TABLE OF CONTENTS—Continued

SATURN

MOTOR
AUTO REPAIR MANUAL
GENERAL MOTORS CORPORATION
58th Edition, Volume 1

First Printing

Published by

MOTOR

A Division of Hearst Business Publishing, Inc.

5600 Crooks Road, Troy, MI 48098

Printed in the U.S.A.

ISBN 0-87851-840-1

VEHICLE IDENTIFICATION

TABLE OF CONTENTS

1992 BUICK

V.I.N. DEFINED

1st POSITION
COUNTRY
1 = United States
2 = Canada

2nd POSITION
MANUFACTURER
G = General Motors

3rd POSITION
DIVISION
4 = Buick
7 = GM of Canada

4th POSITION
CARLINE CODE
A = Century
B = LeSabre, Electra (RWD)
B = Estate Wagon (RWD)
B = Coachbuilder Wagon
B = Roadmaster
C = Electra/Park Ave (FWD)
D = Electra (RWD)
E = Riviera/Reatta
G = Regal
H = LeSabre (FWD)
J = Skyhawk
N = Somerset Regal/Skylark
W = Regal
X = Skylark

5th POSITION, 1985-88
CARLINE SERIES
B = Skylark Custom
C = Skylark Limited
D = Skylark Sport
E = Skylark T-Type
F = Electra T-Type
G = Century Sport
H = Century Custom
J = Regal/Somerset
K = Regal/Somerset
L = Century Limited
M = Regal/Somerset Limited
N = LeSabre Custom
P = Lesabre Limited
R = Electra Limited
S = Skyhawk Custom
T = Skyhawk Limited
U = Park Avenue (RWD)
V = Electra Estate
W = Park Avenue (FWD)
X = Electra Limited (FWD)
Y = Riviera T-TYPE
Z = Riviera Luxury

5th POSITION, 1989-92
CARLINE SERIES
B = Regal Custom
B = Coachbuilder Wagon
C = Reatta
C = Skylark Custom 4 Door
D = Regal/Skylark Limited
E = Skyhawk Sport
F = Electra T-Type
H = Century Custom/Wagon
J = Skylark Custom 2 Door
K = Regal/Somerset

5th POSITION, 89-92 (CONT'D)
L = Century Limited/Wagon
L = Estate Wagon
M = Skylark Limited
M = Skylark Grand Sport
N = Roadmaster
P = Lesabre Custom
R = LeSabre Limited
R = LeSabre Estate Wagon
R = Roadmaster Est Wagon
S = Skyhawk Custom
T = Roadmaster ITT Ltd.
U = Elect Park Ave (Ultra)
V = Electra Estate (RWD)
V = Skylark
W = Electra Park Avenue
X = Electra Limited (FWD)
Z = Riviera Luxury

6th & 7th POSITION, 1985-86
BODY TYPE
19 = 4 Door Sedan
27 = 2 Door Coupe
35 = 4 Door Wagon
37 = 2 Door Coupe
47 = 2 Door Coupe
57 = 2 Door Coupe
67 = 2 Door Convertable
69 = 4 Door Sedan
77 = 2 Door Hatchback
87 = 2 Door Coupe

6th POSITION, 1987-92
BODY TYPE
1 = 2 Door Coupe
2 = 2 Door Hatchback
3 = 2 Door Convertable
5 = 4 Door Sedan
6 = 4 Door Sedan
8 = 4 Door Wagon

7th POSITION, 1987-92
RESTRAINT SYSTEM
1 = Manual Belts
2 = Manual Belts (Built In Safety)
2 = Manual Belts (Dual Air Bags)
3 = Manual Belts (Driver Air Bag)
4 = Automatic Belts
5 = Automatic Belts (Driver Air Bag)

8th POSITION, 1985-88
ENGINE CODE
A = 3.8-V6, 2 Barrel
B = 3.8-V6, 2 Barrel
D = 2.3-L4, Fuel Injected
E = 3.0-V6, 2 Barrel
H = 5.0-V8, 4 Barrel
J = 1.8-L4, MFI
M = 3.0-V6, Fuel Injected
N = 5.7-V8, Diesel
P = 2.0-L4, EFI
R = 2.5-L4, TBI
T = 4.3-V6, Diesel
U = 2.5-L4, TBI
V = 4.3-V6, Diesel
W = 2.8-V6, MFI
X = 2.8-V6, 2 Barrel
Y = 5.0-V8, 4 Barrel
Z = 4.3-V6, TBI

8th POSITION, 85-88 (CONT'D)
0 = 1.8-L4, TBI
1 = 2.0-L4, EFI
3 = 3.8-V6, MFI
7 = 3.8-V6, SFI
9 = 3.8-V6, SFI

8th POSITION, 1989-92
ENGINE CODE
C = 3.8-V6, MFI
D = 2.3-L4, MFI
F = 5.0-V8, TBI
G = 2.2-L4, TBI
L = 3.8-V6, MFI
N = 3.3-V6, MFI
R = 2.5-L4, TBI
T = 3.1-V6, MFI
U = 2.5-L4, TBI
W = 2.8-V6, Fuel Injected
Y = 5.0-V8, 4 Barrel
Z = 4.3-V6, TBI
1 = 2.0-L4, Fuel Injected
1 = 3.8-V6, MFI
3 = 2.3-L4, MFI
4 = 2.2-L4, MFI
7 = 5.7-V8, TBI

9th POSITION
CHECK DIGIT

10th POSITION
MODEL YEAR
F = 1985
G = 1986
H = 1987
J = 1988
K = 1989
L = 1990
M = 1991
N = 1992

11th POSITION
ASSEMBLY PLANT
A = Lakewood, GA
B = Lansing, MI
C = Lansing, MI
D = Doraville, GA
H = Flint, MI
K = Leeds, MO
M = Lansing, MI
P = Pontiac, MI
R = Arlington, TX
S = Ramos Arizpe, Mexico
T = Tarrytown, NY
U = Hamtramck, MI
X = Fairfax, KS
Z = Fremont, Ca
1 = Oshawa #2, Canada
1 = Wentzville, MO
2 = Ste. Therese, Canada
4 = Orion, MI
6 = Oklahoma City, OK
7 = Lordstown, OH
9 = Oshawa #1, Canada

12th Thru 17th POSITION
PRODUCTION SEQUENCE NUMBER

1993–95 BUICK

V.I.N. DEFINED

1st POSITION
COUNTRY
1 = United States
2 = Canada
3 = Mexico
4 = United States

2nd POSITION
MANUFACTURER
G = General Motors
C = CAMI

3rd POSITION
DIVISION
4 = Buick
7 = GM of Canada

4th POSITION
CARLINE CODE
A = Century
B = Estate Wagon (RWD)
B = Coachbuilder Wagon
B = Roadmaster
C = Park Avenue (FWD)
E = Riviera
G = Riviera
H = LeSabre (FWD)
N = Somerset/Skylark
W = Regal

5th POSITION
CARLINE SERIES
B = Regal Custom
B = Regal Gran Sport (2D)
B = Coachbuilder Wagon
D = Regal Limited
D = Riviera
F = Regal Gran Sport (4D)
G = Century Spl & Wagon
H = Century Custom/Wagon
J = Skylark
L = Century Limited Wagon
M = Skylark Gran Sport
N = Roadmaster
P = LeSabre Custom
R = LeSabre Limited
R = Roadmaster Est Wagon
T = Roadmaster Limited
U = Park Avenue - Ultra
V = Somerset
V = Skylark Custom
V = Skylark LTD/Gran Sport
W = Park Avenue
Z = Riviera

6th POSITION
BODY TYPE
1 = 2 Door Coupe
2 = 2 Door
3 = 2 Door Convertable
4 = 2 Door Waqon
5 = 4 Door Sedan
6 = 4 Door
8 = 4 Door Wagon

7th POSITION
RESTRAINT SYSTEM
1 = Manual Belts
2 = Manual Belts (Dual Air Bags)
3 = Manual Belts (Driver Air Bag)
4 = Automatic Belts
5 = Automatic Belts (Driver Air Bag)
6 = Automatic Belts (Dual Air Bags)

8th POSITION
ENGINE CODE
D = 2.3-L4, MFI
K = 3.8-V6, MFI
L = 3.8-V6, MFI
M = 3.1-V6, MFI
N = 3.3-V6, MFI
P = 5.7-V8, MFI
R = 2.5-L4, TBI
T = 3.1-V6, MFI
1 = 3.8-V6, MFI
3 = 2.3-L4, MFI
4 = 2.2-L4, MFI
7 = 5.7-V8, TBI

9th POSITION
CHECK DIGIT

10th POSITION
MODEL YEAR
P = 1993
R = 1994
S = 1995

11th POSITION
ASSEMBLY PLANT

12th Thru 17th POSITION
PRODUCTION SEQUENCE NUMBER

CADILLAC

V.I.N. DEFINED

1st POSITION
COUNTRY
1 = United States
2 = Canada
4 = United States

2nd POSITION
MANUFACTURER
G = General Motors
C = CAMI

3rd POSITION
DIVISION
6 = Cadillac
7 = GM of Canada

4th POSITION
CARLINE CODE
C = Fleetwood/DeVille (FWD)
C = Commercial Chassis
C = Sixty Special
C = DeVille/DeVille Touring
D = Fleetwood/DeVille (RWD)
D = Brougham
D = Commercial Chassis (RWD)
E = Eldorado
E = Eldorado Touring
J = Cimarron
K = Concours
K = DeVille
K = Seville
K = Seville Touring
V = Allante'

5th POSITION
CARLINE SERIES
B = Fleetwood (FWD)
B = Sixty Special
D = DeVille (FWD)
F = Concours
F = Fleetwood Limo
G = Cimarron
G = Fleetwood 60 Special
H = Fleetwood Limo
H = Commercial Chassis (RWD)
L = Eldorado
M = Deville (RWD)
R = Allante' Conv. & HT
S = Seville
S = Allante' Convertible
S = Fleetwood 60 Special
T = Eldorado Touring
T = DeVille Touring
W = Fleetwood Brougham
Y = Seville Touring Sedan
Z = Commercial Chassis

6th & 7th POSITION, 1985-86
BODY TYPE
19 = 4 Door Sedan
27 = 2 Door Coupe
35 = 4 Door Wagon
37 = 2 Door Coupe
47 = 2 Door Coupe
57 = 2 Door Coupe
67 = 2 Door Convertable
69 = 4 Door Sedan
77 = 2 Door Hatchback
87 = 2 Door Coupe

6th POSITION, 1987-95
BODY TYPE
1 = 2 Door Coupe
2 = 2 Door
3 = 2 Door Convertible
5 = 4 Door Sedan
6 = 4 Door

7th POSITION, 1987-95
RESTRAINT SYSTEM
1 = Manual Belts
2 = Manual Belts (Built In Safety)
2 = Manual Belts (Dual Air Bags)
3 = Manual Belts (Driver Air Bag)
4 = Automatic Belts
5 = Automatic Belts (Driver Air Bag)
6 = Automatic Belts (Dual Air Bags)

8th POSITION
ENGINE CODE
B = 4.9-V8, MFI
E = 5.0-V8, TBI
N = 5.7-V8, Diesel
P = 2.0-L4, EFI
P = 5.7-V8, MFI
W = 2.8-V6, MFI
Y = 5.0-V8, 4 Barrel
Y = 4.6-V8, MFI
3 = 4.5-V8, MFI
5 = 4.5-V8, Fuel Injected
6 = 4.5-V8, Fuel Injected
7 = 4.1-V8, Fuel Injected
7 = 5.7-V8, TBI
8 = 4.1-V8, DFI
8 = 4.5-V8, MFI
9 = 5.0-V8, 4 Barrel
9 = 4.6-V8, MFI

9th POSITION
CHECK DIGIT

10th POSITION
MODEL YEAR
F = 1985
G = 1986
H = 1987
J = 1988
K = 1989
L = 1990
M = 1991
N = 1992
P = 1993
R = 1994
S = 1995

11th POSITION
ASSEMBLY PLANT

12th Thru 17th POSITION
PRODUCTION SEQUENCE NUMBER

1992–94 CHEVROLET

V.I.N. DEFINED

1st POSITION
COUNTRY
1 = United States
2 = Canada

2nd POSITION
MANUFACTURER
G = General Motors
Y = N.U.M.M.I.
8 = General Motors

3rd POSITION
DIVISION
1 = Chevrolet
7 = GM of Canada

4th POSITION
CARLINE CODE
A = Celebrity
B = Impala
B = Caprice/Hearse/Limo
F = Camaro & Convertible
G = El Camino, Monte Carlo
J = Cavalier/Conv./Wagon
L = Corsica, Beretta
M = Sprint
R = Spectrum
S = Nova, TVS, Venture
T = Chevette
W = Lumina
X = Citation
Y = Corvette & Convertible

5th POSITION
CARLINE SERIES
B = Chevette
B = Hearse/Limo Chassis
C = Cavalier Cadet
C = Cavalier Conv. & Wag (1992-94)
D = Cavalier CS
D = Corsica
E = Cavalier Hatchback, Type 10
F = Cavalier Convertible (1989-94)
F = Cavalier Z24 (1989-94)
F = Spectrum Level I
G = Spectrum Level II
H = Citation
J = Chevette Scooter
K = Nova, TVX
L = Impala
L = Caprice/Caprice Wagon
L = Lumina
L = Nova Twin Cam
M = Lumina Coupe
N = Caprice Classic LS
N = Lumina Eurosport/LS
P = Camaro Sport Coupe & Conv.
P = Lumina Z34
R = Sprint
S = Camaro Berlinetta
S = Sprint E/R
T = Corsica
T = Corsica LT
T = Sprint
U = Caprice Classic Brougham & LS
V = Beretta & Convertible
W = Celebrity
W = Beretta GT/Z26

5th POSITION (CONTINUED)
X = Citation
Y = Corvette & Convertible
Z = Beretta GTZ
Z = Corsica LTZ
Z = Corvette ZR1
Z = Monte Carlo

6th & 7th POSITION, 1985-86
BODY TYPE
08 = 2 Door Hatchback
19 = 4 Door Sedan
27 = 2 Door Coupe
35 = 4 Door Wagon
37 = 2 Door Coupe
47 = 2 Door Coupe
57 = 2 Door Coupe
67 = 2 Door Convertable
68 = 4 Door Hatchback
69 = 4 Door Sedan
77 = 2 Door Hatchback
87 = 2 Door Coupe

6th POSITION, 1987-94
BODY TYPE
1 = 2 Door Coupe
2 = 2 Door Coupe
2 = 2 Door Hatchback
2 = 2 Door Convertible
3 = 2 Door Convertable
5 = 4 Door Sedan
6 = 4 Door Hatchback
6 = 4 Door Sedan
8 = 4 Door Wagon
8 = Commercial Chassis

7th POSITION, 1987-94
RESTRAINT SYSTEM
1 = Manual Belts
2 = Manual Belts (Built In Safety)
2 = Manual Belts (Dual Air Bags)
3 = Manual Belts (Driver Air Bag)
4 = Automatic Belts
5 = Automatic Belts (Driver Air Bag)
6 = Automatic Belts (Dual Air Bags)

8th POSITION, 1985-88
ENGINE CODE
A = 3.8-V6, 2 Barrel
B = 3.8-V6, 2 Barrel
C = 1.6-L4, 2 Barrel
D = 1.8-L4, Diesel
E = 5.0-V8, Fuel Injected
F = 5.0-V8, Fuel Injected
G = 5.0-V8, 4 Barrel
H = 5.0-V8, 4 Barrel
K = 1.5-L4, 2 Barrel
K = 2.0-L4, EFI
M = 1.3-L3, 2 Barrel
M = 2.0-L4, MFI
N = 5.7-V8, Diesel
P = 2.0-L4, EFI
R = 2.5-L4, TBI
S = 2.8-V6, MFI
T = 4.3-V6, Diesel
V = 4.3-V6, Diesel
W = 2.8-V6, MFI
X = 2.8-V6, 2 Barrel
Z = 4.3-V6, TBI
1 = 2.0-L4, EFI

8th POSITION, 85-88(CONT'D)
2 = 1.0-L3, EFI
2 = 1.0-L3, Turbo
2 = 2.5-L4, TBI
4 = 1.6-L4, 2 Barrel
5 = 1.0-L3, 2 Barrel
5 = 1.5-L4, Diesel
5 = 1.6-L4, EFI
6 = 1.0-L3, TBI
6 = 5.7-V8, Barrel
7 = 1.5-L4, Barrel
8 = 5.7-V8, MFI
9 = 1.5-L4, Fuel Injected
9 = 1.5-L4, Turbocharged

8th POSITION, 1989-94
ENGINE CODE
A = 2.3-L4, MFI
E = 5.0-V8, TBI
F = 5.0-V8, MFI
G = 2.2-L4, TBI
J = 5.7-V8, MFI
P = 5.7-V8, MFI
R = 2.5-L4, TBI
S = 2.8-V6, Fuel Injected
S = 3.4-V6, MFI
T = 3.1-V6, MFI
W = 2.8-V6, Fuel Injected
W = 3.1-V6, MFI
W = 4.3-V6, MFI
X = 3.4-V6, MFI
Y = 5.0-V8, 4 Barrel
Z = 4.3-V6, TBI
1 = 2.0-L4, Fuel Injected
2 = 1.0-L3, MFI
4 = 2.2-L4, MFI
5 = 1.6-L4, MFI
6 = 1.0-L3, TBI
6 = 1.6-L4, MFI
7 = 5.7 V8, TBI
8 = 5.7 V8, MFI

9th POSITION
CHECK DIGIT

10th POSITION
MODEL YEAR
F = 1985
G = 1986
H = 1987
J = 1988
K = 1989
L = 1990
M = 1991
N = 1992
P = 1993
R = 1994

11th POSITION
ASSEMBLY PLANT

12th Thru 17th POSITION
PRODUCTION SEQUENCE NUMBER

1995 CHEVROLET

V.I.N. DEFINED

1st POSITION
COUNTRY
1 = United States
2 = Canada
3 = Mexico
4 = United States

2nd POSITION
MANUFACTURER
C = CAMI
G = General Motors
Y = N.U.M.M.I.

3rd POSITION
DIVISION
1 = Chevrolet
7 = GM of Canada

4th POSITION
CARLINE CODE
B = Impala
B = Caprice
F = Camaro
J = Cavalier
L = Corsica, Beretta
M = GEO
S = GEO
W = Lumina
W = Monte Carlo
Y = Corvette

5th POSITION
CARLINE SERIES
C = Cavalier
D = Corsica
F = Cavalier Convertible
F = Cavalier Z24 & LS
K = Prizm
L = Impala SS
L = Caprice/Caprice Wagon
L = Lumina Sedan
N = Lumina LS
P = Camaro Sport Coupe & Conv.
R = Metro & Metro LSi
V = Beretta
W = Beretta Z26
W = Monte Carlo SS
X = Monte Carlo Z34
Y = Corvette & Convertible
Z = Corvette ZR1

6th POSITION
BODY TYPE
1 = 2 Door Coupe
2 = 2 Door
3 = 2 Door Convertable
4 = 2 Door Wagon
5 = 4 Door Sedan
6 = 4 Door
8 = 4 Door Wagon

7th POSITION
RESTRAINT SYSTEM
1 = Manual Belts
2 = Manual Belts (Dual Air Bags)
3 = Manual Belts (Driver Air Bag)
4 = Automatic Belts
5 = Automatic Belts (Driver Air Bag)
6 = Automatic Belts (Dual Air Bags)

8th POSITION
ENGINE CODE
D = 2.3-L4, MFI
J = 5.7-V8, MFI
K = 3.8-V6, MFI
M = 3.1-V6, MFI
P = 5.7-V8, MFI
S = 3.4-V6, MFI
T = 3.1-V6, MFI
W = 4.3-V8, MFI
X = 3.4-V6, MFI
4 = 2.2-L4, MFI
6 = 1.0-L3, TBI
6 = 1.6-L4, MFI
8 = 1.8-L4, MFI
9 = 1.3-L4, TBI

9th POSITION
CHECK DIGIT

10th POSITION
MODEL YEAR
S = 1995

11th POSITION
ASSEMBLY PLANT

12th Thru 17th POSITION
PRODUCTION SEQUENCE NUMBER

GEO

V.I.N. DEFINED

1st POSITION
COUNTRY
1 = United States
2 = Canada
J = Japan

2nd POSITION
MANUFACTURER
C = Canada
G = General Motors
G = Suzuki
Y = N.U.M.M.I.
8 = General Motors

3rd POSITION
DIVISION
1 = Chevrolet
1 = GEO
7 = GM of Canada
7 = GEO
7 = Pontiac

4th POSITION
CARLINE CODE
M = Metro
R = Spectrum
R = Storm
S = Prizm

5th POSITION
CARLINE SERIES
F = Spectrum Level I
F = Storm Level I
G = Spectrum Level II
G = Storm Level II
K = Prizm
L = Prizm GSI
R = Metro GEO, Base
R = Metro LSI
R = Metro FXI
S = Metro
S = Metro FXI
T = Storm GSI Level II

6th POSITION
BODY TYPE
1 = 2 Door Coupe Sedan
2 = 2 Door Hatchback
2 = 3 Door 2+2 Coupe
3 = 2 Door Convertible
4 = 3 Door Hatchback Cpe/Wagon
5 = 4 Door Sedan
5 = 4 Door Notchback
6 = 4 Door Hatchback
7 = 4 Door Liftback
8 = 4 Door Wagon

7th POSITION
RESTRAINT SYSTEM
1 = Manual Belts
2 = Manual Belts (Built in Safety)
3 = Manual Belts (Driver Air Bag)
4 = Automatic Belts (Passive)

8th POSITION
ENGINE CODE
K = 1.5-L4, 2 Barrel
2 = 1.0-L3, Turbo
5 = 1.6-L4, EFI
6 = 1.0-L3, TBI
6 = 1.6-L4, EFI
7 = 1.5-L4, 2 Barrel
8 = 1.8-L4, EFI
9 = 1.5-L4, Turbo
9 = 1.3-L4, TBI

9th POSITION
CHECK DIGIT

10th POSITION
MODEL YEAR
K = 1989
L = 1990
M = 1991
N = 1992
P = 1993
R = 1994
S = 1995

11th POSITION
ASSEMBLY PLANT
K = Kosia, Japan
Z = Fremont, Ca
6 = Ingersoll, Ont. (CAMI)
7 = Fujisawa, Japan
8 = Fujisawa, Japan

12th Thru 17th POSITION
PRODUCTION SEQUENCE NUMBER

1992 OLDSMOBILE

V.I.N. DEFINED

1st POSITION
COUNTRY
1 = United States
2 = Canada

2nd POSITION
MANUFACTURER
G = General Motors

3rd POSITION
DIVISION
3 = Oldsmobile
7 = GM of Canada

4th POSITION
CARLINE CODE
A = Cutlass Ciera/Cruiser
B = 88 Custom Cruiser (RWD)
C = 98 Touring Sedan
C = 98 Regency/Brougham (FWD)
C = 98 Regency Elite
D = 98 Regency (RWD)
E = Toronado
E = Toronado Trofe'o
G = Cutlass
H = Delta 88 (FWD)
H = 88 Royale/LS (FWD)
J = Firenza
N = Calais
N = Cutlass International
N = Achieva
W = Cutlass Supreme & S
W = Cutlass International
W = Cutlass Convertible

5th POSITION, 1985-88
CARLINE SERIES
C = Firenza
D = Firenza
F = Calais
G = 98 Regency (RWD)
H = 98 Regency (RWD)
J = Cutlass Ciera
K = Cutlass Calais
M = Cutlass Brougham
N = Delta 88
P = Custom Cruiser
R = Cutlass Supreme
W = 98 Regency Brougham
X = 98 Regency
Y = Delta 88 Brougham
Z = Toronado Brougham

5th POSITION, 1989-92
CARLINE SERIES
F = Achieva SL
F = Calais
F = Calais S
H = Cutlass Supreme
J = Cutlass Ciera/Wagon
K = Cutlass International
L = Cutlass Calais
L = Cutlass Ciera
L = Cutlass Ciera S
L = Achieva S
M = Cutlass Ciera SL
M = Cutlass Cruiser SL Wagon
M = Cutlass Brougham
N = Delta 88

5th POSITION, 89-92 (CONT'D)
N = 88 Royale
P = Custom Cruiser
R = Cutlass Supreme Int'l
S = Cutlass Ciera Int'l
S = Cutlass Supreme SL
T = Calais SL
T = Cutlass Convertible
V = Toronado Trofe'o
V = 98 Touring Sedan
W = 98 Regency Brougham
W = 98 Regency Elite
X = 98 Regency (FWD)
Y = Delta 88 Brougham
Y = 88 Royale Brougham
Y = 88 Royale LS
Z = Toronado

6th & 7th POSITION, 1985-86
BODY TYPE
19 = 4 Door Sedan
27 = 2 Door Coupe
35 = 4 Door Wagon
37 = 2 Door Coupe
47 = 2 Door Coupe
57 = 2 Door Coupe
67 = 2 Door Convertible
69 = 4 Door Sedan
77 = 2 Door Hatchback
87 = 2 Door Coupe

6th POSITION, 1987-92
BODY TYPE
1 = 2 Door Coupe
1 = 2 Door Sedan
2 = 2 Door Coupe
3 = 2 Door Convertible
5 = 4 Door Sedan
6 = 4 Door Sedan
8 = 4 Door Wagon

7th POSITION, 1987-92
RESTRAINT SYSTEM
1 = Manual Belts
2 = Manual Belts (Built In Safety)
2 = Manual Belts (Dual Air Bags)
3 = Manual Belts (Driver Air Bag)
4 = Automatic Belts
5 = Automatic Belts (Driver Air Bag)

8th POSITION, 1985-88
ENGINE CODE
A = 3.8-V6, 2 barrel
B = 3.8-V6, 2 barrel
D = 2.3-L4, Fuel Injected
E = 3.0-V6, 2 barrel
H = 5.0-V8, 4 barrel
L = 3.0-V6, MFI
M = 3.0-V6, Fuel Injected
N = 5.7-V8, Diesel
P = 2.0-L4, EFI
R = 2.5-L4, TBI
T = 4.3-V6, Diesel
U = 2.5-L4, TBI
V = 4.3-V6, Diesel
W = 2.8-V6, MFI
X = 2.8-V6, 2 barrel
Y = 5.0-V8, 4 barrel

8th POSITION, 85-88 (CONT'D)
0 = 1.8-L4, TBI
1 = 2.0-L4, EFI
3 = 3.8-V6, MBI
7 = 4.3-V6, Diesel
9 = 5.0-V8, 4 barrel

8th POSITION, 1989-92
ENGINE CODE
A = 2.3-L4, MFI
C = 3.8-V6, MFI
D = 2.3-L4, MFI
E = 5.0-V8, TBI
L = 3.8-V6, MFI
N = 3.3-V6, MFI
R = 2.5-L4, TBI
T = 3.1-V6, MFI
U = 2.5-L4, TBI
W = 2.8-V6, MFI
X = 3.4-V6, MFI
Y = 5.0-V8, 4 Barrel
1 = 3.8-V6, MFI
3 = 2.3-L4, MFI
7 = 3.8-V6, TBI
7 = 5.7-V8, TBI

9th POSITION
CHECK DIGIT

10th POSITION
MODEL YEAR
F = 1985
G = 1986
H = 1987
J = 1988
K = 1989
L = 1990
M = 1991
N = 1992

11th POSITION
ASSEMBLY PLANT
B = Lansing, MI
C = Lansing, MI
D = Doraville, GA
E = Linden, NJ
F = Flint, MI
G = Framingham, MA
K = Leeds, MO
M = Lansing, MI
R = Arlington, TX
U = Hamtramck, MI
W = Willow Run, MI
X = Fairfax, KS
Y = Wilmington, DE
Z = Fremont, Ca
1 = Wentzville, MO
1 = Oshawa #2, Canada
2 = Ste. Therese, Canada
4 = Orion, MI
7 = Lordstown, OH
9 = Oshawa #1, Canada

12th Thru 17th POSITION
PRODUCTION SEQUENCE
NUMBER

1993–95 OLDSMOBILE

V.I.N. DEFINED

1st POSITION
COUNTRY
1 = United States
2 = Canada
3 = Mexico
4 = United States

2nd POSITION
MANUFACTURER
C = CAMI
G = General Motors

3rd POSITION
DIVISION
3 = Oldsmobile
7 = GM of Canada

4th POSITION
CARLINE CODE
A = Cutlass Ciera/Cruiser
B = 88 Custom Cruiser (RWD)
C = 98 Touring Sedan
C = 98 Regency/Elite
E = Toronado
E = Toronado Trofe'o
G = Aurora
H = 88 Royale/LS (FWD)
N = Achieva
W = Cutlass Supreme S
W = Cutlass International
W = Cutlass Convertible

5th POSITION
CARLINE SERIES
F = Achieva SL & SC
G = Cutlass Ciera S
H = Cutlass Supreme S
J = Cutlass S/SL & Wagon
L = Cutlass Ciera S
L = Achieva S
M = Cutlass Ciera SL
M = Cutlass Cruiser SL Wagon
N = 88 Royale
P = Custom Cruiser
R = Cutlass Supreme Int'l
R = Aurora
T = Cutlass Convertible
V = Toronado Trofe'o
V = 98 Touring Sedan
W = 98 Regency Elite
X = 98 Regency (FWD)
X = 98 Regency Elite
Y = 88 Royale LS
Z = Toronado

6th POSITION
BODY TYPE
1 = 2 Door Coupe
2 = 2 Door
3 = 2 Door Convertible
4 = 2 Door Wagon
5 = 4 Door Sedan
6 = 4 Door
8 = 4 Door Wagon

7th POSITION
RESTRAINT SYSTEM
1 = Manual Belts
2 = Manual Belts (Dual Air Bags)
3 = Manual Belts (Driver Air Bag)
4 = Automatic Belts
5 = Automatic Belts (Driver Air Bag)
6 = Automatic Belts (Dual Air Bags)

8th POSITION
ENGINE CODE
A = 2.3-L4, MFI
C = 4.0-V8, MFI
D = 2.3-L4, MFI
E = 5.0-V8, TBI
K = 3.8-V6, MFI
L = 3.8-V6, MFI
M = 3.1-V6, MFI
N = 3.3-V6, MFI
R = 2.5-L4, TBI
T = 3.1-V6, MFI
X = 3.4-V6, MFI
1 = 3.8-V6, MFI
3 = 2.3-L4, MFI
4 = 2.2-L4, MFI
7 = 5.7-V8, TBI

9th POSITION
CHECK DIGIT

10th POSITION
MODEL YEAR
P = 1993
R = 1994
S = 1995

11th POSITION
ASSEMBLY PLANT
B = Lansing, MI
C = Lansing, MI
D = Doraville, GA
E = Linden, NJ
F = Flint, MI
G = Framingham, MA
K = Leeds, MO
M = Lansing, MI
R = Arlington, TX
U = Hamtramck, MI
W = Willow Run, MI
X = Fairfax, KS
Y = Wilmington, DE
Z = Fremont, Ca
1 = Wentzville, MO
1 = Oshawa #2, Canada
2 = Ste. Therese Canada
4 = Orion, MI
7 = Lordstown, OH
9 = Oshawa #1, Canada

12th Thru 17th POSITION
PRODUCTION SEQUENCE NUMBER

1992–93 PONTIAC

V.I.N. DEFINED

1st POSITION
COUNTRY
1 = United States
2 = Canada
K = Korea

2nd POSITION
MANUFACTURER
G = General Motors
L = Daewoo Motors

3rd POSITION
DIVISION
2 = Pontiac
7 = GM of Canada

4th POSITION
CARLINE CODE
A = 6000
B = Parisienne/Safari
F = Firebird
G = Grand Prix Brougham
H = Bonneville
J = Sunbird, 2000 & Conv.
L = Tempest
M = Firefly
N = Grand Am
P = Fiero
T = T-1000/Lemans
W = Grand Prix

5th POSITION
CARLINE SERIES
E = Sunbird, J2000
E = Sunbird LE
B = Sunbird SE & Conv.
C = Sunbird, J2000 LE
D = Sunbird, J2000 SE
D = Sunbird GT
E = Fiero/Grand Am/6000 SE
E = Grand Am LE
F = Fiero SE/6000 LE
G = 6000 LE/Fiero GT
H = 6000 STE
H = Grand Prix LE
J = Grand Prix LE & SE
J = 6000 SE
K = Grand Prix LJ
L = T1000/Parisienne
M = Fiero Sport Coupe
N = Bonneville/Parisienne Brougham
N = Lemans
N = Lemans SE Aero Cpe & Sedan
P = Grand Prix Brougham & SE
P = Grand Prix GT/GTP
R = Bonneville Brougham
R = Firefly
R = Lemans SE
S = Firebird/Bonneville
S = Lemans GSE
T = Grand Prix STE
T = Parisienne Brougham
T = Tempest
U = Sunbird GT/Parisienne Export
V = Grand Am LE
V = Formula
W = Firebird Trans Am
W = Grand Am SE & GT
X = Firebird SE/Bonneville LE
X = Bonneville SE

5th POSITION (CONTINUED)
X = Lemans, Lemans GSE
X = Lemans Aero Coupe
Y = Bonneville SSE, SSEi
Z = Bonneville LE, SE & SSE

6th & 7th POSITION, 1985-86
BODY TYPE
19 = 4 Door Sedan
27 = 2 Door Coupe
35 = 4 Door Wagon
37 = 2 Door Coupe
47 = 2 Door Coupe
57 = 2 Door Coupe
67 = 2 Door Convertable
69 = 4 Door Sedan
77 = 2 Door Hatchback
87 = 2 Door Coupe

6th POSITION, 1987-93
BODY TYPE
1 = 2 Door Coupe
2 = 2 Door Coupe
2 = 2 Door Hatchback
2 = 2 Door Convertible
3 = 2 Door Convertible
5 = 4 Door Sedan
5 = 3 Door Cargo Van
6 = 4 Door Sedan
6 = 4 Door Hatchback
6 = 3 Door Van
8 = 4 Door Wagon

7th POSITION, 1987-93
RESTRAINT SYSTEM
1 = Manual Belts
2 = Manual Belts (Built In Safety)
2 = Manual Belts (Dual Air Bags)
3 = Manual Belts (Driver Air Bag)
4 = Automatic Belts
5 = Automatic Belts (Driver Air Bag)

8th POSITION, 1985-88
ENGINE CODE
A = 3.8-V6, 2 barrel
B = 3.8-V6, 2 barrel
C = 1.6-L4, 2 barrel
D = 1.8-L4, Diesel
E = 5.0-V8, Fuel Injected
F = 5.0-V8, Fuel Injected
G = 5.0-V8, 4 barrel
H = 5.0-V8, 4 barrel
J = 1.8-L4, MFI
L = 3.0-V6, MFI
N = 5.7-V8, Diesel
P = 2.0-L4, EFI
R = 2.5-L4, TBI
S = 2.8-V6, MFI
T = 4.3-V6, Diesel
U = 2.5-L4, TBI
V = 4.3-V6, Diesel
W = 2.8-V6, MFI
X = 2.8-V6, 2 barrel
Z = 4.3-V6, TBI
0 = 1.8-L4, TBI
2 = 2.5-L4, TBI
6 = 1.6-L4, 2 barrel
6 = 1.6-L4, TBI
9 = 2.8-V6, MFI

8th POSITION, 1989-93
ENGINE CODE
A = 2.3-L4, MFI
C = 3.8-V6, MFI
D = 2.3-L4, MFI
E = 5.0-V8, TBI
F = 5.0-V8, MFI
H = 2.0-L4, MFI
K = 2.0-L4, TBI
L = 3.8-V6, MFI
M = 2.0-L4, MFI
N = 3.3-V6, MFI
P = 5.7-V8, MFI
R = 2.5-L4, TBI
S = 2.8-V6, MFI
S = 3.4-V6, MFI
T = 3.1-V6, MFI
U = 2.5-L4, TBI
V = 3.1-V6, MFI
W = 2.8-V6, MFI
X = 3.4-V6, MFI
Y = 5.0-V8, 4 Barrel
Z = 4.3-V6, TBI
1 = 3.8-V6, MFI
3 = 2.3-L4, MFI
6 = 1.6-L4, TBI
7 = 3.8-V6, MFI
8 = 5.7-V8, MFI

9th POSITION
CHECK DIGIT

10th POSITION
MODEL YEAR
F = 1985
G = 1986
H = 1987
J = 1988
K = 1989
L = 1990
M = 1991
N = 1992
P = 1993

11th POSITION
ASSEMBLY PLANT
A = Lakewood, GA
B = Lansing, MI
B = Korea
C = Lansing, MI
F = Flint, MI
L = Van Nuys, CA
M = Lansing, MI
N = Norwood, OH
P = Pontiac, MI
U = Hamtramck, MI
W = Willow Run, MI
X = Fairfax, KS
Y = Wilmington, DE
1 = Wentzville, MO
1 = Oshawa #2, Canada
2 = Ste. Therese, Quebec, Canada
5 = Bowling Green, KY
6 = Oklahoma City, OK
7 = Lordstown, OH
9 = Oshawa #1, Canada

12th Thru 17th POSITION
PRODUCTION SEQUENCE
NUMBER

1994–95 PONTIAC

V.I.N. DEFINED

1st POSITION
COUNTRY
1 = United States
2 = Canada
3 = Mexico
4 = United States

2nd POSITION
MANUFACTURER
C = CAMI
G = General Motors

3rd POSITION
DIVISION
2 = Pontiac
7 = GM of Canada

4th POSITION
CARLINE CODE
F = Firebird/Formula
H = Bonneville
J = Sunbird & Convertible
J = Sunfire
N = Grand Am
W = Grand Prix

5th POSITION
CARLINE SERIES
B = Sunbird SE & Convertible
B = Sunfire SE & Convertible
D = Sunfire GT
E = Grand Am SE
J = Grand Prix SE
L = Sunbird SE
M = Grand Prix
S = Firebird & Convertible
V = Formula & Convertible
V = Trans Am
W = Grand Am GT
X = Bonneville SE
Z = Bonneville SSE

6th POSITION
BODY TYPE
1 = 2 Door Coupe
2 = 2 Door
3 = 2 Door Convertible
4 = 2 Door Wagon
5 = 4 Door Sedan
6 = 4 Door
8 = 4 Door Wagon

7th POSITION
RESTRAINT SYSTEM
1 = Manual Belts
2 = Manual Belts (Dual Air Bags)
3 = Manual Belts (Driver Air Bag)
4 = Automatic Belts
5 = Automatic Belts (Driver Air Bag)
6 = Automatic Belts (Dual Air Bags)

8th POSITION
ENGINE CODE
A = 2.3-L4, MFI
D = 2.3-L4, MFI
H = 2.0-L4, MFI
K = 3.8-V6, MFI
L = 3.8-V6, MFI
M = 3.1-V6, MFI
P = 5.7-V8, MFI
S = 3.4-V6, MFI
T = 3.1-V6, MFI
X = 3.4-V6, MFI
1 = 3.8-V6, MFI
3 = 2.3-L4, MFI
4 = 2.2-L4, MFI

9th POSITION
CHECK DIGIT

10th POSITION
MODEL YEAR
R = 1994
S = 1995

11th POSITION
ASSEMBLY PLANT

12th Thru 17th POSITION
PRODUCTION SEQUENCE NUMBER

SATURN

V.I.N. DEFINED

1st POSITION
COUNTRY
1 = United States

2nd POSITION
MANUFACTURER
G = General Motors

3rd POSITION
DIVISION
8 = Saturn

4th POSITION
CARLINE CODE
Z = SL, SL1&2, SC
Z = SC1&2, SW1&2

5th POSITION
CARLINE SERIES
E = SC1 Coupe
F = SL Sedan, SC1 Coupe
G = SL1 Sedan, SC
G = SC2 Sedan, SW1 Wagon
H = SL1 Sedan, SC
H = SC2 Coupe, SW1 Wagon
J = SL2 Sedan, SW2 Wagon
K = SL2 Sedan, SW2 Wagon

6th POSITION
BODY TYPE
1 = 2 Door Coupe
2 = 2 Door
3 = 2 Door Convertible
4 = 2 Door Wagon
5 = 4 Door Sedan
6 = 4 Door
8 = 5 Door Wagon

7th POSITION
RESTRAINT SYSTEM
1 = Manual Belts
2 = Manual Belts (Dual Air Bags)
3 = Manual Belts (Driver Air Bag)
4 = Automatic Belts
5 = Automatic Belts (Driver Air Bag)
6 = Automatic Belts (Dual Air Bags)

8th POSITION
ENGINE CODE
7 = 1.9-L4, MFI
8 = 1.9-L4, MFI
9 = 1.9-L4, TBI

9th POSITION
CHECK DIGIT

10th POSITION
MODEL YEAR
M = 1991
N = 1992
P = 1993
R = 1994
S = 1995

11th POSITION
ASSEMBLY PLANT
Z = Spring Hill

12th Thru 17th POSITION
PRODUCTION SEQUENCE NUMBER

AIR BAG SYSTEM PRECAUTIONS

INDEX

AIR BAG SYSTEM DISARMING

ACHIEVA, GRAND AM & SKYLARK

The diagnostic energy reserve module or sensing and diagnostic module (DERM/SDM) can maintain enough voltage to cause air bag deployment for up to ten minutes after the ignition switch is turned off and the battery is disconnected. Servicing the SIR system during this period may result in accidental deployment and personal injury.

1. Ensure front wheels are pointed straight ahead.
2. Turn ignition switch to Lock position.
3. Remove AIR BAG fuse from fuse block.
4. Working through trap door located in the lefthand sound insulator, disconnect Connector Position Assurance (CPA) and yellow 2-way connector at base of steering column.

BERETTA & CORSICA

The diagnostic energy reserve module or sensing and diagnostic module (DERM/SDM) can maintain enough voltage to cause air bag deployment for up to ten minutes after the ignition switch is turned off and the battery is disconnected. Servicing the SIR system during this period may result in accidental deployment and personal injury.

1. Ensure front wheels are pointed straight ahead.
2. Turn ignition switch to Lock position and remove SIR or AIR BAG fuse (fuse No. 3 on 1995 models).
3. Remove left sound insulator. **Remove courtesy lamp from sound insulator, if necessary.**
4. Disconnect Connector Position Assurance (CPA), then the yellow two-way SIR electrical connector at base of steering column.

BONNEVILLE, LESABRE, PARK AVENUE, 88 & 98

The diagnostic energy reserve module or sensing and diagnostic module (DERM/SDM) can maintain enough voltage to cause air bag deployment for up to ten minutes after the ignition switch is turned off and the battery is disconnected. Servicing the SIR system during this period may result in accidental deployment and personal injury.

1. Ensure front wheels are pointed straight ahead.
2. Turn ignition switch to Lock position and remove SIR or AIR BAG fuse.
3. Remove left sound insulator. **Remove courtesy lamp from sound insulator, if necessary.**
4. Disconnect Connector Position Assurance (CPA), then the yellow two-way SIR electrical connector at base of steering column.
5. **On models with passenger air bag,** remove righthand sound insulator and disconnect CPA and yellow 2-way connector from passenger inflator pigtail.

CAMARO & FIREBIRD

The diagnostic energy reserve module or sensing and diagnostic module (DERM/SDM) can maintain enough voltage to cause air bag deployment for up to ten minutes after the ignition switch is turned off and the battery is disconnected. Servicing the SIR system during this period may result in accidental deployment and personal injury.

1. Ensure front wheels are pointed straight ahead.
2. Turn ignition switch to Lock position and remove SIR or AIR BAG fuse.
3. Remove left sound insulator. **Remove courtesy lamp from sound insulator, if necessary.**
4. Disconnect Connector Position Assurance (CPA), then the yellow two-way SIR electrical connector at base of steering column.
5. Remove glove compartment door assembly, then CPA and yellow 2-way connector from passenger inflator module.

CAPRICE, CUSTOM CRUISER, IMPALA SS & ROADMASTER

The diagnostic energy reserve module or sensing and diagnostic module (DERM/SDM) can maintain enough voltage to cause air bag deployment for up to ten minutes after the ignition switch is turned off and the battery is disconnected. Servicing the SIR system during this period may result in accidental deployment and personal injury.

1. Ensure front wheels are pointed straight ahead.
2. Turn ignition switch to Lock position and remove SIR or AIR BAG fuse from fuse block.
3. **On 1992-93 models,** remove Connector Position Assurance (CPA), then disconnect yellow two-way SIR electrical connector at base of steering column.
4. **On 1994-95 models,** remove Connector Position Assurance (CPA), then disconnect both yellow two-way SIR electrical connectors at base of steering column.

CAVALIER & SUNFIRE

The diagnostic energy reserve module or sensing and diagnostic module (DERM/SDM) can maintain enough voltage to cause air bag deployment for up to ten minutes after the ignition switch is turned off and the battery is disconnected. Servicing the SIR sys-

tem during this period may result in accidental deployment and personal injury.

1. Ensure front wheels are directed straight ahead, then place ignition switch in Lock position and remove key.
2. Remove "AIR BG 1" fuse from instrument panel fuse block, then remove lefthand lower trim panel.
3. Remove Connector Position Assurance (CPA) and disconnect both yellow SIR connectors at base of steering column.

CENTURY, CUTLASS CIERA & CUTLASS CRUISER

The diagnostic energy reserve module or sensing and diagnostic module (DERM/SDM) can maintain enough voltage to cause air bag deployment for up to ten minutes after the ignition switch is turned off and the battery is disconnected. Servicing the SIR system during this period may result in accidental deployment and personal injury.

1. Ensure front wheels are pointed straight ahead.
2. Turn ignition switch to Lock position and remove SIR or AIR BAG fuse.
3. Remove left sound insulator. **Remove courtesy lamp from sound insulator, if necessary.**
4. Remove Connector Position Assurance (CPA), then disconnect yellow two-way SIR electrical connector at base of steering column.

CORVETTE

The diagnostic energy reserve module (DERM) can maintain enough voltage to cause air bag deployment for up to ten minutes after the ignition switch is turned off and the battery is disconnected. Servicing the SIR system during this period may result in accidental deployment and personal injury.

1992–93

1. Ensure front wheels are pointed straight ahead.
2. Turn ignition switch to Lock position and remove AIR BAG fuse.
3. Remove left sound insulator. **Remove courtesy lamp from sound insulator, if necessary.**
4. Disconnect Connector Position Assurance (CPA), then the yellow two-way SIR electrical connector at base of steering column.

1994–95

1. Ensure front wheels are pointed straight ahead.
2. Turn ignition switch to Lock position and remove key.
3. Remove AIR BAG fuse from instrument panel fuse block.
4. Remove trim panel from under steering column.
5. Remove Connector Position Assurance (CPA), then disconnect both yellow SIR connectors located near base of steering column.

CUTLASS SUPREME & REGAL

The diagnostic energy reserve module or sensing and diagnostic module (DERM/SDM) can maintain enough voltage to cause air bag deployment for up to ten minutes after the ignition switch is turned off and the battery is disconnected. Servicing the SIR system during this period may result in accidental deployment and personal injury.

1992–94

1. Ensure front wheels are pointed straight ahead.
2. Turn ignition switch to the Lock position.
3. Remove "AR BG 1" fuse from fuse block.
4. Remove trim panel from under steering column.
5. Disconnect Connector Position Assurance (CPA) and yellow 2-way connector at base of steering column.

1995

1. Ensure front wheels are directed straight ahead, then turn ignition switch to Lock position and remove key.
2. Remove fuse No. 21 from instrument panel fuse block, then remove lefthand lower trim panel.
3. Remove Connector Position Assurance (CPA) and disconnect yellow 2-way connector at base of steering column, then remove glove compartment door.
4. Remove CPA and disconnect yellow 2-way connector behind glove compartment door area.

DEVILLE & FLEETWOOD

The diagnostic energy reserve module or sensing and diagnostic module (DERM/SDM) can maintain enough voltage to cause air bag deployment for up to ten minutes after the ignition switch is turned off and the battery is disconnected. Servicing the SIR system during this period may result in accidental deployment and personal injury.

1992–93

1. Ensure front wheels are pointed straight ahead.
2. Turn ignition switch to Lock position and remove SIR or AIR BAG fuse.
3. Remove left sound insulator. **Remove courtesy lamp from sound insulator, if necessary.**
4. Disconnect Connector Position Assurance (CPA), then the yellow two-way SIR electrical connector at base of steering column.

1994–95

1. Ensure front wheels are pointed straight ahead.
2. Turn ignition key to the Lock position and remove key.
3. **On Fleetwood (RWD),** remove AIR BAG fuse from instrument panel fuse block.
4. **On all models,** remove lefthand sound insulator from under steering column.
5. **On Fleetwood (RWD),** remove CPAs and disconnect both yellow 2-way connectors located near base of steering column.
6. **On 1995 DeVille,** remove CPA and disconnect yellow 2-way connector at base of steering column; then, working through trap door in glove compartment, remove CPA and disconnect yellow 2-way connector from passenger inflator module pigtail.

AURORA, ELDORADO, RIVIERA, SEVILLE, TORONADO & TROFEO

The diagnostic energy reserve module (DERM) can maintain enough voltage to cause air bag deployment for up to ten minutes after the ignition switch is turned off and the battery is disconnected. Servicing the SIR system during this period may result in accidental deployment and personal injury.

1. Ensure front wheels are pointed straight ahead.
2. Turn ignition switch to Lock position and remove SIR or AIR BAG fuse.
3. Remove left sound insulator. **Remove courtesy lamp from sound insulator, if necessary.**
4. Disconnect Connector Position Assurance (CPA), then the yellow two-way SIR electrical connector at base of steering column.
5. **On models with passenger air bag,** remove righthand sound insulator and disconnect CPA and yellow 2-way connector from passenger inflator pigtail.

GRAND PRIX, LUMINA & MONTE CARLO

The diagnostic energy reserve module or sensing and diagnostic module (DERM/SDM) can maintain enough voltage to cause air bag deployment for up to ten minutes after the ignition switch is turned off and the battery is disconnected. Servicing the SIR system during this period may result in accidental deployment and personal injury.

1. Ensure front wheels are pointed straight ahead.
2. Turn ignition switch to the Lock position and remove key.
3. Remove AIR BAG fuse (No. 21 on 1995 models) from instrument panel fuse block.
4. Remove trim panel from under steering column.
5. Disconnect Connector Position Assurance (CPA) and yellow 2-way connector at base of steering column.
6. Open glove compartment door and disconnect passenger side Connector Position Assurance (CPA) and yellow 2-way connector.

METRO

The diagnostic energy reserve module (DERM) can maintain enough voltage to cause air bag deployment for up to ten minutes after the ignition switch is turned off and the battery is disconnected. Servicing the SIR system during this period may result in accidental deployment and personal injury.

1. **On 1992-93 models,** place steering wheel so that wheels are pointing straight ahead, then turn ignition switch to the Lock position.
2. **On all models,** remove SIR IG fuse from SIR fuse block.
3. Remove rear plastic access cover from inflator module housing.
4. Remove Connector Position Assurance (CPA), then disconnect yellow two-way SIR electrical connector inside inflator module housing.

PRIZM

The diagnostic energy reserve module (DERM) can maintain enough voltage to cause air bag deployment for up to ten minutes after the ignition switch is turned off and the battery is disconnected. Servicing the SIR system during this period may result in accidental deployment and personal injury.

1. Ensure front wheels are pointed straight ahead, then turn ignition switch to Lock position.
2. Remove IGN and CIG & RADIO fuse from junction block No. 1.
3. Remove Connector Position Assurance (CPA) and disconnect lower steering column (yellow two-cavity) connector at base of steering column.
4. **On models with passenger air bag,** open glove box door and gently pry off passenger inflator module connector retainer.
5. Remove CPA and disconnect yellow 2-way connector from passenger inflator module.

STORM

The diagnostic energy reserve module (DERM) can maintain enough voltage to cause air bag deployment for up to ten minutes after the ignition switch is turned off and the battery is disconnected. Servicing the SIR system during this period may result in accidental deployment and personal injury.

1. Place steering wheel so that wheels are pointing straight ahead, then turn ignition switch to Lock position.
2. Remove fuses C-22 and C-23 from fuse block.
3. Remove switch bezel from instrument panel, then disconnect electrical connector from switches.
4. Remove cigar lighter bezel from instrument panel, then disconnect cigar lighter electrical connectors.
5. Remove two screws and hood latch release handle from knee bolster, then the three screws, three bolts and two nuts retaining the knee bolster.
6. Disconnect lap cooler air duct from knee bolster, then remove knee bolster from vehicle.
7. Remove Connector Position Assurance (CPA), then disconnect orange three-way connector at the base of the steering column.

SATURN

The diagnostic energy reserve module (DERM) can maintain enough voltage to cause air bag deployment for up to ten minutes after the ignition switch is turned off and the battery is disconnected. Servicing the SIR system during this period may result in accidental deployment and personal injury.

1. Point wheels straight ahead by turning steering wheel.
2. Turn ignition switch to Off position, then disconnect and tape battery ground terminal.
3. Remove air bag fuse.
4. Remove connector position assurance (CPA) device from yellow two-way SIR connector at base of steering column, then disconnect connector.

AIR BAG SYSTEM ARMING

ACHIEVA, GRAND AM & SKYLARK

1. Turn ignition switch to the Lock position and remove key.
2. Working through trap door located in the lefthand sound insulator, connect Connector Position Assurance (CPA) and yellow 2-way connector at base of steering column.
3. Install AIR BAG fuse.
4. Turn ignition switch to the Run position and verify that the AIR BAG warning lamp flashes seven times and then turns off. If lamp does not operate as specified, refer to "Passive Restraints" section of this manual.

BERETTA & CORSICA

1. Connect yellow two-way SIR electrical connector, then install Connector Position Assurance (CPA).
2. Install left sound insulator. **Install courtesy lamp to sound insulator, if applicable.**
3. Install SIR fuse to fuse block, turn ignition switch to Run position and ensure "Inflatable Restraint" lamp flashes 7 to 9 times, then turns off.

BONNEVILLE, LESABRE, PARK AVENUE, 88 & 98

1. **On models with passenger air bag,** connect CPA and yellow 2-way connector to passenger inflator pigtail, then install righthand sound insulator.
2. **On all models,** connect yellow two-way SIR electrical connector, then install Connector Position Assurance (CPA).
3. Install left sound insulator. **Install courtesy lamp to sound insulator, if applicable.**
4. Install SIR fuse to fuse block, turn ignition switch to Run position and ensure "Inflatable Restraint" lamp flashes 7 to 9 times, then turns off.

CAMARO & FIREBIRD

1. Turn ignition switch to the Lock position and remove key.
2. Connect CPA and yellow 2-way connector to passenger inflator module, then install glove compartment door assembly.
3. Connect yellow two-way SIR electrical connector, then install Connector Position Assurance (CPA) near base of steering column.
4. Install left sound insulator. **Install courtesy lamp to sound insulator, if applicable.**
5. Install SIR fuse to fuse block, then verify that the "Inflatable Restraint" lamp flashes 7 to 9 times and then turns off. If lamp does not operate as specified, refer to "Passive Restraints" section of this manual.

CAPRICE, CUSTOM CRUISER, IMPALA SS & ROADMASTER

1. **On 1992-93 models,** connect yellow two-way SIR electrical connector at base of column, then install Connector Position Assurance (CPA).
2. **On 1994-95 models,** connect both yellow two-way SIR electrical connectors at base of column, then install Connector Position Assurance (CPA).
3. **On all models,** install SIR or AIR BAG fuse into fuse block, turn ignition switch to Run position and ensure "Inflatable Restraint" lamp flashes 7 to 9 times and then turns off. If lamp does not operate as specified, refer to "Passive Restraints" section of this manual.

CAVALIER & SUNFIRE

1. Ensure ignition switch is in Lock position and key is removed, then connect both yellow SIR connectors at base of steering column and install CPAs.
2. Install lefthand lower trim panel and position "AIR BG 1" fuse in instrument panel fuse block.
3. Place ignition switch in Run position and ensure "AIR BG 1" warning lamp flashes 7 times, then turns off. If lamp does not operate as specified, refer to "Passive Restraints" section of this manual.

CENTURY, CUTLASS CIERA & CUTLASS CRUISER

1. Place ignition switch in Lock position and remove key.
2. Connect yellow two-way SIR electrical connector, then install Connector Position Assurance (CPA).
3. Install left sound insulator. **Install courtesy lamp to sound insulator, if applicable.**
4. Install SIR or AIR BAG fuse into fuse block, the turn ignition switch to Run position and ensure AIR BAG warning lamp flashes 7 times and then turns off. If warning lamp does not operate as specified, refer to "Passive Restraints." section of this manual.

CORVETTE

1992–93

1. **On models with passenger air bag,** connect CPA and yellow 2-way connector to passenger inflator pigtail, then install righthand sound insulator.
2. **On all models,** connect yellow two-way SIR electrical connector, then install Connector Position Assurance (CPA).
3. Install left sound insulator. **Install courtesy lamp to sound insulator, if applicable.**
4. Install SIR fuse to fuse block, turn ignition switch to Run position and ensure "Inflatable Restraint" lamp flashes 7 to 9 times, then turns off.

1994–95

1. Turn ignition key to the Lock position.
2. Connect both yellow SIR connectors and corresponding CPAs located near base of steering column.
3. Install trim panel under steering column.
4. Install AIR BAG fuse into instrument panel fuse block.
5. Turn ignition switch to the Run position and verify that the AIR BAG warning lamp flashes seven times and then turns off. If warning lamp does not operate as specified, refer to "Passive Restraints" section of this manual.

CUTLASS SUPREME & REGAL

1992–94

1. Turn ignition switch to the Lock position and remove key.
2. Connect Connector Position Assurance (CPA) and yellow 2-way connector at base of steering column.
3. Install trim panel under steering column.
4. Install "AR BG 1" fuse into fuse block.
5. Turn ignition switch to the Run position and verify that the AIR BAG warning lamp flashes seven times and then turns off. If lamp does not operate as specified, refer to "Passive Restraints" section of this manual.

1995

1. Turn ignition switch to Lock position and remove key, then connect yellow 2-way connector and install CPA behind glove compartment door.
2. Install glove compartment door, then connect yellow 2-way connector and install CPA at base of steering column.
3. Install lefthand lower trim panel and fuse No. 21, then turn ignition switch to Run position and ensure "Air Bag" warning lamp flashes 7 times, then turns off.

DEVILLE & FLEETWOOD

1992–93

1. Connect yellow two-way SIR electrical connector, then install Connector Position Assurance (CPA).
2. Install left sound insulator. **Install courtesy lamp to sound insulator, if applicable.**
3. Install SIR fuse to fuse block, turn ignition switch to Run position and ensure "Inflatable Restraint" lamp flashes 7 to 9 times, then turns off. If lamp does not operate as specified, refer to "Passive Restraints" section of this manual.

1994–95

1. Turn ignition to the Lock position and remove key.
2. **On DeVille,** connect 2-way yellow connector and install CPA at base of steering column.
3. **On Fleetwood (RWD),** connect both yellow 2-way connectors and install CPAs at base of steering column.
4. **On all models,** install lefthand sound insulator.
5. **On Fleetwood (RWD),** install AIR BAG fuse into instrument panel fuse block.
6. **On 1995 DeVille,** connect yellow 2-way connector and install CPA through trap door in glove compartment, then connect yellow 2-way connector at base of steering column and install CPA.
7. **On all models,** turn ignition switch to the Run position and verify that AIR BAG warning lamp flashes seven times and then turns off. If warning lamp does not operate as specified, refer to "Passive Restraints" section of this manual.

AURORA, ELDORADO, RIVIERA, SEVILLE, TORONADO & TROFEO

1. **On models with passenger air bag,** connect CPA and yellow 2-way connector to passenger inflator pigtail, then install righthand sound insulator.
2. **On all models,** connect yellow two-way SIR electrical connector, then install Connector Position Assurance (CPA).
3. Install left sound insulator. **Install courtesy lamp to sound insulator, if applicable.**
4. Install SIR fuse to fuse block, turn ignition switch to Run position and ensure "Inflatable Restraint" lamp flashes 7 to 9 times, then turns off.

GRAND PRIX, LUMINA & MONTE CARLO

1. Turn ignition switch to the Lock position and remove key.
2. Open glove compartment door and connect yellow 2-way connector and Connector Position Assurance (CPA).
3. Connect yellow 2-way connector and Connector Position Assurance (CPA) at base of steering column.
4. Install trim panel under steering column.
5. Install AIR BAG fuse into instrument panel fuse block.
6. Turn ignition switch to the Run position and verify that the INFLATABLE RESTRAINT warning lamp flashes seven times and then turns off. If lamp does not operate as specified, refer to "Passive Restraints" section of this manual.

METRO

1. Turn ignition switch to Lock position.
2. Connect yellow two-way SIR electrical connector inside inflator module housing, then install Connector Position Assurance (CPA).
3. Install SIR IG fuse into SIR fuse block, then the rear plastic access cover onto inflator module housing.
4. Turn ignition switch to Run position and ensure "Inflatable Restraint" lamp flashes 7 to 9 times and then turns off.

PRIZM

1. Turn ignition switch to Lock position.
2. **On models with passenger air bag,** connect passenger inflator module 2-way connector and secure with CPA.
3. **On all models,** connect lower steering column yellow two-cavity connector and secure with CPA.
4. Install IGN and CIG & RADIO fuses.
5. Turn ignition switch to ACC or On positions and verify that the air bag indicator illuminates steady for approximately six seconds and then turns off.

STORM

1. Turn ignition switch to Off position, then connect orange three-way connector at the base of the steering column.
2. Connect lap cooler air duct to knee bolster, then install knee bolster.
3. **Torque** knee bolster bolts and nuts to 89 inch lbs.
4. Install hood latch release handle to knee bolster.
5. Connect cigar lighter electrical connector, then snap cigar lighter bezel into place on instrument panel.
6. Connect switch bezel electrical connectors, then snap switch bezel into place on instrument panel.

SATURN

1. Turn ignition switch to Off position.
2. Connect yellow two-way SIR connector at base of steering column and install Connector Position Assurance (CPA) device to connector.
3. Install air bag fuse.
4. Turn ignition switch to Run position. Ensure "Air Bag" telltale lamp flashes seven times, then remains off.

SERVICE REMINDER & WARNING LAMP RESET PROCEDURES

TABLE OF CONTENTS

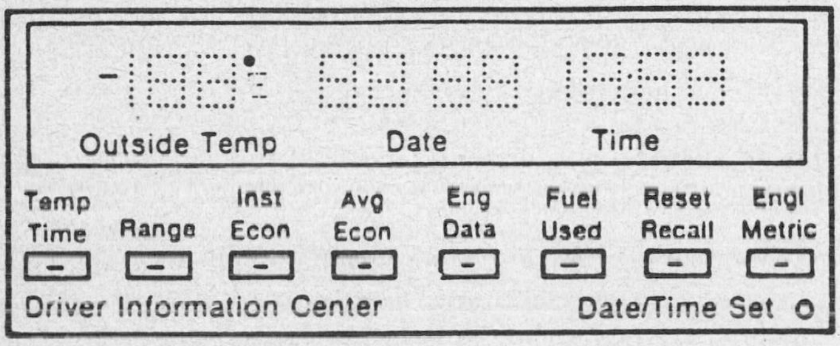

Outside Temp
Date
Time
Temp Time
Range
Inst Econ
Avg Econ
Eng Data
Fuel Used
Reset Recall
Engl Metric
Driver Information Center
Date/Time Set

Fig. 1 Driver Information Center. 1986–92 Cadillac Eldorado & Seville

ANTI-LOCK WARNING LAMP

This lamp will be illuminated when the ignition switch is placed in the ON position. The lamp may be illuminated for as long as 30 seconds as a bulb and system check. If lamp remains illuminated or comes on while operating the vehicle, a problem in the anti-lock brake system is indicated. When lamp is illuminated, place ignition switch in OFF position, then restart engine. If lamp still remains illuminated, the anti-lock brake system should be serviced. The brake system will remain functional, but without the anti-lock function. After servicing the anti-lock brake system the lamp will automatically reset. On some models it may be necessary to operate vehicle at a speed over 18 MPH to reset lamp.

AIR BAG WARNING LAMP

On models equipped with an air bag system, if the air bag warning lamp illuminates and stays on, diagnosis and repair of the air bag system will be necessary to reset the lamp.

CHANGE OIL OR CHANGE OIL NOW MESSAGE

CADILLAC

When the engine oil life index has reached zero, the Change Engine Oil message will be indicated on the Driver Information Display. After performing the engine oil change, the engine Oil Life Index may be reset as follows:

1992–95 Eldorado & Seville

Press the INFORMATION button until oil life index is displayed, then press STORE/RECALL until oil life index resets to 100 (approximately five seconds).

1993–95 DeVille & Sixty Special

Reset the Engine Oil Life Index (EOLI) after each oil change by pressing the RANGE and RESET keys on the Fuel Data Center for 5-50 seconds. The "Change Oil Soon" lamp will flash four times to indicate that the index has been reset.

Fleetwood (RWD)

1. Turn ignition switch to On position, without starting engine.
2. Press accelerator pedal to wide open throttle (WOT) position and release three times within five seconds.
3. If "Change Oil" warning indicator goes out, system has been reset.
4. If "Change Oil" warning indicator does not reset, turn ignition switch Off and repeat procedure.

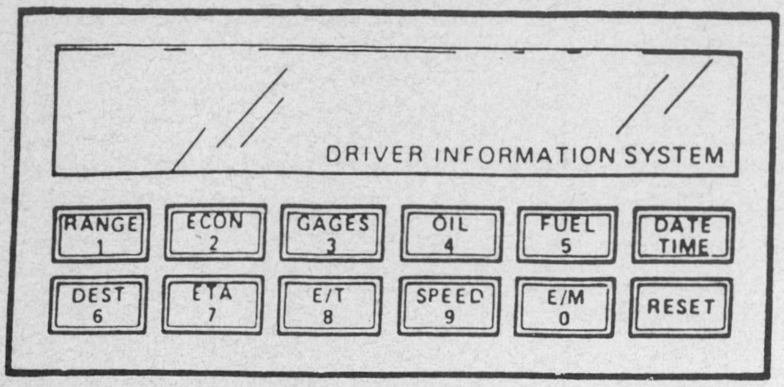
DRIVER INFORMATION SYSTEM
RANGE 1
ECON 2
GAGES 3
OIL 4
FUEL 5
DATE TIME
DEST 6
ETA 7
E/T 8
SPEED 9
E/M 0
RESET

Fig. 2 Driver Information Center. 1988–91 Oldsmobile except Toronado

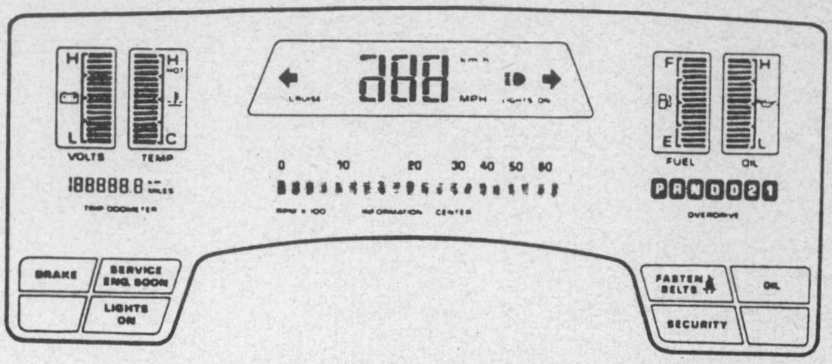
VOLTS
TEMP
MPH
FUEL
OIL
BRAKE
SERVICE ENG. SOON
LIGHTS ON
FASTEN BELTS
SECURITY

Fig. 3 Information Center. 1986–89 Oldsmobile Toronado

OLDSMOBILE

Except Toronado

When the engine oil life index has reached 10 or less, the Driver Information System display will indicate distance to oil change and sound a beep, when ignition switch is placed in the Run or Accessory position for the first time each day. When the engine oil life index has reached 0, the Driver Information System display will indicate Change Oil Now and sound a beep, when ignition switch is placed in the Run or Accessory position for the first time each day. After engine oil change has been performed, the oil life index may be reset by depressing and holding the Oil and Reset buttons for approximately 5 seconds, **Fig. 2.**

1986–89 Toronado

When the engine oil life index has reached 0, the Information System display will indicate Change Oil. After engine oil change has been performed, the oil life index may be reset by depressing and holding the Engine Data and Gauge buttons until Oil Index 100 message appears in Information Display panel, **Fig. 3.**

1990–92 Toronado

When the engine oil life index has reached 0, the Information System display will indicate Change Oil. After engine oil change has been performed, the oil life index may be reset by depressing and holding the reset button for at least five seconds.

Aurora, 1992–95 Eighty-Eight & Ninety-Eight

When the engine oil life index has reached 10 or less, the Driver Information System display will indicate distance to oil change and sound a beep when the ignition switch is placed in the RUN or ACC position for the first time each day. When the engine oil life index has reached zero, the Driver Information System display will indicate "Change Oil Now" and sound a beep, when ignition switch is placed in the RUN or ACC position for the first time each day. After engine oil change has been performed, the oil life index may be reset as follows:

1. **On Aurora, 1992-93 Eighty-Eight & Ninety Eight,** depress the TEST button and release.
2. Depress OIL button and release.
3. **On 1994-95 Eighty-Eight & Ninety-Eight,** select OIL menu by depressing mode button.
4. **On all models,** depress and hold the RESET button for approximately seven seconds.

BUICK

1992–95 LeSabre & Park Avenue

The reset button is located under the passenger side of the instrument panel. With the ignition in the ON position, but the engine not started, use a pencil to push reset button, holding it for five seconds. After this, the "Change Oil Soon" light will flash four times. This indicates that the Oil Life Monitor System has acknowledged the oil change.

PONTIAC

6000 & Bonneville

After changing engine oil and filter, if necessary, reset service interval indicator by depressing and releasing the service reminder button until the desired item is displayed. When the desired item is displayed, do not release service reminder button. After button has been depressed for approximately 10 seconds, the service interval mileage display will begin to count down in 500 mile intervals. When desired service interval mileage is reached, release button. The service interval reminder indicates miles to service, not miles from last service.

CHEVROLET

1992–95 Corvette

1. Turn ignition key to On position, without starting engine.
2. Press ENG MET button on the trip monitor and release, then press and release again within five seconds.
3. Within five seconds of step 2, press and hold GAUGES button on trip monitor. "Change Oil" lamp will flash.
4. Hold GAUGES button until "Change Oil" lamp stops flashing and goes out.
5. When light goes out, the engine oil life monitor is reset. If it does not reset, turn ignition switch Off and repeat procedure.

CHECK ENGINE INDICATOR LAMP (DIESEL ENGINE)

MODELS w/DIESEL ELECTRONIC CONTROL SYSTEM

The check engine lamp will be illuminated when the ignition switch is placed in the On position. When the engine is started, the lamp should go off. If the lamp remains On after the engine is started, the self diagnosis system has detected a problem and has stored a code in the system Electronic Control Module (ECM). After diagnosis and repair, the ECM memory can be cleared of codes when the ignition switch has been placed in the Off position. To clear codes, disconnect battery ground cable for approximately 30 seconds. It should be noted, when battery ground cable is disconnected to clear codes, components such as clocks, electronically tuned radios etc., will have to be reset.

CHECK ENGINE OR SERVICE NOW/SOON ENGINE INDICATOR LAMPS (GASOLINE ENGINES w/ELECTRONIC ENGINE CONTROLS OR EFI)

EXCEPT CHEVROLET SPECTRUM & SPRINT, GEO & PONTIAC LEMANS

The check engine lamp will be illuminated when the ignition switch is placed in the On position. When the engine is started, the lamp should go off. If the lamp remains On for 10 seconds or constantly after the engine is started, the self diagnosis system has detected a problem and has stored a code in the system Electronic Control Module (ECM). After diagnosis and repair, the ECM memory can be cleared of codes as follows:

On models except Cadillac with DEFI and 1986-88 Buick Reatta/Riviera and Oldsmobile Toronado/Trofeo, remove the ECM fuse or disconnect the battery ground cable for approximately 30 seconds, with ignition switch in the Off position. It should be noted, if battery ground cable is disconnected to clear codes, components such as clocks, electronically tuned radios etc., will have to be reset.

On vehicle that are equipped as such, the ECM power feed is connected by a pigtail, inline fuse holder, at the positive battery terminal. To clear codes within the ECM system and protect the components that need resetting, disconnect the inline fuse.

On 1980-85 Cadillac models with DEFI engines, depress Electronic Climate Control Off and Hi buttons to clear codes. On 1986-92 Cadillac DeVille and Fleetwood models, depress Off and Lo button on the Electronic Climate Control to clear stored BCM codes. Depress Off and Hi to clear stored ECM codes.

On Cadillac Eldorado and Seville and 1986-88 Buick Reatta/Riviera and Oldsmobile Toronado/Trofeo models, the stored codes are cleared during the self-diagnostic procedure.

CHEVROLET SPECTRUM

The check engine lamp will be illuminated when the ignition switch is in the On position with engine not operating. When engine is started, the Check Engine lamp should go off. If lamp remains on, a code has been stored by the Electronic Control Module (ECM). After diagnosis and repair, place ignition switch in Off position, then clear codes stored in the ECM memory by removing the Emission or ECM fuse, located in the fuse box under the instrument panel on the lefthand side, for approximately 10 seconds.

CHEVROLET SPRINT

1987–88 Models Less Turbo Engine

The check engine lamp will be illuminated when the ignition switch is in the On position with engine not operating. When engine is started, the Check Engine lamp should go off. If lamp remains on, a code has been stored by the Electronic Control Module (ECM) memory. After diagnosis and repair, with diagnosis switch in Off position, start engine and allow to reach operating temperature. After engine has reached operating temperature, the Check Engine lamp should be off while engine is operating.

1987–88 Models w/Turbo Engine

The check engine lamp will be illuminated when the ignition switch is in the On position with engine not operating. When engine is started, the Check Engine lamp should go off. If lamp remains on, a code has been stored by the Electronic Control Module (ECM) memory. After diagnosis and repair, place ignition switch in Off position, then clear codes stored in the ECM memory by disconnecting the battery ground cable, for approximately 20 seconds.

GEO METRO

The check engine lamp will be illuminated when the ignition switch is in the On position with engine not operating. When engine is started, the Check Engine lamp should go off. If lamp remains on, a code has been stored by the Electronic Control Module (ECM) memory. After diagnosis and repair, place ignition switch in Off position, then clear codes stored in the ECM memory by disconnecting the battery ground cable, for approximately 20 seconds.

GEO PRIZM

The check engine lamp will be illuminated when the ignition switch is in the On position with engine not operating. When engine is started, the Check Engine lamp should go off. If lamp remains on, a code has been stored by the Electronic Unit (ECU) memory. After diagnosis and repair, place ignition switch in Off position, then clear codes stored in the ECU memory by removing the Stop Fuse. The Stop fuse is located in a fuse panel, in the passenger compartment, on driver's side, behind kick panel, **Fig. 4.** The fuse must be removed for 10 seconds or longer, depending on ambient temperature. The lower the ambient temperature, the longer the fuse will have to be removed.

GEO STORM

The check engine lamp will be illuminated when the ignition switch is in the On position with engine not operating. When engine is started, the Check Engine lamp should go off. If lamp remains on, a code has been stored by the Electronic Control Module (ECM) memory. After diagnosis and repair, place ignition switch in Off position, then clear codes stored in the ECM memory by disconnecting the battery ground cable for approximately 30 seconds.

GEO SPECTRUM

The check engine lamp will be illuminated when the ignition switch is in the On position with engine not operating. When engine is started, the Check Engine lamp should go off. If lamp remains on, a code has been stored by the Electronic Control Module (ECM) memory. After diagnosis and repair, place ignition switch in Off position, then clear codes stored in the ECM memory by disconnecting the battery ground cable for approximately 30 seconds.

PONTIAC LEMANS

The check engine lamp will be illuminated when the ignition switch is placed in the On position. When the engine is started, them should go off. If the lamp remains On for 10 seconds or constantly after the engine is started, the self diagnosis system has detected a problem and has stored a code in the system Electronic Control Module (ECM). After diagnosis and repair, the ECM memory can be cleared of codes, by disconnecting battery ground cable for 10 seconds, with ignition switch in the off position.

CHECK INFO CENTER WARNING LAMP

1986–92 CADILLAC ELDORADO & SEVILLE

This lamp will be illuminated for a few seconds when the ignition switch is placed in the On position as a bulb check. If lamp remains illuminated, a message is store in the Driver Information Center. Refer to "Driver Information Center."

CHOKE OR OIL/CHOKE WARNING LAMP

MODELS WITH CARBURETED ENGINE

On models less gauges, the oil/choke warning indicator lamp should be illuminated when the ignition switch is in the Run or Start position. When the engine is started, the choke warning indicator lamp should go off. If the lamp fails to illuminate with ignition switch in Run or Start position with engine not operating, a burned bulb or fuse or defect in choke electrical system is indicated. If lamp remains on after engine has been started, a problem in the engine oil pressure system or electrical choke system exist.

On models equipped with gauges, the choke warning indicator lamp should be illuminated when the ignition switch is in the Run or Start position. When the engine is started, the choke warning indicator lamp should go off. If fails to illuminate with ignition switch in Run or Start position with engine not operating, a burnt out bulb or fuse or defect in choke electrical system is indicated. If lamp remains on after engine has been started, a problem in the alternator circuit is indicated.

After service has been completed, the lamp operation should return to normal.

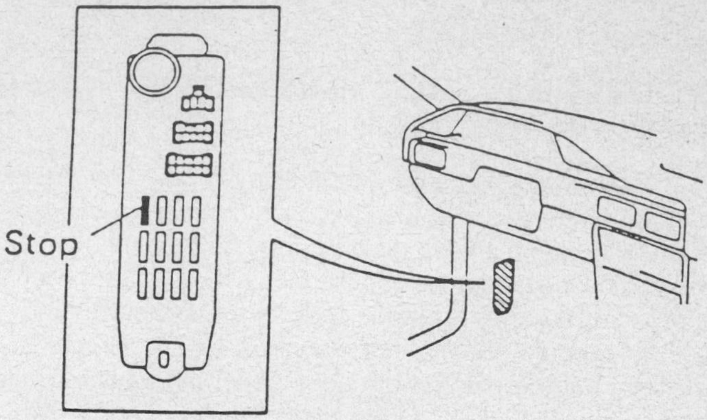
Stop

Fig. 4 Stop fuse location. Geo Prizm

DRIVER INFORMATION CENTER

CADILLAC

1986–88 Cadillac Eldorado & Seville

This system, **Fig. 1,** incorporates a warning lamp, located on the instrument cluster, that is illuminated when the ignition switch is in the On position. After a few seconds the lamp should go off, unless a message in The Driver Information System is present. The driver information center will display the following messages:

A/C Overheated–A/C Compressor Off–This message is displayed when excessive pressure in the refrigerant system is encountered. When this condition is encountered, the A/C compressor clutch will be de-energized and cool air will not be delivered to the vehicle interior. The message will continue to appear and the A/C compressor clutch will continue to be de-energized until the system pressure returns to normal range. If this message frequently appears, the A/C system should be serviced.

A/C Sensor Fault–This message will be displayed when the sensor controlling A/C compressor clutch cycling has failed. When this sensor has failed, the A/C compressor will not operate and the A/C system will emit warmer air. After servicing system and replacing sensor, the display message will be cancelled.

Battery Volts High–This message will appear when the charging system is overcharging the battery. After completing charging system diagnosis and repair, the message will be cancelled when battery voltage returns to 11.5 to 15.5 volts with engine operating. Battery voltage can be displayed on the Drive Information Center Display by depressing the Eng-Data button three times.

Battery Volts Low—If this message is displayed while driving the vehicle or after vehicle has been started, a problem in the charging system is present or battery has been drained. After diagnosing charging system or electrical system for cause of battery drain, the message will be cancelled when engine is operating and battery voltage is between 11.5 to 15.5 volts. Battery voltage can be displayed on the Drive Information Center Display by depressing the Eng-Data button three times.

Engine Hot—A/C Compressor Off—This message will appear when A/C system is on Auto or Defrost and engine coolant temperature is excessive. The A/C compressor clutch will be automatically de-energized when excessive engine coolant temperatures are encountered. When engine coolant temperature returns to normal, the A/C compressor clutch will be energized and the message on the display will be cancelled.

Front Or Rear Door Ajar—This message will appear when the transmission selector lever is moved out of the Park position and a door is not properly closed. The message can be cancelled by properly closing the indicated door.

Fuel Level Very Low—When low fuel level conditions are encountered this message will appear. To cancel message, add fuel.

Headlamps Or Parking Lamps On—This message will be displayed when the headlamp switch is On, vehicle is moving and the sensed level of outside light indicates that headlamps should not be illuminated. This message may be cancelled by placing the headlamp switch in the Off position.

Low A/C Refrigerant—A/C Compressor Off—This message will be displayed when the A/C system detects a refrigerant charge low enough to cause compressor damage. When this condition is encountered, the A/C compressor clutch is de-energized and the A/C system is switched from Auto to Econ. The system will remain in Econ until necessary repairs are made and system is recharged. After completing necessary repairs and recharging the system, A/C system operation will return to normal and the message on the display will be cancelled.

Low A/C Refrigerant—Service A/C Soon—This message will be displayed when the A/C system detects that refrigerant charge is low enough to cause a reduction in cooling capacity. This message will be displayed until system has been recharged.

Low Washer Fluid—This message will appear when windshield washer fluid level is low. To cancel message, refill windshield washer fluid reservoir.

Service Electrical System—This message will appear when a problem in the charging system is present. After repairing charging system, the message will be automatically cancelled.

Service Now Or Service Soon—This message will be displayed when a problem in one the engine monitored systems is present. After diagnosis and repair the message will be automatically cancelled.

System Problem—Service Car Soon—This message will be displayed when one or more of the vehicle computers supplying information to the Driver Information Center become defective. After diagnosis and repair of the defective computer, the message will be automatically cancelled.

Theft System Problem/Car May Not Start—This message will appear when the vehicle security system senses an improper ignition key has been placed in the ignition switch. After removal of key from ignition switch, the Driver Information Center display will indicate "Wait 3 Minutes," "Wait 2 Minutes," Wait 1 Minute" and then "Start Car." When the "Start Car" message appears, insert ignition key and attempt to start vehicle. If message appears again, check ignition key for damage and replace as necessary. If key appears to be satisfactory, clean pellet contacts with a soft cloth and attempt to restart vehicle.

Trunk Open—This message will appear when the ignition switch is the Run position and the trunk is not properly closed. The message can be cancelled by properly closing the trunk.

1989–92 Cadillac Eldorado & Seville

This system incorporates a warning lamp, located on the instrument cluster, that is illuminated when the ignition switch is in the On position. After a few seconds the lamp should go off, unless a message in The Driver Information System is present. The driver information center will display the following messages:

A/C Overheated—A/C Compressor Off—This message is displayed when excessive pressure in the refrigerant system is encountered. When this condition is encountered, the A/C Compressor clutch will be de-energized and cool air will not be delivered to the vehicle interior. The message will continue to appear and the A/C compressor clutch will continue to be de-energized until the system pressure returns to normal range. If this message frequently appears, the A/C system should be serviced.

A/C Sensor Fault—This message will be displayed when the sensor controlling A/C compressor clutch cycling has failed. When this sensor has failed, the A/C compressor will not operate and the A/C system will emit warmer air. After servicing system and replacing sensor, the display message will be cancelled.

Battery Volts High—This message will appear when the charging sys tem is overcharging the battery. After completing charging system diagnosis and repair, the message will be cancelled when battery voltage returns to 11.5 to 15.5 volts with engine operating. Battery voltage can be displayed on the Drive Information Center Display by depressing the Eng-Data button three times.

Battery Volts Low—If this message is displayed while driving the vehicle or after vehicle has been started, a problem in the charging system is present or battery has been drained. After diagnosing charging system or electrical system for cause of battery drain, the message will be cancelled when engine is operating and battery voltage is between 11.5 to 15.5 volts. Battery voltage can be displayed on the Drive Information Center Display by depressing the Eng-Data button three times.

Change Engine Oil—When the engine oil life index has

reached 0, the Change Engine Oil message will be indicated. After performing the engine oil change, the engine Oil Life Index may be reset by depressing and holding the Engine Data and Range buttons for at least 5 seconds

Cooling Fan Fault—This message will appear when the engine cooling fan system inoperative. After repairing cooling fan system the message will be automatically cancelled.

Engine Hot—A/C Compressor Off—This message will appear when A/C system is Auto or Defrost and engine coolant temperature is excessive. The A/C compressor clutch will be automatically de-energized when excessive engine coolant temperatures are encountered. When engine coolant temperature returns to normal, the A/C compressor clutch will be energized and the message on the display will be cancelled.

Front Or Rear Door Ajar—This message will appear when the transmission selector lever is moved out of the Park position and a door is not properly closed. The message can be cancelled by properly closing the indicated door.

Fuel Level Very Low—When low fuel level conditions are encountered this message will appear. To cancel message, add fuel.

Gear Select Problem—This message will appear if a problem in the transaxle gear select system is encountered while operating vehicle. After performing necessary service, the message will automatically be cancelled.

Headlamps Or Parking Lamps On—This message will be displayed when the headlamp switch is On, vehicle is moving and the sensed level of outside light indicates that headlamps should not be illuminated. This message may be cancelled by placing the headlamp switch in the Off position.

Headlamps Suggested—This message will be displayed when the Twilight Sentinel is in the Off position, vehicle is moving and the sensed level of outside light indicates that headlamps should be illuminated. This message may be cancelled by activating the Twilight Sentinel System.

Low A/C Refrigerant—A/C Compressor Off—This message will be displayed when the A/C system detects a refrigerant charge low enough to cause compressor damage. When this condition is encountered, the A/C compressor clutch is de-energized and the A/C system is switched from Auto to Econ. The system will remain in Econ until necessary repairs are made and system is recharged. After completing necessary repairs and recharging the system, A/C system operation will return to normal and the message on the display will be cancelled.

Low A/C Refrigerant—Service A/C Soon—This message will be displayed when the A/C system detects that refrigerant charge is low enough to cause a reduction in cooling capacity. This message will be displayed until system has been recharged.

Low Washer Fluid—This message will appear when windshield washer fluid level is low. To cancel message, refill windshield washer fluid reservoir.

Oil Life Index—The oil life index is a series of numerals ranging from 0 to 100. The 100 is indicated when engine oil has been drained and replacement engine oil has been installed. The 0 is an indication that the engine oil should be changed. The oil life index is accessed by depressing the Engine Data button four times.

Service Electrical System—This message will appear when a problem in the charging system is present. After repairing charging system, the message will be automatically cancelled.

Set Timing Mode—This message will appear if ignition timing is improperly set. After performing necessary service, the message will be automatically cancelled.

Starting Disabled/Due to Theft System/Remove Ignition Key—This message is an indication of a problem in the vehicle security system that may prohibit the vehicle from being restarted after the ignition switch has been placed in the Off position. After servicing the vehicle security system the message will be automatically cancelled.

System Ok—This message will be displayed for approximately 5 seconds after ignition switch has been placed in the On position, unless a problem in the system has been detected. After approximately 5 seconds the display will return to the last display function selected.

System Problem—Service Car Soon—This message will be displayed when one or more of the vehicle computers supplying information to the Driver Information Center become defective. After diagnosis and repair of the defective computer, the message will be automatically cancelled.

Theft System Problem/Car May Not Start—This message will appear when the vehicle security system senses an improper ignition key has been placed in the ignition switch. After remove key from ignition switch, the Driver Information Center display will indicate "Wait 3 Minutes," "Wait 2 Minutes," Wait 1 Minute" and then "Start Car." When the "Start Car" message appears, insert ignition key and attempt to start vehicle. If message appears again, check ignition key for damage and replace as necessary. If key appears to be satisfactory, clean pellet contacts with a soft cloth and attempt to restart vehicle.

Trunk Open—This message will appear when the ignition switch is the Run position and the trunk is not properly closed. The message can be cancelled by properly closing the trunk.

OLDSMOBILE AURORA, 1992–93 EIGHTY-EIGHT & NINETY-EIGHT

The Driver Information Center Display, **Figs. 5 and 6,** is located on the instrument panel (Eighty-Eight models with digital cluster or Touring Sedan gauge cluster). It provides travel and performance information on the following:

1. **Date and Time**—This information is displayed for five seconds when ignition switch is turned On. The DT/TM button may be pressed at any time to display current date and time.
2. **Fuel Economy**—The ECON button displays average fuel economy.
3. **Remaining Fuel/Fuel Used**—Depressing FUEL button displays amount of fuel used since RESET button was last pressed. Depressing FUEL button a second time displays amount of fuel remaining.

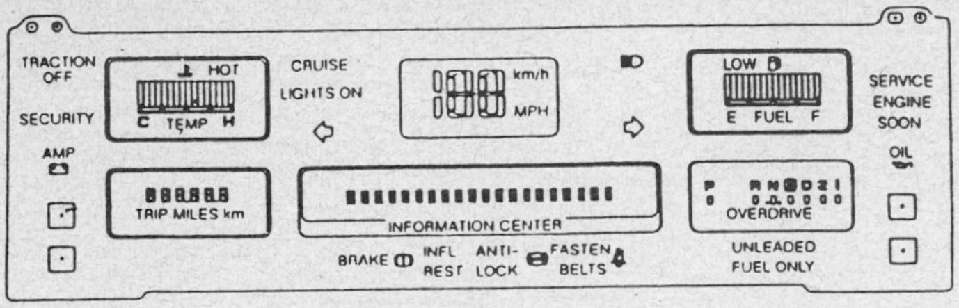
TRACTION OFF
HOT
C TEMP H
SECURITY
AMP
CRUISE
LIGHTS ON
km/h
MPH
LOW
E FUEL F
SERVICE ENGINE SOON
OIL
TRIP MILES km
INFORMATION CENTER
OVERDRIVE
BRAKE
INFL REST
ANTI-LOCK
FASTEN BELTS
UNLEADED FUEL ONLY

Fig. 5 Driver Information Center. 1992–93 Eighty-Eight & Ninety-Eight

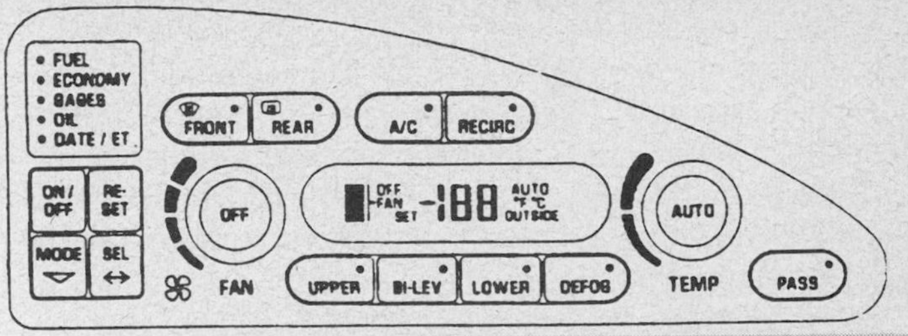
FUEL
ECONOMY
GAGES
OIL
DATE / ET
FRONT
REAR
A/C
RECIRC
ON/ OFF
RE-SET
MODE
SEL
OFF
AUTO
OUTSIDE
FAN
UPPER
BI-LEV
LOWER
DEFOG
TEMP
PASS

Fig. 7 Driver Information Center. 1994–95 Eighty-Eight & Ninety-Eight

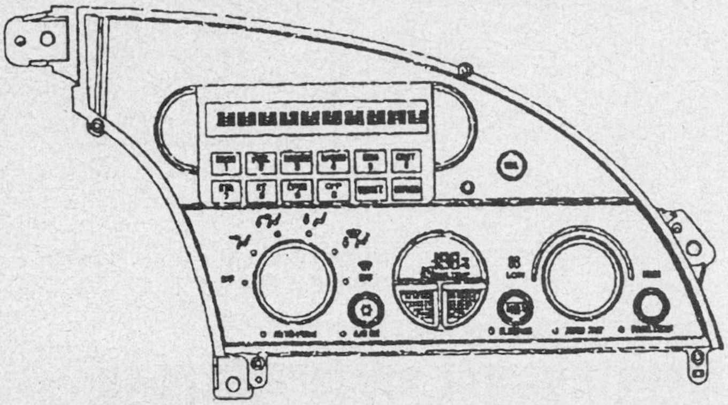

Fig. 6 Driver Information Center. Aurora

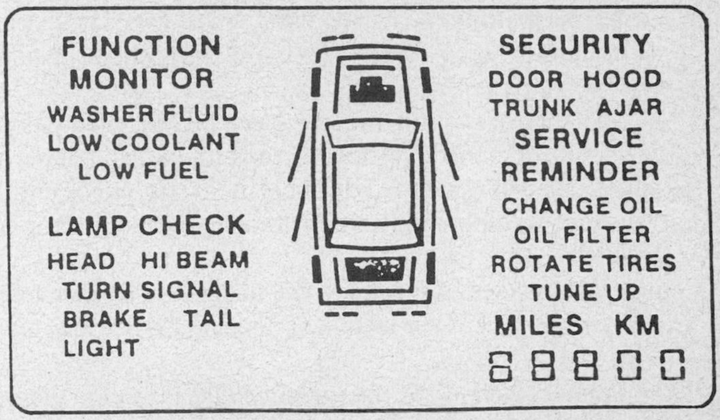
FUNCTION MONITOR
WASHER FLUID
LOW COOLANT
LOW FUEL
LAMP CHECK
HEAD HI BEAM
TURN SIGNAL
BRAKE TAIL
LIGHT
SECURITY
DOOR HOOD
TRUNK AJAR
SERVICE REMINDER
CHANGE OIL
OIL FILTER
ROTATE TIRES
TUNE UP
MILES KM
88800

Fig. 8 Driver Information Center. 1988–90 Pontiac 6000 STE & Bonneville SSE

4. **Fuel Range**—Depress RANGE to display distance that may be driven before refueling. To display amount of fuel used from a specific starting point, press FUEL then RESET.
5. **Average Speed**—Depress SPEED to display average speed. To reset average speed, press SPEED then RESET.
6. **Remaining Oil Life and Oil Change Information**—The OIL button displays information on oil life. Refer to "Change Oil Or Change Oil Now Message" for reset procedure.
7. **Engine Coolant Temperature, Oil Pressure, Battery Voltage and Tachometer**—Depressing GAGES once displays coolant temperature. Pressing GAGES a second time displays oil pressure. Pressing GAGES a third time displays battery voltage and pressing GAGES a fourth time will display tachometer RPM.
8. **Distance To Destination**—Depress DEST then RESET and enter length of trip. Display will then count backwards to zero distance remaining. When display reaches zero, "Trip Complete" message is displayed. This message will clear when the TEST button is pressed or the ignition switch is turned Off.
9. **Estimated Time Of Arrival**—After entering distance to destination, press ETA button to display time remaining to destination (based on average speed).
10. **Elapsed Time**—Depressing the E/T button activates a stopwatch that records up to 100 hours.

1994–95 EIGHTY-EIGHT & NINETY EIGHT

The Driver Information Center display, **Fig. 7**, is located on the instrument panel. When the ignition switch is placed in the On position, the display will go through a system check while the "Monitored Systems OK" message is displayed. If no problems are detected, the screen returns to the mode displayed before the engine was turned off.

There are four buttons that control the functions of the Driver Information Center:

1. The MODE button, when pressed, cycles through a series of displays in the following order:
   a. ECON—Average fuel economy and instantaneous fuel economy.
   b. FUEL—Amount of fuel used since last fuel-used reset, and fuel remaining.
   c. RANGE—Fuel range and low fuel range.
   d. OIL—Oil life index and next required oil change.
   e. GAGES—Oil pressure, tachometer and battery voltage information.
   f. ET—Elapsed time since last reset.
   g. DT/TM—Date and Time.
2. The ON/OFF button is used to input numbers and to blank out the display.
3. The RESET button is used with other buttons to reset the system. Depressing this button once enters the reset mode. Pressing this button a second time aborts the reset.
4. The SEL button is used to select different displays within a specific mode. For example, when the SEL button is depressed while in the GAGES mode, the display will cycle from oil pressure to battery voltage to tachometer.

PONTIAC 6000 & BONNEVILLE

The Driver Information Center Display, **Fig. 8**, is located on the instrument panel. When the ignition switch is placed in the On position, the display will go through a bulb check, in which the vehicle graph and message title will be displayed in sequence. After the sequence has been completed, all messages and vehicle graph will remain illuminated for approximately 2 seconds. After approximately 2 seconds, if all monitored systems are functioning properly, the message titles should go off and only the vehicle outline should be illuminated. If a problem in any of the monitored systems is present, the particular title for the monitored system will be illuminated and its approximate location on the vehicle graphic display will be illuminated. The following messages will be displayed:

1. **Function Monitor**—The coolant level, fuel level and windshield washer levels are monitored when ignition switch is the On position.
   a. Coolant Level—This message will be indicated when engine coolant level in the radiator drops below a pre-determined level. To cancel message, check cooling system, then add coolant to bring system to proper level.
   b. Fuel Level—This message will be indicated when fuel level is 5 gallons or less. To cancel message add fuel to fuel tank.
   c. Washer Fluid—This message will be indicated when windshield washer fluid is at about 40 of capacity. To cancel message, add washer fluid to reservoir.
2. **Lamp Check**—The headlamps, tail lamps, brake lamps and turn signal lamps will be checked whenever the lamp system is activated. To cancel this message, replace bulb or check and repair electrical system as necessary for lamp system indicated.
3. **Security**—Door, Hood Or Trunk Ajar are monitored. This message will appear when the indicated component is open or improperly closed. To cancel message, properly close indicated component.
4. **Service Reminder**—Oil change, oil filter change, engine tune-up and tire rotation intervals are monitored.
   a. After the bulb check sequence has been completed, the service interval can be checked by depressing the service reminder button. Depressing the button once will display the Change Oil indication and mileage remaining to service interval. Depressing the button a second time, will display the Change Oil Filter indication and mileage remaining to service interval. Depressing the button a third time will display the Rotate Tires and mileage to service interval. Depressing the button a fourth time will display Tune-Up indication and mileage to service interval.
   b. After completing the required service, reset service interval indicator by depressing and releasing the service reminder button until the desired item is displayed. When the desired item is displayed, do not release service reminder button. After button has been depressed for approximately 10 seconds, the service interval mileage display will begin to count down in 500 mile intervals. When desired service interval mileage is reached, release button. The service interval reminder indicates miles to service, not miles from last service.

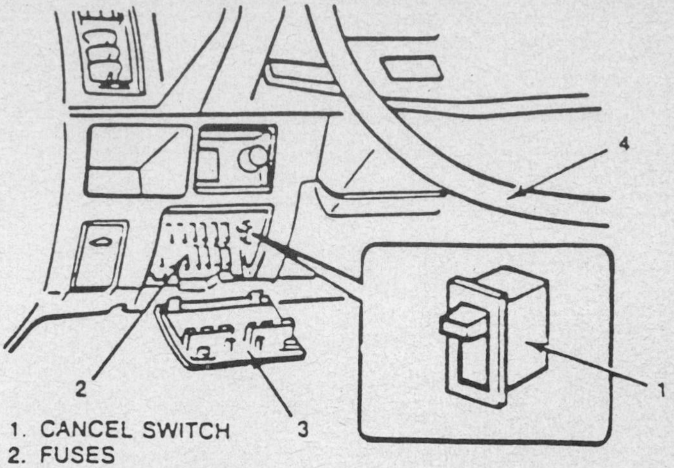
1
2
3
4

1. CANCEL SWITCH
2. FUSES
3. FUSE CASE COVER
4. STEERING WHEEL

Fig. 9 Oxygen sensor indicator lamp cancel switch. 1985–86 Chevrolet Sprint

EMISSION OR SENSOR MAINTENANCE REMINDER FLAG

1980 MODELS & 1981–83 CADILLAC LIMOUSINE & COMMERCIAL CHASSIS

At 30,000 mile intervals, a Emission or Sensor reminder flag, if equipped, will appear across the odometer to indicate the need for oxygen sensor replacement. After performing the required service, the flag must be reset for the next 30,000 mile interval.

On models except Cadillac, this is accomplished by gaining access to the speedometer head and removing the speedometer lens. Using a suitable pointed tool, rotate edge of flag wheel detents downward, until flag wheel can no longer be rotated. Flag wheel alignment mark should center in odometer.

On Cadillac models, remove lower steering column cover, then lightly pull sensor reset cable to reset flag. The sensor reset cable is located to the left of the speedometer cluster.

ENGINE CONTROL SYSTEM WARNING LAMP

1986–88 CADILLAC ELDORADO & SEVILLE

This lamp will be illuminated for a few seconds when the ignition switch is placed in On position as a bulb check. If lamp remains on, a problem in one of the emission control systems is indicated. The Driver Information Center should indicate a Service Soon or Service Now message. Refer to "Driver Information Center."

LOW COOLANT LAMP

This lamp will be illuminated when engine coolant level in the radiator drops below a pre-determined level. To turn lamp off, check cooling system, then add coolant to bring system to proper level.

LOW OIL LEVEL INDICATOR

The low oil ground is controlled by the PCM. To check for a low oil condition, the PCM checks the low oil level sensor after the ignition switch has been turned to the Off or Lock position. The PCM checks for a low oil condition 32 minutes after the ignition switch is turned off if the previous ignition cycle was less than 12 minutes.

LOW WASHER FLUID INDICATOR

The windshield washer solvent tank has a switch that closes when the washer solvent level becomes low, illuminating the "Low Washer Fluid" indicator.

OXYGEN SENSOR MAINTENANCE REMINDER LAMP

1985–86 CHEVROLET SPRINT

A Sensor lamp is located on the instrument panel to indicate proper operation of the oxygen sensor feedback circuit. Every 30,000 miles of vehicle operation, the lamp will begin to flash. When the lamp begins to flash, the feedback circuit should be checked and the lamp reset using the following procedure.

1. Ensure that ignition switch is off, remove fuse panel cover and move cancel switch to on position, **Fig. 9.**
2. Turn ignition switch to On position and observe Sensor lamp. If lamp does not light (without flashing), check for defective bulb or open feed circuit and repair as needed.
3. After illumination of lamp is confirmed, start engine and run until it reaches normal operating temperature.
4. Run engine at 1500-2000 RPM while observing lamp.
5. If lamp flashes, system is operating properly. If lamp does not flash, a problem in the Computer Controlled Emission Control System may be indicated.
6. After proper system operation has been verified, place cancel switch in off position to reset automatic indicator system.

SERVICE AIR COND LAMP

CADILLAC

This lamp will be illuminated when the A/C system detects a low refrigerant charge. The lamp will be illuminated for approximately 2 seconds after ignition switch has been placed in the On position as a bulb check.

If while operating vehicle, the lamp illuminates for approximately 60 seconds and then goes off, the refrigerant level is low enough to cause reduced cooling capacity. At this point the blower motor will increase speed to try to offset the loss in cooling capacity. The lamp will be automatically reset after system has been checked and refrigerant charge has been brought to proper level.

If lamp is illuminated for approximately 60 seconds after engine start up, the refrigerant charge may be low enough to cause A/C compressor damage. When this condition is encountered, the A/C compressor clutch is de-energized and the A/C system is switched from Auto to Econ. The system will remain in Econ until necessary repairs are made and system is recharged. After completing necessary repairs and recharging the system, A/C system operation will return to normal and the lamp will be automatically reset.

SERVICE ELECTRICAL SYSTEM LAMP

CADILLAC

This lamp will be illuminated when a problem in the charging system is present. The lamp will be illuminated during engine starting as a bulb check. If lamp is illuminated while engine is operating, the charging system should be checked. After repairing charging system, the lamp will be automatically reset.

WATER IN FUEL OR DRAIN FUEL FILTER WARNING LAMP

MODELS w/DIESEL ENGINE

The water in fuel indicator will be illuminated when excessive water has entered the fuel system. As the fuel filter becomes plugged, a low pressure sensor activates the lamp. The lamp will be illuminated during engine starting as a bulb check. Once the engine has started, the lamp should go off. If the lamp is illuminated intermittently, drain fuel filter. If lamp remains illuminated, drain fuel filter. If the lamp still remains on after fuel filter has been drained, replace fuel filter. If lamp is illuminated during high speed operation or during heavy acceleration, replace fuel filter. If after starting, the engine stalls and will not restart and lamp remains illuminated, check for plugged fuel filter or fuel lines. If this condition occurs immediately after refueling, check fuel tank for large concentration of water in fuel, and if necessary purge fuel tank and replace fuel filter. After performing the required service, the increased fuel pressure through the fuel filter will reset the water in fuel lamp.

VEHICLE LIFT POINTS

INDEX

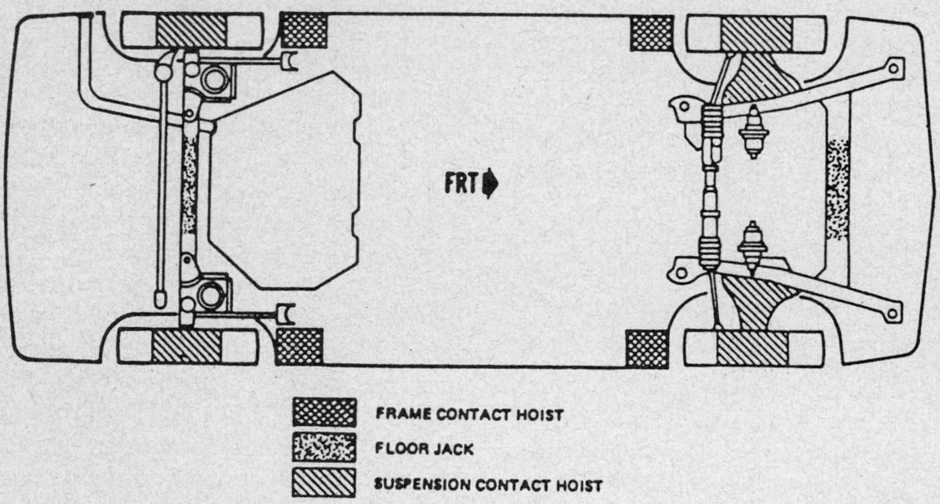

FRT
FRAME CONTACT HOIST
FLOOR JACK
SUSPENSION CONTACT HOIST

Fig. 1 Century, Cutlass Ciera, Cutlass Cruiser, 1992 Achieva, Grand Am & Skylark

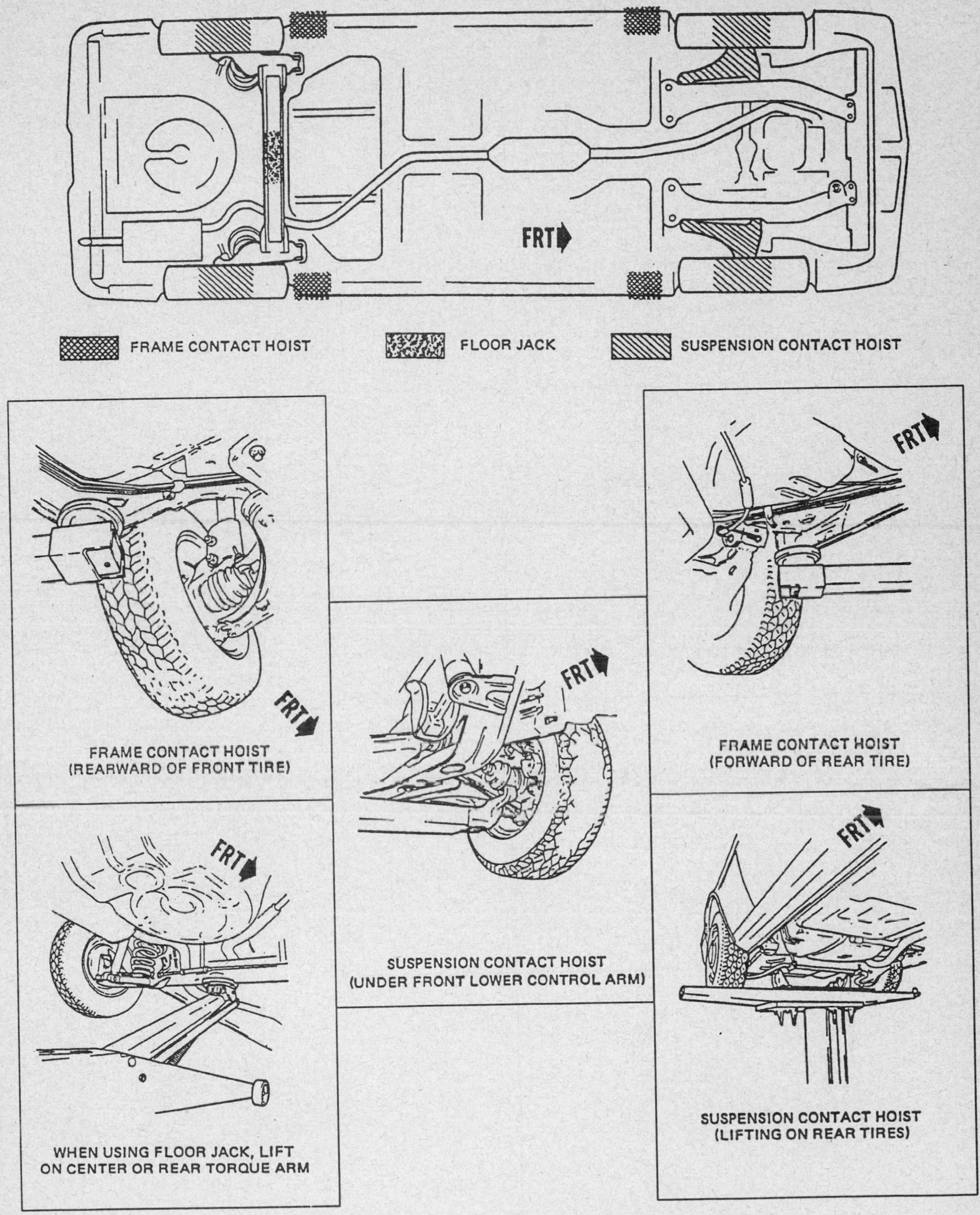
FRT
FRAME CONTACT HOIST
FLOOR JACK
SUSPENSION CONTACT HOIST
FRT
FRAME CONTACT HOIST
(REARWARD OF FRONT TIRE)
FRT
WHEN USING FLOOR JACK, LIFT
ON CENTER OR REAR TORQUE ARM
FRT
SUSPENSION CONTACT HOIST
(UNDER FRONT LOWER CONTROL ARM)
FRT
FRAME CONTACT HOIST
(FORWARD OF REAR TIRE)
FRT
SUSPENSION CONTACT HOIST
(LIFTING ON REAR TIRES)

Fig. 2 1993–95 Achieva, Beretta, Corsica, Grand Am & Skylark

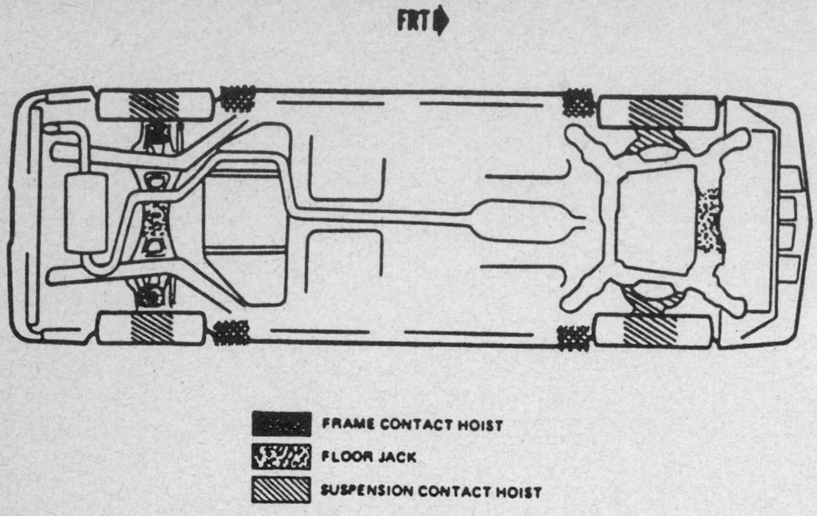
FRT
FRAME CONTACT HOIST
FLOOR JACK
SUSPENSION CONTACT HOIST

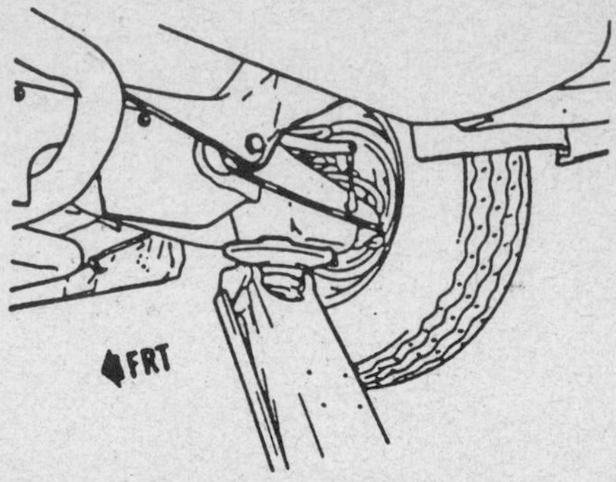
FRT
USING FLOOR JACK UNDER REAR CONTROL ARM

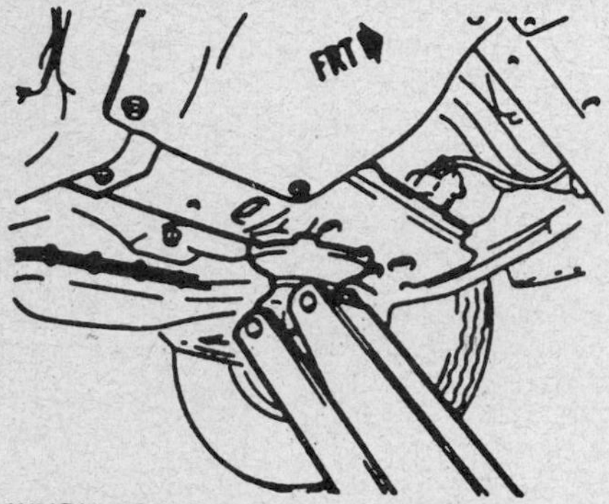
FRT
WHEN USING FLOOR JACK, LIFT ON CENTER OF FRONT CROSSMEMBER

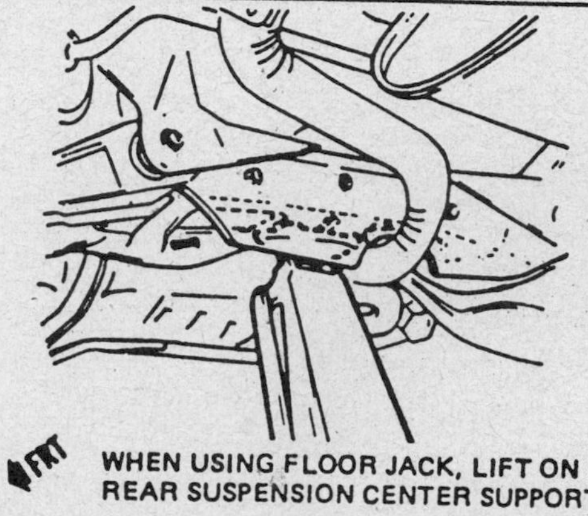
FRT
WHEN USING FLOOR JACK, LIFT ON REAR SUSPENSION CENTER SUPPORT

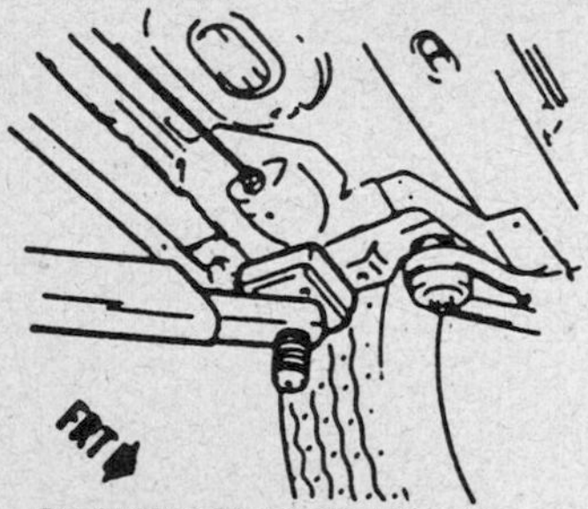
FRT
FRAME CONTACT HOIST (REARWARD OF FRONT TIRE)

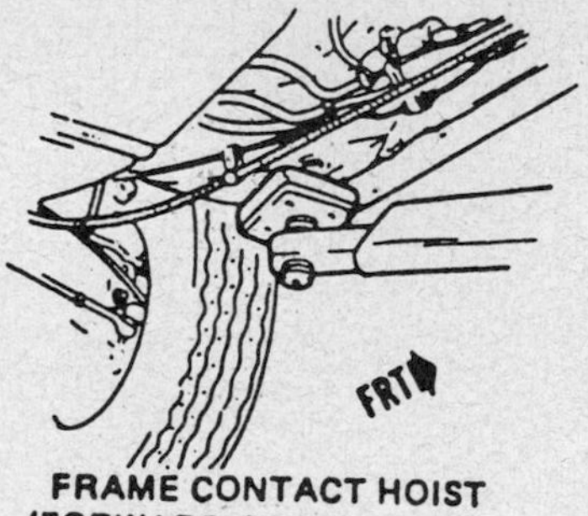
FRT
FRAME CONTACT HOIST (FORWARD OF REAR TIRE)

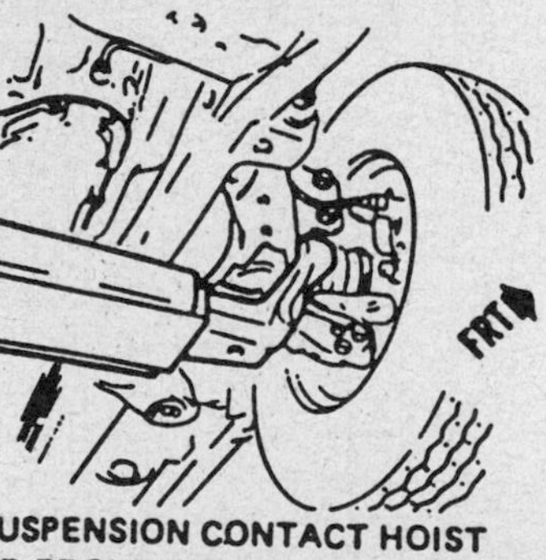
FRT
SUSPENSION CONTACT HOIST (UNDER FRONT LOWER CONTROL ARM)

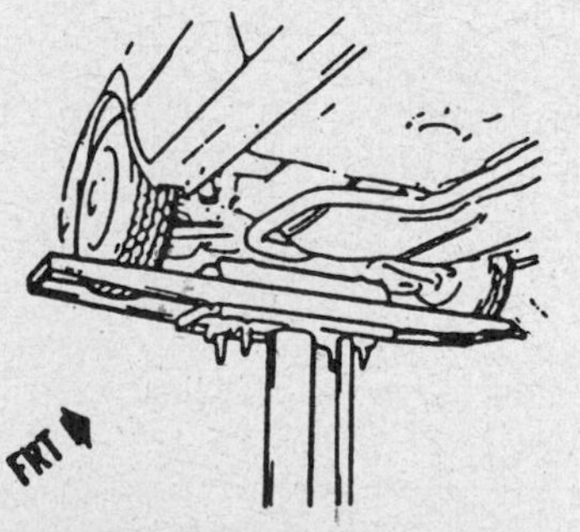
FRT
SUSPENSION CONTACT HOIST (LIFTING ON REAR TIRES)

Fig. 3 Aurora, Bonneville, DeVille, Eighty-Eight, Fleetwood, LeSabre, Ninety-Eight, Park Avenue, Riviera & 1992 Beretta & Corsica

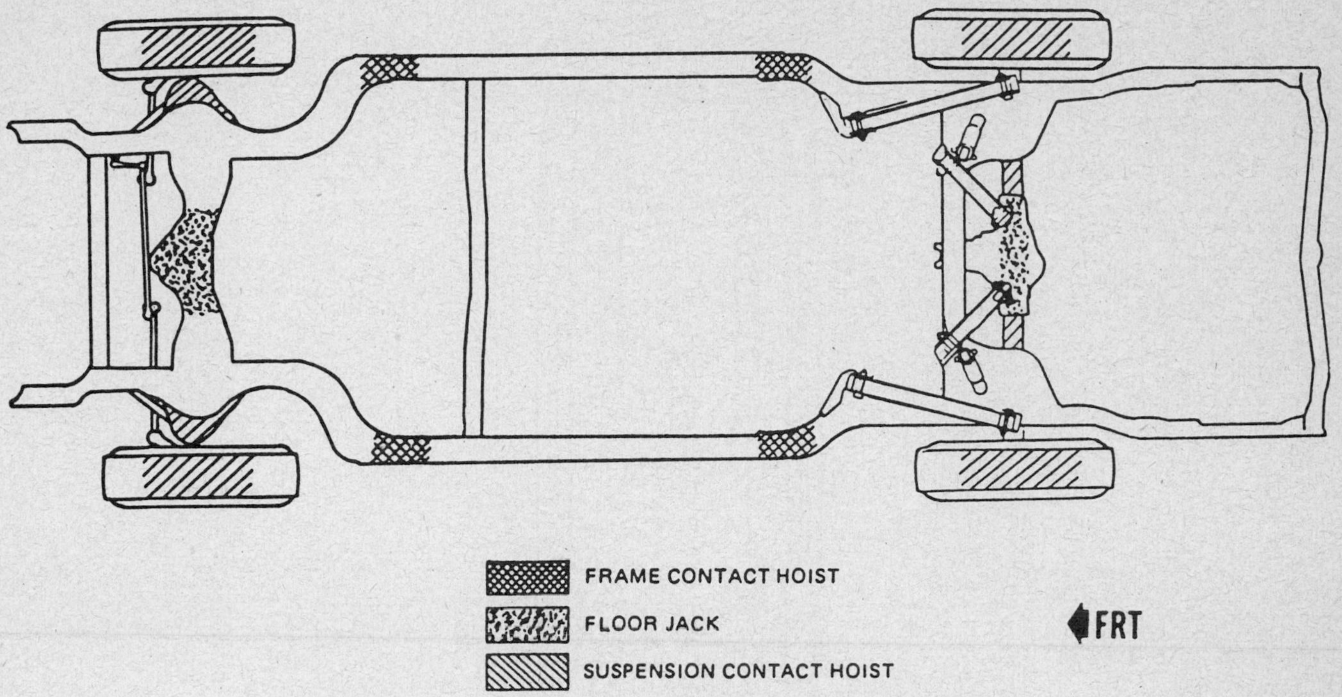
FRAME CONTACT HOIST
FLOOR JACK
SUSPENSION CONTACT HOIST
FRT

Fig. 4 Caprice, Custom Cruiser, Impala SS & Roadmaster

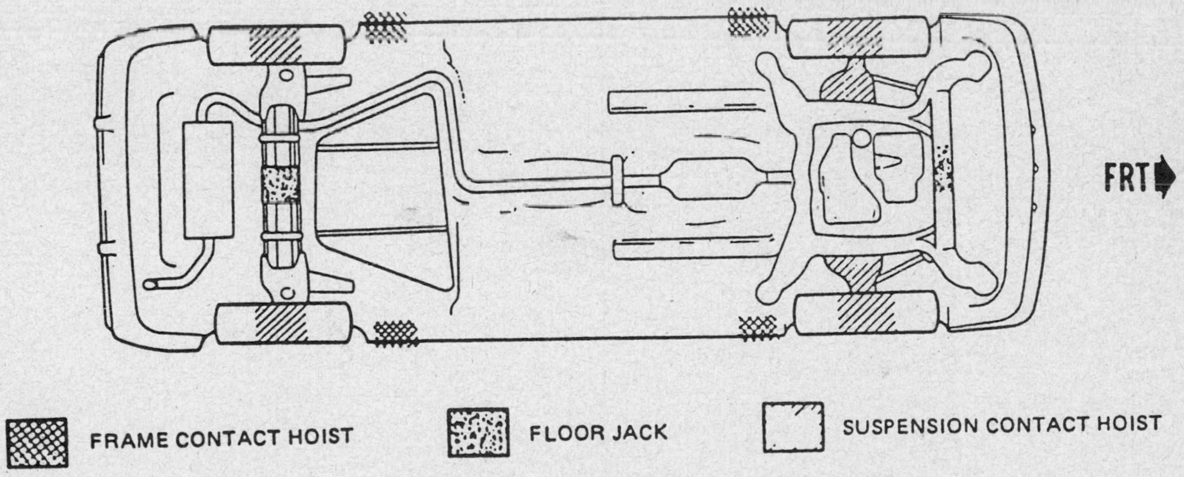
FRT
FRAME CONTACT HOIST
FLOOR JACK
SUSPENSION CONTACT HOIST

Fig. 5 Eldorado, Seville, Reatta, Toronado & Trofeo

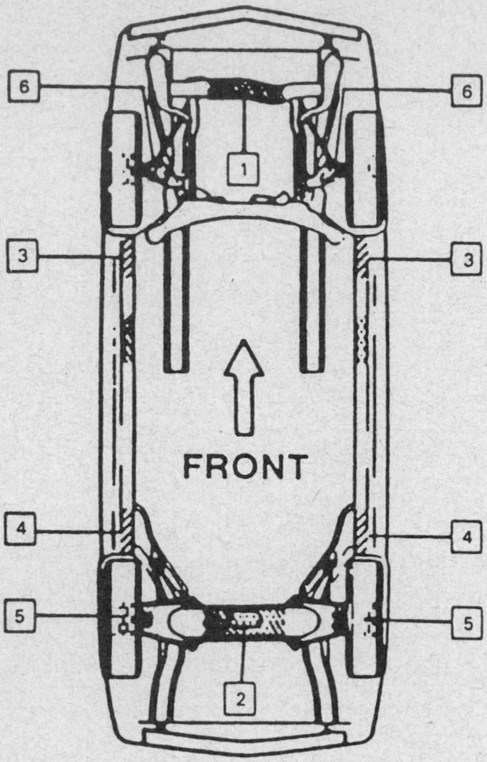
6
6
1
3
3
FRONT
4
4
5
5
2

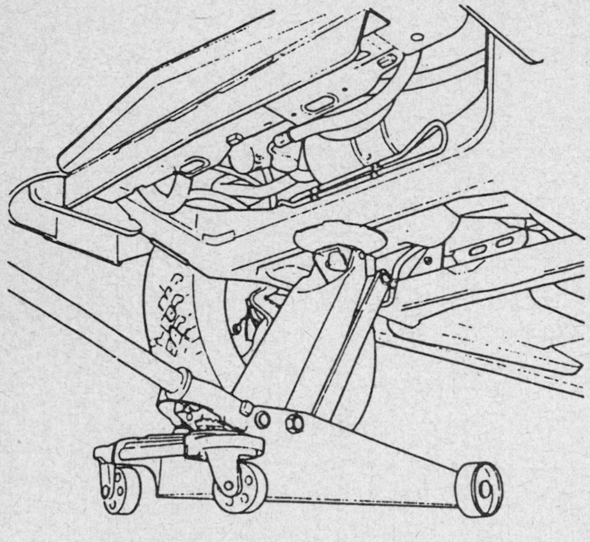

1 WHEN USING FLOOR JACK, LIFT ON CENTER OF FRONT CROSSMEMBER

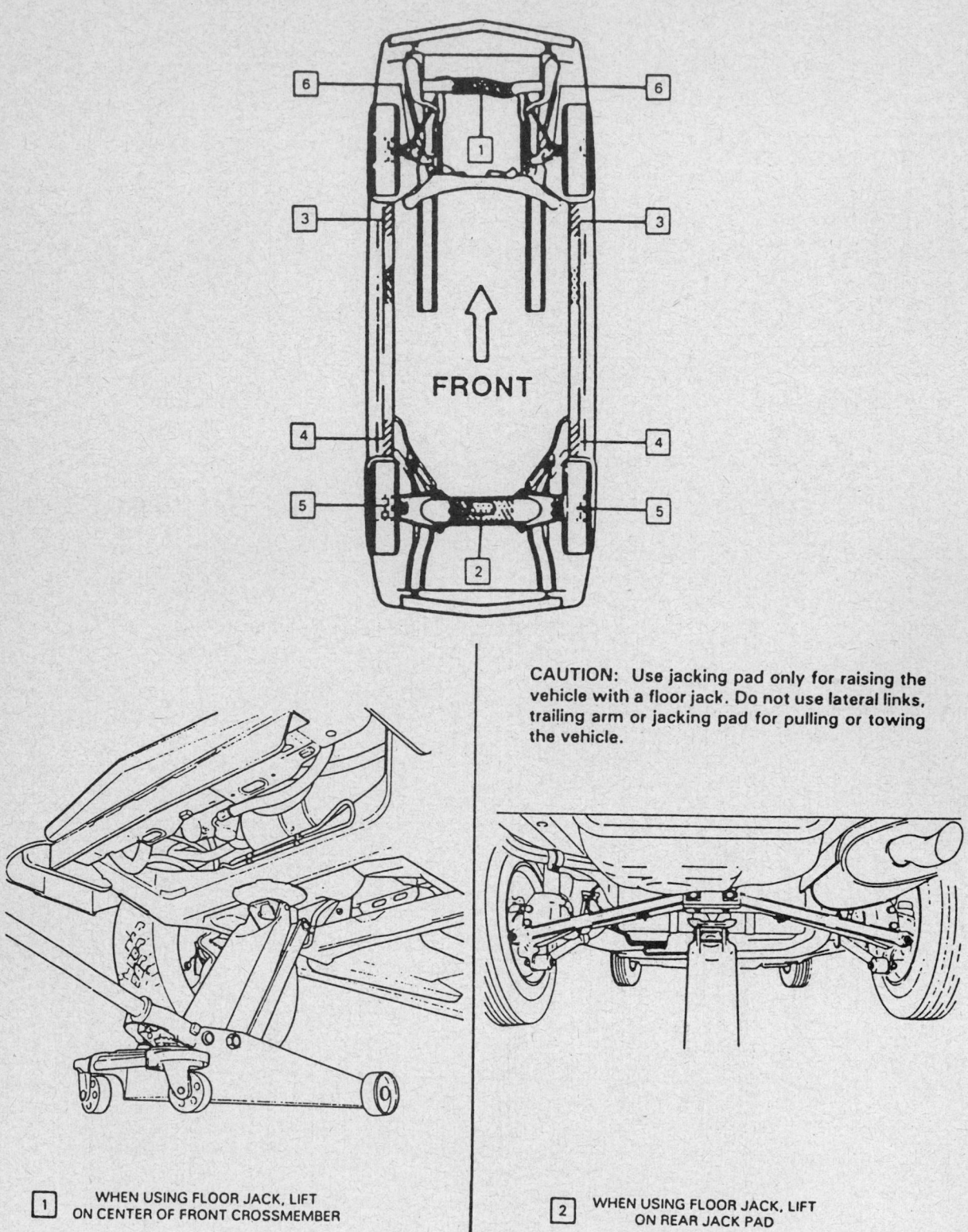

CAUTION: Use jacking pad only for raising the vehicle with a floor jack. Do not use lateral links, trailing arm or jacking pad for pulling or towing the vehicle.

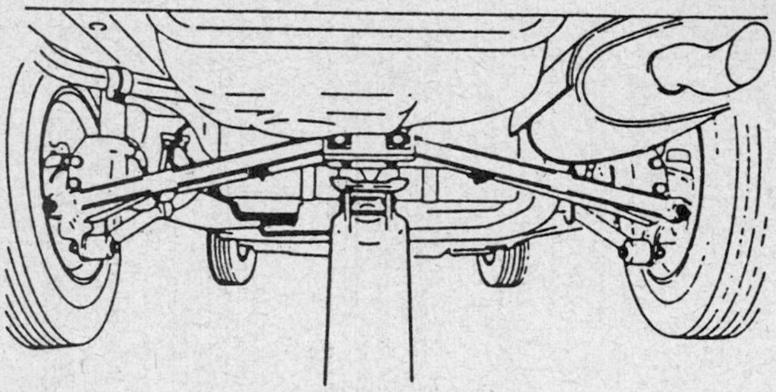

2 WHEN USING FLOOR JACK, LIFT ON REAR JACK PAD

Fig. 6 Cutlass Supreme, Grand Prix, Regal, Lumina & Monte Carlo (Part 1 of 2)

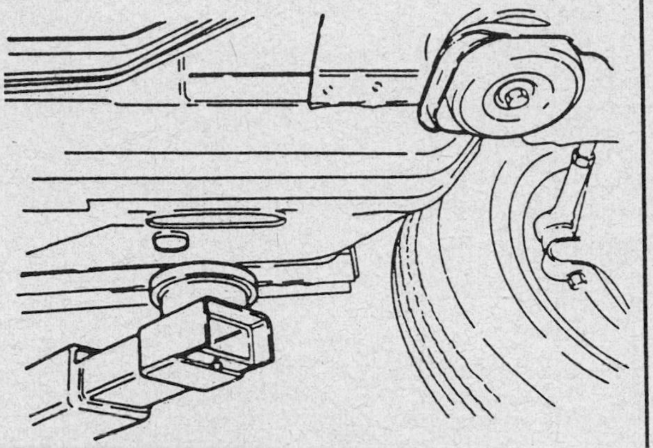

3 FRAME CONTACT HOIST (REARWARD OF FRONT TIRE)

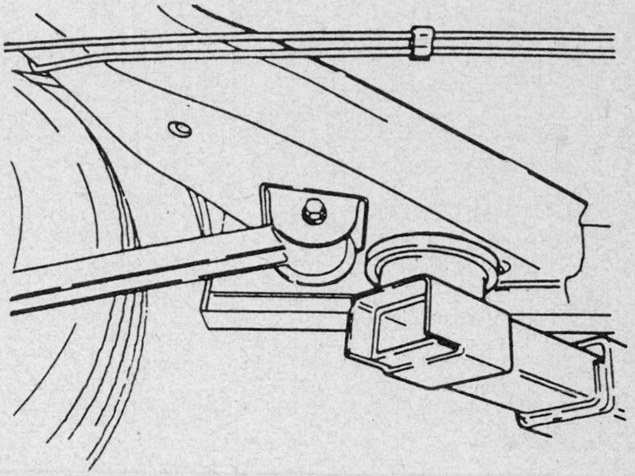

4 FRAME CONTACT HOIST (FORWARD OF REAR TIRE)

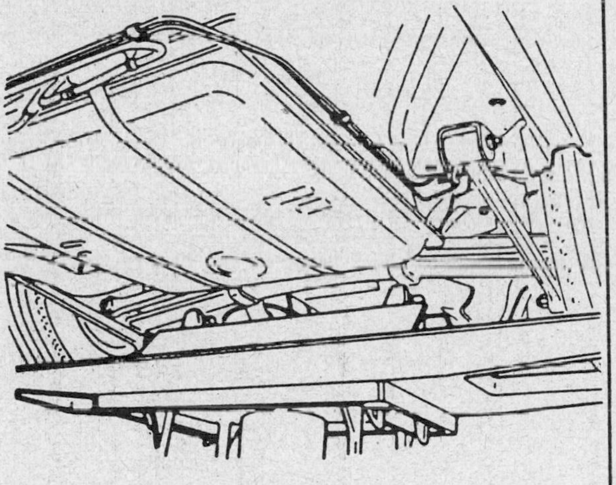

5 SUSPENSION CONTACT HOIST (LIFTING ON REAR TIRES)

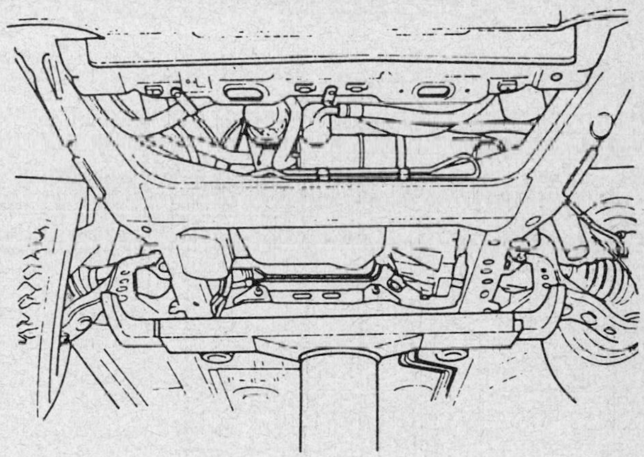

6 SUSPENSION CONTACT HOIST (UNDER FRONT LOWER CONTROL ARM)

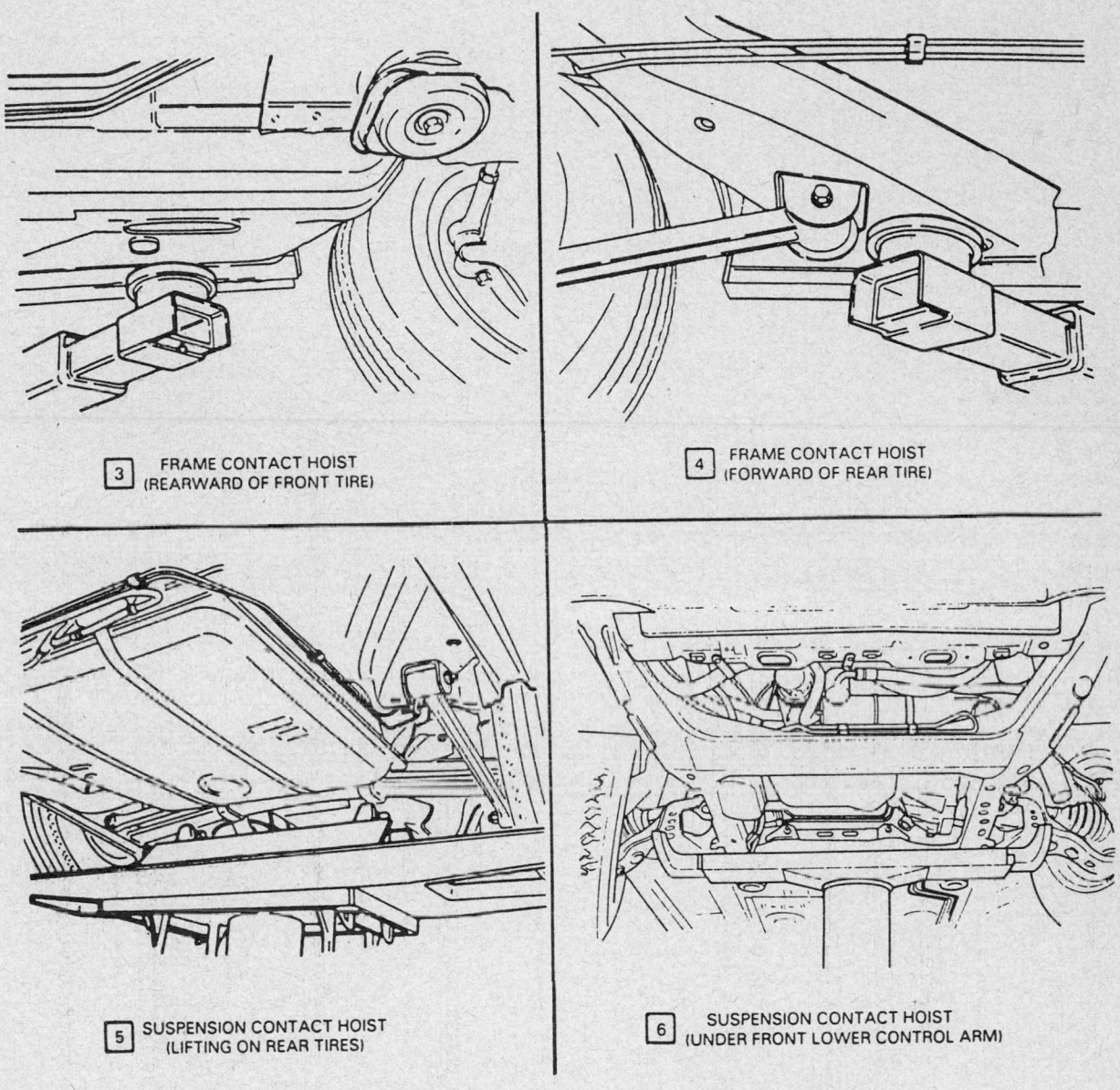

Fig. 6 Cutlass Supreme, Grand Prix, Regal, Lumina & Monte Carlo (Part 2 of 2)

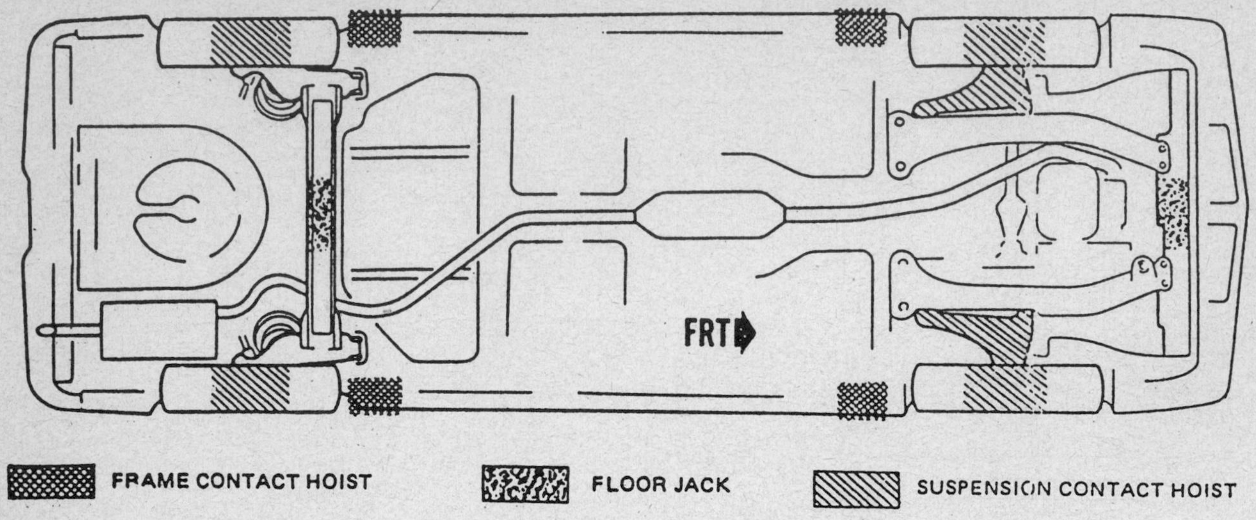
FRT
FRAME CONTACT HOIST
FLOOR JACK
SUSPENSION CONTACT HOIST

Fig. 7 Cavalier, Sunbird & Sunfire

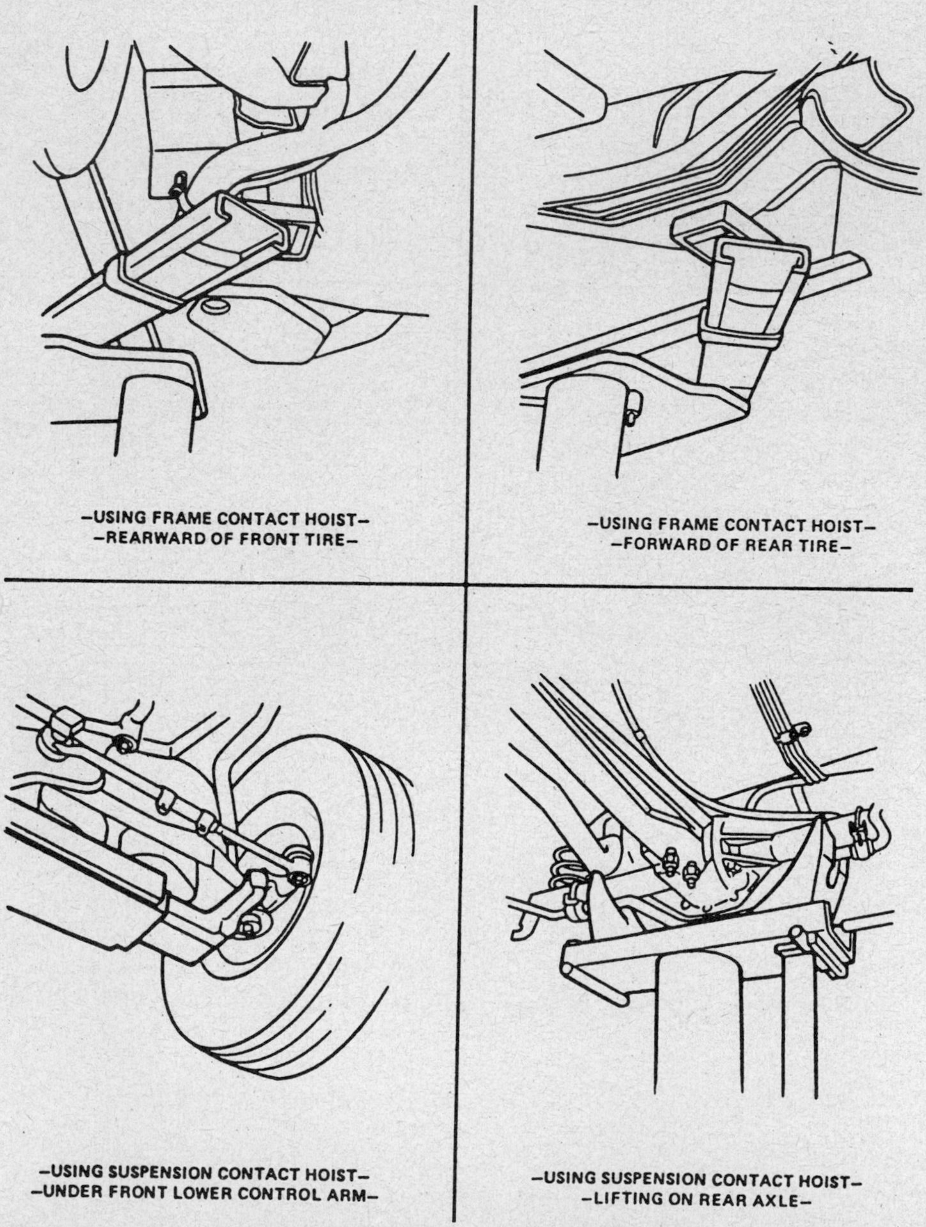
–USING FRAME CONTACT HOIST–
–REARWARD OF FRONT TIRE–
–USING FRAME CONTACT HOIST–
–FORWARD OF REAR TIRE–
–USING SUSPENSION CONTACT HOIST–
–UNDER FRONT LOWER CONTROL ARM–
–USING SUSPENSION CONTACT HOIST–
–LIFTING ON REAR AXLE–

Fig. 8 1992 Camaro & Firebird

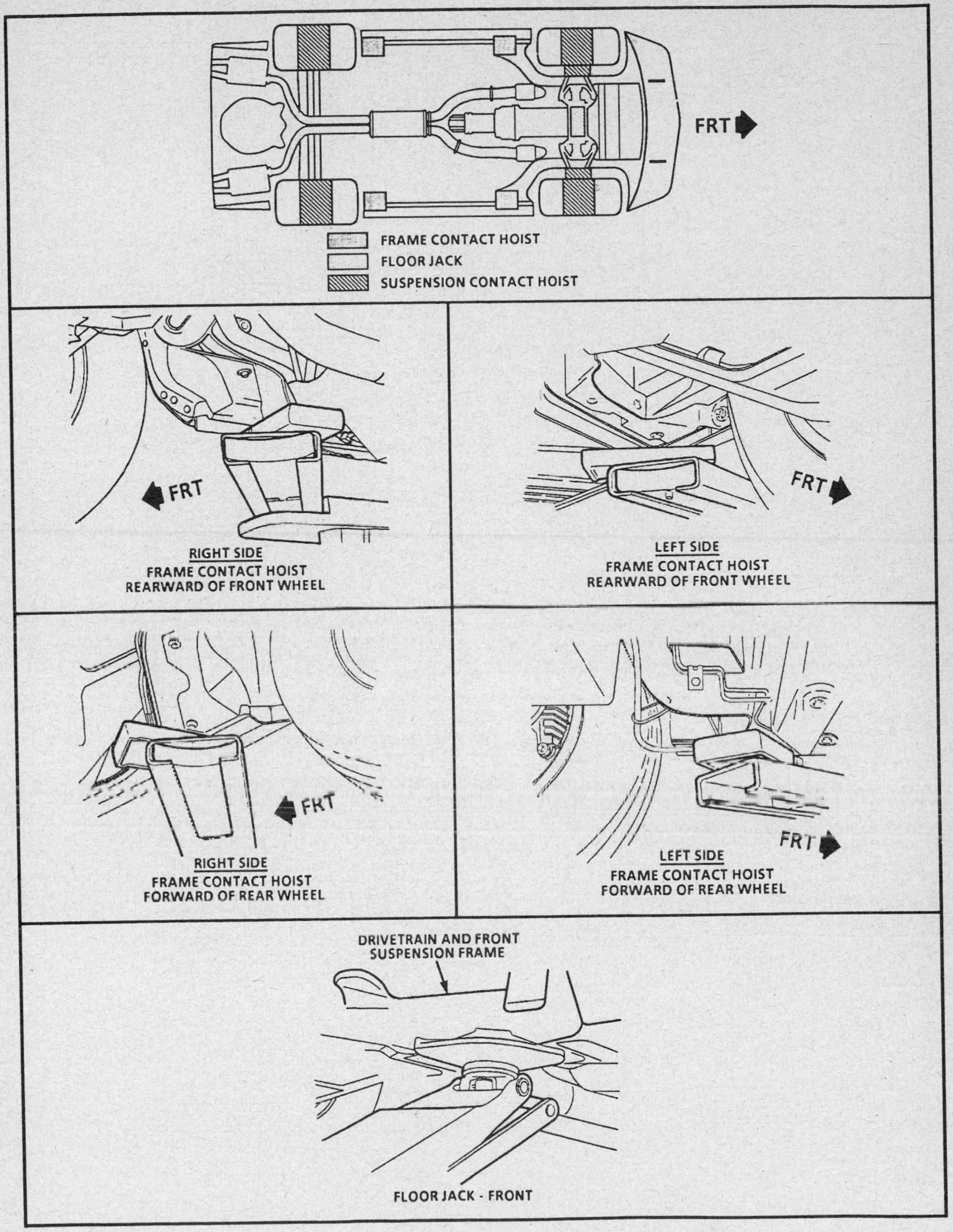
FRT
FRAME CONTACT HOIST
FLOOR JACK
SUSPENSION CONTACT HOIST
FRT
RIGHT SIDE
FRAME CONTACT HOIST
REARWARD OF FRONT WHEEL
FRT
LEFT SIDE
FRAME CONTACT HOIST
REARWARD OF FRONT WHEEL
FRT
RIGHT SIDE
FRAME CONTACT HOIST
FORWARD OF REAR WHEEL
FRT
LEFT SIDE
FRAME CONTACT HOIST
FORWARD OF REAR WHEEL
DRIVETRAIN AND FRONT
SUSPENSION FRAME
FLOOR JACK - FRONT

Fig. 9 Corvette

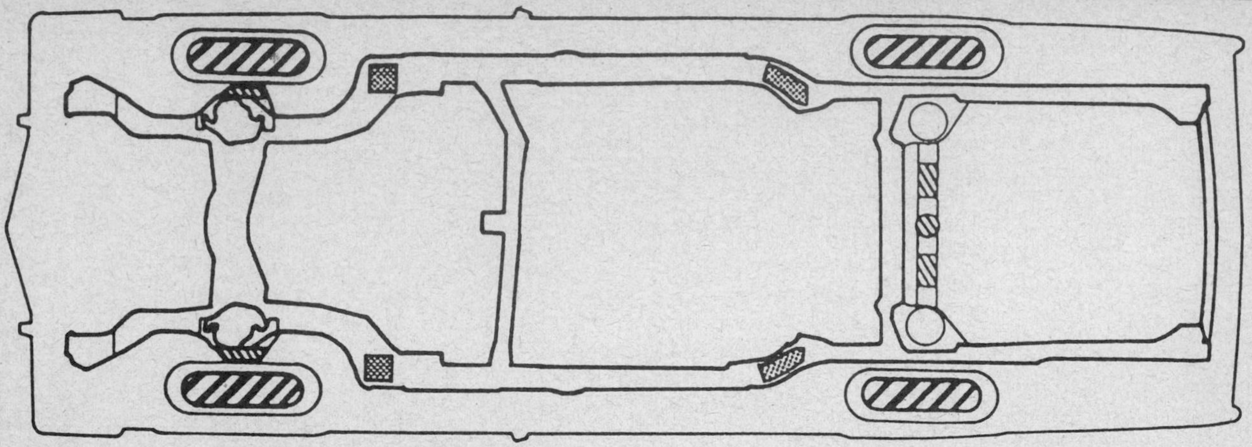

DRIVE ON HOIST

TWIN POST SUSPENSION HOIST

FRAME ENGAGING HOIST

SUPPORTS MUST BE POSITIONED SO AS TO DISTRIBUTE LOAD AND SUPPORT CAR IN A STABLE MANNER. CARE MUST BE EXERCISED TO ENSURE THAT PLACEMENT OF SUPPORTS DOES NOT DAMAGE BRAKE LINES, FUEL LINES, PARKING BRAKE CABLE, OR EXHAUST SYSTEM.

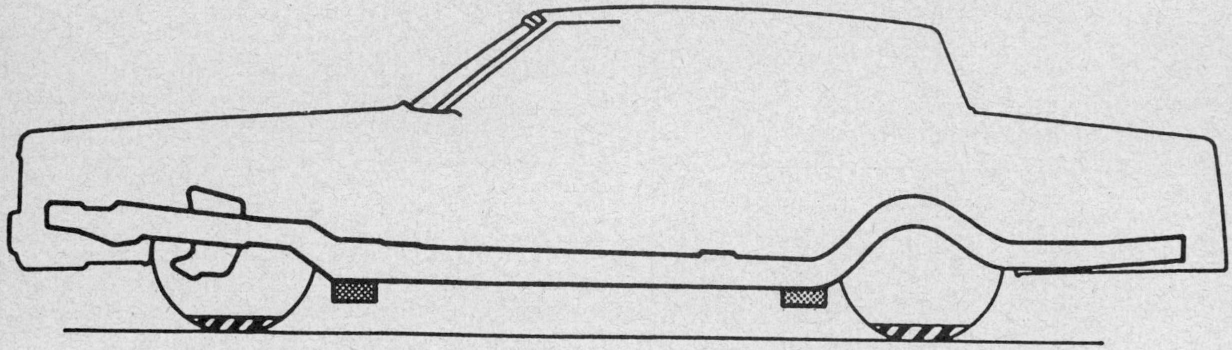

Fig. 10 Brougham

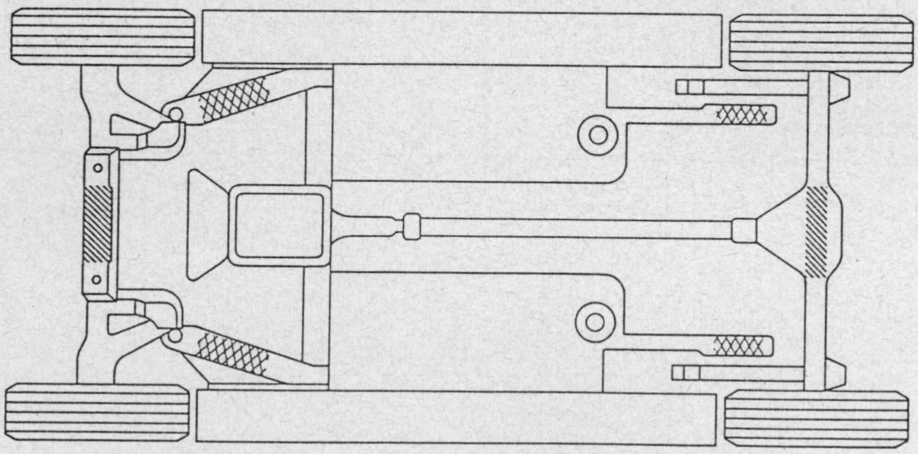

FRAME CONTACT HOIST

FLOOR JACK

Fig. 11 1993 Camaro & Firebird

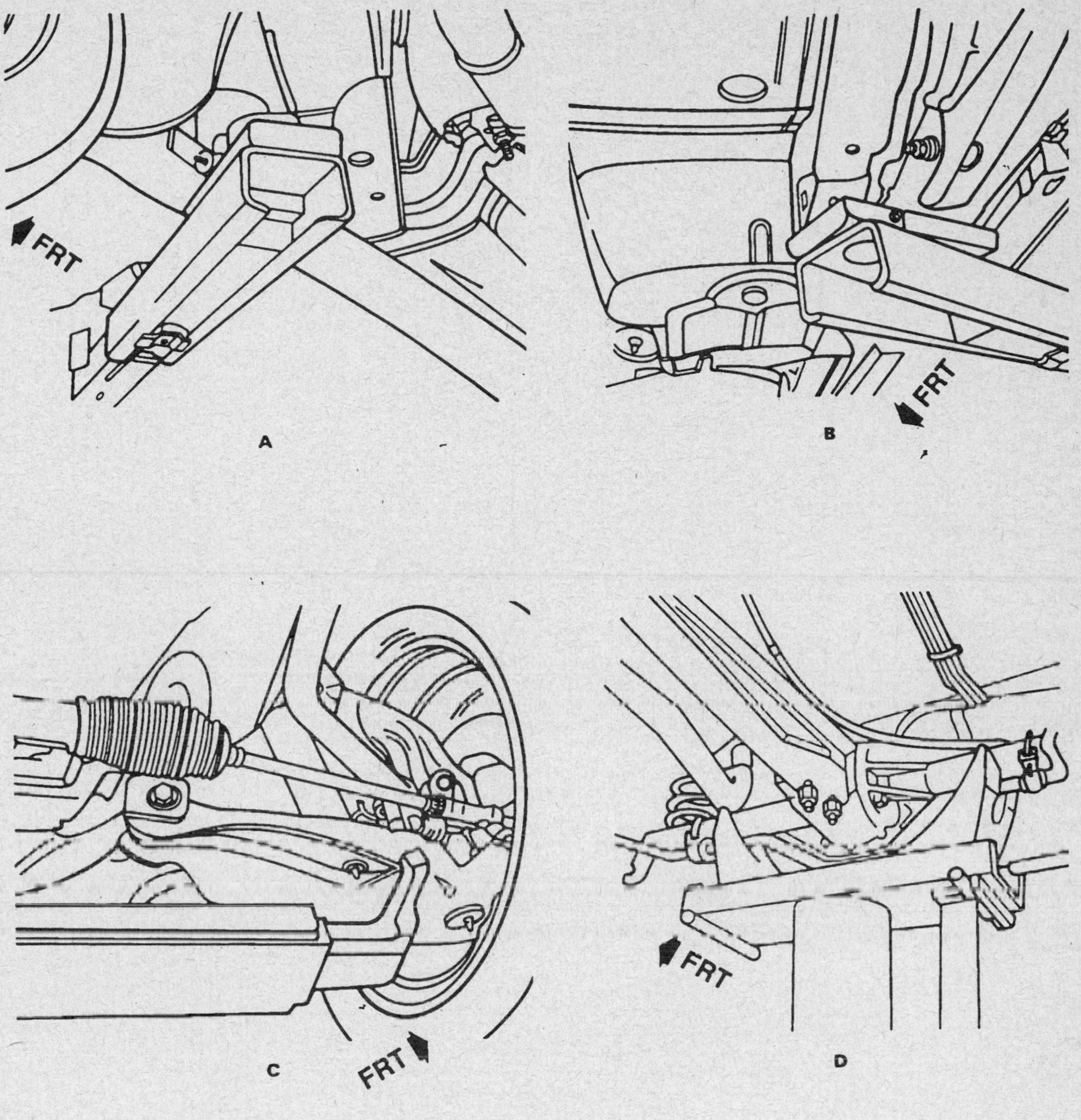
FRT
A
FRT
B
C
FRT
FRT
D

A USING FRAME CONTACT HOIST REARWARD OF FRONT TIRE
B USING FRAME CONTACT HOIST FORWARD OF REAR TIRE
C USING SUSPENSION CONTACT HOIST UNDER FRONT LOWER CONTROL ARM ASSEMBLY
D USING SUSPENSION CONTACT HOIST LIFTING ON REAR AXLE ASSEMBLY

Fig. 12 1994–95 Camaro & Firebird

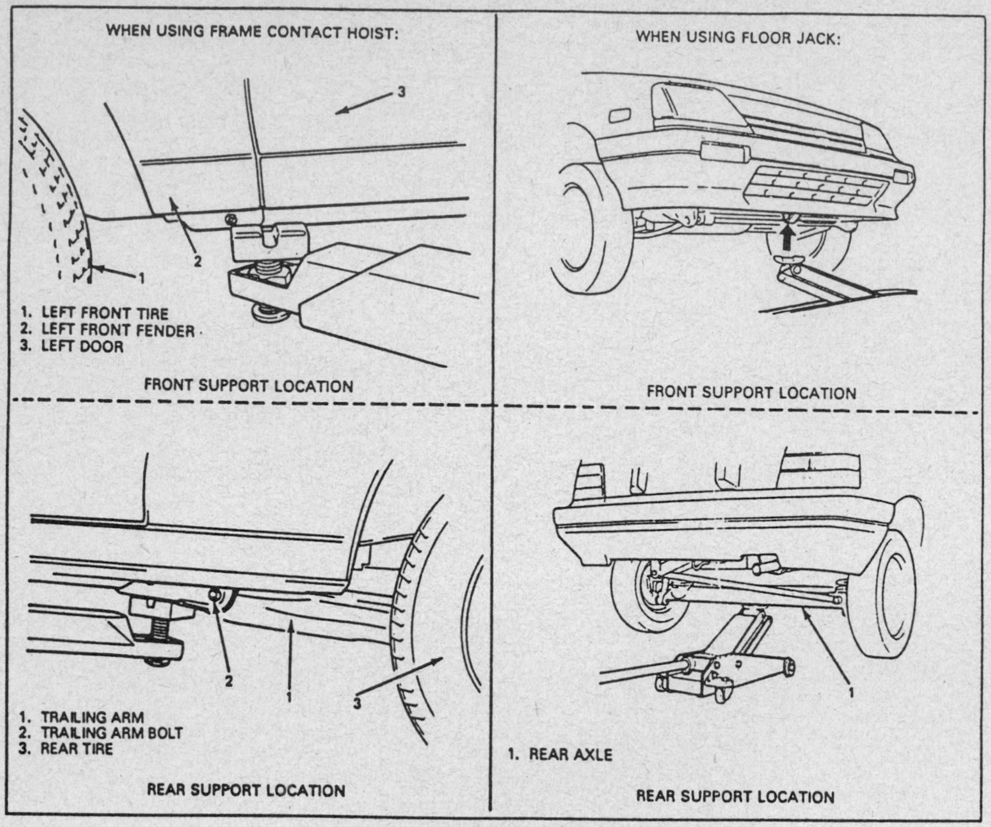

WHEN USING FRAME CONTACT HOIST:
3
2
1
1. LEFT FRONT TIRE
2. LEFT FRONT FENDER
3. LEFT DOOR
FRONT SUPPORT LOCATION
WHEN USING FLOOR JACK:
FRONT SUPPORT LOCATION
2
1
3
1. TRAILING ARM
2. TRAILING ARM BOLT
3. REAR TIRE
REAR SUPPORT LOCATION
1
1. REAR AXLE
REAR SUPPORT LOCATION

Fig. 13 Metro

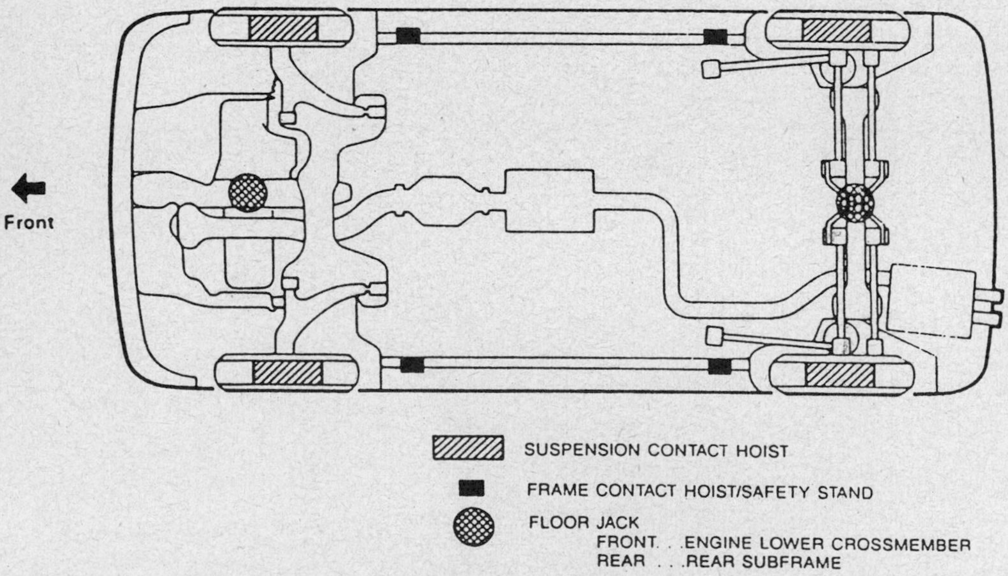

Front
SUSPENSION CONTACT HOIST
FRAME CONTACT HOIST/SAFETY STAND
FLOOR JACK
FRONT. . .ENGINE LOWER CROSSMEMBER
REAR . . .REAR SUBFRAME

Fig. 14 Prizm

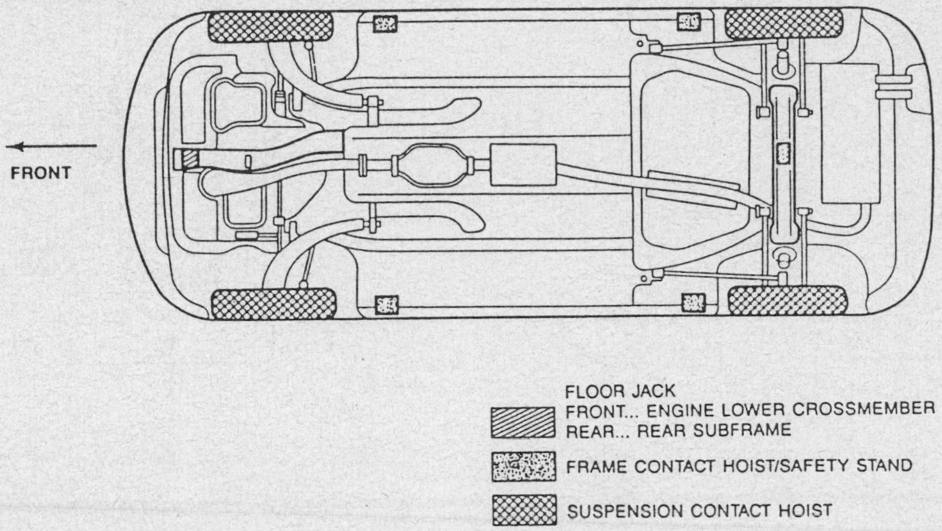
FRONT
FLOOR JACK
FRONT... ENGINE LOWER CROSSMEMBER
REAR... REAR SUBFRAME
FRAME CONTACT HOIST/SAFETY STAND
SUSPENSION CONTACT HOIST

Fig. 15 Storm

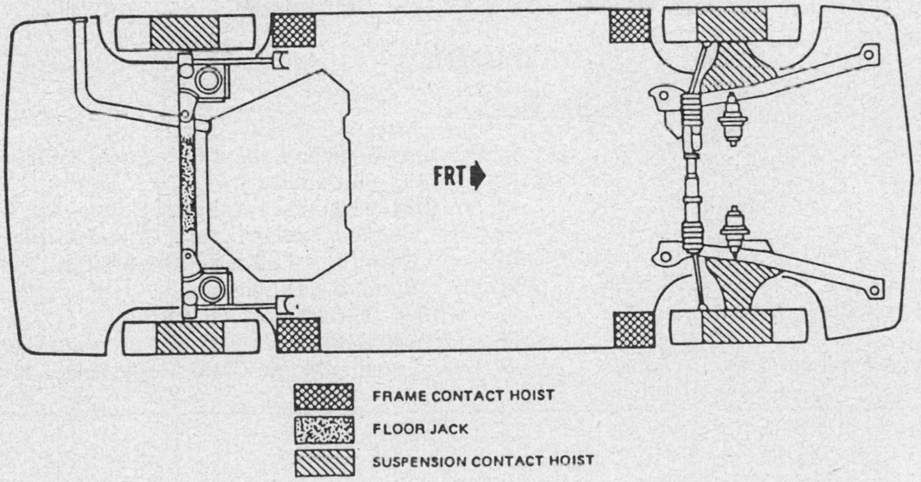
FRT
FRAME CONTACT HOIST
FLOOR JACK
SUSPENSION CONTACT HOIST

Fig. 16 LeMans

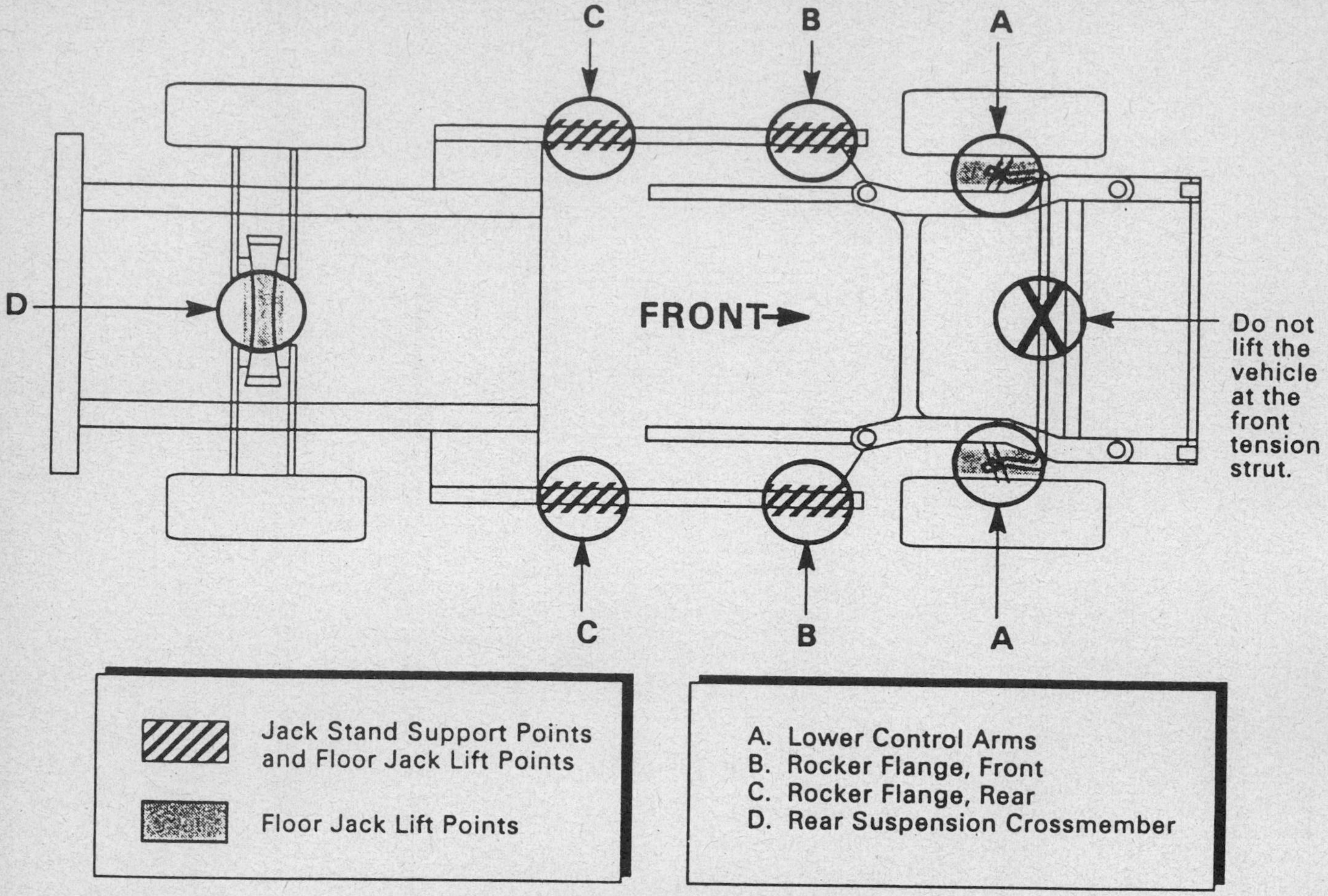
C
B
A
D
FRONT
Do not lift the vehicle at the front tension strut.
C
B
A
Jack Stand Support Points and Floor Jack Lift Points
Floor Jack Lift Points
A. Lower Control Arms
B. Rocker Flange, Front
C. Rocker Flange, Rear
D. Rear Suspension Crossmember

Fig. 17 Saturn

VEHICLE MAINTENANCE SCHEDULES

INDEX

1992 Cadillac Except Brougham & Fleetwood

SCHEDULE I

Follow Schedule I if your car is MAINLY operated under one or more of the following conditions:

- When most trips are less than 4 miles (6 kilometers).
- When most trips are less than 10 miles (16 kilometers) and outside temperatures remain below freezing.
- Idling and/or low speed operation in stop–and–go traffic.
- Towing a trailer. ***
- Operating in dusty areas.

Schedule I should also be followed if the vehicle is used for livery service or other commercial applications.

ITEM NO.	TO BE SERVICED	When To Perform Miles (Kilometers) Or Months Whichever Occurs First	The Services Shown In This Schedule Up To 48,000 Miles (80,000 Km) Are To Be Performed After 48,000 Miles At The Same Intervals															
		MILES (000)	3	6	9	12	15	18	21	24	27	30	33	36	39	42	45	48
		KILOMETERS(000)	5	10	15	20	25	30	35	40	45	50	55	60	65	70	75	80
1	Engine Oil & Oil Filter Change*	Every 3,000 Mi. (5,000 Km) Or 3 Mos.	•	•	•	•	•	•	•	•	•	•	•	•	•	•	•	•
2	Chassis Lubrication	Every Other Oil Change		•		•		•		•		•		•		•		•
3	Throttle Boot Mounting Bolt Torque *	At 6,000 Mi (10,000 Km) Only		•**														
4	Tire & Wheel Inspection & Rotation	At 6,000 Mi. (10,000 Km) And Then Every 15,000 (25,000 Km)		•					•					•				
5	Engine Accessory Drive Belt Inspection *	Every 30,000 Mi. (50,000 Km) Or 24 Mos.										•**						
6	Cooling System Service *											•						
7	Front Wheel Bearing Repack (Brougham Only)																	
8	Transmission/Transaxle Service																	
9	Spark Plug Replacement ****											•**						
10	Spark Plug Wire Inspection**											•						
11	EGR System Check *											•						
12	Air Cleaner Filter & A.I.R. Filter (Brougham Only) Replacement *	Every 30,000 Mi. (50,000 Km)										•**						
13	Engine Timing Check *											•						
14	Fuel Tank, Cap & Lines Inspection *											•						
15	Throttle Body Inspection											•						

SCHEDULE II

Follow Schedule II ONLY IF NONE of the driving conditions specified in Schedule I apply:

ITEM NO.	TO BE SERVICED	When To Perform Miles (Kilometers) Or Months Whichever Occurs First	The Services Shown In This Schedule Up To 45,000 Miles (75,000 Km) Are To Be Performed After 45,000 Miles At The Same Intervals					
		MILES (000)	7.5	15	22.5	30	37.5*	45
		KILOMETERS(000)	12.5	25	37.5	50	62.5	75
1	Engine Oil & Oil Filter Change*	Every 7,500 Mi. (12,500 Km) Or 12 mos.	•	•	•	•	•	•
	Oil Filter Change *	At first and then every other oil change or 12 mos.	•		•		•	
2	Chassis Lubrication	Every 7,500 Mi. (12,500 Km) Or 12 mos.	•	•	•	•	•	•
3	Throttle Body Mounting Bolt Torque *	At 7,500 Mi (12,500 Km) Only	•**					
4	Tire & Wheel Inspection & Rotation	At 7,500 Mi. (12,500 Km) And Then Every 15,000 (25,000 Km)	•		•		•	
5	Engine Accessory Drive Belt Inspection *	Every 30,000 Mi. (50,000 Km) Or 24 mos.				•**		
6	Cooling System Service *					•		
7	Front Wheel Bearing Repack (Brougham Only)	Every 30,000 Mi. (50,000 Km)				•		
8	Transmission/Transaxle Service							
9	Spark Plug Replacement ****					•**		
10	Spark Plug Wire Inspection**					•**		
11	EGR System Check *					•		
12	Air Cleaner Filter & A.I.R. Filter (Brougham Only) Replacement *	Every 30,000 Mi. (50,000 Km) Or 36 Mos.				•**		
13	Engine Timing Check *					•		
14	Fuel Tank, Cap & Lines Inspection *					•		
15	Throttle Body Inspection *					•		

* An Emission Control Service

** The U.S. Environmental Protection Agency has determined that failure to perform this maintenance item will not nullify the emission warranty or limit recall liability prior to the completion of vehicle useful life. General Motors, however, urges that all Emission Control Maintenance Services shown be performed at the indicated intervals and the maintenance be recorded.

[1]Schedule 1 should also be followed if the car is used for livery service or commercial application

*** Trailer pulling is not recommended for some models. See Owner's Manual for details.

**** .. BROUGHAM ONLY. Replace on all other carlines every 100,000 miles (160,000 km).

The services shown in these schedules up to 48,000 miles (80,000 km) are to be performed after 48,000 miles at the same intervals.

1992 Cadillac Brougham & Fleetwood

SCHEDULE I

Follow Schedule I if your car is MAINLY operated under one or more of the following conditions:

- When most trips are less than 4 miles (6 kilometers).
- When most trips are less than 10 miles (16 kilometers) and outside temperatures remain below freezing.
- Idling and/or low speed operation in stop-and-go traffic.
- Towing a trailer. ***
- Operating in dusty areas.

Schedule I should also be followed if the vehicle is used for livery service or other commercial applications.

ITEM NO.	TO BE SERVICED	When To Perform Miles (Kilometers) Or Months Whichever Occurs First		The Services Shown In This Schedule Up To 48,000 Miles (80,000 Km) Are To Be Performed After 48,000 Miles At The Same Intervals														
		MILES (000)	3	6	9	12	15	18	21	24	27	30	33	36	39	42	45	48
		KILOMETERS(000)	5	10	15	20	25	30	35	40	45	50	55	60	65	70	75	80
1	Engine Oil & Oil Filter Change*	Every 3,000 Mi. (5,000 Km) Or 3 Mos.	•	•	•	•	•	•	•	•	•	•	•	•	•	•	•	•
2	Chassis Lubrication	Every Other Oil Change		•		•		•		•		•		•		•		•
3	Throttle Boot Mounting Bolt Torque *	At 6,000 Mi (10,000 Km) Only		•**														
4	Tire & Wheel Inspection & Rotation	At 6,000 Mi. (10,000 Km) And Then Every 15,000 (25,000 Km)		•					•					•				
5	Engine Accessory Drive Belt Inspection *	Every 30,000 Mi. (50,000 Km) Or 24 Mos.										•**						
6	Cooling System Service *											•						
7	Wheel Bearing Repack (Brougham Only)																	
8	Transmission/Transaxle Service																	
9	Spark Plug Replacement	Every 30,000 Mi. (50,000 Km)										•**						
10	Spark Plug Wire Inspections*											•**						
11	PCV Valve Inspection *											•						
12	EGR System Service *											•						
13	Air Cleaner, PCV Filter & A.I.R. Filter Replacement *											•**						
14	Engine Timing Check *											•						
15	Fuel Tank, Cap & Lines Inspection *											•						
16	Throttle Body Inspection											•						

SCHEDULE II

Follow Schedule II ONLY IF NONE of the driving conditions specified in Schedule 1 apply:

ITEM NO.	TO BE SERVICED	When To Perform Miles (Kilometers) Or Months Whichever Occurs First	The Services Shown In This Schedule Up To 45,000 Miles (75,000 Km) Are To Be Performed After 45,000 Miles At The Same Intervals					
		MILES (000)	7.5	15	22.5	30	37.5*	45
		KILOMETERS(000)	12.5	25	37.5	50	62.5	75
1	Engine Oil & Oil Filter Change*	Every 7,500 Mi. (12,500 Km) Or 12 mos.	•	•	•	•	•	•
	Oil Filter Change *	At first and then every other oil change or 12 mos.	•		•		•	
2	Chassis Lubrication	Every 7,500 Mi. (12,500 Km) Or 12 mos.	•	•	•	•	•	•
3	Throttle Body Mounting Bolt Torque *	At 7,500 Mi (12,500 Km) Only	•**					
4	Tire & Wheel Inspection & Rotation	At 7,500 Mi. (12,500 Km) And Then Every 15,000 (25,000 Km)	•		•		•	
5	Engine Accessory Drive Belt Inspection *	Every 30,000 Mi. (50,000 Km) Or 24 mos.				•**		
6	Cooling System Service *					•		
7	Wheel Bearing Repack (Brougham Only)	Every 30,000 Mi. (50,000 Km)				•		
8	Transmission/Transaxle Service					•		
9	Spark Plug Replacement	Every 30,000 Mi. (50,000 Km) Or 36 Mos.				•**		
10	Spark Plug Wire Inspections*					•**		
11	PCV Valve Inspection *					•		
12	EGR System Service *					•		
13	Air Cleaner, PCV Filter & A.I.R. Filter Replacement *					•**		
14	Engine Timing Check *					•		
15	Fuel Tank, Cap & Lines Inspection *					•		
16	Throttle Body Inspection *					•		

* An Emission Control Service

** The U.S. Environmental Protection Agency has determined that failure to perform this maintenance item will not nullify the emission warranty or limit recall liability prior to the completion of vehicle useful life. General Motors, however, urges that all Emission Control Maintenance Services shown be performed at the indicated intervals and the maintenance be recorded.

[1]Schedule 1 should also be followed if the car is used for livery service or commercial application

*** Trailer pulling is not recommended for some models. See Owner's Manual for details.

The services shown in these schedules up to 48,000 miles (80,000 km) are to be performed after 48,000 miles at the same intervals.

1993–95 Cadillac

SCHEDULE I

Follow Schedule I if your car is MAINLY operated under one or more of the following conditions:

- When most trips are less than 4 miles (6 kilometers).
- When most trips are less than 10 miles (16 kilometers) and outside temperatures remain below freezing.
- Idling and/or low speed operation in stop–and–go traffic.
- Towing a trailer. ***
- Operating in dusty areas.

Schedule I should also be followed if the vehicle is used for livery service or other commercial applications.

ITEM NO.	TO BE SERVICED	When To Perform Miles (Kilometers) Or Months Whichever Occurs First	The Services Shown In This Schedule Up To 48,000 Miles (80,000 Km) Are To Be Performed After 48,000 Miles At The Same Intervals															
		MILES (000)	3	6	9	12	15	18	21	24	27	30	33	36	39	42	45	48
		KILOMETERS(000)	5	10	15	20	25	30	35	40	45	50	55	60	65	70	75	80
1	Engine Oil & Oil Filter Change*	Every 3,000 Mi. (5,000 Km) Or 3 Mos.	●	●	●	●	●	●	●	●	●	●	●	●	●	●	●	●
2	Chassis Lubrication	Every Other Oil Change		●		●		●		●		●		●		●		●
3	Throttle Boot Mounting Bolt Torque *	At 6,000 Mi (10,000 Km) Only		●**														
4	Tire & Wheel Inspection & Rotation	At 6,000 Mi. (10,000 Km) And Then Every 15,000 (25,000 Km)		●					●					●				
5	Engine Accessory Drive Belt Inspection *	Every 30,000 Mi. (50,000 Km) Or 24 Mos.										●**						
6	Cooling System Service *											●						
7	Front Wheel Bearing Repack (Brougham Only)																	
8	Transmission/Transaxle Service																	
9	Throttle Body Inspection											●**						
10	Spark Plug Wire Inspection * **											●**						
11	EGR System Check * **											●						
12	Air Cleaner, Filter Replacement *	Every 30,000 Mi. (50,000 Km)										●**						
13	Engine Timing Check *											●						
14	Fuel Tank, Cap & Lines Inspection * **											●						
15	Spark Plug Replacement	Every 100,000 Mi. (160,000 Km)																

SCHEDULE II

Follow Schedule II ONLY IF NONE of the driving conditions specified in Schedule I apply:

ITEM NO.	TO BE SERVICED	When To Perform Miles (Kilometers) Or Months Whichever Occurs First	The Services Shown In This Schedule Up To 45,000 Miles (75,000 Km) Are To Be Performed After 45,000 Miles At The Same Intervals					
		MILES (000)	7.5	15	22.5	30	37.5*	45
		KILOMETERS(000)	12.5	25	37.5	50	62.5	75
1	Engine Oil & Oil Filter Change*	Every 7,500 Mi. (12,500 Km) Or 12 mos.	●	●	●	●	●	●
	Oil Filter Change *	At first and then every other oil change or 12 mos.	●		●		●	
2	Chassis Lubrication	Every 7,500 Mi. (12,500 Km) Or 12 mos.	●	●	●	●	●	●
3	Throttle Body Mounting Bolt Torque *	At 7,500 Mi (12,500 Km) Only	●**					
4	Tire & Wheel Inspection & Rotation	At 7,500 Mi. (12,500 Km) And Then Every 15,000 (25,000 Km)	●		●		●	
5	Engine Accessory Drive Belt Inspection *	Every 30,000 Mi. (50,000 Km) Or 24 mos.				●**		
6	Cooling System Service *					●		
7	Front Wheel Bearing Repack (Brougham Only)	Every 30,000 Mi. (50,000 Km)				●		
8	Transmission/Transaxle Service							
9	Throttle Body Inspection *					●**		
10	Spark Plug Wire Inspection * **					●**		
11	EGR System Check * **					●		
12	Air Cleaner, PCV Filter & A.I.R. Filter Replacement *	Every 30,000 Mi. (50,000 Km) Or 36 Mos.				●**		
13	Engine Timing Check *					●		
14	Fuel Tank, Cap & Lines Inspection * **					●		
15	Spark Plug Replacement	Every 100,000 Mi. (160,000 Km)						

* An Emission Control Service

** The U.S. Environmental Protection Agency has determined that failure to perform this maintenance item will not nullify the emission warranty or limit recall liability prior to the completion of vehicle useful life. General Motors, however, urges that all Emission Control Maintenance Services shown be performed at the indicated intervals and the maintenance be recorded.

[1]Schedule 1 should also be followed if the car is used for livery service or commercial application

*** Trailer pulling is not recommended for some models. See Owner's Manual for details.

The services shown in these schedules up to 48,000 miles (80,000 km) are to be performed after 48,000 miles at the same intervals.

1992-93 Except Cadillac, LeMans, Metro, Prizm & Storm

SCHEDULED MAINTENANCE SERVICES

SCHEDULE I

Follow Schedule I if your vehicle is MAINLY driven under one or more of the following conditions:

- When most trips are less than 6 kilometers (4 miles).
- When most trips are less than 16 kilometers (10 miles) and outside temperatures remain below freezing.
- When most trips include extended idling and/or frequent low-speed operation as in stop-and-go traffic.†
- Towing a trailer.**
- Operating in dusty areas.

ITEM NO.	TO BE SERVICED	WHEN TO PERFORM Kilometers (Miles) or Months, Whichever Occurs First	The services shown in this schedule up to 80 000 km (48,000 miles) are to be performed after 80 000 km (48,000 miles) at the same intervals.															
		KILOMETERS (000)	5	10	15	20	25	30	35	40	45	50	55	60	65	70	75	80
		MILES (000)	3	6	9	12	15	18	21	24	27	30	33	36	39	42	45	48
1.	Engine Oil & Oil Filter Change*	Every 5 000 km (3,000 mi.) or 3 mos.	•	•	•	•	•	•	•	•	•	•	•	•	•	•	•	•
2.	Chassis Lubrication	Every other oil change		•		•		•		•		•		•		•		•
3.	Throttle Body Mounting Bolt Torque*	At 10 000 km (6,000 mi.) only		•														
4.	Tire & Wheel Inspection & Rotation	At 10 000 km (6,000 mi.) and then every 25 000 km (15,000 mi.)		•					•					•				
5.	Engine Accessory Drive Belt Inspection	Every 50 000 km (30,000 mi.) or 24 mos.										•						
6.	Cooling System Service*	Every 50 000 km (30,000 mi.) or 24 mos.										•						
7.	Front Wheel Bearing Repack																	
8.	Transmission Service																	
9.	Spark Plug Replacement*	Every 50 000 km (30,000 mi.).										•						
10.	Spark Plug Wire Inspection*‡	Every 50 000 km (30,000 mi.).										•						
11.	PCV Valve Inspection*‡	Every 50 000 km (30,000 mi.).										•						
12.	Thermostatically Controlled Air Cleaner Inspection	Every 50 000 km (30,000 mi.).										•						
13.	EGR System Inspection*‡	Every 50 000 km (30,000 mi.).										•						
14.	Air Cleaner Filter Replacement*	Every 50 000 km (30,000 mi.).										•						
15.	Engine Timing Check*	Every 50 000 km (30,000 mi.).										•						
16.	Fuel Tank, Cap & Lines Inspection*‡	Every 50 000 km (30,000 mi.).										•						

† Note: Schedule I should also be followed if the vehicle is used for delivery service, police, taxi or other commercial applications.
‡ The U.S. Environmental Protection Agency has determined that the failure to perform this maintenance item will not nullify the emission warranty or limit recall liability prior to the completion of vehicle useful life. General Motors, however, urges that all recommended maintenance services be performed at the indicated intervals and the maintenance be recorded in section C of the owner's maintenance schedule.
* An Emission Control Service
** Trailering is not recommended for some models. See your Owner's Manual for details.

1992-93 Except Cadillac, LeMans, Metro, Prizm & Storm

SCHEDULED MAINTENANCE SERVICES

SCHEDULE II

Follow Schedule II ONLY if none of the driving conditions specified in Schedule I apply.

ITEM NO.	TO BE SERVICED	WHEN TO PERFORM Kilometers (Miles) or Months, Whichever Occurs First	The services shown in this schedule up to 75 000 km (45,000 miles) are to be performed after 75 000 km (45,000 miles) at the same intervals.					
		KILOMETERS (000)	12.5	25	37.5	50	62.5	75
		MILES (000)	7.5	15	22.5	30	37.5	45
1.	Engine Oil Change*	Every 12 500 km (7,500 mi.) or 12 mos.	•	•	•	•	•	•
	Oil Filter Change†*	At first and then every other oil change or 12 mos	•		•		•	
2.	Chassis Lubrication	Every 12 500 km (7,500 mi.) or 12 mos.	•	•	•	•	•	•
3.	Throttle Body Mounting Bolt Torque	At 12 500 km (7,500 mi.) only	•					
4.	Tire & Wheel Inspection & Rotation	At 12 500 km (7,500 mi.) and then every 25 000 km (15,000 mi.)	•		•		•	
5.	Engine Accessory Drive Belt Inspection	Every 50 000 km (30,000 mi.) or 24 mos.				•		
6.	Cooling System Service*					•		
7.	Front Wheel Bearing Repack	Every 50 000 km (30,000 mi.)				•		
8.	Transmission Service							
9.	Spark Plug Replacement*	Every 50 000 km (30,000 mi.).				•		
10.	Spark Plug Wire Inspection*‡					•		
11.	PCV Valve Inspection*‡					•		
12.	Thermostatically Controlled Air Cleaner Inspection					•		
13.	EGR System Inspection*‡					•		
14.	Air Cleaner Filter Replacement*					•		
15.	Engine Timing Check*					•		
16.	Fuel Tank, Cap & Lines Inspection*‡					•		

‡ The U.S. Environmental Protection Agency has determined that the failure to perform this maintenance item will not nullify the emission warranty or limit recall liability prior to the completion of vehicle useful life. General Motors, however, urges that all recommended maintenance services be performed at the indicated intervals and the maintenance be recorded in section C of the owner's maintenance schedule.

*** An Emission Control Service**

1994-95 Caprice, Cutlass Supreme, Grand Prix, Impala SS, Lumina, Monte Carlo, Regal & Roadmaster

SCHEDULED MAINTENANCE SERVICES
SCHEDULE I

Follow Schedule I if the car is MAINLY driven under one or more of the following conditions:

- When most trips are less than 6 kilometers (4 miles).
- When most trips are less than 16 kilometers (10 miles) and outside temperature remains below freezing.
- When most trips include extended idling and/or frequent low-speed operation as in stop-and-go traffic.
- When vehicle is used for delivery service, police, taxi or other commercial applications.
- Towing a trailer.**
- Operating in dusty areas.

ITEM NO.	TO BE SERVICED	WHEN TO PERFORM Kilometers (Miles) or Months, Whichever Occurs First	The services shown in this schedule up to 80 000 km (48,000 miles) are to be performed after 80 000 km (48,000 miles) at the same intervals.															
		KILOMETERS (000)	5	10	15	20	25	30	35	40	45	50	55	60	65	70	75	80
		MILES (000)	3	6	9	12	15	18	21	24	27	30	33	36	39	42	45	48
1.	Engine Oil & Oil Filter change*	Every 5 000 km (3,000 Miles) or 3 mos. or when "CHANGE OIL" light comes on	•	•	•	•	•	•	•	•	•	•	•	•	•	•	•	•
2.	Chassis Lubrication	Every other oil change.		•		•		•		•		•		•		•		•
3.	Tire and Wheel Rotation	At 10 000 km (6,000 mi.) and then every 20,000 km (12,000 mi.)		•				•				•					•	
4.	Serpentine Drive Belt Inspection*	Every 50 000 km (30,000 mi.) or 24 mos.										•						
5.	Cooling System Service*	Every 50 000 km (30,000 mi.) or 24 mos.										•						
6.	Front Wheel Bearing Repack	See explanation for service interval.																
7.	Transmission Service	See explanation for service interval.																
8.	Spark Plug Replacement*	Every 160 000 km (100,000 mi.).																
9.	Spark Plug Wire Inspection* ‡	Every 50 000 km (30,000 mi.).										•						
10.	Positive Carankcase Ventilation (PCV) Valve Inspection* ‡	Every 50 000 km (30,000 mi.).										•						
11.	Fuel Tank, Cap & Lines Inspection* ‡	Every 50 000 km (30,000 mi.).										•						
12.	Air Cleaner Filter Inspection/Replacement*	Inspect air cleaner filter every 25,000 km (15,000 mi.) and replace every 50,000 km (30,000 mi.)					•					•					•	
13.	Rear Axle Lubricant Change	See explanation for service interval.																

† **Note: Schedule I should also be followed if the vehicle is used for delivery service, police, taxi or other commercial applications.**

‡ **The U.S. Enviromental Protection Agency or the California Air Resources Board has determined that the failure to perform this maintenance item will not nullify the emission warranty or limit recall liability prior to the completion of vehicle useful life. General Motors, however, urges that all recommended maintenance services be performed at the indicated intervals and the maintenance be recorded in section E of the owner's maintenance schedule.**

* **An Emission Control Service.**

** **Do not exceed trailering limits.**

1994-95 Caprice, Cutlass Supreme, Grand Prix, Impala SS, Lumina, Monte Carlo, Regal & Roadmaster

SCHEDULED MAINTENANCE SERVICES
SCHEDULE II

* Follow Schedule II only if none of the driving conditions specified in Schedule I apply.

The services shown in this schedule up to 75 000 km (45,000 miles) are to be performed after 75 000 km (45,000 miles) at the same intervals.

ITEM NO.	TO BE SERVICED	WHEN TO PERFORM Kilometers (Miles) or Months, Whichever Occurs First						
		KILOMETERS (000)	12.5	25	37.5	50	62.5	75
		MILES (000)	7.5	15	22.5	30	37.5	45
1	Engine Oil Change•	Every 12 500 km (7,500 mi.) or 12 mos. or when "CHANGE OIL" light comes on	•	•	•	•	•	•
	Oil Filter change•	At first and then every other oil change or 12 mos.	•		•		•	
2.	Chassis Lubrication	Every 12 500 km (7,500 mi.) or 12 mos.	•	•	•	•	•	•
3.	Tire & Wheel Rotation	At 12 500 km (7,500 mi.) and then every 25 000 km (15,000 mi.)	•		•		•	
4.	Serpentine Drive Belt inspection•	At 50 000 km (30,000 mi.) or 24 mos.				•		
5.	Cooling System Service•					•		
6.	Front Wheel Bearing Repack	Every 50 000 km (30,000 mi.).				•		
7.	Transmission Service	See explanation for service interval.						
8.	Spark Plug Replacement•	Every 160 000 km (100,000 mi.).						
9.	Spark Plug Wire Inspection• ‡	Every 50 000 km (30,000 mi.)				•		
10.	Positive Carankcase Ventilation (PCV) Valve Inspection• ‡					•		
11.	Air Cleaner Filter Replacement•					•		
12.	Fuel Tank, Cap & Lines Inspection• ‡					•		
13.	Rear Axle Lubricant Change	See explanation for service interval						

‡ The U.S. Enviromental Protection Agency or the California Air Resources Board has determined that the failure to perform this maintenance item will not nullify the emission warranty or limit recall liability prior to the completion of vehicle useful life. General Motors, however, urges that all recommended maintenance services be performed at the indicated intervals and the maintenance be recorded in section E of the owner's maintenance schedule.

• An Emission Control Service.

1994-95 Achieva, Beretta, Bonneville, Cavalier, Century, Corsica, Cutlass Ciera, Cutlass Cruiser, Eighty-Eight, Grand Am, LeSabre, Ninety- Eight, Park Avenue, Skylark, Sunbird & Sunfire

FOLLOW SCHEDULE I IF THE CAR IS MAINLY OPERATED UNDER ONE OR MORE OF THE FOLLOWING CONDITIONS: WHEN MOST TRIPS ARE LESS THAN 4 MILES (6 KILOMETERS). WHEN MOST TRIPS ARE LESS THAN 10 MILES (16 KILOMETERS) AND OUTSIDE TEMPERATURE REMAINS BELOW FREEZING. WHEN MOST TRIPS INCLUDE EXTENDED IDLING AND/OR FREQUENT LOW-SPEED OPERATION AS IN STOP-AND-GO TRAFFIC. TOWING A TRAILER.** OPERATING IN DUSTY AREAS.

SCHEDULE I SHOULD ALSO BE FOLLOWED IF THE CAR IS USED FOR DELIVERY SERVICE, POLICE, TAXI, OR OTHER COMMERCIAL APPLICATION.

TO BE SERVICED	WHEN TO PREFORM MILES (KILOMETERS) OR MONTHS WHICHEVER OCCURS FIRST	THE SERVICE SHOWN IN THIS SCHEDULE UP TO 60,000 MILES (100,000 KM) ARE TO BE PERFORMED AFTER 60,000 MILES (100,00 KM) AT THE SAME INTERVALS.																			
	MILES (000)	3	6	9	12	15	18	21	24	27	30	33	36	39	42	45	48	51	54	57	60
	KILOMETERS (000)	5	10	15	20	25	30	35	40	45	50	55	60	65	70	75	80	85	90	95	100
ENGINE OIL & OIL FILTER CHANGE *	EVERY 3,000 (5000 KM) OR 3 MOS.	•	•	•	•	•	•	•	•	•	•	•	•	•	•	•	•	•	•	•	•
CHASSIS LUBRICATION	EVERY OTHER OIL CHANGE		•		•		•		•		•		•		•		•		•		•
SERVICE TO BE PERFORMED AT LEAST TWICE A YEAR (SEE EXPLANATION)																					
SERVICE TO BE PERFORMED AT LEAST ONCE A YEAR (SEE EXPLANATION)																					
THROTTLE BODY MOUNT BOLT TORQUE (SOME MODELS) *	AT 6,000 MI (10,000 KM) ONLY		•																		
TIRE & WHEEL INSP. AND ROTATION	AT 6,000 MI. (10,000 KM) AND THEN EVERY 12,000 MI. (20,000 KM)		•				•				•				•				•		
ENGINE ACCESSARY DRIVE BELT(S) INSP.*	EVERY 30,000 MI. (50,000 KM) OR 24 MOS.										•										•
COOLING SYSTEM SERVICE *	EVERY 30,000 MI. (50,000 KM) OR 24 MOS.										•										•
TRANSMISSION/TRANSAXLE SERVICE	SEE EXPLANATION FOR SERVICE INTERVAL																				
SPARK PLUG REPLACEMENT	4 CYL: 100,000 MI. (160,900 KM) 6 CYL: 30,000 MI. (50,000 KM)																				
SPARK PLUG WIRE INSP. (SOME MODELS)*	EVERY 30,000 MI. (50,000 KM)										•										•
EGR SYSTEM INSP.*††	EVERY 30,000 MI. (50,000 KM) OR 36 MOS.										•										•
AIR CLEANER & PVC INLET FILTER ELEMENT REPLACEMENT *	EVERY 30,000 MI. (50,000 KM) OR 36 MOS.										•										•
FUEL TANK, CAP, & LINES INSP.*††	EVERY 30,000 MI. (50,000 KM)										•										•

FOOTNOTES:

* AN EMISSION CONTROL SERVICE

†† THE U.S. ENVIRONMENTAL PROTECTION AGENCY OR CALIFORNIA AIR RESOURCES BOARD HAS DETERMINED THAT THE FAILURE TO PERFORM THIS MAINTENANCE ITEM WILL NOT NULLIFY THE EMISSION WARRANTY OR LIMIT RECALL LIABILITY PRIOR TO THE COMPLETION OF VEHICLE USEFUL LIFE. GENERAL MOTORS, HOWEVER, URGES THAT ALL RECOMMENDED MAINTENANCE SERVICES BE PERFORMED AT THE INDICATED INTERVALS AND THE MAINTENANCE BE RECORDED IN SECTION C OF THE OWNER'S MAINTENANCE SCHEDULE.

1994-95 Achieva, Beretta, Bonneville, Cavalier, Century, Corsica, Cutlass Ciera, Cutlass Cruiser, Eighty-Eight, Grand Am, LeSabre, Ninety- Eight, Park Avenue, Skylark, Sunbird & Sunfire

+ FOLLOW SCHEDULE II ONLY IF NONE OF THE DRIVING CONDITIONS SPECIFIED IN SCHEDULE I APPLY.

TO BE SERVICED	WHEN TO PERFORM MILES (KILOMETERS) OR MONTHS WHICHEVER OCCURS FIRST	THE SERVICES SHOWN IN THIS SCHEDULE UP TO 60,000 MILES (100,000 KM) ARE TO BE PERFORMED AFTER 60,000 MILES (100,000 KM) AT THE SAME INTERVALS.							
	MILES (000)	7.5	15	22.5	30	37.5	45	52.5	60
	KILOMETERS (000)	12.5	25	37.5	50	62.5	75	87.5	100
ENGINE OIL CHANGE*, PLUS OTHER REQUIRED SERVICES (SEE EXPLANATION)	EVERY 7,500 MI. (12,500 KM) OR 12 MONTHS	•	•	•	•	•	•	•	•
OIL FILTER CHANGE*		•		•		•		•	
CHASSIS LUBRICATION	EVERY 7,500 MI. (12,500) OR 12 MOS.	•	•	•	•	•	•	•	•
SERVICES TO BE PERFORMED AT LEAST TWICE A YEAR (SEE EXPLANATION)									
SERVICES TO BE PERFORMED AT LEAST ONCE A YEAR (SEE EXPLANATION)									
THROTTLE BODY MOUNT BOLT TORQUE (SOME MODELS)	AT 7,500 MI. (12,500 KM) ONLY	•							
TIRE & WHEEL INSP. AND ROTATION	AT 7,500 MI. (12,500 KM) AND THEN EVERY 15,000 MI. (25,000 KM)	•		•		•		•	
ENGINE ACCESSORY DRIVE BELT(S) INSP.*	30,000 MI. (50,000 KM) OR 24 MOS.				•				•
COOLING SYSTEM SERVICE*					•				•
TRANSMISSION/TRANSAXLE SERVICE	SEE EXPLANATION FOR SERVICE INTERVAL								
SPARK PLUG REPLACEMENT *	4 CYL: 100,000 MI. (160,900 KM) 6 CYL: 30,000 MI. (50,000 KM)								
SPARK PLUG WIRE INSP. (SOME MODELS)*	EVERY 30,000 MI. (50,000 KM)				•				•
EGR SYSTEM INSP.* ††	EVERY 30,000 MI. (50,000 KM) OR 36 MOS.				•				•
AIR CLEANER & PCV INLET FILTER ELEMENT REPT.*					•				•
FUEL TANK, CAP & LINES INSP.* ††	EVERY 30,000 MI. (50,000 KM)				•				•

FOOTNOTES:

* AN EMISSION CONTROL SERVICE

†† THE U.S. ENVIRONMENTAL PROTECTION AGENCY OR CALIFORNIA AIR RESOURCES BOARD HAS DETERMINED THAT THE FAILURE TO PERFORM THIS MAINTENANCE ITEM WILL NOT NULLIFY THE EMISSION WARRANTY OR LIMIT RECALL LIABILITY PRIOR TO THE COMPLETION OF VEHICLE USEFUL LIFE. GENERAL MOTORS, HOWEVER, URGES THAT ALL RECOMMENDED

Aurora & 1994-95 Riviera

SCHEDULE I

Follow Schedule I if the vehicle is mainly operated under one or more of the following conditions:

- When most trips are less than 4 miles (6 kilometers).
- When most trips are less than 10 miles (16 kilometers) and outside temperatures remain below freezing.
- When most trips include extended idling and/or frequent low-speed operation as in stop-and-go traffic.
- Towing a trailer **
- Operating in dusty areas.

Schedule I should also be followed if the vehicle is used for delivery service, police, taxi or other commercial applications.

ITEM NO.	TO BE SERVICED	WHEN TO PERFORM Miles (Kilometers) or Months, Whichever Occurs First	The services shown in this schedule up to 48,000 miles (80,000)km are to be performed after 48,000 miles at the same intervals															
		Miles (000)	3	6	9	12	15	18	21	24	27	30	33	36	39	42	45	48
		Kilometer (000)	5	10	15	20	25	30	35	40	45	50	55	60	65	70	75	80
1	Engine Oil & Oil Filter Change *	Every 3,000 (5,000 km) or 3 months	•	•	•	•	•	•	•	•	•	•	•	•	•	•	•	•
2	Chassis Lubrication	Every other oil change		•		•		•		•		•		•		•		•
3	Tire & Wheel Insp. and Rotation	At 6,000 mi (10,000 km) and then every 15,000 mi (25,000 km)		•					•					•				
4	Engine Accy. Drive Belt(s) Insp.	Every 30,000 mi (50,000 km) or 24 months										•						
5	Cooling System Service *											•						
6	Transmission/Transaxle Service	See explanation for service interval																
7	Spark Plug Replacement	Every 30,000 mi (50,000 km)										•						
8	Spark Plug Replacement (Premium V8 only)	Every 100,000 mi (160,000 km)																
9	Spark Plug Wiring Insp. • ††	Every 30,000 mi (50,000 km) or 36 months										•						
10	Air Cleaner Filter Replacement *											•						
												•						
11	Fuel Tank, Cap & Pipes Insp. • ††	Every 30,000 mi (50,000 km)										•						
12	Supercharger Oil Check (3.8L Code 1 engine only)	Every 30,000 mi (50,000 km)										•						

SCHEDULE II

Follow Schedule II ONLY if none of the driving conditions specified in Schedule I apply.

ITEM NO.	TO BE SERVICED	WHEN TO PERFORM Miles (Kilometers) or Months, Whichever occurs first	The services shown in this schedule up to 45,000 miles (75,000 km) are to be performed after 45,000 miles at the same intervals.					
		Miles (000)	7.5	15	22.5	30	37.5	45
		Kilometers (000)	12.5	25	37.5	50	62.5	75
1	Engine Oil Change*	Every 7,500 mi (12,500 km) or 12 months	•	•	•	•	•	•
	Filter Change*	At first and every other oil change or 12 months	•		•		•	
2	Chassis Lubrication	Every 7,500 mi. (12,500 km) or 12 months	•	•	•	•	•	•
3	Tire & Wheel Insp. and Rotation	At 7,500 mi (12,500 km) and then every 15,000 mi. (25,000 km) or as necessary	•		•		•	
4	Engine Accy. Drive Belt(s) Insp. *	Every 30,000 mi (50,000 km) or 24 months				•		
5	Cooling System Service *					•		
6	Transmission/Transaxle Service	See explanation for service interval						
7	Spark Plug Replacement	Every 30,000 mi (50,000 km)						
8	Spark Plug Replacement (Premium V8 only)	Every 100,000 mi (160,000 km)				•		
9	Spark Plug Wiring Insp. • ††	Every 30,000 mi (50,000 km) or 36 months				•		
10	Air Cleaner Filter Replacement •							
11	Fuel Tank, Cap & Pipes Insp. • ††	Every 30,000 mi (50,000 km)				•		
12	Supercharger Oil Check (3.8L Code 1 engine only)	Every 30,000 mi (50,000 km)				•		

FOOTNOTES * An Emission Control Service

†† The U.S. Environmental Protection Agency has determined that the failure to perform this maintenance item will not nullify the emmission warranty or limit recall liability prior to the completion of vehicle useful life. General Motors, however , urges that all recommeded maintenance services be performed at the indicated intervals and the maintenance be recorded on Section C of the Owner's Maintenance Schedule.

Aurora & 1994-95 Riviera

SCHEDULED MAINTENANCE SERVICES

SCHEDULE I

Follow Schedule I if your vehicle is MAINLY driven under one or more of the following conditions:

- When most trips are less than 6 kilometers (4 miles).
- When most trips are less than 16 kilometers (10 miles) and outside temperatures remain below freezing.
- When most trips include extended idling and/or frequent low-speed operation as in stop-and-go traffic.†
- Towing a trailer.**
- Operating in dusty areas.

WHEN TO PERFORM: Kilometers (Miles) or Months, Whichever Occurs First

The services shown in this schedule up tp 80 000 km (48,000 miles) are to be performed after 80 000 km (48,000 miles) at the same intervals.

ITEM NO.	TO BE SERVICED	WHEN TO PERFORM	5	10	15	20	25	30	35	40	45	50	55	60	65	70	75	80
		KILOMETERS (000)	5	10	15	20	25	30	35	40	45	50	55	60	65	70	75	80
		MILES (000)	3	6	9	12	15	18	21	24	27	30	33	36	39	42	45	48
1	Engine Oil & Oil Filter Change*	Every 5 000 km (3,000 mi) or 3 mos	•	•	•	•	•	•	•	•	•	•	•	•	•	•	•	•
2	Chassis Lubrication	Every other oil change		•		•		•		•		•		•		•		•
3	Tire & Wheel Assembly Inspection & Rotation	At 10 000 km (6,000 mi) and then every 25 000 km (15,000 mi)		•				•				•				•		
4	Serpentine Drive Belt Inspection	Every 50 000 km (30 000 mi) or 24 mos										•						
5	Cooling System Service*	Every 50 000 km (30 000 mi) or 24 mos										•						
6	Transmission Service	See explanation for service interval																
7	Spark Plug Assembly Replacement*	See explanation for service interval																
8	Spark Plug Wire Assembly Inspection*‡	Every 50 000 km (30,000 mi)										•						
9	Air Cleaner & Crankcase Ventilation Filter Replacement*	Every 50 000 km (30,000 mi)										•						
10	Fuel Tank, Cap & Lines Inspection*‡	Every 50 000 km (30,000 mi)										•						

† Note. Schedule I should also be followed if the vehicle is used for delivery service, police, taxi or other commercial applications.

‡ The U.S. Environmental Protection Agency has determined that the failure to perform this maintenance Item will not nullify the emission warranty or limit recall liability prior to the completion of vehicle useful life. General Motors, however, urges that all recommended maintenance services be performed at the indicated intervals and the maintenance be recorded in section E of the owner's maintenance schedule.

* An Emission Control Service

** Do not exceed trailering limits See your Owner's Manual for details

Aurora & 1994-95 Riviera

SCHEDULED MAINTENANCE SERVICES
SCHEDULE II

Follow schedule II ONLY if none of the driving conditions specified in Schedule I apply.

ITEM NO.	TO BE SERVICED	WHEN TO PERFORM Kilometers (Miles) or Months, Whichever Occurs First	The services shown in this schedule up to 75 000 km (45,000 miles) are to be performed after 75 000 km (45,000 miles) at the same intervals.					
		KILOMETERS (000)	12..5	25	37.5	50	62.5	75
		MILES (000)	7.5	15	22.5	30	37.5	45
1.	Engine Oil Change*	Every 12 500 km (7,500 mi.) or 12 mos.	•	•	•	•	•	•
	Oil Filter Change*	At first and then every other oil change	•		•		•	
2.	Chassis Lubrication	Every 12 500 km (7,500 mi.) or 12 mos.	•	•	•	•	•	•
3.	Tire & Wheel Assembly Inspection & Rotation	At 12 500 km (7,500 mi.) and then every 25 000km (15,000mi.)	•		•		•	
4.	Serpentine Drive Belt Inspection	Every 50 000 km (30,000 mi.) or 24 mos.				•		
5.	Cooling System Service*							
6.	Transmission Service	See explanation for service interval.						
7.	Spark Plug Assembly Replacement*							
8.	Spark Plug Wire Assembly Inspection*‡	Every 50 000 km (30,000 mi.)				•		
9.	Air Cleaner & Crankcase Ventilation Filter Replacement*					•		
10.	Fuel Tank Cap & Lines Inspection*‡					•		

‡ The U.S. Environmental Protection Agency has determined that the failure to perform this maintenance item will not nullify the emission warranty or limit recall liability prior to the completion of vehicle useful life. General Motors, however, urges that all recommended maintenance services be performed at the indicated intervals and the maintenance be recorded in section E of the owner's maintenance schedule.

* An Emission Control Service.

LeMans

Select and follow Schedule I or Schedule II based on how you use your car:

SCHEDULE I

Follow Schedule I if your car is mainly operated under one or more of the following conditions:

- When most trips are less than 4 miles (6 kilometers).
- When most trips are less than 10 miles (16 kilometers) and outside temperatures remain below freezing.
- Idling and/or low speed operation in stop-and-go traffic.
- Operating in dusty areas.

Schedule I should also be followed if the car is used for delivery service, police, taxi or other commercial applications.

ITEM NO.	TO BE SERVICED	WHEN TO PERFORM Miles (kilometers) or Months, Whichever Occurs First	The services shown in this schedule up to 48,000 miles (80 000 km) are to be performed after 48,000 miles at the same intervals.															
		MILES (000)	3	6	9	12	15	18	21	24	27	30	33	36	39	42	45	48
		KILOMETERS (000)	5	10	15	20	25	30	35	40	45	50	55	60	65	70	75	80
1	Engine Oil & Oil Filter Change*	Every 3,000 miles (5 000 km) or 3 months	•	•	•	•	•	•	•	•	•	•	•	•	•	•	•	•
2	Throttle Body Mounting Bolt Torque*	At 6,000 miles (10 000 km) only		•														
3	Tire & Wheel Rotation	At 6,000 miles (10 000 km), and then every 15,000 miles (25 000 km)		•					•					•				
4	Drive Belt Inspection*	Every 30,000 miles (50 000 km) or 24 months										•						
5	Cooling System Service*											•						
6	Brake System Service	See Explanation on Page 1																
7	Transaxle Service																	
8	Spark Plug Service*	Every 30,000 miles (50 000 km)										•						
9	Spark Plug Wire Inspection*											•						
10	Fuel Micro-Filter Replacement*	Every 30,000 miles (50 000 km) or 36 months										•						
11	Air Cleaner Element Replacement*											•						
12	Engine Timing Check*	Every 30,000 miles (50 000 km)										•						
13	Fuel Tank, Cap & Lines Inspection*											•						
14	Thermostatically Controlled Air Cleaner Inspection*											•						

SCHEDULE II

Follow Schedule II **only** if none of the driving conditions specified in Schedule I apply.

ITEM NO.	TO BE SERVICED	WHEN TO PERFORM Miles (kilometers) or Months, Whichever Occurs First	The services shown in this schedule up to 45,000 miles (75 000 km) are to be performed after 45,000 miles at the same intervals					
		MILES (000)	7.5	15	22.5	30	37.5	45
		KILOMETERS (000)	12.5	25	37.5	50	62.5	75
1	Engine Oil & Oil Filter Change*	Every 7,500 miles (12 500 km) or 12 months	•	•	•	•	•	•
2	Throttle Body Mounting Bolt Torque*	At 7,500 miles (12 500 km) only	•					
3	Tire & Wheel Rotation	At 7,500 miles (12 500 km) and then every 15,000 miles (25 000 km)	•		•		•	
4	Drive Belt Inspection*	Every 30,000 miles (50 000 km) or 24 months				•		
5	Cooling System Service*					•		
6	Brake System Service	See Explanation on Page 1						
7	Transaxle Service							
8	Spark Plug Service*	Every 30,000 miles (50 000 km)				•		
9	Spark Plug Wire Inspection*					•		
10	Fuel Micro-Filter Replacement*	Every 30,000 miles (50 000 km) or 36 months				•		
11	Air Cleaner Element Replacement*					•		
12	Engine Timing Check*	Every 30,000 miles (50 000 km)				•		
13	Fuel Tank, Cap & Lines Inspection*					•		
14	Thermostatically Controlled Air Cleaner Inspection*					•		

FOOTNOTES:

* *An Emission Control Service.*

Metro

SCHEDULED MAINTENANCE SERVICES
SCHEDULE I

Follow Schedule I if your vehicle is MAINLY operated under one or more of the following conditions:

- When most trips are less than 4 miles (6 kilometers).
- When most trips are less than 10 miles (16 kilometers) and outside temperatures remain below freezing.
- When most trips include extended idling and/or frequent low-speed operation as in stop-and-go traffic.
- Operating in dusty areas.

Schedule I should also be followed if the vehicle is used for delivery service, police, taxi or other commercial applications.

	TO BE SERVICED	WHEN TO PERFORM Miles (kilometers) or Months, Whichever Occurs First (Also, See Explanation of Services Pages 6–7)*	The services shown in this schedule up to 60 000 miles (100 000 km) are to be performed after 60 000 miles at the same intervals.																			
			MILES (000)																			
			3	6	9	12	15	18	21	24	27	30	33	36	39	42	45	48	51	54	57	60
			KILOMETERS (000)																			
			5	10	15	20	25	30	35	40	45	50	55	60	65	70	75	80	85	90	95	100
1	Engine Oil and Oil Filter Change*	Every 3 000 Miles (5 000 km) or 3 Months	•	•	•	•	•	•	•	•	•	•	•	•	•	•	•	•	•	•	•	•
2	Chassis Lubrication	Every Other Oil Change		•		•		•		•		•		•		•		•		•		•
3	Tire and Wheel Inspection and Rotation	Every 6 000 Miles (10 000 km)		•		•		•		•		•		•		•		•		•		•
4	Water Pump Belt Inspection*	Every 30 000 Miles (50 000 km) or 30 Months										•										•
5	Cooling System Service*	See Explanation of Scheduled Maintenance Services																				
6	Brake Fluid Inspection	Every 15 000 Miles (25 000 km) or 15 Months					•					•					•					•
7	Transaxle Service	See Explanation of Scheduled Maintenance Services																				
8	Spark Plug Replacement*	Every 30 000 Miles (50 000 km)										•										•
9	Spark Plug Wires, Replacement*	Every 60 000 Miles (100 000 km) or 60 Months																				•
10	Air Cleaner Element Replacement*	Every 30 000 Miles (50 000 km) or 30 Months										•										•
11	Fuel Tank, Cap and Lines—Inspection*‡	Every 15 000 Miles (25 000 km) or 15 Months					•					•					•					•

** An Emission Control Service*

‡The U.S. Environmental Protection Agency has determined that the failure to perform this maintenance item will not nullify the emission warranty or limit recall liability prior to the completion of vehicle useful life. General Motors, however, urges that all recommended maintenance services be performed at the indicated intervals and the maintenance be recorded in the Maintenance Schedule Booklet.

Metro

SCHEDULED MAINTENANCE SERVICES
SCHEDULE II

Follow Schedule II only if none of the driving conditions specified in Schedule I apply.

	TO BE SERVICED	WHEN TO PERFORM Miles (kilometers) or Months, Whichever Occurs First (Also, See Explanation of Services Pages 6–7)	The services shown in this schedule up to 60 000 miles (100 000 km) are to be performed after 60 000 miles at the same intervals. MILES (000)							
			7.5	15	22.5	30	37.5	45	52.5	60
			KILOMETERS (000)							
			12.5	25	37.5	50	62.5	75	87.5	100
1	Engine Oil and Oil Filter Change*	Every 7 500 Miles (12 500 km) or 7.5 Months	•	•	•	•	•	•	•	•
2	Chassis Lubrication	Every 7 500 Miles (12 500 km) or 7.5 Months	•	•	•	•	•	•	•	•
3	Tire and Wheel Inspection and Rotation	At 7 500 Miles (12 500 km) and Then Every 15 000 Miles (25 000 km)	•		•		•		•	
4	Water Pump Belt Inspection*	Every 30 000 Miles (50 000 km) or 30 Months				•				•
5	Cooling System Service*	See Explanation of Scheduled Maintenance Services		•		•		•		•
6	Brake Fluid Inspection	Every 15 000 Miles (25 000 km) or 15 Months		•		•		•		•
7	Transaxle Service	See Explanation of Scheduled Maintenance Services								
8	Spark Plug Replacement*	Every 30 000 Miles (50 000 km)				•				•
9	Spark Plug Wires, Replacement*	Every 60 000 Miles (100 000 km) or 60 Months								•
10	Air Cleaner Element Replacement*	Every 30 000 Miles (50 000 km) or 30 Months				•				•
11	Fuel Tank, Cap and Lines—Inspection*‡	Every 15 000 Miles (25 000 km) or 15 Months		•		•		•		•

* An Emission Control Service

‡ The U.S. Environmental Protection Agency has determined that the failure to perform this maintenance item will not nullify the emission warranty or limit recall liability prior to the completion of vehicle useful life. General Motors, however, urges that all recommended maintenance services be performed at the indicated intervals and the maintenance be recorded in the Maintenance Schedule Booklet.

Prizm

TO BE SERVICED	WHEN TO PERFORM MILES (KILOMETERS) OR MONTHS WHICHEVER OCCURS FIRST	THE SERVICES SHOWN IN THIS SCHEDULE UP TO 60,000 MILES (100 000 km) ARE TO BE PERFORMED AFTER 60,000 MILES (100 000 km) AT THE SAME INTERVALS									
	MILES (000)	3.75	7.5	11.25	15	18.75	22.5	26.25	30	33.75	37.5
	KILOMETERS	6 200	12 500	18 700	25 000	31 250	37 500	43 750	50 000	56250	62 500
ENGINE OIL & FILTER CHANGE*	EVERY 3,750 mi. (6 200 km) OR 6 mos. FIRST AND EVERY OTHER OIL CHANGE.	•	•	•	•	•	•	•	•	•	•
CHASSIS LUBRICATION	EVERY OTHER OIL CHANGE.		•		•		•		•		•
VALVE CLEARANCE ADJUSTMENT	EVERY 60,000 mi. (100 000 km) OR 72 mos.										
ENGINE TIMING BELT REPLACEMENT											
ENGINE IDLE SPEED ADJUSTMENT	AT 7,500 mi. (12 500 km) OR 12 mos. AND THEN EVERY 15,000 mi. (25 000 km) OR 24 mos.		•				•				•
TIRE & WHEEL INSPECTION AND ROTATION	AT 6,000 mi. (10 000 km) AND THEN EVERY 15,000 mi. (25 000 km).										
ENGINE ACCESSORY DRIVE BELT(S) INSPECTION*											
COOLING SYSTEM SERVICE*											
TRANSAXLE SERVICE											
SPARK PLUG REPLACEMENT (VIN 5)*	EVERY 60,000 mi. (100 000 km) OR 72 mos.										
SPARK PLUG REPLACEMENT (VIN 6)*	EVERY 30,000 mi. (50 000 km) OR 36 mos.								•		
CHARCOAL CANISTER INSPECTION*	SEE EXPLANATION FOR SERVICE INTERVAL.										
AIR CLEANER FILTER SERVICE*	SEE EXPLANATION FOR SERVICE INTERVAL.										
FUEL TANK, CAP & LINES INSPECTION*††	EVERY 30,000 mi. (50 000 km) OR 36 mos.								•		
FUEL TANK, CAP GASKET REPLACEMENT											

FOOTNOTES: * AN EMISSION CONTROL SERVICE

†† THE U.S. ENVIRONMENTAL AGENCY HAS DETERMINED THAT THE FAILURE TO PERFORM THIS MAINTENANCE ITEM WILL NOT NULLIFY THE EMISSION WARRANTY OR LIMIT RECALL LIABILITY PRIOR TO THE COMPLETION OF VEHICLE'S USEFUL LIFE. GENERAL MOTORS, HOWEVER, URGES THAT ALL RECOMMENDED MAINTENANCE SERVICES BE PERFORMED AT THE INDICATED INTERVALS AND THE MAINTENANCE BE RECORDED IN SECTION E OF THE OWNER'S MAINTENANCE SCHEDULE.

** TRAILERING IS NOT RECOMMENDED FOR SOME MODELS, SEE THE OWNER'S MANUAL FOR DETAILS.

Prizm

TO BE SERVICED	WHEN TO PERFORM MILES (KILOMETERS) OR MONTHS WHICHEVER OCCURS FIRST	THE SERVICES SHOWN IN THIS SCHEDULE UP TO 60.000 MILES (100 000 km) ARE TO BE PERFORMED AFTER 60.000 MILES (100 000 km) AT THE SAME INTERVALS.							
	MILES (000)	7.5	15	22.5	30	37.5	45	52.5	60
	KILOMETERS (000)	12.54	25	37.5	50	62.5	75	87.5	100
ENGINE OIL & OIL FILTER CHANGE*	EVERY 7.500 mi. (12 500 km) OR 12 mos.	•	•	•	•	•	•	•	•
CHASSIS LUBRICATION	EVERY OTHER OIL CHANGE.		•		•		•		•
VALVE CLEARANCE ADJUSTMENT	EVERY 60.000 mi. (100 000 km) OR 72 mos.								•
ENGINE IDLE SPEED ADJUSTMENT	AT 7.500 mi. (12 500 km) OR 12 mos. AND THEN EVERY 15.000 mi. (25 000 km) OR 24 mos.	•		•		•		•	
COOLING SYSTEM SERVICE	AT 45.000 mi. (75 000 km) OR 36 mos AND THEN EVERY 30.000 mi. (50 000 km) OR 24 mos.						•		
CHARCOAL CANISTER INSPECTION									
TIRE & WHEEL INSPECTION AND ROTATION	AT 7.500 mi. (12 500 km) AND THEN EVERY 15.000 mi. (25 000 km).	•		•		•		•	
ENGINE ACCESSORY DRIVE BELT(S) INSPECTION*									
FUEL TANK CAP GASKET REPLACEMENT									
TRANSAXLE SERVICE									
SPARK PLUG REPLACEMENT (VIN 5)*	EVERY 60.000 mi. (100 000 km) OR 72 mos								•
SPARK PLUG REPLACEMENT (VIN 6)*	EVERY 30.000 mi. (50 000 km) OR 36 mos.				•				•
EGR SYSTEM INSPECTION*††	EVERY 30.000 mi. (50 000 km) OR 36 mos.				•				•
AIR CLEANER FILTER REPLACEMENT*	EVERY 30.000 mi. (50 000 km) OR 36 mos.				•				•
FUEL TANK, CAP & LINES INSPECTION*††	EVERY 30.000 mi. (50 000 km) OR 36 mos.				•				•
PCV SYSTEM INSPECTION*									

FOOTNOTES: * AN EMISSION CONTROL SERVICE

†† THE U.S. ENVIRONMENTAL AGENCY HAS DETERMINED THAT THE FAILURE TO PERFORM THIS MAINTENANCE ITEM WILL NOT NULLIFY THE EMISSION WARRANTY OR LIMIT RECALL LIABILITY PRIOR TO THE COMPLETION OF VEHICLE'S USEFUL LIFE. GENERAL MOTORS. HOWEVER. URGES THAT ALL RECOMMENDED MAINTENANCE SERVICES BE PERFORMED AT THE INDICATED INTERVALS AND THE MAINTENANCE BE RECORDED IN SECTION E OF THE OWNER'S MAINTENANCE SCHEDULE.

Storm

SCHEDULED MAINTENANCE SERVICES
SCHEDULE I

Follow Schedule I if your car is MAINLY operated under one or more of the following conditions:

- When most trips are less than 4 miles (6 kilometers).
- When most trips are less than 10 miles (16 kilometers) and outside temperatures remain below freezing.
- When most trips include extended idling and/or frequent low-speed operation as in stop-and-go traffic.
- Towing a trailer.#
- Operating in dusty areas.

Schedule I should also be followed if the car is used for delivery service, police, taxi or other commercial applications.

The services shown in this schedule up to 60 000 miles (100 000 km) are to be performed after 60 000 miles at the same intervals.

	TO BE SERVICED	WHEN TO PERFORM Miles (kilometers) or Months, Whichever Occurs First	3	6	9	12	15	18	21	24	27	30	33	36	39	42	45	48	51	54	57	60
		MILES (000) / KILOMETERS (000)	5	10	15	20	25	30	35	40	45	50	55	60	65	70	75	80	85	90	95	100
1	Engine Oil Replacement*	Every 3 000 Miles (5 000 km) or 3 Months	•	•	•	•	•	•	•	•	•	•	•	•	•	•	•	•	•	•	•	•
	Oil Filter Replacement*	At First and Then Every Other Oil Change	•		•		•		•		•		•		•		•		•		•	•
2	Chassis and Body Lubrication	Every Other Oil Change		•		•		•		•		•		•		•		•		•		•
3	Valve Clearance Adjustment* VIN 6	Every 15 000 Miles (25 000 km)					•					•					•					•
	VIN 5	Every 60 000 Miles (100 000 km)																				•
4	Timing Belt Replacement	Every 60 000 Miles (100 000 km)																				•
5	Tire and Wheel Inspection and Rotation	At 6 000 Miles (10 000 km) and Then Every 15 000 Miles (25 000 km)		•					•					•					•			
6	Drive Belt Inspection*	Every 30 000 Miles (50 000 km)										•										•
7	Cooling System Inspection*	Every 15 000 Miles (25 000 km)					•					•					•					•
	Cooling System Refill*	Every 30 000 Miles (50 000 km)										•										•
8	Manual Transaxle Fluid Replacement	Every 15 000 Miles (25 000 km)					•					•					•					•
	Automatic Transaxle Fluid Replacement	Every 15 000 Miles (25 000 km)					•					•					•					•
9	Spark Plug Replacement*	Every 30 000 Miles (50 000 km)										•										•
10	Power Steering Fluid Replacement	Every 21 000 Miles (35 000 km) or 24 Months							•							•						
11	Power Steering Hose Inspection	Every 42 000 Miles (70 000 km)														•						
12	Air Cleaner Element Replacement*	See Explanation of Scheduled Maintenance Services										•										•
13	Fuel Cap, Lines and Tank Inspection*‡	Every 15 000 Miles (25 000 km)					•					•					•					•
14	PCV Valve Inspection*‡	Every 30 000 Miles (50 000 km)										•										•

** An Emission Control Service.*

‡The U.S. Environmental Protection Agency has determined that the failure to perform this maintenance item will not nullify the emission warranty or limit recall liability prior to the completion of vehicle useful life. General Motors, however, urges that all recommended maintenance services be performed at the indicated intervals and the maintenance be recorded in Section C of the Owner's Maintenance Schedule.

 # Trailering is not recommended for some models. See your Owner's Manual for details.

Storm

SCHEDULED MAINTENANCE SERVICES SCHEDULE II

Follow Schedule II only if none of the driving conditions specified in Schedule I apply.

The services shown in this schedule up to 60 000 miles (96 000 km) are to be performed after 60 000 miles at the same intervals.

	TO BE SERVICED	WHEN TO PERFORM Miles (kilometers) or Months, Whichever Occurs First	MILES (000) 3	6	7.5	9	12	15	18	21	22.5	24	27	30	33	36	37.5	39	42	45	48	51	52.5	54	57	60
			KILOMETERS (000) 5	10	12.5	15	20	25	30	35	37.5	40	45	50	55	60	62.5	65	70	75	80	85	87.5	90	95	100
1	Engine Oil Replacement*	Every 7 500 Miles (12 500 km) or 12 Months			•			•			•			•			•			•			•			•
	Oil Filter Replacement*	At First and Then Every Other Oil Change			•						•						•						•			
2	Chassis and Body Lubrication	Every 7 500 Miles (12 500 km) or 12 Months			•			•			•			•			•			•			•			•
3	Valve Clearance Adjustment* VIN 6	Every 15 000 Miles (25 000 km)						•						•						•						•
	VIN 5	Every 60 000 Miles (100 000 km)																								•
4	Timing Belt Replacement	Every 60 000 Miles (100 000 km)																								•
5	Tire and Wheel Inspection and Rotation	At 7 500 Miles (12 500 km) and Then Every 15 000 Miles (25 000 km)			•						•						•						•			
6	Drive Belt Inspection*	Every 30 000 Miles (50 000 km)												•												•
7	Cooling System Inspection*	Every 15 000 Miles (25 000 km)						•						•						•						•
	Cooling System Refill*	Every 30 000 Miles (50 000 km)												•												•
8	Manual Transaxle Fluid Replacement	Every 30 000 Miles (50 000 km)												•												•
	Automatic Transaxle Fluid Replacement	Every 30 000 Miles (50 000 km)												•												•
9	Spark Plug Replacement*	Every 30 000 Miles (50 000 km)												•												•
10	Power Steering Fluid Replacement	Every 22 500 Miles (37 500 km) or 24 Months									•									•						
11	Power Steering Hose Inspection	Every 45 000 Miles (75 000 km)																		•						
12	Air Cleaner Element Replacement*	Every 30 000 Miles (50 000 km)												•												•
13	Fuel Cap, Lines and Tank Inspection*‡	Every 15 000 Miles (25 000 km)						•						•						•						•
14	PCV Valve Inspection*‡	Every 30 000 Miles (50 000 km)												•												•

*An Emission Control Service.

‡The U.S. Environmental Protection Agency has determined that the failure to perform this maintenance item will not nullify the emission warranty or limit recall liability prior to the completion of vehicle useful life. General Motors, however, urges that all recommended maintenance services be performed at the indicated intervals and the maintenance be recorded in Section C of the Owner's Maintenance Schedule.

Saturn

Follow Schedule I if the car is usually operated under one or more of the following conditions:

- Most trips are less than 8 Km (5 miles).
- It's below freezing outside, day and night.
- It's very humid outside.
- Your engine is often idling or running at low speed, as in heavy traffic.
- You're towing a trailer.
- You drive in dusty places.
- Your Saturn is used for delivery service, police, taxi or other commercial purposes.

Kilometers x 1000 (Miles x 1000)	5 (3)	10 (6)	15 (9)	20 (12)	25 (15)	30 (18)	35 (21)	40 (24)	45 (27)	50 (30)	55 (33)	60 (36)	65 (39)	70 (42)	75 (45)	80 (48)	85 (51)	90 (54)	95 (57)	100 (60)
1. Change engine oil and filter. * Every 3 mos. or 5,000 km (3,000 mi).																				
2. Inspect axle boots, suspension bushings and ball joint seals. Every 6 mos. or 10,000 km (6,000 mi).																				
3. Inspect exhaust system and shields. Every 6 mos. or 10,000 km (6,000 mi).																				
4. Inspect and rotate tires and wheels. At 10,000 km (6,000 mi) and then every 25,000 km (15,000 mi).																				
5. Service manual transaxle, change fluid. At 10,000 km (6,000 mi) only.																				
6. Service automatic transaxle, change fluid. Every 50,000 km (30,000 mi).																				
7. Change automatic transaxle pressure filter. At 50,000 km (30,000 mi) and then every 100,000 km (60,000 mi).																				
8. Replace spark plugs. * Every 50,000 km (30,000 mi).																				
9. Inspect vacuum line/hose. * # Every 24 mos. or 50,000 km (30,000 mi).																				
10. Inspect EGR system. * # Every 24 mos. or 50,000 km (30,000 mi).																				
11. Inspect fuel tank, cap, and pipe/hoses. * # Every 24 mos. or 50,000 km (30,000 mi).																				
12. Inspect engine accessory drive belt and coolant hoses. Every 24 mos. or 50,000 km (30,000 mi).																				
13. Replace engine air filter. * Every 36 mos. or 50,000 km (30,000 mi).																				
14. Flush cooling system, change coolant and check pressure cap. * Every 36 mos. or 60,000 km (36,000 mi).																				
15. Replace fuel filter. Every 48 mos. or 100,000 km (60,000 mi).																				

Saturn

Schedule II should only be followed if none of the conditions for Schedule I apply.

- If trips are more than 8 km (5 miles), more than half of these miles should include non-stop highway driving.

Kilometers x 1000 (Miles x 1000)	5 (3)	10 (6)	15 (9)	20 (12)	25 (15)	30 (18)	35 (21)	40 (24)	45 (27)	50 (30)	55 (33)	60 (36)	65 (39)	70 (42)	75 (45)	80 (48)	85 (51)	90 (54)	95 (57)	100 (60)
1. Change engine oil and filter. * Every 6 mos. or 10,000 km (6,000 mi).																				
2. Inspect axle boots, suspension bushings and ball joint seals. Every 6 mos. or 10,000 km (6,000 mi).																				
3. Inspect exhaust system and shields. Every 6 mos. or 10,000 km (6,000 mi).																				
4. Inspect and rotate tires and wheels. At 10,000 km (6,000 mi) and then every 30,000 km (18,000 mi).																				
5. Service manual transaxle, change fluid. At 10,000 km (6,000 mi).																				
6. Service automatic transaxle, change fluid. Every 50,000 km (30,000 mi).																				
7. Change automatic transaxle pressure filter. At 50,000 km (30,000 mi) and then every 100,000 km (60,000 mi).																				
8. Replace spark plugs. * Every 50,000 km (30,000 mi).																				
9. Inspect vacuum line/hose. * # Every 24 mos. or 50,000 km (30,000 mi).																				
10. Inspect EGR system. * # Every 24 mos. or 50,000 km (30,000 mi).																				
11. Inspect fuel tank, cap, and pipe/hoses. * # Every 24 mos. or 50,000 km (30,000 mi).																				
12. Inspect engine accessory drive belt and coolant hoses. Every 24 mos. or 50,000 km (30,000 mi).																				
13. Replace engine air filter. * Every 36 mos. or 50,000 km (30,000 mi).																				
14. Flush cooling system, change coolant and check pressure cap. * Every 36 mos. or 60,000 km (36,000 mi).																				
15. Replace fuel filter. Every 48 mos. or 100,000 km (60,000 mi).																				

* *An emission control service.*

\# *The U.S. Environmental Protection Agency has determined that the failure to perform the maintenance item will not nullify the emission warranty or limit recall liability prior to the completion of vehicle useful life. Saturn, however, urges that all recommended maintenance services be performed at the indicated intervals and the maintenance be recorded in Section C of the owner's maintenance booklet.*

ELECTRICAL SYMBOL & WIRE COLOR CODE IDENTIFICATION

TABLE OF CONTENTS

Electrical Symbol Identification

INDEX

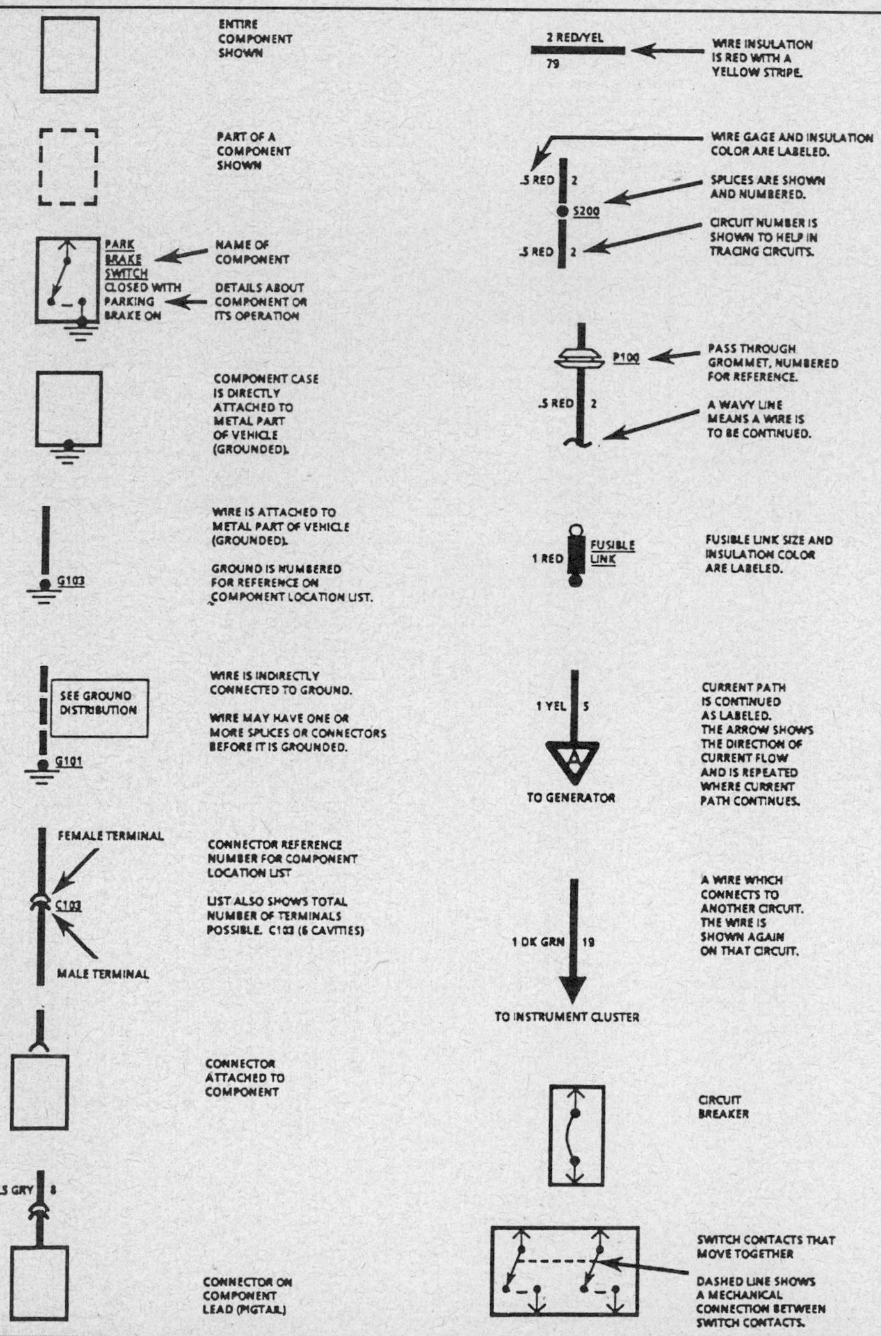

ENTIRE COMPONENT SHOWN
PART OF A COMPONENT SHOWN
PARK BRAKE SWITCH
CLOSED WITH PARKING BRAKE ON
NAME OF COMPONENT
DETAILS ABOUT COMPONENT OR ITS OPERATION
COMPONENT CASE IS DIRECTLY ATTACHED TO METAL PART OF VEHICLE (GROUNDED).
G103
WIRE IS ATTACHED TO METAL PART OF VEHICLE (GROUNDED).
GROUND IS NUMBERED FOR REFERENCE ON COMPONENT LOCATION LIST.
SEE GROUND DISTRIBUTION
G101
WIRE IS INDIRECTLY CONNECTED TO GROUND.
WIRE MAY HAVE ONE OR MORE SPLICES OR CONNECTORS BEFORE IT IS GROUNDED.
FEMALE TERMINAL
C103
MALE TERMINAL
CONNECTOR REFERENCE NUMBER FOR COMPONENT LOCATION LIST
LIST ALSO SHOWS TOTAL NUMBER OF TERMINALS POSSIBLE. C103 (6 CAVITIES)
CONNECTOR ATTACHED TO COMPONENT
.5 GRY
8
CONNECTOR ON COMPONENT LEAD (PIGTAIL)
2 RED/YEL
79
WIRE INSULATION IS RED WITH A YELLOW STRIPE.
WIRE GAGE AND INSULATION COLOR ARE LABELED.
.5 RED
2
S200
SPLICES ARE SHOWN AND NUMBERED.
CIRCUIT NUMBER IS SHOWN TO HELP IN TRACING CIRCUITS.
P100
PASS THROUGH GROMMET, NUMBERED FOR REFERENCE.
A WAVY LINE MEANS A WIRE IS TO BE CONTINUED.
1 RED
FUSIBLE LINK
FUSIBLE LINK SIZE AND INSULATION COLOR ARE LABELED.
1 YEL
5
A
TO GENERATOR
CURRENT PATH IS CONTINUED AS LABELED. THE ARROW SHOWS THE DIRECTION OF CURRENT FLOW AND IS REPEATED WHERE CURRENT PATH CONTINUES.
1 DK GRN
19
TO INSTRUMENT CLUSTER
A WIRE WHICH CONNECTS TO ANOTHER CIRCUIT. THE WIRE IS SHOWN AGAIN ON THAT CIRCUIT.
CIRCUIT BREAKER
SWITCH CONTACTS THAT MOVE TOGETHER
DASHED LINE SHOWS A MECHANICAL CONNECTION BETWEEN SWITCH CONTACTS.

Fig 1 Symbol Identification (Part 1 of 3). Except Saturn

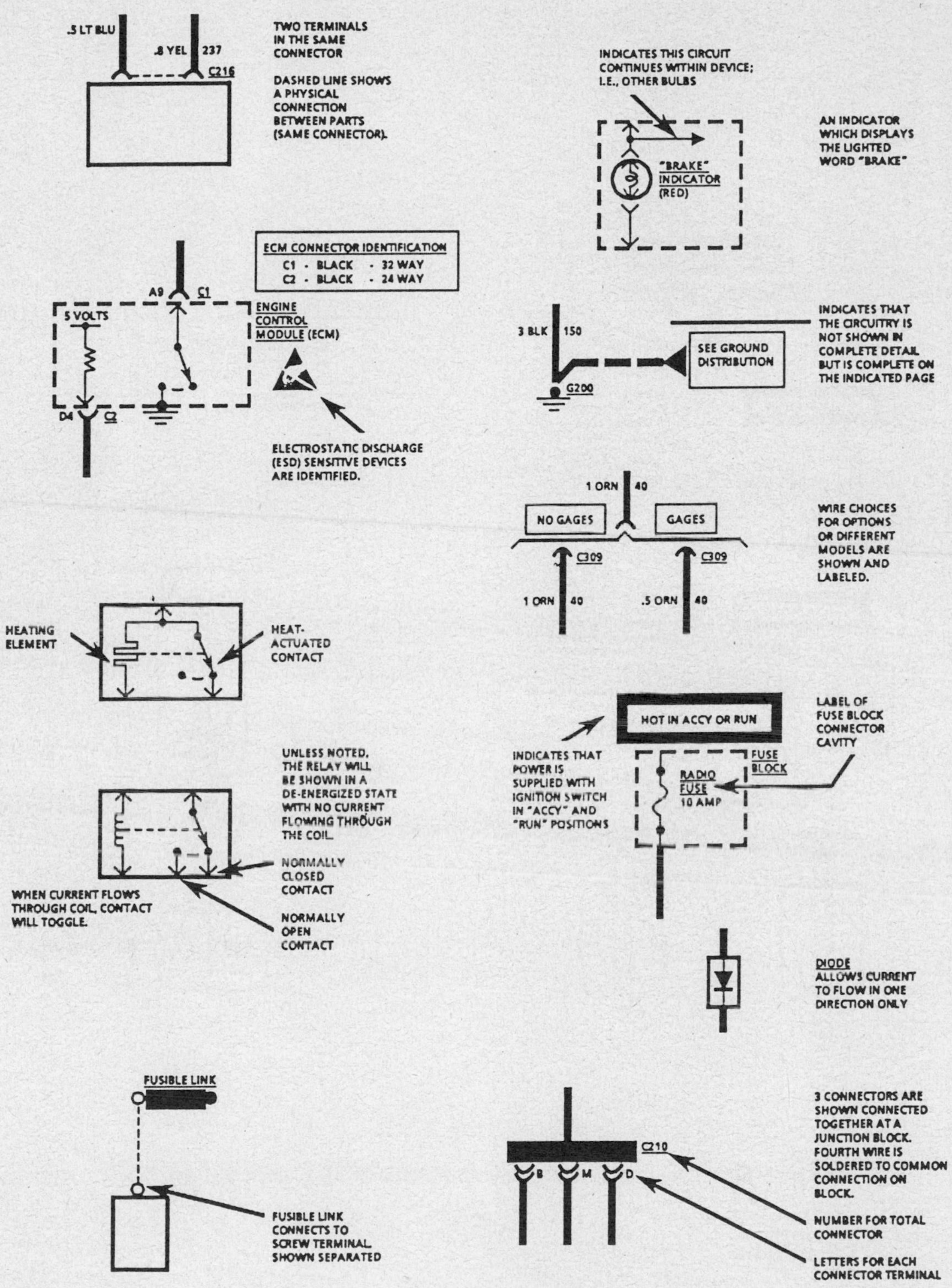

.5 LT BLU
.8 YEL
237
C216
TWO TERMINALS IN THE SAME CONNECTOR
DASHED LINE SHOWS A PHYSICAL CONNECTION BETWEEN PARTS (SAME CONNECTOR).
INDICATES THIS CIRCUIT CONTINUES WITHIN DEVICE; I.E., OTHER BULBS
"BRAKE" INDICATOR (RED)
AN INDICATOR WHICH DISPLAYS THE LIGHTED WORD "BRAKE"
ECM CONNECTOR IDENTIFICATION
C1 - BLACK - 32 WAY
C2 - BLACK - 24 WAY
A9
C1
5 VOLTS
ENGINE CONTROL MODULE (ECM)
D4
C2
ELECTROSTATIC DISCHARGE (ESD) SENSITIVE DEVICES ARE IDENTIFIED.
3 BLK
150
SEE GROUND DISTRIBUTION
G200
INDICATES THAT THE CIRCUITRY IS NOT SHOWN IN COMPLETE DETAIL BUT IS COMPLETE ON THE INDICATED PAGE
1 ORN
40
NO GAGES
GAGES
C309
C309
1 ORN
40
.5 ORN
40
WIRE CHOICES FOR OPTIONS OR DIFFERENT MODELS ARE SHOWN AND LABELED.
HEATING ELEMENT
HEAT-ACTUATED CONTACT
HOT IN ACCY OR RUN
LABEL OF FUSE BLOCK CONNECTOR CAVITY
INDICATES THAT POWER IS SUPPLIED WITH IGNITION SWITCH IN "ACCY" AND "RUN" POSITIONS
FUSE BLOCK
RADIO FUSE 10 AMP
UNLESS NOTED, THE RELAY WILL BE SHOWN IN A DE-ENERGIZED STATE WITH NO CURRENT FLOWING THROUGH THE COIL.
NORMALLY CLOSED CONTACT
WHEN CURRENT FLOWS THROUGH COIL, CONTACT WILL TOGGLE.
NORMALLY OPEN CONTACT
DIODE ALLOWS CURRENT TO FLOW IN ONE DIRECTION ONLY
FUSIBLE LINK
FUSIBLE LINK CONNECTS TO SCREW TERMINAL. SHOWN SEPARATED
C210
B
M
D
3 CONNECTORS ARE SHOWN CONNECTED TOGETHER AT A JUNCTION BLOCK. FOURTH WIRE IS SOLDERED TO COMMON CONNECTION ON BLOCK.
NUMBER FOR TOTAL CONNECTOR
LETTERS FOR EACH CONNECTOR TERMINAL

Fig 1 Symbol Identification (Part 2 of 3). Except Saturn

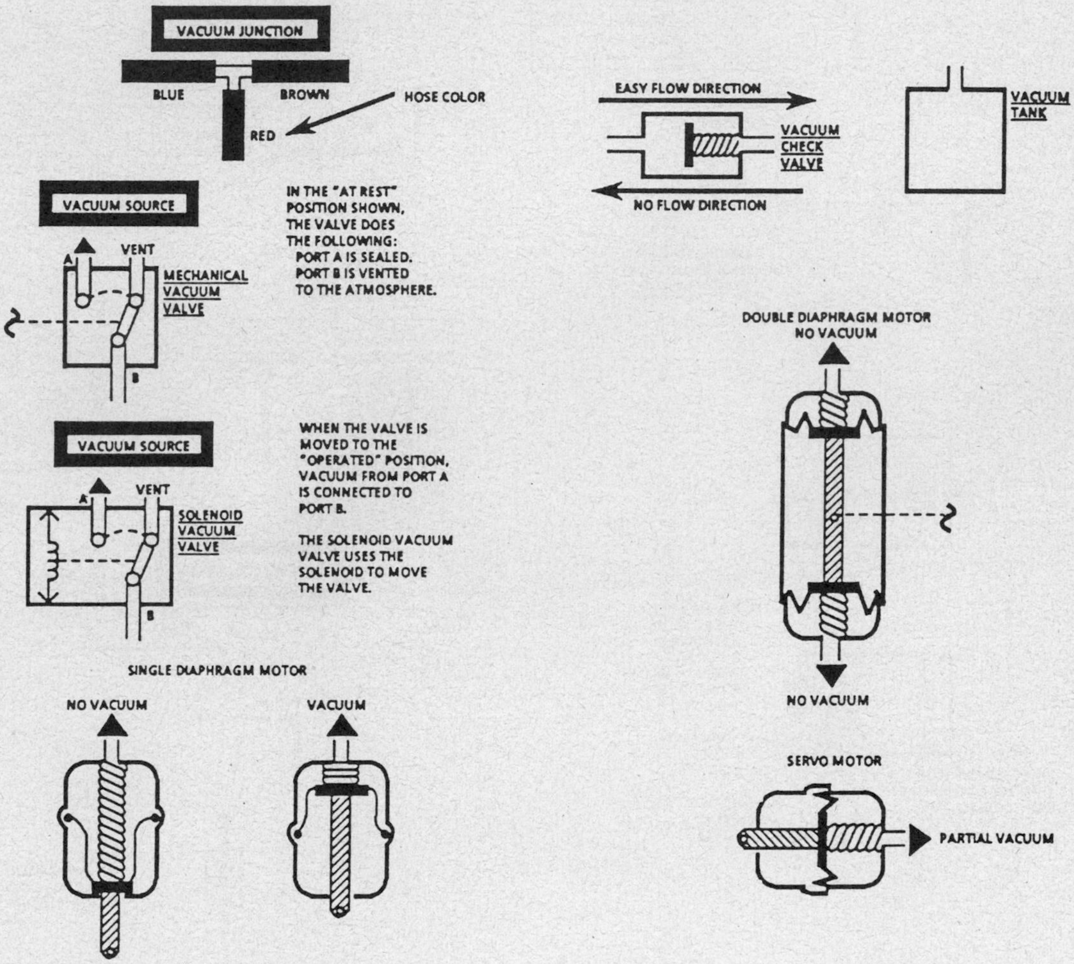
VACUUM JUNCTION
BLUE
BROWN
HOSE COLOR
RED
EASY FLOW DIRECTION
VACUUM CHECK VALVE
NO FLOW DIRECTION
VACUUM TANK
VACUUM SOURCE
VENT
A
MECHANICAL VACUUM VALVE
B
IN THE "AT REST" POSITION SHOWN, THE VALVE DOES THE FOLLOWING:
PORT A IS SEALED.
PORT B IS VENTED TO THE ATMOSPHERE.
VACUUM SOURCE
VENT
A
SOLENOID VACUUM VALVE
B
WHEN THE VALVE IS MOVED TO THE "OPERATED" POSITION, VACUUM FROM PORT A IS CONNECTED TO PORT B.
THE SOLENOID VACUUM VALVE USES THE SOLENOID TO MOVE THE VALVE.
DOUBLE DIAPHRAGM MOTOR
NO VACUUM
NO VACUUM
SINGLE DIAPHRAGM MOTOR
NO VACUUM
VACUUM
SERVO MOTOR
PARTIAL VACUUM

Fig 1 Symbol Identification (Part 3 of 3). Except Saturn

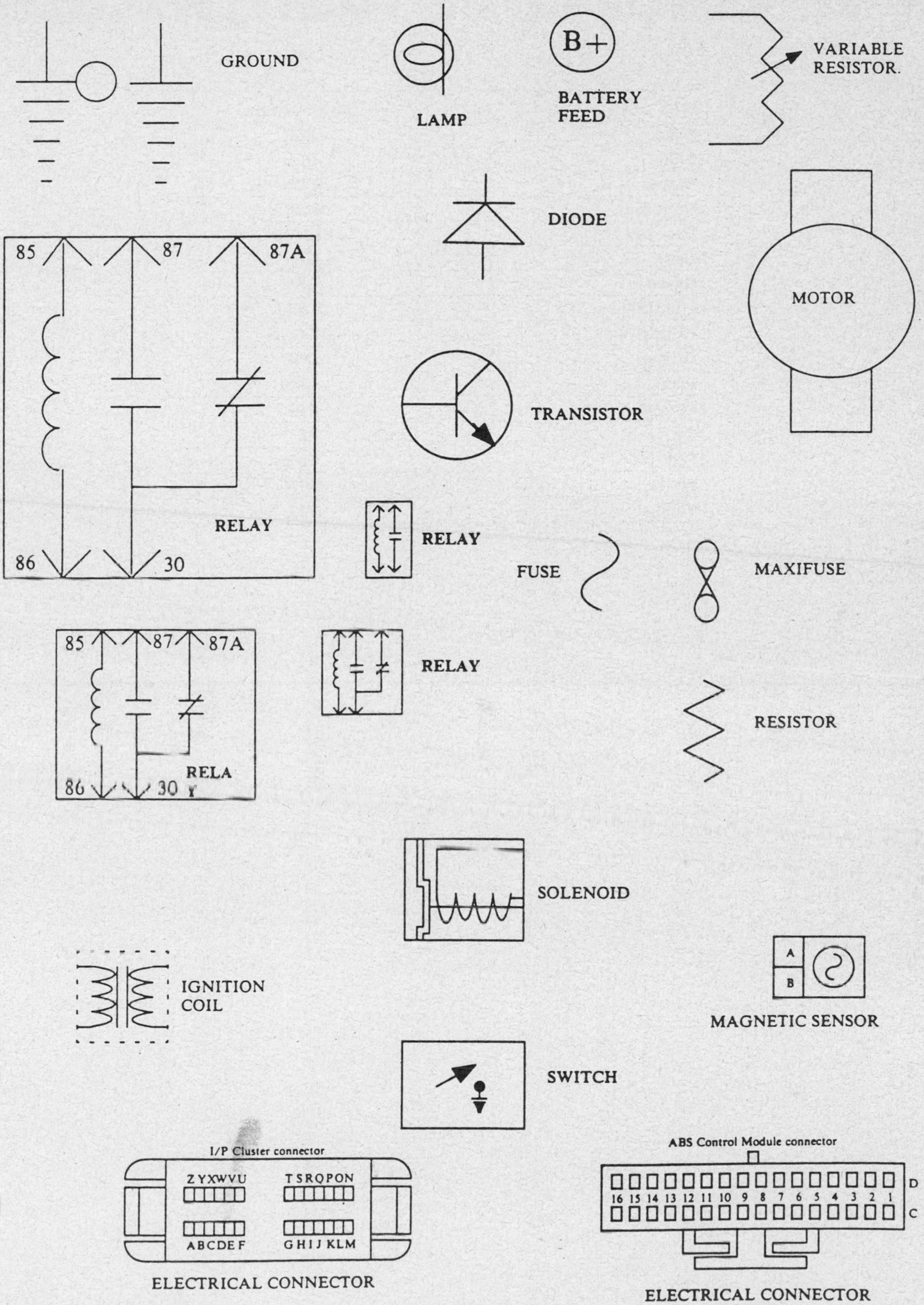
GROUND
LAMP
B+
BATTERY FEED
VARIABLE RESISTOR.
DIODE
MOTOR
85
87
87A
86
30
RELAY
TRANSISTOR
RELAY
FUSE
MAXIFUSE
85
87
87A
86
30
RELA Y
RELAY
RESISTOR
SOLENOID
IGNITION COIL
A
B
MAGNETIC SENSOR
SWITCH
I/P Cluster connector
ZYXWVU
TSRQPON
ABCDEF
GHIJ KLM
ELECTRICAL CONNECTOR
ABS Control Module connector
D
16 15 14 13 12 11 10 9 8 7 6 5 4 3 2 1
C
ELECTRICAL CONNECTOR

Fig. 2 Symbol Identification. Saturn

Wire Color Code Identification

Wire Color	Abbreviation
Black	BLK
Blue	BLU
Brown	BRN
Dark Blue	DK BLU
Dark Green	DK GRN
Gray	GRY
Green	GRN
Light Blue	LT BLU
Light Green	LT GRN
Orange	ORN
Pink	PNK
Purple	PPL
Red	RED
Tan	TAN
White	WHT
Yellow	YEL

BUICK ROADMASTER, CADILLAC BROUGHAM & FLEETWOOD (RWD), CHEVROLET CAPRICE & IMPALA SS & OLDSMOBILE CUSTOM CRUISER (B & D Cars)

NOTE: Refer To Rear Of This Manual For Vehicle Manufacturer's Special Tool Suppliers.

INDEX OF SERVICE OPERATIONS

NOTE: For Service Operations Not Listed Below, Refer To The Table Of Contents In The Front Of This Manual.

Continued

INDEX OF SERVICE OPERATIONS—CONTINUED

Specifications

GENERAL ENGINE SPECIFICATIONS

Year	Engine		Fuel System	Bore & Stroke	Compression Ratio	Net Brake H.P. @ RPM	Maximum Torque Ft. Lbs. @ RPM	Normal Oil Pressure, psi
	CID/Liter	VIN Code ①						
1992	4.3L/V6-262	Z	TBI	4.00 x 3.48	9.3	145 @ 4200	225 @ 2000	②
	5.0L/V8-305	E	TBI	3.74 x 3.48	9.3	170 @ 4200	255 @ 2400	②
	5.7L/V8-350	7	TBI	4.00 x 3.48	9.8	185 @ 3800	300 @ 2400	②
1993	4.3L/V6-262	Z	TBI	4.00 x 3.48	9.3	145 @ 4200	225 @ 2000	②
	5.0L/V8-305	E	TBI	3.74 x 3.48	9.1	170 @ 4100	255 @ 2400	②
	5.7L/V8-350	7	TBI	4.00 x 3.48	9.8	185 @ 3800	300 @ 2400	②
1994	4.3L/V8-265	W	SFI	3.74 x 3.00	9.9	200 @ 5200	235 @ 2400	②
	5.7L/V8-350	P	SFI	4.00 x 3.48	10.5	260 @ 4800	330 @ 3200	②
1995	4.3L/V8-265	W	SFI	3.74 x 3.00	9.9	200 @ 5200	235 @ 2400	②
	5.7L/V8-350	P	SFI	4.00 x 3.48	10.5	260 @ 5000	330 @ 3200	②

CID—Cubic Inch Displacement
TBI—Throttle Body Fuel Injection.
①—The eighth digit of the VIN denotes engine code.
②—Minimum w/engine hot, 6 psi. @ 1000 RPM; 18 psi. @ 2000 RPM; 24 psi. @ 4000 RPM.

TUNE UP SPECIFICATIONS

Year & Engine/ VIN Code ①	Spark Plug Gap, Inch	Ignition Timing			Curb Idle Speed, RPM	Fast Idle Speed, RPM	Fuel Pump Pressure, psi
		Firing Order Fig. ②	Degrees BTDC	Mark Fig.			
1992–93							
4.3L/V6-262/Z	.035	C	⑤	B	⑥	⑥	9-13⑦
5.0L/V8-305 (E)	.035	A	⑧	B	⑥	⑥	9-13⑦
5.7L/V8-350 (7)	.035	A	③	B	⑥	⑥	9-13⑦
1994-95							
4.3L/V8-265/W	.050	D④	③	-	⑥	⑥	41-47
5.7L/V8-350/P	.050	D④	③	-	⑥	⑥	41-47

BTDC—Before Top Dead Center
①—The eighth digit of the VIN denotes engine code.
②—Before removing wires from distributor cap, determine location of No. 1 wire in cap, as distributor position may have been altered from that shown at the end of this chart.
③—Computer controlled, no adjustment.
④—1-8-4-3-6-5-7-2.
⑤—Disconnect set timing bypass connector (tan/black wire) when adjusting ignition timing. The timing bypass connector breaks out of the engine wiring harness on the righthand side of the engine compartment. After completing adjustment, reconnect set timing connector. With engine off, clear trouble code from ECM memory by removing battery voltage to the ECM for 30 seconds.
⑥—Idle speed is controlled by IAC (Idle Air Control) or ILC (Idle Load Compensator).
⑦—Wrap shop towel around fuel hose to steel line connection in engine compartment to prevent fuel spillage. Disconnect hose from steel line & install suitable fuel pressure gauge between hose & line. Ensure gauge connections are tight, then start engine & check fuel pressure readings.
⑧—Disconnect EST bypass electrical connector when checking ignition timing. The bypass connector is located on the AIR control valve tube. After completing adjustment, reconnect EST bypass electrical connector.

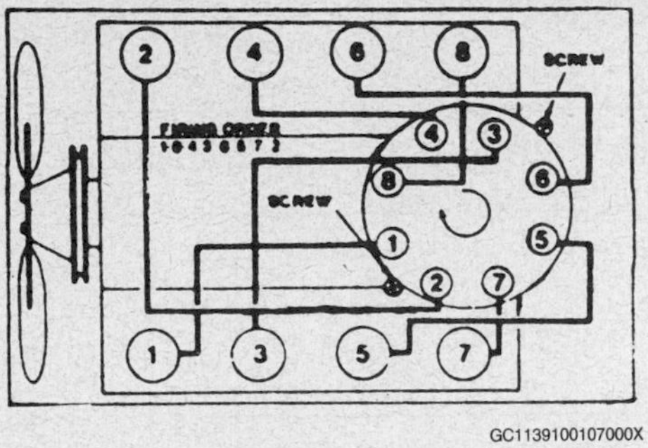

2
4
6
8
SCREW
FIRING ORDER
SCREW
1
3
5
7
GC1139100107000X

Fig. A

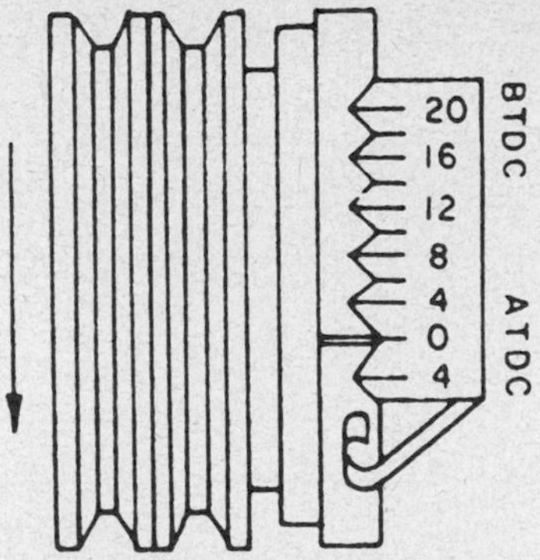

20
16
12
8
4
0
4
BTDC
ATDC
GC1139100108000X

Fig. B

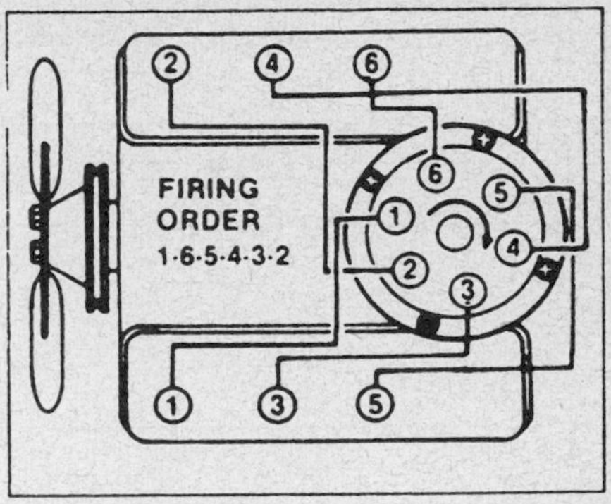

FIRING
ORDER
1-6-5-4-3-2
GC1139100109000X

Fig. C

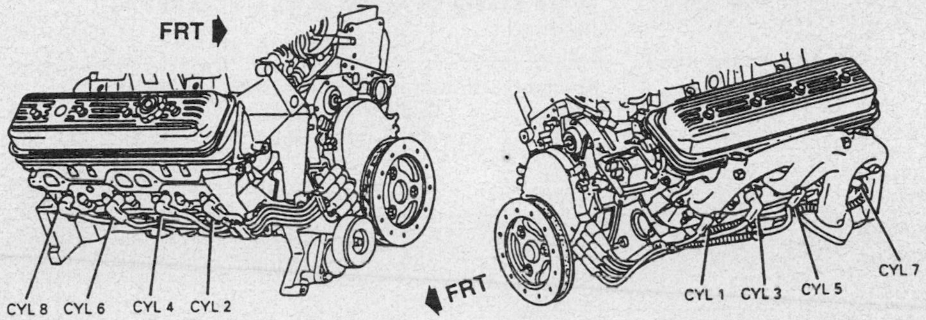

FRT
CYL 8
CYL 6
CYL 4
CYL 2
FRT
CYL 1
CYL 3
CYL 5
CYL 7

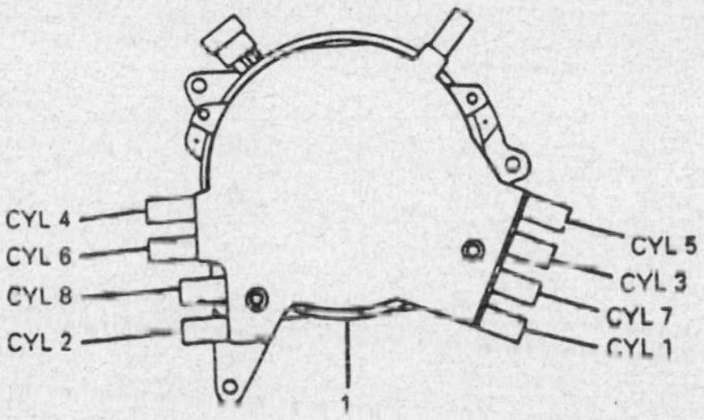

CYL 4
CYL 6
CYL 8
CYL 2
CYL 5
CYL 3
CYL 7
CYL 1
1

1 DISTRIBUTOR ASSEMBLY, IGNITION

GC1139100110000X

Fig. D

FRONT WHEEL ALIGNMENT SPECIFICATIONS

Year	Model	Caster Angle, Degrees		Camber Angle, Degrees		Total Toe, Degrees
		Limits	Desired	Limits	Desired	
1992	Brougham	+2 to +4	+3	-.5 to +.5	0	-.2 to +.2
	Except Brougham	+2.5 to +4.5	+3.5	0 to +1.6	+.8	-.04 to +.36
1993-94	All	+2.5 to +4.5	+3.5	-1 to +1	0	-.04 to +.36
1995	All	①	①	-1 to +1	0	-.04 to +.36

①—Left side, +2.25° to +4.25°; right side, +2.75° to +4.75°.

②—Left side, +3.25°; right side, +3.75°.

REAR WHEEL ALIGNMENT SPECIFICATIONS

Year	Model	Thrust Angle, Degrees
1992–95	All	-.15 to +.15

COOLING SYSTEM & CAPACITY DATA

Make & Year	Model	Engine Liter/ CID	Coolant Capacity, Qts.	Radiator Cap Relief Pressure, psi	Thermo. Opening Temp.°F	Fuel Tank, Gals.	Engine Oil, Qts.②	Auto. Trans. Qts. ③	Rear Axle, Pts.
BUICK									
1992-93	Roadmaster	5.0L/V8-305	⑩	15	195	23	4④	⑨	4.25
1994	Roadmaster	5.7L/V8-350	⑫	15	180	①	4④	⑨	⑬
1995	Roadmaster	5.7L/V8-350	⑫	15	180	⑧	4④	⑨	⑬
CADILLAC									
1992	Brougham	5.0L/V8-305	16.5	15	195	25	4④	⑦	4.2
		5.7L/V8-350	16.5	15	195	25	4④	⑦	4.2
1993	Fleetwood (RWD)	5.7L/V8-350	⑤	15	195	23	4④	⑦	4.2
1994-95	Fleetwood (RWD)	5.7L/V8-350	⑫	15	180	23	4④	⑨	4.2
CHEVROLET									
1992	Caprice Sedan	4.3L/V6-262	⑯	15	195	23	4⑮	⑪	⑭
		5.0L/V8-305	⑩	15	195	23	4④	⑪	⑭
	Caprice Wagon	5.7L/V8-350	14.6	15	195	22	4④	⑪	⑭
1993	Caprice	4.3L/V6-262	⑥ ⑯	15	195	①	4⑮	⑨	⑭
		5.0L/V8-305	⑥ ⑩	15	195	①	4⑮	⑨	⑭
		5.7L/V8-350	⑥ ⑫	15	195	①	4⑮	⑨	⑭
1994	Caprice & Impala SS	4.3L/V6-265	⑫	15	180	①	4④	⑨	⑬
		5.7L/V8-350	⑫	15	180	①	4④	⑨	⑬
1995	Caprice & Impala SS	4.3L/V8-265	⑫	15	180	⑧	4④	⑨	⑬
		5.7L/V8-350	⑫	15	180	⑧	4④	⑨	⑬
OLDSMOBILE									
1992	Custom Cruiser	5.0L/V8-305	⑩	15	195	23	4④	⑨	4.25
		5.7L/V8-350	⑩	15	195	23	4④	⑨	4.25

CID: Cubic Inch Displacement.

①—Sedan 23 gals., wagon 22 gals.

②—Approximate, additional oil may be required.

③—Approximate, make final check w/dipstick.

④—Add 1 qt. w/filter change.

⑤—Less heavy duty radiator, 15 qts., w/heavy duty radiator, 15.7 qts.

⑥—Police option w/heavy duty radiator 15.1 qts.

⑦—Drain & refill, 5 qts., total capacity, 11 qts.

⑧—Sedan 23 gals., wagon 21 gals.

⑨—Drain & refill, 5 qts.; total capacity, 11.2 qts.

⑩—Less heavy duty radiator, 16.7 qts., w/heavy duty radiator, 17.3 qts.

⑪—Drain & refill, 5.3 qts., total capacity, 11 qts.

⑫—Less heavy duty radiator, 14.3 qts., w/heavy duty radiator, 14.6 qts.

⑬—7½ inch ring gear, 3.5 pts., 8½ inch ring gear, 4.25 pts.

⑭—7½ inch ring gear, 2.9 pts., 8½ inch ring gear, 3.5 pts.

⑮—Add ½ qt. w/filter change.

⑯—Less heavy duty radiator, 12.6 qts., w/heavy duty radiator, 13.2 qts.

LUBRICANT DATA

Year	Models	Lubricant Type			
		Automatic Transmission	Rear Axle①	Power Steering	Brake System
1992-93	All	DEXRON IIE	SAE 80W-90 GL-5	Power Steering Fluid②	DOT 3
1994-95	All	DEXRON IIE or III	SAE 80W-90 GL-5	Power Steering Fluid②	DOT 3

①—If equipped w/limited slip, friction modifier will also be required.

②—Meeting GM requirement G985010.

Electrical

NOTE: On Air Bag Equipped Models, Refer To "Air Bag System Precautions" Located In The Front Of This Manual For System Disarming & Arming Procedures.

INDEX

PRECAUTIONS

AIR BAG SYSTEMS

Refer to "Air Bag System Precautions" in the front of this manual for system disarming and arming procedures.

FUSE PANEL & FLASHER LOCATION

The primary fuse panel is located behind the lefthand side of the instrument panel near the shroud. On Police models, the auxiliary fuse panel is located behind the lefthand side of the instrument panel, near the lefthand side of the steering column.

On Brougham and Fleetwood (RWD), the hazard warning flasher is located on the fuse panel. On Caprice, Custom Cruiser and Roadmaster the hazard warning flasher is located on the convenience center near the instrument panel fuse panel.

On Roadmaster, the turn signal flasher is located on the convenience center near the fuse panel. On Brougham and Fleetwood (RWD), the turn signal flasher is located on a bracket behind the instrument panel to the right of the steering column. On Caprice, the turn signal flasher is located on the convenience center next to the auxiliary fuse block. On Custom Cruiser, the turn signal flasher is located on the convenience center near the fuse panel.

RELAY CENTER LOCATION

The relays are located in the underhood electrical center, located in the engine compartment mounted to right side inner fender.

STARTER

REPLACE

If shims are used between starter and engine block, they should be placed in their original location during installation.

1. Disconnect battery ground cable.
2. Raise and support vehicle.

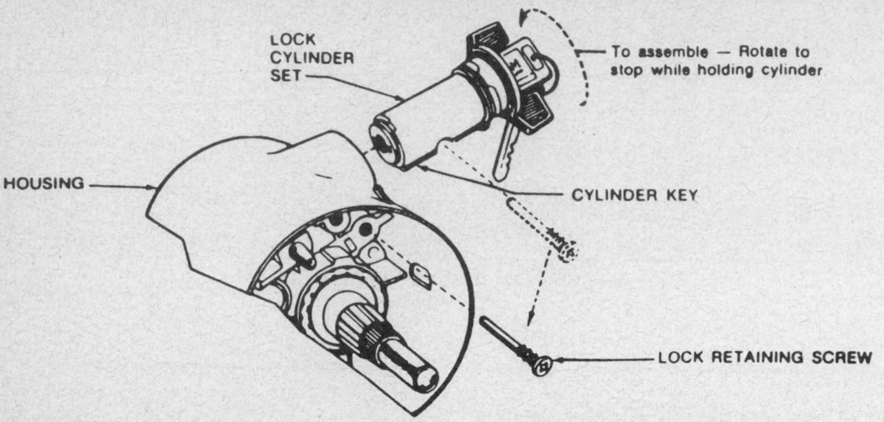
LOCK CYLINDER SET
To assemble — Rotate to stop while holding cylinder
HOUSING
CYLINDER KEY
LOCK RETAINING SCREW
GC9129100015000X

Fig. 1 Ignition lock installation

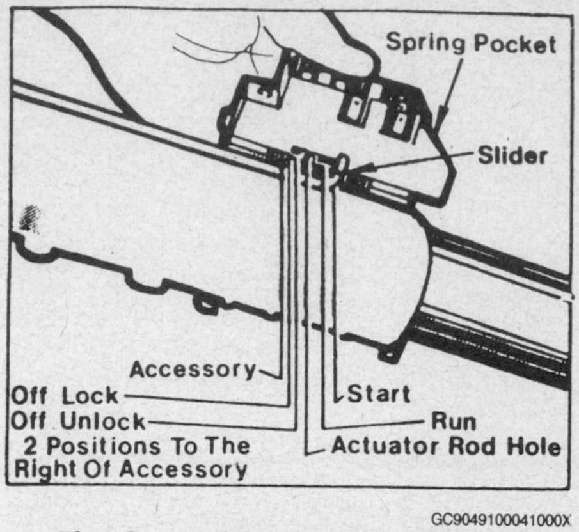
Spring Pocket
Slider
Accessory
Off Lock
Off Unlock
2 Positions To The Right Of Accessory
Start
Run
Actuator Rod Hole
GC9049100041000X

Fig. 2 Ignition switch. Except 1994-95 Fleetwood (RWD)

3. Remove starter to engine brace and starter heat shields, if equipped.
4. Remove flywheel housing cover.
5. Remove starter mounting bolts and lower starter. Note position of shims, if used.
6. Disconnect solenoid wires and the battery cable.
7. Remove starter from vehicle.
8. Reverse procedure to install.

DISTRIBUTOR

REPLACE

1992–93

Removal

1. Disconnect battery ground cable.
2. Disconnect ignition switch feed and tachometer leads from distributor cap. Screwdriver or other tools should not be used to release lead connector locking tab.
3. Remove distributor cap attaching screws, then position cap out of way.
4. Disconnect four terminal ECM electrical connector from distributor electrical connector.
5. Remove distributor hold down clamp and bolt. Mark position of distributor rotor to distributor housing and position of distributor housing to engine for use during installation.
6. Lift distributor upward until rotor stops rotating and mark position of rotor to distributor housing for use during installation.
7. Remove distributor from engine.

Installation

1. Position rotor to mark on distributor housing, then insert distributor into engine aligning rotor to housing and housing to engine marks made during removal.
2. If engine was disturbed while distributor was removed, proceed as follows:
   a. Remove spark plug from No. 1 cylinder.
   b. With transmission in Neutral or Park and parking brake applied, position finger over spark plug opening in cylinder head, then slowly crank engine until compression is felt.
   c. Align crankshaft pulley with TDC (0) mark on timing indicator.
   d. Locate distributor rotor contact between No. 1 and 8 spark plug firing positions on distributor.
   e. Insert distributor into engine.
3. Install distributor hold clamp and bolt. Hand tighten bolt.
4. Connect ECM four terminal electrical connector to distributor.
5. Install distributor cap, then connect ignition switch and tachometer lead connector to cap.
6. Connect battery ground cable, then check and adjust ignition timing as necessary. **Torque** distributor hold down bolt to 27 ft. lbs.

1994–95

Removal

1. Ensure ignition switch is Off and in Lock position.
2. Remove water pump as outlined "Water Pump, Replace."
3. Remove crankshaft balancer assembly as outlined under "Crankshaft Damper, Replace."
4. Disconnect spark plug wire harness assemblies and four-terminal PCM connector from distributor, then vacuum harness from distributor.
5. Remove distributor bolts/screws, then the distributor. Pull distributor assembly forward until coupling disengages from end of camshaft.

Installation

1. Install distributor. Rotate distributor coupling until camshaft sprocket pin slot aligns with camshaft sprocket pin. Slide distributor onto end of camshaft until fully seated on engine front cover.
2. **Do not attempt to fully seat distributor using bolts/screws. If distributor will not seat by hand, it is not properly aligned with camshaft. Rotate crankshaft until engine is at No. 1 cylinder TDC (camshaft at nine o'clock position). Rotate distributor coupling until camshaft sprocket pin slot aligns with distributor base timing mark. Install distributor using hand pressure to fully seat.**
3. Install distributor bolts and screws. **Torque** to 106 inch lbs.
4. Connect four-terminal connector, vacuum harness and spark plug harness assemblies to distributor.
5. Install crankshaft balancer and hub assembly, then tighten to specifications.
6. Install water pump, then tighten to specifications.

IGNITION LOCK

REPLACE

1. Remove steering wheel as described under "Steering Wheel, Replace."
2. Remove turn signal switch as described under "Turn Signal Switch, Replace," then remove buzzer switch.
3. Place ignition switch in Run position, then remove lock cylinder retaining screw and lock cylinder.
4. Install by rotating lock cylinder to stop while holding housing, **Fig. 1.** Align cylinder key with keyway in housing, then push lock cylinder assembly into housing until fully seated.
5. Install lock cylinder retaining screw.
6. Install buzzer switch, turn signal switch and steering wheel.

IGNITION SWITCH

REPLACE

EXCEPT 1994–95 FLEETWOOD (RWD)

The ignition switch is mounted on top of the mast jacket inside the brake pedal support and is actuated by a rod and rack assembly.

1. Disconnect battery ground cable.
2. Disconnect and lower steering column. **It may be necessary, on some models, to remove the upper column mounting bracket if it hinders servicing of switch. Use extreme care when lowering steering column to prevent damage to column assembly. Only lower steering column a sufficient distance to perform ignition switch service.**
3. Rotate ignition lock to Off unlocked position.

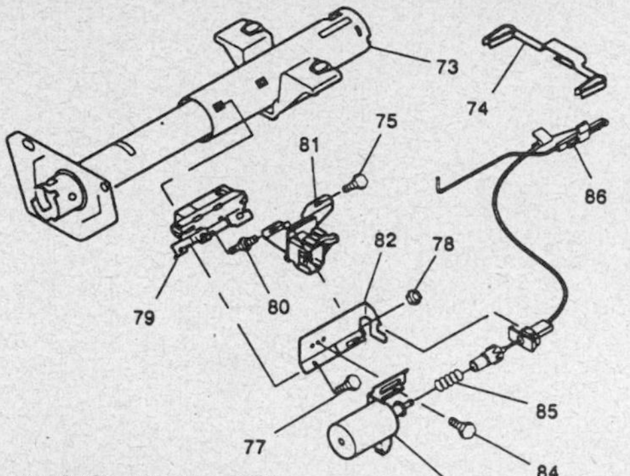
73
74
75
81
86
82
78
79
80
85
77
84
83

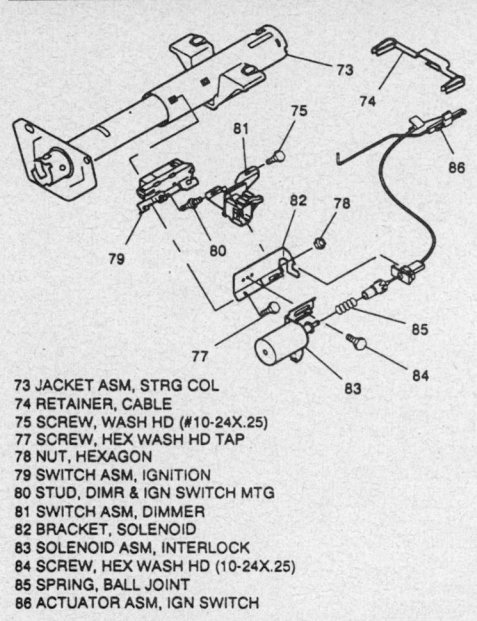

73 JACKET ASM, STRG COL
74 RETAINER, CABLE
75 SCREW, WASH HD (#10-24X.25)
77 SCREW, HEX WASH HD TAP
78 NUT, HEXAGON
79 SWITCH ASM, IGNITION
80 STUD, DIMR & IGN SWITCH MTG
81 SWITCH ASM, DIMMER
82 BRACKET, SOLENOID
83 SOLENOID ASM, INTERLOCK
84 SCREW, HEX WASH HD (10-24X.25)
85 SPRING, BALL JOINT
86 ACTUATOR ASM, IGN SWITCH

GC9049100042000X

Fig. 3 Exploded view of ignition switch, dimmer switch and solenoid. 1994-95 Fleetwood (RWD)

4. If lock cylinder has been removed, pull switch actuator rod up to stop, then push rod down to second detent to place switch in Off unlocked position, **Fig. 2.**
5. Remove column mounted dimmer switch, if equipped, then remove switch retaining screws and switch.
6. Reverse procedure to install, noting the following:
   a. Place gear shift lever in neutral.
   b. Place lock cylinder and switch in Off locked position, **Fig. 2.**
   c. Fit actuator rod into hole in switch slider and secure switch with retaining screws, ensuring switch does not move out of detent.
   d. Install and adjust dimmer switch, if removed, as outlined in "Dimmer Switch, Replace."

1994–95 FLEETWOOD (RWD)

1. Disconnect battery ground cable.
2. Disconnect steering column from vehicle.
3. Remove solenoid cable from interlock solenoid assembly and solenoid bracket, **Fig. 3.** Remove ball joint spring.
4. Remove washer head screw, then interlock solenoid assembly.
5. Remove hexagon head tapping screw and hexagon nut, then solenoid bracket.
6. Remove washer head screw, then dimmer switch assembly.
7. Remove dimmer and ignition switch mounting stud and ignition switch, then disconnect ignition switch from wire harness.
8. Reverse procedure to install noting the following:

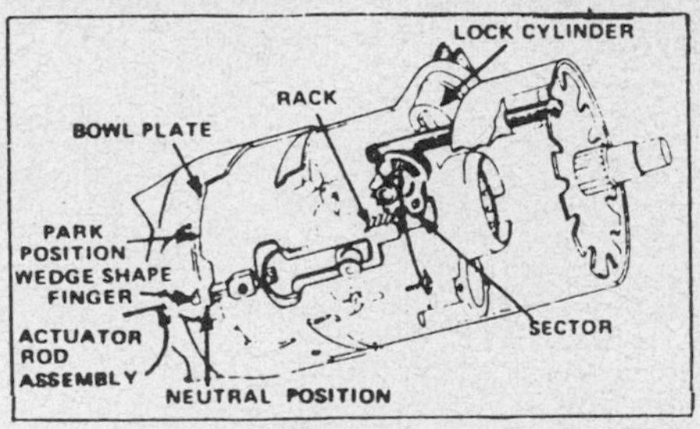
LOCK CYLINDER
RACK
BOWL PLATE
PARK POSITION
WEDGE SHAPE FINGER
ACTUATOR ROD ASSEMBLY
NEUTRAL POSITION
SECTOR

GC9049100043000X

Fig. 4 Mechanical neutral safety system. Models w/tilt column

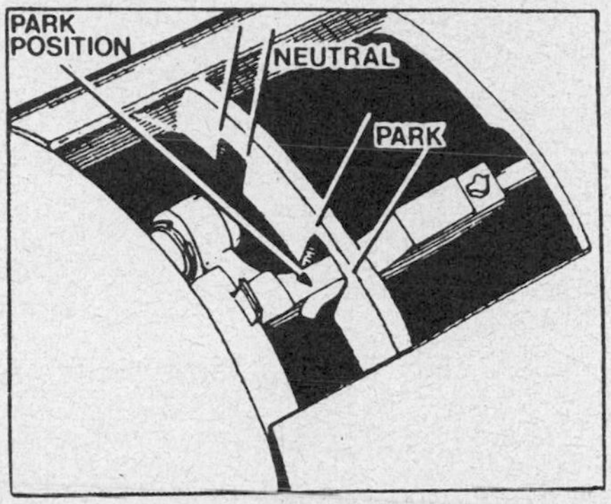
PARK POSITION
NEUTRAL
PARK

GC9049100045000X

Fig. 6 Mechanical neutral safety system in Park position

   a. Remove plastic pin after switch is assembled to column. Failure to do so may cause switch damage.
   b. Adjust ignition switch by moving slider to extreme right position, then move switch slider one detent to left OFF-LOCK position. Install 3/32 inch drill bit in hole on switch to limit travel.
   c. **Torque** dimmer and ignition mounting stud to 35 ft. lbs., then remove drill bit from ignition switch.
   d. Adjust dimmer switch by installing 3/32 inch drill bit in hole on switch to limit travel. Position switch on column and push to remove all lash. Remove drill bit.
   e. **Torque** washer screw and hexagon nut to 35 inch lbs.
   f. **Torque** hexagon washer tap screw to 22 inch lbs.
   g. **Torque** hexagon washer screw to 35 inch lbs.

NEUTRAL SAFETY SWITCH

REPLACE

MECHANICAL

Actuation of the ignition switch is prevented by a mechanical lockout system, **Figs. 4 and 5,** which prevents the lock cylinder from rotating when the selector lever is out of Park or Neutral. When the selector lever is in Park or Neutral, the slots in the bowl plate and the finger on the actuator rod align, allowing the finger to pass through the bowl plate in turn actuating the ignition switch, **Fig. 6.** If the selector lever is in any position other than Park or Neutral, the finger contacts the bowl plate when the lock cylinder is rotated, thereby preventing full travel of the lock cylinder.

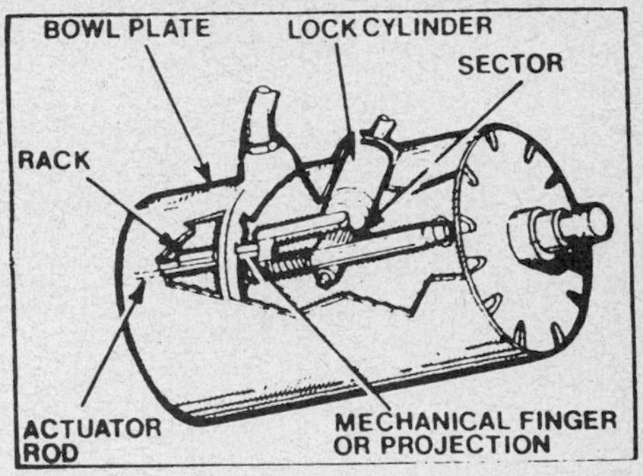
BOWL PLATE
LOCK CYLINDER
SECTOR
RACK
ACTUATOR ROD
MECHANICAL FINGER OR PROJECTION

GC9049100044000X

Fig. 5 Mechanical neutral safety system. Models w/standard column

ELECTRIC

On models incorporating an electric neutral start switch, the start switch, back-up light switch and parking brake vacuum release valve are combined into one unit. This unit is mounted on the steering column under the instrument panel.

HEADLAMP SWITCH

REPLACE

CAPRICE, CUSTOM CRUISER, IMPALA SS & ROADMASTER

1. Disconnect battery ground cable.
2. Remove lower steering column trim panel attaching screws, then pull downward to remove.
3. Through glove compartment, unsnap righthand molding.
4. Loosen steering column support bracket to instrument panel carrier attaching bolts. **Do not remove bolts.**
5. Gently lower steering column assembly. **Use extreme care when lowering steering to prevent damage to column assembly.**
6. Remove lefthand trim plate to instrument panel carrier assembly six attaching screws, then unsnap lefthand trim assembly.
7. Remove headlamp switch attaching screws.
8. Pull switch rearward, then disconnect switch electrical connectors and remove, **Fig. 7.**
9. Reverse procedure to install.

1992 BROUGHAM

1. Disconnect battery ground cable.
2. Remove lefthand instrument panel insert.
3. Remove three screws attaching light switch to instrument panel, **Fig. 8.**
4. **On vehicles equipped with Cruise Control and Twilight Sentinel,** remove two screws retaining Cruise Control switch to instrument panel.

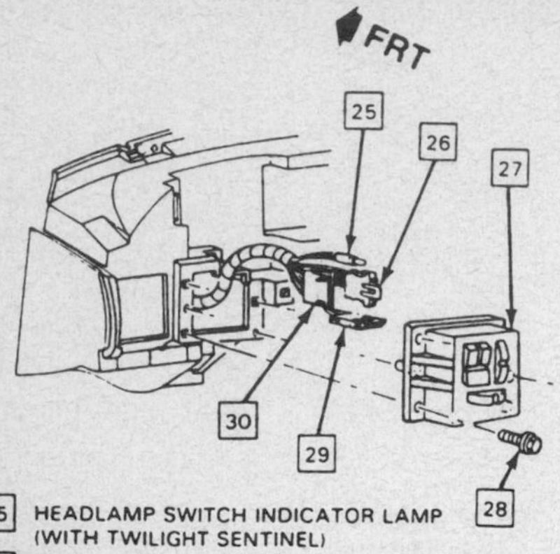
FRT
25
26
27
28
29
30

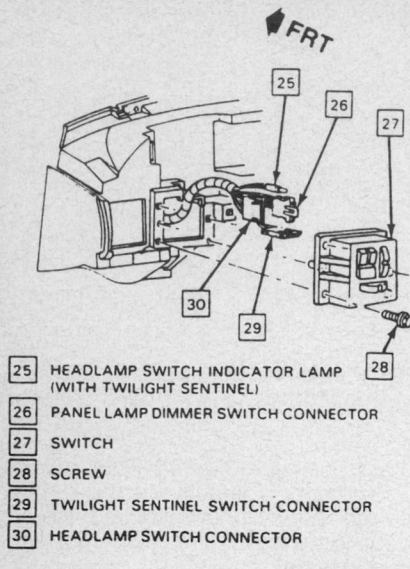

25 HEADLAMP SWITCH INDICATOR LAMP (WITH TWILIGHT SENTINEL)
26 PANEL LAMP DIMMER SWITCH CONNECTOR
27 SWITCH
28 SCREW
29 TWILIGHT SENTINEL SWITCH CONNECTOR
30 HEADLAMP SWITCH CONNECTOR

GC9049100046000X

Fig. 7 Headlamp switch replacement. Caprice, Custom Cruiser, Impala SS & Roadmaster

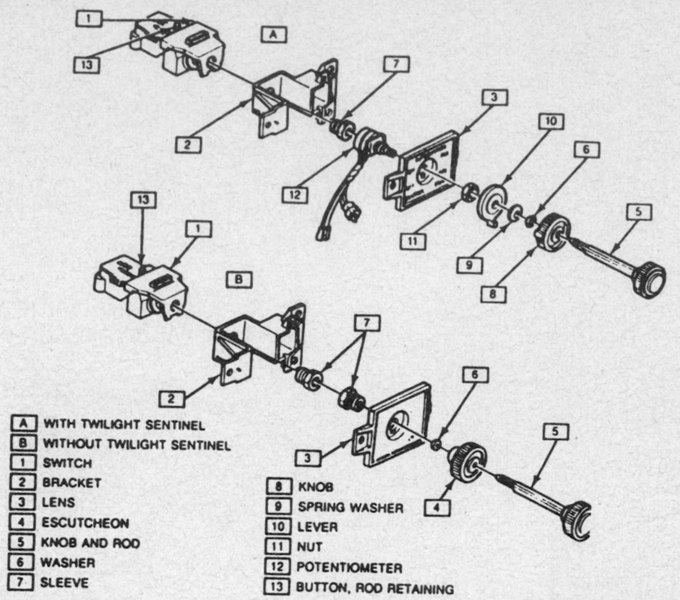
A WITH TWILIGHT SENTINEL
B WITHOUT TWILIGHT SENTINEL
1 SWITCH
2 BRACKET
3 LENS
4 ESCUTCHEON
5 KNOB AND ROD
6 WASHER
7 SLEEVE
8 KNOB
9 SPRING WASHER
10 LEVER
11 NUT
12 POTENTIOMETER
13 BUTTON, ROD RETAINING

GC9049100047000X

Fig. 8 Headlamp switch replacement. 1992 Brougham

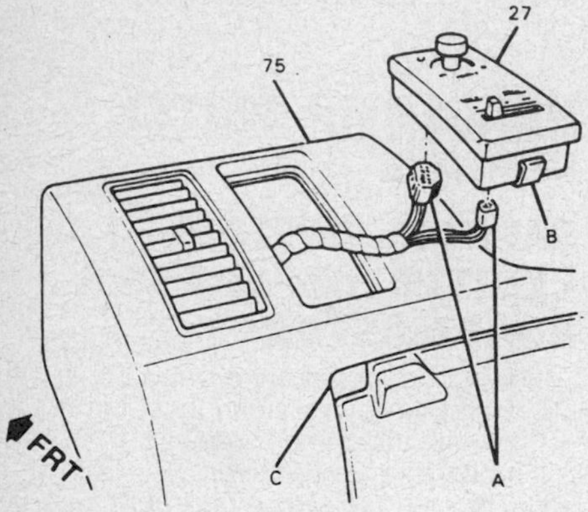
27
75
B
FRT
C
A

A CONNECTOR, ELECTRICAL
B LOCK TANG
C ACCESS HOLE
27 SWITCH ASSEMBLY, HEADLAMP
75 PANEL ASSEMBLY, INSTRUMENT

GC9049300048000X

Fig. 9 Headlamp switch replacement. Fleetwood (RWD)

5. Slide Cruise Control switch forward to remove headlamp switch.
6. Disconnect electrical connector from headlamp switch.
7. While depressing rod retaining button, pull switch knob and rod from switch, **Fig. 8.**
8. Remove nut from switch lens housing, then remove switch.
9. Reverse procedure to install.

FLEETWOOD (RWD)

1. Remove instrument panel left sound insulator assembly.
2. Remove instrument panel driver knee bolster deflector.
3. Using suitable flat bladed tool, pry headlamp switch from instrument panel, **Fig. 9.**
4. Disconnect switch electrical connector, then remove switch.
5. Reverse procedure to install.

STOP LIGHT SWITCH
REPLACE

The stop light switch has a slip fit in the mounting sleeve which permits positive adjustment by pulling the brake pedal up firmly against the stop. The pedal arm forces the switch body to slip in the mounting sleeve bushing to position the switch properly.

1. Disconnect wires from switch and remove switch from bracket.
2. Position replacement switch in bracket and push inward until fully seated. Brake pedal arm moves switch to correct distance on rebound. Check if pedal is in full return position by lifting slightly by hand.
3. Connect switch electrical connector.

TURN SIGNAL SWITCH
REPLACE

1. Disconnect battery cable, then remove steering wheel and column to instrument panel trim cover.
2. **On models with telescoping column,** remove bumper spacer and snap ring retainer.
3. **On models less telescoping column,** remove cover from lock plate.
4. **On all models,** using a suitable tool, compress lock plate (horn contact carrier on tilt models) and remove snap ring (C-ring on tilt models), **Fig. 10.**
5. Remove lock plate, cancelling cam, upper bearing preload spring, thrust washer and signal lever.

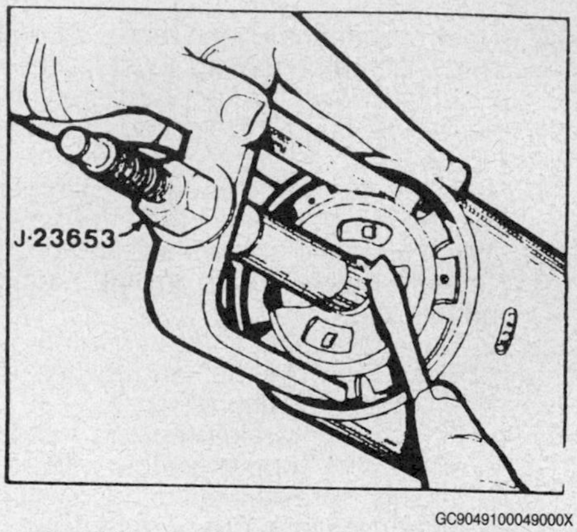
J-23653

GC9049100049000X

Fig. 10 Lock plate retaining ring removal

6. Remove turn signal lever or actuating arm screw, if equipped, or on models with column mounted wiper switch, pull lever straight out of detent. Depress hazard warning button, then unscrew button.
7. Pull connector from bracket and wrap upper part of connector with tape to prevent snagging the wires during removal, **Fig. 11.**
8. **On Tilt models,** position shifter housing in Low position. Remove harness cover.
9. **On models less tilt** remove retaining screws and remove switch, **Fig. 12 and 13.**
10. Reverse procedure to install.

DIMMER SWITCH
REPLACE

1. Disconnect battery ground cable.
2. Remove instrument panel lower trim and on models with A/C, remove A/C duct extension at column.

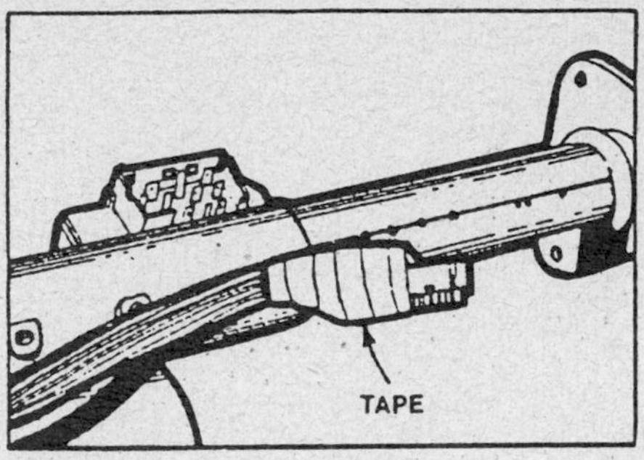
TAPE

GC9049100050000X

Fig. 11 Turn signal electrical connector & wiring isolation

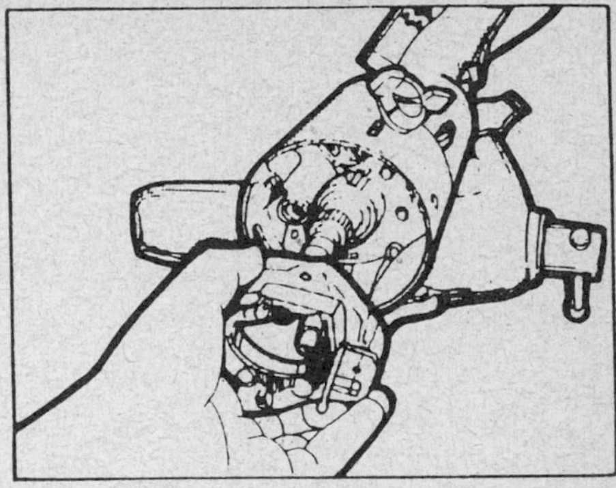

GC9049100051000X

Fig. 12 Turn signal switch removal from column bowl. Less tilt

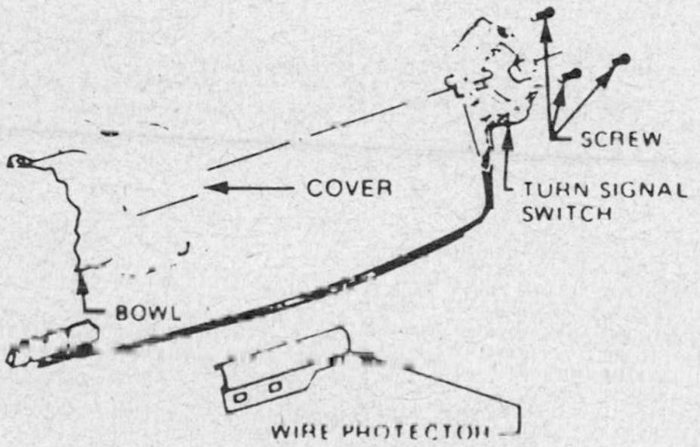
SCREW
COVER
TURN SIGNAL SWITCH
BOWL
WIRE PROTECTOR

Fig. 13 Turn signal switch replacement. Less tilt

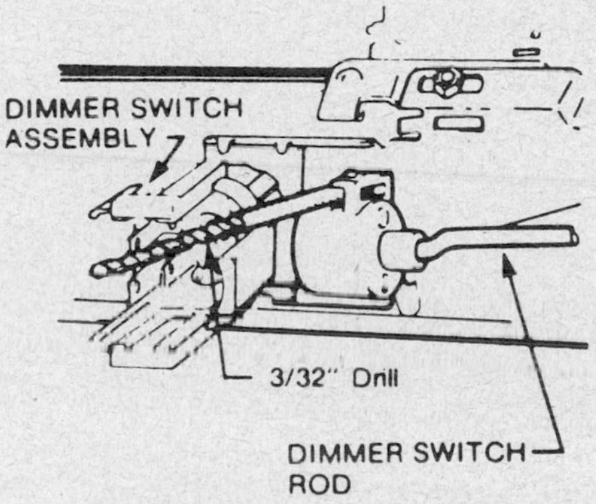
DIMMER SWITCH ASSEMBLY
3/32" Drill
DIMMER SWITCH ROD

GC9049100053000X

Fig. 14 Column mounted dimmer switch installation

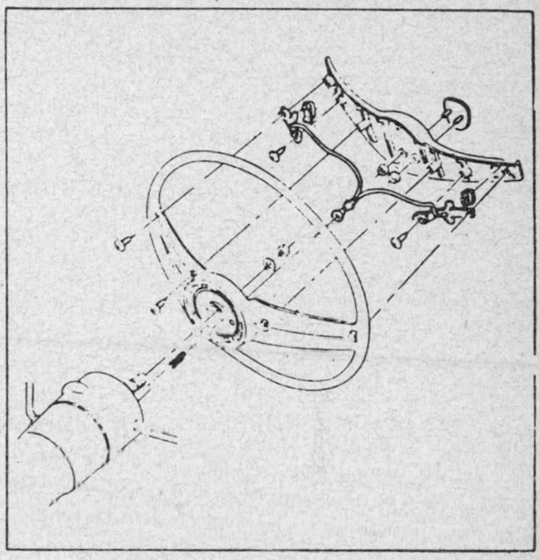

GC6049100133000X

Fig. 15 Steering wheel. Less air bag. Caprice, Custom Cruiser & Roadmaster

3. Disconnect shift indicator from column and remove toe-plate cover screws.
4. Remove two nuts from instrument panel support bracket studs and lower steering column, resting steering wheel on front seat.
5. Remove dimmer switch retaining screws and the switch. Tape actuator rod to column and separate switch from rod.
6. Reverse procedure to install. To adjust switch, depress dimmer switch slightly and install a 3/32 inch twist drill to lock the switch to the body, **Fig. 14.** Force switch upward to remove lash between switch and pivot, then remove tape from actuator rod. Remove twist drill and check for proper operation.

STEERING WHEEL

REPLACE

Mark position of steering wheel in relation to shaft prior to removal to ensure correct installation.

CAPRICE, CUSTOM CRUISER, IMPALA SS & ROADMASTER

Less Air Bag

1. Disconnect battery ground cable.
2. Remove horn pad attaching screws.
3. Pull pad reward, then turn horn lead insulator in counterclockwise direction to disconnect horn lead.
4. Remove steering wheel attaching nut and retainer, **Fig. 15.**
5. Using suitable steering wheel puller, remove steering wheel.
6. Reverse procedure to install.

With Air Bag

1. Disconnect battery ground cable.
2. Using a No. 30 Torx driver, loosen air bag inflator module attaching screws until module can be released from steering wheel, **Fig. 16.**
3. Pull module rearward, then disconnect coil, connector position assurance and horn lead connectors, then remove module. **Do not carry module by connectors or wires, when placing live module on bench, place bag and trim cover upward.**
4. Remove steering wheel attaching nut.
5. Using suitable steering wheel puller, remove steering wheel and horn contact.
6. Reverse procedure to install.

1992 BROUGHAM

1. Disconnect battery ground cable.
2. Remove steering wheel pad attaching screws.
3. Pull pad rearward, then remove horn contact from plastic tower by pushing wire inward and turning counterclockwise.
4. Turn ignition switch to On position.
5. **On models equipped with tilt and telescope wheel,** remove telescoping locking lever to adjuster attaching screws, then remove adjuster.
6. **On models equipped with standard wheel,** remove locking lever assembly.
7. **On all models,** scribe steering wheel with installation alignment mark.
8. Remove steering wheel attaching nut.
9. Using suitable steering wheel puller tool, remove steering wheel.
10. Reverse procedure to install.

FLEETWOOD (RWD)

1. Remove inflatable restraint steering wheel module assembly.
2. Remove nut. **When removing steering wheel assembly, use only specified steering wheel puller. Under no conditions should the end of the steering shaft be hammered on, as hammering could loosen the plastic injections which maintain steering column rigidity. When attaching puller bolts tool No. J-**

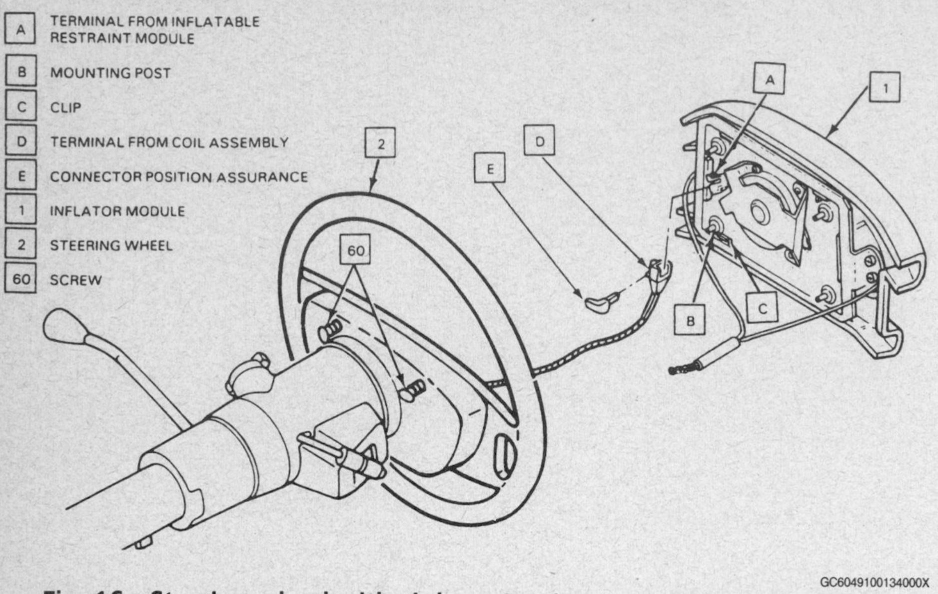
A TERMINAL FROM INFLATABLE RESTRAINT MODULE
B MOUNTING POST
C CLIP
D TERMINAL FROM COIL ASSEMBLY
E CONNECTOR POSITION ASSURANCE
1 INFLATOR MODULE
2 STEERING WHEEL
60 SCREW
GC6049100134000X

Fig. 16 Steering wheel with air bag. Caprice, Impala SS & Roadmaster

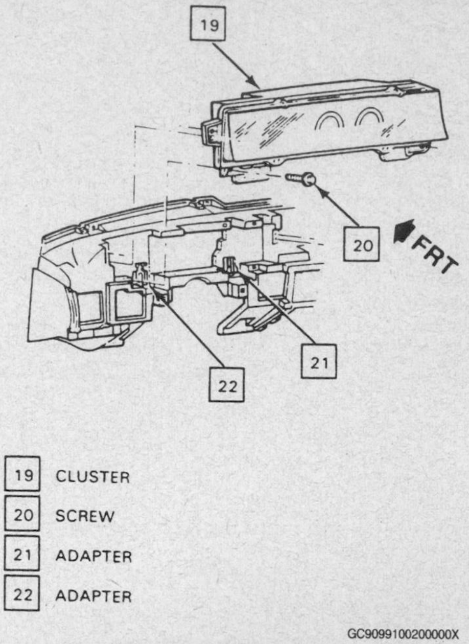
FRT
19 CLUSTER
20 SCREW
21 ADAPTER
22 ADAPTER
GC9099100200000X

Fig. 17 Instrument cluster replacement. Caprice, Custom Cruiser, Impala SS & Roadmaster

1859-A or equivalent and puller tool No. J 38720 or equivalent to steering wheel, use care to prevent threading bolts all the way through the steering wheel hub into the air bag coil and damaging the coil.

3. Remove steering wheel.
4. Reverse procedure to install, noting the following:
   a. Align block tooth on steering wheel with block tooth on steering shaft within one female serration.
   b. **Torque** steering wheel nut to 30 ft. lbs.

INSTRUMENT CLUSTER
REPLACE

CAPRICE, CUSTOM CRUISER, IMPALA SS & ROADMASTER

1. Disconnect battery ground cable.
2. Remove lower steering column trim panel attaching screws, then pull downward to remove.
3. Through glove compartment, unsnap righthand molding.
4. Loosen steering column support bracket to instrument panel carrier attaching bolts. **Do not remove bolts.**
5. Gently lower steering column assembly. **Use extreme care when lowering steering to prevent damage to column assembly.**
6. Remove lefthand trim plate to instrument panel carrier assembly six attaching screws, then unsnap lefthand trim assembly.
7. Remove instrument cluster attaching screws.
8. Pull cluster rearward, then disconnect shift indicator cable.
9. Pull instrument cluster from panel carrier, **Fig. 17,** then remove.
10. Reverse procedure to install.

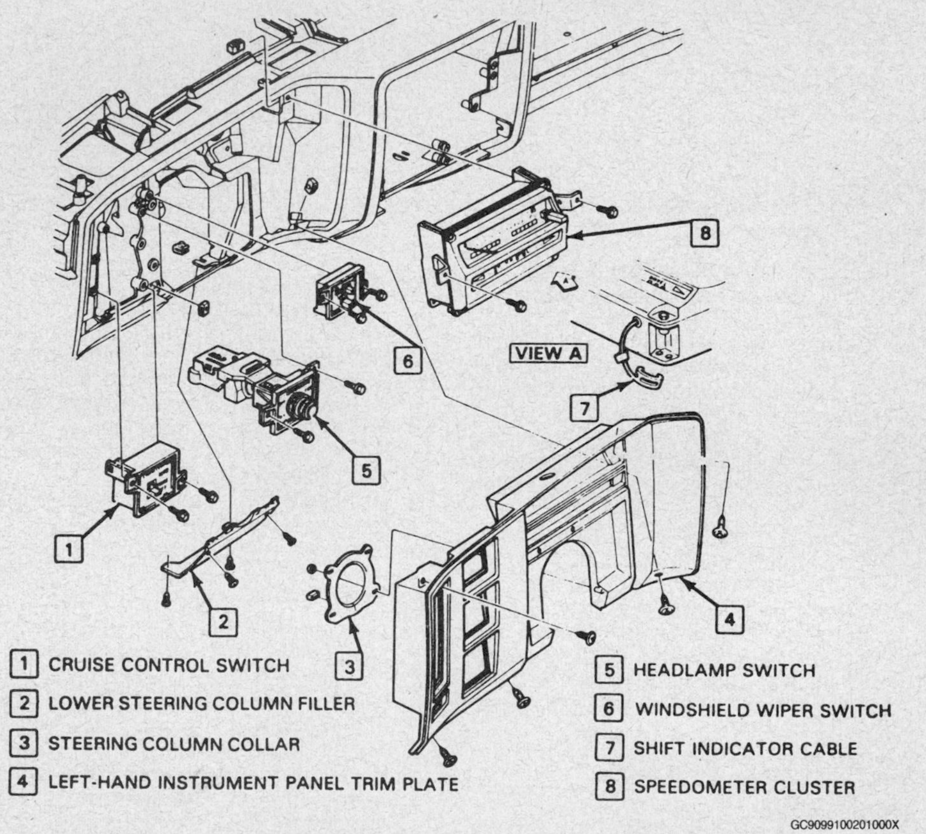
VIEW A
1 CRUISE CONTROL SWITCH
2 LOWER STEERING COLUMN FILLER
3 STEERING COLUMN COLLAR
4 LEFT-HAND INSTRUMENT PANEL TRIM PLATE
5 HEADLAMP SWITCH
6 WINDSHIELD WIPER SWITCH
7 SHIFT INDICATOR CABLE
8 SPEEDOMETER CLUSTER
GC9099100201000X

Fig. 18 Instrument cluster replacement. 1992 Brougham

1992 BROUGHAM

Analog Cluster

1. Disconnect battery ground cable.
2. Remove cluster bezel, then with shift lever in the Park position, remove the screw securing shift indicator cable to steering column.
3. Remove four screws securing cluster to instrument horizontal support, **Fig. 18.**
4. **On vehicles equipped with speed control sensor,** disconnect sensor from cluster before completely removing cluster assembly. This will prevent connector from damaging cluster during removal.

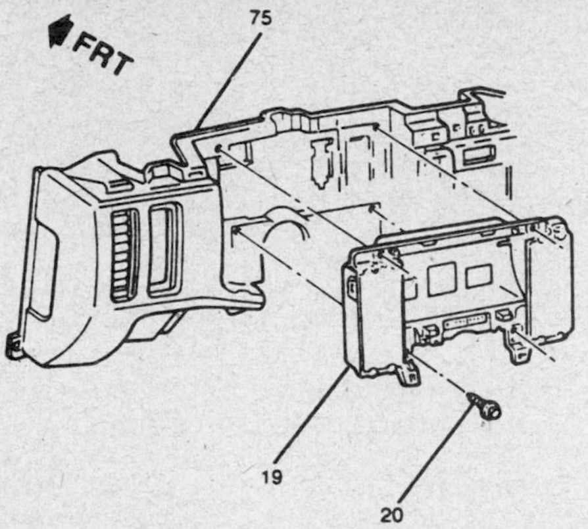
FRT
75
19
20
19 CLUSTER ASSEMBLY, INSTRUMENT
20 BOLT/SCREW, INSTRUMENT CLUSTER, 1.9 N·m (17 LB. IN.)
75 PANEL ASSEMBLY, INSTRUMENT
GC9099100202000X

Fig. 19 Instrument cluster replacement. Fleetwood (RWD)

5. **On all models** disengage speedometer cable at neck by pulling cluster straight out and depressing retaining spring. **To remove cluster, place shift lever in Low range and on models with tilt wheel, place wheel in lowest position.**
6. Rotate cluster downward, disconnect printed circuit connector, then remove cluster.
7. Reverse procedure to install.

Digital Cluster

1. Disconnect battery ground cable.
2. Loosen outlet grille directional knob Allen key, located at bottom of knob, then remove knob.
3. Remove lower steering column cover attaching screws.
4. Remove lefthand trim panel six attaching screws, then place shift level in Park position.
5. Remove lefthand trim panel from instrument column.
6. With shift lever in Park position, remove steering column shift indicator clip.
7. Remove instrument cluster four attaching screws, then tilt steering wheel downward, remove cluster.
8. Reverse procedure to install.

FLEETWOOD (RWD)

1. Remove instrument panel left sound insulator assembly.
2. Remove instrument panel driver knee bolster deflector.
3. Remove steering column tilt lever assembly.
4. Remove cluster trim plate.
5. Disconnect transmission shift indicator cable.
6. Remove instrument cluster attaching screws, **Fig. 19,** then remove cluster.
7. Reverse procedure to install.

RADIO

REPLACE

When installing radio, be sure to adjust antenna trimmer for peak reception. Also, be sure to connect speaker before applying power to radio.

CAPRICE, CUSTOM CRUISER, IMPALA SS & ROADMASTER

1. Disconnect battery ground cable.
2. Remove steering column lower trim panel, then remove lefthand trim panel.
3. Remove radio bracket to instrument carrier attaching screws, then pull radio and bracket assembly outward.
4. Disconnect radio and antenna electrical connectors.
5. Remove radio to bracket attaching nuts, then remove radio.
6. Reverse procedure to install.

1992 BROUGHAM

Radio Control Head

1. Disconnect battery ground cable.
2. Remove set screws at bottom of each A/C vent on/off lever heads, then pull lever heads forward and off.
3. Remove two screws from lower portion of instrument panel trim plate, then remove trim plate from instrument panel.
4. Remove center 7 mm black screw from upper center radio control head upper bracket.
5. Remove two screws from lower ends of bottom radio control bracket.
6. Carefully pull radio control forward.
7. Disconnect electrical connectors from radio control, then remove radio control and bracket.
8. Reverse procedure to install.

Radio Receiver

The radio receiver is located behind the lefthand side of the instrument panel.

1. Disconnect battery ground cable.
2. Remove 4 screws and one wing nut from lefthand side hush panel, then remove panel.
3. Remove attaching screw from lefthand A/C duct, then pull duct down and outward.
4. Remove attaching screw from righthand A/C duct, then pull duct down and outward.
5. Remove two mounting bolts and ground strap from chime module mounting bracket.
6. Remove nut from bottom of radio receiver.
7. Position chime module, bracket and wiring downward and out of way.
8. Disconnect antenna lead from radio receiver.
9. Carefully pull radio receiver downward and toward front of vehicle, then disconnect gray and black electrical connectors from rear of receiver, **Fig. 20.**

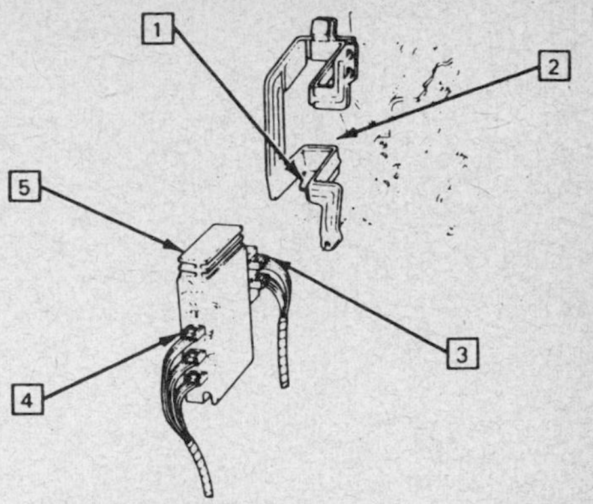
1
2
3
4
5
1 BRACKET LEDGE FOR FULLY SEATED REMOTE CHASSIS
2 REAR CONNECTOR (2) HARNESS ROUTES THROUGH SIDE SLOT IN BRACKET
3 REAR CONNECTORS (2)
4 FRONT CONNECTORS (3)
5 REMOTE RADIO CHASSIS
GC9039100026000X

Fig. 20 Radio receiver replacement. 1992 Brougham

10. Carefully pull radio receiver from behind instrument panel, then disconnect blue, white and black electrical connectors from front radio receiver.
11. Remove radio receiver.
12. Reverse procedure to install.

FLEETWOOD (RWD)

1. Remove instrument panel righthand molding assembly.
2. Remove instrument panel righthand trim plate assembly.
3. Remove radio to instrument panel attaching screws, **Fig. 21.**
4. Pull radio assembly slightly rearward, then disconnect radio electrical connector.
5. Remove upper and lower radio to bracket attaching nuts, then remove radio attaching bolts and screws.
6. Reverse procedure to install.

WIPER MOTOR

REPLACE

1992 BROUGHAM

1. Raise hood and remove cowl screen or grille.
2. Disconnect wiring and washer hoses.
3. Reaching through cowl opening, loosen transmission drive link attaching nuts to motor crank arm.
4. Disconnect drive link from motor crank arm.
5. Remove motor attaching screws.
6. Remove motor while guiding crank arm through hole.
7. Reverse procedure to install.

CAPRICE, CUSTOM CRUISER, FLEETWOOD (RWD), IMPALA SS & ROADMASTER

1. Disconnect battery ground cable.

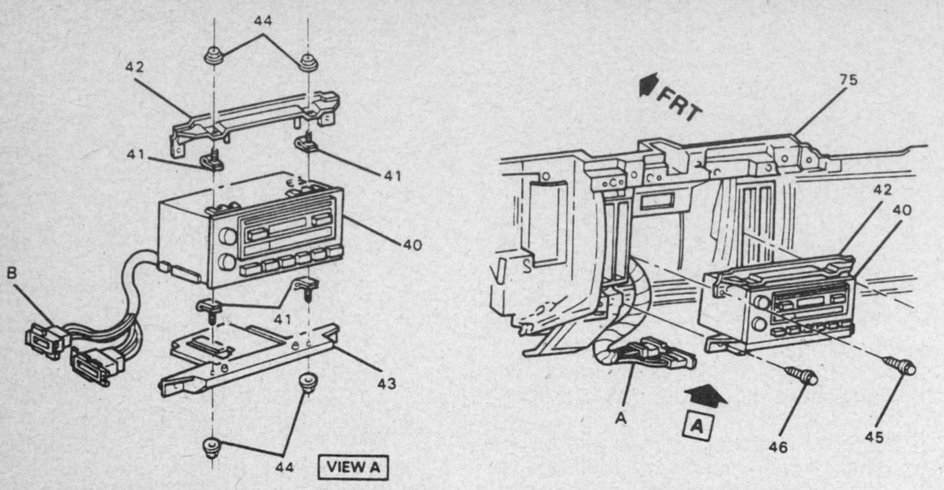
44
42
41
41
40
B
41
43
44
VIEW A
FRT
75
42
40
A
A
46
45

A HARNESS ASSEMBLY, INSTRUMENT PANEL WIRING
B CONNECTOR, ELECTRICAL
40 RADIO ASSEMBLY
41 BOLT/SCREW, RADIO CONTROL
42 BRACKET, RADIO UPPER
43 BRACKET, RADIO LOWER
44 NUT, RADIO CONTROL, 2.8 N•m (25 LB. IN.)
45 BOLT/SCREW, RADIO UPPER BRACKET, 1.9 N•m (17 LB. IN.)
46 BOLT/SCREW, RADIO LOWER BRACKET, 1.9 N•m (17 LB. IN.)
75 PANEL ASSEMBLY, INSTRUMENT

GC9039100027000X

Fig. 21 Radio receiver replacement. Fleetwood (RWD)

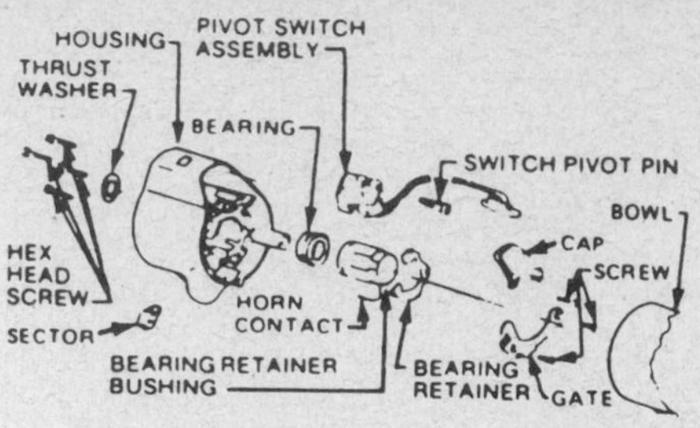
HOUSING
PIVOT SWITCH ASSEMBLY
THRUST WASHER
BEARING
SWITCH PIVOT PIN
BOWL
CAP
SCREW
HEX HEAD SCREW
HORN CONTACT
SECTOR
BEARING RETAINER BUSHING
BEARING RETAINER
GATE

GC9029100229000X

Fig. 22 Windshield wiper switch. Standard steering column

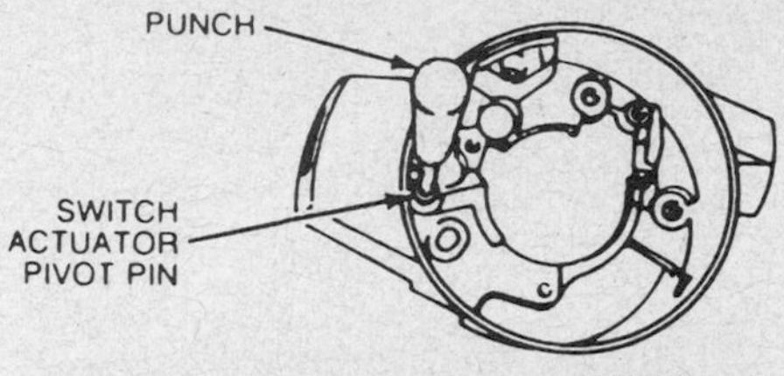
PUNCH
SWITCH ACTUATOR PIVOT PIN

GC9029100231000X

Fig. 24 Windshield wiper switch actuator pivot pin replacement

2. Remove righthand wiper arm and hose.
3. Remove lefthand cowl vent screen, then righthand screen.
4. Remove wiper linkage access hole cover attaching screws, then remove hole cover.
5. Disconnect wiper motor drive link from motor crank arm.
6. Disconnect wiper motor electrical connectors.
7. Remove motor attaching bolts, then remove motor guiding crank arm through access hole.
8. Reverse procedure to install.

WIPER SWITCH
REPLACE

CAPRICE, CUSTOM CRUISER, IMPALA SS & ROADMASTER

1. Disconnect battery ground cable and remove turn signal switch as outlined under "Turn Signal Switch, Replace.".
2. Remove ignition lock, ignition switch and dimmer switch as outlined under "Ignition Switch, Replace" and "Dimmer Switch, Replace".
3. Remove ignition lock housing retaining screws and housing, **Figs. 22 and 23.**
4. Remove pivot bolt and wiper switch from lock housing, **Fig. 24.**
5. Reverse procedure to install.

1992 BROUGHAM

1. Disconnect battery ground cable.
2. Remove lefthand climate control outlet grille.
3. Remove screw securing switch to instrument panel.
4. Pull control switch and electrical connector out, then disconnect from panel.
5. Reverse procedure to install.

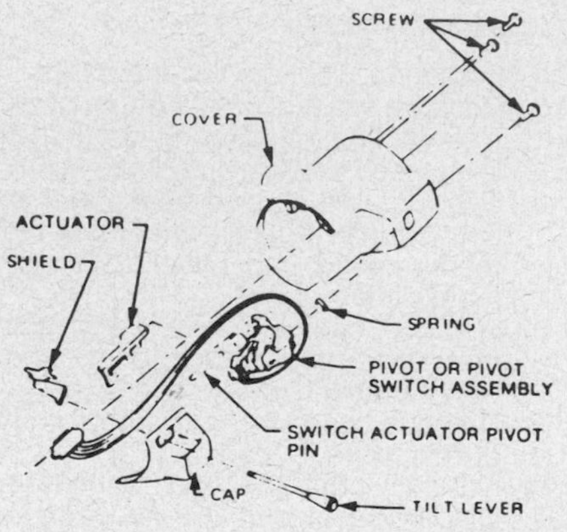
SCREW
COVER
ACTUATOR
SHIELD
SPRING
PIVOT OR PIVOT SWITCH ASSEMBLY
SWITCH ACTUATOR PIVOT PIN
CAP
TILT LEVER

GC9029100230000X

Fig. 23 Windshield wiper switch. Tilt steering column

FLEETWOOD (RWD)

The wiper/washer switch is non-replaceable component of the multi-function lever. The multi-function lever must be replaced as an assembly.

WIPER TRANSMISSION
REPLACE

1992 BROUGHAM

1. Raise hood and remove wiper arm assemblies.
2. Remove lower windshield reveal molding and cowl vent screen.
3. Place suitable lever between drive link and motor crank arm, then pry drive link from crank arm.
4. Remove screws securing transmission pivot retainers to body, then withdraw transmission assembly through plenum opening.
5. Reverse procedure to install.

CAPRICE, CUSTOM CRUISER, FLEETWOOD (RWD), IMPALA SS & ROADMASTER

1. Disconnect battery ground cable.
2. Remove right and lefthand wiper arm and hose.
3. Remove lefthand cowl vent screen, then righthand screen.
4. Disconnect plastic nozzle hose from rubber washer hose.
5. Remove wiper linkage access hole cover attaching screws, then remove cover.
6. Disconnect drive link from motor crank arm.
7. Remove linkage to body attaching screws, then remove linkage through access hole.
8. Reverse procedure to install.

BLOWER MOTOR
REPLACE

1992 BROUGHAM

1. Disconnect battery ground cable.
2. Disconnect blower motor lead wire, then the cooling tube, if equipped.
3. Remove blower motor to case attaching screws, then remove blower motor, **Fig. 25.**
4. Reverse procedure to install.

CAPRICE, CUSTOM CRUISER, FLEETWOOD (RWD), IMPALA SS & ROADMASTER

1. Disconnect battery ground cable.
2. Remove righthand instrument panel sound insulator attaching screws,

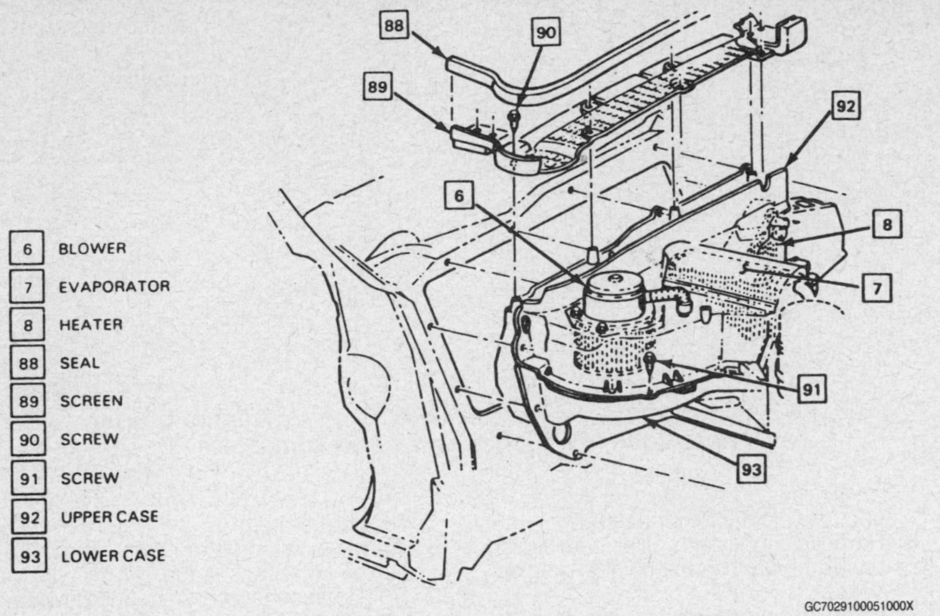

6 BLOWER
7 EVAPORATOR
8 HEATER
88 SEAL
89 SCREEN
90 SCREW
91 SCREW
92 UPPER CASE
93 LOWER CASE
GC7029100051000X

Fig. 25 Blower motor, heater core & evaporator core. 1992 Brougham with A/C

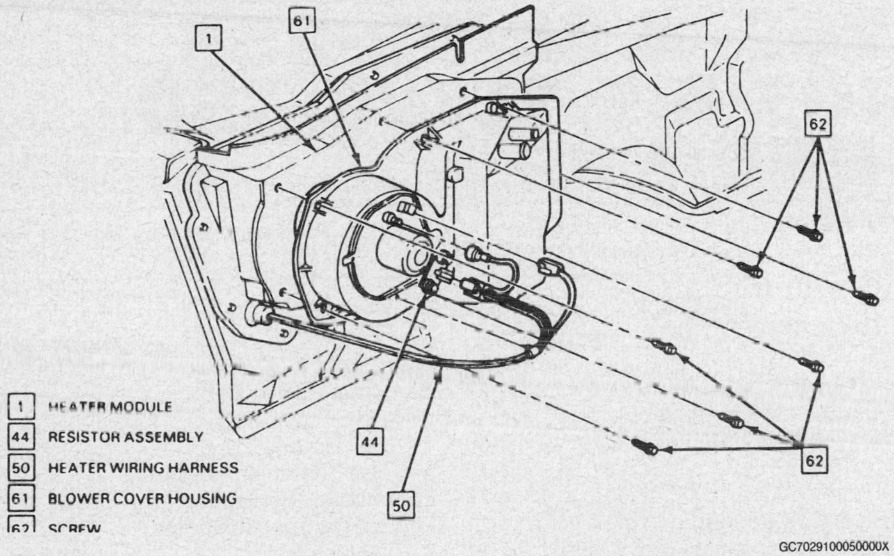

1 HEATER MODULE
44 RESISTOR ASSEMBLY
50 HEATER WIRING HARNESS
61 BLOWER COVER HOUSING
62 SCREW
GC7029100050000X

Fig. 26 Blower motor & heater core. Less A/C

then pull panel rearward disengaging attaching studs.

3. Disconnect blower assembly electrical connector, **Figs. 26 and 27.**
4. Remove righthand hinge pillar trim finish panel.
5. Remove secondary ECM bracket attaching screw, then position secondary ECM and bracket aside.
6. Support blower motor assembly, then remove blower motor assembly attaching screws.
7. Remove blower motor assembly.
8. Reverse procedure to install.

HEATER CORE

REPLACE

LESS A/C

1. Disconnect battery ground cable and drain cooling system.
2. Disconnect heater hoses from heater core. Plug core outlets to prevent coolant spillage.
3. Disconnect electrical connections at blower motor and resistor.
4. Detach heater wiring from clip at blower housing cover.
5. Remove blower housing cover attaching screws, then remove blower housing cover, **Fig. 26.**
6. Remove heater core.
7. Reverse procedure to install.

WITH A/C

1992 Brougham

1. Disconnect battery ground cable and drain cooling system.
2. Disconnect heater hoses at heater core. Cap core outlets to prevent coolant spillage.
3. Pull hood seal from A/C module flange and area above air screen.
4. Remove air inlet screen attaching screws and air inlet screen.
5. Remove righthand windshield wiper arm.
6. Detach A/C module ground strap from dash panel.
7. Disconnect electrical connectors from A/C module upper case components.
8. Remove upper A/C module attaching screws, then remove A/C module upper case, **Fig. 26.**
9. Remove heater core tube seal, then remove heater core retaining clamp and lift heater core from case.
10. Reverse procedure to install.

Caprice, Custom Cruiser, Fleetwood (RWD), Impala SS & Roadmaster

1. Disconnect battery ground cable, then drain cooling system.
2. Remove heater outlet attaching screw.
3. Disconnect heater core pipe fittings, then disengage pipe from fitting.
4. Remove righthand instrument insulator panel attaching screws, then pull panel rearward to disconnect.
5. Remove instrument panel lower reinforcement attaching nut and screw.
6. Disconnect lower evaporator case vacuum electrical connectors.
7. Remove righthand pillar trim finish panel, then roll carpet back to gain access.
8. Remove seven lower evaporator case attaching screws, then remove lower evaporator case.
9. Remove heater core attaching straps and screws, then pull heater core rearward working heater tubes out of seal, **Fig. 27.**
10. Reverse procedure to install.

EVAPORATOR CORE

REPLACE

1992 BROUGHAM

1. Disconnect battery ground cable and discharge refrigerant from A/C system.
2. Disconnect evaporator core inlet and outlet refrigerant lines. Cap lines and outlets.
3. Remove expansion tube from evaporator inlet pipe using tool No. J26549-D or equivalent.
4. Pull hood seal from A/C module flange and area above air screen.
5. Remove air inlet screen attaching screws and air inlet screen.
6. Remove righthand windshield wiper arm.
7. Detach A/C module ground strap from dash panel.
8. Disconnect electrical connectors from A/C module upper case components.
9. Remove upper A/C module attaching screws, then remove A/C module upper case, **Fig. 25.**

10. Remove evaporator core clamp, then lift evaporator core from case.
11. Reverse procedure to install. When installing, ensure evaporator core seal remain properly positioned. After completing installation, add three ounces of refrigerant oil and recharge A/C system as described in "Air Conditioning" section.

CAPRICE, CUSTOM CRUISER, FLEETWOOD (RWD), IMPALA SS & ROADMASTER

1. Disconnect battery ground cable and discharge refrigerant from A/C system.
2. Disconnect evaporator core inlet and outlet refrigerant lines. Cap lines and outlets.
3. Remove righthand instrument insulator panel attaching screws, then pull panel rearward to disconnect.
4. Remove instrument panel lower reinforcement attaching nut and screw.
5. Disconnect lower evaporator case vacuum electrical connectors.
6. Remove righthand pillar trim finish panel, then roll carpet back to gain access.
7. Remove seven lower evaporator case attaching screws, then remove lower evaporator case.
8. Remove evaporator core attaching screw and bracket, **Fig. 27.**
9. Pull heater core rearward and down to remove.
10. Reverse procedure to install.

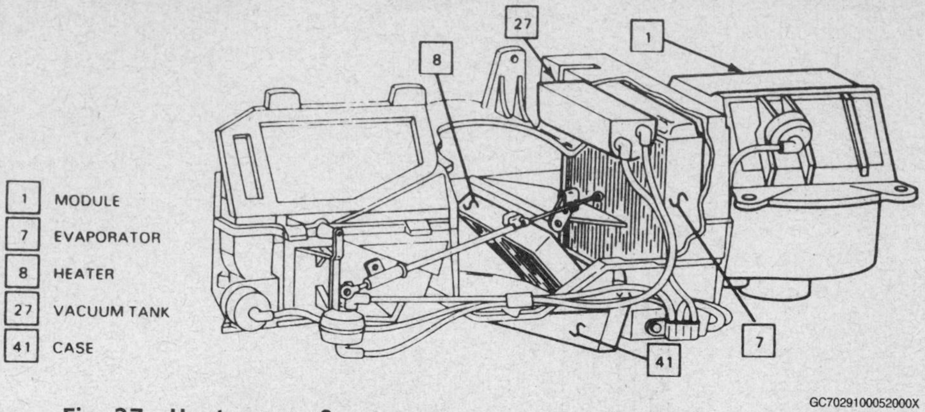
1 MODULE
7 EVAPORATOR
8 HEATER
27 VACUUM TANK
41 CASE
27
1
8
41
7
GC7029100052000X

Fig. 27 Heater core & evaporator core. Caprice, Custom Cruiser, Fleetwood (RWD), Impala SS & Roadmaster

4.3L/V6-262, 4.3L/V8-265, 5.0L/V8-305 & 5.7L/V8-350 ENGINES

NOTE: On Air Bag Equipped Models, Refer To "Air Bag System Precautions" Located In The Front Of This Manual For System Disarming & Arming Procedures.

INDEX

PRECAUTIONS

AIR BAG SYSTEMS

Refer to "Air Bag System Precautions" in the front of this manual for system disarming and arming procedures.

FUEL SYSTEM PRESSURE RELIEF

1. Turn ignition Off, then disconnect battery ground cable.
2. Loosen fuel filler cap to relieve fuel tank pressure. Do not tighten until service has been completed.
3. Connect fuel pressure gauge.
4. Install bleed hose into approved container an open valve to bleed system pressure.
5. Drain any fuel remaining in gauge into approved container.

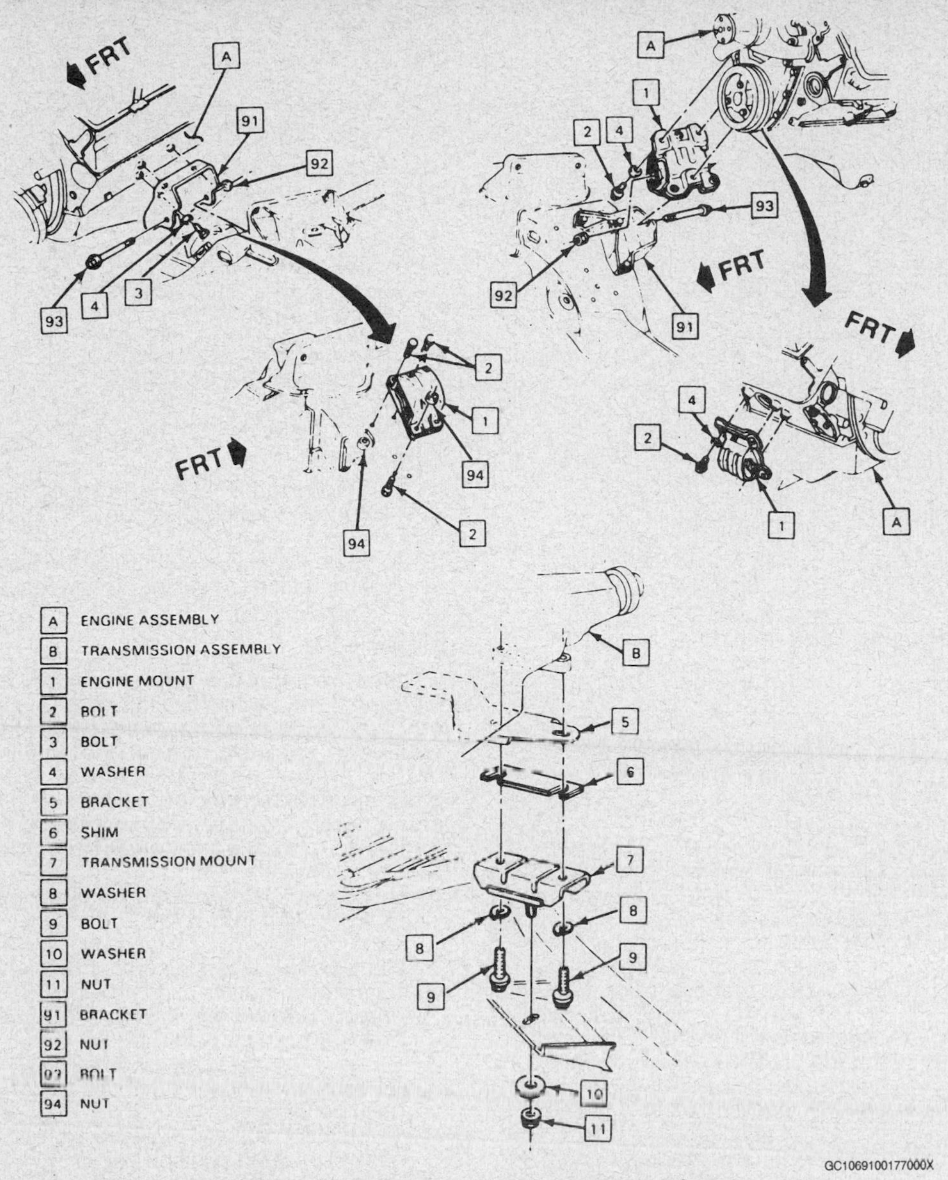
FRT
A ENGINE ASSEMBLY
B TRANSMISSION ASSEMBLY
1 ENGINE MOUNT
2 BOLT
3 BOLT
4 WASHER
5 BRACKET
6 SHIM
7 TRANSMISSION MOUNT
8 WASHER
9 BOLT
10 WASHER
11 NUT
91 BRACKET
92 NUT
93 BOLT
94 NUT
GC1069100177000X

Fig. 1 Engine & transmission mounting

ENGINE MOUNT

REPLACE

1. Remove mount retaining bolt from below frame mounting bracket, **Fig. 1.**
2. Raise front of engine and remove mount to engine bolts and mount.
3. **On models with 4.3L/V6-262 engine,** the righthand mount may be removed by loosening the through bolt.
4. **On all models, raise engine only enough to provide sufficient clearance for mount removal. Check for interference between rear of engine and cowl panel which could result in distributor damage.**
5. Reverse procedure to install.

ENGINE

REPLACE

1992–93

1. Disconnect battery cable from battery, then remove air cleaner assembly.
2. Drain cooling system, then disconnect radiator and heater hoses.
3. Remove upper fan shroud, then remove engine cooling fan.
4. Remove power steering pump from bracket and position aside with hoses attached.
5. Remove A/C compressor from mounting and position aside with hoses attached.
6. Disconnect accelerator and T.V. cables from throttle body.
7. Remove radiator from vehicle.
8. Disconnect electrical wiring and vacuum hoses as necessary to permit engine removal. Tag electrical wiring and vacuum hoses so they may be installed at the same locations.
9. Disconnect ground strap at engine bulkhead.
10. Scribe alignment marks on hinges, then remove hood.
11. **On 1992-93 models,** remove distributor, wiper motor and MAP sensor.
12. **On all models,** disconnect cruise control cable, if equipped.
13. Disconnect battery ground cable from cylinder head.
14. Raise and support vehicle, then drain crankcase.
15. Disconnect electrical wiring from starter motor.
16. Remove exhaust crossover pipe and catalytic convertor as an assembly.
17. Remove flywheel cover, then remove flywheel to converter attaching bolts.
18. Remove engine mount through bolts.
19. **On TBI models,** relieve fuel pressure as outlined under "Precautions," then disconnect fuel hoses from fuel lines.
20. **On all models,** disconnect converter clutch wiring at transmission.
21. Detach transmission oil cooler lines from clip at oil pan.
22. **On 4.3L/V6-262 engine,** remove converter AIR pipe from exhaust manifold.
23. **On all models,** remove transmission to engine attaching bolts.
24. Lower vehicle, then support transmission using a suitable jack.
25. Install a suitable engine lifting fixture to engine, then remove engine from vehicle.
26. Reverse procedure to install.

1994–95

This engine is equipped with a sequential multiport fuel injection system. Fuel injector connectors must be positioned onto the correct fuel injectors or engine performance and exhaust emissions may be seriously affected. Fuel injector connectors are numbered to match the correct injector for that cylinder.

1. Disconnect battery ground cable, then recover R134a refrigerant. Refer to "Air Conditioning" section.
2. Drain coolant into suitable container(s), then remove air cleaner resonator bracket nuts and resonator assembly by loosening clamp at air intake duct and sliding resonator assembly off studs.
3. Remove air intake duct.
4. Disconnect fuel lines at fuel rail.
5. **On models equipped with mechanical fan,** remove radiator fan upper shroud.
6. Remove fan blade clutch nuts and fan blade with clutch attached.
7. Remove fan pulley.
8. **On all models,** disconnect heater hoses from water pump.
9. Disconnect accelerator control cable at throttle body.
10. Disconnect radiator inlet and outlet hoses from water pump and engine, then coolant hose at throttle body.
11. Raise and support vehicle, then remove engine oil filter adapter hose assemblies, if equipped, and drain engine oil.
12. Remove warm up three-way catalytic converters and gaskets from exhaust manifolds.
13. Remove converter cover bolts/screws, then cover.
14. Remove converter bolts/screws.
15. Remove serpentine drive belt as outlined.

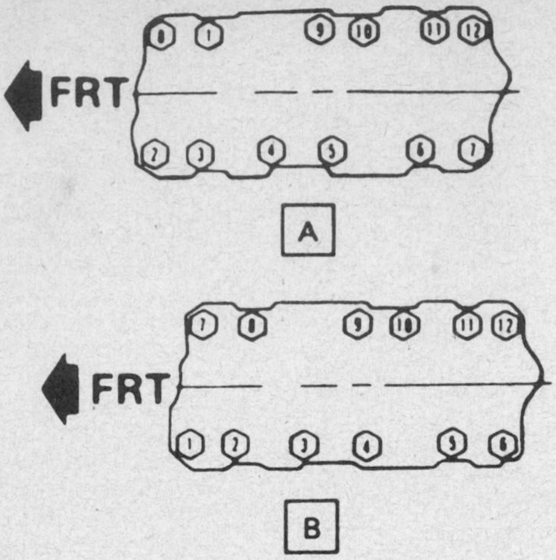
FRT
A
FRT
B

A INITIAL TIGHTENING SEQUENCE

B FINAL TIGHTENING SEQUENCE

GC1059100058000X

Fig. 2 Intake manifold bolt tightening sequence. 4.3L/V6-262

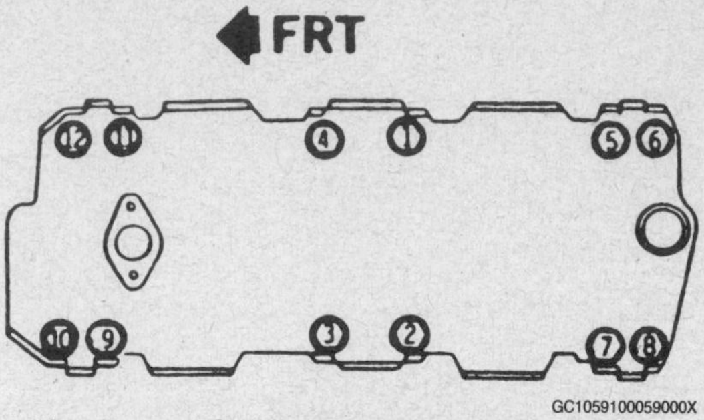
FRT

GC1059100059000X

Fig. 3 Intake manifold bolt tightening sequence. 5.0L/V8-305 & 1992–93 5.7L/V8-350

16. Remove air conditioning hose from compressor, then plug open ends of lines and fittings.
17. Disconnect transmission fluid cooler lines from engine clips.
18. **On models equipped with mechanical fan,** remove radiator fan lower shroud.
19. **On all models,** remove electric engine cooling fans.
20. Disconnect electrical connectors from starter motor, knock sensor, oxygen sensor, engine oil level switch and fuel pump switch/engine oil pressure gage sensor.
21. Lower vehicle, then disconnect power steering inlet and outlet hoses at pump. Siphon fluid from reservoir to prevent excessive spillage.
22. Disconnect brake booster vacuum hose and generator wiring from generator.
23. Disconnect engine wiring harness connectors and ground straps, then raise and support vehicle.
24. Remove transmission-to-engine bolts/screws, then transmission filler tube bolt/screw at rear of right hand cylinder head.
25. Remove engine mount through-bolts/screws, then lower vehicle.
26. Disconnect engine wiring harness support at left front corner of intake manifold.
27. Install engine lifting device to boss at left front corner of intake manifold using a 3/8-16 NC standard thread bolt. Bolt should be long enough to thread into intake manifold at least one inch. Install other end of engine lifting device to fourth studded bolt on right side of intake manifold. Use a 3/8-16 NC nut to secure lifting device to studded bolt.
28. Remove engine.
29. Reverse procedure to install.

INTAKE MANIFOLD

REPLACE

1992–93

1. Disconnect battery ground cable, drain cooling system and remove air cleaner.
2. Disconnect accelerator, transmission and cruise control linkages.
3. Disconnect fuel line from carburetor or TBI unit and remove fuel line clips as needed, then remove carburetor or throttle body from intake manifold.
4. Disconnect necessary vacuum hoses and electrical connectors, noting position for installation.
5. Disconnect upper radiator and heater hoses from manifold.
6. **On Brougham and 1993 Fleetwood (RWD) models,** remove thermostat and housing.
7. **On all models,** remove distributor as described in "Electrical" section under "Distributor, Replace."
8. Remove ignition coil, AIR pump, cruise control servo and brackets, as needed.
9. Remove alternator upper mounting bracket and EGR solenoids.
10. Remove manifold retaining bolts and the manifold.
11. Reverse procedure to install, noting the following:
    a. Ensure surfaces are clean and dry, then apply a 3/16 bead of RTV sealer on each block ridge and apply suitable sealer around water outlets, install gaskets and secure gasket position by extending bead of sealer approximately 1/2 inch onto gasket ends.
    b. Install manifold and retaining bolts, ensuring areas between case ridges and manifold are completely sealed.
    c. Torque manifold bolts to specifications in sequence shown in **Figs. 2 and 3.**
    d. After installing carburetor or TBI unit, check to ensure no fuel leakage is present.

1994–95

These engines are equipped with a sequential multiport fuel injection system. Fuel injector connectors must be positioned onto the correct fuel injectors or engine performance and exhaust emissions may be seriously affected. Fuel injector connectors are numbered to match the correct injector for that cylinder.

1. Disconnect battery ground cable, then drain coolant into suitable container(s).
2. Remove air cleaner resonator bracket nuts and resonator assembly by loosening clamp at air intake duct and sliding resonator assembly off studs.
3. Remove throttle body air duct.
4. Disconnect fuel injector wiring harness connectors.
5. Disconnect left and right wiring harness clips, then position aside.
6. Remove accelerator control cable bracket bolts/screws and bracket from throttle body.
7. Relieve fuel system pressure as outlined.
8. Disconnect fuel pipe connectors from fuel rail, then remove fuel rail bolts/screws.
9. Remove resonator bracket with canister purge solenoid attached.
10. Disconnect fuel pressure regulator vacuum tube, then remove fuel rail from intake manifold and position aside.
11. Disconnect vacuum and crankcase vent hoses.
12. Remove EGR control valve relay nut, then control valve relay.
13. Remove EGR valve pipe nuts, bolt/screw, pipe and gasket. Discard gasket.
14. Disconnect engine wiring harness and remove nuts at left front corner of intake manifold.
15. Disconnect coolant hoses from throttle body, then remove throttle body bolts/screws, throttle body and gasket.

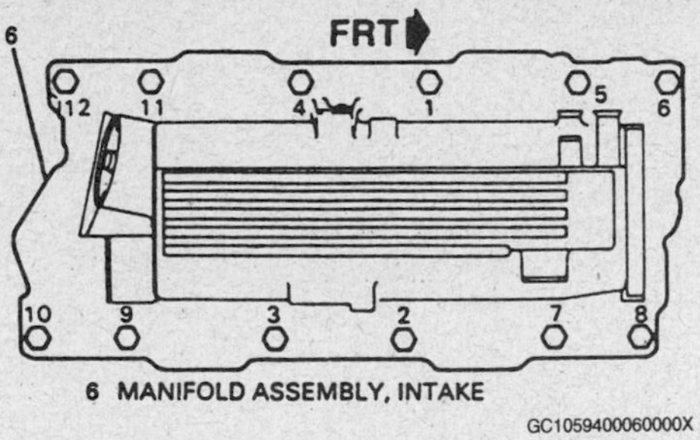
FRT
6
12
11
4
1
5
6
10
9
3
2
7
8
6 MANIFOLD ASSEMBLY, INTAKE
GC1059400060000X

Fig. 4 Intake manifold bolt tightening sequence. 4.3L/V8-265 & 1994–95 5.7L/V8-350

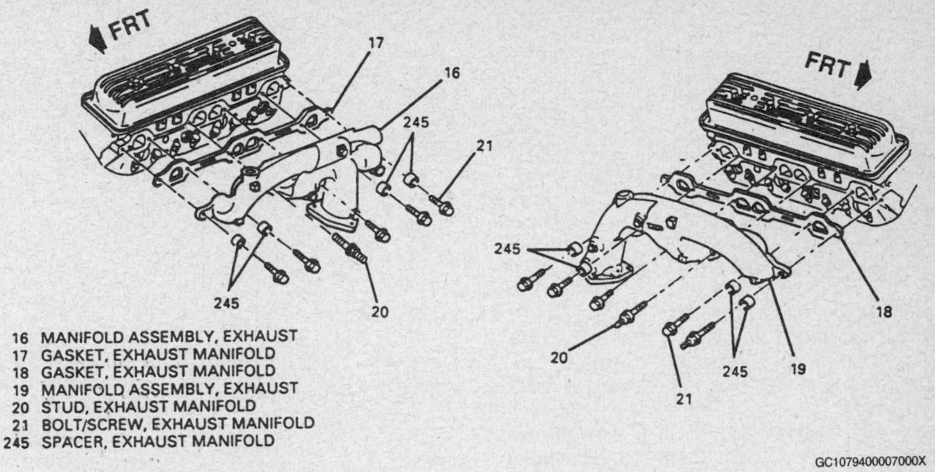
FRT
17
16
245
21
245
20
FRT
245
18
20
245
19
21
16 MANIFOLD ASSEMBLY, EXHAUST
17 GASKET, EXHAUST MANIFOLD
18 GASKET, EXHAUST MANIFOLD
19 MANIFOLD ASSEMBLY, EXHAUST
20 STUD, EXHAUST MANIFOLD
21 BOLT/SCREW, EXHAUST MANIFOLD
245 SPACER, EXHAUST MANIFOLD
GC1079400007000X

Fig. 6 Exhaust manifold installation. 1994–95

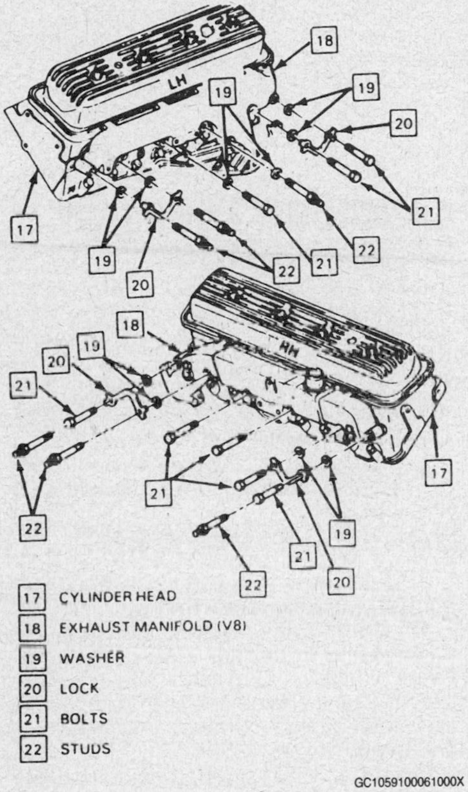
18
19
19
20
21
17
19
22
21
22
20
18
19
20
21
17
21
19
21
22
22
20
17 CYLINDER HEAD
18 EXHAUST MANIFOLD (V8)
19 WASHER
20 LOCK
21 BOLTS
22 STUDS
GC1059100061000X

Fig. 5 Exhaust manifold installation. 1992–93

16. Remove intake manifold bolts/screws and studs, then intake manifold and gaskets. Discard gaskets.
17. Reverse procedure to install, noting the following:
    a. Ensure surfaces are clean and dry, then apply a 3/16 bead of RTV sealer to front and rear of engine block. Extend bead approximately 1/2 inch up each cylinder head.
    b. Install manifold and retaining bolts, ensuring areas between case ridges and manifold are completely sealed.
    c. Tighten manifold bolts to specifications in sequence shown in **Fig. 4.**

EXHAUST MANIFOLD

REPLACE

1992–93

1. Disconnect battery ground cable, then raise and support vehicle.
2. Disconnect crossover pipe from exhaust manifold.
3. Lower vehicle, then remove air cleaner, if necessary.
4. Disconnect spark plug wires and diverter valve, if necessary.
5. Remove hoses, brackets and pipes as necessary to permit exhaust manifold removal. Tag hoses so they can be installed in the same locations.
6. Remove exhaust manifold attaching bolts and studs, then remove exhaust manifold and gasket, **Fig. 5.**
7. Reverse procedure to install. Tighten to specifications.

1994–95

1. Remove warm up three-way catalytic converter and gasket from exhaust manifold.
2. Remove oil level indicator tube.
3. Remove secondary air injection pipe fitting from exhaust manifold.
4. Remove generator rear lower braces.
5. Remove exhaust manifold bolts/screws, studs and spacers, **Fig. 6.**
6. Remove exhaust manifold and gasket.
7. Reverse procedure to install.

CYLINDER HEAD

REPLACE

1992–93

1. Disconnect battery ground cable, then drain cooling system and engine block.
2. Remove intake manifold and exhaust manifolds.
3. Remove rocker arm covers.
4. Remove alternator lower mounting bolt and position alternator aside.
5. Remove dipstick tube and bracket.

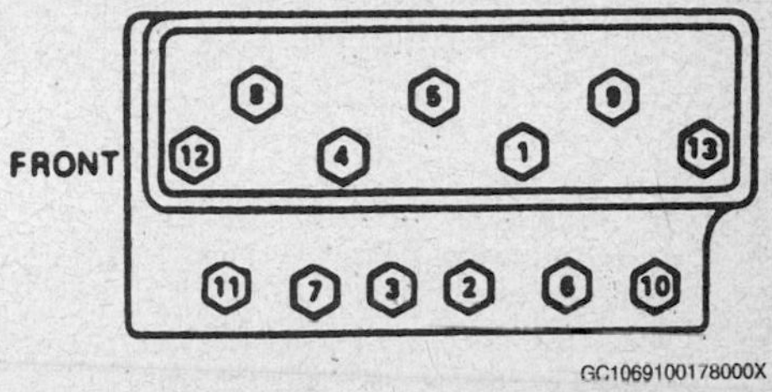
FRONT
9
5
9
12
4
1
13
11
7
3
2
6
10
GC1069100178000X

Fig. 7 Cylinder head bolt tightening sequence. 4.3L/V6-262

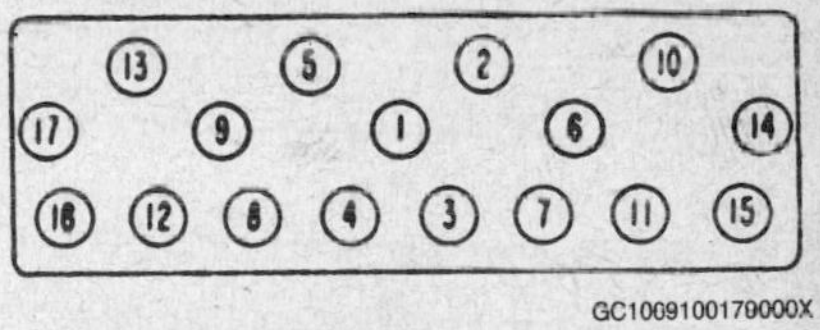
13
5
2
10
17
9
1
6
14
18
12
8
4
3
7
11
15
GC1009100179000X

Fig. 8 Cylinder head bolt tightening sequence. 5.0L/V8-305 & 5.7L/V8-350

6. If equipped with A/C, remove compressor and forward mounting bracket and position aside.
7. Remove power steering pump and bracket, position aside.
8. Remove rocker arm cover, rocker arms and push rods. **Keep rocker arm, rocker arm balls and push rods in order so they can be installed in the same position.**
9. Remove diverter valve, if equipped.
10. Remove cylinder head bolts and cylinder head.
11. Reverse procedure to install. Apply suitable sealer to cylinder head bolts and gradually tighten bolts to specifications, in sequence shown in **Figs. 7 and 8.**

1994–95

Left

1. Raise and support vehicle, then drain coolant into suitable container(s).
2. Remove three-way catalytic converter and gasket from exhaust manifold, then lower vehicle.

3. Remove intake manifold as outlined.
4. Disconnect secondary air injection pipe from check valve.
5. Disconnect coolant air bleed pipe bolt/screw from left cylinder head using a back up wrench on pipe fitting.
6. Remove ignition coil bolts/screws and coil assembly as follows:
   a. Disconnect four-terminal PCM connector at ignition coil module.
   b. Disconnect ignition coil wiring connectors, then coil harness.
   c. Remove studs, then ignition coil. Do not wipe silicone grease from bottom of ignition coil assembly if it is to be reinstalled.
7. Remove left exhaust manifold as outlined.
8. Disconnect spark plug wire harness from clips, then from spark plugs.
9. Remove spark plugs.
10. Disconnect coolant temperature sensor.
11. Remove rocker arm cover bolts/screws, then cover.
12. Remove rocker arm nuts, rocker arms and pushrods.
13. Remove cylinder head bolts/screws, then cylinder head and gasket. Discard gasket.
14. Reverse procedure to install. Apply suitable sealer to cylinder head bolts and gradually tighten bolts to specifications, in sequence shown in **Fig. 9.**

Right

1. Raise and support vehicle, then drain coolant into suitable container(s).
2. Remove serpentine drive belt and belt tensioner as outlined.
3. Disconnect transmission fluid level indicator tube bracket from transmission housing and rear of right cylinder head.
4. Remove air conditioning compressor rear brace bolt/screw from engine block, then disconnect compressor electrical connector.
5. Remove air conditioning compressor front mounting bolts/screws and position compressor aside.
6. Remove three-way catalytic converter and gasket from exhaust manifold, then lower vehicle.
7. Remove right exhaust manifold as outlined.
8. Remove generator.
9. Remove right rocker arm cover.
10. Remove intake manifold as outlined, then disconnect coolant air bleed pipe bolt/screw from both cylinder heads using a back up wrench on pipe fittings.
11. Disconnect radiator outlet hose and heater hoses from water pump and reposition.
12. Remove power steering pump as outlined. Refer to "Front Suspension & Steering" section.
13. Remove generator, power steering pump and air conditioning compressor bracket assembly.
14. Disconnect spark plug wiring harness from spark plugs, then remove spark plugs.
15. Remove rocker arms and pushrods.
16. Disconnect engine coolant temperature sensor electrical connector on side of cylinder head.
17. Remove cylinder head bolts/screws, then cylinder head and gasket. Discard gasket.
18. Reverse procedure to install. Apply suitable sealer to cylinder head bolts and gradually tighten bolts to specifications, in sequence shown in **Fig. 9.**

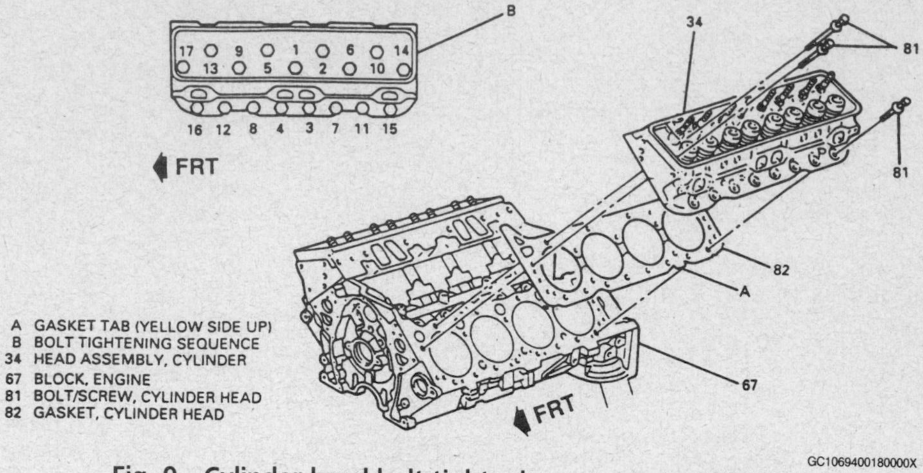
B
17 9 1 6 14
13 5 2 10
16 12 8 4 3 7 11 15
FRT
34
81
81
82
A
67
FRT
A GASKET TAB (YELLOW SIDE UP)
B BOLT TIGHTENING SEQUENCE
34 HEAD ASSEMBLY, CYLINDER
67 BLOCK, ENGINE
81 BOLT/SCREW, CYLINDER HEAD
82 GASKET, CYLINDER HEAD
GC1069400180000X

Fig. 9 Cylinder head bolt tightening sequence. 1994–95

VALVE ARRANGEMENT

FRONT TO REAR

4.3L/V6-262

Right .... E-I-I-E-I-E
Left .... E-I-E-I-I-E

4.3L/V8-265, 5.0L/V8-305 & 5.7L/V8-350

All .... E-I-I-E-E-I-I-E

VALVE LIFT SPECIFICATIONS

Engine/VIN	Year	Int.	Exh.
5.0L/V8-305/E	1992–93	.350	.385
4.3L/V6-262/Z	1992–93	.350	.385
4.3L/V8-265/W	1994–95	.418	.418
5.7L/V8-350/7	1992–93	①	①
5.7L/V8-350/P	1994–95	.418	.430

①—Except police models, intake .350 inch, exhaust .385 inch. Police models, intake .413 inch, exhaust .428 inch.

CAMSHAFT LOBE LIFT SPECIFICATIONS

Engine/VIN	Year	Int.	Exh.
5.0L/V8-305/E	1992	.234	.257
4.3L/V6-262/Z	1992	.234	.257
5.7L/V8-350/7	1992	①	①
All	1993	.233	.257
All	1994–95	.279	.286

①—Except police models, intake .233 inch, exhaust .256 inch. Police models, intake .257 inch, exhaust .269 inch.

VALVE ADJUSTMENT

Adjust valves, **Fig. 10,** with engine at normal operating temperature.

On V6 engines, rotate engine until No. 1 cylinder is in position to fire. Adjust exhaust valves 1-5-6 and intake valves 1-2-3. Crank engine one complete revolution, then adjust exhaust valves 2-3-4 and intake valves 4-5-6.

On V8 engines, rotate engine until No. 1 cylinder is in position to fire. Adjust exhaust valves 1-3-4-8 and intake valves 1-2-5-7. Crank engine one complete revolution, then adjust exhaust valves 2-5-6-7 and intake vales 3-4-6-8.

On all engines, the following procedure, performed with the engine running, should only be performed if readjustment is required.

1. After engine has been warmed up to normal operating temperature, remove valve cover and install a new valve cover gasket.
2. With engine running at idle speed, back off valve rocker arm nut until rocker arm starts to clatter.
3. Turn rocker arm nut down slowly until the clatter just stops. This is the zero lash position.
4. Turn nut down 1/4 additional turn and pause 10 seconds until engine runs smoothly. Repeat additional 1/4 turns, pausing 10 seconds each time, until nut has been turned down the number

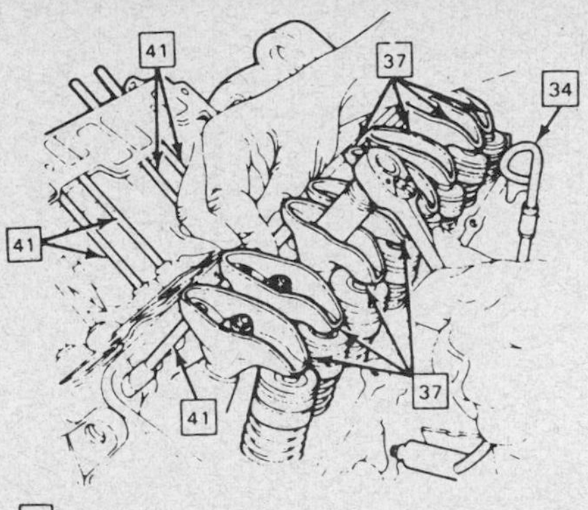
41
37
34
41
41
37

34 OIL LEVEL INDICATOR
37 ROCKER ARM
41 PUSH ROD

GC1069100181000X

Fig. 10 Valve lash adjustment

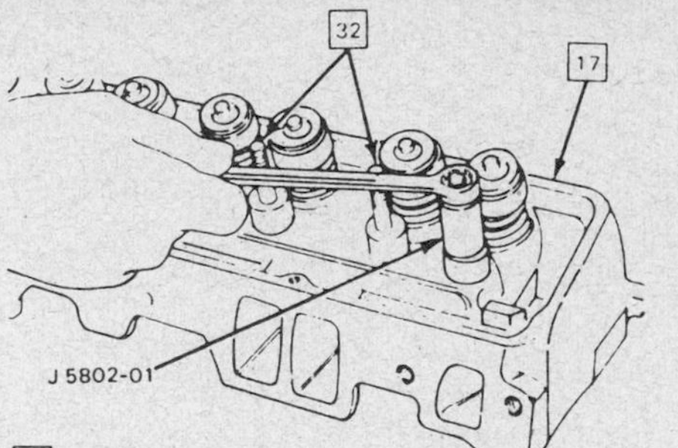
32
17
J 5802-01

17 CYLINDER HEAD
32 ROCKER ARM STUD

GC1069100182000X

Fig. 11 Rocker arm stud removal

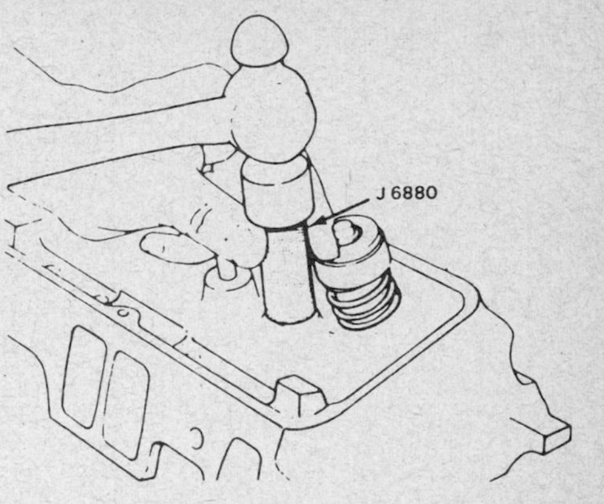
J 6880

GC1069100183000X

Fig. 12 Rocker arm stud installation

of turns listed in the "Valve Lash Specifications" chart from the zero lash position. **This preload adjustment must be done slowly to allow the lifter to adjust itself to prevent the possibility of interference between the valve head and top of piston, which might result in internal damage and/or bent push rods. Noisy lifters should be replaced.**

ROCKER ARMS

When replacing rocker arms or rocker arm balls, bearing surfaces of rocker arms and balls should be coated with pre-lube part No. 3755008 or equivalent.

ROCKER ARM STUDS

If studs are loose in cylinder head, .003 inch or .013 inch oversize studs may be installed after reaming holes with a proper size reamer.

1. Remove the old stud by placing a suitable spacer, **Fig. 11,** over stud. Install nut and flat washer and remove stud by turning nut.
2. Ream hole for oversize stud.
3. Coat press-fit area of stud with rear axle lube. Then install new stud, **Fig. 12.** If tool shown is used, it should bottom on the head.

PUSH RODS

On engines that use push rods with a hardened insert at one end, the hardened end is identified by a color stripe and should always be installed toward the rocker arm during assembly.

VALVE GUIDES

On all engines valves operate in guide holes bored in the head. If clearance becomes excessive, use the next oversize valve and ream the bore to fit. Valves with oversize stems are available in .003, .015 and .030 inch.

HYDRAULIC LIFTERS

REPLACE

Valve lifters can be lifted from their

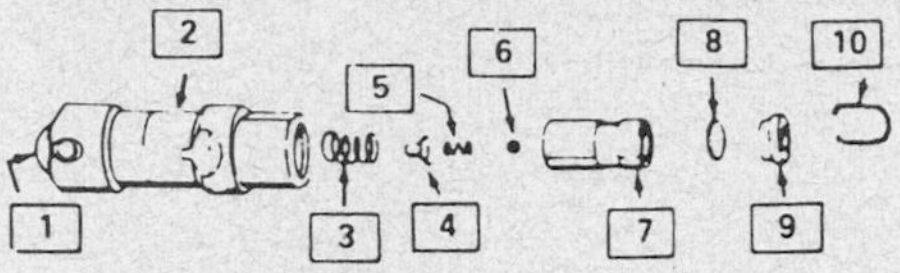
1
2
3
4
5
6
7
8
9
10

1-ROLLER
2-LIFTER BODY
3-PLUNGER SPRING
4-BALL CHECK RETAINER
5-BALL CHECK SPRING
6-BALL CHECK
7-PLUNGER
8-OIL METERING VALVE
9-PUSH ROD SEAT
10-RETAINER RING

GC1069100184000X

Fig. 13 Exploded view of hydraulic valve lifter

bores after removing rocker arms and push rods and intake manifold. Adjustable pliers with protected jaws may be used to remove lifters which are stuck due to carbon or varnish deposits. **Fig. 13** illustrates the type of valve lifter used.

CRANKSHAFT DAMPER

REPLACE

1994–95

1. Raise and support vehicle if equipped with mechanical fan.
2. Remove serpentine drive belt as outlined under "Serpentine Drive Belt".
3. Remove crankshaft pulley bolts/screws and pulley, if equipped with mechanical fan.
4. Remove balancer bolts/screws and balancer.
5. Match mark crankshaft hub to engine front cover. **Do not crank engine after matching crankshaft hub and front cover. Rotating crankshaft will misalign crankshaft hub and balancer with respect to crankshaft, possibly resulting in engine imbalance.**
6. Remove crankshaft hub bolt/screw and washer, crankshaft hub using crankshaft hub remover and installer.
7. Reverse procedure to install. If engine is accidentally turned over, the crankshaft hub can be installed after match marking the hub and front cover using the following procedure:
   a. Set No. 1 piston to TDC. When No. 1 piston is at TDC, crankshaft keyway should be in position shown in **Fig. 14.**
   b. Install crankshaft hub with cast arrow on hub in 12 o'clock position.

FRONT COVER

REPLACE

On all engines the cover oil seal may be replaced without taking off the timing gear cover. After removing the vibration damper, pry out the old seal with a screwdriver. Install the new seal with the lip or open end toward inside of cover and drive it into position.

1. **On 1994-95 models,** proceed as follows:
   a. Remove water pump as outlined under "Water Pump, Replace"
   b. Remove crankshaft balancer and hub as outlined under "Crankshaft Damper, Replace".
   c. Remove distributor as outlined in "Electrical" section.
2. **On 1992-93 models,** disconnect battery ground cable and drain cooling system, then remove vibration damper and water pump.
3. **On all models,** remove oil pan and gasket as outlined under "Oil Pan, Replace".
4. Remove front cover retaining screws and the front cover.
5. Reverse procedure to install.

TIMING CHAIN

REPLACE

1. Remove engine front cover as outlined under "Front Cover, Replace".
2. Remove crankshaft oil slinger.
3. Crank engine until timing markson sprockets are in alignment, **Figs. 14 and 15.**
4. Remove three camshaft to sprocket bolts.
5. Remove camshaft sprocket and timing chain together. Sprocket is a light press fit on camshaft for approximately 1/8 inch. If sprocket does not come off easily, a light blow with a plastic hammer on the lower edge of the sprocket should dislodge it.

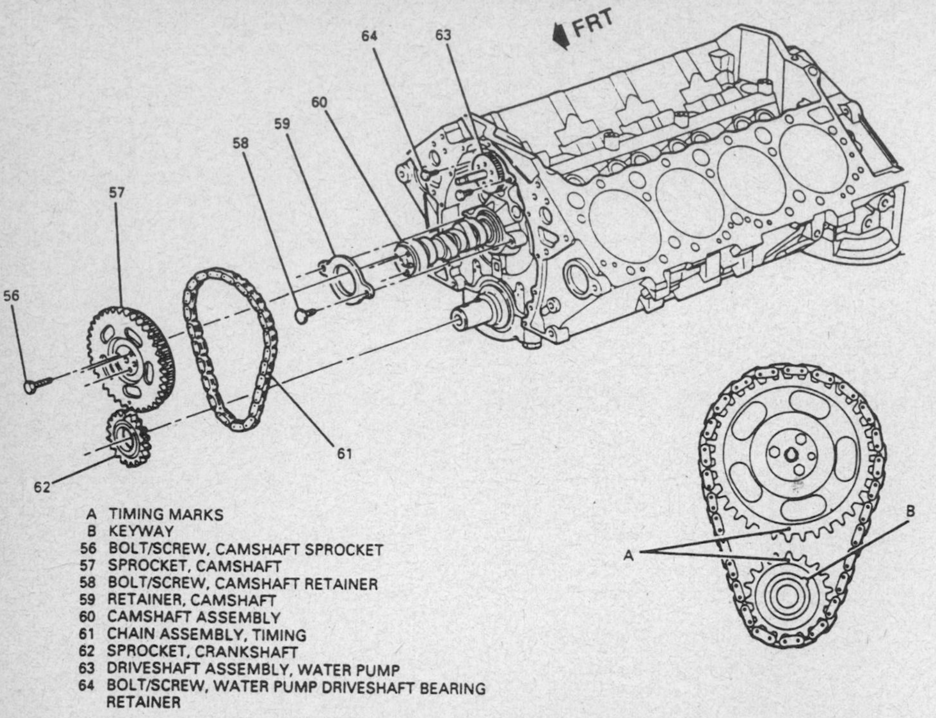
FRT
A TIMING MARKS
B KEYWAY
56 BOLT/SCREW, CAMSHAFT SPROCKET
57 SPROCKET, CAMSHAFT
58 BOLT/SCREW, CAMSHAFT RETAINER
59 RETAINER, CAMSHAFT
60 CAMSHAFT ASSEMBLY
61 CHAIN ASSEMBLY, TIMING
62 SPROCKET, CRANKSHAFT
63 DRIVESHAFT ASSEMBLY, WATER PUMP
64 BOLT/SCREW, WATER PUMP DRIVESHAFT BEARING RETAINER
GC1069400185000X

Fig. 14 Crankshaft assembly, sprockets & sprocket alignment, water pump driveshaft assembly & timing marks. 1994-95

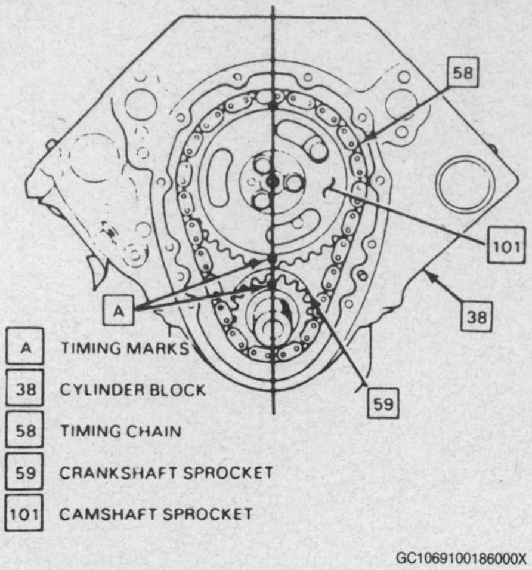
A TIMING MARKS
38 CYLINDER BLOCK
58 TIMING CHAIN
59 CRANKSHAFT SPROCKET
101 CAMSHAFT SPROCKET
GC1069100186000X

Fig. 15 Valve timing marks. 1992–93

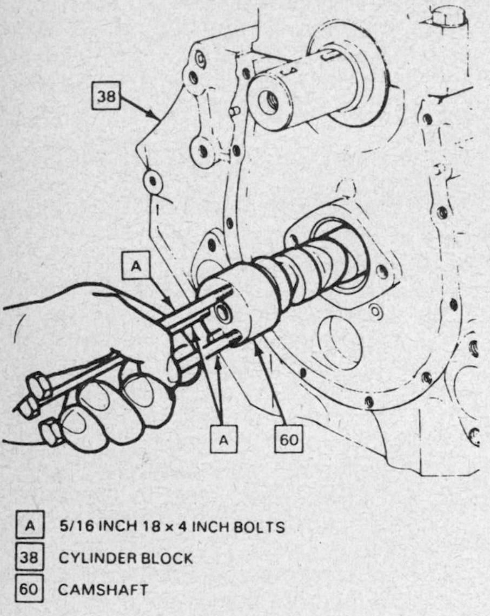
A 5/16 INCH 18 x 4 INCH BOLTS
38 CYLINDER BLOCK
60 CAMSHAFT
GC1069100187000X

Fig. 16 Camshaft removal

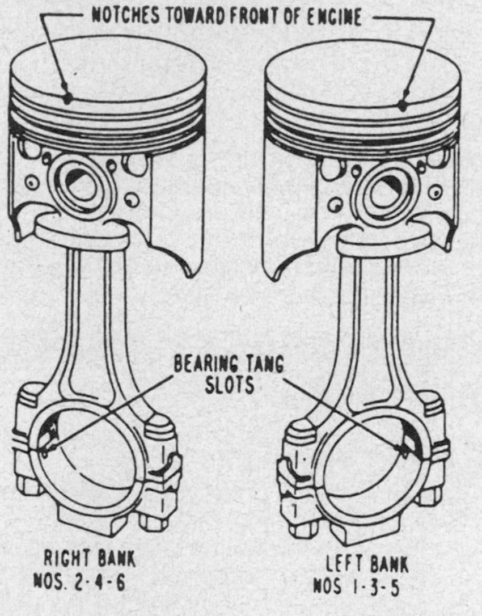
NOTCHES TOWARD FRONT OF ENGINE
BEARING TANG SLOTS
RIGHT BANK NOS. 2-4-6
LEFT BANK NOS 1-3-5
GC1069100188000X

Fig. 17 Piston & rod assembly. 4.3L/V6-262

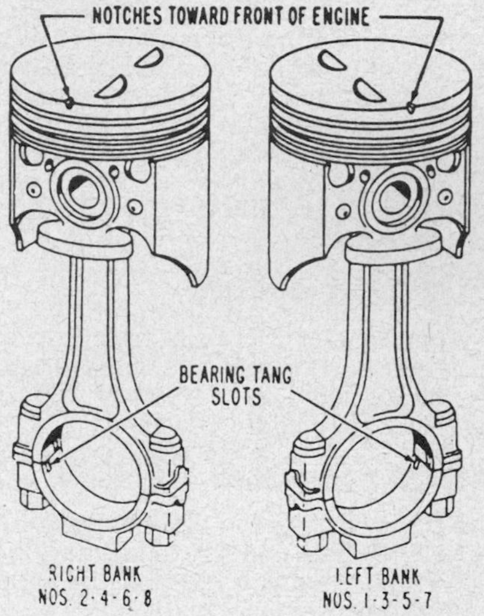
NOTCHES TOWARD FRONT OF ENGINE
BEARING TANG SLOTS
RIGHT BANK NOS. 2-4-6-8
LEFT BANK NOS. 1-3-5-7
GC1069100189000X

Fig. 18 Piston & rod assembly. 5.0L/V8-305 & 1992–93 5.7L/V8-350

6. If crankshaft sprocket is to be replaced, remove it with a suitable gear puller. Install new sprocket, aligning key and keyway.
7. Install chain on camshaft sprocket. Hold sprocket vertical with chain hanging below and shift around to align the timing marks on sprockets.
8. Align dowel in camshaft with dowel hole in sprocket and install sprocket on camshaft. Do not attempt to drive sprocket on camshaft as welch plug at rear of engine can be dislodged.
9. Draw sprocket onto camshaft, using the three mounting bolts. Tighten to specifications.
10. Lubricate timing chain with engine oil and install cover.

CAMSHAFT
REPLACE

1. Remove intake manifold as described under "Intake Manifold, Replace."
2. **On 1994-95 models,** remove oil pump drive and driveshaft.
3. **On all models,** remove valve covers, rocker arms and push rods. Keep rocker arms and push rods in order so they can be installed in the same locations.
4. Remove accessory drive belt(s), then remove upper fan shroud.
5. Remove radiator.
6. **On models equipped with A/C,** discharge refrigerant system and remove condenser.
7. **On all models** remove timing chain as described under "Timing Chain, Replace."
8. Remove grille.
9. Remove valve lifters. Keep valve lifters in order so they can be installed in the same locations.
10. Install three 5/16-18 x 4 inch bolts in camshaft bolt holes, then carefully remove camshaft, **Fig. 16.**
11. Reverse procedure to install.

PISTON & ROD ASSEMBLY

Assemble pistons to connecting rods as shown in **Figs. 17 through 19.**

Upon installation, measure the connecting rod side clearance using a suitable

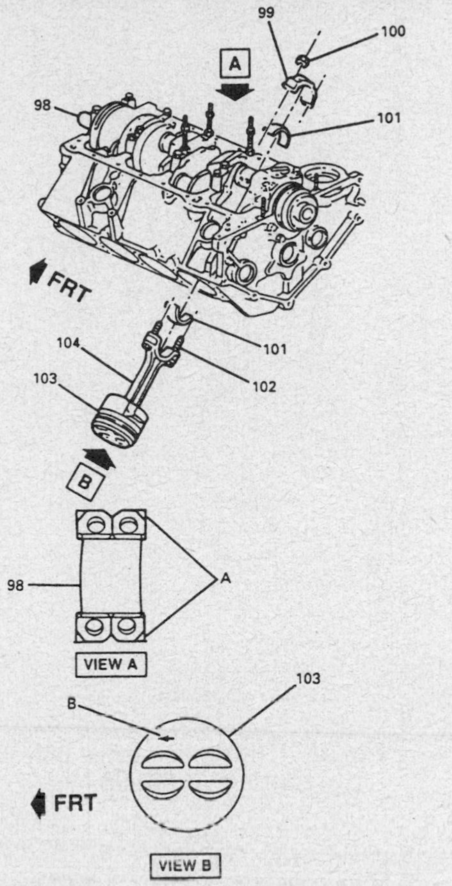
99
100
A
98
101
FRT
104
101
103
102
B
98
A
VIEW A
103
B
FRT
VIEW B

A FLANGES OF CONNECTING RODS MUST FACE TO THE FRONT IN THE LEFT BANK AND TO THE REAR IN THE RIGHT BANK
B ARROW TO BE ORIENTED TO FRONT OF ENGINE
98 CRANKSHAFT ASSEMBLY
99 CAP, CONNECTING ROD
100 NUT, CONNECTING ROD
101 BEARING, CONNECTING ROD
102 BOLT/SCREW, CONNECTING ROD
103 PISTON ASSEMBLY
104 ROD ASSEMBLY, CONNECTING

GC1069100190000X

Fig. 19 Piston & rod assembly. 1994–95

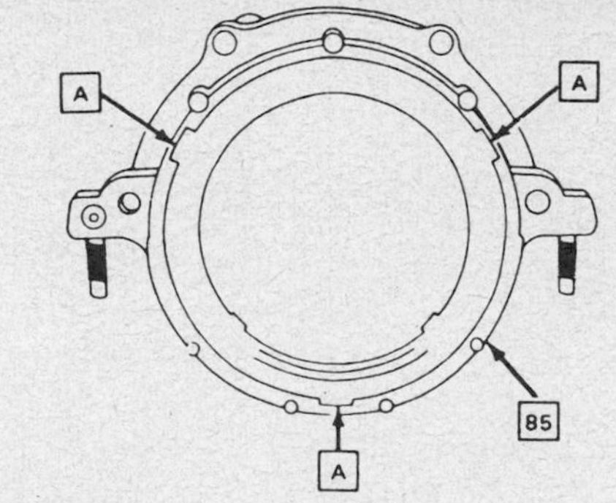
A
A
85
A

A SEAL REMOVAL NOTCHES
85 REAR CRANKSHAFT SEAL RETAINER

GC1069100191000X

Fig. 20 Crankshaft rear oil seal retainer notch locations

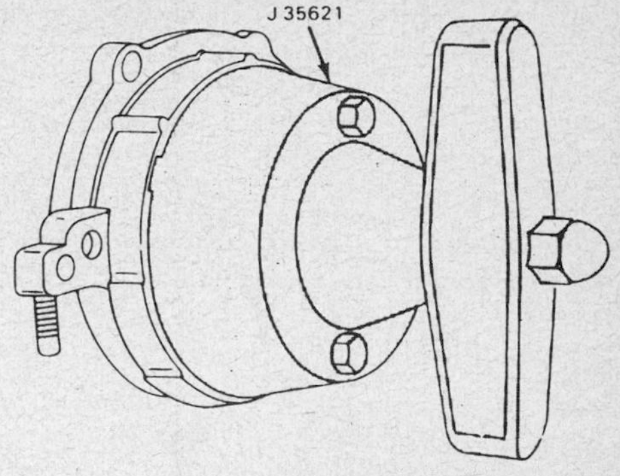
J 35621

GC1069100192000X

Fig. 21 Crankshaft rear oil seal installation

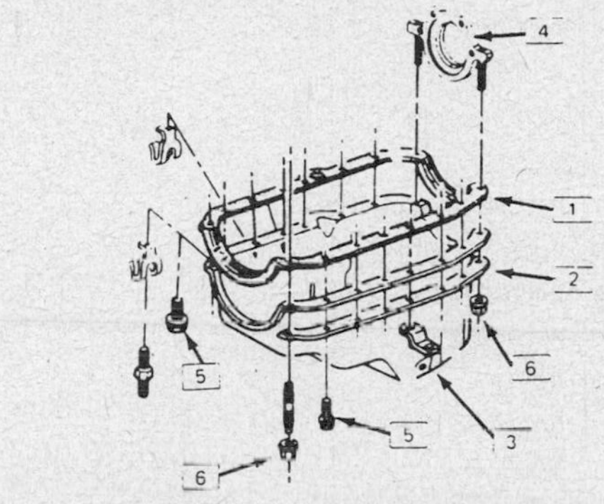
4
1
2
5
6
5
3
6

ENGINE OIL PRESSURE 10 LBS. MINIMUM AT 500 RPM AND 30-55 LBS. AT 2000 RPM.
OIL FILTER BY-PASS VALVE OPERATES AT 9- TO 11 LBS. PRESSURE.

1. GASKET
2. REINFORCEMENT
3. OIL PAN
4. RETAINER
5. 72-130 IN. LBS. (13)
6. 150-250 IN. LBS.

GC1099100019000X

Fig. 22 Oil pan & gasket assembly. 4.3L/V6-262 engine

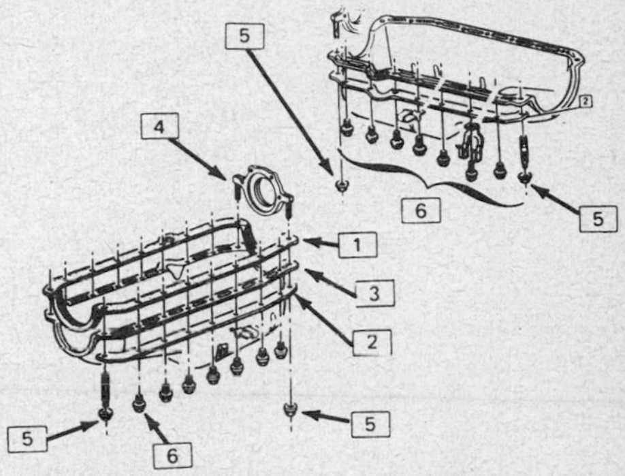
5
4
6
5
1
3
2
5
6
5

ENGINE OIL PRESSURE 10 LBS. MINIMUM AT 500 RPM AND 30-55 LBS. AT 2000 RPM
OIL FILTER BY-PASS VALVE OPERATES AT 9- TO 11 LBS. PRESSURE.

1. GASKET
2. REINFORCEMENT
3. OIL PAN
4. RETAINER
5. 150-250 IN. LBS.
6. 72-130 (14)

GC1099100020000X

Fig. 23 Oil pan & gasket assembly. 5.0L/V8-305 & 1992–93 5.7L/V8-350 engines

feeler gauge. Refer to "Engine Rebuilding Specifications" for connecting rod side clearance.

PISTONS, PINS & RINGS

Pistons are available in standard and oversizes of .010 and .030 inch.

Piston rings are available in standard and oversizes of .030 inch.

MAIN & ROD BEARINGS

Connecting rod bearings are available in standard and undersizes of .001, .002, .010 and .020 inch.

Main bearings are available in standard and undersizes of .001, .002, .009, .010 and .020 inch.

CRANKSHAFT REAR OIL SEAL

REPLACE

These engines are equipped with a one-piece, lip type seal mounted in a separate seal retainer. Seal replacement requires removal of the transmission.

1. **On all models,** raise and support vehicle, then remove transmission and flywheel.
2. Pry seal from retainer, inserting screwdriver in notches provided in seal retainer, **Fig. 20.**
3. Lubricate inner and outer diameters of replacement seal with engine oil, then mount seal on tool No. J-35621 or equivalent, **Fig. 21.**
4. Mount seal installer tool No. J-35621 or equivalent on rear of crankshaft, tightening screws snugly to ensure seal will be installed squarely on crankshaft.
5. Tighten wing nut on tool until it bottoms, then remove tool from crankshaft.
6. Reverse remaining removal steps to complete installation.

OIL PAN

REPLACE

1992–93

1. Disconnect battery ground cable, then remove air cleaner.
2. Remove distributor cap and wires.
3. Remove upper fan shroud.
4. Raise and support vehicle, then disconnect AIR pipe at exhaust manifold.
5. Disconnect AIR hose at converter pipe.
6. Drain crankcase.
7. Disconnect exhaust pipe at exhaust manifold.
8. Remove flywheel cover.
9. Remove transmission dipstick tube assembly.
10. Detach transmission oil cooler lines from oil pan clips.
11. Remove attaching bolts, then remove starter motor.
12. **On 5.0L/V8-305 and 5.7L/V8-350 engines**, remove oil level sensor electrical connector, then remove oil level sensor.
13. **On all engines**, remove both left and righthand engine mount through bolts.
14. Remove oil pan attaching nuts and bolts, then lower oil pan, **Figs. 22 and 23.**
15. Position forward crankshaft counterbalance weight and throw to permit oil pan removal.
16. Raise engine slightly to permit oil pan removal.
17. Remove oil pan and gasket.

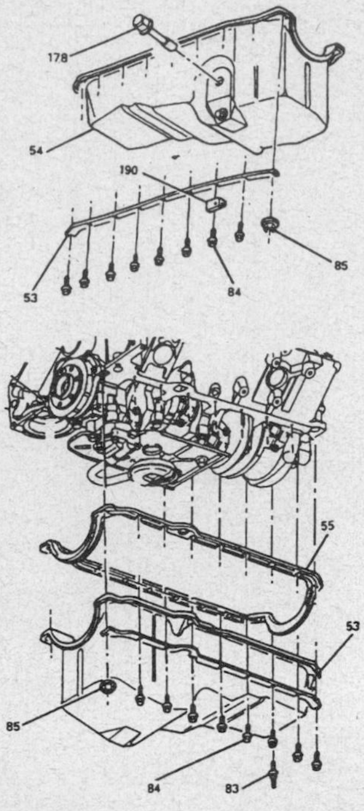
178
54
190
85
53
84
55
53
85
84
83

53 REINFORCEMENT, OIL PAN
54 PAN ASSEMBLY, OIL
55 GASKET, OIL PAN
83 STUD, OIL PAN
84 BOLT/SCREW, OIL PAN
85 NUT, OIL PAN
178 SENSOR ASSEMBLY, ENGINE OIL LEVEL SWITCH
190 BRACKET, ENGINE WIRING HARNESS

GC1099400113000X

Fig. 24 Oil pan & gasket assembly. 1994–95

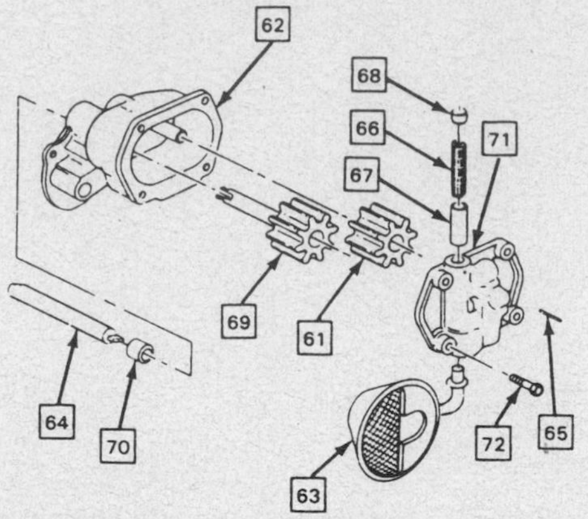
62
68
66
71
67
69
61
64
70
72
65
63

61 IDLER GEAR
62 PUMP BODY
63 PICKUP SCREEN AND PIPE
64 DRIVESHAFT
65 RETAINING PIN
66 SPRING
67 PRESSURE REGULATOR VALVE
68 PLUG
69 DRIVE GEAR AND SHAFT
70 RETAINER
71 COVER
72 COVER BOLT

GC1099100021000X

Fig. 25 Exploded view of oil pump

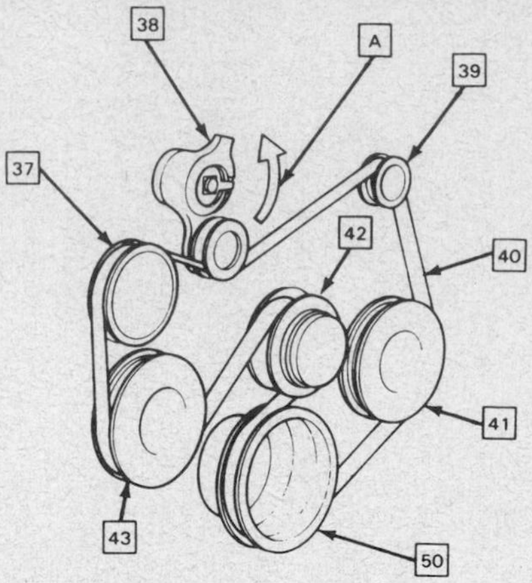
38
A
39
37
42
40
41
43
50

A ROTATE TENSIONER IN DIRECTION SHOWN TO INSTALL OR REMOVE BELT
37 A/C COMPRESSOR
38 BELT TENSIONER
39 GENERATOR ASSEMBLY PULLEY
40 SERPENTINE BELT
41 P/S PUMP PULLEY
42 WATER PUMP PULLEY
43 AIR PUMP PULLEY
50 CRANKSHAFT PULLEY

GC1069100193000X

Fig. 26 Serpentine drive belt routing. 1992–93

18. Reverse procedure to install. Apply a small quantity of sealer part No. 1052914 or equivalent to front cover and engine block junction and rear seal retainer and engine block junction.

1994–95

1. Disconnect battery ground cable, then remove air cleaner, resonator and air intake duct.
2. Remove radiator upper fan shroud if equipped with a mechanical fan.
3. Disconnect windshield wiper motor electrical connector.
4. Raise and support vehicle, then drain engine oil.
5. Disconnect oil level sensor connector, then remove oil level sensor.
6. Remove warm up three-way catalytic converters from exhaust manifolds, then catalytic converter support-to-transmission bolts/screws and washers.
7. Remove engine oil filter adapter, then disconnect transmission fluid cooler lines from clip at oil pan.
8. Remove starter, then converter cover bolt/screws and cover.
9. Rotate crankshaft until arrow on crankshaft balancer is pointing straight down (six o'clock).
10. Remove engine mount through-bolts/screws and nuts, then raise engine with jacking fixture.
11. Remove oil pan bolts, screws, studs & nuts, then oil pan, reinforcements and gaskets Fig. 24.
12. Reverse procedure to install. Apply a small quantity of sealer part No. 1052914 or equivalent to front cover and engine block junction and rear seal retainer and engine block junction.

OIL PUMP

REPLACE

1. Remove oil pan as described under "Oil Pan, Replace".
2. Remove pump to rear main bearing cap bolt and remove pump and extension shaft.
3. Reverse procedure to install. Make sure that installed position of oil pump screen is with bottom edge parallel to oil pan rails.

OIL PUMP SERVICE

1. Remove oil pump as outlined under "Oil Pump, Replace."
2. Remove pump cover screws and pump cover, **Fig. 25.**
3. Mark gear teeth so they can be reassembled with same teeth indexing, then remove drive gear, idler gear and shaft.
4. Remove pressure regulator valve retaining pin, pressure regulator valve and related parts.
5. If pickup screen and pipe require replacement, mount pump in a soft-jawed vise and extract pipe from pump.
6. Wash all parts in cleaning solvent and dry with compressed air.
7. Inspect pump body and cover for cracks and excessive wear.
8. Inspect pump gears for damage or excessive wear.
9. Check drive gear shaft for looseness in pump body.
10. Inspect inside of pump cover for wear that would allow oil to leak past the ends of the gears.
11. Inspect pickup screen and pipe assembly for damage to screen, pipe or relief grommet.
12. Check pressure regulator valve for fit in pump housing.
13. Reverse procedure to assemble. Turn drive shaft by hand to check for smooth operation. **The pump gears and body are not serviced separately. If the pump gears or body are damaged or worn, the pump assembly should be replaced. Also, if the pick-up screen and tube assembly was removed, it should be replaced with a new one as loss of the press fit condition could result in an air leak and loss of oil pressure.**

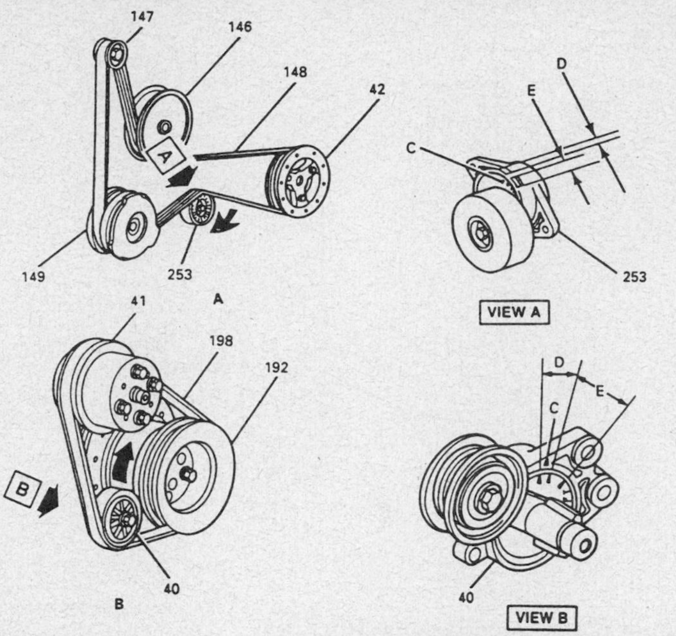
147
146
148
42
D
E
C
149
253
A
253
VIEW A
41
198
192
D
E
C
B
40
B
40
VIEW B

A COOLING SYSTEM WITHOUT MECHANICAL FAN
B COOLING SYSTEM WITH MECHANICAL FAN
C INDICATOR MARK
D ACCEPTABLE OPERATING RANGE
E UNACCEPTABLE OPERATING RANGE
40 TENSIONER ASSEMBLY, DRIVE BELT (WITH MECHANICAL FAN)
41 PULLEY, FAN
42 BALANCER ASSEMBLY, CRANKSHAFT
146 PUMP ASSEMBLY, POWER STEERING
147 GENERATOR ASSEMBLY
148 BELT, SERPENTINE DRIVE
149 COMPRESSOR ASSEMBLY, AIR CONDITIONING
192 PULLEY, CRANKSHAFT
198 BELT, FAN
253 TENSIONER ASSEMBLY, DRIVE BELT

GC1069400194000X

Fig. 27 Serpentine drive belt routing. 1994–95

BELT TENSION DATA

Year	New Lbs.	Used Lbs.
A/C Compressor		
1992–93	105–125	105–125

The serpentine drive belts are automatically tensioned and require no adjustment.

SERPENTINE DRIVE BELT

BELT ROUTING

Refer to **Figs. 26 and 27,** for serpentine belt routing diagrams.

BELT, REPLACEMENT

1992–93

1. Disconnect battery ground cable.
2. Using suitable 1/2 inch breaker bar, push belt tensioner upward, then remove belt.
3. Reverse procedure to install.

1994–95

1. Disconnect battery ground cable.
2. **On models with mechanical cooling fan,** proceed as follows:
   a. Rotate mechanical cooling fan tensioner pulley clockwise using a suitable 13 mm wrench while sliding belt from tensioner pulley.
   b. Remove fan belt from pulleys.
   c. Remove radiator outlet nuts at air conditioning compressor.
3. **On all models,** rotate tensioner pulley clockwise using a suitable 9/16 offset wrench while sliding belt from tensioner, then remove serpentine drive belt.
4. Reverse procedure to install.

BELT TENSIONER, REPLACE

1. Disconnect battery ground cable.
2. Remove serpentine belt as outlined under"Serpentine drive belts."
3. Remove belt tensioner attaching bolt, then belt tensioner.
4. Reverse procedure to install.

COOLING SYSTEM BLEED

These engines do not require a specific bleed procedure. After filling cooling system, start engine and allow to reach operating temperature with radiator cap removed. Air in system will then be automatically bled through cap opening.

THERMOSTAT

REPLACE

1. Disconnect battery negative cable.
2. If necessary, remove air cleaner assembly.
3. With engine cool, drain engine coolant below thermostat level.
4. Disconnect radiator hose from thermostat housing.
5. Remove thermostat housing retaining bolts, then the housing, gasket and thermostat.
6. Reverse procedure to install noting the following:
   a. Ensure thermostat gasket sealing surface is clean.
   b. Install thermostat with new gasket.
   c. Tighten thermostat housing retaining bolts to specifications.
   d. Refill and bleed cooling system as needed.

WATER PUMP

REPLACE

1992–93

1. Disconnect battery ground cable and drain cooling system.
2. Remove upper fan shroud, then remove accessory drive belts.
3. Remove fan and pulley from water pump hub.
4. Remove power steering pump, A/C compressor and AIR pump brackets, as required.
5. Remove radiator lower hose and heater hose from water pump.
6. Remove water pump attaching bolts and the pump, **Fig. 28.** Note position of bolts for assembly reference.
7. Reverse procedure to install.

1994–95

1. Drain cooling system into suitable container(s).
2. **On models equipped with mechanical fan,** remove air cleaner bracket, air cleaner, resonator and air intake duct.
3. Remove upper radiator fan shroud, then remove belts as outlined under "Serpentine Drive Belts."
4. **On all models,** disconnect engine coolant and heater hoses from water pump.
5. **On models equipped with mechanical fan,** remove fan pulley, bracket and nuts.
6. **On all models,** disconnect electrical connector from coolant sensor.
7. Remove secondary air injection pump and bracket.
8. Remove water pump bolts/screws and stud, then water pump, gasket and water pump driveshaft coupling and seals, **Fig. 29.** Discard seals.
9. Reverse procedure to install.

WATER PUMP DRIVESHAFT

REPLACE

1. Remove timing chain as outlined under "Timing Chain, Replace."
2. Remove water pump drive gear and shaft.
3. Reverse procedure to install.

RADIATOR

REPLACE

1. Disconnect battery ground cable, then remove air intake duct and resonator.
2. Drain coolant into suitable containers through valve located in left radiator

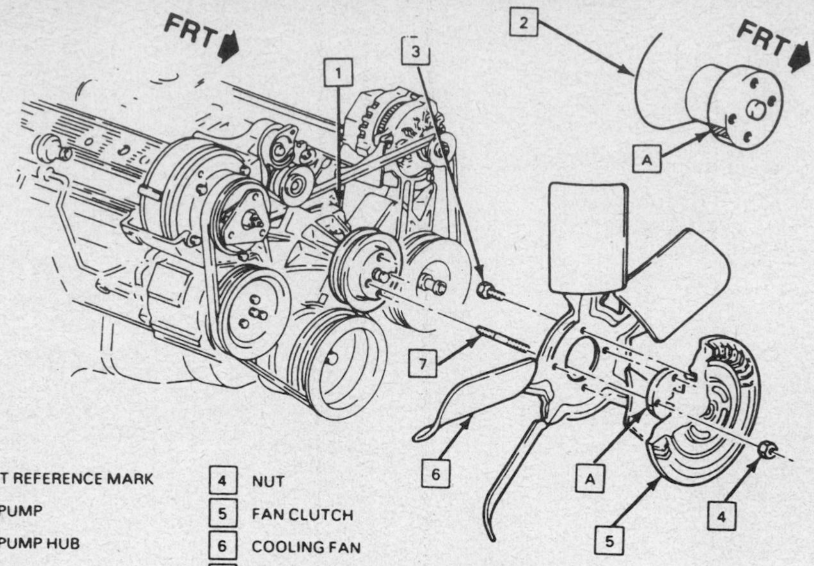
FRT
FRT
1
2
3
A
7
6
A
5
4

A	ALIGNMENT REFERENCE MARK	4	NUT
1	COOLANT PUMP	5	FAN CLUTCH
2	COOLANT PUMP HUB	6	COOLING FAN
3	BOLT	7	STUD

GC1089100127000X

Fig. 28 Water pump replacement. 1992–93

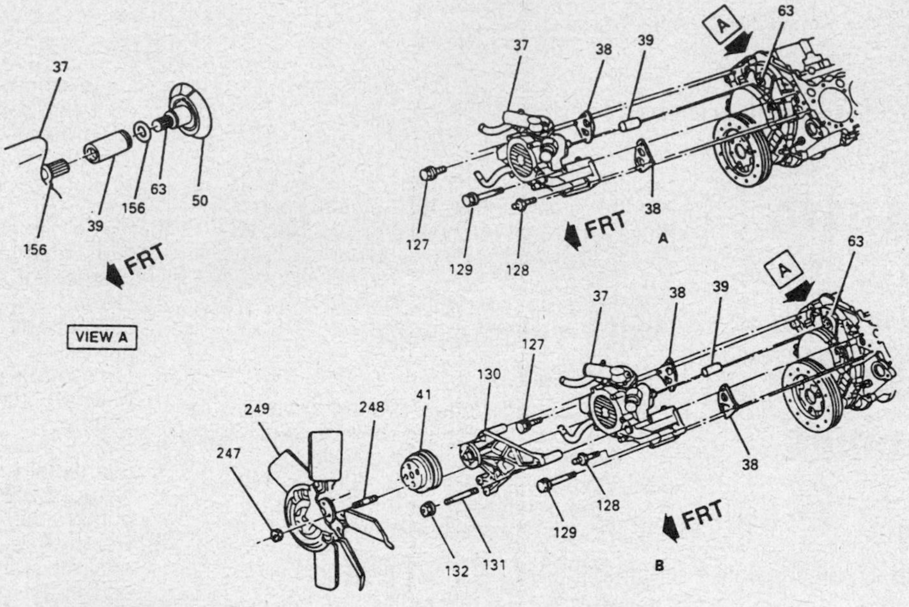
37
156
39
63
50
156
FRT
VIEW A
A
63
37
38
39
127
129
128
38
FRT
A
A
63
37
38
39
127
130
41
248
249
247
132
131
129
128
38
FRT
B

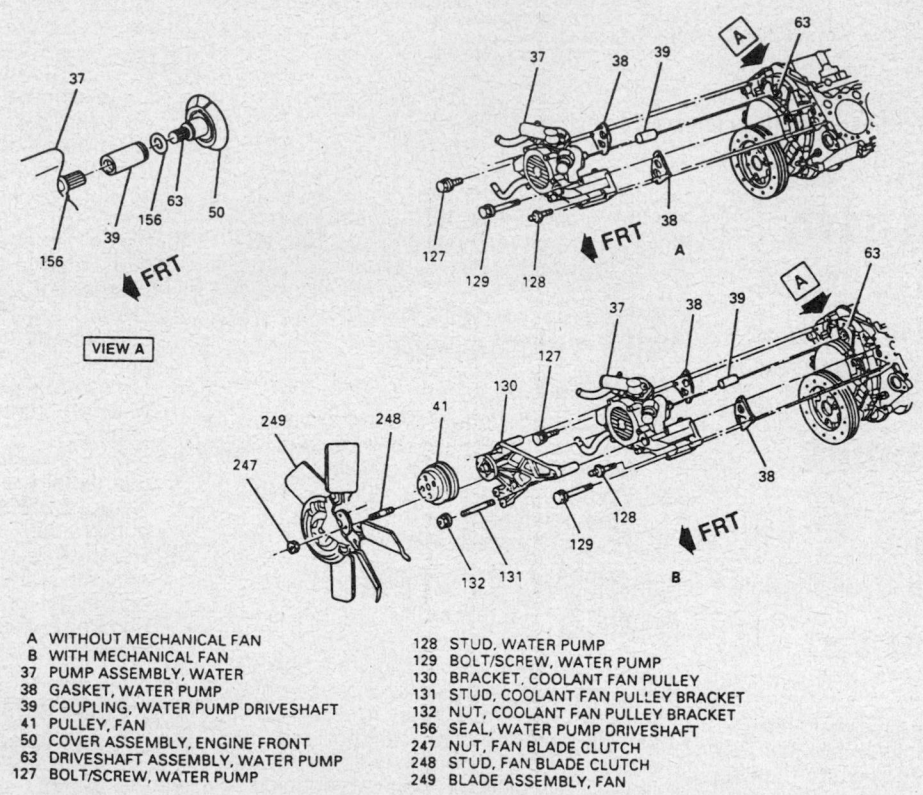

A WITHOUT MECHANICAL FAN
B WITH MECHANICAL FAN
37 PUMP ASSEMBLY, WATER
38 GASKET, WATER PUMP
39 COUPLING, WATER PUMP DRIVESHAFT
41 PULLEY, FAN
50 COVER ASSEMBLY, ENGINE FRONT
63 DRIVESHAFT ASSEMBLY, WATER PUMP
127 BOLT/SCREW, WATER PUMP
128 STUD, WATER PUMP
129 BOLT/SCREW, WATER PUMP
130 BRACKET, COOLANT FAN PULLEY
131 STUD, COOLANT FAN PULLEY BRACKET
132 NUT, COOLANT FAN PULLEY BRACKET
156 SEAL, WATER PUMP DRIVESHAFT
247 NUT, FAN BLADE CLUTCH
248 STUD, FAN BLADE CLUTCH
249 BLADE ASSEMBLY, FAN

GC1089400128000X

Fig. 29 Water pump replacement. 1994–95

end tank.

3. Disconnect engine coolant hoses from radiator, then remove engine cooling fans.
4. Disconnect and plug transmission cooler and engine oil cooler lines, if equipped.
5. Disconnect coolant recovery reservoir, then remove upper mounting panel if not equipped with mechanical fan.
6. Remove radiator.
7. Reverse procedure to install, noting the following.
   a. Ensure radiator is properly seated into lower mount cushions.
   b. **Torque** transmission cooler line fittings to 17 ft. lbs. and if equipped with an engine oil cooler **torque** fittings to 18 ft. lbs.

FUEL PUMP

REPLACE

1. Remove fuel tank filler cap, then disconnect battery ground cable.
2. Drain fuel tank.
3. Remove fuel tank as follows:
   a. Raise and support vehicle.
   b. Disconnect electrical connectors.

   c. Disconnect hoses from sending unit.
   d. Support fuel tank, then disconnect retaining straps.
   e. Lower tank and remove from vehicle.
4. Remove fuel level sending unit and pump assembly by turning cam lock ring counterclockwise.
5. Remove fuel pump from fuel level sending unit by pulling fuel pump up and outward, away from bottom support, **Fig. 30.**
6. Reverse procedure to install.

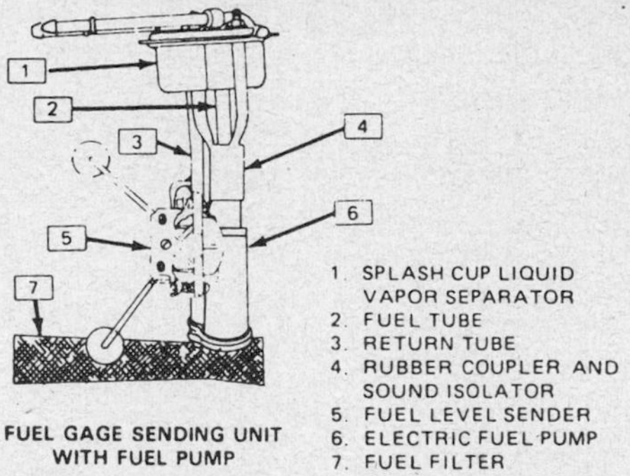
1
2
3
4
5
6
7
FUEL GAGE SENDING UNIT WITH FUEL PUMP
1. SPLASH CUP LIQUID VAPOR SEPARATOR
2. FUEL TUBE
3. RETURN TUBE
4. RUBBER COUPLER AND SOUND ISOLATOR
5. FUEL LEVEL SENDER
6. ELECTRIC FUEL PUMP
7. FUEL FILTER
GC1029102710000X

Fig. 30 Intake electric fuel pump & fuel gauge sending unit

FUEL FILTER

REPLACE

1. Relieve fuel system pressure as outlined under "Precautions".
2. Remove fuel filter bracket attaching bolt.
3. Grasp filter and one fuel line fitting and twist quick connect fitting 1/4 turn in each direction to loosen. Repeat for other fitting.
4. Depress quick connect fitting plastic tabs of male end connector, then pull connector apart, repeat for other fitting.
5. Remove fuel filter.
6. Reverse procedure to install.

TIGHTENING SPECIFICATIONS

1992–93

Year	Component	Torque/Ft. Lbs.
1992-93	AIR Crossover Pipe	24④
	Alternator Bracket	37
	Belt Tensioner Bolt	37
	Camshaft Retainer Bolt	105①
	Camshaft Sprocket	21
	Connecting Rod Cap Bolt	44
	Cooling Fan Shroud	53①
	Crankshaft Pulley Bolt	43
	Cylinder Head Bolt	68
	Engine Block Coolant Drain Plug	16
	Engine Cooling Fan Bolts	18
	Engine Front Cover	100①
	Exhaust Crossover Pipe Nut	15
	Exhaust Manifold Bolt	②
	Flywheel To Crankshaft	74
	Flywheel Housing Cover	89①
	Front Engine Mount Bracket Bolts	70
	Front Engine Mount Bracket Nut	49
	Front Engine Mount Bolts	33
	Front Engine Mount Nut	30
	Fuel Feed/Return Pipes	20
	Fuel Pump & Sender Assembly Nut	27①
	Fuel Pump Lower Cover Bolt	105①
	Fuel Pump Upper Cover Bolt	25
	Fuel Tank Cross Strap Nut	11
	Fuel Tank Front Strap Bolt	24
	Fuel Tank Rear Strap Nut	18
	Ignition Distributor Clamp	27
	Intake Manifold Bolt	②
	Main Bearing Cap Bolt	77

Year	Component	Torque/Ft. Lbs.
1992-93 —Cont'd	Oil Filter Adapter Bolt	18
	Oil Gallery Plug	113①
	Oil Pan Attaching Bolts	101①
	Oil Pan Attaching Nuts	17
	Oil Pump	77
	Oil Pump Cover	80①
	Rear Seal Retainer	11
	Rocker Arm Cover	95
	Spark Plug	③
	Thermostat Housing	21
	Throttle Body To Intake Manifold	16
	Torque Converter To Flywheel Bolts	35
	Transmission Mount Bolt To Engine	70
	Transmission Mount Nut To Engine	35
	Valve Lifter Retainer Bolt	12
	Vibration Damper	70
	Water Pump	⑤

①—Inch lbs.
②—Bolt 26 ft. lbs.; stud, 20 ft. lbs.
③—Except 1992 Brougham, 77 ft. lbs., 1992 Brougham, 75 ft. lbs.
④—Except Brougham & Fleetwood (RWD) 68 ft. lbs., Brougham, 70 ft. lbs., Fleetwood (RWD), 65 ft. lbs.
⑤—Except 1992 Brougham, 30 ft. lbs., 1992 Brougham, to block 22 ft. lbs., to front cover 10 ft. lbs.
⑥—Except 1992 Caprice & 1993 models, 22 ft. lbs., 1992 Caprice & 1993 models, 11 ft. lbs.
⑦—4.3L/V6-262 engine.

1994–95

Year	Component	Torque/Ft. Lbs.
1994–95	Accelerator Control Cable Bracket Bolt/Screw	90①
	Camshaft Retainer Bolt/Screw	108①
	Camshaft Sprocket Bolt/Screw	21
	Connecting Rod Nut	47
	Crankshaft Balancer Bolt/Screw	60
	Crankshaft Balancer Hub Bolt/Screw	75
	Crankshaft Bearing Cap Bolt/Screw & Stud	78
	Crankshaft Rear Oil Seal Housing Nut & Bolt/Screw	11
	Cylinder Head Bolt	②
	Distributor Bolt/Screw	106①
	EGR Control Valve Relay Nut	16
	EGR Valve Nut	16
	EGR Valve Pipe Bolt/Screw & Nut	18
	Engine Coolant Air Bleed Pipe Bolt/Screw	30
	Exhaust Manifold Stud & Bolt/Screw	26
	Fan Pulley Bracket Nut	26
	Front Cover Bolts/Screws	100①
	Fuel Pump Switch & Oil Pressure Gage Sensor	108①
	Fuel Rail Bolt/Screw	89①
	Generator Bracket Bolt/Screw	30
	Ignition Coil Studs	24
	Intake Manifold	③
	Oil Filter Adapter Bolt/Screw	17
1994–95 —Cont'd	Oil Gallery Plug	18
	Oil Level Indicator Nut	100①
	Oil Level Switch Sensor	26
	Oil Pan Corner Bolt/Screw And Nut Or Stud	15
	Oil Pan Drain Plug	16
	Oil Pan Side Rail Bolt/Screw Or Stud	100①
	Oil Pump Bolt/Screw To Rear Crankshaft Bearing Cap	65
	Oil Pump Cover Bolt/Screw	80①
	Oil Pump Driveshaft Bolt/Screw	13
	Rocker Arm Cover Bolt/Screw	100①
	Rocker Arm Stud	50
	Secondary Air Injection Pipe Fitting To Exhaust Manifold	25
	Secondary Air Injection Pump Bracket Bolt/Screw	18
	Spark Plug	11
	Starter Motor Bolt/Screw	35
	Throttle Body Bolt/Screw	19
	Valve Lifter Guide Retainer Bolt/Screw	15
	Water Pump Bolt/Screw & Stud	30
	Water Pump Driveshaft Bearing Retainer Bolt/Screw	108①

①—Inch lbs.
②—Tighten bolts in sequence in three steps to 65 ft. lbs.
③—Bolt 26 ft. lbs.; stud, 20 ft. lbs.

Rear Axle & Suspension

INDEX

DESCRIPTION

In these rear axles, the rear axle housing and differential carrier are cast into an integral housing assembly. The drive pinion assembly is mounted in two opposed tapered roller bearings. The pinion bearings are preloaded by a spacer behind the front bearing. The pinion is positioned by a washer between the head of the pinion and the rear bearing. The differential is supported in the carrier by two tapered roller side bearings. These bearings are preloaded by spacers located between the bearings and carrier housing. The differential assembly is positioned for proper ring gear and pinion backlash by varying these spacers. The differential case houses two side gears in mesh with two pinions mounted on a pinion shaft which is held in place by a lockpin. The side gears and pinions are backed by thrust washers. A limited slip rear axle, available on most models, uses disc or cone type clutches which are splined to the side gears to lock the axle shafts to the case or in effect to each other. Therefore, if one drive wheel is on a slippery surface, the other wheel must develop more torque than on a standard type differential before the differential case will allow wheel spin. However, axle shaft torques produced during cornering are sufficient to overcome the clutch action, allowing axles to rotate at different speeds.

REAR AXLE

REPLACE

Construction of the axle assembly is such that service operations may be performed with the housing installed in the vehicle or with the housing removed and installed in a holding fixture. The following procedure is necessary only when the housing requires replacement.

1. Raise and support vehicle, then support rear axle with a suitable jack.
2. **On models equipped with anti-lock**

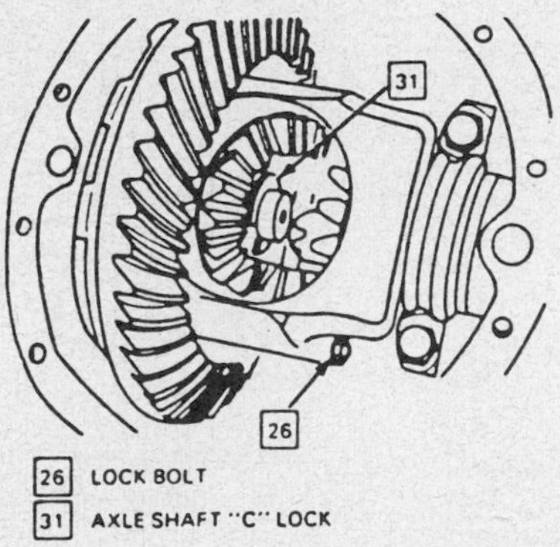
31
26
26 LOCK BOLT
31 AXLE SHAFT "C" LOCK

Fig. 1 Pinion shaft lock bolt & C-lock removal

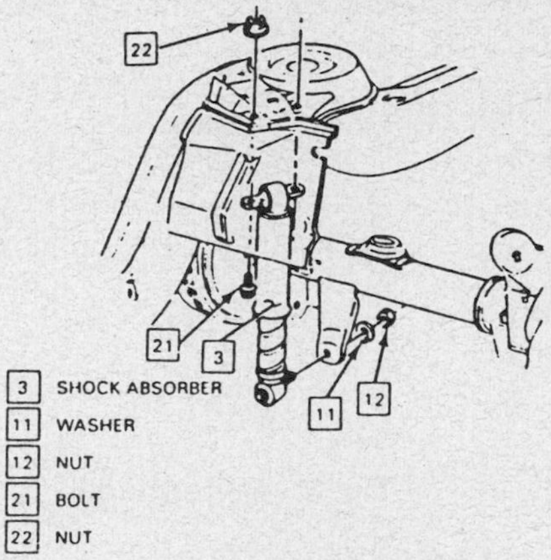
22
21
3
11
12
3 SHOCK ABSORBER
11 WASHER
12 NUT
21 BOLT
22 NUT

Fig. 2 Shock absorber replacement

brake systems, remove rear axle speed sensor as follows:
   a. Disconnect speed sensor electrical harness.
   b. Remove speed sensor harness bracket attaching bolt.
   c. Remove speed sensor to rear axle attaching bolt, then remove speed sensor and bracket assembly and position aside.
   d. Reverse procedure to install. Wheel speed sensors are to installed by hand. **Do not hammer sensors into position, as damage may result.**
3. **On all models,** disconnect shock absorbers from lower mountings.
4. Remove propeller shaft.
5. Disconnect upper control arms from axle housing attachments.
6. Disconnect brake line from axle housing junction block and the parking brake cable.
7. Disconnect lower control arms from axle housing attachments.
8. Lower axle slowly until springs can be moved. Roll axle assembly out from under vehicle.
9. Reverse procedure to install.

REAR AXLE SHAFT
REPLACE

1. Raise vehicle and remove wheel and brake drum or rotor.
2. Drain lube from carrier and remove cover.
3. Remove differential pinion shaft lock bolt and remove differential pinion shaft, **Fig. 1.**
4. Pull flanged end of axle shaft toward center of vehicle and remove C-lock from button end of shaft.
5. Remove axle shaft from housing, being careful not to damage seal.
6. Reverse procedure to install the axle shaft.

PROPELLER SHAFT
REPLACE

1. Raise and support vehicle.
2. Mark position of shaft in relation to pinion flange for reassembly.
3. Remove straps securing universal joint to pinion flange, then disconnect shaft from flange. **Tape bearing cups to universal joint to prevent loss of needle bearings.**
4. Slide yoke out of transmission and remove propeller shaft. Insert suitable plug in transmission to prevent fluid loss.
5. Reverse procedure to install.

SHOCK ABSORBER
REPLACE

1. If equipped with Superlift shock absorbers, disconnect air lines from shock absorber fittings.
2. With rear axle properly supported, disconnect shock absorber from upper and lower mountings, **Fig. 2.**
3. Reverse procedure to install.

COIL SPRING
REPLACE

If more than one coil spring is being replaced, remove and install one spring at a time to prevent axle assembly from slipping or twisting out of position.

1. Support vehicle at frame and rear axle.
2. **On models equipped with anti-lock brake systems,** remove rear axle speed sensor as follows:
   a. Disconnect speed sensor electrical harness.
   b. Remove speed sensor harness bracket attaching bolt.
   c. Remove speed sensor to rear axle attaching bolt, then remove speed sensor and bracket assembly and position aside.
   d. Reverse procedure to install. Wheel speed sensors are to installed by hand. **Do not hammer sensors into position, as damage may result.**
3. **On all models,** disconnect shock absorbers at lower mountings.
4. Disconnect upper control arms from axle housing.
5. Disconnect stabilizer bar from either right or lefthand side of control arm, if equipped.
6. **On models equipped with electronic suspension,** disconnect height sensor arm link.
7. **On all models,** remove brake hose support bolt and support without disconnecting the brake lines.
8. Lower axle until spring can be removed, then remove spring and insulator.
9. Reverse procedure to install. Springs must be installed with an insulator between upper seat and spring and positioned properly, **Fig. 3.**

CONTROL ARM
REPLACE

If more than one control arm is being replaced, remove and install one arm at a time to prevent axle assembly from slipping or twisting out of position.

1. Raise vehicle and support at frame pads. Support nose of axle housing to prevent assembly from twisting when control arm is removed.
2. **On models equipped with anti-lock brake systems,** remove rear axle speed sensor as follows:
   a. Disconnect speed sensor electrical harness.
   b. Remove speed sensor harness bracket attaching bolt.
   c. Remove speed sensor to rear axle attaching bolt, then remove speed sensor and bracket assembly and position aside.

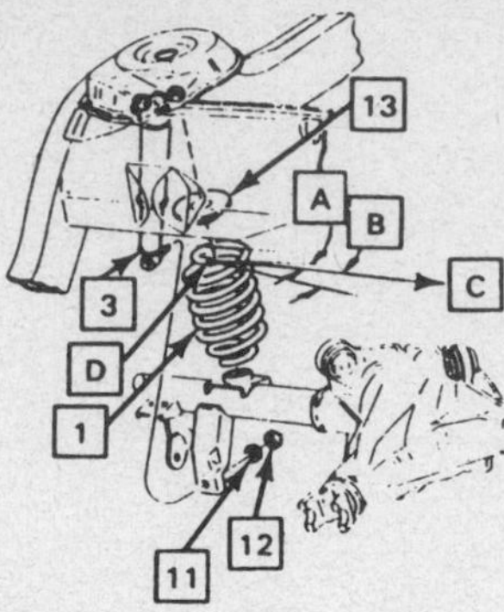
13
A
B
C
3
D
1
11
12

A 5 DEGREES MAXIMUM REARWARD
B 15 DEGREES MAXIMUM FORWARD
C ARROW POINTING TO LEFT SIDE OF CAR, PERPENDICULAR TO CENTERLINE OF CHASSIS
D COIL LEG
1 REAR SPRING
3 SHOCK ABSORBER
11 WASHER
12 NUT
13 INSULATOR

GC2039100023000X

Fig. 3 Coil spring installation

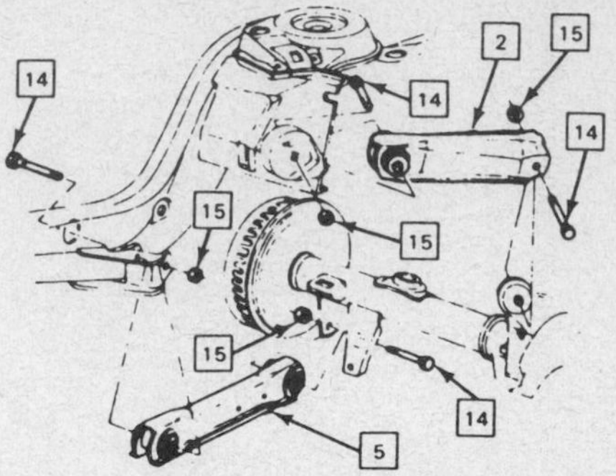
14
2
15
14
14
15
15
15
5
14

2 UPPER CONTROL ARM
5 LOWER CONTROL ARM
14 BOLT
15 NUT

GC2039100024000X

Fig. 4 Control arm replacement

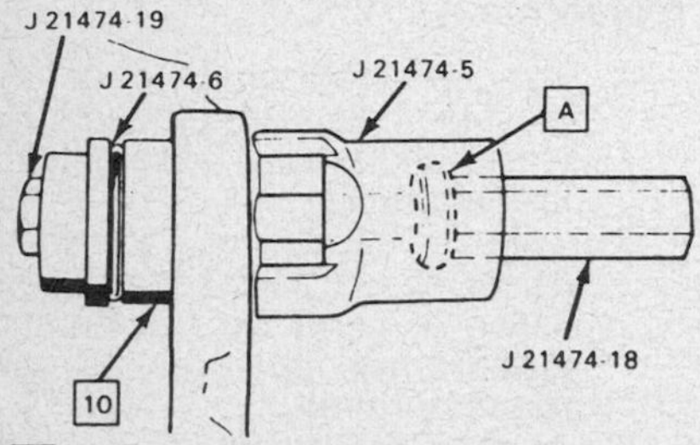
J 21474-19
J 21474-6
J 21474-5
A
J 21474-18
10

A THRUST BEARING (HIDDEN INSIDE J 21474-5)
10 REAR AXLE HOUSING BUSHING

GC2039100025000X

Fig. 5 Upper control arm rear bushing (differential carrier bushing) removal

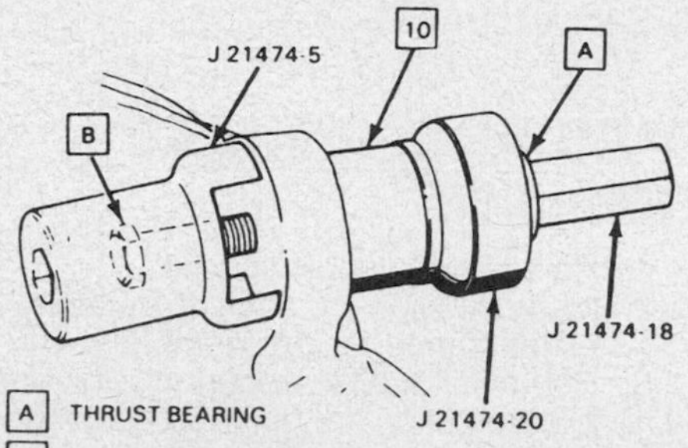
J 21474-5
10
A
B
J 21474-18
J 21474-20

A THRUST BEARING
B J 21474-19 (HIDDEN INSIDE J 21474-5)
10 REAR AXLE HOUSING BUSHING

GC2039100026000X

Fig. 6 Upper control arm rear bushing (differential carrier bushing) installation

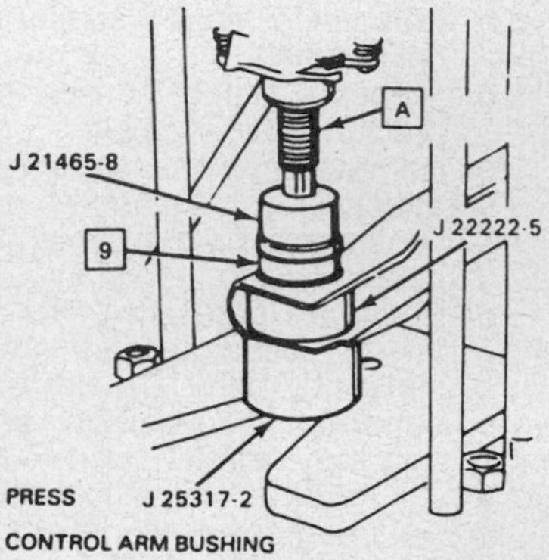
A
J 21465-8
J 22222-5
9
J 25317-2

A PRESS
9 CONTROL ARM BUSHING

GC2039100027000X

Fig. 7 Control arm bushing removal

d. Reverse procedure to install. Wheel speed sensors are to installed by hand. **Do not hammer sensors into position, as damage may result.**

3. **On all models**, if lower control arm is being replaced, remove bolts securing stabilizer bar to control arm, if equipped.
4. Remove bolts securing control arm to chassis and rear axle, and the control arm, **Fig. 4.**
5. Reverse procedure to install, lower vehicle and torque control arm bolts to specifications, with vehicle at normal ride height. **All prevailing torque type fasteners must be tightened at the nut, not at the bolt, to ensure proper clamping force.**

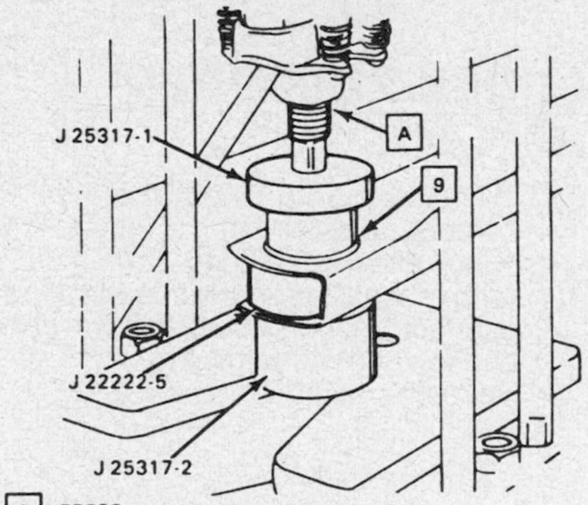
J 25317-1
A
9
J 22222-5
J 25317-2

A PRESS
9 CONTROL ARM BUSHING

GC2039100028000X

Fig. 8 Control arm bushing installation

CONTROL ARM BUSHING
REPLACE

DIFFERENTIAL CARRIER BUSHINGS (UPPER CONTROL ARM REAR BUSHING)

The upper control arm rear bushing, which is pressed into the differential carrier, can be replaced using the following procedure:

1. Raise vehicle and support at frame pads, and support nose of axle housing to prevent assembly from twisting.
2. Lower rear axle to obtain clearance, disconnect upper control arm from axle and position aside.
3. Install suitable bushing removal tool as shown in **Fig. 5,** tighten puller screw and press bushing out of housing.
4. To install replacement bushing, reverse position of removal tool and pull bushing into position by tightening screw, **Fig. 6.**

CONTROL ARM BUSHINGS

1. Raise and support vehicle and remove control arm as outlined previously.
2. Press bushings out of control arm using suitable tools as shown in **Fig. 7.**
3. Reverse procedure to install, ensuring bushing is properly seated in control arm, **Fig. 8. If replacement bushing fits loosely in control arm, or if mounting areas are damaged or deformed, control arm must be replaced.**

STABILIZER BAR
REPLACE

1. Support vehicle at rear axle.
2. Remove bolts securing stabilizer bar to lower control arms.
3. Reverse procedure to install. Use spacer shims, if needed, placed equally on each side of stabilizer bar. Tighten attaching bolts with vehicle at curb height.

TIGHTENING SPECIFICATIONS

Year	Component	Torque/Ft. Lbs.
1992–95	Brake Assembly To Rear Axle	35
	Lower Control Arm Bushing Bolt③	122
	Lower Control Arm Bushing Nut③	92
	Lower Control Arm To Frame Bolt④	89
	Lower Control Arm To Frame Nut④	92
	Propeller Shaft Rear Universal Joint To Pinion Yoke	16
	Rear Axle Filler Plug	26
	Shock Absorber Lower Attachment	48
	Shock Absorber Upper Attachment	①
	Stabilizer Bar To Mounting Bracket	52
	Stabilizer Mounting Bracket To Control Arm	21
	Upper Control Arm Front Bushing Bolt ③	122
1992–95 —Cont'd	Upper Control Arm Front Bushing Nut ③	92
	Upper Control Arm Rear Bushing Bolt③	80
	Upper Control Arm Rear Bushing Nut③	70
	Upper Control Arm To Axle Housing Bolt④	85
	Upper Control Arm To Axle Housing Nut ④	70
	Upper Control Arm To Frame Bolt④	89
	Upper Control Arm To Frame Nut④	92
	Wheel Lug Nuts	②

①—Upper bolt, 20 ft. lbs.; upper nut, 12 ft. lbs..
②—1992-93, except sedan, 100 ft. lbs., sedan, 81 ft. lbs.
③—Except Brougham.
④—Brougham.

Front Suspension & Steering

NOTE: On Air Bag Equipped Models, Refer To "Air Bag System Precautions" Located In The Front Of This Manual For System Disarming & Arming Procedures.

INDEX

PRECAUTIONS

AIR BAG SYSTEMS

Refer to "Air Bag System Precautions" in the front of this manual for system disarming and arming procedures.

FUEL SYSTEM PRESSURE RELIEF

1. Turn ignition Off, then disconnect battery ground cable.
2. Loosen fuel filler cap to relieve fuel tank pressure. Do not tighten until service has been completed.
3. Connect fuel pressure gauge.
4. Install bleed hose into approved container an open valve to bleed system pressure.
5. Drain any fuel remaining in gauge into approved container.

DESCRIPTION

All models use a Short-Long Arm (SLA) type front suspension with independent coil springs riding on lower control arms, **Fig. 1.** Ball joints link upper and lower control arms to a spindle assembly, and tubular shock absorbers are used to dampen spring action. On some models, a spring steel stabilizer shaft is connected between the chassis and lower control arms to control side roll.

WHEEL BEARING

ADJUST

1. While rotating wheel forward, torque spindle nut to 12 ft. lbs., **Fig. 2**
2. Back off nut until just loose then hand tighten nut and back it off again until either hole in spindle lines up with hole in nut. **Do not back off nut more than $\frac{1}{2}$ flat.**
3. Install new cotter pin. With wheel bearing properly adjusted, there will be .001-.005 inch end play.

WHEEL BEARING

REPLACE

1. Raise car and remove front wheels.
2. **On models equipped with anti-lock brake systems,** remove right and left wheel speed sensors as follows:
   a. Under vehicle hood, disconnect speed sensor electrical harness.
   b. Raise and support vehicle, then remove speed sensor harness bracket attaching bolt.
   c. Remove speed sensor to steering knuckle attaching bolt, then remove speed sensor and bracket assembly and position aside.
   d. Reverse procedure to install. Install wheel speed sensors by hand. **Do not hammer sensors into position, as damage may result.**
3. **On all models,** remove bolts holding brake caliper to its mounting and insert a fabricated block ($1\frac{1}{16}$ x $1\frac{1}{16}$ x 2 inches in length) between the brake pads as the caliper is being removed. Once removed, the caliper can be wired or secured in some manner away from the disc.
4. Remove spindle nut and hub and disc assembly. Grease retainer and inner wheel bearing can now be removed, **Fig. 3.**
5. Reverse procedure to install.

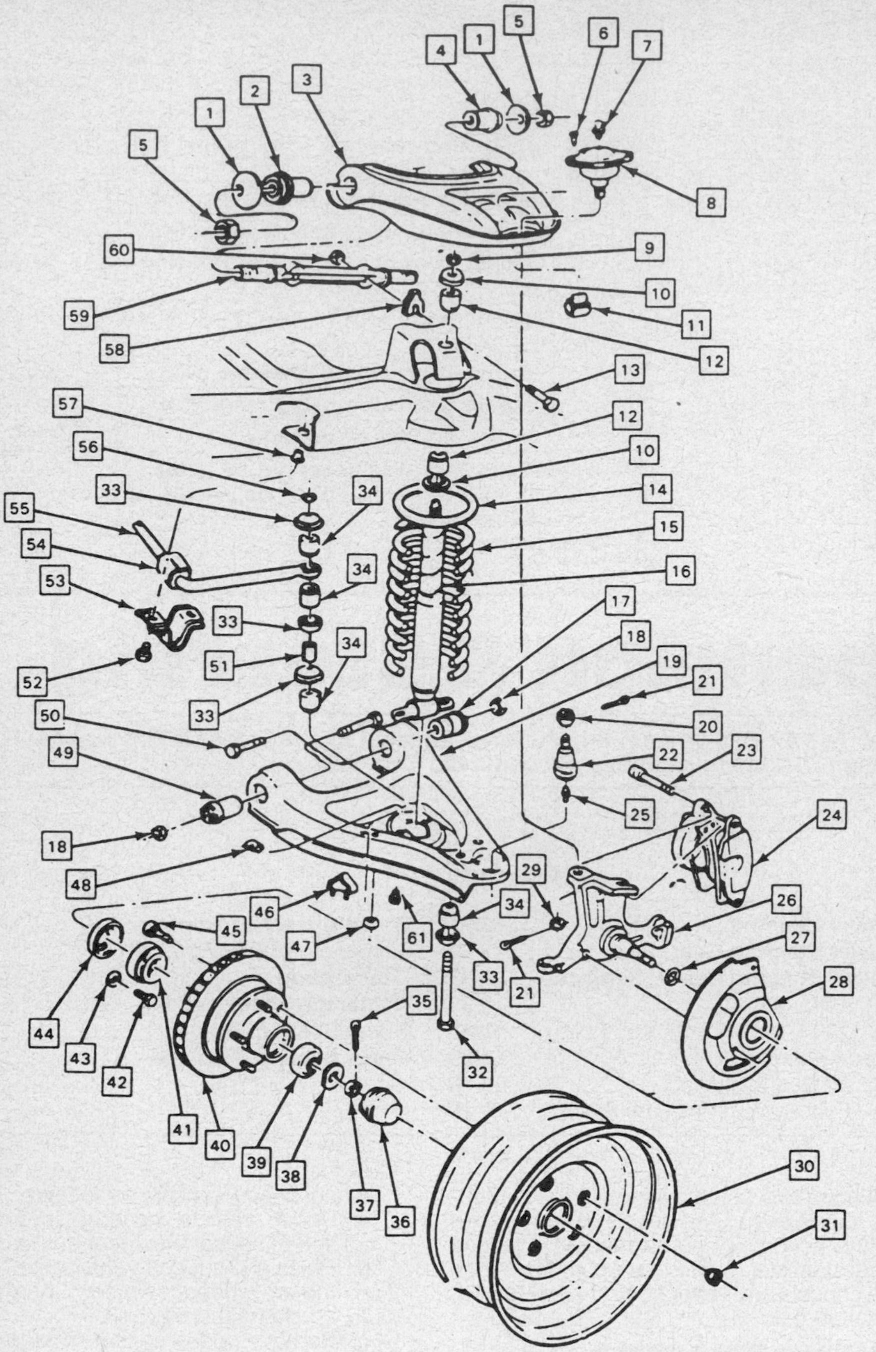

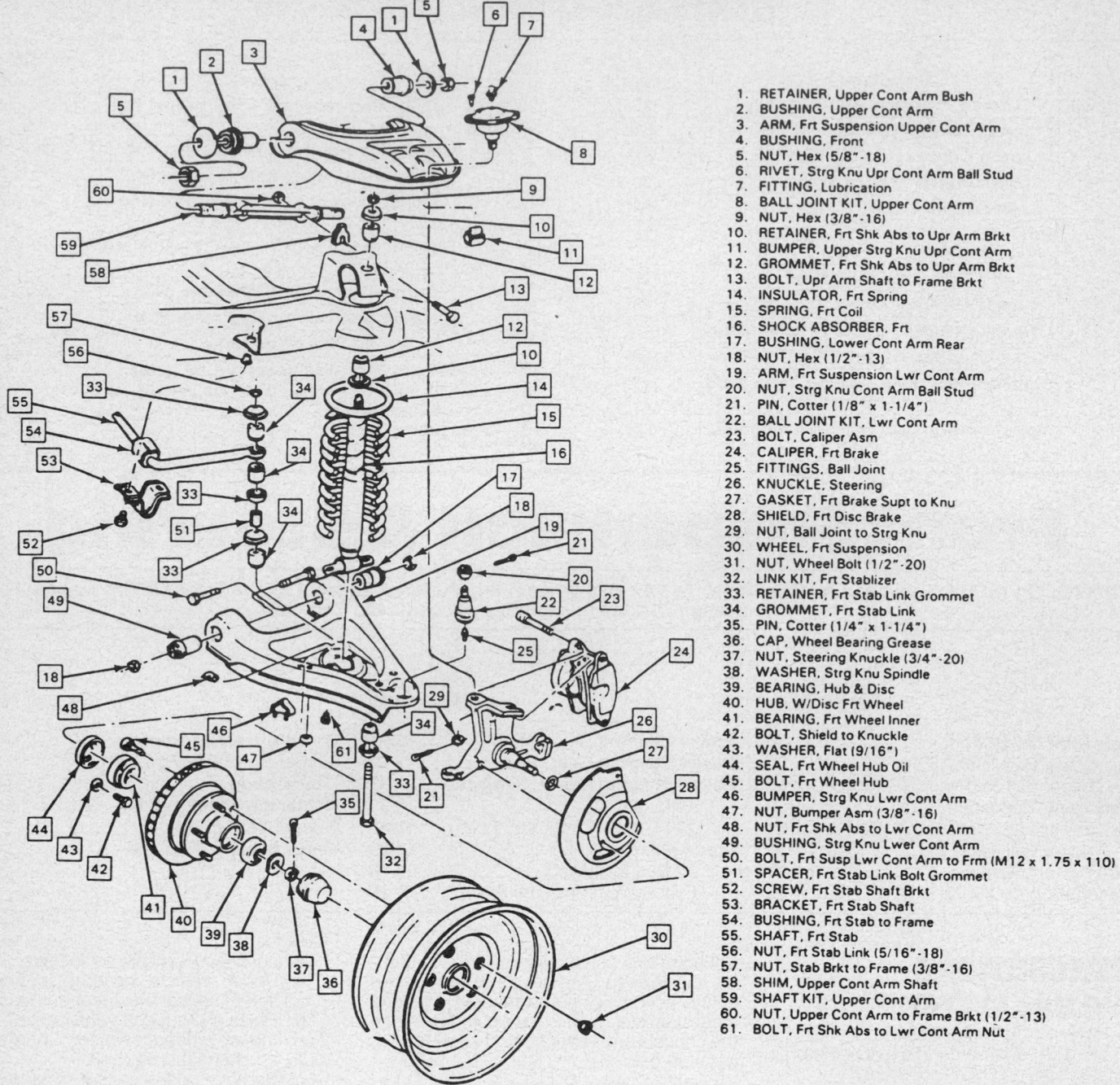

1. RETAINER, Upper Cont Arm Bush
2. BUSHING, Upper Cont Arm
3. ARM, Frt Suspension Upper Cont Arm
4. BUSHING, Front
5. NUT, Hex (5/8"-18)
6. RIVET, Strg Knu Upr Cont Arm Ball Stud
7. FITTING, Lubrication
8. BALL JOINT KIT, Upper Cont Arm
9. NUT, Hex (3/8"-16)
10. RETAINER, Frt Shk Abs to Upr Arm Brkt
11. BUMPER, Upper Strg Knu Upr Cont Arm
12. GROMMET, Frt Shk Abs to Upr Arm Brkt
13. BOLT, Upr Arm Shaft to Frame Brkt
14. INSULATOR, Frt Spring
15. SPRING, Frt Coil
16. SHOCK ABSORBER, Frt
17. BUSHING, Lower Cont Arm Rear
18. NUT, Hex (1/2"-13)
19. ARM, Frt Suspension Lwr Cont Arm
20. NUT, Strg Knu Cont Arm Ball Stud
21. PIN, Cotter (1/8" x 1-1/4")
22. BALL JOINT KIT, Lwr Cont Arm
23. BOLT, Caliper Asm
24. CALIPER, Frt Brake
25. FITTINGS, Ball Joint
26. KNUCKLE, Steering
27. GASKET, Frt Brake Supt to Knu
28. SHIELD, Frt Disc Brake
29. NUT, Ball Joint to Strg Knu
30. WHEEL, Frt Suspension
31. NUT, Wheel Bolt (1/2"-20)
32. LINK KIT, Frt Stablizer
33. RETAINER, Frt Stab Link Grommet
34. GROMMET, Frt Stab Link
35. PIN, Cotter (1/4" x 1-1/4")
36. CAP, Wheel Bearing Grease
37. NUT, Steering Knuckle (3/4"-20)
38. WASHER, Strg Knu Spindle
39. BEARING, Hub & Disc
40. HUB, W/Disc Frt Wheel
41. BEARING, Frt Wheel Inner
42. BOLT, Shield to Knuckle
43. WASHER, Flat (9/16")
44. SEAL, Frt Wheel Hub Oil
45. BOLT, Frt Wheel Hub
46. BUMPER, Strg Knu Lwr Cont Arm
47. NUT, Bumper Asm (3/8"-16)
48. NUT, Frt Shk Abs to Lwr Cont Arm
49. BUSHING, Strg Knu Lwer Cont Arm
50. BOLT, Frt Susp Lwr Cont Arm to Frm (M12 x 1.75 x 110)
51. SPACER, Frt Stab Link Bolt Grommet
52. SCREW, Frt Stab Shaft Brkt
53. BRACKET, Frt Stab Shaft
54. BUSHING, Frt Stab to Frame
55. SHAFT, Frt Stab
56. NUT, Frt Stab Link (5/16"-18)
57. NUT, Stab Brkt to Frame (3/8"-16)
58. SHIM, Upper Cont Arm Shaft
59. SHAFT KIT, Upper Cont Arm
60. NUT, Upper Cont Arm to Frame Brkt (1/2"-13)
61. BOLT, Frt Shk Abs to Lwr Cont Arm Nut

GC2029100061000X

Fig. 1 Front suspension

BALL JOINT INSPECTION

UPPER BALL JOINT

1. Raise and support vehicle. Position jack stands under lower control arm as close to lower ball joint as possible.
2. Position a suitable dial indicator against wheel rim, **Fig. 4.**
3. Grasp wheel at top and bottom, then pull top of wheel outward, while pushing inward on bottom of wheel. Note dial indicator reading.
4. Pull bottom of wheel outward, while pushing inward on top of wheel. Note dial indicator reading.
5. Deflection reading on dial indicator should not exceed .125 inch.
6. If reading exceeds .125 inch, replace upper ball joint.

LOWER BALL JOINT

All models have a wear indicator built into the lower ball joint, **Fig. 5.** When inspecting wear indicator, vehicle must be supported in a normal manner on wheels to properly load ball joint.

BALL JOINT

REPLACE

UPPER BALL JOINT

1. Raise vehicle and support with stands at outer ends of lower control arms.
2. Remove wheel and tire.
3. Remove cotter pin and retaining nut, then separate ball joint stud from knuckle using a suitable tool, **Fig. 6.**
4. Support upper control arm in a raised position.
5. Remove heads of rivets securing joint to arm, then drive out rivets to remove joint.
6. Position replacement joint on top of control arm, insert retaining bolts supplied with joint from under arm, install nuts and tighten to specifications, **Fig. 7.**
7. Remove upper control arm support, assemble ball joint to steering knuck-

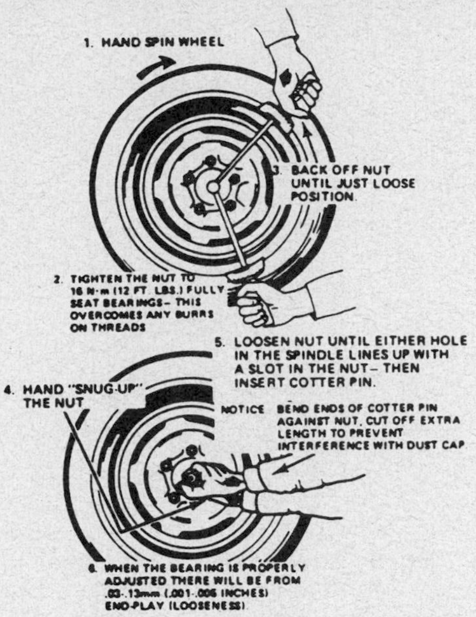
1. HAND SPIN WHEEL
3. BACK OFF NUT UNTIL JUST LOOSE POSITION.
2. TIGHTEN THE NUT TO 16 N·m (12 FT. LBS.) FULLY SEAT BEARINGS– THIS OVERCOMES ANY BURRS ON THREADS
5. LOOSEN NUT UNTIL EITHER HOLE IN THE SPINDLE LINES UP WITH A SLOT IN THE NUT– THEN INSERT COTTER PIN.
4. HAND "SNUG-UP" THE NUT
NOTICE BEND ENDS OF COTTER PIN AGAINST NUT, CUT OFF EXTRA LENGTH TO PREVENT INTERFERENCE WITH DUST CAP
6. WHEN THE BEARING IS PROPERLY ADJUSTED THERE WILL BE FROM .03-.13mm (.001-.005 INCHES) END-PLAY (LOOSENESS)
GC2029100062000X

Fig. 2 Front wheel bearing adjustment

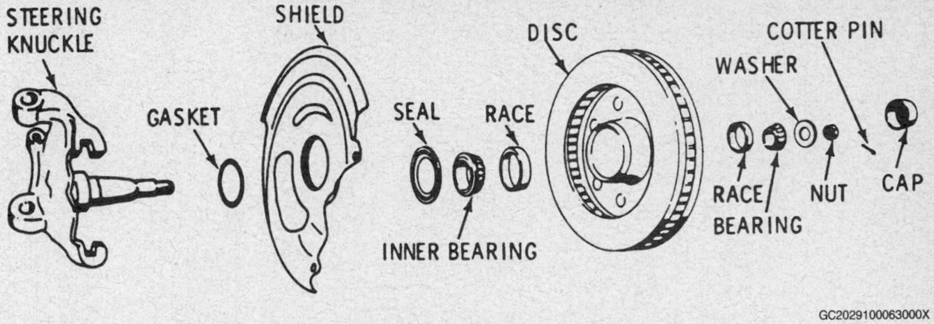
STEERING KNUCKLE
SHIELD
DISC
COTTER PIN
WASHER
GASKET
SEAL
RACE
RACE
BEARING
NUT
CAP
INNER BEARING
GC2029100063000X

Fig. 3 Hub & wheel bearing replacement

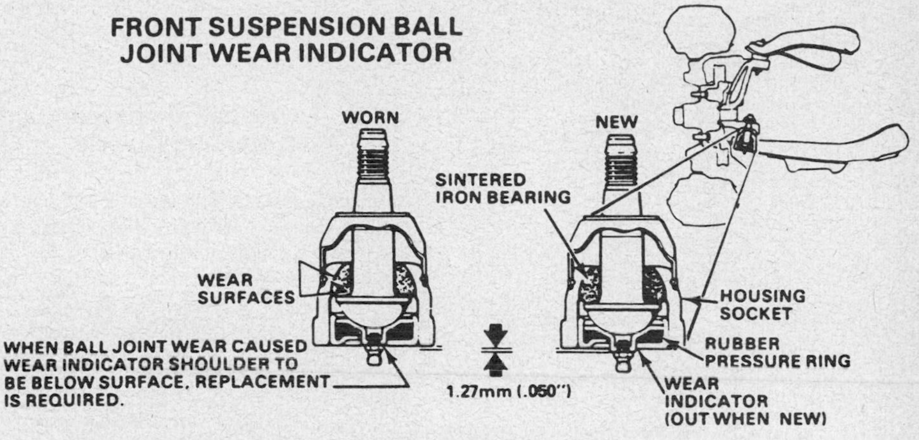
FRONT SUSPENSION BALL JOINT WEAR INDICATOR
WORN
NEW
SINTERED IRON BEARING
WEAR SURFACES
HOUSING SOCKET
RUBBER PRESSURE RING
WHEN BALL JOINT WEAR CAUSED WEAR INDICATOR SHOULDER TO BE BELOW SURFACE, REPLACEMENT IS REQUIRED.
1.27mm (.050")
WEAR INDICATOR (OUT WHEN NEW)
GC2029100065000X

Fig. 5 Lower ball joint wear indicator

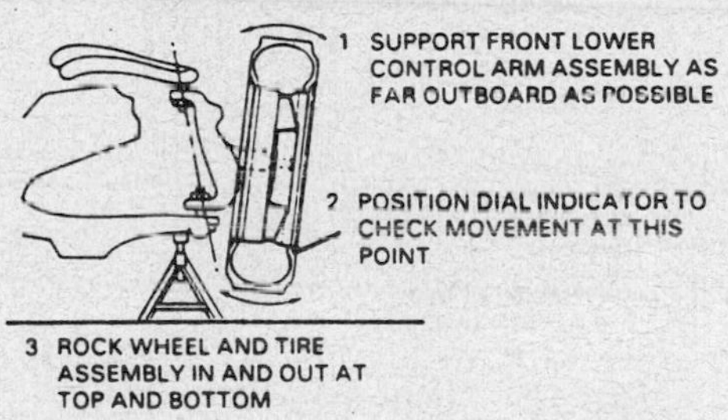
1 SUPPORT FRONT LOWER CONTROL ARM ASSEMBLY AS FAR OUTBOARD AS POSSIBLE
2 POSITION DIAL INDICATOR TO CHECK MOVEMENT AT THIS POINT
3 ROCK WHEEL AND TIRE ASSEMBLY IN AND OUT AT TOP AND BOTTOM
GC2029100064000X

Fig. 4 Upper ball joint wear inspection

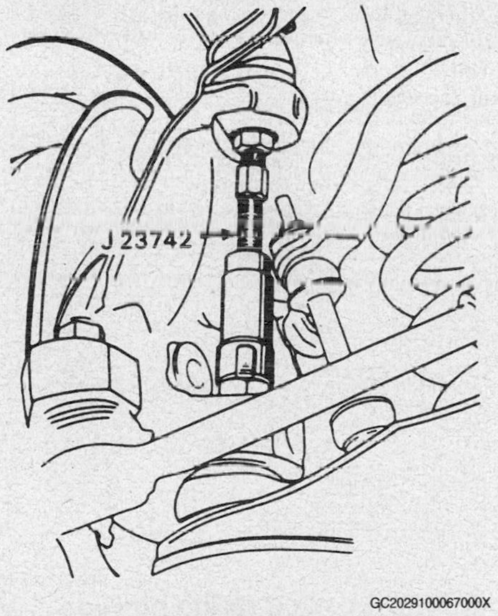
J 23742
GC2029100067000X

Fig. 6 Upper ball joint separation from steering knuckle

le, install washer, if equipped, and retaining nut.

8. Tighten retaining nut to specifications.
9. Tighten retaining nut up to an additional 1/16 turn, if necessary, to align hole in ball stud with nut, then install cotter pin.

LOWER BALL JOINT

1. Raise vehicle and support at frame, and remove wheel and tire.
2. Position a suitable jack under lower control arm spring seat, and raise jack to compress coil spring. **Jack must remain in place during ball joint replacement to hold spring and lower control arm in position.**
3. Remove cotter pin and nut securing ball joint stud to steering knuckle, then disconnect joint from knuckle using a suitable tool, **Fig. 8.**
4. Lift knuckle assembly from ball stud, guiding control arm out of splash shield, then support knuckle aside to allow clearance for joint removal.
5. Remove grease fitting, then press ball joint assembly out of lower control arm using a suitable tool, **Fig. 9.**
6. Press replacement joint into arm using suitable tools, **Fig. 10.** Fit spindle over ball stud, install washer, if equipped, and retaining nut.
7. Tighten retaining nut to specifications.
8. Tighten nut an additional 1/16 turn, if necessary, to align hole in ball stud with nut, then install cotter pin.

COIL SPRING REPLACE

1. Raise and support front of vehicle, then remove wheel and tire assembly. Support vehicle by frame so control arms hang free.
2. **On models equipped with anti-lock brake systems,** remove right and left wheel speed sensors as follows:
   a. Under vehicle hood, disconnect speed sensor electrical harness.
   b. Raise and support vehicle, then remove speed sensor harness bracket attaching bolt.
   c. Remove speed sensor to steering knuckle attaching bolt, then remove speed sensor and bracket assembly and position aside.
   d. Reverse procedure to install. Wheel speed sensors are to installed by hand. **Do not hammer sensors into position, as damage may result.**
3. **On all models,** remove stabilizer to lower control arm attachment.
4. Disconnect tie rod end from steering knuckle.
5. Install a suitable coil spring compressor, then compress coil spring.
6. Remove lower control arm to frame

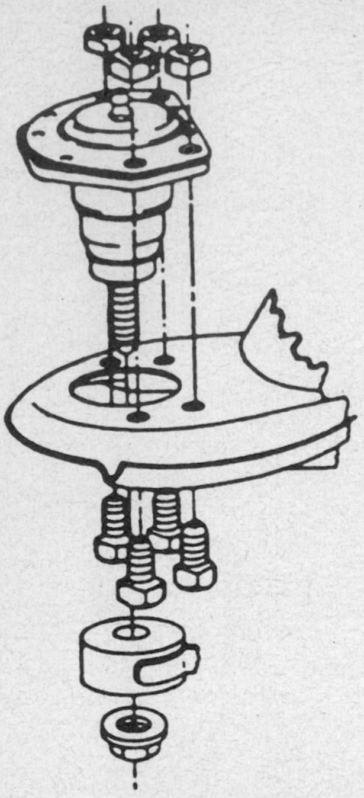

GC2029100068000X

Fig. 7 Upper ball joint installation

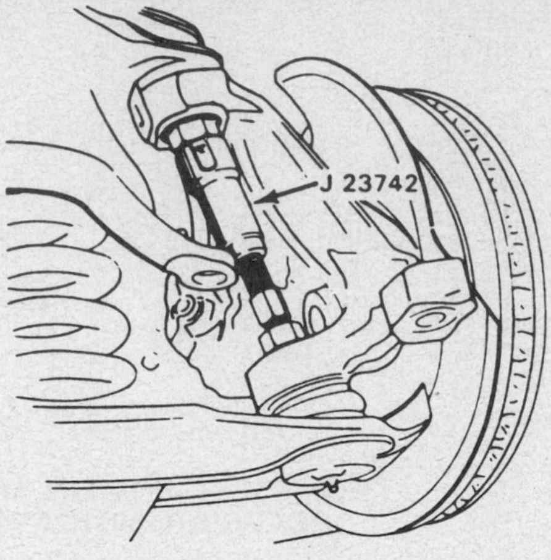
J 23742

GC2029100069000X

Fig. 8 Lower ball joint separation from steering knuckle

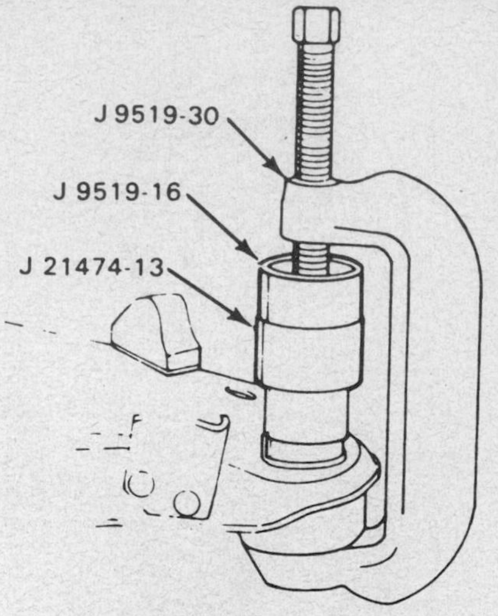
J 9519-30
J 9519-16
J 21474-13

GC2029100070000X

Fig. 9 Lower ball joint removal from lower control arm

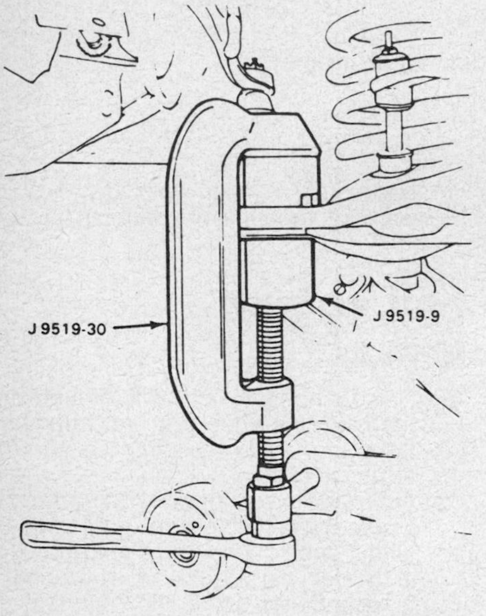
J 9519-30
J 9519-9

GC2029100071000X

Fig. 10 Lower ball joint installation into lower control arm

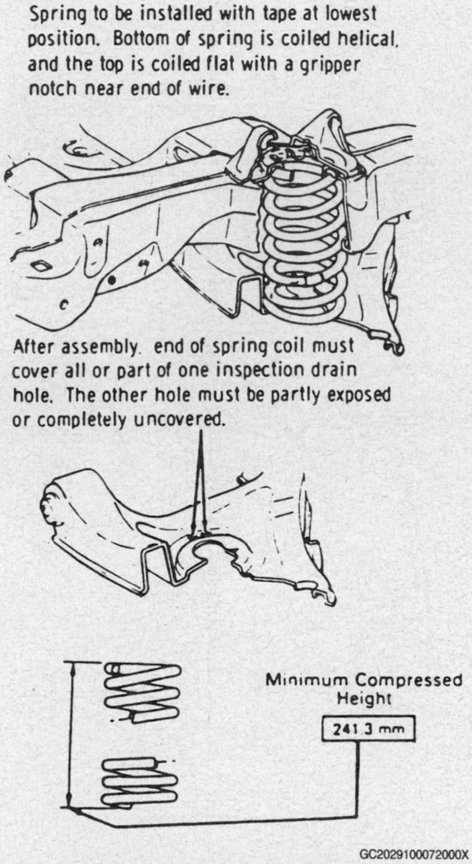
Spring to be installed with tape at lowest position. Bottom of spring is coiled helical, and the top is coiled flat with a gripper notch near end of wire.
After assembly, end of spring coil must cover all or part of one inspection drain hole. The other hole must be partly exposed or completely uncovered.
Minimum Compressed Height
241.3 mm

GC2029100072000X

Fig. 11 Coil spring position

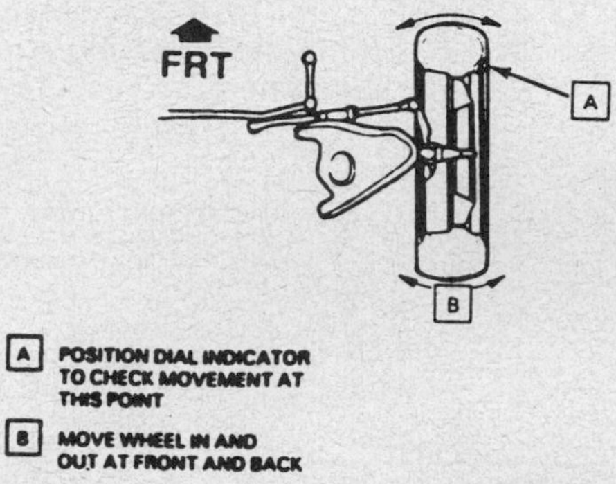
FRT
A
B
A POSITION DIAL INDICATOR TO CHECK MOVEMENT AT THIS POINT
B MOVE WHEEL IN AND OUT AT FRONT AND BACK

GC2029100066000X

Fig. 12 Suspension & steering linkage inspection

bolts, then pivot lower control arm rearward.

7. Carefully loosen coil spring compressor and remove coil spring from vehicle.
8. Reverse procedure to install. Position coil spring as shown in **Fig. 11.** Install front pivot bolt first. **To ensure adequate suspension clearance, install front pivot bolt from front, with nut toward rear of vehicle. Rear bolt can be installed from either direction.**
9. Tighten pivot bolts to specifications.

SHOCK ABSORBER

REPLACE

1. Raise and support vehicle as needed, and remove wheel and tire.
2. Hold shock absorber shaft with a suitable wrench and remove upper retaining nut, washer and bushing.
3. Remove lower retaining bolts and shock absorber.
4. Reverse procedure to install. Tighten upper retaining nut and lower mounting bolts to specifications.

SUSPENSION STEERING LINK INSPECTION

1. Raise vehicle with jack placed under frame torque box behind front wheel.
2. Lock steering wheel with wheels in straight ahead position, then mount dial indicator on a suitable stand with pointer bearing against outer rim of wheel, **Fig. 12.**
3. Move wheel in and out at front and rear, without moving steering wheel, while observing gauge.
4. If gauge reading exceeds .108 inch, check steering linkage and suspension for excessive wear or damage and wheel bearings for proper adjustment.

POWER STEERING GEAR

REPLACE

1. Disconnect battery ground cable.
2. Disconnect pressure and return hoses from power steering gear. Position hoses in upward direction to prevent fluid drainage. Cap lines and fittings.
3. Disconnect intermediate steering shaft from steering gear stub shaft.

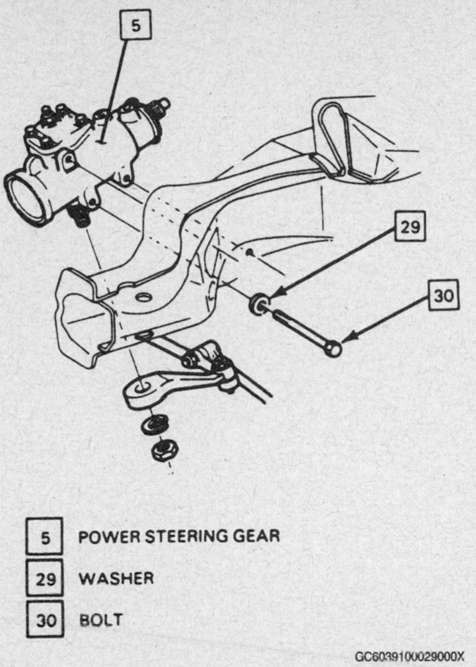
5
29
30
5 POWER STEERING GEAR
29 WASHER
30 BOLT
GC6039100029000X

Fig. 13 Power steering gear mount

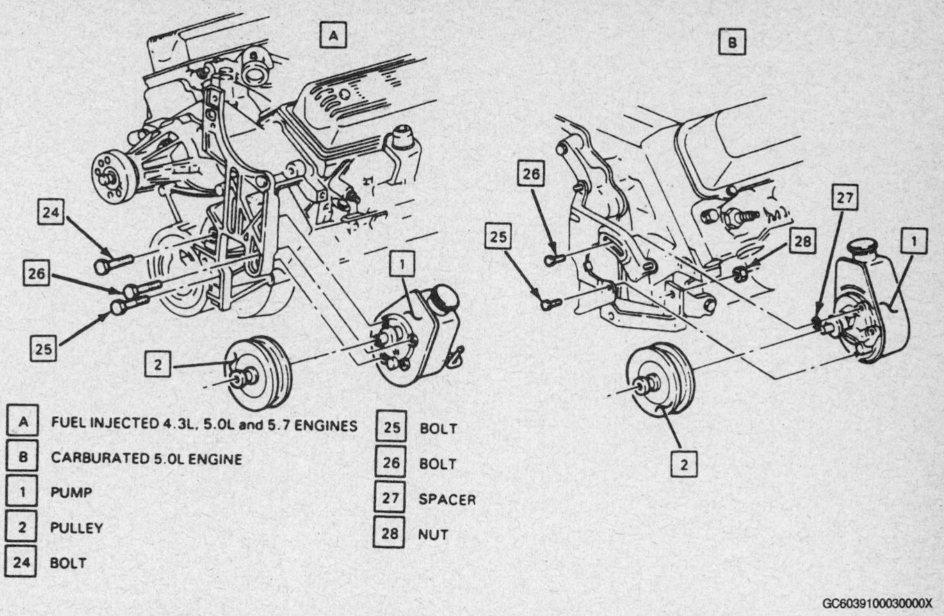
A
B
24
26
25
2
1
26
25
27
28
1
2
A FUEL INJECTED 4.3L, 5.0L and 5.7 ENGINES
B CARBURATED 5.0L ENGINE
1 PUMP
2 PULLEY
24 BOLT
25 BOLT
26 BOLT
27 SPACER
28 NUT
GC6039100030000X

Fig. 14 Power steering pump mount. 1992–93

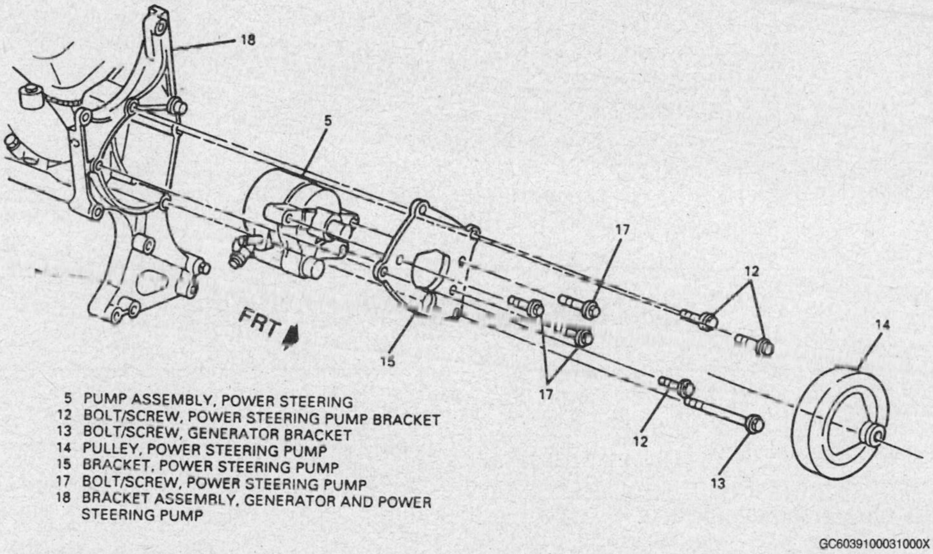
18
5
17
12
14
FRT
15
17
12
13
5 PUMP ASSEMBLY, POWER STEERING
12 BOLT/SCREW, POWER STEERING PUMP BRACKET
13 BOLT/SCREW, GENERATOR BRACKET
14 PULLEY, POWER STEERING PUMP
15 BRACKET, POWER STEERING PUMP
17 BOLT/SCREW, POWER STEERING PUMP
18 BRACKET ASSEMBLY, GENERATOR AND POWER STEERING PUMP
GC6039100031000X

Fig. 15 Exploded view of power steering pump mounting 1994–95

4. Disconnect Pitman arm from steering gear.
5. **On models equipped with ABS brake systems,** remove ABS modulator bracket attaching nut from steering gear.
6. **On all models,** remove steering attaching bolts and washers, then remove steering gear, **Fig. 13.**
7. Reverse procedure to install. Tighten attaching bolts to specifications.

POWER STEERING PUMP

REPLACE

1992–93

1. Disconnect battery ground cable.
2. Disconnect hoses at power steering pump, then plug pump parts and hoses.
3. Loosen pump adjusting bolt and remove pump drive belt.
4. Remove pump to support bracket attaching bolts and the pump, **Fig. 14.**
5. Reverse procedure to install. Tighten attaching bolts to specifications.

1994–95

1. Siphon power steering fluid from reservoir to prevent excess spillage.
2. Drain engine cooling system into suitable container(s), then, if equipped with mechanical fan, remove engine cooling fan bracket.
3. Disconnect heater inlet and outlet hoses from water pump.
4. Remove heater inlet and outlet hose clip bolt/screw from generator and power steering pump bracket, **Fig. 15,** then position aside.
5. Remove drive belt from power steering pump as outlined under "Serpentine Drive Belt."
6. Disconnect power steering gear inlet hose from power steering pump, **Fig. 16.**
7. Disconnect power steering fluid reservoir hose from power steering pump by squeezing clamp and sliding away from pump, then rotating and sliding hose away from power steering pump, **Fig. 16.**
8. Remove pump bracket bolts/screws and generator bracket bolt/screw, then pump and pulley.
9. Reverse procedure to install.

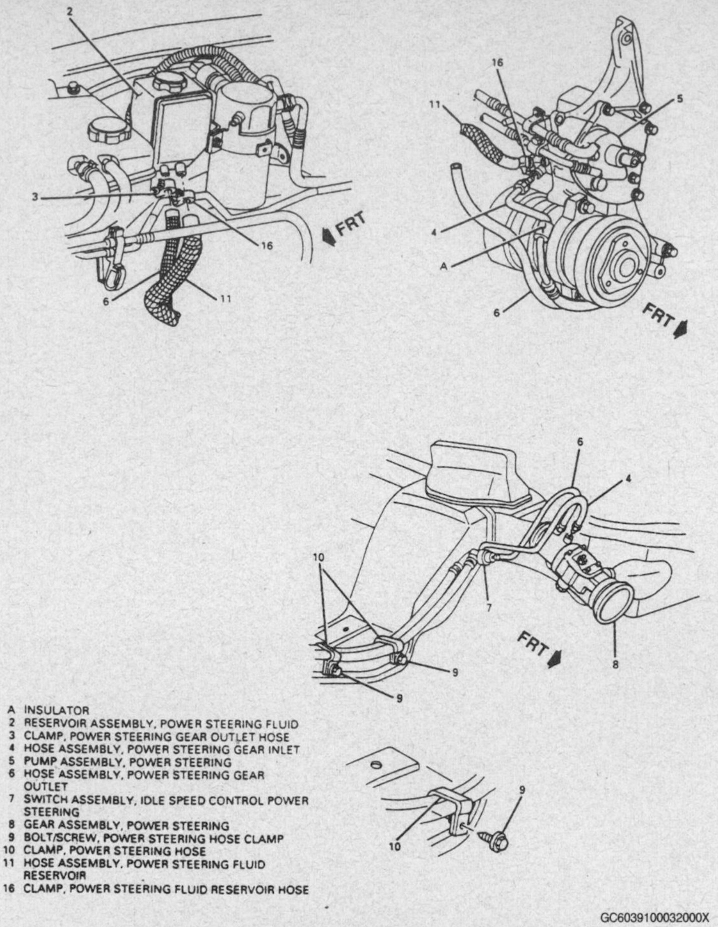
A INSULATOR
2 RESERVOIR ASSEMBLY, POWER STEERING FLUID
3 CLAMP, POWER STEERING GEAR OUTLET HOSE
4 HOSE ASSEMBLY, POWER STEERING GEAR INLET
5 PUMP ASSEMBLY, POWER STEERING
6 HOSE ASSEMBLY, POWER STEERING GEAR OUTLET
7 SWITCH ASSEMBLY, IDLE SPEED CONTROL POWER STEERING
8 GEAR ASSEMBLY, POWER STEERING
9 BOLT/SCREW, POWER STEERING HOSE CLAMP
10 CLAMP, POWER STEERING HOSE
11 HOSE ASSEMBLY, POWER STEERING FLUID RESERVOIR
16 CLAMP, POWER STEERING FLUID RESERVOIR HOSE
FRT
GC6039100032000X

Fig. 16 Power steering gear inlet & outlet hose locations 1994–95

TIGHTENING SPECIFICATIONS

Year	Component	Torque/Ft. Lbs.
1992–93	ABS Modulator Bracket	18
	Idler Arm To Frame Nut	61
	Intermediate Shaft Coupling Flange Bolt	52
	Lower Ball Joint To Knuckle Stud Nut	83
	Lower Control Arm To Frame Nuts	92
	Pitman Shaft Nut	179
	Power Steering Inlet/Outlet Hose Fitting	21
	Power Steering Outlet Hose Clamp	12①
	Power Steering Pump Bracket To Engine	24
	Power Steering Pump To Bracket	37
	Shock Absorber Lower Attachment	20
	Shock Absorber Upper Attachment	97①
	Splash Shield Bolt	124①
	Stabilizer Bar Bracket To Frame	24
	Stabilizer Bar To Idler Arm Nut	40
	Stabilizer Bar To Inner Tie Rod Nut	40
	Stabilizer Bar To Pitman Arm Nut	44

Year	Component	Torque/Ft. Lbs.
1992–93 —Cont'd	Stabilizer Link Nut	13
	Steering Gear To Frame Bolts	70
	Steering Knuckle Hub Nut	125
	Tie Rod Clamp Nuts	14
	Tie Rod End To Steering Knuckle Stud Nut	35
	Upper Ball Joint To Knuckle Stud Nut	60
	Upper Control Arm Bushing Nuts	85
	Upper Control Arm To Frame Nuts	72
	Wheel Bearing Nut	12
	Wheel Lug Nuts	100
1994–95	ABS Modulator Bracket	18
	Idler Arm To Frame Nut	61
	Generator Bracket Bolt/Screw	37
	Heater Inlet & Outlet Hose Clip Bolt/Screw	17①
	Intermediate Shaft Coupling Flange Bolt	52
	Lower Ball Joint To Knuckle Stud Nut	83
	Lower Control Arm To Frame Nuts	92

TIGHTENING SPECIFICATIONS-Continued

Year	Component	Torque/Ft. Lbs.
	Pitman Shaft Nut	179
	Power Steering Hose Clamp Bolt/Screw	44①
	Power Steering Pump Bolt/Screw	37
	Power Steering Pump Bracket Bolt/Screw	30
	Power Steering Gear Inlet Hose Fitting To Power Steering Gear	21
	Power Steering Gear Inlet Hose Fitting To Power Steering Pump	21
	Power Steering Gear Outlet Hose Fitting To Power Steering Gear	21
	Shock Absorber Lower Attachment	20
	Shock Absorber Upper Attachment	97①
	Splash Shield Bolt	124①
	Stabilizer Bar Bracket To Frame	24
	Stabilizer Bar To Idler Arm Nut	40
	Stabilizer Bar To Inner Tie Rod Nut	40
	Stabilizer Bar To Pitman Arm Nut	44
	Stabilizer Link Nut	13
	Steering Gear To Frame Bolts	70
	Steering Knuckle Hub Nut	125
	Tie Rod Clamp Nuts	14
	Tie Rod End To Steering Knuckle Stud Nut	35
	Upper Ball Joint To Knuckle Stud Nut	60
	Upper Control Arm Bushing Nuts	85
	Upper Control Arm To Frame Nuts	72
	Wheel Bearing Nut	12
	Wheel Lug Nuts	100

①—Inch lbs.

Wheel Alignment

INDEX

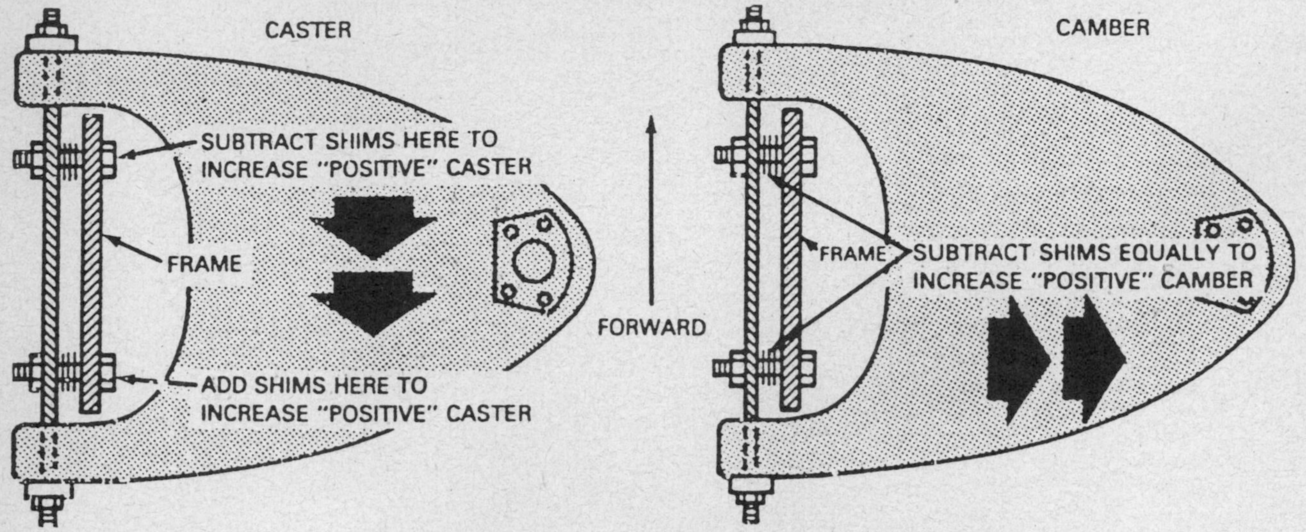

CASTER
SUBTRACT SHIMS HERE TO INCREASE "POSITIVE" CASTER
FRAME
ADD SHIMS HERE TO INCREASE "POSITIVE" CASTER
FORWARD
CAMBER
FRAME
SUBTRACT SHIMS EQUALLY TO INCREASE "POSITIVE" CAMBER

GC2049100036000X

Fig. 1 Caster & camber adjustments

PRELIMINARY INSPECTION

1. Inspect tires for proper inflation and similar tread wear.
2. Inspect hub and bearing for excessive wear, repair as required.
3. Inspect ball joints.
4. Inspect tie rod ends for excessive looseness.
5. Check wheel and tire runout.
6. Inspect vehicle ride height.
7. Inspect rack and pinion for looseness at frame.
8. Ensure proper strut operation.
9. Check suspension and steering components for damage, replace as required.

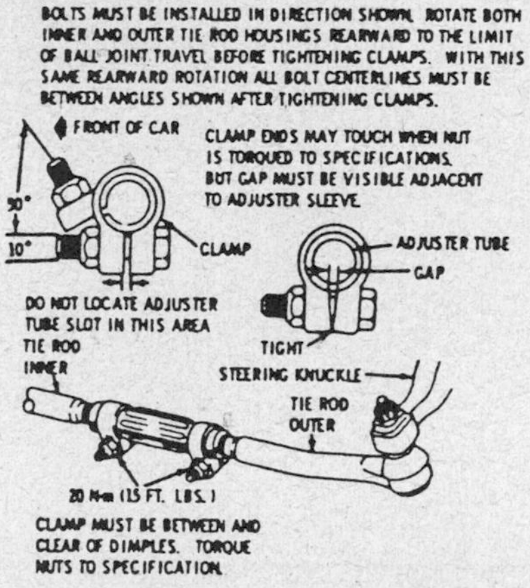

BOLTS MUST BE INSTALLED IN DIRECTION SHOWN. ROTATE BOTH INNER AND OUTER TIE ROD HOUSINGS REARWARD TO THE LIMIT OF BALL JOINT TRAVEL BEFORE TIGHTENING CLAMPS. WITH THIS SAME REARWARD ROTATION ALL BOLT CENTERLINES MUST BE BETWEEN ANGLES SHOWN AFTER TIGHTENING CLAMPS.
FRONT OF CAR
CLAMP ENDS MAY TOUCH WHEN NUT IS TORQUED TO SPECIFICATIONS. BUT GAP MUST BE VISIBLE ADJACENT TO ADJUSTER SLEEVE.
50°
10°
CLAMP
ADJUSTER TUBE
GAP
DO NOT LOCATE ADJUSTER TUBE SLOT IN THIS AREA
TIGHT
TIE ROD INNER
STEERING KNUCKLE
TIE ROD OUTER
20 N·m (15 FT. LBS.)
CLAMP MUST BE BETWEEN AND CLEAR OF DIMPLES. TORQUE NUTS TO SPECIFICATION.

GC2049100037000X

Fig. 2 Toe-in adjustment

FRONT WHEEL ALIGNMENT

CASTER

Caster adjustments are made by means of shims between the upper control arm inner support shaft and the support bracket attached to the frame, **Fig. 1.** Shims may be added, subtracted or transferred to change the readings.

Transfer shims from front to rear or rear to front. The transfer of one shim to the front bolt from the rear bolt will decrease positive caster. One shim ($1/32$ inch) transferred from the rear bolt to the front bolt will change caster about $1/2$ degree.

CAMBER

Camber adjustments are made by means of shims between the upper control arm inner support shaft and the support bracket attached to the frame, **Fig. 1.** Shims may be added, subtracted or transferred to change the readings.

Change shims at both the front and rear of the shaft. Adding an equal number of shims at both front and rear of the support shaft will decrease positive camber. One shim ($1/32$ inch) at each location will move camber approximately $1/6$ degree.

TOE-IN

Toe-in can be adjusted by loosening the clamp bolts at each end of each tie rod and turning each tie rod to increase or decrease its length as necessary until proper toe-in is secured and the steering gear is on the high point for straight-ahead driving, **Fig. 2.**

VEHICLE RIDE HEIGHT

EXCEPT CADILLAC

Refer to **Figs. 3 through 5** for ride height measurements and specifications.

CADILLAC

Refer to **Figs. 6 and 7** for ride height measurements and specifications.

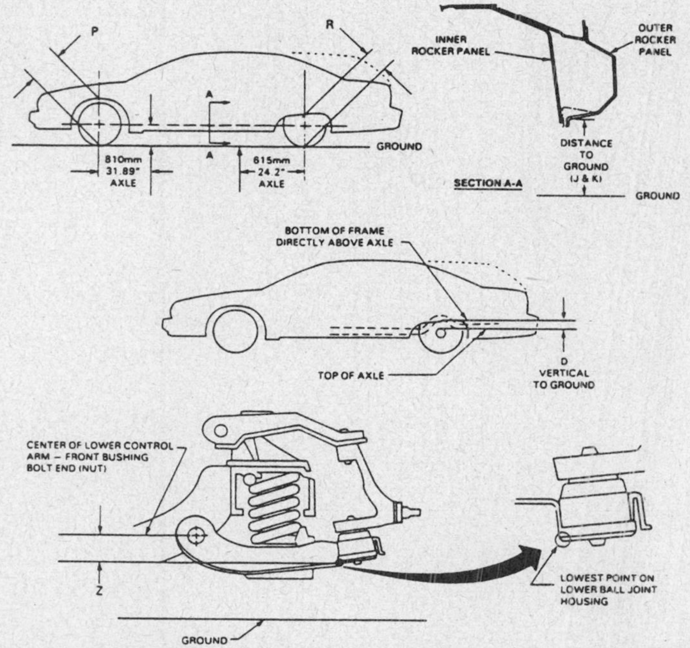
P
R
A
A
810mm
31.89"
AXLE
615mm
24.2"
AXLE
GROUND
INNER
ROCKER PANEL
OUTER
ROCKER
PANEL
DISTANCE
TO
GROUND
(J & K)
SECTION A-A
GROUND
BOTTOM OF FRAME
DIRECTLY ABOVE AXLE
TOP OF AXLE
D
VERTICAL
TO GROUND
CENTER OF LOWER CONTROL
ARM – FRONT BUSHING
BOLT END (NUT)
Z
LOWEST POINT ON
LOWER BALL JOINT
HOUSING
GROUND

MODEL	SUSPENSION	TIRE	J		K		P		R		D		Z	
			mm	INCH	mm	INCH	mm	INCH	mm	INCH	mm	INCH	mm	INCH
SEDAN	FE1	215-75	252	9.9	264	10.4	742	29.2	540	21.3	151	5.9	61	2.4
		225-70	252	9.9	264	10.4	742	29.2	540	21.3	152	6.0	62	2.4
	FE2/F41	225-70	252	9.9	264	10.4	742	29.2	539	21.2	152	6.0	63	2.5
WAGON	F40	225-70	252	9.9	264	10.4	742	29.2	550	21.7	133	5.2	63	2.5
		225-75	252	9.9	264	10.4	742	29.2	550	21.7	122	4.8	53	2.1
POLICE	783	215-75	252	9.9	264	10.4	742	29.2	539	21.2	148	5.8	59	2.3
		225-70	252	9.9	264	10.4	742	29.2	539	21.2	151	5.9	62	2.4
		235-70	252	9.9	264	10.4	742	29.2	539	21.2	144	5.7	54	2.1
TAXI	783	225-70	252	9.9	264	10.4	742	29.2	539	21.2	151	5.9	62	2.4

NOTE: Trim heights should be within ± 10mm (0.4 inch).

GC2049200038000X

Fig. 3 Vehicle ride height measurement locations & specifications. 1992 Custom Cruiser and 1992-93 Caprice & Roadmaster

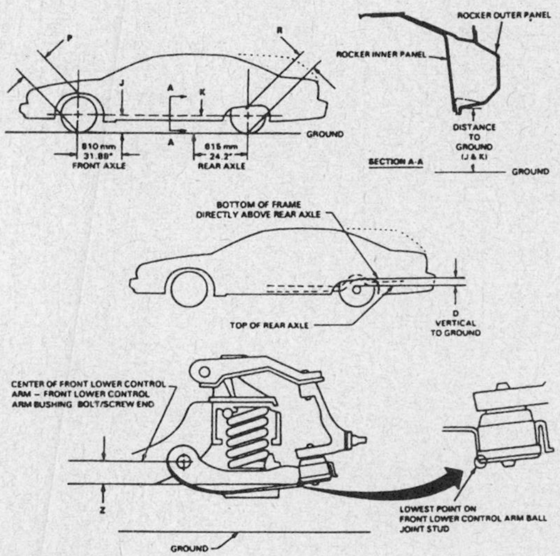
P
R
J
A
K
A
810 mm
31.89"
FRONT AXLE
615 mm
24.2"
REAR AXLE
GROUND
ROCKER OUTER PANEL
ROCKER INNER PANEL
DISTANCE
TO
GROUND
(J & K)
SECTION A-A
GROUND
BOTTOM OF FRAME
DIRECTLY ABOVE REAR AXLE
TOP OF REAR AXLE
D
VERTICAL
TO GROUND
CENTER OF FRONT LOWER CONTROL
ARM – FRONT LOWER CONTROL
ARM BUSHING BOLT/SCREW END
Z
LOWEST POINT ON
FRONT LOWER CONTROL ARM BALL
JOINT STUD
GROUND

MODEL	SUSPENSION	TIRE	J		K		P		R		D		Z	
			mm	INCH	mm	INCH	mm	INCH	mm	INCH	mm	INCH	mm	INCH
BUICK SEDAN	FE1	235-70	252	9.9	264	10.4	737	29.0	546	21.5	147	5.8	57	2.2
	FE2/F41	225-70	252	9.9	264	10.4	737	29.0	546	21.5	154	6.1	64	2.5
	FE3	235-70	252	9.9	264	10.4	737	29.0	546	21.5	147	5.8	58	2.3
BUICK WAGON	F40	225-75	252	9.9	264	10.4	748	29.4	557	21.9	123	4.8	52	2.0

NOTE: Trim heights should be within ± 10 mm (0.4 inch).

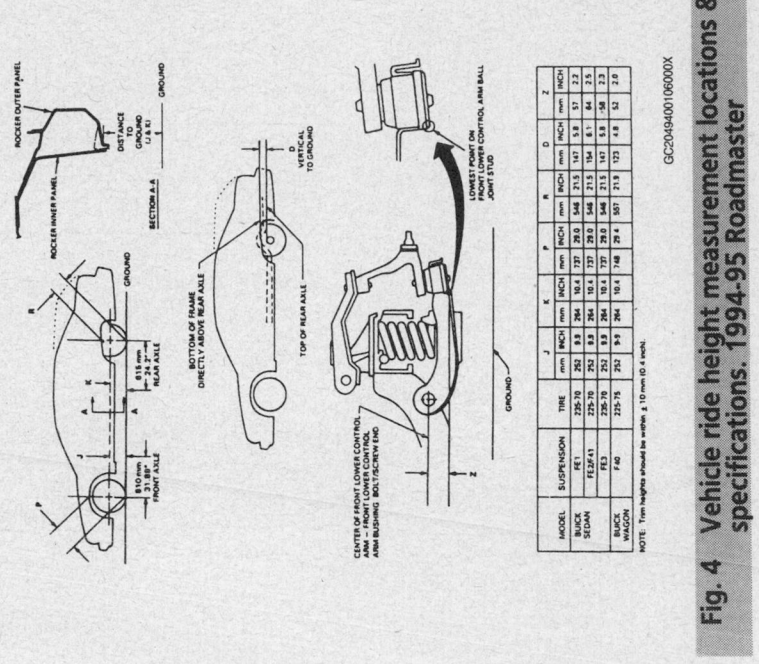

GC2049400106000X

Fig. 4 Vehicle ride height measurement locations & specifications. 1994-95 Roadmaster

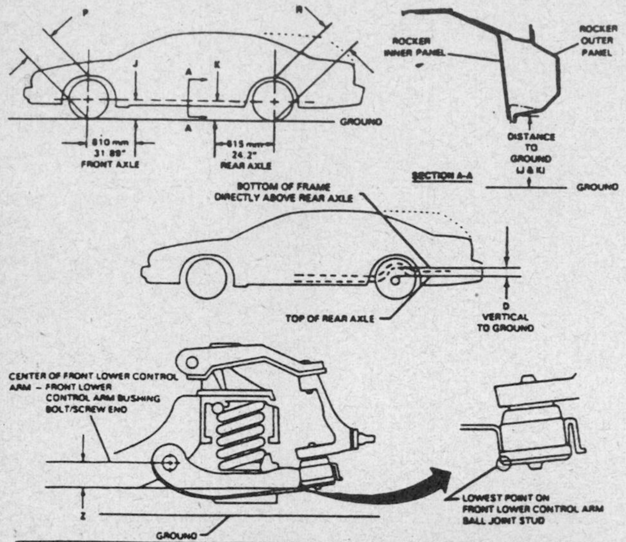
P
R
J
K
A
A
GROUND
610 mm
31.89"
FRONT AXLE
615 mm
24.2"
REAR AXLE
ROCKER INNER PANEL
ROCKER OUTER PANEL
DISTANCE TO GROUND (J & K)
SECTION A-A
GROUND
BOTTOM OF FRAME DIRECTLY ABOVE REAR AXLE
TOP OF REAR AXLE
D
VERTICAL TO GROUND
CENTER OF FRONT LOWER CONTROL ARM – FRONT LOWER CONTROL ARM BUSHING BOLT/SCREW END
Z
GROUND
LOWEST POINT ON FRONT LOWER CONTROL ARM BALL JOINT STUD

MODEL	SUSPENSION	TIRE	J		K		P		R		D		Z	
			mm	INCH	mm	INCH	mm	INCH	mm	INCH	mm	INCH	mm	INCH
CHEVROLET SEDAN	FE1	215-75	257	10.1	259	10.2	738	29.0	723	28.5	142	5.6	71	2.8
		225-70 (SEO ONLY)	252	9.9	264	10.4	726	28.6	732	28.8	152	6.0	61	2.4
	FE2/F41	225-70 (EXC SEO)	252	9.9	254	10.0	731	28.8	718	28.3	140	3.5	69	2.7
		225-70 (SEO)	252	9.9	264	10.4	726	28.6	732	28.8	152	6.0	62	2.4
	FE3	235-70	252	9.9	254	10.0	731	28.8	718	28.3	133	5.2	62	2.4
	7B3 (SEO ONLY)	215-75	252	9.9	264	10.4	726	28.6	732	28.8	150	5.9	60	2.4
		225-70	252	9.9	264	10.4	726	28.6	732	28.8	153	6.0	64	2.5
		235-70	252	9.9	264	10.4	726	28.6	732	28.8	145	5.7	54	2.1
	FE4 (IMPALA SS)	255-50	227	8.9	229	9.0	708	27.8	683	27.3	113	4.4	42	1.7
CHEVROLET WAGON	F40	225-75	252	9.9	264	10.4	742	29.2	551	21.7	123	4.8	52	2.0
		225-70 (SEO)	252	9-9	264	10.4	742	29.2	551	21.7	134	5.3	62	2.4

NOTE. Trim heights should be within ±10 mm (0.4 inch).

GC2049400107000X

Fig. 5 Vehicle ride height measurement locations & specifications. 1994-95 Caprice & Impala SS

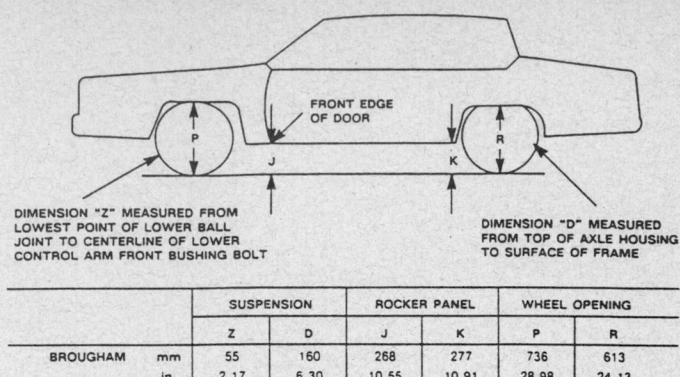

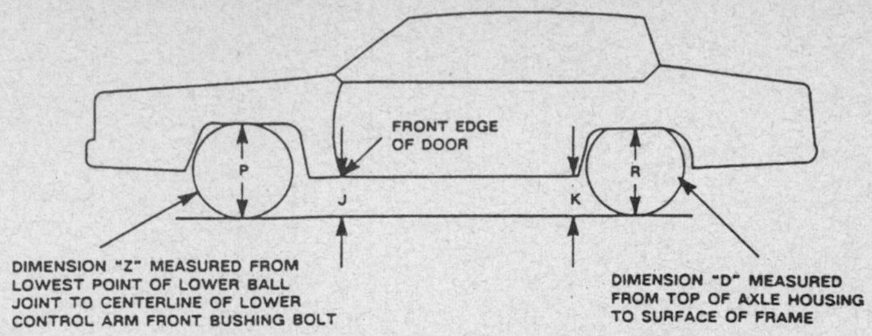
FRONT EDGE OF DOOR
P
R
J
K
DIMENSION "Z" MEASURED FROM LOWEST POINT OF LOWER BALL JOINT TO CENTERLINE OF LOWER CONTROL ARM FRONT BUSHING BOLT
DIMENSION "D" MEASURED FROM TOP OF AXLE HOUSING TO SURFACE OF FRAME

		SUSPENSION		ROCKER PANEL		WHEEL OPENING	
		Z	D	J	K	P	R
BROUGHAM	mm	55	160	268	277	736	613
	in.	2.17	6.30	10.55	10.91	28.98	24.13

GC2049100039000X

Fig. 6 Vehicle ride height measurement locations & specifications. Brougham

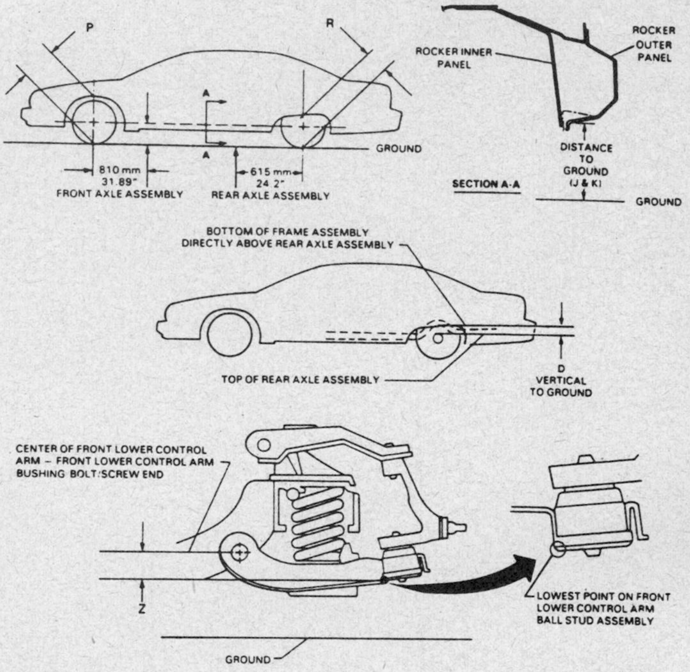
P
R
A
A
GROUND
810 mm
31.89"
FRONT AXLE ASSEMBLY
615 mm
24.2"
REAR AXLE ASSEMBLY
ROCKER INNER PANEL
ROCKER OUTER PANEL
DISTANCE TO GROUND (J & K)
SECTION A-A
GROUND
BOTTOM OF FRAME ASSEMBLY DIRECTLY ABOVE REAR AXLE ASSEMBLY
TOP OF REAR AXLE ASSEMBLY
D
VERTICAL TO GROUND
CENTER OF FRONT LOWER CONTROL ARM – FRONT LOWER CONTROL ARM BUSHING BOLT/SCREW END
Z
GROUND
LOWEST POINT ON FRONT LOWER CONTROL ARM BALL STUD ASSEMBLY

MODEL	SUSPENSION	TIRE	J		K		P		R		D		Z	
			mm	INCH	mm	INCH	mm	INCH	mm	INCH	mm	INCH	mm	INCH
SEDAN	FE1	235-70	252	9.9	264	10.4	737	29.0	546	21.5	147	5.8	56	2.2
	FE2/F41	225-70	252	9.9	264	10.4	737	29.0	546	21.5	152	6.0	61	2.4

NOTE: Trim heights should be within ± 10 mm (0.4 inch).

GC2049300040000X

Fig. 7 Vehicle ride height measurement locations & specifications. 1993-95 Fleetwood (RWD)

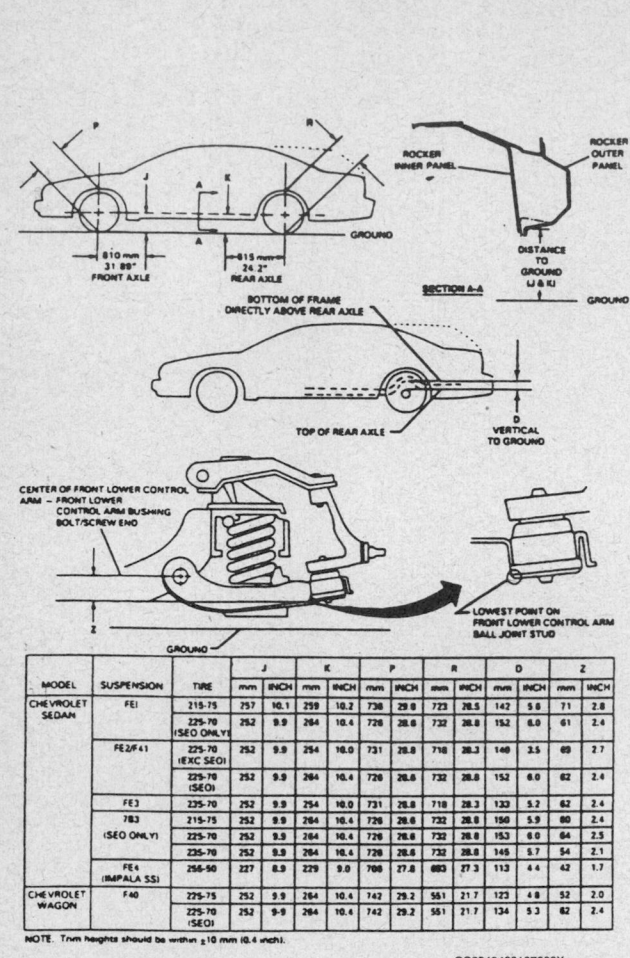

CHEVROLET CAMARO & PONTIAC FIREBIRD (F Cars)

NOTE: Refer To The Rear Of This Manual For Vehicle Manufacturer's Special Tool Suppliers.

INDEX OF SERVICE OPERATIONS

NOTE: For Service Operations Not Listed Below, Refer To The Table Of Contents In The Front Of This Manual.

Continued

INDEX OF SERVICE OPERATIONS—CONTINUED

Specifications

GENERAL ENGINE SPECIFICATIONS

Year	Engine		Fuel System	Bore & Stroke	Compression Ratio	Net Brake H.P. @ RPM ②	Maximum Torque	Normal Oil Pressure, psi
	Liter/CID	VIN Code①						
1992	3.1L/V6-191	T	MFI	3.50 x 3.31	8.5	140 @ 4400	180 @ 3200	⑥
	5.0L/V8-305	E	TBI	3.74 x 3.48	9.3	170 @ 4000	255 @ 2400	③
	5.0L/V8-305	F	TPI	3.74 x 3.48	9.3	205 @ 4200	285 @ 3200	③
	5.7L/V8-350④	8	TPI	4.00 x 3.48	9.8	245 @ 4400	345 @ 3200	③
	5.7L/V8-350⑤	8	TPI	4.00 x 3.48	9.3	230 @ 4400	300 @ 3200	③
1993–95	3.4L/V6-207	S	MFI	3.62 x 3.31	9.0	160 @ 4600	200 @ 3600	⑦
	5.7L/V8-350	P	MFI	4.00 x 3.48	10.5	275 @ 5000	325 @ 2400	③

MFI: Multi-Port Fuel Injection.
TBI: Throttle Body Injection.
TPI: Tune Port Injection.
①—The eighth digit of the VIN denotes engine code.
②—Ratings are net-as installed in vehicle.
③—Minimum, 6 psi @ 1000 RPM; 18 psi @ 2000 RPM; 24 psi @ 4000 RPM.
④—Auto. trans.
⑤—Manual trans.
⑥—8 psi @ 600 RPM minimum.
⑦—50 to 65 psi @ 2400 RPM & oil temperature at 240°F.

TUNE UP SPECIFICATIONS

Year & Engine Liter/ CID (VIN code)①	Spark Plug Gap	Ignition Timing BTDC				Curb Idle Speed②		Fast Idle Speed		Fuel Pump Pressure, psi
		Firing Order Fig.③	Man. Trans.	Auto. Trans.	Mark Fig.	Man. Trans.	Auto. Trans.	Man. Trans.	Auto. Trans.	
1992										
3.1L/V6-191(T)	.045	A	10④	10④	B	800⑤	650D⑤	⑤	⑤	34–47⑥
5.0L/V8-305(E) EFI	.035	C	—	TDC⑦	B	—	600D⑤	—	⑤	9–13⑧
5.0L/V8-305(F) TPI	.035	C	6⑦	6⑦	B	800⑤	800N	⑤	⑤	34–47⑥
5.7L/V8-350(8)	.035	C	—	6⑦	D	—	800N⑤	—	⑤	34–47⑥
1993–95										
3.4L/V6-207(S)	.045	⑨	④	④	⑩	⑤	⑤	⑤	⑤	41–47⑪
5.7L/V8-350(P)	.050	F	④	④	⑩	⑤	⑤	⑤	⑤	41–47⑥

BTDC: Before Top Dead Center.
①—The eighth digit of Vehicle Identification Number (VIN) denotes engine code.
②—D: Drive. N: Neutral. When adjusting idle speed, set parking brake & block drive wheels.
③—Before disconnecting wires from distributor cap, determine location of No. 1 wire in cap, as distributor position may have been altered from that shown at the end of this chart.
④—Computer controlled, no adjustment.
⑤—Idle speed is controlled by an Idle Speed Control (ISC) motor, Idle Air Control (IAC) valve or Idle Load Compensator (ILC).
⑥—With shop towel wrapped around fuel pressure valve to prevent fuel spillage, connect a suitable fuel pressure gauge to fuel pressure valve. Check fuel pressure with ignition switch On, engine not running.
⑦—Disconnect set timing bypass connector (tan/black wire) near the brake booster when adjusting ignition timing. After completing adjustment, reconnect set timing connector. With engine off, clear trouble code from Electronic Control Module memory (ECM) by removing battery voltage to ECM for 30 seconds.
⑧—Wrap shop towel around fuel hose to steel line connection in engine compartment to prevent fuel spillage. Disconnect hose from steel line & install a suitable fuel pressure gauge between hose & line. Ensure gauge connections are tight, then start engine & check fuel pressure readings.
⑨—Cylinder numbering front to rear, left bank 2, 4, 6: right bank, 1, 3, 5. Firing order 1-2-3-4-5-6.. Refer to Fig. E for spark plug wire connections at coil unit.
⑩—Equipped w/crankshaft sensor.
⑪—With ignition switch in the off position, disconnect battery ground cable. Loosen fuel tank filler cap. Disconnect fuel line quick connect

Continued

TUNE UP SPECIFICATIONS—Continued

fittings, then install a suitable fuel pressure test gauge. Tighten fuel tank filler cap & connect battery ground cable. Place ignition switch in On position & check for leaks at gauge connections. With ignition switch in On position note fuel pressure reading.

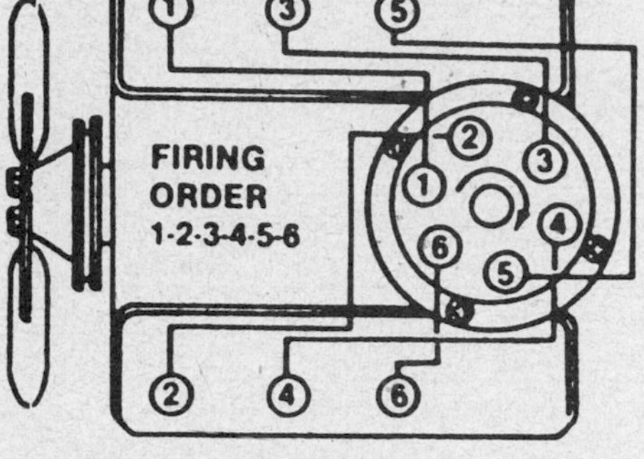
1
3
5
FIRING ORDER 1-2-3-4-5-6
2
4
6

GC1139100111000X

Fig. A

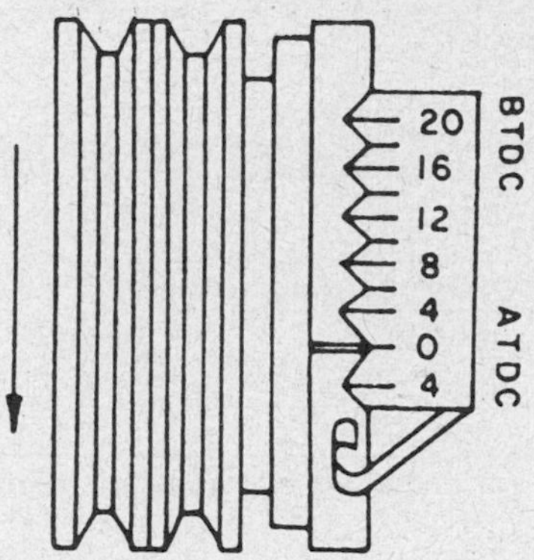
20
16
12
8
4
0
4
BTDC
ATDC

GC1139100112000X

Fig. B

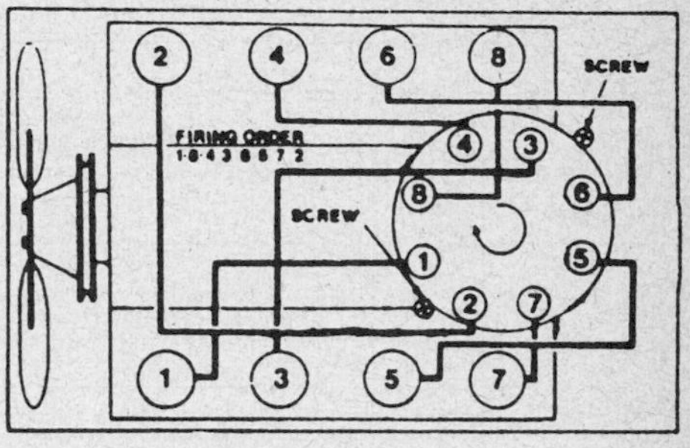
2
4
6
8
SCREW
FIRING ORDER
SCREW
1
3
5
7

GC1139100113000X

Fig. C

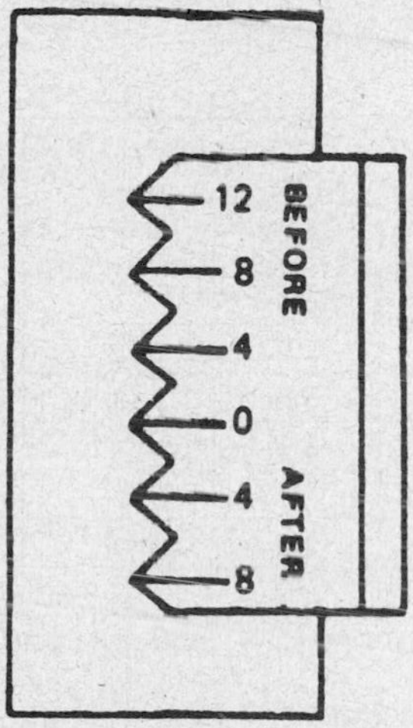
12
8
4
0
4
8
BEFORE
AFTER

GC1139100114000X

Fig. D

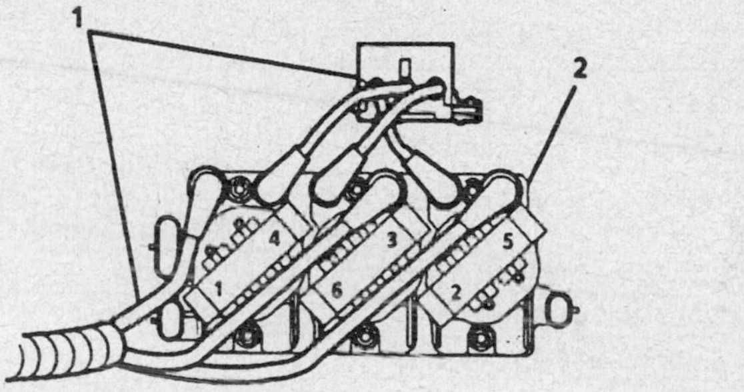
1
2

1 SPARK PLUG WIRE HARNESS ASSEMBLY

2 IGNITION COIL ASSEMBLY

GC1139100115000X

Fig. E

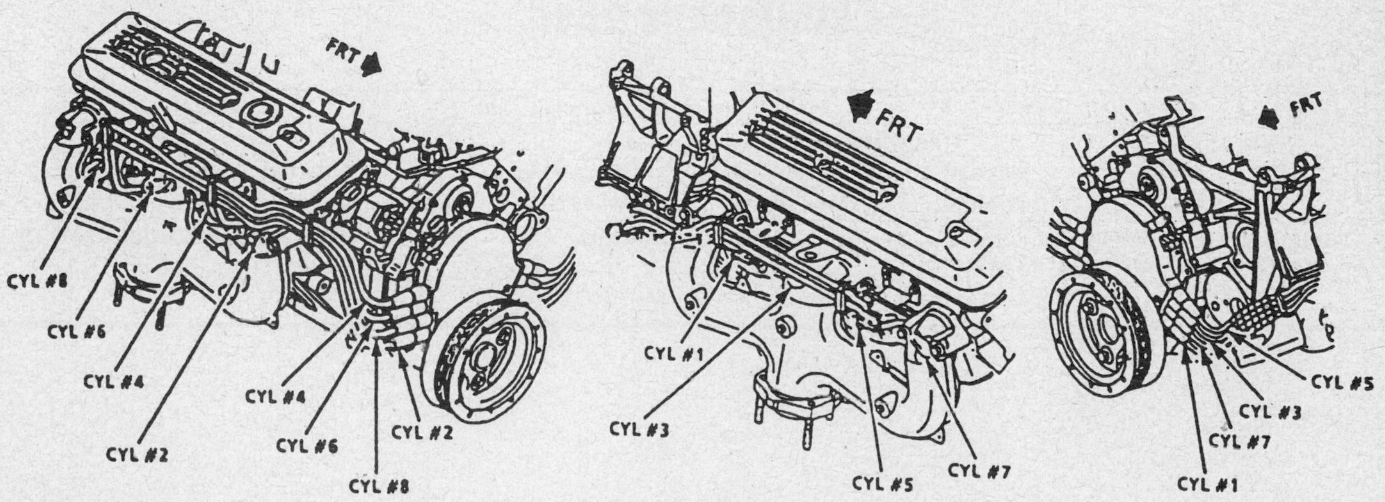
FRT
CYL #8
CYL #6
CYL #4
CYL #2
CYL #4
CYL #6
CYL #2
CYL #8
FRT
CYL #1
CYL #3
CYL #5
CYL #7
FRT
CYL #5
CYL #3
CYL #7
CYL #1

GC1139100116000X

Fig. F

FRONT WHEEL ALIGNMENT SPECIFICATIONS

Year	Model	Caster Angle, Degrees		Camber Angle, Degrees		Toe, Degrees
		Limits	Desired	Limits	Desired	
1992	All	+4.3 to +5.3	+4.8	-.2 to +.8	+.3	0
1993–95	All	+3.9 to +4.9	+4.4	-.1 to +.9	+.4	0

REAR WHEEL ALIGNMENT SPECIFICATIONS

Year	Model	Camber Angle, Degrees①		Total Toe, Degrees①	
		Limits	Desired	Limits	Desired
1992	All	-.5 to +.5	0	-.3 to +.3	0
1993–95	All	-.6 to +.6	0	-.3 to +.3	0

①—Not adjustable. If out of specification, check for worn, bent or damaged axle housing, frame or suspension components.

COOLING SYSTEM & CAPACITY DATA

Year	Engine Liter/CID (VIN)①	Coolant Capacity, Qts.		Radiator Cap Relief Pressure, psi	Thermo. Opening Temp.°F	Fuel Tank, Gals.	Engine Oil Refill Qts.	Transmission Oil		Rear Axle, Pts.
		Less A/C	With A/C					Man Trans., Pts.	Auto. Trans., Qts. ②	
1992	3.1L/V6-191(T)	14.7	14.8	15	195	15.5	4③	5.9	④	3.6
	5.0L/V8-305(E)	17.4	18	15	195	15.5	4⑤	5.9	⑥	3.6
	5.0L/V8-305(F)	17.9	18	15	195	15.5	4⑤	5.9	⑥	3.6
	5.7L/V8-350(8)	16.6	16.7	15	195	15.5	4⑤	—	⑥	3.6
1993–95	3.4L/V6-207(S)	12.5	12.5	15	195	15.5	4③	5.9	④	2.9
	5.7L/V8-350(P)	15.3	15.3	15	180	15.5	4⑤	8.2	⑥	2.9

①—The eighth digit of Vehicle Identification Number (VIN) denotes engine code.
②—Approximate. Make final check with dipstick.
③—Additional oil may be required to bring oil level to full mark when changing filter.
④—Total capacity, 8.35 qts.; pan only, 5 qts.
⑤—Add 1 qt. with filter change.
⑥—Total capacity, 11.2 qts.; pan only, 5 qts.

LUBRICANT DATA

Year	Model	Lubricant Type				
		Transmission		Rear Axle	Power Steering System	Brake System
		Manual	Automatic			
1992-95	All	Dexron IIE	Dexron IIE	80W–90 GL-5①	Power Steering Fluid②	DOT 3

①—Limited slip differentials also require 4 oz. of lubricant additive (GM part No. 1052358 or equivalent).
②—Meeting GM specification 9985010.

Electrical

NOTE: On Air Bag Equipped Models, Refer To "Air Bag System Precautions" Located In The Front Of This Manual For System Disarming & Arming Procedures.

INDEX

PRECAUTIONS

AIR BAG SYSTEMS

Refer to "Air Bag System Precautions" in the front of this manual for system disarming and arming procedures.

FUSE PANEL & FLASHER LOCATION

1992

The fuse panel is located behind the left hand side of the instrument panel. The hazard warning flasher is located behind the instrument panel to the right of the steering column, in the convenience center. The turn signal flasher is located behind the left hand side of the instrument panel, clipped to the fuse block bracket.

1993–95

The instrument panel fuse block is located on the lefthand side of the instrument panel carrier, on the side. The underhood electrical center is located on the lefthand side of the engine compartment, forward of the wheelhouse. The convenience center is located on the lefthand side of the steering column, mounted to the bottom of the instrument panel carrier. The hazard warning flasher is located in the convenience center. The turn signal flasher is mounted to a bracket on the righthand side of the steering column, above the data link.

RELAY CENTER LOCATION

The relay center is located on the front LH side kick panel, mounted on foot rest bracket, under the carpet.

STARTER

REPLACE

1992

If shims are used between starter and engine block, they should be placed in their original location during installation. If starter is noisy during cranking, remove one .015 inch double shim or add one .015 single shim to the outer bolt. If starter makes a high pitched whine after firing, add .015 inch double shims until noise ceases.

1. Disconnect battery ground cable.
2. Raise and support vehicle.
3. Remove starter to engine brace and starter heat shields, if equipped.
4. Remove flywheel housing cover.
5. Remove starter mounting bolts and lower starter. Note position of shims, if used, **Fig. 1.**
6. Disconnect solenoid wires and the battery cable.
7. Remove starter from vehicle.
8. Reverse procedure to install.

1993–95

This vehicle was designed for starter mounting without shims. If single or double shims have been added to correct a noise or engagement problem, they should be reinstalled in their original positions to ensure proper pinion to flywheel assembly engagement.

Removal

1. Disconnect battery ground cable, then raise and support vehicle.
2. Disconnect exhaust crossover pipe at manifolds, then remove starter motor mounting bolts and lower starter motor assembly, **Fig. 2.**
3. Disconnect electrical connectors from starter motor assembly, then remove starter motor assembly.

Installation

Before connecting electrical connectors, tighten inner nuts on the solenoid terminals. If the nuts are not tight, the solenoid cap may be damaged during installation of connectors. Torque inner nut of BAT terminal to 80 inch lbs.

1. Connect electrical connectors to starter motor assembly, then **torque** BAT terminal nut to 80 inch lbs. and S terminal nut to 22 inch lbs.
2. Install starter motor assembly and **torque** mounting bolts to 35 ft. lbs.
3. Measure pinion to flywheel clearance, **Fig. 3**, adding shims if necessary.
4. Connect exhaust crossover pipe to manifolds, then lower vehicle and connect battery ground cable.

ALTERNATOR

REPLACE

Disconnect battery ground cable. Refer to **Figs. 4 through 7** for alternator replacement.

DISTRIBUTOR

REPLACE

1992

Removal

1. Disconnect battery ground cable.

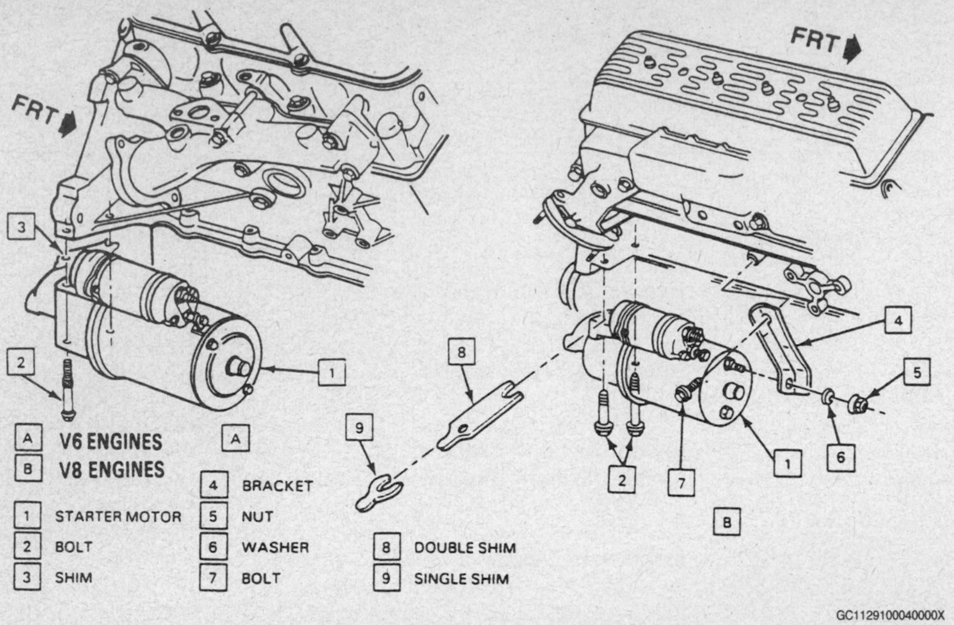
FRT
FRT
A V6 ENGINES
B V8 ENGINES
1 STARTER MOTOR
2 BOLT
3 SHIM
4 BRACKET
5 NUT
6 WASHER
7 BOLT
8 DOUBLE SHIM
9 SINGLE SHIM
GC1129100040000X

Fig. 1 Starter motor replacement. 1992

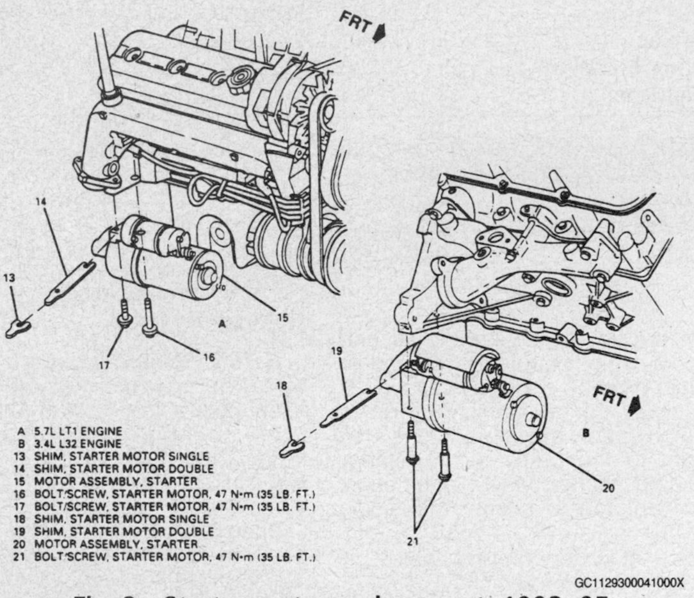
FRT
FRT
A 5.7L LT1 ENGINE
B 3.4L L32 ENGINE
13 SHIM, STARTER MOTOR SINGLE
14 SHIM, STARTER MOTOR DOUBLE
15 MOTOR ASSEMBLY, STARTER
16 BOLT/SCREW, STARTER MOTOR, 47 N•m (35 LB. FT.)
17 BOLT/SCREW, STARTER MOTOR, 47 N•m (35 LB. FT.)
18 SHIM, STARTER MOTOR SINGLE
19 SHIM, STARTER MOTOR DOUBLE
20 MOTOR ASSEMBLY, STARTER
21 BOLT/SCREW, STARTER MOTOR, 47 N•m (35 LB. FT.)
GC1129300041000X

Fig. 2 Starter motor replacement. 1993–95

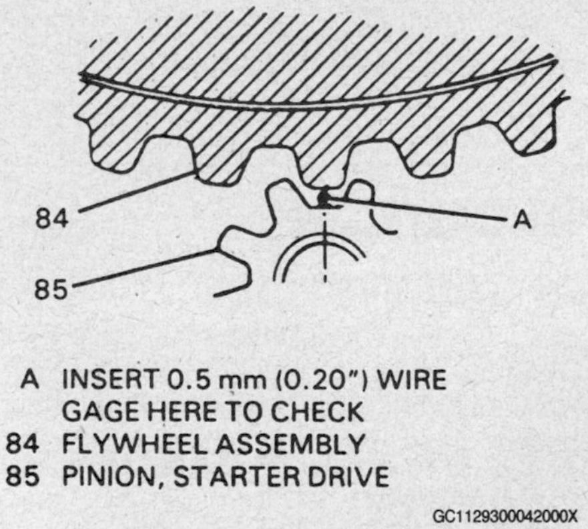
84
85
A
A INSERT 0.5 mm (0.20") WIRE GAGE HERE TO CHECK
84 FLYWHEEL ASSEMBLY
85 PINION, STARTER DRIVE
GC1129300042000X

Fig. 3 Flywheel assembly to pinion clearance check. 1993–95

2. Disconnect ignition switch feed and tachometer leads from distributor cap. Screwdriver or other tools should not be used to release lead connector locking tab.
3. Remove distributor cap attaching screws, then position cap out of way.
4. Disconnect four terminal ECM electrical connector from distributor electrical connector.
5. Remove distributor hold-down clamp and bolt. Mark position of distributor rotor to distributor housing and position of distributor housing to engine for use during installation.
6. Lift distributor upward until rotor stops rotating and mark position of rotor to distributor housing for use during installation.
7. Remove distributor from engine.

Installation

1. Position rotor to mark on distributor housing, then insert distributor into engine aligning rotor to housing and housing to engine marks made during removal.
2. If engine was disturbed while distributor was removed, proceed as follows:
   a. Remove spark plug from No. 1 cylinder.
   b. With transmission in Neutral or Park and parking brake applied, position finger over spark plug opening in cylinder head, then slowly crank engine until compression is felt.
   c. Align crankshaft pulley with TDC (0) mark on timing indicator.
   d. Locate distributor rotor contact between spark plug firing positions No. 1 and 6 on V6 engines, No. 1 and 8 on V8 engines, on distributor.
   e. Insert distributor into engine.
3. Install distributor hold clamp and bolt. Hand tighten bolt.
4. Connect ECM four terminal electrical connector to distributor.
5. Install distributor cap, then connect ignition switch and tachometer lead connector to cap.
6. Connect battery ground cable, then check and adjust ignition timing as necessary. **Torque** distributor hold-down bolt to 27 ft. lbs.

1993–95

Removal

1. Ensure ignition switch is in Off or Lock position, then remove water pump assembly as described under "Water Pump, Replace" in the "5.0L/V8-305 & 5.7L/V8-350 Engines" section.
2. Remove crankshaft balancer assembly as described under "Crankshaft Balancer Assembly & Hub, Replace"

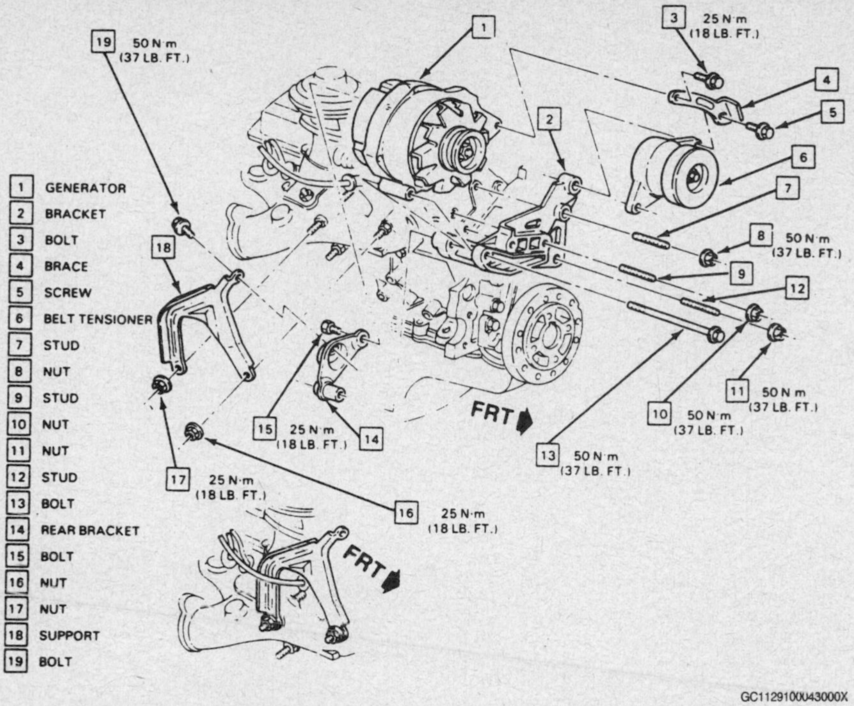
1 GENERATOR
2 BRACKET
3 BOLT
4 BRACE
5 SCREW
6 BELT TENSIONER
7 STUD
8 NUT
9 STUD
10 NUT
11 NUT
12 STUD
13 BOLT
14 REAR BRACKET
15 BOLT
16 NUT
17 NUT
18 SUPPORT
19 BOLT
GC1129100043000X

Fig. 4 Alternator replacement. 3.1L/V6-191 engines

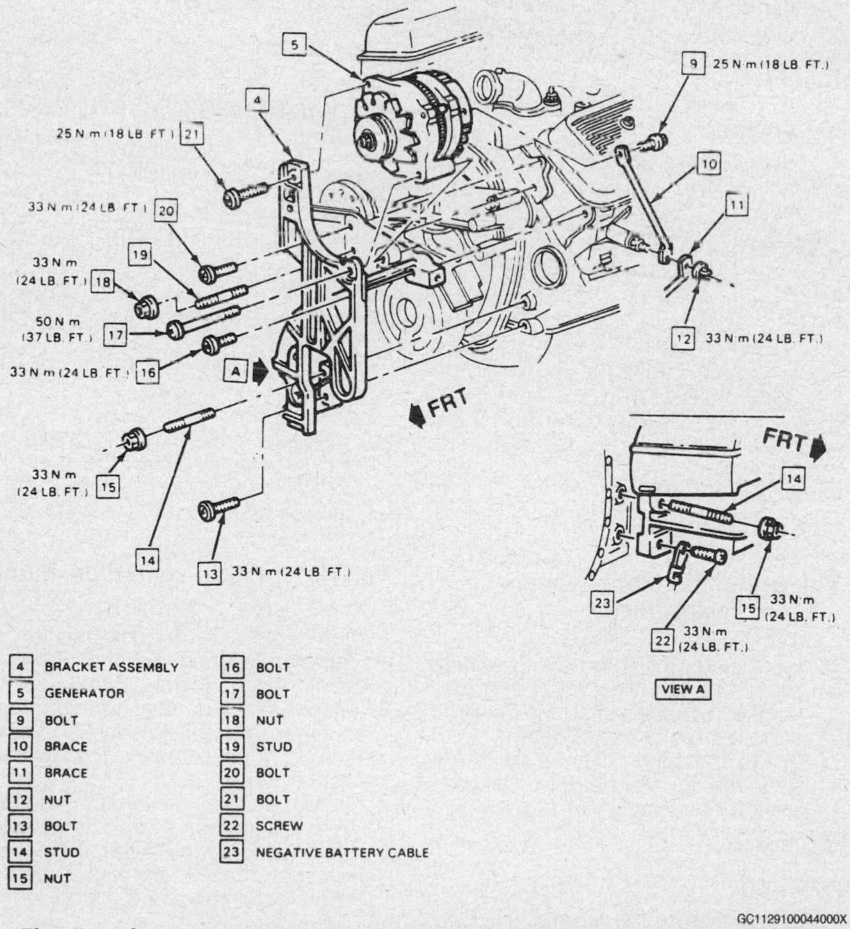
4 BRACKET ASSEMBLY
5 GENERATOR
9 BOLT
10 BRACE
11 BRACE
12 NUT
13 BOLT
14 STUD
15 NUT
16 BOLT
17 BOLT
18 NUT
19 STUD
20 BOLT
21 BOLT
22 SCREW
23 NEGATIVE BATTERY CABLE
VIEW A
GC1129100044000X

Fig. 5 Alternator replacement. 1992 5.0L/V8-305 & 5.7L/V8-350 engines

in the "5.0L/V8-305 & 5.7L/V8-350 Engines" section.

3. Disconnect spark plug wire assemblies and the four-terminal ECM connector from distributor assembly.
4. Remove distributor assembly bolts, then pull distributor assembly forward until driveshaft disengages from end of camshaft assembly, **Fig. 8.**
5. Mark top surface of driveshaft for alignment during installation.

Installation

1. Turn driveshaft until alignment mark made during removal is on top, then install distributor assembly.
2. Install and **torque** distributor bolts to 97 inch lbs.
3. Connect four-terminal ECM connector and spark plug wire assemblies to distributor assembly.
4. Install crankshaft balancer assembly as described under "Crankshaft Balancer Assembly & Hub, Replace" in the "5.0L/V8-305 & 5.7L/V8-350 Engines" section.
5. Install water pump assembly as described under "Water Pump, Replace" in the "5.0L/V8-305 & 5.7L/V8-350 Engines" section.

IGNITION LOCK

REPLACE

1. Remove steering wheel as described under "Steering Wheel, Replace."
2. Remove turn signal switch as described under "Turn Signal Switch, Replace."
3. Remove buzzer switch retaining clip, then the buzzer switch.
4. Place ignition switch in Lock position.
5. Remove lock cylinder retaining screw, **Fig. 9.**
6. Disconnect terminal electrical connector at bulkhead connection to provide slack.
7. Remove wiring connector from steering column.
8. Attach a suitable length of mechanic wire to ignition lock electrical connector for use during installation. Detach wire retaining clip, then carefully pull ignition lock wiring through housing shroud, steering column and lock housing cover.
9. Remove lock cylinder.
10. Reverse procedure to install. Ensure lock cylinder wiring is properly routed through steering column. **Torque** lock cylinder retaining screw to 22 inch lbs.

IGNITION SWITCH

REPLACE

1992

The ignition switch is mounted on top of the mast jacket inside the brake pedal support and is actuated by a rod and rack assembly.

1. Disconnect battery cable.
2. Remove steering column as described in "Steering Columns" section.
3. Rotate ignition lock to Off unlocked position.

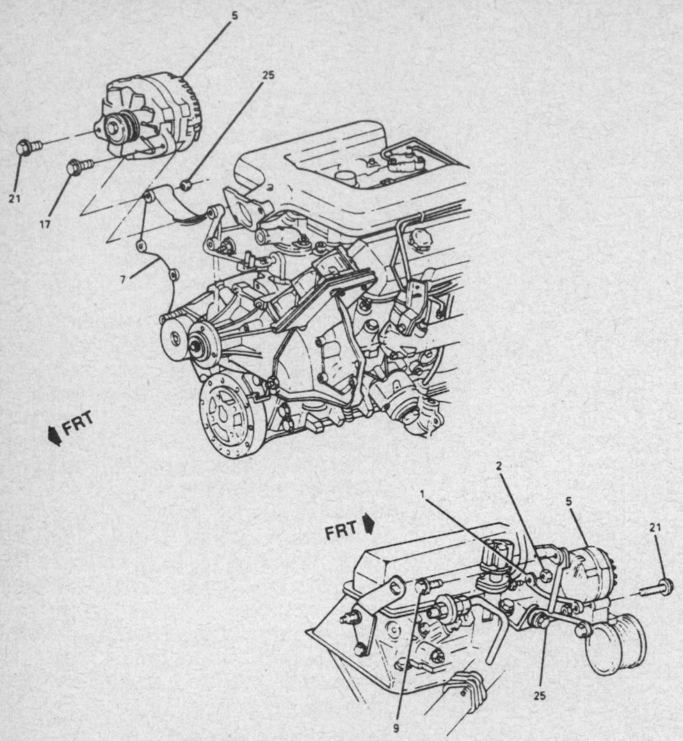
FRT
FRT

1 BRACE, GENERATOR REAR INNER
2 NUT, GENERATOR BRACE, 25 N•m (18 LB. FT.)
5 GENERATOR ASSEMBLY
7 BRACKET, ACCESSORY MOUNTING
9 BOLT/SCREW, GENERATOR REAR BRACE, 25 N•m (18 LB. FT.)
17 BOLT/SCREW, GENERATOR, 50 N•m (37 LB. FT.)
21 BOLT/SCREW, GENERATOR, 50 N•m (37 LB. FT.)
25 NUT, GENERATOR, 50 N•m (37 LB. FT.)

GC1129100045000X

Fig. 6 Alternator replacement. 3.4L/V6-207 engines

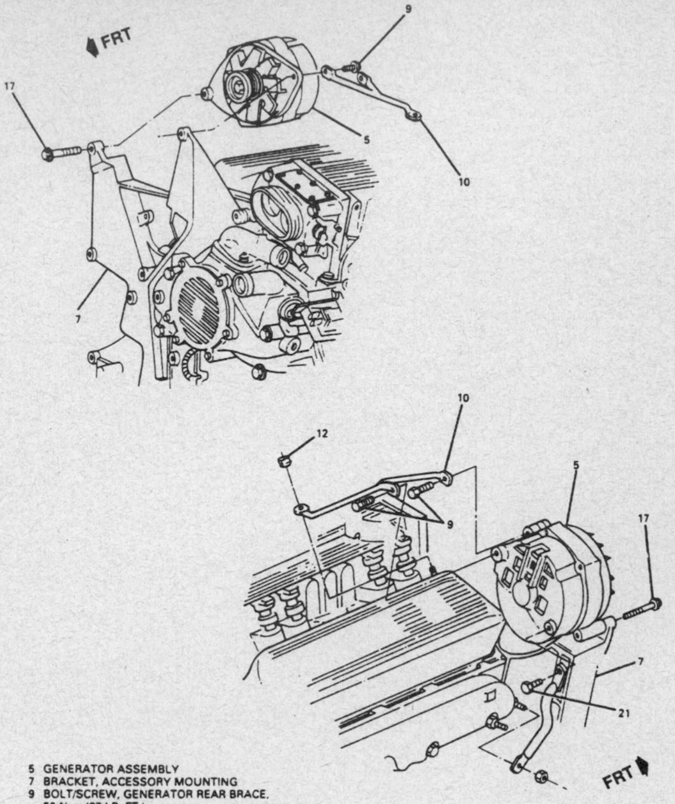
FRT
FRT

5 GENERATOR ASSEMBLY
7 BRACKET, ACCESSORY MOUNTING
9 BOLT/SCREW, GENERATOR REAR BRACE, 50 N•m (37 LB. FT.)
10 BRACE ASSEMBLY, GENERATOR REAR OUTER
12 NUT, GENERATOR REAR BRACE, 33 N•m (24 LB. FT.)
17 BOLT/SCREW, GENERATOR, 50 N•m (37 LB. FT.)
21 BOLT/SCREW, GENERATOR, 25 N•m (18 LB. FT.)

GC1129300046000X

Fig. 7 Alternator replacement. 1993–95 5.7L/V8-350 engines

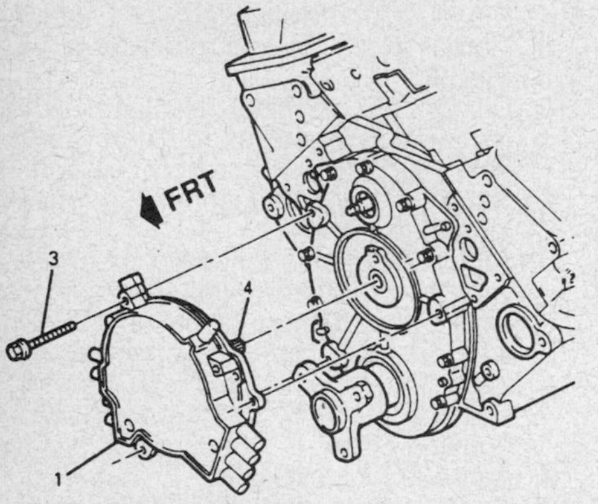
FRT

1 DISTRIBUTOR ASSEMBLY
3 BOLT/SCREW, DISTRIBUTOR
4 DRIVESHAFT, DISTRIBUTOR

GC1119300112000X

Fig. 8 Distributor replacement. 1993–95 5.7L/V8-350 engines

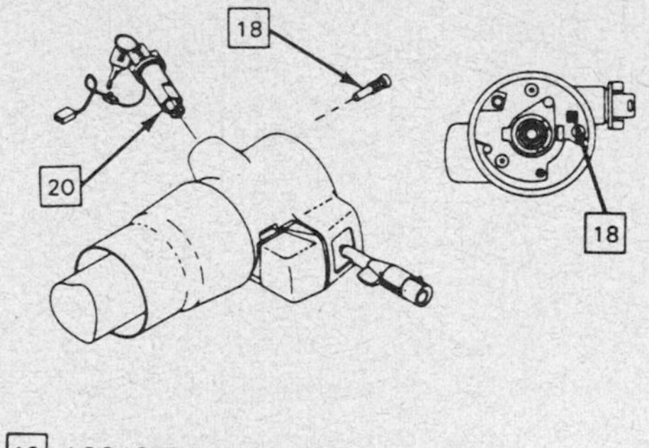

18 LOCK RETAINING SCREW
20 VATS LOCK CYLINDER SET

GC9129100016000X

Fig. 9 Ignition lock cylinder replacement

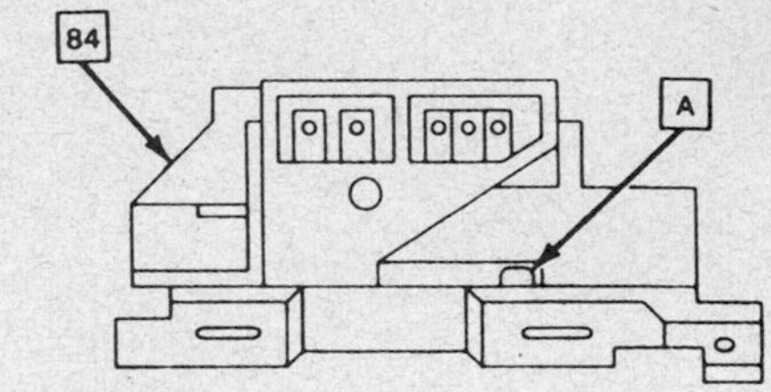

A MOVE SWITCH SLIDER TO EXTREME RIGHT POSITION AND THEN MOVE SLIDER ONE DETENT TO THE LEFT (OFF LOCK)
84 IGNITION SWITCH

GC9049100054000X

Fig. 10 Ignition switch positioning

4. If lock cylinder has been removed, pull switch actuator rod up to stop, then push rod down to second detent to place switch in Off unlocked position, **Fig. 10.**
5. Remove column mounted dimmer switch, if equipped, then remove switch retaining screws and switch.
6. Reverse procedure to install, noting the following:
   a. Place gear shift lever in neutral.
   b. Place lock cylinder and switch in Off unlocked position.
   c. Fit actuator rod into hole in switch slider and secure switch with retaining screws, ensuring switch does not move out of detent.
   d. Install and adjust dimmer switch, if removed, as described in "Dimmer Switch, Replace."

1993–95

Removal

1. Remove lefthand instrument panel sound insulator assembly, then the instrument panel driver knee bolster assembly and deflector.
2. Ensure steering column lock and ignition switch are in Lock position, then remove steering column upper support nuts and lower column assembly.
3. Disconnect electrical connectors from dimmer switch assembly and ignition switch, then remove dimmer switch actuator rod.
4. Remove dimmer switch assembly, then the ignition switch actuator rod.
5. Remove ignition switch, then disconnect automatic transmission park lock cable assembly, if equipped.

Installation

1. Connect automatic transmission park lock cable assembly, if equipped, then ensure ignition switch, steering col-

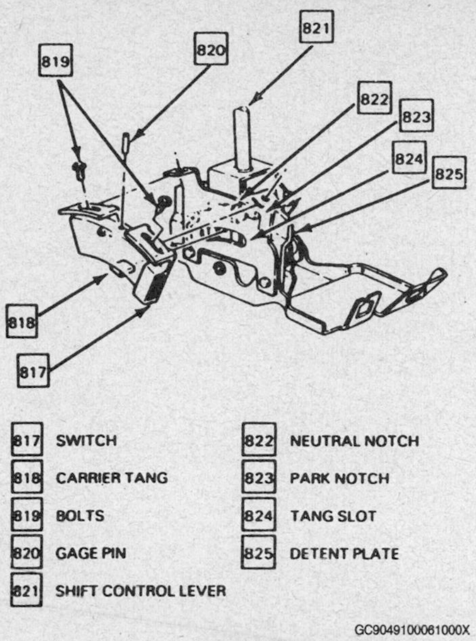
817 SWITCH
818 CARRIER TANG
819 BOLTS
820 GAGE PIN
821 SHIFT CONTROL LEVER
822 NEUTRAL NOTCH
823 PARK NOTCH
824 TANG SLOT
825 DETENT PLATE
GC9049100061000X

Fig. 11 Neutral safety switch replacement

umn lock and ignition cylinder assembly are in LOCK position.

2. Install ignition switch to jacket, then connect ignition switch actuator rod to ignition switch.
3. **Torque** ignition switch mounting screws to 22 inch lbs.
4. Install dimmer switch assembly, then adjust by pressing switch mechanism slightly to insert a 3/32 inch drill bit and moving dimmer switch assembly to remove tool.
5. **Torque** dimmer switch mounting screws to 35 inch lbs.
6. Install dimmer switch actuator rod, then connect electrical connectors to dimmer switch assembly and ignition switch.
7. Raise column assembly and install upper support nuts.
8. Install instrument panel driver knee bolster assembly and deflector, then the lefthand instrument panel sound insulator assembly.

CLUTCH START SWITCH

REPLACE

1992

1. Disconnect battery ground cable.
2. Disconnect wire connector at switch.
3. Remove retaining nut, if so equipped and unscrew switch from bracket.
4. To install, depress clutch pedal, then insert and push switch into clip until shoulder bottoms out.
5. Plug connector on switch and check for proper operation.

1993–95

Refer to "Stop Light Switch, Replace.

NEUTRAL SAFETY SWITCH

REPLACE

1. Disconnect batter ground cable.
2. Remove floor console, then disconnect electrical connectors from switch.
3. Place shift lever in Neutral position of detent plate, then remove switch attaching screws and switch, **Fig. 11.**
4. To install, ensure the shift lever is in Neutral, then position switch on shift lever making sure pin on shaft is in slot of switch.
5. If reinstalling existing switch, rotate switch to align service adjustment hole with carrier tang hole. Insert a 3/32 inch gauge pin and rotate switch until pin drops in to a depth of 19/32 inch. **Torque** switch attaching nut to 18 inch lbs., then remove gauge pin.
6. If installing a new switch, **torque** attaching nuts to 18 inch lbs., then move shift lever out of Neutral to shear pin which is part of new switch.
7. Reconnect electrical connectors to switch, then apply parking brake and start engine. Check back-up lights and seat belt warning system for proper operation and ensure engine will start only in Park or Neutral.
8. Turn ignition off and install floor console.

HEADLAMP SWITCH

REPLACE

CAMARO

1992

1. Disconnect battery ground cable.
2. Open screw covers, then remove knee bolster attaching screws and knee bolster.
3. From under instrument panel, depress release button on light switch, then remove switch knob and shaft assembly from switch, **Fig. 12.**
4. Remove instrument cluster trim plate, then remove switch retaining nut.
5. Lower switch and disconnect electrical connector, then remove switch.
6. Reverse procedure to install.

1993–95

1. Remove switch assembly from bezel assembly, **Fig. 13.**
2. Disconnect electrical connector from switch assembly.
3. Reverse procedure to install.

FIREBIRD

1992

1. Disconnect battery ground cable.
2. Remove left and right hand lower instrument panel trim covers.
3. Remove instrument cluster trim plate.
4. Remove switch attaching screws, then depress switch side tangs and pull switch from instrument panel, **Fig. 14.**
5. Disconnect electrical connector and remove switch.
6. Reverse procedure to install.

1993–95

1. Remove switch assembly from carrier, **Fig. 15.**
2. Disconnect electrical connector from switch assembly.
3. Reverse procedure to install.

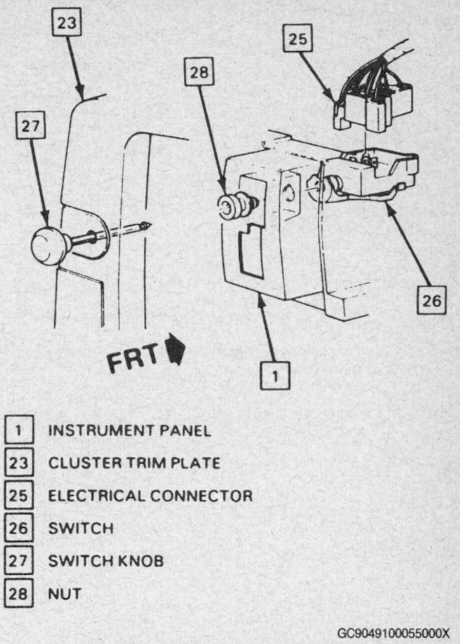
23
25
28
27
26
FRT
1
1 INSTRUMENT PANEL
23 CLUSTER TRIM PLATE
25 ELECTRICAL CONNECTOR
26 SWITCH
27 SWITCH KNOB
28 NUT
GC9049100055000X

Fig. 12 Headlamp switch replacement. 1992 Camaro

STOP LIGHT SWITCH

REPLACE

1992

1. Remove left hand side hush panel.
2. Working from underneath instrument panel, disconnect wire connector from switch at brake pedal support.
3. Remove switch from mounting bracket, **Fig. 16.**
4. Depress brake pedal and install new switch into clip, until switch body bottoms out against clip.
5. Release brake pedal, then pull pedal rearward against internal stop. The switch is properly positioned when no clicks are noticed when brake pedal is against internal stop. Ensure brake lamps remain Off when brake pedal is in the released position, if readjust switch.

1993–95

1. Remove lefthand instrument panel sound insulator assembly, then disconnect electrical connectors, **Fig. 17.**
2. Remove release switch assembly, stoplamp and TCC switch assembly and clutch switch assembly, or clutch anticipate switch assembly, if equipped, from pedal assembly with bracket.
3. Install release switch assembly, stoplamp and TCC switch assembly and clutch switch assembly, or clutch anticipate switch assembly, if equipped, to pedal assembly with bracket.
4. Connect electrical connectors, then adjust switches as follows:
   a. Depress brake pedal assembly or clutch pedal assembly and insert release switch assembly, stoplamp

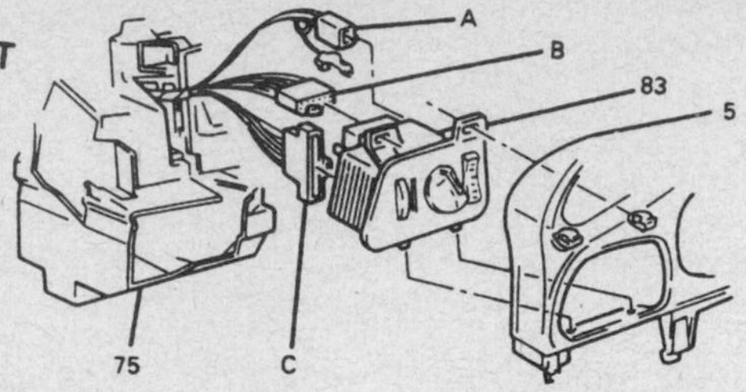
FRT
A
B
83
5
75
C

A CONNECTOR, INSTRUMENT PANEL WIRING HARNESS FOG LAMP ELECTRICAL
B CONNECTOR, INSTRUMENT PANEL WIRING HARNESS ELECTRICAL
C CONNECTOR, INSTRUMENT PANEL WIRING HARNESS DIMMER SWITCH ELECTRICAL
5 BEZEL ASSEMBLY, INSTRUMENT PANEL CLUSTER TRIM PLATE
75 CARRIER, INSTRUMENT PANEL
83 SWITCH ASSEMBLY, HEADLAMP AND INSTRUMENT PANEL LAMP DIMMER

GC9049300056000X

Fig. 13 Headlamp switch replacement. 1993–95 Camaro

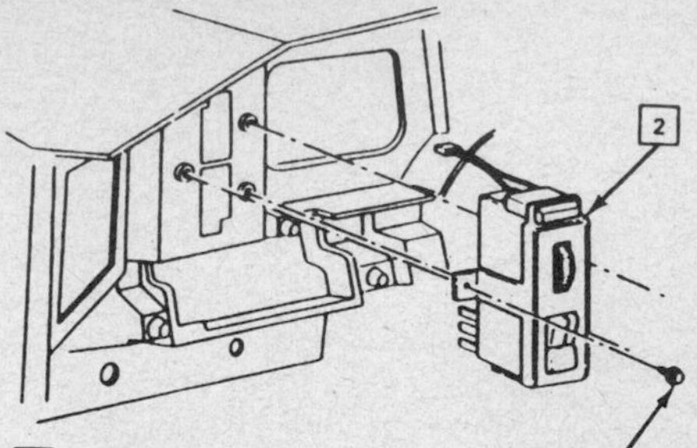
2
1

1 BOLT/SCREW
2 HEADLAMP/PARKING LAMP SWITCH

GC9049100057000X

Fig. 14 Headlamp switch replacement. 1992 Firebird

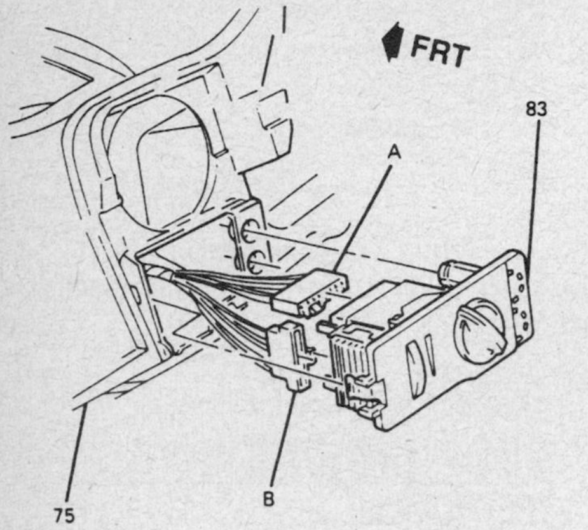
FRT
83
A
75
B

A CONNECTOR, INSTRUMENT PANEL WIRING HARNESS ELECTRICAL
B CONNECTOR, INSTRUMENT PANEL WIRING HARNESS ELECTRICAL
75 CARRIER, INSTRUMENT PANEL
83 SWITCH ASSEMBLY, HEADLAMP AND INSTRUMENT PANEL LAMP DIMMER

GC9049300058000X

Fig. 15 Headlamp switch replacement. 1993–95 Firebird

and TCC switch assembly and clutch switch assembly, or clutch anticipate switch assembly into pedal assembly with bracket until retainer is fully seated.
b. Slowly pull brake or clutch pedal assembly rearward with a force of 50 lbs. until click sounds can no longer be heard.
c. Measure release switch assembly and stoplamp and TCC switch assembly contacts, should be open 1 inch or less of pedal assembly travel, and should occur at the same time or before onset of braking.

5. Install lefthand instrument panel sound insulator assembly.

TURN SIGNAL SWITCH
REPLACE

1. Remove steering wheel as described under "Steering Wheel, Replace."
2. Place ignition switch in Lock position to retain coil assembly in the centered position.
3. Disconnect battery ground cable.
4. Remove coil assembly retaining ring, **Fig. 18.**
5. Lift coil assembly from steering shaft and allow to hang from wire, then remove wave washer.
6. Using a suitable tool, compress lock plate and remove snap ring (C-ring on tilt models), **Fig. 19.**
7. Remove lock plate, turn signal canceling cam and upper bearing spring, inner race seat and inner race.
8. Place turn signal lever in right hand turn position, then remove multifunction lever and hazard warning flasher knob.
9. Remove turn signal switch lever attaching screw, then remove lever.
10. Remove turn signal switch attaching screws.
11. Disconnect turn signal switch electrical connector at lower portion of steering column.
12. Remove turn signal switch wiring protector cover from steering column, **Fig. 20.**
13. Carefully pull turn signal switch wiring up and out of steering column.
14. Reverse procedure to install. If coil assembly has become uncentered, refer to **Fig. 21** for centering procedure.

DIMMER SWITCH
REPLACE

1992

1. Disconnect battery ground cable.
2. Remove instrument panel lower trim.
3. **On models with A/C,** remove A/C duct extension at column.
4. **On all models,** remove steering column as described in "Steering Columns" section.
5. Remove dimmer switch retaining screw(s) and the switch. Tape actuator rod to column and separate switch from rod.
6. Reverse procedure to install. To adjust switch, depress dimmer switch slightly and install a 3/32 inch twist drill to lock the switch to the body, **Fig. 22.** Force switch upward to remove lash. **Torque** retaining screws to 35 inch lbs. and remove tape from actuator rod. Remove twist drill and check for proper operation.

1993–95

Refer to "Ignition Switch, Replace."

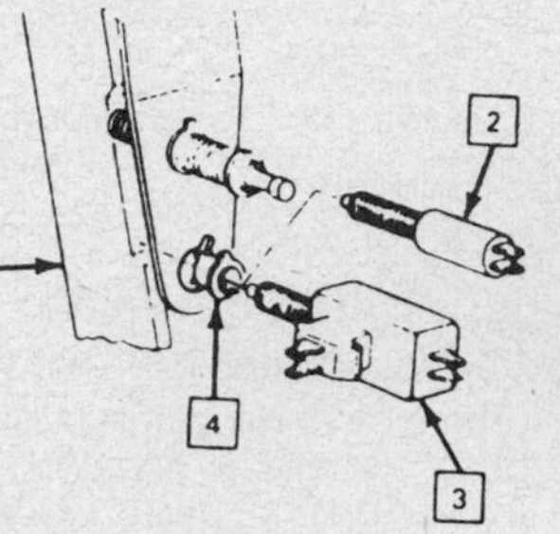
2
1
4
3

1 BRAKE PEDAL
2 SWITCH – WITHOUT CRUISE CONTROL
3 SWITCH – WITH CRUISE CONTROL
4 CLIP

GC9049100059000X

Fig. 16 Stop lamp switch replacement. 1992

STEERING WHEEL
REPLACE

1992

Removal

1. With steering wheel in straight ahead position, place ignition switch in Lock position.
2. Remove air bag (SIR) fuse from fuse panel.
3. Remove lower left hand trim panel, then remove connector position assurance and disconnect yellow two way Supplemental Inflatable Restraint connector at base of steering column.
4. Disconnect battery ground cable and tape cable end.
5. Remove inflator module attaching screws from rear of steering wheel.
6. Lift inflator module from steering wheel, then disconnect electrical connectors from inflator module.
7. Remove steering wheel retaining nut.
8. Using puller tool No. J-1859-03, or equivalent, pull steering wheel from steering shaft.
9. Disconnect horn electrical connect and remove steering wheel.

Installation

1. Connect horn electrical connector.

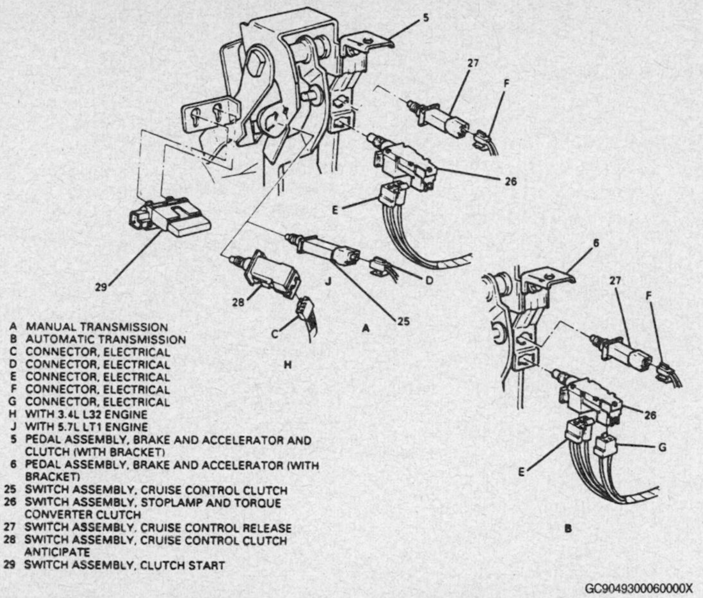
A MANUAL TRANSMISSION
B AUTOMATIC TRANSMISSION
C CONNECTOR, ELECTRICAL
D CONNECTOR, ELECTRICAL
E CONNECTOR, ELECTRICAL
F CONNECTOR, ELECTRICAL
G CONNECTOR, ELECTRICAL
H WITH 3.4L L32 ENGINE
J WITH 5.7L LT1 ENGINE
5 PEDAL ASSEMBLY, BRAKE AND ACCELERATOR AND CLUTCH (WITH BRACKET)
6 PEDAL ASSEMBLY, BRAKE AND ACCELERATOR (WITH BRACKET)
25 SWITCH ASSEMBLY, CRUISE CONTROL CLUTCH
26 SWITCH ASSEMBLY, STOPLAMP AND TORQUE CONVERTER CLUTCH
27 SWITCH ASSEMBLY, CRUISE CONTROL RELEASE
28 SWITCH ASSEMBLY, CRUISE CONTROL CLUTCH ANTICIPATE
29 SWITCH ASSEMBLY, CLUTCH START
GC9049300060000X

Fig. 17 Stop lamp switch replacement. 1993–95

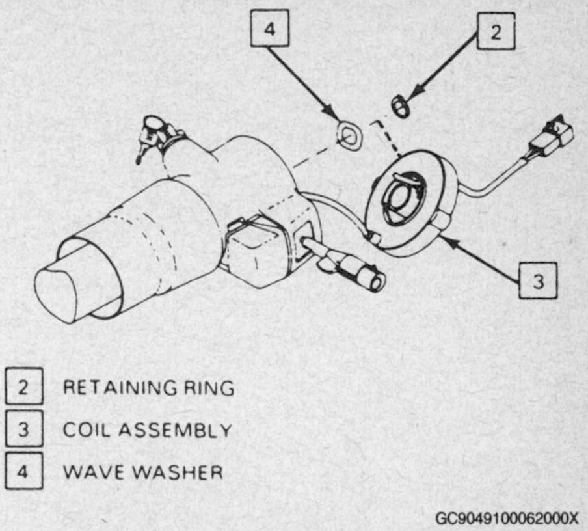
2 RETAINING RING
3 COIL ASSEMBLY
4 WAVE WASHER
GC9049100062000X

Fig. 18 Coil assembly removal

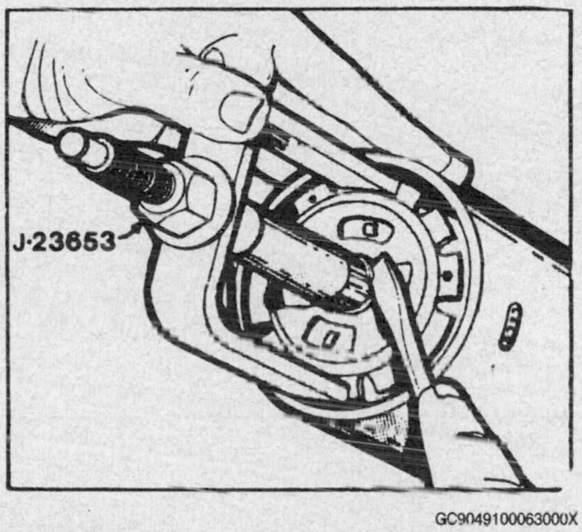
J-23653
GC9049100063000X

Fig. 19 Lock plate retaining ring removal

2. Align block tooth on steering wheel with block tooth on steering shaft, then install steering wheel.
3. Install steering wheel retaining nut and **torque** to 30 ft. lbs.
4. Connect SIR coil electrical connector to inflator module, then install connector position assurance.
5. Position inflator module to steering wheel, then install new mounting screws. **Torque** mounting screws to 25 inch lbs.
6. Ensure ignition switch is in Lock position.
7. Connect yellow SIR two way electrical connector and install connector position assurance at base of steering column.
8. Install lower left hand trim panel.
9. Install air bag (SIR) fuse into fuse panel.
10. Connect battery ground cable.
11. Place ignition switch in Run position and note operation of inflatable Restraint warning lamp. Warning lamp should flash 7 to 9 times and then turn off. If not, refer to "Passive Restraint" section for diagnostic system check.

1993–95

Removal

When removing steering wheel, use only specified puller. Do not hammer on end of steering column shaft. Hammering on shaft may damage plastic injections, affecting column assembly rigidity.

When attaching specified puller to steering wheel, use caution to prevent threading bolts through steering wheel hub into SIR coil assembly, damaging coil assembly.

1. Remove screws from back of steering wheel assembly using a No. 30 TORX driver, then the inflatable restraint steering wheel module assembly from steering wheel assembly.
2. Disconnect SIR coil assembly electrical connector and retainer from inflatable restraint steering wheel module assembly.
3. **On Firebird models,** disconnect radio control switch electrical connector from inflatable restraint steering wheel module assembly, if equipped.
4. **On all models,** disconnect horn lead from column assembly.
5. Remove steering wheel using steering wheel puller tool No. J-1859-A and steering wheel puller bolts tool No. J-38720, or equivalents.

Installation

1. Route SIR coil assembly electrical connector to steering wheel, then install steering wheel, aligning block tooth on steering wheel with block tooth on steering column shaft within one female serration.
2. Install nut and **torque** to 32 ft. lbs.
3. Connect horn lead to column assembly.
4. **On Firebird models,** connect radio control switch electrical connector from inflatable restraint steering wheel module assembly, if equipped.

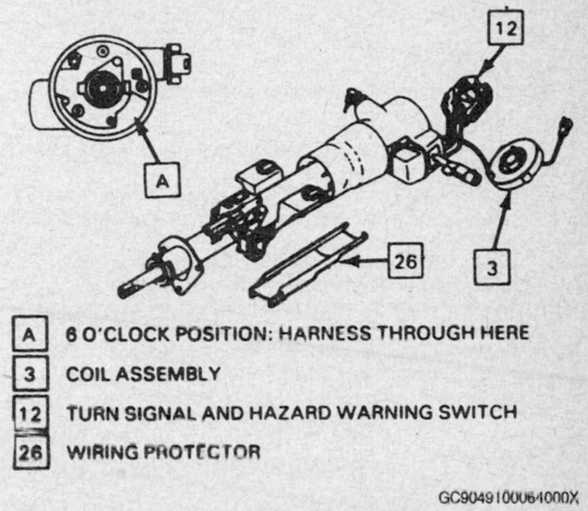
A 6 O'CLOCK POSITION: HARNESS THROUGH HERE
3 COIL ASSEMBLY
12 TURN SIGNAL AND HAZARD WARNING SWITCH
26 WIRING PROTECTOR
GC9049100064000X

Fig. 20 Turn signal switch removal

5. **On all models,** connect SIR coil assembly electrical connector and retainer to inflatable restraint steering wheel module assembly.
6. Secure SIR coil assembly electrical connector to steering wheel by inserting thick section of wire into existing retainers.
7. Position inflatable restraint steering wheel module assembly to steering wheel, ensuring wiring is not exposed or trapped between module assembly and steering wheel.
8. Install inflatable restraint steering wheel module assembly screws and **torque** to 25 inch lbs.

INSTRUMENT CLUSTER REPLACE

1992

Camaro

1. Disconnect battery ground cable.
2. Remove instrument cluster trim panel.
3. Remove cluster retaining screws, then pull cluster back and disconnect speedometer cable and electrical connectors, as equipped, **Fig. 23.**
4. Reverse procedure to install.

Firebird

1. Disconnect battery ground cable, then remove knee bolster.
2. Remove instrument cluster trim plate.
3. Remove cluster attachment screws, **Fig. 24,** pull cluster back and discon-

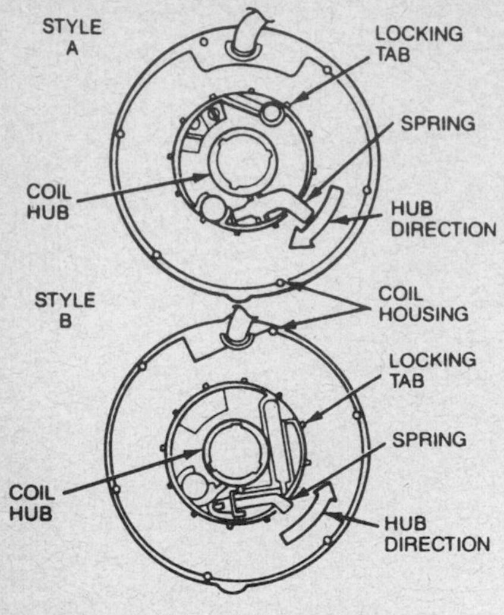
STYLE A
LOCKING TAB
SPRING
COIL HUB
HUB DIRECTION
STYLE B
COIL HOUSING
LOCKING TAB
SPRING
COIL HUB
HUB DIRECTION

Perform the following steps to center coil assembly:

A. Remove coil assembly.
B. Hold coil assembly with clear bottom up to see coil ribbon.
C. NOTE: There are two different styles of coils. One rotates clockwise and the other rotates counterclockwise.
D. While holding coil assembly, depress spring lock to rotate hub in direction of arrow until it stops.
E. The coil ribbon should be wound up snug against center hub.
F. Rotate coil hub in opposite direction approximately two and a half (2-1/2) turns. Release spring lock between locking tabs in front of arrow.

GC9049100065000X

Fig. 21 Centering coil assembly

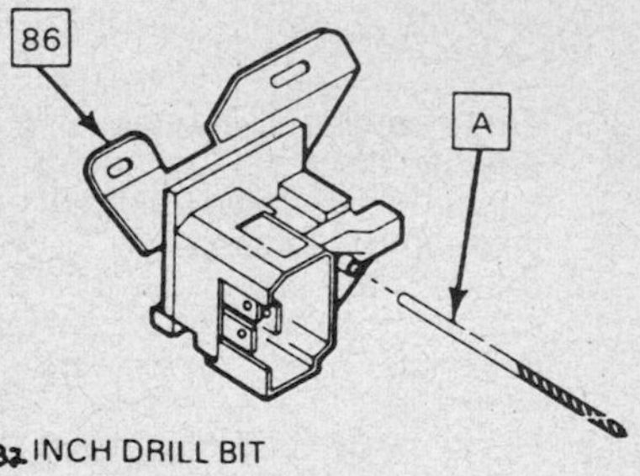
86
A
A 3/32 INCH DRILL BIT
86 DIMMER SWITCH

GC9049100066000X

Fig. 22 Column mounted dimmer switch installation

nect necessary electrical connections.

4. Remove trip odometer reset knob, if equipped, then cluster lens.
5. Reverse procedure to install.

1993–95

1. Disconnect instrument panel upper trim panel assembly from lower windshield support, then remove from carrier.
2. Remove instrument cluster assembly carrier, **Figs. 25 and 26,** then disconnect electrical connector from cluster assembly.
3. Reverse procedure to install.

RADIO

REPLACE

When installing radio, be sure to adjust antenna trimmer for peak reception. Also, be sure to connect speaker before applying power to radio.

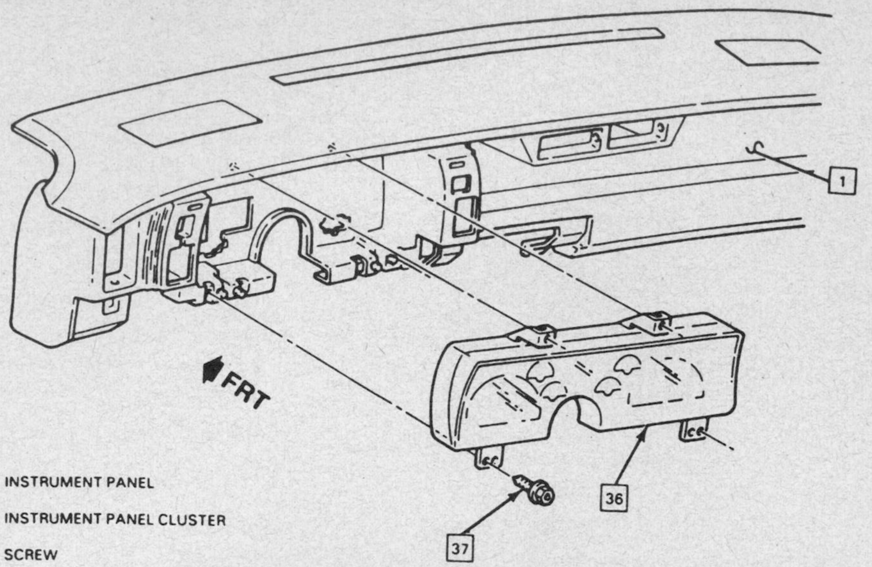
1
FRT
36
37
1 INSTRUMENT PANEL
36 INSTRUMENT PANEL CLUSTER
37 SCREW

GC9099100203000X

Fig. 23 Instrument cluster. 1992 Camaro

1. Disconnect battery ground cable.
2. Remove accessory trim plate, then radio to console attaching screws.
3. Pull radio outward and disconnect electrical connector, then remove radio.
4. Reverse procedure to install.

WIPER MOTOR

REPLACE

1992

1. Raise hood, then remove wiper arms and cowl cover.
2. Disconnect wiring and washer hoses.
3. Reaching through cowl opening, loosen transmission drive link attaching nuts to motor crankarm.
4. Disconnect drive link from motor crankarm.
5. Remove motor attaching screws.
6. Remove motor while guiding crankarm through hole.
7. Reverse procedure to install.

1993–95

Removal

1. Remove wiper arm and blade assemblies as follows:
   a. Operate wipers at lowest delay setting, then shut Off wipers at inner wipe (end of sweep) position.
   b. Mark windshield at tip of blade assembly to aid installation, then lift wiper arm nut cover and remove nut.
   c. Remove wiper arm from linkage drive shaft using wiper arm puller J 39637.
2. Disconnect battery ground cable, then remove lefthand cowl panel and hood seal.
3. Disconnect washer hose assembly from lefthand cowl panel, then the electrical connector from wiper motor assembly.

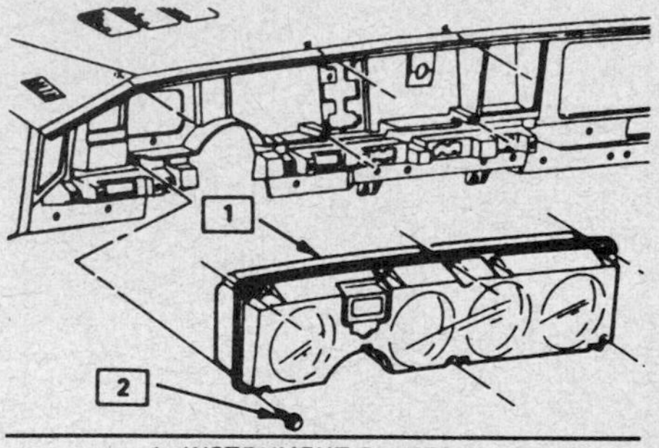
1
2
1–INSTRUMENT CLUSTER
2–SCREW

GC9099100204000X

Fig. 24 Instrument cluster. 1992 Firebird

4. Remove screw and nut from lefthand linkage assembly, **Fig. 27,** then disconnect socket of righthand linkage assembly from ball of lefthand linkage assembly using wiper linkage separator tool No. J-39232, or equivalent.
5. Remove lefthand linkage assembly, then the screw from wiper motor assembly.
6. Pull wiper motor assembly free from slots of bracket, then disconnect socket of righthand linkage assembly from crank arm ball of wiper motor assembly using wiper linkage separator.

Installation

When installing wiper motor assembly, ensure that crank arm is in inner wipe position. Crank arm drive pin must be engaged in cam pocket.

1. Press socket of righthand linkage assembly into engagement with crank arm ball of wiper motor assembly using wiper linkage installer J 39529.
2. Install wiper motor assembly with two locator pads pressed fully into slots of bracket, then the mounting screw and **torque** to 7.5 ft. lbs.

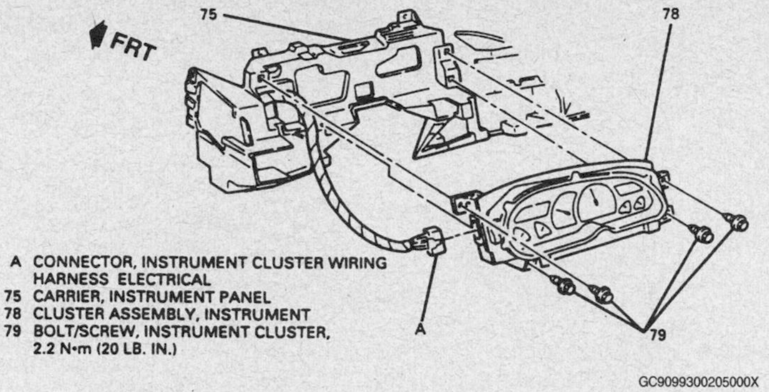
FRT
75
78
A CONNECTOR, INSTRUMENT CLUSTER WIRING HARNESS ELECTRICAL
75 CARRIER, INSTRUMENT PANEL
78 CLUSTER ASSEMBLY, INSTRUMENT
79 BOLT/SCREW, INSTRUMENT CLUSTER, 2.2 N•m (20 LB. IN.)
A
79
GC9099300205000X

Fig. 25 Instrument cluster. 1993–95 Camaro

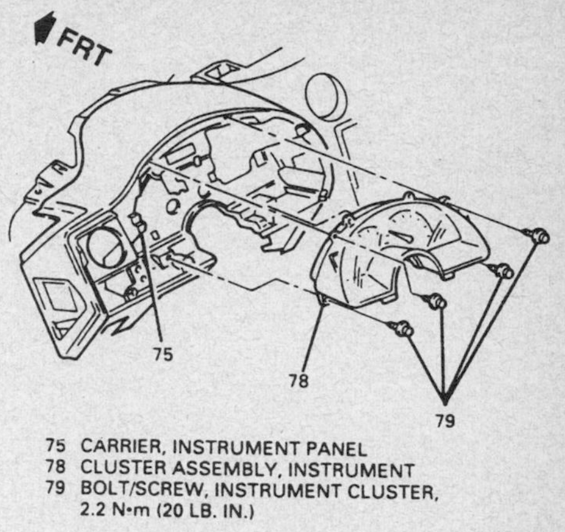
FRT
75
78
79
75 CARRIER, INSTRUMENT PANEL
78 CLUSTER ASSEMBLY, INSTRUMENT
79 BOLT/SCREW, INSTRUMENT CLUSTER, 2.2 N•m (20 LB. IN.)
GC9099300206000X

Fig. 26 Instrument cluster. 1993–95 Firebird

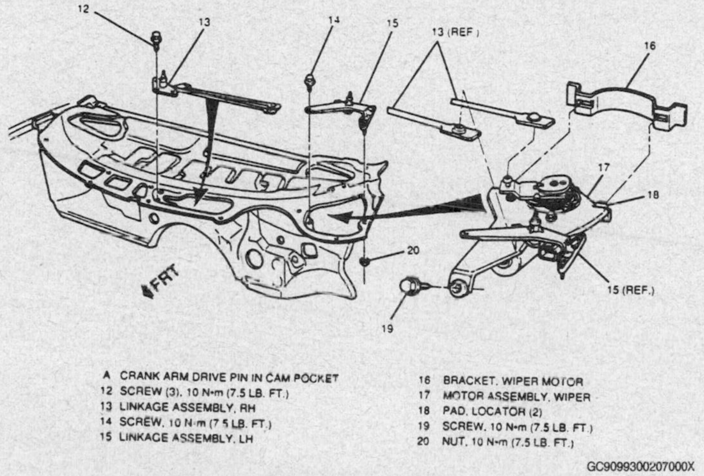
12
13
14
15
13 (REF.)
16
17
18
20
15 (REF.)
19
FRT
A CRANK ARM DRIVE PIN IN CAM POCKET
12 SCREW (3), 10 N•m (7.5 LB. FT.)
13 LINKAGE ASSEMBLY, RH
14 SCREW, 10 N•m (7.5 LB. FT.)
15 LINKAGE ASSEMBLY, LH
16 BRACKET, WIPER MOTOR
17 MOTOR ASSEMBLY, WIPER
18 PAD, LOCATOR (2)
19 SCREW, 10 N•m (7.5 LB. FT.)
20 NUT, 10 N•m (7.5 LB. FT.)
GC9099300207000X

Fig. 27 Windshield wiper motor/transmission assembly. 1993–95

3. Install lefthand linkage assembly without attaching parts, then press socket of righthand linkage assembly into engagement with ball of lefthand linkage assembly using wiper linkage installer.
4. Attach lefthand linkage assembly with screw and nut and **torque** to 7.5 ft. lbs.
5. Connect electrical connector to wiper motor assembly, then the washer hose assembly to lefthand cowl panel and washer nozzle.
6. Install lefthand cowl panel and hood seal, then connect battery ground cable.
7. Install wiper arm and blade assemblies as follows:
   a. Install wiper arm and blade assembly onto linkage drive shaft, with tip of blade assembly aligned with mark made at removal.
   b. Install nut on linkage drive shaft and **torque** to 24 ft. lbs. while holding wiper arm.
   c. Close nut cover, then run wipers and check for proper wipe pattern. Shut Off wipers and check for correct park position.

WIPER SWITCH
REPLACE

1992

1. Disconnect battery ground cable.
2. Remove ignition lock cylinder as described under "Ignition Lock, Replace.
3. Remove housing cover end cap.
4. **On models with cruise control,** unplug connector from housing cover end base plate, then remove multifunction lever.
5. **On all models,** remove lock housing cover screws.
6. Remove housing cover end base plate and dimmer switch rod actuator from lock housing cover, then pull wiper switch wire harness through steering column.
7. Remove wiper switch pivot pin, then the wiper/pivot switch.
8. Reverse procedure to install.

1993–95

1. **On models with cruise control,** remove tilt wheel release lever and access cover, then disconnect electrical connectors.
2. **On all models,** remove wiper switch by grasping firmly and pulling straight out.
3. Reverse procedure to install, noting the following:
   a. Ensure wiper switch is in Off position before installing.
   b. Position tilt lever ±5° from centerline of column assembly.

WIPER TRANSMISSION
REPLACE

1992

1. Ensure motor is in park position.
2. Raise hood and remove wiper arm assemblies.
3. Remove cowl vent screen.
4. Loosen nuts securing pivot at motor crankarm, then disconnect transmission rod from crankarm.
5. Remove retaining nuts or screws securing transmission to body, then withdraw transmission assembly through cowl opening.
6. Reverse procedure to install.

1993–95

Removal

1. Remove wiper arm and blade assemblies as follows:
   a. Operate wipers at lowest delay setting, then shut Off wipers at inner wipe (end of sweep) position.
   b. Mark windshield at tip of blade assembly to aid installation, then lift wiper arm nut cover and remove nut.
   c. Remove wiper arm from linkage drive shaft using wiper arm puller J 39637.
2. Remove lefthand cowl panel and hood seal, then disconnect washer hose assembly from lefthand cowl panel.
3. Remove screw and nut from lefthand linkage assembly, **Fig. 27,** then disconnect socket of righthand linkage assembly from ball of lefthand linkage assembly using wiper linkage separator J-39232.
4. Remove lefthand linkage assembly, then the screws securing righthand linkage assembly.
5. Disconnect socket of righthand linkage assembly from crank arm ball of wiper motor assembly using wiper linkage separator, then remove righthand linkage assembly from slotted plenum access hole.

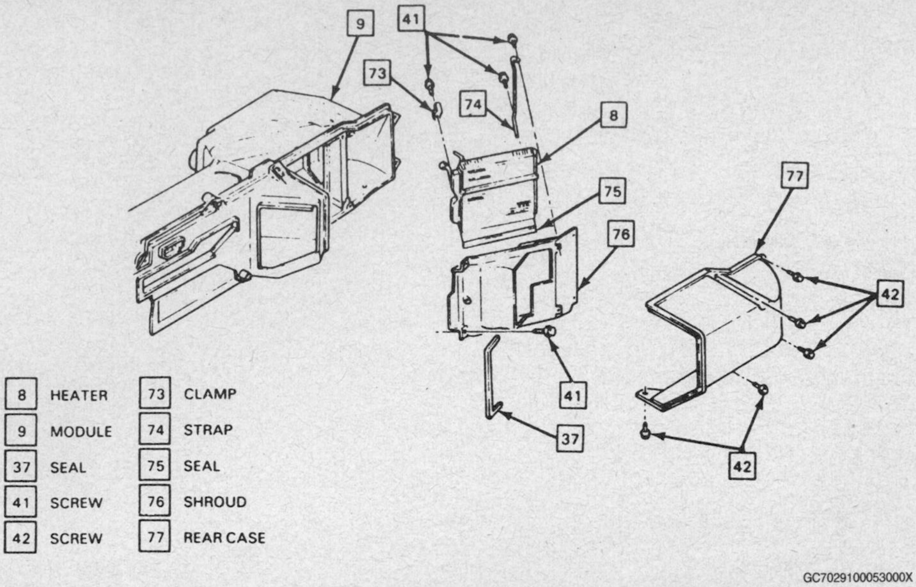
9
41
73
74
8
75
76
77
42
41
37
42
8 HEATER
9 MODULE
37 SEAL
41 SCREW
42 SCREW
73 CLAMP
74 STRAP
75 SEAL
76 SHROUD
77 REAR CASE
GC7029100053000X

Fig. 28 Heater core replacement. 1992

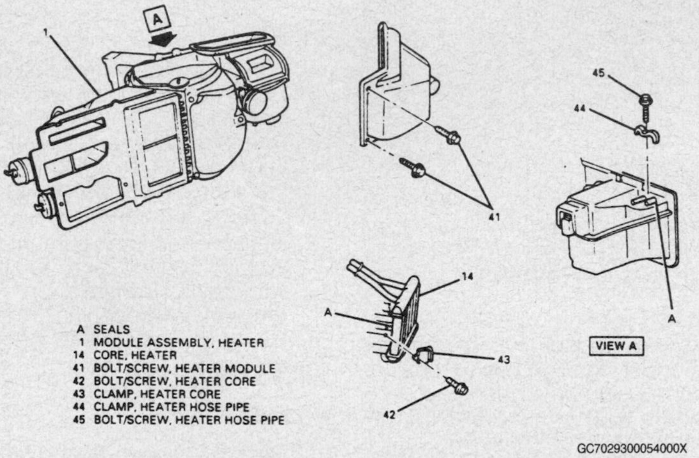
A
1
45
44
41
14
A
43
42
VIEW A
A
A SEALS
1 MODULE ASSEMBLY, HEATER
14 CORE, HEATER
41 BOLT/SCREW, HEATER MODULE
42 BOLT/SCREW, HEATER CORE
43 CLAMP, HEATER CORE
44 CLAMP, HEATER HOSE PIPE
45 BOLT/SCREW, HEATER HOSE PIPE
GC7029300054000X

Fig. 29 Heater core replacement. 1993–95

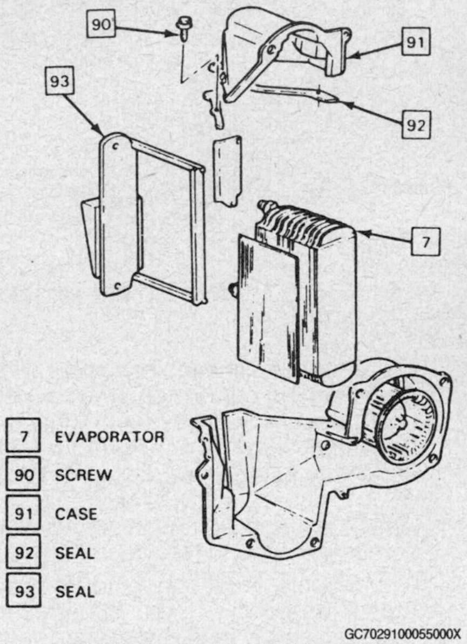
90
91
93
92
7
7 EVAPORATOR
90 SCREW
91 CASE
92 SEAL
93 SEAL
GC7029100055000X

Fig. 30 Evaporator core replacement. 1992

Installation

1. Install righthand linkage assembly from slotted plenum access hole, then the screws securing righthand linkage assembly finger tight.
2. Align righthand linkage assembly, then press socket of righthand linkage assembly into engagement with crank arm ball of wiper motor assembly using wiper linkage installer J 39529.
3. Install lefthand linkage assembly without attaching parts, then press socket of righthand linkage assembly into engagement with ball of lefthand linkage assembly using wiper linkage installer.
4. Attach lefthand linkage assembly with screw and nut and **torque** to 7.5 ft. lbs.
5. Connect washer hose assembly to lefthand cowl panel and washer nozzle.
6. Install lefthand cowl panel and hood seal, then connect battery ground cable.
7. Install wiper arm and blade assemblies as follows:
   a. Install wiper arm and blade assembly onto linkage drive shaft, with tip of blade assembly aligned with mark made at removal.
   b. Install nut on linkage drive shaft and **torque** to 24 ft. lbs. while holding wiper arm.
   c. Close nut cover, then run wipers and check for proper wipe pattern. Shut Off wipers and check for correct park position.

BLOWER MOTOR

REPLACE

1992

1. Disconnect battery ground cable.
2. Remove fender brace at rear right hand corner of engine compartment, if necessary.
3. Disconnect blower motor and resistor wires.
4. Disconnect cooling tube, if equipped.
5. Remove blower motor retaining screws and motor/cage assembly from case.
6. While holding blower motor cage, remove cage retaining screw and slide cage from motor shaft.
7. Reverse procedure to install.

1993–95

1. Ensure ignition switch is in Off position, then remove righthand instrument panel sound insulator assembly and side trim panel.
2. Remove blower motor mounting bolts, then the blower motor.
3. reverse procedure to install. **Torque** mounting bolts to 20 inch lbs.

HEATER CORE

REPLACE

1992

1. Disconnect battery ground cable and drain cooling system.
2. Disconnect heater hoses from heater core tubes.

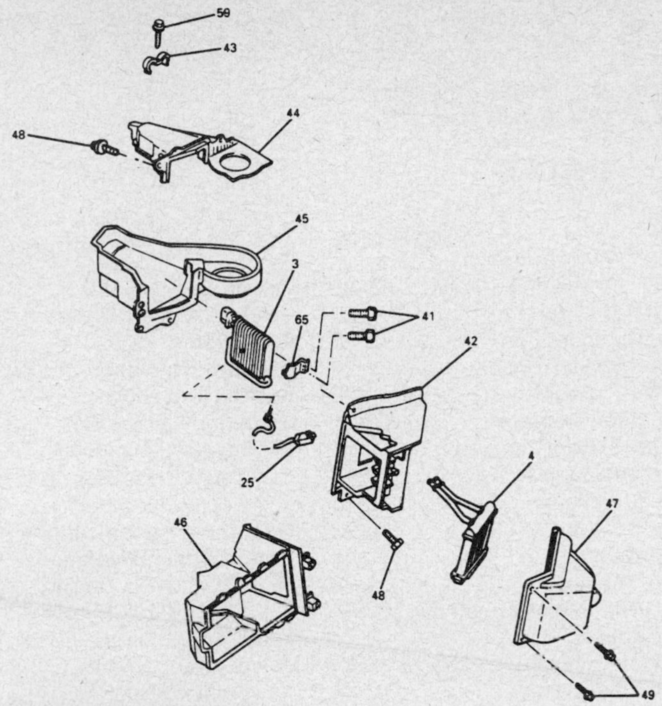
59
43
48
44
45
3
65
41
42
25
4
47
46
48
49

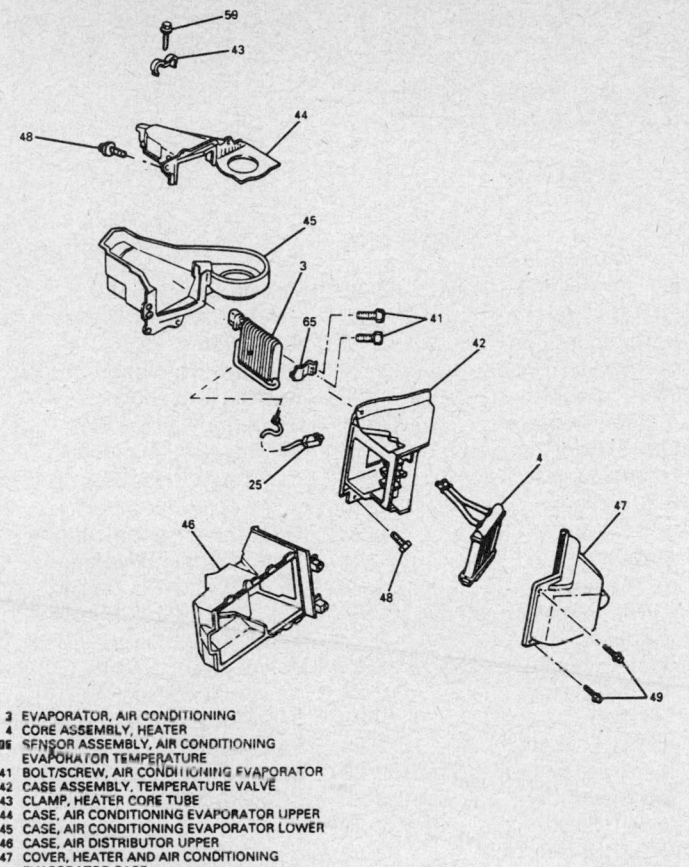

3 EVAPORATOR, AIR CONDITIONING
4 CORE ASSEMBLY, HEATER
25 SENSOR ASSEMBLY, AIR CONDITIONING EVAPORATOR TEMPERATURE
41 BOLT/SCREW, AIR CONDITIONING EVAPORATOR
42 CASE ASSEMBLY, TEMPERATURE VALVE
43 CLAMP, HEATER CORE TUBE
44 CASE, AIR CONDITIONING EVAPORATOR UPPER
45 CASE, AIR CONDITIONING EVAPORATOR LOWER
46 CASE, AIR DISTRIBUTOR UPPER
47 COVER, HEATER AND AIR CONDITIONING EVAPORATOR CASE
48 BOLT/SCREW, TEMPERATURE VALVE CASE ASSEMBLY
49 BOLT/SCREW, HEATER AND AIR CONDITIONING EVAPORATOR CASE COVER
59 BOLT/SCREW, HEATER CORE TUBE CLAMP
65 CLAMP, AIR CONDITIONING EVAPORATOR

GC7029300056000X

Fig. 31 Evaporator core replacement. 1993–95

3. Remove instrument panel and center console.
4. Remove heater case, **Fig. 28.**
5. Remove heater core shroud screws, then separate heater case assembly.
6. Remove core mounting strap, then the core.
7. Reverse procedure to install.

1993–95

1. Open instrument panel compartment by pushing in on sides of compartment to release it.
2. Drain coolant.
3. Remove heater module bolts, then the heater module assembly cover, **Fig. 29.**
4. Remove heater core bolt and heater core clamp, then the hose pipe clamp bolt and hose pipe clamp.
5. Disconnect hose heater hose assembly from heater hose pipes, then carefully pull heater core toward you to remove.
6. Reverse procedure to install, noting the following:
   a. Ensure seals around heater pipes stay in place when installing core.
   b. **Torque** hose pipe clamp bolt and heater core bolt to 16 inch lbs. and heater module bolts to 18 inch lbs.
   c. Operate engine and check for coolant leaks, then check coolant level, adding coolant as necessary.

EVAPORATOR CORE REPLACE

1992

1. Disconnect battery ground cable.
2. Discharge A/C refrigerant system, then remove the accumulator.
3. Remove blower motor resistor assembly.
4. Remove blower motor relay and bracket.
5. Remove upper evaporator case attaching screws, then remove upper evaporator case and seal, **Fig. 30.**
6. Disconnect refrigerant line from lower fitting of evaporator. Cap refrigerant line and evaporator fitting.
7. Remove evaporator and seal.
8. Reverse procedure to install.

1993–95

1. Discharge refrigerant into a recovery station, then drain coolant.
2. Remove righthand instrument panel sound insulator panel assembly, then disconnect heater hoses at heater core assembly.
3. Remove instrument panel compartment, then the heater core as previously described.
4. Remove evaporator temperature sensor assembly, **Fig. 31,** then disconnect temperature control cable assembly at temperature valve case assembly.
5. Remove bolts from temperature valve case assembly, then the temperature valve case assembly by sliding case assembly downward to disengage upper case clip.
6. Remove thermostatic expansion valve assembly.
7. Using a small hand saw, remove perforated section of evaporator module assembly as one piece and retain for reuse.
8. Remove bolts retaining evaporator, then the evaporator from module assembly by sliding evaporator to left and pulling out through opening cut in module.
9. Reverse procedure to install, noting the following:
   a. If replacing evaporator, transfer condensate screen to new evaporator.
   b. If replacing evaporator, add 3 fluid ounces of polyalkylene glycol (PAG) synthetic refrigerant oil to new evaporator.
   c. Apply sealer No. 3012078, or equivalent, between evaporator upper and lower case just behind thermostatic expansion valve assembly to prevent air entry from engine compartment.
   d. Use epoxy glue to adhere perforated section of module assembly to module assembly.
   e. Fill radiator and bleed cooling system.
   f. Partially charge system and perform a leak test, then recover refrigerant and evacuate and charge system.

3.1L/V6-191 & 3.4L/V6-207 Engines

INDEX

PRECAUTIONS

AIR BAG SYSTEMS

Refer to "Air Bag System Precautions" in the front of this manual for system disarming and arming procedures.

FUEL SYSTEM PRESSURE RELIEF

Failure to relieve system pressure prior to disconnecting fuel system components may cause fire or personal injury. Remove fuel tank filler cap to release fuel tank pressure. Connect pressure gauge tool No. J-34730-1, or equivalent, to pressure tap on fuel rail, position bleed hose into suitable container and slowly relieve fuel system pressure. Prior to disconnecting fuel line, position shop towel over fitting.

ENGINE MOUNT

REPLACE

FRONT MOUNT

3.1L/V6-191 Engine

1. Disconnect battery ground cable.
2. Remove upper half of fan shroud, if necessary.
3. Raise and support vehicle.
4. Remove engine mount through bolt, then raise front of engine to release weight from mount.
5. Remove mount to engine bolts and mount, **Fig. 1. Raise engine only enough to provide sufficient clearance for mount removal. Check for interference between rear of engine and cowl panel which could result in distributor damage.**
6. Reverse procedure to install.

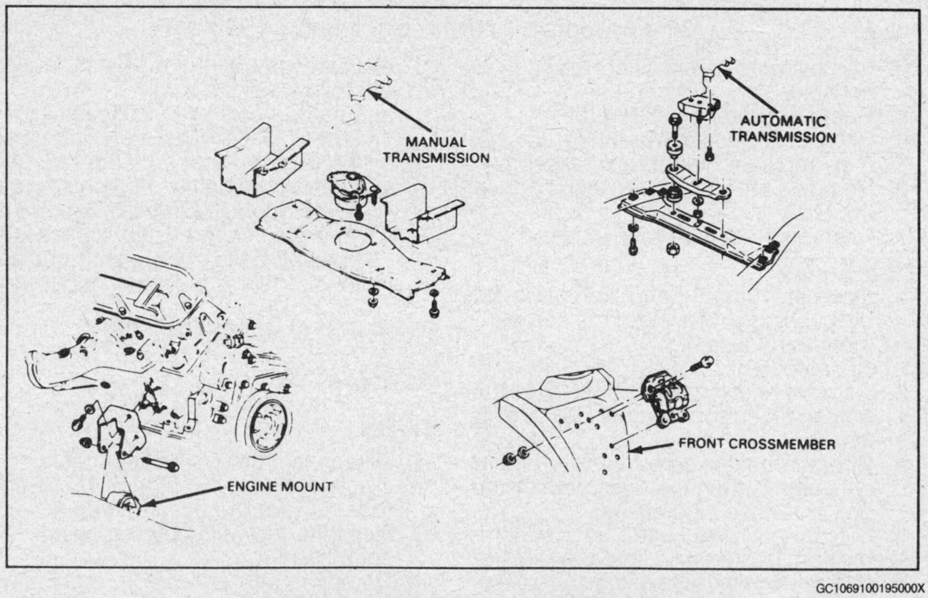
MANUAL TRANSMISSION
AUTOMATIC TRANSMISSION
ENGINE MOUNT
FRONT CROSSMEMBER
GC1069100195000X

Fig. 1 Engine mounting. 3.1L/V6-191 engine

3.4L/V6-207 Engine

1. Raise and support vehicle, then disconnect exhaust crossover pipe.
2. Remove engine mount through bolt and nut, then raise engine with a jack.
3. Remove engine mount, then the engine bracket, if necessary.

4. Reverse procedure to install. Tighten fasteners to specifications.

REAR MOUNT

3.1L/V6-191 Engine

1. Disconnect battery ground cable.
2. Raise and support vehicle, then remove crossmember to transmission mount nuts and washers.
3. **On models with automatic transmission,** raise transmission slightly for clearance, then remove crossmember to transmission support nuts, bolts and insulators and transmission support.
4. **On all models,** remove transmission mount attaching bolts, then remove mount, **Fig. 1.**
5. Reverse procedure to install.

3.4L/V6-207 Engine

Refer to "Front Mount" for procedures.

ENGINE

REPLACE

3.1L/V6-191 ENGINE

1. Disconnect battery ground cable, then remove air cleaner duct.
2. Scribe alignment marks on hood and hood hinge, then remove hood.
3. Remove serpentine drive belt.
4. Remove A/C compressor from bracket and position out of way with refrigerant hoses attached.
5. Drain cooling system, then disconnect upper and lower radiator hoses, coolant recovery hose and heater hose at water pump and valve.
6. Disconnect throttle linkage and cruise control cable, if equipped.
7. Disconnect vacuum hose from power brake unit.
8. Remove distributor cap and position aside with wiring attached.
9. Remove power steering pump from bracket and position out of way with hoses attached.
10. Disconnect and tag all electrical wiring and hoses that may interfere with engine removal.
11. Raise and support vehicle, then detach transmission oil cooler lines at oil pan clips, if equipped.
12. Disconnect exhaust crossover pipe at exhaust manifolds.
13. **On models with automatic transmission,** remove converter housing cover, then remove torque converter to driveplate attaching bolts.
14. **On all models,** disconnect wiring from starter motor.
15. **On models with manual transmission,** remove bellhousing to engine bolts.
16. **On all models,** remove engine mount through bolts, then lower vehicle.
17. Relieve fuel system pressure as described under "Precautions," then disconnect fuel lines.
18. Support transmission using a transmission jack or other suitable support.
19. Attach a suitable engine lifting device

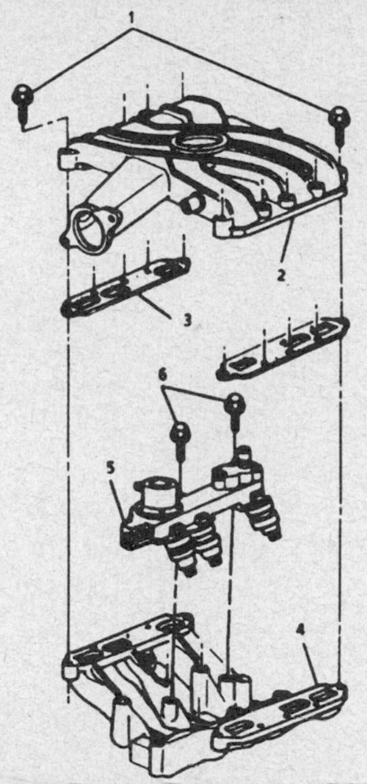
1
2
3
4
5
6

1 PLENUM TO MANIFOLD BOLT	4 INTAKE MANIFOLD
2 INTAKE PLENUM	5 FUEL RAIL ASSEMBLY
3 GASKET	6 FUEL RAIL ATTACHING BOLT

GC1069100196000X

Fig. 2 Fuel rail & plenum replacement. 3.1L/V6-191 engine

to engine, then remove engine from vehicle. When removing engine, detach wire from bracket at left hand rear of engine.

20. Reverse procedure to install.

3.4L/V6-207 ENGINE

1. Disconnect battery ground cable.
2. Raise and support vehicle, then remove wheels.
3. Drain coolant, then disconnect exhaust crossover pipe assembly from intermediate pipe.
4. **On vehicles with automatic transmission,** remove converter cover bolts and converter bolts.
5. **On all vehicles,** remove front fascia lower deflectors, stabilizer bar bolts and the serpentine drive belt.
6. **On vehicles with automatic transmission,** disconnect transmission cooler lines from radiator.
7. **On all vehicles,** disconnect lower radiator hose from radiator and heater hoses from pipes at engine, then the electrical ground straps from right side of engine block and electrical connections from starter motor.
8. Disconnect electrical connectors from knock sensor, oxygen sensor, coolant temperature sensor, camshaft sensor, crankshaft sensor and wheel speed sensor.
9. Disconnect electrical connectors from engine oil level switch and fuel pump switch/engine oil pressure gauge sensor assemblies.
10. Disconnect right front brake line from caliper brake hose, then the wiring harness from transmission.
11. Disconnect shift linkage from transmission, then the propeller shaft from transmission. **Scribe alignment marks on propeller shaft before disconnecting.**
12. Disconnect torque arm from transmission, then the intermediate steering shaft from rack and pinion assembly.
13. Disconnect electrical ground straps from left side of frame rail, then lower vehicle.
14. Remove air intake duct, then the fuel pipe assembly.
15. Disconnect cruise and accelerator control cables from throttle body, then he upper radiator hose from intake manifold and lower radiator hose from front cover.
16. Disconnect radiator fan electrical connections, then remove radiator fan assembly.
17. Disconnect brake booster vacuum hose, then the Y brace from right exhaust manifold.
18. Remove alternator and A/C compressor bracket and reposition, then disconnect engine wiring harness connectors and reposition.
19. Remove brake master cylinder and reposition, then the upper bolts and nuts from strut assemblies.
20. Disconnect right front brake line from modulator valve assembly and clips, then raise and support vehicle.
21. Place a lift table under engine and engine frame assembly, then remove engine frame and transmission support bolts.
22. Raise vehicle from engine, transmission and engine frame assemblies, then secure strut assemblies to engine frame.
23. Disconnect transmission TV cable from throttle body, then remove transmission assembly.
24. **On vehicles with manual transmission,** remove clutch housing and clutch assembly.
25. **On all vehicles,** disconnect power steering lines from power steering pump.
26. Remove engine mount through bolts, then the engine assembly from engine frame.
27. Reverse procedure to install, noting the following:
    a. Tighten fasteners to specifications.
    b. Bleed brake and power steering systems.
    c. Align wheels.

INTAKE MANIFOLD

REPLACE

3.1L/V6-191 ENGINE

1. Disconnect battery ground cable, remove air cleaner and drain cooling system.
2. Relieve fuel system pressure as described under "Precautions."
3. Disconnect air inlet duct, electrical connectors, coolant hoses and vacuum hoses from throttle body, noting position for installation.
4. Disconnect accelerator, cruise control and transmission cables, as equipped.

5. Remove throttle body retaining bolts and the throttle body.
6. Remove EGR pipe retaining bolts and throttle cable bracket.
7. Remove bolts securing plenum to manifold and the plenum, **Fig. 2.**
8. Disconnect fuel lines from fuel rail and remove cold start valve.
9. Disconnect vacuum hose from pressure regulator and remove fuel rail retaining bolts.
10. Disconnect injector harness connectors and remove fuel rail assembly, **Fig. 2.**
11. Disconnect high tension leads from spark plugs and disconnect wiring from coil.
12. Remove distributor cap and plug wire assembly.
13. Rotate crankshaft until No. 1 cylinder is at TDC on compression stroke, mark position of distributor rotor and remove distributor.
14. Remove air injection hose, if equipped, disconnect canister hoses and remove pipe bracket from front of left valve cover.
15. Remove left valve cover and air management bracket, then remove right valve cover.
16. Disconnect upper radiator and heater hoses from manifold.
17. Disconnect coolant switches and remove manifold retaining bolts.
18. Remove manifold and thoroughly clean old gasket and sealer from mating surfaces.
19. Ensure surfaces are clean and dry, then apply 3/16 bead of RTV sealer on each block ridge, install gaskets and secure gasket position by extending bead of sealer approximately 1/4 inch onto gasket ends. **New gaskets must be cut to fit behind pushrods. When installing gaskets, note left and right side markings.**
20. Install manifold and retaining bolts, ensuring areas between case ridges and manifold are completely sealed.
21. Tighten manifold bolts to specifications in sequence shown in **Fig. 3**, then reverse remaining procedure to complete installation.

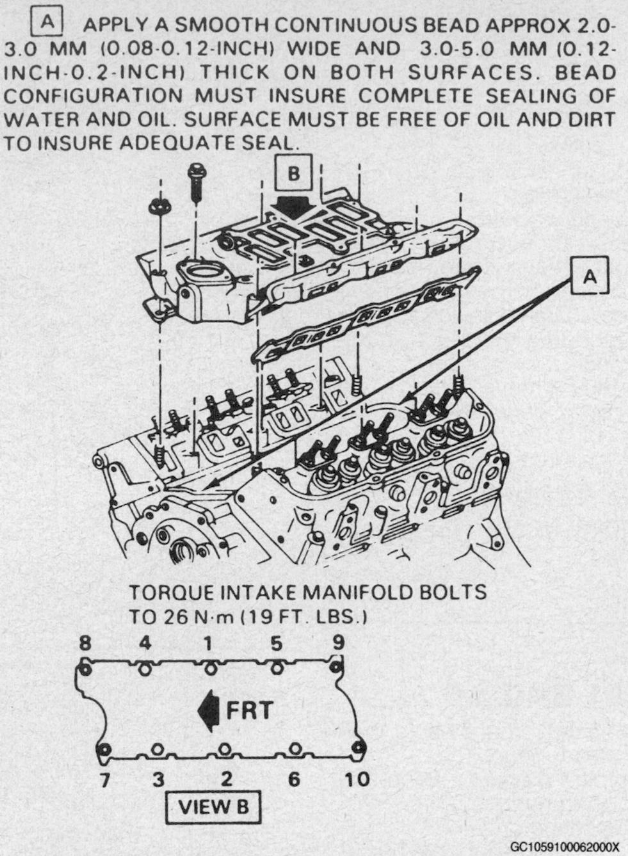

A APPLY A SMOOTH CONTINUOUS BEAD APPROX 2.0-3.0 MM (0.08-0.12-INCH) WIDE AND 3.0-5.0 MM (0.12-INCH-0.2-INCH) THICK ON BOTH SURFACES. BEAD CONFIGURATION MUST INSURE COMPLETE SEALING OF WATER AND OIL. SURFACE MUST BE FREE OF OIL AND DIRT TO INSURE ADEQUATE SEAL.
B
A
TORQUE INTAKE MANIFOLD BOLTS TO 26 N·m (19 FT. LBS.)
8 4 1 5 9
FRT
7 3 2 6 10
VIEW B
GC1059100062000X

Fig. 3 Intake manifold replacement & bolt tightening sequence. 3.1L/V6-191 engine

3.4L/V6-207 Engine

UPPER

1. Disconnect battery ground cable.
2. Drain coolant, then disconnect throttle body air duct.
3. Disconnect fuel rail injector wiring harness connectors, then the wiring harness retaining nut and set harness aside.
4. Remove accelerator cable bracket bolts, then disconnect bracket and cables from throttle body assembly.
5. Disconnect fuel pipe connectors, then remove fuel pipe assembly and reposition.
6. Disconnect coolant hoses from throttle body assembly, then remove fuel rail stud.
7. Disconnect fuel pressure regulator vacuum hose, then the electrical connectors from IAC, TPS, MAP sensor and evaporative emissions canister purge solenoid valve.
8. Blow dirt out of injector bores with compressed air, then remove fuel rail assembly.
9. Disconnect vacuum harness assembly, then EGR flexible pipe assembly from upper intake manifold and reposition.
10. Remove upper intake manifold assembly.
11. Reverse procedure to install, noting the following:
    a. Tighten fasteners to specifications.
    b. Apply teflon sealant No. 1052080, or equivalent, to threads of EGR flexible pipe assembly bolts and fuel pipe hold down plate bolts.
    c. Lightly lubricate fuel injector O-rings with clean engine oil.

LOWER

1. Remove upper intake manifold as previously described, then the rocker arm covers.
2. Disconnect upper radiator hose and heater hose from lower intake manifold assembly, then the wiring harness ground leads.
3. Remove lower intake manifold assembly.
4. Reverse procedure to install, noting the following:
    a. Tighten manifold bolts in sequence shown in **Fig. 4**, to specifications.
    b. Tighten other fasteners to specifications.
    c. Apply sealant No. 1345739, or equivalent, at engine block to manifold mating surface. Bead should be 0.08-0.12 inch wide by 0.12-0.20 inch thick.

EXHAUST MANIFOLD

REPLACE

LEFT SIDE

3.1L/V6-191 Engine

1. Disconnect battery ground cable.
2. Raise and support vehicle.
3. Disconnect exhaust crossover pipe from exhaust manifold, then lower vehicle.
4. Remove power steering pump rear bracket.
5. Remove exhaust manifold attaching bolts and nut, then remove exhaust manifold and gasket, **Fig. 5.**
6. Reverse procedure to install.

3.4L/V6-207 Engine

1. Disconnect battery ground cable, then raise and support vehicle.
2. Disconnect exhaust crossover pipe from manifold, then lower vehicle.
3. Disconnect oxygen sensor electrical connector.

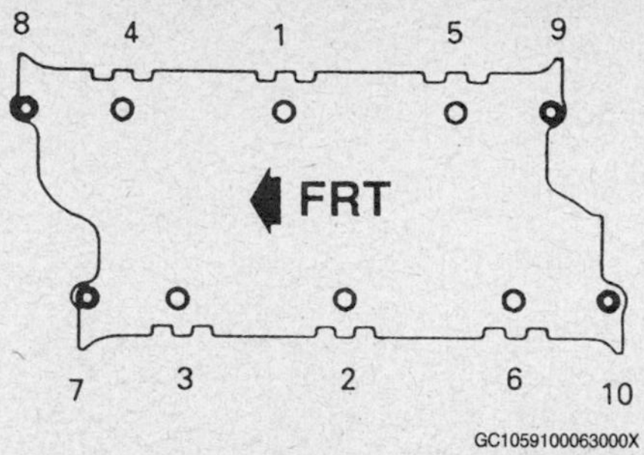
8
4
1
5
9
FRT
7
3
2
6
10
GC1059100063000X

Fig. 4 Lower intake manifold bolt tightening sequence. 3.4L/V6-207 engine

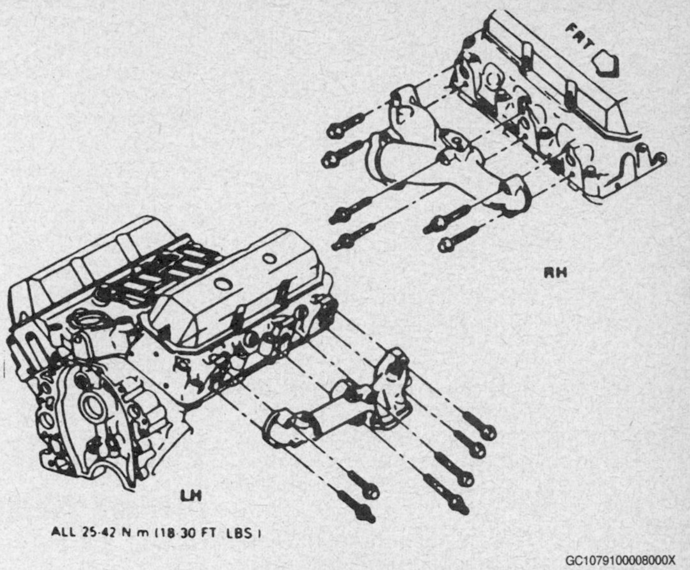
FRT
RH
LH
ALL 25-42 N·m (18-30 FT. LBS.)
GC1079100008000X

Fig. 5 Exhaust manifold replacement. 3.1L/V6-191 engine

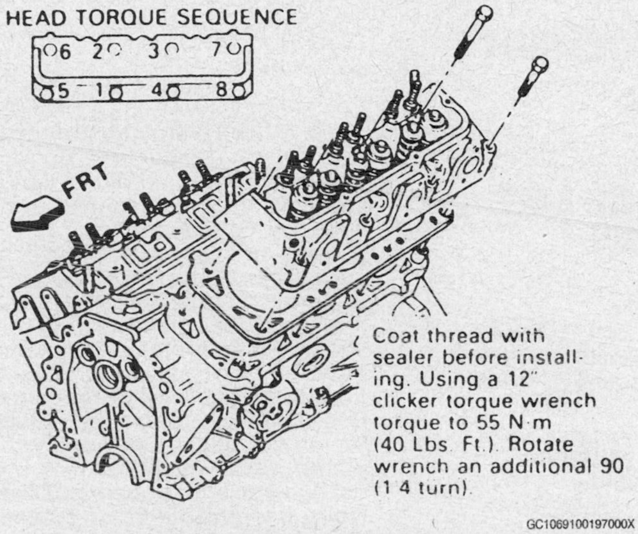
HEAD TORQUE SEQUENCE
6 2 3 7
5 1 4 8
FRT
Coat thread with sealer before installing. Using a 12" clicker torque wrench torque to 55 N·m (40 Lbs. Ft.). Rotate wrench an additional 90 (1/4 turn).
GC1069100197000X

Fig. 6 Cylinder head replace & bolt tightening sequence. 3.1L/V6-191 engine

4. **On vehicles with manual transmission,** remove secondary air injection check valve pipe bracket nut and reposition pipe.
5. **On all vehicles,** remove exhaust manifold.
6. Reverse procedure to install. Tighten fasteners to specifications.

RIGHT SIDE

3.1L/V6-191 Engine

1. Disconnect battery ground cable, then remove throttle body air duct.
2. Disconnect EGR transfer tube at plenum, then remove EGR valve with adapter and shield from exhaust manifold.
3. Remove serpentine drive belt, then remove AIR pump pulley.
4. Remove AIR pump upper bracket, then disconnect AIR hose from check valve.
5. Raise and support vehicle, then remove exhaust crossover pipe nuts from exhaust manifold.
6. Disconnect vacuum line and electrical connector from diverter valve, then lower vehicle.
7. Remove AIR pump to lower bracket attaching bolt, then remove AIR pump with diverter valve.
8. Disconnect AIR pipe from exhaust manifold.
9. Remove alternator brace, then remove exhaust manifold attaching bolts and exhaust manifold, **Fig. 5.**
10. Reverse procedure to install.

3.4L/V6-207 Engine

1. Disconnect battery ground cable, then raise and support vehicle.
2. Disconnect exhaust crossover pipe from manifold, then remove transmission filler tube.
3. Remove A/C compressor rear bracket bolts, then the two rear exhaust manifold bolts.
4. Lower vehicle, then remove serpentine drive belt.
5. Disconnect oxygen sensor electrical connector, then remove alternator.
6. Remove A/C compressor from bracket and reposition, then the alternator rear Y brace.
7. Remove EGR valve, adapter, and flexible pipe.
8. **On models equipped with manual transmission,** disconnect secondary air injection pipe assembly from exhaust manifold.
9. **On all vehicles,** remove exhaust manifold.
10. Reverse procedure to install. Tighten fasteners to specifications.

CYLINDER HEAD REPLACE

LEFT

3.1L/V6-191 Engine

1. Remove intake manifold as described under "Intake Manifold, Replace."
2. Remove spark plugs.
3. Raise and support vehicle, then drain coolant from engine block.
4. Drain crankcase and remove oil filter.
5. Lower vehicle and remove engine oil dipstick and tube.
6. Remove exhaust manifold as described under "Exhaust Manifold, Replace."
7. Remove serpentine drive belt.
8. Remove A/C compressor and bracket and position aside with refrigerant hose attached.
9. Remove engine lift bracket, if equipped.
10. Disconnect engine ground cable from rear of cylinder head.
11. Remove power steering pump and bracket and position aside with hoses attached.
12. Loosen rocker arm nuts until pushrods can be removed.
13. Remove cylinder head attaching bolts, then remove cylinder head.
14. Reverse procedure to install. Prior to installation, coat cylinder head bolts with sealer 1052080 or equivalent. Tighten cylinder bolts in sequence shown in **Fig. 6.**

3.4L/V6-207 Engine

1. Raise and support vehicle and drain coolant, then lower vehicle.
2. Remove upper intake manifold, lower intake manifold and left exhaust manifold as previously described.
3. Remove oil dipstick and tube assembly, then the serpentine drive belt.
4. Disconnect coolant temperature sen-

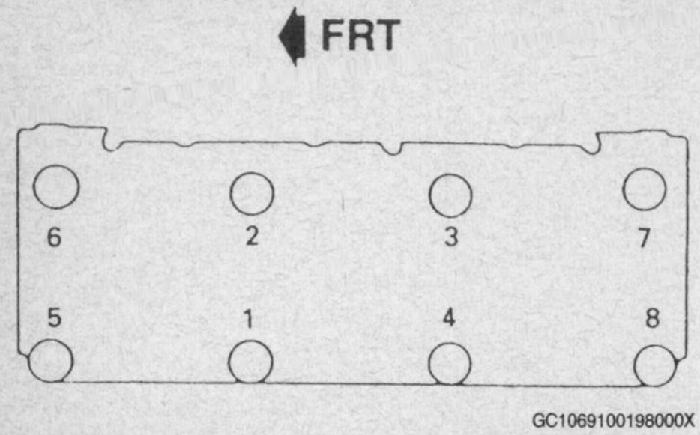
FRT
6
2
3
7
5
1
4
8
GC1069100198000X

Fig. 7 Cylinder head bolt tightening sequence. 3.4L/V6-207 engine

sor electrical connector, then the spark plug wires from spark plugs.

5. Remove spark plugs, engine lift bracket, wiring harness clip from rear of cylinder head and secondary air injection pipe bracket bolt.
6. Remove power steering pump assembly and brackets and set aside, then loosen rocker arms until pushrod assemblies can be removed.
7. Remove cylinder head bolts, then the cylinder head.
8. Reverse procedure to install, noting the following:
   a. Tighten fasteners to specifications.
   b. Coat threads of cylinder head bolts with sealing compound 1052080 and **torque** in sequence shown in **Fig. 7**, to 41 ft. lbs., then in sequence an additional 90 degrees using torque angle meter tool No. J-36660, or equivalent
   c. Adjust valves.

RIGHT

3.1L/V6-191 Engine

1. Remove intake manifold as described under "Intake Manifold, Replace."
2. Remove spark plugs.
3. Remove exhaust manifold as described under "Exhaust Manifold, Replace."
4. Raise and support vehicle, then drain coolant from engine block.
5. Drain crankcase and remove oil filter.
6. Lower vehicle.
7. Loosen rocker arms until pushrods can be removed.
8. Remove serpentine drive belt, then remove belt tensioner.
9. Remove alternator and brackets.
10. Disconnect engine ground cable from rear of cylinder head.
11. Remove cylinder head attaching bolts, then remove cylinder head.
12. Reverse procedure to install. Prior to installation, coat cylinder head bolts with sealer 1052080 or equivalent. Tighten cylinder bolts in sequence shown in **Fig. 6.**

3.4L/V6-207 Engine

1. Raise and support vehicle and drain coolant, then lower vehicle.
2. Remove serpentine drive belt tensioner assembly.
3. Remove upper intake manifold, lower intake manifold and right exhaust manifold as previously described.
4. Remove alternator and brackets, then disconnect spark plug wires from spark plugs.
5. Loosen rocker arms until pushrod assemblies can be removed.
6. Remove cylinder head bolts, then the cylinder head.
7. Reverse procedure to install, noting the following:
   a. Tighten fasteners to specifications.
   b. Coat threads of cylinder head bolts with sealing compound 1052080 and **torque** in sequence shown in **Fig. 7**, to 41 ft. lbs., then in sequence an additional 90 degrees using torque angle meter tool No. J-6660, or equivalent
   c. Adjust valves.

VALVE ARRANGEMENT

FRONT TO REAR

Right .... E-I-E-I-I-E
Left .... E-I-I-E-I-E

CAMSHAFT LOBE LIFT SPECIFICATIONS

Engine (VIN)	Int.	Exh.
3.1L/V6-191(T)	.2626	.2732
3.4L/V6-207(S)	.2626	.2732

VALVE CLEARANCE SPECIFICATIONS

Year	Engine (VIN)	Valve Lash
1992	3.1L/V6-191(T)	1½ Turns ①
1993–95	3.4L/V6-207(S)	1½ Turns ①

①—Turn rocker arm stud nut until all lash is eliminated, then tighten nut the additional turn listed.

VALVE ADJUSTMENT

After the engine has been thoroughly warmed up the valves may be adjusted, **Fig. 8,** with the engine shutoff as follows: With engine in position to fire No. 1 cylinder the following valves may be adjusted: exhaust 1-2-3, intake 1-5-6. Then crank the engine one more complete revolution which will bring No. 4 cylinder to the firing position at which time the following valves may be adjusted: exhaust 4-5-6, intake 2-3-4.

The following procedure, performed with the engine running, should be done only in case readjustment is required.

1. After engine has been warmed up to operating temperature, remove valve cover and install a new valve cover gasket.
2. With engine running at idle speed, back off valve rocker arm nut until rocker arm starts to clatter.
3. Turn rocker arm nut down slowly until the clatter just stops. This is the zero lash position.

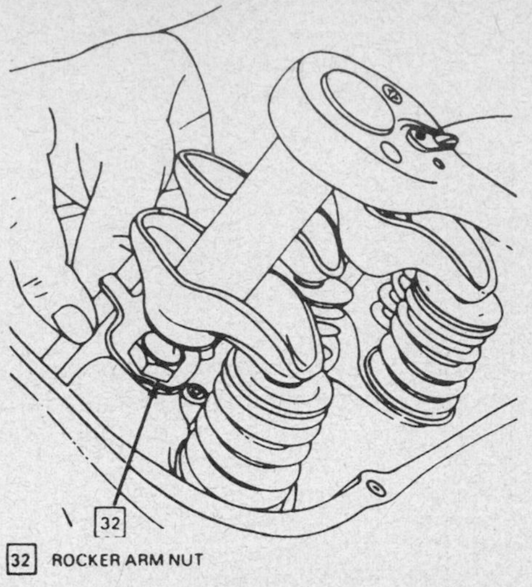
32
32 ROCKER ARM NUT
GC1069100199000X

Fig. 8 Valve lash adjustment

4. Turn nut down ¼ additional turn and pause 10 seconds until engine runs smoothly. Repeat additional ¼ turns, pausing 10 seconds each time, until nut has been turned down the number of turns listed in the Valve Lash Specifications Chart from the zero lash position. **This preload adjustment must be done slowly to allow the lifter to adjust itself to prevent the possibility of interference between the intake valve head and top of piston, which might result in internal damage and/or bent pushrods. Noisy lifters should be replaced.**

ROCKER ARM STUDS

If studs are loose in cylinder head, .003 inch or .013 inch oversize studs may be installed on all engines with pressed-in type studs, after reaming holes with a proper size reamer. On engines with threaded rocker studs, looseness can be corrected by installing the proper size Heli-Coil insert, or by replacing cylinder head. Replace damaged pressed-in rocker arm studs using the following procedure:

1. Remove the old stud by placing a suitable spacer, **Fig. 9,** over stud. Install nut and flat washer and remove stud by turning nut.
2. Ream hole for oversize stud.
3. Coat press-fit area of stud with rear axle lube. Then install new stud, **Fig. 10.** If tool shown is used, it should bottom on the head.

PUSH RODS

On engines that use pushrods with a hardened insert at one end, the hardened end is identified by a color stripe and should always be installed toward the rocker arm during assembly. When installing, ensure pushrods are seated properly in hydraulic lifters.

VALVE GUIDES

Valves operate in guide holes bored in the head. If clearance becomes excessive, use the next oversize valve and ream the

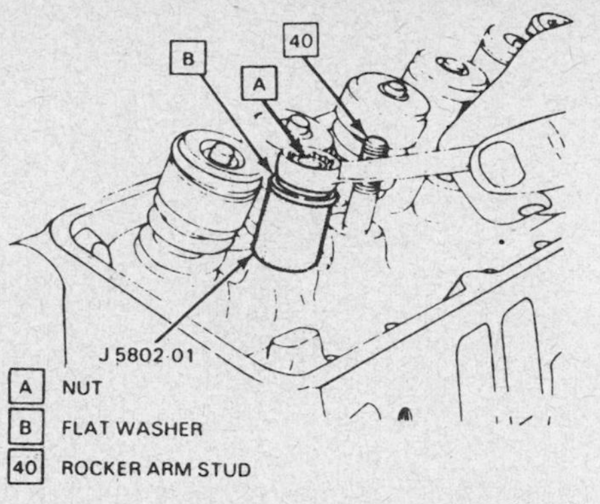

B
40
A
J 5802-01
A NUT
B FLAT WASHER
40 ROCKER ARM STUD
GC1069100200000X

Fig. 9 Pressed-in type rocker arm stud removal

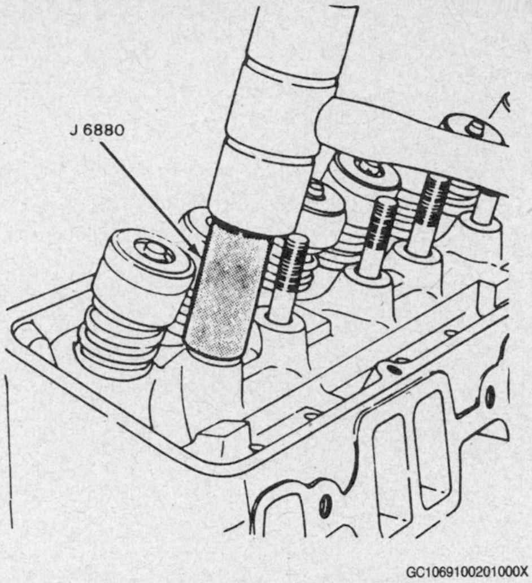

J 6880
GC1069100201000X

Fig. 10 Pressed-in type rocker arm stud installation

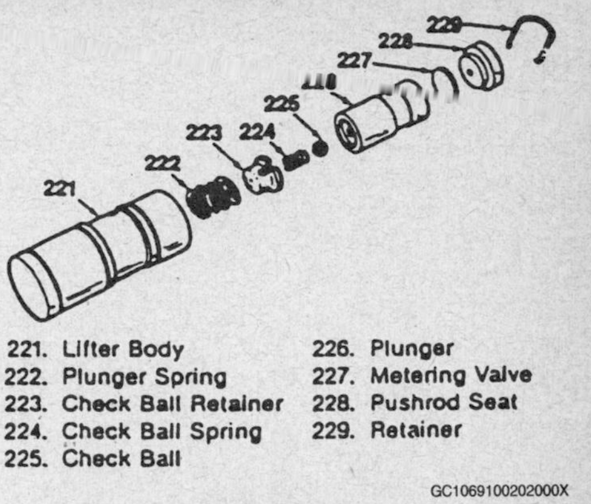

221
222
223
224
225
226
227
228
229
221. Lifter Body
222. Plunger Spring
223. Check Ball Retainer
224. Check Ball Spring
225. Check Ball
226. Plunger
227. Metering Valve
228. Pushrod Seat
229. Retainer
GC1069100202000X

Fig. 11 Hydraulic valve lifter

bore to fit. Valves with oversize stems are available in .003, .015 and .030 inch.

HYDRAULIC LIFTERS

REPLACE

Some engine may be equipped with standard and over size lifters. Lifter bosses where oversize lifters are installed will be marked by dab of white paint or stamped .25 mm O.S.

Valve lifters can be lifted from their bores after removing rocker arms and pushrods and intake manifold. Adjustable pliers with protected jaws may be used to remove lifters which are stuck due to carbon or varnish deposits. Tag lifters so they can be installed at the same location as removed. If new lifters are being installed, coat lifter foot with Molykote or equivalent. Fig. 11 illustrate types of valve lifter used.

FRONT COVER

REPLACE

3.1L/V6-191 ENGINE

1. Remove oil pan as described under "Oil Pan, Replace."
2. Remove power steering pump and bracket.
3. Disconnect heater hose, then remove water pump as described under "Water Pump, Replace."
4. Remove vibration damper, then disconnect lower radiator hose from front cover.
5. Remove front cover retaining bolts and cover.
6. Thoroughly clean sealing surfaces of front cover and engine block surface.
7. Reverse procedure to install.

3.4L/V6-207 ENGINE

1. Disconnect throttle body air duct, then remove serpentine drive belt.
2. Remove water pump as described under "Water Pump, Replace," then the crankshaft balancer assembly using torsional damper remover J 24420.
3. Remove power steering pump and bracket, then the oil pan assembly as described under "Oil Pan, Replace."
4. Disconnect lower radiator hose from front cover assembly, then remove crankshaft sensor.

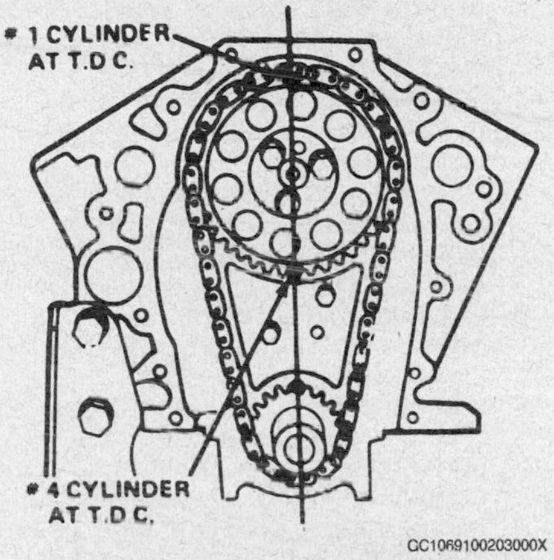

1 CYLINDER AT T.D.C.
4 CYLINDER AT T.D.C.
GC1069100203000X

Fig. 12 Valve timing marks. 3.1L/V6-191 engine

5. Remove front cover assembly.
6. Reverse procedure to install, noting the following:
   a. Tighten fasteners to specifications.
   b. Coat both sides of lower tabs of front cover gasket with sealer 1052080.
   c. Install crankshaft balancer assembly using torsional damper installer J-29113.

FRONT COVER SEAL

REPLACE

The front cover oil seal may be replaced without taking off the front cover. After removing the vibration damper, pry out the old seal with a screwdriver. Install the new seal with the lip or open end toward inside of cover and drive it into position using tool No. J-35468, or equivalent.

TIMING CHAIN

REPLACE

3.1L/V6-191 ENGINE

1. Remove front cover as described previously.
2. Remove crankshaft oil slinger.
3. Crank engine until timing marks on sprockets are in alignment, **Fig. 12.**
4. Remove camshaft to sprocket bolts.
5. Remove camshaft sprocket and timing chain together. If sprocket does not come off easily, a light blow with a plastic hammer to the sprocket should dislodge it.
6. If crankshaft sprocket is to be replaced, remove it with a suitable gear puller.
7. Apply Molykote or equivalent to sprocket thrust surfaces.
8. Install crankshaft sprocket, aligning key and keyway, if removed.
9. Install chain on camshaft sprocket. Hold sprocket vertical with chain hanging below and shift around to align the timing marks on sprockets.
10. Align dowel in camshaft with dowel hole in sprocket and install sprocket on camshaft. Do not attempt to drive sprocket on camshaft as welch plug at rear of engine can be dislodged.
11. Draw sprocket onto camshaft, using the mounting bolts. Tighten to specifications.
12. Lubricate timing chain with engine oil and install front cover.

3.4L/V6-207 ENGINE

1. Remove front cover assembly as previously described, then rotate crankshaft until timing marks on crankshaft sprocket and camshaft sprocket are aligned to marks on engine block or timing chain dampener, **Fig. 13.**
2. Remove camshaft sprocket bolts, then the camshaft sprocket and timing chain assembly.
3. Remove crankshaft sprocket using crankshaft sprocket remover tool No. J-23444-A, or equivalent, then the timing chain dampener.
4. Remove crankshaft sprocket key, if necessary.
5. Reverse procedure to install, noting the following:
   a. Tighten fasteners to specifications.
   b. Install crankshaft sprocket using crankshaft sprocket installer tool No. J-38612, or equivalent.
   c. When installing camshaft sprocket and timing chain assembly, ensure timing marks are aligned as previously described.

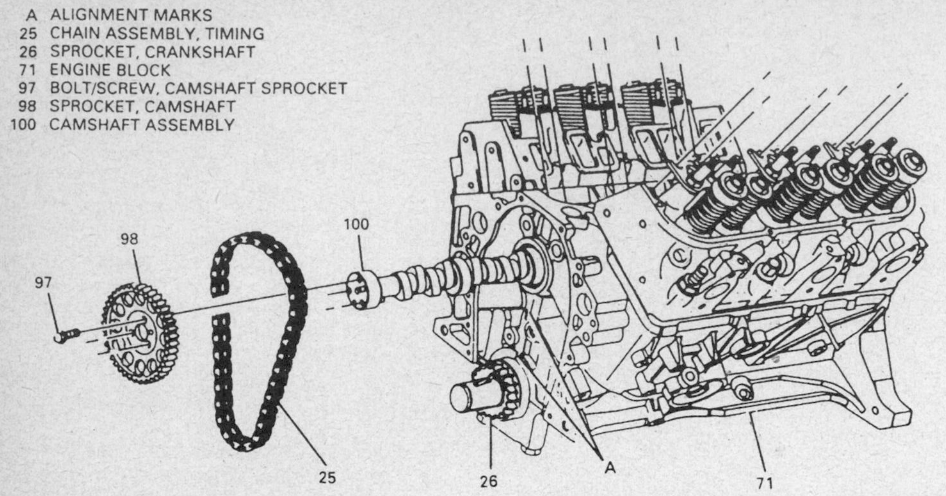
A ALIGNMENT MARKS
25 CHAIN ASSEMBLY, TIMING
26 SPROCKET, CRANKSHAFT
71 ENGINE BLOCK
97 BOLT/SCREW, CAMSHAFT SPROCKET
98 SPROCKET, CAMSHAFT
100 CAMSHAFT ASSEMBLY
98
100
97
25
26
A
71
GC1069100204000X

Fig. 13 Valve timing marks. 3.4L/V6-207 engine

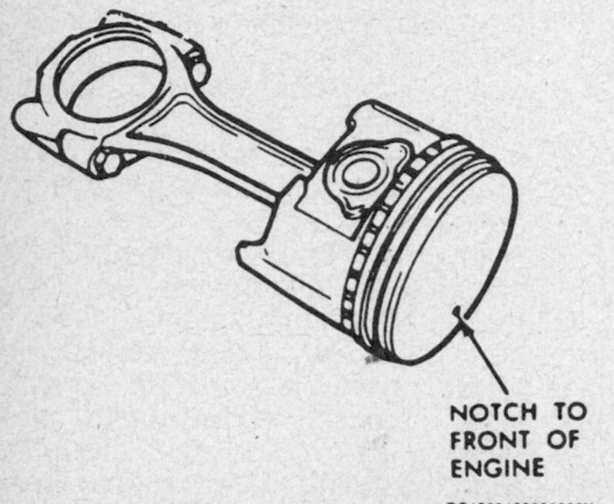
NOTCH TO FRONT OF ENGINE
GC1069100206000X

Fig. 15 Piston & rod assembly. 3.1L/V6-191 engine

d. Coat crankshaft and camshaft sprockets with engine oil.

CAMSHAFT

REPLACE

3.1L/V6-191 ENGINE

1. Remove valve lifters and engine front cover.
2. Remove grille, radiator and condenser.
3. Remove timing chain as described previously.
4. Remove camshaft from engine using care not to damage camshaft bearings, **Fig. 14.**
5. Reverse procedure to install. Coat camshaft journals with engine oil. If installing a new camshaft, coat camshaft lobes with lubricant No. GM ESO, or equivalent, prior to installation.

3.4L/V6-207 ENGINE

1. Remove upper intake manifold assembly, then the lower intake manifold assembly as previously described.
2. Remove rocker arm covers, then the rocker arm nuts and balls.
3. Remove rocker arms and pushrod assemblies. **Place rocker arms, balls and pushrod assemblies in a rack so that they may be reinstalled in same locations from which they were removed.**
4. Remove oil pump drive assembly, then the front cover assembly as previously described.
5. Remove camshaft sprocket as described under "Timing Chain, Replace," then the valve lifter assemblies.
6. Discharge A/C refrigerant into a recovery station, then remove A/C compressor.
7. Disconnect A/C condenser hose and receiver and dehydrator hose from condenser, then remove radiator assembly with A/C condenser.
8. Install three 5/16-18 x 4 inch bolts in camshaft bolt holes, then carefully rotate and pull camshaft assembly out of bearings.
9. Reverse procedure to install, noting the following:
   a. Tighten fasteners to specifications.
   b. If installing new camshaft, coat camshaft lobes with Molykote.
   c. If installing new camshaft, replace all valve lifter assemblies.
   d. Lubricate all camshaft journals and oil pump drive assembly with engine oil.
   e. Lubricate oil pump drive gear with prelube 1052365.

PISTON & ROD ASSEMBLY

3.1L/V6-191 ENGINE

Assemble pistons to connecting rods as shown in **Fig. 15. Numbers on rod & cap must be on same side.**

Upon installation, measure the connecting rod side clearance using a suitable feeler gauge. Refer to "Engine Rebuilding Specifications" for connecting rod side clearance.

3.4L/V6-207 ENGINE

When installing piston and connecting rod assemblies, stamped arrow on piston

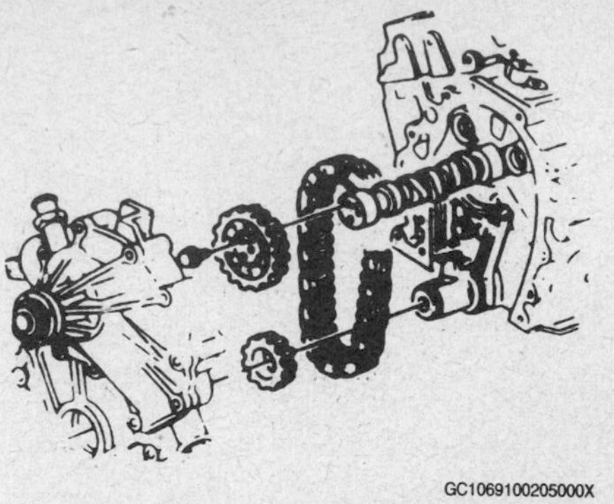
GC1069100205000X

Fig. 14 Front cover, timing chain & camshaft. 3.1L/V6-191 engine

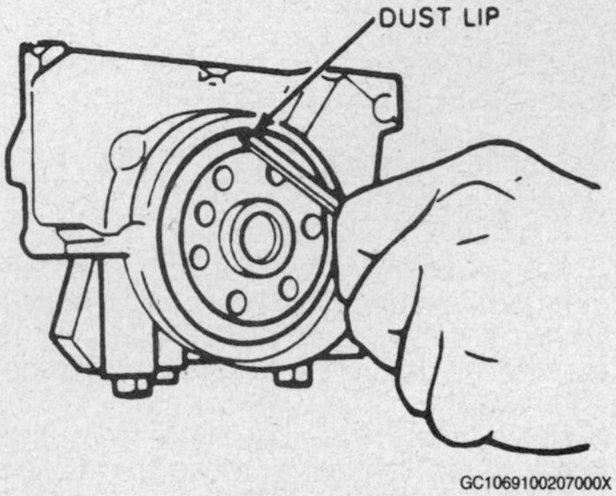
DUST LIP
GC1069100207000X

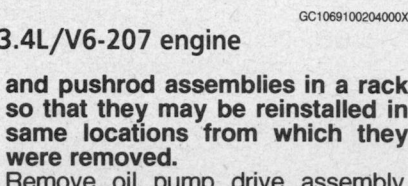

Fig. 16 Crankshaft rear oil seal removal

assembly must point to front of engine while flange on connecting rod must face toward front of piston on lefthand assembly and face toward rear of piston on righthand assembly.

PISTONS, PINS & RINGS

Pistons and piston rings are available in standard and oversizes of .010 and .030 inch.

MAIN & ROD BEARINGS

Connecting rod bearings are available in standard and undersizes of .001, .002, .010 and .020 inch.

Main bearings are available in standard and undersizes of .001, .002, .009, .010 and .020 inch.

CRANKSHAFT REAR OIL SEAL

REPLACE

1. Raise and support vehicle.
2. Support engine as needed, then remove transmission.
3. Remove clutch and pressure plate, if equipped, then remove flywheel or flex plate.
4. Insert screwdriver through seal lip and pry seal from bore, taking care not to damage crankshaft, **Fig. 16.**
5. Clean seal bore and crankshaft, then inspect for burrs, nicks and wear, and repair as needed.
6. Lightly lubricate replacement seal lip with engine oil, mount seal on installer tool No. J-34686, or equivalent, and

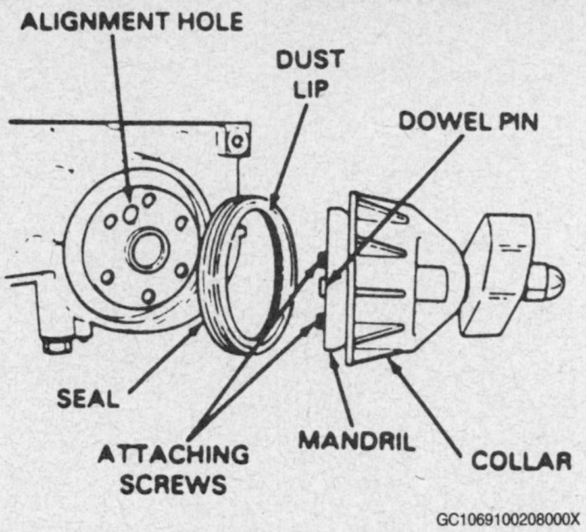
ALIGNMENT HOLE
DUST LIP
DOWEL PIN
SEAL
ATTACHING SCREWS
MANDRIL
COLLAR
GC1069100208000X

Fig. 17 Crankshaft rear oil seal installation

seat dust lip of seal squarely against collar.

7. Lubricate outer diameter of seal with engine oil, align dowel pin of tool with dowel pin hole in crankshaft, mount tool on crankshaft and **torque** to 24 to 60 inch lbs., **Fig. 17.**
8. Rotate T handle of tool clockwise, pressing seal into bore until collar is tight against engine case to ensure seal is fully seated.
9. Rotate T handle of tool counterclockwise to stop, then remove tool and ensure seal is seated squarely in bore.
10. Reverse remaining procedure to complete installation.

OIL PAN

REPLACE

3.1L/V6-191 ENGINE

1. Disconnect battery ground cable.
2. Raise and support vehicle, then remove catalytic converter hanger bolts.
3. Detach transmission oil cooler lines from oil pan clips, if equipped.
4. Place crankshaft damper timing mark at the 7 O'clock position.
5. Drain crankcase, then remove flywheel dust cover, if equipped.
6. Disconnect exhaust crossover pipe from exhaust manifolds.
7. Remove engine mount through bolts, then raise engine slightly permit oil pan removal using a suitable lifting device.
8. Remove oil pan attaching bolts, then remove oil pan, **Fig. 18.**
9. Reverse procedure to install.

3.4L/V6-207 ENGINE

1. Disconnect battery ground cable, then remove air intake duct.
2. Raise and support vehicle, then drain engine oil.
3. Remove wiring harness clips from left side of oil pan assembly, then disconnect oil level sensor connector.
4. Remove oil level sensor assembly, then disconnect exhaust crossover pipes from exhaust manifold assemblies.
5. Remove exhaust pipe hanger bolt and reposition pipe, then disconnect transmission cooler lines from clip at oil pan assembly, if equipped.
6. Remove starter motor assembly, then the converter cover, if equipped.
7. Remove engine mount through bolts, then raise engine with a jacking fixture.
8. Remove oil pan bolts, studs, nuts and reinforcements, then the oil pan assembly.
9. Reverse procedure to install, noting the following:
   a. Tighten fasteners to specifications.
   b. Apply a small amount of sealer 12345739 where oil pan gasket tabs seat on rear crankshaft bearing cap groove.

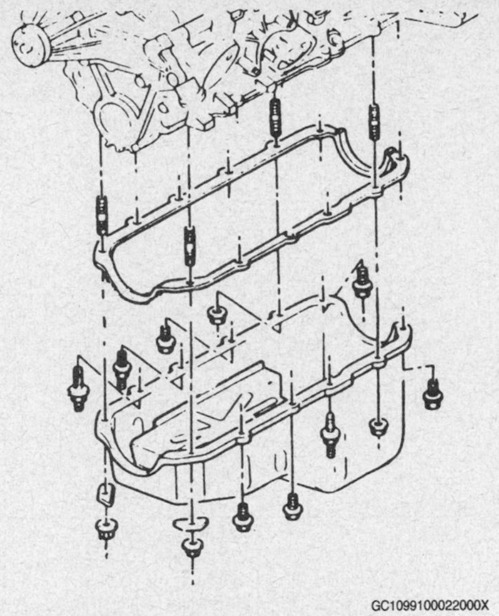
GC1099100022000X

Fig. 18 Oil pan replacement. 3.1L/V6-191 engine

OIL PUMP

REPLACE

3.1L/V6-191 ENGINE

1. Remove oil pan as described previously.
2. Remove pump to rear main bearing cap bolt and remove pump and extension shaft.
3. Reverse procedure to install. Make sure that installed position of oil pump screen is with bottom edge parallel to oil pan rails. Prime oil pump prior to installation.

3.4L/V6-207 ENGINE

1. Remove oil pan as previously described, then the oil pump assembly and driveshaft.
2. Reverse procedure to install, noting the following:
   a. Tighten fasteners to specifications.
   b. Align slot on end of intermediate shaft with drive tang on oil pump drive assembly.

OIL PUMP SERVICE

3.1L/V6-191 ENGINE

1. Remove oil pump as described previously.
2. Remove pump cover screws and pump cover, **Fig. 19.**
3. Mark gear teeth so they can be reassembled with same teeth indexing, then remove drive gear, idler gear and shaft.
4. Remove pressure regulator valve retaining pin, pressure regulator valve and related parts.
5. If pickup screen and pipe require replacement, mount pump in a soft-jawed vise and extract pipe from pump.
6. Wash all parts in cleaning solvent and dry with compressed air.
7. Inspect pump body and cover for cracks and excessive wear.
8. Inspect pump gears for damage or excessive wear.
9. Check drive gear shaft for looseness in pump body.
10. Inspect inside of pump cover for wear that would allow oil to leak past the ends of the gears.
11. Inspect pickup screen and pipe assembly for damage to screen, pipe or relief grommet.
12. Check pressure regulator valve for fit in pump housing.
13. Reverse procedure to assemble. Turn driveshaft by hand to check for smooth operation. **The pump gears and body are not serviced separately. If the pump gears or body are damaged or worn, the pump assembly should be replaced. Also, if the pick-up screen and pump assembly was removed, it should be replaced with a new one as loss of the press fit condition could result in an air leak and loss of oil pressure.**

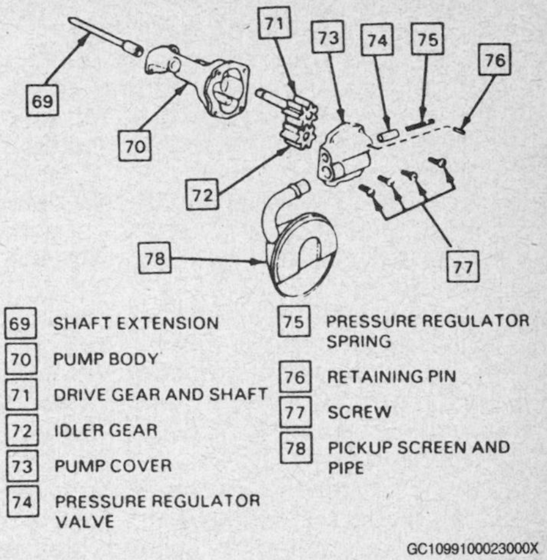
69
70
71
72
73
74
75
76
77
78
69 SHAFT EXTENSION
70 PUMP BODY
71 DRIVE GEAR AND SHAFT
72 IDLER GEAR
73 PUMP COVER
74 PRESSURE REGULATOR VALVE
75 PRESSURE REGULATOR SPRING
76 RETAINING PIN
77 SCREW
78 PICKUP SCREEN AND PIPE
GC1099100023000X

Fig. 19 Exploded view of oil pump. 3.1L/V6-191 engine

3.4L/V6-207 ENGINE

1. Remove oil pump as previously described, then drain oil from pump.
2. Remove drive shaft, then the pump cover.
3. Remove pump gears, then the cotter pin, spring and pressure regulator valve. **Pressure regulator valve**

spring is under pressure in some models, use extreme caution when removing retaining pin. If valve is stuck, soak pump housing in carburetor cleaning solvent.

4. Clean all parts of sludge, oil and varnish.
5. Inspect for foreign material, pump housing and cover for cracks, scoring, casting imperfections and damaged threads.
6. Inspect idler gear shaft. If loose in housing, replace pump.
7. Inspect pressure regulator valve for scoring and sticking and pressure regulator spring for loss of tension or bending.
8. Inspect suction pipe and screen assembly for looseness or broken wire mesh or screen. If suction pipe is loose, bent or broken, pump body cover and suction pipe must be replaced.
9. Inspect gears for chipping, galling or wear and drive shaft and drive shaft extension for looseness or wear.
10. Measure gear lash, pump housing gear pocket, gears, gear side clearance and gear end clearance. **When deciding pump serviceability based on end clearance, consider depth of wear pattern in pump cover.**
11. Reverse steps 1 through 3 to assemble pump. Tighten fasteners to specifications.

BELT TENSION DATA

Engine (VIN)	Year	Less A/C, Lbs.①	With A/C, Lbs.②
3.1L/V6-191(T)	1992	95–140	85–110

①—Checked between tensioner & power steering pump.
②—Checked between tensioner & A/C compressor.

SERPENTINE DRIVE BELT

1. Disconnect battery ground cable.
2. Lift belt tensioner off belt using a socket and breaker bar.
3. Remove drive belt.
4. Reverse procedure to install. Refer to **Figs. 20 and 21** for serpentine belt routing. Start and operate engine for 5 minutes. Check belt tension using a suitable belt tension gauge. **On models less A/C,** check belt tension between tensioner and power steering pump. **On models with A/C,** check belt tension between tensioner and A/C compressor. Refer to "Belt Tension Data" for specifications. Operate engine 30 seconds, then recheck belt tension. If tension is not with in limits, check belt and tensioner and replace as necessary.

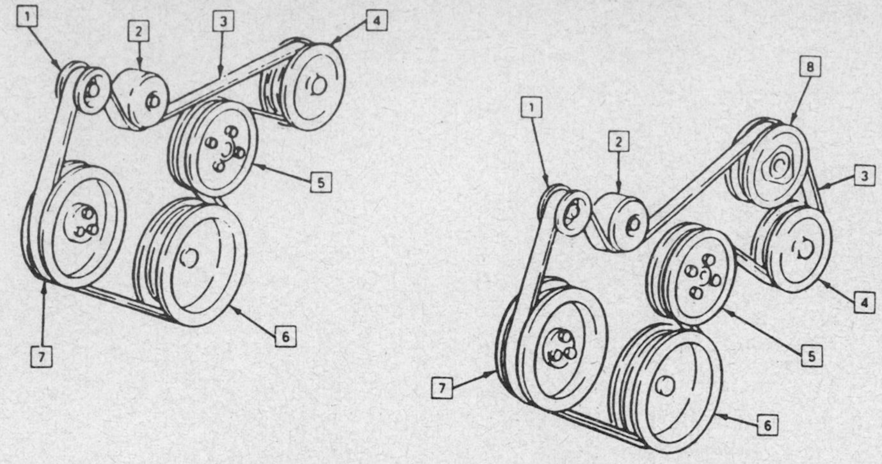
1
2
3
4
5
6
7
8
1
2
3
4
5
6
7

1. GENERATOR
2. TENSIONER
3. BELT
4. P S PUMP
5. WATER PUMP
6. CRANKSHAFT
7. A.I.R. PUMP
8. A/C COMPRESSOR

GC1069100209000X

Fig. 20 Serpentine drive belt routing. 3.1L/V6-191 engine

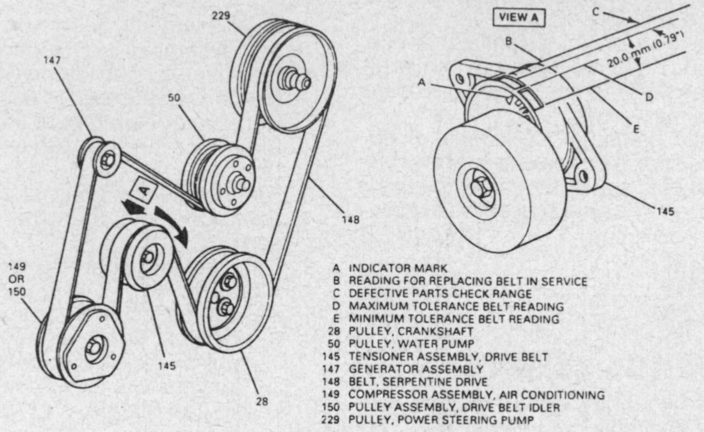
229
147
50
148
149 OR 150
145
28
VIEW A
A
B
C
D
E
20.0 mm (0.79")
145
A INDICATOR MARK
B READING FOR REPLACING BELT IN SERVICE
C DEFECTIVE PARTS CHECK RANGE
D MAXIMUM TOLERANCE BELT READING
E MINIMUM TOLERANCE BELT READING
28 PULLEY, CRANKSHAFT
50 PULLEY, WATER PUMP
145 TENSIONER ASSEMBLY, DRIVE BELT
147 GENERATOR ASSEMBLY
148 BELT, SERPENTINE DRIVE
149 COMPRESSOR ASSEMBLY, AIR CONDITIONING
150 PULLEY ASSEMBLY, DRIVE BELT IDLER
229 PULLEY, POWER STEERING PUMP

GC1069100210000X

Fig. 21 Serpentine drive belt routing. 3.4L/V6-207 engine

COOLING SYSTEM BLEED

After filling cooling system, start engine and allow to reach operating temperature with radiator cap removed. Air in system is bleed through radiator cap opening. Add coolant as necessary to bring to proper level, then install radiator cap and check coolant level in recovery reservoir.

THERMOSTAT

REPLACE

3.1L/V6-191 ENGINE

1. Disconnect battery ground cable, then drain cooling system, until coolant lever is below level of thermostat.
2. Remove air cleaner and air duct, as necessary.
3. Relieve fuel system pressure as described under "Precautions."
4. Remove throttle body and plenum.
5. Disconnect radiator from thermostat housing.
6. Remove thermostat housing attaching bolts, then remove housing and thermostat, **Fig. 22.**
7. Reverse procedure to install.

3.4L/V6-207 ENGINE

1. Disconnect battery ground cable, then drain cooling system, until coolant lever is below level of thermostat.
2. Remove air cleaner, then disconnect radiator inlet hose from thermostat assembly.
3. Remove thermostat housing attaching bolts, then remove housing and thermostat.
4. Reverse procedure to install. Tighten fasteners to specifications.

WATER PUMP

REPLACE

3.1L/V6-191 ENGINE

1. Disconnect battery ground cable and drain cooling system.
2. Remove intake duct, then remove serpentine drive belt.

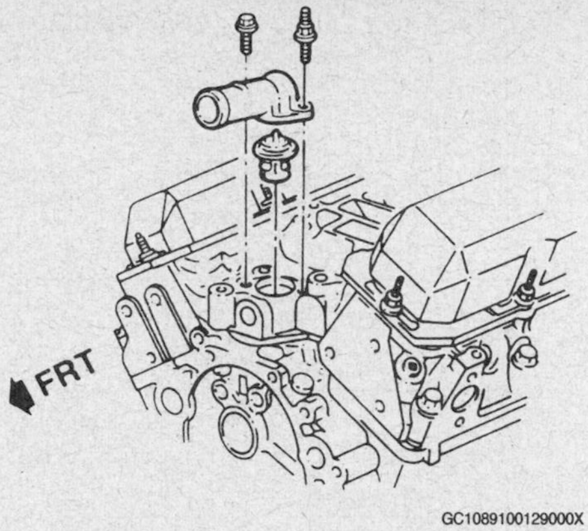
FRT
GC1089100129000X

Fig. 22 Thermostat & housing replacement. 3.1L/V6-191 engine

3. Disconnect heater hose from water pump.
4. Disconnect radiator hose from thermostat housing.
5. Remove power steering pump and bracket and position aside with hoses attached.
6. Remove water pump attaching bolts, then remove water pump and gasket.
7. Reverse procedure to install. Prior to installation, coat water pump bolt threads with a suitable sealer. Refer to **Fig. 23,** for water pump attaching bolt tightness.

3.4L/V6-207 ENGINE

1. Drain cooling system, then disconnect air duct and electrical connector.
2. Disconnect top coil of coil pack, then loosen tensioner pulley bolt.
3. Disconnect heater hose from pump, then loosen water pump pulley bolts.
4. Remove power steering bracket bolts, then the serpentine drive belt.
5. Remove water pump pulley, then the power steering pump bracket and pump.
6. Remove water pump.
7. Reverse procedure to install, noting the following:
   a. Tighten fasteners to specifications.
   b. Bleed cooling system.

RADIATOR

REPLACE

1. Disconnect intake duct, then remove air cleaner assembly.
2. Remove mass air flow sensor (MAF), if equipped.
3. Raise and support vehicle, then drain engine coolant.
4. Disconnect electrical connectors at cooling fans.
5. Remove upper radiator mounting panel, then cooling fan assembly.
6. Disconnect oil cooler lines, then remove coolant sensor, if equipped.
7. Lower vehicle and loosen receiver/dryer bracket.
8. Disconnect upper and lower radiator hoses, then overflow coolant hose.
9. Disconnect heater hose and clamp, if equipped.
10. Remove upper radiator mount, then radiator assembly.

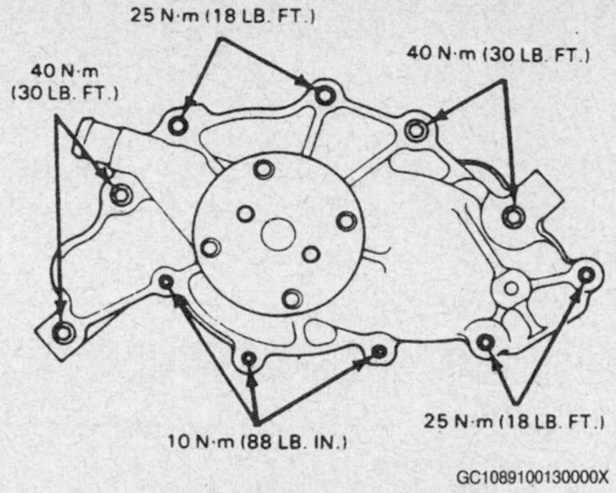
25 N·m (18 LB. FT.)
40 N·m (30 LB. FT.)
40 N·m (30 LB. FT.)
10 N·m (88 LB. IN.)
25 N·m (18 LB. FT.)
GC1089100130000X

Fig. 23 Water pump bolt tightening specifications. 3.1L/V6-191 engine

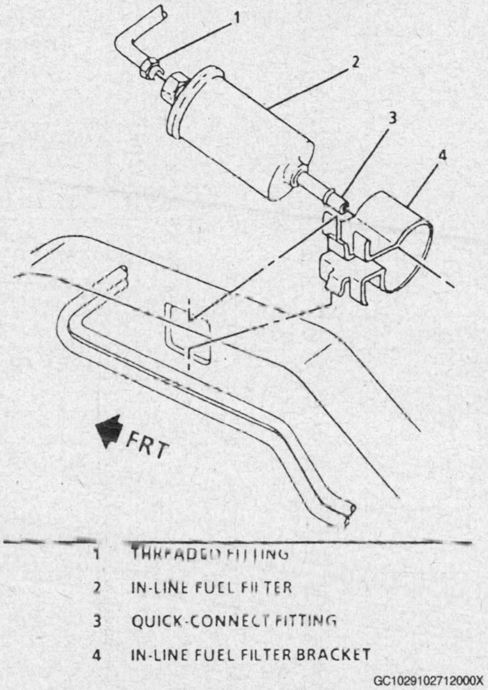
1
2
3
4
FRT
1 THREADED FITTING
2 IN-LINE FUEL FILTER
3 QUICK-CONNECT FITTING
4 IN-LINE FUEL FILTER BRACKET
GC1029102712000X

Fig. 25 Fuel filter replacement. 3.4L/V6-207 engine

11. Reverse procedure to install.

FUEL PUMP

REPLACE

3.1L/V6-191 ENGINE

1. Disconnect battery ground cable, then disconnect engine harness connector at ignition distributor.
2. Relieve fuel system pressure as described under "Precautions."
3. Drain fuel tank. Place fuel in an approved container.
4. Remove filler neck shield.
5. Remove tires, then raise and support vehicle.
6. Remove track bar and brace.
7. Support axle, then disconnect lower shock mount.
8. Remove exhaust from converter back, then the heat shield.
9. Disconnect brake cables from S clips, then from retainers on frame rails.
10. Remove stabilizer bar links.

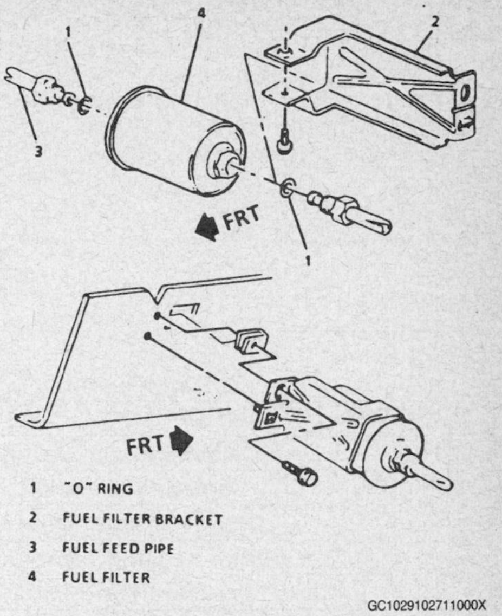
1
2
3
4
FRT
FRT
1 "O" RING
2 FUEL FILTER BRACKET
3 FUEL FEED PIPE
4 FUEL FILTER
GC1029102711000X

Fig. 24 Fuel filter replacement. 3.1L/V6-191 engine

11. Lower axle, then remove rear springs.
12. Disconnect fuel lines and wires.
13. Support fuel tank and remove straps.
14. Remove fuel tank from vehicle.
15. Remove fuel level sending unit and pump assembly by turning cam lock ring counterclockwise.
16. Remove fuel pump from level sending unit by pulling fuel pump upward and outward, away from bottom support.
17. Reverse procedure to install.

3.4L/V6-207 ENGINE

1. Relieve fuel system pressure as described under "Precautions," then drain fuel tank. Place fuel in an approved container.
2. Remove fuel tank as follows:
   a. Raise and support vehicle, then remove fuel filler neck shield.
   b. Remove rear axle assembly as described in "Rear Axle & Suspension" section.
   c. Remove exhaust pipe and muffler and muffler heat shield.
   d. Clean all fuel pipe and hose connections, then disconnect rear fuel feed pipe assembly from fuel sender/pump assembly, fuel return, vapor and vent hoses at fuel sender/pump assembly.
   e. Disconnect electrical connector from fuel sender assembly, then remove fuel tank.
3. Remove fuel sender/pump retaining nuts and retaining ring, then the fuel sender/pump assembly.
4. Reverse procedure to install. Tighten fasteners to specifications.

FUEL FILTER

REPLACE

3.1L/V6-191 ENGINE

1. Relieve fuel system pressure as described under "Precautions."
2. Raise and support vehicle.
3. Clean all fuel filter connections and surrounding areas.

4. Disconnect fuel feed pipes from filter, **Fig. 24,** then drain remaining fuel into suitable container.
5. Remove filter mounting screw, then the fuel filter.
6. Reverse procedure to install.

3.4L/V6-207 ENGINE

1. Relieve fuel system pressure as described under "Precautions," then raise and support vehicle.
2. Clean both fuel feed pipe connections and surrounding areas, then remove fuel filter bracket.
3. Disconnect quick-disconnect fitting at fuel filter inlet, **Fig. 25,** then the threaded outlet fitting from chassis fuel pipe.
4. Remove fuel filter.
5. Reverse procedure to install. Tighten fittings to specifications.

TIGHTENING SPECIFICATIONS

Year	Component	Torque/ Ft. Lbs.
3.1L/V6-191 ENGINES		
1992	Camshaft Rear Cover	89①
	Camshaft Sprocket	21
	Clutch Housing Cover	53①
	Clutch Housing To Engine	70
	Clutch Pressure Plate To Flywheel	15
	Connecting Rod Cap	39
	Crankshaft Damper	70
	Crankshaft Pulley	37
	Cylinder Head	②
	Distributor Hold-Down Bolt	25
	Drive Belt Tensioner Brace To Alternator Bracket	26
	Drive Belt Tensioner Brace To Engine	18
	Engine Coolant Drain Plugs	15
	Engine Front Cover Bolts	15
	Engine Mount Nut	30
	Engine Mount Through Bolt & Nut	50
	Exhaust Crossover Pipe Nut	15
	Exhaust Manifold	25
	Flywheel to Crankshaft	52
	Fuel Line Nuts & Bolts	20
	Fuel Rail	18
	Intake Manifold (Center)	15
	Intake Manifold (Lower)	19
	Intake Plenum Bolts & Studs	15
	Main Bearing Cap	73
	Oil Dipstick Tube Nut	27
	Oil Filter Adapter Bolts	63
	Oil Pan Drain Plug	18
	Oil Pan Rear Two Bolts	18
	Oil Pan Except Rear Two Bolts	89①
	Oil Pump	30
	Rocker Arm Cover	10
	Spark Plug	25
	Starter Motor Mounting Bolts	35
	Thermostat Housing	18
	Throttle Body Bolts	20
	Timing Chain Damper	15
	Torque Converter to Flywheel Bolts (Automatic)	46
	Torque Housing Cover (Automatic)	89①
	Transmission to Crossmember Nut	35

Year	Component	Torque/ Ft. Lbs.
3.1L/V6-191 ENGINES -Continued		
1992 -Cont'd	Transmission Mount to Support Bolt (Manual)	40
	Transmission Mount To Support Nut	35
	Transmission Mount to Transmission	40
	Transmission Support to Frame	40
	Transmission to Engine (Automatic)	35
	Transmission to Flywheel Housing (Manual)	55
	Water Pump	③
3.4L/V6-207 ENGINES		
1993–95	Accelerator Cable Bracket Bolt	90①
	Camshaft Sprocket Bolts	18
	Connecting Rod Nuts	37
	Crankshaft Balancer Bolt	58
	Crankshaft Bearing Cap Bolts	37④
	Crankshaft Pulley Bolts	37
	Cylinder Head	②
	Dipstick Tube Nut	15
	EGR Flexible Pipe Bolts	19
	EGR Valve Adapter Bolt & Stud	23
	Engine Mount Bolts	43
	Engine Mount Through Bolt	70
	Engine Mount Through Bolt Nut	59
	Engine Oil Level Sensor	16
	Exhaust Manifold Bolts	18
	Flywheel Bolts	61
	Front Cover Bolts	15
	Fuel Filter Fitting	20
	Fuel Pipe Bracket-To-Front Brace Bolt	71①
	Fuel Pipe Bracket-To-Intake Manifold Assembly Bolt	89
	Fuel Pipe Hold Down Plate Bolt	18
	Fuel Rail Stud	19
	Fuel Sender Retaining Nuts	63①
	Fuel Tank Strap Attaching Bolts	25
	Lower Intake Manifold Bolts & Nuts	22
	Oil Pan Front Corner Nuts	24
	Oil Pan Rear Corner Bolts	18
	Oil Pan Side Rail Bolts	89①
	Oil Pan Studs	53①
	Oil Pump Bolts	30
	Oil Pump Drive Clamp Bolt	25
	Secondary Air Injection Check Valve Pipe Bracket Nut	18

Continued

TIGHTENING SPECIFICATIONS-Continued

Year	Component	Torque/ Ft. Lbs.
3.4L/V6-207 ENGINES-Continued		
1993-95 -Cont'd	Serpentine Drive Belt Idler Pulley Bolts	37
	Serpentine Drive Belt Tensioner Bolts	24
	Spark Plugs	11
	Thermostat Housing Bolts	21
	Timing Chain Dampener Bolts	15
	Upper Intake Manifold Bolts	18
	Valve Rocker Arm Cover Reinforcement Nuts	89①
	Water Pump Bolts, Large	33
	Water Pump Bolts, Small	89①

①—Inch lbs.
②—Refer to text.
③—Torque to 40 ft. lbs., then tighten an additional 90°
④—Plus an additional 77° using torque angle meter tool No. J-36660, or equivalent.

5.0L/V8-305 & 5.7L/V8-350 Engines

NOTE: On Air Bag Equipped Models, Refer To "Air Bag System Precautions" Located In The Front Of This Manual For System Disarming & Arming Procedures.

NOTE: For 5.7L/V8-350 VIN P Procedures Not Found In This Section, Refer To The 5.7L/V8-350 Single Cam 16 Valve Engine (VIN P) Engine Section In The Chevrolet Corvette Chapter.

INDEX

PRECAUTIONS

AIR BAG SYSTEMS

Refer to "Air Bag System Precautions" in the front of this manual for system disarming and arming procedures.

FUEL SYSTEM PRESSURE RELIEF

5.0L/V8-305 (VIN E) TBI Engine

Remove fuel tank filler cap to release fuel tank pressure. The fuel injection system incorporates an internal constant bleed which releases fuel system pressure whenever engine is off.

5.0L/V8-305 (VIN F) & 5.7/V8-350 Engines

Failure to relieve system pressure prior to disconnecting fuel system components may cause fire or personal injury. Remove fuel tank filler cap to release fuel tank pressure. Connect pressure gauge tool No. J-34730-1, or equivalent, to pressure tap on fuel rail, position bleed hose into suitable container and slowly relieve fuel system pressure. Prior to disconnecting fuel line, position shop towel over fitting.

ENGINE MOUNT

REPLACE

Do not raise or support engine by positioning jack under oil pan, crankshaft damper or other sheet metal components. Raise engine only enough to provide sufficient clearance for mount removal. Check for interference between rear of engine and cowl panel which could result in distributor damage.

FRONT MOUNT

1. Disconnect battery ground cable.
2. Raise and support vehicle.
3. Remove engine mount through bolt, then raise front of engine to release weight from mount.
4. Remove mount to engine bolts and mount, **Fig. 1.**
5. Reverse procedure to install.

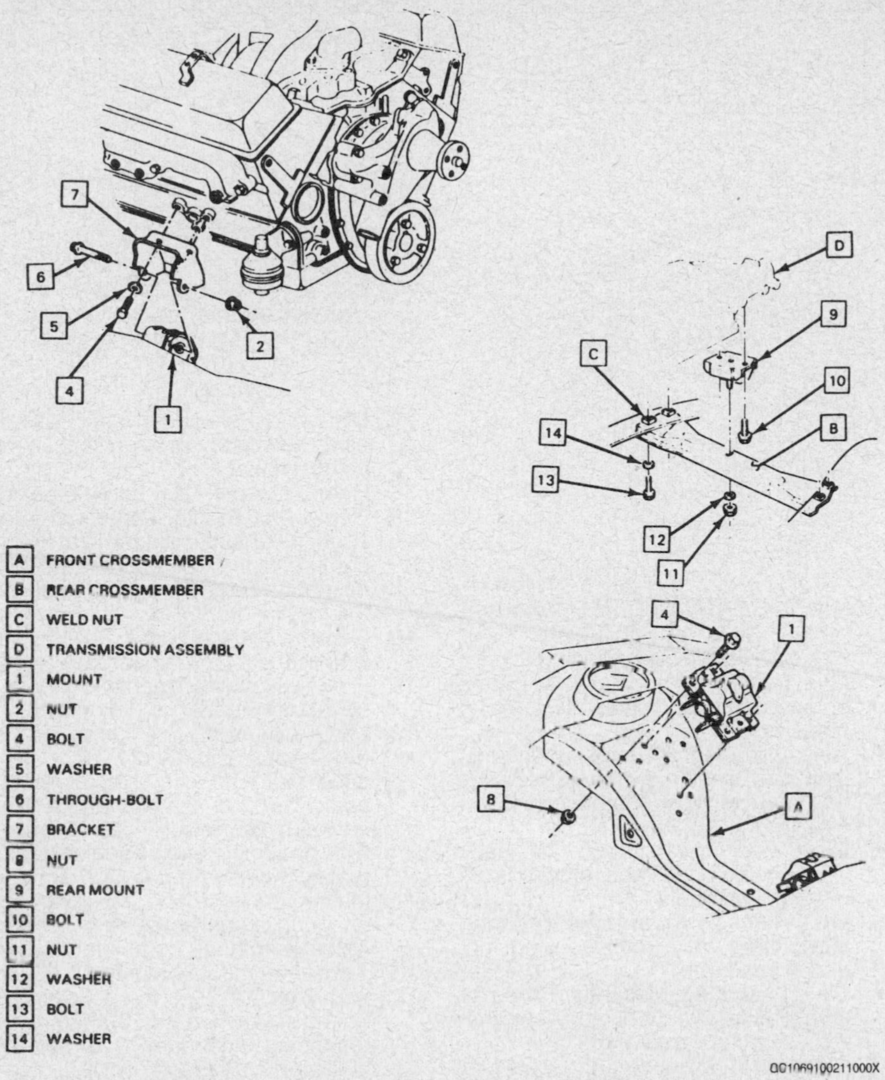
A FRONT CROSSMEMBER
B REAR CROSSMEMBER
C WELD NUT
D TRANSMISSION ASSEMBLY
1 MOUNT
2 NUT
4 BOLT
5 WASHER
6 THROUGH-BOLT
7 BRACKET
8 NUT
9 REAR MOUNT
10 BOLT
11 NUT
12 WASHER
13 BOLT
14 WASHER

Fig. 1 Engine mounting. Except 5.7L/V8-350 (VIN P) engine

REAR MOUNT

Except 5.7L/V8-350 (VIN P) Engine

1. Disconnect battery ground cable.
2. Support rear of engine to relieve weight on rear mount.
3. Remove mount to crossmember nut and washer.
4. Remove mount to transmission attaching bolt, then raise rear of engine slightly and remove mount, **Fig. 1.**
5. Reverse procedure to install.

ENGINE

REPLACE

EXCEPT 5.7L/V8-350 (VIN P) ENGINE

Do not raise or support engine by positioning jack under oil pan, crankshaft damper or other sheet metal components. Raise engine only enough to provide sufficient clearance for mount removal. Check for interference between rear of engine and cowl panel which could result in distributor damage.

1. Disconnect battery ground cable.
2. Scribe alignment marks on hood and hood hinge, then remove hood.
3. Remove air cleaner assembly, then raise and support vehicle.
4. Drain crankcase and cooling system, then disconnect lower radiator hose.
5. Remove lower fan attaching bolts, then disconnect electrical connectors and remove clips from fan.
6. Lower vehicle, then disconnect upper radiator hose.
7. Remove upper shroud and fan assembly.
8. Disconnect transmission oil cooler lines, if equipped, then remove radiator.
9. Remove serpentine drive belt.
10. Disconnect throttle linkage and cruise control cable, if equipped.
11. Remove plenum extension attaching screws and plenum extension, if equipped.
12. Disconnect and tag spark plug leads and wiring at distributor, then remove distributor.
13. Remove ignition coil, if equipped with external coil.
14. Disconnect all electrical wiring and vacuum hoses which would interfere with engine removal.
15. **On 5.0L/V8-305 VIN F and 5.7L/V8-350 engines,** relieve fuel system pressure as described under "Precautions."
16. **On all models,** disconnect fuel hoses at fuel lines.
17. Remove power steering pump pulley, then remove power steering pump.
18. Discharge A/C refrigerant system, then remove A/C compressor.
19. Disconnect battery ground cable from engine block.
20. Disconnect AIR hoses and pipe.
21. Raise and support vehicle, then disconnect crossover pipe from exhaust manifolds.
22. **On models with automatic transmission,** remove torque converter housing cover, then remove torque converter to flywheel attaching bolts. Also detach oil cooler lines at oil pan.
23. **On all models,** remove starter motor.
24. Remove engine mount bolts.
25. Support transmission using a transmission jack or other suitable fixture, then remove transmission crossmember bolts.
26. Lower transmission, then remove bellhousing to engine attaching bolts.
27. Raise transmission and install and tighten two transmission crossmember mounting bolts.
28. Remove transmission support device and lower vehicle.
29. Attach suitable a suitable engine lifting device to engine.
30. Position suitable support under transmission.
31. Disconnect ground wires and remove catalytic converter support bracket from rear of cylinder head.
32. Reverse engine from vehicle. Prior to removing engine, ensure all electrical wiring and hoses which would interfere with engine removal are disconnected.
33. Reverse procedure to install.

5.7L/V8-350 (VIN P) ENGINE

1. Disconnect battery ground cable.
2. Remove air intake duct, then raise and support vehicle and remove wheels.
3. Drain coolant and engine oil, then remove exhaust crossover pipe assembly.
4. **On vehicles with automatic transmission,** remove converter cover and converter bolts.
5. **On all vehicles,** remove front fascia lower deflectors, stabilizer bar bolts and the serpentine drive belt.
6. Remove secondary air injection pump assembly, then disconnect A/C hose assembly from condenser and compressor.
7. **On vehicles with automatic transmission,** disconnect transmission cooler lines from radiator.
8. **On all vehicles,** disconnect lower ra-

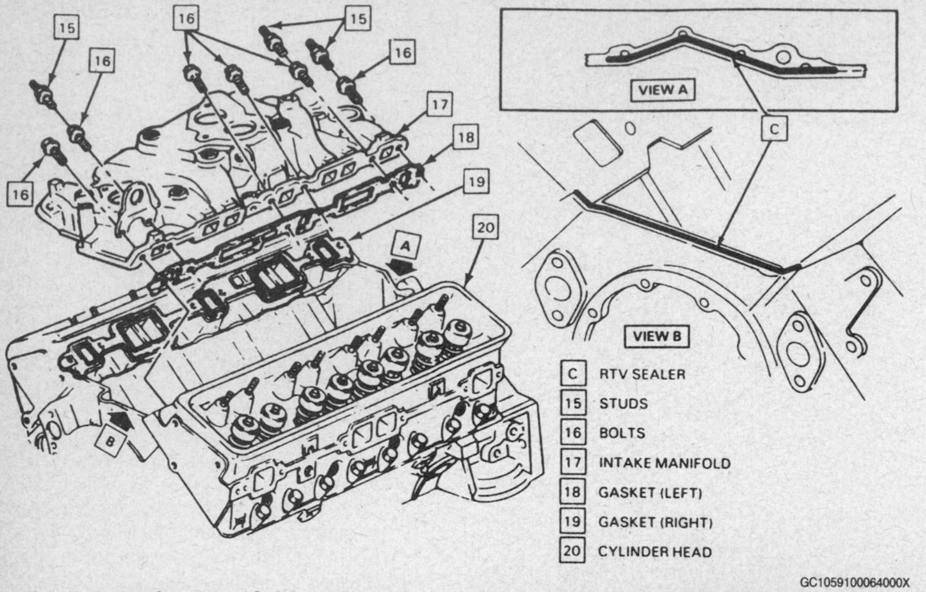
15
16
15
16
16
17
18
19
16
20
A
B
VIEW A
C
VIEW B
C RTV SEALER
15 STUDS
16 BOLTS
17 INTAKE MANIFOLD
18 GASKET (LEFT)
19 GASKET (RIGHT)
20 CYLINDER HEAD
GC1059100064000X

Fig. 2 Intake manifold replacement. Except 5.7L/V8-350 (VIN P) engine

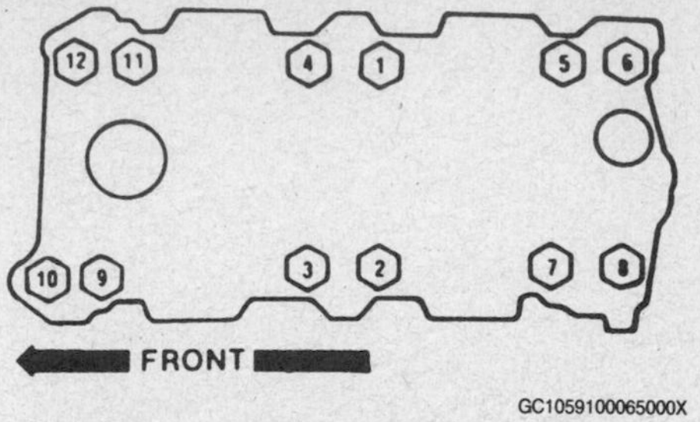
12
11
4
1
5
6
10
9
3
2
7
8
FRONT
GC1059100065000X

Fig. 3 Intake manifold bolt tightening sequence. Except 5.7L/V8-350 (VIN P) engine

diator hose from radiator and lower heater hose from water pump, then the electrical ground straps from right side of engine block and electrical connections from starter motor.

9. Disconnect electrical connectors from knock sensor, oxygen sensor, coolant temperature sensor, wheel speed sensor, engine oil level switch and fuel pump switch/engine oil pressure gauge sensor assemblies.
10. Disconnect left front brake line from caliper brake hose, then the wiring harness from transmission.
11. Disconnect shift linkage from transmission, then the propeller shaft from transmission. **Scribe alignment marks on propeller shaft before disconnecting.**
12. Disconnect torque arm from transmission, then the intermediate steering shaft from rack and pinion assembly.
13. Disconnect electrical ground straps from left side of engine block and frame rail, then lower vehicle.
14. Disconnect fuel lines from fuel rail assembly.
15. Disconnect cruise and accelerator control cables from throttle body, then the upper and lower radiator hoses and upper heater hose from water pump.
16. Disconnect coolant air bleed pipe hose from radiator assembly.
17. Disconnect brake booster vacuum hose, then the alternator.
18. Disconnect engine wiring harness connectors and reposition harness.
19. Disconnect A/C receiver and dehydrator hose from condenser, A/C hose from expansion tube, then the power steering reservoir and reposition.
20. Remove brake master cylinder and reposition, then the upper bolts and nuts from strut assemblies.
21. Disconnect right front brake line from modulator valve assembly and clips, then raise and support vehicle.
22. Place a lift table under engine and engine frame assembly, then remove engine frame and transmission support bolts.
23. Raise vehicle from engine, transmission and engine frame assemblies, then secure strut assemblies to engine frame.
24. Disconnect transmission TV cable from throttle body, then remove transmission assembly.
25. **On vehicles with manual transmission,** remove clutch housing and clutch assembly.
26. **On all vehicles,** disconnect hose assemblies from A/C compressor, then remove compressor.
27. Disconnect power steering lines from power steering pump.
28. Remove engine mount through bolts, then the engine assembly from engine frame.
29. Reverse procedure to install, noting the following:
    a. Tighten fasteners to specifications.
    b. Bleed brake and power steering systems.
    c. Align wheels.

INTAKE MANIFOLD REPLACE

5.0L/V8-305 TBI (VIN E) ENGINE

1. Disconnect battery ground cable, drain cooling system and remove air cleaner.
2. Disconnect accelerator, transmission and cruise control linkages, as equipped.
3. Disconnect fuel line from TBI unit and remove fuel line clips as needed.
4. Remove throttle body.
5. Disconnect ECM control wiring harness and position aside.
6. Disconnect upper radiator and heater hoses from manifold.
7. Disconnect electrical wiring and hoses as necessary to permit intake manifold removal.
8. Remove accelerator cable bracket.
9. Remove distributor cap, rotate crankshaft until No. 1 cylinder is at TDC on compression stroke, mark position of distributor rotor, then remove distributor.
10. Remove ignition coil.
11. Remove coolant temperature sensor.
12. Remove intake manifold retaining bolts and the manifold, **Fig. 2.**
13. Ensure surfaces are clean and dry, then apply 3/16 bead of RTV sealer on each block ridge and apply suitable sealer around water outlets, install gaskets and secure gasket position by extending bead of sealer approximately 1/2 inch onto gasket ends.
14. Install manifold and retaining bolts, ensuring areas between case ridges and manifold are completely sealed.
15. **Torque** manifold bolts first to 89 inch lbs., then to 35 ft. lbs. following sequence shown in **Fig. 3,** then reverse remaining procedure to complete installation.

5.0L/V8-305 (VIN F) TPI & 5.7L/V8-350 (VIN 8) ENGINES

1. Disconnect battery ground cable, drain cooling system and remove air intake duct.
2. Disconnect accelerator, cruise control and transmission cables, as equipped.
3. Disconnect air inlet duct and heater hoses at throttle body.
4. Disconnect and tag electrical connectors and vacuum hoses at throttle body and intake manifold.
5. Relieve fuel system pressure as described under "Precautions," then disconnect fuel lines.
6. Remove vent valve assembly and hoses.
7. Remove vapor pipe assembly.
8. Remove plenum extension.
9. Disconnect and tag spark plug wires at distributor cap.
10. Rotate crankshaft until No. 1 cylinder is at TDC on compression stroke, remove distributor cap and mark position of distributor rotor, then remove distributor.
11. Loosen fuel rail retaining bolts and raise rail assembly.

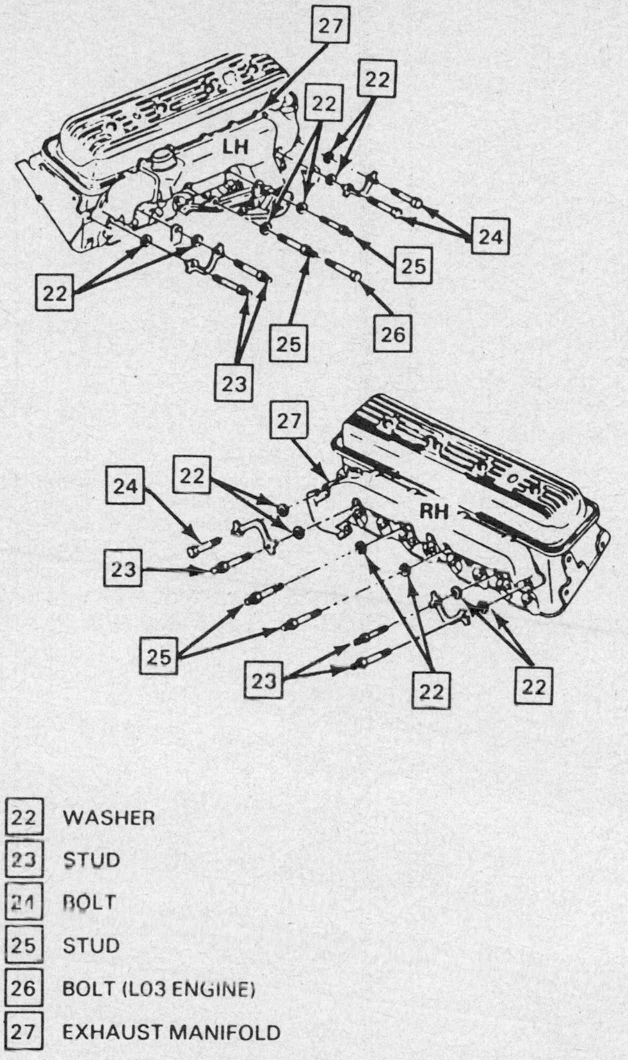
27
22
22
LH
24
25
22
26
25
23
27
24
22
RH
23
25
23
22
22
22 WASHER
23 STUD
24 BOLT
25 STUD
26 BOLT (L03 ENGINE)
27 EXHAUST MANIFOLD
GC1079100009000X

Fig. 4 Exhaust manifold replace. Except 5.7L/V8-350 (VIN P) engine

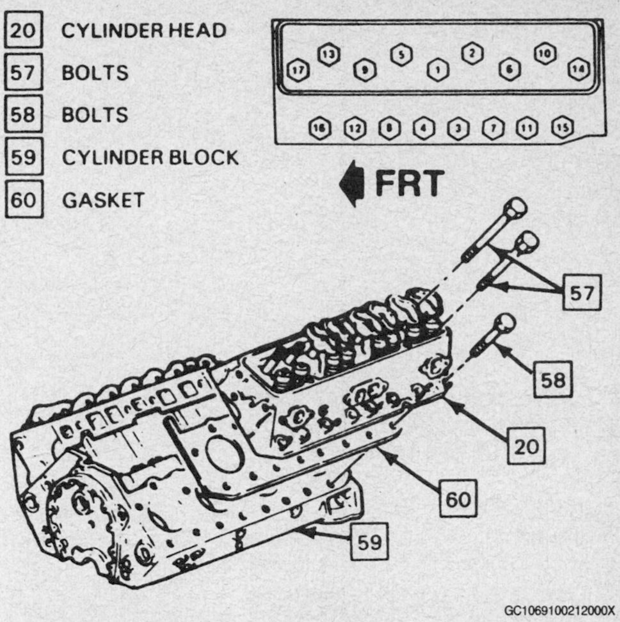
20 CYLINDER HEAD
57 BOLTS
58 BOLTS
59 CYLINDER BLOCK
60 GASKET
FRT
57
58
20
60
59
GC1069100212000X

Fig. 5 Cylinder head replace & bolt tightening sequence. Except 5.7L/V8-350 (VIN P) engine

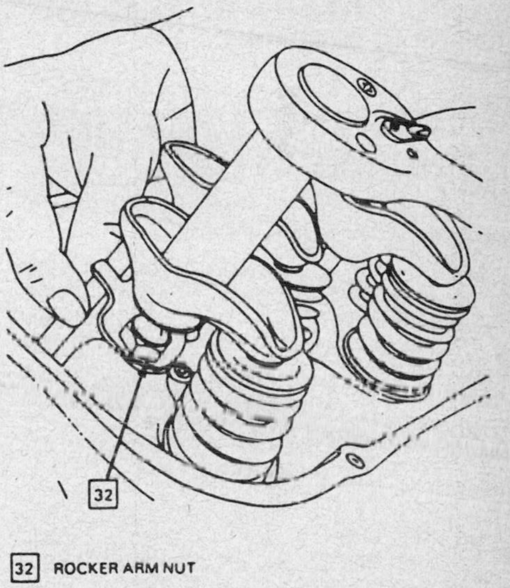
32
32 ROCKER ARM NUT
GC1069100213000X

Fig. 6 Adjusting valve lash. Except 5.7L/V8-350 (VIN P) engine

12. Remove remaining manifold runners and the fuel rail assembly.
13. Remove ignition coil and EGR solenoid.
14. Disconnect upper radiator hose, then remove thermostat housing and gasket.
15. Remove EGR valve and pipe.
16. Disconnect all necessary electrical connectors and vacuum hoses, then remove manifold retaining bolts and the manifold, **Fig. 2.**
17. Ensure surfaces are clean and dry, then apply 3/16 bead of RTV sealer on each block ridge and apply suitable sealer around water outlets, install gaskets and secure gasket position by extending bead of sealer approximately 1/2 inch onto gasket ends.
18. Install manifold and retaining bolts, ensuring areas between case ridges and manifold are completely sealed.
19. Tighten manifold bolts to specifications in sequence shown in **Fig. 3**, then reverse remaining procedure to complete installation.

EXHAUST MANIFOLD

REPLACE
EXCEPT 5.7L/V8-350 (VIN P) ENGINE

1. Disconnect battery ground cable.
2. If necessary, disconnect spark plug wires from spark plugs.
3. Remove AIR pipes and AIR valve.
4. Raise and support vehicle.
5. Disconnect exhaust crossover pipe from exhaust manifold, then lower vehicle.
6. Remove exhaust manifold attaching bolts, then remove exhaust manifold and gasket, **Fig. 4.**
7. Reverse procedure to install.

CYLINDER HEAD

REPLACE
EXCEPT 5.7L/V8-350 (VIN P) ENGINE

1. Disconnect battery ground cable, then drain cooling system and engine block.
2. Remove intake manifold and exhaust manifolds.
3. Remove alternator lower mounting bolt and position alternator aside.
4. Remove dipstick tube and bracket.
5. If equipped with A/C, remove compressor and forward mounting bracket and position aside.
6. Remove power steering pump and bracket, position aside.
7. Remove rocker arm cover, rocker arms and pushrods. **Keep rocker arm, rocker arm balls and pushrods in order so they can be installed in the same position.**
8. Remove diverter valve, if equipped.
9. Remove cylinder head bolts and cylinder head, **Fig. 5.**
10. Reverse procedure to install. Apply

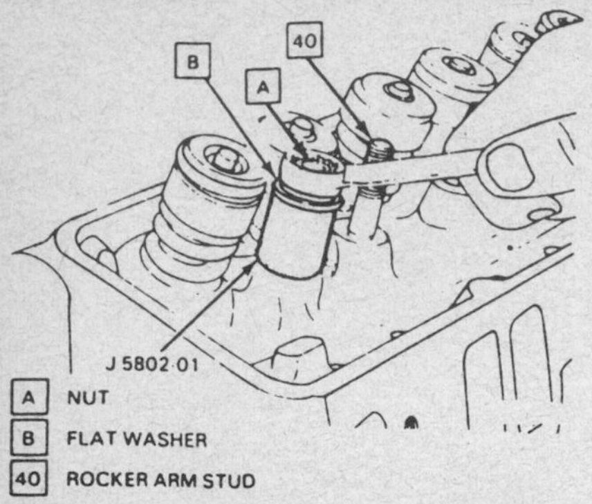
B
40
A
J 5802-01
A NUT
B FLAT WASHER
40 ROCKER ARM STUD
GC1069100214000X

Fig. 7 Pressed-in type rocker arm stud removal. Except 5.7L/V8-350 (VIN P) engine

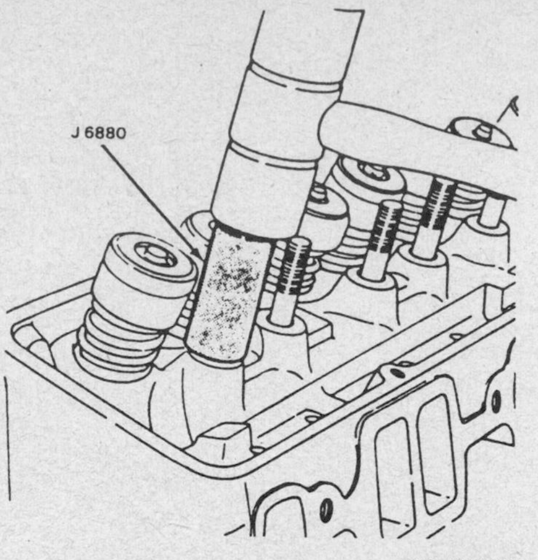
J 6880
GC1069100215000X

Fig. 8 Pressed-in type rocker arm stud installation. Except 5.7L/V8-350 (VIN P) engine

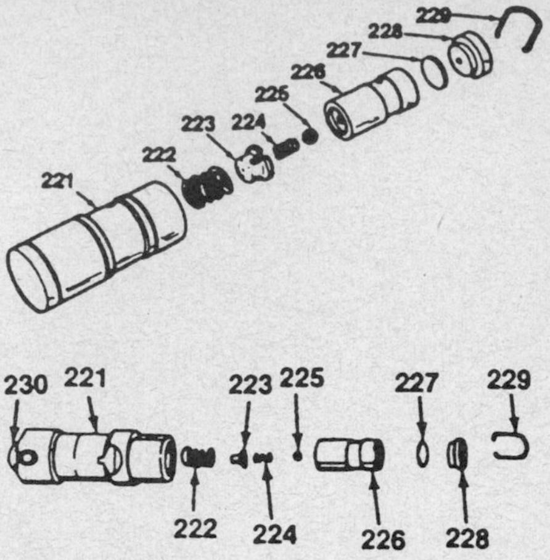
229
228
227
226
225
224
223
222
221
230
GC1069100216000X

221. Lifter Body
222. Plunger Spring
223. Check Ball Retainer
224. Check Ball Spring
225. Check Ball
226. Plunger
227. Metering Valve
228. Pushrod Seat
229. Retainer
230. Roller

Fig. 9 Hydraulic valve lifters. Except 5.7L/V8-350 (VIN P) engine

suitable sealer to cylinder head bolts and gradually tighten bolts to specifications in sequence shown in **Fig. 5.**

VALVE ARRANGEMENT

FRONT TO REAR

5.0L/V8-305 & 5.7L/V8-350 (VIN 8) Engines

All .... E-I-I-E-E-I-I-E

CAMSHAFT LOBE LIFT SPECIFICATIONS

Engine (VIN)	Int.	Exh.
5.0L/V8-305(E)	.234	.257
5.0L/V8-305(F)	.275	.285
5.7L/V8-350(8)	.275	.285

VALVE CLEARANCE SPECIFICATIONS

Engine (VIN)	Int.	Exh.
5.0L/V8-305(E)	.350	.385
5.0L/V8-305(F)	.413	.428
5.7L/V8-350(8)	.413	.428

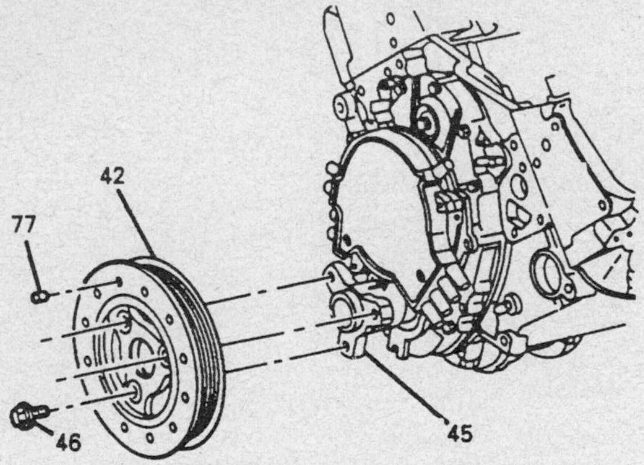
42
77
46
45

42 BALANCER ASSEMBLY, CRANKSHAFT
45 HUB, CRANKSHAFT BALANCER
46 BOLT/SCREW, CRANKSHAFT BALANCER
77 WEIGHT, CRANKSHAFT BALANCER

GC1069500598000X

Fig. 10 Crankshaft balancer assembly & hub removal

VALVE ADJUSTMENT

EXCEPT 5.7L/V8-350 (VIN P) ENGINE

After the engine has been thoroughly warmed up the valves may be adjusted, **Fig. 6,** with the engine shutoff as follows: With engine in position to fire No. 1 cylinder the following valves may be adjusted: exhaust 1-3-4-8, intake 1-2-5-7. Then crank the engine one more complete revolution which will bring No. 6 cylinder on V8 engines, to the firing position at which time the following valves may be adjusted: exhaust 2-5-6-7, intake 3-4-6-8.

The following procedure, performed with the engine running, should be done only in case readjustment is required.

1. After engine has been warmed up to operating temperature, remove valve cover and install a new valve cover gasket.
2. With engine running at idle speed, back off valve rocker arm nut until rocker arm starts to clatter.
3. Turn rocker arm nut down slowly until the clatter just stops. This is the zero lash position.
4. Turn nut down 1/4 additional turn and pause 10 seconds until engine runs smoothly. Repeat additional 1/4 turns, pausing 10 seconds each time, until nut has been turned down the number of turns listed in the "Valve Lash Specifications Chart" from the zero lash position. **This preload adjustment must be done slowly to allow the lifter to adjust itself to prevent the possibility of interference between the intake valve head and top of piston, which might result in internal damage and/or bent push-rods. Noisy lifters should be replaced.**

ROCKER ARM STUDS

EXCEPT 5.7L/V8-350 (VIN P) ENGINE

If studs are loose in cylinder head, .003 inch or .013 inch oversize studs may be installed on all engines with pressed-in type studs, after reaming holes with a proper size reamer. On engines with threaded rocker studs, looseness can be corrected by installing the proper size Heli-Coil insert, or by replacing cylinder head. Replace damaged pressed-in rocker arm studs using the following procedure:

1. Remove the old stud by placing a suitable spacer, **Fig. 7,** over stud. Install nut and flat washer and remove stud by turning nut.

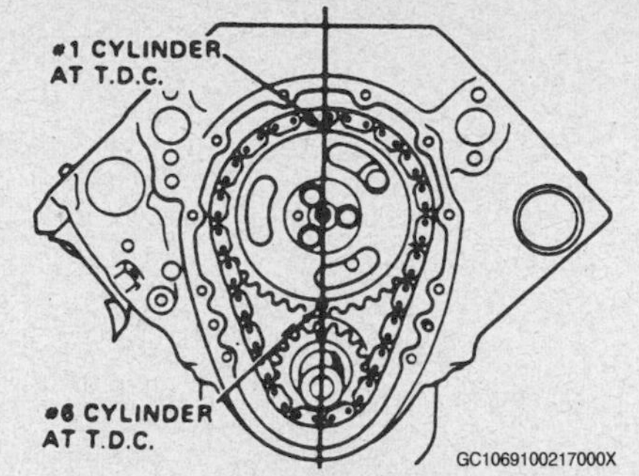
#1 CYLINDER
AT T.D.C.
#6 CYLINDER
AT T.D.C.
GC1069100217000X

Fig. 11 Valve timing marks. Except 5.7L/V8-350 (VIN P) engine

2. Ream hole for oversize stud.
3. Coat press-fit area of stud with rear axle lube. Then install new stud, **Fig. 8.** If tool shown is used, it should bottom on the head.

PUSH RODS

EXCEPT 5.7L/V8-350 (VIN P) ENGINE

On engines that use pushrods with a hardened insert at one end, the hardened end is identified by a color stripe and should always be installed toward the rocker arm during assembly.

VALVE GUIDES

EXCEPT 5.7L/V8-350 (VIN P) ENGINE

Valves operate in guide holes bored in the head. If clearance becomes excessive, use the next oversize valve and ream the bore to fit. Valves with oversize stems are available in .003, .015 and .030 inch.

HYDRAULIC LIFTERS

REPLACE

EXCEPT 5.7L/V8-350 (VIN P) ENGINE

Valve lifters can be lifted from their bores after removing rocker arms and pushrods and intake manifold. Adjustable pliers with protected jaws may be used to remove lifters which are stuck due to carbon or varnish deposits. **Fig. 9** illustrate types of valve lifters used.

CRANKSHAFT BALANCER ASSEMBLY & HUB

REPLACE

1. Raise and support vehicle, then remove serpentine belt.
2. Remove balancer bolts, then balancer assembly**Fig. 10.**
3. Scribe crankshaft hub to engine front cover assembly. **Do not crank engine over after scribing as it will interfere with installation of balancer assembly, resulting in engine imbalance.**
4. Remove crankshaft hub bolts.
5. Using puller tool No. J-39046, or equivalent, remove crankshaft hub.
6. Reverse procedure to install, **torquing** crankshaft balancer hub bolt to 74 ft. lbs.

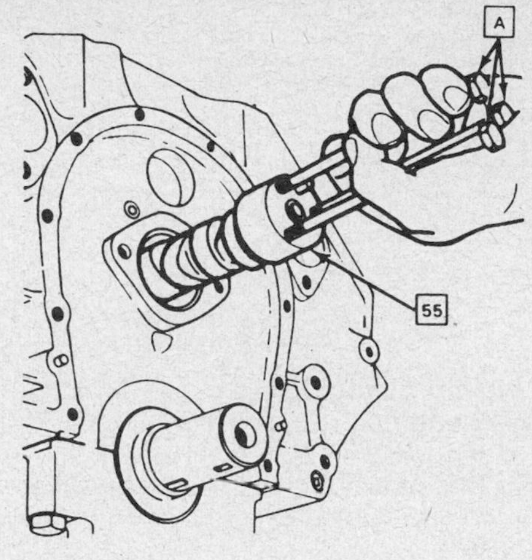
A
55

A BOLTS
55 CAMSHAFT

GC1069100218000X

Fig. 12 Camshaft removal. Except 5.7L/V8-350 (VIN P) engine

FRONT COVER

REPLACE

EXCEPT 5.7L/V8-350 (VIN P) ENGINE

The cover oil seal may be replaced without taking off the front cover. After removing the vibration damper, pry out the old seal with a screwdriver. Install the new seal with the lip or open end toward inside of cover and drive it into position.

1. Disconnect battery ground cable and drain cooling system.
2. Remove vibration damper and water pump.
3. Remove oil pan and gasket as described.
4. Remove timing cover retaining screws and the timing cover.
5. Reverse procedure to install.

TIMING CHAIN

REPLACE

EXCEPT 5.7L/V8-350 (VIN P) ENGINE

1. Remove timing chain cover as described previously.
2. Remove crankshaft oil slinger.
3. Crank engine until timing marks on sprockets are in alignment, **Fig. 11.**
4. Remove three camshaft to sprocket bolts.
5. Remove camshaft sprocket and timing chain together. Sprocket is a light press fit on camshaft for approximately 1/8 inch. If sprocket does not come off easily, a light blow with a plastic hammer on the lower edge of the sprocket should dislodge it.
6. If crankshaft sprocket is to be replaced, remove it with a suitable gear puller. Install new sprocket, aligning key and keyway.
7. Install chain on camshaft sprocket. Hold sprocket vertical with chain hanging below and shift around to align the timing marks on sprockets.
8. Align dowel in camshaft with dowel hole in sprocket and install sprocket on camshaft. Do not attempt to drive sprocket on camshaft as welch plug at rear of engine can be dislodged.
9. Draw sprocket onto camshaft, using the three mounting bolts. Tighten to specifications.
10. Lubricate timing chain and install cover.

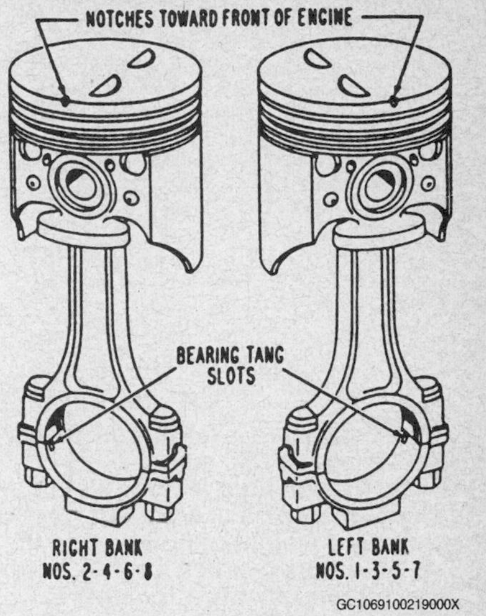
NOTCHES TOWARD FRONT OF ENGINE
BEARING TANG SLOTS
RIGHT BANK
NOS. 2-4-6-8
LEFT BANK
NOS. 1-3-5-7
GC1069100219000X

Fig. 13 Piston & rod assemble. Except 5.7L/V8-350 (VIN P) engine

CAMSHAFT

REPLACE

EXCEPT 5.7L/V8-350 (VIN P) ENGINE

1. Remove valve lifters and engine front cover.
2. Remove grille, radiator, oil cooler and condenser.
3. Remove timing chain as described previously.
4. Install two 5/16-18 x 4 inch bolts in camshaft bolt holes, **Fig. 12.**
5. Remove camshaft from engine using care not to damage camshaft bearings.
6. Reverse procedure to install.

PISTON & ROD ASSEMBLY

EXCEPT 5.7L/V8-350 (VIN P) ENGINE

Assemble pistons to connecting rods as shown in **Fig. 13.**

Upon installation, measure the connecting rod side clearance using a suitable feeler gauge. Refer to "Engine Rebuilding Specifications" for connecting rod side clearance.

PISTONS, PINS & RINGS

EXCEPT 5.7L/V8-350 (VIN P) ENGINE

Pistons are available in standard and oversizes of .010 and .030 inch.

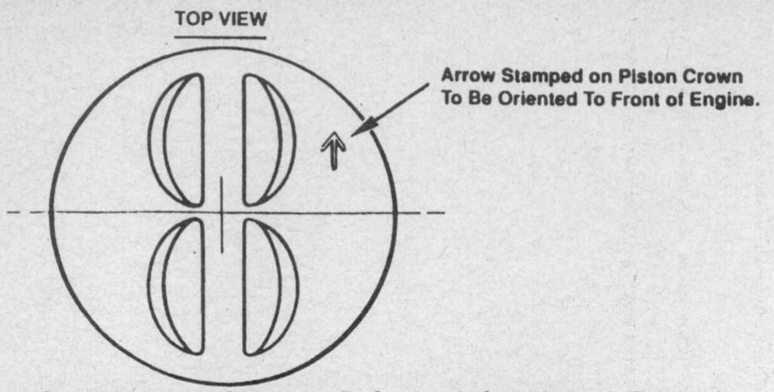
TOP VIEW
Arrow Stamped on Piston Crown
To Be Oriented To Front of Engine.

Fig. 14 Low friction, light weight piston. Except 5.7L/V8-350 (VIN P) engine

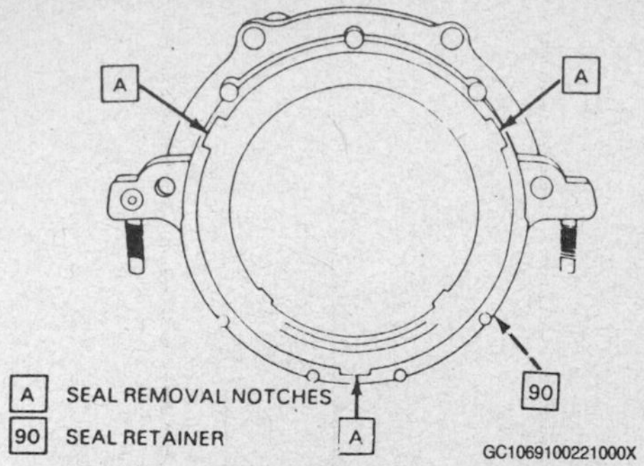
A
A
90
A SEAL REMOVAL NOTCHES
90 SEAL RETAINER
A
GC1069100221000X

Fig. 15 Crankshaft rear oil seal removal. Except 5.7L/V8-350 (VIN P) engine

Piston rings are available in standard and oversizes of .030 inch.

A low friction light weight piston and new design ring pack are used. The low friction light weight piston can be identified by a raised notch on the bottom of the piston pin bore located toward rear of engine, Fig. 14.

MAIN & ROD BEARINGS

EXCEPT 5.7L/V8-350 (VIN P) ENGINE

Connecting rod bearings are available in standard and undersizes of .001, .002, .010 and .020 inch.

Main bearings are available in standard and undersizes of .001, .002, .009, .010 and .020 inch.

CRANKSHAFT REAR OIL SEAL

REPLACE

EXCEPT 5.7L/V8-350 (VIN P) ENGINE

These engines are equipped with a one-piece, lip type seal mounted in a separate seal retainer. Seal replacement requires removal of the transmission.

1. Raise and support vehicle, then remove transmission, clutch assembly and flywheel, as equipped.
2. Pry seal from retainer, inserting screwdriver in notches provided in seal retainer, **Fig. 15.**
3. Lubricate inner and outer diameters of replacement seal with engine oil, then mount seal on tool No. J-35621, or equivalent.
4. Mount tool on rear of crankshaft, tightening screws snugly to ensure seal will be installed squarely on crankshaft.
5. Tighten wing nut on tool until it bottoms, then remove tool from crankshaft.
6. Reverse remaining procedure to complete installation.

OIL PAN

REPLACE

EXCEPT 5.7L/V8-350 (VIN P) ENGINE

1. Disconnect battery ground cable, then remove fan shroud.
2. **On models with TBI,** remove air cleaner.
3. **On all models,** remove plenum extension, if equipped.
4. Disconnect and tag spark plug wires at distributor, then remove distributor cap.
5. Remove A/C compressor and position aside with refrigerant lines attached.
6. Raise and support vehicle, then drain crankcase.
7. Remove AIR pipe, if equipped, and hanger bolts from catalytic converter. On some models it may be necessary to disconnect exhaust crossover pipe at exhaust manifolds.
8. Remove starter motor attaching bolts and position starter motor aside.
9. Remove engine mount through bolts, then raise engine.
10. Remove oil pan attaching bolts and oil pan, **Fig. 16. If oil pan removal is hampered by the forward crankshaft throw and/or counterweight extending downward, turn crankshaft as needed to put throw in a horizontal position.**
11. Reverse procedure to install, using a new gasket and seals.

OIL PUMP

REPLACE

EXCEPT 5.7L/V8-350 (VIN P) ENGINE

1. Remove oil pan as described previously.
2. Remove pump to rear main bearing cap bolt and remove pump and extension shaft.
3. Reverse procedure to install. Make sure that installed position of oil pump screen is with bottom edge parallel to oil pan rails.

OIL PUMP SERVICE

EXCEPT 5.7L/V8-350 (VIN P) ENGINE

1. Remove oil pump as described previously.
2. Remove pump cover screws and pump cover, **Fig. 17.**
3. Mark gear teeth so they can be reassembled with same teeth indexing, then remove drive gear, idler gear and shaft.
4. Remove pressure regulator valve retaining pin, pressure regulator valve and related parts.
5. If pickup screen and pipe require replacement, mount pump in a soft-jawed vise and extract pipe from pump.
6. Wash all parts in cleaning solvent and dry with compressed air.
7. Inspect pump body and cover for cracks and excessive wear.
8. Inspect pump gears for damage or excessive wear.
9. Check drive gear shaft for looseness in pump body.
10. Inspect inside of pump cover for wear that would allow oil to leak past the ends of the gears.
11. Inspect pickup screen and pipe assembly for damage to screen, pipe or relief grommet.
12. Check pressure regulator valve for fit in pump housing.
13. Reverse procedure to assemble. Turn driveshaft by hand to check for smooth operation. **The pump gears and body are not serviced separately. If the pump gears or body are damaged or worn, the pump assembly should be replaced. Also, if the pick-up screen and pump assembly was removed, it should be replaced with a new one as loss of the press fit condition could result in an air leak and loss of oil pressure.**

BELT TENSION DATA

Belt tension is maintained by a spring tensioner and no adjustment is necessary.

SERPENTINE DRIVE BELT

EXCEPT 5.7L/V8-350 (VIN P) ENGINE

1. Disconnect battery ground cable.
2. Using a breaker bar, lift tensioner upward and off drive belt.
3. Remove serpentine drive belt from pulleys.
4. Reverse procedure to install. Refer to **Fig. 18** for serpentine belt routing.

COOLING SYSTEM BLEED

EXCEPT 5.7L/V8-350 (VIN P) ENGINE

After filling cooling system, start engine and allow to reach operating temperature with radiator cap removed. Air in system is bleed through radiator cap opening. Add coolant as necessary to bring to proper level, then install radiator cap and check coolant level in recovery reservoir.

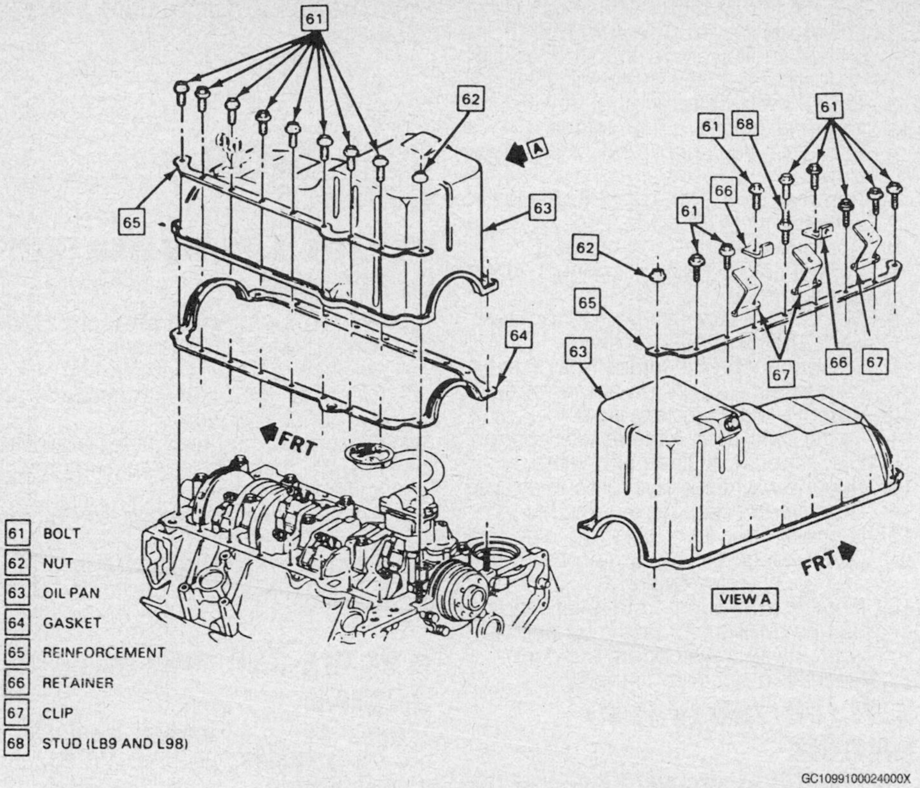
61 BOLT
62 NUT
63 OIL PAN
64 GASKET
65 REINFORCEMENT
66 RETAINER
67 CLIP
68 STUD (LB9 AND L98)
A
FRT
VIEW A
GC1099100024000X

Fig. 16 Oil pan replacement. Except 5.7L/V8-350 (VIN P) engine

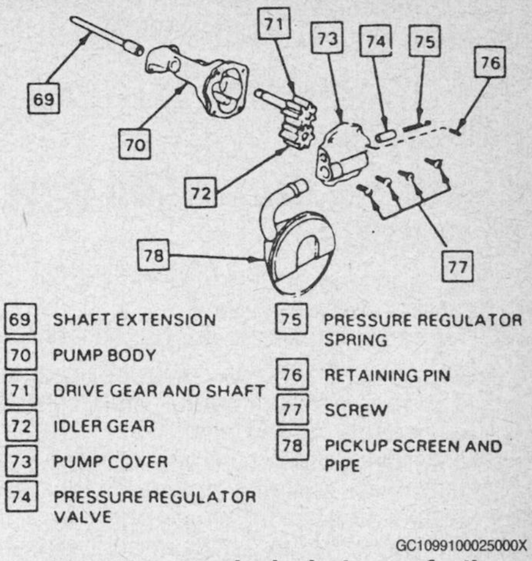
69 SHAFT EXTENSION
70 PUMP BODY
71 DRIVE GEAR AND SHAFT
72 IDLER GEAR
73 PUMP COVER
74 PRESSURE REGULATOR VALVE
75 PRESSURE REGULATOR SPRING
76 RETAINING PIN
77 SCREW
78 PICKUP SCREEN AND PIPE
GC1099100025000X

Fig. 17 Exploded view of oil pump. Except 5.7L/V8-350 (VIN P) engine

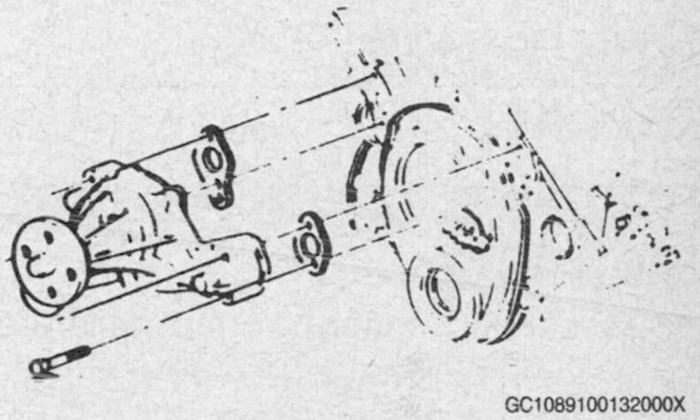
GC1089100132000X

Fig. 20 Water pump replace. Except 5.7L/V8-350 (VIN P) engine

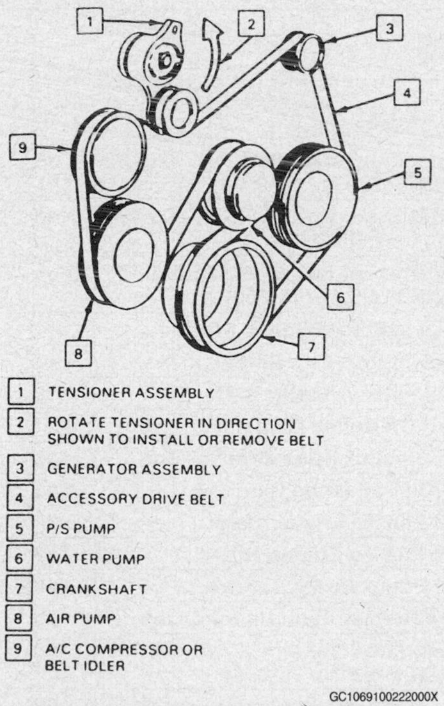
1 TENSIONER ASSEMBLY
2 ROTATE TENSIONER IN DIRECTION SHOWN TO INSTALL OR REMOVE BELT
3 GENERATOR ASSEMBLY
4 ACCESSORY DRIVE BELT
5 P/S PUMP
6 WATER PUMP
7 CRANKSHAFT
8 AIR PUMP
9 A/C COMPRESSOR OR BELT IDLER
GC1069100222000X

Fig. 18 Serpentine drive belt routing. Except 5.7L/V8-350 (VIN P) engine

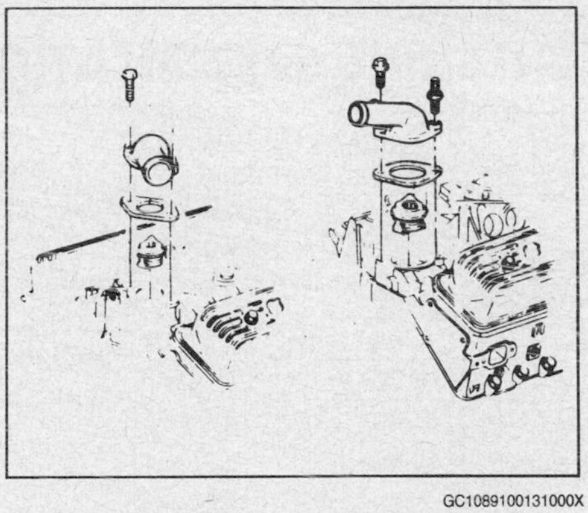
GC1089100131000X

Fig. 19 Thermostat replacement. Except 5.7L/V8-350 (VIN P) engine

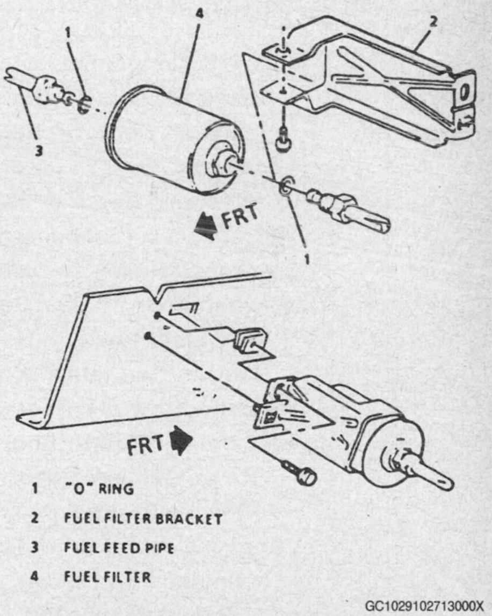
FRT
1 "O" RING
2 FUEL FILTER BRACKET
3 FUEL FEED PIPE
4 FUEL FILTER
GC1029102713000X

Fig. 21 Fuel filter replacement. Except 5.7L/V8-350 (VIN P) engine

THERMOSTAT

REPLACE

EXCEPT 5.7L/V8-350 (VIN P) ENGINE

1. Disconnect battery ground cable, then drain cooling system, until coolant level is below level of thermostat.
2. Remove air cleaner and air duct, as necessary.
3. Relieve fuel system pressure as described under "Precautions."
4. Remove throttle body.
5. Disconnect radiator hose from thermostat housing.
6. Remove thermostat housing attaching bolts, then remove housing and thermostat, **Fig. 19.**
7. Reverse procedure to install.

RADIATOR

REPLACE

1. Disconnect intake duct, then remove air cleaner assembly.
2. Raise and support vehicle, then drain engine coolant.
3. Disconnect electrical connectors at cooling fans.
4. Remove upper radiator mounting panel, then cooling fan assembly.
5. Disconnect oil cooler lines, then remove coolant sensor, if equipped.
6. Lower vehicle and loosen receiver/dryer bracket.
7. Disconnect upper and lower radiator hoses, then overflow coolant hose.
8. Disconnect radiator from air conditioning condenser, then remove radia-

for assembly.
9. Reverse procedure to install.

WATER PUMP

REPLACE

EXCEPT 5.7L/V8-350 (VIN P) ENGINE

1. Disconnect battery ground cable and drain cooling system.
2. Remove intake air duct assembly.
3. Remove fan shroud or upper radiator support, as applicable, then remove accessory drive belts.
4. Remove pulley from water pump hub.
5. Remove radiator lower hose and heater hose from water pump.
6. Remove water pump attaching bolts and the pump, **Fig. 20,** noting position of bolts for assembly reference.
7. Reverse procedure to install.

FUEL PUMP

REPLACE

EXCEPT 5.7L/V8-350 (VIN P) ENGINE

1. Disconnect battery ground cable, then disconnect engine harness connector at ignition distributor.
2. **On models with port fuel injection,** relieve fuel system pressure as described under "Precautions."
3. **On all models,** drain fuel tank. Place fuel in an approved container.
4. Remove gas cap and filler neck shield.
5. Remove tires, then raise and support vehicle.
6. Remove track bar and brace.
7. Support axle, then disconnect lower shock mount.
8. Remove exhaust from converter back, then the heat shield.
9. Disconnect brake cables from S clips, then from retainers on frame rails.
10. Remove stabilizer bar links.
11. Lower axle, then remove rear springs.
12. Disconnect fuel lines and wires.
13. Support fuel tank and remove straps.
14. Remove fuel tank from vehicle.
15. Remove fuel level sending unit and pump assembly by turning cam lock ring counterclockwise.
16. Remove fuel pump from level sending unit by pulling fuel pump up and outward, away from bottom support.
17. Reverse procedure to install.

5.7L/V8-350 (VIN P) ENGINE

Refer to "3.4L/V6-207 Engine" in the "3.1L/V6-191 & 3.4L/V6-207 Engines" section.

FUEL FILTER

REPLACE

EXCEPT 5.7L/V8-350 (VIN P) ENGINE

1. Relieve fuel system pressure as described under "Precautions."
2. Raise and support vehicle.
3. Clean all fuel filter connections and surrounding areas.
4. Disconnect fuel feed pipes from filter, **Fig. 21,** then drain remaining fuel into suitable container.
5. Remove filter mounting screw, then the fuel filter.
6. Reverse procedure to install.

5.7L/V8-350 (VIN P) ENGINE

Refer to "3.4L/V6-207 Engines" in the "3.1L/V6-191 & 3.4L/V6-207 Engines" section.

TIGHTENING SPECIFICATIONS

Year	Component	Torque/ Ft. Lbs.
1992	Camshaft Retainer Nuts	106①
	Camshaft Sprocket Bolts	21
	Clutch Pressure Plate To Flywheel Bolts	30
	Connecting Rod Cap Nuts	44
	Crankshaft Damper Bolt	70
	Crankshaft Pulley To Damper	43
	Crankshaft Rear Oil Seal Retainer	11
	Cylinder Head Bolts	68
	Distributor Clamp Bolt	27
	Drive Belt Idler Pulley (Long Bolt)	61
	Drive Belt Idler Pulley (Short Bolt)	37
	Drive Belt Tensioner	37
	Engine Bracket Bolt	38
	Engine Coolant Drain Plug	15
	Engine Front Cover	97①
	Engine Mount Nut	30
	Engine Mount Through Bolt	50
	Engine Oil Cooler Retainer	17
	Exhaust Crossover Pipe To Exhaust Manifold Nuts	15
	Exhaust Manifold Bolt & Stud (Center)	20
	Exhaust Manifold Bolt & Stud (Outer)	26
	Flywheel To Crankshaft Bolts	74
	Fuel Line Nuts	20
	Fuel Pump Cover Lower Bolt	106①
	Fuel Pump Cover Upper Bolt	25

Year	Component	Torque/ Ft. Lbs.
1992 —Cont'd	Fuel Rail Attaching Bolts (5.0L/V8-305 TPI VIN F & 5.7L/V8-350)	15
	Ignition Coil Bracket Bolt (5.0L/V8-305 TBI VIN E)	16
	Ignition Coil Bracket Bolt (5.0L/V8-305 TPI VIN F & 5.7L/V8-350)	50①
	Intake Manifold Bolt & Stud	②
	Main Rod Cap Bolts	77
	Oil Filter Adapter Bolt	18
	Oil Galley Plug	115①
	Oil Level Dipstick Tube Bracket Bolt	25
	Oil Pan Drain Plug	16
	Oil Pan To Engine Bolts	97①
	Oil Pan To Engine Nuts	17
	Oil Pump Cover Screws	80①
	Oil Pump To Rear Main Bearing Cap	65
	Runner To Manifold Bolts (5.0L/V8-305 TPI VIN F & 5.7L/V8-350)	25
	Spark Plug	20
	Starter Motor Mounting Bolts	35
	Thermostat Housing (5.0L/V8-305 TBI VIN E)	21
	Thermostat Housing (5.0L/V8-305 TPI VIN F & 5.7L/V8-350)	25
	Torque Converter Cover Bolts	89①
	Torque Converter To Flywheel Attaching Bolts	46

Continued

TIGHTENING SPECIFICATIONS-Continued

Year	Component	Torque/ Ft. lbs.
1992 -Cont'd	Throttle Body Attaching Bolts (5.0L/V8-305 TBI VIN E)	16
	Throttle Body Attaching Bolts (5.0L/V8-305 TPI VIN F & 5.7L/V8-350)	18
	Throttle Body Fuel Inlet Line (5.0L/V8-305 TBI VIN E)	30
	Throttle Body Fuel Outlet Line (5.0L/V8-305 TBI VIN E)	21
	Transmission Rear Mount Bolt	40

Year	Component	Torque/ Ft. lbs.
1992 -Cont'd	Transmission Rear Mount Nut	35
	Transmission To Bellhousing Bolts (Manual)	55
	Transmission To Engine Bolts (Automatic)	35
	Valve Cover Bolts	97①
	Valve Lifter Retainer Bolt	15
	Water Pump Bolts	30

①—Inch Lbs.
②—Refer to text.

Clutch & Manual Transmission

NOTE: On Air Bag Equipped Models, Refer To "Air Bag System Precautions" Located In The Front Of This Manual For System Disarming & Arming Procedures.

INDEX

PRECAUTIONS

AIR BAG SYSTEMS

Refer to "Air Bag System Precautions" in the front of this manual for system disarming and arming procedures.

ADJUSTMENTS

The hydraulic clutch system sets the clutch pedal height and provides automatic clutch adjustment. No adjustment of clutch or clutch pedal assembly is necessary.

HYDRAULIC SYSTEM SERVICE

CLUTCH SYSTEM BLEED

1992

1. Clean area around clutch fluid reservoir, then remove cap and add DOT 3 type brake fluid as necessary to bring to proper level, **Fig. 1.**
2. At clutch actuator, fully loosen bleeder screw located near fluid inlet line connection.
3. Allow system to gravity bleed until a steady stream of fluid is expelled from bleeder valve. Maintain reservoir level during gravity bleeding operation.
4. After air has been expelled from slave cylinder, tighten bleeder screw.
5. Push clutch fork lightly toward actuator, then open bleeder screw. While maintaining light force on clutch fork, tighten bleeder screw.
6. Push clutch fork lightly toward actuator with bleeder screw closed. This will force any remaining air into reservoir.
7. Check clutch system by starting vehicle, then select reverse gear with clutch pedal fully depressed. If gears do not grate, system is satisfactory. If gears do grate, repeat bleeding procedure.
8. Check actuator output rod travel. Minimum travel should be .43 inch for V6 engines, .57 inch for V8 engines.

1993-95

1. Loosen clutch master cylinder nuts to end of threads on U-bolt, then clean dirt and grease from reservoir cap, **Figs. 2 and 3.**
2. Remove reservoir cap and diaphragm, then wrap a piece of mechanics wire around lefthand hood strut bracket ensuring wire is accessible from underside of vehicle.
3. Raise and support vehicle, then remove actuator cylinder and retain in engine compartment using mechanics wire previously installed.
4. Lower vehicle, then grasp actuator cylinder and depress pushrod approximately .787 inch (20 mm) into cylinder bore and hold.
5. Install diaphragm and reservoir cap while holding in actuator pushrod, then release actuator pushrod.
6. Hold actuator cylinder vertically with pushrod facing down, then press pushrod into actuator cylinder bore with short .390 inch (10 mm) strokes while inspecting master cylinder reservoir for air bubbles. **Actuator cylinder should be lower than master cylinder.**
7. Continue stroking cylinder until air bubbles are no longer entering reservoir, then raise and support vehicle.
8. Remove actuator cylinder from mechanics wire, then install actuator cylinder and tighten to specifications.
9. Lower vehicle, then remove mechanics wire from lefthand hood strut bracket.
10. Install clutch master cylinder nuts and tighten to specifications, then inspect fluid level, adding fluid if necessary.

CLUTCH ACTUATOR, REPLACE

1992

1. Disconnect battery ground cable.
2. Disconnect input rod from clutch master cylinder, **Fig. 1.** This will prevent damage to actuator if clutch pedal is depressed while actuator is removed.
3. Raise and support vehicle, then disconnect hydraulic hose from clutch actuator.
4. Remove actuator and heat shield attaching bolts, then remove actuator and heat shield.
5. Reverse procedure to install. After completing installation, bleed clutch hydraulic system.

CLUTCH MASTER & ACTUATOR CYLINDER

1993–95

1. Disconnect battery ground cable, then remove instrument panel driver knee bolster assembly.
2. Disconnect clutch master cylinder pushrod from clutch pedal assembly, then remove clutch master cylinder nuts from dash panel assembly.
3. Remove clutch master cylinder U-bolt from dash panel assembly, then the clutch master cylinder from dash panel assembly.
4. Remove clutch master cylinder reservoir retainer, then the clutch master cylinder reservoir from lefthand hood strut bracket.
5. Raise and support vehicle, then remove clutch actuator cylinder from clutch housing.
6. Remove clutch master and actuator cylinder assembly from vehicle.
7. Reverse procedure to install, noting the following:
   a. Tighten fasteners to specifications.
   b. Bleed hydraulic clutch system.

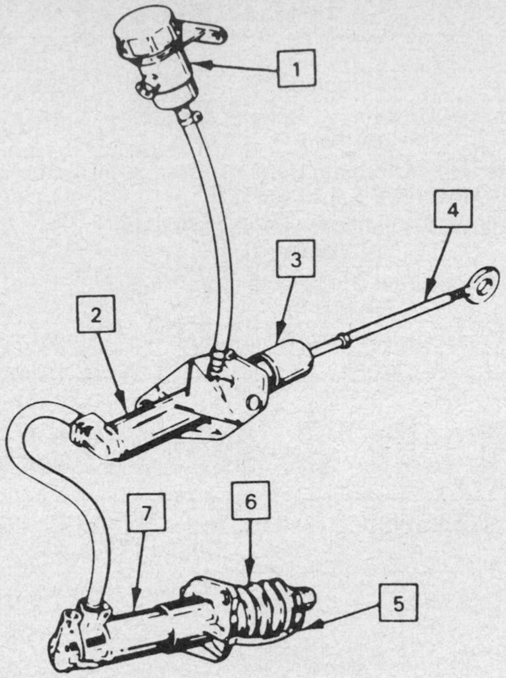
1
2
3
4
5
6
7
1 FLUID RESERVOIR
2 CLUTCH MASTER CYLINDER
3 BOOT
4 CLUTCH MASTER CYLINDER INPUT ROD
5 SHIPPING STRAP
6 BOOT
7 ACTUATOR
GC5049100031000X

Fig. 1 Clutch hydraulic system. 1992

CLUTCH

REPLACE

1992

1. Support engine and remove transmission as described further on.
2. Remove slave cylinder heat shield and cylinder from flywheel housing. Prior to removing slave cylinder, disconnect pushrod from clutch master cylinder.
3. Remove flywheel housing, **Fig. 4.**
4. Slide clutch fork from ball stud and remove fork from dust boot. **Look for X mark on flywheel and on clutch cover. If X mark is not evident, prick punch marks on flywheel and clutch cover for indexing purposes during installation.**
5. Loosen clutch to flywheel attaching bolts evenly one turn at a time until spring pressure is released. Then remove bolts and clutch assembly.
6. Reverse procedure to install. Prior to installation, lubricate pilot bearing sparingly with machine oil. Also apply wheel bearing lubricant 1051344 or equivalent to clutch fork ball socket and fingers and release bearing collar recesses. Use a suitable pilot tool to center clutch disc. Tighten clutch cover bolts evenly and gradually to avoid distorting cover.

1993–95

1. Disconnect battery ground cable, then remove instrument panel driver knee bolster assembly.
2. Disconnect clutch master cylinder pushrod from clutch pedal assembly, then raise and support vehicle.
3. Remove transmission assembly, then the clutch actuator cylinder and retain with mechanics wire.
4. Remove transmission brace, then the flywheel housing cover and flywheel housing assembly, **Figs. 5 and 6.**
5. Remove clutch pressure plate, then the clutch disc.
6. Reverse procedure to install, noting the following:
   a. Tighten fasteners to specifications.
   b. Align clutch disc and pressure plate using clutch alignment arbor tool No. J-33169, or equivalent, for models with five-speed transmission or tool No. J-38836, or equivalent, for models with 6-speed transmission, or equivalents.
   c. Check for proper clutch fork to clutch release bearing engagement.

TRANSMISSION

REPLACE

1992

It may be necessary to remove the catalytic converter and its support bracket to facilitate transmission removal.

1. Disconnect battery ground cable.
2. Raise and support vehicle, then drain lubricant from transmission.
3. Remove propeller shaft.
4. Support left hand side of rear axle with a suitable lifting device.
5. Remove torque arm rear attaching bolts, then remove front torque arm bracket and torque arm.
6. Disconnect speed sensor and back-up lamp switch electrical connectors.
7. Remove catalytic converter hanger bracket.
8. Support engine using a suitable jack stand, then remove transmission mount nuts at support.
9. Remove transmission support bolts, then remove support.
10. Lower transmission just enough to provide access to shift control assembly.
11. Remove shift control assembly attaching bolts, then disconnect shift control from extension housing.
12. Remove transmission to flywheel housing attaching bolts, the remove transmission from vehicle.
13. Reverse procedure to install. Apply a 1/8 bead of sealant No. 12345739, or equivalent, to extension sealing surface.

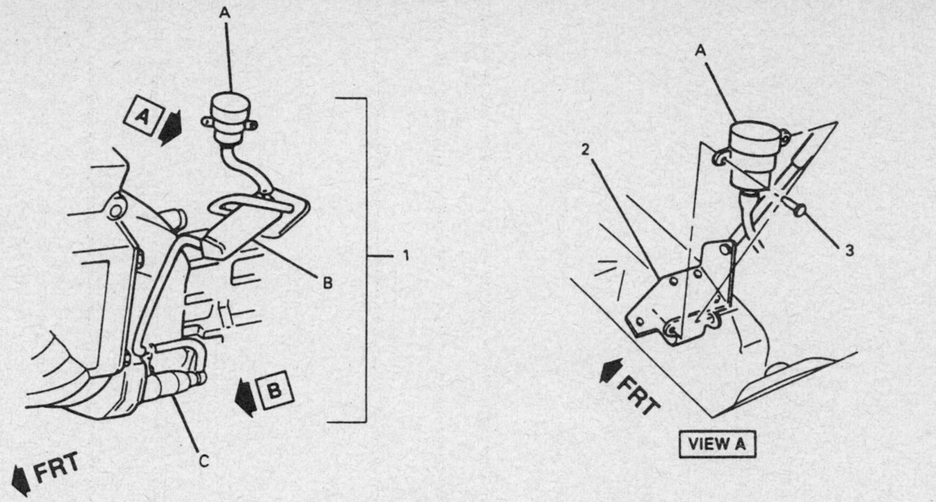
A
B
C
1
FRT
2
3
VIEW A

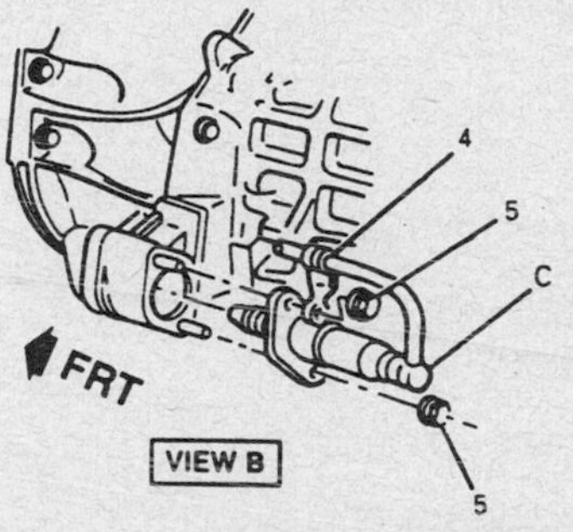
4
5
C
FRT
VIEW B

A RESERVOIR, CLUTCH MASTER CYLINDER
B MASTER CYLINDER, CLUTCH
C ACTUATOR CYLINDER, CLUTCH
1 CYLINDER ASSEMBLY, CLUTCH MASTER AND ACTUATOR
2 BRACKET, HOOD STRUT LEFT-HAND
3 RETAINER, CLUTCH MASTER CYLINDER RESERVOIR
4 HOSE CLIP, CLUTCH MASTER CYLINDER AND ACTUATOR
5 NUT, CLUTCH ACTUATOR CYLINDER, 20 N•m (15 LB. FT.)

GC5049300032000X

Fig. 2 Clutch hydraulic system. 1993–95 models w/5-speed transmission

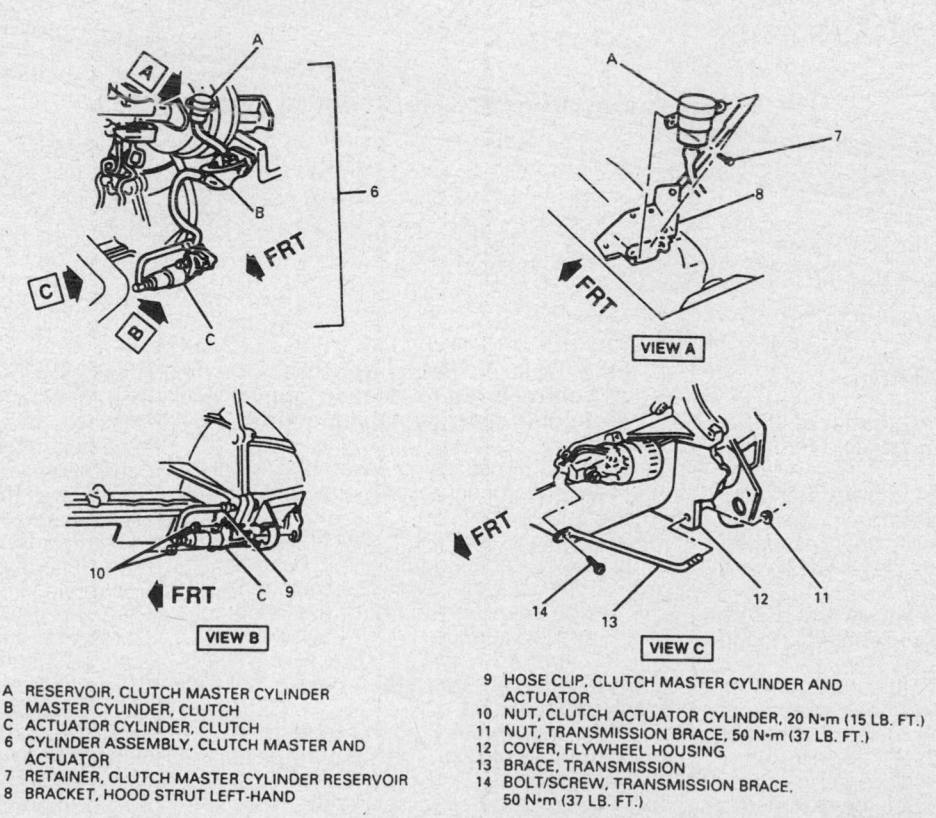

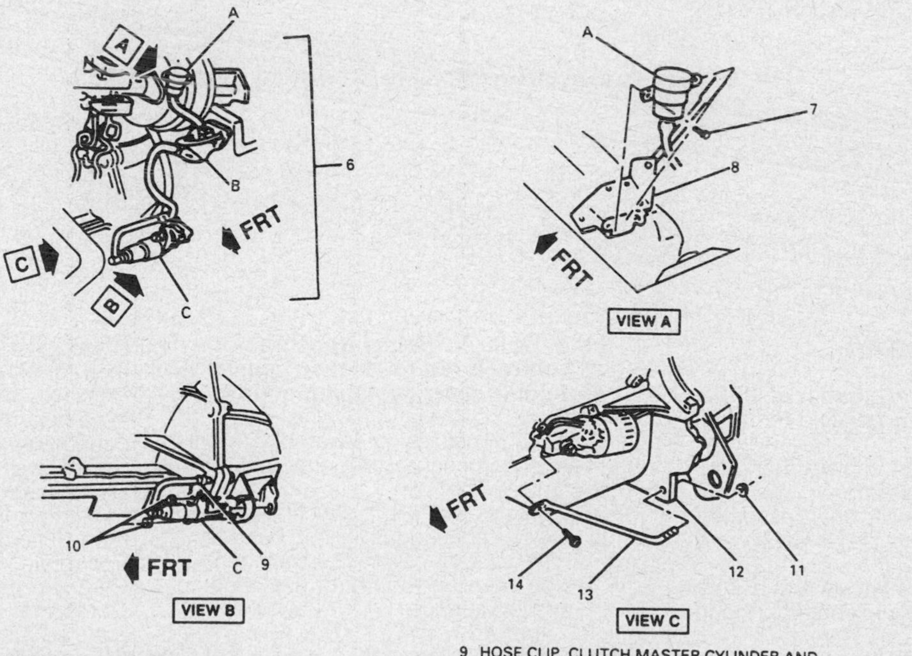
A
B
C
6
FRT
7
8
VIEW A
10
9
VIEW B
11
12
13
14
VIEW C

A RESERVOIR, CLUTCH MASTER CYLINDER
B MASTER CYLINDER, CLUTCH
C ACTUATOR CYLINDER, CLUTCH
6 CYLINDER ASSEMBLY, CLUTCH MASTER AND ACTUATOR
7 RETAINER, CLUTCH MASTER CYLINDER RESERVOIR
8 BRACKET, HOOD STRUT LEFT-HAND
9 HOSE CLIP, CLUTCH MASTER CYLINDER AND ACTUATOR
10 NUT, CLUTCH ACTUATOR CYLINDER, 20 N•m (15 LB. FT.)
11 NUT, TRANSMISSION BRACE, 50 N•m (37 LB. FT.)
12 COVER, FLYWHEEL HOUSING
13 BRACE, TRANSMISSION
14 BOLT/SCREW, TRANSMISSION BRACE, 50 N•m (37 LB. FT.)

GC5049300033000X

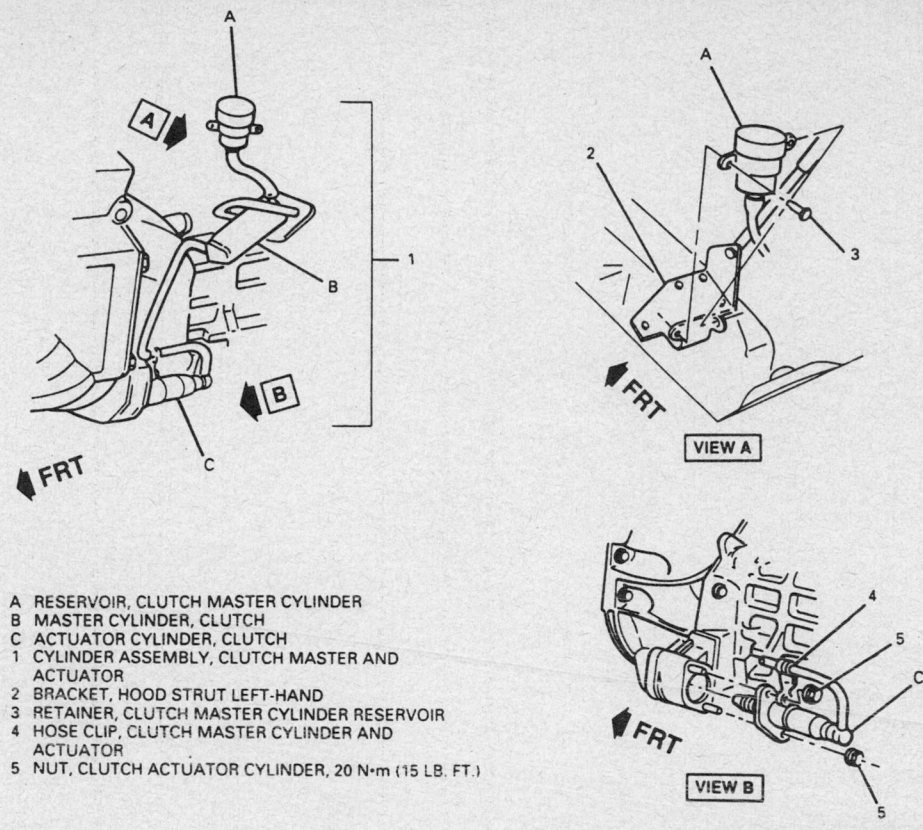

Fig. 3 Clutch hydraulic system. 1993–95 models w/6-speed transmission

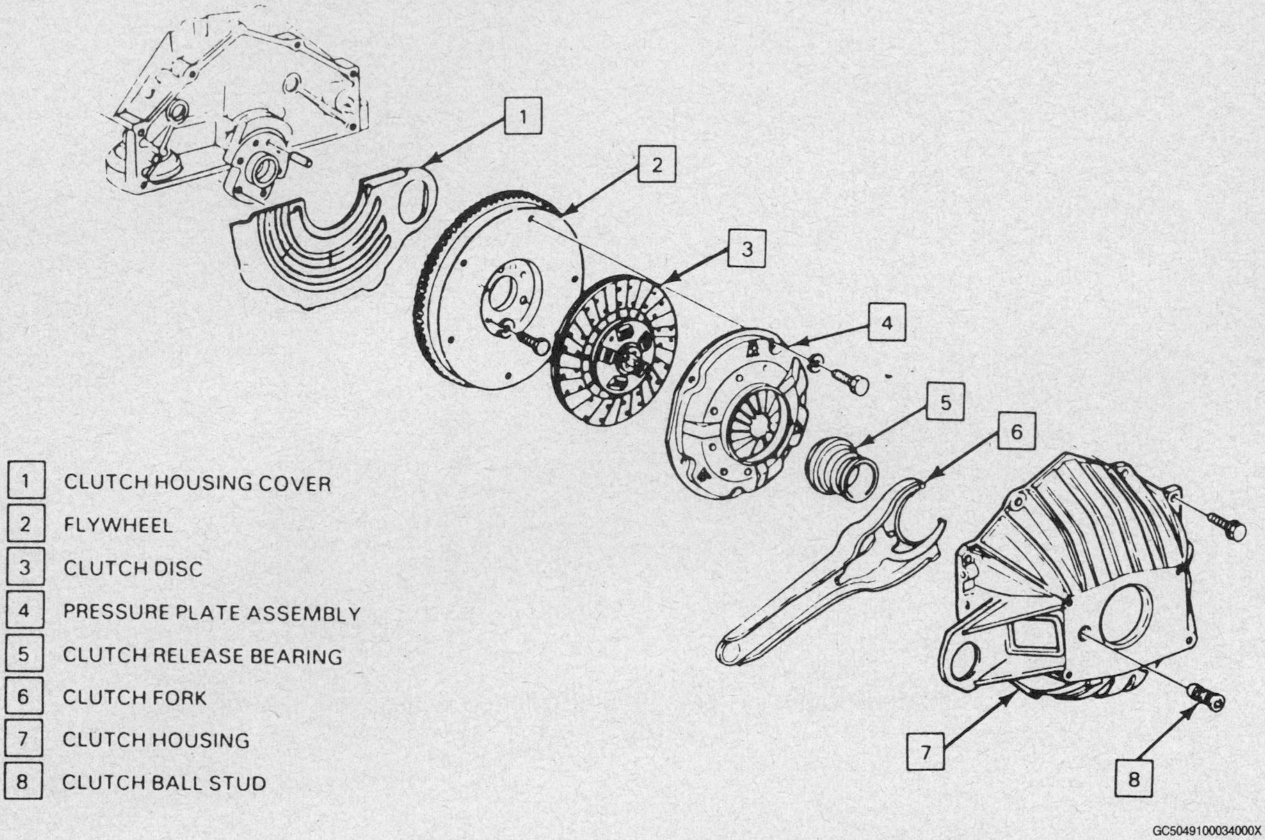
1
2
3
4
5
6
7
8
1 CLUTCH HOUSING COVER
2 FLYWHEEL
3 CLUTCH DISC
4 PRESSURE PLATE ASSEMBLY
5 CLUTCH RELEASE BEARING
6 CLUTCH FORK
7 CLUTCH HOUSING
8 CLUTCH BALL STUD
GC5049100034000X

Fig. 4 Clutch disc, pressure plate & housing assembly. 1992

Models w/5-Speed Transmission

1. Disconnect battery ground cable, then remove front floor console trim plate assembly.
2. Raise and support vehicle, then drain fluid from transmission.
3. Disconnect propeller shaft assembly, then support rear axle assembly with a jack stand.
4. Remove rear axle torque arm assembly, then the catalytic converter hanger assembly.
5. Disconnect electrical connectors from back-up lamp switch and speed sensor, then support engine assembly with a jack stand.
6. Remove transmission support and mount assembly, then lower transmission enough to reach control bolts.
7. Remove transmission control bolts, then lower transmission and remove control assembly. **Control must be held while lowering transmission as control is not retained in vehicle and could drop damaging component.**
8. Remove transmission assembly.
9. Reverse procedure to install, noting the following:
   a. Tighten fasteners to specifications.
   b. Apply a continuous 1/8 inch bead of RTV sealant 12345739 to extension housing to control assembly sealing surface.

Models w/6-Speed Transmission

1. Disconnect battery ground cable, then remove front floor console trim plate assembly.
2. Remove control lever handle, then raise and support vehicle.
3. Drain fluid from transmission, then support rear axle assembly with a jack stand.
4. Disconnect propeller shaft assembly, then remove rear axle torque arm.
5. Remove catalytic converter hanger assembly, then disconnect electrical connectors from back-up lamp switch and reverse lockout solenoid.
6. Disconnect clutch master cylinder pushrod from clutch pedal assembly, then remove clutch actuator cylinder and retain with mechanics wire.
7. Remove actuator spacer, then pull clutch fork assembly down to disengage release bearing.
8. Disconnect electrical connector from electronic speed sensor, then support engine assembly with a jack stand.
9. Support transmission assembly with a jack stand, then remove transmission support and mount assembly.
10. Remove transmission assembly.
11. Reverse procedure to install. Tighten fasteners to specifications.

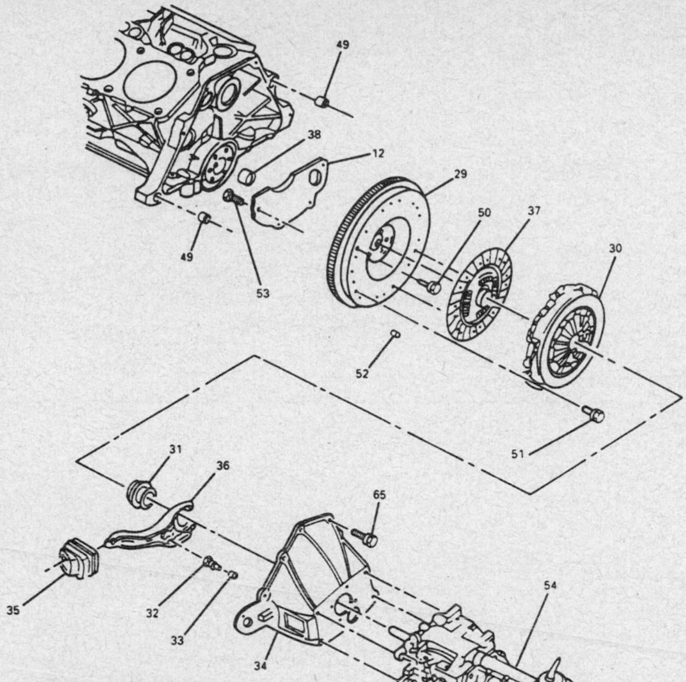
49
38
12
29
50
37
30
49
53
52
51
31
36
65
54
35
32
33
34

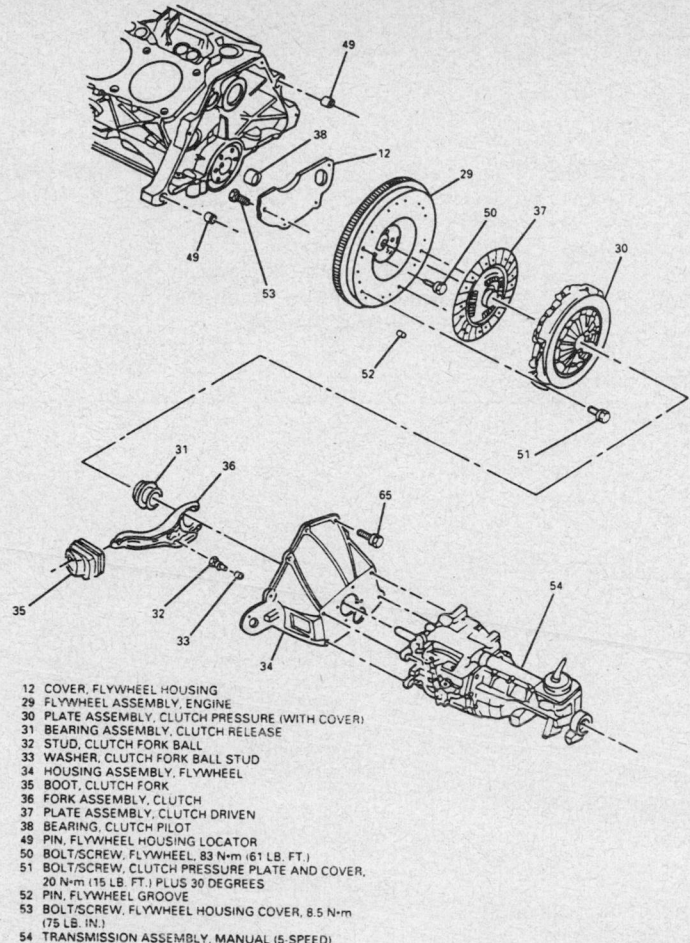

12 COVER, FLYWHEEL HOUSING
29 FLYWHEEL ASSEMBLY, ENGINE
30 PLATE ASSEMBLY, CLUTCH PRESSURE (WITH COVER)
31 BEARING ASSEMBLY, CLUTCH RELEASE
32 STUD, CLUTCH FORK BALL
33 WASHER, CLUTCH FORK BALL STUD
34 HOUSING ASSEMBLY, FLYWHEEL
35 BOOT, CLUTCH FORK
36 FORK ASSEMBLY, CLUTCH
37 PLATE ASSEMBLY, CLUTCH DRIVEN
38 BEARING, CLUTCH PILOT
49 PIN, FLYWHEEL HOUSING LOCATOR
50 BOLT/SCREW, FLYWHEEL, 83 N•m (61 LB. FT.)
51 BOLT/SCREW, CLUTCH PRESSURE PLATE AND COVER, 20 N•m (15 LB. FT.) PLUS 30 DEGREES
52 PIN, FLYWHEEL GROOVE
53 BOLT/SCREW, FLYWHEEL HOUSING COVER, 8.5 N•m (75 LB. IN.)
54 TRANSMISSION ASSEMBLY, MANUAL (5-SPEED)
65 BOLT/SCREW, FLYWHEEL HOUSING, 75 N•m (55 LB. FT.)

GC5049300035000X

Fig. 5 Clutch disc, pressure plate & housing assembly. 1993–95 models w/5-speed transmission

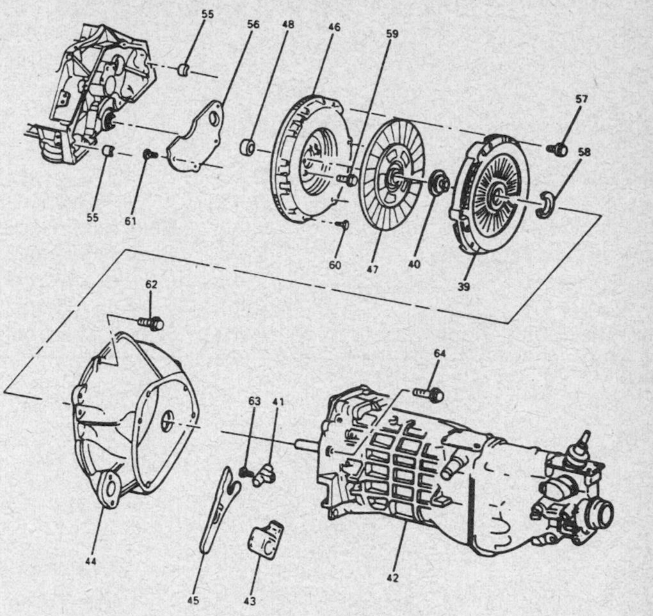
55
56
48
46
59
57
58
55
61
60
47
40
39
62
64
63
41
44
45
43
42

39 PLATE ASSEMBLY, CLUTCH PRESSURE (WITH COVER)
40 BEARING ASSEMBLY, CLUTCH RELEASE
41 T-STUD, CLUTCH FORK
42 TRANSMISSION ASSEMBLY, MANUAL (6-SPEED)
43 SPACER, CLUTCH ACTUATOR CYLINDER
44 HOUSING ASSEMBLY, FLYWHEEL
45 FORK ASSEMBLY, CLUTCH
46 FLYWHEEL ASSEMBLY, ENGINE
47 PLATE ASSEMBLY, CLUTCH DRIVEN
48 BEARING, CLUTCH PILOT
55 PIN, FLYWHEEL HOUSING LOCATOR
56 COVER, FLYWHEEL HOUSING
57 BOLT/SCREW, CLUTCH PRESSURE PLATE AND COVER 30 N•m (22 LB. FT.)
58 RETAINER, CLUTCH RELEASE BEARING
59 BOLT/SCREW, FLYWHEEL, 100 N•m (74 LB. FT.)
60 PIN, FLYWHEEL GROOVE
61 BOLT/SCREW, FLYWHEEL HOUSING COVER, 8.5 N•m (75 LB. IN.)
62 BOLT/SCREW, FLYWHEEL HOUSING, 47 N•m (35 LB. FT.)
63 BOLT/SCREW, CLUTCH FORK T-STUD, 24 N•m (18 LB. FT.)
64 BOLT/SCREW, TRANSMISSION, 35 N•m (26 LB. FT.)

GC5049300036000X

Fig. 6 Clutch disc, pressure plate & housing assembly. 1993–95 models w/6-speed transmission

TIGHTENING SPECIFICATIONS

Year	Component	Torque/ Ft. Lbs.
1992	Actuator Cylinder To Housing	15
	Clutch Housing To Engine (V6)	70
	Clutch Housing To Engine (V8)	35
	Clutch Pedal Mounting Bracket	26
	Extension Housing Bolt	22
	Flywheel To Crankshaft (V6)	52
	Flywheel To Crankshaft (V8)	74
	Heat Shield To Clutch Housing	15
	Master Cylinder To Cowl	10
	Neutral Safety Switch	19①
	Pressure Plate To Flywheel (V6)	15
	Pressure Plate To Flywheel (V8)	30
	Reservoir To Mounting Bracket	53①
	Shift Control Lever Bolt	13
	Transmission Drain & Fill Plugs	20
	Transmission To Flywheel Housing Bolt	55
1993–95	Actuator Cylinder Nuts	15

Year	Component	Torque/ Ft. Lbs.
1993–95 —Cont'd	Clutch Master Cylinder Nuts	20
	Flywheel Housing Bolts. Models w/5-Speed	55
	Flywheel Housing Bolts. Models w/6-Speed	35
	Flywheel Housing Cover Bolts	6
	Pressure Plate To Flywheel. Models w/5-Speed	15②
	Pressure Plate To Flywheel. Models w/6-Speed	22
	Shift Control Lever Bolt. Models w/5-Speed	13
	Shift Control Lever Bolt. Models w/6-Speed	18
	Transmission Brace Nut & Bolt. Models w/5-Speed	37
	Transmission To Flywheel Housing Bolt. Models w/5-Speed	55
	Transmission To Flywheel Housing Bolt. Models w/6-Speed	26

①—Inch lbs.
②—Plus an additional 30 degrees.

Rear Axle & Suspension

INDEX

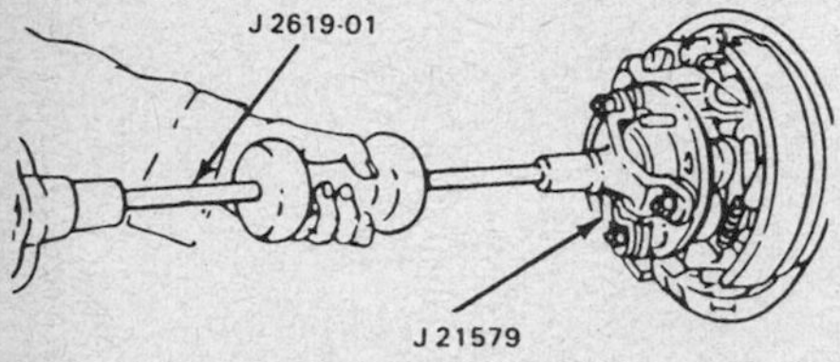
J 2619-01
J 21579
GC3039100213000X

Fig. 1 Axle shaft removal. Borg Warner axle

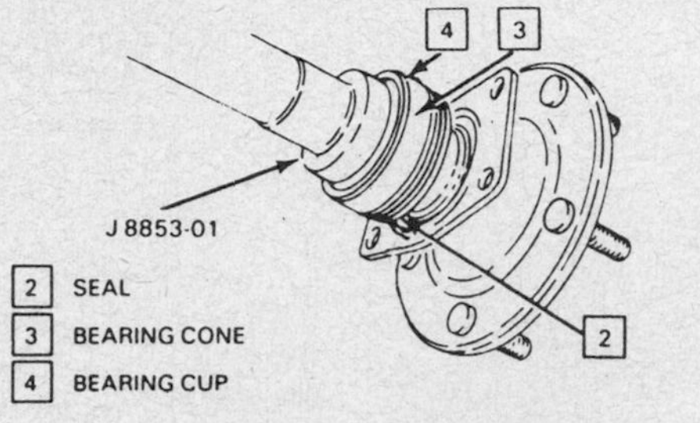
4
3
J 8853-01
2
2 SEAL
3 BEARING CONE
4 BEARING CUP
GC3039100214000X

Fig. 2 Axle shaft bearing retainer nut removal. Borg Warner axle

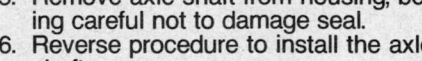

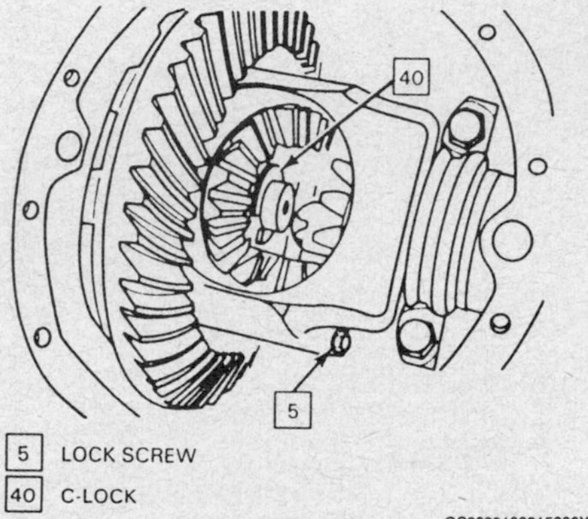
40
5
5 LOCK SCREW
40 C-LOCK
GC3039100215000X

Fig. 3 Pinion shaft lock screw & axle shaft C-lock. GM axle

REAR AXLE
REPLACE

Construction of the axle assembly is such that service operations may be performed with the housing installed in the vehicle or with the housing removed and installed in a holding fixture. The following procedure is necessary only when the housing requires replacement.

1. Raise and support vehicle, then support rear axle with a suitable jack.
2. Disconnect shock absorbers from lower mountings.
3. Remove track bar.
4. Disconnect brake line from axle housing junction block and the parking brake cable.
5. Disconnect lower control arms from axle housing attachments.
6. Remove propeller shaft.
7. Lower axle slowly until springs can be moved. Roll axle assembly out from under vehicle.
8. Reverse procedure to install.

REAR AXLE SHAFT
REPLACE

BORG WARNER AXLE

1. Raise and support rear of vehicle, then remove wheel and tire assembly.
2. Remove brake caliper, then remove brake rotor.
3. Remove four nuts attaching axle shaft bearing retainer to axle housing.
4. Using puller and adapter tools No. J-21579 and J-2619-01, or equivalents, pull axle shaft from housing, **Fig. 1.**
5. To replace axle shaft bearing, split inner retainer with a suitable chisel, then remove retainer from axle shaft, **Fig. 2.** Using tool No. J-22912-01, or equivalent, press bearing and seal from axle shaft.
6. Reverse procedure to install. When replacing oil seals, it should be noted right hand seal is identified by black bands, while left hand seal is identified by gold bands. Prior to installation, seal lips should be lightly coated with a suitable grease. When pressing bearing and seal onto axle shaft, use tool No. J-8853-01, or equivalent. Position chamfer on outer diameter of bearing retainer toward bearing. **On models with limited slip,** both axle shaft splines should be fully engaged before axle shaft is rotated to maintain spline alignment.

GM AXLE

1. Raise vehicle and support vehicle, then remove wheel and brake drum or rotor.
2. Drain lube from carrier and remove cover.
3. Remove differential pinion shaft lock screw and remove differential pinion shaft, **Fig. 3.**
4. Pull flange end of axle shaft toward center of vehicle and remove C-lock from button end of shaft, **Fig. 3.**
5. Remove axle shaft from housing, being careful not to damage seal.
6. Reverse procedure to install the axle shaft.

PROPELLER SHAFT
REPLACE

1992

1. Raise and support vehicle.
2. Mark position of shaft in relation to pinion flange for reassembly.
3. Remove straps securing universal joint to pinion flange, then disconnect shaft from flange. **Tape bearing cups to universal joint to prevent loss of needle bearings.**
4. Slide yoke out of transmission and remove propeller shaft. Insert suitable plug in transmission to prevent fluid loss.
5. Reverse procedure to install.

1993–95

1. Raise and support vehicle, then mark relationship of propeller shaft assembly to pinion gear yoke.

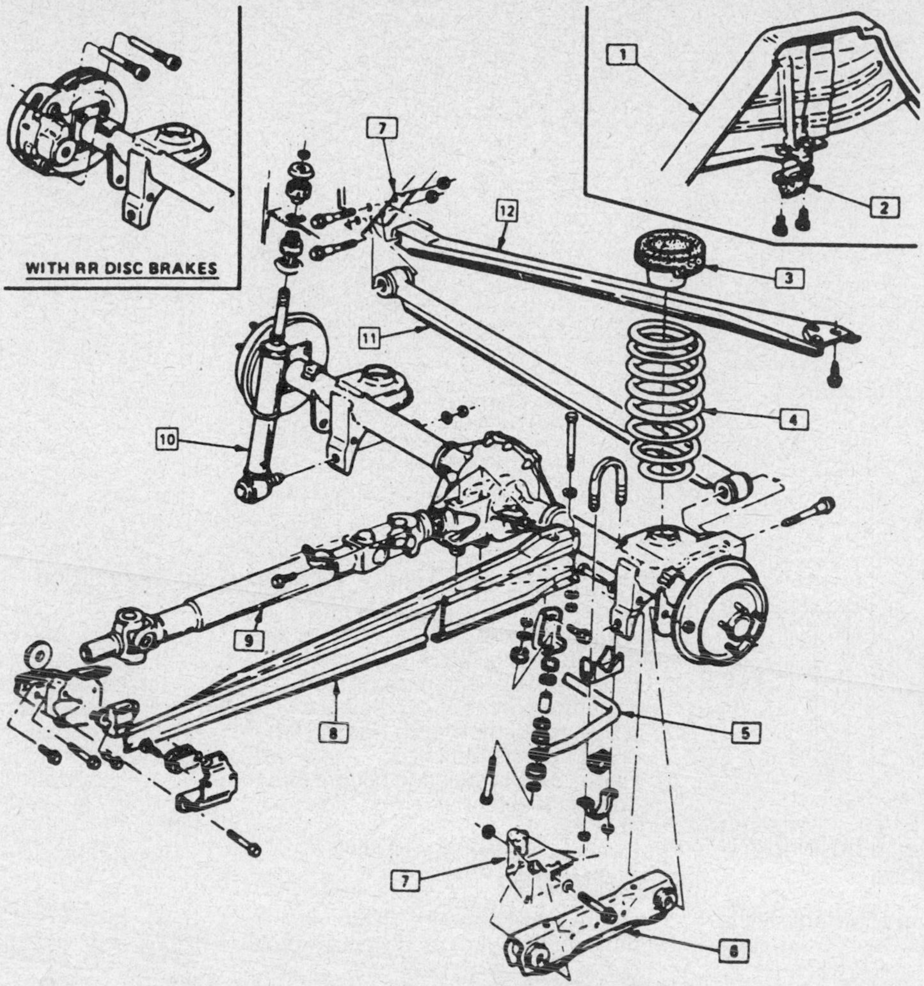
WITH RR DISC BRAKES

1. RAIL
2. JOUNCE BUMPER
3. SPRING INSULATOR ASSEMBLY
4. COIL SPRING
5. OPTIONAL STABILIZER BAR
6. LOWER CONTROL ARM
7. UNDERBODY
8. TORQUE ARM
9. PROP SHAFT
10. SHOCK ABSORBER
11. TRACK BAR
12. TRACK BAR BRACE

GC2039100029000X

Fig. 4 Exploded view of rear suspension

2. **On two-piece propeller shafts,** remove bolts from center support bearing.
3. Remove center support bearing and washers from torque arm assembly.
4. **On all propeller shafts,** remove bolts and retainers, then the propeller shaft.
5. Reverse procedure to install, noting the following:
   a. Tighten fasteners to specifications.
   b. Lubricate slip yoke with .6 ounces of propeller shaft slip yoke lubricant 1050169.
   c. Align marks on pinion gear yoke and propeller shaft.

SHOCK ABSORBER

REPLACE

1992

1. Raise vehicle and support rear axle.
2. Pull back carpeting, then remove shock absorber upper mounting nut.
3. Remove shock absorber lower mounting nut, then remove shock absorber, **Fig. 4.**
4. Reverse procedure to install.

1993–95

1. Fold down seat back frame, then remove quarter trim panel.
2. Pull folding carpet back, then raise and support vehicle.
3. Support rear axle, then remove shock absorber.
4. Reverse procedure to install. Tighten fasteners to specifications.

COIL SPRING

REPLACE

1992

1. Raise and support vehicle and support rear axle with a suitable adjustable jack.
2. Remove track bar mounting bolt from axle and loosen track bar bolt at body brace, **Fig. 4.**
3. Disconnect rear brake hose clip at underbody, then disconnect shock absorbers at lower mountings.
4. Carefully lower rear axle and remove springs and insulators.
5. Reverse procedure to install.

1993–95

1. Raise and support vehicle, then sup-

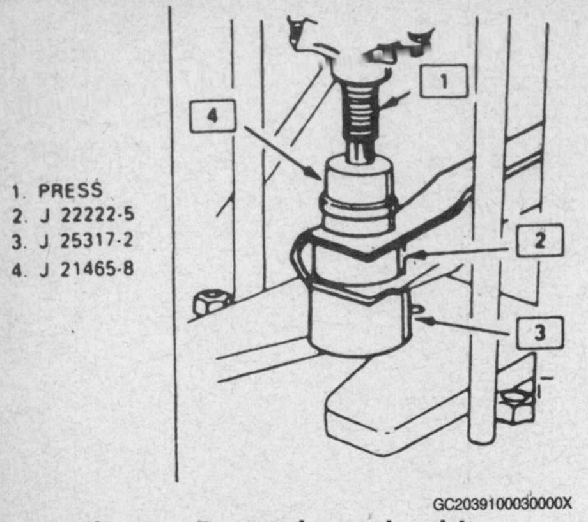
1. PRESS
2. J 22222-5
3. J 25317-2
4. J 21465-8
1
2
3
4
GC2039100030000X

Fig. 5 Control arm bushing removal

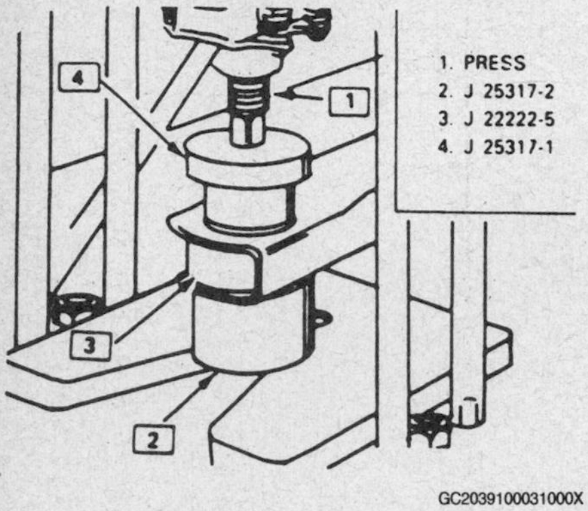
1. PRESS
2. J 25317-2
3. J 22222-5
4. J 25317-1
1
2
3
4
GC2039100031000X

Fig. 6 Control arm bushing installation

port rear axle with an adjustable lifting device. **Do not use twin post type hoist.**

2. Remove shock absorber nuts from rear axle, then lower rear axle.
3. Remove upper insulator assembly, then the rear spring.
4. Reverse procedure to install. Tighten fasteners to specifications.

CONTROL ARM

REPLACE

LOWER

If both control arms are to be removed,

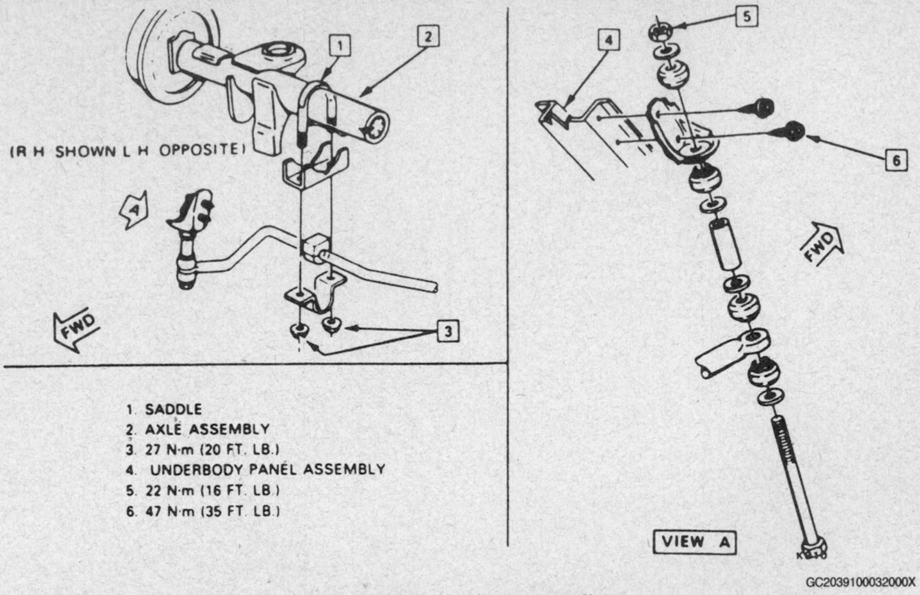
(R H SHOWN L H OPPOSITE)
1. SADDLE
2. AXLE ASSEMBLY
3. 27 N·m (20 FT. LB.)
4. UNDERBODY PANEL ASSEMBLY
5. 22 N·m (16 FT. LB.)
6. 47 N·m (35 FT. LB.)
FWD
VIEW A
GC2039100032000X

Fig. 7 Stabilizer bar installation

remove one control arm at a time to prevent axle from slipping or rolling.

1. Raise vehicle and support at frame pads. Support nose of axle housing to prevent assembly from twisting when control arm is removed.
2. Remove bolts securing control arm to chassis and rear axle, and the control arm, **Fig. 4.**
3. Reverse procedure to install.

BUSHINGS

1. Raise and support vehicle and remove control arm as described previously.
2. Press bushings out of control arm using suitable tools as shown in **Fig. 5.**
3. Reverse procedure to install, ensuring bushing is properly seated in control arm, **Fig. 6. If replacement bushing fits loosely in control arm, or if mounting areas are damaged or deformed, control arm must be replaced.**

STABILIZER BAR

REPLACE

1. Raise and support vehicle.
2. Remove link bolt nuts, washers, bushings, spacers and link bolts securing stabilizer to chassis, **Fig. 7.**
3. Remove clamps securing stabilizer shaft to rear axle and stabilizer shaft.
4. Reverse procedure to install. Tighten link bolts and U-bolt nuts to specifications.

TRACK ROD

REPLACE

1. Raise vehicle and support rear axle at curb height.
2. Remove track bar mounting bolt and nut from rear axle and from body bracket, then remove track bar, **Fig. 4.**
3. Remove heat shield attaching screws from track bar brace.
4. Remove three track bar to body brace screws.
5. Remove nut and bolt from body bracket, then remove track bar brace.
6. Reverse procedure to install.

TIGHTENING SPECIFICATIONS

Year	Component	Torque/ Ft. lbs.
1992	Control Arm To Rear Axle	85
	Control Arm To Underbody	85
	Rear Axle Housing Cover To Axle	22
	Rear Axle Pinion Shaft Lock Screw	27
	Shock Absorber Lower Mounting	66
	Shock Absorber Upper Mounting	13
	Stabilizer Bracket To Body	35
	Stabilizer Clamp To U-Bolt	18
	Stabilizer Shaft To Body Bracket	13
	Torque Arm Outer Bracket	30
	Torque Arm To Rear Axle	98
	Track Bar To Axle	77
	Track Bar To Body Bracket	59
	Track Bar Brace To Body Bracket Nut	61
	Track Bar Brace To Body Bracket Screw	35
	Universal Joint Strap Bolt	16

Year	Component	Torque/ Ft. lbs.
1992	Wheel Lug Nuts	100
1993–95	Control Arm Bolts	74
	Control Arm Nuts	60
	Differential Pinion Gear Shaft Lock Bolt	27
	Shock Absorber Lower Nut	66
	Shock Absorber Upper Nut	13
	Stabilizer Link	16
	Stabilizer Shaft Bracket Bolts	17
	Stabilizer Shaft Nuts	18
	Torque Arm To Rear Axle Bolts	96
	Torque Arm To Rear Axle Nuts	97
	Torque Arm To Transmission Center Bolt	20
	Torque Arm To Transmission Lower & Upper Bolts	37
	Torque Arm To Transmission Nuts	30
	Wheel Lug Nuts	100

Front Suspension & Steering

NOTE: On Air Bag Equipped Models, Refer To "Air Bag System Precautions" Located In The Front Of This Manual For System Disarming & Arming Procedures.

INDEX

PRECAUTIONS

AIR BAG SYSTEMS

Refer to "Air Bag System Precautions" in the front of this manual for system disarming and arming procedures.

DESCRIPTION

1992

A modified strut type suspension is used on Camaro and Firebird, **Fig. 1.** Each wheel is independently connected to the chassis by a lower control arm, spindle and a strut assembly which locates the spindle and controls ride by dampening spring action. Coil springs are mounted between the lower control arm and crossmember, and a stabilizer shaft is connected between the chassis and control arms to control side roll.

1993–95

The short/long arm (SLA) front suspension assembly, **Fig. 2,** is designed to allow each wheel to compensate for changes in road surface level without significantly affecting the opposite wheel. Each wheel is independently connected to the frame by a steering knuckle, wheel hub, shock absorber and spring, upper and lower ball studs and upper and lower control arms.

WHEEL BEARING

ADJUST

1992

1. While rotating wheel forward, **torque spindle nut to 12 ft. lbs., Fig. 3.**
2. Back off nut until just loose then hand tighten nut and back it off again until either hole in spindle lines up with hole in nut. **Do not back off nut more than 1/2 flat.**
3. Install new cotter pin. With wheel bearing properly adjusted, there will be .001-.005 inch endplay.

1993–95

These vehicles use a maintenance-free wheel bearing, which does not require adjustment.

WHEEL BEARING

REPLACE

1992

1. Raise and support vehicle, then remove wheel and tire assembly.

2. Remove disc brake caliper. Once removed, the caliper can be wired or secured in some manner away from the disc. Do not allow caliper to hang from brake hose.
3. Remove spindle nut and hub and disc assembly. Grease retainer and inner wheel bearing can now be removed.
4. Reverse procedure to install.

1993–95

These vehicles use a maintenance-free wheel bearing, which is serviced as an assembly with the wheel hub.

WHEEL HUB

REPLACE

1. Raise and support vehicle, then remove tire and wheel assembly on side to be serviced.
2. Remove brake caliper assembly, and brake disc.
3. Disconnect wheel speed sensor electrical connector and secure aside.
4. Remove bolts and screws from hub assembly, then the hub assembly.
5. Reverse procedure to install, **torquing** retaining bolts to 63 ft. lbs.

BALL JOINT INSPECTION

LOWER

On 1992 models, ball joint seals should be checked for cuts and tears. If cuts and tears are present, replace ball joint.

On 1993-95 models, the lower ball joint has a visual wear indicator. Proceed as follows to inspect:

1. Ensure vehicle is supported by wheel assemblies so weight of vehicle is properly loading ball joints, then wipe grease fitting free of dirt and grease.
2. Wear is indicated by position of 1/2 inch diameter nipple in which grease fitting is threaded. If nipple is flush or inside cover surface, replace ball joint.

UPPER

1992

Ball joint seals should be checked for cuts and tears. If cuts and tears are present, replace ball joint.

1993–95

1. Raise front end of vehicle and position floor stands under both lower control arms as near to ball joints as possible.
2. Position a dial indicator against wheel rim as shown in **Fig. 4.** Push in on bottom of tire while pulling out at top, then reverse procedure.
3. Deflection on dial indicator should not exceed .125 inch. If deflection exceeds specification, replace ball joint.
4. If ball joint is disconnected from steering knuckle, check for looseness or see if ball joint can be twisted in its socket using your fingers.
5. If either of the above conditions exist, replace ball joint.

BALL JOINT

REPLACE

LOWER

1. Raise vehicle and support at frame, and remove wheel and tire.
2. Position a suitable jack under lower control arm spring seat, and raise jack to compress coil spring. **Jack must remain in place during ball joint replacement to hold spring and lower control arm in position.**
3. Remove cotter pin and nut securing ball joint stud to steering knuckle, then disconnect joint from knuckle using a suitable tool.
4. Lift knuckle assembly from ball stud, guiding control arm out of splash shield, then support knuckle aside to allow clearance for joint removal.
5. Remove grease fitting, then press ball joint assembly out of lower control arm using a suitable tool, **Fig. 5.**
6. Press replacement joint into arm by reversing removal tools, fit spindle over ball stud, install washer, if equipped, and retaining nut.
7. Tighten retaining nut to specifications.
8. Tighten nut up to an additional 1/16 turn, if necessary, to align hole in ball stud with nut, then install cotter pin.

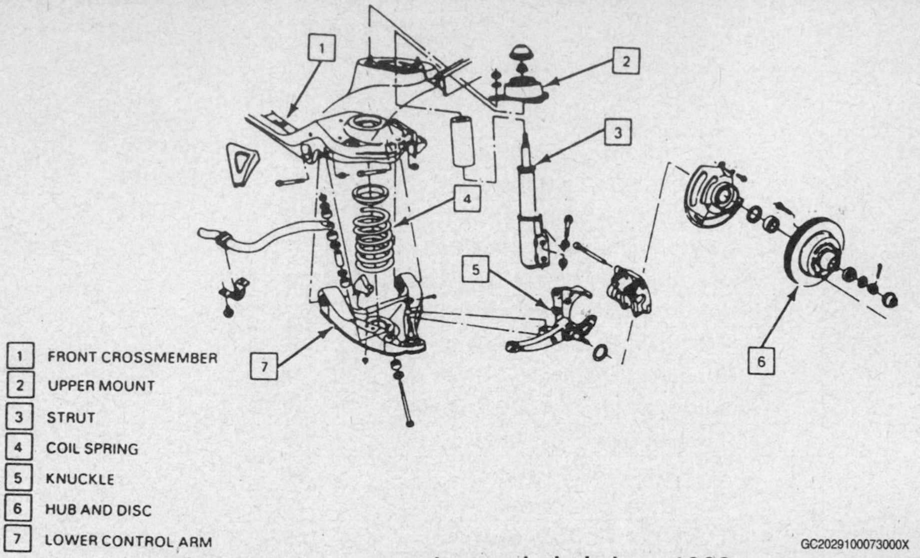
1
2
3
4
5
6
7
1 FRONT CROSSMEMBER
2 UPPER MOUNT
3 STRUT
4 COIL SPRING
5 KNUCKLE
6 HUB AND DISC
7 LOWER CONTROL ARM
GC2029100073000X

Fig. 1 Front suspension exploded view. 1992

UPPER

1993–95

1. Raise and support vehicle, then remove wheel.
2. Place a floor jack under shock absorber mounting location on lower control. **Jack must remain in place during ball joint replacement to hold spring and lower control arm in position.**
3. Loosen ball joint from steering knuckle, then remove cotter pin and nut.
4. Support steering knuckle with floor stands, then disconnect ball joint from upper control arm using ball joint/tie rod separator J 39549.
5. With upper control arm in raised position, drill out four rivets approximately 1/4 inch deep using a 1/8 inch drill bit.
6. Drill off rivet heads using a 1/2 inch drill bit, then punch out rivets using a small punch and remove ball joint.
7. Position new ball joint and install bolts and nuts supplied with new ball joint.
8. Remove support from steering knuckle, then connect ball joint to steering knuckle.
9. tighten nut enough to align slot with stud hole, then tighten nut to specifications and install cotter pin.

COIL SPRING

REPLACE

1992

1. Raise and support vehicle, then remove wheel and tire assembly.
2. Remove stabilizer link and bushings from lower control arm.
3. Remove cotter pin and nut from tie rod end.
4. Using ball joint remover tool No. tool No. J-24292-B, or equivalent, disconnect tie rod end from steering knuckle.
5. Using a suitable spring compressor, compress coil spring, **Fig. 6.**
6. Remove lower control arm pivot bolt, then pivot control arm rearward.
7. Remove spring compressor and coil spring.
8. Reverse procedure to install. When installing, position coil spring as shown in **Fig. 6.** Lower control arm must be positioned at dimension A, **Fig. 7,** when torquing bolts.

STRUT

REPLACE

1992

1. Raise and support vehicle.
2. Remove wheel and support lower control arm with a suitable jack.
3. Remove brake hose bracket and two strut to knuckle bolts, **Fig. 8.**
4. Remove upper mounting assembly cover.
5. Remove nut from upper end of strut, then the strut and shield.
6. Reverse procedure to install.

STRUT SERVICE

1993–95

1. **On models being serviced on driver's side,** remove brake master cylin-

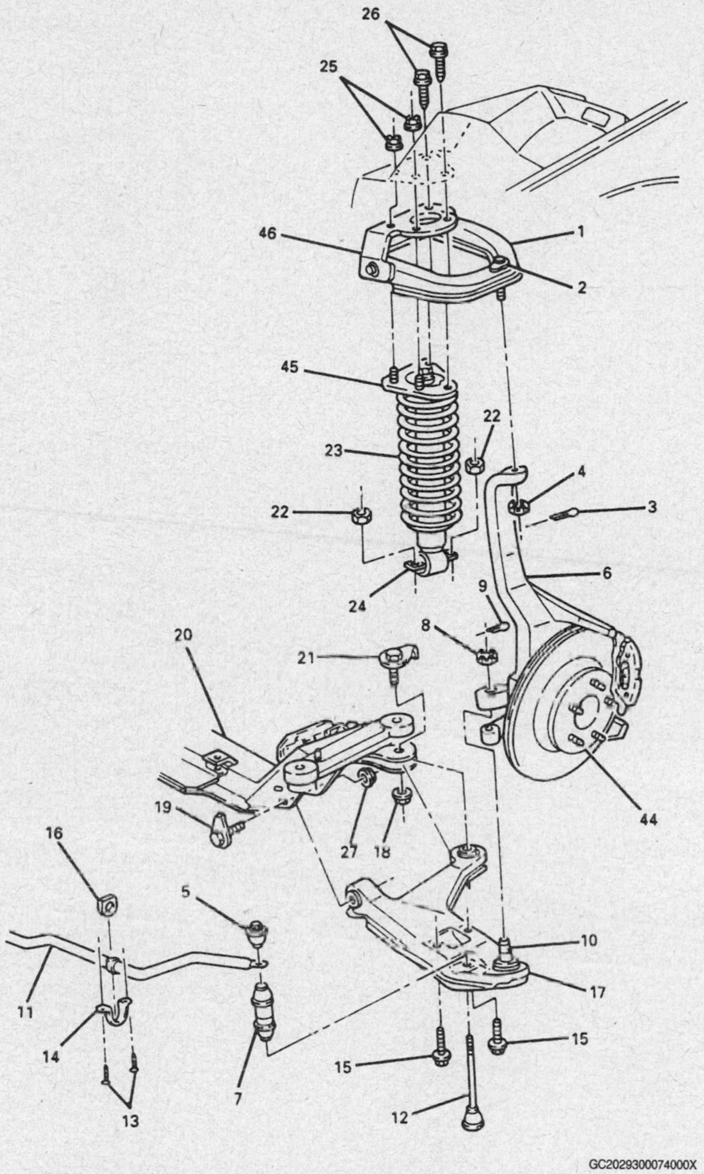
GC2029300074000X

Fig. 2 Front suspension exploded view. 1993–95

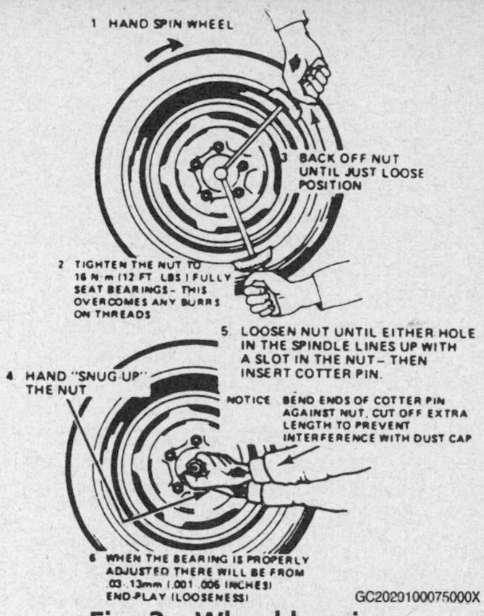
1 HAND SPIN WHEEL
3 BACK OFF NUT UNTIL JUST LOOSE POSITION
2 TIGHTEN THE NUT TO 16 N·m (12 FT. LBS.) FULLY SEAT BEARINGS – THIS OVERCOMES ANY BURRS ON THREADS
5 LOOSEN NUT UNTIL EITHER HOLE IN THE SPINDLE LINES UP WITH A SLOT IN THE NUT – THEN INSERT COTTER PIN.
4 HAND "SNUG UP" THE NUT
NOTICE BEND ENDS OF COTTER PIN AGAINST NUT. CUT OFF EXTRA LENGTH TO PREVENT INTERFERENCE WITH DUST CAP
6 WHEN THE BEARING IS PROPERLY ADJUSTED THERE WILL BE FROM .03-.13mm (.001-.005 INCHES) END-PLAY (LOOSENESS)
GC2029100075000X

Fig. 3 Wheel bearing adjustment. 1992

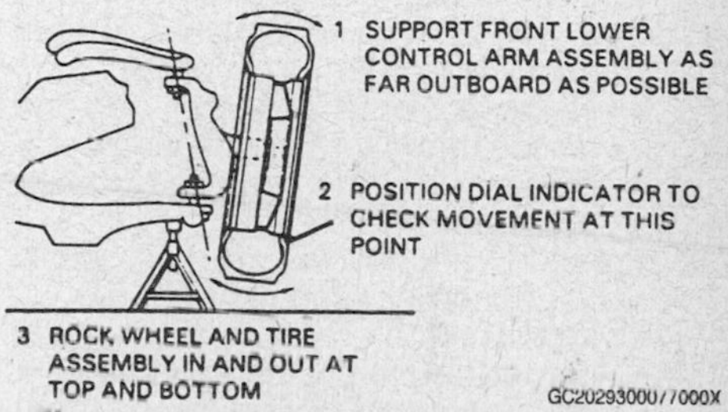
1 SUPPORT FRONT LOWER CONTROL ARM ASSEMBLY AS FAR OUTBOARD AS POSSIBLE
2 POSITION DIAL INDICATOR TO CHECK MOVEMENT AT THIS POINT
3 ROCK WHEEL AND TIRE ASSEMBLY IN AND OUT AT TOP AND BOTTOM

Fig. 4 Upper ball joint inspection. 1993–95

der nuts, then move master cylinder aside.

2. **On all models,** remove upper shock absorber mounting nuts and bolts, then raise and support vehicle.
3. Remove tire and wheel assembly, then disconnect stabilizer shaft link.
4. Remove lower shock absorber mounting nuts and bolts, then separate lower ball joint from steering knuckle.
5. Mark lower mount location relative to upper mount location, then remove shock absorber and spring assembly.
6. Proceed as follows to disassemble shock absorber assembly:
   a. Install modular shock assembly compressor adapter tool No. J-34013-114, or equivalent, onto strut spring compressor tool No. J-34013-B, or equivalent, using wing nuts to secure tool to mounting holes C-H in lower left corner and P in upper right corner for driver side shock absorber assembly, **Figs. 9 and 10,** or to holes A-X-P in upper left corner and C-H in lower right corner for passenger side shock absorber assembly, **Fig. 11.**
   b. Install strut compressor adapter tool No. J-34013-88, or equivalent, and modular shock support tool No. J-34013-218, or equivalent, onto strut spring compressor, **Fig. 12. Ensure strut compressor adapter and modular shock support are aligned so that they can open and close together. If tools are not properly aligned, they will not open.**
   c. Install shock absorber assembly to top of modular shock assembly compressor adapter, **Fig. 13 and 14. Ensure top of shock absorber assembly is flat against modular shock assembly compressor adapter. Shock absorber assembly will not be aligned properly if it does not lay flat against tool.**
   d. Install shock absorber assembly into strut compressor adapter and modular shock support, **Fig. 15,** then close strut compressor adapter and modular shock support and install locking pin. **Ensure mounting ears of shock absorber assembly are facing downward toward rear of strut spring compressor or shock absorber assembly will not align properly.**

e. Turn screw on strut spring compressor counterclockwise to raise shock absorber assembly up to modular shock assembly compressor adapter. Ensure studs go through guide holes in modular shock assembly compressor adapter and top of shock absorber assembly is flat against tool.

f. Compress front spring assembly approximately 1/2 inch or three or four complete turns of screw on modular shock assembly compressor adapter. **Do not over compress front spring assembly. Severe overloading may cause tool failure, possibly resulting in personal injury.**

g. Insert J 39642-1 from modular shock nut removal set tool No. J-39642, or equivalent, on shock absorber nut, then insert tool No. J-39642-2, or equivalent, from modular shock nut removal set tools No. J-39642 through J-39642-1, or equivalents, to hold shock absorber rod in place.

h. Remove shock absorber nut and discard, then turn strut spring compressor clockwise to relieve spring pressure.

7. Proceed as follows to assemble shock absorber assembly:

a. Install shock absorber to strut compressor adapter and modular shock support. **Ensure mounting ears of shock absorber assembly are facing downward toward rear of strut spring compressor or shock absorber assembly will not align properly.**

b. Close strut compressor adapter and modular shock support and install locking pin, then ensure upper and lower spring seats are positioned correctly.

c. Assemble shock absorber assembly to top of modular shock assembly compressor adapter. **Ensure top of shock absorber assembly is flat against modular shock assembly compressor adapter. Shock absorber assembly will not be aligned properly if it does not lay flat against tool.**

d. Turn screw on strut spring compressor counterclockwise to raise shock absorber assembly up to modular shock assembly compressor adapter without compressing spring assembly. Ensure studs on shock absorber assembly go through guide holes in modular shock assembly compressor adapter. **Only turn screw until shock absorber assembly is held in strut spring compressor by itself. Do not load spring assembly.**

e. Place modular shock assembly alignment rod J 34013-115 down through top of strut spring compressor, through top of shock absorber assembly and onto shock absorber rod, **Fig. 16. Ensure shock assembly alignment rod**

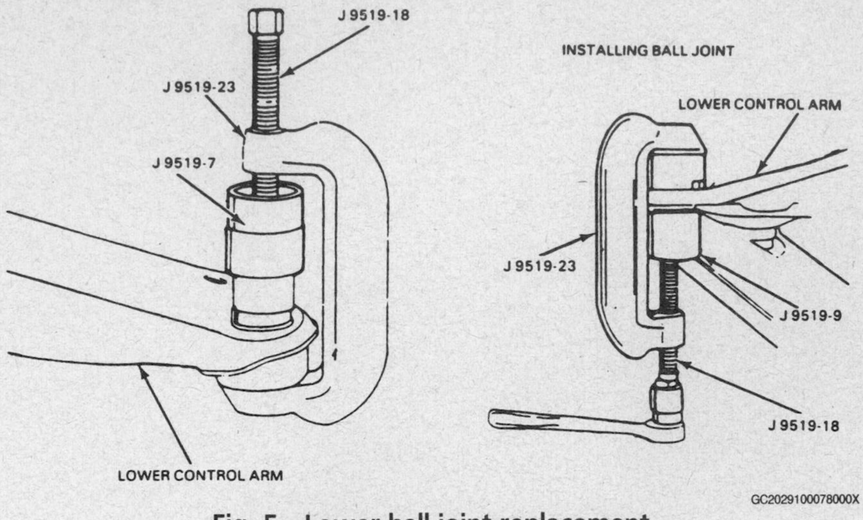
J 9519-18
INSTALLING BALL JOINT
J 9519-23
LOWER CONTROL ARM
J 9519-7
J 9519-23
J 9519-9
J 9519-18
LOWER CONTROL ARM
GC2029100078000X

Fig. 5 Lower ball joint replacement

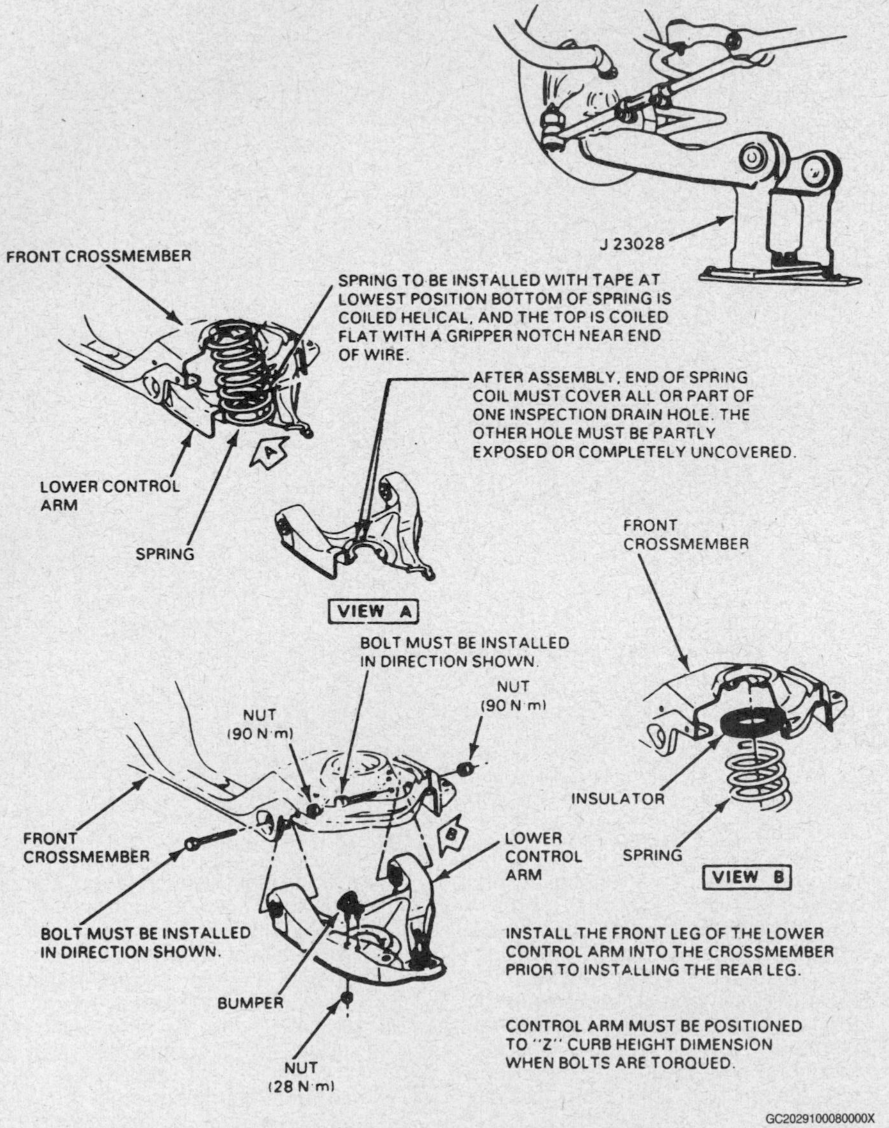
J 23028
FRONT CROSSMEMBER
SPRING TO BE INSTALLED WITH TAPE AT LOWEST POSITION BOTTOM OF SPRING IS COILED HELICAL, AND THE TOP IS COILED FLAT WITH A GRIPPER NOTCH NEAR END OF WIRE.
AFTER ASSEMBLY, END OF SPRING COIL MUST COVER ALL OR PART OF ONE INSPECTION DRAIN HOLE. THE OTHER HOLE MUST BE PARTLY EXPOSED OR COMPLETELY UNCOVERED.
LOWER CONTROL ARM
SPRING
VIEW A
FRONT CROSSMEMBER
BOLT MUST BE INSTALLED IN DIRECTION SHOWN.
NUT (90 N·m)
NUT (90 N·m)
INSULATOR
FRONT CROSSMEMBER
LOWER CONTROL ARM
SPRING
VIEW B
BOLT MUST BE INSTALLED IN DIRECTION SHOWN.
INSTALL THE FRONT LEG OF THE LOWER CONTROL ARM INTO THE CROSSMEMBER PRIOR TO INSTALLING THE REAR LEG.
BUMPER
CONTROL ARM MUST BE POSITIONED TO "Z" CURB HEIGHT DIMENSION WHEN BOLTS ARE TORQUED.
NUT (28 N·m)
GC2029100080000X

Fig. 6 Coil spring replacement. 1992

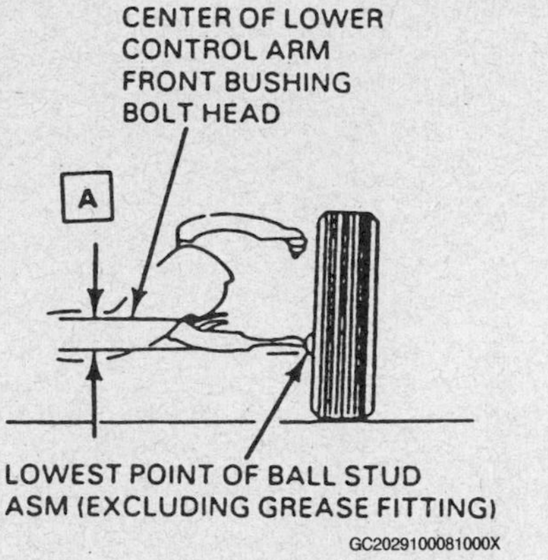
CENTER OF LOWER CONTROL ARM FRONT BUSHING BOLT HEAD
A
LOWEST POINT OF BALL STUD ASM (EXCLUDING GREASE FITTING)
GC2029100081000X

Fig. 7 Lower control arm dimension "A" measurement location (Part 1 of 2). 1992

Year	Model	Suspension (Option Code)	Dimension A, Inches
1992	Camaro Coupe	Soft Ride (FE1)	1.220
		Ride & Handling (FE2)①	1.181
		Ride & Handling (FE2)②	.906
	Firebird Coupe	Soft Ride (FE1)	1.102
		Ride & Handling (FE2)	1.220
		Special Heavy Duty (FE41)	1.181
	Camaro & Firebird Convertible	Soft Ride (FE1)	1.299
		Ride & Handling (FE2)①	1.220
		Ride & Handling (FE2)②	.945

①—With 15 inch wheels.
②—With 16 inch wheels.

Fig. 7 Lower control arm dimension "A" specifications (Part 2 of 2). 1992

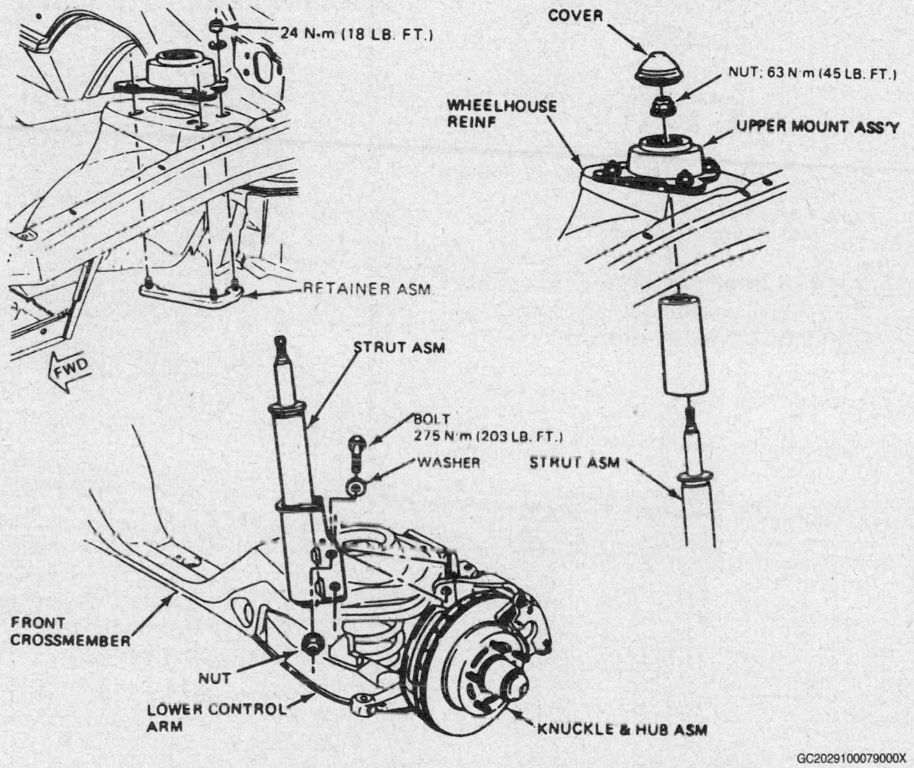
24 N·m (18 LB. FT.)
RETAINER ASM.
FWD
STRUT ASM
BOLT
275 N·m (203 LB. FT.)
WASHER
STRUT ASM
COVER
NUT; 63 N·m (45 LB. FT.)
WHEELHOUSE REINF
UPPER MOUNT ASS'Y
FRONT CROSSMEMBER
NUT
LOWER CONTROL ARM
KNUCKLE & HUB ASM
GC2029100079000X

Fig. 8 Front suspension strut replacement. 1992

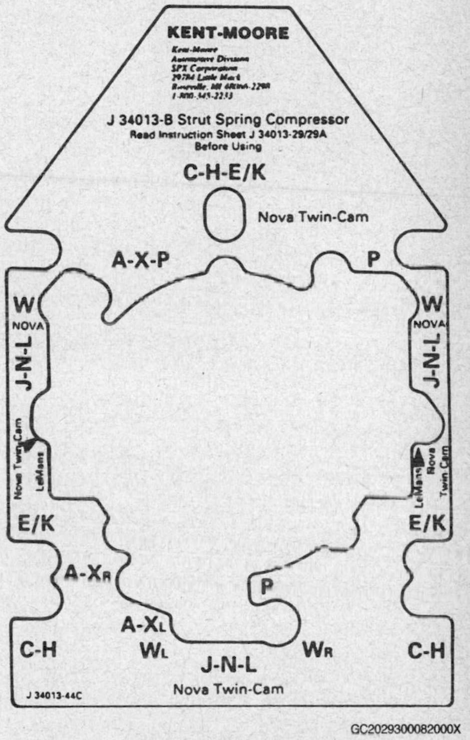
KENT-MOORE
J 34013-B Strut Spring Compressor
Read Instruction Sheet J 34013-29/29A Before Using
C-H-E/K
Nova Twin-Cam
A-X-P
P
W
NOVA
J-N-L
Nova Twin-Cam
LeMans
E/K
A-XR
P
A-XL
C-H
WL
J-N-L
WR
Nova Twin-Cam
J 34013-44C
GC2029300082000X

Fig. 9 Modular shock absorber assembly compressor mounting hole locations. 1993–95

is straight with shock absorber assembly. If shock assembly alignment rod is angled, repeat steps 7a through 7d until tool is straight.

f. Turn operating screw clockwise to compress spring assembly until threaded portion of shock absorber rod is through top of shock absorber assembly. **Do not over compress front spring assembly. Severe overloading may cause tool failure, possibly resulting in personal injury.**

g. Remove modular shock assembly alignment rod, then insert a new shock absorber nut on shock absorber rod. **Always replace shock absorber nut. Do not turn shock absorber rod when tightening nut or shock absorber assembly could be damaged. Retain shock absorber rod in a stationary position when tightening nut.**

h. Place tool No. J-39642-1, or equivalent, from modular shock nut removal set tool No. J-39642, or equivalent, on shock absorber nut, then insert J-39642-2 from modular shock nut removal set J-39642 through J-39642-1 to hold shock absorber rod in place and tighten nut to specifications.

i. Remove shock absorber assembly from strut spring compressor.

8. Reverse steps 1 through 5 to install. Tighten fasteners to specifications

STABILIZER BAR

REPLACE

1. Raise and support vehicle.
2. Remove nut from link bolt located at each side, then remove bolt, grommets and bushings, **Figs. 17 and 18.**
3. Remove stabilizer shaft to body bolts, then remove stabilizer bar.
4. Reverse procedure to install.

SUSPENSION STEERING LINKAGE INSPECTION

1992

1. Raise vehicle with jack placed under frame torque box behind front wheel.

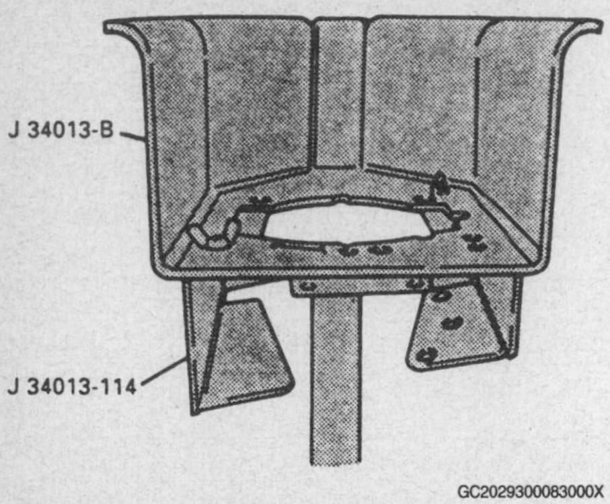
J 34013-B
J 34013-114
GC2029300083000X

Fig. 10 Modular shock absorber assembly compressor adapter, driver side. 1993–95

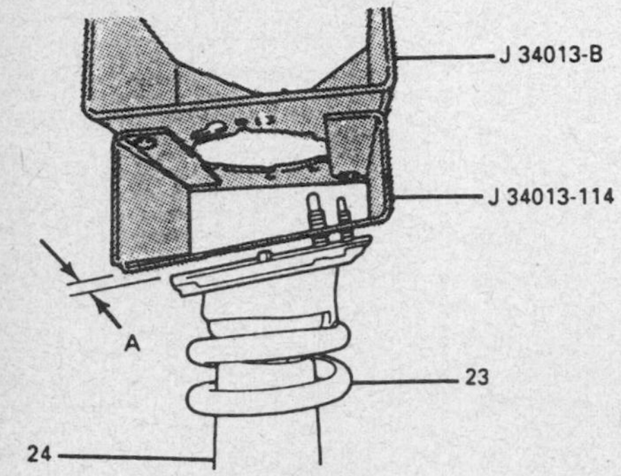
J 34013-B
J 34013-114
23
24
A

A MATCHING ANGLE BETWEEN SHOCK ABSORBER ASSEMBLY AND J 34013-114
23 SPRING ASSEMBLY, FRONT
24 ABSORBER ASSEMBLY, FRONT SHOCK

GC2029300086000X

Fig. 13 Upper driver side shock absorber assembly to strut spring compressor installation. 1993–95

2. Lock steering wheel with wheels in straight ahead position, then mount dial indicator on a suitable stand with pointer bearing against outer rim of wheel, **Fig. 19.**
3. Move wheel in and out at front and rear, without moving steering wheel, while observing gauge.
4. If gauge reading exceeds .108 inches, check steering linkage and suspension for excessive wear or damage.

POWER STEERING GEAR

REPLACE

1992

1. Disconnect pressure hose and cooling pipe from power steering gear. Position pressure hose in upward position to prevent fluid drainage.
2. Disconnect intermediate steering shaft from power steering gear stub shaft.
3. Disconnect Pitman arm from power steering gear.
4. Remove steering gear attaching bolts, then remove power steering gear, **Fig. 20.**
5. Reverse procedure to install.

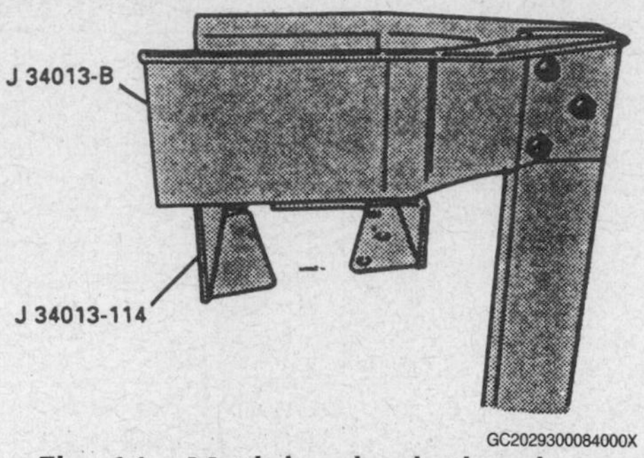
J 34013-B
J 34013-114
GC2029300084000X

Fig. 11 Modular shock absorber assembly compressor adapter, passenger side. 1993–95

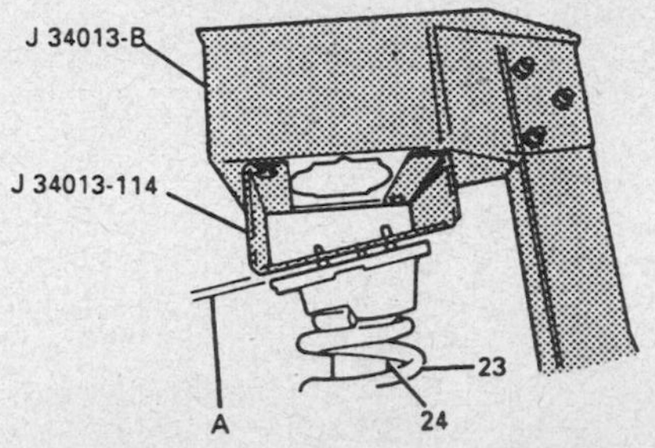
J 34013-B
J 34013-114
23
24
A

A MATCHING ANGLE BETWEEN SHOCK ABSORBER ASSEMBLY AND J 34013-114
23 SPRING ASSEMBLY, FRONT
24 ABSORBER ASSEMBLY, FRONT SHOCK

GC2029300087000X

Fig. 14 Upper passenger side shock absorber assembly to strut spring compressor installation. 1993–95

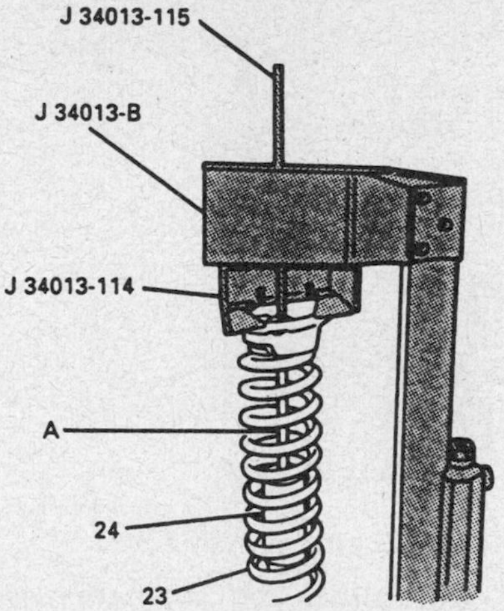
J 34013-115
J 34013-B
J 34013-114
A
24
23

A ROD, FRONT SHOCK ABSORBER
23 SPRING ASSEMBLY, FRONT
24 ABSORBER ASSEMBLY, FRONT SHOCK

GC2029300089000X

Fig. 16 Modular shock assembly alignment rod installation. 1993–95

1993–95

1. Raise and support vehicle, then remove wheels.
2. Disconnect inlet and outlet hoses from steering gear, then the steering linkage outer tie rods from steering knuckles, **Fig. 21.**

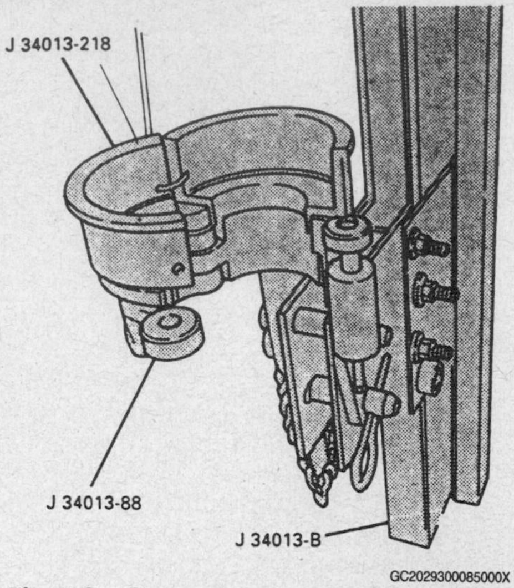
J 34013-218
J 34013-88
J 34013-B
GC2029300085000X

Fig. 12 Strut compressor adapter & modular shock support to strut spring compressor mounting. 1993–95

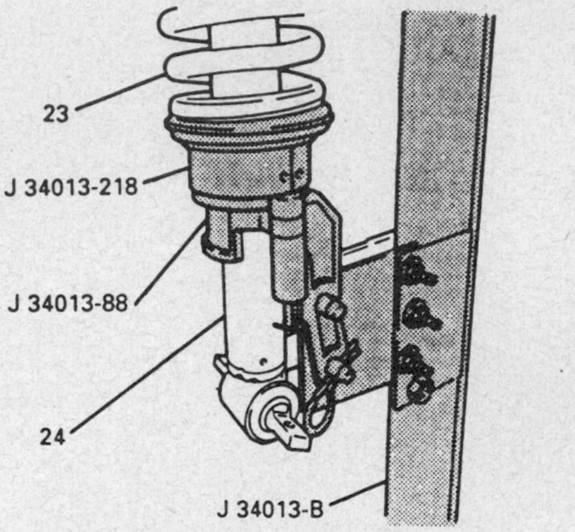
23
J 34013-218
J 34013-88
24
J 34013-B

23 SPRING ASSEMBLY, FRONT
24 ABSORBER ASSEMBLY, FRONT SHOCK

GC2029300088000X

Fig. 15 Shock absorber assembly to strut spring compressor installation. 1993–95

3. Disconnect steering gear coupling shaft from steering gear, then remove steering gear.
4. Reverse procedure to install, noting the following:
   a. Tighten fasteners to specifications.
   b. Adjust steering gear so that it aligns as straight as possible with steering gear coupling shaft.
   c. Refill and bleed power steering system.

POWER STEERING PUMP

REPLACE

1992

1. Remove serpentine drive belt.
2. Remove pulley from power steering pump shaft, **Figs. 22 and 23.**
3. Disconnect hoses at power steering pump, then plug pump ports and hoses.

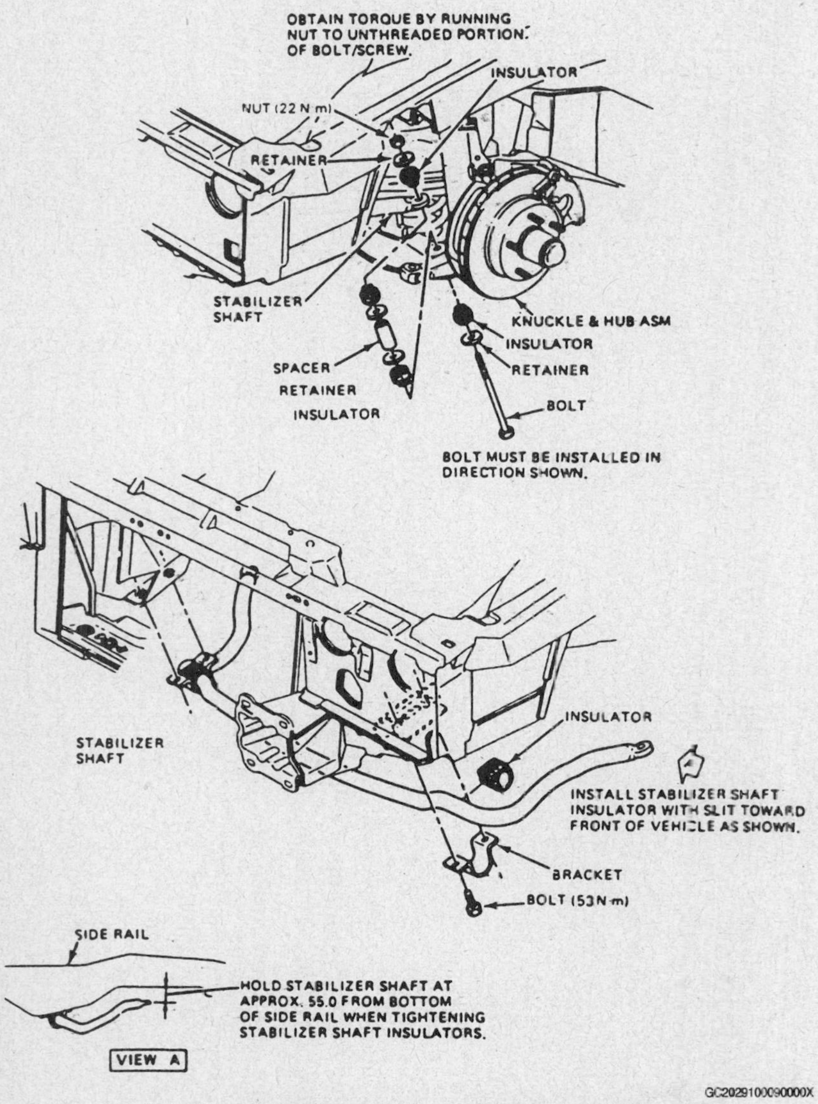
OBTAIN TORQUE BY RUNNING NUT TO UNTHREADED PORTION OF BOLT/SCREW.
INSULATOR
NUT (22 N·m)
RETAINER
STABILIZER SHAFT
SPACER
RETAINER
INSULATOR
KNUCKLE & HUB ASM
INSULATOR
RETAINER
BOLT
BOLT MUST BE INSTALLED IN DIRECTION SHOWN.
STABILIZER SHAFT
INSULATOR
INSTALL STABILIZER SHAFT INSULATOR WITH SLIT TOWARD FRONT OF VEHICLE AS SHOWN.
BRACKET
BOLT (53 N·m)
SIDE RAIL
HOLD STABILIZER SHAFT AT APPROX. 55.0 FROM BOTTOM OF SIDE RAIL WHEN TIGHTENING STABILIZER SHAFT INSULATORS.
VIEW A
GC2029100090000X

Fig. 17 Stabilizer shaft replacement. 1992

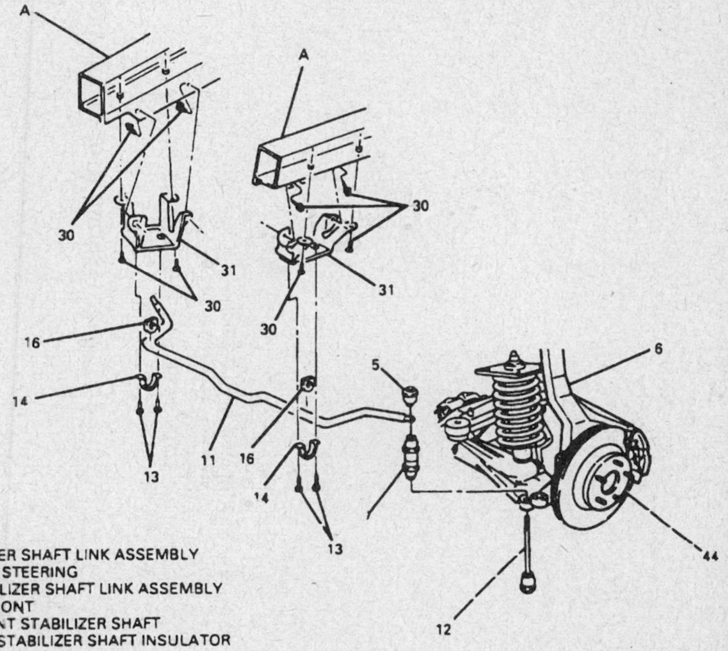
A
A
30
31
30
16
14
11
16
13
14
13
5
6
44
12

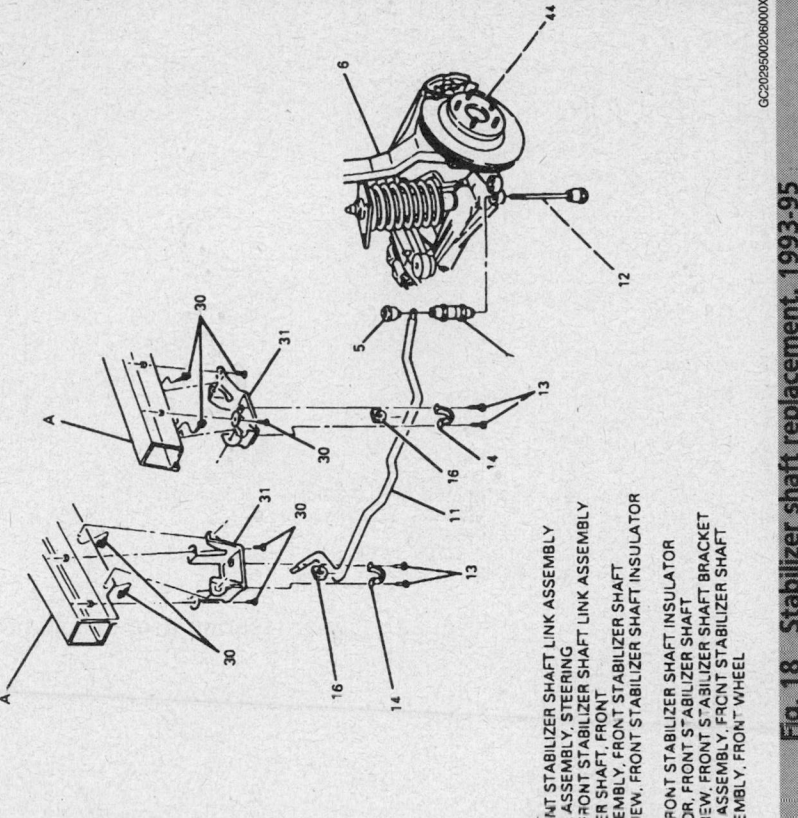

A SIDE RAIL
5 NUT, FRONT STABILIZER SHAFT LINK ASSEMBLY
6 KNUCKLE ASSEMBLY, STEERING
7 SLEEVE, FRONT STABILIZER SHAFT LINK ASSEMBLY
11 STABILIZER SHAFT, FRONT
12 LINK ASSEMBLY, FRONT STABILIZER SHAFT
13 BOLT/SCREW, FRONT STABILIZER SHAFT INSULATOR CLAMP
14 CLAMP, FRONT STABILIZER SHAFT INSULATOR
16 INSULATOR, FRONT STABILIZER SHAFT
30 BOLT/SCREW, FRONT STABILIZER SHAFT BRACKET
31 BRACKET ASSEMBLY, FRONT STABILIZER SHAFT
44 HUB ASSEMBLY, FRONT WHEEL

GC2029500206000X

Fig. 18 Stabilizer shaft replacement. 1993-95

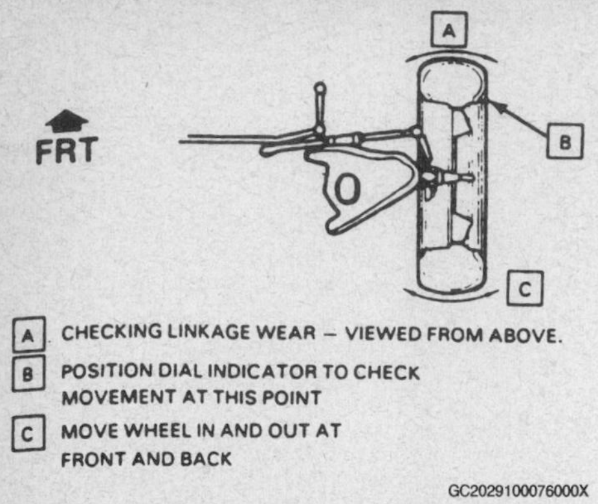

FRT
A
B
C
A CHECKING LINKAGE WEAR — VIEWED FROM ABOVE.
B POSITION DIAL INDICATOR TO CHECK MOVEMENT AT THIS POINT
C MOVE WHEEL IN AND OUT AT FRONT AND BACK
GC2029100076000X

Fig. 19 Suspension & steering linkage check. 1992

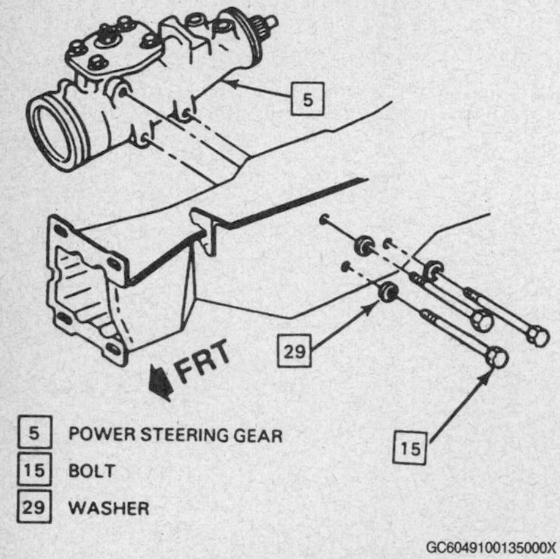

5
FRT
29
15
5 POWER STEERING GEAR
15 BOLT
29 WASHER
GC6049100135000X

Fig. 20 Power steering gear installation. 1992

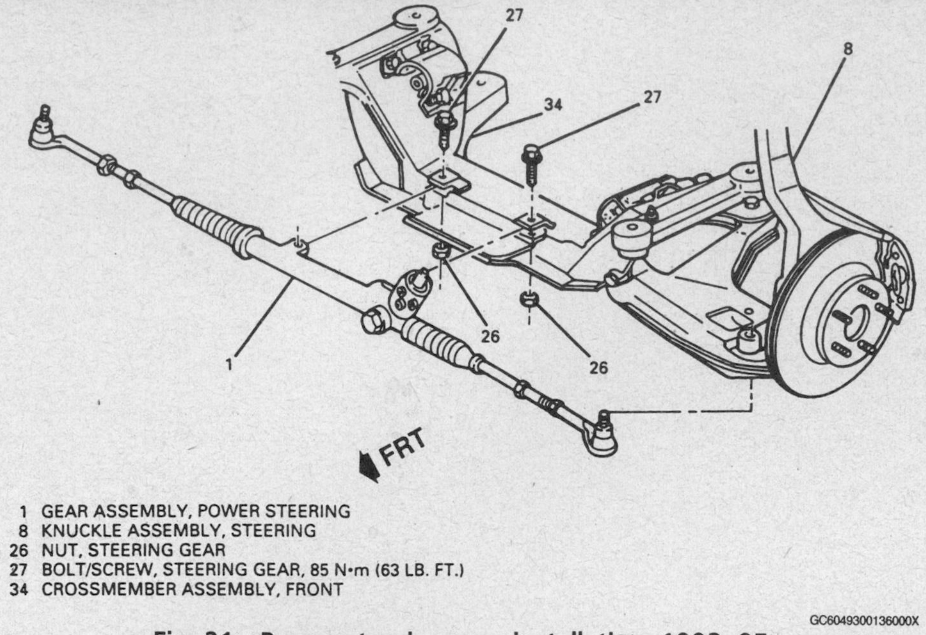

27
8
34
27
26
26
1
FRT
1 GEAR ASSEMBLY, POWER STEERING
8 KNUCKLE ASSEMBLY, STEERING
26 NUT, STEERING GEAR
27 BOLT/SCREW, STEERING GEAR, 85 N•m (63 LB. FT.)
34 CROSSMEMBER ASSEMBLY, FRONT
GC6049300136000X

Fig. 21 Power steering gear installation. 1993–95

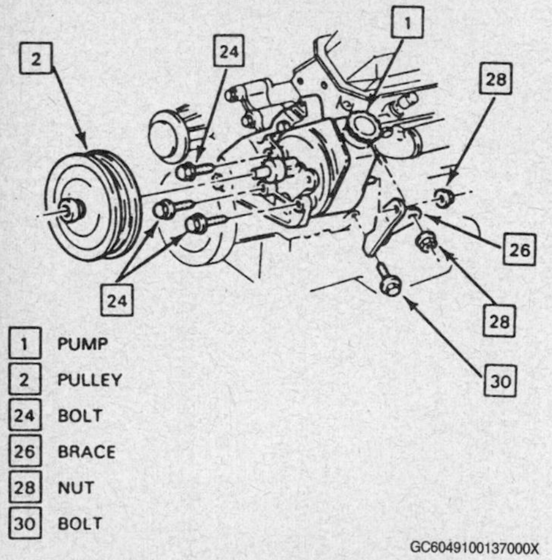

1
2
24
28
26
24
28
30
1 PUMP
2 PULLEY
24 BOLT
26 BRACE
28 NUT
30 BOLT
GC6049100137000X

Fig. 22 Power steering pump installation. 1992 3.1L/V6-191 engine

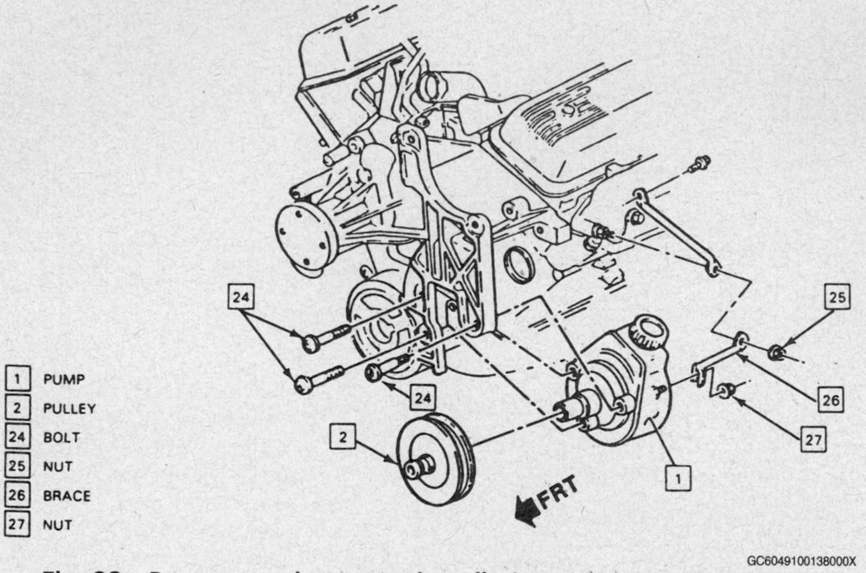

24
25
26
24
27
2
1
FRT
1 PUMP
2 PULLEY
24 BOLT
25 NUT
26 BRACE
27 NUT
GC6049100138000X

Fig. 23 Power steering pump installation. 1992 5.0L/V8-305 & 5.7L/V8-350 engines

4. Remove pump to support bracket attaching bolts and the pump.
5. Reverse procedure to install. Tighten attaching bolts to specifications.

1993–95

3.4L/V6-207 Engine

1. Remove serpentine belt, then the front air intake duct.
2. Disconnect inlet and outlet hoses from pump, then remove pump pulley using pump pulley remover tool No. J-25034-B, or equivalent.
3. Remove pump support from pump, **Fig. 24** then the pump.
4. Reverse procedure to install, noting the following:
   a. Tighten fasteners to specifications.
   b. Install pump pulley using pump pulley installer tool No. J-25033-B, or equivalent. **Face of pulley hub must be flush with end of pump shaft before applying load to pulley hub. Load required to press pulley hub onto pump shaft must be greater than 1500 lbs., but less than 7000 lbs.**
   c. Refill and bleed power steering system.

5.7L/V8-350 Engine

1. Raise and support vehicle, then drain engine coolant.
2. Remove serpentine belt, then lower vehicle.
3. Remove front air intake duct, then the alternator.
4. Disconnect radiator outlet hose from engine, heater inlet and outlet hoses from water pump, then the throttle body heater return hose from heater outlet hose.
5. Remove pump mounting bolts, **Fig. 25,** then disconnect inlet and reservoir hoses from pump and remove pump.
6. Reverse procedure to install, noting the following:
   a. Tighten fasteners to specifications.
   b. Refill and bleed power steering system.

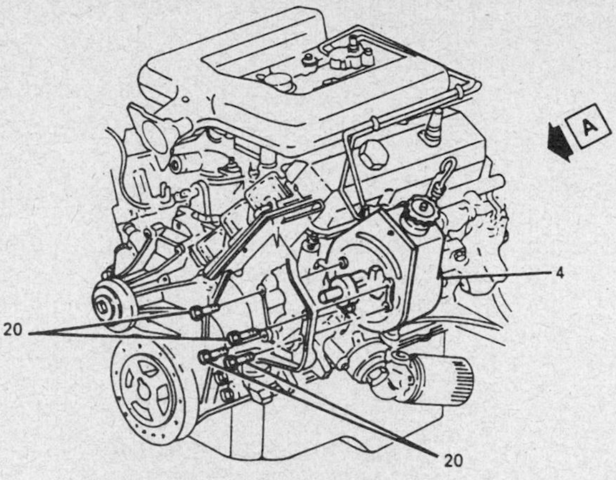

A
4
20
20

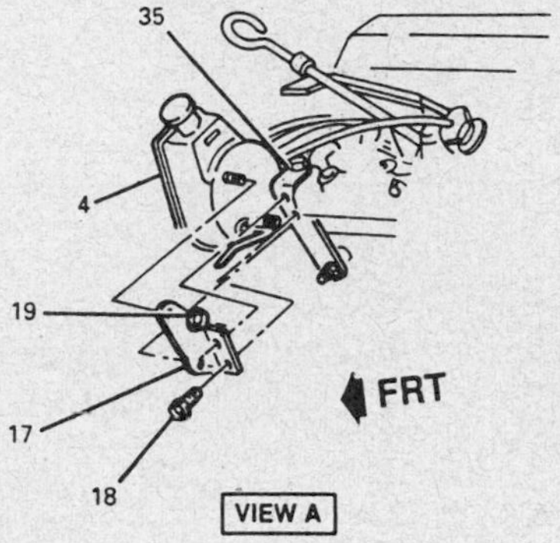

35
4
19
17
18
FRT
VIEW A

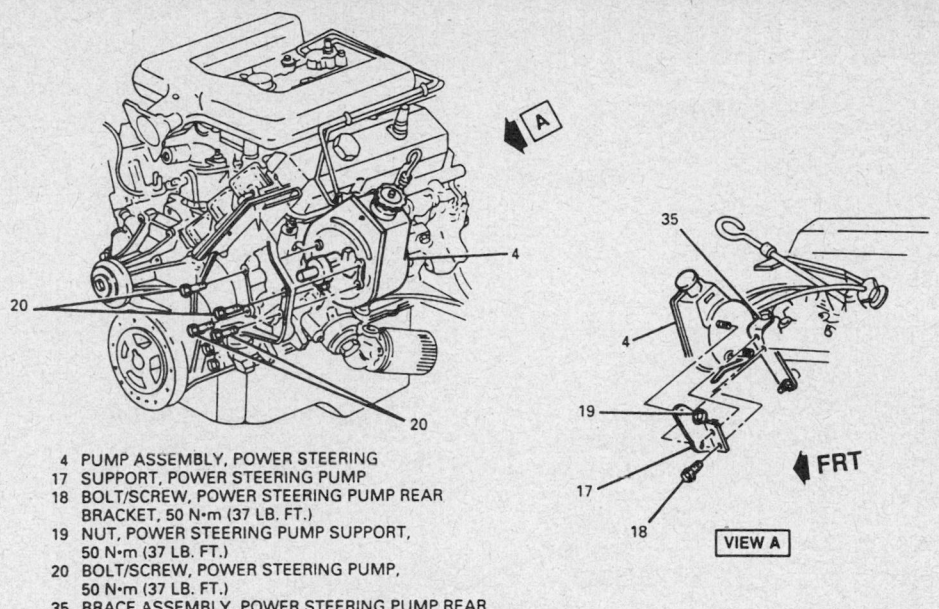

4 PUMP ASSEMBLY, POWER STEERING
17 SUPPORT, POWER STEERING PUMP
18 BOLT/SCREW, POWER STEERING PUMP REAR BRACKET, 50 N•m (37 LB. FT.)
19 NUT, POWER STEERING PUMP SUPPORT, 50 N•m (37 LB. FT.)
20 BOLT/SCREW, POWER STEERING PUMP, 50 N•m (37 LB. FT.)
35 BRACE ASSEMBLY, POWER STEERING PUMP REAR

GC6049100139000X

Fig. 24 Power steering pump installation. 1993–95 3.4L/V6-207 engine

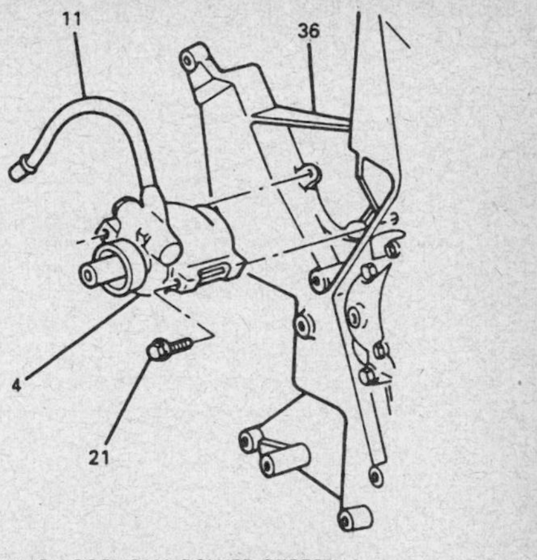

11
36
4
21

4 PUMP ASSEMBLY, POWER STEERING
11 HOSE ASSEMBLY, POWER STEERING FLUID RESERVOIR
21 BOLT/SCREW, POWER STEERING PUMP, 25 N•m (18 LB. FT.)
36 BRACKET ASSEMBLY, GENERATOR AND AIR CONDITIONER COMPRESSOR AND POWER STEERING PUMP AND DRIVE BELT TENSIONER

GC6049300140000X

Fig. 25 Power steering pump installation. 1993–95 5.7L/V8-350 engine

TIGHTENING SPECIFICATIONS

Year	Component	Torque/ Ft. Lbs.
1992	Idler Arm To Frame Nut	63
	Lower Control Arm Ball Joint Stud	80
	Lower Control Arm Pivot Bolt	61
	Pitman Arm Nut	184
	Power Steering Gear Mounting Bolts	73
	Power Steering Pump Brace To Pump Nut (V6 Engine)	18
	Power Steering Pump Brace To Pump Nut (V8 Engine)	37
	Power Steering Pump Bracket To Engine Bolt	24
	Power Steering Pump Bracket To Engine Stud Nut	24
	Relay Rod To Inner Tie Rod Nut	40
	Relay Rod To Pitman Arm Nut	35
	Stabilizer Bracket Bolt	39
	Stabilizer Link Nut	①
	Strut To Steering knuckle	②
	Strut Bottom Upper Nut	40
	Strut Upper Mount To Wheel Housing Tower	14
	Tie Rod Adjuster Clamp Nut	13
	Tie Rod End To Steering Knuckle	35
	Tie Rod (Outer) To Steering Arm Nut	35

Year	Component	Torque/ Ft. Lbs.
	Wheel Lug Nuts	100
1993–95	Lower Ball Joint Nut	81
	Lower Shock Absorber Nuts	48
	Power Steering Gear Mounting Bolts	63
	Power Steering Pump Bolts (V6 Engine)	37
	Power Steering Pump Bolts (V8 Engine)	18
	Power Steering Pump Support To Pump Nuts & Bolts (V6 Engine)	37
	Stabilizer Bracket To Frame Bolts	41
	Stabilizer Clamp To Stabilizer Bracket Bolts	41
	Stabilizer Link Nut	17
	Upper Ball Joint Nut	39
	Upper Shock Absorber Mount To Strut Tower Bolts	37
	Upper Shock Absorber Mount To Strut Tower Nuts	32
	Wheel Lug Nuts	100

①—Less ride & handling suspension, 13 ft. lbs.; w/ride & handling suspension, 18 ft. lbs.

②—Torque nuts to 125 ft. lbs., then tighten each nut an additional 120°. Ensure total torque reading exceeds 148 ft. lbs.

Wheel Alignment

INDEX

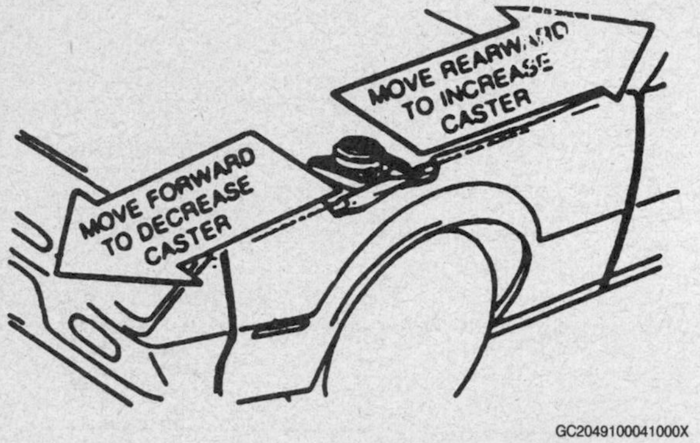

MOVE REARWARD TO INCREASE CASTER
MOVE FORWARD TO DECREASE CASTER
GC2049100041000X

Fig. 1 Caster adjustment. 1992

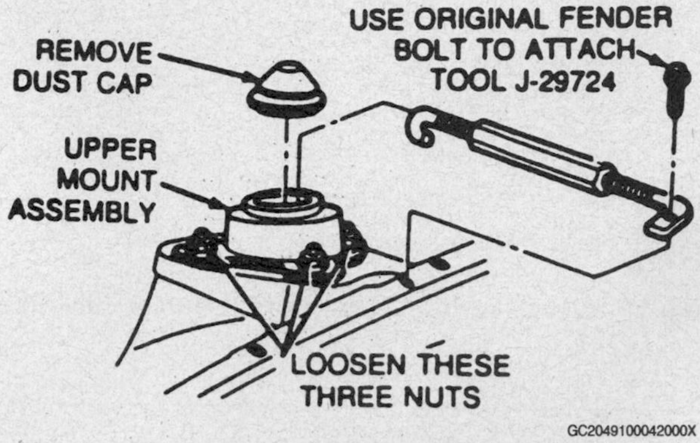

REMOVE DUST CAP
USE ORIGINAL FENDER BOLT TO ATTACH TOOL J-29724
UPPER MOUNT ASSEMBLY
LOOSEN THESE THREE NUTS
GC2049100042000X

Fig. 2 Front caster & camber adjustment tool installation. 1992

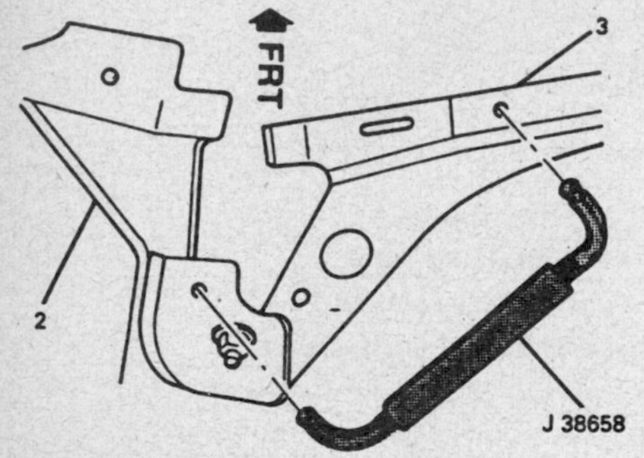

FRT
3
2
J 38658

2 CROSSMEMBER ASSEMBLY, FRONT
3 ARM ASSEMBLY, FRONT LOWER CONTROL

GC2049300043000X

Fig. 3 Front caster adjustment tool installation. 1993–95

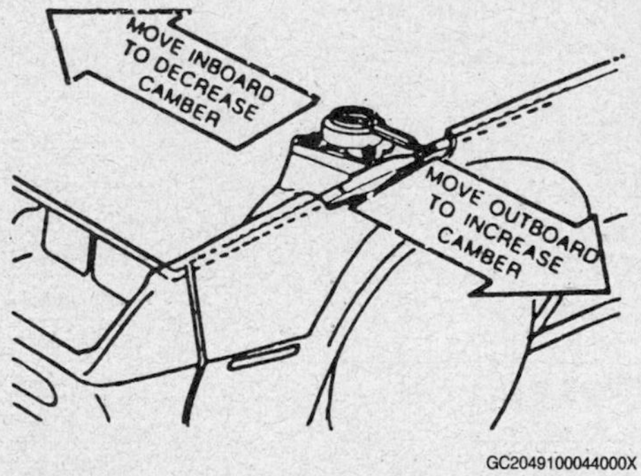

MOVE INBOARD TO DECREASE CAMBER
MOVE OUTBOARD TO INCREASE CAMBER
GC2049100044000X

Fig. 4 Front camber adjustment

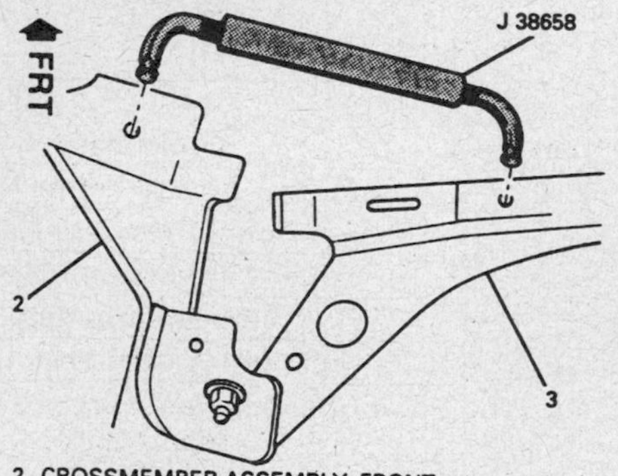

FRT
J 38658
2
3

2 CROSSMEMBER ASSEMBLY, FRONT
3 ARM ASSEMBLY, FRONT LOWER CONTROL

GC2049300045000X

Fig. 5 Front camber adjustment tool installation. 1993–95

FRONT WHEEL ALIGNMENT

Prior to checking or adjusting front suspension alignment, inspect suspension components for damage or excessive wear, and replace as needed. Ensure tire pressures and wheel bearings are properly adjusted, then raise and release front bumper several times to allow vehicle to assume normal ride height.

CASTER

1992

Caster adjustments are made by moving the position of the upper strut mount assembly, **Fig. 1.** To make adjustment, remove dust cap and fender bolt and attach tool No. J-29724, or equivalent, to original fender bolt, **Fig. 2.** Tighten the turnbuckle and loosen the three strut mount attaching nuts.

Adjust caster by lightly tapping the mount assembly forward or rearward. Move mount forward to decrease caster, or rearward to increase caster, **Fig. 1.**

1993–95

1. Jounce front bumper three times to allow vehicle to return to normal ride height, then raise and support vehicle.
2. Loosen front lower control arm nuts, then install camber/caster adjuster tool No. J-38658, or equivalent, to slot holes in lower control arm and front crossmember, **Fig. 3.**
3. Adjust caster to specifications by rotating turnbuckle on camber/caster adjuster. Clockwise increases caster, counterclockwise decreases caster.
4. Remove camber/caster adjuster, then **torque** front lower control arm nuts to 96 ft. lbs.

CAMBER

1992

Camber adjustments are made by moving the position of the upper strut mount assembly, **Fig. 4.** To make adjustment, remove dust cap and fender bolt and attach tool No. J-29724, or equivalent, to original fender bolt, **Fig. 2.** Tighten the turnbuckle and loosen the three strut mount attaching nuts.

Adjust camber by rotating the turnbuckle to move mount assembly inward or outward. Move mount inboard to decrease camber, or outboard to increase camber, **Fig. 4.**

1993–95

1. Jounce front bumper three times to allow vehicle to return to normal ride

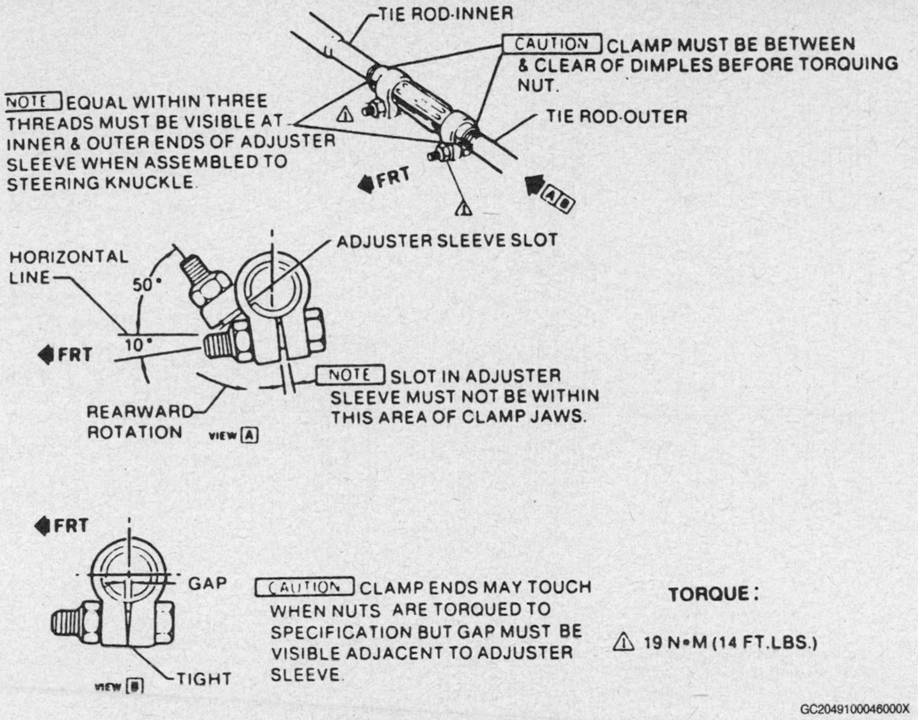
TIE ROD-INNER
CAUTION CLAMP MUST BE BETWEEN & CLEAR OF DIMPLES BEFORE TORQUING NUT.
NOTE EQUAL WITHIN THREE THREADS MUST BE VISIBLE AT INNER & OUTER ENDS OF ADJUSTER SLEEVE WHEN ASSEMBLED TO STEERING KNUCKLE.
TIE ROD-OUTER
FRT
A B
HORIZONTAL LINE
50°
10°
ADJUSTER SLEEVE SLOT
FRT
NOTE SLOT IN ADJUSTER SLEEVE MUST NOT BE WITHIN THIS AREA OF CLAMP JAWS.
REARWARD ROTATION
VIEW A
FRT
GAP
TIGHT
VIEW B
CAUTION CLAMP ENDS MAY TOUCH WHEN NUTS ARE TORQUED TO SPECIFICATION BUT GAP MUST BE VISIBLE ADJACENT TO ADJUSTER SLEEVE.
TORQUE:
19 N•M (14 FT.LBS.)
GC2049100046000X

Fig. 6 Tie rod clamp & sleeve positioning

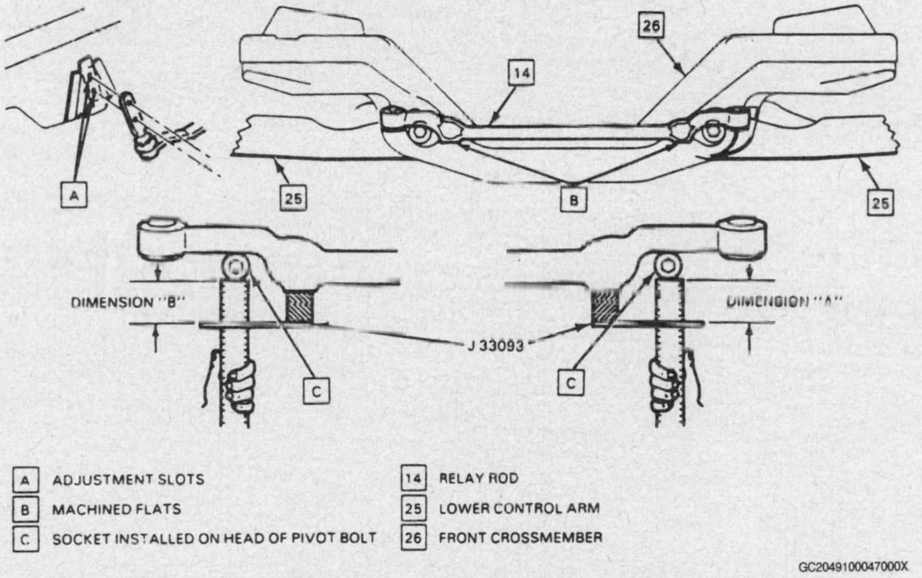
26
14
A
25
B
25
DIMENSION "B"
DIMENSION "A"
J 33093
C
C
A ADJUSTMENT SLOTS
B MACHINED FLATS
C SOCKET INSTALLED ON HEAD OF PIVOT BOLT
14 RELAY ROD
25 LOWER CONTROL ARM
26 FRONT CROSSMEMBER
GC2049100047000X

Fig. 7 Relay rod height adjustment

height, then raise and support vehicle.

2. Loosen front lower control arm nuts, then install camber/caster adjuster tool No. J-38658, or equivalent, to slot holes in lower control arm and front crossmember, **Fig. 5.**
3. Adjust camber to specifications by rotating turnbuckle on camber/caster adjuster. Clockwise increases caster, counterclockwise decreases caster.
4. Remove camber/caster adjuster, then **torque** front lower control arm nuts to 96 ft. lbs.

TOE-IN

1992

1. Loosen clamp bolts at each end of tie rod adjustable sleeves.
2. Set steering wheel in straight-ahead position, then turn tie rods as necessary until toe-in is within specifications.
3. After adjustment is complete, ensure threads exposed on each end of sleeve are equal and tie rod end housings are at right angles to steering arm.
4. Position tie rod clamps and sleeves as shown, **Fig. 6,** then tighten nuts.

1993–95

Toe adjustments are made separately at each individual wheel.

1. Ensure steering wheel is set in a straight ahead position within ± 3.5 degrees.
2. Loosen nut on inner tie rod, then adjust toe to specifications. Left and right toe adjustment should be equal within ± .2 degrees.
3. Ensure steering gear boot is not twisted, then **torque** inner tie rod nut to 35 ft. lbs.

RELAY ROD HEIGHT ADJUSTMENT

1992

Relay rod height should be equal (plus or minus .039 inch) from side to side. If relay rod height is not within specifications,

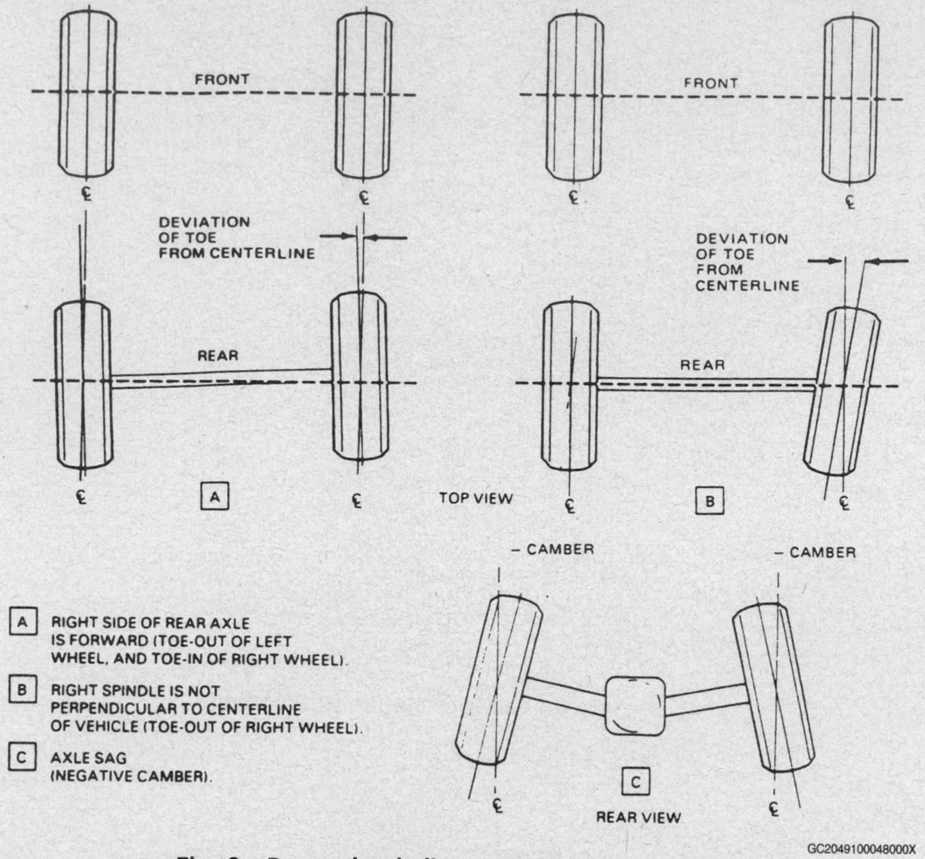
FRONT
FRONT
DEVIATION
OF TOE
FROM CENTERLINE
DEVIATION
OF TOE
FROM
CENTERLINE
REAR
REAR
A
TOP VIEW
B
− CAMBER
− CAMBER
C
REAR VIEW
A RIGHT SIDE OF REAR AXLE IS FORWARD (TOE-OUT OF LEFT WHEEL, AND TOE-IN OF RIGHT WHEEL).
B RIGHT SPINDLE IS NOT PERPENDICULAR TO CENTERLINE OF VEHICLE (TOE-OUT OF RIGHT WHEEL).
C AXLE SAG (NEGATIVE CAMBER).
GC2049100048000X

Fig. 8 Rear wheel alignment inspection. 1992

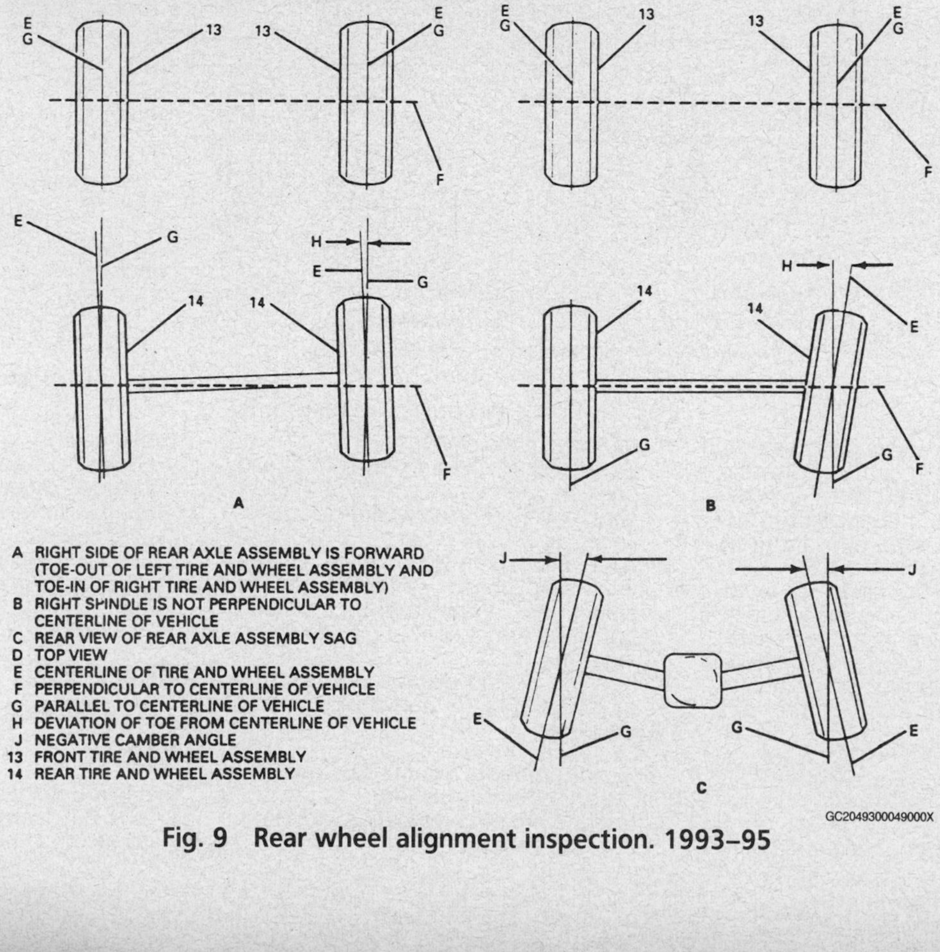
A
B
C
A RIGHT SIDE OF REAR AXLE ASSEMBLY IS FORWARD (TOE-OUT OF LEFT TIRE AND WHEEL ASSEMBLY AND TOE-IN OF RIGHT TIRE AND WHEEL ASSEMBLY)
B RIGHT SPINDLE IS NOT PERPENDICULAR TO CENTERLINE OF VEHICLE
C REAR VIEW OF REAR AXLE ASSEMBLY SAG
D TOP VIEW
E CENTERLINE OF TIRE AND WHEEL ASSEMBLY
F PERPENDICULAR TO CENTERLINE OF VEHICLE
G PARALLEL TO CENTERLINE OF VEHICLE
H DEVIATION OF TOE FROM CENTERLINE OF VEHICLE
J NEGATIVE CAMBER ANGLE
13 FRONT TIRE AND WHEEL ASSEMBLY
14 REAR TIRE AND WHEEL ASSEMBLY
GC2049300049000X

Fig. 9 Rear wheel alignment inspection. 1993–95

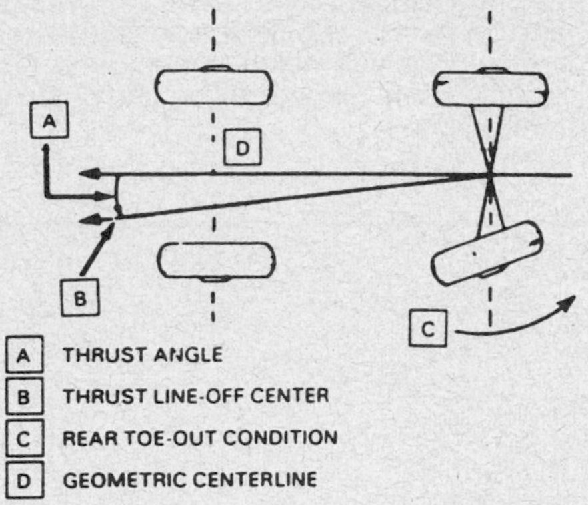

A
D
B
C
A THRUST ANGLE
B THRUST LINE-OFF CENTER
C REAR TOE-OUT CONDITION
D GEOMETRIC CENTERLINE
GC2049100050000X

Fig. 10 Thrust angle inspection

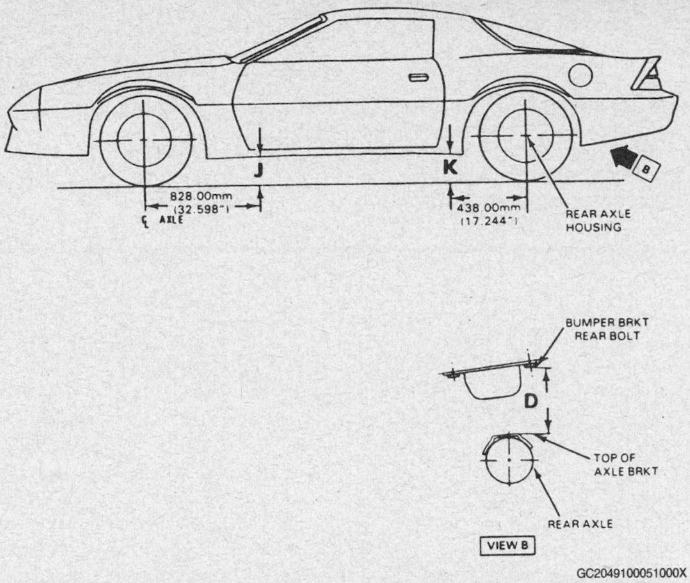

J
K
B
828.00mm
(32.598")
AXLE
438.00mm
(17.244")
REAR AXLE HOUSING
BUMPER BRKT REAR BOLT
D
TOP OF AXLE BRKT
REAR AXLE
VIEW B
GC2049100051000X

Fig. 11 Vehicle ride height measurement locations & specifications (Part 1 of 2)

Year	Make & Model	Suspension (Option Code)	Riding Height Measurements, Inches ①		
			Dimension D	Dimension J	Dimension K
1992	Camaro Coupe	Soft Ride (FE1)	4.409	8.346	8.307
		Ride & Handling (FE2) ②	4.370	8.346	8.307
		Ride & Handling (FE2) ③	4.331	8.031	8.110
	Firebird Coupe	Soft Ride (FE1)	4.370	8.228	8.268
		Ride & Handling (FE2) ③	4.449	8.228	8.268
		Special Heavy Duty (F41) ④	4.370	8.228	8.200
		Special Heavy Duty (F41) ⑤	4.409	8.228	8.268
	Convertibles	Soft Ride (FE1)	4.449	8.346	8.307
		Ride & Handling (FE2) ②	4.370	8.346	8.307
		Ride & Handling (FE2) ③	4.331	8.031	8.110
1993-95	All	Ride & Handling (FE2) ⑥	4.800	8.000	8.200
		Ride & Handling (FE2) ⑦	4.600	8.000	8.400
		Firm Ride (F41) ⑦	4.600	8.000	8.400
		Firm Ride (F41) ⑧	4.900	8.000	8.400

TBI: Throttle Body Injection.
TPI: Tuned Port Injection.
①—Plus or minus .4 inch.
②—With 15 inch wheels.
③—With 16 inch wheels.
④—With 5.0L/V8-305 TBI engine.
⑤—With 5.0L/V8-305 TPI engine.

Fig. 11 Vehicle ride height measurement locations & specifications (Part 2 of 2)

steering and handling problem could be encountered. Relay rod height is adjusted at the idler arm to frame attachment.

1. Raise and support vehicle.
2. Using a suitable wire brush, clean both flats of relay rod.
3. Position tool No. J-33093, or equivalent, on flat of relay rod at Pitman arm end.
4. Position a socket on pivot bolt of left hand lower control arm.
5. Measure distance between bottom socket and tool and note, **Fig. 7.**
6. Loosen idler arm to frame nuts just enough to allow idler arm to slide upward and downward.
7. Position tool No. J-33093, or equivalent, on flat of relay rod at idler arm end.
8. Position a socket on pivot bolt of right hand lower control arm.
9. Measure distance between bottom socket and tool and note, **Fig. 7.**
10. Both reading should be with in .039 inch of each other. If not, adjust position of idle arm at frame until readings are within limits.
11. **Torque** idler arm to frame nuts to 52 ft. lbs., then remove tool and socket and lower vehicle.
12. Check and adjust toe as necessary.

REAR WHEEL ALIGNMENT

After front wheel alignment has been checked or adjusted, rear wheel alignment angles should be checked if vehicle still does not track properly or if excessive rear tire wear is present. Rear wheels should be parallel to and the same distance from the vehicle centerline, **Figs. 8 and 9.**

Rear wheel alignment is not adjustable. If alignment angles are not within specification, check for bent or damaged suspension arms, axle housing or frame.

THRUST ANGLE

1992

The vehicle is steered by the front wheels. The path which the rear wheels follow is the thrust angle, **Fig. 10.** In an ideal setting, the thrust angle would be aligned with that of the vehicle center line.

1993–95

If the thrust angle is not within specifications, inspect upper and lower control arms for damage. If control arms are not damaged, check frame dimensions.

VEHICLE RIDE HEIGHT

1992

Refer to **Fig. 11** for vehicle ride height measurements and specifications. When checking vehicle ride height measurements, fuel tank should be full, tires at should be correct pressure, front seat should be rearward position, truck should be empty except for spare tire and jack and vehicle should be on level ground. If fuel tank is not full, add weight to trunk to compensate for amount fuel vehicle is below the full level.

Prior to checking ride height, lift front bumper upward approximately 1.5 inches and gently release (3 times), then check front ride height. Push front bumper downward approximately 1.5 inches and gently release (3 times), then recheck front ride height. Average of both readings to determine vehicle ride height. Check rear ride height in same manner, lifting and pushing rear bumper.

CHEVROLET CORVETTE (Y Car)

NOTE: Refer To The Rear Of This Manual For Vehicle Manufacturer's Special Tool Suppliers.

INDEX OF SERVICE OPERATIONS

NOTE: For Service Operations Not Listed Below, Refer To The Table Of Contents In The Front Of This Manual.

Continued

INDEX OF SERVICE OPERATIONS—CONTINUED

Specifications

GENERAL ENGINE SPECIFICATIONS

Year	Engine Liter/CID	Engine VIN Code ①	Fuel System	Bore & Stroke	Compression Ratio	Net Brake H.P. @ RPM ②	Maximum Torque	Normal Oil Pressure psi
1992	5.7L/V8-350 ⑥	P	TPI	4.00 x 3.48	10.2	300 @ 5000	330 @ 4000	④
	5.7L/V8-350 ④	J	TPI	3.90 x 3.66	11.0	375 @ 5800	370 @ 4800	⑤
1993–94	5.7L/V8-350 ⑥	P	TPI	4.00 x 3.48	10.5	300 @ 5000	330 @ 4000	③
	5.7L/V8-350 ④	J	TPI	3.90 x 3.66	11.0	375 @ 5800	370 @ 4800	⑤
1995	5.7L/V8-350 ⑥	P	TPI	4.00 x 3.48	10.5	300 @ 5000	340 @ 4000	③
	5.7L/V8-350 ④	J	TPI	3.90 x 3.66	11.0	405 @ 5800	385 @ 5200	⑤

CID—Cubic Inch Displacement.
TPI—Tune Port Injection.
VIN—Vehicle Identification Number
①—The eighth digit of the VIN denotes engine code.
②—Ratings are net, as installed in vehicle.
③—With engine hot, minimum oil pressure at 1000 RPM, 6 psi.; at 2000 RPM, 18 psi.; at 4000 RPM, 24 psi.
④—4 Cam 32 valve engine (ZR-1).
⑤—With engine hot, minimum oil pressure, at idle speed, 12 psi.; above 3000 RPM, 40 psi.
⑥—Single cam 16 valve engine.

TUNE UP SPECIFICATIONS

Year & Engine (VIN code) ①	Spark Plug Gap	Ignition Timing BTDC: Firing Order Fig. ③	Ignition Timing BTDC: Man. Trans.	Ignition Timing BTDC: Auto. Trans.	Ignition Timing BTDC: Mark Fig.	Curb Idle Speed ④: Man. Trans.	Curb Idle Speed ④: Auto. Trans.	Fast Idle Speed: Man. Trans.	Fast Idle Speed: Auto. Trans.	Fuel Pump Pressure psi
1992-95										
5.7L/V8-350 (P) ②	.050	C	⑧	⑧	—	⑤	⑤	⑤	⑤	41-47 ⑥
5.7L/V8-350 (J) ⑦	.035	A	⑧	—	B	⑤	—	⑤	—	48-55 ⑥

BTDC—Before Top Dead Center
VIN—Vehicle Identification Number
①—The eighth digit of the VIN denotes engine code.
②—Single cam 16 valve engine.
③—Before removing from distributor cap, determine location of No. 1 wire in cap, as distributor position may have been altered from that shown at the end of this chart.
④—When checking idle speed, set parking brake & block drive wheels.
⑤—Idle speed is controlled by an idle speed control motor.
⑥—With shop towel wrapped around fuel pressure fitting to prevent fuel spillage, connect a suitable fuel pressure gauge. Check fuel pressure with ignition switch in ON position, engine not running.
⑦—4 cam 32 valve engine (ZR-1).
⑧—Computer controlled, no adjustment.

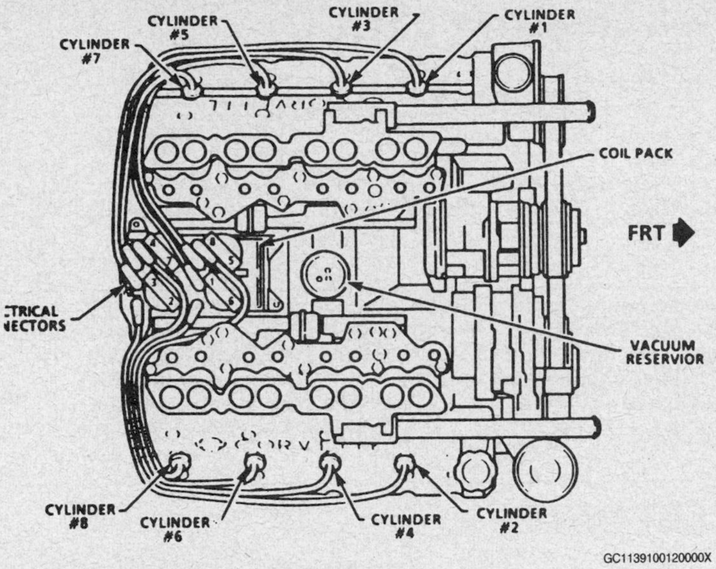
CYLINDER #5
CYLINDER #3
CYLINDER #1
CYLINDER #7
COIL PACK
FRT
TRICAL
NECTORS
VACUUM RESERVIOR
CYLINDER #8
CYLINDER #6
CYLINDER #4
CYLINDER #2
GC1139100120000X

Fig. A

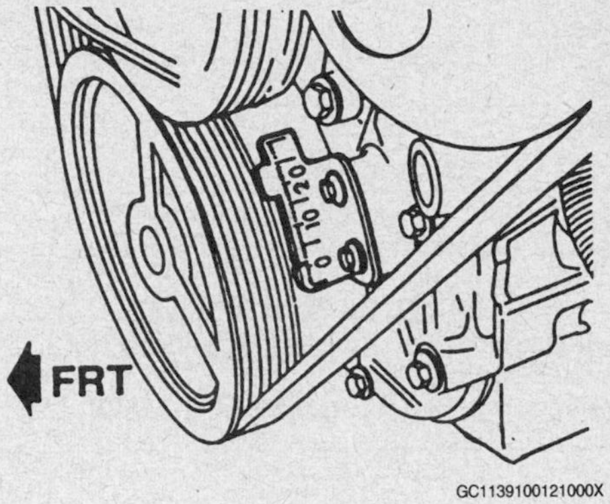
FRT
GC1139100121000X

Fig. B

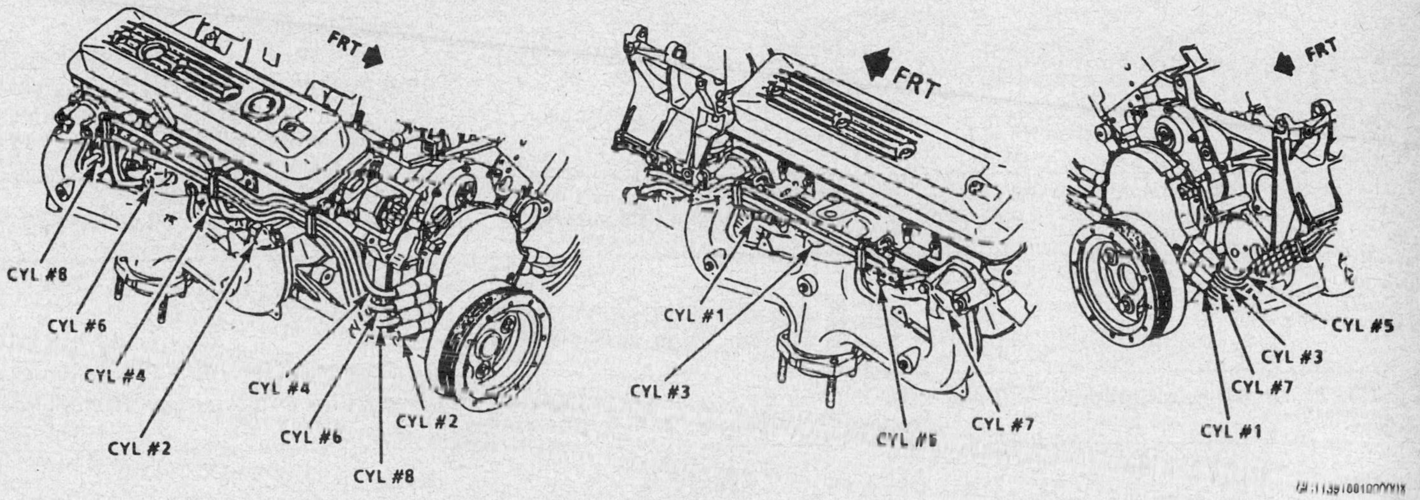
FRT
CYL #8
CYL #6
CYL #4
CYL #2
CYL #4
CYL #6
CYL #2
CYL #8
FRT
CYL #1
CYL #3
CYL #5
CYL #7
FRT
CYL #5
CYL #3
CYL #7
CYL #1

Fig. C

FRONT WHEEL ALIGNMENT SPECIFICATIONS

Year	Model	Caster Angle, Degrees		Camber Angle, Degrees		Toe Per Wheel, Degrees		Steering Wheel Angle, Degrees
		Limits	Desired	Limits	Desired	Limits	Desired	
1992-95	All	+5.5 to +6.5	+6	0 to +1	+.5	-.10 to +.10	0	-1 to +1

REAR WHEEL ALIGNMENT SPECIFICATIONS

Year	Model	Camber Angle, Degrees		Toe Per Wheel, Degrees		Thrust Angle, Degrees	
		Limits	Desired	Limits	Desired	Limits	Desired
1992-95	All	-.5 to +.5	0	-.1 to +.1	0	-.1 to +.1	0

COOLING SYSTEM & CAPACITY DATA

Year	Model Or Engine (VIN)①	Coolant Capacity, Qts.	Radiator Cap Relief Pressure, psi	Thermo. Opening Temp.°F	Fuel Tank, Gals.	Engine Oil, Qts.②		Transmission Oil			Rear Axle Pts.
						Less Filter Change	With Filter Change	Man Trans. Pts.	Auto. Trans. Qts. ③		
									Drain & Refill	Total Capacity	
1992-95	5.7L/V8-350 (P)⑦	17.8	15	180	20	4⑤	5⑤	4.4	5	11.2	⑧
	5.7L/V8-350 (J)⑥	14.7	15	180	20	④	④	4.4	—	—	⑧

VIN—Vehicle Identification Number
①—The eighth digit of the VIN denotes engine code.
②—After refilling, recheck oil level.
③—Approximate, make final check w/dipstick.
④—Recommended engine oil SG SAE 10W-30. Less filter change, 7.6 qts.; w/filter change 8.6 qts. With oil cooler drain & flush, less filter change, 9.6 qts.; w/filter change, 10.6 qts. Total system capacity w/filter removed & oil pan dry, 11.6 qts.
⑤—Recommended engine oil SG SAE 5W-30 synthetic engine oil meeting GM specification GM4718M.
⑥—4 cam 32 valve engine (ZR-1).
⑦—Single cam 16 valve engine.
⑧—1992-93, 4 pts.; 1994-95, 3 pts.

LUBRICANT DATA

Year	Lubricant Type				
	Transmission		Rear Axle	Power Steering System	Brake System
	Automatic	Manual			
1992-94	Dexron IIE	5W-30①	②	Power Steering Fluid ③	DOT 3 Brake Fluid
1995	Dexron IIE or III	5W-30①	②	Power Steering Fluid ③	DOT 3 Brake Fluid

①—Manual transmission fluid, GM part No. 1052931 or equivalent.
②—Use 80W-90 GL-5 gear lubricant & lubricant additive (GM part No. 1052358 or equivalent).
③—Meeting GM specification 9985835.

Electrical

NOTE: On Air Bag Equipped Models, Refer To "Air Bag System Precautions" Located In The Front Of This Manual For System Disarming & Arming Procedures.

INDEX

PRECAUTIONS

AIR BAG SYSTEMS

Refer to "Air Bag System Precautions" in the front of this manual for system disarming and arming procedures.

FUSE PANEL & FLASHER LOCATION

The fuse panel is located behind the far righthand corner of the instrument panel. The hazard warning flasher is located behind the righthand side of the instrument panel near radio receiver. The turn signal flasher is located behind the below lefthand side of the instrument panel to the

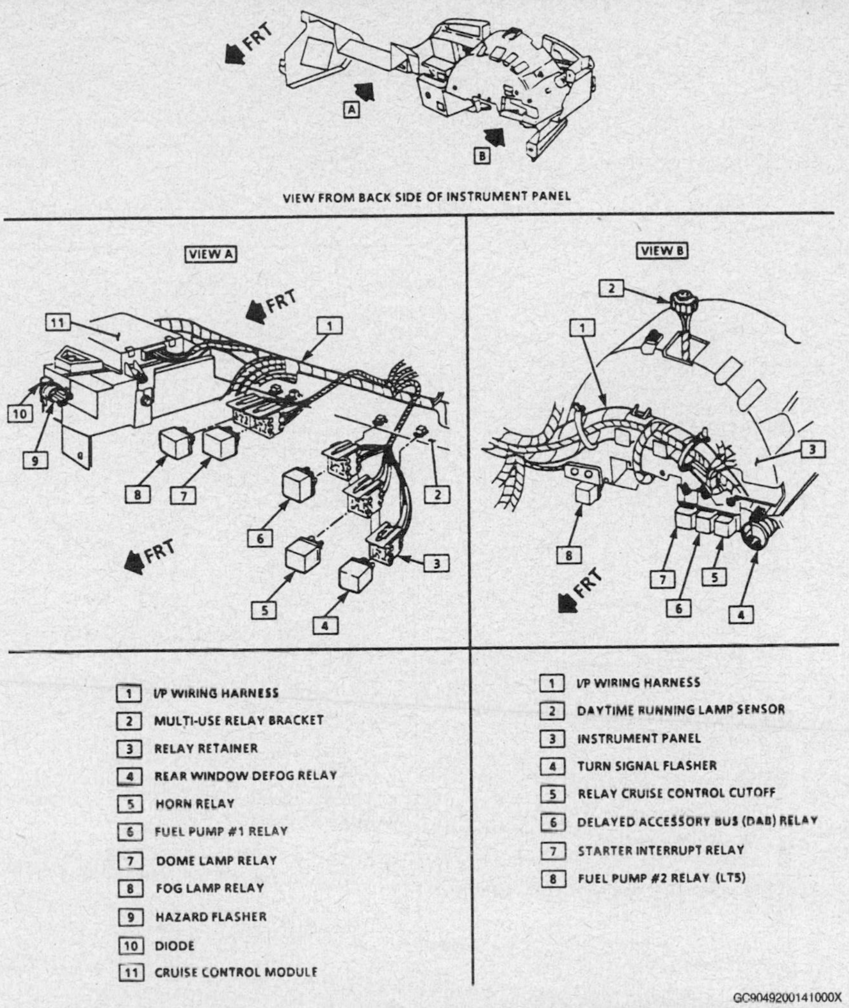

FRT
A
B
VIEW FROM BACK SIDE OF INSTRUMENT PANEL
VIEW A
VIEW B
1 I/P WIRING HARNESS
2 MULTI-USE RELAY BRACKET
3 RELAY RETAINER
4 REAR WINDOW DEFOG RELAY
5 HORN RELAY
6 FUEL PUMP #1 RELAY
7 DOME LAMP RELAY
8 FOG LAMP RELAY
9 HAZARD FLASHER
10 DIODE
11 CRUISE CONTROL MODULE
1 I/P WIRING HARNESS
2 DAYTIME RUNNING LAMP SENSOR
3 INSTRUMENT PANEL
4 TURN SIGNAL FLASHER
5 RELAY CRUISE CONTROL CUTOFF
6 DELAYED ACCESSORY BUS (DAB) RELAY
7 STARTER INTERRUPT RELAY
8 FUEL PUMP #2 RELAY (LT5)
GC9049200141000X

Fig. 1 Instrument panel relay location. 1992–93

left of the steering column.

RELAY CENTER LOCATION

The relay centers are located on the backside of the instrument panel, **Figs. 1 through 3.** The cooling fan relays are located on the upper radiator support, forward of the left front wheellhouse, **Fig. 4.**

STARTER

REPLACE

If shims are used between starter and engine block, they should be placed in their original location during installation. If starter is noisy during cranking, remove one .015 inch double shim or add one .015 single shim to the outer bolt. If starter makes a high pitched whine after firing, add .015 inch double shims until noise ceases.

5.7L/V8-350 SINGLE CAM 16 VALVE ENGINE

1. Disconnect battery ground cable.
2. Raise and support vehicle, then disconnect starter wiring.
3. Remove starter to engine brace and starter heat shields, if equipped.
4. Remove starter mounting bolts and lower starter, **Fig. 5.** Note position of shims, if used.
5. Disconnect solenoid wires and the battery cable.
6. Remove starter from vehicle.
7. Reverse procedure to install, noting the following:
   a. **Torque** starter mounting bolts to 34 ft. lbs.

5.7L/V8-350 4 CAM 32 VALVE (ZR-1) ENGINE

1. Disconnect battery ground cable, then drain cooling system.
2. Remove intake plenum assembly. Refer to "5.7L/V8-350 4 Cam 32 Valve Engine" section; "Plenum Assembly, Replace" procedure.
3. Remove ignition coil pack outlined in the "Distributor, Replace."
4. Disconnect battery positive cable and electrical leads from starter motor.
5. Remove starter motor to engine block attaching bolts, then remove starter motor, **Fig. 6.**
6. Reverse procedure to install, noting the following:
   a. Prior to installation, coat threads of starter mounting bolts with Loctite 262 or equivalent.
   b. **Torque** starter mounting bolts to 38 ft. lbs.

ALTERNATOR

REPLACE

5.7L/V8-350 SINGLE CAM 16 VALVE ENGINE

1. Disconnect battery ground cable, then remove intake air duct.
2. Disconnect regulator electrical connector and battery lead from rear of alternator.
3. **On 1992-94 models,** using a suitable socket and handle on tensioner pulley bolt, lift tensioner upward in the clockwise direction, then remove serpentine drive belt.
4. **On all models,** remove alternator rear mounting bolt and nut, then remove alternator rear mounting bracket,**Fig. 7**
5. Remove two bolts from alternator upper mounting, then remove upper mounting bracket.
6. Remove two bolts from alternator lower mounting, then remove lower mounting bracket.
7. Remove alternator from vehicle.
8. Reverse procedure to install, noting the following:
   a. Do not tighten alternator mounting bolts until all mounting brackets and bolts have been installed.
   b. **Torque** alternator lower and upper mounting bolts to 37 ft. lbs.
   c. **Torque** alternator rear mounting bolt to 17 ft. lbs. and rear mounting nut to 24 ft. lbs.
   d. Lift tensioner using a suitable socket and handle on pulley bolt, then position serpentine drive belt over pulleys and release tensioner.
   e. Ensure belt tension indicator marks are within limit lines on bolt tensioner indicator.

5.7L/V8-350 4 CAM 32 VALVE (ZR-1) ENGINE

1. Disconnect battery ground cable, then remove intake air duct.
2. Remove throttle body extension.
3. Using a 1/2 inch breaker bar, rotate serpentine drive belt tensioner to release belt tension.
4. Remove serpentine drive belt from water pump pulley, then remove belt.
5. Remove alternator lower support bolts and bracket, **Fig. 8.**
6. Remove rear support bracket to alternator retaining bolt.
7. Remove alternator upper support bolts and bracket.
8. Disconnect electrical connector, then remove oil sender unit.
9. Disconnect electrical connectors from alternator, then remove alternator from vehicle.
10. Reverse procedure to install, noting the following:
    a. Apply Loctite 565 or equivalent to threads of alternator mounting bolts prior to installation.
    b. **Torque** alternator mounting bolts

to 19 ft. lbs.

c. When installing serpentine drive belt, position belt over A/C compressor pulley. Retract belt tensioner using a 1/2 inch drive ratchet and route belt over alternator, crankshaft and power steering pump pulleys, then position belt behind water pump pulley. Ensure belt is properly positioned on pulleys, then pull belt forward onto water pump pulley. Release belt tensioner.

d. **Torque** throttle body extension attaching bolts to 53 inch lbs.

DISTRIBUTOR
REPLACE
5.7L/V8-350 SINGLE CAM 16 VALVE ENGINE
Removal

1. Disconnect battery ground cable.
2. Disconnect intake air temperature sensor harness connector.
3. Using a suitable socket and handle on serpentine drive belt tensioner pulley bolt, lift tensioner upward in the clockwise direction, then remove serpentine drive belt.
4. Drain coolant from engine.
5. Disconnect coolant hoses from water pump, then disconnect coolant sensor electrical connector.
6. Remove water pump as described under "Water Pump, Replace."
7. Remove crankshaft pulley attaching bolts, then remove pulley.
8. Remove crankshaft damper as described under "Crankshaft Damper, Replace."
9. Disconnect spark plug cables from distributor, then disconnect four terminal ECM connector at distributor. Note location of spark plug wires in distributor cap for use during installation.
10. Remove distributor attaching bolts, then pull distributor forward until shaft disengages from engine, **Fig. 9.**

Installation

1. Position distributor shaft in engine and place alignment mark at top shaft. Remove distributor shaft from engine and position in distributor. Rotate shaft until alignment mark is located at top.
2. Position distributor and shaft assembly to engine and install, **Fig. 9**.
3. **Torque** distributor to engine attaching bolts to 8 ft. lbs.
4. Connect ECM four terminal connector at distributor, then connect spark plug wires to distributor cap terminals.
5. Install crankshaft damper as described in "Crankshaft Damper & Hub, Replace."
6. Install crankshaft pulley.
7. Install water pump assembly as described under "Water Pump, Replace.
8. Connect coolant sensor electrical connector.
9. Connect coolant hoses to water pump, then fill cooling system.
10. Install serpentine drive belt and air intake duct.
11. Connect intake air temperature sensor harness connector and battery ground cable.

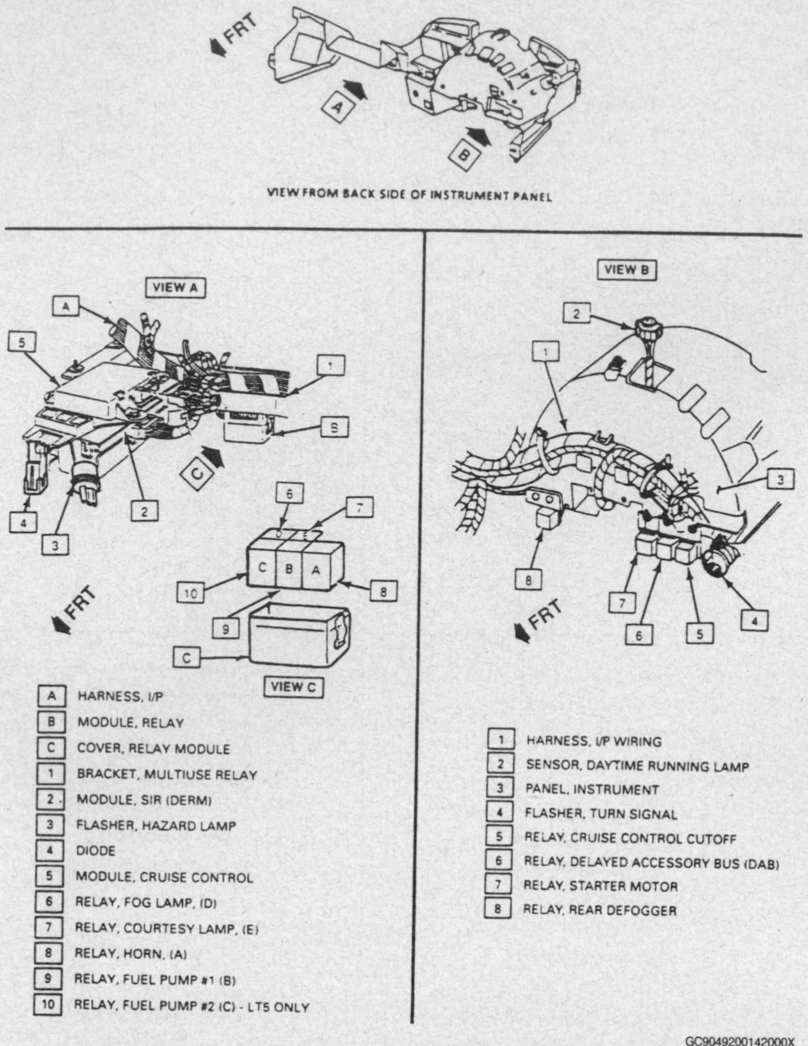

FRT
A
B
VIEW FROM BACK SIDE OF INSTRUMENT PANEL
VIEW A
VIEW B
VIEW C
C B A
A HARNESS, I/P
B MODULE, RELAY
C COVER, RELAY MODULE
1 BRACKET, MULTIUSE RELAY
2 MODULE, SIR (DERM)
3 FLASHER, HAZARD LAMP
4 DIODE
5 MODULE, CRUISE CONTROL
6 RELAY, FOG LAMP, (D)
7 RELAY, COURTESY LAMP, (E)
8 RELAY, HORN, (A)
9 RELAY, FUEL PUMP #1 (B)
10 RELAY, FUEL PUMP #2 (C) - LT5 ONLY
1 HARNESS, I/P WIRING
2 SENSOR, DAYTIME RUNNING LAMP
3 PANEL, INSTRUMENT
4 FLASHER, TURN SIGNAL
5 RELAY, CRUISE CONTROL CUTOFF
6 RELAY, DELAYED ACCESSORY BUS (DAB)
7 RELAY, STARTER MOTOR
8 RELAY, REAR DEFOGGER
GC9049200142000X

Fig. 2 Instrument panel relay location. 1994

IGNITION LOCK
REPLACE

1. Disconnect battery ground cable.
2. Remove steering wheel as described under "Steering Wheel, Replace."
3. Remove turn signal switch as described under "Turn Signal Switch, Replace."
4. Place ignition switch in Lock position.
5. Remove lock cylinder retaining screw.
6. Disconnect terminal electrical connector at bulkhead connection to provide slack.
7. Remove wiring connector from steering column.
8. Attach a suitable length of mechanic wire to ignition lock electrical connector for use during installation. Detach wire retaining clip, then carefully pull ignition lock wiring through housing shroud, steering column and lock housing cover, **Fig. 10.**
9. Remove lock cylinder.
10. Reverse procedure to install, noting the following:
    a. Ensure lock cylinder wiring is properly routed through steering column.
    b. **Torque lock cylinder retaining screw to 22 inch lbs.**

IGNITION SWITCH
REPLACE

The ignition switch is mounted on top of the mast jacket inside the brake pedal support and is actuated by a rod and rack assembly.

1. Disconnect battery ground cable.
2. Remove steering column from vehicle as outlined in the "Steering Columns" section.
3. Remove hex nut and washer head screw.
4. Remove horn pad ground wiring assembly from dimmer and ignition switch mounting stud. Remove wiring assembly from slot D of turn signal switch connector body, if necessary.
5. Remove cable bracket, then the dimmer switch from actuator rod.
6. Remove dimmer and ignition switch mounting stud.

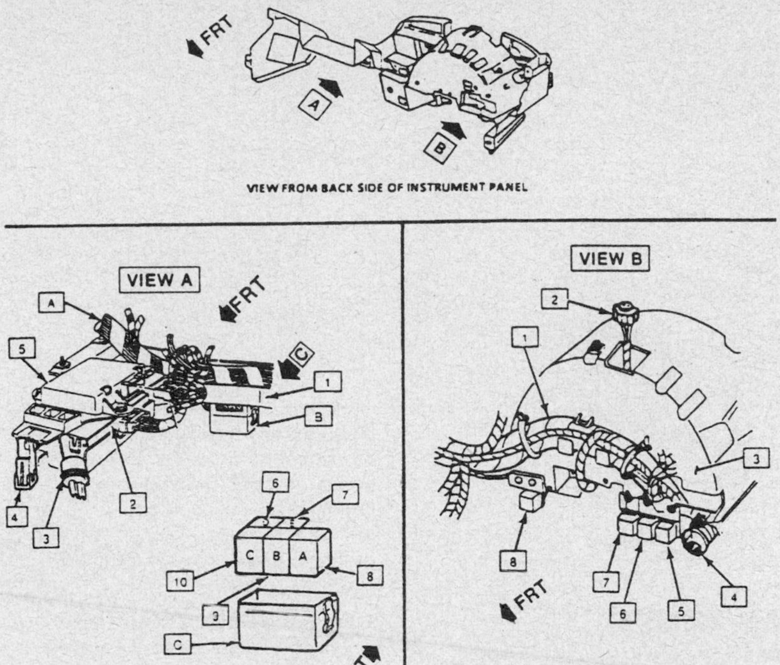
FRT
A
B
VIEW FROM BACK SIDE OF INSTRUMENT PANEL
VIEW A
FRT
VIEW B
VIEW C
FRT

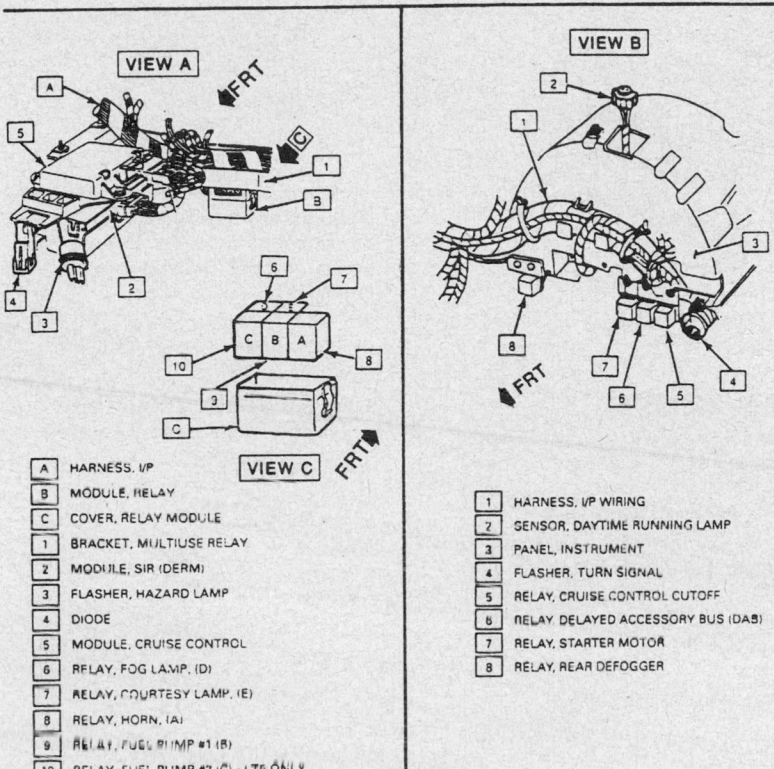

A	HARNESS, I/P
B	MODULE, RELAY
C	COVER, RELAY MODULE
1	BRACKET, MULTIUSE RELAY
2	MODULE, SIR (DERM)
3	FLASHER, HAZARD LAMP
4	DIODE
5	MODULE, CRUISE CONTROL
6	RELAY, FOG LAMP, (D)
7	RELAY, COURTESY LAMP, (E)
8	RELAY, HORN, (A)
9	RELAY, FUEL PUMP #1 (B)
10	RELAY, FUEL PUMP #2 (C) - LT5 ONLY

1	HARNESS, I/P WIRING
2	SENSOR, DAYTIME RUNNING LAMP
3	PANEL, INSTRUMENT
4	FLASHER, TURN SIGNAL
5	RELAY, CRUISE CONTROL CUTOFF
6	RELAY, DELAYED ACCESSORY BUS (DAB)
7	RELAY, STARTER MOTOR
8	RELAY, REAR DEFOGGER

GC9049200143000X

Fig. 3 Instrument panel relay location. 1995

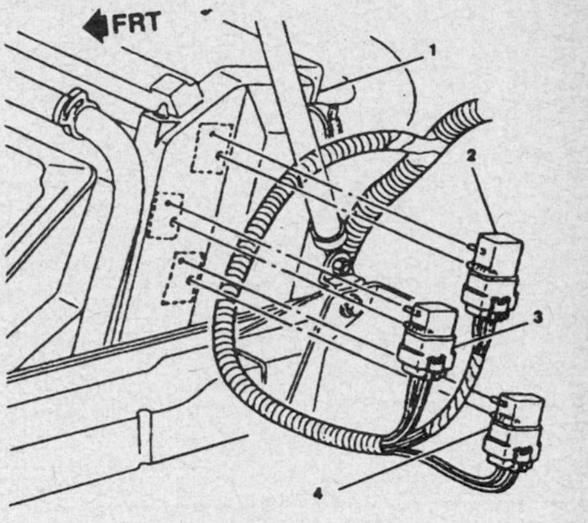
FRT

1 RADIATOR
2 COOLING FAN RELAY #1
3 COOLING FAN RELAY #2
4 COOLING FAN RELAY #3

GC9049200144000X

Fig. 4 Cooling fan relay location

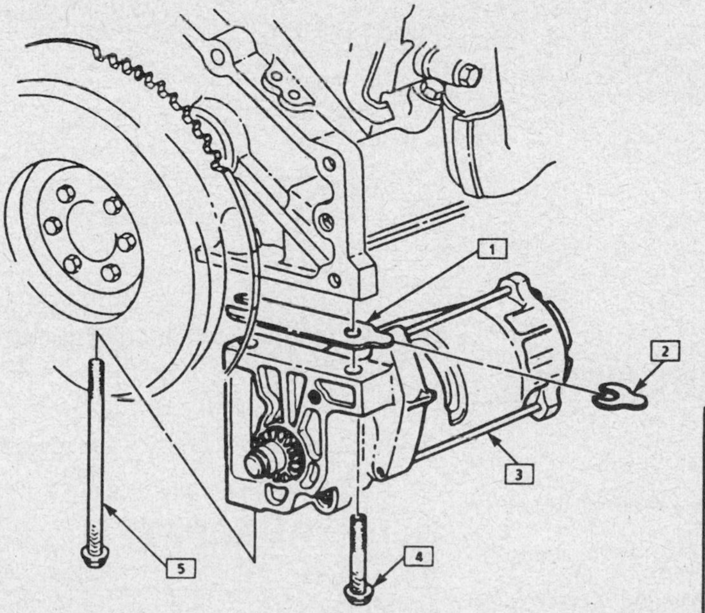

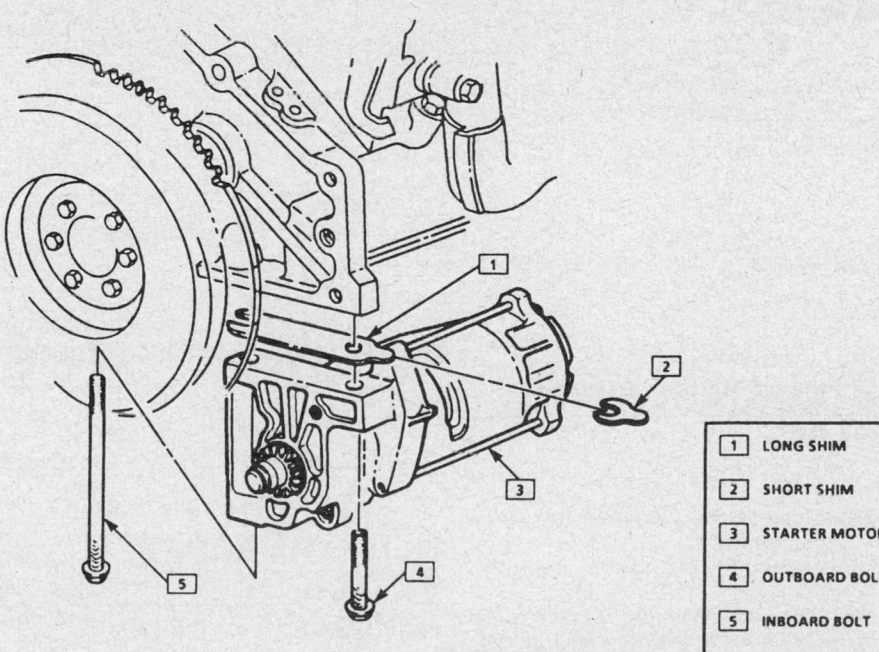

1	LONG SHIM
2	SHORT SHIM
3	STARTER MOTOR
4	OUTBOARD BOLT
5	INBOARD BOLT

GC1129100047000X

Fig. 5 Starter motor replacement. 5.7L/V8-350 single cam 16 valve engine

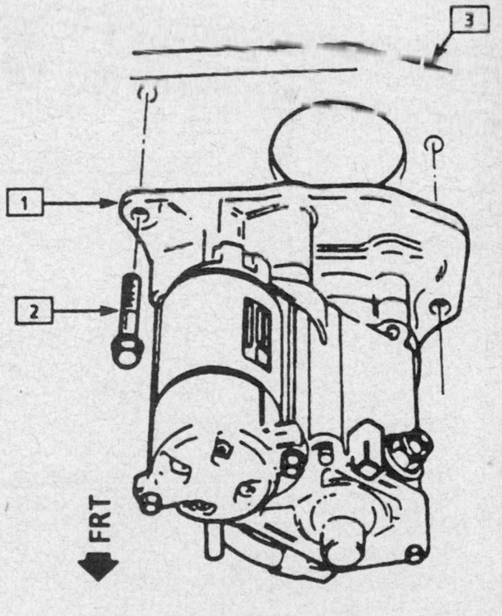
FRT

1	MOTOR, STARTER
2	BOLT, STARTER MOTOR MOUNTING
3	CASE, CYLINDER

GC1129100048000X

Fig. 6 Starter motor replacement. 5.7L/V8-350 4 cam 32 valve (ZR-1) engine

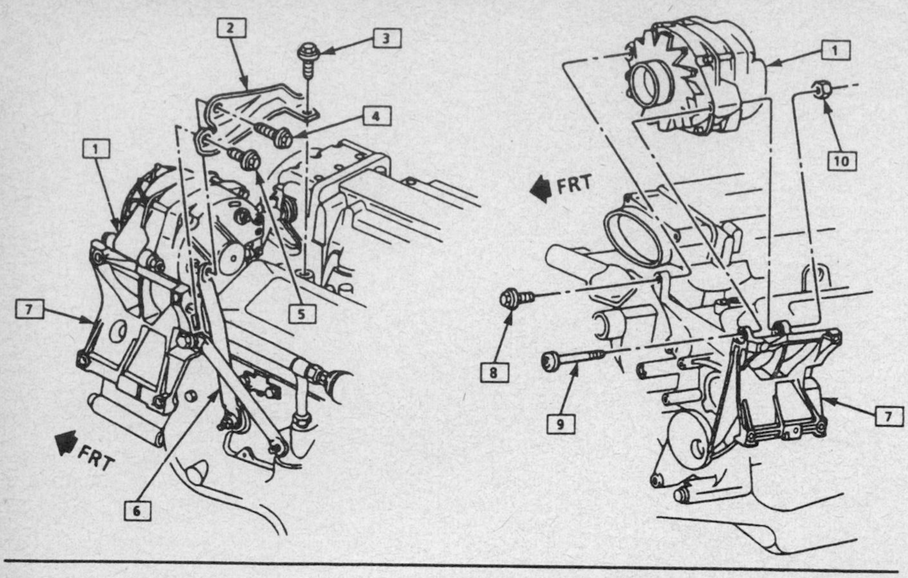
FRT
FRT

[1] GENERATOR
[2] GENERATOR MOUNTING BRACE
[3] BOLT - TIGHTEN TO 33 N·m (24 lb. ft.)
[4] BOLT - TIGHTEN TO 50 N·m (37 lb. ft.)
[5] BOLT - TIGHTEN TO 33 N·m (24 lb. ft.)
[6] GENERATOR REAR BRACE
[7] GENERATOR, A/C COMPRESSOR AND POWER STEERING PUMP BRACKET
[8] BOLT - TIGHTEN TO 50 N·m (37 lb. ft.)
[9] BOLT
[10] NUT - TIGHTEN TO 50 N·m (37 lb. ft.)

GC1129200049000X

Fig. 7 Alternator mounting. 5.7L/V8-350 single cam 16 valve engine

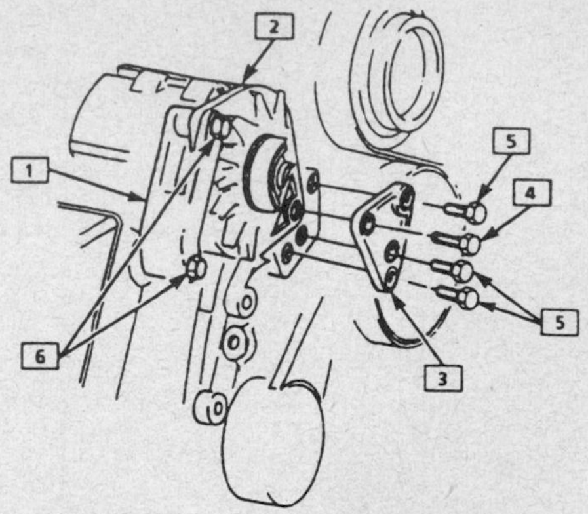

[1] GENERATOR SUPPORT BRACKET
[2] GENERATOR
[3] GENERATOR LOWER SUPPORT BRACKET
[4] GENERATOR LOWER MOUNTING BOLT
[5] GENERATOR BRACKET BOLT
[6] GENERATOR UPPER SUPPORT BRACKET BOLT

GC1129100050000X

Fig. 8 Alternator mounting. 5.7L/V8-350 four cam 32 valve engine

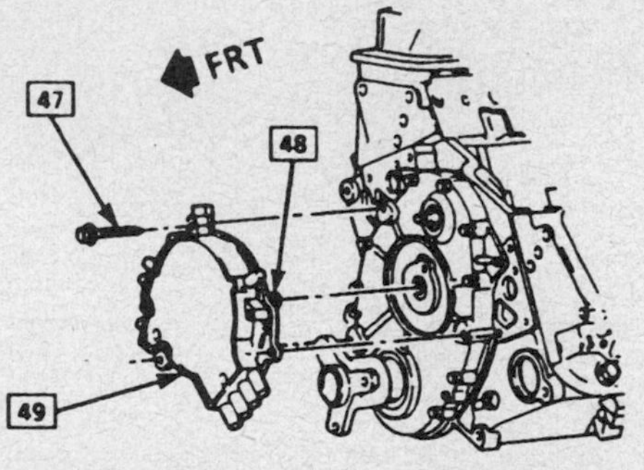
FRT

[47] BOLT
[48] DRIVESHAFT
[49] DISTRIBUTOR

GC1119200113000X

Fig. 9 Distributor replacement. 5.7L/V8-350 single cam 16 valve engine

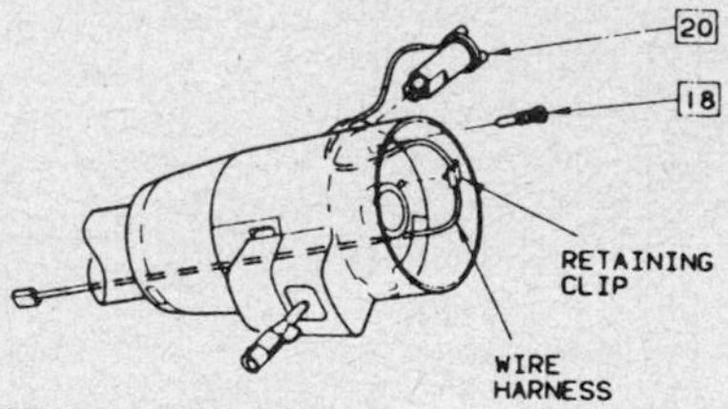
20
18
RETAINING CLIP
WIRE HARNESS

18 SCREW, LOCK RETAINING
20 LOCK CYLINDER SET, STRG COL PASS KEY

GC9129100017000X

Fig. 10 Ignition lock replacement

MOVE SWITCH SLIDER TO EXTREME RIGHT POSITION AND THEN MOVE SLIDER ONE DETENT TO THE LEFT (OFF LOCK)

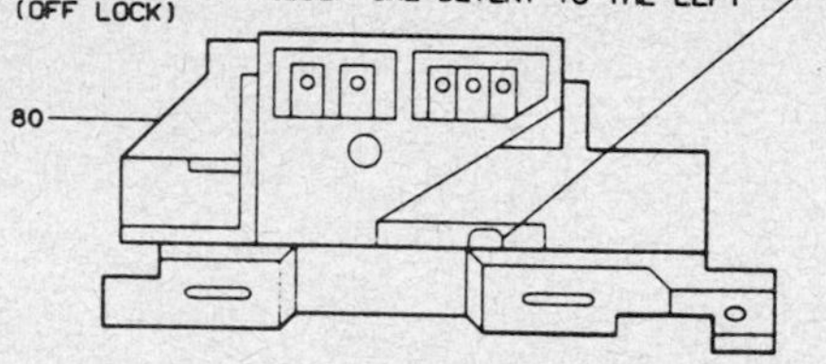
80

80 SWITCH ASM, IGNITION

GC9049100067000X

Fig. 11 Ignition switch adjustment

7. Remove ignition switch assembly from switch actuator assembly, then disconnect wiring harness from switch assembly.
8. Reverse procedure to install, noting the following:
   a. Place lock cylinder and switch in OFF-LOCKED position, **Fig. 12.** A new ignition switch will be pinned in OFF-LOCKED position. Remove plastic pin after switch is assembled to column.
   b. Install and adjust dimmer switch as outlined under "Dimmer Switch, Replace."

CLUTCH START SWITCH

REPLACE

1. Disconnect battery ground cable and set parking brake.
2. Remove hush panel from under instrument panel.
3. Remove clip securing clutch start switch actuating lever to clutch pedal, then disengage lever from pedal arm, **Fig. 12.**
4. Remove clutch start switch to pedal bracket retaining screw, then disconnect electrical connector and remove switch.
5. Reverse procedure to install.

NEUTRAL SAFETY SWITCH

REPLACE

1. Remove floor console cover, then disconnect electrical connectors from switch.
2. Place shift lever in Neutral position of

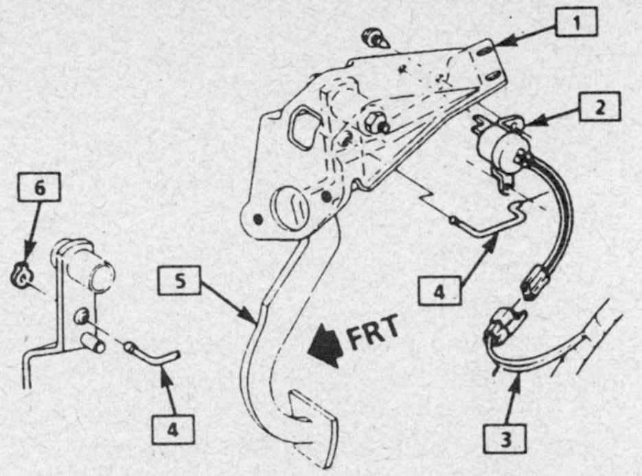
FRT

1 CLUTCH PEDAL ASSEMBLY BRACKET
2 TRANSMISSION CLUTCHSTART SWITCH
3 INSTRUMENT PANEL WIRING HARNESS
4 CLUTCH START SWITCH ROD
5 CLUTCH PEDAL
6 CLUTCH START SWITCH ROD RETAINER

GC9049100068000X

Fig. 12 Clutch start switch replacement

detent plate, then remove switch attaching nuts and switch, **Fig. 13.**

3. To install, ensure the shift lever is in Neutral, then position switch on shift lever making sure pin on shaft is in slot of switch.
4. If reinstalling existing switch, rotate switch to align service adjustment hole with carrier tang hole. Insert a .094 inch gauge pin and rotate switch until pin drops in to a depth of .59 inch. **Torque** switch attaching nut to 26 inch lbs., then remove gauge pin.
5. If installing a new switch, **torque** attaching nuts to 26 inch lbs., then move shift lever out of Neutral to shear pin which is part of new switch.
6. Reconnect electrical connectors to switch, then apply parking brake and start engine. Check back-up lights and seat belt warning system for proper operation and ensure engine will start only in Park or Neutral.
7. Turn ignition off and install floor console.

HEADLAMP SWITCH

REPLACE

1. Disconnect battery ground cable.
2. Remove instrument cluster bezel as described under "Instrument Cluster, Replace."
3. Remove attaching screws from righthand side of switch, **Fig. 14.**
4. Remove switch trim plate attaching screws.
5. Disconnect electrical connectors, then remove switch.
6. Reverse procedure to install.

STOP LIGHT SWITCH

REPLACE

1. Remove lefthand lower trim panel as follows:
   a. Remove retainer securing lower trim panel to stud on steering column.
   b. Remove trim panel mounting screws, then the trim panel.
   c. Remove DLC connector assembly mounting screw, then disconnect courtesy lamp electrical connector.
2. Remove stop lamp electrical connectors, then the vacuum hose for cruise control switch.
3. Depress retainer tabs and remove switch from bracket.
4. Reverse procedure to install, noting the following:
   a. With brake pedal depressed, insert switch assembly into bracket until seated. Audible clicks can be heard as threaded portion is pushed through bracket toward brake pedal.
   b. Pull brake pedal fully rearward against pedal stop until click sounds are not heard. Switch will move in retainer, providing adjustment.
   c. Repeat steps a and b until click sounds are not heard.

TURN SIGNAL SWITCH

REPLACE

1. Remove steering wheel as described under "Steering Wheel, Replace."
2. Place ignition switch in Lock position to retain coil assembly in the centered position.
3. Disconnect battery ground cable.
4. Remove coil assembly retaining ring, **Fig. 15.**
5. Lift coil assembly from steering shaft and allow to hang from wire.
6. Using a suitable tool, compress lock plate and remove retaining ring, **Fig. 16.**
7. Remove lock plate, turn signal canceling cam and upper bearing spring, inner race seat and inner race.
8. Place turn signal lever in righthand turn position, then remove multifunction lever and hazard warning flasher knob.
9. Remove turn signal switch lever attaching screw, then remove lever.
10. Remove turn signal switch attaching screws.
11. Disconnect turn signal switch electrical connector at lower portion of steering column.
12. Remove turn signal switch wiring protector cover from steering column.
13. Carefully pull turn signal switch wiring up and out of steering column, **Fig. 17.**
14. Reverse procedure to install. If coil assembly has become uncentered, refer to **Fig. 18** for centering procedure.

DIMMER SWITCH

REPLACE

1. Disconnect battery ground cable.
2. Remove steering column from vehicle as outlined in the "Steering Columns" section.
3. Remove hex nut and washer head screw.

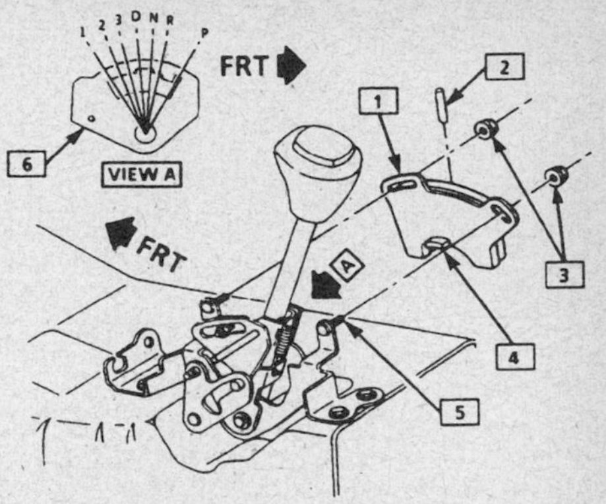
FRT
VIEW A
FRT

1 NEUTRAL START AND BACKUP LAMP SWITCH
2 GAGE PIN
3 NUT
4 CARRIER TANG
5 MOUNTING STUD
6 DETENT PLATE

GC9049100069000X

Fig. 13 Neutral safety switch replacement

4. Remove horn pad ground wiring assembly from dimmer and ignition switch mounting stud. Remove wiring assembly from slot D of turn signal switch connector body, if necessary.
5. Remove cable bracket, then the dimmer switch assembly from actuator rod.
6. Disconnect wiring harness from dimmer switch.
7. Reverse procedure to install. Adjust dimmer switch as follows:
   a. Install a 3/32 inch twist drill, to limit switch travel, **Fig. 19.**
   b. Position switch on column and push against dimmer switch rod to remove all lash.
   c. Remove drill bit and check for proper operation.

STEERING WHEEL

REPLACE

Mark position of steering wheel in relation to shaft prior to removal to ensure correct installation.

REMOVAL

1. Disconnect battery ground cable.
2. Remove steering wheel retaining nut, then disconnect horn electrical connector.
3. Using puller J-1859-03 or equivalent, pull steering wheel from steering shaft, **Fig. 20.**

INSTALLATION

1. Connect horn electrical connector.
2. Position steering wheel spline alignment marks to alignment marks of steering shaft splines, then install steering wheel.
3. Install steering wheel retaining nut and **torque** to 30 ft. lbs.

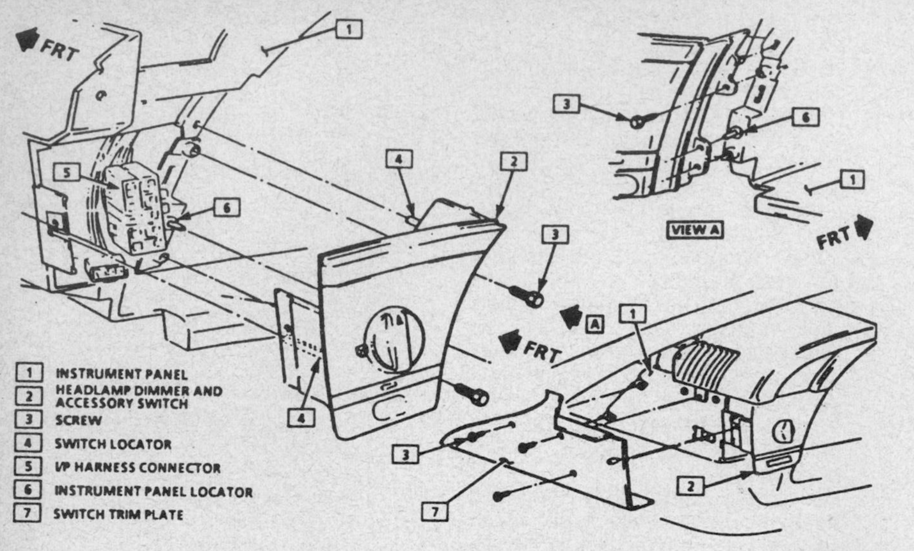
FRT
1
2
3
4
5
6
VIEW A
FRT
A
7
1 INSTRUMENT PANEL
2 HEADLAMP DIMMER AND ACCESSORY SWITCH
3 SCREW
4 SWITCH LOCATOR
5 I/P HARNESS CONNECTOR
6 INSTRUMENT PANEL LOCATOR
7 SWITCH TRIM PLATE
GC9049100070000X

Fig. 14 Headlamp switch replacement

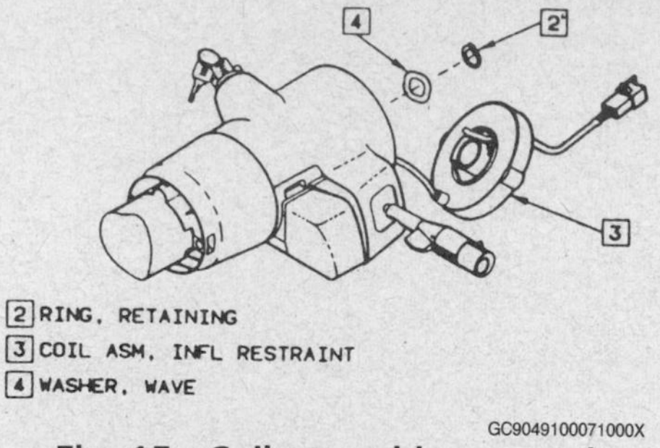
4
2*
3
2 RING, RETAINING
3 COIL ASM, INFL RESTRAINT
4 WASHER, WAVE
GC9049100071000X

Fig. 15 Coil assembly removal

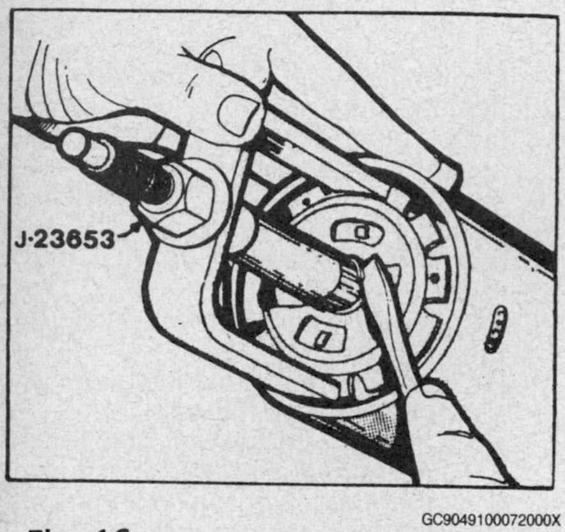
J-23653
GC9049100072000X

Fig. 16 Lock plate retaining ring removal

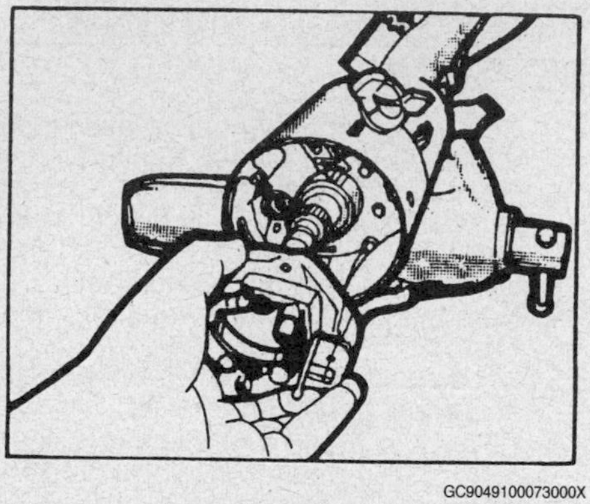
GC9049100073000X

Fig. 17 Turn signal switch removal

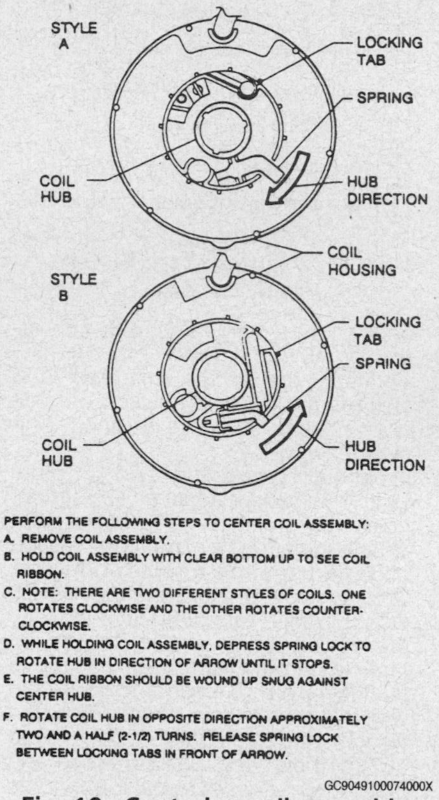
STYLE A
LOCKING TAB
SPRING
COIL HUB
HUB DIRECTION
COIL HOUSING
STYLE B
LOCKING TAB
SPRING
COIL HUB
HUB DIRECTION
PERFORM THE FOLLOWING STEPS TO CENTER COIL ASSEMBLY:
A. REMOVE COIL ASSEMBLY.
B. HOLD COIL ASSEMBLY WITH CLEAR BOTTOM UP TO SEE COIL RIBBON.
C. NOTE: THERE ARE TWO DIFFERENT STYLES OF COILS. ONE ROTATES CLOCKWISE AND THE OTHER ROTATES COUNTER-CLOCKWISE.
D. WHILE HOLDING COIL ASSEMBLY, DEPRESS SPRING LOCK TO ROTATE HUB IN DIRECTION OF ARROW UNTIL IT STOPS.
E. THE COIL RIBBON SHOULD BE WOUND UP SNUG AGAINST CENTER HUB.
F. ROTATE COIL HUB IN OPPOSITE DIRECTION APPROXIMATELY TWO AND A HALF (2-1/2) TURNS. RELEASE SPRING LOCK BETWEEN LOCKING TABS IN FRONT OF ARROW.
GC9049100074000X

Fig. 18 Centering coil assembly

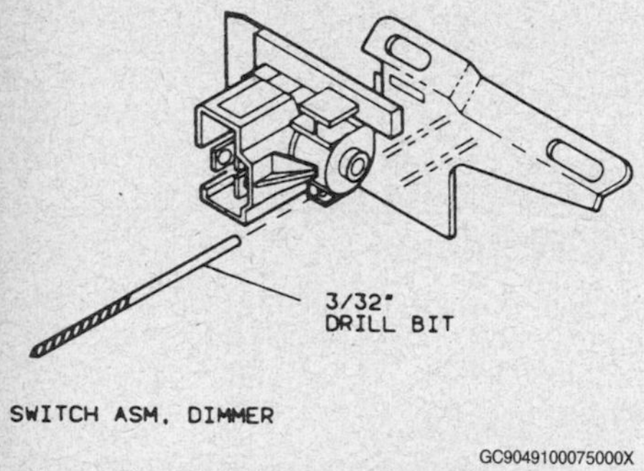
3/32" DRILL BIT
SWITCH ASM, DIMMER
GC9049100075000X

Fig. 19 Column mounted dimmer switch installation

4. Ensure ignition switch is in OFF position, then connect battery ground cable.

INSTRUMENT CLUSTER

REPLACE

1. Remove lefthand lower trim panel as follows:
   a. Remove retainer securing lower trim panel to stud on steering column.
   b. Remove trim panel mounting screws, then the trim panel.
   c. Remove DLC connector assembly mounting screw, then disconnect courtesy lamp electrical connector.
2. Remove driver's knee bolster as follows:
   a. Pull down carpet from upper corner of lefthand console side trim panel.
   b. Remove screws from flip down access door. Bend door down to access bolster retaining screws.
   c. Remove screws from knee bolster brackets, then the knee bolster.
3. Remove steering column support bolts, then lower steering column.
4. Remove cluster bezel attaching screws, then the bezel, **Fig. 21.**
5. Remove cluster mounting screws, **Fig. 22,** then disconnect cluster electrical connectors.
6. Remove instrument cluster from vehicle.
7. Reverse procedure to install, noting the following:
   a. **Torque** cluster mounting screws to 16 inch lbs.
   b. **Torque** bezel mounting screws to 29 inch lbs.

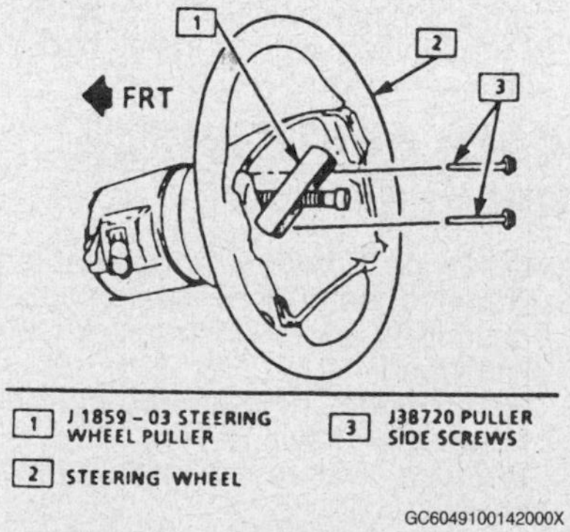
1
2
FRT
3
1 J 1859 - 03 STEERING WHEEL PULLER
3 J38720 PULLER SIDE SCREWS
2 STEERING WHEEL
GC6049100142000X

Fig. 20 Steering wheel removal

RADIO

REPLACE

When installing radio, be sure to adjust antenna trimmer for peak reception. Also, be sure to connect speaker before applying power to radio.

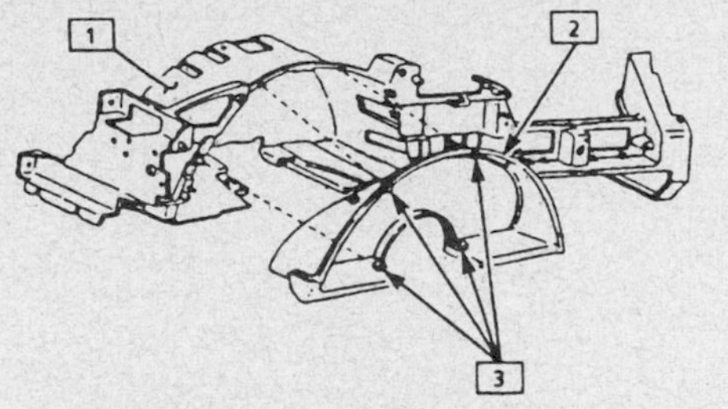
1
2
3

1 INSTRUMENT PANEL CARRIER
2 INSTRUMENT PANEL CLUSTER BEZEL
3 SCREWS

GC6049100143000X

Fig. 21 Instrument cluster bezel replacement

RADIO CONTROL

1. Disconnect battery ground cable.
2. Remove transmission gear selector knob.
3. Remove console trim plate attaching screws from under ash tray.
4. Disconnect electrical connectors from console trim plate components, then remove trim plate.
5. Remove screw attaching center air outlet to instrument panel carrier, then remove outlet.
6. Remove screws attaching accessory trim plate to instrument panel.
7. Disconnect electrical connector to engine power switch, then remove accessory trim plate.
8. Remove console door.
9. Remove screws attaching console righthand side trim panel to instrument panel and console. Remove passenger seat from vehicle to gain access to screws at side of trim panel. After all attaching screws have been removed, remove side trim panel.
10. Remove screws attaching radio control to instrument panel.
11. Pull radio control outward, then disconnect electrical connectors and remove radio control.
12. Reverse procedure to install.

RADIO RECEIVER

1992

1. Disconnect battery ground cable.
2. Remove screws attaching lower righthand trim panel to instrument panel and support.
3. Disconnect courtesy lamp electrical connector and air duct, then remove lower righthand trim panel.
4. Remove radio receiver front attaching nut and loosen side mounting nuts.
5. Slide radio receiver forward to release tab, then disconnect electrical connectors and antenna lead.
6. Remove radio receiver.
7. Reverse procedure to install.

1993-95

1. Disconnect battery ground cable.
2. Open right rear floor storage compartment door, then remove tray.
3. Remove radio receiver by pulling firmly on receiver to separate hook and loop fastener.

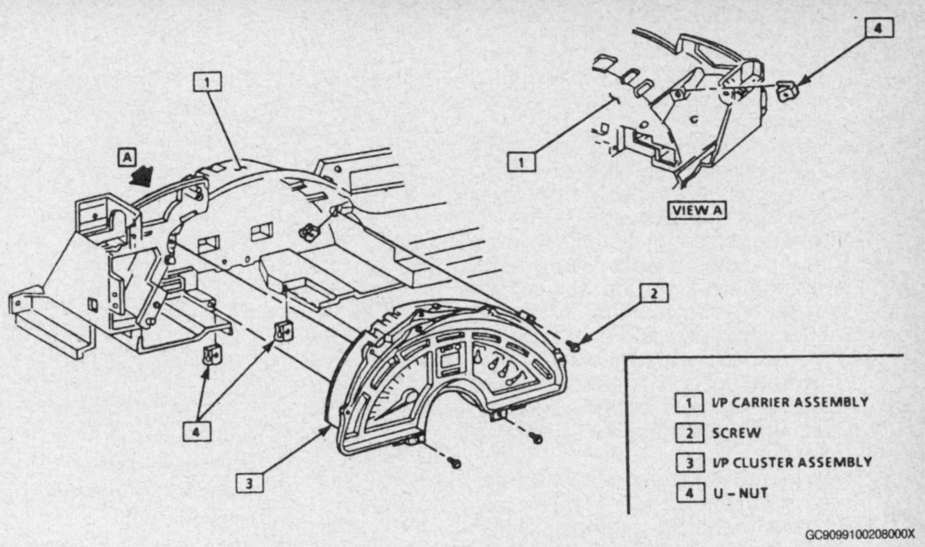
A
1
2
3
4
VIEW A

1 I/P CARRIER ASSEMBLY
2 SCREW
3 I/P CLUSTER ASSEMBLY
4 U-NUT

GC9099100208000X

Fig. 22 Instrument cluster replacement

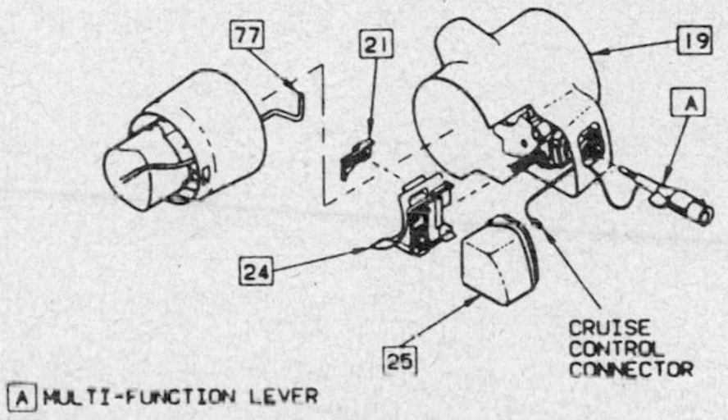
77
21
19
A
24
25
CRUISE
CONTROL
CONNECTOR

A MULTI-FUNCTION LEVER
19 COVER ASM. LOCK HOUSING
21 ACTUATOR. DIMMER SWITCH ROD
24 BASE PLATE. COL HSG COVER END
25 CAP. COL HSG COVER END
77 ROD. DIMMER SWITCH

GC9049100076000X

Fig. 23 Multi-function lever replacement

4. Disconnect antenna cable extension and electrical connectors.
5. Reverse procedure to install.

WIPER MOTOR

REPLACE

1. Disconnect battery ground cable.
2. Remove wiper arms, if necessary.
3. Disconnect wiper motor upper electrical connectors.
4. Remove lefthand plenum screen.
5. Remove left and righthand wiper transmission attaching nuts.
6. Remove left and righthand wiper transmission sockets.
7. **On ZR1 models,** disconnect vacuum booster supply hose at plenum.
8. **On all models,** remove wiper motor attaching bolts, then carefully lift wiper motor from mounting.
9. Disconnect wiper motor lower electrical connectors and remove wiper motor.
10. Reverse procedure to install.

WIPER SWITCH

REPLACE

1. Pull column housing end toward front of vehicle and remove cover, **Fig. 23.**
2. Disconnect electrical connector and grommet.
3. Pull outward on multi-function lever to release from detent, **Fig. 23.**
4. Reverse procedure to install, noting the following:
   a. Position lever in Off position.
   b. Align lever tab with mounting slot.

WIPER TRANSMISSION

REPLACE

1. Ensure motor is in Park position.
2. Raise hood and remove wiper arm assemblies.
3. Remove lefthand cowl vent screen.
4. Loosen nuts securing pivot at motor crankarm, then disconnect transmission rod from crankarm.
5. Remove retaining nuts or screws securing transmission to body, then withdraw transmission assembly through cowl opening.
6. Reverse procedure to install.

BLOWER MOTOR

REPLACE

1. Disconnect battery ground cable.
2. Remove right front wheel housing rear panel, and push housing aside.
3. Remove motor cooling tube and screws securing relay, and set relay aside.
4. Remove motor retaining screws, motor and impeller.
5. Reverse procedure to install.

HEATER CORE

REPLACE

1. Remove lower righthand trim panel as follows:
   a. Remove fuse box cover, then instrument panel side trim panel.
   b. Remove lower trim panel mounting screw, then the trim panel.
   c. Disconnect courtesy lamp harness connector.
2. Remove glovecompartment as follows:
   a. Remove screws from glove compartment lower hinge, then from

latch striker.

b. Remove glove compartment from upper trim pad, then disconnect glove compartment lamp switch connector.

3. Remove righthand outer air outlet mounting screws, then the air outlet.
4. Remove center air outlet mounting screws, then the air outlet.
5. Remove console trim plate as follows:
   a. **On models with automatic transmission,** pry up shifter button, then remove shifter button retainer, snap ring and shift knob.
   b. **On models with manual transmission,** pry up shifter button, then remove shifter button, retainer, shift knob, setscrew and reverse inhibitor.
   c. **On all models,** disconnect electrical connectors for lighter, rear compartment lid release switch and gear indicator lamp, if equipped. Unclip accessory plug harness.
   d. Pry locking tabs on underside of shifter boot from groove in shaft, then remove console trim plate with boot.
6. Remove accessory trim plate mounting screw, then the trim plate.
7. **On ZR-1 models,** disconnect engine power switch from trim plate.
8. **On all models,** remove windshield defroster grill by prying up on rear edge, the disconnect sun load sensor connector.
9. Remove lefthand outer air outlet mounting screws, then the air outlet.
10. Remove upper trim pad mounting screws, **Fig. 24**, then the upper trim pad.
11. Drain cooling system, then remove in vehicle temperature sensor aspirator hose.
12. Disconnect in vehicle temperature sensor connector, the remove floor heat deflector mounting screws.
13. Remove righthand knee bolster brace, then the floor heat deflector.
14. Remove relays from multi use relay bracket, then loosen wiring harness retainer to radio receiver mounting nuts.
15. Remove wiring harness retainer, then the harnesses from wiring harness retainer.
16. Remove carrier nuts from righthand pillar.
17. Remove console righthand side trim panel as follows:
    a. Remove righthand seat, then trim panel to tunnel mounting screws.
    b. Remove console door, then the remaining side trim panel mounting screws.
18. Remove lower trim panel support as follows:
    a. Remove bolts mounting lower trim panel support to passenger inner knee bolster bracket.
    b. Remove bolts mounting trim panel support to passenger knee bolster outer bracket.
    c. Remove lower trim panel support.
19. Remove four passenger knee bolster

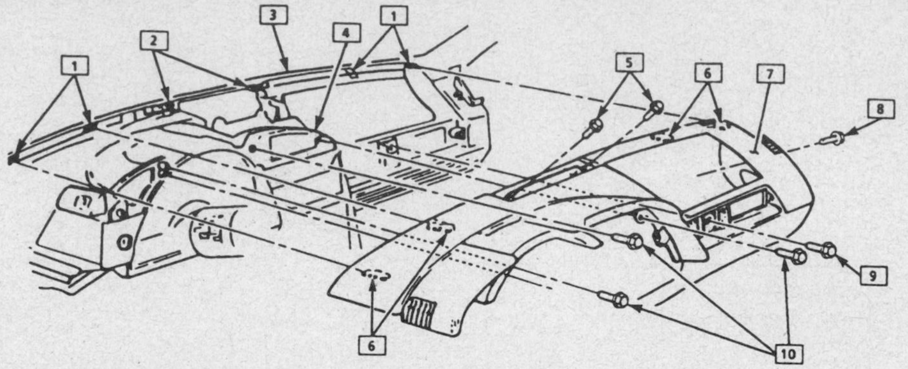
1
2
3
4
5
6
7
8
9
10

1 SLOTS FOR CLIPS
2 RETAINING BRACKETS
3 LOWER WINDSHIELD ASSEMBLY
4 INSTRUMENT PANEL
5 BOLT/SCREWS TO RETAINING BRACKETS
6 TRIM PAD CLIPS
7 UPPER TRIM PAD
8 BOLT/SCREW RIGHT SIDE
9 BOLT/SCREW AIR OUTLET
10 BOLT/SCREWS TO I/P

GC9099100209000X

Fig. 24 Instrument panel trim pad removal

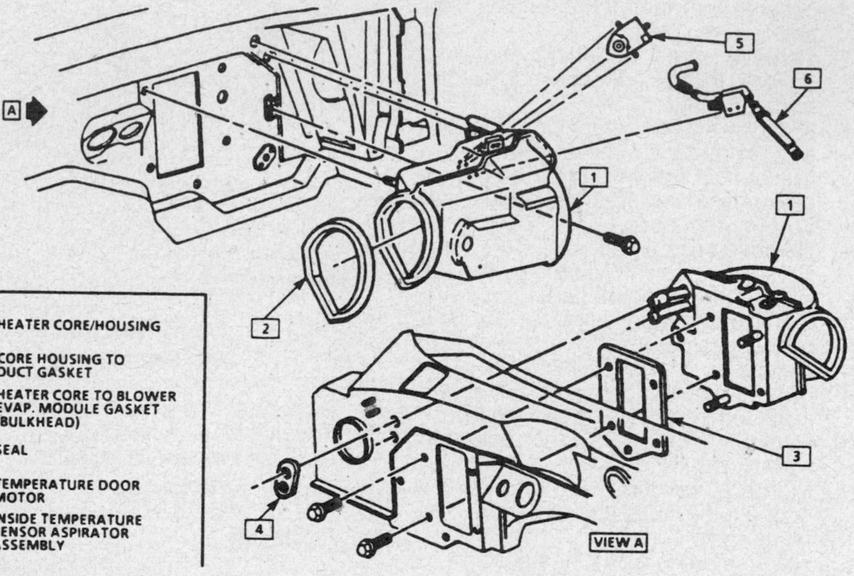
A
1
2
3
4
5
6
VIEW A

1 HEATER CORE/HOUSING
2 CORE HOUSING TO DUCT GASKET
3 HEATER CORE TO BLOWER EVAP. MODULE GASKET (BULKHEAD)
4 SEAL
5 TEMPERATURE DOOR MOTOR
6 INSIDE TEMPERATURE SENSOR ASPIRATOR ASSEMBLY

GC7029100057000X

Fig. 25 Heater core housing

inner bracket fasteners.

20. Remove bolts mounting passenger knee bolster inner bracket to lower instrument panel support.
21. Remove bolts mounting passenger knee bolster inner bracket to bulkhead, then remove passenger knee bolster inner bracket.
22. Remove passenger knee bolster outer bracket as follows:
    a. Remove bolts mounting outer bracket to lower windshield frame assembly.
    b. Remove bolts mounting outer bracket to pillar assembly, then the outer bracket.
23. Remove side window defroster duct mounting clip, then duct hose from knee bolster brace.
24. Pull carrier back and remove passenger knee bolster brace.
25. Disconnect radio receiver electrical connectors.
26. Remove multi use relay bracket and disconnect cruise control module electrical connectors.
27. Remove screws attaching side window defroster duct to rear of heater case.
28. Remove fuse block from carrier, then disconnect vacuum hose from actuator.
29. Remove vacuum line retainer tape on heater, then the harness from retainer clip on bottom of rear heater case.
30. Remove side window defroster center duct extension (in heater case).
31. Remove rear heater case attaching screw, then the rear heater case half, **Fig. 25.**
32. Remove height fill reservoir, then heater hose from heater core.
33. Remove heater core from case.
34. Reverse procedure to install.

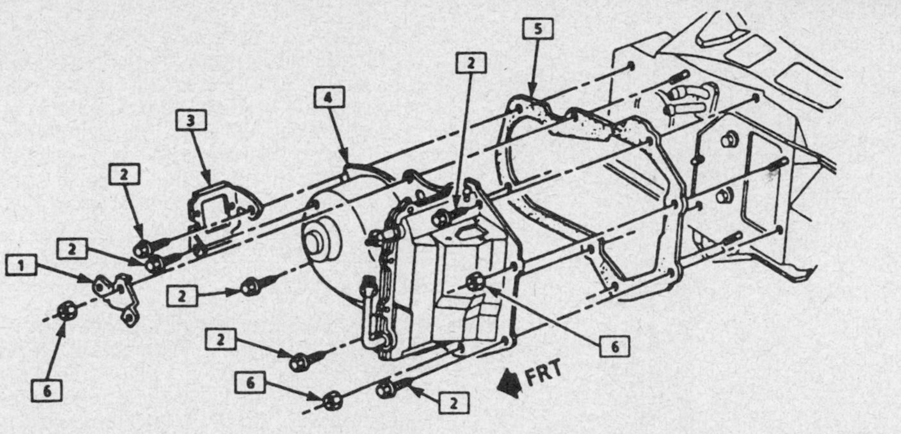
5
2
4
3
2
2
1
2
2
6
6
6
2
FRT

1	AIR CONDITIONING WIRING HARNESS BRACKET	4	AIR CONDITIONING EVAPORATOR AND BLOWER MOTOR MODULE
2	BLOWER MOTOR AND EVAPORATOR MODULE BOLT	5	AIR CONDITIONING EVAPORATOR AND BLOWER MOTOR MODULE GASKET
3	ELECTRONIC SPARK CONTROL BRACKET	6	BLOWER MOTOR AND EVAPORATOR MODULE NUT

GC7029100058000X

Fig. 27 Evaporator core housing

EVAPORATOR CORE

REPLACE

1. Disconnect battery ground cable.
2. Discharge A/C refrigerant system
3. Drain cooling system.
4. Remove front wheel house rear panel and seal.
5. Disconnect electrical connectors from blower motor.
6. Disconnect evaporator outlet hose.
7. Remove pressure cycling switch.
8. Disconnect heater hoses and evaporator inlet hose, then expansion tube.
9. Disconnect vapor pipe bracket from evaporator case.
10. Remove attaching bolt from upper righthand fender apron.
11. Remove nuts and bolts attaching evaporator core and blower housing to dash panel, **Fig. 27.**
12. Remove evaporator housing from vehicle, then separate housing and remove evaporator core.
13. Reverse procedure to install.

5.7L/V8-350 Single Cam 16 Valve Engine (VIN P)

INDEX

PRECAUTIONS

FUEL SYSTEM PRESSURE RELIEF

Failure to relieve system pressure prior to disconnecting fuel system components may cause fire or personal injury. Remove fuel tank filler cap to release fuel tank pressure. Connect pressure gauge J-34730-1 or equivalent to pressure tap on fuel rail, position bleed hose into suitable container and slowly relieve fuel system pressure. Prior to disconnecting fuel line, position shop towel over fitting.

ENGINE MOUNT

REPLACE

Check engine mounts for damage to rubber components or mounting stud and fluid loss, and replace as necessary.

1. Disconnect battery ground cable.
2. Raise and support vehicle.
3. Remove engine mount nuts (128), **Fig. 1,** at each side.
4. Disconnect catalytic converters from exhaust manifolds. Position catalytic converter out of way.
5. Using a suitable engine lifting device, raise engine just enough so that mount studs clear crossmember.
6. Remove engine mount through bolt.
7. Remove engine mount, heat shield and spacers, if equipped.
8. Remove engine bracket attaching bolts, then remove bracket.
9. Reverse procedure to install.

ENGINE

REPLACE

1. Disconnect battery ground cable, then drain cooling system.
2. Remove air intake duct, then disconnect electrical connectors and vacu-

um lines from upper part of engine.

3. Disconnect upper radiator hose at water pump and throttle body coolant hose at radiator tee.
4. Disconnect lower radiator hose and heater hose from water pump.
5. Disconnect coolant hose from righthand side of throttle body.
6. Disconnect pressure hose from power steering pump.
7. Remove alternator upper brace.
8. Remove center panel from lefthand wheelwell.
9. Remove serpentine drive belt.
10. Remove A/C compressor from mounting bracket and position aside with refrigerant lines attached.
11. Disconnect electrical connector from windshield wiper motor, then remove cover.
12. Disconnect hose from AIR diverter valve.
13. Relieve fuel system pressure as described under "Precautions," then disconnect and cap fuel lines at fuel rail.
14. Disconnect hose from power steering reservoir.
15. Disconnect accelerator, cruise control, throttle valve and traction control cables.
16. Raise and support vehicle, then disconnect wiring from starter motor.
17. Disconnect catalytic converters from exhaust manifolds.
18. **On models with manual transmission,** remove transmission as described under "Transmission Replace," in "Clutch & Transmission" section.
19. **On models with automatic transmission,** driveplate to converter attaching bolts.
20. **On models with manual transmission,** remove pressure plate and clutch disk, then the flywheel.
21. **On all models,** disconnect ground leads at rear of engine.
22. Disconnect electrical connectors from coolant temperature sensor, oil pressure sender, oil level indicator and knock sensor.
23. Remove nuts from engine mount studs, then lower vehicle.
24. Install suitable engine lifting device.
25. Ensure all components that would interfere with engine removal are detached, then lift engine from vehicle.
26. Reverse procedure to install.

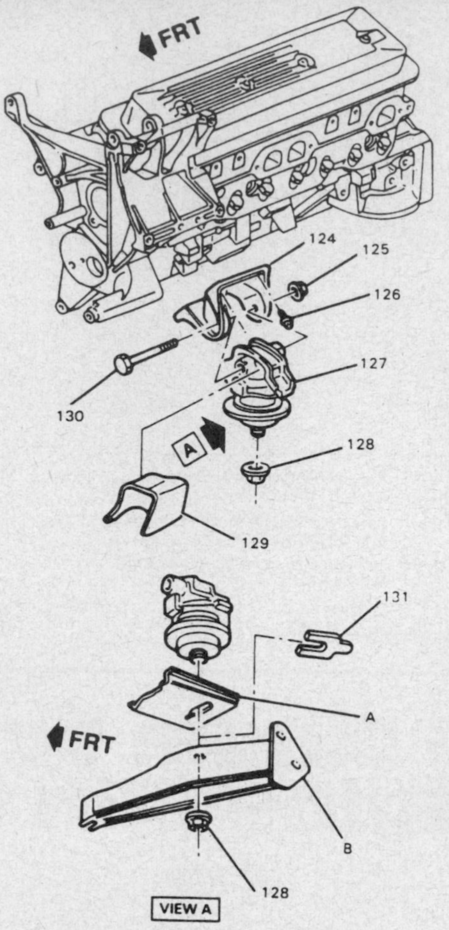
FRT
124
125
126
127
128
129
130
131
A
B
FRT
128
VIEW A

A DRIVETRAIN AND FRONT SUSPENSION FRAME
B FRONT SIDE MEMBER
124 BRACKET
125 NUT
126 BOLT
127 MOUNT
128 NUT
129 HEAT SHIELD
130 THROUGH-BOLT
131 SPACER

GC1069100235000X

Fig. 1 Engine mount replacement

INTAKE MANIFOLD
REPLACE

1. Disconnect battery ground cable, then drain cooling system.
2. Remove throttle body air duct, then disconnect electrical connectors from fuel injectors.
3. Disconnect left and righthand wiring harness and position aside.
4. Remove accelerator cable bracket and disconnect cable from throttle body.
5. Disconnect hoses from AIR diverter valve.
6. Disconnect ground strap from intake manifold.
7. Remove retaining bolts from fuel rail.
8. Disconnect vacuum hose from fuel pressure regulator.
9. Relieve fuel system pressure as described under "Precautions," then disconnect and cap fuel lines at fuel rail.
10. Remove fuel injectors and fuel rail from intake manifold and position aside, **Fig. 2.**
11. Disconnect vacuum and PCV hoses from intake manifold.
12. Remove EGR solenoid bracket and fuel vapor canister purge solenoid bracket.
13. Remove EGR valve.
14. Disconnect air pipe from intake manifold and righthand exhaust manifold.
15. Remove alternator brace.
16. Disconnect coolant hoses from throttle body.
17. Remove throttle body to intake manifold mounting bolts, then remove throttle body and gasket, **Fig. 2.**
18. Remove intake manifold to engine block attaching bolts and studs, then remove intake manifold and gasket, **Fig. 3.**
19. Reverse procedure to install. Prior to installation, apply a 3/16 inch bead of sealer 1052366 or equivalent to front and rear of engine block. Extend bead of sealer 1/2 inch up each cylinder head to seal and retain gaskets. Install manifold and tighten bolts to specifications in sequence shown in **Fig. 4.**

EXHAUST MANIFOLD
REPLACE

The following service procedure has been revised by a "Technical Service Bulletin".

On 1992 models equipped with 5.7L/V8-350 (VIN P) engines, exhaust manifold to heat shield bolts may back out causing an exhaust leak. The ticking sound produced is similar in nature to a piston type noise.

Ensure tightening toque on the three exhaust manifold heat shield bolts is 72-108 inch lbs.

LEFT SIDE

1. Disconnect battery ground cable.
2. Raise and support vehicle, then disconnect catalytic converter from exhaust manifold.
3. Lower vehicle, then remove air intake duct.
4. Remove serpentine drive belt.
5. Remove center panel front lefthand wheelwell.
6. Remove alternator and A/C compressor upper brace.
7. Remove A/C compressor and position aside with refrigerant hoses attached.
8. Disconnect air pipe, check valve and hose as an assembly from exhaust manifold.
9. Disconnect spark plug wires from spark plugs and wire clips from supports.
10. Remove accessory and A/C compressor bracket braces.
11. Remove spark plug wire supports, then remove spark plugs from cylinder head.
12. Remove exhaust manifold attaching bolts and studs, **Fig. 5.**
13. Remove heat shields, exhaust manifold and gasket.
14. Reverse procedure to install. Check **torque**on the three exhaust manifold heat shield bolts, 72-108 inch lbs.

RIGHT SIDE

1. Disconnect battery ground cable.
2. Raise and support vehicle, then disconnect catalytic converter from exhaust manifold.
3. Lower vehicle, then disconnect electrical connectors from fuel injectors.
4. Disconnect vacuum hose from fuel pressure regulator.
5. Relieve fuel system pressure as described under "Precautions," then disconnect and cap fuel lines at fuel rail.
6. Remove fuel rail to intake manifold attaching bolts, then remove fuel injectors and rail.
7. Remove spark plug wires from spark

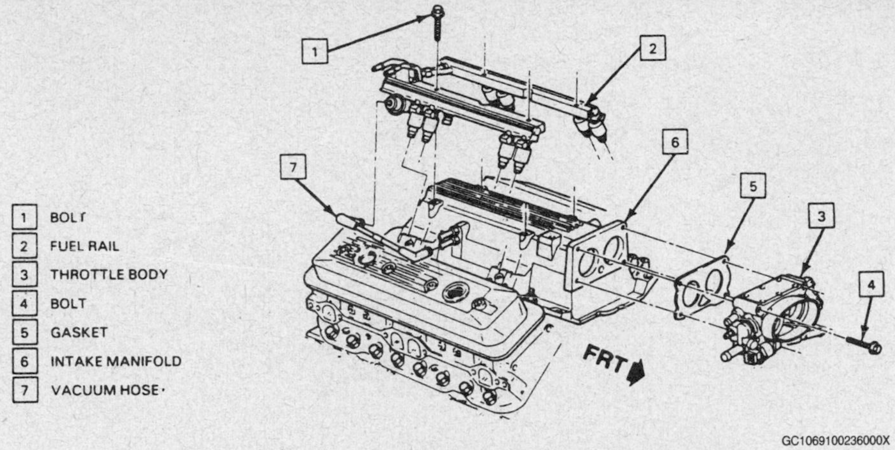
1 BOLT
2 FUEL RAIL
3 THROTTLE BODY
4 BOLT
5 GASKET
6 INTAKE MANIFOLD
7 VACUUM HOSE
FRT
GC1069100236000X

Fig. 2 Fuel rail & throttle body replacement

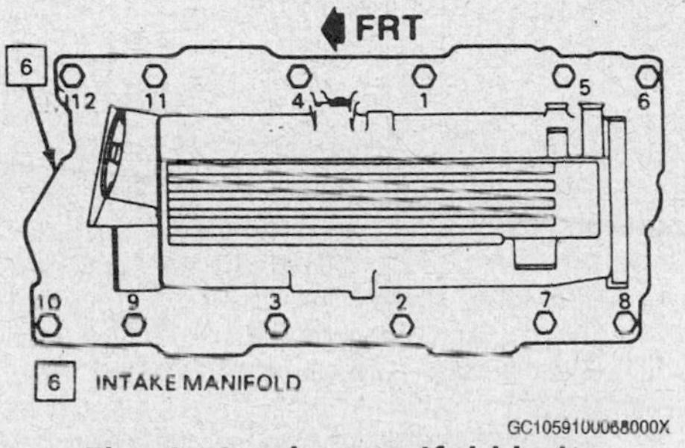
FRT
6
12
11
4
1
5
6
10
9
3
2
7
8
6 INTAKE MANIFOLD
GC1059100068000X

Fig. 4 Intake manifold bolt tightening sequence

plugs and wire clips from supports.

8. Remove spark plugs from cylinder head, then remove front spark plug wire bracket and bolt.
9. Remove oil level dipstick and tube.
10. Disconnect air pipe, gasket and check valve as an assembly from intake and exhaust manifolds and cylinder head.
11. Remove exhaust manifold attaching bolts and studs, **Fig. 5.**
12. Remove heat shields, exhaust manifold and gasket.
13. Reverse procedure to install. Prior to installing oil level dipstick and tube, apply sealer 1052080 or equivalent around tube approximately 1/2 inch below bead. Check **torque** on the three exhaust manifold heat shield bolts, 72-108 inch lbs.

CYLINDER HEAD
REPLACE

LEFT SIDE

1. Disconnect battery ground cable.
2. Raise and support vehicle, then disconnect catalytic converter from exhaust manifold.
3. Drain cooling system, then lower vehicle.
4. Disconnect upper radiator hose, then remove serpentine drive belt.
5. Remove intake manifold as described under "Intake Manifold, Replace."
6. Remove center panel from lefthand wheelwell.
7. Remove A/C compressor and position aside with refrigerant hoses attached.

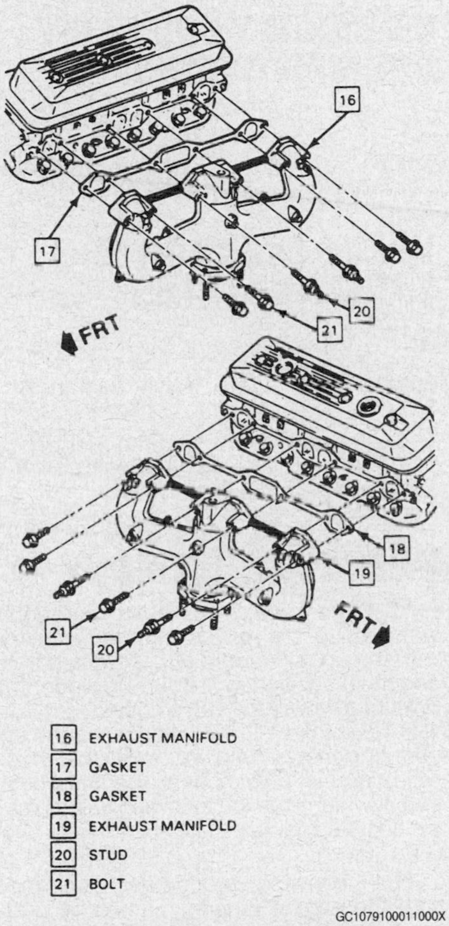
16
17
20
21
FRT
18
19
21
20
FRT
16 EXHAUST MANIFOLD
17 GASKET
18 GASKET
19 EXHAUST MANIFOLD
20 STUD
21 BOLT
GC1079100011000X

Fig. 5 Exhaust manifold replacement

8. Remove alternator and A/C compressor brace.
9. Remove spark plug wire bracket, then disconnect spark plug wires from spark plugs.
10. Remove spark plugs from cylinder head.
11. Remove lefthand exhaust manifold as describe under "Exhaust Manifold, Replace."
12. Remove alternator and brace.
13. Disconnect AIR diverter valve hose.
14. Remove valve cover, then remove drive belt tensioner and idler pulley.

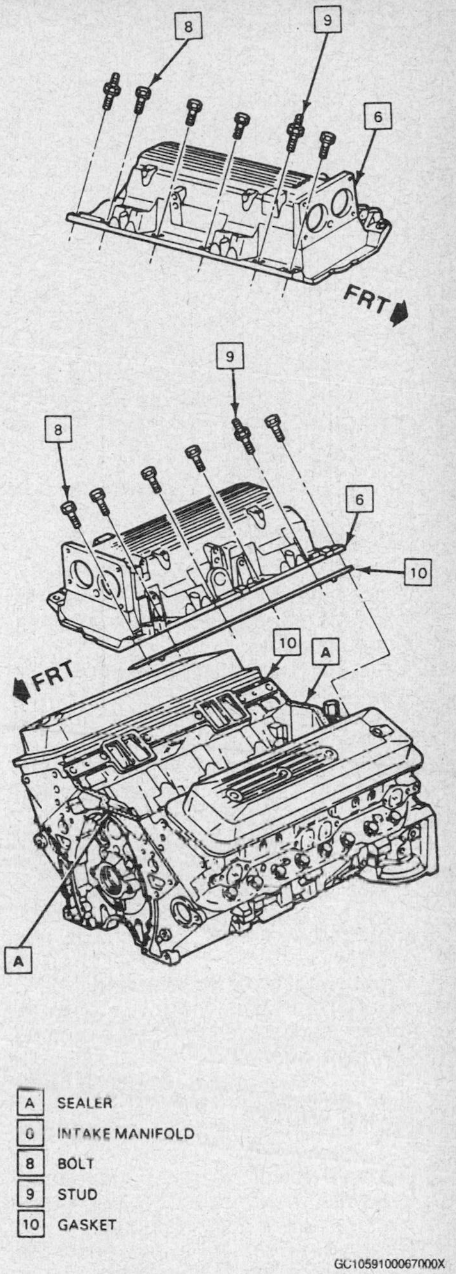
8
9
6
FRT
9
8
6
10
10
A
FRT
A
A SEALER
6 INTAKE MANIFOLD
8 BOLT
9 STUD
10 GASKET
GC1059100067000X

Fig. 3 Intake manifold replacement

15. Remove power steering pump attaching bolts, then disconnect hoses and remove power steering pump.
16. Disconnect spark plug wires and coil wire at distributor.
17. Remove accessory mounting bracket.
18. Remove rocker arms and pushrods. Tag rocker arms and pushrods so they can be installed in the same positions.
19. Remove cylinder head attaching bolts, then remove cylinder head and gasket.
20. Reverse procedure to install. When installing cylinder head gasket, position over dowel pins with bead facing upward. Prior to installing cylinder head bolts, coat threads with sealer 1052080 or equivalent. Tighten cylinder head bolts in sequence shown in **Fig. 6**, to specifications.

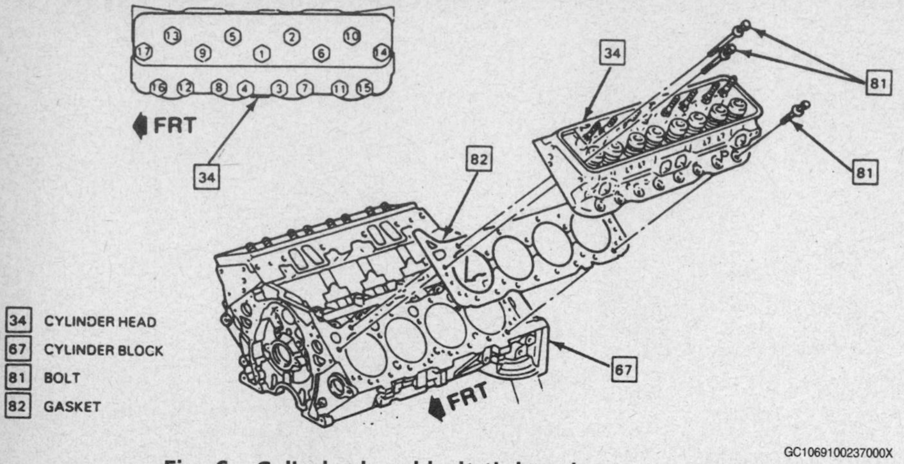
34
81
82
81
34
FRT
34 CYLINDER HEAD
67 CYLINDER BLOCK
81 BOLT
82 GASKET
67
FRT
GC1069100237000X

Fig. 6 Cylinder head bolt tightening sequence

RIGHT SIDE

1. Disconnect battery ground cable.
2. Raise and support vehicle, then disconnect catalytic converter from exhaust manifold.
3. Drain cooling system, then lower vehicle.
4. Disconnect lower radiator and heater hoses.
5. Remove power steering pump reservoir from cylinder head and position out of way.
6. Remove coil and bracket.
7. Remove intake manifold as described under "Intake Manifold, Replace."
8. Remove spark plug wires from clips, then remove front spark plug wire bracket.
9. Remove oil level dipstick and tube.
10. Disconnect spark plug wire, then remove spark plugs from cylinder head.
11. Remove righthand exhaust manifold as described under "Exhaust Manifold, Replace."
12. Remove cylinder head rear vent pipe and valve cover.
13. Remove power steering pump attaching bolts, then disconnect hoses and remove power steering pump.
14. Remove rocker arms and pushrods. Tag rocker arms and pushrods so they can be installed in the same positions.
15. Remove cylinder head attaching bolts, then remove cylinder head and gasket.
16. Reverse procedure to install. When installing cylinder head gasket, position over dowel pins with bead facing upward. Prior to installing cylinder head bolts, coat threads with sealer 1052080 or equivalent. Tighten cylinder head bolts in sequence shown in **Fig. 6**,to specifications.

VALVE ARRANGEMENT

FRONT TO REAR

All . . . . E-I-I-E-E-I-I-E

CAMSHAFT LOBE LIFT SPECIFICATIONS

Engine	Int.	Exh.
5.7L/V8-350	.300	.300

VALVE CLEARANCE SPECIFICATIONS

Engine/VIN	Valve Clearance
5.7L/V8-350 (P)	1 Turn①

①—Turn rocker arm stud nut until all lash is eliminated, then tighten nut the additional turn listed, plus or minus 1/4 turn.

VALVE ADJUSTMENT

After the engine has been thoroughly warmed up the valves may be adjusted with the engine turned off, as follows: with engine in position to fire No. 1 cylinder the following valves may be adjusted: Exhaust 1-3-4-8, intake 1-2-5-7. Then crank the engine one more complete revolution which will bring No. 6 cylinder to the firing position at which time the following valves may be adjusted: Exhaust 2-5-6-7, intake 3-4-6-8.

The following procedure, performed with the engine running, should be done only if readjustment is required.

1. After engine has been warmed up to operating temperature, remove valve cover and install a new valve cover gasket.
2. With engine running at idle speed, back off valve rocker arm nut until rocker arm starts to clatter.
3. Turn rocker arm nut down slowly until the clatter just stops. This is the zero lash position.
4. Turn nut down 1/4 additional turn and pause 10 seconds until engine runs smoothly. Repeat additional 1/4 turns, pausing 10 seconds each time, until nut has been turned down the number of turns listed in the Valve Adjustment Specifications Chart from the zero lash position. **This preload adjustment must be done slowly to allow the lifter to adjust itself to prevent the possibility of interference between the intake valve head and top of piston, which might result in internal damage and/or bent pushrods. Noisy lifters should be replaced.**

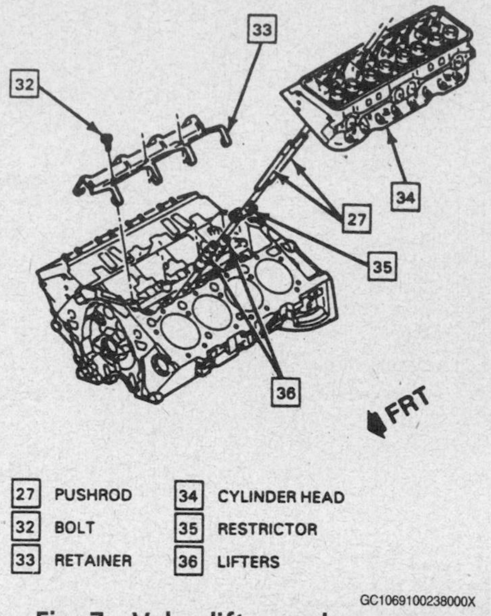
33
32
34
27
35
36
FRT
27 PUSHROD
32 BOLT
33 RETAINER
34 CYLINDER HEAD
35 RESTRICTOR
36 LIFTERS
GC1069100238000X

Fig. 7 Valve lifter replacement

ROCKER ARMS

Tag rocker arms and components during removal so they can be installed in the same positions. When replacing rocker arms or rocker arm balls, bearing surfaces of rocker arms and balls should be coated with prelube 1052365 or equivalent.

ROCKER ARM STUDS

Rocker arm studs with damaged threads should be replaced. Threads of replacement rocker arms studs should be coated with sealing compound 1052080 or equivalent prior to installation. Looseness can be corrected by installing the proper size Heli-Coil insert, or by replacing cylinder head.

PUSH RODS

Tag pushrods during remove so they can be installed in the same positions. When installing, ensure pushrod is seated in lifter sockets.

VALVE GUIDES

Valves operate in guide holes bored in the head. If clearance becomes excessive, use the next oversize valve and ream the bore to fit. Valves with oversize stems are available in .003, .015 and .030 inch.

HYDRAULIC LIFTERS

REPLACE

Valve lifters, **Fig. 7**, can be lifted from their bores after removing rocker arms, pushrods, intake manifold and valve lifter

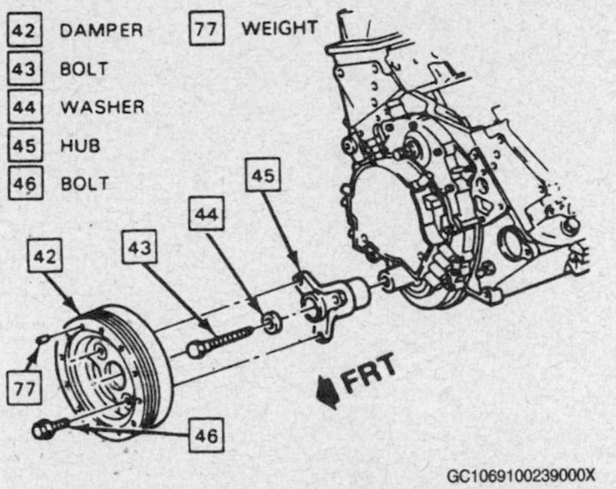
42 DAMPER
43 BOLT
44 WASHER
45 HUB
46 BOLT
77 WEIGHT
FRT
GC1069100239000X

Fig. 8 Crankshaft damper & hub replacement

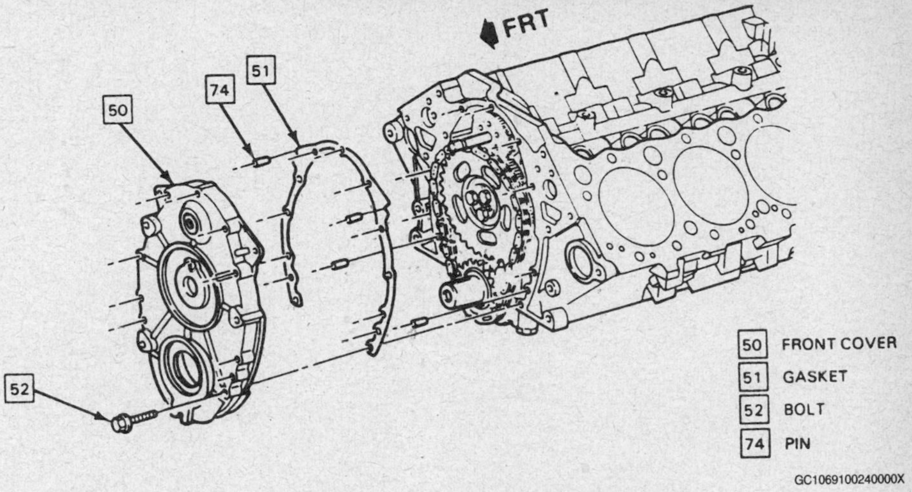
FRT
50 FRONT COVER
51 GASKET
52 BOLT
74 PIN
GC1069100240000X

Fig. 9 Engine front cover replacement

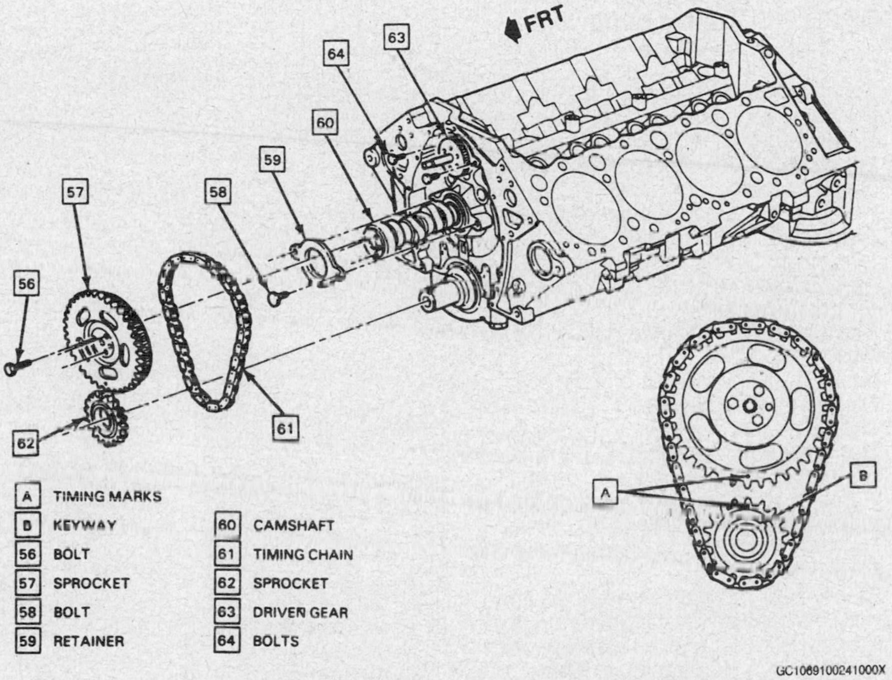
FRT
A TIMING MARKS
B KEYWAY
56 BOLT
57 SPROCKET
58 BOLT
59 RETAINER
60 CAMSHAFT
61 TIMING CHAIN
62 SPROCKET
63 DRIVEN GEAR
64 BOLTS
GC1069100241000X

Fig. 10 Camshaft, sprockets & timing chain

retainer. When removing, position valve lifters in rack so they may be installed at the same location. Adjustable pliers with protected jaws may be used to remove lifters which are stuck due to carbon or varnish deposits. When installing replacement valve lifters, coat roller with prelube 1052365 or equivalent.

CRANKSHAFT DAMPER & HUB

REPLACE

1. Disconnect battery ground cable.
2. Remove air intake duct, then remove serpentine drive belt.
3. Raise and support vehicle, then remove engine mount nuts.
4. Remove power steering fluid cooler.
5. Attach suitable engine lifting device, then raise engine slightly to provide tool access to damper attaching bolts.
6. Remove damper to hub attaching bolts, then remove damper, **Fig. 8.**
7. Disconnect power steering line from steering gear.
8. Place alignment marks on damper hub and front cover for use during installation. **After placing alignment marks on hub and front cover do not rotate crankshaft, as an engine imbalance may result.**
9. Remove crankshaft hub bolt and washer, then remove crankshaft hub using tool No. J39046 or equivalent.
10. Reverse procedure to install. If crankshaft was accidentally rotated after placing alignment marks, position No. 1 cylinder at top dead center, then install hub with arrow casting at 12 o'clock position. If a replacement damper is to be installed, balance weights of the same size as the original damper must be install in the same locations on the new damper.

FRONT COVER

REPLACE

1. Disconnect battery ground cable and drain cooling system.
2. Remove throttle body air duct.
3. Remove water pump as described under "Water Pump, Replace."
4. Remove crankshaft damper and hub as described under "Crankshaft Damper and Hub, Replace."
5. Remove ignition distributor as described under "Distributor, Replace" in the "Electrical" section.
6. Remove oil pan as described under "Oil Pan, Replace."
7. Remove front cover retaining screws and the front cover, **Fig. 9.**
8. Reverse procedure to install.

FRONT COVER SEAL

REPLACE

1. Remove front cover as described under "Front Cover, Replace."
2. Remove oil seal for crankshaft, water pump shaft and distributor shaft as necessary.
3. Properly support front cover in seal area.
4. Using tool No. J-35468 or equivalent, install crankshaft oil seal.
5. Using tool No. J-39090 or equivalent, install distributor shaft oil seal.
6. Using tool No. J-39088 or equivalent, install water pump oil seal.
7. Install engine front cover.

TIMING CHAIN

REPLACE

1. Remove front cover as outlined previously.
2. Remove crankshaft oil slinger.
3. Rotate engine until timing marks on sprockets are in alignment, **Fig. 10.**

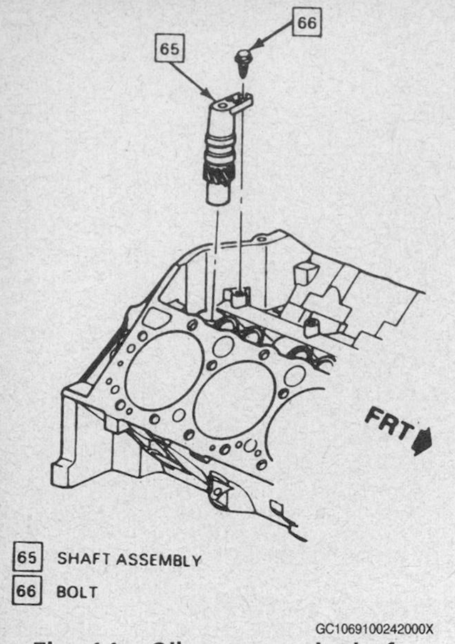
65
66
FRT
65 SHAFT ASSEMBLY
66 BOLT
GC1069100242000X

Fig. 11 Oil pump stub shaft location

4. Remove camshaft to sprocket bolts, **Fig. 10.**
5. Remove camshaft sprocket and timing chain together. Do not rotate crankshaft after timing chain has been removed.
6. If crankshaft sprocket is to be replaced, remove it with a suitable gear puller. Install new sprocket, aligning key and keyway.
7. If water pump driven gear is to be replaced, remove mounting bolts, then remove gear using a suitable gear puller. Install new gear using tool No. J3092 or equivalent, then install mounting bolts.
8. Install chain on camshaft sprocket. Hold sprocket vertical with chain hanging below and shift around to align the timing marks on sprockets. Align dowel in camshaft with dowel hole in sprocket and install sprocket on camshaft. **When installing camshaft sprocket onto camshaft, ensure teeth camshaft sprocket and water pump driven gear mesh. Do not attempt to drive sprocket on camshaft as welch plug at rear of engine can be dislodged.**
9. Using tool No. J39089, install water pump driven gear O-ring.
10. Lubricate timing chain with engine oil, then install front cover.

CAMSHAFT

REPLACE

1. Disconnect battery ground cable, then remove surge tank cap and drain cooling system.
2. Remove engine front cover as described under "Front Cover, Replace."
3. Remove intake manifold as described under "Intake Manifold, Replace."
4. Remove oil pump stub shaft retaining bolt, then remove stub shaft, **Fig. 11.**
5. Remove valve covers, rocker arms and pushrods. Tag rocker arms and

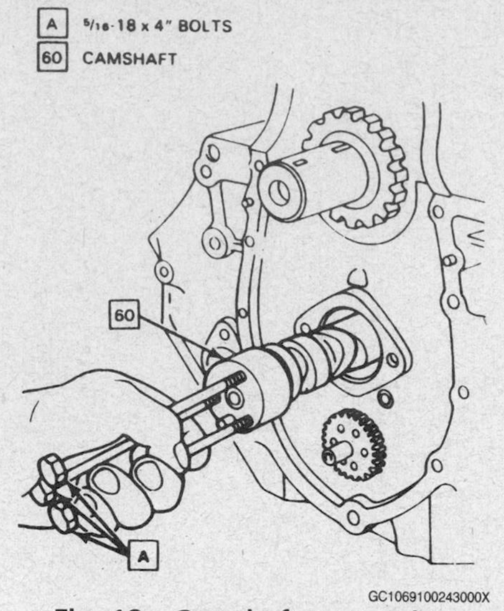
A 5/16-18 x 4" BOLTS
60 CAMSHAFT
60
A
GC1069100243000X

Fig. 12 Camshaft removal & installation

pushrods so they can be installed in the same locations.

6. Remove camshaft sprocket and timing chain as described under "Timing Chain, Replace."
7. Remove air cleaner assembly, then disconnect reservoir hose from radiator.
8. From lefthand side of radiator support, remove relay bracket.
9. Remove AIR pump inlet duct, then remove AIR pump mounting bolts and position AIR pump out of way.
10. Disconnect electrical connectors from engine cooling fans.
11. Remove bolt retaining accumulator bracket to upper radiator support.
12. Remove fan shroud to radiator upper support attaching screws.
13. Remove access plug from upper part of radiator.
14. Disconnect radiator bleed hose, then remove bolts and nuts retaining upper radiator support to front side member.
15. Remove screws attaching upper radiator support to lower support, then remove upper radiator support.
16. Disconnect hoses from radiator.
17. **On models with automatic transmission,** disconnect transmission fluid cooler lines from radiator.
18. **On all models,** remove radiator from vehicle.
19. Raise and support vehicle, then remove lower fan shroud attaching bolts.
20. Lower vehicle, then remove fan shroud and fans.
21. Detach A/C condenser line bracket from front crossmember.
22. Remove engine mount stud nuts, then using a suitable engine lifting fixture, raise front of engine slightly to provide clearance for camshaft removal.
23. Remove camshaft retainer bolts and retainer, **Fig. 10.**
24. Install three 5/16 18 x 4 inch bolts into camshaft bolt holes, **Fig. 12.**
25. Carefully rotate and pull camshaft from engine. Use care when removing

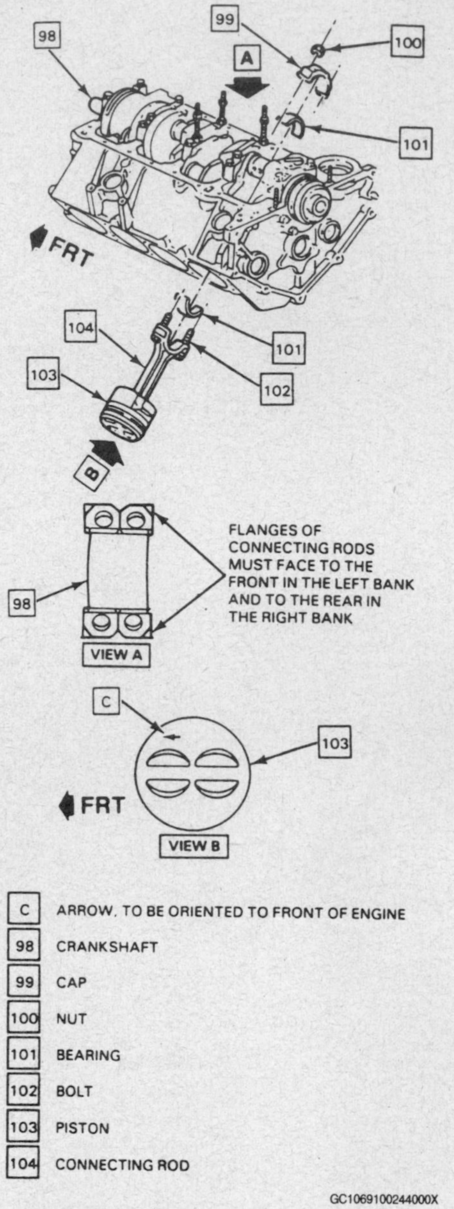
98
99
A
100
101
FRT
104
101
103
102
B
FLANGES OF CONNECTING RODS MUST FACE TO THE FRONT IN THE LEFT BANK AND TO THE REAR IN THE RIGHT BANK
98
VIEW A
C
103
FRT
VIEW B
C ARROW, TO BE ORIENTED TO FRONT OF ENGINE
98 CRANKSHAFT
99 CAP
100 NUT
101 BEARING
102 BOLT
103 PISTON
104 CONNECTING ROD
GC1069100244000X

Fig. 13 Piston & rod assembly

camshaft to prevent damage to camshaft bearings.

26. Reverse procedure to install. Prior to installation, coat camshaft and bearings with engine oil. If installing a new camshaft, coat lobes with Molykote or equivalent and replace roller lifters.

PISTON & ROD ASSEMBLY

Assemble pistons to connecting rods as shown in **Fig. 13.**

Upon installation, measure the connecting rod side clearance using a suitable feeler gauge. Refer to "Engine Rebuilding Specifications" section for connecting rod side clearance.

PISTONS, PINS & RINGS

Pistons are available in standard and oversizes of .010 and .030 inch.

Piston rings are available in standard and oversizes of .030 inch.

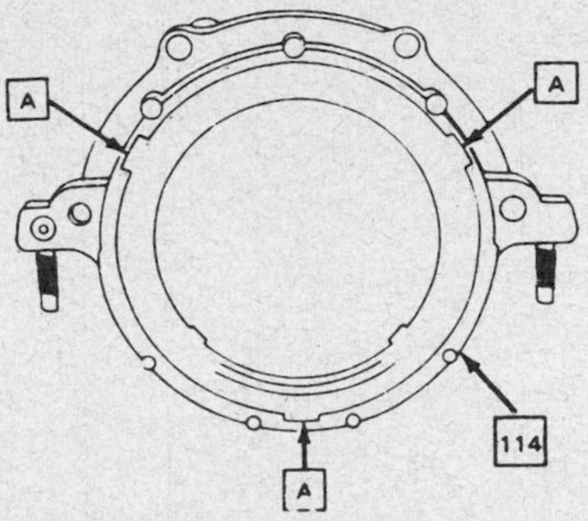
A
A
114
A

A SEAL REMOVAL NOTCHES

114 REAR CRANKSHAFT SEAL RETAINER

GC1069100245000X

Fig. 14 Crankshaft rear oil seal removal

MAIN & ROD BEARINGS

Connecting rod bearings are available in standard and undersizes of .001, .002, .010 and .020 inch.

Main bearings are available in standard and undersizes of .001, .002, .009, .010 and .020 inch.

CRANKSHAFT REAR OIL SEAL

REPLACE

This engine is equipped with a one-piece, lip type seal mounted in a separate seal retainer. Seal replacement requires removal of the transmission.

1. Raise and support vehicle, then remove transmission, clutch assembly and flywheel, as equipped.
2. Pry seal from retainer, inserting screwdriver in notches provided in seal retainer, **Fig. 14.**
3. Lubricate replacement seal with engine oil, then mount seal on tool J-35621 or equivalent, **Fig. 15.**
4. Mount tool on rear of crankshaft, tightening screws snugly to ensure seal will be installed squarely on crankshaft.
5. Tighten wing nut on tool until it bottoms, then remove tool from crankshaft.
6. Reverse remaining procedure to complete installation.

OIL PAN

REPLACE

1. Disconnect battery ground cable.
2. Raise and support vehicle, then drain crankcase.
3. Disconnect oil level sensor electrical connector, then remove oil level sensor, **Fig. 16.**
4. Remove oil filter.
5. Remove starter motor, then remove flywheel cover.
6. Disconnect catalytic converters at exhaust manifolds.
7. Remove nuts from engine mount studs.
8. Remove oil pan attaching bolts, nuts and studs, then the oil pan.

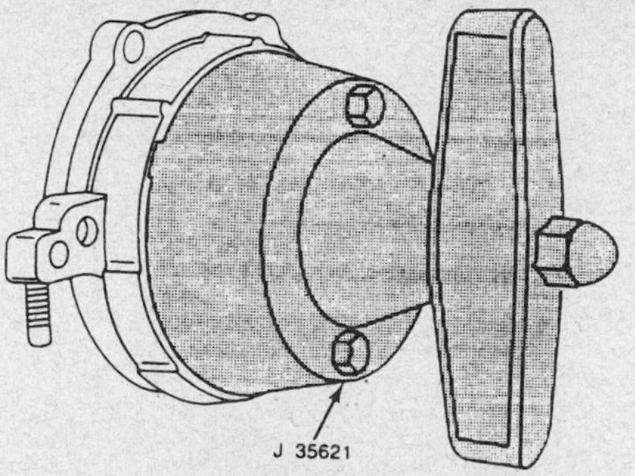
J 35621

GC1069100246000X

Fig. 15 Crankshaft rear oil seal installation

9. Reverse procedure to install. Prior to installation apply a small amount of sealer 1052914 or equivalent to front cover to engine mating surface and rear seal retainer to engine mating surface. Apply sealer 1 inch in each direction of the radius cavity of these mating surfaces. Tighten oil pan retaining bolts to specifications.

OIL PUMP

REPLACE

1. Remove oil pan as described previously.
2. Remove oil pan baffle nuts.
3. Remove pump to rear main bearing cap bolt and remove oil pan baffle, pump intermediate shaft and retainer, **Fig. 17.**
4. Reverse procedure to install. Prime oil pump with clean engine oil prior to installation.

OIL PUMP SERVICE

1. Remove oil pump as described previously.
2. Remove pump cover screws and pump cover, **Fig. 18.**
3. Mark gear teeth so they can be reassembled with same teeth indexing, then remove drive gear, idler gear and shaft.
4. Remove pressure regulator valve retaining pin, pressure regulator valve and related parts.
5. If pickup screen and pipe require replacement, mount pump in a soft-jawed vise and extract pipe from pump.
6. Wash all parts in cleaning solvent and dry with compressed air.
7. Inspect pump body and cover for cracks and excessive wear.
8. Inspect pump gears for damage or excessive wear.
9. Check drive gear shaft for looseness in pump body.
10. Inspect inside of pump cover for wear that would allow oil to leak past the ends of the gears.
11. Inspect pickup screen and pipe assembly for damage to screen, pipe or relief grommet.
12. Check pressure regulator valve for fit in pump housing.

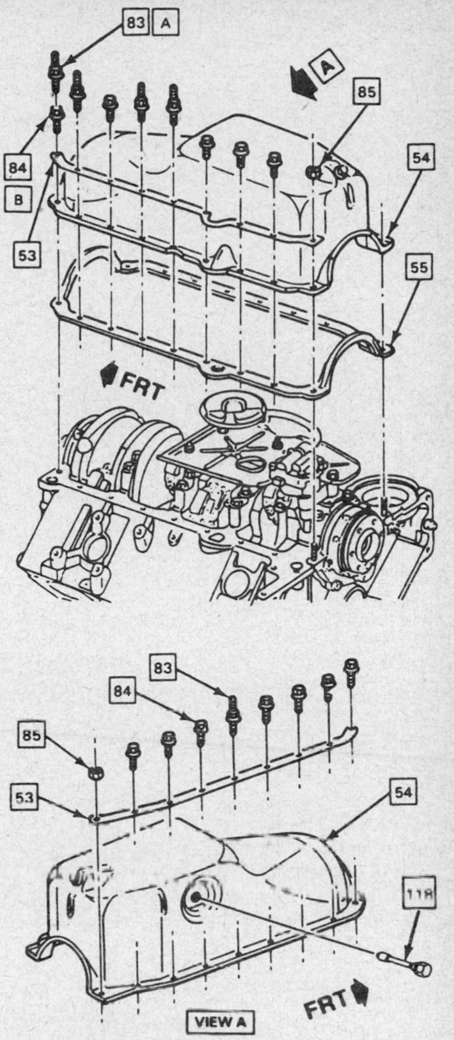
83
A
A
85
84
B
54
53
55
FRT
83
84
85
53
54
118
VIEW A
FRT

A	AUTO TRANSMISSION	83	STUD
B	MANUAL TRANSMISSION	84	BOLT
53	REINFORCEMENT	85	NUT
54	OIL PAN	118	OIL LEVEL SENSOR
55	GASKET		

GC1069100247000X

Fig. 16 Oil pan installation

13. Reverse procedure to assemble. Turn driveshaft by hand to check for smooth operation. **The pump gears and body are not serviced separately. If the pump gears or body are damaged or worn, the pump assembly should be replaced. Also, if the pick-up screen and pump assembly was removed, it should be replaced with a new one as loss of the press fit condition could result in an air leak and loss of oil pressure.**

BELT TENSION DATA

Engine (VIN)	New Lbs.①	Used Lbs.
5.7L/V8-350 (P)	①	①

①—**Indicator located on tensioner housing.**

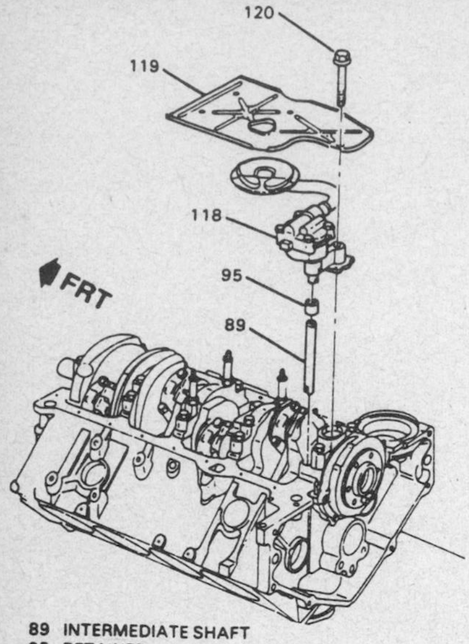

120
119
118
95
89
FRT

89 INTERMEDIATE SHAFT
95 RETAINER
118 OIL PUMP
119 BAFFLE
120 BOLT

GC1099100028000X

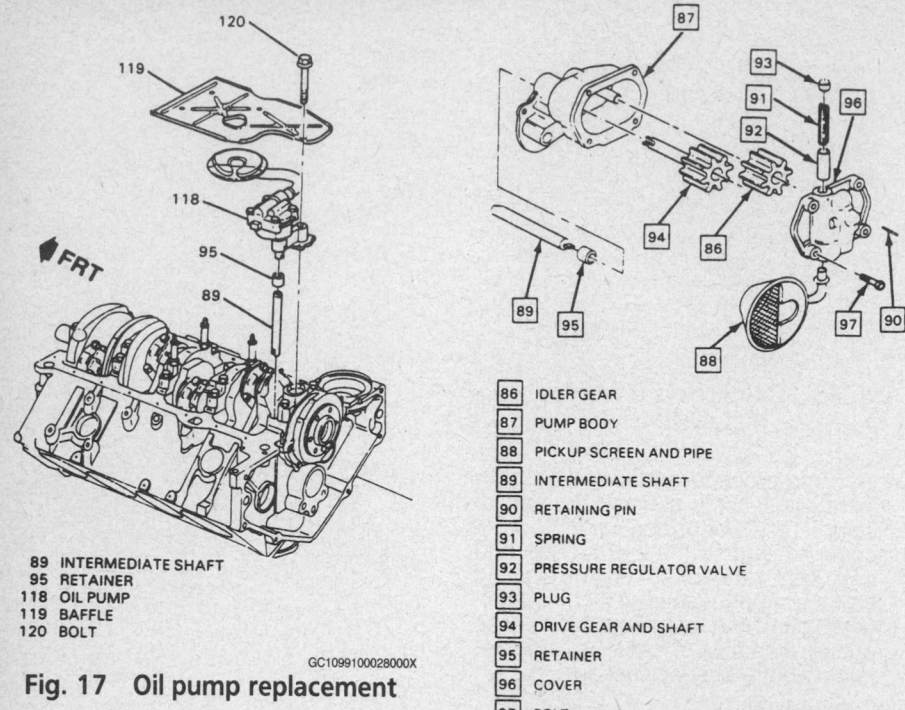

Fig. 17 Oil pump replacement

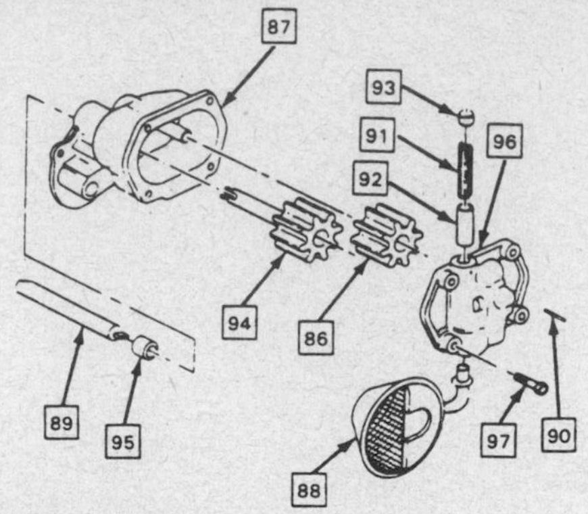

87
93
91
96
92
94
86
89
95
97
90
88

86 IDLER GEAR
87 PUMP BODY
88 PICKUP SCREEN AND PIPE
89 INTERMEDIATE SHAFT
90 RETAINING PIN
91 SPRING
92 PRESSURE REGULATOR VALVE
93 PLUG
94 DRIVE GEAR AND SHAFT
95 RETAINER
96 COVER
97 BOLT

GC1099100029000X

Fig. 18 Exploded view of oil pump

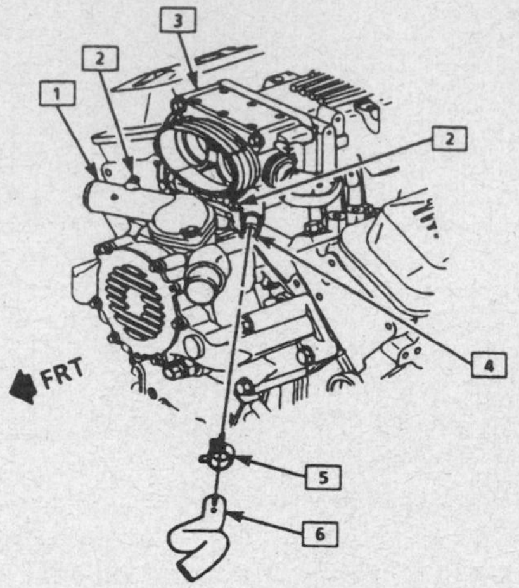

3
2
1
2
FRT
4
5
6

1 THERMOSTAT HOUSING
2 AIR BLEED VALVE
3 THROTTLE BODY ASSEMBLY
4 THROTTLE BODY NIPPLE
5 CLAMP - THROTTLE BODY
6 THROTTLE BODY HOSE

GC1089100134000X

Fig. 20 Cooling system bleed valve locations

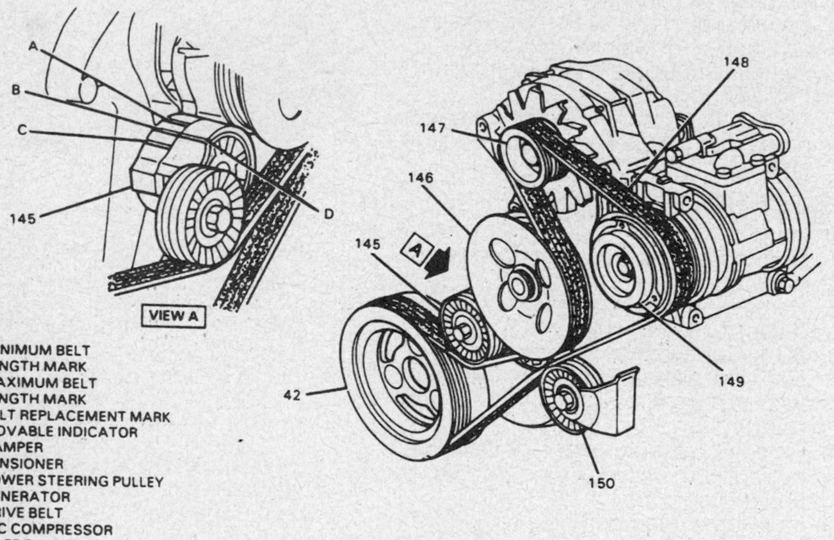

A
B
C
D
145
VIEW A
148
147
146
145
A
42
149
150

A MINIMUM BELT LENGTH MARK
B MAXIMUM BELT LENGTH MARK
C BELT REPLACEMENT MARK
D MOVABLE INDICATOR
42 DAMPER
145 TENSIONER
146 POWER STEERING PULLEY
147 GENERATOR
148 DRIVE BELT
149 A/C COMPRESSOR
150 IDLER PULLEY

GC1069100248000X

Fig. 19 Serpentine drive belt replacement

SERPENTINE DRIVE BELT

1. Using a suitable socket and handle on tensioner pulley bolt, lift tensioner upward in the clockwise direction, then remove serpentine drive belt, **Fig. 19.**
2. Reverse procedure to install. Ensure belt tension indicator marks are within limit lines on belt tensioner indicator.

COOLING SYSTEM BLEED

Open bleed valves, **Fig. 20,** on thermostat housing and throttle body prior to adding coolant. Add coolant through radiator surge tank opening until level is at base of tank neck. Close each bleed valve as solid flow of coolant is emitted from valve. Start engine and operate with surge tank cap removed until engine coolant level is maintained at base of surge tank neck. Add coolant as necessary, then install surge tank cap with arrows facing overflow tube. Fill coolant recovery reservoir to proper level. Start engine and allow reach operating temperature. Turn engine off and allow to cool, then recheck coolant level.

THERMOSTAT

REPLACE

1. Disconnect battery ground cable.
2. Disconnect intake air temperature sensor electrical connector.
3. Remove air cleaner and intake duct assembly.
4. Remove pressure cap from surge tank, then drain cooling system.
5. Disconnect lower radiator hose from thermostat housing on water pump.
6. Remove thermostat housing attaching bolts, then remove housing, **Fig. 21.**
7. Remove thermostat and seal.
8. Reverse procedure to install. When installing thermostat seal, position seal with taper facing upward. Bleed cooling system as described under "Cooling System Bleed."

WATER PUMP

REPLACE

1. Disconnect battery ground cable.
2. Disconnect intake air temperature sensor electrical connector.
3. Remove air cleaner and duct assembly.
4. Remove radiator surge tank cap, then drain cooling system and remove knock sensor.

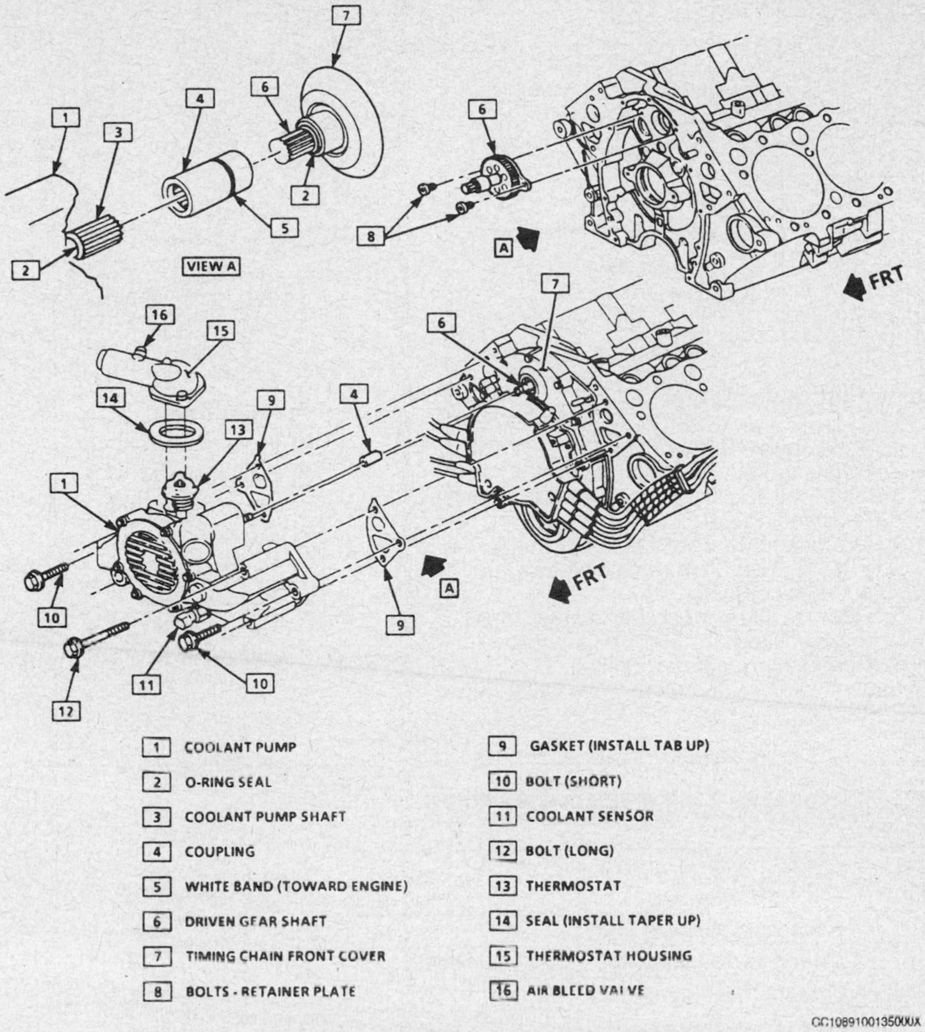
VIEW A
FRT
1 COOLANT PUMP
2 O-RING SEAL
3 COOLANT PUMP SHAFT
4 COUPLING
5 WHITE BAND (TOWARD ENGINE)
6 DRIVEN GEAR SHAFT
7 TIMING CHAIN FRONT COVER
8 BOLTS - RETAINER PLATE
9 GASKET (INSTALL TAB UP)
10 BOLT (SHORT)
11 COOLANT SENSOR
12 BOLT (LONG)
13 THERMOSTAT
14 SEAL (INSTALL TAPER UP)
15 THERMOSTAT HOUSING
16 AIR BLEED VALVE
GC1089100135000X

Fig. 21 Water pump & thermostat replacement

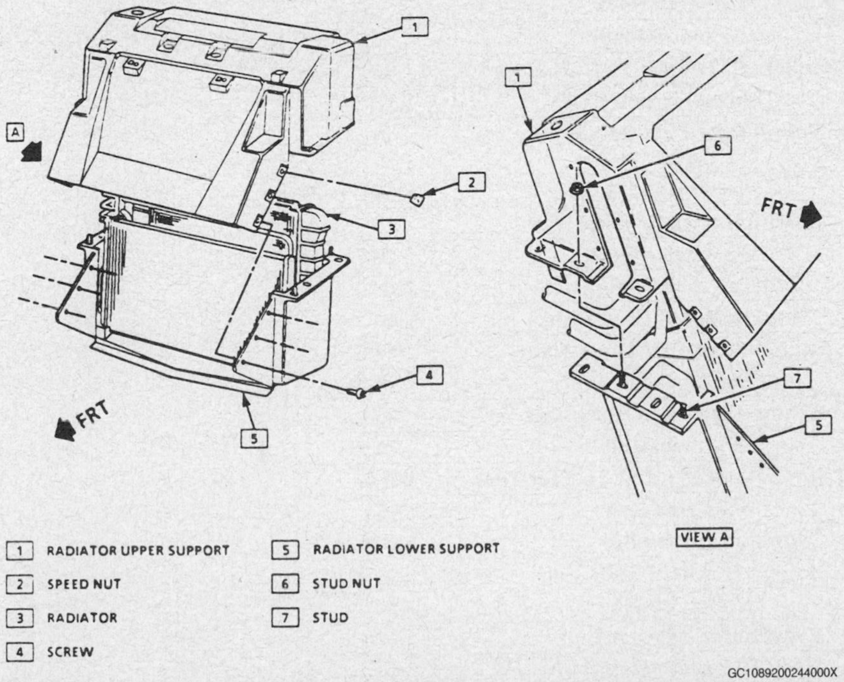
FRT
VIEW A
1 RADIATOR UPPER SUPPORT
2 SPEED NUT
3 RADIATOR
4 SCREW
5 RADIATOR LOWER SUPPORT
6 STUD NUT
7 STUD
GC1089200244000X

Fig. 22 Radiator upper support removal

5. Disconnect upper and lower radiator hose, heater hose and coolant sensor electrical connector from water pump.
6. Remove coolant sensor wire retainer from front of water pump.
7. Using a 5/8 inch box wrench on serpentine drive belt tensioner, left tensioner upward and remove belt from alternator pulley.
8. Remove six water pump to engine attaching bolts, then remove water pump, **Fig. 21.**
9. Reverse procedure to install. Prior to assembling coupling to pump, apply a light coat of grease seals and splines. When installing coupling, white band should face toward engine, **Fig. 21**. Install water pump gaskets with tabs facing upward. After installation bleed cooling system.

RADIATOR
REPLACE

1. Disconnect battery ground cable.
2. Drain coolant from radiator.
3. Remove upper radiator support, **Fig. 22.**
4. Disconnect radiator inlet and outlet hoses at radiator.
5. **On models equipped with automatic transmission,** disconnect transmission oil cooler lines at radiator.
6. **On all models,**remove radiator from vehicle.
7. Reverse procedure to install, noting the following:
   a. **Torque** automatic transmission oil cooler lines to 20 ft. lbs.
   b. Check and fill engine coolant and transmission fluid levels.

FUEL PUMP
REPLACE

The fuel pump is an electric in-tank design attached to the fuel level sending unit. Replace fuel pump as follows:

1. Disconnect battery ground cable.
2. Connect pressure gauge J-34370-1 or equivalent to pressure tap on fuel rail, position bleed hose in suitable container and slowly relieve fuel system pressure. **Failure to relieve system pressure prior to disconnecting fuel system components may cause fire or personal injury.**
3. Remove fuel tank filler cap, then drain fuel tank. Drain fuel into an approved fuel storage container.
4. Remove fuel filler door bezel attaching screws, then remove bezel, **Fig. 23.**
5. Lift fuel filler neck housing and disconnect drain hose.
6. Remove fuel meter and pump attaching screws.
7. Disconnect fuel lines, hoses and electrical connectors from fuel meter and pump assembly. Tag hoses and electrical connectors so they may be installed at the same location.
8. Carefully remove fuel meter and pump assembly.

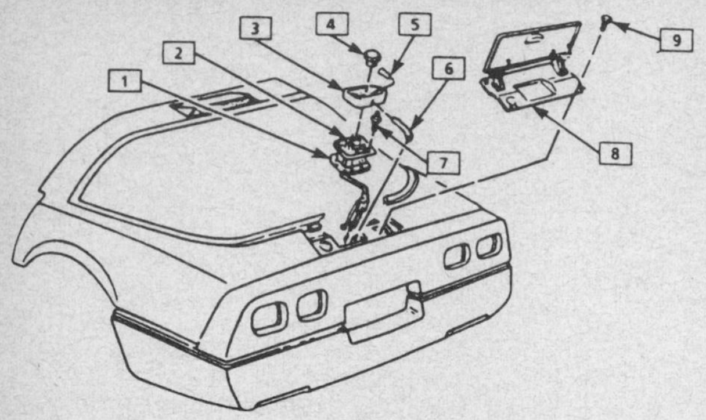
1 GASKET
2 FUEL LEVEL METER ASSEMBLY
3 FILER NECK HOUSING
4 FUEL FILER CAP
5 NIPPLE
6 DRAIN HOSE
7 SCREW ASSEMBLY (WITH O-RING) 4.5 N·m (40 lb. in.)
8 FILLER DOOR BEZEL
9 SCREW
GC1029102716000X

Fig. 23 Fuel pump/sending unit replacement

9. Reverse procedure to install. Prior to installation, position gasket on fuel tank with notch facing forward in right-hand corner of fuel tank. Carefully fold strainer to fit through fuel tank opening. Strainer must unfold when positioned inside tank.

FUEL FILTER

REPLACE

1. Relieve fuel system pressure as outlined under "Precautions."
2. Raise and support vehicle.
3. Clean all fuel filter connections and surrounding areas.
4. Disconnect fuel feed pipes from filter, **Fig. 24**, then drain remaining fuel into suitable container.
5. Remove filter mounting screw, then the fuel filter.
6. Reverse procedure to install.

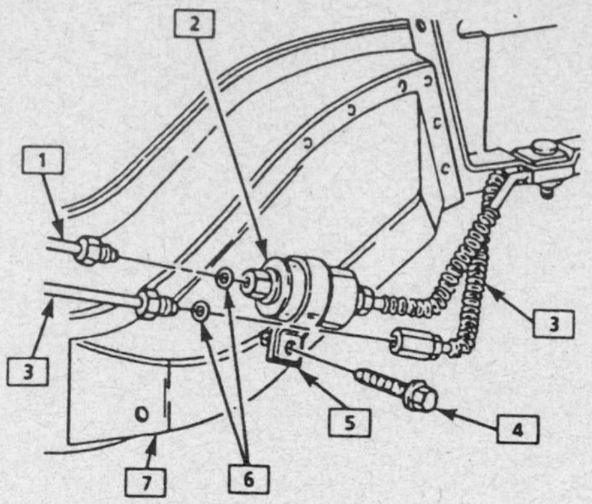
1 FUEL FEED PIPE
2 IN-LINE FUEL FILTER
3 FUEL RETURN PIPE
4 FUEL FILTER ATTACHING SCREW
5 FUEL FILTER BRACKET
6 FUEL PIPE O-RING
7 RIGHT SIDE FRAME
GC1029102717000X

Fig. 24 Fuel filter replacement

TIGHTENING SPECIFICATIONS

Year	Component	Torque/Ft. Lbs.
1992-95	Accessory Bracket Bolt	25
	Camshaft Retainer Bolt	105①
	Camshaft Sprocket Bolt	21
	Connecting Rod Cap Nut	47
	Camshaft Sprocket Bolt	21
	Catalytic Converter To Exhaust Manifold Nuts	21
	Coolant Sensor	17
	Crankshaft Damper To Hub Bolts	60
	Crankshaft Hub Bolt	70
	Crankshaft Rear Seal Retainer Bolt & Nut	11
	Cylinder Head Bolts	65
	EGR Solenoid Bracket Nut	25
	EGR Valve Bolt	16
	Engine Front Cover Bolt	100①
	Engine Mount Stud Nuts	40
	Engine Mount Through Bolts	77
	Engine Oil Galley Plug	18
	Exhaust Manifold Bolt/Stud	26
	Flywheel Bolt	74
	Fuel Pump/Sending Unit To Fuel Tank	45①
	Fuel Rail Bolt	15
	Ignition Distributor Bolt	100①
	Intake Manifold Bolt/Stud	35
	Knock Sensor	14
	Oil Filter Adapter Bolt	17
	Oil Level Sensor	16
	Oil Pan Baffle Nut	25

Continued

TIGHTENING SPECIFICATIONS—Continued

Year	Component	Torque/Ft. Lbs.
1992-95 —Cont'd	Oil Pan Drain Plug	16
	Oil Pressure Fittings (Plus Alignment)	89①
	Oil Pressure Sensor/Switch	105①
	Oil Pump Cover	80①
	Oil Pump Stub Shaft Bolt	13
	Oil Pump To Rear Main Bearing Cap	65
	Oil Temperature Sensor	108①
	Purge Solenoid Bracket Nut	25
	Rocker Arm Stud	50
	Spark Plug	11
	Starter Motor Mounting Bolts	34
	Thermostat Housing To Water Pump	8
	Throttle Body To Intake Manifold	19
	Valve Lifter Retainer	15
	Valve Rocker Arm Cover	75①
	Water Pump Driven Gear Retainer	105①
	Water Pump To Engine Bolt	35

①—Inch lbs.

5.7L/V8-350 4 CAM 32 Valve (ZR-1) Engine

INDEX

PRECAUTIONS

FUEL SYSTEM PRESSURE RELIEF

Failure to relieve system pressure prior to disconnecting fuel system components may cause fire or personal injury. Remove fuel tank filler cap to release fuel tank pressure. Connect pressure gauge J-34730-1 or equivalent to pressure tap on fuel rail, position bleed hose into suitable container and slowly relieve fuel system pressure. Prior to disconnecting fuel line, position shop towel over fitting.

ENGINE MOUNT

REPLACE

Check engine mounts for damage to rubber components or mounting stud and fluid loss, and replace as necessary.

1. Disconnect battery ground cable.
2. Remove exhaust manifold from side on engine mount is to be replaced. Refer to "Exhaust Manifold, Replace."
3. Remove nut attaching engine mount to engine and frame, **Fig. 1.**
4. Support engine.
5. Raise engine slightly to permit removal of engine mount to bracket nut and bolt, then remove nut and bolt.
6. Remove engine mount and heat shield from vehicle.

7. If necessary, remove bolts attaching mount bracket to engine, then remove bracket.
8. Reverse procedure to install.

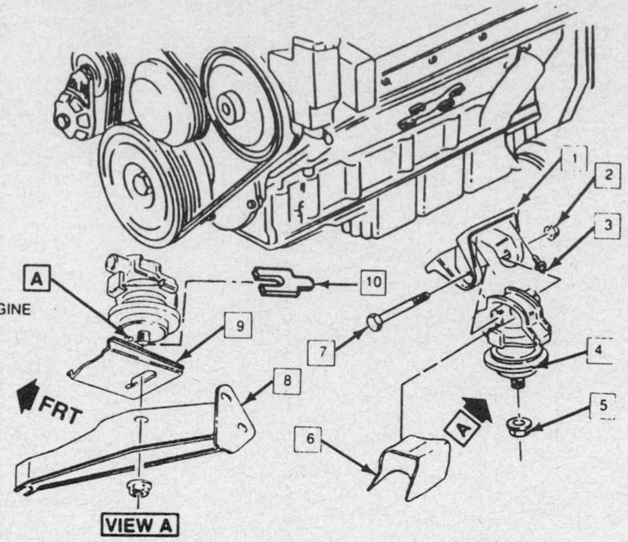
A
1
2
3
4
5
6
7
8
9
10
FRT
A
VIEW A

- A LOCATION PEG
- 1 BRACKET, ENGINE MOUNT
- 2 NUT, ENGINE MOUNT/BRACKET
- 3 BOLT, ENGINE MOUNT BRACKET/ENGINE
- 4 MOUNT, ENGINE HYDRAULIC
- 5 NUT, ENGINE MOUNT/FRAME
- 6 HEAT SHIELD, ENGINE MOUNT
- 7 BOLT, ENGINE MOUNT/BRACKET
- 8 SIDE MEMBER, FRONT
- 9 FRAME, DRIVETRAIN AND FRONT SUSPENSION
- 10 SPACER, ENGINE MOUNT

GC1069100249000X

Fig. 1 Engine mount replacement

ENGINE

REPLACE

1. Disconnect battery ground cable.
2. Raise and support vehicle.
3. Drain cooling system and crankcase.
4. Remove exhaust system from vehicle.
5. Remove driveshaft from vehicle.
6. Position suitable support under transmission.
7. Remove drive line support member from vehicle.
8. Remove transmission from vehicle, refer to "Transmission, Replace."
9. Remove clutch assembly, refer to "Clutch, Replace."
10. Install engine lifting hook J-37307 or equivalent, to rear of engine.
11. Detach AIR tube center section from AIR hose and oil pan.
12. Remove oxygen sensors.
13. Detach lower power steering hose from oil cooler.
14. Disconnect battery ground cable from engine.
15. Remove engine mount to engine and frame attaching nut.
16. Lower vehicle, then remove air cleaner assembly and duct.
17. Disconnect oil cooler lines from oil filter housing.
18. Raise rear of engine.
19. Remove fuel tank filler cap.
20. Relieve fuel system pressure as described under "Precautions."
21. Disconnect fuel lines at fuel rail.
22. Remove evaporator housing panel and restrictor.
23. Remove righthand firewall wiring harness connector retaining bolts.
24. Disconnect engine righthand wiring harness connector.
25. Remove righthand lower instrument panel sound insulator, then disconnect right firewall connector wiring harness from under instrument.
26. Disconnect air bleed hose from at plenum.
27. Disconnect radiator upper and lower hoses.
28. Disconnect vacuum lines from power steering pump.
29. Discharge A/C refrigerant system.
30. Disconnect A/C suction and discharge line flange from A/C compressor.
31. Disconnect A/C compressor to accumulator line at accumulator.
32. Remove A/C accumulator from bracket and position aside, then remove accumulator bracket from vehicle.
33. Disconnect power steering pressure line at power steering gear.
34. Disconnect accelerator and cruise control cables from throttle body and plenum retainers.
35. Install lifting hook J-37307-1 or equivalent, to front of engine.
36. Disconnect electrical connectors from ECM.
37. Remove left front fender from vehicle.
38. Disconnect battery positive cable and remove battery hold-down, then remove battery from vehicle.
39. Disconnect engine lefthand firewall electrical connector.
40. Disconnect engine wiring harness fusible links at junction block.
41. Disconnect electrical connectors from secondary injector modules, battery positive cable junction block, differential pressure switch, A/C cutout relay, A/C high blower relay, transmission shift solenoid relay, fuel pump fuse and forward lamp link.
42. Disconnect battery positive lead, then disconnect electrical connectors at blower motor resistor, blower motor, A/C pressure sensors, A/C cooling fan switch, windshield washer pump, low coolant sensor and ESC knock sensor and sensor relay.
43. Disconnect vacuum pump hose.
44. Disconnect front and rear vacuum connectors.
45. Position engine wiring harness out of way.
46. Disconnect engine ground strap from lefthand frame rail.
47. Position battery positive out of way.
48. Remove lefthand plenum screen.
49. Disconnect vacuum hose from power brake unit.
50. Remove windshield wiper motor.
51. Remove MAP sensor and bracket from plenum.
52. Disconnect AIR hose from lefthand exhaust manifold.
53. Ensure all electrical connector and vacuum hoses that would interfere with engine removal are disconnected.
54. Attach suitable engine lifting fixture and remove engine from vehicle.
55. Reverse procedure to install.

PLENUM ASSEMBLY

REPLACE

1. Disconnect battery ground cable.
2. Drain cooling system, then remove air intake duct.
3. Remove cable shield, then disconnect control cables at throttle body.
4. Remove cable hold-down clamps from plenum.
5. Disconnect fresh air hoses from throttle body extension.
6. Disconnect electrical connectors from TPS, IAC and MAT.
7. Disconnect air bleed hose from plenum.
8. Disconnect power brake unit vacuum hose at plenum.
9. Disconnect vacuum hose located between plenum and fuel pressure regulator.
10. Disconnect vacuum hoses at mid-plenum.
11. Disconnect vacuum hose from MAP sensor and plenum, then disconnect electrical connector from MAP sensor.
12. Relieve fuel system pressure as outlined under "Precautions," then disconnect and cap fuel lines at fuel rail.
13. Remove bolts attaching plenum assembly to injector housing.
14. Disconnect electrical connectors from ignition module.
15. Disconnect PCV and purge canister vacuum hoses from plenum.
16. Disconnect vacuum hose from lower portion of throttle body extension.
17. Remove plenum assembly. Cover injector housing openings.
18. Reverse procedure to install. Tighten plenum assembly attaching bolts in sequence shown in **Fig. 2**, to specifications.

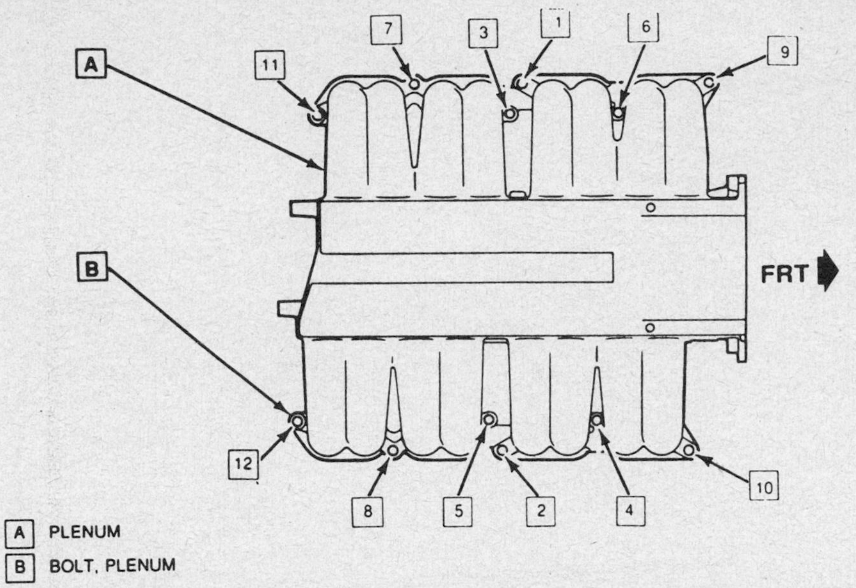
A
B
FRT
7
3
1
6
9
11
12
8
5
2
4
10
A PLENUM
B BOLT, PLENUM
GC1069100250000X

Fig. 2 Plenum assembly bolt tightening sequence

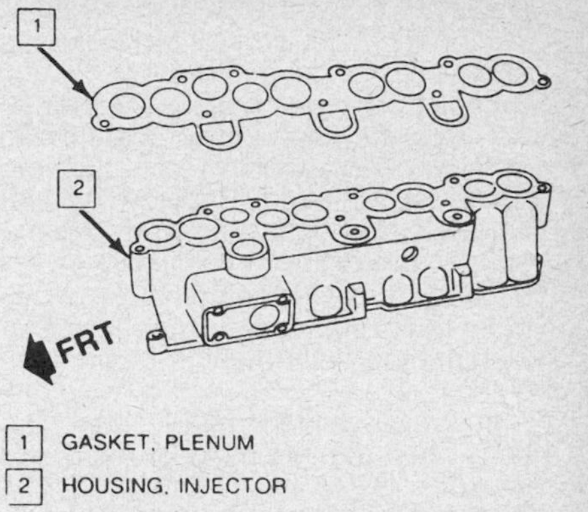
1
2
FRT
1 GASKET, PLENUM
2 HOUSING, INJECTOR
GC1069100251000X

Fig. 3 Injector housing & gasket

INJECTOR HOUSING
REPLACE

1. Disconnect battery ground cable, then drain cooling system.
2. Remove plenum assembly as described under "Plenum Assembly, Replace."
3. Remove fuel tank filler cap.
4. Relieve fuel system pressure as described under "Precautions."
5. Disconnect fuel lines at righthand fuel rail.
6. Disconnect electrical connectors from injectors.
7. Remove bolts attaching fuel rail to injector housing, then remove injectors from housing and remove fuel rail.
8. Disconnect coolant outlet pipe from injector housing being removed.
9. If lefthand injector housing is to be removed, remove bolt retaining outlet pipe bracket to power steering pump bracket.
10. If righthand injector housing is to be removed, remove oil pressure sensor from oil filter housing.
11. Remove PCV grommet from injector housing, then disconnect ventilation hose.
12. If lefthand injector housing is to be removed, disconnect electrical connectors from coolant temperature and cooling fan switches.
13. If righthand injector housing is to be replaced, remove bolt attaching alternator rear support bracket and ventilation pipe bracket to injector housing, then remove ventilation pipe and bracket.
14. Remove injector housing to cylinder head attaching bolts, then remove injector housing and gasket, **Fig. 3.**
15. Reverse procedure to install.

EXHAUST MANIFOLD
REPLACE
LEFT SIDE

1. Disconnect battery ground cable.
2. Raise and support vehicle, then remove wheel and tire assembly.
3. Remove wheel housing lower rear and center panels.
4. Remove exhaust system as follows:
   a. Remove underbody braces, if equipped.
   b. Remove bolt attaching exhaust pipe flange to lefthand catalytic converter.
   c. Loosen clamp securing exhaust pipe to righthand catalytic converter.
   d. Support exhaust system, then remove bolts attaching resonator assembly to front spring hanger.
   e. Remove bolts attaching resonator assembly to rear spring hanger.
   f. Remove nuts attaching mufflers to hanger brackets, then remove exhaust system from vehicle.
5. Remove lefthand floor heat shield, then remove lefthand frame heat shield.
6. Remove engine heat shield, then disconnect oxygen sensor electrical connector.
7. Remove AIR check valves, housings and tubes.
8. Remove manifold outer heat shield.
9. Remove catalytic converter from exhaust manifold.
10. Remove exhaust manifold attaching bolts, nut and spacers, then remove exhaust manifold and gasket, **Fig. 4.**
11. Reverse procedure to install, noting the following:
    a. **Torque** exhaust manifold heat shield bolts to 72-108 inch lbs.

RIGHT SIDE

1. Disconnect battery ground cable.
2. Raise and support vehicle, then remove wheel and tire assembly.
3. Remove wheel housing lower rear and center panels.
4. Remove manifold outer heat shields.
5. Remove exhaust system as follows:
   a. Remove underbody braces, if equipped.
   b. Remove bolt attaching exhaust pipe flange to lefthand catalytic converter.
   c. Loosen clamp securing exhaust pipe to righthand catalytic converter.
   d. Support exhaust system, then remove bolts attaching resonator assembly to front spring hanger.
   e. Remove bolts attaching resonator assembly to rear spring hanger.
   f. Remove nuts attaching mufflers to hanger brackets, then remove exhaust system from vehicle.
6. Remove engine block heat shield.
7. Remove catalytic converter from exhaust manifold.
8. Disconnect oxygen sensor electrical connector.
9. Remove exhaust manifold rear attaching bolts, spacers and nut.
10. Lower vehicle, then remove AIR check valve and hoses from manifold.
11. Remove oil level dipstick tube retaining bolt.
12. Remove remaining exhaust manifold attaching bolts and spacers, then remove exhaust manifold and gasket, **Fig. 4.**
13. Reverse procedure to install.

CYLINDER HEAD
REPLACE
LEFT SIDE

1. Disconnect battery ground cable.
2. Remove lefthand injector housing as described under "Injector Housing, Replace."
3. Disconnect vacuum hose from throttle valve actuator secondary port.
4. Remove power brake unit.
5. Remove valve lash adjusters from lefthand side as described under "Hydraulic Valve Lash Adjusters, Re-

place."
6. Disconnect AIR control valve hoses and electrical connectors.
7. Remove camshaft position sensor.
8. Remove lefthand exhaust manifold to cylinder head attaching bolts. Refer to "Exhaust Manifold, Replace" procedure. It is not necessary to remove exhaust manifold from vehicle.
9. Remove access plug from front of cylinder head, then remove upper bolt attaching secondary timing chain fixed guide.
10. Remove cylinder head attaching bolts, then remove cylinder head and gasket.
11. Reverse procedure to install. Prior to installation of cylinder head bolts, coat threads and washers with engine oil. Tighten cylinder head attaching bolts in sequence shown in **Fig. 5**,to specifications. Prior to installation of secondary timing chain fixed guide upper attaching bolt, apply Loctite 262 or equivalent to bolt threads.

RIGHT SIDE

1. Disconnect battery ground cable.
2. Remove righthand injector housing as described under "Injector Housing, Replace."
3. Remove valve lash adjusters from righthand side as described under "Hydraulic Valve Lash Adjusters, Replace."
4. Remove alternator.
5. Remove righthand exhaust manifold to cylinder head attaching bolts. Refer to "Exhaust Manifold, Replace" procedure. It is not necessary to remove exhaust manifold from vehicle.
6. Remove fuel filter heat shield.
7. Disconnect vacuum hose from throttle valve actuator secondary port.
8. Remove access plug from front of cylinder head, then remove upper bolt attaching secondary timing chain fixed guide.
9. Remove cylinder head attaching bolts, then remove cylinder head and gasket.
10. Reverse procedure to install. Prior to installation of cylinder head bolts, coat threads and washers with engine oil. Tighten cylinder head attaching bolts in sequence shown in **Fig. 5**,to specifications. Prior to installation of secondary timing chain fixed guide upper attaching bolt, apply Loctite 262 or equivalent to bolt threads.

VALVE ARRANGEMENT

Exhaust valve are located on the exhaust manifold side of the cylinder head. Intake valve are located on the plenum side of the cylinder head.

CAMSHAFT LOBE LIFT SPECIFICATIONS

Engine (VIN)	Int.①	Exh.①
5.7L/V8-350 (J)	.3898	.3898

①—Plus or minus .002 inch.

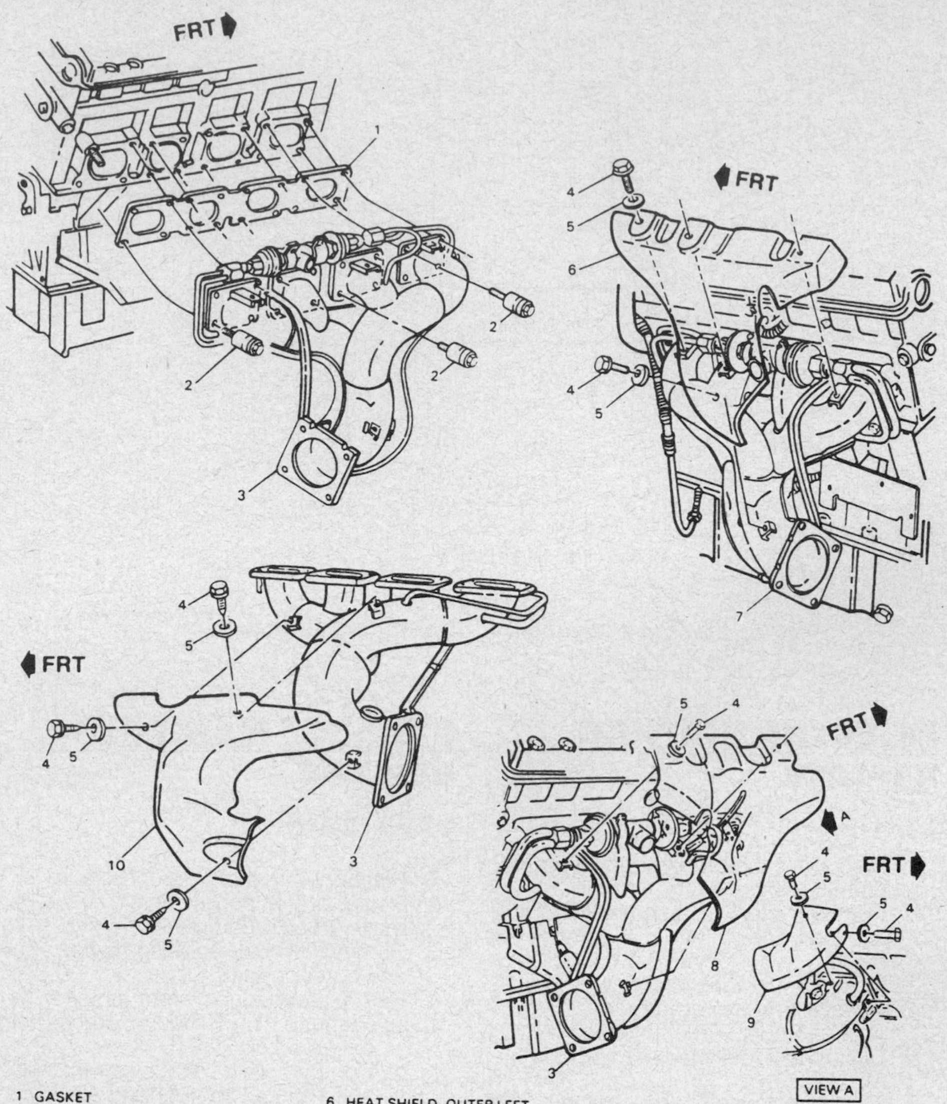
FRT
VIEW A
1 GASKET
2 BOLT W/SPACER
3 EXHAUST MANIFOLD, RIGHT
4 SCREW
5 WASHER
6 HEAT SHIELD, OUTER LEFT
7 EXHAUST MANIFOLD, LEFT
8 HEAT SHIELD, OUTER RIGHT
9 HEAT SHIELD, OUTER RIGHT FRONT
10 HEAT SHIELD, INNER
GC1079200012000X

Fig. 4 Exhaust manifold & converter assembly

VALVE CLEARANCE SPECIFICATIONS

This engine is equipped with hydraulic valve lash adjusters. No adjustment is required.

VALVE ADJUSTMENT

This engine is equipped with hydraulic valve lash adjusters. No adjustment is required.

HYDRAULIC VALVE LASH ADJUSTERS

REPLACE

1. Disconnect battery ground cable.
2. Remove camshaft(s) as described under "Camshaft, Replace."
3. Remove valve lash adjusters from cylinder head, **Fig. 6.**Note position of lash adjusters during removal so they may be reinstalled into the same bore.
4. Check lash adjuster contact surfaces for concave wear using a straightedge and replace as necessary. If camshaft lobe is worn, replace lash adjusters and camshaft as an assembly.
5. Reverse procedure to install. Apply engine oil to lash adjusters and bores prior to installation.

CAMSHAFT COVER

REPLACE

LEFT SIDE

1. Disconnect battery ground cable.
2. Remove power steering pump.
3. Discharge A/C refrigerant system, then disconnect suction and discharge hoses from A/C compressor. Cap refrigerant lines and A/C compressor openings.
4. Disconnect spark plug wires from

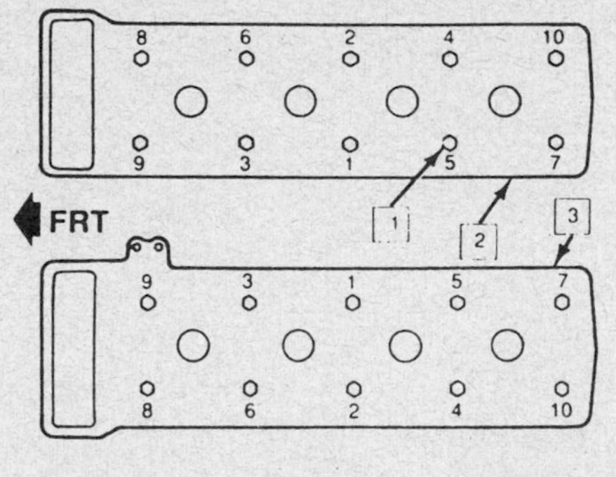
8 6 2 4 10
9 3 1 5 7
FRT
1
2
3
9 3 1 5 7
8 6 2 4 10

1 BOLT, CYLINDER HEAD
2 HEAD, CYLINDER-RH
3 HEAD, CYLINDER-LH

GC1069100252000X

Fig. 5 Cylinder head bolt tightening sequence

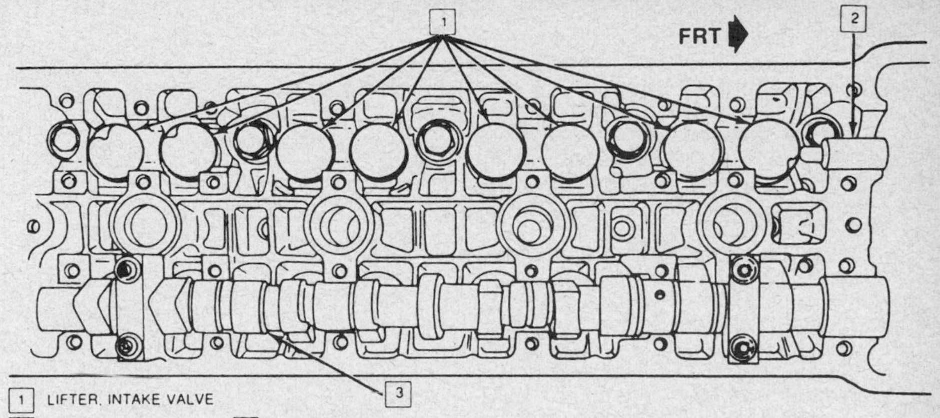
1
2
FRT
3

1 LIFTER, INTAKE VALVE
2 HEAD, CYLINDER
3 CAMSHAFT, EXHAUST-RH

GC1069100253000X

Fig. 6 Hydraulic valve lifter installation

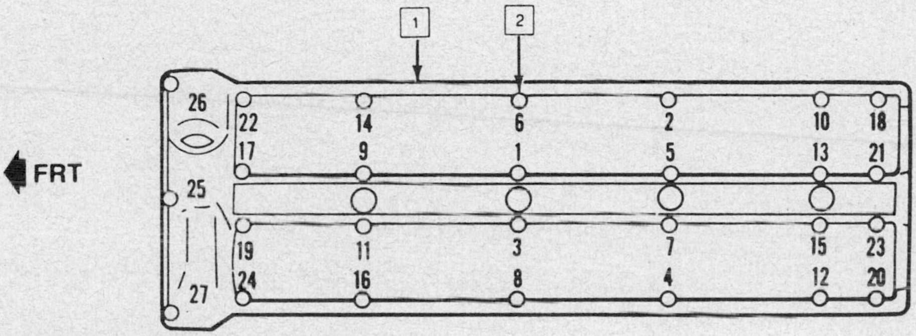
1
2
FRT
26
22 14 6 2 10 18
17 9 1 5 13 21
25
19 11 3 7 15 23
24 16 8 4 12 20
27

1 COVER, CAMSHAFT
2 BOLT, CAMSHAFT COVER

GC1069100254000X

Fig. 7 Camshaft cover bolt tightening sequence

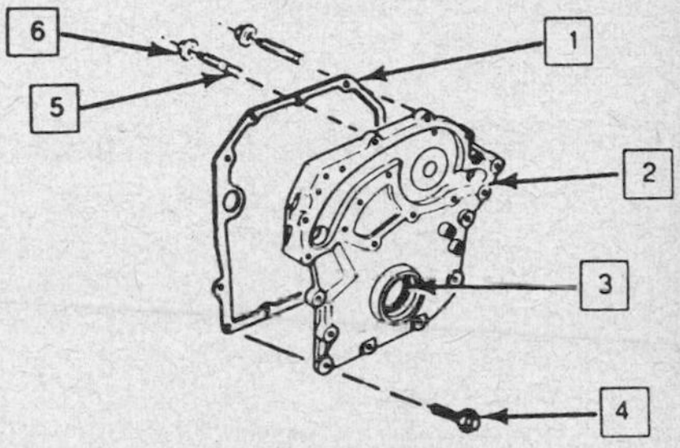
6
5
1
2
3
4

1 GASKET, ENGINE FRONT COVER
2 COVER, ENGINE FRONT
3 SEAL, ENGINE FRONT COVER
4 BOLT, ENGINE FRONT COVER
5 STUD, ENGINE FRONT COVER
6 NUT, ENGINE FRONT COVER STUD

GC1069100255000X

Fig. 8 Engine front cover & gasket

spark plugs.

5. Disconnect ventilation hose from camshaft cover.
6. Remove hold-down clamps retaining throttle and cruise control cables to plenum.
7. Remove throttle body extension and coolant outlet tube.
8. Remove power brake booster from vehicle.
9. **On all models,** remove bolts attaching camshaft cover to cylinder head, then remove cover.
10. Reverse procedure to install, noting the following:
    a. Apply Permabond A136 or equivalent to camshaft cover prior to installation.
    b. Apply Loctite 565 to end plugs.
    c. Ensure camshaft end plugs and spark plug bore O-rings are properly position.
    d. Insert the two rear lower camshaft cover bolts prior to placing cover on cylinder head.
    e. Tighten camshaft cover attaching bolts in sequence shown in **Fig. 7** to specifications.

RIGHT SIDE

1. Disconnect battery ground cable, then drain cooling system.
2. Disconnect spark plug wires from spark plugs.
3. Disconnect blower motor resistor electrical connectors.
4. Remove evaporator housing panel attaching screws, then remove panel.
5. Remove oil pressure sensor from oil filter housing.
6. Remove bolt attaching coolant outlet pipe to alternator bracket.
7. Remove screws attaching coolant outlet to injector housing, then position coolant outlet aside.
8. Remove bolt attaching fresh air pipe bracket to injector housing.
9. Remove camshaft cover to cylinder head attaching bolts, then remove cover.
10. Reverse procedure to install, noting the following:
    a. Apply Permabond A136 or equivalent to camshaft cover prior to installation.
    b. Apply Loctite 565 to end plugs.
    c. Ensure camshaft end plugs and spark plug bore O-rings are properly position.
    d. Tighten camshaft cover attaching bolts in sequence shown in **Fig. 7,** to specifications.
    e. When installing coolant outlet pipe bracket bolt and oil pressure sensor, apply Loctite 565 or equivalent to threads.

FRONT COVER SEAL

REPLACE

REMOVAL

1. Disconnect battery ground cable.
2. Remove water pump as described under "Water Pump, Replace."
3. Discharge A/C refrigerant system, then remove A/C compressor.
4. Remove steering gear, if necessary.
5. Remove serpentine drive belt.
6. Remove crankshaft damper to crankshaft retaining bolt and washer, then remove damper using puller J-24420-C or equivalent.
7. Remove key from crankshaft keyway.
8. Remove front cover attaching screws and nuts, then remove front cover, **Fig. 8.**
9. Using tool No. J-29077-A, remove seal from front cover.

INSTALLATION

1. Apply Loctite 262 or equivalent to front cover stud threads. Apply Loctite 565 or equivalent to front cover bolt

threads.
2. Position front cover and gasket to engine, then install attaching bolts and nuts finger tight.
3. Lubricate front cover seal with engine oil, then install seal using installation tool No. J-37309 or equivalent, **Fig. 9.**
4. Tighten front cover attaching bolts and nuts to specification, then remove seal installation tool.
5. Install water pump and A/C compressor.
6. Apply engine oil to seal surface of crankshaft damper, then position damper to crankshaft.
7. Apply Loctite 262 or equivalent to crankshaft damper attaching bolt, then install bolt and tighten to specification.
8. Install serpentine drive belt and connect battery ground cable.

TIMING CHAIN

REPLACE

PRIMARY TIMING CHAIN

1. Disconnect battery ground cable.
2. Remove engine front cover as described under "Front Cover, Replace."
3. Remove left and righthand intake camshafts as described under "Camshaft, Replace."
4. Remove bolts attaching primary timing chain guide to oil pump, then remove chain guide.
5. Remove idler sprocket assembly attaching bolts, **Fig. 10.**
6. Detach primary timing chain from idler sprocket and crankshaft sprocket, then remove timing chain from engine.
7. Reverse procedure to install, noting the following:
   a. Apply Loctite 262 or equivalent to idle sprocket attaching and primary timing guide bolt threads prior to installation.
   b. When installing primary timing chain guide, use only finger pressure to remove slack from chain.

SECONDARY TIMING CHAINS

Removal

1. Disconnect battery ground cable.
2. Remove camshafts as described under "Camshaft, Replace."
3. Remove primary timing chain as described previously.
4. Disengage left and righthand secondary timing chains from idler sprocket.
5. Remove idler sprocket attaching bolts, then remove idle sprocket, **Fig. 10.**
6. Remove left and righthand secondary timing chains.

Installation

1. Install longer outer secondary timing chain through lefthand cylinder head and hold in position with retainer J-38099 or equivalent, then place chain on inner idler sprocket.

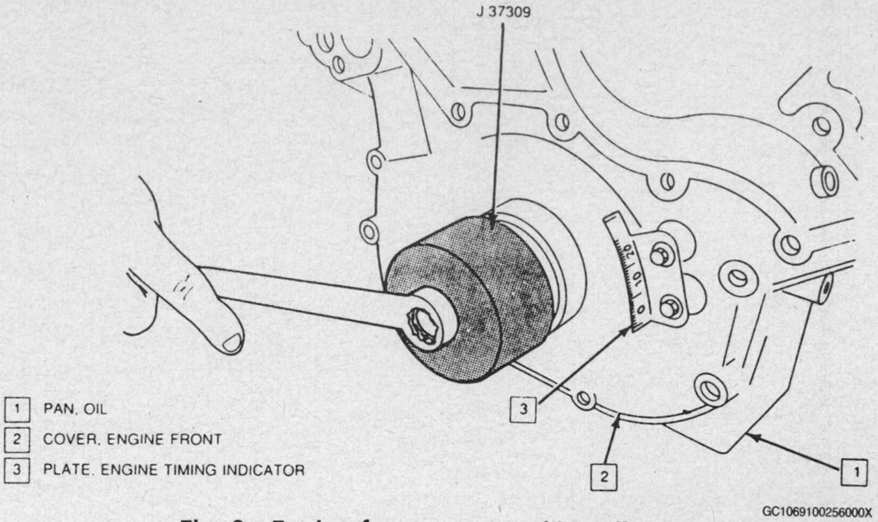
J 37309
1 PAN, OIL
2 COVER, ENGINE FRONT
3 PLATE, ENGINE TIMING INDICATOR
GC1069100256000X

Fig. 9 Engine front cover seal installation

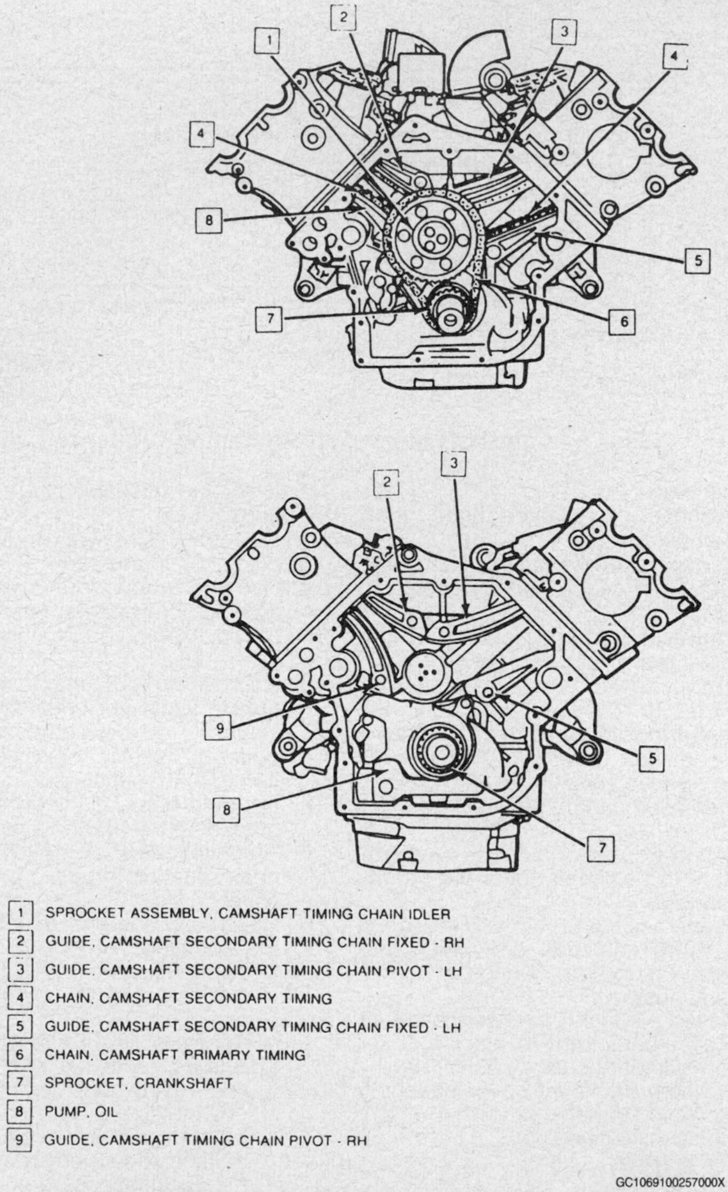
1 SPROCKET ASSEMBLY, CAMSHAFT TIMING CHAIN IDLER
2 GUIDE, CAMSHAFT SECONDARY TIMING CHAIN FIXED - RH
3 GUIDE, CAMSHAFT SECONDARY TIMING CHAIN PIVOT - LH
4 CHAIN, CAMSHAFT SECONDARY TIMING
5 GUIDE, CAMSHAFT SECONDARY TIMING CHAIN FIXED - LH
6 CHAIN, CAMSHAFT PRIMARY TIMING
7 SPROCKET, CRANKSHAFT
8 PUMP, OIL
9 GUIDE, CAMSHAFT TIMING CHAIN PIVOT - RH
GC1069100257000X

Fig. 10 Primary & secondary timing chains & guides

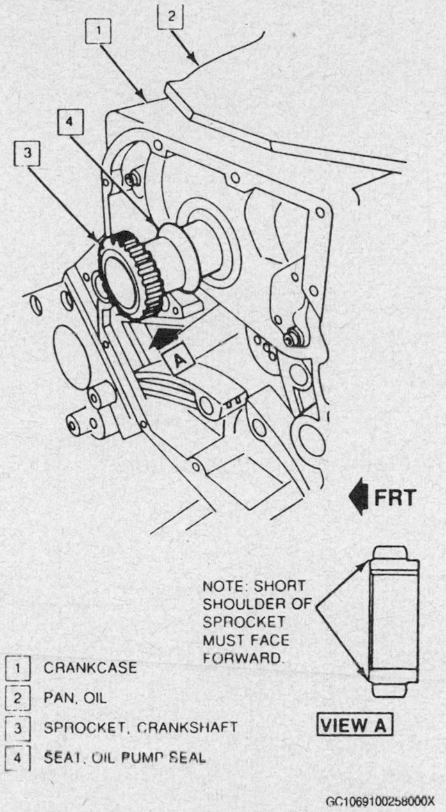
1
2
4
3
A
FRT
NOTE: SHORT SHOULDER OF SPROCKET MUST FACE FORWARD.
VIEW A
1 CRANKCASE
2 PAN, OIL
3 SPROCKET, CRANKSHAFT
4 SEAT, OIL PUMP SEAL
GC1069100258000X

Fig. 11 Crankshaft sprocket installation

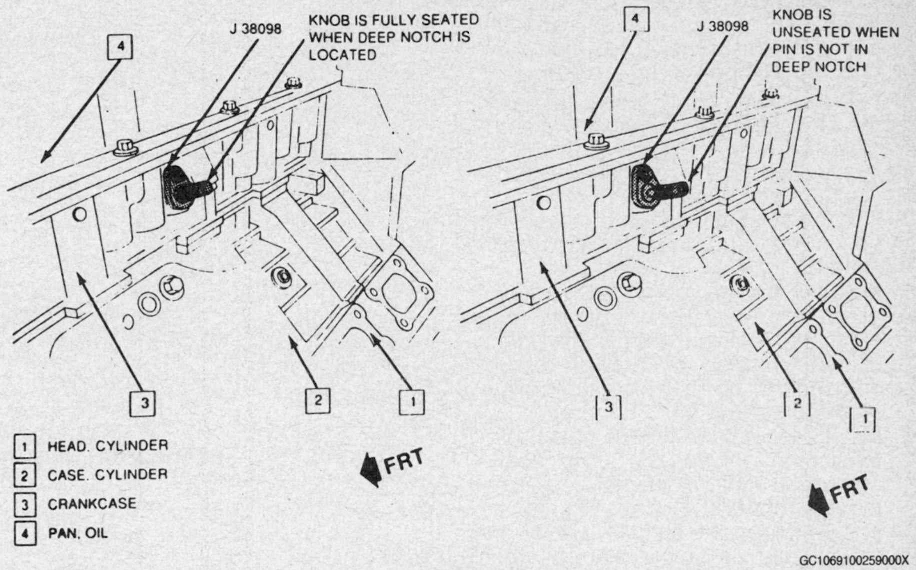
J 38098
KNOB IS FULLY SEATED WHEN DEEP NOTCH IS LOCATED
KNOB IS UNSEATED WHEN PIN IS NOT IN DEEP NOTCH
FRT
1 HEAD, CYLINDER
2 CASE, CYLINDER
3 CRANKCASE
4 PAN, OIL
GC1069100259000X

Fig. 12 Installing tool No. J-38098 into crankshaft position sensor opening

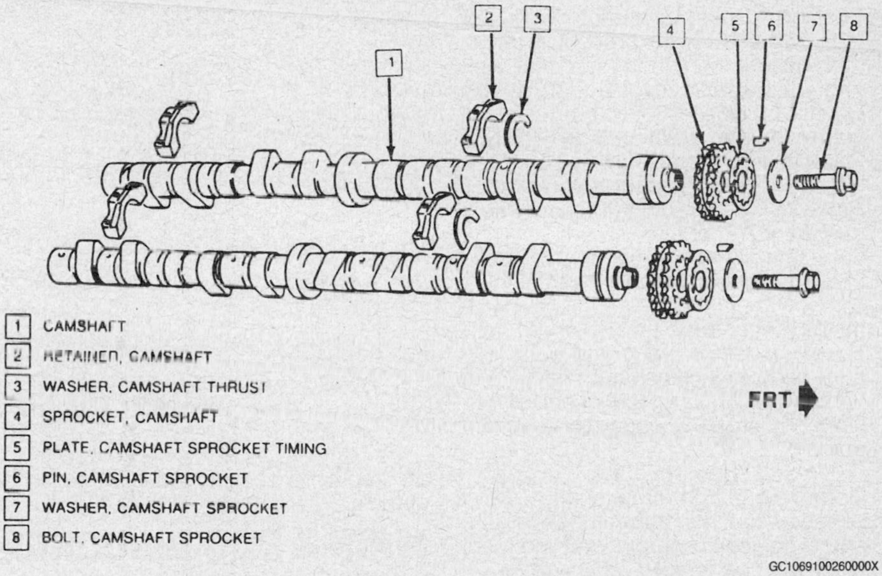
FRT
1 CAMSHAFT
2 RETAINER, CAMSHAFT
3 WASHER, CAMSHAFT THRUST
4 SPROCKET, CAMSHAFT
5 PLATE, CAMSHAFT SPROCKET TIMING
6 PIN, CAMSHAFT SPROCKET
7 WASHER, CAMSHAFT SPROCKET
8 BOLT, CAMSHAFT SPROCKET
GC1069100260000X

Fig. 13 Camshafts, sprocket & retainers

2. Install shorter inner secondary timing chain through righthand cylinder head and hold in position with retainer J-38099 or equivalent, then place chain on outer idler sprocket.
3. Install primary timing chain as described previously.
4. Install camshafts as described under "Camshaft, Replace."
5. Connect battery ground cable.

CRANKSHAFT SPROCKET

REPLACE

1. Disconnect battery ground cable.
2. Remove primary timing chain as described under "Timing Chain, Replace."
3. Using tool No. J-38211 and J-24420-C, remove crankshaft sprocket from crankshaft.
4. Remove key and oil pump seal seat from crankshaft.
5. Reverse procedure to install, noting the following:
   a. Position sprocket to crankshaft with short shoulder toward front, **Fig. 11.**
   b. Use tool No. J-38132, or equivalent, to install crankshaft sprocket.

CAMSHAFT

REPLACE

REMOVAL

1. Disconnect battery ground cable.
2. If camshaft(s) is to be removed from lefthand cylinder head, remove A/C compressor.
3. If camshaft(s) is to be removed from righthand cylinder head, remove oil filter housing.
4. Remove camshaft cover as described under "Camshaft Cover, Replace."
5. Raise and support vehicle.
6. Disconnect electrical connector from crankshaft position sensor, then remove crankshaft position sensor from engine.
7. Install tool No. J-38098 or equivalent into crankshaft position sensor opening. Ensure tool properly positioned in sensor opening, **Fig. 12.**
8. Lower vehicle, then remove secondary timing chain tensioner housing to cylinder head attaching bolts.
9. Remove secondary timing chain tensioner housing, O-ring and tensioner.
10. Position a suitable wrench at rear of camshaft on hex, then remove camshaft sprocket attaching bolt(s) and washer(s), **Fig. 13.**
11. Remove camshaft timing plates and pins, then remove camshaft retainers and thrust washers.
12. Remove camshaft and sprocket. Use tool No. J-38099 or equivalent to retain secondary timing chain, **Fig. 14.**

INSTALLATION

If a replacement camshaft is to be installed, the hydraulic valve lash adjusters should also be replaced to aid in preventing premature camshaft wear.

1. Position camshaft sprocket to secondary timing chain while removing retaining tool(s).

2. Note position of alignment hole for timing pin tool, then slide camshaft into camshaft sprocket. Position camshaft so that no valves are open.
3. Lubricate camshaft lobes, journals, thrust washers and retainers with engine oil.
4. Install camshaft retainers, thrust washers and bolts, **Fig. 13.**
5. If both camshafts where removed, repeat steps 1 through 4 for other camshaft.
6. Install timing pin(s) J-37326 or equivalent into camshaft retainers and alignment hole on camshaft. Use a suitable wrench on hex at rear of camshaft to position camshaft alignment holes, **Fig. 15.**
7. Install secondary timing chain pretensioning tool No. J-37305 or equivalent, then tighten tool until slack is removed from timing chain, **Fig. 16.**
8. Install timing plate and pin. If holes are not aligned on timing plate, reverse plate.
9. Apply Loctite 262 or equivalent to a new camshaft sprocket retaining bolt threads. Apply engine oil to camshaft sprocket washer.
10. Position a suitable wrench on hex at rear of camshaft to prevent rotation, then install camshaft sprocket bolt and washer and **torque** to 19 ft. lbs. Using tool No. J-36660 or equivalent, tighten bolt an additional 80° to 85°.
11. Remove timing pins from camshaft retainer(s) and alignment hole(s).
12. Remove pre-tensioning tool from secondary timing chain.
13. Lubricate a new secondary timing chain tensioner exterior with engine oil.
14. Install secondary timing chain tensioner, housing, O-ring and bolts. Ensure oil hole in tensioner piston is in vertical position and fork at end of tensioner is properly engaged on chain guide.
15. Raise and support vehicle.
16. Remove tool from crankshaft position sensor opening, then install crankshaft position sensor and connect electrical connector.
17. Lower vehicle, then install camshaft cover.
18. If camshaft was removed lefthand cylinder head, install A/C compressor.
19. If camshaft was removed righthand cylinder head, install oil filter housing.
20. Connect battery ground cable.

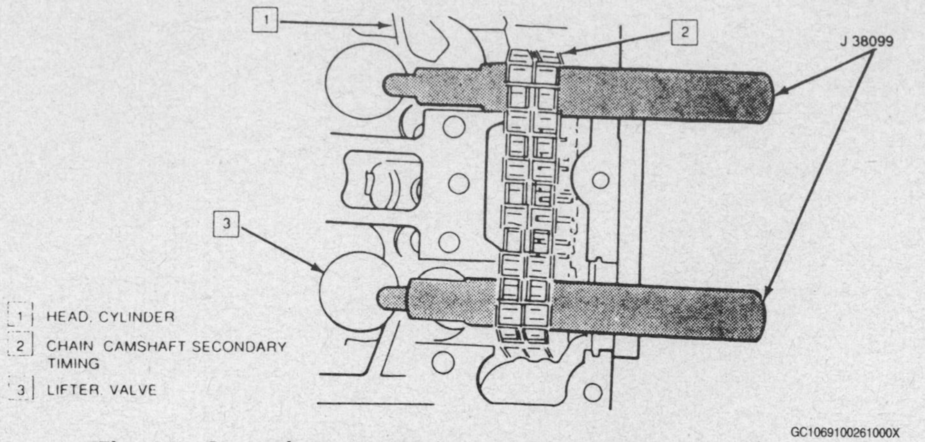
1
2
J 38099
3
1 HEAD, CYLINDER
2 CHAIN, CAMSHAFT SECONDARY TIMING
3 LIFTER, VALVE
GC1069100261000X

Fig. 14 Secondary timing chain retaining tool installation

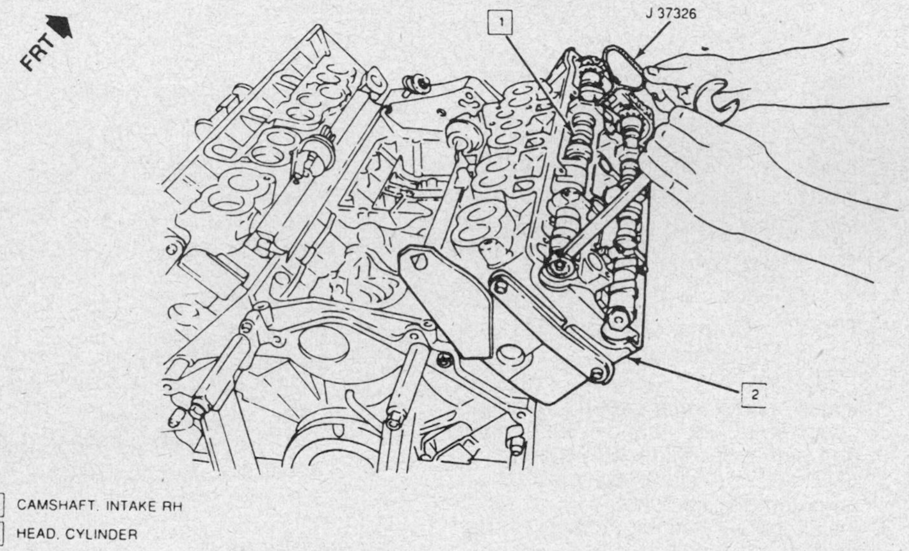
FRT
1
J 37326
2
1 CAMSHAFT, INTAKE RH
2 HEAD, CYLINDER
GC1069100262000X

Fig. 15 Camshaft timing pin installation

PISTON & ROD ASSEMBLY

Assemble pistons to connecting rods as shown in **Fig. 17.** When install piston and rod assembly, arrow on piston head must face front of engine.

Upon installation, measure the connecting rod side clearance using a suitable feeler gauge. Connecting rod side clearance should be .008 to .028 inch.

PISTONS, PINS & RINGS

Pistons, pins, rings and cylinder liners are replaced in matched sets as an assembly.

MAIN & ROD BEARINGS

Main and rod bearing are of the precision insert type and must be replaced in a complete set of upper and lower halves. If main or rod bearing are found to be worn or out of round, the crankshaft must be replaced.

CYLINDER LINER

REPLACE

REMOVAL

1. Disconnect battery ground cable.
2. Remove engine from vehicle as described under "Engine, Replace."
3. Remove flywheel attaching bolts, then remove flywheel from crankshaft.
4. Remove crankshaft rear oil seal housing.
5. Remove cylinder heads from engine.
6. Remove oil pump from engine.
7. Install cylinder liner retainers J-37330 or equivalent, **Fig. 18.**
8. Invert engine, then remove oil pan.
9. Rotate crankshaft until piston is located at bottom of cylinder liner bore.
10. Remove connecting rod bearing cap bolts, then remove cap and bearing. Mark side of rod cap so they can be installed in the same position.
11. Remove piston and rod assemblies from cylinder liner.
12. Remove bolts and washers attaching crankcase at main bearing journals.
13. Remove bolts attaching crankcase to cylinder case, then remove crankcase from cylinder case.
14. Remove crankshaft, then remove main bearing inserts. Tag bearing insert so they can be installed in the same locations.
15. Remove cylinder liner retaining tool, then remove cylinder liner using tool Nos. J-38124 and J-8092 or equivalent, **Fig. 19.**

INSTALLATION

1. Position cylinder liners into cylinder case. Flats on liners should face front and rear of cylinder case.

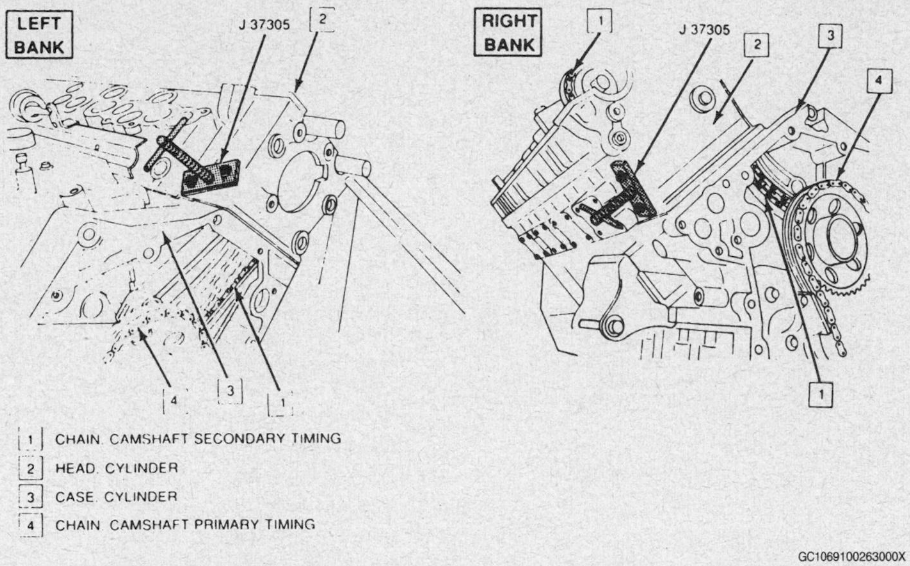
LEFT BANK
J 37305
2
4
3
1
RIGHT BANK
1
J 37305
2
3
4
1
1 CHAIN, CAMSHAFT SECONDARY TIMING
2 HEAD, CYLINDER
3 CASE, CYLINDER
4 CHAIN, CAMSHAFT PRIMARY TIMING
GC1069100263000X

Fig. 16 Secondary timing chain tension tool installation

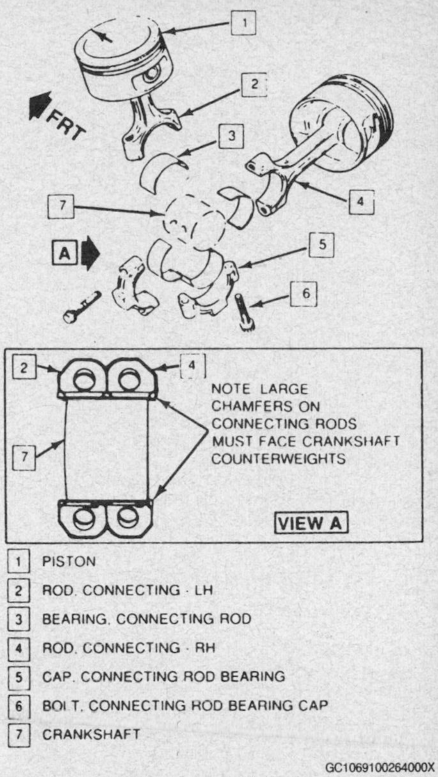
1
2
FRT
3
4
7
A
5
6
2
4
7
NOTE LARGE CHAMFERS ON CONNECTING RODS MUST FACE CRANKSHAFT COUNTERWEIGHTS
VIEW A
1 PISTON
2 ROD, CONNECTING - LH
3 BEARING, CONNECTING ROD
4 ROD, CONNECTING - RH
5 CAP, CONNECTING ROD BEARING
6 BOLT, CONNECTING ROD BEARING CAP
7 CRANKSHAFT
GC1069100264000X

Fig. 17 Piston & rod assembly

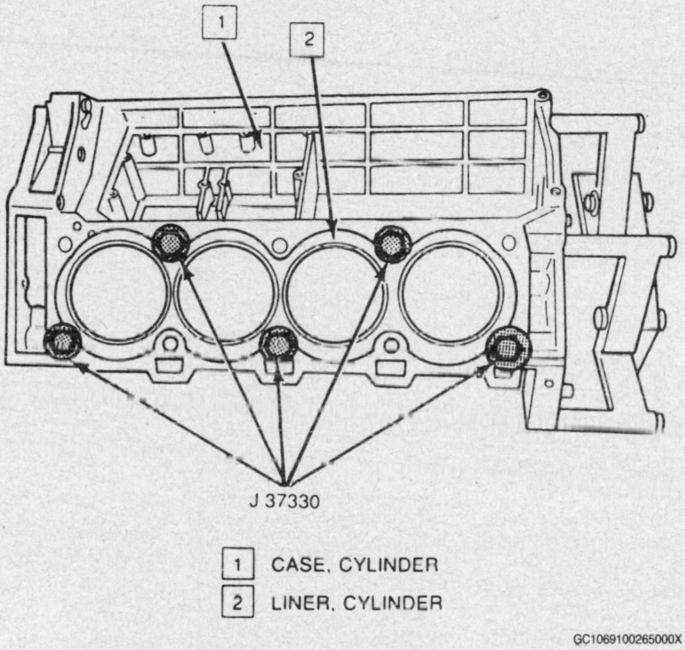
1
2
J 37330
1 CASE, CYLINDER
2 LINER, CYLINDER
GC1069100265000X

Fig. 18 Cylinder liner retainer installation

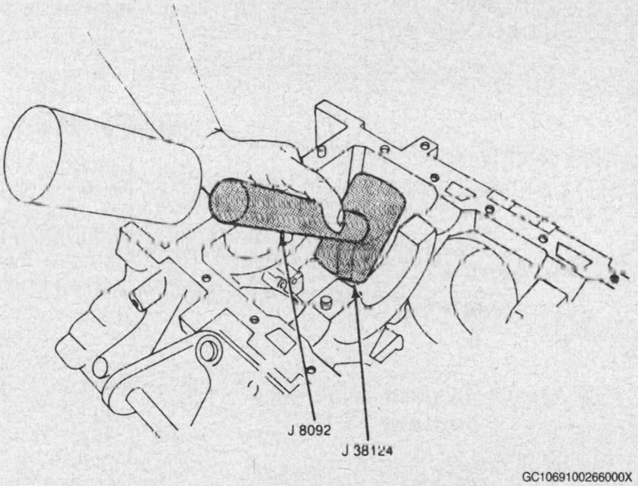
J 8092
J 38124
GC1069100266000X

Fig. 19 Cylinder liner removal

2. Check cylinder liner protrusion. Distance between cylinder case deck and lower ridge at top of liner should be .001 to .003 inch. If protrusion is not within limits, check liner ridge and cylinder case seat for burrs, damage or debris and clean as necessary. If protrusion is still not within limits, replace cylinder liner.
3. After proper cylinder liner protrusion has been obtained, remove liner. Apply a bead of Loctite 565 or equivalent, approximately .47 inch wide, around circumference of liner, 1 inch from liner bottom edge, **Fig. 20.**
4. Position liner into cylinder case and install liner retainer J37330 or equivalent, **Fig. 18.**
5. Lubricate main bearing insert with engine oil. Insert upper main bearing insert into cylinder case bores. Insert lower main bearing inserts into crankcase bores.
6. Position crankshaft on cylinder case.
7. Apply Permabond A136 or equivalent to crankcase on cylinder case sealing surfaces. Be sure to rout sealant around bolt holes.
8. Install crankcase on cylinder case.
9. Coat new bolts and washers located at main bearing journals with engine oil. Do not coat other crankcase to cylinder case attaching bolts.
10. Install all crankcase to cylinder case bolts finger tight. Do not rotate crankshaft until bolts have been tighten to final torque reading.
11. **Torque** crankcase to cylinder case attaching bolts to specified torque in sequence shown in **Fig. 21. Torque** bolts listed in numbered sequence first, then tighten bolts listed in lettered sequence.
12. Lubricate pistons, connecting rod bearings, cylinder liner bores and crank pin journals with engine oil.
13. Using a suitable ring compressor install piston and rod assemblies into cylinder liner bores and locate rod and bearing on crankshaft.
14. Install connecting rod bearings and caps. **Torque** new connecting bolts to 22 ft. lbs., then tighten bolts an additional 80° to 85° using tool No. J-36660 or equivalent. Rotate crankshaft as necessary to install piston and connecting rod assemblies.
15. Install oil pan and gasket, then invert engine. Apply Loctite 242 or equiva-

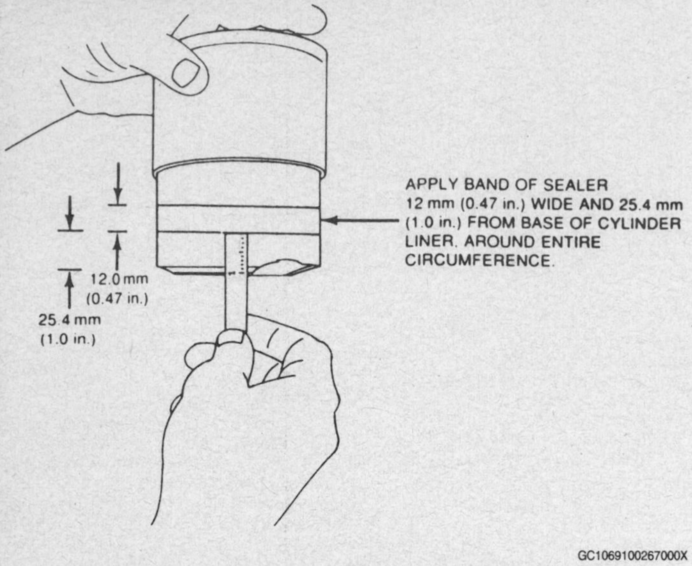
APPLY BAND OF SEALER
12 mm (0.47 in.) WIDE AND 25.4 mm
(1.0 in.) FROM BASE OF CYLINDER
LINER. AROUND ENTIRE
CIRCUMFERENCE.
12.0 mm
(0.47 in.)
25.4 mm
(1.0 in.)
GC1069100267000X

Fig. 20 Applying sealer to cylinder liner outer surface

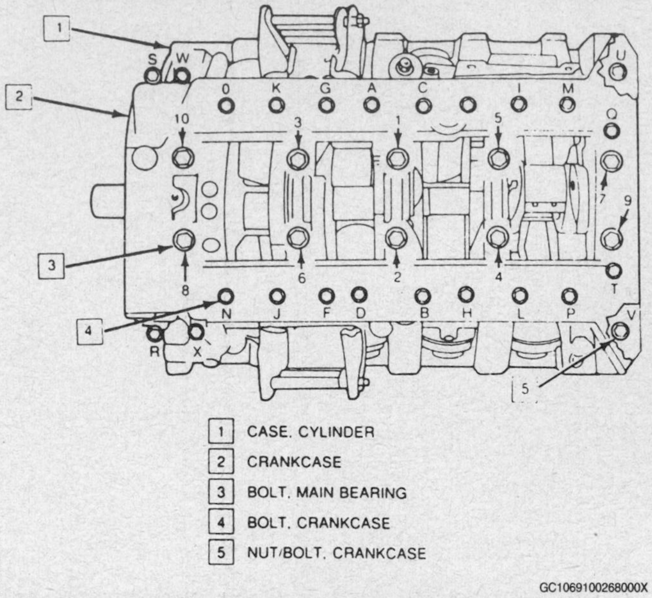
1 CASE, CYLINDER
2 CRANKCASE
3 BOLT, MAIN BEARING
4 BOLT, CRANKCASE
5 NUT/BOLT, CRANKCASE
GC1069100268000X

Fig. 21 Crankcase to cylinder case bolt tightening sequence

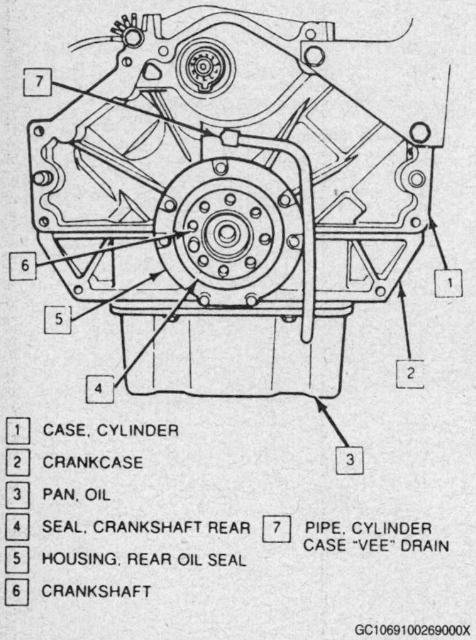
1 CASE, CYLINDER
2 CRANKCASE
3 PAN, OIL
4 SEAL, CRANKSHAFT REAR
5 HOUSING, REAR OIL SEAL
6 CRANKSHAFT
7 PIPE, CYLINDER CASE "VEE" DRAIN
GC1069100269000X

Fig. 22 Crankshaft rear seal & housing

lent to all oil pan attaching screws.
16. Remove cylinder liner retainers, then install oil pump.
17. Install cylinder heads.
18. Install crankshaft rear oil seal housing.
19. Apply Loctite 262 or equivalent to flywheel attaching bolt threads, then install flywheel. Flywheel must be installed with crankshaft dowel pin at the 6 o'clock position.
20. Install engine in vehicle.

CRANKSHAFT REAR OIL SEAL

REPLACE

1. Disconnect battery ground cable.
2. Remove transmission and clutch assembly.
3. Remove flywheel from crankshaft.
4. Remove oil seal housing to cylinder block attaching screws.
5. Remove seal housing assembly from crankshaft, then remove seal from housing, **Fig. 22.**
6. Reverse procedure to install. Using tool J-37312 or equivalent, install seal into housing until it is 1 to 1.5 mm below housing surface. Lubricate seal lip with engine oil prior to installation.

OIL PAN

REPLACE

1. Disconnect battery ground cable.
2. Remove oil level dipstick from tube.
3. Raise and support vehicle, then drain oil from crankcase.
4. Remove flywheel housing cover attaching bolts, then remove cover.
5. Disconnect low oil level sensor electrical connector, then remove oil level sensor, if equipped.
6. Remove bolts attaching AIR pipe bracket to oil pan.
7. Remove converter heat shield attaching screws, then remove heat shields.
8. Remove engine mount retaining nuts at front crossmember rear brace from left and righthand sides.
9. Remove bolts attaching front crossmember rear braces to front crossmember and side crossmembers, then remove braces.
10. Remove bolts attaching oil pan to engine block, then remove oil pan, **Fig. 23.**
11. Disassemble oil pan, if necessary, as follows:
    a. Remove baffle to oil pan attaching bolts, then remove baffle.
    b. Remove bolt and spacer attaching oil pickup assembly to oil pan, then remove pickup assembly. Clean oil pickup assembly with suitable solvent and dry with compressed air.
12. Assemble oil pan, if necessary, as follows:
    a. Install oil pickup assembly to oil pan. Prior to installation, apply Loctite 565 or equivalent to oil pan and oil pickup assembly joint. Also apply Loctite 262 or equivalent to oil pickup assembly mounting bolt threads.
    b. Install baffle to oil pan. Prior to installation, apply Loctite 262 or equivalent to bolt threads.
13. Reverse procedure to install. Apply Loctite 242 or equivalent to all oil pan attaching screws. Tighten bolts in sequence shown in **Fig. 23.**

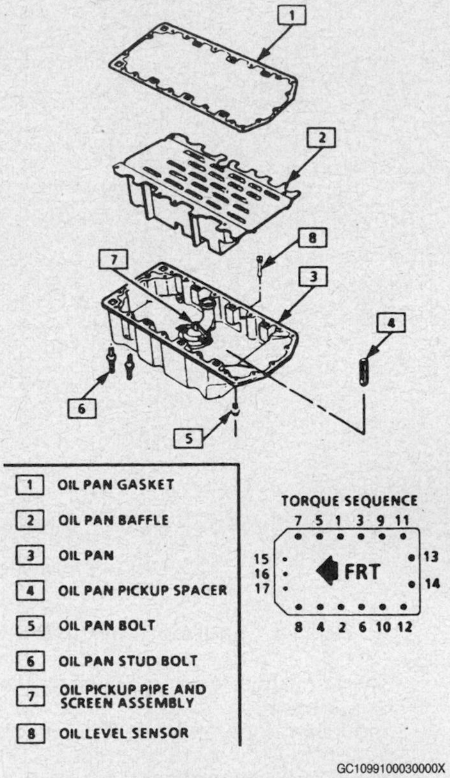
1 OIL PAN GASKET
2 OIL PAN BAFFLE
3 OIL PAN
4 OIL PAN PICKUP SPACER
5 OIL PAN BOLT
6 OIL PAN STUD BOLT
7 OIL PICKUP PIPE AND SCREEN ASSEMBLY
8 OIL LEVEL SENSOR
TORQUE SEQUENCE
7 5 1 3 9 11
15 16 17
FRT
13 14
8 4 2 6 10 12
GC1099100030000X

Fig. 23 Oil pan, baffle & gasket

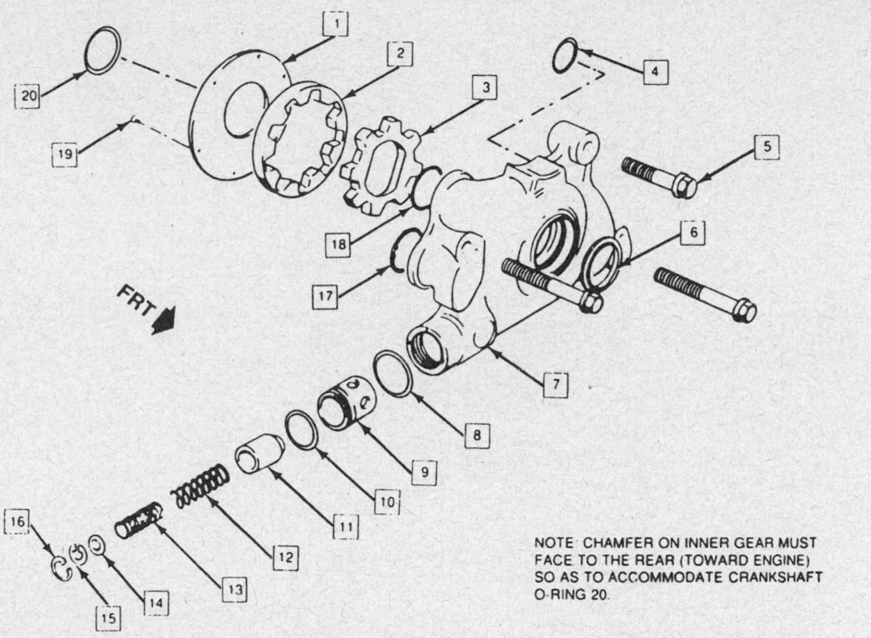
1
2
3
4
5
6
7
8
9
10
11
12
13
14
15
16
17
18
19
20
FRT
NOTE: CHAMFER ON INNER GEAR MUST FACE TO THE REAR (TOWARD ENGINE) SO AS TO ACCOMMODATE CRANKSHAFT O-RING 20.

1	PLATE, OIL PUMP	11	VALVE, OIL PRESSURE REGULATION
2	GEAR, OUTER	12	SPRING, OIL PRESSURE REGULATION VALVE OUTER
3	GEAR, INNER	13	SPRING, OIL PRESSURE REGULATION VALVE INNER
4	O-RING, OIL PUMP BODY	14	STOP, OIL PRESSURE REGULATION VALVE
5	BOLT, OIL PUMP	15	RETAINER, OIL PRESSURE REGULATION VALVE
6	SEAL, OIL PUMP CRANKSHAFT	16	RETAINER, OIL PRESSURE REGULATION VALVE
7	BODY, OIL PUMP	17	O-RING, OIL FILTER FEED RETURN
8	O-RING, OIL PRESSURE REGULATION VALVE	18	O-RING, OIL FILTER FEED RETURN
9	HOUSING, OIL PRESSURE REGULATION VALVE	19	SCREW, OIL PUMP PLATE
10	O-RING, OIL PRESSURE REGULATION VALVE	20	O-RING, OIL PUMP CRANKSHAFT

CC1089100031000X

Fig. 24 Exploded view of oil pump

OIL PUMP

REPLACE

REMOVAL

1. Disconnect battery ground cable.
2. Remove crankshaft sprocket as described under "Crankshaft Sprocket, Replace."
3. Remove bolts attaching oil pump to engine block, then remove oil pump.
4. Remove O-ring from crankshaft.
5. Remove oil pump shaft seal using tool No. J-29077-A or equivalent.

INSTALLATION

1. Position O-ring on crankshaft.
2. Apply Loctite 262 or equivalent to oil pump attaching bolt threads.
3. Position oil pump to engine, aligning flats on oil pump drive gear with flats on crankshaft.
4. Install oil pump to engine block attaching bolts and finger tighten.
5. Using tool No. J-38383 or equivalent, align oil pump on crankshaft, then tighten oil pump to engine block attaching bolts.
6. Install oil pump shaft seal using tool Nos. J-38135 and J-38463 or equivalent.
7. Install crankshaft sprocket.

OIL PUMP SERVICE

DISASSEMBLE

1. Remove oil pump plate to pump housing attaching screws, then remove plate, **Fig. 24.**
2. Remove inner and outer gears from pump housing.
3. Remove snap ring retaining pressure regulator valve to pump housing, then remove pressure regulator valve.
4. Remove snap ring from pressure regulator valve and disassembly valve, if necessary.
5. Remove oil pump shaft seal using tool No. J-29077-A or equivalent, if not removed during disassembly.
6. Remove O-rings from pump housing.

ASSEMBLE

1. Install O-rings into pump housing, **Fig. 24.**
2. Assemble pressure regulator valve and install snap ring.
3. Position pressure regulator valve into pump housing, then install snap ring.
4. Position inner and outer gears into pump housing. Place inner gear into pump housing with chamfer facing rear of pump housing (toward engine). Place outer pump gear in housing with chamfer facing toward recess in pump housing.
5. Position pump plate to pump housing, then install attaching screws.

OIL FILTER

REPLACE

1. Disconnect battery ground cable.
2. Drain cooling system.
3. Remove air intake duct.
4. Disconnect hoses from coolant outlets and radiator inlet.
5. Remove clamps from inlet pipe, then remove inlet pipe and hose assembly.
6. Rotate serpentine belt tensioner, then slip belt behind water pump pulley.
7. Release belt tensioner, then remove belt from pulleys.
8. Remove serpentine drive belt tensioner attaching bolt and tensioner.
9. Remove oil filter.
10. Disconnect electrical connectors from oil pressure, oil temperature and low oil pressure switches.
11. Remove oil pressure sensor from filter housing.
12. Remove bolt attaching outlet pipe to alternator bracket.
13. Disconnect oil cooler lines from oil filter housing.
14. Remove oil filter housing to engine block attaching bolts, then remove oil filter housing, **Fig. 25.**
15. Reverse procedure to install. Apply Loctite 565 or equivalent to threads of oil pressure sensor and outlet pipe bracket to alternator bracket bolt.

OIL COOLER

REPLACE

1. Disconnect battery ground cable.
2. Drain cooling system.
3. Remove air cleaner assembly.
4. Remove radiator upper air deflector.
5. Disconnect electrical connectors from cooling fan relays.
6. Remove accumulator bracket to upper radiator support attaching bolts.
7. Remove fan shroud to upper radiator attaching screws.
8. Remove rubber access plug from upper part of radiator, then disconnect radiator air bleed hose.
9. Remove bolts and nuts attaching upper radiator support to frame side member.
10. Remove oil cooler line to oil cooler attaching bolts, then remove seal retainers and seals from oil cooler and A/C lines.
11. Remove AIR pump.
12. Remove AIR rear bracket bolt and loosen front bracket bolt.
13. Remove AIR pump intake duct, then remove bolt attaching upper radiator support to lower support.

14. Remove upper radiator support from vehicle.
15. Disconnect upper and lower radiator hoses from radiator, then remove radiator from vehicle.
16. Disconnect oil cooler lines from oil cooler. Cap oil cooler lines and fittings.
17. Remove oil cooler to condenser attaching screws, then remove oil cooler, **Fig. 26.**
18. Reverse procedure to install. Ensure oil cooler O-rings are properly positioned prior to installation.

CYLINDER CASE VENTILATION COVER & BAFFLE

REPLACE

1. Disconnect battery ground cable.
2. Remove plenum as described under "Plenum Assembly, Replace."
3. Discharge A/C system, then remove A/C compressor.
4. Disconnect spark plug wires from coil pack, then remove bolts attaching ignition coil pack to ventilation cover and cylinder case.
5. Disconnect electrical connectors, then remove ignition coil pack assembly.
6. Disconnect vacuum hoses from vacuum reservoir, then remove reservoir attaching nuts and reservoir.
7. Disconnect vacuum hoses and electrical connector from vacuum solenoid, then remove vacuum solenoid attaching screw and vacuum solenoid.
8. Disconnect vacuum hoses from secondary port throttle actuators, then remove actuator to bracket attaching nuts and retaining clips and remove actuators.
9. Remove actuator bracket to control cover attaching screws, then remove covers.
10. Disconnect links from lever assemblies.
11. Disconnect electrical connectors from coolant temperature sensor and cooling fan switch, then remove sensor and switch from injector housing.
12. Disconnect hoses from ventilation cover, then remove ventilation cover attaching screws and ventilation cover, **Fig. 27.**
13. Remove cylinder case ventilation baffle attaching screws, then remove baffle, **Fig. 28.**
14. Reverse procedure to install. Prior to installing coolant sensor and cooling fan switch, apply Loctite 565 or equivalent to threads.

BELT TENSION DATA

Engine (VIN)	New Lbs.	Used Lbs.
5.7L/V8-350 (J)	①	①

①—Controlled by belt tensioner.

SERPENTINE DRIVE BELT

1. Disconnect battery ground cable.

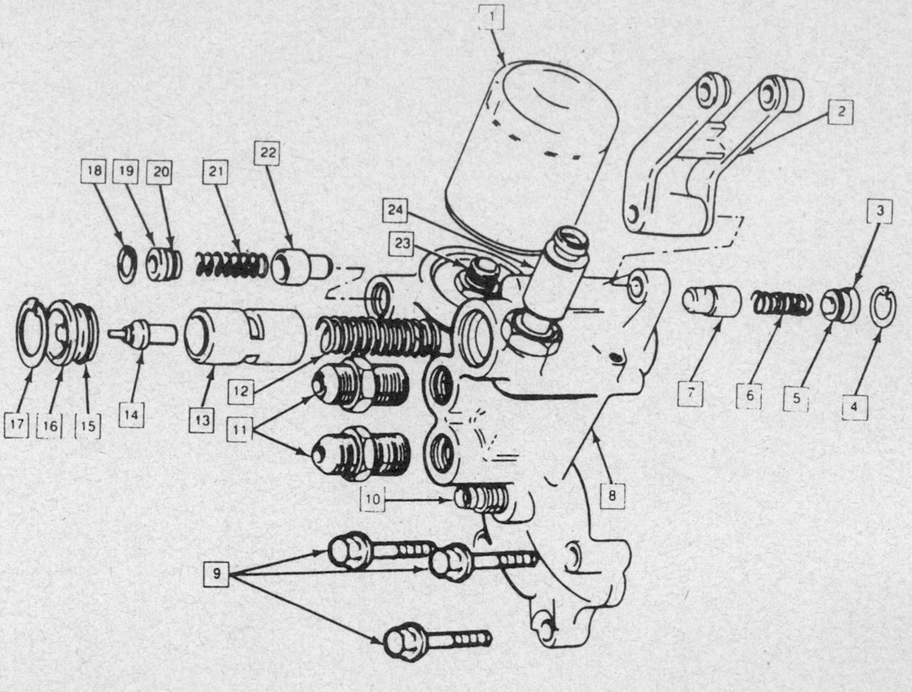

1 FILTER, OIL
2 BRACKET, OIL FILTER HOUSING
3 CAP, OIL COOLER BYPASS SEAL
4 RETAINER, OIL COOLER BYPASS VALVE
5 O-RING, OIL COOLER BYPASS VALVE
6 SPRING, OIL COOLER BYPASS VALVE
7 VALVE, OIL COOLER BYPASS
8 HOUSING, OIL FILTER
9 BOLT, OIL FILTER HOUSING
10 SENSOR, OIL TEMPERATURE
11 ADAPTER, OIL COOLER
12 SPRING, OIL TEMPERATURE CONTROL VALVE
13 SLEEVE, OIL TEMPERATURE CONTROL VALVE
14 VALVE, OIL TEMPERATURE CONTROL
15 O-RING, OIL TEMPERATURE CONTROL VALVE
16 DISC, OIL TEMPERATURE CONTROL VALVE SEAL
17 RETAINER, OIL TEMPERATURE CONTROL VALVE
18 RETAINER, OIL FILTER BYPASS VALVE
19 CAP, OIL FILTER BYPASS VALVE SEAL
20 O-RING, OIL FILTER BYPASS VALVE
21 SPRING, OIL FILTER BYPASS VALVE
22 VALVE, OIL FILTER BYPASS
23 ADAPTER, OIL FILTER
24 SENSOR, OIL PRESSURE

GC1099100032000X

Fig. 25 Oil filter housing assembly

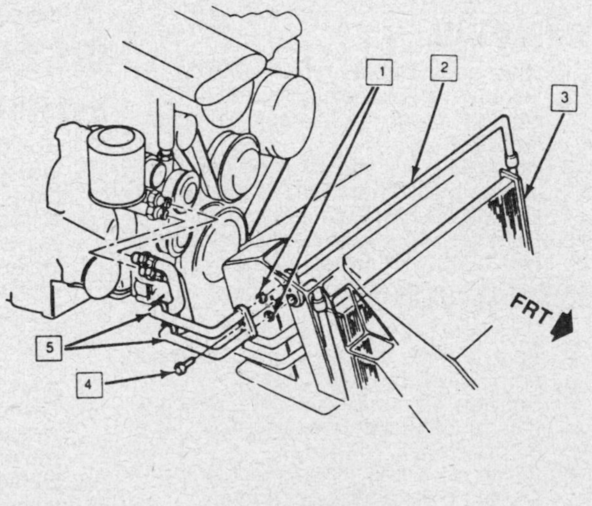
FRT

1 O-RING, ENGINE OIL COOLER
2 PIPE, ENGINE OIL COOLER
3 COOLER, ENGINE OIL
4 BOLT, ENGINE OIL COOLER
5 HOSE, ENGINE OIL COOLER

GC1099100033000X

Fig. 26 Oil cooler assembly replacement

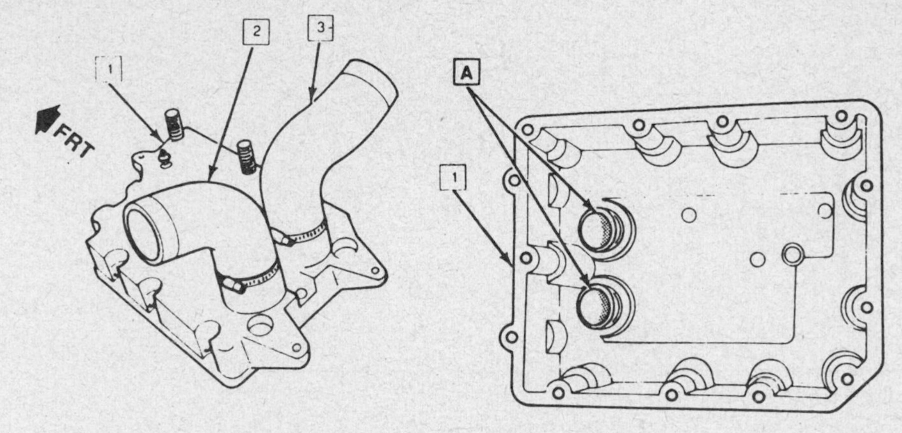
FRT

A PASSAGE. CYLINDER CASE VENTILATION COVER
1 COVER. CYLINDER CASE VENTILATION
2 HOSE. CYLINDER CASE VENTILATION - LEFT HAND
3 HOSE. CYLINDER CASE VENTILATION - RIGHT HAND

GC1069100583000X

Fig. 27 Cylinder case ventilation cover

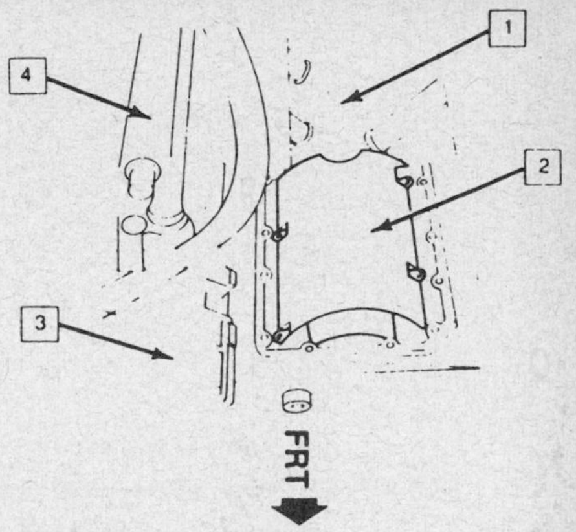
FRT

1 CASE. CYLINDER
2 BAFFLE. CYLINDER CASE VENTILATION
3 HEAD. CYLINDER
4 RAIL. FUEL

GC1069100271000X

Fig. 28 Cylinder case ventilation baffle

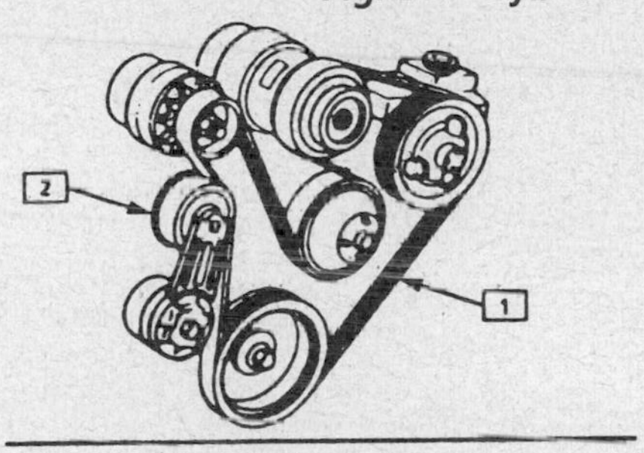

1 SERPENTINE DRIVE BELT
2 BELT TENSIONER

GC1069100272000X

Fig. 29 Serpentine drive belt routing

2. Remove air intake duct from throttle body extension.
3. Using a 1/2 inch ratchet, retract serpentine drive belt tensioner.
4. Lift belt rearward, off water pump pulley, then remove belt from vehicle.
5. Reverse procedure to install. Refer to **Fig. 29.** for serpentine belt routing.

COOLING SYSTEM BLEED

After filling cooling system, start engine and allow to reach operating temperature with radiator cap removed. Air in system will be bled through radiator cap opening. Add coolant as necessary to bring level to bottom of high fill reservoir neck, then install radiator cap and check coolant level in recovery reservoir.

THERMOSTAT

REPLACE

1. Disconnect battery ground cable.
2. Remove surge tank cap, then drain cooling system.
3. Raise and support vehicle.
4. Remove bolts attaching thermostat housing sections, **Fig. 30.**
5. Loosen bolts attaching housing bracket to front side member.
6. Remove thermostat and seal, **Fig. 31.**
7. Reverse procedure to install. Thermostat should be installed with taper toward radiator. Ensure seal is properly in housing.

WATER PUMP

REPLACE

1. Disconnect battery ground cable.
2. Drain cooling system.
3. Remove air intake duct.
4. Remove throttle body extension attaching screws, then remove extension from throttle body.
5. Disconnect hoses from coolant inlets and outlet and radiator upper hose.
6. Remove hose and inlet pipe assembly from vehicle.
7. Remove serpentine drive belt.
8. Remove bolt attaching serpentine drive belt tensioner to water pump, then remove tensioner.
9. Disconnect engine to water pump hose.
10. Remove bolts attaching lower alternator mounting bracket, then remove bracket. Note length and location of bolts for installation.
11. Remove water pump to front cover attaching bolts, **Fig. 32.**
12. Remove bolt attaching A/C compressor to water pump.
13. Remove water pump from engine.
14. Reverse procedure to install. Apply Loctite 565 or equivalent to alternator lower bracket attaching bolt threads prior to installation.

RADIATOR

REPLACE

1. Disconnect battery ground cable.
2. Drain coolant from radiator.
3. Remove upper radiator support, **Fig. 33.**

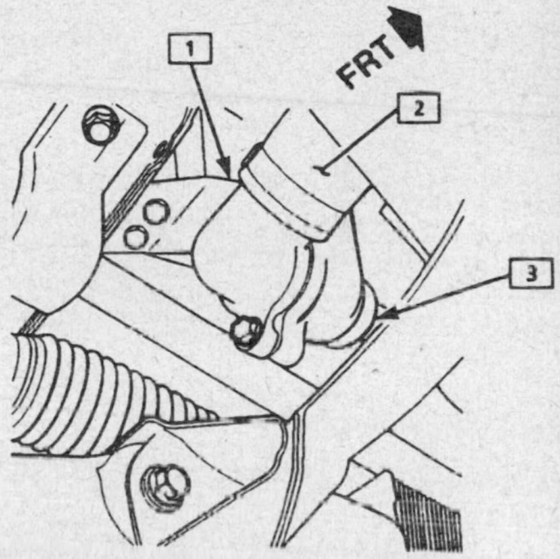
FRT

1 THERMOSTAT BRACKET
2 RADIATOR OUTLET HOSE
3 THERMOSTAT HOUSING

GC1069100136000X

Fig. 30 Thermostat housing location

4. Disconnect radiator inlet and outlet hoses at radiator.
5. **On models equipped with automatic transmission,** disconnect transmission oil cooler lines at radiator.
6. **On all models,**remove radiator from vehicle.
7. Reverse procedure to install, noting the following:
   a. **Torque** automatic transmission oil cooler lines to 20 ft. lbs.
   b. Check and fill engine coolant and transmission fluid levels.

FUEL PUMP

REPLACE

The fuel is an electric in tank design at-

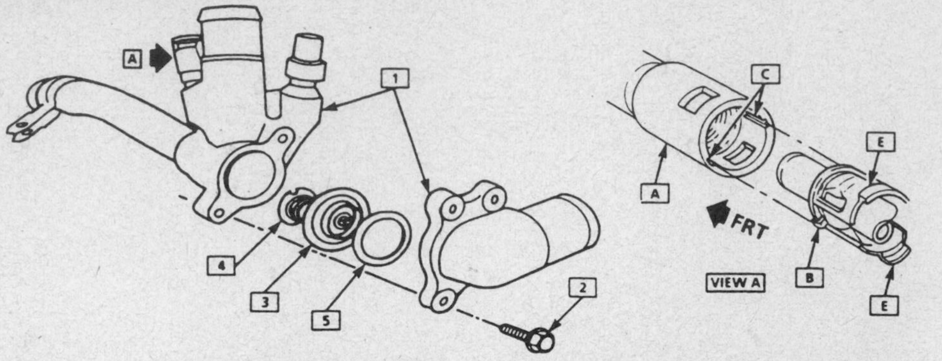
A
1
C
E
A
FRT
4
3
5
2
VIEW A
B
E
A QUICK CONNECT FITTING
B ORIENTATION TAB
C GROOVE
E RELEASE TAB
1 THERMOSTAT HOUSING
2 BOLT
3 THERMOSTAT SEAL
4 THERMOSTAT
5 SEAL
GC1089100137000X

Fig. 31 Thermostat assembly

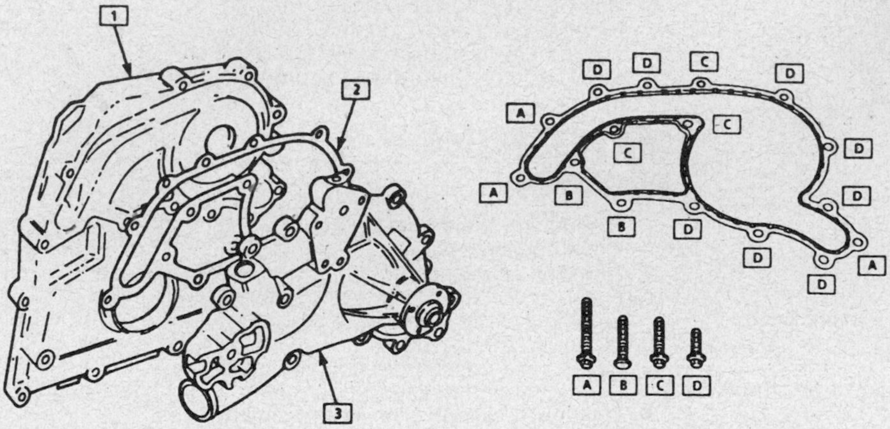
1
2
3
D
D
C
D
A
C
C
D
A
B
D
B
D
D
D
A
D
A B C D
1 ENGINE FRONT COVER
2 COOLANT PUMP GASKET
3 COOLANT PUMP
GC1089100138000X

Fig. 32 Water pump installation & bolt locations

tached to the fuel level sending unit. Replace fuel pump as follows:

1. Disconnect battery ground cable.
2. Connect pressure gauge J-34370-1 or equivalent to pressure tap on fuel rail, position bleed hose in suitable container and slowly relieve fuel system pressure. **Failure to relieve system pressure prior to disconnecting fuel system components may cause fire or personal injury.**
3. Drain fuel tank. Drain fuel into an approved fuel storage container.
4. Remove fuel filler door bezel attaching screws, then remove bezel, **Fig. 34.**
5. Remove fuel filler cap, then lift fuel filler neck housing and disconnect drain hose.
6. Remove fuel meter and pump attaching screws.
7. Disconnect fuel lines, hoses and electrical connectors from fuel meter and pump assembly. Tag hoses and electrical connectors so they may be installed at the same location.
8. Carefully remove fuel meter and pump assembly.
9. Reverse procedure to install.

FUEL FILTER
REPLACE

1. Relieve fuel system pressure as outlined under "Precautions."
2. Raise and support vehicle.
3. Clean all fuel filter connections and surrounding areas.
4. Disconnect fuel feed pipes from filter, **Fig. 35,** then drain remaining fuel into suitable container.
5. Remove filter mounting screw, then the fuel filter.
6. Reverse procedure to install.

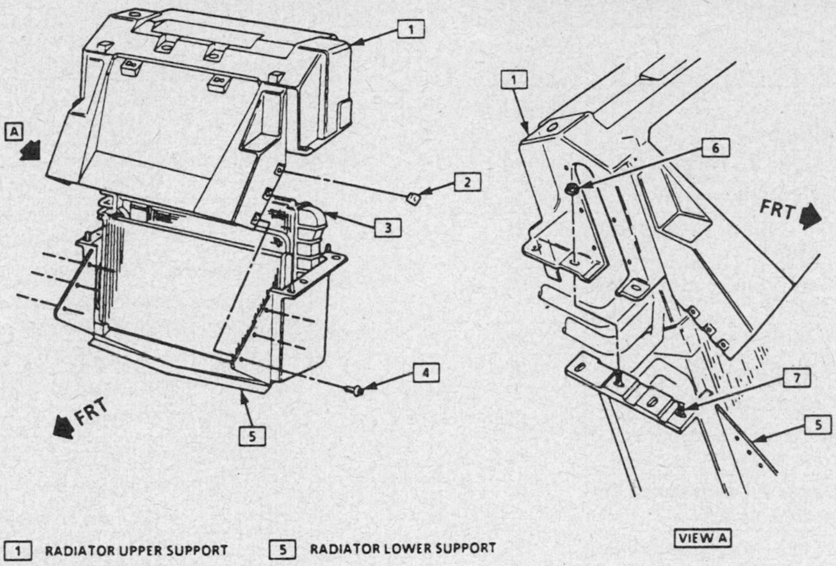
1
A
2
3
4
FRT
5
1
6
FRT
7
5
VIEW A

1 RADIATOR UPPER SUPPORT
2 SPEED NUT
3 RADIATOR
4 SCREW
5 RADIATOR LOWER SUPPORT
6 STUD NUT
7 STUD

GC1089200245000X

Fig. 33 Radiator upper support removal

1 GASKET
2 FUEL LEVEL METER ASSEMBLY
3 FILLER NECK HOUSING
4 FUEL FILLER CAP
5 NIPPLE
6 DRAIN HOSE
7 SCREW ASSEMBLY (WITH O – RING) 4.5 N·m (40 LB. IN.)
8 FILLER DOOR BEZEL
9 SCREW

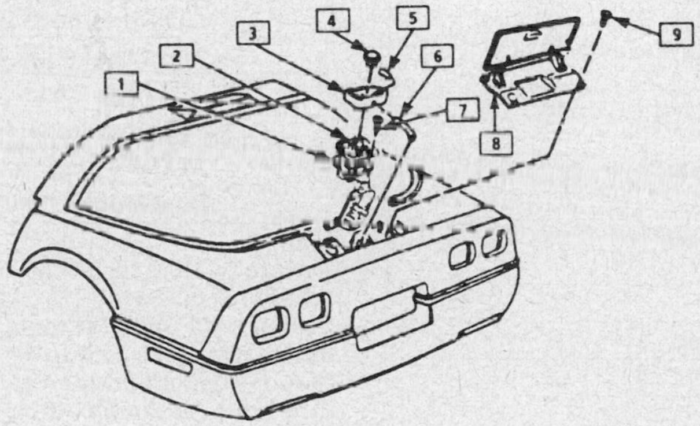
1
2
3
4
5
6
7
8
9

GC1029102718000X

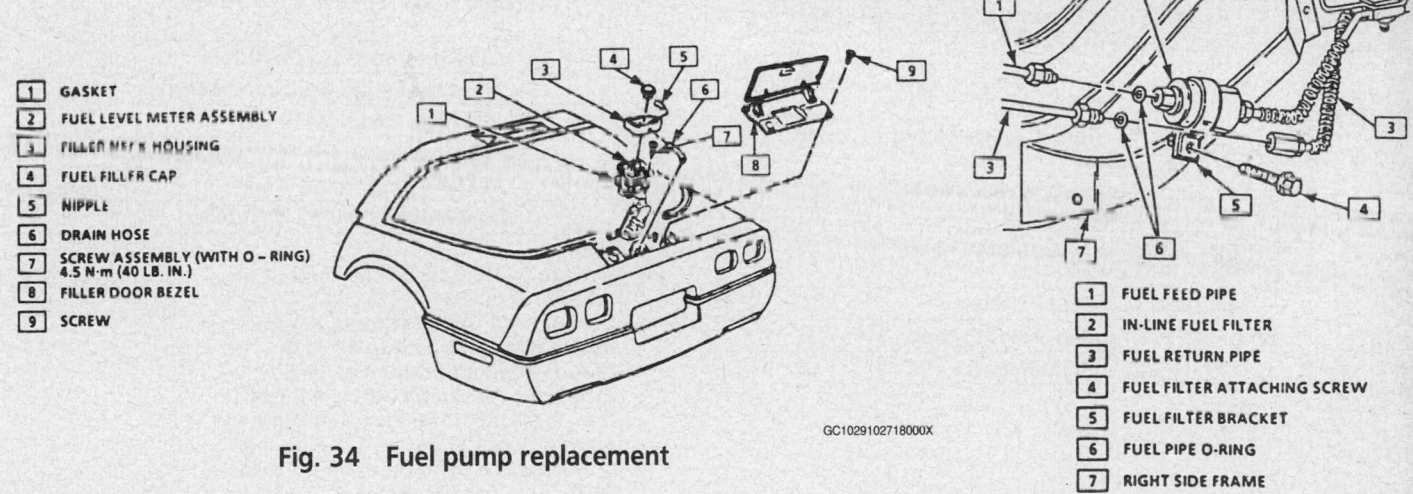

Fig. 34 Fuel pump replacement

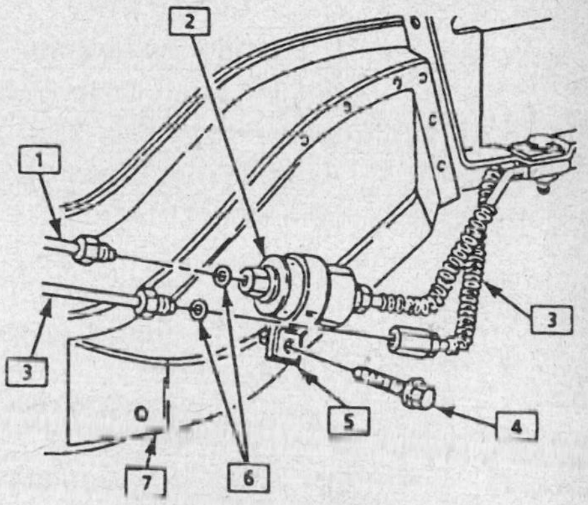
2
1
3
3
5
4
7
6

1 FUEL FEED PIPE
2 IN-LINE FUEL FILTER
3 FUEL RETURN PIPE
4 FUEL FILTER ATTACHING SCREW
5 FUEL FILTER BRACKET
6 FUEL PIPE O-RING
7 RIGHT SIDE FRAME

GC1029102719000X

Fig. 35 Fuel filter replacement

TIGHTENING SPECIFICATIONS

Year	Component	Torque/Ft. Lbs.
1992-95	AIR Pipe Bracket To Oil Pan	19
	Belt Tensioner To Water Pump	45
	Camshaft Cover To Cylinder Head Bolt (M6)	89①
	Camshaft Cover To Cylinder Head Bolt (M8)	15
	Camshaft Position Sensor	71①
	Camshaft Retainer Bolt	89①
	Camshaft Sprocket Bolt	②
	Coolant Outlet Cover To Injector Housing	89①
	Coolant Outlet Cover Pipe Bracket To Alternator Bracket	38
	Coolant Outlet Cover Pipe Bracket To Power Steering Pump Bracket	19
	Crankcase To Cylinder Case Bolts	③
	Crankshaft Damper Bolt	148
	Cylinder Case Ventilation Baffle To Cylinder Case	89①
	Cylinder Case Ventilation Cover To Cylinder Case	89①
	Cylinder Head Bolts	118
	Engine Front Cover Bolt	19
	Engine Front Cover Stud Nut	21
	Engine Front Cover Stud	97①
	Engine Mount To Engine Bolts	38
	Engine Mount To Drivetrain & Frame Nut	40
	Engine Mount To Front Crossmember Nut	40
	Engine Timing Plate To Front Cover Bolts	89①
	Exhaust Manifold To Cylinder Head Bolt & Stud Nut	18
	Exhaust Manifold To Stud	22
	Exhaust Pipe To Converter Flange	15
	Flywheel To Crankshaft	66

Year	Component	Torque/Ft. Lbs.
1992-95	Front Crossmember Rear Brace To Crossmember Bolt	59
	Front Crossmember Rear Brace To Side Member	46
	Fuel Rail To Injector Housing Bolt	19
	Ignition Coil Pack Bracket To Cylinder Case Ventilation Cover	89①
	Injector Housing To Cylinder Head	19
	MAT Sensor Bracket	71①
	Oil Dipstick Tube To Exhaust Manifold	11
	Oil Filter Housing To Cylinder Case	19
	Oil Pan Baffle To Oil Pan Bolt	89①
	Oil Pan Drain Plug	38
	Oil Pan To Crankcase	23
	Oil Pick-up Tube To Oil Pan Bolt	89①
	Oil Pressure Sensor	9
	Oil Pump Plate To Housing	26①
	Oil Pump To Cylinder Case	19
	Plenum To Injector Housing	19
	Secondary Timing Chain Pivot Guide To Cylinder Case	19
	Spark Plug	15
	Thermostat Housing Bolt	18
	Throttle Body Extension To Throttle Body	53①
	Throttle Body To Plenum	11
	Timing Chain Idler Sprocket Bolts	20
	Timing Chain Tensioner	89①
	Transmission To Clutch Housing Bolts	37
	Water Pump Pulley To Hub	89①
	Water Pump To Cylinder Case	20

①—Inch Lbs.
②—Torque to 19 ft. lbs., then tighten an additional 80–85°.
③—Torque M12 bolts (at main bearing journal Nos. 1, 3 & 5) to 30 ft. lbs., then tighten an additional 45–50°; M10 bolts (at main bearing journal Nos. 2 & 4) to 15 ft. lbs., then tighten an additional 77.5–82.5°; remaining crankcase to cylinder case bolts to 20 ft. lbs.

Clutch & Manual Transmission

INDEX

ADJUSTMENTS

CLUTCH PEDAL

The clutch release mechanism on these models is hydraulically operated, and is not adjustable. When the clutch pedal is depressed, the pedal pushrod contacts a plunger in the clutch master cylinder bore. The plunger first closes off the master cylinder fluid return port, then when moved further, forces fluid under pressure into the clutch actuating cylinder. As pressure is applied to the actuating cylinder, the actuating cylinder piston is forced outward activating the clutch release fork. To diagnose malfunctions in the clutch release system, proceed as follows:

SHIFT LINKAGE

The gear shift lever assembly is floor mounted and located on top of extension housing. The shift assembly does not require adjustment.

HYDRAULIC SYSTEM SERVICE

INSPECTION

1. With engine running at normal operating temperature and brakes applied, hold clutch pedal in fully depressed position and move transmission selector between 1st and reverse several times.
2. If transmission selector can be moved without binding or gear clash, clutch is releasing properly.
3. If shifter cannot be moved or if gear clash is evident, inspect clutch pedal bushings for damage and wear, and replace as needed.
4. If bushings are satisfactory, check clutch pedal travel.
5. Clutch pedal travel should be 6.25 inch.

BLEEDING

1. Fill clutch master cylinder reservoir with clutch hydraulic fluid 12345347 or DOT 3 brake fluid. It may be necessary to remove ECM from mounting bracket to gain access to reservoir. If a squeaking noise is present in clutch master cylinder, drain DOT 3 brake fluid from clutch hydraulic system and fill with clutch hydraulic fluid 12345347 or equivalent.
2. Raise and support vehicle.
3. Remove actuating cylinder attaching bolts and lower cylinder to a point below the catalytic converter, then remove bleeder screw cap.
4. Hold cylinder in horizontal position with bleeder screw vertical.
5. Fully depress and hold clutch pedal, then open bleeder screw.
6. Close bleeder screw, then release clutch pedal.
7. Repeat steps 4 and 5 until all air has been purged from system, remount actuating cylinder and repeat inspection. **Check and fill master cylinder reservoir, as needed, to ensure no air is drawn into system during bleeding.**

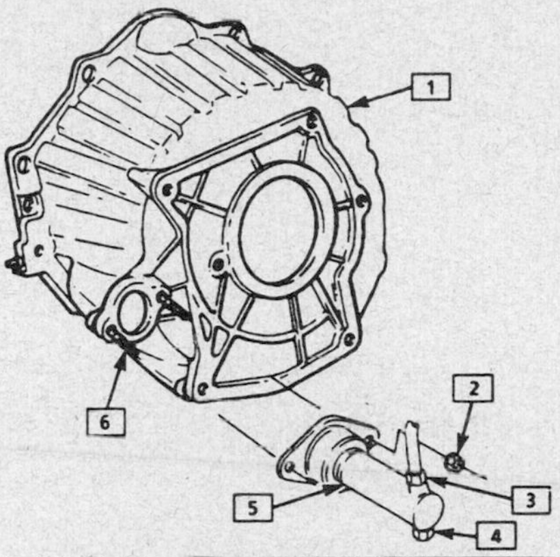

1
2
3
4
5
6

1 CLUTCH HOUSING
2 CLUTCH ACTUATOR CYLINDER STUD NUT
3 HYDRAULIC LINE
4 BLEED SCREW
5 CLUTCH ACTUATOR CYLINDER
6 CLUTCH ACTUATOR CYLINDER STUD

GC5049100037000X

Fig. 1 Clutch actuating cylinder replacement

CLUTCH ACTUATING CYLINDER, REPLACE

1. Disconnect battery ground cable.
2. Raise and support vehicle, then remove actuating cylinder stud nuts.
3. Detach hydraulic line from retaining clip. Note position of line for use during installation.
4. Remove actuating cylinder and pushrod from clutch housing. Do not allow actuating cylinder to be suspended from hydraulic line.
5. Disconnect hydraulic line and remove actuating cylinder, **Fig. 1.**
6. Reverse procedure to install. Bleed clutch hydraulic system.

CLUTCH

REPLACE

On models except ZR-1, a magnesium clutch housing may be used. On these models aluminum spacer plates will be installed between clutch housing and engine and clutch housing and transmission.

1. Disconnect battery ground cable.
2. Remove exhaust system from vehicle.
3. Remove transmission from vehicle as described under "Transmission, Replace."
4. **On models except ZR-1,** disconnect ground connection at lefthand side of clutch housing.
5. **On all models,** remove nuts attaching actuating cylinder to clutch housing, then position actuating cylinder aside. Support actuating cylinder so that hydraulic hose does not become damaged.
6. Remove starter motor from vehicle.
7. **On ZR-1 models,** remove nut attaching lefthand side catalytic converter shield to converter housing.
8. **On all models,** remove clutch cover from clutch housing.
9. Remove bolts attaching clutch housing to engine.
10. **On ZR-1 models,** remove bolt attaching righthand catalytic converter heat shield to clutch housing.
11. **On all models,** remove clutch housing. Align fork with two flats on release bearing, push fork away from bearing. It may be necessary to loosen ball stud locking screw and ball stud to remove housing.
12. Place align marks on clutch cover and flywheel for use during installation.
13. Alternately and evenly loosen clutch cover to flywheel attaching bolts one turn at a time until spring tension is relieved.
14. Remove clutch cover and clutch disc, **Fig. 2.**
15. Check flywheel for signs of lubricant leakage. Also check flywheel friction surfaces for burned or heat checked metal. Flywheel should be checked for internal looseness. Slight movement is normal. If any of the above conditions are present, replace flywheel. The flywheel should not be machined.

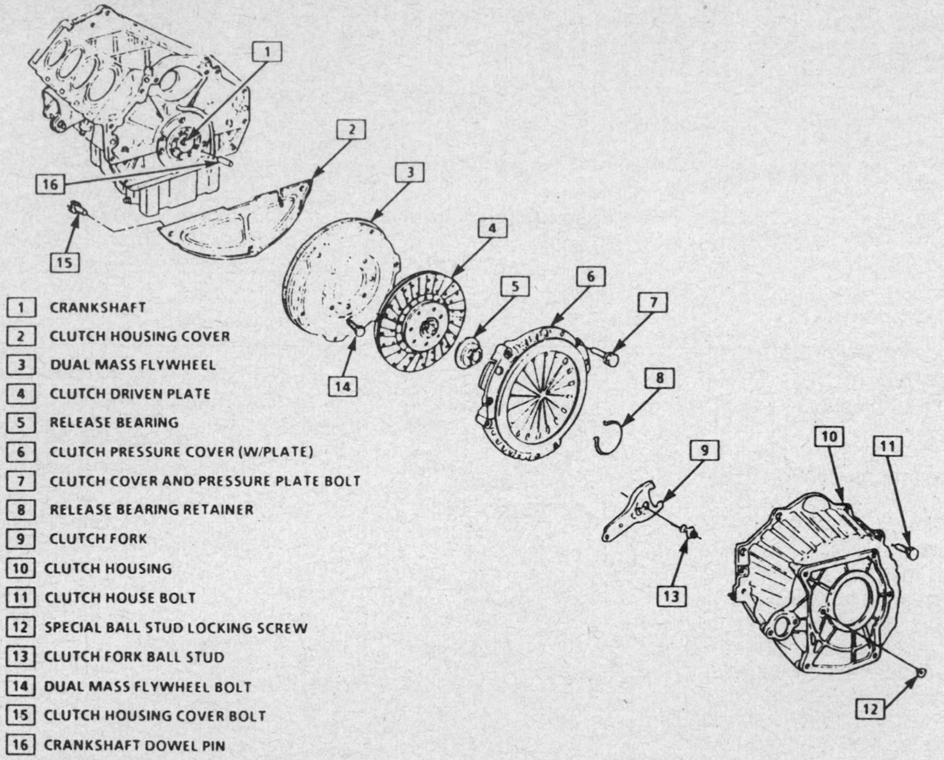
1 CRANKSHAFT
2 CLUTCH HOUSING COVER
3 DUAL MASS FLYWHEEL
4 CLUTCH DRIVEN PLATE
5 RELEASE BEARING
6 CLUTCH PRESSURE COVER (W/PLATE)
7 CLUTCH COVER AND PRESSURE PLATE BOLT
8 RELEASE BEARING RETAINER
9 CLUTCH FORK
10 CLUTCH HOUSING
11 CLUTCH HOUSE BOLT
12 SPECIAL BALL STUD LOCKING SCREW
13 CLUTCH FORK BALL STUD
14 DUAL MASS FLYWHEEL BOLT
15 CLUTCH HOUSING COVER BOLT
16 CRANKSHAFT DOWEL PIN
GC5049100038000X

Fig. 2 Exploded view of clutch assembly

16. Reverse procedure to install, noting the following:
    a. When installing clutch cover to flywheel, align marks made during removal.
    b. When installing clutch cover attaching bolts, tighten alternately and evenly in a side to side-cross pattern.
    c. Lubricate clutch fork ball and release bearing inner and outer circumference with lubricant 1052356 or equivalent

TRANSMISSION
REPLACE

On except ZR-1 models, a magnesium clutch housing may be used. On these models aluminum spacer plates will be installed between clutch housing and engine and clutch housing and transmission.

It may be necessary to remove the catalytic converter and its support bracket to facilitate transmission removal.

1. Disconnect battery ground cable.
2. Remove shift lever.
3. Remove complete exhaust system.
4. Remove front cross over hanger from transmission.
5. Remove propeller shaft.
6. Support transmission with a suitable jack, then remove driveline support beam.
7. Disconnect electrical connectors.
8. Remove transmission to clutch housing attaching bolts, then the transmission from vehicle.
9. Reverse procedure to install. When installing driveline support, apply sealer at locations shown in **Fig. 3.**

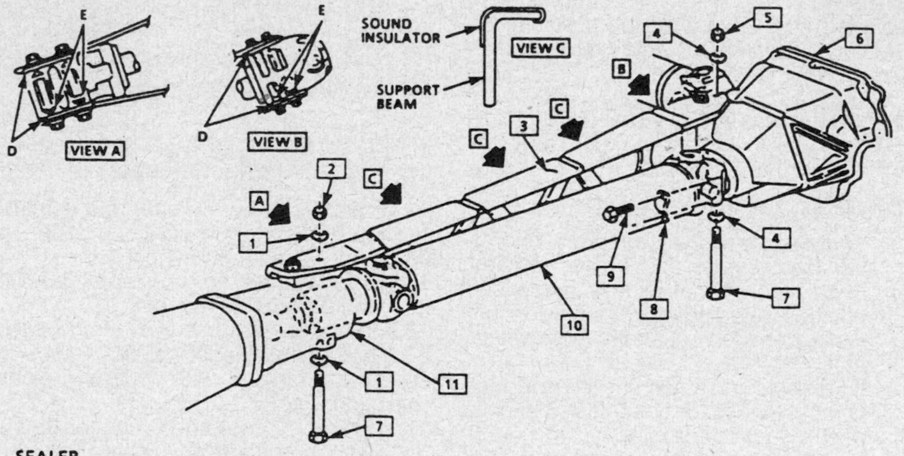
VIEW A
VIEW B
VIEW C
SOUND INSULATOR
SUPPORT BEAM
D
E
A
B
C

SEALER
APPLY A BEAD OF SEALER AROUND THE TOP AND BOTTOM MATING SURFACES OF DRIVELINE TO AXLE AND TRANSMISSION EXTENSION AT POINTS D AND ALSO TO THE CAVITY AROUND THE BOLTS AT POINTS E. USE URETHANE IN CAULKING KIT (P/N 963067) OR EQUIVALENT.

INSULATOR
REMOVE INSULATOR WITH FLAT BLADE SCRAPER AND CLEAN SURFACE. INSTALL INSULATOR BY REMOVING THE BACKING ON THE INSULATOR AND PRESSING THE INSULATOR AS SHOWN IN VIEW C TO OBTAIN ADHESION TO SUPPORT BEAM. TRIM OFF ANY OVERHANG.

1	DRIVELINE SUPPORT FRONT WASHER	5	HEX SELF-LOCKING NUT	9	PROPELLER BOLT
2	SELF-LOCKING NUT	6	REAR AXLE CARRIER	10	PROPELLER SHAFT
3	DRIVELINE SUPPORT	7	HEX BOLT	11	TRANSMISSION EXTENSION HOUSING
4	WASHER	8	PROPELLER SHAFT RETAINER		

GC5049100039000X

Fig. 3 Driveline support installation & sealer application locations

TIGHTENING SPECIFICATIONS

Year	Component	Torque/Ft. Lbs.
1992–95	Clutch Actuating Cylinder Bolts Or Nuts	19
	Clutch Cover To Flywheel	30
	Clutch Fork Ball Stud Nut	33
	Clutch Fork Ball Stud Locking Screw	20
	Clutch Housing To Engine	37
	Clutch Master Cylinder Bolts	12
	Clutch Pedal Pivot Bolt Or Nut	13
	Flywheel Bolt To Crankshaft	①
	Hydraulic Hose Fittings At Clutch Actuating Cylinder	13
1992–95 —Cont'd	Hydraulic Hose Fittings At Clutch Master Cylinder	13
	Support Beam To Differential Carrier Bolt	60
	Support Beam To Transmission Bolt	37
	Transmission Drain Plug	34
	Transmission Fill Plug	34
	Transmission To Clutch Housing Bolt	37

①—Except 1992 ZR-1 engine, 74 ft. lbs.; 1992 ZR-1 engine, 66 ft. lbs.

Rear Axle & Suspension

INDEX

REAR AXLE

REPLACE

1. Raise and support vehicle, and remove spare tire, tire cover and underbody braces, as required.
2. Remove exhaust system assembly as follows:
   a. Disconnect AIR pipe at converter and AIR pipe clamps at manifold.
   b. Disconnect electrical connector from oxygen sensor.
   c. Support exhaust system, remove bolts securing mufflers to hangers, and remove converter bracket.
   d. Disconnect exhaust pipes at manifolds and remove exhaust system.
3. Disconnect leaf spring from spindle support knuckles, then remove bolts securing spring to differential carrier and spring.
4. Scribe mark between cam bolts and brackets, then remove cam bolts and mounting bracket from carrier.
5. Disconnect tie rods from left and right spindle support knuckles.
6. Remove straps securing driveshaft universal joints to differential side yokes, push wheel and tire assemblies outward, and disconnect driveshafts from side yokes. **Tape bearing cups to universal joint yokes to prevent loss of needle bearings.**
7. Remove straps securing propeller shaft universal joint to pinion flange, push propeller shaft forward into transmission and tie shaft to support beam.
8. Support transmission and remove bolts securing differential carrier beam to frame brackets, **Fig. 1.**
9. Remove mounting bolts at front of differential carrier and carrier assembly.
10. Reverse procedure to install. When installing driveline support, apply sealer at locations shown in **Fig. 2.** Check rear suspension alignment.

REAR WHEEL SHAFT

REPLACE

1. Remove center cap from wheel.
2. Remove cotter pin, spindle nut and washer from spindle, **Fig. 3.**
3. Raise and support vehicle, and remove wheel and tire.
4. Disconnect tie rod and spring from spindle support knuckle.
5. Scribe a reference mark between cam bolt and bracket, remove cam bolt and separate spindle support rod from bracket.
6. Remove straps securing inner universal joint to drive yoke, pull knuckle assembly outward, and disconnect shaft from yoke. **Tape bearing cups to universal joint yoke to prevent loss of needle bearings.**
7. Pull spindle out of hub and remove rear wheel shaft.
8. Reverse procedure to install, torquing cam bolt and spindle nut to specifications.

PROPELLER SHAFT

REPLACE

1. With transmission in neutral and parking brake released, raise and support vehicle, then remove underbody braces, as required.
2. Remove exhaust system as follows:
   a. Disconnect AIR pipe from catalytic converter and exhaust pipe.
   b. Disconnect electrical connector to oxygen sensor.
   c. Remove bolts securing muffler to hangers, disconnect exhaust pipes from manifolds and remove exhaust system as an assembly.
3. Support transmission, remove support beam retaining bolts and support beam.
4. Mark position of shaft in relation to pinion flange for installation.
5. Remove straps securing universal joint to pinion flange, then disconnect shaft from flange. **Tape bearing cups to universal joint to prevent loss of needle bearings.**
6. Slide yoke out of transmission and remove propeller shaft. Insert suitable plug in transmission to prevent fluid loss.
7. Reverse procedure to install. When installing driveline support, apply sealer at locations shown in **Fig. 2.**

HUB & BEARING

REPLACE

1. Remove rear wheel shaft assembly

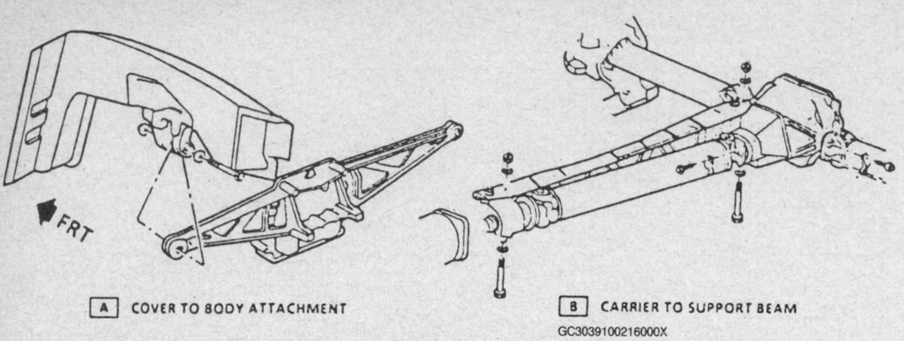
FRT
A COVER TO BODY ATTACHMENT
B CARRIER TO SUPPORT BEAM
GC3039100216000X

Fig. 1 Differential carrier attachment

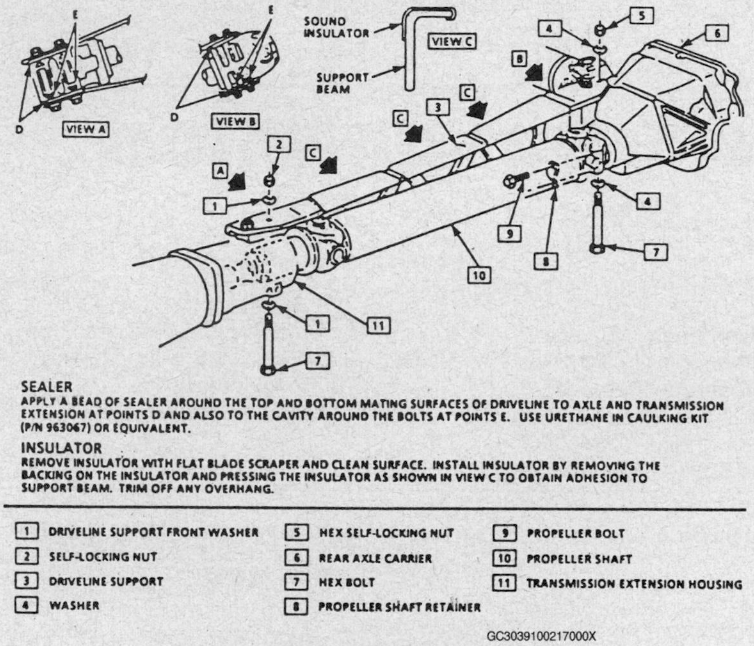
SOUND INSULATOR
SUPPORT BEAM
VIEW C
VIEW A
VIEW B
SEALER
APPLY A BEAD OF SEALER AROUND THE TOP AND BOTTOM MATING SURFACES OF DRIVELINE TO AXLE AND TRANSMISSION EXTENSION AT POINTS D AND ALSO TO THE CAVITY AROUND THE BOLTS AT POINTS E. USE URETHANE IN CAULKING KIT (P/N 963067) OR EQUIVALENT.
INSULATOR
REMOVE INSULATOR WITH FLAT BLADE SCRAPER AND CLEAN SURFACE. INSTALL INSULATOR BY REMOVING THE BACKING ON THE INSULATOR AND PRESSING THE INSULATOR AS SHOWN IN VIEW C TO OBTAIN ADHESION TO SUPPORT BEAM. TRIM OFF ANY OVERHANG.
1 DRIVELINE SUPPORT FRONT WASHER
2 SELF-LOCKING NUT
3 DRIVELINE SUPPORT
4 WASHER
5 HEX SELF-LOCKING NUT
6 REAR AXLE CARRIER
7 HEX BOLT
8 PROPELLER SHAFT RETAINER
9 PROPELLER BOLT
10 PROPELLER SHAFT
11 TRANSMISSION EXTENSION HOUSING
GC3039100217000X

Fig. 2 Driveline support installation & sealer application locations

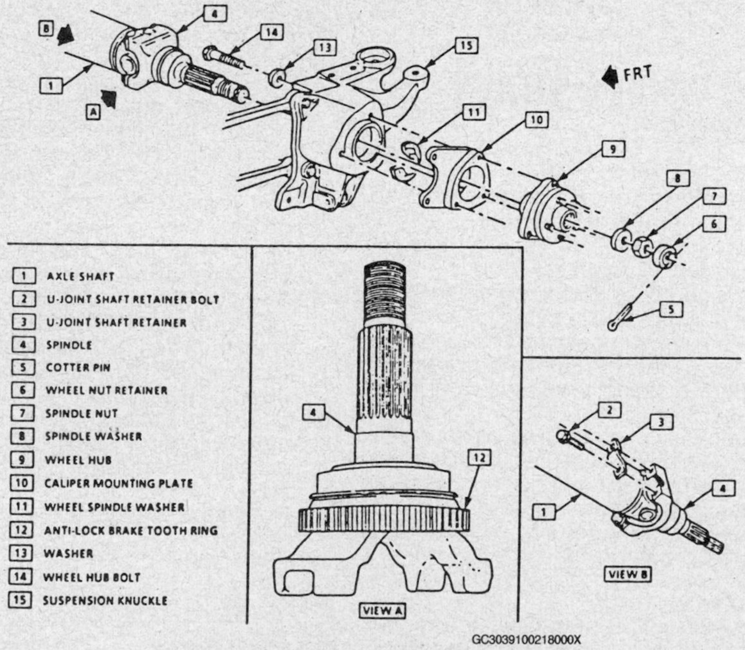
FRT
1 AXLE SHAFT
2 U-JOINT SHAFT RETAINER BOLT
3 U-JOINT SHAFT RETAINER
4 SPINDLE
5 COTTER PIN
6 WHEEL NUT RETAINER
7 SPINDLE NUT
8 SPINDLE WASHER
9 WHEEL HUB
10 CALIPER MOUNTING PLATE
11 WHEEL SPINDLE WASHER
12 ANTI-LOCK BRAKE TOOTH RING
13 WASHER
14 WHEEL HUB BOLT
15 SUSPENSION KNUCKLE
VIEW A
VIEW B
GC3039100218000X

Fig. 3 Rear wheel hub, bearing & spindle removal

as outlined in "Rear Wheel Shaft, Replace."

2. Remove wheel speed sensor.
3. Remove bolts securing brake caliper bracket to support knuckle, secure caliper aside, then remove brake rotor.
4. Remove hub and bearing retaining bolts, **Fig. 3.**
5. Remove cotter pin, wheel nut retainer, nut and washer from spindle.
6. Remove hub and bearing assembly.
7. Reverse procedure to install. Install spindle washer with flat portion against should of wheel spindle and with lip of washer facing spindle splines. Do not allow vehicle to rest on tires until after wheel spindle nut has been tightened to the specified **torque**.

SPINDLE KNUCKLE
REPLACE

1. Remove center cap from wheel, cotter pin and spindle nut.
2. Raise and support vehicle, and remove wheel and tire, then remove wheel speed sensor.
3. Remove bolts securing brake caliper to knuckle, brake caliper assembly and brake rotor.
4. Disconnect tie rod, leaf spring and stabilizer shaft from knuckle as outlined previously.
5. Disconnect shock absorber and support rod from knuckle, using a back-up wrench on shock mounting stud.
6. Disconnect spindle rod from knuckle.
7. Remove bolts securing control arms to knuckle, lower knuckle assembly and slide spindle out of hub and bearing.
8. Reverse procedure to install, then check rear suspension alignment. **Torque** all bolts to specifications.

SPINDLE SUPPORT ROD
REPLACE

1. Raise and support vehicle, and remove wheel and tire.
2. Scribe mark between cam bolt and bracket for reassembly.
3. Remove cam bolt and disconnect support rod from bracket, **Fig. 4.**
4. Remove bolt securing spindle support rod to knuckle and rod.
5. Reverse procedure to install, then check rear suspension alignment. **Torque** retaining bolt at knuckle and cam bolt to specifications.

REAR WHEEL SPINDLE
REPLACE

1. Raise and support vehicle, then remove wheel and tire assembly.
2. Remove wheel speed sensor.
3. Detach rear spring from knuckle.
4. Remove axle outer socket from knuckle.
5. Remove spindle rod from spindle bracket.
6. Remove cotter pin, wheel nut retainer, nut and washer from spindle.
7. Remove rear wheel shaft.
8. Remove spindle from hub and bearing, then remove washer from spindle.

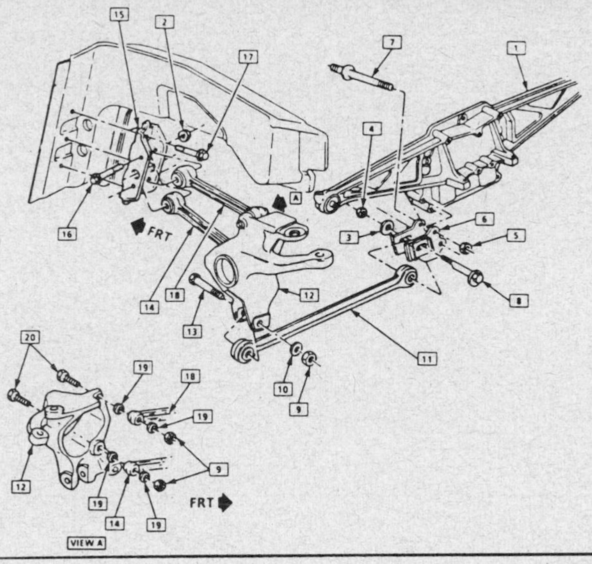
FRT
VIEW A
FRT

1 DIFFERENTIAL CARRIER
2 HEX NUT
3 SPINDLE ROD ADJUSTMENT CAM
4 SPINDLE ROD ADJUSTMENT NUT
5 HEX NUT
6 SPINDLE ROD BRACKET
7 SPINDLE ROD BRACKET STUD
8 WHEEL SPINDLE ROD ADJUSTMENT BOLT
9 HEX NUT
10 SPINDLE ROD WASHER
11 SPINDLE ROD
12 SUSPENSION KNUCKLE
13 HEX BOLT
14 WHEEL SPINDLE LOWER CONTROL ROD
15 SPINDLE CONTROL ROD BRACKET
16 WHEEL SPINDLE ROD BOLT
17 HEX BOLT
18 WHEEL SPINDLE UPPER CONTROL ROD
19 SPINDLE ROD WASHER
20 SPINDLE ROD BOLT

GC2039100033000X

Fig. 4 Knuckle & control arm

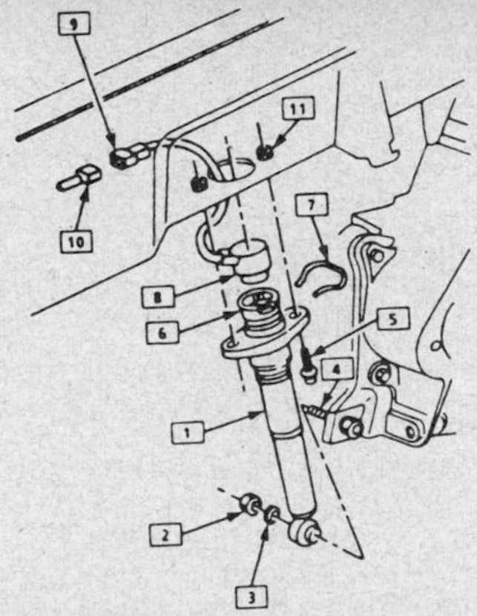

1 SELECTIVE RIDE CONTROL SHOCK ABSORBER
2 HEX NUT
3 SHOCK ABSORBER WASHER
4 SHOCK ABSORBER STUD
5 SHOCK ABSORBER BRACKET BOLT
6 CUP ASSEMBLY RETAINER
7 ACTUATOR RETAINING CLIP
8 SHOCK ABSORBER ELECTRICAL ACTUATOR
9 ACTUATOR ELECTRICAL CONNECTOR
10 WIRING HARNESS CONNECTOR
11 WELD NUT

GC2039100035000X

Fig. 6 Shock absorber replacement. Models w/Selective Ride Control

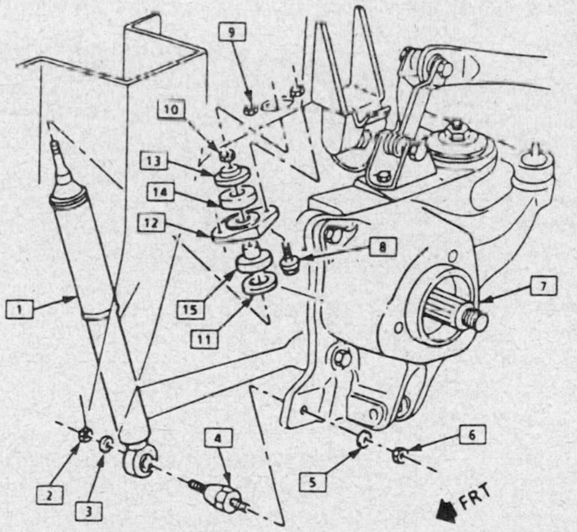
FRT

1 SHOCK ABSORBER
2 HEX NUT
3 SHOCK ABSORBER WASHER
4 SHOCK ABSORBER STUD
5 SHOCK ABSORBER WASHER
6 HEX NUT
7 SUSPENSION KNUCKLE
8 SHOCK ABSORBER BRACKET BOLT
9 WELD NUT
10 HEX NUT
11 SHOCK ABSORBER INSULATION RETAINER
12 SHOCK ABSORBER UPPER BRACKET
13 SHOCK ABSORBER INSULATION RETAINER
14 SHOCK ABSORBER UPPER GROMMET
15 SHOCK ABSORBER UPPER INSULATOR

GC2039100034000X

Fig. 5 Shock absorber replacement. Except Selective Ride Control

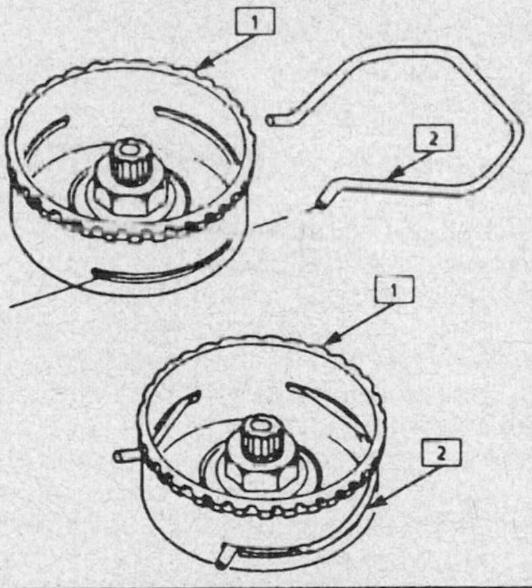

1 CUP ASSEMBLY RETAINER
2 ACTUATOR RETAINING CLIP

GC2039100036000X

Fig. 7 Installing actuator clip. Models w/Selective Ride Control

9. Reverse procedure to install. Install spindle washer with flat portion against should of wheel spindle and with lip of washer facing spindle splines. Do not allow vehicle to rest on tires until after wheel spindle nut has been tightened to the specified **torque.**

SHOCK ABSORBER

REPLACE

If shock absorber is to be discarded, position shock absorber in a suitable vise with piston facing downward. Measure .40 to .60 inch from bottom of shock absorber and drill a .20 inch hole to release gas pressure from shock absorber. Measure 5.5 to 6 inches from gas pressure release drill hole and drill another .20 inch hole to drain oil from shock absorber.

EXCEPT SELECTIVE RIDE CONTROL

1. Raise and support vehicle.
2. Using a suitable jack stand, support knuckle.
3. Disconnect shock absorber from upper and lower mountings, **Fig. 5.**
4. Reverse procedure to install.

SELECTIVE RIDE CONTROL

Removal

1. Disconnect battery ground cable.
2. Raise and support vehicle.
3. Using a suitable jack stand, support knuckle.

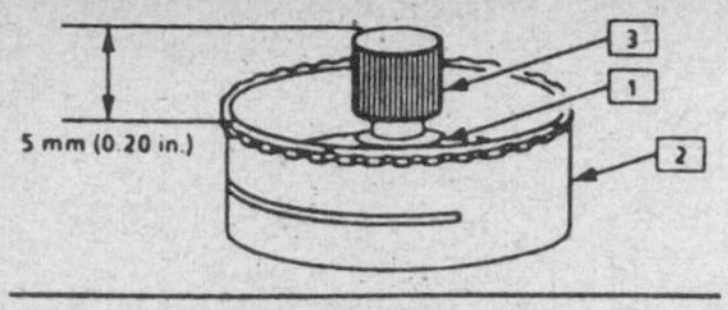
5 mm (0.20 in.)
1
2
3
1 HEX PREVAILING TORQUE NUT
2 CUP ASSEMBLY RETAINER
3 SELECTOR GEAR
GC2039100037000X

Fig. 8 Positioning selector gear. Models w/Selective Ride Control

4. Disconnect shock absorber from upper and lower mountings, **Fig. 6.** Do not allow shock absorber to hang from wiring harness.
5. Remove retaining clip, then remove electrical actuator from shock absorber.
6. Remove shock absorber from vehicle.

Installation

1. Install retaining clip onto cup assembly retainer, **Fig. 7.**
2. Install electrical actuator into cup retainer with electrical lead facing toward front of vehicle. A click should be noted when actuator is properly seated. Selector gear should be located a minimum of .20 inch top of retainer, **Fig. 8.**
3. Ensure actuator is properly seated in cup retainer, then position shock absorber to lower mounting.
4. Position shock absorber to upper mounting.
5. Position vehicle at proper trim height using jack stands, then tighten upper shock absorber attaching bolts.
6. Install shock absorber lower attaching nut and washer.
7. Lower vehicle and connect battery ground cable.

LEAF SPRING

REPLACE

When servicing, use care not to scratch the fiber glass leaf spring. Also do not use any cleaning solvent on spring.

1. Raise and support vehicle and remove wheel and tire assembly.
2. Using tool No. J-33432 or equivalent to compress spring.
3. Remove cotter pin, retaining nuts, bushings and link bolts securing spring to spindle support knuckles, **Fig. 9.**
4. Release spring and remove compressing tool J-33432 or equivalent.
5. Remove bolts securing spring anchor plate to rear axle carrier, **Fig. 10.**
6. Reverse procedure to install.

CONTROL ARM

REPLACE

1. Raise and support vehicle, and remove wheel and tire assembly.
2. Remove bolts securing control arm to spindle support knuckle, **Fig. 4.**
3. Remove control arm bolt at mounting bracket and control arm.
4. Reverse procedure to install. **Torque** control arm to bracket bolt and control arm to knuckle bolt to specifications.

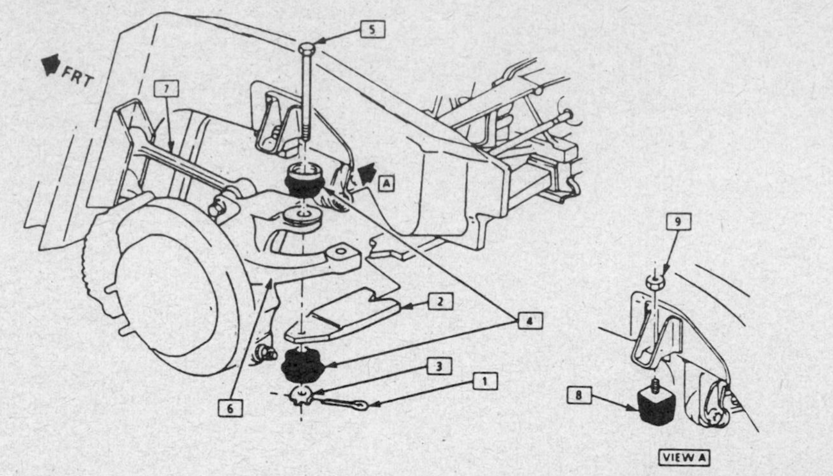
FRT
A
VIEW A
1 COTTER PIN
2 REAR SPRING
3 SLOTTED SPRING NUT
4 SPRING INSULATOR
5 SPRING BOLT
6 SUSPENSION KNUCKLE
7 WHEEL SPINDLE UPPER CONTROL ROD
8 SUSPENSION BUMPER
9 HEX NUT
GC2039100038000X

Fig. 9 Leaf spring to knuckle attachment

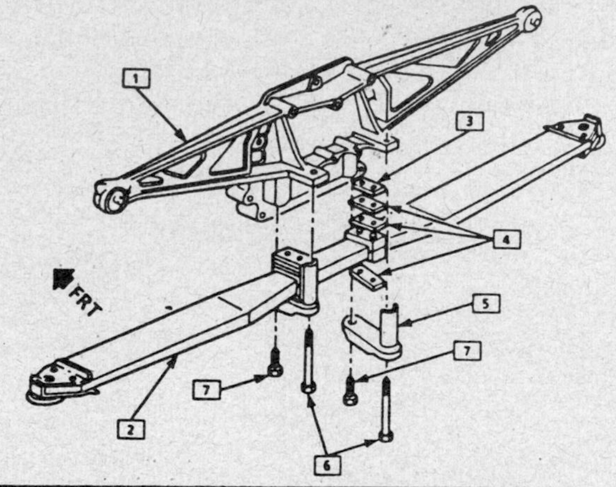
FRT
1 DIFFERENTIAL CARRIER
2 REAR SPRING
3 SPRING INSULATOR
4 SPRING SPACER
5 SPRING ANCHOR PLATE
6 HEX FLANGED HEAD BOLT
7 HEX FLANGED HEAD BOLT
GC2039100039000X

Fig. 10 Leaf spring to differential carrier attachment

TIE ROD

REPLACE

1. Raise and support vehicle, then remove wheel and tire.
2. Loosen outer tie rod jam nuts, then remove cotter pin and nut securing tie rod to spindle support knuckle, **Fig. 11.**
3. Press tie rod from knuckle using tool J-24319-01 or equivalent.
4. Remove tie rod from adjusting sleeve, counting number of turns necessary.
5. Reverse procedure to install, then check rear suspension alignment. Tighten tie rod nut specifications.

STABILIZER SHAFT

REPLACE

1. Raise and support vehicle, then remove wheel and tire assemblies.
2. Remove spare tire and carrier.
3. Remove bolts and nuts attaching stabilizer shaft links to stabilizer shaft link brackets, **Fig. 12.**
4. Remove nuts attaching fuel tank safety straps to stabilizer shaft brackets, then remove safety straps.
5. Remove stabilizer shaft bracket nuts, brackets and insulators.
6. Remove nuts, then detach mufflers from hanger brackets.
7. Remove stabilizer shaft from vehicle.
8. Reverse procedure to install. Tighten bushing retaining nuts and bolts securing stabilizer links to knuckles to specifications, and bolts securing links to stabilizer shaft to specifications.

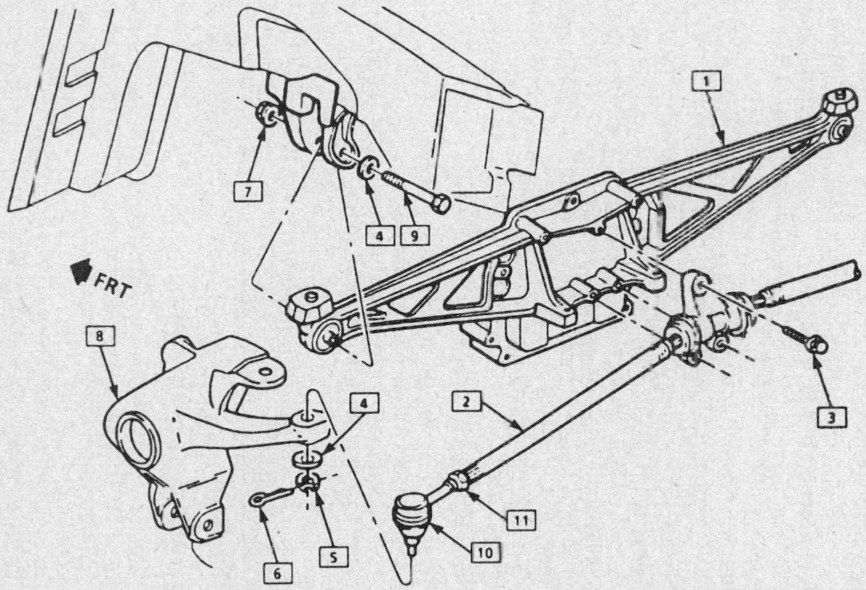
FRT

1 DIFFERENTIAL CARRIER
2 AXLE TIE ROD
3 AXLE TIE BOLT
4 WASHER
5 AXLE TIE ROD NUT
6 COTTER PIN
7 HEX NUT
8 SUSPENSION KNUCKLE
9 DIFFERENTIAL CARRIER BOLT
10 AXLE OUTER SOCKET
11 JAM NUT

GC2039100043000X

Fig. 11 Tie rod replacement

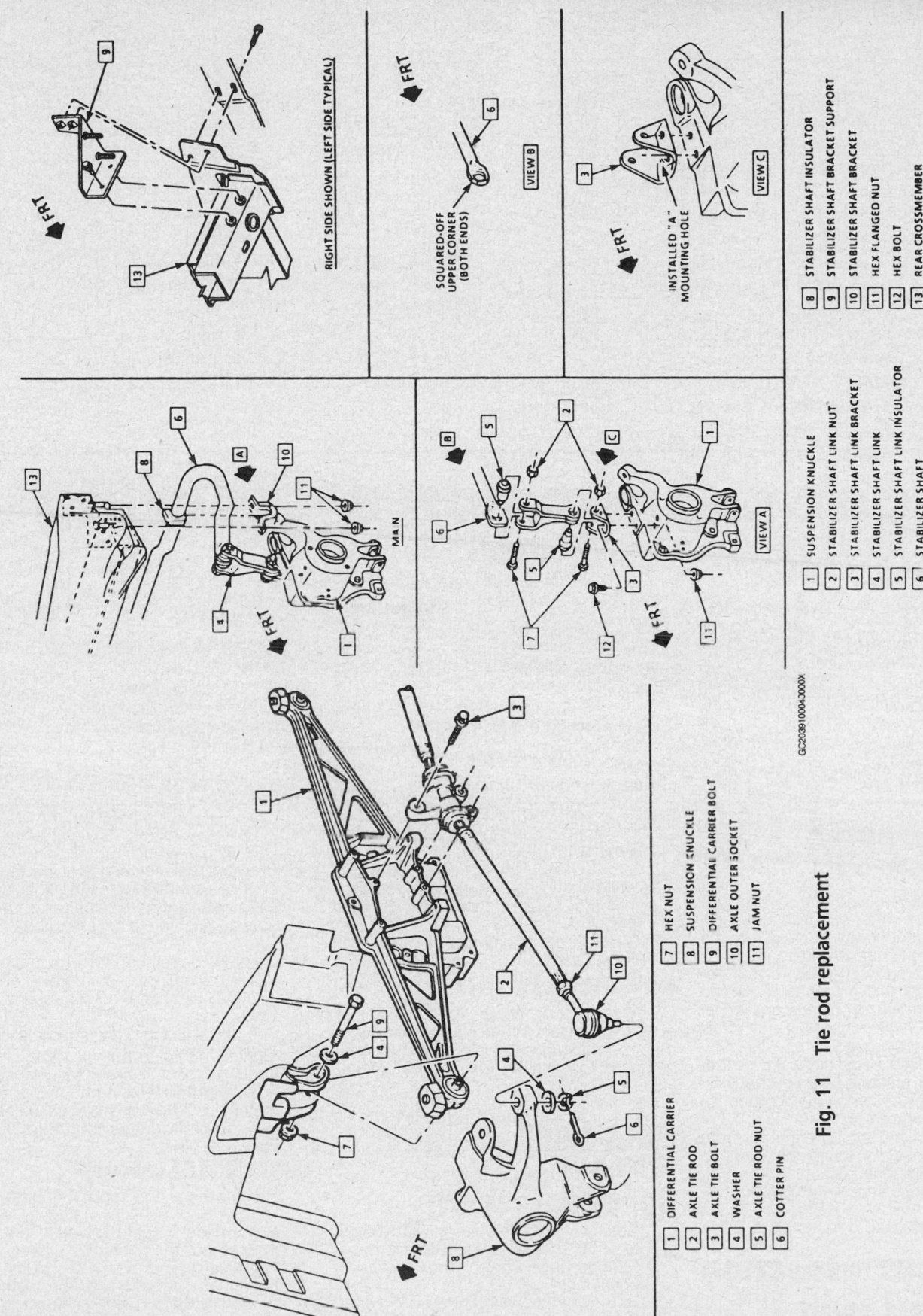

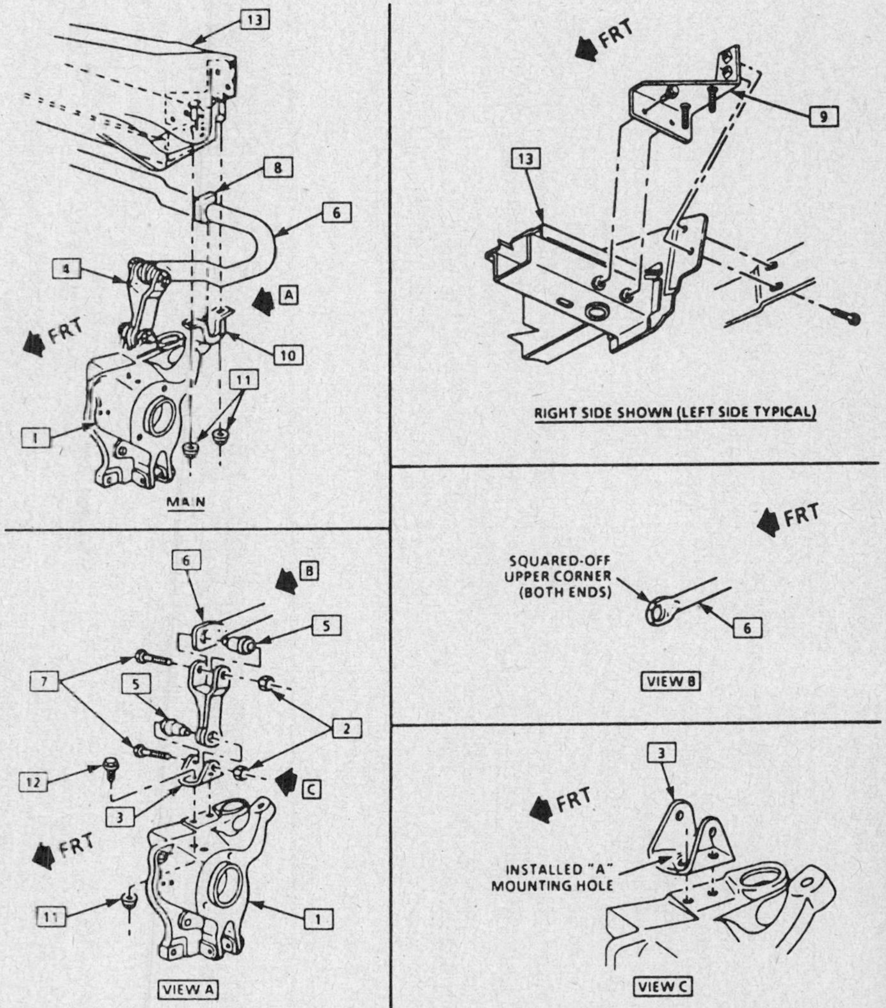
FRT
MAIN
VIEW A
RIGHT SIDE SHOWN (LEFT SIDE TYPICAL)
SQUARED-OFF UPPER CORNER (BOTH ENDS)
VIEW B
INSTALLED "A" MOUNTING HOLE
VIEW C

1 SUSPENSION KNUCKLE
2 STABILIZER SHAFT LINK NUT
3 STABILIZER SHAFT LINK BRACKET
4 STABILIZER SHAFT LINK
5 STABILIZER SHAFT LINK INSULATOR
6 STABILIZER SHAFT
7 STABILIZER SHAFT LINK BOLT
8 STABILIZER SHAFT INSULATOR
9 STABILIZER SHAFT BRACKET SUPPORT
10 STABILIZER SHAFT BRACKET
11 HEX FLANGED NUT
12 HEX BOLT
13 REAR CROSSMEMBER

GC2039100041000)

Fig. 12 Stabilizer bar replacement

TIGHTENING SPECIFICATIONS

Year	Component	Torque/Ft. Lbs.
1992-95	Cam Bolt To Spindle Rod	187
	Control Rods To Knuckle	140
	Control Rods To Spindle Control Rod	63
	Differential Cover To Body	89
	Hub & Bearing To Knuckle	66
	Shock Absorber To Body Bolt	22
	Shock Absorber To Knuckle	61
	Shock Absorber Stud To Knuckle Nut	89
	Spindle Nut	164
	Spindle Rod To Differential Carrier	60
	Spindle Rod To Knuckle	107
	Stabilizer Shaft To Body	18
	Stabilizer Shaft To Link Bracket To Knuckle	18
1992-95 —Cont'd	Stabilizer Link To Bracket & Shaft	39
	Support Beam To Differential Carrier Bolt	59
	Support Beam To Transmission	37
	Tie Rod End To Knuckle	33
	Tie Rod Jam Nut	50
	Tie Rod To Differential Carrier	54
	Transverse Spring To Differential Carrier	37
	Trunnion Strap (Pinion)	17
	Trunnion Strap (Yoke)	26
	Wheel Lug Nuts	100

Front Suspension & Steering

INDEX

WHEEL BEARING
REPLACE

The wheel bearing and hub assembly is a sealed unit. If endplay exceeds .005 inch, or if noise or roughness is detected, the unit must be replaced as an assembly.

1. Raise and support vehicle, and remove wheel and tire. Prior to raising vehicle, remove tie offs and grommets to provide ABS sensor wire to lower control arm clearance.
2. Remove bolts securing brake caliper bracket to steering knuckle and secure caliper assembly aside, then remove brake rotor.
3. Disconnect electrical connector from speed sensor, then remove speed sensor cable bracket.
4. Remove bolts securing hub to knuckle and hub assembly, **Fig. 1.**
5. Reverse procedure to install.

BALL JOINT INSPECTION
UPPER BALL JOINT

1. Raise and support front of vehicle, then position jack stands under lower control arms.
2. Position a suitable dial indicator against wheel rim, **Fig. 2.**
3. Move wheel inward and outward, while observing dial indicator reading. Indicator reading should not exceed .125 inch.
4. Replace upper ball joint if looseness is indicated.

LOWER BALL JOINT

Lower ball joints are equipped with visual wear indicators. When checking, vehicle must be supported by wheel and tire assemblies to maintain load on ball joints. Refer to **Fig. 3.**

BALL JOINT
REPLACE

UPPER BALL JOINT

1. Raise vehicle and support with stands at outer ends of lower control arms.
2. Support upper control arm in a raised position.
3. Remove wheel and tire assembly.
4. Remove cotter pin and retaining nut, then separate ball joint stud from knuckle using a suitable tool, **Fig. 4.**
5. Remove heads of rivets securing joint to arm, then drive out rivets to remove joint, **Fig. 4.**
6. Position replacement joint on top of control arm, insert retaining bolts supplied with joint from under arm, install nuts and tighten to specifications, **Fig. 5.**
7. Remove upper control arm support, assemble ball joint to steering knuckle, install washer, if equipped, and retaining nut.
8. Tighten retaining nut to specifications.
9. Tighten retaining nut up to an additional 1/16 turn, if necessary, to align hole in ball stud with nut, then install cotter pin. Cotter pin must be installed in direction from rear to front of vehicle.

LOWER BALL JOINT

1. Raise vehicle and support front of vehicle.
2. Support lower control using a suitable jack stand, then remove wheel and tire assembly.
3. Remove cotter pin and nut securing ball joint stud to steering knuckle, then disconnect joint from knuckle using a suitable tool, **Fig. 6.**
4. Lift knuckle assembly from ball stud, guiding control arm out of splash

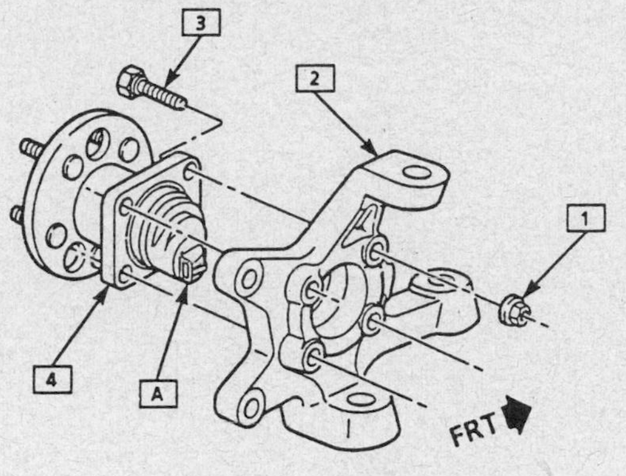
3
2
1
4
A
FRT

1 HEX FLANGE TORQUE NUT

2 STEERING KNUCKLE

3 WHEEL HUB BOLT

4 WHEEL HUB

A SPEED SENSOR CONNECTOR MUST BE FACING THE REAR OF THE VEHICLE

GC3039100219000X

Fig. 1 Hub & bearing assembly replacement

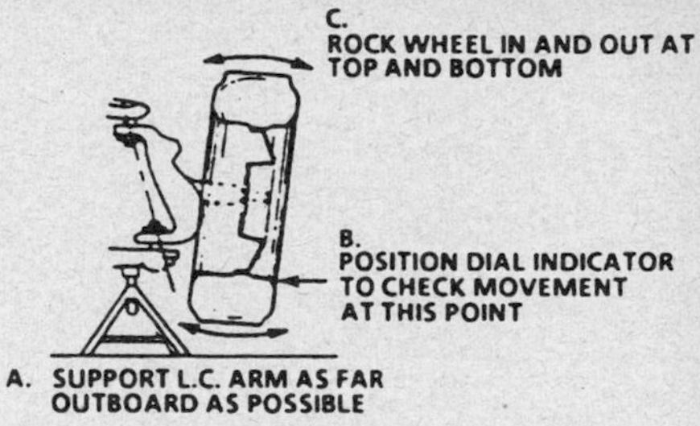
C.
ROCK WHEEL IN AND OUT AT TOP AND BOTTOM
B.
POSITION DIAL INDICATOR TO CHECK MOVEMENT AT THIS POINT
A. SUPPORT L.C. ARM AS FAR OUTBOARD AS POSSIBLE

GC2029100091000X

Fig. 2 Upper ball joint inspection

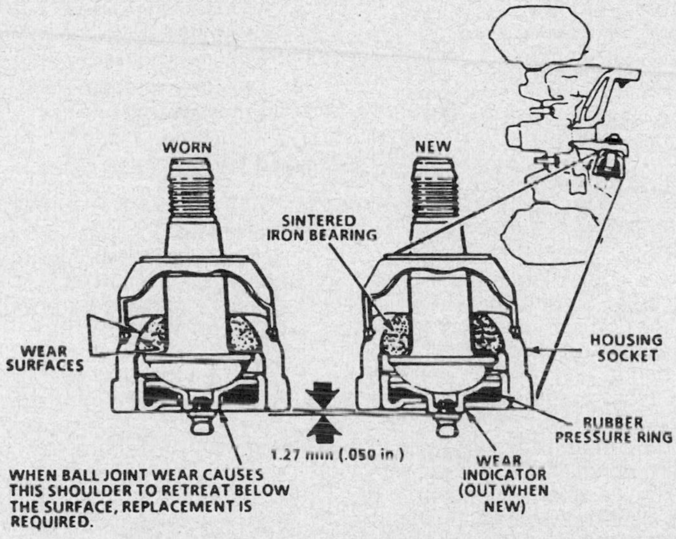
WORN
NEW
SINTERED IRON BEARING
WEAR SURFACES
HOUSING SOCKET
RUBBER PRESSURE RING
1.27 mm (.050 in.)
WHEN BALL JOINT WEAR CAUSES THIS SHOULDER TO RETREAT BELOW THE SURFACE, REPLACEMENT IS REQUIRED.
WEAR INDICATOR (OUT WHEN NEW)

GC2029100092000X

Fig. 3 Lower ball joint inspection

shield, then support knuckle aside to allow clearance for joint removal.

5. Remove grease fitting, then press ball joint assembly out of lower control arm using a suitable tool, **Fig. 6.**
6. Press replacement joint into arm by reversing removal tools, fit spindle over ball stud, install washer, if equipped, and retaining nut, **Fig. 7.**
7. Tighten retaining nut to specifications.
8. Tighten nut up to an additional $1/16$ turn, if necessary, to align hole in ball stud with nut, then install cotter pin. Cotter pin must be installed in direction from rear to front of vehicle.

SHOCK ABSORBER

REPLACE

If shock absorber is to be discarded, position shock absorber in a suitable vise with piston facing downward. Measure approximately .50 inch from bottom of shock absorber and drill a .20 inch hole to release gas pressure from shock absorber. Measure 5.5 to 6 inches from gas pressure release drill hole and drill another .20 inch hole to drain oil from shock absorber.

EXCEPT SELECTIVE RIDE CONTROL

1. Raise and support vehicle as needed, and remove wheel and tire.
2. Remove shock absorber from upper and lower attachments, **Fig. 8.** If upper retaining nut is difficult to remove, wheel housing lower center panel to gain access to nut.
3. Reverse procedure to install.

SELECTIVE RIDE CONTROL

1. Disconnect battery ground cable.
2. Raise and support front of vehicle, then remove wheel and tire assembly.
3. Support lower control arm with suitable jack stand.
4. Remove actuator retaining clip, then remove actuator from cup retainer.

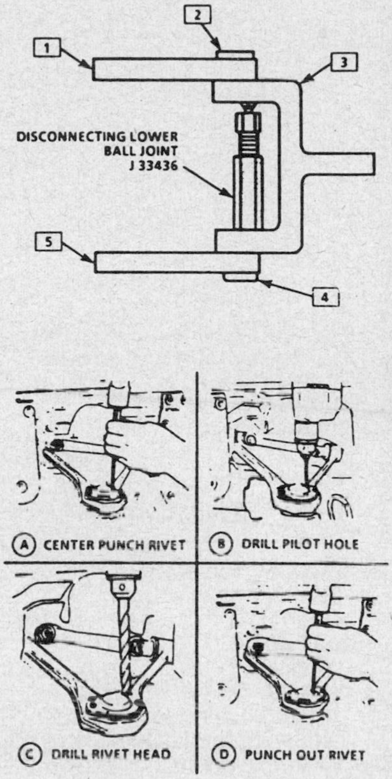
1
2
3
DISCONNECTING LOWER BALL JOINT J 33436
5
4
A CENTER PUNCH RIVET
B DRILL PILOT HOLE
C DRILL RIVET HEAD
D PUNCH OUT RIVET

1 UPPER CONTROL ARM

2 UPPER CONTROL ARM BALL STUD

3 STEERING KNUCKLE

4 LOWER CONTROL ARM BALL STUD

5 LOWER CONTROL ARM

GC2029100093000X

Fig. 4 Upper ball joint removal

Note position of electrical connector for use during installation.

5. Remove shock absorber upper retaining nut, then remove cup retainer, **Fig. 9.**
6. Remove shock absorber retainer and upper insulator.
7. Remove shock absorber lower attaching nuts and bolts, then compress shock absorber and remove from vehicle.
8. Reverse procedure to install, noting the following:
   a. When installing actuator, a click should be noted when actuator is

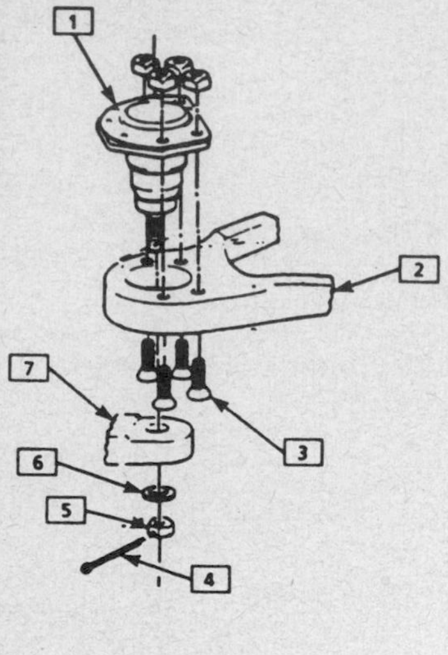

1 UPPER CONTROL ARM BALL STUD
2 UPPER CONTROL ARM
3 BOLTS MUST BE MOUNTED IN THE DIRECTION SHOWN
4 COTTER PIN
5 UPPER CONTROL ARM BALL STUD NUT
6 UPPER CONTROL ARM BALL STUD MUST BE REPLACED WASHER
7 STEERING KNUCKLE

GC2029100094000X

Fig. 5 Upper ball joint installation

properly seated.

b. Selector gear should be located a minimum of .178 inch top of retainer, **Fig. 10.**

c. A minimum clearance of .315 inch should be maintained between wheel housing lower center panel and actuator electrical lead, **Fig. 9.** Electrical connector should be positioned as noted during removal.

LEAF SPRING

REPLACE

When servicing, use care not to scratch the fiber glass leaf spring. Also do not use any cleaning solvent on spring.

1. Disconnect battery ground cable.
2. Raise and support vehicle, and remove front wheel and tire assembly.
3. Remove shock absorber to lower control arm attachments.
4. Remove bolts and nuts attaching stabilizer shaft links to lower control arms.
5. **On models with Selective Ride Control,** disconnect electrical connector and detach sensor cable from bracket.
6. **On all models,** disconnect wheel speed sensor electrical connector and sensor cable from bracket.
7. **On all models,** remove both spring protectors, **Fig. 11.**
8. Install spring compressor J-33432 or equivalent, **Fig. 12.**
9. Disconnect lower ball joints from steering knuckles.

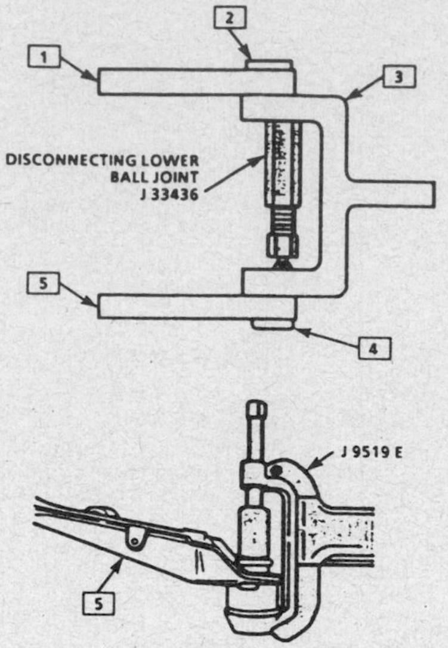
DISCONNECTING LOWER BALL JOINT J 33436
J 9519 E

1 UPPER CONTROL ARM
2 UPPER CONTROL ARM BALL STUD
3 STEERING KNUCKLE
4 LOWER CONTROL ARM BALL STUD
5 LOWER CONTROL ARM

GC2029100095000X

Fig. 6 Lower ball joint removal

10. Compress spring by rotating turnbuckle on spring compressor.
11. Remove bolts securing shock brackets to lower control arms and spring mounting bolts.
12. Release tension on spring compressor and remove compressor.
13. Remove spring and retainer shims, if equipped. Note number of shims removed.
14. Reverse procedure to install. Prior to installation, lubricate spring pads with a suitable rubber lubricant. If equipped, install spring retainer shims. The number of spring retaining shims can be determined by the color code located on the spring. If color code is blue, no shims are required; yellow or white, 1 shim; green, 2 shims. Tighten spring mounting bolts to specifications, with vehicle on ground.

CONTROL ARM

REPLACE

UPPER CONTROL ARM

1. Disconnect battery ground cable.
2. Raise and support vehicle, then remove wheel and tire assembly.
3. Remove wheel housing seal and lower center panel.
4. **On models equipped with Selective Ride Control,** disconnect shock absorber actuator electrical connector.
5. **On all models,** using a suitable jack stand, support lower control arm.
6. Disconnect wheel speed sensor electrical connector and detach speed sensor cable from bracket.

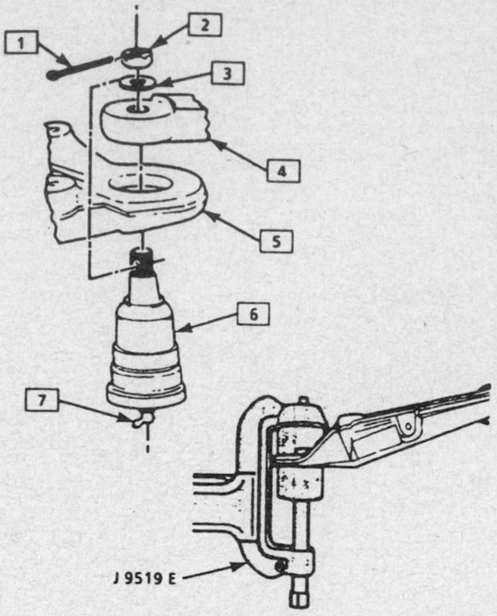
J 9519 E

1 COTTER PIN
2 HEX SLOTTED NUT
3 LOWER CONTROL ARM BALL STUD MUST BE REPLACED WASHER
4 STEERING KNUCKLE
5 LOWER CONTROL ARM
6 LOWER CONTROL ARM BALL STUD
7 INSTALL ZERK FITTING AS SHOWN

GC2029100096000X

Fig. 7 Lower ball joint installation

7. Using tool No. J-33436 or equivalent, detach upper ball joint from steering knuckle.
8. Remove upper control arm to frame member attaching bolts and shims, **Fig. 13.** Note location and number of shims for installation.
9. Remove upper control arm from vehicle.
10. Reverse procedure to install. Install shims in same location as removed. Install upper ball joint stud cotter pin from rear to front of vehicle. After completing installation, check wheel alignment and adjust as necessary.

LOWER CONTROL ARM

1. Disconnect battery ground cable.
2. Raise and support vehicle, then remove wheel and tire assembly.
3. Remove both spring protectors, then install spring compressor J-33432 or equivalent.
4. Compress front spring with tool, then support lower control arm with suitable jack stand.
5. Disconnect shock absorber and stabilizer shaft link from lower control arm.
6. Disconnect front wheel speed sensor electrical connector, then detach speed sensor cable from bracket.
7. Disconnect lower ball joint from steering knuckle.
8. Remove lower control arm to frame member attaching bolts, then remove lower control arm, **Fig. 14.**
9. Reverse procedure to install. When installing, position lower ball joint stud so that cotter pin can be installed from rear to front of vehicle. When tighten-

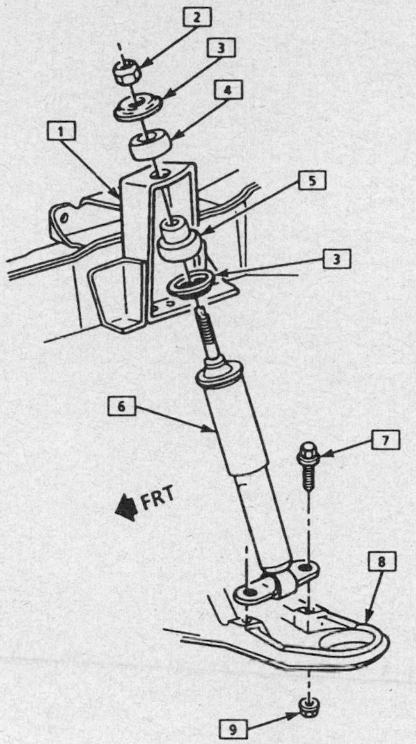
FRT

1 SHOCK ABSORBER TOWER
2 HEX PREVAILING TORQUE NUT
3 SHOCK ABSORBER INSULATOR RETAINER
4 SHOCK ABSORBER UPPER INSULATOR
5 SHOCK ABSORBER LOWER INSULATOR
6 SHOCK ABSORBER
7 HEX FLANGE HEAD BOLT
8 LOWER CONTROL ARM
9 HEX FLANGE NUT

GC2029100097000X

Fig. 8 Shock absorber replacement. Models less Selective Ride Control

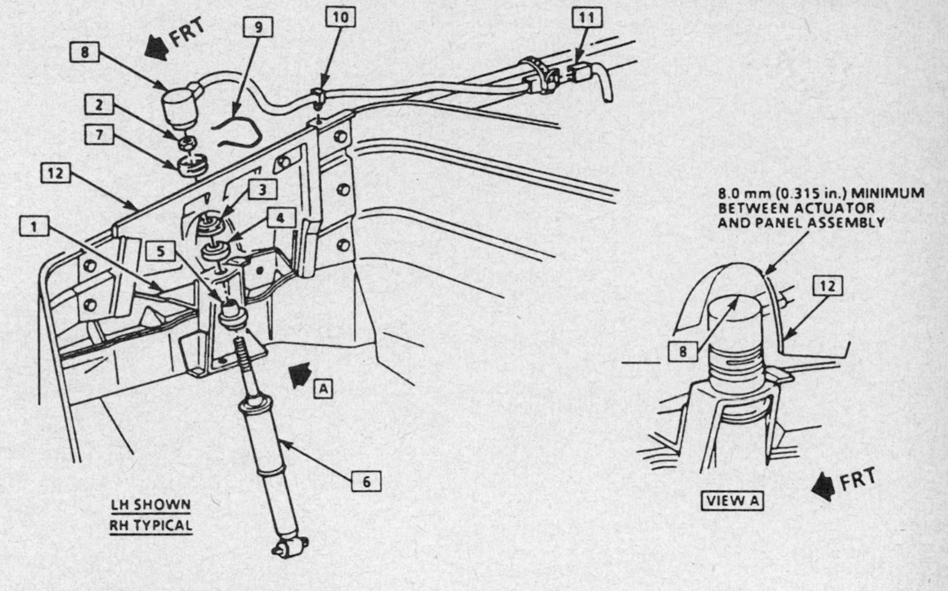
FRT
LH SHOWN
RH TYPICAL
8.0 mm (0.315 in.) MINIMUM
BETWEEN ACTUATOR
AND PANEL ASSEMBLY
VIEW A
FRT

1 SHOCK ABSORBER TOWER
2 HEX PREVAILING TORQUE NUT
3 SHOCK ABSORBER INSULATOR RETAINER
4 SHOCK ABSORBER UPPER INSULATOR
5 SHOCK ABSORBER LOWER INSULATOR
6 SHOCK (SELECTIVE RIDE) ABSORBER
7 CUP ASSEMBLY RETAINER
8 SHOCK ABSORBER ELECTRICAL ACTUATOR
9 ACTUATOR RETAINING CLIP
10 ROSEBUD CLIP
11 ACTUATOR ELECTRICAL CONNECTOR
12 FRONT WHEELHOUSE LOWER CENTER PANEL

GC2029100098000X

Fig. 9 Shock absorber replacement. Selective Ride Control

ing stabilizer shaft link, lower control arm and shock absorber lower attaching bolts and nuts, use jack stands to hold suspension at proper trim height.

STEERING KNUCKLE

REPLACE

1. Disconnect battery ground cable.
2. Raise and support vehicle, then remove wheel and tire assembly.
3. Remove brake caliper and rotor.
4. Disconnect wheel speed sensor electrical connector, then detach speed sensor cable from bracket.
5. Remove hub assembly attaching bolts and nuts, then remove hub assembly.
6. Support lower control arm using a suitable jack stand.
7. Disconnect upper and lower control arms from steering knuckle, **Fig. 15.**
8. Disconnect tie rod end from steering knuckle.
9. Remove steering knuckle.
10. Reverse procedure to install, noting the following:
    a. When installing, position ball joint studs so that cotter pins can be installed from rear to front of vehicle.
    b. When installing wheel hub, speed sensor cable should be facing rearward.

STABILIZER BAR

REPLACE

1. Raise and support vehicle, then remove wheel and tire assembly.
2. Support lower control arm with a suitable jack stand.
3. Remove stabilizer shaft attaching bolts, insulator clamps and brackets from frame, **Fig. 16.**
4. Remove stabilizer shaft from vehicle.
5. Reverse procedure to install. When tightening stabilizer shaft link attaching bolts and nuts, use jack stands to hold suspension at proper trim height. Refer to **Fig. 16** for bolt installation direction.

POWER STEERING GEAR

REPLACE

1. Disconnect battery ground cable.
2. Position drain pan under vehicle, then disconnect inlet and outlet hoses from steering gear.
3. Disconnect power steering fluid cooling pipes, if equipped.
4. Disconnect intermediate steering shaft from power steering gear.

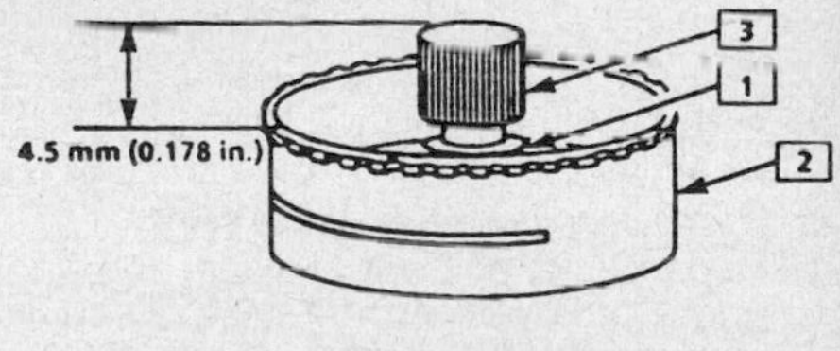
4.5 mm (0.178 in.)

1 HEX PREVAILING TORQUE NUT
2 CUP ASSEMBLY RETAINER
3 SELECTOR GEAR

GC2029100099000X

Fig. 10 Positioning selector gear

5. Raise and support vehicle, and remove wheel and tire assemblies.
6. Disconnect outer tie rods from steering knuckles, **Fig. 17.**
7. Remove power steering fluid oil cooler, if equipped.
8. Remove stabilizer shaft from vehicle as describe under "Stabilizer Shaft, Replace."
9. Remove steering gear to frame attaching bolts and nuts, then remove steering gear.
10. Reverse procedure to install. Top off fluid reservoir, bleed system and check for leaks. After completing installation, check front toe setting.

POWER STEERING PUMP

REPLACE

EXCEPT ZR-1

1. Disconnect battery ground cable.

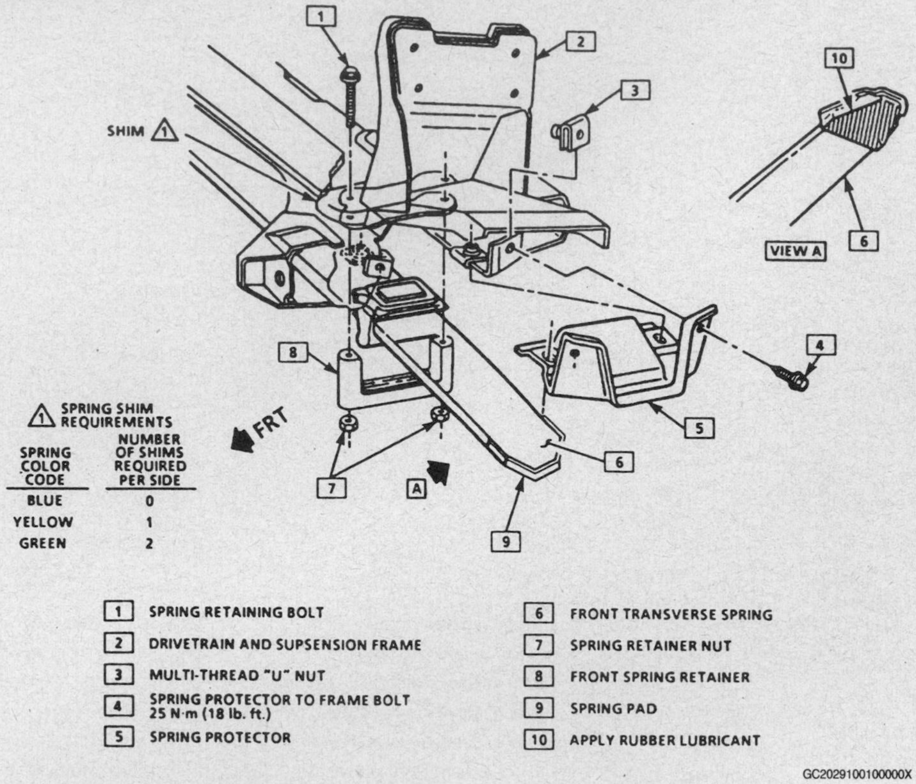
SHIM
SPRING SHIM REQUIREMENTS
SPRING COLOR CODE
NUMBER OF SHIMS REQUIRED PER SIDE
BLUE 0
YELLOW 1
GREEN 2
FRT
VIEW A
A
1 SPRING RETAINING BOLT
2 DRIVETRAIN AND SUPSENSION FRAME
3 MULTI-THREAD "U" NUT
4 SPRING PROTECTOR TO FRAME BOLT 25 N·m (18 lb. ft.)
5 SPRING PROTECTOR
6 FRONT TRANSVERSE SPRING
7 SPRING RETAINER NUT
8 FRONT SPRING RETAINER
9 SPRING PAD
10 APPLY RUBBER LUBRICANT
GC2029100100000X

Fig. 11 Front leaf spring replacement

2. Position suitable drain pan under vehicle.
3. Remove serpentine drive belt.
4. Remove cap from power steering pump pulley, then remove pulley using a suitable puller.
5. Disconnect power steering hoses from pump.
6. Remove power steering pump mounting bolts, then remove power steering pump and front bracket, **Fig. 18.**
7. Reverse procedure to install. Bleed power steering system as outlined in "Power Steering" section.

ZR-1

1. Disconnect battery ground cable.
2. Drain cooling system, then remove air intake duct.
3. Drain power steering fluid.
4. Remove vacuum hose retainer from power steering fluid reservoir, then disconnect and position hoses aside.
5. Remove lefthand coolant outlet housing and hose.
6. Remove serpentine drive belt.
7. Remove power steering pump to cylinder head bracket attaching bolts, **Fig. 19.**
8. Remove power steering pump to A/C compressor bracket bolt.
9. Disconnect power steering fluid cooler hose from reservoir.
10. Disconnect power steering gear inlet hose from power steering pump.
11. Remove power steering pump from vehicle.
12. Reverse procedure to install.

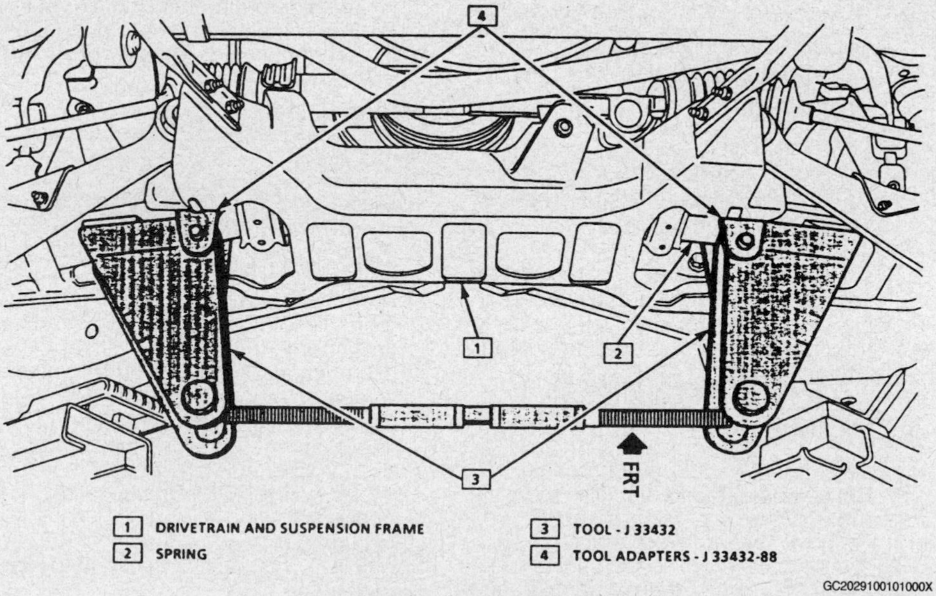
FRT
1 DRIVETRAIN AND SUSPENSION FRAME
2 SPRING
3 TOOL - J 33432
4 TOOL ADAPTERS - J 33432-88
GC2029100101000X

Fig. 12 Front leaf spring compression

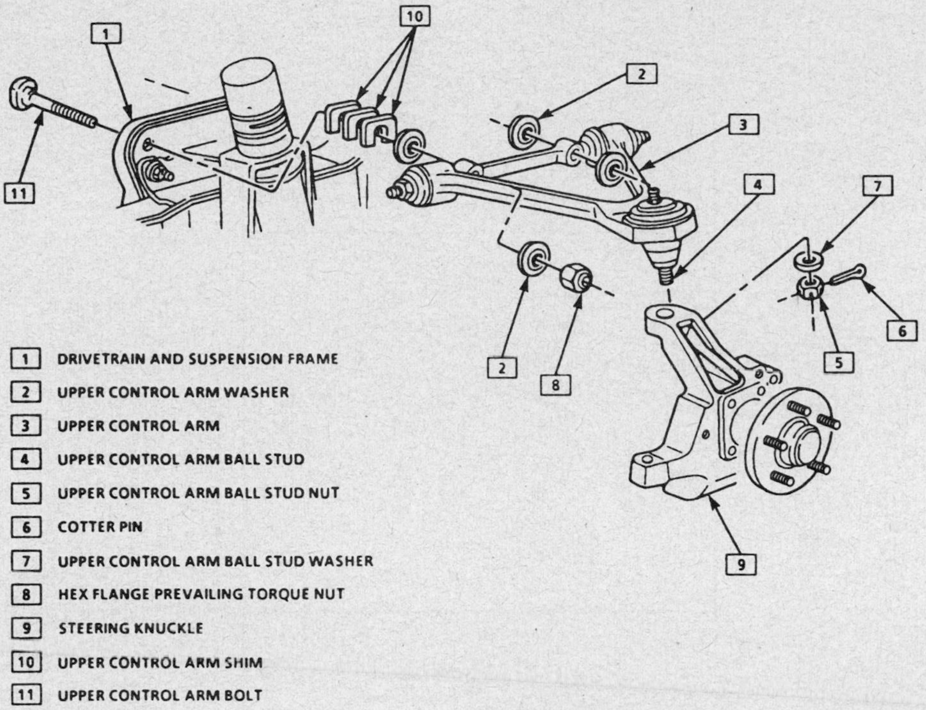
1 DRIVETRAIN AND SUSPENSION FRAME
2 UPPER CONTROL ARM WASHER
3 UPPER CONTROL ARM
4 UPPER CONTROL ARM BALL STUD
5 UPPER CONTROL ARM BALL STUD NUT
6 COTTER PIN
7 UPPER CONTROL ARM BALL STUD WASHER
8 HEX FLANGE PREVAILING TORQUE NUT
9 STEERING KNUCKLE
10 UPPER CONTROL ARM SHIM
11 UPPER CONTROL ARM BOLT
GC2029100102000X

Fig. 13 Upper control arm replacement

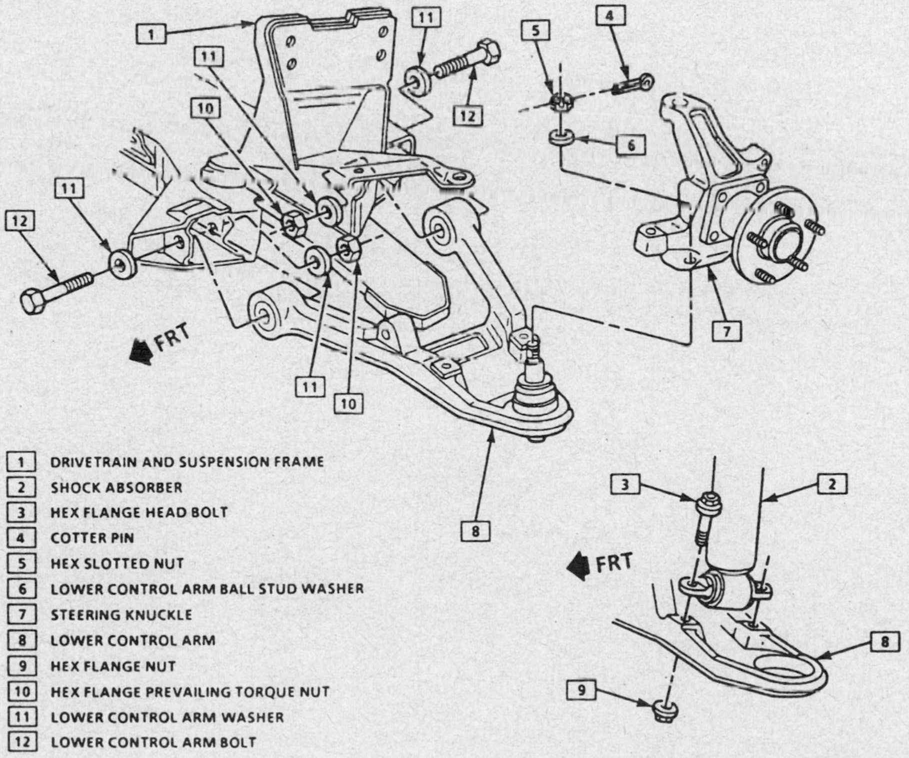
FRT
FRT
1 DRIVETRAIN AND SUSPENSION FRAME
2 SHOCK ABSORBER
3 HEX FLANGE HEAD BOLT
4 COTTER PIN
5 HEX SLOTTED NUT
6 LOWER CONTROL ARM BALL STUD WASHER
7 STEERING KNUCKLE
8 LOWER CONTROL ARM
9 HEX FLANGE NUT
10 HEX FLANGE PREVAILING TORQUE NUT
11 LOWER CONTROL ARM WASHER
12 LOWER CONTROL ARM BOLT
GC2029100103000X

Fig. 14 Lower control arm replacement

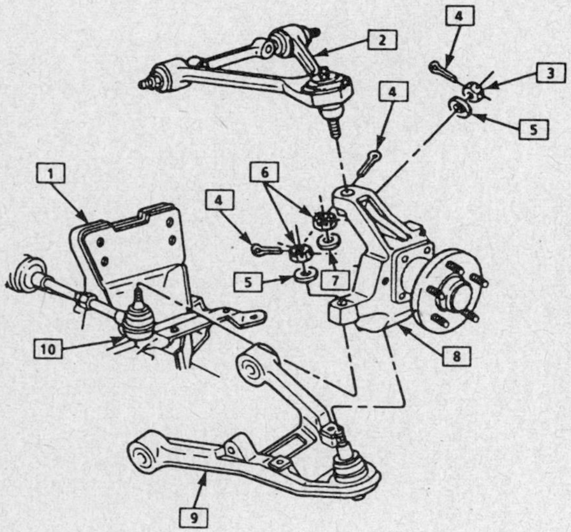
1
2
3
4
5
6
7
8
9
10

1 DRIVETRAIN AND SUSPENSION FRAME
2 UPPER CONTROL ARM
3 UPPER CONTROL ARM BALL STUD NUT
4 COTTER PIN
5 UPPER CONTROL ARM BALL STUD WASHER
6 HEX SLOTTED NUT
7 LOWER CONTROL ARM BALL STUD WASHER
8 STEERING KNUCKLE
9 LOWER CONTROL ARM
10 STEERING GEAR TIE ROD BALL STUD

GC2029100104000X

Fig. 15 Steering knuckle replacement

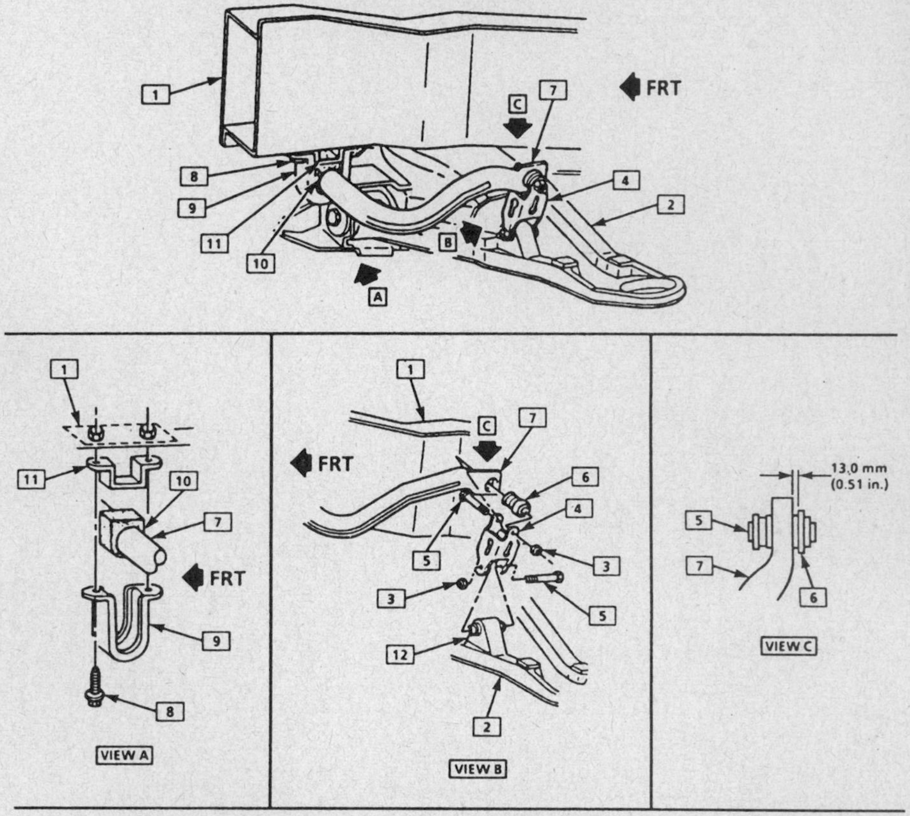
FRT
A
B
C
VIEW A
VIEW B
VIEW C
13.0 mm
(0.51 in.)

1 DRIVETRAIN AND SUSPENSION FRAME
2 LOWER CONTROL ARM
3 HEX NUT
4 STABILIZER SHAFT LINK
5 HEX BOLT
6 STABILIZER SHAFT LINK UPPER INSULATOR
7 STABILIZER SHAFT
8 BOLT
9 STABILIZER SHAFT INSULATOR CLAMP
10 STABILIZER SHAFT INSULATOR
11 STABILIZER SHAFT BRACKET
12 STABILIZER SHAFT LINK LOWER INSULATOR

GC2029100105000X

Fig. 16 Stabilizer bar replacement

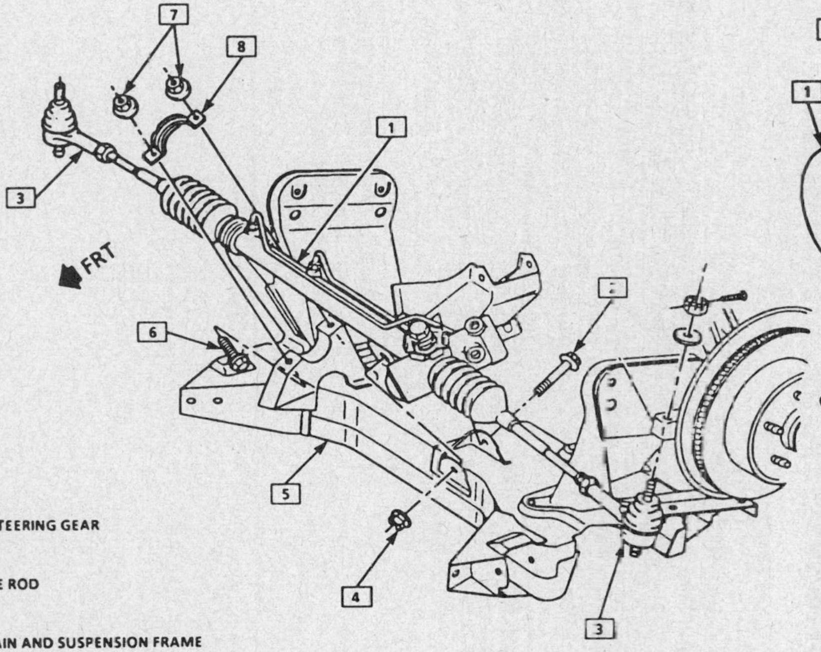
FRT
1 POWER STEERING GEAR
2 BOLT
3 OUTER TIE ROD
4 NUT
5 DRIVETRAIN AND SUSPENSION FRAME
6 BOLT
7 NUT
8 STEERING GEAR TO FRAME CLAMP

GC6039100033000X

Fig. 17 Steering gear attachment

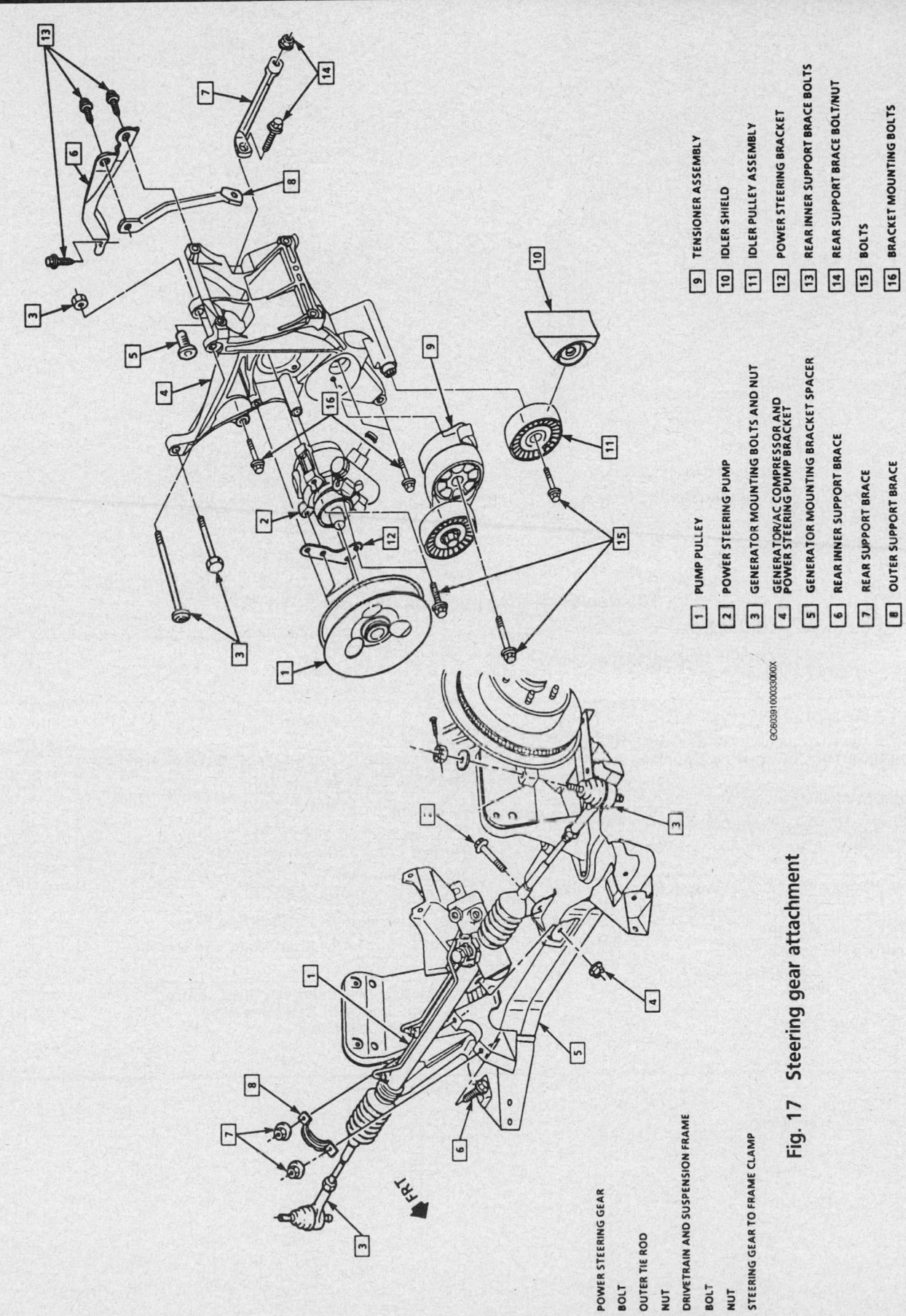

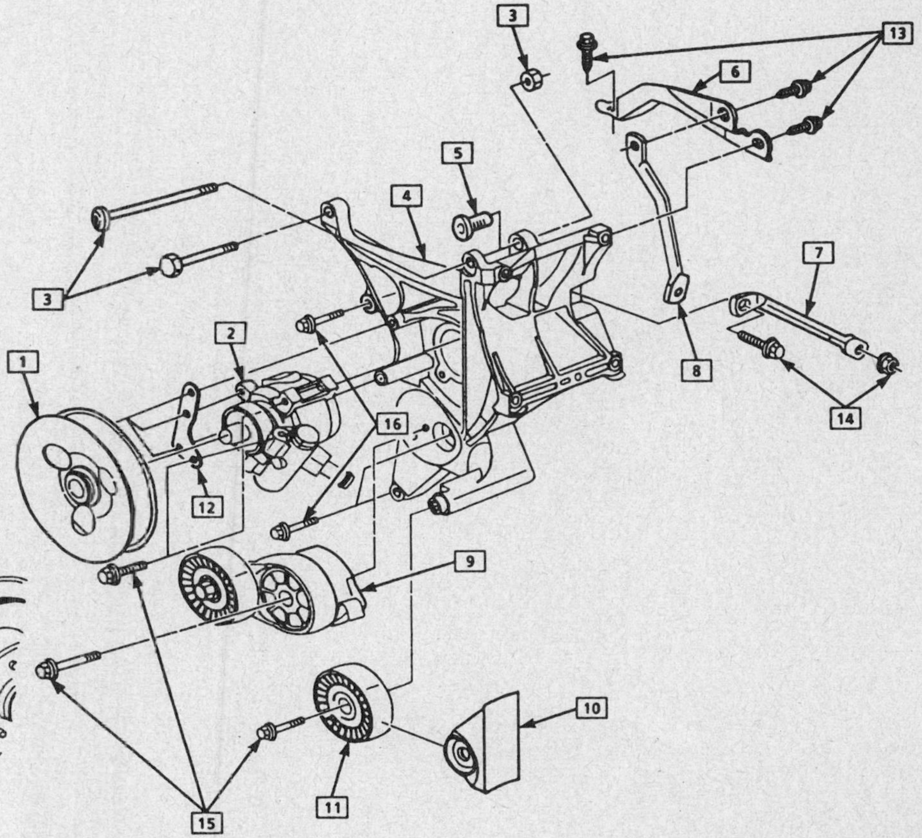
1 PUMP PULLEY
2 POWER STEERING PUMP
3 GENERATOR MOUNTING BOLTS AND NUT
4 GENERATOR/AC COMPRESSOR AND POWER STEERING PUMP BRACKET
5 GENERATOR MOUNTING BRACKET SPACER
6 REAR INNER SUPPORT BRACE
7 REAR SUPPORT BRACE
8 OUTER SUPPORT BRACE
9 TENSIONER ASSEMBLY
10 IDLER SHIELD
11 IDLER PULLEY ASSEMBLY
12 POWER STEERING BRACKET
13 REAR INNER SUPPORT BRACE BOLTS
14 REAR SUPPORT BRACE BOLT/NUT
15 BOLTS
16 BRACKET MOUNTING BOLTS

GC6039200034000X

Fig. 18 Power steering pump installation. Except ZR-1

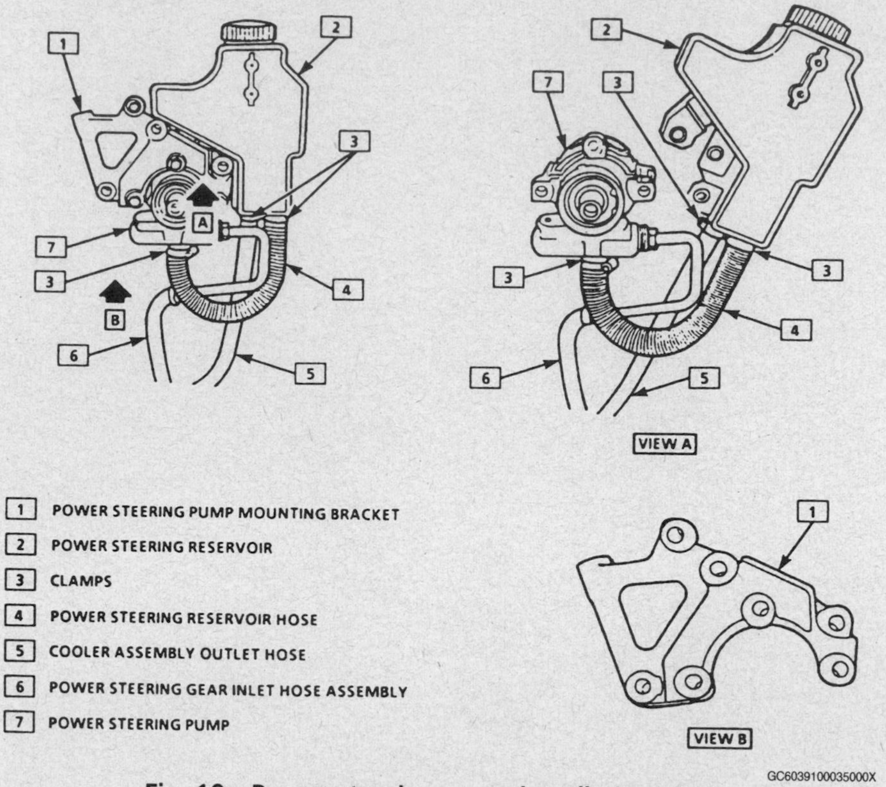
1
2
3
3
7
3
A
B
4
6
5
2
7
3
3
3
4
6
5
VIEW A
1
VIEW B
1 POWER STEERING PUMP MOUNTING BRACKET
2 POWER STEERING RESERVOIR
3 CLAMPS
4 POWER STEERING RESERVOIR HOSE
5 COOLER ASSEMBLY OUTLET HOSE
6 POWER STEERING GEAR INLET HOSE ASSEMBLY
7 POWER STEERING PUMP
GC6039100035000X

Fig. 19 Power steering pump installation. ZR-1

TIGHTENING SPECIFICATIONS

Component	Torque/Ft. Lbs.
Hub & Bearing Assembly To Steering Knuckle Bolts	46
Lower Ball Joint Stud Nut	50
Lower Control Arm Shaft To Frame Member	82
Power Steering Pump & Bracket Mounting Bolts (Except ZR-1)	18
Power Steering Pump & Bracket Mounting Bolts (ZR-1)	19
Shock Absorber Lower Attaching Bolt	19
Shock Absorber Upper Attaching Nut	①
Spring Protector To Crossmember Bolt	18
Spring Retainer Bolts	48
Stabilizer Shaft Clamp Bolts	40

Component	Torque/Ft. Lbs.
Stabilizer Shaft Link To Lower Control Arm Bolt	35
Stabilizer Shaft To Link Bolt	35
Steering Gear Clamp Bolts	18
Steering Gear To Crossmember	30
Tie Rod End To Steering Knuckle Stud Nut	33
Tie Rod Jam Nut	50
Upper Ball Joint Stud Nut	33
Upper Ball Joint To Control Arm Bolts	13
Upper Control Arm Shaft To Frame Member	37
Wheel Lug Nuts	100

①—Models less Selective Ride Control, 19 ft. lbs.; with Selective Ride Control, 31 ft. lbs.

Wheel Alignment

INDEX

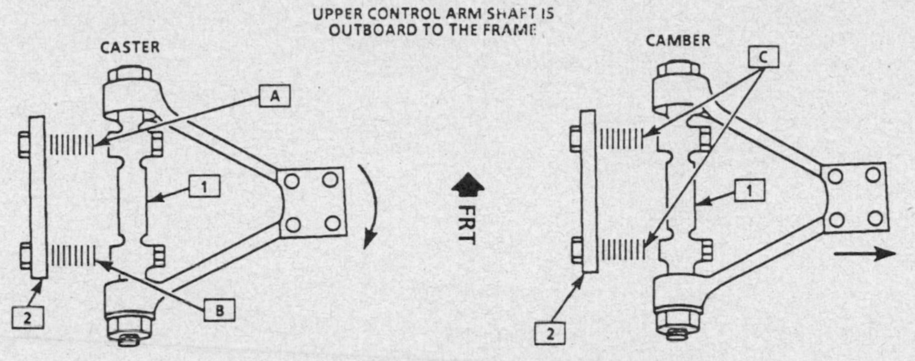

UPPER CONTROL ARM SHAFT IS OUTBOARD TO THE FRAME
CASTER
CAMBER
A
B
C
1
2
FRT

A ADD SHIMS HERE TO INCREASE POSITIVE CASTER
B SUBTRACT SHIMS HERE TO INCREASE POSITIVE CASTER
C ADD SHIMS EQUALLY TO INCREASE POSITIVE CAMBER
1 UPPER CONTROL ARM SHAFT
2 DRIVETRAIN AND FRONT SUSPENSION FRAME

Fig. 1 Front caster & camber adjustments

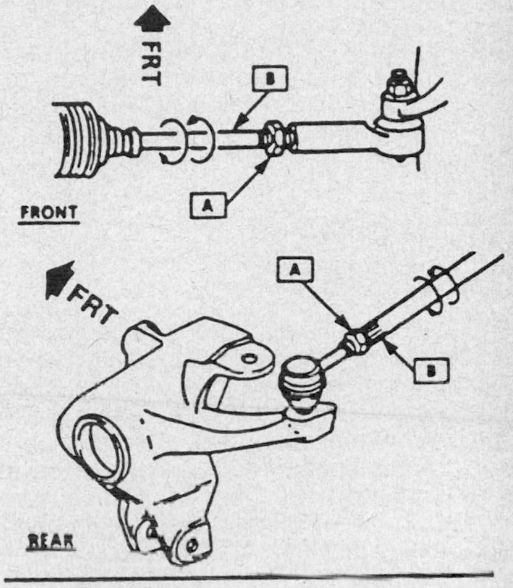

FRT
FRONT
REAR
A
B

A LOOSEN LOCK NUT
B ADJUST TOE BY ROTATING TIE ROD

Fig. 2 Toe-in adjustment

PRELIMINARY INSPECTION

Prior to checking or adjusting front suspension alignment, inspect suspension components and wheel bearings for damage or excessive wear, and replace as needed. Ensure tire pressure is properly adjusted, then raise and release front bumper several times to allow vehicle to assume normal ride height. The following items should be inspected prior to performing wheel alignment procedures:

1. Check all tires for proper inflation pressure.
2. Check hubs and bearings for excessive wear.
3. Check ball joints and tie rod ends for looseness and wear.
4. Check for bent wheel rims, wheel runout, and defective tires (belt shift).
5. Measure vehicle trim height.
6. Check all suspension and steering components for looseness and wear.
7. Check for excessive cargo loads, correct if necessary.

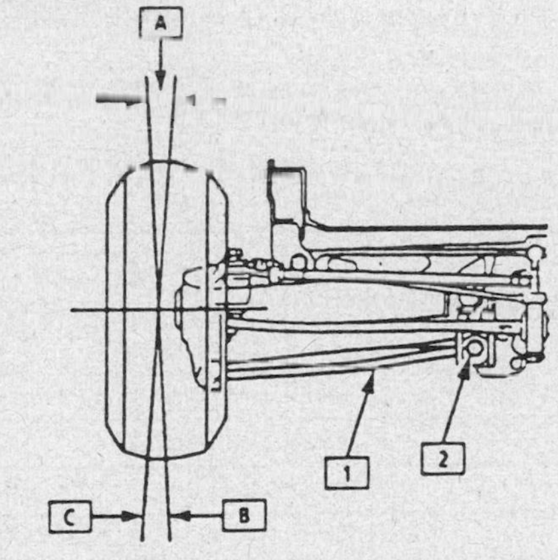

A
B
C
1
2

A NEGATIVE CAMBER ANGLE
B VERTICAL
C CENTERLINE OF WHEEL
1 SPINDLE ROD
2 WHEEL SPINDLE ROD ADJUSTMENT BOLT

Fig. 3 Rear camber adjustment

FRONT WHEEL ALIGNMENT

CASTER

Caster adjustments are made by means of shims between the upper control arm shaft and the support bracket attached to the frame. Shims may be added, subtracted or transferred to change the readings.

Transfer shims from front to rear or rear to front. The transfer of one shim to the front bolt from the rear bolt will decrease positive caster. One shim transferred from the rear bolt to the front bolt will change caster about .36°. Refer to **Fig. 1**, and note the effect of shim placement.

CAMBER

Camber adjustments are made by means of shims between the upper control arm shaft and the support bracket attached to the frame, **Fig. 1.** Shims may be added, subtracted or transferred to change the readings.

Change shims at both the front and rear of the shaft. Adding an equal number of shims at both front and rear of the support shaft will decrease positive camber.

TOE-IN

Toe-in can be adjusted by loosening the

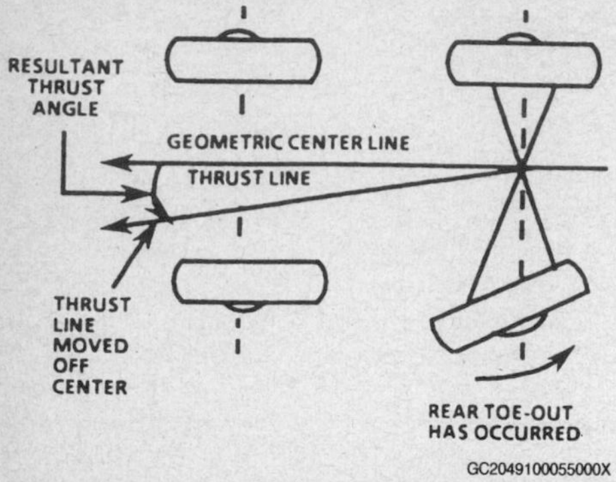
RESULTANT
THRUST
ANGLE
GEOMETRIC CENTER LINE
THRUST LINE
THRUST
LINE
MOVED
OFF
CENTER
REAR TOE-OUT
HAS OCCURRED
GC2049100055000X

Fig. 4 Vehicle thrust angle

clamp bolts at each end of each tie rod and turning each tie rod to increase or decrease its length as necessary until proper toe-in is secured and the steering gear is on the high point for straight-ahead driving, **Fig. 2.**

REAR WHEEL ALIGNMENT

Rear wheel alignment should be checked and adjusted periodically, when rear tires indicate abnormal wear, or when suspension components are replaced. Prior to rear wheel alignment, check suspension components for damage or excessive wear and repair as needed. Also ensure tires are properly inflated, and wheel bearing endplay is within specifications.

CAMBER

Camber is adjusted by rotating the eccentric cam and bolt located at the inboard end of the spindle support rod, **Fig. 3.** To check and adjust camber, proceed as follows:

1. Place rear wheels of vehicle on suitable alignment equipment following manufacturer's instructions, then check camber reading.
2. If wheel camber is not within specifications, loosen cam bolt retaining nut.
3. Rotate cam bolt, **Fig. 3,** until camber reading is within specifications listed at the front of this chapter.

TOE-IN

Toe-in is adjusted by loosening locknuts on tie rod ends and rotating adjuster sleeves until desired setting is obtained, **Fig. 2.**

THRUST ANGLE

The vehicle is steered by the front wheels. The path which the rear wheels follow is the thrust angle, **Fig. 4.** In an ideal setting, the thrust angle would be aligned with that of the vehicle center line.

VEHICLE RIDE HEIGHT

Refer to **Figs. 5 and 6**for ride height measurements and specifications.

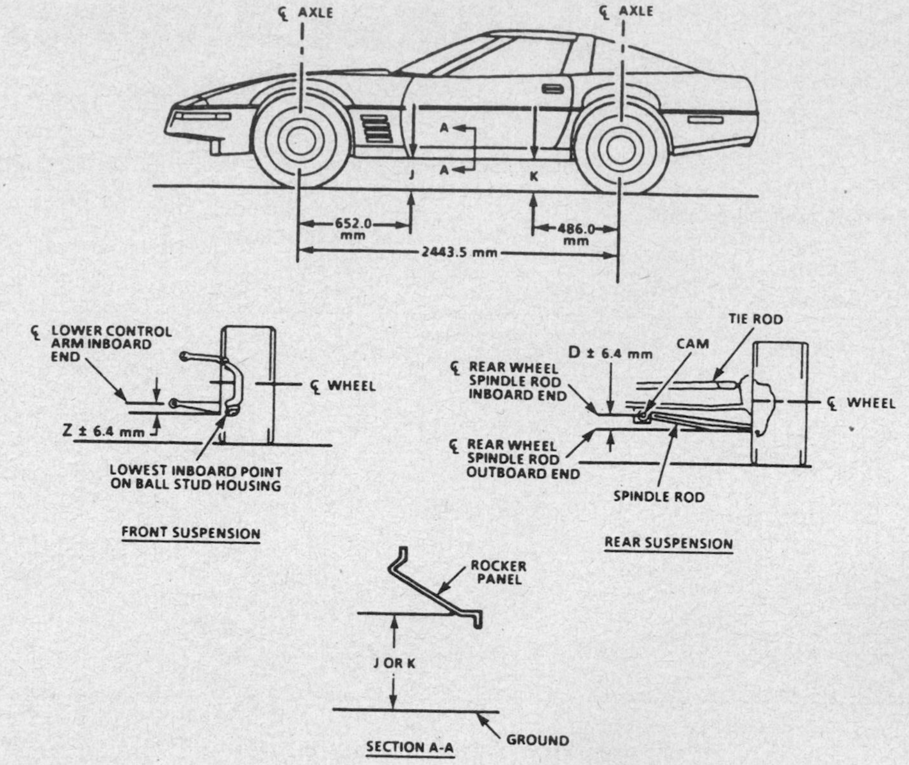
℄ AXLE
℄ AXLE
A
A
J
K
652.0 mm
486.0 mm
2443.5 mm
℄ LOWER CONTROL ARM INBOARD END
℄ WHEEL
Z ± 6.4 mm
LOWEST INBOARD POINT ON BALL STUD HOUSING
FRONT SUSPENSION
TIE ROD
D ± 6.4 mm
CAM
℄ REAR WHEEL SPINDLE ROD INBOARD END
℄ WHEEL
℄ REAR WHEEL SPINDLE ROD OUTBOARD END
SPINDLE ROD
REAR SUSPENSION
ROCKER PANEL
J OR K
GROUND
SECTION A-A

VERTICAL HEIGHTS: "Z" AND "J" DIMENSIONS - LIFT FRONT BUMPER OF VEHICLE UP APPROXIMATELY 38.0 mm. GENTLY REMOVE HANDS AND LET VEHICLE SETTLE ON ITS OWN. REPEAT TWICE FOR A TOTAL OF 3 TIMES. MEASURE "Z" AND "J" DIMENSIONS. PUSH FRONT BUMPER OF VEHICLE DOWN APPROXIMATELY 38.0 mm. GENTLY REMOVE HANDS AND LET VEHICLE RISE ON ITS OWN. REPEAT TWICE FOR A TOTAL OF 3 TIMES. MEASURE "Z" AND "J" DIMENSIONS. TRUE HEIGHTS ARE THE AVERAGE OF THE HIGH AND LOW MEASUREMENTS.

"D" AND "K" DIMENSIONS - SAME PROCEDURE AS "Z" AND "J" DIMENSIONS USING REAR BUMPER.

RECOMMENDED TIRE PRESSURE: TRIM HEIGHT. SET TIRE PRESSURE TO AGREE WITH VEHICLE'S TIRE PRESSURE STICKER FOR LOADING "UP TO VEHICLE CAPACITY."

NOTE: LOAD CONDITIONS: SHIPPING WEIGHT - VEHICLE IS BUILT TO PARTS LIST SPECIFICATIONS INCLUDING COOLANT TO CAPACITY AND 20.8 LITERS (5.5 GALLONS) OF GASOLINE. CURB WEIGHT - VEHICLE IS BUILT TO PARTS LIST SPECIFICATIONS INCLUDING COOLANT TO CAPACITY AND FULL TANK OF GASOLINE.

GC2049200056000X

Fig. 5 Ride height measurement locations

MODEL	SUSP.	ENG.	OPT. PKG.	Z		D		J		K	
				SHIPPED	CURB	SHIPPED	CURB	SHIPPED	CURB	SHIPPED	CURB
1YY07	FE1	VIN P	BASE CPE.	54.3	56.5	58.6	47.4	194.6	193.2	202.0	192.8
1YY07	FE1	VIN P	FX 3 & ZO7	52.1	54.0	54.3	46.0	191.8	190.9	198.1	191.2
1YY67	FE1	VIN P	BASE CONV.	62.8	65.0	66.4	55.2	201.8	200.3	208.8	199.6
1YZ07	FE1	VIN J	FX3 & ZR1	5.3	7.5	59.8	46.7	195.1	193.1	208.8	199.6

IMPORTANT: All dimensions in mm.
Dimension "Z", "J", "K", and "D"... Vertical to ground and apply to all vehicles.

GC2049200057000X

Fig. 6 Ride height specifications (FE1 = Soft Ride Suspension; FE7 = Heavy Duty Suspension; VIN P = V8-350/5.7L Single Cam Engine; VIN J = V8-350/5.7L 4 Cam Engine; 1YY07 = Hatchback; 1YY67 = Convertible; 1YZ07 = ZR-1 Hatchback)

BUICK CENTURY, OLDSMOBILE CUTLASS CIERA & CUTLASS CRUISER (A Cars)

NOTE: Refer To The Rear Of This Manual For Vehicle Manufacturer's Special Service Tool Suppliers.

INDEX OF SERVICE OPERATIONS

NOTE: For Service Operations Not Listed Below, Refer To The Table Of Contents In The Front Of This Manual.

Continued

INDEX OF SERVICE OPERATIONS—CONTINUED

Specifications

GENERAL ENGINE SPECIFICATIONS

Year	Engine: Liter/CID	Engine: VIN Code ①	Fuel System	Bore & Stroke	Compression Ratio	Net H.P. @ RPM ②	Maximum Torque Ft. Lbs. @ RPM	Normal Oil Pressure psi
1992	2.5L/4-151	R	TBI	4.00 x 3.00	8.3	110 @ 5200	135 @ 3200	50
	3.3L/V6-204	M	SFI	3.70 x 3.16	9.0	160 @ 5200	185 @ 2000	45③
1993	2.2L/4-134	4	MFI	3.50 x 3.46	8.85	110 @ 5200	130 @ 3200	56④
	3.3L/V6-204	M	SFI	3.70 x 3.16	9.0	160 @ 5200	185 @ 2000	45③
1994-95	2.2L/4-134	4	MFI	3.50 x 3.46	9.0	120 @ 5200	130 @ 4000	12-20④
	3.1L/V6-191	M	MFI	3.50 x 3.31	9.6	160 @ 5200	185 @ 4000	40-52⑤

①—The eighth digit denotes engine code.
②—Ratings are net-as installed in vehicle.
③—psi @ 2000 RPM.
④—psi @ 3000 RPM.
⑤—psi @ 2400 RPM.

TUNE UP SPECIFICATIONS

Engine: Liter/CID	Engine: VIN Code ①	Spark Plug Gap	Ignition Timing BTDC: Firing Order Fig.	Ignition Timing BTDC: Auto. Trans.	Ignition Timing BTDC: Mark Fig.	Curb Idle Speed	Fast Idle Speed	Fuel Pump Pressure
1992								
2.5L/4-151	R	.060	⑦	③	④	⑤	⑤	9–13⑥
3.3L/V6-204	N	.060	②	③	④	⑤	⑤	41–47⑨
1993–95								
2.2L/4-134	4	.045	⑧	③	④	⑤	⑤	41–47⑥
3.1L/V6-191	N	—	—	—	—	—	—	—
3.3L/V6-204	N	.060	②	③	④	⑤	⑤	41–47⑨

BTDC—Before top dead center.
①—The eighth digit of the Vehicle identification Number (V.I.N.) denotes engine code.
②—Refer to A for cylinder numbering. Firing order is 1-6-5-4-3-2.
③—No adjustment.
④—Equipped with crankshaft position sensor.
⑤—Idle speeds are controlled by the idle air control (IAC) valve or idle speed control (ISC) motor.
⑥—Wrap shop towel around fuel hose to steel line connection to prevent fuel spillage. Disconnect fuel hose from steel line & connect suitable fuel pressure gauge. Ensure pressure gauge connections are tight, then start engine & note fuel pressure reading.
⑦—Refer to B for cylinder numbering. Firing order 1-3-4-2.
⑧—Refer to Fig. C for cylinder numbering. Firing order 1-3-4-2.
⑨—With shop towel wrapped around fuel pressure valve to prevent fuel spillage, connect a suitable fuel pressure gauge to fuel pressure valve. Check fuel pressure with ignition switch On, engine not running.

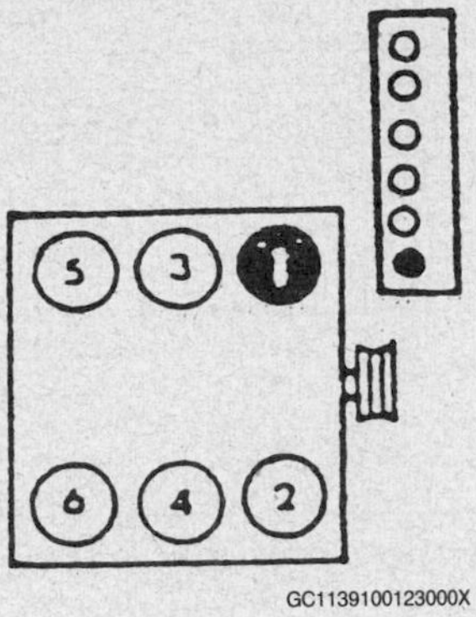
5
3
1
6
4
2
GC1139100123000X

Fig. A

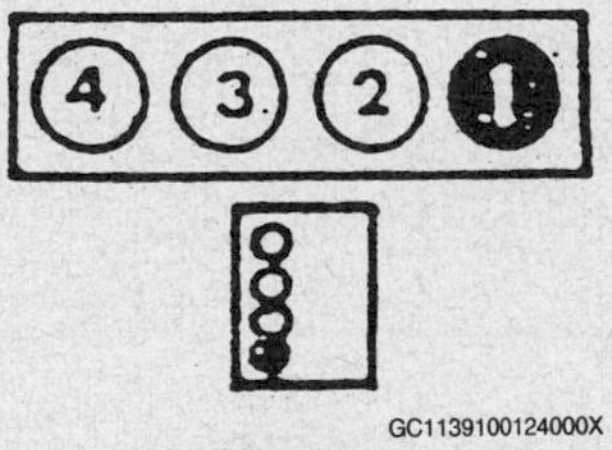
4
3
2
1
GC1139100124000X

Fig. B

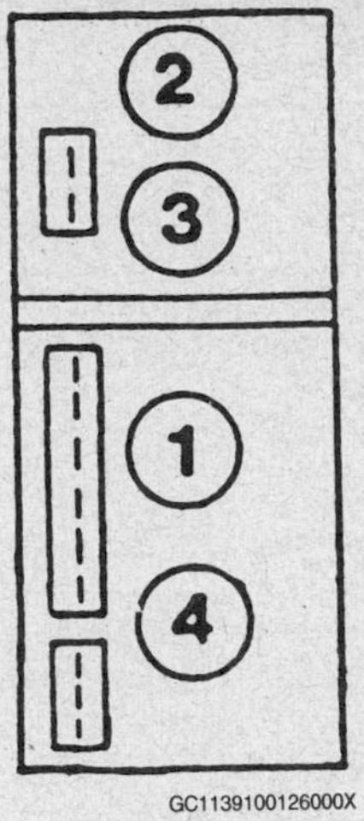
2
3
1
4
GC1139100126000X

Fig. C

FRONT WHEEL ALIGNMENT SPECIFICATIONS

Year	Model	Caster Angle, Degrees ①		Camber Angle, Degrees				Toe-In Inch
				Limits		Desired		
		Limits	Desired	Left	Right	Left	Right	
1992-93	All	+.7 to +2.7	+1.7	-.5 to +.5	-.5 to +.5	0	0	0
1994-95	All	+2.3 to +3.7	3.0	-.5 to +.5	-.5 to +.5	0	0	0

①—Non-adjustable.

REAR WHEEL ALIGNMENT SPECIFICATIONS

Year	Model	Camber Angle, Degrees ①				Toe-In Inch ①
		Limits		Desired		
		Left	Right	Left	Right	
1992-95	All	-.3 to +.3	-.3 to +.3	0	0	0

①—Non-adjustable.

COOLING SYSTEM & CAPACITY DATA

Year	Engine		Coolant Capacity, Qts.		Radiator Cap Relief Pressure, Lbs.	Thermo. Opening Temp. °F	Fuel Tank Gals.	Engine Oil Refill Qts. ②	Automatic Transaxle Oil, Qts. ①
	Liter/CID	VIN	Less A/C	With A/C					
1992	2.5L/4-151	R	9.7	9.9	15	195	15.7	4.0	③
	3.3L/V6-204	M	12.9	13.2	15	195	15.7	4.0	③
1993	2.2L/4-134	4	7.6	7.6	15	195	16.5	4.0	③
	3.3L/V6-204	M	12.9	13.2	15	195	16.5	4.0	③
1994-95	2.2L/4-134	4	—	8.7	15.9	192	16.5	4.0	③
	3.1L/V6-191	M	—	11.6	15	195	16.5	4.0	③

①—Approximate, make final check w/dipstick.

②—Additional oil may be required to bring oil level to full mark when changing oil filter.

③—Oil pan only, 4 qts. w/3T40 trans. or 6 qts. w/4T60 trans.; Total capacity, 7 qts. w/3T40 trans. or 8 qts. w/4T60 trans.

LUBRICANT DATA

Year	Model	Lubricant Type				
		Automatic	Rear Axle	Power Steering ①	Brake System	
1992-95	All	Dexron IIE	—	GM Power Steering	DOT 3	

①—An equivalent fluid meeting GM requirements can be used.

Electrical

NOTE: On Air Bag Equipped Models, Refer To "Air Bag System Precautions" Located In The Front Of This Manual For System Disarming & Arming Procedures.

INDEX

PRECAUTIONS

AIR BAG SYSTEMS

Refer to "Air Bag System Precautions" in the front of this manual for system disarming and arming procedures.

FUSE PANEL & FLASHER LOCATION

CENTURY

The fuse panel is located behind the righthand side of the instrument panel, in or near the glove box.

The hazard flasher is located in the convenience center behind the instrument panel, to the left of the steering column and the turn signal flasher is located on the accelerator pedal bracket.

CUTLASS CIERA & CUTLASS CRUISER

The fuse panel is located behind the righthand side of the instrument panel, in or near the glove box.

The hazard flasher is located in the convenience center behind the righthand side of instrument panel and the turn signal flasher is located on the instrument panel brace to the right side of the steering column.

RELAY CENTER LOCATION

The relay center is located at the front righthand side of the the engine compartment.

STARTER

REPLACE

Upon removal of starter, note if any shims are used. If shims are used, they should be reinstalled in their original location during installation.

If starter is noisy during cranking, remove one .015 inch double shim or add one .015 inch single shim to the outer bolt. If starter makes a high pitched whine after firing, add .015 inch double shims until noise ceases.

2.2L/4-134 ENGINE

1. Disconnect battery ground cable.
2. Remove engine torque strut bracket pencil brace.
3. Raise and support vehicle.
4. Remove bolts from flexplate inspection cover, then the cover.
5. Remove starter attaching bolts, then disconnect starter wiring.
6. Carefully lower starter. Note position of shims, if used.
7. Reverse procedure to install.

2.5L/4-151 ENGINE

1. Disconnect battery ground cable.
2. Raise and support vehicle.
3. Remove all electrical wiring from starter.
4. Remove dust cover attaching bolts, then dust cover.
5. Remove starter motor attaching bolts, then the nut securing starter bracket to rear of starter.
6. Remove starter from vehicle. **If starter needs additional room, remove engine brace and roll engine rearward.**

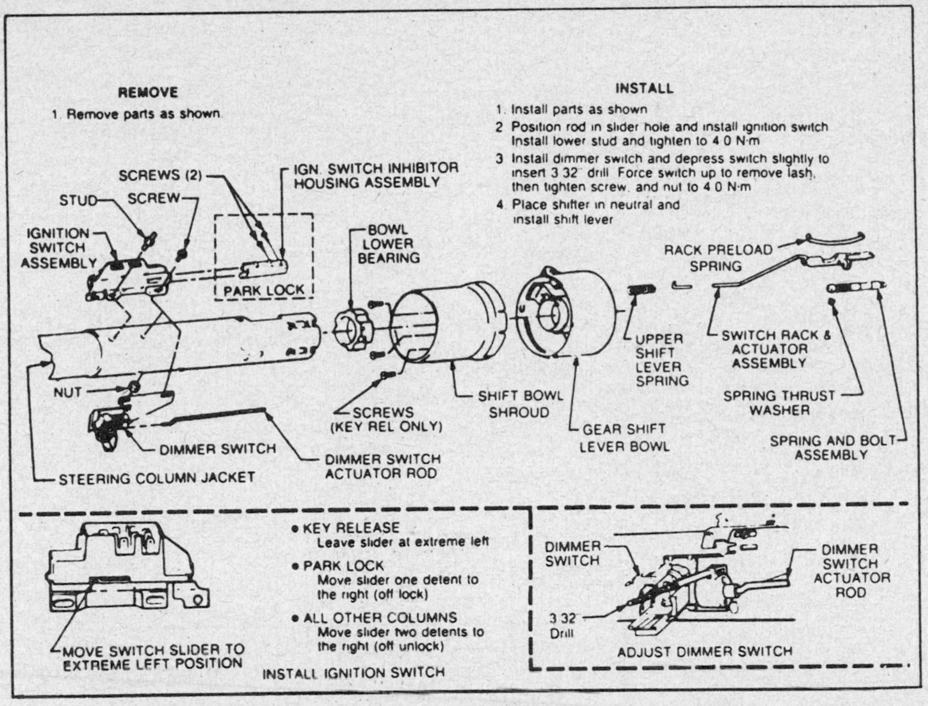
REMOVE
1. Remove parts as shown.
INSTALL
1. Install parts as shown
2. Position rod in slider hole and install ignition switch. Install lower stud and tighten to 4.0 N·m
3. Install dimmer switch and depress switch slightly to insert 3/32" drill. Force switch up to remove lash, then tighten screw, and nut to 4.0 N·m
4. Place shifter in neutral and install shift lever
SCREWS (2)
STUD
SCREW
IGN. SWITCH INHIBITOR HOUSING ASSEMBLY
IGNITION SWITCH ASSEMBLY
BOWL LOWER BEARING
PARK LOCK
RACK PRELOAD SPRING
UPPER SHIFT LEVER SPRING
SWITCH RACK & ACTUATOR ASSEMBLY
NUT
SHIFT BOWL SHROUD
SPRING THRUST WASHER
SCREWS (KEY REL ONLY)
GEAR SHIFT LEVER BOWL
SPRING AND BOLT ASSEMBLY
DIMMER SWITCH
DIMMER SWITCH ACTUATOR ROD
STEERING COLUMN JACKET
• KEY RELEASE
Leave slider at extreme left
• PARK LOCK
Move slider one detent to the right (off lock)
• ALL OTHER COLUMNS
Move slider two detents to the right (off unlock)
MOVE SWITCH SLIDER TO EXTREME LEFT POSITION
INSTALL IGNITION SWITCH
DIMMER SWITCH
DIMMER SWITCH ACTUATOR ROD
3/32 Drill
ADJUST DIMMER SWITCH
GC9049100077000X

Fig. 1 Ignition & dimmer switch replacement. Fixed column.

7. Reverse procedure to install. **Torque** starter motor attaching bolts to 32 ft. lbs.

3.1L/V6-189 ENGINE

1. Disconnect battery negative cable.
2. Raise and support vehicle, then remove nut from brace at A/C compressor.
3. Disconnect wiring from front of frame.
4. Remove dust cover attaching bolts, then dust cover.
5. Remove all electrical wiring from starter, then remove starter from vehicle.
6. Remove starter attaching bolts, then lower starter.
7. Reverse procedure to install.

3.3L/V6-204 ENGINE

1. Disconnect battery ground cable.
2. Raise and support vehicle.
3. Remove flywheel cover attaching bolts, then the cover.
4. Disconnect all electrical wires from starter.
5. Remove starter motor attaching bolts, then the motor by rotating the solenoid side toward the vehicle.
6. Reverse procedure to install. **Torque** starter attaching bolts to 32 ft. lbs. and inspection cover bolts to 89 inch lbs.

IGNITION LOCK

REPLACE

1. Remove turn signal switch as outlined under "Turn Signal Switch, Replace."
2. Remove buzzer switch and spring clip. Ignition key must be removed from lock to remove buzzer switch. Switch and spring clip are one assembly.
3. Turn lock cylinder to Run position, then remove lock cylinder retaining screw and the lock cylinder.
4. To install, rotate lock cylinder to the stop while holding housing. Align cylinder key with keyway in housing, then push lock cylinder into housing until fully seated. Lock cylinder must be in Run position to install buzzer switch.
5. Install lock cylinder retaining screw, then the buzzer switch, turn signal switch and steering wheel.

IGNITION SWITCH

REPLACE

FIXED COLUMN

1. Remove ignition lock as outlined under "Ignition Lock, Replace."
2. Refer to **Fig. 1** for ignition and dimmer switch replacement procedures.
3. Remove washer and hex nut.
4. Disconnect dimmer switch assembly from rod.
5. Remove dimmer switch and ignition switch mounting stud.
6. Remove ignition switch from ignition switch actuator assembly.
7. Disconnect turn signal switch assembly electrical connector from bulkhead connector.
8. Remove pivot and switch assembly connector from bulkhead connector.
9. Reverse procedure to install.

TILT COLUMN

1. Remove ignition lock as outlined under "Ignition Lock, Replace."
2. Remove housing as follows:
   a. Install tilt lever and place column in full Up position.
   b. Pull upward on tilt lever and pull housing upward until it stops.
   c. Move housing to right to disengage rack from actuator, then remove housing from steering column.
3. Refer to **Fig. 2** for ignition and dimmer switch replacement procedures.
4. Install housing as follows:
   a. While holding up on tilt lever to disengage lock shoes install over steering shaft.
   b. Move rack downward and hold. Tip housing to the left until rack engages pin on actuator rod.
   c. Push housing down until pivot pin holes are in alignment.

NEUTRAL SAFETY SWITCH

REPLACE

REMOVAL

1. Disconnect battery ground cable.
2. Apply parking brake and block wheels, then place transaxle in the NEUTRAL position.
3. Disconnect shift linkage from transmission, then the electrical connector from the neutral switch, **Fig. 3**.
4. Remove two switch mounting bolts, then the switch.

INSTALLATION

1. Place shift shaft in neutral.
2. Align flats in shift shaft with flats in switch.
3. Install mounting bolts, if bolt holes will not align with mounting boss on the transmission, proceed as follows:
   a. Ensure shift shaft is in neutral position. **Do not rotate switch. Switch is pinned in a neutral position.**
   b. Install mounting bolts loosely.
   c. Align slot in support with slot in back and insert a $^{3}/_{32}$ drill bit horizontally into both pieces.
4. **Torque** mounting bolts to 18 ft. lbs.
5. Remove drill bit, if used, then reconnect electrical connector and shift linkage.
6. Verify that engine will start only in neutral or park position, if engine starts in any other position, adjust switch as follows:
   a. Place shifter in NEUTRAL position, then loosen switch attaching screws.
   b. Rotate switch on shifter assembly to align service adjustment hole with carrier tang hole, **Fig. 3**.
   c. Insert a $^{3}/_{32}$ inch gauge pin to a depth of $^{5}/_{8}$ inch.
   d. **Torque** mounting bolts to 18 ft. lbs., then remove gauge pin.
7. Release parking brake and remove wheel blocks.

HEADLAMP SWITCH

REPLACE

CENTURY

1. Disconnect battery ground cable.

2. Remove left instrument panel trim plate as follows:
   a. Remove screws holding ALDL connector, then lower connector.
   b. Remove filler panel attaching screws, then lap vent hose.
   c. Remove filler panel by swinging down and pulling out.
   d. Remove steering column opening filler attaching screws, then opening filler.
   e. Remove left trim plate attaching screw, then trim plate. On vehicles with column shift, shift transaxle to First gear.
3. Remove switch trim plate attaching screws, then trim plate.
4. Remove switch attaching screws, then switch.
5. Reverse procedure to install.

CUTLASS CIERA & CRUISER

1. Disconnect battery ground cable, then remove upper console, if equipped.
2. Remove accessory trim plate as follows:
   a. Pry steering column collar rearward, using a suitable tool, and remove.
   b. Remove outer air deflectors, then the two screws behind the deflector openings.
   c. Remove screw from behind steering column collar.
   d. **On models less console,** open ashtray and remove trim plate attaching screws.
   e. **On models with console,** remove four screws from ashtray trim cover, then ashtray trim cover. Remove trim plate attaching screws.
   f. **On all models,** pull trim plate rearward to release clips, then remove trim plate.
3. Remove 3 switch to panel attaching screws.
4. Pull switch rearward and remove from panel.
5. Reverse procedure to install.

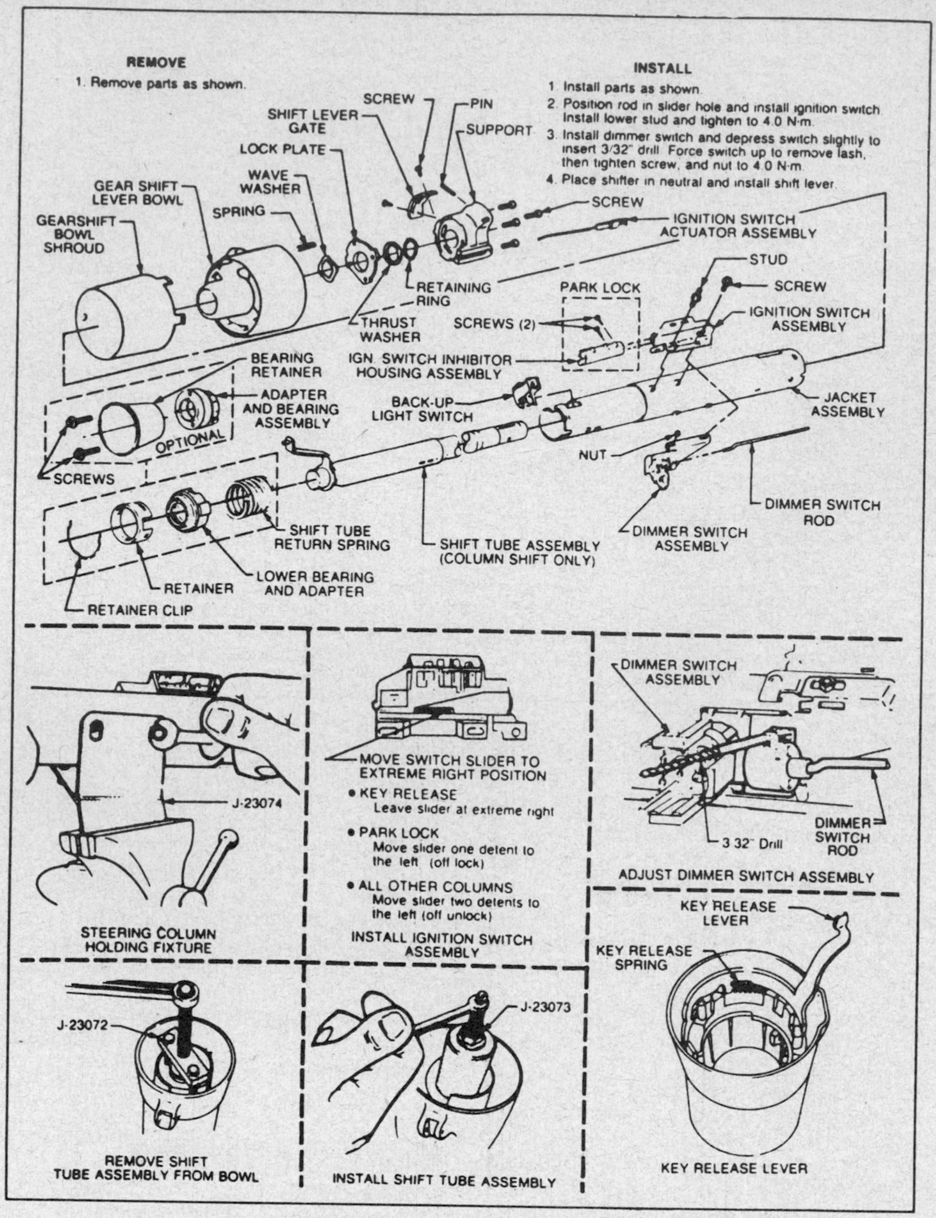
REMOVE
1. Remove parts as shown.
INSTALL
1. Install parts as shown.
2. Position rod in slider hole and install ignition switch. Install lower stud and tighten to 4.0 N·m.
3. Install dimmer switch and depress switch slightly to insert 3/32" drill. Force switch up to remove lash, then tighten screw, and nut to 4.0 N·m.
4. Place shifter in neutral and install shift lever.
SCREW
PIN
SUPPORT
SHIFT LEVER GATE
LOCK PLATE
WAVE WASHER
GEAR SHIFT LEVER BOWL
GEARSHIFT BOWL SHROUD
SPRING
SCREW
IGNITION SWITCH ACTUATOR ASSEMBLY
STUD
RETAINING RING
PARK LOCK
SCREW
IGNITION SWITCH ASSEMBLY
THRUST WASHER
SCREWS (2)
BEARING RETAINER
IGN. SWITCH INHIBITOR HOUSING ASSEMBLY
ADAPTER AND BEARING ASSEMBLY
BACK-UP LIGHT SWITCH
JACKET ASSEMBLY
OPTIONAL
SCREWS
NUT
DIMMER SWITCH ROD
SHIFT TUBE RETURN SPRING
SHIFT TUBE ASSEMBLY (COLUMN SHIFT ONLY)
DIMMER SWITCH ASSEMBLY
RETAINER
LOWER BEARING AND ADAPTER
RETAINER CLIP
J-23074
STEERING COLUMN HOLDING FIXTURE
MOVE SWITCH SLIDER TO EXTREME RIGHT POSITION
• KEY RELEASE
Leave slider at extreme right
• PARK LOCK
Move slider one detent to the left (off lock)
• ALL OTHER COLUMNS
Move slider two detents to the left (off unlock)
INSTALL IGNITION SWITCH ASSEMBLY
DIMMER SWITCH ASSEMBLY
3 32" Drill
DIMMER SWITCH ROD
ADJUST DIMMER SWITCH ASSEMBLY
KEY RELEASE LEVER
KEY RELEASE SPRING
J-23072
REMOVE SHIFT TUBE ASSEMBLY FROM BOWL
J-23073
INSTALL SHIFT TUBE ASSEMBLY
KEY RELEASE LEVER
GC9049100078000X

Fig. 2 Ignition & dimmer switch replacement. Tilt column

STOP LIGHT SWITCH

REPLACE

1. Disconnect battery ground cable.
2. Disconnect electrical connector from stop lamp switch.
3. Remove stop lamp switch from brake pedal support bracket, **Fig. 4.**
4. Reverse procedure to install.

ADJUSTMENT

Insert switch into tubular clip until the switch body seats on the tube clip. Pull the brake pedal rearward against internal pedal stop. This will properly position switch in tubular clip.

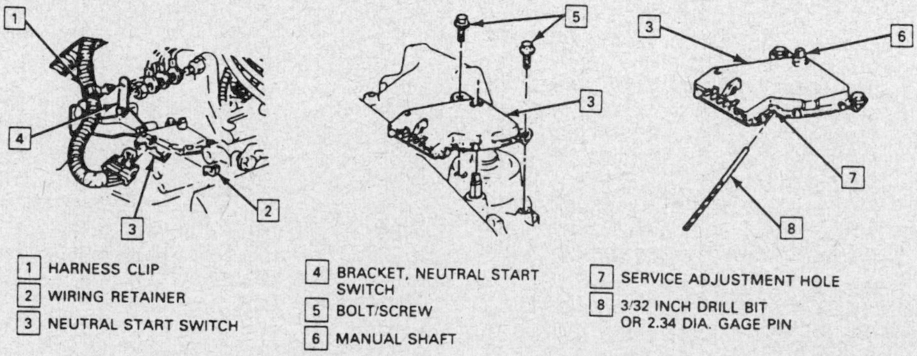
1 HARNESS CLIP
2 WIRING RETAINER
3 NEUTRAL START SWITCH
4 BRACKET, NEUTRAL START SWITCH
5 BOLT/SCREW
6 MANUAL SHAFT
7 SERVICE ADJUSTMENT HOLE
8 3/32 INCH DRILL BIT OR 2.34 DIA. GAGE PIN
GC9049100079000X

Fig. 3 Neutral switch removal & adjustment

TURN SIGNAL SWITCH

REPLACE

1. Disconnect battery ground cable.
2. Remove steering wheel as outlined under "Steering Wheel, Replace" procedure.
3. Using a screwdriver, pry cover from housing.
4. Using lock plate compressing tool No. J-23653, or equivalent, compress lock plate, and pry snap ring from groove on shaft, **Fig. 5.** Slowly release lock plate compressing tool, then remove tool and lock plate from shaft end.
5. Slide canceling cam and upper bearing preload spring from end of shaft.

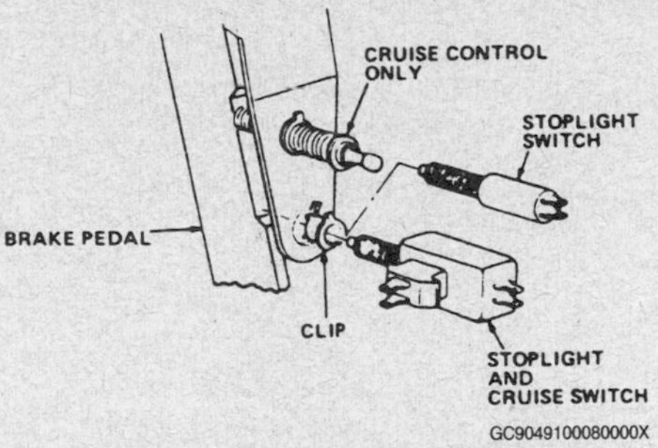
CRUISE CONTROL ONLY
STOPLIGHT SWITCH
BRAKE PEDAL
CLIP
STOPLIGHT AND CRUISE SWITCH
GC9049100080000X

Fig. 4 Stoplamp switch replacement

6. Remove turn signal (multi-function) lever.
7. Remove hazard warning knob retaining screw, button, spring and knob.
8. Remove pivot arm.
9. Wrap upper part of electrical connector with tape to prevent snagging of wires during switch removal.
10. Remove switch retaining screws and pull switch up from column, guiding wire harness through column.
11. Reverse procedure to install.

DIMMER SWITCH

REPLACE

Refer to "Ignition Switch, Replace" for procedure.

STEERING WHEEL

REPLACE

1. Disconnect battery ground cable.
2. Remove horn button or pad
3. Disconnect horn pad and lead by pushing down and turning counterclockwise.
4. **On models equipped with air bag,** remove air bag inflator module as outlined under "Air Bag Systems."
5. **On all models,** remove retainer and steering wheel retaining nut.
6. Using steering wheel puller No. J-1859-03 or equivalent, remove steering wheel. With steering wheel controls, puller bolts should not be turned in more than five complete turns.
7. Reverse procedure to install.

INSTRUMENT CLUSTER

REPLACE

CENTURY

1. Disconnect battery ground cable.
2. Remove steering column filler panel as follows:
   a. Remove ALDL connector attaching screws, then lower ALDL connector.
   b. Remove filler panel attaching screws, then lap vent hose.
   c. Remove filler panel by swinging down and pulling out.
3. Remove left trim plate as follows:
   a. Remove steering column opening filler attaching screws, then opening filler.

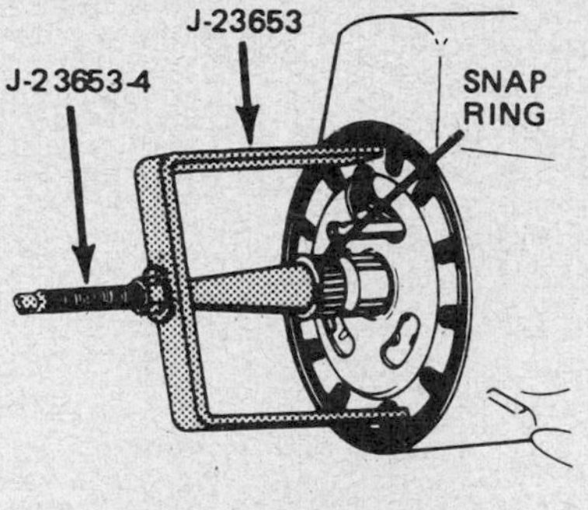
J-23653
J-23653-4
SNAP RING
Tighten nut until tool slightly depresses lock plate
GC9129100018000X

Fig. 5 Lock plate compression

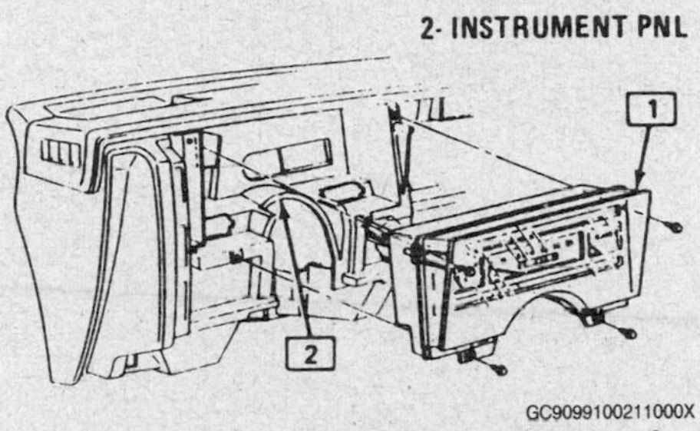
1- CLUSTER ASM
2- INSTRUMENT PNL
1
2
GC9099100211000X

Fig. 7 Instrument cluster removal. Century

   b. Remove ashtray, then trim plate attaching screws, **Fig. 6.**
   c. Pull trim panel straight forward to release two retaining clips in center of panel, then remove panel.
4. Disconnect speedometer cable from transmission. If two piece cable is used, disconnect in engine compartment to ensure there is cable slack.
5. Remove shift indicator clip from steering column shift bowl, then cluster attaching screws, **Fig. 7.**
6. Pull cluster assembly out far enough to reach behind and disconnect speedometer cable.
7. Remove cluster.
8. Reverse procedure to install.

CUTLASS CIERA & CRUISER

1. Disconnect battery ground cable, then remove upper console, if equipped.
2. Remove accessory trim plate as follows:
   a. Pry steering column collar rearward, using a suitable tool, and remove.
   b. Remove outer air deflectors, then the two screws behind the deflector openings.
   c. Remove screw from behind steering column collar.
   d. **On models less console,** open ashtray and remove trim plate attaching screws.
   e. **On models with console,** remove four screws from ashtray trim cover, then ashtray trim cover. Remove trim plate attaching screws.

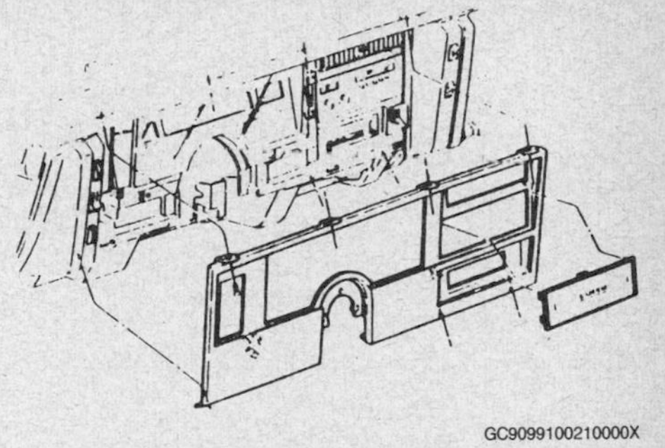
GC9099100210000X

Fig. 6 Left trim plate removal. Century

   f. **On all models,** pull trim plate rearward to release clips, then remove accessory trim plate, **Fig. 8.**
3. Remove screws attaching cluster trim plate, then trim plate, **Fig. 9.**
4. Remove steering column trim collar and trim plate.
5. Disconnect shift indicator clip from steering column shift bowl.
6. Remove cluster assembly attaching bolts, **Fig. 10,** then pull cluster rearward.
7. Disconnect speedometer cable from cluster.
8. Remove cluster assembly.
9. Reverse procedure to install.

RADIO

REPLACE

CENTURY

1. Disconnect battery ground cable.
2. Remove steering column filler panel as follows:
   a. Remove ALDL connector attaching screws, then lower ALDL connector.
   b. Remove filler panel attaching screws, then lap vent hose.
   c. Remove filler panel by swinging down and pulling out.
3. Remove left trim plate as follows:
   a. Remove steering column opening filler attaching screws, then opening filler.
   b. Remove ashtray, then trim plate attaching screws, **Fig. 6.**
   c. Pull trim panel straight forward to release two retaining clips in center of panel, then remove panel.
4. Remove right cluster trim plate attaching screws, then trim plate.
5. Remove radio assembly attaching screws, then pull out radio.
6. Disconnect all electrical connectors from radio, then remove radio.
7. Reverse procedure to install.

CUTLASS CIERA & CRUISER

1. Disconnect battery ground cable, then remove upper console, if equipped.
2. Remove accessory trim plate as follows:
   a. Pry steering column collar rearward, using a suitable tool, and remove.

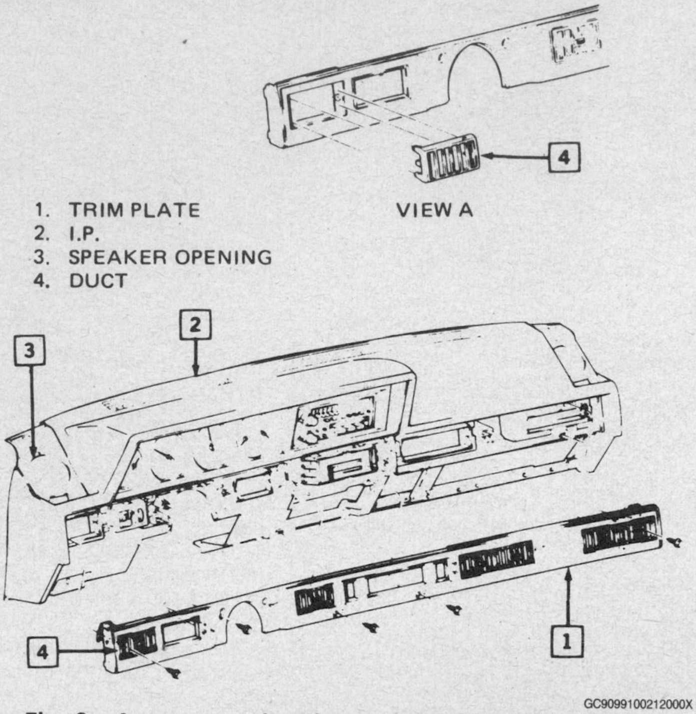
1. TRIM PLATE
2. I.P.
3. SPEAKER OPENING
4. DUCT
VIEW A
GC9099100212000X

Fig. 8 Accessory trim plate removal. Cutlass Ciera & Cruiser

b. Remove outer air deflectors, then the two screws behind the deflector openings.
c. Remove screw from behind steering column collar.
d. **On models less console,** open ashtray and remove trim plate attaching screws.
e. **On models with console,** remove four screws from ashtray trim cover, then ashtray trim cover. Remove trim plate attaching screws.
f. **On all models,** pull trim plate rearward to release clips, then remove accessory trim plate, **Fig. 8.**

3. Remove screws attaching cluster trim plate, then trim plate, **Fig. 9.**
4. Remove radio attaching bolts, then pull out radio.
5. Disconnect all electrical connectors from radio, then remove radio.
6. Reverse procedure to install.

WIPER MOTOR
REPLACE
FRONT

1. Raise hood, then remove right and left wiper arm and blade assemblies.
2. Remove shroud grille to body attaching screws, then shroud grille.
3. Loosen, but do not remove nuts securing transmission drive link to motor crank arm, then disconnect drive link.
4. Disconnect wiring connectors and washer hoses.
5. Remove three screws attaching wiper motor to firewall.
6. Remove motor while guiding crank arm through hole.
7. Reverse procedure to install. Motor must be in "Park" position before assembling transmission drive link to crank arm. **Torque** transmission drive link to 48-75 inch lbs.

REAR

1. Remove wiper arm, then nut on transmission shaft.
2. Remove liftgate glass opening upper finishing molding, then disconnect electrical connector from motor.
3. Remove upper mounting screw (second screw is a dowel).
4. Rotate motor assembly to 12 o'clock position, guide motor pivot out of tailgate assembly.
5. Reverse procedure to install.

WIPER SWITCH
REPLACE
FRONT

Refer to **Figs. 11 through 14** during the following procedure.

Fixed Column

1. Remove ignition and dimmer switches as outlined under "Ignition Switch, Replace."
2. Disconnect battery ground cable.
3. Remove shaft lock cover, then shaft retaining ring using tool No. J 23653-C, or equivalent, to push down shaft lock. Dispose of ring.
4. Remove shaft lock, then turn signal cancelling cam assembly.
5. Remove upper bearing spring and thrust washer.
6. Turn lever to "Right" position, then remove multi-function lever and hazard knob assembly.
7. Remove screw and switch arm, then multi-function switch screws.

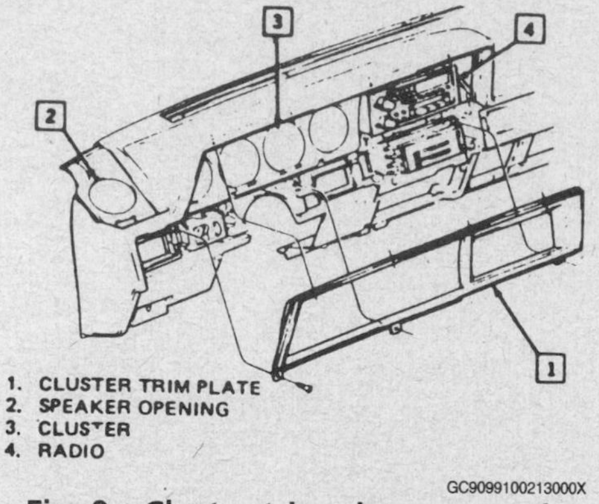
1. CLUSTER TRIM PLATE
2. SPEAKER OPENING
3. CLUSTER
4. RADIO
GC9099100213000X

Fig. 9 Cluster trim plate removal. Cutlass Ciera & Cruiser

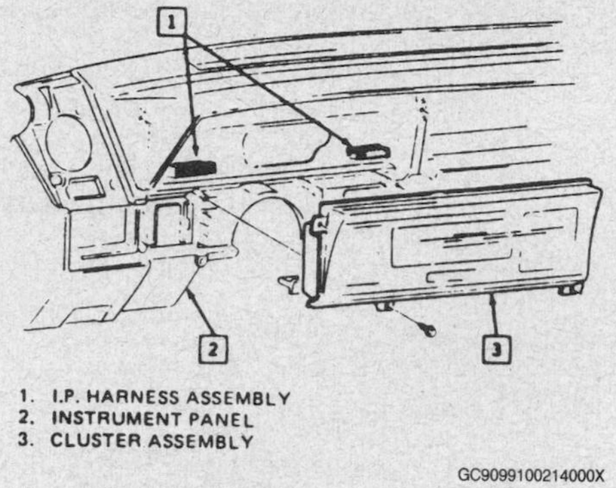
1. I.P. HARNESS ASSEMBLY
2. INSTRUMENT PANEL
3. CLUSTER ASSEMBLY
GC9099100214000X

Fig. 10 Instrument cluster removal. Cutlass Ciera & Cruiser

8. Remove switch assembly as follows:
   a. Disconnect switch connector from bulkhead connector and wire harness strap.
   b. Remove wiring protector.
   c. Remove key from lock cylinder set, then buzzer switch assembly.
   d. Reinsert key into lock cylinder, then turn to "Lock" position.
   e. Remove lock retaining screw, then lock cylinder set.
9. Reverse procedure to install.

Tilt Column

1. Remove ignition lock as outlined under "Ignition Lock, Replace."
2. Refer to **Fig. 15** for wiper switch replacement.

REAR

1. Disconnect battery ground cable.
2. Remove lefthand trim panel, then right side switch trim cover.
3. Remove switch attaching screws, then switch.
4. Reverse procedure to install.

WIPER TRANSMISSION
REPLACE

1. Raise hood, then remove right and left wiper arm and blade assemblies.
2. Loosen, but do not remove nuts securing transmission drive link to motor crank arm.
3. Remove air inlet panel attaching screw, then panel.
4. Disconnect transmission drive link from motor crank arm, **Fig. 16.**

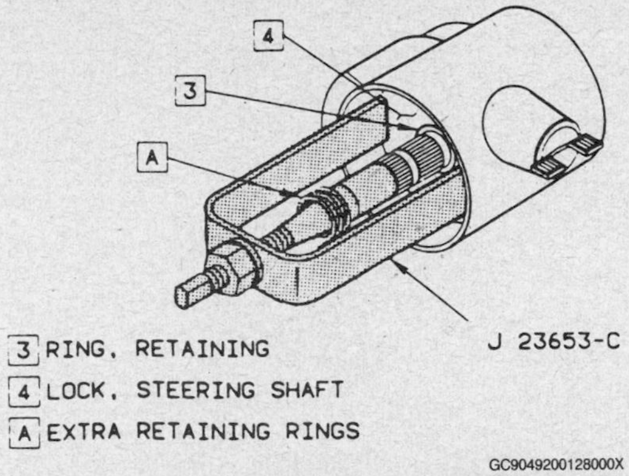
4
3
A
J 23653-C
3 RING, RETAINING
4 LOCK, STEERING SHAFT
A EXTRA RETAINING RINGS
GC9049200128000X

Fig. 11 Shaft lock retaining ring removal

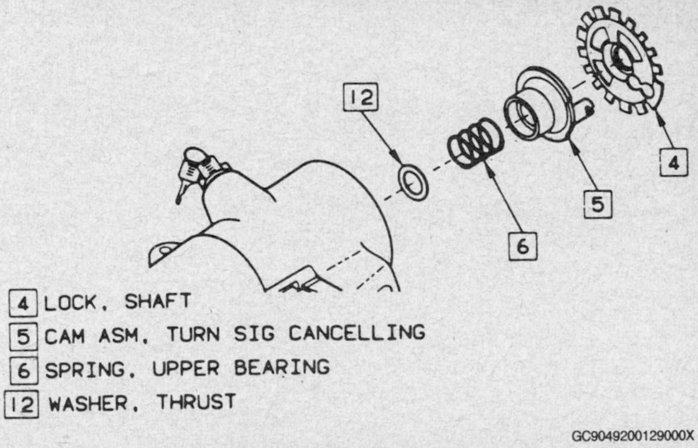
12
4
5
6
4 LOCK, SHAFT
5 CAM ASM, TURN SIG CANCELLING
6 SPRING, UPPER BEARING
12 WASHER, THRUST
GC9049200129000X

Fig. 12 Upper shaft component removal

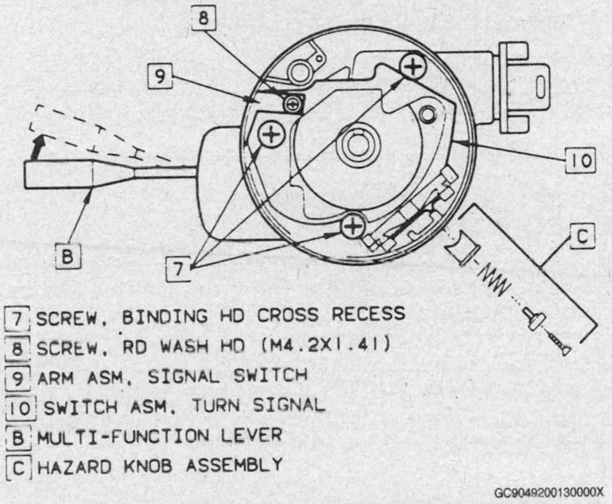
8
9
10
C
B
7
7 SCREW, BINDING HD CROSS RECESS
8 SCREW, RD WASH HD (M4.2X1.41)
9 ARM ASM, SIGNAL SWITCH
10 SWITCH ASM, TURN SIGNAL
B MULTI-FUNCTION LEVER
C HAZARD KNOB ASSEMBLY
GC9049200130000X

Fig. 13 Switch removal preparation

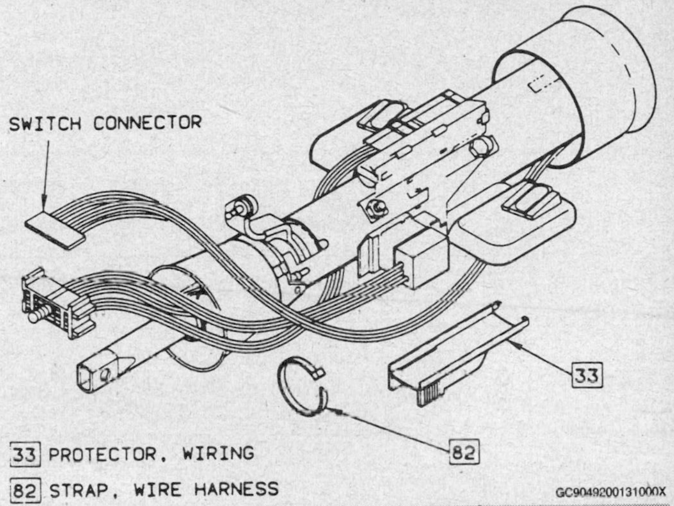
SWITCH CONNECTOR
33
82
33 PROTECTOR, WIRING
82 STRAP, WIRE HARNESS
GC9049200131000X

Fig. 14 Switch removal

5. Remove wiper transmission to body attaching screw.
6. Carefully guide transmission assembly through access hole in upper shroud panel to remove.
7. Reverse procedure to install. **Torque** transmission drive link nuts to 53-75 inch lbs.

BLOWER MOTOR

REPLACE

CENTURY

1. Disconnect battery ground cable.
2. Disconnect engine torque strut and rotate engine forward.
3. Disconnect blower motor electrical connectors and vent tube, then remove blower motor attaching screws.
4. Remove fan retaining nut from blower motor shaft.
5. Holding fan securely, remove fan from blower motor while removing blower motor from vehicle. **Failure to hold fan securely can cause fan to fall into heater A/C module.**
6. Reverse procedure to install.

CUTLASS CIERA & CUTLASS CRUISER

1. Disconnect battery ground cable.
2. Disconnect blower motor electrical connections.

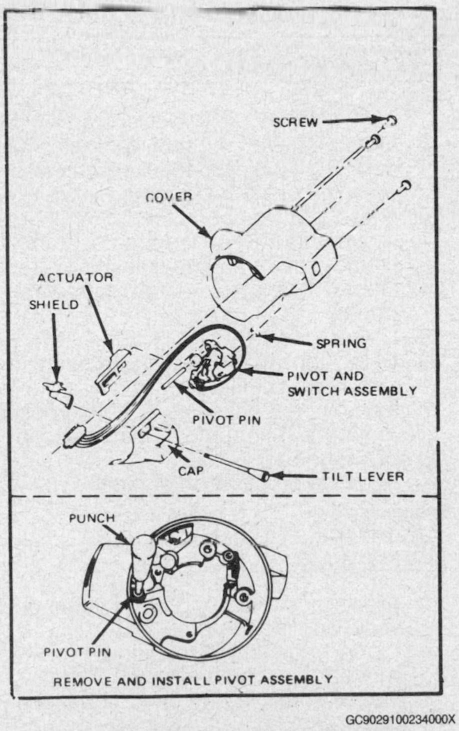
SCREW
COVER
ACTUATOR
SHIELD
SPRING
PIVOT AND
SWITCH ASSEMBLY
PIVOT PIN
CAP
TILT LEVER
PUNCH
PIVOT PIN
REMOVE AND INSTALL PIVOT ASSEMBLY
GC9029100234000X

Fig. 15 Cover & wiper switch replacement. Tilt column

3. Remove serpentine drive belt, then the alternator bracket bolts. Position alternator aside.
4. Remove vent tube.
5. Remove blower motor attaching screws, then the blower motor.
6. Reverse procedure to install.

HEATER CORE

REPLACE

LESS A/C

1. Drain cooling system.
2. Disconnect heater inlet and outlet hoses.
3. Remove lower instrument panel sound insulator, then radio noise suppression strap.
4. Remove cover retaining screws and cover.
5. Remove heater core strap, then heater core.
6. Reverse procedure to install.

WITH A/C

1. Drain cooling system.
2. Disconnect heater inlet and outlet hoses.
3. Remove lower instrument panel sound insulator, then heater floor outlet duct.
4. Remove heater core cover screws and clips securing cover to air valve housing, then heater core cover.

5. Remove heater core retaining straps, then heater core.
6. Reverse procedure to install.

EVAPORATOR CORE

REPLACE

1. Disconnect battery ground cable, then discharge and recover A/C system.
2. **On models with 3.1L/V6-189 engine,** disconnect throttle modulator assembly.
3. **On all models,** disconnect A/C heater module electrical connectors, then harness straps. Move harness aside.
4. Remove heater hose routing bracket and resistor from cover, if equipped, then the vacuum tank.
5. Disconnect liquid line at evaporator inlet and low pressure line at evaporator outlet.
6. Dismount alternator and move away from module, if necessary.

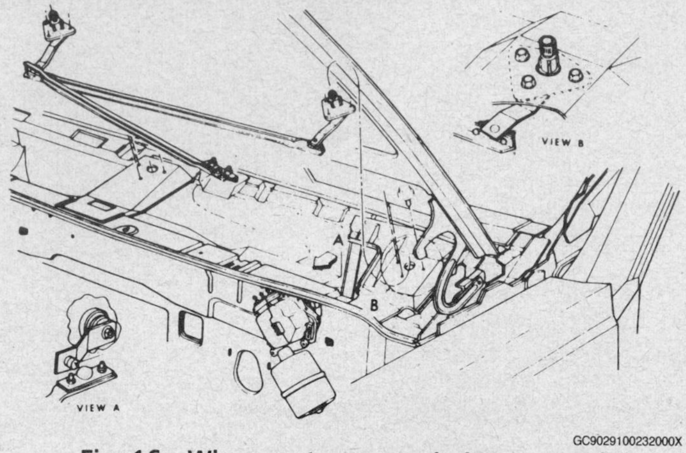
VIEW B
A
B
VIEW A
GC9029100232000X

Fig. 16 Wiper motor transmission removal

7. Remove evaporator core cover retaining screws (loosen bottom screws only), then remove evaporator core cover.
8. Remove evaporator core.
9. Reverse procedure to install.

2.2L/4-134 Engine

NOTE: On Air Bag Equipped Models, Refer To "Air Bag System Precautions" Located In The Front Of This Manual For System Disarming & Arming Procedures.

NOTE: For Procedures Not Found In This Section, Refer To The 2.2L/4-134 Engine Section In The Chevrolet Cavalier, Pontiac Sunbird & Sunfire Chapter.

INDEX

PRECAUTIONS

AIR BAG SYSTEMS

Refer to "Air Bag System Precautions" in the front of this manual for system disarming and arming procedures.

FUEL SYSTEM PRESSURE RELIEF

Whenever the fuel lines are to be disconnected for engine service on fuel injected engines, relieve fuel system pressure following the procedures outlined below. Failure to follow these procedures exactly, may result in personal injury.

1. Disconnect battery ground cable, then loosen filler cap to relieve tank vapor pressure.
2. Connect fuel pressure gauge No. J-34730-1 or equivalent to fuel pressure valve. Wrap a shop towel around fitting while connecting gauge to avoid spillage.
3. Install bleed hose into an approved container and open valve to bleed system pressure. Fuel connections are now safe for servicing.
4. Drain any fuel remaining in gauge into approved container.

ENGINE MOUNT

REPLACE

1. Install engine support tool Nos. J-28467-A and J-36462, or equivalent, then remove engine mount strut.
2. Raise and support vehicle, then remove right wheel and tire assembly.
3. Remove right engine splash shield.
4. Remove engine mount nuts from frame.
5. Lower vehicle.
6. Using tool No J-28467-A or equivalent, raise engine off mount.
7. Remove nut attaching engine bracket to mount, then remove mount assembly, **Fig. 1.**
8. Reverse procedure to install.

ENGINE

REPLACE

1. Disconnect battery ground cable and drain cooling system.
2. Open hood to full position, then remove gas support at cowl.
3. Remove air cleaner and duct assembly.
4. Remove throttle control cable bracket at intake and rocker cover.
5. Relieve fuel pressure as follows:
   a. Loosen fuel tank filler cap to relieve tank pressure.
   b. Raise and support vehicle, then disconnect fuel pump electrical connector.
   c. Lower vehicle.
   d. Start and operate engine until fuel supply is consumed.
   e. Crank engine for approximately 3 seconds to relieve remaining pressure.
   f. Disconnect battery ground cable, then reconnect fuel pump connector.
6. Disconnect fuel line, then the vacuum, radiator and heater hoses.
7. Remove engine mount strut and bracket pencil brace, then disconnect engine electrical connector.
8. Rotate engine forward.
9. Remove power steering pump and electrical connectors at rear of engine.
10. Disconnect transaxle fluid level indicator, then remove transaxle engine bolts except two upper bolts.
11. Rotate engine rearward, then raise and support vehicle.
12. Remove front wheel and tire assembly.

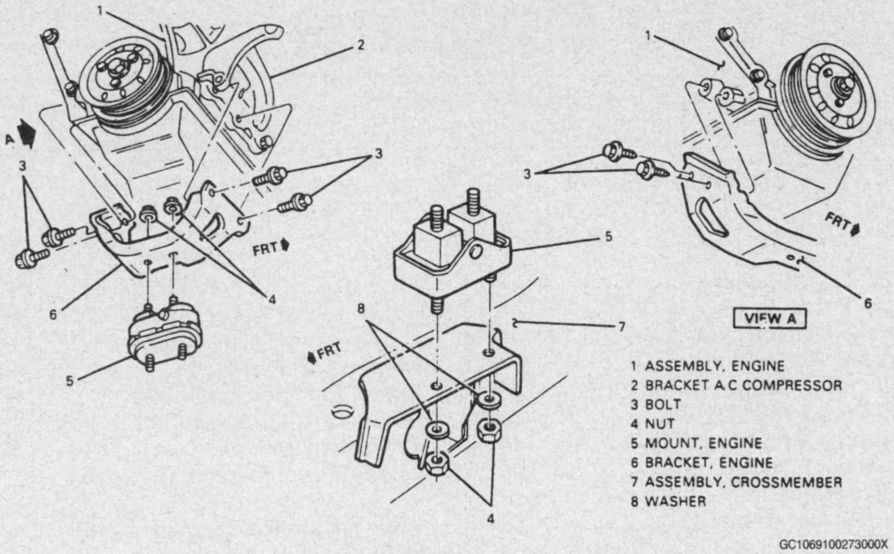

VIEW A
FRT
1 ASSEMBLY, ENGINE
2 BRACKET A.C COMPRESSOR
3 BOLT
4 NUT
5 MOUNT, ENGINE
6 BRACKET, ENGINE
7 ASSEMBLY, CROSSMEMBER
8 WASHER
GC1069100273000X

Fig. 1 Engine mounts

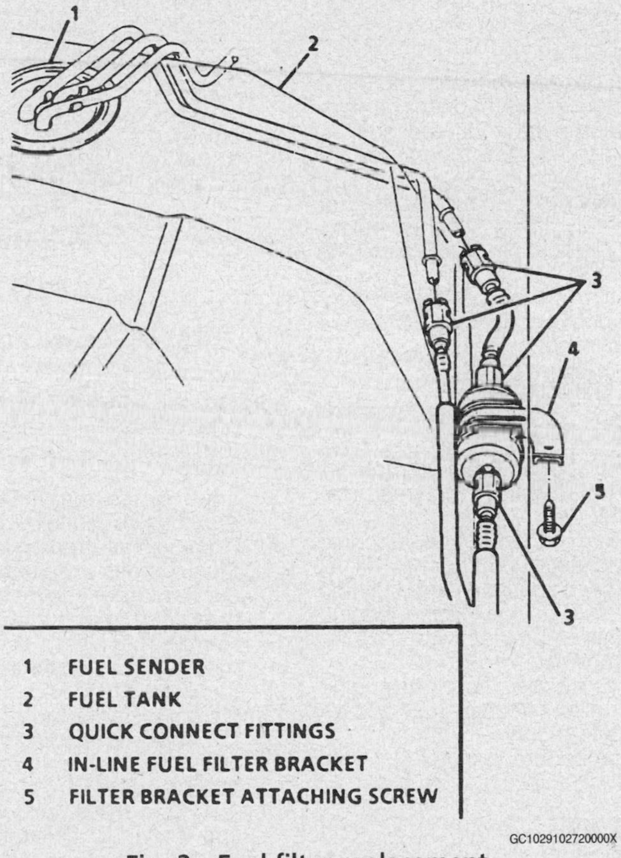

1 FUEL SENDER
2 FUEL TANK
3 QUICK CONNECT FITTINGS
4 IN-LINE FUEL FILTER BRACKET
5 FILTER BRACKET ATTACHING SCREW
GC1029102720000X

Fig. 2 Fuel filter replacement

13. Remove right side engine splash shield, then disconnect exhaust pipe from crossover.
14. Remove flywheel cover and starter motor.
15. Remove engine mount to frame nuts.
16. Remove converter to flywheel bolts.
17. Disconnect A/C compressor, leaving hoses attached, then position compressor aside.
18. Disconnect front exhaust pipe support bracket at transaxle.
19. Remove transaxle support bracket to transaxle bolt, then lower vehicle.
20. Rotate engine forward and rearward, then remove rear and front transaxle attaching bolts to engine.
21. Attach suitable lifting device to engine.
22. Remove engine.
23. Reverse procedure to install.

RADIATOR

REPLACE

1. Remove air cleaner assembly and resonator.
2. Drain engine coolant, then disconnect cooling fan electrical connector.
3. Remove cooling fan screws, then the cooling fan assembly.
4. Remove engine mount strut and mounting bracket from radiator upper mounting panel.
5. Remove radiator mounting panel.
6. Disconnect oil cooler lines.
7. Disconnect coolant recovery hose, then the upper and lower radiator hoses.
8. Remove radiator.
9. Reverse procedure to install.

FUEL FILTER

REPLACE

1. Relieve fuel system pressure as outlined under "Precautions."
2. Raise and support vehicle.
3. Remove bracket attaching screw and filter bracket, **Fig. 2.**
4. Grasp filter and fuel line fitting. Twist quick-connect fitting 1/4 turn in each direction to loosen any dirt within fitting.
5. Using compressed air, blow out dirt from quick-connect fitting.
6. Remove feed pipe nut from fuel filter, then drain any remaining fuel into an suitable container.
7. Remove fuel filter.
8. Reverse procedure to install.

2.5L/4-151 Engine

NOTE: On Air Bag Equipped Models, Refer To "Air Bag System Precautions" Located In The Front Of This Manual For System Disarming & Arming Procedures.

INDEX

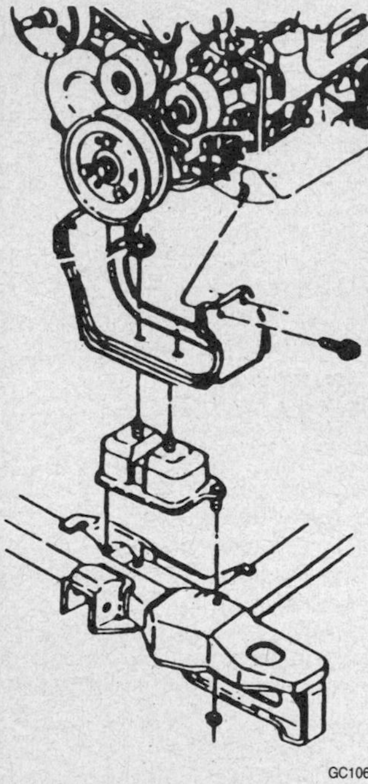
GC1069100274000X

Fig. 1 Engine mounts

PRECAUTIONS

AIR BAG SYSTEMS

Refer to "Air Bag System Precautions" in the front of this manual for system disarming and arming procedures.

FUEL SYSTEM PRESSURE RELIEF

Whenever the fuel lines are to be disconnected for engine service on fuel injected engines, relieve fuel system pressure following the procedures outlined below. Failure to follow these procedures exactly, may result in personal injury.

1. Place transmission in Park or Neutral.
2. Disconnect fuel pump at rear body connector or remove fuel pump inline fuse located in the engine compartment, behind righthand headlights.
3. Start engine and allow to run until engine stalls.
4. After engine stalls, engage starter for approximately three seconds to relieve any residual pressure remaining in system.
5. Turn ignition switch off, then reconnect fuel pump connector or replace fuel pump inline fuse.

ENGINE MOUNT

REPLACE

1. Raise and support front of vehicle, then remove chassis to mount attaching nuts, **Fig. 1.**
2. Remove forward torque rod attaching bolts at radiator support panel.
3. Raise engine slightly using a suitable engine lifting device. Raise engine only enough to provide clearance for mount removal.
4. Remove two upper mount to engine support bracket attaching nuts and remove engine mount.
5. Reverse procedure to install.

ENGINE

REPLACE

1. Disconnect cables from battery, then drain cooling system.
2. Remove air cleaner assembly, then disconnect engine electrical harness connector.
3. Remove hood support, then prop hood up.
4. Disconnect all external vacuum hose connections, then remove radiator and heater hoses.
5. **On models equipped with A/C,** disconnect compressor and position aside. Do not disconnect refrigerant lines from compressor.

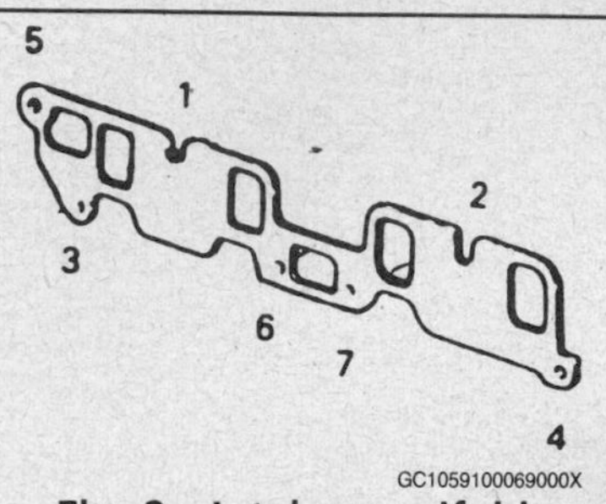
5
1
2
3
6
7
4
GC1059100069000X

Fig. 2 Intake manifold tightening sequence

6. **On all models,** remove alternator and alternator bracket, then engine torque strut.
7. Remove throttle and transaxle linkages at the throttle body assembly and intake manifold.
8. Remove all transaxle-to-engine attaching bolts except the top two bolts.
9. Remove front engine mount-to-cradle nuts, then front exhaust pipe.
10. Remove flywheel inspection cover, then tighten converter-to-flywheel attaching bolts.
11. Remove starter motor.
12. **On models equipped with power steering,** remove power steering pump and bracket and position aside.
13. **On all models,** disconnect fuel feed line. Refer to "Precautions" for fuel pressure relief procedure.
14. Remove 2 rear transaxle support bracket bolts.
15. Using a suitable jack and a block of wood placed under transaxle, raise engine and transaxle until engine front mount studs clear cradle bracket.
16. Attaching suitable lifting equipment to engine. Put tension on engine and remove 2 remaining transaxle to engine attaching bolts.
17. Slide engine assembly forward and lift from vehicle.
18. Reverse procedure to install.

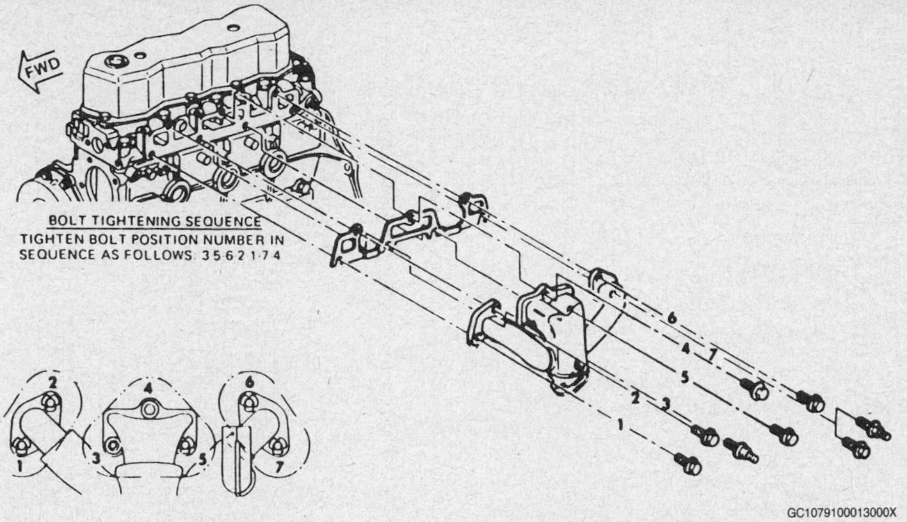
FWD
BOLT TIGHTENING SEQUENCE
TIGHTEN BOLT POSITION NUMBER IN SEQUENCE AS FOLLOWS: 3 5 6 2 1 7 4
GC1079100013000X

Fig. 3 Exhaust manifold tightening sequence

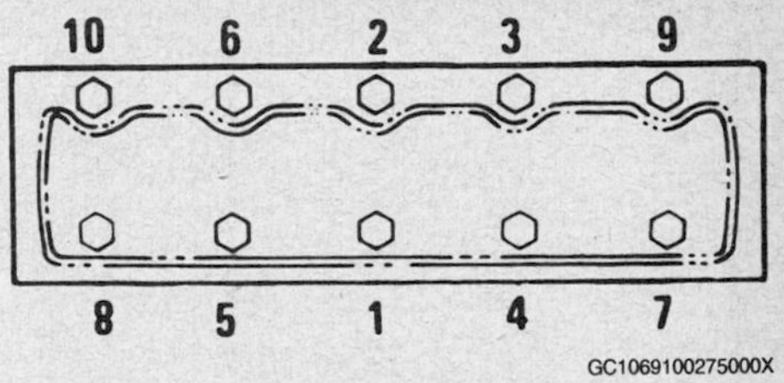
10 6 2 3 9
8 5 1 4 7
GC1069100275000X

Fig. 4 Cylinder head tightening sequence

INTAKE MANIFOLD

REPLACE

1. Disconnect battery ground cable, then remove air cleaner.
2. Disconnect PCV valve and hose at TBI unit, then drain cooling system.
3. Disconnect fuel line and all vacuum hoses that will interfere with manifold removal. **Refer to "Precautions" for fuel pressure bleed procedure.**
4. Disconnect all electrical connections and throttle linkage from TBI unit.
5. Disconnect downshift and cruise control linkage, if applicable.
6. Disconnect throttle linkage and TV cables, position cables aside.
7. Disconnect heater hose.
8. Remove intake manifold attaching bolts, then the intake manifold.
9. Reverse procedure to install. Tighten bolts to specification in sequence shown in **Fig. 2.**

EXHAUST MANIFOLD

REPLACE

1. Remove air cleaner, then torque rod strut.
2. Remove oxygen sensor connector, then dipstick tube.
3. Raise and support vehicle, then remove exhaust pipe from manifold.
4. Lower vehicle, then remove exhaust manifold attaching bolts and washers.
5. Remove exhaust manifold and gasket.
6. Reverse procedure to install. **Torque** exhaust manifold bolt Nos. 1, 2, 6 and 7 to 28 ft. lbs. and bolt Nos. 3, 4 and 5 to 37 ft. lbs. in sequence shown in **Fig. 3.**

CYLINDER HEAD

REPLACE

1. Disconnect battery ground cable, then drain cooling system.
2. Raise and support vehicle, then disconnect exhaust pipe from exhaust manifold.
3. Disconnect oxygen sensor connector, then lower vehicle.
4. Remove battery (auxiliary) ground cable, then oil dipstick tube and air cleaner.
5. Disconnect wire connectors, throttle linkage and fuel lines from TBI unit. **Refer to "Precautions" for fuel pressure bleed procedure.**
6. Disconnect heater hose from intake manifold, then all wiring connections from intake manifold and cylinder head.
7. Remove all vacuum lines that will interfere with manifold or cylinder head removal.
8. Remove engine torque strut rod bolts from upper support, then serpentine drive belt.
9. Remove alternator brackets and position alternator aside.
10. **On vehicles equipped w/top mounted A/C compressor,** remove compressor brackets and position compressor aside.
11. **On vehicles equipped w/top mounted power steering pump,** remove pump upper bracket.
12. **On all models,** remove radiator hoses, then rocker arm and push rod covers.
13. Remove rocker arms, push rods, then cylinder head attaching bolts.
14. Lift cylinder head with intake and exhaust manifolds as an assembly from cylinder block.
15. Reverse procedure to install. Coat heads and threads of cylinder bolts with a suitable sealing compound, then install bolts finger tight.
16. Tighten cylinder head bolts in sequence shown in **Fig. 4** as follows:
    a. **Torque** all bolts to 18 ft. lbs.
    b. **Torque** all bolts except No. 9 to 26 ft. lbs. **Torque** No. 9 bolt to 18 ft. lbs.
    c. Repeat sequence again, turning all bolts an additional 90 degrees or (1/4 turn).
17. Tighten intake manifold bolts in sequence shown in **Fig. 2,** if necessary.
18. Tighten exhaust manifold bolts in sequence shown in **Fig. 3,** if necessary.

VALVE ARRANGEMENT

FRONT TO REAR

2.5L/4-151 .... I-E-I-E-E-I-E-I

VALVE LIFTERS

Failure of a hydraulic valve lifter, **Fig. 5,** is generally caused by an inadequate oil supply or dirt. An air leak at the intake side of the oil pump or too much oil in the engine will cause air bubbles in the oil supply to the lifters, causing them to collapse. This is a probable cause of trouble if several lifters fail to function, but air in oil is an unlikely cause of failure of a single unit.

Valve lifters can be removed after removing rocker arm cover, intake manifold, pushrod cover and pushrod retainer and guide, if applicable. Loosen rocker arm stud nut and rotate rocker arm so that pushrod can be removed, then remove valve lifter. It may be necessary to use lifter remover No. J-3049 or equivalent to facilitate lifter removal.

CAMSHAFT LOBE LIFT SPECIFICATIONS

Engine	Year	Int.	Exh.
2.5L/4-151	1992	.248	.248

VALVE CLEARANCE SPECIFICATIONS

These engines are equipped with hydraulic lifters, no provision for adjustment is provided.

VALVE ADJUSTMENT

These engines are equipped with hydraulic lifters, no provision for adjustment is provided.

ROCKER ARM STUDS

Rocker arm studs that are cracked or have damaged threads can be removed from the cylinder head using a deep well socket. Install and tighten new rocker arm stud to specifications.

VALVE GUIDES

Valve guides are an integral part of the cylinder head and are not removable. If valve stem clearance becomes excessive, the valve guide should be reamed to the next oversize and the appropriate oversize valves installed. Valves are available in .003 and .005 inch oversizes.

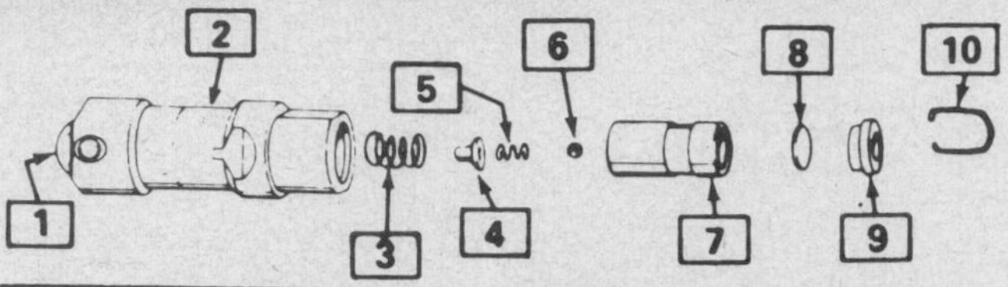
2
6
8
10
5
1
3
4
7
9
1 ROLLER
2 LIFTER BODY
3 PLUNGER SPRING
4 BALL CHECK RETAINER
5 BALL CHECK SPRING
6 BALL CHECK
7 PLUNGER
8 OIL METERING VALVE
9 PUSH ROD SEAT
10 RETAINER RING
GC1069100276000X

Fig. 5 Exploded view of roller type hydraulic lifter

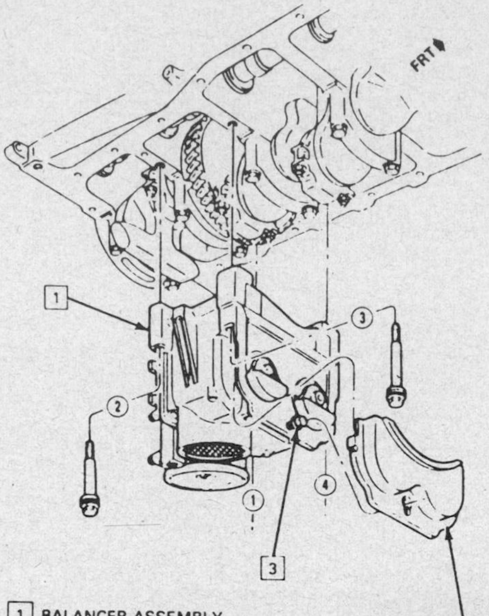
FRT
1
2
3
4
1 BALANCER ASSEMBLY
2 BAFFLE
3 10 N·m (90 LB. IN.)
* CIRCLED NUMBERS SHOW BOLT POSITION (SEE TEXT FOR TIGHTENING SEQUENCE)
GC1069100279000X

Fig. 6 Force balancer tightening sequence

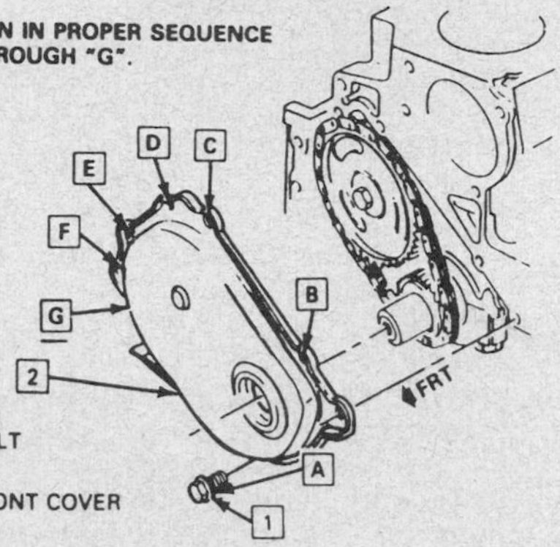
TIGHTEN IN PROPER SEQUENCE "A" THROUGH "G".
E
D
C
F
G
B
2
FRT
A
1
1 BOLT
2 FRONT COVER
GC1069100277000X

Fig. 7 Front cover tightening sequence

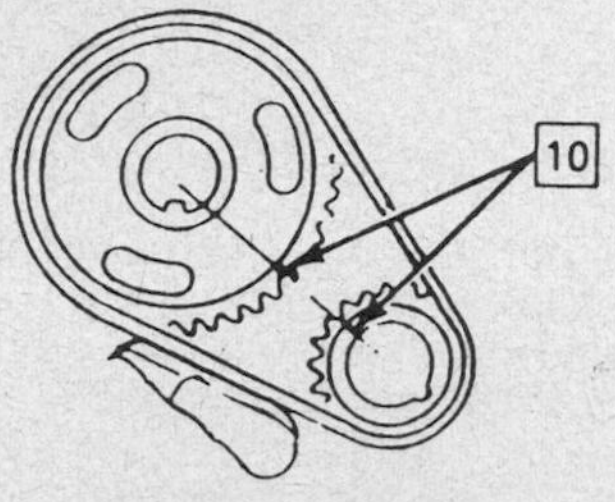
10
10 TIMING MARKS TO BE ALIGNED AS SHOWN WHEN ENGINE IS ROTATED TO T.D.C.
GC1069100278000X

Fig. 8 Timing mark alignment

CRANKSHAFT DAMPER

REPLACE

1. Remove oil pan as outlined further on.
2. Remove balancer assembly to crankcase attaching bolts, then balancer assembly.
3. To install, proceed as follows:
   a. position No. 1 and No. 4 cylinders at TDC (crank counterweights at BTDC). **When installing balancer, the end of the housing without dowel pins must remain in contact with block surface. If it loses contact, gear engagement may be lost and permanent damage to either the crank or balancer gears may result.**
   b. Install balancer onto crankshaft with balancer weights at BTDC (plus or minus one half gear tooth).
   c. **Torque** bolts in sequence, 3-1-2-4, shown in **Fig. 6.**
   d. Following sequence shown in step c, **torque** short bolts to 11 ft. lbs. plus 75° and long bolts to 11 ft. lbs. plus 90°.
   e. Rotate crankshaft four times and check for clearance between the fourth counterweight and balancer weights.
   f. Reinstall oil pan.

FRONT COVER

REPLACE

1. Disconnect battery ground cable, then remove serpentine drive belt tensioner and drive belt.
2. Raise and support vehicle, then remove right hand wheel assembly.
3. Remove right fender splash shield, then flywheel cover. Install suitable tool to prevent flywheel from rotating.
4. Remove crankshaft harmonic balancer attaching bolt, then balancer and key.
5. Remove front cover attaching screws, then front cover.
6. Using flathead screwdriver, remove oil seal. Do not distort cover.
7. Reverse procedure to install, noting the following:
   a. Position centering tool No. J-34995 or equivalent, into cover, then install and partially tighten two opposing cover screws.
   b. Tighten bolts to specifications in sequence shown in **Fig. 7.**

TIMING CHAIN

REPLACE

1. Remove front cover as outlined under "Front Cover, Replace."
2. Loosen but do not remove camshaft bolt.
3. Align timing marks on camshaft and crankshaft gears, then remove camshaft bolt.
4. Remove timing chain and sprocket.
5. Reverse procedure to install, noting the following:
   a. Align timing marks as shown in **Fig. 8.**

CAMSHAFT

REPLACE

ENGINE IN VEHICLE

1. Disconnect battery ground cable, then drain cooling system.
2. Remove air cleaner assembly, PCV hose, EGR valve, spark plug wires and clips.
3. Remove fuel line bracket and fuel lines. **Refer to "Precautions" for fuel pressure bleed procedure.**
4. Remove vacuum hoses including power brake booster hose.
5. Remove all wiring and throttle linkage from TBI assembly.
6. Remove transaxle downshift bracket, then heater hose from intake manifold.
7. Remove serpentine drive belt, then tensioner to engine attaching bolts. Position tensioner/power steering pump assembly aside.
8. Remove intake manifold, pushrod cover and valve lifters.
9. Disconnect electrical connections from DIS assembly, then remove DIS assembly.
10. Remove bolt from torque strut at engine bracket, then swing strut aside.
11. Install engine lift bracket, then engine support fixtures No. J-28467-A and J-36462.
12. Raise and support vehicle, then remove both front wheel assemblies.
13. Drain engine oil, then move steering column intermediate shaft cover aside.
14. Remove steering shaft to steering gear pinch bolt, then right front lower ball joint pinch bolt.

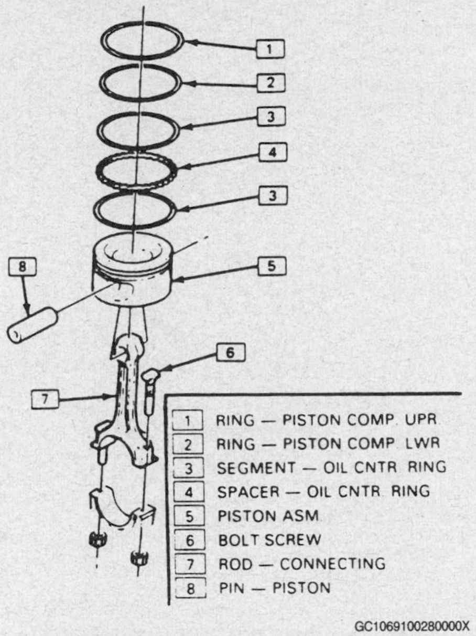
1 RING — PISTON COMP. UPR
2 RING — PISTON COMP. LWR
3 SEGMENT — OIL CNTR. RING
4 SPACER — OIL CNTR. RING
5 PISTON ASM.
6 BOLT SCREW
7 ROD — CONNECTING
8 PIN — PISTON
GC1069100280000X

Fig. 9 Piston & rod assembly

15. Remove right front ball joint from knuckle, then lower air deflector.
16. Remove right front wheelhouse engine splash shield.
17. Remove flywheel cover, then crankshaft balancer retaining bolt. **Have an assistant hold flywheel from turning while removing bolt.**
18. Remove crankshaft balancer, then front cover.
19. Remove frame bolts and insulators, then brake line to frame bracket and bolt.
20. Remove oil filter, then lower frame/powertrain assembly with support fixtures. **Lower passenger side just enough to access camshaft gear area.**
21. Align timing marks on camshaft and crankshaft sprockets, then remove camshaft sprocket bolt.
22. Remove timing chain and sprockets, then camshaft thrust plate.
23. Remove camshaft. Use care not to damage camshaft bearings.
24. Reverse procedure to install, noting the following:
    a. Ensure crankshaft and camshaft timing marks on gears are aligned, **Fig. 8.**
    b. Tighten all bolts/nuts to specifications.

ENGINE REMOVED

1. Remove engine from vehicle as outlined under "Engine, Replace."
2. Remove rocker arm cover, then push rods.
3. Remove pushrod cover, then valve lifters.
4. Remove crankshaft harmonic balancer, then front cover.
5. Remove camshaft sprocket bolt, then timing chain and sprockets.
6. Remove camshaft thrust plate, then pull camshaft from engine block. Use care not to damage camshaft bearings.
7. Reverse procedure to install, noting the following:
    a. Ensure crankshaft and camshaft timing marks on gears are aligned, **Fig. 8.**
    b. Tighten all bolts/nuts to specifications.

PISTON & ROD ASSEMBLY

Assemble piston to rod with mark on piston and rod both facing toward front of engine. Rod may not be marked, **Fig. 9.**

PISTONS, PINS & RINGS

Install rings on pistons as shown in **Fig. 10.**

Pistons, pins and rings are available in standard and oversizes.

MAIN & ROD BEARINGS

Main and rod bearings are available in standard size and undersizes.

CRANKSHAFT REAR OIL SEAL

REPLACE

The rear main oil seal is a one piece unit and is replaced without removing the oil pan or crankshaft.

1. Remove transaxle and flywheel.
2. **On models equipped w/manual transaxle,** remove pressure plate and disc.
3. **On all models,** using a suitable screwdriver, remove rear main bearing oil seal. Use care not to scratch crankshaft.
4. Lubricate inside and outside diameters of replacement seal with engine oil. Install seal using seal installer No. J-34924-A onto rear crankshaft flange with helical lip side facing toward engine. Ensure seal is firmly and evenly seated.
5. Install flywheel and transaxle.

OIL PAN

REPLACE

1. Disconnect battery ground cable, then remove coolant reservoir bottle.
2. Remove engine torque strut, then air cleaner assembly.
3. Remove air inlet, then serpentine drive belt.
4. Remove A/C compressor from brackets and set aside, then engine oil level indicator.
5. Support engine using support fixture No. J-28467-A, then raise and support vehicle.
6. Drain engine oil, then remove starter and support bracket. Position starter aside.
7. Remove flywheel covers, then turn front wheels to full right position.
8. Remove engine wiring harness retainer screws under both sides of oil pan.
9. Remove right side engine splash shield, then front engine mount bracket bolts/nuts.

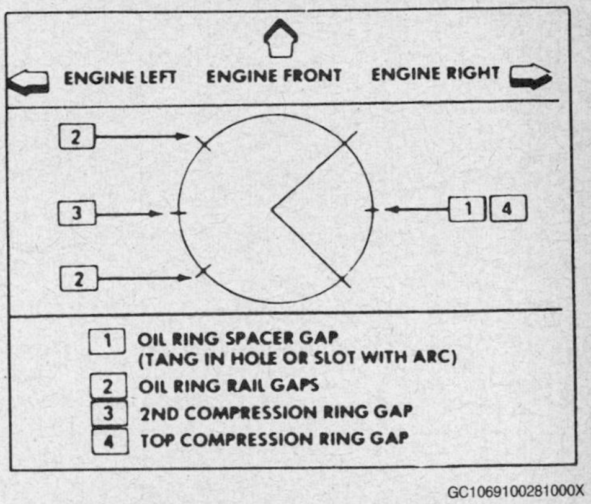
ENGINE LEFT
ENGINE FRONT
ENGINE RIGHT
1 OIL RING SPACER GAP (TANG IN HOLE OR SLOT WITH ARC)
2 OIL RING RAIL GAPS
3 2ND COMPRESSION RING GAP
4 TOP COMPRESSION RING GAP
GC1069100281000X

Fig. 10 Pin ring gap locations

10. Remove transaxle mount nuts.
11. Using support fixture installed in step 5, raise engine approximately two inches, then remove front engine mount and bracket.
12. Loosen frame bolts, then remove oil pan attaching bolts.
13. Remove oil pan.
14. Reverse procedure to install, noting the following:
    a. Apply RTV sealant as shown in **Fig. 11.**
    b. Tighten all bolts/nuts to specifications.

OIL PUMP

REPLACE

The oil pump can be serviced without removing the balancer assembly.

1. Remove oil pan as outlined under "Oil Pan, Replace."
2. Remove restrictor, oil filter, oil pump cover assembly and gears, then the pressure regulator plug or pin, spring and valve. **Use caution when removing plug or pin, since spring pressure can cause personal injury.**
3. Clean all parts in solvent and dry with compressed air.
4. Inspect pump housing, cover assembly, regulator valve and spring and screen assembly for excessive wear or damage.
5. Inspect depth of wear pattern in gear housing pocket and face of oil pump cover assembly, then the gear thickness. Gear pocket depth should be .514-.516 inch, while gear thickness should be .511-.512 inch.
6. Lubricate all internal parts with engine oil.
7. Pack all pump cavities with petroleum jelly, then install gears.
8. Install oil pump cover assembly, then the pressure regulator valve, spring and pin or plug. Tighten pump cover attaching bolts to specifications.
9. Clean intake screen, then install oil filter and restrictor.

BELT TENSION DATA

Belt tension is maintained automatically by a spring tensioned idler pulley. No adjustment is necessary.

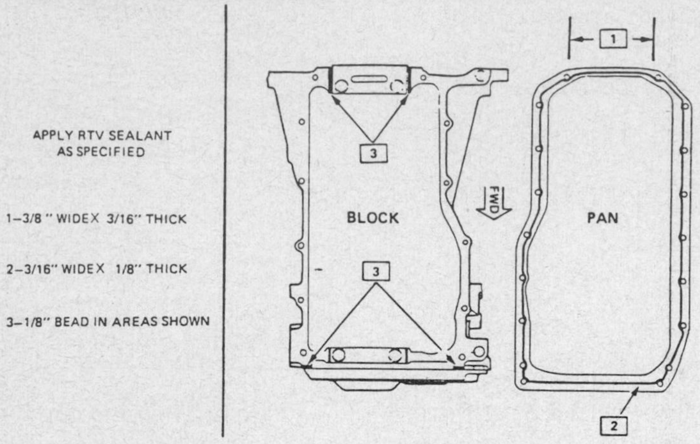
APPLY RTV SEALANT
AS SPECIFIED
1–3/8" WIDE X 3/16" THICK
2–3/16" WIDE X 1/8" THICK
3–1/8" BEAD IN AREAS SHOWN
BLOCK
PAN
FWD
1
2
3
3
GC1099100034000X

Fig. 11 Oil pan sealer application

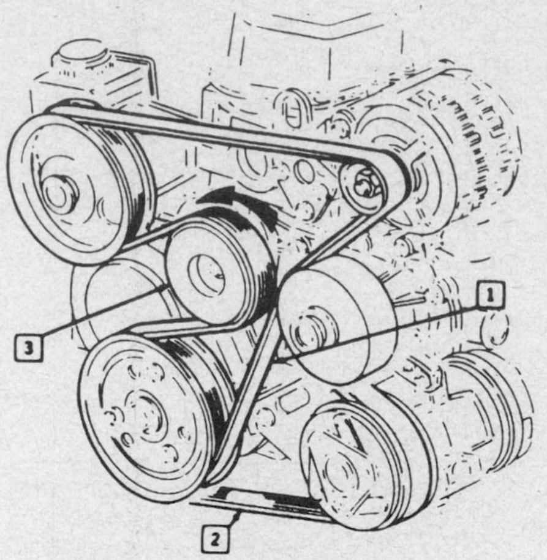
1
2
3

1. ROUTING WITHOUT AIR CONDITIONING
2. ROUTING WITH AIR CONDITIONING
3. TENSIONER – ROTATE DRIVE BELT TENSIONER IN DIRECTION OF ARROW TO INSTALL OR REMOVE DRIVE BELT.

GC1069100282000X

Fig. 12 Serpentine drive belt routing

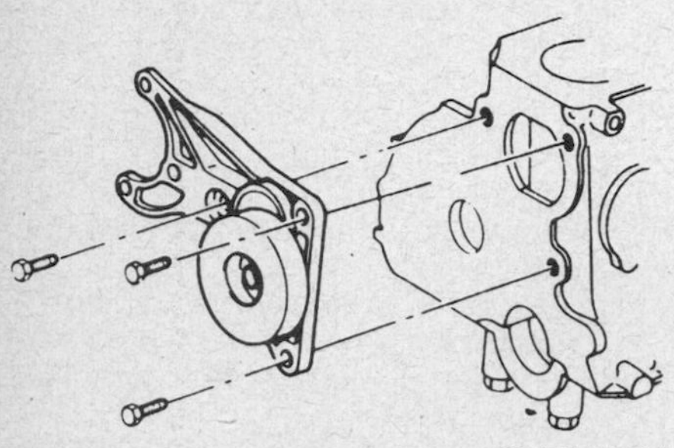
GC1069100283000X

Fig. 13 Drive belt tensioner removal

SERPENTINE DRIVE BELT

BELT ROUTING

Refer to **Fig. 12** for routing of serpentine drive belt.

TENSIONER INSPECTION

1. Run engine, with no accessories on, until normal operating temperature is reached. Shut engine off and read belt tension using belt tension gauge J-23600-B or equivalent. Place gauge halfway between alternator and power steering pump.
2. Start engine, with accessories off, and allow system to stabilize for 15 seconds. Turn engine off. Using a 15 mm socket, apply clockwise force to tensioner pulley bolt. Release force and immediately take a tension reading without disturbing belt tensioner position.
3. Using 15 mm socket, apply counterclockwise force to tensioner pulley bolt, raise pulley to eliminate all tension. Slowly lower pulley to belt and take a tension reading without disturbing belt tensioner position.
4. Average three readings. If average is not between 50-70 lbs. and belt is within tensioner's operating range, replace belt tensioner.

TENSIONER, REPLACE

1. Partially drain cooling system, then remove serpentine drive belt.

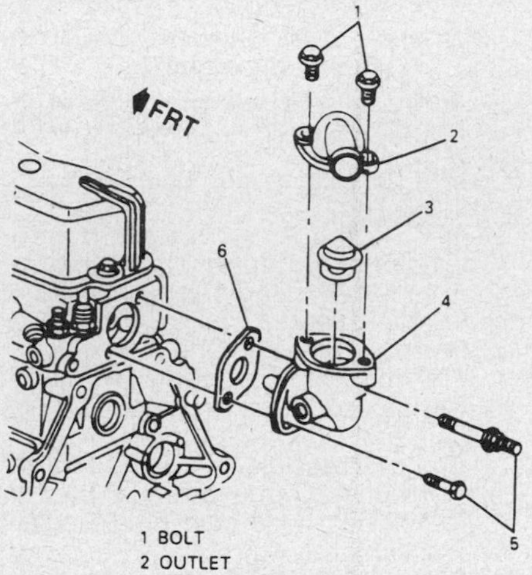
FRT
1
2
3
4
5
6

1 BOLT
2 OUTLET
3 THERMOSTAT ASSEMBLY
4 HOUSING
5 BOLT
6 GASKET

GC1089100139000X

Fig. 14 Thermostat & housing assembly

2. Remove power steering pump bolt from tensioner. Position pump aside.
3. Remove tensioner attaching bolts, then tensioner, **Fig. 13.**
4. Reverse procedure to install. Tighten bolts to specifications.

COOLING SYSTEM BLEED

This engine does not require a specified bleed procedure. After filling cooling system, run engine to operating temperature with radiator/pressure cap off. Air will then be automatically bled through cap opening.

THERMOSTAT

REPLACE

Refer to **Fig. 14** when performing the following procedure.

1. Disconnect battery ground cable.
2. If necessary, remove air cleaner assembly.

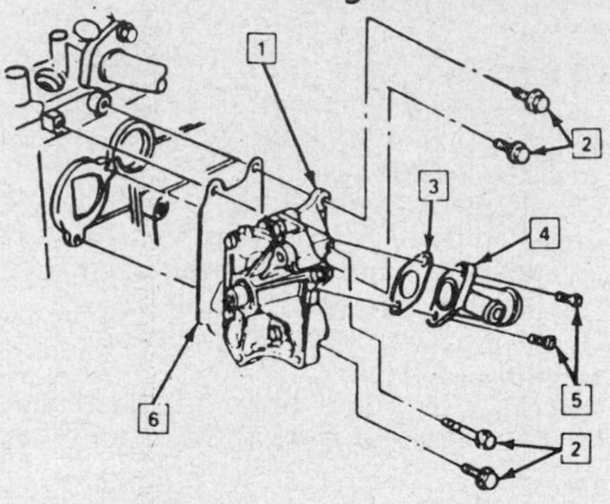
1
2
3
4
5
6
2

1 COOLANT PUMP
2 BOLT/SCREW
3 GASKET, COOLANT PUMP INLET
4 INLET, COOLANT PUMP
5 BOLT/SCREW
6 GASKET, COOLANT PUMP

GC1089100140000X

Fig. 15 Water pump removal

3. With engine cool, drain engine coolant below thermostat level. **Never open cooling system with engine hot.**
4. Disconnect radiator hose from thermostat housing.
5. Remove thermostat housing retaining bolts, then the housing, gasket and thermostat.
6. Reverse procedure to install, noting the following:
   a. Ensure thermostat gasket area is thoroughly clean.
   b. Install thermostat with new gasket.
   c. Apply a suitable sealer to thermostat housing retaining bolts. Install and **torque** bolts to 20 ft. lbs.
   d. Refill and bleed cooling system as necessary.

WATER PUMP

REPLACE

1. Disconnect battery ground cable, then drain cooling system.

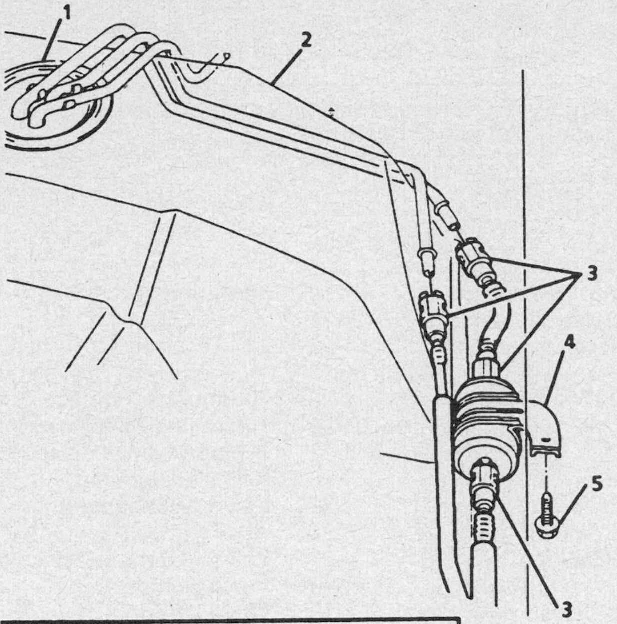
1
2
3
4
5
3

1 FUEL SENDER
2 FUEL TANK
3 QUICK CONNECT FITTINGS
4 IN-LINE FUEL FILTER BRACKET
5 FILTER BRACKET ATTACHING SCREW

GC1029102721000X

Fig. 16 Fuel filter replace

2. Remove alternator, then disconnect radiator and heater hoses from inlet.
3. Remove water pump attaching bolts **Fig. 15**, then water pump and pulley assembly.
4. Separate pulley and water pump.
5. Reverse procedure to install. Tighten to specifications.

RADIATOR

REPLACE

1. Remove air cleaner assembly and resonator.
2. Drain engine coolant, then disconnect cooling fan electrical connector.
3. Remove cooling fan screws, then the cooling fan assembly.
4. Remove engine mount strut and mounting bracket from radiator upper mounting panel.
5. Remove radiator mounting panel screws and panel.
6. Disconnect oil cooler lines.
7. Disconnect coolant recovery hose, then the upper and lower radiator hoses.
8. Remove radiator.
9. Reverse procedure to install.

FUEL PUMP

REPLACE

1. Relieve fuel pressure as outlined under "Precautions," then disconnect battery ground cable.
2. Remove fuel tank.
3. Remove fuel pump assembly by turning cam lock ring counterclockwise. Lift assembly from fuel tank and remove fuel pump from fuel tank sending unit.
4. Reverse procedure to install.

FUEL FILTER

REPLACE

1. Relieve fuel system pressure as outlined under "Precautions."
2. Raise and support vehicle.
3. Remove bracket attaching screw and filter bracket, **Fig. 16.**
4. Grasp filter and fuel line fitting. Twist quick-connect fitting 1/4 turn in each direction to loosen any dirt within fitting.
5. Using compressed air, blow out dirt from quick-connect fitting.
6. Remove feed pipe nut from fuel filter, then drain any remaining fuel into an suitable container.
7. Remove fuel filter.
8. Reverse procedure to install.

TIGHTENING SPECIFICATIONS

Year	Component	Torque/Ft. Lbs.
1992	Belt Tensioner Bolt	37
	Camshaft Thrust Plate Bolt	7.5
	Connecting Rod Nuts	29
	Cylinder Head Bolts	①
	EGR Valve To Manifold Bolt	16
	Engine Bracket To Engine Bolt	40
	Engine Lift Brackets	37
	Engine Mount To Bracket Nut	35
	Engine Mount To Frame Nut	35
	Engine Torque Strut Bolt/Nut	41
	Engine Torque Strut Bracket Bolt	17
	Exhaust Manifold Bolt	①
	Flywheel To Crankshaft Bolt (Automatic)	55
	Flywheel To Crankshaft Bolt (Manual)	69
	Force Balancer to Block Bolts	①
	Front Cover Bolt	7.5
	Harmonic Balancer Bolt	162
	Intake Manifold Bolt	25①

Year	Component	Torque/Ft. Lbs.
1992 —Cont'd	Main Bearing To Block Bolt	65
	Oil Filter Access Plug	②
	Oil Indicator Fill Tube Nut	17
	Oil Pan Bolt	7.5
	Oil Pan Drain Plug	25
	Oil Pump Cover Bolt	7.5
	Pushrod Cover Nut	7.5
	Rocker Arm Bolt	20
	Rocker Arm Cover Bolt	6.6
	Stud Roller Lifter Guide Retainer To Block	7.5
	Thermostat Housing Bolt	20
	Throttle Body Injection Assembly	18
	Transaxle Mount To Bracket Nut	33
	Transaxle Mount To Frame Nut	33
	Water Outlet Housing Bolt	20
	Water Pump To Block	25

①—Refer to text.
②—Finger tight, then an additional 1/4 turn.

3.1L/V6-189 Engine

NOTE: On Air Bag Equipped Models, Refer To "Air Bag System Precautions" Located In The Front Of This Manual For System Disarming & Arming Procedures.

INDEX

PRECAUTIONS

AIR BAG SYSTEMS

Refer to "Air Bag System Precautions" in the front of this manual for system disarming and arming procedures.

FUEL SYSTEM PRESSURE RELIEF

Whenever the fuel lines are to be disconnected for engine service on fuel injected engines, relieve fuel system pressure following the procedures outlined below. Failure to follow these procedures exactly, may result in personal injury.

1. Disconnect battery ground cable, then loosen filler cap to relieve tank vapor pressure.
2. Connect fuel pressure gauge No. J-34730-1 or equivalent to fuel pressure valve. Wrap a shop towel around fitting while connecting gauge to avoid spillage.
3. Install bleed hose into an approved container and open valve to bleed system pressure. Fuel connections are now safe for servicing.
4. Drain any fuel remaining in gauge into approved container.

ENGINE MOUNT

REPLACE

1. Disconnect battery ground cable, then remove mount retaining nuts from below frame mounting bracket.
2. Remove transaxle mount nuts, then install suitable engine support fixture.
3. Raise engine only enough to provide clearance for mount removal.
4. Remove mount to engine bracket nuts, then mount, **Fig. 1.**
5. Reverse procedure to install. Tighten to specifications.

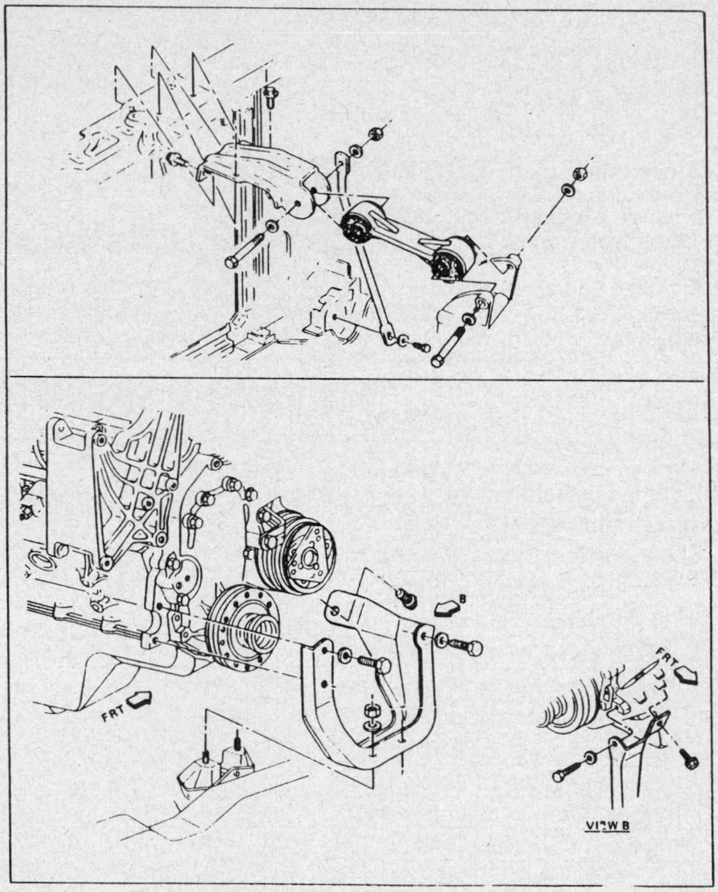

FRT
B

GC1069100284000X

Fig. 1 Engine mounts

ENGINE

REPLACE

1. Disconnect battery cables, then drain cooling system.
2. Remove air cleaner assembly, including air flow duct from throttle body, then all necessary wiring.
3. Remove hood, then disconnect throt-

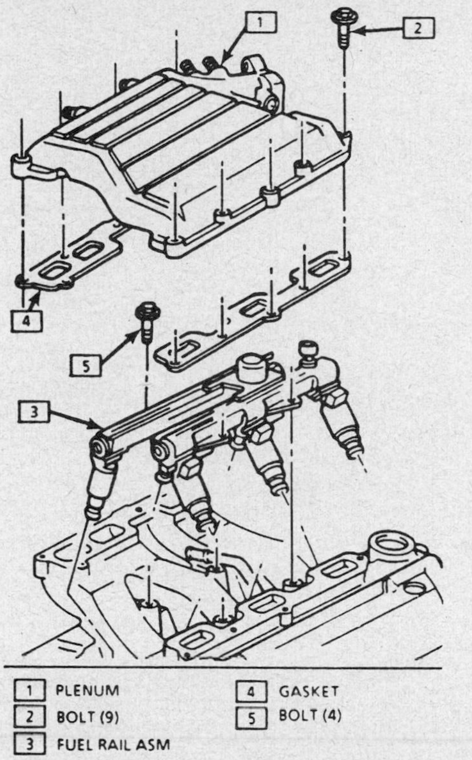
1 PLENUM
2 BOLT (9)
3 FUEL RAIL ASM
4 GASKET
5 BOLT (4)
GC1069100285000X

Fig. 2 Plenum & fuel rail removal

tle, TV and cruise control cables.
4. Remove fuel lines. Refer to "Precautions" for fuel pressure bleed procedure.
5. Remove crossover pipe from manifolds, then serpentine drive belt.
6. Remove radiator and heater hoses from engine, then A/C bolts at front bracket.
7. Remove power steering pump and position aside, then remove alternator, if necessary.
8. Remove brake booster vacuum supply line, then EGR at exhaust, if equipped.
9. Raise and support vehicle, then remove A/C compressor bolts at rear bracket. Position compressor aside.
10. Remove A.I.R. pump, if equipped, then flywheel cover.
11. Remove starter, then torque converter bolts.
12. Remove transaxle bracket. then exhaust pipe from manifold.
13. Remove engine front mount retaining nuts, then lower vehicle.
14. Remove engine torque strut(s), then bulkhead connector.
15. Support transaxle, then remove transaxle attaching bolts.
16. Attach suitable lifting device to engine, then remove engine from vehicle.
17. Reverse procedure to install. Tighten to specifications.

INTAKE MANIFOLD

REPLACE

1. Remove air cleaner assembly, including air flow duct from throttle body, then disconnect battery ground cable.
2. Remove all cables at throttle body, then disconnect brake vacuum pipe at plenum.
3. Remove cable bracket at plenum, then all necessary vacuum lines.
4. Remove EGR valve, throttle body and ignition wire plastic shield bolts from plenum.
5. Remove plenum attaching bolts, then plenum, **Fig. 2.**
6. Relieve fuel pressure as outlined under "Precautions," then remove fuel lines at fuel rail.
7. Remove serpentine drive belt, then alternator. Position alternator aside.
8. Remove power steering lines at alternator bracket, then power steering pump mounting bolts. Position pump aside.
9. Remove wiring from fuel injectors, then drain cooling system.
10. Remove bypass hose at water pump and cylinder head.
11. Remove PCV hose, then front valve cover.
12. Remove alternator brace and bracket, then rear valve cover.
13. Remove upper radiator hose, then all necessary wiring.
14. Remove coolant sensor, then fuel lines at bracket.
15. Remove throttle body heater hose, then heater pipe at intake.
16. Remove intake manifold attaching bolts, then intake manifold. **Ensure washers are retained in their original positions on four center bolts.**
17. Loosen rocker arms, then remove pushrods. **Intake and exhaust pushrods are different lengths with exhaust pushrods being longer of the two.**
18. Reverse procedure to install, noting the following:
    a. Place 3 mm bead of suitable RTV sealer on each ridge where front and rear of intake manifold contacts the block.
    b. **Torque** intake manifold attaching bolts to 15 ft. lbs. in sequence shown in **Fig. 3**, then retighten to 24 ft. lbs. in sequence shown in **Fig. 3.**
    c. Tighten all bolts/nuts to specifications.

EXHAUST MANIFOLD

REPLACE

LEFT

1. Remove battery ground cable, then air cleaner assembly.
2. Remove coolant recovery bottle, then serpentine drive belt.
3. Remove A/C compressor. Position compressor aside.
4. Remove right side torque strut, then strut mounting bracket.
5. Remove heat shield, then crossover pipe at manifolds.
6. Remove exhaust manifold attaching bolts, then manifold, **Fig. 4.**
7. Reverse procedure to install. Tighten to specifications.

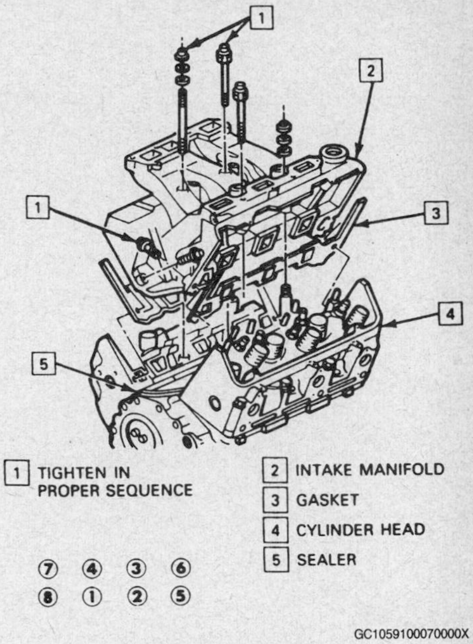
1 TIGHTEN IN PROPER SEQUENCE
2 INTAKE MANIFOLD
3 GASKET
4 CYLINDER HEAD
5 SEALER
⑦ ④ ③ ⑥
⑧ ① ② ⑤
GC1059100070000X

Fig. 3 Intake manifold tightening sequence

RIGHT

1. Remove battery ground cable, then air cleaner assembly.
2. Raise and support vehicle, then remove exhaust pipe from manifold.
3. Lower vehicle, then remove breather and mass air flow sensor.
4. Remove heat shield, then crossover at manifold.
5. Remove throttle and TV cables from throttle body, then throttle and TV cable bracket at plenum.
6. Remove oxygen sensor, then exhaust manifold attaching bolts.
7. Remove exhaust manifold, **Fig. 4.**
8. Reverse procedure to install. Tighten to specifications.

CYLINDER HEAD

REPLACE

LEFT BANK

1. Remove intake manifold as outlined under "Intake Manifold, Replace."
2. Remove left exhaust manifold as outlined under "Exhaust Manifold, Replace."
3. Remove oil level indicator, then plug wires from left cylinder head.
4. Loosen rocker arms, then remove pushrods. **Intake and exhaust pushrods are different lengths with exhaust pushrods being longer of the two.**
5. Remove cylinder head attaching bolts, then cylinder head, **Fig. 5.**
6. Reverse procedure to install, noting the following:
    a. Coat cylinder head bolt threads with a suitable sealing compound.
    b. **Torque** cylinder head attaching bolts to 33 ft. lbs. in sequence shown in **Fig. 5.**
    c. Turn bolts and additional 1/4 turn in sequence shown in **Fig. 5.**

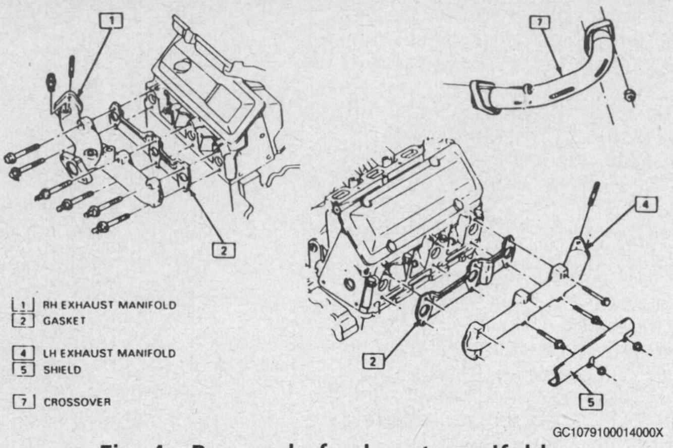
1 RH EXHAUST MANIFOLD
2 GASKET
4 LH EXHAUST MANIFOLD
5 SHIELD
7 CROSSOVER
GC1079100014000X

Fig. 4 Removal of exhaust manifolds

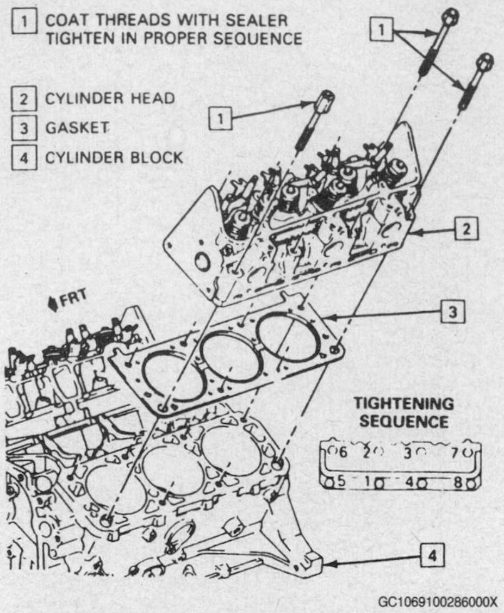
1 COAT THREADS WITH SEALER TIGHTEN IN PROPER SEQUENCE
2 CYLINDER HEAD
3 GASKET
4 CYLINDER BLOCK
FRT
TIGHTENING SEQUENCE
GC1069100286000X

Fig. 5 Cylinder head tightening sequence

d. Tighten all bolts/nuts to specifications.

RIGHT

1. Remove intake manifold as outlined under "Intake Manifold, Replace."
2. Remove right exhaust manifold as outlined under "Exhaust Manifold, Replace."
3. Remove plug wires from right cylinder head.
4. Loosen rocker arms, then remove pushrods. **Intake and exhaust pushrods are different lengths with exhaust pushrods being longer of the two.**
5. Remove cylinder head attaching bolts, then cylinder head, **Fig. 5.**
6. Reverse procedure to install, noting the following:
   a. Coat cylinder head bolt threads with a suitable sealing compound.
   b. **Torque** cylinder head attaching bolts to 33 ft. lbs. in sequence shown in **Fig. 5.**
   c. Turn bolts and additional 1/4 turn in sequence shown in **Fig. 5.**
   d. Tighten all bolts/nuts to specifications.

VALVE ARRANGEMENT

FRONT TO REAR

Left .... E-I-I-E-I-E
Right .... E-I-E-I-I-E

VALVE LIFTERS

Some engines will be equipped with both standard and .010 inch oversize valve lifters. The cylinder case will be marked where the oversize valve lifters are installed with a dab of white paint and .25 mm. O.S. will be stamped on the valve lifter boss, **Fig. 6.**

Failure of a hydraulic valve lifter is generally caused by an inadequate oil supply or dirt. An air leak at the intake side of the oil pump or too much oil in the engine will cause air bubbles in the oil supply to the lifters, causing them to collapse. This is a probable cause of trouble if several lifters fail to function, but air in oil is an unlikely cause of failure of a single unit.

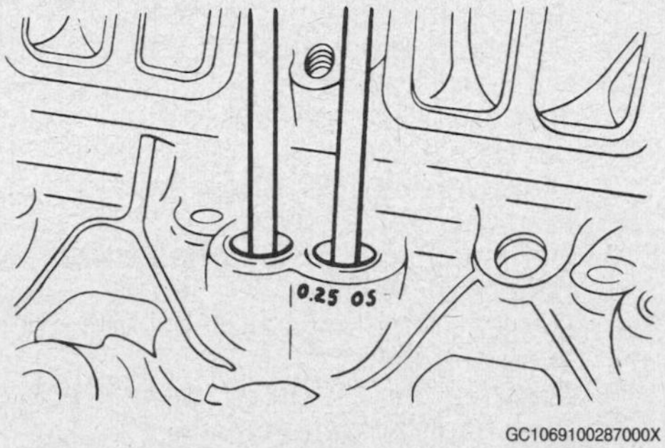
0.25 OS
GC1069100287000X

Fig. 6 Oversize valve lifter marking

Valve lifters can be removed after removing rocker arm covers, intake manifold, rocker stud nuts, rocker arm balls, rocker arms and pushrods.

VALVE CLEARANCE SPECIFICATIONS

This engine uses hydraulic valve lifters. No clearance specifications are available.

VALVE ADJUSTMENT

1. Crank engine until mark on torsional damper is aligned with TDC mark on timing tab. Check to ensure engine is in the No. 1 cylinder firing position by placing fingers on No. 1 cylinder rocker arms as mark on damper comes near TDC mark on timing tab. If valves are not moving, the engine is in the No. 1 firing position. If valves move as damper mark nears TDC mark on timing tab, engine is in the No. 4 cylinder firing position and should be rotated one revolution to reach the No. 1 cylinder firing position.
2. With engine in the No. 1 cylinder firing position, adjust the following valves: Exhaust-1, 2, 3; Intake-1, 5, 6. To adjust valves, back off adjusting nut until lash is felt at push rod, then tighten adjusting nut until all lash is removed. This can be determined by rotating the push rod while tightening the adjusting nut. When all lash has been eliminated, turn adjusting nut an additional 1 1/2 turns.
3. Crank engine one revolution until mark on torsional damper and TDC mark are again aligned. This is the No. 4 cylinder firing position. With engine in this position, the following valves can be adjusted: Exhaust-4, 5 & 6; Intake-2, 3 & 4.
4. Install rocker arm covers, then start engine and check timing and idle speed.

ROCKER ARM STUDS

Rocker arm studs that are cracked or have damaged threads can be replaced. If threads in cylinder head are damaged or stripped, the head can be retapped and a helical type insert added. When installing a new rocker arm stud, tighten stud to specifications.

VALVE GUIDES

Valve guides are an integral part of the cylinder head and are not removable. If valve stem clearance becomes excessive, the valve guide should be reamed to the next oversize and the appropriate oversize valves installed. Valves are available in oversizes of .003, .015 and .030 inch.

FRONT COVER

REPLACE

1. Disconnect battery ground cable, then drain cooling system.
2. Remove serpentine drive belt, then drive belt tensioner.
3. Remove alternator and power steering pump. Position pump aside.
4. Raise and support vehicle, then remove inner splash shield.
5. Remove flywheel cover at transaxle, then starter.
6. Remove harmonic balancer as follows:
   a. Remove balancer retaining bolt. Have an assistant keep flywheel from turning.
   b. Using harmonic balancer puller No. J-24420-B, remove balancer.

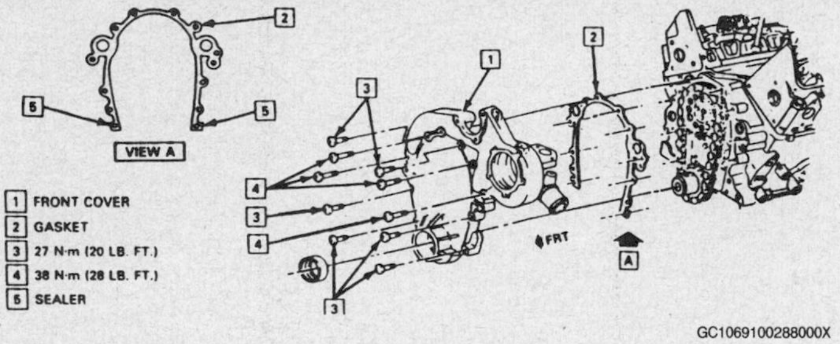
VIEW A
1 FRONT COVER
2 GASKET
3 27 N·m (20 LB. FT.)
4 38 N·m (28 LB. FT.)
5 SEALER
FRT
A
GC1069100288000X
Fig. 7 Front cover assembly removal

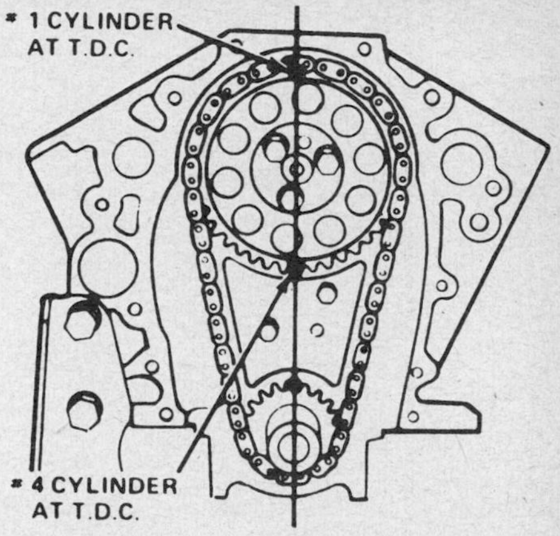
* 1 CYLINDER AT T.D.C.
* 4 CYLINDER AT T.D.C.
GC1069100289000X
Fig. 8 Timing mark alignment

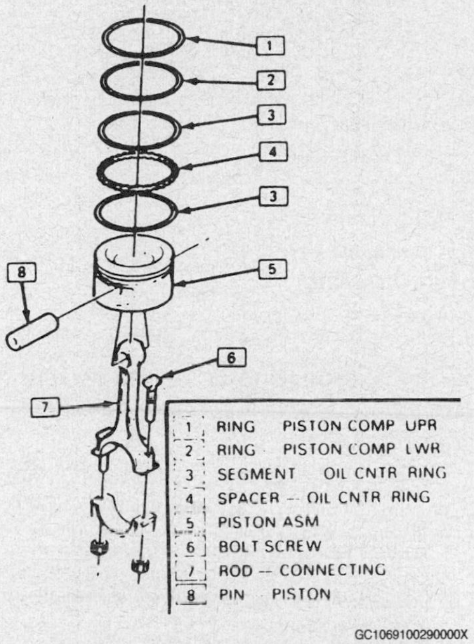
1 RING PISTON COMP UPR
2 RING PISTON COMP LWR
3 SEGMENT OIL CNTR RING
4 SPACER – OIL CNTR RING
5 PISTON ASM
6 BOLT SCREW
7 ROD – CONNECTING
8 PIN PISTON
GC1069100290000X
Fig. 9 Piston & rod assembly

7. Remove serpentine belt idler pulley, then lower oil pan.
8. Remove lower cover bolts, then lower vehicle.
9. Remove radiator hose at water pump, then heater hose at cooling system fill pipe.
10. Remove bypass and overflow hoses, then canister purge hose.
11. Remove upper cover bolts, then front cover, **Fig. 7.**
12. Reverse procedure to install. Tighten to specifications.

TIMING CHAIN

REPLACE

1. Remove front cover as outlined under "Front Cover, Replace."
2. Place No. 1 piston at top dead center with marks on camshaft and crankshaft sprockets aligned, **Fig. 8.**
3. Remove camshaft sprocket bolts, then remove sprocket and timing chain. If sprocket does not come off easily, tap lower edge of sprocket with a plastic mallet.
4. If crankshaft sprocket is to be replaced, remove sprocket using a suitable puller. Install new sprocket, aligning key and keyway.
5. Install timing chain on camshaft sprocket. Hold sprocket vertically with chain hanging down and align marks on camshaft and crankshaft sprockets.

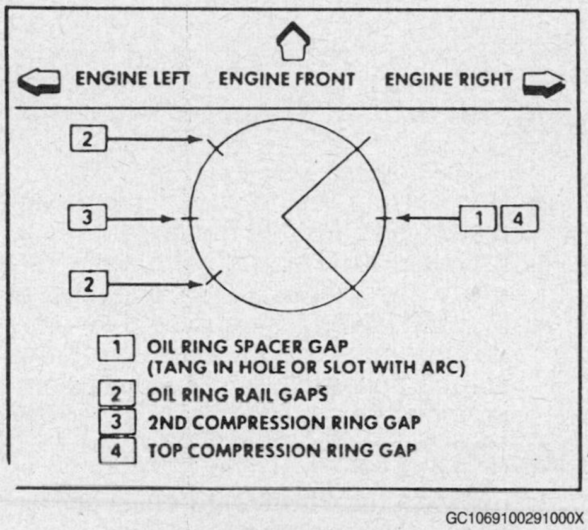
ENGINE LEFT ENGINE FRONT ENGINE RIGHT
2
3
2
1 4
1 OIL RING SPACER GAP (TANG IN HOLE OR SLOT WITH ARC)
2 OIL RING RAIL GAPS
3 2ND COMPRESSION RING GAP
4 TOP COMPRESSION RING GAP
GC1069100291000X
Fig. 10 Pin ring gap locations

6. Align dowel pin hole in sprocket with dowel pin on camshaft, then install sprocket on camshaft.
7. Using camshaft sprocket attaching bolts, draw sprocket on camshaft. Tighten bolts to specifications.
8. Lubricate timing chain with engine oil, then install front cover as outlined previously.

CAMSHAFT

REPLACE

1. Remove engine from vehicle as described under "Engine, Replace."
2. Remove pushrods and valve lifters.
3. Remove front cover as outlined under "Front Cover, Replace."
4. Remove timing chain and sprocket as outlined under "Timing Chain, Replace."
5. Withdraw camshaft from engine, using care not to damage camshaft bearings.
6. Reverse procedure to install. When installing timing chain, align valve timing marks as shown in **Fig. 8.**

PISTON & ROD ASSEMBLY

Assemble piston to rod with mark on piston and rod both facing toward front of engine, **Fig. 9.** Rod may not be marked.

PISTONS, PINS & RINGS

Install rings on pistons as shown in **Fig. 10.**

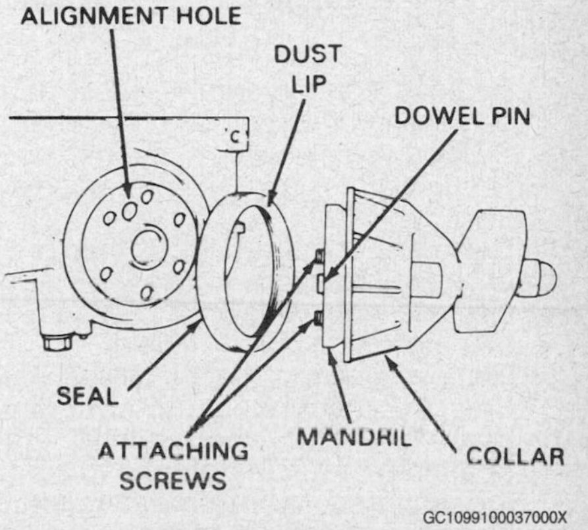
ALIGNMENT HOLE
DUST LIP
DOWEL PIN
SEAL
ATTACHING SCREWS
MANDRIL
COLLAR
GC1099100037000X
Fig. 11 Rear main bearing oil seal installation

Pistons, pins and rings are available in standard and oversizes.

MAIN & ROD BEARINGS

Main and rod bearings are available in standard size and undersizes.

CRANKSHAFT REAR OIL SEAL

REPLACE

1. Remove transaxle and flywheel.
2. Using a screwdriver, pry out old seal. Use care to avoid damaging crankshaft. File all burrs or nicks as required.
3. Install new seal using seal installer No. J-34686 or equivalent, as follows:
   a. Apply a light coat of engine oil to I.D. and O.D. of oil seal.
   b. Slide seal over tool mandrel until dust lip bottoms squarely against collar of tool.
   c. Align dowel pin of tool with dowel pin hole in crankshaft, **Fig. 11,** then attach tool to crankshaft with screw provided.
   d. Turn handle of tool until seal is pushed into bore and collar is positioned firmly against case. Remove tool.
4. Install flywheel and transmission, then start engine and check for leaks.

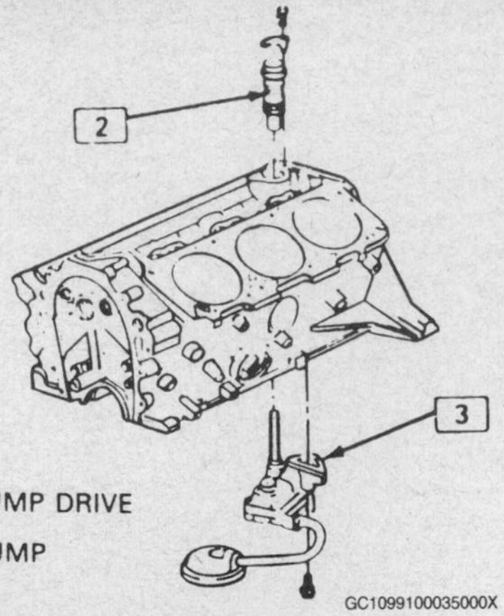
2
3
2 OIL PUMP DRIVE
3 OIL PUMP
GC1099100035000X

Fig. 12 Oil pump removal

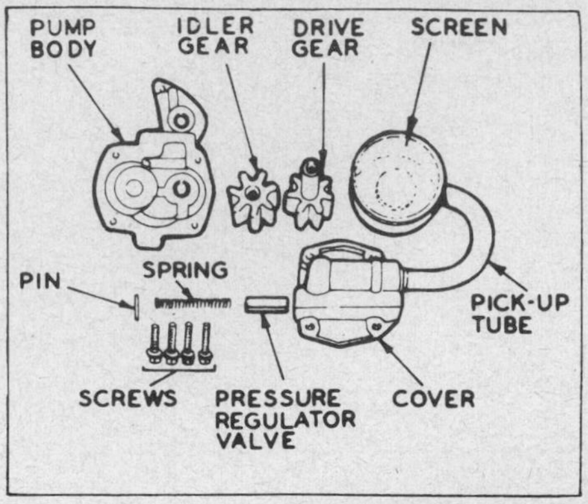
PUMP BODY
IDLER GEAR
DRIVE GEAR
SCREEN
PIN
SPRING
PICK-UP TUBE
SCREWS
PRESSURE REGULATOR VALVE
COVER
GC1099100036000X

Fig. 13 Exploded view of oil pump

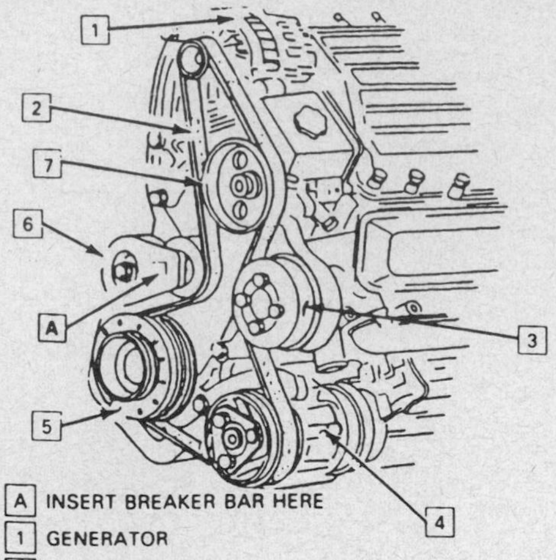
1
2
7
6
A
3
5
4
A INSERT BREAKER BAR HERE
1 GENERATOR
2 SERPENTINE BELT
3 WATER PUMP
4 AIR CONDITIONING COMPRESSOR
5 CRANKSHAFT
6 BELT TENSIONER
7 POWER STEERING PUMP
GC1069100292000X

Fig. 14 Serpentine drive belt routing

OIL PAN

REPLACE

1. Remove battery ground cable, then serpentine drive belt and tensioner.
2. Support vehicle using support fixtures No. J-28467-A and J-36462 or equivalent.
3. Raise and support vehicle, then drain engine oil from crankcase.
4. Remove right side wheel assembly, then right side splash shield.
5. Remove steering gear pinch bolt. **Failure to disconnect intermediate shaft from rack and pinion stub shaft can result in damage to steering gear and/or intermediate shaft.**
6. Remove transaxle mount retaining nut, then engine to frame mount nuts.
7. Remove front engine mount bracket from block, then outboard flywheel/starter plastic shield.
8. Remove inboard flywheel metal shield, then start.
9. Place jack stand under frame front center crossmember, then loosen rear frame bolts. **Do not remove rear frame bolts.**
10. Remove front frame bolts, then lower front of frame.
11. Disconnect DIS sensor wire, then remove oil pan retaining bolts.
12. Remove oil pan retaining nuts, then oil pan.
13. Reverse procedure to install. Tighten to specifications.

OIL PUMP SERVICE

REMOVAL

1. Remove oil pan as described under "Oil Pan, Replace."
2. Remove pump to rear main bearing cap bolt and remove pump and extension shaft, **Fig. 12.**

DISASSEMBLE

1. Remove pump cover attaching bolts and pump cover, **Fig. 13.**
2. Mark drive and idler gear teeth so they can be installed in the same position, then remove idler and drive gear and shaft from pump body.
3. Remove pin, spring and pressure regulator valve from pump cover.
4. If pickup tube and screen assembly are to be replaced, mount pump cover in a soft jawed vise and remove pickup tube from cover. Do not remove screen from pickup tube, these components are serviced as an assembly.

INSPECTION

1. Inspect pump body and cover for excessive wear and cracks.
2. Inspect pump gear for damage or excessive wear. If pump gears are damaged or worn, the entire pump assembly must be replaced.
3. Check drive gear shaft for looseness in pump body.
4. Inspect pump cover for wear that would allow oil to leak past gear teeth.
5. Inspect pickup tube and screen assembly for damage.
6. Check pressure regulator valve for fit in pump cover.

ASSEMBLE

1. If pickup tube and screen were removed, apply sealer to end of pickup tube, then mount pump cover in a soft jawed vise and using mounting tool No. J-8369 or equivalent, tap pickup tube into position using a plastic mallet. **Whenever the pickup tube and screen assembly has been removed, a new pickup tube and screen assembly should be installed. Use care when installing pickup tube and screen assembly so that tube does not twist, shear or collapse. Loss of a press fit condition could result in an air leak and a loss of oil pressure.**
2. Install pressure regulator valve, spring and pin, **Fig. 13.**
3. Install drive gear and shaft in pump body.
4. Align marks made during disassembly, then install idler gear.
5. Install pump cover gasket, cover and attaching bolts. Tighten bolts to specifications.
6. Rotate pump drive shaft by hand and check pump for smooth operation.

INSTALLATION

1. Assemble pump and extension shaft with retainer to rear main bearing cap, aligning extension shaft with drive gear.
2. Install pump to rear main bearing cap bolt.
3. Install oil pan as described under "Oil Pan, Replace."

BELT TENSION DATA

Belt tension is maintained automatically by a spring tensioned pulley. No adjustment is necessary.

SERPENTINE DRIVE BELT

BELT ROUTING

Refer to **Fig. 14** for routing of serpentine drive belt.

TENSIONER INSPECTION

1. Run engine, with no accessories on, until normal operating temperature is reached. Turn engine off and read belt tension using belt tension gauge J-23600-B or equivalent. Place gauge halfway between alternator and power steering pump.
2. Start engine, with accessories off, and allow system to stabilize for 15 seconds. Turn engine off. Using a 15 mm socket, apply clockwise force to tensioner pulley bolt. Release force and immediately take a tension reading without disturbing belt tensioner position.
3. Using a 15 mm socket, apply counterclockwise force to tensioner pulley bolt, raise pulley to eliminate all tension. Slowly lower pulley to belt and take a tension reading without disturbing belt tensioner position.

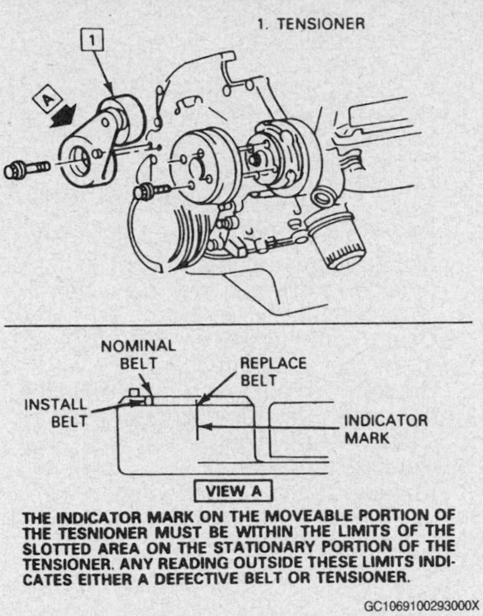
1. TENSIONER
1
A
NOMINAL BELT
REPLACE BELT
INSTALL BELT
INDICATOR MARK
VIEW A
THE INDICATOR MARK ON THE MOVEABLE PORTION OF THE TESNIONER MUST BE WITHIN THE LIMITS OF THE SLOTTED AREA ON THE STATIONARY PORTION OF THE TENSIONER. ANY READING OUTSIDE THESE LIMITS INDICATES EITHER A DEFECTIVE BELT OR TENSIONER.
GC1069100293000X

Fig. 15 Belt tensioner replacement

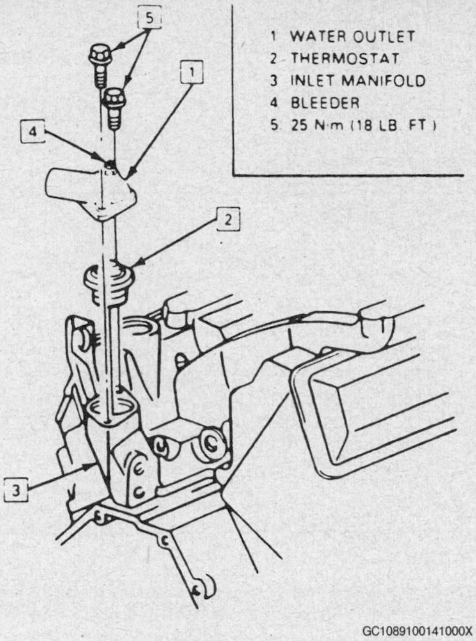
1 WATER OUTLET
2 THERMOSTAT
3 INLET MANIFOLD
4 BLEEDER
5 25 N·m (18 LB. FT.)
GC1089100141000X

Fig. 16 Thermostat & housing assembly

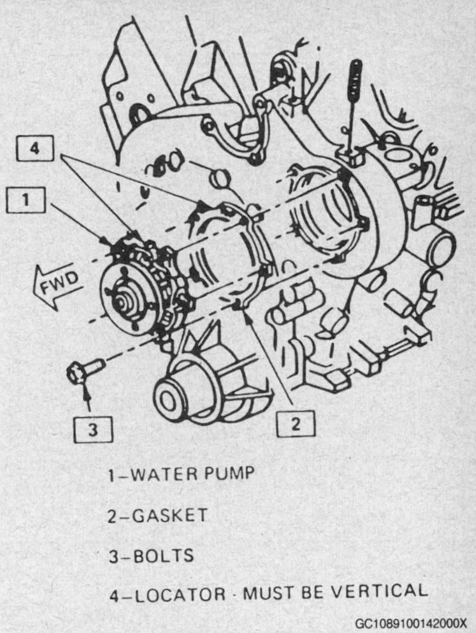
FWD
1–WATER PUMP
2–GASKET
3–BOLTS
4–LOCATOR - MUST BE VERTICAL
GC1089100142000X

Fig. 17 Water pump assembly replacement

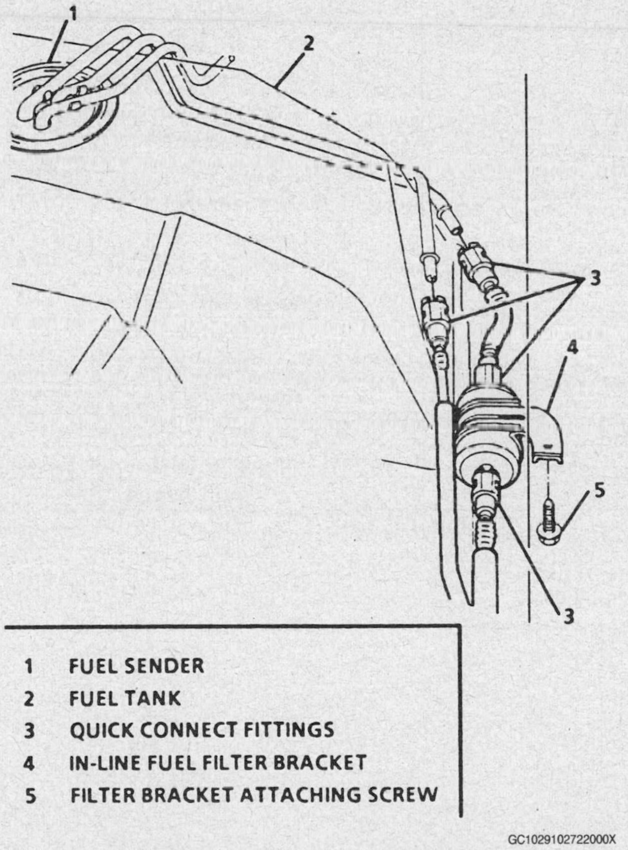
1 FUEL SENDER
2 FUEL TANK
3 QUICK CONNECT FITTINGS
4 IN-LINE FUEL FILTER BRACKET
5 FILTER BRACKET ATTACHING SCREW
GC1029102722000X

Fig. 18 Fuel filter replacement

4. Average three readings. If average is not between 50-70 lbs. and belt is within tensioner's operating range, replace belt tensioner.

TENSIONER, REPLACE

1. Remove serpentine drive belt.
2. Remove tensioner attaching bolts, then tensioner, **Fig. 15.**
3. Reverse procedure to install. Tighten to specifications.

COOLING SYSTEM BLEED

These engines do not require a specified bleed procedure. After filling cooling system, run engine to operating temperature with radiator/pressure cap off. Air will then be automatically bled through cap opening.

Open air bleed vent on bypass pipe three turns when draining system. The engine has two engine drain plug.

THERMOSTAT
REPLACE

Refer to **Fig. 16** when performing the following procedure.

1. Disconnect battery ground cable.
2. With engine cool, drain engine coolant below thermostat level. **Never open cooling system with engine hot.**
3. Disconnect radiator hose from thermostat housing.
4. Remove thermostat housing retaining bolts, then the housing, gasket and thermostat.
5. Reverse procedure to install, noting the following:
   a. Ensure thermostat gasket area is thoroughly clean.
   b. Install thermostat with new gasket.
   c. Apply a suitable sealer to thermostat housing retaining bolts. Install and **torque** bolts to 18 ft. lbs.
   d. Refill and bleed cooling system as necessary.

WATER PUMP
REPLACE

1. Disconnect battery ground cable, then drain cooling system.
2. Remove vacuum line from top of coolant pump.
3. Remove serpentine drive belt, then water pump pulley.
4. Remove water pump attaching bolts, then water pump, **Fig. 17.**
5. Reverse procedure to install. Tighten all bolts/nuts to specifications.

RADIATOR
REPLACE

1. Remove air cleaner assembly and resonator.
2. Drain engine coolant, then disconnect cooling fan electrical connector.
3. Remove cooling fan screws, then the cooling fan assembly.
4. Remove engine mount strut and mounting bracket from radiator upper mounting panel.
5. Remove radiator mounting panel.
6. Disconnect oil cooler lines.
7. Disconnect coolant recovery hose, then the upper and lower radiator hoses.
8. Remove radiator.
9. Reverse procedure to install.

FUEL PUMP
REPLACE

1. Relieve fuel pressure as outlined under "Precautions," then disconnect battery ground cable.
2. Remove fuel tank.
3. Remove fuel pump assembly by turning cam lock ring counterclockwise. Lift assembly from fuel tank and remove fuel pump from fuel tank sending unit.
4. Reverse procedure to install.

FUEL FILTER
REPLACE

1. Relieve fuel system pressure as outlined under "Precautions."
2. Raise and support vehicle.
3. Remove bracket attaching screw and filter bracket, **Fig. 18.**
4. Grasp filter and fuel line fitting. Twist quick-connect fitting 1/4 turn in each direction to loosen any dirt within fitting.
5. Using compressed air, blow out dirt from quick-connect fitting.
6. Remove feed pipe nut from fuel filter, then drain any remaining fuel into an suitable container.
7. Remove fuel filter.
8. Reverse procedure to install.

TIGHTENING SPECIFICATIONS

Year	Component	Torque/Ft. Lbs.
1992–93	Camshaft Sprocket Bolt	21
	Connecting Rod Nut	37
	Cylinder Head Bolt	①
	Drive Belt Tensioner Bolt	37
	Engine Bracket To Engine Bolt	81
	Engine Bracket To Engine Mount Nut	34
	Engine Mount To Frame Nut	34
	Engine Strut Bracket To Engine Bolt	17
	Engine Strut To Tie Bar Bracket	41
	Engine Strut To Upper Tie Bar	17
	Exhaust Crossover Nut	18
	Exhaust Manifold Heat Shield Nut	7
	Exhaust Manifold To Cylinder Head Bolt	18
	Flywheel Bolt	52
	Front Cover Bolt	①
	Intake Manifold Bolt	①
	Main Bearing Cap Bolt	73
	Oil Filter	11

Year	Component	Torque/Ft. Lbs.
1992–93 —Cont'd	Oil Filter Adapter Connector	50
	Oil Filter Drip Shield	7
	Oil Level Indicator Retaining Nut	18
	Oil Pan Bottom Bolts	18
	Oil Pan Rear Bolts (2)	18
	Oil Pan Stud To Cylinder Block	7
	Oil Pump Drive Bolt	25
	Oil Pump Mounting Bolt	30
	Oxygen Sensor	31
	Rocker Arm Cover Bolt	7
	Rocker Arm Nut	18
	Spark Plug	10-25
	Thermostat Housing	15-23
	Timing Chain Dampener Bolt	15
	Torsional Dampener (Harmonic Balancer)	76
	Water Pump	7

①—Refer to text.

3.3L/V6-204 Engine

NOTE: On Air Bag Equipped Models, Refer To "Air Bag System Precautions" Located In The Front Of This Manual For System Disarming & Arming Procedures.

INDEX

PRECAUTIONS

AIR BAG SYSTEMS

Refer to "Air Bag System Precautions" in the front of this manual for system disarming and arming procedures.

FUEL SYSTEM PRESSURE RELIEF

Whenever the fuel lines are to be disconnected for engine service on fuel injected engines, relieve fuel system pressure following the procedures outlined below. Failure to follow these procedures exactly, may result in personal injury.

1. Disconnect battery ground cable, then loosen filler cap to relieve tank vapor pressure.
2. Connect fuel pressure gauge No. J-34730-1 or equivalent to fuel pressure valve. Wrap a shop towel around fitting while connecting gauge to avoid spillage.
3. Install bleed hose into an approved container and open valve to bleed system pressure. Fuel connections are now safe for servicing.
4. Drain any fuel remaining in gauge into approved container.

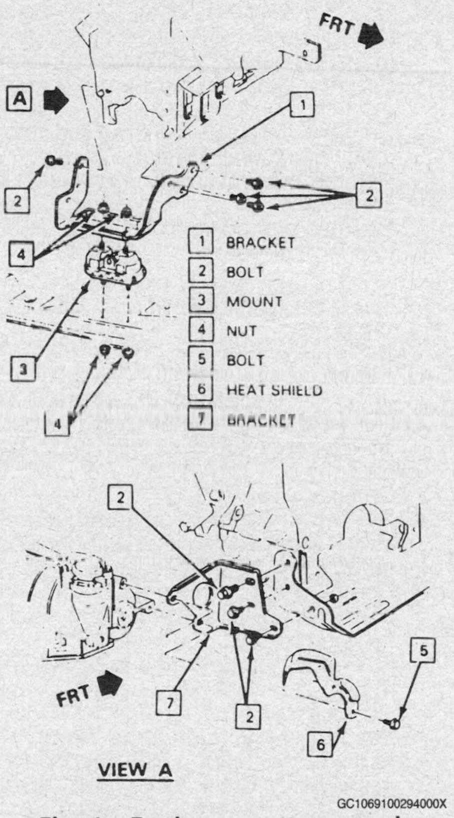

FRT
A
1 BRACKET
2 BOLT
3 MOUNT
4 NUT
5 BOLT
6 HEAT SHIELD
7 BRACKET
FRT
VIEW A
GC1069100294000X

Fig. 1 Engine mount removal

ENGINE MOUNT

REPLACE

1. Attach suitable engine lifting fixture to engine.
2. Raise and support front of vehicle.
3. Remove mount to engine mount bracket nuts. Raise engine slightly and remove mount to frame nuts. Remove mount, **Fig. 1.**
4. Reverse procedure to install. Tighten to specifications.

ENGINE

REPLACE

1. Remove hood, then disconnect battery ground cable.
2. Drain cooling system, then remove radiator and heater hoses.
3. Remove upper engine torque strut, then engine cooling fan.
4. Remove air intake duct from throttle body, then vacuum hosing to all non-engine mounted components.
5. Relieve fuel pressure as outlined under "Precautions," then remove fuel lines from fuel rail.
6. Remove all cables from throttle body, then cable bracket.
7. Remove serpentine drive belt, then disconnect all necessary electrical connections.
8. Remove power steering pump from mounting bracket. Position pump aside.
9. Remove upper transaxle to engine bolts, then raise and support vehicle.
10. Remove A/C compressor. Position compressor aside.
11. Remove engine mount to frame nuts, then exhaust pipe from exhaust manifold.
12. Remove flywheel dust cover, then flywheel to converter bolts. Mark torque converter and flywheel to assure proper assembly.
13. Remove lower engine to transaxle bolts. **One bolt is located between transaxle case and engine block and is installed in the opposite direction.**
14. Lower car, then install engine lift fixture.
15. Remove engine.
16. Reverse procedure to install. Tighten to specifications.

INTAKE MANIFOLD

REPLACE

1. Disconnect battery ground cable, then drain cooling system.
2. Remove serpentine drive belt, then alternator and bracket.
3. Remove power steering pump braces, then coolant bypass hose.
4. Remove air inlet duct, heater pipe and upper radiator hose.
5. Remove throttle cable bracket and cables from throttle body.
6. Remove vacuum lines and wiring connectors as necessary.

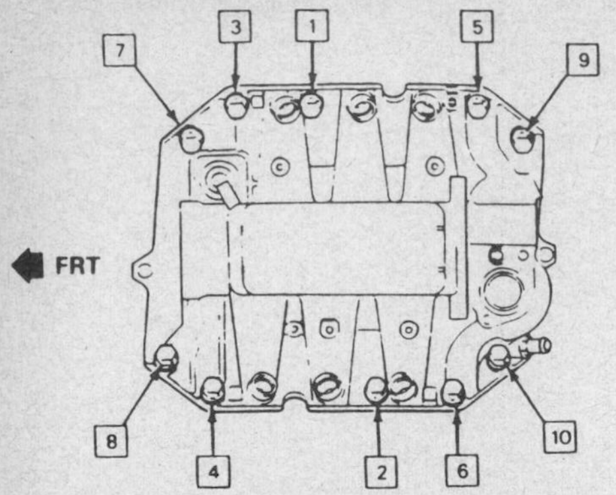
FRT
1
2
3
4
5
6
7
8
9
10

GC1059100071000X

Fig. 2 Intake manifold tightening sequence

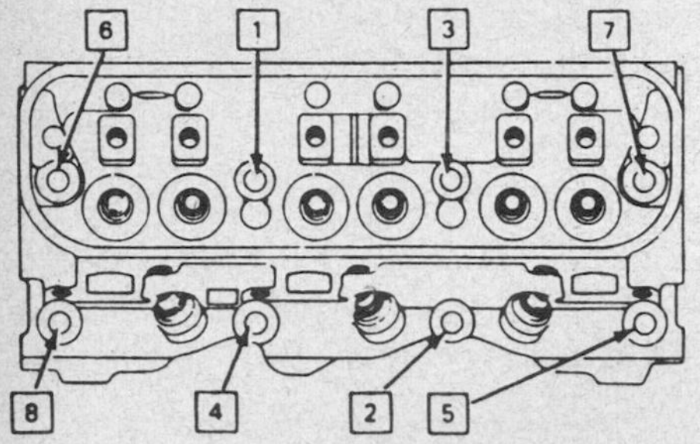
1
2
3
4
5
6
7
8

GC1069100295000X

Fig. 3 Cylinder head tightening sequence

7. Relieve fuel pressure as outlined under "Precautions," then remove fuel lines.
8. Remove heater hose from throttle body.
9. Remove intake manifold attaching bolts, then intake manifold.
10. Reverse procedure to install, noting the following:
    a. Apply suitable sealer to ends of manifold seals.
    b. Apply thread lock compound No. 12345493 or equivalent, to intake manifold bolt threads before assembly.
    c. **Torque** intake manifold bolts **twice** to 89 inch lbs., in sequence shown in **Fig. 2.**

EXHAUST MANIFOLD
REPLACE

LEFT

1. Disconnect battery ground cable, then remove air cleaner inlet duct.
2. Remove spark plug wires, then exhaust crossover pipe to manifold attaching bolts.
3. Remove engine lift hook, then manifold heat shield.
4. Remove oil level indicator tube, then manifold studs.
5. Remove exhaust manifold.
6. Reverse procedure to install. Tighten to specifications.

RIGHT

1. Disconnect battery ground cable, then remove spark plug wires.
2. Disconnect oxygen sensor lead, then remove throttle cable bracket and cables from throttle body.
3. Remove brake booster hose from manifold, then exhaust crossover pipe to manifold attaching bolts.
4. Remove exhaust pipe from manifold, then engine lift hook.
5. Remove transaxle oil level indicator tube, then manifold heat shield.
6. Remove manifold studs, then exhaust manifold.
7. Reverse procedure to install. Tighten to specifiations.

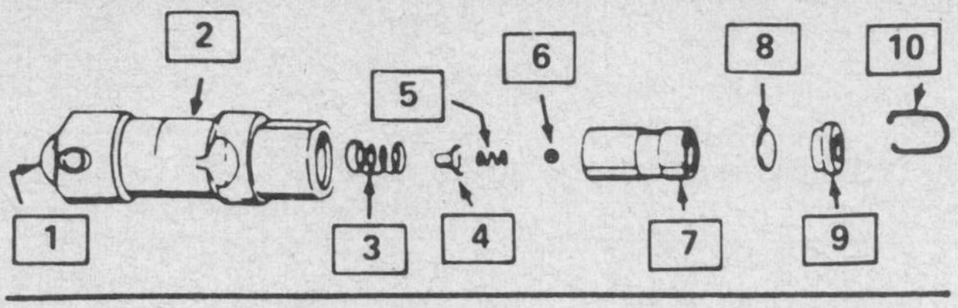
1
2
3
4
5
6
7
8
9
10

1–ROLLER
2–LIFTER BODY
3–PLUNGER SPRING
4–BALL CHECK RETAINER
5–BALL CHECK SPRING
6–BALL CHECK
7–PLUNGER
8–OIL METERING VALVE
9–PUSH ROD SEAT
10–RETAINER RING

GC1069100296000X

Fig. 4 Exploded view of roller type hydraulic valve lifter

CYLINDER HEAD
REPLACE

1. Remove intake manifold as outlined under "Intake Manifold, Replace."
2. Remove exhaust manifolds as outlined under "Exhaust Manifold, Replace."
3. Remove valve covers.
4. **For left cylinder head removal,** remove alternator bracket with ignition module and coils attached.
5. Remove A/C compressor bracket bolt, then power steering pump. Position pump aside.
6. **For right cylinder head removal,** remove serpentine drive belt, then tensioner assembly.
7. **For either cylinder head removal,** remove spark plug wires, rocker arm assemblies, guide plate and pushrods.
8. Remove cylinder head attaching bolts, then cylinder head.
9. Reverse procedure to install, noting the following:
    a. Apply sealant No. 1052080 or equivalent to underside of cylinder head bolt heads.
    b. Apply thread locker No. 12345382 or equivalent to bolt threads.
    c. **Torque** cylinder head bolts in sequence shown in **Fig. 3,** to 35 ft. lbs.
    d. Tighten each bolt an additional 130° in same sequence, then tighten center four bolts an additional 30° in same sequence.
    e. Apply thread locker No. 12345493 or equivalent to rocker arm pedestal bolts before assembly.
    f. Tighten all remaining bolts/nuts to specifications.

VALVE ARRANGEMENT

FRONT TO REAR

Left side .... E-I-E-I-I-E
Right side .... E-I-I-E-I-E

VALVE LIFTERS

Failure of an hydraulic valve lifter, **Fig. 4,** is generally caused by dirt or an inadequate oil supply. An air leak at the intake side of the oil pump or too much oil in the engine will cause air bubbles in the oil supply to the lifters, causing them to collapse. This is a probable cause of trouble if several lifters fail to function, but air in the oil is an unlikely cause of failure of a single unit.

The valve lifters may be lifted out of their bores after removing the rocker arms, pushrods and intake manifold. Adjustable pliers with taped jaws may be used to remove lifters that are stuck due to varnish, carbon, etc. Roller type lifters are used to reduce friction and improve performance. The lifters are cylindrical with the exception of two parallel flats milled into the upper part of the body. Slotted guides which hold the lifters in pairs fit over the milled area to keep the lifters from turning in their bores.

VALVE CLEARANCE SPECIFICATIONS

These engines are equipped with hydraulic lifters. No provision for specifications is provided.

VALVE ADJUSTMENT

These engines are equipped with hydraulic lifters. No provision for adjustment is provided.

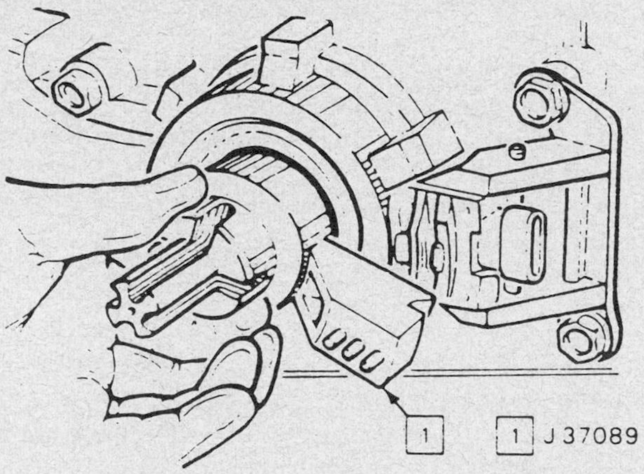
1
1 J 37089
GC1069100297000X

Fig. 5 Crankshaft sensor adjustment

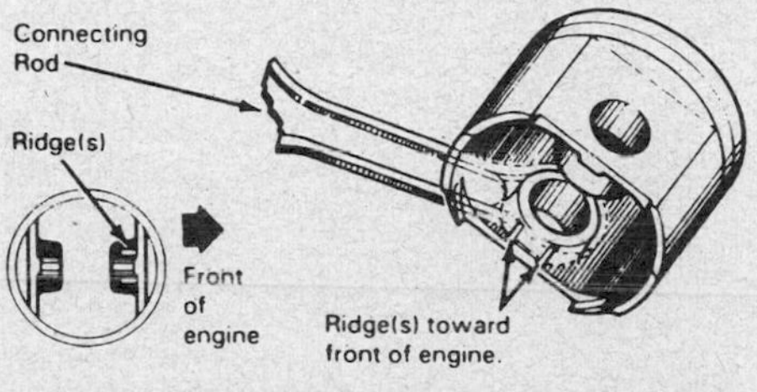
Connecting Rod
Ridge(s)
Front of engine
Ridge(s) toward front of engine.
GC1069100299000X

Fig. 7 Piston and rod assembly

ROCKER ARMS

Rocker arms are mounted to the cylinder head via individual iron pedestals and are retained by hardened steel bolts.

To install rocker arms, position pedestal retainer, rocker arm and pedestal onto cylinder head. Install retaining bolts and tighten to specification.

VALVE GUIDES

The valve guides are an integral part of the cylinder head and cannot be replaced.

If valve stem clearance is excessive, the valve guide must be reamed and an oversize valve installed. Valves are available in oversize of .010 inch.

FRONT COVER

REPLACE

1. Disconnect battery ground cable and drain cooling system.
2. Remove serpentine drive belt, then heater hoses.
3. Disconnect lower radiator and coolant bypass hoses from cover.
4. Raise and support vehicle, then remove right front wheel.
5. Remove right inner fender splash shield.
6. Remove torque converter cover, then prevent flywheel from turning using suitable tool.
7. Remove balancer bolt and washer, then remove balancer assembly.
8. Disconnect electrical connections at camshaft, crankshaft and oil pressure sensors.
9. Remove bolts attaching front cover to

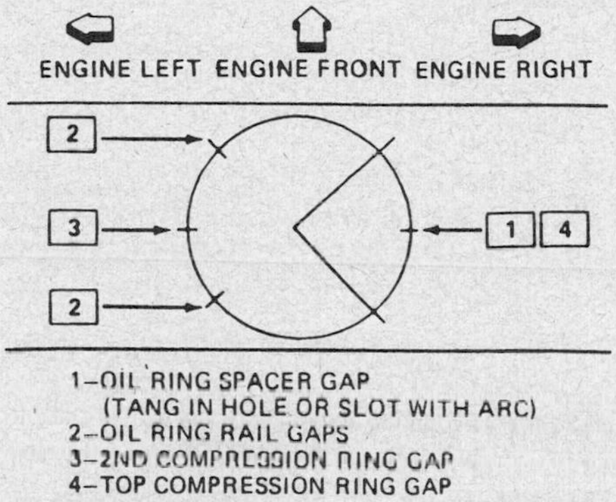
ENGINE LEFT ENGINE FRONT ENGINE RIGHT
2
3
2
1
4
1–OIL RING SPACER GAP
(TANG IN HOLE OR SLOT WITH ARC)
2–OIL RING RAIL GAPS
3–2ND COMPRESSION RING GAP
4–TOP COMPRESSION RING GAP
GC1069100300000X

Fig. 8 Piston ring end gap locations

cylinder block, then oil pan to front cover bolts.

10. Remove front cover assembly and gasket.
11. Reverse procedure to install, noting the following:
    a. Adjust crankshaft sensor using tool shown in **Fig. 5.**
    b. When reinstalling front cover bolts, apply a suitable sealer to the threads to prevent leakage.
    c. Tighten all bolts/nuts to specifications.

TIMING CHAIN

REPLACE

1. Remove front cover as outlined under "Front Cover, Replace."
2. Temporarily install balancer bolt and washer in end of crankshaft. Turn crankshaft so timing marks on sprockets are as close together as possible. Remove balancer bolt and washer using a sharp blow on wrench handle, so bolt can be removed without changing position of sprockets.
3. Remove timing chain dampener, then and camshaft sprocket bolts.
4. Using two large screwdrivers, alternately pry off sprockets and chain.
5. Reverse procedure to install. Assemble timing chain on sprockets and slide sprockets and chain assembly onto camshaft and crankshaft with

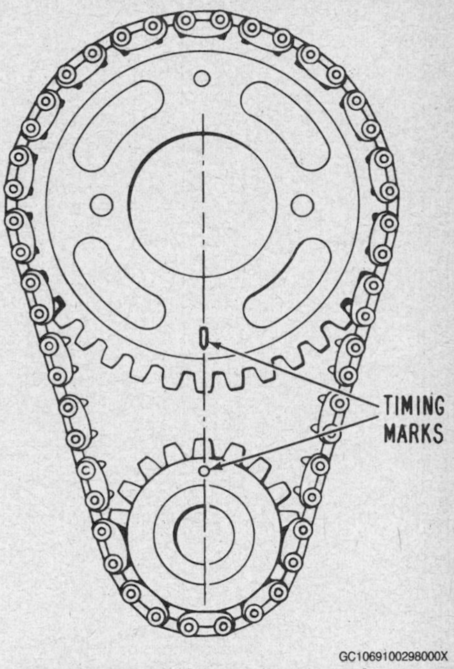
TIMING MARKS
GC1069100298000X

Fig. 6 Valve timing marks

timing marks aligned as shown in **Fig. 6.**

6. Tighten all bolts and nuts to specifications.

CAMSHAFT

REPLACE

1. Remove engine as outlined under "Engine, Replace."
2. Remove intake manifold as outlined under "Intake Manifold, Replace."
3. Remove rocker arm covers.
4. Remove rocker arms, pushrods and valve lifters.
5. Remove front cover as outlined under "Front Cover, Replace."
6. Align timing marks of camshaft and crankshaft sprocket. Remove timing chain and sprockets.
7. Remove cam sensor magnet assembly and camshaft thrust plate if applicable.
8. Slide camshaft forward out of bearing bores, using care so as not to damage bearing surfaces.
9. Reverse procedure to install, noting the following:
    a. Ensure crankshaft and camshaft timing marks as shown in **Fig. 6.**
    b. Tighten all bolts/nuts to specifications.

PISTON & ROD ASSEMBLY

Pistons can be installed on connecting rod in either direction.

Piston/connecting rod assembly must be installed in engine as shown in **Fig. 7.**

PISTONS, PINS & RINGS

Install rings on piston as shown in **Fig. 8.**

Pistons are available in standard sizes and oversize of .010 inch. Rings are avail-

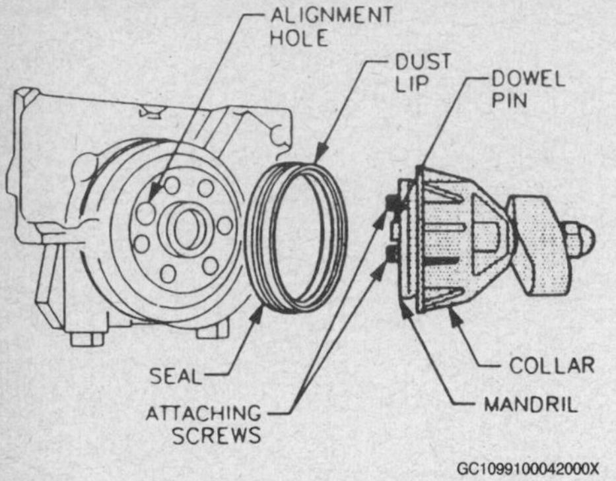
ALIGNMENT HOLE
DUST LIP
DOWEL PIN
SEAL
ATTACHING SCREWS
COLLAR
MANDRIL
GC1099100042000X

Fig. 9 Rear main seal installation

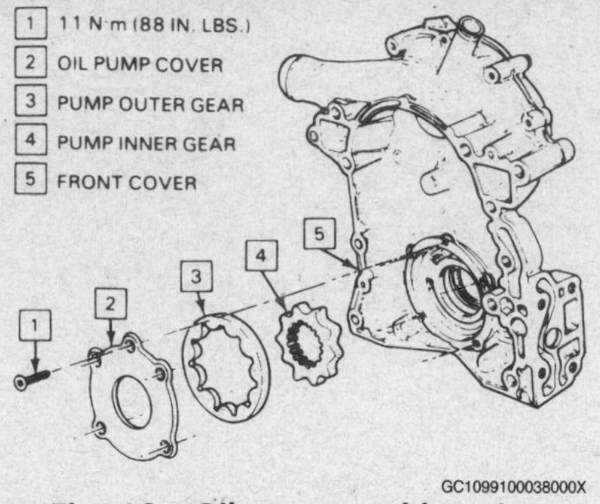
1 11 N·m (88 IN. LBS.)
2 OIL PUMP COVER
3 PUMP OUTER GEAR
4 PUMP INNER GEAR
5 FRONT COVER
GC1099100038000X

Fig. 10 Oil pump and housing assembly

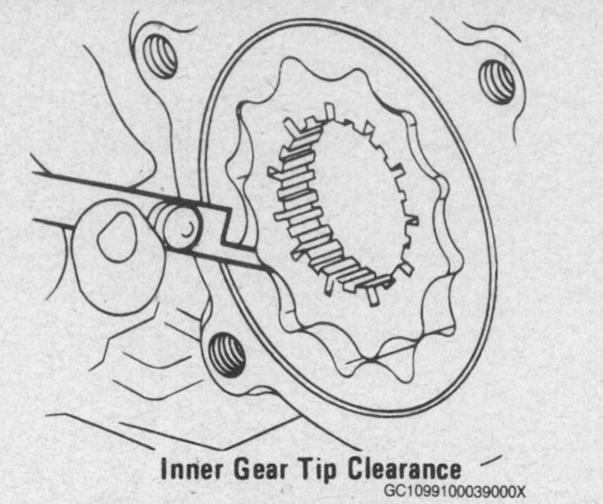
Inner Gear Tip Clearance
GC1099100039000X

Fig. 11 Inner gear tip clearance check

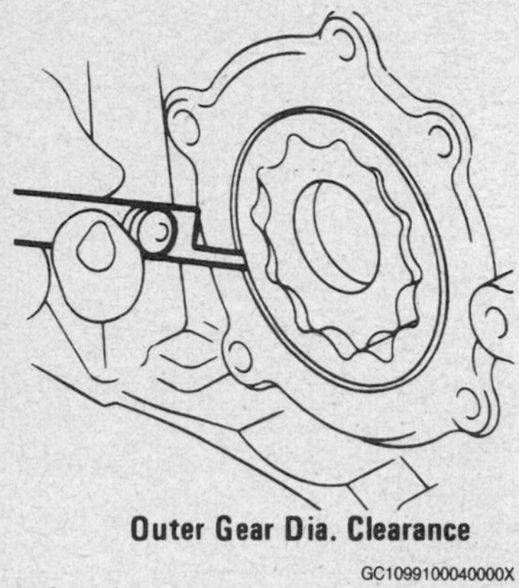
Outer Gear Dia. Clearance
GC1099100040000X

Fig. 12 Outer gear diameter clearance check

able in standard sizes and oversize of .010 inch. Piston pins are supplied with piston and available only in standard sizes.

MAIN & ROD BEARINGS

Main and connecting rod bearings are available in standard sizes and undersizes of .0005, .0010 and .0015 inch.

CRANKSHAFT REAR OIL SEAL

REPLACE

1. Remove transaxle and flywheel.
2. Using a screwdriver, pry out old seal. Use care to avoid damaging crankshaft. File all burrs or nicks as required.
3. Install new seal using seal installer No. J-38196 or equivalent, as follows:
   a. Apply a light coat of engine oil to I.D. and O.D. of oil seal.
   b. Slide seal over tool mandrel until dust lip bottoms squarely against collar of tool.
   c. Align dowel pin of tool with dowel pin hole in crankshaft, **Fig. 9**, then attach tool to crankshaft with screw provided.
   d. Turn handle of tool until seal is pushed into bore and collar is positioned firmly against case. Remove tool.
4. Install flywheel and transmission, then start engine and check for leaks.

OIL PAN

REPLACE

1. Disconnect battery ground cable, then raise and support vehicle.
2. Drain engine oil, then remove flywheel cover.
3. Remove starter, then oil filter.
4. Remove oil pan attaching bolts, then oil pan.
5. Remove and discard old oil pan gasket.
6. Reverse procedure to install. Tighten to specifications.

OIL PUMP SERVICE

REMOVAL & INSPECTION

1. Remove front cover, then the oil filter adapter, pressure regulator valve and valve spring.
2. Remove oil pump cover attaching screws, cover and gears, **Fig. 10.**
3. Inspect pump cover and housing for cracks, scoring, porosity and damaged threads, pressure regulator valve and spring for sticking, scoring or tension loss and gears for chipping, galling or excessive wear. Replace as necessary.
4. Check gear clearance as follows:
   a. Check inner gear tip clearance with feeler gauge as shown in **Fig. 11.** Maximum clearance should not exceed .006 inch.
   b. Check outer gear diameter clearance with feeler gauge as shown in **Fig. 12.** Clearance should be .008-.015 inch.
   c. Check gear end clearance (gear drop in housing) as shown in **Fig. 13.** Clearance should be .001-.0035 inch.
5. Replace parts as necessary.

INSTALLATION

1. Lubricate gears with petroleum jelly, then install into oil pump housing.
2. Pack gear cavity with petroleum jelly, then install pump cover and attaching screws. Tighten attaching screws to specifications.
3. Install pressure regulator valve spring and valve.
4. Install oil filter adapter using new gasket. Tighten adapter bolts to specifications.
5. Reinstall front cover onto engine.

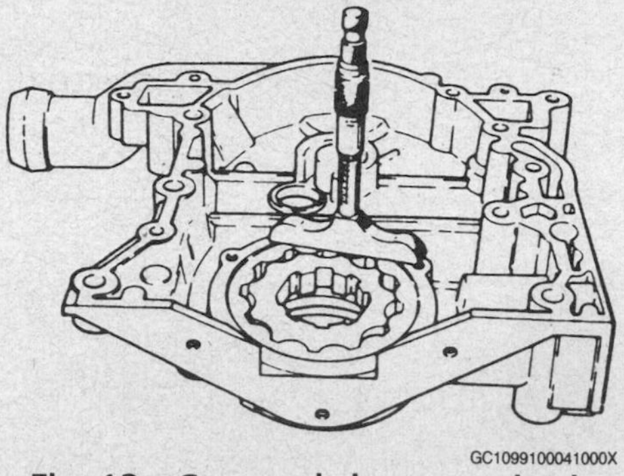
GC1099100041000X

Fig. 13 Gear end clearance check

BELT TENSION DATA

Belt tension is maintained automatically by a spring tensioned pulley. No adjustment is necessary.

SERPENTINE DRIVE BELT

BELT ROUTING

Refer to **Fig. 14** for routing of serpentine drive belt.

TENSIONER INSPECTION

1. Run engine, with no accessories on, until normal operating temperature is reached. Turn engine off and read belt tension using belt tension gauge J-23600-B or equivalent. On models equipped with A/C, place gauge halfway between alternator and A/C compressor. On models less A/C, place gauge halfway between power steering pump and crankshaft pulley.
2. Start engine, with accessories off, and allow system to stabilize for 15 seconds. Turn engine off. Using a 18 mm socket, apply clockwise force to tensioner pulley bolt. Release force and immediately take a tension reading without disturbing belt tensioner position.
3. Using a 18 mm socket, apply counterclockwise force to tensioner pulley bolt, raise pulley to eliminate all tension. Slowly lower pulley to belt and take a tension reading without disturbing belt tensioner position.

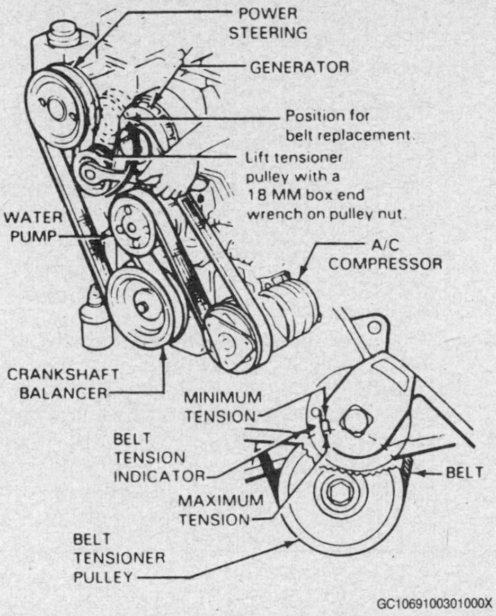
POWER
STEERING
GENERATOR
Position for
belt replacement.
Lift tensioner
pulley with a
18 MM box end
wrench on pulley nut.
WATER
PUMP
A/C
COMPRESSOR
CRANKSHAFT
BALANCER
MINIMUM
TENSION
BELT
TENSION
INDICATOR
BELT
MAXIMUM
TENSION
BELT
TENSIONER
PULLEY
GC1069100301000X

Fig. 14 Serpentine drive belt routing

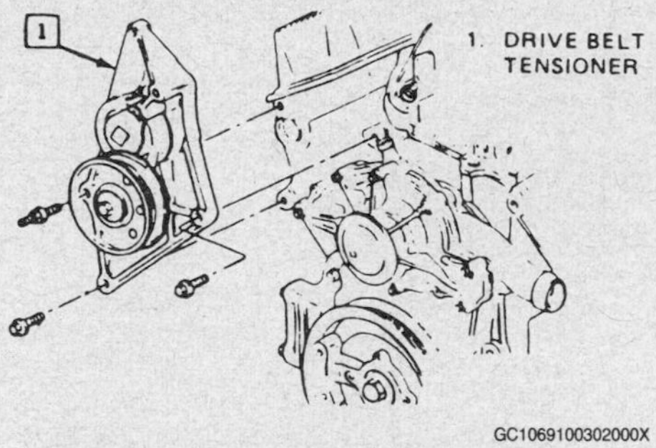
1
1. DRIVE BELT
TENSIONER
GC1069100302000X

Fig. 15 Tensioner replacement

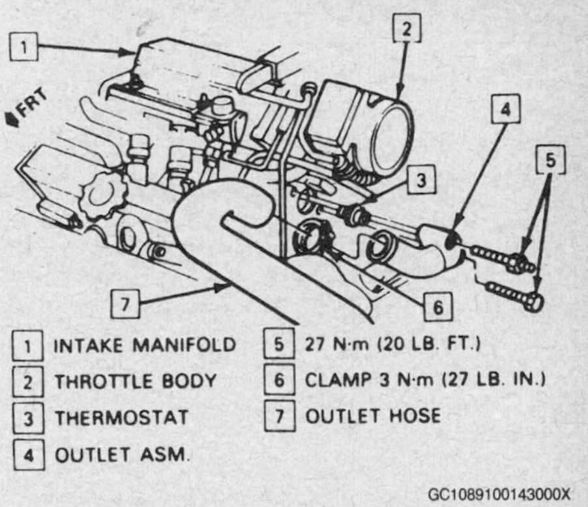
1
2
FRT
4
5
3
7
6
1 INTAKE MANIFOLD
2 THROTTLE BODY
3 THERMOSTAT
4 OUTLET ASM.
5 27 N·m (20 LB. FT.)
6 CLAMP 3 N·m (27 LB. IN.)
7 OUTLET HOSE
GC1089100143000X

Fig. 16 Thermostat & housing assembly

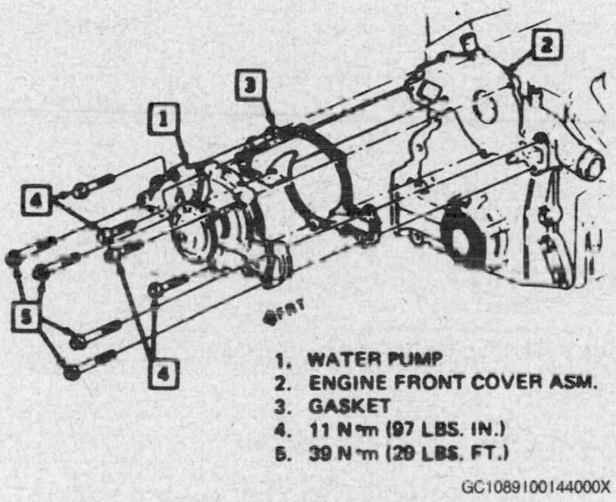
2
3
1
4
5
4
FRT
1. WATER PUMP
2. ENGINE FRONT COVER ASM.
3. GASKET
4. 11 N·m (97 LBS. IN.)
5. 39 N·m (29 LBS. FT.)
GC1089100144000X

Fig. 17 Water pump removal & installation

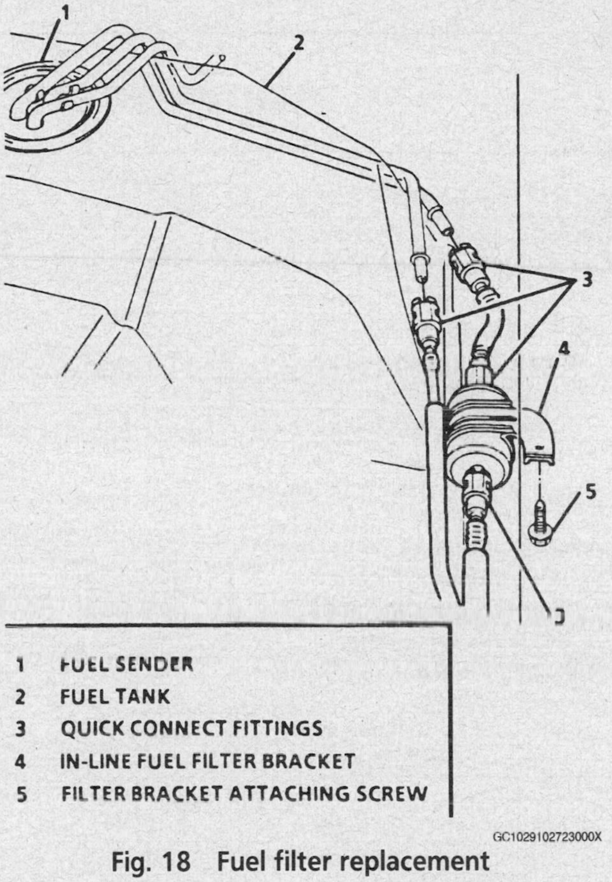
1
2
3
4
5
1 FUEL SENDER
2 FUEL TANK
3 QUICK CONNECT FITTINGS
4 IN-LINE FUEL FILTER BRACKET
5 FILTER BRACKET ATTACHING SCREW
GC1029102723000X

Fig. 18 Fuel filter replacement

4. Average three readings. If average is lower than 67 lbs. and belt is within tensioner's operating range, replace belt tensioner.

TENSIONER, REPLACE

1. Remove serpentine drive belt.
2. Remove tensioner attaching bolts, then tensioner, **Fig. 15.**
3. Reverse procedure to install. Tighten to specifications.

COOLING SYSTEM BLEED

These engines do not require a specified bleed procedure. After filling cooling system, run engine to operating temperature with radiator pressure cap off. Air will then be automatically bled through cap opening.

THERMOSTAT

REPLACE

Refer to **Fig. 16** when performing the following procedure.

1. Disconnect battery negative cable.
2. If necessary, remove air cleaner assembly.
3. With engine cool, drain engine coolant below thermostat level. **Never open cooling system with engine hot.**
4. Disconnect radiator hose from thermostat housing.
5. Remove thermostat housing retaining bolts, then the housing, gasket and thermostat.
6. Reverse procedure to install noting the following:
   a. Ensure thermostat gasket area is thoroughly clean.
   b. Install thermostat with new gasket.
   c. Apply a suitable sealer to thermostat housing retaining bolts. Install and **torque** bolts to 20 ft. lbs.
   d. Refill and bleed cooling system as necessary.

WATER PUMP

REPLACE

1. Disconnect battery ground cable.
2. Drain cooling system, then remove serpentine drive belt.
3. Remove lower radiator hose and heater hose at pump.
4. Remove water pump pulley attaching bolts. Long bolt is removed through access hole located in the body side rail.
5. Remove water pump pulley.
6. Remove water pump attaching bolts, then the water pump, **Fig. 17.**
7. Reverse procedure to install. Tighten bolts to specifications.

RADIATOR

REPLACE

1. Remove air cleaner assembly and resonator.
2. Drain engine coolant, then disconnect cooling fan electrical connector.
3. Remove cooling fan screws, then the cooling fan assembly.
4. Remove engine mount strut and mounting bracket from radiator upper mounting panel.
5. Remove radiator mounting panel.
6. Disconnect oil cooler fines.
7. Disconnect coolant recovery hose, then the upper and lower radiator hoses.
8. Remove radiator.
9. Reverse procedure to install.

FUEL PUMP

REPLACE

1. Relieve fuel pressure as outlined under "Precautions," then disconnect battery ground cable.
2. Remove fuel tank.
3. Remove fuel pump assembly by turning cam lock ring counterclockwise. Lift assembly from fuel tank and remove fuel pump from fuel tank sending unit.
4. Reverse procedure to install.

FUEL FILTER

REPLACE

1. Relieve fuel system pressure as outlined under "Precautions."
2. Raise and support vehicle.
3. Remove bracket attaching screw and filter bracket, **Fig. 18.**
4. Grasp filter and fuel line fitting. Twist quick-connect fitting 1/4 turn in each direction to loosen any dirt within fitting.
5. Using compressed air, blow out dirt from quick-connect fitting.
6. Remove feed pipe nut from fuel filter, then drain any remaining fuel into an suitable container.
7. Remove fuel filter.
8. Reverse procedure to install.

TIGHTENING SPECIFICATIONS

Year	Component	Torque/Ft. Lbs.
1992–93	Alternator Support To Cylinder Head	37
	Alternator Support Through Generator	37
	Balancer Assembly To Crankshaft	219
	Camshaft Sensor To Front Cover	80③
	Camshaft Sprocket Bolt	26
	Camshaft Thrust Plate Bolt	11③
	Connecting Rod Bolts	①
	Coolant Temperature Sensor To Intake	15
	Crankshaft Bearing Caps To Cylinder Block	90
	Crankshaft Sensor To Front Cover	22
	Crankshaft Sensor Clamp Bolt	40③
	Cylinder Block Drain Plug	25
	Cylinder Head Bolts	②
	Engine Mount Bracket To Cylinder Block	44
	Engine Mount To Cylinder Block	70
	Engine Mount To Frame	33
	Engine Mount To Engine Mount Bracket	33
	ESC Knock Sensor To Cylinder Block	13
	Exhaust Manifold To Cylinder Head	30
	Flywheel Cover To Transaxle	48③
	Flywheel To Crankshaft	61
	Front Cover To Block	22
	Fuel Feed & Return Pipes To Fuel Rail	22
	Fuel Rail To Intake Manifold	11
	Heater Hose Pipe To Throttle Body	20
	Ignition Module To Alternator Support	18
	Intake Manifold To Cylinder Head	②
	Oil Filter Adapter To Front Cover	24
	Oil Filter Assembly To Filter Adapter	18
1992–93 —Cont'd	Oil Galley Plugs	25
	Oil Pan Drain Plug	30
	Oil Pan To Cylinder Block	10.3
	Oil Pan To Front Cover	10.3
	Oil Pressure Switch To Oil Filter Adapter	24
	Oil Pump Cover To Timing Chain Cover	8
	Oil Screen Housing To Cylinder Block	9.5
	Oxygen Sensor To Exhaust Manifold	31
	Rocker Arm Cover To Cylinder Head	7.3
	Rocker Arm Pedestal To Cylinder Head	28
	Serpentine Belt Tensioner To Cylinder Head	37
	Spark Plug	20
	Starting Motor To Cylinder Block	35
	Strut Bracket To Manifold Studs	24
	Strut Bracket To Cylinder Head	37
	Thermostat Housing To Intake Manifold	20
	Throttle Body To Intake Manifold	20
	Throttle Cable Bracket To Throttle Body	36③
	Timing Chain Dampener	14
	Torque Converter To Flywheel	46
	Transaxle To Cylinder Block	46
	Vacuum Harness To Intake Manifold	9.5
	Valve Lifter Guide Retainer Bolts	27
	Water Pump To Front Cover	7
	Water Pump Pulley To Hub	9.5

①—20 ft. lbs., plus an additional 1/2 turn.
②—Refer to text.
③—Inch lbs.

Rear Axle & Suspension

NOTE: On Air Bag Equipped Models, Refer To "Air Bag System Precautions" Located In The Front Of This Manual For System Disarming & Arming Procedures.

INDEX

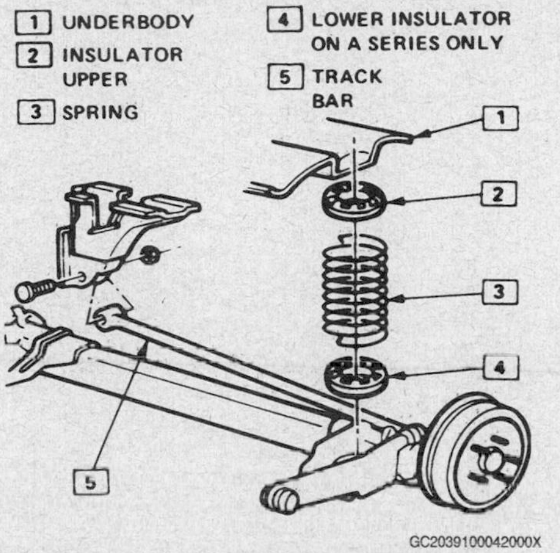

1 UNDERBODY
2 INSULATOR UPPER
3 SPRING
4 LOWER INSULATOR ON A SERIES ONLY
5 TRACK BAR
1
2
3
4
5
GC2039100042000X

Fig. 1 Rear axle & suspension

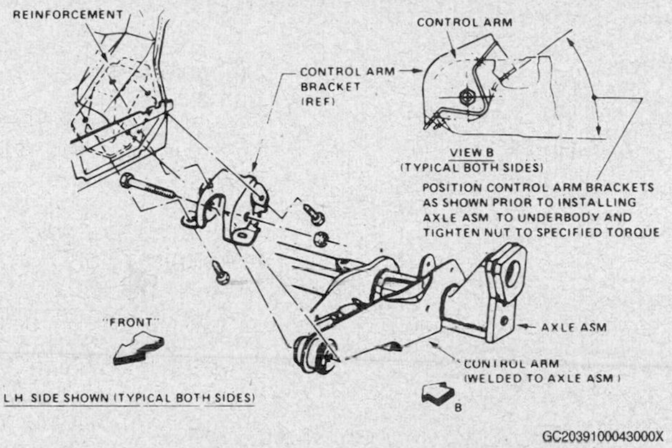

REINFORCEMENT
CONTROL ARM
CONTROL ARM BRACKET (REF)
VIEW B (TYPICAL BOTH SIDES)
POSITION CONTROL ARM BRACKETS AS SHOWN PRIOR TO INSTALLING AXLE ASM TO UNDERBODY AND TIGHTEN NUT TO SPECIFIED TORQUE
"FRONT"
AXLE ASM
CONTROL ARM (WELDED TO AXLE ASM)
L.H. SIDE SHOWN (TYPICAL BOTH SIDES)
B
GC2039100043000X

Fig. 2 Control arm bracket installation

PRECAUTIONS

AIR BAG SYSTEMS

Refer to "Air Bag System Precautions" in the front of this manual for system disarming and arming procedures.

DESCRIPTION

The rear suspension, **Fig. 1,** consists of a rear axle assembly, control arms, coil springs, shock absorbers, track bar and a track bar brace. The rear axle is trailing arm type design. A non-serviceable stabilizer bar is welded to the inside of the axle housing and is an integral part of the axle assembly. A single unit hub and bearing assembly is bolted to each end of the axle assembly. The hub and bearing assembly is a sealed unit and must be replaced as an assembly.

REAR AXLE

REPLACE

When removing rear axle assembly, do not use twin-post type hoist. The swing arc tendency of this axle may cause it to slip from hoist. Perform axle removal on floor if necessary.

1. Raise rear of vehicle and support rear axle using a jack.
2. Remove rear wheel assembly and brake drum. **Do not hammer on brake drum since damage to bearings may result.**
3. Disconnect parking brake cable from equalizer, then remove brake line brackets from frame.
4. Disconnect shock absorber from lower mountings on axle housing.
5. Remove track bar attaching nut and bolt, then disconnect track bar. **Do not suspend rear axle by brake hoses, otherwise damage to hoses may result.**
6. Carefully lower rear axle assembly, then remove coil spring and insulators.
7. Disconnect brake lines from control arm attachments.
8. Remove parking brake cable from rear axle attachments.
9. Remove hub attaching bolts, then the hub and bearing assembly. Position backing plate out of way.
10. Remove control arm bracket to underbody attaching bolts (four each side), then lower axle assembly and remove from vehicle.
11. Reverse procedure to install, noting the following:
    a. If control arm brackets were removed from control arms, install control arm bracket at a 40-44° angle as shown in **Fig. 2.**
    b. Tighten all bolts/nuts to specifications.

HUB & BEARING

REPLACE

1. Raise and support rear of vehicle, then remove wheel and tire assembly and brake drum. **Do not hammer on brake drum since damage to bearing may result.**
2. Remove hub and bearing assembly attaching bolts, then hub and bearing assembly. Do not support brake assembly by brake line.
3. Reverse procedure to install. Tighten to specifications.

SHOCK ABSORBER

REPLACE

1. Open deck lid and remove trim cover, then remove shock absorber upper attaching nut.
2. Raise rear of vehicle and support rear axle using a jack.
3. Disconnect shock absorber from lower attachment and remove shock absorber from vehicle.
4. Reverse procedure to install. Tighten to specifications.

COIL SPRING

REPLACE

1. Raise rear of vehicle and support rear axle using a jack.
2. Remove right and left brake line bracket attaching bolts from frame and allow brake lines to hang freely.
3. Remove track bar attaching nut and bolt at rear axle, then disconnect track bar.
4. Disconnect shock absorbers at lower mountings. **Do not suspend rear axle by brake hoses since damage to hoses may result.**
5. Carefully lower rear axle assembly,

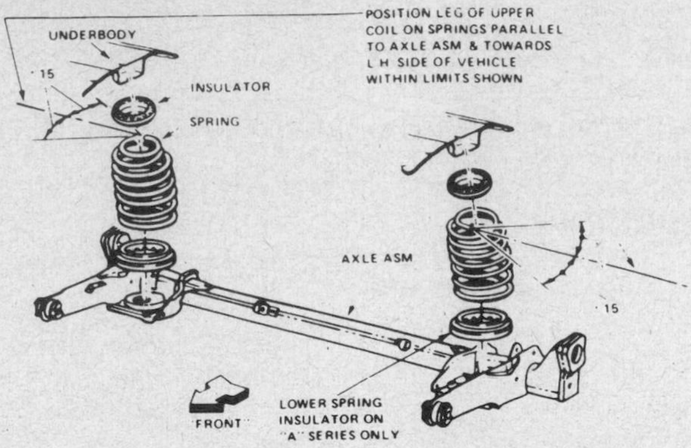
UNDERBODY
POSITION LEG OF UPPER COIL ON SPRINGS PARALLEL TO AXLE ASM & TOWARDS L H SIDE OF VEHICLE WITHIN LIMITS SHOWN
15
INSULATOR
SPRING
AXLE ASM
15
FRONT
LOWER SPRING INSULATOR ON "A" SERIES ONLY

GC2039100044000X

Fig. 3 Coil spring & insulator installation

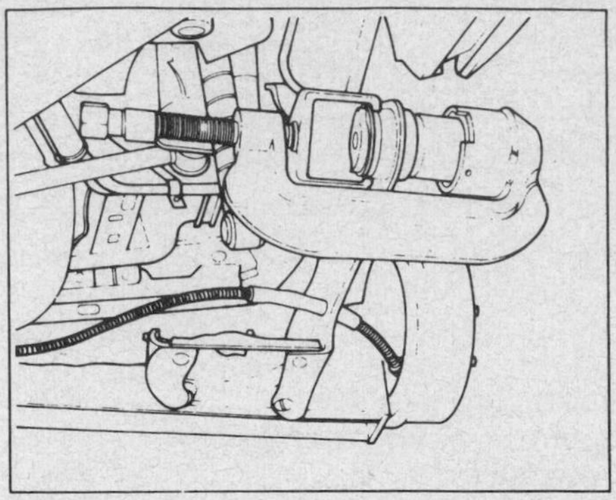

GC2039100045000X

Fig. 4 Control arm bushing removal

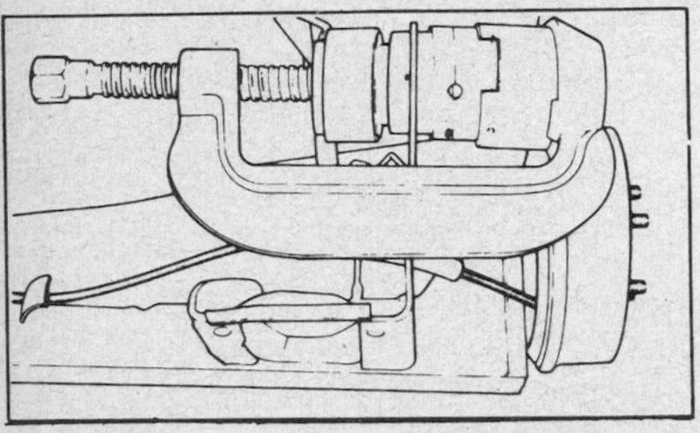

GC2039100046000X

Fig. 5 Control arm bushing installation

then remove springs and insulators.

6. Reverse procedure to install, as shown in **Fig. 3.**

CONTROL ARM BUSHING
REPLACE

1. Raise rear of vehicle and support rear axle under front side of spring seat using a jack.
2. If right hand side bushing is to be replaced, disconnect parking brake cable from equalizer.
3. Remove parking brake cables from bracket attachment, then position out of way.
4. Disconnect brake line bracket from frame.
5. Disconnect shock absorber from lower mounting, then pull spring out of way.
6. Remove four control arm to underbody attaching bolts, then allow control arm to rotate downward.
7. Remove nut and bolt from bracket attachment, then remove bracket.
8. The bushing can now be replaced using tools shown in **Figs. 4 and 5.** When installing bushing, the cutouts on rubber portion of bushing must face front and rear of vehicle. Press bushing in until end of bushing is aligned with scribed line on tool No. J-28685-2, **Fig. 5.**
9. Reverse procedure to install control arm. Install bracket to control arm as shown in **Fig. 2.**

TRACK ROD
REPLACE

1. Raise rear of vehicle and support rear axle using a jack.
2. Remove nut and bolt attaching track bar to axle housing and underbody, then remove track bar, **Fig. 6.**

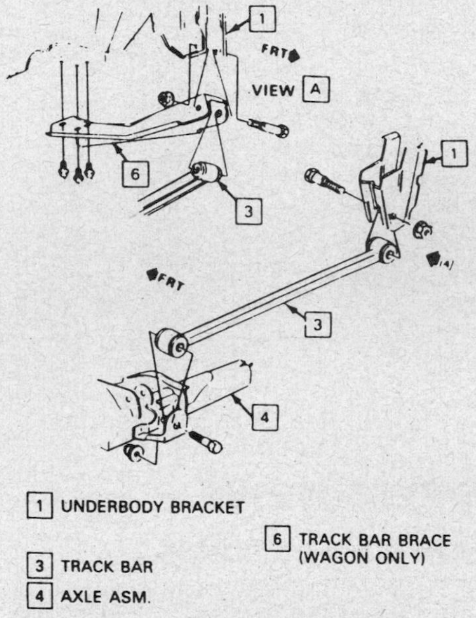
1
FRT
VIEW A
1
6
3
FRT
3
4
1 UNDERBODY BRACKET
3 TRACK BAR
4 AXLE ASM.
6 TRACK BAR BRACE (WAGON ONLY)

GC2039100047000X

Fig. 6 Track bar removal

3. Reverse procedure to install. Tighten to specifications.

TIGHTENING SPECIFICATIONS

Year	Component	Torque/Ft. Lbs.
1992–95	Brake Line Bracket Screw	8
	Control Arm Bracket To Underbody	28
	Control Arm To Bracket Nut	84
	Hub & Bearing Assembly Bolts	44
	Shock Absorber Lower Nut	44
	Shock Absorber Mount To Body	16
	Shock Absorber Upper Nut	16
	Track Bar Bolt At Axle	44
	Track Bar Nut At Brace Or Underbody Bracket	35
	Wheel Lug Nuts	92

Front Suspension & Steering

NOTE: On Air Bag Equipped Models, Refer To "Air Bag System Precautions" Located In The Front Of This Manual For System Disarming & Arming Procedures.

INDEX

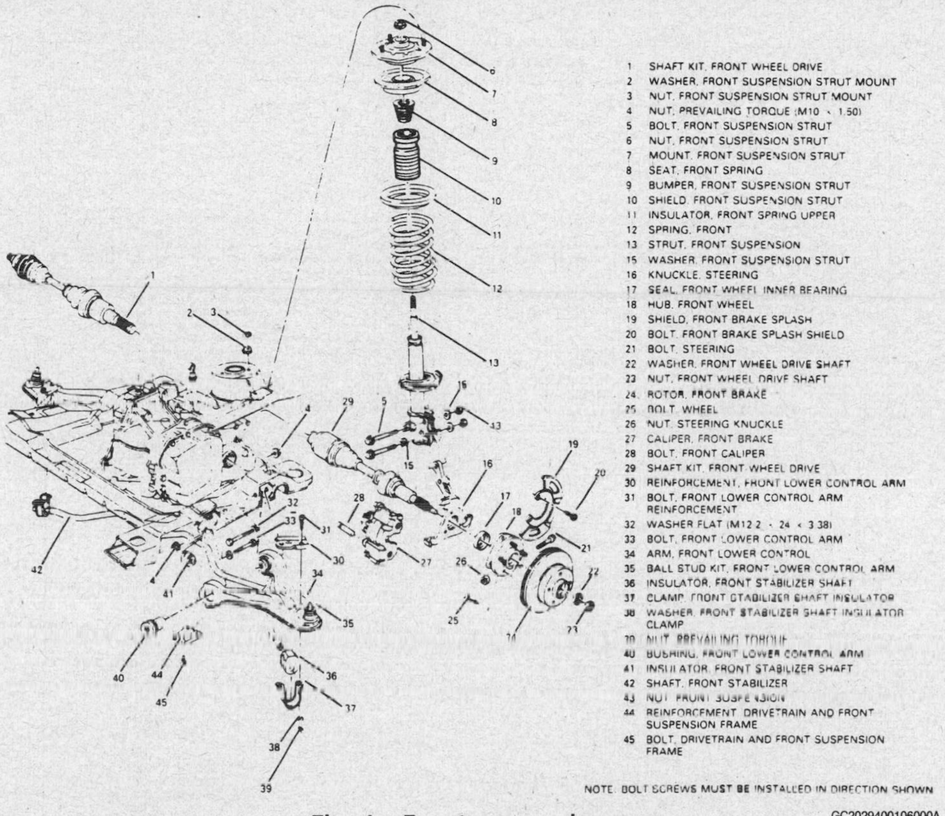

1 SHAFT KIT, FRONT WHEEL DRIVE
2 WASHER, FRONT SUSPENSION STRUT MOUNT
3 NUT, FRONT SUSPENSION STRUT MOUNT
4 NUT, PREVAILING TORQUE (M10 × 1.50)
5 BOLT, FRONT SUSPENSION STRUT
6 NUT, FRONT SUSPENSION STRUT
7 MOUNT, FRONT SUSPENSION STRUT
8 SEAT, FRONT SPRING
9 BUMPER, FRONT SUSPENSION STRUT
10 SHIELD, FRONT SUSPENSION STRUT
11 INSULATOR, FRONT SPRING UPPER
12 SPRING, FRONT
13 STRUT, FRONT SUSPENSION
15 WASHER, FRONT SUSPENSION STRUT
16 KNUCKLE, STEERING
17 SEAL, FRONT WHEEL INNER BEARING
18 HUB, FRONT WHEEL
19 SHIELD, FRONT BRAKE SPLASH
20 BOLT, FRONT BRAKE SPLASH SHIELD
21 BOLT, STEERING
22 WASHER, FRONT WHEEL DRIVE SHAFT
23 NUT, FRONT WHEEL DRIVE SHAFT
24 ROTOR, FRONT BRAKE
25 BOLT, WHEEL
26 NUT, STEERING KNUCKLE
27 CALIPER, FRONT BRAKE
28 BOLT, FRONT CALIPER
29 SHAFT KIT, FRONT WHEEL DRIVE
30 REINFORCEMENT, FRONT LOWER CONTROL ARM
31 BOLT, FRONT LOWER CONTROL ARM REINFORCEMENT
32 WASHER FLAT (M12.2 × 24 × 3.38)
33 BOLT, FRONT LOWER CONTROL ARM
34 ARM, FRONT LOWER CONTROL
35 BALL STUD KIT, FRONT LOWER CONTROL ARM
36 INSULATOR, FRONT STABILIZER SHAFT
38 WASHER, FRONT STABILIZER SHAFT INSULATOR CLAMP
40 BUSHING, FRONT LOWER CONTROL ARM
41 INSULATOR, FRONT STABILIZER SHAFT
42 SHAFT, FRONT STABILIZER
44 REINFORCEMENT, DRIVETRAIN AND FRONT SUSPENSION FRAME
45 BOLT, DRIVETRAIN AND FRONT SUSPENSION FRAME
NOTE: BOLT SCREWS MUST BE INSTALLED IN DIRECTION SHOWN
GC2029400106000A

Fig. 1 Front suspension

PRECAUTIONS

AIR BAG SYSTEMS

Refer to "Air Bag System Precautions" in the front of this manual for system disarming and arming procedures.

DESCRIPTION

The front suspension, **Fig. 1**, on these vehicles is a McPherson strut design. The lower control arms pivot from the engine cradle. This engine cradle has isolation mounts to the body and conventional rubber bushings are used for the lower control arm pivots. The upper end of the strut is isolated by a rubber mount incorporating a bearing for wheel turning. The lower end of the steering knuckle pivots on a ball stud which is retained in the lower control arm with rivets and is clamped to the steering knuckle. Sealed wheel bearings are used and are bolted to the steering knuckle.

HUB, BEARING & SEAL

REPLACE

Hub and bearing are replaced as an assembly. Refer to **Fig. 1** during service procedure.

1. Loosen hub nut with vehicle on ground.
2. Raise and support vehicle, then remove front wheel.
3. Install drive axle seal protectors. **These protectors should be used any time service is performed on or near drive axle. Failure to use them may result in interior joint or seal damage.**
4. Remove, then discard hub nut and washer.
5. Remove brake caliper from support and suspend caliper from frame with a length of wire. **Do not suspend caliper by the brake hose.** Remove rotor.
6. Using tool No. J-28733, or equivalent, separate hub and drive axle.
7. Remove hub and bearing attaching bolts, then shield, hub and bearing assembly and O-ring.
8. To remove factory seal, tap seal toward engine. When seal is removed from steering knuckle, cut it off drive axle using side cutters. **Factory seal is installed from engine side of steering knuckle. Replacement seal is installed from wheel side of steering knuckle.**
9. Reverse procedure to install, noting the following:
   a. Lubricate seal, then install using seal installer No. J-28671 or equivalent.
   b. Tighten bolts/nuts to specifications.

BALL JOINT INSPECTION

1. Raise and support front of vehicle allowing suspension to hang free.
2. Grasp tire at the top and bottom, then move top of tire in an in-and-out motion.
3. Check for any horizontal movement of the knuckle relative to the control arm.
4. If any movement or looseness is detected in the joint or if the joint seal is cut, the ball joint must be replaced.

BALL JOINT

REPLACE

1. Raise and support vehicle, then place jack stands under suspension.
2. Lower vehicle slightly so weight of vehicle rests on jack stands, then remove wheel assembly.
3. Install drive axle seal protectors. **These protectors should be used any time service is performed on or near drive axle. Failure to use them may result in interior joint or seal damage.**
4. Remove pinch bolt, then ball joint from steering knuckle.
5. Drill out three rivets retaining ball joint. Use a 1/8 inch drill to make a pilot hole through rivets. Finish drilling rivets with 1/2 inch drill bit.
6. Loosen stabilizer shaft bushing assembly nut, then remove ball joint from control arm.
7. Reverse procedure to install. Tighten to specifications.

STRUT

REPLACE

1. Remove strut top attaching nuts, then raise and support vehicle.
2. Place jack stands under suspension support, the lower vehicle slightly so weight of vehicle rests on jack stands.
3. Remove wheel assemblies, then install drive axle seal protectors.
4. Disconnect front wheel sensor, if equipped w/anti-lock brakes.
5. Remove brake line bracket from strut assembly, then strut to steering knuckle attaching bolts.
6. Remove strut from vehicle, **Fig. 2.**
7. Reverse procedure to install. Tighten to specifications.

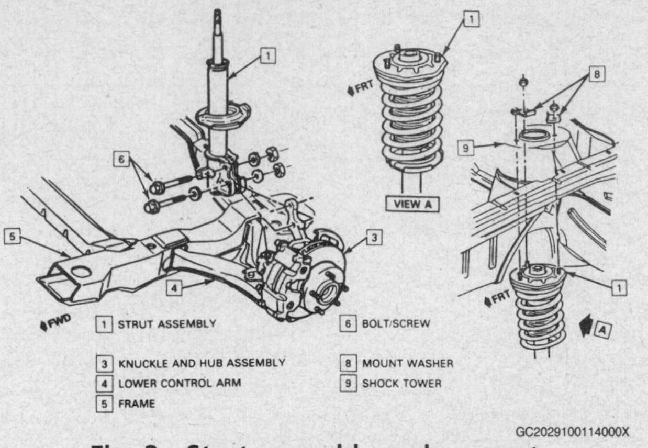
FRT
VIEW A
FWD
1 STRUT ASSEMBLY
3 KNUCKLE AND HUB ASSEMBLY
4 LOWER CONTROL ARM
5 FRAME
6 BOLT/SCREW
8 MOUNT WASHER
9 SHOCK TOWER
A
GC2029100114000X

Fig. 2 Strut assembly replacement

STRUT SERVICE

Refer to **Fig. 3** for strut assembly service.

CONTROL ARM

REPLACE

1. Raise and support vehicle, then place jack stands under suspension.
2. Lower vehicle slightly so weight of vehicle rests on jack stands, then remove wheel assembly.
3. Install drive axle seal protectors. **These protectors should be used any time service is performed on or near drive axle. Failure to use them may result in interior joint or seal damage.**
4. Remove pinch bolt holding ball joint to steering knuckle, then control arm mounting bolts.
5. Remove control arm from vehicle, **Fig. 4.**
6. Refer to **Fig. 5** for bushing replacement procedure.
7. Reverse procedure to install, noting the following:
   a. Weight of vehicle must be supported by control arms when tightening control arm mounting nuts.
   b. Tighten bolts/nuts to specifications.

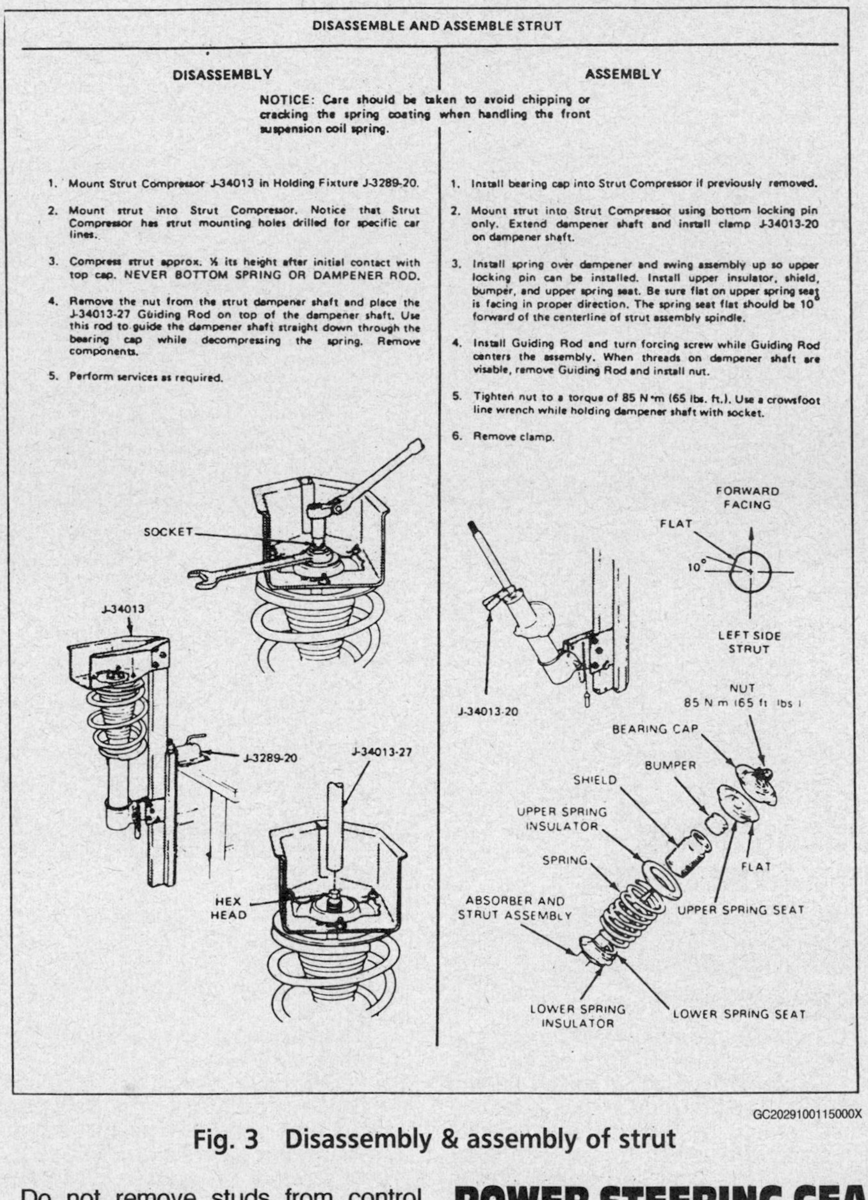
DISASSEMBLE AND ASSEMBLE STRUT
DISASSEMBLY
ASSEMBLY
NOTICE: Care should be taken to avoid chipping or cracking the spring coating when handling the front suspension coil spring.
1. Mount Strut Compressor J-34013 in Holding Fixture J-3289-20.
2. Mount strut into Strut Compressor. Notice that Strut Compressor has strut mounting holes drilled for specific car lines.
3. Compress strut approx. ½ its height after initial contact with top cap. NEVER BOTTOM SPRING OR DAMPENER ROD.
4. Remove the nut from the strut dampener shaft and place the J-34013-27 Guiding Rod on top of the dampener shaft. Use this rod to guide the dampener shaft straight down through the bearing cap while decompressing the spring. Remove components.
5. Perform services as required.
1. Install bearing cap into Strut Compressor if previously removed.
2. Mount strut into Strut Compressor using bottom locking pin only. Extend dampener shaft and install clamp J-34013-20 on dampener shaft.
3. Install spring over dampener and swing assembly up so upper locking pin can be installed. Install upper insulator, shield, bumper, and upper spring seat. Be sure flat on upper spring seat is facing in proper direction. The spring seat flat should be 10° forward of the centerline of strut assembly spindle.
4. Install Guiding Rod and turn forcing screw while Guiding Rod centers the assembly. When threads on dampener shaft are visable, remove Guiding Rod and install nut.
5. Tighten nut to a torque of 85 N·m (65 lbs. ft.). Use a crowsfoot line wrench while holding dampener shaft with socket.
6. Remove clamp.
SOCKET
J-34013
J-3289-20
J-34013-27
HEX HEAD
FORWARD FACING
FLAT
10°
LEFT SIDE STRUT
NUT
85 N m (65 ft lbs)
J-34013-20
BEARING CAP
BUMPER
SHIELD
UPPER SPRING INSULATOR
SPRING
FLAT
ABSORBER AND STRUT ASSEMBLY
UPPER SPRING SEAT
LOWER SPRING INSULATOR
LOWER SPRING SEAT
GC2029100115000X

Fig. 3 Disassembly & assembly of strut

CONTROL ARM BUSHING

REPLACE

Refer to "Control Arm, Replace" for procedure.

STEERING KNUCKLE

REPLACE

For removal and installation procedures, refer to **Fig. 6.**

STABILIZER BAR BUSHING

REPLACE

1. Raise and support vehicle.
2. Remove stabilizer shaft insulator clamp and insulator at control arms. Do not remove studs from control arms.
3. Remove plates from frame, then stabilizer bar and insulator bushings, **Fig. 7.**
4. Reverse procedure to install. Tighten to specifications.

POWER STEERING GEAR

REPLACE

1. Install engine support fixture No. J-28467-A or equivalent.
2. Raise and support vehicle, then remove both front wheel assemblies.

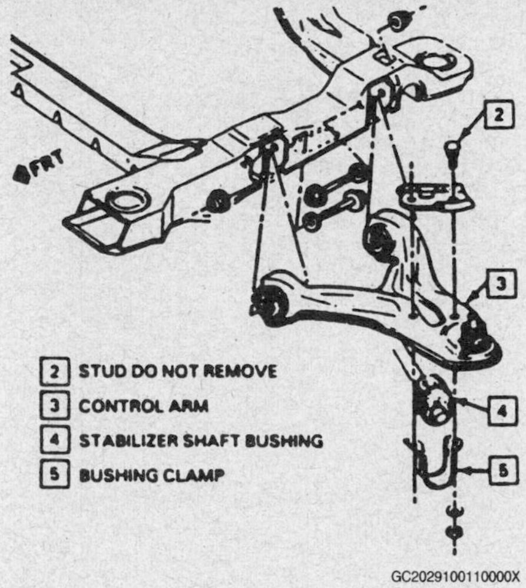
FRT
2 STUD DO NOT REMOVE
3 CONTROL ARM
4 STABILIZER SHAFT BUSHING
5 BUSHING CLAMP
GC2029100110000X

Fig. 4 Control arm replacement

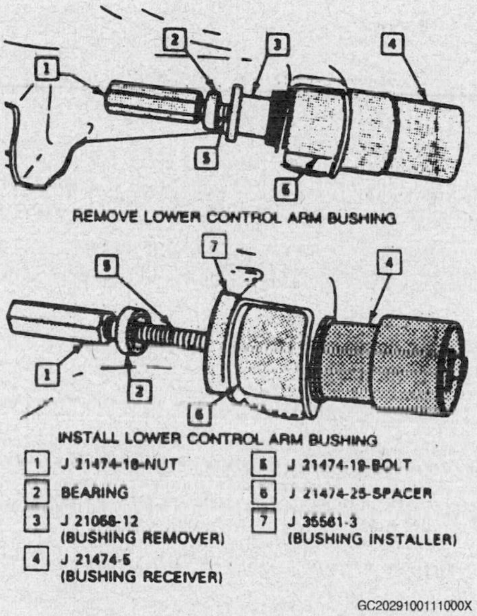
REMOVE LOWER CONTROL ARM BUSHING
INSTALL LOWER CONTROL ARM BUSHING
1 J 21474-18-NUT
2 BEARING
3 J 21058-12 (BUSHING REMOVER)
4 J 21474-5 (BUSHING RECEIVER)
5 J 21474-19-BOLT
6 J 21474-25-SPACER
7 J 35561-3 (BUSHING INSTALLER)
GC2029100111000X

Fig. 5 Control arm bushing replacement

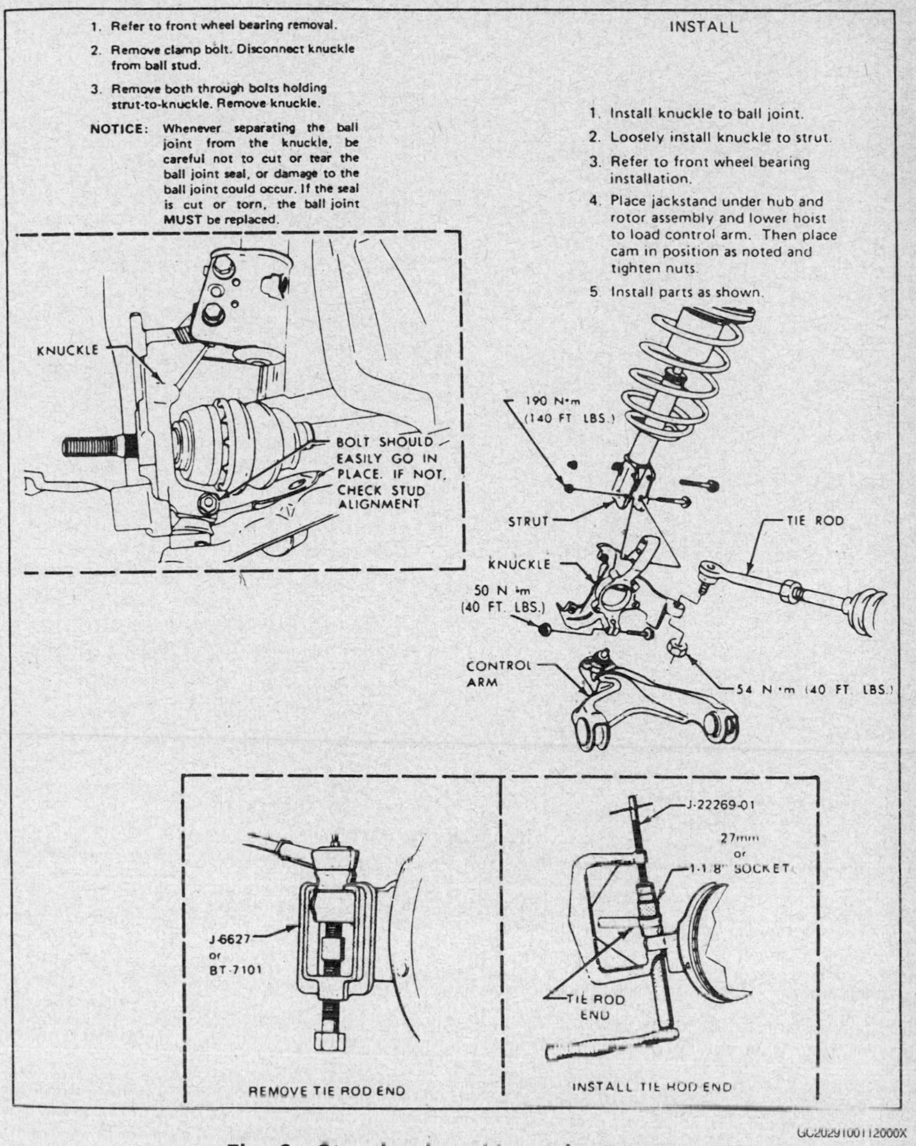
1. Refer to front wheel bearing removal.
2. Remove clamp bolt. Disconnect knuckle from ball stud.
3. Remove both through bolts holding strut-to-knuckle. Remove knuckle.
NOTICE: Whenever separating the ball joint from the knuckle, be careful not to cut or tear the ball joint seal, or damage to the ball joint could occur. If the seal is cut or torn, the ball joint MUST be replaced.
KNUCKLE
BOLT SHOULD EASILY GO IN PLACE. IF NOT, CHECK STUD ALIGNMENT
INSTALL
1. Install knuckle to ball joint.
2. Loosely install knuckle to strut.
3. Refer to front wheel bearing installation.
4. Place jackstand under hub and rotor assembly and lower hoist to load control arm. Then place cam in position as noted and tighten nuts.
5. Install parts as shown.
190 N·m (140 FT. LBS.)
STRUT
TIE ROD
KNUCKLE
50 N·m (40 FT. LBS.)
CONTROL ARM
54 N·m (40 FT. LBS.)
J-6627 or BT-7101
REMOVE TIE ROD END
J-22269-01
27mm or 1-1/8" SOCKET
TIE ROD END
INSTALL TIE ROD END
GC2029100112000X

Fig. 6 Steering knuckle replacement

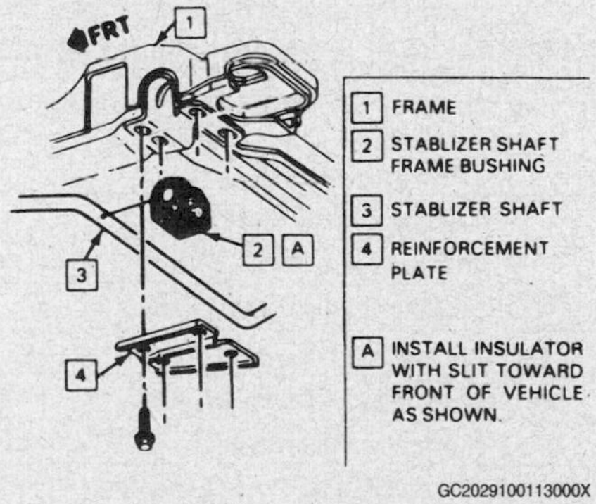
FRT
1 FRAME
2 STABLIZER SHAFT FRAME BUSHING
3 STABLIZER SHAFT
4 REINFORCEMENT PLATE
A INSTALL INSULATOR WITH SLIT TOWARD FRONT OF VEHICLE AS SHOWN.
GC2029100113000X

Fig. 7 Stabilizer bar replacement

3. Remove intermediate shaft lower pinch bolt, then intermediate shaft from stub shaft.
4. Disconnect tie rod ends from steering knuckles.
5. If equipped, remove brake line retaining bolts from heat shield, then heat shield.
6. Support engine frame at rear with jack stand, then remove engine mounts to frame attaching bolts.
7. Remove rear engine frame retaining bolts, then loosen front engine retaining bolts. **Do not remove front engine retaining bolts.**
8. Lower engine frame at rear 4 to 5 inches. **Do not lower frame more than specified, as damage to engine components may result.**
9. Remove steering gear heat shield, then line retaining clip from steering gear.
10. Disconnect and cap pump lines at steering gear.
11. Remove steering gear assembly mounting bolts, **Fig. 8**, then steering gear assembly through left wheel opening.
12. Reverse procedure to install. Tighten to specifications.

POWER STEERING PUMP

REPLACE

1. Remove serpentine drive belt from pulley, then disconnect power steering lines at pump.
2. Remove pump retaining bolts, then pump, **Figs. 9 through 12.**
3. Reverse procedure to install. Tighten to specifications.

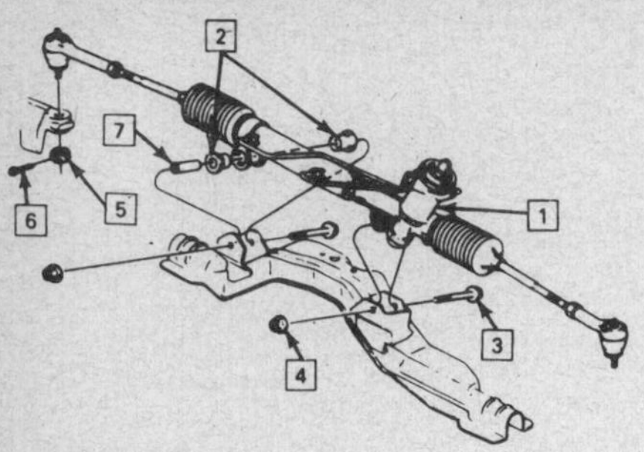

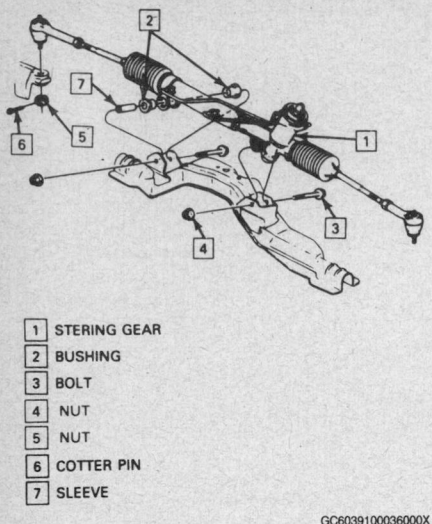

1 STERING GEAR
2 BUSHING
3 BOLT
4 NUT
5 NUT
6 COTTER PIN
7 SLEEVE

GC6039100036000X

Fig. 8 Steering gear replacement

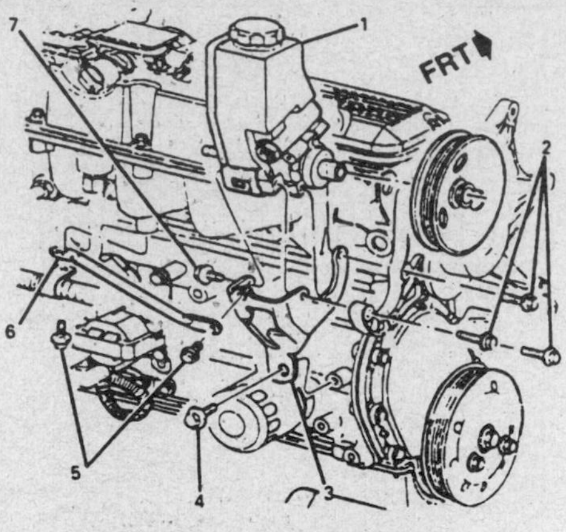
FRT

1 PUMP ASSEMBLY, POWER STEERING
2 BOLT/SCREW, POWER STEERING PUMP
3 BRACKET ASSEMBLY, POWER STEERING PUMP
4 BOLT/SCREW, POWER STEERING PUMP BRACKET
5 BOLT/SCREW, POWER STEERING PUMP BRACE
6 BRACE, POWER STEERING PUMP BRACKET
7 BOLT/SCREW, POWER STEERING PUMP BRACKET

GC6039100037000X

Fig. 9 Power steering pump replacement. 2.2L/4-134 engine

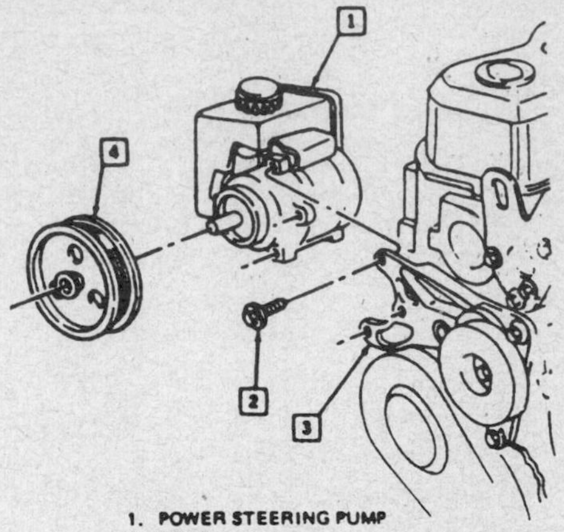

1. POWER STEERING PUMP
2. BOLT
3. TENSIONER ASSY.
4. PULLEY

GC6039100038000X

Fig. 10 Power steering pump replacement. 2.5L/4-151 engine

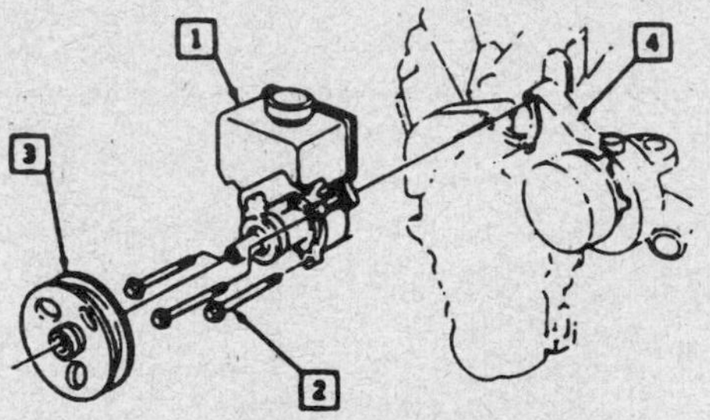

1. POWER STEERING PUMP
2. BOLT
3. PULLEY
4. COVER

GC6039100039000X

Fig. 11 Power steering pump replacement. 3.1L/V6-189 engine

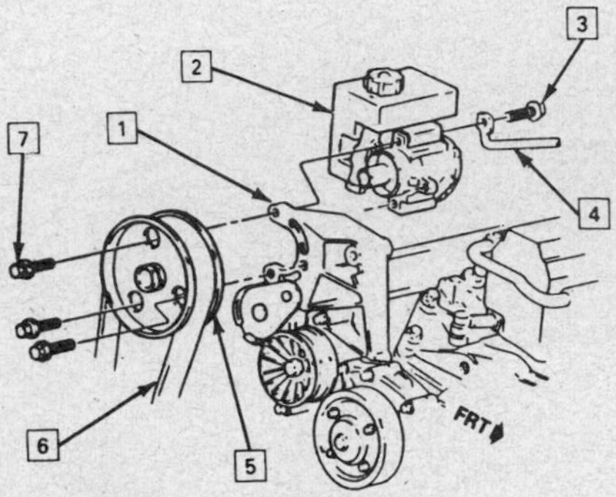
FRT

1 BELT TENSIONER ASM.
2 POWER STEERING PUMP
3 BOLT/SCREW
4 BELT TENSIONER BRACE
5 PULLEY
6 ACCESSORY DRIVE BELT
7 BOLT

GC6039100040000X

Fig. 12 Power steering pump replacement. 3.3L/V6-204 engine

TIGHTENING SPECIFICATIONS

Year	Component	Torque/Ft. Lbs.
1992–95	Ball Joint Pinch Bolt Nut	33
	Brake Line Bracket Bolt	13
	Control Arm Pivot Bolt Nut	61
	Caliper Bolt	38
	Hub & Bearing Retaining Bolt	①
	Insulator Clamp Nut	33
	Reinforcement Plate To Frame Bolt	40
	Stabilizer Shaft Bushing Clamp Nut	33
	Steering Knuckle To Strut Assembly Bolt	140
	Strut Assembly To Body Nut	18
	Strut Dampener Shaft Nut	65
	Wheel Lug Nut	92

①—Standard brakes, 63 ft. lbs.; heavy duty brakes, 70 ft. lbs.

Wheel Alignment

NOTE: On Air Bag Equipped Models, Refer To "Air Bag System Precautions" Located In The Front Of This Manual For System Disarming & Arming Procedures.

INDEX

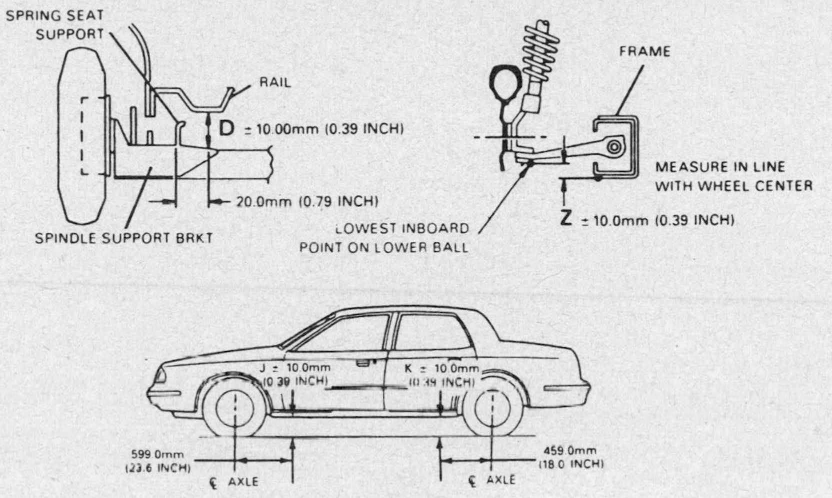

SPRING SEAT SUPPORT
RAIL
D ± 10.00mm (0.39 INCH)
20.0mm (0.79 INCH)
SPINDLE SUPPORT BRKT
FRAME
MEASURE IN LINE WITH WHEEL CENTER
Z ± 10.0mm (0.39 INCH)
LOWEST INBOARD POINT ON LOWER BALL
J ± 10.0mm (0.39 INCH)
K ± 10.0mm (0.39 INCH)
599.0mm (23.6 INCH)
℄ AXLE
459.0mm (18.0 INCH)
℄ AXLE

GC2049400052000A

Fig. 1 Measurement point locations

MODEL	SUSPENSION	TIRE SIZE	Z (CURB)	D (CURB)	J (CURB)	K (CURB)
WAGON	FE1	P185-75R14	−1mm (−.04 IN.)	191mm (7.52 IN.)	236mm (9.29 IN.)	240mm (9.44 IN.)
WAGON	FE1	P195-75R14	−1mm (−.04 IN.)	191mm (7.52 IN.)	242mm (9.53 IN.)	246mm (9.69 IN.)
COUPE	FE1	P185-75R14	−1mm (−.04 IN.)	191mm (7.52 IN.)	236mm (9.29 IN.)	242mm (9.53 IN.)
SEDAN	FE1	P185-75R14	−1mm (−.04 IN.)	191mm (7.52 IN.)	236mm (9.29 IN.)	242mm (9.53 IN.)
SEDAN	F41	P195-75R14	−1mm (−.04 IN.)	191mm (7.52 IN.)	243mm (9.57 IN.)	249mm (9.80 IN.)

GC2049100053000X

Fig. 2 Vehicle ride height specifications. Century

MODEL	SUSPENSION	TIRE SIZE	Z (CURB)	D (CURB)	J (CURB)	K (CURB)
WAGON	FE1	P185-75R14	−1mm (−.04 IN.)	191mm (7.52 IN.)	234mm (9.21 IN.)	238mm (9.37 IN.)
WAGON	FE1	P195-75R14	−1mm (−.04 IN.)	191mm (7.52 IN.)	234mm (9.21 IN.)	246mm (9.68 IN.)
WAGON	FE1	P195-70R14	−1mm (−.04 IN.)	191mm (7.52 IN.)	232mm (9.13 IN.)	237mm (9.33 IN.)
COUPE/SEDAN	FE1	P185-75R14	−1mm (−.04 IN.)	191mm (7.52 IN.)	234mm (9.21 IN.)	240mm (9.45 IN.)
COUPE/SEDAN	FE1	P195-75R14	−1mm (−.04 IN.)	191mm (7.52 IN.)	241mm (9.48 IN.)	247mm (9.72 IN.)
COUPE/SEDAN	FE1	P195-70R14	−1mm (−.04 IN.)	191mm (7.52 IN.)	232mm (9.13 IN.)	238mm (9.68 IN.)
SEDAN	FE3	P195-75R14	−1mm (−.04 IN.)	191mm (7.52 IN.)	241mm (9.48 IN.)	248mm (9.76 IN.)

GC2049100054000X

Fig. 3 Vehicle ride height specifications. 1992 Cutlass Ciera & Cruiser

PRECAUTIONS

AIR BAG SYSTEMS

Refer to "Air Bag System Precautions" in the front of this manual for system disarming and arming procedures.

FRONT WHEEL ALIGNMENT

CAMBER

The camber angle is adjusted by loosening the strut cam bolt and the through bolt, then rotating the cam bolt to move the upper portion of the steering knuckle inward or outward. When correct camber angle is obtained, **torque** cam and through bolts to 140 ft. lbs.

When performing this adjustment, the top through bolt must be loosened to prevent damage to the outer cam guide.

TOE-IN

Toe-in is controlled by tie rod position. Adjustment is made by loosening the nuts at the steering knuckle end of the tie rods and rotating the rods to obtain proper toe-in setting. When adjusting toe-in, the tie rod boot clamps must be removed. After correct toe-in setting is obtained, **torque** tie rod nuts to 45 ft. lbs.

VEHICLE RIDE HEIGHT

Refer to **Figs. 1 through 4,** for vehicle ride height specifications and measurement location points.

MODEL	SUSPENSION	TIRE SIZE	Z (CURB)	D (CURB)	J (CURB)	K (CURB)
WAGON	FE1	P185-75R14	– 1mm (– .04 IN.)	191mm (7.52 IN.)	239mm (9.41 IN.)	246mm (9.69 IN.)
WAGON	FE1	P195-75R14	– 1mm (– .04 IN.)	191mm (7.52 IN.)	245mm (9.65 IN.)	252mm (9.92 IN.)
SEDAN	FE1	P185-75R14	– 1mm (– 0.4 IN.)	191mm (7.52 IN.)	239mm (9.41 IN.)	247mm (9.72 IN.)
SEDAN	FE1	P195-75R14	– 1mm (– 0.4 IN.)	191mm (7.52 IN.)	245mm (9.65 IN.)	253mm (9.97 IN.)

GC2049300055000X

Fig. 4 Vehicle ride height specifications. 1993–95 Cutlass Ciera & Cruiser

BUICK LESABRE & PARK AVE., CADILLAC DEVILLE & FLEETWOOD (FWD), OLDSMOBILE EIGHTY EIGHT & NINETY EIGHT & PONTIAC BONNEVILLE (C & H Cars)

NOTE: Refer To The Rear Of This Manual For Vehicle Manufacturer's Special Service Tool Suppliers.

INDEX OF SERVICE OPERATIONS

NOTE: For Service Operations Not Listed Below, Refer To The Table Of Contents In The Front Of This Manual.

Continued

INDEX OF SERVICE OPERATIONS—CONTINUED

Specifications

GENERAL ENGINE SPECIFICATIONS

Year	Engine		Fuel System	Bore and Stroke	Compression Ratio	Net H.P. @ RPM②	Maximum Torque Ft. Lbs. @ RPM	Normal Oil Pressure Psi
	Liter/CID	VIN Code①						
1992	3800/V6-231	L	SFI⑦	3.80 x 3.40	8.5	170 @ 4800	220 @ 2000	60⑤
	3800/V6-231 ③	1	SFI⑦	3.80 x 3.40	8.5	205 @ 4400	260 @ 2800	60⑤
	4.9L/V8-300	B	SFI⑦	3.62 x 3.62	9.5	200 @ 4100	275 @ 3000	④
1993	3800/V6-231	L	SFI⑦	3.80 x 3.40	9.0	170 @ 4800	225 @ 3200	60⑤
	3800/V6-231 ③	1	SFI⑦	3.80 x 3.40	8.5	205 @ 4400	260 @ 2600	60⑤
	4.9L/V8-300	B	SFI⑦	3.62 x 3.62	9.5	200 @ 4100	275 @ 3000	④
1994	3800/V6-231	L	SFI⑦	3.80 x 3.40	9.0	170 @ 4800	225 @ 3200	60⑤
	3800/V6-231 ③	1	SFI⑦	3.80 x 3.40	8.5	205 @ 4400	260 @ 2600	60⑤
	4.6L/V8-279	Y	TPI⑧	3.66 x 3.31	10.3	270 @ 5600	300 @ 4000	⑥
	4.9L/V8-300	B	SFI⑦	3.62 x 3.62	9.5	200 @ 4100	275 @ 3000	④
1995	3800/V6-231	L	SFI⑦	3.80 x 3.40	9.0	170 @ 4800	225 @ 3200	60⑤
	3800/V6-231	K	SFI⑦	3.80 x 3.40	9.0	205 @ 5200	230 @ 4000	60⑤
	3800/V6-231 ③	1	SFI⑦	3.80 x 3.40	8.5	225 @ 5000	275 @ 3200	60⑤
	4.6L/V8-279	Y	TPI⑧	3.66 x 3.31	10.3	275 @ 5600	300 @ 4000	⑥
	4.9L/V8-300	B	SFI⑦	3.62 x 3.62	9.5	200 @ 4400	275 @ 3000	④

①—The eighth digit denotes engine code.
②—Ratings are net-as installed in vehicle.
③—Supercharged.
④—Minimum oil pressure at normal operating temperature, 11 psi. @ 2000 RPM.
⑤—At 1850 RPM using SAE 10W-30 motor oil.
⑥—Minimum oil pressure at normal operating remperature, 5 psi. @ idle; 35 psi. @ 2000 RPM.
⑦—Sequential Port Fuel Injection.
⑧—Tuned Port Fuel Injection.

TUNE UP SPECIFICATIONS

Year & Engine/VIN Code ①	Spark Plug Gap	Ignition Timing			Curb Idle Speed	Fast Idle Speed	Fuel Pump Pressure
		Firing Order Fig.②	°BTDC	Mark Fig.			
1992-93							
3800/V6-231/1	.060	⑥	⑦	⑧	③	③	40-47⑤
3800/V6-231/L	.060	⑥	⑦	⑧	③	③	40-47⑤
4.9L/V8-300/B	.060	A	10④	B	③	③	32-38⑨
1994							
3800/V6-231/1	.060	⑥	⑦	⑧	③	③	40-47⑤
3800/V6-231/L	.060	⑥	⑦	⑧	③	③	40-47⑤
4.6L/V8-279/Y	.050	⑩	10⑦	⑧	③	③	41-47⑤
4.9L/V8-300/B	.060	A	10④	B	③	③	32-38⑨
1995							
3800/V6-231/1	.060	⑥	⑦	⑧	③	③	41-47⑤
3800/V6-231/K	.060	⑥	⑦	⑧	③	③	48-55⑤
3800/V6-231/L	.060	⑥	⑦	⑧	③	③	41-47⑤
4.6L/V8-279/Y	.050	⑩	10⑦	⑧	③	③	41-47⑤
4.9L/V8-300/B	.060	A	10④	B	③	③	40-50⑤

BTDC—Before Top Dead Center

①—The eighth digit of the Vehicle Identification Number (VIN) denotes engine code.

②—Before removing wires from distributor cap, determine location of No. 1 wire in cap, as distributor position may have been altered from that shown at the end of this chart.

③—Idle speed is controlled by an idle speed control (ISC) motor or an idle air control (IAC) valve.

④—Connect jumper wire between ALCL connector terminals A & B. The ALCL connector is located under the instrument panel to the right of the steering column. After completing adjustment, disconnect jumper wire from between terminals A & B. With engine off, clear trouble code from Electronic Control Module (ECM) memory by removing battery voltage from ECM for 30 seconds.

⑤—With shop towel wrapped around fuel pressure valve to prevent fuel spillage, connect a suitable fuel pressure gauge to fuel pressure valve. Check fuel pressure with ignition switch in the On position, engine not running.

⑥—Cylinder numbering left to right as viewed from front of vehicle, front bank, 1, 3, 5; rear bank, 2, 4, 6. Firing order 1-6-5-4-3-2. Two different types computer controlled coil ignition systems are used. Refer to C. & D for spark plug wire connections at coil unit.

⑦—Computer controlled, no adjustment.

⑧—Equipped with crankshaft position sensor.

⑨—With shop towel wrapped around fitting to prevent spillage, connect a suitable fuel pressure gauge to fuel line service fitting. Check fuel pressure while cranking engine.

⑩—Cylinder numbering from left to right as viewed from front of vehicle, front bank, 2, 4, 6, 8; rear bank, 1, 3, 5, 7. Firing order 1-2-7-3-4-5-6-8. Refer to E for plug wire connections at the coil unit.

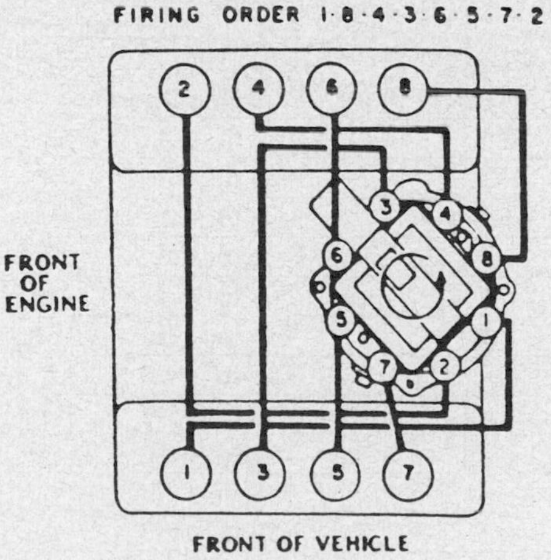
FIRING ORDER 1·8·4·3·6·5·7·2
FRONT OF ENGINE
FRONT OF VEHICLE

GC1139100127000X

Fig. A

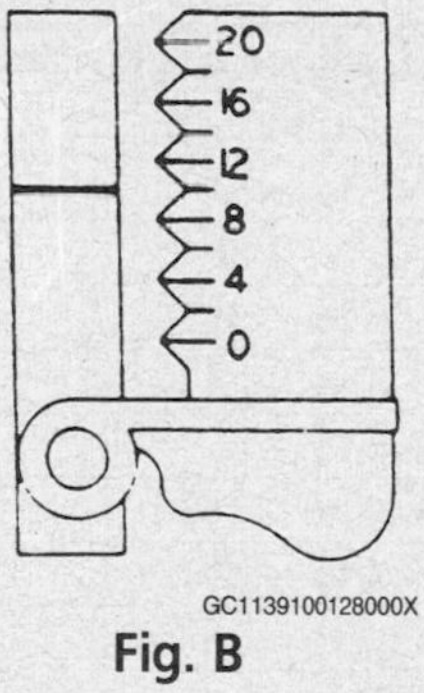
20
16
12
8
4
0

GC1139100128000X

Fig. B

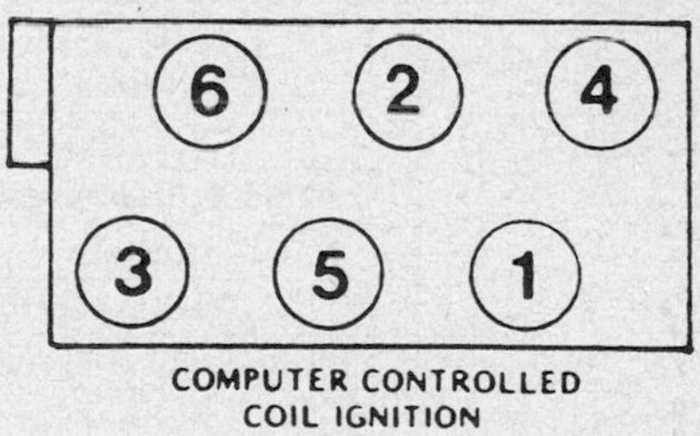
6
2
4
3
5
1
COMPUTER CONTROLLED
COIL IGNITION

GC1139100129000X

Fig. C

Continued

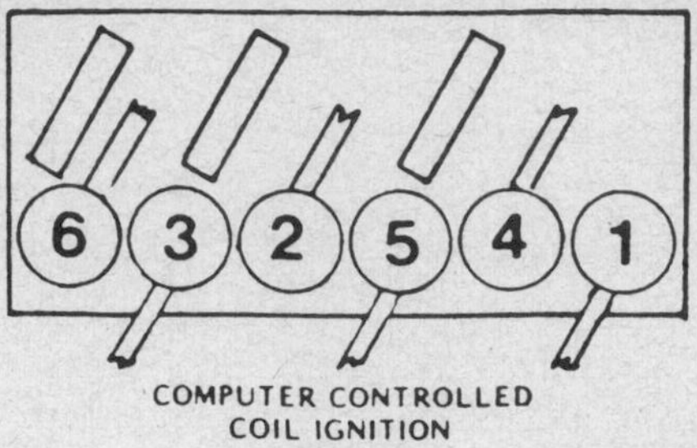
6
3
2
5
4
1
COMPUTER CONTROLLED
COIL IGNITION

GC1139100130000X

Fig. D

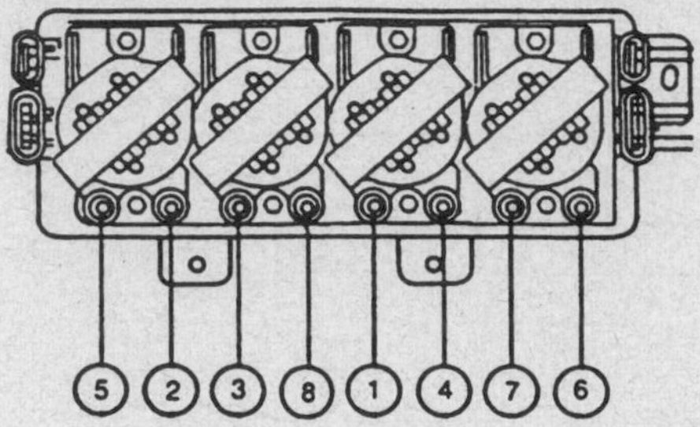
5
2
3
8
1
4
7
6

GC1139100131000X

Fig. E

FRONT WHEEL ALIGNMENT SPECIFICATIONS

Year	Model	Caster Angle, Degrees		Camber Angle, Degrees				Total Toe, Degree
				Limits		Desired		
		Limits	Desired	Left	Right	Left	Right	
1992	Bonneville	+2.5 to +3.5	+3	-.3 to +.7	-.3 to +.7	+.2	+.2	0
	DeVille & Fleetwood (FWD)	+2.5 to +3.5	+3	-1 to 0	0 to +1	-.5	+.5	0
	LeSabre	+2.5 to +3.5	+3	-.3 to +.7	-.3 to +.7	+.2	+.2	0
	Park Avenue	+2.5 to +3.5	+3	-.3 to +.7	-.3 to +.7	+.2	+.2	0
	Eighty-Eight & Ninety-Eight	+2.5 to +3.5	+3	-.3 to +.7	-.3 to +.7	+.2	+.2	0
1993	Bonneville	+2.5 to +3.5	+3	-.55 to +.95	-.3 to +.7	+.2	+.2	0
	DeVille & Sixty Special	+2.5 to +3.5	+3	-1 to 0	0 to +1	-.5	+.5	0
	LeSabre	+2.5 to +3.5	+3	-.55 to +.95	-.3 to +.7	+.2	+.2	0
	Park Avenue	+2.5 to +3.5	+3	-.55 to +.95	-.3 to +.7	+.2	+.2	0
	Eighty-Eight & Ninety-Eight	+2.5 to +3.5	+3	-.55 to +.95	-.3 to +.7	+.2	+.2	0
1994-95	Bonneville	+2.5 to +3.5	+3	-.55 to +.95	-.3 to +.7	+.2	+.2	0
	Concours	+2.5 to +3.5	+3	-1 to 0	0 to +1	-.5	+.5	0
	DeVille	+2.5 to +3.5	+3	-1 to 0	0 to +1	-.5	+.5	0
	LeSabre	+2.5 to +3.5	+3	-.55 to +.95	-.3 to +.7	+.2	+.2	0
	Park Avenue	+2.5 to +3.5	+3	-.55 to +.95	-.3 to +.7	+.2	+.2	0
	Eighty-Eight & Ninety-Eight	+2.5 to +3.5	+3	-.55 to +.95	-.3 to +.7	+.2	+.2	0

REAR WHEEL ALIGNMENT SPECIFICATIONS

Year	Model	Camber Angle, Degrees		Total Toe, Degrees	Thrust Angle, Degrees
		Limits	Desired		
1992	Bonneville	-.8 to +.2	-.3	+.1	-.1 to +.1
	DeVille & Fleetwood (FWD)	-.8 to +.2	-.3	+.1	-.15 to +.15
	LeSabre	-.8 to +.2	-.3	+.1	-.1 to +.1
	Park Avenue	-.8 to +.2	-.3	+.1	-.1 to +.1
	Eighty-Eight & Ninety-Eight	-.8 to +.2	-.3	+.1	-.1 to +.1
1993	Bonneville	-1.05 to +.45	-.3	+.1	-.15 to +.15
	DeVille & Sixty Special	-.8 to +.2	-.3	+.1	-.15 to +.15
	LeSabre	-1.05 to +.45	-.3	+.1	-.15 to +.15
	Park Avenue	-1.05 to +.45	-.3	+.1	-.15 to +.15
	Eighty-Eight & Ninety-Eight	-1.05 to +.45	-.3	+.1	-.15 to +.15
1994-95	Bonneville	-1.05 to +.45	-.3	+.1	-.15 to +.15
	Concours	-.8 to +.2	-.3	+.1	-.15 to +.15
	DeVille	-.8 to +.2	-.3	+.1	-.15 to +.15
	LeSabre	-1.05 to +.45	-.3	+.1	-.15 to +.15
	Park Avenue	-1.05 to +.45	-.3	+.1	-.15 to +.15
	Eighty-Eight & Ninety-Eight	-1.05 to +.45	-.3	+.1	-.15 to +.15

COOLING SYSTEM & CAPACITY DATA

Year	Model	Engine/VIN	Coolant Capacity, Qts.	Radiator Cap Relief Pressure, Lbs.	Thermo. Opening Temp.	Fuel Tank Gals.	Engine Oil Refill Qts.	Auto. Transaxle Qts.①
1992–93	Bonneville SE & SSE	3800/V6-231/L	13	15	195	19	4②	③
	Bonneville SSEi	3800/V6-231/1⑥	13	15	195	19	4②	8⑤
	DeVille/Fleetwood (FWD)	4.9L/V8-300/B	13.2	15	195	19	5④	③
	LeSabre	3800/V6-231/C	13	15	195	19	4②	③
	Park Avenue	3800/V6-231/L	13	15	195	19	4②	③
	Park Avenue Ultra	3800/V6-231/1⑥	13	15	195	19	4②	8⑤
	Eighty-Eight	3800/V6-231/L	13	15	195	18	4②	③
	Ninety-Eight Regency	3800/V6-231/L	13	15	195	18	4②	③
	Ninety-Eight Touring Sedan	3800/V6-231/1⑥	13	15	195	18	4②	8⑤
1994	Bonneville	3800/V6-231/L,1	12.5	15	195	18	4④	⑦
	Concours	4.6L/V8-279/Y	13.2	15	180	24	7④	⑧
	DeVille	4.9L/V8-300/B	13.2	15	195	19	5④	③
	LeSabre	3800/V6-231/C	13	15	195	19	4②	③
	Park Avenue	3800/V6-231/L	13	15	195	19	4②	③
	Park Avenue Ultra	3800/V6-231/1⑥	13	15	195	19	4②	8⑤
	Eighty-Eight	3800/V6-231/L	13	15	195	18	4②	③
	Ninety-Eight Regency	3800/V6-231/L	13	15	195	18	4②	③
	Ninety-Eight Touring Sedan	3800/V6-231/1⑥	13	15	195	18	4②	8⑤
1995	Bonneville	3800/V6-231/K,L,1	13	15	195	18	⑨	③
	Concours	4.6L/V8-279/Y	10.7	15	180	20	7④	⑧
	DeVille	4.9L/V8-300/B	10.7	15	195	20	5④	③
	LeSabre	3800/V6-231/K,L	13	15	195	18	4②	③
	Park Avenue	3800/V6-231/K,L	13	15	195	18	4②	③
	Park Avenue Ultra	3800/V6-231/1⑥	13	15	195	18	4②	③
	Eighty-Eight	3800/V6-231/K,L	13	15	195	18	4②	③
	Ninety-Eight	3800/V6-231/K,L	13	15	195	18	4②	③
	Ninety-Eight Touring Sedan	3800/V6-231/1⑥	13	15	195	18	4②	③

①—Approximate, make final check with dipstick.
②—Add 1 qt. w/filter change.
③—Oil pan capacity, 6 qts.; total capacity, 11 qts.
④—Add ½ qt. w/filter change.
⑤—Drain & refill.
⑥—Supercharged.
⑦—Oil pan capacity, 8 qts.; total capacity, 11 qts.
⑧—Oil pan capacity, 8 qts.; total capacity, 12.6 qts.

LUBRICANT DATA

Year	Model	Lubricant Type		
		Automatic Transaxle	Power Steering	Brake System
1992–95	All	Dexron IIE Or III	Power Steering Fluid①	DOT 3

①—Meeting GM specification 9985010.

Electrical

NOTE: On Air Bag Equipped Models, Refer To "Air Bag System Precautions" Located In The Front Of This Manual For System Disarming & Arming Procedures.

INDEX

PRECAUTIONS

AIR BAG SYSTEMS

Refer to "Air Bag System Precautions" in the front of this manual for system disarming and arming procedures.

FUSE PANEL & FLASHER LOCATION

BUICK, OLDSMOBILE & PONTIAC

The instrument panel fuse panel is located behind the lefthand side of the instrument panel, behind the trim panel. The engine compartment fuse panel is located at the rear center of the engine compartment.

The hazard flasher is located behind the lefthand side of the instrument panel, on the righthand side of the steering column. The turn signal flasher is located behind the lefthand side of the instrument panel, left of the steering column.

CADILLAC

1992–93

The instrument panel fuse panel is located under the lefthand side of the instrument panel. The engine compartment fuse panel is located at the rear of the engine compartment at the bulkhead.

The turn signal flasher is located behind the lefthand side of the instrument panel on the lefthand side of the steering column. The hazard flasher is located below the lefthand side of the instrument panel at the top of the brake pedal support.

1994–95

The engine compartment fuse block is mounted on the lefthand side wheelhouse. The trunk compartment fuse block is located on the rear lefthand side of the luggage compartment.

The hazard flasher is located behind the lefthand side of the instrument panel, above the steering column. The turn flasher module is located behind the lefthand side of the instrument panel, left of the steering column.

RELAY CENTER LOCATION

BUICK, OLDSMOBILE & PONTIAC

The passenger compartment relay center is located behind the righthand side of the instrument panel, at the top of the righthand kick panel. The engine compartment relay center is located at the rear center of the engine compartment.

CADILLAC

The engine compartment relay center is located on the front lefthand side of the engine compartment. The luggage compartment relay center is located on the front righthand side of the luggage compartment.

STARTER

REPLACE

When removing starter, note if any shims are used between the starter and mounting surface. If shims are found, reinstall in original locations.

If starter is noisy during cranking, remove one .015 inch double shim or add one .015 inch single shim to the outer bolt. If starter makes a high pitched whine after engine start, add .015 inch double shims until noise ceases.

1. Disconnect battery ground cable, then raise and support vehicle.
2. Remove starter braces, shields or other components that may hinder starter removal.
3. Support starter and remove mounting bolts.
4. Lower starter and disconnect solenoid wires and battery cable.
5. Remove starter from vehicle.
6. Reverse procedure to install.

IGNITION LOCK

REPLACE

REMOVAL

1. Remove steering wheel as described in "Steering Wheel, Replace."
2. Remove turn signal switch as described in "Turn Signal Switch, Replace."
3. Disconnect "RSWC" connector from turn signal wire harness, **Fig. 1.**
4. Disconnect SIR wiring harness from

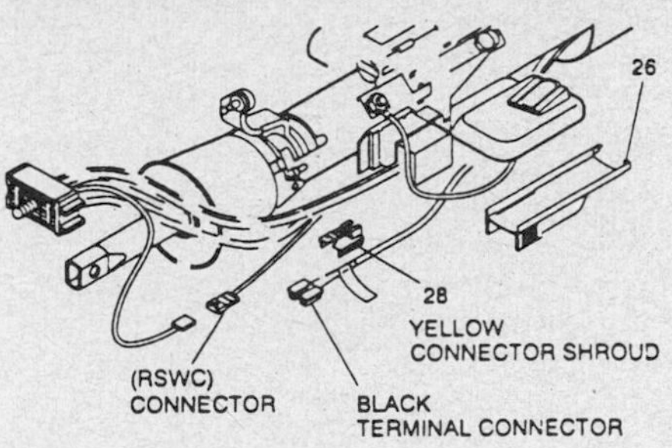
26
28
YELLOW
CONNECTOR SHROUD
(RSWC)
CONNECTOR
BLACK
TERMINAL CONNECTOR

26 PROTECTOR, WIRING
28 SHROUD, CONNECTOR

GC8019201342000X

Fig. 1 SIR coil assembly removal

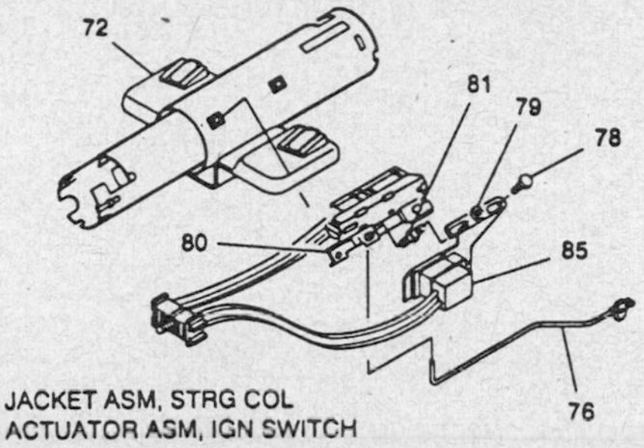
72
81
79
78
80
85
76

72 JACKET ASM, STRG COL
76 ACTUATOR ASM, IGN SWITCH
78 SCREW, WASH HD (#10-24X.25)
79 NUT, HEXAGON (#10-24)
80 SWITCH ASM, IGNITION & DIMR
81 STUD, DIMR & IGN SW MTG
85 SWITCH ASM, DIMMER

GC9049200137000X

Fig. 4 Ignition & dimmer switch replacement

wiring protector and wire harness strap.

5. Attach a length of mechanics wire to both coil terminal connectors to aid in reassembly.
6. Gently pull wire through column.
7. Remove key from lock cylinder, then remove buzzer switch from column housing.
8. Reinsert key and turn lock cylinder to LOCK position, then remove lock cylinder retaining screw.
9. To remove pass key lock cylinder and wire harness from steering column, proceed as follows:
   a. Disconnect pivot and pulse switch connector from bulkhead connector, then remove 13-way secondary lock, **Fig. 2.**
   b. Disconnect two terminals of pass key wire harness from cavities 12 and 13 of pivot and pulse switch connector.
   c. Disconnect pass key wiring harness from wiring protector and wire harness strap.
   d. Attach a length of mechanics sire to SIR terminals aid in reassembly.
   e. Remove retaining clip from lock housing cover and gently pull wire harness through column, **Fig. 3.**

INSTALLATION

1. Insert ignition lock cylinder wires through column and snap retaining clip into hole in lock housing.

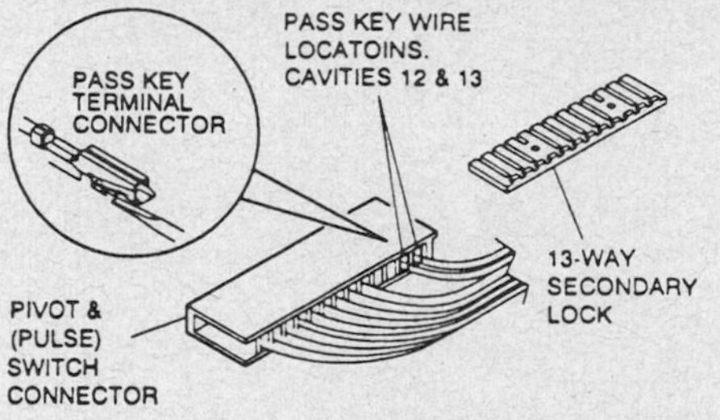
PASS KEY WIRE
LOCATOINS.
CAVITIES 12 & 13
PASS KEY
TERMINAL
CONNECTOR
13-WAY
SECONDARY
LOCK
PIVOT &
(PULSE)
SWITCH
CONNECTOR

GC9049200135000X

Fig. 2 Pass key wire connections

2. Insert two terminals of pass key wire harness into cavities 12 and 13 of pivot and pulse switch connector, **Fig. 3.**
3. Install 13-way secondary lock onto pivot and pulse switch connector.
4. Connect switch connector to bulkhead connector.
5. Install ignition lock retaining screw, **torque** screw to 22 inch lbs.
6. Install buzzer switch assembly.
7. Install key into pass key lock cylinder set and turn key to the "LOCK" position.
8. Install turn signal switch as described in "Turn Signal Switch, Replace."
9. Install steering wheel as described in "Steering Wheel, Replace."

IGNITION SWITCH

REPLACE

1. Remove steering wheel as described in "Steering Wheel, Replace."
2. Remove turn signal switch as outlined under "Turn Signal Switch, Replace" procedure.
3. Refer to **Fig. 4** to remove ignition and dimmer switches.
4. Refer to **Fig. 5** to disconnect dimmer switch from bulkhead connector.
5. When installing dimmer switch, depress switch slightly to install a 3/32 inch twist drill. Force switch upward to remove lash and tighten retaining screw.

NEUTRAL SAFETY SWITCH

REPLACE

1. Disconnect battery ground cable.
2. Disconnect shift cable from transaxle.
3. Disconnect electrical connector from switch.
4. Remove two switch mounting bolts and the switch.
5. Align flats on switch with flats on transaxle shaft and push switch over shaft and fully seat on transaxle.
6. Install and **torque** switch mounting bolts to 20 ft. lbs. **If switch was rotated and the pin broken, the switch will be automatically reset to the neutral position as follows:**
   a. Place transaxle shaft in neutral position.
   b. Install switch on transaxle as outlined previously and loosely install mounting bolts.

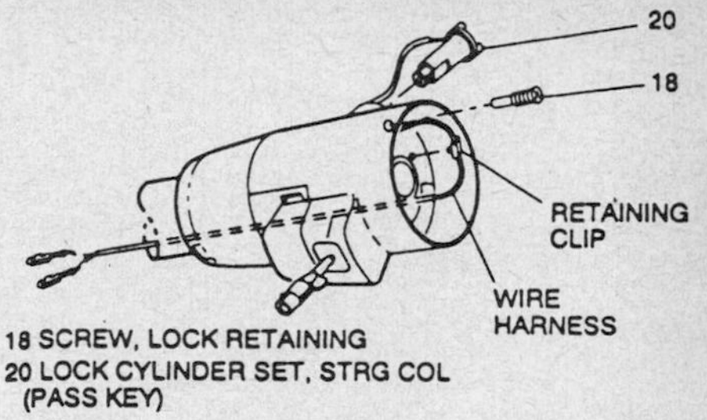
20
18
RETAINING
CLIP
WIRE
HARNESS

18 SCREW, LOCK RETAINING
20 LOCK CYLINDER SET, STRG COL (PASS KEY)

GC9049200136000X

Fig. 3 Lock cylinder replacement

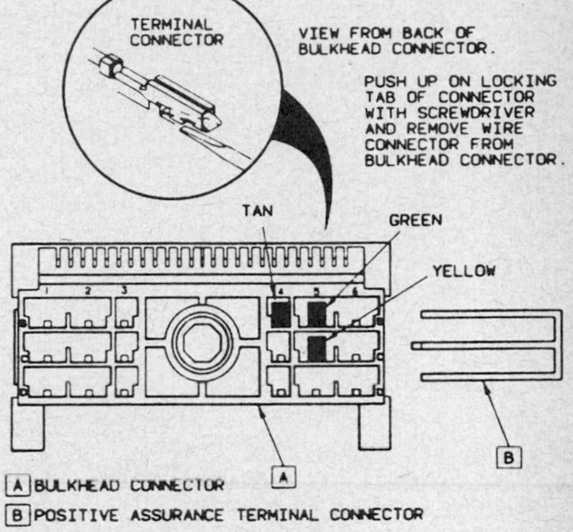
TERMINAL
CONNECTOR
VIEW FROM BACK OF
BULKHEAD CONNECTOR.
PUSH UP ON LOCKING
TAB OF CONNECTOR
WITH SCREWDRIVER
AND REMOVE WIRE
CONNECTOR FROM
BULKHEAD CONNECTOR.
TAN
GREEN
YELLOW
A
B
A BULKHEAD CONNECTOR
B POSITIVE ASSURANCE TERMINAL CONNECTOR

GC9049100083000X

Fig. 5 Disconnecting dimmer switch from bulkhead connector

   c. Insert a 3/32 inch gauge pin into service adjustment hole of switch.
   d. Rotate switch until pin drops in detent.
   e. **Torque** mounting bolts to 20 ft. lbs.

BACK-UP LAMP SWITCH

REPLACE

Refer to "Neutral Safety Switch, Replace for procedure.

HEADLAMP SWITCH

REPLACE

BUICK

Refer to **Figs. 6 and 7,** for switch replacement.

CADILLAC

Refer to **Fig. 8,** for switch replacement.

OLDSMOBILE

Refer to **Fig. 9** for switch replacement.

PONTIAC

Refer to **Fig. 10** for switch replacement.

TURN SIGNAL SWITCH

REPLACE

1. Remove steering wheel as described in "Steering Wheel, Replace."
2. Using lock plate compressor tool No. J 23653-C or equivalent, push down

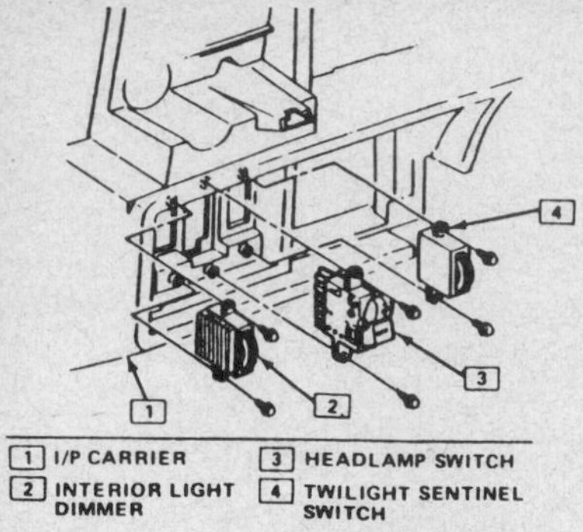
1 I/P CARRIER
2 INTERIOR LIGHT DIMMER
3 HEADLAMP SWITCH
4 TWILIGHT SENTINEL SWITCH
GC9049100084000X

Fig. 6 Headlamp switch removal. LeSabre

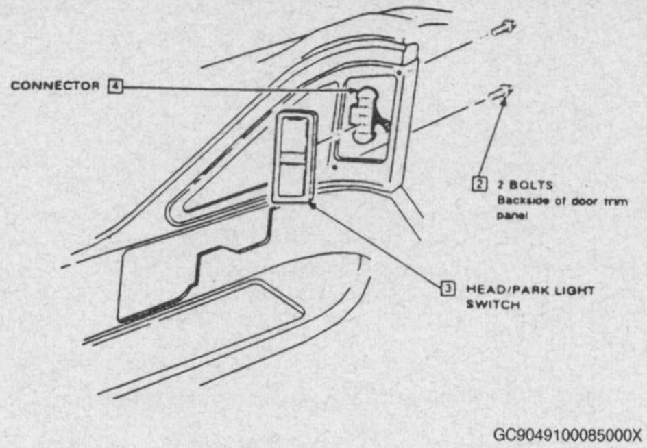
CONNECTOR 4
2 2 BOLTS Backside of door trim panel
3 HEAD/PARK LIGHT SWITCH
GC9049100085000X

Fig. 7 Headlamp switch removal. Park Avenue

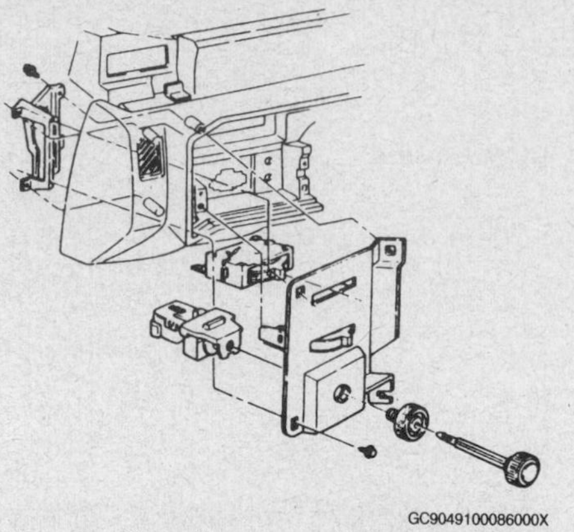
GC9049100086000X

Fig. 8 Headlamp switch removal. DeVille & Fleetwood (FWD)

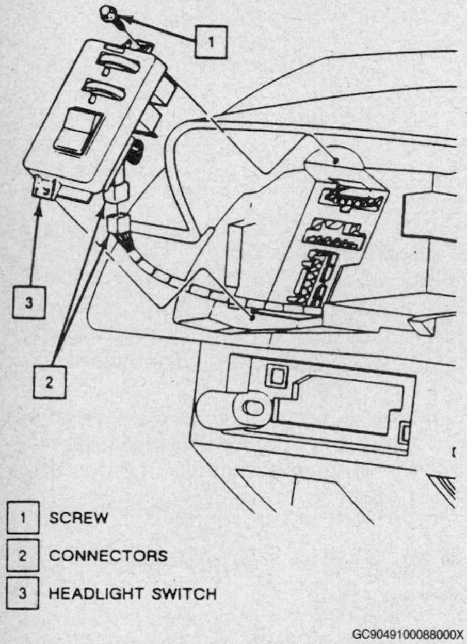
1 SCREW
2 CONNECTORS
3 HEADLIGHT SWITCH
GC9049100088000X

Fig. 9 Headlamp switch removal. Eighty Eight & Ninety Eight

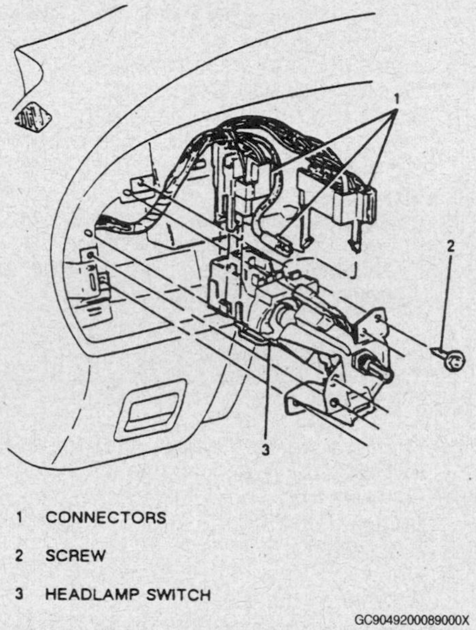
1 CONNECTORS
2 SCREW
3 HEADLAMP SWITCH
GC9049200089000X

Fig. 10 Headlamp switch removal. Bonneville

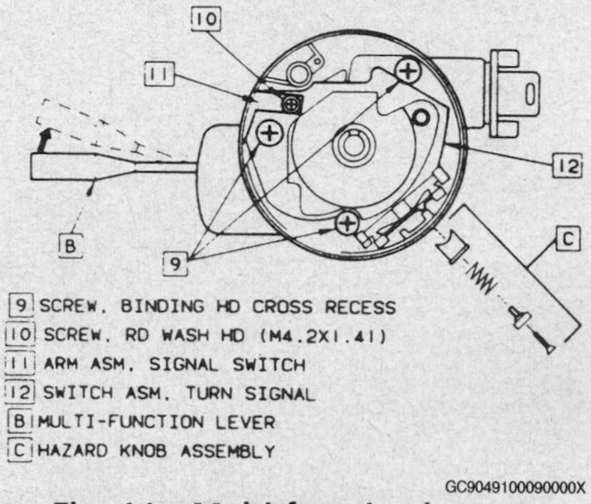
9 SCREW, BINDING HD CROSS RECESS
10 SCREW, RD WASH HD (M4.2X1.41)
11 ARM ASM, SIGNAL SWITCH
12 SWITCH ASM, TURN SIGNAL
B MULTI-FUNCTION LEVER
C HAZARD KNOB ASSEMBLY
GC9049100090000X

Fig. 11 Multi-function lever & hazard knob assembly removal

shaft lock and remove shaft lock retaining ring.

3. Remove shaft lock, turn signal cancelling cam assembly, upper bearing spring, upper bearing inner race seat and inner race.
4. Set turn signal to RIGHT TURN position, then remove multi-function lever and hazard knob assembly, **Fig. 11.**
5. Remove signal switch arm retaining screw and switch arm.
6. Remove turn signal switch attaching screws, then signal switch as follows:
   a. Disconnect turn signal switch connector from bulkhead connector and wire harness strap, **Fig. 12.**
   b. Disconnect E & C module connector from signal switch harness.
   c. Remove wiring protector, then nut holding ground wire to stud.
   d. Gently pull wire harness through column.
7. Reverse procedure to install.

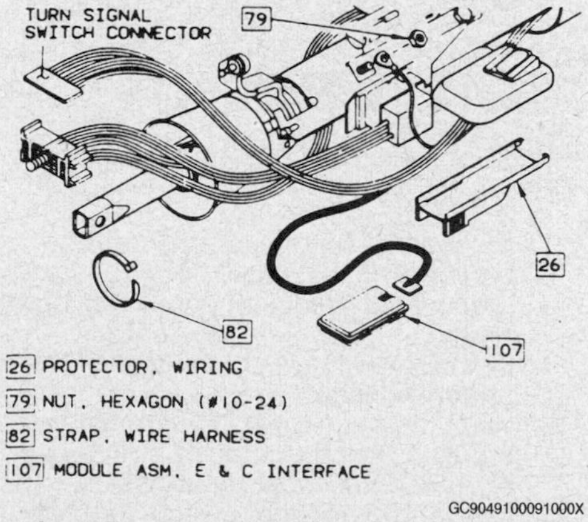
TURN SIGNAL SWITCH CONNECTOR
26 PROTECTOR, WIRING
79 NUT, HEXAGON (#10-24)
82 STRAP, WIRE HARNESS
107 MODULE ASM, E & C INTERFACE
GC9049100091000X

Fig. 12 Turn signal switch removal

DIMMER SWITCH

REPLACE

Refer to "Ignition Switch, Replace" for procedure.

STEERING WHEEL

REPLACE

EXCEPT MODELS W/INFLATABLE RESTRAINT SYSTEM

STANDARD & TILT WHEEL

1. Disconnect battery ground cable.
2. **On models with control pad assembly,** pry out control pad using a thin bladed tool.
3. **On models less control pad assembly,** remove two steering wheel pad retaining screws.
4. **On all models,** disconnect horn wire from cam tower.
5. **On models with control pad assembly,** pry rocker button and push button from control pad.
6. **On all models,** remove steering wheel nut retainer.
7. Remove steering wheel retaining nut.
8. Using a suitable puller, remove steering wheel.
9. Reverse procedure to install.

TELESCOPING WHEEL

Except Cadillac

1. Disconnect battery ground cable.
2. Remove two steering wheel pad retaining screws.

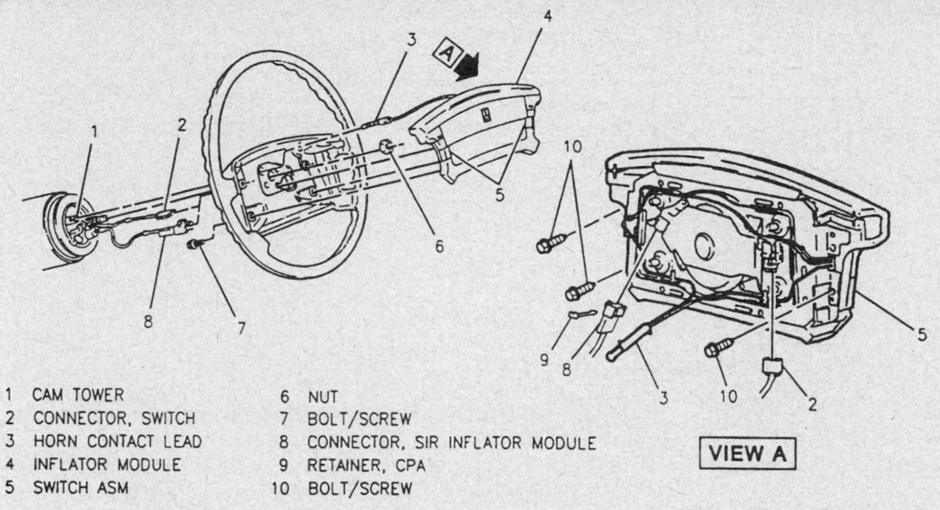
A
VIEW A
1 CAM TOWER
2 CONNECTOR, SWITCH
3 HORN CONTACT LEAD
4 INFLATOR MODULE
5 SWITCH ASM
6 NUT
7 BOLT/SCREW
8 CONNECTOR, SIR INFLATOR MODULE
9 RETAINER, CPA
10 BOLT/SCREW
GC6049100144000X

Fig. 13 Inflator module assembly

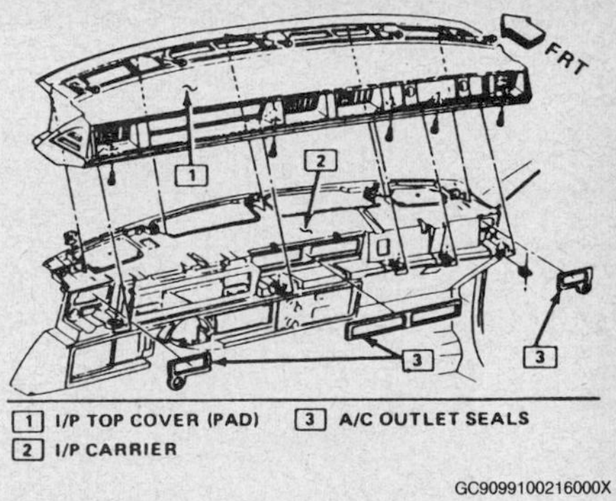
FRT
1 I/P TOP COVER (PAD)
2 I/P CARRIER
3 A/C OUTLET SEALS
GC9099100216000X

Fig. 14 Instrument panel top cover pad removal. LeSabre

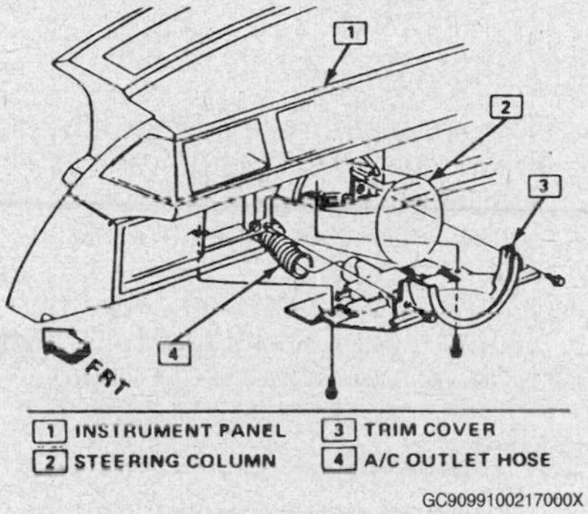
FRT
1 INSTRUMENT PANEL
2 STEERING COLUMN
3 TRIM COVER
4 A/C OUTLET HOSE
GC9099100217000X

Fig. 15 Steering column cover to disconnect shift cable removal. LeSabre

3. Disconnect horn wire from steering wheel pad.
4. Remove steering shaft lock knob bolt positioning screws, then the lock knob bolt from steering shaft.
5. Remove steering wheel nut retainer and the steering wheel nut. Using a suitable puller, remove steering wheel.
6. Reverse procedure to install.

Cadillac

1. Disconnect battery ground cable.
2. Remove two steering wheel pad retaining screws.
3. Disconnect horn wire from steering wheel pad.
4. Remove three screws from telescoping adjusting lever.
5. Remove steering shaft lock knob from steering shaft.
6. Remove steering wheel nut.
7. Using a suitable puller, remove steering wheel.
8. Reverse procedure to install.

MODELS w/INFLATABLE RESTRAINT SYSTEM

1. Remove module retaining screws from back of steering wheel.
2. Remove module from steering wheel, then disconnect horn contact, by pushing slightly and twisting counterclockwise.
3. Remove connector position assurance, then disconnect coil assembly connector, **Fig. 13.**
4. Remove steering wheel retaining nut.
5. Using suitable steering wheel puller, remove wheel.
6. Reverse procedure to install.

INSTRUMENT CLUSTER REPLACE

BUICK

LeSabre

1. Disconnect battery ground cable.
2. Remove upper trim pad, **Fig. 14,** as follows:
   a. Remove defroster grille, then the A/C outlets from upper trim pad.
   b. Remove instrument panel trim plates, then 10 instrument panel pad retaining screws.
   c. **On models equipped with twilight sentinel,** pop up photocell retainer, then remove photocell by turning counterclockwise.
   d. **On all models,** slide panel pad out far enough to disconnect aspirator tube and in-car temperature sensor electrical connector.
   e. Remove pad.
3. **On models with analog cluster,** Remove steering column filler panel, **Fig. 15,** then disconnect shift indicator cable from steering column.
4. **On all models,** remove five instrument cluster attaching screws, then the cluster, **Fig. 16.**

Park Avenue

1. Disconnect battery ground cable.
2. Remove right and left side sound insulators.
3. Remove instrument panel lower trim plates, **Fig. 17.**
4. Remove air vent deflectors, then three glove box attaching bolts.

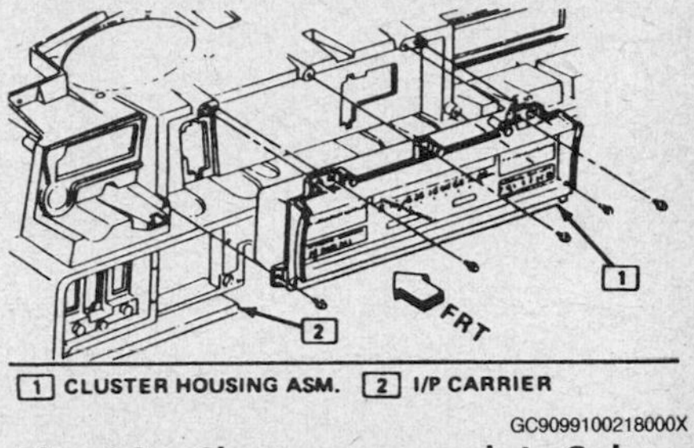
FRT
1 CLUSTER HOUSING ASM.
2 I/P CARRIER
GC9099100218000X

Fig. 16 Cluster removal. LeSabre

5. Remove five instrument panel trim plate attaching screws, then trim plate.
6. Remove seven lower instrument panel trim pad to instrument panel attaching screws.
7. Slide rubber collar up steering column, then slide clip off with gear selector as shown in **Fig. 18.**
8. Remove five instrument cluster to instrument panel attaching bolts, then pull cluster straight out.
9. Reverse procedure to install.

CADILLAC

1. Disconnect battery ground cable.
2. Remove upper trim pad as follows:
   a. Remove A/C outlets from upper trim pad.
   b. Remove screws locations 2 and 3 from both side of pad, **Fig. 19.**
   c. Remove upper trim pad.
3. Remove screw (88) and plate (87), **Fig. 20.**
4. Remove cluster attaching screws.
5. Disconnect wiring from rear of cluster and remove cluster from vehicle.
6. Reverse procedure to install.

OLDSMOBILE

1. Disconnect battery ground cable.
2. Remove cluster trim plate to instrument panel attaching screws, **Fig. 21.**
3. Tilt trim plate rearward and disconnect driver information display and defogger/heated windshield connectors.
4. Remove cluster trim plate, then cluster to instrument panel attaching screws, **Fig. 22.**
5. Pull cluster rearward, then disconnect

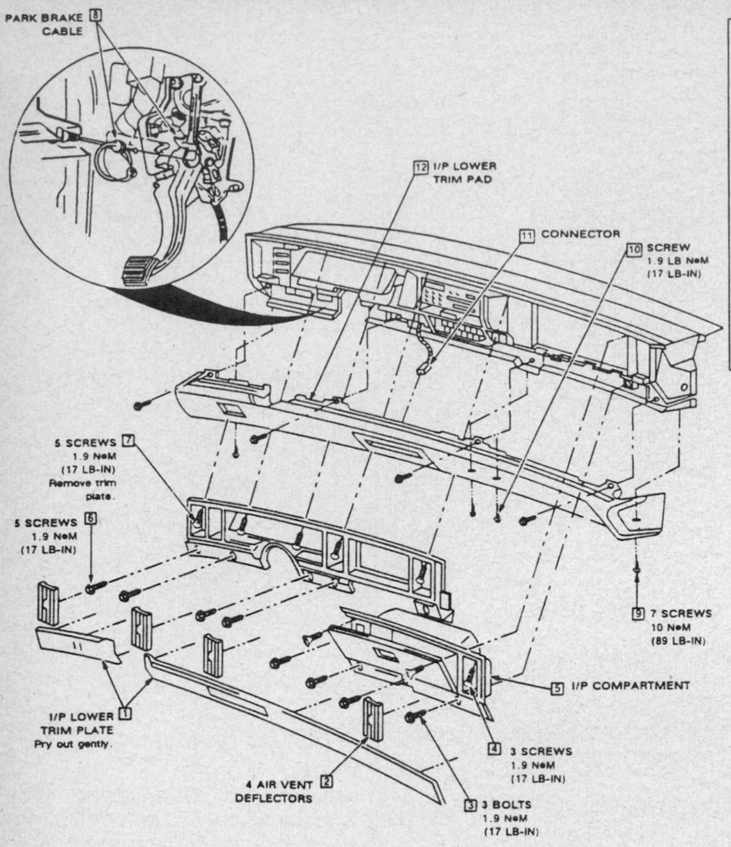
PARK BRAKE 8
CABLE
12 I/P LOWER
TRIM PAD
11 CONNECTOR
10 SCREW
1.9 LB N•M
(17 LB-IN)
5 SCREWS 7
1.9 N•M
(17 LB-IN)
Remove trim
plate.
5 SCREWS 6
1.9 N•M
(17 LB-IN)
9 7 SCREWS
10 N•M
(89 LB-IN)
5 I/P COMPARTMENT
I/P LOWER
TRIM PLATE
Pry out gently.
1
4 3 SCREWS
1.9 N•M
(17 LB-IN)
4 AIR VENT 2
DEFLECTORS
3 3 BOLTS
1.9 N•M
(17 LB-IN)
GC9099100219000X

Fig. 17 I/P trim pad & trim panels removal. Park Avenue

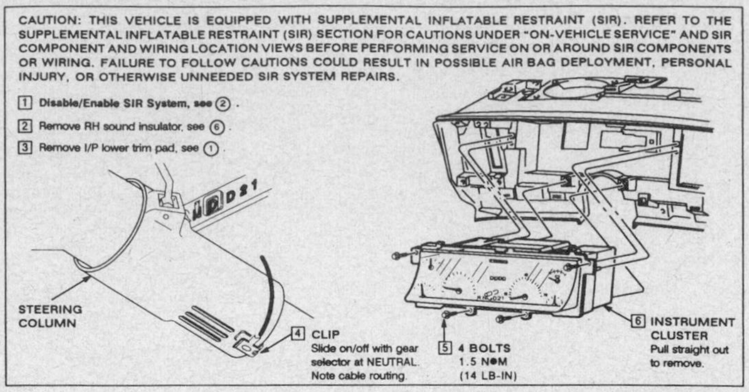
CAUTION: THIS VEHICLE IS EQUIPPED WITH SUPPLEMENTAL INFLATABLE RESTRAINT (SIR). REFER TO THE SUPPLEMENTAL INFLATABLE RESTRAINT (SIR) SECTION FOR CAUTIONS UNDER "ON-VEHICLE SERVICE" AND SIR COMPONENT AND WIRING LOCATION VIEWS BEFORE PERFORMING SERVICE ON OR AROUND SIR COMPONENTS OR WIRING. FAILURE TO FOLLOW CAUTIONS COULD RESULT IN POSSIBLE AIR BAG DEPLOYMENT, PERSONAL INJURY, OR OTHERWISE UNNEEDED SIR SYSTEM REPAIRS.
1 Disable/Enable SIR System, see 2.
2 Remove RH sound insulator, see 6.
3 Remove I/P lower trim pad, see 1.
STEERING
COLUMN
4 CLIP
Slide on/off with gear
selector at NEUTRAL.
Note cable routing.
5 4 BOLTS
1.5 N•M
(14 LB-IN)
6 INSTRUMENT
CLUSTER
Pull straight out
to remove.
GC9099100220000X

Fig. 18 Instrument cluster removal. Park Avenue

cluster electrical connector and PRNDL cable.
6. Remove cluster assembly.
7. Reverse procedure to install.

PONTIAC

1. Disconnect battery ground cable.
2. Remove steering column lower filler attaching screws, then remove.
3. Remove steering column support attaching bolts, then carefully lower steering column and cover to prevent damage.
4. Remove instrument panel trim plate attaching screws.
5. Pull headlamp dimmer and twilight sentinel control knob rearward.
6. Pull panel cluster plate rearward to remove.
7. Remove headlamp switch attaching screws, pull rearward, then remove dimmer and twilight sentinel control knob from switch.
8. Remove instrument panel cluster trim plate.
9. Remove instrument cluster attaching screws, then pull righthand side of cluster rearward, **Fig. 23.**
10. Depress cluster electrical connector locking tab through top right side of assembly.
11. Pull bottom of cluster rearward, then rotate cluster to face upward, then pull rearward to remove.
12. Reverse procedure to install.

RADIO

REPLACE

BUICK

LeSabre

1. Remove lower RH trim plate.
2. Remove four radio retaining screws, then pull radio out of dash and disconnect electrical connectors and antenna lead.
3. Remove radio, **Fig. 24.**
4. Reverse procedure to install.

Park Avenue

1. Disconnect battery ground cable.
2. Remove instrument panel lower trim plates and four air vent deflectors by prying gently.
3. Remove bolts and screws that attach the glove box to the instrument panel, **Fig. 25.**
4. Remove five instrument panel trim plate attaching screws.
5. Remove five radio to instrument panel attaching bolts and nuts, **Fig. 25.**
6. Pull radio straight back and disconnect electrical connectors and antenna.
7. Reverse procedure to install.

CADILLAC

1. Disconnect battery ground cable.
2. Remove radio trim plate, **Fig. 26.**
3. Open ashtray and remove one screw from rear support bracket.
4. Remove two screws from front of radio, then pull radio straight out and disconnect electrical connectors and antenna.
5. Remove four bracket retaining nuts and brackets.
6. Reverse procedure to install.

OLDSMOBILE

1. Remove instrument cluster trim plate as described in "Instrument Cluster, Replace."
2. Remove five radio to instrument panel attaching screws.
3. Pulling radio rearward, disconnect electrical connectors and antenna.
4. Remove radio mounting brackets.
5. Reverse procedure to install.

PONTIAC

1. Disconnect battery ground cable.
2. Carefully pry instrument panel trim panel, pull panel upward, then rearward to remove.
3. Remove radio attaching screws, then pull rearward.
4. Disconnect electrical connector and antenna lead.
5. Remove radio assembly, **Fig. 27.**
6. Reverse procedure to install.

WIPER MOTOR

REPLACE

1. Remove wiper arms.
2. Remove cowl cover.
3. Remove air inlet screen assembly.
4. **On all models,** disconnect wiper arm drive link from crank arm.
5. Disconnect motor electrical connectors.
6. Remove wiper motor attaching screws, then remove motor guiding cranking arm through hole.
7. Reverse procedure to install.

WIPER SWITCH

REPLACE

1. Remove turn signal switch as outlined under "Turn Signal Switch, Replace" procedure.
2. Refer to **Figs. 28 through 31,** for switch replacement.

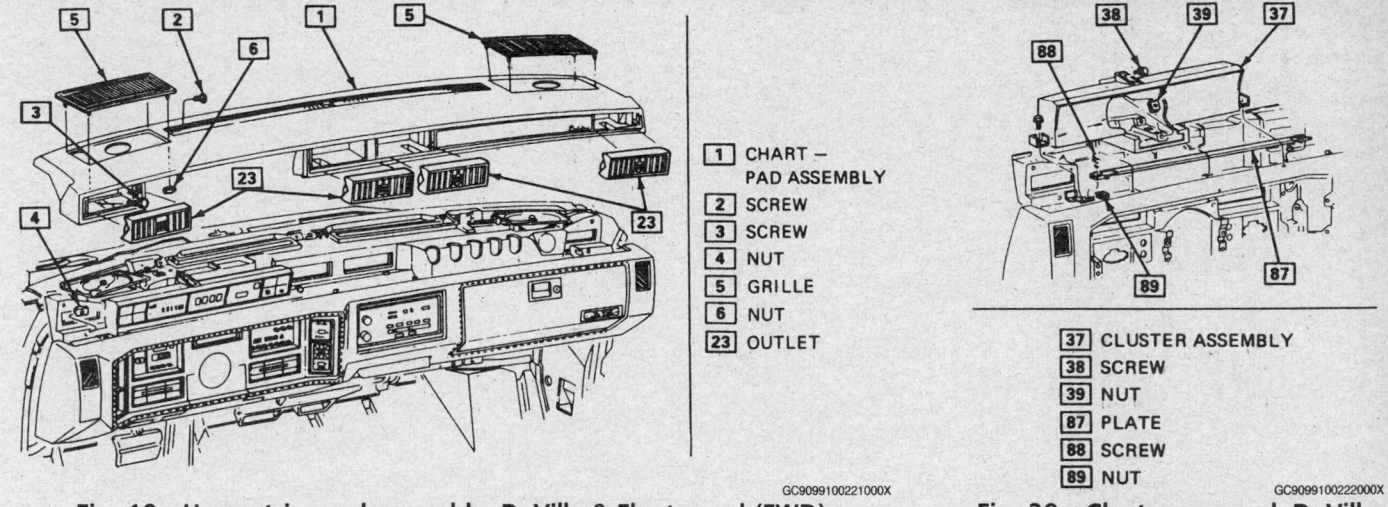

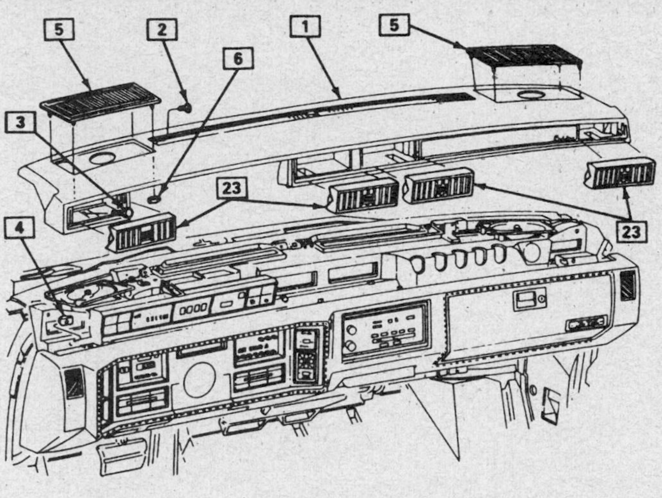
1 CHART – PAD ASSEMBLY
2 SCREW
3 SCREW
4 NUT
5 GRILLE
6 NUT
23 OUTLET
GC9099100221000X

Fig. 19 Upper trim pad assembly. DeVille & Fleetwood (FWD)

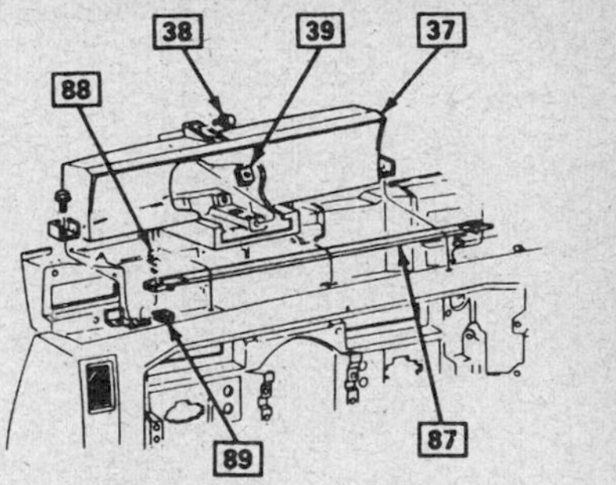
37 CLUSTER ASSEMBLY
38 SCREW
39 NUT
87 PLATE
88 SCREW
89 NUT
GC9099100222000X

Fig. 20 Cluster removal. DeVille & Fleetwood (FWD)

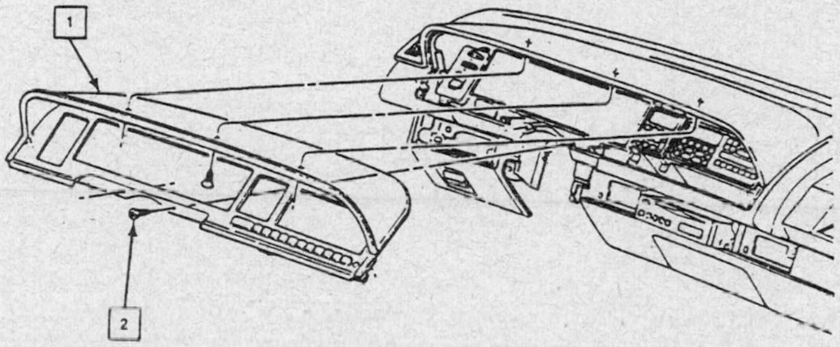
1 IP CLUSTER TRIM PLATE
2 SCREW
GC9099100225000X

Fig. 21 Cluster trim plate removal. Eighty-Eight & Ninety-Eight

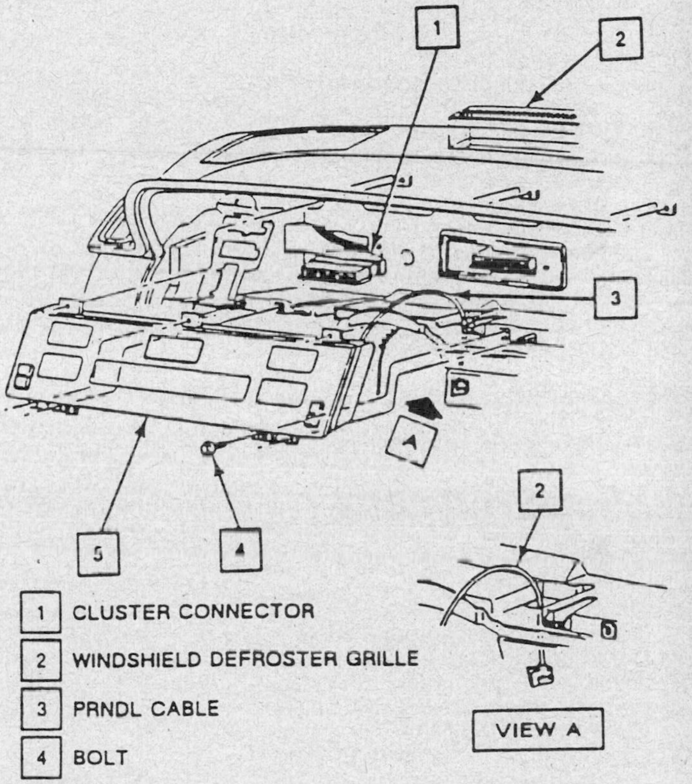
1 CLUSTER CONNECTOR
2 WINDSHIELD DEFROSTER GRILLE
3 PRNDL CABLE
4 BOLT
5 CLUSTER ASSEMBLY
VIEW A
GC9099100226000X

Fig. 22 Cluster removal. Eighty-Eight & Ninety-Eight

WIPER TRANSMISSION

REPLACE

1. Disconnect washer hoses, then remove wiper arms.
2. Remove air inlet screen assembly.
3. Disconnect drive link from motor crank arm.
4. Remove linkage attaching screws, the pull transmission through access hole in shroud upper panel.
5. Reverse procedure to install.

BLOWER MOTOR

REPLACE

1. Disconnect battery ground cable.
2. Disconnect cooling tube and blower motor electrical connector.
3. Remove blower motor attaching screws and the blower motor.
4. Reverse procedure to install.

HEATER CORE

REPLACE

EXCEPT CADILLAC

1. Disconnect battery ground cable.
2. Drain cooling system.
3. Remove right sound insulator.
4. Remove center and lower instrument panel trim plates.
5. **On models with automatic climate control,** remove speaker grille and speaker for access to programmer attaching bolt.
6. Disconnect wiring and hoses from programmer.
7. Remove programmer linkage cover and disconnect linkage.
8. Remove programmer attaching bolt and the programmer.
9. **On all models,** remove heater core cover, then the splash cover for access to heater hoses.
10. Disconnect heater hoses from heater core.
11. Remove heater core cover, then the heater core.
12. Reverse procedure to install.

CADILLAC

1. Disconnect battery ground cable.
2. Remove glove box attaching screws, then the glove box.
3. Remove lower sound insulator attaching screws and nuts, then the lower sound insulator.
4. Remove programmer as follows:

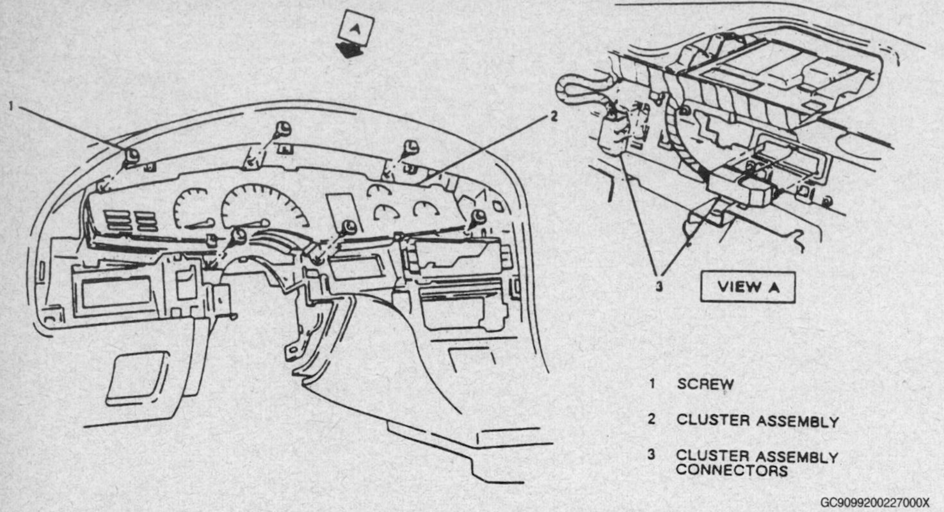
A
1
2
3
VIEW A
1 SCREW
2 CLUSTER ASSEMBLY
3 CLUSTER ASSEMBLY CONNECTORS
GC9099200227000X

Fig. 23 Cluster removal. Bonneville

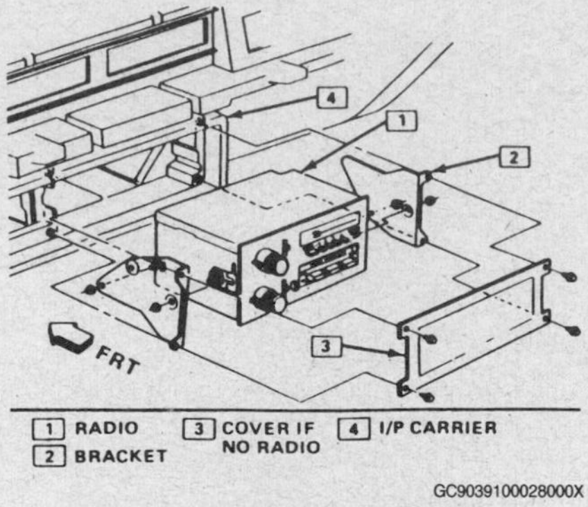
4
1
2
3
FRT
1 RADIO
2 BRACKET
3 COVER IF NO RADIO
4 I/P CARRIER
GC9039100028000X

Fig. 24 Radio installation. LeSabre

a. Remove programmer shield attaching screws, then the programmer shield.
b. Disconnect threaded rod from programmer.
c. Disconnect programmer electrical and vacuum connector, then remove programmer.

5. Disconnect body control module electrical connector, then remove module attaching screws and module.
6. Remove relay panel from module assembly, then the module assembly heater core cover.
7. Disconnect heater hoses from heater core.
8. Remove two heater core attaching screws, then the heater core.
9. Reverse procedure to install.

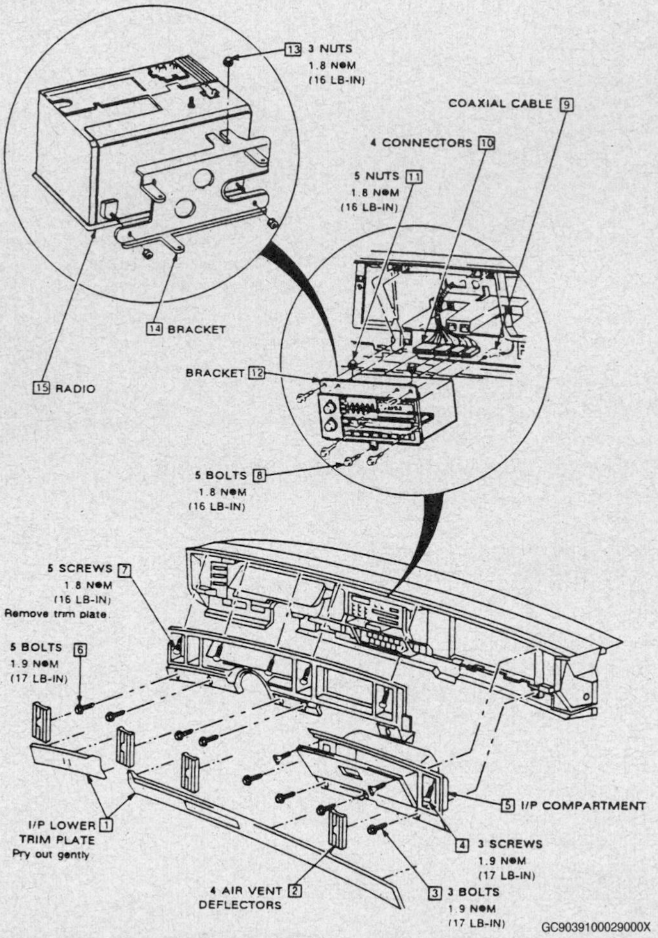
13 3 NUTS 1.8 N●M (16 LB-IN)
COAXIAL CABLE 9
4 CONNECTORS 10
5 NUTS 11 1.8 N●M (16 LB-IN)
14 BRACKET
BRACKET 12
15 RADIO
5 BOLTS 8 1.8 N●M (16 LB-IN)
5 SCREWS 7 1.8 N●M (16 LB-IN) Remove trim plate
5 BOLTS 6 1.9 N●M (17 LB-IN)
5 I/P COMPARTMENT
I/P LOWER TRIM PLATE 1 Pry out gently
4 3 SCREWS 1.9 N●M (17 LB-IN)
4 AIR VENT DEFLECTORS 2
3 3 BOLTS 1.9 N●M (17 LB-IN)
GC9039100029000X

Fig. 25 Radio removal & installation. Park Avenue

EVAPORATOR CORE
REPLACE

CADILLAC

1. Disconnect battery ground cable.
2. Drain coolant, then remove front dash cover and vacuum tank.
3. Remove relay pack, EGR solenoid valve and related parts.
4. Loosen wiring harness from front of dash and position aside.
5. Disconnect heater hoses from evaporator module.
6. Remove MAP sensor, sensor bracket and attaching rods from dash panel.
7. Remove wiring harness brackets from lift cover and position out of the way.
8. Discharge A/C system.
9. Remove washer reservoir, then disconnect all accumulator lines.
10. Disconnect upper hose from power steering pump and position aside.
11. Remove blower motor and exhaust manifold heat shield, **Fig. 32.**
12. Disconnect all wiring and connectors attached to evaporator and blower module.
13. Remove all brackets around barrier insulator, then all screws and bolts around insulator.
14. Raise and support vehicle.
15. Cut barrier insulator on mark line, located on right side of barrier insulator.
16. Remove evaporator core.
17. Reverse procedure to install.

PARK AVENUE

Brazed fittings are used on the condenser and evaporator. These fittings cannot be turned. It is important that the service technician recognize which fitting is to be turned and use back-up wrenches. The brazed fitting that should not be turned is always the same color as the pipe it is brazed to.

1. Disconnect battery ground cable.
2. Discharge A/C system, then remove vacuum tank.
3. Remove rear sight shield, then disconnect positive battery booster cable from underhood fuse block.
4. Remove underhood fuse block from relay bracket and position aside.

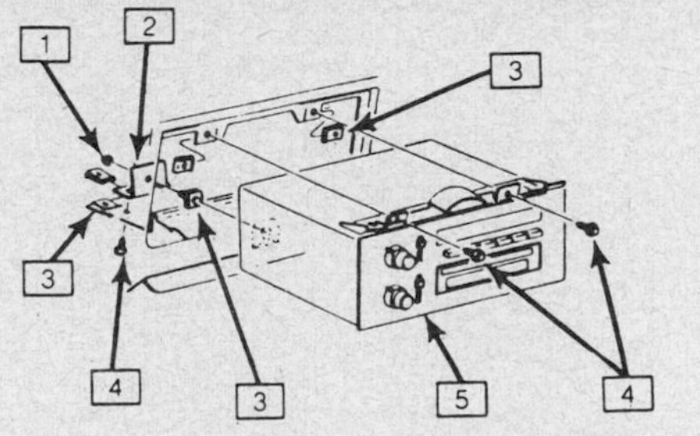
1
2
3
3
4
3
5
4

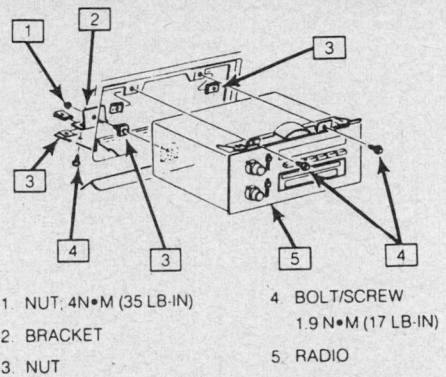

1. NUT; 4N•M (35 LB-IN)
2. BRACKET
3. NUT
4. BOLT/SCREW 1.9 N•M (17 LB-IN)
5. RADIO

GC9039100030000X

Fig. 26 Radio installation. DeVille & Fleetwood (FWD)

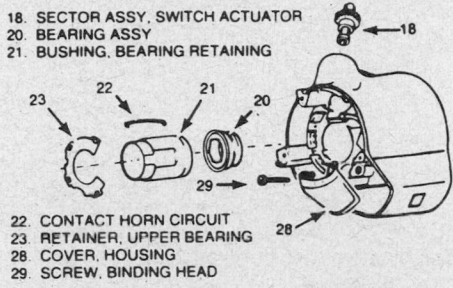

18. SECTOR ASSY. SWITCH ACTUATOR
20. BEARING ASSY
21. BUSHING. BEARING RETAINING

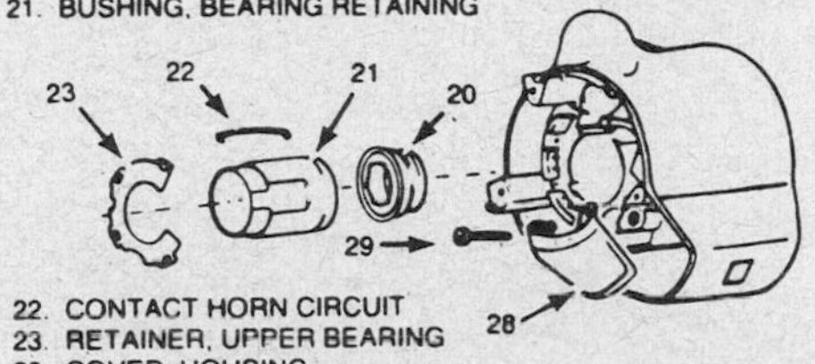
18
23
22
21
20
29
28

22. CONTACT HORN CIRCUIT
23. RETAINER, UPPER BEARING
28. COVER, HOUSING
29. SCREW, BINDING HEAD

GC9049100092000X

Fig. 28 Lock housing cover removal. Standard column

5. Remove relay bracket from dash panel, then the blower resistor from top of evaporator/heater module casing.
6. Disconnect A/C module to accumulator tube from accumulator.
7. Disconnect A/C compressor and condenser hose from the accumulator.
8. Remove clamp from accumulator, then disconnect electrical connector from the pressure cycling switch.
9. Disconnect evaporator to condenser tube from evaporator case and condenser.
10. Disengage tube from clips holding evaporator tube to fender, then remove tube from vehicle.
11. Remove blower motor, the all brackets from evaporator/heater module, **Fig. 33.**
12. Remove heat shield from bottom of evaporator/heater module, then the three screws attaching bottom of module to dash panel.
13. Remove five screws attaching top and side of module to the dash panel.
14. Cut insulator on module along line indicated.
15. Remove four module to insulator attaching screws, located behind insulator.
16. Remove Electronic Brake Control Module (EBCM) as follows:
    a. Remove two screws attaching the Assembly Line Diagnostic Link (ALDL) connector to the righthand side sound insulator.
    b. Remove push-on nuts and attaching bolts from left and right sound insulators, **Fig. 34.**

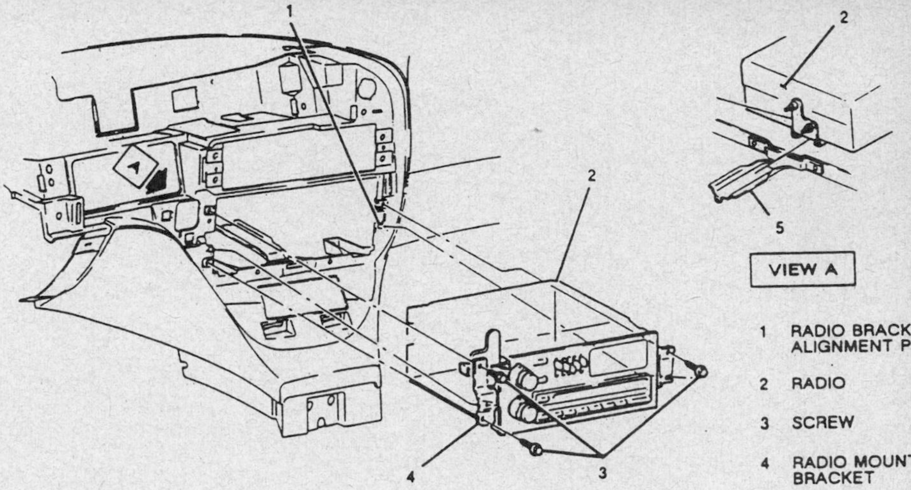
1
2
5
VIEW A
2
4
3

1. RADIO BRACKET ALIGNMENT PIN
2. RADIO
3. SCREW
4. RADIO MOUNTING BRACKET
5. IP RADIO MOUNT BRACKET

GC9039200031000X

Fig. 27 Radio replace. Bonneville

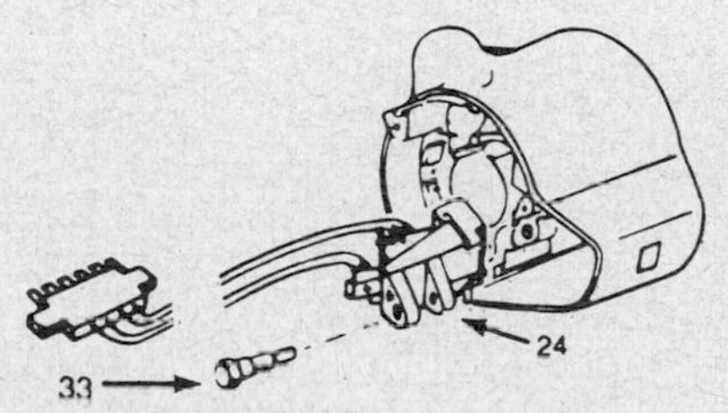
24
33

24. SWITCH ASSY. PIVOT &
33. PIN, SWITCH ACTUATOR PIVOT

GC9049100093000X

Fig. 29 Wiper switch removal. Standard column

19
B
21
77
24
F
25

19 COVER ASM. LOCK HOUSING
21 ACTUATOR, DIMMER SW ROD
24 BASE PLATE, COL HSG CVR END
25 CAP, COL HSG COVER END
77 ROD, DIMMER SWITCH
B MULTI-FUNCTION LEVER
F CRUISE CONTROL PLUG

GC9049100094000X

Fig. 30 Lock housing cover removal. Tilt column & columns w/SIR

19
22
SWITCH CONNECTOR
23

19 COVER ASM. LOCK HOUSING
22 PIN, SWITCH ACTUATOR PIVOT
23 SWITCH ASM, PIVOT & (PULSE)

GC9049100095000X

Fig. 31 Wiper switch removal. Tilt column & columns w/SIR

    c. Remove righthand footwell courtesy light and oil life module from right side sound insulator, then the insulator from vehicle.
    d. Remove left footwell courtesy light from left side sound insulator, then the insulator from the vehicle.
    e. Remove two floor outlet assembly to instrument panel attaching screws.
    f. Remove four EBCM bracket to instrument panel attaching screws.
    g. Pull bracket away from the instrument panel and remove EBCM to bracket attaching bolt, then slide EBCM out of bracket.
17. Pull down rug and padding, then remove dash panel to evaporator/heater module case attaching screw.
18. Pull module case away from dash panel and remove evaporator.
19. Reverse procedure to install.

BUICK LESABRE, OLDSMOBILE & PONTIAC

Brazed fittings are used on the condenser and evaporator. These fittings cannot be turned. It is important that the service technician recognize which fitting is to be turned and use back-up wrenches. The brazed fitting that should not be turned is always the same color as the pipe it is brazed to.

1. Disconnect battery ground cable.
2. Discharge A/C system, then remove engine rear sight shield.
3. Disconnect electrical connector from pressure cycling switch.
4. Remove accumulator clamp screw.
5. Disconnect accumulator inlet and outlet connections, then remove accumulator from the vehicle.
6. Remove blower motor resistor, then the vacuum tank.
7. Remove engine coolant reservoir,

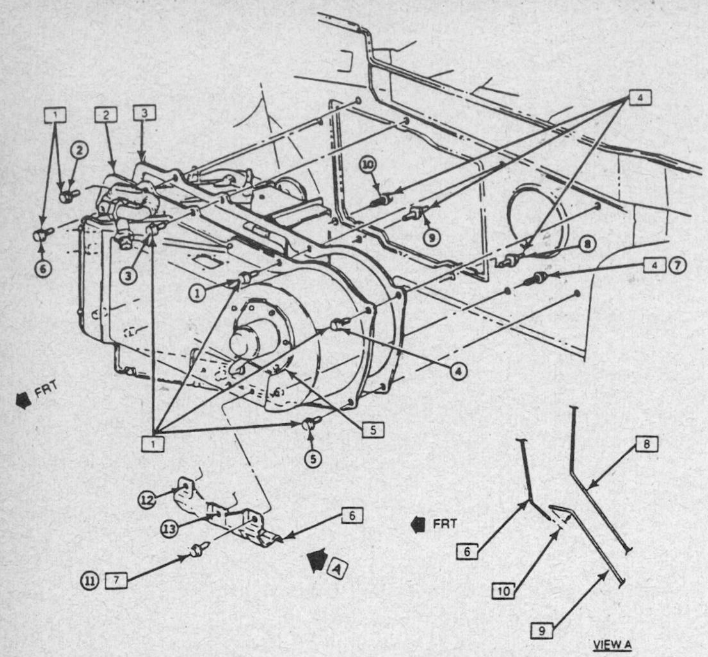
FRT
FRT
A
VIEW A

1. BOLT/SCREW: 3 N•M (27 LB-IN)
2. EVAPORATOR AND BLOWER MODULE
3. GASKET
4. BOLT/SCREW: 3.4 N•M (30 LB-IN)
5. BLOWER MOTOR
6. SHIELD
7. BOLT/SCREW: 1.9 N•M (17 LB-IN)
8. DASH PANEL
9. CATALYTIC CONVERTER HEAT SHIELD
10. 13.0 MM (APPROXIMATELY)

GC7029100059000X

Fig. 32 Evaporator removal. DeVille, Fleetwood (FWD) & Sixty Special

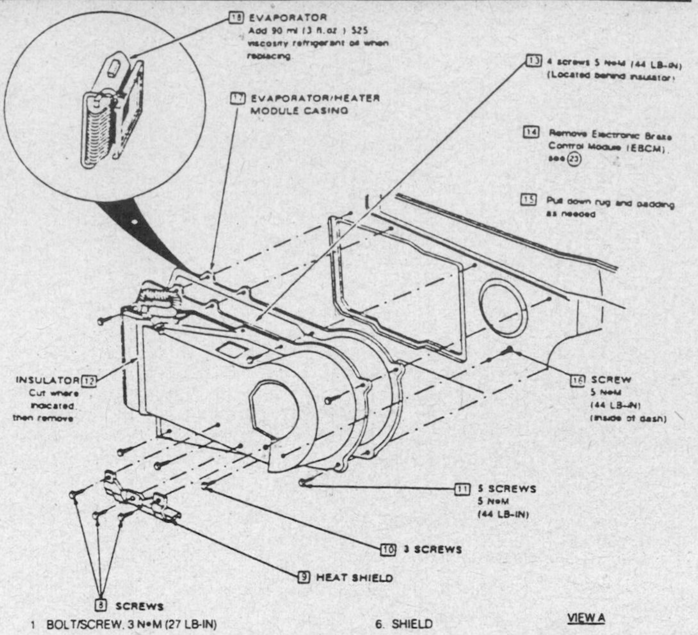
18 EVAPORATOR
17 EVAPORATOR/HEATER MODULE CASING
14 Remove Electronic Brake Control Module (EBCM), see 33
15 Pull down rug and padding as needed
INSULATOR 12 Cut where indicated, then remove
16 SCREW 5 N•M (44 LB-IN) (inside of dash)
11 5 SCREWS 5 N•M (44 LB-IN)
10 3 SCREWS
9 HEAT SHIELD
8 SCREWS
VIEW A

1. BOLT/SCREW: 3 N•M (27 LB-IN)
2. EVAPORATOR AND BLOWER MODULE
3. GASKET
4. BOLT/SCREW: 3.4 N•M (30 LB-IN)
5. BLOWER MOTOR
6. SHIELD
7. BOLT/SCREW: 1.9 N•M (17 LB-IN)
8. DASH PANEL
9. CATALYTIC CONVERTER HEAT SHIELD
10. 13.0 MM (APPROXIMATELY)

GC7029100060000X

Fig. 33 Evaporator/heater module assembly. Park Avenue

then the evaporator tube from condenser outlet.

8. Disconnect A/C lines from clamp near the shock tower, then remove evaporator tube from vehicle.
9. Remove blower motor, then the brackets and heat shield from blower module assembly.
10. Cut blower module assembly along indicated line, then remove bolts attaching blower module assembly to front of dash (driver's side only).
11. Remove large piece of blower module assembly insulation.
12. Remove screws from evaporator cover, then the evaporator.
13. Reverse procedure to install.

TECHNICAL SERVICE BULLETINS

BLOWER MOTOR NOISE

1994 Cadillac DeVille

Some of these models may exhibit a blower motor whine noise that varies in frequency as motor speed changes. This whine noise could be caused by the motor generated torque, amplified by the fan motor mounting and the vehicle structure. To repair this condition, an inertia plate will have to be installed on the back of the blower motor. Use the following procedure to install the inertia plate.

1. Disconnect battery ground cable.
2. Disconnect blower motor electrical connector.
3. Remove three blower motor cover retaining screws and washers. Discard screws. **Do not push inward when removing last screw or the motor could be pushed out of the cover assembly.**
4. Install inertia disc service kit part No. 22137062 over blower motor cover assembly and install new screw and washer assemblies.
5. **Torque** screws to 62 inch lbs.

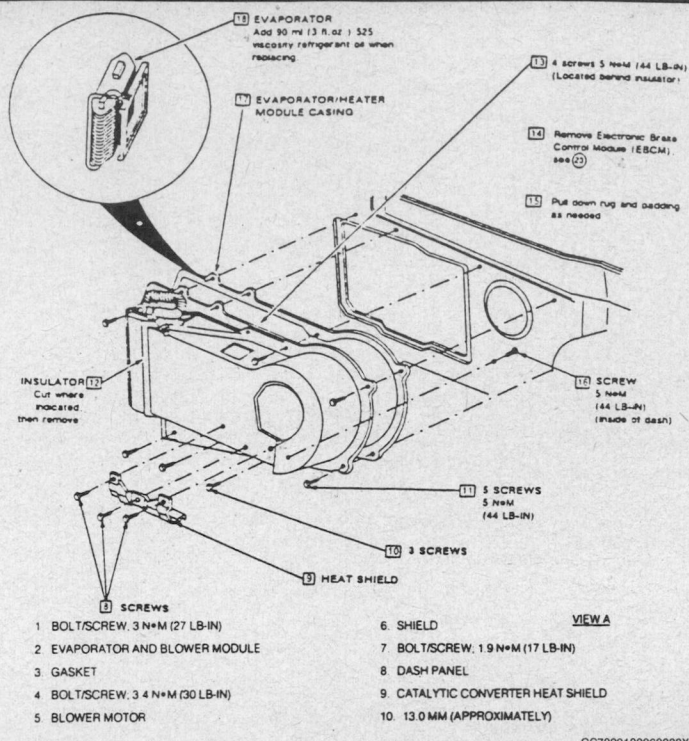

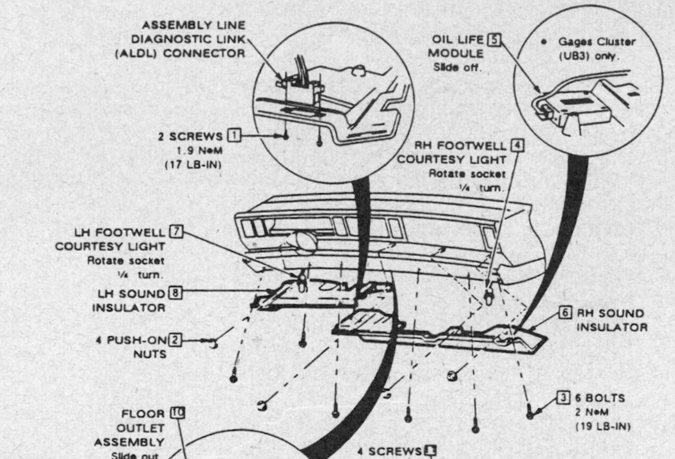
ASSEMBLY LINE DIAGNOSTIC LINK (ALDL) CONNECTOR
OIL LIFE 5 MODULE Slide off.
• Gages Cluster (UB3) only.
2 SCREWS 1 1.9 N•M (17 LB-IN)
RH FOOTWELL 4 COURTESY LIGHT Rotate socket 1/4 turn.
LH FOOTWELL 7 COURTESY LIGHT Rotate socket 1/4 turn.
LH SOUND 8 INSULATOR
6 RH SOUND INSULATOR
4 PUSH-ON 2 NUTS
3 6 BOLTS 2 N•M (19 LB-IN)
FLOOR 10 OUTLET ASSEMBLY Slide out.
4 SCREWS 11 1.4 N•M (12 LB-IN)
SCREWS 9 1.5 N•M (13 LB-IN)
12 BRACKET
15 CONNECTOR
BOLT 13 2.3 N•M (19 LB-IN)
14 ELECTRONIC BRAKE CONTROL MODULE (EBCM) Slide out of bracket.

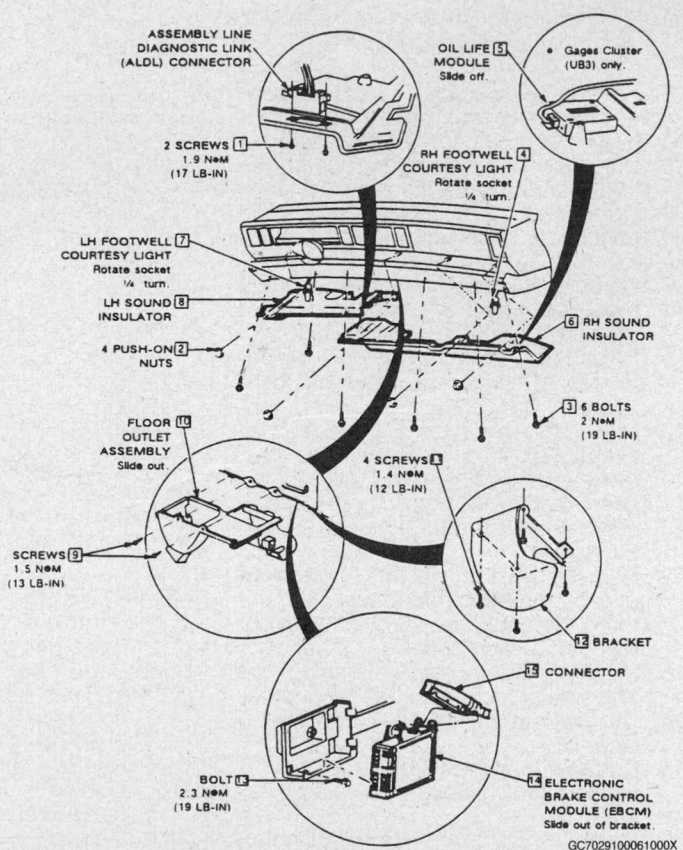

GC7029100061000X

Fig. 34 Electronic Brake Control Module (EBCM) assembly removal. Park Avenue

3800/V6-231 Engines

NOTE: On Air Bag Equipped Models, Refer To "Air Bag System Precautions" Located In The Front Of This Manual For System Disarming & Arming Procedures.

INDEX

PRECAUTIONS

AIR BAG SYSTEMS

Refer to "Air Bag System Precautions" in the front of this manual for system disarming and arming procedures.

FUEL SYSTEM PRESSURE RELIEF

After relieving fuel system pressure, a small amount of fuel may be released when servicing fuel pipes or connections. In order to reduce the risk of personal injury, cover fuel pipe fittings with a suitable shop towel before disconnecting to catch any fuel that may leak.

1. Disconnect battery ground cable, then loosen fuel filler cap to relieve tank pressure.
2. Connect fuel pressure gauge tool No. J 34370-1 or equivalent to fuel pressure connection. Wrap fitting in suitable shop towel.
3. Install bleed hose to suitable container, then open valve and bleed off pressure.
4. Disconnect fuel pressure gauge, then drain gauge in suitable container.

ENGINE MOUNT

REPLACE

1. Disconnect battery ground cable.
2. Attach suitable lifting equipment to engine, then raise engine slightly to remove weight from engine mounts.
3. Remove accessory drive belt.
4. Remove through bolt from front engine mount, **Fig. 1.**
5. Lift engine until power steering reservoir touches strut tower cross brace, then loosen bottom two bolts on front engine mount.
6. Remove A/C line clip, then the top two bolts from front engine mount and remove mount.
7. Reverse procedure to install.

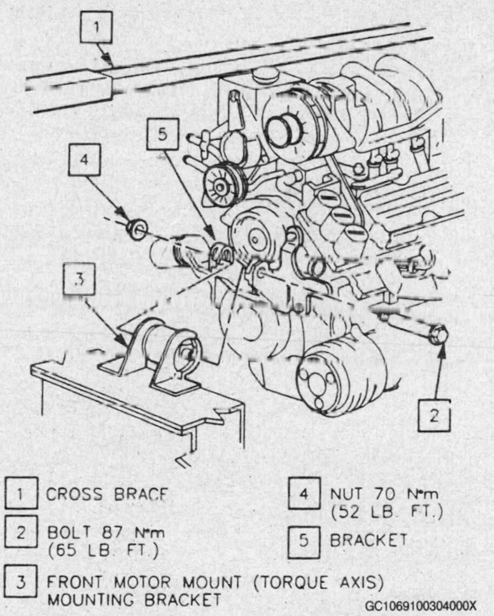
1
2
3
4
5
1 CROSS BRACE
2 BOLT 87 N·m (65 LB. FT.)
3 FRONT MOTOR MOUNT (TORQUE AXIS) MOUNTING BRACKET
4 NUT 70 N·m (52 LB. FT.)
5 BRACKET
GC1069100304000X

Fig. 1 Engine mount

ENGINE

REPLACE

1. Relieve fuel pressure as outlined under "Precautions."
2. Scribe alignment marks on hood for installation reference, then remove hood.
3. Disconnect battery leads, then drain engine coolant.
4. **On VIN L engines,** remove strut tower cross brace.
5. **On all models,** disconnect windshield washer, radiator and heater supply hoses.
6. Disconnect starter electrical connector and wiring.
7. Disconnect main engine harness and battery harness electrical connectors at relay center.
8. Remove accessory drive belt.
9. Remove power steering pump and position aside.
10. Remove air intake duct and air cleaner assembly.
11. Remove throttle cable from linkage bracket, then other applicable cables.
12. Disconnect electrical connectors from the following:
    a. MAT sensor.
    b. Throttle position switch.
    c. Idle air control valve.
    d. Oxygen sensor.
    e. A/C compressor.
    f. Oil pressure switch.
    g. Power steering cutout switch.
    h. Vehicle speed sensor.
    i. Low oil level sensor.
13. Remove ignition coil ground strap attaching screws.
14. Disconnect fuel feed and return lines from fuel rail and pressure regulator.
15. Disconnect throttle body canister hoses.
16. Disconnect brake booster and heater control hoses from engine vacuum connection.
17. Disconnect cruise control servo vacuum hoses.
18. Raise and support vehicle.
19. Remove exhaust pipe from right manifold.
20. Install suitable engine lifting equipment, then raise engine slightly.

21. Remove A/C compressor and position aside.
22. Disconnect engine oil cooler lines, if equipped.
23. Remove front engine mount.
24. Remove right front engine to transaxle bracket.
25. Using suitable jack stands, support transaxle, then remove engine to transaxle attaching bolts.
26. Remove flywheel cover.
27. Scribe flywheel installation alignment mark, then remove torque converter to flywheel attaching bolts.
28. Lower vehicle and remove torque axis engine mount.
29. Separate engine from transaxle, then remove engine assembly.
30. Reverse procedure to install.

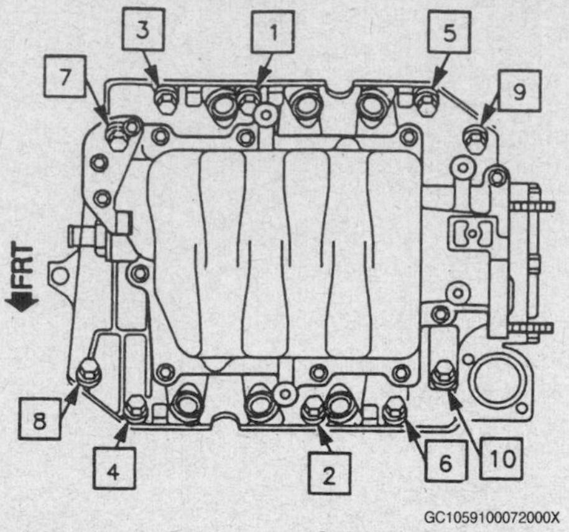
3
1
5
7
9
FRT
8
4
2
6
10
GC1059100072000X

Fig. 2 Intake manifold tightening sequence

INTAKE MANIFOLD
REPLACE
VIN K & L

1. Remove upper intake manifold as described under "Upper Intake Manifold, Replace."
2. Drain cooling system and remove upper radiator hose from coolant outlet.
3. Remove alternator and set aside.
4. Remove drive belt tensioner.
5. Remove EGR valve outlet pipe.
6. Remove intake manifold bolts, then the manifold.
7. Reverse procedure to install, noting the following:
   a. Clean cylinder block, heads and intake manifold sealing surface of all oil using a suitable solvent.
   b. Remove adhesive compound from intake manifold bolts and bolt holes.
   c. Apply thread lock compound part No. 12345493 or equivalent to intake manifold bolt threads prior to installation.
   d. Tighten intake manifold bolts in two steps to specifications in sequence shown in **Fig. 2.**

VIN 1

1. Relieve fuel pressure as outlined under "Precautions."
2. Remove fuel injector sight shield.
3. Remove plastic engine cover and air intake duct.
4. Disconnect manifold vacuum source, then drain cooling system.
5. Disconnect righthand side spark plug wires and position aside.
6. Remove fuel rail, then exhaust manifold heat shield.
7. Disconnect upper radiator and bypass hoses from coolant outlet.
8. Disconnect electrical connectors from the following:
   a. Throttle position sensor.
   b. Idle air control valve.
   c. Fuel injectors.
   d. MAP sensor.
9. Remove EGR outlet pipe.
10. Remove throttle and cruise control cables.
11. Remove throttle bracket with power steering reservoir and set aside.
12. Remove inner accessory drive belt, then disconnect heater hose from intake.
13. Using standard double nut procedure, remove tensioner bracket to supercharger retaining stud.
14. Remove intake manifold attaching bolts, then the manifold.
15. Reverse procedure to install, noting the following:
    a. Clean cylinder block, heads and intake manifold sealing surface of all oil using a suitable solvent.
    b. Remove adhesive compound from intake manifold bolts and bolt holes.
    c. Apply thread lock compound part No. 12345493 or equivalent to intake manifold bolt threads prior to installation.
    d. Tighten intake manifold bolts in two steps to specifications in sequence shown in **Fig. 2.**

UPPER INTAKE MANIFOLD
REPLACE
VIN K & L

1. Relieve fuel pressure as outlined under "Precautions."
2. Disconnect battery ground cable.
3. Remove fuel injector sight shield and air intake duct.
4. Remove spark plug wires on right (rear) side of engine and position aside.
5. Remove fuel rail, then the exhaust manifold heat shield.
6. Remove throttle cable bracket to cylinder head mounting bolt.
7. Remove throttle body support bracket.
8. Remove upper intake manifold attaching bolts, then the manifold, **Figs. 3 and 4.**
9. Reverse procedure to install.

EXHAUST MANIFOLD
REPLACE
LEFT SIDE (FRONT)
VIN K & L

1. Relieve fuel pressure as outlined under "Precautions."
2. Disconnect battery ground cable, then remove two crossover pipe to manifold attaching bolts.
3. Disconnect spark plug wires at spark plugs.
4. Remove oil dipstick tube and dipstick.
5. Remove manifold attaching bolts, then the manifold.
6. Reverse procedure to install.

VIN 1

1. Disconnect battery ground cable.
2. Remove two left exhaust manifold to right exhaust manifold attaching bolts.
3. Disconnect spark plug wires at spark plugs.
4. Remove oil dipstick tube and dipstick.
5. Remove manifold attaching bolts and studs, then the manifold.
6. Reverse procedure to install.

RIGHT SIDE (REAR)
1992–93

1. Relieve fuel pressure as outlined under "Precautions."
2. Disconnect battery ground cable, then disconnect spark plug wires from spark plugs and position aside.
3. Remove throttle cable bracket, then the crossover pipe heat shield.
4. Remove transaxle dipstick and dipstick tube.
5. Disconnect oxygen sensor lead, then remove EGR pipe.
6. Remove two exhaust pipe to manifold attaching bolts.
7. Remove plastic vacuum tank mounted on cowl, then raise and support vehicle.
8. Remove catalytic converter heat shield and pipe hanger.
9. Remove front exhaust pipe to manifold attaching nuts, then the pipe from manifold.
10. Lower vehicle, then remove engine lift bracket.
11. Remove exhaust manifold attaching nuts, then the manifold.
12. Reverse procedure to install.

1994–95

1. Disconnect battery ground cable.
2. Disconnect spark plug wires from spark plugs and position aside.
3. **On VIN 1 engines,** remove throttle cable bracket and crossover pipe heat shield.
4. **On all engines,** remove transaxle oil level indicator and indicator tube.
5. Disconnect oxygen sensor wire.
6. **On VIN K and L engines,** remove two right exhaust manifold to crossover pipe attaching bolts.
7. **On VIN 1 engines,** remove two right manifold to left manifold attaching bolts.

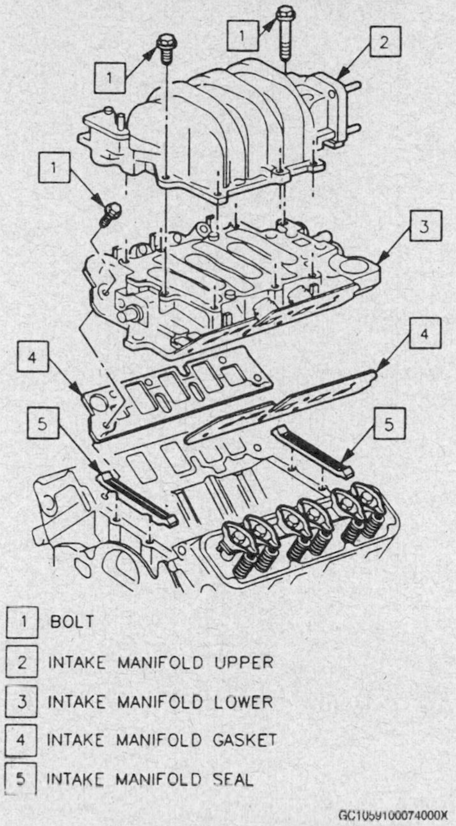
1
1
2
1
3
4
4
5
5
1 BOLT
2 INTAKE MANIFOLD UPPER
3 INTAKE MANIFOLD LOWER
4 INTAKE MANIFOLD GASKET
5 INTAKE MANIFOLD SEAL
GC1059100074000X

Fig. 3 Upper intake manifold. VIN L

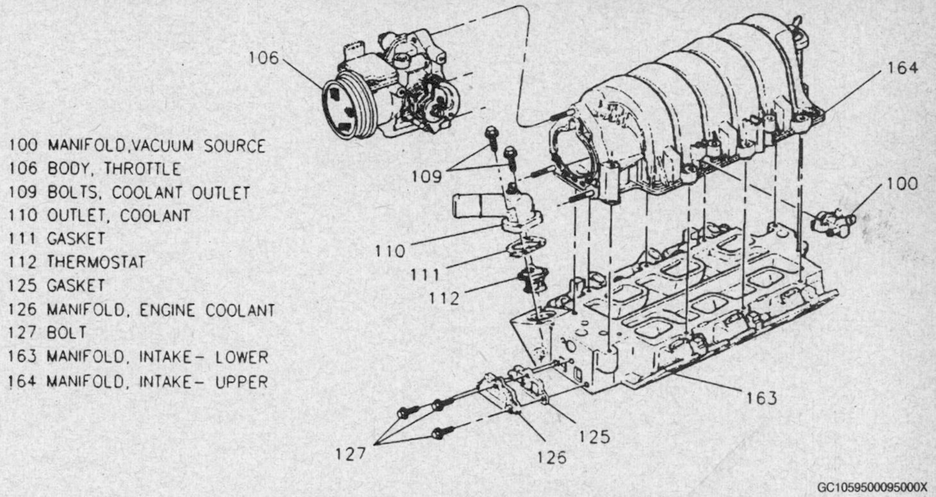
100 MANIFOLD,VACUUM SOURCE
106 BODY, THROTTLE
109 BOLTS, COOLANT OUTLET
110 OUTLET, COOLANT
111 GASKET
112 THERMOSTAT
125 GASKET
126 MANIFOLD, ENGINE COOLANT
127 BOLT
163 MANIFOLD, INTAKE- LOWER
164 MANIFOLD, INTAKE- UPPER
106
164
109
100
110
111
112
163
125
127
126
GC1059500095000X

Fig. 4 Upper intake manifold. VIN K

8. **On all engines,** remove vacuum reservoir from cowl.
9. Raise and support vehicle.
10. Remove exhaust pipe to exhaust manifold retaining nuts, then disconnect exhaust pipe from exhaust manifold.
11. Lower vehicle, then remove engine lift bracket.
12. Remove exhaust manifold attaching bolts and studs, then the manifold.
13. Reverse procedure to install. Tighten to specifications.

CYLINDER HEAD

REPLACE

1. Relieve fuel pressure as outlined under "Precautions."
2. Disconnect battery ground cable, then remove intake and exhaust manifolds as described previously.
3. To remove left (front) valve cover, proceed as follows:
   a. Disconnect C3I and spark plug wires.
   b. Remove alternator bracket.
   c. Remove A/C compressor bracket bolt.
4. To remove right (rear) valve cover, proceed as follows:
   a. Remove power steering pump.
   b. Remove belt tensioner assembly.
   c. Remove fuel line heat shield.
5. Remove rocker arm assemblies, guide plate and pushrods.
6. Remove cylinder head attaching bolts, then remove.

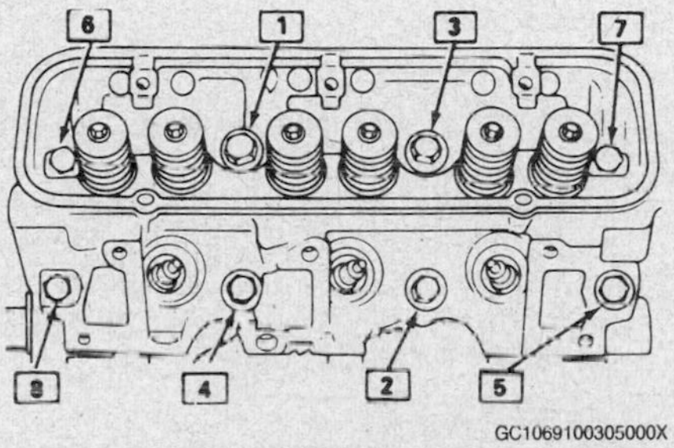
6
1
3
7
8
4
2
5
GC1069100305000X

Fig. 5 Cylinder head tightening sequence

7. Reverse procedure to install, noting the following:
   a. Clean all gasket mating surfaces and cylinder head bolt holes in block.
   b. Clean threads in block with appropriate tap.
   c. Apply suitable sealant to bolt threads.
   d. **Torque** cylinder head bolts to 35 ft. lbs., in sequence shown in **Fig. 5.**
   e. Tighten each bolt an additional 130° in sequence.
   f. Tighten center four bolts an additional 30° in sequence.

VALVE ARRANGEMENT

FRONT TO REAR

Left Side

VIN L .... E-I-E-I-I-E

Right Side

VIN L .... E-I-I-E-I-E

CAMSHAFT LOBE LIFT SPECIFICATIONS

Engine/VIN	Year	Int.	Exh.
3800/V6-231	1992–95	.250	.255

VALVE CLEARANCE SPECIFICATIONS

These engines are equipped with hydraulic valve lifters, valve clearance should be zero.

VALVE ADJUSTMENT

These engines are equipped with hydraulic valve lifters, there is no provision for adjustment.

ROCKER ARMS

Rocker arms are pedestal mounted, over support plates, **Fig. 6.** To replace rocker arms, remove valve cover, pedestal retaining bolt(s), pedestal and the rocker arm. Replace rocker arms and pedestals as an assembly if they are damaged or excessively worn. If rocker arms are to be reused, they must be installed in original position.

VALVE GUIDES

The valve guides are an integral part of the cylinder head and cannot be replaced. If excessive valve stem clearance is noted, the valve guide must be reamed and an oversize valve guide installed. Valves are available in an oversize of .010 inch.

FRONT COVER

REPLACE

1. Disconnect battery ground cable.
2. Remove torque axis engine mount.
3. Remove serpentine belt.
4. Using pulling tool No. J38197 or equivalent, remove crankshaft pulley.
5. Remove crankshaft sensor shield, then oil pan to front cover attaching bolts.
6. Remove front cover attaching bolts, then the front cover.
7. Reverse procedure to install, noting the following:
   a. Inspect timing chain for in and out

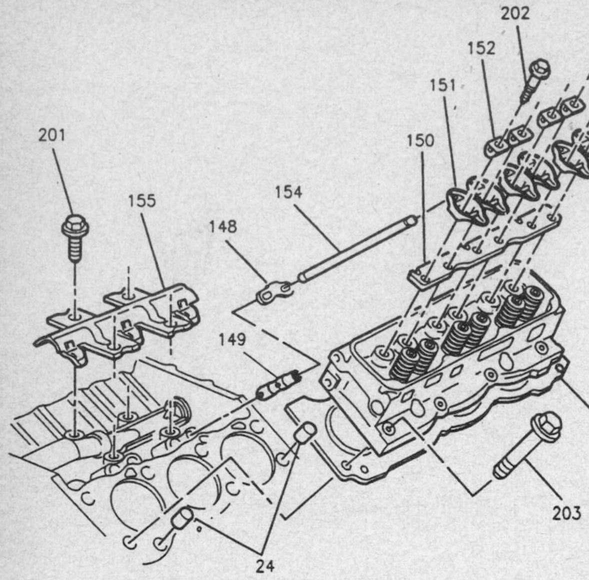
202
152
151
201
150
155
154
148
149
143
203
24

24 DOWEL PIN
143 HEAD GASKET
148 LIFTER GUIDE
149 VALVE LIFTER
150 PUSHROD GUIDE
151 ROCKER ARM
152 ROCKER ARM PIVOT
154 PUSHROD
155 LIFTER GUIDE RETAINER
201 BOLT
202 BOLT
203 HEAD BOLT

GC1069100306000X

Fig. 6 Rocker arm assembly

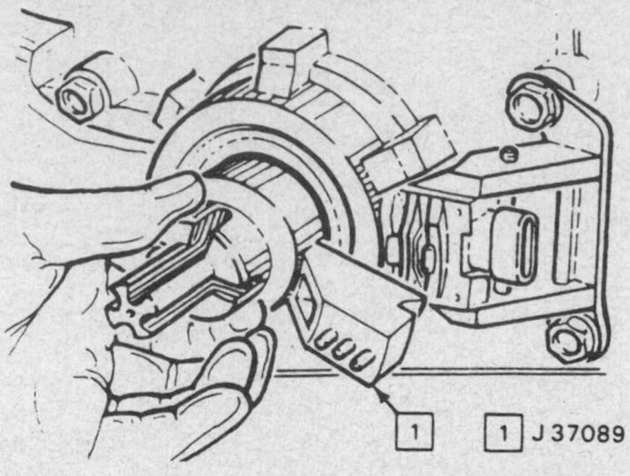
1
1 J 37089

GC1069100307000X

Fig. 7 Crankshaft sensor adjustment

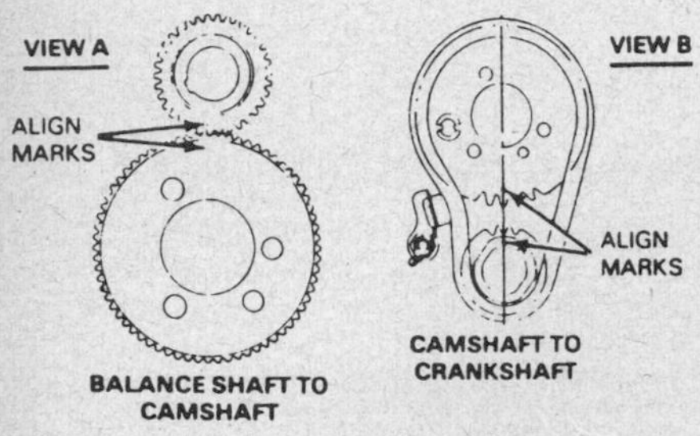
VIEW A
ALIGN MARKS
BALANCE SHAFT TO CAMSHAFT
VIEW B
ALIGN MARKS
CAMSHAFT TO CRANKSHAFT

GC1069100308000X

Fig. 8 Timing balance shaft & camshaft marks

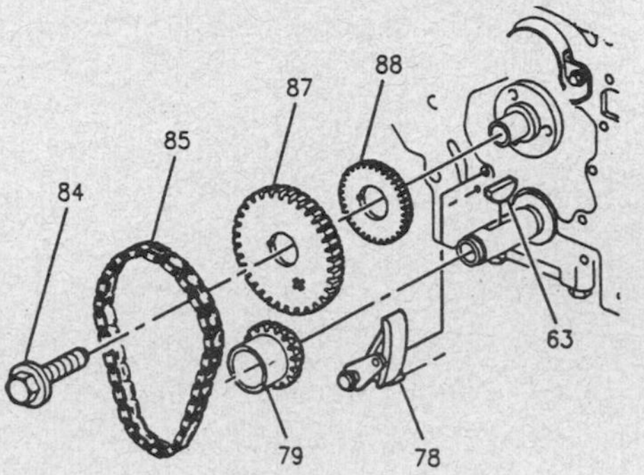
88
87
85
84
63
79
78

63 KEY
78 DAMPER ASSEMBLY
79 CRANKSHAFT SPROCKET
84 BOLT
85 TIMING CHAIN
87 CAMSHAFT SPROCKET
88 CAMSHAFT GEAR

GC1069100310000X

Fig. 9 Timing chain & sprockets

movement, movement should not exceed 1 inch.
- b. Check timing chain sprockets for any signs of wear.
- c. Clean gasket mating surfaces at timing chain cover and cylinder block.
- d. Apply sealant part No. 1052080 or equivalent to bolt threads prior to installation.
- e. Adjust crankshaft sensor using tool No. J37087 or equivalent as shown in **Fig. 7.**

TIMING CHAIN
REPLACE

1. Remove front cover as outlined under "Front Cover, Replace."
2. Align timing marks on sprockets, **Fig. 8,** so that they are as close together as possible.
3. Remove timing chain dampener.
4. Remove camshaft sprocket bolts, **Fig. 9**
5. Remove camshaft sprocket and chain, then the crankshaft sprocket.
6. Reverse procedure to install, noting the following:
   - a. Ensure No. 1 piston is at TDC.
   - b. Ensure camshaft and balance shaft timing marks are straight down, **Fig. 8.**
   - c. Assemble timing chain on sprockets with their timing marks in their closest together position.
   - d. Torque camshaft sprocket bolts specifications.

CAMSHAFT
REPLACE

1. Relieve fuel pressure as outlined under "Precautions."
2. Disconnect battery ground cable, then remove intake manifold as described previously.
3. Remove valve cover, rocker arms, pushrods and valve lifters.
4. Remove crankshaft pulley and crankshaft sensor cover.
5. Remove front cover, timing chain and sprockets.
6. Remove camshaft thrust plate and camshaft. **When removing or installing camshaft, avoid marring the bearing surface.**
7. Reverse procedure to install, coating camshaft and valve lifters with prelube part No. 1052365 or equivalent prior to installation.

BALANCE SHAFT
REPLACE
REMOVAL

1. Remove engine as previously described.
2. Remove flywheel, then the intake manifold.
3. Remove lifter guide retainer, then the front cover.
4. Remove balance shaft drive gear bolt, **Fig. 10,** then the camshaft sprocket and timing chain.
5. Remove balance shaft retainer bolts, retainer and gear.
6. Using tool J-6125-B, remove balance shaft. **The balance shaft and both bearings are serviced as a complete package. Use only the correct tools for bearing and shaft removal and installation. Inspect balance shaft drive gear and the camshaft drive gear for nicks and burrs.**
7. Remove balance shaft rear plug.
8. Using tool J-36995-5, remove balance shaft rear bearing.

INSTALLATION

1. Dip balance shaft rear bearing in clean engine oil, then, using tool J-36995-1, install bearing with rolled edge facing into engine and Manufacturer's markings facing flywheel side.
2. Dip front balance shaft bearing into clean engine oil, then, using tool J-36996, install balance shaft into block.
3. Temporarily install balance shaft bearing retainer and bolts.
4. Install balance shaft drive gear, then apply suitable sealant to and install bolt, tightening to specifications.
5. Install balance shaft rear plug.
6. Measure balance shaft endplay, **Fig. 11.**. Endplay should be 0-.008 inch.
7. Measure balance shaft radial play at both front and rear, **Figs. 12 and 13.** Front radial play should be 0-.0011 inch and rear radial play should be .0005-.0047 inch.

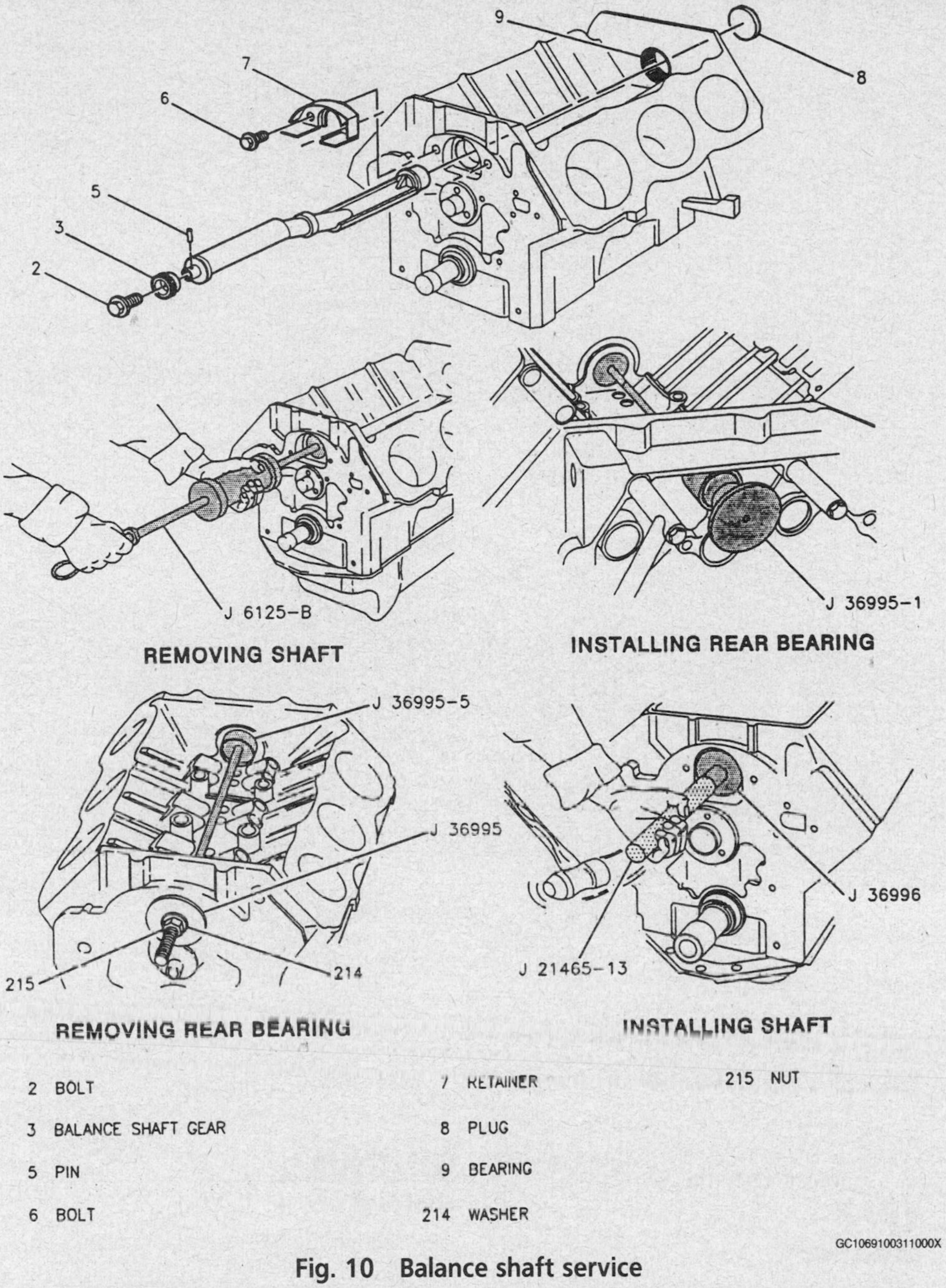
9
7
6
8
5
3
2
J 6125–B
REMOVING SHAFT
J 36995–1
INSTALLING REAR BEARING
J 36995–5
J 36995
J 36996
J 21465–13
215
214
REMOVING REAR BEARING
INSTALLING SHAFT
2 BOLT
3 BALANCE SHAFT GEAR
5 PIN
6 BOLT
7 RETAINER
8 PLUG
9 BEARING
214 WASHER
215 NUT
GC1069100311000X

Fig. 10 Balance shaft service

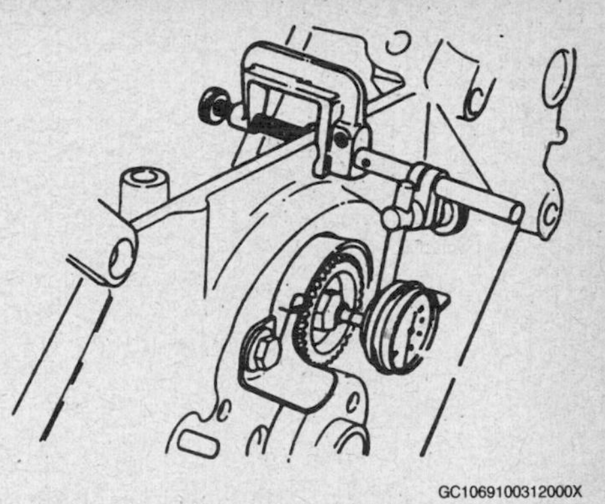
GC1069100312000X

Fig. 11 Measuring balance shaft endplay

GC1069100313000X

Fig. 12 Measuring balance shaft front radial play

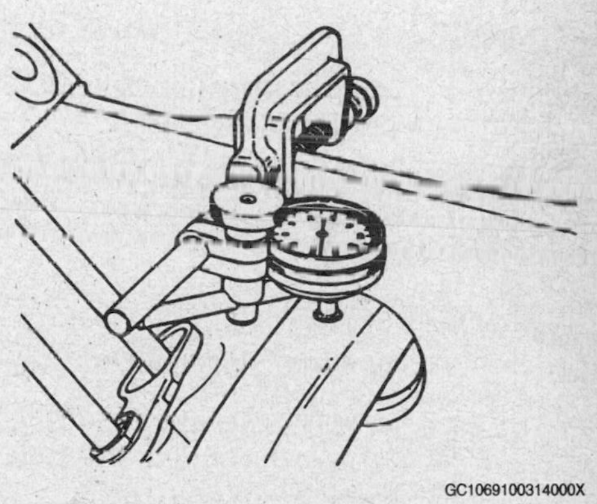
GC1069100314000X

Fig. 13 Measuring balance shaft rear radial play

8. Turn camshaft so, with camshaft sprocket temporarily installed, timing mark is straight down.
9. With camshaft sprocket and camshaft gear removed, turn balance shaft so that the timing mark on gear points straight down.
10. Install camshaft gear, aligning marks on balance shaft gear and camshaft gear by turning balance shaft, **Fig. 8.**
11. Turn crankshaft so that No. 1 piston is at TDC.
12. Install timing chain and camshaft sprocket.
13. Measure gear lash, **Fig. 14,** at four places, every 1/4 turn. Lash should be .002-.005 inch.
14. Install balance shaft front bearing retainer and bolts, then tighten to specifications.
15. Install front cover, then the lifter guide retainer.
16. Install intake manifold, then the flywheel. Torque flywheel bolts to specifications.
17. Install engine in vehicle.

PISTON & ROD ASSEMBLY

Pistons should be assembled to rods and installed as shown in **Fig. 15.**

After piston and rod installation, measure connecting rod side clearance. Side clearance should be .003-.015 inch.

PISTONS, PINS & RINGS

Pistons and ring are available in standard sizes and oversizes of .010. Piston pins are supplied with the piston and are available in standard size only.

To check piston fit in bore, measure bore diameter using suitable telescoping gauges and record reading. Measure piston across skirt at a point 3/4 inch below piston pin center line and record reading. Subtract piston diameter from bore diameter and compare to specified clearance.

MAIN & ROD BEARINGS

Main bearings are available in standard sizes and undersizes of .001 and .002 inch. Rod bearings are available in standard size and an undersize of .008 inch.

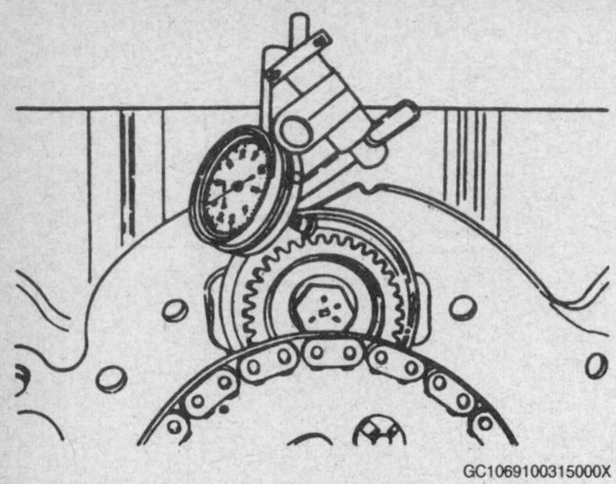
GC1069100315000X

Fig. 14 Measuring balance shaft gear lash

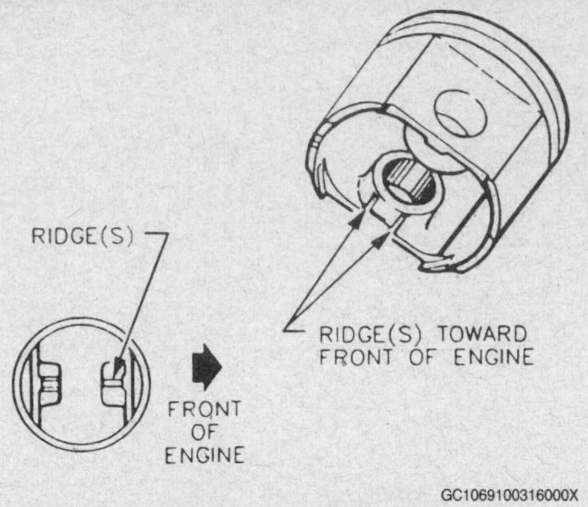
RIDGE(S)
RIDGE(S) TOWARD FRONT OF ENGINE
FRONT OF ENGINE
GC1069100316000X

Fig. 15 Piston installation direction

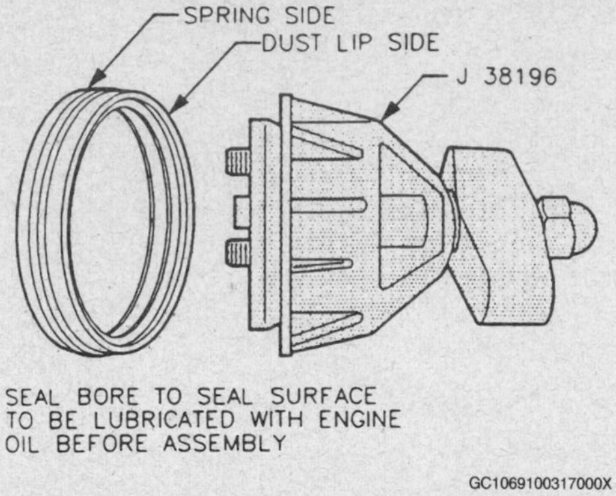
SPRING SIDE
DUST LIP SIDE
J 38196
SEAL BORE TO SEAL SURFACE TO BE LUBRICATED WITH ENGINE OIL BEFORE ASSEMBLY
GC1069100317000X

Fig. 16 Crankshaft rear oil seal (rear main) & tool. VIN L & 1

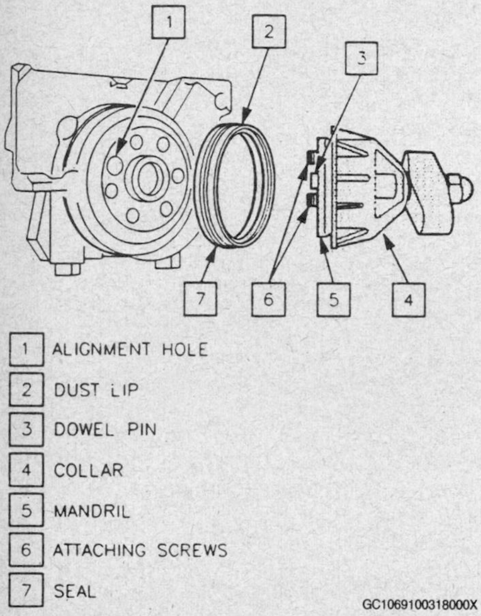
1
2
3
7
6
5
4
1 ALIGNMENT HOLE
2 DUST LIP
3 DOWEL PIN
4 COLLAR
5 MANDRIL
6 ATTACHING SCREWS
7 SEAL
GC1069100318000X

Fig. 17 Crankshaft rear oil seal installation (rear main). VIN L & 1

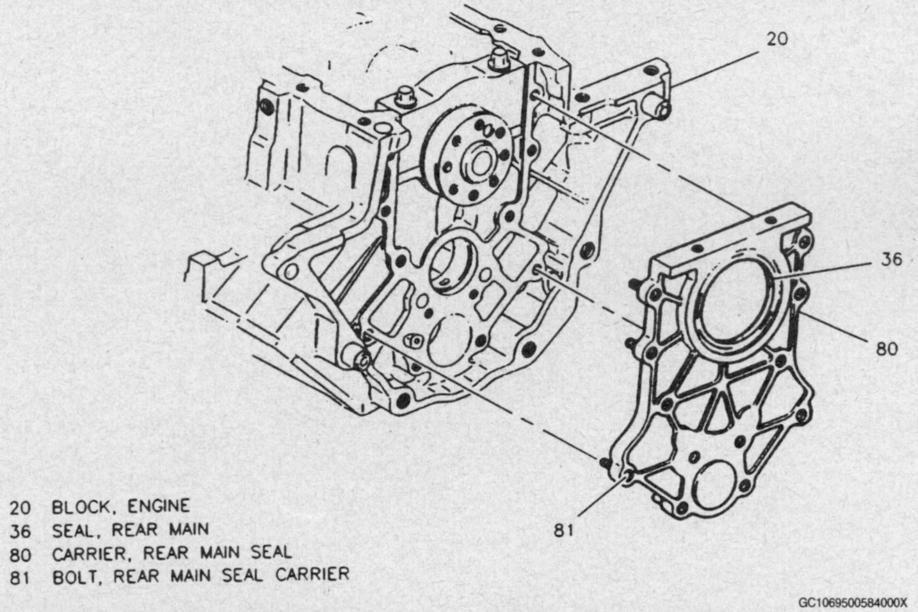
20
36
80
81
20 BLOCK, ENGINE
36 SEAL, REAR MAIN
80 CARRIER, REAR MAIN SEAL
81 BOLT, REAR MAIN SEAL CARRIER
GC1069500584000X

Fig. 18 Rear main seal replacement. VIN K

CRANKSHAFT SEAL
REPLACE

VIN L & 1

1. Remove flexplate and confirm rear seal leak.
2. Insert a screwdriver through oil seal dust lip and pry seal out towards end of crankshaft pilot.
3. Reverse procedure to install, noting the following:
   a. Check inside of bore and crankshaft for nicks or burrs. Repair or replace as required.
   b. Apply engine oil to inside and outside surfaces of the new seal, then slide seal over seal installation tool No. J38196 or equivalent as shown in **Fig. 16,** until seal bottoms squarely against bottom of tool.
   c. Align dowel pin of tool with dowel pin in crankshaft and attach tool to crankshaft by hand and tighten attaching screws to 60 inch lbs., **Fig. 17.**
   d. Turn T-handle of tool so that collar pushes seal into bore, turn handle until collar is tight against case.
   e. Loosen T-handle, remove attaching screws and the tool.

VIN K

Removal

1. Remove flywheel.
2. Remove oil pan as described in "Oil Pan, Replace."
3. Remove rear main seal carrier attaching bolts, then the seal carrier, **Fig. 18.**
4. Remove rear main seal from seal carrier.

Installation

1. Install seal into seal carrier.
2. Install seal carrier and finger tighten attaching bolts.
3. Wipe a thin film of oil on both sides of rear cover aligning tool No. J 41349 or equivalent.
4. Install aligning tool over crankshaft, twist and turn tool as necessary.
5. Tighten housing bolts to specification, then remove alignment tool.
6. Tighten housing bolts to specification.
7. Install flywheel and oil pan.

OIL PAN
REPLACE

1. Relieve fuel pressure as outlined under "Precautions."
2. Raise and support vehicle, then drain engine oil.
3. Disconnect oil level sensor electrical connector.
4. Remove oil pan retaining bolts, then the oil pan.
5. Remove old oil pan gasket and discard.
6. Reverse procedure to install.

OIL PUMP SERVICE
REMOVAL & INSPECTION

1. Remove front cover, refer to "Front Cover, Replace" procedure.
2. Remove oil filter adapter, pressure regulator valve and spring.
3. Remove oil pump cover attaching screws, then the cover and gears, **Fig. 19.**

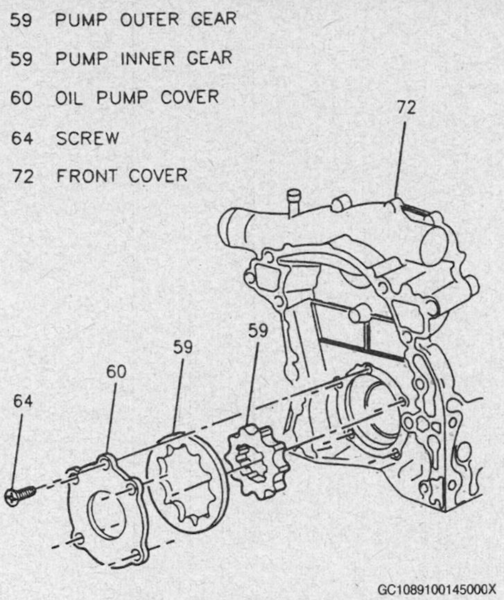
59 PUMP OUTER GEAR
59 PUMP INNER GEAR
60 OIL PUMP COVER
64 SCREW
72 FRONT COVER
72
59
59
60
64
GC1089100145000X

Fig. 19 Oil pump

4. Check pump cover and housing for cracks, scoring, porous or damaged casting, damaged threads or excessive wear or galling. Replace as required.
5. Check pressure regulator valve for scoring, burrs or sticking in valve bore. Replace as required.
6. Check pressure regulator valve spring for tension loss or bending. Replace spring as required.
7. Check gears for chipping galling or excessive wear. Replace as required.

ASSEMBLY & INSTALLATION

1. Measure oil pump inner gear tip clearance, **Fig. 20.** Maximum clearance should be .006 inch.
2. Measure oil pump outer gear diameter clearance, **Fig. 21.** Clearance should be .008-.015 inch.
3. Measure oil pump gear end clearance with gear dropped in housing, **Fig. 22.** Clearance should be .0010-.0035 inch.
4. Measure pressure regulator valve for valve to bore clearance of .0015-.003 inch.
5. Lubricate all gears with clean motor oil, then install gears in housing.
6. Pack pump cavity with suitable petroleum jelly.
7. Install pump cover and cover attaching screws. Tighten cover attaching screws to specifications.
8. Install pressure regulator valve and spring.
9. Install oil filter adapter using a new gasket. Torque oil filter adapter attaching bolts to specifications.
10. Install front cover on engine. **During front cover installation, ensure inner pump gear is properly engaged on crankshaft sprocket.**

BELT TENSION DATA

Belt	New Lbs.	Used Lbs.
Serpentine	①	①

①—Equipped with auto-tensioner.

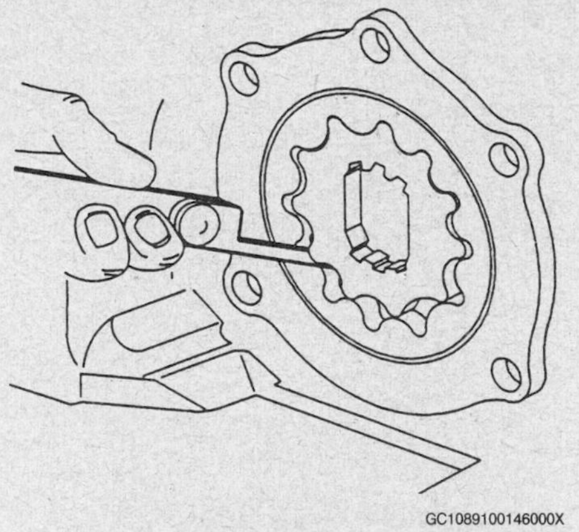
GC1089100146000X

Fig. 20 Measuring oil pump inner gear tip clearance

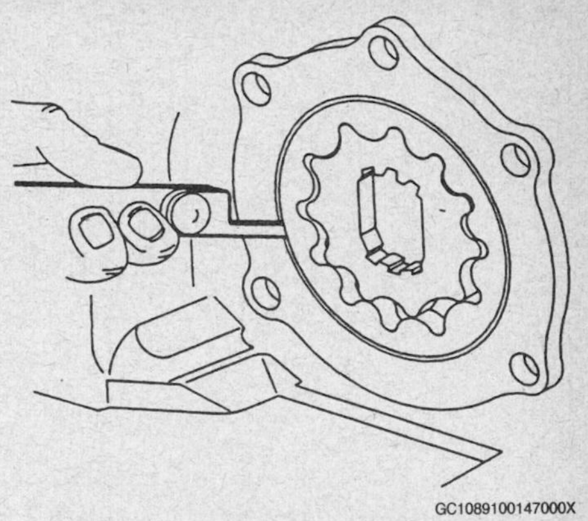
GC1089100147000X

Fig. 21 Measuring oil pump outer gear diameter clearance

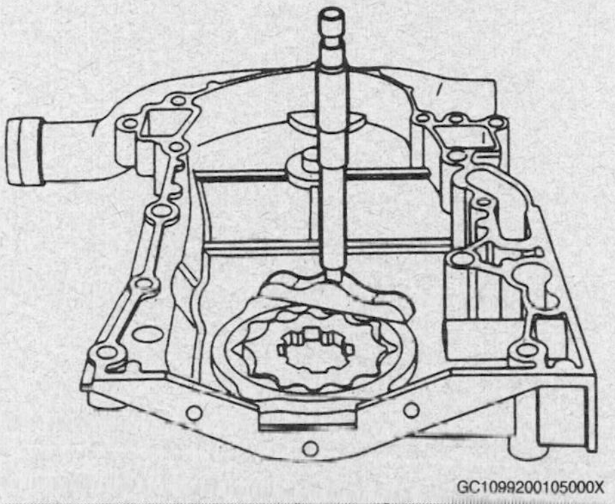
GC1099200105000X

Fig. 22 Measuring oil pump gear end clearance

SERPENTINE DRIVE BELT

BELT ROUTING

Refer to **Figs. 23 through 25** for serpentine drive belt routing.

BELT TENSIONER, REPLACE

VIN L

1. Disconnect battery ground cable.
2. Remove accessory drive, **Fig. 23.**
3. Remove tensioner pulley attaching bolt, then remove pulley.
4. Remove power steering pump from bracket and position aside.
5. Loosen, but do not remove, alternator attaching bolts, then remove alternator to tensioner attaching bolt.
6. Remove tensioner attaching bolt and studs, then remove.
7. Reverse procedure to install.

VIN 1

1. Disconnect battery ground cable.
2. Remove inner and outer accessory drive belts, **Fig. 24.**
3. Remove alternator attaching bolts, then position aside.
4. Drain engine coolant.
5. Disconnect heater hoses from pipes and pipes from engine.
6. Raise and support vehicle.
7. Remove lower bracket to transaxle bracket attaching bolt.
8. Drain power steering fluid, then disconnect power steering hoses.
9. Remove power steering pump attaching bolts, then position aside.
10. Lower vehicle.
11. Remove tensioner bracket attaching bolts, supercharger to bracket attaching nut, then remove tensioner and bracket.
12. Reverse procedure to install.

VIN K

1. Disconnect battery ground cable.
2. Drain engine coolant, then remove accessory drive belt, **Fig. 25.**
3. Remove alternator and heater hoses.
4. Remove tensioner attaching bolts, then the tensioner.
5. Reverse procedure to install.
6.

BELT, REPLACE

1. Disconnect battery ground cable.
2. **On VIN L engines,** refer to **Fig. 23.**
3. **On VIN 1 engines,** refer to **Fig. 24.**
4. **On VIN K engines,** refer to **Fig. 25.**
5. **On all engines,** reverse procedure to install.

COOLING SYSTEM BLEED

1. Fill cooling system and leave radiator cap off.
2. Turn A/C-heater control to any A/C mode and set temperature to the highest setting.
3. Start engine and allow engine to idle until bottom radiator hose is hot.
4. Cycle engine speed up to 3000 RPM and back to idle five times. This should expel any trapped air in the system.
5. Refill radiator and install pressure cap.
6. Allow engine to return to outside temperature, then fill coolant reservoir to FULL COLD mark.

THERMOSTAT

REPLACE

1. Disconnect battery negative cable.
2. With engine cool, drain engine coolant

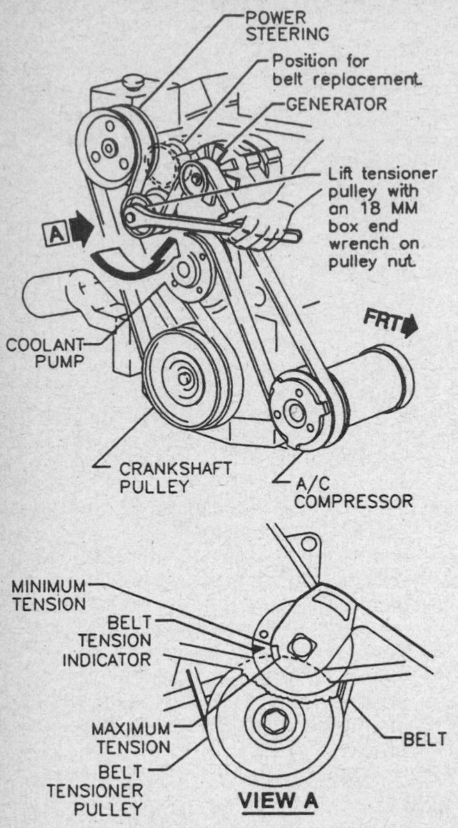
POWER STEERING
Position for belt replacement.
GENERATOR
Lift tensioner pulley with an 18 MM box end wrench on pulley nut.
A
FRT
COOLANT PUMP
CRANKSHAFT PULLEY
A/C COMPRESSOR
MINIMUM TENSION
BELT TENSION INDICATOR
MAXIMUM TENSION
BELT TENSIONER PULLEY
BELT
VIEW A

GC1069100319000X

Fig. 23 Serpentine belt routing & replacement. VIN L

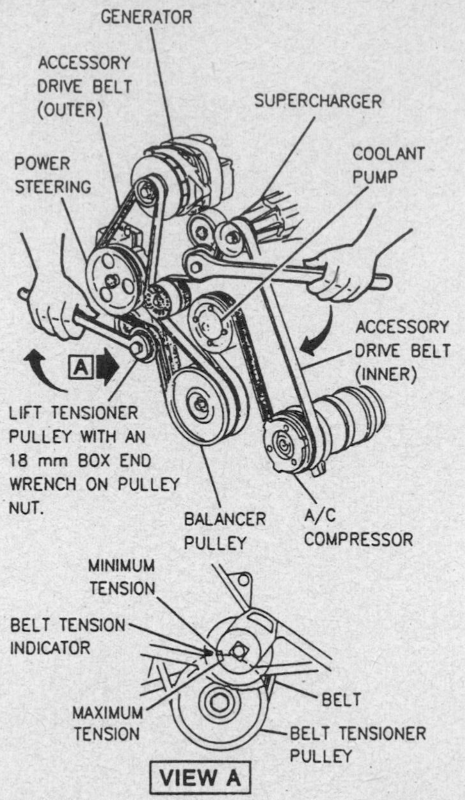
GENERATOR
ACCESSORY DRIVE BELT (OUTER)
SUPERCHARGER
POWER STEERING
COOLANT PUMP
ACCESSORY DRIVE BELT (INNER)
A
LIFT TENSIONER PULLEY WITH AN 18 mm BOX END WRENCH ON PULLEY NUT.
BALANCER PULLEY
A/C COMPRESSOR
MINIMUM TENSION
BELT TENSION INDICATOR
MAXIMUM TENSION
BELT
BELT TENSIONER PULLEY
VIEW A

GC1069100320000X

Fig. 24 Serpentine belt routing & replacement. VIN 1

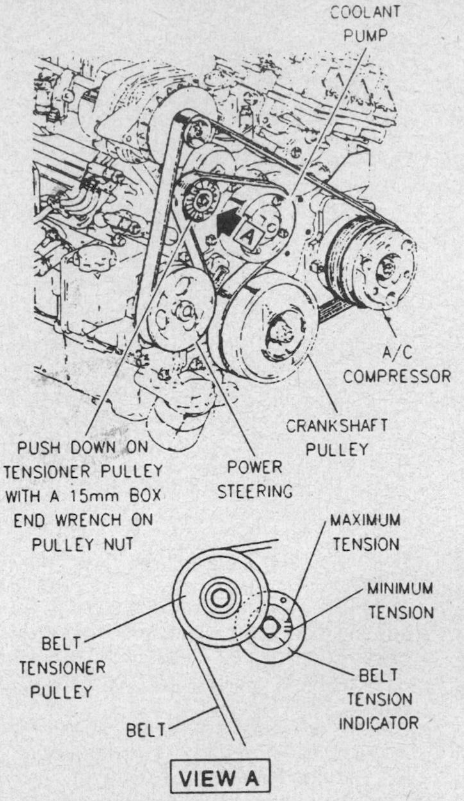
COOLANT PUMP
A
A/C COMPRESSOR
CRANKSHAFT PULLEY
PUSH DOWN ON TENSIONER PULLEY WITH A 15mm BOX END WRENCH ON PULLEY NUT
POWER STEERING
MAXIMUM TENSION
MINIMUM TENSION
BELT TENSIONER PULLEY
BELT TENSION INDICATOR
BELT
VIEW A

GC1069500585000X

Fig. 25 Serpentine belt routing & replacement. VIN K

below thermostat level. **Never open cooling system with engine hot. Failure to follow this warning may cause personal injury.**

3. Disconnect radiator hose from thermostat housing.
4. Remove thermostat housing retaining bolt(s), then the housing, gasket and thermostat.
5. Reverse procedure to install noting the following:
   a. Prior to installation, ensure thermostat gasket area is thoroughly clean.
   b. Install thermostat with new gasket.
   c. Tighten thermostat housing retaining bolt(s) to specifications.
   d. Refill and bleed cooling system as needed.

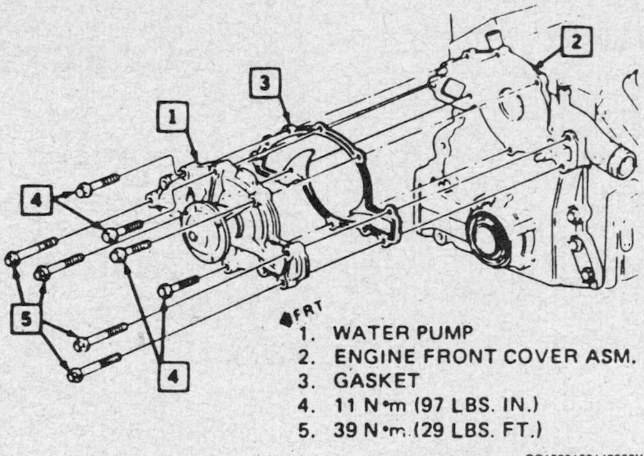
1
2
3
4
5
4
FRT
1. WATER PUMP
2. ENGINE FRONT COVER ASM.
3. GASKET
4. 11 N•m (97 LBS. IN.)
5. 39 N•m (29 LBS. FT.)

GC1089100148000X

Fig. 26 Water pump assembly

WATER PUMP
REPLACE

1. Disconnect battery ground cable and drain cooling system.
2. Remove drive belts and disconnect radiator hoses and heater hoses from pump.
3. Remove water pump pulley attaching bolts, **Fig. 26.** The long bolt is accessed through hole in body side rail. Remove pump pulley.
4. Remove water pump attaching bolts and the water pump.
5. Reverse procedure to install.

RADIATOR
REPLACE

1. Disconnect battery ground cable.
2. Drain engine coolant.
3. Remove upper fan mounting bolts.
4. Remove upper radiator panel.
5. Remove coolant hoses from radiator and coolant recovery tank hose from radiator neck.
6. Disconnect coolant fan electrical connector.
7. Disconnect transaxle oil cooler lines from radiator side tank.
8. Remove radiator from vehicle.
9. Reverse procedure to install.

FUEL PUMP
REPLACE

1. Relieve fuel pressure as outlined under "Precautions."
2. Disconnect battery ground cable.
3. Drain fuel tank and disconnect tank unit wire from connector in rear compartment.
4. Remove ground wire retaining screw from underbody.
5. Disconnect hoses from tank unit.
6. Support fuel tank and release the two retaining straps. Lower tank from vehicle.

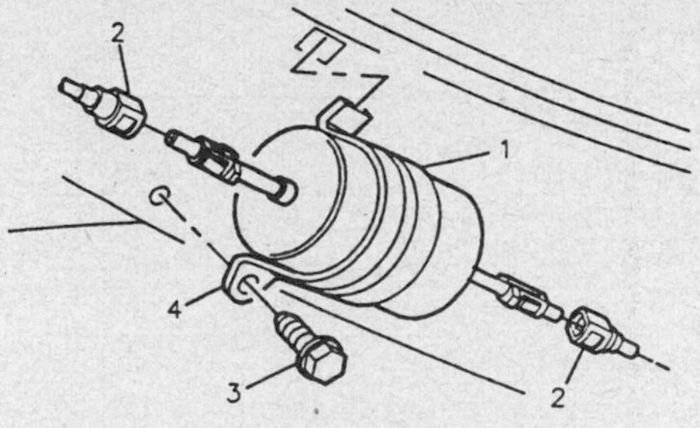
1 FUEL FILTER
2 QUICK CONNECTOR
3 BOLT/SCREW
4 FUEL FILTER BRACKET
GC1029102724000X

Fig. 27 Fuel filter replacement

7. Remove fuel gauge sender and pump assembly by turning cam lock counterclockwise, then remove.
8. Remove pump from sending unit.
9. Reverse procedure to install.

FUEL FILTER

REPLACE

1. Relieve fuel pressure as outlined under "Precautions."
2. Raise and support vehicle.
3. Disconnect fuel pipe inlet connector, then loosen filter from bracket, **Fig. 27.**
4. Disconnect outlet connector, then remove filter.
5. Reverse procedure to install.

SUPERCHARGER

REPLACE

1. Relieve fuel pressure as outlined under "Precautions."

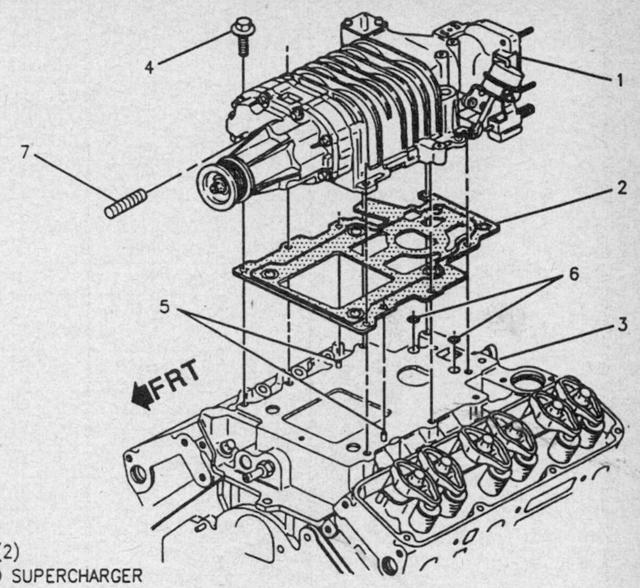
1 SUPERCHARGER
2 GASKET, SUPERCHARGER
3 LOWER INTAKE MANIFOLD
4 BOLTS, SUPERCHARGER (8)
5 LOCATOR PINS
6 O-RINGS, COOLANT PASSAGE (2)
7 STUD, TENSIONER BRACKET TO SUPERCHARGER
FRT
GC1059100073000X

Fig. 28 Supercharger. VIN 1

2. Disconnect battery ground cable.
3. Remove accessory drive belt.
4. Remove fuel injector sight shield.
5. Disconnect fuel pipe from fuel rail.
6. Disconnect pressure regulator vacuum hose.
7. Disconnect injector electrical connectors.
8. Remove fuel rail attaching bolts, then remove rail with injectors.
9. Disconnect idle air control, throttle position switch, MAF, EGR and boost control solenoid electrical connectors, then position aside.
10. Remove air intake duct.
11. Disconnect throttle and cruise control cables.
12. Remove cable bracket.
13. Remove tensioner bracket to supercharger mounting stud with suitable stud removal tool or install two 8 mm nut together on stud, then install suitable wrench to inner nut and turn counterclockwise to remove stud.
14. Remove supercharger to intake manifold attaching bolts, **Fig. 28,** then remove and discard gasket and O-rings.
15. Reverse procedure to install.

TIGHTENING SPECIFICATIONS

Year	Component	Torque/Ft. Lbs.
1992–95	Accessory Drive Belt Tensioner	37
	Balance Shaft Gear Bolt	①
	Balance Shaft Retainer	22
	Boost Control Solenoid To Bypass Actuator	22⑧
	Bypass Actuator To Supercharger	22⑧
	Camshaft Sensor To Front Cover	75②
	Camshaft Sprocket Bolts	⑥
	Connecting Rod Bolts	⑦
	Coolant Temperature Sensor To Intake	15
	Coolant Plug	32
	Crankshaft Balancer	⑨
	Crankshaft Sensor To Front Cover	22
	Crankshaft Sensor Clamp Bolt	40②
	Cylinder Block Drain Plug	25
	Cylinder Head To Block	③
	EGR Valve Adapter	37
1992–95 —Cont'd	EGR Pipe To Exhaust Manifold	15
	EGR Pipe To EGR Valve	22
	EGR Valve To Intake Manifold Adapter	22
	Engine Mount To Cylinder Block	70
	ESC Knock Sensor	13
	Exhaust Manifold To Cylinder Head	38
	Exhaust Pipe To Exhaust Manifold	18
	Flywheel Cover To Transaxle	48②
	Flywheel To Crankshaft	⑪
	Front Cover To Block	22
	Fuel Feed & Return Pipes To Fuel Rail	22
	Fuel Rail To Intake Manifold	11
	Generator Support To Cylinder Head	36
	Generator Support Through Generator	36
	Heater Hose Fitting To Intake	11
	Ignition Module To Generator Support	18

Continued

TIGHTENING SPECIFICATIONS—Continued

Year	Component	Torque/Ft. Lbs.
1992–95 —Cont'd	Intake Manifold To Cylinder Head	88②
	Intake Manifold (Upper) To Lower Manifold	22
	Main Bearing Cap Bolts (1992-94)	⑫
	Main Bearing Cap Bolts (1995 VIN L)	⑤
	Main Bearing Cap Bolts (1995 VIN K & 1)	⑬
	Oil Filter Adapter To Front Cover	22
	Oil Galley Plugs	25
	Oil Level Indicator Tube	11
	Oil Level Sensor To Oil Pan	16
	Oil Pan Drain Plug	30
	Oil Pan To Block	124②
	Oil Pan To Front Cover	124②
	Oil Pressure Switch	24
	Oil Pump Cover To Front Cover	97②
	Oil Screen Housing To Cylinder Block	134②
	Oxygen Sensor	31
	Pulley Assembly To Crankshaft	⑨
	Right Exhaust Manifold To Left Exhaust Manifold	15
	Rocker Arm Cover	88②
	Rocker Arm Pedestal	⑩
	Spark Plug	12
	Starter Motor	35
	Supercharger To Lower Intake Manifold	19–22
	Thermostat Housing	20
	Throttle Body Adapter To Intake	20
	Throttle Body To Throttle Body Adapter	20
	Throttle Cable Bracket	35②

Year	Component	Torque/Ft. Lbs.
1992–95 —Cont'd	Timing Chain Damper	④
	Torque Converter To Flywheel	46
	Transaxle To Cylinder Block	55
	Valve Lifter Guide Bolts	22
	Water Pump Cover To Timing Chain Cover	11
	Water Pump Pulley	114②

①—16 ft. lbs., then tighten an additional 70°.
②—Inch lbs.
③—Refer to text for procedure.
④—1992-94, 16 ft. lbs.; 1995 VIN L, 14 ft. lbs.; VIN K & 1, 16 ft. lbs.
⑤—29 ft. lbs., then tighten an additional 90°.
⑥—74 ft. lbs., then tighten an additional 105°.
⑦—20 ft lbs., then tighten an additional 50°.
⑧—VIN 1, supercharged.
⑨—110 ft. lbs., then tighten an additional 76°.
⑩—19 ft. lbs., then tighten an addtional 90°.
⑪—11 ft. lbs., then tighten an additional 50°.
⑫—Torque bolts to 26 ft. lbs., then tighten each bolt an additional 50°.
⑬—Torque bolts to 51 ft. lbs. to seat bearings. Loosen all bolts 1 turn. Torque bolts to 14 ft. lbs. Torque all bolts to 29 ft. lbs. Tighten each bolt an additional 105° in 35° increments. Torque side bolts to 11 ft. lbs., then tighten each bolt an additional 45°.

4.6L/V8-279 Engine

NOTE: Refer To The 4.6L/V8-279 Engine Section In The Buick Riviera: Cadillac Eldorado & Seville: Oldsmobile Toronado & Trofeo Section For Repair Procedures On This Engine.

4.9L/V8-300 Engines

NOTE: On Air Bag Equipped Models, Refer To "Air Bag System Precautions" Located In The Front Of This Manual For System Disarming & Arming Procedures.

INDEX

PRECAUTIONS

AIR BAG SYSTEMS

Refer to "Air Bag System Precautions" in the front of this manual for system disarming and arming procedures.

FUEL SYSTEM PRESSURE RELIEF

After relieving fuel system pressure, a small amount of fuel may be released when servicing fuel pipes or connections. In order to reduce the risk of personal injury, cover fuel pipe fittings with a suitable shop towel before disconnecting to catch any fuel that may leak.

1. Disconnect battery ground cable, then loosen fuel filler cap to relieve tank pressure.
2. Connect fuel pressure gauge tool No. J 34370-1 or equivalent to fuel pressure connection. Wrap fitting in suitable shop towel.
3. Install bleed hose to suitable container, then open valve and bleed off pressure.
4. Disconnect fuel pressure gauge, then drain gauge in suitable container.

ENGINE MOUNT

REPLACE

RIGHT SIDE

1. Relieve fuel pressure as outlined under "Precautions."
2. Open hood, then remove engine bracket to engine brace.
3. Remove engine bracket to mount attaching nuts.
4. Raise and support vehicle.
5. Using suitable jack stands, support vehicle at each front frame horn.
6. Remove two engine mount to frame attaching nut, **Fig. 1.**
7. Remove two transaxle bracket to mount attaching nuts.
8. Install engine support tool No. J 28467 or equivalent, then raise engine until bracket is clear of mounts.
9. Remove bracket to block stud and bolts, then pull mount and bracket forward to remove.
10. Remove transaxle mount bracket, then mount assembly.
11. Reverse procedure to install.

LEFT FRONT TRANSAXLE MOUNT

1. Relieve fuel pressure as outlined under "Precautions."
2. Raise and support vehicle.
3. Using suitable jack stands, support vehicle at each front frame horn.
4. Remove mount to transaxle bracket and frame attaching nuts.
5. Install engine support tool No. J 28467 or equivalent, raise engine, then remove bracket to transaxle attaching bolts.
6. Raise engine assembly until brackets are clear.
7. Pull mount and bracket upward to remove.
8. Reverse procedure to install.

LEFT REAR TRANSAXLE MOUNT

1. Relieve fuel pressure as outlined under "Precautions."
2. Raise vehicle hood, install engine support tool No. J 28467 or equivalent, then raise and support vehicle.
3. Remove rack and pinion three right-hand attaching bolts.
4. Remove mount attaching nuts and bolts.
5. While moving rack and pinion up and forward, remove mount assembly.
6. Reverse procedure to install.

ENGINE

REPLACE

1. Relieve fuel pressure as outlined under "Precautions."
2. Disconnect battery ground cable.
3. Drain engine coolant and oil.
4. Remove air cleaner assembly.
5. Mark hood installation alignment mars, then remove.
6. Remove cooling fan.
7. Remove accessory drive belt.
8. Remove upper radiator and heater hoses from thermostat housing.
9. Disconnect and position aside the following electrical connectors:
   a. Oil pressure switch.
   b. distributor.
   c. EGR solenoid.
   d. Engine temperature switch.
   e. Idle speed control (ISC).
   f. Throttle position sensor (TPS).
   g. Coolant temperature sensor and fuel injectors at rail connector.
   h. MAT sensor.
   i. Oxygen sensor.
   j. Alternator.
   k. Ground wire at alternator bracket.
10. Disconnect throttle cable from throttle lever.
11. Disconnect cruise control diaphragm with bracket and position aside.
12. Remove exhaust crossover pipe.
13. Disconnect oil and transmission cooler lines at radiator.
14. Remove radiator.
15. Disconnect oil and transmission cooler lines from oil filter adapter, then remove lines.
16. Remove oil cooler line bracket at

transmission, then air cleaner bracket.
17. Remove oil filter housing adapter.
18. Remove strut tower cross-car brace.
19. Remove right front heater hose.
20. Remove power steering line bracket from right cylinder head.
21. Disconnect power steering tensioner assembly and position aside.
22. Discharge A/C system, then disconnect accumulator and condenser lines.
23. Disconnect fuel rail fuel lines, then remove fuel line bracket to transmission and position aside.
24. Disconnect vacuum modulator line and power brake vacuum line and position aside.
25. Raise and support vehicle.
26. Remove starter heat shield.
27. Disconnect starter electrical connectors and engine block ground wires.
28. Disconnect exhaust pipe to converter at RH manifold.
29. Remove starter, then two flexplate covers.
30. Remove three flexplate attaching bolts, then remove.
31. Remove A/C compressor lower dust shield.
32. Remove right front wheel and tire assembly.
33. Remove wheelwell plastic shield.
34. Remove right rear transaxle to engine mount.
35. Remove lower engine mount attaching nut.
36. Remove front engine mount attaching nuts, then right rear transaxle mount attaching bolts.
37. Disconnect oxygen sensor electrical connector and heater bypass bracket front righthand side of vehicle.
38. Lower vehicle, then remove five upper engine to transaxle attaching bolts.
39. Install suitable engine lifting equipment, ensuring A/C accumulator line clearance.
40. Support transmission using suitable jack stand, then remove engine to transmission attaching bolts, then remove engine assembly.
41. Reverse procedure to install.

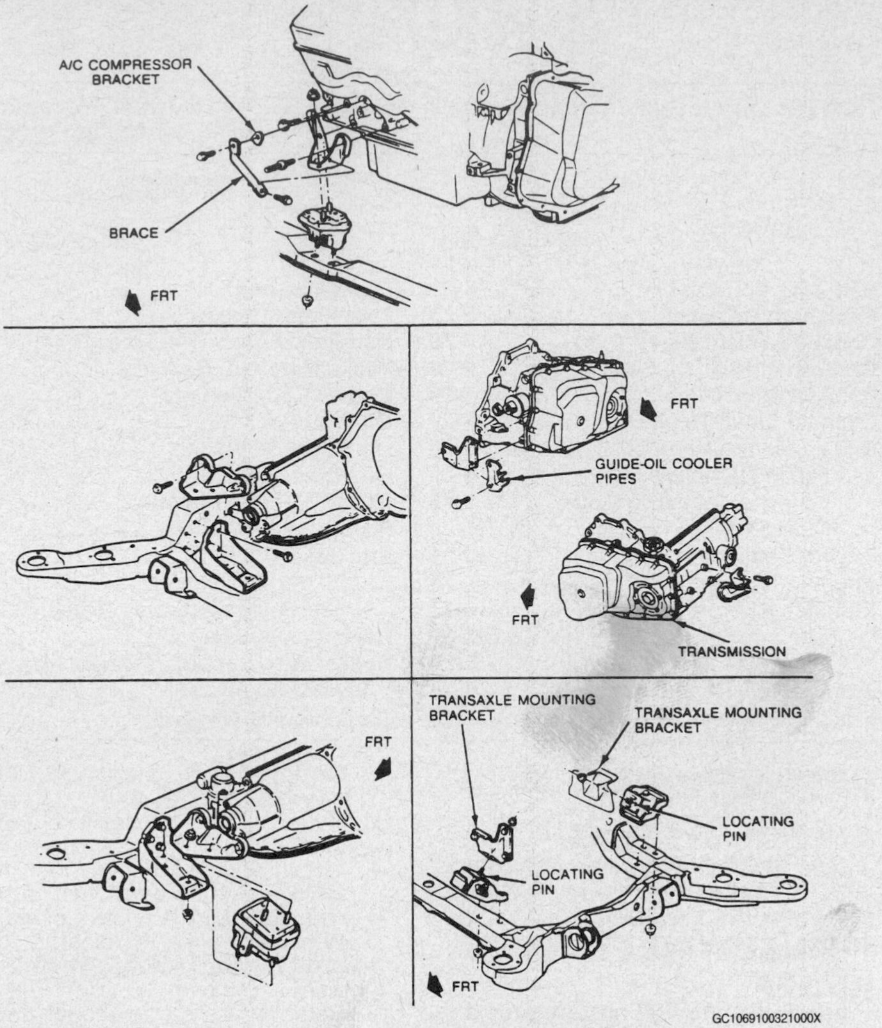
A/C COMPRESSOR BRACKET
BRACE
FRT
FRT
GUIDE-OIL COOLER PIPES
FRT
TRANSMISSION
TRANSAXLE MOUNTING BRACKET
TRANSAXLE MOUNTING BRACKET
FRT
LOCATING PIN
LOCATING PIN
FRT
GC1069100321000X

Fig. 1 Engine & transaxle mounts

INTAKE MANIFOLD

REPLACE

1. Relieve fuel pressure as outlined under "Precautions."
2. Disconnect battery ground cable.
3. Remove air cleaner assembly, then drain engine coolant.
4. Remove cross car brace, then accessory drive belt.
5. Disconnect power steering and tensioner bracket assembly and position aside.
6. Remove alternator and bracket.
7. Disconnect throttle cable from throttle body.
8. Disconnect the following electrical connectors and position aside:
   a. Distributor.
   b. Oil pressure switch.
   c. Coolant sensor.
   d. EGR solenoid.
   e. ISC motor.
   f. TP sensor.
   g. Fuel injectors.
   h. MAT sensor.
9. Remove MAP hoses.
10. Disconnect thermostat housing attaching hoses.
11. Remove A/C hose bracket.
12. Remove distributor cap, spark plug wire protectors and position aside.
13. Mark distributor rotor installation alignment, then remove rotor.
14. Disconnect fuel lines at transmission bracket.
15. Disconnect throttle body fuel and vacuum lines.
16. Disconnect throttle body and transmission modulator line vacuum supply lines.
17. Loosen vacuum line clip at lift bracket.
18. Remove valve covers.
19. Mark pushrods with installation positions, then remove rocker arms and pushrods. **Ensure pushrods are installed in original positions.**
20. Remove bracket at power steering.
21. Remove right front and rear lift brackets.
22. Remove intake manifold attaching bolts, then remove.
23. Reverse procedure to install. Refer to **Fig. 2,** for torque specifications and tightening sequence.

EXHAUST MANIFOLD

REPLACE

RIGHT SIDE

1. Relieve fuel pressure as outlined under "Precautions."
2. Disconnect battery ground cable, then remove air cleaner assembly.
3. Disconnect oxygen sensor and coolant temperature sensor electrical connectors.
4. Remove two forward, upper exhaust manifold to cylinder head attaching bolts.
5. Raise and support vehicle.
6. Remove manifold to converter exhaust pipe attaching bolts.
7. Using suitable jack stands, support engine cradle.
8. Remove rear engine cradle bolts, loosen, but do not remove, front cradle bolts.
9. Lower engine cradle slightly, then remove exhaust manifold attaching bolts, remove manifold.
10. Reverse procedure to install.

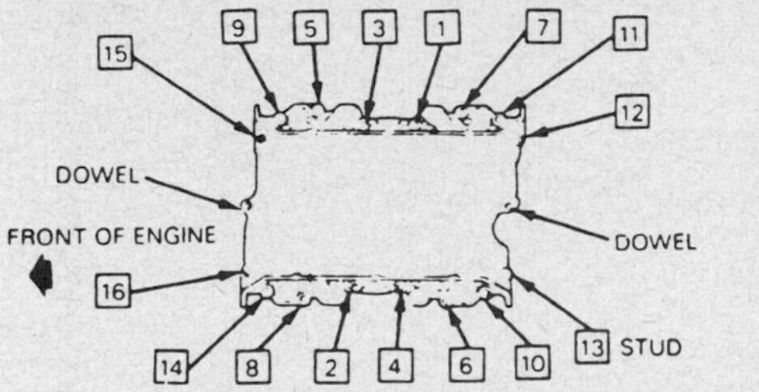
15
9
5
3
1
7
11
12
DOWEL
FRONT OF ENGINE
DOWEL
16
13 STUD
14
8
2
4
6
10

BOLT TIGHTENING SEQUENCE

1. TIGHTEN BOLTS 1, 2, 3, & 4 IN SEQUENCE TO 12.0 N·m (8 FT-LBS).
2. TIGHTEN BOLTS 5 THRU 16 IN SEQUENCE TO 12.0 N·m (8 FT-LBS).
3. RETIGHTEN ALL BOLTS IN SEQUENCE TO 16.0 N·m (12 FT-LBS).
4. REPEAT STEP 3 UNTIL TORQUE LEVEL IS MAINTAINED.

BOLT POSITION	BOLT LENGTH (MM)	BOLT POSITION	BOLT LENGTH (MM)
1	55	9	40
2	55	10	40
3	55	11	40
4	55	12	55
5	30	13	40 W Studhead
6	30	14	40
7	30	15	55
8	30	16	40

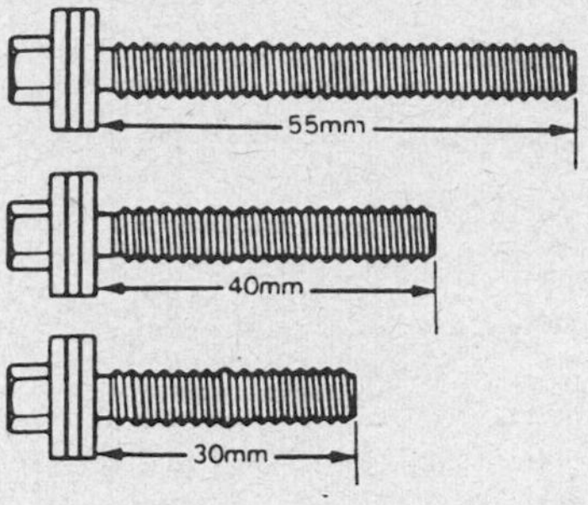
55mm
40mm
30mm

GC1059100075000X

Fig. 2 Intake manifold bolt size & bolt torque sequence

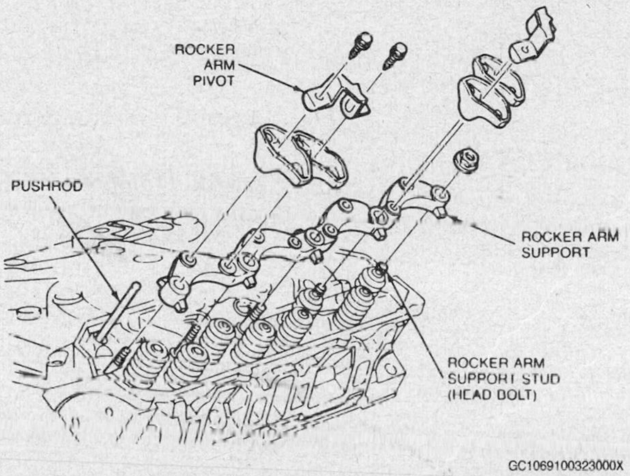
ROCKER ARM PIVOT
PUSHROD
ROCKER ARM SUPPORT
ROCKER ARM SUPPORT STUD (HEAD BOLT)

GC1069100323000X

Fig. 4 Rocker arm support, rocker arms & pivots

LEFT SIDE

1. Relieve fuel pressure as outlined under "Precautions."
2. Disconnect battery ground cable.
3. Remove both cooling fans.
4. Remove exhaust crossover pipe.
5. Remove accessory drive belt.
6. Remove power steering and tensioner covering manifolds.
7. Remove manifold attaching bolts, then remove.
8. Reverse procedure to install.

CYLINDER HEAD

REPLACE

1. Relieve fuel pressure as outlined under "Precautions."
2. Disconnect battery ground cable, then drain cooling system.
3. Remove intake manifold as outlined under "Intake Manifold, Replace" procedure.
4. If removing left side cylinder head, remove the two cooling fans.
5. Remove appropriate exhaust manifold as outlined under "Exhaust Manifold, Replace," procedure.
6. Remove dipstick tube when lefthand cylinder head is to be replaced.
7. Remove ten cylinder head bolts.
8. Reverse procedure to install, referring to **Fig. 3,** for bolt tightening sequence. Tighten cylinder head bolts in 3 steps as follows:
   a. **Torque** all bolts in sequence to 38 ft. lbs.
   b. **Torque** all bolts in sequence to 68 ft. lbs.
   c. **Torque** bolts 1, 3 and 4 to 90 ft. lbs.

VALVE CLEARANCE SPECIFICATIONS

These engines are equipped with hydraulic valve lifters. Valve clearance should be zero.

VALVE ADJUSTMENT

These engines are equipped with hydraulic valve lifters, there is no provision for adjustment.

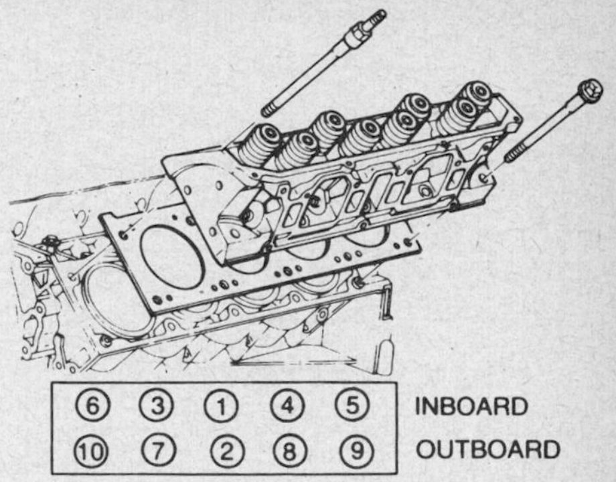
6 3 1 4 5 INBOARD
10 7 2 8 9 OUTBOARD

GC1069100322000X

Fig. 3 Cylinder head bolt tightening sequence

VALVE LIFT SPECIFICATIONS

Engine	Year	Int.	Exh.
All	1992-95	.384	.396

VALVE TIMING

INTAKE OPENS BEFORE TDC

Engine	Year	Degrees
4.9L/V8-300	1992-95	21

ROCKER ARM SUPPORT, ROCKER ARM & PIVOT

REPLACE

1. Remove rocker arm covers.
2. Remove rocker arm support retaining nuts from stud headed cylinder head bolts, Fig. 4. **Removing the rocker arm support with the rocker arms and pivots attached is recommended since the pivot assemblies may be damaged if pivot bolt torque is not removed evenly against valve spring pressure.**
3. Secure support in a suitable vise and remove rocker arms and pivots.
4. Reverse procedure to install. Torque pivot bolts to specifications.

VALVE GUIDES

Check valve stem to valve guide clearance. Clearance should be .005 inch or less. Service valves are available in standard size (.343 inch) or oversizes of .003 and .006 inch. If clearance is excessive, ream valve guide to accommodate next oversize valve. Some engines are factory fitted with .003 inch oversize valve guides and valves and are identified by a "3" stamped on the cylinder head gasket surface in-line with the oversize valve.

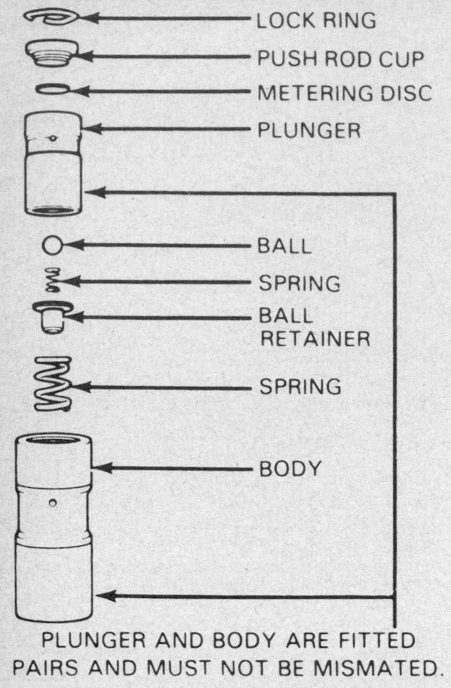
LOCK RING
PUSH ROD CUP
METERING DISC
PLUNGER
BALL
SPRING
BALL RETAINER
SPRING
BODY
PLUNGER AND BODY ARE FITTED PAIRS AND MUST NOT BE MISMATED.
GC1069100324000X

Fig. 5 Hydraulic valve lifter

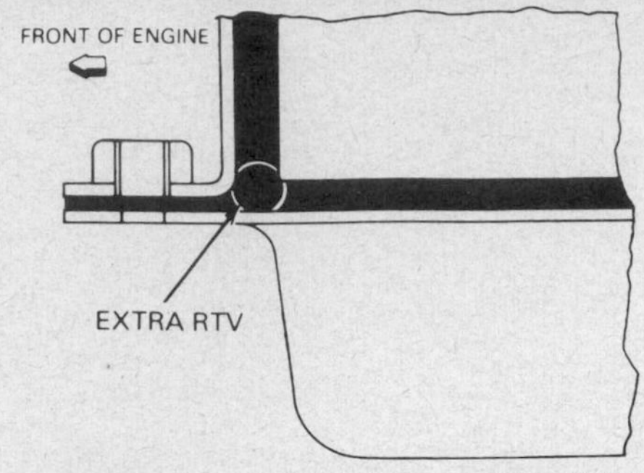
FRONT OF ENGINE
EXTRA RTV
GC1069100325000X

Fig. 6 RTV sealant application

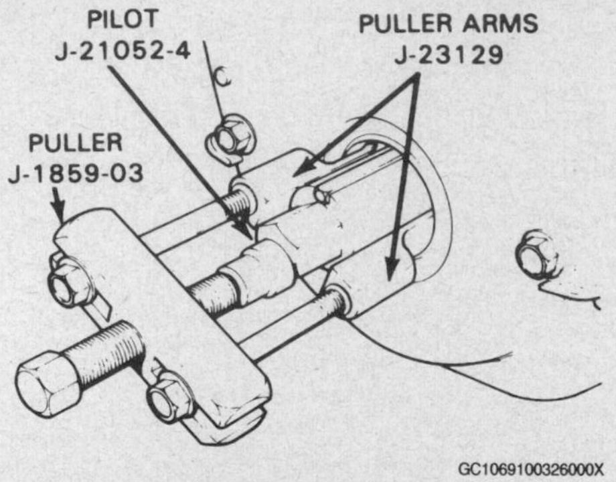
PILOT J-21052-4
PULLER ARMS J-23129
PULLER J-1859-03
GC1069100326000X

Fig. 7 Timing case oil seal removal

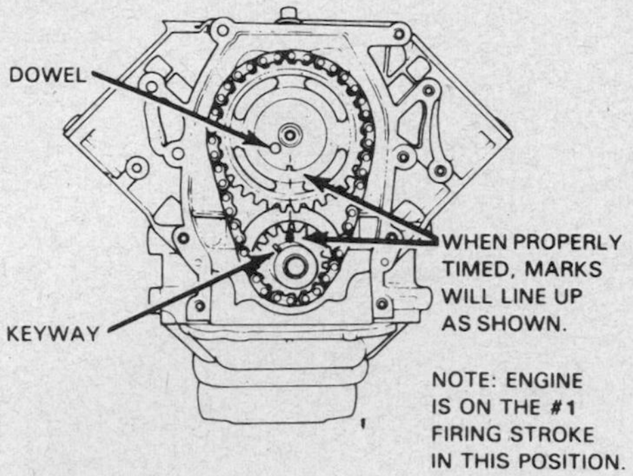
DOWEL
KEYWAY
WHEN PROPERLY TIMED, MARKS WILL LINE UP AS SHOWN.
NOTE: ENGINE IS ON THE #1 FIRING STROKE IN THIS POSITION.
GC1069100327000X

Fig. 8 Camshaft timing marks

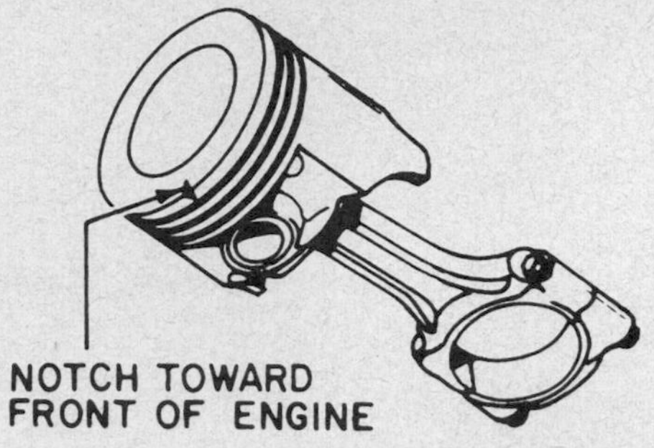
NOTCH TOWARD FRONT OF ENGINE
GC1069100328000X

Fig. 9 Piston & rod assembly

HYDRAULIC LIFTERS

REPLACE

Valve lifters may be removed from their bores after the intake manifold, rocker arms and pushrods are removed. Adjustable pliers with taped jaws may be used to remove lifters that are stuck due to varnish, carbon, etc. **Fig. 5,** illustrates the type of lifter used.

FRONT COVER

REPLACE

1. Disconnect battery ground cable.
2. Drain cooling system.
3. Remove air cleaner.
4. Remove drive belt.
5. Remove alternator and position aside.
6. Remove A/C accumulator from bracket and position aside.
7. Remove idler pulley, water pump pulley and water pump.
8. Raise and support vehicle.
9. Remove crankshaft puller and hub.
10. Remove cover attaching bolts and the cover.
11. Reverse procedure to install. When installing, place a bead of RTV sealer on the front cover lip on the oil pan sealing surface and a 1/4 inch bead of RTV sealer on the oil pan where the oil pan, cylinder block and cover join together, **Fig. 6.** The 1/4 inch bead is needed because the cover has a rounded corner instead of a square corner. If the extra RTV is not applied an oil leak may occur.

FRONT COVER SEAL

REPLACE

1. Remove crankshaft pulley and vibration damper.

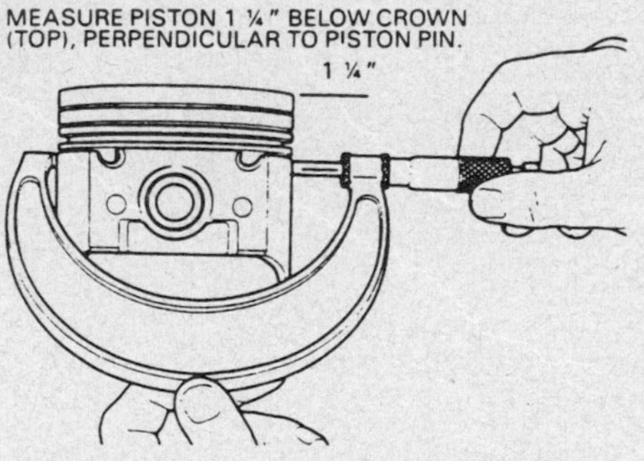
MEASURE PISTON 1 ¼" BELOW CROWN (TOP), PERPENDICULAR TO PISTON PIN.
1 ¼"
GC1069100329000X

Fig. 10 Measuring piston diameter

2. Remove oil seal with tools J-1859-03 and J-23129 or equivalents, **Fig. 7.**
3. Lubricate new oil seal with engine oil and install with tool J-29662 or equivalent.
4. Install crankshaft puller and vibration damper.

TIMING CHAIN

REPLACE

1. Remove front cover as outlined under "Front Cover, Replace."
2. Remove oil slinger from crankshaft.
3. Rotate crankshaft to align camshaft and crankshaft sprocket timing marks, **Fig. 8.**
4. Remove screw attaching camshaft sprocket to camshaft, then the camshaft and crankshaft sprockets with the timing chain attached.
5. Reverse procedure to install. Ensure that timing marks are aligned, **Fig. 8.**

CAMSHAFT

REPLACE

1. Remove engine as outlined under "Engine, Replace" procedure.
2. Remove front cover and timing chain.
3. Remove intake manifold and valve lifters.
4. Slide camshaft forward carefully from engine.
5. Reverse procedure to install.

PISTON & ROD ASSEMBLY

Assemble pistons to rods as shown in **Fig. 9.** Measure connecting rod side clearance with a suitable feeler gauge after installation. Clearance should be .008 to .020 inch.

PISTONS, PINS & RINGS

When measuring piston diameter, place micrometer 1 1/4 inch below crown (top) of piston, perpendicular to piston pin, **Fig. 10.**

Cylinder liner diameter is measured two inches down from top of liner and perpendicular to the cylinder centerline. The difference between the two readings should be .0004-.0020 inch. Cylinder bore out of round should not exceed .0008 inch. If any reading is not within specifications, the piston and cylinder liner must be replaced. No attempt should be made to rebore or hone the cylinder liner. Refer to "Cylinder Liner, Replace" procedure.

Piston pins are a matched fit with the piston and are not available for separate replacement. Piston pins are pressed into the connecting rods and will not become loose enough to cause a knock or tapping until after very high mileage.

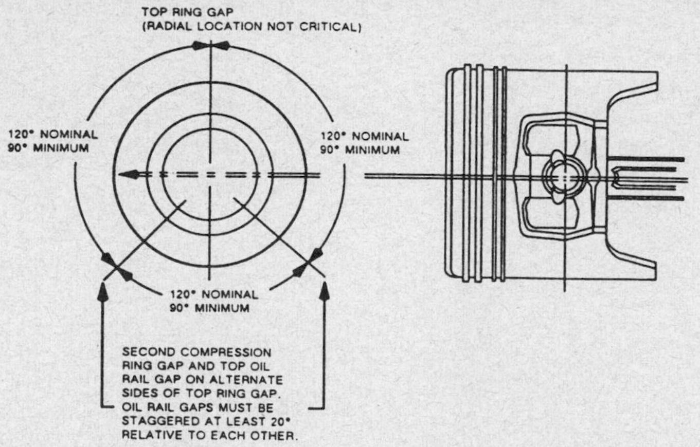
TOP RING GAP
(RADIAL LOCATION NOT CRITICAL)
120° NOMINAL
90° MINIMUM
120° NOMINAL
90° MINIMUM
120° NOMINAL
90° MINIMUM
SECOND COMPRESSION RING GAP AND TOP OIL RAIL GAP ON ALTERNATE SIDES OF TOP RING GAP. OIL RAIL GAPS MUST BE STAGGERED AT LEAST 20° RELATIVE TO EACH OTHER.

GC1069100330000X

Fig. 11 Piston ring end gap location

On these engines, replacement rings are available in standard size only. If piston ring clearance is excessive, the piston and cylinder liner must be replaced. Refer to "Cylinder Liner, Replace" procedure. Arrange piston rings as shown in **Fig. 11.**

MAIN & ROD BEARINGS

Main and rod bearings are supplied in standard sizes only.

CYLINDER LINER

REPLACE

1. Remove cylinder heads, pistons and connecting rods must be removed before replacing cylinder liner. After removing cylinder heads, install tool J-29775 to retain the cylinder liners not being replaced.
2. If original liners are to be reinstalled, mark position of cylinder liner in cylinder block and keep piston with original liner for reference during installation.
3. Pull cylinder liner from cylinder block. Discard O-ring from base of liner.
4. Check cylinder liner and cylinder block mating surfaces.
5. If original cylinder liner is to be installed and engine has not experienced overheating, install new O-ring onto bottom of liner. Align reference marks made during removal and install liner into cylinder block.
6. If new liner is being installed or if original liner is being installed and the engine has experienced overheating, then cylinder liner height must be measured as follows:
   a. Place liner in cylinder block without O-ring.
   b. Place gauge J-29776 or equivalent on cylinder liner. Check that spring-loaded guide pins fit into liner with machined pads resting on edge of liner and dial indicator plunger contacting block deck face. Apply moderate pressure to gauge until dial indicator stops moving. Record this reading. If reading is on the + side of dial indicator, cylinder liner is higher than block face. If reading is on the - side, the liner is lower than the block face.

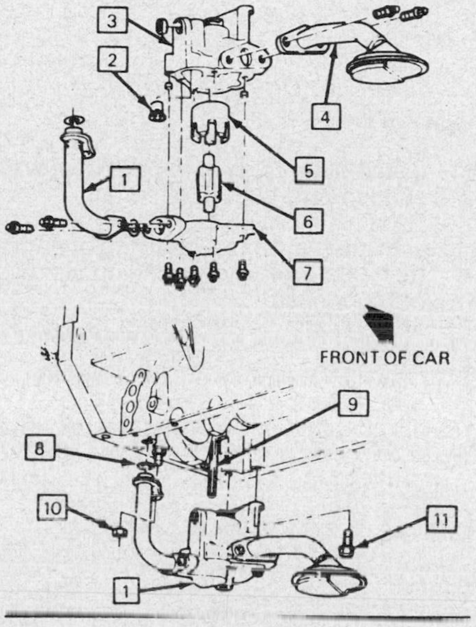
FRONT OF CAR

1 SUPPLY TUBE	7 PUMP COVER
2 PRESSURE RELIEF VALVE	8 "O" RING
3 PUMP BODY	9 DRIVE SHAFT
4 PICKUP	10 NUT
5 OUTER ROTOR	11 BOLT
6 INNER ROTOR	

GC1099100044000X

Fig. 13 Oil pump assembly

   c. Repeat step b at two other locations on the liner. Use average of the three readings as actual liner height.
   d. Cylinder liner height should be 0-.003 inch above cylinder deck face.
   e. Check liner-to-liner height with tool J-29766 or equivalent. Install adjacent liners with O-ring. Liner-to-liner height should be -.002 to +.002 inch. Mark liners in measured positions.
7. When installing liners into block, check alignment marks. Be sure to install O-ring onto liner.

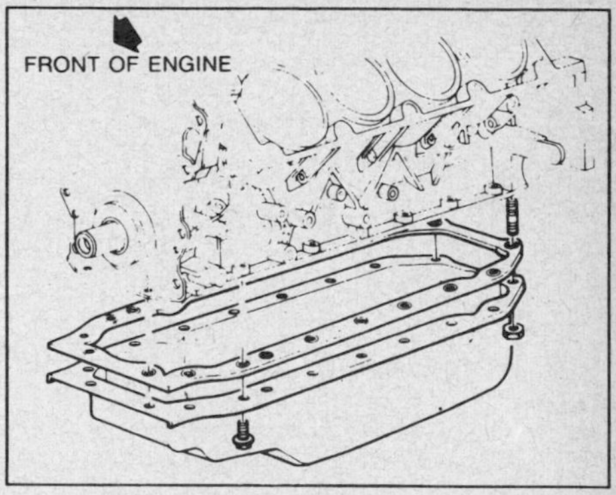
FRONT OF ENGINE

GC1099100043000X

Fig. 12 Oil pan removal & installation

CRANKSHAFT REAR OIL SEAL

REPLACE

Before replacing the crankshaft oil seal, be sure that the apparent oil seal leak is not actually a leak between the sides of the rear main cap and crankcase.

1. Remove transaxle, then the flex plate from crankshaft.
2. Remove old seal with tool J-26868 or equivalent.
3. Lubricate new seal lip with wheel bearing grease and place on crankshaft with spring facing inside of engine.
4. Press seal into position with tool J-34604 or equivalent. Seal is fully installed when flush with block or slightly below. The use of the tool is recommended since the seal must fit squarely on the crankshaft, otherwise an oil leak could result.

OIL PAN

REPLACE

1. Disconnect battery ground cable.
2. Raise and support vehicle.
3. Drain oil pan.
4. Remove two flexplate covers.
5. Remove oil pan attaching bolts and the two nuts from studs.
6. Remove oil pan, **Fig. 12.**
7. Reverse procedure to install. RTV sealer is used to seal the oil pan.

OIL PUMP

REPLACE

1. Remove oil pan as outlined under "Oil Pan, Replace" procedure.
2. Remove bolts securing oil pump to engine, **Fig. 13.**
3. Remove oil pump.
4. Reverse procedure to install.

OIL PUMP SERVICE

1. Remove oil pump cover to housing attaching screws, **Fig. 13.**
2. Remove inlet and outlet pipes attaching screws, then remove and discard O-rings.
3. Slide inner and outer rotors from

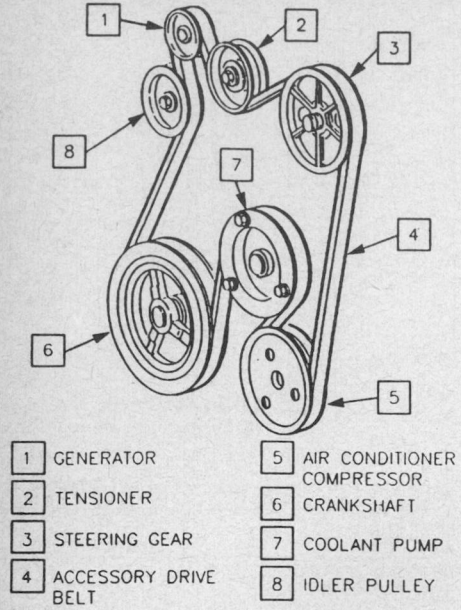

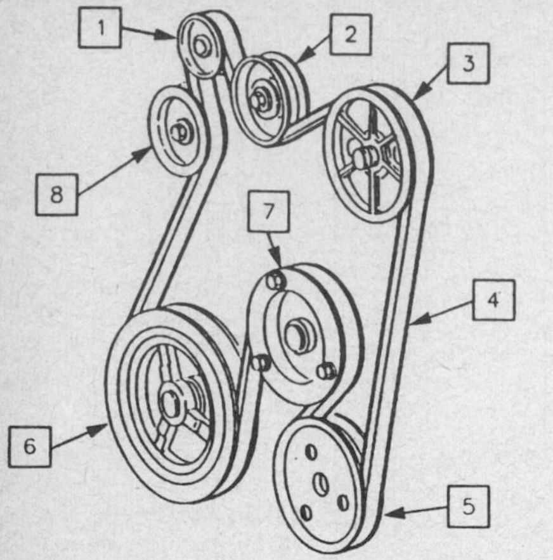
1
2
3
4
5
6
7
8
1 GENERATOR
2 TENSIONER
3 STEERING GEAR
4 ACCESSORY DRIVE BELT
5 AIR CONDITIONER COMPRESSOR
6 CRANKSHAFT
7 COOLANT PUMP
8 IDLER PULLEY
GC1069100331000X

Fig. 14 Serpentine drive belt routing

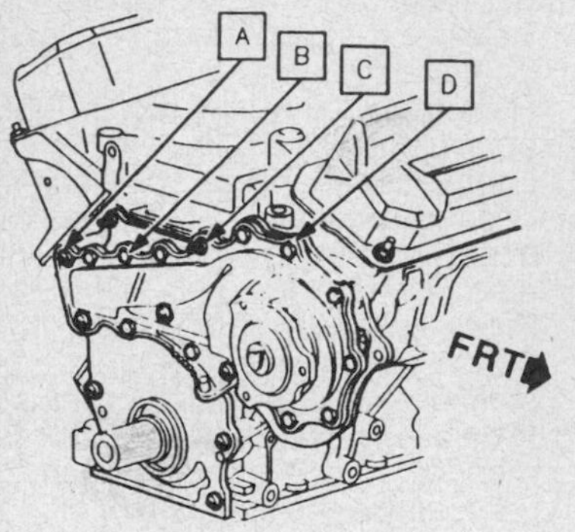
A
B
C
D
FRT

KEY	FASTENER TYPE	QTY.	TORQUE	
			N•m	FT. LBS.
A	TORX SCREW	4	40	30
B	NUT	7	7	5
C	STUD	1	40	30
D	HEX SCREW	7	7	5

GC1089100150000X

Fig. 17 Water pump tightening sequence & specifications

housing. **Pressure relief valve is not removable.**

4. Inspect pump housing for damage that may cause a leak or binding condition in rotor pocket.
5. Inspect drive and driven rotors for nicks and burrs.
6. Inspect interior pump surface for excessive wear or scoring.
7. Inspect pump housing cover, inlet and outlet pipes for flatness.
8. Inspect inlet screen and pipe for debris.
9. Inspect pump driveshaft for wear or twisting.
10. Ensure pressure relief valve closes by filling housing valve cavity with suitable light oil, not oil leakage should be indicated.

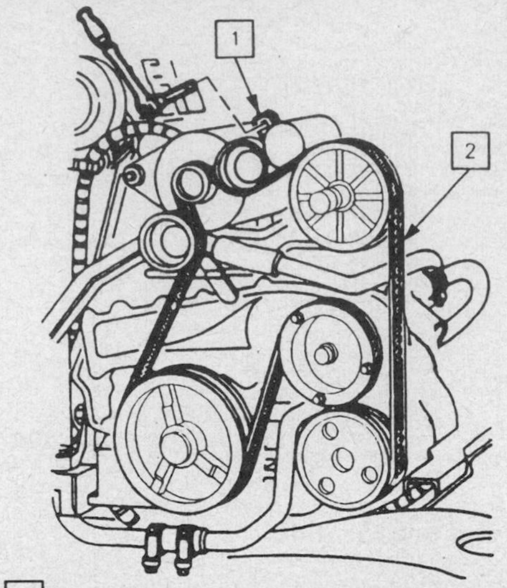
1
2
1 DRIVE BELT TENSIONER
2 ACCESSORY DRIVE BELT
GC1069100332000X

Fig. 15 Drive belt removal

11. Install outer rotor in rotor pocket with slots toward bottom of pump.
12. Slide inner rotor inside driven rotor with internal hex towards top of pump, then rotate gears ensuring not binding or roughness.
13. Install pump cover, tighten to specifications.
14. Install inlet pipe to housing, tighten to specifications.
15. Temporarily install driveshaft to pump, then rotate gears ensuring no binding or roughness.

BELT TENSION DATA

Engine	Year	Lbs.
4.9L/V8-300	1992-94	120

SERPENTINE DRIVE BELT

BELT ROUTING

Refer to **Fig. 14**, for serpentine drive belt routing.

BELT, REPLACE

1. Using suitable 1/2 inch breaker bar, rotate belt tensioner upward from drive belt, **Fig. 15.**
2. Remove accessory drive belt.
3. Reverse procedure to install.

COOLING SYSTEM BLEED

1. Fill cooling system and leave radiator cap off.
2. Start engine, then and push front "DEF" button and increase temperature to 90°.
3. Run engine at 2000 RPM for approximately 10 minutes, then refill radiator until full and install radiator cap with engine running.

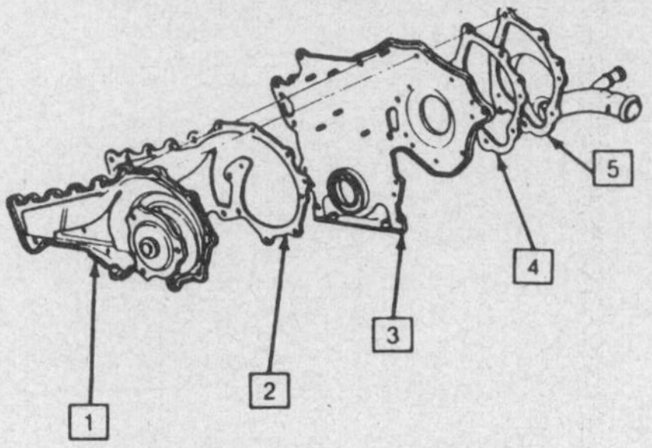
1
2
3
4
5
1 WATER PUMP ASSEMBLY
2 WATER PUMP GASKET
3 FRONT COVER
4 WATER PUMP INLET GASKET
5 WATER PUMP INLET
GC1089100149000X

Fig. 16 Water pump assembly

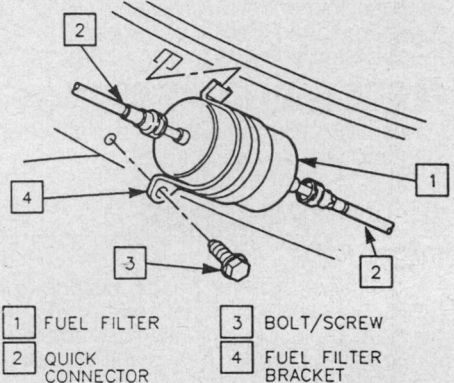

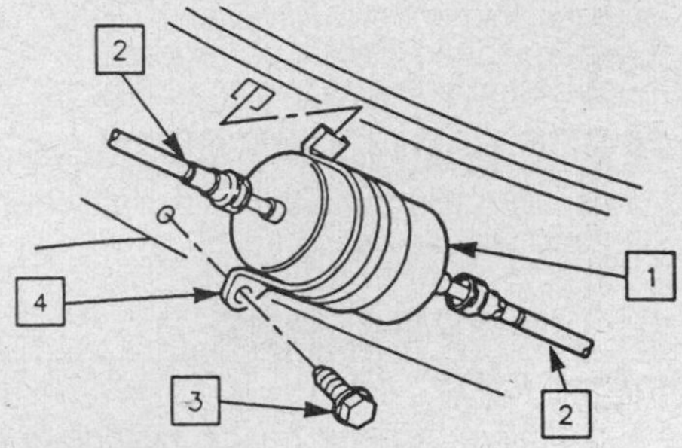
1
2
3
4
1 FUEL FILTER
2 QUICK CONNECTOR
3 BOLT/SCREW
4 FUEL FILTER BRACKET
GC1029102725000X

Fig. 18 Fuel filter replacement

4. Fill coolant reservoir to the "FULL" mark.

THERMOSTAT

REPLACE

1. Disconnect battery negative cable.
2. With engine cool, drain engine coolant below thermostat level. **Never open cooling system with engine hot. Failure to follow this warning may cause personal injury.**
3. Remove two thermostat housing retaining bolts, then the upper thermostat housing.
4. Remove thermostat and gasket from lower housing, then clean both mating surfaces.
5. Reverse procedure to install. Replace gasket and tighten thermostat housing retaining bolts to specifications.
6. With installation done, ensure that draincock is closed, refill radiator with proper coolant mixture, replace pressure cap and start engine. Check for leaks.

WATER PUMP

REPLACE

1. Disconnect battery ground cable and drain cooling system.

2. Remove A/C accumulator from bracket and position aside.
3. Remove A/C accumulator bracket from wheel house.
4. Remove right hand cross-car brace.
5. Remove drive belt as outlined previously.
6. Remove drive belt idler puller and bracket.
7. Remove water pump pulley.
8. Remove water pump attaching bolts and the water pump, **Fig. 16.**
9. Reverse procedure to install. Tighten bolts to specifications, **Fig. 17.**

RADIATOR

REPLACE

1. Disconnect battery ground cable.
2. Drain engine coolant, then raise and support vehicle.
3. Disconnect left and right cooling fan electrical connectors.
4. Remove cooling fan to lower engine cradle attaching bolts.
5. Lower vehicle and remove air cleaner intake duct.
6. Remove cooling fan to upper radiator mounting panel attaching bolts.
7. Remove upper radiator mounting panel, then the cooling fans.
8. Disconnect coolant reservoir hose from radiator filler neck.
9. Disconnect upper radiator hose from radiator.
10. Disconnect engine and transaxle oil cooler lines from radiator.
11. Disconnect lower radiator hose from radiator.
12. Remove radiator from vehicle.
13. Reverse procedure to install.

FUEL PUMP

REPLACE

1. Remove fuel tank.
2. Remove cam lock with tool J-24187 or equivalent.
3. Remove fuel sending unit and fuel pump assembly from tank.
4. Remove fuel pump from sending unit.
5. Reverse procedure to install.

FUEL FILTER

REPLACE

1. Release fuel system pressure as outlined under "Precautions."
2. Raise and support vehicle.
3. Twist quick-connect fitting 1/4 turn in each direction to loosen dirt within fitting.
4. Using compressed air, clean quick-connect fitting at ends of filter.
5. Disconnect quick-connect fittings by squeezing plastic tabs of male end connector and pulling apart.
6. Remove filter from bracket, then the fuel filter, **Fig. 18.**
7. Reverse procedure to install.

TIGHTENING SPECIFICATIONS

4.9L/V8-300 ENGINE

Year	Component	Torque/Ft. Lbs.
1992-95	Connecting Rod Bolts	25
	Coolant Fan To Radiator Support Bolts	84①
	Coolant Hose Clamps	15①
	Coolant Temperature Sensor	15
	Cylinder Head Bolts	②
	Damper To Crankshaft	70
	Distributor Hold-Down Nut	20
	Distributor Hold-Down Stud	26
	EGR Valve Screws	18
	Engine Oil Cooler Fittings	29
	Exhaust Manifold Bolts	16
	Exhaust Outlet Flange Studs	15
	Flywheel To Crankshaft	70
	Front Cover Screws (Lower 4)	17
	Front Cover Screws (Upper 4)	30
	Intake Manifold Bolts	②
	Lift Bracket To Cylinder Head	29
	Main Bearing Caps	85
	MAT Sensor	20
	Oil Filter Adapter To Block	14
	Oil Gallery Plug At Rear Of Block	32
	Oil Pan Bolts	14
1992-95 —Cont'd	Oil Drain Plug	22
	Oil Pressure Switch	10
	Oil Pump Cover Screws	7
	Oil Pump Mounting Nut To Stud	22
	Oil Pump Mounting Screws To Block	14
	Oxygen Sensor	30
	Radiator	88①
	Rocker Arm Cover Screws	8
	Rocker Arm Pivot To Support	22
	Rocker Arm Support To Head Bolts	36
	Spark Plugs	23
	Thermostat Housing To Intake Manifold	23
	Timing Sprocket To Camshaft	36
	Transaxle Oil Cooler Fittings	20
	Upper Thermostat Housing To Lower Housing	19
	Water Passage Plugs	5
	Water Pump Pulley To Pump Bolts	115①
	Water Pump To Block	29
	Water Pump To Front Cover Bolts	97①

①—Inch lbs.
②—Refer to text.

Rear Suspension

INDEX

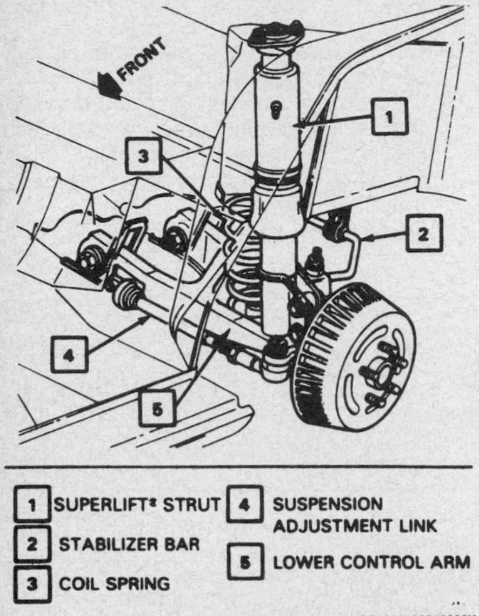
FRONT
1
2
3
4
5
1 SUPERLIFT® STRUT
2 STABILIZER BAR
3 COIL SPRING
4 SUSPENSION ADJUSTMENT LINK
5 LOWER CONTROL ARM
GC2039100048000X

Fig. 1 Rear suspension

DESCRIPTION

These vehicles use an independent rear suspension consisting of lower control arms, coil springs, toe links, suspension knuckles, superlift struts and stabilizer bar, **Fig. 1.** The hub and wheel bearing is an assembly and does not require periodic lubrication.

HUB & BEARING
REPLACE

1. Raise and support rear of vehicle.
2. Remove wheel assembly and brake drum. **Do not hammer on drum as damage to bearing may occur.**
3. Disconnect ABS sensor wire.
4. Remove four hub and bearing assembly to axle attaching bolts. **These four bolts also support the brake assembly. When removing these bolts, support the brake assembly with a wire. Do not let the brake line or ABS electrical wire support the brake assembly.**
5. , Remove hub and bearing assembly from axle, **Fig. 2.**
6. Reverse procedure to install. Tighten attaching bolts to specifications.

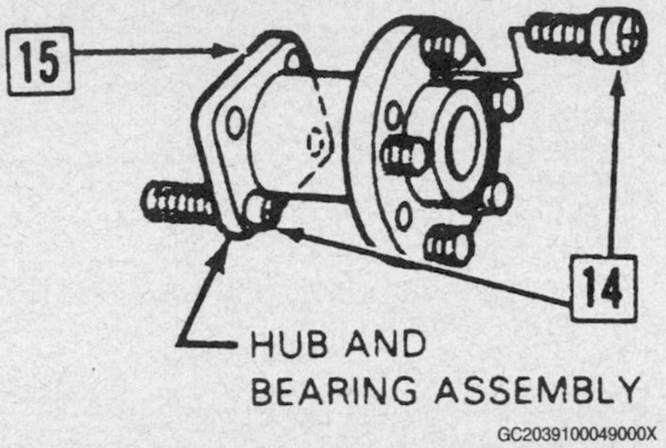
15
14
HUB AND
BEARING ASSEMBLY
GC2039100049000X

Fig. 2 Hub & bearing assembly

STRUT
REPLACE

1. Raise and support vehicle.
2. **On 1992-93 Ninety Eight and Park Avenue and 1992-94 Bonneville, DeVille, Eighty Eight and LeSabre models,** remove trunk side cover.
3. **On 1994-95 Ninety Eight and Park Avenue and all 1995 models,** remove rear seat cushion and seat back to gain access to strut tower mounting nuts.
4. Remove tire and wheel assembly.
5. Disconnect air tube from strut, **Fig. 3.**
6. Support lower control arm with suitable jack stand.
7. Remove two strut tower mount nuts.
8. Remove two strut anchor bolts, washers and nuts from knuckle, then the knuckle bracket.
9. Remove strut from vehicle.
10. Reverse procedure to install.

COIL SPRING
REPLACE

1. Support vehicle so the rear wheel and control arm hang free, then remove rear wheel.
2. Disconnect rear stabilizer bar from knuckle bracket.
3. Disconnect electronic level control height sensor link if removing right control arm.
4. Disconnect parking brake cable clip from frame if removing left control arm.
5. Place tool J-23028-01 in position to cradle control arm bushings, **Fig. 4. Tool J-23028-01 should be secured to a suitable jack, otherwise, personal injury could result.**

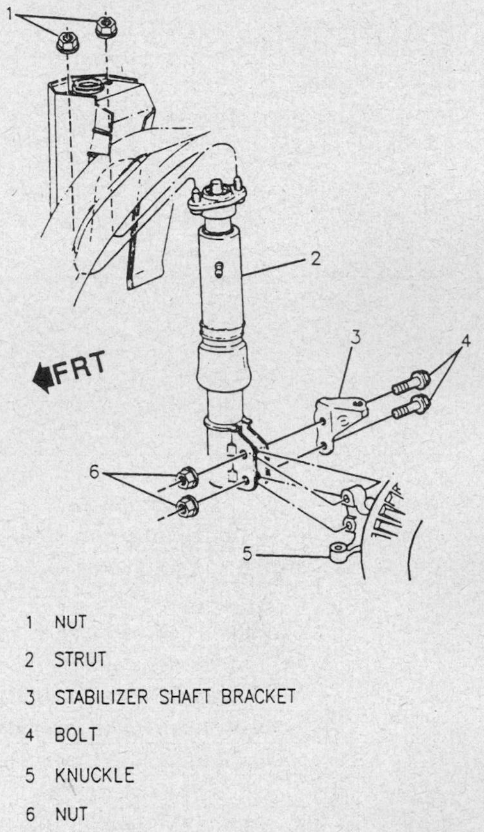
1
2
3
4
5
6
FRT
1 NUT
2 STRUT
3 STABILIZER SHAFT BRACKET
4 BOLT
5 KNUCKLE
6 NUT
GC2039100057000X

Fig. 3 Strut assembly

6. Raise jack to relieve tension from control arm pivot bolts.
7. Place a chain around spring and control for safety.
8. Remove rear control arm pivot bolt and nut, **Fig. 5.**
9. Slowly lower jack until front bolt and nut can be removed.
10. Remove coil spring. **Do not apply force on lower arm and ball joint to remove spring. Maneuver spring to remove.**
11. Reverse procedure to install, noting the following:
    a. Replace spring insulators that are damaged or if vehicle has been in service for more than 50,000 miles
    b. Install springs so that end of spring is as shown in **Fig. 6.**
    c. Tighten suspension fasteners sufficiently to retain position of components, lower vehicle so that it

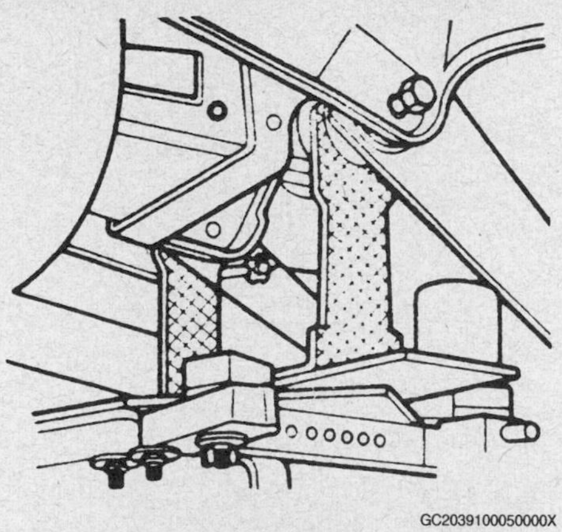
GC2039100050000X

Fig. 4 Installing tool J-23028-01

rests on the wheels at normal ride height, then tighten fasteners in the following order: tighten control arm pivot nuts to specifications, tighten control arm pivot bolts to specifications, tighten stabilizer shaft link bolt to specifications.

d. **Failure to tighten fasteners in correct sequence may adversely affect ride and handling.**

BALL JOINT INSPECTION

The ball joint has a visual wear indicator. Checking the condition of the ball joint is a simple procedure but must be followed accurately to prevent unnecessary ball joint replacement.

The vehicle must be supported by the wheels during inspection to ensure that the vehicle weight is properly loading the ball joints.

The ball joint is inspected for wear by visual observation alone. Wear is indicated by retraction of the 1/2 inch diameter nipple into the ball joint cover (the ball joint grease fitting is threaded into this nipple). The nipple protrudes .050 inch beyond the surface of the ball joint cover on a new unworn joint. Normal wear will result in the surface of this nipple retracting very slowly inward. The ball joint should be replaced if the nipple is flush or below the cover surface, **Fig. 7.**

Ball stud tightness in the knuckle boss should also be checked when inspecting the ball joint. This may be done by shaking the wheel and feeling for movement of the stud end or castellated nut at the knuckle boss.

Checking the fastener tightness at the castellated nut is an alternative method of inspecting (a loose nut can indicate a bent stud or an "opened up" hole in the knuckle boss). If worn, the ball joint and knuckle must be replaced.

If the ball joint is separated from the knuckle for suspension service, the ball joint seal should be inspected for damage. A damaged seal will cause joint failure. If seal damage is found the ball joint should be replaced.

BALL JOINT

REPLACE

1. Raise and support vehicle.

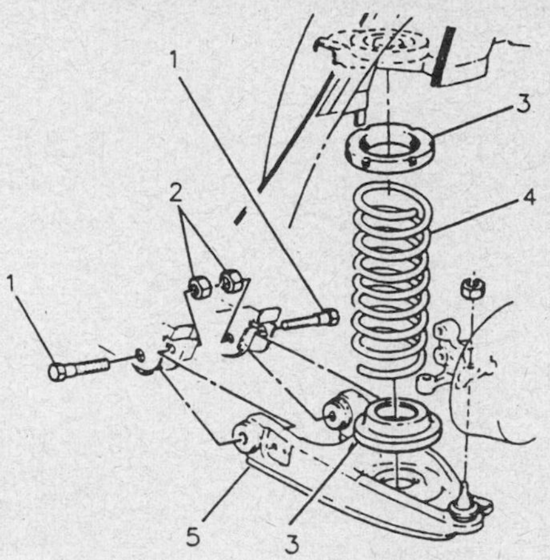
1
2
3
4
1
5
3

1 PIVOT BOLT

2 PIVOT NUT

3 INSULATOR

4 COIL SPRING

5 CONTROL ARM

GC2039100051000X

Fig. 5 Coil spring replacement

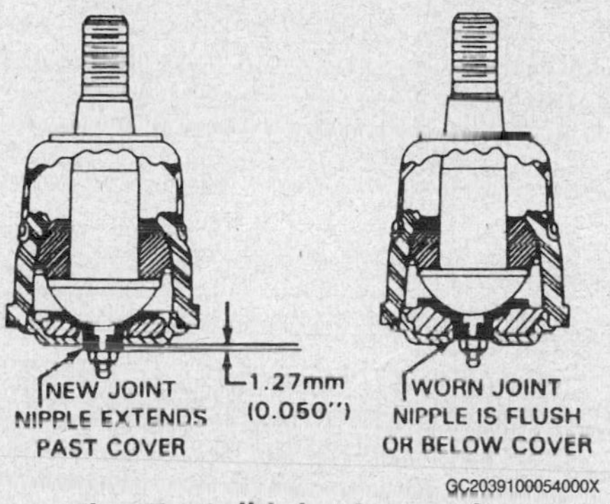
NEW JOINT NIPPLE EXTENDS PAST COVER
1.27mm (0.050")
WORN JOINT NIPPLE IS FLUSH OR BELOW COVER
GC2039100054000X

Fig. 7 Ball joint inspection

2. Remove wheel assembly, cotter key and castle nut.
3. Disconnect outer tie rod/adjustment link from knuckle as outlined previously.
4. Disconnect electronic level control height sensor link from right side control arm.
5. Support control arm with a suitable jack.
6. Remove ball joint cotter pin and nut.
7. Using tool J-29330, disconnect ball joint from knuckle, **Fig. 8.**
8. Using tool J-9519-7, remove ball joint from control arm.
9. Reverse procedure to install.

CONTROL ARM

REPLACE

1. Remove coil spring as outlined under "Coil Spring, Replace" procedure.
2. Remove control arm front pivot bolt.
3. Remove control arm from vehicle.
4. Reverse procedure to install.

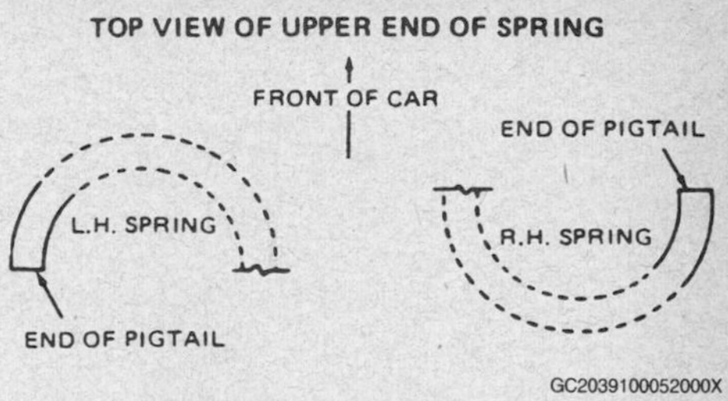
TOP VIEW OF UPPER END OF SPRING
FRONT OF CAR
END OF PIGTAIL
L.H. SPRING
R.H. SPRING
END OF PIGTAIL
GC2039100052000X

Fig. 6 Rear spring positioning

CONTROL ARM BUSHING

REPLACE

These vehicles incorporate control arm configuration with two different sized bushings, **Fig. 9.** These bushings are not interchangeable, and require different combinations of special tools for removal and installation. The following service procedure refer to these bushings as A and B.

REMOVAL

1. Remove control arm from vehicle.
2. Place control arm onto a suitable work bench, up side down.
3. For bushing A, install spacer tool J-22222-5, for bushing B, install spacer tool J-33793-5 onto control arm.
4. Position receiver tube J-25317-2 and cap tool J-29376-7 on outer side of control arm. Ensure receiver tube does not contact the bushing flange.
5. Coat threaded area of long bolt J-21474-19 with extreme pressure lubricant J-23444-A, then install bolt through receiver, cap and bushing.
6. Install remover tool J-22222-2 for bushing A or tool J-28685-2 for bushing B onto bolt at inner side of control arm. Position remover so small diameter portion contacts bushing.
7. Place bearing on bolt and install long nut tool J21474-18. Bearing must be installed between nut and remover.
8. Draw bushing out of control arm by tightening the nut.

INSTALLATION

1. With control arm up side down on work bench, position new bushing into control arm. **When installing new bushings, the flanged end of the bushing must face outward when installed in the control arm.**
2. Install spacer tool J-22222-5 for bushing A or tool J-33793-5 for bushing B.
3. Position receiver tube J-25317-2 and cap tool J-29376-7 onto inner side of control arm. Receiver tube should be centered over the hole.
4. Coat threaded area of long bolt with extreme pressure lubricant J-23444-A and install through receiver, cap and bushing.
5. Position installer J-28685-2 onto bolt at outer side of control arm. Installer should be positioned with large diameter end contacting bushing flange.
6. Place bearing on bolt and install long nut J-21474-18. Bearing must be positioned between nut and installer.

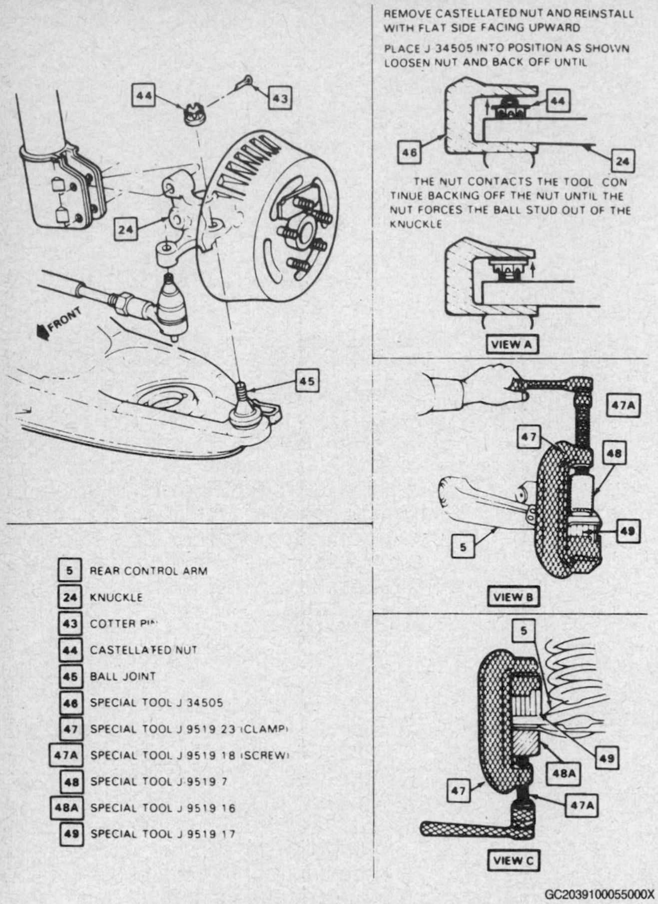
REMOVE CASTELLATED NUT AND REINSTALL WITH FLAT SIDE FACING UPWARD
PLACE J 34505 INTO POSITION AS SHOWN LOOSEN NUT AND BACK OFF UNTIL
THE NUT CONTACTS THE TOOL CONTINUE BACKING OFF THE NUT UNTIL THE NUT FORCES THE BALL STUD OUT OF THE KNUCKLE
FRONT
VIEW A
VIEW B
VIEW C
5 REAR CONTROL ARM
24 KNUCKLE
43 COTTER PIN
44 CASTELLATED NUT
45 BALL JOINT
46 SPECIAL TOOL J 34505
47 SPECIAL TOOL J 9519 23 (CLAMP)
47A SPECIAL TOOL J 9519 18 (SCREW)
48 SPECIAL TOOL J 9519 7
48A SPECIAL TOOL J 9519 16
49 SPECIAL TOOL J 9519 17
GC2039100055000X

Fig. 8 Ball joint replacement

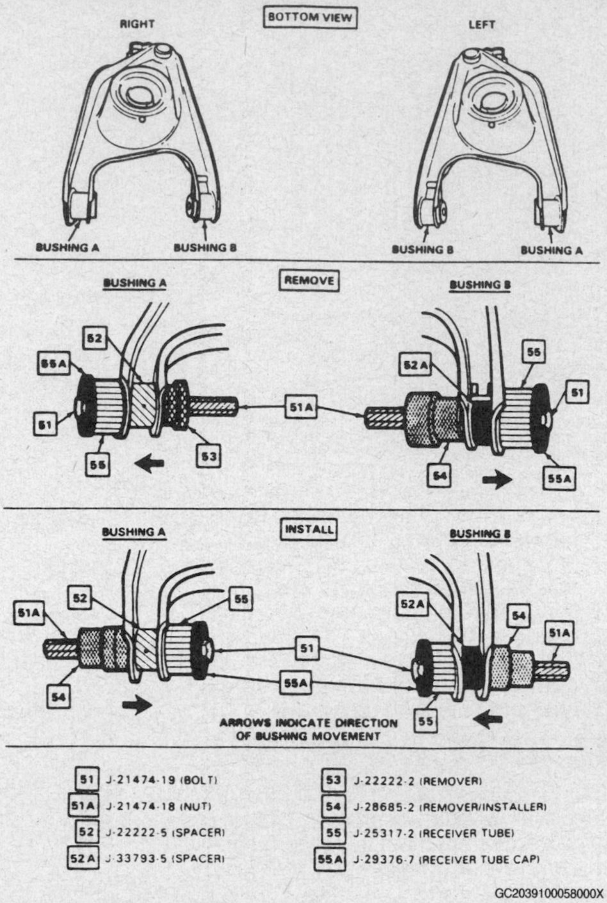
RIGHT
BOTTOM VIEW
LEFT
BUSHING A
BUSHING B
REMOVE
INSTALL
ARROWS INDICATE DIRECTION OF BUSHING MOVEMENT
51 J-21474-19 (BOLT)
51A J-21474-18 (NUT)
52 J-22222-5 (SPACER)
52A J-33793-5 (SPACER)
53 J-22222-2 (REMOVER)
54 J-28685-2 (REMOVER/INSTALLER)
55 J-25317-2 (RECEIVER TUBE)
55A J-29376-7 (RECEIVER TUBE CAP)
GC2039100058000X

Fig. 9 Control arm bushing removal/installation

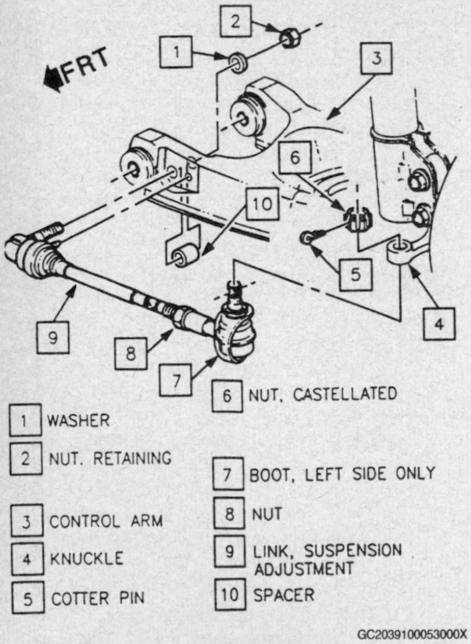
FRT
1 WASHER
2 NUT, RETAINING
3 CONTROL ARM
4 KNUCKLE
5 COTTER PIN
6 NUT, CASTELLATED
7 BOOT, LEFT SIDE ONLY
8 NUT
9 LINK, SUSPENSION ADJUSTMENT
10 SPACER
GC2039100053000X

Fig. 10 Tie rod/adjustment link installation

7. Draw bushing into control arm by tightening nut. Tighten nut until bushing flange seats firmly against control arm.
8. Install control arm into vehicle, adjust rear wheel alignment, if necessary.

TIE ROD

REPLACE

1. Raise and support vehicle.
2. Remove wheel assembly, cotter key and castle nut, **Fig. 10.**
3. Using tool J-24319-01, disconnect outer tie rod/adjustment from knuckle. **When disconnecting the tie rod/adjustment from knuckle, do not use a wedge since seal damage will occur.**
4. Remove rod/link assembly retaining nut and retainer.
5. Remove rod/link assembly from lower control arm.
6. Reverse procedure to install. **Torque** link retaining nut to specifications and castellated nut securing ball stud to 37 ft. lbs. Install cotter pin retaining castellated nut, tightening nut as needed to insert pin through hole in stud. Do not loosen nut to align slots with hole.

STABILIZER BAR

REPLACE

1. Remove rear wheels and tires.
2. Remove stabilizer shaft support bolt, nut, retainer and insulators from knuckle bracket, **Fig. 11.**
3. Remove bushing clip bolt.
4. Bend open end of support assembly downward.
5. Remove stabilizer shaft and bushings.

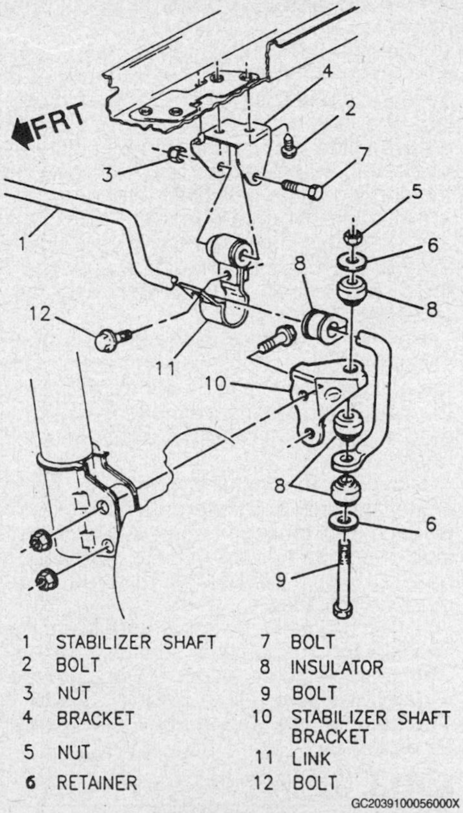
FRT
1 STABILIZER SHAFT
2 BOLT
3 NUT
4 BRACKET
5 NUT
6 RETAINER
7 BOLT
8 INSULATOR
9 BOLT
10 STABILIZER SHAFT BRACKET
11 LINK
12 BOLT
GC2039100056000X

Fig. 11 Stabilizer bar & bushing assembly

TIGHTENING SPECIFICATIONS

Year	Component	Torque/Ft. Lbs.
1992-95	Ball Joint Nut	88①②
	Control Arm Pivot Bolts	138
	Control Arm Pivot Nuts	85
	Hub & Bearing Assembly Bolts	52
	Stabilizer Shaft Bushing Assembly Nut	35–37
	Stabilizer Shaft Bushing Clip Bolt	37
	Stabilizer Shaft Link Bolt	13-14
	Stabilizer Shaft Mounting Bracket Bolt	14
	Stabilizer Shaft Support Nut	14
1992-95 —Cont'd	Strut To Knuckle Bolts	140
	Strut Mount To Underbody	18–19
	Strut Tower Mounting Nut	35
	Suspension Adjustment Link At Knuckle	33
	Suspension Adjustment Link At Control Arm	63
	Suspension Adjustment Link Locknut	48
	Wheel Lug Nuts	100

①—Inch lbs. ②—Tighten nut an additional 2/3 of a turn.

Front Suspension & Steering

NOTE: On Air Bag Equipped Models, Refer To "Air Bag System Precautions" Located In The Front Of This Manual For System Disarming & Arming Procedures.

INDEX

PRECAUTIONS

AIR BAG SYSTEMS

Refer to "Air Bag System Precautions" in the front of this manual for system disarming and arming procedures.

DESCRIPTION

The front suspension is of the McPherson design, **Fig. 1.** The control arm pivots from the cradle and is mounted in rubber bushings. The upper end of the strut is isolated by a rubber mount and contains a non-serviceable bearing to allow for rotation. The lower end of the steering knuckle pivots on a ball joint riveted to the control arm. The ball joint is fastened to the steering knuckle with a castle nut and cotter pin.

HUB & BEARING

REPLACE

1. Raise and support vehicle and remove wheel assembly.
2. Install drive axle boot protector tool J-28712 on outer joints and J-34754 on inner joints.
3. Insert a suitable drift through opening in caliper into rotor cooling fins to prevent assembly from rotating, then remove hub nut and washer.
4. Remove caliper bracket mounting bolts and the caliper and bracket assembly, then secure assembly aside taking care not to stretch brake hose. Use care not to damage brake hose.
5. Disconnect ABS front wheel speed sensor connector and unclip connector from dust shield.
6. Remove rotor, then press drive axle from hub using J-28733 or equivalent, **Fig. 2.**
7. Remove hub assembly retaining bolts, shield, hub and bearing assembly, and O-ring, **Fig. 3.**
8. Reverse procedure to install. Fill area between seal and bearing assembly with GM lubricant part NO. 1052497 or equivalent. Tighten hub attaching bolts, caliper bolts and hub nut to specifications.

BALL JOINT INSPECTION

Ball joints must be replace if any looseness is detected or ball joint seal is cut or damaged.

To inspect ball joints, raise the front of the vehicle, allowing suspension to hang freely. Grasp the tire at the top and bottom, an move the top of the tire in an in and out motion. Check for any horizontal movement of the knuckle relative to the control arm. If the ball stud is disconnected from the knuckle and looseness is detected, or if the ball stud can be twisted using finger pressure, replace the ball joint.

Ball stud tightness in the knuckle boss should also be inspected. This may be done by shaking the wheel and feeling for movement of the stud end or nut at the knuckle boss. Worn or damaged ball joints and knuckles must be replaced.

BALL JOINT

REPLACE

1. Raise and support vehicle and place jackstands under cradle. **Vehicle weight should not be placed on the control arms.**
2. Remove wheel assembly.
3. Install drive axle boot protectors.
4. Remove cotter key from ball joint nut and, using tool J-34505, separate ball joint from steering knuckle, **Fig. 4.**
5. Drill out ball joint retaining rivets.
6. Remove stabilizer bar bushing to control arm bolt.
7. Pull control arm downward and remove ball joint from steering knuckle and control arm.
8. Reverse procedure to install. Tighten new ball joint attaching nuts to specifications, **Fig. 5.**

STRUT

REPLACE

1. Remove three nuts attaching top of strut to body, **Fig. 6.**
2. Raise and support vehicle and place jackstands under cradle. Vehicle weight should not be placed on the control arms.

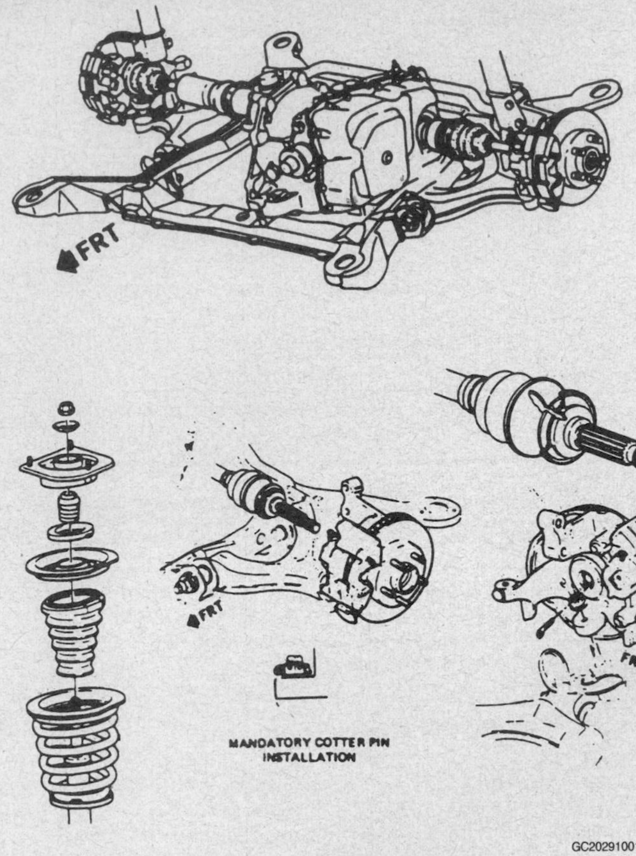
FRT
FRT
FRT
MANDATORY COTTER PIN INSTALLATION
GC2029100116000X

Fig. 1 Front suspension

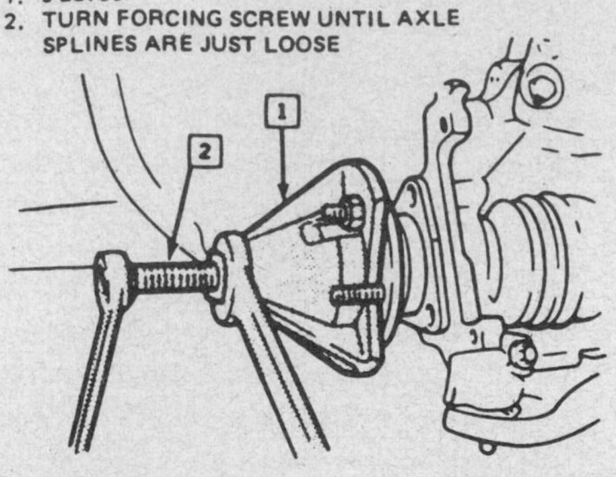
1. J-28733
2. TURN FORCING SCREW UNTIL AXLE SPLINES ARE JUST LOOSE
1
2
GC2029100117000X

Fig. 2 Separating drive axle from hub

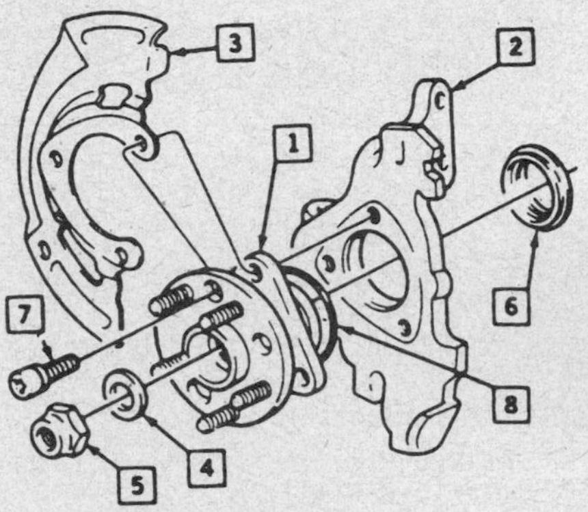
1
2
3
4
5
6
7
8
1. HUB AND BEARING ASSEMBLY
2. STEERING KNUCKLE
3. SHIELD
4. WASHER
5. HUB NUT 245 N·m (180 LBS. FT.)
6. SEAL
7. HUB AND BEARING RETAINING BOLT (55 TORX) 95 N·m (70 LBS. FT.)
8. "O" RING
GC2029100118000X

Fig. 3 Hub & bearing assembly

3. Remove wheel assembly.
4. Install drive axle boot protectors.
5. Remove brake line bracket bolt from strut assembly.
6. Remove strut to steering knuckle attaching bolts.
7. Remove strut assembly from vehicle.
8. Reverse procedure to install. Tighten strut mounting bolts to specifications.

STRUT SERVICE

Refer to **Figs. 7 and 8** when performing the following procedure.

1. Remove strut as outlined under "Strut, Replace" procedure.
2. Mount strut in compressor tool J-34013 and holding fixture J-3289-20.
3. Rotate compressor forcing screw until spring compresses slightly.
4. Hold damper shaft from rotating and remove nut from top of strut assembly.
5. Use tool J-34013-30 to guide damper shaft from assembly.
6. Loosen compressor forcing screw while guiding damper shaft from assembly. Continue to loosen nut until strut damper and spring can be removed.
7. Reverse procedure to assemble. When assembling spring, the flat on upper spring seat must face outward 90 degrees from centerline of vehicle or when mounted in the strut compressor, the seat faces in the same direction as the steering knuckle mounting flange.

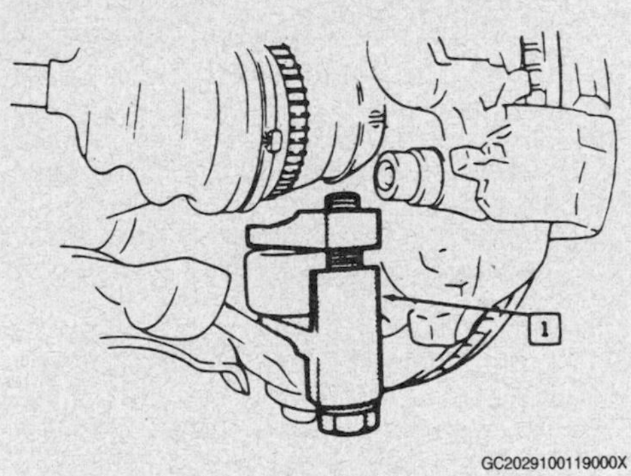
1. J 36226 BALL JOINT SEPARATOR
1
GC2029100119000X

Fig. 4 Separating ball joint from steering knuckle

CONTROL ARM
REPLACE

1. Raise and support vehicle and place jackstands under cradle. **Vehicle weight should not be placed on the control arms.**
2. Remove wheel assembly.
3. Install drive axle boot protectors.
4. Remove cotter key from ball joint nut and, using tool J-34505, separate ball joint from steering knuckle.
5. Remove stabilizer bar bushing to control arm bolt.
6. Remove control arm mounting bolts and the control arm, **Fig. 9.**
7. Reverse procedure to install. When installing control arms, install but do not torque control arm mounting bolts. Sufficiently tighten bolts to assure security but final tightening should done when vehicle weight is supported by control arms. Tighten rear arm bolt and front bolt to specifications.

STABILIZER BAR
REPLACE

1. Raise and support vehicle and place jackstands under cradle. Vehicle weight should
2. Remove wheel assembly.
3. Install drive axle boot protectors.
4. Remove nuts, washers, bushings and bolt securing stabilizer shaft to each control arm, **Fig. 10.**
5. Remove stabilizer bar mounting bolts, two bolts from each side, **Fig. 11.**
6. Disconnect tie rods from steering knuckles.
7. Remove exhaust pipe between exhaust manifold and catalytic converter.
8. Rotate right side strut assembly completely to the right.
9. Slide stabilizer bar to the right over the steering knuckle and pull downward on left side until stabilizer bar clears the cradle, **Fig. 12.**
10. Reverse procedure to install.

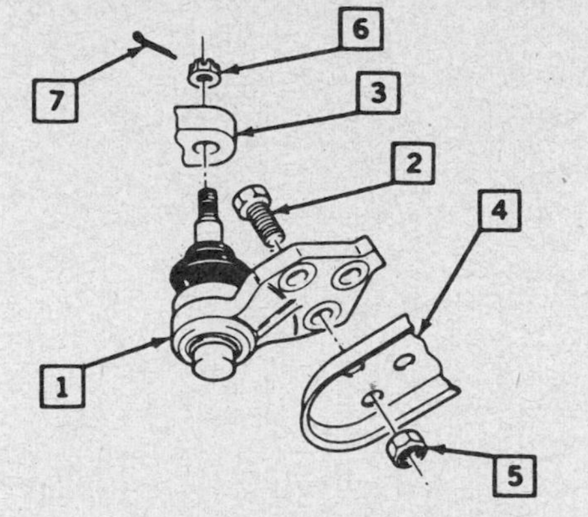

1. SERVICE BALL JOINT
2. BALL JOINT MOUNTING BOLTS MUST FACE DOWN
3. STEERING KNUCKLE
4. CONTROL ARM
5. BALL JOINT MOUNTING NUTS 68 N·m (50 LBS. FT.)
6. BALL JOINT TO STEERING KNUCKLE NUT 110 N·m (81 LBS. FT.) BEFORE COTTER PIN INSTALLATION
7. COTTER PIN

GC2029100120000X

Fig. 5 Service ball joint attachment

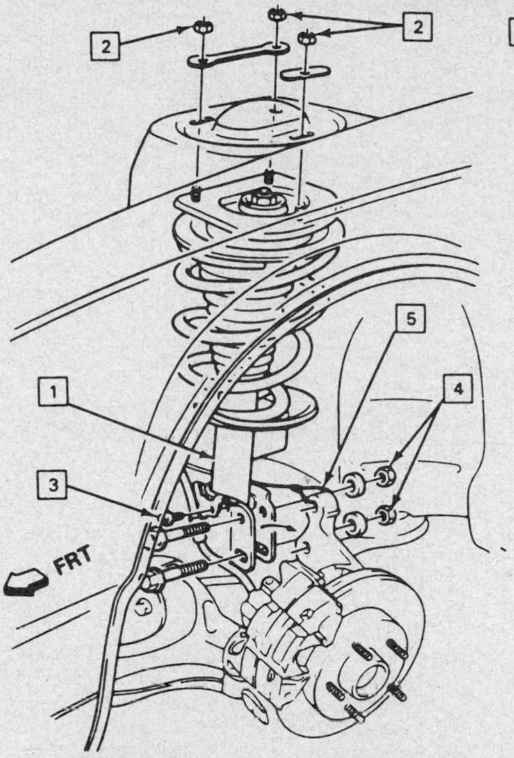
FRT

1. STRUT ASSEMBLY
2. STRUT TO BODY NUTS 24N·m (18 LBS.FT.)
3. BRAKE LINE BRACKET BOLT 17 N·m (13 LBS.FT.)
4. STRUT TO STEERING KNUCKLE NUTS 195 N·m (144 LBS. FT.)
5. Retain STEERING KNUCKLE with wire once STRUT ASSEMBLY is removed

GC2029100125000X

Fig. 6 Strut assembly

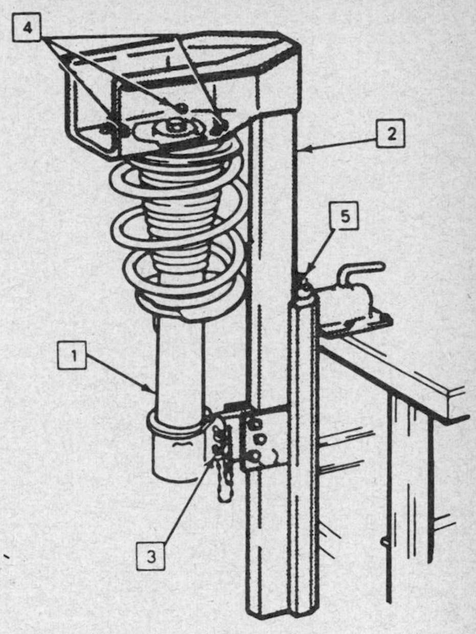

1. STRUT ASSEMBLY
2. STRUT COMPRESSOR J-34013
3. Install LOCKING PINS through STRUT ASSEMBLY
4. Tighten NUTS till flush with STRUT COMPRESSOR
5. COMPRESSOR FORCING SCREW

GC2029100126000X

Fig. 7 Disassembling strut

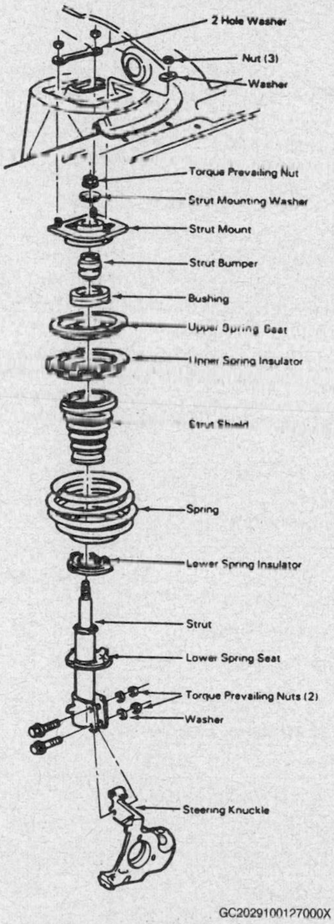
2 Hole Washer
Nut (3)
Washer
Torque Prevailing Nut
Strut Mounting Washer
Strut Mount
Strut Bumper
Bushing
Upper Spring Seat
Upper Spring Insulator
Strut Shield
Spring
Lower Spring Insulator
Strut
Lower Spring Seat
Torque Prevailing Nuts (2)
Washer
Steering Knuckle

GC2029100127000X

Fig. 8 Exploded view of strut assembly

1. CONTROL ARM
2. FRAME
3. FRAME MOUNTED BUSHING
4. CONTROL ARM MOUNTED BUSHING
5. FRAME MOUNTED BUSHING NUT 190 N·m (140 LBS. FT.)
6. CONTROL ARM MOUNTED BUSHING NUT 123 N·m (90 LBS. FT.)
7. WASHER

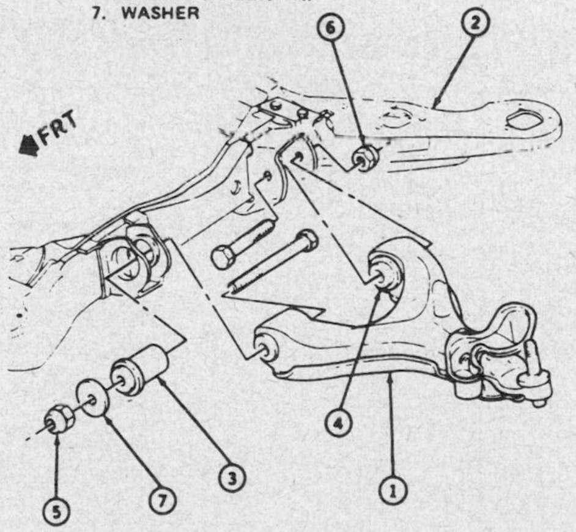
FRT

GC2029100121000X

Fig. 9 Control arm assembly

1. Stabilizer Bar
2. Control Arm
3. Insulator (4)
4. Retainer (4)
5. Bolt
6. Nut 17 N·m (13 LBS. FT.)

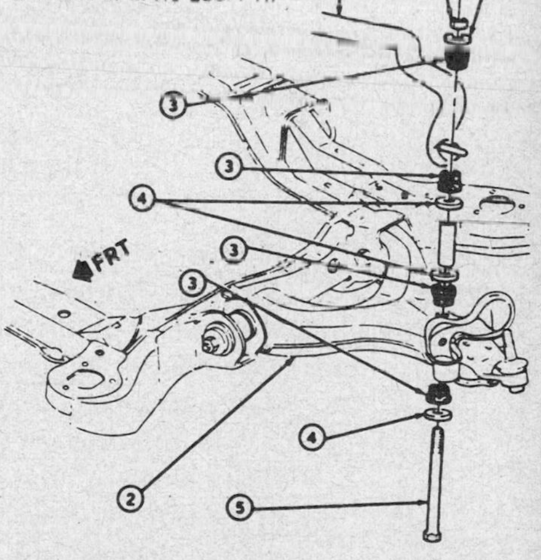
FRT

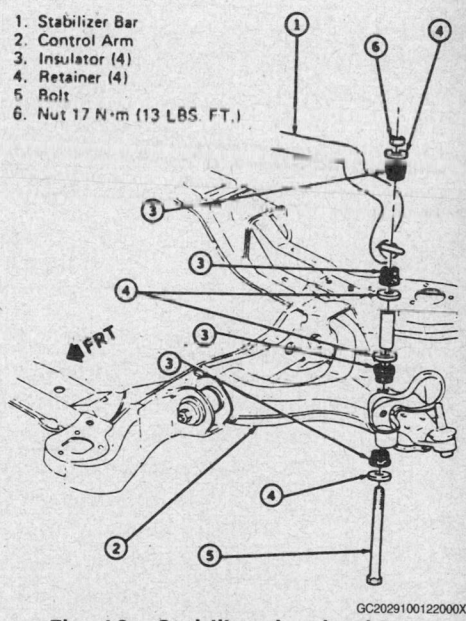

GC2029100122000X

Fig. 10 Stabilizer bar bushing assembly

POWER STEERING GEAR

REPLACE

1. Raise and support vehicle with weight resting on suspension.
2. Remove front wheel assemblies.
3. Disconnect intermediate shaft from steering gear stub shaft.
4. Disconnect both tie rod ends from steering knuckles.
5. Remove line retainers and disconnect hydraulic lines from steering gear.
6. Remove five steering gear attaching bolts, **Fig. 13.**
7. Remove steering gear from vehicle by sliding out to the side.
8. Reverse procedure to install. Refer to **Fig. 13,** for tightening sequence.

1. STABILIZER BAR
2. STABILIZER BAR MOUNTING BRACKET
3. STABILIZER BAR MOUNTING BUSHING
4. 50 N·m (37 LBS. FT.)
5. FRAME WELDED NUTS
6. FRAME

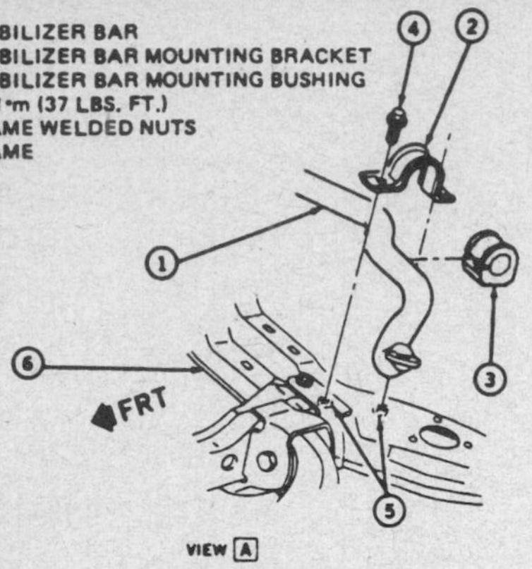
FRT
VIEW A

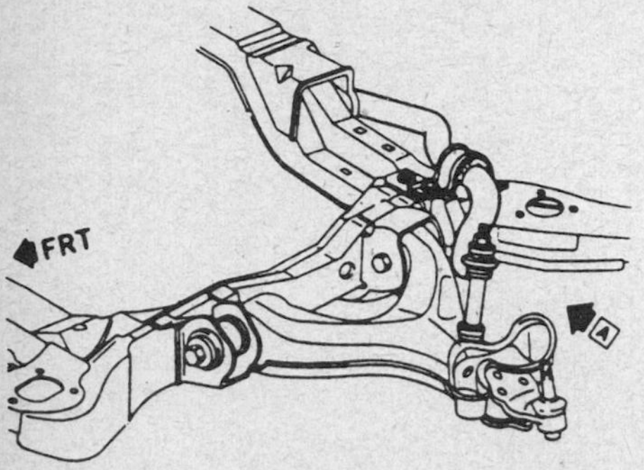
FRT
A

GC2029100123000X

Fig. 11 Stabilizer bar mounting

POWER STEERING PUMP

REPLACE

3800/V6-231 ENGINE

1. Disconnect battery ground cable.
2. Remove air cleaner, if necessary.
3. Remove alternator drive belt and alternator.
4. Raise and support vehicle.
5. Disconnect hydraulic lines from pump.
6. Remove rear pump adjustment bracket to pump nut.
7. Remove pump drive belt.
8. Lower vehicle.
9. Remove pump rear adjustment bracket.
10. Remove power steering pump from vehicle.
11. Reverse procedure to install.

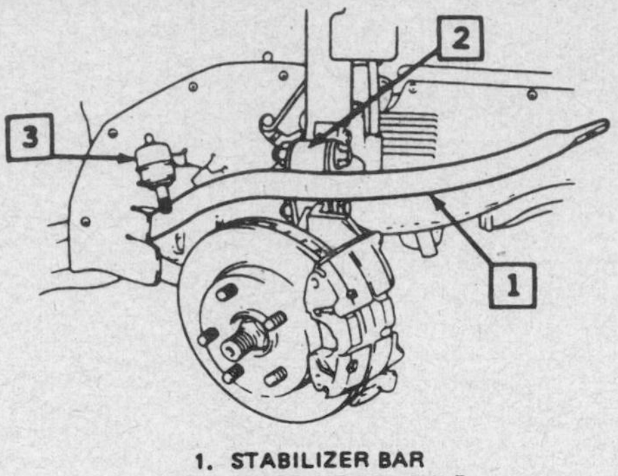
1
2
3

1. STABILIZER BAR
2. STEERING KNUCKLE
3. TIE ROD

GC2029100124000X

Fig. 12 Stabilizer bar replacement

4.6L/V8-279 & 4.9L/V8-300 ENGINES

1. Disconnect battery ground cable.
2. Remove pump drive belt and the pulley.
3. Disconnect hydraulic lines from pump.
4. Remove two pump mounting bolts.
5. Remove power steering pump from vehicle.
6. Reverse procedure to install.

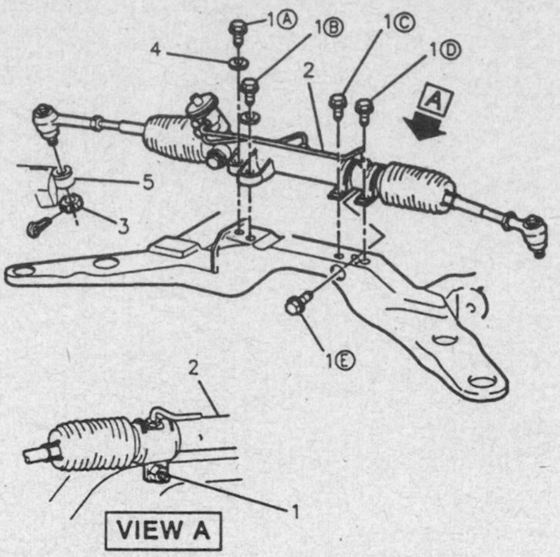
VIEW A

1 BOLT
TIGHTEN IN SEQUENCE A THRU E.
2 STEERING GEAR
3 NUT; 47 N·m (35 LB. FT.). MAXIMUM PERMISSIBLE TORQUE TO ALIGN COTTER PIN SLOT IS 70 N·m (52 LB. FT.).
4 WASHER
5 STEERING KNUCKLE

GC6039100041000X

Fig. 13 Steering gear replacement

TIGHTENING SPECIFICATIONS

Year	Component	Torque/Ft. Lbs.
1992-95	Ball Joint To Knuckle	88①②
	Brake Caliper To Knuckle	38
	Brake Line Bracket To Underbody	13
	Control Arm Mounting Nut (Front)	140-144
	Control Arm Mounting Nut (Rear)	88-90
	Drive Axle Shaft Nut	107
	Hub & Bearing To Knuckle	70
	Power Steering Gear	50
	Power Steering Gear Inlet Hose To Pump	20
	Power Steering Gear Lines To Gear	70①
1992-95 —Cont'd	Power Steering Pump	20
	Service Ball Joint To Control Arm	50
	Stabilizer Shaft Bushing Nut	13
	Stabilizer Shaft Mounting Bracket	37
	Steering Knuckle To Strut Bolts	140-144
	Strut Assembly To Body Nuts	18
	Strut Mount Nut	55
	Tie Rod To Knuckle	35③
	Wheel Lug Nut	100

①—Inch lbs.
②—Tighten an additional 120°.
③—Tighten to align cotter pin.

Wheel Alignment

NOTE: On Air Bag Equipped Models, Refer To "Air Bag System Precautions" Located In The Front Of This Manual For System Disarming & Arming Procedures.

INDEX

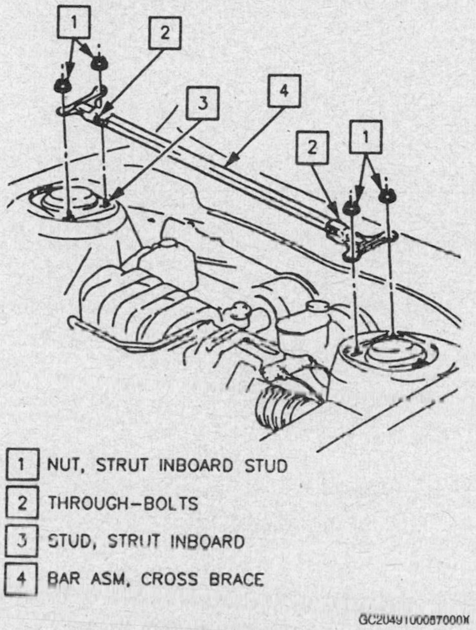

1
2
3
4
2
1
1 NUT, STRUT INBOARD STUD
2 THROUGH-BOLTS
3 STUD, STRUT INBOARD
4 BAR ASM, CROSS BRACE
GC2049100057000X

Fig. 1 Cross brace removal

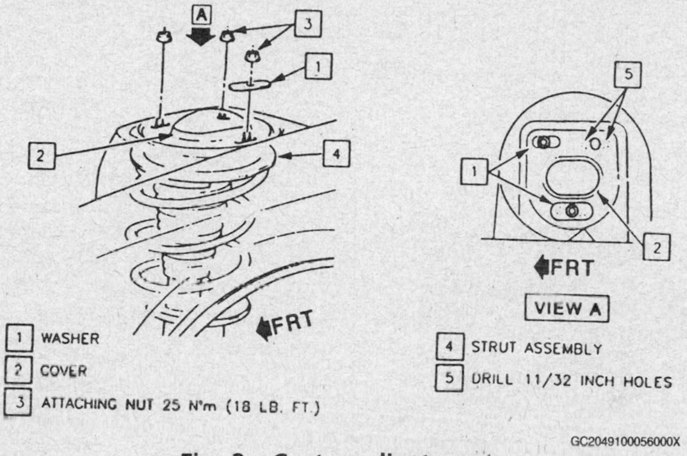

A
3
1
2
4
FRT
1 WASHER
2 COVER
3 ATTACHING NUT 25 N·m (18 LB. FT.)
5
1
2
FRT
VIEW A
4 STRUT ASSEMBLY
5 DRILL 11/32 INCH HOLES
GC2049100056000X

Fig. 2 Caster adjustment

PRECAUTIONS

AIR BAG SYSTEMS

Refer to "Air Bag System Precautions" in the front of this manual for system disarming and arming procedures.

PRELIMINARY INSPECTION

1. Inspect tires for proper inflation and similar tread wear.
2. Inspect hub and bearing for excessive wear, repair as required.
3. Inspect ball joints.
4. Inspect tie rod ends for excessive looseness.
5. Check wheel and tire runout.
6. Inspect vehicle ride height.
7. Inspect rack and pinion for looseness at frame.
8. Ensure proper strut operation.
9. Inspect control arm bushings.
10. Inspect stabilizer shaft for loose or missing parts.
11. Check suspension and steering components for damage, replace as required.

FRONT WHEEL ALIGNMENT

CASTER

1. Loosen cross brace assembly through bolts, **Fig. 1.**
2. Remove inboard strut nuts, then the brace assembly.
3. Remove remaining nut over oval strut mounting hole, **Fig. 2.**
4. Lift front of vehicle by body to separate strut from inner wheelhouse.
5. Drill two 11/32 inch holes at front and rear of oval strut mounting hole.
6. File excess metal to elongate original holes, then paint exposed metal with primer.
7. Lower front of vehicle.
8. Place cross brace assembly on inboard strut studs and install strut attaching nuts.
9. Set caster to specifications by moving strut forward or rearward as necessary.
10. **Torque** strut attaching nuts to 18 ft. lbs.
11. **Torque** cross brace bar through bolts to 21 ft. lbs.

CAMBER

1. Loosen both strut to knuckle attaching nuts, **Fig. 3.**
2. Install camber adjusting tool J-29862.
3. Set camber to specifications.
4. Remove adjusting tool and **torque** strut to knuckle attaching nuts to 144 ft. lbs.
5. Recheck camber.

TOE

1. Loosen locknuts on both inner tie rods, **Fig. 4.**
2. Adjust toe to specifications by rotating inner tie rod.
3. **Torque** locknuts to 50 ft. lbs.
4. Recheck toe setting.

REAR WHEEL ALIGNMENT

When checking rear wheel alignment, the electronic leveling system must have the superlift struts inflated with residual pressure only.

Place a weight in trunk and turn ignition on and move transmission selector from Park to Reverse position and back. This will activate the compressor. Turn ignition off and remove weight from trunk. Wait 30 seconds for the system to exhaust. Roll vehicle forward one complete wheel rotation. Jounce vehicle before checking alignment.

CAMBER

1. Loosen strut to knuckle attaching nuts.
2. Install camber adjusting tool J-29862, **Fig. 5.**
3. Move strut to set camber to specifications.
4. Remove camber adjusting tool and **torque** strut to knuckle nuts to 144 ft. lbs.
5. Recheck camber setting.

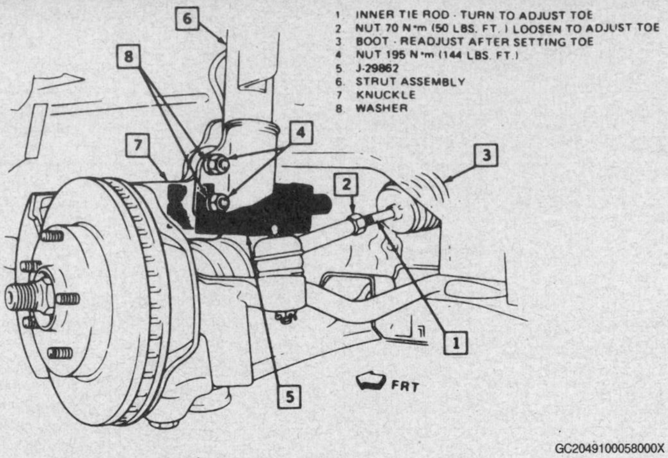
1 INNER TIE ROD - TURN TO ADJUST TOE
2 NUT 70 N·m (50 LBS. FT.) LOOSEN TO ADJUST TOE
3 BOOT - READJUST AFTER SETTING TOE
4 NUT 195 N·m (144 LBS. FT.)
5 J-29862
6 STRUT ASSEMBLY
7 KNUCKLE
8 WASHER
FRT

GC2049100058000X

Fig. 3 Camber adjustment

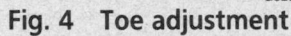

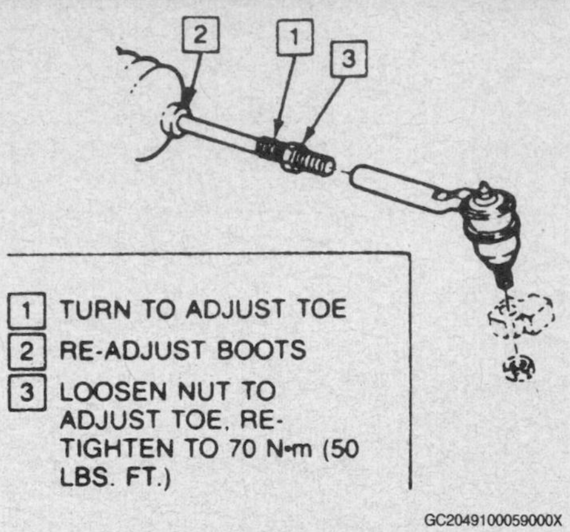
1 TURN TO ADJUST TOE
2 RE-ADJUST BOOTS
3 LOOSEN NUT TO ADJUST TOE, RE-TIGHTEN TO 70 N·m (50 LBS. FT.)

GC2049100059000X

Fig. 4 Toe adjustment

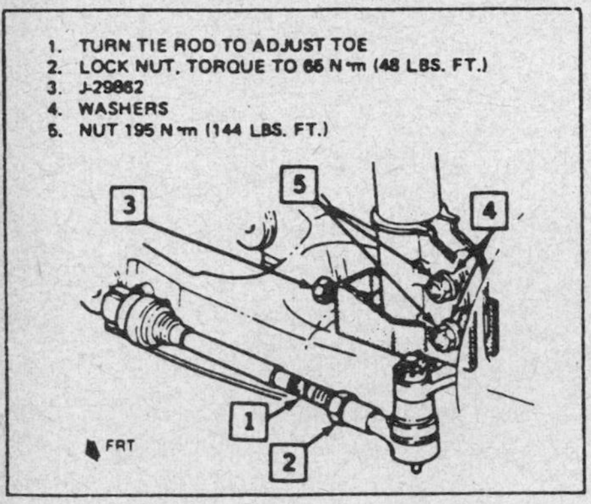
1. TURN TIE ROD TO ADJUST TOE
2. LOCK NUT, TORQUE TO 65 N·m (48 LBS. FT.)
3. J-29862
4. WASHERS
5. NUT 195 N·m (144 LBS. FT.)
FRT

GC2049100060000X

Fig. 5 Rear camber & toe adjustments

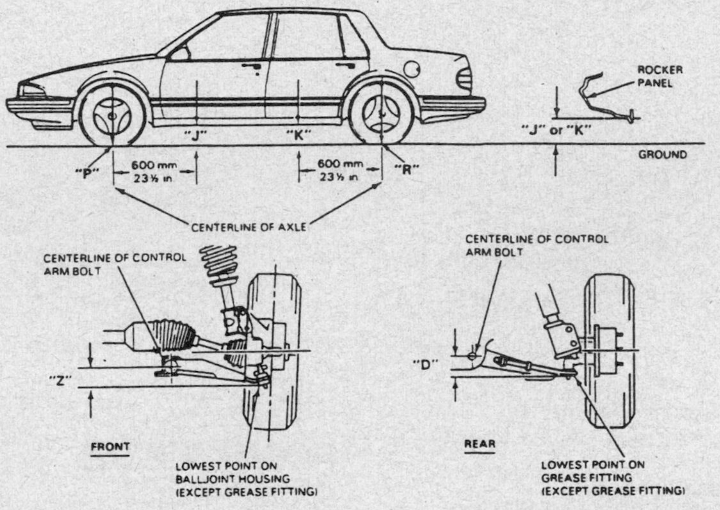
ROCKER PANEL
"J" or "K"
GROUND
"J"
"K"
"P"
600 mm 23½ in
600 mm 23½ in
"R"
CENTERLINE OF AXLE
CENTERLINE OF CONTROL ARM BOLT
CENTERLINE OF CONTROL ARM BOLT
"Z"
"D"
FRONT
REAR
LOWEST POINT ON BALLJOINT HOUSING (EXCEPT GREASE FITTING)
LOWEST POINT ON GREASE FITTING (EXCEPT GREASE FITTING)

GC2049100061000X

Fig. 6 Ride height measurements

TOE

Toe adjustment is made by loosening the locknut at tie rod end and turning inner tie rod to set toe to specifications, **Fig. 5.**

VEHICLE RIDE HEIGHT

Refer to **Figs. 6 and 7** for ride height specifications and measurement locations. Check ride height as follows:

1. Ensure vehicle is on level ground.
2. Ensure tires are inflated to proper pressures.
3. Fuel tank should be full to obtain accurate readings.
4. Trunk should be empty except for spare tire and jack.
5. Place the front seat in the far rearward position, then turn ignition to On position to activate the electronic level control, if equipped.
6. Bounce the car three times at the front and rear to normalize suspension.
7. Measure from lowest point on the ball joint housing to control arm bolt centerline, "D" and "Z" positions.
8. Measure from level floor to rocker panel at "J" and "K" positions.

Make & Model	Year	Riding Height Measurements In Inches			
		Dimension Z	**Dimension D**	**Dimension J**	**Dimension K**
BUICK					
LeSabre	**1992-95**	**1 15/16-2 3/4**	**2 11/16-3 7/16**	**9-9 13/16**	**9 9/32-10 1/16**
Park Avenue	**1992-95**	**1 15/16-2 3/4**	**2 11/16-3 7/16**	**9-9 13/16**	**9 1/16-9 27/32**
CADILLAC					
Concours/DeVille/Fleetwood (FWD)/Sixty Special	**1992-95**	**1 15/16-2 3/4**	**2 11/16-3 7/16**	**9-9 13/16**	**9 1/16-9 27/32**
OLDSMOBILE					
Eighty-Eight	**1992-95**	**1 15/16-2 3/4**	**2 11/16-3 7/16**	**9-9 13/16**	**9 9/32-10 1/16**
Ninety-Eight	**1992-95**	**1 15/16-2 3/4**	**2 11/16-3 7/16**	**9-9 13/16**	**9 1/16-9 27/32**
PONTIAC					
Bonneville	**1992①**	**1 15/16-2 3/4**	**2 11/16-3 7/16**	**9-9 13/16**	**9 5/16-10 1/16**
	1992②	**1 15/16-2 3/4**	**2 11/16-3 7/16**	**9-9 13/16**	**9 1/16-9 27/32**
	1993-95	**1 15/16-2 3/4**	**2 11/16-3 7/16**	**9-9 13/16**	**9 9/32-10 1/16**

①—SE.
②—Except SE

Fig. 7 Ride height specifications

CADILLAC ELDORADO & SEVILLE: OLDSMOBILE TORONADO & TROFEO: 1992–93 BUICK RIVIERA

(E & K Cars)

NOTE: Refer To Rear Of This Manual For Vehicle Manufacturer's Special Service Tool Suppliers.

INDEX OF SERVICE OPERATIONS

NOTE: For Service Operations Not Listed Below, Refer To The Table Of Contents In The Front Of This Manual.

Specifications

GENERAL ENGINE SPECIFICATIONS

Year	Engine Liter/CID	Engine VIN Code ②	Fuel Injection System	Bore & Stroke	Compression Ratio	Net H.P. @ RPM ③	Maximum Torque Ft. Lbs. @ RPM	Normal Oil Pressure Pounds
1992	3.8L/V6-231	L	TPI④	3.80 X 3.40	8.5	170 @ 4800	220 @ 3200	60⑤
1993	3.8L/V6-231	L	TPI④	3.80 X 3.40	8.5	170 @ 4800	220 @ 3200	60⑤
	4.6L/V8-279	9	TPI④	3.66 x 3.31	10.3	295 @ 6000	290 @ 4400	35①
	4.6L/V8-279	Y	TPI④	3.66 x 3.31	10.3	270 @ 5600	300 @ 4000	35①
	4.9L/V8-300	B	SFI⑥	3.62 x 3.62	9.5	200 @ 4400	275 @ 3000	—
1994	4.6L/V8-279	9	TPI④	3.66 x 3.31	10.3	295 @ 6000	290 @ 4400	35⑦
	4.6L/V8-279	Y	TPI④	3.66 x 3.31	10.3	270 @ 5600	300 @ 4000	35⑦
1995	4.6L/V8-279	9	TPI④	3.66 x 3.31	10.3	295 @ 6000	290 @ 4400	35⑦
	4.6L/V8-279	Y	TPI④	3.66 x 3.31	10.3	270 @ 5600	300 @ 4000	35⑦

①—At 2000 RPM.
②—The eighth digit denotes engine code.
③—Ratings are net-as installed in vehicle.
④—Tuned Port Fuel Injection.
⑤—At 1850 RPM, w/10W-30 engine oil.
⑥—Sequential Fuel Injection.
⑦—At 2000 RPM.
⑧—Sequential Port Fuel Injection

TUNE UP SPECIFICATIONS

Year & Engine/ VIN Code ①	Spark Plug Gap	Ignition Timing: Firing Order Fig. ④	Ignition Timing: Degrees BTDC	Ignition Timing: Mark Fig.	Curb Idle Speed ③	Fast Idle Speed	Fuel Pump Pressure, Psi
1992							
3.8L/V6-231(L)	.060	⑨	⑤	⑩	⑥	⑥	41–47⑦
4.9L/V8-300(B)	.060	C	10⑧	D	⑥	⑥	40–50⑦
1993							
3.8L/V6-231(L)	.060	⑨	⑤	⑩	⑥	⑥	41–47⑦
4.6L/V8-279(9)	.050	②	10⑤	⑩	⑥	⑥	40–50⑦
4.6L/V8-279(Y)	.050	②	10⑤	⑩	⑥	⑥	40–50⑦
4.9L/V8-300(B)	.060	C	10⑧	D	⑥	⑥	40–50⑦
1994							
4.6L/V8-279(9)	.050	②	10⑤	⑩	⑥	⑥	40–50⑦
4.6L/V8-279(Y)	.050	②	10⑤	⑩	⑥	⑥	40–50⑦
1995							
4.6L/V8-279(9)	.050	②	10⑤	⑩	⑥	⑥	40–50⑦
4.6L/V8-279(Y)	.050	②	10⑤	⑩	⑥	⑥	40–50⑦

BTDC—Before top dead center.
①—The eighth digit of the Vehicle Identification Number (VIN) denotes engine code.
②——Cylinder numbering from left to right as viewed from front of vehicle, front bank, 2, 4, 6, 8; rear bank, 1, 3, 5, 7. Firing order 1-2-7-3-4-5-6-8. Refer to Fig. for spark plug wire connections at coil unit.
③—On auto. trans. models, idle speed is adjusted in Drive. When adjusting idle speed, set parking brake & block drive wheels.
④—Before disconnecting wires from distributor cap, determine location of No. 1 wire in cap, as distributor position may have been altered from that shown at the end of this chart.
⑤—Computer controlled, no adjustment.
⑥—Idle speed is controlled by an idle speed control (ISC) motor or an idle air control (IAC) valve.
⑦—With shop towel wrapped around fuel pressure valve to prevent fuel spillage, connect a suitable fuel pressure gauge to fuel pressure valve. Check fuel pressure with ignition switch in the On position, engine not running.
⑧—Connect jumper wire between ALCL connector terminals A & B. The ALCL connector is located under the instrument panel to the right of the steering column. After completing adjustment, disconnect jumper wire from between terminals A & B. With engine off, clear trouble code from Electronic Control Module (ECM) by removing battery voltage to ECM for 30 seconds.
⑨—Cylinder numbering from left to right as viewed from front of vehicle, front bank, 1, 3, 5; rear bank, 2, 4, 6. Firing order 1-6-5-4-3-2. Refer to Figs. A & B for spark plug wire connections at coil unit.
⑩—Equipped with crankshaft position sensor.

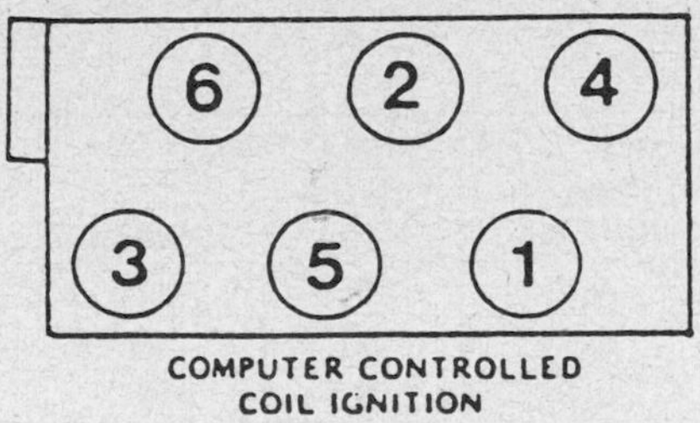

6
2
4
3
5
1
COMPUTER CONTROLLED
COIL IGNITION

GC1139100132000X

Fig. A

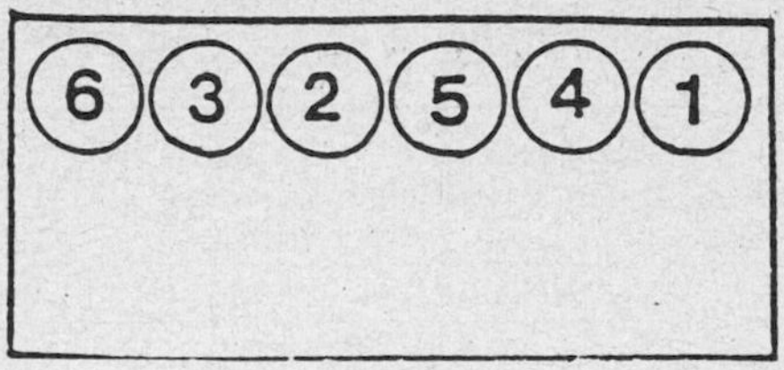

6 3 2 5 4 1

GC1139100133000X

Fig. B

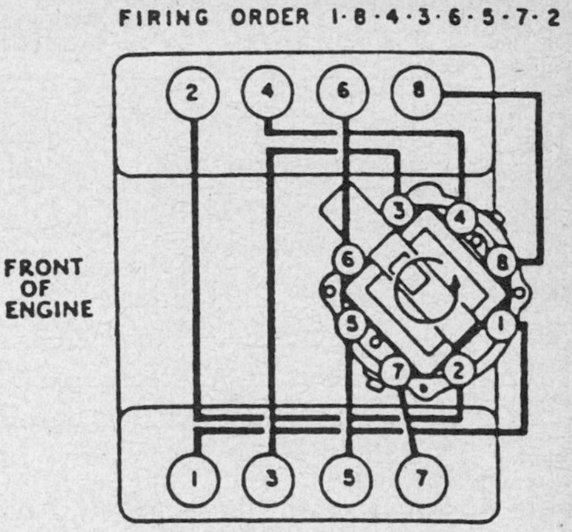

FIRING ORDER 1·8·4·3·6·5·7·2
FRONT OF ENGINE
2 4 6 8
1 3 5 7

GC1139100134000X

Fig. C

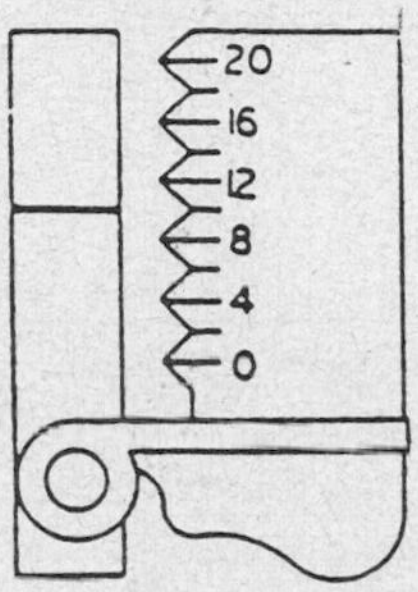

20
16
12
8
4
0

GC1139100135000X

Fig. D

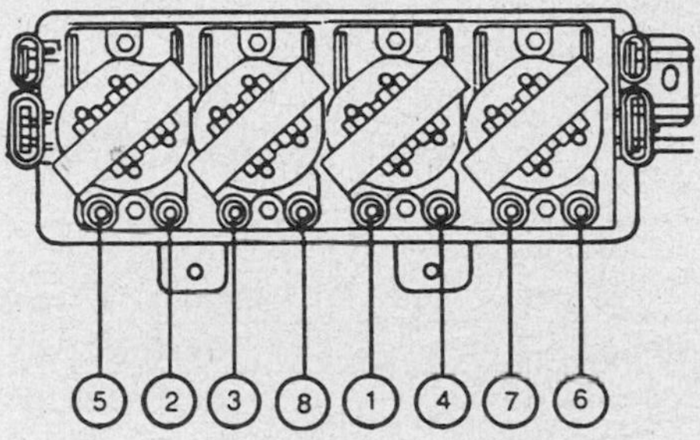

5 2 3 8 1 4 7 6

GC1139100136000X

Fig. E

FRONT WHEEL ALIGNMENT SPECIFICATIONS

Year	Model	Caster Angle, Degrees		Camber Angle, Degrees				Total Toe Degrees
				Limits		Desired		
		Limits	Desired	Left	Right	Left	Right	
1992	Toronado & Trofeo	+1.3 to +3.0	+2.3	-.8 to +.8	-.8 to +.8	0	0	+.2
1992-93	Riviera	+1.3 to +3.3	+2.3	-.8 to +.8	-.8 to +.8	0	0	+.2
1992-95	Eldorado & Seville	+1.5 to +3.5	+2.5	-1 to +1	0 to +1.0	-.5	+.5	+.2

REAR WHEEL ALIGNMENT SPECIFICATIONS

Year	Model	Camber Angle, Degrees				Total Toe Degrees	Thrust Angle, Degrees
		Limits		Desired			
		Left	Right	Left	Right		
1992	Tornado & Trofeo	—	—	—	—	+.2	-.1 to +.1
1992-93	Riviera	—	—	—	—	+.2	-.1 to +.1
1992–95	Elorado & Seville	+.5 to -.5	+.5 to -.5	0	0	+.2	-.1 to +.1

COOLING SYSTEM & CAPACITY DATA

Year	Liter/CID/VIN	Coolant Capacity, Qts.	Radiator Cap Relief Pressure, Lbs.	Thermo. Opening Temp.°F	Fuel Tank Gals	Engine Oil Refill Qts.	Auto Transaxle Qts.①	
							Drain & Refill	Overhaul
1992	3.8L/V6-231(L)	13	15	195	18	4②	6	11
	4.9L/V8-300(B)	12.1	15	195	18.8	5③	6	8
1993	3.8L/V6-231(L)	13	15	195	18	4②	6	11
	4.6L/V8-279 (9 or Y)	12.3	15	180	20	7③	8	12.6
	4.9L/V8-300(B)	12.3	15	195	20	5③	6	8
1994–95	4.6L/V8-279 (9 or Y)	12.5	15	180	20	7③	8	12.6

①—Approximate. Make final check w/dipstick.
②—Additional oil will be necessary when changing filter.
③—Add 1/2 qt. w/filter change.

LUBRICANT DATA

Year	Model	Lubricant Type		
		Automatic Transaxle	Power Steering	Brake System
1992	Toronado, Trofeo	Dexron IIE or III	GM Power Steering Fluid①	DOT 3
	Eldorado, Seville	Dexron IIE or III	GM Power Steering Fluid①	DOT 3
	Riviera	Dexron IIE or III	GM Power Steering Fluid①	DOT 3
1993	Eldorado, Seville	Dexron IIE or III	GM Power Steering Fluid①	DOT 3
	Riviera	Dexron IIE or III	GM Power Steering Fluid①	DOT 3
1994–95	Eldorado, Seville	Dexron IIE or III	GM Power Steering Fluid①	DOT 3

①—Meeting GM requirements 9985010.

Electrical

NOTE: On Air Bag Equipped Models, Refer To "Air Bag System Precautions" Located In The Front Of This Manual For System Disarming & Arming Procedures.

INDEX

PRECAUTIONS

AIR BAG SYSTEMS

Refer to "Air Bag System Precautions" in the front of this manual for system disarming and arming procedures.

FUSE PANEL & FLASHER LOCATION

On Riviera, Toronado and Trofeo models, the fuse panel is located inside the glove compartment. On Eldorado and Seville models, the fuse panel is located behind the center of the instrument panel, behind the glove box door.

On Toronado and Trofeo models, the hazard flasher and turn signal flasher are located behind the instrument panel, on the righthand side of the steering column support. On Eldorado, Riviera and Seville models, the turn/hazard module is located behind the lefthand side of the instrument panel above the steering column.

RELAY CENTER LOCATION

The relay center is located in the lefthand side of the engine compartment, on the wheel house.

STARTER

REPLACE

If shims are used between starter and engine block, they should be placed in original position during installation. If starter is noisy during cranking, remove double .015 inch shim or add .015 inch shim at outer bolt only. If high pitched whine is observed after engine starts, add double .015 inch shims (to maximum of .045 inch) until noise is corrected.

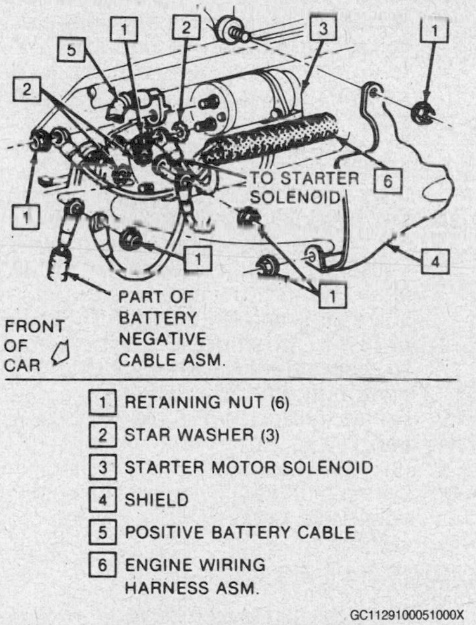

1
2
3
5
TO STARTER SOLENOID
6
4
PART OF BATTERY NEGATIVE CABLE ASM.
FRONT OF CAR
1 RETAINING NUT (6)
2 STAR WASHER (3)
3 STARTER MOTOR SOLENOID
4 SHIELD
5 POSITIVE BATTERY CABLE
6 ENGINE WIRING HARNESS ASM.
GC1129100051000X

Fig. 1 Starter wiring. Eldorado & Seville w/4.9L/V8-300

ELDORADO & SEVILLE

4.9L/V8-300 Engine

1. Disconnect battery ground cable, then raise and support vehicle.
2. Remove nuts securing starter shield and the shield.
3. Disconnect front and rear exhaust pipe if necessary.
4. Remove nuts securing solenoid wires and battery cable, then disconnect wiring, **Fig. 1.**
5. Remove starter brace, mounting bolts and the starter motor.
6. Reverse procedure to install.

4.6L/V8-279 Engine

1. Remove intake manifold as outlined under "Intake Manifold, Replace" in "4.6L/V8-279 Engine" section.
2. Remove starter electrical connectors, then the starter mounting bolts.
3. Remove starter from vehicle.
4. Reverse procedure to install.

RIVIERA, TORONADO & TROFEO

1. Disconnect battery ground cable, then raise and support vehicle.
2. Remove flywheel inspection cover, then the starter splash shield, if equipped.
3. Remove two bolts securing starter to engine block, then lower starter motor.
4. Remove retaining nuts and disconnect electrical connectors, noting position for installation.
5. Reverse procedure to install.

DISTRIBUTOR

REPLACE

ELDORADO & SEVILLE

1. Remove distributor appearance cover and retainer.

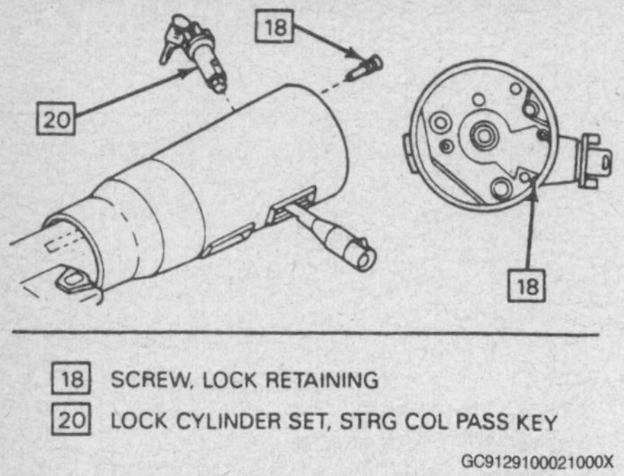
18
20
18
18 SCREW, LOCK RETAINING
20 LOCK CYLINDER SET, STRG COL PASS KEY
GC9129100021000X
Fig. 2 Lock cylinder set removal

2. Disconnect ignition switch battery feed wire from distributor cap.
3. Disconnect coil connections from cap. **Do not use a screwdriver or other tool to release locking tabs.**
4. Remove four bolts from distributor cap, note position of cap ignition coil then move cap aside.
5. Disconnect six terminal ECM harness from distributor.
6. Remove distributor clamp nut and hold-down clamp. Use tool No. J-29791 or equivalent to remove hold-down nut.
7. Note position of rotor. Pull distributor up until rotor stops turning counterclockwise, then note position of rotor.
8. Remove distributor. **A thrust washer is used between distributor drive gear and crankcase. This washer may stick to bottom of distributor when removed. Before replacing distributor, ensure thrust washer is located in crankcase at bottom of distributor bore.**
9. Reverse procedure to install, noting the following:
   a. If distributor position was lost, or set incorrectly, remove No. 1 spark plug wire.
   b. Place a finger over No. 1 spark plug hole while an assistant slowly cranks engine until compression is felt.
   c. Align timing mark on pulley with "0 mark on timing indicator.
   d. Turn rotor to point between No. 1 and No. 8 spark plug towers on distributor cap.
   e. Install distributor.

IGNITION LOCK

REPLACE

1. Disconnect battery ground cable, then remove steering wheel as outlined under "Steering Wheel, Replace."
2. Remove turn signal switch as outlined under "Turn Signal Switch, Replace."
3. Remove key from lock, then the buzzer switch assembly.
4. Place key in "Lock" position, then remove lock retaining screw, **Fig. 2.**
5. Disconnect electrical connector, retaining clip from housing cover, then withdraw lock cylinder assembly from column.
6. Reverse procedure to install. **Torque** lock retaining screw to 22 inch lbs.

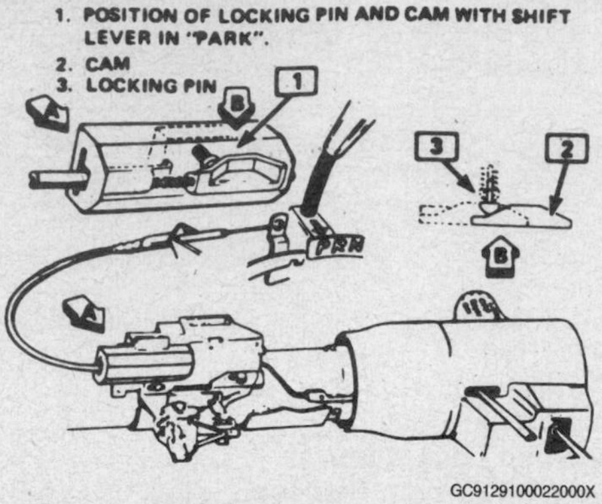
1. POSITION OF LOCKING PIN AND CAM WITH SHIFT LEVER IN "PARK".
2. CAM
3. LOCKING PIN
1
B
3
2
B
PRN
GC9129100022000X
Fig. 3 Park-lock cable. With floor shift

IGNITION SWITCH

REPLACE

REMOVAL

1. Disconnect battery ground cable.
2. **On models with floor shift,** place transmission selector in park and rotate ignition lock to "Run" position.
3. **On all models,** remove left hush panel, lower steering column cover, insulator at toe plate, and the lower steering column mounting screws.
4. Remove nuts securing upper steering column bracket to instrument panel, then carefully lower column. **Disconnect shift indicator cable and electrical connectors, as needed, prior to lowering column. Do not force column down as it may be damaged.**
5. Remove dimmer switch mounting nut, screw and the dimmer switch, then tape actuator rod to steering column.
6. **On models with floor shift,** insert screwdriver into slot in ignition switch inhibitor, depress park-lock cable latch and disconnect cable from inhibitor, **Fig. 3. Ignition switch must be in "Run" position. Do not attempt to disconnect park-lock cable with switch in any other position.**
7. Rotate ignition key to "Off-Lock" position.
8. **On all models,** remove ignition switch stud bolt, disconnect electrical connector, then remove switch assembly.

INSTALLATION

1. Move ignition switch slider to extreme right, then one detent to the left to place switch in "Off-Lock" position.
2. Connect electrical connector to ignition switch, install switch assembly on column ensuring actuator is properly engaged, and **torque** stud bolt to 35 inch lbs.
3. Install dimmer switch assembly, depress switch against actuator and insert $3/32$ inch drill into adjustment slot, **Fig. 4,** then **torque** nut and retaining screw to 35 inch lbs.
4. **On models with floor shift,** rotate ignition lock to "Run" position, then install shift-lock cable on inhibitor.

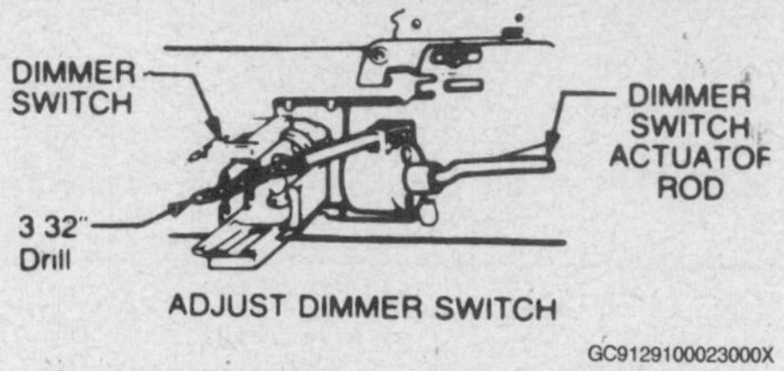
DIMMER SWITCH
DIMMER SWITCH ACTUATOR ROD
3 32" Drill
ADJUST DIMMER SWITCH
GC9129100023000X
Fig. 4 Dimmer switch installation

5. **On all models,** reverse remaining procedure to complete installation. **Torque** upper column bracket bolts to 20 ft. lbs. and lower column bolts to 25 ft. lbs.

NEUTRAL SAFETY SWITCH

REPLACE

ELDORADO & SEVILLE

1. Remove shift linkage, electrical connector and vacuum hose.
2. Remove attaching nut and shift lever, then the fuel line bracket.
3. Remove switch attaching screws, then the switch **Fig. 5.**
4. Reverse procedure to install, noting the following:
   a. **Torque** Attaching screws to 20 ft. lbs.
   b. Adjust switch as outlined under "Adjustments."

RIVIERA, TORONADO & TROFEO

1. Set parking brake, place gear selector in "Neutral" position.
2. Remove linkage bracket attaching nut, then the linkage bracket, **Fig. 6.**
3. Remove switch attaching bolts, then the switch.
4. Reverse procedure to install, noting the following:
   a. **Torque** switch attaching bolts to 20 ft. lbs.
   b. Adjust switch as described under "Adjustments."

ADJUSTMENT

Eldorado & Seville

1. Position transaxle shifter assembly in N notch in detent plate, then loosen switch attaching screws.
2. Rotate switch on shifter assembly until adjustment hole aligns with carrier tang hole.
3. Insert $3/32$ inch gauge pin into adjustment hole to a depth of $15/32$ inch.
4. Tighten switch mounting bolts, then remove gauge pin.

Riviera, Toronado & Trofeo

1. Place transaxle control shifter in the "Neutral" notch in detent plate.
2. Loosen switch attaching bolts, then rotate switch on shifter assembly to align service adjustment slot.
3. Insert $3/32$ drill bit into service slots, then **torque** attaching bolts to 20 ft. lbs.
4. Remove drill bit.

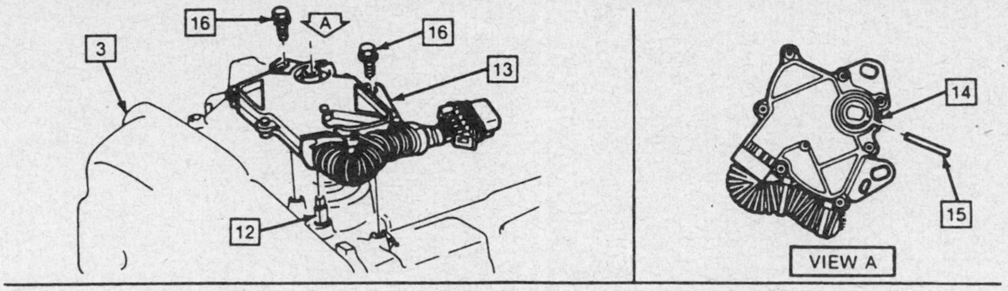
VIEW A

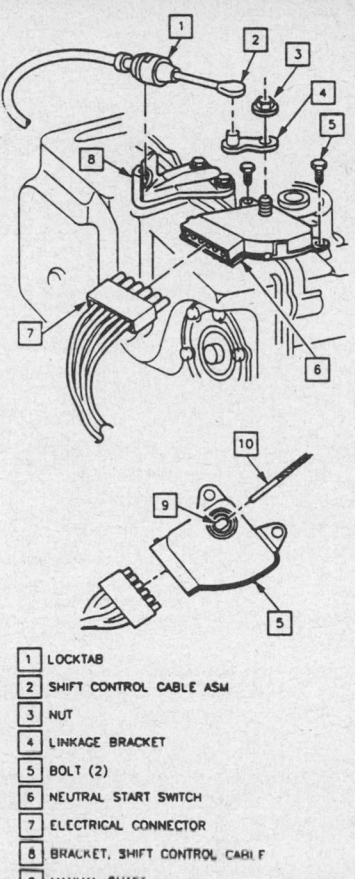

3 TRANSAXLE ASSEMBLY
12 TRANS MANUAL SHAFT
13 NEUTRAL START & BACK UP LAMP SW.
14 SERVICE ADJUSTMENT SLOT
15 SERVICE GAGE PIN (2.34 MM — 3/32 IN.)
16 NUT (27 N·m/20 FT. LBS.)

GC9049100096000X

Fig. 5 Back-up/neutral safety switch replacement. Eldorado & Seville

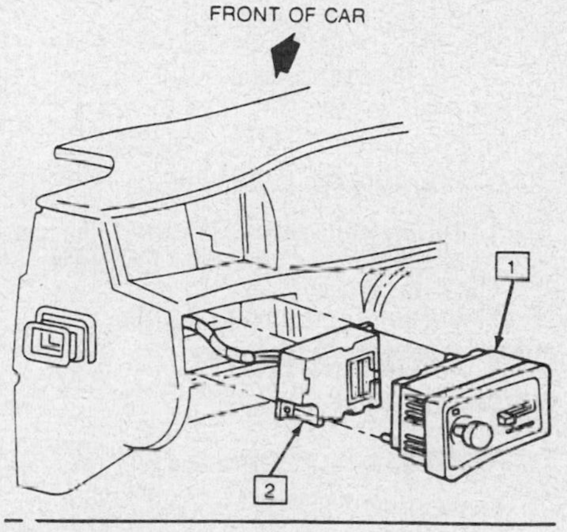
FRONT OF CAR

1 HEADLAMP SWITCH
2 TWILIGHT SENTINEL/DRL MODULE

GC9049200098000X

Fig. 7 Headlamp switch replacement. Eldorado & Seville

HEADLAMP SWITCH REPLACE

ELDORADO & SEVILLE

1. Disconnect battery ground cable.
2. Remove headlamp switch module from instrument panel by firmly pulling outward on headlamp switch knob, **Fig. 7.**
3. Disconnect electrical connector from switch.
4. Reverse procedure to install.

RIVIERA

1. Turn ignition switch to the Off position.
2. Remove two upper panel cluster attaching screws, then pull trim plate out of lower retaining clips.
3. Remove two switch attaching screws, then the switch assembly, **Fig. 8.**
4. Disconnect electrical connectors.
5. Reverse procedure to install.

TORONADO & TROFEO

1. Disconnect battery ground cable.
2. Remove left side insulator and knee bolster.

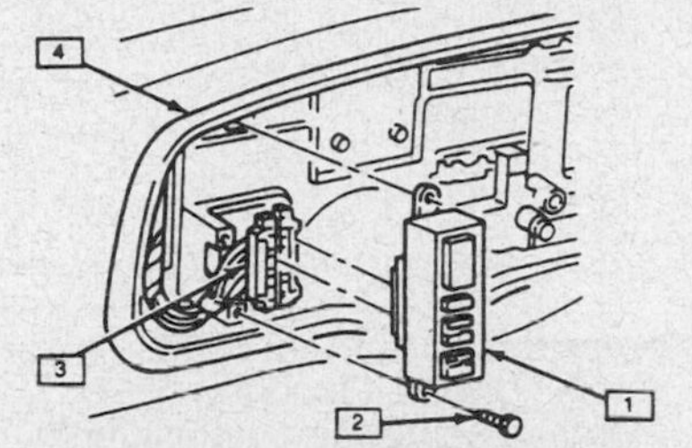

1 HEADLAMP SWITCH ASSEMBLY
2 SCREW (2)
3 ELECTRICAL CONNECTOR
4 I/P CLUSTER HOUSING

GC0049100099000X

Fig. 8 Headlamp switch replacement. Riviera

3. Remove switch attaching screws, then pull switch assembly from electrical connector.
4. Reverse procedure to install.

TURN SIGNAL SWITCH REPLACE

1. Disconnect battery ground cable, then remove steering wheel and inflator module (if equipped), as described under "Steering Wheel, Replace."
2. Remove lower steering column trim cover.
3. Mount spring compressor J-23653 or equivalent on steering shaft, **Fig. 9.**
4. Remove lock plate retaining ring and telescoping wheel components, as equipped, then remove spring compressor.
5. Remove lock plate, canceling cam, upper bearing spring, then upper bearing inner race and seat.
6. Remove multi-function lever.
7. Remove turn signal switch retaining screws, then the switch assembly.
8. Reverse procedure to install.

DIMMER SWITCH REPLACE

Refer to "Ignition Switch, Replace" for procedure.

STEERING WHEEL REPLACE

If the air bag has been deployed, inspect coil for signs of scorching, melting, or other

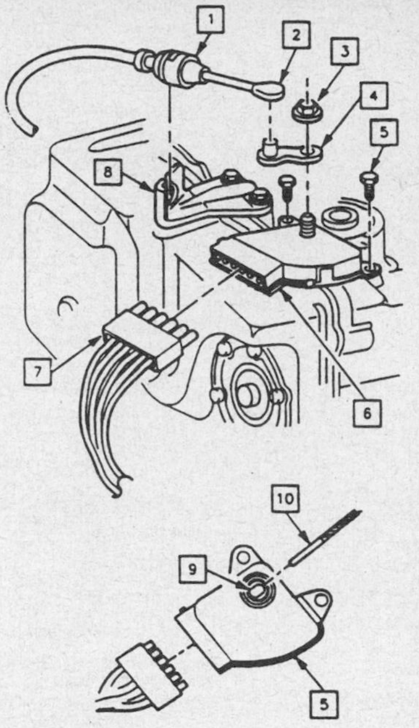

1 LOCKTAB
2 SHIFT CONTROL CABLE ASM
3 NUT
4 LINKAGE BRACKET
5 BOLT (2)
6 NEUTRAL START SWITCH
7 ELECTRICAL CONNECTOR
8 BRACKET, SHIFT CONTROL CABLE
9 MANUAL SHAFT
10 2.34 MM DIA. GAGE PIN, OR 3/32 IN. DRILL BIT

GC9049100097000X

Fig. 6 Back-up/neutral safety switch replacement. Riviera, Toronado & Trofeo

damage. Coil must be replaced if damaged.

1. Turn ignition switch to the Off position, disconnect battery ground cable.
2. Remove Torx screws from back of steering wheel.
3. Remove inflator module from wheel. **Always carry live inflator modules with the trim cover facing away from you. Never carry module by the wiring. Always place module on a flat surface with the trim cover facing up.**
4. Remove horn contact by pushing slightly and twisting counterclockwise.
5. Disconnect Connector Position Assurance (CPA) and coil assembly connector from inflator module.
6. Remove steering column shaft nut.
7. Remove steering wheel using puller No. J-1859-03 or equivalent. **Do not thread puller bolts too far in steering wheel. Threading puller bolts too far into steering wheel could damage SIR coil assembly. Four turns is sufficient.**
8. Reverse procedure to install, noting the following:
   a. **Torque** steering wheel shaft nut to 30 ft. lbs.
   b. **Torque** SIR module retaining screws to 27 inch lbs.

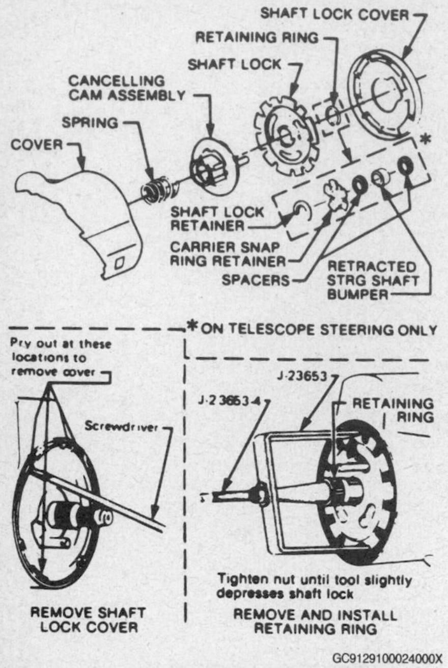
SHAFT LOCK COVER
RETAINING RING
SHAFT LOCK
CANCELLING CAM ASSEMBLY
SPRING
COVER
SHAFT LOCK RETAINER
CARRIER SNAP RING RETAINER
SPACERS
RETRACTED STRG SHAFT BUMPER
*ON TELESCOPE STEERING ONLY
Pry out at these locations to remove cover
Screwdriver
J-23653
J-23653-4
RETAINING RING
Tighten nut until tool slightly depresses shaft lock
REMOVE SHAFT LOCK COVER
REMOVE AND INSTALL RETAINING RING
GC9129100024000X

Fig. 9 Lock plate & cancelling cam removal

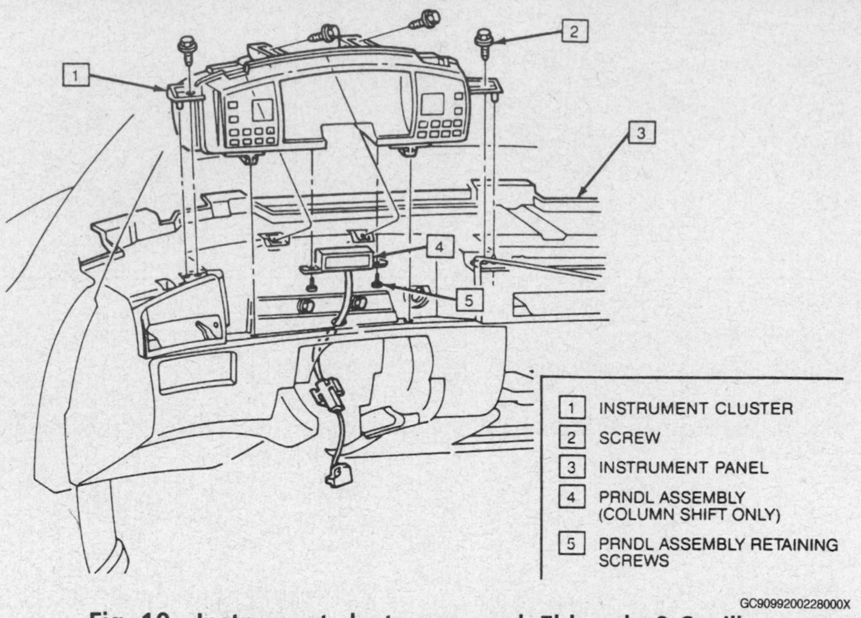
1 INSTRUMENT CLUSTER
2 SCREW
3 INSTRUMENT PANEL
4 PRNDL ASSEMBLY (COLUMN SHIFT ONLY)
5 PRNDL ASSEMBLY RETAINING SCREWS
GC9099200228000X

Fig. 10 Instrument cluster removal. Eldorado & Seville

INSTRUMENT CLUSTER REPLACE

ELDORADO & SEVILLE

1. Remove fuses A5 and B5 from rear compartment fuse panel and fuse A3 from engine compartment fuse panel.
2. Using a small flat-bladed tool, remove defroster grill.
3. Remove sunload and headlamp auto control sensors from defroster grill.
4. Remove three upper trim panel retaining screws, through defroster grill opening.
5. Remove heater and A/C vents from instrument panel.
6. Remove four upper trim panel retaining screws, through vent openings.
7. Remove upper trim panel.
8. Disconnect two electrical connectors from top of instrument panel.
9. Remove four instrument cluster to instrument panel attaching screws, **Fig. 10.**
10. Raise cluster, remove two screws securing PRNDL mechanism on digital clusters.
11. Remove instrument cluster.
12. Reverse procedure to install.

RIVIERA

1. Place ignition switch in Off position.
2. Remove left-side sound insulator retaining screws and nuts.
3. Remove courtesy lamp from sound insulator, then the lefthand side sound insulator from the vehicle.
4. Disconnect Connector Position Assurance (CPA) and yellow two-way connector from base of the steering column.
5. Disconnect battery ground cable.
6. Remove four trim plate retaining screws, then pull trim plate from lower retaining clips, **Fig. 11.**
7. Remove center air duct assembly.
8. Remove 13 screws retaining housing to back of instrument panel.
9. Remove two screws from front of instrument panel.
10. Reverse procedure to install.

TORONADO & TROFEO

1. Disconnect battery ground cable.
2. Remove two front retaining screws, two rear retaining nuts, then the courtesy lamp from lefthand side sound insulator.
3. Remove sound insulator from vehicle.
4. Remove two retaining screws from knee bolster, then the bolster from the vehicle.
5. Remove trim plate retaining screws, then the trim plate from vehicle.
6. Remove screws retaining cluster to instrument panel.
7. Pull cluster forward enough to disconnect electrical connectors, then remove cluster from vehicle.
8. Reverse procedure to install.

Cathode Ray Tube (CRT) Replace

CRT's are located in the center of the instrument panel assembly and may also be known as a visual information center (VIC), driver information display (DID), electronic control center (ECC), or a graphic control center (GCC).

Some of the CRT's have a controller built in. For those which do not, refer to "CRT Controller, Replace."

1. Disconnect battery ground cable.
2. Remove instrument panel trim plate attaching screws, then the trim plate.
3. Remove four attaching bolts securing CRT to instrument panel and mounting bracket assembly.
4. Carefully pull out CRT, then disconnect electrical connector from rear of CRT assembly.
5. Reverse procedure to install.

CRT CONTROLLER, REPLACE

Toronado & Trofeo

1. Disconnect battery ground cable.
2. Remove console compartment retaining screws, then the compartment.
3. Gently pry off compact disc trim plate, if equipped.
4. Disconnect console trim plate electrical connectors, then remove console trim plate.
5. Remove compact disc player, if equipped.
6. Remove screws and nuts retaining console assembly to the floor.
7. Disconnect electrical connectors, then remove console.
8. Remove four nuts retaining controller to retaining bracket.
9. Disconnect electrical connectors, then remove controller from vehicle.
10. Reverse procedure to install.

RADIO REPLACE

MODELS LESS CRT

ELDORADO & SEVILLE

Models w/Console Shift

1. Using a putty knife, remove radio trim plate, **Fig. 12.**
2. Remove console trim plate by pulling up the upper edge first.
3. Remove two nuts from bottom of control head.
4. Position control head so that the right side is removed first, to clear connectors on left side.
5. Disconnect electrical connectors, then remove radio.

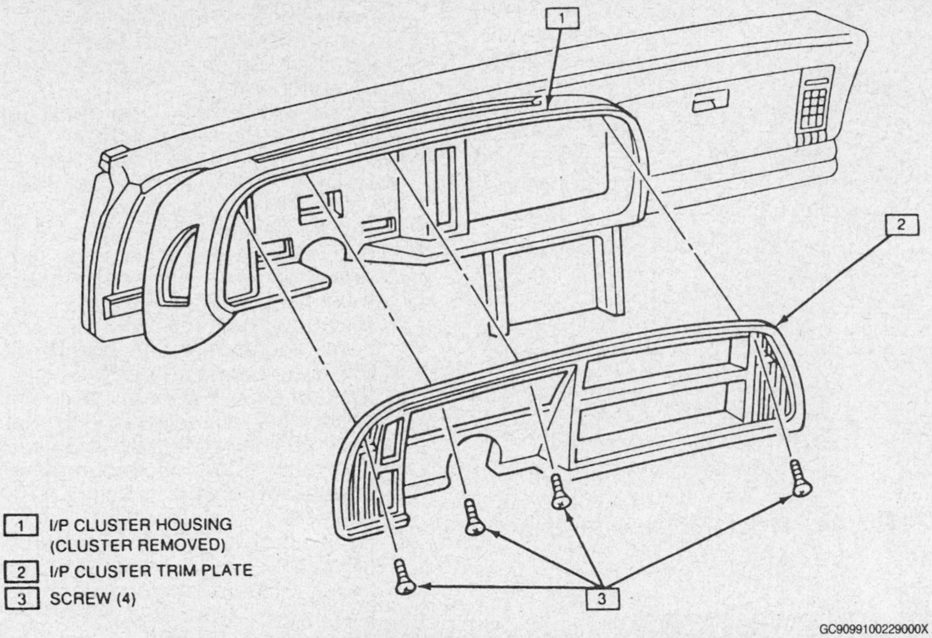
1
2
3
1 I/P CLUSTER HOUSING (CLUSTER REMOVED)
2 I/P CLUSTER TRIM PLATE
3 SCREW (4)
GC9099100229000X

Fig. 11 Trim plate retaining screw locations. Riviera.

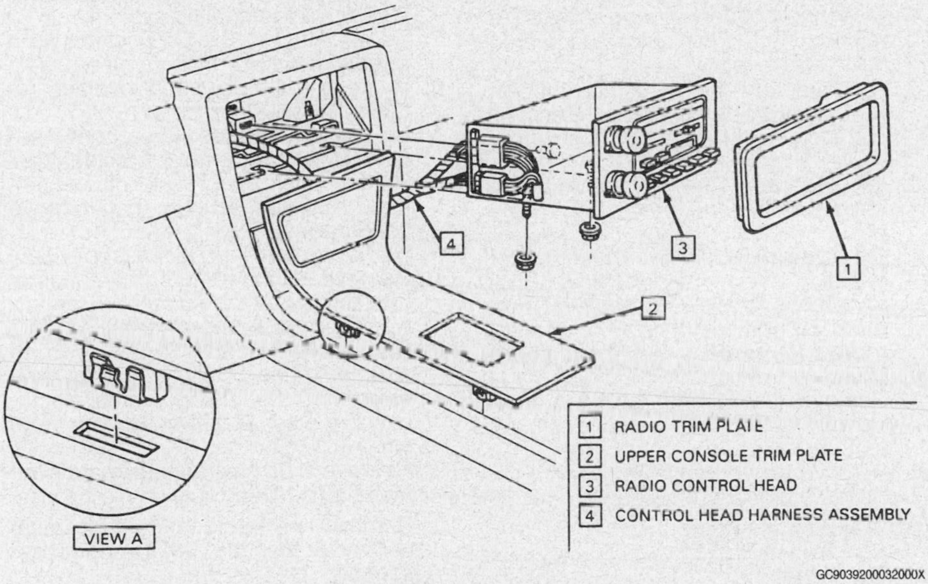
1
2
3
4
VIEW A
1 RADIO TRIM PLATE
2 UPPER CONSOLE TRIM PLATE
3 RADIO CONTROL HEAD
4 CONTROL HEAD HARNESS ASSEMBLY
GC9039200032000X

Fig. 12 Radio removal. Eldorado & Seville w/console shift

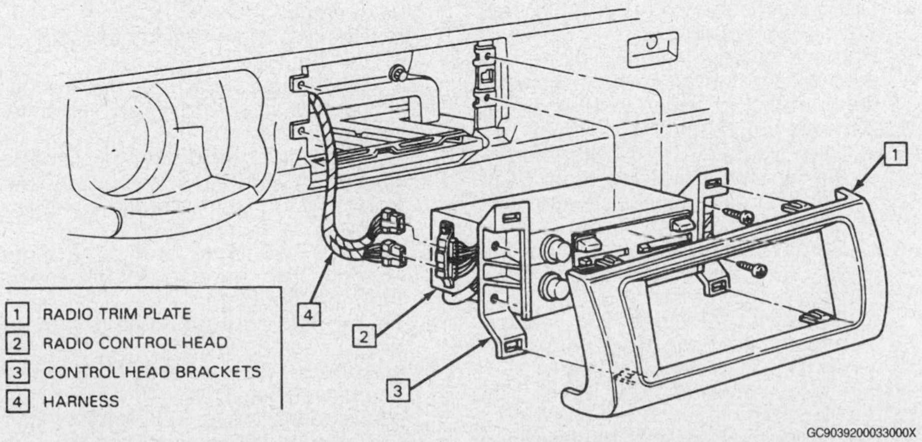
1
2
3
4
1 RADIO TRIM PLATE
2 RADIO CONTROL HEAD
3 CONTROL HEAD BRACKETS
4 HARNESS
GC9039200033000X

Fig. 13 Radio removal. Eldorado & Seville w/column shift

6. Reverse procedure to install.

Models w/Column Shift

1. Remove radio trim, then the four screws from side bracket, **Fig. 13.**
2. Remove control head, then disconnect electrical connectors.
3. Reverse procedure to install.

RIVIERA

1. Disconnect battery ground cable.
2. Remove top of instrument panel plate, then the screws retaining radio and ECC bracket.
3. Remove bracket from radio and disconnect electrical connector.
4. Reverse procedure to install.

TORONADO & TROFEO

Radio

1. Disconnect battery ground cable.
2. Remove screws securing instrument cluster bezel, then pull bezel away from instrument panel to disengage retaining clips.
3. Disconnect electrical connectors and remove cluster bezel.
4. Remove screws securing ECC panel and radio brackets to instrument panel and pull assembly away from panel.
5. Disconnect electrical connectors, noting position for installation, then remove ECC panel and radio assembly.
6. Remove nuts securing radio to brackets, then the radio.
7. Reverse procedure to install.

Console Mounted Tape Player & Booster

1. Disconnect battery ground cable, then carefully pull trim plate from console.
2. Lift out shift indicator assembly and disconnect bulbs from indicator.
3. Remove screws securing console mounting plate.
4. Disconnect electrical connectors, then remove mounting plate assembly.
5. Remove nuts securing tape player or booster to mounting plate, then the components as required.
6. Reverse procedure to install, pressing console trim plate into retaining clip until trim plate is secured.

MODELS W/CRT

1. Disconnect battery ground cable.
2. Pull shift indicator trim plate up and out slowly. Place selector in neutral if necessary.
3. Remove indicator lamp bulbs.
4. Remove lumbar/bolster control switch, if equipped.
5. Remove outer console trim plate.
6. Remove attaching screws securing graphic equalizer and tape mounting plate.
7. Remove mounting plate.
8. Disconnect electrical connector from tape deck and graphic equalizer.
9. Pull tape holder out of console bucket.
10. Remove screws at bottom of console compartment liner and screws at top of liner, then pull liner out.

11. Remove nuts attaching console to floor pan.
12. Pull console upward and slide back toward rear seat.
13. Pull radio remote chassis out to the right.
14. Disconnect radio chassis electrical connectors.
15. Reverse procedure to install.

WIPER MOTOR

REPLACE

1. Disconnect battery ground cable.
2. Remove wiper arm assemblies, then air conditioning pipe shroud.
3. Remove shroud air inlet grille panel.
4. Disconnect electrical connectors from wiper motor.
5. Disconnect wiper transmission drive link socket from wiper motor crank arm using tool No. J-39232, or equivalent.
6. Remove sir conditioning shroud pipe from wheel house.
7. Remove three screws, then the wiper motor.
8. Reverse procedure to install.

WIPER SWITCH

REPLACE

ELDORADO & SEVILLE

1. Remove steering wheel as outlined under "Steering Wheel, Replace."
2. Slide connector cover toward front of vehicle, then unplug electrical connector.
3. Push lever in and rotate clockwise 1/4 turn and pull out switch.
4. Reverse procedure to install.

RIVIERA

1. Remove steering wheel as outlined under "Steering Wheel, Replace."
2. Remove access cover from steering column housing.
3. Disconnect electrical connectors, pull lever straight out of switch.
4. Reverse procedure to install.

TORONADO & TROFEO

1. Remove steering wheel as outlined under "Steering Wheel, Replace."
2. Remove access cover from steering column housing.
3. Disconnect electrical connectors, pull lever straight out of switch. **The switch must be in the OFF position before removing lever and do not extend lever wire beyond its normal length.**
4. Reverse procedure to install.

WIPER TRANSMISSION

REPLACE

1. Disconnect battery ground cable, then remove wiper arm assemblies
2. Remove shroud air inlet grille panel.
3. Using tool No. J-39232, or equivalent, remove drive link from wiper motor crank arm.
4. Remove six screws, then the wiper transmission assembly.
5. Reverse procedure to install.

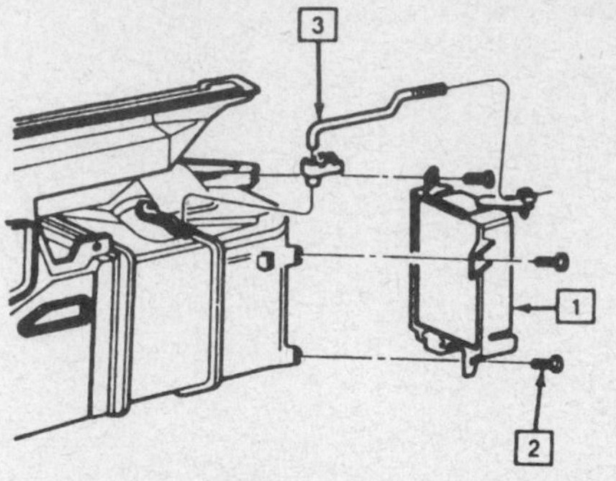
3
1
2
1 PROGRAMMER
2 PROG. MTG. SCREW (3 REQ'D)
3 THREADED ROD
GC9039100034000X

Fig. 14 Programmer mounting bolt locations

BLOWER MOTOR

REPLACE

1. Disconnect battery ground cable, then remove strut tower cross brace (two nuts each side).
2. Remove cowl relay center bracket (two nuts), then disconnect electrical connector and cooling hose from blower motor.
3. **On Eldorado and Seville models,** remove MAP sensor mounting bracket.
4. **On all models,** remove blower motor retaining screws, then tilt blower motor in case to allow fan removal. **Fan must be removed prior to blower motor to prevent fan from being bent.**
5. Remove fan retainer and fan from blower motor, then remove blower motor.
6. Remove blower fan from case.
7. Reverse procedure to install.

HEATER CORE

REPLACE

ELDORADO & SEVILLE

1. Disconnect battery ground cable, then drain cooling system.
2. Remove screws securing glove box module and the glove box, then the righthand lower sound insulator.
3. Remove programmer as follows:
   a. Remove two ECM bracket mounting screws, then position ECM aside to gain access to rear programmer mounting screw.
   b. Remove threaded rod, then the vacuum connector retaining nut from programmer.
   c. Disconnect electrical and vacuum connectors from programmer assembly, then remove three mounting screws and programmer, **Fig. 14.**
4. Disconnect electrical connections from ECM, then remove the ECM and mounting bracket from vehicle.
5. **On all models,** remove heater core cover, then disconnect heater hoses from heater core.
6. Remove two heater core retaining screws, then the heater core.
7. Reverse procedure to install. Prior to installing glove box module, adjust air mix door link rod as follows:
   a. Set temperature control for 90°F and allow 1-2 minutes for programmer arm to travel to maximum heat position, **Fig. 15.**
   b. Disconnect air mix door link rod from programmer and ensure air mix door operated freely.
   c. Preload air mix door in maximum heat position by pulling rod to seat door against seal, then snap rod into connector on programmer arm, taking care not to disturb position of arm or air mix door.
   d. Set control for 60°F and ensure programmer arm and air mix door travel to maximum cooling position.

RIVIERA

1. Disconnect negative battery cable, then drain the cooling system.
2. Turn ignition to the Off position, then remove fuse No. 14 from fuse panel.
3. Remove left side sound insulator retaining screws and nuts.
4. Disconnect courtesy lamp from insulator panel and remove from vehicle.
5. Remove instrument panel cluster trim plate retaining screws, then remove plate from vehicle.
6. Remove center air duct assembly.
7. Remove 13 instrument panel cluster retaining screws, then pull cluster outward from instrument panel.
8. Remove two headlamp switch to instrument panel retaining screws, then disconnect headlamp switch electrical connector and remove from vehicle.
9. Remove four electronic climate control head retaining screws, if equipped.
10. Remove climate control electrical connector then the climate control assembly.
11. **On models equipped with integral radio unit,** proceed as follows:
    a. Remove radio/ECC retaining screws.
    b. Remove radio bracket to radio retaining nuts.
    c. Disconnect radio electrical connectors and remove radio from vehicle.
12. **On models equipped with cassette tape/compact disc,** remove holder from rear console storage compartment.
13. Remove two outer and three inner console trim plate retaining screws, then the trim plate.
14. **On models equipped with CD player,** proceed as follows:
    a. Remove CD trim plate from instrument panel.
    b. Disconnect two CD player electrical connectors accessed through ashtray.

c. Remove two T-15 Torx retaining screws to CD mounting bracket, then pull player and bracket forward.
d. Remove two 10mm bracket to CD retaining nuts.

15. **On all models,** remove two front storage compartment retaining screws, then the storage compartment.
16. Remove right side sound insulator retaining screws and nuts.
17. Disconnect courtesy lamp from panel and remove sound insulator from vehicle.
18. Remove six knee bolster retaining screws, then remove bolster from vehicle.
19. Remove four steering column reinforcement plate retaining screws, then remove plate from vehicle.
20. Remove glove box door and glove box unit retaining screws.
21. Remove three upper trim pad retaining screws, then pull trim pad up and out of retaining clips to remove from vehicle.
22. Remove lower left side instrument panel retaining bolt.
23. Remove hood release retaining screws.
24. Remove two instrument panel brace retaining screws, then the brace.
25. Remove four inflator module retaining screws located on back of steering wheel assembly.
26. Remove inflator module from vehicle. **When carrying a live inflator, ensure the bag and trim cover are pointed away in case of accidental deployment. Do not carry inflator module by wires of connector on underside of module. When placing a live inflator module on a bench or other surface, ensure the bag and trim cover faces in a upward direction. Never rest steering column assembly on the steering wheel with the inflator module face down and column vertical. This is necessary in case of accidental deployment. Otherwise, personal injury may result.**
27. Disconnect ignition wiring and multifunction switch electrical connectors.
28. Remove pinch bolt from intermediate shaft.
29. Remove upper and lower steering column support brackets, then remove steering column from vehicle.
30. Remove lower right instrument panel retaining bolt and three upper instrument panel retaining screws.
31. Disconnect instrument panel electrical connectors, then remove instrument panel from vehicle.
32. Disconnect programmer electrical connectors, then remove programmer from vehicle, **Fig. 14.**
33. Disconnect BCM electrical connectors, then remove BCM and mounting bracket from vehicle.
34. Disconnect ECM electrical connectors, then remove ECM and mounting bracket from vehicle.
35. Remove heater core cover, then the hoses from heater core.
36. Remove two heater core retaining screws, then the heater core from vehicle.
37. Reverse procedure to install.

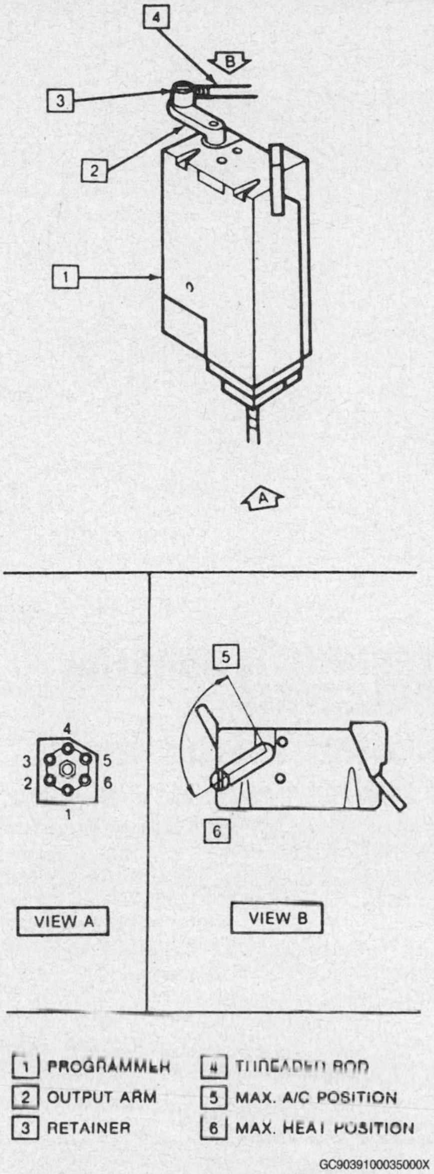
4
B
3
2
1
A
5
6
VIEW A
VIEW B
1 PROGRAMMER
2 OUTPUT ARM
3 RETAINER
4 THREADED ROD
5 MAX. A/C POSITION
6 MAX. HEAT POSITION
GC9039100035000X

Fig. 15 Programmer linkage positioning

TORONADO & TROFEO

1. Disconnect battery ground cable and drain cooling system, then remove righthand sound insulator.
2. Remove knee bolster, then the instrument panel column reinforcement plate.
3. Remove instrument panel cluster trim plate, then the lefthand side switch assembly.
4. Remove righthand side switch plate assembly, then the instrument panel cluster.
5. Remove climate control head, if equipped.
6. Remove four bolts retaining driver information display (DID), then the DID.
7. Remove center A/C deflectors, then unsnap and remove defroster grille.
8. Remove upper, then the lower-left instrument panel mounting screws and bolts.
9. Remove hood release assembly, retaining bolts and center instrument panel brace.
10. Remove steering column, then the glove box.
11. Remove lower-right instrument panel retaining bolt, then the fuse box retaining screws and fuse box.
12. Remove console, then the instrument panel. Disconnect instrument panel electrical connectors.
13. Disconnect programmer electrical connectors, then remove programmer, **Fig. 14.**
14. Disconnect BCM electrical connections, then remove BCM and mounting bracket.
15. Disconnect ECM electrical connections, then remove ECM and mounting bracket.
16. Remove heater core from housing, then the hoses from the core.
17. Remove two heater core retaining screws, then the heater core from vehicle.
18. Reverse procedure to install.

EVAPORATOR CORE REPLACE

ELDORADO & SEVILLE

1. Discharge refrigerant from system. Refer to "A/C Refrigerant Recovery" in "Air Conditioning" chapter.
2. Drain radiator and cooling system.
3. Remove two bolts from each side of cross-tower support bracket.
4. Remove two nuts from cowl relay center bracket, then position relay bracket aside.
5. Disconnect electrical connectors from power module, blower motor and blower motor resistor.
6. Disconnect both heater core hoses from heater core.
7. Remove evaporator line retaining bracket.
8. Remove evaporator core refrigerant lines. **Cap all open fittings to prevent contamination of system.**
9. Remove heater hose T-connector.
10. Remove two heat shield screws from engine compartment.
11. Raise and support vehicle, then remove the remaining two heat shield retaining screws from under the vehicle.
12. Remove heat shield, then the two A/C module retaining screws (one 7 mm and one 10 mm).
13. Lower vehicle and remove MAP sensor bracket.
14. Remove diverter valve from righthand side valve cover.
15. Remove two harness hold-down brackets from valve cover.
16. Remove power module, blower motor and sound insulator.
17. Remove A/C module cover screws,

module cover, sound insulator and the seal.

18. Remove evaporator retaining clamp, then pull evaporator core from evaporator case.
19. Reverse procedure to install, noting the following:
    a. **Torque** module cover retaining screws to 27 inch lbs.
    b. **Torque** line fitting bolt to 18 ft. lbs.
    c. Leak test all refrigerant connections.

RIVIERA, TORONADO & TROFEO

1. Discharge refrigerant from system. Refer to "A/C Refrigerant Recovery" in "Air Conditioning" chapter.
2. Drain cooling system, remove cross tower support bracket attaching nuts and bolts.
3. Remove relay center, set aside.
4. Remove heater hoses from heater core, then the evaporator core retaining bracket.
5. Disconnect refrigerant inlet and outlet lines from evaporator.
6. Remove heater hose T connector.
7. Remove two engine compartment heat shield attaching screws, then raise vehicle and remove two remaining heat shield attaching screws from under the vehicle. Remove heat shield.
8. Remove two A/C module attaching screws, then lower vehicle.
9. Disconnect electrical connectors from power module and blower motor.
10. Remove power module, then the blower motor.
11. Remove module cover, sound insulator, seal and evaporator core.
12. Reverse procedure to install.

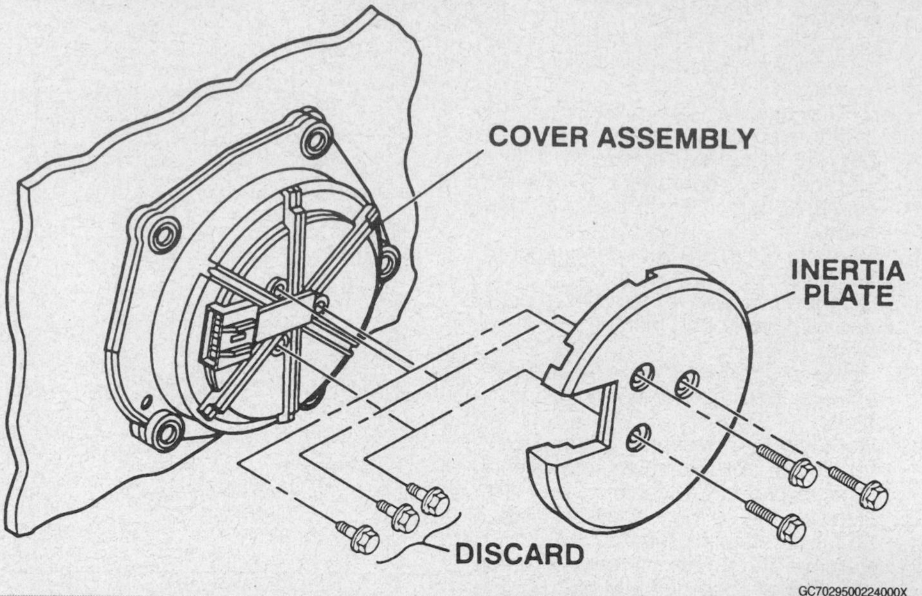
COVER ASSEMBLY
INERTIA PLATE
DISCARD
GC7029500224000X

Fig. 16 Inertia plate installation

TECHNICAL SERVICE BULLETINS

BLOWER MOTOR NOISE

1994–95 Eldorado & Seville

A blower motor noise may be noted that varies in frequency as motor speed changes. This noise should not be confused with normal air rush noise which can also be heard and varies in intensity.

The cause is motor-created torque, amplified by fan motor mounting and vehicle structure.

To repair this condition, install inertia disc kit, part No. 22137062, **Fig. 16**, as follows:

1. Disconnect electrical connector at blower motor.
2. Remove three screw and washer assemblies, ONE at a time, from cover assembly and discard. **Do not push inward when removing last screw to motor could be pushed out of cover assembly.**
3. Firmly hold inertia plate in position, then hand tighten new screw and washer assemblies.
4. **Torque** fasteners to 62 inch lbs.
5. Connect electrical connector at blower motor. **Ensure that spark plug wires are routed a minimum of 1 inch from motor exterior surface. Failure to do so may result in premature motor failure.**

3.8L/V6-231 & 4.9L/V8-300 Engines

NOTE: On Air Bag Equipped Models, Refer To "Air Bag System Precautions" Located In The Front Of This Manual For System Disarming & Arming Procedures.

NOTE: For Service Procedures Not Found In This Section, Refer To 3.8L/V6-231 & 4.9L/V8-300 Engine Section in the Buick LeSabre & Park Avenue, Cadillac DeVille & Fleetwood, Oldsmobile Eighty Eight & Ninety Eight & Pontiac Bonneville Chapter.

INDEX

PRECAUTIONS

AIR BAG SYSTEMS

Refer to "Air Bag System Precautions" in the front of this manual for system disarming and arming procedures.

FUEL SYSTEM PRESSURE RELIEF

1. Loosen fuel filler cap, then connect gauge J-34700 1, or equivalent, to fuel pressure connection. Wrap shop towel around fitting while connecting gauge.
2. Install bleed hose into approved container, then open valve on gauge to bleed system pressure.

ENGINE MOUNT

REPLACE

ELDORADO & SEVILLE

RIGHT SIDE ENGINE & TRANSAXLE MOUNT

Removal

Refer to **Fig. 1,** for engine and transaxle mount position.

1. Open hood, then remove brace between engine bracket and engine.
2. Remove two nuts securing mount to engine bracket.
3. Raise vehicle on a hoist and support with stands at each front frame horn.
4. Remove two nuts securing engine mount to frame.
5. Remove two nuts securing transaxle bracket to mount.
6. Remove two nuts securing transaxle mount to frame bracket.
7. Raise engine using support J-28467 or equivalent, lifting engine until bracket is free from engine and transaxle mounts.
8. Remove stud and two bolts securing bracket to block, then the bracket and mount by pulling forward.
9. Remove transaxle mounting bracket from transaxle, then the mount.

Installation

Refer to **Fig. 1,** for engine and transaxle mount position.

1. Position engine mount and bracket between block and frame, then tighten bracket bolts and stud to specifications.
2. Position transaxle mount and bracket between transaxle and frame, then tighten bracket retaining bolts to specifications.
3. Guide mounts into position while lowering engine and reverse remaining procedure to complete installation, tighten all fasteners to specifications.

LEFT ENGINE MOUNT

Refer to **Fig. 1,** for engine and transaxle mount position.

1. Disconnect battery ground cable, then remove air cleaner assembly.
2. Remove serpentine drive belt, then discharge A/C system and recover coolant. Refer to "A/C Refrigerant Recovery" in "Air Conditioning."
3. Install engine support tool No. J-28467, or equivalent.
4. Remove lower center exhaust manifold nut, then the top nut from engine damper.
5. Raise and support vehicle, remove right engine splash shield and A/C splash shield.
6. Remove engine damper.
7. Remove two A/C compressor brackets, then the A/C compressor.
8. Remove water pipe bracket bolt.
9. Remove bolts securing engine mount bracket to block and cradle.
10. Remove engine mount and bracket assembly through right wheelwell.
11. Remove engine mount from bracket.
12. Reverse procedure to install, tighten engine mount bolts and nuts to specifications.

RIVIERA, TORONADO & TROFEO

1. Support engine using tool J-28467, or equivalent.
2. Raise and support vehicle.
3. Remove nuts securing engine mount to bracket, **Fig. 2 and 3,** then raise engine slightly.
4. Remove nuts securing mount to frame and engine mount.
5. Reverse procedure to install. Tighten mount fasteners to specifications as shown in **Fig. 2 and 3.**

ENGINE

REPLACE

ELDORADO & SEVILLE

1. Relieve fuel system pressure as described under "Precautions."
2. Disconnect battery ground cable.
3. Drain cooling system.
4. Remove air cleaner assembly.
5. Mark position of hood hinges, disconnect necessary electrical connectors, then remove hood hinge bolts and the hood.
6. Remove engine cooling fan and serpentine drive belt.
7. Disconnect upper radiator and heater hoses from thermostat housing.
8. Disconnect and mark the electrical connectors from the following components:
   a. Oil pressure switch.

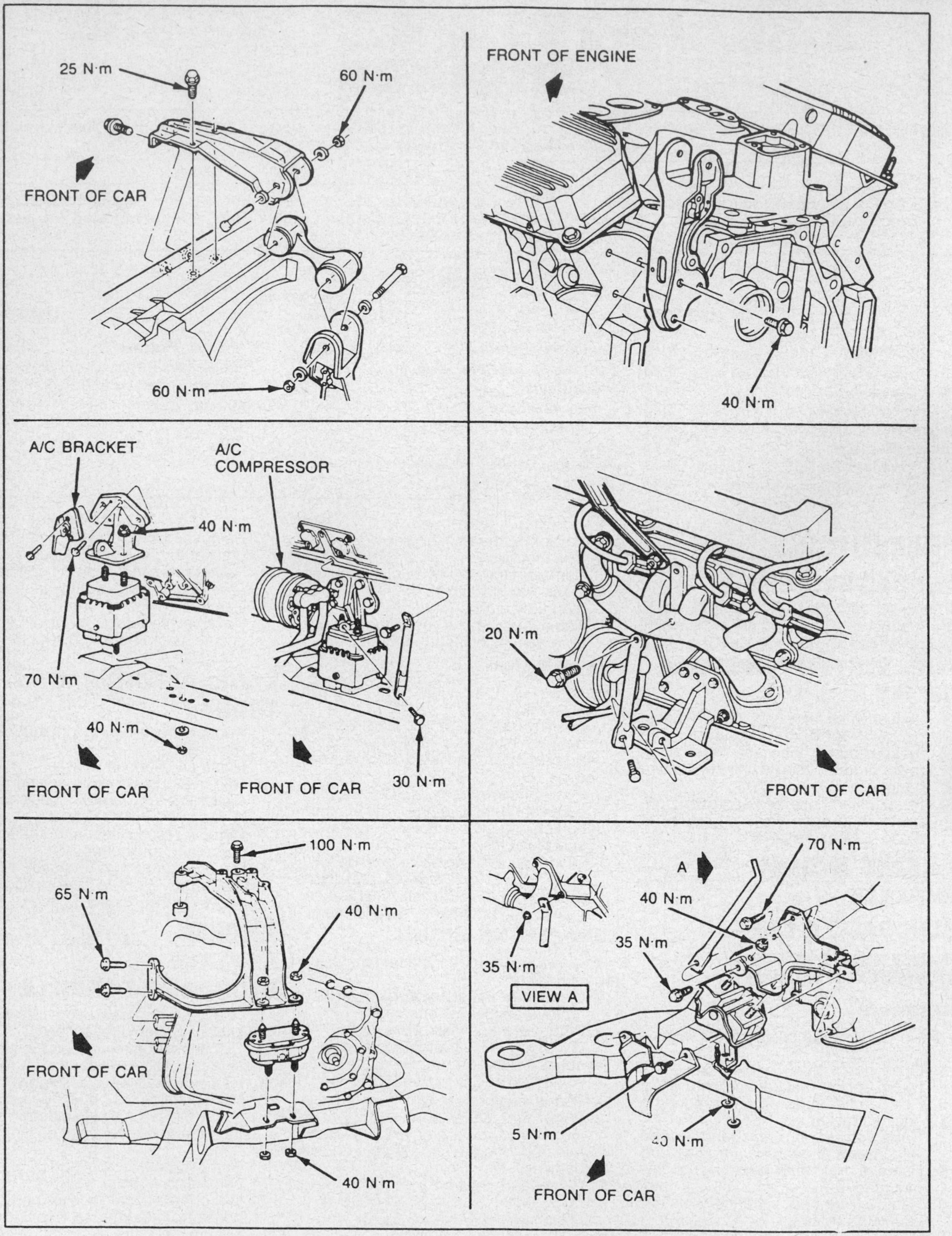
25 N·m
60 N·m
FRONT OF CAR
60 N·m
FRONT OF ENGINE
40 N·m
A/C BRACKET
A/C
COMPRESSOR
40 N·m
70 N·m
40 N·m
FRONT OF CAR
FRONT OF CAR
30 N·m
20 N·m
FRONT OF CAR
100 N·m
65 N·m
40 N·m
FRONT OF CAR
40 N·m
A
70 N·m
40 N·m
35 N·m
35 N·m
VIEW A
5 N·m
40 N·m
FRONT OF CAR
GC1069100333000X

Fig. 1 Engine & transaxle mounts. Eldorado & Seville

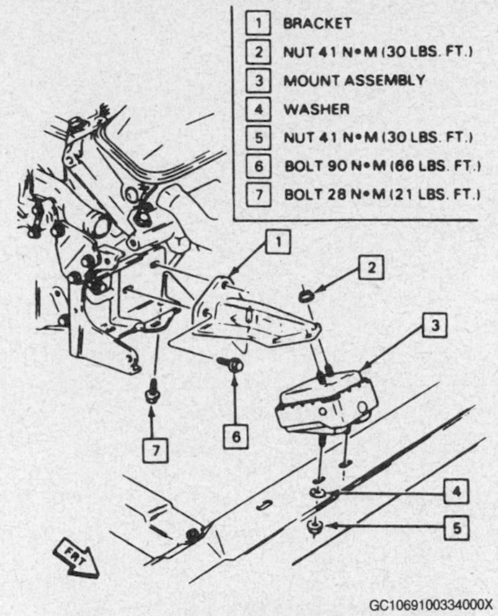

1 BRACKET
2 NUT 41 N•M (30 LBS. FT.)
3 MOUNT ASSEMBLY
4 WASHER
5 NUT 41 N•M (30 LBS. FT.)
6 BOLT 90 N•M (66 LBS. FT.)
7 BOLT 28 N•M (21 LBS. FT.)
1
2
3
7
6
4
5
GC1069100334000X

Fig. 2 Front engine mount. Riviera, Toronado & Trofeo

b. Coolant temperature sensor.
c. Distributor.
d. EGR solenoid.
e. Engine temperature switch.
f. ISC motor.
g. Throttle position switch.
h. Injectors.
i. MAT sensor.
j. Oxygen sensor.
k. Throttle body base warmer.
l. Alternator and ground wiring at alternator bracket.
m. Electric EFE grid.

9. Release engine harness from retainers and secure aside.
10. Disconnect accelerator, cruise control and transmission cables from throttle body.
11. Remove cruise control diaphragm brackets and secure assembly aside.
12. Disconnect oil and transmission cooler lines from radiator.
13. Disconnect remaining hoses and remove radiator.
14. Disconnect oil cooler lines at filter adapter and remove lines.
15. Remove oil cooler line bracket at transaxle and the air cleaner bracket.
16. Remove oil filter adapter housing.
17. Disconnect AIR tubes from diverter valve, if equipped.
18. Remove front right and rear body cross braces.
19. Disconnect and remove right front heater hose and coolant reservoir.
20. Remove AIR filter box and bracket, if equipped.
21. Disconnect power steering line bracket from right cylinder head, remove power steering pump and tensioner retaining bolts and secure assembly aside.
22. Discharge A/C system, disconnect A/C lines at accumulator and condenser, plug lines and fittings.
23. Disconnect fuel lines at throttle body and fuel line bracket from transaxle, then position fuel lines aside.
24. Remove EGR lines and brackets.
25. Disconnect vacuum modulator line, then the power brake vacuum line.
26. Raise and support vehicle, remove starter shield, then disconnect starter wiring and block ground straps.
27. Remove exhaust crossover pipe and starter motor.
28. Remove both flexplate dust shields, then the three bolts securing torque converter to flexplate.
29. Remove A/C compressor dust shield.
30. Remove right front tire and wheel, then the outer wheelhouse plastic shield.
31. Remove right rear engine to transaxle mounting bolt and lower engine damper nut.
32. Remove front (left) engine mount nuts and right rear engine/transaxle mount bolts, **Fig. 1.**
33. Disconnect alternator and oxygen sensor wiring, then remove heater bypass bracket from right side of vehicle.
34. Remove right engine brace, then lower vehicle.
35. Remove five top engine to transaxle mounting bolts.
36. Install lift equipment and support transaxle with a jack.
37. Raise engine, separate engine from transaxle, then remove engine from vehicle.
38. Reverse procedure to install.

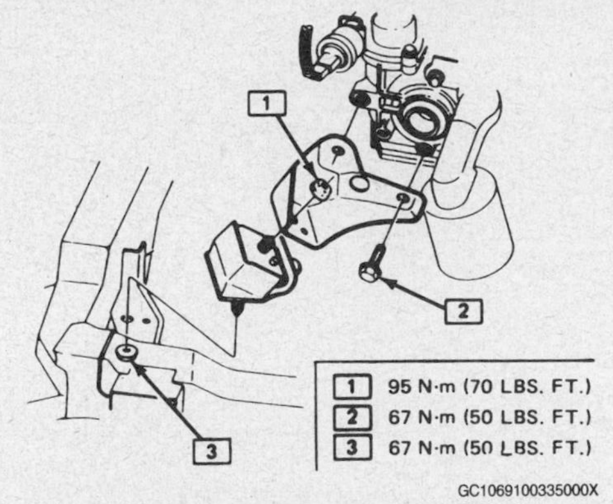

1
2
3
1 95 N·m (70 LBS. FT.)
2 67 N·m (50 LBS. FT.)
3 67 N·m (50 LBS. FT.)
GC1069100335000X

Fig. 3 Rear engine mount. Riviera, Toronado & Trofeo

RIVIERA, TORONADO & TROFEO

1. Disconnect battery ground cable.
2. Remove air intake duct.
3. Remove throttle cable bracket and throttle cables from throttle body.
4. Drain engine coolant.
5. Raise and support vehicle.
6. Remove exhaust pipe from rear exhaust manifold, then the engine mount bolts.
7. Disconnect starter wiring, then remove starter.
8. Remove A/C compressor and secure aside.
9. Disconnect power steering hoses at steering gear.
10. Remove lower transaxle-to-engine bolts. **Note location and direction of bolts for assembly reference.**

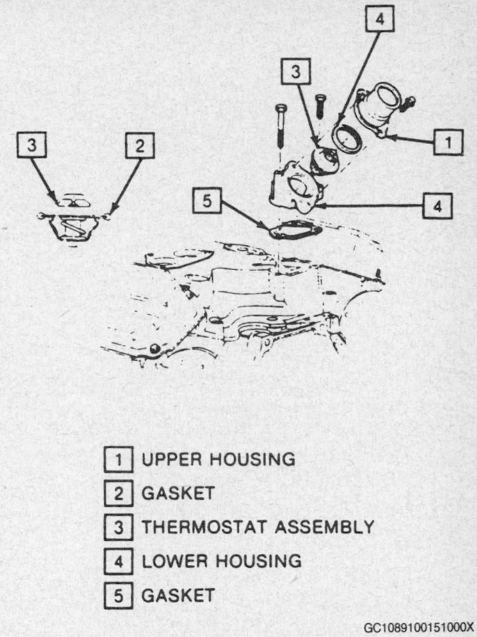

4
3
3
2
1
5
4
1 UPPER HOUSING
2 GASKET
3 THERMOSTAT ASSEMBLY
4 LOWER HOUSING
5 GASKET
GC1089100151000X

Fig. 4 Thermostat replacement. Eldorado & Seville

11. Remove torque converter dust shield, then scribe an alignment mark between converter and flexplate, remove converter bolts.
12. Remove engine support bracket at transaxle.
13. Lower vehicle, then disconnect radiator hoses and heater hoses at engine.
14. Disconnect vacuum modulator and canister purge lines.
15. Disconnect engine wiring harness, then remove remaining transaxle to engine bolts.
16. Attach lifting equipment to engine and support transaxle.
17. Raise engine, separate engine from transaxle and remove engine from vehicle.
18. Reverse procedure to install.

COOLING SYSTEM BLEED

To be performed after cooling system has been drained, flushed and is ready to be refilled.

1. Fill cooling system with a 50/50 mixture of antifreeze and water, to just below the filler neck.
2. Fill coolant recovery reservoir to specified fill mark on outside of reservoir.
3. Run engine with radiator cap removed until normal operating temperature is achieved.
4. With engine running at idle, add coolant to radiator, until it reaches the bottom of the filler neck.
5. Cycle the engine to 5000 RPM, then back to idle at least five times. This will help expel any air trapped in the system.
6. Install radiator cap. **Arrows on the cap must line up with the coolant recovery reservoir hose.**

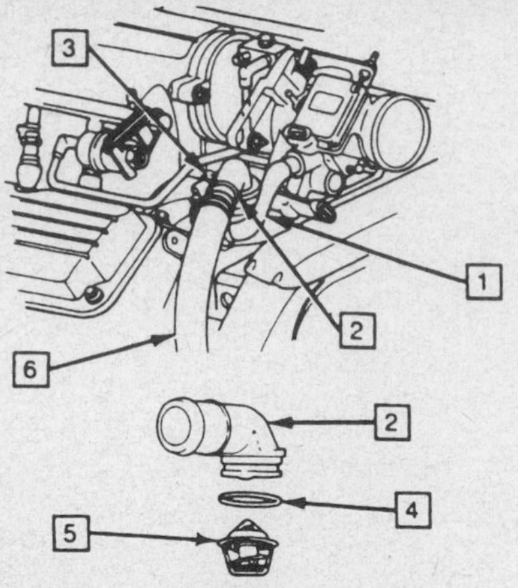
1
2
3
4
5
6

1 THROTTLE BODY INLET COOLANT HOSE
2 MANIFOLD COOLANT OUTLET
3 BOLT
4 O-RING
5 THERMOSTAT
6 RADIATOR HOSE

GC1089100152000X

Fig. 5 Thermostat replacement. Riviera, Toronado & Trofeo

THERMOSTAT
REPLACE

ELDORADO & SEVILLE

1. Drain coolant level below that of thermostat housing.
2. Remove upper air filter assembly if necessary.
3. Remove upper thermostat housing attaching bolts, **Fig. 4.**
4. Remove upper thermostat housing, then thermostat and gasket from lower housing.
5. Reverse procedure to install, noting the following:
   a. Tighten upper thermostat attaching bolts to specifications.
   b. Fill cooling system, bleed system as outlined under "Cooling System Bleed."

RIVIERA, TORONADO & TROFEO

1. Drain coolant until level is below that of the thermostat housing.
2. Remove fuel rail cover from engine.
3. Remove thermostat upper housing attaching bolt, **Fig. 5.**
4. Remove upper thermostat housing, then the thermostat.
5. Reverse procedure to install, noting the following:
   a. Install new rubber O-ring on upper thermostat housing, lubricate with coolant.
   b. Tighten thermostat attaching bolt to specifications.
   c. Fill cooling system, then bleed system as outlined under "Cooling System Bleed."

RADIATOR
REPLACE

1. Drain cooling system, then remove plastic radiator support cover.
2. Remove cooling fan, then the coolant reservoir hose at filler neck.
3. Disconnect upper and lower radiator hoses.
4. Disconnect oil cooler lines at radiator.
5. Remove radiator top support, then the radiator.
6. Reverse procedure to install.

FUEL PUMP
REPLACE

Remove fuel pump as described in the "4.6L/V8-279 Northstar Engine" section.

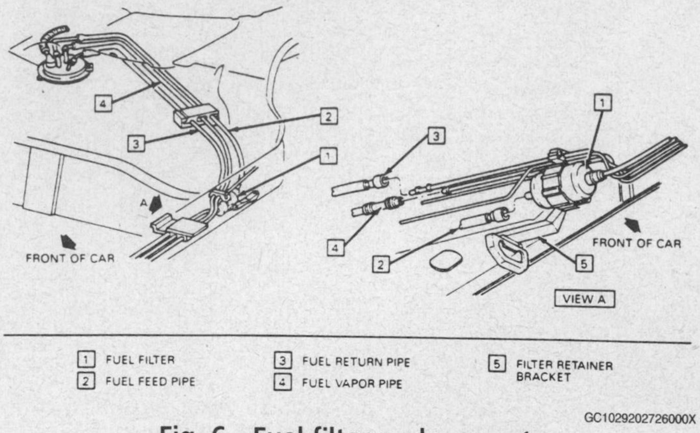
FRONT OF CAR
A
FRONT OF CAR
VIEW A
1 FUEL FILTER
2 FUEL FEED PIPE
3 FUEL RETURN PIPE
4 FUEL VAPOR PIPE
5 FILTER RETAINER BRACKET
GC1029202726000X

Fig. 6 Fuel filter replacement

FUEL FILTER
REPLACE

1. Disconnect battery ground cable.
2. Release fuel system pressure as described under "Precautions."
3. Disconnect fuel filter bracket release tabs.
4. Twist quick-connect fitting 1/4 turn in each direction to loosen dirt within fitting.
5. Using compressed air, clean quick-connect fitting at ends of filter.
6. Disconnect quick-connect fittings by squeezing plastic tabs of male end connector and pulling apart.
7. Remove fuel filter, **Fig. 6.**
8. Reverse procedure to install.

TECHNICAL SERVICE BULLETINS

OIL LEAK DIAGNOSIS

When diagnosing oil leaks from rear of engine, use of a high intensity black light is the recommended procedure. This will help eliminate improper diagnosis, as various seals at rear of engine, if leaking, may appear to be a defective rear main seal.

TIGHTENING SPECIFICATIONS

Torque Specifications Are For Clean And Lightly Lubricated Threads Only. Dry Or Dirty Threads Produce Increased Friction Which Prevents Accurate Measurement Of Tightness.

3.8L/V6-231 ENGINE

Year	Component	Torque/Ft. Lbs.
1992-93	Alternator Support To Cylinder Head	36
	Alternator Support Through Alternator	36
	Engine Mount To Cylinder Block	70
	Flywheel To Crankshaft	61
	Heater Hose Fitting To Intake	11
	Ignition Module To Alternator Support	18
	Oil Level Switch To Oil Pan	40
	Oil Pan Drain Plug	18
	Oxygen Sensor To Exhaust Manifold	31
	Spark Plug To Cylinder Head	20
	Starter Motor To Cylinder Block	35
	Thermostat Housing To Intake Manifold	10
	Water Pump Cover To Timing Chain Cover	7
	Water Pump Pulley To Hub	12

4.9L/V8-300 ENGINE

Year	Component	Torque/Ft. Lbs.
1992-95	Air Pipe To Cylinder Head	22
	Coolant Temperature Sensor	22
	Distributor Hold-Down Nut	18
	Distributor Hold-Down Stud	26
	Engine Metal Temperature Switch	6
	Flywheel To Crankshaft	70
	Heater Water Valve	22
	Lower Thermostat Housing To Water Pump Bolt	7
	Lower Thermostat Housing To Water Pump Stud	30
	MAT Sensor	22
	Oil Filter Adapter To Block Screws	15
	Oil Pressure Switch	10
	Oxygen Sensor	30
	Spark Plugs	11
	Thermal Vacuum Switch (TVS)	15
	Upper Thermostat Housing To Lower Thermostat Housing Screws	20

4.6L/V8-279 Engine

NOTE: On Air Bag Equipped Models, Refer To "Air Bag System Precautions" Located In The Front Of This Manual For System Disarming & Arming Procedures.

INDEX

PRECAUTIONS

AIR BAG SYSTEMS

Refer to "Air Bag System Precautions" in the front of this manual for system disarming and arming procedures.

FUEL SYSTEM PRESSURE RELIEF

1. Remove fuel pump fuse B1 in console fuse block.
2. Loosen fuel filler cap, then connect gauge J-34730-1 to fuel pressure connection. Wrap shop towel around fitting while connecting gauge.
3. Install bleed hose into approved container, then open valve on gauge to bleed system pressure.

THROTTLE POSITION (TP) SENSOR LEARN PROCEDURE

Ensure nothing is touching or obstructing the accelerator or brake pedals during this procedure.

1. Turn ignition to On (engine Off) position.
2. Depress OFF and WARMER buttons of the Electronic Climate Control (ECC) until all segments of the display are illuminated.
3. Turn ignition switch Off, then wait 20 seconds.
4. Repeat steps 1 through 3 two more times.

IDLE LEARN PROCEDURE

This procedure must be performed after throttle position sensor learn procedure.

Air temperature must be at least 50°F to perform this test.

1. Start and run engine until coolant temperature is 176°F, then allow to idle for an additional 5 minutes.
2. Apply brakes and place transaxle in Drive range.
3. Turn ECC to Off position and allow engine to idle for 30 seconds.
4. Turn ECC to Auto position and allow engine to idle for another 30 seconds.
5. Place transaxle in Park range and turn ignition to Off position.

ENGINE MOUNT

REPLACE

1. Remove righthand and lefthand engine cooling fan.
2. Remove right and left torque struts, **Fig. 1.**
3. Install engine support fixture No. J-28467-A. Use only one support at left rear engine bracket.
4. Raise and support vehicle, then remove nuts securing mount to engine cradle, **Fig. 2.**
5. Remove bolts securing motor mount bracket to crankcase, then lower vehicle.
6. Remove bolts securing mount to cylinder head and bracket.
7. Raise engine by tightening support chain until mount and bracket can be separated and removed.
8. Reverse procedure to install.

ENGINE

REPLACE

1. Release fuel system pressure as outlined under "Precautions."
2. Remove hood, then disconnect both battery cables.
3. Remove air cleaner inlet duct, then drain cooling system.
4. Remove left and right torque struts. Reinstall bolts in torque strut bracket at left front of engine as this will be used as an engine lift point.
5. Disconnect radiator hoses from water crossover.
6. Remove both engine cooling fans, then the serpentine drive belt.
7. Disconnect cruise control servo connections, then the ISC electrical connector.
8. Disconnect throttle cable from throttle body cam.
9. Disconnect shift cable from park/neutral switch and cable bracket at transmission. Remove park/neutral switch.
10. Disconnect power brake vacuum hose, then the cylinder head temperature switch.
11. Remove bellhousing bolts, **Fig. 3,** then the ignition coils and spark plug wires.
12. Raise and support vehicle, then remove oil pan to transmission brace.
13. Remove torque converter splash shield, then converter to flywheel bolts.
14. Disconnect oil cooler lines at oil filter adapter.
15. Remove A/C compressor. Position compressor aside leaving lines attached.

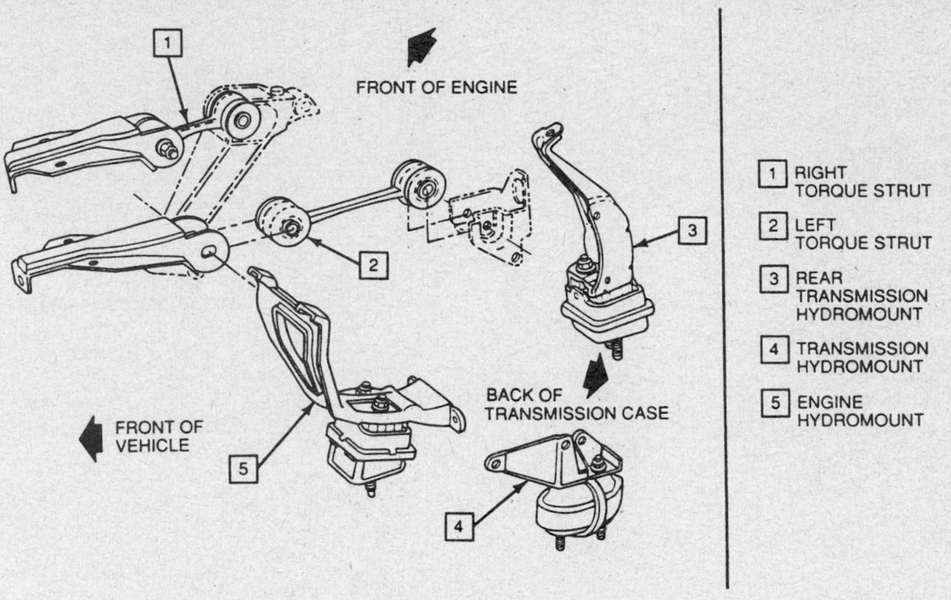

1
FRONT OF ENGINE
2
3
BACK OF TRANSMISSION CASE
FRONT OF VEHICLE
5
4
1 RIGHT TORQUE STRUT
2 LEFT TORQUE STRUT
3 REAR TRANSMISSION HYDROMOUNT
4 TRANSMISSION HYDROMOUNT
5 ENGINE HYDROMOUNT
GC1069100336000X

Fig. 1 Engine/transaxle mounts

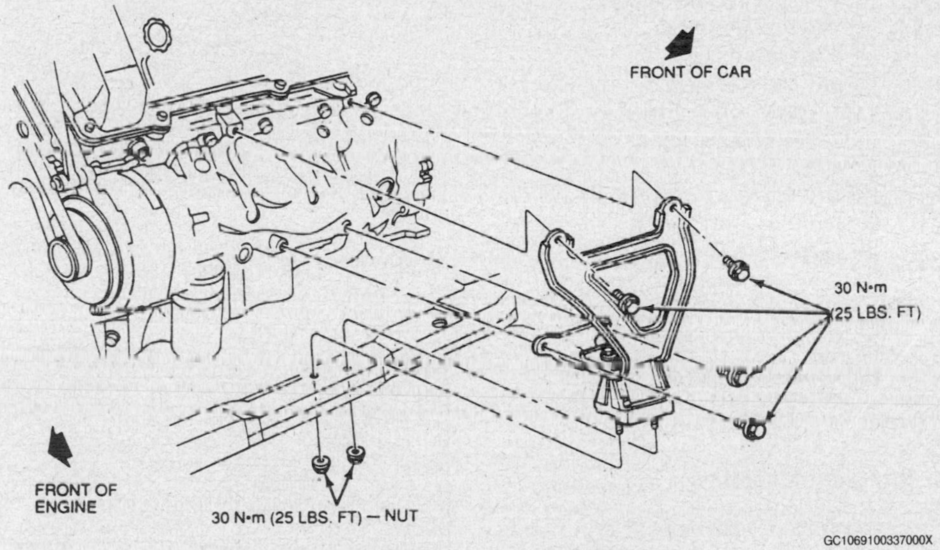

FRONT OF CAR
30 N•m (25 LBS. FT)
FRONT OF ENGINE
30 N•m (25 LBS. FT) — NUT
GC1069100337000X

Fig. 2 Front engine mount replacement

16. disconnect electrical connections from harness along lefthand side of engine, **Fig. 4.** Move harness out from behind exhaust manifold.
17. Remove nuts securing motor mount to engine cradle front crossmember, then the exhaust pipe.
18. Remove right front wheel, then the crankcase to transmission bracket at transmission tail shaft.
19. Disconnect knock sensor, then remove bolts from transmission to cylinder head brace at cylinder head.
20. Lower vehicle, then using fuel line remover No. J-37088 or equivalent, disconnect fuel lines.
21. Disconnect injector harness connector, then the hoses from coolant reservoir. Remove coolant reservoir.
22. Disconnect cam position sensor, then the heater hoses from water pipes at front of right cylinder head.
23. Disconnect battery cable from junction block, then remove retainer at cylinder head.
24. Disconnect starter cable from junction block, then the power steering pump line at pump.
25. Remove power steering line retainer at right front of crankcase, then disconnect rear oxygen sensor connector.
26. Remove screws securing wiring harness retainer to right cam cover. Position harness aside.
27. Connect suitable engine lifting fixture to engine using support hooks at left rear and right rear of engine. Use torque strut bracket at left front of engine for third lift point.
28. Remove engine from vehicle.
29. Reverse procedure to install.

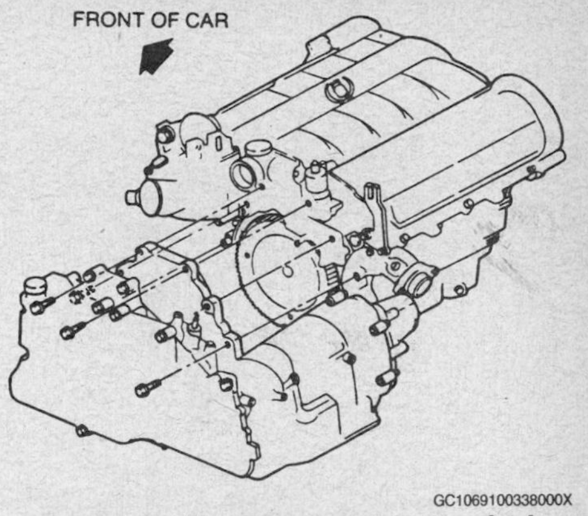

FRONT OF CAR
GC1069100338000X

Fig. 3 Bellhousing mounting bolt locations

INTAKE MANIFOLD

REPLACE

1. Remove air intake duct from throttle body.
2. Disconnect and plug coolant hoses at throttle body and coolant reservoir.
3. Disconnect electrical connectors from intake manifold, TP sensor, ISC motor, EEC solenoid and cruise control servo.
4. Disconnect vacuum hoses from brake booster, fuel pipe bundle and body.
5. Disconnect PCV hose at manifold, then the accelerator cable at throttle body. Position cable aside.
6. Release fuel system pressure as outlined under "Precautions."
7. Disconnect fuel pipe quick connects at fuel pipe bundle in engine compartment.
8. Remove EEC solenoid bracket at rear cam cover, then reposition transaxle range control cable away from cruise control servo.
9. Remove intake manifold bolts, then the intake manifold/throttle body assembly.
10. Reverse procedure to install. Tighten manifold bolts to specifications in sequence shown in **Fig. 5.**

THROTTLE BODY, REPLACE

1. Remove intake manifold/throttle body assembly as outlined under "Intake Manifold, Replace."
2. Disconnect vacuum manifold at throttle body, then the vacuum hoses at cruise control servo.
3. Disconnect cruise control cable at servo. Cable can be removed at servo blade without removing plastic retainer.
4. Remove cruise control servo and bracket from throttle body, then disconnect cruise control cable at throttle body.
5. Remove throttle position sensor, then disconnect fuel pipe retainer at ISC bracket.
6. Remove throttle body from intake manifold, then the ISC motor and bracket from throttle body.
7. Reverse procedure to install.

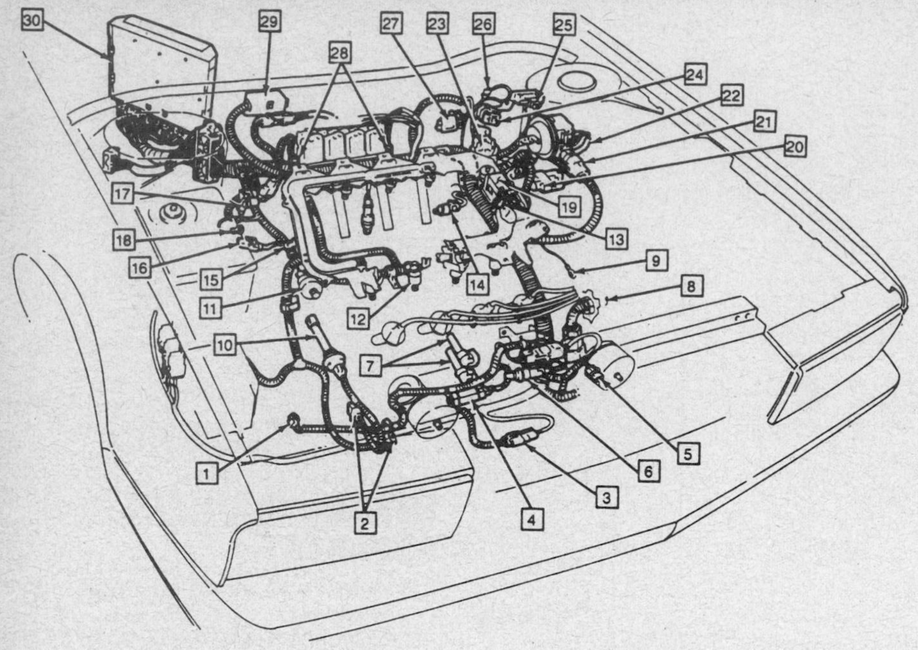

1 COMPRESSOR CLUTCH
2 GENERATOR CONN
3 RIGHT PULLER FAN
4 OIL PRESSURE SWITCH
5 LEFT PULLER FAN
6 O_2 SENSOR
7 CRANKSHAFT POSITION SENSORS (2)
8 TRANSMISSION
9 GROUND
10 OIL LEVEL SWITCH
11 KNOCK SENSOR
12 STARTER
13 MAT SENSOR
14 COOLANT TEMPERATURE SENSOR
15 VEHICLE SPEED SENSOR
16 POWER STEERING PRESSURE SWITCH
17 CAM POSITION SENSOR
18 PCM & DIS GROUNDS
19 MAP SENSOR
20 IDLE SPEED CONTROL
21 THROTTLE POSITION SENSOR
22 CRUISE CONTROL SERVO
23 EGR
24 PARK/NEUTRAL SAFETY SWITCH
25 BRAKE BOOSTER SENSOR
26 SPEED SENSING SWITCH
27 CANISTER PURGE SOLENOID
28 DIS MODULE
29 BATTERY/STARTER JUNCTION BOX
30 POWERTRAIN CONTROL MODULE

GC1069100339000X

Fig. 4 Engine electrical connection locations

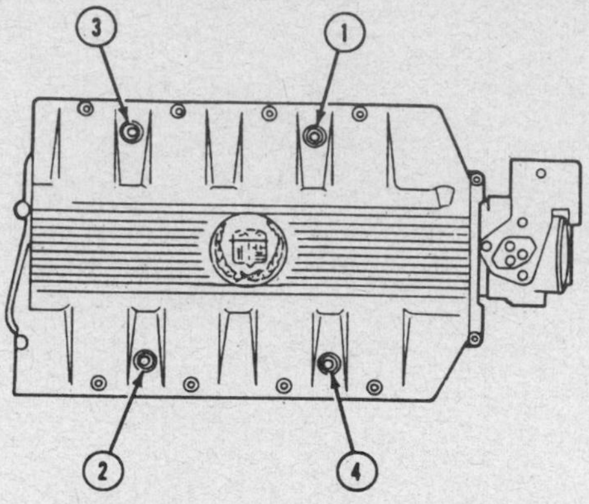

GC1059100076000X

Fig. 5 Intake manifold tightening sequence

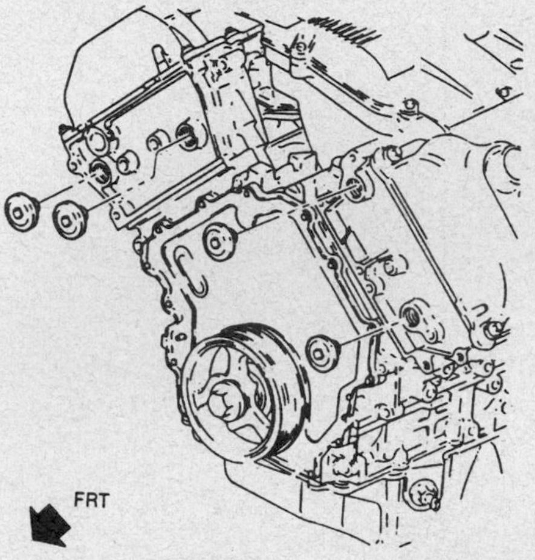
FRT

GC1069100341000X

Fig. 6 Chain guide access plugs removal

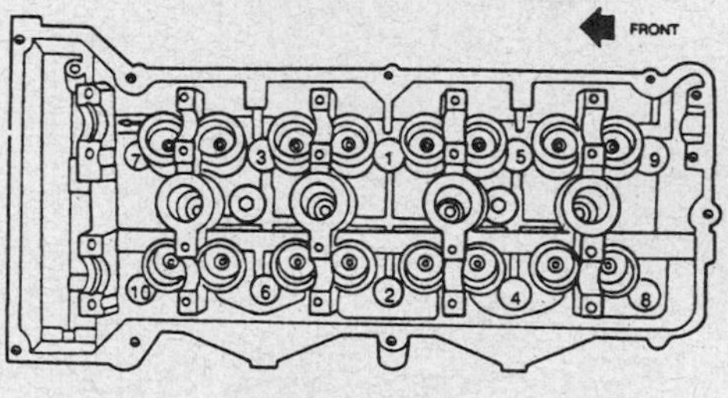
FRONT

GC1069100342000X

Fig. 7 Cylinder head bolt tightening sequence

8. Reverse procedure to install. **Perform TP sensor learn and idle learn procedures.**

EXHAUST MANIFOLD

REPLACE

LEFT SIDE

1. Remove motor mount as outlined under "Engine Front Mount, Replace."
2. Remove rear alternator bracket, then remove two bolts at manifold outlet flange.
3. Disconnect oxygen sensor electrical connector, then remove manifold attaching bolts.
4. Remove exhaust manifold, then the oxygen sensor.
5. Reverse procedure to install. Coat oxygen sensor threads with high temperature anti-seize compound.

RIGHT SIDE

1. Disconnect both battery cables, then the rear oxygen sensor and harness clip.
2. Raise and support vehicle, then disconnect exhaust pipe from catalytic converter.
3. Disconnect suspension position sensor at both lower control arms.
4. Support rear crossmember of engine cradle with suitable screw jack, then remove 4 cradle to body bolts.
5. Carefully lower rear of engine cradle.
6. Remove pipe to exhaust manifold and crossover exhaust pipe mounting bolts.
7. Remove exhaust manifold mounting nuts, then the exhaust manifold.
8. Reverse procedure to install. Coat oxygen sensor threads with high temperature anti-sieze compound.

CYLINDER HEAD

REPLACE

1. Remove intake manifold as described under "Intake Manifold, Replace."
2. Remove cam covers as described under "Valve Cover, Replace."
3. Remove crankshaft damper as described under "Crankshaft Damper, Replace."
4. Remove front cover as described under "Front Cover, Replace."
5. Remove oil pump as described under "Oil Pump, Replace."
6. Remove chain tensioner from timing chain for cylinder head being removed.
7. Remove cam sprockets from head being removed. **Timing chains should remain in chain case.**
8. Remove timing chain guide retaining screws through access plugs at front of cylinder head, **Fig. 6.**

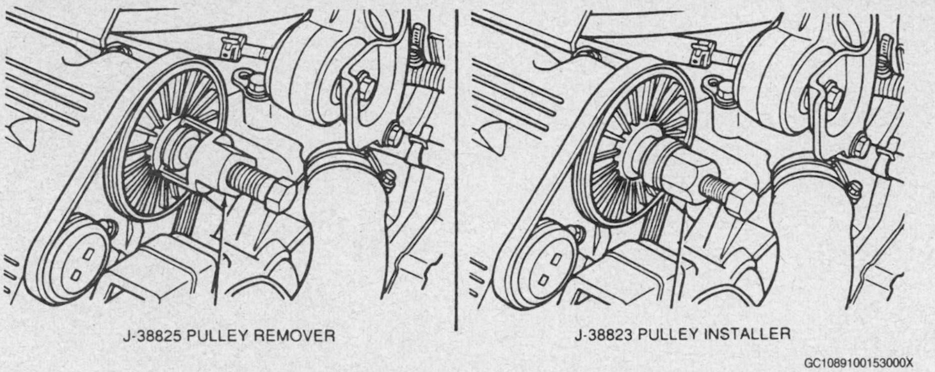
J-38825 PULLEY REMOVER
J-38823 PULLEY INSTALLER
GC1089100153000X

Fig. 8 Water pump pulley removal

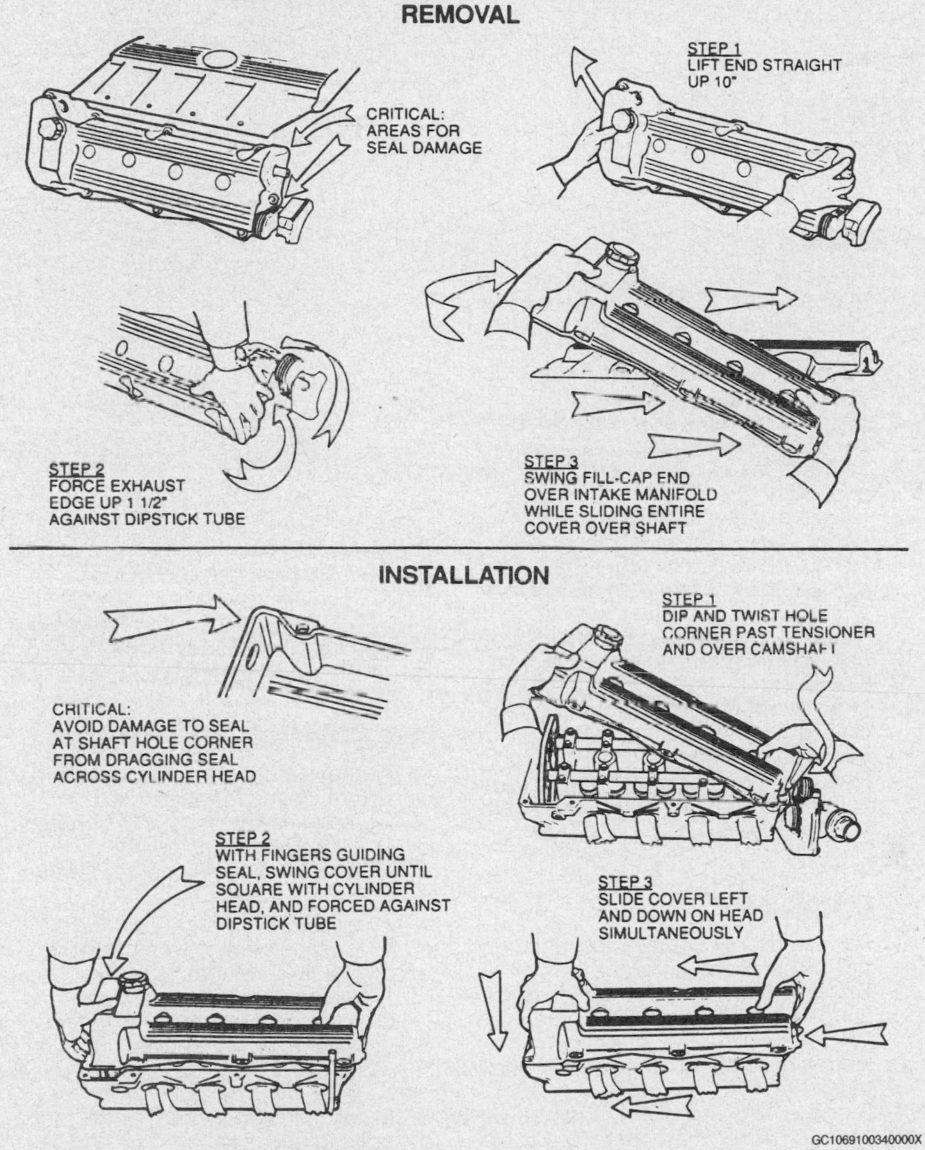
REMOVAL
CRITICAL:
AREAS FOR
SEAL DAMAGE
STEP 1
LIFT END STRAIGHT
UP 10"
STEP 2
FORCE EXHAUST
EDGE UP 1 1/2"
AGAINST DIPSTICK TUBE
STEP 3
SWING FILL-CAP END
OVER INTAKE MANIFOLD
WHILE SLIDING ENTIRE
COVER OVER SHAFT
INSTALLATION
STEP 1
DIP AND TWIST HOLE
CORNER PAST TENSIONER
AND OVER CAMSHAFT
CRITICAL:
AVOID DAMAGE TO SEAL
AT SHAFT HOLE CORNER
FROM DRAGGING SEAL
ACROSS CYLINDER HEAD
STEP 2
WITH FINGERS GUIDING
SEAL, SWING COVER UNTIL
SQUARE WITH CYLINDER
HEAD, AND FORCED AGAINST
DIPSTICK TUBE
STEP 3
SLIDE COVER LEFT
AND DOWN ON HEAD
SIMULTANEOUSLY
GC1069100340000X

Fig. 9 Valve cover replacement

9. Remove water crossover, then the exhaust manifold as described under "Exhaust Manifold, Replace."
10. Remove cylinder head bolts, then the cylinder head and gasket. **When camshafts remain in the cylinder head some valves will be open at all times. Do not rest the cylinder head on a flat surface with cylinder face down.**
11. Reverse procedure to install. Tighten cylinder head bolts in sequence shown in **Fig. 7,** as follows:
    a. **Torque** ten M11 bolts to 22 ft. lbs. plus an additional 90°.
    b. Tighten an additional 90° in same sequence.
    c. **Torque** M6 bolts to 10 ft. lbs.

VALVE COVER
REPLACE
LEFT SIDE

1. Disconnect both battery cables, then partially drain cooling system.
2. Disconnect upper radiator hose at water crossover, then the spark plug wires.
3. Remove right cooling fan, then disconnect PCV fresh air tube from cam cover.
4. Remove right and left torque struts, then disconnect water pump drive belt.
5. Remove water pump pulley using tools shown in **Fig. 8.**
6. Remove camshaft seal retainer screws, then seal.
7. Disconnect battery cable retainer at front of valve cover, then remove valve cover retaining screws.
8. Remove valve cover as shown in **Fig. 9.**
9. Reverse procedure to install.

RIGHT SIDE

1. Disconnect both battery cables, then remove tower to tower brace.
2. Disconnect DIS wiring connectors and mounting bolts, then remove DIS and right bank spark plug wires.
3. Disconnect PCV valve, then remove purge canister solenoid from rear of cover.
4. Remove wiring harness from cover, then the cam cover mounting screws.
5. Support front of engine cradle and remove front cradle mounting screws.
6. Remove right and left torque struts.
7. Lower engine cradle to provide clearance at rear of engine compartment.
8. Remove cam cover.
9. Reverse procedure to install.

VALVE ADJUSTMENT

This engine is equipped with hydraulic lifters. Valve adjustment is not necessary.

CRANKSHAFT DAMPER
REPLACE

1. Release tension from accessory drive belt, then raise and support vehicle.
2. Remove right front wheel, then the splash shields from wheelwell.
3. Remove brace between engine oil pan and transmission case, then install flywheel holder No. J-39411 or equivalent.
4. Remove balancer bolt, then support engine cradle with suitable jack screw and remove 3 engine cradle bolts at right side of cradle.
5. Disconnect RSS sensor from right-hand lower control arm, then lower engine cradle to obtain clearance below body rail for balancer puller.

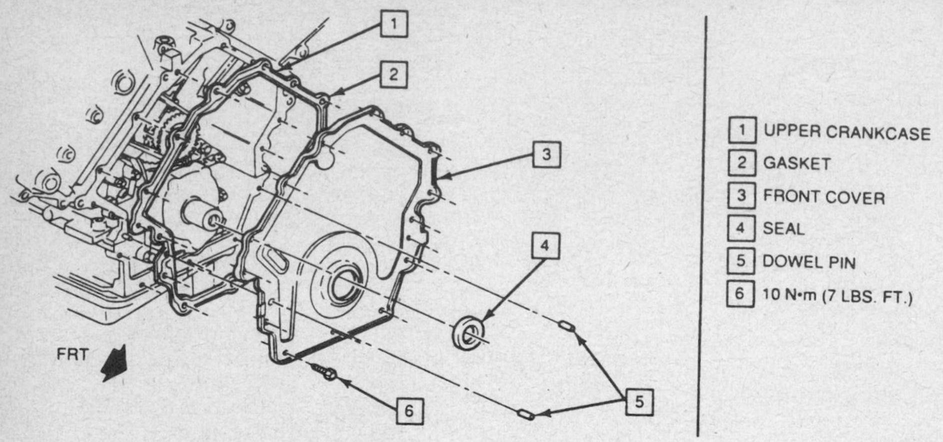
1
2
3
4
5
6
FRT
1 UPPER CRANKCASE
2 GASKET
3 FRONT COVER
4 SEAL
5 DOWEL PIN
6 10 N•m (7 LBS. FT.)
GC1069100344000X

Fig. 10 Front cover replacement

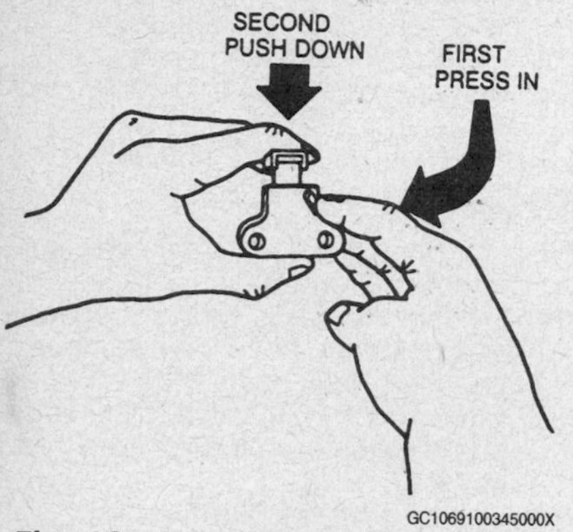
SECOND
PUSH DOWN
FIRST
PRESS IN
GC1069100345000X

Fig. 12 Tensioner release lever rotating

6. Install pilot No. J-39344-2 into end of crankshaft.
7. Using puller No. J-38416 or equivalent, remove crankshaft damper.
8. Reverse procedure to install.

FRONT COVER

REPLACE

1. Remove serpentine drive belt.
2. Remove crankshaft damper as outlined under "Crankshaft Damper, Replace."
3. Remove belt tensioner, then the belt idler pulley.
4. Remove front cover mounting bolts, **Fig. 10,** then the front cover.
5. Reverse procedure to install.

FRONT COVER SEAL

REPLACE

1. Remove crankshaft damper as outlined under "Crankshaft Damper, Replace."
2. Using screwdriver behind front cover seal, pry out seal. Do not score cover bore for seal or crankshaft.
3. Lubricate seal lips with engine oil and position seal to front cover with garter spring side toward engine.
4. Using seal installer No. J-38818 and harmonic balancer installer No. J-39344 or equivalents, push seal into front cover until it bottoms on cover.
5. Install harmonic balancer.

TIMING CHAIN

REPLACE

PRIMARY

1. Remove engine assembly as described under "Engine, Replace," then place engine assembly on a suitable stand.
2. Remove serpentine drive belt, idler pulley and belt tensioner.
3. Remove front cover as described under "Front Cover, Replace."
4. Remove oil pump assembly as described under "Oil Pump, Replace."
5. Remove valve covers as described under "Valve Cover, Replace."
6. Remove three timing chain tensioners, then all four camshaft sprockets.
7. Remove secondary drive chains from around intermediate shaft sprocket.
8. Remove one bolt from intermediate shaft sprocket and slide gears and primary drive chain off crankshaft and intermediate shaft.
9. Reverse procedure to install, time camshafts as described under "Camshaft, Replace."

SECONDARY

1. Remove front cover as described under "Front Cover, Replace."
2. Remove lefthand valve cover as described under "Valve Cover, Replace."
3. Remove lefthand secondary chain tensioner.
4. Remove lefthand chain guide as described under "Cylinder Head, Replace."
5. Remove lefthand cam sprocket bolts and sprockets.
6. Remove lefthand secondary drive chain, **Fig. 11.**
7. To remove righthand secondary drive chain, refer to steps 2 through 6 and substitute righthand for lefthand.
8. Reverse procedure to install, time camshafts as described under "Camshaft, Replace."

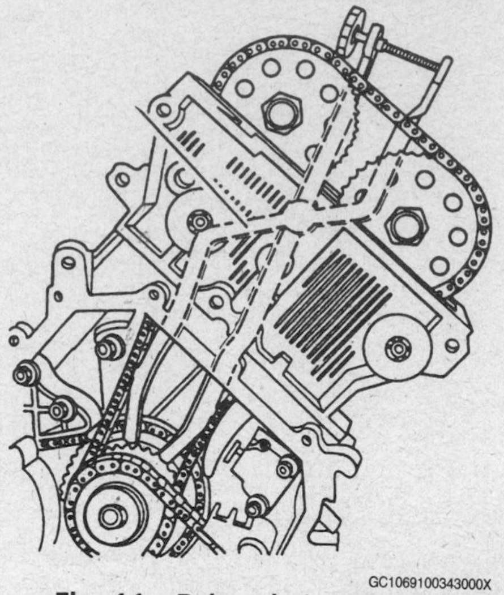
GC1069100343000X

Fig. 11 Drive chain tension

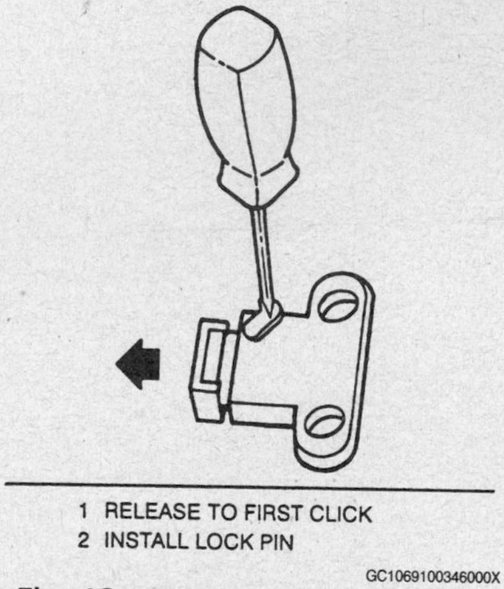
1 RELEASE TO FIRST CLICK
2 INSTALL LOCK PIN
GC1069100346000X

Fig. 13 Tensioner in collapsed position

TENSIONER, REPLACE

1. Remove front cover as described in "Front Cover, Replace."
2. Remove two tensioner mounting bolts, then the tensioner.
3. Collapse new tensioner as follows:
   a. Rotate ratchet release lever counter clockwise and hold, **Fig. 12.**
   b. Collapse tensioner shoe and hold.
   c. Release ratchet lever and slowly release pressure on shoe.
   d. As ratchet lever moves to first click hold tensioner shoe inward and insert a pin through hole in release lever, **Fig. 13.**
4. Install tensioner and bolts, tighten bolts to specification.
5. Remove retaining pin allowing tensioner shoe to extend.
6. Install front cover.

CAMSHAFT

REPLACE

REMOVAL

1. Remove cam cover as described in "Valve Cover, Replace."

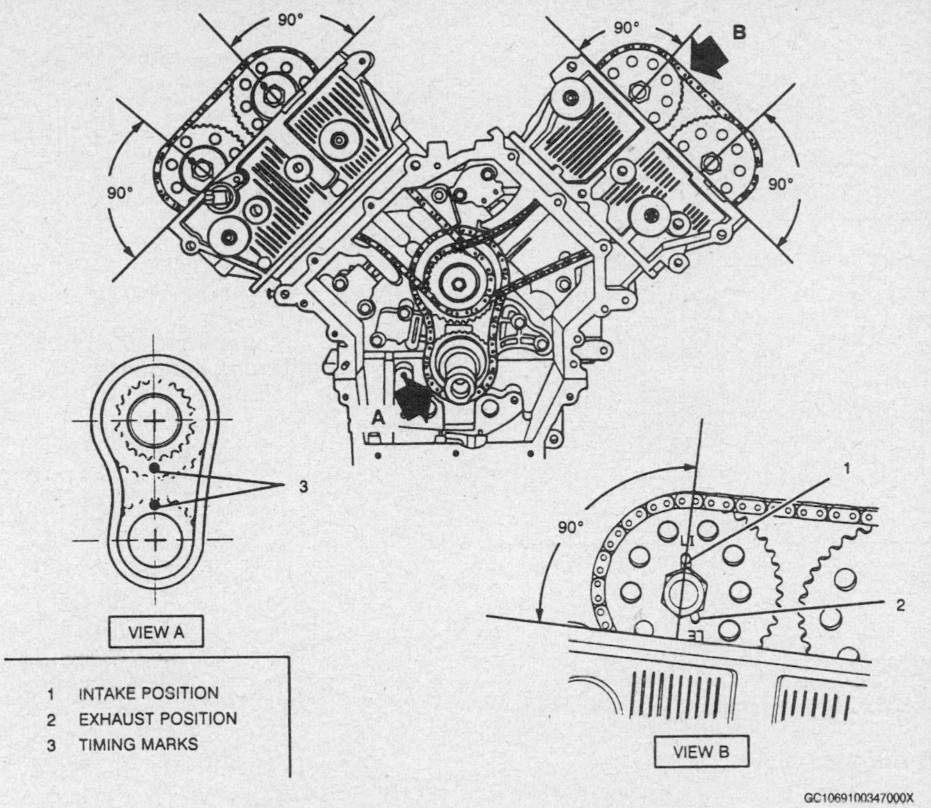
90°
90°
90°
90°
B
A
3
1
2
90°
VIEW A
VIEW B
1 INTAKE POSITION
2 EXHAUST POSITION
3 TIMING MARKS
GC1069100347000X

Fig. 14 Camshaft timing procedure

2. Secure cam sprocket to timing chain by installing tie-wraps through sprocket holes. Use two tie-wraps per sprocket. **The sprocket-chain relationship must be maintained throughout this procedure or camshaft timing will be lost and require further engine disassembly to time.**
3. Install cam chain holder tool No. J-38815 or equivalent behind camshaft sprockets so that it is positioned between chain tensioner and chain guide, **Fig. 11.** Apply tension to tool by tightening tension adjusting screw.
4. Remove both camshaft sprocket bolts. **Note location of cam drive pins in end of camshafts.**
5. Work sprockets off of cams using play in chain.
6. Loosen cam bearing cap bolts a few turns at a time until all valve spring pressure has been released.
7. Remove bolts and bearing caps, then the camshaft.

INSTALLATION

1. Apply camshaft prelube part No. 1052365, or equivalent, to face of each cam lobe.
2. Install camshaft, then position cam bearing caps to cylinder head noting the following:
   a. Arrow on top of bearing cap points towards front of engine.
   b. The "E" mark on top of bearing cap indicates a cap for the exhaust cam.
   c. The "I" mark on top of bearing cap indicates a cap for the intake cam.
   d. The No. "1" mark on top of the bearing cap should be towards front of engine.
3. Loosely install cam bearing cap bolts, then alternately tighten each bearing cap bolt a few turns at a time against valve spring pressure until all bolts are snug.
4. Tighten bearing cap bolts to specification.
5. Rotate camshaft until drive pins are in position to engage cam sprockets over cams, then install retaining bolts. Tighten sprocket bolts to specification.
6. Remove chain holder tool, then the tie-wraps from cam sprockets.
7. Install cam cover.

CAMSHAFT TIMING

Setting camshaft timing is necessary whenever the cam drive system has been disturbed such that the relationship between any chain and sprocket has been lost.

1. Remove valve covers as described under "Valve Cover, Replace."
2. Remove front cover as described under "Front Cover, Replace."
3. Remove or retract three chain tensioners. **Tensioners may be in their installed positions but must be fully retracted as described under "Timing Chain, Replace."**
4. Remove oil pump assembly as described in "Oil Pump, Service."
5. Rotate crankshaft until sprocket drive key is at approximately the 1 o'clock position.
6. Install crankshaft and intermediate shaft sprockets to primary drive chain with their timing marks aligned as shown in **Fig. 14.**
7. Install crank and intermediate shaft sprockets over their respective shafts.
8. Rotate crankshaft so that crankshaft key engages the sprocket without changing timing mark position.
9. Install intermediate sprocket retaining bolt, tighten bolt to specification.
10. Install primary chain tensioner and release tensioner shoe. Tighten tensioner mounting bolts to specification.
11. Install flywheel holder tool No. J-39411, or equivalent, to lock crankshaft in this position.
12. Route secondary drive chain for left-hand cylinder head over inner row of intermediate shaft teeth.
13. Route secondary drive chain over chain guide and install exhaust cam sprocket to chain so that the camshaft drive pin engages sprocket. There should be no slack in lower section of chain and cam drive pin must be perpendicular to cylinder head face as shown in **Fig. 14. LH cam sprocket must contain cam position sensor pickup.**
14. Install intake cam sprocket into chain so sprocket engages cam drive pin while pin remains perpendicular to cylinder head face as shown in **Fig. 14.**
15. A hex is cast into camshafts so that an open end wrench can be used to provide minor repositioning of the cams.
16. Loosely install exhaust and intake cam sprocket bolts.
17. Install chain tensioner and release tension on shoe, then tighten tensioner mounting bolts to specifications.
18. Tighten cam sprocket bolts to specifications.
19. Route secondary drive chain for right-hand cylinder head over outer row of intermediate shaft teeth and repeat steps 13 through 18 for righthand cams.

PISTON & ROD ASSEMBLY

Refer to **Fig. 15** for correct piston and rod assembly installation.

Ensure piston and rod assemblies are coated with suitable lubricant before installation.

MAIN & ROD BEARINGS

Shell type main bearings of steel backed aluminum are used at all positions. The upper halves are all interchangeable, as are all of the lower halves except for the thrust bearings in the No. 3 position. If bearing clearance is greater than .003 inch and new bearings do not reduce the clearance to .0005-.002 inch, a new crankshaft will be required. Undersized bearing are not available and crankshaft grinding is not allowed. When installing main bearing bolts, **torque** bolts in to 15 ft. lbs. plus an additional 65° using sequence shown in **Fig. 16.** Maximum crankshaft endplay is .019 inch.

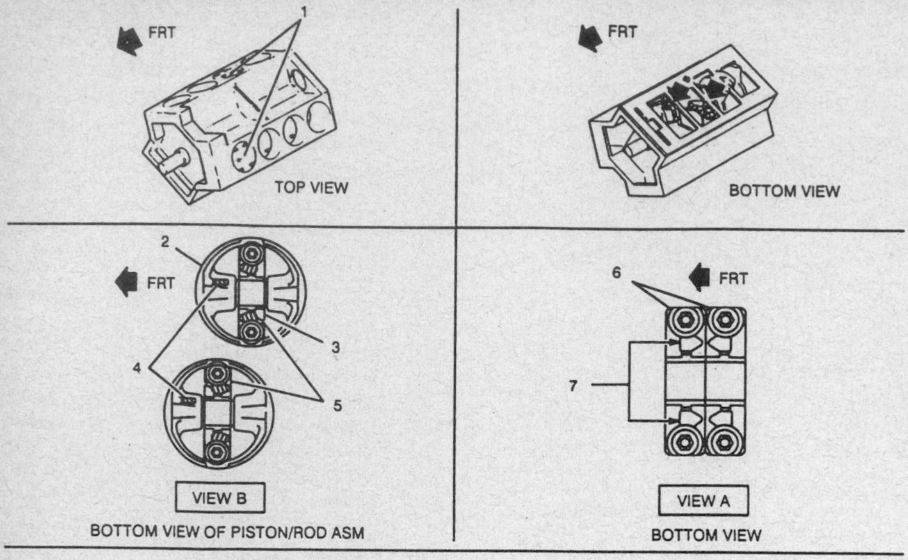
FRT
TOP VIEW
BOTTOM VIEW
VIEW B
BOTTOM VIEW OF PISTON/ROD ASM
VIEW A
BOTTOM VIEW

1 PISTON ARROW TOWARD CHAIN CASE ON BOTH SIDES
2 PISTON
3 ROD CAP
4 LOCATER LUGS INDICATE PISTON FRONT TOWARDS ENGINE FRONT
5 BEARING CAP ARROWS POINT TOWARD EACH OTHER ON PAIRED RODS
6 ROD CAPS
7 BEARING CAP ARROWS POINT TOWARD EACH OTHER ON PAIRED RODS

GC1069100349000X

Fig. 15 Piston & rod assembly

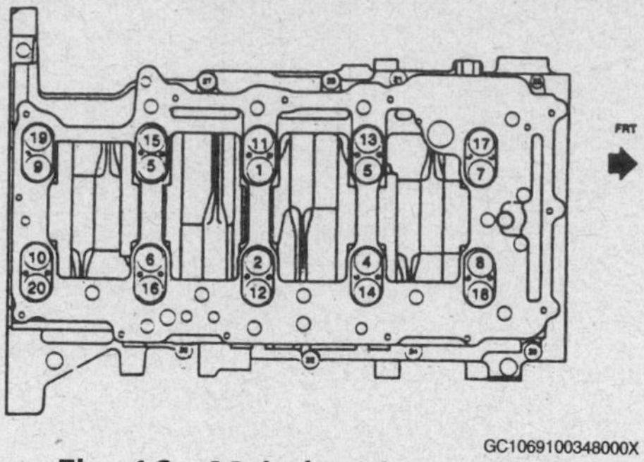

GC1069100348000X

Fig. 16 Main bearing cap bolt tightening sequence

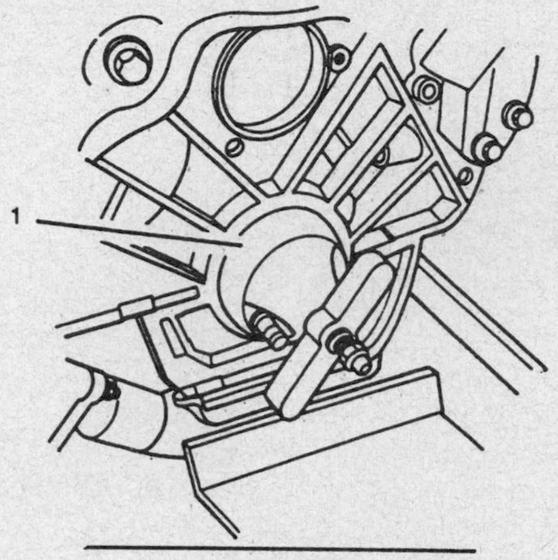

1 J 38817

GC1099100047000X

Fig. 17 Rear main seal installation

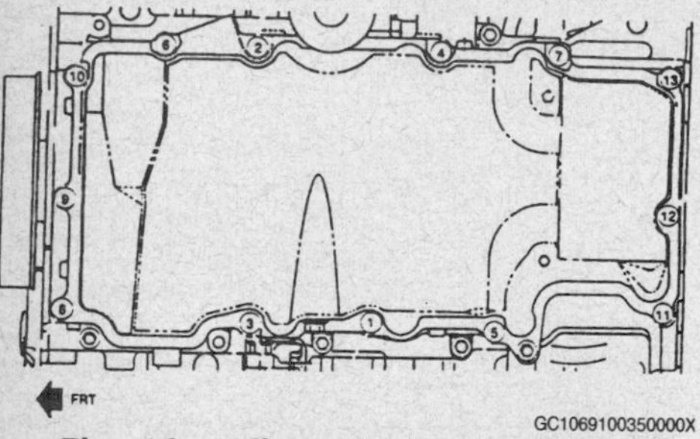
FRT

GC1069100350000X

Fig. 18 Oil pan bolt tightening sequence

Ensure that bearings are coated with a suitable lubricant and crankshaft journals are covered completely with lubricant.

CRANKSHAFT REAR OIL SEAL

REPLACE

1. Remove transaxle assembly, refer to "Automatic Transmissions/Transaxles."
2. Remove eight flywheel mounting bolts, then the flywheel.
3. Drill a 1/8 inch hole into metal body of rear main seal, then remove seal using a slide hammer.
4. Place a small dab of RTV sealant at crankcase split line across end of upper/lower crankcase seal.
5. Lubricate new oil seal with engine oil, then slide seal over arbor of seal installation tool No. J-38817 or equivalent.
6. Thread seal-installer tool No. J-38818 in crankshaft flange and install seal by turning handle until tool bottoms against crankcase, **Fig. 17.**
7. Install flywheel and transaxle assembly.

OIL PAN

REPLACE

1. Remove engine assembly and place on suitable engine stand.
2. Drain engine oil.
3. Remove oil pan bolts, then the pan.
4. Reverse procedure to install, noting the following:
   a. Gasket is reusable unless damaged. **Do not remove gasket from oil pan groove unless replacement is required.**
   b. Using sequence shown in **Fig. 18,** tighten oil pan bolts to specification.

OIL PUMP SERVICE

Refer to "Technical Service Bulletins" for additional instruction for oil pump servicing.

REMOVAL

1. Remove front cover as described in "Front Cover, Replace."
2. Remove three oil pump mounting bolts, **Fig. 19.**
3. Remove pump and drive spacer.

DISASSEMBLE

1. Remove drive spacer from pump housing, **Fig. 20.**
2. Remove two screws holding pump housing halves together.
3. Remove inner and outer rotors from housing. **Mark mating surfaces.**
4. Remove pressure relief valve.

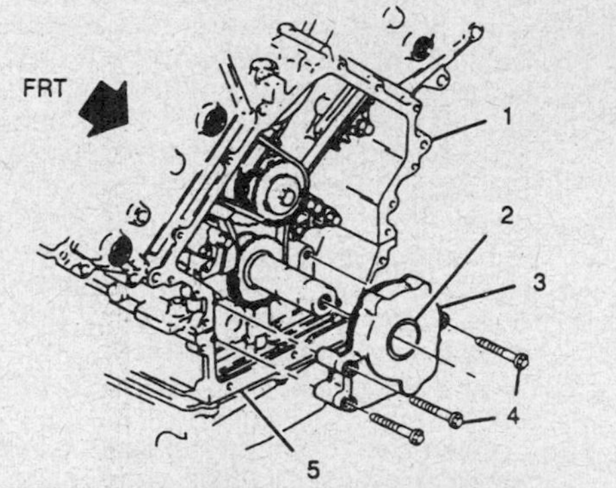
FRT

1 ENGINE UPPER CRANKCASE
2 OIL PUMP DRIVE SPACER
3 OIL PUMP
4 BOLT (3)
5 LOWER CRANKCASE

GC1099100045000X

Fig. 19 Oil pump removal

INSPECTION

1. Inspect pump housing for nicks, burrs, chips or debris that may cause a leak or binding condition in rotor pocket.
2. Inspect drive or driven rotors for nicks or burrs.
3. Check pump cover and interior surface for excessive wear or score marks.

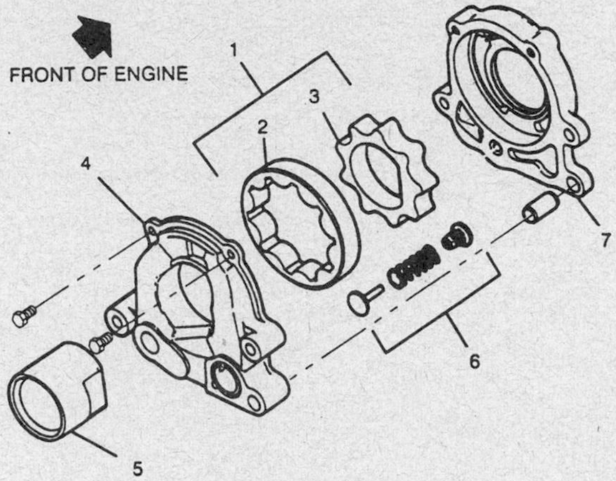
FRONT OF ENGINE
1
2
3
4
5
6
7

1 GEROTOR ASSEMBLY
2 OUTER GEAR
3 INNER GEAR
4 HOUSING
5 DRIVE SPACER
6 RELIEF VALVE
7 COVER

GC1099100046000X

Fig. 20 Exploded view of oil pump

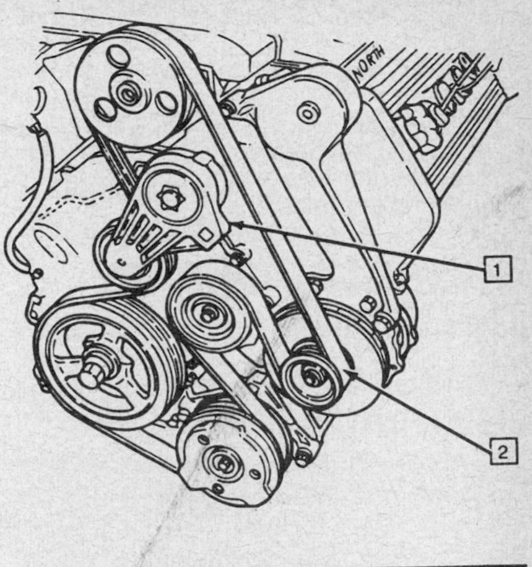
1
2

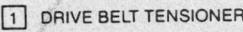

1 DRIVE BELT TENSIONER
2 SERPENTINE DRIVE BELT

GC1069100351000X

Fig. 21 Serpentine drive belt routing

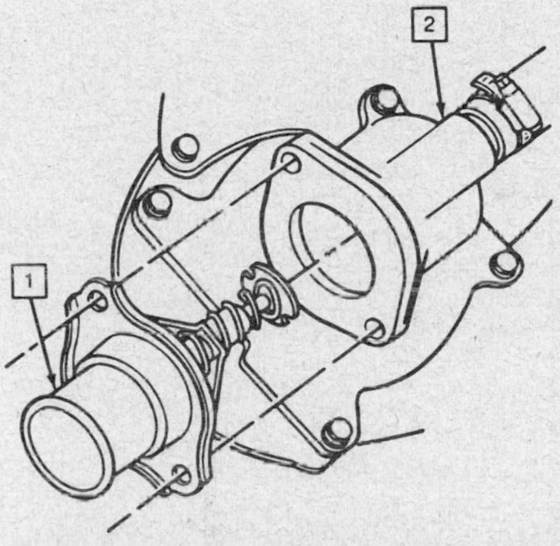
2
1

1 THERMOSTAT
2 THERMOSTAT HOUSING

GC1089100155000X

Fig. 22 Thermostat replacement

ASSEMBLE

1. Install inner and outer rotors to pump cover. **Align marks made during pump disassemble procedure.**
2. Install pressure relief valve seat, spring and pilot in pump housing.
3. Assemble housing and cover over locating dial.
4. Insert a 3/8 inch drill bit in pump mounting hole on opposite side to aid in alignment of housing and cover.
5. Install two bolts and **torque** to 9 ft. lbs.

INSTALLATION

1. Install oil pump drive spacer into oil pump from rear so that drive flat engages pump rotor.
2. Position pump over crankshaft, then loosely install bolts.
3. Holding pump up as high as possible, **torque** pump retaining bolts to 7 ft. lbs. plus an additional 35°.
4. Install front cover assembly as described in "Front Cover, Replace."

SERPENTINE DRIVE BELT

1. Rotate drive belt tensioner mechanism upward, away from drive belt using a 1/2 inch breaker bar.
2. Remove serpentine drive belt.
3. Reverse procedure to install. Refer to **Fig. 21**, for serpentine drive belt routing.

COOLING SYSTEM BLEED

This engine does not require a specified bleed procedure. After filling cooling system, run engine to operating temperature with radiator/pressure cap off. Air will then be automatically bled through cap opening.

THERMOSTAT

REPLACE

1. Drain cooling system, then remove front end beauty panel and air cleaner.
2. Remove thermostat housing mounting bolts, then the housing, **Fig. 22.**
3. Remove thermostat and O-ring from housing.
4. Reverse procedure to install.

WATER PUMP

REPLACE

1. Drain cooling system, then remove air cleaner.
2. Remove water pump housing retaining bolts, then the water pump housing, **Fig. 23.**
3. Remove water pump drive belt, then the water pump.
4. Reverse procedure to install.

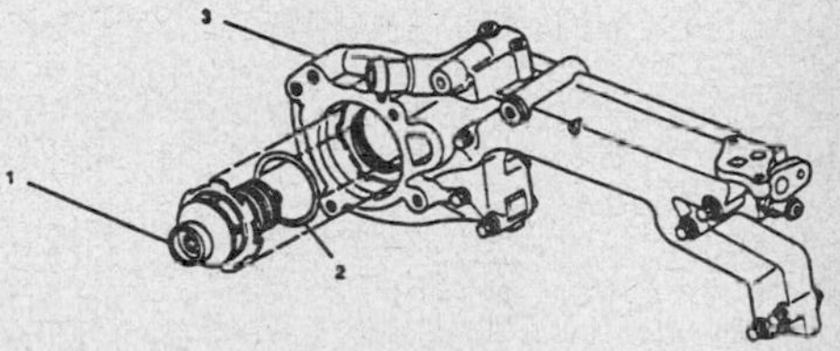
3
1
2

1 WATER PUMP ASM.
2 O-RING SEAL
3 WATER PUMP HOUSING ASM.

GC1089100154000X

Fig. 23 Water pump assembly & housing

RADIATOR

REPLACE

1. Drain cooling system, then remove plastic radiator support cover.
2. Remove cooling fan, then the coolant reservoir hose at filler neck.
3. Disconnect upper and lower radiator hoses.
4. Disconnect oil cooler lines at radiator.
5. Remove radiator top support, then the radiator.
6. Reverse procedure to install.

FUEL PUMP

REPLACE

1. Relieve fuel pressure as outlined under "Precautions."
2. Raise and support vehicle, then remove fuel tank.
3. Remove locking nut using tool No. J-39348, or equivalent, **Fig. 24.**
4. Remove modular fuel tank sending unit/fuel pump from tank, then fuel pump from modular fuel sending unit, **Fig.25.**
5. Reverse procedure to install.

FUEL FILTER

REPLACE

1. Disconnect battery ground cable.
2. Release fuel system pressure as outlined under "Precautions."
3. Disconnect fuel filter bracket release tabs.
4. Twist quick-connect fitting 1/4 turn in

each direction to loosen dirt within fitting.
5. Clean quick-connect fitting at ends of filter.
6. Disconnect quick-connect fittings by squeezing plastic tabs of male end connector and pulling apart.
7. Remove fuel filter.
8. Reverse procedure to install.

TECHNICAL SERVICE BULLETINS

1993–94 CADILLAC ELDORADO & SEVILLE

When servicing engine and oil pump removal is required, the following procedures must be followed to prime engine's lubrication system:

1. Thoroughly pack oil pump with Amojell (R) or white petroleum jelly during assembling and fill new oil filter with correct specification engine oil before installation.
2. Ensure engine oil is at proper level. **System capacity is 7 qts. with oil filter full. Fill to capacity if necessary.**
3. Disconnect right front connect from DIS module and crank engine for 30 seconds.
4. Reconnect power lead to DIS and start engine. Check DIC for "Low Oil Pressure" message and listen for any audible engine noise (i.e., lifters "ticking", rod knocks, etc.).
5. If engine noise exists, stop engine and remove oil pressure switch from oil filter adapter and install oil pressure gauge.
6. If oil pressure is indicated on gauge and no unusual sounds are heard, oil pressure should be present and both the oil pump and engine lubrication system are primed. If no oil pressure is indicated, repeat step 3, then proceed to next step.
7. If no oil pressure after repeating process, remove oil filter adapter and using compressed air, force engine oil into engine block outlet port closest to front of engine. Install oil filter adapter and restart engine.
8. If oil pressure is indicated, stop engine and install oil pressure switch in oil filter adapter. Once connected, check instrument panel display once more for no oil pressure or message "Low Oil Pressure."

CYLINDER HEAD FLATNESS MEASUREMENT

The dimension between combustion chamber gauge pad and cylinder head deck must be 10.5 mm or greater after cylinder head deck resurfacing.

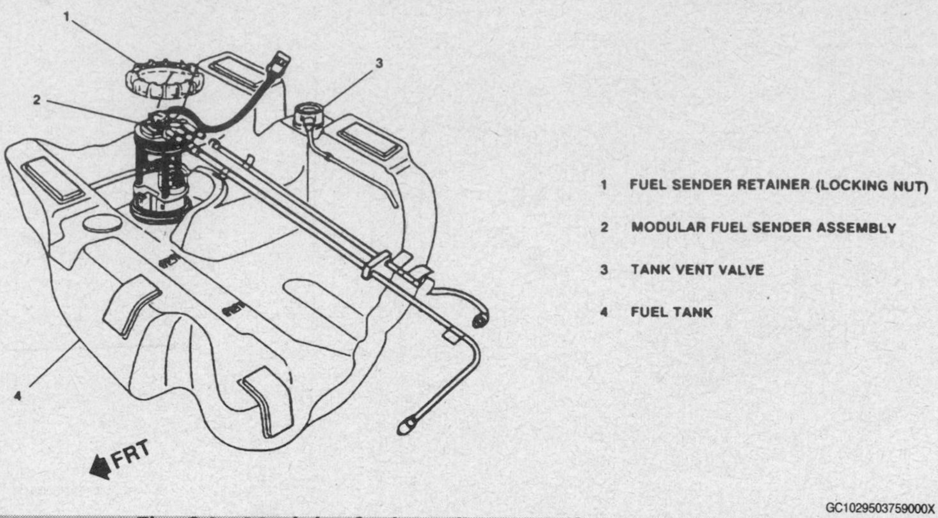
1
2
3
4
FRT
1 FUEL SENDER RETAINER (LOCKING NUT)
2 MODULAR FUEL SENDER ASSEMBLY
3 TANK VENT VALVE
4 FUEL TANK
GC1029503759000X

Fig. 24 Modular fuel sending unit/fuel pump removal

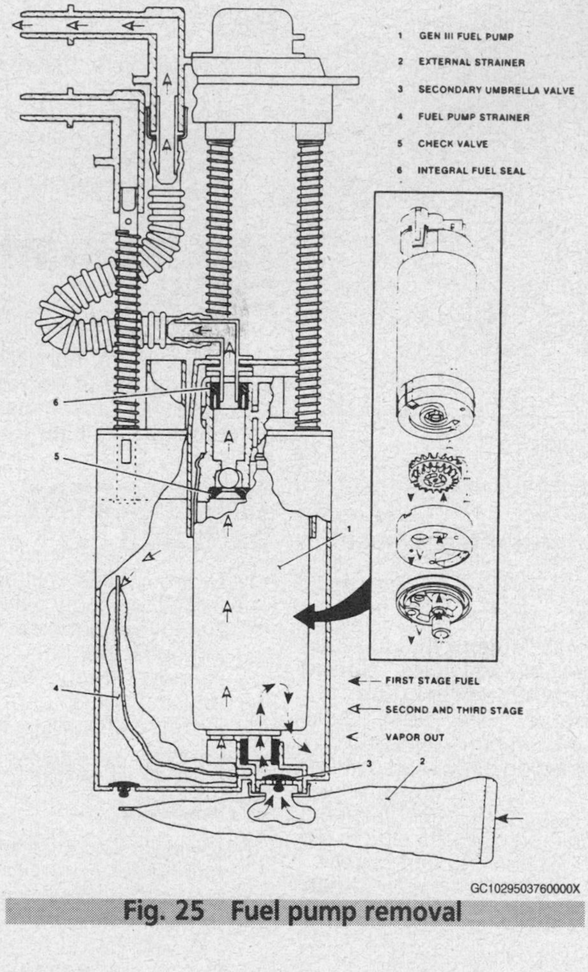
1 GEN III FUEL PUMP
2 EXTERNAL STRAINER
3 SECONDARY UMBRELLA VALVE
4 FUEL PUMP STRAINER
5 CHECK VALVE
6 INTEGRAL FUEL SEAL
FIRST STAGE FUEL
SECOND AND THIRD STAGE
VAPOR OUT
GC1029503760000X

Fig. 25 Fuel pump removal

TIGHTENING SPECIFICATIONS

Year	Component	Torque/Ft. Lbs.
1993-95	Belt Tensioner	35
	Cam Cover	7
	Camshaft Bearing Cap	9
	Camshaft Drive Chain Tensioner	20
	Camshaft Seal Retainer To Cover	10①
	Camshaft Sprocket	90
	Connecting Rod Nut	20⑦
	Coolant Drain Plug	6
	Cooling Fan Mounting Bolts	88①
	Cylinder Head Bolts	③
	Engine To Transmission	35
	Exhaust Manifold To Cylinder Head Bolt	20
	Exhaust Manifold To Cylinder Head Locknut	25
	Flywheel	11⑤
	Flywheel Housing Cover	12①
	Front Cover	7
	Fuel Filter Bolt	88①
	Intake Manifold Bolts	4②
	Intake Manifold Cover Bolts	106①
	Main Bearing Cap Bolts	③

Year	Component	Torque/Ft. Lbs.
1993-95 —Cont'd	Oil Filter Adapter	20
	Oil Pan	7
	Oil Pan Drain Plug	15
	Oil Pump To Lower Crankcase	7⑥
	Oil Pump To Suction Pipe	7
	Oxygen Sensor	30
	Thermostat Housing Bolts	18
	Throttle Body Bolts	106①
	Torque Strut Bracket To Cylinder Head	35
	Torque Strut Bracket To Water Manifold	20
	Torsional Damper	105④
	Transmission Brace	35
	Water Pump Housing	20
	Water Pump Pulley Mounting Bolts	22
	Water Pump Stud Nuts	62①

①—Inch pounds.
②—Plus an additional 1/3 turn (120°).
③—Refer to text.
④—Plus an additional 120°.
⑤—Plus an additional 50°.
⑥—Plus an additional 35°.
⑦—Plus an additional 90°.

Rear Suspension

NOTE: On Air Bag Equipped Models, Refer To "Air Bag System Precautions" Located In The Front Of This Manual For System Disarming & Arming Procedures.

INDEX

PRECAUTIONS

AIR BAG SYSTEMS

Refer to "Air Bag System Precautions" in the front of this manual for system disarming and arming procedures.

DESCRIPTION

All rear suspension components are mounted on a suspension support assembly, **Fig. 1**, which is attached to the body at four points. The transverse leaf spring is fully isolated from the crossmember and is held in position by left and right retainers and insulators. On their inboard end, the control arms pivot on the suspension support, allowing each end of the leaf spring to act directly on the control arm surface. A suspension knuckle pivots on the outboard end of each control arm, and each knuckle contains a sealed hub and wheel bearing assembly. Each knuckle is located at the top by an air adjustable strut assembly which is connected to the suspension support.

On some models, a stabilizer shaft is used to further locate the knuckle assemblies and provide increased roll stiffness. Strut charging is controlled by an Electronic Level Control (ELC) system, which maintains a standard rear trim height under a variety of load conditions.

HUB & BEARING

REPLACE

1. Raise and support vehicle.
2. Remove tire and wheel assembly.
3. Remove brake caliper attaching bolts and position caliper aside. **Do not suspend caliper by brake line.**
4. Remove rotor retainers, if equipped. Retainers may be discarded after removal.
5. Remove rotor.
6. Remove four hub mounting bolts, then the hub and bearing assembly.
7. Reverse procedure to install, tightening to specifications.

STRUT

REPLACE

1. Raise and support vehicle on frame contact type hoist, then remove wheel and tire assembly.
2. If left strut is to be replaced, disconnect ELC height sensor link.
3. Reinstall two wheel nuts to retain brake rotor, then remove stabilizer shaft mounting bolt at strut, if equipped.
4. Remove brake caliper as outlined, then secure aside leaving hoses connected.

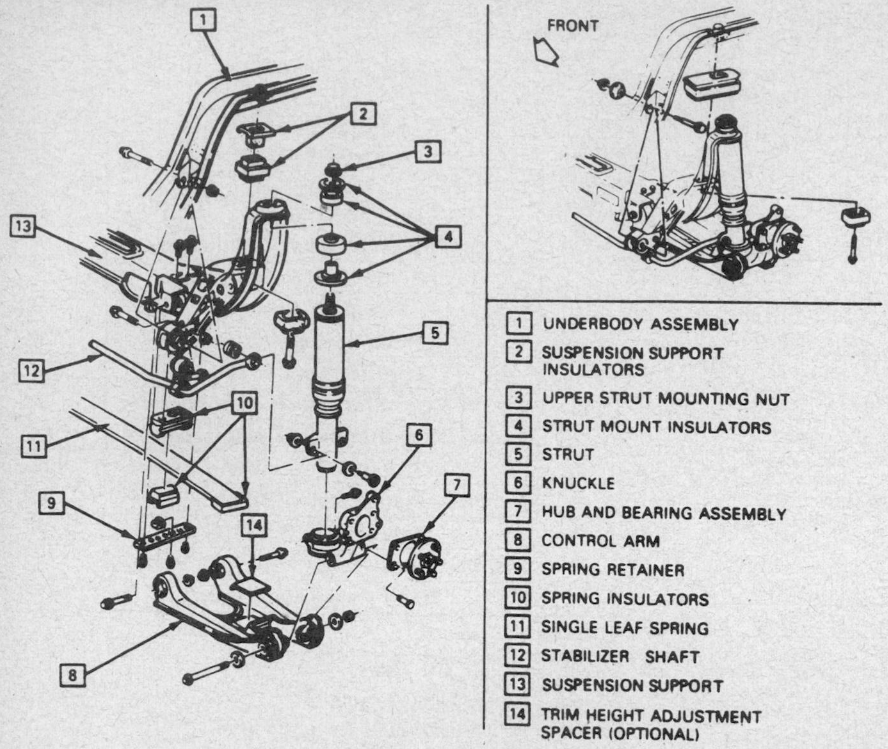
FRONT
1 UNDERBODY ASSEMBLY
2 SUSPENSION SUPPORT INSULATORS
3 UPPER STRUT MOUNTING NUT
4 STRUT MOUNT INSULATORS
5 STRUT
6 KNUCKLE
7 HUB AND BEARING ASSEMBLY
8 CONTROL ARM
9 SPRING RETAINER
10 SPRING INSULATORS
11 SINGLE LEAF SPRING
12 STABILIZER SHAFT
13 SUSPENSION SUPPORT
14 TRIM HEIGHT ADJUSTMENT SPACER (OPTIONAL)
GC2039100059000X

Fig. 1 Rear suspension exploded view. Left side

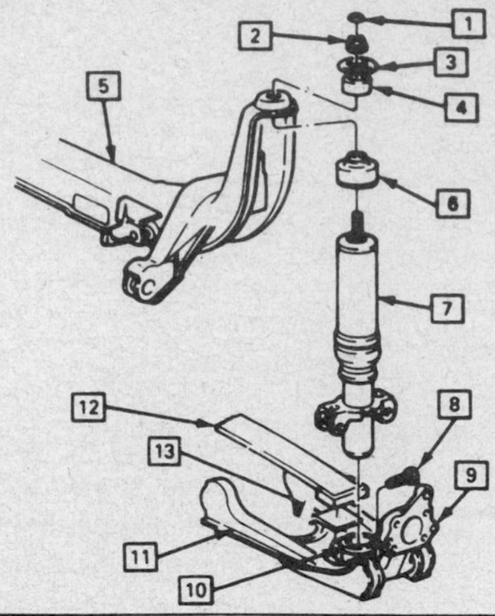

1. STRUT ROD CAP
2. NUT 88 N·m (65 LBS. FT.)
3. RETAINER
4. UPPER INSULATOR
5. SUSPENSION SUPPORT
6. LOWER INSULATOR
7. STRUT
8. LOWER PINCH BOLT 55 N·m (40 LBS. FT.)
9. KNUCKLE
10. LOCATING SLOT
11. CONTROL ARM
12. SPRING
13. TRIM HEIGHT ADJUSTMENT SPACER (OPTIONAL)

GC2039100060000X

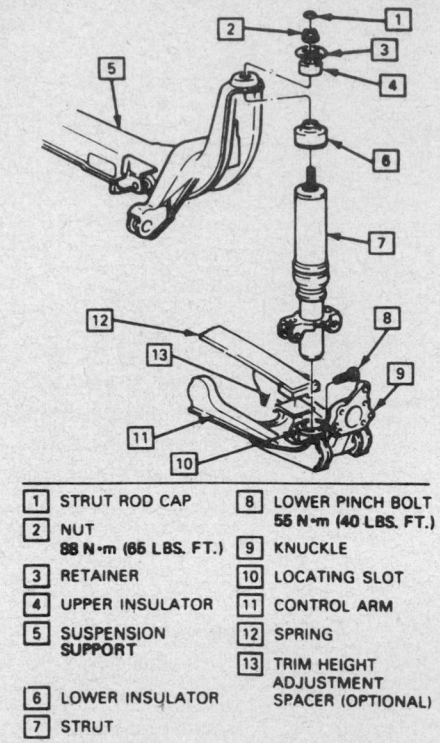

Fig. 2 Rear strut replacement

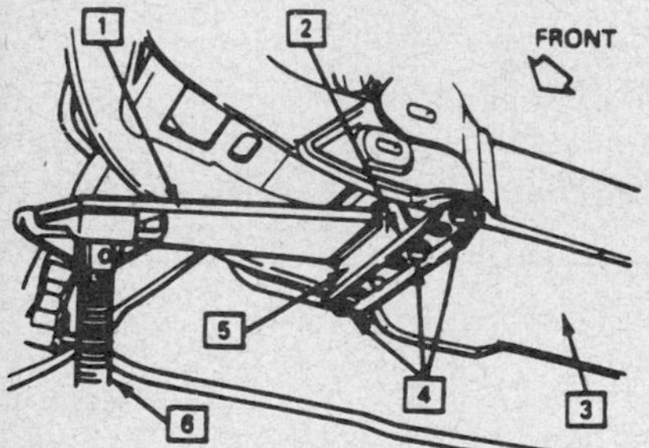
FRONT

1. SPRING
2. SPRING RETAINER
3. SUSPENSION CROSSMEMBER ASSEMBLY
4. RETAINER BOLTS (28 N·m/21 FT. LBS.)
5. LOWER OUTBOARD INSULATOR
6. JACKSTAND

GC2039100064000X

Fig. 3 Spring replacement

5. Loosen, but do not remove, knuckle pivot bolt at outboard end of control arm. **Support outboard end of control arm with a jackstand to slightly compress spring. Jackstand must be of adequate strength to support vehicle weight and be properly positioned to prevent personal injury.**
6. Remove upper strut rod cap, mounting nut and insulator, **Fig. 2.**
7. Slowly remove jackstand to relieve spring pressure, compress strut by hand, then remove lower insulator.
8. Rotate strut and knuckle assembly outward, remove pinch bolt, then separate strut from knuckle.
9. Reverse procedure to install, ensuring strut is fully seated with tang on strut bottomed in steering knuckle slot. When suspension is fully assembled, tighten bolts to specifications.

LEAF SPRING
REPLACE

Removal of rear spring requires disassembly of either left or right side of the suspension while leaving opposite side intact. Spring may be removed from either side of vehicle.

1. Remove lower control arm as outlined.
2. Place a support under outboard end of spring as shown in **Fig. 3,** then lower vehicle so weight of vehicle compresses spring. **Ensure jack stand can support weight of vehicle and is properly positioned under spring.**
3. Remove three spring retainer bolts, retainer and lower insulator, **Fig. 4,** from end of spring nearest support stand.
4. Slowly raise vehicle, allowing spring to deflect downward until spring no longer exerts force on stand.
5. Remove retainer bolts, retainer and insulator from opposite end of spring, then withdraw spring from crossmember.
6. Remove upper spring insulators.
7. Inspect spring insulators and retainers and replace as needed.
8. Install center and upper outboard insulators in crossmember, then tighten bolts to specifications. **Ensure arrows on upper outboard insulators point toward centerline of vehicle.**

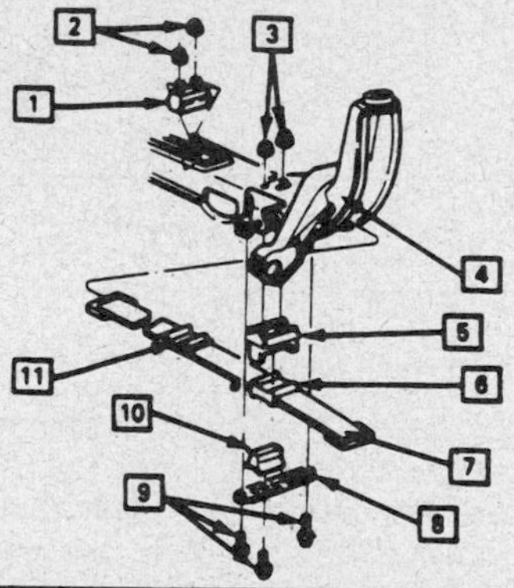

1. CENTER INSULATOR
2. CENTER INSULATOR NUTS (28 N·m/21 FT. LBS.)
3. OUTBOARD INSULATOR NUTS (28 N·m/21 FT. LBS.)
4. SUSPENSION CROSSMEMBER ASSEMBLY
5. UPPER OUTBOARD INSULATOR
6. OUTBOARD INSULATOR LOCATING BAND
7. SPRING
8. SPRING RETAINER
9. RETAINER BOLTS (28 N·m/21 FT. LBS.)
10. LOWER OUTBOARD INSULATOR
11. CENTER INSULATOR LOCATING BAND

GC2039100065000X

Fig. 4 Exploded view of spring

9. Position spring in suspension support by inserting through disassembled side of suspension. Ensure outboard and center insulator bands are centered on spring insulators.
10. Install lower insulator and retainer on side opposite disassembled portion of suspension, tighten retaining bolts to

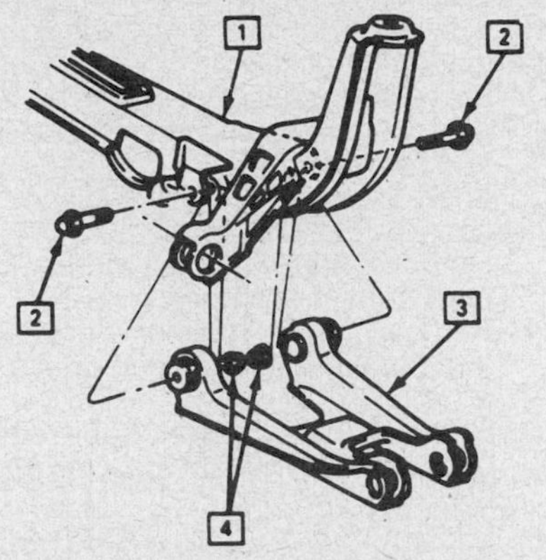
1
2
2
3
4

1 SUSPENSION CROSSMEMBER ASSEMBLY
2 INNER CONTROL ARM BOLTS
3 CONTROL ARM
4 NUTS (90 N•m/66 FT. LBS.)

GC2039100062000X

Fig. 5 Lower control arm replacement

specifications, then place a stand under free end of spring, **Fig. 3.**

11. Lower vehicle, allowing weight to load spring and deflect free end of spring into position in suspension support.
12. Install lower insulator and spring retainer on disassembled side of suspension support, then tighten bolts to specifications.
13. Raise vehicle and remove stand.
14. Reverse remaining procedure to complete installation.

CONTROL ARM

REPLACE

1. Raise and support vehicle on frame contact type hoist, then remove wheel and tire assembly.
2. If left control arm is to be replaced, disconnect ELC height sensor link.
3. Remove stabilizer shaft mounting bolt from strut, if equipped.
4. Reinstall two wheel nuts to retain brake rotor, then remove brake caliper as outlined and secure aside leaving hoses connected.
5. Loosen, but do not remove, knuckle pivot bolt at outboard end of control arm.
6. Support outboard end of control arm with a proper jackstand.
7. Remove upper strut rod cap, mounting nut and insulator, **Fig. 2.**
8. Slowly remove jackstand to relieve spring pressure.
9. Compress strut by hand and remove lower insulator.
10. Remove wheel speed sensor from knuckle if equipped with anti-lock brakes.
11. Support knuckle assembly, remove knuckle pivot bolt, then remove strut, knuckle, hub, bearing and rotor as an assembly.
12. Remove both inner control arm bolts, then the control arm, **Fig. 5.**
13. Reverse procedure to install, ensuring strut is fully seated with tang on strut bottomed in steering knuckle slot. When suspension is fully assembled, tighten bolts to specifications.

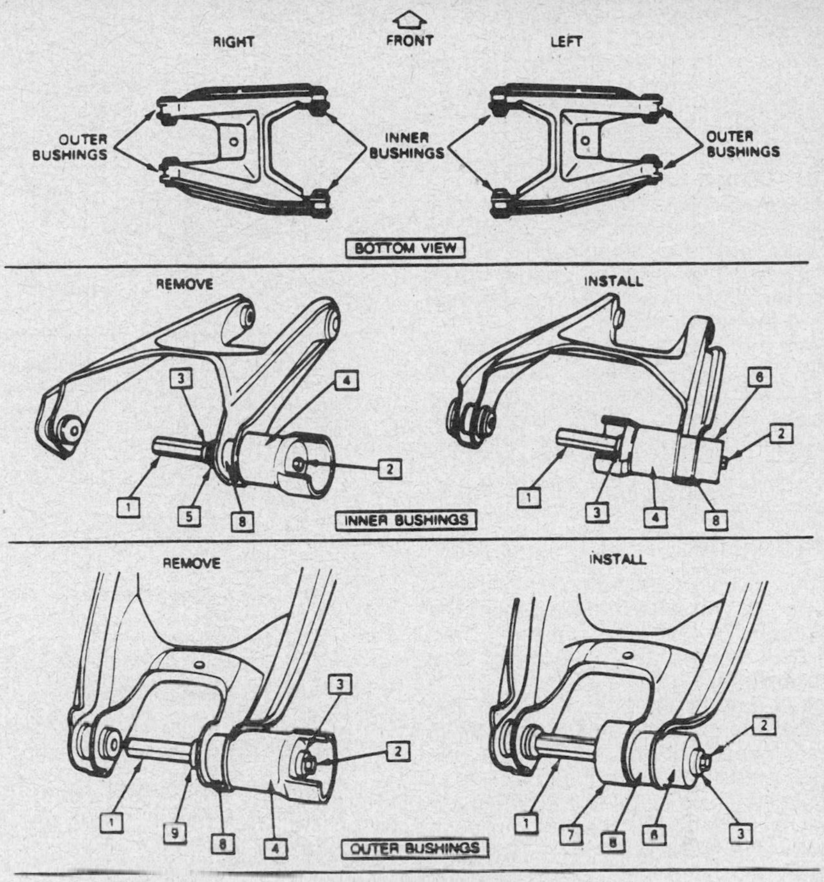
RIGHT
FRONT
LEFT
OUTER BUSHINGS
INNER BUSHINGS
OUTER BUSHINGS
BOTTOM VIEW
REMOVE
INSTALL
INNER BUSHINGS
REMOVE
INSTALL
OUTER BUSHINGS

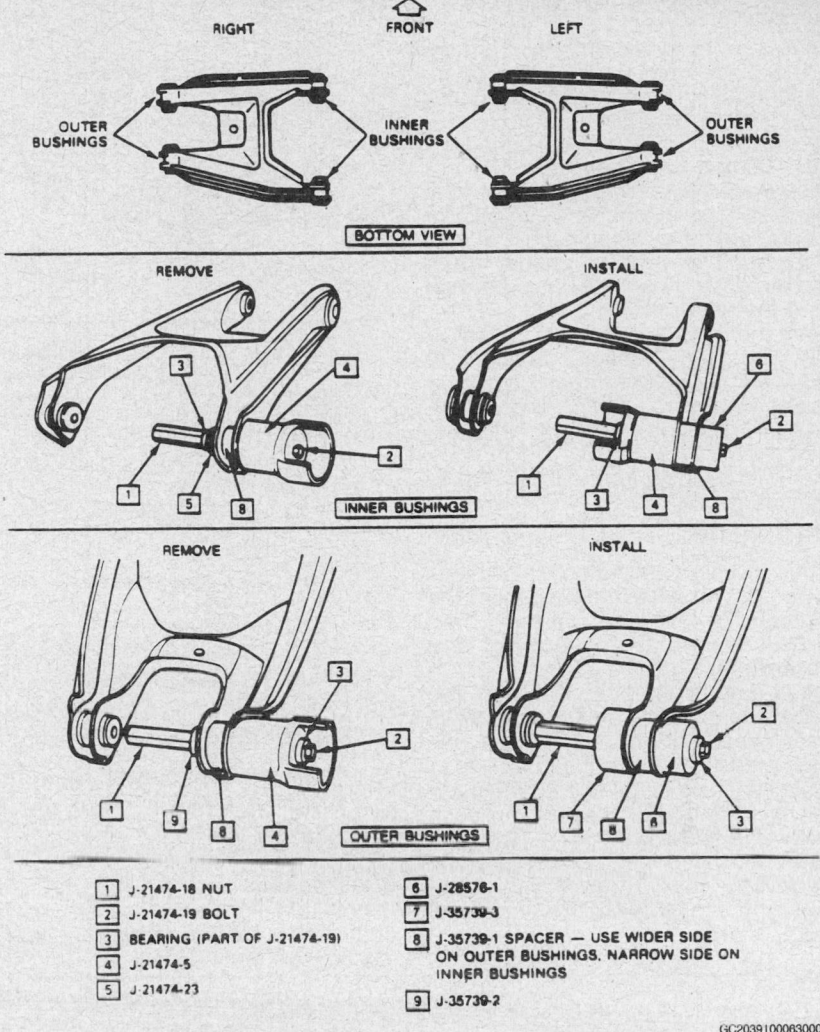

1 J-21474-18 NUT
2 J-21474-19 BOLT
3 BEARING (PART OF J-21474-19)
4 J-21474-5
5 J-21474-23
6 J-28576-1
7 J-35739-3
8 J-35739-1 SPACER — USE WIDER SIDE ON OUTER BUSHINGS, NARROW SIDE ON INNER BUSHINGS
9 J-35739-2

GC2039100063000X

Fig. 6 Control arm bushings replacement

CONTROL ARM BUSHING

REPLACE

OUTER

Removal

If inner control arm bolts are not loosened, or removed, alignment will not be disturbed and it will not be necessary to perform wheel alignment after outer bushing replacement.

1. Outer control arm bushings can be replaced without removing control arm from vehicle after performing steps 1-12 of "Control Arm, Replace" procedure.
2. Insert spacer between control arm flanges. Special tool No. J-35739-1, or equivalent, is a combination of two spacers. **The wide spacer must be used for outer bushing removal and installation.**
3. Coat the threads of tool No. J-21474-19 bolt with high pressure lubricant J-23444-A, or equivalent, to prevent thread damage.
4. Install tool Nos. J-35739-2 remover, J-21474-5 receiver, bearing, J-21474-18 nut and J-21474-19 bolt, or equivalents, as shown in **Fig. 6.**
5. Remove bushing from control arm by tightening nut.

Installation

1. Position new bushing for installation on control arm. Bushing must be installed from the outside of the control arm, then drawn inward toward the control arm centerline.
2. Insert wide end of J-35739-1 spacer between control arm flanges.
3. Coat threads of bolt J-21474-19 with high pressure lubricant J-23444-A.
4. Install bushing installer J-28576-1, receiver J-35739-3, bearing, nut J-21474-18 and bolt J-21474-19, **Fig. 6.**
5. Draw bushing into control arm by tightening nut. Tighten nut until bushing flange seats firmly against control arm.
6. Refer to "Control Arm, Replace" for suspension assembly.

INNER

Control arm must be removed from vehicle to replace inner control arm bushings. After replacing inner bushings, check wheel alignment as outlined.

1. Remove control arm as described under "Control Arm, Replace."
2. Insert spacer between control arm flanges. Special tool No. J-35739-1 or equivalent is a combination of two spacers. **The narrow spacer must be used for inner bushing removal and installation.**
3. Coat the threads of bolt No. J-21474-19 with high pressure lubricant J-23444-A to prevent thread damage.
4. Install remover J-21474, receiver J-21474-5, bearing, nut J-21474-18 and bolt J-21474-19, **Fig. 6.**
5. Remove bushing from control arm by tightening nut.

Installation

1. Position new bushing on control arm. **Bushing must be installed from the outside of the control arm, then drawn inward to the control arm centerline.**
2. Insert narrow end of spacer J-35739-1 between control arm flanges, then coat threads of bolt J-21474-19 with high pressure lubricant J-23444-A.
3. Install bushing installer J-28576-1, receiver J-21474-5, bearing, nut J-21474-18 and bolt J-21474-19, **Fig. 6.**
4. Draw bushing into control arm by tightening nut. **Tighten nut until bushing flange seats firmly against control arm.**

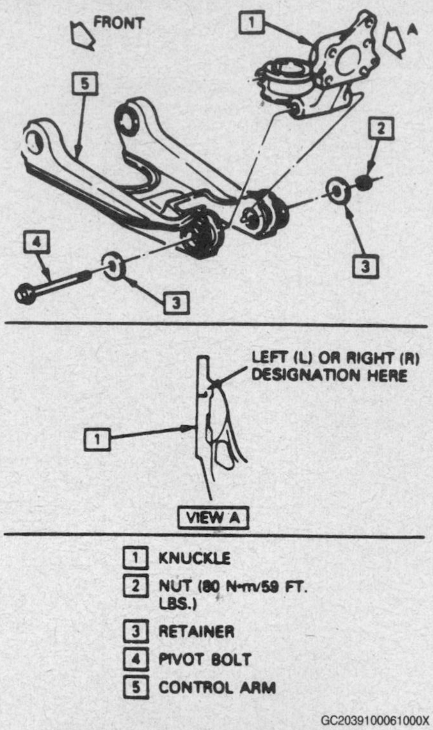
FRONT
A
1
2
3
3
4
5
LEFT (L) OR RIGHT (R) DESIGNATION HERE
1
VIEW A
1 KNUCKLE
2 NUT (80 N-m/59 FT. LBS.)
3 RETAINER
4 PIVOT BOLT
5 CONTROL ARM
GC2039100061000X

Fig. 7 Knuckle replacement

5. Refer to "Control Arm, Replace," for suspension assembly.

KNUCKLE

REPLACE

Left and right knuckles are not interchangeable. When replacing knuckles, check knuckle for the L or R designation stamped on knuckle.

1. Raise and support vehicle on frame contact type hoist, then remove wheel and tire assembly.
2. If left knuckle is to be replaced, disconnect ELC height sensor link.
3. Remove stabilizer shaft mounting bolt from strut, if equipped.
4. Remove brake caliper as outlined, and secure aside leaving hoses connected.
5. Remove brake rotor, hub retaining bolts and the hub and bearing assembly.
6. Loosen, but do not remove, knuckle pivot bolt at outboard end of control arm.
7. Support outboard end of control arm with a proper jackstand. **Jack stand must be securely positioned or personal injury may result.**
8. Remove upper strut rod cap, mounting nut and insulator, **Fig. 2.**
9. Compress strut by hand and remove lower insulator.
10. Rotate strut and knuckle assembly outward, remove pinch bolt, then separate strut from knuckle.
11. Remove speed sensor from knuckle if equipped with anti-lock brakes.
12. Remove knuckle pivot bolt and the knuckle, **Fig. 7.**
13. Reverse procedure to install, ensuring strut is fully seated with tang on strut bottomed in steering knuckle slot. When suspension is fully assembled, tighten bolts and wheel lug nut to specifications.

TIGHTENING SPECIFICATIONS

Year	Component	Torque/Ft. Lbs.
1992-95	Caliper Mounting Bracket Bolts	83
	Center Insulator Nuts	21
	Hub Mounting Bolts	52
	Inner Control Arm To Suspension Support	66
	Knuckle Pinch Bolt	40
	Knuckle Pivot Bolt	59
	Spring Retainer Bolts	21
	Stabilizer Shaft Bracket Bolt	43
	Stabilizer Shaft Mounting Bolt	43
	Stabilizer Shaft Mounting Nut	43
	Strut Bracket Bolt	43
	Suspension Support Forward Arm Bolts	66
	Suspension Support Upper Mounting Bolts	66
	Upper Outboard Insulator Nuts	21
	Upper Strut Nut	65
	Wheel Lug Nuts	100

Front Suspension & Steering

NOTE: On Air Bag Equipped Models, Refer To "Air Bag System Precautions" Located In The Front Of This Manual For System Disarming & Arming Procedures.

INDEX

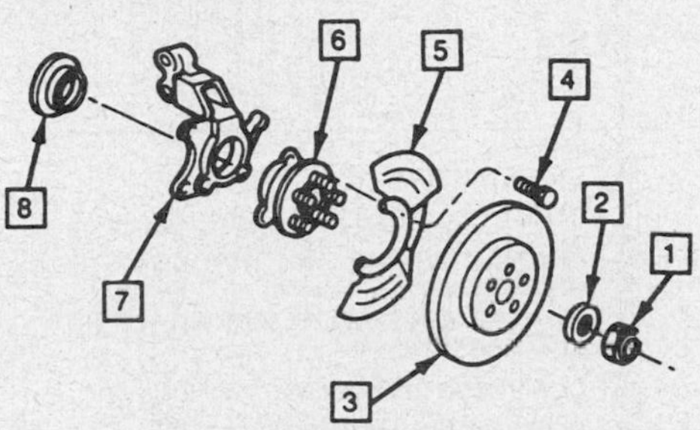

1
2
3
4
5
6
7
8

1 NUT 245 N·m (180 FT. LBS.)
2 WASHER
3 ROTOR
4 BOLT 95 N·m (70 FT. LBS.)
5 FRONT BRACE SHIELD
6 HUB AND BEARING
7 KNUCKLE
8 SEAL

GC2020100131000X

Fig. 1 Drive axle from hub separation

PRECAUTIONS

AIR BAG SYSTEMS

Refer to "Air Bag System Precautions" in the front of this manual for system disarming and arming procedures.

HUB & BEARING

REPLACE

1. Siphon 2/3 of the brake fluid from master cylinder, then raise vehicle and support frame with stands.
2. Remove wheel and tire assembly.
3. Insert a drift through rotor and remove hub nut and washer.
4. Remove caliper boots, lift caliper off rotor and bracket, then secure caliper aside.
5. Remove bolts securing caliper bracket, bracket and the brake rotor. **Prevailing torque bolts used to secure mounting bracket cannot be reused. If bolts become loose or are removed, bolts must be replaced.**
6. Mount tool J-28733 or equivalent on hub, **Fig. 1**, then tighten screw just enough to separate drive axle from hub.
7. Remove hub retaining bolts and the hub and bearing assembly, **Fig. 2.**
8. If seal is being replaced, drive seal toward engine, then cut seal off drive axle.
9. Lubricate seal lip and install using a driver, install O-ring and fill cavity between seal and bearing with grease.
10. Install hub and bearing assembly over drive axle and tighten bolts to specifications.
11. Install rotor and caliper mounting bracket and tighten new bracket bolts to specifications.
12. Install caliper ensuring insulators are properly positioned, coat mounting bolt shafts with silicone grease and tighten to specifications.
13. Install hub nut and washer, insert drift through rotor and tighten nut securely.
14. Remove drift, install wheel and tire assembly and lower vehicle, then tighten hub nut to specifications.

BALL JOINT

REPLACE

1. Raise and support vehicle.
2. Remove tire and wheel assembly.
3. **On models with road sensing suspension,** disconnect position sensor from lower control arm.
4. **On all models,** remove ball joint from knuckle.
5. Drill out three rivets retaining ball joint. Start with a 1/4 inch drill bit, then use a 1/2 inch bit.
6. Remove ball joint.
7. Reverse procedure to install, noting the following:
   a. **Torque** ball joint to control arm nut to 84 inch lbs. using 90° adapter J-35551 or equivalent.
   b. Tighten nut an additional 120°, noting torque reading.
   c. Tighten nut up to an additional 60° to align holes and install cotter pin. **When tightening nut, minimum torque (as listed in "Tightening Specifications") must be obtained. If minimum torque cannot be obtained, check for stripped threads and repair as needed. If threads are satisfactory, replace ball joint and steering knuckle.**

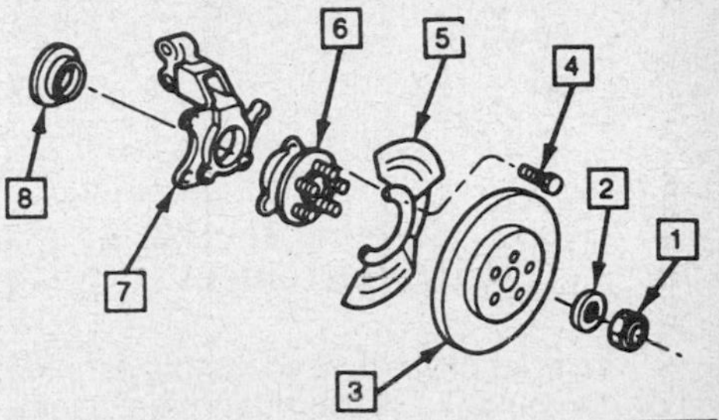

1
2
3
4
5
6
7
8

1 NUT 245 N·m (180 FT. LBS.)
2 WASHER
3 ROTOR
4 BOLT 95 N·m (70 FT. LBS.)
5 FRONT BRACE SHIELD
6 HUB AND BEARING
7 KNUCKLE
8 SEAL

GC2029100132000X

Fig. 2 Hub & bearing assembly replacement

STRUT

REPLACE

Care must be taken not to overextend driveshaft Tri-Pot joints when replacing suspension components. Overextending joint could cause separation of internal joint components, resulting in failure of the joint.

1. Remove nuts securing top of strut assembly to body, **Fig. 3.**
2. Raise vehicle and support frame with stands, then remove wheel and tire.
3. Scribe reference marks between strut and steering knuckle as follows:
   a. Scribe strut along lower outboard strut radius (A), **Fig. 4.**
   b. Scribe strut flange on inboard side along curve of knuckle (B).
   c. Scribe mark along strut/knuckle interface (C).
4. Disconnect brake line bracket from strut.
5. Remove bolt securing strut to stabilizer link, then the stabilizer link.
6. Remove bolts securing strut to steering knuckle, support knuckle with wire and remove strut.

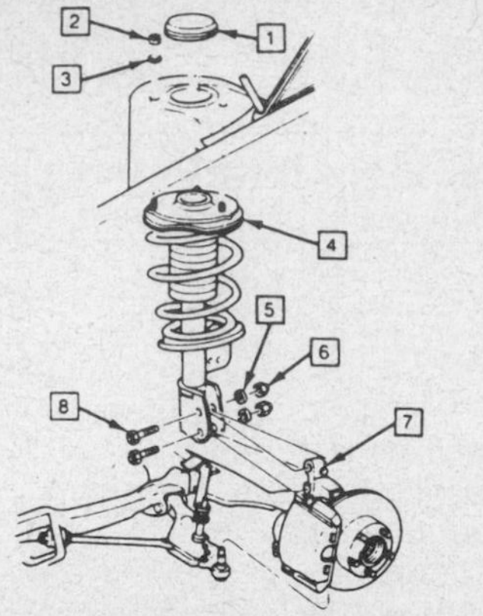

1 COVER
2 NUT 24 N m (18 FT. LBS.)
3 WASHER
4 STRUT AND SPRING ASSEMBLY
5 WASHER
6 NUT 184 N m (136 FT. LBS.)
7 KNUCKLE
8 BOLT — INSTALL IN DIRECTION SHOWN

GC2029100133000X

Fig. 3 Steering knuckle & strut replacement

7. Reverse procedure to install, aligning scribe marks made during disassembly. tighten nuts and bolts to specifications, then check alignment.

STRUT SERVICE

1. Place strut assembly in strut compressor J-34013, **Fig. 5.**
2. Turn compressor forcing screw until spring compresses slightly.
3. Keep dampener shaft from turning with a T-50 Torx bit and remove nut from top of dampener shaft.
4. Using tool J-34013-38 or equivalent, guide dampener shaft out of assembly.
5. Loosen compressor screw while guiding dampener shaft out of assembly, continually loosening compressor screw till strut dampener and spring can be removed. **Be careful to avoid chipping or cracking the spring coating when handling the front suspension coil spring.**
6. Install strut dampener in strut compressor J-34013 with clamp J-34013-20 clamped on dampener shaft.
7. Install spring over strut in correct position and move assembly upright in strut compressor and install upper locking pin. **Flat on upper spring seat must face out from centerline of vehicle, Fig. 6, or when mounted in strut compressor spring seat faces same direction as steering knuckle mounting flange.**
8. Install rod J-34013-38 or equivalent into strut assembly to guide dampener shaft on reassembly of strut.
9. Start turning compressor screw clockwise on J-34013 while guiding J-34013-38 which will center dampener shaft in the assembly.
10. Continue turning compressor screw until dampener shaft threads are visible through top of strut assembly.

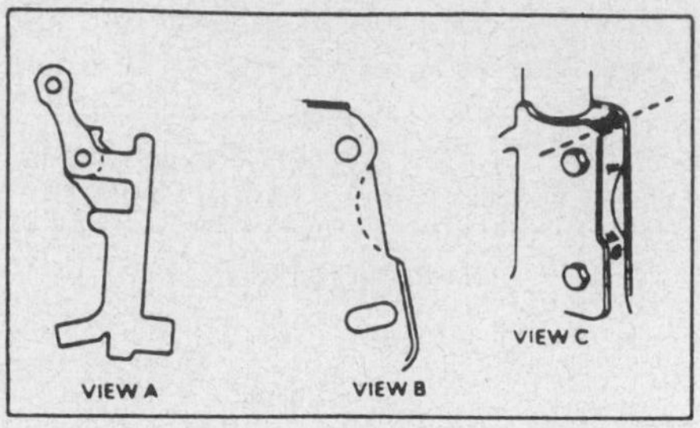
VIEW A
VIEW B
VIEW C

GC2029100134000X

Fig. 4 Steering knuckle & strut alignment marking

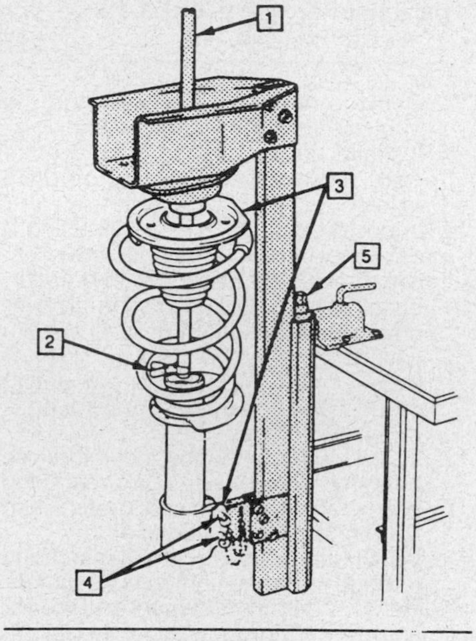

1 ROD J-34013-38 INSTALLED
2 CLAMP J-34013-20 INSTALLED
3 FLAT ON SPRING SEAT MUST FACE SAME DIRECTION AS STEERING KNUCKLE FLANGE
4 BOTH LOCKING PINS INSTALLED
5 COMPRESSOR FORCING SCREW

GC2029100136000X

Fig. 6 Flat on upper spring seat alignment

11. Install washer and nut, then remove J-34013-20 from dampener shaft.
12. Hold dampener shaft with socket, then tighten dampener shaft nut to specifications.
13. Remove three nuts securing strut assembly to strut compressor, the two locking pins at bottom of strut compressor and the strut assembly.

CONTROL ARM
REPLACE

Care must be taken not to overextend driveshaft Tri-Pot joints when replacing suspension components. Overextending joint could cause separation of internal joint components, resulting in failure of the joint.

1. Remove ball joint from steering knuckle as outlined under "Ball Joint, Replace."

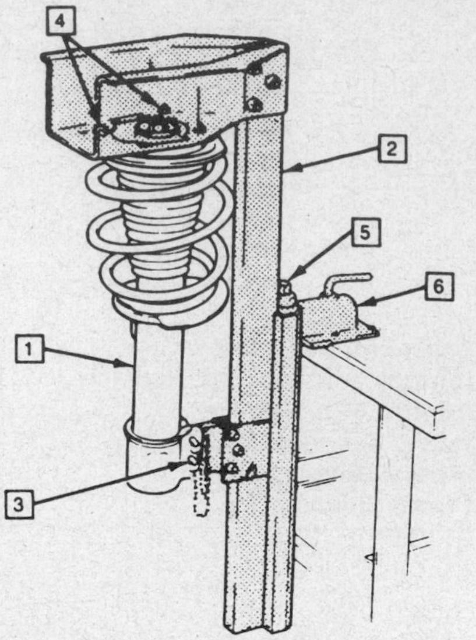

1 STRUT ASSEMBLY
2 STRUT COMPRESSOR J-34013
3 INSTALL LOCKING PINS THROUGH STRUT ASSEMBLY
4 TIGHTEN NUTS TILL FLUSH WITH STRUT COMPRESSOR
5 COMPRESSOR FORCING SCREW
6 HOLDING FIXTURE J3289-20

GC2029100135000X

Fig. 5 Strut assembly installation in strut compressor

2. Remove control arm bushing bolt and brake reaction rod nut, retainer and insulator, **Fig. 7.**
3. Remove control arm from frame.
4. Install control arm on frame.
5. Install control arm bushing bolt and nut, retainer and insulator but do not tighten bolt.
6. Install lower ball joint in steering knuckle as outlined.
7. Reverse remaining procedure to complete installation. Tighten bolts to specifications as shown in **Fig. 8 and 7.**

CONTROL ARM BUSHING
REPLACE

When replacing lower control arm bushings, refer to **Fig. 9.**

1. Remove lower control arm as outlined under "Control Arm, Replace."
2. Install driver, tool No. J-35561-1, receiver No. J-35561-2 and installing cup No. J-35561-3, or equivalents.
3. Press out bushing.
4. Lubricate new bushing with rubber lube.
5. Install tools, then press in new bushing.
6. Install lower control arm.

STEERING KNUCKLE
REPLACE

1. Remove hub and bearing assembly as outlined under "Hub & Bearing Assembly, Replace."

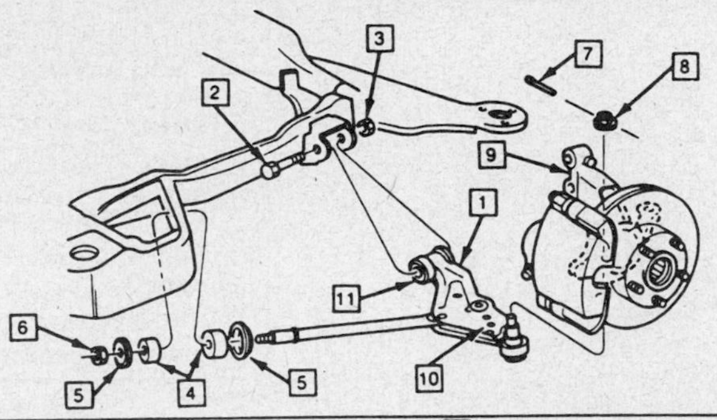

1 CONTROL ARM
2 BOLT — 140 N·m (100 FT. LBS.) TIGHTEN WITH CAR AT PROPER TRIM HEIGHT
3 NUT — 123 N·m (91 FT. LBS.) TIGHTEN WITH CAR AT PROPER TRIM HEIGHT
4 INSULATOR
5 RETAINER
6 NUT — 70 N·m (52 FT. LBS.)
7 PIN
8 NUT — TIGHTEN NUT TO 10 N·m (88 IN. LBS.) CONTINUE TIGHTENING BY ROTATING NUT AN ADDITIONAL 120°, DURING WHICH A MINIMUM TORQUE OF 50 N·m (37 FT. LBS.) MUST BE OBTAINED. INSTALL COTTER PIN
9 KNUCKLE
10 BALL JOINT ATTACHMENT RIVETS
11 BUSHING

GC2029100129000X

Fig. 7 Lower control arm replacement

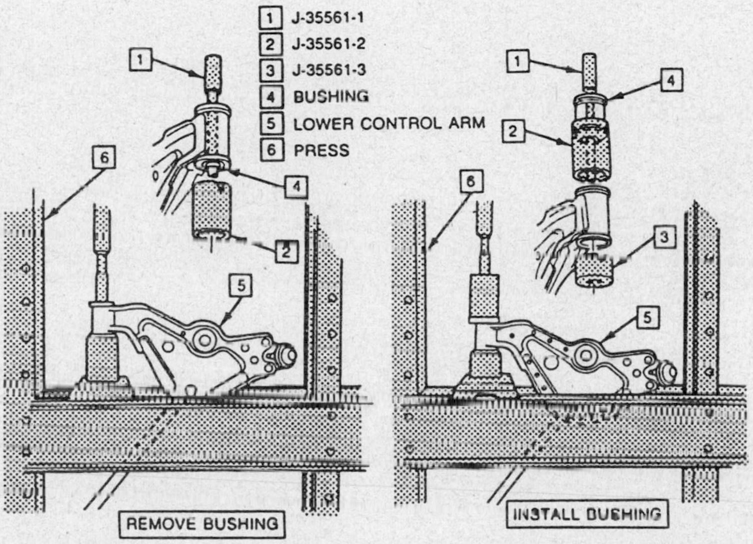
1 J-35561-1
2 J-35561-2
3 J-35561-3
4 BUSHING
5 LOWER CONTROL ARM
6 PRESS
REMOVE BUSHING
INSTALL BUSHING

GC2029100130000X

Fig. 9 Lower control arm bushings replacement

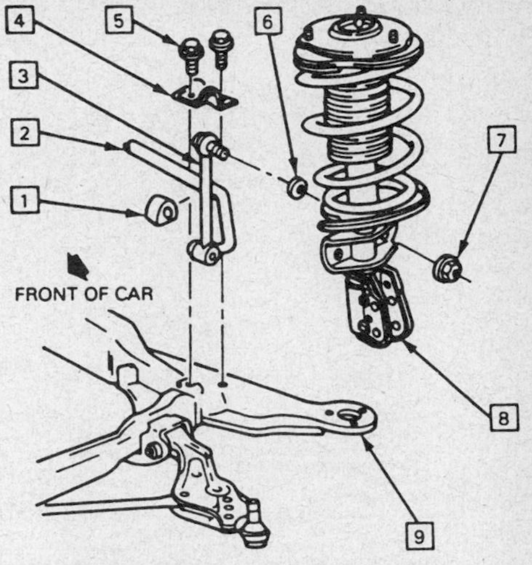
FRONT OF CAR

1 INSULATOR – INSTALL WITH SLIT TO REAR OF CAR
2 STABILIZER SHAFT
3 STABILIZER LINK
4 BRACKET
5 BOLT – 47 N·m (35 lbs. ft.)
6 WASHER
7 NUT – 65 N·m (48 lbs. ft.)
8 SPRING & STRUT ASSEMBLY
9 FRAME

GC2029100128000X

Fig. 8 Stabilizer shaft replacement

2. Remove nut securing tie rod, then separate tie rod from knuckle.
3. Cut inner tabs from boot protector tool No. J-34754 or equivalent and install protector over drive axle outer joint.
4. Remove cotter pin and nut securing lower ball joint and separate ball stud from steering knuckle.
5. Remove bolts securing strut to steering knuckle, **Fig. 3,** and the steering knuckle.
6. Reverse procedure to install.

STABILIZER BAR

REPLACE

1. Raise vehicle and support with weight of vehicle resting on frame, not the lower control arms.
2. Remove right front wheel and tire.
3. **On models with road sensing suspension,** disconnect position sensor from lower control arm.
4. **On all models,** remove left and right insulators, retainers, spacers and bolts, **Fig. 8.**
5. Remove left and right bracket bolts, brackets and insulators.
6. Disconnect exhaust pipe from rear manifold, raise pipe to gain clearance, then withdraw stabilizer shaft.
7. Reverse procedure to install.

POWER STEERING GEAR

REPLACE

1. Raise vehicle and support vehicle on frame contact hoist, then remove front wheels.
2. Remove pinch bolt and disconnect intermediate shaft from steering gear.
3. Disconnect tie rods from steering knuckles.
4. Remove power steering line retainer, then disconnect pressure and return lines from steering gear.
5. Remove steering gear mounting bolts, **Fig. 10 and 11,** then withdraw gear through wheel opening.

6. Reverse procedure to install. Tighten tie rod nuts to specifications. After tightening nut as specified, continue tightening nut to align cotter pin holes, then install new cotter pins.

POWER STEERING PUMP

REPLACE

ELDORADO & SEVILLE

1. Remove serpentine drive belt.
2. Remove pump pulley using a puller, **Fig. 12.**
3. Disconnect pressure and return lines from pump, noting position for installation.
4. Remove two pump mounting bolts, **Fig. 13,** and the pump.
5. Reverse procedure to install.

RIVIERA, TORONADO & TROFEO

1. Remove drive belt.
2. Disconnect pressure and return lines from pump.
3. Remove pump mounting bolts, **Fig. 14,** and the pump.
4. Reverse procedure to install.

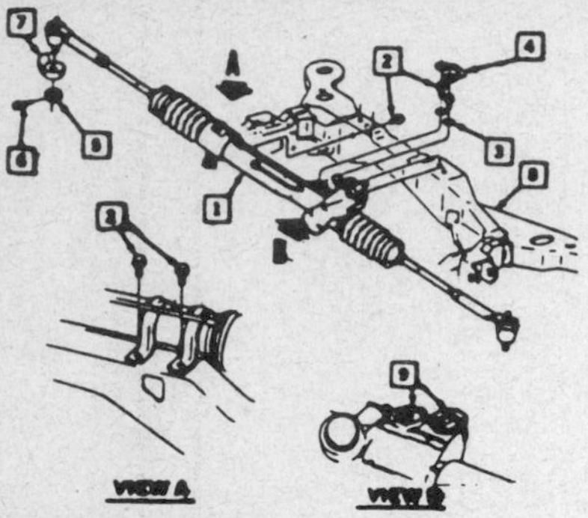
VIEW A
VIEW B

1. STEERING GEAR
2. BOLT – 68 N·m (50 LBS. FT.) AFTER SECOND REUSE OF BOLT, LOCKTITE THREAD LOCKING KIT NO. 1052624 MUST BE USED.
3. WASHER
4. RETAINER
5. NUT – TIGHTEN NUT TO 10 N·m (7 LBS. FT.) THEN TIGHTEN NUT AN ADDITIONAL 120 DEGREES (2 FLATS) DURING WHICH A MINIMUM TORQUE OF 45 N·m (33 LBS. FT.) IS TO BE OBTAINED. IF 45 N·m (33 LBS. FT.) IS NOT OBTAINED, INSPECT FOR STRIPPED THREADS. IF THREADS ARE SATISFACTORY, REPLACE KNUCKLE.
6. PIN
7. KNUCKLE
8. FRAME
9. RTV SEALER AROUND INSERTS

GC6039100045000X

Fig. 10 Power steering gear installation. Riviera, Toronado & Trofeo

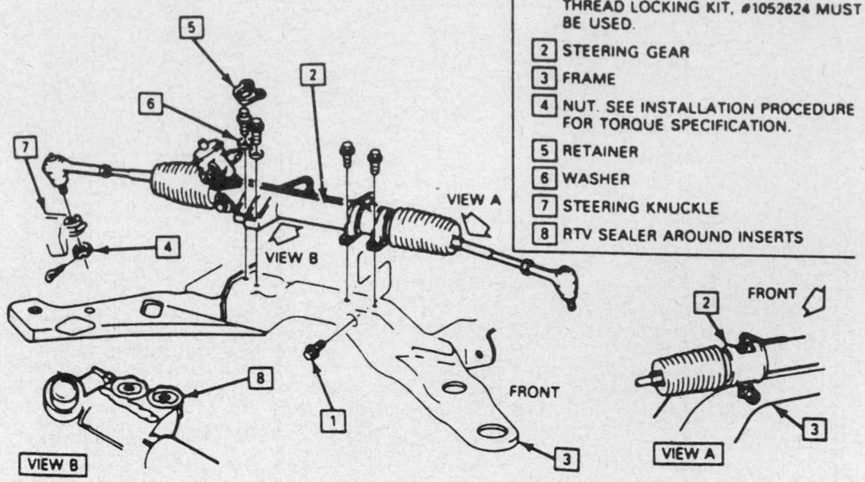
VIEW A
VIEW B
FRONT
FRONT
VIEW B
VIEW A

[1] BOLT 68 N·m (50 LBS. FT.) AFTER SECOND REUSE OF BOLT, LOCTITE THREAD LOCKING KIT, #1052624 MUST BE USED.
[2] STEERING GEAR
[3] FRAME
[4] NUT. SEE INSTALLATION PROCEDURE FOR TORQUE SPECIFICATION.
[5] RETAINER
[6] WASHER
[7] STEERING KNUCKLE
[8] RTV SEALER AROUND INSERTS

GC6039100046000X

Fig. 11 Power steering gear installation. Eldorado & Seville

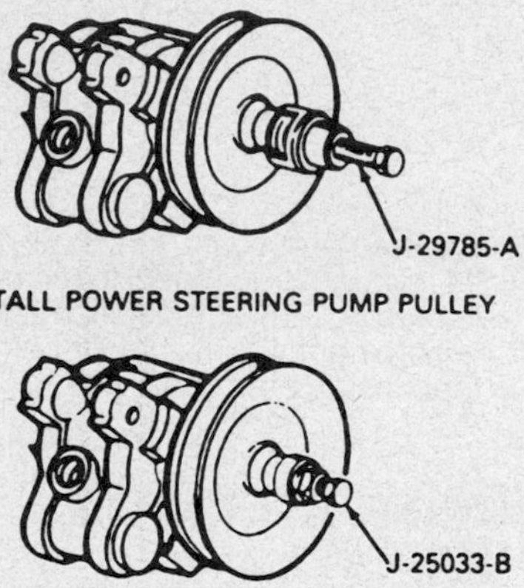
J-29785-A
INSTALL POWER STEERING PUMP PULLEY
J-25033-B

FLAT WASHER MUST BE USED TO POSITION PULLEY FLUSH WITH END OF SHAFT.

GC6039100042000X

Fig. 12 Power steering pump pulley removal. Eldorado & Seville

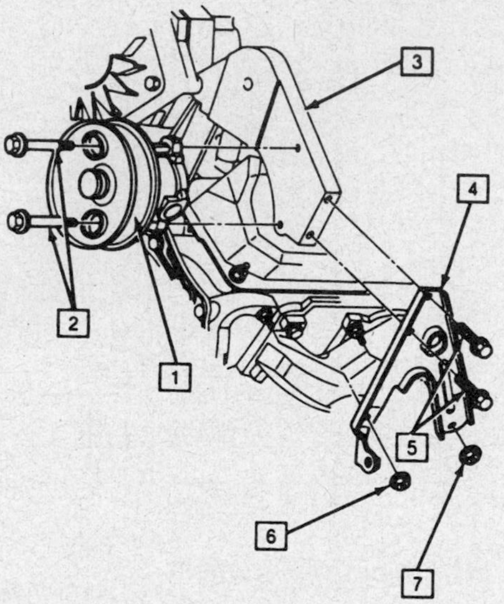

[1] PUMP
[2] PUMP MOUNTING BOLTS (25 N·m/18 FT. LBS.)
[3] PUMP AND TENSIONER BRACKET
[4] BRACE
[5] BOLTS (45 N·m/33 FT. LBS.)
[6] NUT (45 N·m/33 FT. LBS.)
[7] NUT (25 N·m/18 FT. LBS.)

GC6039100043000X

Fig. 13 Power steering pump installation. Eldorado & Seville

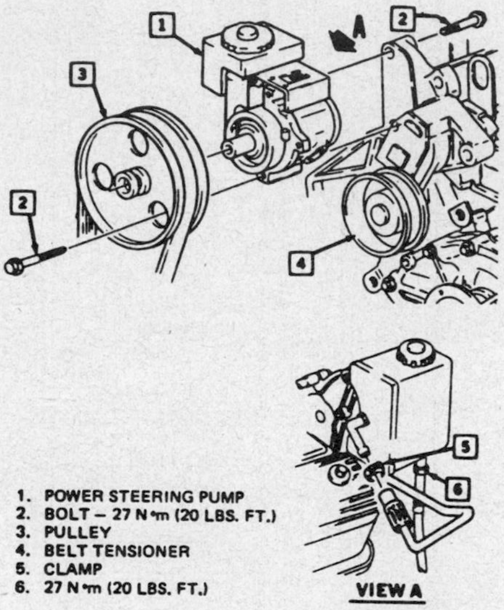
VIEW A

1. POWER STEERING PUMP
2. BOLT – 27 N·m (20 LBS. FT.)
3. PULLEY
4. BELT TENSIONER
5. CLAMP
6. 27 N·m (20 LBS. FT.)

GC6039100044000X

Fig. 14 Power steering pump installation. Riviera, Toronado & Trofeo

TIGHTENING SPECIFICATIONS

Year	Component	Torque/Ft. Lbs.
1992-95	Adjuster Plug Locknut	50
	Ball Joint To Control Arm	50
	Ball Joint To Knuckle	37
	Brake Reaction Rod To Frame	58
	Caliper Attaching Bolts	63
	Caliper Mounting Bracket	83
	Control Arm Bushing Nuts	103
	Cylinder Line Fittings	15
	Dampener Shaft	55
	Hub & Bearing To Knuckle	70
	Hub To Drive Axle	180
	Inner Tie Rod Housing To Rack	70
	Intermediate Shaft Pinch Bolts	35
	Outer Tie Rod Jam Nut	30
	Pinion Locknut	26
	Pinion Preload	1.4
	Power Steering Line Fittings	20
	Stabilizer Bracket To Frame	35
	Stabilizer Link Nut	48
	Strut Mount To Body	18
	Strut To Knuckle	136
	Strut To Strut Top Mount	①
	Tie Rod Nuts	②
	Tie Rod Pinch Bolts	41
	Wheel Lug Nuts	100

①—Tighten old design (flanged) nut to 75 ft. lbs. & new design (non-flanged) nut to 55 ft. lbs.
②—Tighten to 7.5 ft. lbs., then an additional 1/3 turn.

Wheel Alignment

INDEX

FRONT WHEEL ALIGNMENT

Steering and vibration complaints are not always the result of improper alignment. Another possibility is tire "lead" due to worn or improperly manufactured tires. "Lead" is the vehicles's deviation from a straight path on a level road without pressure on the steering wheel.

Before making any adjustment affecting wheel alignment, make the following checks to ensure correct alignment readings and alignment adjustments.

1. Check all tires for proper inflation pressures and ensure all tires have approximately equal tread wear.
2. Check hub and bearing assemblies for excessive wear, correcting as necessary.
3. Check ball joints and tie rod ends. If they are excessively loose, correct before making adjustment.
4. Check runout of wheels and tires.
5. Check vehicle trim height, correcting as necessary before adjusting alignment.
6. Check for proper operation of the Electronic Level Control system.
7. Check strut dampers for proper operation.
8. Check control arms for loose bushings.
9. Check stabilizer bar for loose or missing parts.

Consideration must also be given to excess loads, such as tool boxes or sample cases. If these items are normally carried in the vehicle, they should remain in the vehicle during alignment adjustments. Consideration should be given to condition of equipment being used to adjust alignment. Be sure to follow equipment manufacturer's instructions. Regardless of equipment being used, vehicle must be on level surface, both fore and aft and sideways.

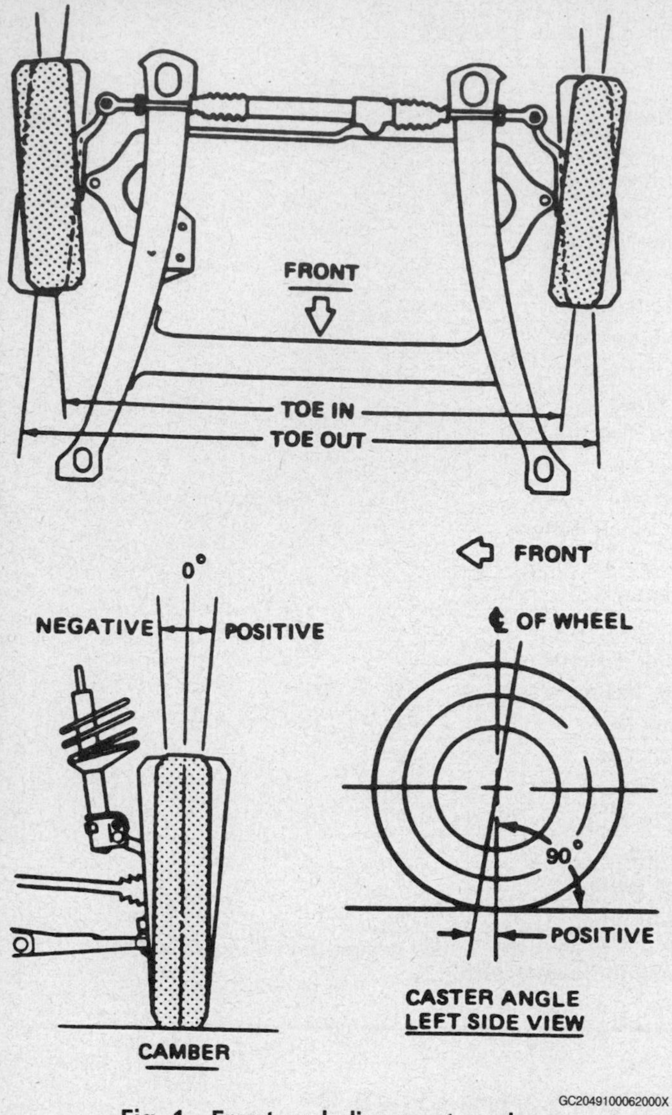
FRONT
TOE IN
TOE OUT
FRONT
0°
NEGATIVE
POSITIVE
℄ OF WHEEL
90°
POSITIVE
CAMBER
CASTER ANGLE
LEFT SIDE VIEW
GC2049100062000X

Fig. 1 Front end alignment angles

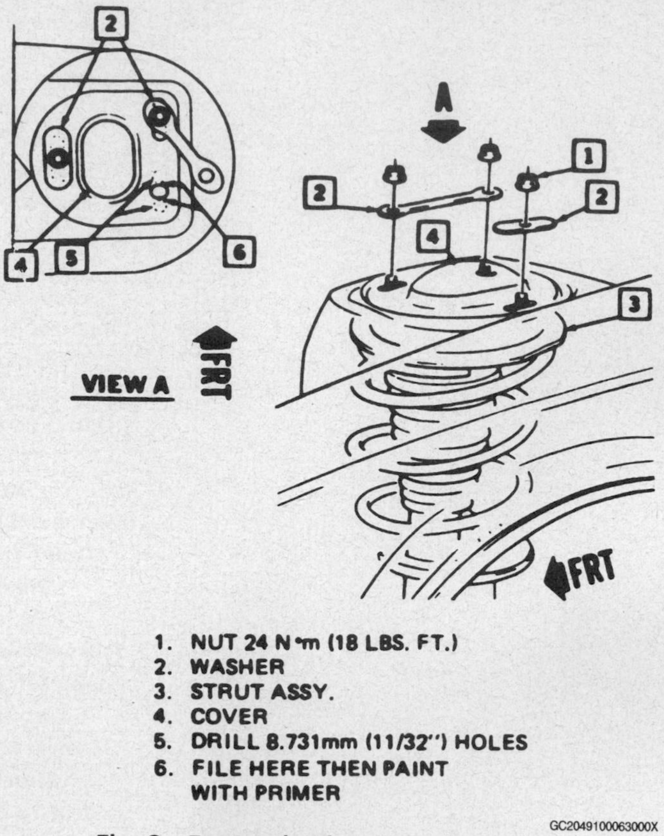
A
VIEW A
FRT
FRT
1. NUT 24 N·m (18 LBS. FT.)
2. WASHER
3. STRUT ASSY.
4. COVER
5. DRILL 8.731mm (11/32") HOLES
6. FILE HERE THEN PAINT WITH PRIMER
GC2049100063000X

Fig. 2 Front wheel caster adjustment

MEASURING FRONT ALIGNMENT ANGLES

Install alignment equipment following equipment manufacturer's instructions. Measure alignment angles, **Fig. 1**, and record the readings. If adjustments are necessary, they must be made in order; caster first, camber second and toe third. Jounce front and rear bumpers three times to normalize suspension prior to measuring angles.

CASTER ADJUSTMENT

1. With car supported by its wheels, remove the three top strut mounting nuts and washers, **Fig. 2.**
2. Lift front of car by the body to separate top strut mount from inner wheelhouse. **Do not raise control arms or tires.**
3. Drill two 11/32 inch holes at the front and rear of outboard strut mounting holes. Use a rat-tail file to slot the outboard hole.
4. Paint any bare metal areas with a corrosion protective primer or paint.
5. Reposition strut mount in holes, then lower front of car.
6. Reinstall washers and nuts.
7. Set caster to specifications by moving top of strut forward or rearward as required. 1 mm of movement is equivalent to 0.1° of caster.
8. **Torque** top strut mounting bolts to 18 ft. lbs.

CAMBER ADJUSTMENT

1. Loosen both strut to knuckle bolts just enough to allow movement.
2. Adjust camber by turning camber adjustment bolt, **Fig. 3.**
3. **Torque** strut to knuckle nuts to 136 ft. lbs.
4. **Torque** camber adjustment bolt to 7 ft. lbs.

TOE ADJUSTMENT

1. Loosen locknut on inner tie rods, **Fig. 4.**
2. Adjust toe by turning inner tie rods.
3. Adjust boots so that they are not twisted.
4. **Torque** locknuts to 45 ft. lbs.

REAR WHEEL ALIGNMENT

Rear wheel toe is the only adjustable angle. If camber is not within specifications, inspect for worn or damaged rear suspension components.

Before checking rear trim height or measuring rear alignment angles, the following procedure should be performed to ensure the rear air-adjustable struts are filled with residual pressure only.

1. Place a weight of at least 300 lbs. in vehicle trunk.
2. Turn ignition On, then wait for the Car Is Leveling light to illuminate.
3. Turn ignition Off and remove weight from trunk.
4. Wait at least 30 seconds for ELC system to exhaust.
5. Roll car forward or backward several complete tire rotations to eliminate the effects of tire camber change.
6. Jounce front and rear bumpers 3 times to normalize suspension prior to measuring angles.

TOE ADJUSTMENT

1. Loosen front and rear inside control arm mounting bolts, **Fig. 5.**

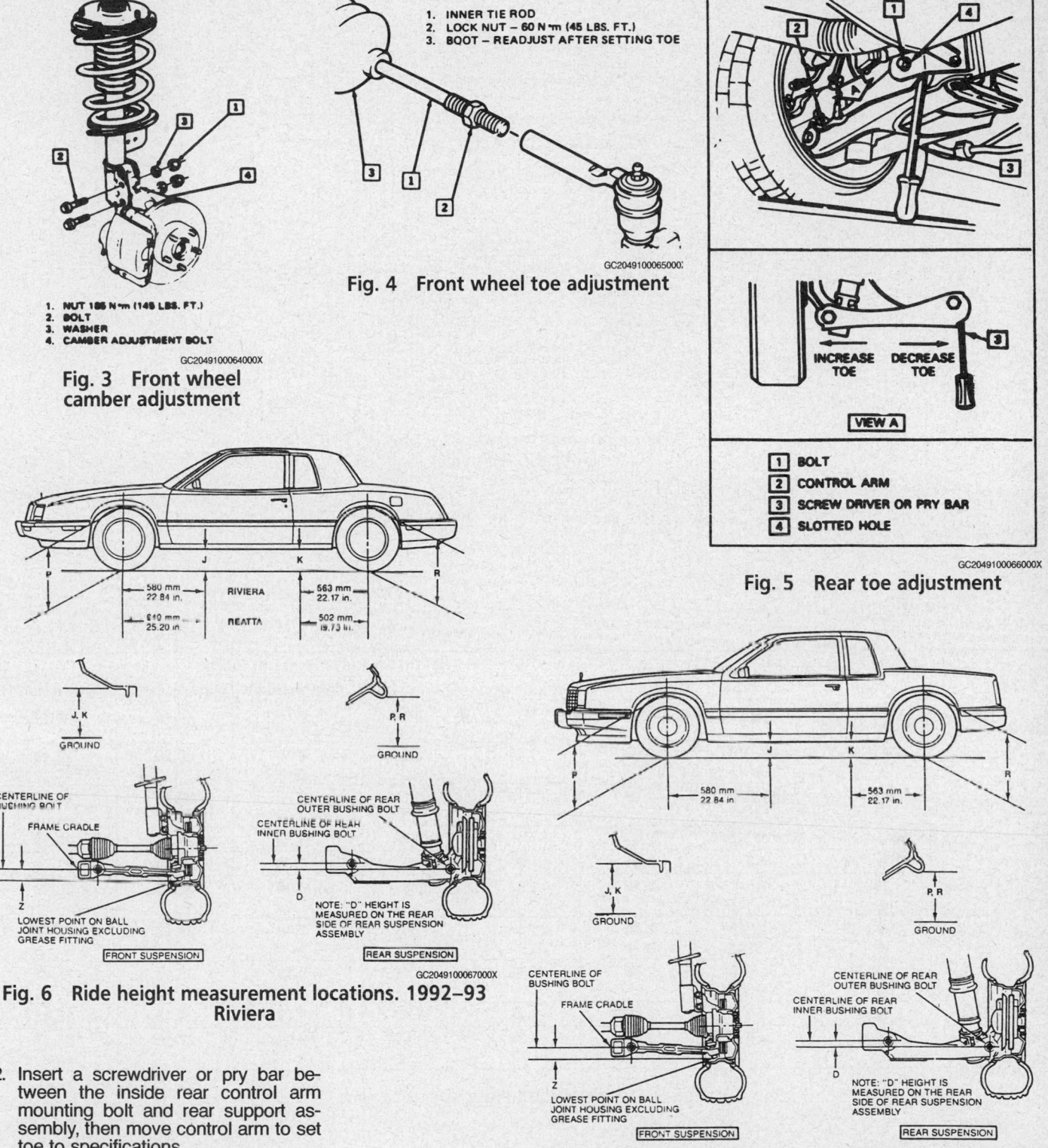

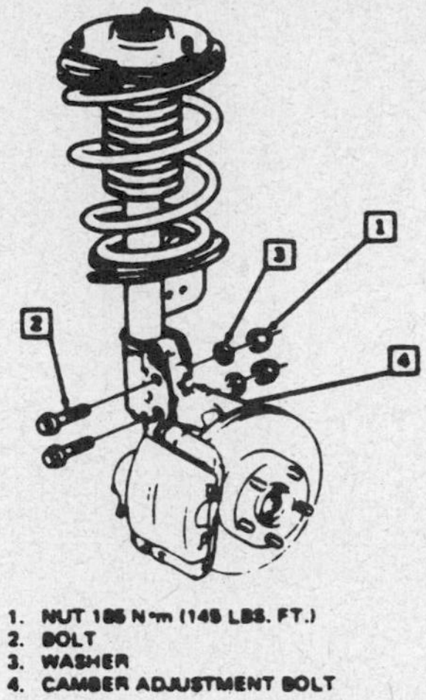
1
2
3
4
1. NUT
2. BOLT
3. WASHER
4. CAMBER ADJUSTMENT BOLT
GC2049100064000X

Fig. 3 Front wheel camber adjustment

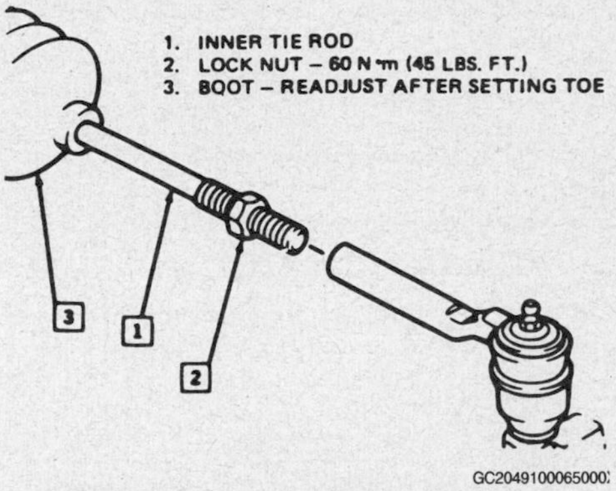
1. INNER TIE ROD
2. LOCK NUT – 60 N·m (45 LBS. FT.)
3. BOOT – READJUST AFTER SETTING TOE
1
2
3

Fig. 4 Front wheel toe adjustment

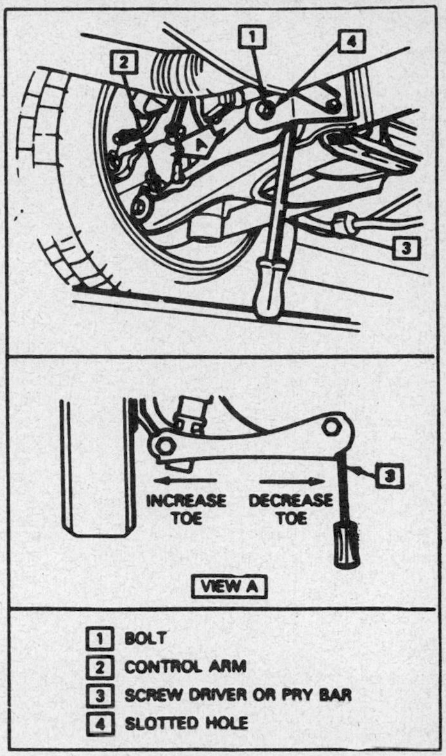
1
2
3
4
A
INCREASE TOE
DECREASE TOE
VIEW A
1 BOLT
2 CONTROL ARM
3 SCREW DRIVER OR PRY BAR
4 SLOTTED HOLE
GC2049100066000X

Fig. 5 Rear toe adjustment

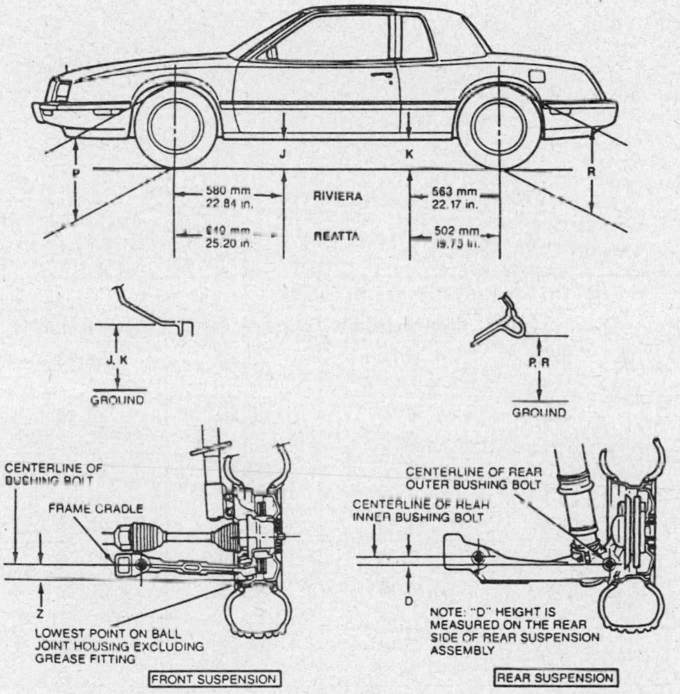
P
J
K
R
580 mm 22.84 in.
RIVIERA
563 mm 22.17 in.
REATTA
502 mm 19.75 in.
J, K
GROUND
P, R
GROUND
CENTERLINE OF BUSHING BOLT
FRAME CRADLE
Z
LOWEST POINT ON BALL JOINT HOUSING EXCLUDING GREASE FITTING
FRONT SUSPENSION
CENTERLINE OF REAR OUTER BUSHING BOLT
CENTERLINE OF REAR INNER BUSHING BOLT
D
NOTE: "D" HEIGHT IS MEASURED ON THE REAR SIDE OF REAR SUSPENSION ASSEMBLY
REAR SUSPENSION
GC2049100067000X

Fig. 6 Ride height measurement locations. 1992–93 Riviera

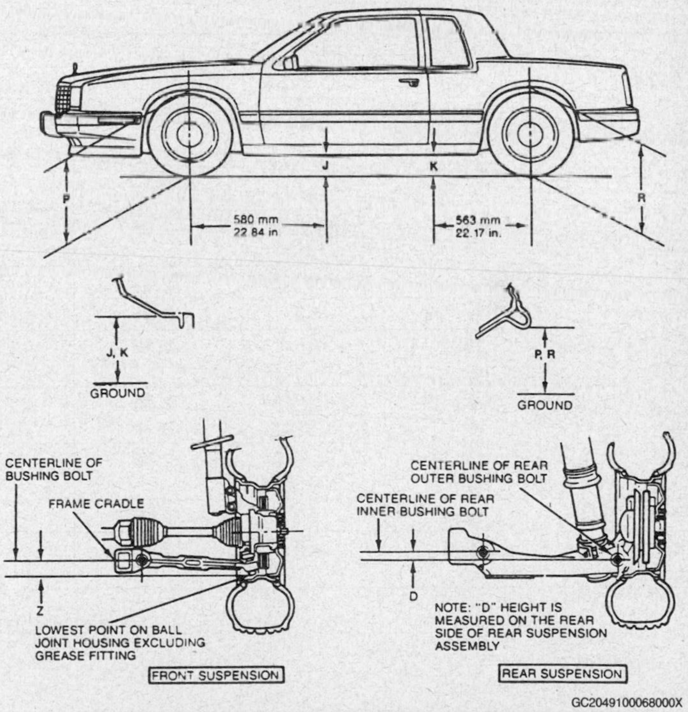
P
J
K
R
580 mm 22.84 in
563 mm 22.17 in.
J, K
GROUND
P, R
GROUND
CENTERLINE OF BUSHING BOLT
FRAME CRADLE
Z
LOWEST POINT ON BALL JOINT HOUSING EXCLUDING GREASE FITTING
FRONT SUSPENSION
CENTERLINE OF REAR OUTER BUSHING BOLT
CENTERLINE OF REAR INNER BUSHING BOLT
D
NOTE: "D" HEIGHT IS MEASURED ON THE REAR SIDE OF REAR SUSPENSION ASSEMBLY
REAR SUSPENSION
GC2049100068000X

Fig. 7 Ride height measurement locations. 1992 Eldorado, Seville; 1992 Toronado & Trofeo

2. Insert a screwdriver or pry bar between the inside rear control arm mounting bolt and rear support assembly, then move control arm to set toe to specifications.
3. **Torque** inside front and rear control arm mounting bolt to 66 ft. lbs.

VEHICLE RIDE HEIGHT

Refer to **Figs. 6 through 8**, for ride height measurements and **Fig. 9**, for specifications. When checking ride height measurements, fuel tank should be full, tires at should be correct pressure, front seat should be rearward position, truck should be empty except for spare tire and jack and vehicle should be on level ground. If fuel tank is not full, add weight to trunk to compensate for amount fuel vehicle is below the full level.

Prior to checking ride height, lift front bumper upward approximately 1.5 inches and gently release (3 times), then check front ride height. Push front bumper downward approximately 1.5 inches and gently release (3 times), then recheck front ride height. Average of both readings to determine vehicle ride height. Check rear ride height in same manner, lifting and pushing rear bumper.

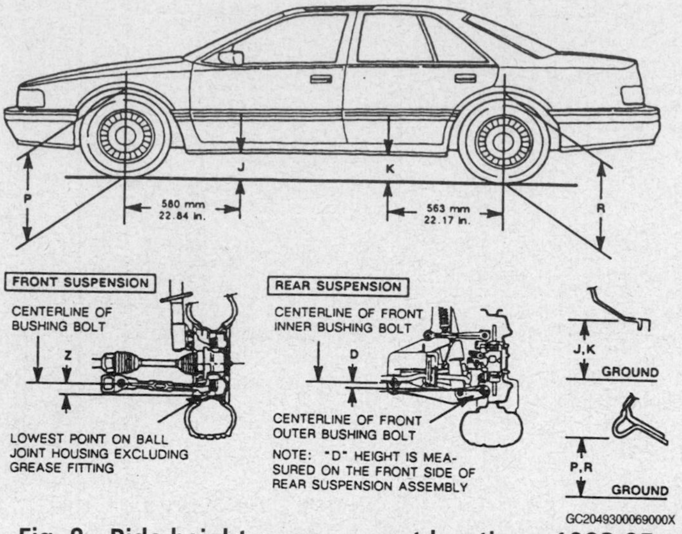
J
K
P
R
580 mm
22.84 in.
563 mm
22.17 in.
FRONT SUSPENSION
CENTERLINE OF
BUSHING BOLT
Z
LOWEST POINT ON BALL
JOINT HOUSING EXCLUDING
GREASE FITTING
REAR SUSPENSION
CENTERLINE OF FRONT
INNER BUSHING BOLT
D
CENTERLINE OF FRONT
OUTER BUSHING BOLT
NOTE: "D" HEIGHT IS MEA-
SURED ON THE FRONT SIDE OF
REAR SUSPENSION ASSEMBLY
J,K
GROUND
P,R
GROUND
GC2049300069000X

Fig. 8 Ride height measurement locations. 1993-95 Eldorado & Seville

Model	Year	Engine Liter/ CID (VIN)	Ride Height Measurements In Inches					
			Dimension Z	Dimension D	Dimension J	Dimension K	Dimension P	Dimension R
Eldorado & Seville	1992	All	2.05	1.18	8.78	8.70	28.23	28.19
	1993-95	4.6L/V8-279(Y)	2.09	1.46	8.78	8.70	28.23	28.19
		4.6L/V8-279(9)	2.09	1.14	8.78	8.70	28.23	28.19
		4.9L/V8-300	2.01	1.46	8.78	8.70	28.23	28.19
Riviera	1992-93	All	1.81	1.10	8.62	8.74	27.40	27.76
Seville Except STS	1992	All	2.21	1.34	9.65	9.65	28.68	28.68
	1993-95	4.6L/V8-279(9)	2.09	1.46	9.49	9.49	28.43	28.43
		4.9L/V8-300(B)	2.05	1.46	9.49	9.49	28.43	28.43
Seville STS	1992	All	2.05	1.22	9.49	9.49	28.43	28.43
Tornado & Trofeo	1992	All	2.24	1.34	9.09	9.09	27.80	28.27

Fig. 9 Vehicle ride height specifications

OLDSMOBILE AURORA & 1995 BUICK RIVIERA G CARS

INDEX OF SERVICE OPERATIONS

NOTE: For Service Operations Not Listed Below, Refer To The Table Of Contents In The Front Of This Manual.

Specifications

GENERAL ENGINE SPECIFICATIONS

Year	Engine Liter/CID	Engine VIN Code①	Fuel System	Bore & Stroke	Compression Ratio	Net H.P. @ RPM ②	Maximum Torque Ft. Lbs. @ RPM	Normal Oil Pressure
1995	3800/V6-231	K	SFI	3.80 X 3.40	9.0	205 @ 5200	230 @ 4000	60
	3800/V6-231③	1	SFI	3.80 X 3.40	8.5	225 @ 5000	275 @ 3200	60
	4.0L/V8-244	C	SFI	3.43 X 3.31	10.2	250 @ 5600	245 @ 4400	④

①—The eighth digit of the Vehicle Identification Number (VIN) denotes engine code.

②—Ratings are net-as installed in vehicle.

③—Supercharged.

④—5 psi at idle speed, 30 psi at 2000 RPM.

TUNE UP SPECIFICATIONS

Year	Engine/VIN Code①	Spark Plug Gap	Ignition Timing Firing Order	Ignition Timing Wire Connections Fig.	Idle Speed	Fuel Pump Pressure
1995	3800/V6-231/K	.060	②	A	③	48-55⑤
	3800/V6-231/1	.060	②	A	③	41-47⑤
	4.0L/V8-244/C	.050	④	B	⑥	41-47⑤

①—The eighth digit of the Vehicle Identification Number (VIN) denotes engine code.

②—Firing order, 1-6-5-4-3-2.

③—Idle speed is controlled by the Idle Air Control (IAC) Valve.

④—Firing order, 1-2-7-3-4-5-6-8.

⑤—With shop towel wrapped around fuel pressure gauge and fuel pressure test port to prevent spillage, connect fuel pressure gauge to fuel pressure test port. Check fuel pressure with ignition key in the ON position and engine not running.

⑥—Idle speed is controlled by the Idle Speed Control (ISC) Actuator.

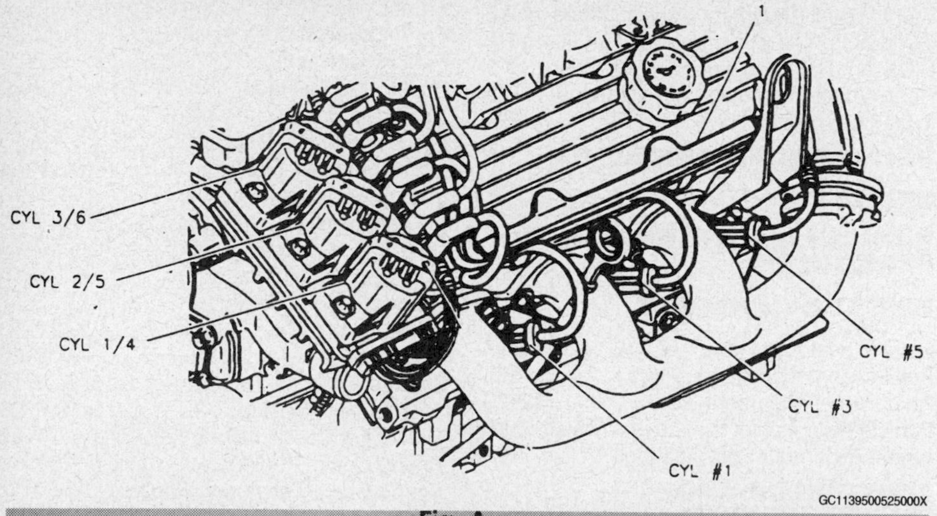
1
CYL 3/6
CYL 2/5
CYL 1/4
CYL #5
CYL #3
CYL #1
GC1139500525000X

Fig. A

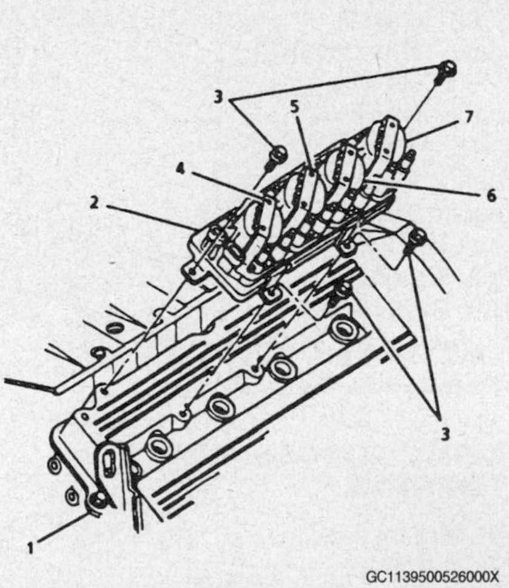
1
2
3
4
5
6
7
GC1139500526000X

Fig. B

FRONT WHEEL ALIGNMENT SPECIFICATIONS

Year	Model	Caster Angle, Degrees		Camber Angle, Degrees		Total Toe, Degree	Steering Angle, Degrees
		Limits	Desired	Limits	Desired		
1995	All	+4.5 to +6.5	+5.5	-.8 to -1.2	+.2	0	-.3 to +.3

REAR WHEEL ALIGNMENT SPECIFICATIONS

Year	Model	Camber Angle, Degrees		Total Toe, Degrees	Thrust Angle, Degrees
		Limits	Desired		
1995	All	-.8 to +.2	-.3	+.2	-.1 to +.1

COOLING SYSTEM & CAPACITY DATA

Year	Model	Engine/VIN	Coolant Capacity, Qts.	Radiator Cap Relief Pressure, Lbs.	Thermo Opening Temp.	Fuel Tank, Gallons	Engine Oil Refill, Qts. ①	Auto Transaxle, Qts.
1995	Aurora	4.0L/V8-244/C	13.2	15	195	20	5	②
	Riviera	3800/V6-231/K	13	15	195	18	5	②
		3800/V6-231/1	13	15	195	18	7.5	②

①—With filter change.
②—Oil pan capacity, 6 qts.; total capacity, 11 qts.

LUBRICANT DATA

Year	Model	Lubricant Type		
		Automatic	Power Steering System	Brake System
1995	All	Dexron III	Power Steering Fluid	DOT 3

Electrical

NOTE: On Air Bag Equipped Models, Refer To "Air Bag System Precautions" Located In The Front Of This Manual For System Disarming & Arming Procedures.

INDEX

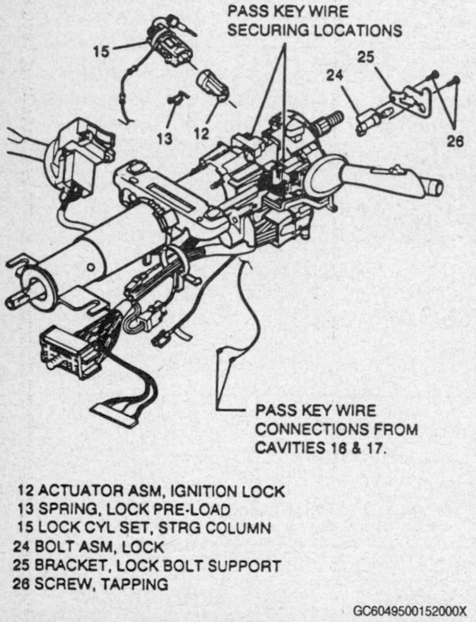

PASS KEY WIRE SECURING LOCATIONS
15
25
24
13
12
26
PASS KEY WIRE CONNECTIONS FROM CAVITIES 16 & 17.
12 ACTUATOR ASM, IGNITION LOCK
13 SPRING, LOCK PRE-LOAD
15 LOCK CYL SET, STRG COLUMN
24 BOLT ASM, LOCK
25 BRACKET, LOCK BOLT SUPPORT
26 SCREW, TAPPING
GC6049500152000X

Fig. 1 Lock cylinder & lock bolt removal

PRECAUTIONS

AIR BAG SYSTEMS

Refer to "Air Bag System Precautions" in the front of this manual for system disarming and arming procedures.

FUSE PANEL & FLASHER LOCATION

The instrument panel fuse block is located behind the lefthand side of the instrument panel, behind the trim panel. The rear fuse block is located under the rear seat.

The hazard flasher is located behind the lefthand side of the instrument panel, right of the steering column support. The turn signal flasher is located behind the lefthand side of the instrument panel, attached to the lefthand sound insulator.

RELAY CENTER LOCATION

The passenger compartment relay center is located under the rear seat. The engine compartment relay center is located on the front righthand side of the engine compartment.

STARTER

REPLACE

3800/V6-231 ENGINE

1. Disconnect battery ground cable.
2. Raise and support vehicle.
3. Disconnect starter wiring.
4. Remove flywheel inspection cover attaching bolts, then the cover.
5. Remove starter to engine attaching bolts, then the starter.
6. Reverse procedure to install, noting the following:
   a. **Torque** starter to engine bolts to 32 ft. lbs.
   b. **Torque** nut on solenoid battery terminal to 12 ft. lbs.
   c. **Torque** nut on solenoid "S" terminal to 22 inch lbs.
   d. **Torque** flywheel inspection cover bolts to 62 inch lbs.

4.0L/V8-244 ENGINE

1. Disconnect battery ground cable, then the positive battery cable.
2. Remove intake manifold as described under "Intake Manifold, Replace" in the "4.0L/V8-244 Engine" section.
3. Disconnect electrical connectors from starter solenoid "S" and battery terminals.
4. Remove starter mounting bolts, then the starter.
5. Reverse procedure to install, noting the following:
   a. **Torque** inner nuts on the solenoid terminals to 70 inch lbs.
   b. **Torque** "S" terminal nut to 20 inch lbs.
   c. **Torque** battery terminal nut to 70 inch lbs.
   d. **Torque** starter mounting bolts to 22 ft. lbs.

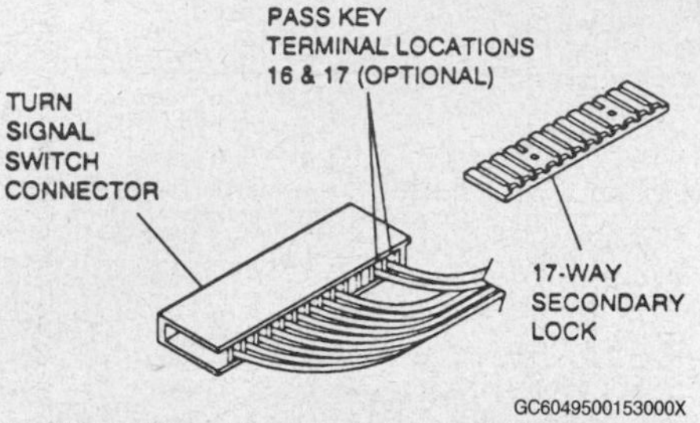

PASS KEY TERMINAL LOCATIONS 16 & 17 (OPTIONAL)
TURN SIGNAL SWITCH CONNECTOR
17-WAY SECONDARY LOCK
GC6049500153000X

Fig. 2 Pass Key wire connector removal

IGNITION LOCK

REPLACE

REMOVAL

1. Disconnect battery ground cable.
2. Tilt column to the "CENTER" position.
3. Remove three upper steering column cover attaching screws, then the upper cover.
4. Remove pivot and pulse switch as described under "Pivot & Pulse Switch, Replace,", allow switch to hang freely from column.
5. Turn lock cylinder to the RUN position.
6. Push against locking button located on back side of bearing and housing assembly and remove lock cylinder.
7. Remove lock preload spring, **Fig. 1.**
8. To remove "Pass Key" wiring harness from steering column, proceed as follows:
   a. Disconnect bulkhead connector from vehicle wire harness.
   b. Disconnect gray turn signal switch connector from bulkhead connector, **Fig. 2.**

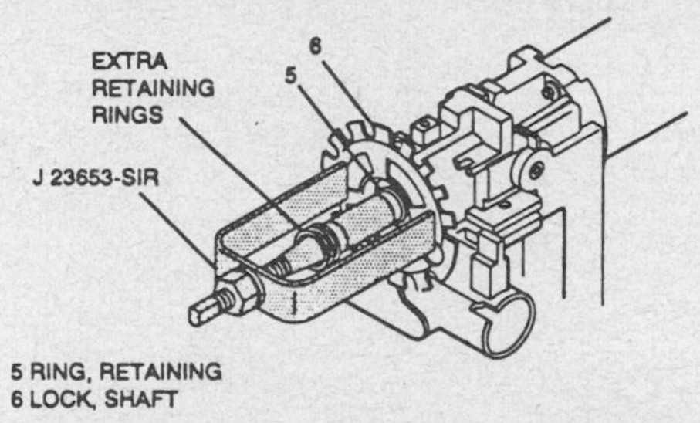
EXTRA RETAINING RINGS
6
5
J 23653-SIR
5 RING, RETAINING
6 LOCK, SHAFT
GC6049500154000X

Fig. 3 Shaft lock retaining ring removal & installation

c. Remove 17-way secondary lock from turn signal switch connector.
d. Disconnect two "Pass Key" terminals from cavities 16 and 17 of gray turn signal switch connector.
e. Disconnect "Pass Key" wire harness from wire harness strap, multi-function switch and upper head housing assembly.

9. Using needle nose pliers, remove ignition lock actuator assembly from upper head housing assembly.
10. Remove lock bolt assembly as follows:
    a. Remove tilt lever knob attaching screw and the knob.
    b. Pry close out knob locking tabs from bearing and housing assembly, then remove close out knob.
    c. Remove three lower steering column cover attaching screws, then the lower cover.
    d. Remove steering wheel as described under "Steering Wheel, Replace."
    e. Remove SIR coil assembly retaining ring, then the coil assembly from the column. Allow coil assembly to hang freely from steering column.
    f. Using lock plate compressor tool No. J 23653-SIR or equivalent to push down shaft lock, remove shaft lock retaining ring, **Fig. 3.**
    g. Remove shaft lock from steering column.
    h. Remove turn signal cancel cam, upper bearing spring, upper bearing inner race seat, inner race and tilt lever bracket, **Fig. 4.**
    i. Remove two lock bolt support bracket attaching bolts, then the bracket.
    j. Remove lock bolt from housing assembly.

INSTALLATION

1. Install lock bolt and support bracket into housing assembly, **torque** support bracket attaching screws to 46 inch lbs.
2. Ensure end of lock bolt is flush with support bracket, **Fig. 1,** install ignition lock actuator assembly into housing.
3. Rotate actuator counterclockwise until it pushes out lock bolt and actuator seats into housing assembly.
4. Rotate actuator clockwise to the RUN position.
5. Align inner block tooth of lock plate to block tooth of upper shaft assembly.

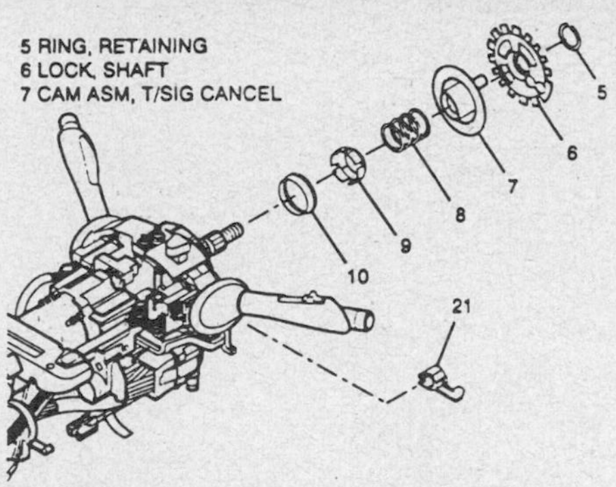
5 RING, RETAINING
6 LOCK, SHAFT
7 CAM ASM, T/SIG CANCEL
5
6
7
8
9
10
21
8 SPRING, UPPER BEARING
9 SEAT, UPPER BEARING INNER RACE
10 RACE, INNER
21 BRACKET, TILT LEVER
GC6049500155000X

Fig. 4 Upper steering shaft components

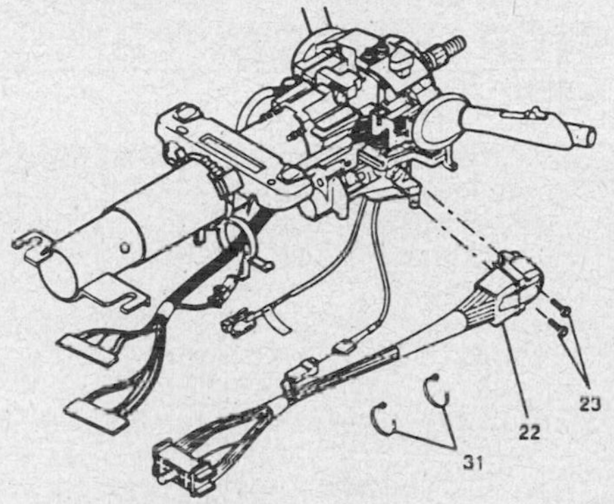
22
23
31
22 SWITCH ASM, IGN & KEY ALARM
23 SCREW, TAPPING
31 STRAP, WIRE
GC6049500156000X

Fig. 6 Ignition & key alarm switch removal

6. Install tilt lever bracket, inner race, upper bearing inner race seat, upper bearing spring and turn signal cam assembly.
7. Lubricate shaft lock with suitable synthetic grease, then install shaft lock into housing.
8. Using lock plate compressor tool No. J 23653-SIR or equivalent to push down shaft lock, install shaft lock retaining ring, **Fig. 3. Ensure ring is seated firmly in groove on shaft.**
9. Insert key into lock cylinder, then with lock cylinder in the RUN position, align locking tab with slot in housing assembly and push into position.
10. Insert "Pass Key" wire harness into column and route wire harness through wiring protector.
11. Secure wiring harness to housing assembly and multi-function switch, then route through wiring harness strap.
12. Connect terminals of wiring harness to cavities 16 and 17 in gray turn signal switch connector.
13. Install 17-way secondary lock onto turn signal switch connector.
14. Connect gray turn signal switch connector to bulkhead connector.
15. Connect bulkhead connector to vehicle wiring harness.

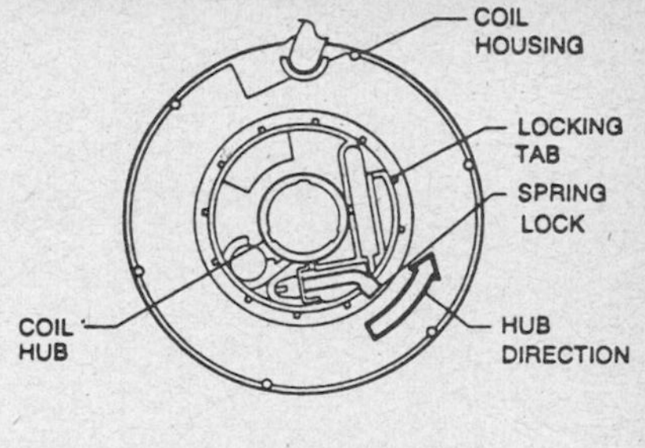
COIL HOUSING
LOCKING TAB
SPRING LOCK
COIL HUB
HUB DIRECTION
PERFORM THE FOLLOWING STEPS TO CENTER COIL ASSEMBLY
A. WHEELS STRAIGHT AHEAD.
B. REMOVE COIL ASSEMBLY.
C. HOLD COIL ASSEMBLY WITH BOTTOM UP.
D. WHILE HOLDING COIL ASSEMBLY, DEPRESS SPRING LOCK TO ROTATE HUB IN DIRECTION OF ARROW UNTIL IT STOPS.
E. THE COIL RIBBON SHOULD BE WOUND UP SNUG AGAINST CENTER HUB.
F. ROTATE COIL HUB IN OPPOSITE DIRECTION APPROXIMATELY TWO AND A HALF (2-1/2) TURNS. RELEASE SPRING LOCK BETWEEN LOCKING TABS.
GC8019501343000X

Fig. 5 SIR coil assembly installation

16. Install pivot and pulse switch assembly as described under "Pivot & Pulse Switch, Replace."
17. Install upper steering column cover, **torque** cover attaching screws to 46 inch lbs.
18. Install multi-function switch as described under "Multi-Function Switch, Replace."
19. Install and center SIR coil assembly as shown in **Fig. 5.**
20. Install steering wheel as described under "Steering Wheel, Replace."
21. Install battery ground cable.

IGNITION SWITCH
REPLACE

1. Disconnect battery ground cable.
2. Tilt column to the "CENTER" position.
3. Remove three upper steering column cover attaching screws, then the upper cover.
4. Remove tilt lever knob attaching screw and the knob.
5. Pry close out knob locking tabs from bearing and housing assembly, then remove close out knob.
6. Remove three lower steering column cover attaching screws, then the lower cover.
7. Remove two wire straps from steering column wiring harness, **Fig. 6.**
8. Disconnect steering column bulkhead connector from vehicle wiring harness.
9. Disconnect ignition key and alarm switch assembly from wire harness strap.
10. Disconnect gray and black connectors of turn signal and multi-function switch from column bulkhead connector.
11. Remove two ignition and key alarm switch attaching screws, then the ignition and key alarm switch from the column.
12. Reverse procedure to install.

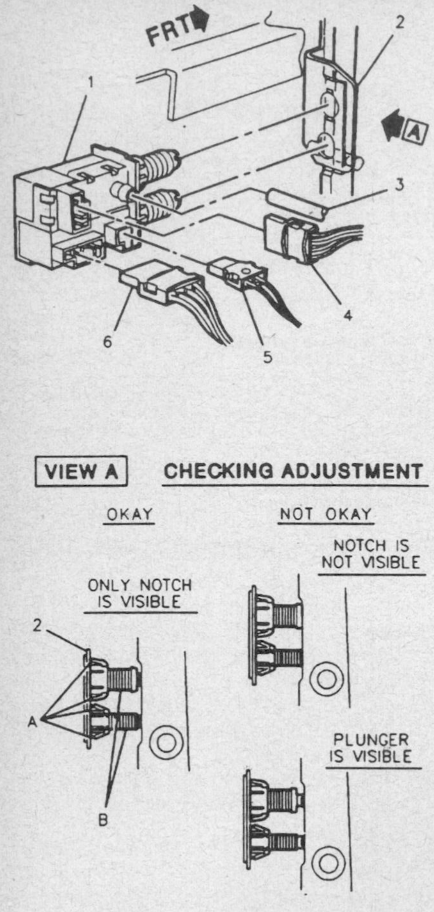
FRT
2
1
A
3
4
6
5
VIEW A
CHECKING ADJUSTMENT
OKAY
NOT OKAY
NOTCH IS NOT VISIBLE
ONLY NOTCH IS VISIBLE
2
A
B
PLUNGER IS VISIBLE

A RETAINING TABS
B SWITCH BARRELS
1 SWITCH
2 MOUNTING BRACKET
3 CRUISE VACUUM LINE
4 CONNECTOR, TCC/ABS (BLACK)
5 CONNECTOR, STOPLAMP SW (GRAY)
6 CONNECTOR, SHIFT-INTERLOCK/CRUISE (BLUE)

GC9049500138000X

Fig. 7 Stop lamp switch removal & adjustment

NEUTRAL SAFETY SWITCH

REPLACE

1. Set parking brake and set gear selector to the "Neutral" position.
2. Remove linkage cable bracket to transaxle shaft retaining nut.
3. Remove linkage cable bracket from transaxle shaft.
4. Remove Park/Neutral position switch attaching bolts.
5. Disconnect Park/Neutral position switch electrical connector.
6. Remove terminal nut on starter solenoid, then disconnect cable from starter.
7. Remove Park/Neutral position switch from vehicle.
8. Reverse procedure to install.

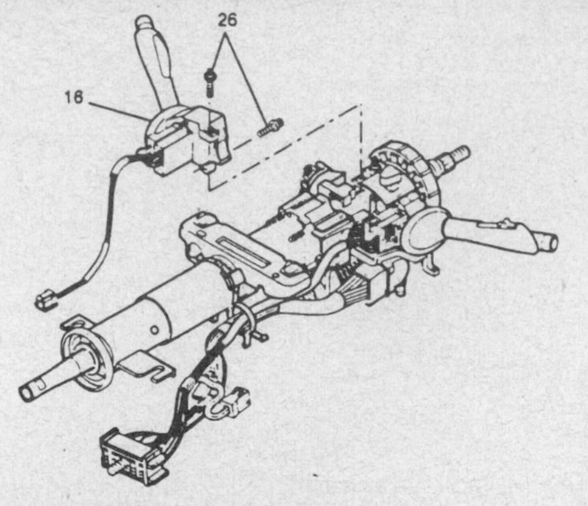
26
16

16 SWITCH ASM, PIVOT & (PULSE)
26 SCREW, TAPPING

GC9049500139000X

Fig. 8 Pivot & pulse switch assembly removal

STOP LIGHT SWITCH

REPLACE

1. Disconnect battery ground cable.
2. Remove lefthand side instrument panel sound insulator.
3. Disconnect switch electrical connectors, **Fig. 7.**
4. Disconnect vacuum hose from switch.
5. Remove switch from brake pedal support.
6. Reverse procedure to install, adjust switch as follows:
   a. After installing switch, press brake pedal rearward until no audible clicks remain, then release the pedal.
   b. Press brake pedal again to ensure no clicks are heard.
   c. Compare switch adjustment to **Fig. 7.**
   d. Only notch should be visible. If plunger is visible or notch is not, repeat adjustment.

PIVOT & PULSE SWITCH

REPLACE

1. Disconnect battery ground cable.
2. Tilt column to the "CENTER" position.
3. Remove three upper steering column cover attaching screws, then the upper cover.
4. Remove two wire straps from steering column wire harness.
5. Disconnect pivot and pulse switch connector from turn signal and multi-function switch wire harness connector.
6. Disconnect pivot and pulse switch harness from wire harness strap.
7. Remove two pivot and pulse switch attaching screws, then the pivot and pulse switch assembly from the column, **Fig. 8.**
8. Reverse procedure to install.

MULTI-FUNCTION SWITCH

REPLACE

1. Disconnect battery ground cable.

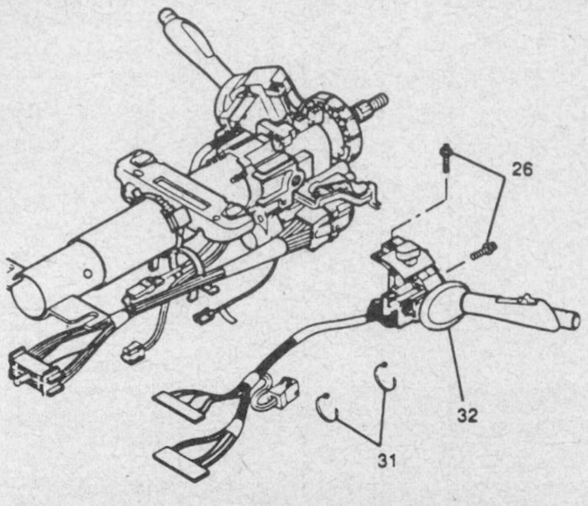
26
32
31

26 SCREW, TAPPING
31 STRAP, WIRE
32 SWITCH ASM, T/S & MULTIFUNC

GC9049500140000X

Fig. 9 Turn signal & multi-function switch removal

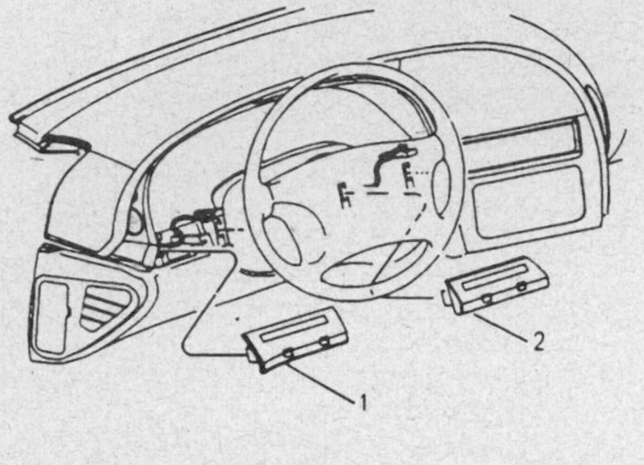
2
1

1 SWITCH ASSEMBLY, INTERIOR LAMP/ TWILIGHT SENTINAL
2 SWITCH ASSEMBLY, R/CMPT LID FUEL DOOR RELEASE

GC9099500267000X

Fig. 10 Instrument cluster filler trim plate removal. Aurora

2. Tilt column to the "CENTER" position.
3. Remove three upper steering column cover attaching screws, then the upper cover.
4. Remove two wire straps from steering column wire harness.
5. Disconnect steering column bulkhead connector from vehicle wiring harness.
6. Disconnect turn signal and multi-function switch wiring harness from wiring harness strap.
7. Disconnect pivot and pulse switch assembly connector from multi-function switch wire harness connector.
8. Disconnect gray and black multi-function switch connectors from column bulkhead connector.
9. Remove 17-way secondary lock from turn signal switch connector.
10. Disconnect two "Pass Key" terminals from cavities 16 and 17 of the gray turn signal switch connector.
11. Remove two multi-function switch attaching screws, then the multi-function switch from the column, **Fig. 9.**
12. Reverse procedure to install.

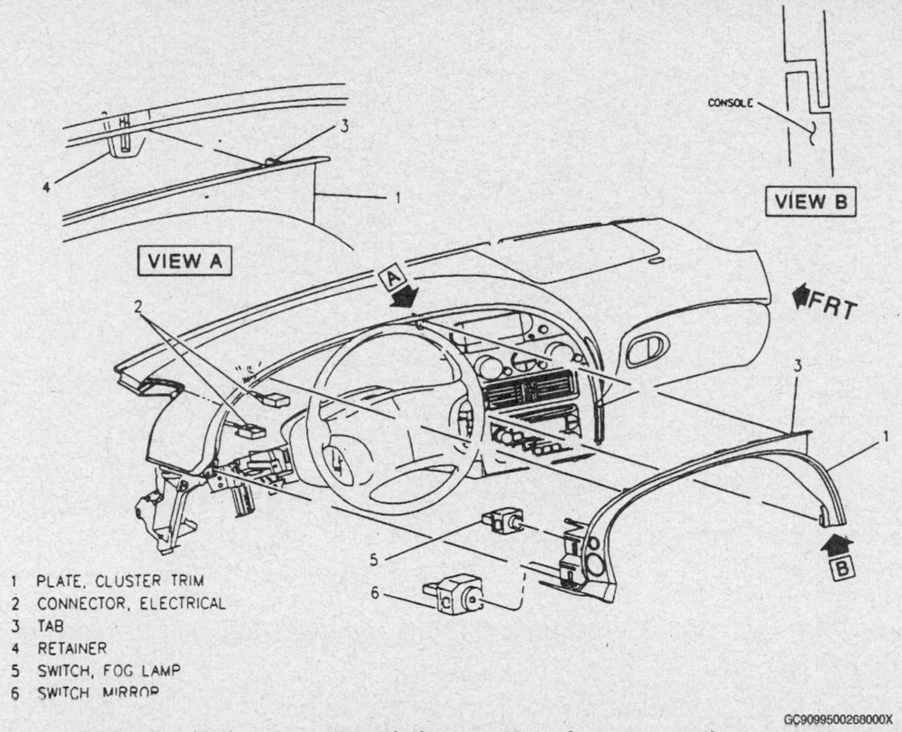
CONSOLE
VIEW B
VIEW A
FRT
A
B
1 PLATE, CLUSTER TRIM
2 CONNECTOR, ELECTRICAL
3 TAB
4 RETAINER
5 SWITCH, FOG LAMP
6 SWITCH, MIRROR
GC9099500268000X

Fig. 11 Instrument panel cluster trim plate removal. Aurora

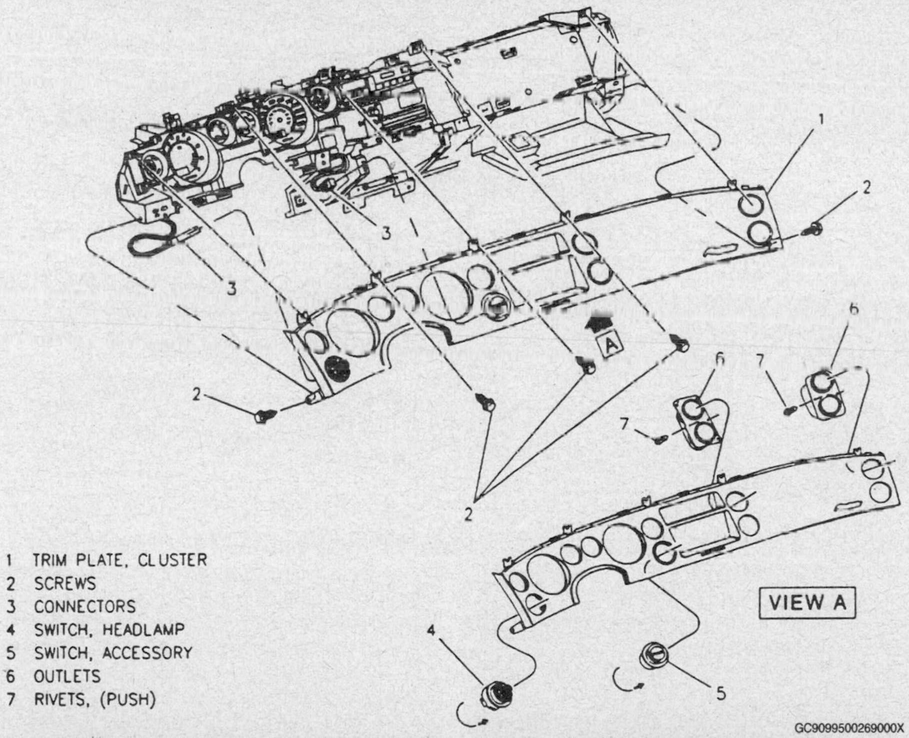
A
VIEW A
1 TRIM PLATE, CLUSTER
2 SCREWS
3 CONNECTORS
4 SWITCH, HEADLAMP
5 SWITCH, ACCESSORY
6 OUTLETS
7 RIVETS, (PUSH)
GC9099500269000X

Fig. 12 Instrument panel cluster trim plate removal. Riviera

STEERING WHEEL
REPLACE

1. Disconnect battery ground cable.
2. **On Aurora models,** remove steering wheel inserts covering inflator module mounting screws.
3. **On all models,** remove SIR inflator module mounting screws, then the inflator module from the steering wheel. **Note inflator wire routing for installation reference.**
4. Remove steering wheel retaining nut.
5. Using pulling tool Nos. J1859-03 and J38720 or equivalent, remove steering wheel from steering shaft.
6. Reverse procedure to install, noting the following:
   a. Align mark on steering shaft with steering wheel.
   b. **Torque** steering wheel retaining nut to 30 ft. lbs.
   c. **Torque** inflator module retaining screws to 27 inch lbs.

INSTRUMENT CLUSTER
REPLACE

1. **On Aurora models,** remove instrument panel cluster trim plate as follows:
   a. Remove instrument cluster filler trim plates as shown in **Fig. 10.**
   b. Carefully pull instrument panel cluster trim plate rearward, **Fig. 11.**
   c. Disconnect three wire harnesses from trim plate.
   d. Remove fog lamp and mirror control switches from cluster trim plate by disengaging tabs on switches from retainers on trim plate.
   e. Remove trim plate from vehicle.
2. **On Riviera models,** remove instrument panel cluster trim plate as follows:
   a. Remove switches and air deflectors from cluster trim plate, **Fig. 12.**
   b. Remove cluster trim plate attaching screws.
   c. Remove cluster trim plate from instrument panel.
3. **On all models,** remove instrument cluster retaining screws.
4. Disconnect cluster electrical connectors, **Figs. 13 and 14.**
5. Remove instrument cluster from vehicle.
6. Reverse procedure to install.

RADIO
REPLACE
AURORA

1. Disconnect battery ground cable.
2. Remove instrument panel center trim plate by pulling rearward to disengage retainers.
3. Remove two radio assembly retaining screws.
4. Pull radio outward and disconnect antenna lead and electrical connectors.
5. Remove radio from vehicle.
6. Reverse procedure to install.

RIVIERA

1. Disconnect battery ground cable.
2. Remove instrument cluster trim plate as described under "Instrument Cluster, Replace."
3. Remove two radio assembly retaining screws.
4. Pull radio outward and disconnect antenna lead and electrical connectors.
5. Remove radio from vehicle.
6. Reverse procedure to install.

WIPER MOTOR
REPLACE

1. Turn ignition switch to the "ACCY" position, then set wiper switch to the "PULSE" position.
2. Turn ignition switch off when wiper arms are at bottom of innerwipe and not moving.
3. Lift wiper blade assembly up from windshield.

4. Pull out retaining latch with a screwdriver.
5. Pull wiper arm assembly off transmission driveshaft.
6. Disconnect battery ground cable.
7. Disconnect hose from washer hose.
8. Remove five air inlet panel retainers.
9. Push washer hose into firewall.
10. Remove air inlet panel from vehicle.
11. Using wiper transmission separator tool No. J39232 or equivalent, remove transmission drive link socket from wiper motor crank arm.
12. Pull two harness connector retainers out of wiper motor connector.
13. Disconnect two harness connectors from wiper motor.
14. Remove wiper motor attaching bolts and stud, then the wiper motor from the vehicle.
15. Reverse procedure to install.

BLOWER MOTOR
REPLACE

1. Disconnect battery ground cable.
2. Remove righthand side sound insulator.
3. Disconnect blower motor electrical connector.
4. Disconnect cooling tube from blower motor.
5. Remove blower motor to heater and A/C control module attaching screws.
6. Remove blower motor and fan assembly from vehicle.
7. Reverse procedure to install.

HEATER CORE
REPLACE

1. Disconnect battery ground cable.
2. Drain cooling system.
3. Disconnect heater hoses from heater core.
4. Remove righthand and lefthand sound insulators.
5. Remove heater core cover from heater and A/C module.
6. Remove heater core retaining straps.
7. Remove heater core from vehicle.
8. Reverse procedure to install. To aid installation the sound insulator seal may be cut in half. Each half should be placed into the respective sides of the heater and A/C module.

EVAPORATOR CORE
REPLACE

1. Disconnect battery ground cable.
2. Remove storage compartment bin from center console.
3. Remove shifter handle retainer, then lift shifter handle.
4. Disconnect shift handle electrical connector and remove handle.
5. **On Aurora models,** remove shifter trim plate as follows:
   a. Pull shifter trim plate up to disengage retaining tabs.
   b. Disconnect all trim plate electrical connectors, then remove shifter trim plate from center console.

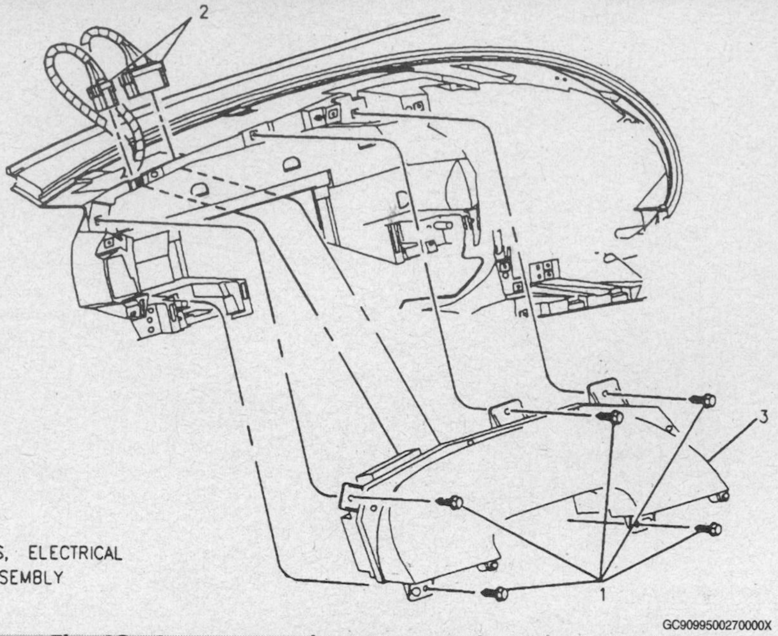
2
3
1
1 SCREWS
2 CONNECTORS, ELECTRICAL
3 CLUSTER ASSEMBLY
GC9099500270000X

Fig. 13 Instrument cluster removal. Aurora

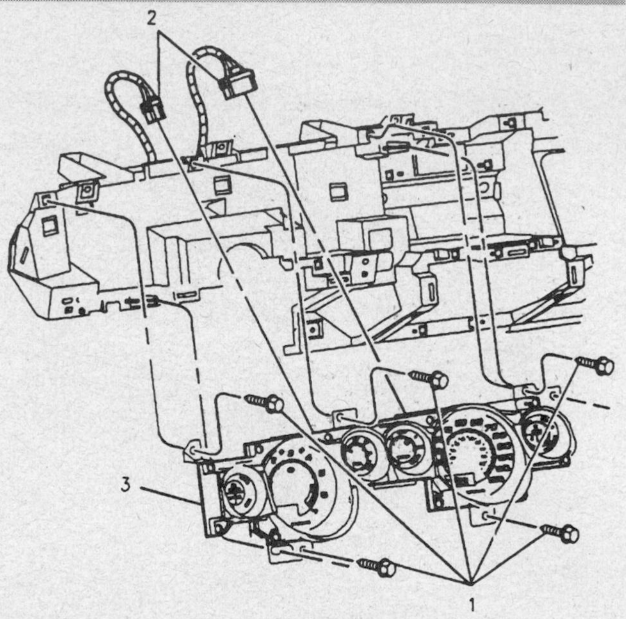
2
3
1
1 SCREWS
2 CONNECTORS, ELECTRICAL
3 CLUSTER ASSEMBLY
GC9099500271000X

Fig. 14 Instrument cluster removal. Riviera

6. **On Riviera models,** remove shifter trim plate as follows:
   a. Remove upper console trim plate by pulling outward.
   b. Remove shifter trim plate attaching screws.
   c. Pull shifter trim plate upward and disconnect electrical connectors.
   d. Remove trim plate from center console.
7. **On all models,** remove center console attaching nuts and bolts.
8. Disconnect console electrical connectors and remove console assembly from vehicle.
9. Remove cluster trim plate as described under "Instrument Cluster, Replace."
10. **On Aurora models,** remove instrument panel upper trim pad attaching screws, then the upper trim pad attaching screws.
11. **On Riviera models,** remove instrument panel upper trim pad as follows:
    a. Carefully pry windshield defroster grill upward.
    b. Disconnect sunload temperature and twilight sentinel sensors from defroster grill.
    c. Remove defroster grill from vehicle.
    d. Remove upper trim pad to instrument panel attaching screws.
    e. Remove upper trim pad from instrument panel.
12. **On all models,** remove "A" pillar trim pads.
13. Remove left and right sound insulators.
14. **On Aurora models,** remove knee bolster attaching screws, then the knee bolster.

15. **On Riviera models,** remove knee bolster attaching screws. Disconnect electrical connectors, traction control switch and air temperature sensor, then remove knee bolster.
16. **On all models,** remove glove box from instrument panel.
17. Remove radio as described under "Radio, Replace."
18. Remove HVAC control head retaining screws.
19. Disconnect HVAC control head electrical connector, then remove control head from instrument panel.
20. Remove instrument panel to dash panel attaching screws.
21. Pull instrument panel carrier away from dash and disconnect electrical connectors and antenna cable.
22. Remove instrument panel from vehicle.
23. Recover refrigerant from A/C system.
24. Remove engine compartment vacuum tank.
25. Remove multi-use bracket to gain access to A/C lines.
26. Remove A/C lines from evaporator, then drain cooling system.
27. Disconnect heater hoses from heater core.
28. Remove PCM/Programmer bracket.
29. Remove passenger air bag module retaining screws, then the module from the vehicle.
30. Remove defroster duct, then disconnect electrical connector near blower housing.
31. Remove connector duct from case and floor.
32. Remove side window ducts.
33. Remove right center instrument panel mounting bracket.
34. Remove heater and A/C module retaining nuts.
35. Remove heater and A/C module.
36. Remove evaporator access panel from heater and A/C module.
37. Remove evaporator retaining straps, then the evaporator from heater and A/C module.
38. Reverse procedure to install.

3800/V6-231 Engine

NOTE: On Air Bag Equipped Models, Refer To "Air Bag System Precautions" Located In The Front Of This Manual For System Disarming & Arming Procedures.

NOTE: Refer To "3800/V6-231 Engines" Section In The "Buick LeSabre & Park Avenue, Cadillac DeVille & Fleetwood (FWD), Oldsmobile Eighty Eight & Ninety Eight & Pontiac Bonneville" Chapter For Procedures Not Covered In This Section.

INDEX

PRECAUTIONS

AIR BAG SYSTEMS

Refer to "Air Bag System Precautions" in the front of this manual for system disarming and arming procedures.

FUEL SYSTEM PRESSURE RELIEF

After relieving fuel system pressure, a small amount of fuel may be released when servicing fuel pipes or connections. In order to reduce the risk of personal injury, cover fuel pipe fittings with shop towel before disconnecting to catch any fuel that may leak.

1. Disconnect battery ground cable.
2. Loosen fuel filler cap to relieve tank pressure.
3. Connect suitable fuel pressure gauge to fuel pressure test connector. **Wrap a shop towel around connection to avoid fuel spillage.**
4. Insert bleed hose into a suitable container and open valve to bleed system.
5. Drain any fuel remaining in fuel gauge into suitable container.

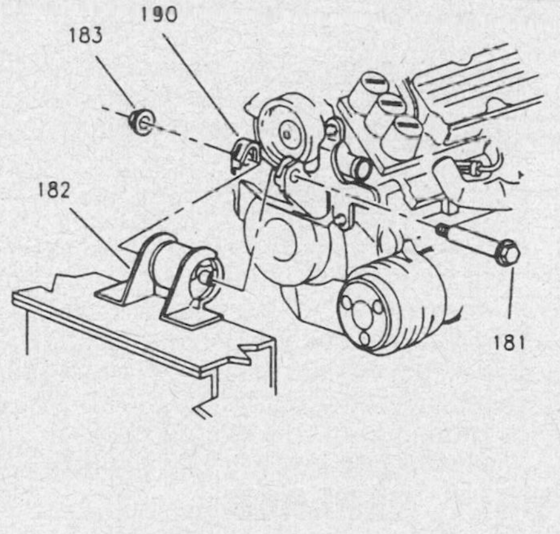

190
183
182
181
181 BOLT 87 N•m (65 LB. FT.)
183 NUT 70 N•m (52 LB. FT.)
182 TORQUE AXIS MOUNT
190 BRACKET
GC1069500602000X

Fig. 1 Engine mount replacement

ENGINE MOUNT

REPLACE

1. Disconnect battery ground cable.
2. Remove vacuum reservoir.
3. Raise engine slightly using the following engine support tools or equivalents:
   a. Engine support fixture tool No. J28467-A.
   b. Engine lifting bracket tool No. J38854.
   c. Engine core support wedges tool No. J28467-350.
   d. Engine core support arm tool No. J28467-330,
4. Remove two torque axis engine mount attaching bolts, **Fig. 1.**
5. Remove two torque axis to engine through bolts.
6. Remove serpentine drive belt as described under "Serpentine Drive Belt Service."
7. **On models less supercharger,** remove power steering pump and position aside.
8. **On all models,** raise engine to obtain enough clearance to remove engine mount from front of engine.
9. Reverse procedure to install.

ENGINE

REPLACE

1. Disconnect battery ground cable.

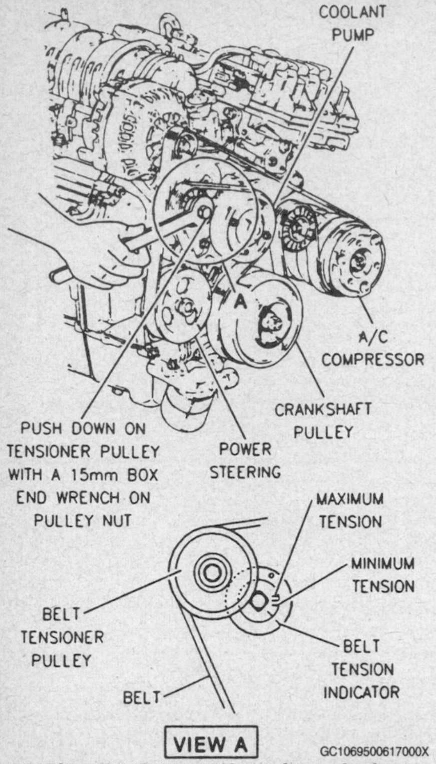
COOLANT PUMP
A/C COMPRESSOR
CRANKSHAFT PULLEY
PUSH DOWN ON TENSIONER PULLEY WITH A 15mm BOX END WRENCH ON PULLEY NUT
POWER STEERING
MAXIMUM TENSION
MINIMUM TENSION
BELT TENSIONER PULLEY
BELT TENSION INDICATOR
BELT
VIEW A
GC1069500617000X

Fig. 2 Serpentine drive belt routing. Except supercharged engine

2. Remove engine hood. **Mark hood for installation reference.**
3. Relieve fuel system pressure as described under "Precautions."
4. Drain coolant and engine oil.
5. Remove radiator and heater hoses.
6. Disconnect battery ground cable from engine.
7. Disconnect engine harness at bulkhead connector.
8. Remove serpentine drive belt.
9. Remove power steering pump from engine and position aside.
10. Remove air flow duct.
11. Disconnect throttle cable from throttle linkage mounting bracket, and other applicable cables.
12. Disconnect the following wiring harness connectors:
    a. MAT sensor.
    b. Throttle position sensor.
    c. Idle air control valve.
    d. Oxygen sensor.
    e. A/C compressor.
    f. Oil pressure switch.
    g. Power steering cutout switch.
    h. Vehicle speed sensor.
    i. Low oil level sensor.
13. Disconnect ignition coil ground strap from fender inner panel attaching screws.
14. Disconnect fuel feed and return lines from fuel rail and fuel pressure regulator.
15. Disconnect emission control canister hoses from throttle body connections.
16. Disconnect brake booster and heater control hoses from engine vacuum connections.
17. Disconnect vacuum hoses from cruise control and servo assembly.
18. Raise and support vehicle.
19. Remove exhaust pipe from righthand side exhaust manifold.
20. Remove A/C compressor and position aside.
21. Remove right front engine to transaxle bracket.
22. Remove flywheel cover, then the starter motor.
23. Remove flywheel to torque converter bolts. **Scribe marks on the flywheel and torque converter for reassembly reference.**
24. Lower vehicle.
25. Attach suitable lifting device to engine lifting brackets
26. Raise engine slightly and remove torque axis engine mount.
27. Support transaxle, then remove engine to transaxle bolts.
28. Separate engine from transaxle, then remove engine from vehicle.
29. Reverse procedure to install.

SERPENTINE DRIVE BELT

BELT TENSION INSPECTION

1. Run engine, with no accessories on, until engine is warmed up.
2. Shut engine off and read belt tension using belt tension gauge tool No. J23600-B or equivalent. Place gauge between alternator and power steering pump.
3. **On supercharged engines,** check inner belt tension between supercharger and idler pulley.
4. **On all engines,** note readings, then remove belt tension gauge.
5. Start engine and with accessories off and allow system to stabilize for 15 seconds.
6. Turn engine off and using a 15mm socket, apply clockwise force to tensioner pulley bolt. Release force and immediately take a tension reading without disturbing belt tensioner position.
7. Using 15mm socket, apply a counterclockwise force to tensioner pulley bolt and raise pulley to eliminate all tension. Slowly lower pulley to belt and take a tension reading without disturbing belt tensioner position.
8. Average three readings, if average of readings is not 50-70 lbs. and belt is within tensioners operating range, replace tensioner.

BELT, REPLACE

Refer to **Figs. 2 and 3** for serpentine drive belt replacement.

BELT TENSIONER, REPLACE

Except Supercharged Engine

1. Disconnect battery ground cable.
2. Drain engine coolant, then remove drive belt.
3. Remove alternator.

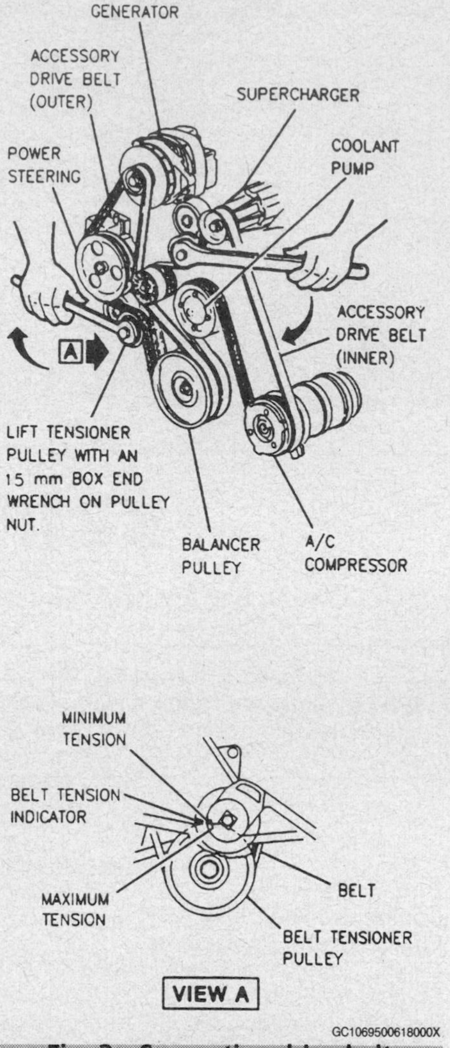
GENERATOR
ACCESSORY DRIVE BELT (OUTER)
SUPERCHARGER
POWER STEERING
COOLANT PUMP
ACCESSORY DRIVE BELT (INNER)
A
LIFT TENSIONER PULLEY WITH AN 15 mm BOX END WRENCH ON PULLEY NUT.
BALANCER PULLEY
A/C COMPRESSOR
MINIMUM TENSION
BELT TENSION INDICATOR
BELT
MAXIMUM TENSION
BELT TENSIONER PULLEY
VIEW A
GC1069500618000X

Fig. 3 Serpentine drive belt routing. Supercharged engine

4. Remove heater hoses.
5. Remove tensioner attaching bolts, then the tensioner.
6. Reverse procedure to install.

Supercharged Engine

1. Disconnect battery ground cable.
2. Remove outer and inner drive belts.
3. Remove alternator attaching bolts, then set alternator aside.
4. Drain cooling system, then disconnect heater hoses and pipes from engine.
5. Raise and support vehicle.
6. Remove lower bracket to transaxle bracket bolt.
7. Disconnect power steering hoses from power steering pump.
8. Remove power steering pump and set aside.
9. Lower vehicle.
10. Remove tensioner bracket bolts and nut from supercharger to bracket stud.
11. Remove tensioner bracket,
12. Reverse procedure to install.

COOLING SYSTEM BLEED

1. After filling cooling system, place heater and A/C control to any A/C mode except MAX. Set temperature to

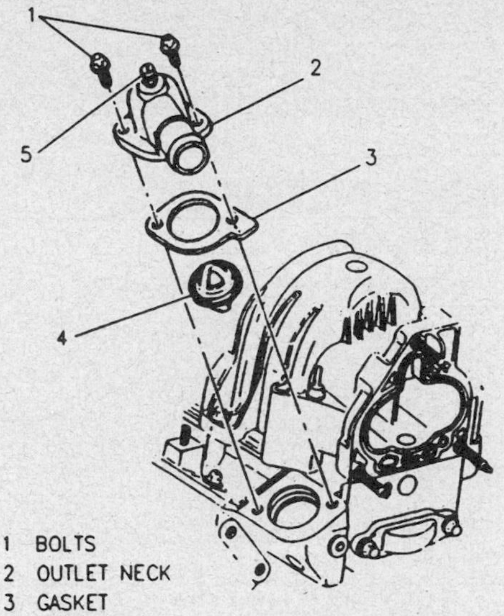
1
2
3
4
5

1 BOLTS
2 OUTLET NECK
3 GASKET
4 THERMOSTAT
5 BLEEDER VALVE

GC1089500245000X

Fig. 4 Thermostat & housing. Except supercharged engine

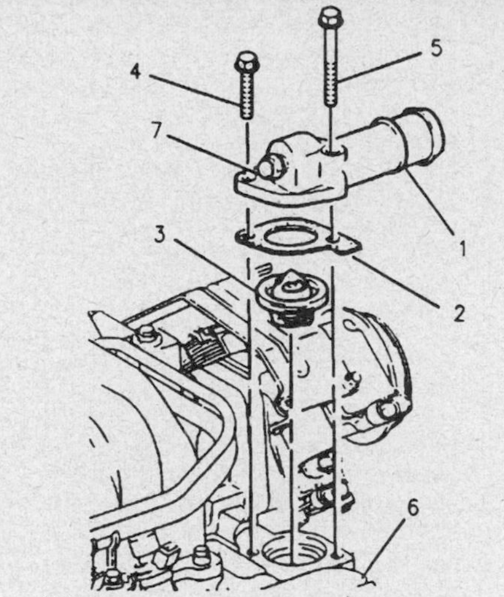
1
2
3
4
5
6
7

1 OUTLET
2 GASKET
3 THERMOSTAT
4 BOLT/SCREW
5 BOLT/SCREW
6 INTAKE MANIFOLD
7 BLEEDER VALVE

GC1089500246000X

Fig. 5 Thermostat & housing. Supercharged engine

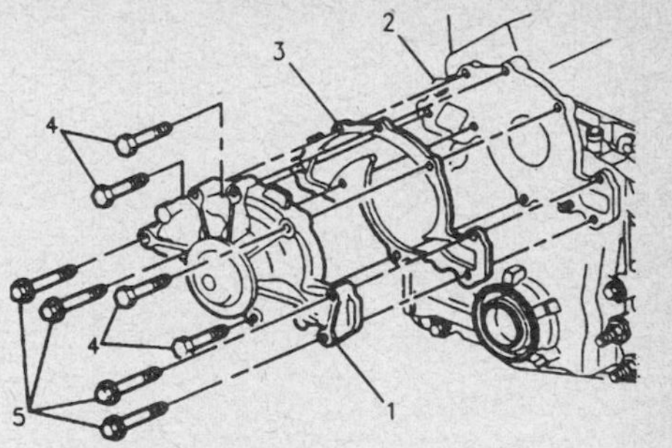
1
2
3
4
5

1 COOLANT PUMP
2 ENGINE FRONT COVER
3 GASKET
4 11 N·m (97 LB. IN.)
5 39 N·m (29 LB. FT.)

GC1089500247000X

Fig. 6 Water pump removal

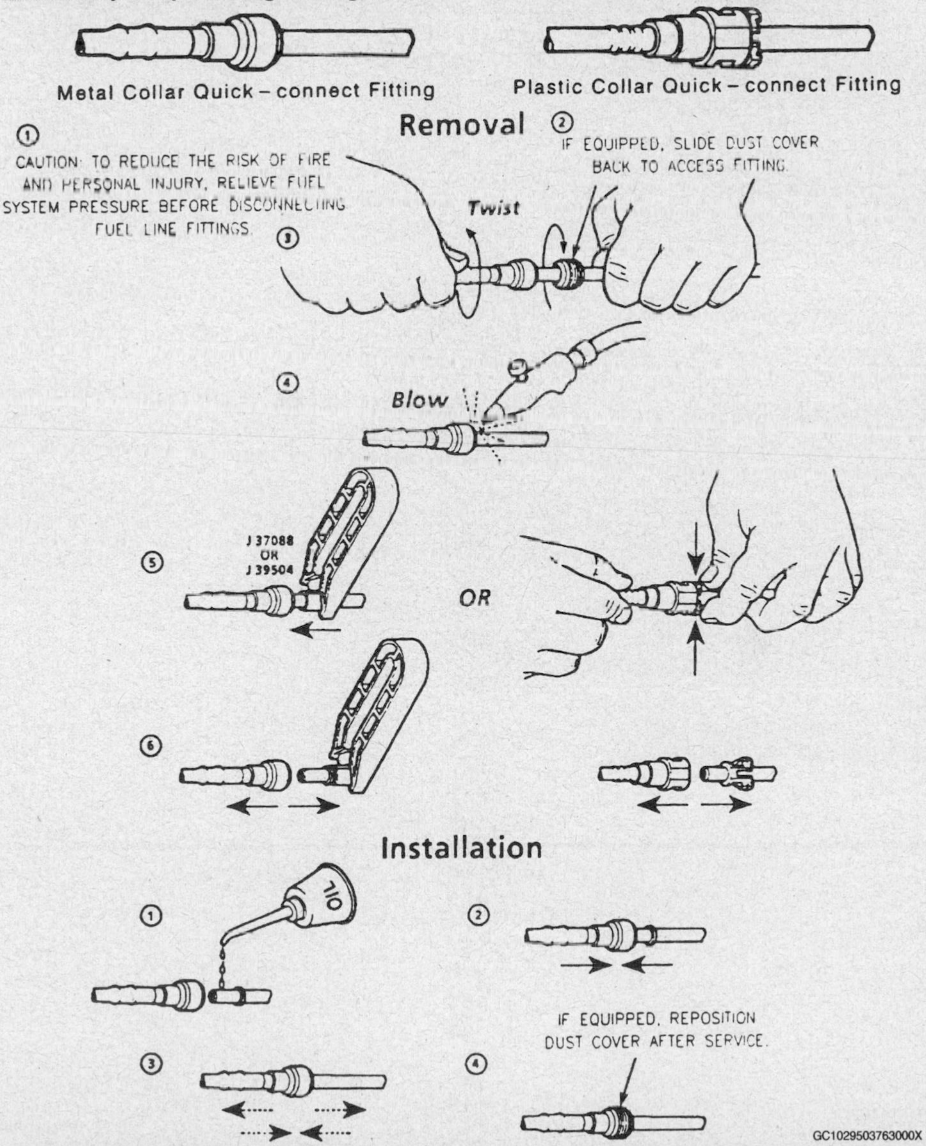
Metal Collar Quick – connect Fitting
Plastic Collar Quick – connect Fitting
Removal
① CAUTION: TO REDUCE THE RISK OF FIRE AND PERSONAL INJURY, RELIEVE FUEL SYSTEM PRESSURE BEFORE DISCONNECTING FUEL LINE FITTINGS.
② IF EQUIPPED, SLIDE DUST COVER BACK TO ACCESS FITTING.
③
Twist
④
Blow
⑤
J 37088 OR J 39504
OR
⑥
Installation
①
OIL
②
③
④
IF EQUIPPED, REPOSITION DUST COVER AFTER SERVICE.

GC1029503763000X

Fig. 7 Servicing fuel line quick-connect fittings

its highest setting.

2. Allow engine to continue idling until lower radiator hose to coolant pump is hot.
3. Cycle engine speed up to about 3000 rpm and back to idle five times.
4. Slowly open bleed valve on rear of thermostat housing for approximately 15 seconds to expel any air in the cooling system.
5. After air has been expelled, fill cooling system.

THERMOSTAT

REPLACE

1. Disconnect battery ground cable.
2. Drain cooling system.
3. Remove upper radiator hose from thermostat housing.
4. Remove thermostat housing attaching bolts, then the housing, **Figs. 4 and 5.**
5. Remove thermostat.
6. Reverse procedure to install.

WATER PUMP

REPLACE

1. Disconnect battery ground cable.
2. Drain cooling system.
3. Remove drive belt.
4. Disconnect coolant hoses from water pump.
5. Remove water pump pulley attaching bolts. Remove long bolt through access hole in body side rail.
6. Remove engine mount as described under "Engine Mount, Replace."
7. Remove water pump attaching bolts, then the pump, **Fig. 6.**
8. Reverse procedure to install.

RADIATOR

REPLACE

1. Disconnect battery ground cable.
2. Raise and support vehicle.
3. Remove lower air dam, then drain cooling system.
4. Install lower air dam and lower vehicle.
5. Remove upper tie bar.
6. Disconnect cooling fan electrical connectors.

7. Remove left and right cooling fans.
8. Disconnect coolant level sensor electrical connector.
9. Disconnect coolant recovery hose from radiator filler neck.
10. Remove upper and lower radiator hoses from radiator.
11. Remove condenser to radiator attaching bolts.
12. Remove transaxle cooler lines from radiator.
13. Remove radiator from vehicle.
14. Reverse procedure to install.

FUEL PUMP

REPLACE

1. Drain fuel tank to at least 3/4 of a tank.
2. Relieve fuel system pressure as described under "Precautions."
3. Remove spare tire cover, jack and tire.
4. Pull back trunk liner, then remove fuel sender access panel.
5. Disconnect quick-connect fittings from fuel pump as shown in **Fig. 7.**
6. Disconnect fuel pump electrical connectors.
7. Using retaining ring removal tool No. J39765 or equivalent, remove fuel pump retaining ring.
8. Pull fuel pump straight up and hold while pumping fuel from reservoir. **When removing fuel pump from fuel tank, the reservoir bucket on the fuel pump is full of fuel. It must be tipped slightly during removal to avoid damage to the float assembly. Place remaining fuel into an approved container once fuel pump is removed from fuel tank. Discard fuel pump assembly gasket.**
9. Reverse procedure to install.

FUEL FILTER

REPLACE

1. Relieve fuel system pressure as described under "Precautions."
2. Raise and support vehicle.
3. Disconnect quick-connect fittings from fuel filter shown in **Fig. 7.**
4. Disconnect fuel feed pipe from fuel filter and drain any remaining fuel into an approved container.
5. Remove fuel filter.
6. Reverse procedure to install.

TIGHTENING SPECIFICATIONS

Year	Component	Torque Ft. Lbs.
1995	Alternator Support To Cylinder Head	11
	Alternator Support Through Alternator	36
	Coolant Temperature Sensor	15
	Drive Belt Tensioner Bracket	33
	Engine Mount To Cylinder Block	70
	Flywheel Cover	48①
	Flywheel To Crankshaft	②
	Fuel Feed & Return Pipes	22
	Heater Hose Fitting To Intake	11
	Ignition Module To Alternator	18
	Oil Level Sensor	16
	Oil Pan Drain Plug	30
	Starter Motor	35
	Thermostat Housing	20
	Throttle Cable Bracket	35①
	Torque Converter To Flywheel	46
	Transaxle To Cylinder Block	55
	Water Pump Pulley	114①
	Water Pump To Front Cover	③

①—Inch lbs.
②—11 ft. lbs. plus an additional 50°.
③—11 ft. lbs. plus an additional 80°.

4.0L/V8-244 Engine

NOTE: On Air Bag Equipped Models, Refer To "Air Bag System Precautions" Located In The Front Of This Manual For System Disarming & Arming Procedures.

INDEX

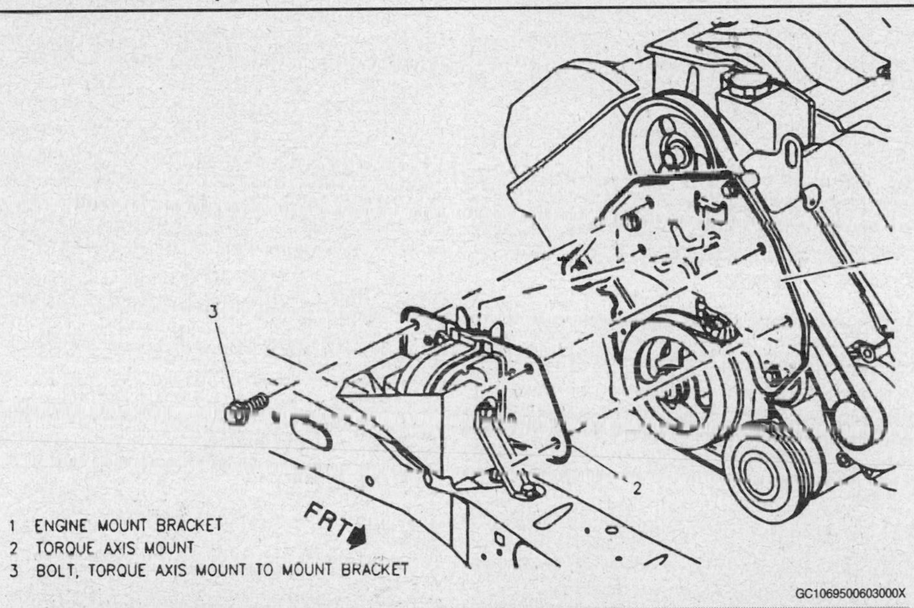

3
2
FRT
1 ENGINE MOUNT BRACKET
2 TORQUE AXIS MOUNT
3 BOLT, TORQUE AXIS MOUNT TO MOUNT BRACKET
GC1069500603000X

Fig. 1 Front engine mount

PRECAUTIONS

AIR BAG SYSTEMS

Refer to "Air Bag System Precautions" in the front of this manual for system disarming and arming procedures.

FUEL SYSTEM PRESSURE RELIEF

After relieving fuel system pressure, a small amount of fuel may be released when servicing fuel pipes or connections. In order to reduce the risk of personal injury, cover fuel pipe fittings with shop towel before disconnecting to catch any fuel that may leak.

1. Disconnect battery ground cable.
2. Loosen fuel filler cap to relieve tank pressure.
3. Connect suitable fuel pressure gauge to fuel pressure test connector. **Wrap a shop towel around connection to avoid fuel spillage.**
4. Insert bleed hose into a suitable container and open valve to bleed system.
5. Drain any fuel remaining in fuel gauge into suitable container.

ENGINE MOUNT

REPLACE

1. Install engine support fixture tool No. J28467-A, core support wedges tool No. J28467-350 and core support bar tool No. J28467-330 or equivalent lifting devices to engine.
2. Remove engine mount to body through bolt.
3. Remove torque axis engine mount from engine mount bracket, **Fig. 1.**
4. Raise and support vehicle.
5. Remove right front tire and wheel assembly.
6. Remove splash shield from wheel well.
7. Remove lower center air deflector.
8. Remove left transaxle mount to cradle through bolt.
9. Remove lower retaining bolt/nut from engine mount bracket.
10. Remove power steering pump and set aside.
11. Raise engine with support fixture.
12. Remove engine mount bracket from engine.
13. Remove torque axis mount from body.
14. Reverse procedure to install.

ENGINE

REPLACE

1. Disconnect battery ground cable.
2. Drain cooling system and oil from crankcase.
3. Relieve fuel system pressure as described under "Precautions."
4. Recover refrigerant from A/C system.
5. Disconnect fuel feed and return lines.
6. Disconnect vacuum harness from rear of intake.
7. Disconnect engine wire harness at bulkhead.
8. Disconnect coolant hoses from overflow reservoir.
9. Remove upper radiator hose from coolant crossover.
10. Remove lower radiator hose at thermostat housing.
11. Disconnect upper transaxle cooler hose at radiator.
12. Disconnect lower transaxle cooler hose at transaxle.
13. Remove heater hoses from coolant pipes at rear of engine.
14. Disconnect brake booster vacuum hose.
15. Remove shift control cable retaining bracket from transaxle.

16. Remove shift control cable from lever on transaxle.
17. Remove vacuum reservoir.
18. Disconnect vacuum and electrical connectors at cruise control servo.
19. Install engine support fixture.
20. Disconnect positive battery cable at junction block.
21. Remove through bolt from front engine mount.
22. Remove front engine mount bolts from front plate.
23. Disconnect battery ground cable from engine block.
24. Raise and support vehicle.
25. Remove both front wheels.
26. Remove right and left splash shields.
27. Disconnect steering gear electrical connector.
28. Remove cotter pin from lefthand side ball joint, then separate ball joint from steering knuckle.
29. Remove hub assembly from left axle shaft.
30. Remove exhaust pipe to exhaust manifold attaching bolts and nuts, then separate exhaust system from exhaust manifold.
31. Remove engine oil cooler hoses at adapter.
32. Remove engine to transaxle brace.
33. Remove flywheel cover.
34. Remove flywheel to converter bolts.
35. Remove oil cooler adapter from engine block.
36. Disconnect A/C hose and muffler from rear of A/C compressor.
37. Position cradle support table under engine and lower vehicle.
38. Remove left transaxle mount.
39. Support front of lower engine with a block of wood.
40. Release engine support.
41. Remove engine cradle bolts.
42. Raise vehicle and remove engine and transaxle assembly from under vehicle.
43. Reverse procedure to install. **When refilling cooling system refer to "Cooling System Bleed" procedure for important cooling system refill information.**

INTAKE MANIFOLD
REPLACE

1. Disconnect battery ground cable.
2. Relieve fuel system pressure as described under "Precautions."
3. Remove air intake duct from throttle body.
4. Disconnect intake manifold, throttle position sensor, ISC motor, EEC solenoid and cruise control servo electrical connectors.
5. Disconnect brake booster, fuel rail and throttle body vacuum hoses.
6. Disconnect PCV hose at manifold.
7. Disconnect throttle cable at throttle body and position aside.
8. Disconnect fuel pipe quick connect fittings at fuel rail.
9. Remove EEC solenoid bracket at rear cam cover, then reposition transaxle range control cable away from cruise control servo.
10. Remove intake manifold attaching bolts, then the intake manifold and throttle body assembly.
11. Reverse procedure to install.

EXHAUST MANIFOLD
REPLACE

LEFT SIDE

1. Disconnect battery ground cable.
2. Remove drive belt from power steering and generator pulleys and set aside.
3. Remove alternator upper retaining bolt.
4. Raise and support vehicle.
5. Remove righthand side splash shield from wheel well.
6. Remove lower center air deflector.
7. Remove rear alternator bracket, then the lower alternator retaining bolt, position alternator aside.
8. Remove exhaust manifold to crossover exhaust pipe bolts.
9. Disconnect oxygen sensor electrical connector.
10. Remove exhaust manifold to cylinder head attaching bolts.
11. Remove exhaust manifold and gasket from cylinder head.
12. Remove oxygen sensor from manifold.
13. Reverse procedure to install, coat oxygen sensor threads with suitable high temperature anti-seize lubricant prior to installation.

RIGHT SIDE

1. Disconnect battery ground cable.
2. Raise and support vehicle.
3. Remove exhaust "Y" pipe from front of catalytic converter.
4. Remove exhaust "Y" pipe from exhaust manifold.
5. Remove heat shield and knock sensor.
6. Disconnect oxygen sensor electrical connector.
7. Remove exhaust manifold retaining nuts.
8. Remove exhaust manifold and gasket.
9. Remove oxygen sensor from exhaust manifold.
10. Reverse procedure to install, coat oxygen sensor threads with suitable high temperature anti-seize lubricant prior to installation.

CYLINDER HEAD
REPLACE

Align all timing marks before removing cylinder heads and timing chains. Especially if only removing one cylinder head.

1. Remove engine assembly as described under "Engine, Replace."
2. Remove intake manifold as described under "Intake Manifold, Replace."
3. Remove cam covers as described in "Cam Covers, Replace."
4. Remove harmonic balancer as described in "Harmonic Balancer, Replace."
5. Remove front cover as described in "Front Cover, Replace."
6. Remove oil pump as described in "Oil Pump, Replace."
7. Remove chain tensioner from timing chain, then the cam sprocket. Timing chain should remain in case.
8. Remove timing chain guides and lever. Access for retaining bolts is through plugs at front of cylinder head.
9. Remove water crossover.
10. Remove exhaust manifold.
11. Remove cylinder head bolts, then the cylinder head and gasket.
12. Reverse procedure to install, noting the following:
    a. Clean any remaining gasket material from cylinder head and cylinder head mating surface. **Extreme care must be taken when cleaning aluminum gasket surfaces to prevent damage to the sealing surfaces. Use only plastic, wood or dull gasket scrapers. Chemical agents can be used to dissolve gasket materials, follow manufacturers recommendations carefully.**
    b. Coat washers and underside of cylinder bolt heads with suitable anti-seize lubricant, prior to installation.
    c. Tighten ten M11 cylinder head bolts in three steps in sequence shown in **Fig. 2.** First **torque** to 22 ft. lbs., then an additional 60°, then final tighten in sequence an additional 60°.
    d. **Torque** three cylinder head M6 bolts to 10 ft. lbs.

CAM COVERS
REPLACE

LEFT

1. Disconnect battery ground cable.
2. Remove intake manifold sight shield.
3. Partially drain cooling system, then remove upper radiator hose.
4. Disconnect lefthand side spark plug wires from plugs.
5. Remove upper core support brace.
6. Remove PCV fresh air tube from cam cover.
7. Remove air intake hose and EGR outlet pipe.
8. Remove coolant drive belt shield and coolant pump drive belt.
9. Remove coolant pump drive belt tensioner and coolant pump pulley.
10. Remove oil level dipstick and tube.
11. Remove camshaft seal retainer screws and seal.
12. Remove cam cover attaching bolts.
13. Remove cam cover by moving cam drive end cover up and then pivot entire cover around water pump drive shaft. Continue moving cover upward and pivoting such that edge of cover closely follows the left edge of intake manifold cover. Remove cover, **Fig. 3.**

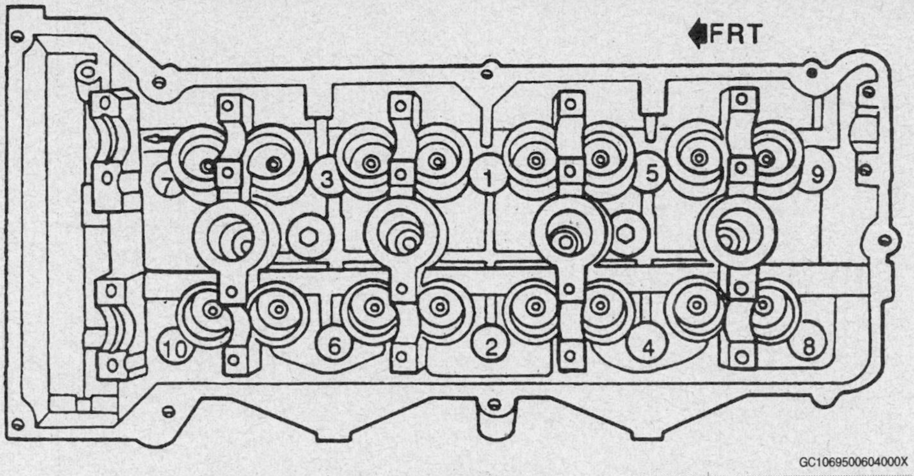
FRT
1
2
3
4
5
6
7
8
9
10
GC1069500604000X

Fig. 2 Cylinder head tightening sequence

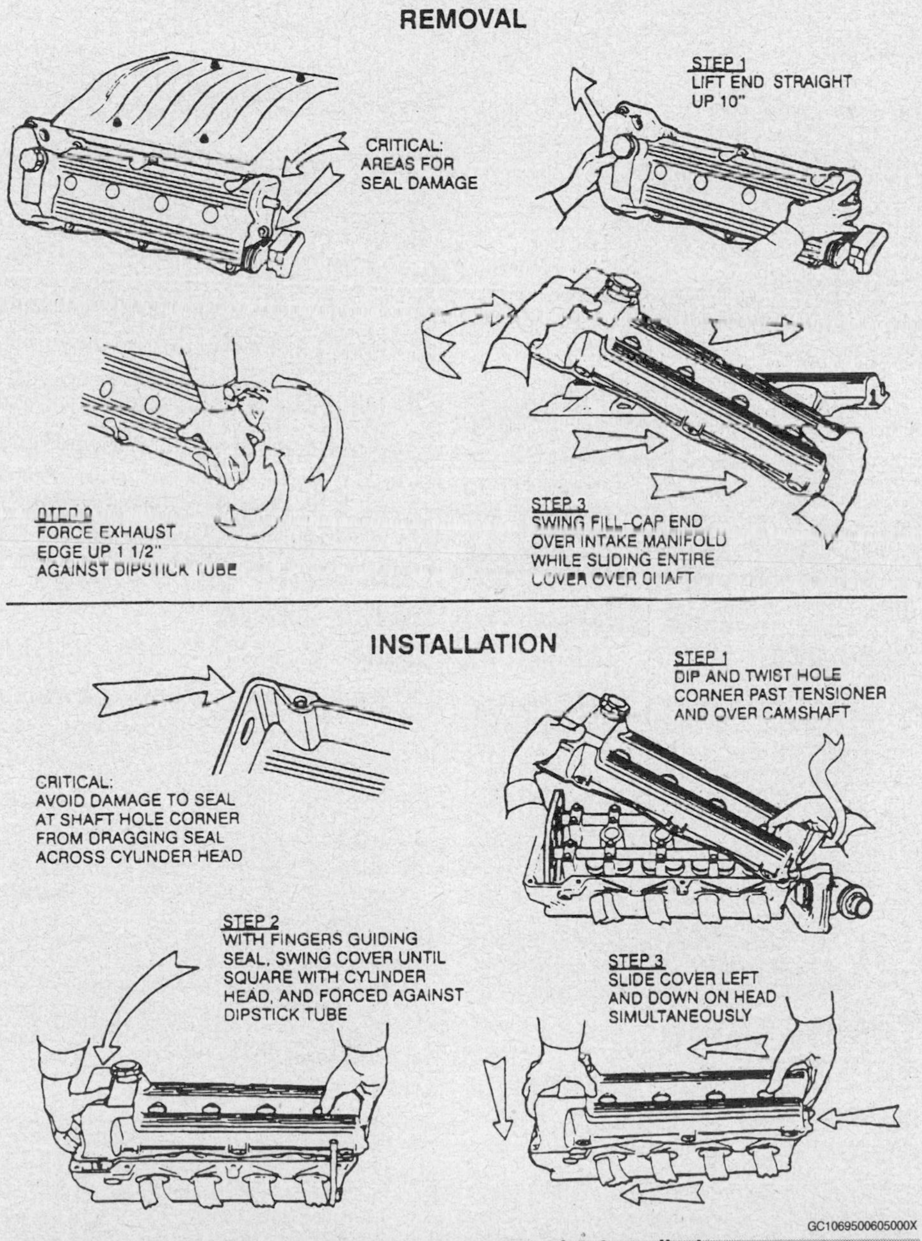
REMOVAL
STEP 1
LIFT END STRAIGHT UP 10"
CRITICAL:
AREAS FOR SEAL DAMAGE
STEP 2
FORCE EXHAUST EDGE UP 1 1/2" AGAINST DIPSTICK TUBE
STEP 3
SWING FILL-CAP END OVER INTAKE MANIFOLD WHILE SLIDING ENTIRE COVER OVER SHAFT
INSTALLATION
STEP 1
DIP AND TWIST HOLE CORNER PAST TENSIONER AND OVER CAMSHAFT
CRITICAL:
AVOID DAMAGE TO SEAL AT SHAFT HOLE CORNER FROM DRAGGING SEAL ACROSS CYLINDER HEAD
STEP 2
WITH FINGERS GUIDING SEAL, SWING COVER UNTIL SQUARE WITH CYLINDER HEAD, AND FORCED AGAINST DIPSTICK TUBE
STEP 3
SLIDE COVER LEFT AND DOWN ON HEAD SIMULTANEOUSLY
GC1069500605000X

Fig. 3 Left cam cover removal & installation

14. Reverse procedure to install, noting the following:
    a. Insert intake cam through hole in cam cover and use fingers to guide cam cover up over edge of cylinder head. **Use care to prevent exposed section of cam cover seal from being damaged by edge of cylinder head casting.**
    b. Work cover into position by allowing top edge of cover to follow left-hand edge of intake manifold.
    c. **When refilling cooling system refer to "Cooling System Bleed" procedure for important cooling system refill information.**

RIGHT

1. Disconnect battery ground cable.
2. Remove intake manifold sight shield.
3. Remove vacuum reservoir.
4. Remove cruise control servo and position aside.
5. Disconnect DIS ignition module wiring connectors, then remove DIS module attaching bolts.
6. Remove DIS ignition module and spark plug wires from cam cover.
7. Remove PCV valve and canister purge solenoid from cam cover.
8. Raise and support vehicle.
9. Disconnect the following electrical connectors:
    a. Knock sensor.
    b. Vehicle speed sensor.
    c. Power steering pressure switch.
10. Lower vehicle, then remove wiring harness retainers from cover.
11. Remove cam cover attaching bolts, then the cam cover.
12. Reverse procedure to install.

VALVE CLEARANCE SPECIFICATIONS

These engines are equipped with hydraulic valve lifters. Valve clearance should be zero.

VALVE ADJUSTMENT

These engines are equipped with hydraulic valve lifters. No adjustment is required.

VALVE GUIDES

Check valve stem to valve guide clearance. Clearance should be .005 inch or less. Service valves are available in standard size (.235 inch). If clearance is excessive and new standard size valve stem will not bring clearance within specifications, cylinder head must be replaced.

HYDRAULIC LIFTERS

REPLACE

1. Remove cylinder head as described in "Cylinder Head, Replace."
2. If camshafts remain in cylinder head some valves will always be held open and cylinder head cannot be set on workbench with cylinder head face down. Damage to valves and/or gasket surface will result.

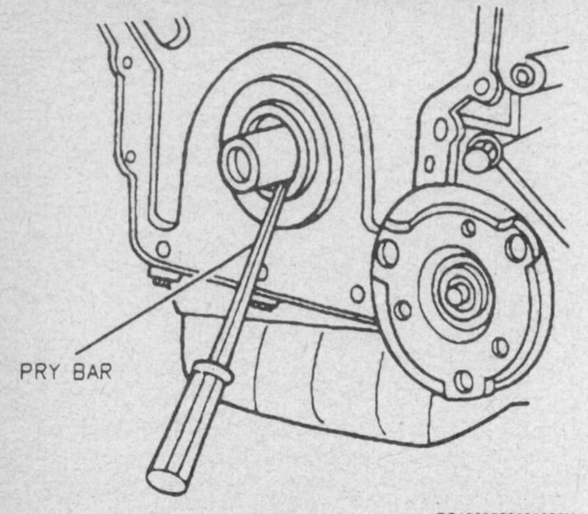
PRY BAR

GC1069500606000X

Fig. 4 Front cover seal removal

3. Remove intake and exhaust camshafts by alternately loosening each cam bearing cap bolt two turns at a time until valve spring pressure is completely released. **Do not mix cam bearing caps between positions or between heads. Each cap must be reassembled in the position from which it was removed and in the original orientation (arrow points toward front of engine).**
4. Remove valve lifters and arrange them so they may be installed in their original position.
5. Reverse procedure to install, noting the following:
   a. Lubricate camshaft bearing journals with engine oil prior to installation.
   b. Alternately tighten camshaft bearing cap bolts one turn at a time to specifications.

HARMONIC BALANCER

REPLACE

1. Release accessory drive belt tension.
2. Remove torque axis engine mount as described in "Engine Mount, Replace.
3. Remove brace between engine oil pan and transaxle case and install flywheel holder tool No. J39411 or equivalent.
4. Remove harmonic balancer attaching bolt.
5. Lower engine at support fixture to obtain clearance for pulling tool J38416-A or equivalent below body rail.
6. Install pilot tool No. J39344-2 or equivalent into end of crankshaft.
7. Install pulling tool No. J38416-A or equivalent onto balancer, then remove balancer from end of crankshaft.
8. Reverse procedure to install, noting the following:
   a. Thoroughly clean balancer bolt threads.
   b. Apply clean engine oil to balancer bolt threads prior to installation.
   c. Tighten bolt to specification.

FRONT COVER

REPLACE

1. Remove accessory drive belt.
2. Remove harmonic balancer as described in "Harmonic Balancer, Replace."
3. Remove drive belt tensioner and belt idler pulley.
4. Remove front cover attaching bolts, then the cover and gasket.
5. Reverse procedure to install. Front cover seal is reusable, do not discard unless seal is damaged.

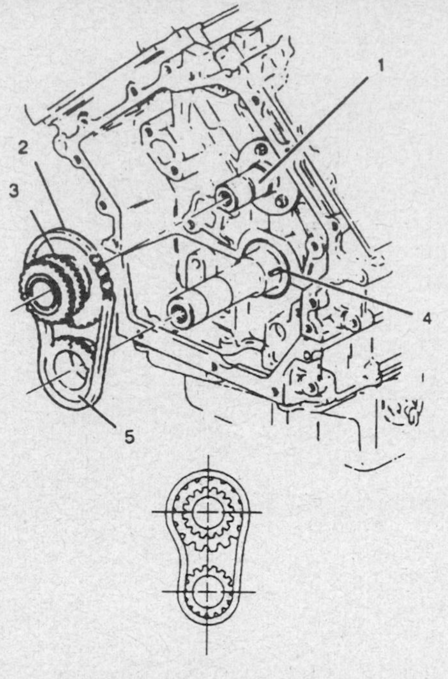
1
2
3
4
5

1 INTERMEDIATE SHAFT
2 PRIMARY CHAIN
3 INTERMEDIATE SHAFT SPROCKET
4 CRANKSHAFT SPROCKET KEY
5 SPROCKET

GC1069500607000X

Fig. 5 Primary drive chain removal

FRONT COVER SEAL

REPLACE

1. Remove harmonic balancer as described in "Harmonic Balancer, Replace."
2. Using a flat-bladed screwdriver, pry front cover seal out of front cover, **Fig. 4.**
3. Reverse procedure to install, noting the following:
   a. Lubricate seal lips with clean engine oil prior to installation.
   b. Use seal installer tool No. J38818 or equivalent to push seal into front cover until tool bottoms on cover.

TIMING CHAIN

REPLACE

CAMSHAFT PRIMARY DRIVE CHAIN

1. Remove accessory drive belt, idler pulley and belt tensioner.
2. Remove front cover as described in "Front Cover, Replace."

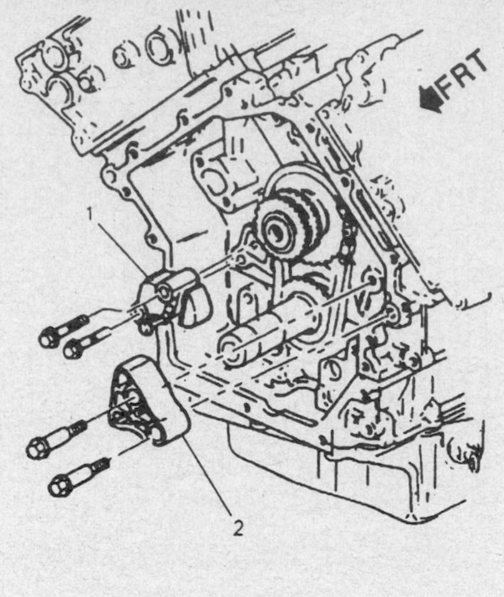
FRT
1
2

1 PRIMARY CHAIN TENSIONER
2 PRIMARY CHAIN GUIDE

GC1069500608000X

Fig. 6 Primary chain tensioner removal

3. Remove oil pump as described in "Oil Pump, Replace."
4. Remove cam covers as described in "Cam Covers, Replace."
5. Remove three timing chain tensioners.
6. Remove camshaft sprockets from all camshafts.
7. Remove secondary drive chains from around intermediate shaft sprocket.
8. Remove bolt from intermediate shaft sprocket and slide gears and primary drive chain off crankshaft and intermediate shaft, **Fig. 5.**
9. Reverse procedure to install, set camshaft timing as described in "Setting Camshaft Timing."

CAMSHAFT SECONDARY DRIVE CHAIN

Right

1. Remove front cover as described in "Front Cover, Replace."
2. Remove right side cam cover as described in "Cam Cover, Replace."
3. Remove righthand side secondary chain tensioner.
4. Remove righthand chain guide. Access upper chain guide mounting bolt through hole in cylinder head covered with plastic plug.
5. Remove right side camshaft sprockets.
6. Remove secondary drive chain.
7. Reverse procedure to install, set camshaft timing as described in "Setting Camshaft Timing."

Left

1. Remove front cover as described in "Front Cover, Replace."
2. Remove left side cam cover as described in "Cam Cover, Replace."
3. Remove lefthand side secondary chain tensioner.
4. Remove lefthand chain guide. Access

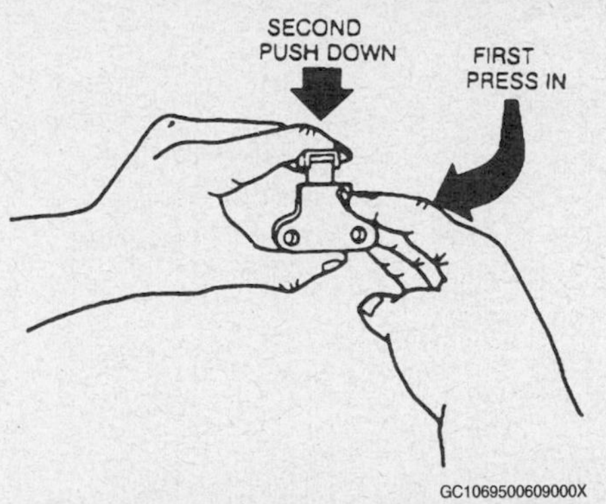
SECOND
PUSH DOWN
FIRST
PRESS IN
GC1069500609000X

Fig. 7 Rotating tensioner release lever

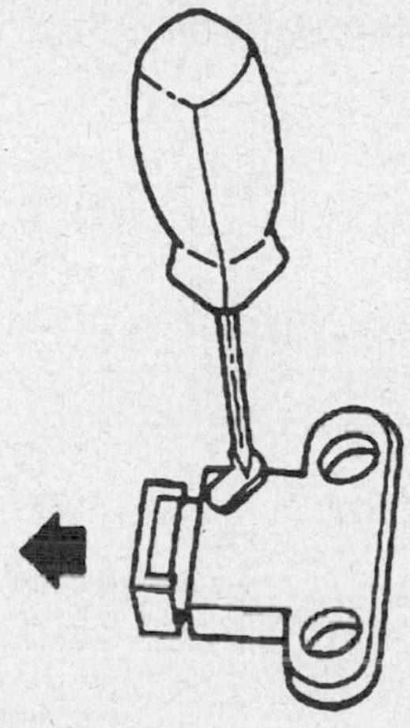
1 RELEASE TO FIRST CLICK
2 INSTALL LOCK PIN
GC1069500610000X

Fig. 8 Locking tensioner

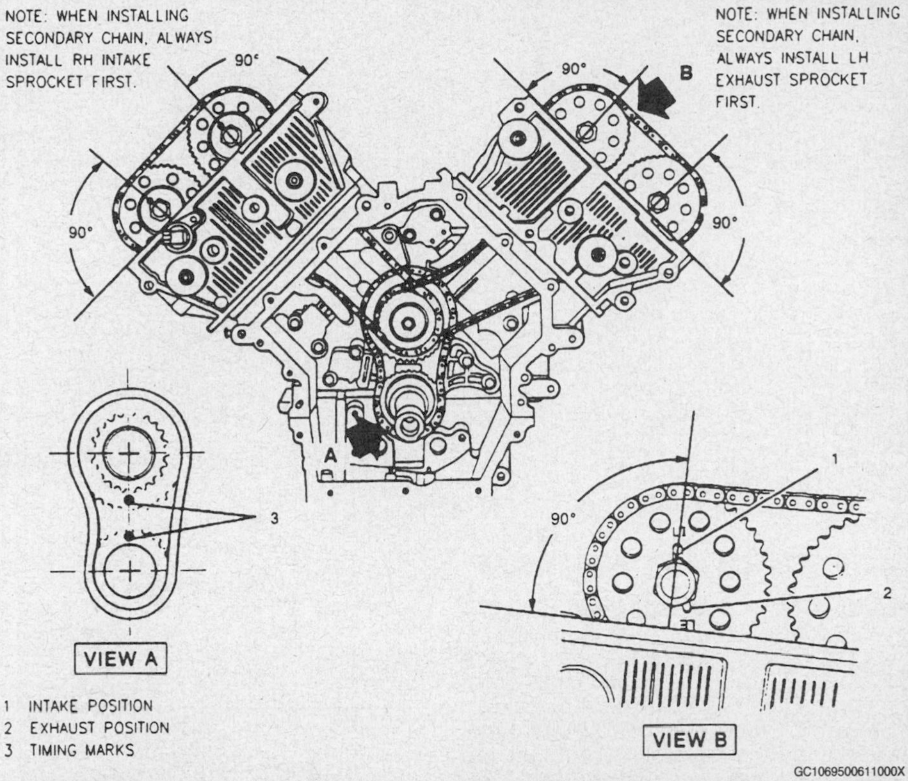
NOTE: WHEN INSTALLING SECONDARY CHAIN, ALWAYS INSTALL RH INTAKE SPROCKET FIRST.
NOTE: WHEN INSTALLING SECONDARY CHAIN, ALWAYS INSTALL LH EXHAUST SPROCKET FIRST.
90°
B
A
VIEW A
VIEW B
1 INTAKE POSITION
2 EXHAUST POSITION
3 TIMING MARKS
GC1069500611000X

Fig. 9 Setting camshaft timing

upper chain guide mounting bolt through hole in cylinder head covered with plastic plug.
5. Remove left side camshaft sprockets.
6. Remove secondary drive chain.
7. Reverse procedure to install, set camshaft timing as described in "Setting Camshaft Timing."

TIMING CHAIN TENSIONER

REPLACE

1. Remove front cover as described in "Front Cover, Replace."
2. Remove two tensioner mounting bolts, then the tensioner, **Fig. 6.**
3. Reverse procedure to install, collapse and install tensioner as follows:
   a. Rotate ratchet release lever counterclockwise and hold, **Fig. 7.**
   b. Collapse tensioner retainer shoe and hold.
   c. Release ratchet lever and slowly release pressure on shoe.
   d. As ratchet lever moves to first click hold tensioner shoe at this point and insert a pin through hole and release lever, **Fig. 8.**
   e. Install tensioner and bolts, then remove retaining pin allowing tensioner shoe to extend.

SETTING CAMSHAFT TIMING

Any references to right and left cylinder heads are from rear of engine. This engine is an interference fit engine, meaning that the engine is not free spinning and pistons will strike valves if crankshaft is rotated with camshaft drive disconnected or if camshafts are not properly timed. The camshaft levers are not interchangeable and are marked with left and right designations. The secondary chains, chain guides and chain tensioners are interchangeable.

1. Remove cam covers as described in "Cam Covers, Replace."
2. Remove front engine mount as described in "Engine Mount, Replace."
3. Support front of engine, then remove front cover as described in "Front Cover, Replace."
4. Remove three chain tensioners. Chain tensioners may remain in their installed position, but must be fully retracted.
5. Remove oil pump as described "Oil Pump, Replace."
6. Using suitable socket, rotate crankshaft until No. 1 piston is at Top Dead Center (TDC) and sprocket drive key is at approximately the 1 o'clock position.
7. Install crankshaft and intermediate shaft sprockets to primary drive chain with their timing marks adjacent to each other, **Fig. 9.**
8. Install crank and intermediate sprockets over their respective shafts.
9. Rotate crankshaft as necessary to engage crankshaft key in sprocket without changing relationship of timing marks to each other.
10. Install intermediate sprocket retainer bolt and tighten bolt to specification.
11. Install primary chain tensioner and release tensioner shoe.
12. Install flywheel holding tool No. J39411 or equivalent to lock crankshaft into position.
13. Route secondary drive chain for left-hand side cylinder head over inner row of intermediate shaft teeth.
14. Route secondary drive chain over chain guide and install left exhaust cam sprocket to chain so that camshaft drive pin engages sprocket notch marked "LE." There should be no slack in lower section of chain and cam drive pin must be perpendicular to cylinder head face. "RE" cam sprocket should contain cam position sensor pickup.
15. Loosely install exhaust cam sprocket retainer bolt.
16. Install intake cam sprocket into chain so that sprocket notch marked "LI" engages cam drive pin while pin remains perpendicular to cylinder head face. A hex is cast into camshaft behind lobes for cylinder No. 1 (or No. 2 left) so that an open end wrench may be used to provide minor repositioning of cams.
17. Loosely install cam sprocket retaining bolt.
18. Install chain tensioner and release tension on shoe. Tighten tensioner and cam sprocket bolts to specifications.

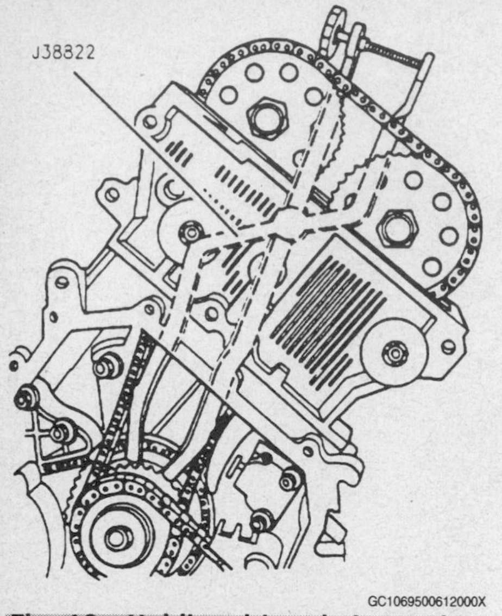
J38822
GC1069500612000X

Fig. 10 Holding drive chain tension

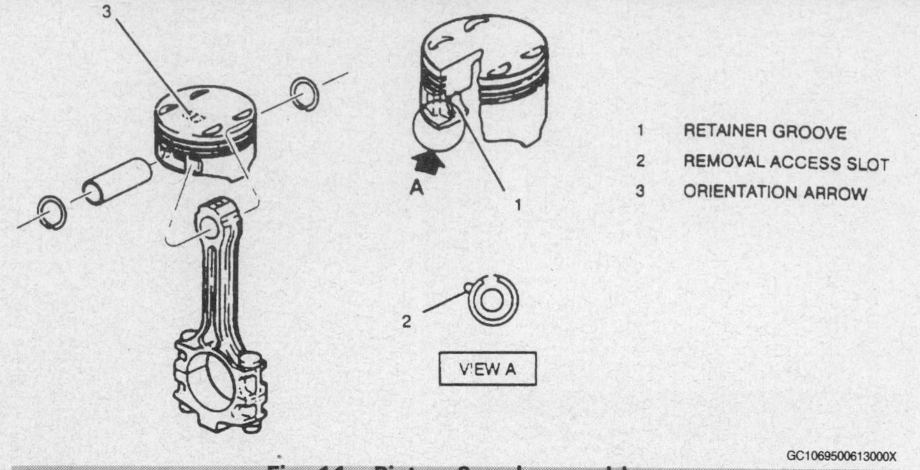
1 RETAINER GROOVE
2 REMOVAL ACCESS SLOT
3 ORIENTATION ARROW
A
VIEW A
GC1069500613000X

Fig. 11 Piston & rod assembly

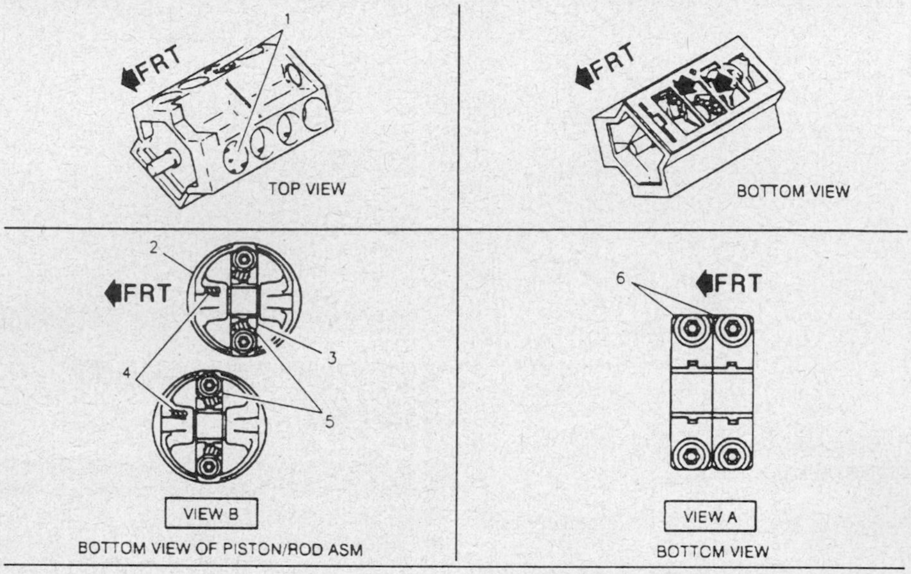
FRT
TOP VIEW
BOTTOM VIEW
VIEW B
BOTTOM VIEW OF PISTON/ROD ASM
VIEW A
BOTTOM VIEW

1 PISTON ARROW TOWARD CHAIN CASE ON BOTH SIDES
2 PISTON
3 ROD CAP
4 LOCATER LUGS INDICATE PISTON FRONT TOWARDS ENGINE FRONT
5 BEARING CAP NOTCHES POINT TOWARD EACH OTHER ON PAIRED RODS
6 ROD CAPS

GC1069500614000X

Fig. 12 Piston installation

19. Route secondary drive chain for righthand cylinder head over outer row of intermediate shaft teeth and repeat steps 6 through 18 for righthand cams. Righthand side cam sprockets are identified "RI" (right intake) and "RE" (right exhaust). There should be no slack on "RI" sprocket side of chain, install "RI" sprocket first for right cylinder head.

CAMSHAFT

REPLACE

1. Remove cam cover as described in "Cam Cover, Replace."
2. Set engine at TDC (No. 1 piston) and align timing marks to correct position.
3. Secure cam sprocket to timing chain using tie-raps through cam sprocket holes. Use two tie-raps per sprocket. **Sprocket to chain relationship must be maintained throughout this procedure or camshaft timing will be lost and require further engine disassembly for retiming.**
4. Working behind sprockets, install cam chain holder J38822 or equivalent so that it is positioned between chain tensioner and chain guide, **Fig. 10.** Apply tension to tool by tightening tension adjusting screw. **When using cam chain holder tool on right cylinder bank it is necessary to remove wiper motor to gain enough clearance for tool usage.**
5. Remove camshaft sprocket bolts. Note relative location of cam drive pins in ends of camshafts.
6. Work sprockets off of cams using play in chain.
7. Remove intake and exhaust camshafts by alternately loosening each cam bearing cap bolt two turns at a time until valve spring pressure is completely released. **Do not mix cam bearing caps between positions or between heads. Each cap must be reassembled in the position from which it was removed and in the original orientation (arrow points toward front of engine).**
8. Reverse procedure to install.

PISTON & ROD ASSEMBLY

Refer to **Fig. 11** for piston and rod assembly. Refer to **Fig. 12** for piston installation.

MAIN & ROD BEARINGS

Shell type main bearings of steel backed aluminum are used at all positions. The upper and lower bearing halves are all interchangeable except for the upper bearing in the No. 3 position as this is the thrust bearing. Maximum crankshaft endplay is .019 inch.

With the crankcase disassembled the main bearing clearance can be measured using a suitable plastic gauging material. Wipe oil from crankshaft journals and bearing inserts. Place plastic gauging material across journals to be measured. Install lower crankcase and oil manifold. Install main bearing bolts and using sequence shown in **Fig. 13,** tighten bolts to specifications. Determine clearance by comparing width of flattened plastic gauging material with measurement increments on plastic gauging package. If bearing clearance is greater than .003 inch and new bearings do not reduce clearance to .0005 to .002 inch a new crankshaft is required. Undersized bearings are not available and no crankshaft grinding is allowed.

CRANKSHAFT SEAL

REPLACE

1. Remove powertrain assembly as described in "Engine, Replace."

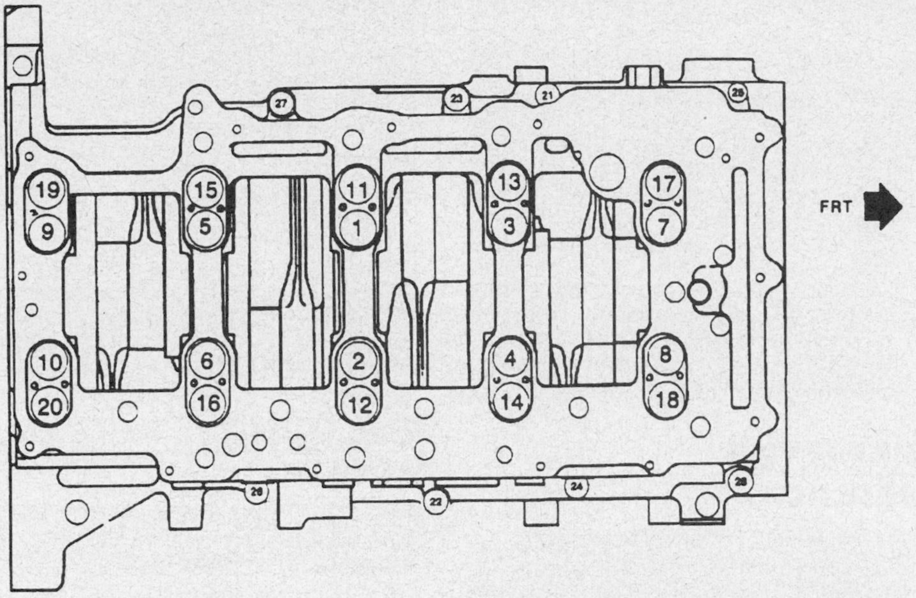
FRT
GC1069500615000X

Fig. 13 Main bearing bolt tightening sequence

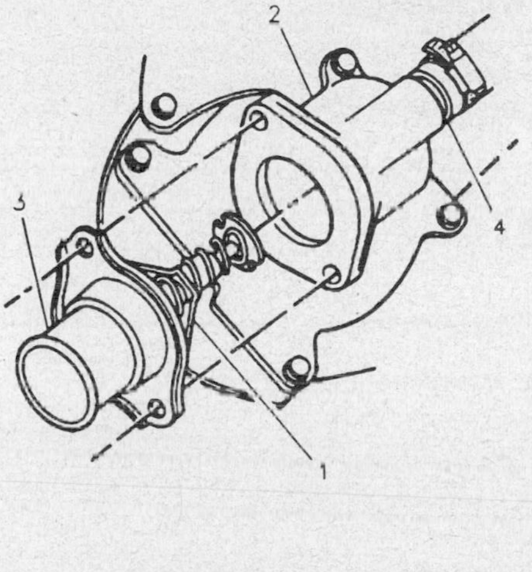
1 THERMOSTAT
2 THERMOSTAT HOUSING
3 COOLANT PUMP INLET
4 THERMOSTAT BY-PASS HOSE
GC1089500248000X

Fig. 15 Thermostat removal

2. Remove transaxle to cylinder block attaching bolts, then separate transaxle from engine.
3. Remove flywheel attaching bolts, then the flywheel.
4. Remove seal by drilling a 1/8 inch hole in metal body of seal and using a suitable slide hammer to remove seal. **Seal removal can also be done using a flat-bladed screwdriver between seal lip and crankshaft. However, extreme care is required when using this method so as to avoid any damage to sealing surface of crankshaft.**
5. Reverse procedure to install, noting the following:
   a. Place a small amount of RTV sealant at crankcase split line across end of upper and lower crankcase seal.
   b. Lubricate rear main seal with clean engine oil prior to installation.

OIL PAN

REPLACE

1. Remove powertrain assembly as described in "Engine, Replace."
2. Remove transaxle to cylinder block attaching bolts, then separate transaxle from engine.
3. Remove oil pan retaining bolts, then the oil pan.
4. Reverse procedure to install. Gasket is reusable unless damaged. **Do not remove gasket from oil pan groove unless replacement is required. If replacing gasket do not expose new gasket to oil before inserting gasket into pan groove, gasket will expand when exposed to oil and will not stay in pan groove.**

OIL PUMP

REPLACE

1. Remove front cover as described in "Front Cover, Replace."
2. Remove three oil pump mounting bolts.
3. Remove oil pump and drive spacer, **Fig. 14.**
4. Reverse procedure to install.

OIL PUMP SERVICE

DISASSEMBLE

1. Remove drive spacer from pump housing.
2. Remove two screws holding pump housing halves together.
3. Remove inner (drive) and outer (driven) rotors out of housing. Mark mating surfaces.
4. Remove pressure relief valve.

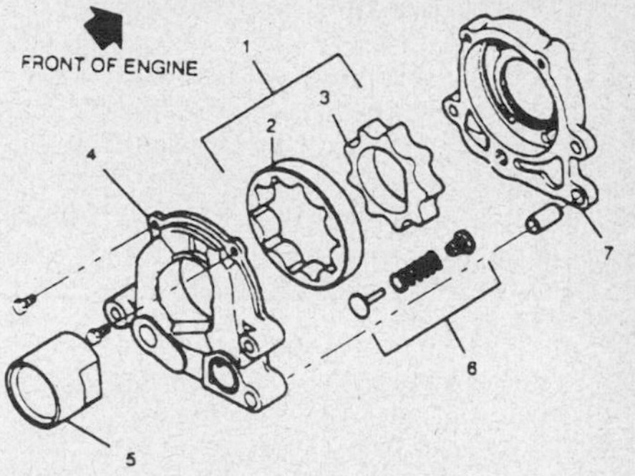
FRONT OF ENGINE
1 GEROTOR ASSEMBLY
2 OUTER GEAR
3 INNER GEAR
4 HOUSING
5 DRIVE SPACER
6 RELIEF VALVE
7 COVER
GC1069500616000X

Fig. 14 Exploded view of oil pump

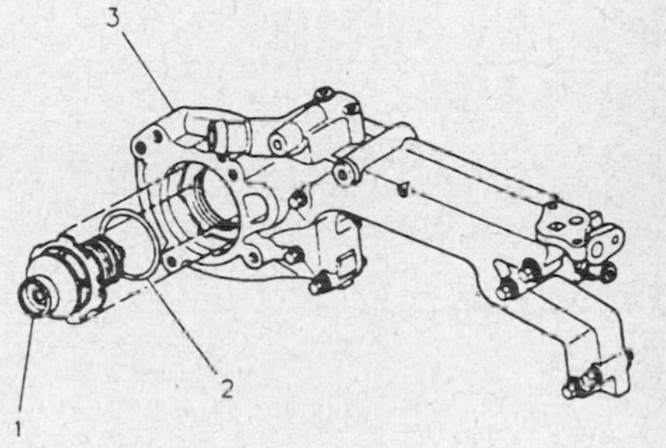
1 WATER PUMP ASSEMBLY
2 O RING SEAL
3 WATER PUMP HOUSING ASSEMBLY
GC1089500249000X

Fig. 16 Coolant pump removal

ASSEMBLE

1. Install inner and outer rotors to pump cover in same position as they were removed (dimples out).
2. Install pressure relief valve seat, spring and pilot in pump housing.
3. Assemble housing and cover over locating dowel.
4. Insert a 3/8 inch drill in pump mounting hole on opposite side to aid in alignment of housing and cover.
5. Install screws and tighten to specifications.

COOLING SYSTEM BLEED

This engine does not require a cooling system bleed procedure. However, when refilling the cooling system on aluminum engines a special coolant solution along with GM coolant supplement (sealant) part No. 3634621 or equivalent must be used. **Failure to add the sealant or the approved coolant solution could result in major engine damage.** When refilling cooling system add three pellets of engine coolant supplement (sealant) part No. 3634621 or equivalent to lower radiator hose. **Under some conditions, the ethylene glycol engine coolant is combustible. To avoid being burned, do not spill antifreeze or coolant on the exhaust system or hot engine parts.**

THERMOSTAT

REPLACE

1. Disconnect battery ground cable.
2. Drain cooling system.
3. Remove air intake duct.
4. Disconnect radiator housing from thermostat housing.
5. Remove thermostat housing attaching bolts, then the housing, **Fig. 15.**
6. Remove thermostat from thermostat housing.
7. Reverse procedure install. **When refilling cooling system refer to "Cooling System Bleed" procedure for important cooling system refill information.**

WATER PUMP

REPLACE

1. Disconnect battery ground cable.
2. Drain engine coolant.
3. Remove air intake duct.
4. Remove coolant pump drive belt cover.
5. Remove coolant pump drive belt and set aside.
6. Remove lower radiator hose and bypass hose.
7. Remove thermostat housing from coolant pump housing, **Fig. 16.**
8. Remove coolant pump by turning locking ring with coolant remover/installer tool No. J38816 or equivalent.
9. Reverse procedure to install. **When refilling cooling system refer to "Cooling System Bleed" procedure for important cooling system refill information.**

RADIATOR

REPLACE

1. Disconnect battery ground cable.
2. Raise and support vehicle.
3. Remove lower air dam, then drain cooling system.
4. Install lower air dam and lower vehicle.
5. Remove upper tie bar.
6. Disconnect cooling fan electrical connectors.
7. Remove left and right cooling fans.
8. Disconnect coolant level sensor electrical connector.
9. Disconnect coolant recovery hose from radiator filler neck.
10. Remove upper and lower radiator hoses from radiator.
11. Remove condenser to radiator attaching bolts.
12. Remove transaxle cooler lines from radiator.
13. Remove radiator from vehicle.
14. Reverse procedure to install. **When refilling cooling system refer to "Cooling System Bleed" procedure for important cooling system refill information.**

FUEL PUMP

REPLACE

Refer to "Fuel Pump, Replace" in "3800/V6-231 Engine" section for fuel pump replacement procedure.

FUEL FILTER

REPLACE

Refer to "Fuel Filter, Replace" in "3800/V6-231 Engine" section for fuel filter replacement procedure.

TIGHTENING SPECIFICATIONS

Year	Component	Torque Ft. lbs.
1995	Alternator Bracket	25
	Belt Idler Pulley	35
	Belt Tensioner	35
	Cam Cover Bolts	84①
	Camshaft Bearing Cap	9
	Camshaft Drive Chain Tensioner	20
	Camshaft Sprocket Bolts	90
	Connecting Rod Bearing Cap	⑥
	Cylinder Head	④
	Exhaust Manifold Outlet Flange	35
	Exhaust Manifold To Cylinder Head	25
	Exhaust Y Pipe	26
	Flywheel To Converter	③
	Flywheel To Crankshaft	③
	Front Cover	7
	Harmonic Balancer	②

Year	Component	Torque/Ft. Lbs.
	Intake Manifold	25
	Intermediate Sprocket	45
	Main Bearing Cap	⑦
	Oil Filter Adapter	20
	Oil Manifold	7
	Oil Pan	9
	Oil Pump	⑤
	Oxygen Sensor	30
	Primary Chain Tensioner	20
	Transaxle Brace	35
	Upper Crankcase To Lower Crankcase	22

①—Inch lbs.
②—105 ft. lbs. plus an additional 120°.
③—11 ft. lbs. plus an additional 50°.
④—Refer to text.
⑤—7 ft. lbs. plus an additional 35°.
⑥—20 ft. lbs. plus an additional 90°.
⑦—15 ft. lbs. plus an additional 65°.

Rear Suspension

INDEX

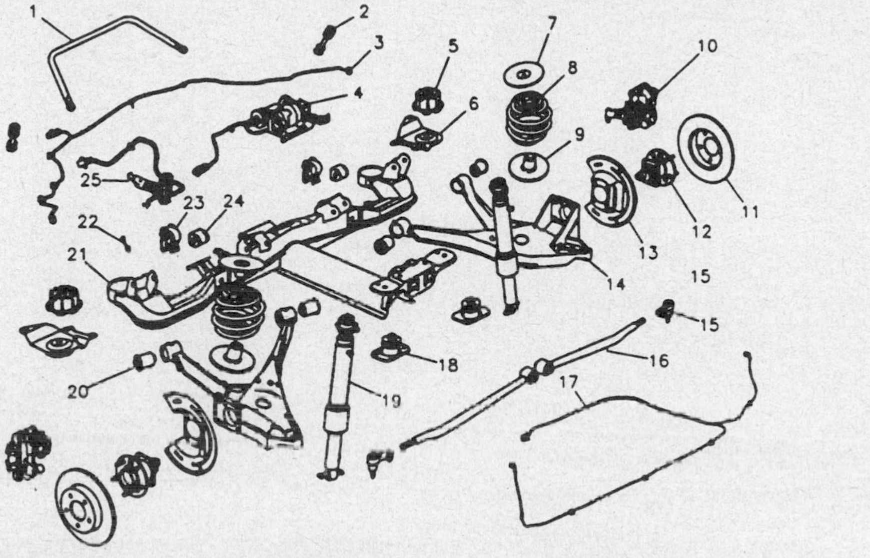

1 STABILIZER BAR
2 STABILIZER BAR LINK
3 ABS ELECTRICAL HARNESS
4 ELC COMPRESSOR
5 FORWARD BODY MOUNT
6 SUPPORT BRACKET
7 JOUNCE BUMPER
8 SPRING
9 LOWER SPRING INSULATOR
10 BRAKE CALIPER
11 BRAKE ROTOR
12 HUB AND BEARING
13 BRAKE SHIELD
14 CONTROL ARM
15 OUTER ADJUSTMENT LINK
16 INNER ADJUSTMENT LINK
17 ELC AIR LINE
18 REAR BODY MOUNT
19 SHOCK
20 CONTROL ARM BUSHING
21 REAR SUSPENSION SUPPORT ASSEMBLY
22 ELC HEIGHT SENSOR LINK
23 STABILIZER BAR CLAMP
24 STABILIZER BAR INSULATOR
25 ELC HEIGHT SENSOR

GC2039500107000X

Fig. 1 Exploded view of rear suspension

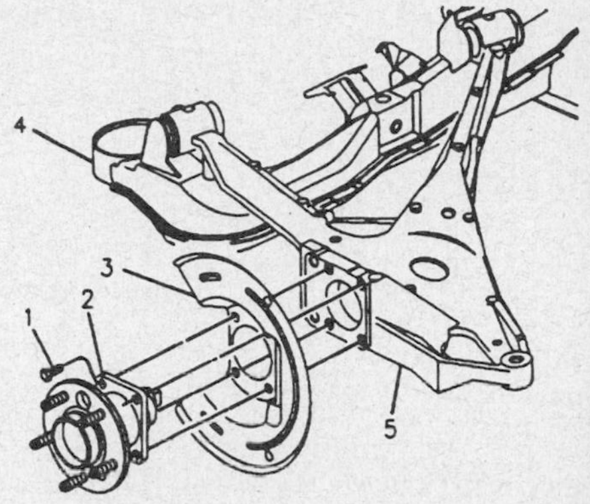

1 BOLT
2 HUB & BEARING
3 BRAKE SHIELD
4 REAR SUSPENSION SUPPORT ASSEMBLY
5 CONTROL ARM

GC2039500108000X

Fig. 2 Hub & bearing replacement

DESCRIPTION

These models utilize an independent rear suspension, **Fig. 1,** that is secured to the vehicle body at four points. Control arms, a stabilizer bar and adjustment links are connected to the rear suspension support assembly to provide side to side stability and to allow for rear toe adjustment.

The Electronic Level Control (ELC) system employs rear air adjustable shocks which are anchored at the control arms and allow the system to maintain proper vehicle ride height under various load conditions. The shocks are not manually adjustable and must be replaced if they lose their resistance or begin leaking fluid.

The rear wheel bearings have been integrated into the hubs to eliminate the necessity of adjustments and periodic maintenance. This integral hub and bearing also incorporates a wheel speed sensor ring for anti-lock brake operation.

HUB & BEARING REPLACE

1. Raise and support vehicle, then remove wheel and disc brake caliper. **It is not necessary to disconnect hydraulic line from caliper; support caliper assembly from frame to prevent hydraulic line damage.**
2. Remove brake rotor and ABS sensor wire connector.
3. Remove 4 bolts, then lift hub and bearing assembly and brake shield from control arm, **Fig. 2.**
4. Reverse procedure to install. Tighten bolts and wheel lug nuts to specifications.

HUB & BEARING SERVICE

WHEEL STUD REPLACEMENT

It is not necessary to remove the hub and bearing assembly from the vehicle to replace wheel studs.

Removal

1. Raise and support vehicle, then remove wheel and disc brake caliper. **It is not necessary to disconnect hydraulic line from caliper; support caliper assembly from frame to prevent hydraulic line damage.**
2. Remove brake rotor; then, using wheel stud remover tool No. J6627-A or equivalent, press wheel stud out rear of hub.

Installation

1. Position new wheel stud in hole from rear side of hub, then place 4 flat washers on outer portion of stud.
2. Place wheel lug nut on new stud with flat side toward washers, then tighten nut until stud is seated fully in hub flange.
3. Remove wheel lug nut and 4 washers, then install brake rotor and caliper.

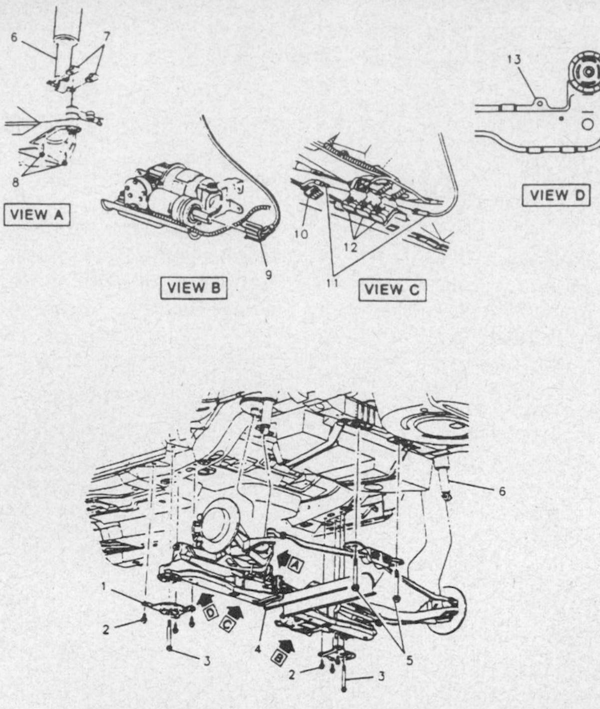
VIEW A
VIEW B
VIEW C
VIEW D

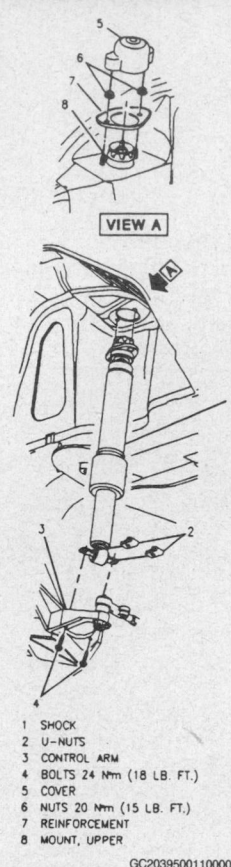

1 SUPPORT BRACKET
2 BOLT 86 N•m (63 LB. FT.)
3 BOLT 191 N•m (141 LB. FT.)
4 REAR SUSPENSION SUPPORT ASSEMBLY
5 BOLT 165 N•m (122 LB. FT.)
6 SHOCK
7 U-NUT
8 BOLT 24 N•m (18 LB. FT.)
9 ELC AIR LINE
10 ELC COMPRESSOR ELECTRICAL CONNECTOR
11 ELC COMPRESSOR VENT TUBE
12 ELECTRICAL CONNECTORS, (ELC HEIGHT SENSOR, FUEL PUMP, ABS HARNESS)
13 GAUGE HOLE

GC2039500109000X

Fig. 3 Rear suspension assembly replacement

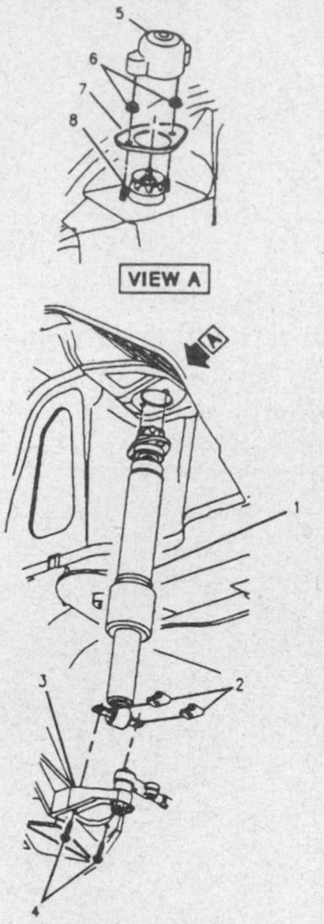
VIEW A

1 SHOCK
2 U-NUTS
3 CONTROL ARM
4 BOLTS 24 N•m (18 LB. FT.)
5 COVER
6 NUTS 20 N•m (15 LB. FT.)
7 REINFORCEMENT
8 MOUNT, UPPER

GC2039500110000X

Fig. 4 Shock absorber replacement

4. Install wheel and tighten wheel lug nuts to specifications, then lower vehicle.

WHEEL BEARING
ADJUST

Because the hub and bearing are integral parts, the bearing is non-adjustable and is not independently serviceable. If the bearing requires service, the entire hub assembly must be replaced.

REAR SUSPENSION
REPLACE

1. Raise and support vehicle, then remove rear wheels and disconnect exhaust system components as necessary to provide clearance.
2. Remove rear springs as described under "Coil Spring, Replace," then remove brake calipers from control arms. **It is not necessary to disconnect hydraulic line at caliper; support caliper from frame to prevent hydraulic line damage.**
3. Disconnect parking brake cables at calipers and at rear suspension support assembly.
4. Disconnect rear suspension support assembly electrical connectors from electrical harness, then disconnect Electronic Level Control (ELC) electrical connector and vent hose.
5. Disconnect ELC air tube from ELC compressor, then support rear suspension assembly, **Fig. 3**, with a suitable jack.
6. Remove 3 support bracket to body bolts from each side of vehicle.
7. Remove 2 front and 2 rear anchor bolts, then lower rear suspension support assembly from vehicle.
8. Reverse procedure to install, noting the following:
   a. Tighten all bolts and nuts to specifications.
   b. Adjust parking brake cable as necessary.

SHOCK ABSORBER
REPLACE

1. Raise and support vehicle, then remove wheel and support control arm with a suitable jack stand.
2. Disconnect Electronic Level Control (ELC) at shock absorber, then remove 2 shock to control arm bolts, **Fig. 4.**
3. Remove luggage compartment trim as necessary to gain access to shock absorber upper mounting nuts, then remove shock upper cover.
4. Remove upper mounting nuts and reinforcement, then the shock absorber.
5. Reverse procedure to install. Tighten mounting bolts and nuts to specifications.

COIL SPRING
REPLACE

1. Raise and support vehicle so as to allow control arm to hang freely, then remove wheel.
2. Support control arm with a suitable jack, then disconnect Electronic Level Control (ELC) air tube from shock absorber.
3. Disconnect shock absorber at control arm, then remove cotter pin and slotted nut securing adjustment link to knuckle.
4. Using universal steering linkage puller tool No. J24319-B, separate adjustment link from knuckle, then slowly lower control arm until it bottoms on rear suspension support assembly.
5. Pry under lower coil spring insulator and remove spring with insulator, **Fig. 5;** then, if necessary, remove jounce bumper by pulling downward.
6. Reverse procedure to install. Tighten all bolts and nuts to specifications.

CONTROL ARM
REPLACE

1. Remove rear suspension support assembly as described under "Rear Suspension, Replace."
2. If left control arm is being replaced, remove Electronic Level Control (ELC) height sensor link.
3. Remove stabilizer link bolt and nut, then disconnect ABS electrical connector.
4. Remove hub and bearing assembly as described under "Hub & Bearing, Replace," then remove bolt and nut securing control arm to rear suspension support assembly.
5. Reverse procedure to install, noting the following:

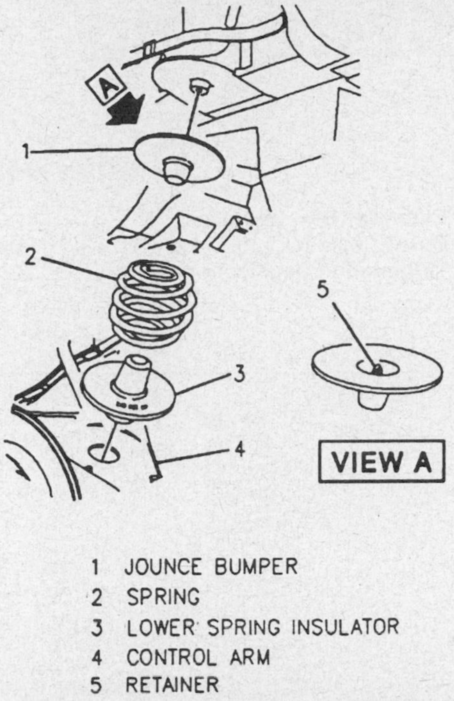
A
1
2
3
4
5
VIEW A
1 JOUNCE BUMPER
2 SPRING
3 LOWER SPRING INSULATOR
4 CONTROL ARM
5 RETAINER
GC2039500111000X

Fig. 5 Coil spring replacement

a. Tighten control arm nuts with vehicle weight resting on rear wheels.
b. Tighten all bolts and nuts to specifications.

CONTROL ARM BUSHING

REPLACE

REMOVAL

1. Remove control arm as described under "Control Arm, Replace," then assemble bushing replacement tools as

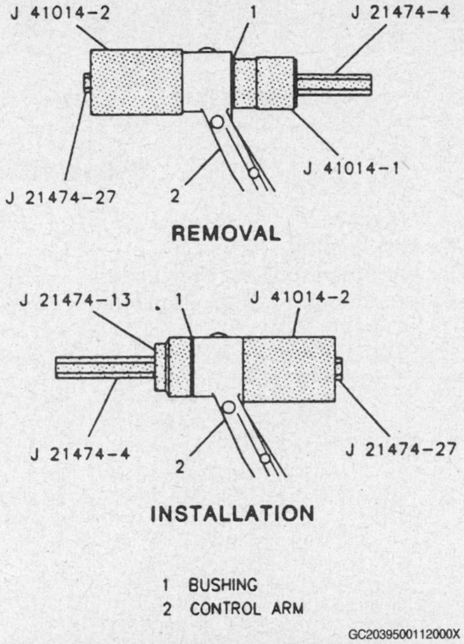
J 41014-2
1
J 21474-4
J 41014-1
J 21474-27
2
REMOVAL
J 21474-13
1
J 41014-2
J 21474-4
2
J 21474-27
INSTALLATION
1 BUSHING
2 CONTROL ARM
GC2039500112000X

Fig. 6 Control arm bushing replacement tool installation

shown in **Fig. 6.**

2. Tighten nut until bushing is driven from control arm, then remove bushing replacement tools.

INSTALLATION

1. Start new bushing into control arm with flat on bushing positioned vertically and rearward.
2. Assemble bushing tools as shown in **Fig. 6**, then tighten bolt until bushing is seated fully in control arm.
3. Remove bushing tools, then install control arm as described under "Control Arm, Replace."

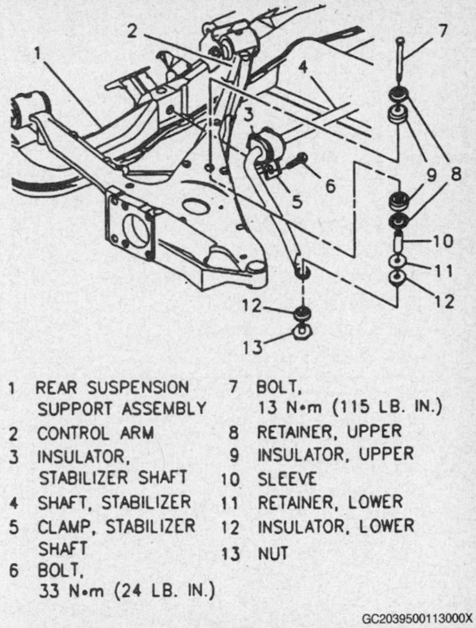
1
2
3
4
5
6
7
8
9
10
11
12
13
1 REAR SUSPENSION SUPPORT ASSEMBLY
2 CONTROL ARM
3 INSULATOR, STABILIZER SHAFT
4 SHAFT, STABILIZER
5 CLAMP, STABILIZER SHAFT
6 BOLT, 33 N•m (24 LB. IN.)
7 BOLT, 13 N•m (115 LB. IN.)
8 RETAINER, UPPER
9 INSULATOR, UPPER
10 SLEEVE
11 RETAINER, LOWER
12 INSULATOR, LOWER
13 NUT
GC2039500113000X

Fig. 7 Stabilizer shaft replacement

STABILIZER SHAFT

REPLACE

1. Raise and support vehicle, then remove wheels and disconnect Electronic Level Control (ELC) height sensor link at control arm.
2. Remove 2 bolts and position ELC height sensor aside, then remove stabilizer shaft link assembly bolt, nut, retainer and insulators from control arm, **Fig. 7.**
3. Remove clamp bolt and bend open end of clamp upward, then remove stabilizer shaft and insulators.
4. Reverse procedure to install, noting the following:
   a. Ensure stabilizer shaft is centered before tightening clamp bolt.
   b. Tighten all bolts and nuts to specifications.

TIGHTENING SPECIFICATIONS

Year	Component	Torque/Ft. Lbs.
	Adjustment Link Pinch Bolt	35
	Adjustment Link To Control Arm Nut	7-8①
	Adjustment Link To Rear Suspension Support Assembly	55
	Control Arm Nuts	78
	ELC Height Sensor Bolts	62②
	Rear Body Mount Bolts	38
	Rear Suspension Support Assembly Bracket Bolts	63

Year	Component	Torque/Ft. Lbs.
	Rear Suspension Support Assembly To Body Rear Bolts	122
	Shock Absorber To Control Arm Bolts	18
	Shock Tower Mounting Nut	15
	Stabilizer Link Bolt	13
	Stabilizer Shaft Clamp Bolt	24
	Stabilizer Shaft Link Bolt	9-10
	Wheel Lug Nuts	100

①—Plus an additional ½ turn.
②—Inch lbs.

Front Suspension & Steering

INDEX

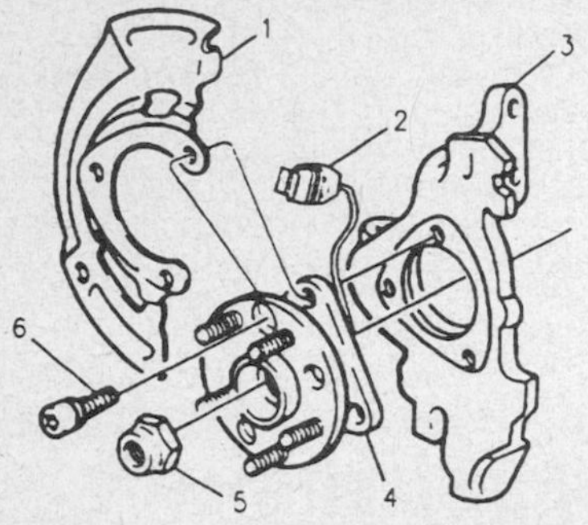

1 DUST SHIELD
2 WHEEL SPEED SENSOR CONNECTOR
3 STEERING KNUCKLE
4 HUB AND BEARING
5 NUT, DRIVE AXLE, 145 N•m (107 LB. FT.)
6 RETAINING BOLT, 95 N•m (75 LB. FT.)

GC2029500207000X

Fig. 1 Hub & Bearing Replacement

HUB & BEARING
REPLACE

REMOVAL

1. Raise and support vehicle.
2. Remove tire and wheel assembly.
3. Remove drive axle nut, **Fig. 1**. Insert suitable drift punch or screwdriver into caliper and rotor to prevent rotor from turning.
4. Remove caliper bolts; support caliper.
5. Remove rotor.
6. Remove ABS front wheel speed sensor connector and unclip from dust shield.
7. Remove hub and bearing retaining bolts and dust shield.
8. Place transmission in PARK.
9. Using tool No. J28733-B or equivalent, separate hub and bearing from drive axle.

INSTALLATION

1. Apply light coating of grease to knuckle bore, then install hub and bearing to drive axle. **Do not handle knuckle or hub near ABS sensor wire.**
2. Install new drive axle nut, and draw hub and bearing onto axle.
3. Place transmission in NEUTRAL.
4. Install dust shield.
5. Tighten hub and bearing bolts to specifications.
6. Connect ABS front wheel speed sensor connector and clip to dust shield.
7. Install rotor, then the caliper. Tighten caliper mounting bolts to specifications.
8. Install suitable drift or screwdriver into caliper and rotor to prevent rotor from turning.
9. Tighten drive axle nut to specification.
10. Install wheel and tire, tighten wheel lug nuts to specifications.
11. Lower vehicle.

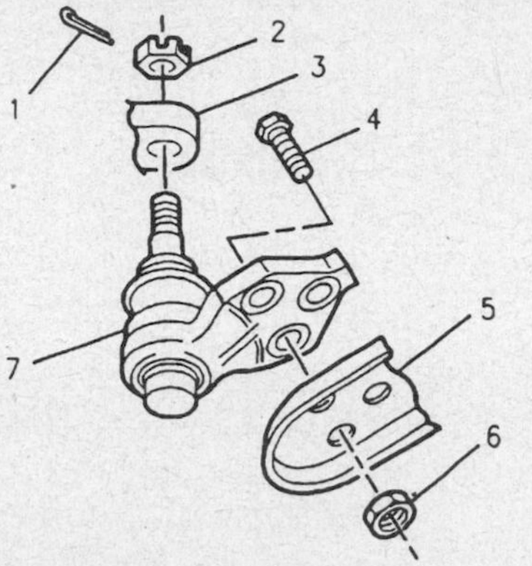

1 PIN
2 NUT, BALL JOINT TO KNUCKLE; TIGHTEN TO 10 N•m (88 LB. IN.) THEN TIGHTEN 2 FLATS TO 55 N•m (41 LB. FT.), MIN.
3 KNUCKLE
4 BALL JOINT MOUNTING BOLTS MUST FACE DOWN
5 CONTROL ARM
6 BALL JOINT MOUNTING NUTS 68 N•m (50 LB. FT.)
7 SERVICE BALL JOINT

GC2029500208000X

Fig. 2 Ball joint replacement

BALL JOINT INSPECTION

Ball joints must be replaced if any looseness is detected in the joint, or the ball joint seal is cut. To inspect ball joints, raise and support the front of the vehicle, allowing the suspension to hang free. Move the tires at top and bottom and move the top of the tires in an in-and-out motion. If any ball stud looseness is visible, or the ball stud can be twisted in its socket easily, replace the ball joint.

BALL JOINT
REPLACE

1. Raise and support vehicle, then remove tire and wheel assembly.
2. Remove cotter pin from ball joint and loosen nut.
3. Using tool No. J-36226 or equivalent, separate ball joint from steering knuckle, **Fig. 2**.
4. Loosen stabilizer shaft link nut.
5. Drill out three rivets or grind off rivet heads retaining ball joint. **Do not damage drive axle seals when drilling or grinding.**
6. Remove ball joint from knuckle and control arm.
7. Reverse procedure to install. Tighten ball joint and stabilizer shaft nuts to specifications.

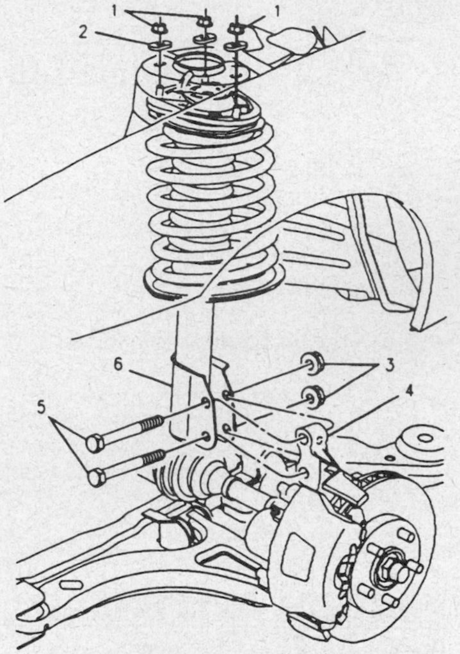

1 NUTS, 47 N•m (35 LB. FT.)
2 WASHER
3 NUTS, 185 N•m (136 LB. FT.)
4 KNUCKLE
5 BOLT
6 STRUT

GC2029500210000X

Fig. 3 Strut replacement

STRUT
REPLACE

1. From engine compartment, remove three strut mount nuts and washers, **Fig. 3**.
2. Raise and support vehicle.
3. Remove wheel and tire assembly.
4. Disconnect ABS front wheel speed sensor connector.
5. Remove speed sensor bracket from

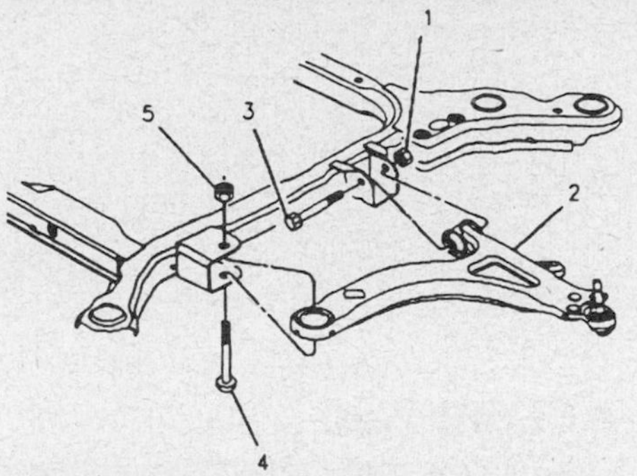
1
2
3
4
5

1 NUT
2 CONTROL ARM
3 BOLT, 158 N•m (117 LB. FT.)
4 BOLT
5 NUT, 126 N•m (93 LB. FT.)

GC2029500209000X

Fig. 4 Control arm mounting bolt removal

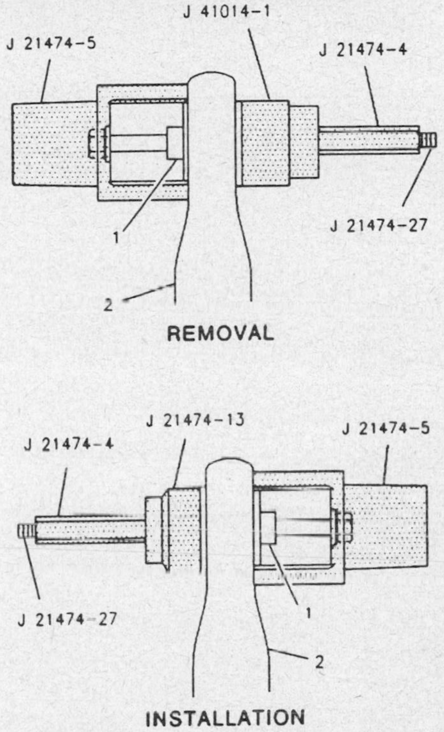
J 41014-1
J 21474-5
J 21474-4
J 21474-27
1
2
REMOVAL
J 21474-13
J 21474-4
J 21474-5
J 21474-27
1
2
INSTALLATION

1 BUSHING
2 CONTROL ARM

GC2029500212000X

Fig. 5 Control arm bushing replacement

strut.
6. Remove strut to knuckle bolts.
7. Remove strut from vehicle.
8. Reverse procedure to install.

CONTROL ARM

REPLACE

1. Raise and support vehicle.
2. Remove wheel and tire assembly.
3. Remove stabilizer link to control arm bolt.
4. Remove cotter pin and loosen nut from ball stud.
5. Using tool No. J-36226, separate ball joint from steering knuckle.

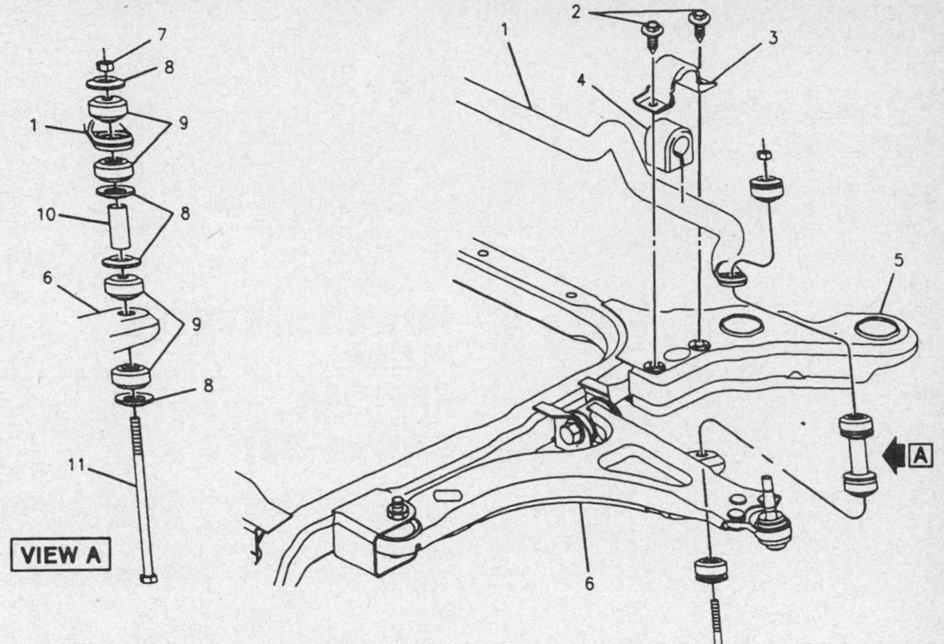
1
2
3
4
5
6
7
8
9
10
11
A
VIEW A

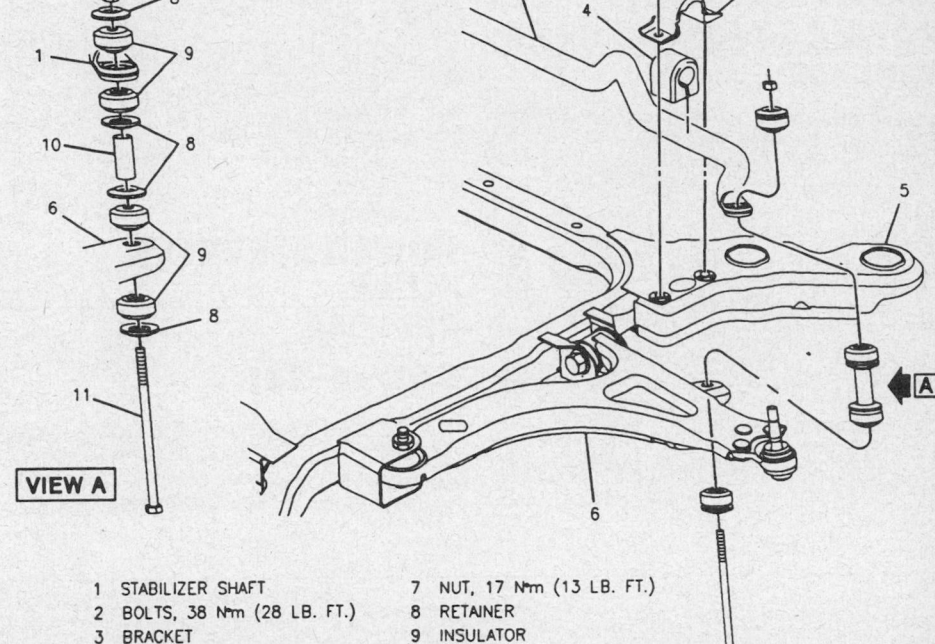

1 STABILIZER SHAFT
2 BOLTS, 38 N•m (28 LB. FT.)
3 BRACKET
4 INSULATOR
5 FRAME
6 CONTROL ARM
7 NUT, 17 N•m (13 LB. FT.)
8 RETAINER
9 INSULATOR
10 SLEEVE
11 BOLT

GC2029500211000X

Fig. 6 Stabilizer shaft & link assembly

6. Remove control arm mounting bolts, **Fig. 4**.
7. Remove control arm from frame.
8. Reverse procedure to install. Tighten control arm mounting bolts to specifications.

CONTROL ARM BUSHING

REPLACE

The rear horizontal control arm bushing is serviced with the control arm and cannot be serviced separately.

1. Remove control arm as described under "Control Arm, Replace."
2. Assemble specified bushing tools or equivalent substitutes as follows:
   a. Bolt tool No. J-21474-27 with washer through bushing receiver, tool No. J-21474-5, with larger diameter end over bushing against control arm, **Fig. 5**.
   b. Coat bolt threads with high pressure lubricant part No. J-23444A, or equivalent.
   c. Install bushing remover tool No. J-41014-1, thrust bearing and nut (tool No. J-21474-4) onto bolt (tool No. J-21474-27).
3. Tighten nut until bushing is driven out of control arm.
4. Remove bushing tools.
5. To install bushing, assemble bushing tools as described in step 2, using bushing installer tool No. J-21474-13 instead of bushing remover.

STABILIZER BAR

REPLACE

1. Raise and support vehicle.

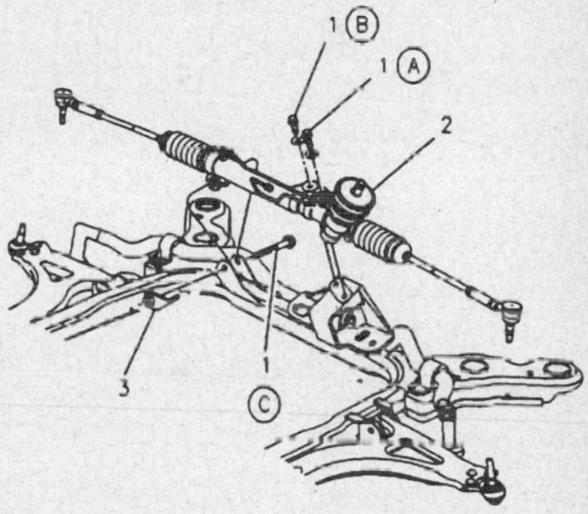
1 (B)
1 (A)
2
3
1 (C)

1 BOLT, 65 N•m (48 LB. FT.) TIGHTEN BOLTS IN SEQUENCE A THRU C
2 STEERING GEAR
3 TAB NUT

GC6029500120000X

Fig. 7 Power steering gear mounting bolts

2. Remove front wheels.
3. Remove left side and right side stabilizer link bolts, **Fig. 6**.
4. Remove left side and right side stabilizer shaft brackets.
5. Using tool No. J-24319B or equivalent, separate left side tie rod end from knuckle.
6. Remove lower exhaust pipe by disconnecting from exhaust manifold and intermediate exhaust hangers.
7. Turn left strut completely to the right. Slide stabilizer shaft outboard over the left steering knuckle until right end comes free.

8. Remove stabilizer shaft from center of vehicle.
9. Reverse procedure to install

POWER STEERING GEAR

REPLACE

1. Ensure front wheels are in straight ahead position.
2. Raise and support vehicle.
3. Remove both front wheels.
4. Remove exhaust system.
5. Remove fasteners and fold back wheelhouse molding enough to remove steering gear.
6. Disconnect intermediate shaft lower connection.
7. Using tool No. J-24319-01 or equivalent, separate tie rod ends from steering knuckles.
8. Unsnap and remove power steering heat shield.
9. Disconnect Magnasteer electrical connector.
10. Disconnect power steering gear inlet and outlet hoses from steering gear.
11. Remove steering gear mounting bolts, Fig. 7.
12. Support rear of frame, then remove rear frame bolts and lower rear frame to allow steering gear removal.
13. Remove steering gear through right side wheel opening.
14. Reverse procedure to install. Tighten steering gear mounting bolts to specifications.

POWER STEERING PUMP

REPLACE

3.8L/V6-231

1. Remove power steering pump drive belt.
2. Disconnect power steering gear inlet and outlet hoses from pump. On supercharged engines, also disconnect remote reservoir hose from pump reservoir.
3. Remove two pump mounting bolts.
4. Raise and support vehicle.
5. Remove pump from beneath engine.
6. Reverse procedure to install. Tighten pump mounting bolts to specifications.

4.0L/V8-244

1. Remove power steering pump drive belt.
2. Disconnect power steering gear inlet and outlet hoses from pump.
3. Remove pump mounting bolt.
4. Remove pump and bracket from engine.
5. Reverse procedure to install. Tighten pump mounting bolt to specification, then fill and bleed power steering system.

TIGHTENING SPECIFICATIONS

Year	Component	Torque/Ft. Lbs.
1995	Ball Joint Nut	88 ①
	Ball Joint To Control Arm Nuts	50
	Brake Line & Speed Sensor Bracket Bolts	13
	Caliper Mounting Bolts	38
	Control Arm Bolt	117
	Control Arm Nut	93
	Drive Axle Nut	107
	Hub & Bearing Bolts	70
	Power Steering Gear Hose Connections	20
	Power Steering Gear Mounting Bolts	48
	Power Steering Pump Bolts	20
	Stabilizer Bracket Bolts	28
	Stabilizer Shaft Link Nut	13
	Strut To Body Attaching Nuts	35
	Strut To Knuckle Bolts	136
	Tie Rod End To Knuckle Nuts	35-52 ②
	Wheel Lug Nuts	100

①—Inch lbs.
②—Do not counter-rotate nut for cotter pin insertion.

Wheel Alignment

INDEX

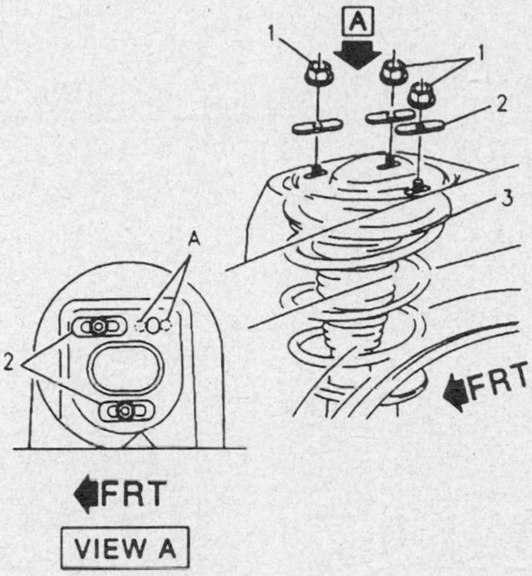

A
1
2
3
FRT
VIEW A

A DRILL 13/32 IN HOLES
1 NUT, 47 N•m (35 LB. FT.)
2 WASHERS
3 STRUT

GC2049500108000X

Fig. 1 Front caster adjustment

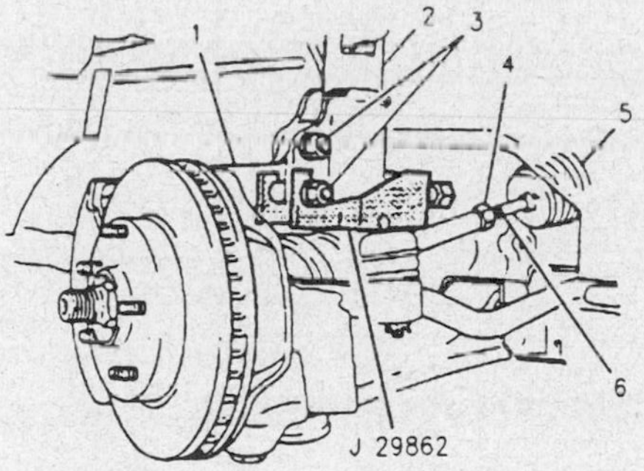

1
2
3
4
5
6
J 29862

1 KNUCKLE
2 STRUT
3 NUT, 185 N•m (136 LB. FT.)
4 LOCK NUT, 64 N•m (47 LB. FT.)
5 BOOT
6 INNER TIE ROD

GC2049500109000X

Fig. 2 Camber & toe adjustment

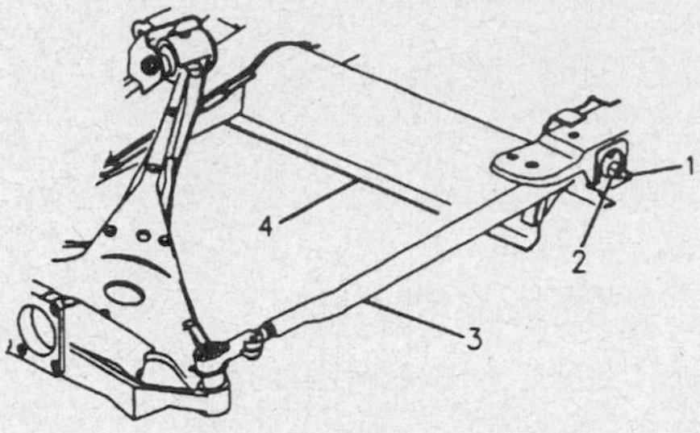

1
2
3
4

1 CAM BOLT
2 NUT, 75 N•m (55 LB. FT.)
3 INNER ADJUSTMENT LINK
4 REAR SUSPENSION SUPPORT ASSEMBLY

GC2049500110000X

Fig. 3 Rear toe adjustment

PRELIMINARY INSPECTION

Inspect all tires for proper inflation.

Inspect tie rods for lateral end motion relative to the steering knuckle and tie rod end seals for any visible signs of damage. Replace tie rod end if either of these conditions exist.

Inspect runout of wheels and tires.

Inspect trim height. If out of specifications, correct before alignment. Inspect shocks, rack and pinion and control arms for looseness and proper operation. Replace any damaged steering/suspension components.

If any excess weight is normally carried in the trunk of vehicle, alignment is recommended with load in place.

Ensure vehicle is level.

FRONT WHEEL ALIGNMENT

CASTER

1. Remove top strut nuts and washers.
2. Raise and support front of vehicle to separate strut from inner wheel housing.
3. Drill two 12/32 inch holes at front and rear of oval strut mounting hole on left and right strut towers, **Fig. 1**, then file excess metal to create slotted holes. **Paint exposed metal with rust resistant paint or primer.**
4. Lower front of vehicle.
5. Install strut attaching nuts, but do not tighten at this time.
6. Adjust caster by moving top of strut forward or rearward. A .040 inch position change at the tower is approximately 0.1 degree change in caster.
7. When caster is within specifications, **torque** strut attaching nuts to 35 ft. lbs.

CAMBER

1. Loosen both strut to steering knuckle nuts, then install camber adjusting tool No. J-29862, **Fig. 2** and set camber to specifications.
2. **Torque** strut to steering knuckle bolts to 136 ft. lbs.

TOE

1. Loosen lock nuts on tie rod ends. **Ensure boots are not twisted or damaged during adjustment.**
2. Rotate inner tie rod, **Fig. 2**, to adjust toe to specifications.
3. **Torque** lock nuts to 47 ft. lbs.

REAR WHEEL ALIGNMENT

Make left and right toe adjustments separately, per wheel.

1. Loosen inner adjustment link cam nut, **Fig. 3.**
2. Rotate cam bolt using an 8 mm wrench or socket and adjust toe to specifications.
3. **Torque** cam nut to 55 ft. lbs.

VEHICLE RIDE HEIGHT

Refer to **Fig. 4** while inspecting vehicle ride height. Ensure vehicle is on level ground and fuel tank is full. Ensure no extra weight is in passenger compartment or trunk.

On vehicle equipped with electronic level control (ELC), ensure ELC is functioning properly.

1. Place front seat to rear position.
2. Bounce vehicle three times at front and rear to normalize suspension.
3. Make measurement D, C, S and Z, **Fig. 4.**
4. Refer to table in **Fig. 5** for specifications.

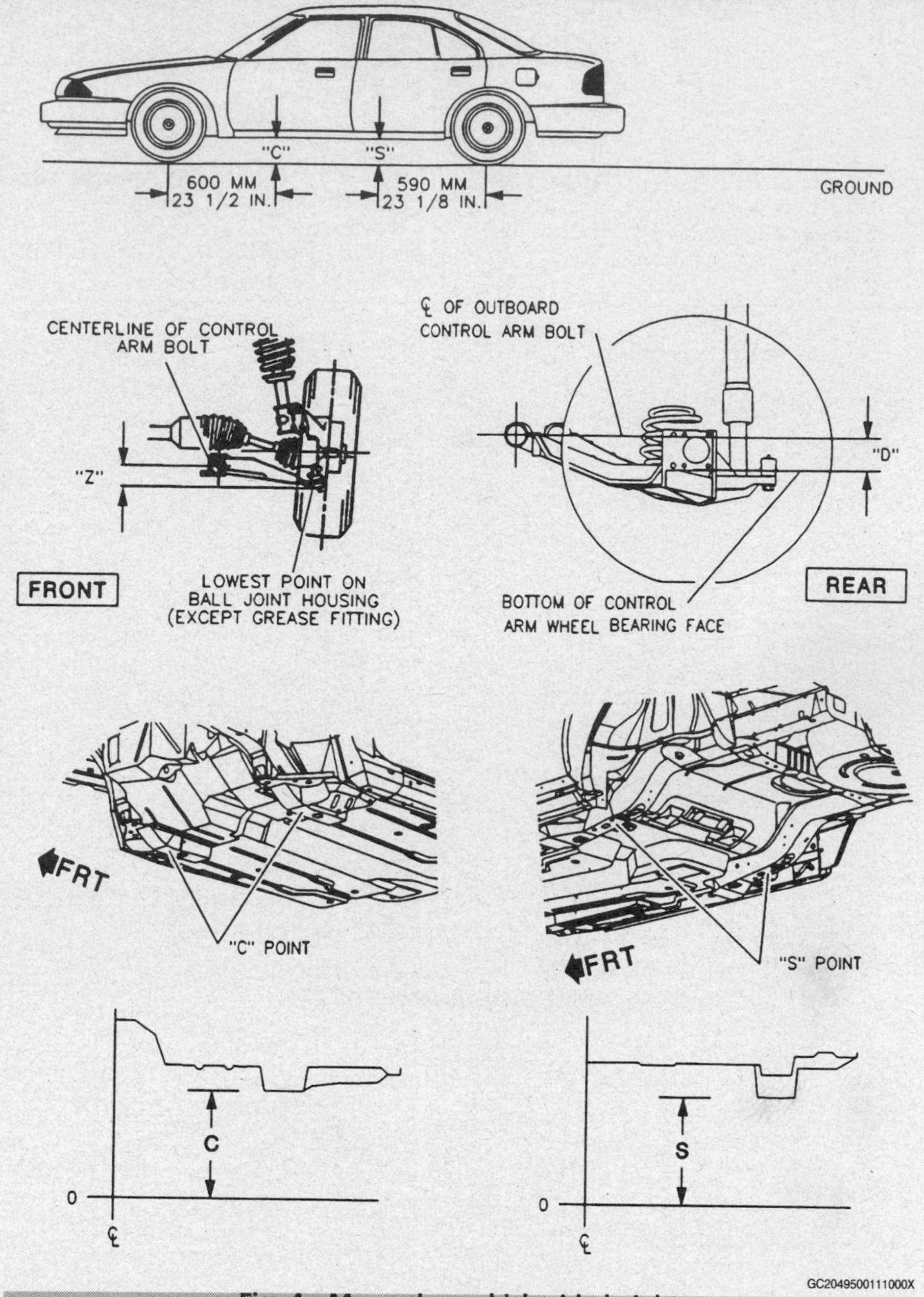
"C"
"S"
600 MM
23 1/2 IN.
590 MM
23 1/8 IN.
GROUND
CENTERLINE OF CONTROL ARM BOLT
"Z"
FRONT
LOWEST POINT ON BALL JOINT HOUSING (EXCEPT GREASE FITTING)
℄ OF OUTBOARD CONTROL ARM BOLT
"D"
REAR
BOTTOM OF CONTROL ARM WHEEL BEARING FACE
FRT
"C" POINT
FRT
"S" POINT
C
0
℄
S
0
℄
GC2049500111000X

Fig. 4 Measuring vehicle ride height

Year	Model	Ride Height (Inches)			
		C	D	S	Z
1995	Aurora	6 11/16	3 to 3 3/4	8 5/8 to 9 13/32	1 3/16 to 2
	Riviera	6 7/16 to 7 1/4	3 to 3 3/4	8 3/8 to 9 3/16	1 3/16 to 2

Fig. 5 Vehicle ride height specifications

CHEVROLET CAVALIER, PONTIAC SUNBIRD & SUNFIRE (J Cars)

NOTE: Refer To The Rear Of This Manual For Manufacturer's Special Service Tool Suppliers.

INDEX OF SERVICE OPERATIONS

NOTE: For Service Operations Not Listed Below, Refer To The Table Of Contents In The Front Of This Manual.

Continued

INDEX OF SERVICE OPERATIONS—CONTINUED

Specifications

GENERAL ENGINE SPECIFICATIONS

Year	Engine		Fuel System	Bore & Stroke	Compression Ratio	Net H.P. @ RPM③	Maximum Torque Ft. Lbs. @ RPM	Normal Oil Pressure psi
	Liter/CID①	VIN Code②						
1992-94	2.0L/4-121 OHC④	H	MFI⑩	3.38 x 3.38	9.2	110 @ 5200	123 @ 3600	65⑨
	2.2L/4-134 OHV⑤	4	MFI⑩	3.50 x 3.46	9.0	120 @ 5200	130 @ 4000	56⑥
	3.1L/V6-192	T	MFI⑩	3.50 x 3.31	8.9	140 @ 4200	185 @ 3200	15⑦
1995	2.2L/4-134 OHV⑤	4	MFI⑩	3.50 x 3.46	9.0	120 @ 5200	130 @ 4000	56
	2.3L/4-138	D	MFI⑩	3.62 x 3.35	9.5⑥	150 @ 6000	145 @ 4800	⑧

①—CID-cubic inch displacement.
②—The eighth digit denotes engine code.
③—Ratings are net as installed in vehicle.
④—Overhead cam engine.
⑤—Overhead valve engine.
⑥—At 3000 RPM.
⑦—At 1100 RPM.
⑧—15 psi @ 900 RPM minimum; 30 2000 RPM minimum.
⑨—At 2500 RPM.
⑩—Multi-point fuel injection.

TUNE UP SPECIFICATIONS

Year & Engine/ VIN Code ①	Spark Plug Gap	Firing Order Fig. ②	Ignition Timing BTDC Man. Trans.	Ignition Timing BTDC Auto. Trans.	Ignition Timing BTDC Mark Fig.	Curb Idle Speed ③ Man. Trans.	Curb Idle Speed ③ Auto. Trans.	Fast Idle Speed Man. Trans.	Fast Idle Speed Auto Trans.	Fuel Pump Pressure
1992-94										
2.0L/4-121(H) OHC	.045	⑩	⑦	⑦	⑧	④	④	④	④	41-47 ⑪
2.2L/4-134(4)	.045	⑥	⑦	⑦	⑧	④	④	④	④	41-47 ⑪
3.1L/V6-192(T)	.045	⑨	⑦	⑦	⑧	④	④	④	④	41-47 ⑤
1995										
2.2L/4-134(4)	.060	⑥	⑦	⑦	⑧	④	④	④	④	41-47 ⑫
2.3L/4-138(D)	.060	⑥	⑦	⑦	⑧	④	④	④	④	41-47 ⑫

BTDC—Before top dead center.

①—The eighth digit of the Vehicle Identification Number (VIN) denotes engine code.

②—Cylinder numbering from front of engine to rear of engine, 1,2,3,4. Firing order 1-3-4-2. Refer to Fig. A for coil connections.

③—Not adjustable.

④—Idle speeds are controlled by the idle air control (IAC) valve.

⑤—With shop towel wrapped around fuel pressure valve to prevent fuel spillage, connect a suitable fuel pressure gauge to fuel pressure valve. Check fuel pressure with ignition switch in the On position, engine not running.

⑥—Cylinder numbering from front of engine to rear of engine, 1, 2, 3, 4. Firing order 1-3-4-2. Refer to Fig. B for spark plug wire connections at coil unit.

⑦—No adjustment.

⑧—Equipped with crankshaft sensor.

⑨—Cylinder numbering left to right as viewed from front of vehicle, front bank, 2, 4, 6; rear bank, 1, 3, 5. Firing order 1-2-3-4-5-6. Refer to Fig. C for spark plug wire connections at coil unit.

⑩—Cylinder numbering from front of engine to rear of engine, 1, 2, 3, 4. Firing order 1-3-4-2. Refer to Fig. D for spark plug wire connection at coil unit.

⑪—To relieve fuel pressure, loosen fuel tank filler cap. Remove fuel pup fuse from fuse panel, then start engine and allow to run until fuel supply is deleted. When engine has stopped, engage starter for 3 seconds to dissipate remaining fuel system pressure. Disconnect battery ground cable. Locate fuel feed quick connect fitting in engine compartment. Install a suitable fuel pressure gauge between fuel feed quick connect fittings. Connect battery ground cable. Start engine and note fuel pressure reading. Before removing fuel gauge, relieve fuel system pressure.

⑫—Loosen fuel tank filler cap to relieve fuel tank pressure. Disconnect fuel pump electrical connector, then start & operate engine. After engine has stalled, crank starter for 3 seconds to deplete remaining fuel pressure. Place ignition switch in Off position, then reconnect fuel pump electrical connector. Disconnect battery ground cable. Connect suitable fuel pressure gauge between fuel line & fuel rail. Connect battery ground cable. Place ignition switch in On position & note fuel pressure reading.

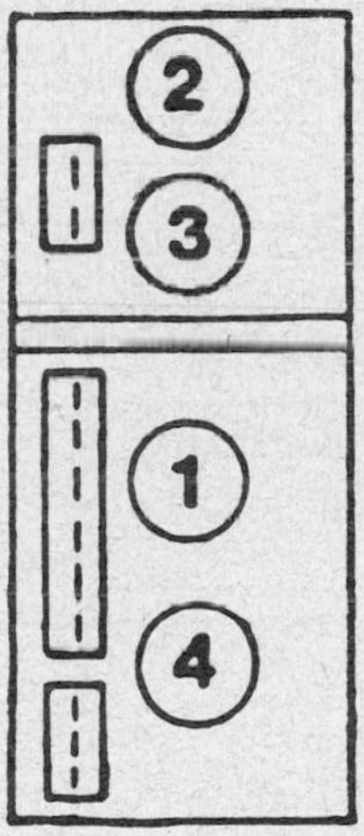
2
3
1
4
GC1139100139000X

Fig. A

1 4 6 3 2 5

Fig. B

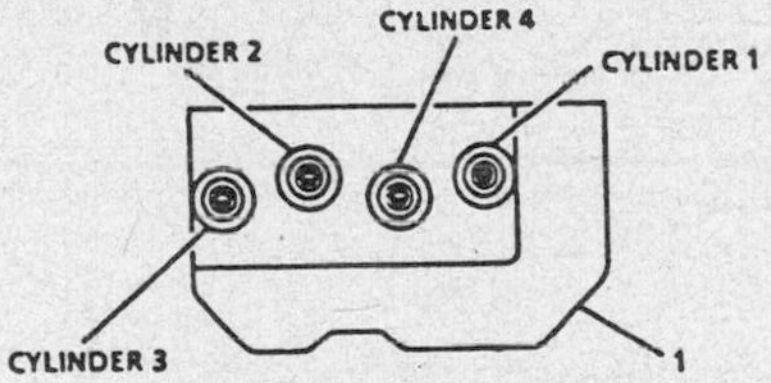
CYLINDER 2
CYLINDER 4
CYLINDER 1
CYLINDER 3
1

1 DIRECT IGNITION SYSTEM (DIS) MODULE/COIL ASSEMBLY

GC1139100141000X

Fig. C

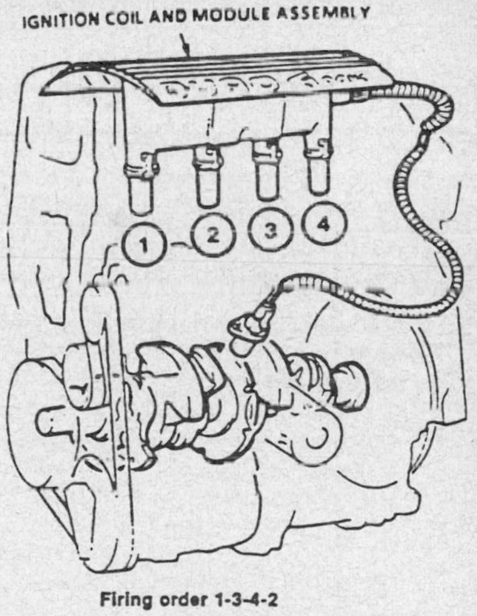
IGNITION COIL AND MODULE ASSEMBLY
1 2 3 4
Firing order 1-3-4-2

Fig. D

FRONT WHEEL ALIGNMENT SPECIFICATIONS

Year	Model	Caster Angle, Degrees Limits	Caster Angle, Degrees Desired	Camber Angle, Degrees Limits Left	Camber Angle, Degrees Limits Right	Camber Angle, Degrees Desired Left	Camber Angle, Degrees Desired Right	Total Toe, Degrees
1992-94	All	+.7 to +2.7	+1.7	-.7 to +.7	-.7 to +.7	0	0	0
1995	All	—	4.3①	—	—	-0.2	-0.2	+0.1

①—Non-adjustable, for inspection purposes only.

REAR WHEEL ALIGNMENT SPECIFICATIONS

Year	Model	Camber Angle, Degrees ①	Thrust Angle, Degrees ①	Total Toe, Degrees ①
1992-94	All	-.82 to +.32	-.31 to +.31	+.25
1995	All	-.25	0	+0.2

①—Non-adjustable, for inspection purposes only.

COOLING SYSTEM & CAPACITY DATA

Year	Model or Engine/ VIN ④	Coolant Capacity, Qts.		Radiator Cap Relief Pressure, Lbs.	Thermo. Opening Temp.	Fuel Tank Gals.	Engine Oil Refill Qts.	Transaxle Oil	
		Less A/C	With A/C					Manual Transaxle Pts.	Auto. Transaxle Qts. ①
1992–93	2.0L/4-121(H)	11.7	11.7	15	195	15.2	4②	4	③
	2.2L/4-134(4)	9.2	9.2	15	195	15.2	4②	4	③
	3.1L/V6-192(T)	⑤	⑤	15	195	15.2	4②	4	③
1994	2.0L/4-121(H)	10.7	10.7	15	195	15.2	4②	4	⑥
	2.2L/4-134(4)	10.7	10.7	15	195	15.2	4②	4	⑥
	3.1L/V6-192(T)	13.7	13.7	15	195	15.2	4②	4	⑥
1995	2.2L/4-138(4)	10.7	10.7	15	195	15.2	4②	5.4	③
	2.3L/4-138(D)	10.4	10.4	15	180	15.2	4②	5.4	⑦

①—Approximate, make final check with dipstick.

②—When changing engine oil filter additional oil may be required.

③—Oil pan only, 4 qts. After overhaul, less torque converter drain, 6 qts.; with torque converter drain, 9 qts.

④—The eighth digit of VIN denotes engine code.

⑤—Cavalier, 13.1 qts.; Sunbird, 14.2 qts.

⑥—Oil pan only, 4 qts.; complete overhaul, 7 qts.; dry, 9 qts.

⑦—3T40 auto. trans., oil pan only, 4 qts; complete overhaul, 7 qts.; dry, 9 qts. 4T40E auto. trans, oil pan only, 7.4 qts.; complete overhaul, 10.6 qts.; new converter, 2.6 qts.

LUBRICANT DATA

Year	Model	Lubricant Type			
		Transaxle			
		Manual	Automatic	Power Steering	Brake System
1992-95	All	①	DEXRON IIE & III	②	DOT-3

①—Manual transmission fluid GM specification No. 12345349 or equivalent.

②—Synchromesh steering fluid GM part No. 9985010 or equivalent.

Electrical

NOTE: On Air Bag Equipped Models, Refer To "Air Bag System Precautions" Located In The Front Of This Manual For System Disarming & Arming Procedures.

INDEX

PRECAUTIONS

AIR BAG SYSTEMS

Refer to "Air Bag System Precautions" in the front of this manual for system disarming and arming procedures.

FUSE PANEL & FLASHER LOCATION

The fuse panel is located on the left side of the instrument panel. To gain access to the panel, pivot access door downward.

The hazard flasher is located under dash panel, left side of steering column.

The turn signal flasher is located under dash panel, right side of steering column.

RELAY CENTER LOCATION

The relay center is located in the LH front of the engine compartment, by the strut tower.

STARTER

REPLACE

2.0L/4-121 ENGINE

Manual Transaxle

1. Disconnect battery ground cable.
2. Remove wiring strap from upper starter mounting bolt.
3. Disconnect shifter cables at selector lever.
4. Remove upper and lower transaxle control lever cable bracket and cables.
5. Remove drive axle support brace.
6. Disconnect wiring from starter motor, then remove starter motor mounting bolts and starter motor.
7. Reverse procedure to install.

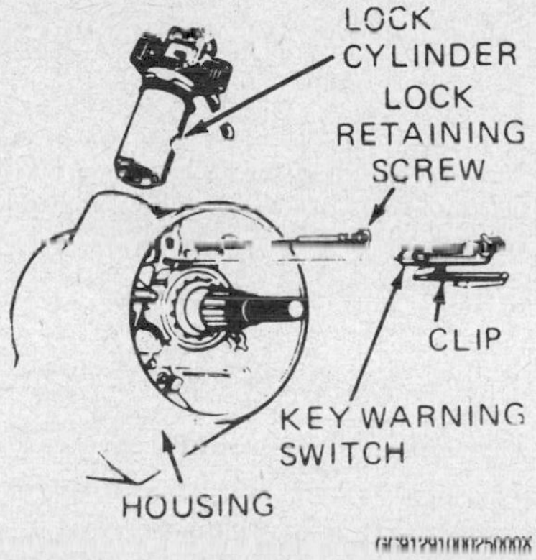

LOCK CYLINDER
LOCK RETAINING SCREW
CLIP
KEY WARNING SWITCH
HOUSING

Fig. 1 Lock cylinder removal

Automatic Transaxle

1. Disconnect battery ground cable.
2. Remove blower motor as described under "Blower Motor, Replace."
3. Disconnect wiring from starter motor.
4. Remove starter motor bracket, then disconnect wiring loom from upper starter mounting bolt and remove bolt.
5. Remove starter motor lower mounting bolt, then remove starter motor through blower motor opening.
6. Reverse procedure to install.

2.2L/4-134 ENGINE

1. Disconnect battery ground cable.
2. Raise and support vehicle, then remove bolts attaching starter motor and bracket to engine.
3. Lower starter motor and disconnect leads at solenoid.
4. Remove starter motor from vehicle. Note position of shims for installation, if used.
5. Reverse procedure to install.

2.3L/4-183 ENGINE

1. Disconnect battery ground cable.
2. Raise and support vehicle.
3. Remove starter electrical connections.
4. Remove starter bolt, then the starter.
5. Reverse procedure to install.

3.1L/V6-192 ENGINE

1. Disconnect battery ground cable, then raise and support vehicle.
2. Remove starter motor to engine attaching bolts.
3. Disconnect starter electrical connectors, then lower starter out of vehicle.
4. Note installation position of starter shim, if equipped.
5. Reverse procedure to install.

ALTERNATOR

REPLACE

1. Disconnect battery ground cable.
2. Disconnect electrical connections to alternator, then the drive belt.
3. Remove three retaining bolts to alternator, then the alternator.
4. Reverse procedure to install.

IGNITION LOCK

REPLACE

1992–94

1. Remove steering wheel as outlined under "Steering Wheel, Replace" procedure.
2. Remove turn signal switch as outlined under "Turn Signal Switch, Replace" procedure.
3. Remove buzzer switch.
4. Turn lock cylinder to "Run" position, then remove the lock cylinder retaining screw and lock cylinder, **Fig. 1.**
5. To install, rotate lock cylinder to stop while holding housing. Align cylinder key with keyway in housing, then push cylinder into housing until fully seated.
6. Install lock cylinder retaining screw.

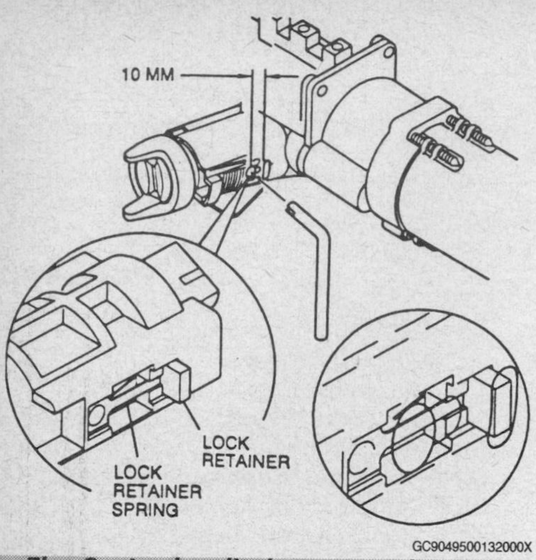
10 MM
LOCK RETAINER
LOCK RETAINER SPRING
GC9049500132000X

Fig. 2 Lock cylinder removal. 1995 Cavalier & Sunfire

7. Install buzzer switch, turn signal switch and steering wheel.

1995

1. Disconnect battery ground cable.
2. Disconnect wiring harness from ignition switch assembly.
3. Disconnect steering column from body as outlined under "Steering Columns."
4. Drill a 9/32 hole on back of steering column housing assembly.
5. Insert suitable tool, **Fig. 2,** into hole to retain lock retainer spring, then turn tool to break retainer spring.
6. Hold column vertical and tap on housing assembly to dislodge retainer.
7. Remove lock retainer and lock cylinder from housing.
8. Reverse procedure to install.

IGNITION SWITCH

REPLACE

CAVALIER

1992–94

1. Remove steering wheel as outlined under "Steering Wheel, Replace" procedure.
2. Remove turn signal switch as outlined under "Turn Signal Switch, Replace" procedure.
3. Remove windshield wiper switch as outlined under "Windshield Wiper Switch, Replace" procedure.
4. Remove ignition switch to ignition switch housing attaching screws.
5. Depress ignition switch locking tab, then disconnect switch electrical connectors.
6. Reverse procedure to install, noting the following:
   a. Ensure lock cylinder shaft aligns with slotted opening on ignition switch.
   b. **Torque** ignition switch attaching screws to 21 inch lbs.

1995

Refer to "Sunfire" for ignition switch replacement procedure.

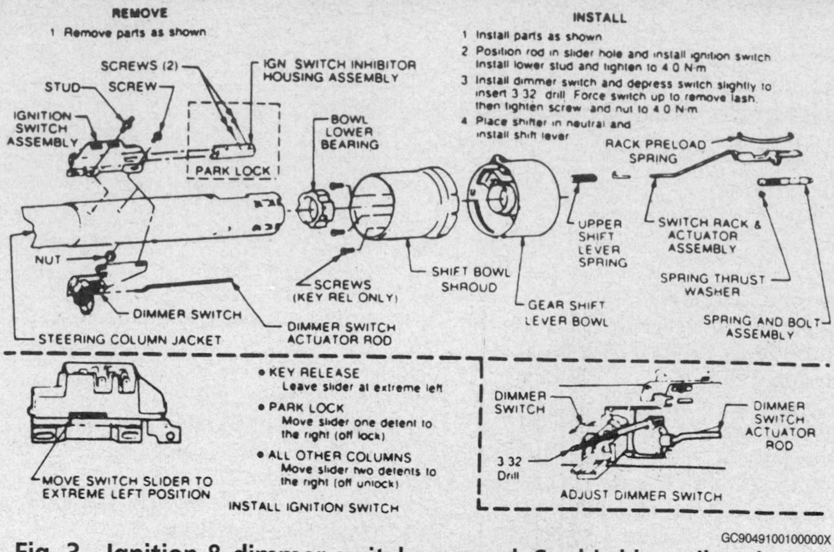
REMOVE
1 Remove parts as shown
INSTALL
1 Install parts as shown
2 Position rod in slider hole and install ignition switch Install lower stud and tighten to 4.0 N·m
3 Install dimmer switch and depress switch slightly to insert 3/32 drill. Force switch up to remove lash then tighten screw and nut to 4.0 N·m
4 Place shifter in neutral and install shift lever
SCREWS (2)
IGN SWITCH INHIBITOR HOUSING ASSEMBLY
STUD
SCREW
IGNITION SWITCH ASSEMBLY
PARK LOCK
BOWL LOWER BEARING
RACK PRELOAD SPRING
UPPER SHIFT LEVER SPRING
SWITCH RACK & ACTUATOR ASSEMBLY
NUT
SCREWS (KEY REL ONLY)
SHIFT BOWL SHROUD
SPRING THRUST WASHER
DIMMER SWITCH
GEAR SHIFT LEVER BOWL
SPRING AND BOLT ASSEMBLY
STEERING COLUMN JACKET
DIMMER SWITCH ACTUATOR ROD
• KEY RELEASE
Leave slider at extreme left
• PARK LOCK
Move slider one detent to the right (off lock)
• ALL OTHER COLUMNS
Move slider two detents to the right (off unlock)
MOVE SWITCH SLIDER TO EXTREME LEFT POSITION
INSTALL IGNITION SWITCH
DIMMER SWITCH
DIMMER SWITCH ACTUATOR ROD
3/32 Drill
ADJUST DIMMER SWITCH
GC9049100100000X

Fig. 3 Ignition & dimmer switch removal. Sunbird less tilt column

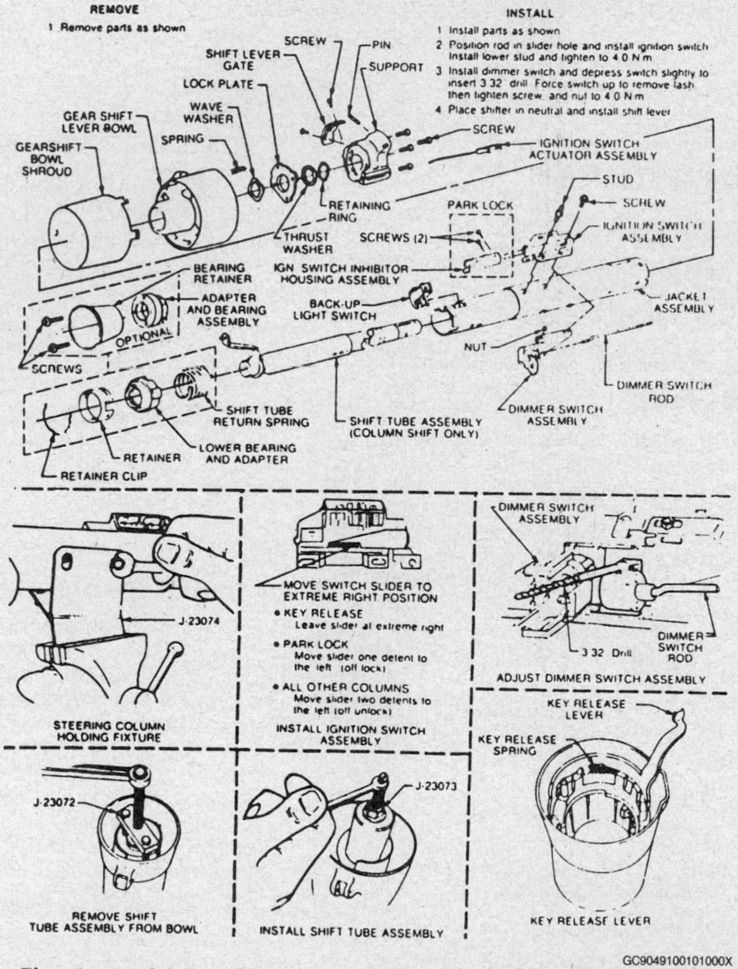
REMOVE
1 Remove parts as shown
INSTALL
1 Install parts as shown
2 Position rod in slider hole and install ignition switch Install lower stud and tighten to 4.0 N·m
3 Install dimmer switch and depress switch slightly to insert 3/32 drill. Force switch up to remove lash then tighten screw and nut to 4.0 N·m
4 Place shifter in neutral and install shift lever
SCREW
PIN
SHIFT LEVER GATE
SUPPORT
LOCK PLATE
GEAR SHIFT LEVER BOWL
WAVE WASHER
SPRING
GEARSHIFT BOWL SHROUD
SCREW
IGNITION SWITCH ACTUATOR ASSEMBLY
STUD
RETAINING RING
PARK LOCK
SCREW
THRUST WASHER
SCREWS (2)
IGNITION SWITCH ASSEMBLY
BEARING RETAINER
IGN SWITCH INHIBITOR HOUSING ASSEMBLY
ADAPTER AND BEARING ASSEMBLY
BACK-UP LIGHT SWITCH
JACKET ASSEMBLY
OPTIONAL
SCREWS
NUT
DIMMER SWITCH ROD
SHIFT TUBE RETURN SPRING
SHIFT TUBE ASSEMBLY (COLUMN SHIFT ONLY)
DIMMER SWITCH ASSEMBLY
RETAINER
LOWER BEARING AND ADAPTER
RETAINER CLIP
J-23074
MOVE SWITCH SLIDER TO EXTREME RIGHT POSITION
• KEY RELEASE
Leave slider at extreme right
• PARK LOCK
Move slider one detent to the left (off lock)
• ALL OTHER COLUMNS
Move slider two detents to the left (off unlock)
STEERING COLUMN HOLDING FIXTURE
INSTALL IGNITION SWITCH ASSEMBLY
DIMMER SWITCH ASSEMBLY
3/32 Drill
DIMMER SWITCH ROD
ADJUST DIMMER SWITCH ASSEMBLY
KEY RELEASE LEVER
KEY RELEASE SPRING
J-23072
J-23073
REMOVE SHIFT TUBE ASSEMBLY FROM BOWL
INSTALL SHIFT TUBE ASSEMBLY
KEY RELEASE LEVER
GC9049100101000X

Fig. 4 Ignition & dimmer switch removal. Sunbird w/tilt column

SUNBIRD

1. Remove steering wheel as outlined under "Steering Wheel, Replace" procedure, then the turn signal switch and lock cylinder as previously described.
2. Refer to **Figs. 3 and 4** to remove ignition .
3. When installing dimmer switch, depress switch slightly and install a 3/32 drill into switch. Force switch upward to remove lash and tighten retaining screw.

SUNFIRE

Refer to **Fig. 5,** for ignition switch removal.

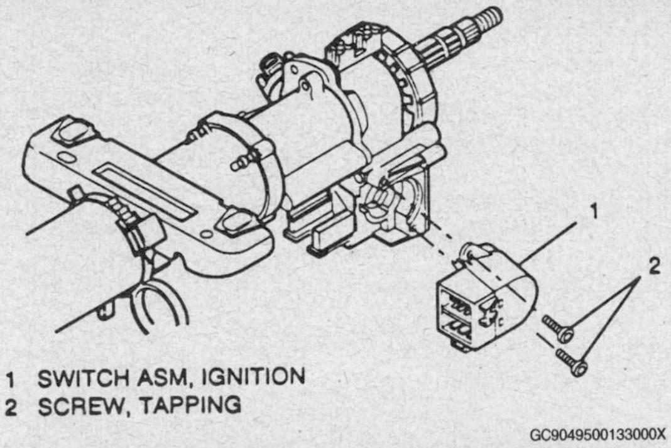
1
2
1 SWITCH ASM, IGNITION
2 SCREW, TAPPING
GC9049500133000X

Fig. 5 Ignition switch removal. 1995 Cavalier & Sunfire

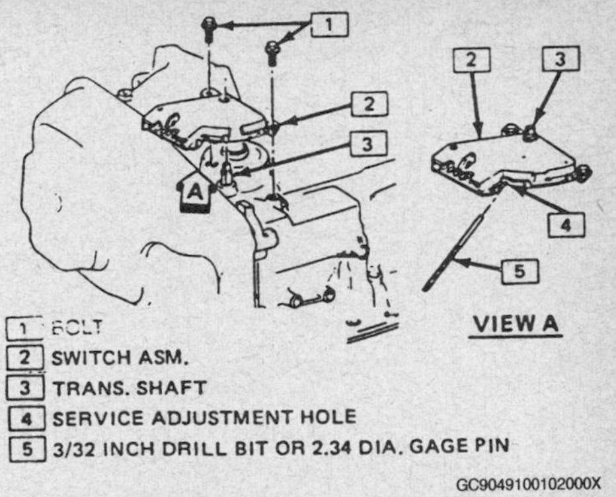
1
2
3
4
5
A
VIEW A
1 BOLT
2 SWITCH ASM.
3 TRANS. SHAFT
4 SERVICE ADJUSTMENT HOLE
5 3/32 INCH DRILL BIT OR 2.34 DIA. GAGE PIN
GC9049100102000X

Fig. 6 Back-up light/neutral start switch replacement

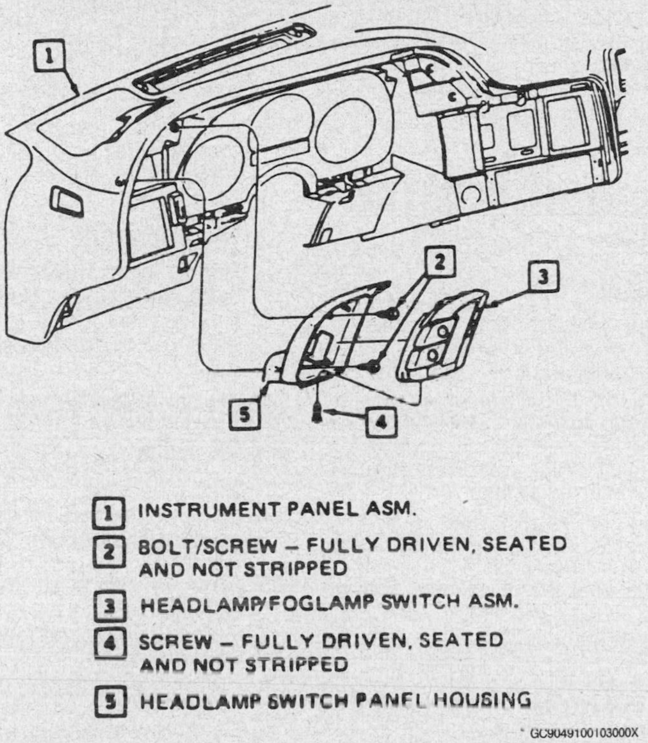
1
2
3
4
5
1 INSTRUMENT PANEL ASM.
2 BOLT/SCREW – FULLY DRIVEN, SEATED AND NOT STRIPPED
3 HEADLAMP/FOGLAMP SWITCH ASM.
4 SCREW – FULLY DRIVEN, SEATED AND NOT STRIPPED
5 HEADLAMP SWITCH PANEL HOUSING
GC9049100103000X

Fig. 7 Headlamp/fog lamp switch replacement. Sunbird

CLUTCH START SWITCH

REPLACE

1. Disconnect clutch switch electrical connector.
2. Remove clutch bracket and switch attaching nuts, then remove switch.
3. Reverse procedure to install. **Torque** switch attaching nuts to 53 inch lbs.

NEUTRAL SAFETY SWITCH

REPLACE

On vehicles equipped with automatic transmission, the neutral start and back-up light switches are combined into one unit and must be replaced as an assembly.

1. Disconnect battery ground cable and shift linkage.
2. Disconnect electrical connector from switch.
3. Remove switch mounting bolts, then switch assembly, **Fig. 6.**
4. If same switch is to be reinstalled, proceed as follows:
   a. Place shift shaft in Neutral position.
   b. Align flats of shift shaft with switch, then install switch.
   c. Loosely install mounting bolts.
   d. Insert gauge pin, **Fig. 6,** in service adjustment hole and rotate switch until pin drops in to a depth of 9 mm ($^9/_{64}$ inch).
   e. **Torque** mounting bolts to 18 ft. lbs.
5. If a new switch is to be installed, proceed as follows:
   a. Place shift shaft in Neutral position.
   b. Align flats of shift shaft with switch, then install switch.
   c. If bolt holes do not align with mounting boss on transaxle, verify shift shaft is in Neutral position, do not rotate switch. Switch is pinned in Neutral position. If switch has been rotated and the pin broken, use procedure outlined in step 4.
   d. **Torque** mounting bolts to 18 ft. lbs.
6. Verify engine will only start in Park or Neutral positions.

HEADLAMP SWITCH

REPLACE

CAVALIER & SUNFIRE

The headlamp switch is part of the turn signal lever assembly and is not serviceable. The headlamp switch, turn signal lever and cruise control switch must be replaced as an assembly.

SUNBIRD

1. Disconnect battery ground cable.
2. Remove left hand sound insulator.
3. Remove two screws attaching left hand trim panel, then remove trim panel by gently prying from instrument panel.
4. Remove screw attaching headlamp switch to housing, then disconnect electrical connector and remove switch, **Fig. 7.**
5. Reverse procedure to install.

STOP LIGHT SWITCH

REPLACE

1. Disconnect battery ground cable.
2. Remove drivers' side hash panel.
3. Disconnect switch electrical connector.
4. Remove switch from brake pedal support bracket.
5. Reverse procedure to install. Adjust switch as follows:
   a. Insert stop lamp switch in retainer until switch body seats on retainer. Pull brake pedal upward against internal pedal stop. Switch will be moved in retainer providing proper adjustment.
   b. Proper switch adjustment is achieved when no audible clicks are heard when the pedal is pulled upward and the brake lights do not remain on without brake application.

TURN SIGNAL SWITCH

REPLACE

CAVALIER

1992–94

1. Disconnect battery ground cable.
2. Remove steering wheel as outlined

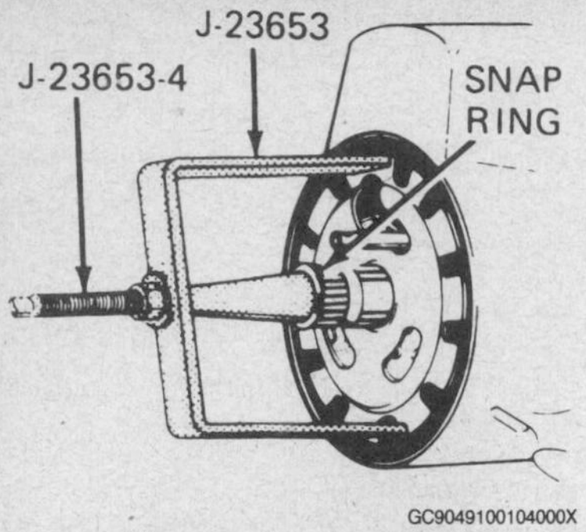
J-23653
J-23653-4
SNAP RING
GC9049100104000X

Fig. 8 Lock plate compression. Sunbird

under "Steering Wheel, Replace."
3. Remove lower steering column cover upper and lower attaching bolts, then remove lower steering column cover.
4. Separate rose bud fastener, integral to wiring harness, from jacket assembly.
5. Remove turn signal switch attaching screws, the depress locking tab and remove turn signal switch electrical connectors.
6. Reverse procedure to install. **Torque** turn signal switch attaching screws to 48 inch lbs.

1995

Refer to "Sunfire" for turn signal switch replacement procedure.

SUNBIRD

1. Disconnect battery ground cable.
2. Remove steering wheel as outlined under "Steering Wheel, Replace" procedure.
3. Using a suitable screwdriver, pry cover from housing.
4. Using lock plate compressing tool J-23653-4, compress lock plate and pry snap ring from groove on steering shaft, **Fig. 8.** Slowly release compressing tool, then remove tool and lock plate from shaft.
5. Slide canceling cam and bearing preload spring from steering shaft.
6. Remove turn signal (multi-function) lever.
7. Remove hazard warning knob retaining screw, button, spring and knob.
8. Remove actuator arm screw and actuator arm.
9. Remove switch retaining screws and pull switch upward from column, guiding wire harness through column.
10. Reverse procedure to install.

SUNFIRE

1. Disconnect battery ground cable.
2. Remove steering wheel as outlined under "Steering Wheel, Replace."
3. **On models with tilt steering,** remove lever.
4. **On all models,** Remove upper and lower steering column covers.
5. Remove dampner assembly, then switch assembly.
6. Reverse procedure to install.

DIMMER SWITCH

REPLACE

Refer to "Ignition Switch, Replace" for procedure.

STEERING WHEEL

REPLACE

1. Disconnect battery ground cable.
2. Remove steering wheel center pad attaching screws.
3. **On models with air bag,** remove inflator module as outlined in "Air Bag Systems."
4. **On all models,** disconnect horn electrical connector, then remove steering wheel center pad.
5. Remove steering wheel retaining nut and retainer.
6. Remove steering dampener, if equipped.
7. Scribe alignment marks on steering wheel and shaft to aid installation.
8. Using tool J-1859-03 or BT-61-9 or equivalent, remove steering wheel from shaft.
9. Reverse procedure to install. **Torque** steering wheel attaching nut to 30 ft. lbs.

INSTRUMENT CLUSTER

REPLACE

CAVALIER

1. Disconnect battery ground cable.
2. Remove steering column opening filler attaching screws, then remove steering opening filler.
3. Pull down slightly on steering column cover to remove bottom cluster extension attaching screws, then remove cluster extension.
4. Disconnect instrument panel dimmer and interior lamp control switches electrical connectors.
5. Remove instrument cluster top attaching screws, **Fig. 9.**
6. Pull instrument cluster rearward to remove.
7. Reverse procedure to install. **Torque** instrument cluster attaching bolts to 19 inch lbs.

SUNBIRD & SUNFIRE

1. Disconnect battery ground cable.
2. Remove four screws attaching instrument cluster trim plate to instrument panel, then pull trim plate outward to remove.
3. Remove four screws attaching instrument cluster to instrument panel, **Fig. 10.**
4. Remove steering column cover, then remove instrument cluster from instrument panel.
5. Reverse procedure to install. **Torque** instrument cluster attaching bolts to 12 inch lbs.

WIPER MOTOR

REPLACE

1. Disconnect battery ground cable.
2. Remove wiper arms from transmission spindle shafts.
3. Remove shroud top vent grille panel and screen.
4. Loosen, but do not remove, transmission drive link to motor crank arm attaching nuts, then pull drive link out of motor crank arm.
5. Disconnect wiper motor electrical connections and remove wiper motor attaching bolts.
6. Rotate wiper motor upward and outward, and remove from vehicle.
7. Reverse procedure to install. **Torque** wiper motor attaching bolts to 80 inch lbs.

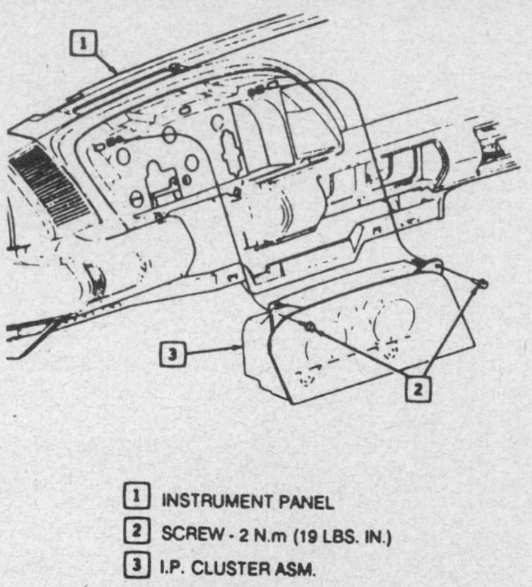
1
2
3
1 INSTRUMENT PANEL
2 SCREW - 2 N.m (19 LBS. IN.)
3 I.P. CLUSTER ASM.
GC9099100230000X

Fig. 9 Instrument cluster. Cavalier

WIPER SWITCH

REPLACE

1. Disconnect battery ground cable.
2. Remove horn pad and steering wheel as described under "Steering Wheel, Replace."
3. Remove tilt lever from column, if equipped, **Fig. 11.**
4. Remove upper and lower steering column covers.
5. Remove dampener assembly, then the headlight switch assembly.
6. Remove windshield wiper switch assembly.
7. Reverse procedure to install.

WIPER TRANSMISSION

REPLACE

1. Remove wiper arms from transmission spindle shafts.
2. Remove shroud top vent grille panel and screen.
3. Loosen, but do not remove, transmission drive link to motor crank arm attaching nuts then pull drive link from motor crank arm.
4. Remove transmission to cowl panel attaching screws and the transmission assembly.
5. Reverse procedure to install. **Torque** wiper transmission attaching screws and nuts to 71 inch lbs.

BLOWER MOTOR

REPLACE

1. Disconnect battery ground cable.
2. Disconnect blower motor electrical connections.

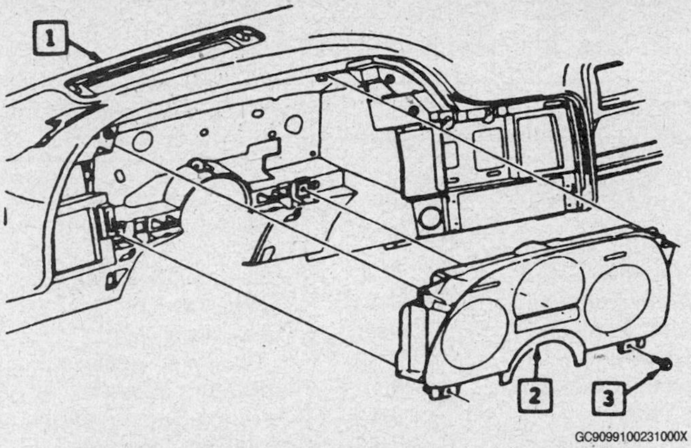
1
2
3
GC9099100231000X

Fig. 10 Instrument cluster. Sunbird & Sunfire

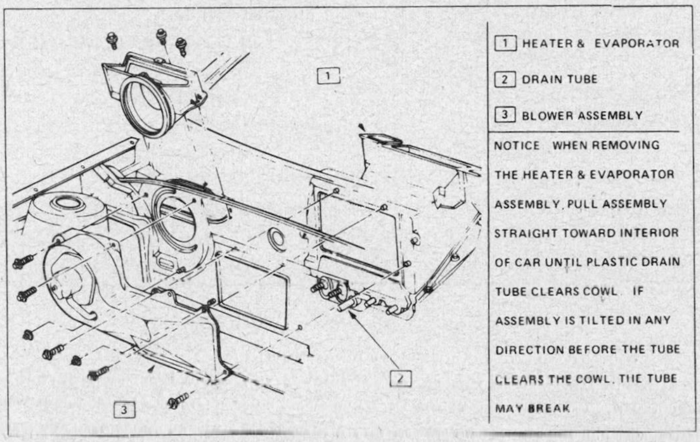
1 HEATER & EVAPORATOR
2 DRAIN TUBE
3 BLOWER ASSEMBLY
NOTICE WHEN REMOVING THE HEATER & EVAPORATOR ASSEMBLY, PULL ASSEMBLY STRAIGHT TOWARD INTERIOR OF CAR UNTIL PLASTIC DRAIN TUBE CLEARS COWL. IF ASSEMBLY IS TILTED IN ANY DIRECTION BEFORE THE TUBE CLEARS THE COWL, THE TUBE MAY BREAK
GC7029100062000X

Fig. 12 Heater core & blower motor

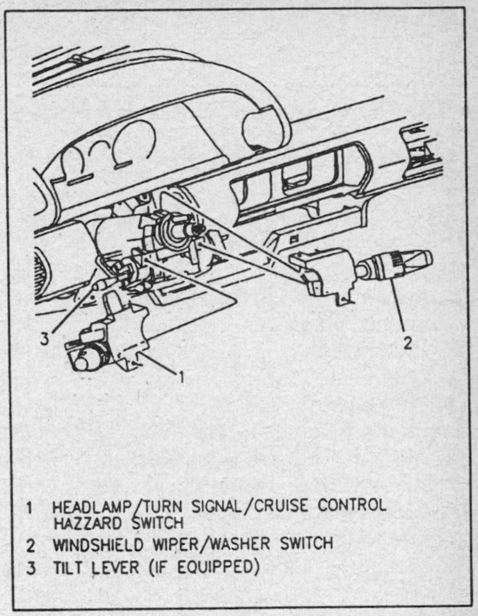
1
2
3
1 HEADLAMP/TURN SIGNAL/CRUISE CONTROL HAZZARD SWITCH
2 WINDSHIELD WIPER/WASHER SWITCH
3 TILT LEVER (IF EQUIPPED)
GC9049100105000X

Fig. 11 Wiper switch removal

3. **On 3.1L/V6-192 engines,** remove tower to tower brace assembly.
4. **On all models,** remove blower motor retaining screws and blower motor.
5. Reverse procedure to install.

HEATER CORE

REPLACE

1. Disconnect battery ground cable and drain cooling system.
2. Raise and support vehicle.
3. Remove rear lateral transaxle strut and mount, if equipped.
4. Disconnect heater case drain tube, then disconnect heater core heater hoses.
5. Lower vehicle and remove right and left hush panels, steering column trim cover and glove compartment.
6. Remove heater duct retaining screw and heater duct.
7. Remove heater core cover attaching screws, then gently pull cover rearward and out of vehicle, **Fig. 12. When removing heater core assembly, pull assembly straight toward interior of vehicle until plastic drain tube clears cowl. If assembly is tilted in any direction before tube clears cowl, the drain tube may break.**
8. Remove heater core retaining clamps and heater core from case.
9. Reverse procedure to install.

EVAPORATOR CORE

REPLACE

1. Disconnect battery ground cable.
2. Discharge air conditioning system, then drain cooling system.
3. Raise and support vehicle.
4. Remove rear lateral transaxle strut and mount, if equipped.
5. Disconnect heater core heater hoses.
6. Disconnect evaporator lines at evaporator core.
7. Disconnect heater and evaporator assembly drain tube.
8. Lower vehicle and remove right and left hush panels, steering column trim cover and glove compartment.
9. Remove heater duct retaining screw and heater duct.
10. Remove heater core cover attaching screws, then gently pull cover rearward and out of vehicle, **Fig. 12. When removing heater core assembly, pull assembly straight toward interior of vehicle until plastic drain tube clears cowl. If assembly is tilted in any direction before tube clears cowl, the drain tube may break.**
11. Remove heater core retaining clamps and heater core from case.
12. Remove defroster vacuum actuator to module case attaching screw.
13. Remove evaporator cover and core.
14. Reverse procedure to install.

2.0L/4-121 Engine

NOTE: On Air Bag Equipped Models, Refer To "Air Bag System Precautions" Located In The Front Of This Manual For System Disarming & Arming Procedures.

INDEX

PRECAUTIONS

AIR BAG SYSTEMS

Refer to "Air Bag System Precautions" in the front of this manual for system disarming and arming procedures.

FUEL SYSTEM PRESSURE RELIEF

1. Loosen fuel filler cap, then remove the fuel pump fuse.
2. Start engine and run until remaining fuel is consumed.
3. Engage starter for approximately three seconds, to ensure relief of any reaming pressure.
4. Disconnect battery ground cable to avoid possible fuel discharge if any attempt is made to start the engine.

ENGINE MOUNT

REPLACE

FRONT

1. Disconnect battery ground cable.
2. Support engine using tool No. J-28467-A or equivalent, then remove two mount to bracket attaching bolts, **Fig. 1.**
3. Remove two top mount attaching bolts, then raise and support vehicle.
4. Remove lower mount attaching bolt, then the engine mount.
5. Reverse procedure to install. Tighten front engine mount attaching bolts to specifications.

REAR

1. Disconnect battery ground cable.
2. Support engine using tool No. J-28467-A or equivalent, then remove two mount to bracket attaching bolts, **Fig. 2.**
3. Raise and support vehicle.
4. Remove two lower mount attaching nuts and reinforcement, then the engine mount.
5. Reverse procedure to install. Tighten rear engine mount attaching bolts to specifications.

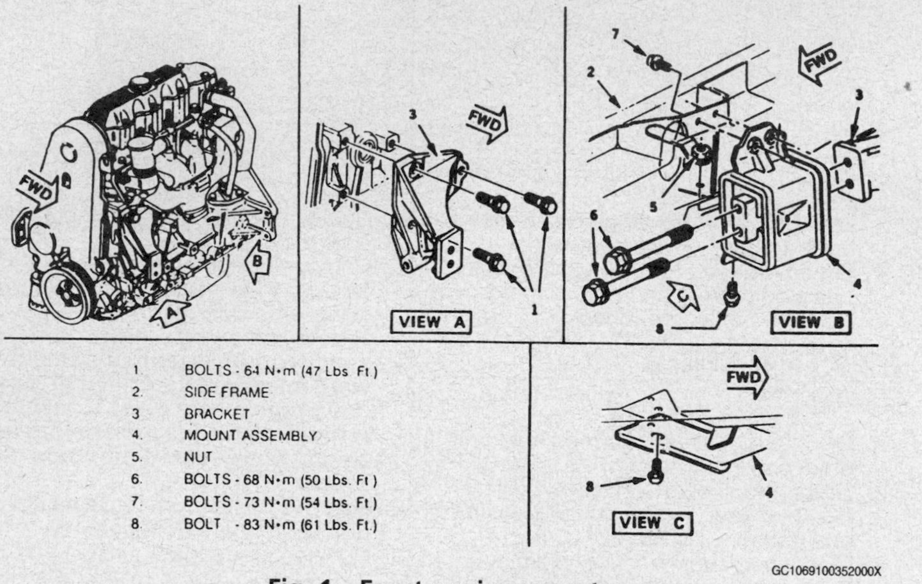

FWD
A
B
C
VIEW A
VIEW B
VIEW C
1. BOLTS - 64 N•m (47 Lbs. Ft.)
2. SIDE FRAME
3. BRACKET
4. MOUNT ASSEMBLY
5. NUT
6. BOLTS - 68 N•m (50 Lbs. Ft.)
7. BOLTS - 73 N•m (54 Lbs. Ft.)
8. BOLT - 83 N•m (61 Lbs. Ft.)
GC1069100352000X

Fig. 1 Front engine mounts

ENGINE

REPLACE

1. Relieve fuel system pressure as outlined under "Precautions."
2. Disconnect battery cables and engine ground wire, then drain cooling system.
3. Remove battery and battery tray.
4. Remove air cleaner.
5. Disconnect engine electrical harness connectors at bulkhead, brake cylinder, wiper motor, cooling fan, relays and grounds.
6. Disconnect throttle cable from bracket and throttle body assembly.
7. Disconnect vacuum hoses from throttle body assembly, then disconnect power steering high pressure hose at cut-off switch.
8. Disconnect vacuum hoses at map sensor and canister, then disconnect air conditioning relay cluster switches.
9. Disconnect power steering return hose at power steering pump.
10. Disconnect ECM electrical connectors, then pull harness through bulkhead and position harness over engine.

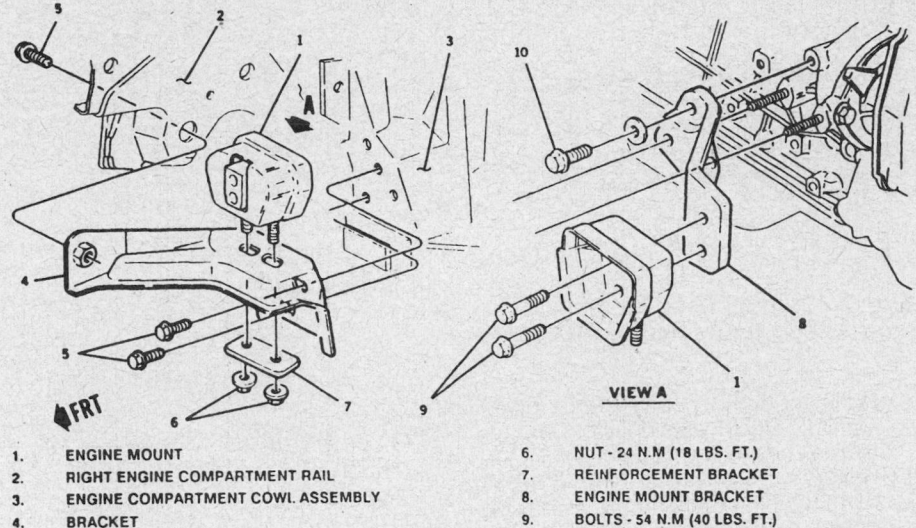

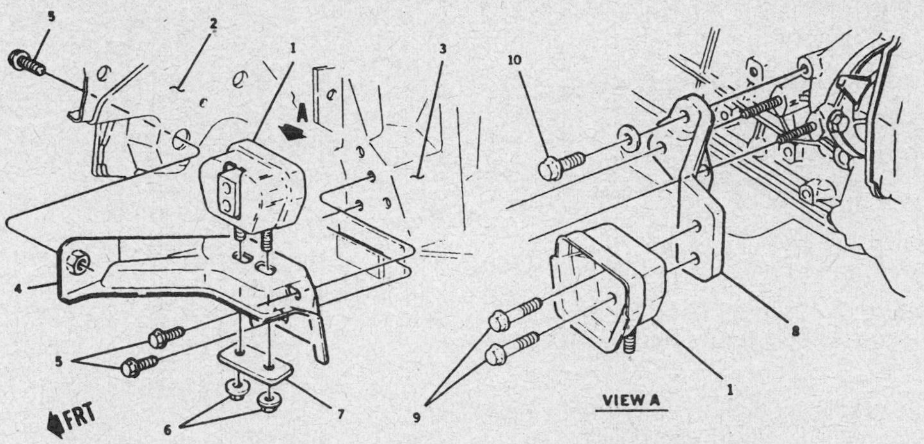
VIEW A
FRT
1. ENGINE MOUNT
2. RIGHT ENGINE COMPARTMENT RAIL
3. ENGINE COMPARTMENT COWL ASSEMBLY
4. BRACKET
5. BOLT - 61 N.M (45 LBS. FT.)
6. NUT - 24 N.M (18 LBS. FT.)
7. REINFORCEMENT BRACKET
8. ENGINE MOUNT BRACKET
9. BOLTS - 54 N.M (40 LBS. FT.)
10. BOLT - 54 N.M (40 LBS. FT.)
GC1069100353000X

Fig. 2 Rear engine mounts

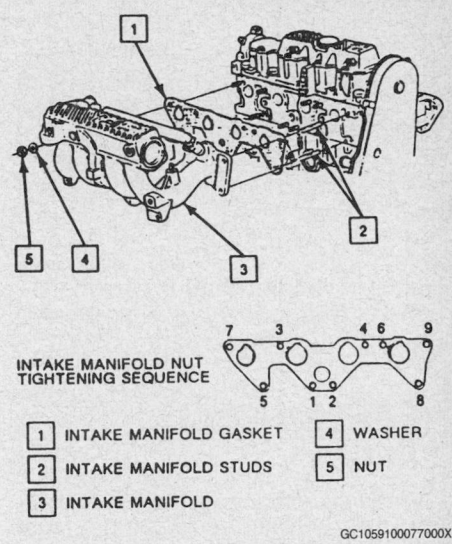

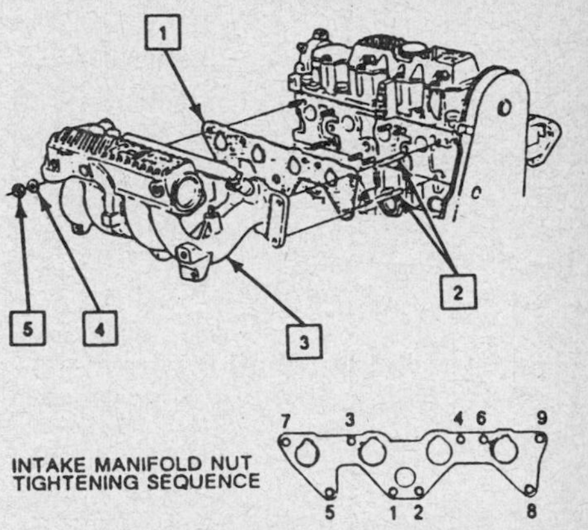
INTAKE MANIFOLD NUT TIGHTENING SEQUENCE
1 INTAKE MANIFOLD GASKET
2 INTAKE MANIFOLD STUDS
3 INTAKE MANIFOLD
4 WASHER
5 NUT
GC1059100077000X

Fig. 3 Intake manifold tightening sequence

11. Disconnect upper and lower radiator hoses from engine, then disconnect wire connector at temperature switch on thermostat housing.
12. Disconnect transmission shift cable at transmission, then raise and support vehicle.
13. Disconnect vehicle speed sensor electrical connector.
14. Disconnect exhaust pipe at exhaust manifold and remove exhaust pipe from converter.
15. Remove heater hoses from heater core, fuel lines at flex hoses and transmission cooler lines at flex hoses. **Place shop towel over fuel line and fitting when disconnecting.**
16. Remove front wheels, right hand spoiler section and splash shield.
17. Remove and support right and left brake calipers.
18. Discharge A/C system, disconnect electrical connectors at A/C compressor, then remove A/C compressor and mounting brackets. Using a piece of wire, support compressor in wheel opening.
19. Remove center front suspension support attachment bolts, then remove one bolt at each end, then loosen remaining bolt.
20. **On automatic transaxle vehicles,** remove rear transaxle lateral strut.
21. **On all models,** remove front transaxle strut.
22. Lower vehicle and support front end by placing jack stands under core support.
23. Using a suitable hoist, position front post of hoist to rear of cowl.
24. Using a suitable piece of wood (4 inch x 4 inch x 6 ft.), position onto front post of hoist.
25. Raise vehicle slightly and remove jack stands from front end.
26. Position a suitable dolly under engine and transaxle assembly.

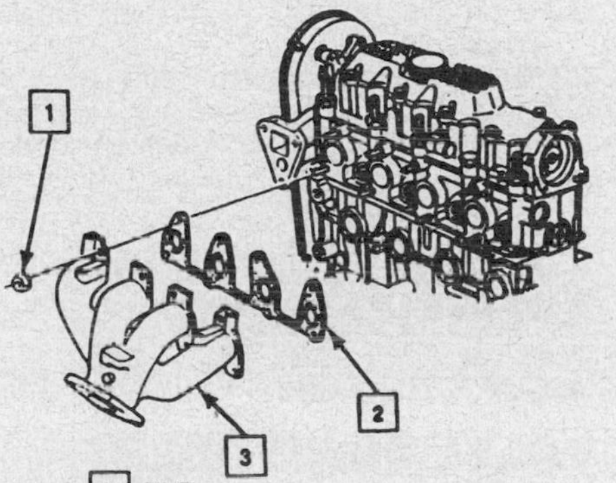
1 NUT
2 EXHAUST MANIFOLD GASKET
3 EXHAUST MANIFOLD
TORQUE #2 AND #3 MANIFOLD RUNNERS PRIOR TO #1 AND #4
GC107910001500X

Fig. 4 Exhaust manifold replacement

27. Position three pieces of wood (4 inch x 4 inch x 12 inch) under engine and transaxle assembly only.
28. Slightly lower vehicle onto dolly and remove right and left front suspension support remaining bolts.
29. Remove transaxle mount to bracket attaching bolt.
30. Remove front and rear engine mount to bracket attaching bolts.
31. Remove right and left steering knuckle to strut attaching bolts.
32. Remove engine and transaxle as an assembly.
33. Position engine and transaxle assembly into vehicle.
34. Loosely install transaxle and left front mounts to side rail bolts.
35. Install right rear mount to body bolts.
36. Position a suitable jack under control arms and raise struts into position, then install retaining nuts.
37. Reverse procedure to complete installation. Tighten all nuts, bolts and screws to specifications.

INTAKE MANIFOLD

REPLACE

1. Disconnect battery ground cable.
2. Remove air cleaner duct from manifold.
3. Remove direct ignition unit, then drain engine coolant.
4. Disconnect coolant and vacuum hoses from manifold.
5. Remove throttle body, gasket, fuel injectors and fuel rail.
6. Remove EGR and PCV hose from manifold.
7. Remove generator and generator bracket at camshaft carrier.
8. Remove power steering bracket from intake manifold, then set power steering and bracket assembly aside.
9. Remove ECM harness to gain access to intake manifold lower retaining nuts.
10. Remove intake manifold attaching nuts, then the manifold.
11. Reverse procedure to install, using sequence shown in **Fig. 3** tighten manifold attaching nuts to specification.

EXHAUST MANIFOLD

REPLACE

1. Disconnect battery ground cable.
2. Remove air cleaner, then remove spark plug wires and retainers.
3. Remove oil dipstick tube and breather.
4. Disconnect oxygen sensor electrical connectors.
5. Remove exhaust pipe, then remove exhaust manifold attaching nuts.
6. Remove exhaust manifold and gasket.
7. Reverse procedure to install. Refer to **Fig. 4,** for manifold bolt tightening sequence. Tighten attaching nuts to specifications.

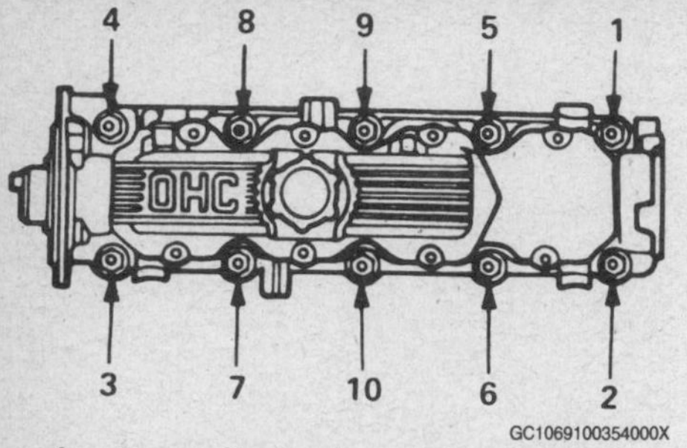
4 8 9 5 1
OHC
3 7 10 6 2
GC1069100354000X

Fig. 5 Cylinder head & camshaft carrier bolt loosening sequence

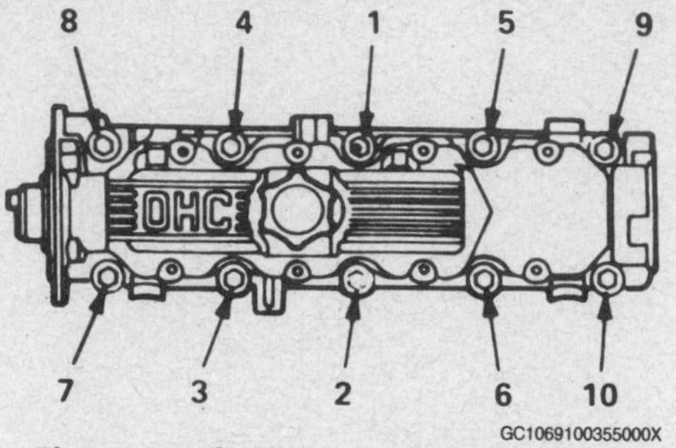
8 4 1 5 9
OHC
7 3 2 6 10
GC1069100355000X

Fig. 6 Cylinder head & camshaft carrier bolt tightening sequence

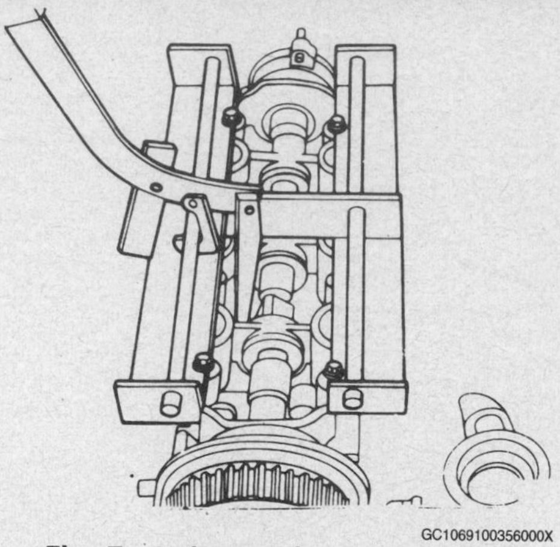
GC1069100356000X

Fig. 7 Using tool No. 33302 to compress valve spring

CYLINDER HEAD

REPLACE

Cylinder head bolts should only be loosened when engine is cold. Do not reuse cylinder head bolts.

1. Relieve fuel system pressure as outlined under "Precautions."
2. Disconnect battery ground cable and drain coolant.
3. Remove air filter housing assembly.
4. Remove coolant reservoir tank.
5. Remove fuel vapor pipe assembly. **Place shop towel over fuel line and fitting when disconnecting.**
6. Remove serpentine belt and front timing cover upper attaching bolts.
7. Loosen serpentine belt tensioner and position aside.
8. Raise and support vehicle, then remove righthand inner splash shield and lower righthand splash shield.
9. Remove air conditioning belt.
10. Remove crankshaft pulley as outlined under "Crankshaft Damper, Replace."
11. Remove flywheel inspection cover.
12. Remove front timing belt cover lower attaching bolts, then remove cover, then align timing marks.
13. Loosen water pump attaching bolts and release timing belt tension using tool No. J-33039-A or equivalent, then remove timing belt.
14. Remove exhaust pipe to manifold.
15. **On all models,** lower vehicle and remove fuel vapor pipe. **Place shop towel over fuel line and fitting when disconnecting.**
16. Remove rear timing cover attaching bolts, then remove rear timing cover.
17. Remove PCV attaching hose.
18. Disconnect intake manifold and cylinder head electrical connectors.
19. Remove exhaust manifold attaching bolts.
20. Remove power steering pump pressure and return lines.
21. Remove alternator and alternator bracket with power steering pump.
22. Disconnect front and rear engine lift brackets, then remove coil assembly.
23. Remove breather tube bracket and breather tube.
24. Remove accelerator linkage and bracket, then remove attaching fuel lines. **Place shop towel over fuel line and fitting when disconnecting.**
25. Remove cylinder head and intake manifold electrical connectors and attaching hoses and coolant lines.
26. Remove cylinder head and camshaft carrier attaching bolts in sequence shown in **Fig. 5.**
27. Remove camshaft carrier, them remove rocker arms, lash compensators and thrust pieces.
28. Remove cylinder head and intake manifold.
29. Reverse procedure to install. Refer to **Fig. 6,** for cylinder head and camshaft carrier attaching bolt tightening sequence. Tighten attaching bolts to specifications.

CAMSHAFT LOBE LIFT SPECIFICATIONS

Year	Int.	Exh.
1992-94	.263	.263

VALVE ADJUSTMENT

Valve lash is obtained through the use of hydraulic valve lash compensators. No provision for adjustment is provided.

ROCKER ARMS

REPLACE

1. Disconnect battery ground cable.
2. Remove camshaft carrier cover.
3. Using tool No. J-33302-25 or equivalent, **Fig. 7,** compress valve springs and remove rocker arms. Place rocker arms in a suitable rack so they can be installed in the same location.
4. Remove hydraulic lash compensators and place them in a rack so they can be installed in the same location.
5. Reverse procedure to install. **The preload of the hydraulic valve lash compensator is automatic and servicing of the compensator requires only care and cleanliness be exercised in the handling of these components.**

VALVE GUIDES

Valve guides are an integral part of the cylinder head. If valve stem to guide clearance is excessive, the guide should be reamed to the next oversize and the appropriate oversize valve installed. Valves are available in standard sizes and oversizes of .00295 inch, .0059 inch and .00984 inch.

VALVE SPRING & STEM OIL SEAL

Removal

1. Disconnect battery ground cable.
2. Remove camshaft carrier cover as described under "Camshaft, Replace."
3. Remove rocker arms and spark plugs.
4. Install air line adapter tool No. J-22794 or equivalent, into spark plug port and apply compressed air to hold valves in place.
5. Using tool No. J-33302-25 or equivalent, **Fig. 7,** compress valve spring and remove rocker guides, valve locks, caps and valve spring.
6. Remove valve stem oil seal.

Installation

1. Using clean engine oil, lubricate valve stem and install new valve stem oil seal over valve stem and seat onto valve guide.
2. Position valve spring and cap over valve stem. Using tool No. J-33302-25 or equivalent, compress valve spring and install valve locks.
3. Install rocker guides and rocker arms, then remove tool No. J-33302-25.
4. Remove air line adapter tool and install spark plugs.
5. Install camshaft carrier cover. Tighten bolts to specifications.

VALVE SEATS

Using a suitable dial indicator measure valve seat concentricity. Valve seat should be concentric to within .002 inch of total indicator reading. Ensure valve guide bores are free from carbon or dirt to allow proper seating of the pilot in the valve guide. When reconditioning the valve seats, use a 45° stone to rough the valve seat and another stone with the same angle to finish the valve seat. Narrow down the valve seats to the proper width, .0050-.0701 inch for both intake and exhaust.

GC1069100358000X

Fig. 8 Camshaft sprocket removal

HYDRAULIC LIFTERS
REPLACE

Refer to "Rocker Arms, Replace" for replacement procedures.

CRANKSHAFT DAMPER
REPLACE

1. Disconnect battery ground cable.
2. Remove inner fender shield.
3. Remove air conditioning belt, if equipped, then remove serpentine belt.
4. Remove crankshaft pulley bolts and pulley.
5. Reverse to install, noting the following:
   a. Using a suitable sealer, coat threads of pulley bolts and install onto pulley.
   b. Tighten bolts to specifications.

FRONT COVER
REPLACE

1. Remove serpentine belt.
2. Loosen serpentine belt tensioner attaching bolt, then allow tensioner to swing downward.
3. Remove timing cover attaching bolts and nut, then remove cover.
4. Reverse procedure to install.

TIMING GEARS
CAMSHAFT SPROCKET, REPLACE

1. Disconnect battery ground cable.
2. Remove camshaft carrier cover.
3. Remove timing belt as outlined under "Timing Belt, Replace."
4. Using a suitable tool, secure camshaft and remove camshaft sprocket bolt, washer and sprocket, **Fig. 8.**
5. Reverse procedure to install. Tighten camshaft sprocket bolt and camshaft carrier cover to specification.

CRANKSHAFT SPROCKET, REPLACE

1. Disconnect battery ground cable.
2. Remove timing belt as described under "Timing Belt, Replace."
3. Remove crankshaft sprocket bolt, washer and sprocket.
4. Reverse procedure to install.

TIMING BELT
REPLACE

1. Disconnect battery ground cable.
2. Remove serpentine belt, then remove timing belt cover as outlined under "Front Cover, Replace" procedure.
3. Loosen water pump attaching bolts and release tension with tool No. J-33039-A or equivalent.
4. Raise and support vehicle.
5. Lower vehicle, then remove timing belt.
6. Reverse procedure to install, noting the following:
   a. Turn crankshaft and camshaft gears clockwise to align timing marks on gears with timing marks on rear cover.
   b. Install timing belt, ensuring portion between camshaft gear and crankshaft gear is in tension.
   c. Using tool No. J-33039-A or equivalent, turn water pump eccentric clockwise until tensioner arm contacts high torque stop, **Fig. 9.** Tighten water pump attaching screws slightly.
   d. Turn engine by crankshaft gear bolt two complete turns clockwise to seat belt to gear teeth.
   e. Turn water pump eccentric counterclockwise until hole in tensioner arm aligns with hole in base. Perform operation with engine at room temperature, approximately 68°F.
   f. Tighten water pump attaching bolts to specifications ensuring tensioner holes remain as adjusted.

TIMING BELT REAR COVER, REPLACE

1. Disconnect battery ground cable.
2. Remove air cleaner and disconnect breather hoses.
3. remove carrier cover bolts and cover.
4. Remove timing belt as described under "Timing Belt, Replace."
5. Remove camshaft and crankshaft sprockets as described under "Timing Gears."
6. Remove timing belt tensioner assembly.
7. Remove timing belt rear cover bolts and cover.
8. Reverse procedure to install. Tighten bolts to specifications.

CAMSHAFT
REPLACE
REMOVAL

1. Disconnect battery ground cable.
2. Remove camshaft carrier cover.
3. Using tool No. J-33302-25 or equivalent, **Fig. 7,** compress valve springs and remove rocker arms.
4. Remove camshaft sprocket as described under "Timing Gears."
5. Remove washer fluid container assembly.

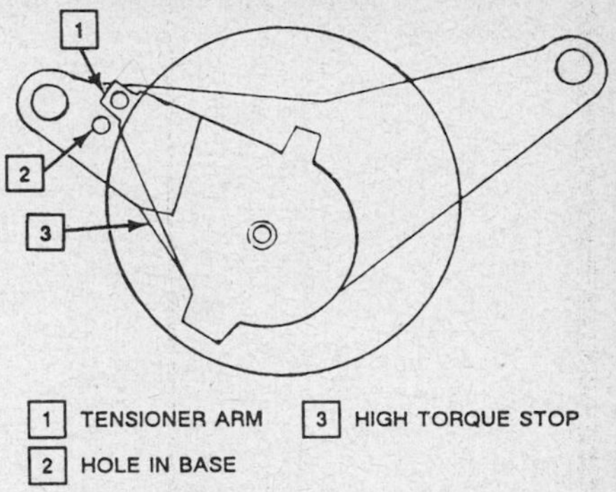
1
2
3
1 TENSIONER ARM
3 HIGH TORQUE STOP
2 HOLE IN BASE
GC1069100357000X

Fig. 9 Timing belt tensioner positions

6. Disconnect spark plug wires from spark plugs, then remove distributor from engine.
7. Remove camshaft thrust plate from rear of camshaft carrier.
8. Slide camshaft rearward and remove camshaft from carrier.

INSTALLATION

1. Install new front oil seal onto camshaft carrier using fingers.
2. Position camshaft into carrier. **Ensure not to damage front oil seal when installing camshaft.**
3. Install camshaft thrust plate and bolts. Tighten bolts to specifications.
4. Check camshaft endplay. Endplay should be within .016 to .064 inch.
5. Install distributor, camshaft sprocket, timing belt and timing belt front cover.
6. Using tool No. J-33302-25 or equivalent, **Fig. 7,** compress valve springs and install rocker arms.
7. Install camshaft carrier cover. Tighten bolts to specifications.

PISTON & ROD ASSEMBLY

Assemble piston to rod, with arrow on piston facing toward front of engine and numbered side toward intake manifold side of engine, **Fig. 10.** Upon installation, measure connecting rod side clearance using a suitable feeler gauge. Side clearance should be .0028 to .0095 inch.

PISTONS, PINS & RINGS

Pistons and rings are available in standard size and oversize of .020 inch (.5 mm). Piston pins are available in standard size only.

MAIN & ROD BEARINGS

Main and rod bearings are available in standard sizes and undersizes of .010 inch (.25 mm) and .020 inch (.5 mm).

CRANKSHAFT SEAL
REPLACE

1. Disconnect battery ground cable.
2. Remove crankshaft sprocket as described under "Timing Gears."
3. Remove key and rear thrust washer from end of crankshaft.
4. Remove rear timing cover as described under "Timing Belt, Replace."

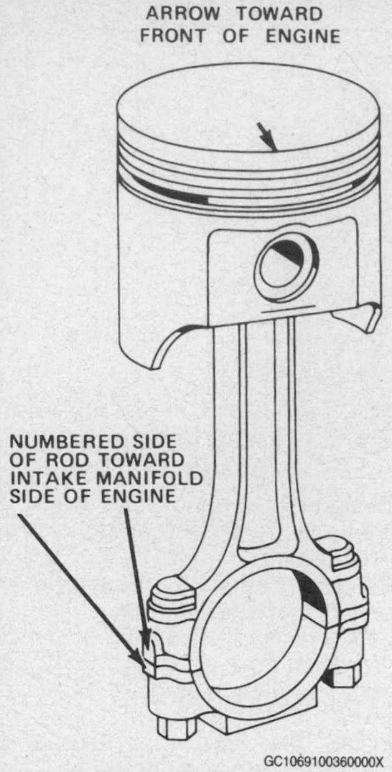
ARROW TOWARD
FRONT OF ENGINE
NUMBERED SIDE
OF ROD TOWARD
INTAKE MANIFOLD
SIDE OF ENGINE
GC1069100360000X

Fig. 10 Piston & rod assembly

5. Using a suitable tool, remove crankshaft front oil seal.
6. During installation of crankshaft front oil seal, position tool No. J-33083 or equivalent, **Fig. 11,** onto crankshaft. Lubricate front oil seal lip and install onto crankshaft.
7. Reverse procedure to complete installation.

CRANKSHAFT REAR OIL SEAL

REPLACE

1. Remove transaxle from vehicle as described under "Transaxle, Replace."
2. Remove flywheel attaching bolts and flywheel or flexplate.
3. **On models with manual transaxle,** remove pressure plate and clutch disc.
4. **On all models,** using a suitable tool, pry crankshaft rear oil seal from bore.
5. Clean engine block and crankshaft to seal mating surfaces.
6. Lubricate crankshaft rear oil seal.
7. Use seal installer J-36227 to press seal evenly into position.
8. **On models with manual transaxle,** tighten flywheel attaching bolts to specifications.
9. **On models with automatic transaxle,** tighten flexplate attaching bolts to specifications.
10. **On models with manual transaxle,** install clutch disc and pressure plate.
11. **On all models,** install transaxle assembly.

OIL PAN

REPLACE

1. Disconnect battery ground cable.

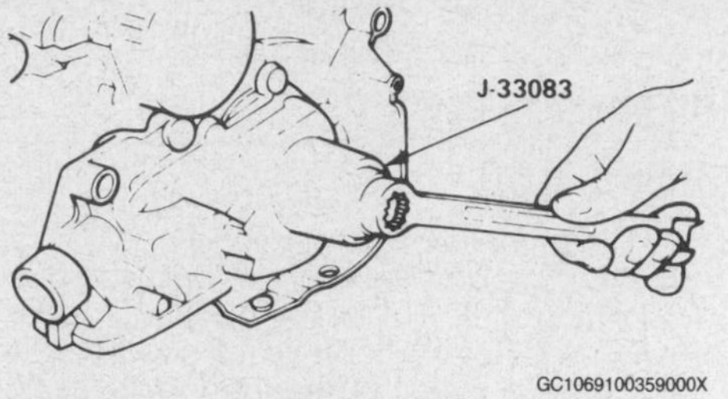
J-33083
GC1069100359000X

Fig. 11 Crankshaft front oil seal installation

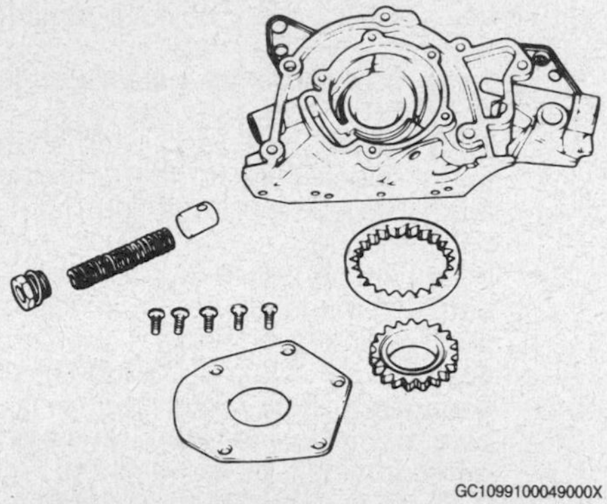
GC1099100049000X

Fig. 13 Oil pump disassembled

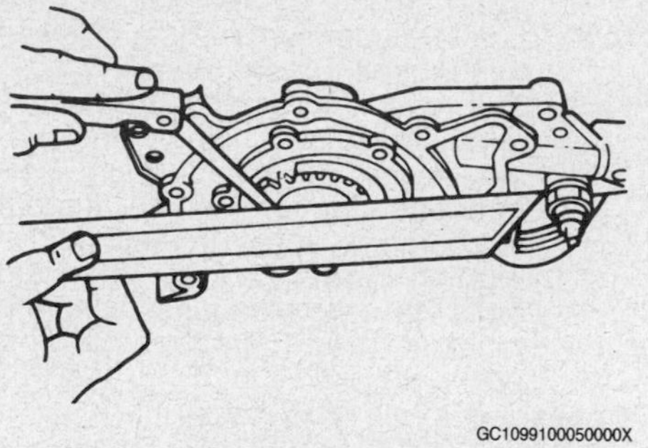
GC1099100050000X

Fig. 14 Drive gear to oil pump housing clearance inspection

2. Raise and support vehicle.
3. Drain engine oil.
4. Disconnect exhaust pipe from exhaust manifold or wastegate, as required.
5. Remove flywheel cover attaching bolts.
6. Remove oil pan bolts and oil pan.
7. Reverse procedure to install. Apply sealer to oil pan and oil pan gasket as shown in **Fig. 12.** Also coat threads of oil pan bolts with sealer. Tighten bolts to specifications.

OIL PUMP SERVICE

REMOVAL

1. Disconnect battery ground cable and drain engine oil.
2. Remove crankshaft sprocket as outlined under "Timing Gears."
3. Remove timing belt rear cover as outlined under "Timing Belt, Replace."
4. Disconnect engine oil pressure switch electrical connector from the switch.
5. Remove oil pan and oil filter.
6. Remove pickup tube to engine block bolts, pickup tube and oil pump.

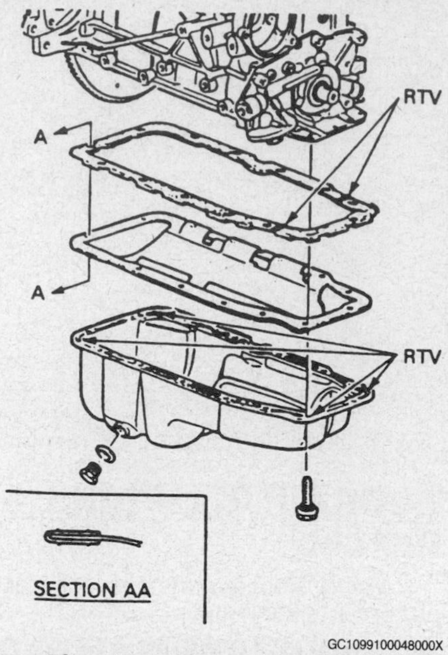
RTV
A
A
RTV
SECTION AA
GC1099100048000X

Fig. 12 Oil pan installation

DISASSEMBLE

1. Remove five screws and rear cover from oil pump, **Fig. 13.**
2. Remove gears, plug, pressure regulator valve plunger and spring.
3. If necessary, remove pickup tube and O-ring from oil pump body.

INSPECTION

After disassembling the oil pump, thoroughly clean all oil pump components and check them for excessive wear and damage.

1. Using a suitable straightedge and feeler gauge, **Fig. 14,** check oil pump clearances.
2. Check clearances for the following oil pump components:
   a. Clearance between idler gear and oil pump body should be .004-.007 inch.
   b. Clearance between drive gear and oil pump body should be .014-.018 inch.
   c. End clearance should be .001-.004 inch.
3. If clearances obtained are not within specified limits, replace worn or damaged oil pump components.

ASSEMBLE

1. Install valve plunger and spring.
2. Using a suitable sealer, coat threads of pressure regulator valve plunger plug and install. Tighten plug and attaching bolts to specifications.
3. Install oil pump gears into oil pump body.

INSTALLATION

1. Install gasket and oil pump onto engine. Tighten oil pump bolts specifications.
2. Install pickup tube and bolts, **torquing** pick-up tube bolts to 71 inch lbs. and pick-up tube support block to 53 inch lbs.

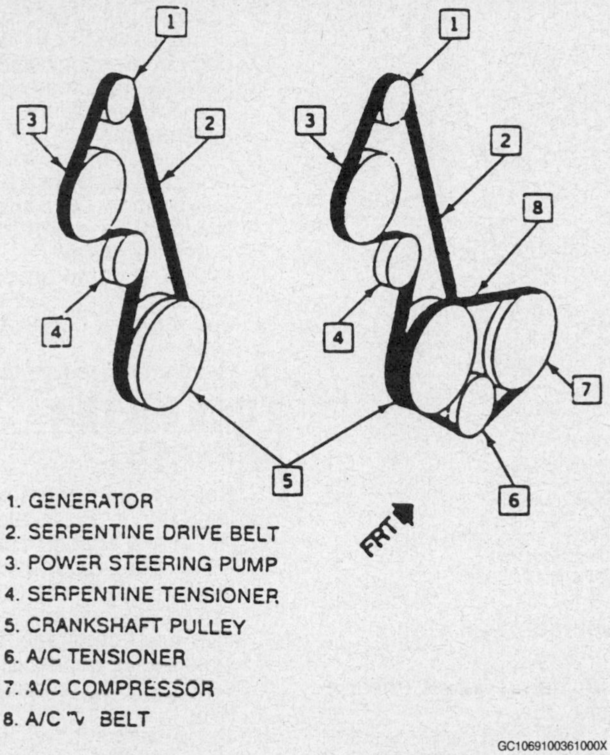
1
1
2
3
3
2
8
4
4
7
5
6
FRT
1. GENERATOR
2. SERPENTINE DRIVE BELT
3. POWER STEERING PUMP
4. SERPENTINE TENSIONER
5. CRANKSHAFT PULLEY
6. A/C TENSIONER
7. A/C COMPRESSOR
8. A/C V BELT
GC1069100361000X

Fig. 15 Serpentine belt routing

3. Install oil pan and oil filter.
4. Connect engine oil pressure switch electrical connector to switch.
5. Install timing belt rear covers and crankshaft sprocket.

BELT TENSION DATA

Belt tension is maintained by a spring-loaded tensioner. No adjustment is necessary.

SERPENTINE DRIVE BELT

ROUTING

Refer to **Fig. 15,** for drive belt routing.

REPLACEMENT

1. Disconnect battery ground cable, then remove coolant recovery tank.
2. Using 19 mm wrench, pivot tensioner and remove belt from alternator.
3. Raise and support vehicle, then remove inner fender splash shield.
4. Remove A/C belt, if equipped.
5. Remove serpentine drive belt.
6. Reverse procedure to install. Refer to **Fig. 15,** for drive belt routing.

TENSIONER, REPLACE

1. Remove drive belt from alternator.
2. Remove bolt from rear of tensioner, then the tensioner.
3. Reverse procedure to install, tighten bolt to specifications.

COOLING SYSTEM BLEED

To ensure sufficient engine cooling, freezing and corrosion protection, maintain

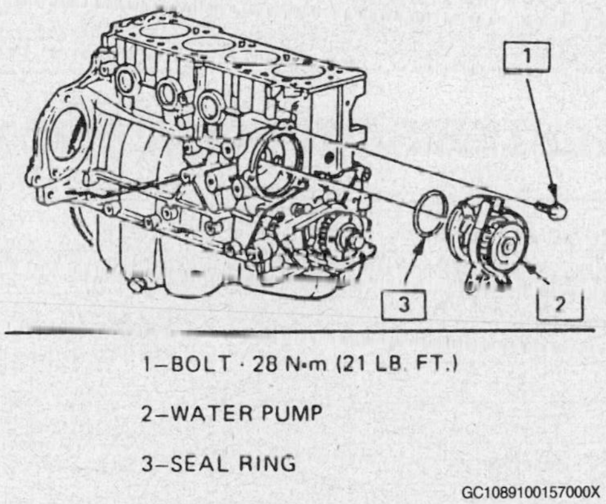
1
3
2
1—BOLT · 28 N·m (21 LB. FT.)
2—WATER PUMP
3—SEAL RING
GC1089100157000X

Fig. 17 Water pump removal & installation

the protection level at -34°F or lower. Use a solution of antifreeze and water, ensuring solution is no more than 70 percent antifreeze.

1. Fill surge tank or radiator to base of filler neck, then install pressure cap.
2. Block the drive wheel and apply parking brake.
3. **On models equipped with automatic transaxle,** place shifter in Park position.
4. **On models equipped with manual transaxle,** place transaxle in Neutral position.
5. **On all models,** start engine and allow to run until upper radiator hose is hot.
6. Turn engine Off, check level of coolant in surge tank or radiator.
7. Allow engine to cool, then add coolant as necessary.

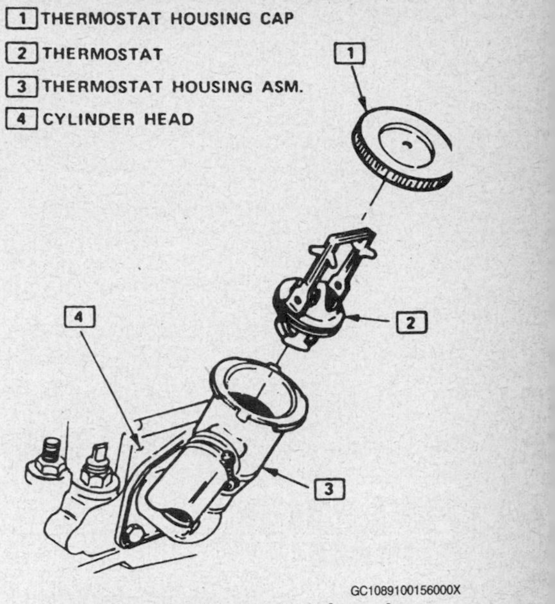
1 THERMOSTAT HOUSING CAP
2 THERMOSTAT
3 THERMOSTAT HOUSING ASM.
4 CYLINDER HEAD
1
4
2
3
GC1089100156000X

Fig. 16 Thermostat & housing assembly

THERMOSTAT

REPLACE

Refer to **Fig. 16** when performing the following procedure.

1. Disconnect battery negative cable.
2. With engine cool, drain engine coolant below thermostat level. **Never open cooling system with engine hot. Failure to follow this warning may cause personal injury.**
3. Remove thermostat housing cap, then the thermostat.
4. Reverse procedure to install.

WATER PUMP

REPLACE

1. Disconnect battery ground cable.
2. Drain cooling system, then remove timing belt. Refer to "Timing Belt, Replace" for procedure.
3. Remove timing belt rear protective covers, as required.
4. Remove lower radiator hose from water pump.
5. Remove water pump attaching bolts then the water pump and sealing ring, **Fig. 17.**
6. Clean engine block and water pump sealing surfaces, then apply a 3/32 inch of RTV sealant to sealing surfaces. While RTV sealant is still wet, install water pump. Tighten attaching bolts finger tight.
7. Install lower radiator hose on water pump, then timing belt rear protective covers.
8. Install timing belt. Refer to "Timing Belt, Replace" for procedure.

RADIATOR

REPLACE

1. Disconnect battery ground cable, then discharge and recover air conditioning refrigerant.

2. Drain and recover engine coolant.
3. Remove hood latch from mounting plate, then both headlight assemblies.
4. Remove radiator mounts, then raise and support vehicle.
5. Disconnect forward SIR sensor harness, then remove cooling fan assembly.
6. Disconnect radiator hoses, then transmission oil cooler lines from radiator.
7. Lower vehicle, then remove hood latch support and forward sensor with wiring harness.
8. Disconnect compressor and accumulator hoses from condenser, discarding O-rings.
9. Disconnect coolant overflow line, then remove radiator.
10. Reverse procedure to install, installing new air conditioning O-rings

FUEL PUMP
REPLACE

1. Depressurize fuel system as outlined under "Precautions."
2. Disconnect battery ground cable.
3. Raise and support vehicle.
4. Remove fuel tank as follows:
   a. Drain fuel tank. **Place shop towel over fuel line and fitting when disconnecting.**
   b. Disconnect tank meter assembly harness from body harness electrical connectors.
   c. Remove tank filler hoses and vent pipes. **Place shop towel over fuel line and fitting when disconnecting.**
   d. Support fuel tank with suitable equipment, then disconnect fuel tank attaching straps.
   e. Carefully lower fuel tank, if required remove fuel tank meter assembly and seal using tool No. J-24187 or equivalent.
5. Remove fuel tank sending unit and pump assembly by turning cam lock ring counterclockwise.
6. Remove fuel meter pump assembly from fuel tank and fuel pump from fuel sending unit.
7. Pull fuel pump upward into fuel hose while pulling outward away from bottom support. **Do not damage rubber insulator and strainer during fuel pump removal.**
8. After fuel pump assembly is clear of bottom support, pull pump assembly out of rubber connector and from vehicle.
9. Reverse procedure to install.

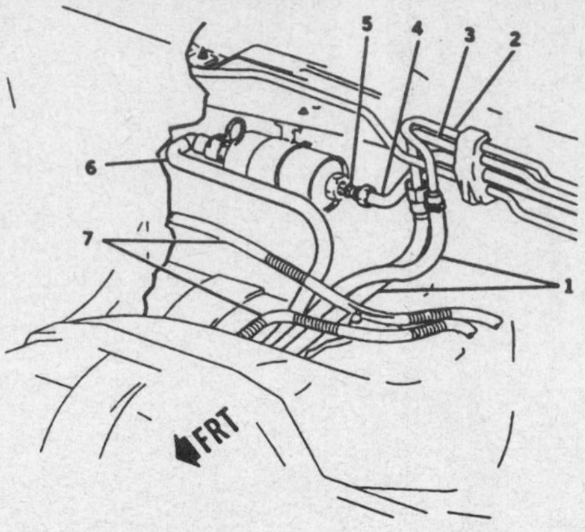
5
4
3
2
6
7
1
FRT

1. HOSE-PART OF FUEL SENDER
2. FUEL VAPOR PIPE
3. FUEL RETURN PIPE
4. FUEL FEED PIPE
5. FUEL FEED PIPE NUT
6. HOSE-PART OF FUEL SENDER
7. ABS AND FUEL SENDER HARNESS

GC1029202727000X

Fig. 18 Fuel filter replacement

FUEL FILTER
REPLACE

1. Relieve fuel system pressure as outlined under "Precautions."
2. Raise and support vehicle.
3. Using back-up wrench, remove filter fitting. If nylon fuel lines become kinked and cannot be straightened, they must be replaced.
4. Twist quick-connect fitting 1/4 turn in each direction to loosen dirt within fitting.
5. Using compressed air, clean quick-connect fitting at ends of filter.
6. Disconnect quick-connect fittings by squeezing plastic tabs of male end connector and pulling apart.
7. Remove fuel filter, **Fig. 18.**
8. Reverse procedure to install.

TIGHTENING SPECIFICATIONS

Component	Torque/Ft. Lbs.
Camshaft Carrier & Cylinder Head	①
Camshaft Carrier Cover	71⑤
Camshaft Sprocket	33
Camshaft Rear Thrust Plate	71⑤
Connecting Rod Cap	26②
Crankshaft Pulley To Sprocket	13
Crankshaft Sprocket	114
Cylinder Head	①
Engine Mount (Front)	⑦
Engine Mount (Rear)	⑥
Exhaust Manifold Attaching Nuts	16
Exhaust Pipe To Manifold	19
Flexplate, Auto. Trans.	48
Flywheel, Manual Trans.	48④
Fuel Tank Strap Bolt (Front)	25
Fuel Tank Strap Nut (Rear)	106⑤
Heater Pipe To Intake	18
Intake Manifold	15-20
Main Bearing Caps	44③
Oil Pan Bolts	44⑤
Oil Pan Drain Plug	34
Oil Pump	62⑤

Component	Torque/Ft. Lbs.
Oil Pump Cover	71⑤
Oil Pump Drive	15-22
Oil Pump Pressure Regulating Valve	22
Oil Pump Suction Tube Bolts	71⑤
Pressure Plate To Flywheel	18
Serpentine Drive Belt Tensioner	35
Spark Plug	15
Suspension Support (Front)	65
Thermostat Housing	20
Throttle Body Injector Assembly	16
Timing Belt Front Cover	89⑤
Timing Belt Rear Cover	89⑤
Timing Belt Tensioner	18
Transaxle Mount Bolt	22⑧
Transaxle To Engine	55⑧
Transaxle Strut To Body Bolt (Front)	40
Transaxle Strut To Body Bolt (Rear)	23
Transaxle Strut To Transaxle (Front	50
Water Inlet	15-22

TIGHTENING SPECIFICATIONS-Continued

Component	Torque/Ft. Lbs.
Water Outlet To Cam Carrier	11
Water Pump	18

①—Torque cylinder head & camshaft carrier bolts to 18 ft. lbs., then tighten bolts an additional 180° in 60° increments. Start engine & allow to reach operating temperature, then tighten bolts an additional 30° to 50°.

Component	Torque/Ft. Lbs.
Wheel And Tire Assembly	100

②—Plus an additional 40–45°.
③—Plus an additional 40–50°.
④—Plus an additional 30°.
⑤—Inch lbs.
⑥—Refer to 2, for specifications.
⑦—Refer to 1, for specifications.
⑧—Vehicles equipped with automatic transmission.

2.2L/4-134 Engine

NOTE: On Air Bag Equipped Models, Refer To "Air Bag System Precautions" Located In The Front Of This Manual For System Disarming & Arming Procedures.

INDEX

PRECAUTIONS

AIR BAG SYSTEMS

Refer to "Air Bag System Precautions" in the front of this manual for system disarming and arming procedures.

FUEL SYSTEM PRESSURE RELIEF

1. Loosen fuel filler cap, then remove the fuel pump fuse.
2. Start engine and run until remaining fuel is consumed.
3. Engage starter for approximately three seconds, to ensure relief of any reaming pressure.
4. Disconnect battery ground cable to avoid possible fuel discharge if any attempt is made to start the engine.

ENGINE MOUNT

REPLACE

FRONT MOUNT

1. Disconnect battery ground cable.
2. Remove upper engine mount to body bolts, **Fig. 1.**
3. Remove upper engine mount to engine bracket bolt.
4. Raise and support vehicle.
5. Using a suitable jack, support engine assembly.
6. Remove inner fender shield.
7. Remove lower engine mount to body bolt.
8. Remove lower engine mount to engine mount bracket bolt, then remove mount.
9. Reverse procedure to install, tighten bolts and nuts to specifications.

REAR MOUNT

1. Disconnect battery ground cable.
2. Raise and support vehicle.
3. Remove engine mount retaining bolts and nuts, **Fig. 2,** then remove mount.
4. Reverse procedure to install, tighten bolts and nuts to specifications.

ENGINE

REPLACE

Refer to **Fig. 3,** when performing the following procedure.

1. Disconnect battery ground cable.
2. Loosen fuel filler cap to relieve tank vapor pressure.
3. Drain engine coolant, then disconnect hood lamp wiring.
4. Mark position of hood for assembly reference, then remove hood retaining bolts and remove hood.
5. Remove throttle body intake duct, then rear sight shields.
6. Remove the battery, then air cleaner housing.
7. Remove upper radiator hose, then disconnect brake booster vacuum hose.
8. Remove alternator top brace, then disconnect wiring.
9. Disconnect upper engine wiring harness from engine.
10. Discharge A/C system, then remove compressor to condenser and accumulator lines.
11. Raise and support vehicle.
12. Remove left splash shield, then disconnect exhaust system from the engine.
13. Disconnect lower engine wiring, then remove flywheel inspection cover.
14. Remove front wheels and lower radiator hose.
15. Disconnect heater hoses from the heater core, then remove brake calipers from the steering knuckle. Use wire to support brake calipers.
16. Disconnect tie rod ends from struts, then lower the vehicle.
17. Remove left side sound insulator from under dash panel, then disconnect the clutch master cylinder pushrod from the clutch pedal.
18. Remove clutch slave cylinder retaining nuts at front of dash and disconnect remote reservoir, if equipped.
19. Disconnect fuel feed and return lines, **Fig. 4. Place shop towel over fuel line and fitting when disconnecting.**
20. Disconnect transaxle linkage at the transaxle.
21. Disconnect accelerator, cruise control and TV cables from throttle body.

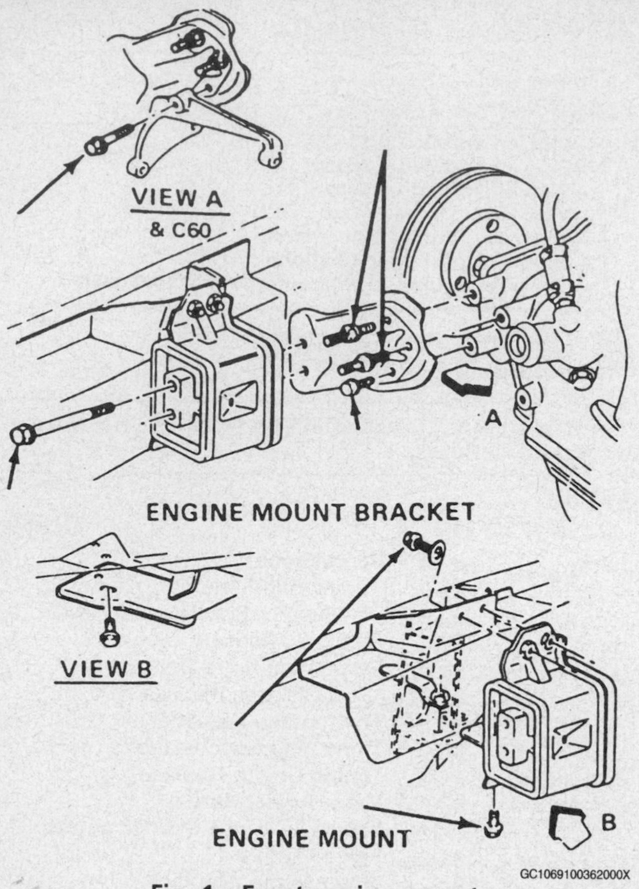
VIEW A
& C60
ENGINE MOUNT BRACKET
VIEW B
A
B
ENGINE MOUNT
GC1069100362000X

Fig. 1 Front engine mount

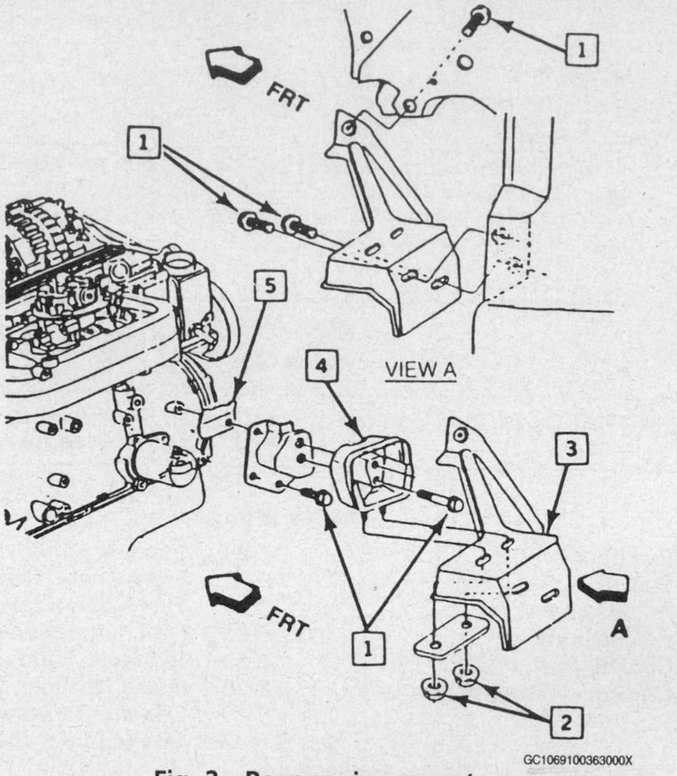
FRT
1
1
5
4
VIEW A
3
FRT
1
A
2
GC1069100363000X

Fig. 2 Rear engine mount

22. **On models equipped with automatic transaxle,** disconnect transmission cooling lines from the transaxle.
23. **On all models,** disconnect power steering hoses from the power steering pump.
24. Remove four center carriage support bolts, then align dolly under frame and lower vehicle to dolly and add support under engine.
25. Support rear of vehicle, then remove upper transaxle mount.
26. Remove upper strut bolts and nuts.
27. Remove front engine mount, then rear engine mount.
28. Remove four rear, then four front carriage retaining bolts.
29. Wire front carriage bolt holes together to prevent axle separation.
30. Raise vehicle and remove engine and transaxle assembly on dolly.
31. Reverse procedure to install.

INTAKE MANIFOLD
REPLACE

1. Remove air intake duct.
2. Drain coolant and disconnect all attaching vacuum lines and wires.
3. Disconnect throttle linkage, then remove MAP sensor and EGR solenoid valve.
4. Remove the power steering pump and position aside.
5. Remove upper intake manifold assembly, EGR valve injector, fuel injector retainer bracket, regulator injectors and fuel lines.
6. Disconnect accelerator and TV cables, then remove cable bracket.
7. Raise and support vehicle.
8. Remove intake manifold lower nuts, then lower vehicle.
9. Remove intake manifold upper nuts.
10. Remove lower intake manifold and gasket.
11. Reverse procedure to install, tighten bolts to specifications in sequence shown in **Fig. 5.**

EXHAUST MANIFOLD
REPLACE

1. Disconnect battery ground cable.
2. Disconnect oxygen sensor lead, then remove serpentine belt.
3. Remove alternator and position aside.
4. Raise and support vehicle.
5. Disconnect exhaust pipe from the exhaust manifold, then lower the vehicle.
6. Remove exhaust manifold attaching bolts and oil fill tube, then remove exhaust manifold.
7. Reverse procedure to install, tighten manifold retaining bolts to specifications.

CYLINDER HEAD
REPLACE

1. Disconnect battery ground cable, then loosen fuel filler cap to relieve tank vapor pressure.
2. Remove air cleaner assembly, then drain cooling system.
3. Disconnect attaching vacuum hoses, electrical connectors and accelerator cable.
4. Remove coolant reservoir tank.
5. Remove serpentine belt, then remove alternator.
6. Loosen power steering pump attaching bolts, then position away.
7. Remove serpentine belt tensioner.
8. Remove ignition wires, then remove canister purge line beneath manifold.
9. Remove upper radiator hose, then remove upper and lower heater hose at manifold.
10. Remove throttle body cables from bracket.
11. Remove cylinder head coolant inlet hose.
12. Remove intake manifold brace to power steering bracket attaching bolts.
13. Remove attaching fuel lines. **Place shop towel over fuel line and fitting when disconnecting.**
14. Remove rocker arm cover attaching bolts, then remove rocker arm cover.
15. Remove rocker arms and pushrods.
16. Remove ignition cable bracket.
17. Disconnect exhaust pipe at exhaust manifold.
18. Remove cylinder head attaching bolts.
19. **On models equipped with automatic transaxle,** remove transaxle fluid level indicator bracket.
20. **On all models,** remove cylinder head assembly.
21. Reverse procedure to install. Refer to **Fig. 6,** for cylinder head bolt tightening sequence. Tighten attaching bolts to specifications.

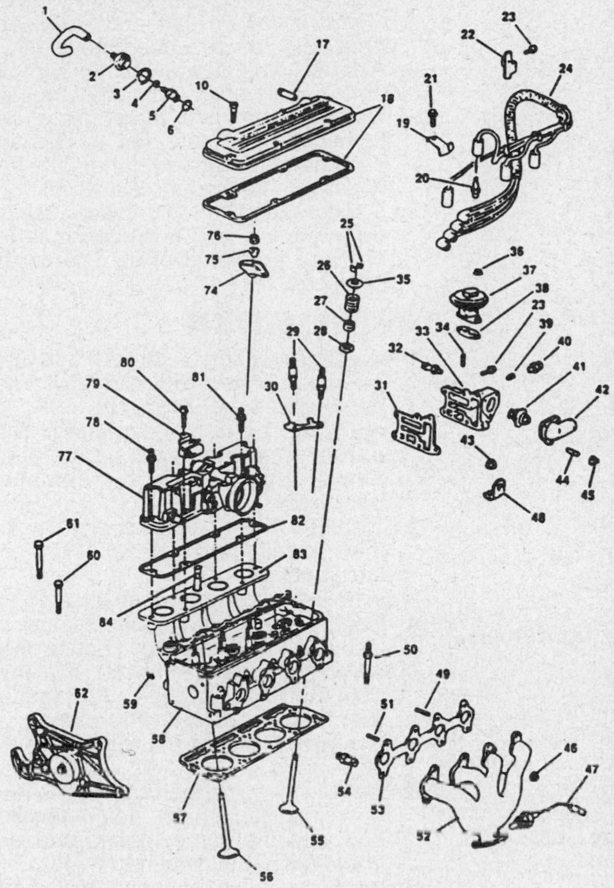

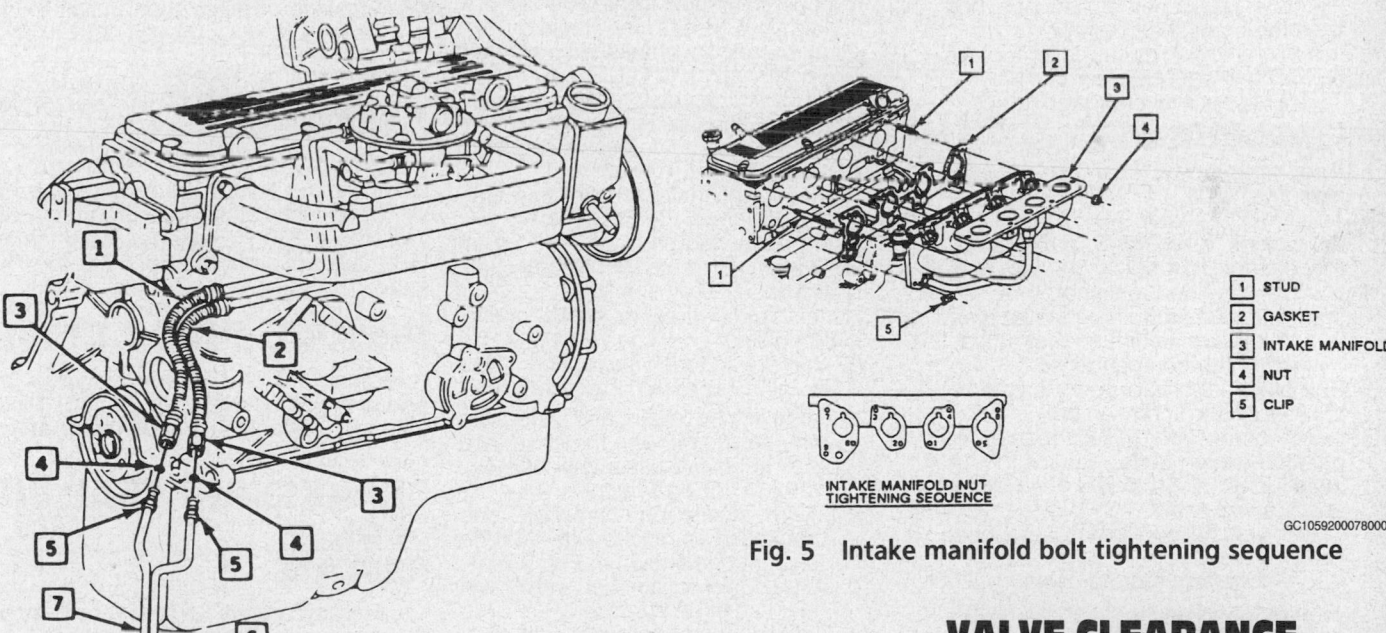

1 PCV HOSE
2 PCV VALVE CAP
3 PCV CAP O-RING
4 PCV VALVE UPPER O-RING
5 PCV VALVE LOWER O-RING
6 PCV VALVE LOWER O-RING
10 BOLT
17 CRANK CASE VENT TUBE
18 ROCKER COVER AND GASKET
19 BRACKET
20 SPARK PLUG
21 BOLT
22 BRACKET
23 BOLT
24 SECONDARY IGNITION CABLES
25 KEY
26 VALVE SPRING
27 VALVE STEM OIL SEAL
28 VALVE SPRING SEAT
29 ROCKER ARM STUD
30 PUSHROD GUIDE
31 COOLANT OUTLET GASKET
32 COOLANT PIPE ADAPTER
33 COOLANT OUTLET ADAPTER
34 STUD
35 VALVE SPRING CAP
36 NUT
37 EGR VALVE
38 EGR VALVE GASKET
39 PLUG
40 COOLANT SENSOR
41 THERMOSTAT
42 COOLANT OUTLET
43 NUT
44 STUD
45 NUT
46 NUT
47 OXYGEN
48 ENGINE LIFT BRACKET
49 STUD
50 STUD
51 STUD
52 EXHAUST MANIFOLD
53 EXHAUST MANIFOLD GASKET
54 HOSE NIPPLE
55 EXHAUST VALVE
56 INTAKE VALVE
57 CYLINDER HEAD GASKET
58 CYLINDER HEAD
59 COOLANT JACKET PLUG
60 BOLT
61 BOLT
62 SERPENTINE DRIVE BELT TENSIONER
74 ROCKER ARM
75 ROCKER ARM BALL
76 NUT
77 UPPER INTAKE MANIFOLD ASSEMBLY
78 STUD
79 EGR VALVE SOLENOID
80 BOLT
81 STUD
82 UPPER INTAKE MANIFOLD ASSEMBLY GASKET
83 LOWER INTAKE MANIFOLD
84 EGR VALVE INJECTOR

Fig. 3 Exploded view of cylinder head assembly

GC1069100364000X

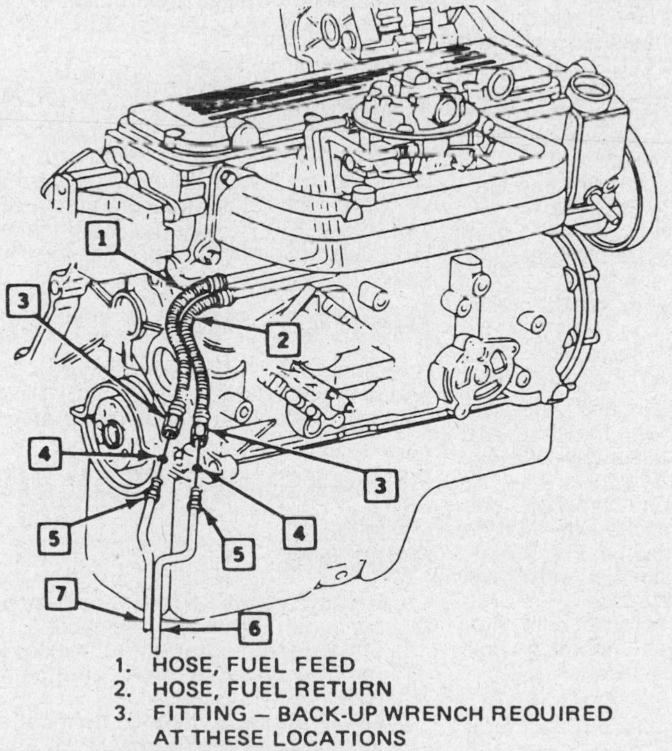

1. HOSE, FUEL FEED
2. HOSE, FUEL RETURN
3. FITTING – BACK-UP WRENCH REQUIRED AT THESE LOCATIONS
4. SEAL – O-RING
5. FITTING – 27 N·m (20 LBS. FT.)
6. PIPE, FUEL RETURN
7. PIPE, FUEL FEED

GC1069100365000X

Fig. 4 Engine fuel hoses & pipes

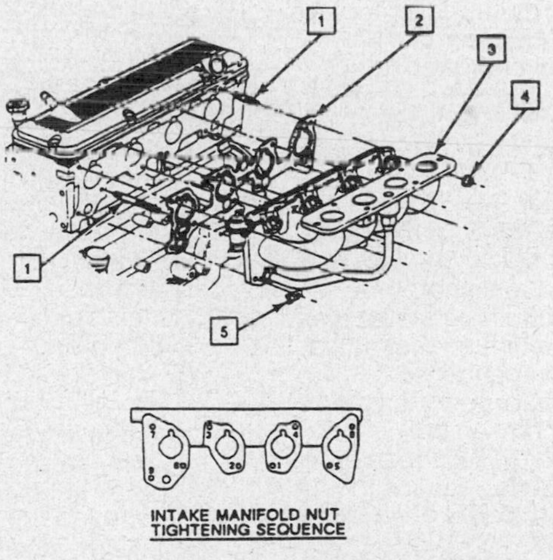
INTAKE MANIFOLD NUT TIGHTENING SEQUENCE

1 STUD
2 GASKET
3 INTAKE MANIFOLD
4 NUT
5 CLIP

GC1059200078000X

Fig. 5 Intake manifold bolt tightening sequence

VALVE CLEARANCE SPECIFICATIONS

This engine is equipped with hydraulic lifters. No adjustment is necessary.

VALVE ADJUSTMENT

Valve lash is obtained through the use of hydraulic valve lifters. No adjustment is necessary.

VALVE GUIDES

Valve guides are an integral part of the cylinder head and are not removable. If valve stem clearance becomes excessive, the valve guide should be reamed to the next oversize and the appropriate oversize valves installed. Valves are available in .00295, .0059 and .00984 inch oversizes.

HYDRAULIC LIFTERS

REPLACE

1. Remove rocker cover as described previously.
2. Loosen rocker arm nut and swing rocker arm aside.
3. Remove pushrod, then using a flexible magnetic wand remove lifter.
4. Inspect lifter for any signs of damage or wear, replacing as necessary.
5. Reverse procedure to install.

CRANKSHAFT DAMPER

REPLACE

REMOVAL

Refer to **Fig. 7,** when performing the following any procedures.

1. Disconnect battery ground cable.
2. Remove serpentine belt, then raise and support vehicle.
3. Remove wheel and tire assembly, then inner fender splash shield.
4. Remove three crankshaft pulley retaining bolts.
5. Remove crankshaft pulley hub bolt, then the crankshaft pulley.
6. Install crankshaft pulley puller tool No. J-24420-B or equivalent on hub.
7. Turn puller screw and remove hub.

INSTALLATION

1. Coat front cover seal contact area with engine oil.
2. Apply RTV sealer No. 1052917 or equivalent, to keyway in pulley hub.
3. Place crankshaft pulley hub into position over key on crankshaft.
4. Install crankshaft pulley installer No. J 29113 into crankshaft so that at least 1/4 inch of thread is engaged.
5. Pull pulley hub into position and remove tool from crankshaft.
6. Install crankshaft pulley, then three pulley retaining bolts.
7. Install inner slash shield, then wheel and tire assembly.
8. Lower vehicle and install serpentine belt.
9. Connect battery ground cable.

FRONT COVER

REPLACE

1. Disconnect battery ground cable.
2. Remove serpentine belt, then the belt tensioner.
3. Raise and support vehicle, then remove oil pan as described in "Oil Pan, Replace."
4. Remove crankshaft pulley and hub as described in "Crankshaft Pulley and Hub, Replace."
5. Remove front cover retaining bolts, then remove front cover.
6. Reverse procedure to install.

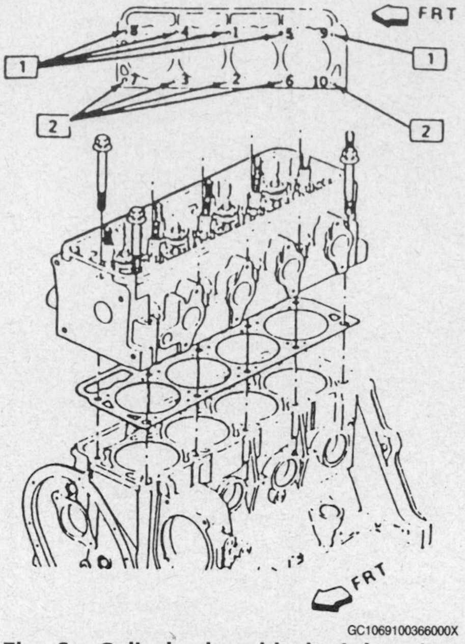
FRT
1
1
2
2
FRT
GC1069100366000X

Fig. 6 Cylinder head bolt tightening sequence

TIMING CHAIN

REPLACE

1. Disconnect battery ground cable, then remove crankcase front cover as described in "Front Cover, Replace."
2. Align marks on crankshaft sprocket and camshaft sprocket, **Fig. 8.**
3. Remove timing chain tensioner upper bolt, then loosen timing chain tensioner Torx as far as possible, but do not remove.
4. Remove camshaft sprocket and timing chain.
5. Using puller tool No. J 22888-20 or equivalent, remove crankshaft sprocket.
6. Reverse procedure to install, noting the following:
   a. Compress tensioner spring, then install a cotter pin or nail into hole
   b. Lube timing chain and sprockets with engine oil, lube thrust surface with camshaft assembly lube No. 1052365 or equivalent.
   c. Align marks on camshaft and crankshaft sprockets with tabs on tensioner as shown in **Fig. 9.**
   d. Align dowel in camshaft with dowel hole camshaft sprocket.
   e. Draw camshaft sprocket onto camshaft using the mounting bolt. Tighten to specifications.

CAMSHAFT

REPLACE

REMOVAL

1. Remove engine assembly as described in "Engine, Replace."
2. Drain engine oil and remove oil filter.
3. Remove valve lifters and crankcase front cover as described previously.
4. Remove oil pump drive, then remove timing chain and camshaft sprocket.
5. Remove camshaft thrust plate and camshaft. Use care not to damage camshaft bearings with the camshaft when withdrawing the camshaft.
6. Inspect camshaft for wear, galling, wear, gouges and overheating. If any of these problems exist, replace the camshaft.

INSTALLATION

1. Install camshaft and thrust plate. **Coat camshaft lobes and bearings with camshaft lube No. 1051396, or equivalent. Insert camshaft with extreme care to avoid personal injury and gouging of the camshaft bearings.**
2. Tighten thrust plate specifications, then install camshaft sprocket and timing chain.
3. Install crankcase front cover.
4. Replace valve lifters. Lifters must be installed in the same bores from which they were removed. **If a new camshaft is installed, replace all valve lifters. Some lifters may be oversized, verify marking near the lifter bore.**
5. Install valve mechanism, parts must be reinstalled in the same position and with the same mating surfaces from which they were removed.
6. Install rocker cover, then the oil pump drive.
7. Replace oil filter, then install engine assembly.

PISTON & ROD ASSEMBLY

Assemble piston to rod, with arrow on piston facing toward front of engine **Fig. 10.** Upon installation measure connecting rod side clearance using a feeler gauge. Side clearance should be .0039 to .0149 inch.

PISTONS, PINS & RINGS

Pistons are available in standard size and oversize of .020 inch (.5 mm). Piston pins are available in standard size only.

CRANKSHAFT REAR OIL SEAL

REPLACE

1. Remove transaxle from vehicle as described in "Transaxle, Replace."
2. **On models with manual transaxle,** remove pressure plate and clutch disc.
3. **On all models,** remove flywheel attaching bolts and flywheel.
4. Insert a screwdriver or similar tool in through the dust lip as shown in **Fig. 11,** pry out seal.
5. Reverse procedure to install, noting the following:

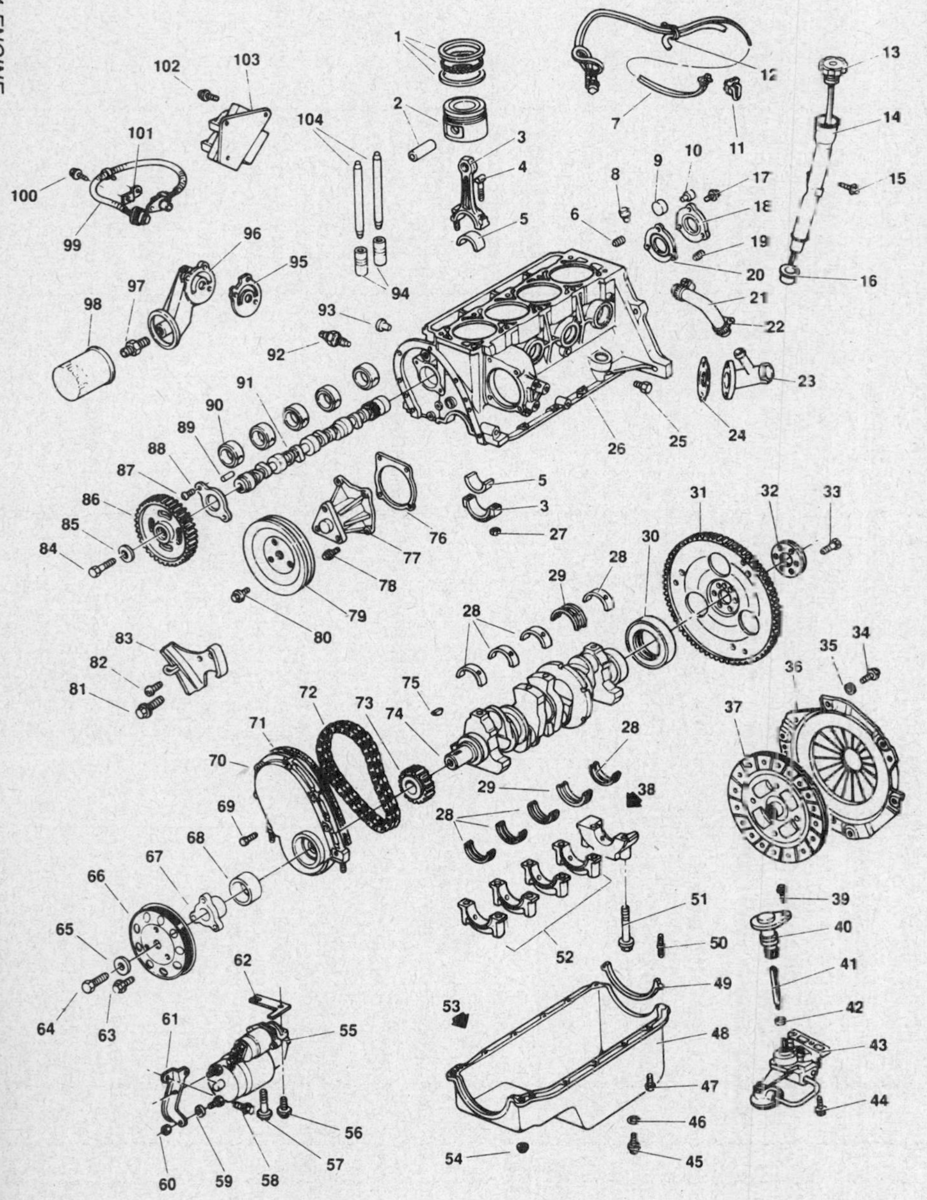

1. PISTON RINGS
2. PISTON AND PIN
3. CONNECTING ROD
4. CONNECTING ROD BOLT
5. CONNECTING ROD BEARING
6. CYLINDER BLOCK OIL GALLERY HOLE PLUG
7. COOLANT HEATER CORD
8. CYLINDER HEAD DOWEL PIN
9. COOLANT JACKET PLUG
10. CLUTCH HOUSING PIN
11. COOLANT HEATER
12. ADJUSTABLE RETAINER
13. OIL LEVEL RETAINER
14. OIL FILL TUBE
15. BOLT
16. OIL FILL TUBE SEAL
17. BOLT
18. CAMSHAFT REAR COVER
19. PLUG
20. CAMSHAFT REAR COVER GASKET
21. COOLANT INLET HOSE
22. CLAMP
23. COOLANT INLET
24. COOLANT INLET GASKET
25. COOLANT DRAIN PLUG
26. CYLINDER BLOCK
27. CONNECTING ROD NUT
28. CRANKSHAFT BEARING
29. CRANKSHAFT BEARING
30. CRANKSHAFT REAR OIL SEAL
31. FLYWHEEL
32. FLYWHEEL RETAINER (AUTOMATIC TRANSAXLE)
33. BOLT
34. BOLT
35. WASHER
36. PRESSURE PLATE
37. CLUTCH DISC
38. SEALANT
39. BOLT
40. OIL PUMP DRIVE ASSEMBLY
41. OIL PUMP DRIVE SHAFT
42. RETAINER
43. OIL PUMP
44. BOLT
45. OIL DRAIN PLUG
46. OIL DRAIN PLUG GASKET
47. BOLT
48. OIL PAN
49. OIL PAN REAR SEAL
50. STUD
51. BOLT
52. MAIN BEARING CAP
53. SEALER
54. NUT
55. STARTER MOTOR
56. BOLT
57. BOLT
58. BOLT
59. WASHER
60. NUT
61. STARTER MOTOR BRACKET
62. SHIM
63. BOLT
64. BOLT
65. WASHER
66. CRANKSHAFT PULLEY
67. CRANKSHAFT PULLEY HUB
68. SEAL
69. BOLT
70. CRANKCASE
71. CRANKCASE FRONT COVER OIL SEAL
72. TIMING CHAIN
73. CRANKSHAFT SPROCKET
74. CRANKSHAFT
75. KEY
76. COOLANT PUMP GASKET
77. COOLANT PUMP
78. BOLT
79. COOLANT PUMP PULLEY
80. BOLT
81. BOLT
82. BOLT
83. TIMING CHAIN TENSIONER
84. BOLT
85. WASHER
86. CAMSHAFT SPROCKET
87. SCREW
88. THRUST PLATE
89. PIN CAMSHAFT BEARING
90. CAMSHAFT BEARING
91. CAMSHAFT
92. FUEL PUMP SWITCH
93. OIL FILTER BY-PASS VALVE
94. LIFTER
95. OIL FILTER ADAPTER GASKET
96. OIL FILTER ADAPTER
97. OIL FILTER CONNECTOR
98. OIL FILTER
99. CRANKSHAFT SENSOR
100. BOLT
101. RETAINER
102. BOLT
103. COIL
104. PUSHROD

GC106910036800AX

Fig. 7 Exploded view of cylinder block assembly

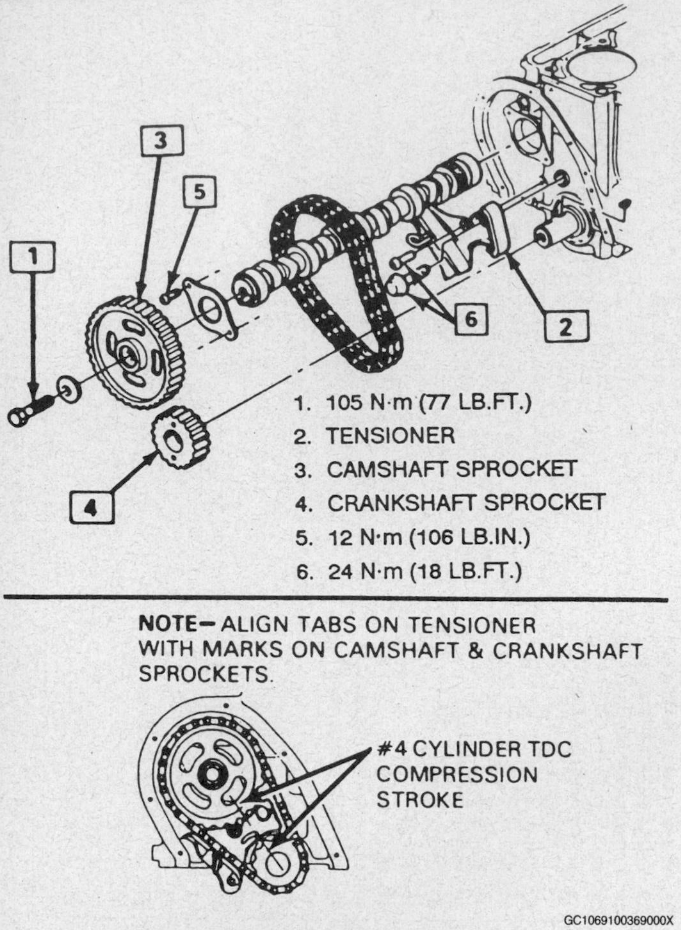
3
5
1
6
2
4
1. 105 N·m (77 LB.FT.)
2. TENSIONER
3. CAMSHAFT SPROCKET
4. CRANKSHAFT SPROCKET
5. 12 N·m (106 LB.IN.)
6. 24 N·m (18 LB.FT.)
NOTE— ALIGN TABS ON TENSIONER WITH MARKS ON CAMSHAFT & CRANKSHAFT SPROCKETS.
#4 CYLINDER TDC COMPRESSION STROKE
GC1069100369000X

Fig. 8 Timing chain & sprockets

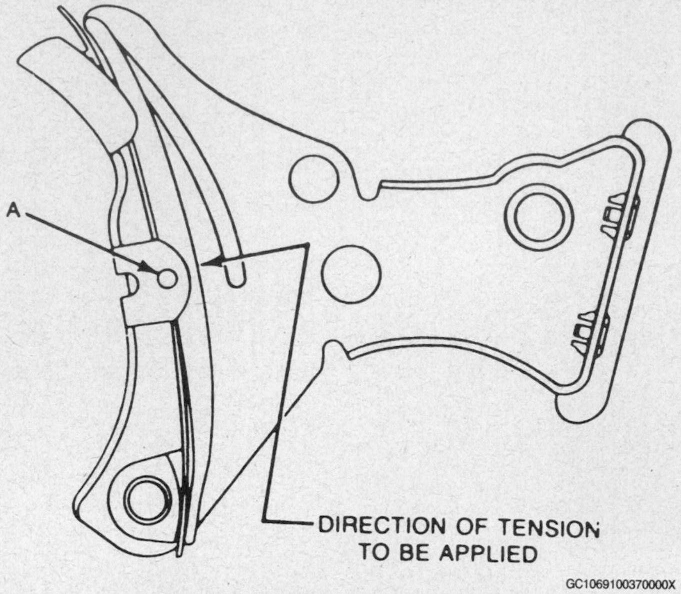
A
DIRECTION OF TENSION TO BE APPLIED
GC1069100370000X

Fig. 9 Timing chain tensioner

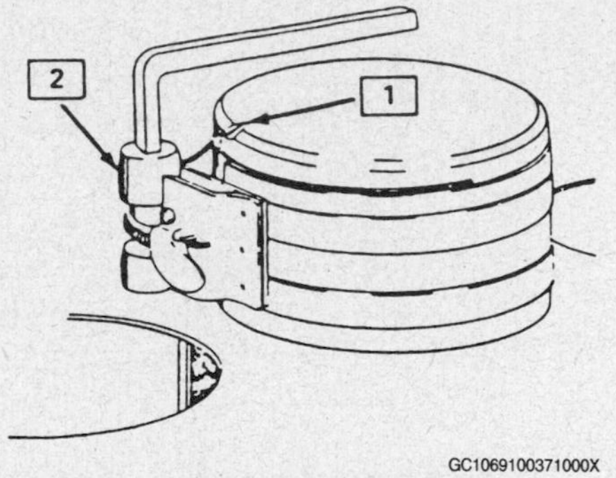
2
1
GC1069100371000X

Fig. 10 Piston installation

a. Lubricate seal bore to seal surface with engine oil.
b. Using seal installation tool No. J 34686 or equivalent, align dowel pin of tool with dowel pin hole in crankshaft and attach tool to crankshaft.
c. **Torque** tool attaching screws to 27-62 inch lbs., then tighten tool T handle to push seal into bore. Continue to tighten until tool is flush against block.

OIL PAN

REPLACE

1. Disconnect battery ground cable.
2. Raise and support vehicle, then disconnect exhaust pipe from the exhaust manifold.
3. Drain engine oil, then remove starter bracket at block.
4. Remove starter and position aside, then remove flywheel cover.
5. Remove four right side engine support bolts, then lower support slightly to gain clearance for oil pan removal.
6. **On models with automatic transaxle,** remove oil filter and extension.
7. **On all models,** remove oil pan retaining bolts and oil pan.
8. Reverse procedure to install, noting the following:
   a. Apply a 1/16 inch diameter bead of GM 1052914 RTV or equivalent, on oil pan to block sealing flanges.
   b. Apply RTV sealer or equivalent to oil pan surface which fits to engine front cover.
   c. Using a new oil pan rear seal, apply a thin coat of RTV sealer or equivalent on ends down to ears, install pan against cylinder case and install bolts.
   d. **On models with automatic transaxle,** replace oil filter adapter seal and install oil filter adapter.

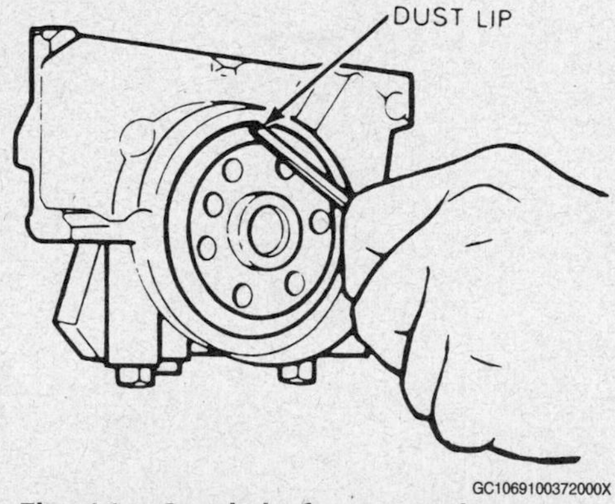
DUST LIP
GC1069100372000X

Fig. 11 Crankshaft rear seal removal

OIL PUMP SERVICE

REMOVAL

1. Remove oil pan as described previously.
2. Remove pump to rear main bearing cap bolt, then remove pump and extension shaft.

DISASSEMBLY

1. Drain oil from pump, then remove driveshaft, **Fig. 12.**
2. Remove pump cover, **Do not remove pickup tube from cover unless loose or broken.**
3. Remove pump gears, then the pressure regulator valve. **The pressure regulator valve spring is under pressure. Exercise caution when removing the retaining pin, as bodily injury may result.**
4. Remove plug, spring and valve. If valve is stuck, soak the pump housing in carburetor cleaning solvent.

INSPECTION

Thoroughly clean all oil pump components and check them for excessive wear or damage.

1. Using a straightedge and feeler

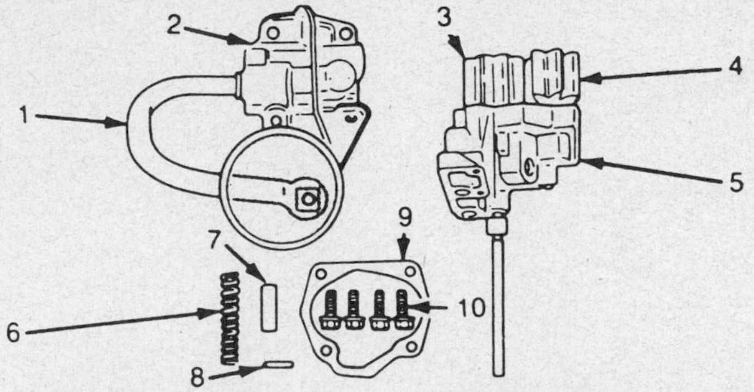
1
2
3
4
5
6
7
8
9
10

1. PICK UP TUBE AND SCREEN.
2. PUMP COVER.
3. DRIVE GEAR AND SHAFT.
4. IDLER GEAR.
5. PUMP BODY.
6. PRESSURE REGULATOR SPRING
7. PRESSURE REGULATOR VALVE.
8. RETAINING PIN.
9. GASKET.
10. ATTACHING BOLTS.

GC1099100051000X

Fig. 12 Exploded view of oil pump

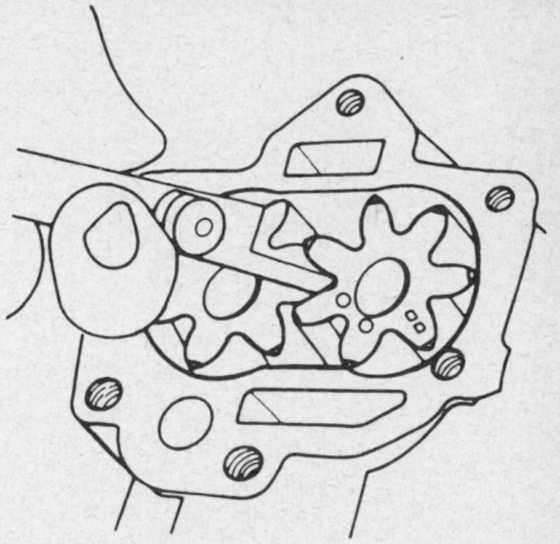

GC1099100052000X

Fig. 13 Oil pump gear lash measurement

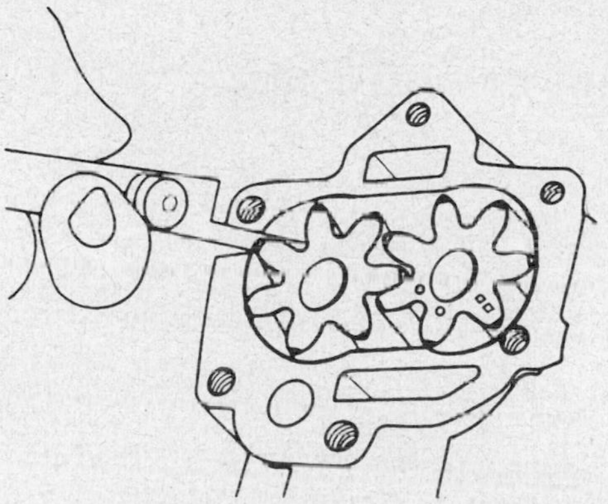

GC1099100053000X

Fig. 14 Gear side clearance measurement

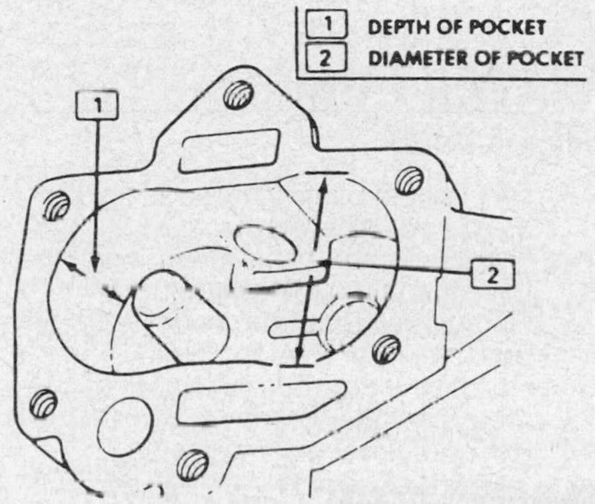
1 DEPTH OF POCKET
2 DIAMETER OF POCKET
1
2

GC1099100054000X

Fig. 15 Oil pump gear pocket measurement

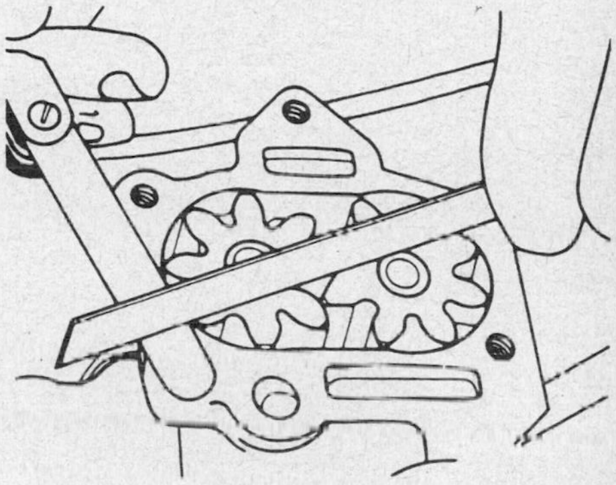

GC1099100055000X

Fig. 16 Oil pump end clearance measurement

gauge, check oil pump clearances as shown in **Figs. 13 through 16.**

2. Install gears and measure in several places, gear lash should be within .004-.008 inch.
3. Measure depth and diameter of oil pump gear pocket, depth should be 1.195-1.198 inch and diameter should be 1.503-1.506 inch.
4. Measure gear side clearance, side clearance should be .0015-.004.
5. Measure gear end clearance, end clearance should be .002-.006. When deciding pump serviceability based on end clearance, consider depth of wear pattern in the pump cover and/or cover plate.

ASSEMBLY

1. Lubricate all internal parts with engine oil during assembly.
2. Install pump gears. **To avoid engine damage, all pump cavities must be packed with petroleum jelly before installing gears to assure priming.**
3. Install oil pump cover and gasket.
4. Install pressure regulator valve, spring and retaining pin.
5. Tighten pump cover bolts to specifications. Whenever the oil pump is overhauled, clear the oil pan of oil and sludge, replace oil filter and fill crankcase with clean oil.

INSTALLATION

1. Install pump and extension shaft, then tighten main bearing cap bolt to specification.
2. Install oil pan.

BELT TENSION DATA

The serpentine belt is automatically adjusted by a spring tensioner. No adjustment is necessary.

SERPENTINE DRIVE BELT

1. Remove coolant reservoir.
2. Rotate tensioner clockwise with a 15 mm wrench and slide belt from generator pulley. Release tensioner and remove belt.
3. Reverse procedure to install, routing belt as shown in **Fig. 17.**

TENSIONER, REPLACE

1. Disconnect negative battery cable and romove coolant reservoir.
2. Remove serpentine belt as described under "Serpentine Drive Belt, Replace.
3. Remove two generator bolts.
4. Remove power steering pump and position aside.
5. Remove tensioner bolts and tensioner.
6. Reverse procedure to install, **Torquing** tensioner bolts to 37 ft. lbs.

COOLING SYSTEM BLEED

To ensure sufficient engine cooling, freezing and corrosion protection, maintain the protection level at -34°F or lower. Use a solution of antifreeze and water, ensuring solution is no more than 70 percent antifreeze.

1. Fill surge tank or radiator to base of filler neck, then attach pressure cap.
2. Block the drive wheel and apply parking brake.
3. **On models equipped with automatic transaxle,** place shifter in Park position.
4. **On models equipped with manual transaxle,** place transaxle in Neutral position.
5. **On all models,** start engine and allow to run until upper radiator hose is hot.
6. Turn engine Off, check level of coolant in surge tank or radiator.

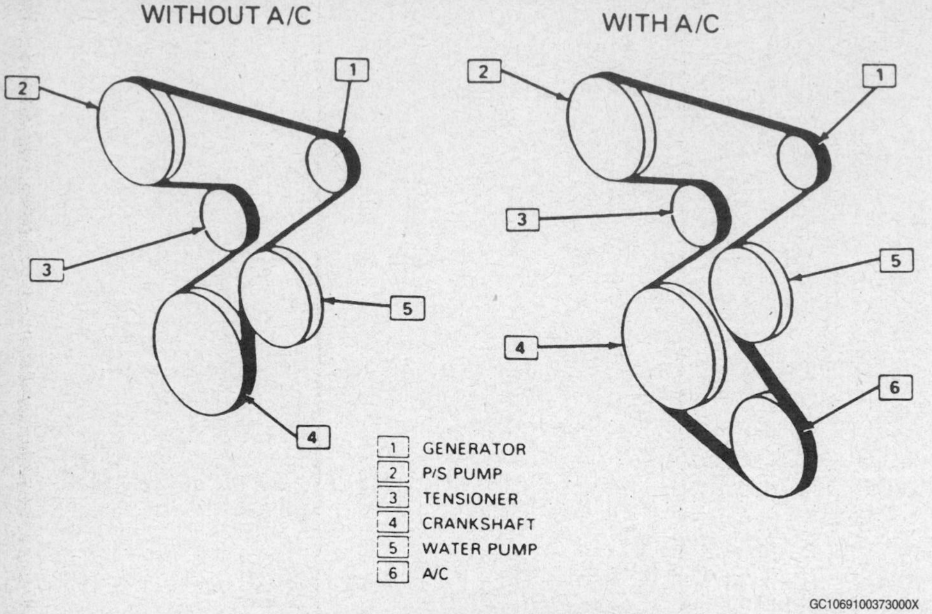
WITHOUT A/C
WITH A/C
1 GENERATOR
2 P/S PUMP
3 TENSIONER
4 CRANKSHAFT
5 WATER PUMP
6 A/C
GC1069100373000X

Fig. 17 Serpentine drive belt routing

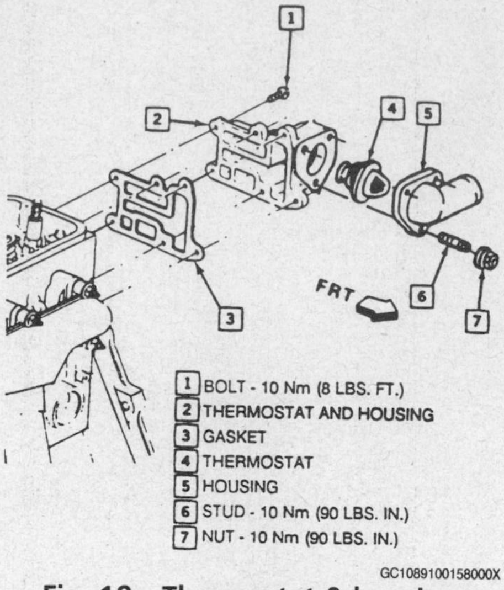
1 BOLT - 10 Nm (8 LBS. FT.)
2 THERMOSTAT AND HOUSING
3 GASKET
4 THERMOSTAT
5 HOUSING
6 STUD - 10 Nm (90 LBS. IN.)
7 NUT - 10 Nm (90 LBS. IN.)
FRT
GC1089100158000X

Fig. 18 Thermostat & housing assembly

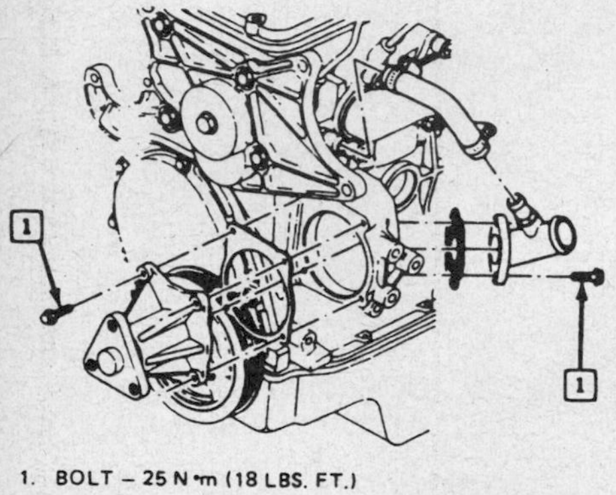
1. BOLT – 25 N·m (18 LBS. FT.)
GC1089100159000X

Fig. 19 Water pump installation

7. Allow engine to cool, then add coolant as necessary.

THERMOSTAT

REPLACE

Refer to **Fig. 18** when performing the following procedure.

1. Disconnect battery negative cable.
2. Remove air intake duct.
3. With engine cool, drain engine coolant below thermostat level. **Never open cooling system with engine hot. Failure to follow this warning may cause personal injury.**
4. Disconnect radiator hose from thermostat housing.
5. Remove thermostat housing retaining nuts, then the housing, gasket and thermostat.
6. Reverse procedure to install noting the following:
   a. Prior to installation, ensure thermostat gasket area is thoroughly clean.
   b. Install thermostat with new gasket.
   c. **Torque** thermostat housing retaining nuts to 89 inch lbs.
   d. Refill and bleed cooling system as needed.

WATER PUMP

REPLACE

1. Disconnect battery ground cable, then drain cooling system.
2. Remove serpentine drive belt, then the alternator and bracket.
3. Remove water pump pulley attaching bolts, then remove the pulley, **Fig. 19.**
4. Remove water pump attaching bolts, then the water pump.
5. Reverse procedure to install.

RADIATOR

REPLACE

1. Disconnect battery ground cable, then discharge and recover air conditioning refrigerant.
2. Drain and recover engine coolant.
3. Remove hood latch from mounting plate, then both headlight assemblies.
4. Remove radiator mounts, then raise and support vehicle.
5. Disconnect forward SIR sensor harness, then remove cooling fan assembly.
6. Disconnect radiator hoses, then transmission oil cooler lines from radiator.
7. Lower vehicle, then remove hood latch support and forward sensor with wiring harness.
8. Disconnect compressor and accumulator hoses from condenser, discarding O-rings.
9. Disconnect coolant overflow line, then remove radiator.
10. Reverse procedure to install, installing new air conditioning O-rings

FUEL PUMP

REPLACE

1. Release fuel system pressure as outlined under "Precautions."
2. Disconnect battery ground cable, then drain fuel tank.

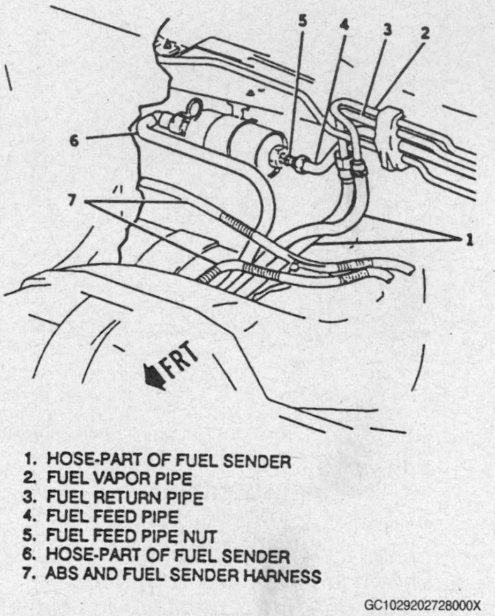
1. HOSE-PART OF FUEL SENDER
2. FUEL VAPOR PIPE
3. FUEL RETURN PIPE
4. FUEL FEED PIPE
5. FUEL FEED PIPE NUT
6. HOSE-PART OF FUEL SENDER
7. ABS AND FUEL SENDER HARNESS
FRT
GC1029202728000X

Fig. 20 Fuel filter replacement

3. Raise and support vehicle.
4. Disconnect tank meter assembly harness from body harness connector.
5. Remove ground wire retaining screw from underbody, then disconnect hoses from fuel meter assembly.
6. Disconnect hoses at tank from filler and vent pipes.
7. Support fuel tank with jack, then disconnect two fuel tank retaining straps.
8. Remove tank assembly.
9. Remove fuel tank sending unit and pump assembly by turning cam lock ring counterclockwise.
10. Lift assembly from fuel tank and remove fuel pump from fuel tank sending unit.
11. Pull fuel pump up into attaching hose while pulling outward away from bottom support. Take care to prevent damage to rubber insulator and strainer during removal. After pump assembly is clear of bottom support, pull pump assembly out of rubber

connector for removal.
12. Reverse procedure to install.

FUEL FILTER
REPLACE

1. Release fuel system pressure as outlined under "Precautions."
2. Raise and support vehicle.
3. Using back-up wrench, remove filter fitting. If nylon fuel lines become kinked and cannot be straightened, they must be replaced.
4. Twist quick-connect fitting 1/4 turn in each direction to loosen dirt within fitting.
5. Using compressed air, clean quick-connect fitting at ends of filter.
6. Disconnect quick-connect fittings by squeezing plastic tabs of male end connector and pulling apart.
7. Remove fuel filter, **Fig. 20.**
8. Reverse procedure to install.

TIGHTENING SPECIFICATIONS

Component	Torque/Ft. Lbs.
Brake Booster Vacuum Fitting	10
Battery Ground Cable	13
Camshaft Pulley	77
Camshaft Thrust Plate	106②
Coolant Drain Plug (Cylinder Block)	11
Coolant Outlet To Cylinder Head	8
Crankcase Front Cover Bolts	97②
Crankshaft Pulley & Hub To Crankshaft	77
Crankshaft Pulley To Hub	37
Cylinder Head Bolts	①
DIS Coil Assembly	18
Exhaust Manifold Nuts	115②
Exhaust Manifold Studs	9-10
Exhaust Pipe To Manifold	18
Engine Mount Bracket To Engine, Front	50
Engine Mount, Lower, To Bracket, Rear	18
Engine Mount To Bracket, Front	74
Engine Mount To Bracket, Rear	50
Flywheel To Crankshaft, Auto. Trans.	52
Flywheel To Crankshaft, Manual Trans.	55
Intake Manifold	22
Main Bearing Cap Bolts	70

Component	Torque/Ft. Lbs.
Oil Fill Tube To Cylinder Block	18
Oil Filter Adapter To Cylinder Block	18
Oil Pan Bolts	71②
Oil Pump Cover Bolts	89②
Oil Pump Drive Assembly Bolt	18
Oil Pump To Bearing Cap	32
Pressure Plate To Flywheel	15
Rear Engine Lift Bracket	32
Rocker Arm Cover	89②
Rocker Arm Nuts	22
Rod Bearing Cap Nut	38
Serpentine Tensioner Assembly	37
Spark Plugs	11
Timing Chain Cover	8
Timing Chain Tensioner	18
Water Pump	18
Water Pump Inlet	18
Wheel Lug Nuts	100

①—Torque long bolts to 46 ft. lbs. and short bolts to 43 ft. lbs. Tightening all bolts an additional 90° in sequence.
②—Inch lbs.

2.3L/4–138 Engine

NOTE: On Air Bag Equipped Models, Refer To "Air Bag System Precautions" Located In The Front Of This Manual For System Disarming & Arming Procedures.

NOTE: Refer To "Oldsmobile Achieva & Pontiac Grand Am" Section Of This Manual For Any Procedure Not Covered.

INDEX

PRECAUTIONS

AIR BAG SYSTEMS

Refer to "Air Bag System Precautions" in the front of this manual for system disarming and arming procedures.

FUEL SYSTEM PRESSURE RELIEF

1. Loosen fuel filler cap, then remove the fuel pump fuse.
2. Start engine and run until remaining fuel is consumed.
3. Engage starter for approximately three seconds, to ensure relief of any reaming pressure.
4. Disconnect battery ground cable to avoid possible fuel discharge if any attempt is made to start the engine.

ENGINE MOUNT
REPLACE

1. Disconnect battery ground cable.
2. Remove bolt attaching coolant recov-

ery tank and position tank aside.
3. Install engine support tool NO. J-28467-A, or equivalent, and raise engine.
4. Remove body to mount retaining nuts, then mount assembly.
5. Reverse procedure to install, **torquing** engine mount bolts to 88 ft. lbs.

ENGINE

REPLACE

1. Disconnect battery ground cable, then drain coolant.
2. **On models equipped with air conditioning,** discharge and recover refrigerant, then disconnect compressor/condenser hose assembly at compressor.
3. **On all models,** remove left sound insulator and disconnect clutch pushrod from pedal assembly.
4. Disconnect heater hose at thermostat housing, then the upper radiator hose.
5. Remove air cleaner and coolant fan assembly.
6. Disconnect all vacuum hoses and electrical connectors.
7. Disconnect throttle cable and bracket.
8. Remove power steering rear bracket and power brake vacuum tube as an assembly.
9. Disconnect and position aside power steering pump.
10. Relive fuel pressure as outlined under "Precautions," then disconnect fuel lines.
11. **On models with automatic transaxle,** disconnect shift cables.
12. **On models with manual transaxle,** disconnect clutch actuator line.
13. Remove exhaust manifold and heat shields.
14. Disconnect lower radiator hose, then install engine support tool No. J-28467-A, or equivalent, and remove engine mount assembly.
15. Raise and support vehicle, then remove both front tire and wheel assemblies.
16. Remove righthand side splash shield and radiator air deflector.
17. Remove engine and transaxle mount, then separate ball joints from steering knuckles.
18. Remove suspension supports, crossmember, and stabilizer shaft as an assembly.
19. Disconnect air conditioning lines from oil pan.
20. Remove air flywheel housing cover.
21. Position suitable support beneath engine and carefully lower vehicle.
22. Mark threads on support fixture hooks so that setting can be duplicated when installing engine.
23. Remove engine support J hooks, then slowly raise vehicle away from engine and transaxle assembly.
24. Reverse procedure to install.

RADIATOR

REPLACE

1. Disconnect battery ground cable, then discharge and recover air conditioning refrigerant.
2. Drain engine coolant.
3. Remove hood latch, and both headlight assemblies.
4. Remove radiator mounts, then raise and support vehicle.
5. Remove cooling fan assembly, then lower radiator hose and oil cooler lines.
6. Lower vehicle, then remove hood latch support and forward sensor w/harness.
7. Disconnect upper radiator hose, overflow hose, then compressor and accumulator hoses.
8. Remove radiator/condenser assembly.
9. Reverse procedure to install.

3.1L/V6-192 Engine

INDEX

PRECAUTIONS

AIR BAG SYSTEMS

Refer to "Air Bag System Precautions" in the front of this manual for system disarming and arming procedures.

FUEL SYSTEM PRESSURE RELIEF

1. Loosen fuel filler cap, then remove the fuel pump fuse.
2. Start engine and run until remaining fuel is consumed.
3. Engage starter for approximately three seconds, to ensure relief of any reaming pressure.
4. Disconnect battery ground cable to avoid possible fuel discharge if any attempt is made to start the engine.

IDLE LEARN PROCEDURE

On models with 3.1L/V6-192 port fuel injected (PFI) engine, any time vehicle power has been interrupted the programed position of the IAC valve pintle is lost. The following procedure must be performed to update the ECM memory with the correct IAC valve pintle position for the vehicle and provide a stable idle speed.

1. Restore vehicle power.
2. Place transaxle in Park or Neutral position.
3. Connect TECH I scan tool to ALDL connector located under the left hand side of the dash panel.

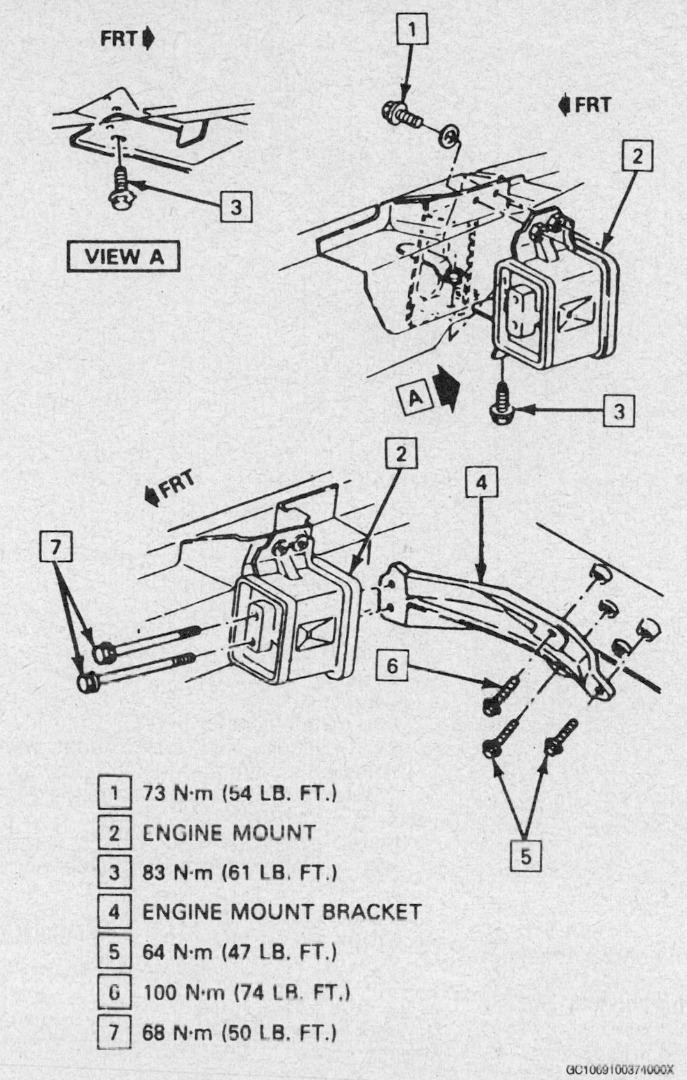
FRT
VIEW A
FRT
A
FRT
1 73 N·m (54 LB. FT.)
2 ENGINE MOUNT
3 83 N·m (61 LB. FT.)
4 ENGINE MOUNT BRACKET
5 64 N·m (47 LB. FT.)
6 100 N·m (74 LB. FT.)
7 68 N·m (50 LB. FT.)
GC1069100374000X

Fig. 1 Front engine mount

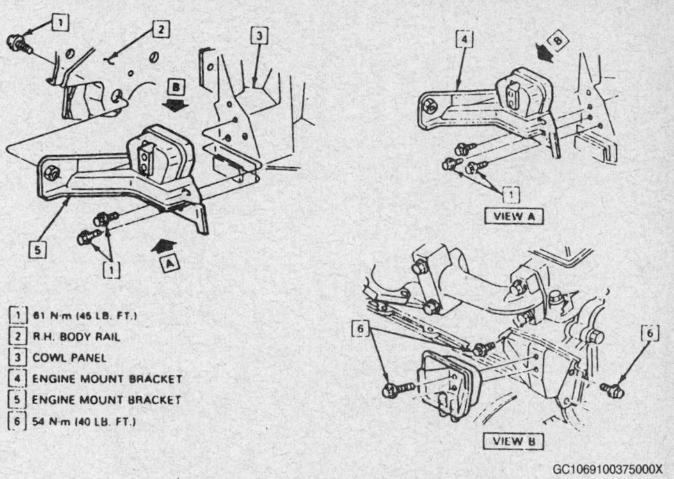
1 61 N·m (45 LB. FT.)
2 R.H. BODY RAIL
3 COWL PANEL
4 ENGINE MOUNT BRACKET
5 ENGINE MOUNT BRACKET
6 54 N·m (40 LB. FT.)
VIEW A
VIEW B
GC1069100375000X

Fig. 2 Rear engine mount

4. Select "IAC System."
5. Select "Idle Learn" in the "Misc. Test" mode.
6. Proceed as directed.

ENGINE MOUNT

REPLACE

FRONT MOUNT

1. Disconnect battery ground cable.
2. Remove engine mount nuts, then raise and support vehicle.
3. Support engine with suitable jack.
4. Remove inner fender shield.
5. Remove and discard engine mount bolts, **Fig. 1.**
6. Remove engine mount from vehicle.
7. Reverse procedure to install, using new engine mount bolts. Remove alignment bolt. Refer to **Fig. 1,** for tightening specifications. **If excessive force is required to remove alignment bolt, loosen transaxle adjusting bolts to align power train components.**

REAR MOUNT

1. Disconnect battery ground cable, then raise and support vehicle.
2. Support engine with suitable jack.
3. Remove motor mount nuts and attaching bolts, **Fig. 2.**
4. Reverse procedure to install. Refer to **Fig. 2,** for tightening specifications.

ENGINE

REPLACE

1. Disconnect battery ground cable and drain cooling system.
2. Remove air cleaner and duct assembly.
3. Remove exhaust crossover heat shield and the exhaust crossover pipe.
4. Remove serpentine belt, tensioner and idler, if equipped.
5. Disconnect radiator hose at engine.
6. Disconnect accelerator and T.V. cables at throttle valve.
7. Remove alternator and disconnect wiring harness at engine.
8. Loosen fuel filler cap to relieve tank vapor pressure, then disconnect fuel hoses and the coolant bypass and overflow hoses at engine.
9. Raise and support vehicle, then remove right inner fender splash shield.
10. Remove harmonic balance and the flywheel cover.
11. Remove starter attaching bolts, disconnect electrical connectors at starter and remove starter.
12. Remove A/C compressor and its mounting bracket(s).
13. Disconnect exhaust pipe at rear of manifold.
14. Remove flex plate to torque converter attaching bolts and the transaxle to engine brace bolts.
15. Remove front and rear engine mount to frame attaching bolts.
16. Disconnect shift cable bracket at transaxle.
17. Remove lower bellhousing bolts and lower vehicle.
18. Disconnect heater hoses at engine.
19. Install suitable engine lifting device and support transaxle with suitable jack.
20. Remove transaxle attaching bolts.
21. Remove engine from vehicle.
22. Reverse procedure to install.

INTAKE MANIFOLD

REPLACE

1. Disconnect battery ground cable.
2. Disconnect accelerator and T.V. cable bracket at plenum.
3. Disconnect brake vacuum pipe and plug harness at plenum.
4. Disconnect throttle body at plenum.
5. Disconnect EGR pipe at EGR valve, then remove plenum.
6. Disconnect fuel inlet and return pipes at fuel rail.
7. Remove serpentine belt, then disconnect alternator assembly and position aside.
8. Remove power steering lines at alternator bracket, then remove power steering pump attaching bolts and position aside.
9. Loosen alternator bracket attaching bolts.
10. Remove idle air to throttle body vacuum hose, then disconnect fuel injector electrical connectors.

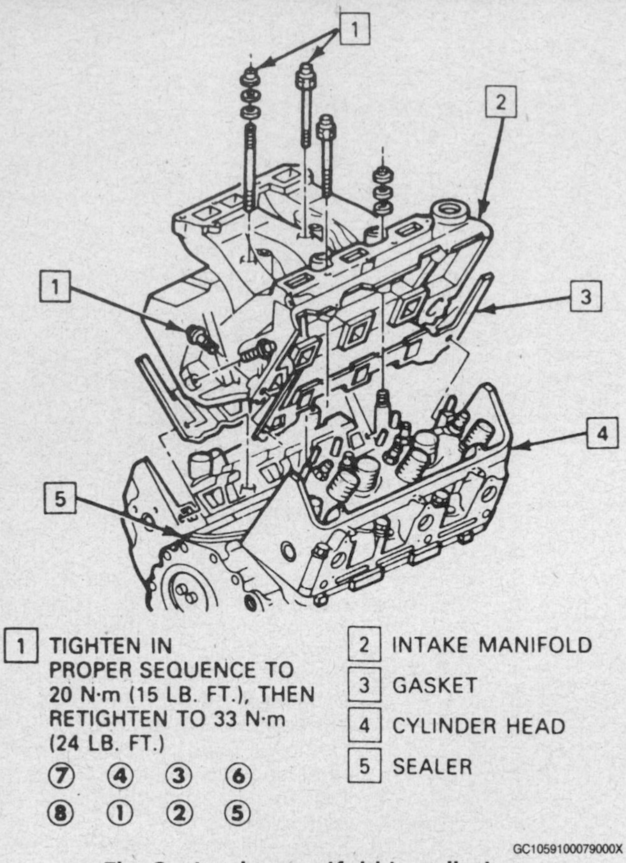
1
2
1
3
4
5
1 TIGHTEN IN PROPER SEQUENCE TO 20 N·m (15 LB. FT.), THEN RETIGHTEN TO 33 N·m (24 LB. FT.)
⑦ ④ ③ ⑥
⑧ ① ② ⑤
2 INTAKE MANIFOLD
3 GASKET
4 CYLINDER HEAD
5 SEALER
GC1059100079000X

Fig. 3 Intake manifold installation

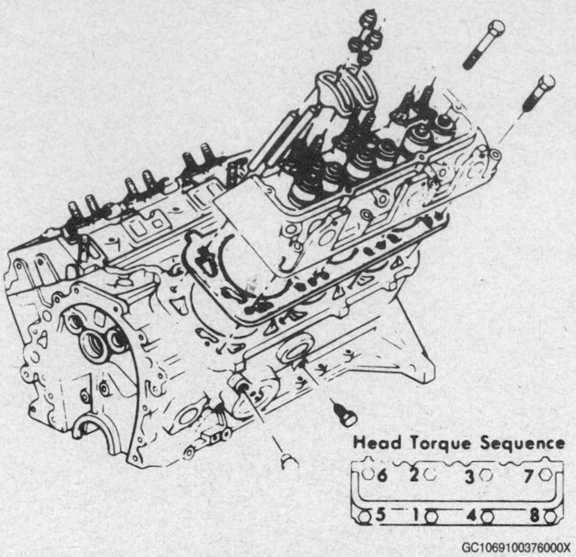
Head Torque Sequence
6 2 3 7
5 1 4 8
GC1069100376000X

Fig. 4 Cylinder head installation

11. Remove fuel rail and breather tube.
12. Remove plug wires at intake manifold.
13. Remove rocker arm covers and drain cooling system.
14. Remove radiator hose at thermostat outlet.
15. Disconnect coolant sensor and oil sending switch electrical connectors, then remove coolant sensor.
16. Remove filler neck to cylinder head bypass hose, then remove heater inlet pipe at manifold.
17. Remove intake manifold attaching bolts, then remove intake manifold.
18. Reverse procedure to install. Refer to **Fig. 3**, for intake manifold tightening sequence and specifications.

EXHAUST MANIFOLD
REPLACE
LEFT SIDE

1. Disconnect battery ground cable and remove air cleaner and inlet hose.
2. Drain cooling system, then remove coolant bypass pipe.
3. Disconnect crossover pipe at manifold, then remove manifold attaching bolts and the manifold.
4. Reverse procedure to install.

RIGHT SIDE

1. Disconnect battery ground cable and remove air cleaner.
2. Raise and support vehicle, then remove heat shield.
3. Remove exhaust pipe at crossover, then lower the vehicle.
4. Disconnect oxygen sensor electrical connector.
5. Remove exhaust manifold attaching bolts, then remove manifold.
6. Reverse procedure to install, tighten attaching nuts, bolts and screws to specifications.

CYLINDER HEAD
REPLACE
REMOVAL

1. Disconnect battery ground cable.
2. Remove intake manifold and plenum assembly as described under "Intake Manifold, Replace."
3. Remove exhaust manifold as described under "Exhaust Manifold, Replace."
4. Disconnect wiring harness at cylinder head.
5. Remove spark plug wires and the spark plugs.
6. Remove rocker arm covers, rocker arm nuts, rocker arm balls, rocker arms and pushrods.
7. Remove cylinder head attaching bolts and the cylinder head.

INSTALLATION

Gasket surfaces on cylinder head and case must be clean and free of nicks or heavy scratches. Cylinder bolt threads in case and threads on cylinder head bolts must be clean to obtain true torque.

1. Place gasket in position over dowel pins with note "This Side Up" showing and install cylinder head.
2. Coat cylinder head bolt threads with suitable sealant and install bolts.
3. Tighten bolts in proper sequence, **Fig. 4.**
4. Install pushrods and loosely retain with rocker arms, ensuring lower ends of pushrods are in lifter seats.
5. Install spark plugs and wires.
6. Install intake and exhaust manifolds, then adjust valves as necessary.

VALVE COVER
REPLACE
LEFT SIDE

1. Disconnect battery ground cable and drain cooling system.
2. Loosen bypass tube at intake, then remove rocker arm cover to air inlet attaching tube.
3. Remove rocker arm cover attaching bolts, then remove rocker arm cover.
4. Reverse procedure to install. Tighten rocker arm cover attaching bolts to specifications.

RIGHT SIDE

1. Disconnect battery ground cable.
2. Remove brake booster vacuum line at bracket, then remove cable bracket at plenum.
3. Remove vacuum line bracket at cable bracket, then remove lines at alternator bracket stud.
4. Remove rear alternator attaching brace, then remove serpentine belt.
5. Remove alternator attaching bolts and position alternator aside.
6. Remove PCV valve, then remove rocker arm cover attaching bolts.
7. Remove spark plug wires, then remove rocker arm cover assembly.
8. Reverse procedure to install. Tighten attaching bolts to specifications.

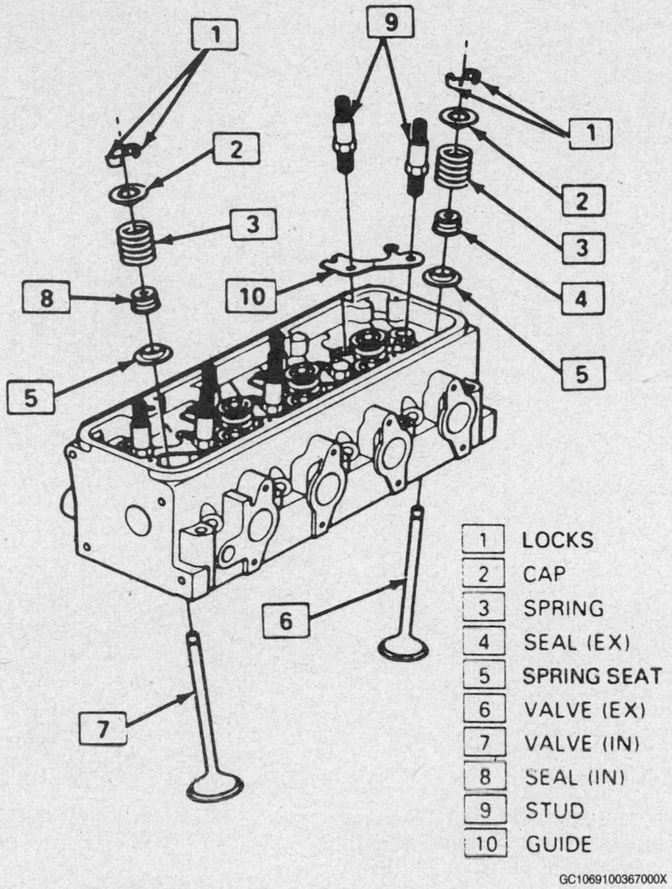
1
9
1
2
2
3
3
4
8
10
5
5
6
7
1 LOCKS
2 CAP
3 SPRING
4 SEAL (EX)
5 SPRING SEAT
6 VALVE (EX)
7 VALVE (IN)
8 SEAL (IN)
9 STUD
10 GUIDE
GC1069100367000X

Fig. 5 Valves, valve seals & valve springs

VALVE ARRANGEMENT

FRONT TO REAR

Right .... E-I-E-I-I-E
Left .... E-I-I-E-I-E

CAMSHAFT LOBE LIFT SPECIFICATIONS

Engine	Intake	Exhaust
3.1/V6-192	.2626	.2732

VALVE ADJUSTMENT

Vehicles are equipped with a non-adjustable rocker arm studs. If valve reconditioning is required, the non-adjustable rocker arm stud must be replaced with an adjustable rocker arm stud and the following procedure must be performed.

1. Remove rocker arm covers.
2. Crank engine until mark on torsional damper lines up with O mark on timing tab. The engine should also be in the No. 1 firing position. This can be determined by placing fingers on No. 1 rocker arms as mark on damper approaches O mark.
3. If valves are not moving, engine is in No. 1 firing position. If valves move as the mark comes up to the timing tab, engine is in No. 4 firing position and should be rotated one revolution to reach No. 1 position.
4. With engine in No. 1 firing position, adjust exhaust valves 1, 2 and 3 and intake valves 1, 5 and 6, as follows:
   a. Back out adjusting nut until lash is felt at pushrod, then turn in adjusting nut until all lash is removed.
   b. When lash has been removed, turn adjusting nut in additional 1 1/2 turns to center lifter plunger.
5. Crank engine one revolution until timing tab O mark and torsional damper mark are again in alignment.
6. With the engine in this, the No. 4 firing position. adjust exhaust valves 4, 5 and 6 and intake valves 2, 3 and 4 as previously described.
7. Install rocker arm covers, then start engine and check timing and idle speed.

VALVE GUIDES

Valve guides are an integral part of the cylinder head and are not removable. If valve stem clearance becomes excessive, the valve guide should be reamed to the next oversize and the appropriate oversize valves installed. Valves are available in .003, .015 and .030 inch over sizes.

VALVE SPRING & STEM OIL SEAL, REPLACE

Removal

1. Disconnect battery ground cable, then remove rocker cover.
2. With engine cold, remove spark plug and clean debris from plug recess.
3. Remove rocker arm and pushrod on cylinders to be serviced.
4. Install air line adapter tool No. J 23590 or equivalent in spark plug thread and apply compressed air to hold valves in place.
5. With valve spring compressor tool No. J-5892-C or equivalent, compress valve spring and remove valve lock and cap, **Fig. 5.**
6. Remove spring, valve stem oil seal and shim.

Installation

1. Install shim if required, then new valve stem oil seal.
2. Set valve spring and cap in place.
3. Using valve spring compressor tool No. J-5892-C or equivalent, compress valve spring.
4. Install valve locks and release compressor. **Make sure locks seat properly in the upper groove of the valve stem. Grease may be used to hold the locks in place while releasing the compressor tool.**
5. Install spark plug, pushrods, rocker arms and rocker cover.

HYDRAULIC LIFTERS

REPLACE

1. Remove intake manifold as previously described.
2. Remove valve mechanism, then the valve lifters.
3. Install valve lifters. When installing new lifters, coat foot of valve lifters with Molykote or equivalent, ensuring lifter foot is convex.
4. Install intake manifold as previously described.
5. Install and adjust valve mechanism.

FRONT COVER

REPLACE

1. Disconnect battery ground cable and drain cooling system.
2. Remove serpentine belt and tensioner.
3. Disconnect alternator and position aside.
4. Disconnect power steering pump and position aside.
5. Raise and support vehicle, then remove inner splash shield.
6. Remove flywheel cover attaching bolts at transaxle, then remove flywheel cover.
7. Remove harmonic balancer with pulling tool No. J-24420-B or equivalent.
8. Remove starter assembly.
9. Remove serpentine belt idler pulley.
10. Remove oil pan as outlined under "Oil

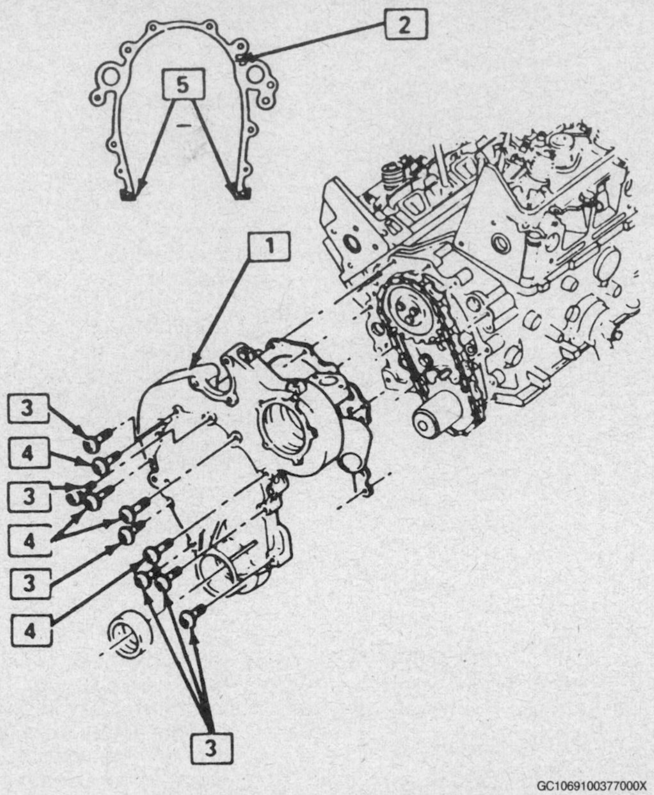
2
5
1
3
4
3
4
3
4
3
GC1069100377000X
Fig. 6 Front cover installation

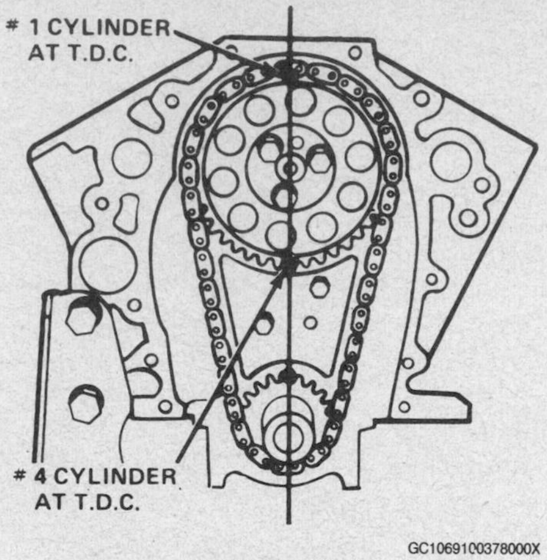
1 CYLINDER
AT T.D.C.
4 CYLINDER
AT T.D.C.
GC1069100378000X
Fig. 7 Valve timing marks

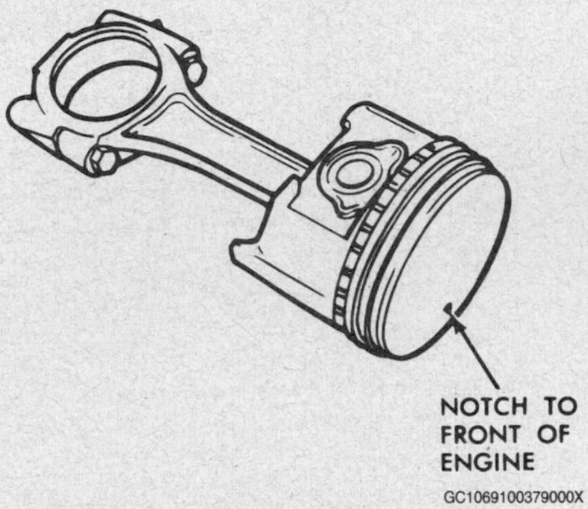
NOTCH TO
FRONT OF
ENGINE
GC1069100379000X
Fig. 8 Piston & rod assembly

Pan, Replace."

11. Remove front cover lower attaching bolts.
12. Lower vehicle, then remove water pump attaching radiator hose.
13. Remove heater hose at cooling system fill pipe, then remove bypass and overflow hoses.
14. Remove water pump pulley, the remove spark plug wire shield at water pump.
15. Remove canister purge hose.
16. Remove upper front cover attaching bolts, then remove front cover, **Fig. 6.**
17. Reverse to install. Tighten all attaching nuts, bolts or screws to specifications.

FRONT COVER SEAL
REPLACE

1. Remove front wheel and tire assemblies.
2. Remove inner splash shield and torsional damper, then pry seal from cover using a suitable screwdriver. **Use caution not to damage crankshaft surface during seal removal.**
3. Install new seal using tool No. J 35468 or equivalent, so open end faces toward inside of cover, then drive seal into position using suitable tool.

TIMING CHAIN
REPLACE

1. Remove crankcase front cover, refer to "Front Cover, Replace" procedure.
2. Place No. 1 cylinder at TDC and align timing marks on crankshaft and camshaft sprockets, **Fig. 7.**
3. Remove camshaft sprocket attaching bolts. Tap lower edge of sprocket with plastic mallet and remove sprocket and timing chain.
4. Align timing marks, **Fig. 7,** and install timing chain on sprockets.
5. Align dowel on camshaft with dowel hole on camshaft sprocket, then install sprocket to camshaft, using attaching bolts to draw sprocket fully to camshaft. Tighten attaching bolts to specification.
6. Lubricate timing chain with engine oil, then install front cover.

CAMSHAFT
REPLACE

1. Remove engine from vehicle, refer to "Engine, Replace" procedure.
2. Remove valve lifters, refer to "Hydraulic Valve Lifters, Replace" procedure.
3. Remove crankcase front cover, refer to "Front Cover, Replace" procedure.
4. Remove fuel pump and pushrod, then the timing chain and sprocket. Refer to "Timing Chain, Replace" procedure.
5. Remove timing chain tensioner.
6. Remove oil pump drive shaft extension.
7. Remove camshaft. **Use caution not to damage bearings during camshaft removal.**
8. Reverse procedure to install. Coat camshaft lobes with GM EOS 1052367 or other suitable lubricant before installation.

PISTON & ROD ASSEMBLY

There is a machined hole or cast notch in the top of all pistons. The piston assemblies should always be installed with the hole or notch toward front of engine, **Fig. 8.**

PISTONS, PINS & RINGS

Pistons and rings are available in standard and oversize. Piston pins are available in standard size only.

MAIN & ROD BEARINGS

Main and rod bearing are available in standard sizes and undersizes.

CRANKSHAFT REAR OIL SEAL
REPLACE

1. Support engine using tool No. J-28467-A or equivalent, then remove transaxle assembly.
2. Remove flywheel assembly.
3. Remove oil seal as shown in **Fig. 9.** Use caution not to damage crankshaft surface with removal tool.
4. Check inside diameter of bore and crankshaft for nicks or burrs. Repair as required.
5. Apply oil to inside diameter of new seal, then install seal on mandrel of

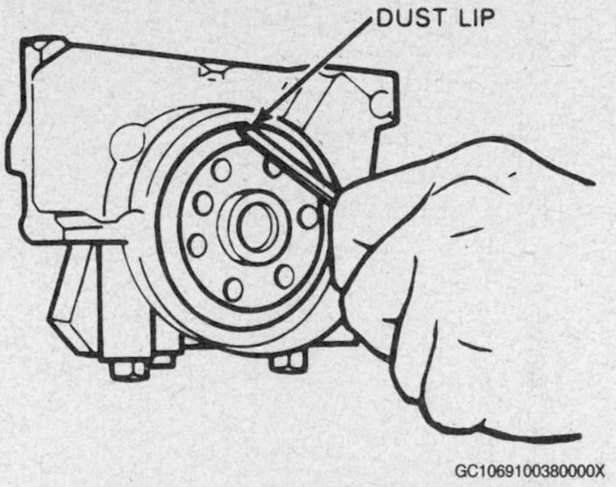
DUST LIP
GC1069100380000X

Fig. 9 Oil seal removal

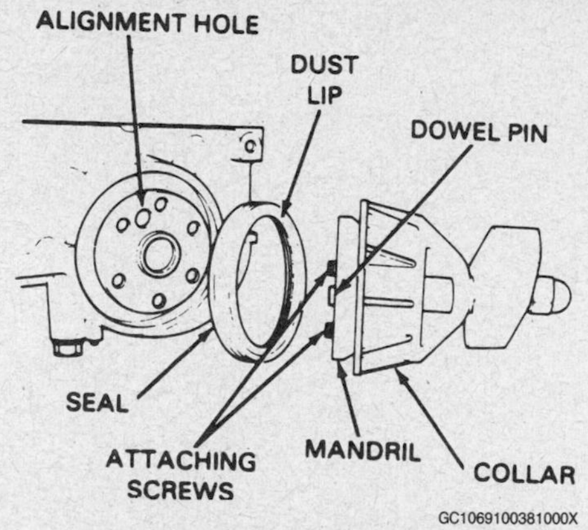
ALIGNMENT HOLE
DUST LIP
DOWEL PIN
SEAL
ATTACHING SCREWS
MANDRIL
COLLAR
GC1069100381000X

Fig. 10 Oil seal installation

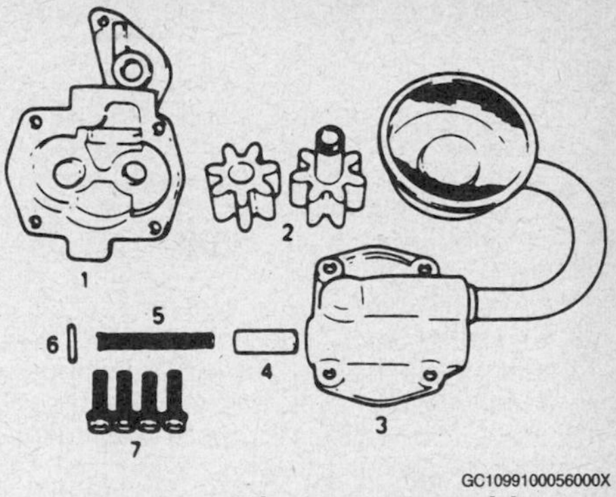
1
2
3
4
5
6
7
GC1099100056000X

Fig. 11 Oil pump assembly

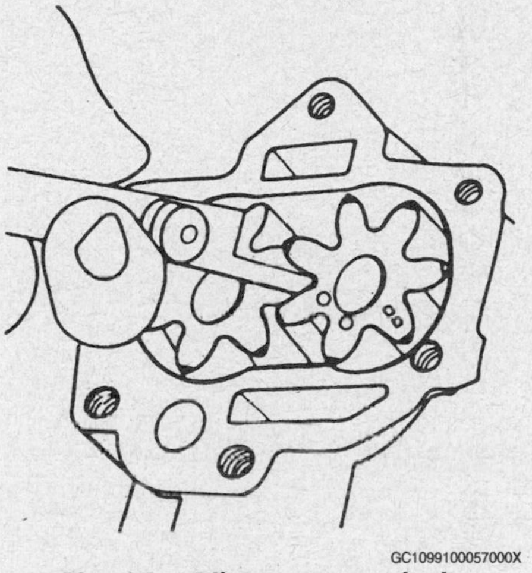
GC1099100057000X

Fig. 12 Oil pump gear lash measurement

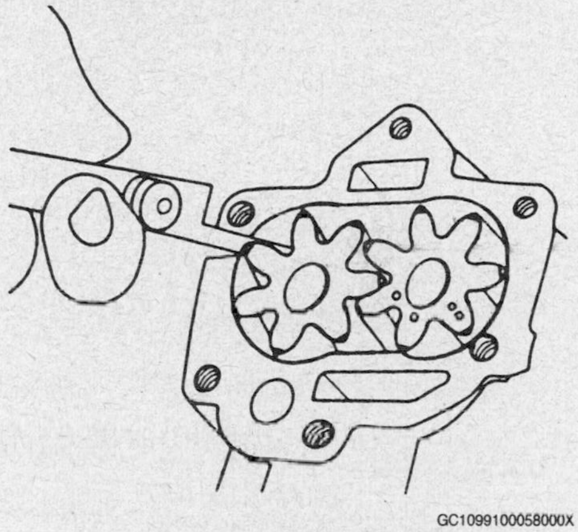
GC1099100058000X

Fig. 13 Gear side clearance measurement

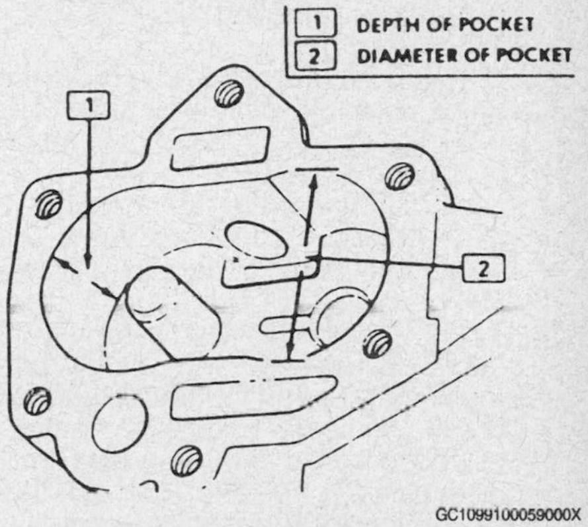
1 DEPTH OF POCKET
2 DIAMETER OF POCKET
1
2
GC1099100059000X

Fig. 14 Oil pump gear pocket measurement

tool No. J-34686 until back of seal bottoms squarely against collar of tool, **Fig. 10.**

6. Align dowel pin of tool with dowel pin of crankshaft, then attach tool to crankshaft. **Torque** attaching screws to 45 inch lbs.
7. Turn "T" handle of tool so collar pushes seal into bore. Ensure seal is properly seated.
8. Loosen "T" handle of tool until it comes to a stop, then remove tool attaching screws. Ensure seal is seated squarely in bore.
9. Install flywheel and transaxle assembly.

OIL PAN

REPLACE

1. Disconnect battery ground cable.
2. Remove serpentine belt and belt tensioner.
3. Raise and support vehicle, then drain engine oil.
4. Remove starter assembly, then remove outer plastic flywheel and starter shield.
5. Remove inner metal flywheel shield.
6. Remove engine to frame mount attaching nuts as outlined under "Engine Mounts, Replace."
7. Lower vehicle and support engine using tool No. J-28467-A or equivalent.
8. Raise and support vehicle, then re-

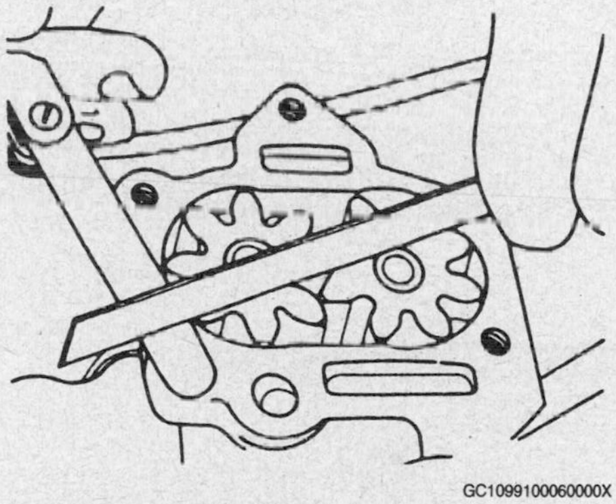
GC1099100060000X

Fig. 15 Oil pump end clearance measurement

move inner fender splash shield.

9. Remove oil pan attaching nuts and bolts, then remove oil pan.
10. Reverse procedure to install. Tighten attaching nuts and bolts to specifications.

OIL PUMP SERVICE

REMOVAL

1. Remove oil pan, refer to "Oil Pan, Replace" procedure.
2. Remove pump to rear main bearing attaching bolt, then the pump and extension shaft.

DISASSEMBLE

1. Remove pump cover attaching bolts (7), **Fig. 11**, and pump cover (3). **Mark gear teeth to ensure correct position during assembly.**
2. Remove idler gear and drive gear (2), then the shaft from pump body (1).
3. Remove pressure regulator valve retaining pin (6), pressure regulator spring (5) and valve (4).
4. If pickup screen and pipe assembly need to be replaced, mount pump in a suitable vise, then remove pipe from pump cover. **Do not remove pickup screen from pipe. This is serviced as an assembly.**

CLEANING & INSPECTION

1. Wash all parts in suitable cleaning solvent, then dry with compressed air.
2. Inspect pump body and cover for cracks or excessive wear.
3. Inspect pump gears for damage or excessive wear. Pump gears and body are not serviced separately. If pump gears are defective, replace entire oil pump assembly.
4. Check drive gear shaft for looseness in the pump body.
5. Inspect inside of pump cover for wear that would permit oil to leak past ends of gears.
6. Inspect pickup screen and pipe assembly for looseness or damage.
7. Check pressure regulator valve for damage and proper fit.
8. Using a straightedge and feeler gauge, check clearances as shown in **Figs. 12 through 15.**
9. Install gears and measure in several

places, gear lash should be within .0037-.0077 inch.

10. Measure depth and diameter of oil pump gear pocket, depth should be 1.202-1.205 inch and diameter should be 1.504-1.506 inch.
11. Measure gear side clearance, gear side clearance should be .003-.004 inch.
12. Measure gear end clearance, gear and clearance should be .002-.006 inch. **When determining pump service ability based on end clearance, consider depth of wear pattern in pump cover.**

ASSEMBLE

1. Lubricate all internal parts with engine oil during assembling.
2. Install pump gears.
3. Prime engine oil galleries by removing engine oil pump drive unit and rotate oil pump using suitable drill motor, socket and extension.
4. Install oil pump cover and gasket.
5. Install pressure regulator valve and spring, then install cotter pin or plug, if equipped.
6. If pipe assembly was removed, it should be replaced with a new part. Mount pump in suitable vise and apply suitable sealer to outside diameter of swaged end of pipe, then tap pipe in place using a suitable tool. **Loss of press fit condition could result in an air leak and loss of oil pressure. Also use caution not to twist, shear or collapse pipe during installation.**
7. Turn driveshaft by hand to ensure smooth operation.

INSTALLATION

1. Install pump and extension shaft with retainer to rear main bearing cap, aligning top end of hexagon extension shaft with hexagon socket of distributor drive gear.
2. Install pump to rear bearing cap bolt and tighten to specifications.
3. Install oil pan, refer to "Oil Pan, Replace" procedure.

BELT TENSION DATA

Year	Belt	New Lbs.	Used Lbs.
1992–94	—	225-236	112-124

SERPENTINE DRIVE BELT

ROUTING

1. Remove belt guard.
2. Lift or rotate tensioner using a 1/2 inch breaker bar.
3. Remove serpentine drive belt.
4. Reverse procedure to install, routing belt as shown in **Fig. 16.**

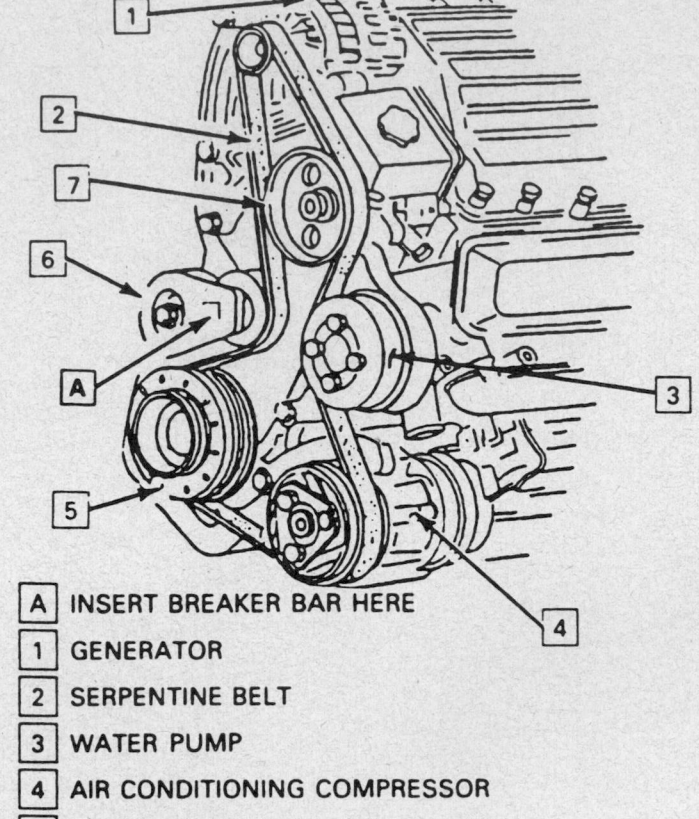

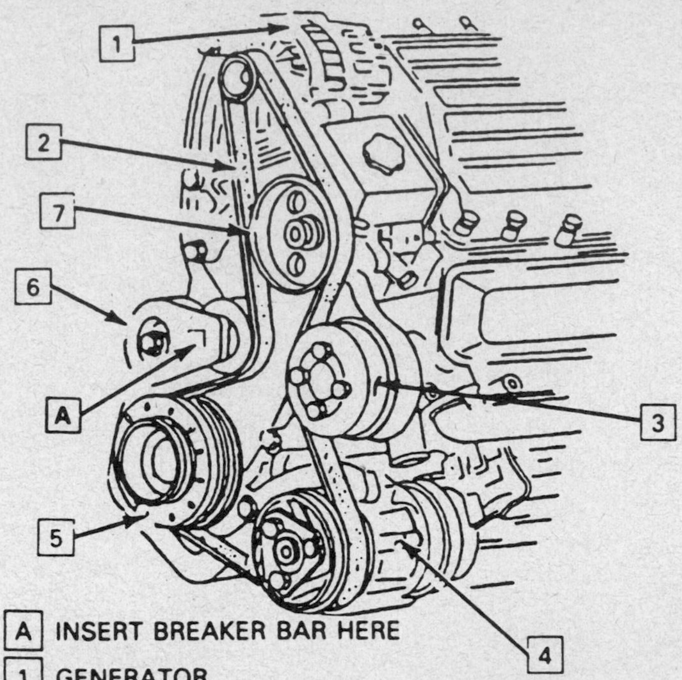
1
2
7
6
A
5
3
4
A INSERT BREAKER BAR HERE
1 GENERATOR
2 SERPENTINE BELT
3 WATER PUMP
4 AIR CONDITIONING COMPRESSOR
5 CRANKSHAFT
6 BELT TENSIONER
7 POWER STEERING PUMP
GC1069100382000X

Fig. 16 Serpentine belt routing

TENSIONER, REPLACE

1. Remove serpentine belt as described under "Serpentine Drive Belt, Replace.
2. Raise and support vehicle.
3. Remove inner splash shield, tensioner bolt and tensioner.
4. Reverse procedure to install, **Torquing** tensioner bolt to 35 ft. lbs.

COOLING SYSTEM BLEED

To ensure sufficient engine cooling, freezing and corrosion protection, maintain the protection level at -34°F or lower. Use a solution of antifreeze and water, ensuring solution is no more than 70 percent antifreeze.

1. Fill surge tank or radiator to base of filler neck, then attach pressure cap.
2. Block the drive wheel and apply parking brake.
3. **On models equipped with automatic transaxle,** place shifter in Park position.
4. **On models equipped with manual transaxle,** place transaxle in Neutral position.
5. **On all models,** start engine and allow to run until upper radiator hose is hot.
6. Stop engine, check level of coolant in surge tank or radiator.
7. Allow engine to cool, then add coolant as necessary.

THERMOSTAT

REPLACE

1. Disconnect negative battery cable.
2. Drain coolant and remove air cleaner assembly.
3. Remove coolant outlet to inlet manifold attaching bolt and nut, coolant outlet and thermostat.
4. Reverse procedure to install.

WATER PUMP

REPLACE

1. Disconnect battery ground cable, then drain cooling system.
2. Disconnect serpentine belt at the water pump pulley.
3. Remove water pump pulley, then the water pump, **Fig. 17.**
4. Reverse procedure to install.

RADIATOR

REPLACE

1. Disconnect battery ground cable, then discharge and recover air conditioning refrigerant.
2. Drain and recover engine coolant.
3. Remove hood latch from mounting

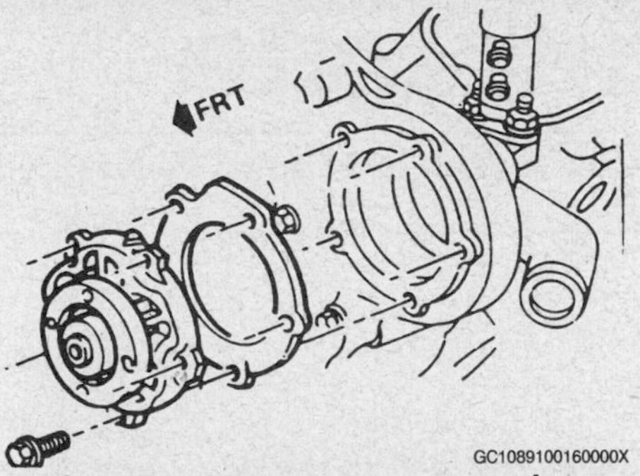
FRT

GC1089100160000X

Fig. 17 Water pump mounting

plate, then both headlight assemblies.
4. Remove radiator mounts, then raise and support vehicle.
5. Disconnect forward SIR sensor harness, then remove cooling fan assembly.
6. Disconnect radiator hoses, then transmission oil cooler lines from radiator.
7. Lower vehicle, then remove hood latch support and forward sensor with wiring harness.
8. Disconnect compressor and accumulator hoses from condenser, discarding O-rings.
9. Disconnect coolant overflow line, then remove radiator.
10. Reverse procedure to install, installing new air conditioning O-rings

FUEL PUMP

REPLACE

1. Loosen fuel filler cap to relieve tank vapor pressure, then disconnect battery ground cable.
2. Remove fuel tank as follows:
   a. Drain fuel tank, then raise and support vehicle. **Ensure additional support to the opposite end from which components are being replaced, to avoid personal injury.**
   b. Disconnect fuel tank harness from body harness electrical connectors.
   c. Remove ground wire attaching screw, if equipped.
   d. Remove tank meter assembly, filler and vent pipe hoses.
   e. Support fuel tank with suitable tool, then disconnect fuel tank attaching straps.
   f. Lower fuel tank, then remove fuel tank meter assembly and gasket using tool No. J 24187 or equivalent.
   g. Remove sound insulators.
3. Remove fuel lever sending unit and pump assembly by turning cam lock ring counterclockwise. Lift assembly from fuel tank, then remove fuel pump from fuel lever sending unit.
4. Pull fuel pump up to attaching hose or pulsator while pulling outward away from bottom support. After pump assembly is clear of bottom support, remove assembly from rubber connector or pulsator. **Use caution not to damage rubber insulator and strainer during removal.**
5. Reverse procedure to install.

FUEL FILTER

REPLACE

1. Relieve fuel system pressure as outlined under "Precautions."

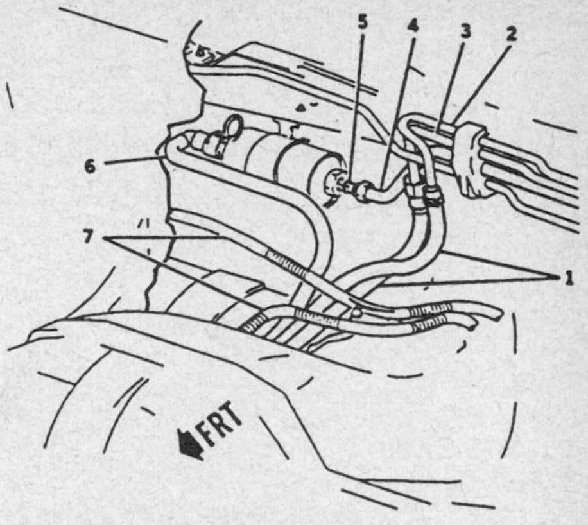
1
2
3
4
5
6
7
FRT

1. HOSE-PART OF FUEL SENDER
2. FUEL VAPOR PIPE
3. FUEL RETURN PIPE
4. FUEL FEED PIPE
5. FUEL FEED PIPE NUT
6. HOSE-PART OF FUEL SENDER
7. ABS AND FUEL SENDER HARNESS

GC1029202729000X

Fig. 18 Fuel filter replacement

2. Raise and support vehicle.
3. Using back-up wrench, remove filter fitting. If nylon fuel lines become kinked and cannot be straightened, they must be replace.
4. Twist quick-connect fitting 1/4 turn in each direction to loosen dirt within fitting.
5. Using compressed air, clean quick-connect fitting at ends of filter.
6. Disconnect quick connect fittings by squeezing plastic tabs of male end connector and pulling apart.
7. Remove fuel filter, **Fig. 18.**
8. Reverse procedure to install.

TIGHTENING SPECIFICATIONS

Component	Torque/Ft Lbs.
Camshaft Rear Cover	6-9
Camshaft Sprocket	21
Connecting Rod Nut	39
Crankshaft Balancer	76
Cylinder Head	③
Distributor hold-down	20-31
Drive Belt Tensioner Bolt	35
Engine Mount Bracket To Body Lower Bolt	74
Exhaust Crossover To Right Manifold	18
Exhaust Manifold	18
Front Cover	①
Front Engine Mount To Bracket Bolt	50
Front Engine Mount To Frame Bolt (Top)	54
Front Engine Mount To Bracket Bolt (Bottom)	61
Front Engine Mount Bracket Body Upper Bolt	74
Heat Shield	89④
Intake Manifold	13-25
Main Bearing Cap	63-83
Negative Battery Cable	11
Oil Level Indicator Nut	18

Component	Torque/Ft. Lbs.
Oil Pan	②
Oil Pump Drive	25
Oil Pump To Rear Bearing Cap	30
Rear Engine Mount To Engine Bolt	40
Rear Engine Bracket To Body Bolt	45
Rocker Arm Covers	89④
Rocker Arm Nuts	18
Spark Plugs	18
Thermostat Housing	15-23
Timing Chain Dampener	15
Torsional Dampener	67-85
Water Pump Pulley To Pump Bolts	15
Water Pump To Block	18
Water Pump To Front Cover Bolts	90④

①—8 mm bolts, 20 ft. lbs.; 10 mm bolts, 28 ft. lbs.
②—6 mm bolts, 71 inch lbs.; 8 mm bolts, 18 ft. lbs.
③—Torque bolts in sequence to 33 ft. lbs., then turn an additional 90°.
④—Inch Lbs.

Clutch & Manual Transaxle

NOTE: On Air Bag Equipped Models, Refer To "Air Bag System Precautions" Located In The Front Of This Manual For System Disarming & Arming Procedures.

INDEX

PRECAUTIONS

AIR BAG SYSTEMS

Refer to "Air Bag System Precautions" in the front of this manual for system disarming and arming procedures.

ADJUSTMENTS

CLUTCH PEDAL

On these models, a hydraulic clutch system is used, **Fig. 1.** The system consists of a dash mounted master cylinder with integral reservoir, a transmission mounted slave cylinder and high pressure tubing to connect the two components.

The hydraulic clutch system provides automatic clutch adjustment, therefore, there is no provision for adjustment.

SHIFT CABLE

Muncie Transaxle

Refer to **Fig. 2** for exploded view of shifter cables.

HYDRAULIC SYSTEM SERVICE

HYDRAULIC SYSTEM BLEED

1. Fill reservoir with a suitable DOT 3 type brake fluid.
2. Fully loosen bleeder screw located on slave cylinder near inlet connection.
3. While maintaining reservoir fluid level, allow fluid to flow from bleeder valve until a steady stream of fluid with no air bubbles is present, then tighten bleeder screw.
4. Fill reservoir to proper level, then start engine.
5. Depress clutch for approximately ten seconds, then select reverse gear. If no gear clash is present, system is satisfactory. If gear clash is present, repeat bleeding procedure.

INSPECTION

1. While observing clutch slave cylinder pushrod travel, have an assistant depress clutch pedal.
2. If slave cylinder pushrod moves .433

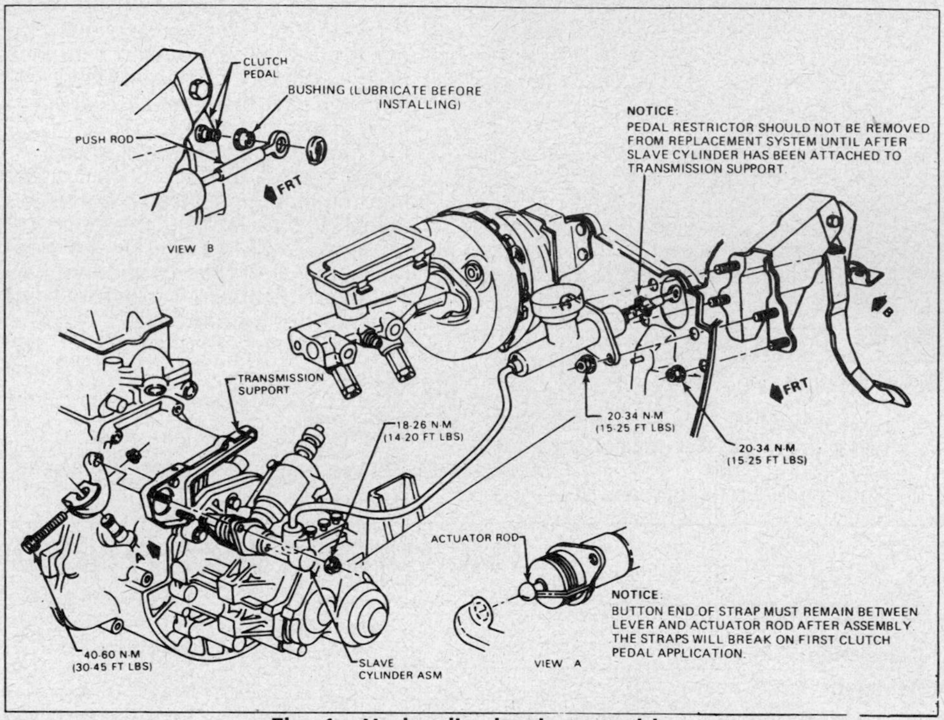

CLUTCH PEDAL
BUSHING (LUBRICATE BEFORE INSTALLING)
PUSH ROD
FRT
VIEW B
NOTICE:
PEDAL RESTRICTOR SHOULD NOT BE REMOVED FROM REPLACEMENT SYSTEM UNTIL AFTER SLAVE CYLINDER HAS BEEN ATTACHED TO TRANSMISSION SUPPORT.
B
FRT
TRANSMISSION SUPPORT
18-26 N·M (14-20 FT LBS)
20-34 N·M (15-25 FT LBS)
20-34 N·M (15-25 FT LBS)
ACTUATOR ROD
NOTICE:
BUTTON END OF STRAP MUST REMAIN BETWEEN LEVER AND ACTUATOR ROD AFTER ASSEMBLY. THE STRAPS WILL BREAK ON FIRST CLUTCH PEDAL APPLICATION.
40-60 N·M (30-45 FT LBS)
SLAVE CYLINDER ASM
VIEW A

Fig. 1 Hydraulic clutch assembly

GC5049100040000X

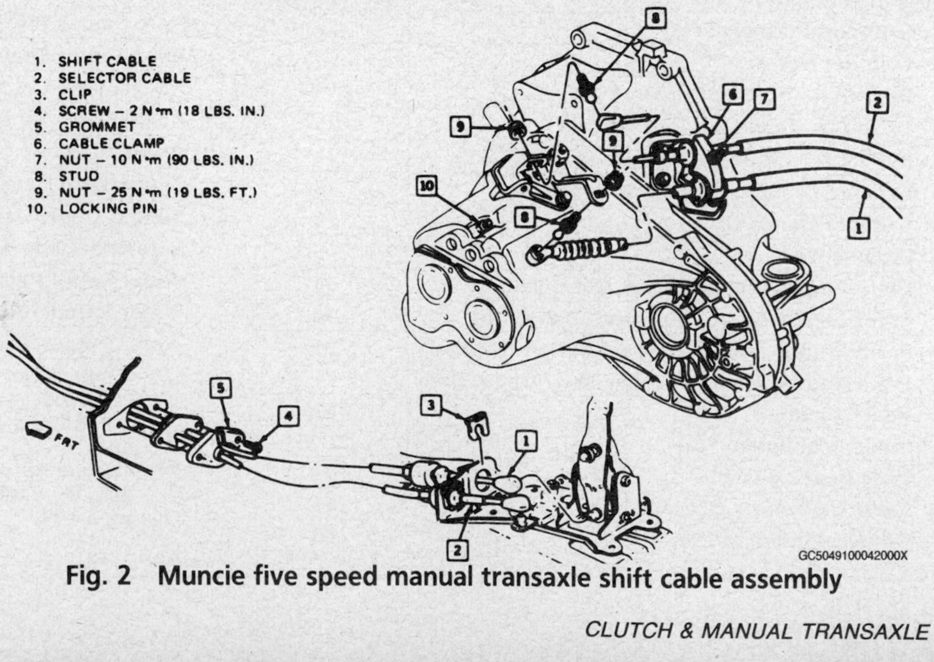

1. SHIFT CABLE
2. SELECTOR CABLE
3. CLIP
4. SCREW – 2 N·m (18 LBS. IN.)
5. GROMMET
6. CABLE CLAMP
7. NUT – 10 N·m (90 LBS. IN.)
8. STUD
9. NUT – 25 N·m (19 LBS. FT.)
10. LOCKING PIN
FRT

GC5049100042000X

Fig. 2 Muncie five speed manual transaxle shift cable assembly

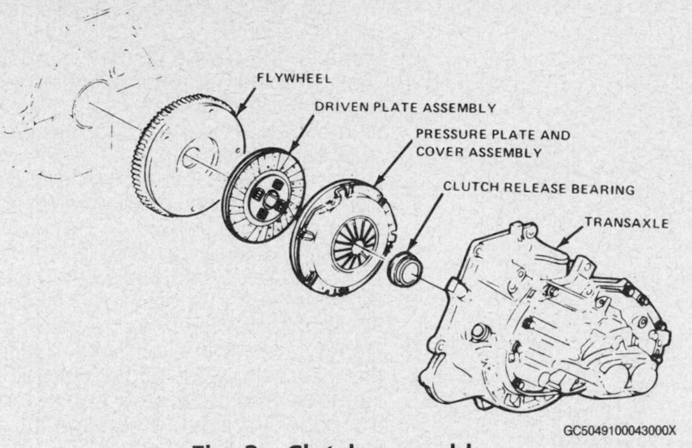
FLYWHEEL
DRIVEN PLATE ASSEMBLY
PRESSURE PLATE AND COVER ASSEMBLY
CLUTCH RELEASE BEARING
TRANSAXLE
GC5049100043000X

Fig. 3 Clutch assembly

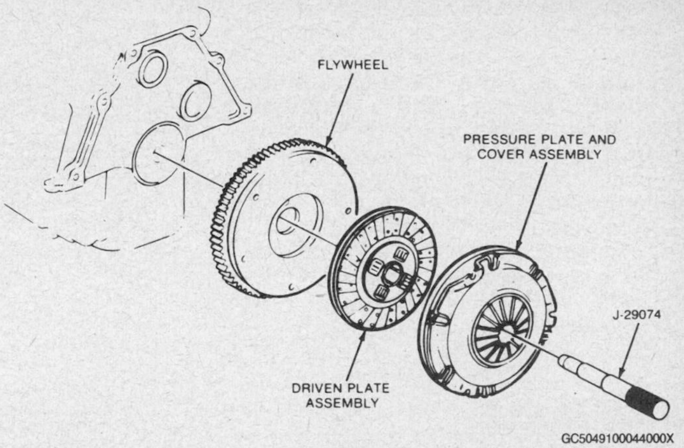
FLYWHEEL
PRESSURE PLATE AND COVER ASSEMBLY
J-29074
DRIVEN PLATE ASSEMBLY
GC5049100044000X

Fig. 4 Clutch disc & pressure plate alignment

inch or more, hydraulic system is operating properly.

3. If slave cylinder pushrod did not move .433 inch, proceed as follows:
   a. Check clutch master cylinder fluid level. The clutch slave cylinder must be installed during this operation. Refill as necessary.
   b. If master cylinder requires fluid, check hydraulic system components for leakage. Remove rubber boots from cylinders and check for leakage past pistons. A slight wetting of piston and wall surfaces is acceptable.
   c. If excessive leakage is indicated, entire hydraulic system must be replaced.

CLUTCH MASTER & ACTUATOR CYLINDERS, REPLACE

FOUR CYLINDER ENGINE

Removal

1. Disconnect negative battery cable.
2. Remove sound insulator from inside of vehicle.
3. Disconnect clutch master cylinder pushrod from clutch pedal.
4. Remove clutch master cylinder retaining nuts at front of dash and disconnect remote reservoir, if equipped.
5. Remove actuator retaining nuts at transaxle.
6. Remove hydraulic system as a unit from vehicle.

Installation

1. Install actuator cylinder to transaxle support bracket aligning pushrod into pocket on lever. **Torque** nuts evenly to 16 ft. lbs.
2. Install clutch master cylinder to front of dash. **Torque** nuts evenly to 16 ft. lbs. **Do not remove plastic pushrod retainer from actuator cylinder. Retainer will break off on first clutch pedal application.**
3. Connect remote reservoir, if equipped.
4. Remove pedal restrictor from pushrod, then lubricate pushrod bushing on clutch pedal.
5. Connect pushrod with clutch pedal and install retaining clip.
6. Install sound insulator.
7. Press clutch pedal down several times. This will break plastic retaining straps on actuator cylinder pushrod. **Do not remove plastic button on pushrod.**
8. Connect negative battery cable.

SIX CYLINDER ENGINE

Removal

1. Remove air intake duct from air cleaner.
2. Disconnect negative and positive battery cables from battery.
3. Remove left fender brace and battery.
4. Disconnect MAT sensor lead at air cleaner.
5. Disconnect mass air flow sensor lead, then remove PCV retaining clamp from air intake duct.
6. Remove clamp retaining air intake duct to throttle body.
7. Remove mass air flow mounting bolt and air cleaner bracket mounting bolts at battery tray.
8. Remove air cleaner, mass air flow sensor and air intake duct as an assembly.
9. Disconnect electrical lead at washer bottle, then remove attaching bolts and washer bottle.
10. Remove cruise control mounting bracket retaining nuts from strut tower, if equipped.
11. Remove sound insulator from inside of vehicle.
12. Disconnect clutch master cylinder pushrod from clutch pedal.
13. Remove clutch master cylinder retaining nuts at front of dash.
14. Remove actuator cylinder retaining nuts at transaxle.
15. Remove hydraulic system as a unit from vehicle.

Installation

1. Install actuator cylinder to transaxle support bracket aligning pushrod into pocket on lever. **Do not remove plastic pushrod retainer from actuator cylinder. Retainer will break off on first clutch pedal application. Torque** nuts evenly to 16 ft. lbs.
2. Install clutch master cylinder to front of dash. **Torque** nuts evenly to 16 ft. lbs.
3. Remove pedal restrictor from pushrod. Lubricate pushrod bushing on clutch pedal, then connect pushrod to clutch pedal and install retaining clip.
4. Check cruise control switch adjustment at clutch pedal. **If adjustment is necessary, do not exert an upward force on clutch pedal pad of more than 20 ft. lbs. or damage to master cylinder pushrod retaining ring may result.**
5. Install sound insulator.
6. Press clutch pedal down several times. This will break plastic retaining straps on actuator cylinder pushrod. **Do not remove plastic button on pushrod.**
7. Install washer bottle.
8. Install air cleaner, mass air flow sensor and air intake duct.
9. Install clamp retaining air intake duct to throttle body.
10. Install PCV pipe retaining clamp.
11. Connect mass air flow and MAT sensor leads.
12. Install battery and left fender brace.
13. Connect positive and negative battery cables, then air intake duct to air cleaner.

CLUTCH

REPLACE

1. Disconnect battery ground cable.
2. Remove hush panel from driver's foot well, as required, then disconnect clutch master cylinder pushrod from clutch pedal.
3. Remove transaxle as outlined under "Manual Transaxle, Replace" procedure.
4. Mark position of pressure plate to flywheel to aid assembling.
5. Gradually loosen pressure plate to flywheel attaching bolts until spring tension is relieved.
6. Support pressure plate and remove attaching bolts, pressure plate and driven disc, **Fig. 3.**
7. Clean pressure plate and flywheel mounting surfaces. Inspect bearing retainer outer surface of the transaxle.

8. Place pressure plate and driven disc in position and support with tool No. J-29074, **Fig. 4. The driven disc is installed with the damper springs offset toward the transaxle. Stamped letters found on the driven disc identify the "Flywheel Side.**
9. Install and gradually tighten the pressure plate to flywheel attaching bolts. Remove support tool.
10. Lubricate the release bearing outside diameter groove and inside diameter recess with lubricant 1051344 or equivalent.
11. Install transaxle.

TRANSAXLE

REPLACE

FOUR CYLINDER ENGINE

1. Disconnect battery ground cable.
2. Install engine support fixture J-28467-A or equivalent, then raise engine enough to take pressure off motor mounts, **Fig. 5.**
3. Remove left sound insulator.
4. Remove clutch master cylinder pushrod from clutch pedal.
5. Remove wire harness at mount bracket.
6. Remove clutch slave cylinder from transaxle support bracket and position aside.
7. Remove transaxle mount and mount bracket attaching bolts.
8. Remove shift cables and retaining clamp at transaxle.
9. Remove ground cable at transaxle attaching bolts, then disconnect backup switch electrical connector.
10. Raise and support vehicle, then drain transaxle fluid.
11. Remove left front wheel and inner splash shield.
12. Remove transaxle front strut and front strut bracket.
13. Remove clutch housing cover attaching bolts, then the vehicle speed sensor at transaxle.
14. Remove stabilizer shaft at left suspension support and control arm.
15. Remove left suspension support attaching bolts and swing aside.
16. Remove drive axles and left shaft at transaxle.
17. Position suitable jack under transaxle, then remove transaxle to engine attaching bolts.
18. Slide transaxle towards drivers side, away from engine, then lower transaxle from vehicle while guiding right drive axle out of transaxle.
19. Reverse procedure to install. When installing transaxle, carefully guide right hand drive axle shaft into transaxle bore as transaxle is being raised. The right hand drive axle shaft cannot be installed once the transaxle has been connected to the engine.

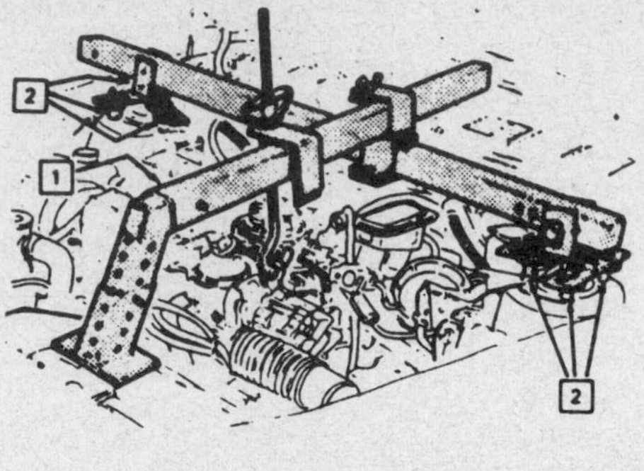
2
1
2

1. TOOL J-28467
2. THREAD ONTO STRUT ATTACHING BOLTS ABOVE NUTS – 3 PER SIDE

GC5049100045000X

Fig. 5 Engine support fixture installation

SIX CYLINDER ENGINE

1. Disconnect battery ground cable.
2. Install engine support fixture J-28467-A or equivalent, then raise engine enough to take pressure off motor mounts, **Fig. 5.**
3. Remove left sound insulator.
4. Remove clutch master cylinder pushrod from clutch pedal.
5. Remove air cleaner and air intake duct assembly.
6. Remove clutch slave cylinder from transaxle support bracket and position aside.
7. Remove transaxle mount through bolt, then raise and support vehicle.
8. Remove exhaust crossover bolts at RH manifold, then lower vehicle.
9. Remove left hand exhaust manifold, then the transaxle mount bracket.
10. Remove transaxle shift cables, then the upper transaxle to engine attaching bolts.
11. Remove transaxle vent tube
12. Raise and support vehicle, then remove left front tire and inner splash shield.
13. Remove transaxle strut and bracket.
14. Drain transaxle, then remove clutch housing cover attaching bolts.
15. Remove speedometer cable, then the stabilizer shaft at left suspension support and control arm.
16. Remove left hand suspension support attaching bolts and swing aside.
17. Remove left hand drive axle from transaxle.
18. Remove intermediate shaft housing to transaxle attaching bolts, then slide housing away from transaxle. Using a suitable tool, disconnect intermediate shaft from transaxle.
19. Position suitable jack under transaxle, then remove remaining transaxle to engine attaching bolts.
20. Lower transaxle assembly from vehicle.
21. Reverse procedure to install. When installing transaxle, carefully guide right hand drive axle shaft into transaxle bore as transaxle is being raised. The right hand drive axle shaft cannot be installed once the transaxle has been connected to the engine.

TIGHTENING SPECIFICATIONS

Component	Torque/Ft. Lbs.
Back-up Switch Assembly To Transaxle	24
Clutch Bleed Screw	17①
Clutch Cover To Flywheel	18②
Clutch Cover To Transaxle	115①
Clutch Master Cylinder	16
Clutch Slave Cylinder Nut	16
Clutch Release Lever (Isuzu)	37
Front Transaxle Strut To Transaxle	50
Front Transaxle To Body Bolt	40
Rear Mount Bracket To Transaxle	40
Rear Transaxle Mount To Body	23
Shift Cable Grommet To Shroud	18①
Shift Control Box To Transaxle (Isuzu)	13
Shift Control To Floor	18

Component	Torque/Ft. Lbs.
Shift Linkage Retainer To Transaxle Case	17
Shift Retainer To Transaxle Case (Isuzu)	18
Shift Shaft Lever Nut	61
Speedometer/VSS Housing To Transaxle	84①
Transaxle Mount To Transaxle	37
Transaxle Shift Cable Bracket To Cables	90①
Transaxle Shift Lever To Cable Stud	18
Transaxle To Engine Bolts and Studs (Isuzu)	55
Transaxle To Engine Nut	55
Transaxle To Engine Stud	106①
Transaxle To Engine Stud/Bolts	55
Wheel Lug Nuts	100

①—Inch lbs.
②—Plus 30° turn.

Rear Axle & Suspension

NOTE: On Air Bag Equipped Models, Refer To "Air Bag System Precautions" Located In The Front Of This Manual For System Disarming & Arming Procedures.

INDEX

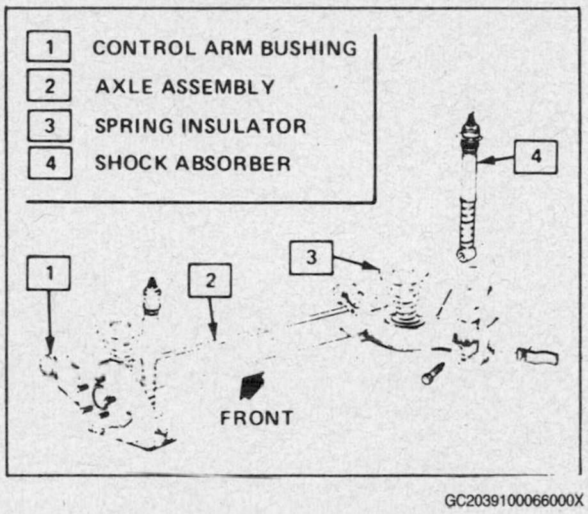

1 CONTROL ARM BUSHING
2 AXLE ASSEMBLY
3 SPRING INSULATOR
4 SHOCK ABSORBER
4
3
1
2
FRONT
GC2039100066000X

Fig. 1 Rear suspension

PRECAUTIONS

AIR BAG SYSTEMS

Refer to "Air Bag System Precautions" in the front of this manual for system disarming and arming procedures.

DESCRIPTION

The rear suspension, **Fig. 1**, is a semi-independent type suspension consisting of an axle assembly with trailing arms and twisting cross beam, coil springs and double action shock absorbers. A stabilizer bar is available and is attached to the inside of the axle beam and to the lower end of the control arms. A single unit hub and bearing assembly is bolted to each end of the axle assembly. The hub and bearing assembly is a sealed, non-serviceable unit and must be replaced as an assembly.

REAR AXLE

REPLACE

1. Raise vehicle and support vehicle. Support rear suspension with suitable jack.
2. Disconnect stabilizer bar at axle assembly, if equipped, **Fig. 2.**
3. Remove rear wheel assembly and brake drum. Do not hammer on brake drum since damage to bearings may result.
4. Remove shock absorber to lower mounting bracket attaching bolts, then disconnect shock absorbers from axle assembly, **Fig. 2.**
5. Disconnect parking brake cable and brake lines at axle brackets.
6. Carefully lower rear axle assembly and remove coil springs and insulators.
7. Remove control arm to underbody bracket bolts, then lower the axle assembly and remove from vehicle.
8. Remove hub to rear axle attaching bolts, then the hubs, bearings and backing plates from rear axle assembly.
9. Reverse procedure to install and bleed brake system.

HUB & BEARING

REPLACE

1. Raise and support vehicle, then remove wheel and tire assembly and brake drum. **Do not hammer brake drum since damage to bearing may result.**
2. Remove four hub/bearing assembly to rear axle attaching bolts, then the hub/bearing assembly from axle. **The upper rear hub attaching bolt may not clear brake shoe when removing hub and bearing assembly. Partially remove hub and bearing assembly prior to removing this bolt.**
3. Reverse procedure to install. Tighten hub attaching bolts to specification. **Use care not to drop hub/bearing assembly since damage to bearing may result.**

SHOCK ABSORBER

REPLACE

1. Open deck lid, then remove trim cover and shock absorber upper retaining nut.
2. Raise rear of vehicle and support rear axle using a suitable jack.
3. Remove shock absorber lower attaching bolt, then disconnect shock absorber from mounting bracket, **Fig. 2.** Remove shock absorber from vehicle.
4. Reverse procedure to install. Tighten attaching bolt to specification.

COIL SPRING

REPLACE

1. Raise and support rear of vehicle. Support rear axle using a suitable jack.
2. Remove wheel and tire assemblies.
3. Remove brake line bracket attaching bolts from frame, **Fig. 2,** and allow brake lines to hang freely.
4. Remove shock absorber to lower mounting bracket bolts, then disconnect shock absorbers from axle assembly. **Do not suspend rear axle by brake hoses since damage to hoses may result.**
5. Carefully lower rear axle assembly and remove springs and insulators.
6. Reverse procedure to install. Position ends of upper coil in seat of body and within limits shown in **Fig. 3.**

CONTROL ARM BUSHING

REPLACE

1. Raise rear of vehicle and support rear axle under front side of spring seat using a suitable jack.
2. Remove wheel and tire assembly.
3. If right hand side bushing is to be replaced, disconnect brake line bracket from body. If left hand side bushing is to be replaced, disconnect brake line bracket from frame and parking brake cable at hook guide.
4. Remove control arm to mounting bracket attaching nut, bolt and washer, then allow control arm to rotate downward.
5. The bushing can now be replaced using tools shown in **Fig. 4.** When installing bushing, the arrow on the installer must align with arrow on the receiver, **Fig. 4.**
6. Reverse procedure to complete installation. **The control arm attaching bolt must be tightened after vehicle is lowered to floor and is in its standing height position. Tighten attaching bolt to specifications.**

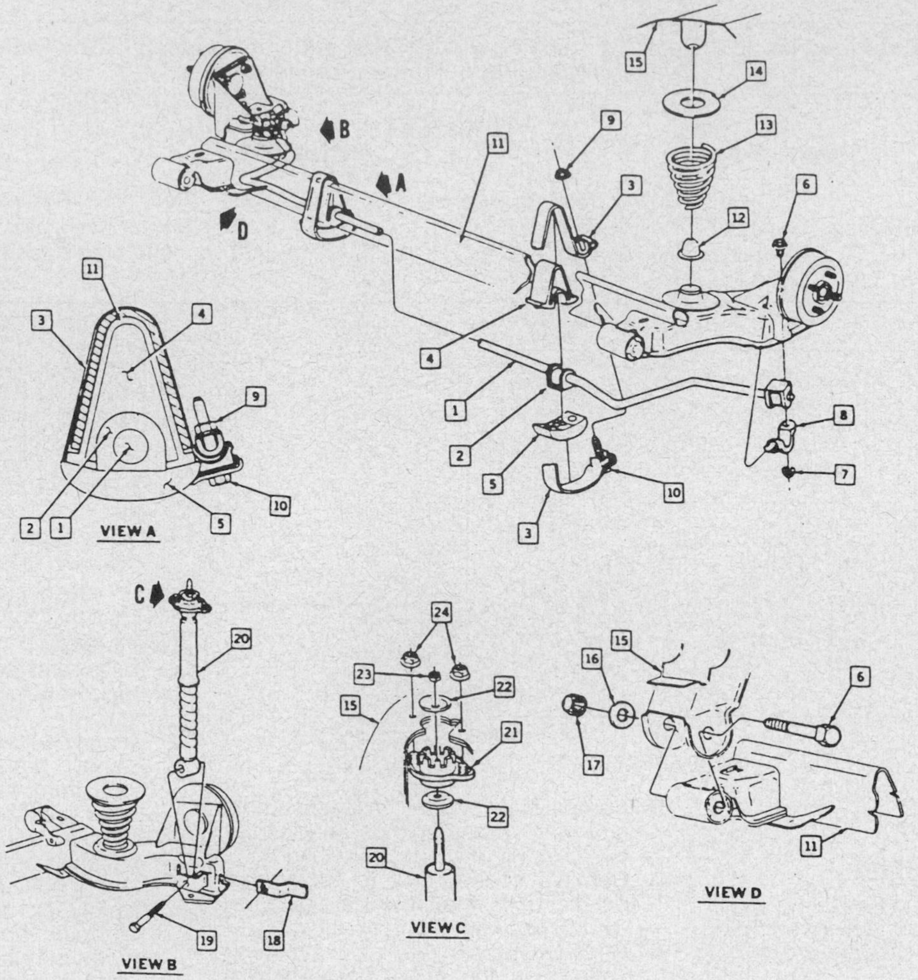
VIEW A
VIEW B
VIEW C
VIEW D

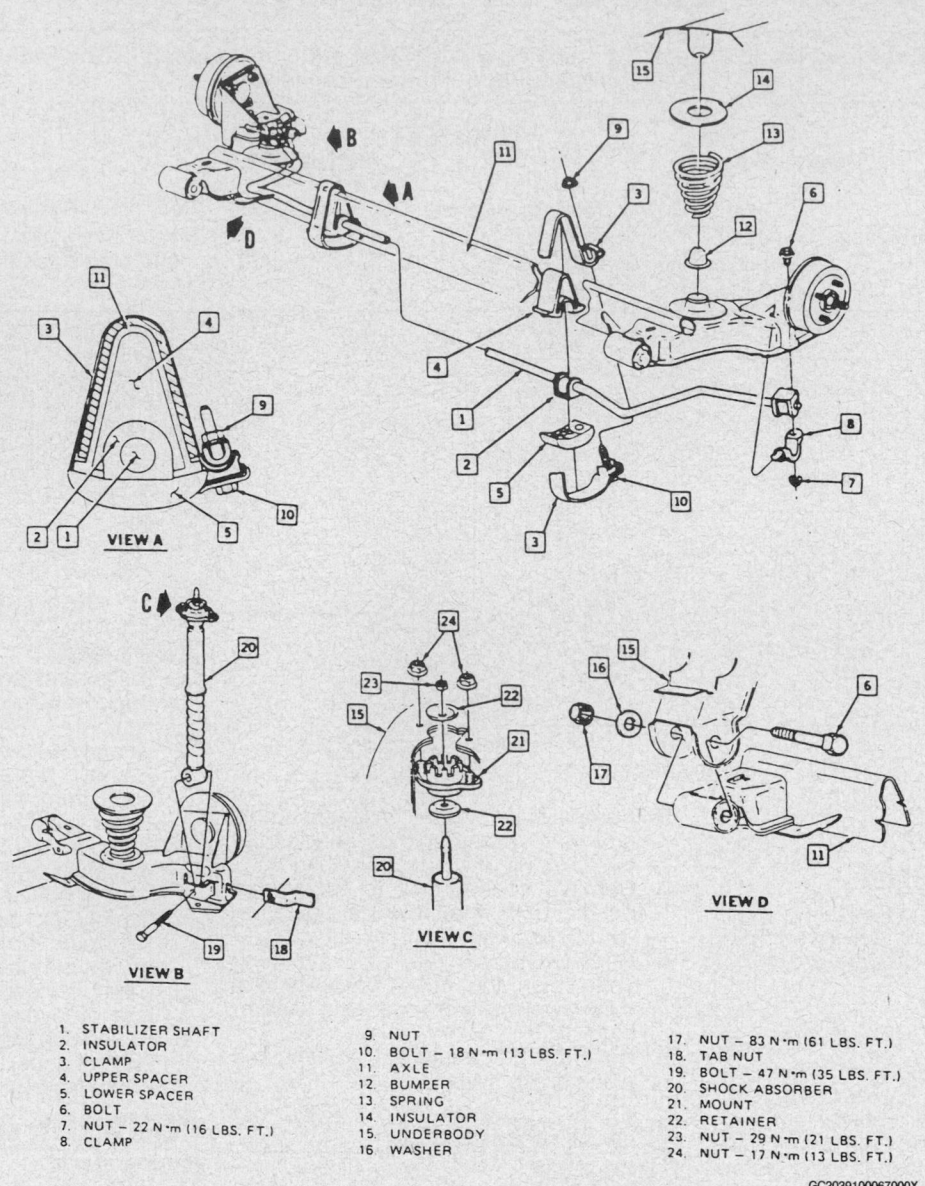

1. STABILIZER SHAFT
2. INSULATOR
3. CLAMP
4. UPPER SPACER
5. LOWER SPACER
6. BOLT
7. NUT – 22 N·m (16 LBS. FT.)
8. CLAMP
9. NUT
10. BOLT – 18 N·m (13 LBS. FT.)
11. AXLE
12. BUMPER
13. SPRING
14. INSULATOR
15. UNDERBODY
16. WASHER
17. NUT – 83 N·m (61 LBS. FT.)
18. TAB NUT
19. BOLT – 47 N·m (35 LBS. FT.)
20. SHOCK ABSORBER
21. MOUNT
22. RETAINER
23. NUT – 29 N·m (21 LBS. FT.)
24. NUT – 17 N·m (13 LBS. FT.)

GC2039100067000X

Fig. 2 Exploded view of rear suspension

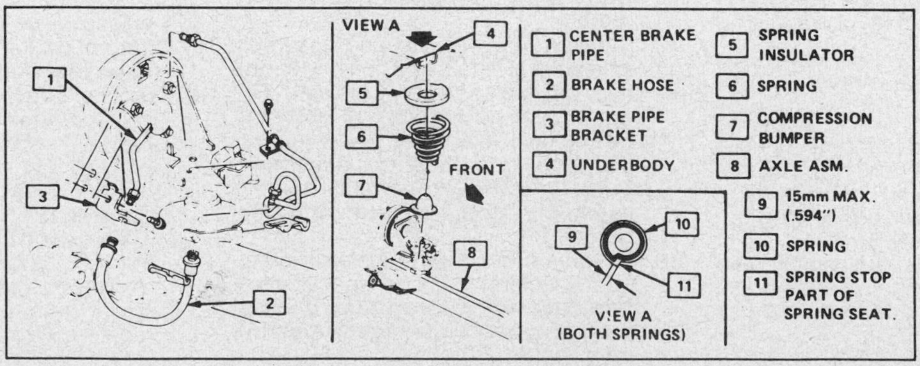
VIEW A
FRONT
1 CENTER BRAKE PIPE
2 BRAKE HOSE
3 BRAKE PIPE BRACKET
4 UNDERBODY
5 SPRING INSULATOR
6 SPRING
7 COMPRESSION BUMPER
8 AXLE ASM.
9 15mm MAX. (.594")
10 SPRING
11 SPRING STOP PART OF SPRING SEAT.
VIEW A (BOTH SPRINGS)

GC2039100068000X

Fig. 3 Coil spring installation

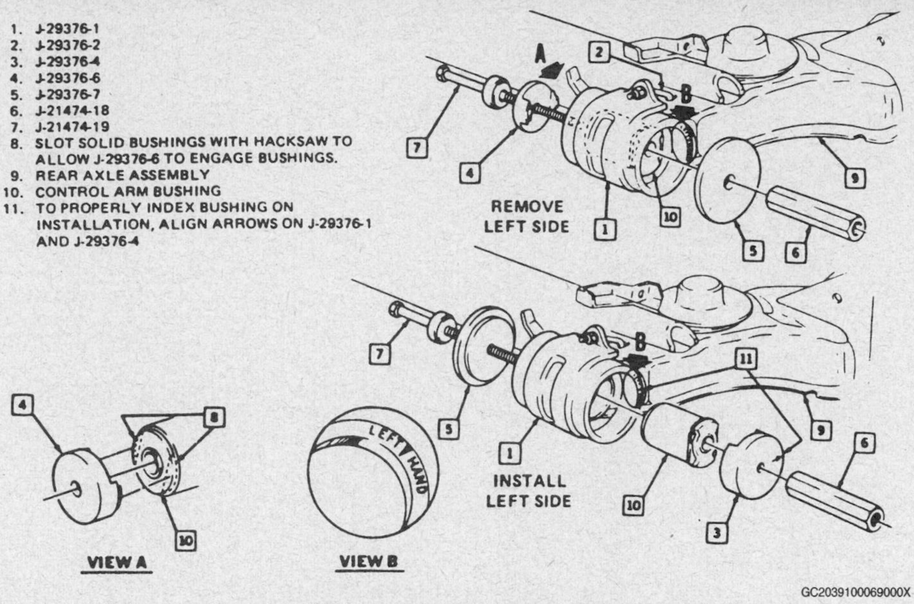
1. J-29376-1
2. J-29376-2
3. J-29376-4
4. J-29376-6
5. J-29376-7
6. J-21474-18
7. J-21474-19
8. SLOT SOLID BUSHINGS WITH HACKSAW TO ALLOW J-29376-6 TO ENGAGE BUSHINGS.
9. REAR AXLE ASSEMBLY
10. CONTROL ARM BUSHING
11. TO PROPERLY INDEX BUSHING ON INSTALLATION, ALIGN ARROWS ON J-29376-1 AND J-29376-4
REMOVE LEFT SIDE
INSTALL LEFT SIDE
LEFT HAND
VIEW A
VIEW B
GC2039100069000X

Fig. 4 Control arm bushing replacement

TIGHTENING SPECIFICATIONS

Component	Torque/Ft. Lbs.
Axle To Body Bracket	68
Brake Line Bracket To Axle	11
Brake Line Bracket To Frame	8
Hub & Bearing Assembly	37
Shock Absorber Bolt At Axle	35

Component	Torque/Ft. Lbs.
Shock Absorber Mount To Body	13
Shock Absorber To Mount	21
Stabilizer Shaft Clamp Bolts At Axle	13
Stabilizer Shaft Clamp Nuts	16
Wheel Lug Nuts	100

Front Suspension & Steering

NOTE: On Air Bag Equipped Models, Refer To "Air Bag System Precautions" Located In The Front Of This Manual For System Disarming & Arming Procedures.

INDEX

PRECAUTIONS

AIR BAG SYSTEMS

Refer to "Air Bag System Precautions" in the front of this manual for system disarming and arming procedures.

DESCRIPTION

The front suspension, **Fig. 1,** on these vehicles is of the MacPherson strut design. The lower control arms pivot from the lower side rails through rubber bushings. The upper end of the strut is isolated by a rubber mount incorporating a non-serviceable bearing for wheel turning. The tie rods connect to the steering arm on the strut, below the spring seat. The lower end of the steering knuckle pivots on a ball stud which is retained to the lower control arm by rivets and is secured to the steering knuckle with a nut and cotter pin. The sealed wheel bearings are integral with the hub and are serviced as an assembly.

WHEEL BEARING

REPLACE

REMOVAL

1. Raise and support vehicle.
2. Remove tire and wheel assembly, then install modified outer seal protector No. J 34754 or equivalent, **Fig. 2.**

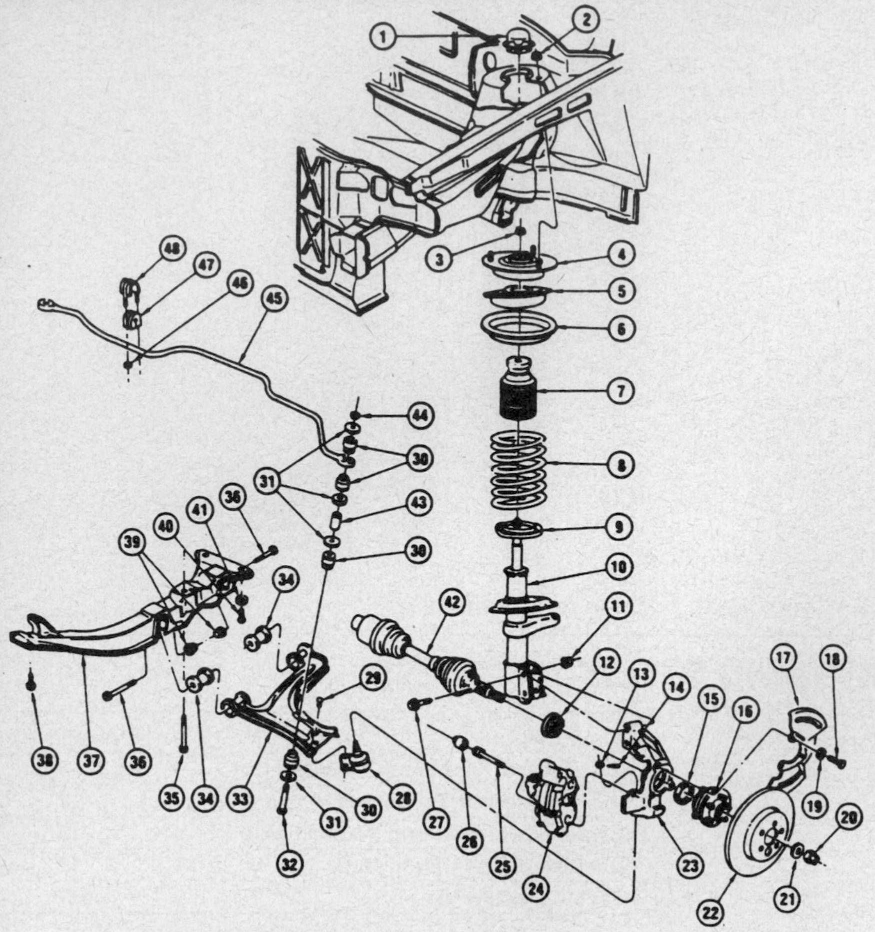

1. COVER
2. NUT
3. NUT
4. MOUNT
5. SEAT
6. INSULATOR
7. BUMPER
8. SPRING
9. INSULATOR
10. STRUT
11. NUT
12. SEAL
13. NUT
14. PIN
15. SEAL
16. HUB
17. SHIELD
18. BOLT
19. WASHER
20. NUT
21. WASHER
22. ROTOR
23. KNUCKLE
24. CALIPER
25. BOLT
26. COVER
27. BOLT
28. BALL JOINT
29. RIVET
30. GROMMET
31. WASHER
32. BOLT
33. ARM
34. BUSHING
35. BOLT
36. BOLT
37. SUPPORT
38. BOLT
39. NUT
40. BOLT
41. WASHER
42. AXLE
43. SPACER
44. NUT
45. SHAFT
46. NUT
47. INSULATOR
48. CLAMP

GC2029100137000X

Fig. 1 Exploded view of front suspension

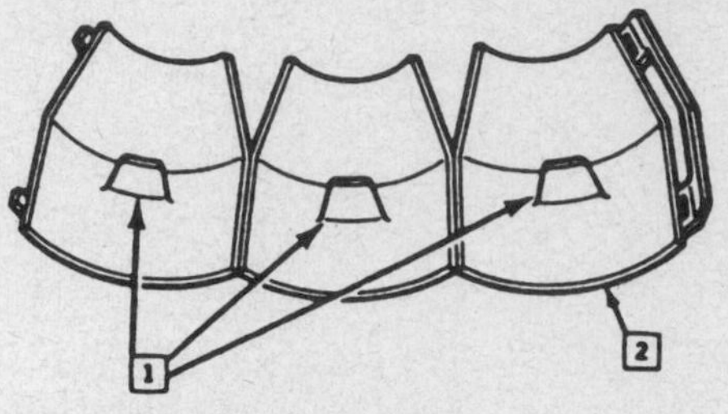

1 REMOVE TABS
2 J 34754 DRIVE AXLE SEAL PROTECTOR

GC2029100138000X

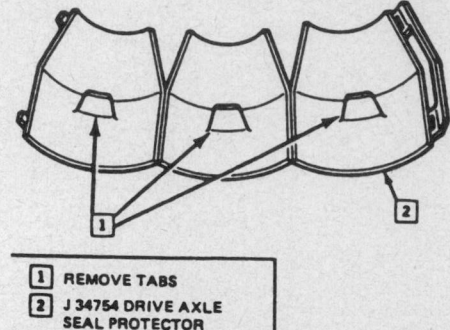

Fig. 2 Modified outer seal protector

1. DRIFT PUNCH
2. 6 POINT DEEP WELL SOCKET

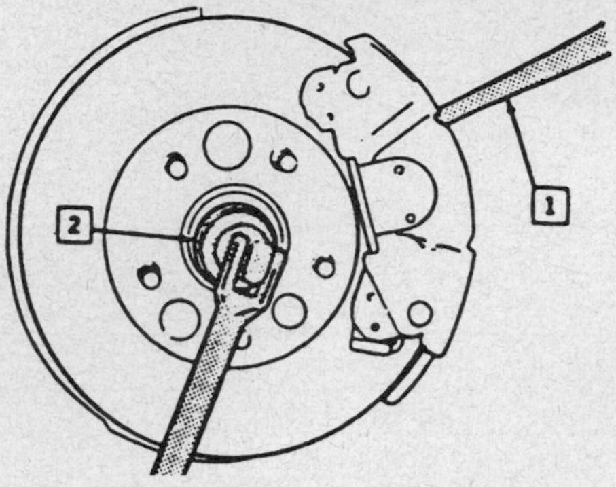

GC2029100139000X

Fig. 3 Shaft nut replacement

3. Insert a drift punch through the rotor, **Fig. 3,** then remove axle shaft nut and washer.
4. Remove ball joint, then using tool No. J-28733-A or equivalent, disengage axle from hub and bearing assembly.
5. **On all models,** move axle shaft inward, then remove caliper attaching bolts and support caliper.
6. Remove brake rotor, then hub and bearing assembly attaching bolts.
7. Remove hub and bearing assembly.

INSTALLATION

1. Install hub and bearing assembly, tighten attaching bolts to specification.
2. Install hub and bearing seal, then the brake rotor.
3. Install caliper, tighten attaching bolts to specification.
4. Move axle shaft outward, then insert drift punch through rotor, **Fig. 3.**
5. Install washer and new shaft nut, tighten shaft nut to specification.
6. Install ball joint, then remove drift punch and seal protector.
7. Install tire and wheel assembly, then lower vehicle.

BALL JOINT INSPECTION

1. Raise and support vehicle so that suspension is allowed to hang free.
2. Grasp wheel and tire assembly at top and bottom, then rock top of wheel and tire assembly inward and outward.
3. While rocking wheel and tire assembly, observe movement between steering knuckle and control arm. If any horizontal movement is present, replace ball joint.
4. If ball joint is disconnected from steering knuckle, use finger to try to twist ball joint in its socket. If ball joint can be twisted in its socket, replace ball joint.

BALL JOINT

REPLACE

1. Raise and support vehicle, then remove wheel and tire.
2. Install modified tool No. J 34754 or equivalent, then remove ball joint attaching cotter pin.
3. Remove ball joint stud retaining nut, then, using tool No. J-38892, or equivalent, separate ball joint from steering knuckle.
4. Using a 1/8 inch drill, drill pilot holes completely through the rivets. Using a 1/2 inch drill, drill final holes through rivets to ensure fitting of new ball joint.
5. Loosen stabilizer shaft assembly bushing attaching nut.
6. Remove ball joint from steering knuckle and control arm.
7. Assemble new ball joint to lower control arm with bolts provided in service package, **Fig. 4.** Tighten bolts to specification.
8. Insert ball joint stud into steering knuckle and tighten nut to specifications.
9. Install wheel and tire.

STRUT

REPLACE

1. Raise hood and remove strut protective cap and three strut to body attaching nuts.

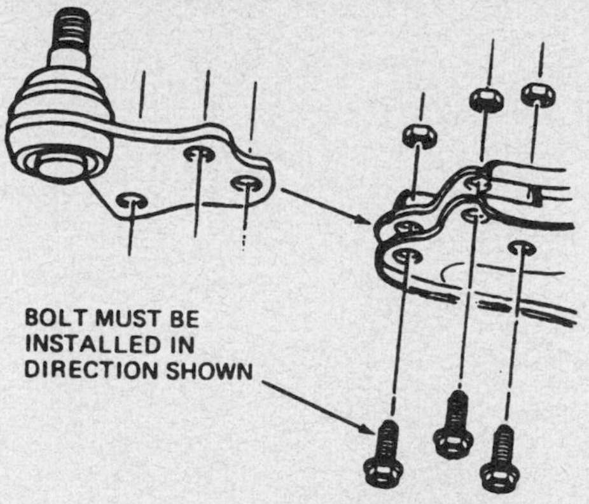
BOLT MUST BE
INSTALLED IN
DIRECTION SHOWN
GC2029100140000X

Fig. 4 Lower ball joint to lower control arm assembly

2. Raise and support vehicle, support suspension using suitable jack stands.
3. Remove wheel and tire assembly, then install modified inner drive joint boot protector tool No. J-34754.
4. Using tool J-24319, disconnect tie rod from strut assembly.
5. Remove strut to steering knuckle attaching bolts, **Fig. 5**, then remove strut from vehicle.
6. Reverse procedure to install.

STRUT SERVICE

DISASSEMBLE

1. Position strut compressor tool No. J-34013 in holding fixture tool No. J-3289-20, or equivalents.
2. Position strut in strut compressor, then compress strut approximately ½ of its height. Use care not to bottom spring or damper rod.
3. Remove nut from strut dampener shaft, then position guide rod J-34013-27 on dampener shaft. Use guide rod J-34013-27 to position dampener shaft down through bearing cap while compressing coil spring.
4. Remove components from coil strut unit.

ASSEMBLE

1. Position bearing cap on strut compressor.
2. Position strut to strut compressor and install compressor bottom locking pin.
3. Extend dampener shaft and install clamp tool No. J-34013-20 or equivalent, to hold shaft in position, **Fig. 6.**
4. Position spring over dampener, then position strut to strut compressor upper locking pin hole and install pin.
5. Install upper insulator, shield, bumper and upper spring seat. The flat on the upper spring seat should face in the same direction as the centerline of the strut assembly spindle, **Fig. 6.**
6. Install guide rod J-34013-27 onto dampener shaft, the compress strut unit until dampener shaft threads are visible. Remove guide rod and install retaining nut.

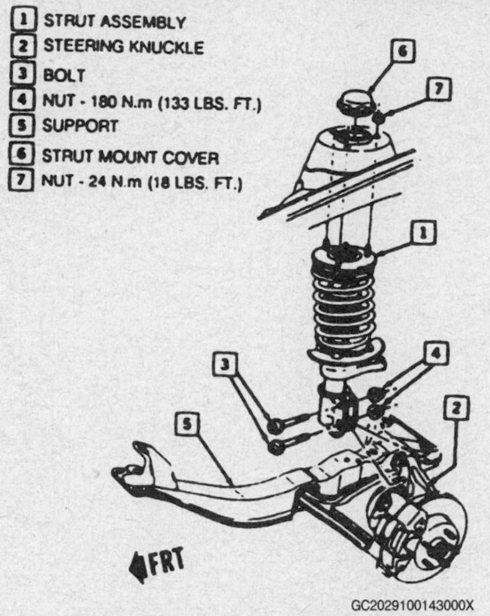
1 STRUT ASSEMBLY
2 STEERING KNUCKLE
3 BOLT
4 NUT - 180 N.m (133 LBS. FT.)
5 SUPPORT
6 STRUT MOUNT COVER
7 NUT - 24 N.m (18 LBS. FT.)
FRT
GC2029100143000X

Fig. 5 Strut assembly installation

7. While holding dampener shaft in position with a suitable wrench, tighten retaining nut to specification. After tightening nut, remove clamp from dampener shaft clamp J-34013-20.

CONTROL ARM

REPLACE

1. Raise and support vehicle, then remove wheel and tire.
2. Disconnect stabilizer bar at lower control arm and control arm support.
3. Install modified seal protector tool No. J 34754 or equivalent.
4. Using tool No. No. J 38892, or equivalents, separate ball joint from steering knuckle.
5. Remove control arm support to chassis retaining bolts and remove control arm support and control arm as an assembly.
6. Separate control arm from support, then using tool Nos. J-29792-1 and J-29792-2 or equivalent, remove bushings from control arm.
7. Lubricate new bushings and install into control arm using tool Nos. J-29792-1, J-29792-2 and J-29792-3 or equivalent.
8. Attach lower control arm to control arm support. **Torque** pivot bolts to 61 ft. lbs.
9. Install control arm support to chassis. Refer to **Fig. 7,** for attaching bolt torques.
10. Reverse procedure to complete installation. Check toe setting and adjust as required.

STEERING KNUCKLE

REPLACE

1. Raise and support vehicle, then remove wheel and tire.
2. Remove front hub and bearing as outlined under "Wheel Bearing, Replace" procedure.
3. Using tool No. J-38892, or equivalent, separate ball joint from steering knuckle.

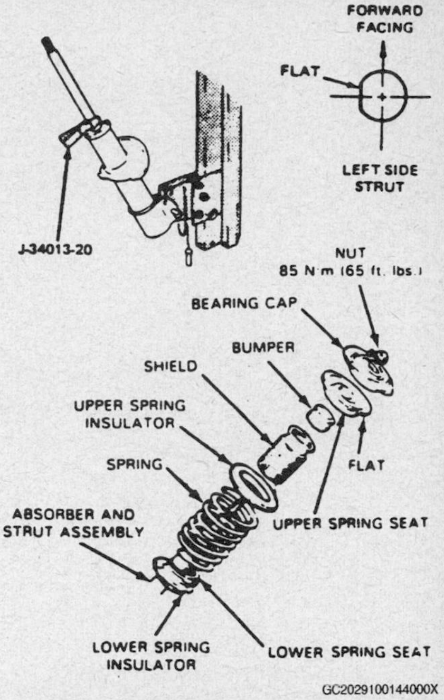
FORWARD
FACING
FLAT
LEFT SIDE
STRUT
J-34013-20
NUT
85 N·m (65 ft. lbs.)
BEARING CAP
BUMPER
SHIELD
UPPER SPRING
INSULATOR
SPRING
FLAT
ABSORBER AND
STRUT ASSEMBLY
UPPER SPRING SEAT
LOWER SPRING
INSULATOR
LOWER SPRING SEAT
GC2029100144000X

Fig. 6 Strut unit assembling

4. Remove strut to steering knuckle attaching bolts, then disconnect strut from steering knuckle.
5. Assemble strut to new steering knuckle and install attaching bolts finger tight.
6. Insert ball joint stud into steering knuckle and tighten stud nut to specification.
7. Tighten strut to steering knuckle bolts to specification.
8. Reverse removal procedure to complete installation.

STABILIZER BAR

REPLACE

1. Raise and support vehicle, allowing control arms to hang freely.
2. Remove left front wheel and tire assembly.
3. Disconnect stabilizer bar at control arms and control arm supports.
4. Disconnect stabilizer bar from control arms, **Fig. 8.**
5. Loosen front and remove rear and center bolts from suspension support assembly. Lower support enough to allow stabilizer bar removal.
6. Remove stabilizer bar with insulators.
7. Reverse procedure to install. Tighten suspension support assembly in a manner which will allow front suspension to hang free.

POWER STEERING GEAR

REPLACE

1. Disconnect battery ground cable.
2. Remove left hand sound insulator.
3. From under instrument panel, pull downward on steering column seal, then remove upper pinch bolt from flexible coupling.
4. Disconnect pressure line from steer-

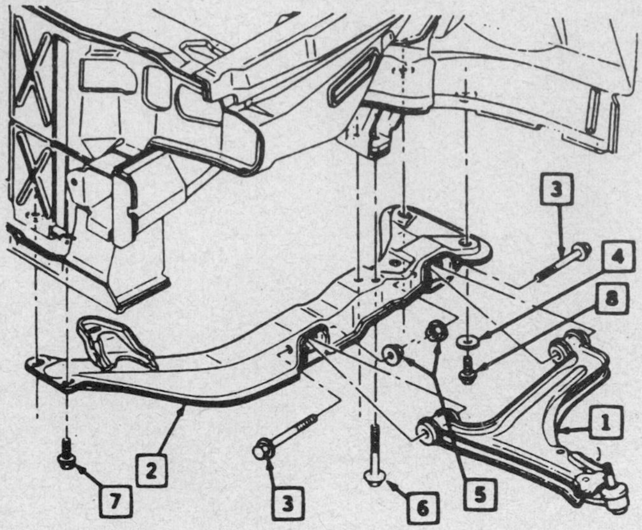
3
4
8
1
2
7
3
6
5

1. CONTROL ARM
2. SUSPENSION SUPPORT
3. BOLT – 83 N·m (61 LBS. FT.)
4. WASHER
5. NUT
6. BOLT – 90 N·m (66 LBS. FT.) TIGHTEN FIRST
7. BOLT – 88 N·m (65 LBS. FT.) TIGHTEN SECOND
8. BOLT – 88 N·m (65 LBS. FT.) TIGHTEN THIRD

GC2029100141000X

Fig. 7 Lower control arm replacement

1
10
2
7
8
9
7
8
11
3
5
7
8
6

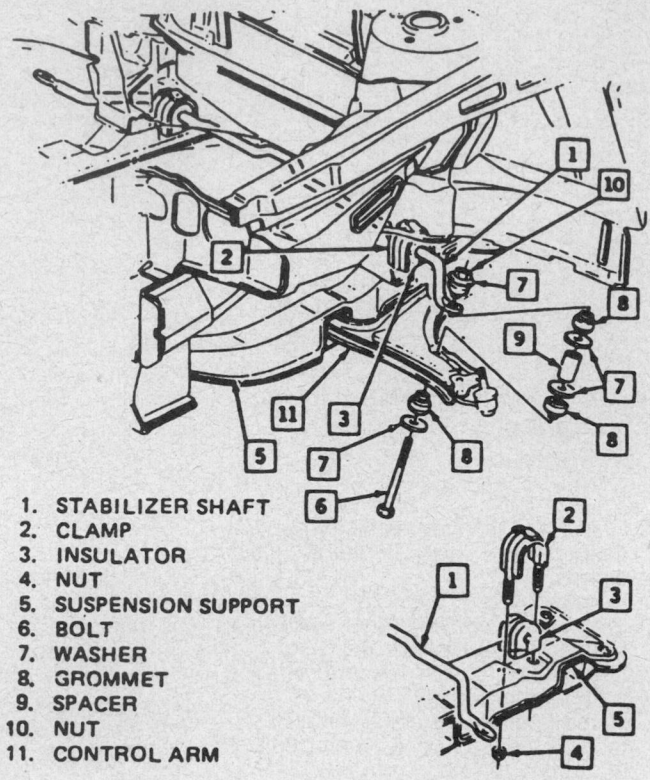

1. STABILIZER SHAFT
2. CLAMP
3. INSULATOR
4. NUT
5. SUSPENSION SUPPORT
6. BOLT
7. WASHER
8. GROMMET
9. SPACER
10. NUT
11. CONTROL ARM

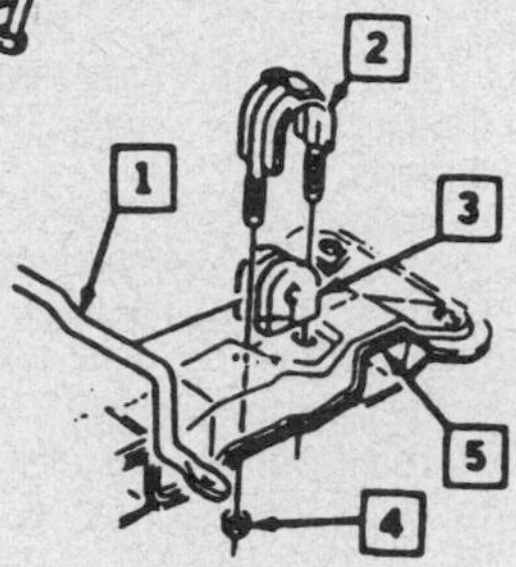
2
1
3
5
4

GC2029100142000X

Fig. 8 Stabilizer bar installation

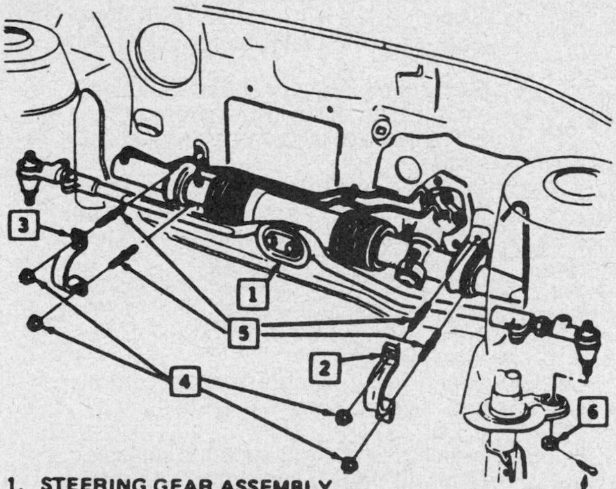
3
1
5
2
4
6
7

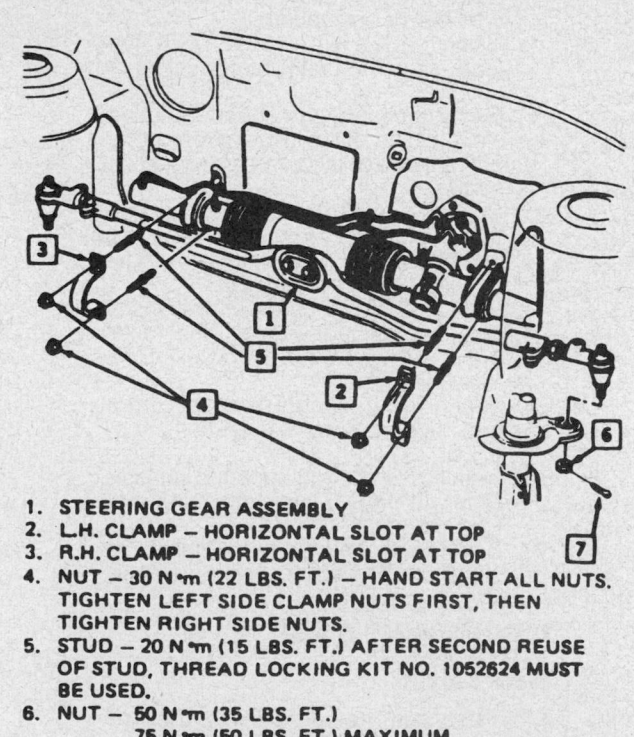

1. STEERING GEAR ASSEMBLY
2. L.H. CLAMP – HORIZONTAL SLOT AT TOP
3. R.H. CLAMP – HORIZONTAL SLOT AT TOP
4. NUT – 30 N·m (22 LBS. FT.) – HAND START ALL NUTS. TIGHTEN LEFT SIDE CLAMP NUTS FIRST, THEN TIGHTEN RIGHT SIDE NUTS.
5. STUD – 20 N·m (15 LBS. FT.) AFTER SECOND REUSE OF STUD, THREAD LOCKING KIT NO. 1052624 MUST BE USED.
6. NUT – 50 N·m (35 LBS. FT.) 75 N·m (50 LBS. FT.) MAXIMUM TO INSTALL COTTER PIN.
7. COTTER PIN

GC6039100047000X

Fig. 9 Rack & pinion steering gear removal

ing gear and remove screw attaching line bracket to cowl.
5. Raise and support front of vehicle, then remove both front wheel and tire assemblies.
6. Disconnect tie rods from struts using tool No. J-24319-01, then lower vehicle.
7. Remove steering gear mounting clamps, **Fig. 9.**
8. Move steering gear slightly forward, then disconnect return line from gear and drain power steering fluid.
9. Remove lower pinch bolt from flexible coupling, then detach coupling from steering gear stub shaft and remove dash seal.
10. Raise and support front of vehicle, then remove splash shield from left inner fender.
11. Place steering knuckle and hub assembly into the full left turn position, then remove steering gear through access hole in left hand inner fender.
12. Reverse procedure to install, noting the following:
    a. If steering gear mounting clamps have backed out during removal, install double nuts on stud and **Torque** to 22 ft. lbs.
    b. **Torque** coupling to stub shaft pinch bolt to 30 ft. lbs.
    c. Tighten pressure and return line fittings to specifications.

POWER STEERING PUMP

REPLACE

1. Disconnect battery ground cable.
2. Remove serpentine belt.
3. Remove power steering pump attaching pressure lines.
4. Remove power steering pump attaching bolts.
5. Remove pump assembly, then transfer power steering pump pulley.
6. Reverse to install. Tighten attaching bolts to specifications.

MANUAL STEERING GEAR

REPLACE

1. Disconnect battery ground cable.
2. Remove left hand sound insulator.
3. From under instrument panel, pull downward on steering column seal, then remove upper pinch bolt from flexible coupling.
4. Raise and support front of vehicle, then remove both front wheel and tire assemblies.
5. Disconnect tie rods from struts using tool No. J-24319-01, then lower vehicle.
6. Remove steering gear mounting clamps, **Fig. 9.**
7. Move steering gear assembly slightly forward, then remove lower pinch bolt from flexible coupling and detach coupling from steering gear stub shaft.
8. Remove dash panel seal from steering gear.
9. Raise and support front of vehicle, then remove splash shield from left inner fender.
10. Place left hand knuckle and hub assembly in the full left turn position, then remove steering gear through access hole in left hand inner fender.
11. Reverse procedure to install. Tighten attaching nuts, bolts and screws to specifications.

TIGHTENING SPECIFICATIONS

Component	Torque/Ft. Lbs.
Ball Joint To Knuckle	41-50
Caliper Bolts	38
Control Arm Pivot Bolt	61
Hub & Bearing Assembly	70
Hub Nut	185
Inner Tie Rod End Bolts	65
Power Coupling To Steering Column	30
Power Coupling To Stub Shaft	30
Power Rack & Pinion Mounts	22
Power Steering Return Lines	19
Stabilizer Shaft To Control Arm	13
Stabilizer To Support Assembly	16
Steering Knuckle To Strut Assembly	133
Strut Assembly To Body	18
Strut Cartridge Retaining Nut	65
Suspension Support Assembly	①
Tie Rod Pinch Bolts	41
Tie Rod To Steering Knuckle	37
Tie Rod To Strut	37
Wheel Lug Nuts	100

①—Torque suspension support assembly center bolts to 66 ft. lbs.; then front bolts to 65 ft. lbs.; then rear bolts to 65 ft. lbs.

Wheel Alignment

INDEX

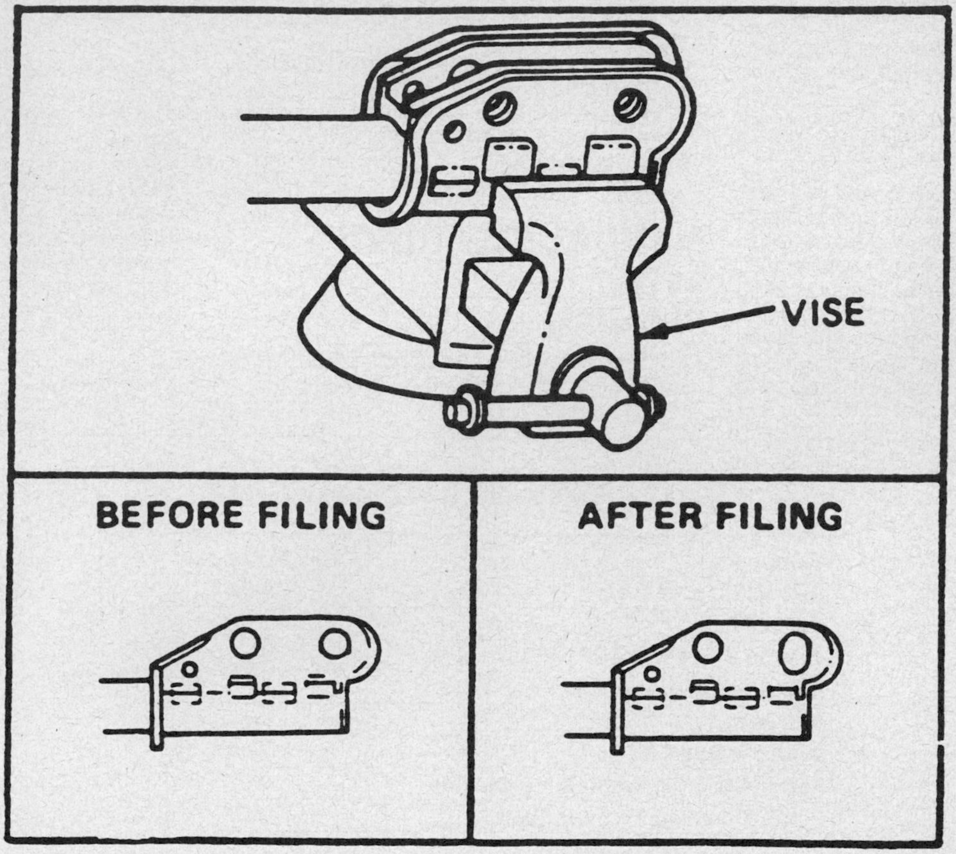

VISE
BEFORE FILING
AFTER FILING
GC2049100070000X

Fig. 1 Strut bracket modification to adjust camber

FRONT WHEEL ALIGNMENT

CASTER

Caster is not adjustable. If caster angle is not within specifications, inspect for suspension support misalignment or front suspension damage.

CAMBER

Toe setting is the only adjustment normally required. However, in special circumstances, such as damage due to road hazard or collision, camber may be adjusted by modifying the strut assembly.

1. Secure bottom of strut assembly in a suitable vise.
2. Enlarge bottom holes in outer flanges with a round file until holes in outer flanges match slots in inner flanges, **Fig. 1.**
3. Connect strut to steering knuckle and install bolts finger tight.
4. Grasp top of tire firmly, then move tire inboard or outboard until correct camber reading is obtained. Tighten retaining bolts enough to secure camber setting.
5. Remove wheel and tire and tighten strut to steering knuckle retaining bolts. **Torque** strut to steering knuckle attaching bolt to 133 ft. lbs.

TOE

Toe-out is controlled by tie rod position. Adjustment is made by loosening the clamp bolts at the steering knuckle end of the tie rods and rotating the rods to obtain proper toe setting, **Fig. 2.** After correct toe setting is obtained, tighten clamp bolts. **Torque** clamp bolts to 41 ft. lbs.

VEHICLE RIDE HEIGHT

Refer to **Fig. 3,** for ride height measurements and **Fig. 4,** for specifications. When checking ride height measurements, fuel tank should be full, tires at should be correct pressure, front seat should be rearward position, truck should be empty except for spare tire and jack and vehicle should be on level ground. If fuel tank is not full, add weight to trunk to compensate for amount fuel vehicle is below the full level.

Prior to checking ride height, lift front bumper upward approximately 1.5 inches and gently release (3 times), then check front ride height. Push front bumper downward approximately 1.5 inches and gently release (3 times), then recheck front ride height. Average of both readings to determine vehicle ride height. Check rear ride height in same manner, lifting and pushing rear bumper.

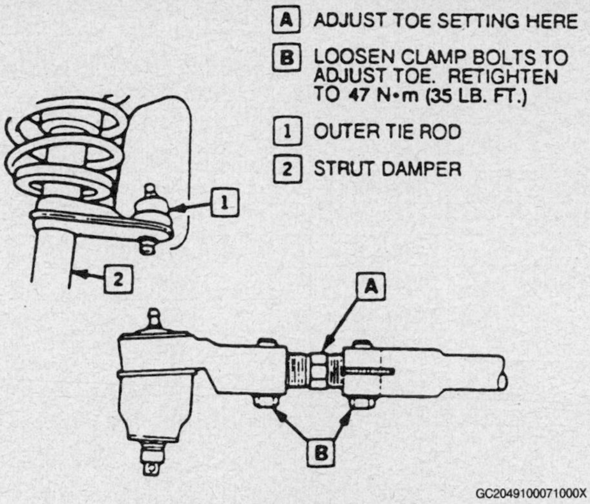
A ADJUST TOE SETTING HERE
B LOOSEN CLAMP BOLTS TO ADJUST TOE. RETIGHTEN TO 47 N•m (35 LB. FT.)
1 OUTER TIE ROD
2 STRUT DAMPER
GC2049100071000X

Fig. 2 Toe adjustment

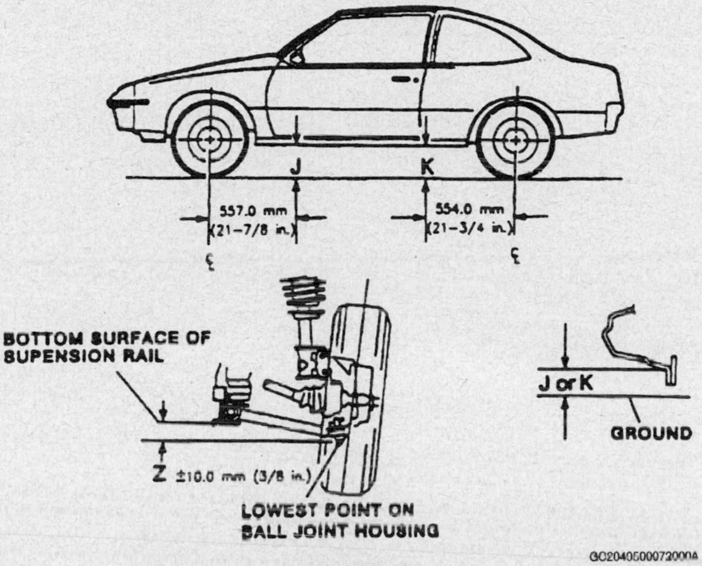
J
K
557.0 mm (21-7/8 in.)
554.0 mm (21-3/4 in.)
BOTTOM SURFACE OF SUPENSION RAIL
Z ±10.0 mm (3/8 in.)
LOWEST POINT ON BALL JOINT HOUSING
J or K
GROUND

Fig. 3 Vehicle ride height measurement locations. 1992-94

Year	Model	Tire Size	Engine Liter/CID	Ride Height Measurements In Inches ①		
				Dimension Z	Dimension J	Dimension K
1992-94	Cavalier Station Wagon	185/75R x 14	2.2L/4-134	3.62	9.53	9.65
		195/70R x 14	2.2L/4-134	3.78	9.53	9.65
		195/70R x 14	3.1L/V6-192	3.82	9.53	9.65
	Cavalier Coupe & Sedan	185/75R x 14	2.2L/4-134	3.42	9.26	9.13
		195/70R x 14	2.2L/4-134	3.58	9.26	9.13
		195/70R x 14	3.1L/V6-192	3.62	9.26	9.13
	Cavalier Z34	205/60R x 15	3.1L/V6-192	3.58	9.26	9.13
	Sunbird LE Coupe & Sedan, Sunbird SE Coupe	185/75R x 14	2.0L/4-121	3.42	9.26	9.13
		195/70R x 14	2.0L/4-121	3.58	9.26	9.13
		195/70R x 14	3.1L/V6-192	3.62	9.26	9.13
	Sunbird LE Convertible	185/75R x 14	2.0L/4-121	3.46	9.26	9.13
		195/70R x 14	2.0L/4-121	3.62	9.26	9.13
		195/70R x 14	3.1L/V6-192	3.66	9.26	9.13
	Sunbird GT	215/60R x 14	3.1L/V6-192	3.86	9.26	9.13
		205/60R x 15	3.1L/V6-192	3.58	9.26	9.13

Fig. 4 Vehicle ride height specifications (Part 1 of 2)

Year	Model	Tire Size	Engine Liter/CID	Ride Height Measurements In Inches ①		
				Dimension Z	Dimension J	Dimension K
1992-94	Cavalier Station Wagon	185/75R x 14	2.2L/4-134	9/32	9.53	9.65
		195/70R x 14	2.2L/4-134	7/16	9.53	9.65
		195/70R x 14	3.1L/V6-192	31/64	9.53	9.65
	Cavalier Convertible	185/75R x 14	All	5/64	9.26	9.13
	Cavalier Coupe & Sedan	195/70R x 14	All	5/64	9.26	9.13
	Cavalier Z34	205/60R x 15	3.1L/V6-192	15/64	9.26	9.13
	Sunbird Except GT Series	185/75R x 14	All	5/64	9.26	9.13
		195/70R x 14	All	13/64	9.26	9.13
		195/65R x 15	All	9/32	9.26	9.13
	Sunbird GT	205/60R x 15	All	15/64	9.26	9.13
1995	Cavalier	195/70R x 14	All	23/64	9.17	9.45
	Sunfire	195/70R x 14	All	25/64	9.17	9.45
		195/70R x 14	All	25/64	9.17	9.45
		195/65R x 15	All	5/32	9.17	9.45
		205/55R x 16	All	7/64	9.17	9.45
		205/55R x 15	All	5/32	9.17	9.45

① —Maximum variation side to side and front to rear is 3/4 inch.

Fig. 4 Vehicle ride height specifications (Part 2 of 2)

CHEVROLET BERETTA & CORSICA (L Cars)

NOTE: Refer To The Rear Of This Manual For Vehicle Manufacturer's Special Service Tool Suppliers.

INDEX OF SERVICE OPERATIONS

NOTE: For Service Operations Not Listed Below, Refer To The Table Of Contents In The Front Of This Manual.

Continued

INDEX OF SERVICE OPERATIONS—CONTINUED

Specifications

GENERAL ENGINE SPECIFICATIONS

Year	Engine		Fuel System	Bore & Stroke	Compression Ratio	Net H.P. @ RPM	Maximum Torque Ft. Lbs. @ RPM	Normal Oil Pressure, psi
	Liter/CID	VIN Code②						
1992-93	2.2L/4-134	4	MPFI	3.50 x 3.46	8.85	—	—	63-77③
	2.3L/4-138	A	MPFI	3.62 x 3.35	10.0	180 @ 6200	160 @ 5000	15-30
	3.1L/V6-192	T	MPFI	3.50 x 3.31	8.8	140 @ 4200	185 @ 3600	15④
1994	2.2L/4-134	4	MPFI	3.50 x 3.46	9.0	120 @ 5200	130 @ 4000	63-77③
	2.3L/4-138	A	MPFI	3.63 x 3.35	10.0	170 @ 6200	150 @ 5200	30①
	3.1L/V6-192	T	MPFI	3.50 x 3.31	9.6	160 @ 5200	185 @ 4000	15④
1995	2.2L/4-134	4	MPFI	3.50 x 3.46	9.0	120 @ 5200	130 @ 4000	63-77③
	3.1L/V6-192	T	MPFI	3.50 x 3.31	9.5	160 @ 5200	185 @ 4000	15④

CID-cubic inch displacement.
①—At 2000 RPM.
②—The eighth digit denotes engine code.
③—At 1200 RPM.
④—At 1100 RPM.

TUNE UP SPECIFICATIONS

Year & Engine/ V.I.N. Code①	Spark Plug Gap	Ignition Timing BTDC				Curb Idle Speed③		Fast Idle Speed		Fuel Pump, psi
		Firing Order Fig. ②	Man. Trans.	Auto. Trans.	Mark Fig.	Man. Trans.	Auto. Trans.	Man. Trans.	Auto Trans.	
1992-93										
2.2L/4-134/4	.035	④	③	③	⑥	⑦	⑦	⑦	⑦	43–47
2.3L/4-138/A	.035	C	⑤	—	⑥	⑦	—	⑦	—	51⑧
3.1L/V6-192/T	.045	⑨	③	③	⑥	⑦	⑦	⑦	⑦	40.5–47⑧
1994										
2.2L/4-134/4	.035	④	③	③	⑥	⑦	⑦	⑦	⑦	43–44
2.3L/4-138/A	.035	C	⑤	—	⑥	⑦	—	⑦	—	43
3.1L/V6-192/T	.045	⑨	③	③	⑥	⑦	⑦	⑦	⑦	—
1995										
2.2L/4-134/4	.035	④	③	③	⑥	⑦	⑦	⑦	⑦	43–44
3.1L/V6-192/T	.045	⑨	③	③	⑥	⑦	⑦	⑦	⑦	41–47

BTDC—Before Top Dead Center
①—The eighth digit of Vehicle Identification Number (V.I.N.) denotes engine code.
②—Before removing wires from distributor cap, determine location of No. 1 wire in cap, as distributor position may have been altered from that shown at the end of this chart.
③—Not adjustable.
④—Cylinder numbering front to rear, 1, 2, 3, 4. Firing order 1-3-4-2. Refer to A for spark plug wire connections at coil unit.
⑤—Computer controlled, no adjustment.
⑥—Equipped w/crankshaft position sensor.
⑦—Idle speeds are controlled by the idle air control assembly.
⑧—With shop towel wrapped around fuel pressure valve to prevent fuel spillage, connect a suitable fuel pressure gauge to fuel pressure valve. Check fuel pressure with ignition switch On, engine not running.
⑨—Cylinder numbering left to right as viewed from front of vehicle, front bank 2, 4, 6; rear bank 1, 3, 5. Firing order, 1-2-3-4-5-6. Refer to B for spark plug wire connections at coil unit.

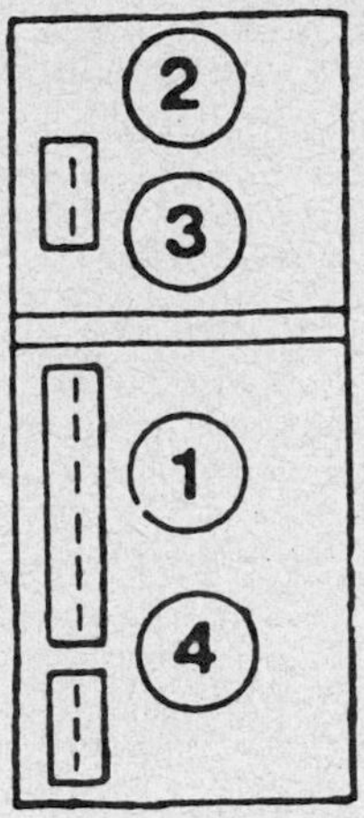
2
3
1
4

GC1139100142000X

Fig. A

1 4 6 3 2 5

GC1139100143000X

Fig. B

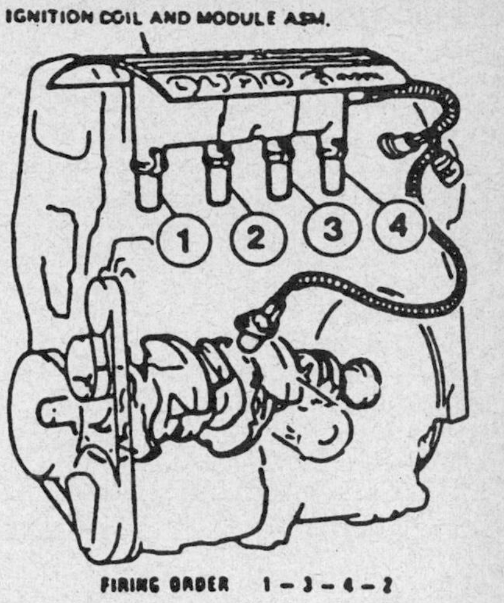
IGNITION COIL AND MODULE ASM.
1 2 3 4
FIRING ORDER 1-3-4-2

GC1139100144000X

Fig. C

FRONT WHEEL ALIGNMENT SPECIFICATIONS

Year	Model	Caster Angle, degrees		Camber Angle, degrees				Toe, degrees
				Limits		Desired		
		Limits	Desired	Left	Right	Left	Right	
1992	①	+.4 to +1.9	+1.15	+.6 to +.8	+.6 to +.8	+.7	+.7	0
	②	+.4 to +1.9	+1.15	-.8 to +.4	-.8 to +.4	-.2	-.2	0
1993–95	①	+.2 to +2.2	+1.2	-.7 to +.7	-.7 to +.7	0	0	0
	②	+.2 to +2.2	+1.2	-.85 to +.55	-.85 to +.55	-.15	-.15	0

①—Except GTZ.
②—GTZ.

REAR WHEEL ALIGNMENT SPECIFICATIONS

Year	Model	Camber Angle, Degrees				Toe, Degrees①
		Limits		Desired		
		Left	Right	Left①	Right①	
1992	Beretta	-.89 to +.39①	-.89 to + .39①	-.25	-.25	.20
	Corsica	-.82 to +.32①	-.82 to + .32	-.25	-.25	.25
1993–95	All	-.85 to +.35①	-.85 to + .35①	-.25	-.25	0

①—Not adjustable.

COOLING SYSTEM & CAPACITY DATA

Year	Model or Engine/ VIN	Coolant Capacity, Qts.		Radiator Cap Relief Pressure, psi	Thermo. Opening Temp.°F	Fuel Tank Gals.	Engine Oil Refill Qts. ④	Transaxle Oil	
		Less A/C	With A/C					Manual Transaxle Pts.	Auto. Transaxle Qts. ①
1992-93	2.2L/4-134/4	8.7	8.7	15	195	15.6	4	4.2	③
	2.3L/4-138/A	9.2	9.2	15	192	15.6	4	4.2	③
	3.1L/V6-192/T	13.1	13.1	15	195	15.6	4	4.2	②
1994	2.2L/4-134/4	9.2	9.2	15	195	15.2	4	4.2	③
	2.3L/4-138/A	10.4	10.4	15	192	15.2	4	4.2	③
	3.1L/V6-192/T	12.7	12.7	15	195	15.2	4	4.2	②

COOLING SYSTEM & CAPACITY DATA-Continued

Year	Model or Engine/ VIN	Coolant Capacity, Qts. Less A/C	Coolant Capacity, Qts. With A/C	Radiator Cap Relief Pressure, psi	Thermo. Opening Temp.°F	Fuel Tank Gals.	Engine Oil Refill Qts. ④	Transaxle Oil Manual Transaxle Pts.	Transaxle Oil Auto. Transaxle Qts. ①
1995	2.2L/4-134/4	9.2	9.2	15	195	15.2	4	4.2	③
	3.1L/V6-192/T	12.7	12.7	15	195	15.2	4	4.2	③

①—Approximate, make final check with dipstick.
②—With heavy duty radiator, 9.4 qts.
③—Oil pan only, 4 qts. After overhaul, less torque converter drain, 6 qts.; with torque converter drain, 9 qts.
④—When changing engine oil filter additional oil may be required.

LUBRICANT DATA

Model	Lubricant Type: Transaxle, Manual	Lubricant Type: Transaxle, Automatic	Power Steering	Brake System
All	Manual Transmission Fluid①	Dexron IIE	Power Steering Fluid②	DOT 3

①—GM part No. 12345349 or equivalent.
②—Meeting requirements of GM 9985010.

Electrical

NOTE: On Air Bag Equipped Models, Refer To "Air Bag System Precautions" Located In The Front Of This Manual For System Disarming & Arming Procedures.

INDEX

PRECAUTIONS

AIR BAG SYSTEMS

Refer to "Air Bag System Precautions" in the front of this manual for system disarming and arming procedures.

FUSE PANEL & FLASHER LOCATION

The fuse panel is located behind the lefthand side of the instrument panel, near the shroud.

The hazard warning flasher is located behind the lefthand side of the instrument panel in the convenience center. The turn signal flasher is located next to the convenience center.

RELAY CENTER LOCATION

The relay center is located at the righthand rear side of the engine compartment, behind the strut tower.

STARTER

REPLACE

2.2L/4-134 ENGINE

1. Disconnect battery ground cable.
2. Raise and support front of vehicle.
3. Disconnect solenoid wires and battery cable at starter motor.
4. Disconnect wiring clamp at starter support bracket, then remove the support bracket to engine attaching bolt.
5. Remove starter attaching bolts, then carefully lower starter. Note position of shims, if used.
6. Reverse procedure to install.

2.3L/4-138 ENGINE

1. Disconnect battery ground cable, then remove serpentine drive belt.
2. Remove coolant reservoir.
3. Disconnect A/C line rail clip.
4. Remove alternator, then the oil fill tube and dipstick assembly.
5. Remove alternator bracket, then the air cleaner assembly.
6. Place a suitable drain pan under engine oil pan, then remove oil filter.

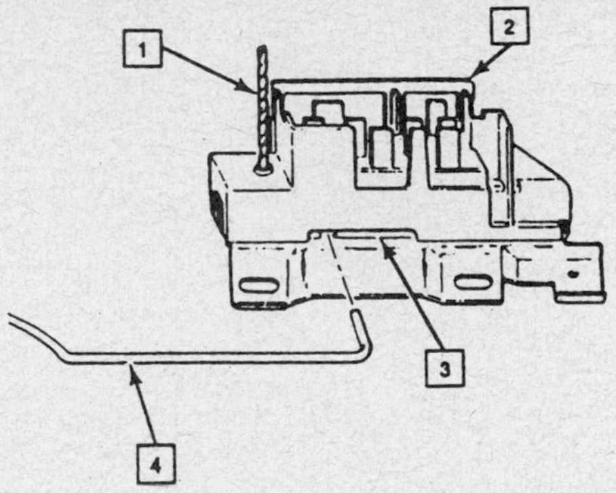
1
2
3
4

1 3/32" INCH DRILL BIT
2 IGNITION SWITCH ASSEMBLY
3 SWITCH SLIDER
4 IGNITION SWITCH ROD

GC9049100107000X

Fig. 1 Ignition switch adjustment

7. Remove starter as follows:
   a. Remove upper and lower starter mounting bolts.
   b. Position starter for access to solenoid wiring, then disconnect wiring.
   c. Remove starter from near front of engine between intake manifold and engine block.
8. Reverse procedure to install.

3.1L/V6-192 ENGINE

1. Remove air cleaner assembly.
2. Disconnect battery ground cable.
3. Raise and support front of vehicle.
4. **On models with engine oil cooler,** remove oil filter, then position oil cooler hose out of the way.
5. **On all models,** remove A/C compressor brace attaching nuts, then the starter support brace-to-engine attaching nut.
6. Remove flywheel inspection cover attaching bolts, then the cover.
7. Remove starter attaching bolts, then carefully lower starter. Note position of shims, if used.
8. Disconnect starter wiring at solenoid.
9. Reverse procedure to install. On models with engine oil cooler, check engine oil level after installing filter.

IGNITION LOCK

REPLACE

1. Remove Steering wheel as outlined in "Steering wheel Replace."
2. Disconnect battery ground cable, remove coil assembly retaining clip, then coil assembly. Let coil assembly hang freely.
3. Remove wave washer, then on standard columns remove spacer shaft lock.
4. Attach tool No. J-23563-C or equivalent, compress shaft lock, then pry off retaining ring.
5. Remove shaft lock, then turn signal canceling cam assembly.
6. Remove upper bearing spring, then place turn signal to right turn position.
7. Remove multi-function lever, then hazard knob assembly.
8. **On models with tilt and cruise control,** remove signal switch arm assembly.
9. **On all models** remove turn signal switch attaching screws, then turn signal switch.
10. Remove buzzer switch assembly, then ignition lock retaining screw.
11. Place cylinder lock in "Lock" position, then remove cylinder lock.
12. Reverse procedure to install noting the following:
    a. After cylinder lock is installed place lock in "Run" position.

IGNITION SWITCH

REPLACE

1. Place ignition switch in the "Off-Lock" position.
2. Remove steering column support bracket bolts, then flexible coupling bolts.
3. Remove upper and lower steering column bolts, then lower steering column.
4. Remove electrical connectors from ignition and dimmer switch.
5. Remove hex nut from stud, dimmer switch actuator rod, then dimmer switch.
6. Remove ignition switch stud, then actuator rod.
7. Remove park lock cable from ignition switch, then ignition switch.
8. Reverse position to install noting the following:
   a. When installing ignition switch place slider in far left position and move back one detent to the right. Insert a 3/32 drill bit in adjustment hole **Fig. 1** to hold switch slider in proper position when installing ignition switch.
   b. When installing dimmer switch place and 3/32 drill bit into hole on switch to limit travel **Fig. 2**, then position switch onto column and push against dimmer switch rod to remove lash. Tighten down switch.

CLUTCH START SWITCH

REPLACE

1. **On all models,** disconnect battery ground cable.
2. Disconnect wiring connector from switch located on clutch pedal support above clutch pedal.
3. Disconnect switch link from pedal, then remove switch retaining link and switch.
4. Reverse procedure to install.

NEUTRAL SAFETY SWITCH

REPLACE

1. Disconnect battery ground cable.
2. Disconnect shift linkage from transaxle.

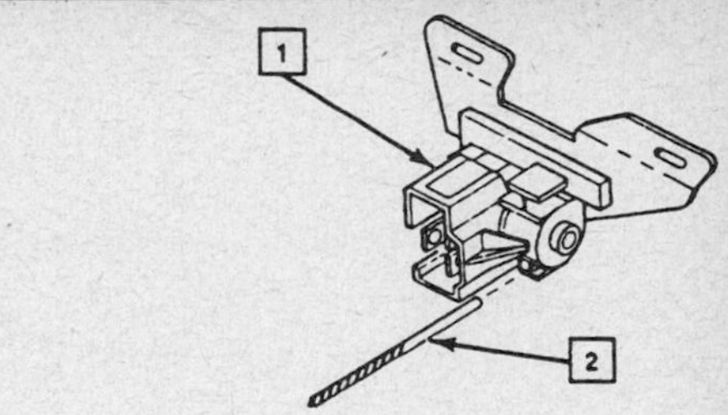
1
2

1 DIMMER SWITCH
2 3/32" INCH DRILL BIT

GC9049100108000X

Fig. 2 Dimmer switch adjustment

3. Disconnect electrical connector from neutral start switch.
4. Remove neutral start switch attaching screws, then the switch.
5. Ensure transaxle shift shaft is in Neutral position.
6. If installing new switch, align new back-up light/neutral start switch flats with flats of shift shaft, then install switch. **Torque** attaching bolts to 22 ft. lbs.
7. If used switch is being installed, proceed as follows:
   a. Align back-up light/neutral start switch flats with flats of shift shaft, then install switch. Loosely install attaching bolts.
   b. Insert 3/32 inch drill in service adjustment hole, then rotate switch until drill drops to a depth of 9/64 inch.
   c. **Torque** attaching bolts to 22 ft. lbs.
8. With either new or used switch, ensure engine will only start in Neutral and Start positions.

HEADLAMP SWITCH

REPLACE

Refer to **Figs. 3 and 4** when performing the following procedure.

1. Disconnect battery ground cable.
2. Remove instrument cluster bezel.
3. Squeeze small switch knob at side and pull straight out.
4. Insert a suitable flat blade screwdriver into slots adjacent to center of inner knob and disengage knob from switch.
5. Remove switch to bezel screws, then switch.
6. Reverse procedure to install noting the following:
   a. When positioning inner knob to switch, make certain tabs align with slots, then press to secure.
   b. Position outer knob on switch and align "D" shaped hole in knob to shaft on switch, then press to secure.

STOP LIGHT SWITCH

ADJUST

Insert stop lamp switch into tubular clip above brake pedal until switch body seats fully into clip. Pull brake pedal rearward

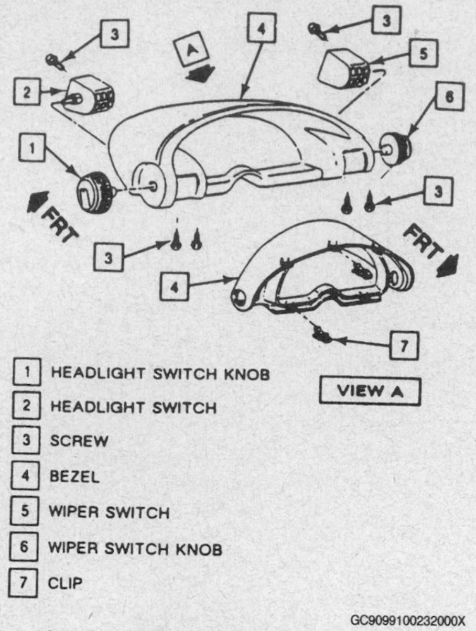
1 HEADLIGHT SWITCH KNOB
2 HEADLIGHT SWITCH
3 SCREW
4 BEZEL
5 WIPER SWITCH
6 WIPER SWITCH KNOB
7 CLIP
VIEW A
FRT
GC9099100232000X

Fig. 3 Instrument cluster bezel removal

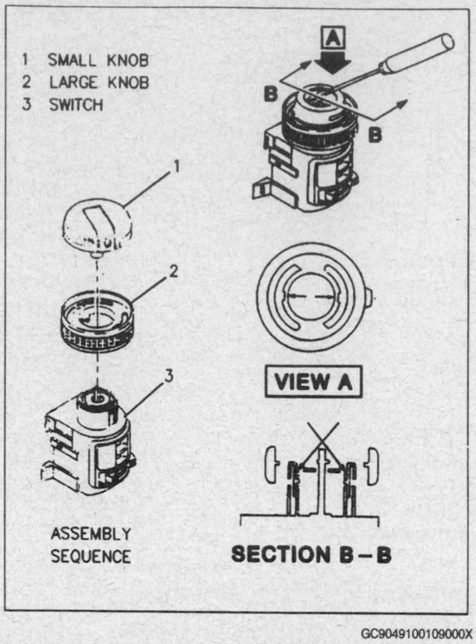
1 SMALL KNOB
2 LARGE KNOB
3 SWITCH
ASSEMBLY SEQUENCE
VIEW A
SECTION B – B
GC9049100109000X

Fig. 4 Headlamp & windshield wiper assembly switch

against internal pedal stop. The switch will be properly positioned in the tubular clip automatically. **Rotate switch 1/2 turn counterclockwise to ensure that switch does not hold brake pedal down after adjustment.**

TURN SIGNAL SWITCH

REPLACE

1. Remove Steering wheel as outlined in "Steering wheel Replace."
2. Disconnect battery ground cable, remove coil assembly retaining clip, then coil assembly. Let coil assembly hang freely.
3. Remove wave washer, then on standard columns remove spacer shaft lock.
4. Attach tool No. J-23563-C or equivalent, compress shaft lock, then pry off retaining ring.
5. Remove shaft lock, then turn signal canceling cam assembly.
6. Remove upper bearing spring, then place turn signal to right turn position.
7. Remove multi-function lever, then hazard knob assembly.
8. **On models with tilt and cruise control,** remove signal switch arm assembly.
9. **On all models** remove turn signal switch attaching screws, then turn signal switch.
10. Reverse procedure to install.

DIMMER SWITCH

REPLACE

Refer to "Ignition Switch, Replace" for dimmer switch replacement.

STEERING WHEEL

REPLACE

1. Remove four Torx screw from back of steering wheel, then connector position assurance (CPA) electrical connector from rear of inflator module.
2. Remove horn slip ring connectors, then horn ring.
3. Remove steering column locknut.
4. Using puller J 1859-03 or equivalent, remove steering wheel.
5. Reverse procedure to install. **Torque** steering wheel locknut to 31 ft. lbs.

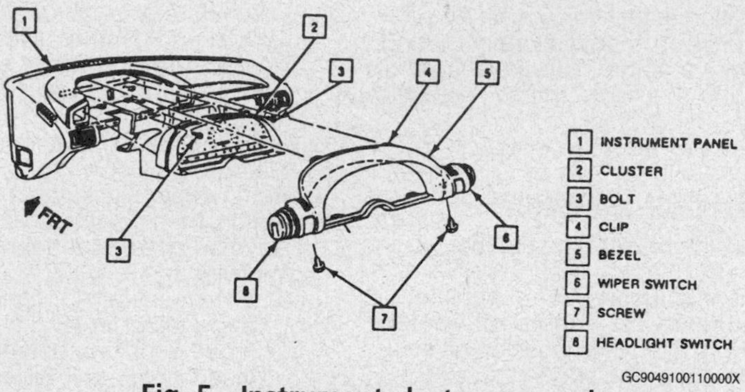
1 INSTRUMENT PANEL
2 CLUSTER
3 BOLT
4 CLIP
5 BEZEL
6 WIPER SWITCH
7 SCREW
8 HEADLIGHT SWITCH
FRT
GC9049100110000X

Fig. 5 Instrument cluster removal

INSTRUMENT CLUSTER

REPLACE

Refer to **Fig. 5** for instrument cluster replacement procedures.

RADIO

REPLACE

Refer to **Fig. 6,** for replacement of radio.

WIPER MOTOR

REPLACE

1. Disconnect battery ground cable.
2. Remove left side wiper arm using following procedure:
   a. Remove plastic cap from end of wiper arm shaft.
   b. Remove nut from end of wiper arm shaft.
   c. Using suitable tool, pry wiper arm from wiper arm shaft.
3. Remove wiper drive link from crank arm.
4. Disconnect electrical connectors and washer hoses from wiper motor.
5. Remove wiper motor attaching bolts, then remove wiper motor, guiding crank arm through drive hole.
6. Reverse procedure to install.

WIPER SWITCH

REPLACE

Refer to "Headlamp Switch, Replace" for procedure.

WIPER TRANSMISSION

REPLACE

1. Disconnect battery ground cable.
2. Remove left and right side wiper arms using following procedure:
   a. Remove plastic cap from end of wiper arm shaft.
   b. Remove nut from end of wiper arm shaft.
   c. Using suitable tool, pry wiper arm from wiper arm shaft.

3. Loosen, but do not remove, transmission drive link(s) to wiper motor crank arm attaching screws.
4. Remove air inlet screen.
5. Disconnect transmission drive link(s) from wiper motor crank arm.
6. Remove wiper transmission to body attaching bolts.
7. Remove wiper transmission by guiding it through shroud upper panel access hole.
8. Reverse procedure to install.

BLOWER MOTOR

REPLACE

LESS A/C

On Models with 3.1L/V6-192 engines it is necessary to remove the serpentine belt and alternator to prior to performing the following procedure.

1. Disconnect blower motor and blower motor resistor electrical connections.
2. Remove plastic water shield from right side of cowl.
3. Remove blower motor attaching screws, then the blower motor.
4. Remove blower motor cage attaching nut, then the cage.

WITH A/C

On Models with 3.1L/V6-192 engines it is necessary to remove the serpentine belt and alternator to prior to performing the following procedure.

1. **On all models,** disconnect battery ground cable.
2. Disconnect blower motor electrical connections.
3. Disconnect blower motor attaching screws, then pull blower motor and cage out.
4. Remove plastic water shield from right side of cowl.
5. Remove blower motor.
6. Remove blower cage attaching nut, then the blower cage.
7. Reverse procedure to install.

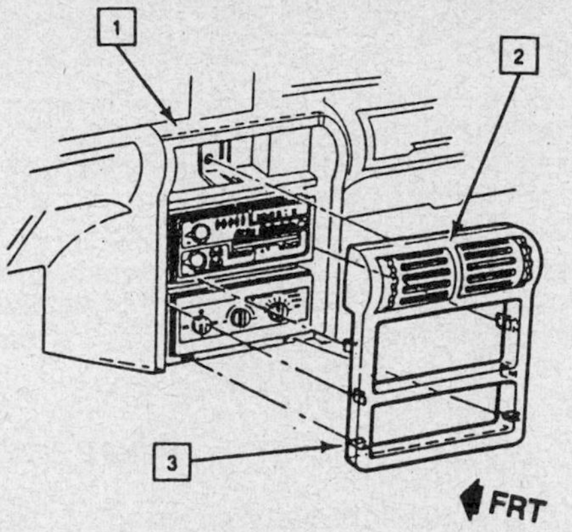
1
2
3
FRT
1 INSTRUMENT PANEL PAD
2 TRIM BEZEL
3 RETAINERS
GC9039100035000X

Fig. 6 Radio removal

HEATER CORE

REPLACE

LESS A/C

1. Remove radio assembly, through opening of radio release heater core cover retaining clips.
2. Remove screw attaching floor outlet, turning clockwise and to the right release rear floor air outlet.
3. Drain engine coolant, raise and support vehicle, then disconnect hoses from heater core.
4. Remove elbow tube from heater core case, then lower vehicle.
5. Remove heater core cover screws, then cover.
6. Remove heater core attaching screws, clamps, then heater core from vehicle.
7. Reverse procedure to install noting the following:

WITH A/C

1. Disconnect battery ground cable, then drain cooling system.
2. Raise and support vehicle, then disconnect drain tube from heater core.
3. Remove heater hoses from heater core, then lower vehicle.
4. Remove console if equipped, then right and left sounder insulator.
5. Remove steering column opening filler, then floor air outlet duct.
6. Remove heater core cover, heater core mounting clamps, then heater core.
7. Reverse procedure to install noting the following:

EVAPORATOR CORE

REPLACE

1. Discharge and recover refrigerant, as outlined in "Discharging & Evacuating System" in the "Air Conditioning" section.
2. Disconnect battery ground cable, then raise and support vehicle.
3. Remove front exhaust shield, then three cradle cross brace attaching bolts and swing brace to the side.
4. Remove A/C lines from evaporator, then lower vehicle.
5. Remove under dash insulator panel from right side.
6. Remove electrical junction box from heater core cover, then left side insulator panel.
7. Remove steering column filler, then partially remove shift console if equipped.
8. Remove floor duct, heater core cover, shroud, then straps.
9. Remove evaporator assembly.
10. Reverse procedure to install.
11. Evacuate and recharge system.

2.2L/4-134 Engine

NOTE: On Air Bag Equipped Models, Refer To "Air Bag System Precautions" Located In The Front Of This Manual For System Disarming & Arming Procedures.

NOTE: Refer To 2.2L/4-134 Engine Section In The "Chevrolet Cavalier & Pontiac Sunbird" Chapter For Service Procedures Not Covered In This Section.

INDEX

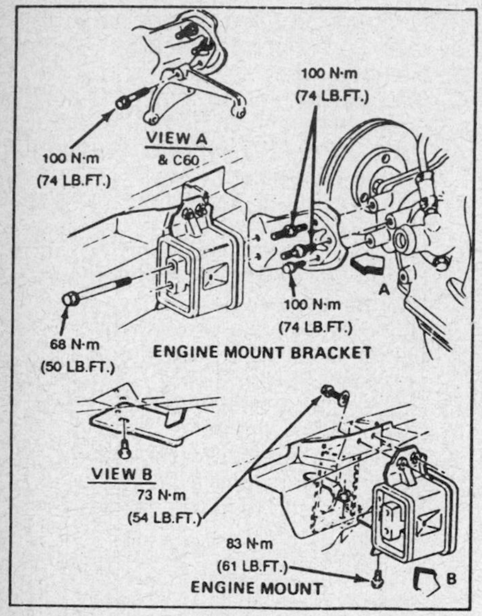
100 N·m
(74 LB.FT.)
VIEW A
& C60
100 N·m
(74 LB.FT.)
A
100 N·m
(74 LB.FT.)
68 N·m
(50 LB.FT.)
ENGINE MOUNT BRACKET
VIEW B
73 N·m
(54 LB.FT.)
83 N·m
(61 LB.FT.)
ENGINE MOUNT
B

GC1069100383000X

Fig. 1 Front engine mount assembly

PRECAUTIONS

AIR BAG SYSTEMS

Refer to "Air Bag System Precautions" in the front of this manual for system disarming and arming procedures.

ENGINE MOUNT

REPLACE

FRONT

Refer to **Fig. 1** when performing the following procedure.

1. Disconnect battery ground cable.
2. Remove two bolts retaining upper engine mount to body.
3. Remove bolt retaining upper engine mount to engine bracket.
4. Raise and support vehicle.
5. Support the engine.
6. Remove inner fender shield.
7. Remove bolt retaining lower engine mount to body.
8. Remove bolt retaining lower engine mount to engine mount bracket, then remove the mount.
9. Reverse procedure to install noting the following:
   a. Clean threads of all bolts removed. Prior to installation apply a suitable lock compound to bolt threads.
   b. Refer to **Fig. 1** for torque values.

REAR

Refer to **Fig. 2** when performing the following procedure.

Removal

1. Disconnect battery ground cable.
2. Raise and support vehicle.
3. Remove engine mount nuts and bolts, then the engine mount.
4. If necessary, remove engine mount bracket.

Installation

1. Clean threads of all bolts removed. Prior to installation apply a suitable lock compound to bolt threads.
2. Install engine mount bracket if removed. Do not tighten bracket bolts at this time.
3. Slightly raise engine and transaxle.
4. Install engine mount. Refer to **Fig. 2** for torque values.
5. Lower vehicle.
6. Install battery ground cable.

ENGINE

REPLACE

1. Disconnect battery cables, then remove the battery.
2. Relieve fuel tank vapor pressure by loosening the fuel filler cap.

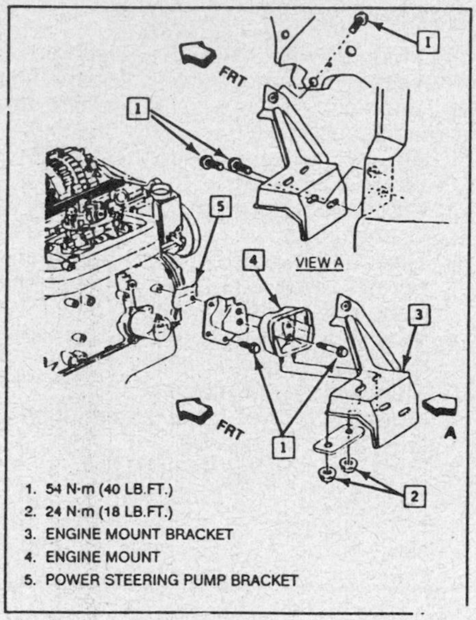
1
FRT
1
5
4
VIEW A
3
FRT
1
A
2
1. 54 N·m (40 LB.FT.)
2. 24 N·m (18 LB.FT.)
3. ENGINE MOUNT BRACKET
4. ENGINE MOUNT
5. POWER STEERING PUMP BRACKET

GC1069100384000X

Fig. 2 Rear engine mount assembly

3. Drain cooling system.
4. Disconnect hood lamp wiring. Remove the hood.
5. Remove throttle body intake duct.
6. Remove rear sight shields.
7. Remove air cleaner housing.
8. Remove upper radiator hose.
9. Disconnect vacuum hose from brake booster.
10. Disconnect alternator electrical connector, then remove the top brace, **Fig. 3.**
11. Remove upper engine wiring harness from engine.
12. Properly discharge A/C system. Refer to "Air Conditioning" in the "General Services" section for procedure.
13. Remove compressor-to-condenser, and accumulator refrigerant lines.

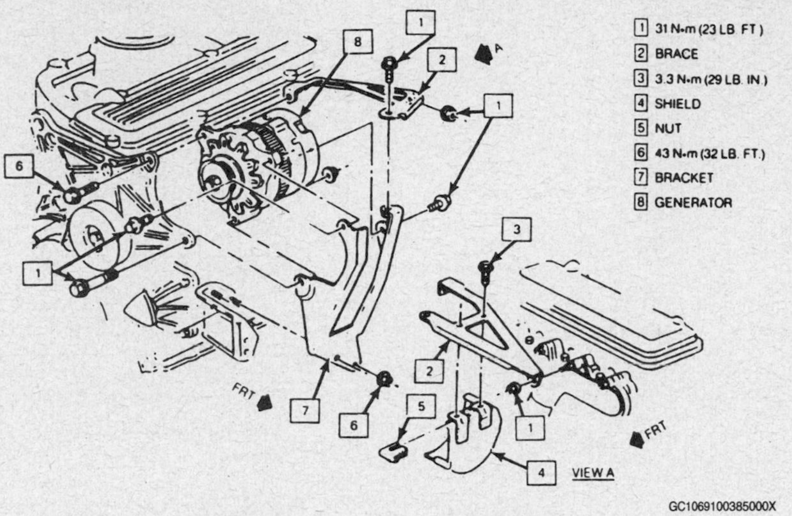
1 31 N•m (23 LB FT)
2 BRACE
3 3.3 N•m (29 LB IN)
4 SHIELD
5 NUT
6 43 N•m (32 LB FT)
7 BRACKET
8 GENERATOR
VIEW A
FRT
GC1069100385000X

Fig. 3 Alternator assembly

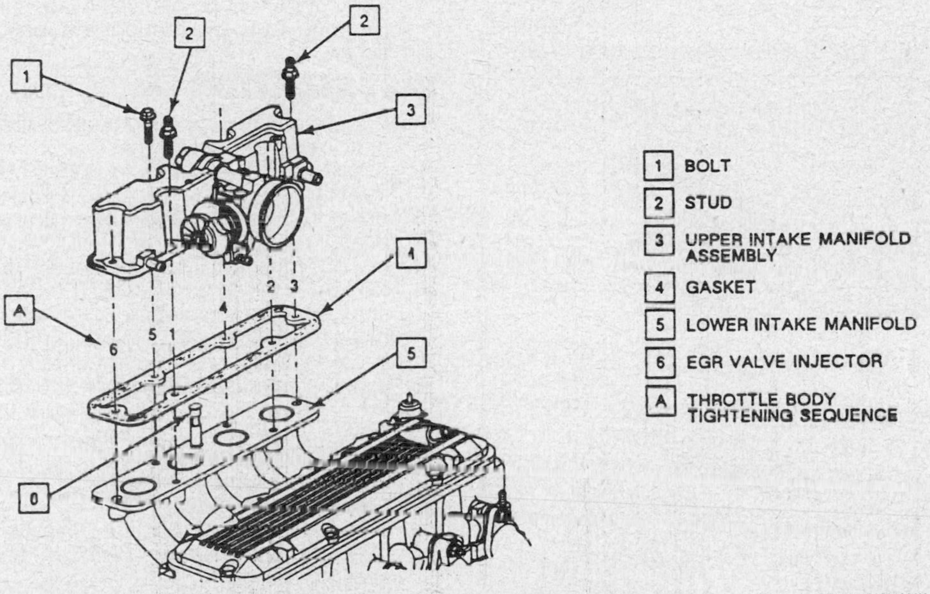
1 BOLT
2 STUD
3 UPPER INTAKE MANIFOLD ASSEMBLY
4 GASKET
5 LOWER INTAKE MANIFOLD
6 EGR VALVE INJECTOR
A THROTTLE BODY TIGHTENING SEQUENCE
GC1059100081000X

Fig. 4 Upper intake manifold replacement

14. Raise and support vehicle.
15. Remove left splash shield.
16. Remove exhaust system.
17. Remove lower engine wiring harness.
18. Remove flywheel inspection cover.
19. Remove front wheels.
20. Remove lower radiator hose.
21. Disconnect heater hoses from heater core.
22. Remove calipers from steering knuckle. Properly support calipers.
23. Remove tie rod ends from struts.
24. Lower the vehicle.
25. **On models with manual transaxle,** remove clutch slave cylinder as follows:
    a. Remove slave cylinder to transaxle attaching bolts.
    b. Using Hydraulic Line Separating Tool No. J-36221 or equivalent, disconnect hydraulic line quick connect fitting.
    c. Remove the slave cylinder.
26. **On all models,** ensure engine compartment fuel line connections are clean, then using Connector Tool Set No. J-37088 or equivalent, disconnect the fuel line quick connect fittings. Plug all fittings.
27. Disconnect linkage from transaxle.
28. Disconnect accelerator, cruise control, and T.V. cables from the TBI unit.
29. **On models with automatic transaxle,** disconnect cooling lines from transaxle.
30. **On all models,** disconnect hoses from power steering pump.
31. Remove four center carriage bolts.
32. Position a dolly with added engine support under the vehicle, then lower vehicle onto the dolly.
33. Support rear of vehicle.
34. Remove upper transaxle mount.
35. Remove upper strut mounting nuts and bolts.
36. Remove front and rear engine mounts as described previously.
37. Remove eight front and rear carriage bolts. **To prevent axle separation, wire front carriage bolt holes together.**
38. Raise the vehicle.
39. Remove engine and transaxle assembly on the dolly.
40. Reverse procedure to install noting the following:
    a. **On models with manual transaxle,** bleed the hydraulic clutch system as described in "Clutch And Manual Transaxle" section.
    b. **On all models,** replenish all fluids as needed.
    c. When recharging the A/C system refer to "Air Conditioning" in the "General Services" section for procedure.
    d. Check wheel Alignment, refer to "Wheel Alignment" section in this chapter.

INTAKE MANIFOLD

REPLACE

1. Relieve fuel system pressure, then remove air intake duct.
2. Drain engine coolant, then disconnect vacuum line and electrical wires as necessary.
3. Remove throttle linkage, then power steering pump.
4. Remove MAP sensor and EGR solenoid valve.
5. Remove upper intake manifold assembly, then EGR valve injector, **Fig. 4.**
6. Remove fuel injector retainer bracket, regulator, then injectors.
7. Remove accelerator and T.V. cables, then cable bracket.
8. Raise and support vehicle, then remove intake manifold lower attaching bolts.
9. Lower vehicle, remove intake manifold upper attaching nuts, then intake manifold and gasket.
10. Reverse procedure to install noting the following:
    a. Tighten intake manifold attaching nut in sequence as shown in **Fig. 5.**
    b. **Torque** intake manifold attaching nut to 22 inch lbs.
    c. **Torque** accelerator bracket attaching bolts to 18 inch lbs.

EXHAUST MANIFOLD

REPLACE

1. Disconnect battery ground cable.
2. Disconnect oxygen sensor.
3. Loosen drive belt tensioner and remove drive belt.
4. Remove alternator, **Fig. 3.**
5. Raise and support vehicle.
6. Disconnect exhaust pipe from manifold.
7. Lower the vehicle.
8. Remove eight exhaust manifold retaining bolts, **Fig. 6.**
9. Remove oil filler tube.
10. Remove exhaust manifold and gasket.
11. Reverse procedure to install noting the following:

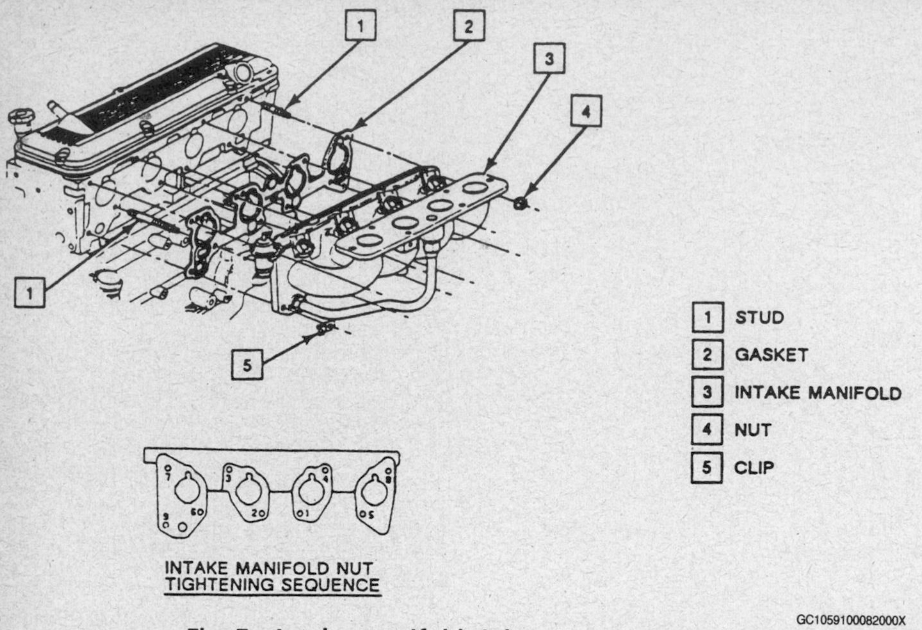
1
2
3
4
1
5
1 STUD
2 GASKET
3 INTAKE MANIFOLD
4 NUT
5 CLIP
INTAKE MANIFOLD NUT TIGHTENING SEQUENCE
GC1059100082000X

Fig. 5 Intake manifold tightening sequence

a. Install exhaust manifold with new gasket. Refer to **Fig. 6** for torque values.
b. When installing alternator, refer to **Fig. 3** for torque values.
c. When installing serpentine drive belt, refer to "Belt Tension Data" in this section.

CYLINDER HEAD

REPLACE

1. Relieve fuel pressure, then remove air inlet duct.
2. Disconnect vacuum lines and electrical connectors.
3. Remove accelerator linkage, then coolant reservoir.
4. Remove serpentine belt, alternator, power steering pump, then serpentine drive belt tensioner.
5. Remove secondary ignition wires, then canister purge line from under manifold.
6. Remove upper radiator hose, throttle body cables from bracket, then coolant inlet hose on cylinder head.
7. Remove intake manifold brace from power steering bracket, then fuel lines.
8. Remove rocker arm cover, rocker arms, then pushrods, **Fig. 7. When valve train components are removed they should be kept in order. Install in same location with same mating surfaces as when removed.**
9. Remove secondary ignition cable bracket, engine lift bracket, then front exhaust pipe.
10. Remove head bolts, then on models equipped with automatic transaxle remove fluid level indicator bracket.
11. Remove cylinder head.
12. Reverse procedure to install, noting the following:
    a. Ensure mating surfaces are clean, then install head using new gasket.

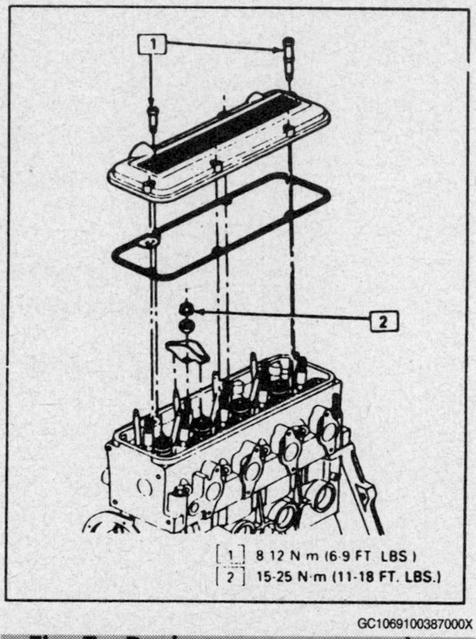
1
2
1 8-12 N·m (6-9 FT. LBS.)
2 15-25 N·m (11-18 FT. LBS.)
GC1069100387000X

Fig. 7 Rocker arm cover, rocker arms & pushrod replacement

b. Refer to **Fig. 8** for cylinder head bolts tightening sequence and tightening specifications.
c. Tighten rocker arms to specifications.

CRANKSHAFT PULLEY & HUB

REPLACE

REMOVAL

1. Disconnect battery ground cable.
2. Loosen drive belt tensioner and remove drive belt.
3. Raise and support vehicle.
4. Remove wheel and tire assembly.
5. Remove inner fender shield.
6. Remove three crankshaft pulley bolts,

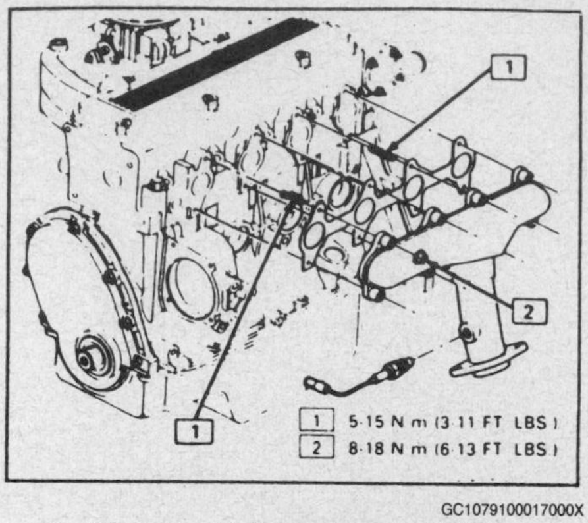
1
2
1
1 5-15 N·m (3-11 FT. LBS.)
2 8-18 N·m (6-13 FT. LBS.)
GC1079100017000X

Fig. 6 Exhaust manifold replacement

Fig. 9, the pulley and hub bolt, then the pulley.
7. Install Crankshaft Pulley Puller Tool No. J-24420-B or equivalent to hub. Remove hub by turning the puller screw.

INSTALLATION

1. Apply clean engine oil to contact area of front cover seal.
2. Apply a suitable sealer to pulley hub keyway.
3. Position pulley hub over key on crankshaft.
4. Install Crankshaft Pulley Installer Tool No. J-29113 or equivalent, to crankshaft. Ensure a minimum of 1/4 inch of threads are engaged. Pull pulley hub into position, then remove the tool.
5. Install crankshaft pulley, then the pulley and hub bolts. Refer to **Fig. 9** for torque values.
6. Install inner fender shield.
7. Install wheel and tire assembly.
8. Lower the vehicle.
9. When installing serpentine drive belt, refer to "Belt Tension Data" in this section.
10. Reconnect battery ground cable.

FRONT COVER

REPLACE

1. Disconnect battery ground cable.
2. Loosen drive belt tensioner and remove drive belt.
3. Remove tensioner, **Fig. 10.**
4. Raise and support vehicle.
5. Remove oil pan as described previously.
6. Remove crankshaft pulley and hub as described previously.
7. Remove eight front cover attaching bolts, **Fig. 11**, then the front cover and gasket.
8. Reverse procedure to install noting the following:
    a. Ensure front cover mating surfaces are thoroughly clean.
    b. Install front cover with new gasket. Refer to **Fig. 11** for torque values.
    c. Clean tensioner bolts and prior to installation apply a suitable lock compound to bolt threads. Refer to **Fig. 10** for torque values.

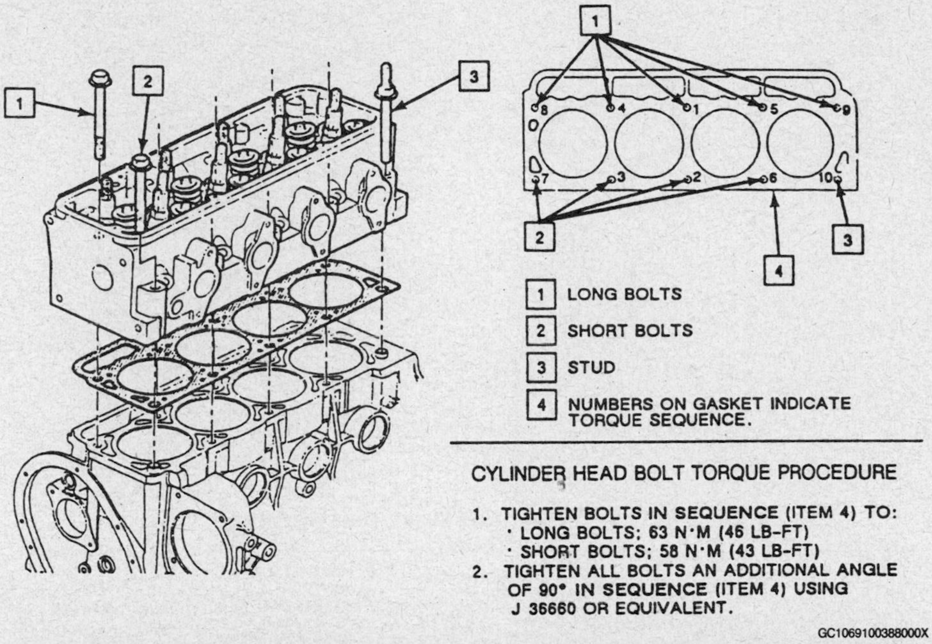
1
2
3
4
1 LONG BOLTS
2 SHORT BOLTS
3 STUD
4 NUMBERS ON GASKET INDICATE TORQUE SEQUENCE.
CYLINDER HEAD BOLT TORQUE PROCEDURE
1. TIGHTEN BOLTS IN SEQUENCE (ITEM 4) TO:
· LONG BOLTS; 63 N·M (46 LB-FT)
· SHORT BOLTS; 58 N·M (43 LB-FT)
2. TIGHTEN ALL BOLTS AN ADDITIONAL ANGLE OF 90° IN SEQUENCE (ITEM 4) USING J 36660 OR EQUIVALENT.
GC1069100388000X

Fig. 8 Cylinder head bolt tightening sequence

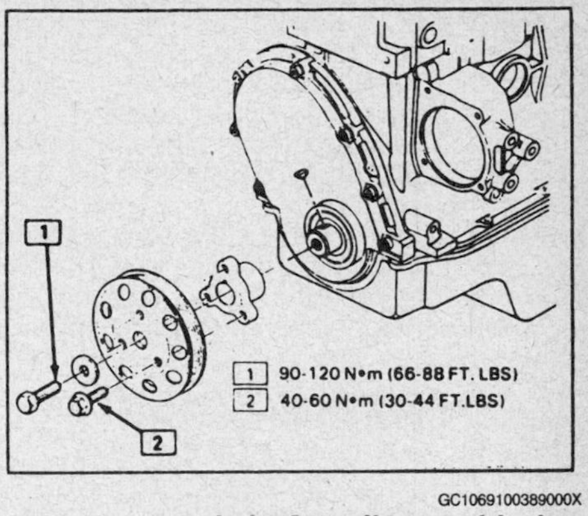
1 90-120 N•m (66-88 FT. LBS)
2 40-60 N•m (30-44 FT.LBS)
GC1069100389000X

Fig. 9 Crankshaft pulley and hub replacement

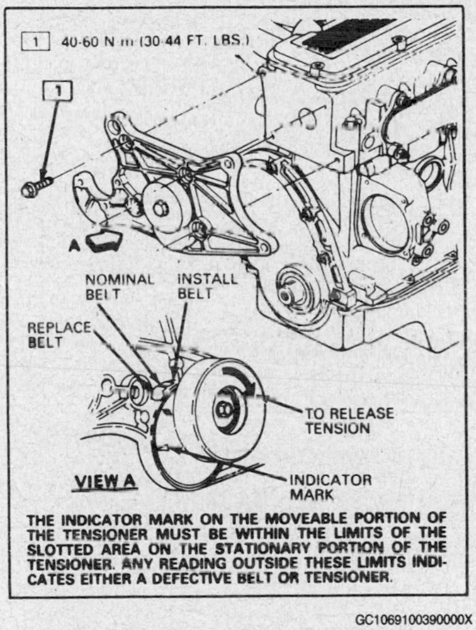
1 40-60 N·m (30-44 FT. LBS.)
A
NOMINAL BELT
INSTALL BELT
REPLACE BELT
TO RELEASE TENSION
VIEW A
INDICATOR MARK
THE INDICATOR MARK ON THE MOVEABLE PORTION OF THE TENSIONER MUST BE WITHIN THE LIMITS OF THE SLOTTED AREA ON THE STATIONARY PORTION OF THE TENSIONER. ANY READING OUTSIDE THESE LIMITS INDICATES EITHER A DEFECTIVE BELT OR TENSIONER.
GC1069100390000X

Fig. 10 Drive belt tensioner assembly

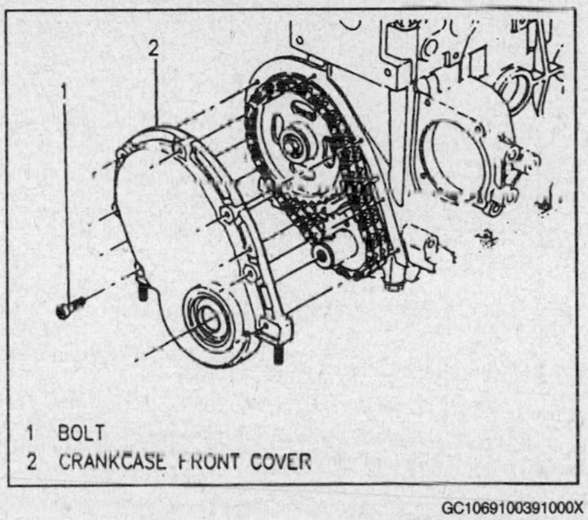
1 BOLT
2 CRANKCASE FRONT COVER
GC1069100391000X

Fig. 11 Front cover replacement

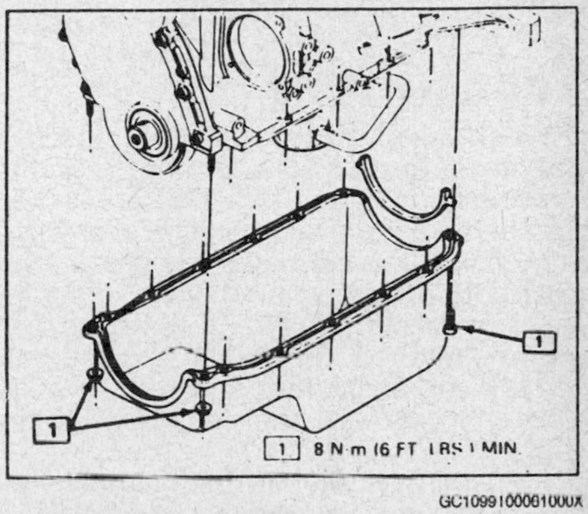
1 8 N·m (6 FT. LBS.) MIN.
GC1099100061000X

Fig. 12 Oil pan replacement

d. When installing serpentine drive belt, refer to "Belt Tension Data" in this section.

OIL PAN

REPLACE

REMOVAL

1. Disconnect battery ground cable.
2. Disconnect exhaust pipe from manifold.
3. Raise and support vehicle.
4. Drain the crankcase.
5. Remove starter bracket, and the starter.
6. Remove flywheel inspection cover.
7. Remove four right side support bolts, then slightly lower the support.
8. **On models with automatic transaxle,** remove oil filter and extension.
9. **On all models,** remove twelve bolts and two nuts retaining the oil pan, **Fig. 12.**
10. Remove oil pan and gasket.

INSTALLATION

1. Ensure oil pan mating surfaces are thoroughly clean.
2. Apply a 1/8 inch diameter bead of suitable sealer on the oil pan to engine block sealing flanges.
3. Apply suitable sealer on the oil pan to front cover mating surface.
4. Apply suitable sealer on ends to the ears of a new oil pan rear seal.
5. Install oil pan to engine block. Refer to **Fig. 12** for torque values.
6. **On models with automatic transaxle,** install oil filter adapter with a new seal, then the oil filter.
7. **On all models,** install exhaust pipe to manifold.
8. Install right side support with attaching bolts.
9. Install starter.
10. Lower the vehicle.
11. Refill crankcase.
12. Connect battery ground cable.

OIL PUMP

REPLACE

1. Remove oil pan as previously described.
2. Remove pump to rear main bearing cap bolt, then the pump and extension shaft.
3. Remove extension shaft and retainer.
4. Reverse procedure noting the following:
   a. Heat retainer in hot water prior to assembling extension shaft.
   b. **Torque** oil pump bolt to 32 ft. lbs.

BELT TENSION DATA

1. Check belt tensioner indicator marks, **Fig. 10,** to ensure belt is in operating range. Replace belt as needed, refer to **Fig. 13** for belt routing.
2. With all accessories Off, run engine until operating temperature is achieved.
3. Turn ignition switch to Off.
4. Position Belt Tensioner Tool No. J-23600 or equivalent, on the drive belt between power steering pump and alternator. Note reading, and remove the tool.
5. Run engine for 15 seconds, then turn the ignition switch to Off.
6. Using a 15 mm socket, apply counterclockwise force to tensioner pulley bolt. Release the pulley, then take a reading as described in step 4.

7. Using a 15 mm socket, apply clockwise force to tensioner pulley bolt until the install position is reached. Slowly release pulley to rest position, then take a reading as described in step 4. Use caution not to disturb the belt tensioner position.
8. If average of the three readings taken is 63-77 lbs., and the belt is in the tensioners operating range, replace the belt tensioner as described in this section.

SERPENTINE DRIVE BELT

BELT ROUTING

Refer to **Fig. 13** for serpentine drive belt routing.

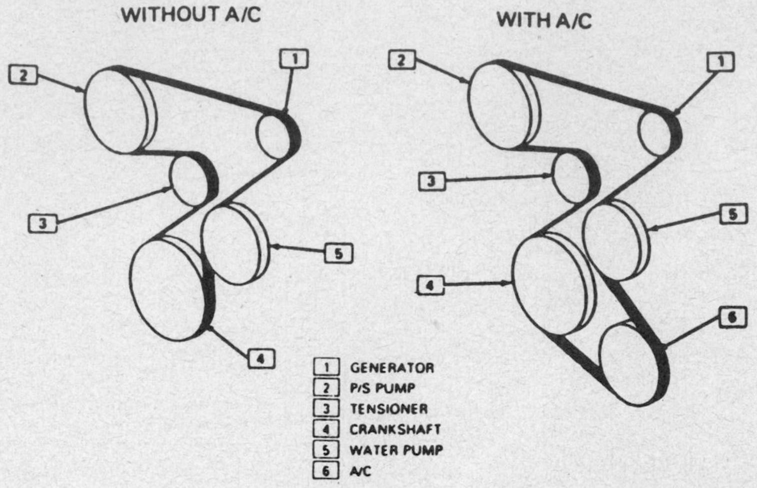
WITHOUT A/C
WITH A/C
1 GENERATOR
2 P/S PUMP
3 TENSIONER
4 CRANKSHAFT
5 WATER PUMP
6 A/C

GC1069100392000X

Fig. 13 Serpentine drive belt routing

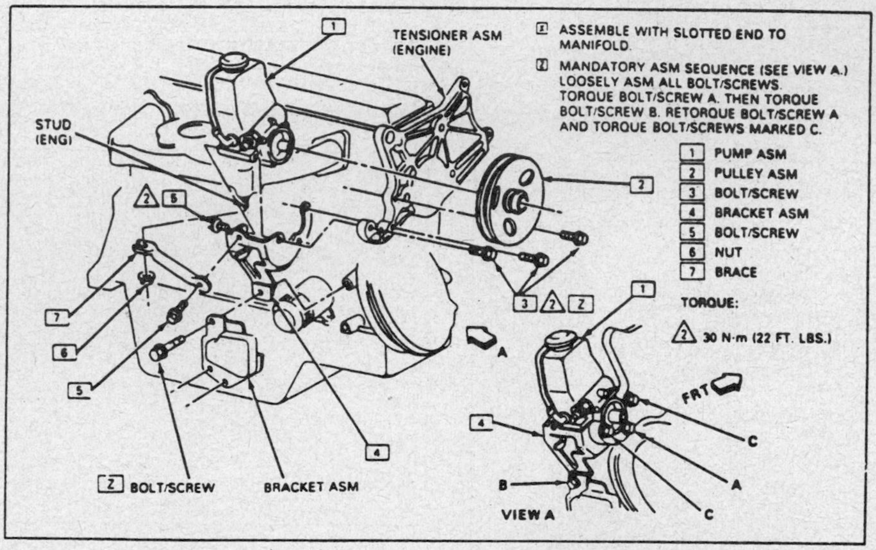
TENSIONER ASM (ENGINE)
Z ASSEMBLE WITH SLOTTED END TO MANIFOLD.
Z MANDATORY ASM SEQUENCE (SEE VIEW A.) LOOSELY ASM ALL BOLT/SCREWS. TORQUE BOLT/SCREW A. THEN TORQUE BOLT/SCREW B. RETORQUE BOLT/SCREW A AND TORQUE BOLT/SCREWS MARKED C.
STUD (ENG)
1 PUMP ASM
2 PULLEY ASM
3 BOLT/SCREW
4 BRACKET ASM
5 BOLT/SCREW
6 NUT
7 BRACE
TORQUE:
2 30 N·m (22 FT. LBS.)
FRT
Z BOLT/SCREW
BRACKET ASM
VIEW A

GC1069100386000X

Fig. 14 Power steering pump replacement

PRECAUTIONS

When installing or removing the drive belt, never exceed 30 ft. lbs. torque on the tensioner center bolt, **Fig. 10.** Care should also be taken to avoid bending or twisting the tensioner. If the belt tensioner or idler assembly produces a whining noise, inspect for bearing failure. If the drive belt becomes frayed, check belt tensioner assembly alignment and ensure belt edge does not contact the tensioner pulley flange.

Serpentine drive belt performance will not be impaired by cracks in the belt ribs. However belt replacement will be required if any of the following conditions occur: Belt ribs are missing, the belt slips or is frayed, or the belt tensioner runs out of travel before adjustment is proper.

BELT TENSIONER REPLACEMENT

1. Disconnect battery ground cable.
2. Remove coolant reservoir.
3. Loosen drive belt tensioner and remove drive belt.
4. Remove two alternator bolts.
5. Remove belt tensioner pulley.
6. Remove power steering pump as follows:
   a. Disconnect return and pressure hoses from the pump.
   b. Loosen drive belt tensioner. Separate belt from power steering pulley.
   c. Remove three front pump retaining bolts, **Fig. 14.** Bolts can be accessed through hole in the pulley.
   d. Remove one retaining bolt from rear of the pump, then remove the pump.
7. Remove four tensioner retaining bolts, **Fig. 10,** then the tensioner.
8. Reverse procedure to install noting the following:
   a. Clean tensioner bolts and prior to installation apply a suitable lock compound to bolt threads. Refer to **Fig. 10** for torque values.
   b. When installing power steering pump, refer to **Fig. 14** for bolt tightening sequence and torque values.
   c. When installing alternator bolts, refer to **Fig. 3** for torque values.
   d. When installing serpentine drive belt, refer to **Fig. 13** for belt routing.

COOLING SYSTEM BLEED

These engines do not require a specified bleed procedure. After filling cooling system, run engine to operating temperature with radiator pressure cap off. Air will then be automatically bled through cap opening.

THERMOSTAT

REPLACE

1. Remove air cleaner duct, then disconnect battery ground cable.
2. Drain cooling system below level of thermostat housing.
3. Remove radiator hose from water outlet, then remove three water outlet attaching nuts.
4. Remove outlet, then thermostat.
5. Reverse procedure to install. **Torque** water outlet attaching nut to 89 inch lbs.

WATER PUMP

REPLACE

1. Disconnect battery ground cable.
2. Drain cooling system.
3. Loosen drive belt tensioner and remove drive belt.
4. Remove water pump pulley attaching bolts, **Fig. 15,** then the pulley.
5. Remove alternator, **Fig. 3.**
6. Remove alternator side bracket.
7. Remove water pump attaching bolts, **Fig. 16,** then the pump and gasket.
8. Reverse procedure to install noting the following:
   a. Ensure water pump mating surface is thoroughly clean.
   b. Install water pump with new gasket. Refer to **Fig. 15 and 16** for torque values.
   c. When installing alternator, refer to **Fig. 3** for torque values.
   d. When installing serpentine drive belt, refer to "Belt Tension Data" in this section.

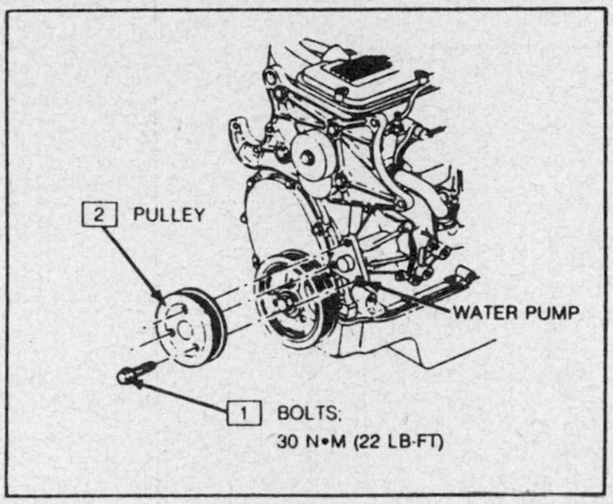
2 PULLEY
WATER PUMP
1 BOLTS:
30 N•M (22 LB-FT)

GC1089100161000X

Fig. 15 Water pump pulley installation

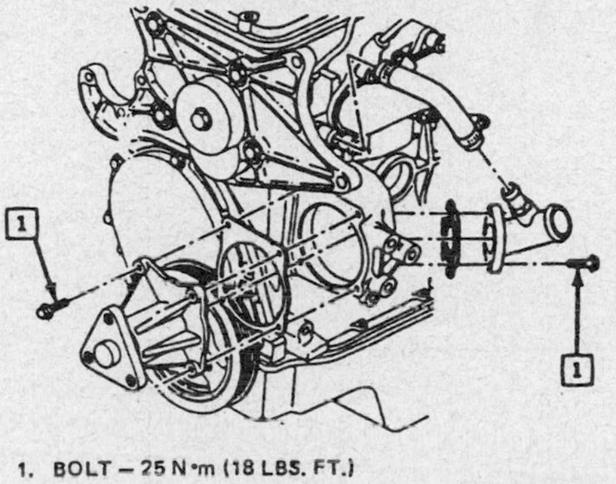
1
1
1. BOLT – 25 N·m (18 LBS. FT.)

GC1089100162000X

Fig. 16 Water pump replacement

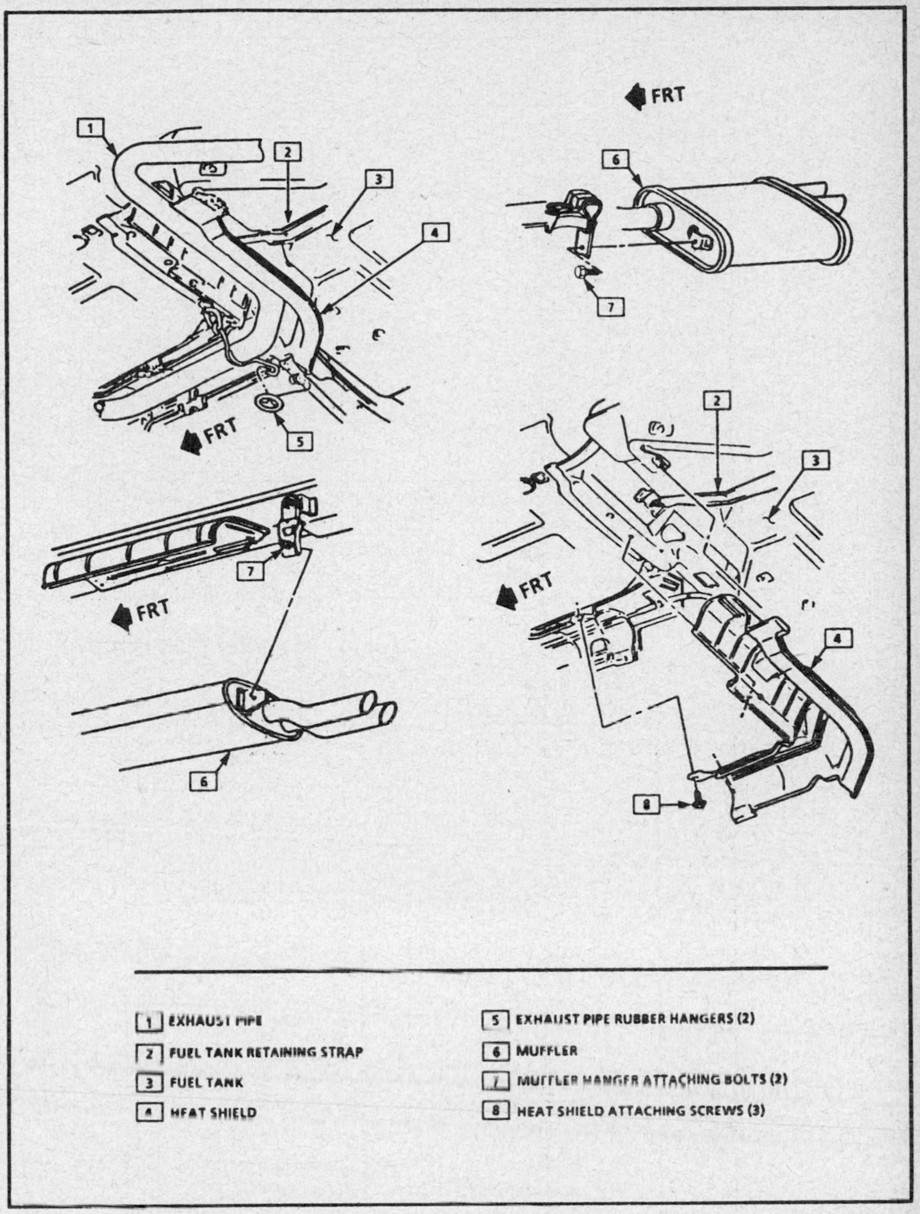
FRT
1
2
3
4
5
6
7
FRT
7
FRT
6
2
3
FRT
4
8
1 EXHAUST PIPE
2 FUEL TANK RETAINING STRAP
3 FUEL TANK
4 HEAT SHIELD
5 EXHAUST PIPE RUBBER HANGERS (2)
6 MUFFLER
7 MUFFLER HANGER ATTACHING BOLTS (2)
8 HEAT SHIELD ATTACHING SCREWS (3)

GC1079100018000X

Fig. 17 Exhaust assembly

RADIATOR
REPLACE

1. Disconnect battery ground cable.
2. Drain coolant system.
3. Disconnect air intake duct assembly.
4. Disconnect upper transaxle cooler line.
5. Disconnect upper radiator hose.
6. Disconnect lower transaxle cooler line.
7. Disconnect cooling fan electrical connector and remove retaining bolt.
8. Remove cooling fan.
9. Remove splash guard below lower radiator hose.
10. Disconnect lower radiator hose from radiator.
11. **On models equipped with A/C,** remove condenser line retaining clip and condenser mounting bolts.
12. **On all models,** disconnect coolant surge tank hose.
13. Remove radiator retaining bolts, then the radiator.
14. Reverse procedure to install. **Torque** radiator retaining bolts to 89 inch lbs.

FUEL PUMP
REPLACE

1. Disconnect battery ground cable.
2. Relieve fuel tank vapor pressure by loosening the fuel filler cap.
3. Using a suitable siphon, drain the fuel tank.
4. Remove fuel tank as follows:
   a. Raise and support vehicle.
   b. Remove two rubber exhaust pipe hangers, **Fig. 17.**
   c. Remove two muffler hanger retaining bolts.
   d. Remove three heat shield attaching screws, then the heat shield.
   e. Remove fuel tank filler tube, vent tube, vent hose, and clamps.
   f. Disconnect electrical connector, **Fig. 18.**
   g. Disconnect fuel level meter vapor hose.
   h. Ensure fuel line connections are clean. Disconnect fuel return quick connect fitting by squeezing plastic tab on male end of the fitting. Using Fuel Line Separator Tool Set No. J-37088 or equivalent, disconnect fuel line quick connect fitting. Plug all fittings.
   i. Properly support tank.
   j. Remove two rear retaining strap attaching bolts, then the fuel tank and retaining straps.
5. Thoroughly clean fuel level meter assembly connection and surrounding area, **Fig. 19.**
6. Using Fuel Sender Spanner Wrench tool No. J-35731, remove fuel level meter assembly lock ring. Remove assembly from tank, and discard the O-ring.
7. Disassemble fuel level meter assembly as follows:
   a. Note orientation of fuel filter for proper installation.
   b. To remove fuel filter, rotate it while pulling fuel pump in opposite direction, **Fig. 20.**
   c. Disconnect fuel pump electrical connector.
   d. Position fuel level meter assembly

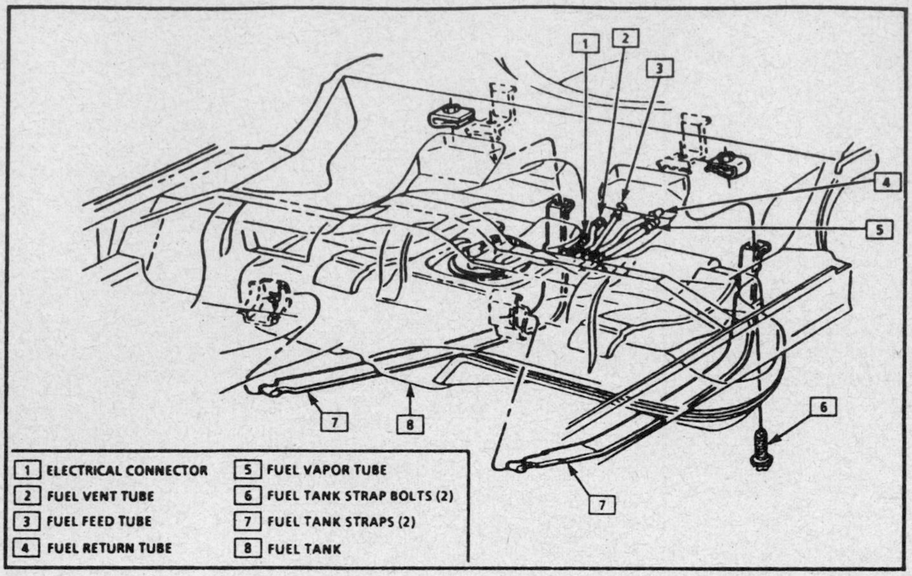
1
2
3
4
5
6
7
8
7
1 ELECTRICAL CONNECTOR
2 FUEL VENT TUBE
3 FUEL FEED TUBE
4 FUEL RETURN TUBE
5 FUEL VAPOR TUBE
6 FUEL TANK STRAP BOLTS (2)
7 FUEL TANK STRAPS (2)
8 FUEL TANK

GC1029102730000X

Fig. 18 Fuel tank removal

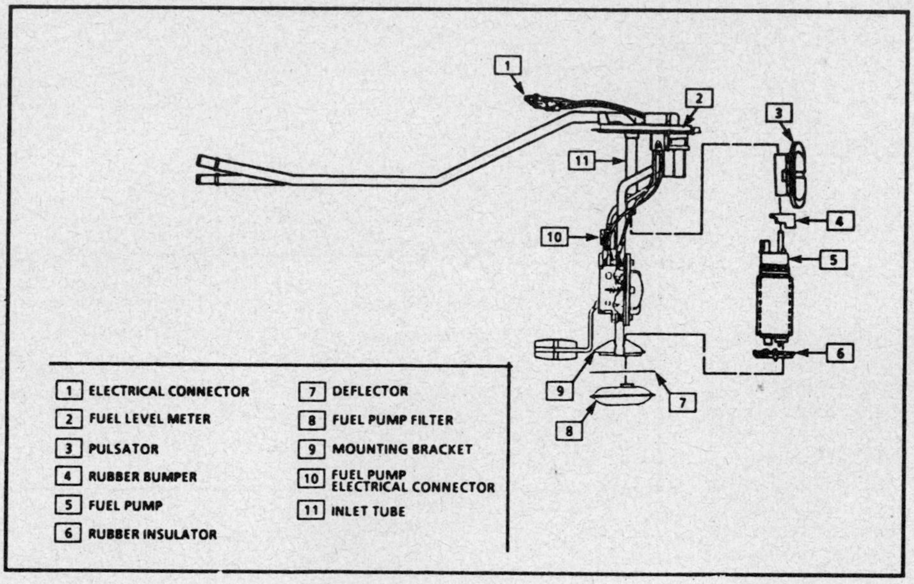
1
2
3
4
5
6
7
8
9
10
11
1 ELECTRICAL CONNECTOR
2 FUEL LEVEL METER
3 PULSATOR
4 RUBBER BUMPER
5 FUEL PUMP
6 RUBBER INSULATOR
7 DEFLECTOR
8 FUEL PUMP FILTER
9 MOUNTING BRACKET
10 FUEL PUMP ELECTRICAL CONNECTOR
11 INLET TUBE

GC1029102731000X

Fig. 19 Fuel level meter assembly

upside down on work area.

e. Pull downward on fuel pump to separate it from mounting bracket. Tilt pump outward and remove it from pulsator.

8. Reverse procedure to install noting the following:
   a. Never run fuel pump unless submerged in fuel.
   b. Always replace fuel filter when installing fuel pump.
   c. Always use new O-ring when installing fuel level meter assembly.

FUEL FILTER

REPLACE

1. Raise and support vehicle.
2. Grasp filter and one nylon fuel connecting line fitting. Twist quick connect fitting 1/4 turn in each direction to loosen any dirt within fitting.
3. Repeat Step 2 for the other connector.
4. Remove fuel filter retaining screw, then squeeze plastic tabs of male end connector of filter connections and pull apart.
5. Using compressed air, blow the quick connectors clean or dirt. **Safety glasses must be worn during this procedure.**
6. Remove protective caps from new filter.
7. Apply a few drops of clean engine oil to the male tubes ends of the filter assembly.
8. Push connectors together to cause the retaining tabs/fingers to snap into place.
9. Once installed, pull on both ends of each connection to ensure they are secure.
10. Turn the ignition switch to the On Position, engine Off, for two seconds.
11. Turn ignition switch to the Off position for ten seconds, then to the ON position. Check fuel filter for leaks.

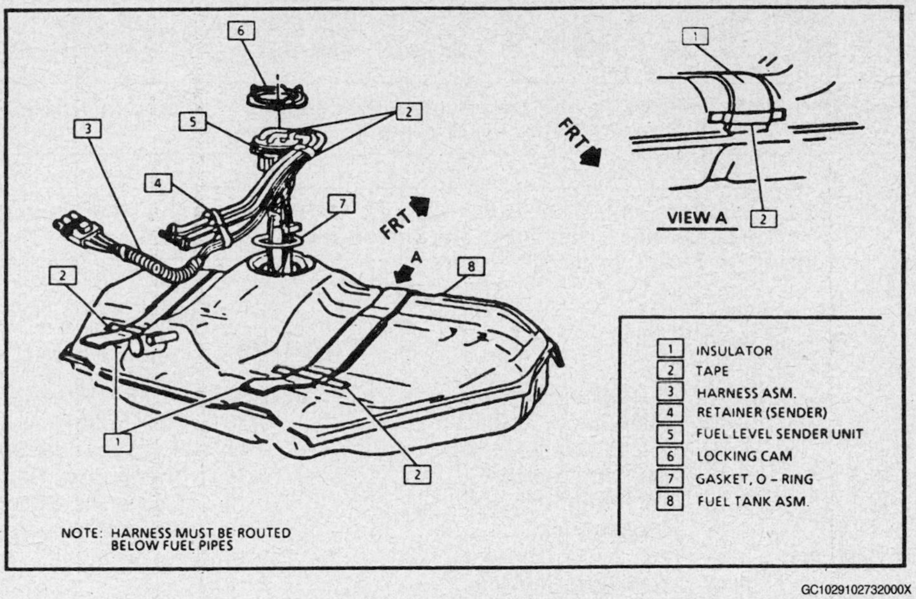
6
5
2
3
4
7
FRT
A
8
2
1
2
1
VIEW A
2
FRT
1 INSULATOR
2 TAPE
3 HARNESS ASM.
4 RETAINER (SENDER)
5 FUEL LEVEL SENDER UNIT
6 LOCKING CAM
7 GASKET, O - RING
8 FUEL TANK ASM.
NOTE: HARNESS MUST BE ROUTED BELOW FUEL PIPES
GC1029102732000X

Fig. 20 Fuel tank assembly

TIGHTENING SPECIFICATIONS

Year	Component	Torque/Ft. Lbs.
1992–95	Accelerator Cable Mounting Bracket	18
	Camshaft Pulley	77
	Camshaft Thrust Plate	9
	Coolant Drain Plug (Cylinder Block)	11
	Coolant Outlet To Cylinder Head	8
	Crankcase Front Cover Bolts	97②
	Crankshaft Pulley & Hub To Crankshaft	85
	Crankshaft Pulley To Hub	37
	Crankshaft Sensor	80②
	Cylinder Head Bolts	①
	DIS Coil Assembly	18
	EGR Valve	16
	Exhaust Manifold Nuts	16
	Exhaust Manifold Studs	9–10
	Flywheel To Crankshaft	52
	Heater Hose To Intake Manifold	24
	Intake Manifold	18
	Main Bearing Cap Bolts	70
	Oil Fill Tube To Cylinder Block	18
	Oil Filter Adapter To Cylinder Block	18
1992-95 —Cont'd	Oil Pan	7-8
	Oil Pump Drive Assembly Bolt	18
	Oil Pump To Bearing Cap	31
	Oxygen Sensor	31
	PCV Valve Cap	89②
	Power Brake Hose Vacuum Fitting	115②
	Pressure Plate To Flywheel	15
	Rear Engine Lift Bracket	32
	Rocker Arm Cover	7-8
	Rocker Arm Nuts	22
	Rod Bearing Cap Nut	38
	Serpentine Tensioner Assembly	37
	Spark Plugs	11
	Timing Chain Cover	8
	Timing Chain Tensioner	18
	Water Pump	18
	Water Pump Inlet	18

①—Refer to text.
②—Inch lbs.

2.3L/4-138 Engine

NOTE: On Air Bag Equipped Models, Refer To "Air Bag System Precautions" Located In The Front Of This Manual For System Disarming & Arming Procedures.

NOTE: Refer To 2.3L/4-138 Engine Section In The "Buick Skylark, Oldsmobile Achieva & Pontiac Grand Am" Chapter For Service Procedures Not Covered In This Section.

INDEX

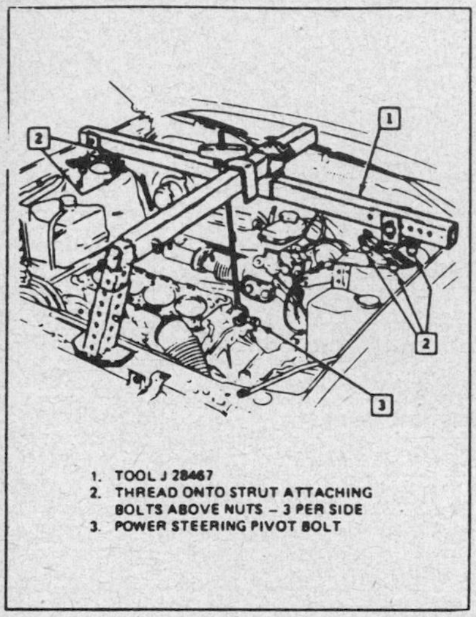

1
2
2
3
1. TOOL J 28467
2. THREAD ONTO STRUT ATTACHING BOLTS ABOVE NUTS – 3 PER SIDE
3. POWER STEERING PIVOT BOLT

GC1069100394000X

Fig. 1 Engine support tool installation

PRECAUTIONS

AIR BAG SYSTEMS

Refer to "Air Bag System Precautions" in the front of this manual for system disarming and arming procedures.

ENGINE MOUNT

REPLACE

RIGHT MOUNT

1. Disconnect battery ground cable.
2. Install Engine Support tool No. J-28467-A or equivalent **Fig. 1,** then raise engine off mount.
3. Raise and support vehicle, remove right side wheel, then right side splash shield.
4. Remove two front engine mount lower attaching bolts.
5. Lower vehicle, remove nut holding lower mounting bolt.
6. Remove bracket to mount attaching nut, then mount assembly.
7. Reverse procedure to install.

ENGINE MOUNT STRUT

1. Disconnect battery ground cable, then raise and support vehicle.
2. Remove bolts attaching engine mount strut to body and engine mount strut bracket.
3. Remove engine mount strut.
4. Reverse procedure to install.

TRANSAXLE MOUNT

1. Disconnect battery ground cable.
2. Install Engine Support tool No. J-28467-A or equivalent **Fig. 1,** then raise engine off mount.
3. Remove through bolt at transaxle mount, then bolts attaching mount to transaxle, **Fig. 2.**
4. Remove mount.
5. Reverse procedure to install.

ENGINE

REPLACE

1. Relieve fuel system pressure as follows:
   a. Disconnect battery negative cable.
   b. Relieve fuel tank vapor pressure by loosening the fuel filler cap.
   c. Install Fuel Pressure Gauge Tool, No. J-34730 or equivalent, to fuel pressure valve. **To avoid spilling fuel when connecting the gauge wrap fitting with a towel.**
   d. Position end of bleed hose into a suitable container. Open the bleeder valve until system pressure is gone.
2. Drain cooling system.
3. Raise and support vehicle.
4. Remove front wheels.
5. Remove air cleaner assembly.
6. Disconnect heater hoses.
7. Remove upper radiator hose.

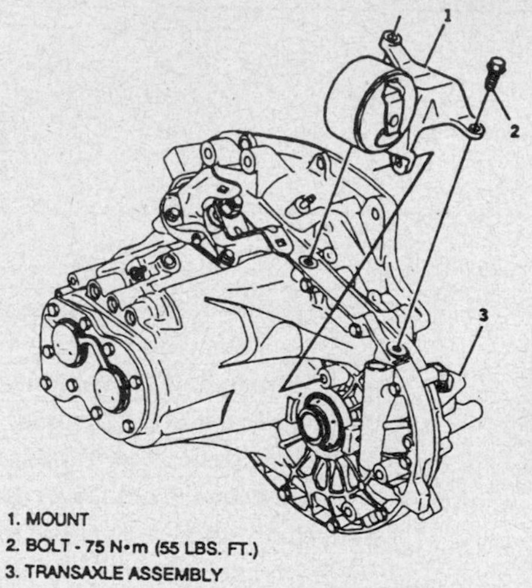

1
2
3
1. MOUNT
2. BOLT - 75 N•m (55 LBS. FT.)
3. TRANSAXLE ASSEMBLY

GC1069100396000X

Fig. 2 Transaxle mount

8. Remove coolant fan.
9. Properly discharge A/C system. Refer to "Air Conditioning" in the "General Services" section for procedure.
10. Remove oil filter.
11. Remove A/C compressor to condenser refrigerant line.
12. Disconnect all electrical connectors and vacuum lines necessary to facilitate engine removal.
13. Remove battery ground cable to engine block retaining bolt, then the battery cable.
14. Separate shift cable from bracket.
15. Disconnect vacuum hose from brake booster.
16. Disconnect accelerator cable, then remove the bracket, **Fig. 3.**
17. Remove power steering pump assembly with hoses attached, **Fig. 4,** and position aside.
18. Remove oil/air separator.
19. Disconnect engine compartment fuel lines.

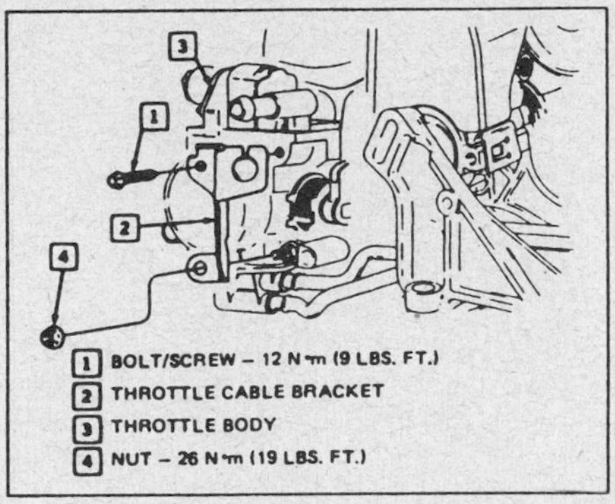
1
2
3
4
1 BOLT/SCREW – 12 N·m (9 LBS. FT.)
2 THROTTLE CABLE BRACKET
3 THROTTLE BODY
4 NUT – 26 N·m (19 LBS. FT.)

GC1069100397000X

Fig. 3 Accelerator cable bracket

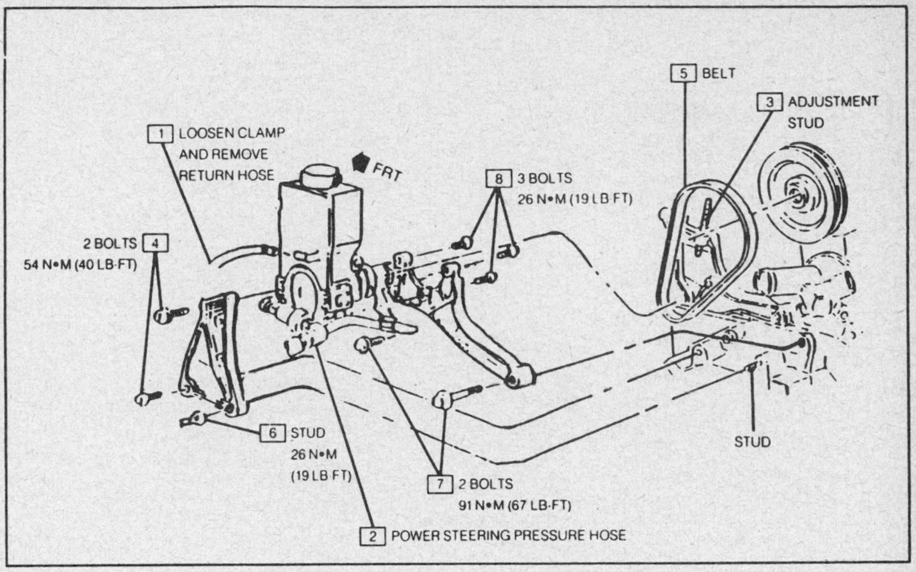
5 BELT
3 ADJUSTMENT STUD
1 LOOSEN CLAMP AND REMOVE RETURN HOSE
FRT
8 3 BOLTS 26 N•M (19 LB FT)
2 BOLTS 4 54 N•M (40 LB·FT)
6 STUD 26 N•M (19 LB FT)
STUD
7 2 BOLTS 91 N•M (67 LB·FT)
2 POWER STEERING PRESSURE HOSE

GC1069100398000X

Fig. 4 Power steering pump assembly

20. **On models with manual transaxle,** remove clutch actuator.
21. **On all models,** disconnect engine oil cooler lines from adapter.
22. Remove exhaust manifold as described later in this section.
23. Remove front engine mount retaining nut, **Fig. 5.**
24. Remove lower radiator hose and heater hose.
25. Install Engine Support Tool No. J-28467 or equivalent, **Fig. 1.**
26. Remove splash shields.
27. Separate ball joints from steering knuckles, then stabilizer shafts from both control arms.
28. Remove drive axles as described in the "Front Wheel Drive" section.
29. Remove suspension support.
30. Remove ground strap from block.
31. Remove rear engine mount assembly as described previously.
32. Remove transaxle mount through bolt.
33. Lower the engine.
34. Disconnect starter wires.
35. **On models equipped with manual transmission,** the throttle body coolant pipes must be removed before engine is removed. **Do not bent coolant pipes to gain clearance.**
36. Remove engine and transaxle assembly.
37. Reverse procedure to install noting the following:
    a. **On models with manual transaxle,** bleed the hydraulic clutch system as described in "Clutch And Manual Transaxle" section.
    b. Replenish all fluids as needed.
    c. When recharging the A/C system refer to "Air Conditioning" in the "General Services" section for procedure.
    d. Check wheel Alignment, refer to "Wheel Alignment" section in this chapter.

INTAKE MANIFOLD

REPLACE

1. Disconnect battery ground cable.
2. Drain cooling system.
3. Disconnect MAP sensor electrical connector and vacuum hose.

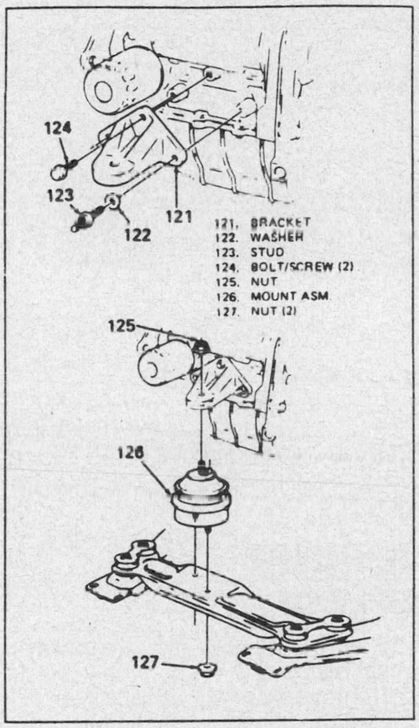
124
123
121
122
121. BRACKET
122. WASHER
123. STUD
124. BOLT/SCREW (2)
125. NUT
126. MOUNT ASM
127. NUT (2)
125
126
127

GC1069100393000X

Fig. 5 Front engine mount retaining nut removal

4. Disconnect MAT sensor, purge solenoid, and fuel injector harness electrical connectors.
5. Disconnect intake manifold vacuum hoses.
6. Disconnect fuel regulator, and purge solenoid-to-canister hoses.
7. Remove throttle body-to-air cleaner duct, then separate vent tube from the duct.
8. Remove accelerator cable bracket, **Fig. 3.**
9. Remove brake booster vacuum hose, along with retaining bracket to power steering bracket.
10. Disconnect throttle body coolant lines.
11. Remove oil/air separator with hoses, **Fig. 6.** Disconnect hoses from the oil filler, chain cover, intake duct, and intake manifold.
12. Remove oil filler cap/level indicator assembly from filler tube, **Fig. 6.**
13. Remove bolt/screw retaining the oil filler tube to engine. Pull tube upward to separate it from the block.
14. Disconnect injector harness electrical connector.
15. Remove oil filler tube by pulling upward while rotating it between intake tubes and fuel rail electrical harness. Discard oil filler tube O-ring.
16. Remove intake manifold support brace, **Fig. 7.**
17. Remove five bolts and two nuts retaining the intake manifold, **Fig. 8.**
18. Remove intake manifold and gasket.
19. Reverse procedure to install noting the following:
    a. Install intake manifold with new gasket. Ensure numbers stamped on the gasket face the manifold surface. Refer to **Fig. 8** for tightening sequence, and to specifications for torque values.
    b. Install a new O-ring to oil filler tube. Refer to **Fig. 6** when installing oil filler tube to engine.

EXHAUST MANIFOLD

REPLACE

1. Disconnect battery ground cable.
2. Disconnect oxygen sensor.
3. Raise and support vehicle.
4. Remove exhaust manifold brace, **Fig. 9.**
5. Remove exhaust pipe from manifold, **Fig. 10.**
6. Lower the vehicle.
7. Remove exhaust manifold heat shields, **Fig. 11.**
8. Remove exhaust manifold and gasket, **Fig. 12.**
9. Reverse procedure to install noting the following:

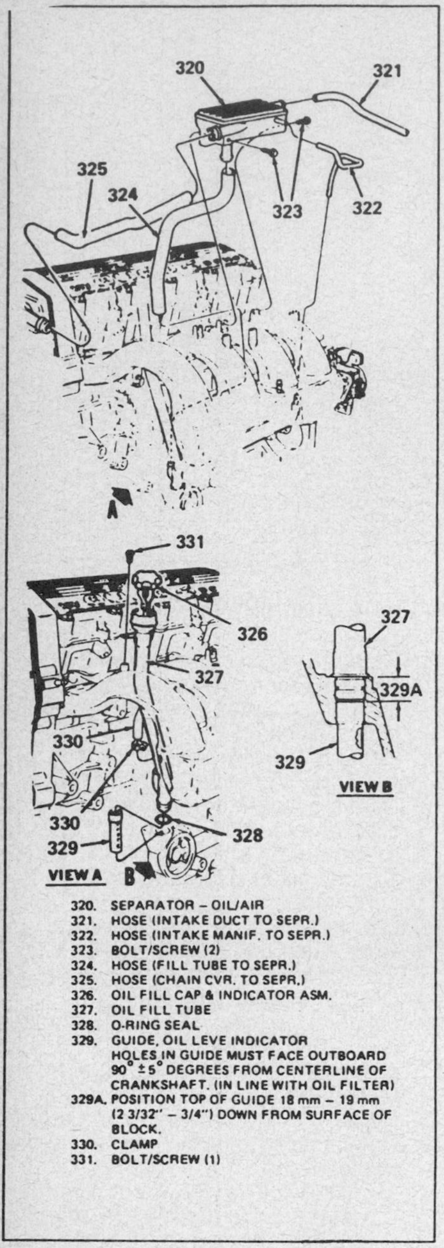
320
321
325
324
323
322
331
326
327
327
329A
330
329
VIEW B
330
329
328
VIEW A
320. SEPARATOR – OIL/AIR
321. HOSE (INTAKE DUCT TO SEPR.)
322. HOSE (INTAKE MANIF. TO SEPR.)
323. BOLT/SCREW (2)
324. HOSE (FILL TUBE TO SEPR.)
325. HOSE (CHAIN CVR. TO SEPR.)
326. OIL FILL CAP & INDICATOR ASM.
327. OIL FILL TUBE
328. O-RING SEAL
329. GUIDE, OIL LEVE INDICATOR HOLES IN GUIDE MUST FACE OUTBOARD 90° ± 5° DEGREES FROM CENTERLINE OF CRANKSHAFT. (IN LINE WITH OIL FILTER)
329A. POSITION TOP OF GUIDE 18 mm – 19 mm (2 3/32" – 3/4") DOWN FROM SURFACE OF BLOCK.
330. CLAMP
331. BOLT/SCREW (1)

GC1069100399000X

Fig. 6 Crankcase ventilation components

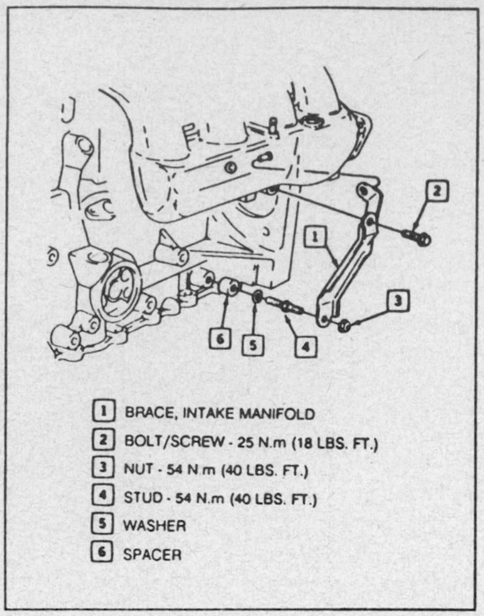
1 BRACE, INTAKE MANIFOLD
2 BOLT/SCREW - 25 N.m (18 LBS. FT.)
3 NUT - 54 N.m (40 LBS. FT.)
4 STUD - 54 N.m (40 LBS. FT.)
5 WASHER
6 SPACER

GC1059100083000X

Fig. 7 Intake manifold support brace

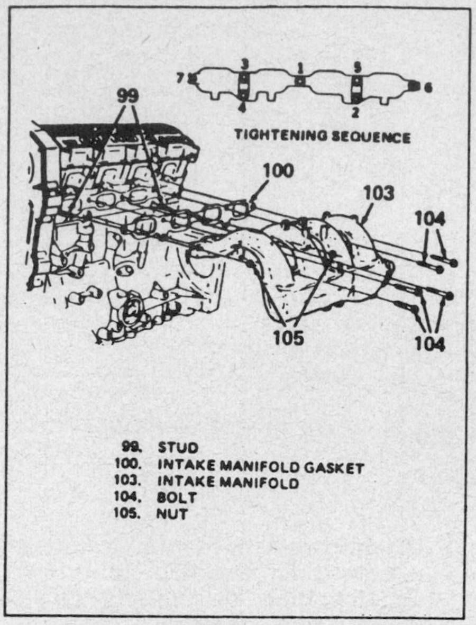
TIGHTENING SEQUENCE
99
100
103
104
105
104
99. STUD
100. INTAKE MANIFOLD GASKET
103. INTAKE MANIFOLD
104. BOLT
105. NUT

GC1059100084000X

Fig. 8 Intake manifold replacement

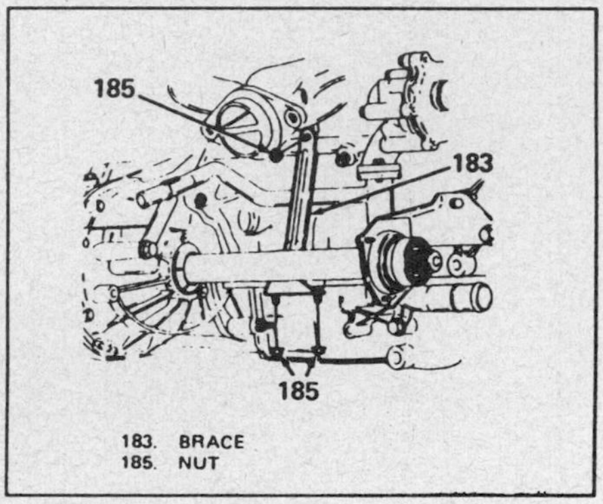
185
183
185
183. BRACE
185. NUT

GC1079100019000X

Fig. 9 Exhaust manifold brace

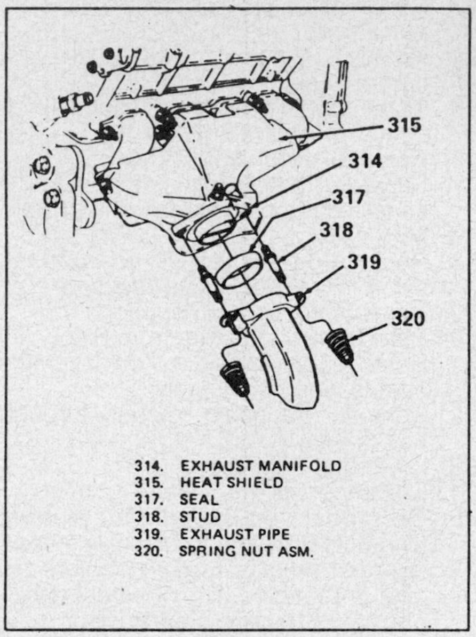
315
314
317
318
319
320
314. EXHAUST MANIFOLD
315. HEAT SHIELD
317. SEAL
318. STUD
319. EXHAUST PIPE
320. SPRING NUT ASM.

GC1079100020000X

Fig. 10 Exhaust pipe installation

a. Install exhaust manifold with new gasket. Refer to specifications for torque values.
b. Coat threads of Oxygen sensor with suitable anti-seize compound before installing.

OIL PAN

REPLACE

1. Disconnect battery ground cable.
2. Drain engine oil.
3. Remove flywheel cover, then the exhaust manifold brace.
4. Disconnect radiator outlet pipe to oil pan bolt, then transaxle to oil pan nut.
5. Remove oil pan to transaxle stud, then the oil pan bolts.
6. Remove oil pan.
7. Reverse procedure to install.

OIL PUMP

REPLACE

1. Remove oil pan as previously described.
2. Remove oil pump assembly bolts.
3. Remove oil pump assembly.
4. Reverse procedure to install.

BELT TENSION DATA

1. Check belt tensioner indicator marks, **Fig. 13,** to ensure belt is in operating range. Replace belt as needed, refer to **Fig. 14** for belt routing.
2. With all accessories Off, run engine until operating temperature is achieved.
3. Turn ignition switch to Off.
4. Position Belt Tensioner Tool No. J-36018 or equivalent, on the drive belt between idler pulley and alternator (models less A/C), or between A/C compressor and alternator (models with A/C). Note reading, and remove the tool.
5. Run engine for 15 seconds, then turn the ignition switch to Off.
6. Using a 13 mm socket, apply clockwise force to tensioner pulley bolt. Release the pulley, then take a reading as described in step 4.
7. Using a 13 mm socket, apply counterclockwise force to tensioner pulley bolt until the Install position is reached. Slowly release pulley to Rest position, then take a reading as described in step 4. Use caution not to disturb the belt tensioner position.
8. If average of the three readings taken is 50 lbs., and the belt is in the tensioners operating range, replace the tensioner bracket assembly as described in this section.

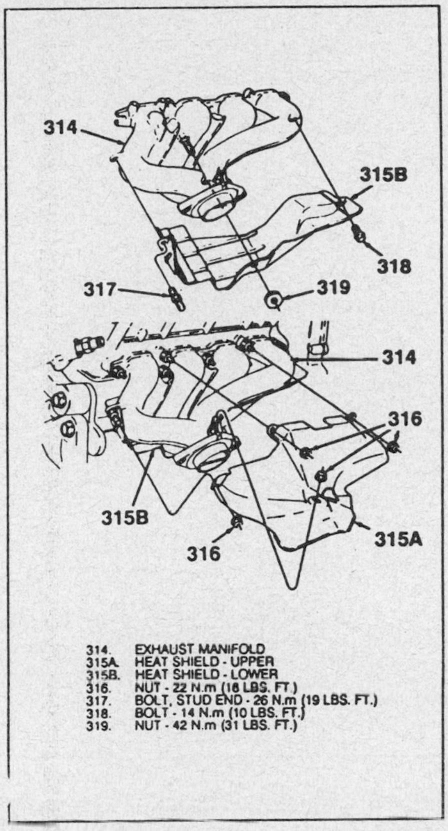
314
315B
318
317
319
314
316
315B
316
315A
314. EXHAUST MANIFOLD
315A. HEAT SHIELD - UPPER
315B. HEAT SHIELD - LOWER
316. NUT - 22 N.m (16 LBS. FT.)
317. BOLT, STUD END - 26 N.m (19 LBS. FT.)
318. BOLT - 14 N.m (10 LBS. FT.)
319. NUT - 42 N.m (31 LBS. FT.)

Fig. 11 Exhaust manifold heat shield installation

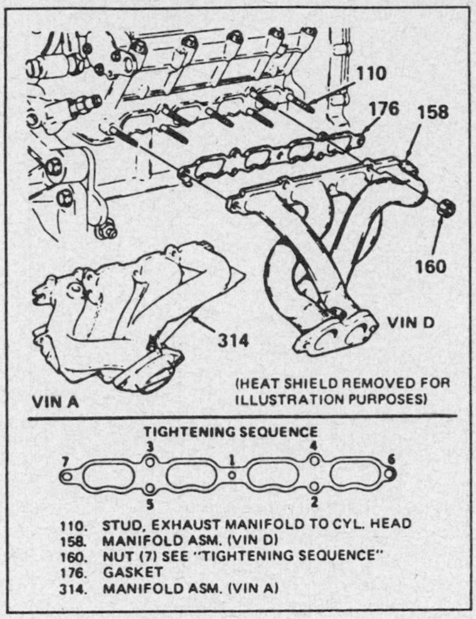
110
176
158
160
VIN D
314
VIN A
(HEAT SHIELD REMOVED FOR ILLUSTRATION PURPOSES)
TIGHTENING SEQUENCE
7 3 1 4 6
5 2
110. STUD, EXHAUST MANIFOLD TO CYL. HEAD
158. MANIFOLD ASM. (VIN D)
160. NUT (7) SEE "TIGHTENING SEQUENCE"
176. GASKET
314. MANIFOLD ASM. (VIN A)

GC1079100022000X

Fig. 12 Exhaust manifold replacement

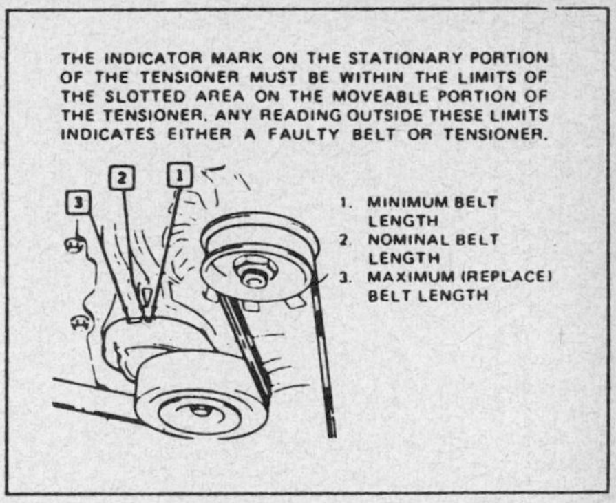
THE INDICATOR MARK ON THE STATIONARY PORTION OF THE TENSIONER MUST BE WITHIN THE LIMITS OF THE SLOTTED AREA ON THE MOVEABLE PORTION OF THE TENSIONER. ANY READING OUTSIDE THESE LIMITS INDICATES EITHER A FAULTY BELT OR TENSIONER.
3
2
1
1. MINIMUM BELT LENGTH
2. NOMINAL BELT LENGTH
3. MAXIMUM (REPLACE) BELT LENGTH

GC1069100403000X

Fig. 13 Drive belt tensioner indicator marks

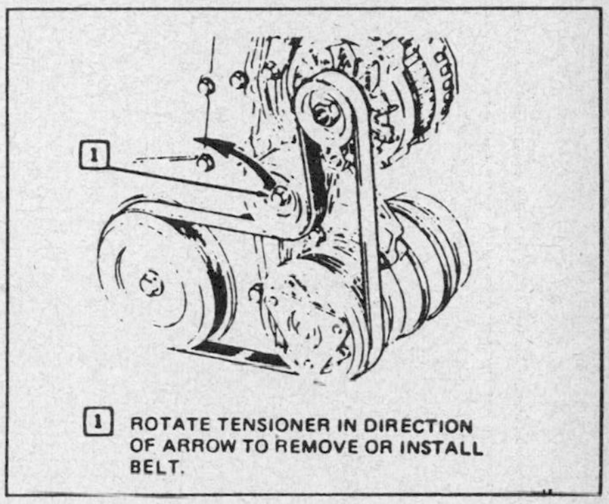
1
1 ROTATE TENSIONER IN DIRECTION OF ARROW TO REMOVE OR INSTALL BELT.

Fig. 14 Serpentine drive belt routing

SERPENTINE DRIVE BELT

BELT ROUTING

Refer to **Fig. 14** for serpentine drive belt routing.

PRECAUTIONS

When installing or removing the drive belt care should be taken to avoid bending or twisting the tensioner. Inspect bearings if belt tensioner or idler assembly produce a whining noise. If the drive belt becomes frayed, check belt tensioner assembly alignment and ensure belt edge does not contact the tensioner pulley flange.

Serpentine drive belt performance will not be impaired by cracks in the belt ribs. However belt replacement will be required if any of the following conditions occur: Belt ribs are missing, the belt slips or is frayed, or the belt tensioner runs out of travel before adjustment is proper.

TENSIONER BRACKET REPLACEMENT

1. Disconnect battery ground cable.
2. Loosen drive belt tensioner and remove drive belt.
3. Remove alternator assembly, **Fig. 15.**
4. **On models with A/C,** remove oil filter.
5. **On models with A/C,** remove rear compressor bracket.
6. **On models less A/C,** remove bolts retaining the idle pulley brace. Remove the brace.
7. **On all models,** raise and support vehicle.
8. Remove right splash shield.
9. **On models with A/C,** remove front compressor mounting bolts and position compressor aside.
10. **On all models,** remove chain housing to belt tensioner bracket brace, **Fig. 16.**
11. Remove five bolts retaining bracket to block.
12. Remove bracket from wheel opening.
13. Reverse procedure to install. Refer to specifications for torque values.

COOLING SYSTEM BLEED

These engines do not require a specified bleed procedure. After filling cooling system, run engine to operating temperature with radiator/pressure cap off. Air will then be automatically bled through cap opening.

THERMOSTAT

REPLACE

1. Disconnect battery ground cable, then drain coolant until level is below that thermostat housing.
2. Remove upper radiator hose and heater hose from housing, place aside.
3. Remove electrical connector from coolant sensor, then throttle body coolant hose.
4. Remove two thermostat housing attaching bolts, thermostat housing, then thermostat.
5. Reverse procedure to install. **Torque** thermostat housing attaching bolts to 19 ft. lbs.

WATER PUMP

REPLACE

1. Disconnect negative battery cable.
2. Drain cooling system.
3. Raise and support vehicle.
4. Disconnect oxygen sensor connector, then the exhaust pipe from exhaust manifold.
5. Remove radiator outlet pipe from oil pan and transaxle.
6. Lower vehicle.
7. Remover upper and lower exhaust manifold heat shields.
8. Remove exhaust manifold to cylinder head retaining nuts, then the exhaust manifold seals and gaskets.
9. Disconnect radiator outlet pipe assembly to coolant pump cover bolts.
10. Remove coolant cover to cylinder block bolts, then coolant pump assembly to timing chain housing nuts, **Fig. 17.**
11. Remove coolant pump and cover assembly.
12. Reverse procedure to install noting the following:
    a. Ensure water pump mating surfaces are clean.
    b. Lube O-ring on radiator outlet pipe with coolant prior to installing,

RADIATOR

REPLACE

Refer to "2.2L/4-134 Engine" section for radiator replacement procedure.

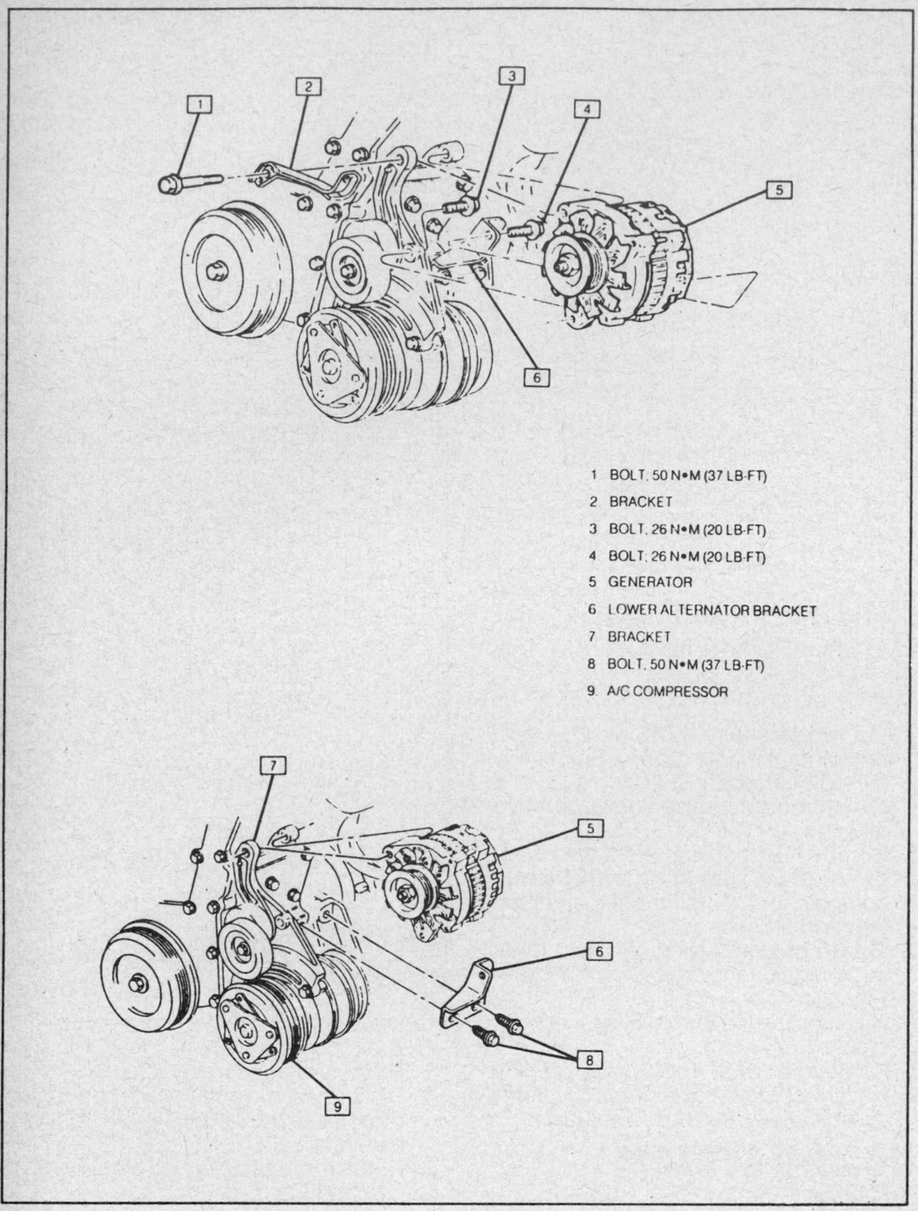
1
2
3
4
5
6
1 BOLT, 50 N•M (37 LB-FT)
2 BRACKET
3 BOLT, 26 N•M (20 LB-FT)
4 BOLT, 26 N•M (20 LB-FT)
5 GENERATOR
6 LOWER ALTERNATOR BRACKET
7 BRACKET
8 BOLT, 50 N•M (37 LB-FT)
9 A/C COMPRESSOR
7
5
6
8
9

GC1069100401000X

Fig. 15 Alternator assembly

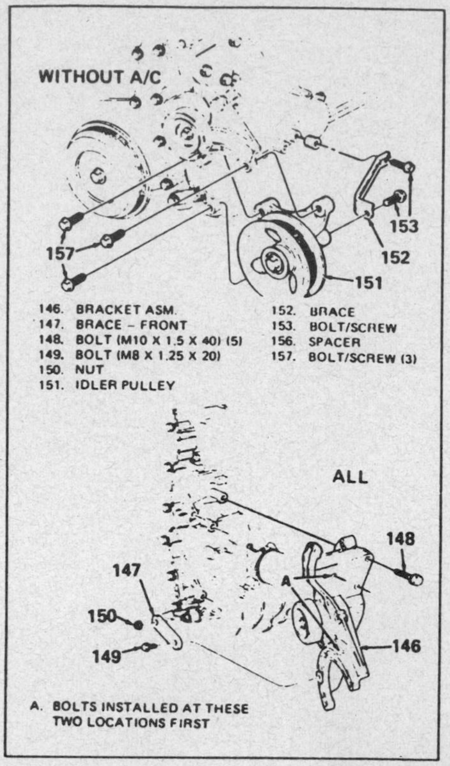
WITHOUT A/C
153
157
152
151
146. BRACKET ASM.
147. BRACE - FRONT
148. BOLT (M10 X 1.5 X 40) (5)
149. BOLT (M8 X 1.25 X 20)
150. NUT
151. IDLER PULLEY
152. BRACE
153. BOLT/SCREW
156. SPACER
157. BOLT/SCREW (3)
ALL
148
147
A
150
149
146
A. BOLTS INSTALLED AT THESE TWO LOCATIONS FIRST

GC1069100402000X

Fig. 16 Tensioner bracket assembly

FUEL PUMP
REPLACE

1. Disconnect battery ground cable.
2. Relieve fuel tank vapor pressure by loosening the fuel filler cap.
3. Using a suitable siphon, drain the fuel tank.
4. Remove fuel tank as follows:
   a. Raise and support vehicle.
   b. Remove two rubber exhaust pipe hangers, **Fig. 18.**
   c. Remove two muffler hanger retaining bolts.
   d. Remove three heat shield attaching screws, then the heat shield.
   e. Remove fuel tank filler tube, vent tube, vent hose, and clamps.
   f. Disconnect electrical connector, **Fig. 19.**
   g. Disconnect fuel level meter vapor hose.
   h. Ensure fuel line connections are clean. Disconnect fuel return quick connect fitting by squeezing plastic tab on male end of the fitting. Using Fuel Line Separator Tool Set No. J-37088 or equivalent, disconnect fuel line quick connect fitting. Plug all fittings.
   i. Properly support tank.
   j. Remove two rear retaining strap attaching bolts, then the fuel tank and retaining straps.
5. Thoroughly clean fuel level meter assembly connection and surrounding area, **Fig. 20.**
6. Using Fuel Sender Spanner Wrench tool No. J-35731 or equivalent, remove fuel level meter assembly lock ring. Remove assembly from tank, and discard the O-ring.
7. Disassemble fuel level meter assembly as follows:
   a. Note orientation of fuel filter for proper installation.
   b. To remove fuel filter, rotate it while pulling fuel pump in opposite direction, **Fig. 21.**
   c. Disconnect fuel pump electrical connector.
   d. Position fuel level meter assembly upside down on work area.
   e. Pull downward on fuel pump to separate it from mounting bracket. Tilt pump outward and remove it from pulsator.
8. Reverse procedure to install noting the following:
   a. Never run fuel pump unless submerged in fuel.
   b. Always replace fuel filter when installing fuel pump.
   c. Always use new O-ring when installing fuel level meter assembly.

FUEL FILTER
REPLACE

1. Loosen fuel filler cap to relieve tank pressure. Do not tighten at this time.
2. Raise and support vehicle, then disconnect fuel pump electrical connector from fuel tank.
3. Lower vehicle.
4. Start engine and run until fuel supply remaining in fuel lines is consumed. Engage starter for 3.0 seconds to ensure relief of any remaining pressure.
5. Raise and support vehicle, then connect fuel tank electrical connector.
6. Grasp filter and one nylon fuel connecting line fitting. Twist quick connect fitting 1/4 turn in each direction to

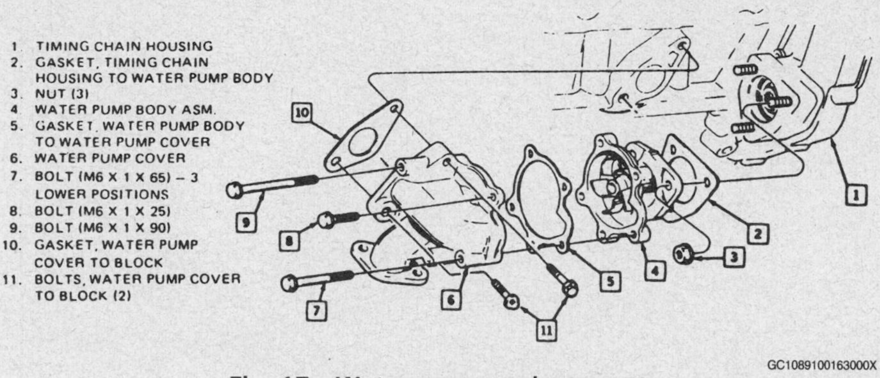
1. TIMING CHAIN HOUSING
2. GASKET, TIMING CHAIN HOUSING TO WATER PUMP BODY
3. NUT (3)
4. WATER PUMP BODY ASM.
5. GASKET, WATER PUMP BODY TO WATER PUMP COVER
6. WATER PUMP COVER
7. BOLT (M6 X 1 X 65) – 3 LOWER POSITIONS
8. BOLT (M6 X 1 X 25)
9. BOLT (M6 X 1 X 90)
10. GASKET, WATER PUMP COVER TO BLOCK
11. BOLTS, WATER PUMP COVER TO BLOCK (2)
GC1089100163000X

Fig. 17 Water pump replacement

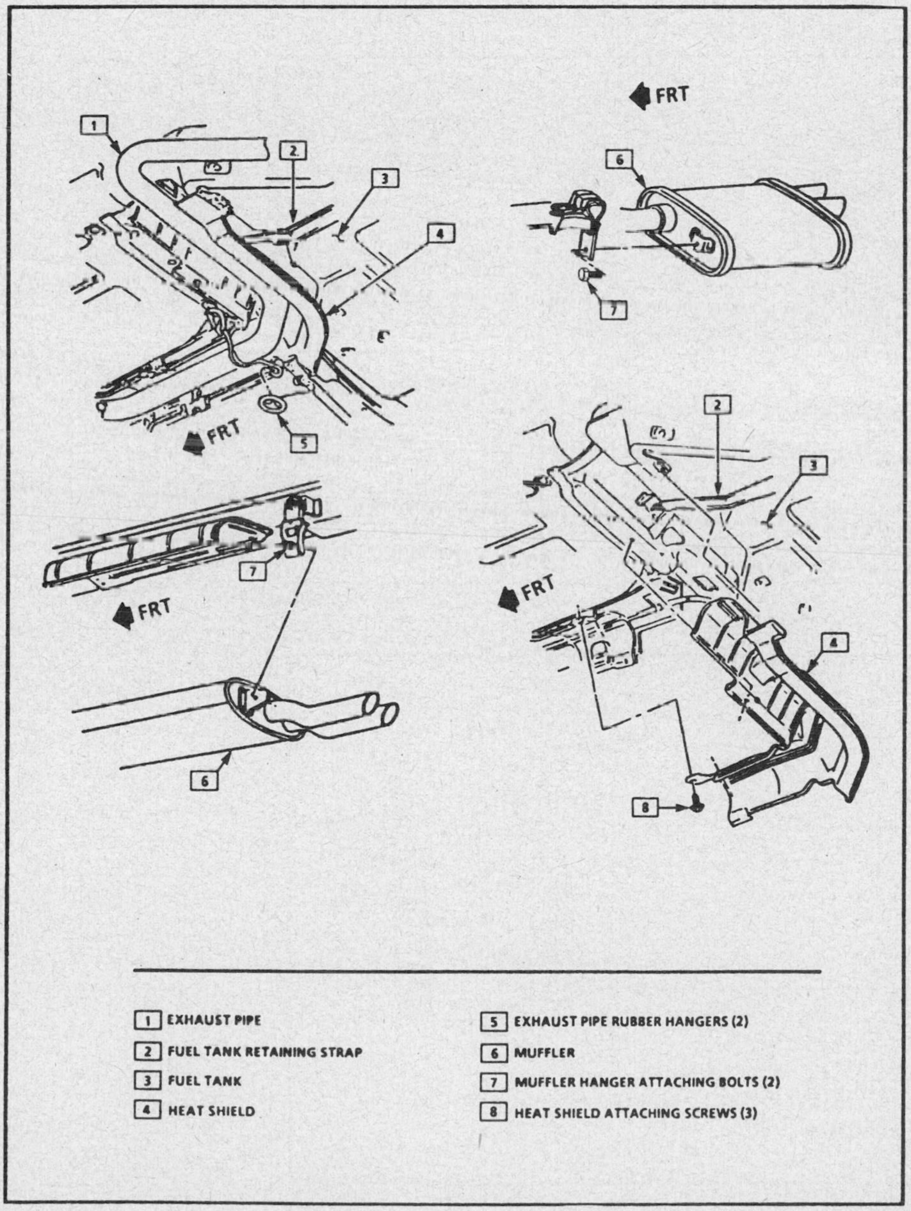
FRT
1 EXHAUST PIPE
2 FUEL TANK RETAINING STRAP
3 FUEL TANK
4 HEAT SHIELD
5 EXHAUST PIPE RUBBER HANGERS (2)
6 MUFFLER
7 MUFFLER HANGER ATTACHING BOLTS (2)
8 HEAT SHIELD ATTACHING SCREWS (3)
GC1079100023000X

Fig. 18 Exhaust assembly

loosen any dirt within fitting.

7. Repeat Step 2 for the other connector.
8. Remove fuel filter retaining screw, then squeeze plastic tabs of male end connector of filter connections and pull apart.
9. Using compressed air, blow the quick connectors clean or dirt. **Safety glasses must be worn during this procedure.**
10. Remove protective caps from new filter.
11. Apply a few drops of clean engine oil to the male tubes ends of the filter assembly.
12. Push connectors together to cause the retaining tabs/fingers to snap into place.
13. Once installed, pull on both ends of each connection to ensure they are secure.
14. Turn the ignition switch to the On Position, engine Off, for two seconds.
15. Turn ignition switch to the Off position for ten seconds, then to the ON position. Check fuel filter for leaks.

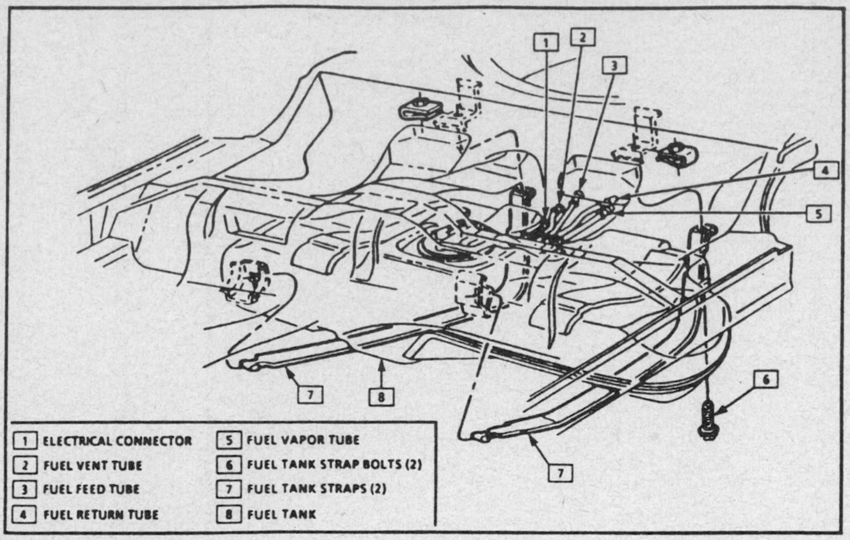
1 ELECTRICAL CONNECTOR
2 FUEL VENT TUBE
3 FUEL FEED TUBE
4 FUEL RETURN TUBE
5 FUEL VAPOR TUBE
6 FUEL TANK STRAP BOLTS (2)
7 FUEL TANK STRAPS (2)
8 FUEL TANK

GC1029102733000X

Fig. 19 Fuel tank removal

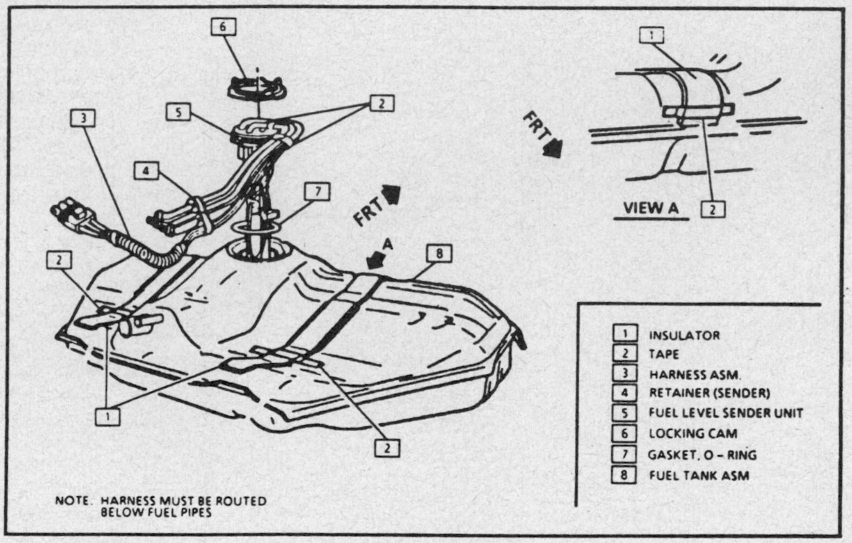
FRT
A
VIEW A
1 INSULATOR
2 TAPE
3 HARNESS ASM.
4 RETAINER (SENDER)
5 FUEL LEVEL SENDER UNIT
6 LOCKING CAM
7 GASKET, O - RING
8 FUEL TANK ASM
NOTE. HARNESS MUST BE ROUTED BELOW FUEL PIPES

GC1029102734000X

Fig. 20 Fuel tank assembly

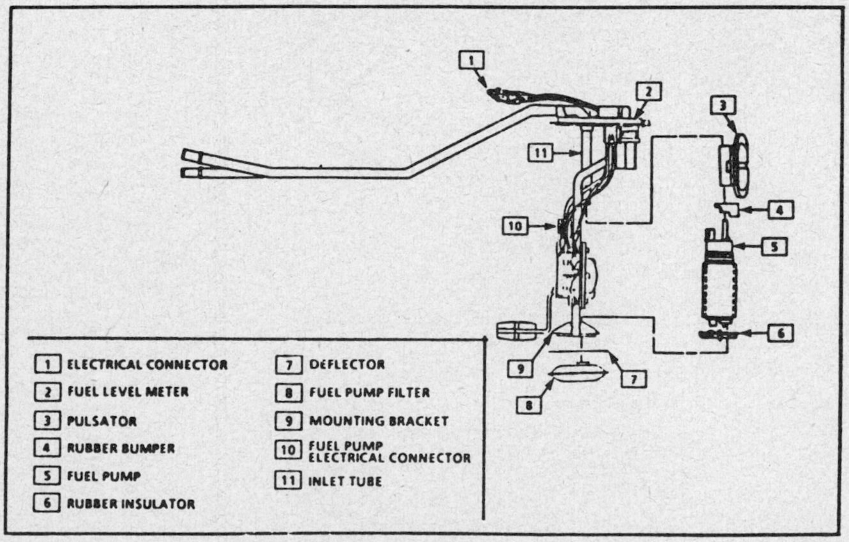
1 ELECTRICAL CONNECTOR
2 FUEL LEVEL METER
3 PULSATOR
4 RUBBER BUMPER
5 FUEL PUMP
6 RUBBER INSULATOR
7 DEFLECTOR
8 FUEL PUMP FILTER
9 MOUNTING BRACKET
10 FUEL PUMP ELECTRICAL CONNECTOR
11 INLET TUBE

GC1029102735000X

Fig. 21 Fuel level meter assembly

TIGHTENING SPECIFICATIONS

Year	Component	Torque/Ft. Lbs.
1992–95	Camshaft Rear Cover	10
	Camshaft Sprocket To Cam Bolt	⑤
	Coolant Outlet To Cylinder Head	19
	Crankshaft Position Sensor To Block	80①
	Cylinder Head Threaded Plug	④
	Engine Mount Strut Bracket Attaching Bolt	49
	Engine Mount Strut Through Bolt	89
	ESC Knock Sensor	15
	Exhaust Manifold To Cylinder Head Nuts	27
	Exhaust Manifold To Cylinder Head Studs	106①
	Exhaust Manifold To Exhaust Pipe	22
	Exhaust Manifold To Oil Pan Brace	19
	Exhaust Manifold Studs To Manifold	22
	Front Cover To Timing Chain Housing	106①
	Front Engine Mount Bracket To Block	40
	Front Engine Mount To Cylinder Block Bracket	55
	Front Engine Mount To Engine Mount Crossmember	30
	Fuel Rail To Camshaft Housing	19
	Ignition Coil And Module Assembly To Camshaft Housing	15
	Intake Manifold Brace Bolts	19
	Intake Manifold To Cylinder Head	18
	Oil/Air Separator To Intake Manifold	71①
	Oil Cooler lines To Oil Cooler Adapter	26
	Oil Filter Connector To Block	21
	Oil Fill Tube Bolt	72①
	Oil Filter To Block	②
	Oil Pan Baffle Bolts	30
	Oil Pan Bolts	17
	Oil Pan Drain Plug	19
	Oil Pump To Block	40
	Oil Pump Cover To Oil Pump Body	106①
	Rear Crankshaft Seal Housing To Block	106①
	Rear Engine Mount Bracket To Body	40
	Rear Engine Mount Bracket To Engine	44
	Rear Engine Mount To Body Bracket	55
	Rear Engine Mount Through Bolt Nut	55
	Right Engine Mount Attaching Bolt	42
	Spark Pugs To Cylinder Head	17
	Starter To Block Bolt	71
	Tensioner Bracket Assembly Bracket To Block	40
	Tensioner Bracket Assembly Bracket To Front Brace	19
	Tensioner Bracket Assembly Bracket To Idler	40
	Tensioner Bracket Assembly Rear Brace To Block Or Idler	40
	Timing Chain Housing To Block	19
	Timing Chain Tensioner To Housing	③
	Throttle Body To Intake Manifold	19
	Transaxle Mount To Body	40
	Water Pump To Timing Chain Housing	19
	Water Pump To Water Pump Cover	10

①—Inch lbs.
②—3/4 to one turn after initial gasket contact.
③—1992 models, 115 inch lbs.; 1993–95 models, 89 inch lbs.
④—1992 models, 19 ft. lbs.; 1993–95 models, 40 ft. lbs.
⑤—1992 models, 40 ft. lbs.; 1993–95 models, 52 ft. lbs.

3.1L/V6-192 Engine

NOTE: On Air Bag Equipped Models, Refer To "Air Bag System Precautions" Located In The Front Of This Manual For System Disarming & Arming Procedures.

NOTE: Refer To 3.1L/V6-192 Engine Section In "Buick Regal, Chevrolet Lumina & Monte Carlo, Oldsmobile Cutlass Supreme & Pontiac Grand Prix" Chapter For Service Procedures Not Covered In This Section.

INDEX

PRECAUTIONS

AIR BAG SYSTEMS

Refer to "Air Bag System Precautions" in the front of this manual for system disarming and arming procedures.

FUEL SYSTEM PRESSURE RELIEF

1. Disconnect battery ground cable.
2. Relieve fuel tank vapor pressure by loosening fuel filler cap.
3. Install Fuel Pressure Gauge tool No. J-34730 or equivalent, to fuel pressure valve. **To avoid spilling fuel when connecting the gauge, wrap fitting with a shop towel.**
4. Position end of bleed hose into a suitable container, then open bleeder valve until system pressure is relieved.

IDLE LEARN PROCEDURE

Any time vehicle power has been interrupted (battery disconnected), the programed position of the IAC valve pintle is lost. The following procedure must be performed to update the ECM memory with the correct IAC valve pintle position, enabling the ECM to provide a stable idle speed.

1. Restore vehicle power.
2. Connect suitable scan tool to ALDL connector, located under the lefthand side of the dash panel.
3. Select "IAC System."
4. Select "Idle Learn" in the "Misc. Test" mode.
5. Proceed as directed by scan tool.

ENGINE MOUNT

REPLACE

FRONT MOUNT

1. Disconnect battery ground cable.
2. Remove two engine mount to body bracket bolts, then the upper engine mount to engine bracket bolt. Raise and support vehicle.
3. Support engine with suitable jack.
4. Remove inner fender shield.
5. Remove lower engine mount to body bracket bolt, **Fig. 1.**
6. Remove lower engine mount to engine bracket bolt, then remove mount.
7. Reverse procedure to install. Clean all bolts with suitable solvent and apply suitable locking compound to threads prior to installation. Torque bolts to specifications given in **Fig. 1.**

REAR MOUNT

1. Disconnect battery ground cable, then raise and support vehicle.
2. Support engine with suitable jack.
3. Remove motor mount nuts and attaching bolts, **Fig. 2.**
4. Reverse procedure to install.

ENGINE

REPLACE

1. Removed air cleaner assembly.
2. Remove battery cables and battery.
3. Drain cooling system, then disconnect transaxle cooler lines at radiator.
4. Disconnect transaxle fluid level indicator.
5. Disconnect upper and lower radiator hoses from engine.
6. Disconnect heater outlet hose from water pump, then the heater inlet hose at rear of engine.
7. Remove serpentine belt.
8. Disconnect shift cable linkage and cable from mounting bracket. It may be necessary to place transaxle in low gear.
9. Disconnect accelerator and cruise control cable, if equipped, from throttle linkage.
10. Disconnect A/C pressure switch electrical connector.
11. Disconnect vacuum check valve from power brake booster, then the canister purge vacuum line from the engine.
12. Disconnect upper engine electrical connectors, then the vacuum hose from vacuum reservoir.
13. Raise and support vehicle.
14. Remove front wheel and tire assemblies.
15. Remove righthand splash shield, then the oil filter.
16. Disconnect lower engine electrical connectors.
17. Disconnect A/C compressor, leaving hoses and rear bracket attached, then secure compressor out of the way.
18. Disconnect exhaust pipe from crossover.
19. Disconnect brake hose bracket at strut, then the brake calipers.
20. Disconnect tie rods from strut assemblies.
21. Place suitable engine table under front of vehicle, then lower vehicle

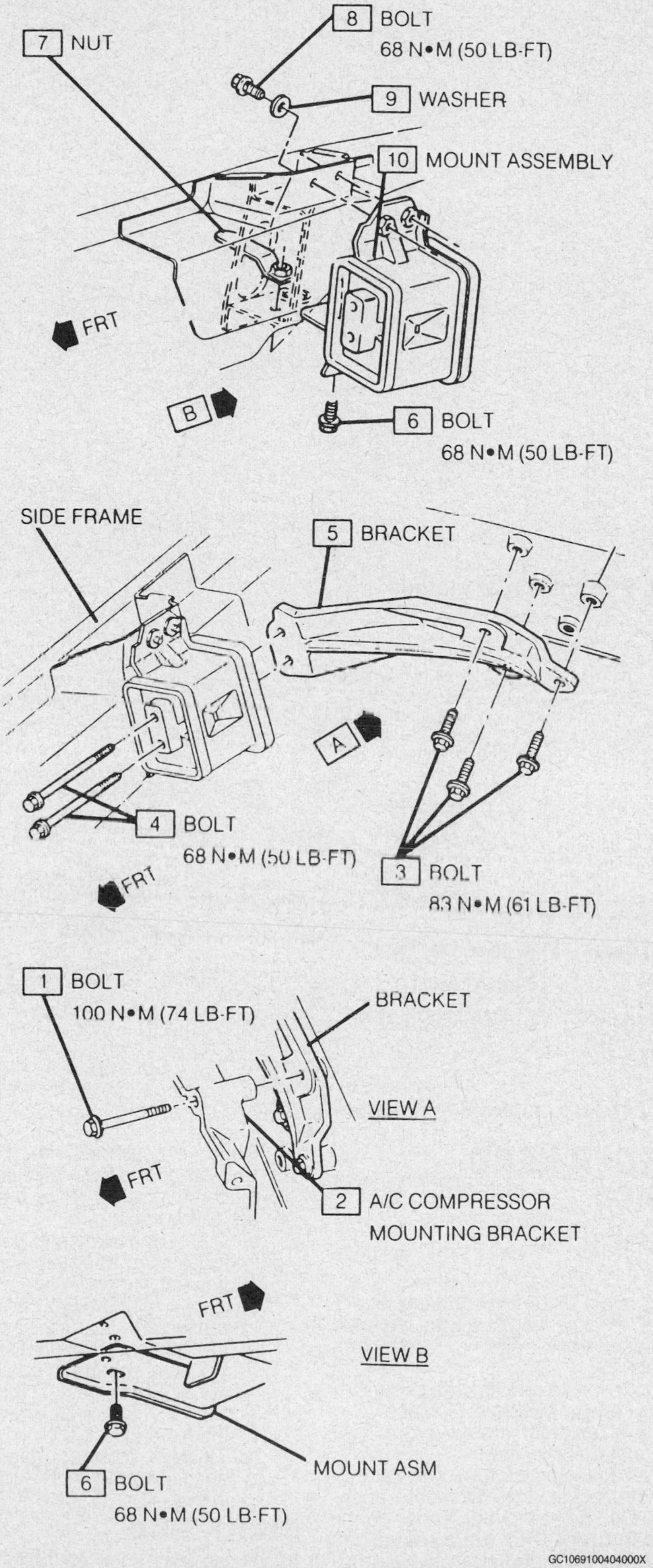

7 NUT
8 BOLT
68 N•M (50 LB-FT)
9 WASHER
10 MOUNT ASSEMBLY
FRT
B
6 BOLT
68 N•M (50 LB-FT)
SIDE FRAME
5 BRACKET
A
4 BOLT
68 N•M (50 LB-FT)
FRT
3 BOLT
83 N•M (61 LB-FT)
1 BOLT
100 N•M (74 LB-FT)
BRACKET
VIEW A
FRT
2 A/C COMPRESSOR
MOUNTING BRACKET
FRT
VIEW B
MOUNT ASM
6 BOLT
68 N•M (50 LB-FT)
GC1069100404000X

Fig. 1 Engine front mount

enough to place engine and transaxle assembly onto table.

22. Lower table with engine and transaxle assembly, then raise vehicle.
23. Reverse procedure to install.

INTAKE MANIFOLD

REPLACE

1. Disconnect battery ground cable.
2. Disconnect accelerator and TV. cable bracket at plenum.
3. Disconnect throttle body at plenum.
4. Disconnect EGR pipe at EGR valve, then remove plenum.
5. Disconnect fuel inlet and return pipes at fuel rail.
6. Remove auxiliary drive belt.
7. Remove power steering pump and position aside.
8. Remove alternator with wiring attached and position aside.
9. Loosen alternator bracket.
10. Disconnect idle air vacuum hose at throttle body and the electrical connectors at injectors.
11. Remove fuel rail, breather tube and the runners.
12. Remove both rocker arm covers.
13. Drain cooling system into suitable container.
14. Disconnect radiator hose at thermostat outlet.
15. Disconnect coolant sensor and oil sender switch electrical connectors.
16. Remove coolant sensor, then disconnect cooling system bypass hose and heater inlet pipe at manifold.
17. Remove intake manifold attaching bolts, then the intake manifold.
18. Loosen rocker arm nuts until pushrods can be removed. **Keep pushrods in order they are removed so they can be installed in their original position.**
19. Reverse procedure to install, noting the following:
    a. When installing gaskets, install only on right or left side as marked.
    b. Clean cylinder case sealing surface front and rear ridges and apply a 3/16 inch bead of suitable RTV sealant on each cylinder block ridge.
    c. Install new intake gaskets on cylinder heads, then install pushrods. Tighten rocker arm attaching nuts to specifications.
    d. When installing intake manifold, ensure areas between case ridges and manifold are completely sealed.
    e. Install manifold retaining bolts and nuts, tighten to specifications.

EXHAUST MANIFOLD

REPLACE

LEFT SIDE

1. Remove air cleaner assembly.
2. Disconnect negative battery cable.
3. Remove coolant fan, then the heat shield.
4. Remove exhaust crossover pipe at manifold.

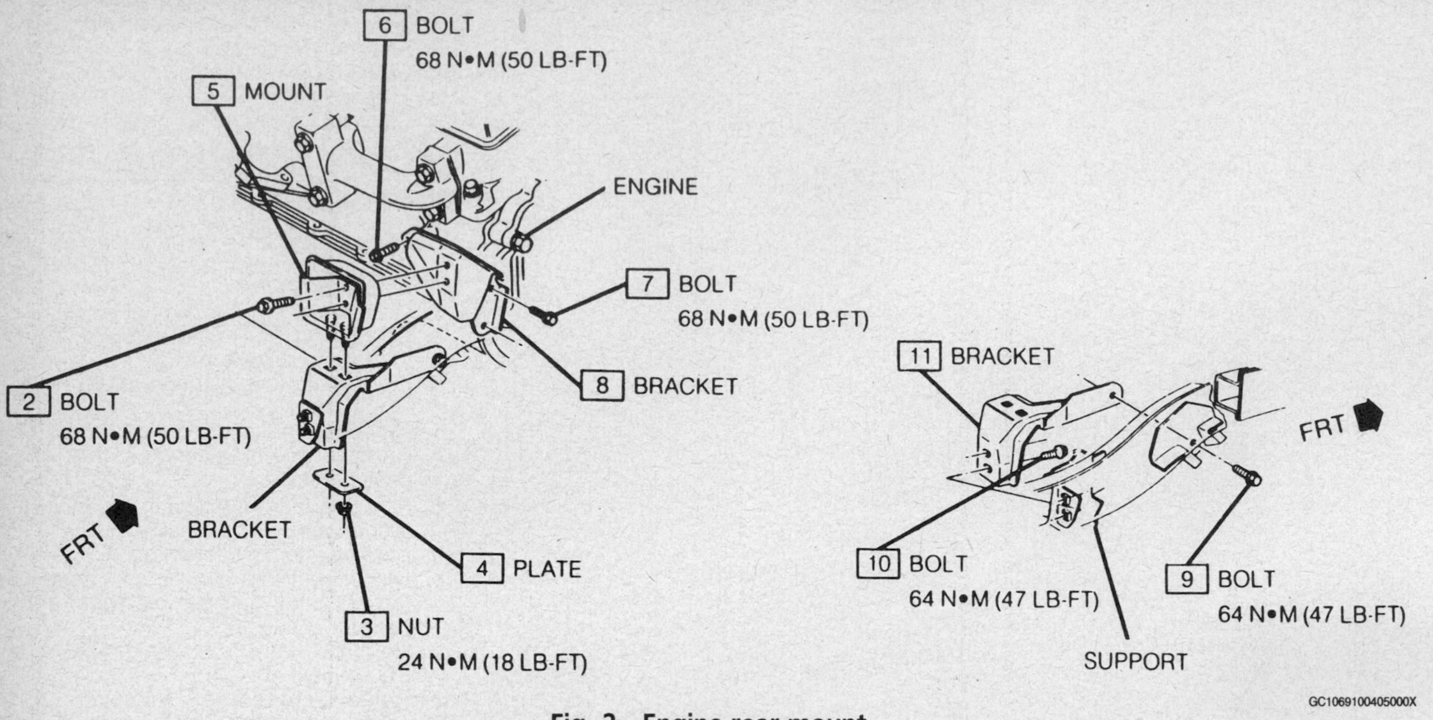
6 BOLT
68 N•M (50 LB-FT)
5 MOUNT
ENGINE
7 BOLT
68 N•M (50 LB-FT)
8 BRACKET
2 BOLT
68 N•M (50 LB-FT)
FRT
BRACKET
4 PLATE
3 NUT
24 N•M (18 LB-FT)
11 BRACKET
FRT
10 BOLT
64 N•M (47 LB-FT)
9 BOLT
64 N•M (47 LB-FT)
SUPPORT
GC1069100405000X

Fig. 2 Engine rear mount

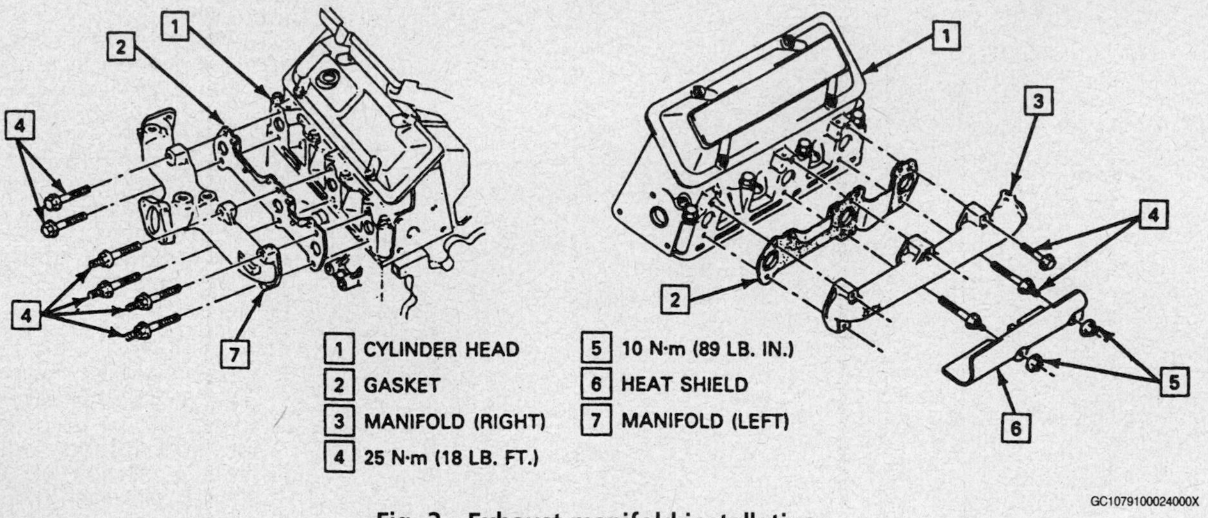
1 CYLINDER HEAD
2 GASKET
3 MANIFOLD (RIGHT)
4 25 N·m (18 LB. FT.)
5 10 N·m (89 LB. IN.)
6 HEAT SHIELD
7 MANIFOLD (LEFT)
GC1079100024000X

Fig. 3 Exhaust manifold installation

5. Remove exhaust manifold bolts, then the exhaust manifold, **Fig. 3.**
6. Reverse procedure to install.

RIGHT SIDE

1. Remove air cleaner assembly.
2. Disconnect negative battery cable.
3. Raise and support vehicle.
4. Remove exhaust pipe at crossover, then lower vehicle.
5. Remove heatshield, then the crossover at manifold.
6. Disconnect accelerator and T.V. cables, then remove bracket.
7. Remove oxygen sensor.
8. Remove exhaust manifold bolts, then the exhaust manifold, **Fig. 3.**
9. Reverse procedure to install.

CYLINDER HEAD
REPLACE
LEFT SIDE

1. Disconnect battery ground cable.
2. Drain engine coolant into suitable container, then remove rocker arm cover.
3. Remove intake manifold as described under "Intake Manifold, Replace."
4. Remove exhaust crossover at right side exhaust manifold.
5. Remove oil dipstick tube bracket.
6. Loosen rocker arm nuts until pushrods can be removed. **Keep pushrods in order they are removed so they can be installed in their original position.**
7. Remove cylinder head attaching bolts, then the cylinder head.
8. Reverse procedure to install, noting the following:
   a. Clean cylinder head bolts and cylinder head bolt holes with suitable solvent.
   b. Apply GM 1052080 sealer or equivalent to cylinder head bolt threads prior to installation.
   c. Position new head gasket on deck surface over dowel pins with "This Side Up" facing up, then install cylinder head.
   d. Tighten cylinder head bolts to specifications, in sequence shown in **Fig. 4.**

RIGHT SIDE

1. Raise and support vehicle, then remove right side exhaust manifold.

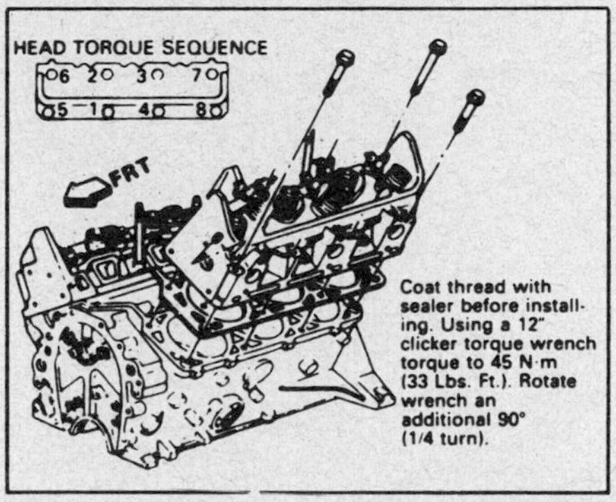
HEAD TORQUE SEQUENCE
6 2 3 7
5 1 4 8
FRT
Coat thread with sealer before installing. Using a 12" clicker torque wrench torque to 45 N·m (33 Lbs. Ft.). Rotate wrench an additional 90° (1/4 turn).

GC1069100406000X

Fig. 4 Cylinder head installation

2. Lower vehicle, then remove rocker arm cover.
3. Remove intake manifold. Refer to "Intake Manifold, Replace" for procedure.
4. Loosen rocker arm nuts until pushrods can be removed. **Keep pushrods in order they are removed so they can be installed in their original position.**
5. Remove cylinder head attaching bolts, then the cylinder head.
6. Reverse procedure to install, noting the following:
   a. Clean cylinder head bolts and cylinder head bolt holes with suitable solvent.
   b. Apply GM 1052080 sealer or equivalent to cylinder head bolt threads prior to installation.
   c. Position new head gasket on deck surface over dowel pins with "This Side Up" facing up, then install cylinder head.
   d. Tighten cylinder head bolts to specifications, in sequence shown in **Fig. 4.**

VALVE ARRANGEMENT

FRONT TO REAR

Right .... E-I-E-I-I-E
Left .... E-I-I-E-I-E

VALVE LIFTERS

1. Remove intake manifold as previously described.
2. Remove valve mechanism, then the valve lifters.
3. Install valve lifters. When installing new lifters, coat foot of valve lifters with "Molykote" or equivalent, ensuring lifter foot is convex.
4. Install intake manifold as previously described.
5. Install and adjust valve mechanism.

CAMSHAFT LOBE LIFT SPECIFICATIONS

Engine	Int.	Exh.
3.1L/V6-192	.2626	.2732

VALVE ADJUSTMENT

1. Remove rocker arm covers.
2. Crank engine until assembly alignment mark on front face of torsional damper lines up with the arrow on the front cover. The engine should also be in the No. 1 firing position. This can be determined by placing fingers on No. 1 rocker arms as mark on torsional damper approaches arrow on front cover.
3. If valves are not moving, engine is in No. 1 firing position. If valves move as the mark comes up to the arrow on front cover, engine is in No. 4 firing position and should be rotated one revolution to reach No. 1 position.
4. With engine in No. 1 firing position, adjust exhaust valves 1, 2 and 3 and intake valves 1, 5 and 6, as follows:
   a. Back out adjusting nut until lash is felt at pushrod, then turn in adjusting nut until all lash is removed.
   b. When lash has been removed, turn adjusting nut in additional 1 1/2 turns to center lifter plunger.
5. Crank engine one revolution until arrow on front cover and torsional damper mark are again in alignment.
6. With the engine in this, the No. 4 firing position. adjust exhaust valves 4, 5 and 6 and intake valves 2, 3 and 4 as previously described.
7. Install rocker arm covers.

VALVE STEM OIL SEAL & VALVE SPRING

REPLACE

1. Remove rocker arm cover, then the spark plug, rocker arm and pushrod on cylinder(s) being serviced. **Keep valve train parts in order they are removed so they can be installed in their original position.**
2. Install Air Line Adapter tool No. J-23590 or equivalent, to spark plug port and apply compressed air to hold valves in place.
3. Using Valve Spring Compressor tool No. J-5892 or equivalent, to compress valve spring, remove valve locks, valve caps, valve spring and seat.
4. Remove valve stem oil seal.
5. Reverse procedure to install.

VALVE GUIDES

Valve guides are an integral part of the cylinder head and are not removable. If valve stem clearance becomes excessive, the valve guide should be reamed to the next oversize and the appropriate oversize valves installed. Valves are available in .003, .015 and .030 inch oversizes.

FRONT COVER

REPLACE

1. Disconnect battery ground cable, then drain cooling system.
2. Remove auxiliary drive belt and tensioner.
3. Remove alternator with wiring connected and position aside.
4. Loosen alternator bracket.
5. Remove power steering pump and position aside.

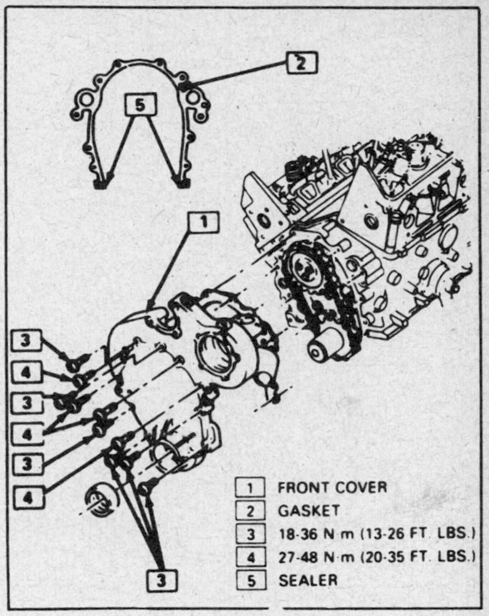
1 FRONT COVER
2 GASKET
3 18-36 N·m (13-26 FT. LBS.)
4 27-48 N·m (20-35 FT. LBS.)
5 SEALER

GC1069100407000X

Fig. 5 Engine front cover installation

6. Remove idler (if equipped).
7. Raise and support vehicle, then remove inner splash shield.
8. Remove flywheel cover from transaxle, then using Torsional Dampener tool No. J-24420 or equivalent, remove damper.
9. Remove starter, then the oil pan.
10. Disconnect radiator hose at water pump, then the heater hose from cooling system fill pipe.
11. Disconnect bypass and overflow hoses.
12. Remove water pump pulley.
13. Remove plug wire shield at water pump.
14. Remove canister purge hose.
15. Remove front cover attaching bolts, then the front cover.
16. Reverse procedure to install, noting the following:
    a. Clean all parts in suitable solvent.
    b. Apply sealer, GM 1052080 or equivalent to bolts as shown, **Fig. 5.**

FRONT COVER SEAL

REPLACE

1. Remove inner splash shield and torsional damper, then pry seal from cover using a suitable screwdriver. **Use caution not to damage crankshaft surface during seal removal.**
2. Install new seal so open end faces toward inside of cover, then drive seal into position using suitable tool.

TIMING CHAIN

REPLACE

1. Remove crankcase front cover, refer to "Front Cover, Replace" for procedure.
2. Place No. 1 cylinder at TDC and align timing marks on crankshaft and camshaft sprockets, **Fig. 6.**
3. Remove camshaft sprocket attaching

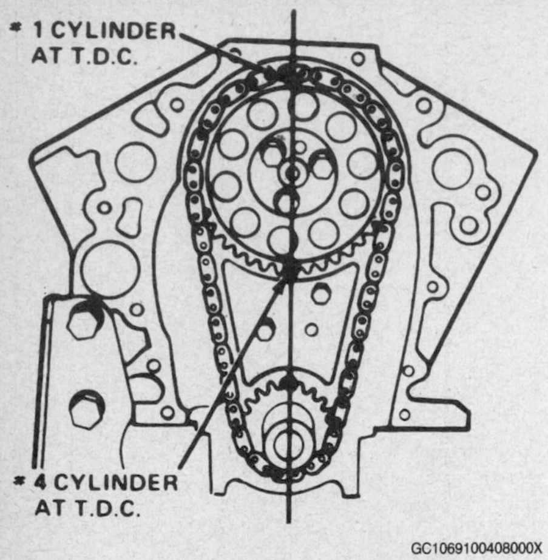
* 1 CYLINDER AT T.D.C.
* 4 CYLINDER AT T.D.C.
GC1069100408000X

Fig. 6 Timing gear mark alignment

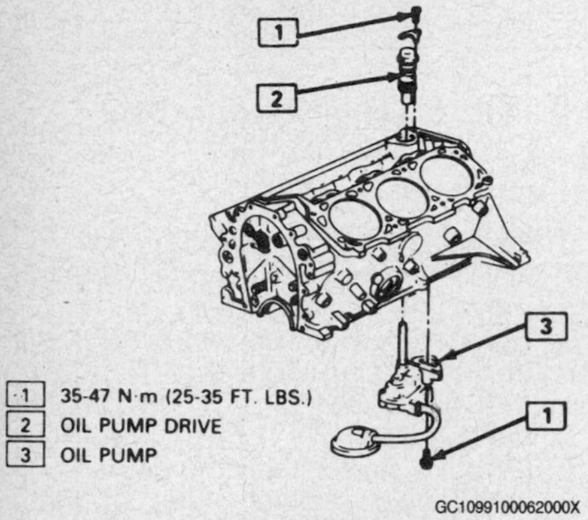
1
2
3
1
1 35-47 N·m (25-35 FT. LBS.)
2 OIL PUMP DRIVE
3 OIL PUMP
GC1099100062000X

Fig. 9 Oil pump removal

bolts. Tap lower edge of sprocket with plastic mallet and remove sprocket and timing chain.
4. If necessary, replace crankshaft sprocket.
5. Apply Molykote or equivalent to sprocket thrust surface.
6. Align timing marks, **Fig. 6**, and install timing chain on sprockets.
7. Position sprocket onto camshaft by aligning dowel hole with the dowel pin. Use retaining bolt to seat sprocket fully onto the camshaft. Tighten retaining bolt to specifications.
8. Lubricate timing chain with engine oil, then install front cover.

CAMSHAFT

REPLACE

1. Remove engine from vehicle, refer to "Engine, Replace" for procedure.
2. Remove valve lifters, refer to "Valve Lifter, Replace" for procedure.
3. Remove engine front cover, refer to "Front Cover, Replace" procedure.
4. Remove timing chain and sprocket. Refer to "Timing Chain & Sprocket, Replace" for procedure.
5. Remove camshaft. **Use caution not to damage bearings during camshaft removal.**
6. Reverse procedure to install. Coat camshaft lobes with GM E.O.S. 1052367 or equivalent prior to installation.

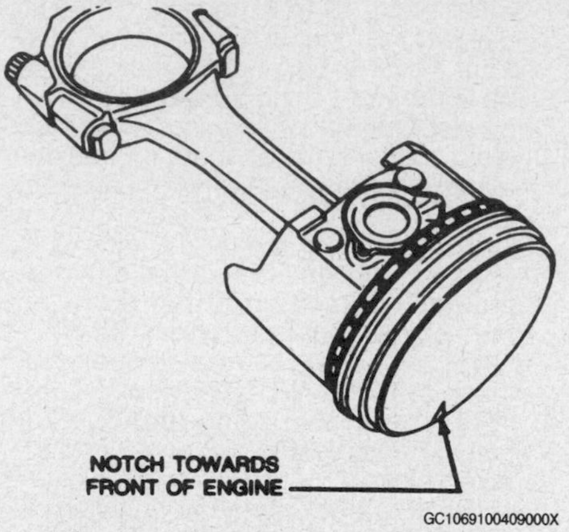
NOTCH TOWARDS FRONT OF ENGINE
GC1069100409000X

Fig. 7 Piston & rod assembly

PISTON & ROD ASSEMBLY

There is a machined hole or cast notch in the top of all pistons. The piston assemblies should always be installed with the hole or notch toward front of engine, **Fig. 7.**

PISTONS, PINS & RINGS

Pistons and rings are available in standard and oversize. Piston pins are available in standard size only.

MAIN & ROD BEARINGS

Main and rod bearing are available in standard sizes and undersizes.

CRANKSHAFT REAR OIL SEAL

REPLACE

1. Support engine and remove transaxle.
2. Remove flywheel.
3. Remove seal by carefully inserting screwdriver in through dust lip and prying towards end of crankshaft. Repeat as necessary around circumference of seal until seal is removed, taking care not to damage crankshaft circumference.
4. Check inside of seal bore for nicks or burrs and correct as necessary. Inspect crankshaft for burrs or nicks on seal contact surface. Repair or replace crankshaft as necessary.
5. Install new seal using Rear Main Seal Installer tool No. J-34686 or equivalent.
6. Place seal on mandrel, making sure that dust lip on seal bottoms squarely against collar of tool, **Fig. 8.**
7. After aligning dowel pin with dowel pin hole in crankshaft, attach tool to crankshaft and **torque** screws to 2-5 ft. lbs.
8. Turn T-handle of tool until collar is tight against engine block to ensure that seal is seated properly in block.
9. Loosen T-handle of tool until it comes to a stop. Remove attaching screws.
10. Check that seal is seated squarely in bore.
11. Install flywheel and transaxle.
12. Start engine and check for leaks.

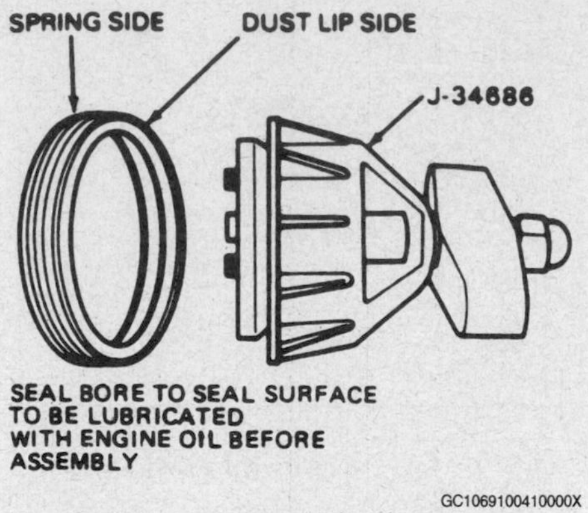
SPRING SIDE
DUST LIP SIDE
J-34686
SEAL BORE TO SEAL SURFACE TO BE LUBRICATED WITH ENGINE OIL BEFORE ASSEMBLY
GC1069100410000X

Fig. 8 Rear main oil seal installation

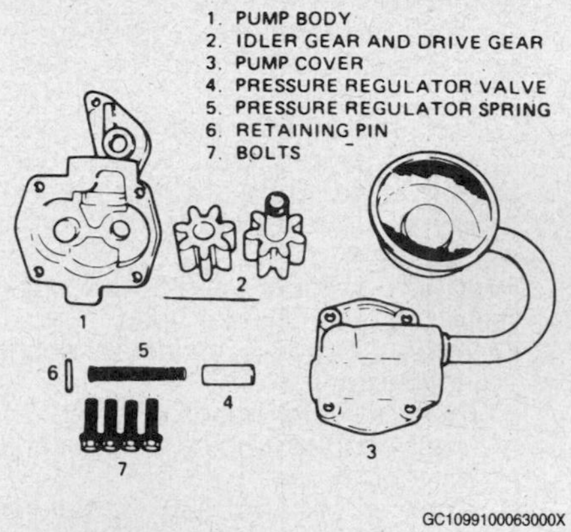
1. PUMP BODY
2. IDLER GEAR AND DRIVE GEAR
3. PUMP COVER
4. PRESSURE REGULATOR VALVE
5. PRESSURE REGULATOR SPRING
6. RETAINING PIN
7. BOLTS
GC1099100063000X

Fig. 10 Oil pump assembly

OIL PAN

REPLACE

1. Disconnect battery ground cable.
2. Raise and support vehicle, then drain crankcase.
3. Remove flywheel dust cover, then the starter motor.
4. Remove oil pan attaching bolts, then the oil pan.
5. Reverse procedure to install. Apply suitable sealer to oil pan mating surfaces. Tighten attaching bolts to specifications.

OIL PUMP

REPLACE

REMOVAL

1. Drain crankcase, then remove oil pan as previously described.
2. Remove pump to rear main bearing attaching bolt, then remove pump, **Fig. 9.**

DISASSEMBLY

1. Drain oil from pump, then remove driveshaft and driveshaft extension.
2. Remove pickup tube and screen.
3. Remove four pump cover to body attaching bolts, then remove cover, idler and drive gears, **Fig. 10. Place alignment mark on oil pump drive and idler gear teeth so they can be installed in the same position.**
4. Remove pressure regulator valve retaining pin, spring and the valve from pump body.

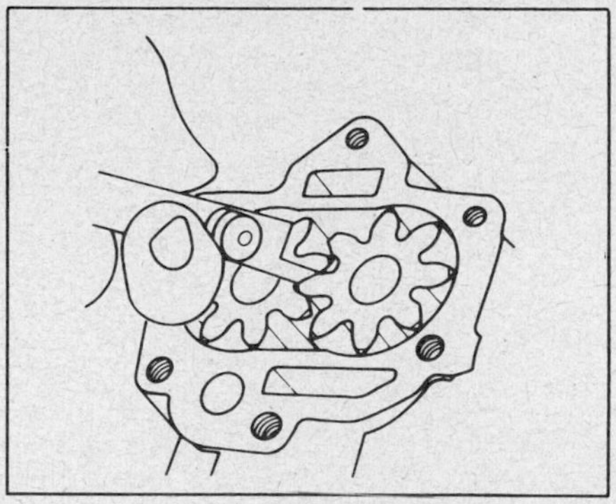
GC1099100064000X

Fig. 11 Oil pump gear lash measurement

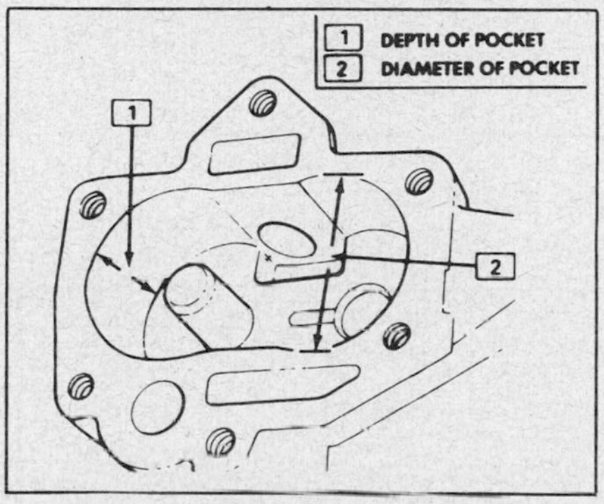
1 DEPTH OF POCKET
2 DIAMETER OF POCKET
1
2
GC1099100065000X

Fig. 12 Oil pump housing pocket measurement

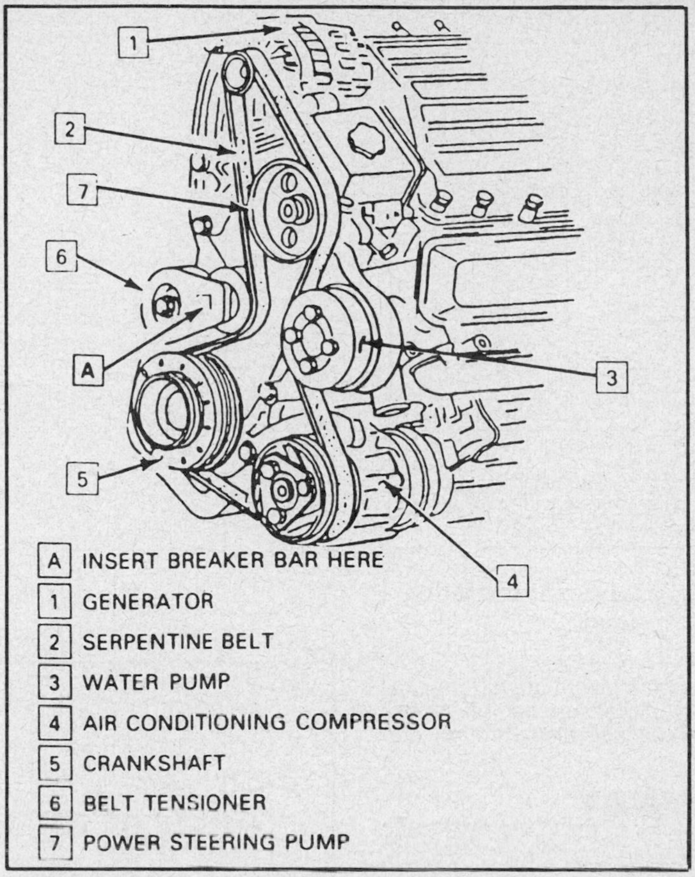
A INSERT BREAKER BAR HERE
1 GENERATOR
2 SERPENTINE BELT
3 WATER PUMP
4 AIR CONDITIONING COMPRESSOR
5 CRANKSHAFT
6 BELT TENSIONER
7 POWER STEERING PUMP
GC1069100411000X

Fig. 13 Serpentine drive belt routing

INSPECTION

1. Inspect pump components and should any of the following conditions exist, the oil pump assembly should be replaced.
   a. Inspect pump body, gears and cover for cracks or excessive wear.
   b. Check drive gear shaft for looseness in housing.
   c. Check inside of pump cover for wear that would allow oil to leak past ends of gears.
   d. Check oil pickup screen assembly for damage to screen or pickup tube.
   e. Check pressure regulator valve for fit in pump body.
2. Install pump gears, then using a feeler gauge, measure oil pump gear lash at several locations, **Fig. 11.** Clearance should be .0037-.0077 inch on 3.1L/V6-192 engines.
3. Remove pump gears, then measure depth of oil pump housing pocket, **Fig. 12.** Depth should be 1.195-1.198 inch on engines with aluminum pump bodies, and 1.202-1.205 on engines with cast iron pump bodies.
4. Measure pump gear length. Length should be 1.199-1.2 inch.
5. Measure pump gear diameters. Diameters should be 1.498-1.5 inch on engines with aluminum pump bodies, and 1.504-1.506 on engines with cast iron pump bodies.
6. Install pump gears, then measure side clearance between pump gears and oil pump housing. Side clearance should be .003-.004 inch.
7. If oil pump components are not within specifications, it should be replaced.

ASSEMBLY

Lubricate internal parts with engine oil during assembly.

1. Install replacement pickup screen and tube assembly, if removed. Position pump in a soft jawed vise, then apply sealer to end of tube and tap into position using Suction Tube Installer Tube tool No. J-8369 or equivalent and a plastic hammer. Use care not to damage inlet screen and tube assembly when installing into pump housing.
2. Place pressure regulator valve, spring and retaining pin into pump body, then install drive gear and shaft.
3. Install idler gear into pump body, then the pump cover gasket. **Fig. 10.**
4. Install pump cover, tighten retaining bolts to specifications.

INSTALLATION

1. Align oil pump extension shaft drive gear socket and pump housing, then install pump assembly. Tighten pump assembly retaining bolts to specifications.
2. Install oil pan as previously described.

SERPENTINE DRIVE BELT

BELT ROUTING

Refer to **Fig. 13** for serpentine drive belt routing.

BELT TENSIONER ADJUSTMENT

Belt tension is maintained by a spring loaded belt tensioner. To remove or install drive belt, rotate tensioner with a 3/4 inch socket. If belt tension is not satisfactory, ensure belt tensioner is within operating limits, **Fig. 14.** If belt tensioner is allowed to operate outside its operating limits, damage to belt tensioner may result.

BELT TENSIONER REPLACEMENT

1. Remove serpentine belt guard, **Fig. 13.**
2. Lift or rotate tensioner using a 1/2 inch breaker bar.
3. Remove serpentine belt, then the tensioner bolt.
4. Remove tensioner.
5. Reverse procedure to install.

COOLING SYSTEM BLEED

These engines do not require a specified bleed procedure. After filling cooling

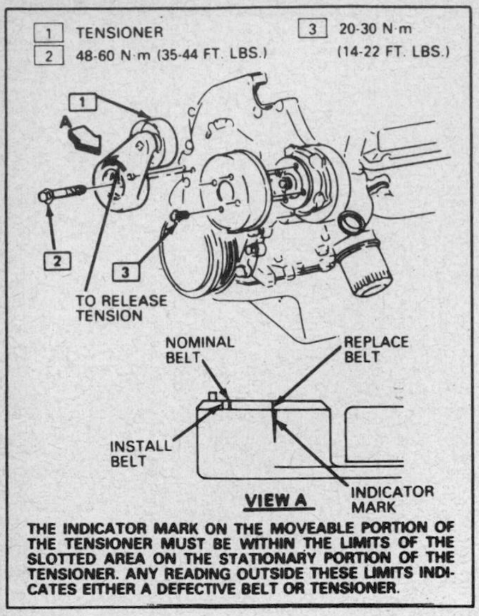
1 TENSIONER
2 48-60 N·m (35-44 FT. LBS.)
3 20-30 N·m (14-22 FT. LBS.)
TO RELEASE TENSION
NOMINAL BELT
REPLACE BELT
INSTALL BELT
VIEW A
INDICATOR MARK
THE INDICATOR MARK ON THE MOVEABLE PORTION OF THE TENSIONER MUST BE WITHIN THE LIMITS OF THE SLOTTED AREA ON THE STATIONARY PORTION OF THE TENSIONER. ANY READING OUTSIDE THESE LIMITS INDICATES EITHER A DEFECTIVE BELT OR TENSIONER.

GC1069100412000X

Fig. 14 Belt tensioner operating range

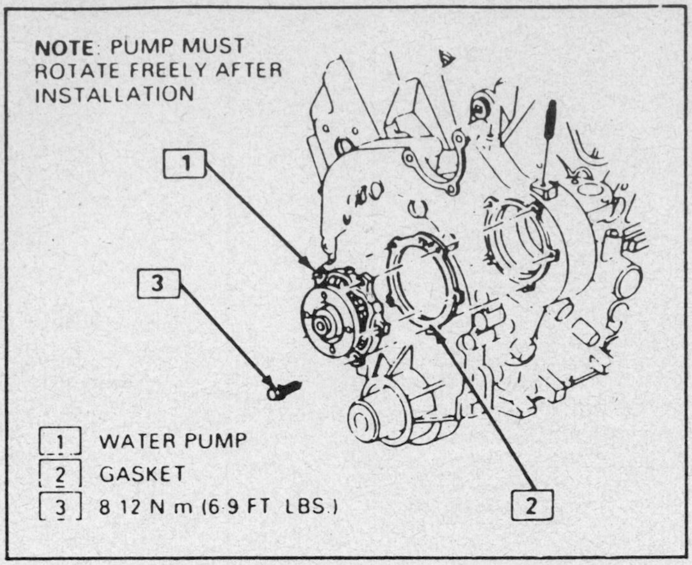
NOTE: PUMP MUST ROTATE FREELY AFTER INSTALLATION
1 WATER PUMP
2 GASKET
3 8-12 N·m (6-9 FT. LBS.)

GC1089100164000X

Fig. 15 Water pump installation

system, run engine to operating temperature with radiator/pressure cap off. Air will then be automatically bled through cap opening.

THERMOSTAT
REPLACE

1. Disconnect battery ground cable.
2. Drain engine coolant below level of thermostat housing.
3. **On 3.1L/V6-192 engine,** remove crankcase vent tube.
4. **On all models,** remove upper radiator hose from housing.
5. Remove housing attaching bolts, water outlet, then thermostat.
6. Reverse procedure to install. **Torque** attaching bolts to 19 ft. lbs.

WATER PUMP
REPLACE

1. Disconnect battery ground cable, then drain cooling system.
2. Remove accessory drive belt.
3. Remove water pump pulley, then the water pump, **Fig. 15.**
4. Reverse procedure to install.

RADIATOR
REPLACE

Refer to "2.2L/4-134 Engine" section for radiator replacement procedure.

FUEL PUMP
REPLACE

1. Disconnect battery ground cable.
2. Raise and support vehicle.
3. Drain, then remove fuel tank as follows:
   a. Raise and support vehicle.
   b. Remove two rubber exhaust pipe hangers, **Fig. 16.**
   c. Remove two muffler hanger retaining bolts.

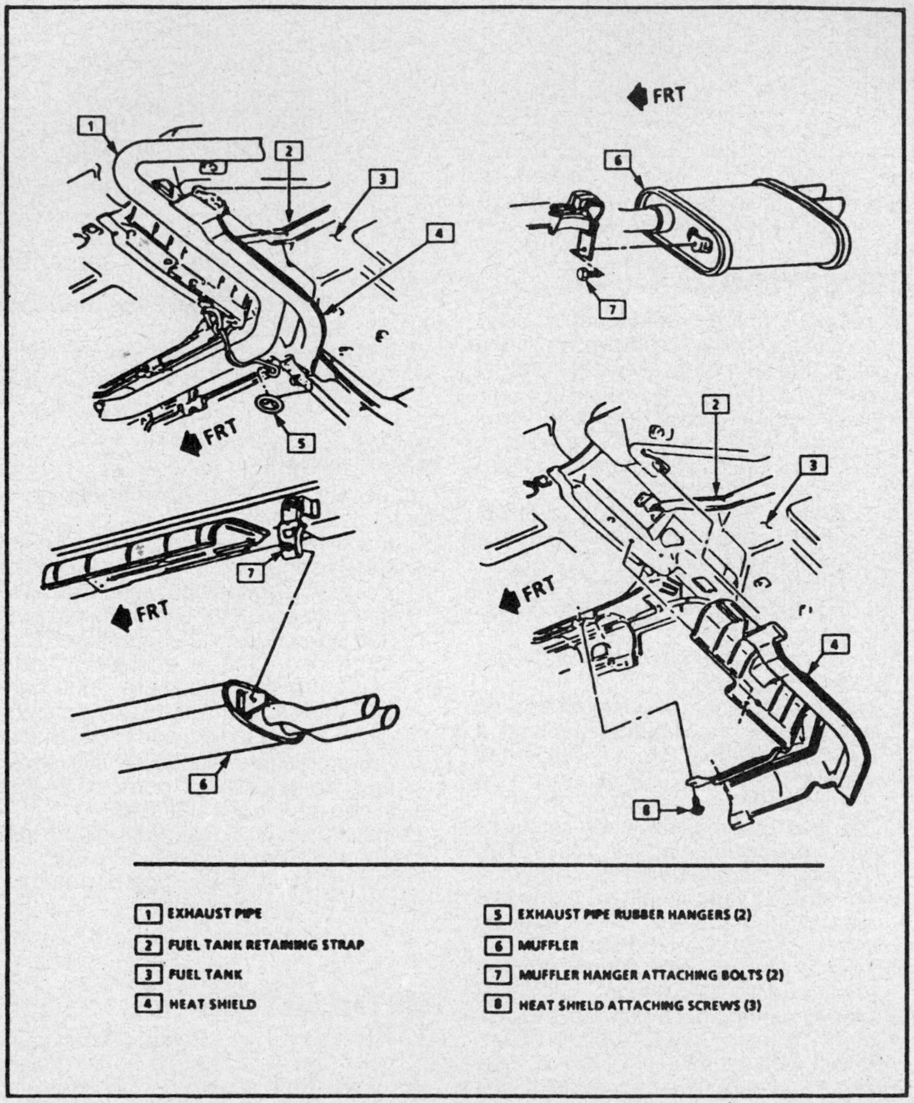
FRT
1 EXHAUST PIPE
2 FUEL TANK RETAINING STRAP
3 FUEL TANK
4 HEAT SHIELD
5 EXHAUST PIPE RUBBER HANGERS (2)
6 MUFFLER
7 MUFFLER HANGER ATTACHING BOLTS (2)
8 HEAT SHIELD ATTACHING SCREWS (3)

GC1079100025000X

Fig. 16 Exhaust assembly

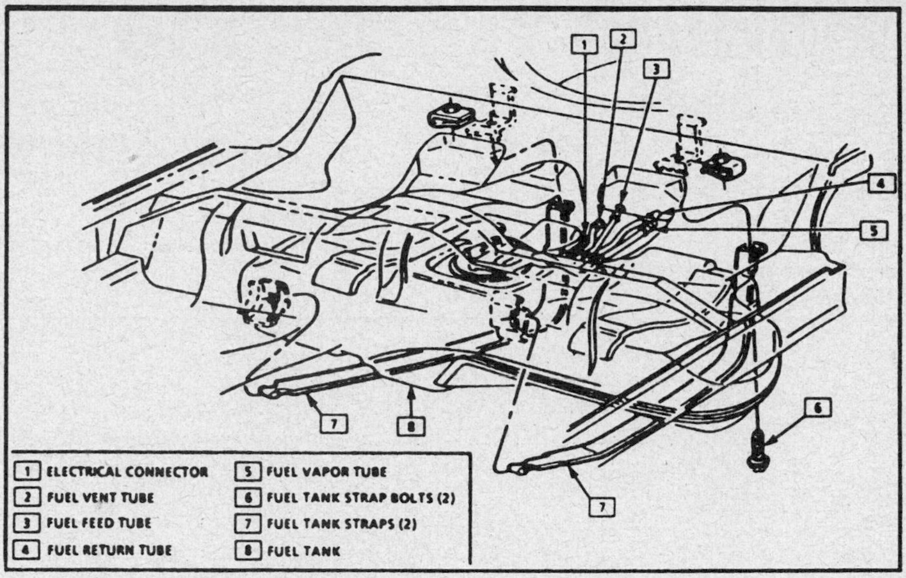
1 ELECTRICAL CONNECTOR
2 FUEL VENT TUBE
3 FUEL FEED TUBE
4 FUEL RETURN TUBE
5 FUEL VAPOR TUBE
6 FUEL TANK STRAP BOLTS (2)
7 FUEL TANK STRAPS (2)
8 FUEL TANK
GC1029102736000X

Fig. 17 Fuel tank removal

d. Remove three heat shield attaching screws, then the heat shield.
e. Remove fuel tank filler tube, vent tube, vent hose, and clamps.
f. Disconnect electrical connector, **Fig. 17.**
g. Disconnect fuel level meter vapor hose.
h. Ensure fuel line connections are clean. Disconnect fuel return quick connect fitting by squeezing plastic tab on male end of the fitting. Using Connector Tool Set No. J-37088 or equivalent, disconnect fuel line quick connect fitting. Plug all fittings.
i. Properly support tank.
j. Remove two rear retaining strap attaching bolts, then the fuel tank and retaining straps.

4. Rotate fuel sender/pump assembly cam lock ring, then lift out fuel sender/pump assembly.
5. Remove fuel pump from fuel sender by pulling fuel pump up into attaching hose while pulling outwards from lower support.
6. Reverse procedure to install noting the following:
   a. Install new fuel sender/pump assembly O-ring onto fuel tank before installation.
   b. Always replace fuel filter when installing new pump.
   c. Never run fuel pump unless submerged in fuel.

FUEL FILTER

REPLACE

1. Disconnect battery ground cable.
2. Loosen fuel filler cap to relieve tank pressure. Do not tighten at this time.
3. Connect Fuel Pressure Gage tool No. J-34730-1 or equivalent to fuel pressure valve. **Wrap a shop towel around fitting while connecting gage to avoid spillage.**
4. Install bleed hose into approved container and open valve to bleed system pressure.
5. Drain any fuel remaining in gage into an approved container.
6. Raise and support vehicle.
7. Grasp filter and one nylon fuel connecting line fitting. Twist quick connect fitting 1/4 turn in each direction to loosen any dirt within fitting.
8. Repeat Step 2 for the other connector.
9. Remove fuel filter retaining screw, then squeeze plastic tabs of male end connector of filter connections and pull apart.
10. Using compressed air, blow the quick connectors clean of dirt. **Safety glasses must be worn during this procedure.**
11. Remove protective caps from new filter.
12. Apply clean engine oil to the male tubes ends of the filter assembly.
13. Push connectors together to cause the retaining tabs/fingers to snap into place.
14. Once installed, pull on both ends of each connection to ensure they are secure.
15. Turn the ignition switch to the On position for two seconds.
16. Turn ignition switch to the Off position for ten seconds, then to the ON position. Check fuel filter for leaks.

TIGHTENING SPECIFICATIONS

Year	Component	Torque/Ft. Lbs.
1992–95	Camshaft Rear Cover	7
	Camshaft Sprocket	18
	Connecting Rod Cap	37
	Cylinder Head Bolts	①
	Drive Belt Tensioner Belt	37
	Engine Strut Bracket To Engine	34
	Exhaust Crossover Nut	18
	Exhaust Manifold	21
	Exhaust Manifold To Heat Shield	89③
	Flywheel to Crankshaft	52
	Intake Manifold	18
	Main Bearing Cap	④
	Oil Filter	11
	Oil Filter Adapter Connector	46
	Oil Level Indicator Retaining Nut	18
	Oil Pan	②
	Oil Pump	⑤
	Oil Pump Cover	8

Year	Component	Torque/Ft. Lbs.
1992–95 —Cont'd	Rocker Arm Nuts	20
	Rocker Arm Stud	47
	Rocker Arm Cover	6-9
	Spark Plugs	10-25
	Strut Brackets To Upper Tie Bar	16
	Strut To Tie Bar Brackets	32
	Thermostat Housing	19
	Timing Chain Dampener Pulley	15
	Vibration Damper or Pulley	67-85
	Water Pump	7

①—Torque to 33 ft. lbs., then tighten an additional 90° in sequence.
②—1992 models, torque 6mm bolts to 6–9 ft. lbs. and 8 mm bolts to 15–23 ft. lbs.; 1993–95 models, torque to 89 inch lbs.
③—Inch lbs.
④—1992 models, 63–83 ft. lbs.; 1993–95 models, 37 ft. lbs. plus an additional 77° turn.
⑤—1992 models, 25-38 ft. lbs.; 1993–95 models, 30 ft. lbs.

Clutch & Manual Transaxle

INDEX

ADJUSTMENTS

CLUTCH

On these models, a hydraulic clutch system is used, **Fig. 1.** The system consists of a dash mounted master cylinder with integral reservoir, a transmission mounted slave cylinder and high pressure tubing to connect the two components.

The hydraulic clutch system provides automatic clutch adjustment, therefore, there is no provision for adjustment.

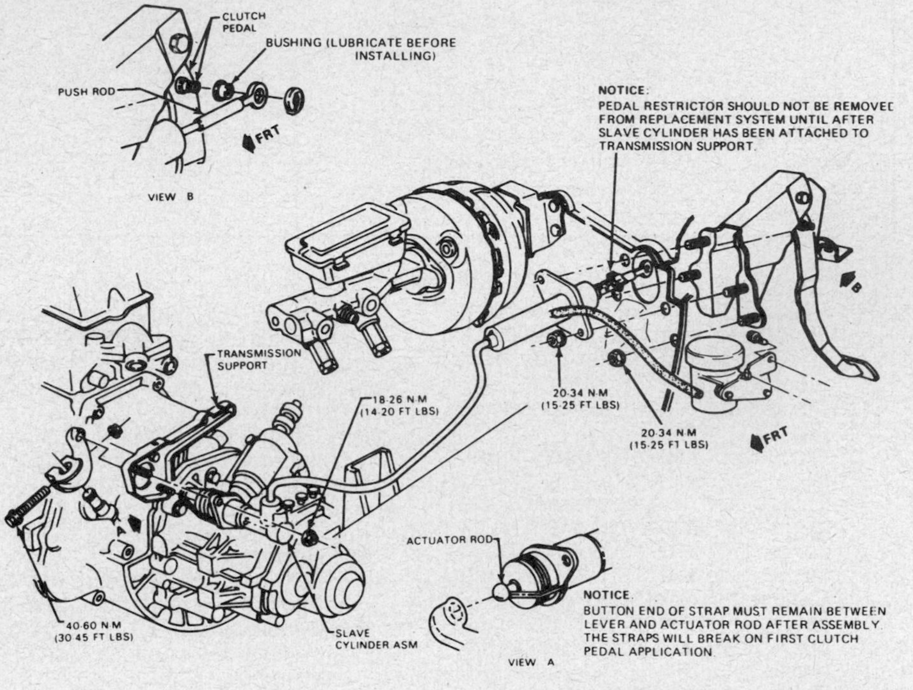

CLUTCH PEDAL
BUSHING (LUBRICATE BEFORE INSTALLING)
PUSH ROD
FRT
VIEW B
NOTICE:
PEDAL RESTRICTOR SHOULD NOT BE REMOVED FROM REPLACEMENT SYSTEM UNTIL AFTER SLAVE CYLINDER HAS BEEN ATTACHED TO TRANSMISSION SUPPORT.
TRANSMISSION SUPPORT
18-26 N·M (14-20 FT LBS)
20-34 N·M (15-25 FT LBS)
20-34 N·M (15-25 FT LBS)
FRT
ACTUATOR ROD
NOTICE:
BUTTON END OF STRAP MUST REMAIN BETWEEN LEVER AND ACTUATOR ROD AFTER ASSEMBLY. THE STRAPS WILL BREAK ON FIRST CLUTCH PEDAL APPLICATION.
40-60 N·M (30-45 FT LBS)
SLAVE CYLINDER ASM
VIEW A

GC5049100046000X

Fig. 1 Hydraulic clutch assembly

HYDRAULIC SYSTEM SERVICE

CLUTCH BLEED

1. Clean dirt and grease from the cap to ensure no foreign substances enter the system.
2. Remove cap and diaphragm and fill reservoir to the top with hydraulic clutch fluid No. 12345347 or an equivalent fluid that meets Dot 3 specifications.
3. Loosen bleed screw which is located on the slave cylinder body next to the inlet connection.
4. Fluid will now begin to move from the master cylinder down the tube to the slave. It is important that for efficient gravity fill, the reservoir must be kept full all the time.
5. It will be noticeable at this point, that bubbles will appear at the bleed screw outlet. This means that air is being expelled from the system. When the slave is full, a steady stream of fluid will come from the slave outlet. At this point, tighten bleed screw.
6. Assemble diaphragm and cap to the reservoir, fluid in reservoir should be level with step.
7. The hydraulic system should now be fully bled and should release the clutch. Check vehicle by starting the engine, pushing clutch pedal to the floor and selecting reverse gear. There should be no grating of gears, if there is, the hydraulic system still contains air. If this is the case, repeat bleed procedure.

CLUTCH

REPLACE

INSPECTION

1. While observing clutch slave cylinder pushrod travel, have an assistant depress clutch pedal. Brake pedal should travel approximately 7.4 inches.
2. If slave cylinder pushrod moves .433 inch or more, hydraulic system is operating properly.
3. If slave cylinder pushrod did not move .433 inch, proceed as follows:
   a. Check clutch master cylinder fluid level. The clutch slave cylinder must be installed during this operation. Refill as necessary.
   b. If master cylinder requires fluid, check hydraulic system components for leakage. Remove rubber boots from cylinders and check for leakage past pistons. A slight wetting of piston and wall surfaces is acceptable.
   c. If excessive leakage is indicated, entire hydraulic system must be replaced.

REPLACEMENT

1. Disconnect battery ground cable.
2. Remove hush panel from driver's footwell, then disconnect clutch master cylinder pushrod from clutch pedal.
3. Remove transaxle as outlined under "Manual Transaxle, Replace" procedure.
4. Mark position of pressure plate to flywheel to aid reassembly.
5. Gradually loosen pressure plate to flywheel attaching bolts until spring tension is relieved.
6. Support pressure plate and remove attaching bolts, pressure plate and driven disc, **Fig. 2.**
7. Clean pressure plate and flywheel mounting surfaces. Inspect bearing retainer outer surface of the transaxle.
8. Place pressure plate and driven disc in position and support with clutch Alignment Arbor tool No. J-29074 or equivalent, **Fig. 3. The driven disc is installed with the damper springs offset toward the transaxle. Stamped letters found on the driven disc identify the "Flywheel Side.**
9. Install and gradually **torque** the pressure plate to flywheel attaching bolts to 15 ft. lbs. Remove support tool.
10. Lubricate the clutch throwout fork where it contacts the release bearing and pack the release bearing inside

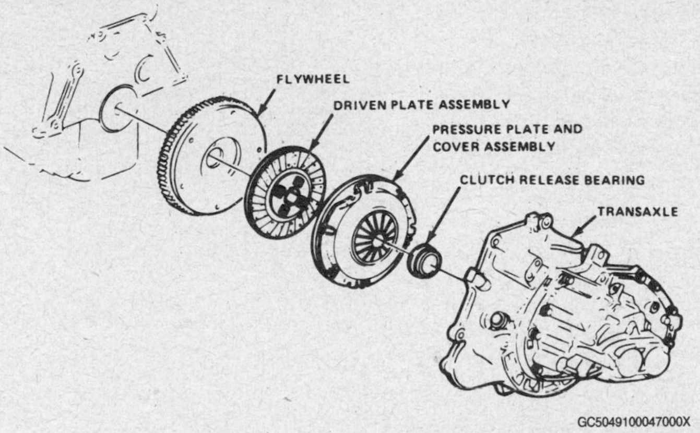
FLYWHEEL
DRIVEN PLATE ASSEMBLY
PRESSURE PLATE AND COVER ASSEMBLY
CLUTCH RELEASE BEARING
TRANSAXLE
GC5049100047000X

Fig. 2 Clutch assembly

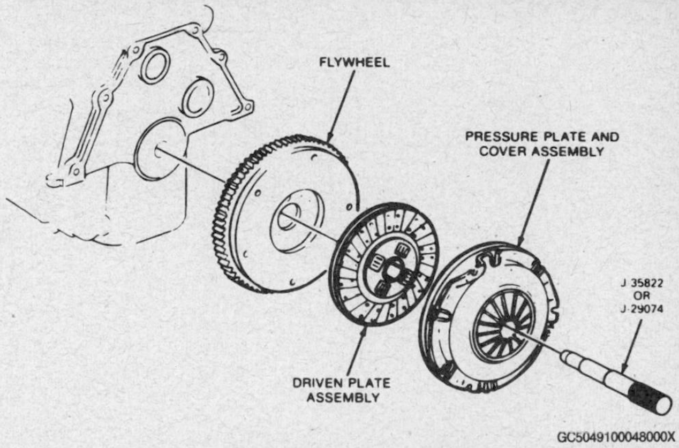
FLYWHEEL
PRESSURE PLATE AND COVER ASSEMBLY
J 35822 OR J-29074
DRIVEN PLATE ASSEMBLY
GC5049100048000X

Fig. 3 Clutch disc & pressure plate alignment

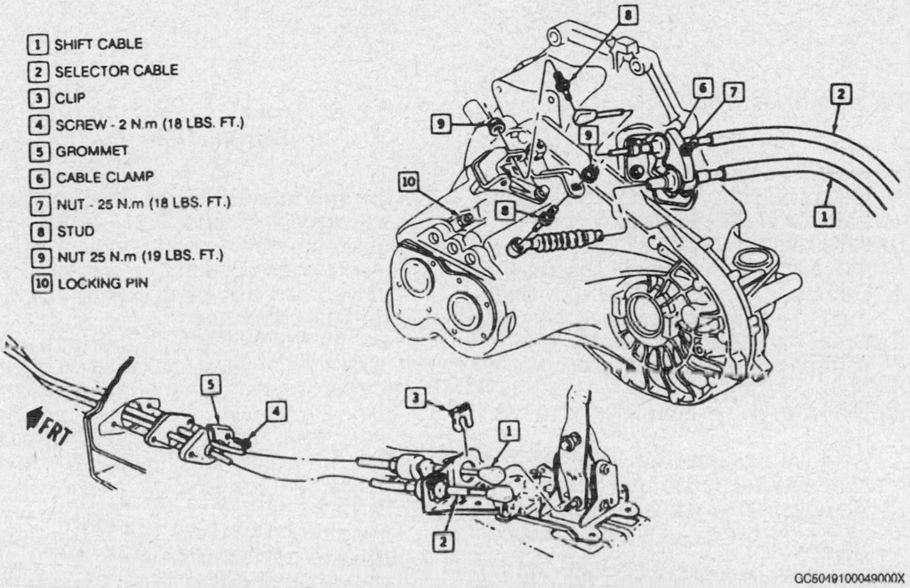
1 SHIFT CABLE
2 SELECTOR CABLE
3 CLIP
4 SCREW - 2 N.m (18 LBS. FT.)
5 GROMMET
6 CABLE CLAMP
7 NUT - 25 N.m (18 LBS. FT.)
8 STUD
9 NUT 25 N.m (19 LBS. FT.)
10 LOCKING PIN
FRT
GC5049100049000X

Fig. 4 Shift cable replacement. Muncie

diameter recess with suitable grease.
11. Install transaxle and hush panel, then connect battery ground cable.

SHIFT CABLE

REPLACE

Refer to **Figs. 4 and 5,** when replacing manual shift cables.

1. Disconnect battery ground cable.
2. Remove clamp and nut from each transaxle shift lever.
3. Remove shift knob, console and shift boot.
4. Remove shift cables from shifter control assembly by twisting between cable socket and control lever with suitable screwdriver.
5. Remove spring clips retaining cables to control assembly.
6. Remove right front sill plate, then pull back carpet to gain access to shift cables.
7. Remove shift cable grommet cover attaching screws, then remove cable cover at floor pan and remove shift cables.
8. Reverse procedure to install.

SHIFT CONTROL ASSEMBLY

REPLACE

1. Disconnect battery ground cable.
2. Remove shift knob, console and shift boot.
3. Remove shift cables from shifter control assembly by twisting between cable socket and control lever with suitable screwdriver.
4. Remove spring clips retaining cables to control assembly.
5. Remove shift control assembly.
6. Reverse procedure to install.

TRANSAXLE

REPLACE

ISUZU TRANSAXLE

1. Disconnect battery ground cable.
2. Install engine support fixture, **Fig. 6.** Connect fixture hook to engine lift ring and raise engine enough to relieve weight from engine mounts. The engine support fixture must be positioned in the center of the cowl and the attaching parts properly tightened before supporting engine.
3. Remove left sound insulator from under instrument panel, then disconnect clutch master cylinder pushrod from clutch pedal.
4. Remove clutch slave cylinder from transaxle support and position aside.
5. Remove transaxle mount attaching bolts.
6. Remove transaxle mount bracket attaching bolts and nuts.
7. Disconnect shift cables and remove retaining clips at transaxle.
8. Disconnect ground cable at transaxle mounting stud, then the shift light wiring.
9. Raise and support vehicle, then remove left front wheel.
10. Remove left front inner splash shield retaining screws and the splash shield.
11. Remove transaxle front strut and front strut bracket.
12. Remove clutch housing cover attaching bolts, then disconnect speedometer cable at transaxle.
13. Disconnect stabilizer bar at the left suspension support and control arm.
14. Remove left side support attaching bolts, then swing support aside.
15. Install boot protectors at drive axles, then disengage both drive axles at transaxle. Remove left drive axle from transaxle housing bore.
16. Attach the transaxle case to a suitable jack, then remove transaxle to engine mounting bolts.
17. Slide transaxle away from engine, lower jack and guide right drive axle from transaxle housing bore. Remove transaxle from vehicle.
18. Reverse procedure to install. **When installing transaxle, guide the right drive axle into transaxle bore as transaxle is being raised. The right drive axle cannot be installed after the transaxle is connected to engine.**

MUNCIE TRANSAXLE (NEW VENTURE)

1. Disconnect battery ground cable.
2. Install engine support fixture, **Fig. 6.**

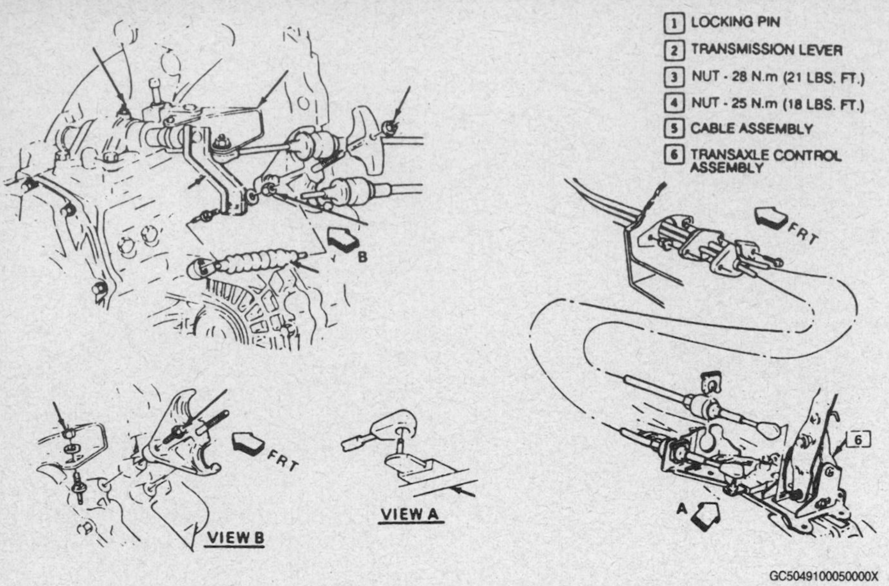
1 LOCKING PIN
2 TRANSMISSION LEVER
3 NUT - 28 N.m (21 LBS. FT.)
4 NUT - 25 N.m (18 LBS. FT.)
5 CABLE ASSEMBLY
6 TRANSAXLE CONTROL ASSEMBLY
FRT
B
FRT
VIEW B
VIEW A
FRT
6
A
GC5049100050000X

Fig. 5 Shift cable replacement. Isuzu

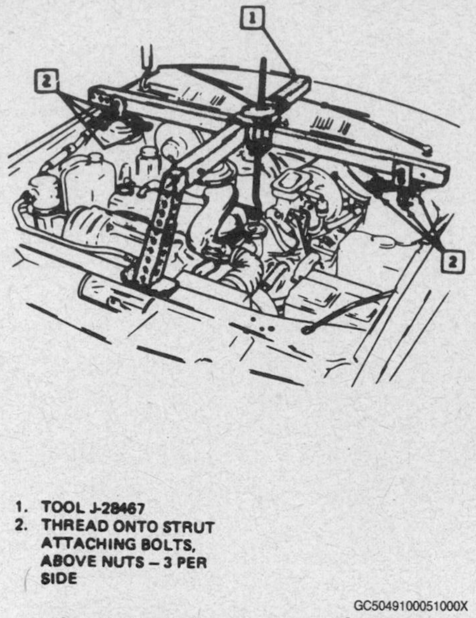
1
2
2
1. TOOL J-28467
2. THREAD ONTO STRUT ATTACHING BOLTS, ABOVE NUTS – 3 PER SIDE
GC5049100051000X

Fig. 6 Engine support fixture installation

Connect fixture hook to engine lift ring and raise engine enough to relieve weight from engine mounts. The engine support fixture must be positioned in the center of the cowl and the attaching parts properly tightened before supporting engine.

3. Remove left sound insulator from under instrument panel, then disconnect clutch master cylinder pushrod from clutch pedal.
4. Remove air cleaner and air intake duct assembly.
5. Remove clutch slave cylinder from transaxle brace and position aside.
6. Remove transaxle mount through bolt.
7. Raise and support vehicle, then remove two exhaust crossover bolts from right side manifold.
8. Lower vehicle, then remove left side exhaust manifold.
9. Remove shift cables, then upper transaxle to engine attaching bolts.
10. Raise and support vehicle, then remove left tire and wheel assembly.
11. Remove left front inner splash shield, then the transaxle strut and bracket.
12. Drain transaxle into suitable container, then remove clutch housing cover bolts.
13. Disconnect speedometer wire connector.
14. Remove stabilizer bar from left side suspension support and control arm.
15. Remove left side suspension support attaching bolts, then swing support aside.
16. Install boot protectors at drive axles, then disengage both drive axles at transaxle. Remove left drive axle from transaxle housing bore.
17. **On models equipped with manual transmission and 2.3L/4-138 engine,** the throttle body coolant pipes must be removed before engine is removed. **Do not bent coolant pipes to gain clearance.**
18. **On all Models,** attach the transaxle case to a suitable jack, then remove transaxle to engine mounting bolts.
19. Slide transaxle away from engine, lower jack and guide right drive axle from transaxle housing bore. Remove transaxle from vehicle.
20. Reverse procedure to install. **When installing transaxle, guide the right drive axle into transaxle bore as transaxle is being raised. The right drive axle cannot be installed after the transaxle is connected to engine.**

TIGHTENING SPECIFICATIONS

Year	Component	Torque/Ft. Lbs.
1992–95	Actuator Cylinder Support To Transaxle	37
	Alternate Oil Level Check/Fill Plug	18
	Back-Up Lamp Switch Assembly To Transaxle	①
	Clutch Actuator Cylinder Nut	16
	Clutch Cover To Flywheel Bolt	③
	Clutch Housing Cover To Transaxle	89②
	Clutch Master Cylinder Nut	20
	Clutch Pedal Bracket Nut	20
	Clutch Start Switch Nuts	53②
	Electronic Speed Sensor Retainer	7
	Fluid Drain Plug	18
	Fluid Reservoir Bolt	80②
1992–95 —Cont'd	Fluid Reservoir Bracket Bolt	16
	Flywheel To Crankshaft	52
	Front Transaxle Strut To Body Bolt	44
	Front Transaxle Strut To Transaxle	44
	Rear Mount Bracket To Mount	72
	Rear Mount Bracket To Transaxle	44
	Rear Transaxle Mount To Body Bolt	41
	Rear Transaxle Mount To Body Nuts	24
	Shift Cable Grommet To Shroud	12②
	Shift Control To Floor	18
	Shift Control Box To Transaxle	13
	Shift Linkage Retainer To Transaxle Case	17
	Shift Retainer To Transaxle Case	90②

Continued

TIGHTENING SPECIFICATIONS-Continued

Year	Component	Torque/Ft. Lbs.
1992–95 —Cont'd	Shift Shaft To Lever Nut	61
	Speedometer To Vehicle Speed Sensor	84②
	Transaxle Shift Cable Bracket To Cables	18
	Transaxle Shift Lever To Cable Stud	18

Year	Component	Torque/Ft. Lbs.
1992–95	Transaxle To Engine Bolts	55

①—Muncie, 24 ft. lbs.; Isuzu, 7 ft. lbs.
②—Inch lbs.
③—Except 2.3L/4-138, 18 ft. lbs.; 2.3L/4-138, 22 ft. lbs.

Rear Axle & Suspension

INDEX

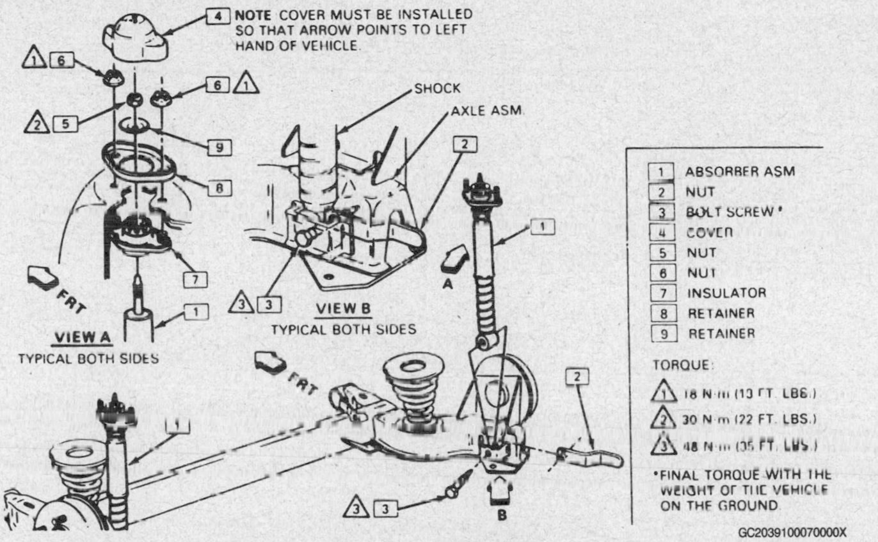

NOTE COVER MUST BE INSTALLED SO THAT ARROW POINTS TO LEFT HAND OF VEHICLE.
SHOCK
AXLE ASM
FRT
VIEW A
TYPICAL BOTH SIDES
VIEW B
TYPICAL BOTH SIDES
A
B
1 ABSORBER ASM
2 NUT
3 BOLT SCREW *
4 COVER
5 NUT
6 NUT
7 INSULATOR
8 RETAINER
9 RETAINER
TORQUE:
18 N·m (13 FT. LBS.)
30 N·m (22 FT. LBS.)
*FINAL TORQUE WITH THE WEIGHT OF THE VEHICLE ON THE GROUND
GC2039100070000X

Fig. 1 Rear suspension. Corsica

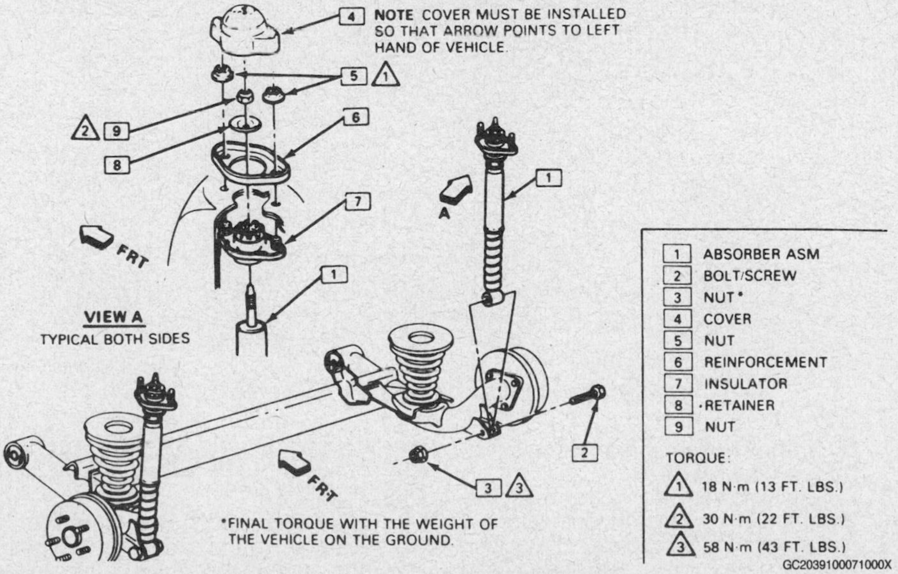

NOTE COVER MUST BE INSTALLED SO THAT ARROW POINTS TO LEFT HAND OF VEHICLE.
FRT
A
VIEW A
TYPICAL BOTH SIDES
*FINAL TORQUE WITH THE WEIGHT OF THE VEHICLE ON THE GROUND.
1 ABSORBER ASM
2 BOLT/SCREW
3 NUT *
4 COVER
5 NUT
6 REINFORCEMENT
7 INSULATOR
8 RETAINER
9 NUT
TORQUE:
18 N·m (13 FT. LBS.)
30 N·m (22 FT. LBS.)
58 N·m (43 FT. LBS.)
GC2039100071000X

Fig. 2 Rear suspension. Beretta

DESCRIPTION

This rear suspension is a semi-independent type suspension consisting of an axle assembly with trailing arms and twisting cross beam, coil springs and double action shock absorbers. A stabilizer bar is available and is attached to the inside of the axle beam and to the lower end of the control arms. A single unit hub and bearing assembly is bolted to each end of the axle assembly. The hub and bearing assembly is a sealed, non-serviceable unit and must be replaced as an assembly.

REAR AXLE

REPLACE

1. Raise vehicle and support vehicle. Support rear suspension with suitable jack.
2. Disconnect stabilizer bar at axle assembly, if equipped.
3. Remove rear wheel assembly and brake drum. **Do not hammer on brake drum since damage to bearings may result.**
4. Remove shock absorber to lower mounting bracket attaching bolts, then disconnect shock absorbers from axle assembly, **Figs. 1 and 2.**
5. Disconnect parking brake cable and brake lines at axle brackets.
6. Carefully lower rear axle assembly and remove coil springs and insulators.
7. Remove control arm to underbody bracket bolts, then lower the axle assembly and remove from vehicle.
8. Remove hub to rear axle attaching bolts, then the hubs, bearings and backing plates from rear axle assembly.
9. Reverse procedure to install and bleed brake system.

HUB & BEARING

REPLACE

1. Raise and support vehicle, then remove wheel and tire assembly and

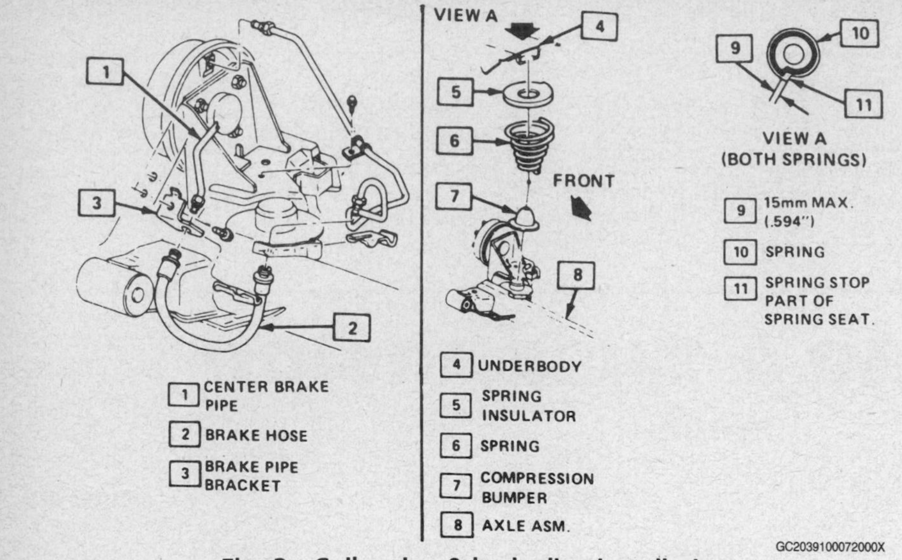

VIEW A
FRONT
1 CENTER BRAKE PIPE
2 BRAKE HOSE
3 BRAKE PIPE BRACKET
4 UNDERBODY
5 SPRING INSULATOR
6 SPRING
7 COMPRESSION BUMPER
8 AXLE ASM.
VIEW A (BOTH SPRINGS)
9 15mm MAX. (.594")
10 SPRING
11 SPRING STOP PART OF SPRING SEAT.
GC2039100072000X

Fig. 3 Coil spring & brake line installation

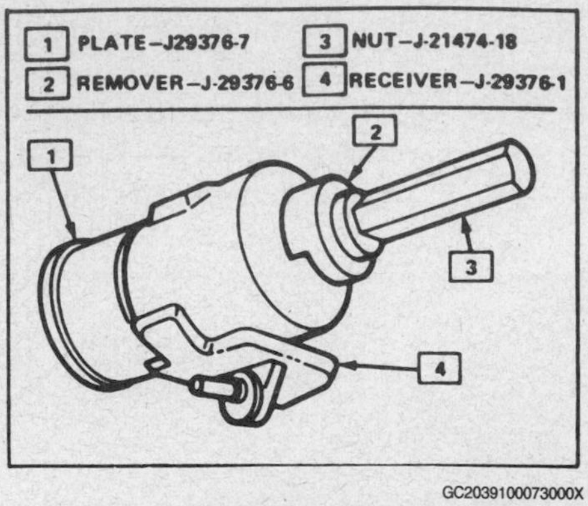

1 PLATE–J29376-7
2 REMOVER–J-29376-6
3 NUT–J-21474-18
4 RECEIVER–J-29376-1
GC2039100073000X

Fig. 4 Control bushing removal

brake drum. **Do not hammer brake drum since damage to bearing may result.**

2. Remove four hub/bearing assembly to rear axle attaching bolts, then the hub/bearing assembly from axle. **The upper rear hub attaching bolt may not clear brake shoe when removing hub and bearing assembly. Partially remove hub and bearing assembly prior to removing this bolt.**
3. Reverse procedure to install. Tighten hub to axle attaching bolts to specifications. **Use care not to drop hub/bearing assembly since damage to bearing may result.**

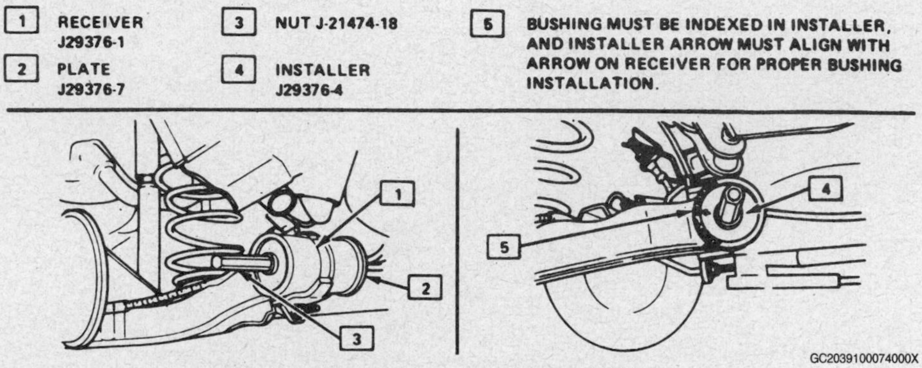

1 RECEIVER J29376-1
2 PLATE J29376-7
3 NUT J-21474-18
4 INSTALLER J29376-4
5 BUSHING MUST BE INDEXED IN INSTALLER, AND INSTALLER ARROW MUST ALIGN WITH ARROW ON RECEIVER FOR PROPER BUSHING INSTALLATION.
GC2039100074000X

Fig. 5 Control arm bushing installation

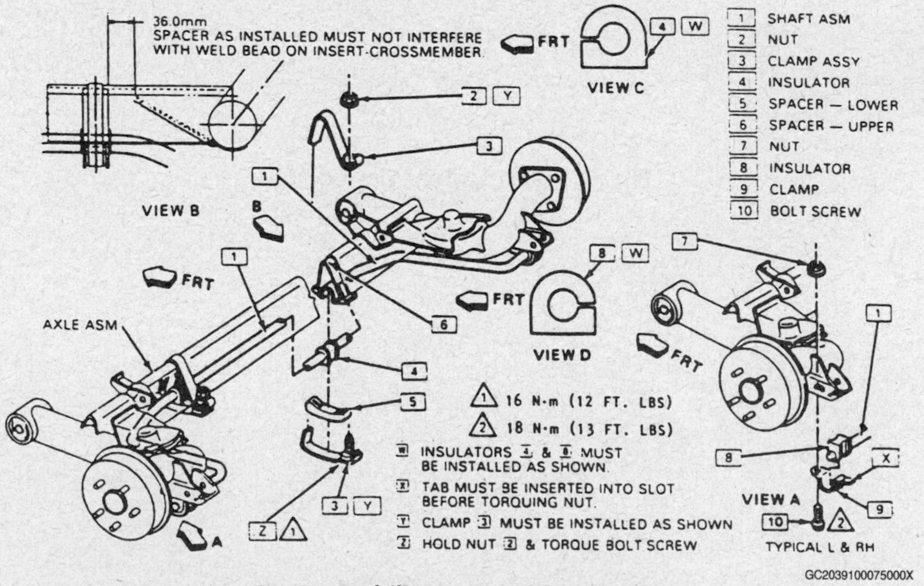

36.0mm
SPACER AS INSTALLED MUST NOT INTERFERE WITH WELD BEAD ON INSERT-CROSSMEMBER.
FRT
VIEW C
VIEW B
AXLE ASM
VIEW D
VIEW A
1 SHAFT ASM
2 NUT
3 CLAMP ASSY
4 INSULATOR
5 SPACER — LOWER
6 SPACER — UPPER
7 NUT
8 INSULATOR
9 CLAMP
10 BOLT SCREW
1 16 N·m (12 FT. LBS)
2 18 N·m (13 FT. LBS)
W INSULATORS 4 & 8 MUST BE INSTALLED AS SHOWN.
X TAB MUST BE INSERTED INTO SLOT BEFORE TORQUING NUT.
Y CLAMP 3 MUST BE INSTALLED AS SHOWN
Z HOLD NUT 2 & TORQUE BOLT SCREW
TYPICAL L & RH
GC2039100075000X

Fig. 6 Stabilizer assembly. Beretta

SHOCK ABSORBER
REPLACE

1. Open deck lid, then remove trim cover (if equipped) and shock absorber upper retaining nut.
2. Raise rear of vehicle and support rear axle using a suitable jack.
3. Remove shock absorber lower attaching bolt, then disconnect shock absorber from mounting bracket, **Fig. 1 and 2.** Remove shock absorber from vehicle.
4. Reverse procedure to install. Tighten attaching bolts to specifications.

COIL SPRING
REPLACE

1. Raise and support rear of vehicle. Support rear axle using a suitable jack.
2. Remove wheel and tire assemblies.
3. Remove brake line bracket attaching bolts, **Fig. 3,** from frame and allow brake lines to hang freely.
4. Remove shock absorber to lower mounting bracket bolts, then disconnect shock absorbers from axle assembly. **Do not suspend rear axle by brake hoses since damage to hoses may result.**
5. Carefully lower rear axle assembly and remove springs and insulators.
6. Reverse procedure to install. Position ends of upper coil in seat of body and within limits shown in **Fig. 3.**

CONTROL ARM BUSHING
REPLACE

1. Raise and support rear of vehicle.
2. Remove wheel and tire assembly, then support body with suitable jack stands

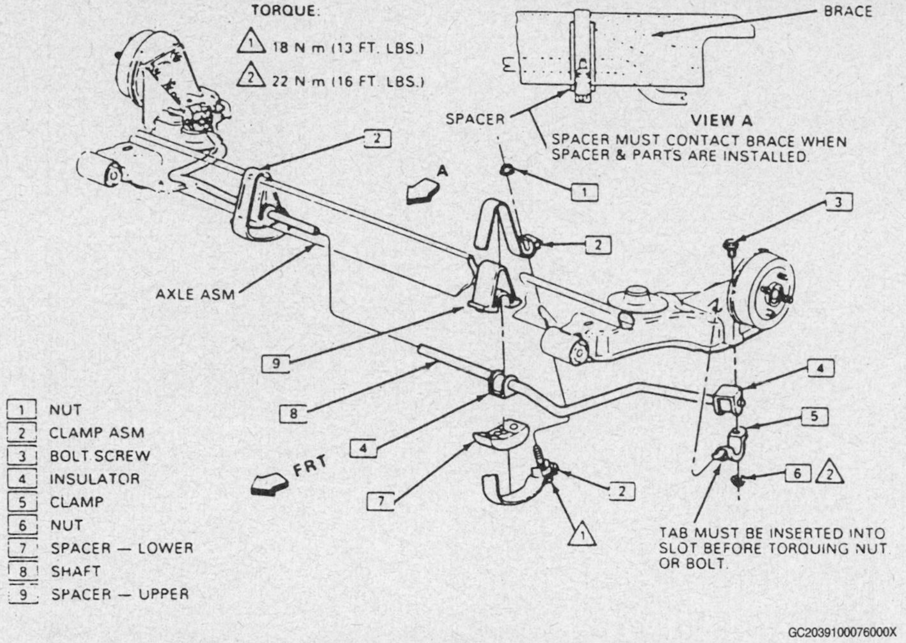

TORQUE:
1 18 N m (13 FT. LBS.)
2 22 N m (16 FT. LBS.)
BRACE
SPACER
VIEW A
SPACER MUST CONTACT BRACE WHEN SPACER & PARTS ARE INSTALLED
A
AXLE ASM
FRT
TAB MUST BE INSERTED INTO SLOT BEFORE TORQUING NUT OR BOLT.
1 NUT
2 CLAMP ASM
3 BOLT SCREW
4 INSULATOR
5 CLAMP
6 NUT
7 SPACER — LOWER
8 SHAFT
9 SPACER — UPPER
GC2039100076000X

Fig. 7 Stabilizer assembly. Corsica

3. Remove brake line bracket to body attaching screws from both sides.
4. Remove control arm to mounting bracket attaching nut, bolt and washer, then allow control arm to rotate downward.
5. The bushing can now be replaced using tools shown in **Figs. 4 and 5.** When installing bushing, the arrow on the installer must align with arrow on the receiver, **Fig. 4.**
6. Reverse procedure to complete installation. **The control arm attaching bolt must be torqued to specifications after vehicle is lowered to floor and is in its standing height position.**

STABILIZER BAR
REPLACE

1. Raise vehicle on hoist and support body with jack stands.
2. Remove nuts and bolts at both the axle and control arm attachments and remove bracket, insulator and stabilizer shaft, **Figs. 6 and 7.**
3. Reverse procedure to install.

TIGHTENING SPECIFICATIONS

Year	Component	Torque/Ft. Lbs.
1992–95	Brake Line Bracket To Control Arm	11
	Brake Line Bracket To Frame	8
	Control Arm Pivot Bolts	66①
	Control Arm To Underbody Attaching Nut	③
	Hub To Axle	④
	Shock Absorber Lower Attaching Bolt	35
	Shock Absorber Upper Shaft Nut	22
	Stabilizer Bar To Axle	16
	Stabilizer Bar To Control Arm	16
1992–95 —Cont'd	Stabilizer Shaft To Rear Axle Assembly Nut②	103
	Upper Shock Mount	21
	Upper Shock Mount Bolt To Body	13
	Wheel Lug Nuts	100

①—Torque control arm attaching bolt after vehicle is lowered to floor and is in its' standing height position.
②—Beretta.
③ 52 ft. lbs., plus 120° rotation.
④—1992 models, 38 ft. lbs.; 1993–95 models, 43 ft. lbs.

Front Suspension & Steering

INDEX

DESCRIPTION

The front suspension, **Figs. 1 through 3,** on these vehicles is of the McPherson strut design. The lower control arms pivot from the lower side rails through rubber bushings. The upper end of the strut is isolated by a rubber mount incorporating a non-serviceable bearing for wheel turning. The tie rods connect to the steering arm on the strut, below the spring seat. The lower end of the steering knuckle pivots on a ball stud which is retained to the lower control arm by rivets and is secured to the steering knuckle with a nut and cotter pin. The sealed wheel bearings are integral with the hub and are serviced as an assembly.

WHEEL BEARING
REPLACE

REMOVAL

1. Loosen hub nut with vehicle on ground.
2. Raise and support vehicle, then remove front wheel.
3. Install Drive Axle Protective Boot Cover tool No. J-28712 or equivalent.
4. Remove hub nut.
5. Remove brake caliper from support and suspend caliper from flame with a length of wire. Do not suspend caliper by brake hose.
6. Remove brake rotor.
7. Remove three hub and bearing attaching bolts, then the splash shield. If the old bearing is being reinstalled, mark attaching bolts and corresponding holes for reinstallation, **Fig. 4.**
8. Using Front Hub Spindle Remover tool No. J-28733 or equivalent, remove bearing from steering knuckle, **Fig. 5. If excessive corrosion is present, ensure that bearing is loose in the knuckle before using puller tool.**
9. If installing new bearing, replace steering knuckle seal. **Do not move drive axle until hub nut is installed and tighten to specifications.**

INSTALLATION

1. Clean and inspect bearing mating surfaces and steering knuckle bore for dirt, nicks and burrs.
2. If installing new steering knuckle seal, apply grease to seal and knuckle bore, then press seal into steering knuckle.
3. Push bearing onto axle shaft, then install splash shield and hub to steering knuckle attaching bolts. Tighten attaching bolts to specifications. Install hub to axle retaining nut and apply a partial **torque** of 74 ft. lbs., **Fig. 6.**
4. Install rotor, brake caliper and wheel assembly.
5. Lower vehicle and **torque** hub nut to 191 ft. lbs.

BALL JOINT
REPLACE

LOWER

1. Raise and support vehicle, then remove wheel and tire.
2. Locate center of rivet body and mark with a center punch.
3. Using a 1/8 inch drill, drill pilot holes completely through the rivets. Using a 1/2 inch drill, drill final holes through rivets to ensure fitting of new ball joint.
4. Remove ball joint stud retaining nut, then, using Ball Joint Separator tool No. J-29330 or equivalent, separate ball joint from steering knuckle. Remove ball joint from lower control arm.
5. Assemble new ball joint to lower control arm with bolts provided in service package, **Fig. 7,** and tighten bolts to specifications.
6. Insert ball joint stud into steering knuckle and tighten nut to specifications.
7. Install wheel and tire, check toe setting and adjust as required.

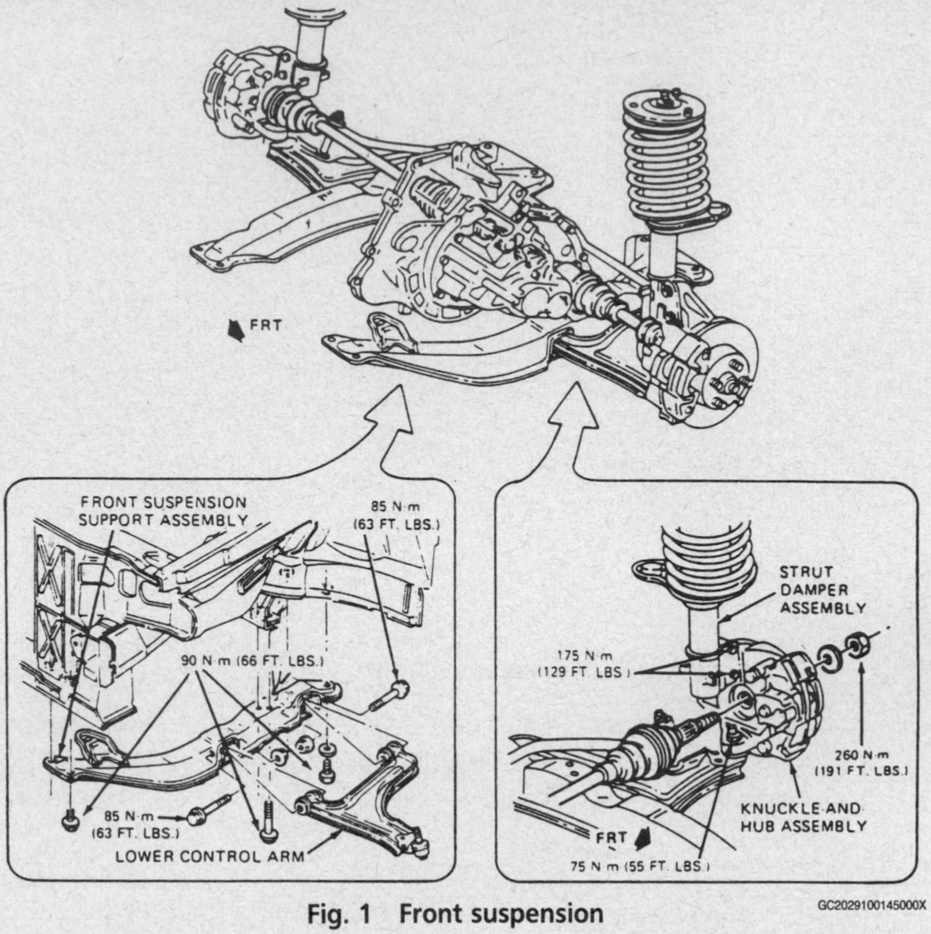
FRT
FRONT SUSPENSION SUPPORT ASSEMBLY
85 N·m (63 FT. LBS.)
90 N·m (66 FT. LBS.)
85 N·m (63 FT. LBS.)
LOWER CONTROL ARM
STRUT DAMPER ASSEMBLY
175 N·m (129 FT. LBS.)
260 N·m (191 FT. LBS.)
KNUCKLE AND HUB ASSEMBLY
FRT
75 N·m (55 FT. LBS.)
GC2029100145000X

Fig. 1 Front suspension

STRUT
REPLACE

1. Raise hood and remove strut protective cap and three strut to body attaching nuts **Fig. 8.**
2. Raise and support vehicle, allowing suspension to hang freely.
3. Remove wheel and tire, then install Drive Axle Protective Cover tool No. J-28712 or equivalent.
4. Using Steering Linkage Puller tool No. J-24319 or equivalent, disconnect tie rod from strut assembly.
5. Remove strut to steering knuckle attaching bolts, then remove strut from vehicle.
6. Reverse procedure to install. Position flats of strut mounting bolts as shown in **Fig. 9.** Tighten all nuts and bolts to specifications.

STRUT SERVICE

DISASSEMBLY

Care must be taken not to damage special coating on coil springs. If special coating is damaged, coil spring damage could occur.

1. Clamp Strut Compressor tool No. J-26584 or equivalent in a suitable vise.
2. Place strut assembly in compressor tool and install Bottom Adapter tool No. J-26584-400 or equivalent, making sure that adapter captures strut and locating pins are fully engaged, **Fig. 10.**
3. Position Top Adapter tool No. J-26584-430 or equivalent on strut cap, aligning mounting holes as necessary.
4. Rotate compressor forcing screw clockwise until top support flange contacts top adapter. Continue rotating forcing screws until strut spring is compressed to approximately 1/2 its height. **Do not bottom the spring or strut damper rod.**
5. Remove damper top nut, then place alignment rod on strut shaft. Use alignment rod to guide shock shaft through spring cap during removal.
6. Remove strut components, then relieve compressor tension.

ASSEMBLY

1. Perform Steps 1 & 2 as outlined in the Disassembly procedure.
2. Position spring on strut, making sure spring is properly seated on bottom spring plate.
3. Install shields, bumpers and insulators on spring seat, then install coil spring seat on top of spring, **Fig. 11.**
4. Install bearing cap on spring seat, ensuring they are centered together and properly aligned.

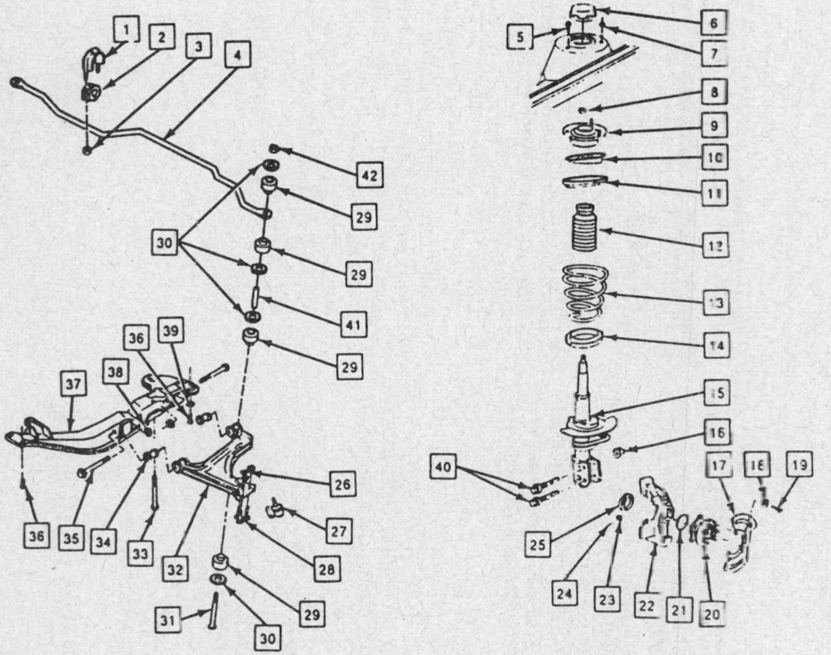

1. CLAMP, STABILIZER SHAFT
2. INSULATOR, STABILIZER SHAFT
3. NUT
4. STABILIZER SHAFT
5. BOLT
6. COVER, STRUT MOUNT
7. NUT
8. NUT, STRUT DAMPENER SHAFT
9. STRUT MOUNT
10. SPRING SEAT
11. UPPER SPRING INSULATOR
12. STRUT BUMPER AND SHIELD
13. SPRING
14. LOWER SPRING INSULATOR
15. STRUT
16. NUT
17. DISK BRAKE SPLASH SHIELD
18. WASHER
19. BOLT
20. HUB AND BEARING ASSEMBLY
21. SEAL (PART OF 25)
22. STEERING KNUCKLE
23. NUT, BALL JOINT
24. COTTER PIN
25. HUB AND BEARING SEAL
26. NUT
27. BALL JOINT
28. BOLT
29. INSULATOR, STABIL ZER LINK
30. WASHER, STABILIZER LINK
31. BOLT, STABILIZER LINK
32. CONTROL ARM
33. BOLT
34. BUSHING, CONTROL ARM
35. BOLT
36. BOLT
37. SUSPENSION SUPPORT
38. NUT
39. WASHER
40. BOLT
41. SPACER, STABILIZER LINK
42. NUT STABILIZER LINK

GC2029100146000X

Fig. 2 Exploded view of front suspension. Except GTZ models

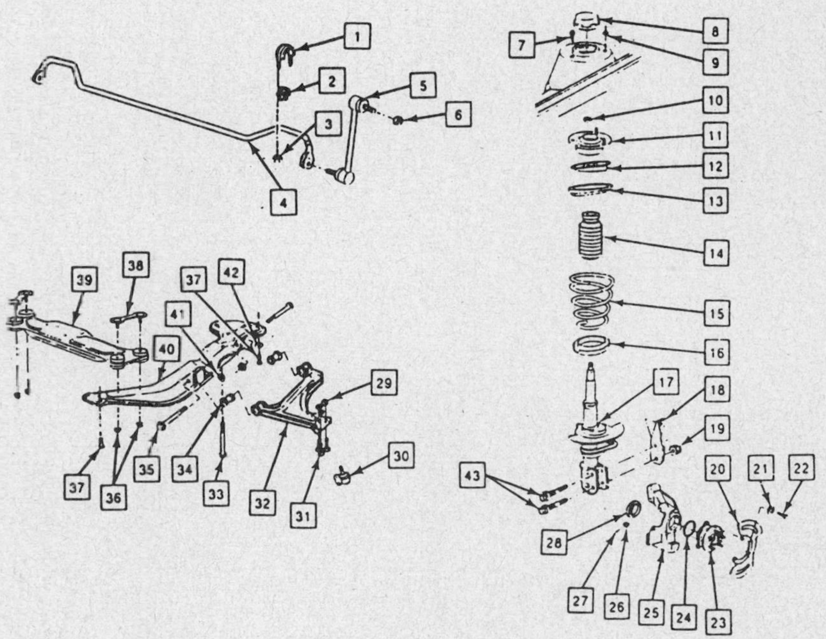

1. CLAMP, STABLIZER SHAFT
2. INSULATOR, STABILIZER SHAFT
3. NUT
4. STABILIZER SHAFT
5. STABILIZER LINK
6. NUT
7. BOLT
8. COVER, STRUT MOUNT
9. NUT
10. NUT, STRUT DAMPENER SHAFT
11. STRUT MOUNT
12. SPRING SEAT
13. UPPER SPRING INSULATOR
14. STRUT BUMPER AND SHIELD
15. SPRING
16. LOWER SPRING INSULATOR
17. STRUT
18. BRACKET, STABILIZER LINK
19. NUT
20. DISK BRAKE SPLASH SHIELD
21. WASHER
22. BOLT
23. HUB AND BEARING ASSEMBLY
24. SEAL (PART OF)
25. STEERING KNUCKLE
26. NUT, BALL JOINT
27. COTTER PIN
28. HUB AND BEARING SEAL
29. NUT
30. BALL JOINT
31. BOLT
32. CONTROL ARM
33. BOLT
34. BUSHING, CONTROL ARM
35. BOLT
36. NUT
37. BOLT
38. PLATE, FRONT ENGINE MOUNT CROSSMEMBER
39. CROSSMEMBER, FRONT ENGINE MOUNT
40. SUSPENSION SUPPORT
41. NUT
42. WASHER
43. BOLT

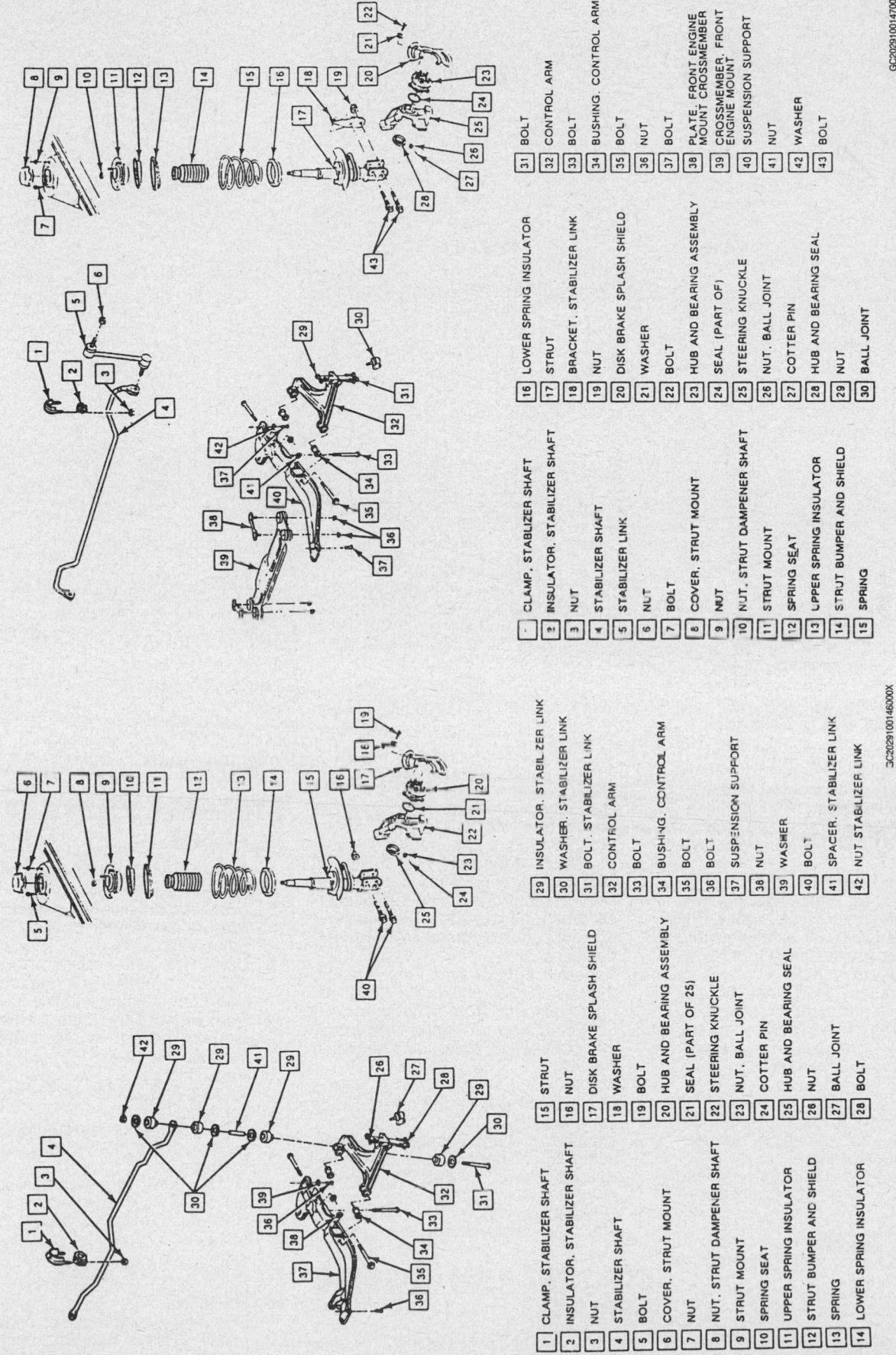

GC2029100147000X

Fig. 3 Exploded view of front suspension. GTZ models

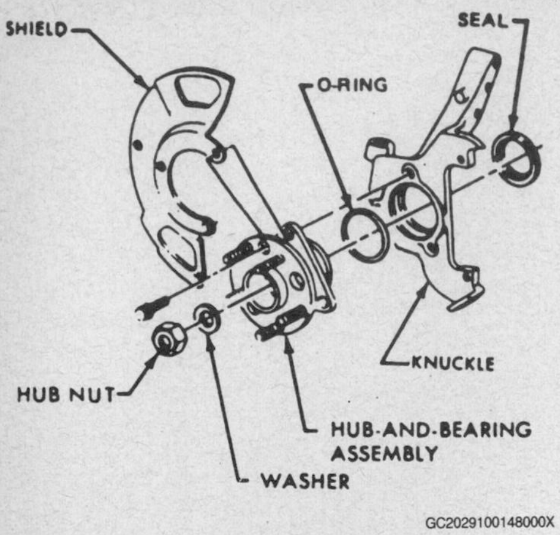
SHIELD
SEAL
O-RING
KNUCKLE
HUB NUT
HUB-AND-BEARING ASSEMBLY
WASHER
GC2029100148000X

Fig. 4 Front hub & wheel bearing assembly

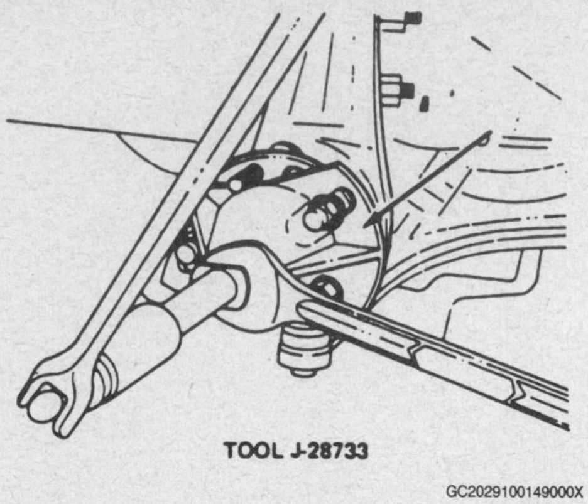
TOOL J-28733
GC2029100149000X

Fig. 5 Front hub & bearing assembly removal

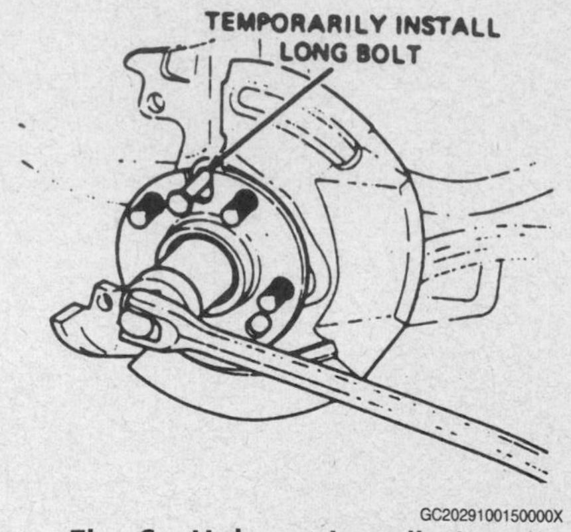
TEMPORARILY INSTALL LONG BOLT
GC2029100150000X

Fig. 6 Hub nut installation

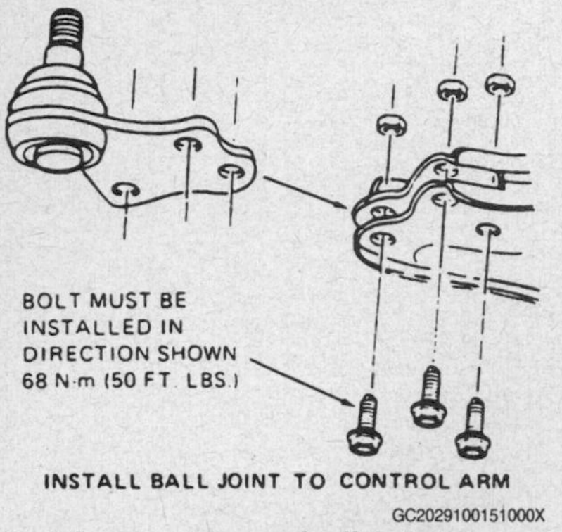
BOLT MUST BE INSTALLED IN DIRECTION SHOWN 68 N·m (50 FT. LBS.)
INSTALL BALL JOINT TO CONTROL ARM
GC2029100151000X

Fig. 7 Lower ball joint to lower control arm installation

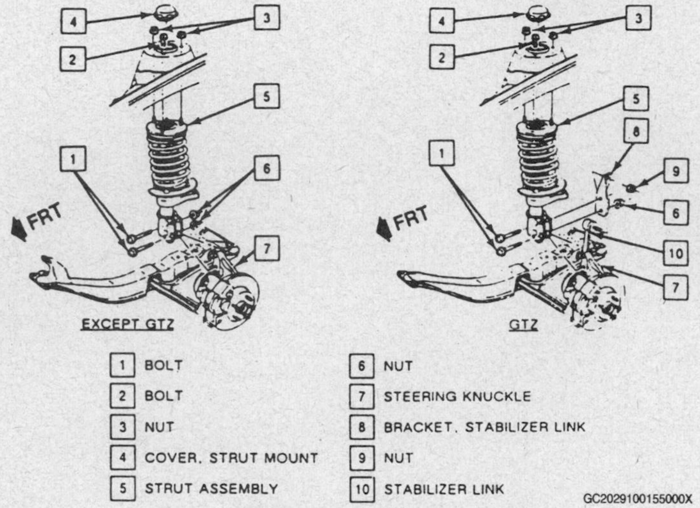
FRT
EXCEPT GTZ
GTZ
1 BOLT
2 BOLT
3 NUT
4 COVER, STRUT MOUNT
5 STRUT ASSEMBLY
6 NUT
7 STEERING KNUCKLE
8 BRACKET, STABILIZER LINK
9 NUT
10 STABILIZER LINK
GC2029100155000X

Fig. 8 Strut assembly mounting

5. Rotate spring as necessary to have upper end of spring located within 10 mm from end of groove in upper insulator and lower end of spring located 10-15 mm from end of groove in lower insulator.
6. Position Top Adapter tool No. J-26584-430 or equivalent on strut cap, then engage compressor slightly. Pull up strut rod to its full extension and clamp in place with Clamp tool No. J-34013-20 or equivalent.
7. Insert Alignment Rod tool No. J-34013-27 or equivalent through bearing and spring cap and position on top of strut rod. Compress spring slowly while guiding strut rod through bearing cap with alignment rod.
8. Continue compressing spring until one inch of strut rod is above bearing cap. Install strut attaching nut and tighten to specifications.
9. Remove strut rod clamp, then release tension on coil spring and remove compressor.

CONTROL ARM

REPLACE

LOWER

1. Raise and support vehicle, then remove wheel and tire.
2. Disconnect stabilizer bar at lower control arm and control arm support.
3. Using Ball Joint Separator tool No. J-29330 or equivalent, separate ball joint from steering knuckle.
4. Remove control arm support to chassis retaining bolts and remove control arm support and control arm as an assembly.
5. Separate control arm from support, then using tools shown in **Fig. 12,** remove bushings from control arm.
6. Lubricate new bushings and install into control arm using tools shown in **Fig. 12.**
7. Attach lower control arm to control arm support and tighten pivot bolts to specifications.
8. Install control arm support to chassis, using attaching bolt tightening sequence shown in **Fig. 13.** Tighten bolts to specifications.
9. Reverse procedure to complete installation. Check wheel alignment.

CONTROL ARM BUSHING

REPLACE

Refer to "Control Arm, Replace" for control arm bushing replacement procedure.

STEERING KNUCKLE

REPLACE

1. Raise and support vehicle, then remove wheel and tire.
2. Remove front hub and bearing as outlined under Wheel Bearing, Replace procedure.
3. Using Ball Joint Separator tool No. J-29330 or equivalent, separate ball joint from steering knuckle.
4. Remove strut to steering knuckle attaching bolts, then disconnect strut from steering knuckle.
5. Assemble strut to new steering knuckle and install attaching bolts finger tight.
6. Insert ball joint stud into steering knuckle and tighten stud nut to specifications.
7. Tighten strut to steering knuckle attaching bolts to specifications.
8. Reverse removal procedure to complete installation.

STABILIZER BAR

REPLACE

1. Disconnect battery ground cable.
2. Install Engine Support tool No. J-28467 or equivalent.

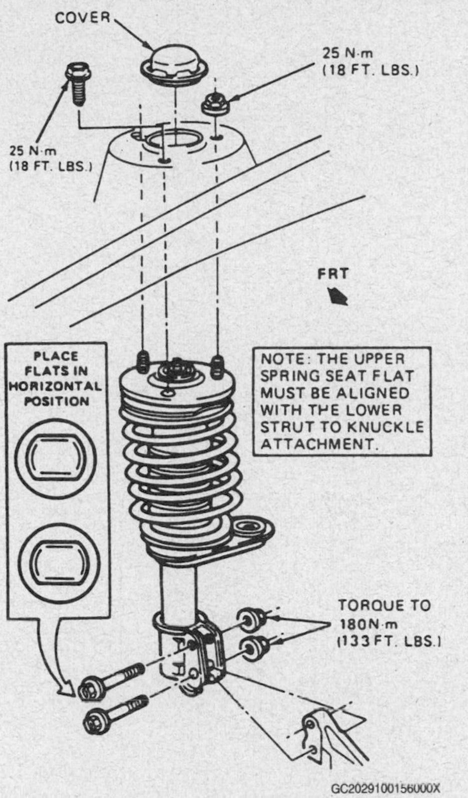
COVER
25 N·m
(18 FT. LBS.)
25 N·m
(18 FT. LBS.)
FRT
PLACE
FLATS IN
HORIZONTAL
POSITION
NOTE: THE UPPER
SPRING SEAT FLAT
MUST BE ALIGNED
WITH THE LOWER
STRUT TO KNUCKLE
ATTACHMENT.
TORQUE TO
180N·m
(133 FT. LBS.)
GC2029100156000X

Fig. 9 Strut assembly installation

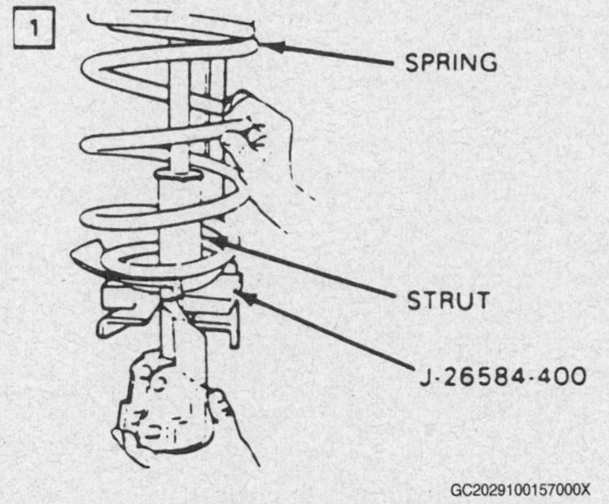
1
SPRING
STRUT
J-26584-400
GC2029100157000X

Fig. 10 Damper & coil spring from strut removal

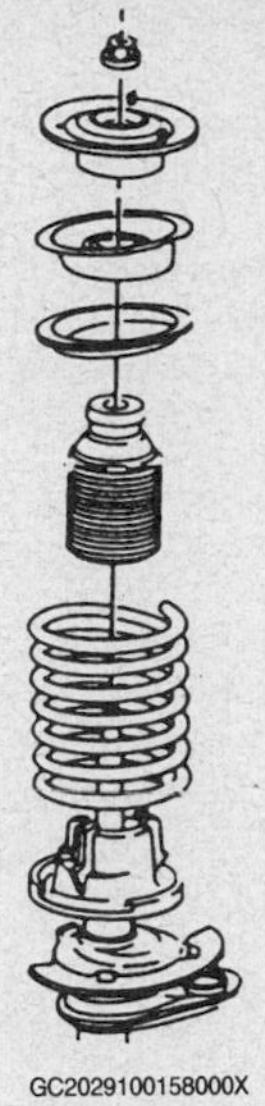
GC2029100158000X

Fig. 11 Strut coil spring & upper mounting installation

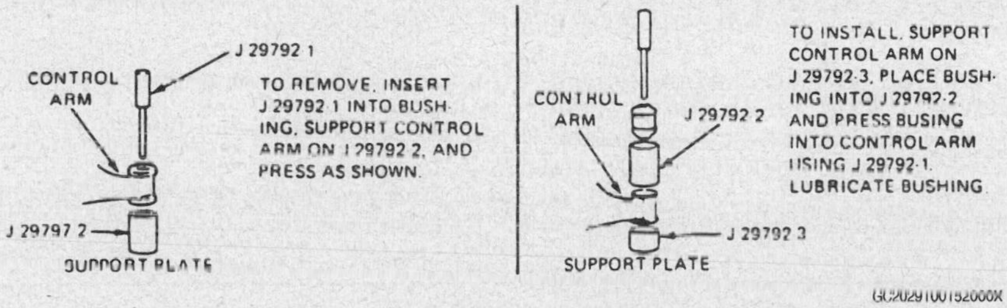
J 29792 1
CONTROL
ARM
TO REMOVE, INSERT
J 29792 1 INTO BUSH-
ING, SUPPORT CONTROL
ARM ON J 29792 2, AND
PRESS AS SHOWN.
J 29792 2
SUPPORT PLATE
CONTROL
ARM
J 29792 2
TO INSTALL, SUPPORT
CONTROL ARM ON
J 29792-3, PLACE BUSH-
ING INTO J 29792-2
AND PRESS BUSING
INTO CONTROL ARM
USING J 29792-1.
LUBRICATE BUSHING.
J 29792 3
SUPPORT PLATE

Fig. 12 Lower control arm bushing replacement

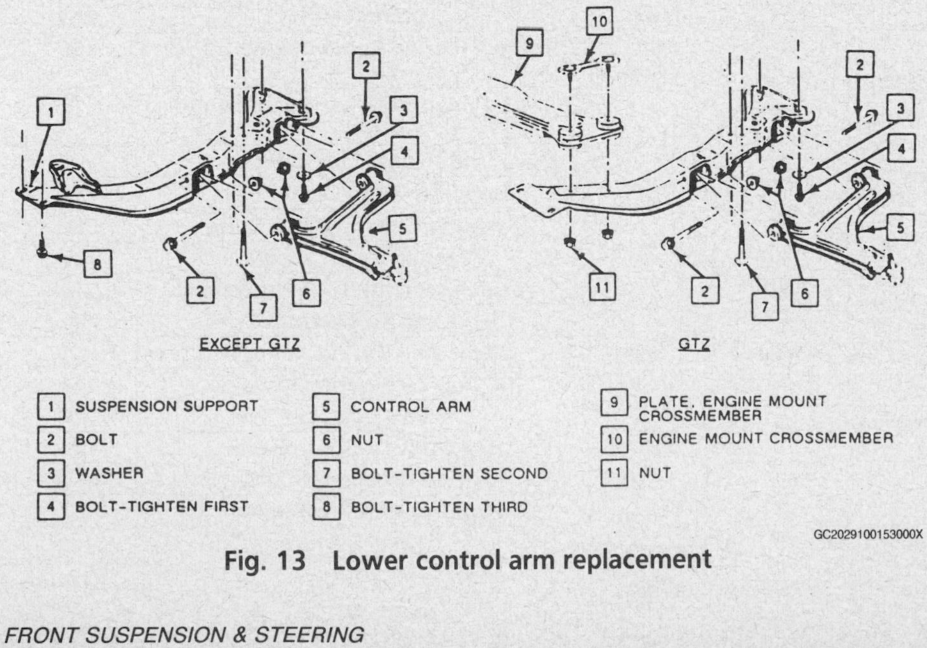
EXCEPT GTZ
GTZ
1 SUSPENSION SUPPORT
2 BOLT
3 WASHER
4 BOLT-TIGHTEN FIRST
5 CONTROL ARM
6 NUT
7 BOLT-TIGHTEN SECOND
8 BOLT-TIGHTEN THIRD
9 PLATE, ENGINE MOUNT CROSSMEMBER
10 ENGINE MOUNT CROSSMEMBER
11 NUT
GC2029100153000X

Fig. 13 Lower control arm replacement

3. Raise and support vehicle, allowing control arms to hang free.
4. Remove left front tire and wheel assembly.
5. Disconnect stabilizer bar from arms, then from support assemblies.
6. Loosen front support attaching bolts, then remove rear and center support bolts. Allow supports to drop down enough to remove stabilizer bar, **Fig. 14.**
7. Reverse procedure to install. Before tightening any attaching bolts, ensure stabilizer bar is centered in chassis. Refer to **Fig. 14,** for tighten specifications.

STABILIZER BAR BUSHING

REPLACE

Refer to "Stabilizer Bar, Replace" for stabilizer bushing replacement.

POWER STEERING GEAR

REPLACE

1. Disconnect battery ground cable.
2. Remove lefthand sound insulator.
3. Remove steering column coupling upper pinch bolt.
4. Remove hydraulic line retainer, then disconnect pump pressure and return lines from steering gear.
5. Raise and support vehicle.
6. Remove front wheel and tire assemblies.
7. Disconnect tie rods from steering knuckles.

8. Lower vehicle, then remove steering gear mounting clamps.
9. Move steering gear forward, then remove steering column coupling lower pinch bolt.
10. Remove steering column coupling and dash seal from steering gear.
11. Raise and support vehicle, then remove steering gear through left front wheel opening.
12. Reverse procedure to install. Tighten all bolts to specifications noting the following:
    a. When installing steering gear, attach clamps and finger tighten all attaching nuts prior to tightening. Ensure dash seal is indexed and flush with steering gear.

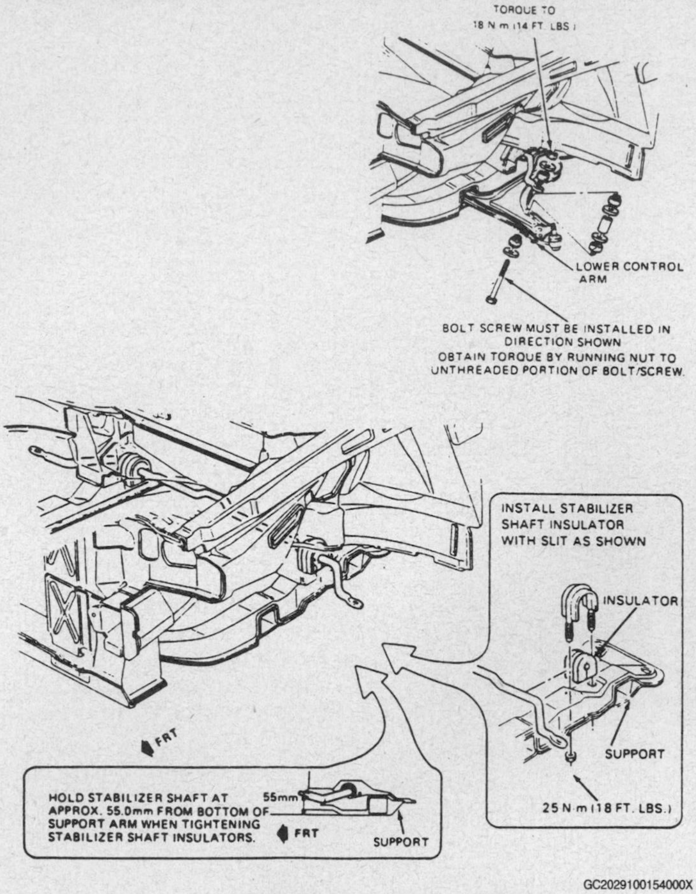

TORQUE TO
18 N·m (14 FT. LBS.)
LOWER CONTROL ARM
BOLT SCREW MUST BE INSTALLED IN DIRECTION SHOWN
OBTAIN TORQUE BY RUNNING NUT TO UNTHREADED PORTION OF BOLT/SCREW.
INSTALL STABILIZER SHAFT INSULATOR WITH SLIT AS SHOWN
INSULATOR
SUPPORT
25 N·m (18 FT. LBS.)
FRT
HOLD STABILIZER SHAFT AT APPROX. 55.0mm FROM BOTTOM OF SUPPORT ARM WHEN TIGHTENING STABILIZER SHAFT INSULATORS.
55mm
FRT
SUPPORT
GC2029100154000X

Fig. 14 Stabilizer bar installation

POWER STEERING PUMP

REPLACE

EXCEPT 2.3L/4-138 ENGINE

1. Disconnect battery ground cable.
2. Place suitable container under pump to catch fluid.
3. Disconnect pressure and return lines at pump, then plug open ends at hoses and pump.
4. Remove auxiliary drive belt.
5. Working through holes in pump pulley, remove pump attaching bolts.
6. Remove power steering pump.
7. Reverse procedure to install.

2.3L/4-138 ENGINE

1. Disconnect negative battery cable.
2. Remove air cleaner assembly, then the pump drive belt.
3. Disconnect power brake booster vacuum line, then the power steering pressure switch electrical connector.
4. Remove pump bracket bolts and bracket.
5. Disconnect pressure and return lines at pump, then plug open ends at hoses and pump.
6. Remove pump pivot bracket bolts and bracket.
7. Remove power steering pump.
8. Reverse procedure to install.

TIGHTENING SPECIFICATIONS

Year	Component	Torque/Ft. Lbs.
1992	Ball Joint To Control Arm	50
	Ball Joint To Steering Knuckle Nuts	26(1)
	Control Arm Pivot Bolts	63
	Control To Suspension Support Bolts	44(1)
	Front Engine Mount Lower Nuts	30
	Front Engine Mount Upper Nut	55
	Gear Inlet & Outlet Pipes To Rack & Pinion Steering Gear	20
	Gear Inlet Pipe To Pump	18
	Hub & Bearing Assembly Bolts	70
	Hub To Axle Nut	192
	Hub To Steering Knuckle	70
	Inner Tie Rod To Rack & Pinion Steering Gear Bolts	66
	Outer Tie Rod End Nuts	55
	Pinion Locknut	26
	Pivot Bracket To Power Steering Pump Bolts(4)	23
1992—Cont'd	Power Steering Pump O-Ring Union Fitting	55
	Rack & Pinion Steering Gear Mounting Stud	15
	Stabilizer Link Nuts	(3)
	Stabilizer Shaft Clamp Nuts	17
	Steering Column Pinch Bolts	(2)
	Steering Gear Clamps	28
	Strut Assembly To Body Bolts	18
	Strut Rod To Bearing Cap	60
	Strut To Steering Knuckle	129
	Tie Rod To Steering Knuckle	44
	Wheel Lug Nuts	100
1993–95	Ball Joint To Control Arm	50
	Ball Joint To Steering Knuckle Nuts	55(1)
	Control Arm Pivot Bolts	63

Continued

TIGHTENING SPECIFICATIONS-Continued

Year	Component	Torque/Ft. Lbs.
1992 —Cont'd	Control To Suspension Support Bolts	89
	Front Engine Mount Lower Nuts	30
	Front Engine Mount Upper Nut	55
	Gear Inlet & Outlet Pipes To Rack & Pinion Steering Gear	20
	Gear Inlet Pipe To Pump	18
	Hub And Bearing Assembly Bolts	70
	Hub To Axle Nut	192
	Hub To Steering Knuckle	70
	Inner Tie Rod To Rack & Pinion Steering Gear Bolts	65
	Outer Tie Rod End Nuts	55
	Pinion Locknut	26
	Pivot Bracket To Power Steering Pump Bolts④	23
	Power Steering Pump O-Ring Union Fitting	55
	Rack & Pinion Steering Gear Mounting Stud	15

Year	Component	Torque/Ft. Lbs.
1992 —Cont'd	Stabilizer Link Nuts	15
	Stabilizer Shaft Clamp Nuts	15
	Steering Column Pinch Bolts	②
	Steering Gear Clamps	22
	Strut Assembly To Body	19
	Strut Rod To Bearing Cap	60
	Strut To Steering Knuckle	133
	Suspension Support Bolts	89
	Tie Rod To Steering Knuckle	44
	Wheel Lug Nuts	100

①—Plus 60° rotation.
②—Torque upper pinch bolt to 29 ft. lbs., torque lower pinch bolt to 37 ft. lbs.
③—Except GTZ models; 13 ft. lbs., GTZ models; 70 ft. lbs.
④—2.3L/4-138 models.

Wheel Alignment

INDEX

PRELIMINARY INSPECTION

1. Inspect tires for proper inflation and similar tread wear.
2. Inspect hub and bearing for excessive wear, repair as required.
3. Inspect ball joints.
4. Inspect tie rod ends for excessive looseness.
5. Check wheel and tire runout.
6. Inspect vehicle ride height.
7. Inspect rack and pinion for looseness at frame.
8. Ensure proper strut operation.
9. Check suspension and steering components for damage, replace as required.

FRONT WHEEL ALIGNMENT

Toe setting is the only adjustment normally required. However, in special circumstances, such as damage due to road hazard or collision, camber may be adjusted by modifying the strut assembly. Caster is not adjustable.

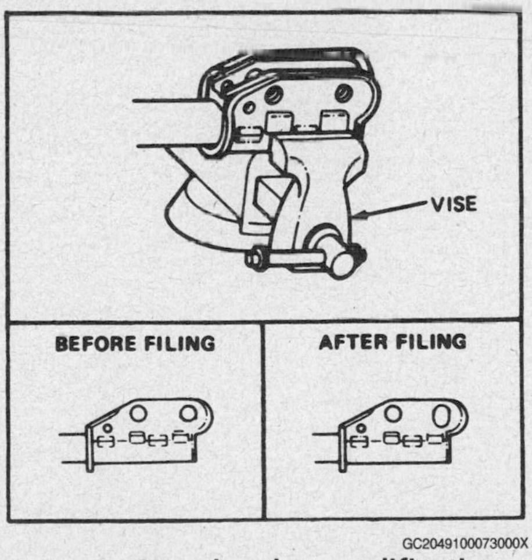
VISE
BEFORE FILING
AFTER FILING
GC2049100073000X

Fig. 1 Strut bracket modification

CAMBER

1. Secure bottom of strut assembly in a suitable vise.
2. Enlarge bottom holes in outer flanges with a round file until holes in outer flanges match slots in inner flanges, **Fig. 1.**
3. Connect strut to steering knuckle and install bolts finger tight.
4. Grasp top of tire firmly, then move tire inboard or outboard until correct camber reading is obtained. Tighten retaining bolts enough to secure camber setting.
5. Remove wheel and tire and **torque** strut to steering knuckle retaining bolts to 133 ft. lbs.

TOE-IN

Toe is controlled by tie rod position. Adjustment is made by loosening the clamp bolts at the steering knuckle end of the tie rods and rotating the adjuster to obtain proper toe setting. After correct toe setting is obtained, **torque** clamp bolts to 35 ft. lbs.

REAR WHEEL ALIGNMENT

There are no adjustments to be made on this rear suspension. If alignment is outside specifications, check for broken or bent parts and replace as necessary.

VEHICLE RIDE HEIGHT

Refer to **Fig. 2,** for ride height specifications and measurement locations. Check ride height as follows:

1. Ensure vehicle is on level ground.
2. Ensure tires are inflated to proper pressures.
3. Fuel tank should be full to obtain accurate readings.
4. Trunk should be empty except for spare tire and jack.
5. Bounce the car three times at the front and rear to normalize suspension.
6. Measure from lowest point on the ball joint housing to control arm bolt centerline, "D" and "Z" positions.
7. Measure from level floor to rocker panel at "J" and "K" positions.

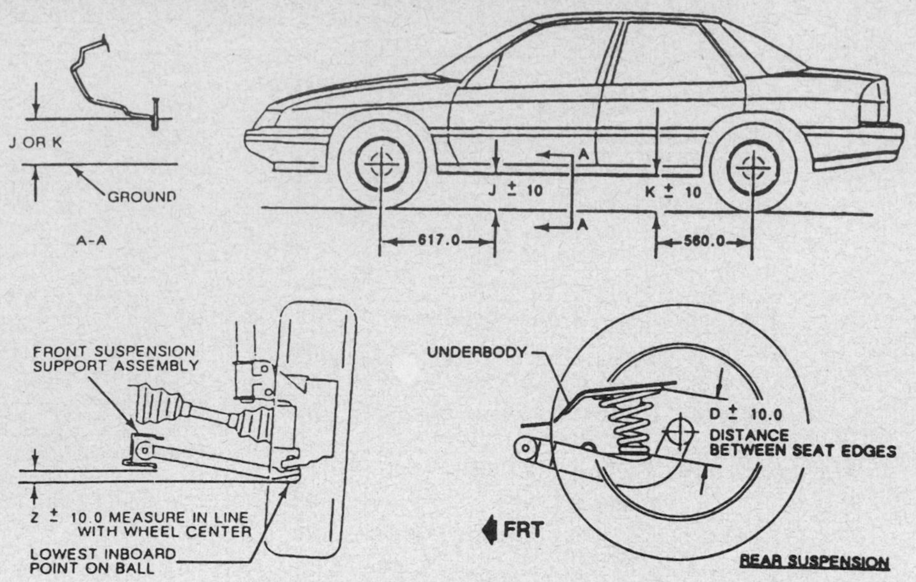
J OR K
GROUND
A-A
A
J ± 10
K ± 10
A
617.0
560.0
FRONT SUSPENSION SUPPORT ASSEMBLY
Z ± 10.0 MEASURE IN LINE WITH WHEEL CENTER
LOWEST INBOARD POINT ON BALL
UNDERBODY
D ± 10.0
DISTANCE BETWEEN SEAT EDGES
FRT
REAR SUSPENSION

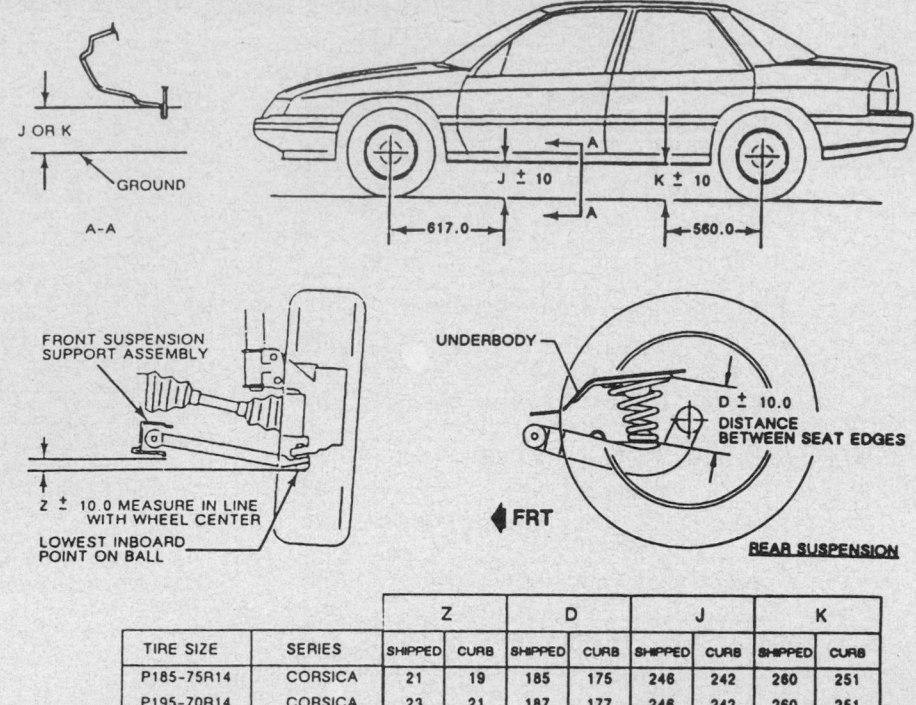

		Z		D		J		K	
TIRE SIZE	SERIES	SHIPPED	CURB	SHIPPED	CURB	SHIPPED	CURB	SHIPPED	CURB
P185-75R14	CORSICA	21	19	185	175	246	242	260	251
P195-70R14	CORSICA	23	21	187	177	246	242	260	251
P205-55R16	BERETTA	2	0	167	157	233	229	249	238
P205-60R15	CORSICA	8	6	173	163	233	229	246	238
P195-70R14	BERETTA	18	16	183	173	243	239	257	248
P205-60R15	BERETTA	8	6	172	164	232	229	246	235
P205-55VR16	BERETTA	2	0	168	159	233	229	253	243

GC2049100074000X

Fig. 2 Vehicle ride height measurements & specifications

BUICK SKYLARK, OLDSMOBILE ACHIEVA & PONTIAC GRAND AM (N Cars)

NOTE: Refer To Rear Of This Manual For Vehicle Manufacturer's Special Service Tool Suppliers.

INDEX OF SERVICE OPERATIONS

NOTE: For Service Operations Not Listed Below, Refer To The Table Of Contents In The Front Of This Manual.

Continued

INDEX OF SERVICE OPERATIONS—CONTINUED

Specifications

GENERAL ENGINE SPECIFICATIONS

Year	Engine Liter/CID	Engine VIN Code (2)	Fuel Injection System	Bore & Stroke	Compression Ratio	Net H.P. @ RPM (3)	Maximum Torque Ft. Lbs. @ RPM	Normal Oil Pressure psi.
1992–93	2.3L/4-138	3	MFI	3.62 x 3.35	9.5	120 @ 5200	140 @ 3200	(4)
	2.3L/4-138	D	MFI	3.62 x 3.35	9.5	160 @ 6200	155 @ 5200	(4)
	2.3L/4-138 HO	A	MFI	3.62 x 3.35	10.0	180 @ 6200	160 @ 5200	(4)
	3.3L/V6-204 (3300)	N	MFI	3.70 x 3.16	9.0	160 @ 5200	185 @ 2000	60(1)
1994	2.3L/4-138	D	MFI	3.62 x 3.35	9.5	155 @ 6200	150 @ 5200	(4)
	2.3L/4-138 HO	A	MFI	3.62 x 3.35	10.0	175 @ 6200	155 @ 5200	(4)
	3.1L/V6-192	M	SFI	3.50 x 3.31	9.5	155 @ 5200	185 @ 4000	15(5)
1995	2.3L/4-138	D	MFI	3.62 x 3.35	9.5	155 @ 6200	150 @ 5200	(4)
	3.1L/V6-192	M	SFI	3.50 x 3.31	9.5	155 @ 5200	185 @ 4000	15(5)

CID-Cubic inch displacement.
MFI: Multi-Port Fuel Injection.
SFI: Sequential Fuel Injection.
TBI: Throttle Body Fuel Injection.

(1)—At 1850 RPM, with engine at operating temperature.
(2)—The eighth digit denotes engine code.
(3)—Ratings are as installed in vehicle.
(4)—At 900 RPM, 15 psi. minimum; at 2000 RPM, 30 psi. minimum.
(5)—Minimum at 1100 RPM.

TUNE UP SPECIFICATIONS

Year & Engine (VIN Code) (1)	Spark Plug Gap, Inch	Ignition Timing, Deg. BTDC: Firing Order, Fig. (2)	Ignition Timing: Man. Trans.	Ignition Timing: Auto. Trans.	Ignition Timing: Mark Fig.	Curb Idle Speed RPM (3): Man. Trans.	Curb Idle Speed RPM (3): Auto. Trans.	Fast Idle Speed RPM: Man. Trans.	Fast Idle Speed RPM: Auto Trans.	Fuel Pump Pressure, psi
1992										
2.3L/4-138 (3)	.035	(10)	(7)	(7)	(8)	900(4)	700D(4)	(4)	(4)	41–47(9)
2.3L/4-138 (D)	.035	(10)	(7)	(7)	(8)	900(4)	700D(4)	(4)	(4)	41–47(9)
2.3L/4-138 (A) HO	.035	(10)	(7)	—	(8)	900(4)	—	(4)	—	41–47(9)
3.3L/V6-204 (N)	.060	(6)	—	(7)	(8)	—	675D(4)	—	(4)	41–47(9)
1993										
2.3L/4-138 (3)	.035	(10)	(7)	(7)	(8)	900(4)	700D(4)	(4)	(4)	41–47(5)
2.3L/4-138 (D)	.035	(10)	(7)	(7)	(8)	900(4)	700D(4)	(4)	(4)	41–47(5)
2.3L/4-138 (A) HO	.035	(10)	(7)	—	(8)	900(4)	—	(4)	—	41–47(5)
3.3L/V6-204 (N)	.060	(6)	—	(7)	(8)	—	675D(4)	—	(4)	41–47(9)

Continued

TUNE UP SPECIFICATIONS—Continued

Year & Engine (VIN Code) (1)	Spark Plug Gap, Inch	Ignition Timing, Deg. BTDC				Curb Idle Speed RPM (3)		Fast Idle Speed RPM		Fuel Pump Pressure, psi
		Firing Order, Fig. (2)	Man. Trans.	Auto. Trans.	Mark Fig.	Man. Trans.	Auto. Trans.	Man. Trans.	Auto Trans.	
1994										
2.3L/4-138 (D)	.035	C	(7)	(7)	(8)	900 (4)	700D (4)	(4)	(4)	41–47 (5)
2.3L/4-138 (A) HO	.035	C	(7)	—	(8)	900 (4)	—	(4)	—	41–47 (5)
3.1L/V6-191 (M)	.060	(2)	(7)	(7)	(8)	(4)	(4)	(4)	(4)	41-47 (9)
1995										
2.3L/4-138 (D)	.035	C	(7)	(7)	(8)	900 (4)	700D (4)	(4)	(4)	41–47 (5)
3.1L/V6-192 (M)	.060	(2)	(7)	(7)	(8)	(4)	(4)	(4)	(4)	41-47 (9)

BTDC-Before top dead center

(1)—The eighth digit of the Vehicle Identification Number (VIN) denotes engine code.

(2)—Cylinder numbering from front of engine to rear: right bank, 1–3–5; left bank, 2–4–6. Firing order 1–2–3–4–5–6. Refer to Fig. D for spark plug wire connections at ignition coil.

(3)—P: Park. When adjusting idle speed, set parking brake & block drive wheels.

(4)—Idle speed is controlled by an idle air control (IAC) valve or an idle speed control (ISC) motor.

(5)—Loosen fuel tank filler cap, then raise vehicle & disconnect fuel pump electrical connector. Start engine & operate until fuel supply is depleted. Crank engine for approximately 3 seconds, then place ignition switch in off position. Connect fuel pump electrical connector, then disconnect battery ground cable. Disconnect fuel line quick connect fittings, then install a suitable fuel pressure test gauge. Tighten fuel tank filler cap & connect battery ground cable. Place ignition switch in On position & check for leaks at gauge connections. With ignition switch in On position note fuel pressure reading.

(6)—Cylinder numbering left to right as viewed from front of vehicle, front bank, 1, 3, 5; rear bank, 2, 4, 6. Firing order, 1-6-5-4-3-2. Two different types of coil units are used, refer to Figs. A & B for spark plug wire connections at coil unit.

(7)—Computer controlled, no adjustment.

(8)—Equipped with crankshaft position sensor.

(9)—With shop towel wrapped around fuel pressure valve to prevent fuel spillage, connect a suitable fuel pressure gauge to fuel pressure valve. Check fuel pressure with ignition switch in the On position, engine not running.

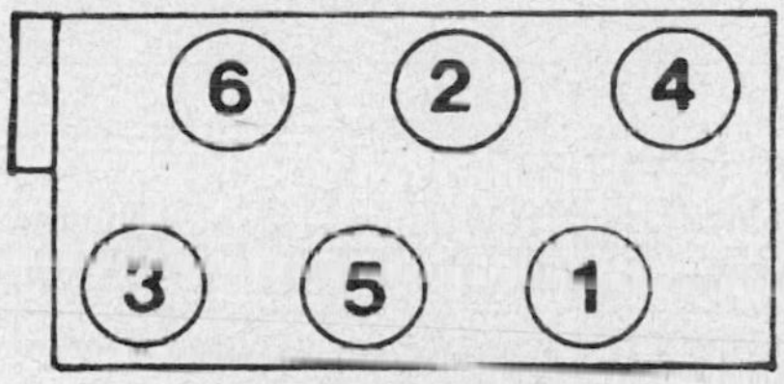
6
2
4
3
5
1
COMPUTER CONTROLLED
COIL IGNITION

GC1139100145000X

Fig. A

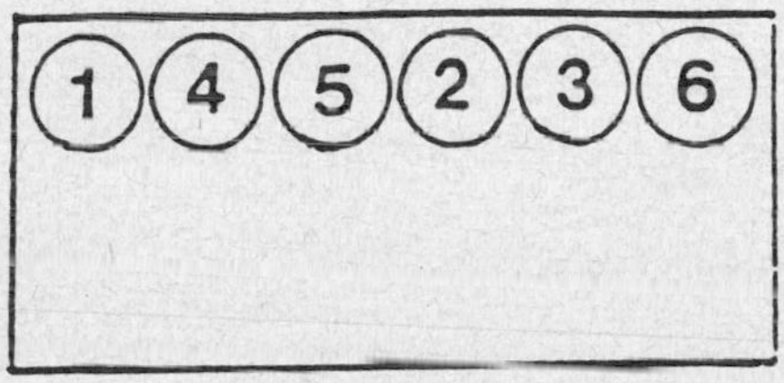
1
4
5
2
3
6
COMPUTER CONTROLLED
COIL IGNITION

GC1139100146000X

Fig. B

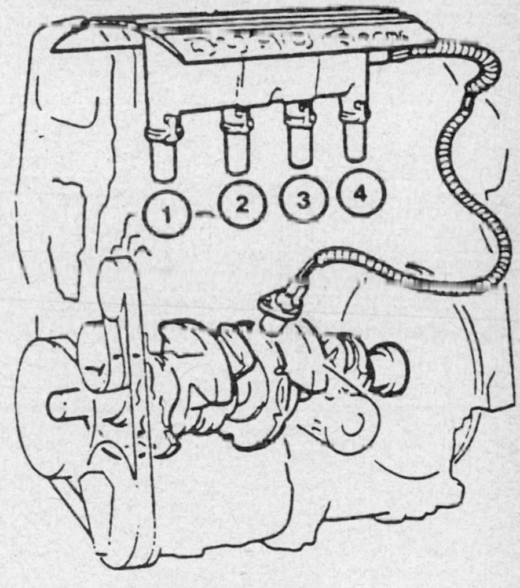
1
2
3
4

Firing order 1-3-4-2

GC1139100147000X

Fig. C

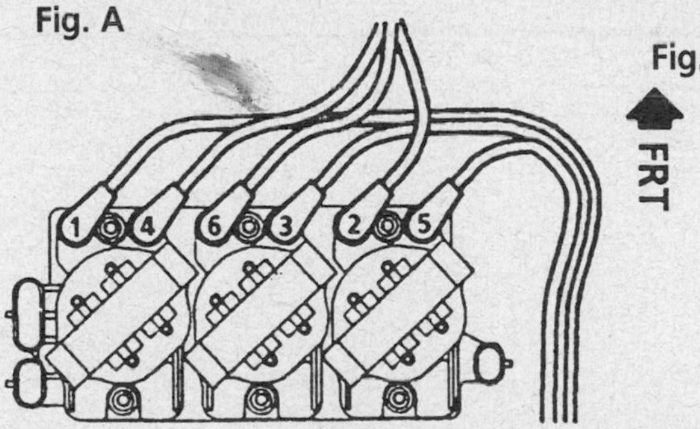
FRT
1
4
6
3
2
5

Fig. D

FRONT WHEEL ALIGNMENT SPECIFICATIONS

Year	Model	Caster Angle, Degrees		Camber Angle, Degrees		Total Toe Deg.
		Limits	Desired	Limits	Desired	
1992	All	+.70 to +2.70	+1.70	-.7 to +.7	0	-.2 to +.2
1993-95	All	+.45 to +2.45	+1.45	-.7 to +.7	0	-.2 to +.2

REAR WHEEL ALIGNMENT SPECIFICATIONS

Year	Model	Camber Angle, Degrees Limits	Camber Angle, Degrees Desired	Total Toe Deg.	Thrust Angle Deg.
1992	All	-.82 to +.32	-.25	-.06 to +.56	-.31 to +.31
1993-95	All	-.85 to +.35	-.25	-.35 to +.35	-.35 to +.35

COOLING SYSTEM & CAPACITY DATA

Year	Model or Engine (VIN)	Coolant Capacity, Qts.		Surge Tank Cap Relief Pressure, psi.	Thermo. Opening Temp. Deg. F	Fuel Tank Gals.	Engine Oil Refill Qts.②	Transaxle Oil	
		Less A/C	With A/C					Manual Transaxle Pts.	Auto. Transaxle Qts.①
1992–93	2.3L/4-138 (3, A & D)	9.5	9.5	18	180	13.6	4	4	③
	3.3L/V6-204 (N)	12.7	12.7	18	195	13.6	4	4	③
1994-95	2.3L/4-138 (A & D)	10.4	10.4	15	180	15.2	4	4	③
	3.1L/V6-192 (M)	13.1	13.1	15	195	15.2	4	4	④

①—Approximate; make final check with dipstick.
②—When changing filter, additional oil may be required.
③—Oil pan capacity, 4 qts.; total capacity, 7 qts.
④—Oil pan capacity, 6 qts.; total capacity, 8 qts.

LUBRICANT DATA

Year	Model	Lubricant Type: Transaxle Automatic	Transaxle Manual	Clutch Hydraulic System	Power Steering System	Brake System
1992-95	All	Dexron IIE or III	①	③	Power Steering Fluid②	DOT 3 Brake Fluid

①—Synchromesh transaxle fluid (GM part No. 12345349 or equivalent).
②—Meeting GM specification 9985010.
③—Hydraulic clutch fluid GM Part No. 12345347 or equivalent.

Electrical

NOTE: On Air Bag Equipped Models, Refer To "Air Bag System Precautions" Located In The Front Of This Manual For System Disarming & Arming Procedures.

INDEX

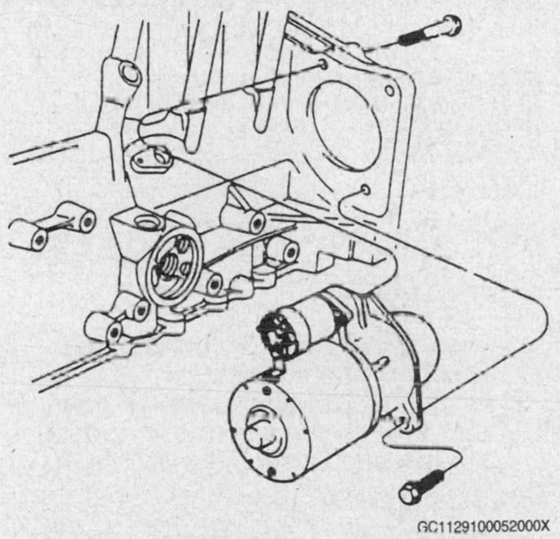
GC1129100052000X

Fig. 1 Starter motor replacement. 2.3L/4-138

PRECAUTIONS

AIR BAG SYSTEMS

Refer to "Air Bag System Precautions" in the front of this manual for system disarming and arming procedures.

FUSE PANEL & FLASHER LOCATION

The fuse panel is located behind the lefthand side of instrument panel.

The turn signal flasher is located behind the instrument panel on right hand side of steering column bracket. The hazard warning flasher is located on the convenience center, behind the left hand side of the instrument panel to the left of the steering column.

RELAY CENTER LOCATION

The relay center is located in the rear of the engine compartment, behind the center of the dash panel. This unit houses the fuel pump, coolant fan, high blower, A/C compressor control & electronic brake control relays.

STARTER

REPLACE

2.3L/4-138 ENGINE

1. Disconnect battery ground cable.
2. Remove air induction tube as necessary.
3. Disconnect coolant fan connector and remove coolant fan.
4. Remove oil filter and intake manifold brace.
5. Remove starter bolts and pull starter motor towards the passenger side of vehicle, **Fig. 1.**
6. Disconnect electrical connections and remove starter by lifting out between intake manifold and radiator.
7. Reverse procedure to install.

3.1L/V6-192 ENGINE

1. Disconnect battery ground cable.
2. Raise and support vehicle.
3. Remove starter motor mounting bolts, then lower starter.
4. Disconnect starter electrical connectors.
5. Remove starter from vehicle.
6. Reverse procedure to install.

3.3L/V6-204 ENGINE

1. Disconnect battery ground cable.
2. Raise and support vehicle, if necessary.

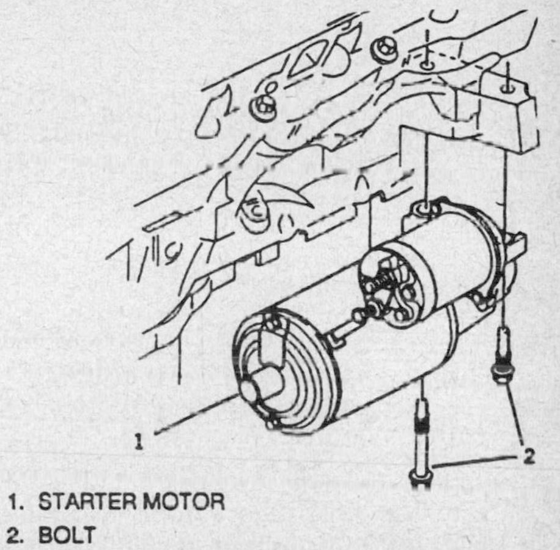
1
2
1. STARTER MOTOR
2. BOLT
GC1129100054000X

Fig. 2 Starter motor replacement. 3.3L/V6-204

3. Remove starter motor mounting bolts, then lower the starter motor, **Fig. 2.**
4. Disconnect starter leads and remove starter from vehicle.
5. Reverse procedure to install.

ALTERNATOR

REPLACE

2.3L/4-138 ENGINE

1. Disconnect battery ground cable.
2. Remove serpentine drive belt, refer to "Serpentine Drive Belt, Replace" in the "2.3L/4-138 Engine" section.
3. Disconnect oil/air separator hose, then vacuum harness bracket and position vacuum harness aside.
4. Remove two (one 10 mm and one 13 mm head) lower mounting bolts at rear of alternator **Fig. 3. Use care not to damage radiator core when removing lower mounting bolts.**

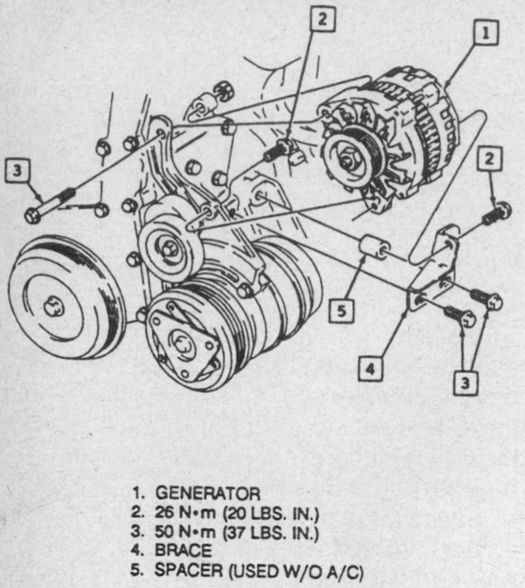
1. GENERATOR
2. 26 N•m (20 LBS. IN.)
3. 50 N•m (37 LBS. IN.)
4. BRACE
5. SPACER (USED W/O A/C)
GC1129100057000X

Fig. 3 Alternator mounting. 2.3L/4-138

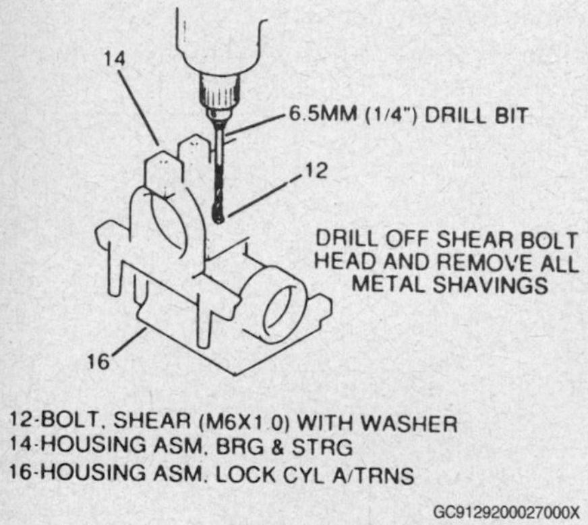
14
6.5MM (1/4") DRILL BIT
12
DRILL OFF SHEAR BOLT HEAD AND REMOVE ALL METAL SHAVINGS
16
12-BOLT, SHEAR (M6X1 0) WITH WASHER
14-HOUSING ASM, BRG & STRG
16-HOUSING ASM, LOCK CYL A/TRNS
GC9129200027000X

Fig. 6 Ignition lock cylinder housing replacement

5. Remove alternator front mounting bolt, then disconnect electrical leads and remove alternator.
6. Reverse procedure to install.

3.1L/V6–192 ENGINE

1. Disconnect battery ground cable.
2. Disconnect alternator electrical connectors.
3. Remove serpentine drive belt.
4. Remove alternator mounting bolts, **Fig. 4.**
5. Disconnect alternator air inlet connector.
6. Remove alternator.
7. Reverse procedure to install.

IGNITION LOCK

REPLACE

1. Disconnect battery ground cable.
2. Remove steering wheel as described under "Steering Wheel, Replace," then remove upper steering column covers.
3. Remove windshield wiper switch as described under "Windshield Wiper Switch, Replace."

A
FRT
GC1129500061000X

Fig. 4 Alternator removal. 3.1L/V6-192

4. Using tool No. J-23653 or equivalent, compress plate cam, then remove snap ring, plate cam and upper bearing spring, **Fig. 5.**
5. Remove thrust washer, then remove upper bearing.
6. Disconnect steering column shaft from coupling and remove column to mounting bracket bolts.
7. Remove steering column from vehicle.
8. With ignition lock in Run position, use a 1/4 inch drill bit to remove heads of shear bolts, **Fig. 6.**
9. Remove lock cylinder housing.
10. Using locking type pliers , remove threaded portion of shear bolts from lock cylinder housing.
11. Reverse procedure to install. Clean metal particles from steering column. Ignition lock should be Run position during installation. When installing lock cylinder, heads of bolts should shear at approximately 97 inch lbs. of torque.

IGNITION SWITCH

REPLACE

1. Disconnect battery ground cable.
2. Remove steering wheel and covers as described under "Steering Wheel, Replace."
3. Place ignition key in the Off/Lock position.
4. Remove two ignition switch mounting screws, then disconnect electrical connectors and remove switch, **Fig. 7.**
5. Reverse procedure to install.

CLUTCH START SWITCH

REPLACE

1. Disconnect battery ground cable.
2. Disconnect switch electrical connector.
3. Remove nuts attaching switch to mounting, then remove switch.
4. Reverse procedure to install. After installation, check switch for proper operation.

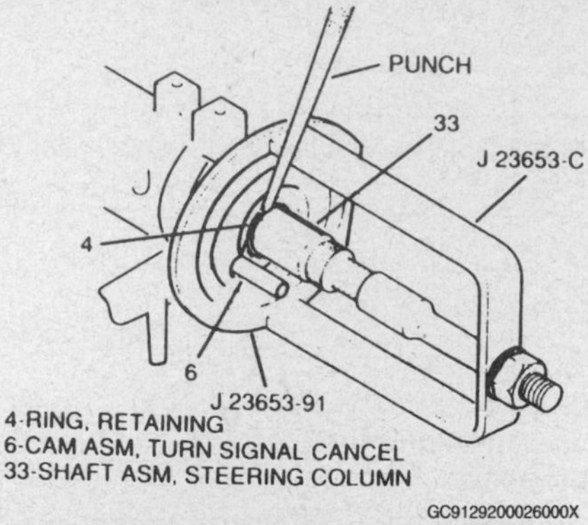
PUNCH
33
J 23653-C
4
6
J 23653-91
4-RING, RETAINING
6-CAM ASM, TURN SIGNAL CANCEL
33-SHAFT ASM, STEERING COLUMN
GC9129200026000X

Fig. 5 Upper plate snap ring removal

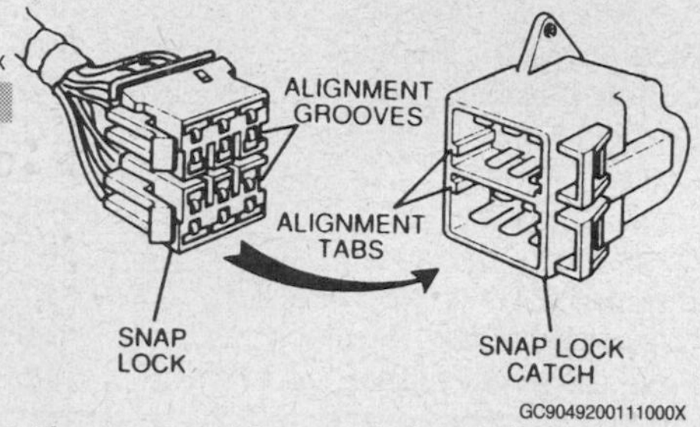
ALIGNMENT GROOVES
ALIGNMENT TABS
SNAP LOCK
SNAP LOCK CATCH
GC9049200111000X

Fig. 7 Ignition switch & electrical connections

NEUTRAL SAFETY SWITCH

REPLACE

AUTOMATIC TRANSAXLE

Removal

1. Disconnect battery ground cable.
2. Disconnect shift linkage.
3. Disconnect switch electrical connector, then remove switch mounting screws and switch, **Fig. 8.**

Installation

1. Place shift shaft in Neutral position, then align flats on shaft with flats on switch.
2. Loosely install switch.
3. If original switch is being installed, insert a 3/32 inch drill bit into switch adjustment hole, **Fig. 8.** Move switch until drill bit drops to depth of 9/64 inch, then tighten switch mounting screws and remove drill bit.
4. New switches are pinned in Neutral position. If installation is difficult, ensure shift shaft is Neutral. Do not rotate switch. Tighten switch mounting screws.

HEADLAMP SWITCH

REPLACE

1. Disconnect battery ground cable.
2. Remove horn pad and steering wheel as described under "Steering Wheel, Replace."
3. Remove tilt lever from steering column, if equipped. If necessary position spark plug boot or other suitable de-

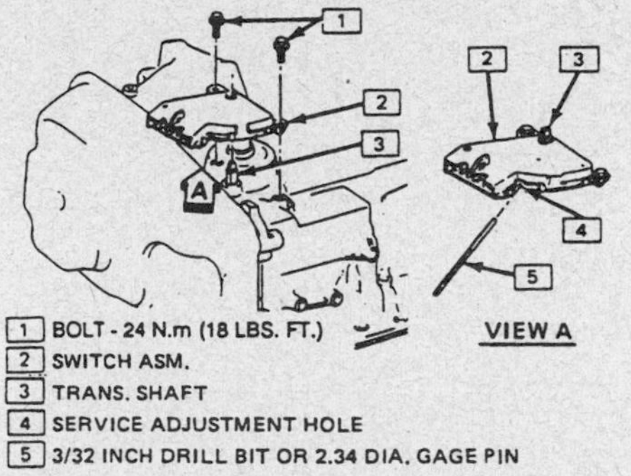
1
2
3
4
5
A
VIEW A
1 BOLT - 24 N.m (18 LBS. FT.)
2 SWITCH ASM.
3 TRANS. SHAFT
4 SERVICE ADJUSTMENT HOLE
5 3/32 INCH DRILL BIT OR 2.34 DIA. GAGE PIN
GC9049100113000X

Fig. 8 Neutral safety/back-up lamp switch replacement

vice over tilt lever (to prevent damage), then remove tilt lever using locking pliers.

4. Remove steering column upper and lower covers, then remove dampener assembly.
5. Remove switch assembly attaching screw, then remove switch, **Fig. 9.**
6. Reverse procedure to install.

STOP LIGHT SWITCH
REPLACE

1. Disconnect battery ground cable.
2. Disconnect electrical connectors from switch, then pull switch out of retaining clip on brake pedal support.
3. Depress brake pedal and push replacement switch into retainer until switch shoulder is bottomed against bracket.
4. Adjust switch by pulling brake pedal back against stop.
5. Ensure switch has continuity when pedal is depressed from normal rest position and when pedal fully returns to rest position stop lamps are off.

TURN SIGNAL SWITCH
REPLACE

Refer to "Headlamp Switch, Replace" for column-mounted switch replacement.

DIMMER SWITCH
REPLACE

Refer to "Headlamp Switch, Replace" for column-mounted switch replacement.

STEERING WHEEL
REPLACE

1. Disconnect battery ground cable, then remove the attaching screws for the steering pad.
2. Remove the pad and horn lead, then remove the steering wheel retainer and nut.
3. Remove the steering wheel with a suitable steering wheel puller.
4. Reverse procedure to install.

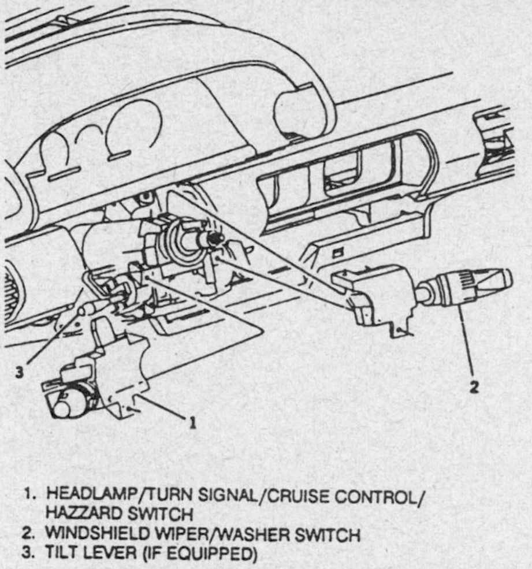
1
2
3
1. HEADLAMP/TURN SIGNAL/CRUISE CONTROL/ HAZZARD SWITCH
2. WINDSHIELD WIPER/WASHER SWITCH
3. TILT LEVER (IF EQUIPPED)
GC9049200112000X

Fig. 9 Column mounted switch replacement

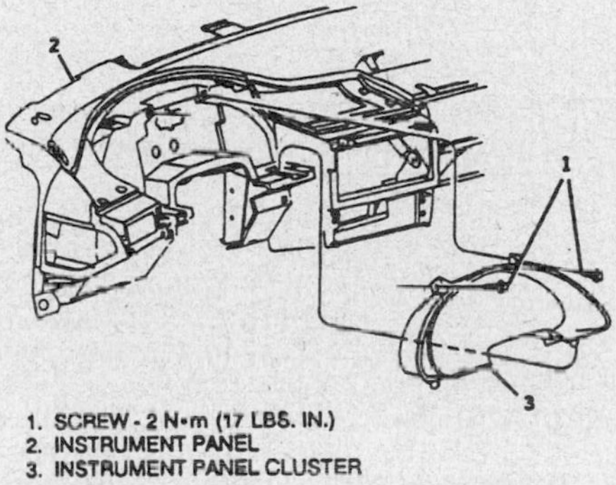
1
2
3
1. SCREW - 2 N•m (17 LBS. IN.)
2. INSTRUMENT PANEL
3. INSTRUMENT PANEL CLUSTER
GC9099200234000X

Fig. 11 Instrument cluster installation. Grand Am

BACK-UP LAMP SWITCH
REPLACE
MANUAL TRANSAXLE

1. Disconnect battery ground cable.
2. Disconnect back-up lamp switch electrical connector.
3. Remove back-up lamp switch from top of transaxle case.
4. Reverse procedure to install. Prior to installation, apply sealant No. 1052080 or equivalent to switch threads.

INSTRUMENT CLUSTER
REPLACE
ACHIEVA

1. Disconnect battery ground cable.
2. Remove steering wheel as outlined under "Steering Wheel, Replace."
3. Remove steering column covers.
4. Remove instrument cluster trim plate eight attaching screws, **Fig. 10.**
5. Pull trim plate rearward to disconnect electrical connectors, then remove plate.
6. Remove instrument cluster four attaching screws, them remove cluster.

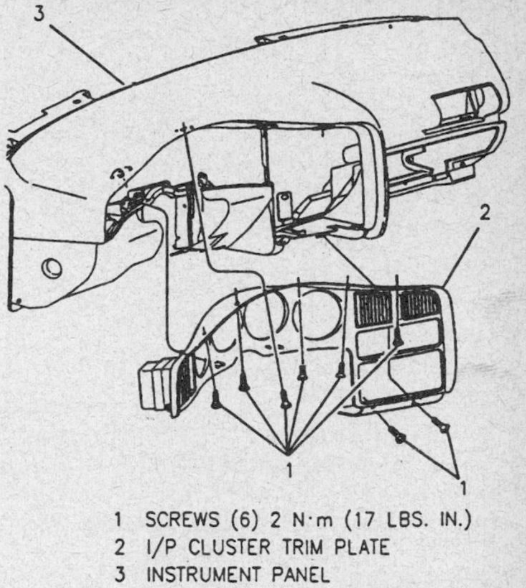
1
2
3
1 SCREWS (6) 2 N·m (17 LBS. IN.)
2 I/P CLUSTER TRIM PLATE
3 INSTRUMENT PANEL
GC9099200233000X

Fig. 10 Instrument cluster trim plate removal. Achieva

7. Reverse procedure to install. **Torque** instrument cluster trim plate attaching screws to 17 inch lbs.

GRAND AM

1. Disconnect battery ground cable.
2. Remove three lower left hand sound insulator attaching screws.
3. Disconnect cruise control module electrical connector and lamp, then remove lower left hand sound insulator panel.
4. Remove ALDL connector attaching screws, then remove steering column filler panel attaching screws and filler panel.
5. Carefully pull driver's side air deflectors rearward.
6. In a rocking motion, alternately and carefully pry left and right hand instrument panel cover retaining clips upward, then remove instrument panel cover.
7. Remove fuse panel cover, then remove left hand instrument panel trim plate. Pull trim plate rearward to disengage retaining clips.
8. Open upper instrument panel compartment door, then remove four compartment to instrument panel attaching screws.
9. Remove upper instrument panel compartment from instrument panel.
10. Press release tab upward, then remove lower instrument panel compartment door.
11. Remove lower instrument panel compartment to instrument panel attaching screws, then disconnect electrical connector and remove compartment.
12. Remove right hand instrument panel trim plate attaching screws.
13. Carefully pull right hand instrument panel trim plate rearward to disengage retaining clips, then remove trim panel.
14. Remove instrument cluster attaching screws, then pull cluster forward and disconnect electrical connectors.

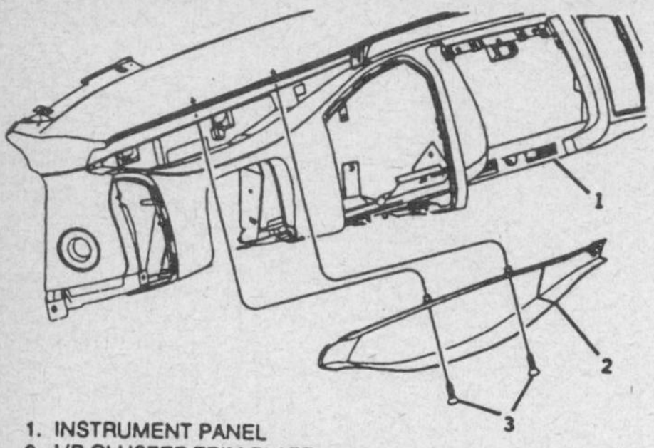
1
2
3
1. INSTRUMENT PANEL
2. I/P CLUSTER TRIM PLATE
3. SCREWS - 2 N·m (17 LBS. IN.)
GC9099200235000X

Fig. 12 Instrument cluster trim plate removal. Skylark

15. Remove instrument cluster, **Fig. 11.**
16. Reverse procedure to install.

SKYLARK

1. Disconnect battery ground cable.
2. Remove instrument panel trim plate attaching screws, **Fig. 12.**
3. Pull trim plate rearward to disengage plate clips, then remove plate.
4. Remove instrument cluster attaching screws.
5. Pull top of cluster rearward to remove.
6. Reverse procedure to install. **Torque** instrument cluster trim plate attaching screws to 17 inch lbs.

RADIO

REPLACE

ACHIEVA

1. Disconnect battery ground cable.
2. Remove steering wheel as outlined under "Steering Wheel, Replace."
3. Remove steering column covers.
4. Remove instrument cluster trim plate attaching screws, **Fig. 10.**
5. Pull trim plate rearward to disconnect electrical connectors, then remove plate.
6. Remove radio to radio bracket attaching nuts.
7. Pull radio rearward to disconnect antenna and electrical connectors, then remove radio assembly.
8. Reverse procedure to install. **Torque** radio to radio bracket attaching nuts to 35 inch lbs.

GRAND AM

1. Disconnect battery ground cable.
2. Remove three lower left hand sound insulator attaching screws.
3. Disconnect cruise control module electrical connector and lamp, then remove left hand sound insulator panel.
4. Remove ALDL connector attaching screws, then remove steering column filler panel attaching screws and filler panel.
5. Open upper instrument panel compartment door, then remove four compartment to instrument panel attaching screws.
6. Remove upper instrument panel compartment from instrument panel.
7. Press release tab upward, then remove lower instrument panel compartment door.
8. Remove lower instrument panel compartment to instrument panel attaching screws, then disconnect electrical connector and remove compartment.
9. Remove right hand instrument panel trim plate attaching screws.
10. Carefully pull right hand instrument panel trim plate rearward to disengage retaining clips, then remove trim panel.
11. Remove radio upper retaining nuts.
12. Pull radio rearward and disconnect electrical connectors and antenna lead.
13. Remove radio from instrument panel.
14. Reverse procedure to install.

SKYLARK

1. Disconnect battery ground cable.
2. Remove instrument panel trim plate two attaching screws, **Fig. 12.**
3. Pull trim plate rearward to disengage plate clips, then remove plate.
4. Remove two radio to radio bracket attaching nuts.
5. Pull radio rearward to disconnect antenna and electrical connectors, then remove radio assembly.
6. Reverse procedure to install. **Torque** radio to radio bracket attaching nuts to 35 inch lbs.

WIPER MOTOR

REPLACE

1. Disconnect battery ground cable.
2. Remove wiper arm and blade assemblies.
3. Remove cowl cover assembly, then disconnect drive link from crank arm.
4. Disconnect wiper motor electrical connectors.
5. Remove wiper motor attaching bolts, then the wiper motor.
6. Reverse procedure to install.

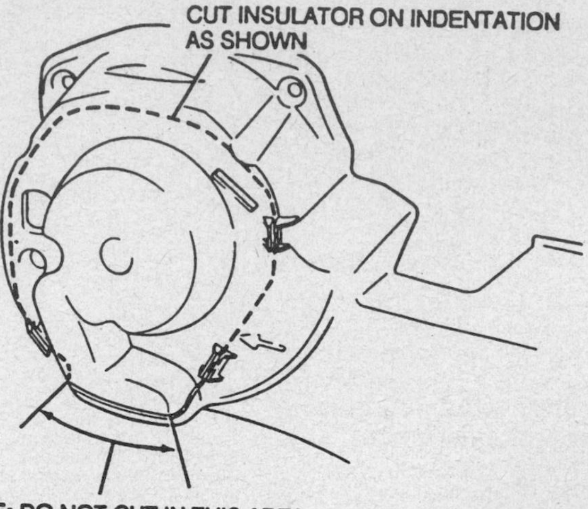
CUT INSULATOR ON INDENTATION AS SHOWN
NOTE: DO NOT CUT IN THIS AREA
GC7029200063000X

Fig. 13 Blower motor removal pattern

WIPER SWITCH

REPLACE

1. Disconnect battery ground cable.
2. Remove headlamp, hazard warning, turn signal and cruise control switch as described previously.
3. Remove windshield wiper/washer to steering column attaching screws, then remove switch, **Fig. 9.**
4. Reverse procedure to install.

WIPER TRANSMISSION

REPLACE

1. Disconnect battery ground cable.
2. Remove wiper arm and blades assemblies.
3. Remove cowl cover assembly, then disconnect drive link from crank arm.
4. Remove windshield wiper transmission to body attaching screws, then guide linkage out through access hole.
5. Reverse procedure to install.

BLOWER MOTOR

REPLACE

1. Disconnect battery ground cable.
2. **On models with 3.3L/V6-204 engines,** remove power steering pump from mounting bracket and position aside with hoses attached.
3. **On all models,** disconnect electrical connectors from blower motor.
4. Partially cut blower motor case cover as indicated in **Fig. 13.** The cutting pattern is also indicated on the blower case cover. Cover thickness is approximately 1/8 inch. Cut just through thickness of cover. Any cut deeper than thickness of cover may cause damage to cooling tube.
5. Move cut portion of cover downward and disconnect blower motor cooling tube.

6. Remove blower motor retaining screws and blower motor.
7. Reverse procedure to install. Use three retaining clips to attach cut portion of blower motor cover.

HEATER CORE

REPLACE

1. Disconnect battery ground cable.
2. Drain cooling system.
3. Raise and support vehicle.
4. Disconnect heater hoses from heater core assembly.
5. Remove drain tube.
6. Lower vehicle.
7. If equipped, remove console as follows:
   a. Apply parking brake and block drive wheels.
   b. Position transaxle shift lever in Neutral.
   c. **On models with automatic transaxle,** remove clip retaining shift lever handle to lever, then remove shift lever handle.
   d. **On models with manual transaxle,** turn shift lever handle counterclockwise to remove from lever.
   e. **On all models,** carefully pry upward on outer edges of console trim plate.
   f. Disconnect electrical connectors and ashtray lamp from console trim plate, then remove trim plate from console.
   g. Remove console to mounting bracket attaching screws, then remove console.
8. Remove three lower left hand sound insulator attaching screws.
9. Disconnect cruise control module electrical connector and lamp, then remove left hand sound insulator panel.
10. Remove two lower right hand sound insulator attaching screws and two nuts.
11. Disconnect EVO controller electrical connector and lamp, then remove right hand sound insulator panel.
12. Remove ALDL connector attaching screws, then remove steering column filler panel attaching screws and filler panel.
13. Remove floor outlet duct.
14. Remove heater core cover attaching screws, then remove heater core cover.
15. Remove heater core mounting clamps, then remove heater core.
16. Reverse procedure to install.

EVAPORATOR CORE

REPLACE

1. Discharge and recover refrigerant from A/C system.
2. Disconnect battery ground cable.
3. Raise and support vehicle, then remove front exhaust system heat shield.
4. Remove three attaching bolts, then swing cradle cross brace aside.
5. Disconnect refrigerant lines from evaporator, then lower vehicle.
6. Remove under dash insulator panel from right hand side.
7. Disconnect electrical connector at heater core cover on heater A/C module.
8. Remove steering column filler panel.
9. Remove center console to gain access to floor duct and heater core cover.
10. Remove heater core shroud and straps. Use care when removing evaporator core, as heater core is only suspended by heater core pipes.
11. Remove evaporator core from vehicle.
12. Reverse procedure to install. When connecting refrigerant lines, use new O-rings.

2.3L/4-138 Engine

NOTE: On Air Bag Equipped Models, Refer To "Air Bag System Precautions" Located In The Front Of This Manual For System Disarming & Arming Procedures.

INDEX

PRECAUTIONS

AIR BAG SYSTEMS

Refer to "Air Bag System Precautions" in the front of this manual for system disarming and arming procedures.

FUEL SYSTEM PRESSURE RELIEF

Failure to relieve system pressure prior to disconnecting fuel system components may cause fire or personal injury.

1. Loosen fuel tank filler cap to relieve tank pressure.
2. Raise and support vehicle, then disconnect fuel pump electrical connector.
3. Start and operate engine until fuel supply is consumed.
4. Crank engine for approximately 3 seconds to relieve remaining pressure.
5. Disconnect battery ground cable, then reconnect fuel pump connector.

ENGINE MOUNT

REPLACE

FRONT MOUNT

1. Disconnect battery ground cable.
2. Using engine support tool No. J-28467-A or equivalent, raise engine off mount.
3. Raise and support vehicle, then remove righthand wheel and tire assembly.
4. Remove righthand splash shield.
5. Remove two front engine mount lower attaching bolts.

6. Lower vehicle, then remove nut attaching mount to body.
7. Remove nut attaching engine bracket to mount, then remove mount assembly, **Fig. 1.**
8. Reverse procedure to install.

ENGINE MOUNT STRUT

1. Disconnect battery ground cable.
2. Raise and support vehicle.
3. Remove bolts attaching engine mount strut to body and engine mount strut bracket, **Fig. 2.**
4. Remove engine mount strut.
5. Reverse procedure to install.

ENGINE

REPLACE

1. Disconnect battery ground cable, then drain cooling system.
2. Disconnect heater hose at thermostat housing, then upper radiator hose.
3. Disconnect air cleaner to throttle body duct.
4. Remove upper radiator support.
5. Remove engine cooling fan.
6. **On models equipped with A/C,** discharge A/C system, then disconnect hoses from A/C compressor and discard O-rings.
7. **On all models,** disconnect two vacuum lines at front of engine.
8. Disconnect electrical connectors from alternator, A/C compressor (if equipped), injector harness, idle air control and throttle position sensor at throttle body and position aside.
9. Disconnect electrical connections from starter motor solenoid.
10. Disconnect ground connections at engine front mount and battery ground cable at transaxle.
11. Disconnect electrical connectors at ignition coil and module assembly, both coolant sensors, oil pressure switch, power steering switch, knock sensor, oxygen sensor, crankshaft position sensor, vehicle speed sensor, neutral safety or back-up lamp switch and starter solenoid connector.
12. Disconnect power brake unit vacuum hose from throttle body and power brake unit vacuum tube to check valve hose from tube.
13. Disconnect throttle cable and remove throttle cable bracket.
14. Remove power steering pump rear bracket and power brake vacuum tube as an assembly.
15. Remove power steering pivot bolt, pump and drive belt. Position pump aside with lines attached.
16. De-pressurize fuel system, then disconnect fuel lines.
17. **On models with manual transaxle,** disconnect shift cables, then remove clutch slave cylinder.
18. **On models with automatic transaxle,** disconnect shift cable, throttle valve cables and transaxle oil cooler lines.
19. **On all models,** remove exhaust manifold and heat shield, then lower radiator hose.

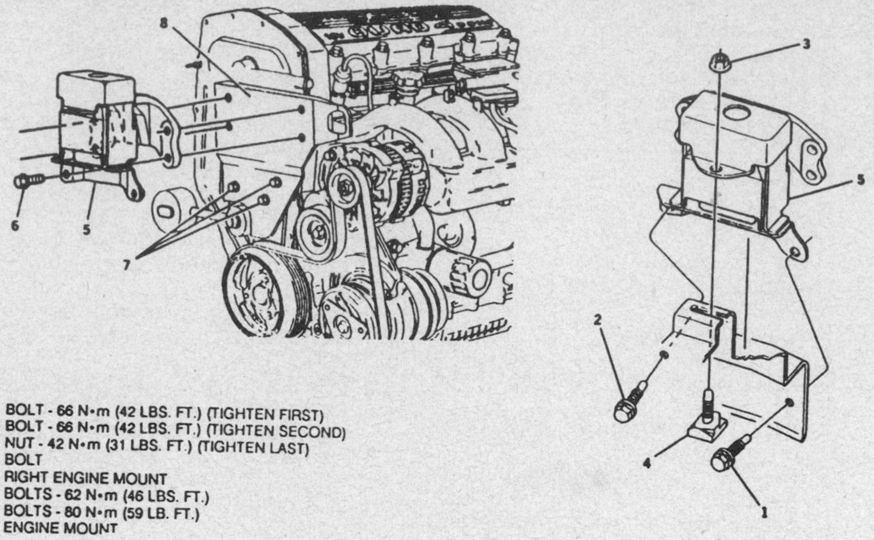

1. BOLT - 66 N•m (42 LBS. FT.) (TIGHTEN FIRST)
2. BOLT - 66 N•m (42 LBS. FT.) (TIGHTEN SECOND)
3. NUT - 42 N•m (31 LBS. FT.) (TIGHTEN LAST)
4. BOLT
5. RIGHT ENGINE MOUNT
6. BOLTS - 62 N•m (46 LBS. FT.)
7. BOLTS - 80 N•m (59 LB. FT.)
8. ENGINE MOUNT

GC1069200413000X

Fig. 1 Right engine mount

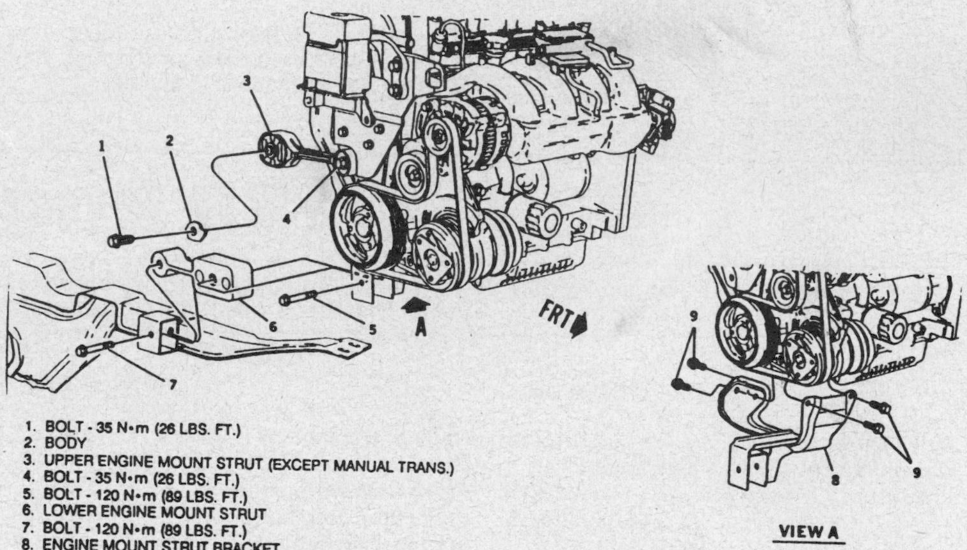
A
FRT
VIEW A

1. BOLT - 35 N•m (26 LBS. FT.)
2. BODY
3. UPPER ENGINE MOUNT STRUT (EXCEPT MANUAL TRANS.)
4. BOLT - 35 N•m (26 LBS. FT.)
5. BOLT - 120 N•m (89 LBS. FT.)
6. LOWER ENGINE MOUNT STRUT
7. BOLT - 120 N•m (89 LBS. FT.)
8. ENGINE MOUNT STRUT BRACKET
9. BOLTS - 66 N•m (49 LBS. FT.)

GC1069200414000X

Fig. 2 Engine mount & strut

20. Remove nut from front engine mount, then install engine support tool J-28467 or equivalent.
21. Raise and support vehicle, then remove front wheel and tire assemblies.
22. Remove right hand lower splash shield and radiator air deflector.
23. Separate ball joints from steering knuckles.
24. Using a suitable holding fixture, support front suspension, then remove suspension support attaching bolts. Remove suspension supports, crossmember and stabilizer bar as an assembly. Then remove heater outlet hose from radiator outlet pipe.
25. Position tool J-34754 or equivalent on drive axle boots, then remove axle shafts from transaxle and position aside.
26. Remove transaxle rear mount through bolt nut, then remove nut from engine rear mount through bolt.
27. Remove rear engine mount body bracket, then position suitable support under engine and lower vehicle to engine support.
28. Remove transaxle mount through bolt.
29. Mark engine support fixture hook threads so that engine can be returned to this position for installation, then remove engine support fixture.
30. Slowly and carefully raise vehicle off engine and transaxle assembly. It may be necessary to move engine and transaxle assembly slightly rearward to provide for intake manifold clearance.
31. Separate engine from transaxle.
32. Reverse procedure to install.

INTAKE MANIFOLD

REPLACE

1. Disconnect battery ground cable, then

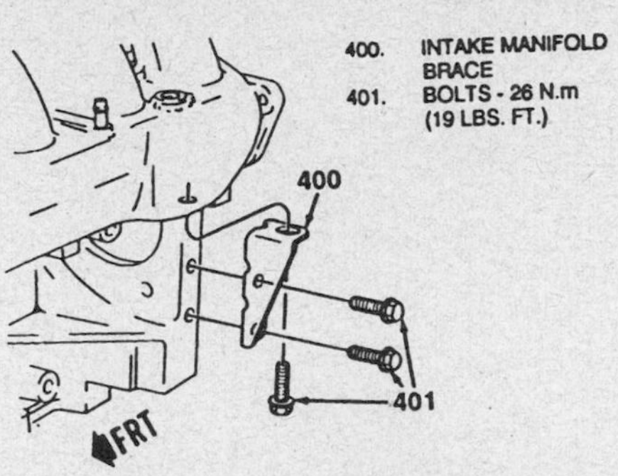
400
401
FRT
400. INTAKE MANIFOLD BRACE
401. BOLTS - 26 N.m (19 LBS. FT.)
GC1059200085000X

Fig. 3 Intake manifold brace removal

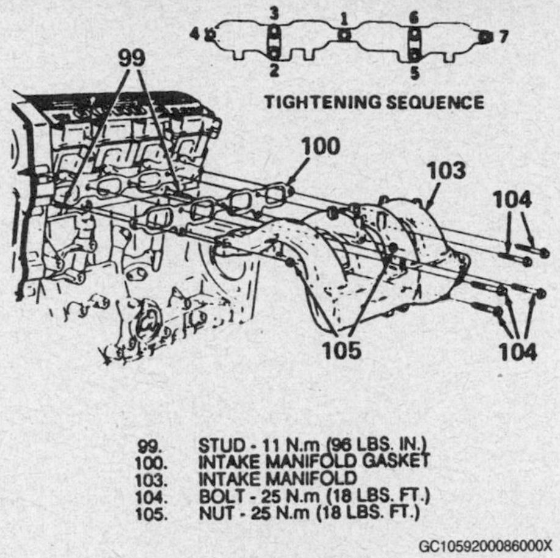
TIGHTENING SEQUENCE
99
100
103
104
105
104
99. STUD - 11 N.m (96 LBS. IN.)
100. INTAKE MANIFOLD GASKET
103. INTAKE MANIFOLD
104. BOLT - 25 N.m (18 LBS. FT.)
105. NUT - 25 N.m (18 LBS. FT.)
GC1059200086000X

Fig. 4 Intake manifold installation & bolt tightening sequence

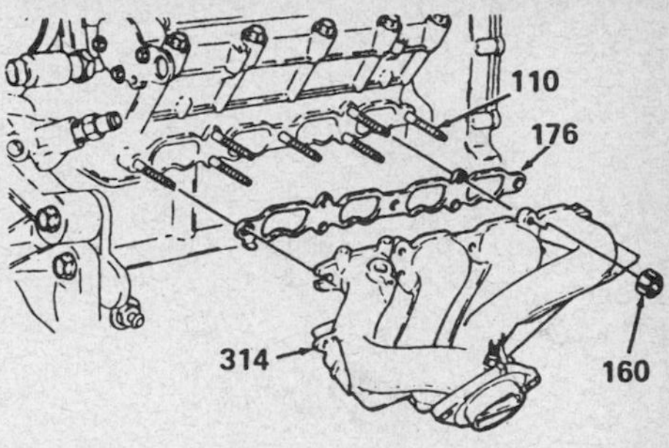
110
176
314
160
(HEAT SHIELD REMOVED FOR ILLUSTRATION PURPOSES)

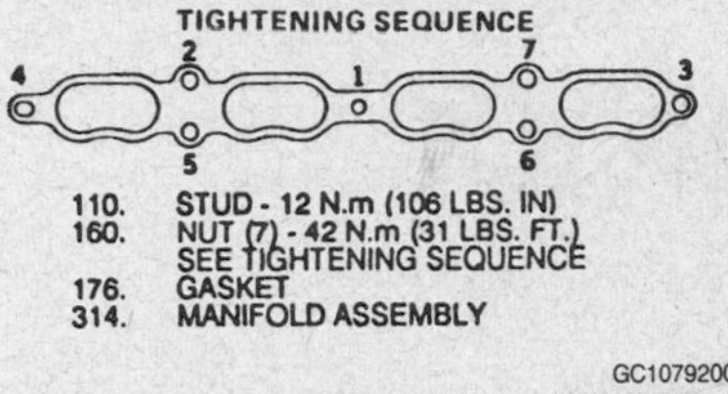
TIGHTENING SEQUENCE
110. STUD - 12 N.m (106 LBS. IN)
160. NUT (7) - 42 N.m (31 LBS. FT.) SEE TIGHTENING SEQUENCE
176. GASKET
314. MANIFOLD ASSEMBLY
GC1079200026000X

Fig. 5 Exhaust manifold installation & bolt tightening sequence

drain coolant to appropriate level.
2. Disconnect vacuum hose and electrical connector from MAP sensor.
3. Disconnect electrical connectors from the MAP sensor, MAT sensor, purge solenoid and fuel injector harness and position aside, then disconnect hoses from intake manifold and hose at fuel regulator and purge solenoid to canister.
4. Disconnect air cleaner to throttle body duct.
5. Disconnect vent tube to air cleaner duct.
6. Remove throttle cable bracket, then disconnect power brake unit vacuum hose with retaining bracket to power steering bracket and position aside.
7. Disconnect coolant lines from throttle body.
8. Remove oil/air separator, leaving hoses attached to the separator. Disconnect hoses from the oil fill, chain housing, chain cover, intake duct and intake manifold and remove as an assembly.
9. Remove oil fill cap and dipstick assembly, then pull oil fill tube upward to unseat from engine block.
10. Disconnect injector wiring harness connector.
11. Remove oil fill tube out top, rotating as necessary to gain clearance for oil/air separator nipple between intake tubes and fuel rail electrical harness.
12. Remove intake manifold support bracket, **Fig. 3.**
13. Remove remaining intake manifold attaching bolts and nuts, then remove intake manifold and gasket.
14. Reverse procedure to install. Tighten intake manifold bolts in sequence shown in **Fig. 4.**

EXHAUST MANIFOLD
REPLACE

1. Disconnect battery ground cable.
2. Disconnect electrical connector from oxygen sensor.
3. Remove heat shield, then raise and support vehicle.
4. Remove exhaust manifold brace to manifold bolt.
5. Remove manifold to exhaust pipe spring loaded nuts, then pull down and back on exhaust pipe to disengage from manifold.

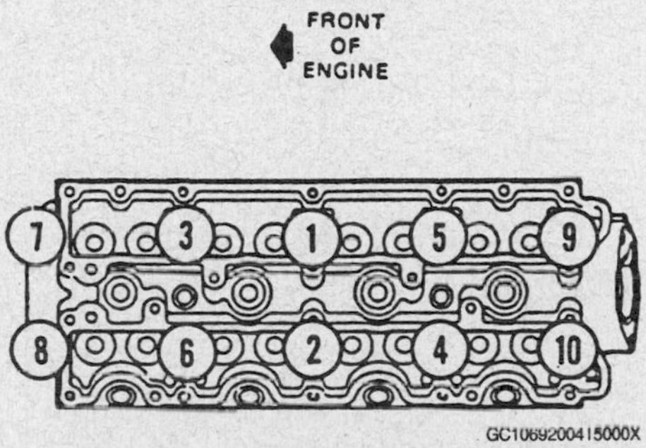
FRONT OF ENGINE
7
3
1
5
9
8
6
2
4
10
GC1069200415000X

Fig. 6 Cylinder head bolt tightening sequence

6. Lower vehicle and remove exhaust manifold to cylinder head retaining nuts, then manifold seals and gaskets.
7. Reverse procedure to install. Tighten exhaust manifold attaching bolts in sequence shown in **Fig. 5.**

CYLINDER HEAD
REPLACE

1. Disconnect battery ground cable, then drain cooling system.
2. Disconnect upper radiator hose, heater hose and throttle body heater hoses from coolant outlets.
3. Remove exhaust manifold as described under "Exhaust Manifold, Replace."
4. **On DOHC engine,** remove intake camshaft housing.
5. **On SOHC engine,** remove camshaft housing. Refer to "Camshaft, Housing and Valve Lash Adjusters, Replace."
6. **On DOHC engine,** remove exhaust camshaft housing as described under "Camshaft, Housing and Valve Lash Adjusters, Replace."
7. **On all models,** remove engine oil filler cap and dipstick from engine.
8. Pull oil fill tube upward to unseat from engine.
9. Disconnect injector wiring harness.
10. Remove oil fill tube out top rotating as necessary to gain clearance for oil/air separator nipple, located between intake manifold tubes.
11. Remove air cleaner to throttle body duct.
12. Disconnect power brake unit vacuum hose from throttle body.
13. Remove throttle cable bracket.
14. Remove throttle body from intake manifold and position aside with throttle cable, coolant hoses and electrical connectors attached.
15. Disconnect MAP sensor vacuum hose at intake manifold.
16. Remove intake manifold brace, then disconnect electrical connectors from the MAP sensor, MAT sensor and purge solenoid.
17. Disconnect upper radiator hose from water outlet.
18. Disconnect both coolant temperature sensor electrical connectors.
19. Loosen cylinder head attaching bolts in reverse order of tightening sequence, **Fig. 6.**
20. Remove cylinder head and gasket.
21. Reverse procedure to install. Tighten cylinder head attaching bolts using torque angle meter tool No. J-36660 or equivalent, as follows:
    a. **On 1992 models, torque** cylinder head bolts 1 through 6 to 26 ft. lbs., bolts 7 and 8 to 15 ft. lbs., and bolts 9 and 10 to 22 ft. lbs., in sequence shown in **Fig. 6,** then tighten all bolts in sequence an additional 90°. In sequence, loosen each bolt one turn and retighten to specifications, then tighten all cylinder head bolts an additional 90°.
    b. **On 1993-95 VIN A and D engines, torque** cylinder head bolts 1 through 6 to 18 ft. lbs., bolts 7 and 8 to 22 ft. lbs., and bolts 9 and 10 to 26 ft. lbs., in sequence shown in **Fig. 6.** Tighten cylinder head bolts 1 through 6 in sequence an additional 90°, then tighten bolts 7 through 10 in sequence an additional 60°. In sequence, loosen each bolt one turn and retighten to specifications, then tighten cylinder

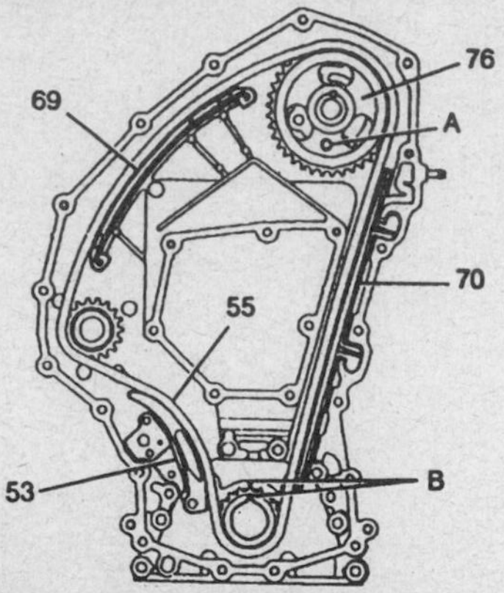
76
69
A
70
55
53
B

A. CAMSHAFT TIMING ALIGNMENT PIN LOCATIONS
B. CRANKSHAFT GEAR TIMING MARKS

53. SHOE AND TENSIONER ASSEMBLY
55. TIMING CHAIN
69. GUIDE - R.H. TIMING CHAIN
70. GUIDE - L.H. TIMING CHAIN
76. SPROCKET, CAMSHAFT

GC1069100416000X

Fig. 7 Valve timing marks. SOHC engine

head bolts 1 through 6 an additional 90° and bolts 7 through 10 an additional 60°.

c. **On 1993 VIN 3 engines, torque** cylinder head bolts 1 through 6 to 18 ft. lbs., bolts 7 and 8 to 26 ft. lbs., and bolts 9 and 10 to 30 ft. lbs., in sequence, **Fig. 6.** Tighten cylinder head bolts 1 through 6 in sequence an additional 90°, then tighten bolts 7 through 10 in sequence an additional 60°. In sequence, loosen each bolt one turn and retighten to torque specifications, then tighten cylinder head bolts 1 through 6 an additional 90° and bolts 7 through 10 an additional 60°.

CAMSHAFT LOBE LIFT SPECIFICATIONS

Year & Engine (VIN)	Int.	Exh.
1992–95		
2.3L/4-138 (A)	.410	.410
2.3L/4-138 (D)	.375	.375
1992–93		
2.3L/4-138 (3)	.410	.410

VALVE ADJUSTMENT

These engines are equipped with hydraulic valve lash adjusters. No adjustment is required.

VALVE GUIDES

Valve guides are an integral part of the cylinder head and are not removable. If valve stem clearance becomes excessive, the valve guide should be reamed to the next oversize and the appropriate oversize valves installed. Valves are available in .010 inch oversize.

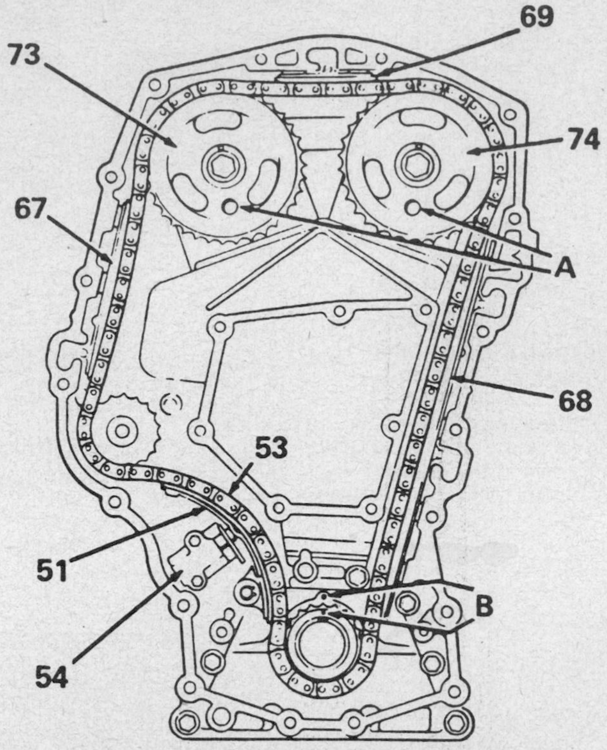
69
73
74
67
A
68
53
51
B
54

A. CAMSHAFT TIMING ALIGNMENT PIN LOCATIONS
B. CRANKSHAFT GEAR TIMING MARKS
51. SHOE ASM. TIMING CHAIN TENSIONER
53. TIMING CHAIN
54. TENSIONER, TIMING CHAIN
67. GUIDE – R.H. TIMING CHAIN
68. GUIDE – L.H. TIMING CHAIN
69. GUIDE – UPPER TIMING CHAIN
73. SPROCKET, EXHAUST CAMSHAFT
74. SPROCKET, INTAKE CAMSHAFT

GC1069100417000X

Fig. 8 Valve timing marks. DOHC engine

VALVE LASH ADJUSTERS

These engines use hydraulic valve lash adjusters. The valve lash adjusters can be replaced after the intake camshaft and housing or exhaust camshaft and housing on DOHC engine, or camshaft and camshaft housing on SOHC engine, are removed. Refer to "Camshaft, Housing and Valve Lash Adjusters, Replace."

FRONT COVER

REPLACE

1. Disconnect battery ground cable, then remove coolant reservoir.
2. Remove serpentine drive belt.
3. Remove alternator from mounting bracket and position aside. Reinstall alternator mount through bolt and attach engine support fixture.
4. Remove upper front cover attaching screws.
5. **On DOHC engine,** remove cover vent hose.
6. Remove right hand front engine mount and engine lift bracket. On automatic transaxle models, also remove upper engine strut.
7. **On all models,** raise and support vehicle, then remove right hand wheel and tire assembly.
8. Remove right hand lower splash shield.
9. Using harmonic balancer tool No. J-38122, or equivalent, to hold crankshaft balancer in position, remove retaining bolt, then remove balancer using puller No. J-24420-B, or equivalent.
10. Remove fasteners attaching lower portion of front cover, then lower vehicle.
11. Remove front cover and gaskets.
12. Reverse procedure to install.

TIMING CHAIN

REPLACE

REMOVAL

1. Remove front cover as described under "Front Cover, Replace."
2. Remove crankshaft oil slinger.
3. Rotate crankshaft in clockwise direction until camshaft and crankshaft timing marks are aligned, **Figs. 7 and 8.**
4. Remove three timing chain guides.
5. Raise and support vehicle.

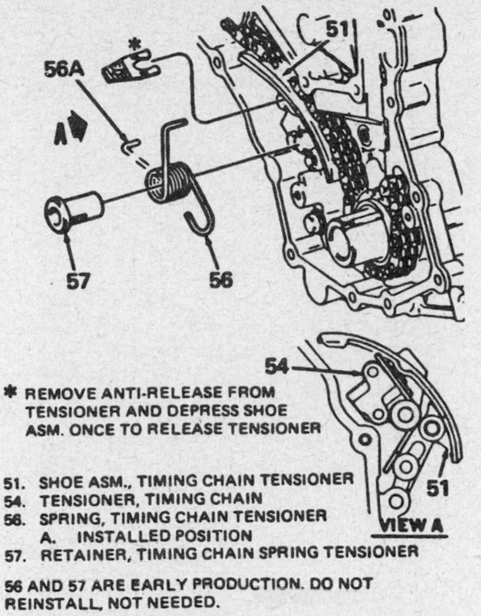
56A
A
57
56
51
54
51
VIEW A
* REMOVE ANTI-RELEASE FROM TENSIONER AND DEPRESS SHOE ASM. ONCE TO RELEASE TENSIONER
51. SHOE ASM., TIMING CHAIN TENSIONER
54. TENSIONER, TIMING CHAIN
56. SPRING, TIMING CHAIN TENSIONER
A. INSTALLED POSITION
57. RETAINER, TIMING CHAIN SPRING TENSIONER
56 AND 57 ARE EARLY PRODUCTION. DO NOT REINSTALL. NOT NEEDED.
GC1069100418000X

Fig. 9 Timing chain tensioner spring & retainer

6. **On early production engines,** gently pry off timing chain tensioner spring retainer and remove spring, **Fig. 9.**
7. **On all models,** removing timing chain tensioner shoe retainer.
8. Ensure slack in timing chain is above tensioner shoe, then remove chain tensioner shoe. The timing chain must be disengaged from grooves in tensioner shoe to permit removal of shoe. Position a suitable screwdriver under timing chain while pulling shoe outward to disengage. If difficulty is encountered in removing tensioner shoe, proceed as follows:
   a. Lower vehicle, then while holding intake camshaft sprocket in position with camshaft sprocket wrench No. J-36013, or equivalent, remove sprocket bolt and washer.
   b. Remove washer, then install bolt into camshaft by hand.
   c. Position a suitable three jaw puller into intake camshaft sprocket relief holes and remove sprocket. Do not pry on camshaft sprocket as damage to sprocket or timing chain housing may result.
9. Remove tensioner assembly attaching bolts and tensioner assembly. Use care when removing, as tensioner is spring loaded.
10. Remove timing chain tensioner shoe pivot stud, then remove timing chain.

INSTALLATION

1. While holding camshaft sprocket in position with camshaft sprocket tool No. J-36013, or equivalent, install attaching and washer, if removed. Tighten to specifications.
2. Install timing pins No. J-36008 or equivalent through holes in camshaft sprockets into holes in timing chain housing to position camshafts for proper timing, **Figs. 7 and 8.** If camshafts are out of position and must be rotated more that 1/8 turn to insert timing pins, the crankshaft should be rotated in the clockwise direction to a position 90° off TDC. After camshafts have been positioned and timing pins have been installed rotate crankshaft in counterclockwise direction to TDC.
3. **On DOHC engine,** place timing chain cover exhaust camshaft sprocket, idler sprocket and crankshaft sprocket.
4. Remove timing pin from intake camshaft and attach camshaft sprocket tool No. J-36013, or equivalent, to camshaft sprocket. Using camshaft sprocket wrench, rotate camshaft sprocket counterclockwise until timing chain can be installed over sprocket. Release tool after timing chain has been installed over sprocket. The timing chain tension between intake and exhaust camshaft sprockets should tighten. The timing pin should easily fit through intake camshaft sprocket timing hole into timing chain housing timing hole. If timing pin does not fit easily, repeat procedure..
5. **On SOHC engine,** remove timing pin from camshaft and attach tool No. J-36013, or equivalent, to camshaft sprocket. Using camshaft sprocket wrench, rotate camshaft sprocket counterclockwise until timing chain can be installed over sprocket. Release tool after timing chain has been installed over sprocket. The timing chain tension should tighten. The timing pin should easily fit through camshaft sprocket timing hole into timing chain housing timing hole. If timing pin does not fit easily, repeat procedure.
6. **On all engines,** with timing pins installed, raise and support vehicle.
7. With slack removed from timing chain between intake camshaft sprocket on DOHC engine, camshaft sprocket on SOHC engine, and crankshaft sprocket, timing marks on crankshaft and engine block should be aligned. If crankshaft timing marks are not aligned, move timing chain one tooth forward or rearward to align marks.
8. Install timing chain tensioner shoe pivot.
9. Reset timing chain tensioner, **Fig. 10,** as follows:
   a. Position restraint cylinder, spring and nylon plug into plunger. Align slot in restraint cylinder with peg in plunger. Rotate restraint cylinder in a clockwise direction and push into plunger until it is bottomed. Keep rotating restraint cylinder clockwise, until spring force pushes the restraint cylinder away from the plunger. The plunger peg will lock the restraint cylinder in the loaded position.
   b. Position timing chain tensioner spacer tool No. J-36589, or equivalent, on plunger assembly.
   c. Position plunger assembly into tensioner body, so that long end of plunger will be toward crankshaft when installed.

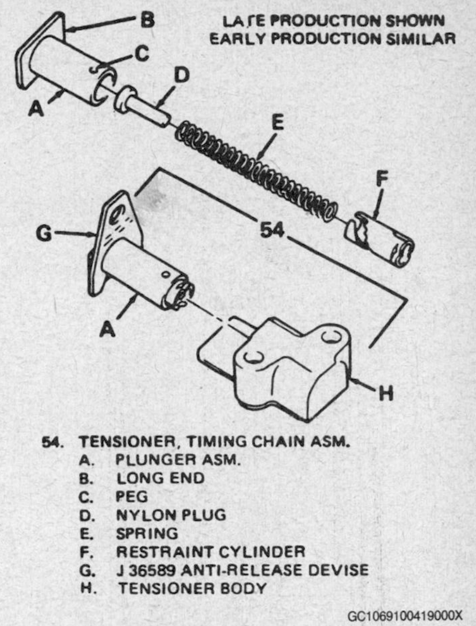
LATE PRODUCTION SHOWN
EARLY PRODUCTION SIMILAR
A
B
C
D
E
F
G
54
A
H
54. TENSIONER, TIMING CHAIN ASM.
A. PLUNGER ASM.
B. LONG END
C. PEG
D. NYLON PLUG
E. SPRING
F. RESTRAINT CYLINDER
G. J 36589 ANTI-RELEASE DEVISE
H. TENSIONER BODY
GC1069100419000X

Fig. 10 Timing chain tensioner

10. Install timing chain tensioner assembly with long end of plunger toward crankshaft. Torque to specifications.
11. Install timing chain tensioner shoe and retainer.
12. Remove tool No. J-36589, or equivalent, from timing chain tensioner, then press timing chain tensioner plunger into tensioner body to unload plunger.
13. Lower vehicle to point where timing pins can be removed from camshaft sprockets, then rotate crankshaft two revolutions in the clockwise direction. Align crankshaft timing marks, then insert timing pins through camshaft sprockets into timing chain housing timing holes. Timing pins should slide easily through timing holes. If timing pins cannot be insert easily, repeat procedure to properly time engine.
14. Install three timing chain guides, then install crankshaft oil slinger.
15. Install engine front cover.

CAMSHAFT, HOUSING & VALVE LASH ADJUSTERS

REPLACE

Whenever camshaft housing to cylinder head attaching bolts are loosened, the camshaft housing to cylinder head gasket must be replaced.

DOHC INTAKE OR SOHC CAMSHAFT HOUSING

1. Disconnect battery ground cable, then disconnect ignition coil and module electrical connectors.
2. Remove four bolts attaching ignition coil and module assembly to camshaft housings, then pull upward on assembly to remove, **Figs. 11 and 12.** If connectors are stuck to spark plugs, use spark plug connector remover No. J-36011, or equivalent, to remove.
3. Disconnect power steering idle speed

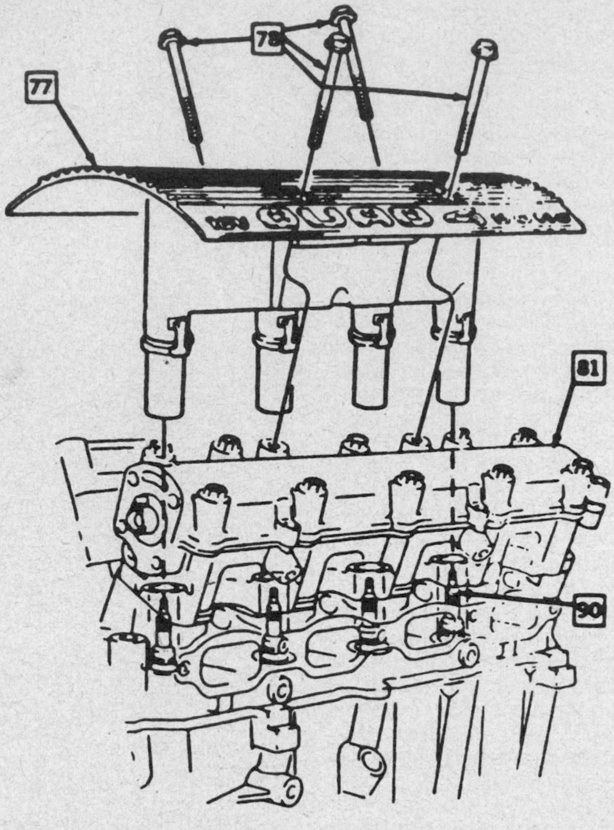
77
78
81
90

77. IGNITION COIL AND MODULE ASM.
78. BOLTS, IGNITION COIL AND MODULE ASM. TO CAMSHAFT HOUSINGS
81. COVER, CAMSHAFT HOUSING (INTAKE SHOWN)
90. SPARK PLUG

GC1069100420000X

Fig. 11 Ignition coil & module assembly removal. DOHC engine

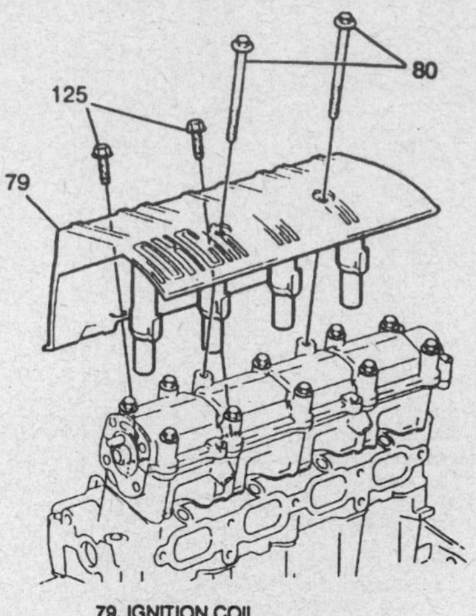
125
80
79

79. IGNITION COIL
80. BOLTS - 22 N•m (16 LBS. FT.)
125. BOLTS - 22 N•m (16 LBS. FT.)

GC1069100421000X

Fig. 12 Ignition coil & module assembly removal. SOHC engine

switch electrical connector.

4. Remove power steering pump and position aside with hoses attached.
5. Using power steering pulley tool Nos. J-36014 and J-29785-A, or equivalents, remove power steering pump drive pulley from camshaft.
6. Remove oil/air separator assembly.
7. Disconnect vacuum line from fuel pressure regulator, then disconnect injector wiring harness.
8. Remove fuel line bracket from top of intake camshaft housing.
9. De-pressurize fuel system, then remove fuel rail retaining bolts and fuel rail. Leave fuel lines attached and position fuel rail over master cylinder. Cover openings in cylinder head and injector nozzles.
10. Disconnect timing chain housing as follows:
    a. Remove coolant recovery tank, then serpentine drive belt.
    b. Raise and support vehicle, then remove right front wheel and tire assembly.
    c. Remove right lower splash shield, then balancer bolt using tool No. J 37086 or equivalent to prevent crankshaft rotation when loosening bolt.
    d. Remove balancer using tool No. J24420-B or equivalent, then front cover lower bolts and nut.
    e. Lower vehicle, then remove water pump assembly to timing chain housing nuts. If not previously removed.
    f. Remove front cover upper bolts and nuts, then front cover.
    g. Remove timing chain as described under "Timing Chain, Replace."
    h. Remove chain housing to belt tensioner bracket brace.
    i. Remove timing chain housing to block lower fasteners, then four oil pan to front cover bolts.
    j. Remove oil/air separator hose from chain housing.
    k. Remove camshaft sprocket retaining bolts and washers while holding sprockets with tool No. J36013 or equivalent camshaft sprocket wrench.
    l. Remove camshaft sprockets. Note: sprockets are identical and interchangeable, no marking is necessary.
    m. Remove chain housing to camshaft housing bolts, then timing chain housing and gaskets.
11. Remove camshaft housing cover attaching bolts, **Fig. 13.**
12. Loosen camshaft housing to cylinder head attaching bolts in reverse order of tightening sequence, **Fig. 14.**
13. Leave two camshaft housing to cylinder head attaching bolts loosely installed. Thread four of the camshaft housing to cylinder head bolts into tapped holes on camshaft housing cover to separate cover from housing.
14. Remove the two camshaft housing to cylinder head bolts and remove camshaft housing cover.
15. Note position of timing chain sprocket dowel pin for reassembly, then remove camshaft, using care not to damage journals.
16. Remove oil seal from camshaft. This seal must be replaced any time the cover and camshaft housing are separated.
17. Remove valve lash adjuster. Keep valve lash adjusters in order for reassembly. Store valve lash adjusters in the upside down position in clean engine oil to prevent lifter bleed down.
18. Remove camshaft housing and gasket from cylinder head.
19. Reverse procedure to install. Prior to installation, lubricate camshaft journals and valve lash adjusters with lubricant No. 1052365 or equivalent. Apply suitable sealant to threads of camshaft housing and cover retaining bolts and ignition coil and module assembly attaching bolts. When installing camshaft housing cover to camshaft housing, refer to **Fig. 15 for seal positioning. Tighten camshaft housing and cover bolts in sequence shown in Fig. 14. Torque** bolts in position 1 through 10, **Fig. 14,** to 11 ft. lbs., then tighten an additional

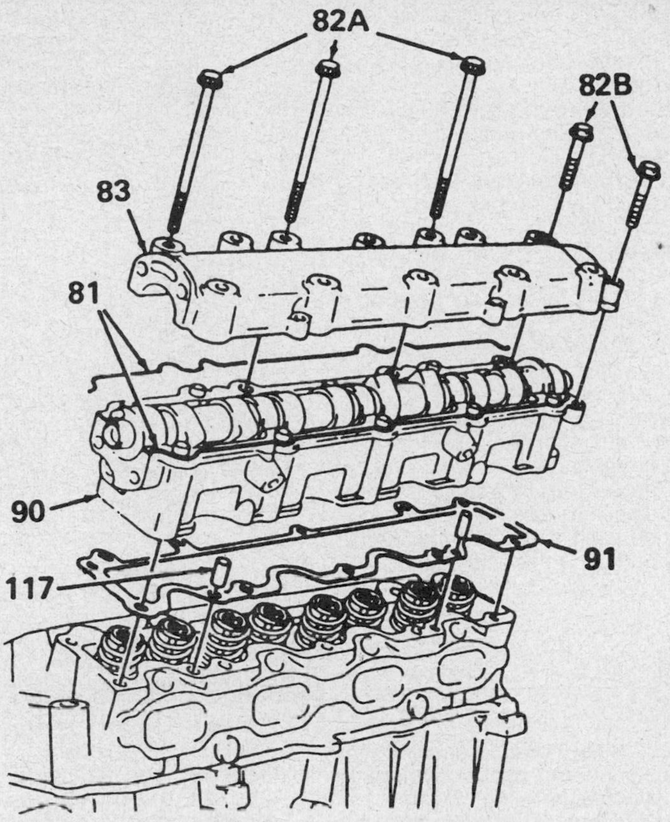
82A
82B
83
81
90
91
117

81. SEALS, CAMSHAFT HOUSING TO CAMSHAFT HOUSING COVER (EACH SEAL IS DIFFERENT)
82A. BOLT, CAMSHAFT HOUSING TO CYLINDER HEAD
82B. BOLT, CAMSHAFT HOUSING COVER TO CAMSHAFT HOUSING
83. COVER, CAMSHAFT
90. CAMSHAFT HOUSING (INTAKE SHOWN)
91. GASKET, CAMSHAFT HOUSING TO CYLINDER HEAD
117. DOWEL PIN (2)

GC1069100422000X

Fig. 13 Camshaft housing & cover

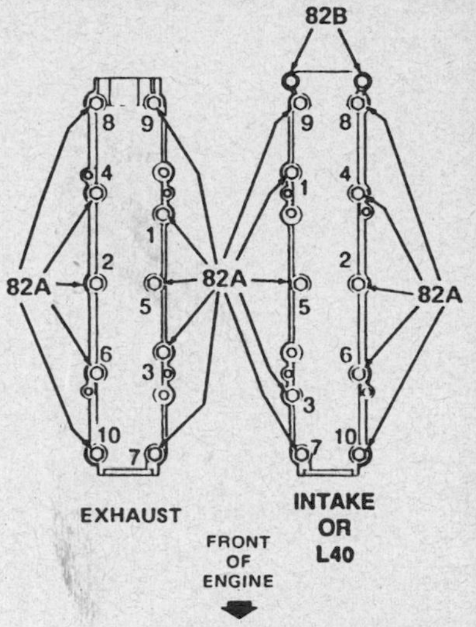
82B
82A
82A
82A
EXHAUST
INTAKE
OR
L40
FRONT
OF
ENGINE

GC1069100423000X

Fig. 14 Camshaft housing bolt tightening sequence

75°. Tighten bolts in positions 11 and 12, **Fig. 14**, to 11 ft. lbs., then tighten an additional 25°. Tighten timing chain housing to engine and camshaft housing fasteners to specifications.

DOHC EXHAUST

1. Disconnect battery ground cable, then disconnect ignition coil and module electrical connectors.
2. Remove four bolts attaching ignition coil and module assembly to camshaft housings, then pull upward on assembly to remove, **Fig. 11.** If connectors are stuck to spark plugs, use tool no. J-36011, or equivalent, to remove.
3. Disconnect oil pressure switch electrical connector.
4. Remove transaxle dipstick and tube assembly from camshaft cover and position aside.
5. Remove exhaust camshaft cover and gasket.
6. Disconnect timing chain housing as follows:
   a. Remove coolant recovery tank, then serpentine drive belt.
   b. Raise and support vehicle, then remove right front wheel and tire assembly.
   c. Remove right lower splash shield, then balancer bolt using tool No. J 37086 or equivalent to prevent crankshaft rotation when loosening bolt.
   d. Remove balancer using tool No. J 24420-B or equivalent, then front cover lower bolts and nut.
   e. Lower vehicle, then remove water pump assembly to timing chain housing nuts. If not previously removed.
   f. Remove front cover upper bolts and nuts, then front cover.
   g. Remove timing chain as described under "Timing Chain, Replace."
   h. Remove chain housing to belt tensioner bracket brace.
   i. Remove timing chain housing to block lower fasteners, then four oil pan to front cover bolts.
   j. Remove oil/air separator hose from chain housing.
   k. Remove camshaft sprocket retaining bolts and washers while holding sprockets with tool No. J 36013 or equivalent camshaft sprocket wrench.
   l. Remove camshaft sprockets. Because sprockets are identical and interchangeable, no marking is necessary.
   m. Remove eight chain housing to camshaft housing bolts, then timing chain housing and gaskets.
7. Loosen camshaft housing to cylinder head attaching bolts in reverse order of tightening sequence, **Fig. 14.**
8. Leave two camshaft housing to cylinder head attaching bolts loosely installed. Thread four of the camshaft housing to cylinder head bolts into tapped holes on camshaft housing cover to separate cover from housing.
9. Remove the two camshaft housing to cylinder head bolts and remove camshaft housing cover.
10. Note position of timing chain sprocket dowel pin for reassembly, then remove camshaft, using care not to damage journals.
11. Remove oil seal from camshaft. This seal must be replaced any time the cover and camshaft housing are separated.
12. Remove valve lash adjuster. Keep valve lash adjusters in order for reassembly. Store valve lash adjusters in the upside down position in clean engine oil to prevent lifter bleed down.
13. Remove camshaft housing and gasket from cylinder head.
14. Reverse procedure to install. Prior to installation, lubricate camshaft journals and valve lash adjusters with lu-

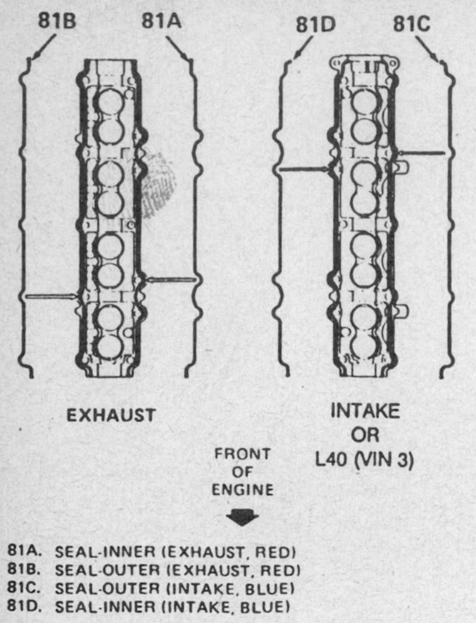
81B
81A
81D
81C
EXHAUST
INTAKE
OR
L40 (VIN 3)
FRONT
OF
ENGINE
81A. SEAL-INNER (EXHAUST, RED)
81B. SEAL-OUTER (EXHAUST, RED)
81C. SEAL-OUTER (INTAKE, BLUE)
81D. SEAL-INNER (INTAKE, BLUE)
GC1069100424000X

Fig. 15 Camshaft housing cover seal installation & identification

bricant No. 1052365 or equivalent. Apply suitable sealant to threads of camshaft housing and cover retaining bolts and ignition coil and module assembly attaching bolts. When installing camshaft housing cover to camshaft housing, refer to **Fig. 15 for seal positioning. Tighten camshaft housing and cover bolts in sequence shown in Fig. 14. Torque** bolts to 11 ft. lbs., then tighten an additional 75°. Tighten timing chain housing to engine and camshaft housing fasteners to 19 ft. lbs.

PISTON & ROD ASSEMBLY

Assemble piston to rod with arrow on piston toward front of engine and oil squirt hole on rod toward exhaust side of engine, **Fig. 16.**

Upon installation, measure connecting rod side clearance using a suitable feeler gauge. Connecting rod side clearance should be .0059 to .0177 inch.

PISTONS, PINS & RINGS

Pistons and rings are available in standard size and oversize of .010 inch. Piston pins and pistons are serviced as an assembly.

MAIN & ROD BEARINGS

Main and rod bearings are available in standard size only.

CRANKSHAFT REAR OIL SEAL

REPLACE

1. Remove transaxle assembly as described under "Transaxle, Replace" in the appropriate transaxle section.
2. **On models with manual transaxle,** remove clutch as described under "Clutch, Replace" in the appropriate transaxle section.
3. **On all models,** remove flywheel to crankshaft attaching bolts, then remove flywheel.
4. Remove oil pan to crankshaft rear seal housing attaching bolts.
5. Remove crankshaft rear seal housing to engine attaching screws, then remove housing and gasket, **Fig. 17.**
6. Support crankshaft rear seal housing on two wooden blocks of equal thickness with crankshaft side facing upward, then drive seal out through transaxle side of housing.
7. Press replacement seal into housing using rear crankshaft seal installer No. J-36005, or equivalent.
8. Reverse procedure to install. Lubricate seal lips with engine oil prior to installing housing. Tighten crankshaft rear seal housing to specifications.

OIL PAN

REPLACE

1. Disconnect battery ground cable.
2. Drain crankcase and cooling system.
3. Remove flywheel housing cover.
4. Remove right hand front wheel and tire assembly, then remove splash shield.
5. Relieve serpentine drive belt tension.
6. Remove engine mount strut from strut bracket.
7. Remove A/C compressor from bracket and support with refrigerant hoses attached.
8. Remove engine mount strut bracket bolts and position bracket aside.
9. Remove radiator outlet pipe bolts, then detach A/C and radiator outlet pipes from suspension supports.
10. Remove exhaust manifold brace.
11. Remove oil pan to flywheel cover nut and bolt.
12. Remove radiator outlet pipe from lower radiator hose and oil pan.
13. Disconnect oil level sensor electrical connector.
14. Remove oil pan attaching bolts and oil pan.
15. Reverse procedure to install. Refer to **Fig. 18** for oil pan bolt identification and tighten specifications.

OIL PUMP SERVICE

REPLACEMENT

1. Remove oil pan as described under "Oil Pan, Replace."
2. Remove oil pump attaching bolts, then remove oil pump and shims, if equipped, **Fig. 19.**
3. Reverse procedure to install. Torque oil pump to engine attaching bolts to specifications. Torque oil pump screen to engine attaching nut to specifications.

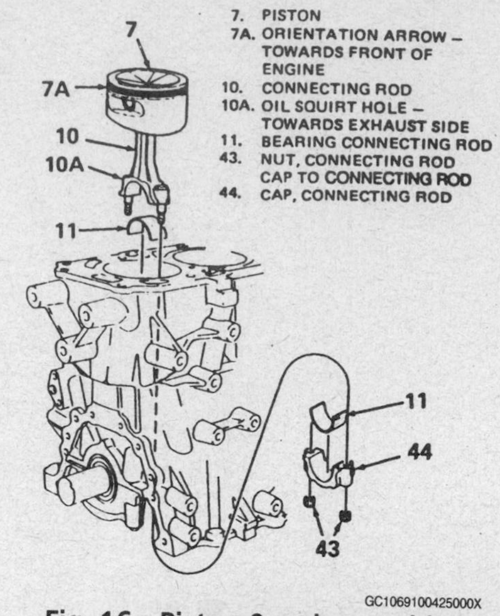
7
7A
10
10A
11
11
44
43
7. PISTON
7A. ORIENTATION ARROW – TOWARDS FRONT OF ENGINE
10. CONNECTING ROD
10A. OIL SQUIRT HOLE – TOWARDS EXHAUST SIDE
11. BEARING CONNECTING ROD
43. NUT, CONNECTING ROD CAP TO CONNECTING ROD
44. CAP, CONNECTING ROD
GC1069100425000X

Fig. 16 Piston & rod assembly

OIL PUMP GEAR BACKLASH ADJUSTMENT

1. Remove oil pump as described under "Oil Pump, Replace."
2. Remove four attaching bolts, then separate the driven gear cover and screen assembly from the oil pump, **Fig. 20.**
3. Position oil pump housing to engine with original shim(s), then install attaching bolts and torque to specifications.
4. Using dial indicator assembly, measure oil pump driven gear to drive gear backlash, **Fig. 21.** Crankshaft should not move during check. Backlash should be .0091 to .0201 inch. To decrease backlash, remove shims. To increase backlash, add shims.
5. After obtaining proper backlash setting, rotate crankshaft 180° and recheck backlash setting.
6. Remove oil pump from engine.
7. Install oil pump cover and pickup tube to oil pump housing. Torque oil pump cover to oil pump housing attaching screws to specifications.
8. Install oil pump and shims.

BELT TENSION DATA

Year	Engine	Belt Tension, Lbs.①
1992-95	2.3L/4-138	50

①—**On models less A/C, take reading between alternator & idler pulley. On models with A/C, take reading between alternator & A/C compressor. If reading is less than listed, replace belt tensioner.**

DRIVE BELT

REPLACE

Refer to **Fig. 22** for serpentine drive belt replacement.

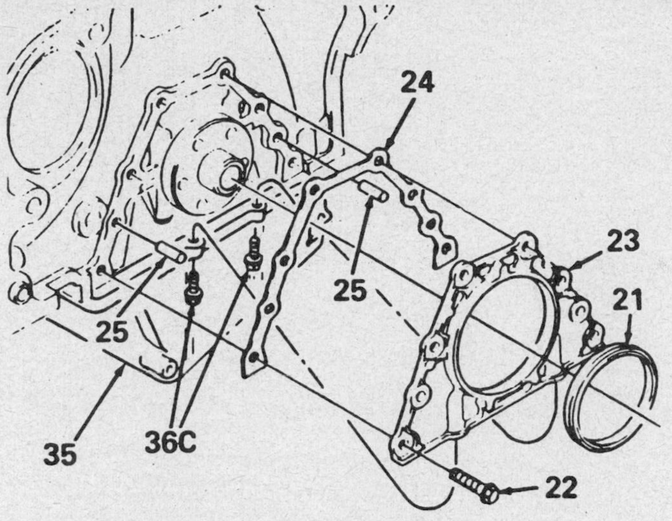

24
23
25
21
25
35
36C
22

21. SEAL, REAR CRANKSHAFT
22. BOLT, REAR CRANKSHAFT SEAL HOUSING TO BLOCK (6)
23. HOUSING, REAR CRANKSHAFT SEAL
24. GASKET, REAR CRANKSHAFT SEAL HOUSING TO BLOCK
25. DOWEL PIN, REAR CRANKSHAFT SEAL HOUSING TO BLOCK
35. OIL PAN
36C. BOLT, TO SEAL HOUSING

GC1069100426000X

Fig. 17 Crankshaft rear oil seal replacement

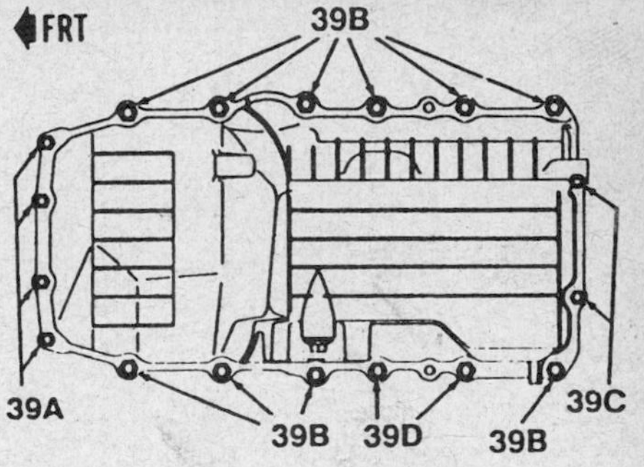

FRT
39B
39A
39B
39D
39B
39C

39A. BOLT (4) (M6 X 1.0 X 25) - 12 N.m (106 LBS. IN.)
39B. BOLT (10) (M8 X 1.25 X 22) - 24 N.m (18 LBS. FT.)
39C. BOLT (10) (M6 X 1.0 X 25) - 12 N.m (106 LBS. IN.)
39D. STUD OR BOLT (2) (M8 X 1.25 X 22) - 26 N.m (19 LBS. FT.)

GC1099200066000X

Fig. 18 Oil pan bolt identification & locations

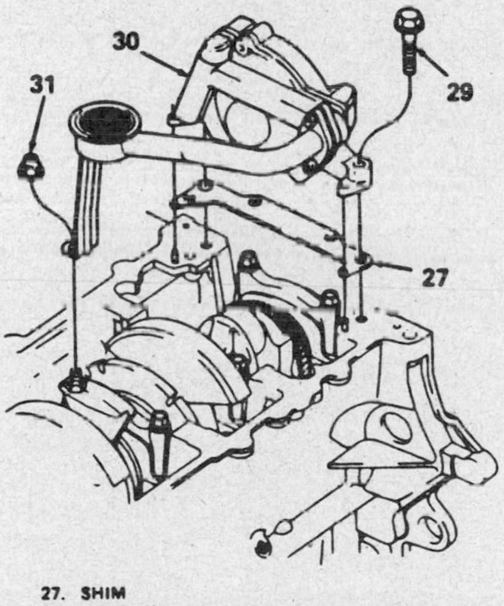

30
31
29
27

27. SHIM
29. BOLT (2)
30. OIL PUMP AND SCREEN
31. NUT – SCREEN TO BLOCK

GC1099100067000X

Fig. 19 Oil pump removal

28. OIL PUMP
28A. DRIVEN GEAR COVER – OIL PUMP
28B. BOLT/SCREW (3)
30. SCREEN ASM. – OIL PUMP
30A. GASKET – SCREEN TO PUMP
30B. BOLT/SCREW (2)

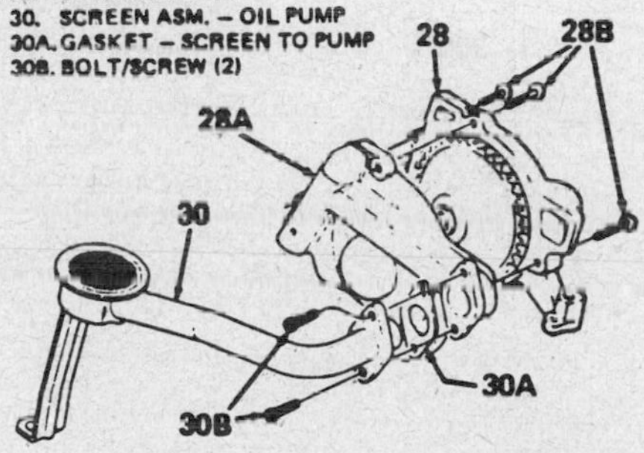

28
28B
28A
30
30A
30B

GC1099100068000X

Fig. 20 Oil cover removal

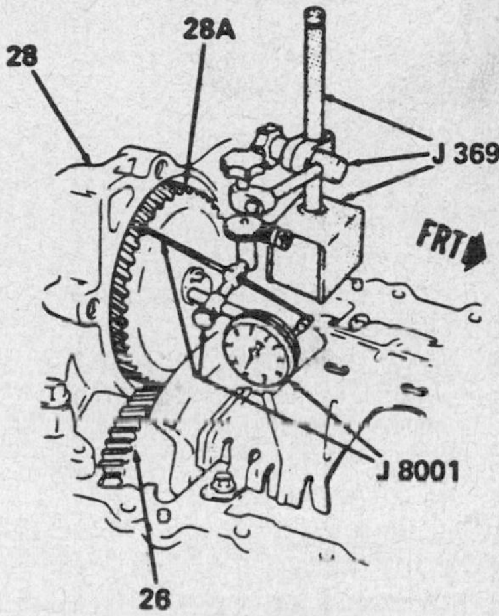

28
28A
J 36900-B
FRT
J 8001
26

26. OIL PUMP DRIVE GEAR
28. OIL PUMP – COVER REMOVED
28A. OIL PUMP DRIVEN GEAR

GC1099100069000X

Fig. 21 Oil pump gear backlash measurement

COOLING SYSTEM BLEED

After filling cooling system, start engine and allow to reach operating temperature with surge tank pressure cap removed. Air will bleed through surge cap opening. Add coolant as necessary to bring to proper level, then install surge tank pressure cap.

THERMOSTAT

REPLACE

1. Disconnect battery ground cable.
2. Drain cooling to level below thermostat.
3. Disconnect radiator hose and heater hose from thermostat housing.
4. Disconnect electrical connector from coolant sensor.
5. Remove throttle body cooling hose.
6. Remove thermostat housing attaching bolts, then remove thermostat housing and thermostat, **Fig. 23.**
7. Reverse procedure to install.

WATER PUMP

REPLACE

1. Disconnect battery ground cable, then drain cooling system. Disconnect heater hose from thermostat housing for more complete coolant drain.
2. Disconnect electrical connector from oxygen sensor.
3. Remove upper and lower exhaust manifold heat shields.
4. Remove bolt attaching exhaust manifold brace to exhaust manifold.
5. Loosen exhaust manifold to exhaust pipe spring loaded bolts using a 13mm wrench.
6. Remove radiator outlet pipe to water pump cover bolts.
7. Raise and support vehicle.
8. Remove manifold to exhaust pipe spring loaded nuts.
9. Pull down and back on exhaust pipe to disengage from manifold bolts.
10. Remove radiator outlet pipe from oil pan and transaxle. On vehicles equipped with manual transaxle, exhaust manifold brace must be removed.
11. Leave the lower radiator hose attached and pull down gently on the radiator outlet pipe to disengage it from the water pump. Leave outlet pipe to hang.
12. Lower vehicle, then remove exhaust manifold to cylinder head retaining

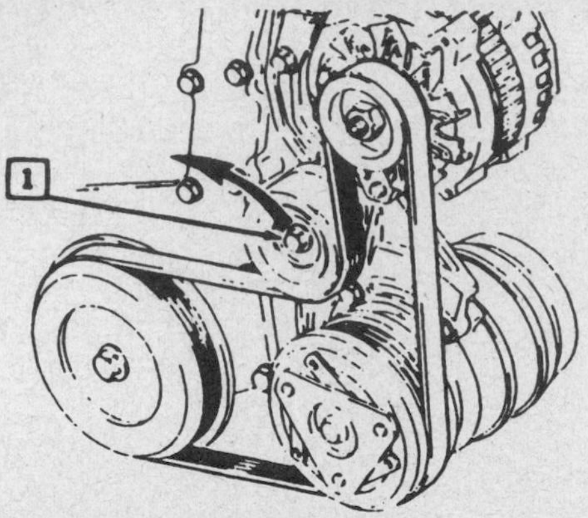

1 ROTATE TENSIONER IN DIRECTION OF ARROW TO REMOVE OR INSTALL BELT.

GC1069100427000X

Fig. 22 Drive belt replacement

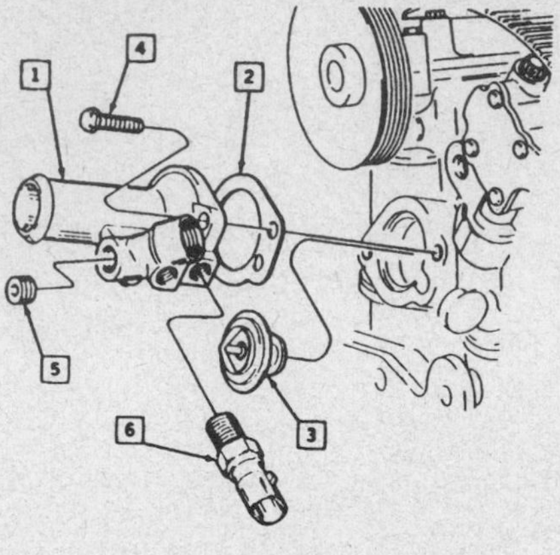

1. OUTLET ASM. – WATER
2. GASKET
3. THERMOSTAT ASM.
4. BOLT (2) (M8 X 1.25 X 30)
5. PLUG – WATER OUTLET
6. SENSOR, COOLANT

GC1089100165000X

Fig. 23 Thermostat replacement

1. TIMING CHAIN HOUSING
2. GASKET, TIMING CHAIN HOUSING TO WATER PUMP BODY
3. NUT (3)
4. WATER PUMP BODY ASM.
5. GASKET, WATER PUMP BODY TO WATER PUMP COVER
6. WATER PUMP COVER
7. BOLT (M6 X 1 X 65) – 3 LOWER POSITIONS
8. BOLT (M6 X 1 X 25)
9. BOLT (M6 X 1 X 90)
10. GASKET, WATER PUMP COVER TO BLOCK
11. BOLTS, WATER PUMP COVER TO BLOCK (2)

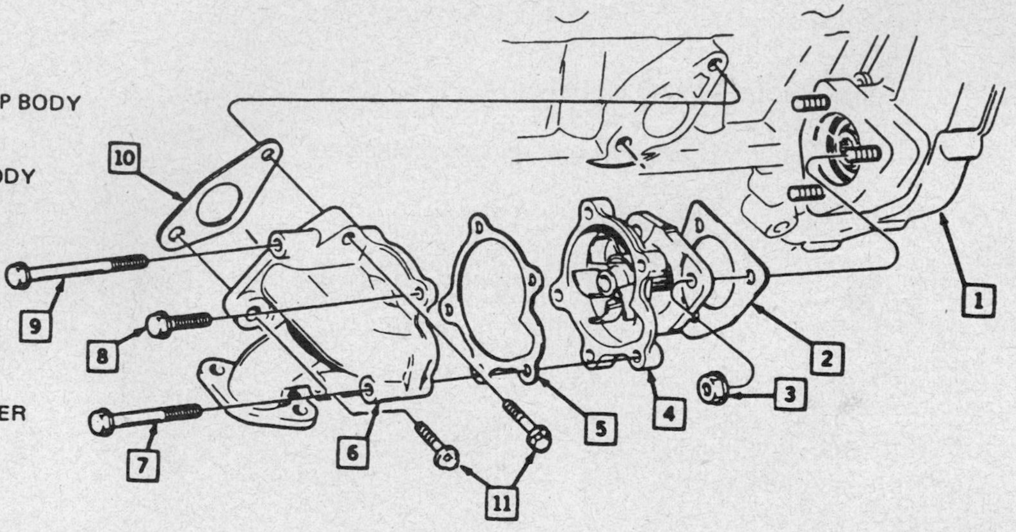

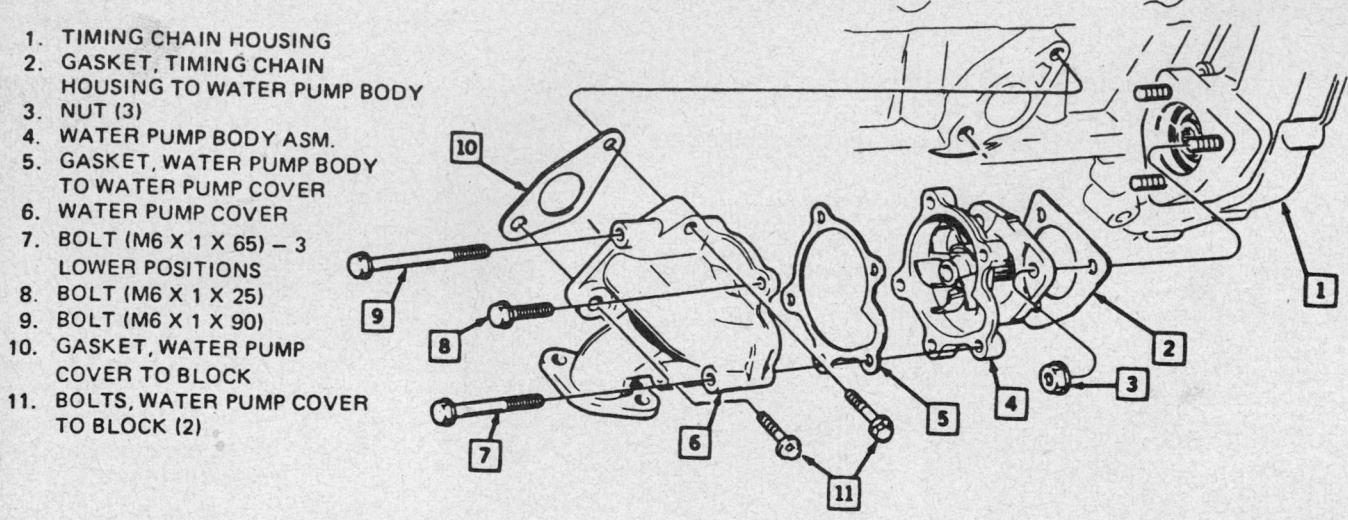

GC1089100166000X

Fig. 24 Water pump replacement

nuts and exhaust manifold, seals and gaskets.

13. Remove water pump cover to cylinder block bolts.
14. Remove water pump assembly to timing chain housing nuts. Note: on early production models it may be necessary to loosen and reposition the rear engine mount, mount to engine block bracket to gain clearance.
15. Remove water pump and cover assembly.
16. Remove water pump cover to water pump assembly, **Fig. 24.**
17. Reverse procedure to install. Tighten water pump to water pump cover attaching bolts to specifications. Tighten water pump to engine and timing chain cover attaching bolts to specifications.

RADIATOR
REPLACE

1. Disconnect battery ground cable.
2. Drain cooling system.
3. Remove air intake duct assembly.
4. Disconnect upper transaxle cooler line.
5. Disconnect upper radiator hose.
6. Disconnect lower transaxle cooler line.
7. Disconnect cooling fan electrical connector, then remove cooling fan mounting bolts.
8. Remove cooling fan.
9. Remove splash guard below lower radiator hose.
10. Disconnect lower radiator hose from radiator.
11. Remove condenser line retaining clip.
12. Remove condenser to radiator attaching bolts.
13. Disconnect coolant surge tank hose.
14. Remove radiator mounting bolts, then the radiator.
15. Reverse procedure to install.

FUEL PUMP
REPLACE

1. Disconnect battery ground cable, then drain fuel tank.
2. Disconnect tank unit harness connector.
3. Remove ground wire retaining screw

from underbody.
4. Disconnect hoses from tank meter assembly, then hoses at tank from filler and vent pipes.
5. Support fuel tank and disconnect the two fuel tank retaining straps.
6. Remove fuel tank from vehicle.
7. Remove fuel tank sending unit and pump assembly by turning cam lock ring counterclockwise. Lift assembly from fuel tank and remove pump from sending unit.
8. Pull fuel pump up into attaching hose while pulling outward away from bottom support. Take care to prevent damage to rubber insulator and strainer during removal.
9. After pump assembly is clear of bottom support, pull pump assembly out of rubber connector for removal.
10. Reverse procedure to install.

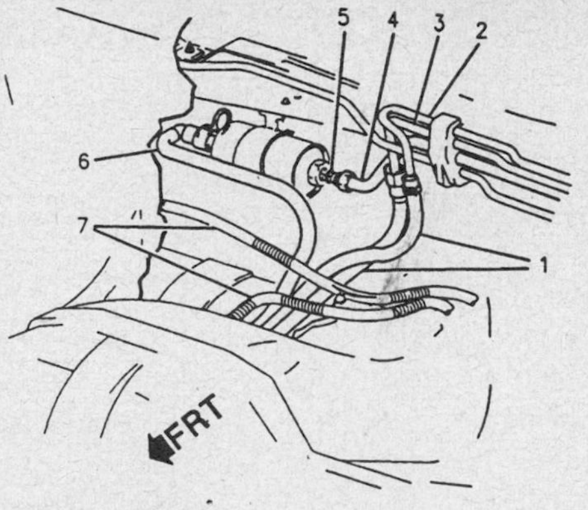
5
4
3
2
6
7
1
FRT

1 HOSE – PART OF FUEL SENDER
2 FUEL VAPOR PIPE
3 FUEL RETURN PIPE
4 FUEL FEED PIPE
5 FUEL FEED PIPE NUT – 27 N·m (20 LBS. FT.)
6 HOSE – PART OF FUEL SENDER
7 ABS AND FUEL SENDER HARNESS

GC1029102737000X

Fig. 25 Fuel filter replacement

FUEL FILTER

REPLACE

The fuel filter is located below the rear of the vehicle, rearward of the fuel tank.

1. Relieve fuel system pressure as outlined under "Precautions."
2. Raise and support vehicle.
3. Using suitable back-up wrench, remove fuel filter fitting, **Fig. 25.**
4. Grasp filter and one nylon fuel connection line fitting, then twist quick connect fitting 1/4 turn in each direction to loosen dirt in fitting.
5. Using compressed air, clean dirt from quick connect fitting.
6. Depress quick connect fitting plastic tabs of male end connector and pull apart.
7. Remove fuel filter.
8. Reverse procedure to install.

TIGHTENING SPECIFICATIONS

Year	Component	Torque/ Ft. Lbs.
1992	Camshaft Housing & Cover To Cylinder Head	11①
	Camshaft Sprocket To Cam Bolt	40
	Connecting Rod Nuts	②
	Coolant Outlet To Cylinder Head	19
	Crankshaft Balancer To Crankshaft	74③
	Crankshaft Bearing Cap Bolts	15③
	Crankshaft Position Sensor To Block	80④
	Cylinder Head Bolts	⑤
	Exhaust Camshaft Housing Rear Cover	10
	Exhaust Manifold Lower Heat Shield Bolt	120④
	Exhaust Manifold To Cylinder Head Nuts	31
	Exhaust Manifold To Cylinder Head Studs	106④
	Exhaust Manifold To Exhaust Pipe	19
	Exhaust Manifold To Oil Pan	19
	Exhaust Manifold Studs To Manifold	19
	Flywheel To Clutch Cover	22
	Flywheel To Converter	46
	Flywheel To Crankshaft	22⑥
	Front Cover To Timing Chain Housing	106④
	Fuel Pipe Bracket To Camshaft Housing	⑧
	Fuel Rail To Camshaft Housing	19
	Ignition Coil & Module Assembly To Camshaft Housing	15
	Intake Manifold Brace Bolts	19
	Intake Manifold To Cylinder Head Nuts	18
	Intake Manifold To Cylinder Head Studs	96④
	Oil/Air Separator To Intake Manifold	72④
	Oil Filter Connector To Block	21
	Oil Filter To Block	⑦
	Oil Pan Bolts	⑤
1992 —Cont'd	Oil Pan Drain Plug	19
	Oil Pump To Block	40
	Oil Pump Cover To Oil Pump Body	106④
	Oil Pump Screen To Pump	30
	Radiator Mounting Bolts	89
	Rear Crankshaft Seal Housing To Block	106④
	Spark Plugs To Cylinder Head	17
	Starter To Block Or Transaxle To Starter	71
	Thermostat Housing	19
	Throttle Body To Intake Manifold	19
	Timing Chain Housing To Block Or Camshaft Housing	19
	Timing Chain Housing To Block Stud	19
	Timing Chain Tensioner To Housing & Block	84④
	Water Pump To Timing Chain Housing	19
	Water Pump To Water Pump Cover	10
	Water Pump Cover To Block	10
1993-95	Camshaft Housing & Cover To Cylinder Head	11③
	Camshaft Sprocket To Cam Bolt	52
	Connecting Rod Nuts	②
	Coolant Outlet To Cylinder Head	19
	Crankshaft Balancer To Crankshaft	110③
	Crankshaft Bearing Cap Bolts	15③
	Crankshaft Position Sensor To Block	80④
	Cylinder Head Bolts	⑤
	Exhaust Camshaft Housing Rear Cover	10
	Exhaust Manifold Lower Heat Shield Bolt	124④
	Exhaust Manifold To Cylinder Head Nuts	31
	Exhaust Manifold To Cylinder Head Studs	106④
	Exhaust Manifold To Exhaust Pipe	19

TIGHTENING SPECIFICATIONS-Continued

Year	Component	Torque/ Ft. Lbs.
1992	Exhaust Manifold To Oil Pan	19
	Exhaust Manifold Studs To Manifold	19
	Flywheel To Clutch Cover	22
	Flywheel To Converter	46
	Flywheel To Crankshaft	22⑥
	Front Cover To Timing Chain Housing	106④
	Fuel Pipe Bracket To Camshaft Housing	⑧
	Fuel Rail To Camshaft Housing	19
	Ignition Coil & Module Assembly To Camshaft Housing	16
	Intake Manifold Brace Bolts	19
	Intake Manifold To Cylinder Head Nuts	18
	Intake Manifold To Cylinder Head Studs	96④
	Oil/Air Separator To Intake Manifold	71④
	Oil Filter Connector To Block	21
	Oil Filter To Block	⑦
	Oil Pan Bolts	⑤
	Oil Pan Drain Plug	19

Year	Component	Torque/ Ft. Lbs.
1992 —Cont'd	Oil Pump To Block	40
	Oil Pump Cover To Oil Pump Body	106④
	Oil Pump Screen To Pump	30
	Radiator Mounting Bolts	89
	Rear Crankshaft Seal Housing To Block	106④
	Spark Plugs To Cylinder Head	16
	Starter To Block Or Transaxle To Starter	71
	Thermostat Housing	19
	Throttle Body To Intake Manifold	19
	Timing Chain Housing To Block Or Camshaft Housing	19
	Timing Chain Housing To Block Stud	19
	Timing Chain Tensioner To Housing & Block	84④
	Water Pump To Timing Chain Housing	19
	Water Pump To Water Pump Cover	124④
	Water Pump Cover To Block	19

①—Plus an additional 75°.
②—18 ft. lbs. plus an additional 80°.
③—Plus an additional 90°.
④—Inch lbs.
⑤—Refer to text.
⑥—Plus an additional 45°.
⑦—¾ to 1 turn after initial gasket contact.
⑧—11 ft. lbs. plus an additional 25°.

3.1L/V6–192 Engine

NOTE: On Air Bag Equipped Models, Refer To "Air Bag System Precautions" Located In The Front Of This Manual For System Disarming & Arming Procedures.

NOTE: For Procedures Not Found In This Section, Refer To 3.1L/V6-192 Engine Section In Buick Regal, Chevrolet Lumina, Cutlass Supreme, Monte Carlo & Pontiac Grand Prix Chapter.

INDEX

PRECAUTIONS

AIR BAG SYSTEMS

Refer to "Air Bag System Precautions" in the front of this manual for system disarming and arming procedures.

FUEL SYSTEM PRESSURE RELIEF

1. Disconnect battery ground cable.
2. Loosen fuel tank filler cap to relieve tank pressure. Wrap shop towel around fitting while connecting gauge to avoid spillage.
3. Install bleed hose into suitable container and open valve to bleed system pressure.
4. Drain any fuel remaining in gauge into suitable container.

ENGINE MOUNT

REPLACE

1. Disconnect battery ground cable.
2. Support engine by oil pan, then remove engine mount assembly to engine mount bracket support bolts, **Fig. 1**.
3. Remove engine mount to body bolts and nut.
4. Remove engine mount assembly.
5. Reverse procedure to install. Tighten mount to body fasteners and mount to engine bracket support bolts to specifications.

ENGINE MOUNT STRUT

REPLACE

1. Disconnect battery ground cable.
2. Raise and support vehicle.
3. Remove right splash shield.
4. Remove engine mount strut bolts, **Fig. 2**.
5. Remove engine mount strut.
6. Reverse procedure to install. Refer to **Fig. 2** for engine mount strut bolt tightening specifications.

ENGINE

REPLACE

1. Relieve fuel system pressure as de-

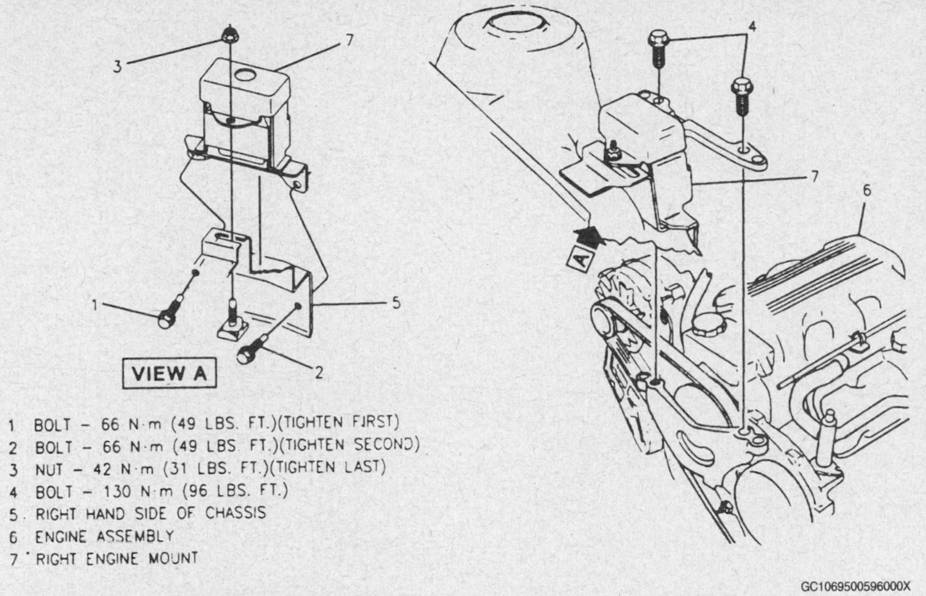

VIEW A
1 BOLT – 66 N·m (49 LBS. FT.)(TIGHTEN FIRST)
2 BOLT – 66 N·m (49 LBS. FT.)(TIGHTEN SECOND)
3 NUT – 42 N·m (31 LBS. FT.)(TIGHTEN LAST)
4 BOLT – 130 N·m (96 LBS. FT.)
5 RIGHT HAND SIDE OF CHASSIS
6 ENGINE ASSEMBLY
7 RIGHT ENGINE MOUNT
GC1069500596000X

Fig. 1 Engine mount assembly. 3.1L/V6-192

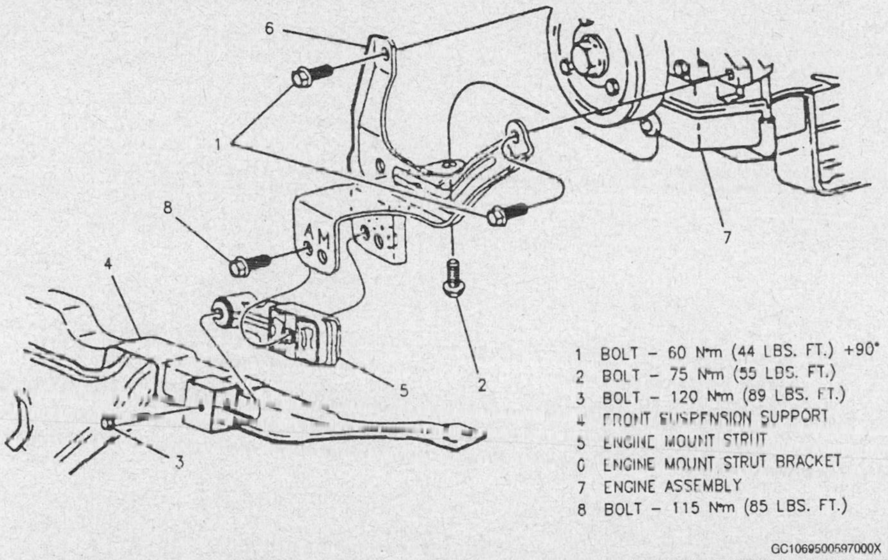

1 BOLT – 60 N·m (44 LBS. FT.) +90°
2 BOLT – 75 N·m (55 LBS. FT.)
3 BOLT – 120 N·m (89 LBS. FT.)
4 FRONT SUSPENSION SUPPORT
5 ENGINE MOUNT STRUT
6 ENGINE MOUNT STRUT BRACKET
7 ENGINE ASSEMBLY
8 BOLT – 115 N·m (85 LBS. FT.)
GC1069500597000X

Fig. 2 Engine mount strut bolt removal. 3.1L/V6-192

scribed under "Precautions".
2. Disconnect battery ground cable.
3. Remove top half of air cleaner assembly and throttle body duct.
4. Drain cooling system.
5. Disconnect upper radiator hose from engine and position aside.
6. Disconnect lower radiator hose from engine and position aside.
7. Disconnect coolant inlet line from surge tank.
8. Disconnect following vacuum hoses:
   a. Vacuum modulator.
   b. EVAP canister purge.
   c. Power brake booster line.
9. Disconnect heater outlet hose from water pump.
10. Remove serpentine drive belt.
11. Disconnect accelerator and cruise control cable from throttle linkage.
12. Remove upper wiring from engine as follows:
   a. Electronic ignition.
   b. Heated oxygen sensor.
   c. Injector harness.
   d. IAC.
   e. Throttle position sensor.
   f. Engine coolant temperature sensor.
   g. Park/Neutral position switch.
   h. Transaxle shift solenoid and TCC solenoid.
   i. EGR.
   j. Ground at transaxle.
13. Remove alternator as described under "Alternator, Replace" in Electrical section.
14. Disconnect power steering lines at power steering pump.
15. Disconnect fuel lines.
16. Remove cooling fan assembly.
17. Disconnect shift cable linkage and cable from mounting bracket. Transaxle should be in low gear for better accessibility.
18. Disconnect transaxle vent tube from transaxle.
19. Disconnect vacuum hose at vacuum reservoir.
20. Remove engine support fixture.
21. Loosen but do not remove top two A/C compressor bolts.
22. Raise and support vehicle.
23. Remove front tire and wheel assemblies.
24. Remove right and left splash shields.
25. Remove engine mount strut as described under "Engine Mount Strut, Replace."
26. Remove both front ABS speed sensor connectors and harness from suspension supports.
27. Remove both ball joints.
28. Remove suspension support assembly.
29. Remove drive axles from transaxle and support.
30. Remove oil filter and adapter.
31. Remove transaxle converter cover.
32. Remove starter as described under "Starter, Replace" in the Electrical section.
33. Disconnect lower engine wiring as follows:
   a. Knock sensor.
   b. Front crankshaft position sensor.
   c. Side crankshaft position sensor.
   d. Oil level sensor.
   e. VSS.
   f. Transaxle ground.
34. Disconnect heater hoses.
35. Remove A/C compressor lower bolts, then position compressor aside.
36. Remove vacuum reserve tank.
37. Remove exhaust pipe from manifold and position aside.
38. Remove engine mount strut bracket.
39. Disconnect transaxle cooling lines at radiator.
40. Remove fluid level indicator and tube.
41. Lower vehicle and engine/transaxle onto suitable table.
42. Remove transaxle mount to body bolts, **Fig. 1.**
43. Remove intermediate bracket from right engine mount support bracket.
44. Raise and support vehicle, leaving powertrain on table.
45. Separate engine and transaxle assembly.
46. Reverse procedure to install, noting the following:
   a. After connecting engine to transaxle, loosely install serpentine drive belt to hold engine design together.
   b. Torque engine fasteners and components to specifications.
   c. Bleed power steering system after engine installation.

INTAKE MANIFOLD

REPLACE

1. Relieve fuel system pressure as described under precautions.
2. Remove top half of air cleaner assembly and throttle body duct.
3. Drain cooling system.
4. Disconnect EGR pipe from exhaust manifold.

5. Remove serpentine drive belt.
6. Disconnect brake vacuum pipe at plenum.
7. Disconnect power steering lines at alternator bracket.
8. Remove alternator as described under "Alternator, Replace" in Electrical section.
9. Disconnect secondary ignition wires from spark plugs and harness at plenum.
10. Remove electronic ignition coil/module assembly and the EVAP canister purge solenoid.
11. Disconnect upper engine wire harness connectors.
12. Disconnect vacuum modulator, fuel pressure regulator and PCV vacuum lines.
13. Remove MAP sensor from upper intake manifold.
14. Remove upper intake manifold, **Fig. 3**.
15. Disconnect fuel lines at fuel rail and remove from bracket.
16. Install engine support fixture.
17. Remove engine mount assembly as described under "Engine Mounts, Replace."
18. Remove power steering pump mounting bolts and position pump aside.
19. Disconnect coolant inlet pipe from coolant outlet housing.
20. Remove coolant bypass at coolant pump and cylinder head.
21. Disconnect radiator hose at coolant outlet housing.
22. Remove coolant outlet housing.
23. Remove both valve rocker covers.
24. Remove lower intake manifold bolts.
25. Loosen rocker arms and remove pushrods.
26. Remove intake manifold and gasket.
27. Reverse procedure to install. Tighten intake manifold upper and lower bolts to specifications.

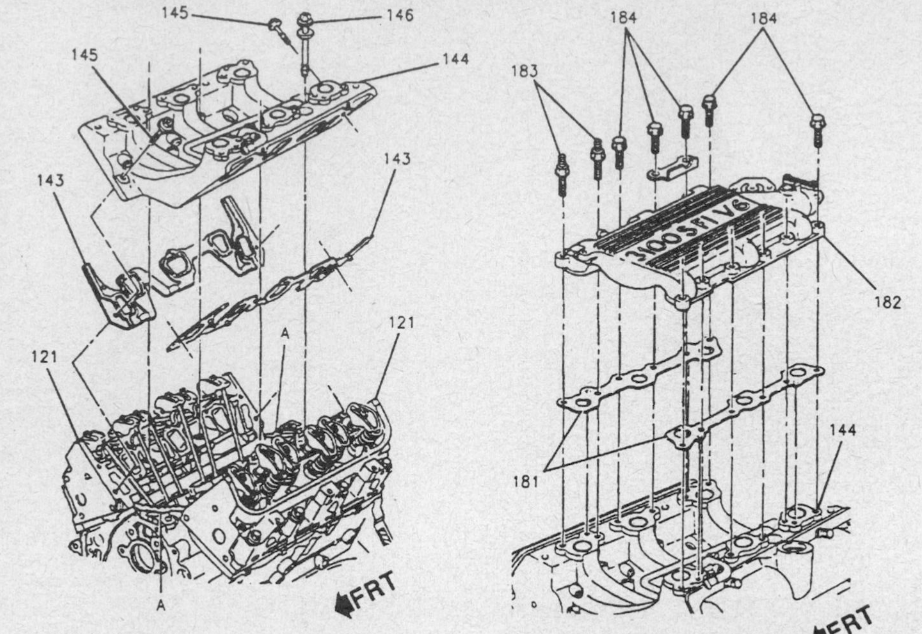
FRT
FRT

A APPLY SEALANT
121 HEAD ASSEMBLY, CYLINDER
143 GASKET, LOWER INTAKE MANIFOLD
144 BOLT, LOWER INTAKE
145 BOLT, LOWER INTAKE MANIFOLD
146 BOLT, LOWER INTAKE MANIFOLD

144 MANIFOLD, LOWER INTAKE
181 GASKET, UPPER INTAKE MANIFOLD
182 MANIFOLD, UPPER INTAKE
183 STUD, UPPER INTAKE MANIFOLD
184 BOLT, UPPER INTAKE MANIFOLD

GC1069500599000X

Fig. 3 Intake manifold assembly. 3.1L/V6-192

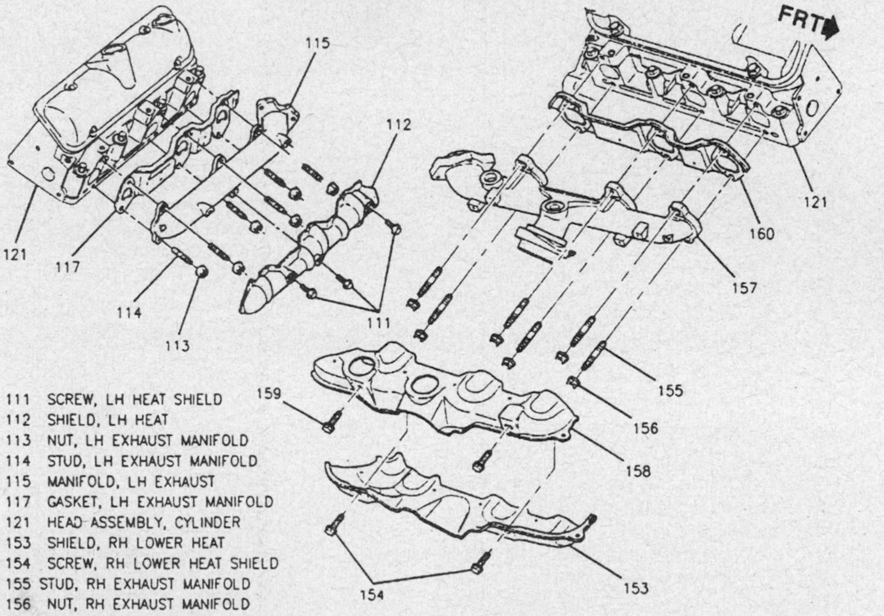
FRT

111 SCREW, LH HEAT SHIELD
112 SHIELD, LH HEAT
113 NUT, LH EXHAUST MANIFOLD
114 STUD, LH EXHAUST MANIFOLD
115 MANIFOLD, LH EXHAUST
117 GASKET, LH EXHAUST MANIFOLD
121 HEAD ASSEMBLY, CYLINDER
153 SHIELD, RH LOWER HEAT
154 SCREW, RH LOWER HEAT SHIELD
155 STUD, RH EXHAUST MANIFOLD
156 NUT, RH EXHAUST MANIFOLD
157 MANIFOLD, RH EXHAUST
158 SHIELD, RH UPPER HEAT
159 SCREW, RH UPPER HEAT SHIELD
160 GASKET, RH EXHAUST MANIFOLD

GC1069500600000X

Fig. 4 Exhaust manifold assembly. 3.1L/V6-192

EXHAUST MANIFOLD
REPLACE
LEFT

1. Disconnect battery ground cable.
2. Remove top half of air cleaner assembly and throttle cable duct.
3. Partially drain cooling system, then disconnect radiator hose from thermostat housing.
4. Disconnect coolant bypass pipe at coolant pump and from exhaust manifold.
5. Remove exhaust crossover heat shield.
6. Remove exhaust crossover pipe from manifold.
7. Disconnect secondary ignition wires from spark plugs.
8. Remove exhaust manifold heat shield, **Fig. 4**.
9. Remove exhaust manifold retaining nuts, then the exhaust manifold.
10. Reverse procedure to install. Tighten exhaust manifold and heat shield to specifications.

RIGHT

1. Disconnect battery ground cable.
2. Remove top half of air cleaner assembly and throttle cable duct.
3. Remove exhaust crossover heat shield.
4. Remove crossover at exhaust manifold.
5. Remove heated oxygen sensor.
6. Disconnect EGR pipe at exhaust manifold.
7. Raise and support vehicle.

8. Remove transaxle oil fill tube and level indicator assembly.
9. Remove exhaust pipe from exhaust manifold.
10. Disconnect exhaust pipe from converter flange, and support converter.
11. Remove converter heat shield from body.
12. Remove exhaust manifold heat shield.
13. Remove exhaust manifold mounting nuts, **Fig. 4** then pull exhaust manifold from bottom of vehicle
14. Reverse procedure to install.

RADIATOR

REPLACE

1. Disconnect battery ground cable.
2. Drain cooling system.
3. Remove air intake duct assembly.
4. Disconnect upper transaxle cooler line.
5. Disconnect upper radiator hose.
6. Lower transaxle cooler line.
7. Disconnect cooling fan electrical connector, then remove cooling fan mounting bolts.
8. Remove cooling fan.
9. Remove splash guard below lower radiator hose.
10. Disconnect lower radiator hose from radiator.
11. Remove condenser line retaining clip.
12. Remove condenser to radiator attaching bolts.
13. Disconnect coolant surge tank hose.
14. Remove radiator mounting bolts, then the radiator.
15. Reverse procedure to install. Tightening to specifications.

TIGHTENING SPECIFICATIONS

Year	Component	Torque/Ft. Lbs.
1994-95	Coolant Drain Plug	14
	Coolant Outlet Bolt	18
	Drive Belt Tensioner Bolt	37
	Engine Mount Strut Bolts	①
	Engine Mount To Body Bolts	49
	Engine Mount To Body Nut	31
	Exhaust Manifold Bolts	12
	Exhaust Manifold Heat Shield	89②
	Lower Intake Manifold Bolts	10
	Oil Filter	9-10
	Upper Intake Manifold Bolts	18

①—Refer to text.
②—Inch Lbs.

3.3L/V6-204 Engine

NOTE: On Air Bag Equipped Models, Refer To "Air Bag System Precautions" Located In The Front Of This Manual For System Disarming & Arming Procedures.

INDEX

PRECAUTIONS

AIR BAG SYSTEMS

Refer to "Air Bag System Precautions" in the front of this manual for system disarming and arming procedures.

FUEL SYSTEM PRESSURE RELIEF

Failure to relieve system pressure prior to disconnecting fuel system components may cause fire or personal injury. Remove fuel tank filler cap to release fuel tank pressure. Connect pressure gauge No. J-34730-1 or equivalent to pressure tap on fuel rail, position bleed hose into suitable container and slowly relieve fuel system pressure. Prior to disconnecting fuel line, position shop towel over fitting.

ENGINE MOUNT

REPLACE

RIGHT ENGINE MOUNT

1. Disconnect battery ground cable.
2. Support engine using tool No. J28476-A or equivalent.
3. Raise and support vehicle, then remove mount to engine mount bracket nuts.
4. Raise engine slightly, then remove mount to frame nuts.
5. Remove engine mount, **Fig. 1.**
6. Reverse procedure to install.

ENGINE MOUNT STRUT

1. Disconnect battery ground cable.
2. Raise and support vehicle.
3. Remove bolts attaching engine

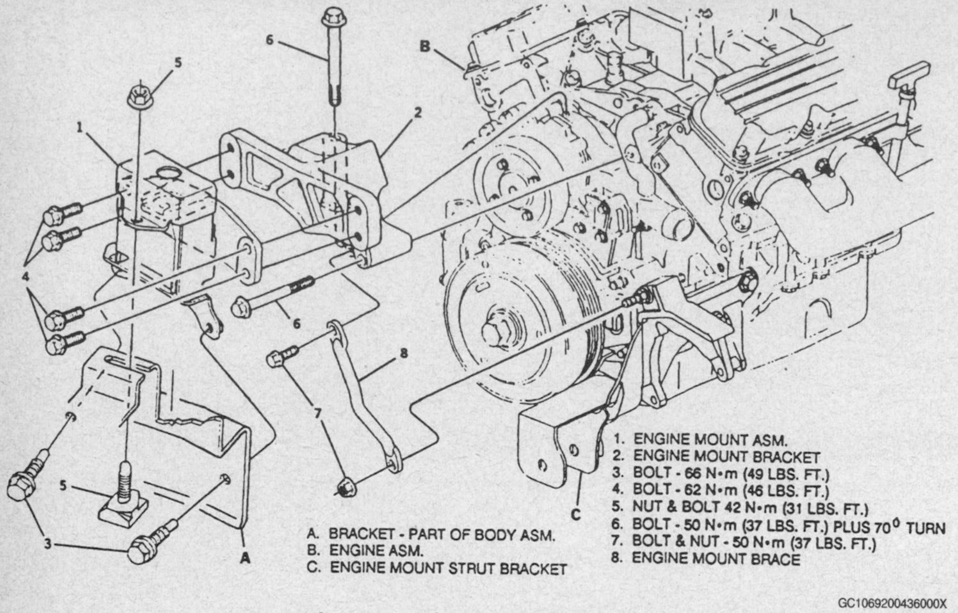

A. BRACKET - PART OF BODY ASM.
B. ENGINE ASM.
C. ENGINE MOUNT STRUT BRACKET
1. ENGINE MOUNT ASM.
2. ENGINE MOUNT BRACKET
3. BOLT - 66 N•m (49 LBS. FT.)
4. BOLT - 62 N•m (46 LBS. FT.)
5. NUT & BOLT 42 N•m (31 LBS. FT.)
6. BOLT - 50 N•m (37 LBS. FT.) PLUS 70° TURN
7. BOLT & NUT - 50 N•m (37 LBS. FT.)
8. ENGINE MOUNT BRACE
GC1069200436000X

Fig. 1 Right engine mount

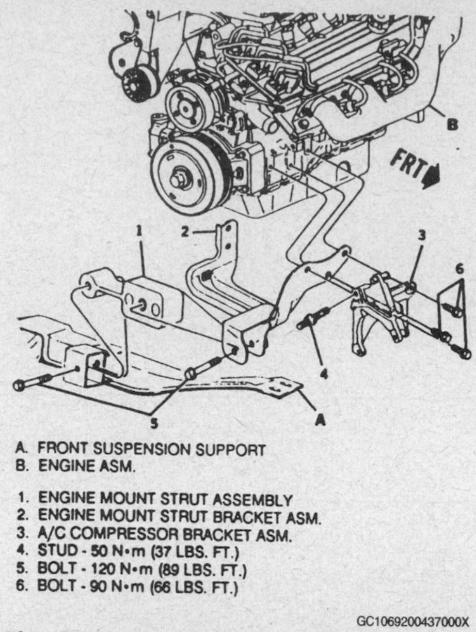

FRT
A. FRONT SUSPENSION SUPPORT
B. ENGINE ASM.
1. ENGINE MOUNT STRUT ASSEMBLY
2. ENGINE MOUNT STRUT BRACKET ASM.
3. A/C COMPRESSOR BRACKET ASM.
4. STUD - 50 N•m (37 LBS. FT.)
5. BOLT - 120 N•m (89 LBS. FT.)
6. BOLT - 90 N•m (66 LBS. FT.)
GC1069200437000X

Fig. 2 Engine mount strut & bracket

mount strut to body.
4. Remove engine mount strut, **Fig. 2.**
5. Reverse procedure to install.

ENGINE

REPLACE

1. Remove hood and cover fenders.
2. Depressurize and disconnect fuel lines from fuel rail.
3. Disconnect battery ground cable, then drain engine coolant.
4. Remove radiator and heater hoses, then engine cooling fan.
5. Remove air intake duct from throttle body, then vacuum lines from the brake power booster and evaporative canister purge.
6. Remove cable bracket and cables from throttle body, then the drive belt.
7. Remove power steering pump and position aside, then disconnect electrical connectors.
8. Remove upper transaxle to engine bolts, then raise and support vehicle.
9. **On models with A/C,** remove A/C compressor and position aside.
10. **On all models,** remove rear engine mount to mount bracket bolts.
11. Remove flywheel dust cover, then flywheel to torque converter bolts. Use a scribe to mark flywheel to torque converter relationship to ensure proper reassembly.
12. Remove lower engine to transaxle bolts. One bolt is located between the transaxle case and engine block and is installed in the opposite direction.
13. Lower vehicle, then remove front engine mount to bracket bolts, then engine assembly.
14. Reverse procedure to install.

INTAKE MANIFOLD

REPLACE

1. Depressurize and disconnect fuel lines from fuel rail, then disconnect battery ground cable.

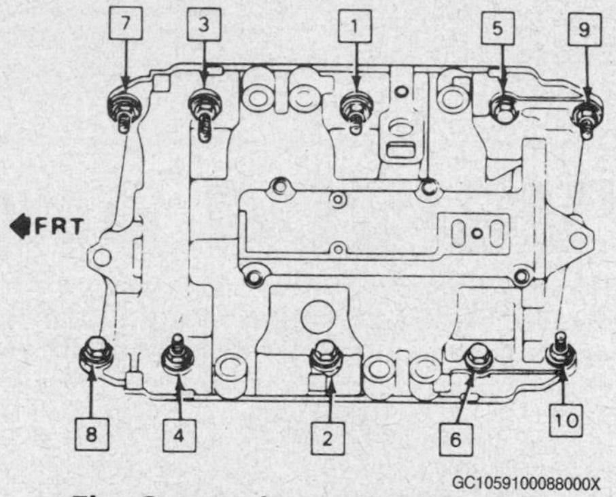

7
3
1
5
9
FRT
8
4
2
6
10
GC1059100088000X

Fig. 3 Intake manifold bolt tightening sequence

2. Remove serpentine drive belt, then the alternator and braces.
3. Remove power steering pump and braces and position aside.
4. Remove coolant bypass hose, then the heater pipe.
5. Remove upper radiator hose, then the air inlet duct.
6. Remove throttle cable bracket and cables from throttle body.
7. Disconnect vacuum hoses, then the electrical connectors.
8. Remove the fuel rail, then disconnect the vapor canister purge line.
9. Remove heater hose from the throttle body, then disconnect the rear spark plug wires.
10. Remove the intake manifold bolts, then the manifold.
11. Reverse procedure to install, noting the following:
    a. Clean the intake manifold bolts and bolt holes of adhesive compound.
    b. Apply sealant No. 12345336 or equivalent, to the ends of the manifold seals.
    c. Apply thread lock compound No. 12345493 or equivalent, to the manifold bolt threads.
    d. Tighten the manifold bolts following the sequence in **Fig. 3,** to specifications.
    e. Lubricate throttle body coolant and heater pipe O-rings with antifreeze before assembly.

EXHAUST MANIFOLD

REPLACE

FRONT

1. Disconnect battery ground cable.
2. Remove air cleaner inlet duct, then disconnect spark plug wires at spark plugs. Tag spark plug wires for installation reference.
3. Disconnect exhaust crossover pipe from exhaust manifold.
4. Remove engine lifting hook.
5. Remove heat shield from exhaust manifold.
6. Remove engine oil dipstick and tube.
7. Remove exhaust manifold attaching studs, then remove exhaust manifold.
8. Reverse procedure to install.

REAR

1. Disconnect battery ground cable.
2. Disconnect spark plug wires at spark plugs. Tag spark plug wires so they can be installed in the same locations.
3. Disconnect electrical connector at oxygen sensor.
4. Disconnect throttle cables at throttle body, then remove throttle cable bracket.
5. Disconnect power brake unit vacuum hose at intake manifold.
6. Disconnect exhaust crossover pipe and exhaust pipe from exhaust manifold.
7. Remove engine lifting hook.
8. Remove transaxle dipstick and tube.
9. Remove heat shield from exhaust manifold.

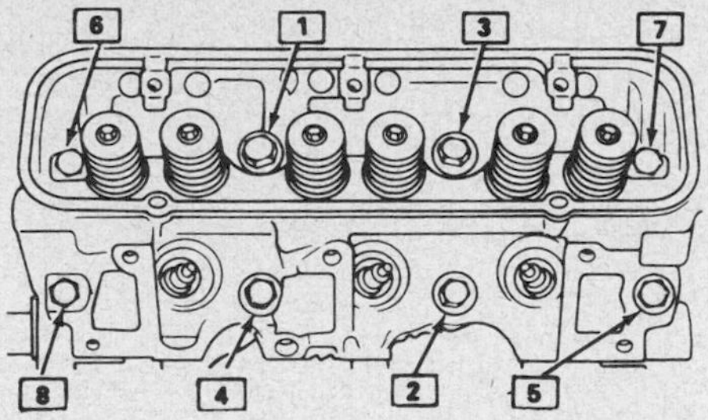
6
1
3
7
8
4
2
5
GC1069100438000X

Fig. 4 Cylinder head bolt tightening sequence

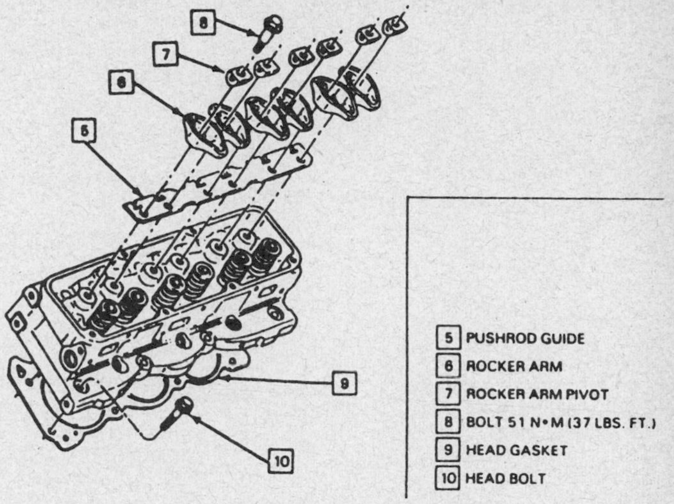
8
7
6
5
9
10
5 PUSHROD GUIDE
6 ROCKER ARM
7 ROCKER ARM PIVOT
8 BOLT 51 N•M (37 LBS. FT.)
9 HEAD GASKET
10 HEAD BOLT
GC1069100439000X

Fig. 5 Rocker arm installation

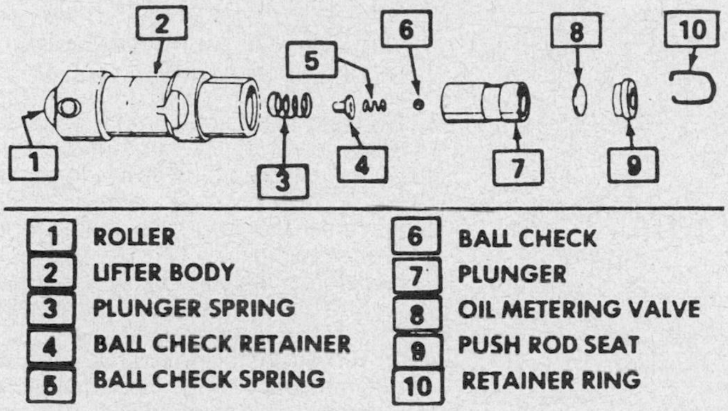
2
5
6
8
10
1
3
4
7
9
1 ROLLER
2 LIFTER BODY
3 PLUNGER SPRING
4 BALL CHECK RETAINER
5 BALL CHECK SPRING
6 BALL CHECK
7 PLUNGER
8 OIL METERING VALVE
9 PUSH ROD SEAT
10 RETAINER RING
GC1069100440000X

Fig. 6 Hydraulic roller valve lifter

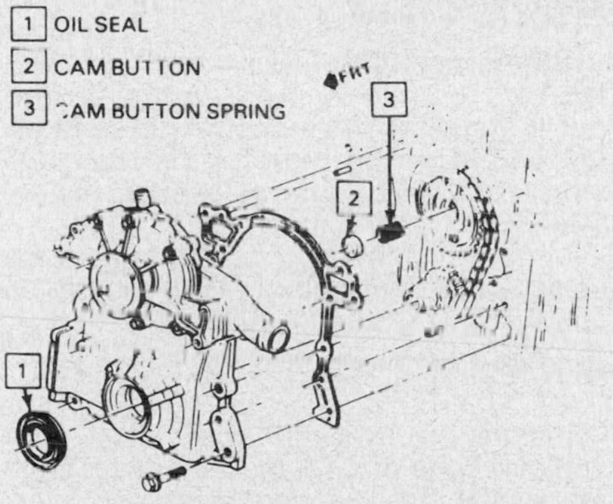
1 OIL SEAL
2 CAM BUTTON
3 CAM BUTTON SPRING
FRT
3
2
1
GC1069100441000X

Fig. 7 Engine front cover replacement

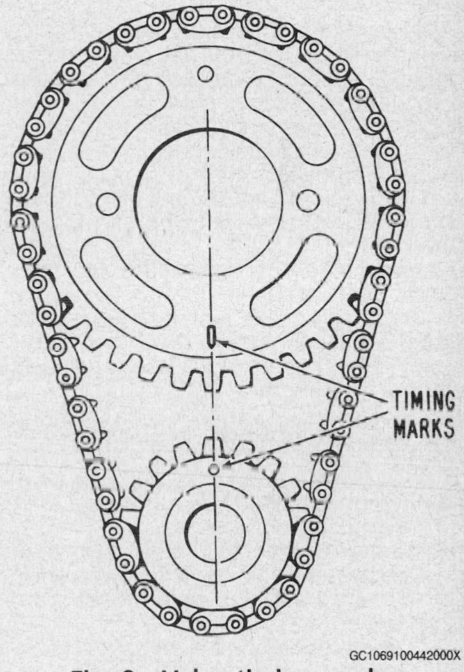
TIMING MARKS
GC1069100442000X

Fig. 8 Valve timing marks

10. Remove exhaust manifold attaching studs and bolt, then remove exhaust manifold.
11. Reverse procedure to install.

CYLINDER HEAD

REPLACE

1. Disconnect battery ground cable.
2. Remove intake manifold as described under "Intake Manifold, Replace."
3. Remove exhaust manifold as described under "Exhaust Manifold, Replace."
4. Remove valve covers, then disconnect spark plug wires.
5. If right hand cylinder is to be removed, proceed as follows:
   a. Remove power steering pump and position aside with hose attached.
   b. Remove belt tensioner assembly.
6. If left hand cylinder head is to be removed, proceed as follows:
   a. Remove alternator bracket with ignition module and coil units attached.
   b. Remove A/C compressor mounting bolt from cylinder head.
7. Remove rocker arm assemblies, guide plate and pushrods.
8. Remove cylinder head attaching bolts and cylinder heads.
9. Reverse procedure to install noting the following:
   a. Clean threads in the block using a 7/16-14 tap, then clean bolt threads.
   b. Apply sealant No. 1052080 or equivalent, to the underside of the bolt heads.
   c. Apply thread locker No. 12345382 or equivalent, to the bolt threads.
   d. Install cylinder head bolts and tighten in sequence shown in **Fig. 4. Torque** each cylinder head bolt to 35 ft. lbs., then tighten an additional 130° using torque angle meter No. J-36660, or equivalent. Tighten the center four cylinder head attaching bolts an additional 30° using torque angle meter J-36660, or equivalent.

VALVE ADJUSTMENT

These engines are equipped with hydraulic valve lifters. No adjustment is required.

ROCKER ARMS

1. Remove valve cover.
2. Remove rocker arm pedestal retaining bolts.
3. Remove pedestal and rocker arm assembly, **Fig. 5.** Keep rocker arms and pedestals together and note installation position. Components that are to be reused should be installed in original position.
4. Reverse procedure to install, **torquing** pedestal retaining bolts to 28 ft. lbs. Clean bolt threads and apply thread locking compound No. 112345493, or equivalent, to bolt threads prior to installation.

VALVE GUIDES

The valve guides are an integral part of the cylinder head and cannot be replaced.

If the valve stem clearance is excessive, the valve guide must be reamed and an oversize valve installed. Valves are available in oversize of .010 inch.

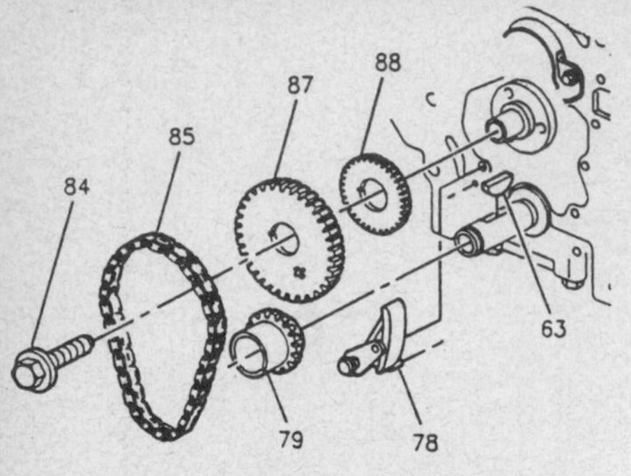
84
85
87
88
63
79
78

63 KEY
78 DAMPER ASSEMBLY
79 CRANKSHAFT SPROCKET
84 BOLT
85 TIMING CHAIN
87 CAMSHAFT SPROCKET
88 CAMSHAFT GEAR

GC1069200443000X

Fig. 9 Timing chain replacement

HYDRAULIC LIFTERS

REPLACE

Failure of a hydraulic valve lifter, **Fig. 6,** is generally caused by dirt or an inadequate oil supply. An air leak at the intake side of the oil pump or too much oil in the engine will cause air bubbles in the oil supply to the lifters, causing them to collapse. This is a probable cause of trouble if several lifters fail to function, but air in the oil is an unlikely cause of failure of a single unit.

The valve lifters may be lifted out of their bores after removing the rocker arms, pushrods and intake manifold. Adjustable pliers with taped jaws may be used to remove lifters that are stuck due to varnish, carbon, etc.

FRONT COVER

REPLACE

1. Disconnect battery ground cable, then drain cooling system.
2. Remove serpentine drive belt, then the heater pipes. Remove lower radiator and coolant bypass hoses from front cover.
3. **On all models,** raise and support vehicle.
4. Remove right front wheel and tire assembly, then remove inner fender splash shield.
5. Remove right front axle, then support engine using fixture No. J-28467 or equivalent.
6. Remove torque converter cover, then install flywheel holder No. J-37096 or equivalent to hold fly wheel in position.
7. Remove crankshaft balancer bolt, then remove balancer.
8. Remove crankshaft sensor shield.
9. Disconnect electrical connectors at camshaft and crankshaft sensors and oil pressure sender switch.
10. Remove oil pan to front cover attaching bolts.
11. Remove front cover to engine attaching bolts, then remove front cover, **Fig. 7.**

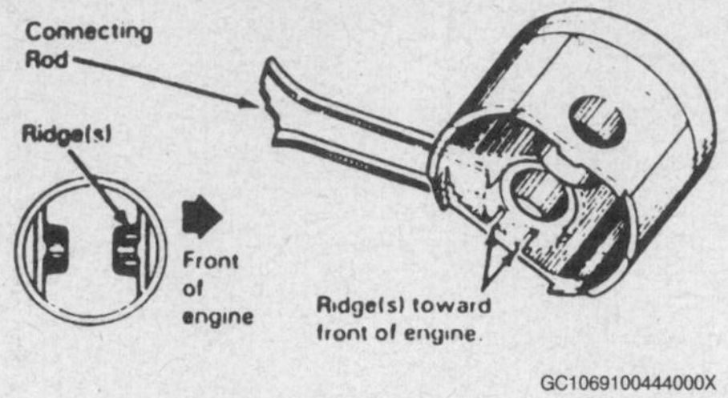
Connecting Rod
Ridge(s)
Front of engine
Ridge(s) toward front of engine.
GC1069100444000X

Fig. 10 Piston installation direction

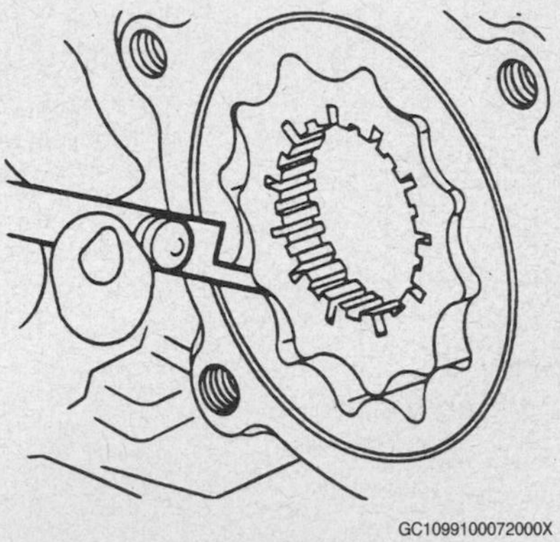
GC1099100072000X

Fig. 12 Inner gear tip clearance inspection

12. Reverse procedure to install. Apply sealant No. 1052080 or equivalent, to front cover bolt threads. Adjust crankshaft sensor using tool No. J-37087 or equivalent. Hold flywheel in place using tool No. J-37096 or equivalent, when tightening balancer bolt.

TIMING CHAIN

REPLACE

1. Remove front cover as described under "Front Cover, Replace."
2. Align timing marks on sprockets so they are as close together as possible, **Fig. 8.**
3. Remove camshaft sprocket attaching bolts, then the camshaft sprocket, chain and crankshaft sprocket, **Fig. 9.**
4. Reverse procedure to install. Install chain with No. 1 piston at TDC, timing mark on camshaft sprocket facing straight down and timing marks on sprockets as close together as possible, **Fig. 8.**

CAMSHAFT

REPLACE

1. Disconnect battery ground cable, then remove engine as described in "Engine, Replace."
2. Remove intake manifold as described in "Intake Manifold, Replace."
3. Remove valve covers, then rocker arms, pushrods and valve lifters.
4. Remove crankshaft balancer assembly.
5. Remove crankshaft sensor shield.
6. Remove front cover as described in "Front Cover, Replace."

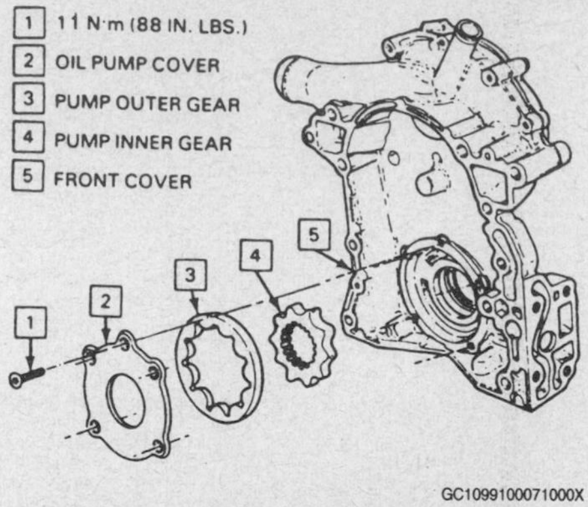
1 11 N·m (88 IN. LBS.)
2 OIL PUMP COVER
3 PUMP OUTER GEAR
4 PUMP INNER GEAR
5 FRONT COVER
GC1099100071000X

Fig. 11 Oil pump & housing assembly

7. Remove timing chain and sprockets.
8. Slide camshaft forward out of bearing bores, using care so as not to damage bearing surfaces.
9. Reverse procedure to install noting the following:
   a. Prior to installation, coat camshaft and dip valve lifters in lubricant No. 12345501 or equivalent.
   b. When installing camshaft, align crankshaft and camshaft timing marks as shown in **Fig. 8.**

PISTON & ROD ASSEMBLY

When installing piston and connecting rod in cylinder bore, ridge on the outer diameter of the piston pin bore on the inside of the piston must face toward front of engine as shown in Fig. 10.

Measure connecting rod side clearance using a suitable feeler gauge. Clearance should be .003 to .015 inch.

PISTONS, PINS & RINGS

Pistons are available in standard sizes and oversizes of .010 and .020 inch. Rings are available in standard sizes and oversizes of .010 and .020 inch. Piston pins are supplied with piston and available only in standard sizes.

MAIN & ROD BEARINGS

Main bearings are available in standard sizes and undersize of .001 inch. Rod bearings are available in standard sizes and in undersize of .008 inch.

CRANKSHAFT REAR OIL SEAL

REPLACE

1. Remove flywheel, then confirm rear seal leak.
2. Insert a screwdriver or similar tool in through the dust lip at any angle and pry seal out by moving the handle of the tool towards the end of the crankshaft pilot. Repeat as required around the seal until seal is removed. Care must be taken not to damage crankshaft OD surface or chamfer with pry tool.

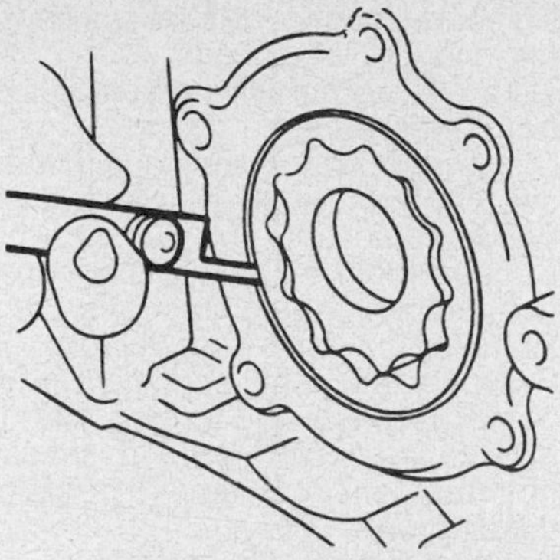

GC1099100073000X

Fig. 13 Outer gear diameter clearance inspection

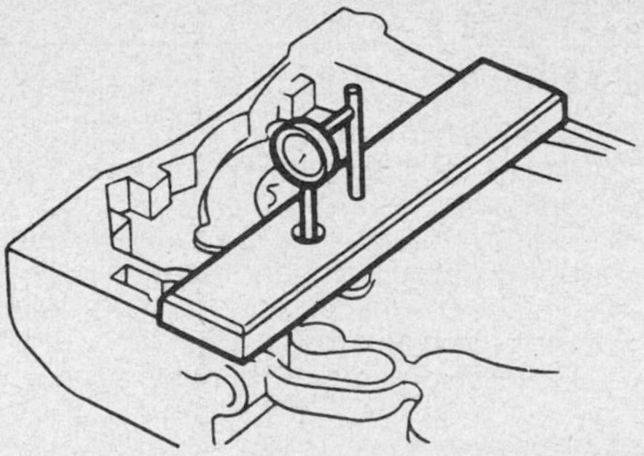

GC1099100074000X

Fig. 14 Gear end clearance inspection

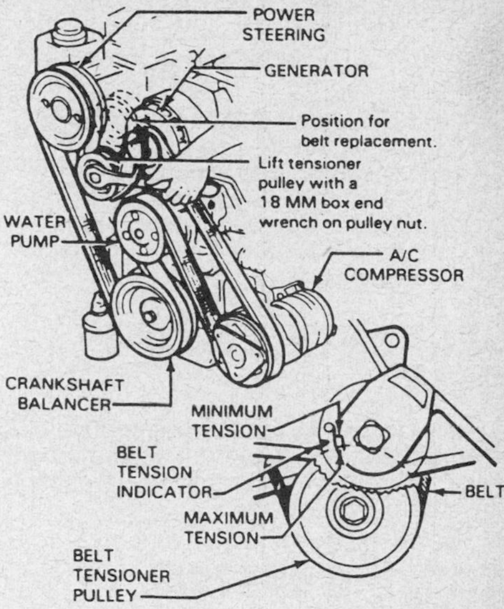
POWER STEERING
GENERATOR
Position for belt replacement.
Lift tensioner pulley with a 18 MM box end wrench on pulley nut.
WATER PUMP
A/C COMPRESSOR
CRANKSHAFT BALANCER
MINIMUM TENSION
BELT TENSION INDICATOR
BELT
MAXIMUM TENSION
BELT TENSIONER PULLEY

GC1069100445000X

Fig. 15 Serpentine belt routing

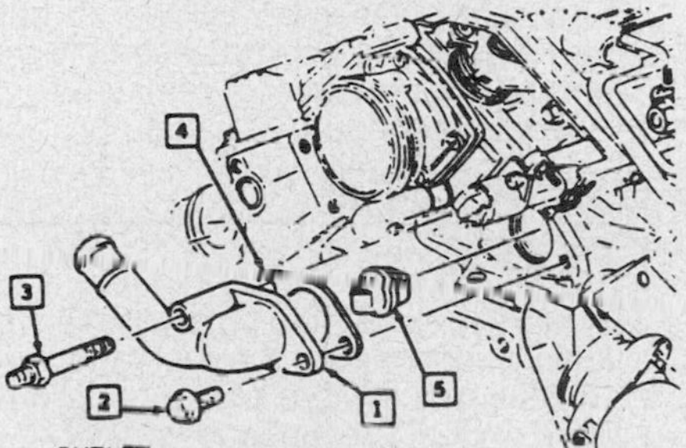

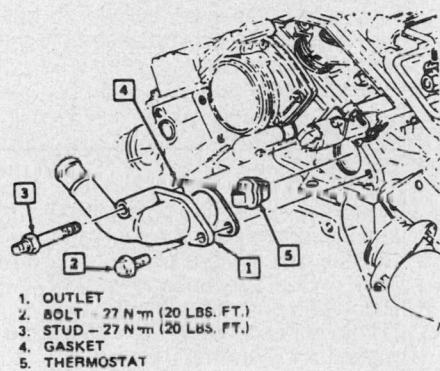

1. OUTLET
2. BOLT – 27 N·m (20 LBS. FT.)
3. STUD – 27 N·m (20 LBS. FT.)
4. GASKET
5. THERMOSTAT

GC1089100169000X

Fig. 16 Thermostat replacement

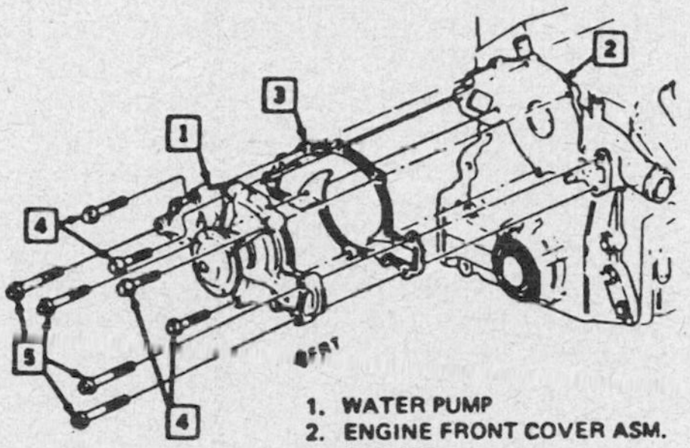

1. WATER PUMP
2. ENGINE FRONT COVER ASM.
3. GASKET
4. 11 N·m (97 LBS. IN.)
5. 39 N·m (29 LBS. FT.)

GC1089100170000X

Fig. 17 Water pump replacement

3. Using tool No. J-38196 or equivalent, apply engine oil to the ID and OD of new seal. Slide new seal over mandrel until back of seal bottom squarely fits against collar.
4. Install seal as follows:
   a. Align dowel pin of tool with dowel pin in crankshaft and attach tool to crankshaft by hand, or **torque** attaching screws to 60 inch lbs.
   b. Turn T-handle of tool so that collar pushes seal into bore, turn the handle until the collar is tight against the case. This will ensure the seal is seated properly.
   c. Loosen the T-handle of the tool until it comes to a stop, then remove attaching screws.
5. Install flywheel.

OIL PAN

REPLACE

1. disconnect battery ground cable.
2. Raise and support vehicle, then drain crankcase.
3. Remove lower splash shield and flap.
4. Remove crankshaft pulley and crankshaft sensor cover.
5. Disconnect A/C compressor electrical connector and hose support from suspension support.
6. Remove A/C compressor from mounting bracket and position aside with refrigerant hoses attached.
7. Remove right hand suspension support front bolts.

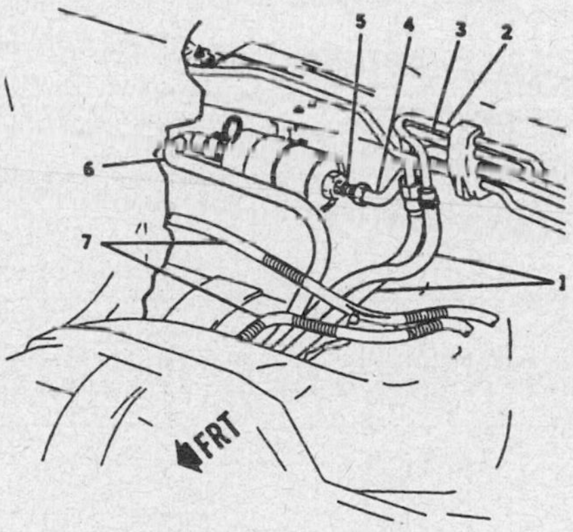
FRT

1. HOSE-PART OF FUEL SENDER
2. FUEL VAPOR PIPE
3. FUEL RETURN PIPE
4. FUEL FEED PIPE
5. FUEL FEED PIPE NUT - 27 NKm (20 LBS. FT.)
6. HOSE-PART OF FUEL SENDER
7. ABS AND FUEL SENDER HARNESS

GC1029202739000X

Fig. 18 Fuel filter replacement

8. Loosen all suspension support attaching bolts so that support will drop approximately 1.5 inches at front.
9. Remove oil lever sensor from oil pan.
10. Remove flywheel housing cover.
11. Remove oil pan attaching bolts and oil pan. Move A/C refrigerant line as necessary to obtain clearance for oil pan removal.
12. Reverse procedure to install.

OIL PUMP SERVICE

REMOVAL & INSPECTION

1. Remove engine front cover as described under "Front Cover, Replace," then the oil filter adapter, pressure regulator valve and valve spring.
2. Remove oil pump cover attaching screws, cover and gears, **Fig. 11.**
3. Inspect pump cover and housing for cracks, scoring, porosity and damaged threads, pressure regulator valve and spring for sticking, scoring or tension loss and gears for chipping, galling or excessive wear. Replace as necessary.
4. Check gear clearance as follows:
   a. Check inner gear tip clearance with feeler gauge as shown in **Fig. 12.** Maximum clearance should not exceed .006 inch.
   b. Check outer gear diameter clearance with feeler gauge as shown in **Fig. 13.** Clearance should be .008-.015 inch.
   c. Check gear end clearance (gear drop in housing) with suitable dial indicator as shown in **Fig. 14.** Clearance should be .001-.0035 inch.
5. Replace parts as necessary.

ASSEMBLY & INSTALLATION

1. Lubricate gears with petroleum jelly, then install into oil pump housing.
2. Pack pump cavity with petroleum jelly, then install pump cover and attaching screws. **Torque** attaching screws to 97 inch lbs.
3. Install pressure regulator valve spring and valve.
4. Install oil filter adapter using new gasket. **Torque** adapter to 24 ft.lbs.
5. Reinstall front cover onto engine.

BELT TENSION DATA

Year	Belt Tension, Lbs.①
1992-93	67

①—On models less A/C, take reading between power steering pump & crankshaft pulley. On models with A/C, take reading between alternator & A/C compressor. If reading is less than listed, replace belt tensioner.

SERPENTINE DRIVE BELT

Refer to **Fig. 15** for serpentine drive belt replacement. The right front engine mount must be removed to replace serpentine drive belt.

COOLING SYSTEM BLEED

After filling cooling system, start engine and allow to reach operating temperature with surge tank pressure cap removed. Air will bleed through surge cap opening. Add coolant as necessary to bring to proper level, then install surge tank pressure cap.

THERMOSTAT

REPLACE

1. Disconnect battery ground cable.
2. Drain cooling system until level is below thermostat.
3. Remove air cleaner assembly.
4. Remove thermostat housing and thermostat, **Fig. 16.**
5. Reverse procedure to install. Apply sealer to bolt threads prior to installation.

WATER PUMP

REPLACE

1. Disconnect battery ground cable.
2. Drain cooling system, then remove serpentine belt.
3. Remove idler pulley bolt, then water pump pulley bolts and remove pulley.
4. Remove water pump attaching bolts, then the water pump, **Fig. 17.**
5. Reverse procedure to install.

RADIATOR

REPLACE

1. Disconnect battery ground cable.
2. Drain cooling system.
3. Remove air intake duct assembly.
4. Disconnect upper transaxle cooler line.
5. Disconnect upper radiator hose.
6. Lower transaxle cooler line.
7. Disconnect cooling fan electrical connector, then remove cooling fan mounting bolts.
8. Remove cooling fan.
9. Remove splash guard below lower radiator hose.
10. Disconnect lower radiator hose from radiator.
11. Remove condenser line retaining clip.
12. Remove condenser to radiator attaching bolts.
13. Disconnect coolant surge tank hose.
14. Remove radiator mounting bolts, then the radiator.
15. Reverse procedure to install. Tighten to specifications.

FUEL PUMP

REPLACE

1. Disconnect battery ground cable, then drain fuel tank.
2. Disconnect tank unit harness connector.
3. Remove ground wire retaining screw from underbody.
4. Disconnect hoses from tank meter assembly, then hoses at tank from filler and vent pipes.
5. Support fuel tank and disconnect the two fuel tank retaining straps.
6. Remove fuel tank from vehicle.
7. Remove fuel tank sending unit and pump assembly by turning cam lock ring counterclockwise. Lift assembly from fuel tank and remove pump from sending unit.
8. Pull fuel pump up into attaching hose while pulling outward away from bottom support. Take care to prevent damage to rubber insulator and strainer during removal.
9. After pump assembly is clear of bottom support, pull pump assembly out of rubber connector for removal.
10. Reverse procedure to install.

FUEL FILTER

REPLACE

The fuel filter is located below the rear of the vehicle, rearward of the fuel tank.

1. Relieve fuel system pressure as outlined under "Precautions."
2. Raise and support vehicle.
3. Using suitable back-up wrench, remove fuel filter fitting, **Fig. 18.**
4. Grasp filter and one nylon fuel connection line fitting, twist quick connect fitting 1/4 turn in each direction to loosen dirt in fitting.
5. Using compressed air, clean dirt from quick connect fitting.
6. Depress quick connect fitting plastic tabs of male end connector and pull apart.
7. Remove fuel filter.
8. Reverse procedure to install.

TIGHTENING SPECIFICATIONS

Year	Component	Torque/Ft. Lbs.
1992	Balance Shaft Gear Bolt	14⑦
	Balance Shaft Retainer	22
	Camshaft Sprocket Bolts	74⑧
	Connecting Rod Bolts	20①
	Coolant Temperature Sensor To Intake	15
	Crankshaft Bearing Caps To Cylinder Block	26①
	Cylinder Block Drain Plug	22
	Cylinder Head To Block	②
	ESC Knock Sensor To Cylinder Block	13
	Exhaust Manifold To Cylinder Head	38
	Flywheel Cover To Transaxle	48③
	Front Cover To Block	22
	Intake Manifold To Cylinder Head	88③

Year	Component	Torque/Ft. Lbs.
1992	Oil Pan Drain Plug	30
—Cont'd	Oil Pan To Cylinder Block	124③
	Oil Pan To Front Cover	124③
	Oil Pump Cover To Timing Chain Cover	97③
	Oxygen Sensor To Exhaust Manifold	31
	Radiator Mounting Bolts	89
	Rocker Arm Pedestal To Cylinder Head	88③
	Serpentine Belt Tensioner To Cylinder Head	38
	Spark Plug To Cylinder Head	12
	Starting Motor To Cylinder Block	35
	Thermostat Housing	20
	Timing Chain Dampener	16

Continued

TIGHTENING SPECIFICATIONS-Continued

Year	Component	Torque/Ft. Lbs.
	Torque Converter To Flywheel	46
	Transaxle To Cylinder Block	55
	Valve Lifter Guide Retainer Bolts	22
	Water Pump To Front Cover	11
	Water Pump Pulley To Hub	114③
1993	Alternator Bracket To Cylinder Head	36
	Alternator Through Bolt	36
	Balancer To Crankshaft	111④
	Camshaft Sprocket Bolts	74⑨
	Connecting Rod Bolts	20①
	Coolant Temperature Sensor To Intake	15
	Crankshaft Bearing Caps To Cylinder Head	26①
	Crankshaft Sensor To Front Cover	22
	Crankshaft Sensor Clamp Bolt	40③
	Cylinder Block Drain Plug	15
	Cylinder Head Bolts	②
	Engine Mount To Cylinder Block	70
	ESC Knock Sensor To Cylinder Block	13
	Exhaust Manifold To Cylinder Head	38
	Flywheel Cover To Transaxle	48③
	Flywheel To Crankshaft	11⑦
	Front Cover To Block	22
	Fuel Feed & Return Pipes To Fuel Rail	22
	Fuel Rail To Intake Manifold	11
	Heater Hose Fitting To Intake	11
	Ignition Module To Alternator Bracket	18
	Intake Manifold To Cylinder Head	89③
	Oil Drain Plug	30
	Oil Filter Adapter To Front Cover	22

Year	Component	Torque/Ft. Lbs.
	Oil Gallery Plugs	25
	Oil Level Sensor To Oil Pan	16
	Oil Pan	124③
	Oil Pressure Switch	24
	Oil Pump Cover To Front Cover	97③
	Oil Screen Housing To Cylinder Block	11
	Oxygen Sensor To Exhaust Manifold	31
	Radiator Mounting Bolts	89
	Rocker Arm Pedestal To Cylinder Head	18⑤
	Spark Plug	20
	Starter Motor To Cylinder Head	35
	Thermostat Housing	20
	Throttle Body To Intake Manifold	21
	Throttle Body Cable Bracket To Throttle Body	35③
	Timing Chain Damper	16
	Torque Converter To Flywheel	46
	Transaxle To Cylinder Block	55
	Valve Cover	89③
	Valve Lifter Guide Bolts	22
	Water Pump To Front Cover	11⑥
	Water Pump Pulley To Hub	114③

①—Plus an additional 50° rotation.
②—Refer to text.
③—Inch lbs.
④—Plus an additional 76° rotation.
⑤—Plus an additional 70° rotation
⑥—Plus an additional 80° rotation
⑦—Plus an additional 35° rotation.
⑧—Plus an additional 105° rotation.
⑨—Plus an additional 90° rotation.

Clutch & Manual Transaxle

NOTE: For Service Procedures Refer To Clutch & Manual Transaxle Section In Chevrolet Cavalier, Pontiac Sunbird & Sunfire Chapter.

Rear Axle & Suspension

INDEX

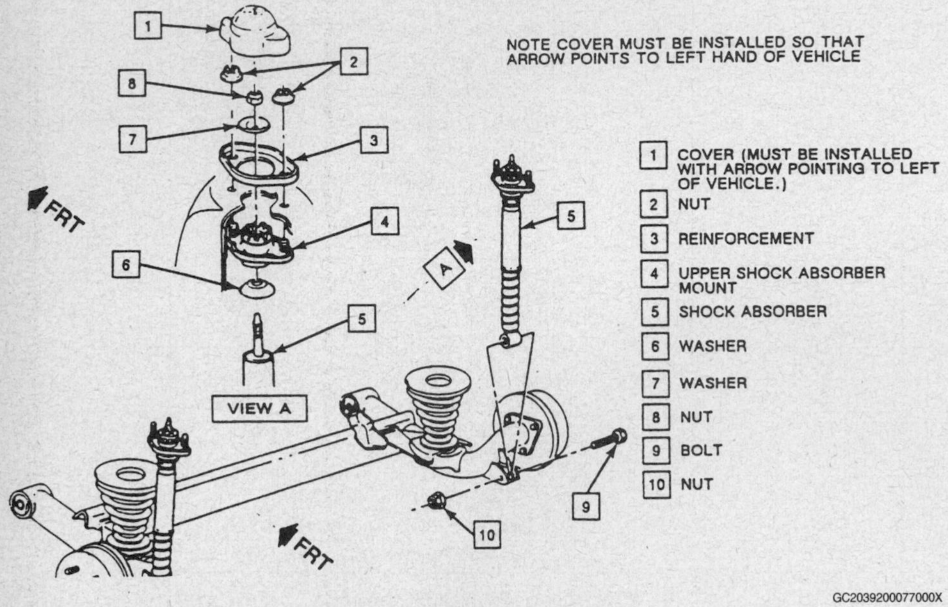

NOTE COVER MUST BE INSTALLED SO THAT ARROW POINTS TO LEFT HAND OF VEHICLE
FRT
VIEW A
A
FRT
1 COVER (MUST BE INSTALLED WITH ARROW POINTING TO LEFT OF VEHICLE.)
2 NUT
3 REINFORCEMENT
4 UPPER SHOCK ABSORBER MOUNT
5 SHOCK ABSORBER
6 WASHER
7 WASHER
8 NUT
9 BOLT
10 NUT
GC2039200077000X

Fig. 1 Rear suspension

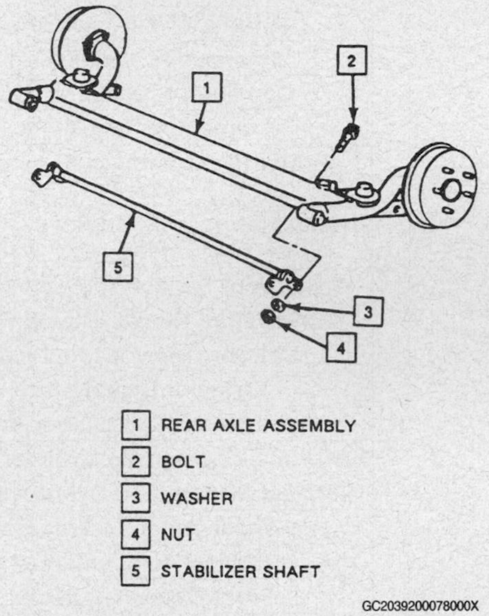

1 REAR AXLE ASSEMBLY
2 BOLT
3 WASHER
4 NUT
5 STABILIZER SHAFT
GC2039200078000X

Fig. 2 Stabilizer bar attachments

DESCRIPTION

The rear suspension, **Fig. 1,** is a semi-independent type suspension consisting of an axle assembly with trailing arms and cross beam, coil springs and shock absorbers. A stabilizer bar is available and is attached to the inside of the axle beam and to the lower end of the control arms. A single unit hub and bearing assembly is bolted to each end of the axle assembly. The hub and bearing assembly is a sealed, non-serviceable unit and must be replaced as an assembly.

REAR AXLE

REPLACE

1. Raise and support vehicle. Support rear suspension with suitable jack.
2. Remove rear wheel and tire assembly.
3. Disconnect brake lines from axle brackets.
4. Disconnect stabilizer bar at axle assembly, if equipped, **Fig. 2.**
5. Remove shock absorber to lower mounting bracket attaching bolts, then disconnect shock absorbers from axle assembly, **Fig. 1.**
6. Disconnect parking brake cable.
7. Carefully lower rear axle assembly and remove coil springs and insulators.
8. If equipped, disconnect ABS electrical connector and mount clip.
9. Disconnect brake lines at left and right hand wheels.
10. Remove control arm to underbody bracket bolts, then lower the axle assembly and remove from vehicle.
11. Reverse procedure to install and bleed brake system.

HUB & BEARING

REPLACE

1. Raise and support vehicle, then remove wheel and tire assembly and brake drum. **Do not hammer brake drum since damage to bearing may result.**
2. Remove four hub/bearing assembly to rear axle attaching bolts, then the hub/bearing assembly from axle. **The upper rear hub attaching bolt may not clear brake shoe when removing hub and bearing assembly. Partially remove hub and bearing assembly prior to removing this bolt. Also if equipped, disconnect ABS wheel sensor electrical connector.**
3. Reverse procedure to install. Tighten hub attaching bolts to specification. **Use care not to drop hub/bearing assembly since damage to bearing may result.**

SHOCK ABSORBER

REPLACE

1. Open deck lid, then remove trim cover and shock absorber upper retaining nut.
2. Raise rear of vehicle and support rear axle using a suitable jack.
3. Remove shock absorber lower attaching bolt, then disconnect shock absorber from mounting bracket, **Fig. 1.** Remove shock absorber from vehicle.
4. Reverse procedure to install. Tighten attaching bolt to specification. **When installing upper shock absorber attachment components, refer to Fig. 1 for proper installation order.**

COIL SPRING

REPLACE

1. Raise and support rear of vehicle. Support rear axle using a suitable jack.
2. Remove wheel and tire assemblies.
3. Remove brake line bracket attaching bolts from body and allow brake lines to hang freely.
4. Remove shock absorber to lower mounting bracket bolts, then disconnect shock absorbers from axle assembly. **Do not suspend rear axle by brake hoses since damage to hoses may result.**

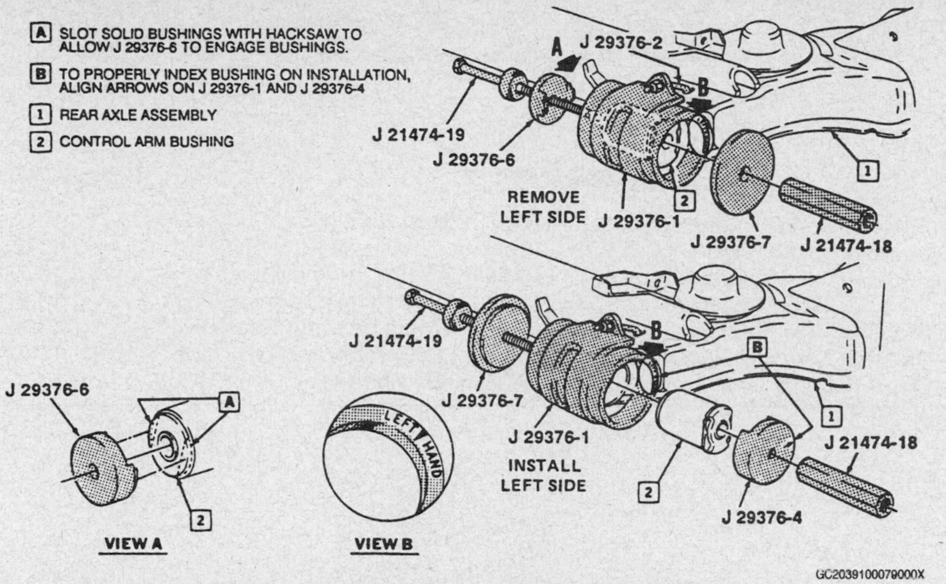
A SLOT SOLID BUSHINGS WITH HACKSAW TO ALLOW J 29376-6 TO ENGAGE BUSHINGS.
B TO PROPERLY INDEX BUSHING ON INSTALLATION, ALIGN ARROWS ON J 29376-1 AND J 29376-4
1 REAR AXLE ASSEMBLY
2 CONTROL ARM BUSHING
J 29376-2
J 21474-19
J 29376-6
REMOVE LEFT SIDE
J 29376-1
J 29376-7
J 21474-18
J 21474-19
J 29376-6
J 29376-7
J 29376-1
INSTALL LEFT SIDE
J 21474-18
J 29376-4
LEFT HAND
VIEW A
VIEW B
GC2039100079000X

Fig. 3 Control arm bushing installation

5. Carefully lower rear axle assembly and remove springs and insulators.
6. Reverse procedure to install. Upper ends of spring must be properly positioned in spring seat and with in 9/16 inch of spring stop.

STABILIZER BAR

REPLACE

1. Raise and support vehicle. Support vehicle body with jack stands.
2. Remove stabilizer bar attachments to axle and control arms, then remove stabilizer bar, **Fig. 2.**
3. Reverse procedure to install.

CONTROL ARM BUSHING

REPLACE

1. Raise rear of vehicle and support rear axle under front side of spring seat using a suitable jack.
2. Remove stabilizer bar from axle.
3. Remove wheel and tire assembly.
4. If right hand side bushing is to be replaced, disconnect brake line bracket from body. If left hand side bushing is to be replaced, disconnect brake line bracket from body and parking brake cable at hook guide.
5. Remove control arm to mounting bracket attaching nut, bolt and washer, then allow control arm to rotate downward.
6. The bushing can now be replaced using tools shown in **Fig. 3.** When installing bushing, the arrow on the installer must align with arrow on the receiver, **Fig. 3.**
7. Reverse procedure to complete installation. **The control arm attaching bolt must be torqued after vehicle is lowered to floor and is in its standing height position.** Tighten attaching bolt to specifications.

TIGHTENING SPECIFICATIONS

Year	Component	Torque/Ft. Lbs.
1992-95	Axle To Body Bracket	68
	Control Arm To Underbody Nuts	①
	Hub & Bearing To Axle Bolts	37
	Shock Absorber Upper Mounting Bolt To Body	13
	Shock Absorber Upper Mounting Nut	21
	Shock Absorber Lower Mounting Bolt To Axle	35
	Stabilizer Bar To Axle Clamp Nuts To Axle	13
	Stabilizer Bar To Axle Nuts	103
	Stabilizer Bar To Control Arm Clamp Nuts	16
	Wheel Lug Nuts	100

①—Torque to 52 ft. lbs., then tighten an additional 120° rotation.

Front Suspension & Steering

INDEX

DESCRIPTION

The front suspension, **Fig. 1**, on these vehicles is of the strut and spring design. The lower control arms pivot from the lower side rails through rubber bushings. The upper end of the strut is isolated by a rubber mount incorporating a bearing for wheel turning. The tie rods connect to the steering arm on the strut, below the spring seat. The lower end of the steering knuckle pivots on a ball stud which is retained to the lower control arm by rivets and is secured to the steering knuckle with a nut and cotter pin. The sealed wheel bearings are integral with the hub and are serviced as an assembly.

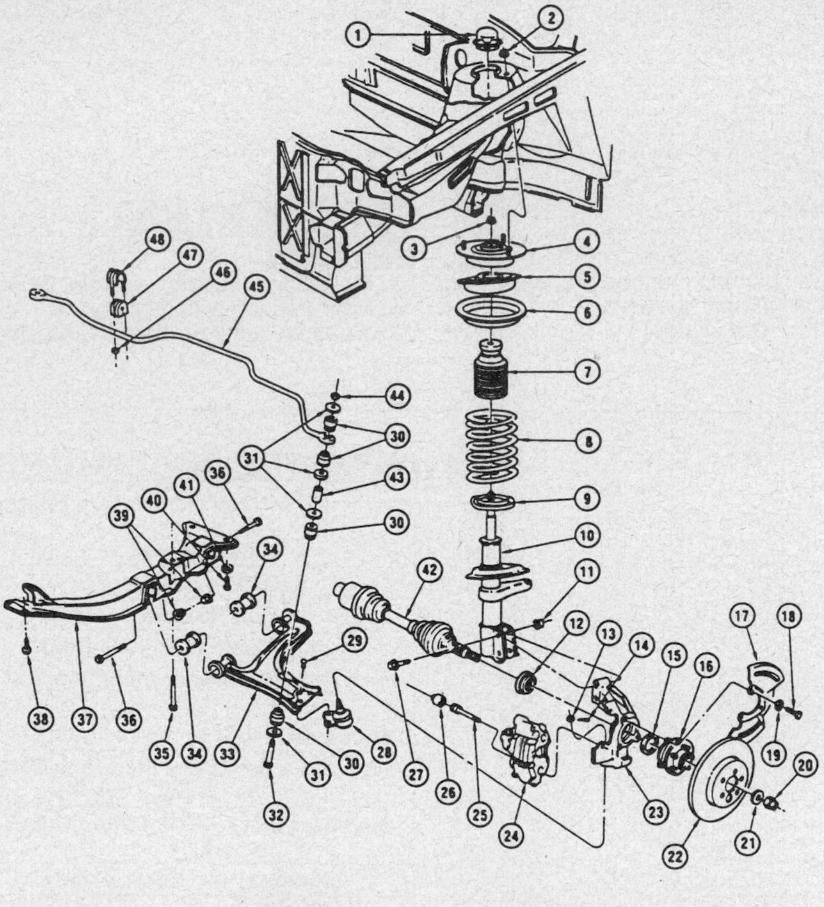

1. COVER
2. NUT
3. NUT
4. MOUNT
5. SEAT
6. INSULATOR
7. BUMPER
8. SPRING
9. INSULATOR
10. STRUT
11. NUT
12. SEAL
13. NUT
14. PIN
15. SEAL
16. HUB
17. SHIELD
18. BOLT
19. WASHER
20. NUT
21. WASHER
22. ROTOR
23. KNUCKLE
24. CALIPER
25. BOLT
26. COVER
27. BOLT
28. BALL JOINT
29. RIVET
30. GROMMET
31. WASHER
32. BOLT
33. ARM
34. BUSHING
35. BOLT
36. BOLT
37. SUPPORT
38. BOLT
39. NUT
40. BOLT
41. WASHER
42. AXLE
43. SPACER
44. NUT
45. SHAFT
46. NUT
47. INSULATOR
48. CLAMP

GC2029100159000X

Fig. 1 Exploded view of front suspension

WHEEL BEARING

REPLACE

REMOVAL

1. Raise and support vehicle.
2. Remove wheel and tire assembly, then install modified outer seal protector No. J34754 or equivalent, **Fig. 2.**
3. Insert a drift punch through the rotor, **Fig. 3,** then remove axle shaft nut and washer.
4. Remove lower ball joint cotter pin and nut, then loosen ball joint from steering knuckle using tool No. J29330 or equivalent.
5. If left hand drive axle shaft is being remove, turn wheel to right. If right hand drive axle shaft is being removed, turn wheel left.
6. Position a suitable pry bar between suspension support and lower control arm and separate lower ball joint from steering knuckle. On some models, it may be necessary to remove nut attaching link to stabilizer shaft.
7. Use tool No. J28733-A to separate drive axle shaft from hub and bearing assembly, **Fig. 4.**
8. Separate drive axle shaft from hub and wheel bearing assembly, then move strut and knuckle assembly rearward. Use wire or rope to suspend drive axle shaft from underbody. Use care not to overextend driveshaft joints.
9. Remove caliper attaching bolts and brake caliper with brake hose attached. Use wire to suspend caliper from underbody. Do not allow caliper to hang from brake hose.
10. Remove brake rotor, then hub and bearing assembly attaching bolts, **Fig. 5.**
11. Remove hub and bearing assembly.

INSTALLATION

1. Install hub and bearing assembly, **Fig. 5,** and tighten attaching bolts to specification.
2. Install brake rotor, then install caliper and torque attaching bolts to specifications.

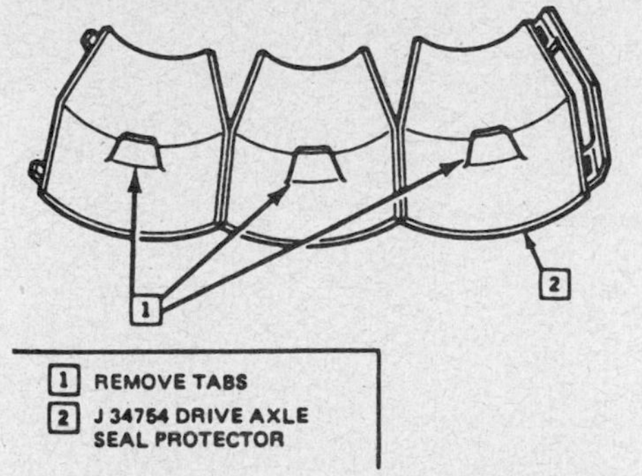
1
2
1 REMOVE TABS
2 J 34754 DRIVE AXLE SEAL PROTECTOR
GC2029100160000X

Fig. 2 Modified outer seal protector

3. Install hub and bearing seal into steering knuckle. Lubricate inner diameter of seal lips and fill cavity hub and bearing and seal with grease No. 09985254 or equivalent.
4. Install modified outer seal protector No. J34754 or equivalent, **Fig. 2,** then insert drive axle shaft into hub and bearing assembly.
5. Position lower ball joint to steering knuckle, then install lower ball joint stud nut and cotter pin.
6. Insert drift punch through rotor, **Fig. 3.**
7. Install washer and new shaft nut, and tighten shaft nut to specifications.
8. Remove drift punch and seal protector.
9. Install tire and wheel assembly, then lower vehicle and check front wheel alignment.

BALL JOINT

REPLACE

1. Raise and support vehicle.
2. Remove tire and wheel assembly, then install modified outer seal protector No. J34754 or equivalent, **Fig. 2.**
3. Remove lower ball joint cotter pin and nut, then loosen ball joint from steering knuckle using tool No. J29330 or equivalent.
4. Position a suitable pry bar between suspension support and lower control arm and separate lower ball joint from steering knuckle. On some models, it may be necessary to remove nut attaching link to stabilizer shaft.
5. Locate center of rivet body and mark with a center punch.
6. Using a 1/8 inch drill, drill pilot holes completely through the rivets. Using a 1/2 inch drill, drill final holes through rivets to ensure fitting of new ball joint.
7. Remove ball joint from lower control arm.
8. Assemble new ball joint to lower control arm with bolts provided in service package, **Fig. 6.** Tighten bolts to specifications.
9. Insert ball joint stud into steering knuckle and tighten nut to specifications, then install cotter pin.
10. Install wheel and tire and check front wheel alignment.

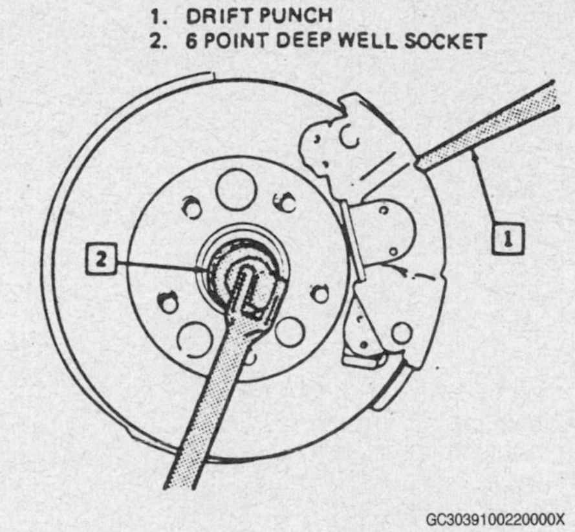
1. DRIFT PUNCH
2. 6 POINT DEEP WELL SOCKET
1
2
GC3039100220000X

Fig. 3 Drive axle shaft nut replacement

STRUT

REPLACE

1. Raise hood and remove strut protective cap and three strut to body attaching nuts.
2. Raise and support vehicle, allowing suspension to hang freely.
3. Remove wheel and tire, then install modified outer seal protector No. J-34754, or equivalent.
4. Remove tie rod end cotter pin and nut, then using tool No. J-24319-01, or equivalent, disconnect tie rod from strut assembly.
5. Scribe alignment marks on strut flange, **Fig. 7.**
6. Remove strut to steering knuckle attaching bolts, then remove strut from vehicle, **Fig. 8.** Use care not to damage spring coating.
7. Reverse procedure to install. Align marks on strut flange and steering knuckle made during removal, then tighten bolts to specifications.

STRUT SERVICE

DISASSEMBLE

1. Position strut compressor No. J-34013, or equivalent, in holding fixture J-3289-20. Use care not to damage spring coating.
2. Position strut in strut compressor, then compress strut approximately 1/2 of its height. Use care not to bottom spring or damper rod.
3. Remove nut from strut dampener shaft, then position guide rod No. J-34013-27, or equivalent, on dampener shaft. Use guide rod No. J-34013-27, or equivalent, to position dampener shaft down through bearing cap while compressing coil spring.
4. Remove components from coil strut unit, **Fig. 9.**

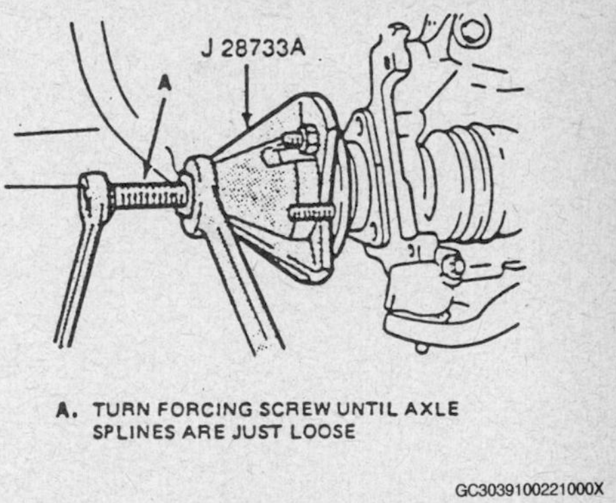
J 28733A
A
A. TURN FORCING SCREW UNTIL AXLE SPLINES ARE JUST LOOSE
GC3039100221000X

Fig. 4 Drive axle shaft from hub removal

ASSEMBLE

1. Position bearing cap on strut compressor.
2. Position strut to strut compressor and install compressor bottom locking pin.
3. Extend dampener shaft and install clamp No. J-34013-20, or equivalent, to hold shaft in position.
4. Position spring over dampener, then position strut to strut compressor upper locking pin hole and install pin. Use care not to damage spring coating.
5. Install upper insulator, shield, bumper and upper spring seat. The flat on the upper spring seat should face in the same direction as the centerline of the strut assembly spindle, **Fig. 10.**
6. Install guide rod No. J-34013-27, or equivalent, onto dampener shaft, the compress strut unit until dampener shaft threads are visible. Remove guide rod and install retaining nut.
7. While holding dampener shaft in position with a suitable wrench, torque retaining nut to specification. After tightening nut, remove clamp from dampener shaft clamp No. J-34013-20, or equivalent.

CONTROL ARM

REPLACE

1. Raise and support vehicle, then remove wheel and tire assembly.
2. Disconnect stabilizer bar at lower control arm and control arm support.
3. Using tool J-29330, separate ball joint from steering knuckle.
4. Position a suitable pry bar between suspension support and lower control arm and separate lower ball joint from steering knuckle. On some models, it may be necessary to remove nut attaching link to stabilizer shaft.
5. Remove control arm support to chassis retaining bolts and remove control arm support and control arm as an assembly, **Fig. 11.**
6. Separate control arm from support, then using tool No. J29792, or equivalent, remove bushings from control arm. Coat threads of tool with extreme pressure lubricant.
7. Lubricate new bushings and install into control arm using tool No.

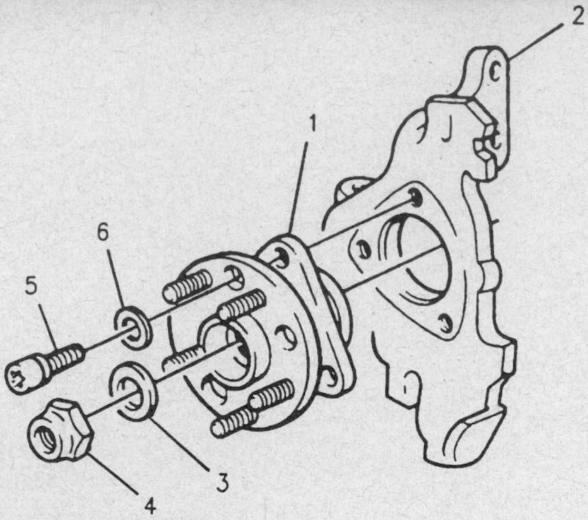
1
2
3
4
5
6

1 HUB AND BEARING ASSEMBLY
2 STEERING KNUCKLE
3 WASHER
4 DRIVE AXLE NUT – 260 N·m (192 LBS. FT.)
5 HUB AND BEARING RETAINING BOLT
6 WASHER

GC3039100222000X

Fig. 5 Front hub & wheel bearing assembly

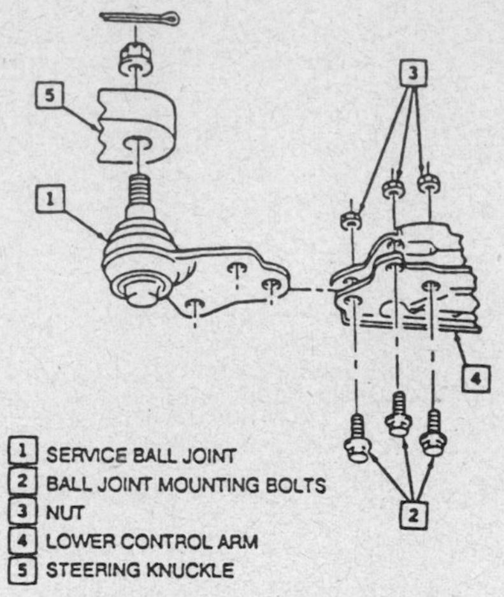
1 SERVICE BALL JOINT
2 BALL JOINT MOUNTING BOLTS
3 NUT
4 LOWER CONTROL ARM
5 STEERING KNUCKLE

GC2029100161000X

Fig. 6 Lower ball joint to lower control arm assembly

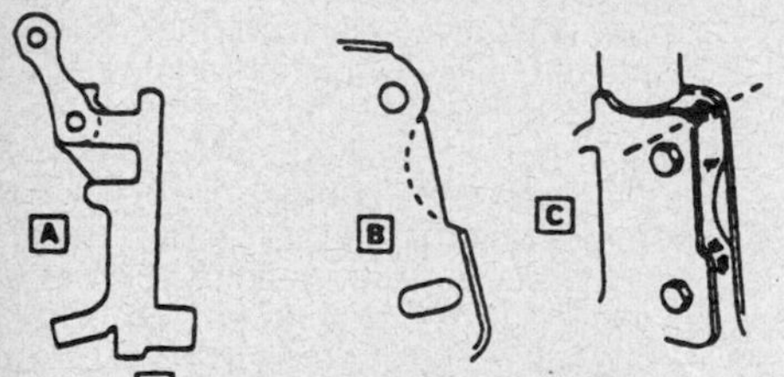
A
B
C

A SCRIBE KNUCKLE ALONG LOWER OUTBOARD STRUT RADUIS
B SCRIBE STRUT FLANGE ON INBOARD SIDE ALONG CURVE OF KNUCKLE
C SCRIBE ACROSS STRUT/KNUCKLE INTERFACE

GC2029100165000X

Fig. 7 Strut & knuckle alignment marks

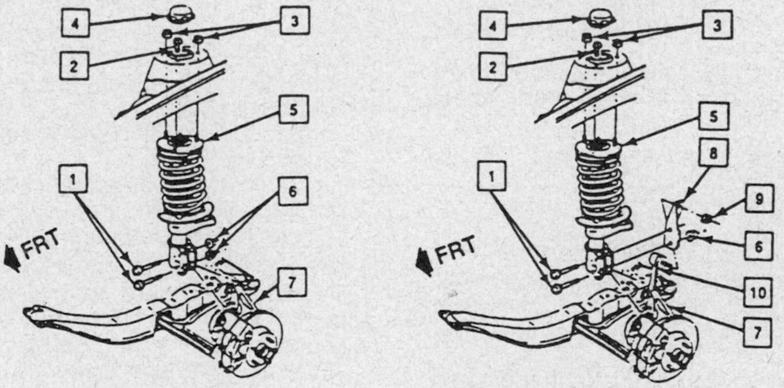
FRT
FRT

BASE SUSPENSION

DIRECT ACTING STABILIZER SUSPENSION

1. BOLT
2. BOLT
3. NUT
4. COVER, STRUT MOUNT
5. STRUT ASSEMBLY
6. NUT
7. STEERING KNUCKLE
8. BRACKET, STABILIZER LINK
9. NUT
10. STABILIZER LINK

GC2029100166000X

Fig. 8 Strut assembly replacement

J29792, or equivalent. Coat threads of tool with extreme pressure lubricant.

8. Reverse procedure to install. Check front wheel alignment and adjust as required.

STEERING KNUCKLE
REPLACE

1. Raise and support vehicle, then remove wheel and tire.
2. Remove front hub and bearing as outlined under "Wheel Bearing, Replace" procedure.
3. Remove strut to steering knuckle attaching bolts, then disconnect strut from steering knuckle.
4. Assemble strut to steering knuckle and install attaching bolts finger tight.
5. Insert ball joint stud into steering knuckle and tighten stud nut to specification, then install cotter pin.
6. Tighten strut to steering knuckle bolts to specification.
7. Reverse removal procedure to complete installation.

STABILIZER BAR
REPLACE

1. Raise and support vehicle, allowing control arms to hang freely.
2. Remove left front wheel and tire assembly.
3. Disconnect stabilizer bar at control arms and suspension support assemblies, **Figs. 12 and 13.**
4. Loosen front and remove rear and center bolts from suspension support assembly. Lower support enough to allow stabilizer bar removal.
5. Remove stabilizer bar with insulators.
6. Reverse procedure to install.

POWER STEERING GEAR
REPLACE

1. Disconnect battery ground cable.
2. Remove left hand sound insulator.
3. From under instrument panel, pull downward on steering column seal, then remove upper pinch bolt from flexible coupling.

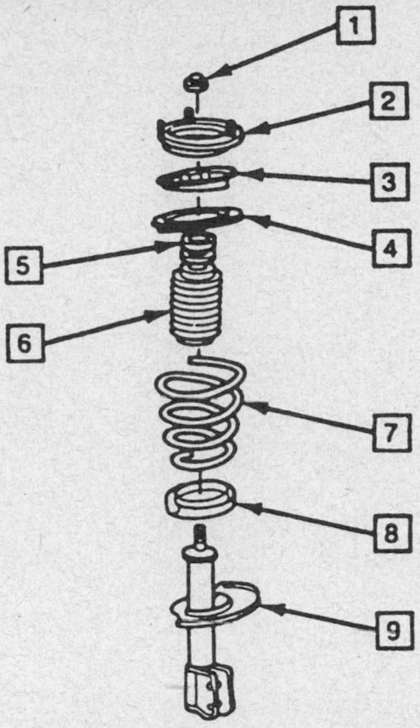
1
2
3
4
5
6
7
8
9
1 STRUT MOUNT NUT
2 STRUT MOUNT
3 SPRING SEAT
4 SPRING UPPER INSULATOR
5 JOUNCE BUMPER
6 STRUT DUST SHIELD
7 SPRING
8 SPRING LOWER INSULATOR
9 STRUT
GC2029100167000X
Fig. 9 Exploded view of strut assembly

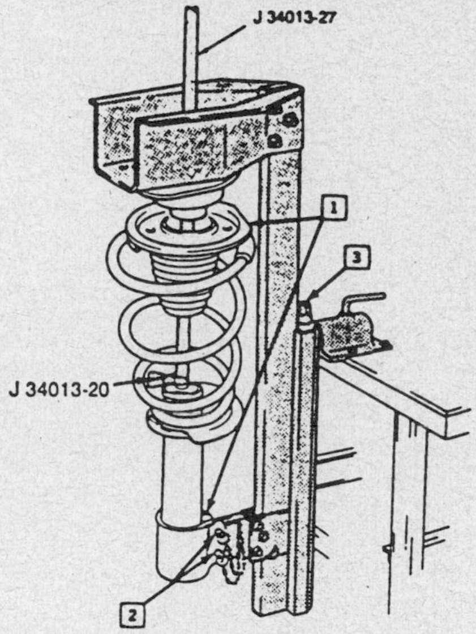
J 34013-27
J 34013-20
1
2
3
1 FLAT ON SPRING SEAT MUST FACE SAME DIRECTION AS STRUT ASSEMBLY SPINDLE
2 BOTH LOCKING PINS INSTALLED
3 COMPRESSOR FORCING SCREW
GC2029100168000X
Fig. 10 Strut unit assembly

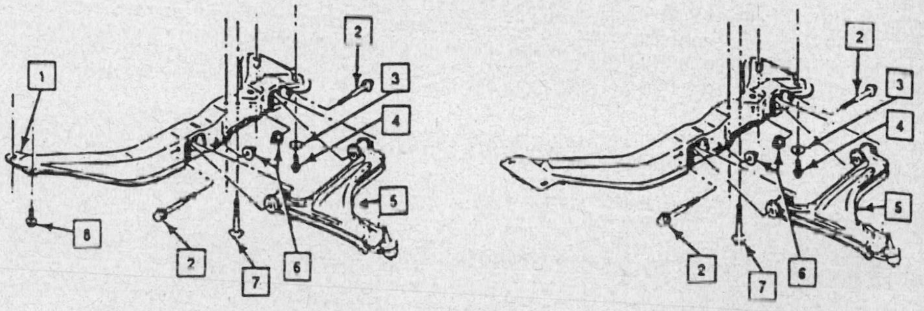
DIRECT ACTING STABILIZER SUSPENSION
BASE SUSPENSION
1. SUSPENSION SUPPORT
2. BOLT
3. WASHER
4. BOLT
5. CONTROL ARM
6. NUT
7. BOLT
8. BOLT
GC2029100162000X
Fig. 11 Lower control arm replacement

4. Remove line retainer.
5. Raise and support front of vehicle, then remove both front wheel and tire assemblies.
6. Disconnect tie rods from struts using tool No. J24319-01, or equivalent, then lower vehicle.
7. Remove steering gear mounting clamps, **Fig. 14.**
8. Disconnect power steering hydraulic lines form steering gear.
9. Move steering gear slightly forward and remove lower pinch bolt from flexible coupling, then detach coupling from steering gear stub shaft and remove dash seal.
10. Remove steering gear through left hand wheel opening.
11. Reverse procedure to install. If steering gear mounting clamp studs have backed out during removal, reinstall studs to cowl and tighten until stud is fully seated. **Torque** should not exceed 15 ft. lbs. After second reuse of studs, thread locking kit No. 1052624 must be used.

POWER STEERING PUMP

REPLACE

2.3L/4-138 ENGINE

1. Disconnect pressure and return lines from power steering pump. Allow fluid to drain into a suitable container.
2. Loosen adjusting stud, then remove outer bracket.
3. Remove drive belt from pump pulley and position aside.
4. Remove bracket to pump bolts, **Fig. 15.**
5. Remove pump and bracket assembly from vehicle. Separate pump from bracket as necessary.
6. Reverse procedure to install.

3.1L/V6-192 ENGINE

1. Remove power steering drive belt.
2. Remove nut from bracket retaining hose on alternator.
3. Remove engine mount as described under "Engine Mount, Replace" in the "3.1L/V6-192 Engine" section.
4. Remove power steering pump bolts to aid in removing power steering lines.
5. Disconnect power steering pump lines at pump, then remove pump.
6. Remove transfer pulley, if necessary.
7. Reverse procedure to install. **Torque** power steering pump mounting bolts to 20 ft. lbs.

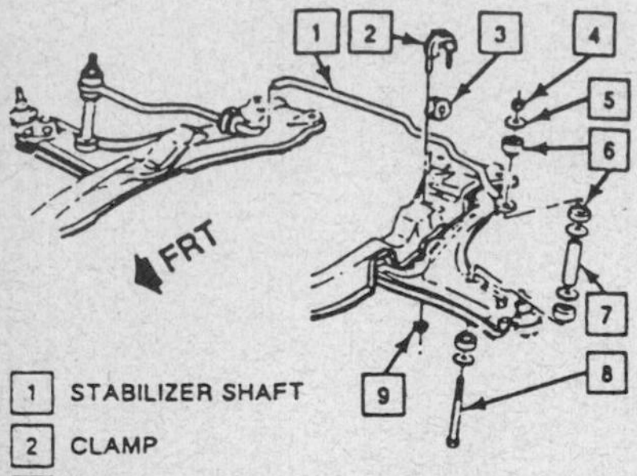
FRT

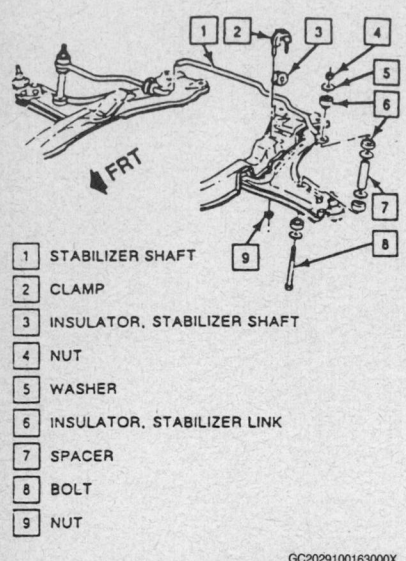

1 STABILIZER SHAFT
2 CLAMP
3 INSULATOR, STABILIZER SHAFT
4 NUT
5 WASHER
6 INSULATOR, STABILIZER LINK
7 SPACER
8 BOLT
9 NUT

GC2029100163000X

Fig. 12 Stabilizer bar installation. Less direct acting stabilizer system

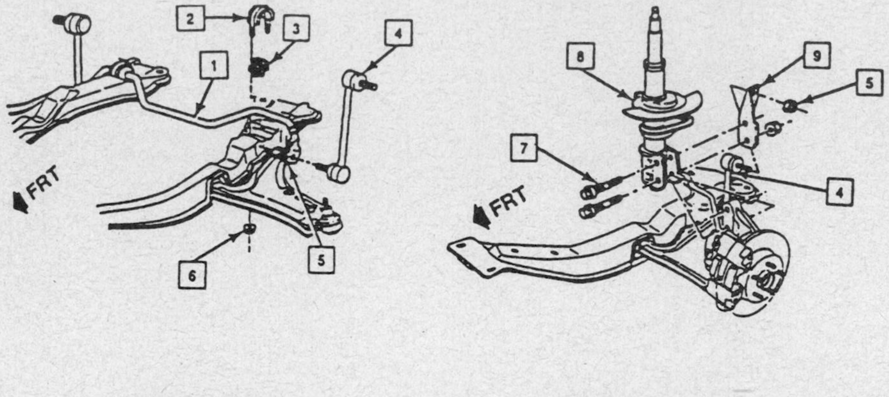
FRT
FRT

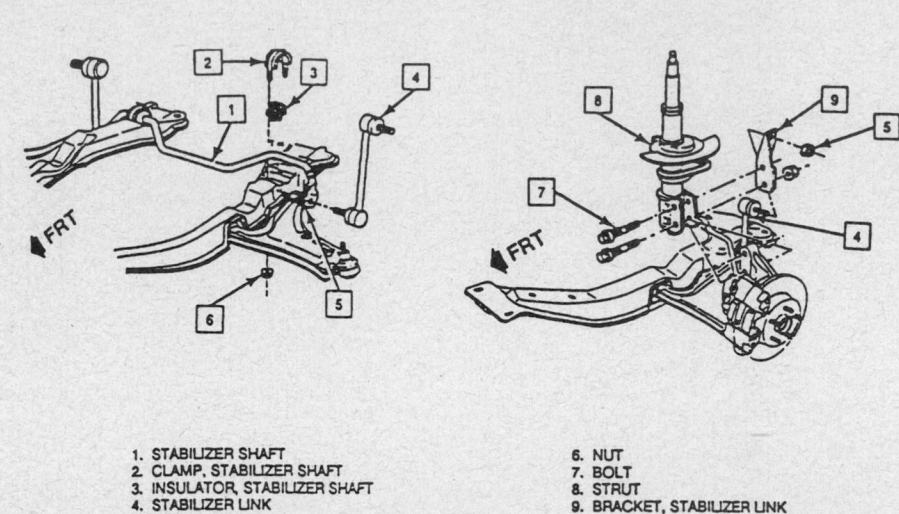

1. STABILIZER SHAFT
2. CLAMP, STABILIZER SHAFT
3. INSULATOR, STABILIZER SHAFT
4. STABILIZER LINK
5. NUT
6. NUT
7. BOLT
8. STRUT
9. BRACKET, STABILIZER LINK

GC2029100164000X

Fig. 13 Stabilizer bar installation. With direct acting stabilizer system

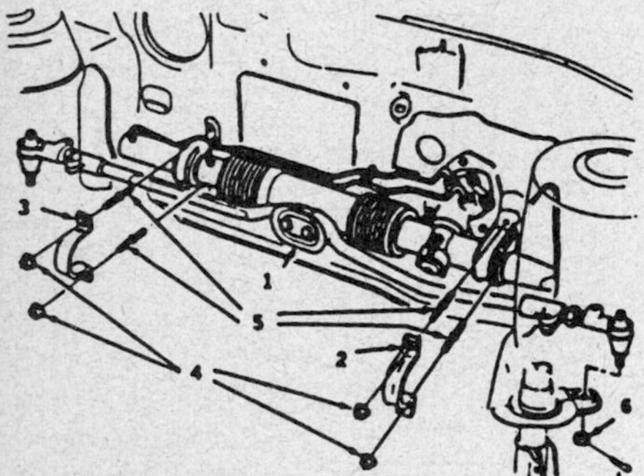

1. RACK AND PINION.
2. L.H. CLAMP - HORIZONTAL SLOT AT TOP
3. R.A. CLAMP HORIZONTAL SLOT AT TOP
4. NUT - 30 N•m (22 LBS.FT.) - HAND START ALL NUTS. TIGHTEN LEFT HAND SIDE CLAMP NUTS FIRST, THEN TIGHTEN RIGHT SIDE NUTS.
5. STUD - 20 N•m (15 LBS.FT.) AFTER SECOND REUSE OF STUD, THREAD LOCKING KIT NO.1052624 MUST BE USED.
6. NUT
7. COTTER PIN

GC2029100169000X

Fig. 14 Power rack & pinion steering gear mounting

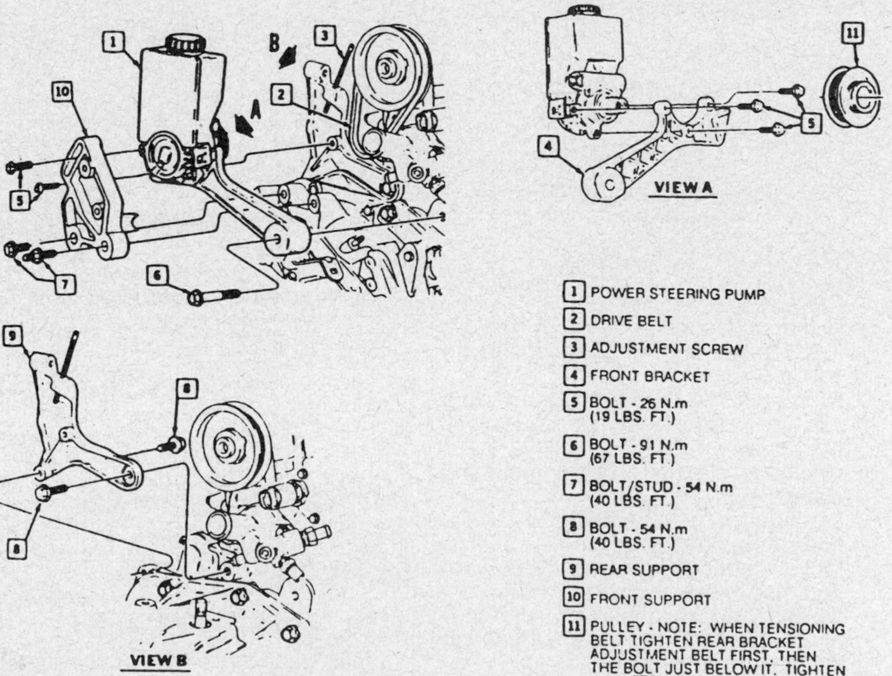
VIEW A
VIEW B

1 POWER STEERING PUMP
2 DRIVE BELT
3 ADJUSTMENT SCREW
4 FRONT BRACKET
5 BOLT - 26 N.m (19 LBS. FT.)
6 BOLT - 91 N.m (67 LBS. FT.)
7 BOLT/STUD - 54 N.m (40 LBS. FT.)
8 BOLT - 54 N.m (40 LBS. FT.)
9 REAR SUPPORT
10 FRONT SUPPORT
11 PULLEY - NOTE: WHEN TENSIONING BELT TIGHTEN REAR BRACKET ADJUSTMENT BELT FIRST, THEN THE BOLT JUST BELOW IT. TIGHTEN BOLT 6 LAST.

GC6039100048000X

Fig. 15 Power steering pump mounting. 2.3L/4-138

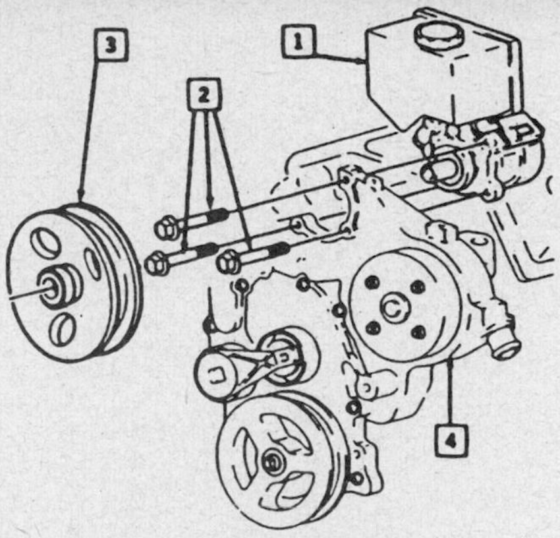
1
2
3
4
1 POWER STEERING PUMP
2 BOLT - 25 N.m (18 LBS. FT.)
3 PULLEY
4 COVER
GC6039100050000X

Fig. 16 Power steering pump mounting. 3.3L/V6-204

3.3L/V6-204 ENGINE

1. Remove drive belt.
2. Remove pump mounting bolts, **Fig. 16.**
3. Remove pump from mounting bracket.
4. Disconnect pressure and return lines from power steering pump, then remove pump. Allow fluid to drain into a suitable container.
5. Reverse procedure to install.

TIGHTENING SPECIFICATIONS

Year	Component	Torque/Ft. Lbs.
1992–95	Disc Brake Caliper Bolts	38
	Driveshaft Hub Nut	185
	Control Arm Pivot Bolt	61
	Hub & Bearing Assembly	70
	Lower Ball Joint To Knuckle	41–50
	Power Steering Line Fittings	19
	Stabilizer Shaft To Control Arm	13
	Stabilizer To Support Assembly	16
	Steering Gear Mounting Clamp	22
	Steering Coupling To Steering Column	30

Year	Component	Torque/Ft. Lbs.
1992–95 —Cont'd	Steering Coupling To Stub Shaft	30
	Steering Knuckle To Strut Assembly	133
	Strut Assembly To Body	18
	Suspension Support Assembly	①
	Strut Cartridge Retaining Nut	65
	Tie Rod End To Steering Knuckle	37
	Tie Rod (Inner) Bolts	65
	Tie Pinch Bolts	41
	Wheel Lug Nuts	100

① Torque suspension support assembly center bolts to 66 ft. lbs., front bolts to 65 ft. lbs., and rear bolts to 65 ft. lbs.

Wheel Alignment

INDEX

PRELIMINARY INSPECTION

Before measuring and setting front wheel alignment, rest front wheels on turn plates.

Before setting rear toe, rest rear wheels on slider plates or turn plates. Before setting any alignment angle, jounce the vehicle three times at each end to establish trim height.

Special adapters are available for using a magnetic hub gauge at rear wheels. Depending on type of equipment used, these may not be necessary. After removing hub cap and bearing cap, hub gauge will snap into place on brake drum. Magnetic mounting toe gauges may also be installed in the same manner.

Always perform wheel alignment on a level alignment rack. Before doing alignment, perform the following:

1. Check for worn suspension components.
2. Inspect standing curb height.
3. Remove heavy weights from trunk.
4. Inspect wheel bearings for excessive free play.
5. Ensure gas tank is full.
6. Place front seats in full rear position.
7. Check rear toe adjustment.
8. Always road test vehicle after adjusting alignment. If vehicle still pulls, switch front tires. If vehicle still pulls in same direction, check alignment and

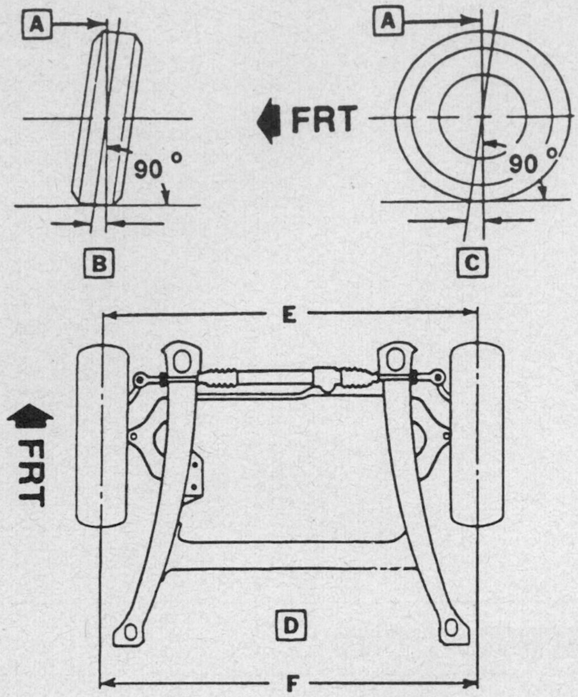
A
A
FRT
90 °
90 °
B
C
E
FRT
D
F

A CENTER OF WHEEL

B CAMBER ANGLE - LEFT FRONT VIEW

C CASTER ANGLE - LEFT SIDE VIEW

D TOE-IN - DIMENSION "E" SHOULD BE LESS THAN "F" FOR TOE-IN.

GC2049100073000X

Fig. 1 Caster, camber & toe angles

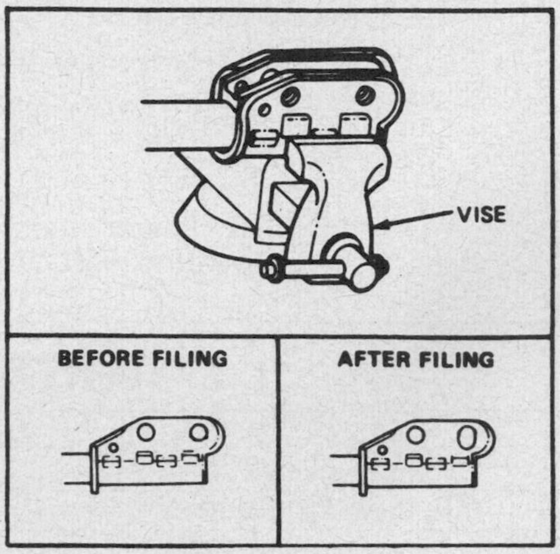
VISE
BEFORE FILING
AFTER FILING

GC2049100074000X

Fig. 2 Strut bracket modification for camber adjustment

A ADJUST TOE SETTING HERE

B LOOSEN CLAMP BOLTS TO ADJUST TOE. RETIGHTEN TO 47 N•m (35 LB. FT.)

1 OUTER TIE ROD

2 STRUT DAMPER

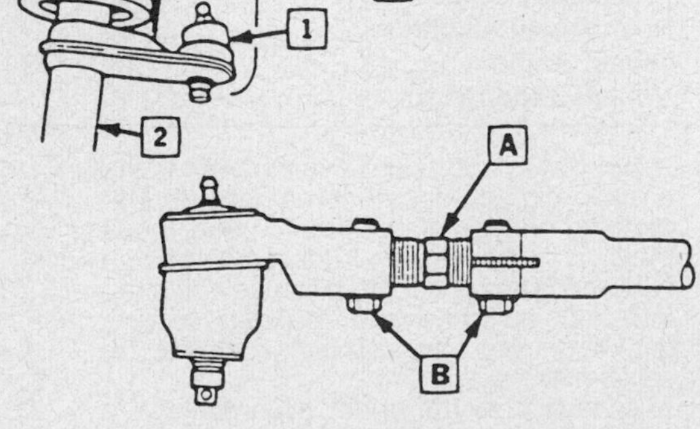
1
2
A
B

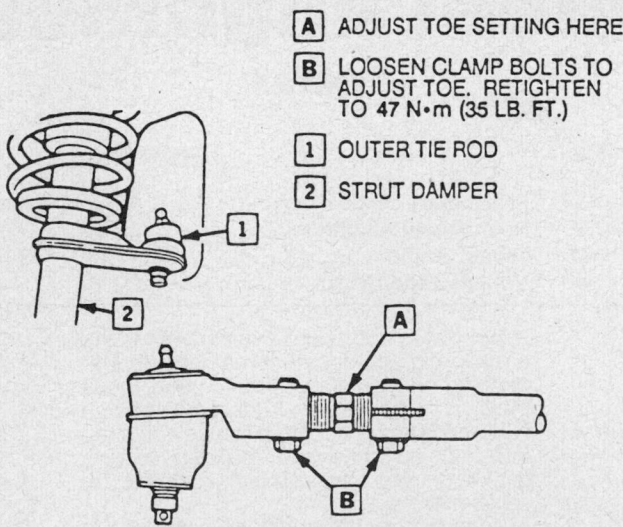

GC2049100075000X

Fig. 3 Toe adjustment

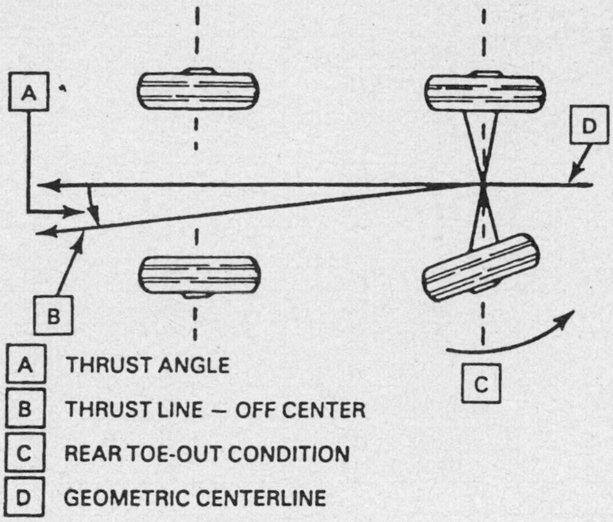
A
B
C
D
A THRUST ANGLE
B THRUST LINE – OFF CENTER
C REAR TOE-OUT CONDITION
D GEOMETRIC CENTERLINE

GC2049100076000X

Fig. 4 Thrust angle

TRIM HEIGHTS CHECKED WITH CORRECT TIRE PRESSURES, FUEL TANK FULL OR EQUIVALENT WEIGHT IN THE TRUNK. NO PASSENGERS OR ADDED WEIGHT IN CAR. FRONT SEAT IN REAR POSITION. TRUNK MUST BE EMPTY EXCEPT FOR SPARE TIRE AND JACK OR SIMULATED FUEL LOAD. MEASURE FROM KNOWN LEVEL FLOOR TO ROCKER PANEL WITH STEERING WHEEL IN THE CENTERED POSITION.

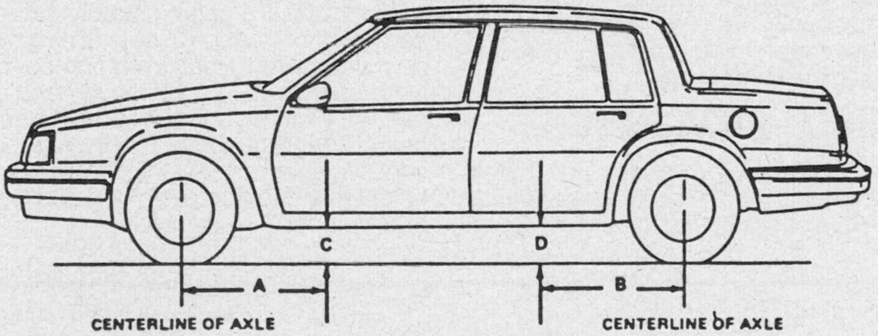
C
D
A
B
CENTERLINE OF AXLE
CENTERLINE OF AXLE

C & D DIMENSION

LIFT CENTER OF FRONT BUMPER UP APPROXIMATELY 38mm (1-½") AND LET VEHICLE SETTLE GENTLY. REPEAT TWO MORE TIMES, THEN MEASURE "C" DIMENSION. PUSH CENTER OF BUMPER DOWN 38mm (1-½") AND LET VEHICLE SETTLE GENTLY. REPEAT TWO MORE TIMES, THEN MEASURE "C" DIMENSION. THE "C" DIMENSION IS AN AVERAGE OF THE HIGH AND LOW MEASUREMENTS. REPEAT PROCEDURE ON THE REAR BUMPER FOR THE "D" DIMENSION.

GC2049200077000X

Fig. 5 Vehicle ride height measurement locations

rear tracking. If vehicle pulls in opposite direction, rotate tires, then road test again.

FRONT WHEEL ALIGNMENT

CASTER

Caster angle is not adjustable. If caster angle, **Fig. 1,** is not with in specifications, check suspension support for improper alignment and suspension components for damage. Replace damaged components as necessary.

CAMBER

Toe setting is the only adjustment normally required. However, in special circumstances, such as damage due to road hazard or collision, camber angle, **Fig. 1,** may be adjusted by modifying the strut assembly.

1. If strut is on vehicle, disconnect strut from steering knuckle. If strut is off vehicle, secure bottom of strut assembly in a suitable vise.
2. Enlarge bottom holes in outer flanges with a round file, until holes in outer flanges match slots in inner flanges, **Fig. 2.**
3. Install or connect strut to steering knuckle and install bolts finger tight.
4. Grasp top of tire firmly, then move tire inboard or outboard until correct camber reading is obtained. Tighten retaining bolts enough to secure camber setting.
5. Remove wheel and tire assembly, if necessary, then **torque** strut to steering knuckle retaining bolts to 133 ft. lbs.

Make & Model	Year	Riding Height Measurements, Inches			
		Tire Size	Dimension Z	Dimension J	Dimension K
BUICK					
Skylark	1992-93	185/75R14	13/32	9.30	9.40
		195/65R15	23/64	9.30	9.40
		205/55R16	9/32	9.30	9.40
	1994-95	P185/75R14	33/64	9.30	9.40
		P195/65R15	23/64	9.30	9.40
		P205/55R16	②	9.30	9.40
OLDSMOBILE					
Achieva	1992-93	185/75R14	13/32	9.30	9.40
		195/70R14	9/16	9.30	9.40
		195/65R15	①	9.30	9.40
		205/55R16	1/4	9.30	9.40
	1994-95	P185/75R14	15/32	9.30	9.40
		P195/65R15	23/64	9.30	9.40
		P205/55R16	9/32	9.30	9.40
PONTIAC					
Grand Am	1992-95	185/75R14	7/16	9.30	9.40
		195/70R14	19/32	9.30	9.40
		195/65R15	5/16	9.30	9.40
		205/55R16	1/4	9.30	9.40
	1994-95	P185/75R14	33/64	9.30	9.40
		P195/70R14	19/32	9.30	9.40
		P195/65R15	23/64	9.30	9.40
		P205/55R16	③	9.30	9.40

①—Achieva S models, 5/16; Achieva SL models, 15/16.

②—Except Grand Sport, 9/32 inch; Grand Sport, 5/16 inch.

③—SE models, 1/4 inch; GT models, 9/32 inch.

Fig. 6 Vehicle ride height specification

TOE

Toe, **Fig. 1,** is controlled by tie rod position. Adjustment is made by loosening the clamp bolts at the steering knuckle end of the tie rods and rotating the rods to obtain proper toe setting, **Fig. 3**. After correct toe setting is obtained, tighten clamp bolts. **Torque** clamp bolts to 41 ft. lbs.

REAR WHEEL ALIGNMENT

After front wheel alignment has been checked or adjusted, rear wheel alignment angles should be checked if vehicle still does not track properly or if excessive rear tire wear is present. Rear wheels should be parallel to and the same distance from the vehicle centerline.

Rear wheel alignment is not adjustable. If alignment angles are not within specification, check for bent or damaged suspension arms, components or underbody.

THRUST ANGLE

The vehicle is steered by the front wheels. The path the rear wheels follow is the thrust angle, **Fig. 4.** In an ideal setting, the thrust angle would be aligned with that of the vehicle center line.

VEHICLE RIDE HEIGHT

Refer to **Fig. 5** for vehicle ride height measurements and **Fig. 6** for specifications. When checking ride height measurements, fuel tank should be full, tires at should be correct pressure, front seat should be in the rearward position, trunk should be empty except for spare tire and jack and vehicle should be on level ground. If fuel tank is not full, add weight to trunk to compensate for amount fuel the vehicle is below the full level.

Prior to checking ride height, lift front bumper upward approximately 1.5 inches and gently release (3 times), then check front ride height. Push front bumper downward approximately 1.5 inches and gently release (3 times), then recheck front ride height. Average both readings to determine vehicle ride height. Check rear ride height in same manner, lifting and pushing rear bumper.

BUICK REGAL, CHEVROLET LUMINA & MONTE CARLO, OLDSMOBILE CUTLASS SUPREME & PONTIAC GRAND PRIX (W Cars)

NOTE: Refer To Rear Of This Manual For Vehicle Manufacturer's Special Service Tool Suppliers.

INDEX OF SERVICE OPERATIONS

NOTE: For Service Operations Not Listed Below, Refer To The Table Of Contents In The Front Of This Manual.

Continued

INDEX OF SERVICE OPERATIONS—CONTINUED

Specifications

GENERAL ENGINE SPECIFICATIONS

Year	Engine		Fuel System	Bore and Stroke	Compression Ratio	Net H.P. @ RPM ③	Maximum Torque Ft. Lbs. @ RPM	Normal Oil Pressure, psi
	Liter/CID ①	VIN Code ②						
1992	2.5L/4-151	R	MFI ⑩	4.00 x 3.00	8.30	110 @ 5200	135 @ 3200	26 ④
	3.1L/V6-192	T	MFI ⑩	3.50 x 3.31	8.80	135 @ 4400	180 @ 3600	15 ⑤
	3.4L/V6-204	X	MFI ⑩	3.62 x 3.31	9.25–9.50	⑨	215 @ 4000	15 ⑤
	3.8L/V6-231	L	MFI ⑩	3.80 x 3.40	8.50	170 @ 4800	220 @ 3200	60 ⑥
1993	2.2L/4-134	4	MFI ⑩	3.50 x 3.46	8.85	110 @ 5200	130 @ 3200	56 ⑦
	3.1L/V6-192	T	MFI ⑩	3.50 x 3.31	8.80	135 @ 4400	180 @ 3600	15 ⑤
	3.4L/V6-204	X	MFI ⑩	3.62 x 3.31	9.25–9.50	⑨	215 @ 4000	15 ⑤
	3.8L/V6-231	L	MFI ⑩	3.80 x 3.40	8.50	170 @ 4800	220 @ 3200	60 ⑥
1994	3.1L/V6-192	T	SFI ⑪	3.50 x 3.31	9.60	165 @ 5200	190 @ 4000	40-52 ⑧
	3.1L/V6-192	T	MFI ⑩	3.50 x 3.31	8.90	140 @ 4400	185 @ 3200	50-65 ⑨
	3.4L/V6-204	X	SFI ⑪	3.62 x 3.31	9.25	210 @ 5200	215 @ 4000	40 ⑧
	3.8L/V6-231	L	MFI ⑩	3.80 x 3.40	8.50	170 @ 4800	220 @ 3200	60 ⑥
1995	3.1L/V6-192	M	SFI ⑪	3.50 x 3.31	9.60	165 @ 5200	190 @ 4000	40-52 ⑧
	3.1L/V6-192	M	MFI ⑩	3.50 x 3.31	8.90	140 @ 4400	185 @ 3200	50-65 ⑨
	3.4L/V6-204	X	SFI ⑪	3.62 x 3.31	9.25	210 @ 5200	215 @ 4000	40 ⑧
	3.8L/V6-231	L	MFI ⑩	3.80 x 3.40	8.50	170 @ 4800	220 @ 3200	60 ⑥

①—CID-Cubic inch displacement.
②—The eighth digit of the VIN denotes engine code.
③—Ratings are net-as installed in vehicle.
④—At 800 RPM.
⑤—At 1100 RPM.
⑥—At 1850 RPM.
⑦—At 3000 RPM.
⑧—At 2000 RPM.
⑨—210 net H.P. @ 5200 RPM with manual transaxle; 200 net H.P. @ 5000 RPM with automatic transaxle.
⑩—Multi-Port fuel injection.
⑪—Sequential-Port fuel injection.

TUNE UP SPECIFICATIONS

Year & Engine, VIN Code ①	Spark Plug Gap	Ignition Timing BTDC				Curb Idle Speed②		Fast Idle Speed		Fuel Pump Pressure, Psi
		Firing Order Fig. ③	Man. Trans.	Auto. Trans.	Mark Fig.	Man. Trans.	Auto. Trans.	Man. Trans.	Auto Trans.	
1992										
2.5L/4-151 (R)	.060	⑨	—	④	⑤	—	⑥	—	⑥	26-32⑩
3.1L/V6-192 (T)	.045	⑪	④	④	⑥	⑥	⑥	⑥	⑥	40-46⑦
3.4L/V6-204 (X)	.045	⑪	④	④	⑤	⑥	⑥	⑥	⑥	40-47⑦
3.8L/V6-231(L)	.060	⑧	—	④	⑤	—	⑥	—	⑥	40-47⑦
1993										
2.2L/4-134 (4)	.045	⑨	—	④	⑤	—	⑥	—	⑥	41-47⑦
3.1L/V6-192(T)	.045	⑪	④	④	⑤	⑥	⑥	⑥	⑥	40-46⑦
3.4L/V6-204 (X)	.045	⑪	④	④	⑤	⑥	⑥	⑥	⑥	40-47⑦
3.8L/V6-231(L)	.060	⑧	—	④	⑤	—	⑥	—	⑥	40-47⑦
1994										
3.1L/V6-192(T)	.045	⑪	④	④	⑤	⑥	⑥	⑥	⑥	40-46⑦
3.4L/V6-204 (X)	.045	⑪	④	④	⑤	⑥	⑥	⑥	⑥	40-47⑦
3.8L/V6-231(L)	.060	⑧	—	④	⑤	—	⑥	—	⑥	40-47⑦
1995										
3.1L/V6-192 (M)	.045	⑪	④	④	⑤	⑥	⑥	⑥	⑥	40-46⑦
3.4L/V6-204 (X)	.045	⑪	④	④	⑤	⑥	⑥	⑥	⑥	40-47⑦
3.8L/V6-231(L)	.060	⑧	—	④	⑤	—	⑥	—	⑥	40-47⑦

BTDC: Before top dead center.

① —The eighth digit of Vehicle Identification Number (VIN) denotes engine code.

② —Idle speed on manual transmission models is adjusted in neutral. On automatic transmission models, idle is adjusted in drive. When adjusting idle speed, set parking brake and block drive wheels. Where two idle speeds are listed, the higher speed is with the idle or A/C solenoid energized.

③ —Before removing wires from distributor cap, determine location of No. 1 wire in cap, as distributor position may have been altered from that shown at the end of this chart.

④ —Computer controlled, no adjustment.

⑤ —Equipped with a crankshaft position sensor.

⑥ —Idle speed is controlled by an idle air control (IAC) valve or idle speed control (ISC) motor.

⑦ —With shop towel wrapped around fuel pressure valve to prevent fuel spillage, connect a suitable fuel pressure gauge to fuel pressure valve. Check fuel pressure with ignition switch On, engine not running.

⑧ —Cylinder numbering as viewed from front of vehicle, front bank, 1, 3, 5; rear bank, 2, 4, 6. Firing order 1-6-5-4-3-2. Two different types of computer controlled coil ignition systems are used. Refer to B and C for spark plug wire connections at coil unit.

⑨ —Cylinder numbering from front of engine, 1, 2, 3, 4. Firing order 1-3-4-2. Refer to D for spark plug wire connections at coil unit.

⑩ —Wrap shop towel around fuel hose to steel line connection in engine compartment to prevent fuel spillage. Disconnect fuel hose from steel line and install a suitable fuel pressure gauge between hose and line. Ensure gauge connections are tight, then start engine and check fuel pressure readings.

⑪ —Cylinder numbering left to right as viewed from front of vehicle, front bank, 2, 4, 6; rear bank, 1, 3, 5. Firing order 1-2-3-4-5-6. Refer to A for spark plug wire connections at coil unit.

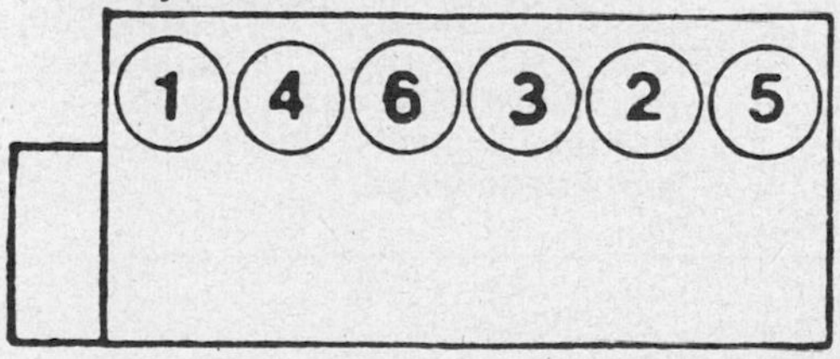
1
4
6
3
2
5
GC1139100148000X

Fig. A

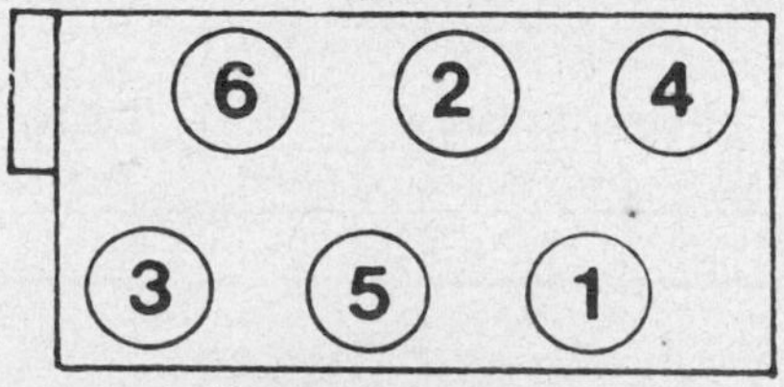
6
2
4
3
5
1
COMPUTER CONTROLLED
COIL IGNITION
GC1139100149000X

Fig. B

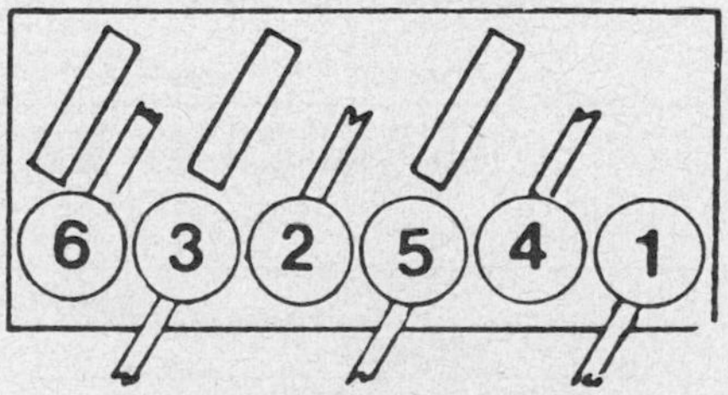
6
3
2
5
4
1
COMPUTER CONTROLLED
COIL IGNITION
GC1139100150000X

Fig. C

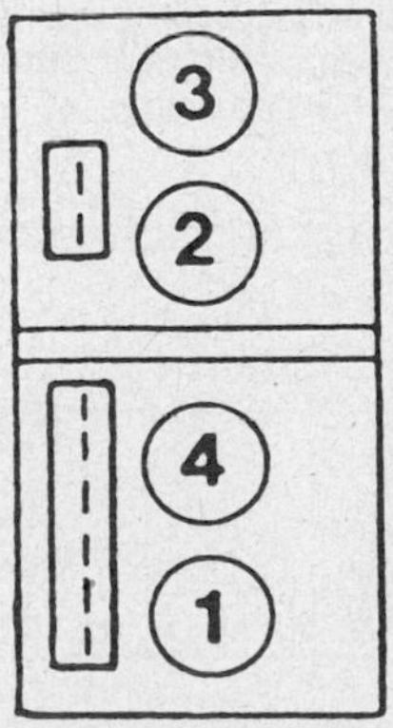
3
2
4
1
GC1139100151000X

Fig. D

FRONT WHEEL ALIGNMENT SPECIFICATIONS

Year	Model	Caster Angle, Degrees		Camber Angle, Degrees		Toe-In Degrees
		Limits	Desired	Limits	Desired	
1992–95	All	+1.5 to +2.5	+2.0	+.20 to +1.2	+.7	0

REAR WHEEL ALIGNMENT SPECIFICATIONS

Year	Model	Camber Angle, Degrees		Toe-In, Degrees
		Limits	Desired	
1992-95	14 inch tires	+.5 to +1.5	+1.0	-.1
	15 & 16 inch tires	+.27 to +.37	+.32	-.1

COOLING SYSTEM & CAPACITY DATA

Year	Model or Engine/ VIN①	Coolant Capacity, Qts.		Radiator Cap Relief Pressure, psi.	Thermo. Opening Temp.°F	Fuel Tank Gals.	Engine Oil Refill Qts.	Transaxle Oil	
		Less A/C	With A/C					Manual Transaxle Pts.	Auto. Transaxle Qts. ②
1992	2.5L/4-151(R)	9.1	9.1	15	195	16.0	4③	4.2	⑥
	3.1L/V6-192(T)	12.0	12.0	15	195	16.0	4③	4.2	⑥
	3.4L/V6-204 (X)	12.6	12.6	15	195	16.0	6⑦	4.2	⑥
1993	2.2L/4-134(4)	11.7	11.7	15	195	17.1	4③	—	④
	3.1L/V6-192(T)	12.0	12.0	15	195	16.0	4③	4.2	⑥
	3.4L/V6-204 (X)	12.6	12.6	15	195	16.0	6⑦	4.2	⑥
	3.8L/V6-231(L)	11.1	11.1	15	195	16.0	4③	—	⑤
1994	3.1L/V6-192(T)	12.0	12.0	15	195	16.0	4③	4.2	⑥
	3.4L/V6-204 (X)	12.6	12.6	15	195	16.0	6⑦	4.2	⑥
	3.8L/V6-231(L)	11.1	11.1	15	195	16.0	4③	—	⑥
1995	3.1L/V6-192 (M)	12.7	12.7	15	195	16.0	4③	4.2	⑥
	3.4L/V6-204 (X)	12.6	12.6	15	195	16.0	5③	4.2	⑥
	3.8L/V6-231(L)	11.1	11.1	15	195	16.0	4③	—	⑥

①—The eight digit of vehicle identification number (VIN) denotes engine code.

②—Capacity approximate. Make final check with dipstick and add fluid as necessary.

③—Additional oil may be required to bring oil level to full mark when changing oil filter.

④—Drain & refill, 6 qts.; total capacity, 9 qts.

⑤—Drain & refill, 6 qts.; total capacity, 8 qts.

⑥—THM 3T40 transaxle, drain & refill, 4 qts.; total capacity, 7 qts.; THM 4T60, drain & refill, 6 qts.; total capacity, 8 qts.; THM 4T60-E, drain & refill, 7.4 qts.; total capacity, 10 qts.

⑦—With filter change.

LUBRICANT DATA

Year	Model	Lubricant Type			
		Transaxle			
		Manual	Automatic	Power Steering	Brake System
1992–95	All	GM Synchromesh Transmission Fluid	Dexron IIE	GM Type Power Steering Fluid	DOT 3

Electrical

NOTE: On Air Bag Equipped Models, Refer To "Air Bag System Precautions" Located In The Front Of This Manual For System Disarming & Arming Procedures.

INDEX

PRECAUTIONS

AIR BAG SYSTEMS

Refer to "Air Bag System Precautions" in the front of this manual for system disarming and arming procedures.

FUSE PANEL & FLASHER LOCATION

On all models, the fuse panel is located behind the instrument panel, under the glove compartment. The turn signal flasher is located under the instrument panel, to the right of the steering column. The hazard warning flasher is located in the convenience center, under the glove box assembly.

RELAY CENTER LOCATION

The relay centers are located on both sides of the instrument panel, under the dash.

STARTER

REPLACE

2.2L/4-134 & 2.5L/4-151 ENGINES

1. Disconnect battery ground cable.
2. Raise and support vehicle.
3. Remove flywheel cover attaching bolts, then the cover.
4. Remove stud from starter motor bracket.
5. Remove starter motor attaching bolts, lower starter and disconnect starter wiring.
6. Remove starter motor, then the bracket from starter.
7. Reverse procedure to install, noting the following:
   a. When removing starter, note if any shims are used between starter and mounting surface. If shims are found, reinstall in original location.
   b. **Torque** starter motor attaching bolts to 32 ft. lbs.
   c. **Torque** starter motor bracket stud to 18 ft. lbs.

3.1L/V6-192 ENGINE

1. Disconnect battery ground cable.
2. Remove air cleaner assembly.
3. Raise and support vehicle.
4. **On models with engine oil cooler,** proceed as follows:
   a. Position a suitable drain pan under vehicle, then remove oil filter.
   b. Position hose next to starter motor aside.
5. **On all models,** remove nut attaching starter brace to A/C compressor.
6. Remove nut attaching starter brace to engine, then the brace.
7. Remove bolts attaching flywheel inspection cover, then the cover.
8. Remove starter motor attaching bolts, lower starter and disconnect starter wiring.
9. Remove starter motor and shims (if used).
10. Reverse procedure to install, noting the following:
    a. When removing starter, note if any shims are used between starter and mounting surface. If shims are found, reinstall in original location.
    b. **Torque** startor motor attaching bolts to 32 ft. lbs.
    c. **Torque** starter brace nuts to 22 ft. lbs.
    d. **On models with oil cooler,** check engine oil level, adding oil as necessary.

3.4L/V6-204 ENGINE

Manual Transaxle

1. Disconnect battery ground cable.
2. Remove air cleaner assembly.
3. Raise and support vehicle.
4. Place a suitable drain pan under vehicle and remove oil filter.
5. Disconnect electrical connections from oil pressure sensor.
6. Disconnect the crank sensor wire from ignition module.
7. Remove oil cooler adapter stud and set oil cooler aside.
8. Disconnect starter electrical connections.
9. Remove starter mounting bolts and starter.
10. Reverse procedure to install, **Torquing** starter bolts to 32 ft. lbs.

Automatic Transaxle

1. Disconnect battery ground cable.
2. Remove air cleaner assembly.
3. Raise and support vehicle.
4. Place a suitable drain pan under vehicle and remove oil filter.
5. Disconnect electrical connections from oil pressure sensor.
6. Disconnect the crank sensor wire from ignition module.
7. Remove oil cooler adapter stud and

set oil cooler aside.
8. Remove wiring harness from bell-housing clamp and lower radiator tie bar.
9. Disconnect power steering oil cooler lines from front crossmember.
10. Remove flywheel inspection cover.
11. Disconnect electrical connections from starter. **Disconnect and move electrical connections on cooling fan if necessary to gain access.**
12. Remove starter mounting bolts and starter assembly from vehicle.
13. Reverse procedure to install, **Torquing** starter mounting bolts to 32 ft. lbs.

3.8L/V6-231 ENGINE

1. Disconnect battery ground cable.
2. Remove cooling fan assembly.
3. Remove serpentine drive belt.
4. Remove A/C compressor upper support brace.
5. Lay A/C compressor in fan opening.
6. Raise and support vehicle.
7. Disconnect engine oil cooler lines at flex connection.
8. Remove bolts from flywheel inspection cover.
9. Remove bolts from starter.
10. Disconnect starter motor wiring.
11. Remove starter motor.
12. Reverse procedure to install, **Torquing** starter motor attaching bolts to 32 ft. lbs.

ALTERNATOR

REPLACE

2.2L/4-134 & 2.5L/4-151 ENGINES

The CS130 alternator cannot be serviced and must be replaced as an assembly.

1. Disconnect battery ground cable.
2. Remove serpentine belt, then rear bracket/heat shield nuts from exhaust manifold.
3. Remove rear bracket/heat shield bolts from engine block.
4. Disconnect electrical connectors from alternator.
5. Remove front attaching bolts to alternator, then the alternator.
6. Reverse procedure to install.

3.1LV6-192 ENGINE

1. Disconnect battery ground cable.
2. Remove serpentine belt at alternator assembly.
3. Remove bolts from alternator assembly.
4. Remove power steering gear clip and nut.
5. Remove alternator stud, then disconnect alternator wiring.
6. Loosen alternator front and rear braces from upper intake manifold.
7. Remove alternator assembly.
8. Reverse procedure to install.

3.4L/V6–204 ENGINE

1. Disconnect battery ground cable, then remove air cleaner assembly.
2. Remove coolant recovery tank, then serpentine belt.
3. Disconnect power steering gear pipes from clip mounted to upper alternator stud.
4. Remove alternator upper stud.
5. Raise and support vehicle, then remove right side tire and wheel assembly.
6. Remove right side engine splash shield, then front exhaust pipe and converter.
7. Remove alternator cooling duct, if equipped.
8. Loosen alternator rear brace.
9. Disconnect intermediate shaft lower pinch bolt at steering gear.
10. Install suitable jack to support engine, then remove rear cradle bolts.
11. Remove steering gear heat shield assembly.
12. Disconnect electrical connector from alternator regulator terminal.
13. Disconnect electrical connector from speed sensor.
14. Remove power steering gear pipe clip from steering gear.
15. Disconnect power steering gear inlet hose assembly from steering gear.
16. Remove alternator assembly.
17. Reverse procedure to install.

3.8L/V6–231 ENGINE

The CS130 alternator cannot be serviced and must be replaced as an assembly.

1. Disconnect battery ground cable.
2. Remove serpentine belt, then disconnect alternator electrical connections.
3. Remove bolts from alternator, then the alternator
4. Reverse procedure to install.

IGNITION LOCK

REPLACE

1. Disconnect battery ground cable.
2. Remove steering column from vehicle. On vehicles with tilt column, column should be tilted to the full up position for removal.
3. Remove and discard two lower spring retainers.
4. Remove lower bearing spring and lower bearing seat.
5. Remove nut retainer and jam nut, then the steering wheel.
6. Remove cancel cam assembly, then the hazard knob screw and hazard warning knob.
7. Position turn signal switch so that turn signal switch screws and housing screw can be removed through opening in switch.
8. Remove housing screw and column housing cover, then the turn signal switch screws.
9. Remove wiring protector from opening in instrument panel bracket on jacket assembly and separate from wires.
10. Disconnect pivot/pulse switch connector then remove the pivot screw and pivot/pulse switch assembly.
11. Disconnect turn signal switch connector from ignition and dimmer switch assembly connector.
12. Disconnect 17 way secondary lock from turn signal connector.
13. Using terminal remover tool No. J-35689-A or equivalent, disconnect wires on buzzer switch from turn signal connector and wrap wire ends with tape.
14. Remove turn signal switch assembly from column.
15. Remove and discard two lower spring retainers.
16. Remove lower bearing spring and seat.
17. Remove adapter screws then the adapter and bearing assembly.
18. **On models with tilt columns,** proceed as follows:
    a. Insert Phillips head screwdriver into square opening in spring retainer, push down and turn left to release retainer and wheel tilt spring.
    b. Remove spring retainer, tilt spring and tilt spring guide.
    c. Using pivot pin remover tool No. J-21854-01 or equivalent, remove two pivot pins.
19. **On all models,** place lock cylinder in Run position.
20. **On models with tilt column,** pull tilt lever to release steering column housing. Remove the steering shaft assembly and steering column housing as a complete unit.
21. **On non-tilt models,** proceed as follows:
    a. Place opening in retaining ring over flat on steering shaft.
    b. Remove retaining ring using a suitable screwdriver.
    c. Remove thrust washer, upper bearing spring and washer.
    d. Remove steering shaft from lower end of jacket and bowl assembly.
    e. Remove housing screws and steering column housing.
    f. Remove housing spacer the bearing using a suitable drift. Discard bearing.
22. **On all models,** place lock cylinder in Off-Lock position and remove key.
23. Remove buzzer switch by lifting switch tab with screwdriver and pulling gently on wires.
24. Remove lock retaining screw and the lock cylinder.
25. Reverse procedure to install, noting the following:
    a. **Torque** lock retaining screw to 22 inch lbs.
    b. **Torque** steering column housing screws to 88 inch lbs.
    c. **Torque** turn signal switch and column housing cover screws to 35 inch lbs.
    d. **Torque** hazard knob screw to 7 inch lbs.
    e. **Torque** jam nut to 30 ft. lbs.
    f. Install new lower spring retainers, compressing spring until retainers are positioned 1.14 inch from lower end of steering shaft.

IGNITION SWITCH

REPLACE

REMOVAL

1. Place shift lever in P position and the

lock cylinder in Off-Lock position.
2. Disconnect battery ground cable.
3. Remove steering column from vehicle.
4. Disconnect turn signal switch connector from ignition and dimmer switch assembly connector.
5. Disconnect pivot and pulse switch connector from ignition and dimmer switch connector.
6. Remove bowl shield screw, bowl shield nut and the bowl shield.
7. Remove dimmer and ignition switch assembly as follows:
   a. Remove dimmer switch nut, then the upper mounting stud.
   b. Remove dimmer switch, then the dimmer switch actuator rod.
   c. Remove lower mounting stud, then the ignition switch from ignition switch actuator rod.

INSTALLATION

Lock cylinder set must be in the Off-Lock position when installing ignition switch to insure proper switch slider positioning.

1. Place ignition switch slider in far left position and move back one detent to right, then insert a 3/32 inch drill bit in adjustment hole on ignition switch to hold switch slider in proper position during installation.
2. Install ignition switch to switch rod.
3. Install ignition switch to steering column jacket assembly with lower mounting stud, **Torquing** to 35 inch lbs.
4. Remove adjustment tool from ignition switch.
5. Install dimmer switch actuator rod through hole in instrument panel bracket and into hole in dimmer switch rod cap.
6. Install dimmer switch assembly on lower mounting stud with dimmer switch nut and upper mounting stud but do not tighten.
7. To adjust dimmer switch, insert a 3/32 inch drill bit and push switch against actuator rod to remove all lash.
8. **Torque** dimmer switch nut and upper mounting stud to 35 inch lbs., then remove adjustment tool from dimmer switch.
9. Install bowl shield to column bowl and upper mounting stud, then install shield screw, **Torquing** to 35 inch lbs.
10. Install bowl shield nut, **Torquing** to 35 inch lbs.
11. Connect turn signal switch connector to ignition and dimmer switch assembly connector and snap in place.
12. Connect pivot and pulse switch connector to ignition and dimmer switch connector.
13. Install steering column and connect battery ground cable.

NEUTRAL SAFETY SWITCH

REPLACE

1. Place vehicle in N.
2. Disconnect battery ground cable, then raise and support vehicle.

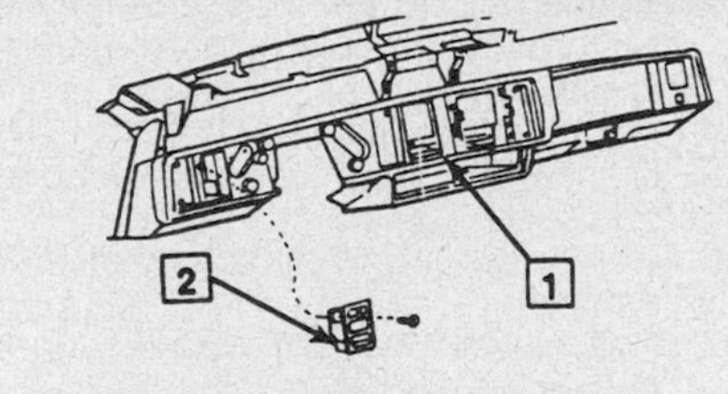
2
1
1- INSTRUMENT PANEL CARRIER
2- HEADLIGHT SWITCH
GC9049300114000X

Fig. 1 Headlamp switch removal. 1994–95

3. Disconnect electrical connector.
4. Remove switch harness from two retention clips, then lower vehicle.
5. Disconnect vacuum lines and electrical connector at cruise control servo, if equipped.
6. Detach servo, if equipped, and position out of way.
7. Disconnect shift lever at transaxle. Do not disconnect lever from cable.
8. Remove switch.
9. Reverse procedure to install, noting the following:
   a. Align groove on inner sleeve of switch with groove on switch body.
   b. **Torque** switch attaching bolts to 18 ft. lbs.
   c. **Torque** shift lever attaching nut to 15 ft. lbs.
   d. **Torque** cruise control servo retaining nut to 27 inch lbs.

HEADLAMP SWITCH

REPLACE

1992–93

Cutlass Supreme

1. Disconnect battery ground cable.
2. Remove five Phillips head screws at top of trim plate and pull top of trim plate out.
3. Starting at either side, carefully pull bottom of trim plate to release five spring clips.
4. Remove trim plate.
5. Remove two screws securing left air outlet trim plate.
6. Remove left air outlet trim plate by pulling carefully at bottom to release spring clips.
7. Disconnect electrical connector.
8. Remove headlight switch retaining screws and the switch.
9. Reverse procedure to install.

Grand Prix

1. Remove screw from instrument panel, under switch.
2. Remove switch assembly by carefully pulling out to release two spring clips at top.
3. Reverse procedure to install.

Lumina

1. Disconnect battery ground cable.
2. Remove left instrument panel trim plate by pulling rearward to disengage retaining clips.
3. Remove two switch assembly attaching screws, pull switch out far enough to disconnect wiring connectors, then remove switch assembly.
4. Reverse procedure to install.

Regal

1. Disconnect battery ground cable.
2. Carefully pry off speaker grilles.
3. Remove screw from under each speaker grille.
4. Remove five screws from under lower edge of instrument panel pad.
5. Remove pad by lifting front and pulling rearward to release, then lifting up and out.
6. Remove cluster trim plate attaching screw and the trim plate.
7. Remove four switch assembly attaching bolts and the switch assembly.
8. Reverse procedure to install.

1994–95

1. Disconnect battery ground cable.
2. Remove instrument panel trim plate.
3. Remove headlight switch mounting bolts, then the switch, **Fig. 1.**
4. Reverse procedure to install.

STOP LIGHT SWITCH

REPLACE

1. Disconnect battery ground cable.
2. Remove left side sound insulator panel.
3. Slide steering shaft protective sleeve toward front of dash.
4. Disconnect air distribution tube and pull down.
5. Remove retainer pin which holds stop light switch to steering column bracket.
6. Disconnect switch arm from pedal by pushing arm over and off of brake pedal pin.
7. Release switch by pulling down and releasing top snap clip.
8. Remove connector position assurance locking pins from four wire and two wire connector.
9. Disconnect two wire and four wire connectors.
10. Reverse procedure to install, then adjust switch as follows:
    a. Depress brake pedal as far as possible and hold.
    b. Using a stiff wire with a hooked end, gently pull on switch set lever and listen for an audible click.
11. Install left sound insulator panel.

TURN SIGNAL SWITCH

REPLACE

1. Disconnect battery ground cable.
2. Remove nut retainer and jam nut, then the steering wheel.
3. Remove turn signal cancel cam assembly.
4. Remove hazard knob screw and the hazard warning knob.
5. Position turn signal switch so that turn signal switch screws and housing screw can be removed through openings in switch.
6. Remove housing screw and the column housing cover.

7. **On models with tilt columns,** remove shoe pin retainer cap.
8. **On all models,** remove pivot switch screw and the pivot and pulse switch assembly.
9. Remove turn signal switch screws.
10. Remove wiring protector from opening in instrument panel bracket on jacket assembly and separate from wires.
11. Disconnect turn signal switch connector from ignition and dimmer switch assembly connector.
12. Disconnect 17 way lock from turn signal connector.
13. Using terminal remover tool No. J-35689-A, or equivalent, disconnect wires on buzzer switch assembly from turn signal connector.
14. Remove turn signal switch assembly from column.
15. Reverse procedure to install, noting the following:
    a. **Torque** turn signal switch and column housing cover screws to 35 inch lbs.
    b. **Torque** pivot switch screw to 20 inch lbs.
    c. **Torque** hazard knob screw to 7 inch lbs.
    d. **Torque** jam nut to 30 ft. lbs.

DIMMER SWITCH

REPLACE

Refer to "Ignition Switch, Replace" for procedure.

STEERING WHEEL

REPLACE

1. Disconnect battery ground cable.
2. Remove trim plate and retainer.
3. Disconnect horn wire from cam tower.
4. Turn ignition switch to On position.
5. Scribe an alignment mark on steering wheel hub inline with slash mark on steering shaft.
6. Loosen steering wheel nut, positioning it flush with end of shaft.
7. Using a suitable puller, loosen steering wheel. **When removing a steering wheel with accessory controls in the hub, use caution to avoid damaging the electronic circuits. Steering wheel puller bolts should be turned in no more than four to six threads to avoid contact with the electronic circuits.**
8. Remove steering shaft nut and steering wheel.
9. Reverse procedure to install, aligning scribe mark and **Torquing** steering shaft nut to 30 ft. lbs.

INSTRUMENT CLUSTER

REPLACE

1992–93

Cutlass Supreme

1. Disconnect battery ground cable.
2. Remove five Phillips head screws at top of trim plate and pull top of trim plate out.
3. Starting at either side, carefully pull bottom of trim plate to release five spring clips.
4. Remove trim plate.
5. Disconnect shift indicator cable, if equipped.
6. Remove four bolts attaching cluster to carrier.
7. Pull cluster forward and disconnect cluster connector.
8. Remove cluster.
9. Reverse procedure to install.

Grand Prix

1. Disconnect battery ground cable.
2. Remove two screws at top of instrument cluster trim plate.
3. Remove two Phillips head screws from under glove compartment.
4. remove two Phillips head screws connecting door hinges to instrument panel.
5. Open glove compartment door, holding at bottom, then lift door up and pull out to release door stops.
6. Remove three Phillips head screws at top of glove compartment.
7. Remove two Phillips head screws holding plastic clips under compartment.
8. Slide glove compartment out of instrument panel.
9. Disconnect electrical connectors for light and trunk release switch.
10. Remove one screw above glove compartment, then lift front of pad and pull rearward to release clips.
11. Remove four instrument cluster attaching screws.
12. Lift cluster and disconnect electrical connector, then remove cluster.
13. Reverse procedure to install.

Lumina

1. Disconnect battery ground cable.
2. Remove instrument panel pad as follows:
    a. Remove five screws from under lower edge of instrument panel pad.
    b. Remove pad by lifting front and pulling rearward to release, then lifting up and out.
3. Disconnect electrical connectors from cluster.
4. Remove three cluster attaching screws, disconnect shift indicator cable, then remove cluster assembly.
5. Reverse procedure to install.

Regal

1. Disconnect battery ground cable.
2. Carefully pry off speaker grilles.
3. Remove screw from under each speaker grille.
4. Remove five screws from under lower edge of instrument panel pad.
5. Remove pad by lifting front and pulling rearward to release, then lifting up and out.
6. Remove cluster trim plate attaching screw and the trim plate.
7. Disconnect electrical connector at cluster.
8. Remove six cluster attaching bolts and the cluster.
9. Reverse procedure to install.

1994–95

1. Disconnect battery ground cable.
2. Remove air cleaner assembly.
3. Remove instrument pad cover and instrument cluster trim plate.
4. Remove LH sound insulator.
5. Remove steering column trim panel.
6. Remove shift control cable at bracket and lever.
7. Remove shift indicator cable.
8. Disconnect electrical connectors, then remove cluster mounting bolts and instrument cluster.
9. Reverse procedure to install. **Torque** cluster mounting bolts to 18 inch lbs.

RADIO

REPLACE

CUTLASS SUPREME

1. Disconnect battery ground cable.
2. Remove radio mounting screws.
3. Pull radio out far enough to disconnect antenna, speaker and electrical connectors, then remove radio.
4. Reverse procedure to install.

GRAND PRIX

1. Remove steering column trim cover as follows:
    a. Disconnect ALDL connector from trim cover.
    b. Remove attaching screws from bottom of trim cover.
    c. Remove cover by carefully pulling rearward to disengage from three retaining clips on top of cover.
2. Remove bolts from left side of accessory trim plate.
3. Open glove compartment door, remove bolts from right side of accessory trim plate, then the trim plate.
4. Remove bolts attaching top of radio and nuts attaching bottom of radio.
5. Pull radio out and disconnect electrical and antenna connectors, then remove radio.
6. Reverse procedure to install.

LUMINA & MONTE CARLO

1. Remove right side instrument panel trim plate by unsnapping from instrument panel carrier.
2. Remove two screws retaining radio and pull out far enough to disconnect antenna, speaker and electrical connectors, then remove radio.
3. Reverse procedure to install.

REGAL

1. Disconnect battery ground cable.
2. Remove right sound insulator.
3. Remove bolt holding courtesy lamp, then courtesy lamp and connector.
4. Remove radio receiver mounting screws, then disconnect electrical and antenna connectors.
5. Remove radio receiver.
6. Reverse procedure to install.

WIPER MOTOR

REPLACE

1. Remove module as previously out-

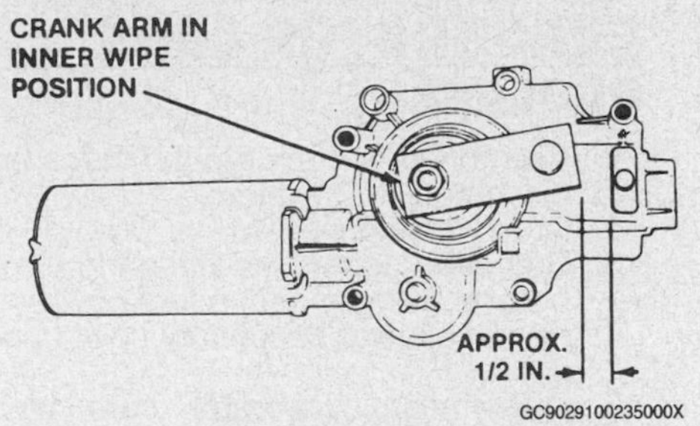
CRANK ARM IN
INNER WIPE
POSITION
APPROX.
1/2 IN.
GC9029100235000X

Fig. 2 Placing crank arm in inner wipe position

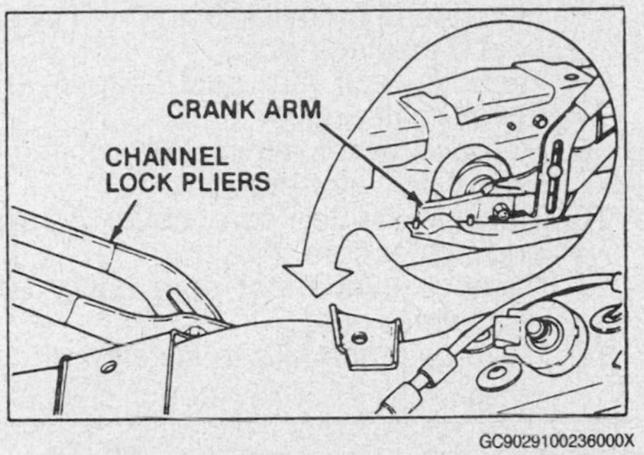
CRANK ARM
CHANNEL
LOCK PLIERS
GC9029100236000X

Fig. 3 Crank arm to inner wipe position

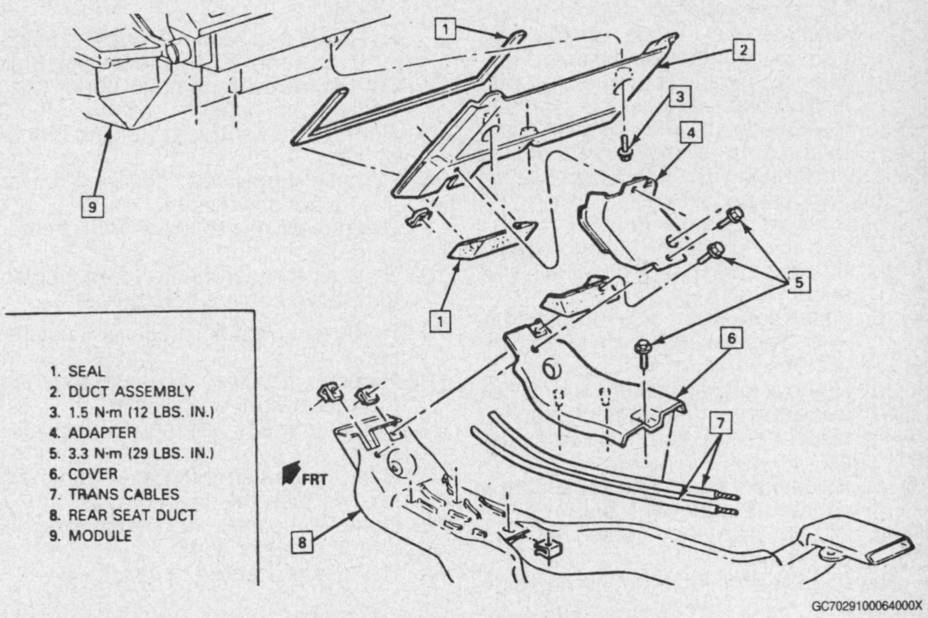
1. SEAL
2. DUCT ASSEMBLY
3. 1.5 N·m (12 LBS. IN.)
4. ADAPTER
5. 3.3 N·m (29 LBS. IN.)
6. COVER
7. TRANS CABLES
8. REAR SEAT DUCT
9. MODULE
FRT
GC7029100064000X

Fig. 4 Heater core removal

lined.

2. Remove crank arm from motor. **Do not remove crank arm from transmission.**
3. Reverse procedure to install, **torquing** crank arm nut to 25-38 ft. lbs.

WIPER SWITCH

REPLACE

Refer to procedure outlined under "Pivot & Pulse Switch & Turn Signal Switch Assembly, Replace."

WIPER TRANSMISSION

REPLACE

1. Remove module as previously outlined.
2. Remove two transmission socket screws, then remove socket from link ball.
3. Remove righthand, lefthand, and bellcrank mounting screws and remove transmission from module.
4. Connect new transmission to module.
5. Ensure wiper motor is in inner wipe position, **Fig. 2.**
6. Using suitable tool, align holes in module and bellcrank and install transmission socket screws.
7. Ensure body seal is in proper place on righthand side of module and install wiper module as previously described.
8. Install passenger side wiper arm and blade. Measure from tip of blade to bottom edge of glass, ensuring distance is approximately $9^1/_8$ inches (231 mm), then tighten nut install protective cap and reconnect washer hose.
9. Install driver side wiper arm and blade. Measure from tip of blade to bottom edge of glass, ensuring distance is approximately 2 inches (53 mm), then tighten nut, install protective cap and reconnect washer hose.
10. Run wiper at high and low speeds with wet and tacky windshield, ensuring wiper parks properly and there is no interference between blades.

WIPER MODULE

REPLACE

The windshield wiper module consists of both the wiper motor and the wiper transmission.

1. Disconnect battery ground cable.
2. Raise hood and remove washer hose, protective cap and nut from each wiper arm.
3. Lift each wiper arm and insert a suitable pin or pop rivet completely through the two holes located next to pivot of arm, then, using wiper arm removal tool No. J-8966 or equivalent, lift each arm off its transmission shaft.
4. Remove lower reveal molding attaching screws, then lower hood and remove lower reveal molding upward and rearward.
5. Raise hood, then remove air inlet panel screws, underhood lamp switch (if equipped) and the air inlet panel. **Attach holding wire or string to upper portion of switch before removing retaining nut to prevent switch from falling between panels.**
6. Disconnect wiring harness connectors at motor and the washer hose at firewall.
7. If motor is inoperative, motor crank arm must be rotated to inner wipe position, **Fig. 2.** Engage upper jaw of pliers against top edge of crank arm and lower jaw against crank arm nut, **Fig. 3.**
8. Remove three screws from bellcrank housing, then lower transmission.
9. Remove wiper module from vehicle.
10. Reverse procedure to install.

BLOWER MOTOR

REPLACE

1. Disconnect battery ground cable.
2. Remove right sound insulator panel from under instrument panel.
3. Remove rear retaining screws from electrical convenience center, then loosen front screw and slide convenience center out.
4. Disconnect electrical connector at motor and remove harness from clip.
5. remove blower motor mounting screws and the blower motor.
6. Reverse procedure to install.

HEATER CORE

REPLACE

WITH A/C

1. Disconnect battery ground cable and drain cooling system.
2. Remove upper dash weather-stripping and the upper secondary cowl.
3. Disconnect heater hoses from heater core.
4. Remove sound insulator, rear seat duct adapter and the heater duct, **Fig. 4.**
5. Remove heater core cover and the heater core.
6. Reverse procedure to install.

LESS A/C

1. Disconnect battery ground cable and drain cooling system.
2. **On models with 2.5L engine,** rotate engine as follows:
   a. Position transaxle in N.
   b. Remove coolant reservoir and position aside. It is not necessary to disconnect coolant reservoir hoses.
   c. Remove torque strut-to-engine

bracket nut and bolt.
   d. Using a prybar at engine torque strut bracket, rotate engine and transaxle assembly forward.
   e. Align slave hole in torque strut with engine bracket hole.
   f. Retain engine in this position using torque strut-to-engine bracket bolt.
3. **On models with 3.1L engines,** rotate engine as follows:
   a. Position transaxle in N.
   b. Remove torque strut-to-engine bracket bolts and position strut aside.
   c. Install passenger side torque strut-to-engine bracket bolt in engine bracket.
   d. Remove coolant reservoir and position aside. It is not necessary to disconnect coolant reservoir hoses.
   e. Place a pry bar in bracket so that it contacts bracket and bolt.
   f. Rotate engine by pulling forward on pry bar.
   g. Align slave hole in driver side torque strut with engine bracket hole.
   h. Retain engine in this position using torque strut-to-engine bracket bolt.
4. **On all models,** remove upper secondary cowl panel.
5. Remove heater hose retaining bracket nuts.
6. Remove upper nut securing lower secondary cowl panel.
7. Disconnect heater hoses from heater core.
8. Blow air through heater core nipples to remove coolant from core.
9. Remove lower right sound insulator panel.
10. Remove rear seat duct adapter, then the heater floor duct, **Fig. 4.**
11. Remove lower left sound insulator panel.
12. Remove heater core cover attaching screws, then the cover,**Fig. 4.**
13. Remove heater core retaining bolt, then the heater core.
14. Reverse procedure to install.

EVAPORATOR CORE

REPLACE

1. Disconnect battery ground cable and discharge A/C system.
2. Drain cooling system.
3. Remove upper weatherstrip from body and upper secondary cowl.
4. Remove lower secondary cowl upper nut.
5. Disconnect evaporator core block connections at cowl.
6. Disconnect heater hoses from heater core.
7. Remove right lower instrument panel sound insulator panel.
8. Remove rear seat duct adapter and lower heater duct.
9. Remove lower left instrument panel sound insulator panel.
10. Remove heater core cover screws and heater core.
11. Remove evaporator core cover and evaporator core.
12. Reverse procedure to install.

2.2L/4-134 Engine

NOTE: On Air Bag Equipped Models, Refer To "Air Bag System Precautions" Located In The Front Of This Manual For System Disarming & Arming Procedures.

NOTE: For Procedures Not Found In This Section, Refer To The 2.2L/4-134 Engine Section In The Chevrolet Cavalier, Pontiac Sunbird & Sunfire Chapter.

INDEX

PRECAUTIONS

AIR BAG SYSTEMS

Refer to "Air Bag System Precautions" in the front of this manual for system disarming and arming procedures.

FUEL SYSTEM PRESSURE RELIEF

To reduce the risk of fire and personal injury, it is necessary to relieve the fuel system pressure before servicing fuel system components.

1. Disconnect battery ground cable.
2. Loosen fuel tank filler cap to relieve tank pressure.
3. Connect fuel pressure gage tool No. J-34730-1, or equivalent, to the fuel pressure valve. Wrap a shop towel around fitting while connection gage to avoid spillage.
4. Install bleed hose into an approved container and open valve to bleed system pressure.

ENGINE MOUNT

REPLACE

1. Remove air cleaner duct assembly.
2. Disconnect engine torque struts.
3. Install engine support tool Nos. J-28467-A, J-28467-90, J-35953 and J-36462, or equivalent, then raise and support vehicle.
4. Remove engine mount nuts at frame.
5. Lower vehicle and raise engine.
6. Remove upper engine mount nuts at mount.
7. Remove mount.
8. Reverse procedure to install.

ENGINE

REPLACE

1. Disconnect battery ground cable.
2. Mark and remove hood assembly.
3. Remove air cleaner and duct assembly.
4. Drain cooling system, then disconnect engine torque strut completely.
5. Remove air intake silencer assembly.
6. Remove coolant recovery reservoir, then disconnect upper and lower radiator hose at engine.
7. Disconnect brake booster vacuum hose at intake manifold and throttle control cable at throttle body.
8. Remove serpentine drive belt, then disconnect electrical connectors and remove retaining screws at engine cooling fan.
9. Remove power steering pump and position aside.
10. Disconnect fuel lines from engine.
11. Remove alternator heat shield, then disconnect electrical connections at alternator and exhaust oxygen sensor.
12. Remove engine torque strut mount at engine lift bracket.
13. Raise and support vehicle.
14. Remove flywheel and torque converter cover.
15. Remove motor mounts as outlined under "Engine Mount, Replace."
16. Disconnect front exhaust pipe from

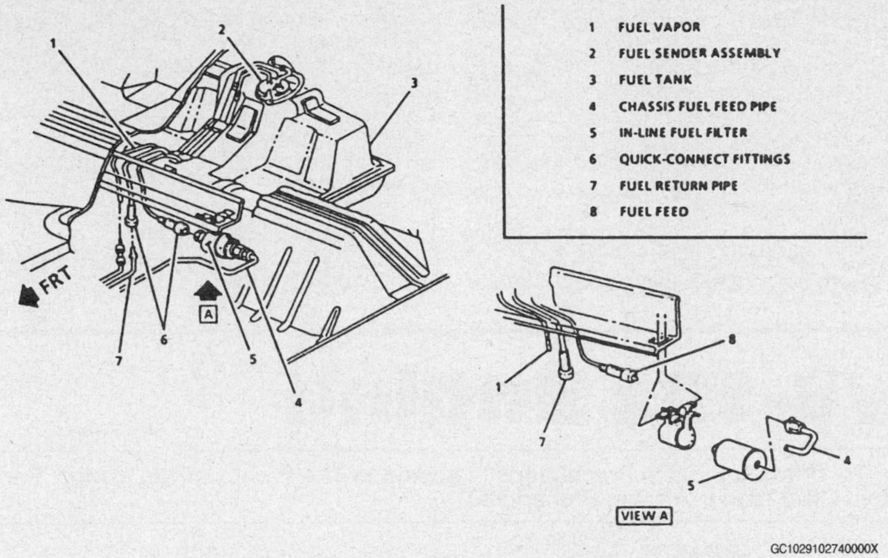
1 FUEL VAPOR
2 FUEL SENDER ASSEMBLY
3 FUEL TANK
4 CHASSIS FUEL FEED PIPE
5 IN-LINE FUEL FILTER
6 QUICK-CONNECT FITTINGS
7 FUEL RETURN PIPE
8 FUEL FEED
FRT
A
VIEW A
GC1029102740000X

Fig. 1 Fuel filter replacement

exhaust manifold.
17. Lower vehicle.
18. Rotate engine, then install strut to bolt hole in engine lift bracket and torque strut mount bracket. This holds engine forward and gives access to rear of engine.
19. Disconnect electrical connectors at starter motor and ground wires at engine block in front of starter.
20. Remove A/C compressor bolts at bracket, then position compressor aside.
21. Remove engine to transaxle bracket at transaxle.
22. Disconnect vacuum hose at intake manifold.
23. Disconnect electrical connectors at speed sensor, knock sensor, engine block ground wires and wire harness clamp nut under intake manifold.
24. Disconnect electrical connectors at throttle body and injector harness. Leave harness on injectors and pull harness from manifold.
25. Remove bellhousing to engine attaching bolts.
26. Remove engine torque struts.
27. Install engine lifting device, then disconnect electrical connectors from electronic ignition module.
28. Remove engine from vehicle.
29. Reverse procedure to install.

FUEL PUMP

REPLACE

1. Disconnect battery ground cable.
2. Relieve fuel system pressure as outlined under "Precautions."
3. Drain fuel tank, then remove fuel tank assembly.
4. Remove fuel sender assembly.
5. Reverse procedure to install.

FUEL FILTER

REPLACE

1. Relieve fuel system pressure as outlined under "Precautions."
2. Raise and support vehicle.
3. Remove bracket attaching screw and filter bracket, **Fig. 1.**
4. Grasp filter and fuel line fitting. Twist quick-connect fitting 1/4 turn in each direction to loosen any dirt within fitting.
5. Using compressed air, blow out dirt from quick-connect fitting.
6. Remove feed pipe nut from fuel filter, then drain any remaining fuel into a suitable container.
7. Remove fuel filter.
8. Reverse procedure to install.

2.5L/4-151 Engine

NOTE: On Air Bag Equipped Models, Refer To "Air Bag System Precautions" Located In The Front Of This Manual For System Disarming & Arming Procedures.

NOTE: For Procedures Not Found In This Section, Refer To The 2.5L/4-151 Engine Section In The Buick Century, Oldsmobile Cutlass Ciera & Cutlass Cruiser Chapter.

INDEX

PRECAUTIONS

AIR BAG SYSTEMS

Refer to "Air Bag System Precautions" in the front of this manual for system disarming and arming procedures.

FUEL SYSTEM PRESSURE RELIEF

To reduce the risk of fire and personal injury, it is necessary to relieve the fuel system pressure before servicing fuel system components.

1. Disconnect battery ground cable.
2. Loosen fuel tank filler cap to relieve tank pressure.
3. Connect fuel pressure gage tool No. J-34730-1, or equivalent, to the fuel pressure valve. Wrap a shop towel around fitting while connection gage to avoid spillage.
4. Install bleed hose into an approved container and open valve to bleed system pressure.

ENGINE

REPLACE

1. Disconnect battery ground cable, then scribe and remove hood.
2. Drain engine coolant and remove coolant recovery bottle.
3. Remove air cleaner assembly.
4. Remove plastic ECM cover, then serpentine drive belt.
5. Disconnect radiator hoses at engine.
6. Disconnect throttle control cables
7. Rotate engine forward, then disconnect power steering pump and set aside.

8. Rotate engine back, then raise and support vehicle.
9. Disconnect front exhaust pipe at converter and manifold.
10. Remove starter motor and righthand engine splash shield.
11. Remove flywheel to torque converter bolts, then the transaxle to support bracket
12. Remove engine and transaxle mount nuts at frame.
13. Lower vehicle.
14. Disconnect front exhaust pipe, then all engine electrical connectors.
15. Disconnect, but do not discharge A/C compressor and secure aside.
16. Relieve fuel pressure as outlined under "Precautions" then disconnect fuel lines to engine and fuel line bracket at transaxle.
17. Disconnect all vacuum lines, then remove exhaust pipe to transaxle bracket bolts.
18. Remove engine to transaxle bolts, then support transaxle with suitable floor jack.
19. Attaching engine lifting device and remove engine.
20. Reverse procedure to install, noting the following:
    a. **Torque** engine to transaxle bolt 55 ft. lbs.
    b. **Torque** Flywheel to torque converter bolts 44 ft. lbs.
    c. **Torque** engine and transaxle mount nuts to 35 ft. lbs.

3.1L/V6-192 Engine

NOTE: On Air Bag Equipped Models, Refer To "Air Bag System Precautions" Located In The Front Of This Manual For System Disarming & Arming Procedures.

INDEX

PRECAUTIONS

AIR BAG SYSTEMS

Refer to "Air Bag System Precautions" in the front of this manual for system disarming and arming procedures.

FUEL SYSTEM PRESSURE RELIEF

To reduce the risk of fire and personal injury, it is necessary to relieve the fuel system pressure before servicing fuel system components.

1. Disconnect battery ground cable.
2. Loosen fuel tank filler cap to relieve tank pressure.
3. Connect fuel pressure gage tool No. J-34730-1, or equivalent, to the fuel pressure valve. Wrap a shop towel around fitting while connection gage to avoid spillage.
4. Install bleed hose into an approved container and open valve to bleed system pressure.

IDLE LEARN PROCEDURE

On models with 3.1L/V6-192 engine, any time vehicle power has been interrupted the programmed position of the IAC valve pintle is lost. The following procedures must be performed to update the ECM memory with the correct IAC valve pintle position for the vehicle and provide a stable idle speed.

1. Restore vehicle power.
2. Connect TECH I scan tool to ALDL connector located under the lefthand side of the dash panel.
3. Select "IAC System."
4. Select "Idle Learn" in the "Misc. Test" mode.
5. Proceed as directed.

ENGINE MOUNT

REPLACE

ENGINE MOUNT

1992

1. Disconnect battery ground cable.
2. Remove mount retaining nuts from below cradle mounting bracket, **Fig. 1.**
3. Raise engine enough to provide clearance, then remove mount to engine bracket attaching nuts and the mount.
4. Reverse procedure to install, torquing nuts and bolts to specifications.

1993–95

1. Disconnect battery ground cable, then scribe and remove hood.
2. Remove engine strut bracket and cooling fan assemblies.
3. Install support tools No. J-28467-A, J-36462, J-28467-90, and J-25953, or equivalents, then raise and support vehicle.
4. Disconnect front exhaust manifold pipe.
5. Disconnect intermediate steering shaft bolt and move cover aside.
6. Drain engine oil, and remove engine splash shield.
7. Suitably support frame assembly with floor stands, then remove transaxle mount frame side bracket nuts from

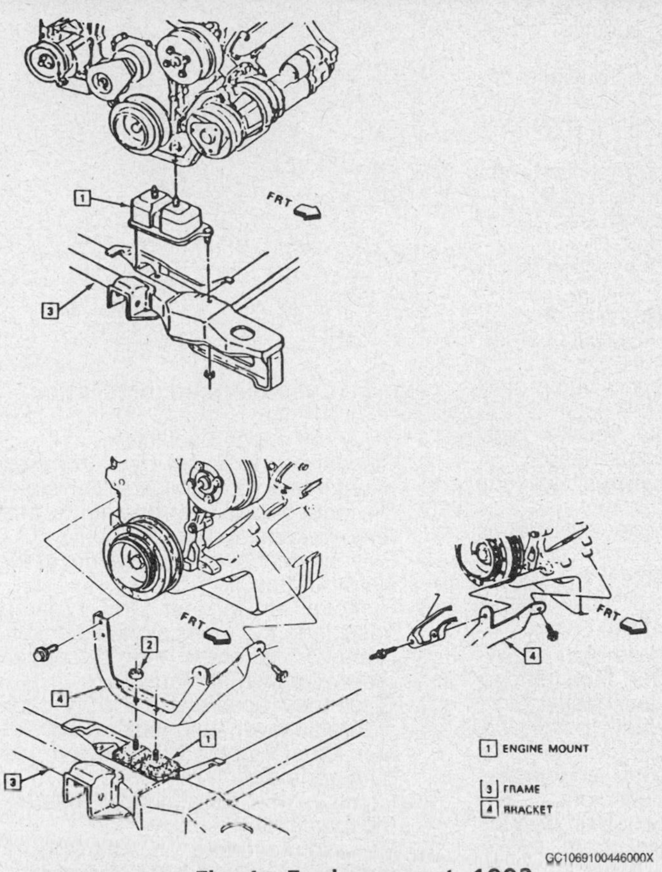
1 ENGINE MOUNT
3 FRAME
4 BRACKET
FRT
GC1069100446000X

Fig. 1 Engine mount. 1992

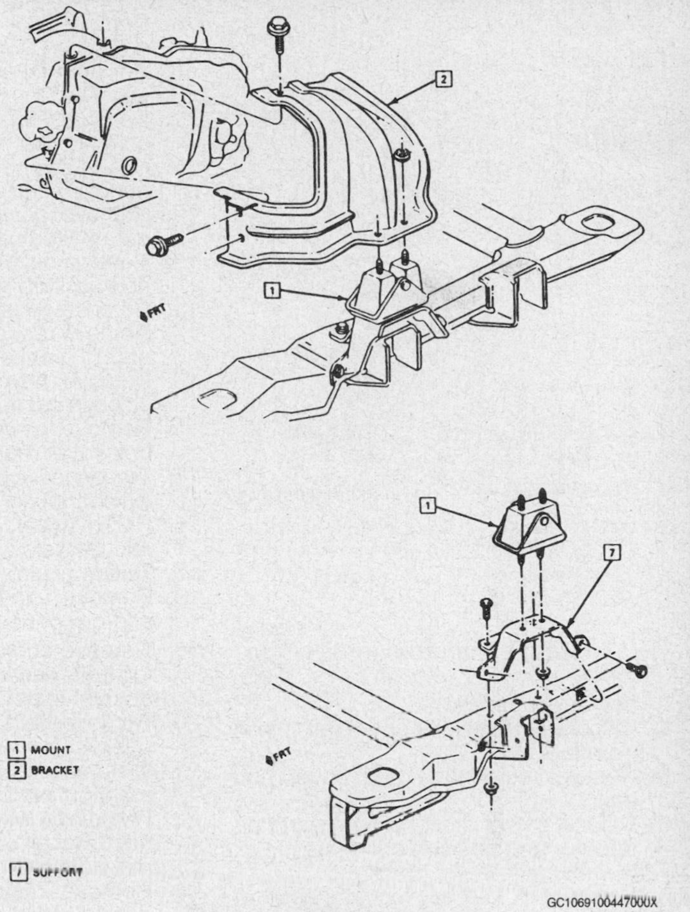
1 MOUNT
2 BRACKET
7 SUPPORT
FRT
GC1069100447000X

Fig. 2 Transaxle mount

frame assembly.

8. Remove rear drivetrain frame and front suspension frame bolts, then lower drivetrain and front suspension assembly.
9. Reverse procedure to install. Tighten to specifications.

ENGINE STRUT

1. Disconnect battery ground cable.
2. Remove radiator inlet hose clip from bolt on dogbone-style strut assembly.
3. Remove bolt from engine mount strut bracket, then bolt from bracket.
4. Remove strut assembly.
5. Reverse procedure to install. Tighten to specifications.

TRANSAXLE MOUNT

1. Disconnect battery ground cable.
2. Support transaxle with suitable jack.
3. Remove crossmember to mount attaching nuts, **Fig. 2.**
4. Remove bracket to transaxle attaching bolts.
5. Remove mount and bracket assembly.
6. Separate mount from bracket.
7. Reverse procedure to install, torquing nuts and bolts to specifications.

ENGINE

REPLACE

1. Disconnect battery ground cable, then drain coolant and engine oil.
2. Relieve fuel pressure as outlined under "Precautions."
3. Scribe alignment marks, then remove hood.
4. Remove air flow tube from air cleaner and throttle valve, then the air cleaner assembly.
5. Remove transaxle filler tube assembly.
6. Disconnect necessary electrical wiring, then the throttle and TV cables.
7. Remove engine mount strut bracket.
8. Disconnect fuel lines.
9. Remove AIR pump belt, then the serpentine drive belt cover and belt.
10. Disconnect radiator hoses at engine.
11. Remove A/C compressor bolts from front bracket.
12. Remove power steering pump and position aside.
13. Disconnect heater hoses from engine.
14. Disconnect brake booster vacuum supply line.
15. Disconnect EGR from exhaust.
16. Raise and support vehicle.
17. Remove starter motor assembly.
18. Remove A/C compressor bolts at rear bracket, then position compressor aside.
19. Remove flywheel cover, then disconnect starter and position aside.
20. Remove torque converter bolts, then the transaxle mount bracket.
21. Remove engine front mount retaining nuts.
22. Disconnect exhaust pipe at crossover, then lower vehicle.
23. Remove coolant recovery bottle.
24. Disconnect accelerator control cable bracket and move assemblies aside.
25. Disconnect crossover pipe at left manifold.
26. Remove serpentine belt, then the alternator.
27. Remove power steering pump assembly.
28. Remove plastic cover front shock tower, then the automatic transaxle modulator pipe assembly.
29. **On models except Lumina and Monte Carlo,** pull engine assembly forward and support in this position.
30. **On all models,** disconnect crossover pipe at right manifold.
31. Disconnect bulkhead connector.
32. **On models except Lumina and Monte Carlo,** remove engine support and allow engine to roll to normal position.
33. **On all models,** remove engine to transaxle attaching bolts, attach lifting device to engine and support transaxle.
34. Remove engine assembly.
35. Reverse procedure to install.

INTAKE MANIFOLD

REPLACE

1992

1. Disconnect battery ground cable.
2. Remove accelerator cable and TV cable bracket, throttle body and EGR valve, then the plenum.
3. Relieve fuel pressure as outlined un-

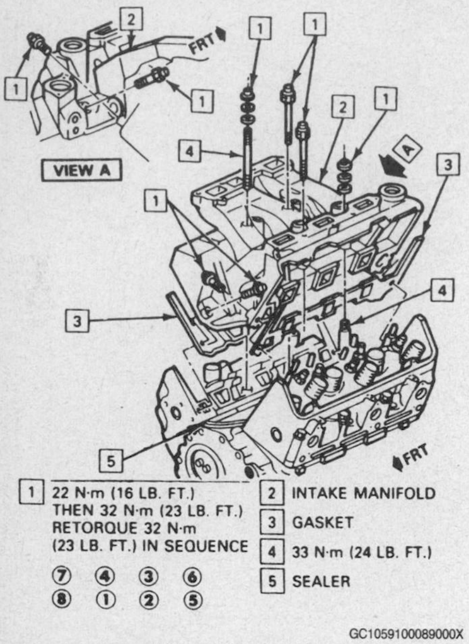

VIEW A
FRT
A
1 22 N·m (16 LB. FT.) THEN 32 N·m (23 LB. FT.) RETORQUE 32 N·m (23 LB. FT.) IN SEQUENCE
⑦ ④ ③ ⑥
⑧ ① ② ⑤
2 INTAKE MANIFOLD
3 GASKET
4 33 N·m (24 LB. FT.)
5 SEALER
GC1059100089000X

Fig. 3 Intake manifold installation

der "Precautions."
4. Disconnect fuel inlet and return pipes from fuel rail.
5. Remove serpentine belt cover and belt.
6. Detach power steering pump and alternator and position out of way.
7. Remove alternator bracket.
8. Disconnect idle air vacuum hose at throttle body.
9. Disconnect wires at injectors and remove fuel rail.
10. Remove breather tube and runners, then the rocker arm covers.
11. Drain cooling system.
12. Disconnect radiator hose from thermostat outlet.
13. Disconnect wires at coolant sensor and oil sending switch, then remove coolant sensor.
14. Disconnect bypass hose at fill neck and head.
15. Disconnect heater inlet pipe from manifold.
16. Remove manifold attaching bolts and the manifold. **Retain Belleville washers in same positions on four center bolts.**
17. Reverse procedure to install, noting the following:
    a. Remove old gasket material and the loose sealant from front and rear ridges of cylinder block, then clean sealing surfaces.
    b. Apply bead of suitable sealant as shown, **Fig. 3.**
    c. Tighten intake manifold nuts and bolts to specification, **Fig. 3.**

1993–95

1. Disconnect battery ground cable.
2. Remove air cleaner assembly.
3. Remove strut bolts and nuts at engine brackets, and pull struts up out of the way.
4. Drain cooling system, then remove throttle body and EGR valve at plenum.
5. Remove brake booster valve at plenum, then the plenum.
6. Relieve fuel pressure as outlined under "Precautions."
7. Remove fuel line bracket, then disconnect fuel lines at fuel rail.
8. Rotate engine assembly forward, then remove alternator and set aside.
9. Remove power steering line clamp nut at alternator bracket.
10. Remove secondary air injection pump and position aside.
11. Remove generator mounting bracket.
12. Remove rear engine lift bracket studs and lift bracket.
13. Remove power steering pump and position aside.
14. Remove power brake booster pipe bracket at rear of cylinder head.
15. Disconnect spark plug wires from rear cylinder head.
16. Remove rear valve cover bolts, cover and gasket.
17. Rotate engine assembly back.
18. Remove upper radiator hose clamp and disconnect hose from engine.
19. Remove coolant bypass pipe retaining bolts and bracket nut, then remove coolant bypass pipe and gasket.
20. Remove front cover bolts, cover and gasket.
21. Disconnect fuel injector and intake manifold electrical connectors.
22. Remove coolant sensor, then disconnect heater inlet pipe from intake manifold and cylinder head.
23. Remove intake manifold bolts, then disconnect necessary vacuum hoses.
24. Remove manifold attaching bolts and the manifold. **Retain Belleville washers in same positions on four center bolts.**
25. Reverse procedure to install, noting the following:
    a. Remove old gasket material and the loose sealant from front and rear ridges of cylinder block, then clean sealing surfaces.
    b. Apply bead of suitable sealant as shown, **Fig. 3.**
    c. Tighten intake manifold nuts and bolts to specification, **Fig. 3.**

EXHAUST MANIFOLD

REPLACE

LEFT

1. Disconnect battery ground cable.
2. Remove air cleaner and breather hose.
3. Disconnect torque struts from engine.
4. Remove coolant recovery bottle, then the serpentine belt cover and belt.
5. Remove A/C compressor, then the A/C strut and bracket.
6. Remove heat shield, then disconnect exhaust crossover pipe.
7. Remove manifold attaching bolts, then the manifold.
8. Reverse procedure to install, torquing manifold attaching bolts to specifications.

RIGHT

1. Disconnect battery ground cable, then

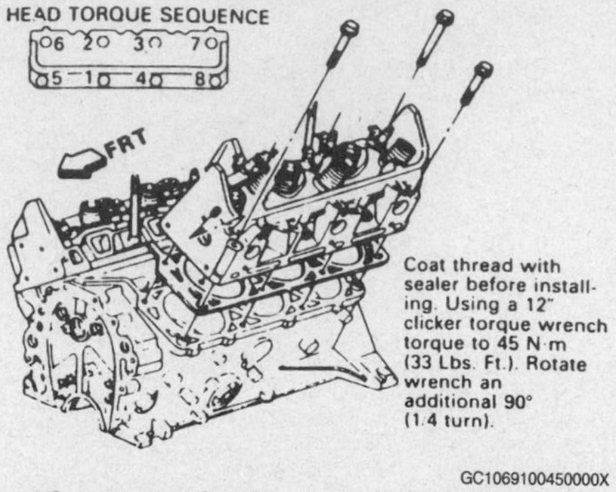

HEAD TORQUE SEQUENCE
6 2 3 7
5 1 4 8
FRT
Coat thread with sealer before installing. Using a 12" clicker torque wrench torque to 45 N·m (33 Lbs. Ft.). Rotate wrench an additional 90° (1/4 turn).
GC1069100450000X

Fig. 4 Cylinder head installation

raise and support vehicle.
2. Disconnect exhaust pipe from exhaust manifold, then lower vehicle.
3. Disconnect engine torque struts, then remove coolant recovery bottle.
4. Pull engine forward and secure in forward position.
5. Remove air cleaner and breather hose, then the mass air flow sensor.
6. Remove heat shield, then disconnect crossover pipe at manifold.
7. Disconnect accelerator and TV cable at throttle lever, then remove accelerator and TV cable bracket from plenum and position out of way.
8. Remove manifold attaching bolts and the manifold.
9. Reverse procedure to install, torquing manifold attaching bolts to specifications.

CYLINDER HEAD

REPLACE

LEFT

1. Disconnect battery ground cable, then drain coolant.
2. Remove rocker covers and intake manifold as previously outlined.
3. Remove exhaust crossover, then the oil lever indicator bracket.
4. Remove left exhaust manifold as previously outlined.
5. Disconnect plug wires at left head, then remove pushrods. Intake and exhaust pushrods are different lengths (exhaust pushrods are longer). Intake pushrods are marked orange and are 6 inches long, exhaust pushrods are marked blue and are 6 3/8 inches long.
6. Remove cylinder head attaching bolts, then the cylinder head.
7. Reverse procedure to install, noting the following:
    a. Clean gasket surfaces on head, cylinder block and intake manifold, cylinder block bolt threads and the cylinder head bolts.
    b. Place gasket in position over dowel pins with "This Side Up" marking facing upward.
    c. Coat cylinder head bolt threads with suitable sealant.
    d. Tighten cylinder head bolts to specifications in sequence shown in **Fig. 4.**
    e. Tighten rocker arm nuts to specifications.

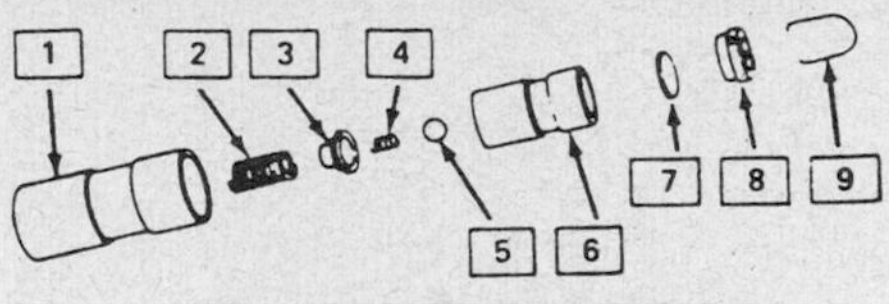
1
2
3
4
5
6
7
8
9
1-LIFTER BODY
2-PLUNGER SPRING
3-BALL CHECK RETAINER
4-BALL CHECK SPRING
5-BALL CHECK
6-PLUNGER
7-OIL METERING VALVE
8-PUSH ROD SEAT
9-RETAINER RING
GC1069100448000X

Fig. 5 Exploded view of valve lifter

RIGHT

1. Disconnect battery ground cable, then drain cooling system.
2. Raise and support vehicle and disconnect exhaust from crossover, then lower vehicle.
3. Disconnect torque struts from engine.
4. Detach coolant recovery bottle and position aside.
5. Pull engine forward and secure.
6. Remove exhaust crossover heat shield and disconnect crossover from right manifold.
7. Remove right exhaust manifold as previously outlined.
8. Disconnect spark plug wires from right cylinder head.
9. Remove rocker covers and intake manifold as previously outlined.
10. Remove pushrods. Intake and exhaust pushrods are different lengths (exhaust pushrods are longer). Intake pushrods are marked orange and are 6 inches long, exhaust pushrods are marked blue and are 6³/₈ inches long.
11. Remove cylinder head attaching bolts, then the cylinder head.
12. Reverse procedure to install, noting the following:
    a. Clean gasket surfaces on head, cylinder block and intake manifold, cylinder block bolt threads and the cylinder head bolts.
    b. Place gasket in position over dowel pins with "This Side Up" marking facing upward.
    c. Coat cylinder head bolt threads with suitable sealant.
    d. Tighten cylinder head bolts to specification in sequence shown in **Fig. 4.**
    e. Tighten rocker arm nuts to specifications.

VALVE COVER

REPLACE

LEFT

1. Disconnect battery ground cable and drain coolant.
2. Disconnect ignition wire clamps from coolant tube, then loosen coolant tube below thermostat housing at engine block.
3. Disconnect coolant tube at each end.
4. Disconnect coolant tube hose at water pump.
5. Remove coolant tube.
6. Remove tube from between rocker cover and air inlet hose.
7. Remove ignition wire guide.
8. Remove cover attaching bolts and the cover. **If cover adheres to cylinder head, shear off by bumping end of cover with palm of hand or soft rubber mallet. If cover still will not come loose, carefully pry until loose. Do not distort sealing flange.**
9. Reverse procedure to install, noting the following:
    a. Clean sealing surfaces on cylinder head and cover.
    b. Use new gasket, ensuring gasket is seated properly in rocker cover groove.
    c. Apply suitable sealer in notch in cylinder head.
    d. Tighten attaching bolts to specifications.

RIGHT

1. Disconnect battery ground cable and drain coolant.
2. Disconnect vacuum hoses at plenum.
3. Remove air cleaner assembly.
4. Disconnect EGR tube at crossover pipe.
5. Remove ignition wire guide, then disconnect ignition wire harness at plenum and spark plugs.
6. Disconnect two coolant hoses at throttle base.
7. Disconnect necessary electrical connectors at plenum.
8. Disconnect throttle, TV and cruise control cables.
9. Disconnect bracket at right side of plenum.
10. Disconnect brake booster vacuum supply hose from plenum.
11. Remove serpentine belt cover and the belt.
12. Detach coolant recovery bottle and position out of way.
13. Remove engine struts, then pull engine forward and secure in forward position, using slave feature on strut.
14. Remove alternator attaching bolts and position alternator out of way.
15. Remove PCV valve.
16. Remove cover attaching bolts and the cover. **If cover adheres to cylinder head, shear off by bumping end of cover with palm of hand or soft rubber mallet. If cover still will not come loose, carefully pry until loose. Do not distort sealing flange.**
17. Reverse procedure to install, noting the following:
    a. Clean sealing surfaces on cylinder head and cover.
    b. Use new gasket, ensuring gasket is seated properly in rocker cover groove.
    c. Apply suitable sealer in notch in cylinder head.
    d. Tighten attaching bolts to specifications.

VALVE ARRANGEMENT

FRONT TO REAR

Cowl side	E-I-E-I-I-E
Radiator side	E-I-I-E-I-E

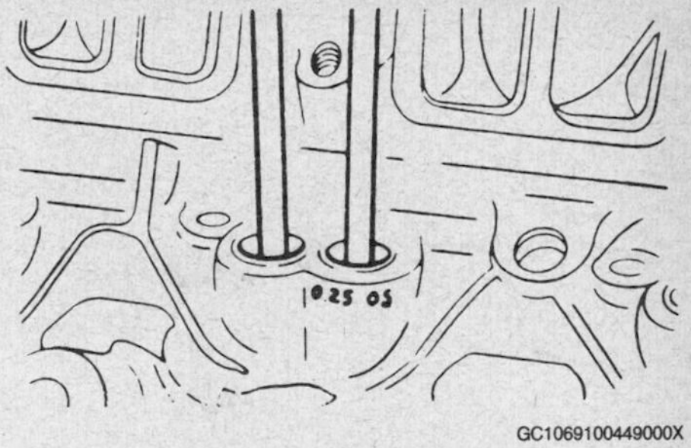
.025 OS
GC1069100449000X

Fig. 6 Oversize lifter marking

VALVE LIFTERS

Roller type valve lifters, **Fig. 5,** are used in this engine. Valve lifters must be replaced whenever camshaft is replaced.

Valve lifters should be kept in order so that they will be reinstalled in their original positions. Some engines will have both standard and .010 inch oversize valve lifters.

Where oversize lifters are used, the cylinder case will be marked "0.25 OS" with white paint on the lifter boss, **Fig. 6.**

If lifters are removed, they must be installed in their original location. If replacement is necessary, use lifters with a narrow flat ground along the lower ³/₄ of the lifter. These flats provide additional oil to the cam lobe and lifter surfaces.

VALVE STEM OIL SEAL & SPRING

REPLACE

1. Remove rocker arm cover, then the spark plug.
2. Remove rocker arm and pushrod.
3. Install air line adapter tool No. J-23590 or equivalent to spark plug port and apply compressed air to hold valves in place.
4. Using valve spring compressor tool No. J-5892 or equivalent, compress valve spring and disassemble valve assembly.
5. Remove valve stem oil seal.
6. Reverse procedure to install, noting the following:
    a. When assembling valve assembly, use plastic seat provided and press over valve guide boss.
    b. If necessary, use grease to retain valve locks.

CAMSHAFT LOBE LIFT SPECIFICATIONS

Intake	.2626
Exhaust	.2732

VALVE CLEARANCE SPECIFICATIONS

This engine is equipped with hydraulic lifters. There is no provision for valve clearance specification available.

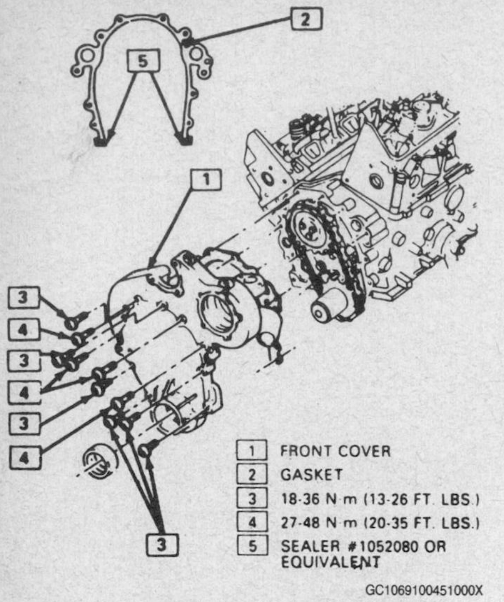
2
5
1
3
4
3
4
3
4
3
1 FRONT COVER
2 GASKET
3 18-36 N·m (13-26 FT. LBS.)
4 27-48 N·m (20-35 FT. LBS.)
5 SEALER #1052080 OR EQUIVALENT
GC1069100451000X

Fig. 7 Front cover installation

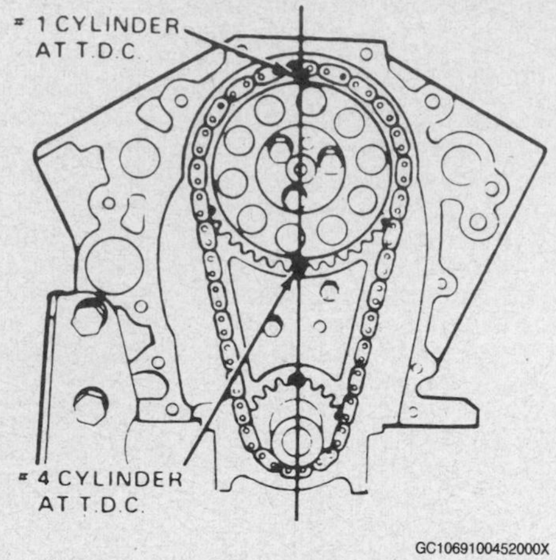
#1 CYLINDER AT T.D.C.
#4 CYLINDER AT T.D.C.
GC1069100452000X

Fig. 8 Timing mark alignment

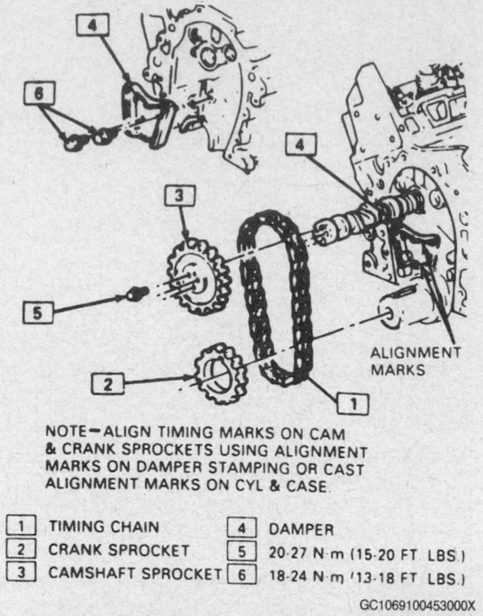
4
6
4
3
5
2
1
ALIGNMENT MARKS
NOTE—ALIGN TIMING MARKS ON CAM & CRANK SPROCKETS USING ALIGNMENT MARKS ON DAMPER STAMPING OR CAST ALIGNMENT MARKS ON CYL & CASE.
1 TIMING CHAIN
2 CRANK SPROCKET
3 CAMSHAFT SPROCKET
4 DAMPER
5 20-27 N·m (15-20 FT. LBS.)
6 18-24 N·m (13-18 FT. LBS.)
GC1069100453000X

Fig. 9 Timing chain & sprockets replacement

VALVE ADJUSTMENT

1. Crank engine until mark on torsional damper is aligned with TDC mark on timing tab. Check to ensure engine is in the No. 1 cylinder firing position by placing fingers on No. 1 cylinder rocker arms as mark on damper comes near TDC mark on timing tab. If valves are not moving, the engine is in the No. 1 firing position. If valves move as damper mark nears TDC mark on timing tab, engine is in the No. 4 cylinder firing position and should be rotated one revolution to reach the No. 1 cylinder firing position.
2. With engine in the No. 1 cylinder firing position, adjust the following valves: Exhaust-1, 2,3; Intake-1, 5, 6. To adjust valves, back off adjusting nut until lash is felt at pushrod, then tighten adjusting nut until all lash is removed. This can be determined by rotating the pushrod while tightening the adjusting nut. When all lash has been eliminated, turn adjusting nut an additional 1 1/2 turns.
3. Crank engine one revolution until mark on torsional damper and TDC mark are again aligned. This is the No. 4 cylinder firing position. With engine in this position, the following valves can be adjusted: Exhaust-4, 5 & 6; Intake-2, 3 & 4.
4. Install rocker arm covers, then start engine and check timing and idle speed.

PUSH RODS

1. Remove rocker arm covers and rocker arms, identifying components so that they can be installed in same location.
2. Remove rocker arm pivot balls and rocker arms, then the pushrods. Intake and exhaust pushrods are different lengths (exhaust pushrods are longer). Intake pushrods are marked orange, exhaust pushrods are marked blue.

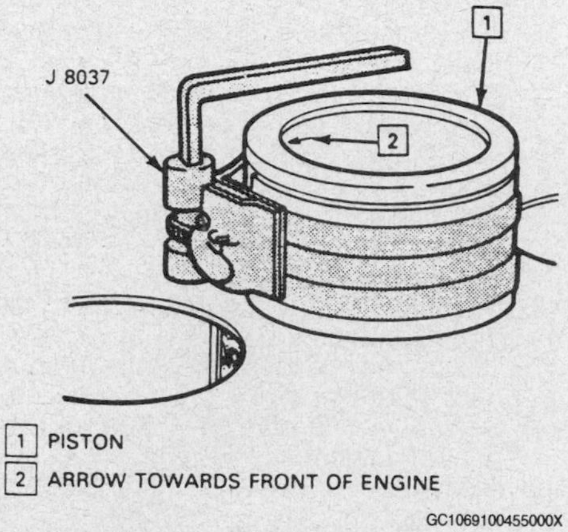
J 8037
1
2
1 PISTON
2 ARROW TOWARDS FRONT OF ENGINE
GC1069100455000X

Fig. 10 Piston marking

3. Reverse procedure to install, noting the following:
   a. Ensure pushrods seat in lifter.
   b. Coat bearing surfaces of rocker arms and pivot balls with Molykote or equivalent lubricant.
   c. Tighten rocker arm nuts to specifications.

FRONT COVER
REPLACE

1. Disconnect battery ground cable and drain cooling system.
2. Remove serpentine drive belt tensioner, then the alternator.
3. Remove serpentine drive belt cover, then the drive belt.
4. Detach power steering pump and position aside.
5. Raise and support vehicle.
6. Remove inner splash shield, then the flywheel cover.
7. Remove starter, then, using torsional dampener remover tool No. J-24420 or equivalent, the crankshaft balancer.
8. Remove serpentine drive belt idler pulley, then the oil pan.
9. Remove lower front cover attaching bolts, then lower vehicle.
10. Disconnect radiator hose at water pump and heater coolant hose from cooling system fill pipe.
11. Disconnect bypass, overflow and canister purge hoses.
12. Remove upper front cover attaching bolts, then the cover.
13. Reverse procedure to install, noting the following:
    a. Clean sealing surfaces on front cover and cylinder block.
    b. Use new gasket and be careful not to damage sealing surfaces.
    c. Apply sealant and tighten front cover attaching bolts as shown, **Fig. 7.**

FRONT COVER SEAL
REPLACE

1. Remove inner splash shield.
2. Using torsional dampener remover tool No. J-24420 or equivalent, remove crankshaft balancer.
3. Using suitable tool, pry out seal, being careful not to damage crankshaft.
4. Reverse procedure to install, noting the following:
   a. Lubricate new seal with clean engine oil and insert in front cover with lip facing engine.
   b. Use front cover alignment and oil seal installer tool No. J-35468 or equivalent to drive seal into place.

TIMING CHAIN
REPLACE
REMOVAL

1. Remove front cover as previously outlined.
2. Position No. 1 piston at TDC with marks on camshaft and crankshaft sprockets aligned, **Fig. 8.**
3. Remove camshaft sprocket and chain. If sprocket does not come off easily, a light blow on lower edge of sprocket should dislodge it.
4. Remove crankshaft sprocket.

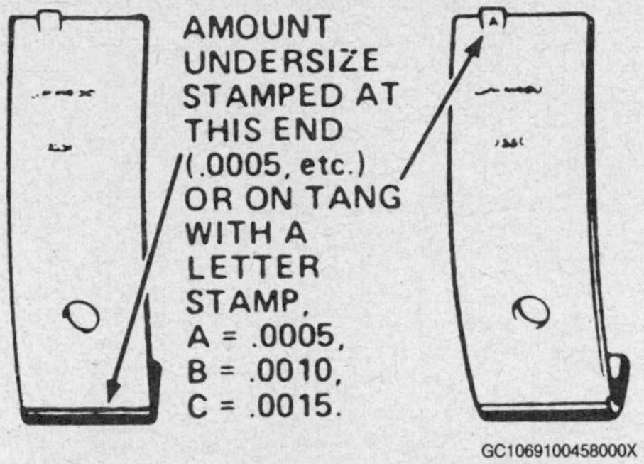
AMOUNT UNDERSIZE STAMPED AT THIS END (.0005, etc.) OR ON TANG WITH A LETTER STAMP, A = .0005, B = .0010, C = .0015.
GC1069100458000X

Fig. 11 Main bearing insert markings

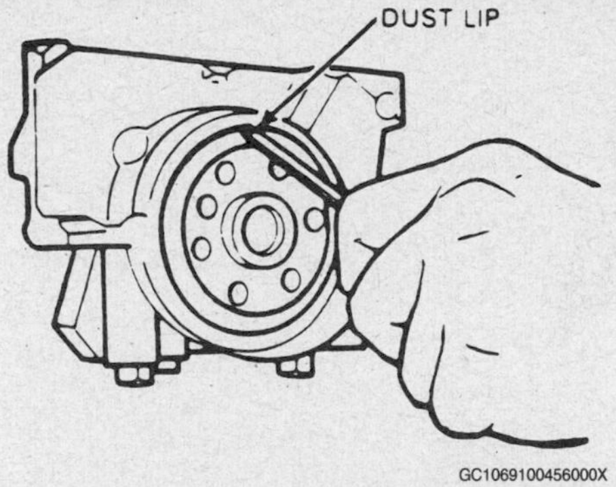
DUST LIP
GC1069100456000X

Fig. 12 Rear main seal removal

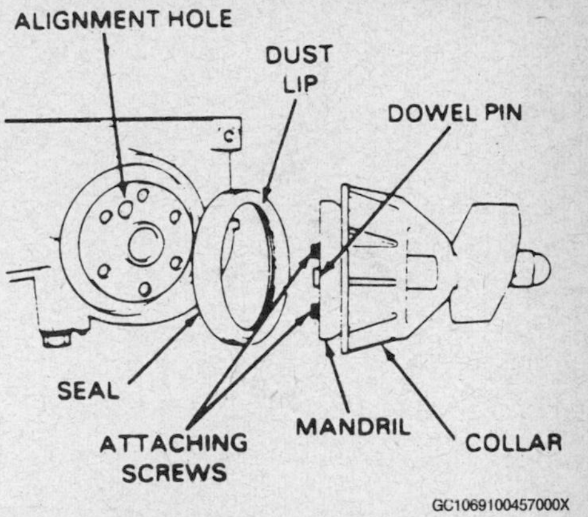
ALIGNMENT HOLE
DUST LIP
DOWEL PIN
SEAL
ATTACHING SCREWS
MANDRIL
COLLAR
GC1069100457000X

Fig. 13 Rear main seal installation

INSTALLATION

1. Install crankshaft sprocket.
2. Apply Molykote or equivalent to sprocket thrust surface.
3. Hold sprocket with chain hanging down and align marks on camshaft and crankshaft sprockets, **Fig. 9.**
4. Align dowel in camshaft with dowel hole in camshaft sprocket.
5. Draw camshaft sprocket onto camshaft using attaching bolts, then tighten bolts to specification, **Fig. 9.**
6. Lubricate timing chain with engine oil.
7. Install timing cover.

CAMSHAFT

REPLACE

1. Remove engine as previously outlined.
2. Remove valve lifters, then the timing cover as previously outlined.
3. Remove timing chain and sprocket as previously outlined, then the camshaft.
4. Reverse procedure to install, noting the following:
   a. If installing new camshaft, coat camshaft lobes with GM E.O.S. 1052367 or equivalent.
   b. Lubricate camshaft journals with engine oil.

PISTON & ROD ASSEMBLY

When installing piston and rod assemblies into cylinder block, ensure arrow on top of piston faces toward front of engine, **Fig. 10.**

MAIN & ROD BEARINGS

Engine bearings are of the precision insert type. They are available for service use in standard and various undersizes, **Fig. 11.**

To determine correct replacement insert size, bearing clearance must be measured as follows:

1. Measure crankshaft journal diameter in several places, approximately 90° apart and average the measurements.
2. Measure taper and runout, which should be .0002 inch (maximum).
3. Install bearing inserts and tighten rod and main bearing cap bolts to specification, then measure I.D. with an inside micrometer. Measure connecting rod I.D. in same direction as length of rod.
4. Select a suitable set of inserts to provide specified clearance limits. **Do not mix inserts of different nominal size in same bearing bore.** If clearance limits cannot be met, crankshaft journal must be reconditioned and undersized bearing inserts installed.

CRANKSHAFT REAR OIL SEAL

REPLACE

REMOVAL

1. Disconnect battery ground cable.
2. Using engine support fixture tool No. J-28467 or equivalent, and an extra support leg, support engine, then remove transaxle.
3. Remove flywheel.
4. Using suitable tool, remove seal by inserting tool in through dust lip at an angle, **Fig. 12,** and pry seal out by moving handle of tool toward end of crankshaft pilot, repeating around circumference of seal as necessary. **Be careful not to damage crankshaft O.D. surface.**

INSTALLATION

1. Check I.D. of bore for nicks or burrs and repair as required.
2. Inspect crankshaft for burrs or nicks on surface which contacts seal, repairing or replacing crankshaft as necessary.
3. Install seal as follows:
   a. Apply engine oil to I.D. and O.D. of new seal, then slide seal over mandrel until back of seal bottoms squarely against collar of rear main bearing seal installer tool No. J-34686 or equivalent, **Fig. 13.**
   b. Align dowel pin of tool with dowel pin in crankshaft by hand, or by **Torquing** attaching screws to 45 inch lbs., **Fig. 13.**
   c. Turn "T" handle of tool so that collar pushes seal into bore, turning handle until collar is tight against case.
   d. Loosen "T" handle of tool until it comes to a stop, then remove attaching screws.
   e. Ensure seal is seated squarely in bore.
4. Install flywheel, then the transaxle.

OIL PAN

REPLACE

1. Disconnect battery ground cable, then remove serpentine drive belt cover, drive belt and belt tensioner.
2. Using engine support fixture tool No. J-28467, or equivalent, and an extra support leg, support engine.
3. Raise and support vehicle, then drain engine oil.
4. Remove right wheel and tire assembly, then the right splash shield.
5. Remove steering gear pinch bolt, then the transaxle mount retaining nuts. **Failure to disconnect intermediate shaft from rack and pinion stub shaft may cause damage to steering gear and/or intermediate shaft. This damage may cause loss of steering control.**
6. Remove engine to cradle mount retaining nuts.
7. Remove front engine horse collar bracket from block.
8. Remove outboard flywheel/starter plastic shield, then the inboard flywheel metal shield.
9. Detach starter and allow to hang from body.
10. Place jack under cradle front center crossmember.
11. Loosen rear cradle bolts. **Do not remove.**
12. Remove front cradle bolts and lower front of cradle.
13. Disconnect DIS sensor wire.
14. Remove eight oil pan retaining bolts and four oil pan retaining nuts, then the oil pan.
15. Reverse procedure to install, noting the following:
    a. Clean oil pan flanges, oil pan rail, front cover, rear main bearing cap and the threaded holes.
    b. Use new gasket.
    c. Apply suitable sealant as shown and tighten nuts and bolts to specification, **Fig. 14.**

OIL PUMP SERVICE

REMOVAL

1. Remove oil pan as previously de-

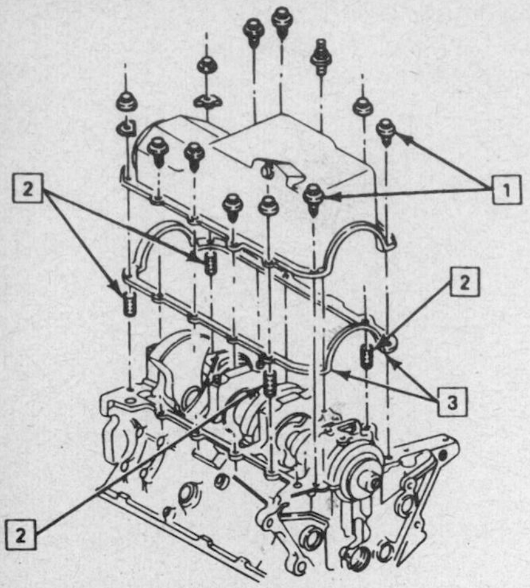
1
2
3

1 25 N·m (18 LB. FT.)
2 17 N·m (13 LB. FT.)
ALL OTHERS 10 N·m (89 LB. IN.)
3 SEALER (1052917)

GC1069100454000X

Fig. 14 Oil pan installation

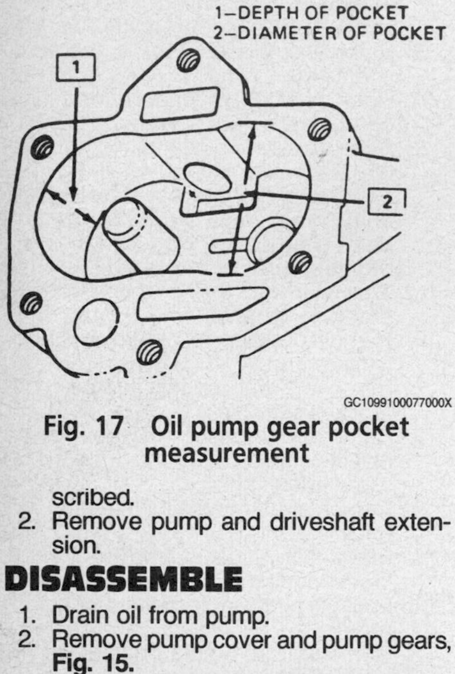
1–DEPTH OF POCKET
2–DIAMETER OF POCKET
1
2

GC1099100077000X

Fig. 17 Oil pump gear pocket measurement

scribed.

2. Remove pump and driveshaft extension.

DISASSEMBLE

1. Drain oil from pump.
2. Remove pump cover and pump gears, **Fig. 15.**
3. Remove pressure regulator valve. If valve is stuck, sock pump housing in carburetor cleaning solvent. **Pressure regulator valve spring may be under pressure. Remain retaining pin carefully.**
4. Clean sludge, oil and/or varnish from all parts. Varnish may be removed by soaking in carburetor or cleaning solvent.

INSPECTION

1. Inspect pump housing and cover for cracks or damaged threads, replacing as necessary. **Do not attempt to repair pump housing.** Replace spring as necessary.
2. Inspect idler gear shaft. If loose in housing, replace pump.

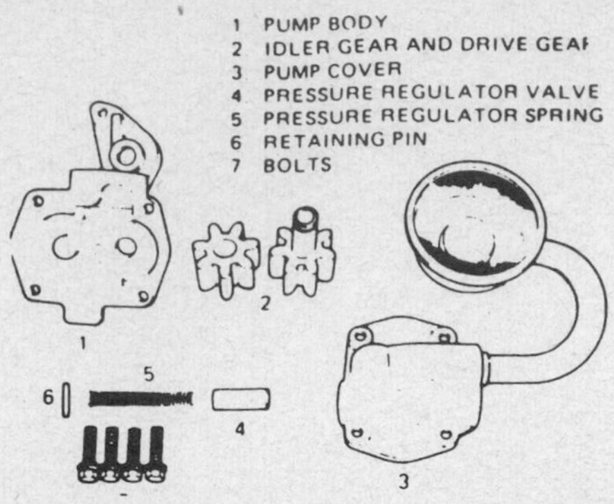
1 PUMP BODY
2 IDLER GEAR AND DRIVE GEAI
3 PUMP COVER
4 PRESSURE REGULATOR VALVE
5 PRESSURE REGULATOR SPRING
6 RETAINING PIN
7 BOLTS
1
2
3
4
5
6

GC1099100075000X

Fig. 15 Exploded view of oil pump

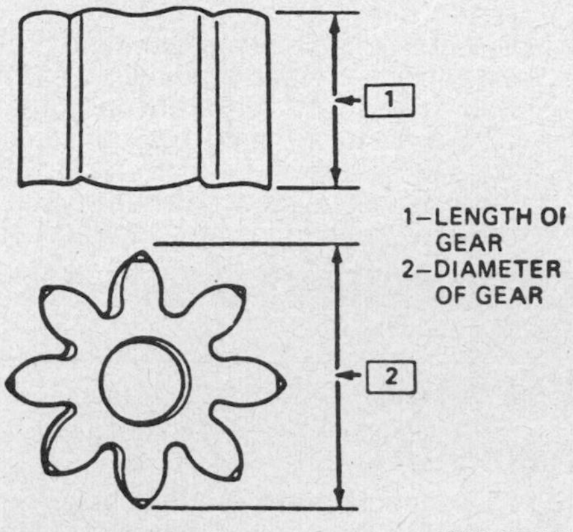
1
2
1–LENGTH OI
GEAR
2–DIAMETER
OF GEAR

GC1099100078000X

Fig. 18 Oil pump gears measurement

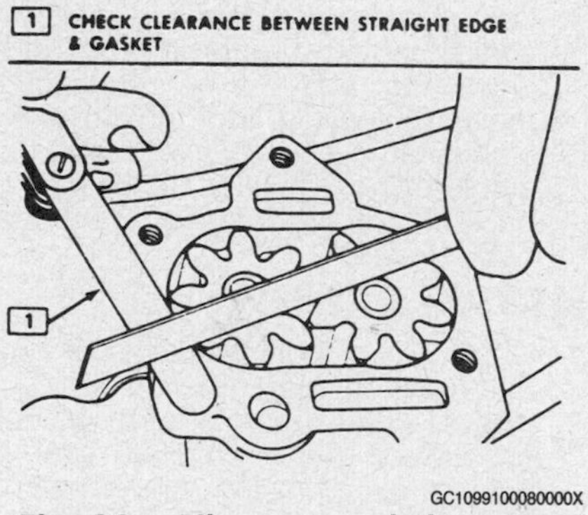
1 CHECK CLEARANCE BETWEEN STRAIGHT EDGE & GASKET
1

GC1099100080000X

Fig. 20 Oil pump end clearance measurement

3. Inspect pressure regulator valve for scoring or sticking. Burrs may be removed with a fine oil stone.
4. Inspect pressure regulator valve spring for loss of tension or bending.
5. Inspect suction pipe and screen assembly for looseness if permanently pressed into pump body. If pipe is loose or has been removed, pump body cover must be replaced. Check for broken wire mesh or screen.
6. Inspect gears for chipping, galling or wear.
7. Measure gear lash in several positions, **Fig. 16.** Gear lash should be .0037-.0077 inch.
8. Measure pump housing gear pocket depth, **Fig. 17.** as follows:

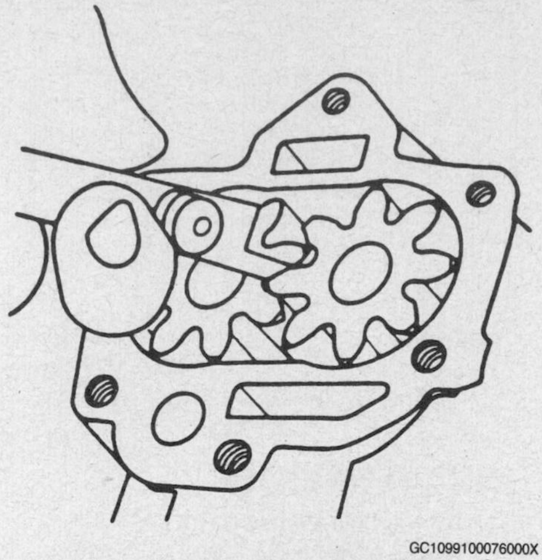

GC1099100076000X

Fig. 16 Oil pump gear lash measurement

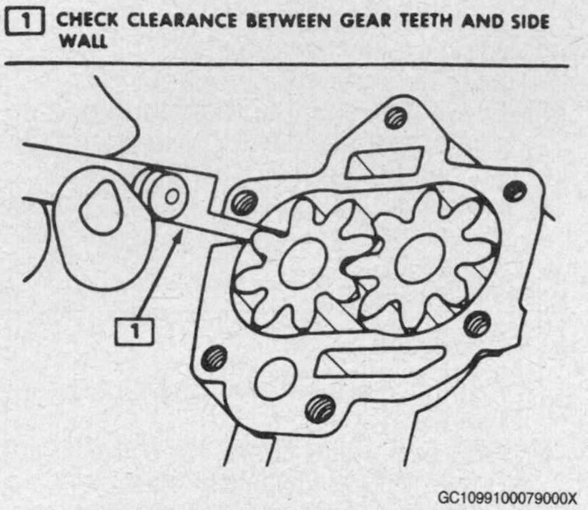
1 CHECK CLEARANCE BETWEEN GEAR TEETH AND SIDE WALL
1

GC1099100079000X

Fig. 19 Gear side clearance measurement

   a. **On models with an aluminum pump body,** pump depth should be 1.195-1.198 inches.
   b. **On models with a cast pump body,** pump depth should be 1.202-1.205 inches.
9. Measure pump housing gear pocket diameter, **Fig. 17.** Pump housing diameter should be 1.503-1.506 inches.
10. Measure pump gear diameters, **Fig. 18.** Gear diameter should be 1.498-1.500 inches.
11. Measure pump gear side clearance, **Fig. 19.** Gear side clearance should be .003-.004 inches.
12. Measure oil pump end clearance, **Fig. 20,** as follows:
   a. **On models with an aluminum pump body** end clearance should be .0016-.0067 inch.
   b. **On models with a cast pump body,** end clearance should be .002-.006 inch.

ASSEMBLE

1. Lubricate all internal parts with engine oil.
2. Install pump gears.
3. Prime engine oil galleries by removing engine oil pump drive unit and rotating oil pump, using drill motor, appropriate socket and extension.

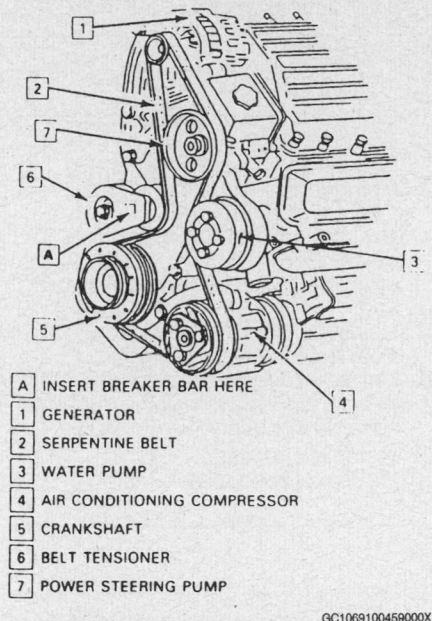

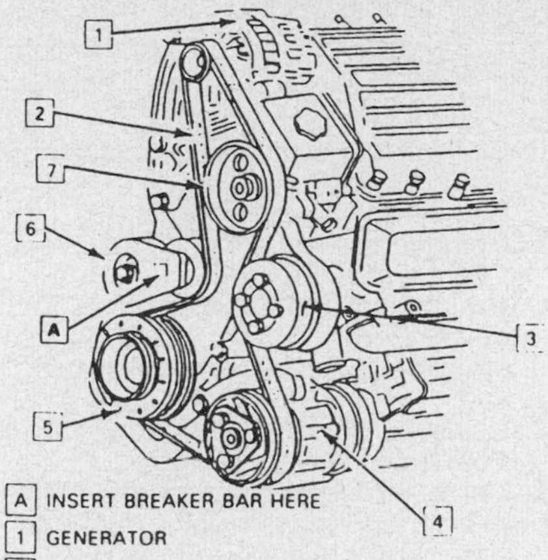
A INSERT BREAKER BAR HERE
1 GENERATOR
2 SERPENTINE BELT
3 WATER PUMP
4 AIR CONDITIONING COMPRESSOR
5 CRANKSHAFT
6 BELT TENSIONER
7 POWER STEERING PUMP
GC1069100459000X

Fig. 21 Serpentine drive belt routing

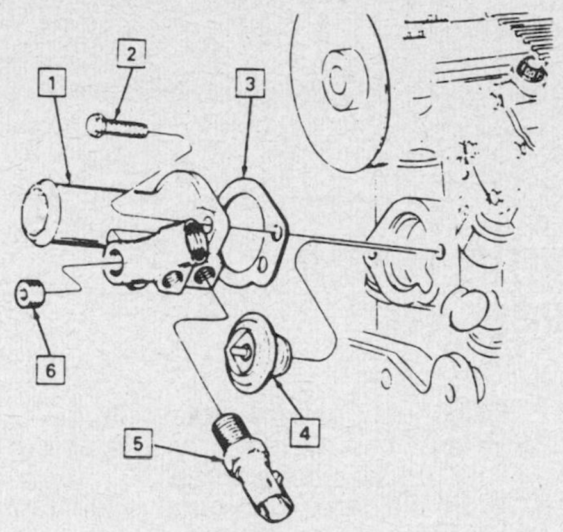
1 WATER OUTLET
2 26 N·m (19 LB. FT.)
3 GASKET
4 THERMOSTAT
5 COOLANT SENSOR
6 PLUG
GC1089100172000X

Fig. 22 Cooling system bleed vent

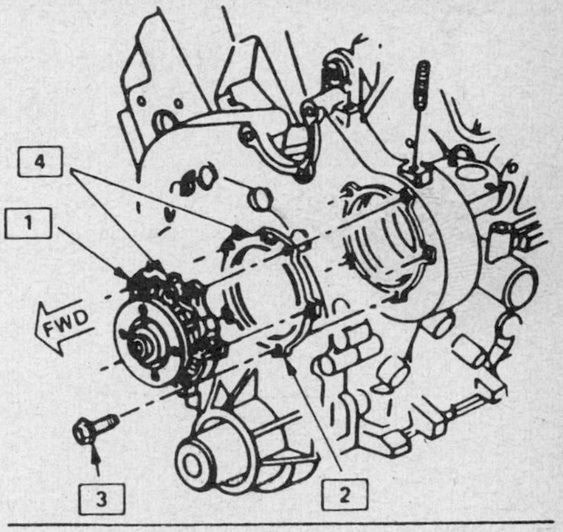
FWD
1. WATER PUMP
2. GASKET
3. 10 N·m (89 LB. IN.)
4. LOCATOR – MUST BE VERTICAL
GC1089100171000X

Fig. 23 Water pump mounting

2. Lift or rotate tensioner using a 1/2 inch breaker bar.
3. Remove serpentine belt.
4. Reverse procedure to install, routing drive belt as shown in **Fig. 21.**

COOLING SYSTEM BLEED

1. Open vent valves located on the thermostat housing and throttle body return pipe above the water pump, **Fig. 22.** Turn both vents screws two to three turns.
2. Fill cooling system to the base of the radiator neck.
3. Close both vent valves. **Do not over tighten vent valves.**
4. Install radiator cap.
5. Add sufficient coolant to the recovery tank.
6. Start engine and observe low coolant warning lamp.
7. If lamp remains On, repeat bleed procedure.

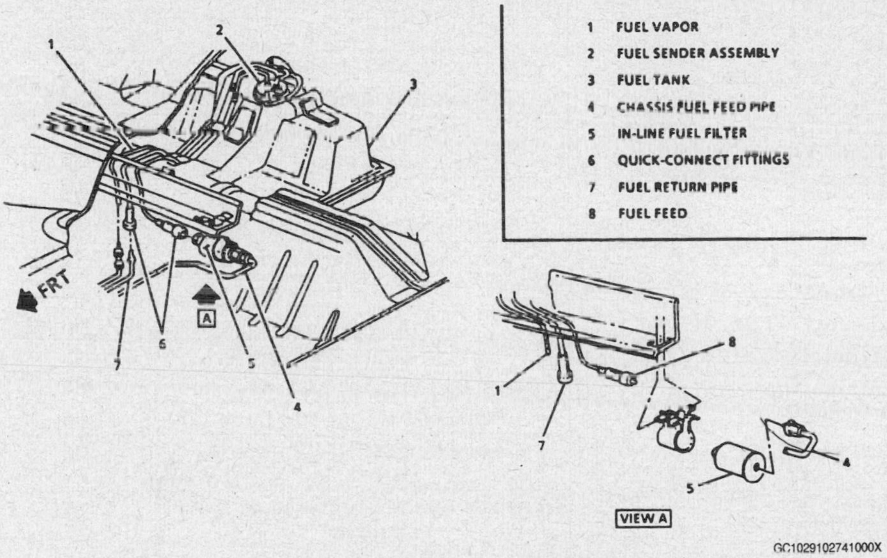
1 FUEL VAPOR
2 FUEL SENDER ASSEMBLY
3 FUEL TANK
4 CHASSIS FUEL FEED PIPE
5 IN-LINE FUEL FILTER
6 QUICK-CONNECT FITTINGS
7 FUEL RETURN PIPE
8 FUEL FEED
FRT
VIEW A
GC1029102741000X

Fig. 24 Fuel filter replacement

4. Install cover and gasket. **Use only original equipment gaskets as gasket thickness is critical to proper pump operation.**
5. Install pin, ensuring it is properly secured.
6. **Torque** pump cover attaching bolts to 89 inch. lbs.

INSTALLATION

1. Apply sealer No. 1050026, Fel-Pro set and seal, or equivalents to new pipe and tap into place with a plastic hammer, using oil suction pipe installer tool No. J-21182, or equivalent.
2. Install oil pump and driveshaft extension, engaging driveshaft extension into drive gear.
3. Install pump to rear bearing cap bolt, tightening to specifications.
4. Clean oil pan of oil and sludge and replace oil filter.
5. Install oil pan, then fill crankcase and check oil pressure. If pressure does not build up almost immediately, remove oil pan and check oil pump suction pipe attachment to pump. If necessary, disassemble oil pump, fill all cavities with petroleum jelly and reassemble. **Running engine without measurable oil pressure will cause extensive damage.**

BELT TENSION DATA

Belt tension is maintained automatically by a spring tensioned idler pulley. Adjustment of serpentine belt is not necessary.

SERPENTINE DRIVE BELT

1. Remove belt guard.

THERMOSTAT

REPLACE

1. Drain coolant.
2. Disconnect radiator hose from thermostat housing.
3. Remove thermostat housing bolts, thermostat housing and thermostat.
4. Reverse procedure to install.

WATER PUMP

REPLACE

1. Disconnect battery ground cable and drain engine coolant.
2. Remove serpentine drive belt, then disconnect radiator and heater hose.
3. Remove water pump attaching bolts, then the water pump, **Fig. 23.**
4. Reverse procedure to install. noting the following:

a. Clean water pump mating surfaces.
b. **Torque** water pump attaching bolts to 89 inch lbs.

RADIATOR
REPLACE

1. Remove air cleaner assembly, then drain coolant.
2. Remove engine strut upper brace bolts from upper tie bar and rotate strut and brace rearward.
3. Disconnect upper radiator mounting panel bolts and clamps.
4. Disconnect cooling fan electrical connector.
5. Remove cooling fan mounting bolts and fan, then upper radiator bracket.
6. Remove upper and lower radiator hoses at radiator.
7. Disconnect low coolant sensor wiring.
8. Disconnect oil cooler lines, then remove radiator.
9. Reverse procedure to install.

FUEL PUMP
REPLACE

1. Disconnect battery ground cable.
2. Relieve fuel system pressure as outlined under "Precautions."
3. Drain fuel tank, then remove fuel tank assembly.
4. Remove fuel sender assembly.
5. Reverse procedure to install.

FUEL FILTER
REPLACE

1. Relieve fuel system pressure as outlined under "Precautions."
2. Raise and support vehicle.
3. Remove bracket attaching screw and filter bracket, **Fig. 24.**
4. Grasp filter and fuel line fitting. Twist quick-connect fitting 1/4 turn in each direction to loosen any dirt within fitting.
5. Using compressed air, blow out dirt from quick-connect fitting.
6. Remove feed pipe nut from fuel filter, then drain any remaining fuel into a suitable container.
7. Remove fuel filter.
8. Reverse procedure to install.

TIGHTENING SPECIFICATIONS

Year	Component	Torque/Ft. Lbs.
1992–95	Camshaft Rear Cover	7
	Camshaft Sprocket	21
	Connecting Rod Bearing Cap Nuts	39
	Crankshaft Balancer	77
	Cylinder Head Bolts	②
	Drive Belt Tensioner Bolt	37
	Engine Bracket To Engine Bolt	④
	Engine Mount Bracket To Engine	63
	Engine Mount To Engine Mount Bracket	32
	Engine Mount To Frame	32
	Engine Strut Bracket To Engine	34
	Exhaust Crossover Nut	18
	Exhaust Manifold Bolts	19
	Exhaust Manifold Heat Shield	90①
	Flywheel Bolts	60
	Fuel Filter	22
	Fuel Tank Bolts	35
	Intake Manifold Bolts	24
	Intake Manifold Nuts	23
	Intake Manifold Studs	23
	Intercooler To Support	89①
	Main Bearing Cap Bolts	73
	Oil Cooler Connector	29
	Oil Filter	11
	Oil Level Indicator Retainer Nut	18

Year	Component	Torque/Ft. Lbs.
1992–95 -Cont'd	Oil Pan	③
	Oil Pump Drive Bolt	25
	Oil Pump	25–35
	Oxygen Sensor	31
	Rocker Arm Adjusting Nuts	14–20
	Rocker Arm Covers	7
	Spark Plugs	20
	Strut Bracket To Upper Tie Bar	16
	Strut To Engine Bracket Bolt	41
	Strut To Tie Bar Bracket	32
	Thermostat Housing	19
	Timing Chain Cover	③
	Timing Chain Dampener	15
	Transaxle Bracket To Transaxle	60
	Transaxle Mount To Frame	38
	Transaxle Mount To Transaxle Bracket	30
	Transaxle Mount To Transaxle Mount Support	38
	Water Pump	19

①—Inch lbs.
②—Torque in sequence to 33 ft. lbs. then turn an each bolt an additional 90° in sequence.
③—Refer to text.
④—Bracket side bolts, 59 ft. lbs.; bracket front bolts, 81 ft. lbs.

3.4L/V6-204 ENGINE

NOTE: On Air Bag Equipped Models, Refer To "Air Bag System Precautions" Located In The Front Of This Manual For System Disarming & Arming Procedures.

INDEX

PRECAUTIONS

AIR BAG SYSTEMS

Refer to "Air Bag System Precautions" in the front of this manual for system disarming and arming procedures.

FUEL SYSTEM PRESSURE RELIEF

To reduce the risk of fire and personal injury, it is necessary to relieve the fuel system pressure before servicing fuel system components.

1. Disconnect battery ground cable.
2. Loosen fuel tank filler cap to relieve tank pressure.
3. Connect fuel pressure gage tool No. J-34730-1, or equivalent, to the fuel pressure valve. Wrap a shop towel around fitting while connection gage to avoid spillage.
4. Install bleed hose into an approved container and open valve to bleed system pressure.

IDLE LEARN PROCEDURE

On models with 3.4L/V6-204 engine, any time vehicle power has been interrupted the programed position of the IAC valve pintle is lost. The following procedures must be performed to update the ECM memory with the correct IAC valve pintle position for the vehicle and provide a stable idle speed.

1. Restore vehicle power.
2. Connect TECH I scan tool to ALDL connector located under the lefthand side of the dash panel.
3. Select "IAC System."
4. Select "Idle Learn" in the "Misc. Test" mode.
5. Proceed as directed.

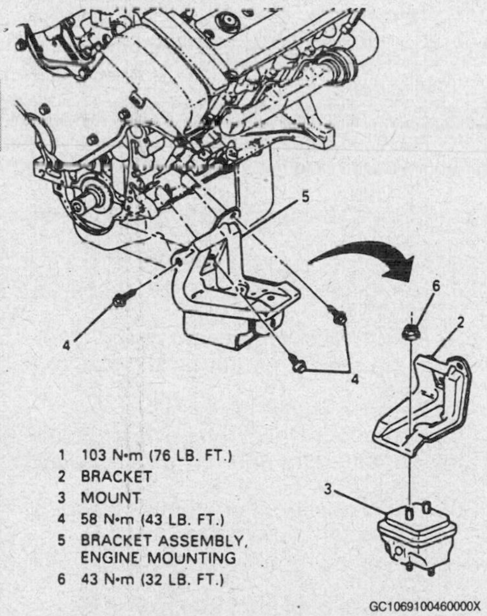

5
6
2
4
4
3
1 103 N•m (76 LB. FT.)
2 BRACKET
3 MOUNT
4 58 N•m (43 LB. FT.)
5 BRACKET ASSEMBLY, ENGINE MOUNTING
6 43 N•m (32 LB. FT.)
GC1069100460000X

Fig. 1 Front engine mounting bracket

ENGINE MOUNT

REPLACE

FRONT

1. Remove air cleaner assembly.
2. Disconnect engine torque strut.
3. Install engine support tool Nos. J-28467, J-28467-90 and J-36462, or equivalent.
4. Raise and support vehicle.
5. Remove right front tire and wheel assembly.
6. Remove righthand engine splash shield.
7. Drain engine oil into a suitable container and remove oil filter.
8. Remove front engine mount nuts at mount bracket and frame, **Fig. 1.**
9. Install drive axle boot protector and lower vehicle.
10. Raise engine.
11. Raise and support vehicle.
12. Remove front mount.
13. Reverse procedure to install.

REAR

1. Remove air cleaner assembly and disconnect engine torque strut.
2. Install engine support tool Nos. J-28467, J-28467-90 and J-36462, or equivalent, then raise and support vehicle.
3. Remove right front tire and wheel assembly, righthand engine and drive axle splash shields.
4. Install drive axle boot protector.

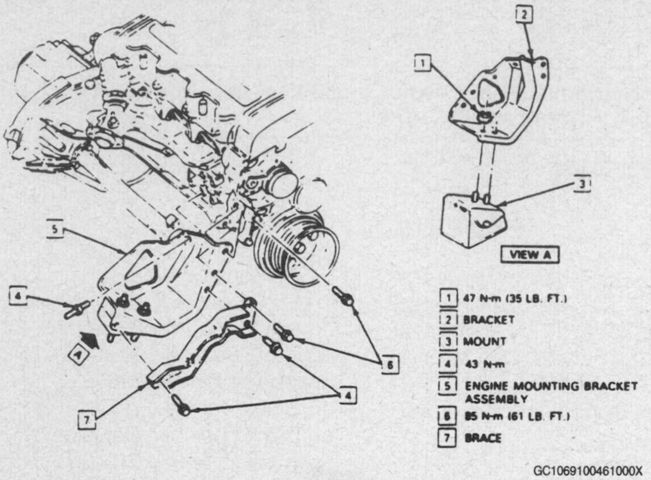
VIEW A
1 47 N·m (35 LB. FT.)
2 BRACKET
3 MOUNT
4 43 N·m
5 ENGINE MOUNTING BRACKET ASSEMBLY
6 85 N·m (61 LB. FT.)
7 BRACE
GC1069100461000X

Fig. 2 Rear engine mounting bracket. Manual transaxle

5. Remove engine mount nuts at frame, **Fig. 2 and 3.**
6. Lower vehicle and raise engine.
7. Raise and support vehicle.
8. Remove power rack and pinion mounting bolts and hang rack on frame.
9. Disconnect right ball joint from lower control arm.
10. Install a suitable jack under righthand side of frame.
11. Remove righthand frame mounting bolts.
12. Loosen lefthand frame mounting bolts.
13. Lower righthand side of frame approximately three inches.
14. Remove upper engine mount nuts at mount.
15. Remove mount.
16. Reverse procedure to install.

ENGINE

REPLACE

MANUAL TRANSAXLE

1. Disconnect battery cables and remove battery jump terminal.
2. Remove air cleaner and duct assembly.
3. Drain cooling system and remove coolant recovery tank.
4. Disconnect control cables at throttle body.
5. Remove serpentine drive belt as outlined under "Serpentine Drive Belt."
6. Disconnect wiring harness cover and upper engine wire connectors at right strut tower.
7. Disconnect engine ground near air cleaner bracket.
8. Relieve fuel system pressure as outlined under "Precautions," then disconnect fuel lines at fuel rail.
9. Disconnect heater hose quick connect at intake manifold and bracket.
10. Disconnect and remove engine torque strut.
11. Remove upper and lower radiator hoses.
12. Disconnect heater hoses at water pump.
13. Remove engine torque strut bracket at frame.
14. Remove right and left engine coolant fan retaining screws.
15. Remove upper radiator support.
16. Remove both engine cooling fans.
17. Disconnect electrical bulkhead connector at right fire wall.
18. Disconnect ECM and set on engine.
19. Remove convenience center, wiring harness cover, harness clips and low coolant sensor connector and position entire harness assembly on top of engine.
20. Discharge A/C system and disconnect A/C lines near accumulator.
21. Remove shift control cable at lever bracket.
22. Mark then disconnect all necessary vacuum lines.
23. Raise and support vehicle.
24. Remove both front tire and wheel assemblies.
25. Remove both flywheel covers.
26. Drain engine oil into a suitable container.
27. Remove starter motor.
28. Remove flywheel to converter bolts.
29. Remove right and left engine splash shields.
30. Disconnect front brake ABS electrical connectors, if equipped.
31. Disconnect front exhaust pipe and converter assembly.
32. Remove both front brake calipers and support on body.
33. Disconnect steering column intermediate shaft pinch bolt and remove shaft from stub.
34. Position transaxle jack under power train.
35. Disconnect and plug transaxle cooler lines.
36. Remove frame bolts.
37. Lower powertrain from vehicle.
38. Disconnect electrical connectors and harness from left lower side of engine.
39. Remove A/C compressor with lines attached.
40. Disconnect electrical, alternator and sensor connectors and ground connections from rear of engine.
41. Remove exhaust crossover pipe.
42. Remove right axle from transaxle as outlined under "Drive Axle, Replace" in the "Front Wheel Drive Axles" section.
43. Remove drive axle shield.
44. Remove engine mounts as outlined under "Engine Mount, Replace."
45. Remove power steering pump assembly.
46. Remove transaxle to engine bolts.
47. Install engine lifting device and remove engine assembly from transaxle.
48. Reverse procedure to install.

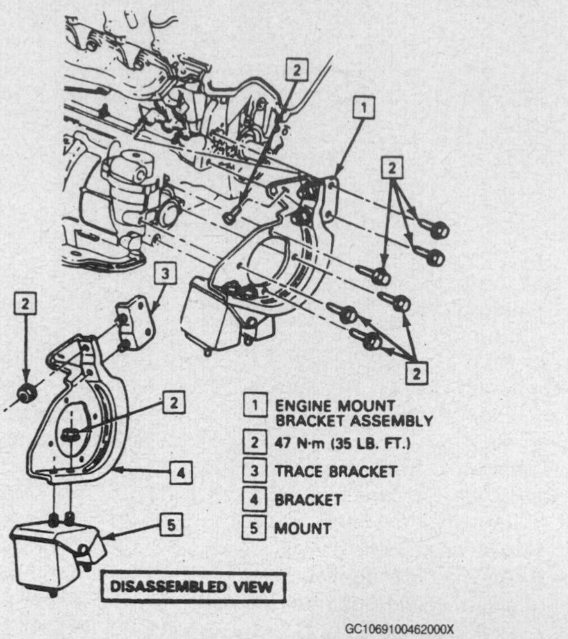
DISASSEMBLED VIEW
1 ENGINE MOUNT BRACKET ASSEMBLY
2 47 N·m (35 LB. FT.)
3 TRACE BRACKET
4 BRACKET
5 MOUNT
GC1069100462000X

Fig. 3 Rear engine mounting bracket. Automatic transaxle

AUTOMATIC TRANSAXLE

1. Relieve fuel system pressure as outlined under "Precautions."
2. Remove air cleaner assembly.
3. Mark and remove hood assembly.
4. Disconnect battery ground cable and drain cooling system.
5. Discharge A/C system and remove coolant recovery tank.
6. Remove heater hoses from engine.
7. Disconnect engine torque strut mount and stud.
8. Disconnect and remove engine cooling fans.
9. Remove radiator hoses from engine.
10. Disconnect control cables from bracket and throttle body.
11. Disconnect bulkhead connections from cowl.
12. Disconnect fuel lines from engine.
13. Remove exhaust crossover pipe.
14. Remove lower transaxle to engine bolts including ground wires.
15. Remove power steering pump from

engine and position aside.
16. Disconnect EGR pipe from EGR valve.
17. Raise and support vehicle.
18. Remove right tire and wheel assembly then the right splash shield.
19. Disconnect A/C manifold from A/C compressor.
20. Remove flywheel and steel torque converter inspection covers then starter.
21. Remove front exhaust pipe and converter.
22. Disconnect motor mounts as outlined under "Engine Mount, Replace."
23. Disconnect electrical connections at front and rear of engine then from alternator.
24. Remove torque converter bolts.
25. Remove right ball joint bolt and separate joint from control arm.
26. Remove drive axle assembly.
27. Lower vehicle.
28. Support transaxle using a suitable jack and install lifting device on engine.
29. Disconnect quick connects near ECM.
30. Remove remaining transaxle to engine bolts.
31. Disconnect necessary vacuum lines from rear of engine.
32. Remove engine assembly.
33. Reverse procedure to install.

INTAKE MANIFOLD

REPLACE

1. Relieve fuel system pressure as outlined under "Precautions."
2. Remove air cleaner assembly.
3. Disconnect battery ground cable and drain cooling system.
4. Remove control cables at throttle body.
5. Disconnect fuel rail cover bolts and remove fuel pipes at fuel rail.
6. Disconnect heater hose at intake manifold.
7. Disconnect vacuum lines from PCV valve and throttle body of plenum.
8. Disconnect AIR solenoid, EGR valve, canister purge solenoid, MAP sensor and throttle position sensor connectors.
9. Remove EGR bolts and EGR valve.
10. Disconnect fuel line bracket and heater hose at throttle body of plenum.
11. Disconnect all necessary vacuum lines at plenum.
12. Remove wire loom bracket for rear bank of spark plug wires.
13. Remove nuts at plenum and plenum bracket.
14. Remove plenum from vehicle.
15. Disconnect fuel rail as follows:
    a. Remove fuel line bracket bolts.
    b. Disconnect fuel lines at fuel rail using a suitable back-up wrench on the fuel rail fittings.
    c. Disconnect vacuum lines at pressure regulator.
    d. Remove fuel rail bolts.
    e. Disconnect injector electrical connectors.
    f. Remove fuel rail from vehicle.
16. Disconnect heater hose pipe bracket

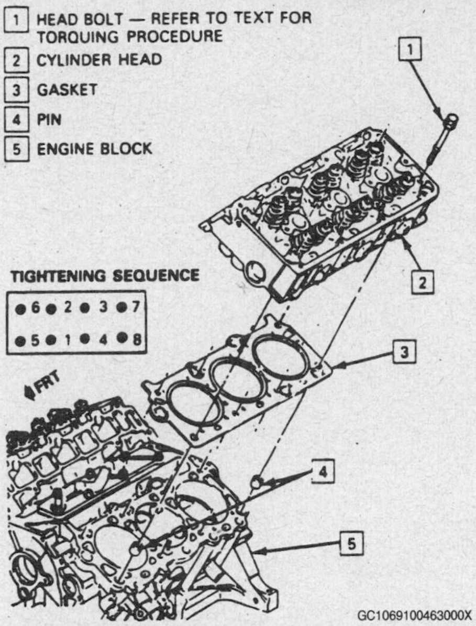
1 HEAD BOLT — REFER TO TEXT FOR TORQUING PROCEDURE
2 CYLINDER HEAD
3 GASKET
4 PIN
5 ENGINE BLOCK
TIGHTENING SEQUENCE
6 2 3 7
5 1 4 8
FRT
GC1069100463000X

Fig. 4 Cylinder head bolt tightening sequence

from thermostat housing.
17. Remove temperature sensor from intake manifold.
18. Disconnect radiator hose from thermostat housing.
19. Remove intake manifold bolts and intake manifold.
20. Reverse procedure to install, inserting rubber isolators fully into manifold flange before tightening fasteners to specifications.

EXHAUST MANIFOLD

REPLACE

FRONT

1. Remove air cleaner assembly.
2. Remove exhaust crossover pipe.
3. Remove engine torque strut bracket to frame bolts and lift strut out of the way.
4. Remove upper radiator shroud, right side cooling fan heat shield and right cooling fan assembly.
5. **On models with manual transaxle,** remove front hose from air pipe.
6. **On all models,** remove exhaust manifold nuts then the manifold and heat shield.
7. Reverse procedure to install.

REAR

Automatic Transaxle

1. Remove rear cam carrier as outlined under "Camshaft Carrier, Replace."
2. Remove exhaust crossover pipe.
3. Raise and support vehicle.
4. Disconnect front exhaust pipe at manifold.
5. Lower vehicle.
6. Disconnect oxygen sensor connector.
7. Remove exhaust manifold nuts then the manifold and heat shield.
8. Reverse procedure to install.

Manual Transaxle

1. Remove air cleaner assembly.
2. Disconnect battery ground cable.
3. Remove exhaust crossover pipe.
4. Raise and support vehicle.
5. Disconnect front exhaust manifold pipe.
6. Disconnect and remove oxygen sensor.
7. Remove exhaust manifold heat shield and disconnect EGR pipe at manifold.
8. Remove exhaust manifold nuts then the exhaust manifold.
9. Reverse procedure to install.

CYLINDER HEAD

REPLACE

FRONT

1. Relieve fuel system pressure as outlined under "Precautions."
2. Remove intake manifold, camshaft carrier and exhaust manifold as outlined under "Intake Manifold, Replace, "Camshaft Carrier, Replace" and "Exhaust Manifold, Replace."
3. Remove right cooling fan assembly.
4. Remove oil level indicator tube.
5. Disconnect temperature sending unit connector.
6. Remove cylinder head bolts then the cylinder head.
7. Reverse procedure to install, noting the following:
    a. Install cylinder head gasket with metal tabs between cylinders facing up.
    b. **Torque** cylinder head bolts in sequence shown in **Fig. 4** to 33 ft. lbs. plus an additional 90° turn using torque/angle meter tool No. J-36660, or equivalent.

REAR

1. Relieve fuel system pressure as outlined under "Precautions."
2. Remove intake manifold, camshaft carrier and exhaust manifold as outlined under "Intake Manifold, Replace, "Camshaft Carrier, Replace" and "Exhaust Manifold, Replace."
3. Disconnect oxygen sensor connector.
4. Remove rear timing belt tensioner bracket.
5. Remove cylinder head bolts then the cylinder head and gasket.
6. Reverse procedure to install, noting the following:
    a. Install cylinder head gasket with metal tabs between cylinders facing up.
    b. **Torque** cylinder head bolts in sequence shown in **Fig. 4** to 33 ft. lbs. plus an additional 90° using torque/angle meter tool No. J-36660, or equivalent.

VALVE LIFTERS

1. Remove camshaft carrier as outlined under "Camshaft Carrier, Replace."
2. Remove six lifter hold-down hoses.
3. Remove lifters.
4. Reverse procedure to install.

VALVE STEM OIL SEAL & SPRING

Head On Engine

1. Remove camshaft carrier as outlined under "Camshaft Carrier, Replace."
2. Remove spark plugs and install spark plug port adapter tool No. J-22794, or equivalent, and apply compressed air to hold valves in place.
3. Compress valve spring using valve

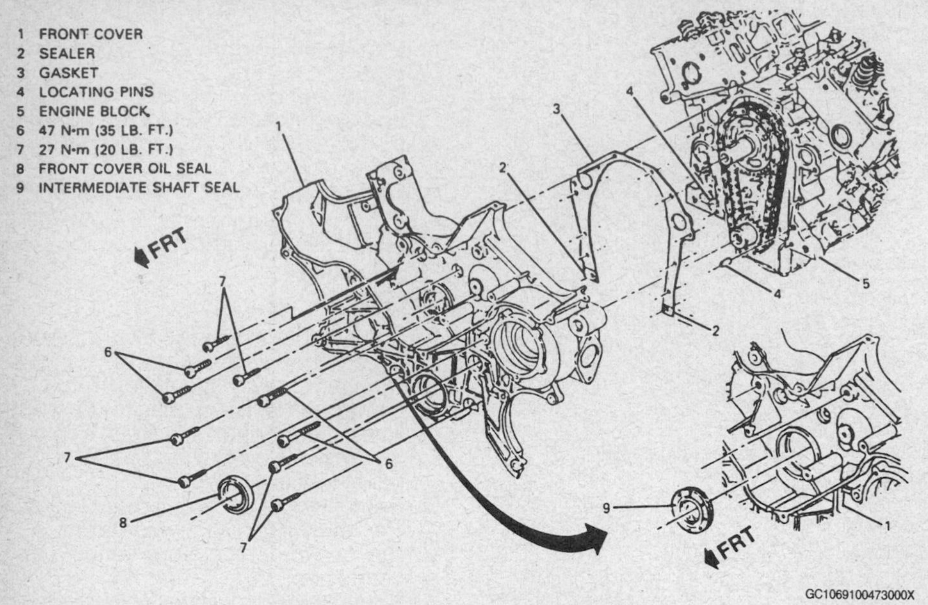
1 FRONT COVER
2 SEALER
3 GASKET
4 LOCATING PINS
5 ENGINE BLOCK
6 47 N•m (35 LB. FT.)
7 27 N•m (20 LB. FT.)
8 FRONT COVER OIL SEAL
9 INTERMEDIATE SHAFT SEAL
FRT
FRT
GC1069100473000X

Fig. 5 Front cover & oil seal

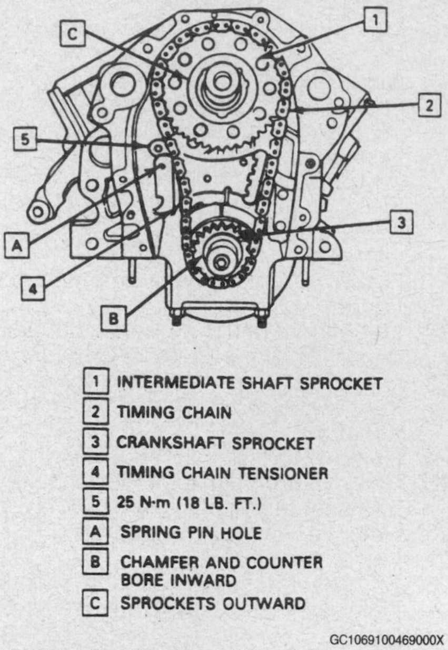
1 INTERMEDIATE SHAFT SPROCKET
2 TIMING CHAIN
3 CRANKSHAFT SPROCKET
4 TIMING CHAIN TENSIONER
5 25 N•m (18 LB. FT.)
A SPRING PIN HOLE
B CHAMFER AND COUNTER BORE INWARD
C SPROCKETS OUTWARD
GC1069100469000X

Fig. 6 Timing chain assembly

spring compressor tool No. J-38606, or equivalent.

4. Remove valve stem locks and release spring tension.
5. Remove valve cap, valve spring and valve stem oil seal. **Wrap tape over valve lock grooves to prevent damage to valve seals.**
6. Reverse procedure to install.

Head Off Engine

1. Compress valve spring using valve spring compressor tool No. J-38606, or equivalent.
2. Remove valve stem locks and release spring tension.
3. Remove valve cap, valve spring and valve stem oil seal. **Wrap tape over valve lock grooves to prevent damage to valve seals.**
4. Reverse procedure to install.

CAMSHAFT LOBE LIFT SPECIFICATIONS

Intake	.370 inch
Exhaust	.370 inch

CRANKSHAFT DAMPER

REPLACE

1. Remove serpentine drive belt as outlined under "Serpentine Drive Belt."
2. Raise and support vehicle.
3. Remove right tire and wheel assembly then the engine splash shield.
4. Remove starter as outlined under "Starter, Replace" in the "Electrical" section.
5. Remove crankshaft damper bolt using flywheel holding tool No. J-37096, or equivalent.
6. Remove crankshaft pulley bolt and pulley.
7. Remove crankshaft damper using crankshaft damper removal tool No. J-24430, or equivalent.
8. Reverse procedure to install, noting the following:
   a. Coat front cover oil seal with engine oil.
   b. Install suitable sealant to keyway of damper before installation.
   c. Install damper using crankshaft damper installer tool No. J-29113, or equivalent.

FRONT COVER

REPLACE

1. Remove secondary timing belt tensioner mounting bracket and idler pulleys as outlined under "Timing Belt, Replace."
2. Remove engine front lift hook.
3. Remove engine torque strut bracket from frame and pull strut and bracket out of the way.
4. Remove upper radiator support.
5. Remove righthand cooling fan heat shield then the cooling fan assembly.
6. Remove lower radiator hose from coolant pump.
7. **On models with manual transaxles,** remove front air hose at air pipe.
8. **On all models,** remove heater hose at front cover and heater pipe bracket at frame.
9. Raise and support vehicle.
10. Remove right tire and wheel assembly then the engine splash shield.
11. Remove crankshaft pulley and damper as outlined under "Crankshaft Damper, Replace."
12. Drain engine oil into a suitable container and remove oil filter.
13. Remove A/C compressor mounting bolts.
14. Remove lower front cover bolts, **Fig. 5.**
15. **On models with automatic transaxle,** remove drive axle assembly.
16. **On all models,** remove rear alternator bracket then the starter motor.
17. Lower vehicle.
18. Remove intermediate timing belt sprocket as outlined under "Intermediate Shaft Belt Sprocket & Oil Seal, Replace," in "Camshaft, Replace" section.
19. Remove upper alternator retaining bolts.
20. Remove forward lamp relay center screws and position relay center aside.
21. Remove oil cooler hose from front cover.
22. Remove water pump pulley.
23. Remove front cover upper bolts then the front cover and gasket.
24. Reverse procedure to install, noting the following:
    a. Apply GM sealer part No. 1052080, or equivalent, to lower edges of sealing surface of front cover.
    b. Apply suitable thread sealant to large bolts.
    c. Tighten attaching bolts to specifications.

FRONT COVER SEAL

REPLACE

1. Remove crankshaft pulley and damper as outlined under "Crankshaft Damper, Replace."
2. Pry out seal using a suitable pry tool.
3. Reverse procedure to install, lubricate seal with oil and install using seal installer tool No. J-34995, or equivalent.

TIMING CHAIN

REPLACE

1. Raise and support vehicle.
2. Remove starter and flywheel cover.
3. Remove oil pan as outlined under "Oil Pan, Replace."
4. Remove engine as outlined under "Engine, Replace."
5. Remove front cover as outlined under "Front Cover, Replace."
6. Mark reference points on the intermediate sprocket, chain link, front face of

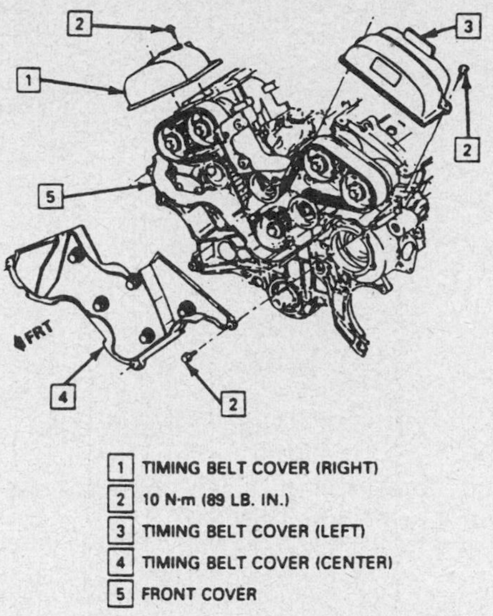
1 TIMING BELT COVER (RIGHT)
2 10 N·m (89 LB. IN.)
3 TIMING BELT COVER (LEFT)
4 TIMING BELT COVER (CENTER)
5 FRONT COVER
FRT

GC1069100464000X

Fig. 7 Timing belt covers

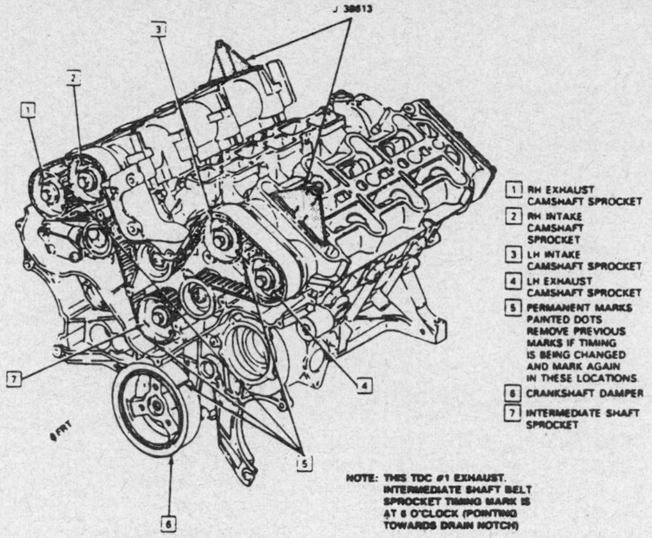
J 38613
1 RH EXHAUST CAMSHAFT SPROCKET
2 RH INTAKE CAMSHAFT SPROCKET
3 LH INTAKE CAMSHAFT SPROCKET
4 LH EXHAUST CAMSHAFT SPROCKET
5 PERMANENT MARKS PAINTED DOTS REMOVE PREVIOUS MARKS IF TIMING IS BEING CHANGED AND MARK AGAIN IN THESE LOCATIONS.
6 CRANKSHAFT DAMPER
7 INTERMEDIATE SHAFT SPROCKET
NOTE: THIS TDC #1 EXHAUST. INTERMEDIATE SHAFT BELT SPROCKET TIMING MARK IS AT 6 O'CLOCK (POINTING TOWARDS DRAIN NOTCH)
FRT

GC1069100465000X

Fig. 8 Engine timing marks

cylinder and crankshaft sprocket, **Fig. 6.**

7. Retract timing chain tensioner as outlined under "Timing Chain Tensioner, Replace."
8. Remove timing chain and crankshaft sprocket using universal puller bridge tool No. J-8433, or equivalent, and special legs and protector tool No. J-38611, or equivalent. If intermediate gear does not slide off easily with timing chain, rotate crankshaft back and forth to help loosen gear.
9. Reverse procedure to install, noting the following:
   a. Aligning marks made during dis assembling.
   b. Large chamfer and counterbore of crankshaft sprocket are installed toward the crankshaft.
   c. Intermediate shaft sprocket spline sockets are installed away from the case.
   d. Crankshaft sprocket must be pressed on for the final .31 inch to seated position using crankshaft gear installer tool No. J-38612, or equivalent.

TIMING BELT

REPLACE

REMOVAL

1. Remove secondary timing belt actuator as outlined under "Tensioner Plate & Actuator, Replace" in this section.
2. If belt is to be reused, mark rotation direction on timing belt.
3. Remove tensioner pulley/arm assembly as outlined under "Tensioner Plate & Actuator, Replace" in this section.
4. Remove timing belt, by carefully sliding it off pulleys.

INSTALLATION

1. Install actuator and side plate. **Ensure reference marks on sprockets are properly aligned.**
2. Install timing belt by routing it around idlers and sprockets as follows:
   a. Start at intermediate camshaft sprocket and work counterclockwise.
   b. Ensure belt is installed in direction of rotation.
   c. Engage teeth into sprockets, place rubber hose behind belt at intermediate sprocket and accumulate slack at tensioner location.
3. Install tensioner pulley to mounting base as follows:
   a. Use a flat magnet, tape or cup plug to hold pivot tube in pulley during this step.
   b. After starting pivot bolt, rotate arm counterclockwise to position square lug at 6 o'clock position.
   c. **Torque** pivot bolt to 37 ft. lbs.
4. Install actuator.

COVER, REPLACE

Right

1. Disconnect battery ground cable.
2. Remove secondary timing belt right cover bolts then the belt cover, **Fig. 7.**
3. Reverse procedure to install.

Left

1. Disconnect battery ground cable.
2. Remove spark plug cover as follows:
   a. Disconnect vacuum hose from camshaft carrier cover.
   b. Remove spark plug cover bolts then the cover.
3. Remove secondary timing belt left cover bolts then the cover, **Fig. 7.**
4. Reverse procedure to install.

Center

1. Disconnect battery ground cable.
2. Remove ECM harness cover.
3. Remove serpentine belt tensioner as outlined under "Serpentine Drive Belt.
4. Remove secondary timing belt right and left covers as outlined under previously.
5. Disconnect power steering pipe retaining clip nut at alternator stud.
6. Remove secondary timing belt center cover bolts then the belt cover, **Fig. 7.**
7. Reverse procedure to install.

TENSIONER PLATE & ACTUATOR, REPLACE

Removal

1. Remove power steering pump as outlined under "Power Steering Pump, Replace" in the "Front Suspension & Steering" section.
2. Remove secondary timing belt center cover as outlined under "Cover, Replace"in this section.
3. Rotate engine clockwise to align timing marks on camshaft sprockets, **Fig. 8.**
4. Verify tensioner pulley position to determine if length of belt is satisfactory as follows:
   a. Insert a flat, narrow .02 inch thick, ruler along the tensioner pulley and engage the steps in the tensioner base and note the reading at the top of the tensioner pulley, **Fig. 9.**
   b. If reading is 1.56-1.68 inch, belt is in acceptable range.
   c. If reading is 1.70-1.84 inch, belt is to be replaced.
5. Loosely clamp two camshaft sprockets on each side of engine together using clamping pliers, or equivalent. **Do not mar camshaft sprockets with clamping device.**
6. Hold belt to righthand exhaust camshaft sprocket with a C-clamp and a wide pad on belt. **No deflection of camshaft sprocket should be noted, if deflection is noted, loosen clamping device.**
7. Remove tensioner side plate retaining bolts from tensioner and remove the side plate from the actuator and base, **Fig. 10.**
8. Rotate actuator assembly around the

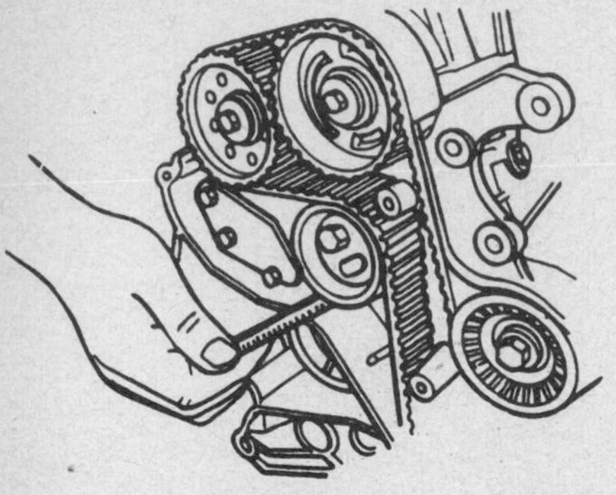

GC1069100466000X

Fig. 9 Actuator measurement

arm pivot and out of the mounting base. Removal of tensioner from base allows it to extend to its maximum travel. **Do not lose or damage tapered bushing when removing tensioner assembly.**

9. Set actuator on table in vertical position to allow oil to drain to boot end, for 5 minutes prior to refilling.
10. Form a double loop in a .032 inch diameter paper clip leaving a 1.85 inch straight length as shown in **Fig. 11.**
11. Remove rubber end plug from rear of tensioner assembly. The assembly is filled with oil and removal of plug may allow oil to escape.
12. Insert paper clip through center hole in vent plug and into pilot hole.
13. Insert a small screwdriver into screw slot inside end of tensioner.
14. Retract tensioner plunger by rotating screw in a clockwise direction while pushing rod tip against the table top, until fully retracted.
15. Rotate screw slot to align with vent hole, and push the straight section of paper clip into screw slot to retain plunger in retracted position.
16. If tensioner oil has been lost, fill tensioner with SAE 5W-30 Mobil 1, or equivalent, engine oil through end hole. Fill to bottom of plug hole only when plunger is fully retracted and pin is installed.

Installation

1. Install rubber end plug to rear of actuator assembly.
2. Insert actuator bushing into side plate.
3. Install actuator assembly into mounting base by inserting tapered trunnion of tensioner into matching hole of bushing in bracket and installing side plate bolts. Ensure installed actuator assembly rotates freely.
4. Gently rotate tensioner pulley 11 ft. lbs. counterclockwise into belt using square lug in arm and engage actuator shaft in arm socket.
5. Pull out paper clip and allow pulley to move into belt.
6. Remove sprocket clamp and any other belt holding device.
7. Repeat step 4 and **torquing** 12-15 ft. lbs. to set initial tension on belt.
8. Rotate engine clockwise three times to seat belt. Ensure sprocket reference marks are aligned properly.

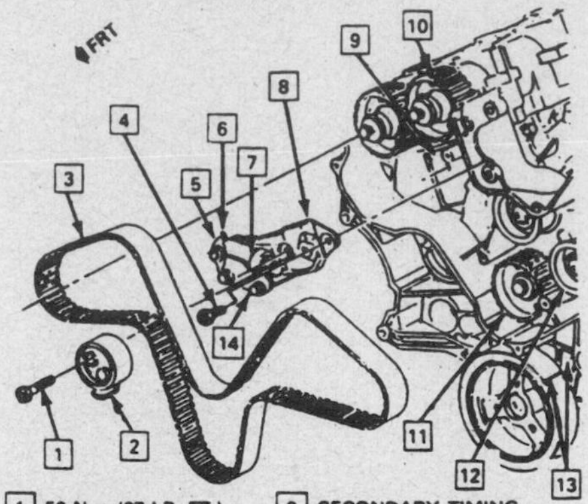
FRT

1 50 N·m (37 LB. FT.)
2 PULLEY ASSEMBLY
3 SECONDARY TIMING BELT
4 50 N·m (37 LB. FT.)
5 ACTUATOR
6 LOCK PIN (PAPER CLIP)
7 SIDE PLATE
8 SECONDARY TIMING BELT TENSIONER BRACKET
9 CYLINDER HEAD
10 DRIVEN SPROCKET
11 DRIVE SPROCKET
12 IDLER ASSEMBLY
13 CRANKSHAFT REFERENCE MARKS
14 25 N·m (18 LB. FT.)

GC1069100467000X

Fig. 10 Timing belt system

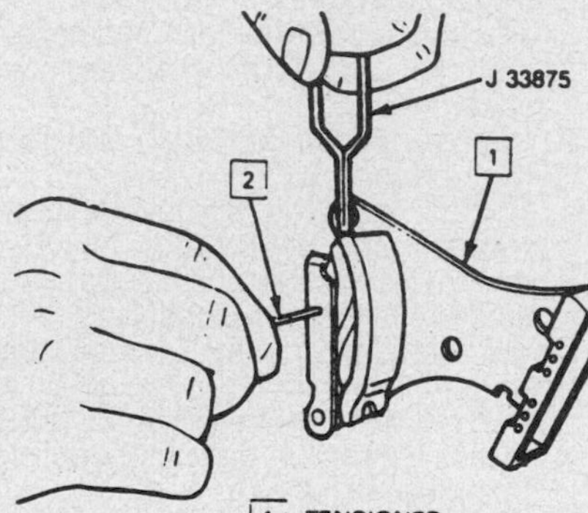
J 33875

1 TENSIONER
2 PIN

GC1069100470000X

Fig. 12 Retracting timing chain tensioner

9. Verify tensioner pulley position to determine if length of belt is satisfactory as follows:
   a. Insert a flat, narrow .02 inch thick ruler along the tensioner pulley and engage the steps in the tensioner base and note the reading at the top of the tensioner pulley, **Fig. 9.**
   b. If reading is 1.56-1.68 inch, belt is in acceptable range.
   c. If reading is 1.70-1.84 inch, belt is to be replaced.
10. Install secondary timing belt center cover as outlined under "Timing Belt, Replace."
11. Install power steering pump as outlined under "Power Steering Pump, Replace" in the "Front Suspension & Steering" section.

TENSIONER PULLEY, ARM & BRACKET, REPLACE

1. Remove secondary timing belt tensioner plate and actuator as outlined under "Secondary Timing Belt, Service."

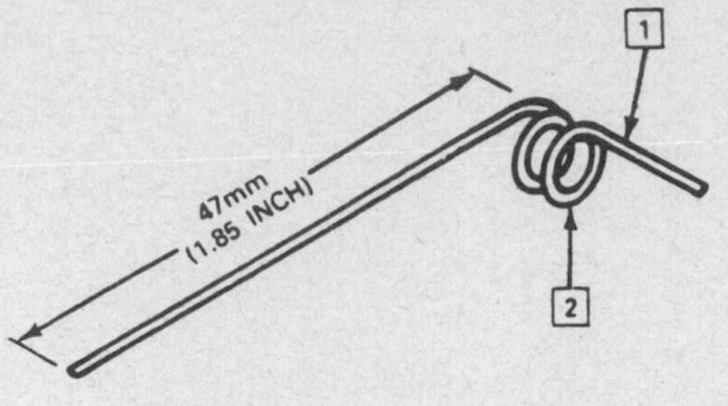
47mm
(1.85 INCH)

1 PAPER CLIP
2 DOUBLE LOOP

GC1069100468000X

Fig. 11 Paper clip retooling

2. Remove tensioner pulley bolt and pulley/arm assembly.
3. Remove mounting bracket bolts then the mounting bracket.
4. Reverse procedure to install, ensuring correct replacement color code on bracket is used.

TIMING CHAIN TENSIONER

REPLACE

1. Remove timing chain as outlined under "Timing Chain, Replace."
2. Retract tensioner shoe using tensioner retractor tool No. J-33875, or equivalent, as follows, **Fig. 12.**
   a. Insert tool on both sides of tensioner. Pull on through pin in tensioner arm to retract spring located in tensioner arm.
   b. While compressing spring, use a suitable tool and insert in hole to retain spring.
3. Remove timing chain and sprockets as outlined under "Timing Chain & Sprockets, Replace."
4. Remove tensioner mounting bolts then the tensioner.
5. Inspect tensioner for wear, cracks or other damage.
6. With tensioner shoe retracted, install tensioner to engine block.
7. Lightly coat tensioner chain surfaces with oil.
8. Install timing chain as outlined under "Timing Chain, Replace."

CAMSHAFT CARRIER COVER

REPLACE

FRONT

1. Disconnect oil/air breather hose from cover.
2. Remove spark plug wires from plugs.
3. Remove rear spark plug wire cover.
4. Remove camshaft carrier cover bolts then the cover and O-ring.
5. Reverse procedure to install, ensuring bolt isolators are fully seated into cover before tightening cover bolts.

REAR

1. Remove intake plenum as outlined under "Intake Manifold, Replace."

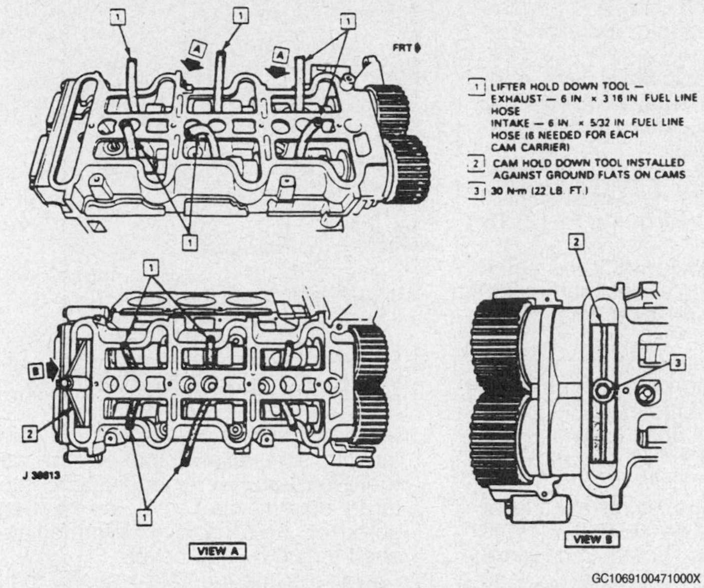
FRT
1 LIFTER HOLD DOWN TOOL —
EXHAUST — 6 IN. × 3/16 IN. FUEL LINE HOSE
INTAKE — 6 IN. × 5/32 IN. FUEL LINE HOSE (6 NEEDED FOR EACH CAM CARRIER)
2 CAM HOLD DOWN TOOL INSTALLED AGAINST GROUND FLATS ON CAMS
3 30 N·m (22 LB. FT.)
J 38613
VIEW A
VIEW B
GC1069100471000X

Fig. 13 Lifter & camshaft hold-down tool

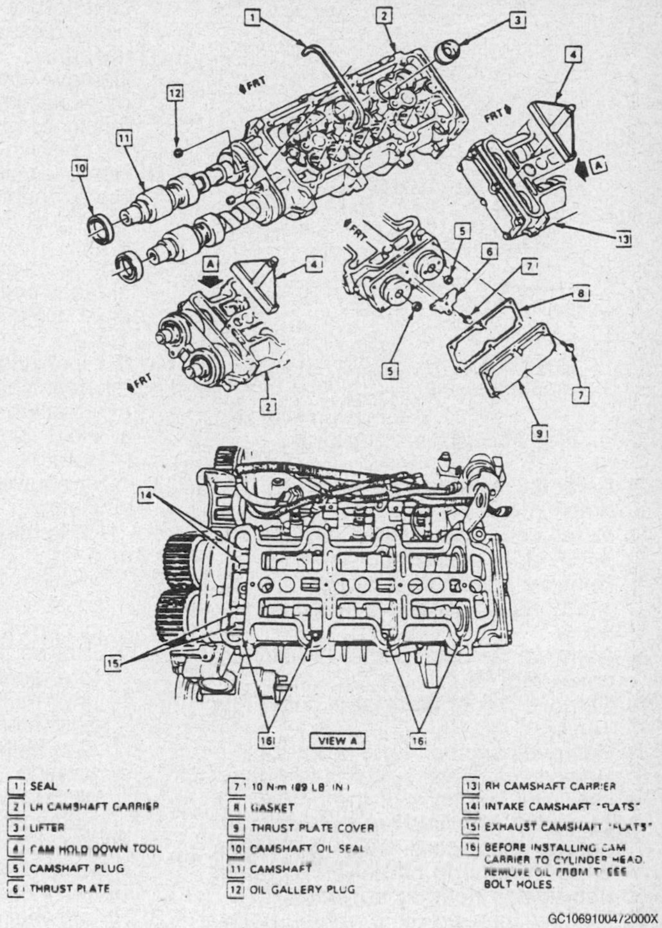
FRT
VIEW A
1 SEAL
2 LH CAMSHAFT CARRIER
3 LIFTER
4 CAM HOLD DOWN TOOL
5 CAMSHAFT PLUG
6 THRUST PLATE
7 10 N·m (89 LB. IN.)
8 GASKET
9 THRUST PLATE COVER
10 CAMSHAFT OIL SEAL
11 CAMSHAFT
12 OIL GALLERY PLUG
13 RH CAMSHAFT CARRIER
14 INTAKE CAMSHAFT "FLATS"
15 EXHAUST CAMSHAFT "FLATS"
16 BEFORE INSTALLING CAM CARRIER TO CYLINDER HEAD, REMOVE OIL FROM THESE BOLT HOLES.
GC1069100472000X

Fig. 14 Camshaft carrier components

2. Remove secondary timing belt right cover as outlined under "Timing Belt, Replace."
3. Remove spark plug wires and oil/air separator hose at camshaft cover.
4. Remove camshaft cover bolts then the camshaft cover and gaskets.
5. Reverse procedure to install, ensuring bolt isolators are fully seated into cover before tightening cover bolts.

CAMSHAFT CARRIER

REPLACE

FRONT

1. Remove left camshaft carrier cover as outlined under "Camshaft Carrier Cover, Replace."
2. Remove secondary timing belt as outlined under "Timing Belt, Replace."
3. Install fuel line hoses under camshaft and between lifters to hold lifters in carrier as shown in **Fig. 13.**
4. Remove exhaust crossover pipe.
5. Remove engine torque strut and strut bracket on engine.
6. Remove camshaft carrier bolts and nut then the camshaft carrier and gasket.
7. Reverse procedure to install, noting the following:
   a. Remove oil from camshaft carrier to cylinder head bolt holes, **Fig. 14.**
   b. Use petroleum jelly in lifter bores, along with hoses to keep lifters in place.

REAR

1. Remove right camshaft carrier cover as outlined under "Camshaft Carrier Cover, Replace."
2. Remove secondary timing belt as outlined under "Timing Belt, Replace."
3. Install fuel line hoses under camshaft and between lifters to hold lifters in carrier as shown in **Fig. 13.**
4. Remove front engine lift hook.
5. Remove camshaft carrier bolts and nut then the camshaft carrier and gasket.
6. Reverse procedure to install, noting the following:
   a. Remove oil from camshaft carrier to cylinder head bolt holes **Fig. 14.**
   b. Use petroleum jelly in lifter bores, along with hoses to keep lifters in place.

CAMSHAFT SPROCKET

REPLACE

REMOVAL

1. Remove camshaft carrier covers as outlined under "Camshaft Carrier Cover, Replace."
2. Remove secondary timing belt and covers as outlined under "Timing Belt, Replace."
3. Remove clamping device from sprocket.
4. Rotate camshafts so flats on camshaft to be serviced are facing up, **Fig. 14.**
5. Install camshaft hold-down tool No. J-38613, or equivalent, and **Torque** bolt to 22 ft. lbs., **Fig. 13.**
6. Remove camshaft sprocket bolt and washer using camshaft holding tool Nos. J38613 and J-38614, or equivalent.
7. Remove camshaft sprocket using sprocket remover tool No. J-38616, or equivalent.
8. Remove flat ring from sprocket bore.

INSTALLATION

1. Install new flat ring to large bore of sprocket.
2. Wipe camshaft noses with a light coat of oil.
3. Install camshaft sprocket on camshaft.
4. Install lock ring far enough to minimize tipping.
5. Lightly oil camshaft sprocket bolt threads and washer before using. Install bolt and washer into camshaft and seat bolt finger tight then back off 1/4-1/2 turn. **Final tightening specification will be reached after performing procedure outlined under "Camshaft, Replace."**
6. Repeat steps 1 through 5 for remaining camshafts.
7. Check each sprocket for binding by rotating it around the camshaft.
8. Install secondary timing belt as outlined under "Timing Belt, Replace."
9. Set camshaft timing as outlined under "Camshaft, Replace."

CAMSHAFT

REPLACE

1. Remove camshaft carrier as outlined under "Camshaft Carrier, Replace."

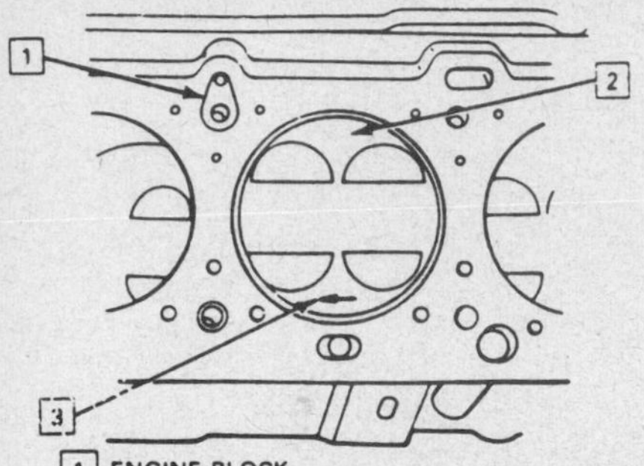
1
2
3
1 ENGINE BLOCK
2 PISTON
3 ARROW FACES TOWARDS FRONT OF ENGINE
GC1069100474000X

Fig. 15 Piston marking

2. Remove lifters as outlined under "Hydraulic Lifter, Replace."
3. Install cam shaft hold-down tool No. J-38613, or equivalent.
4. Remove camshaft sprockets as outlined under "Camshaft Sprocket, Replace."
5. Remove camshaft carrier thrust plate cover, **Fig. 14.**
6. Remove thrust plate and bolts, **Fig. 14.**
7. Remove camshaft hold-down tool.
8. Remove camshaft by carefully removing it out the back of the carrier. **All camshaft journals are the same diameter and care must be taken when removing camshaft to avoid damage to bearing surfaces.**
9. Reverse procedure to install, noting the following:
   a. Coat camshaft lobes and journals with GM engine oil supplement (EOS), or equivalent.
   b. Adjust camshaft timing as outlined under "Camshaft Timing" section.

CAMSHAFT OIL SEAL

1. Remove camshaft as outlined previously.
2. Remove camshaft seal by prying seal out with a suitable screwdriver.
3. Reverse procedure to install, using seal installation tool No. J-38619, or equivalent.

CAMSHAFT TIMING

If only one bank is to be timed, ensure bank to bank camshaft timing relationship is one revolution apart. Timing flats should be 180° opposite when finally timed.

1. Remove spark plugs.
2. Remove camshaft sprockets as outlined under "Camshaft Sprocket, Replace."
3. Rotate camshaft flats Up and install camshaft hold-down tool No. J-38613, or equivalent. **Torque** tool bolt to 22 ft. lbs.
4. Install secondary timing belt and tensioner pulley arm assembly as outlined under "Timing Belt, Replace."
5. Ensure freeness of rotation of tensioner pulley arm assembly.
6. Rotate tensioner pulley 11 ft. lbs. counterclockwise into the belt using cast square lug on body and engage ball end of actuator into socket on pulley arm.
7. Remove tensioner lockpin, using needle nose pliers, or equivalent, allowing tensioner shaft to extend and the pulley to move into belt.
8. Remove sprocket and belt holding devices, then rotate tensioner pulley counterclockwise **torquing** to 12-15 ft. lbs.
9. Rotate engine clockwise three times to seat belt. Align crankshaft reference marks during final rotation to TDC.
10. Set lock ring on right exhaust and intake camshaft into bore by threading in attaching bolt as follows:
    a. Hold sprocket from turning using sprocket holding tool No. J-38614, or equivalent.
    b. Running **Torque**, before seating, of bolt should be 44-66 ft. lbs.
    c. If less tightening is required before seating, the shim and lock rings must be replaced and inspect nose of camshaft for foreign material.
    d. If more tightening is required before seating, the shim and lock rings must be replaced and inspect bolt threads for burrs and/or foreign material.
    e. Seating of lock ring is accomplished when edge of ring is flush with sprocket hub.
    f. **Torque** sprocket bolt to 81 ft. lbs. to complete this step.
11. Remove camshaft holding tool.
12. Rotate engine clockwise an odd number of revolutions and realign the intermediate shaft marks at TDC. Ensure timing marks on damper lines up with front cover marks.
13. Repeat steps 2 through 9 for left intake and exhaust camshaft then repeat step 10.
14. Remove holding tools then the old timing marks.
15. Mark the position of each sprocket at TDC of number one exhaust position with permanent paint, **Fig. 8.**
16. Install secondary timing belt and covers as outlined under "Timing Belt, Replace."
17. Install camshaft carrier covers as outlined under "Camshaft Carrier Cover, Replace."

INTERMEDIATE SHAFT BELT SPROCKET & OIL SEAL

Removal

1. Verify the relationship of intermediate sprocket to front cover.
2. Raise and support vehicle.
3. Remove starter motor and install flywheel holding tool No. J-37096, or equivalent.
4. Lower vehicle.
5. Rotate engine and position to factory alignment marks. Remove sprocket bolt and washer.
6. Mark position of sprocket on nose end of intermediate shaft.

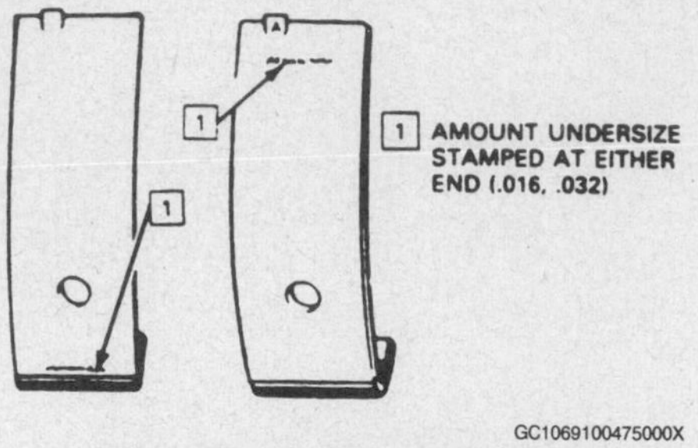
A
1
1
1 AMOUNT UNDERSIZE STAMPED AT EITHER END (.016, .032)
GC1069100475000X

Fig. 16 Bearing marking

7. Remove secondary timing belt as outlined under "Secondary Timing Belt, Service."
8. Reverse center bolt and engage self-tapping screws of sprocket remover tool No. J-38616, or equivalent, into three equally spaced holes on belt sprocket and remove intermediate shaft timing belt sprocket.
9. Remove intermediate shaft belt sprocket oil seal.

Installation

1. Install oil seal using seal installer tool No. J-38619, or equivalent.
2. Lubricate seal surfaces of intermediate shaft sprocket.
3. Align timing marks and install sprocket into position engaging locating tangs of sprocket into mating sockets of chain sprocket.
4. Verify engagement by measuring from face of belt sprocket to front cover. If measurement is more than 1.65 inches, tangs are not engaged.
5. Install O-ring in position on end of intermediate shaft.
6. Lightly lubricate threads of sprocket bolt and tighten bolt to specification.
7. Raise and support vehicle. Remove flywheel holding tool and install starter assembly.
8. Lower vehicle and install secondary timing belt and covers.

INTERMEDIATE SHAFT & BEARINGS

1. Remove engine assembly as outlined under "Engine, Replace."
2. Remove oil pump drive assembly as outlined under "Oil Pump, Service."
3. Remove timing chain as outlined under "Timing Chain & Sprockets, Replace."
4. Remove intermediate shaft thrust plate and screws.
5. Remove intermediate shaft. **All intermediate shaft journals are the same diameter and care should be taken not to damage bearings or journals during removal.**
6. Remove intermediate shaft bearing using bearing remover/installer tool No. J-33049, or equivalent.
7. Reverse procedure to install, noting the following:
   a. Align oil holes in bearing with oil holes in cylinder block. install oil feed holes at 4 and 7 o'clock for front bearing and 4 o'clock for bearings 2, 3 and 4.

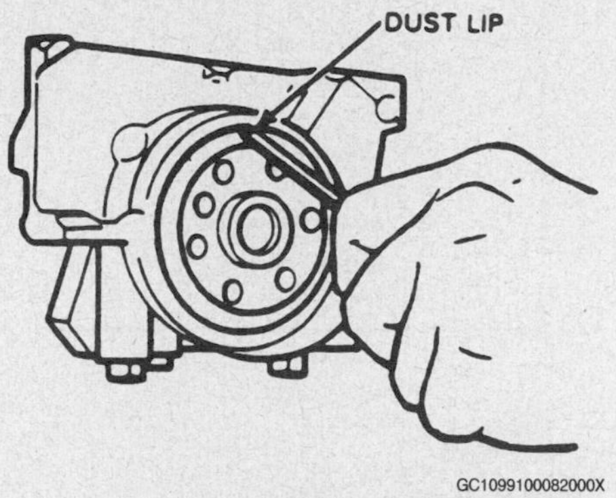
DUST LIP
GC1099100082000X

Fig. 17 Rear main seal removal

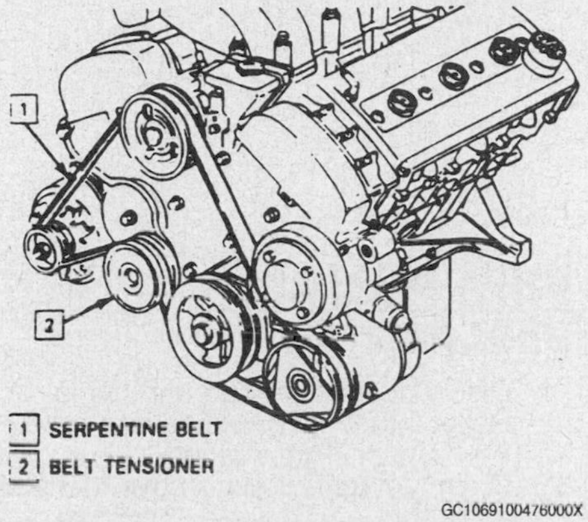
1 SERPENTINE BELT
2 BELT TENSIONER

Fig. 19 Serpentine drive belt routing

b. Apply oil to intermediate shaft journals prior to installation.
c. Replace O-ring seal after sprocket installation.

INTERMEDIATE SHAFT REAR COVER

1. Remove transaxle assembly as outlined under "Transaxle, Replace" in the "Clutch & Manual Transaxle" or the "Automatic Transaxle" section.
2. Remove intermediate shaft rear cover bolts then the cover and gasket.
3. Reverse procedure to install.

PISTON & ROD ASSEMBLY

When installing piston and rod assemblies into cylinder block, ensure arrow on top of piston faces toward the front of the engine, **Fig. 15.**

MAIN & ROD BEARINGS

Connecting rod and main bearing are of the precision insert type. They are available for service use in standard and two undersizes of .016 and .032 inch. Bearing undersize amount is stamped at either end of the bearing, **Fig. 16.**

CRANKSHAFT REAR OIL SEAL

REPLACE

1. Remove transaxle assembly as outlined under "Transaxle, Replace" in the "Clutch & Manual Transaxle" or the "Automatic Transaxle" section.
2. Remove flywheel assembly.
3. Remove oil seal using a suitable pry tool as shown in **Fig. 17.**
4. Reverse procedure to install, using seal installer tool No. J-34686, or equivalent.

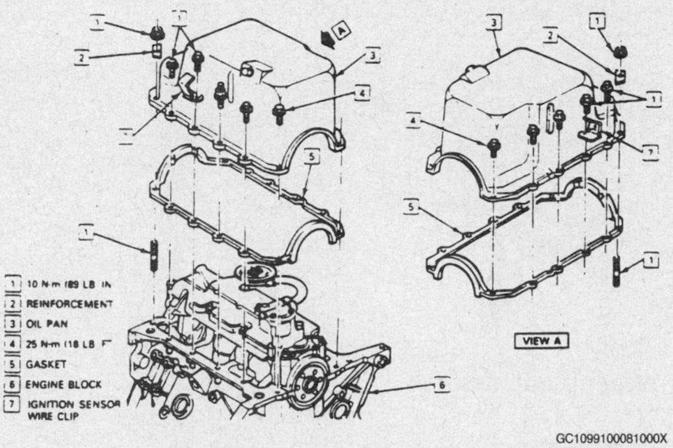
1 10 N·m (89 LB IN
2 REINFORCEMENT
3 OIL PAN
4 25 N·m (18 LB F
5 GASKET
6 ENGINE BLOCK
7 IGNITION SENSOR WIRE CLIP
VIEW A
GC1099100081000X

Fig. 18 Oil pan assembly

OIL DISTRIBUTION COVER, REPLACE

1. Remove intake manifold as outlined under "Intake Manifold, Replace."
2. Remove oil distribution cover mounting bolts then the cover and gasket.
3. Reverse procedure to install.

OIL PAN

REPLACE

1. Remove air cleaner assembly.
2. Install engine support fixture tool Nos. J-28467-A, J-28467-90 and J-36462, or equivalent.
3. Raise and support vehicle.
4. Remove right tire and wheel assembly and steering gear heat shield.
5. Remove steering gear bolts then hang steering gear from frame.
6. Separate ball joints from control arms.
7. Remove power steering cooler line clips from frame.
8. Disconnect engine mounts at frame as outlined under "Mounts, Replace."
9. Support frame assembly and remove frame bolts then remove frame assembly.
10. Disconnect and remove starter assembly.
11. Remove flywheel cover.
12. Remove oil pan nuts and bolts then the oil pan and gasket.
13. Remove oil baffle nuts. Rotate pick up tube and remove oil baffle.
14. Reverse procedure to install, tightening oil pan bolts to specifications shown in **Fig. 18.**

OIL PUMP

REPLACE

1. Remove oil pan and baffle as outlined under "Oil Pan & Baffle, Replace."
2. Remove oil pump bolt then the oil pump and driveshaft extension.

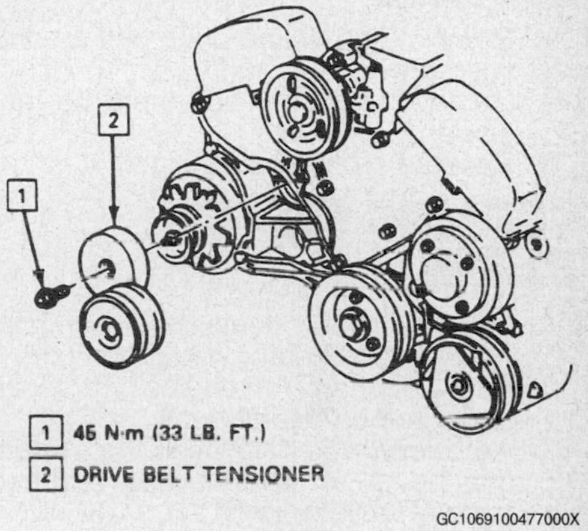
1 45 N·m (33 LB. FT.)
2 DRIVE BELT TENSIONER
GC1069100477000X

Fig. 20 Serpentine drive belt tensioner

3. Install shaft extension on oil pump, engage shaft extension into drive gear.
4. Tighten oil pump bolt to specification.
5. Install oil pan and baffle.

OIL PUMP DRIVE

REPLACE

1. Remove rear cylinder head as outlined under "Cylinder Head, Replace."
2. Remove oil pump drive bolt and clamp.
3. Remove oil pump drive assembly and O-ring.
4. Reverse procedure to install.

BELT TENSION DATA

Belt tension is maintained automatically by a spring tensioned idler pulley. No adjustment of serpentine belt is necessary.

SERPENTINE DRIVE BELT

BELT, REPLACE

1. Remove coolant recovery reservoir.
2. Rotate tensioner clockwise using a box end wrench.
3. Remove serpentine belt.
4. Reverse procedure to install, routing belt as shown in **Fig. 19.**

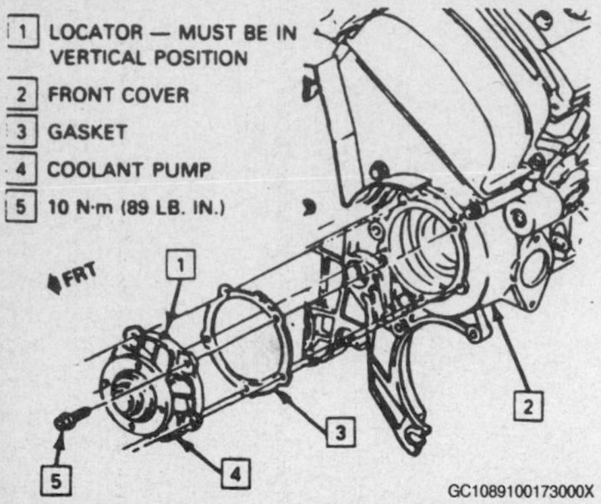
1 LOCATOR — MUST BE IN VERTICAL POSITION
2 FRONT COVER
3 GASKET
4 COOLANT PUMP
5 10 N·m (89 LB. IN.)
FRT
GC1089100173000X

Fig. 21 Water pump assembly

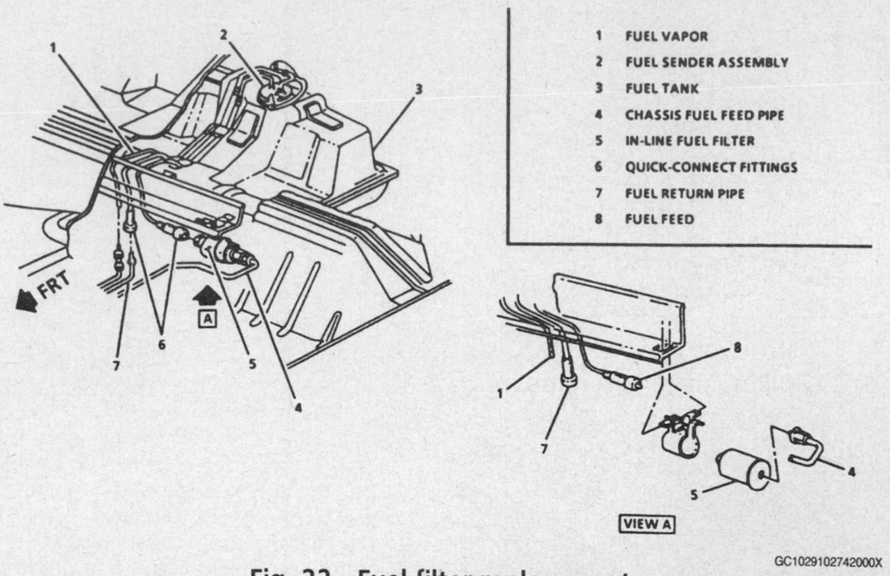
1 FUEL VAPOR
2 FUEL SENDER ASSEMBLY
3 FUEL TANK
4 CHASSIS FUEL FEED PIPE
5 IN-LINE FUEL FILTER
6 QUICK-CONNECT FITTINGS
7 FUEL RETURN PIPE
8 FUEL FEED
FRT
A
VIEW A
GC1029102742000X

Fig. 22 Fuel filter replacement

BELT TENSIONER, REPLACE

1. Remove serpentine drive belt as outlined previously.
2. Remove tensioner bolt then the tensioner, **Fig. 20.**
3. Reverse procedure to install.

COOLING SYSTEM BLEED

1. Open air bleed vents on thermostat housing and heater water inlet pipe.
2. Add 3.6 quarts of engine antifreeze through the radiator neck.
3. Add clean water slowly to the system until level of coolant has reached base of radiator neck.
4. Close bleed vents and add clean water if necessary to bring coolant level to the base of radiator neck.

THERMOSTAT

REPLACE

1. Remove air cleaner and duct assembly.
2. Drain coolant.
3. Remove engine torque strut bolt at engine.
4. Disconnect upper radiator hose at thermostat housing.
5. Release fuel pressure as previously described under "Precautions."
6. Disconnect fuel lines at fuel rail.
7. Remove heater hose bracket at thermostat housing stud.
8. Disconnect heater hose at throttle body.
9. Remove thermostat housing bolts, thermostat housing and thermostat.
10. Reverse procedure to install.

WATER PUMP

REPLACE

1. Remove air cleaner assembly.
2. Disconnect battery ground cable.
3. Drain engine coolant into a suitable container.
4. Remove serpentine drive belt as outlined under "Serpentine Drive Belt, Replace."
5. Remove water pump pulley.
6. Remove water pump bolts then the water pump and gasket, **Fig. 21.**
7. Reverse procedure to install.

RADIATOR

REPLACE

1. Remove air cleaner assembly, then drain coolant.
2. Remove engine strut upper brace bolts from upper tie bar and rotate strut and brace rearward.
3. Disconnect upper radiator mounting panel bolts and clamps.
4. Disconnect cooling fan electrical connector.
5. Remove cooling fan mounting bolts and fan, then upper radiator bracket.
6. Remove upper and lower radiator hoses at radiator.
7. Disconnect low coolant sensor wiring.
8. Disconnect oil cooler lines, then remove radiator.
9. Reverse procedure to install.

FUEL PUMP

REPLACE

1. Disconnect battery ground cable.
2. Relieve fuel system pressure as outlined under "Precautions."
3. Drain fuel tank, then remove fuel tank assembly.
4. Remove fuel sender assembly.
5. Reverse procedure to install.

FUEL FILTER

REPLACE

1. Relieve fuel system pressure as outlined under "Precautions."
2. Raise and support vehicle.
3. Remove bracket attaching screw and filter bracket, **Fig. 22.**
4. Grasp filter and fuel line fitting. Twist quick-connect fitting 1/4 turn in each direction to loosen any dirt within fitting.
5. Using compressed air, blow out dirt from quick-connect fitting.
6. Remove feed pipe nut from fuel filter, then drain any remaining fuel into a suitable container.
7. Remove fuel filter.
8. Reverse procedure to install.

TIGHTENING SPECIFICATIONS

Year	Component	Torque/Ft. Lbs.
1992–95	A/C Compressor To Front Cover Bolt	37
	AIR Pipe	15
	Camshaft Carrier Bolt	18
	Camshaft Carrier Cover Bolt	89①
	Camshaft Carrier Thrust Plate Bolt	89①
	Camshaft Sprocket Bolt	81
	Clutch Cover Bolt	18
	Cooling Fan Attaching Bolt	89①
	Connecting Rod Cap Nut	39
	Crankshaft Damper Mounting Bolt	78
	Crankshaft Main Cap Bolt	②
	Crankshaft Pulley To Crankshaft Damper Bolt	37
	Crankshaft Sensor Bolt	14
	Cylinder Head Bolt	③
	EGR Tube Assembly Bolt	18
	EGR Valve Assembly Bolt	18
	Engine Mount To Bracket Nut	35
	Engine Mounting Bracket To Engine Bolt	61④
	Exhaust Crossover Nut	18
	Exhaust Heat Shield Nut	116①
	Exhaust Mounting Nut	116①
	Exhaust Stud	13
	Flywheel To Engine Bolt	61
	Front Cover Bolts (Large)	35
	Front Cover Bolts (Small)	18
	Front Engine Mounting Bracket To Engine Bolt	63
	Fuel Filter	22
	Fuel Pipe Clip Bolt	53①
	Fuel Pipe Retaining Screw	89①
	Fuel Rail Bolt	89①
	Fuel Tank Bolts	35
	Idler Pulley Bolt	37
	Ignition Coil Bolt	18
	Ignition Coil Nut	18
	Intake Manifold Bolt	18
	Intake Plenum Bolt	18
	Intake Plenum Nut	89①

Year	Component	Torque/Ft. Lbs.
1992–95 —Cont'd	Intermediate Shaft Thrust Plate Screw	89①
	Intermediate Shaft Belt Sprocket Bolt	96①
	Knock Sensor	71①
	Oil Cooler Connector	24
	Oil Cooler Fitting	13
	Oil Distribution Cover Bolt	18
	Oil Level Indicator Bolt	89①
	Oil Pan Baffle Nut	18
	Oil Pan Bolt	89① ⑤
	Oil Pan Bolt	18⑥
	Oil Pan Nut	89①
	Oil Pump Drive Bolt	27
	Oil Pump To Rear Main Bolt	40
	Power Steering Pump To Bracket Bolt	25
	Rear Camshaft Cover Bolt	89①
	Rear Engine Mounting Brace To Bracket Bolt	61
	Rear Engine Mounting Brace To Bracket Nut	35④
	Secondary Timing Belt Idler Bolt	37
	Secondary Timing Belt Tensioner Bracket Bolt	37
	Secondary Timing Belt Tensioner Pulley Bolt	37
	Secondary Timing Belt Tensioner Side Plate Bolt	18
	Serpentine Drive Belt Tensioner Bolt	33
	Spark Plug	11
	Starter Mounting Bolt	32
	Tensioner Mounting Bolt	18
	Timing Belt Cover Bolt	89①
	Timing Chain Tensioner Bolt	18
	Torque Strut and Engine Lift Bracket Bolt	52
	Trace Bracket To Rear Engine Mounting Bracket Bolt	35⑦
	Upper Radiator Mounting Panel Bolt	89①
	Water By-Pass Nut	18
	Water Outlet Bolt	18
	Water Pump Bolt	89①

①—Inch lbs.
②—Torque to 37 ft. lbs. plus an additional 3/4 turn.
③—Refer to text.
④—Manual Transaxle.
⑤—Except two rear bolts.
⑥—Two rear bolts.
⑦—Automatic Transaxle.

3.8L/V6-231 Engine

NOTE: On Air Bag Equipped Models, Refer To "Air Bag System Precautions" Located In The Front Of This Manual For System Disarming & Arming Procedures.

NOTE: For Procedures Not Found In This Section, Refer To The 3.8L/V6-231 Engine Section In The Buick LeSabre & Park Ave., Cadillac DeVille & Fleetwood, Oldsmobile Eighty Eight & Ninety Eight & Pontiac Bonneville Chapter.

INDEX

PRECAUTIONS

AIR BAG SYSTEMS

Refer to "Air Bag System Precautions" in the front of this manual for system disarming and arming procedures.

FUEL SYSTEM PRESSURE RELIEF

To reduce the risk of fire and personal injury, it is necessary to relieve the fuel system pressure before servicing fuel system components.

1. Disconnect battery ground cable.
2. Loosen fuel tank filler cap to relieve tank pressure.
3. Connect fuel pressure gage tool No. J-34730-1, or equivalent, to the fuel pressure valve. Wrap a shop towel around fitting while connection gage to avoid spillage.
4. Install bleed hose into an approved container and open valve to bleed system pressure.

ENGINE MOUNT

REPLACE

1. Disconnect battery ground cable.
2. Remove mount nuts from below frame mounting bracket.
3. Raise and support engine to gain clearance using engine support fixture tool Nos. J-28467-A, J-28467-90 and J-35953, or equivalent.
4. Remove mount to engine nuts then the mount.
5. Reverse procedure to install, **Torquing** nuts to 32 ft. lbs. and bolts to 70 ft. lbs.

TRANSMISSION MOUNT

1. Disconnect battery ground cable.
2. Remove engine torque strut from engine.
3. Raise and support vehicle.
4. Remove left tire and wheel assembly and lower splash shield.
5. Support transaxle using a suitable jack.
6. Remove mount nuts then the mount.
7. Reverse procedure to install, noting the following:
   a. **Torque** upper bracket to engine bolts to 61 ft. lbs.
   b. **Torque** lower bracket to engine bolts to 35 ft. lbs.
   c. **Torque** upper bracket to engine mount nuts to 22 ft. lbs.
   d. **Torque** lower bracket to frame bolts to 38 ft. lbs.
   e. **Torque** frame bracket to mount nuts to 35 ft. lbs.

ENGINE

REPLACE

1. Mark and remove hood assembly.
2. Disconnect battery ground cable.
3. Remove air cleaner assembly.
4. Relieve fuel system pressure as follows:
   a. Disconnect battery ground cable.
   b. Loosen fuel filler cap.
   c. Connect fuel pressure gauge tool No. J-34730-1, or equivalent, to the fuel pressure valve.
   d. Place bleed hose into a suitable container.
   e. Open valve and relieve fuel system pressure.
5. Remove fuel lines from rail and mounting bracket.
6. Remove coolant bottle and inner fender electrical cover.
7. Remove fuel injector sight cover.
8. Remove throttle cables, bracket and vacuum line from throttle body.
9. Remove heat shield from exhaust crossover pipe then crossover pipe.
10. Remove engine torque strut from engine.
11. Remove the engine cooling fan.
12. Remove vacuum line from transaxle module.
13. Remove serpentine drive belt.
14. Remove power steering pump and alternator from engine.
15. Disconnect all necessary electrical connectors.
16. Remove upper and lower radiator and heater hoses from engine.
17. Remove transaxle to engine bolts and ground wire harness with bolt.
18. Raise and support vehicle.
19. Remove right tire and wheel assembly and inner splash shield.
20. Remove flywheel cover and scribe torque converter to flywheel for installation.
21. Remove flywheel to converter bolts.
22. Disconnect wire harness clamps from frame near radiator.
23. Remove A/C compressor and position aside.
24. Remove starter motor.
25. Remove transaxle to engine bolt through wheelwell using suitable extension.
26. Disconnect engine mount to frame nuts.
27. Remove oil filter.
28. Disconnect front exhaust pipe from manifold.
29. Disconnect oil cooler piper from hose connections.
30. Lower vehicle.
31. Install lifting device and remove engine assembly.
32. Reverse procedure to install, noting the following:
   a. Align engine with transaxle dowel pins.
   b. **Torque** torque strut bolts to 41 ft. lbs.
   c. **Torque** flywheel to converter bolts to 46 ft. lbs.

FUEL PUMP

REPLACE

1. Disconnect battery ground cable.
2. Relieve fuel system pressure as outlined under "Precautions."
3. Drain fuel tank, then remove fuel tank assembly.
4. Remove fuel sender assembly.
5. Reverse procedure to install.

FUEL FILTER

REPLACE

1. Relieve fuel system pressure as outlined under "Precautions."
2. Raise and support vehicle.
3. Remove bracket attaching screw and filter bracket, **Fig. 1.**
4. Grasp filter and fuel line fitting. Twist quick-connect fitting 1/4 turn in each direction to loosen any dirt within fitting.

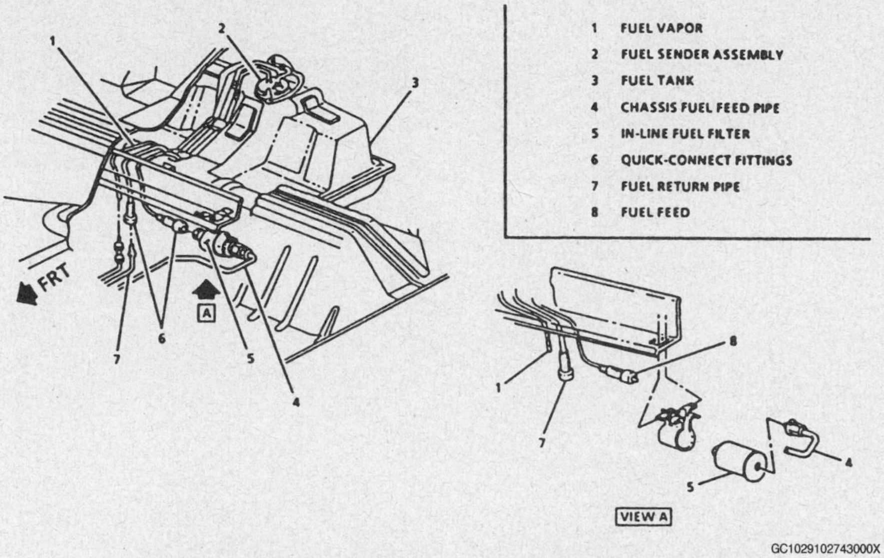
1 FUEL VAPOR
2 FUEL SENDER ASSEMBLY
3 FUEL TANK
4 CHASSIS FUEL FEED PIPE
5 IN-LINE FUEL FILTER
6 QUICK-CONNECT FITTINGS
7 FUEL RETURN PIPE
8 FUEL FEED
FRT
A
VIEW A
GC1029102743000X

Fig. 1 Fuel filter replacement

5. Using compressed air, blow out dirt from quick-connect fitting.
6. Remove feed pipe nut from fuel filter, then drain any remaining fuel into a suitable container.
7. Remove fuel filter.
8. Reverse procedure to install.

Clutch & Manual Transaxle

NOTE: On Air Bag Equipped Models, Refer To "Air Bag System Precautions" Located In The Front Of This Manual For System Disarming & Arming Procedures.

INDEX

PRECAUTIONS

AIR BAG SYSTEMS

Refer to "Air Bag System Precautions" in the front of this manual for system disarming and arming procedures.

DESCRIPTION

The hydraulic system components (master cylinder and clutch actuator) **Fig. 1** can be serviced separately. If a component fails, that component may be replaced. The clutch hydraulic system is serviced as two major assemblies, the master cylinder and actuator assemblies. Each assembly has been bled of air and filled with brake fluid. Individual components of these assemblies are not available separately.

Whenever powertrain components are lowered for any reason (removal or access to other components), the clutch actuator must be removed from the transaxle case. Refer to procedure outlined under "Clutch Actuator." **Failure to remove actuator may result in hydraulic system damage.**

Prior to any operation that requires removal of the actuator, the clutch master cylinder pushrod must be disconnected from the clutch pedal. **Failure to disconnect pushrod will result in permanent damage to the actuator if the clutch pedal is depressed without resistance from clutch loads.** Master cylinder pushrod bushing must also be replaced whenever it has been removed from the clutch pedal.

ADJUSTMENTS

This clutch is equipped with a hydraulic slave cylinder (actuator) and there is no provision for adjustment.

HYDRAULIC SYSTEM SERVICE

MASTER CYLINDER

1. Disconnect battery ground cable.
2. Remove sound insulator, then disconnect master cylinder pushrod from clutch pedal.
3. Remove two nuts attaching master cylinder reservoir to strut tower.
4. Remove anti-rotational screw located next to master cylinder flange at pedal support plate.
5. Using wrench flats on front end of master cylinder, twist master cylinder counterclockwise to release twist lock to plate attachment. **Do not twist hose connections on top of master cylinder body.**
6. Remove two nuts attaching clutch actuator to transaxle case, then the actuator from transaxle housing with pushrod attached forward out of pedal plate.
7. Pull master cylinder assembly. Lift reservoir off strut tower studs, then remove complete hydraulic assembly from vehicle.
8. Reverse procedure to install, noting the following:
   a. Install master cylinder into opening in pedal plate and rotate 45° by applying torque on wrench flats only.
   b. **Torque** anti-rotational screw to 18 inch lbs.
   c. **Torque** reservoir attaching nuts to 36 inch lbs.
   d. Install actuator on transaxle housing. Actuator pushrod busing and retaining straps should be left assembled. Actuator straps will break during normal operation. Pushrod bushing must enter pocket in inter-

nal fork housing as actuator is installed on housing studs.

e. **Torque** actuator attaching nuts evenly to 18 ft. lbs.
f. Install new bushing in master cylinder pushrod. Lubricate bushing prior to installation.
g. Connect master cylinder pushrod to clutch pedal, with bushing tangs snapped into pedal pin groove.
h. Press clutch pedal down several times, ensuring pedal effort is normal and firm.
i. **On models equipped with cruise control,** adjust cruise control clutch switch. Refer to procedure outlined under "Cruise Control, Adjust" in the "Cruise Control" section.

ACTUATOR

Removal

Whenever powertrain components are lowered for any reason (removal or access to other components), the clutch actuator must be removed from the transaxle case. **Failure to remove actuator may result in hydraulic system damage.**

1. Disconnect battery ground cable.
2. Remove air cleaner assembly and sound insulator.
3. Disconnect master cylinder pushrod from clutch pedal, **Fig. 2.**
4. Disconnect hydraulic system at quick connect fitting using tool J-36221.
5. Remove two bolts holding canister bracket to transaxle.
6. Remove two actuator attaching nuts, then the actuator from transaxle housing.

Installation

1. Inspect actuator pushrod for lever bushing and replace if missing.
2. Install actuator on transaxle housing studs with pushrod centered in pocket of internal lever in housing. An axial load on pushrod may be required to compress actuator piston spring.
3. Install actuator attaching nuts, **Torquing** nuts evenly to 18 ft. lbs.
4. Install new bushing in master cylinder pushrod. Lubricate bushing prior to installation.
5. Connect master cylinder pushrod to clutch pedal, with bushing tangs snapped into pedal pin groove, **Fig. 2 & 3.**
6. Press clutch pedal down several times, ensuring pedal effort is normal and firm.
7. **On models equipped with cruise control,** adjust cruise control clutch switch. Refer to procedure outlined under "Cruise Control, Adjust."
8. Install sound insulator and air cleaner, then connect battery ground cable.

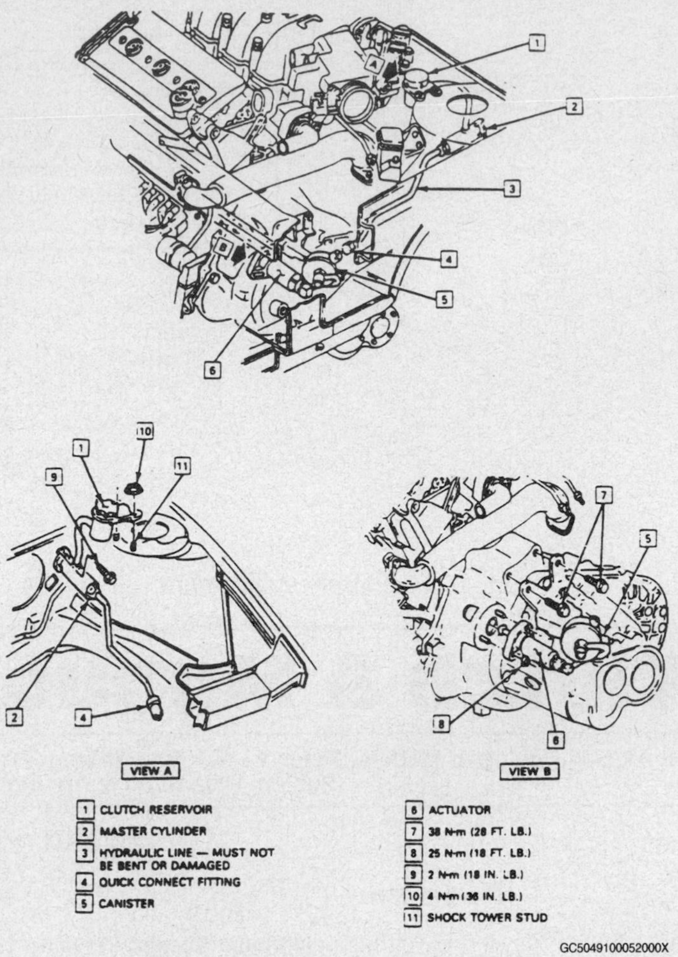
VIEW A
VIEW B
1 CLUTCH RESERVOIR
2 MASTER CYLINDER
3 HYDRAULIC LINE — MUST NOT BE BENT OR DAMAGED
4 QUICK CONNECT FITTING
5 CANISTER
6 ACTUATOR
7 38 N·m (28 FT. LB.)
8 25 N·m (18 FT. LB.)
9 2 N·m (18 IN. LB.)
10 4 N·m (36 IN. LB.)
11 SHOCK TOWER STUD
GC5049100052000X

Fig. 1 Clutch hydraulic system

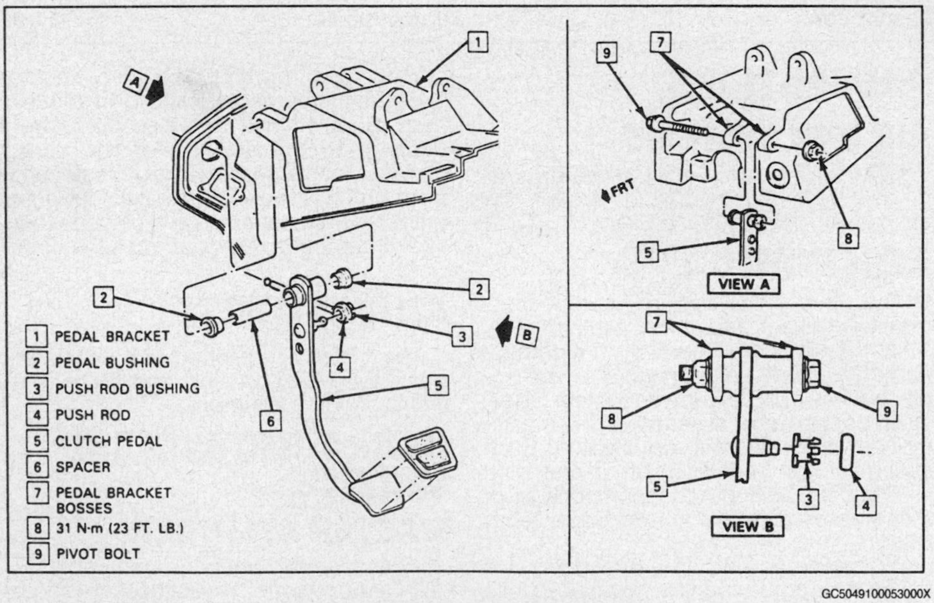
1 PEDAL BRACKET
2 PEDAL BUSHING
3 PUSH ROD BUSHING
4 PUSH ROD
5 CLUTCH PEDAL
6 SPACER
7 PEDAL BRACKET BOSSES
8 31 N·m (23 FT. LB.)
9 PIVOT BOLT
FRT
VIEW A
VIEW B
GC5049100053000X

Fig. 2 Clutch pedal assembly

MASTER CYLINDER BLEED

Manual Method

During this procedure, fluid level in master cylinder must be maintained.

Use a maximum of 50 lbs. pedal pressure to check pedal firmness.

1. Disconnect quick connect fittings in clutch hydraulic line. Insert quick disconnect tool No. J-36221 or equivalent and depress white plastic sleeve to separate connection.
2. Remove cap and diaphragm, and fill reservoir with DOT 3 brake fluid.
3. Remove lefthand upper secondary cowl, then remove air from supply hose by squeezing it until no more air bubbles are seen in reservoir.
4. Pump clutch pedal slowly by hand un-

til slight resistance is felt.

5. Holding pedal pressure, bleed air from system by depressing internal valve at quick connect fitting. **Do not use a sharp object.**
6. Repeat steps 4 and 5 until pedal is firm and no air bubbles are seen.
7. Reconnect clutch hydraulic line, then replace reservoir cap and diaphragm.

Pressure Method

During this procedure, fluid level in master cylinder must be maintained.

1. Disconnect quick connect fittings in clutch hydraulic line. Insert quick disconnect tool No. J-36221, or equivalent, and depress white plastic sleeve to separate connection.
2. Remove cap and diaphragm, and fill reservoir with DOT 3 brake fluid.
3. Install pressure bleed adapter cap No. J-36234 or equivalent to reservoir and connect pressure bleeder.
4. Apply pressure not to exceed 30 lbs., to hydraulic system.
5. Depress internal valve at quick connect fitting. **Do not use a sharp object.**
6. Release internal valve when air is no longer visible.
7. Open internal valve and slowly depress clutch pedal. **Close internal valve before releasing clutch pedal.**
8. Repeat this procedure until air is no longer visible.
9. Reconnect clutch hydraulic line, then replace reservoir cap and diaphragm.

CLUTCH

REPLACE

REMOVAL

Prior to any operation that requires removal of the actuator, the master cylinder pushrod must be disconnected from the clutch pedal. **Failure to disconnect pushrod will result in permanent damage to the actuator if the clutch pedal is depressed without resistance from clutch loads.** Master cylinder pushrod bushing must also be replaced whenever it has been removed from the clutch pedal.

1. Disconnect battery ground cable.
2. Remove sound insulator from inside vehicle, then disconnect clutch master cylinder pushrod from clutch pedal.
3. Disconnect quick connect fittings in clutch hydraulic line. Insert tool No. J-36221 or equivalent and depress white plastic sleeve to separate connection.
4. Remove actuator to transaxle attaching nuts, then the actuator.
5. Remove transaxle assembly. Refer to procedure outlined under "Transaxle, Replace."
6. Place alignment marks on clutch cover assembly and flywheel to ensure reassembly in same position.
7. Loosen attaching bolts one turn at a time, until spring pressure is relieved.
8. Support clutch cover, then remove bolts.
9. Remove clutch cover and driven disc.

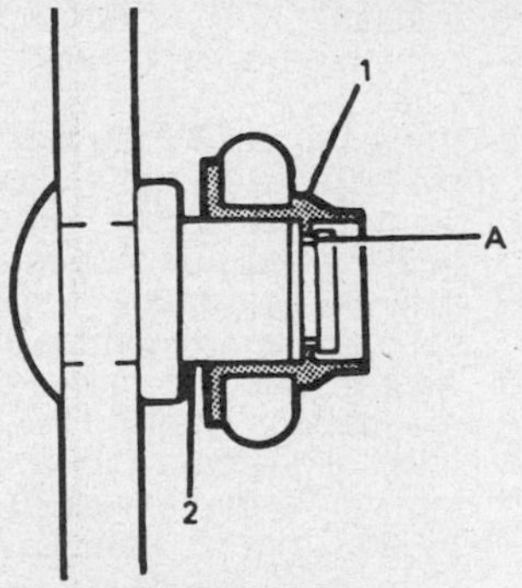
1
A
2

A 3 TANGS ON BUSHING MUST BE IN GROOVE ON PIN
1 BUSHING
2 PIN

GC5049100054000X

Fig. 3 Bushing tang engagement

INSTALLATION

1. Position clutch disc and clutch cover, matching light side of clutch cover (marked with paint) with heavy side of flywheel (stamped with an X). Stamped letters on clutch disc identify "flywheel side." Support clutch disc and clutch cover with clutch alignment arbor tool No. J-35822 or equivalent.
2. Install clutch cover to flywheel bolts in three holes marked "L," then install remaining clutch cover to flywheel bolts, remove tool and **Torque** bolts to 15 ft. lbs. plus a 30° turn.
3. Lightly lubricate clutch fork ends which contact bearing and completely pack I.D. recess of release bearing with suitable grease. Levers on clutch fork shaft must bear on large ears of release bearing. Levers fit between large ears and small tangs on bearing. Fork shaft must move freely with bearing in place.
4. Tie actuator lever through actuator hole to studs, holding release bearing in position.
5. Install transaxle assembly. **Clutch lever must not be moved toward flywheel until transaxle is bolted to engine.**
6. Align actuator and master cylinder quick connect fittings in hydraulic line and insert master cylinder fitting into actuator fitting until it locks in place.
7. **On all models,** remove tie from actuator lever.
8. Inspect actuator rod for lever bushing and replace if missing.
9. Install actuator on housing studs with pushrod bushing centered in pocket of internal lever in housing. It may require an axial load on the pushrod to compress the actuator piston spring.
10. Install actuator retaining nuts, **Torquing** evenly to 18 ft. lbs.
11. Install new bushing in master cylinder pushrod, lubricating before installation.
12. Connect master cylinder pushrod to clutch pedal, with bushing tangs snapped into pedal pin groove.
13. Depress clutch pedal several times, ensuring effort is normal and firm.
14. Readjust cruise control, if necessary, by pulling upward on clutch pedal with a force of not more than 20 lbs.
15. Install sound insulator and connect battery ground cable.

TRANSAXLE

REPLACE

Prior to any operation that requires removal of the actuator, the master cylinder pushrod must be disconnected from the clutch pedal. **Failure to disconnect pushrod will result in permanent damage to the actuator if the clutch pedal is depressed without resistance from clutch loads.** Master cylinder pushrod bushing must also be replaced whenever it has been removed from the clutch pedal.

1. Disconnect battery ground cable.
2. Install engine support fixture tool No. J-28467-A, or equivalent, together with support leg tool No. J-36462 or equivalent.
3. Remove air cleaner housing and air intake tube.
4. Remove clutch actuator from transaxle. Refer to procedure outlined under "Clutch Hydraulic System, Service."
5. Disconnect electrical connector at speedometer driven gear sensor.
6. Remove nut and retaining clamp securing shift and select cables to transaxle.
7. Remove two nuts from cable ball studs at transaxle levers.
8. Disconnect exhaust crossover pipe at left exhaust manifold.
9. Disconnect EGR tube from crossover pipe.
10. Remove crossover to exhaust pipe connecting bolts.
11. Loosen crossover to right exhaust manifold clamp.
12. Swing crossover upward to gain access to top transaxle bolts.
13. Remove two upper transaxle mounting bolts and two upper transaxle mounting studs, leaving one lower mounting bolt and one lower mounting stud attached.
14. Disconnect electrical connector at back-up lamp switch.
15. Raise and support vehicle, then remove drain plug to drain transaxle fluid.
16. Remove four clutch housing cover retaining screws.
17. Remove both front tire and wheel assemblies, then the left and right wheelhouse splash shields.
18. Disconnect power steering cooler lines from frame, then remove power steering rack and pinion heat shield.
19. Disconnect power steering rack and pinion at frame.
20. Disconnect ball joints at steering knuckle.
21. Remove transaxle mount upper retaining bolts, then the engine mount lower retaining nuts.
22. Remove subframe retaining bolts from body, then remove subframe from vehicle.

23. Remove drive axles from transaxle and support from body.
24. Detach starter assembly and support from body.
25. Securely attach transaxle to suitable jack, then remove remaining transaxle mounting bolt and stud and remove transaxle.
26. Reverse procedure to install, noting the following:
    a. **Torque** transaxle to engine attaching bolts and studs to 55 ft. lbs.
    b. Using frame or lower control arm for leverage, seat drive axle into transaxle, using screwdriver/pry bar at groove provided on inner joint.
    c. Verify that axle snap ring is seated by tapping on inner groove with screwdriver. Also, grasp inner housing and pull outboard. **Do not pull on axle shaft.** If snap ring is seated, axle will remain in place.
    d. After positioning frame with body mount bolts installed but not tightened, align frame to body by inserting two 19 mm (.74 inch) diameter by 203 mm (8 inch) long pins in alignment holes on right side of frame, then **Torque** body mount bolts to 100 ft. lbs. **Alignment pins must not be removed until all body mount bolts are tightened to specification. Alignment pins must be kept perpendicular to frame. Right side body mounts (nearest alignment pins) should be tightened first to maintain correct front wheel alignment.**
    e. **Torque** clutch housing cover retaining screws to 115 inch lbs.

TIGHTENING SPECIFICATIONS

Year	Component	Torque/Ft. Lbs.
1992–95	Back-Up Lamp Switch	25
	Cable Ball Stud Nut	18
	Cable Retaining Clamp Nut	89①
	Clutch Actuator Nut	18
	Clutch Canister Bracket Bolts	28
	Clutch Cover To Flywheel	②
	Clutch Fluid Reservoir Nut	36①
	Clutch Housing Cover Screw	116①
	Clutch Master Cylinder Anti-Rotation Screw	18①
	Clutch Pedal Pivot Nut	23

Year	Component	Torque/Ft. Lbs.
1992–95 —Cont'd	Control Assembly Bolt	18
	Flywheel To Crankshaft Bolt	61
	Shift Lever Nut	61
	Shift Linkage Bracket Bolt	17
	Speedometer Signal Assembly Bolt	80①
	Transaxle Mount To Frame Nut	42
	Transaxle Mount To Transaxle Bolt	35
	Transaxle Mounting Bolt	55

①—Inch lbs.
②—15 ft. lbs. plus 30°.

Rear Axle & Suspension

INDEX

DESCRIPTION

These vehicles use a tri-link independent rear suspension system with a transverse leaf spring and tubular struts with large lateral links attached to the body crossmember. The three mounting points are the crossmember, strut tower and trailing arm. The crossmember is stamped steel and the composite fiberglass mono leaf spring is transversely mounted to the under side of the crossmember, with its padded ends free riding on the cast knuckle assembly.

HUB & BEARING

REPLACE

The rear hub and bearing assembly is not serviceable. If the hub and/or bearing is damaged, the complete assembly must be replaced.

1. Raise and support vehicle, then remove tire and wheel assembly.
2. Remove brake caliper, leaving hose attached, and suspend out of way.
3. Remove brake rotor.
4. Disconnect anti-lock brake system electrical harness connector, if equipped.
5. Remove hub and bearing assembly mounting bolts, then the assembly.
6. Reverse procedure to install, torquing hub and bearing assembly mounting bolts to specifications.

STRUT

REPLACE

The following procedure has been modified by technical service bulletin No. 89-3-23.

1. Remove upper strut mount cover from inside rear compartment, then raise and support vehicle and remove tire and wheel assembly.
2. Place scribe marks on strut and knuckle to ensure installation in same position.
3. Remove jack pad.
4. Install rear leaf spring compressor tool No. J-35778 or equivalent onto transverse spring assembly and tighten to hold spring pressure. **Do not remove spring or retention plates.**
5. Remove auxiliary spring as previously outlined.
6. Remove brake hose bracket at strut.
7. Remove upper strut attaching bolts at body and allow assembly to drop down.
8. Remove stabilizer shaft bracket by removing strut to knuckle attaching nuts.
9. Remove strut to knuckle attaching bolts, then the strut assembly.

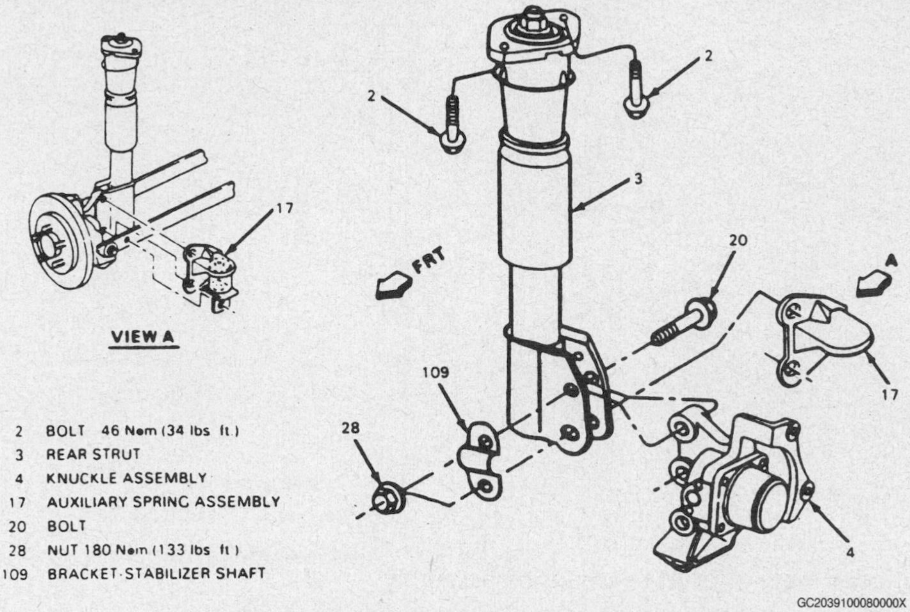
VIEW A
FRT
2
3
17
20
109
28
4
2 BOLT 46 N•m (34 lbs. ft.)
3 REAR STRUT
4 KNUCKLE ASSEMBLY
17 AUXILIARY SPRING ASSEMBLY
20 BOLT
28 NUT 180 N•m (133 lbs. ft.)
109 BRACKET-STABILIZER SHAFT
GC2039100080000X

Fig. 1 Auxiliary spring replacement

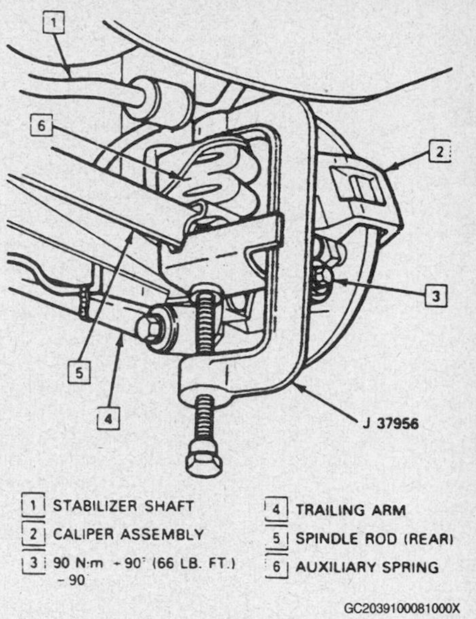
1
2
3
4
5
6
J 37956
1 STABILIZER SHAFT
2 CALIPER ASSEMBLY
3 90 N·m + 90° (66 LB. FT.) + 90°
4 TRAILING ARM
5 SPINDLE ROD (REAR)
6 AUXILIARY SPRING
GC2039100081000X

Fig. 2 Auxiliary spring compression

10. Reverse procedure to install, torquing upper strut attaching bolts to specifications.

LEAF SPRING SERVICE

AUXILIARY SPRING ASSEMBLY, REPLACE

1. Raise and support vehicle, then remove wheel and tire assembly.
2. Remove leaf spring rear retention plate bolt.
3. Remove leaf spring retention bolt only enough to rotate plate clear of rod.
4. Install rear auxiliary spring compressor tool No. J-37956 or equivalent ensuring pin in stationary end of clamp is inserted in hole of upper auxiliary spring bracket, **Fig. 1 and 2.**
5. Remove plug from upper bracket, then seat rod in tool channel and hand tighten.
6. Remove rod-to-knuckle bolt, then loosen tool forcing screw to allow spring to expand.
7. Remove auxiliary spring attaching bolts, then the spring and tool. **When removing auxiliary spring, ensure rod/bushing clears transverse spring and boss on knuckle.**
8. Reverse procedure to install, noting the following:
   a. Compress auxiliary spring with spring compressor tool enough to install rod-to-knuckle bolt.
   b. Install rod-to-knuckle bolt, using Loctite or equivalent. Tighten to specifications.
   c. Properly position leaf spring retention plate, install bolt and tighten to specifications.

TRANSVERSE SPRING ASSEMBLY, REPLACE

Do not use corrosive cleaning agents, engine degreaser or solvents

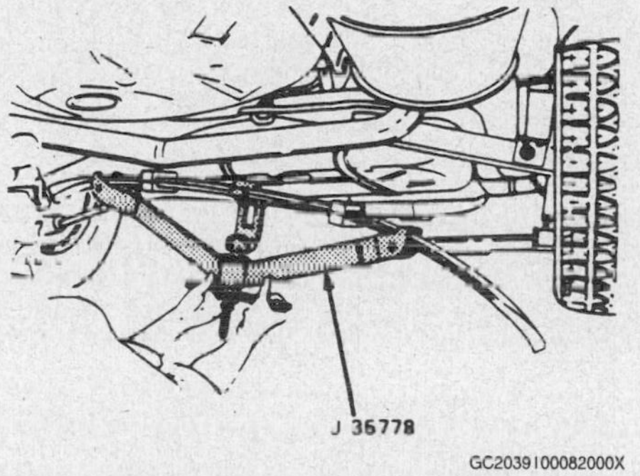
J 35778
GC2039100082000X

Fig. 3 Transverse spring assembly removal

on or near the fiberglass leaf spring.

1. Raise and support vehicle.
2. Remove three jack pad attaching bolts and the pad.
3. Remove left and right spring retention plate attaching bolts.
4. Remove right side trailing link to knuckle attaching nut and bolt.
5. Disconnect anti-lock brake system electrical harness connector, if equipped.
6. Assemble rear spring leaf spring compressor tool No. J-35778 or equivalent to transverse spring.
7. Loosen tool handle to base of tool shank.
8. Hang center shank of tool at spring center. It is not necessary to separate tool body and shank. **Attach from front side of vehicle only.**
9. Attach tool body to spring. **Always center spring on roller of tool.**
10. Fully compress spring, then slide spring to left side. It may be necessary to pry the spring, using a screwdriver/pry bar, to the opposite side, using the wheel for leverage.
11. Relax the spring until removal clearance is achieved, then remove spring, **Fig. 3.**
12. Reverse procedure to install, noting the following:
    a. Tighten trailing link to knuckle attaching bolt to specifications.
    b. Tighten spring retention plate mounting bolts to specifications. **Rear spring retention plates are designed with tabs on one end. Tabs must be aligned with support assembly.**
    c. Tighten jack pad mounting bolts to specifications.

KNUCKLE

REPLACE

The following procedure has been added by technical service bulletin No. 89-3-23.

1. Raise and support vehicle, then remove tire and wheel assembly.
2. Place scribe marks on strut and knuckle to ensure installation in same position.
3. Remove jack pad.
4. Install rear leaf spring compressor tool No. J-35778 or equivalent onto transverse spring assembly and tighten to hold spring pressure. **Do not remove spring or retention plates.**
5. Remove auxiliary spring as previously outlined.
6. Disconnect front link from knuckle.
7. Remove brake caliper, leaving hose attached, and suspend caliper out of way.
8. Remove brake rotor, then the hub and bearing assembly as previously described.
9. Disconnect anti-lock brake system electrical harness connector, if equipped.
10. Remove hub and bearing assembly.
11. Disconnect trailing link from knuckle, **Fig. 4.**
12. Remove strut to knuckle attaching nuts, then the stabilizer shaft bracket.
13. Remove strut to knuckle attaching bolts, then the knuckle.

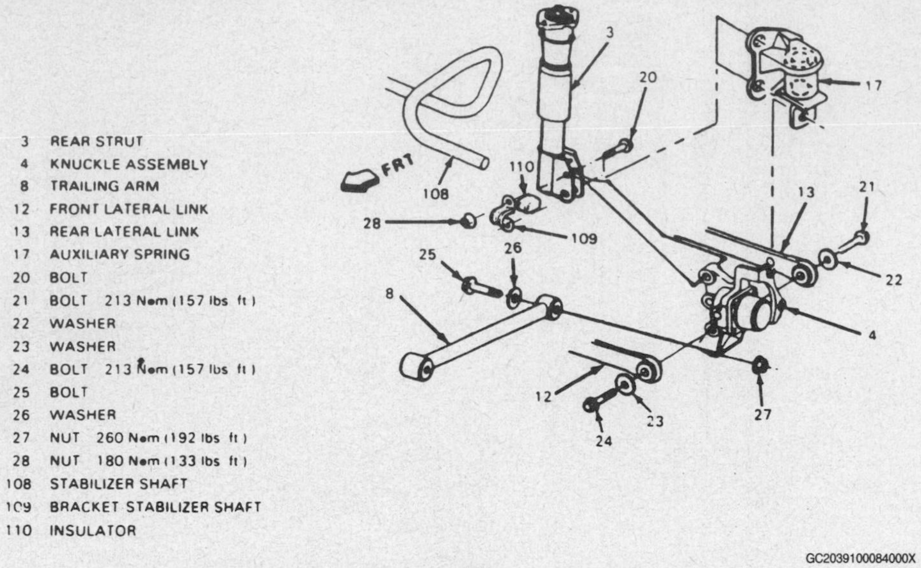
3 REAR STRUT
4 KNUCKLE ASSEMBLY
8 TRAILING ARM
12 FRONT LATERAL LINK
13 REAR LATERAL LINK
17 AUXILIARY SPRING
20 BOLT
21 BOLT 213 N·m (157 lbs ft)
22 WASHER
23 WASHER
24 BOLT 213 N·m (157 lbs ft)
25 BOLT
26 WASHER
27 NUT 260 N·m (192 lbs ft)
28 NUT 180 N·m (133 lbs ft)
108 STABILIZER SHAFT
109 BRACKET STABILIZER SHAFT
110 INSULATOR
FRT
GC2039100084000X

Fig. 4 Exploded view of tri-link suspension assembly

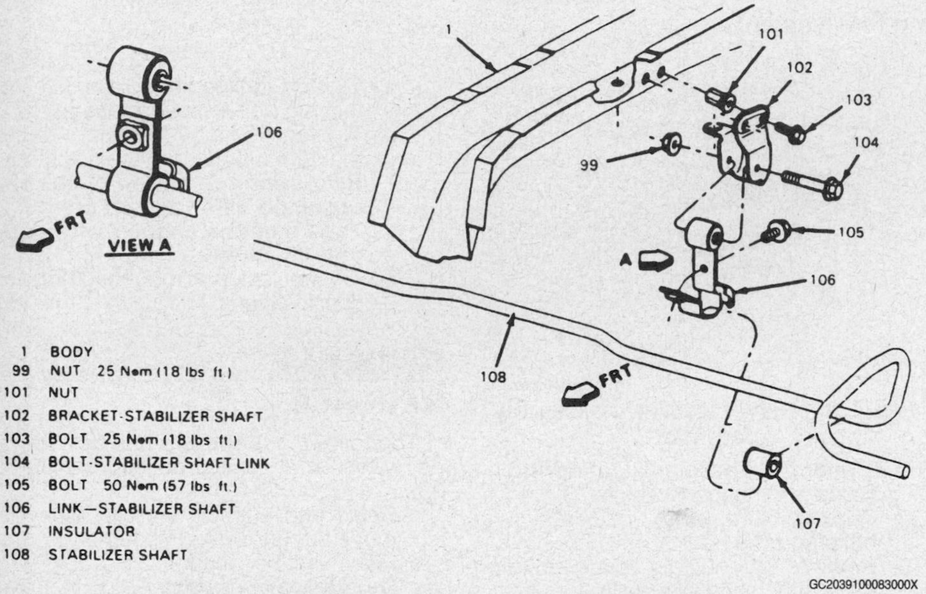
VIEW A
FRT
1 BODY
99 NUT 25 N·m (18 lbs ft)
101 NUT
102 BRACKET-STABILIZER SHAFT
103 BOLT 25 N·m (18 lbs ft)
104 BOLT-STABILIZER SHAFT LINK
105 BOLT 50 N·m (57 lbs ft)
106 LINK—STABILIZER SHAFT
107 INSULATOR
108 STABILIZER SHAFT
GC2039100083000X

Fig. 5 Stabilizer shaft assembly replacement

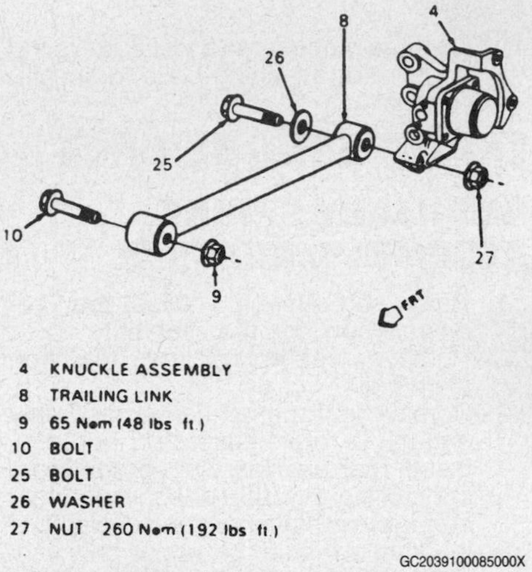
4 KNUCKLE ASSEMBLY
8 TRAILING LINK
9 65 N·m (48 lbs ft)
10 BOLT
25 BOLT
26 WASHER
27 NUT 260 N·m (192 lbs ft)
GC2039100085000X

Fig. 6 Exploded view of trailing link

14. Reverse procedure to install, torquing strut to knuckle attaching bolts and trailing link retaining nut to specifications.

STABILIZER BAR

REPLACE

1. Raise and support vehicle, then remove rear wheel and tire assemblies.
2. Remove right and lefthand stabilizer shaft link bolts, then open brackets to remove insulator.
3. Remove right and lefthand strut to knuckle to stabilizer shaft nuts, **Fig. 5. Do not remove strut to knuckle bolts.**
4. Remove insulator brackets from bolts and from stabilizer shaft, then the stabilizer shaft.
5. Reverse procedure to install, noting the following:
   a. It may be necessary to pry stabilizer shaft to one side for installation clearance at strut. Use caution when prying.
   b. Torquing stabilizer shaft link bolts and strut to knuckle bolts to specifications.

LATERAL LINK

REPLACE

TRAILING

1. Raise and support vehicle.
2. Disconnect anti-lock brake system electrical harness connector, if equipped.
3. Remove trailing link to knuckle attaching nut and bolt, then the trailing link to body attaching nut and bolt, **Figs. 4 and 6.**
4. Remove trailing link.
5. Reverse procedure to install, torquing trailing link to body nut and trailing link to knuckle nut to specifications.

FRONT

1. Raise and support vehicle, then remove tire and wheel assembly.
2. Remove rod to knuckle bolt, then the exhaust pipe heat shield.
3. Lower to fuel tank to gain access.
4. Remove lateral link to knuckle attaching bolt.
5. Remove lateral link to suspension crossmember attaching nut and bolt, then the lateral link.
6. Reverse procedure to install, **Torquing** lateral link to suspension crossmember nut to 140 ft. lbs. and the lateral link to knuckle attaching bolt to 157 ft. lbs.

REAR

1. Raise and support vehicle, then remove tire and wheel assembly.
2. Remove transverse spring as previously outlined.
3. Remove lower auxiliary spring bracket from rod.
4. Remove rear lateral link attaching nut

from crossmember.

5. Push bolt forward enough to provide clearance for link removal, then remove rear lateral link.
6. Reverse procedure to install, **Torquing** lateral link to crossmember attaching nut to 157 ft. lbs. and the rear lateral link to knuckle attaching bolt to 140 ft. lbs.

TIGHTENING SPECIFICATIONS

Year	Component	Torque/Ft. Lbs.
1992–95	Caliper Bleeder Valve	62①
	Front Caliper Mounting Bolt	79
	Front Caliper Mounting Bracket To Knuckle	148
	Jack Pad Bolt	18
	Proportioning Valve Caps	20
	Rear Caliper Mounting Bolt	92
	Rod To Knuckle	66②
	Rod To Support Crossmember	81③
	Spring Retention Plate Bolt	15
	Stabilizer Shaft Link Bolt	40
	Stabilizer Shaft Link To Body Bracket Nut	18
1992–95 —Cont'd	Strut To Knuckle Nut	133
	Suspension Crossmember To Body Bolt	85
	Trailing Arm To Knuckle	192
	Trailing Link To Body Nut	48
	Upper Strut Bolt	34
	Wheel/Hub/Bearing To Knuckle Bolt	52
	Wheel Lug Nuts	100

①—Inch lbs.
②—Turn an additional 90° after reaching specified torque.
③—Turn an additional 60° after reaching specified torque.

Front Suspension & Steering

NOTE: On Air Bag Equipped Models, Refer To "Air Bag System Precautions" Located In The Front Of This Manual For System Disarming & Arming Procedures.

INDEX

PRECAUTIONS

AIR BAG SYSTEMS

Refer to "Air Bag System Precautions" in the front of this manual for system disarming and arming procedures.

DESCRIPTION

The front suspension system on these vehicles is of the McPherson strut design. This design incorporates McPherson struts with coil springs and a one piece configuration with lower control arms. The use of tapered top coil springs on top of the struts provides a well controlled ride and allows a lower hood profile.

HUB & BEARING

REPLACE

1. Remove wheel cover, then loosen drive axle shaft nut and washer one turn. **Do not remove nut at this time. Failure to follow proper removal sequence may cause bearing damage.**
2. Raise and support vehicle, then remove wheel and tire assembly.
3. Remove brake caliper and bracket assembly, then the brake rotor, **Fig. 1.**
4. Remove drive axle shaft nut and washer.
5. Loosen hub and bearing assembly to knuckle attaching bolts.
6. Using front hub spindle remover tool No. J-28733-A or equivalent, push axle splines back out of hub and bearing assembly.
7. Remove hub and bearing assembly to knuckle attaching bolts.
8. **On models with ABS**, remove ABS sensor mounting bolt and position sensor aside.
9. **On all models**, remove hub and bearing assembly. **Protect axle boots from damage during handling.**
10. Reverse procedure to install, **Torquing** all bolts to specifications.

STRUT

REPLACE

Do not service strut unless weight of vehicle is on suspension.

REMOVAL

1. Scribe alignment marks on cover plate, remove cover plate retaining nuts, then the cover plate.
2. Using No. 50 Torx bit and strut rod remover/installer tool No. J-35669, or equivalents, remove strut shaft.
3. Remove strut mount bushing by prying with suitable tool.
4. Using strut mount plate wrench tool No. J-35670, or equivalent, remove jounce bumper retainer.
5. Attach strut extension rod tool No. J-35668, or equivalent, to strut shaft and compress shaft down into cartridge, then remove tool and pull out jounce bumper.
6. Attach strut extension rod tool No. J-

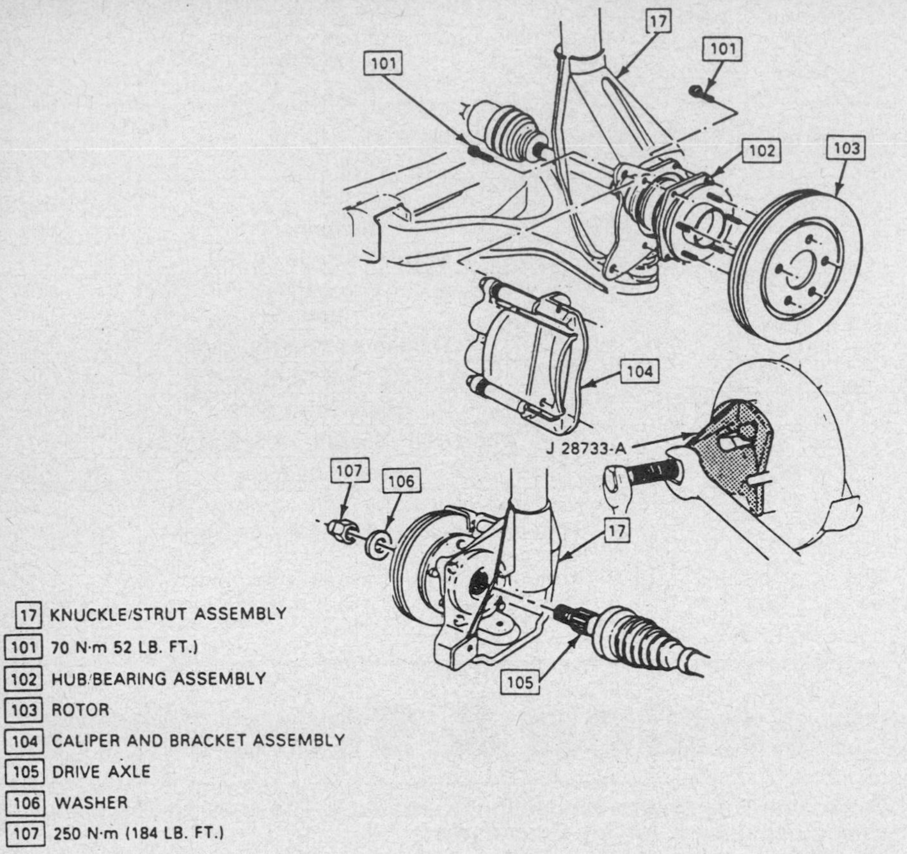
17
101
101
102
103
104
J 28733-A
107
106
17
105
17 KNUCKLE/STRUT ASSEMBLY
101 70 N·m 52 LB. FT.)
102 HUB/BEARING ASSEMBLY
103 ROTOR
104 CALIPER AND BRACKET ASSEMBLY
105 DRIVE AXLE
106 WASHER
107 250 N·m (184 LB. FT.)
GC2029100170000X

Fig. 1 Hub & bearing assembly removal

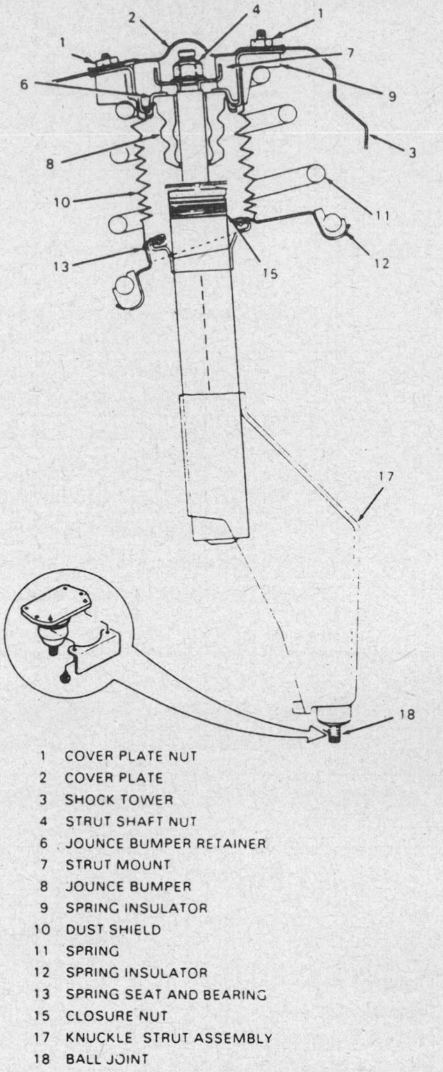
1 COVER PLATE NUT
2 COVER PLATE
3 SHOCK TOWER
4 STRUT SHAFT NUT
6 JOUNCE BUMPER RETAINER
7 STRUT MOUNT
8 JOUNCE BUMPER
9 SPRING INSULATOR
10 DUST SHIELD
11 SPRING
12 SPRING INSULATOR
13 SPRING SEAT AND BEARING
15 CLOSURE NUT
17 KNUCKLE STRUT ASSEMBLY
18 BALL JOINT
GC2029100172000X

Fig. 2 Cross-sectional view of strut & knuckle assembly

35668, or equivalent, to strut shaft and extend shaft, then remove tool and, using strut cap nut wrench tool No. J-35671, or equivalent, unscrew closure nut.

7. Remove strut cartridge.
8. Remove oil from strut tube using suction device.

INSTALLATION

1. Using strut cap nut wrench tool No. J-35671, or equivalent, install self contained replacement cartridge.
2. Install jounce bumper, then using strut mount plate wrench tool No. J-35670 or equivalent, the jounce bumper retainer.
3. Install strut mount bushing. If necessary, use strut extension rod tool No. J-35668 or equivalent after bushing is partially installed and position strut shaft as required. Lubricate bushing with a soap solution to ease installation.
4. Using No. 50 Torx bit and strut rod remover/installer tool No. J-35669, or equivalents, install strut shaft nut, torquing to specifications.
5. Install strut mount cover, aligning scribe marks. Tighten cover plate nuts to specifications.

STRUT SERVICE

REMOVAL

1. Disconnect battery ground cable.
2. Scribe alignment marks on cover plate, then loosen three cover plate retaining nuts.
3. Raise and support vehicle, then remove wheel and tire assembly.
4. Remove brake caliper and bracket assembly, leaving hose attached, and support caliper out of way.
5. Remove brake rotor, then the hub and bearing to knuckle attaching bolts.
6. **On models with ABS,** remove ABS sensor mounting bolt and position sensor aside.
7. **On all models,** separate axle from transaxle and carefully remove drive axle assembly.
8. Remove tie rod to knuckle attaching nut.
9. Using tie rod puller/ball joint remover tool No. J-35917, or equivalent, separate tie rod from knuckle.
10. Remove lower ball joint to knuckle attaching nut.
11. Using tool No. J-35917, or equivalent, separate ball joint from lower control arm.
12. Remove ball joint heat shield, then the cover plate retaining nuts.
13. Remove strut and knuckle assembly.

SERVICE

Springs are under high tension. Do not remove strut shaft nut without using a suitable spring compressing tool.

1. Mount strut and knuckle assembly into strut spring compressor tool No. J-34013-A and strut compressor adapter tool No. J-34013-88, or equivalents, then compress spring with compressor forcing screw just enough to release tension from upper spring insulator.
2. Using Torx bit and strut rod nut remover/installer tool No. J-35669, or equivalents, remove strut shaft nut.
3. Relieve all spring tension, then remove spring and strut components, **Fig. 2.**
4. Install spring seat and bearing.
5. Install lower spring insulator. Lower spring coil end must be visible between the step and the first retention tab of insulator.
6. Install front suspension spring.
7. Install dust shield to lower spring seat.
8. Install jounce bumper.
9. Install upper spring insulator. Upper spring coil end must be between step and location mark on insulator.
10. Using strut mount plate wrench tool No. J-35670 or equivalent, install jounce bumper retainer to strut mount.
11. Install strut mount and upper strut mount bushing.
12. Using strut spring compressor and

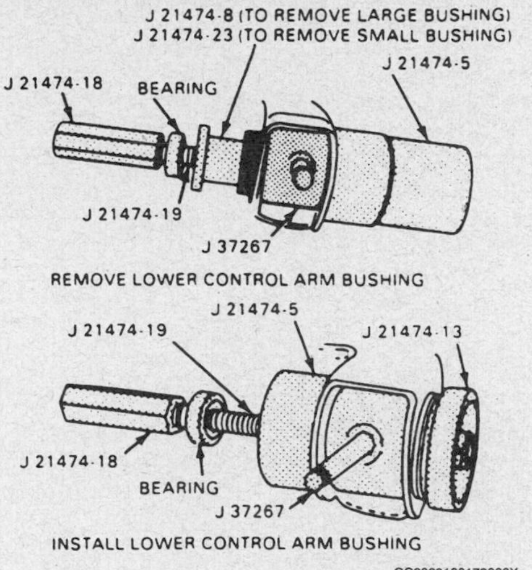
J 21474-8 (TO REMOVE LARGE BUSHING)
J 21474-23 (TO REMOVE SMALL BUSHING)
J 21474-5
J 21474-18
BEARING
J 21474-19
J 37267
REMOVE LOWER CONTROL ARM BUSHING
J 21474-5
J 21474-19
J 21474-13
J 21474-18
BEARING
J 37267
INSTALL LOWER CONTROL ARM BUSHING
GC2029100173000X

Fig. 3 Lower control arm bushings replacement

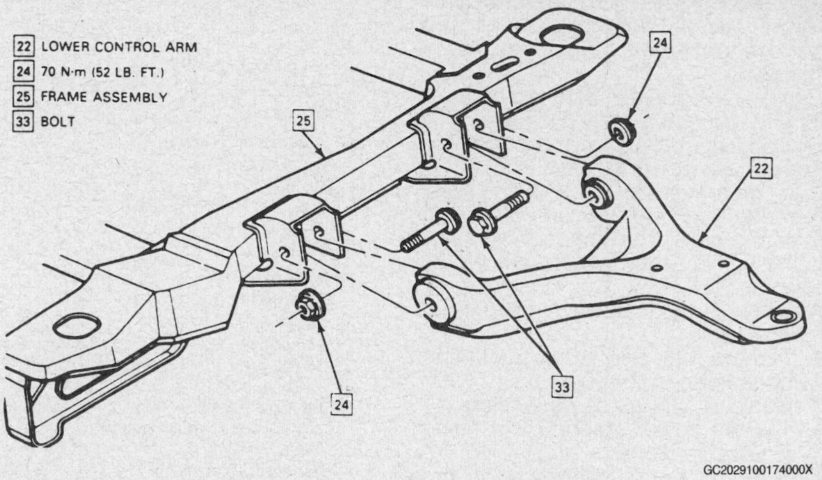
22 LOWER CONTROL ARM
24 70 N·m (52 LB. FT.)
25 FRAME ASSEMBLY
33 BOLT
24
25
22
24
33
GC2029100174000X

Fig. 4 Lower control arm installation

strut compressor adapter tools Nos. J-34013-A and J-34013-88, or equivalents, compress strut assembly.

13. Align strut cartridge shaft with strut extension rod tool No. J-35668, or equivalent.
14. Using strut rod nut remover/installer tool No. J-35669, or equivalent, and Torx bit, install strut shaft nut, torquing to specifications.

INSTALLATION

1. Install strut mount cover plate and upper strut mount to body attaching nuts. Do not tighten nuts until vehicle is lowered to floor.
2. Install ball joint heat shield.
3. Install lower ball joint to control arm attaching nut, **Torquing** to 15 ft. lbs., then tighten an addition 90°.
4. Further tighten to next slot in nut with cotter pin hole in stud and install new cotter pin. **Do not tighten more than an additional 60° to align with hole and do not loosen nut at any time during installation.**
5. Install tie rod to knuckle attaching nut, torquing to specifications, and install cotter pin.
6. Carefully install drive axle assembly through opening in knuckle and insert drive axle into transaxle.
7. Install hub and bearing to knuckle attaching bolts, torquing to specifications.
8. **On models with ABS,** position ABS sensor and install mounting bolt.
9. **On all models,** install brake rotor, then the brake caliper and bracket assembly.
10. Install wheel and tire assembly and lower vehicle.
11. **Torque** lug nuts to 100 ft. lbs. and tighten the cover plate nuts to specifications.
12. Connect battery ground cable.

CONTROL ARM

REPLACE

1. Raise and support vehicle, then remove wheel and tire assembly.
2. **On 3.4L/V6-204 engine models,** remove engine splash shields.
3. **On all models,** remove stabilizer shaft to lower control arm insulator bracket bolts.
4. Remove lower ball joint cotter pin and nut, then, using tie rod puller/ball joint remover tool No. J-35917, or equivalent, separate ball joint from lower control arm.
5. Remove lower control arm to frame attaching nuts and bolts, then the lower control arms.
6. If bushing replacement is necessary, refer to **Fig. 3.** Coat threads of control arm bushing service tool set No. J-21474-19, or equivalent, with an extreme pressure lubricant. To facilitate installation, coat outer casing of bushing with suitable lubricant.
7. Reverse procedure to install, noting the following:
   a. Lower control arm to frame bolts must be installed as shown, **Fig. 4.**
   b. Tighten lower control arm to frame bolts to specifications.
   c. **Torque** lower ball joint nut 15 ft. lbs. and tighten an additional 90°, then further tighten to align next slot in nut with cotter pin hole in stud. **Do not tighten more than 60° to align with hole and do not loosen nut at any time during installation.**
   d. Tighten stabilizer shaft bolts to specifications.
   e. **Torque** lug nuts to 100 ft. lbs.

STABILIZER BAR

REPLACE

1. Raise and support vehicle, then remove wheel and tire assembly.
2. Move steering shaft dust shield to gain access to pinch bolt.
3. Remove pinch bolt from lower intermediate steering shaft.
4. Loosen all insulator clamp attaching nuts and bolts, **Fig. 5.**
5. Place suitable jack under center of rear frame crossmember.
6. Loosen two front frame to body bolts four turns.
7. Remove two rear frame to body bolts.
8. Lower rear of frame just enough to gain access for stabilizer shaft removal.
9. Remove insulators and clamps from frame and control arms.
10. Pull stabilizer shaft rearward, swing down and remove from left side of vehicle.
11. Reverse procedure to install, noting the following:
    a. Coat new insulators with rubber lubricant.
    b. Tighten clamp to frame nuts and clamp to lower control arm bolts to specifications.
    c. **Torque** frame attaching bolts to 100 ft. lbs.
    d. Tighten pinch bolt to specifications.
    e. **Torque** lug nuts to 100 ft. lbs.

POWER STEERING GEAR

REPLACE

EXCEPT 3.4L/V6-204 ENGINE

1. Remove air cleaner, then raise and support vehicle. **Provide additional support at rear of vehicle.**
2. Remove front wheel and tire assemblies.
3. Remove intermediate shaft lower pinch bolt at steering gear.
4. Remove intermediate shaft from stub shaft. **Failure to disconnect intermediate shaft from rack and pinion shaft stub may result in damage to steering gear and/or intermediate shaft. This damage can cause loss of steering control.**
5. Disconnect electrical connector at switch.
6. Using tie rod puller/ball joint remover tool No. J-35917 or equivalent, disconnect tie rod ends from knuckle and strut assembly.
7. Support body with suitable stands, then remove rear frame mounting bolts and lower rear frame no more

than five inches. **Do not lower rear of frame too far. Damage to engine components nearest to cowl may result.**

8. Remove heat shield, then the pipe retaining clip from steering gear.
9. Disconnect inlet pipes and outlet line from power steering gear.
10. Remove remaining brackets and clips.
11. Remove rack and pinion mounting nuts and bolts, then the rack and pinion assembly through the left wheel opening.
12. Reverse procedure to install, noting the following:
    a. Tighten rack and pinion mounting bolts to specifications.
    b. Replace O-rings as necessary.
    c. Tighten power steering line fitting to specifications.
    d. Tighten heat shield attaching screws to specifications.
    e. **Torque** rear frame attaching bolts to 100 ft. lbs.
    f. Tighten tie rod end castle nuts to specifications.
    g. Tighten intermediate shaft lower pinch bolt to specifications.
13. After completing installation, bleed power steering system as follows:
    a. Turn wheels all the way to left.
    b. Add power steering to Cold mark on fluid level indicator.
    c. Start engine and run at fast idle, then add fluid, if necessary, to bring level to Cold mark.
    d. Bleed system by turning wheels from side to side without hitting stops. Keep fluid level at Cold mark.
    e. Return wheels to center position and continue running engine for 2-3 minutes.
    f. Road test vehicle to ensure steering functions normally and is free of noise.
    g. Check fluid level and ensure level is at Hot mark after system has stabilized at its normal operating temperature.

3.4L/V6–204 ENGINE

1. Remove air cleaner and duct assembly.
2. Install engine support tools J-28467-A, J-28467-90 and J-36462, or equivalents.
3. Raise and support vehicle, then remove both front wheel and tire assemblies.
4. Loosen right side engine splash shield.
5. Disconnect both left and right tie rods from steering knuckles.
6. Remove intermediate shaft from stub shaft. **Failure to disconnect intermediate shaft from rack and pinion shaft stub may result in damage to steering gear and/or intermediate shaft. This damage can cause loss of steering control.**

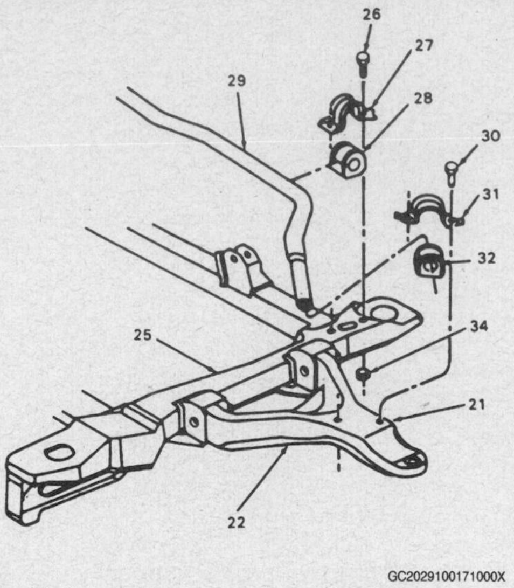

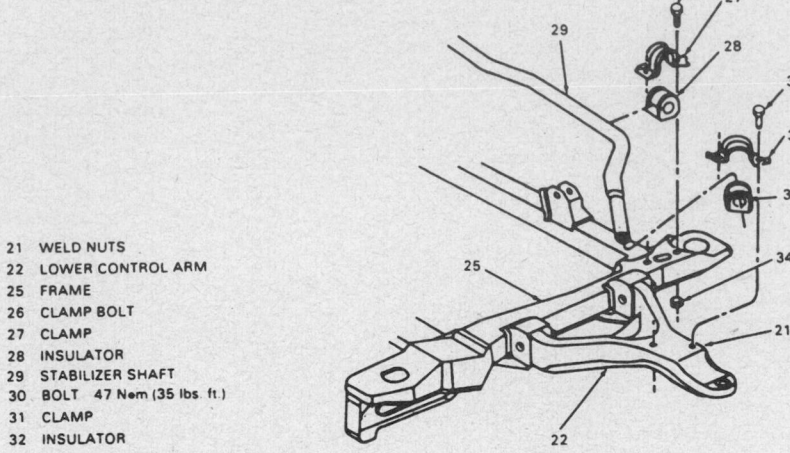

21 WELD NUTS
22 LOWER CONTROL ARM
25 FRAME
26 CLAMP BOLT
27 CLAMP
28 INSULATOR
29 STABILIZER SHAFT
30 BOLT 47 Nem (35 lbs. ft.)
31 CLAMP
32 INSULATOR
34 NUT 47 Nem (35 lbs. ft.)
GC2029100171000X

Fig. 5 Stabilizer shaft & insulators replacement

7. Disconnect electrical connector at pressure switch.
8. Remove exhaust pipe and catalytic converter assembly.
9. Support frame at center rear using jack stands.
10. Remove frame retaining bolts, then lower frame three inches.
11. Remove power steering gear heat shield.
12. Remove power steering line clamp at steering gear.
13. Remove both power steering gear mounting bolts, then disconnect pressure and return lines at steering gear.
14. Remove steering gear through left wheel opening.
15. Replace stub shaft seals.
16. Reverse procedure to install, noting the following:
    a. Tighten rack and pinion mounting bolts to specifications.
    b. Replace O-rings as necessary.
    c. Tighten power steering line fitting to specifications.
    d. Tighten heat shield attaching screws to specifications.
    e. **Torque** rear frame attaching bolts to 100 ft. lbs.
    f. Tighten tie rod end castle nuts to specifications.
    g. Tighten intermediate shaft lower pinch bolt to specifications.
17. After completing installation, bleed power steering system as follows:
    a. Turn wheels all the way to left.
    b. Add power steering to Cold mark on fluid level indicator.
    c. Start engine and run at fast idle, then add fluid, if necessary, to bring level to Cold mark.
    d. Bleed system by turning wheels from side to side without hitting stops. Keep fluid level at Cold mark.
    e. Return wheels to center position and continue running engine for 2-3 minutes.
    f. Road test vehicle to ensure steering functions normally and is free of noise.
    g. Check fluid level and ensure level is at Hot mark after system has stabilized at its normal operating temperature.

POWER STEERING PUMP

REPLACE

1. Disconnect battery ground cable.
2. Disconnect inlet and outlet hoses from pump.
3. Remove serpentine belt guard as necessary.
4. Remove belt from pulley, using 1/2 inch breaker bar.
5. Remove coolant recovery bottle as necessary.
6. Remove pump assembly.
7. Transfer pulley as necessary.
8. Reverse procedure to install, them bleed power steering system as follows:
    a. Turn wheels all the way to left.
    b. Add power steering to Cold mark on fluid level indicator.
    c. Start engine and run at fast idle, then add fluid, if necessary, to bring level to Cold mark.
    d. Bleed system by turning wheels from side to side without hitting stops. Keep fluid level at Cold mark.
    e. Return wheels to center position and continue running engine for 2-3 minutes.
    f. Road test vehicle to ensure steering functions normally and is free of noise.
    g. Check fluid level and ensure level is at Hot mark after system has stabilized at its normal operating temperature.

TIGHTENING SPECIFICATIONS

Year	Component	Torque/Ft. Lbs.
1992–95	Adjuster Plug Locknut	50
	Ball Joint Heat Shield Retaining Nuts	54①
	Cylinder End Fittings	20
	Drive Axle Nut	184
	Engine Torque Strut Bracket Bolt	40
	Front Bracket To Engine Bolt	67
	Front Strut Closure Nut	82
	Front Strut Piston Shaft Nut	72
	Front Wheel Hub/Bearing To Knuckle Bolts	52
	Heat Shield Screws	54①
	Idle Speed Power Steering Pressure Switch	116①
	Inner Tie Rod To Rack	70
	Intermediate Shaft Pinch Bolt	35
	Lower Ball Joint Nut	②
	Lower Control Arm To Frame Bolts	56
	Pinion Locknut	26
	Pinion Preload	16① ③
1992–95 —Cont'd	Power Steering Cooler Pipe Retaining Screw	71①
	Pump Mounting Bolt	21
	Pump To Front Or Rear Bracket Bolt	19
	Rack And Pinion Fittings	20
	Rack And Pinion Mounting Bolts	59
	Stabilizer Bar Insulator Clamp To Frame Nuts	35
	Stabilizer Bar Insulator Clamp To Lower Control Arm Bolt	39
	Strut Mount Cover Plate Nuts	18
	Tie Rod End Jam Nut	50
	Tie Rod End Nuts	40
	Union Fitting To Hydraulic Pump Housing	55
	Valve End Fittings	12
	Wheel Lug Nuts	100

①—Inch lbs.
②—Refer to text.
③—Maximum.

Wheel Alignment

INDEX

PRELIMINARY INSPECTION

1. Ensure tires are inflated to correct pressure, and check for uneven wear.
2. Check front wheel bearings and related suspension components for damage and replace as necessary, to eliminate improper alignment due to faulty components.
3. Check ball joints and tie rods.
4. Check vehicle trim heights.
5. Check steering gear for looseness at frame.
6. Check struts for improper operation.
7. Check for loose control arms.
8. Check for loose or missing stabilizer shaft attachments.

FRONT WHEEL ALIGNMENT

When adjusting wheel alignment, always adjust both front and rear alignment, proceeding in the following order.

1. Rear wheel camber
2. Rear wheel toe and tracking
3. Front wheel camber and toe.

CAMBER

Front

1. Open hood and remove three strut cover plate nuts and the cover plate.
2. Lift front of vehicle just to the point that strut stud clears strut tower and cover top of strut. **Do not over extend drive axle. Do not lift by suspension.**
3. Use strut alignment templet tool No. J-36892, or equivalent, to mark holes, then file three holes. File inboard or outboard of existing hole depending or camber requirement. Do not file more than .2 inch in either direction. **Paint exposed metal with red oxide primer and, after primer has dried, paint area with paint matching body color.**
4. Lower front of vehicle and guide strut studs into slotted holes.
5. Install three strut cover plate nuts.
6. Set camber to specifications by moving strut, then **Torque** strut cover plate nuts to 17 ft. lbs.

Rear

Refer to **Fig. 1** when adjusting rear wheel alignment.

1. Raise and support vehicle.
2. Remove tire and wheel assembly.
3. Remove auxiliary spring as outlined under "Auxiliary Spring Assembly, Replace."
4. Remove strut/upper auxiliary spring bracket/stabilizer shaft bracket, if equipped.
5. Place strut in vise.
6. File lower strut to knuckle attaching hole oblong.
7. Place auxiliary spring assembly in vise.
8. File lower strut attaching hole oblong.
9. Place stabilizer bracket in vise.
10. File lower stabilizer bracket to strut attaching hole oblong.
11. Attach strut assembly/stabilizer shaft bracket/upper auxiliary spring bracket to knuckle.
12. Install strut to body bolts and break hose bracket.
13. Install auxiliary spring and install tire and wheel assembly.
14. Adjust camber then **Torque** strut to knuckle nuts to 136 ft. lbs.
15. Check and adjust toe if necessary.

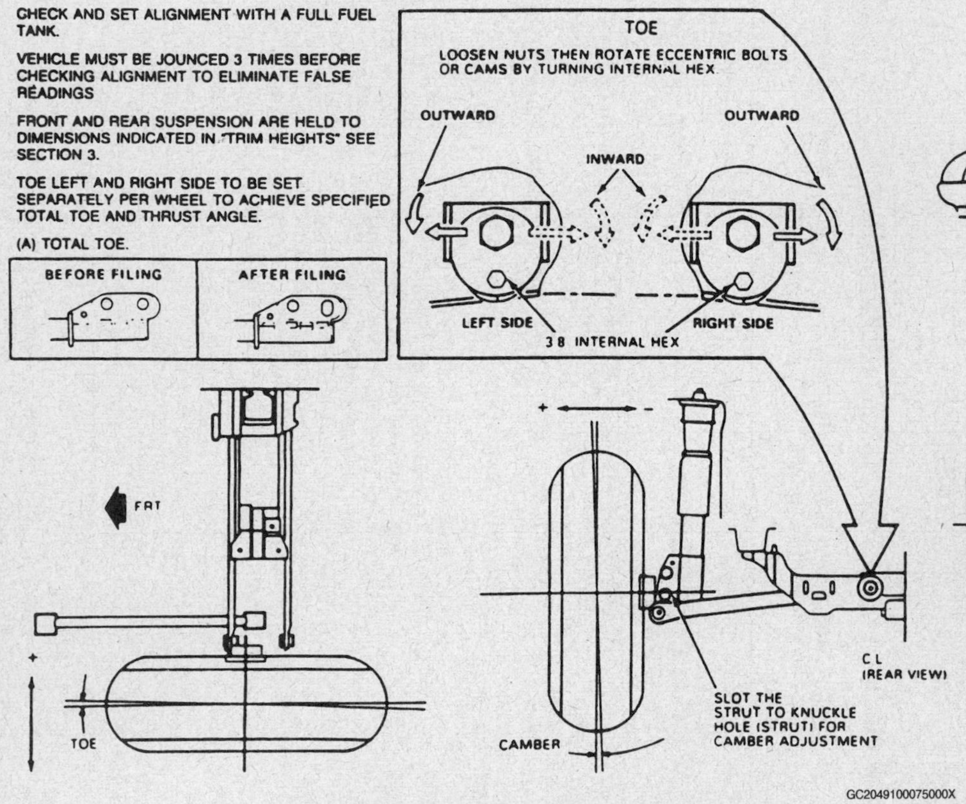
CHECK AND SET ALIGNMENT WITH A FULL FUEL TANK.
VEHICLE MUST BE JOUNCED 3 TIMES BEFORE CHECKING ALIGNMENT TO ELIMINATE FALSE READINGS
FRONT AND REAR SUSPENSION ARE HELD TO DIMENSIONS INDICATED IN "TRIM HEIGHTS" SEE SECTION 3.
TOE LEFT AND RIGHT SIDE TO BE SET SEPARATELY PER WHEEL TO ACHIEVE SPECIFIED TOTAL TOE AND THRUST ANGLE.
(A) TOTAL TOE.
BEFORE FILING
AFTER FILING
TOE
LOOSEN NUTS THEN ROTATE ECCENTRIC BOLTS OR CAMS BY TURNING INTERNAL HEX
OUTWARD
INWARD
OUTWARD
LEFT SIDE
RIGHT SIDE
3 8 INTERNAL HEX
FRT
+
TOE
CAMBER
SLOT THE STRUT TO KNUCKLE HOLE (STRUT) FOR CAMBER ADJUSTMENT
C L (REAR VIEW)
GC2049100075000X

Fig. 1 Rear alignment inspection & adjustment

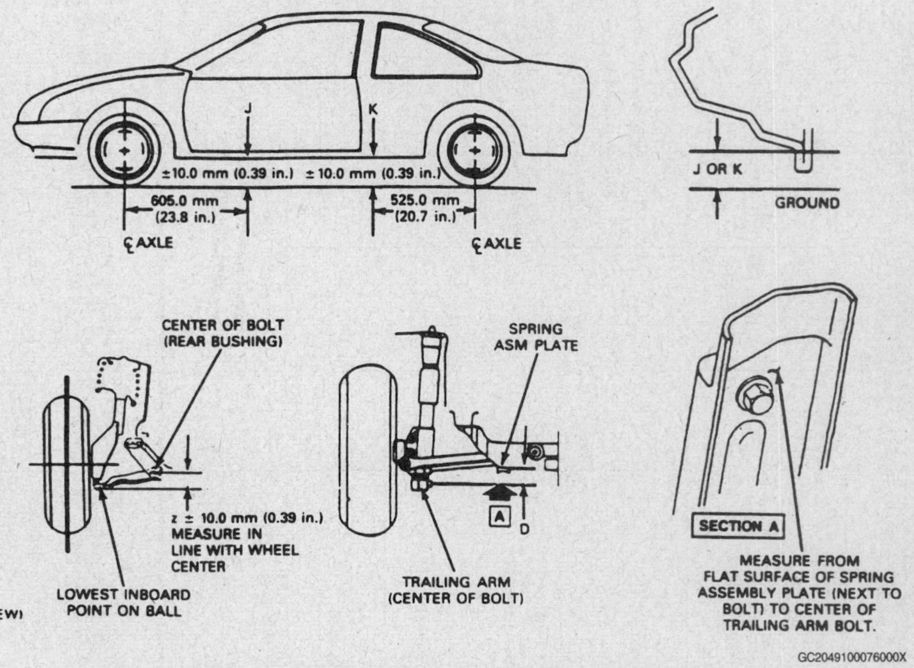
J
K
±10.0 mm (0.39 in.)
± 10.0 mm (0.39 in.)
605.0 mm (23.8 in.)
525.0 mm (20.7 in.)
℄ AXLE
℄ AXLE
J OR K
GROUND
CENTER OF BOLT (REAR BUSHING)
z ± 10.0 mm (0.39 in.) MEASURE IN LINE WITH WHEEL CENTER
LOWEST INBOARD POINT ON BALL
SPRING ASM PLATE
A
D
TRAILING ARM (CENTER OF BOLT)
SECTION A
MEASURE FROM FLAT SURFACE OF SPRING ASSEMBLY PLATE (NEXT TO BOLT) TO CENTER OF TRAILING ARM BOLT.
GC2049100076000X

Fig. 2 Ride height measurement location

MODEL		Z	D	J	K
SUSP	TIRE SIZE	CURB	CURB	CURB	CURB
FE1 (A)	P205/70R15/N	72 mm (2.83 in.)	93 mm (3.66 in.)	249 mm (9.80 in.)	249 mm (9.80 in.)
FE1 (A)	P215/60R16/N	71 mm (2.79 in.)	93 mm (3.66 in.)	249 mm (9.80 in.)	249 mm (9.30 in.)
FE1 (B)	P205/70R15/N	73 mm (2.87 in.)	94 mm (3.70 in.)	249 mm (9.80 in.)	249 mm (9.30 in.)
FE1 (B)	P215/60R16/N	72 mm (2.83 in.)	93 mm (3.66 in.)	249 mm (9.80 in.)	249 mm (9.80 in.)
FE3 (A)	P225/60R16/N	66 mm (2.60 in.)	87 mm (3.43 in.)	249 mm (9.80 in.)	249 mm (9.80 in.)
FE3 (C)	P225/60R16/N	66 mm (2.60 in.)	88 mm (3.46 in.)	249 mm (9.30 in.)	249 mm (9.80 in.)
FE3 (D)	P225/60R16/N	66 mm (2.60 in.)	88 mm (3.46 in.)	249 mm (9.30 in.)	249 mm (9.80 in.)
FE3 (E)	P225/60R16/N	67 mm (2.64 in.)	88 mm (3.46 in.)	249 mm (9.30 in.)	249 mm (9.80 in.)

A. Coupe
B. Sedan
C. Convertible
D. 3.1L (LHO) Engine — Sedan
E. 3.4L (LQI) Engine — Sedan

GC2049200077000X

Fig. 3 Ride height specification chart. 1992 Cutlass Supreme

MODEL		Z	D	J	K
SUSP	TIRE SIZE	CURB	CURB	CURB	CURB
FE1 (A)	P195/75R14/N	83 mm (3.27 in.)	104 mm (4.09 in.)	249 mm (9.80 in.	249 mm (9.80 in.)
FE1 (B)	P195/75R14/N	83 mm (3.27 in.)	105 mm (4.13 in.)	249 mm (9.80 in.	249 mm (9.80 in.)
FE2 (A)	P205/70R15/N	72 mm (2.83 in.)	92 mm (3.62 in.)	249 mm (9.80 in.	249 mm (9.80 in.)
FE2 (B)	P205/70R15/N	73 mm (2.87 in.)	93 mm (3.66 in.)	249 mm (9.80 in.	249 mm (9.80 in.)
F41 (A)	P215/60R16/N	71 mm (2.80 in.)	92 mm (3.62 in.)	249 mm (9.80 in.	249 mm (9.80 in.)
F41 (B)	P215/60R16/N	72 mm (2.83 in.)	92 mm (3.62 in.)	249 mm (9.80 in.	249 mm (9.80 in.)
FE3 (A, B)	P225/60R16/N	67 mm (2.64 in.)	86 mm (3.39 in.)	249 mm (9.80 in.	249 mm (9.80 in.)

A. Coupe B. Sedan

GC2049200078000X

Fig. 4 Ride height specification chart. 1992 Lumina

SUSP	MODEL	ENG	STYLE	TIRE SIZE	Z	D	J	K
FE1	SE	LHO	2 DR	P205/70R15/N	73 mm (2.87 in.)	93 mm (3.66 in.)	249 mm (9.80 in.)	249 mm (9.80 in.)
FE1	SE	LHO	2 DR	P215/60R16/N	72 mm (2.83 in.)	92 mm (3.62 in.)	249 mm (9.80 in.)	249 mm (9.80 in.)
FE1	SE	LHO	4 DR	P205/70R15/N	73 mm (2.87 in.)	92 mm (3.62 in.)	249 mm (9.80 in.)	249 mm (9.80 in.)
FE1	SE	LHO	4 DR	P215/65R15/N	75 mm (2.95 in.)	95 mm (3.70 in.)	249 mm (9.80 in.)	249 mm (9.80 in.)
FE1	SE	LHO	4 DR	P215/60R16/N	72 mm (2.83 in.)	92 mm (3.62 in.)	249 mm (9.80 in.)	249 mm (9.80 in.)
FE1	LE	LHO	4 DR	P205/70R15/N	73 mm (2.87 in.)	92 mm (3.62 in.)	249 mm (9.80 in.)	249 mm (9.80 in.)
FE1	LE	LHO	4 DR	P215/65R15/N	75 mm (2.95 in.)	95 mm (3.70 in.)	249 mm (9.80 in.)	249 mm (9.80 in.)
FE3	SE	LHO	4 DR	P215/65R15/N	75 mm (2.95 in.)	95 mm (3.70 in.)	249 mm (9.80 in.)	249 mm (9.80 in.)
FE3	SE	LQ1	4 DR	P225/60R16/N	68 mm (2.68 in.)	87 mm (3.43 in.)	249 mm (9.80 in.)	249 mm (9.80 in.)
FE3	LE	LHO	4 DR	P205/70R15/N	73 mm (2.87 in.)	92 mm (3.62 in.)	249 mm (9.80 in.)	249 mm (9.80 in.)
FE3	LE	LHO	4 DR	P215/65R15/N	75 mm (2.95 in.)	95 mm (3.70 in.)	249 mm (9.80 in.)	249 mm (9.80 in.)
FE3	LE	LQ1	4 DR	P225/60R16/N	68 mm (2.68 in.)	87 mm (3.43 in.)	249 mm (9.80 in.)	249 mm (9.80 in.)
FE3	STE	LHO	4 DR	P225/60R16/N	67 mm (2.64 in.)	87 mm (3.43 in.)	249 mm (9.80 in.)	249 mm (9.80 in.)
FE3	STE	LQ1	4 DR	P225/60R16/N	68 mm (2.68 in.)	87 mm (3.43 in.)	249 mm (9.80 in.)	249 mm (9.80 in.)
FE3	SE	LHO	2 DR	P215/65R15/N	74 mm (2.91 in.)	95 mm (3.70 in.)	249 mm (9.80 in.)	249 mm (9.80 in.)
FE3	SE	LHO	2 DR	P225/60R16/N	66 mm (2.60 in.)	87 mm (3.43 in.)	249 mm (9.80 in.)	249 mm (9.80 in.)
FE3	SE	LQ1	2 DR	P225/60R16/N	67 mm (2.64 in.)	87 mm (3.43 in.)	249 mm (9.80 in.)	249 mm (9.80 in.)
FE3	GT/GTP	LHO	2 DR	P225/60R16/N	67 mm (2.64 in.)	87 mm (3.43 in.)	249 mm (9.80 in.)	249 mm (9.80 in.)
FE3	GT/GTP	LQ1	2 DR	P225/60R16/N	67 mm (2.64 in.)	87 mm (3.43 in.)	249 mm (9.80 in.)	249 mm (9.80 in.)
FE3	GT/GTP	LQ1	2 DR	P245/50ZR16/N	76 mm (2.99 in.)	97 mm (3.82 in.)	249 mm (9.80 in.)	249 mm (9.80 in.)

GC2049200079000X

Fig. 5 Ride height specification chart. 1992 Grand Prix

MODEL		Z	D	J	K
SUSP	TIRE SIZE	CURB	CURB	CURB	CURB
FE1	P205/70R14/N	86 mm (3.39 in.)	106 mm (4.22 in.)	249 mm (9.80 in.)	249 mm (9.80 in.)
FE1	P205/70R15/N	73 mm (2.87 in.)	93 mm (3.66 in.)	249 mm (9.80 in.)	249 mm (9.80 in.)
FE3	P225/60R16/N	66 mm (2.60 in.)	87 mm (3.43 in.)	249 mm (9.80 in.)	249 mm (9.80 in.)

GC2049200080000X

Fig. 6 Ride height specification chart. 1992 Regal

SUSP	MODEL	ENGINE	STYLE	TIRE	Z (CURB)	D (CURB)
FE1	Z7P w/o BYP	LHO	2 DR.	P205/70R15	72.2 mm (2.84 in.)	92.3 mm (3.63 in.)
FE1	Z7P with BYP	LHO	2 DR.	P215/60R16	71.3 mm (2.81 in.)	92.3 mm (3.63 in.)
FE1	Z7P with BYP	L82	2 DR.	P215/60R16	71.3 mm (2.81 in.)	92.3 mm (3.63 in.)
FE3	Z7P w/o BYP	LQ1	2 DR.	P225/60R16	66.1 mm (2.60 in.)	87.4 mm (3.44 in.)
FE3	Z7P with BYP	LQ1	2 DR.	P225/60R16	66.1 mm (2.60 in.)	87.4 mm (3.44 in.)
FE3	Z7Q w/o BYP	LHO	2 DR.	P225/60R16	65.7 mm (2.59 in.)	87.4 mm (3.44 in.)
FE3	Z7Q w/o BYP	LQ1	2 DR.	P225/60R16	66.9 mm (2.63 in.)	87.4 mm (3.44 in.)
FE3	Z7S w/o BYP	LHO	2 DR.	P225/60R16	66.4 mm (2.62 in.)	89.0 mm (3.50 in.)
FE3	Z7S withBYP	LQ1	2 DR.	P225/60R16	67.7 mm (2.67 in.)	89.0 mm (3.50 in.)
FE1	Z7P w/o BYP	LHO	4 DR.	P205/70R15	72.8 mm (2.87 in.)	93.5 mm (3.68 in.)
FE1	Z7P with BYP	LHO	4 DR.	P215/60R16	71.9 mm (2.83 in.)	93.3 mm (3.67 in.)
FE1	Z7P with BYP	L82	4 DR.	P215/60R16	71.9 mm (2.83 in.)	93.3 mm (3.67 in.)
FE3	Z7P w/o BYP	LQ1	4 DR.	P225/60R16	66.9 mm (2.63 in.)	87.9 mm (3.46 in.)
FE3	Z7P with BYP	LQ1	4 DR.	P225/60R16	66.9 mm (2.63 in.)	87.9 mm (3.46 in.)
FE3	Z7Q w/o BYP	LHO	4 DR.	P225/60R16	66.5 mm (2.62 in.)	88.0 mm (3.46 in.)
FE3	Z7Q w/o BYP	LQ1	4 DR.	P225/60R16	66.9 mm (2.63 in.)	87.9 mm (3.46 in.)

- NOTE: All measurements are ± 10 mm (0.39 in.)
- NOTE: "J" and "K" curb heights are 249 mm (9.80 in.) for all model combinations

GC2049300081000X

Fig. 7 Ride height specification chart. 1993–95 Cutlass

SUSP	MODEL	ENGINE	STYLE	TIRE	Z (CURB)	D (CURB)
FE1	LUMINA	LHO	2 DR.	P195/75R14	83.8 mm (3.30 in.)	103.9 mm (4.09 in.)
FE1	LUMINA	LN2/LHO	4 DR.	P195/75R14	83.2 mm (3.28 in.)	104.5 mm (4.11 in.)
FE2	EUROSPORT	LHO	2 DR.	P205/70R15	72.7 mm (2.86 in.)	92.3 mm (3.63 in.)
FE2	LUMINA 9C6	LN2	4 DR.	P205/70R15	71.4 mm (2.81 in.)	92.8 mm (3.65 in.)
FE2	LUMINA	LHO	4 DR.	P205/70R15	72.7 mm (2.86 in.)	92.8 mm (3.65 in.)
FE3	LUMINA Z34	LQ1	2 DR.	P225/60R16	66.8 mm (2.63 in.)	86.0 mm (3.39 in.)
FE3	EUROSPORT Z34	LQ1	4 DR.	P225/60R16	66.8 mm (2.63 in.)	86.0 mm (3.39 in.)
F41	LUMINA	LHO	2 DR.	P215/60R16	71.7 mm (2.82 in.)	91.6 mm (3.61 in.)
F41	EUROSPORT	LHO	2 DR.	P215/60R16	71.7 mm (2.82 in.)	91.7 mm (3.61 in.)
F41	LUMINA	LN2/LHO	4 DR.	P215/60R16	71.0 mm (2.80 in.)	92.1 mm (3.63 in.)
F41	LUMINA B4C	LHO	4 DR.	P205/70R15	72.6 mm (2.86 in.)	92.3 mm (3.63 in.)
F41	LUMINA B4C	LHO	4 DR.	P215/65R15	73.8 mm (2.91 in.)	94.3 mm (3.71 in.)
F41	EUROSPORT	LHO	4 DR.	P215/60R16	71.7 mm (2.82 in.)	92.2 mm (3.63 in.)

- NOTE: All measurements are ± 10 mm (0.39 in.)
- NOTE: "J" and "K" curb heights are 249 mm (9.80 in.) for all model combinations

GC2049300082000X

Fig. 8 Ride height specification chart. 1993–95 Lumina & Monte Carlo

TOE

Front

1. Remove small seal clamps.
2. With steering wheel in straight ahead position, loosen jam nuts on tie rods.
3. Rotate inner tie rod to obtain proper toe angle, then ensure number of threads showing on each tie rod is approximately equal.
4. Ensure tie rod ends are square, then **Torque** jam nuts to 46 ft. lbs.
5. Ensure seals are not twisted and install seal clamps.

Rear

1. Install rear toe adjusting tool No. J-38118, or equivalent, after lubricating threads.
2. Hand tighten turnbuckle portion of tool in direction of adjustment. Equal amounts of threads should be showing on both sides of turnbuckle.
3. Loosen rear rod nut at crossmember a minimum of four turns.
4. Rotate turnbuckle portion of tool to reach correct toe specification.
5. **Torque** rear rod to crossmember nut to 81 ft. lbs. plus an additional 60° turn.
6. Remove tool.

VEHICLE RIDE HEIGHT

Check ride height as follows, refer to **Fig. 2** for ride height location and **Figs. 2 through 10** for specification charts:

1. Ensure vehicle is on level ground.
2. Ensure tires are inflated to proper pressures.
3. Fuel tank should be full to obtain accurate readings.
4. Trunk should be empty except for spare tire and jack.
5. Bounce the car three times at the front and rear to normalize suspension.
6. Measure from lowest point on the ball joint housing to control arm bolt centerline, "D" and "K" positions.
7. Measure from level floor to rocker panel at "Z" and "J" positions.

SUSP	MODEL	ENGINE	STYLE	TIRE	Z (CURB)	D (CURB)
FE1	SEw o B4U	LHO	4 DR.	P205 70R15	73.4 mm (2.89 in.)	92.3 mm(3.63 in.)
FE1	SE w o B4U	LHO	4 DR.	P215 65R15	75.2 mm (2.96 in.)	94.8 mm (3.73 in.)
FE1	SE w o B4U	LHO	4 DR.	P215 60R16	72.4 mm (2.85 in.)	92.2 mm (3.63 in.)
FE3	SE w o B4U	LHO	4 DR.	P215 65R15	75.2 mm (2.96 in.)	94.8 mm (3.73 in.)
FE3	SE w/o B4U	LQ1	4 DR.	P215 65R15	76.7 mm (3.02 in.)	94.7 mm (3.73 in.)
FE3	SE w/o B4U	LQ1	4 DR.	P225 60R16	68.4 mm (2.69 in.)	86.7 mm (3.41 in.)
FE1	LE w/o B4U	LHO	4 DR.	P205 70R15	74.1 mm (2.92 in.)	92.3 mm (3.63 in.)
FE3	LE w/o B4U	LQ1	4 DR.	P225 60R16	68.4 mm (2.69 in.)	87.3 mm (3.44 in.)
FE3	STE w o B4U	LHO	4 DR.	P225 60R16	67.1 mm (2.64 in.)	86.9 mm (3.42 in.)
FE3	STE w/o B4U	LQ1	4 DR.	P225 60R16	68.5 mm (2.70 in.)	86.7 mm (3.41 in.)
FE1	LE EXPORT	LHO	4 DR.	P205 70R15	74.1 mm (2.92 in.)	92.3 mm (3.63 in.)
FE1	LE EXPORT	LHO	4 DR.	P215 65R15	75.2 mm (2.96 in.)	94.8 mm (3.73 in.)
FE3	LE EXPORT	LHO	4 DR.	P205 70R15	74.1 mm (2.92 in.)	92.3 mm (3.63 in.)
FE3	LE EXPORT	LHO	4 DR.	P215 65R15	75.2 mm (2.96 in.)	94.8 mm (3.73 in.)
FE3	LE EXPORT	LQ1	4 DR.	P225 60R16	68.4 mm (2.69 in.)	87.3 mm (3.44 in.)
FE1	SE w/o B4U	LHO	2 DR.	P205/70R15	73.6 mm (2.90 in.)	92.5 mm (3.64 in.)
FE1	SE w/o B4U	LHO	2 DR.	P215/60R16	72.6 mm (2.86 in.)	92.4 mm (3.64 in.)
FE3	SE w/o B4U	LHO	2 DR.	P215/65R15	74.7 mm (2.94 in.)	94.5 mm (3.72 in.)
FE3	SE w/o B4U	LHO	2 DR.	P225/60R16	66.5 mm (2.62 in.)	86.5 mm (3.41 in.)
FE3	SE with B4U	LHO	2 DR.	P225/60R16	66.5 mm (2.62 in.)	86.5 mm (3.41 in.)
FE3	SE w/o B4U	LQ1	2 DR.	P225/60R16	67.7 mm (2.67 in.)	86.2 mm (3.39 in.)
FE3	SE with B4U	LQ1	2 DR.	P225/60R16	67.7 mm (2.67 in.)	86.2 mm (3.39 in.)
FE3	GT w/o B4U	LHO	2 DR.	P225/60R16	67.2 mm (2.65 in.)	87.0 mm (3.43 in.)
FE3	GT with B4U	LHO	2 DR.	P225/60R16	67.2 mm (2.65 in.)	87.0 mm (3.43 in.)
FE3	GT w/o B4U	LQ1	2 DR.	P225/60R16	67.8 mm (2.67 in.)	86.9 mm (3.42 in.)
FE3	GT with B4U	LQ1	2 DR.	P245/50ZR16	76.4 mm (3.01 in.)	96.6 mm (3.80 in.)
FE3	GT with B4U	LQ1	2 DR.	P225/60R16	67.8 mm (2.67 in.)	86.9 mm (3.42 in.)

- NOTE: All measurements are ± 10 mm (0.39 in.)
- NOTE: "J" and "K" curb heights are 249 mm (9.80 in.) for all model combinations

GC2049300083000X

Fig. 9 Ride height specification chart. 1993–95 Grand Prix

SUSP	MODEL	ENGINE	STYLE	TIRE	Z (CURB)	D (CURB)
FE1	REGAL	LH0	4 DR.	P205/70R15	72.7 mm (2.86 in.)	93.4 mm (3.68 in.)
FE1	REGAL	LHO	4 DR.	P205/70R14	86.2 mm (3.39 in.)	106.3 mm (4.19 in.)
FE3	REGAL	LHO	4 DR.	P225/60R16	66.7 mm (2.63 in.)	87.2 mm (3.43 in.)
FE1	REGAL	L27	4 DR.	P205/70R15	73.4 mm (2.89 in.)	93.4 mm (3.68 in.)
FE1	REGAL	LHO	2 DR.	P205/70R15	72.7 mm (2.86 in.)	92.9 mm (3.66 in.)
FE1	REGAL	LHO	2 DR.	P205/70R14	86.2 mm (3.39 in.)	105.7 mm (4.16 in.)
FE3	REGAL	LHO	2 DR.	P225/60R16	65.9 mm (2.59 in.)	87.2 mm (3.43 in.)
FE1	REGAL	L27	2 DR.	P205/70R15	73.4 mm (2.89 in.)	92.9 mm (3.66 in.)

GC2049300084000X

Fig. 10 Ride height specification chart. 1993–95 Regal

GEO PRIZM
(S Car)

NOTE: Refer To Rear Of This Manual For Vehicle Manufacturer's Special Service Tool Suppliers.

INDEX OF SERVICE OPERATIONS

NOTE: For Service Operations Not Listed Below, Refer To The Table Of Contents In The Front Of This Manual.

Specifications

GENERAL ENGINE SPECIFICATIONS

Year	Engine Liter/CID	Engine VIN Code②	Fuel System	Bore & Stroke	Compression Ratio	Net H.P. @ RPM③	Maximum Torque Ft. Lbs. @ RPM	Normal Oil Pressure Pounds
1992	1.6L/4-97	5	Fuel Injection	3.19 x 3.08	9.4	108 @ 6600	97 @ 4800	①
	1.6L/4-97	6	Fuel Injection	3.19 x 3.08	9.5	102 @ 5800	101 @ 4800	①
1993-95	1.6L/4-97	6	Fuel Injection	3.19 x 3.08	9.5	105 @ 5800	100 @ 4800	①
	1.8L/4-107.5	8	Fuel Injection	3.19 x 3.37	9.5	115 @ 5600	115 @ 2800	—

CID—Cubic inch displacement.
①—At idle, 4.3 psi; At 3000 RPM, 36-71 psi.
②—The eighth digit of the VIN denotes engine code.
③—Ratings are net-as installed in vehicle.

TUNE UP SPECIFICATIONS

Year & Engine/VIN ①	Spark Plug Gap	Ignition Timing BTDC				Curb Idle Speed ③		Fast Idle Speed		Fuel Pump Pressure
		Firing Order Fig. ②	Man. Trans.	Auto. Trans.	Mark Fig.	Man. Trans.	Auto. Trans.	Man. Trans.	Auto Trans.	
1992										
1.6L/4-97 (5)	.031	A	10° ⑤	10° ⑤	B	700	700N	④	④	38-44
1.6L/4-97 (6)	.031	⑥	10° ⑤	10° ⑤	C	800	800N	④	④	38-44
1993–95										
1.6L/4-97 (6)	.031	⑦	10° ⑤	10° ⑤	F	700	700N	④	④	38-44
1.8L/4-107.5 (8)	.031	⑦	10° ⑤	10° ⑤	F	700	700N	④	④	38-44

BTDC — Before Top Dead Center
N — Neutral
D — Drive
①—The eighth digit of the Vehicle Identification Number (VIN) denotes engine code.
②—Before removing wires from distributor cap, determine location of No. 1 wire in cap, as distributor position may have been altered from that shown at the end of this chart.
③—When adjusting idle speed, set parking brake & block drive wheels.
④—Electronically controlled.
⑤—At 700 RPM w/jumper wire connected between terminals of check engine connector. The check engine connector is located in the engine compartment on the left hand inner fender.
⑥—Cylinder numbering front of engine to rear 1, 2, 3, 4. Firing, 1-3-4-2. Refer to Fig. D for spark plug wire connections at distributor cap.
⑦—Cylinder numbering front of engine to rear 1, 2, 3, 4. Firing, 1-3-4-2. Refer to Fig. E for spark plug wire connections at distributor cap.

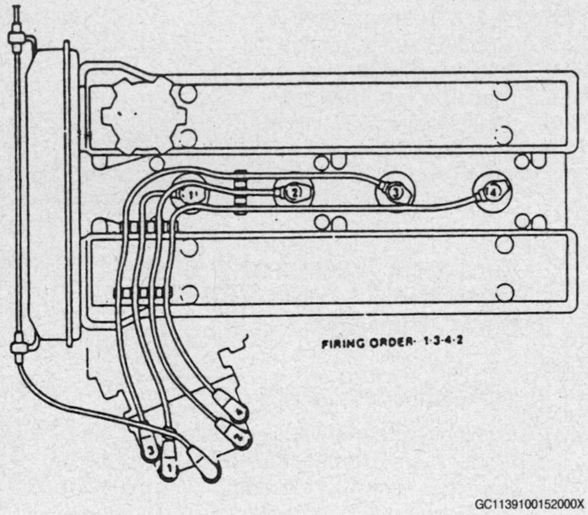
FIRING ORDER· 1·3·4·2
GC1139100152000X

Fig. A

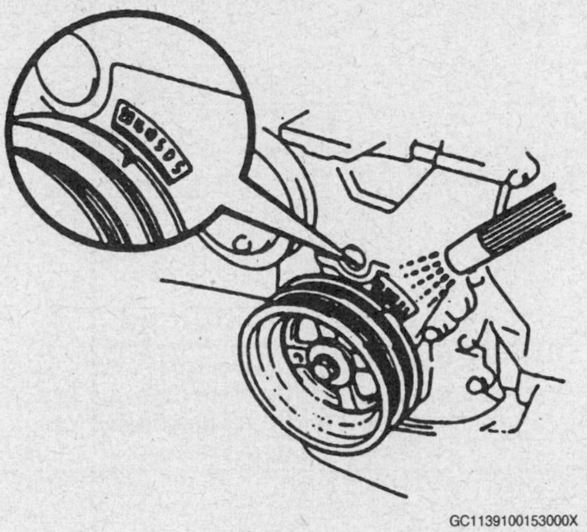

GC1139100153000X

Fig. B

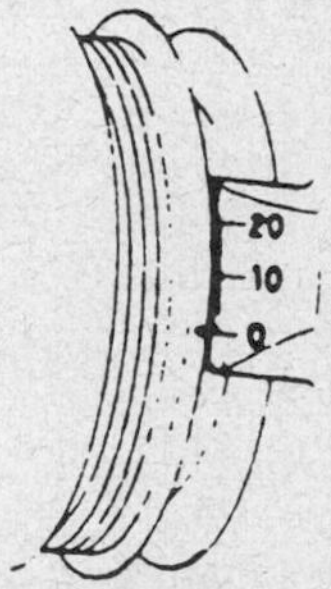
20
10
0

GC1139100154000X

Fig. C

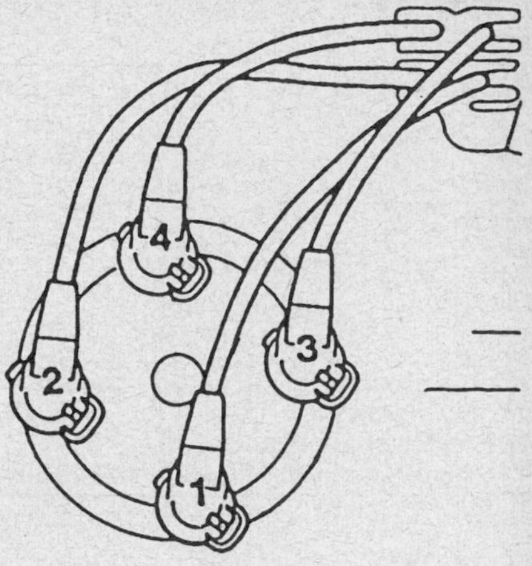
4
3
2
1

GC1139100155000X

Fig. D

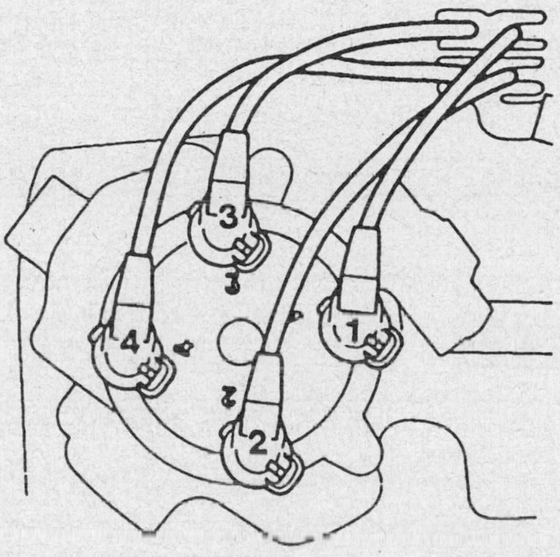
3
4
1
2

GC1139100156000X

Fig. E

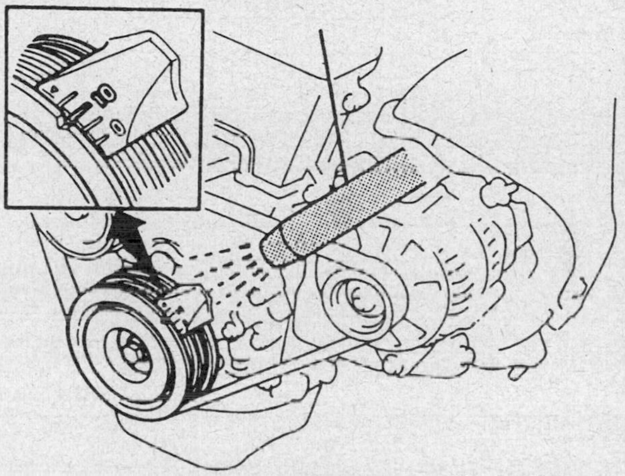
10
0

GC1139100157000X

Fig. F

FRONT WHEEL ALIGNMENT SPECIFICATIONS

Year	Model	Caster Angle, Degrees		Camber Angle, Degrees				Toe-In, Inch	Toe Out on Turns, Degrees	
				Limits		Desired				
		Limits	Desired	Left	Right	Left	Right		Outer Wheel	Inner Wheel
1992	Except GSi	+.61 to +2.11	+1.36	-.9 to +.6	-.9 to +.6	-.15	-.15	.04	—	—
	GSi①	+.7 to +2.2	+1.45	-.95 to +.55	-.95 to +.55	-.20	-.20	.04	—	—
	GSi②	+.61 to +2.11	+1.36	-1.02 to +.48	-1.02 to +.48	-.27	-.27	.04	—	—
1993-95	All	+.58 to +2.08	+1.33	-.92 to +.58	-.92 to +.58	-.17	-.17	.08	33	37–41

①—Models w/automatic transaxle.
②—Models w/manual transaxle.

REAR WHEEL ALIGNMENT SPECIFICATIONS

Year	Model	Camber Angle, Degrees				Toe-In, Inch
		Limits		Desired		
		Left	Right	Left	Right	
1992	Except GSi	-1.33 to +.17	-1.33 to +.17	-.58	-.58	.04
	GSi	-1.43 to +.07	-1.43 to +.07	-.68	-.68	.04
1993-95	All	-1.67 to -.17	-1.67 to -.17	-.92	-.92	.24

COOLING SYSTEM & CAPACITY DATA

Year	Engine (VIN)	Coolant Capacity, Qts. Manual Trans.	Coolant Capacity, Qts. Auto. Trans.	Radiator Cap Relief Pressure, Lbs.	Thermo. Opening Temp. Deg. F	Fuel Tank Gals.	Engine Oil Refill Qts.	Transaxle Oil Man. Transaxle Qts.	Transaxle Oil Auto. Transaxle Qts.①
1992	1.6L/4-97 (5)	6.0	③	14.2	180	13.2	3.6④	2.7	⑤
	1.6L/4-97 (6)	6.0	③	14.2	180	13.2	3.2②	2.7	⑤
1993-95	1.6L/4-97 (6)	6.3	6.2	13.1	180	13.2	3.1②	1.5	⑥
	1.8L/4-107.5 (8)	6.6	6.4	13.1	180	13.2	3.7②	1.5	⑥

①—Approximate. Make final check w/dipstick.
②—Filter change, add .2 qt.
③—3 speed automatic transaxle, 5.8 qts. 4 speed automatic transaxle, 6.1 qts.
④—Filter change add .3 qt.
⑤—3 speed automatic transaxle, 5.8 qts. 4 speed automatic transaxle, 7.6 qts.
⑥—3 speed automatic transaxle, 2.6 qts. 4 speed automatic transaxle, 3.5 qts.

LUBRICANT DATA

Year	Model	Lubricant Type: Transmission Or Transaxle, Manual	Lubricant Type: Transmission Or Transaxle, Automatic	Power Steering	Brake System
1992	All	75W-90 GL-5	Dexron II/IIE	Dexron II/IIE	DOT-3
1993-94	All	75W-90 GL-4	Dexron II/IIE	Power Steering Fluid ①	DOT-3
1995	All	75W-90 GL-4	Dexron III	Dexron III	DOT-3

①—Meeting GM specification 9985010.

Electrical

NOTE: On Air Bag Equipped Models, Refer To "Air Bag System Precautions" Located In The Front Of This Manual For System Disarming & Arming Procedures.

INDEX

PRECAUTIONS

AIR BAG SYSTEMS

Refer to "Air Bag System Precautions" in the front of this manual for system disarming and arming procedures.

FUSE PANEL & FLASHER LOCATION

1992

There are four fuse blocks; the first is behind the left front kick panel, the second is behind the right front kick panel, the third is left of the battery and the fourth is in the lefthand front corner of the engine compartment. The flasher is located under the instrument panel, left of the steering column.

1993–94

There are three fuse blocks; the first is behind the left front kick panel, the second is behind the right front kick panel and the third is left of the air cleaner at the lefthand

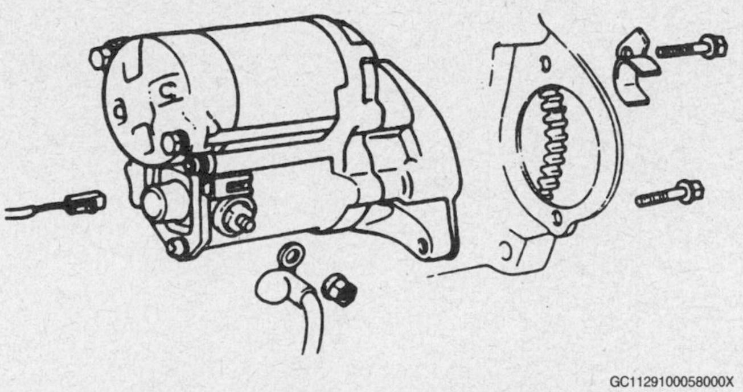
GC1129100058000X

Fig. 1 Starter motor installation

front of the engine compartment. The flasher is located under the instrument panel, left of the steering column.

1995

The power distribution fuse and relay box is located left of the air cleaner at the lefthand front of the engine compartment. The A/C fuse and relay box is located at the lefthand front of the engine compartment, left of the battery. The relay block cassette is located under the lefthand side of the instrument panel. The hazard flasher is located in the relay block cassette.

RELAY CENTER LOCATION

1992

The relay center is located in the lefthand front corner of the engine compartment.

1993–94

The main fuse and relay box is located on the left side of the engine compartment, in front of the strut tower. The A/C fuse and relay box is located at the lefthand front of the engine compartment, left of the battery

1995

The power distribution fuse and relay box is located left of the air cleaner at the lefthand front of the engine compartment. The A/C fuse and relay box is located at the lefthand front of the engine compartment, left of the battery. The relay block cassette is located under the lefthand side of the instrument panel.

STARTER

REPLACE

EXCEPT GSI MODELS

1. Disconnect battery ground cable.
2. Disconnect electrical connectors from starter motor, **Fig. 1.**
3. Remove starter motor retaining bolts.
4. Remove starter motor.
5. Reverse procedure to install.

GSI MODELS

1. Disconnect battery ground cable.
2. Remove rear cooling fan.
3. Raise and support vehicle.
4. Remove right and left splash shields.
5. Disconnect oxygen sensor connector.
6. Disconnect forward exhaust pipe.
7. Disconnect electrical connections from starter assembly.
8. Remove starter assembly attaching bolts.
9. Remove starter assembly from vehicle.
10. Reverse procedure to install.

DISTRIBUTOR

REPLACE

1. Disconnect battery ground cable.
2. Disconnect distributor electrical connectors.
3. Remove distributor cap and spark plug cables and position aside.
4. Mark distributor housing and rotor position.
5. Remove distributor mounting bolts.
6. Remove distributor and O-ring from engine.
7. Reverse procedure to install.

IGNITION LOCK

REPLACE

1. Remove steering wheel as outlined under "Steering Wheel, Replace."
2. Remove upper and lower steering column covers, **Fig. 2 and 3.**
3. Disconnect ignition switch electrical connections.
4. Using a center punch, mark center of tapered-head bolts securing lock cylinder housing.
5. Drill into tapered-head bolts using a .12-.16 inch (3-4 mm) drill bit.
6. Remove tapered-head bolts using a bolt extractor.
7. Place ignition switch in ACC position.
8. Push down stop key and remove cylinder, **Fig. 4.**
9. Reverse procedure to install. Tighten new tapered-head bolts until bolt heads break off.

IGNITION SWITCH

REPLACE

1. Remove ignition lock as outlined under "Ignition Lock, Replace."
2. Remove ignition switch from ignition switch housing.
3. Reverse procedure to install.

COMBINATION SWITCH

REPLACE

1992

1. Disconnect battery ground cable.
2. Remove steering wheel cover and steering wheel as previously outlined under "Steering Wheel, Replace."
3. Remove instrument lower finish panel, air duct and column upper and lower covers.
4. Disconnect electrical connector from ignition/turn signal switch, **Fig. 5.**
5. Remove combination switch assembly.
6. Reverse procedure to install.

1993–95

1. Remove steering wheel as outlined under "Steering Wheel Replace."
2. Remove upper and lower steering column covers.
3. Unclip and set aside left front carpet retainer.
4. Disconnect hood release lever.
5. Remove knee bolster.
6. Untape SRS coil assembly harness from combination switch harness.
7. Disconnect connector from SRS coil.
8. Remove SRS coil assembly from combination switch.
9. Disconnect electrical connector from ignition/turn signal switch, **Fig. 2.**
10. Remove combination switch assembly.
11. Align the SRS coil prior to installation as follows:
    a. Ensure front wheels are in a straight ahead position.
    b. Turn SRS coil counterclockwise by hand until it becomes harder to turn.
    c. Turn the SRS coil clockwise about three turns to align the red marks, **Fig. 6.**
    d. Install and connect the SRS coil.
12. Reverse procedure to install.

STEERING WHEEL

REPLACE

1992

1. Disconnect battery ground cable.
2. Remove steering column center cover and pad assembly.
3. Mark the end of the steering shaft in relation to steering wheel so the wheel and shaft can be aligned properly during installation.
4. Remove steering wheel retaining nut.
5. Using Steering Wheel Puller tool No. J-1859-03, or equivalent, remove steering wheel.
6. Reverse procedure to install, ensuring proper position of steering wheel.

1993–95

1. Place front wheels in a straight ahead position.

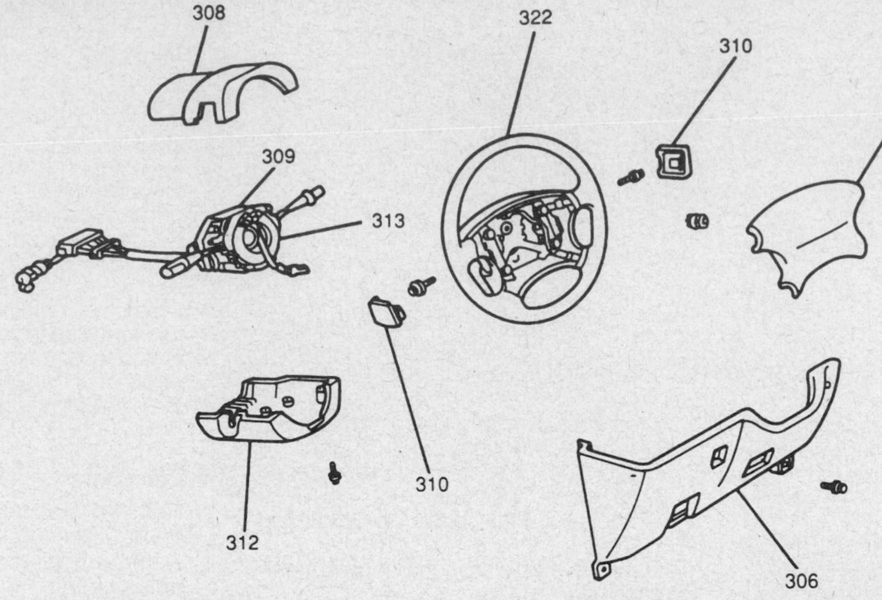
308
322
310
311
309
313
310
312
306

306 KNEE BOLSTER
308 UPPER STEERING COLUMN COVER
309 COMBINATION SWITCH
310 SIDE TRIM COVERS
311 INFLATOR MODULE
312 LOWER STEERING COLUMN COVER
313 SRS COIL ASSEMBLY
322 STEERING WHEEL

GC6049300145000X

Fig. 2 Steering column assembly. 1993–95

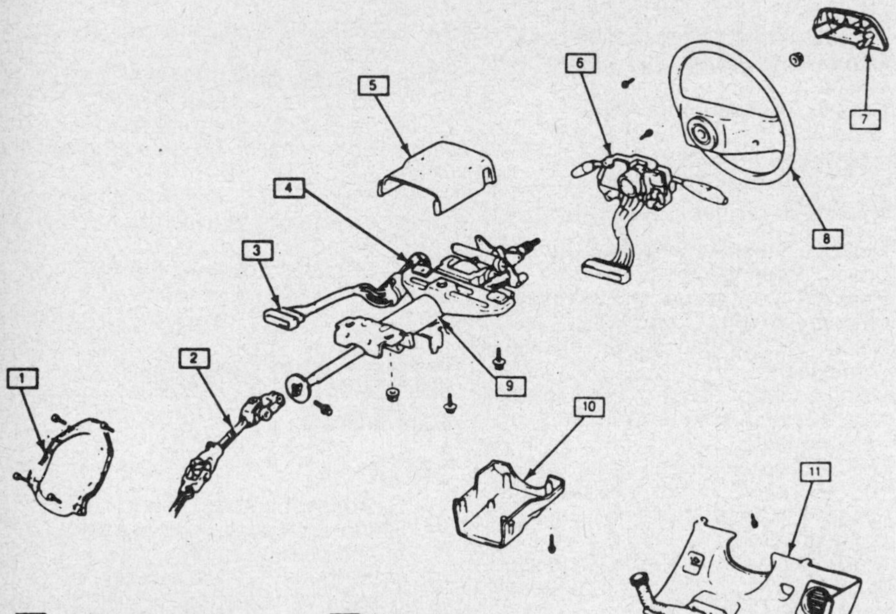
1
2
3
4
5
6
7
8
9
10
11

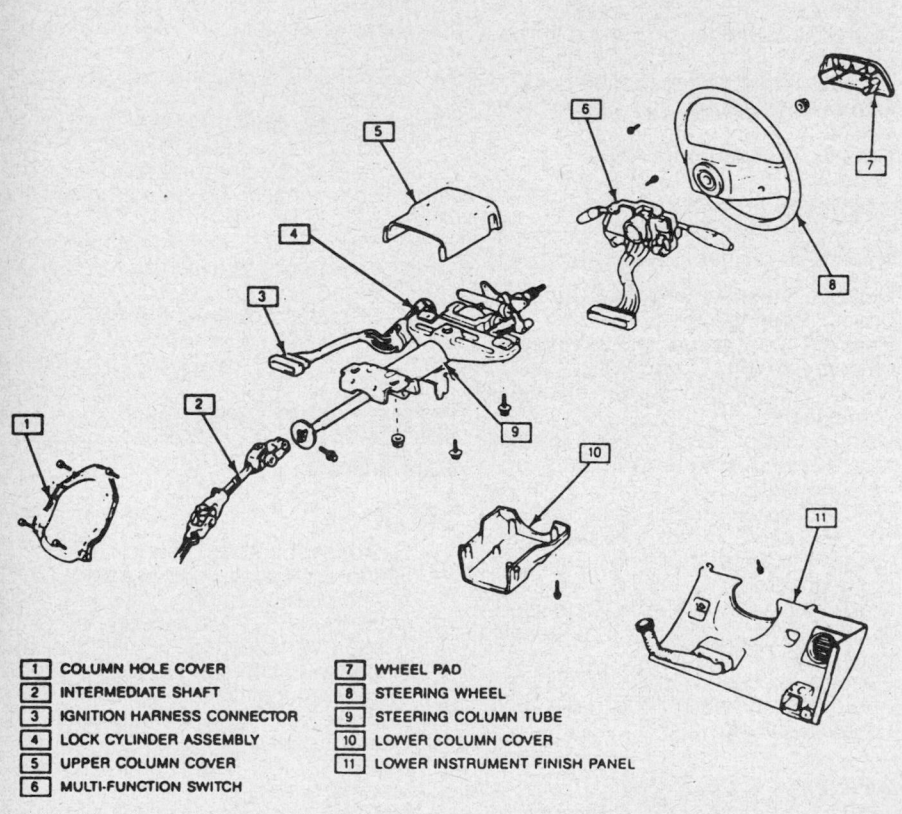

1 COLUMN HOLE COVER
2 INTERMEDIATE SHAFT
3 IGNITION HARNESS CONNECTOR
4 LOCK CYLINDER ASSEMBLY
5 UPPER COLUMN COVER
6 MULTI-FUNCTION SWITCH
7 WHEEL PAD
8 STEERING WHEEL
9 STEERING COLUMN TUBE
10 LOWER COLUMN COVER
11 LOWER INSTRUMENT FINISH PANEL

GC8019100115000X

Fig. 3 Steering column assembly. 1992

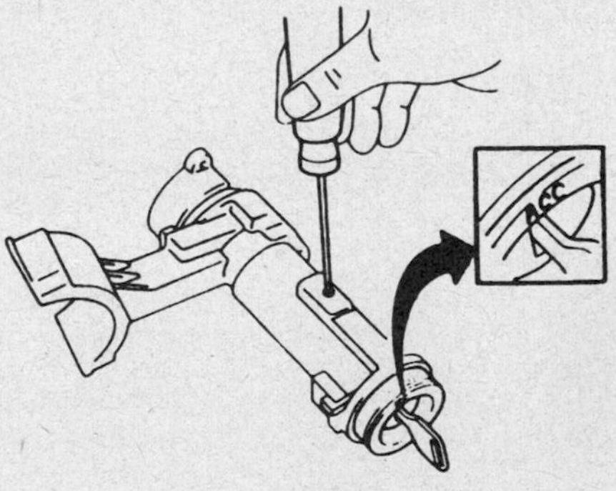
ACC

GC9129100028000X

Fig. 4 Ignition cylinder removal

2. Remove two side trim covers from steering column, **Fig. 2.**
3. Remove two Torx head screws, release Connector Position Assurance (CPA) and disconnect upper steering column connector, **Fig. 7.**
4. Remove air bag from steering wheel.
5. Disconnect horn connector.
6. Remove steering wheel retaining nut.
7. Mark the end of the steering shaft in relation to steering wheel so the wheel and shaft can be aligned properly during installation.
8. Remove steering wheel retaining nut.
9. Using Steering Wheel Puller tool No. J-1859-03, or equivalent, remove steering wheel.
10. Reverse procedure to install, noting the following:
    a. Install air bag module and **torque** Torx head screws to 78 inch lbs.
    b. Ensure proper position of steering wheel.
    c. **Torque** steering wheel nut to 25 ft. lbs.

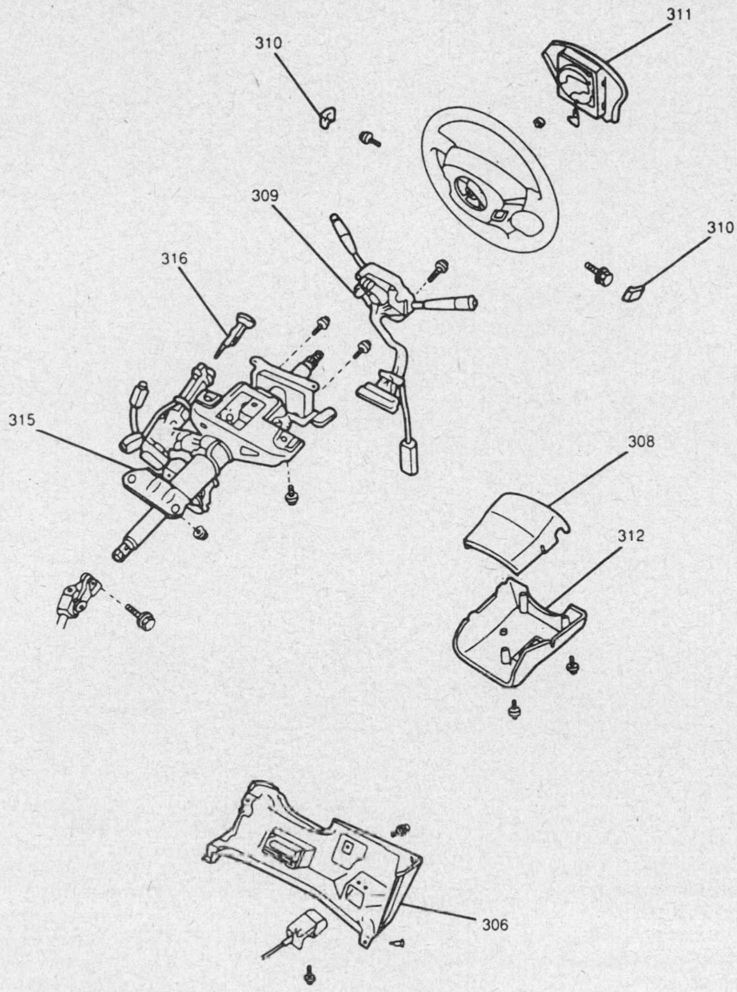

310
311
309
310
316
315
308
312
306

306 KNEE BOLSTER
308 UPPER STEERING COLUMN COVER
309 COMBINATION SWITCH
310 SIDE TRIM COVERS
311 INFLATOR MODULE
312 LOWER STEERING COLUMN COVER
315 STEERING COLUMN ASSEMBLY
316 IGNITION SWITCH

GC9049100115000X

Fig. 5 Steering column switch installation

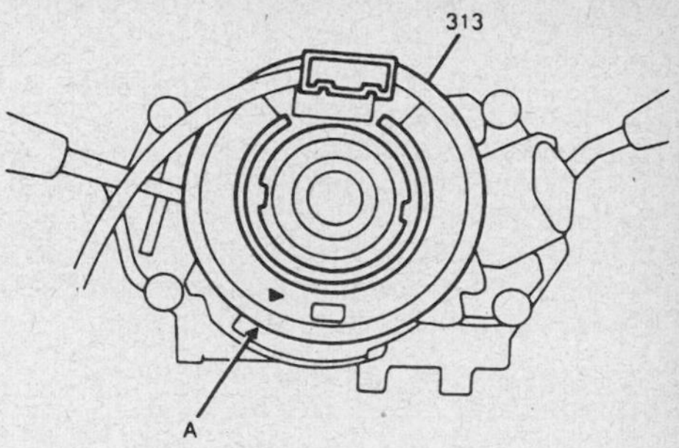

313
A

A ALIGNMENT MARKS
313 SRS COIL ASSEMBLY

GC8019300116000X

Fig. 6 SRS coil alignment. 1993–95

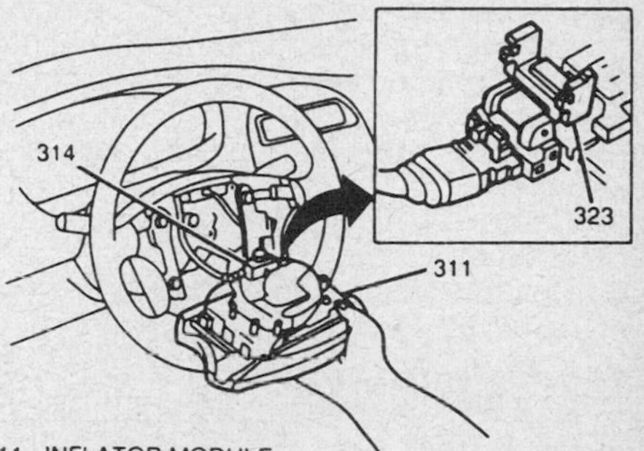

314
323
311

311 INFLATOR MODULE
314 UPPER STEERING COLUMN CONNECTOR
323 CONNECTOR POSITION ASSURANCE (CPA)

GC8019300114000X

Fig. 7 Air bag module removal. 1993–95

INSTRUMENT CLUSTER
REPLACE

1992

1. Disconnect battery ground cable.
2. Disconnect hood release lever.
3. Remove lefthand lower dash trim panel screws and pull out trim, **Fig. 8.**
4. Disconnect speaker connector.
5. Remove A/C duct from lower A/C register, if equipped.
6. Remove lefthand lower trim panel.
7. Remove upper and lower steering column covers.
8. Remove center console trim panel screws and pull out trim.
9. Disconnect and remove cigar lighter lamp from trim panel.
10. Remove center trim panel.
11. Remove cluster bezel attaching screws.
12. Disconnect hazard flasher and dimmer switch electrical connections.
13. Remove cluster bezel.
14. Remove instrument cluster attaching screws.
15. Disconnect speedometer cable and electrical connectors from cluster.
16. Remove instrument cluster.
17. Reverse procedure to install.

1993–95

1. Disconnect battery ground cable.
2. Remove instrument cluster bezel screws, then the bezel by disengaging two lower clips.
3. Remove instrument cluster screws then the cluster disconnecting three electrical connectors.
4. Reverse procedure to install.

RADIO
REPLACE

1. Remove steering column covers.
2. Remove console trim bezel.
3. Disconnect rear wiper/washer, cruise control and defogger electrical connections.
4. Remove radio attaching screws.
5. Remove radio from console.
6. Disconnect radio connections and antenna cable.
7. Reverse procedure to install.

WIPER MOTOR
REPLACE

FRONT

1. Disconnect battery ground cable.
2. Disconnect wiper motor electrical connection.
3. Remove wiper motor attaching bolts.
4. Disconnect wiper linkage from wiper motor output arm.
5. Remove wiper motor.
6. Reverse procedure to install.

REAR

1. Disconnect battery ground cable.
2. Remove wiper arm assembly.
3. Remove liftgate trim panel.
4. Disconnect wiper motor electrical connector.
5. Remove wiper motor attaching bolts.
6. Remove rear wiper motor assembly.
7. Reverse procedure to install.

BLOWER MOTOR

REPLACE

The blower motor is located underneath the instrument panel at the far right side of the vehicle. It is accessible from below the instrument panel.

1. Disconnect battery ground cable.
2. Disconnect rubber air duct running between motor and heater assembly.
3. Disconnect blower motor electrical connectors.
4. Remove blower motor attaching screws.
5. Remove blower motor from under instrument panel.
6. Reverse procedure to install.

HEATER CORE

REPLACE

1992

1. Remove steering wheel as outlined under "Steering Wheel, Replace."
2. Remove trim bezel, instrument panel assembly, cluster assembly, center console and all console trim as outlined under "Dash Panel Service."
3. Remove cup holder from console.
4. Remove radio as outlined under "Radio, Replace."
5. Drain cooling system.
6. Disconnect all cables and ducts from heater case.
7. Disconnect blower switch harness and heater control assembly.
8. Remove two center console support braces.
9. Remove heater hoses from case and grommets from cowl.
10. Remove mounting bolts, nuts and clips from heater and air distribution cases.
11. Remove heater and air distribution cases.
12. Remove screws and clips from case, separate case halves.
13. Remove heater core from case.
14. Reverse procedure to install.

1993–95

1. Disconnect battery ground cable.
2. Remove evaporator case assembly as outlined under "Evaporator Core, Replace."
3. Drain cooling system into a suitable container.
4. Loosen and remove heater core hoses.
5. Remove heater core pipe grommet from vehicle.
6. Remove instrument panel as outlined under "Dash Panel Service."

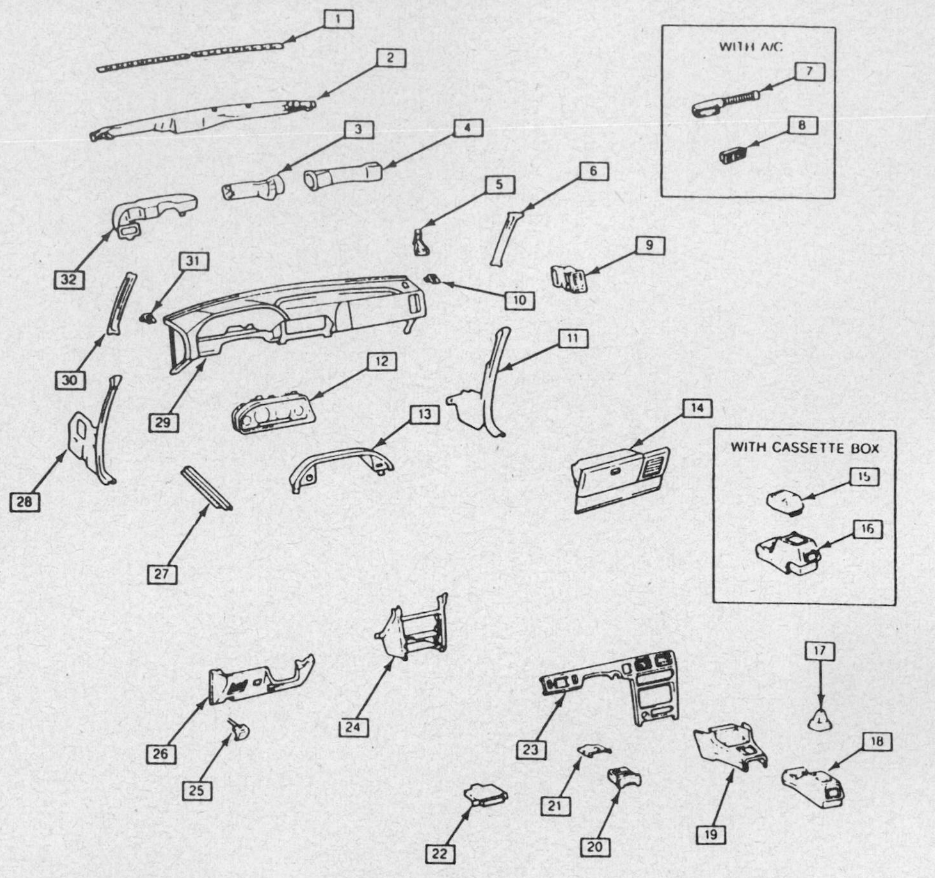
WITH A/C
WITH CASSETTE BOX
1
2
3
4
5
6
7
8
9
10
11
12
13
14
15
16
17
18
19
20
21
22
23
24
25
26
27
28
29
30
31
32

1 DEFROSTER GRILLE
2 DEFROSTER DUCT
3 CENTER VENTILATION DUCT
4 RIGHT VENTILATION DUCT
5 BRACE
6 "A" PILLAR TRIM
7 A/C DUCT
8 LOWER A/C DEFLECTOR
9 RIGHT VENTILATION DEFLECTOR
10 RIGHT WINDOW DEFLECTOR
11 COWL SIDE TRIM
12 INSTRUMENT CLUSTER
13 CLUSTER BEZEL
14 GLOVE BOX AND TRIM ASSEMBLY
15 CASSETTE BOX
16 REAR CONSOLE
17 SHIFT LEVER BOOT (M/T)
18 REAR CONSOLE
19 FRONT CONSOLE
20 ASHTRAY
21 RETAINER
22 CUP HOLDER
23 TRIM BEZEL
24 CENTER CONSOLE TRIM
25 HOOD RELEASE LEVER
26 LEFT LOWER DASH TRIM
27 SCUFF PLATE
28 COWL SIDE TRIM
29 INSTRUMENT PANEL
30 "A" PILLAR TRIM
31 LEFT WINDOW DEFLECTOR
32 LEFT VENTILATION DUCT

GC9099100236000X

Fig. 8 Instrument panel & related components. 1992

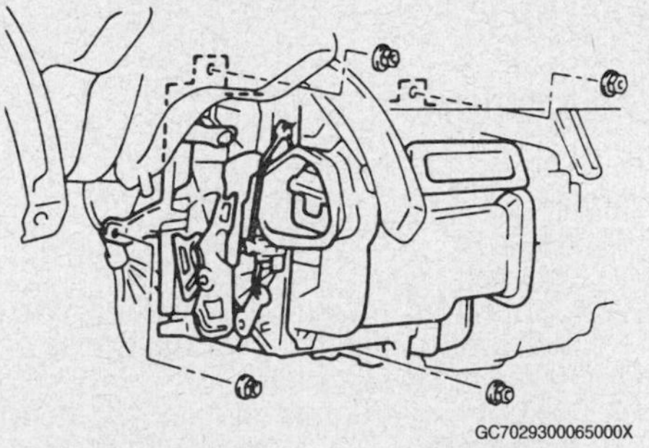
GC7029300065000X

Fig. 9 Heater case. 1993–95

7. Remove right and left instrument panel brace.
8. Remove left and center ventilation ducts.
9. Remove heater case from vehicle, **Fig. 9.**
10. Remove two heater core brackets then slide the heater core from vehicle.
11. Reverse procedure to install.

EVAPORATOR CORE

REPLACE

1992

1. Disconnect battery ground cable.
2. Discharge refrigeration system.
3. Remove and cap suction and liquid tube from evaporator case outlet and inlet fittings.
4. Remove right lower instrument panel trim assembly as outlined under Instrument Panel, Replace.
5. Remove grommets from inlet and outlet fittings.
6. Remove glove box compartment.
7. Disconnect wiring harness connectors.
8. Remove case attaching screws and remove evaporator case from behind instrument panel.
9. Separate upper and lower case halves, **Fig. 10.**

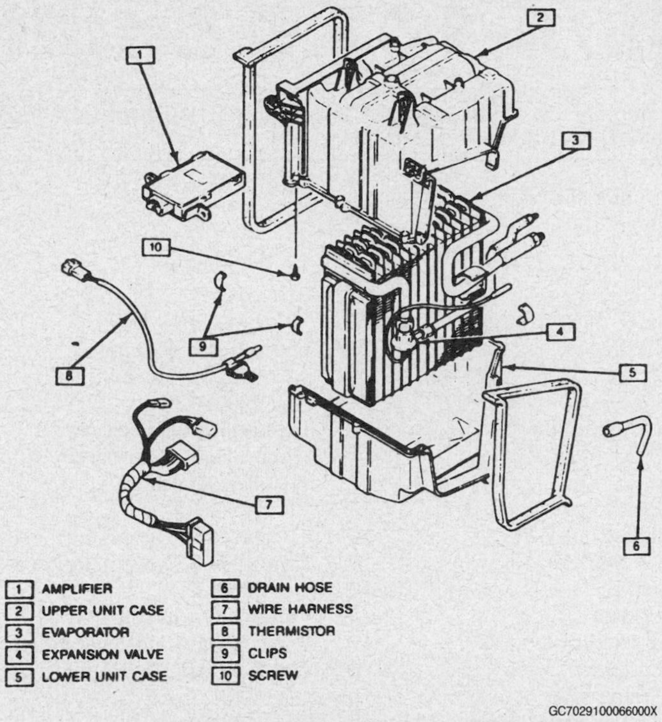
1 AMPLIFIER
2 UPPER UNIT CASE
3 EVAPORATOR
4 EXPANSION VALVE
5 LOWER UNIT CASE
6 DRAIN HOSE
7 WIRE HARNESS
8 THERMISTOR
9 CLIPS
10 SCREW
GC7029100066000X

Fig. 10 Evaporator case. 1992

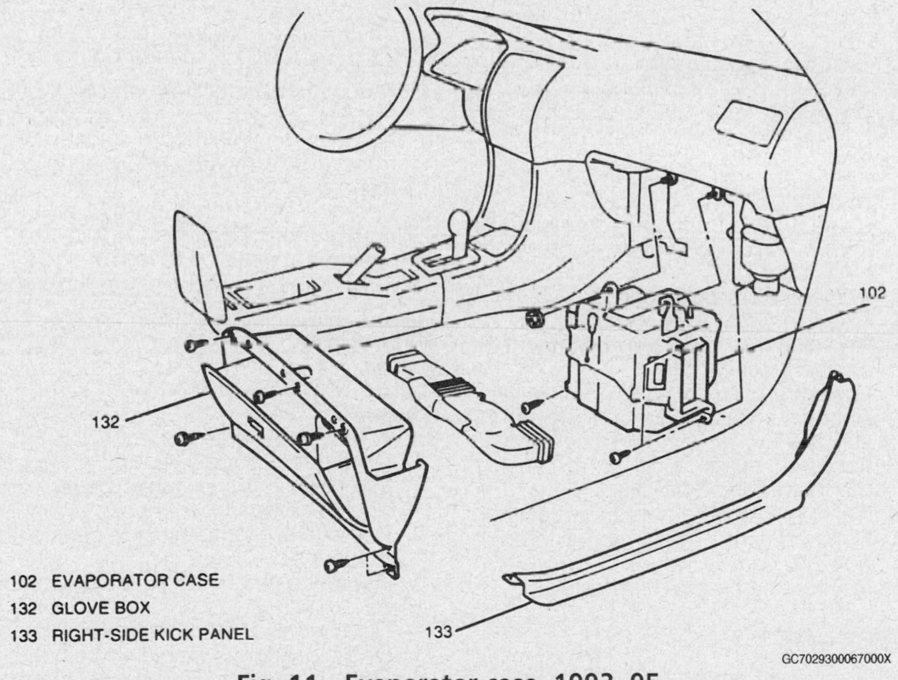
102 EVAPORATOR CASE
132 GLOVE BOX
133 RIGHT-SIDE KICK PANEL
GC7029300067000X

Fig. 11 Evaporator case. 1993–95

10. Disconnect liquid tube from inlet fitting of the expansion tube.
11. Remove packing and heat sensing tube from suction tube of evaporator.
12. Remove expansion valve.
13. Reverse procedure to install.

1993–95

1. Discharge air conditioning system using a suitable A/C recovery system.
2. Disconnect battery ground cable.
3. Remove right side kick panel and glove box assembly.
4. Disconnect evaporator outlet and inlet pipe and plug hoses and evaporator openings.
5. Disconnect hold-down brackets for inlet and outlet pipes.
6. Remove air conditioning amplifier electrical connector then the amplifier.
7. Disconnect evaporator thermister connector.
8. Remove evaporator case from vehicle, **Fig. 11.**
9. Separate evaporator case halves then remove thermister from evaporator.
10. Remove evaporator from case.
11. Reverse procedure to install.

1.6L/4-97 & 1.8L/4-107.5 Engines

NOTE: On Air Bag Equipped Models, Refer To "Air Bag System Precautions" Located In The Front Of This Manual For System Disarming & Arming Procedures.

INDEX

PRECAUTIONS

AIR BAG SYSTEMS

Refer to "Air Bag System Precautions" in the front of this manual for system disarming and arming procedures.

FUEL SYSTEM PRESSURE RELEASE

1992

1. Loosen fuel filler cap to release fuel tank pressure.
2. Disconnect battery ground cable.
3. Wrap a shop towel around the fuel supply fitting.
4. Slowly loosen fuel fitting.
5. Close fuel fitting.

1993–95

1. Loosen fuel filler cap to release fuel tank pressure.
2. Remove radio as outlined under "Radio, Replace" in the "Electrical" section.
3. Disconnect circuit opening relay connector.
4. Start engine and allow to stall.
5. Crank engine for an additional three seconds to release remaining fuel pressure.
6. Disconnect battery ground cable.
7. Connect circuit opening relay connector.
8. Install radio and tighten fuel filler cap.

ENGINE MOUNT

REPLACE

1992

1. Disconnect battery ground cable.
2. Using Engine Support Fixture tool No. J-28467-A or equivalent, support engine assembly.
3. Raise and support vehicle.
4. Remove right lower stone shield.
5. Remove two lower engine mount to engine bracket nuts.
6. Lower vehicle.
7. Remove bolts and right engine mount support.
8. Remove upper bolt from engine mount to engine bracket.
9. Remove windshield washer reservoir.
10. Remove right engine mount through bolt and engine mount.
11. Reverse procedure to install.

1993–95

1. Disconnect battery ground cable.
2. Using Engine Support Fixture tool No. J-28467-A or equivalent, support engine assembly.
3. Remove cruise control actuator and position aside.
4. Remove cruise control actuator bracket.
5. Disconnect two piece air conditioning pipe bracket.
6. Remove bolts from engine mount bracket and engine mount.
7. Raise and support vehicle.
8. Remove engine splash shields.
9. Remove nuts from underside of engine mount bracket.
10. Lower vehicle.
11. Remove insulator from engine mount bracket.
12. Remove engine mount and bracket from vehicle, moving A/C pipe to gain clearance.
13. Remove mount through bolt and the engine mount, **Fig. 1**
14. Reverse procedure to install.

ENGINE

REPLACE

1992

1. Disconnect battery ground and positive cables, then remove battery and engine compartment hood.
2. Remove right and left side engine undercovers.
3. Drain engine oil into suitable container.
4. Drain coolant from radiator and engine block into suitable container.
5. **On models equipped with manual transaxle,** drain transaxle fluid into suitable container.
6. **On all models,** remove air cleaner assembly and coolant reservoir tank.
7. Remove radiator and coolant fan as an assembly.
8. Disconnect heater hoses from coolant inlet housing.
9. Disconnect fuel pressure hose from fuel filter, then the heater and air hoses from air valve.
10. Disconnect fuel return hose from fuel pressure regulator.
11. **On models equipped with manual transaxle,** remove clutch slave cylin-

der without disconnecting hydraulic line and position aside.
12. **On all models,** disconnect vacuum hose from charcoal canister.
13. Disconnect transaxle shift control cables from transaxle.
14. Disconnect speedometer cable, then the cruise control cable (if equipped), accelerator cable and accelerator link.
15. **On models equipped with cruise control,** remove cruise control actuator.
16. Disconnect engine main electrical harness from all related sensors and switches.
17. **On all models,** disconnect brake booster hose from intake manifold.
18. Remove A/C compressor and power steering pump (if equipped) with lines attached and position aside.
19. Disconnect oxygen sensor electrical connector, then remove oxygen sensor.
20. Disconnect oil cooler hoses from oil cooler.
21. Raise and support vehicle, then disconnect catalytic converter clamp, engine pipe clamp and engine pipe from exhaust manifold.
22. Disconnect front and rear engine mounts to center member attaching bolts, then remove front mount through bolt and mount.
23. Remove center member to frame attaching bolts, then the center member.
24. Remove axle to side gear shaft attaching bolts, then disconnect right side lower arm from steering knuckle and separate. Remove axle shafts from side gear shafts and position aside with suitable wire.
25. Lower vehicle to ground level.
26. Attach suitable lifting equipment to engine and transaxle assembly, then remove right and left side mounts.
27. Carefully lift engine and transaxle assembly from vehicle and place on suitable stand.
28. Remove radiator fan temperature switch connector and cold start injector time switch connector.
29. Disconnect vacuum hoses from Bi-Metal Vacuum Switching Valves (BVSV), then remove coolant inlet housing attaching bolts and nut.
30. Disconnect hoses from coolant by-pass tubes, then remove coolant inlet housing.
31. Disconnect back-up lamp switch connector, water temperature sensor connector and water temperature switch connector.
32. **On models equipped with automatic transaxle,** disconnect neutral start switch connectors and transaxle solenoid connector.
33. Rotate crankshaft as necessary to gain access to and remove six torque converter attaching bolts.
34. **On all models,** remove starter assembly, then separate transaxle from engine.
35. Reverse procedure to install.

1993–95

1. Release fuel system pressure as outlined under "Precautions."
2. Disconnect and remove battery.
3. Drain cooling system, engine and transaxle oil into suitable containers.
4. Mark hood hinge position on hood, then remove hood assembly.
5. Remove two splash shields.
6. Disconnect accelerator and kickdown cables.
7. Remove radiator and engine cooling fan assembly.
8. Disconnect necessary electrical harness and vacuum hose connections.
9. Remove air cleaner hose and air cleaner upper and lower cases.
10. Remove coolant reservoir bracket.
11. Remove washer reservoir.
12. Remove cruise control actuator.
13. Disconnect heater hose from thermostat housing and coolant inlet pipe.
14. Disconnect fuel feed pipe from the fuel rail and intake manifold.
15. Disconnect fuel return hose from fuel pressure regulator.
16. **On models with manual transmission,** remove clutch release cylinder.
17. **On all models,** disconnect transaxle control cables.
18. Remove left and right scuff plates.
19. Remove shift lever knob.
20. Remove knee bolster, glove box door, instrument panel trim bezel, front and rear console and lefthand cowl side trim panel.
21. Remove radio as outlined under "Radio, Replace" in the "Electrical" section.
22. Disconnect and remove engine control module.
23. Disconnect cowl panel harness connector and pull harness from the cowl panel.
24. Remove air conditioner compressor and power steering oil pump leaving hoses attached and position in a out of the way location. **Do not allow compressor or oil pump to be supported by the hoses.**
25. Raise and support vehicle.
26. Disconnect front exhaust pipe, exhaust pipe support brackets and oxygen sensor.
27. Disconnect front drive axles as outlined in the "Front Drive Axles" section.
28. Lower vehicle.
29. Attach an engine lifting device to the engine then disconnect engine and transaxle mounts.
30. Ensure all electrical, vacuum and fuel hoses connections are disconnected.
31. Remove engine with transaxle attached from vehicle.
32. Reverse procedure to install.

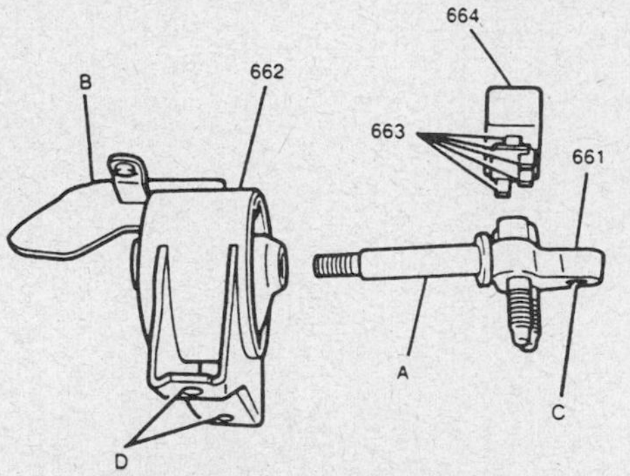
664
662
B
663
661
A
C
D

A THROUGH BOLT PART OF ENGINE MOUNT
B BOLT A HOLE
C BOLT B HOLE
B BOLT C HOLES
661 ENGINE MOUNT BRACKET
662 ENGINE MOUNT
663 TANG
664 INSULATOR

GC1069300478000X

Fig. 1 Engine mount replace. 1993–95

INTAKE MANIFOLD
REPLACE

1992

1. Disconnect battery ground cable.
2. Drain cooling system.
3. Remove air cleaner assembly.
4. **On GSi models,** remove upper radiator hose.
5. **On all models,** disconnect throttle and accelerator cables.
6. Mark then remove all necessary vacuum hoses.
7. **On except GSi models,** proceed as follows:
   a. Disconnect throttle position, cold start, air control valve and vacuum sensors and injector electrical connectors.
   b. Remove cold start injector pipe.
   c. Remove water hose from air valve.
8. **On GSi models,** proceed as follows:
   a. Remove fuel delivery pipe and injectors then the temperature sensor connector.
   b. Remove water outlet bypass pipe.
9. **On all models,** raise and support vehicle.
10. Remove intake manifold bracket.
11. Lower vehicle.
12. Remove intake manifold attaching bolts.
13. Remove intake manifold.
14. Reverse procedure to install.

1993–95

1. Release fuel system pressure as outlined under "Precautions."
2. Disconnect vacuum hoses from vacuum sensor on fuel filter, brake booster and A/C actuator hoses.
3. Disconnect exhaust gas recirculation

(EGR) solenoid valve, vacuum hose from EGR valve then remove the EGR valve.
4. Remove intake manifold brace.
5. Disconnect fuel return hose from pressure regulator.
6. Disconnect TPS sensor and accelerator bracket then remove the throttle body from intake manifold.
7. Remove air intake chamber brace and gasket.
8. Disconnect PCV hoes from cylinder head cover.
9. Remove air intake chamber cover and gasket.
10. Disconnect fuel inlet pipe from fuel rail.
11. Disconnect injector electrical connectors.
12. Remove fuel rail with injectors attached.
13. Remove intake manifold bolts and the intake manifold.
14. Reverse procedure to install.

EXHAUST MANIFOLD
REPLACE

1. Disconnect battery ground cable.
2. Remove exhaust manifold heat shield or insulator.
3. Raise and support vehicle.
4. Disconnect front exhaust pipe.
5. **On except GSi models,** remove exhaust manifold support bracket.
6. **On all models,** lower vehicle.
7. **On except GSi models,** disconnect oxygen sensor.
8. **On all models,** remove exhaust manifold attaching bolts then exhaust manifold.
9. Reverse procedure to install.

CYLINDER HEAD
REPLACE

1992

Except GSi

1. Disconnect battery ground cable.
2. Drain coolant into a suitable container.
3. Raise and support vehicle.
4. Remove righthand lower stone shield.
5. Disconnect two mount nut and stud protectors, then remove two rear transaxle mount to main crossmember mount nuts.
6. Remove two center mount to center crossmember nuts.
7. Lower vehicle.
8. Remove air cleaner assembly.
9. Disconnect throttle, cruise control and transaxle kickdown cables.
10. Mark then disconnect all necessary electrical and vacuum connections.
11. Disconnect fuel inlet line.
12. Disconnect cold start injector pipe and the fuel rail.
13. Remove heater hoses water outlet and inlet housings, **Fig. 2.**
14. Remove spark plugs and PCV valve.
15. Remove cylinder head cover.

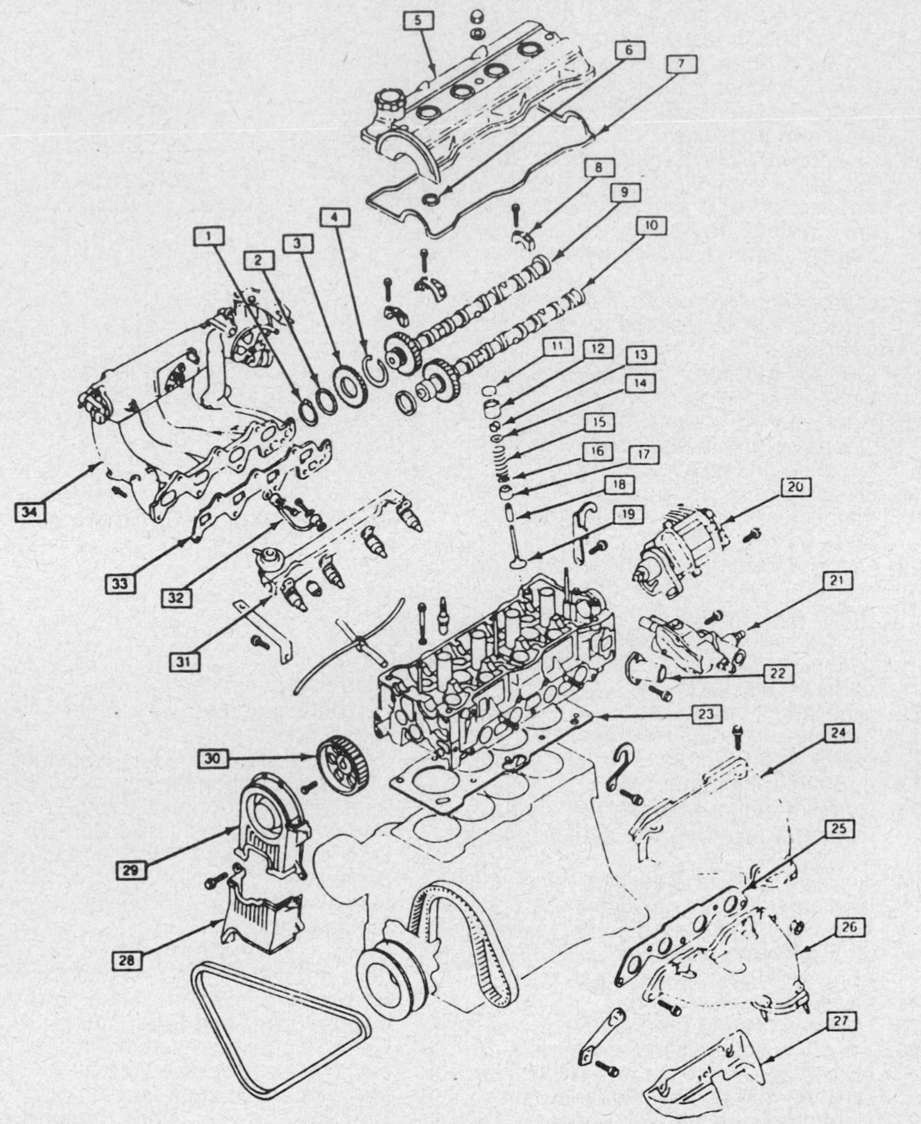

1 CAMSHAFT SNAP RING
2 WAVE WASHER
3 CAMSHAFT SUB-GEAR
4 CAMSHAFT GEAR SPRING
5 CYLINDER HEAD COVER
6 SPARK PLUG TUBE GASKET
7 CYLINDER HEAD COVER GASKET
8 CAMSHAFT BEARING CAP
9 CAMSHAFT (INTAKE)
10 CAMSHAFT (EXHAUST)
11 ADJUSTING SHIM
12 VALVE LIFTER
13 VALVE KEEPERS
14 VALVE SPRING RETAINER
15 VALVE SPRING
16 VALVE SPRING SEAT
17 VALVE STEM OIL SEAL
18 VALVE GUIDE BUSHING
19 VALVE
20 DISTRIBUTOR
21 WATER INLET HOUSING
22 WATER OUTLET HOUSING
23 HEAD GASKET
24 EXHAUST MANIFOLD UPPER INSULATOR
25 EXHAUST MANIFOLD GASKET
26 EXHAUST MANIFOLD
27 EXHAUST MANIFOLD LOWER INSULATOR
28 CENTER TIMING BELT COVER
29 UPPER TIMING BELT COVER
30 CAMSHAFT TIMING GEAR
31 FUEL RAIL
32 COLD-START INJECTOR PIPE
33 INTAKE MANIFOLD GASKET
34 INTAKE MANIFOLD

GC1069100479000X

Fig. 2 Cylinder head & related components. Except GSi models

16. Loosen the A/C compressor, power steering pump and alternator brackets then remove accessory drive belts.
17. Remove A/C idler pulley.
18. Remove cruise control actuator and bracket.
19. Remove windshield washer reservoir.
20. Support engine using Engine Support Fixture tool No. J-28467-A, or equivalent.
21. Remove right engine mount through bolt and raise engine.
22. Remove water pump pulley and lower engine.
23. Remove engine wiring harness from upper timing belt cover.
24. Raise and support vehicle.
25. Remove cylinder head to cylinder block bracket then the exhaust manifold support bracket.
26. Disconnect exhaust pipe from exhaust manifold.
27. Remove upper and center timing belt covers.
28. Remove right engine mount bracket.
29. Remove distributor as outlined under "Distributor, Replace" in the "Electrical" section.

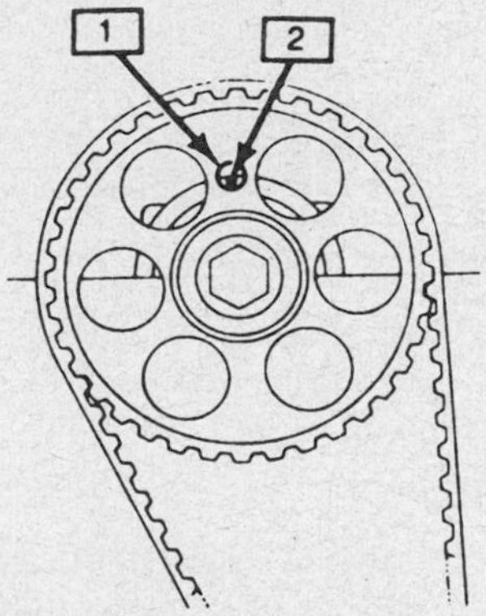
1
2

1 CAMSHAFT GEAR HOLE
2 EXHAUST CAMSHAFT CAP MARK

GC1069100480000X

Fig. 3 Camshaft gear hole alignment. Except GSi models

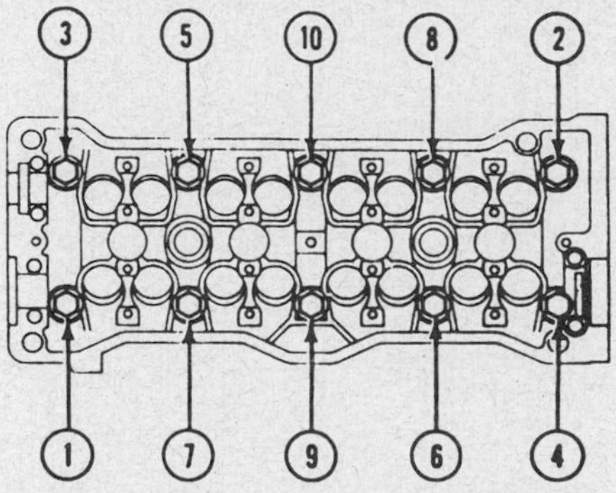
3
5
10
8
2
1
7
9
6
4

GC1069100481000X

Fig. 4 Cylinder bolt removal sequence. Except GSi models

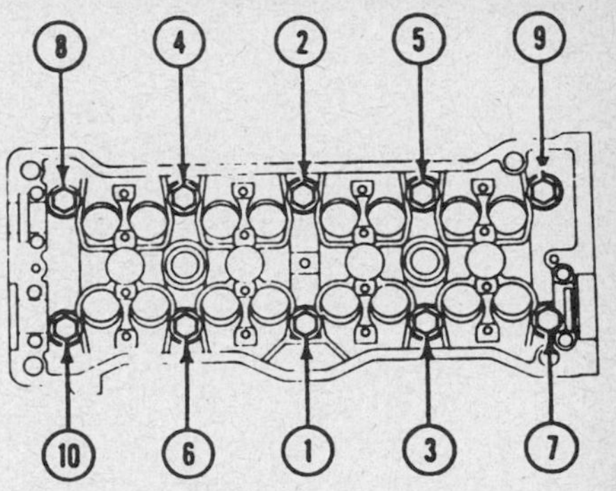
8
4
2
5
9
10
6
1
3
7

GC1069100482000X

Fig. 5 Cylinder bolt tightening sequence. Except GSi models

30. Place No. 1 cylinder at TDC on its compression stroke. Turn crankshaft pulley and align its groove with the "0 mark of timing belt cover. **Ensure that camshaft gear hole is aligned with exhaust camshaft cap mark, Fig. 3.**
31. Remove plug from lower timing belt cover and place alignment marks on camshaft timing gear and belt.
32. Loosen idler pulley mount bolt and push idler pulley toward left then tighten temporarily.
33. Remove timing belt from camshaft timing gear. **Support timing belt so meshing of crankshaft timing gear and belt do not shift. Do not allow oil, water or dust to come in contact with timing belt.**
34. Remove cylinder head bolts in sequence shown in **Fig. 4.**
35. Remove cylinder head with intake and exhaust manifolds attached.
36. Reverse procedure to install, noting the following:
    a. Apply a light coat of clean engine oil to cylinder head bolt threads and under the bolt head before installation.
    b. **Torque** cylinder head bolts, in four incremental steps, in sequence shown in **Fig. 5** ending with a final torque of 44 ft. lbs.

GSi

1. Disconnect battery ground cable.
2. Drain cooling system into a suitable container.
3. Remove air cleaner assembly, then disconnect cruise control cable (if equipped), accelerator cable and link.
4. Disconnect heater hose from rear cylinder head cover.
5. Mark position of vacuum hoses for assembly, then disconnect vacuum hoses from throttle body.
6. Remove cruise control actuator (if equipped), ignition coil and coolant outlet hose.
7. Remove ignition coil.
8. Remove water outlet hose and outlet from cylinder head, **Fig. 6.**
9. Remove brake booster vacuum hose,

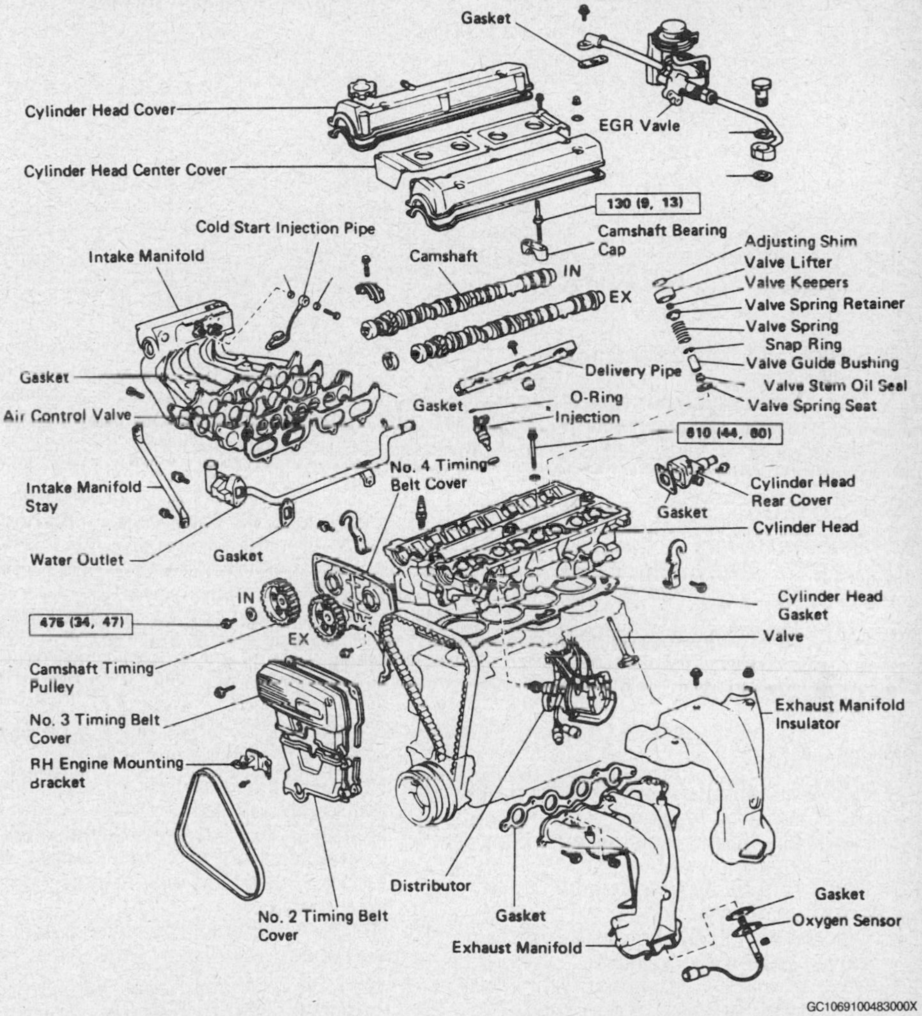
Gasket
Cylinder Head Cover
EGR Vavle
Cylinder Head Center Cover
130 (9, 13)
Cold Start Injection Pipe
Camshaft Bearing Cap
Intake Manifold
Camshaft
IN
EX
Adjusting Shim
Valve Lifter
Valve Keepers
Valve Spring Retainer
Valve Spring
Snap Ring
Valve Guide Bushing
Valve Stem Oil Seal
Valve Spring Seat
Gasket
Delivery Pipe
O-Ring
Gasket
Injection
Air Control Valve
610 (44, 60)
No. 4 Timing Belt Cover
Intake Manifold Stay
Cylinder Head Rear Cover
Gasket
Cylinder Head
Water Outlet
Gasket
IN
476 (34, 47)
EX
Cylinder Head Gasket
Valve
Camshaft Timing Pulley
No. 3 Timing Belt Cover
Exhaust Manifold Insulator
RH Engine Mounting Bracket
Distributor
No. 2 Timing Belt Cover
Gasket
Gasket
Oxygen Sensor
Exhaust Manifold

GC1069100483000X

Fig. 6 Cylinder head & related components. GSi models

then the PCV hose.

10. Remove EGR valve and tubes, then the cold start injector pressure hose.
11. Disconnect water bypass hoses from auxiliary air valve.
12. Remove vacuum pipe and cylinder rear cover.
13. Remove distributor as outlined under "Distributor, Replace" in the "Electrical" section.
14. Disconnect exhaust manifold from cylinder head as outlined under "Exhaust Manifold, Replace."
15. Remove delivery pipe with injectors.
16. Remove intake manifold as outlined under "Intake Manifold, Replace."
17. Remove power steering and alternator drive belts.
18. Remove cylinder head cover and spark plugs.
19. Set crankshaft pulley at TDC of compression stroke. **Ensure valve lifters for No. 1 cylinder are loose. If not, rotate crankshaft pulley an additional 360° to set engine at TDC compression.**

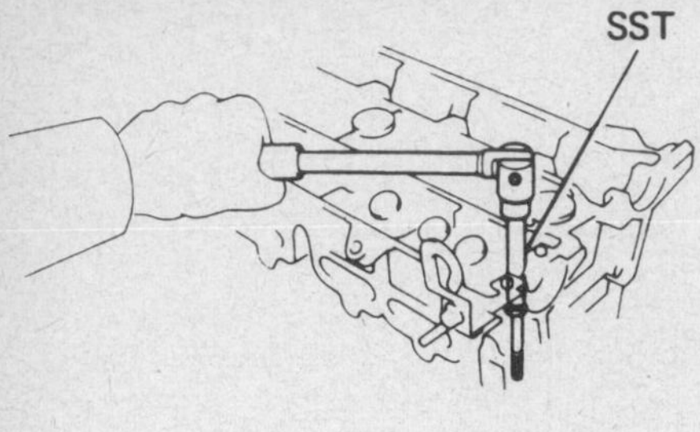
SST

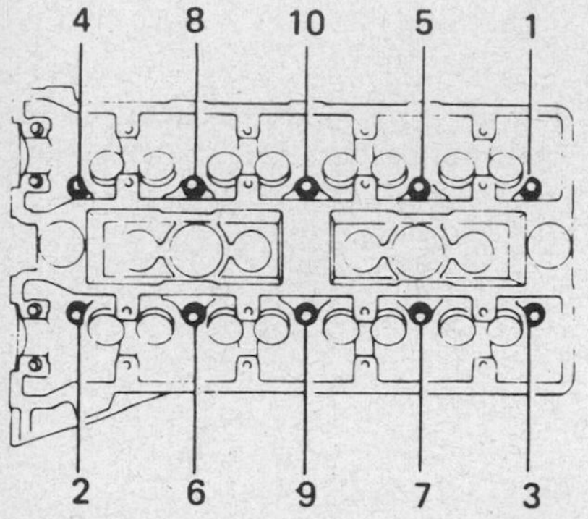
4 8 10 5 1
2 6 9 7 3

GC1069100484000X

Fig. 7 Cylinder head bolt loosening sequence. GSi model

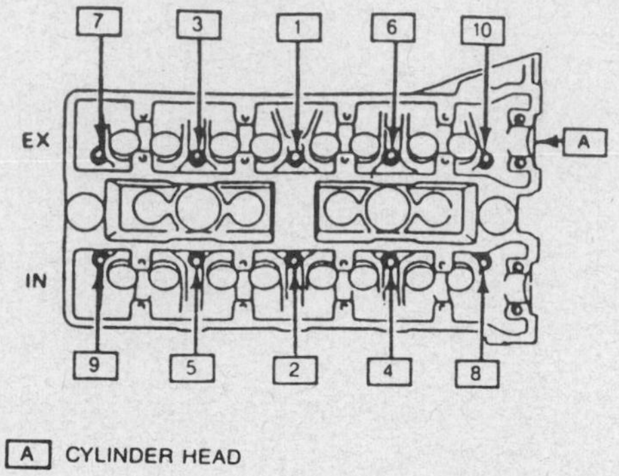
7 3 1 6 10
EX
A
IN
9 5 2 4 8
A CYLINDER HEAD

GC1069100485000X

Fig. 8 Cylinder head bolt tightening sequence. GSi models

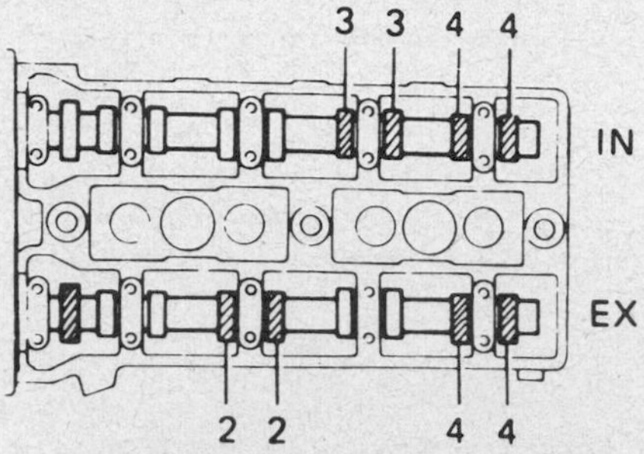
3 3 4 4
IN
EX
2 2 4 4

GC1069100487000X

Fig. 10 Second valve clearance adjustment

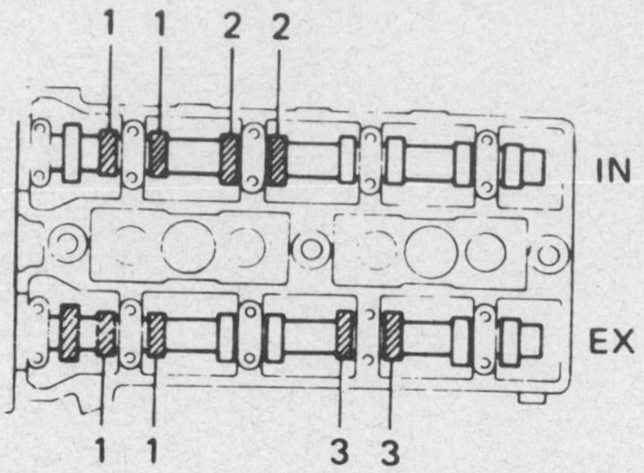
1 1 2 2
IN
EX
1 1 3 3

GC1069100486000X

Fig. 9 First valve clearance adjustment

20. Disconnect right engine mount.
21. Remove water pump pulley then timing belt covers and timing belt as outlined under "Timing Belt Cover, Replace" and "Timing Belt & Camshaft Timing Pulley, Replace."
22. Remove camshaft as outlined under "Camshaft, Replace."
23. Remove cylinder head bolts in sequence shown in **Fig. 7.**
24. Remove cylinder head from engine block.
25. Reverse procedure to install. **Torque cylinder head bolts to 44 ft. lbs. in sequence shown in Fig. 8.**

1993–95

1. Remove camshafts as described under "Camshaft Replace."
2. Remove vacuum hoses from intake chamber.
3. Remove A/C actuator electrical connector, if equipped.
4. Disconnect EGR solenoid vacuum valve electrical connector, vacuum hose from EGR, mounting bolt, then EGR solenoid valve, if equipped.
5. Remove engine wire clamp, intake manifold brace attaching bolts, then brace.
6. Remove fuel return hose from pressure regulator.
7. Remove EGR valve and EGR vacuum modulator, if equipped.
8. Disconnect throttle body position sensor electrical connector, remove accelerator bracket mounting bolts, accelerator bracket, throttle body mounting bolts, then throttle body.
9. Remove fuel inlet hose clamp bolt, then air intake chamber brace and gasket.
10. Remove PCV valves, vacuum hose from pressure regulator, air intake chamber cover nuts and bolts, then air intake chamber cover.
11. Remove union bolt, two gaskets, then fuel inlet pipe from fuel rail.
12. Remove injector electrical connectors, fuel rail attaching bolts, then fuel rail with injectors attached.
13. Remove four insulators, then two spacers from cylinder head.
14. Remove intake manifold attaching bolts, then intake manifold.
15. Remove oxygen sensor electrical connector, front pipe to manifold attaching nuts and bolts, then upper heat insulator.
16. Remove exhaust manifold brace, if equipped.
17. Remove cylinder head bolts in sequence as shown in **Fig. 4,** using a 10 MM 12 point socket. **Note bolt lengths and location when removing bolts from head.**
18. Remove cylinder head from dowels.
19. Reverse procedure to install noting the following:
    a. Install head bolts in proper location. **Torque** bolts in several passes and in sequence shown in **Fig. 5** to 22 ft lbs., tighten head bolts in sequence an additional 90°, then in sequence again an additional 90°.
    b. Tighten all attaching nuts and bolts to specification.

VALVE CLEARANCE SPECIFICATIONS

Year	Engine	Intake Inches	Exhaust Inches
1992–95	1.6L/4-97	.006–.010	.008–.012

VALVE ADJUSTMENT

Measure and adjust valve clearance while the engine is cold.

1. Disconnect battery ground cable.
2. Remove cylinder head cover.
3. Set No. 1 cylinder at TDC on the compression stroke.
4. Turn crankshaft to align groove in crankshaft pulley with "0" mark on No. 1 timing belt cover. **Ensure that valve lifters on No. 1 cylinder have freeplay. If not, rotate crankshaft pulley 360° and align the "0" mark on timing belt cover.**
5. Measure and record valve lash clearance between the cam lobe and the adjusting shim on cylinders shown in **Fig. 9.**
6. Rotate crankshaft 360° and align groove with "0" mark timing belt cover.
7. Measure and record valve lash clearance between the cam lobe and the adjusting shim on cylinders shown in **Fig. 10.**
8. If clearance is not within specifications, obtain the Valve Clearance Adjustment Set tool No. J-37141-A, or equivalent.
9. Insert Valve Spring Compression Tool No. J-37141-1, or equivalent, between the camshaft and lifter adjusting shim. This action will compress the valve spring and push lifter down.
10. Insert Lifter Holding Tool No. J-37141-2A, or equivalent, between camshaft and lifter. Position bottom edge of tool on lifter and not on adjusting shim. The lifter appears to be a sleeve around the adjusting shim. This action will hold the lifter away from camshaft, **Fig. 11.**
11. Remove Spring Compression Tool No. J-37141-1. Lifter Holding Tool No. J-37141-2A should hold lifter down away from camshaft.
12. Remove adjusting shim with a small screwdriver and magnetic finger, **Fig. 12.**

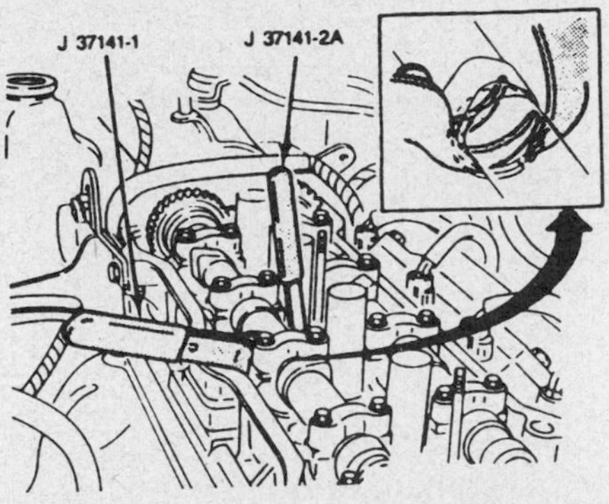
J 37141-1
J 37141-2A
GC1069100488000X

Fig. 11 Depressing valve spring

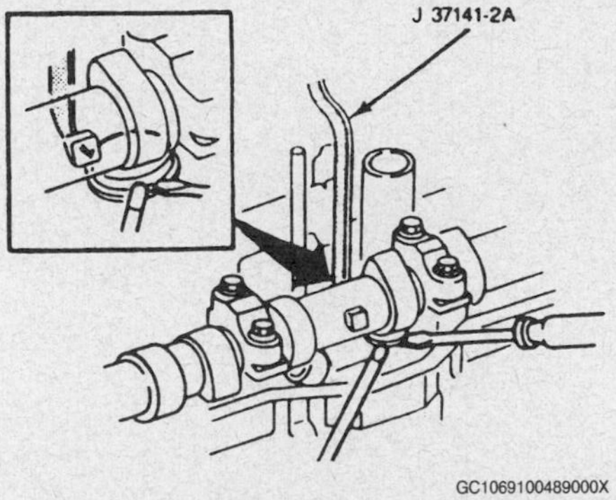
J 37141-2A
GC1069100489000X

Fig. 12 Adjusting shim removal

AVAILABLE SHIMS

Shim No.	Thickness	Shim No.	Thickness
02	2.500 (0.0984)	20	2.950 (0.1161)
04	2.550 (0.1004)	22	3.000 (0.1181)
06	2.600 (0.1024)	24	3.050 (0.1201)
08	2.650 (0.1043)	26	3.100 (0.1220)
10	2.700 (0.1063)	28	3.150 (0.1240)
12	2.750 (0.1083)	30	3.200 (0.1260)
14	2.800 (0.1102)	32	3.250 (0.1280)
16	2.850 (0.1122)	34	3.300 (0.1299)
18	2.900 (0.1142)		

Intake valve clearance (cold): 0.15 – 0.25 mm (0.006 – 0.010 in.)
Example: A 2.800 mm shim is installed and the measured clearance is 0.450 mm. Replace the 2.800 mm shim with shim No. 24 (3.050 mm).

GC1069100490000X

Fig. 13 Valve shim size chart

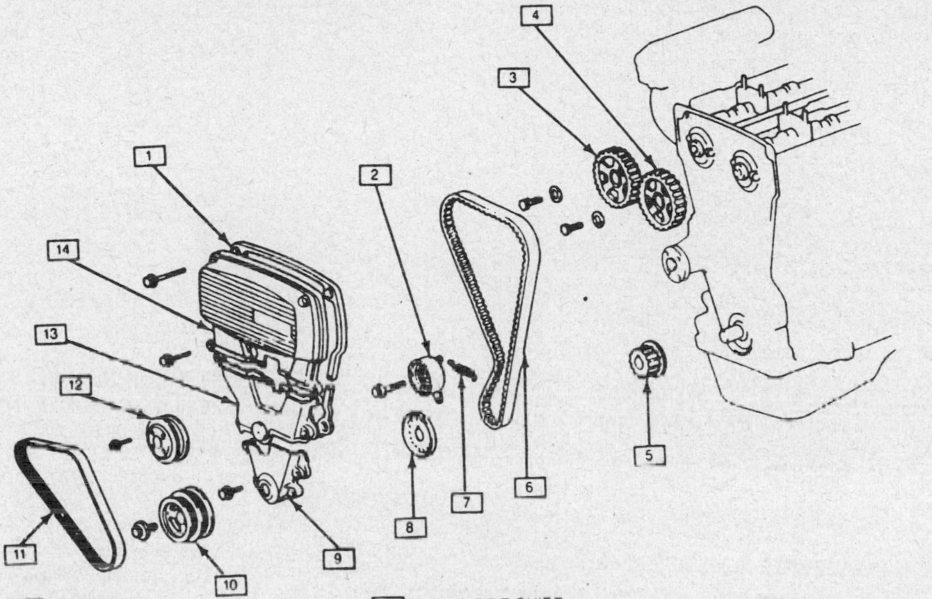

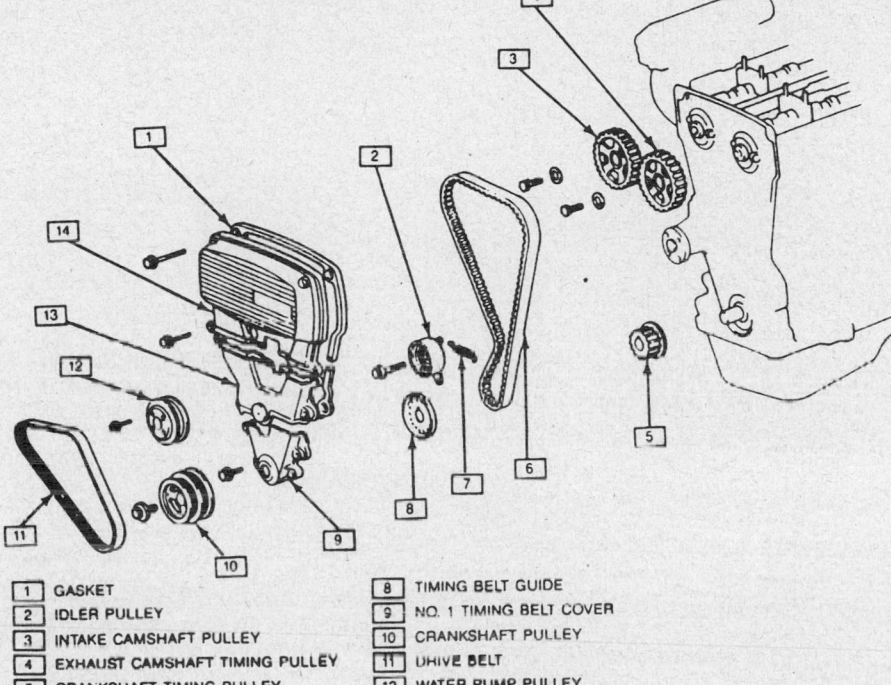

1 GASKET
2 IDLER PULLEY
3 INTAKE CAMSHAFT PULLEY
4 EXHAUST CAMSHAFT TIMING PULLEY
5 CRANKSHAFT TIMING PULLEY
6 TIMING BELT
7 TENSION SPRING
8 TIMING BELT GUIDE
9 NO. 1 TIMING BELT COVER
10 CRANKSHAFT PULLEY
11 DRIVE BELT
12 WATER PUMP PULLEY
13 NO. 2 TIMING BELT COVER
14 NO. 3 TIMING BELT COVER

GC1069100401000X

Fig. 14 Timing belt components. 1992 GSi models

13. Measure thickness of removed shim.
14. Calculate thickness of new shim required by using the following formula:
    a. T = Thickness of shim removed.
    b. A = Valve clearance measured.
    c. N = Thickness of shim required.
    d. For intake valves use formula; N = T + (A - .008 inch (.20 mm)).
    e. For exhaust valves use formula; N = T + (A - .010 inch (.25 mm)).
    f. Select a shim from **Fig. 13** with a thickness as close as possible to the calculated valve.
15. Install new adjusting shims as required.
16. Depress valve spring using Spring Compressor tool No. J-37141-1 and remove the Lifter Holding tool No. J-37141-2A.
17. Install cylinder head cover and connect battery ground cable.

TIMING BELT COVER REPLACE

1992

GSi Models

1. Disconnect battery ground cable.
2. Remove righthand wheel and lower splash shield.
3. Drain coolant.
4. Disconnect accelerator and cruise control cables.
5. Remove cruise control actuator and ignition coil.
6. Remove water outlet hose.
7. Remove accessory drive belts.
8. Remove spark plugs.
9. Set No. 1 cylinder at TDC on the compression stroke. Turn crankshaft pulley to align its groove with idler pulley bolt. Remove oil filter cap and ensure that you see hole in camshaft. **If hole cannot be seen, turn crankshaft 360° and check again.**
10. Disconnect righthand engine mount.
11. Remove water pump pulley.
12. Remove crankshaft pulley using Holder tool No. J-8614-0, or equivalent and Puller tool No.J-1859-03, or equivalent.
13. Remove timing belt cover attaching screws and belt covers, **Fig. 14.**
14. Reverse procedure to install.

Except GSi Models

1. Disconnect battery ground cable.
2. Raise and support vehicle.
3. Remove right lower stone shield.
4. Lower vehicle.
5. Disconnect engine wiring harness from upper timing belt cover.
6. Remove accessory drive belts.
7. Remove crankshaft pulley using Puller tool No. J-1859-03, or equivalent.
8. Remove cylinder head cover and windshield washer reservoir.
9. Support engine using Engine Support Fixture tool No. J-28467-A, or equivalent.
10. Remove right engine mount through bolt.
11. Raise and support vehicle.
12. Remove two rear transaxle mount to main crossmember nuts.
13. Remove two center transaxle mount to center crossmember nuts.
14. Lower vehicle.
15. Raise engine and remove water pump pulley.
16. Remove timing belt covers attaching screws and timing belt covers, **Fig. 15.**
17. Reverse procedure to install.

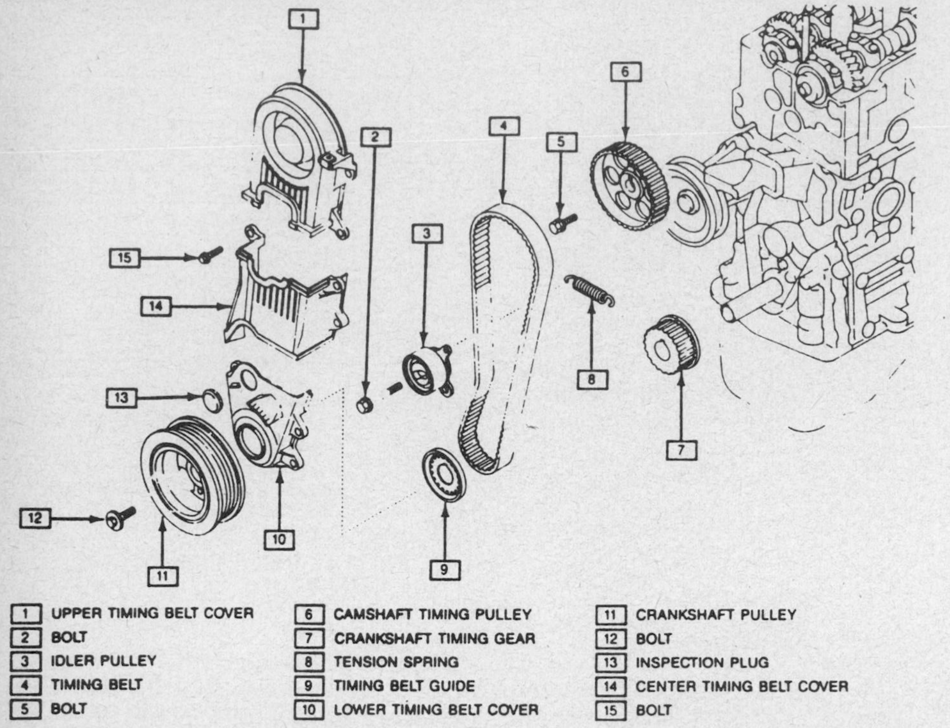
1 UPPER TIMING BELT COVER
2 BOLT
3 IDLER PULLEY
4 TIMING BELT
5 BOLT
6 CAMSHAFT TIMING PULLEY
7 CRANKSHAFT TIMING GEAR
8 TENSION SPRING
9 TIMING BELT GUIDE
10 LOWER TIMING BELT COVER
11 CRANKSHAFT PULLEY
12 BOLT
13 INSPECTION PLUG
14 CENTER TIMING BELT COVER
15 BOLT
GC1069100492000X

Fig. 15 Timing belt components. 1992 Except GSi models

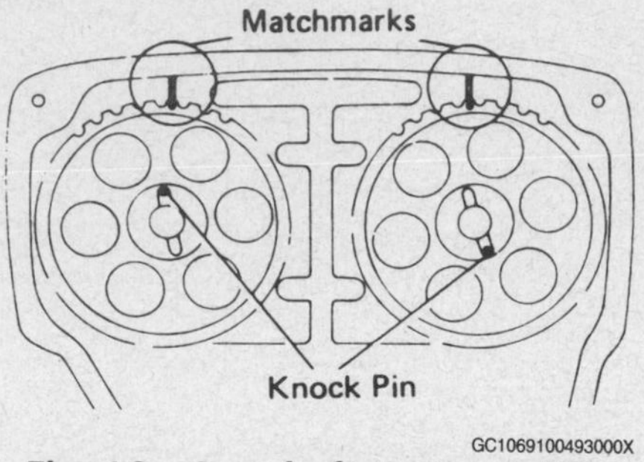
Matchmarks
Knock Pin
GC1069100493000X

Fig. 16 Camshaft timing pulley alignment. 1992 GSi models

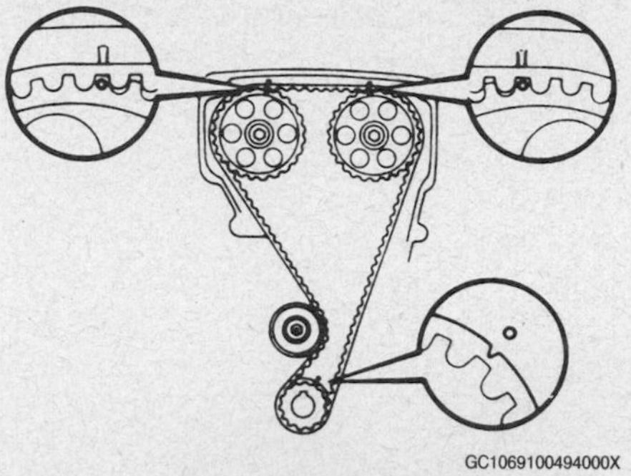
GC1069100494000X

Fig. 17 Belt & pulley alignment. 1992 GSi models

TIMING BELT & CAMSHAFT TIMING PULLEY

REPLACE

1992

GSI MODELS

Removal

1. Disconnect battery ground cable, then remove right front wheel and engine undercover.
2. Drain radiator coolant, then disconnect cruise control cable (if equipped), accelerator cable and link.
3. Remove cruise control actuator (if equipped), then the ignition coil and coolant outlet hose.
4. Remove accessory drive belts, then the spark plugs.
5. Turn crankshaft pulley and align groove with "0" mark on the No. 1 timing belt cover, then remove oil filler cap and ensure cavity in camshaft is visible indicating TDC compression. If camshaft cavity is not visible, rotate crankshaft an additional 360° to set engine at TDC compression.
6. Raise engine with suitable jack, then remove right side engine mount through bolt and the mount. **Insert suitable piece of wood between jack and engine to prevent damage.**
7. Remove crankshaft pulley using suitable tools.
8. Remove timing belt covers and gaskets, then the timing belt guide from crankshaft sprocket.
9. Loosen idler pulley bolt, then push idler pulley as far left as possible and temporarily tighten idler pulley bolt.

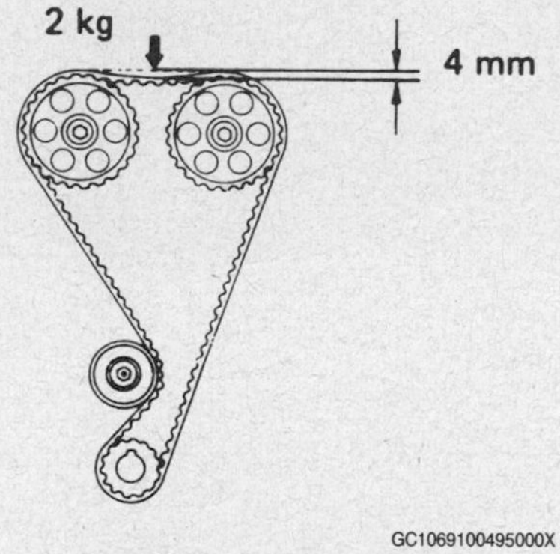
2 kg
4 mm
GC1069100495000X

Fig. 18 Measuring belt deflection. 1992 GSi models

10. Remove timing belt, idler pulley bolt, pulley and tension spring. **If timing belt is to reused, mark direction and belt-to-sprocket reference marks to ensure correct position during installation.**
11. Remove cylinder head covers, then using suitable wrench positioned on camshaft flats, remove camshaft sprocket attaching bolts and sprockets.

Installation

1. Install camshaft sprockets, aligning marks as shown in **Fig. 16.** Install sprocket attaching bolts and tighten to specifications.
2. Install cylinder head covers, then the crankshaft sprocket, idler pulley and tension spring. Pry idler pulley towards the left as far as possible and temporarily tighten attaching bolt.
3. Install timing belt. **If belt is being reused, ensure it is installed in the same position as removed.**
4. Slowly loosen timing belt idler bolt, then temporarily install crankshaft pulley bolt.
5. Turn crankshaft two complete revolutions clockwise from TDC of compression stroke to TDC of compression stroke.
6. Check valve timing. Ensure each sprocket is aligned as shown in **Fig. 17.**
7. Tighten timing belt idler pulley bolt to 27 ft. lbs.
8. Measure timing belt deflection as shown in **Fig. 18.** If deflection is not .16 inch with 4.4 lbs. of pressure, readjust as necessary with idler pulley.
9. Remove crankshaft pulley bolt, then install timing belt guide. Ensure guide cup side is facing outward.
10. Install timing belt covers and gaskets.
11. Reverse steps 1 through 5 of removal procedure to complete installation. When installing crankshaft pulley, tighten pulley bolt to specification.

EXCEPT GSI MODELS

Removal

1. Disconnect battery ground cable.
2. Remove timing belt covers as outlined under "Timing Belt Cover, Replace." **If timing belt is to be reused, mark direction and belt to sprocket reference marks to ensure correct position during installation.**
3. Remove timing belt guide from crankshaft sprocket.
4. Loosen idler pulley bolt, then push idler pulley as far left as possible and

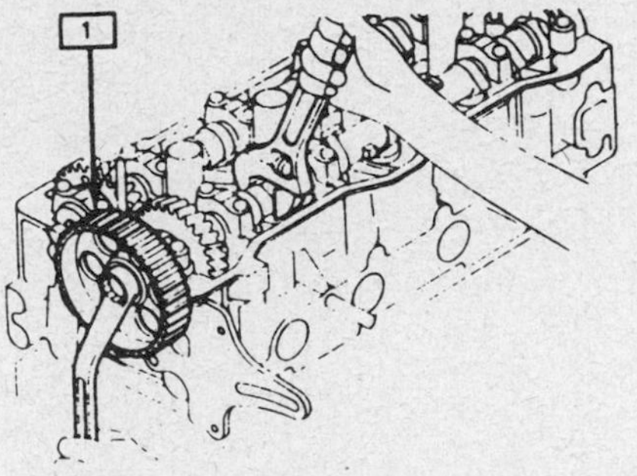
1

1 CAMSHAFT TIMING GEAR

GC1069100496000X

Fig. 19 Camshaft timing gear. 1992 Except GSi models

temporarily tighten idler pulley bolt.

5. Remove timing belt, idler pulley bolt, pulley and tension spring.
6. Remove idler pulley bolt, pulley and return spring.
7. Remove crankshaft timing pulley.
8. Remove camshaft timing gear by securing the camshaft with a wrench and removing the bolt, **Fig. 19. Ensure not to damage cylinder head or camshaft with wrench.**

Installation

1. Install camshaft timing gear.
2. Install crankshaft timing gear.
3. Position No. 1 cylinder at TDC.
4. Align camshaft timing gear hole with the exhaust camshaft cap mark, **Fig. 3.**
5. Install idler pulley, mount bolt and tensioner spring. Pry idler to left and temporarily tighten.
6. Install timing belt. If reusing original timing belt, align points made during disassembly with arrow pointing in proper direction.
7. Loosen timing belt idler pulley mount bolt.
8. Temporarily install crankshaft pulley bolt and turn crankshaft 2 revolutions from TDC to TDC. **Always turn the crankshaft clockwise.**
9. Ensure all components are properly aligned.
10. Install the timing belt idler pulley bolt.
11. Ensure timing belt deflection is .20-.24 inch. If belt is not within specification, the idler pulley must be adjusted.
12. Reverse remaining removal procedure to complete procedure.

1993–95

Removal

1. Disconnect battery ground cable.
2. Remove wiper reservoir, cruise control actuator cover and cable.
3. Remove cruise control actuator.
4. Raise and support engine.
5. Remove right tire and wheel assembly then the wheel housing.
6. Remove accessory drive belts.
7. Lower vehicle.
8. Remove A/C compressor keeping hoses attached. Position in a out of the way location.

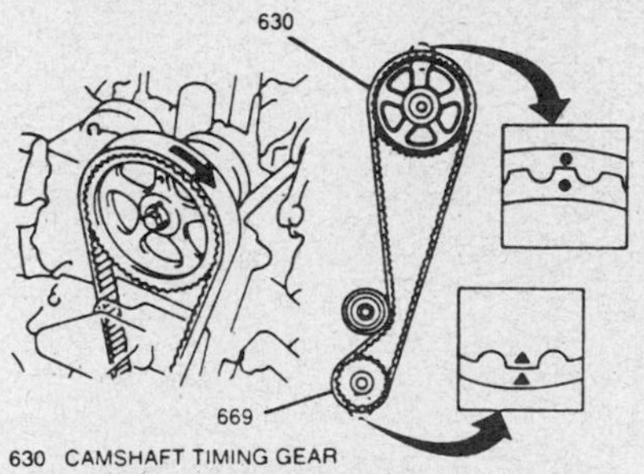
630
669

630 CAMSHAFT TIMING GEAR
669 CRANKSHAFT TIMING GEAR

GC1069300497000X

Fig. 20 Engine timing marks. 1993–95 models

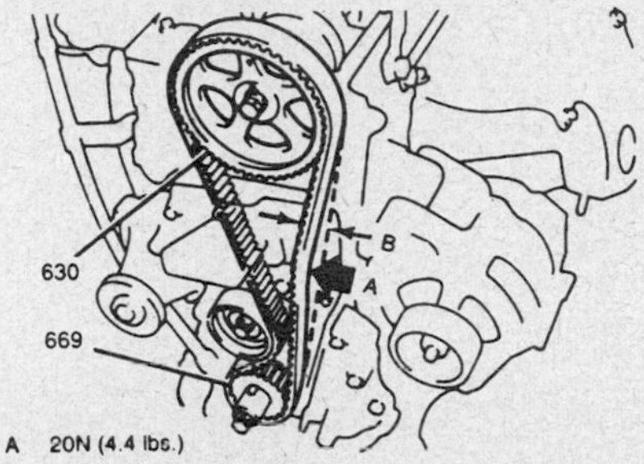
630
669
B
A

A 20N (4.4 lbs.)
B 5 – 6 mm (0.20 – 0.24")
630 CAMSHAFT TIMING GEAR
669 CRANKSHAFT TIMING GEAR

GC1069300499000X

Fig. 22 Timing belt tension check. 1993–94

9. Remove A/C compressor bracket.
10. Remove power steering pump keeping hoses attached. Position out of the way.
11. Disconnect alternator and oil pressure switch electrical connections.
12. Remove wiring harness cover and harness from cylinder head.
13. Remove spark plug wires and plugs.
14. Remove PCV hoses from cylinder head covers.
15. Remove cylinder head covers and gaskets.
16. Turn crankshaft to position No. 1 cylinder at TDC on its compression stroke. Valve lifters for No. 1 cylinder should be loose.
17. Disconnect engine ground wire from right fender apron.
18. Disconnect engine mounts as outlined under "Engine Mount Replace."
19. Remove water pump and crankshaft pulleys using puller tool No. J 1859-03 or equivalent.
20. Remove timing belt cover bolts and the timing belt covers.
21. Slide timing belt guide from crankshaft.
22. Ensure timing marks are aligned, **Fig. 20.**
23. If timing belt is to reused, mark timing belt with arrow showing direction of engine rotation.
24. Remove idler pulley bolt, idler pulley and tension spring.
25. Remove timing belt from camshaft and crankshaft timing gears.

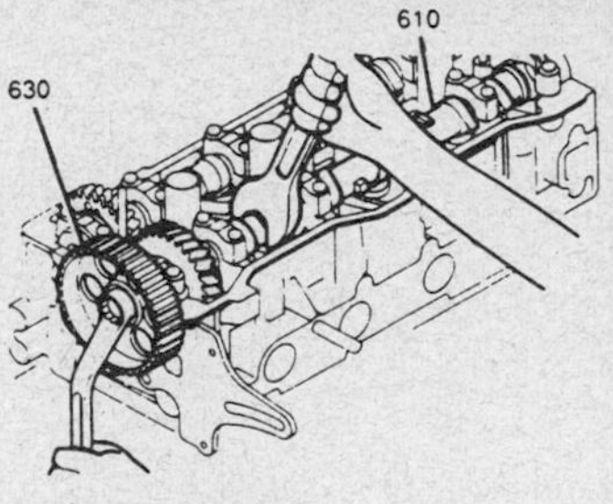
610
630

610 EXHAUST CAMSHAFT
630 CAMSHAFT TIMING GEAR

GC1069300498000X

Fig. 21 Camshaft timing gear replacement. 1993–95 models

26. Remove camshaft timing gear while holding camshaft by the hexagonal wrench head section, **Fig. 21.**
27. Remove crankshaft timing gear using two flat blade screwdrivers to pry off.

Installation

1. Install camshaft and crankshaft timing gear aligning keyways on shafts.
2. Tighten camshaft timing gear while holding camshaft by the hexagonal wrench head section, **Fig. 21.**
3. Install idler pulley and idler pulley spring.
4. Push idler pulley to its extreme left travel and tighten idler pulley.
5. Install timing belt to camshaft and crankshaft timing gears and idler pulley.
6. Loosen idler pulley bolt allowing spring to pull pulley to the right.
7. Temporarily install crankshaft pulley bolt and turn crankshaft two complete revolutions clockwise.
8. Ensure timing marks are still aligned.
9. Measure timing belt deflection as shown in **Fig. 22.** Belt deflection should be .20-.24 inch with 4.4 lbs. of pressure applied.
10. Replace timing belt if not with specification.
11. If timing belt is within specification, tighten idler pulley.
12. Install timing belt guide, facing cupped side outward.
13. Install timing belt covers starting with the lowest cover to the highest.
14. Install crankshaft pulley and secure with one bolt.
15. Install engine mount to body.
16. Raise and support vehicle.
17. Install mounting brackets to engine mount.
18. Install right side wheelhousing and tire and wheel assembly.
19. Lower vehicle.
20. Install A/C pipe bracket and engine ground wire to right front fender.
21. Install new cylinder cover gasket and cover.
22. Install PCV hoses, spark plugs and wires.
23. Install engine wiring harness and cover.
24. Connect alternator and oil pressure switch electrical connectors.

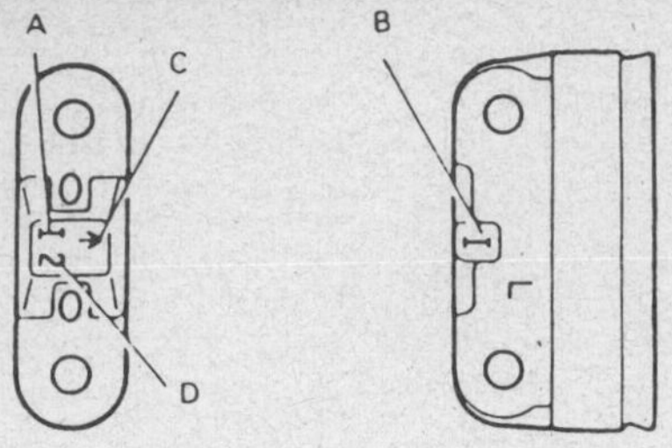
A
B
C
D

A I = INTAKE E = EXHAUST
B I = INTAKE E = EXHAUST
C FRONT MARK
D I.D FOR BEARING NO. 2 THRU NO. 5

GC1069100500000X

Fig. 23 Camshaft bearing caps installation. GSi models

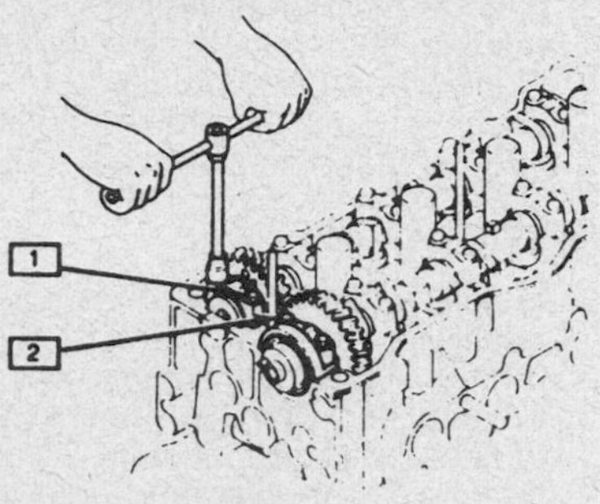
1
2

1 INTAKE BEARING CAP BOLT
2 EXHAUST BEARING CAP BOLT

GC1069100503000X

Fig. 26 Number 1 bearing cap bolts. Except GSi models

25. Install power steering oil pump and air conditioner compressor.
26. Install and adjust accessory drive belts.
27. Install cruise control actuator and windshield washer reservoir.
28. Connect battery ground cable.

CAMSHAFT

REPLACE

GSI MODELS

Removal

1. Disconnect battery ground cable.
2. Remove cylinder head cover.
3. Remove timing belt covers as outlined under "Timing Belt Cover, Replace."
4. Remove timing belt as outlined under "Timing Belt & Camshaft Timing Pulley, Replace."
5. Remove camshaft bearing caps.
6. Remove camshaft.

Installation

1. Install camshaft(s). Exhaust camshaft has distributor drive gear.
2. Install camshaft bearing caps on each journal with arrows pointed toward the front, **Fig. 23.**
3. Tighten cap bolts in three passes to specification in sequence shown in **Fig. 24.**
4. Install timing belt and covers as previously described.

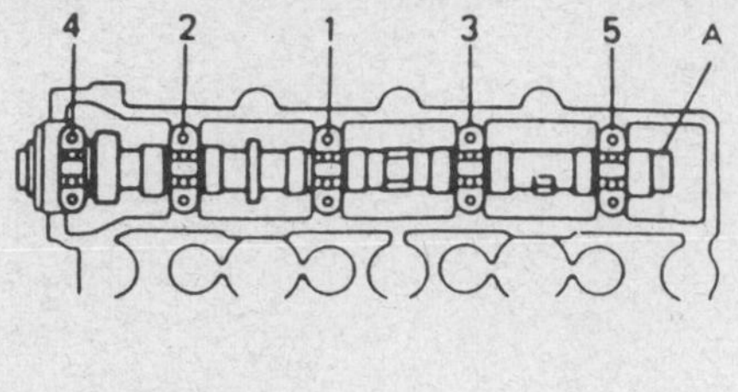
4
2
1
3
5
A

A CAMSHAFT

GC1069100501000X

Fig. 24 Camshaft bearing caps tightening sequence. GSi models

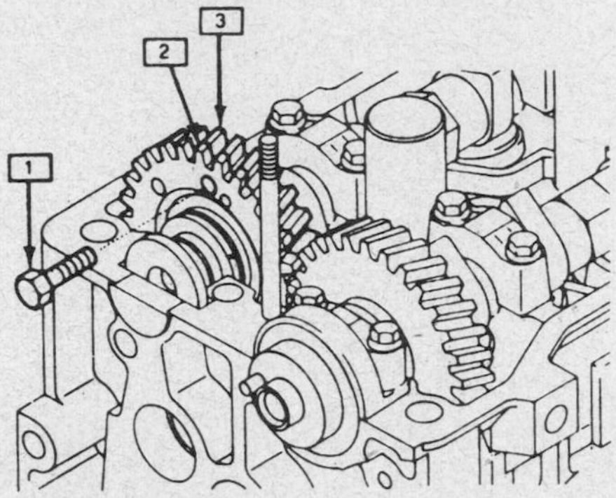
1
2
3

1 SERVICE BOLT
2 SUB-GEAR
3 MAIN GEAR

GC1069100504000X

Fig. 27 Fastening sub-gear to main gear. Except GSi models

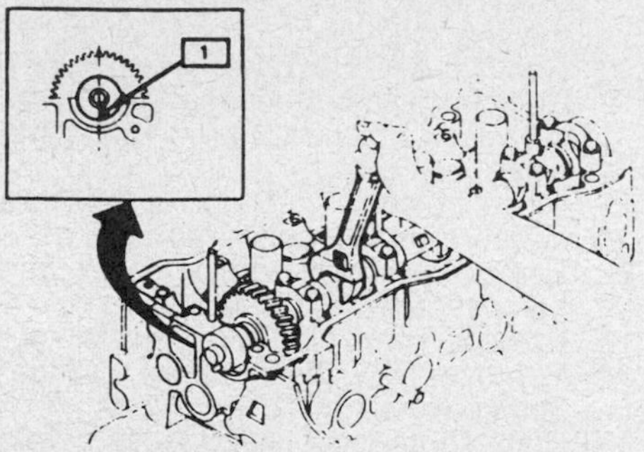
1

1 KNOCKPIN POSITION

GC1069100506000X

Fig. 29 Knockout pin position. Except GSi models

5. Install cylinder head cover and connect battery ground cable.

EXCEPT GSI MODELS

Removal

1. Disconnect battery ground cable.
2. Remove cylinder head cover.
3. Remove timing belt covers as outlined under "Timing Belt Cover, Replace."
4. Remove timing belt as outlined under "Timing Belt & Camshaft Timing Pulley, Replace."
5. Remove camshaft timing gear by holding the camshaft with a wrench and removing the camshaft bolt. **Use caution not to damage camshaft or cylinder head with wrench.**

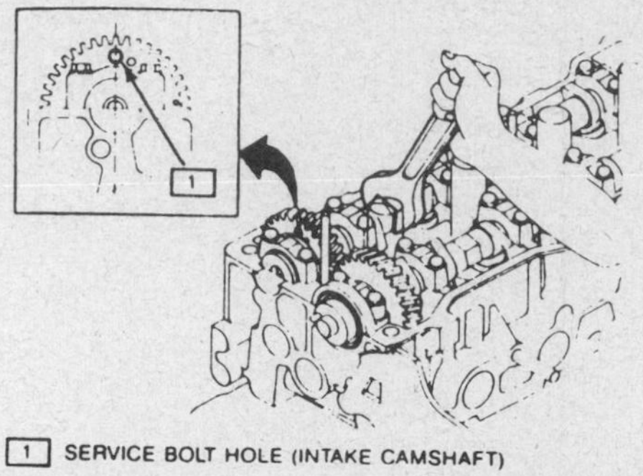
1

1 SERVICE BOLT HOLE (INTAKE CAMSHAFT)

GC1069100502000X

Fig. 25 Service bolt hole alignment. Except GSi models

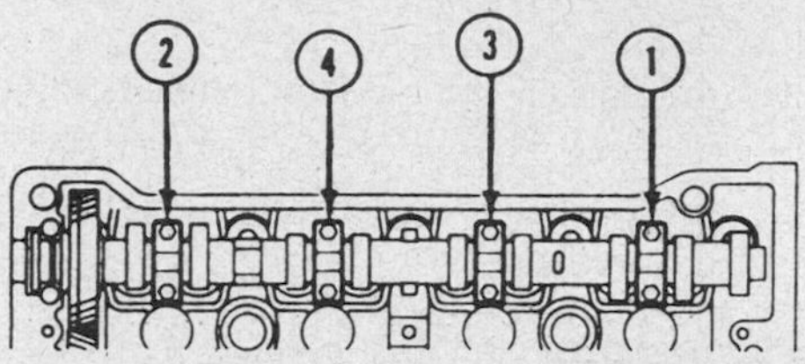
2
4
3
1

GC1069100505000X

Fig. 28 Intake camshaft removal sequence. Except GSi models

6. With the No. 1 cylinder in TDC position, the service bolt hole of the intake camshaft gear should be in position as shown in **Fig. 25.**
7. Alternately loosen the No. 1 (front) intake and exhaust camshaft bearing cap bolts in several steps, **Fig. 26.**
8. Remove No. 1 bearing caps.
9. Fasten the intake camshaft sub-gear to the main gear with a service bolt, **Fig. 27.**
10. Uniformly loosen each intake camshaft bearing cap bolt in several steps in sequence shown in **Fig. 28.**
11. Remove intake camshaft bearing caps and camshaft. **The camshaft must be held level while it is being removed. If the camshaft is not kept level, the portion of the cylinder head receiving the shaft trust may crack or be damaged. If the camshaft cannot be lifted out straight and level, retighten the No. 3 bearing cap and alternately loosen the bolts of the bearing cap in several steps while pulling up on the camshaft gear.**
12. Rotate exhaust camshaft 105°, using a suitable wrench.
13. Place lockpin in position shown in **Fig. 29.**
14. Uniformly loosen each exhaust camshaft bearing cap bolt in several steps in sequence shown in **Fig. 30.**
15. Remove exhaust camshaft bearing caps and camshaft.
16. Disassemble intake camshaft by inserting pins into service holes in camshaft sub-gear, **Fig. 31**
17. Using a screwdriver, turn sub-gear clockwise and remove pin C.
18. Remove snap ring, wave washer, camshaft sub gear, and camshaft gear spring.
19. Remove exhaust camshaft oil seal.

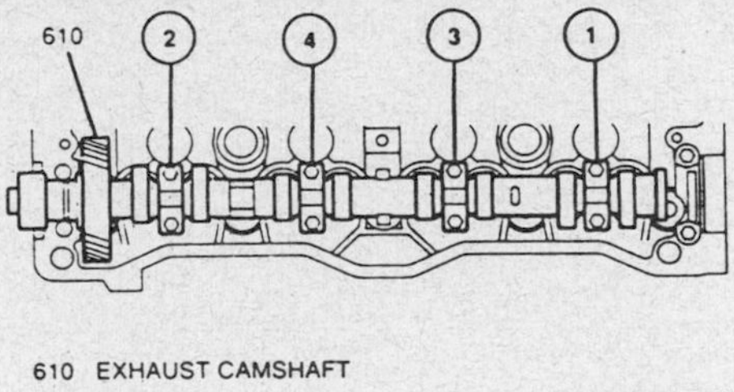
610
2
4
3
1
610 EXHAUST CAMSHAFT
GC1069100507000X

Fig. 30 Exhaust camshaft removal sequence. Except GSi models

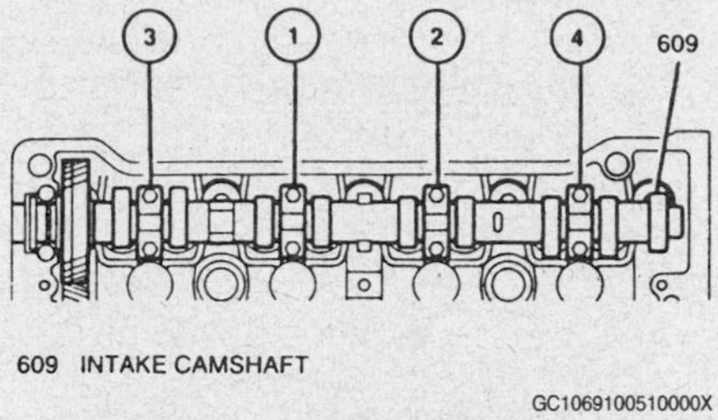
3
1
2
4
609
609 INTAKE CAMSHAFT
GC1069100510000X

Fig. 33 Intake camshaft tightening sequence. Except GSi models

Installation

1. Install ring, wave washer, camshaft sub-gear and camshaft gear spring.
2. Install pins A and B, **Fig. 31,** into service holes of camshaft sub-gear.
3. Using a screwdriver, align holes of camshaft drive gear and sub-gear by turning camshaft sub-gear clockwise.
4. Install pin C.
5. Install the exhaust camshaft on cylinder head so that No. 1 and No. 3 cam lobes push their valves lifters evenly.
6. Install bearing caps on journals with arrows pointing toward the crankshaft pulley.
7. Tighten each bearing cap to specification in several steps in sequence shown in **Fig. 32.**
8. Apply multi-purpose grease to a new exhaust camshaft oil seal and install oil seal using Seal Installer tool No. J-35403 or equivalent.
9. Position lockpin of exhaust camshaft so that No. 4 cylinder cam lobes push their lifters.
10. Engage intake camshaft gear with exhaust camshaft gear by matching alignment marks.
11. Roll camshaft into position keeping timing gears engaged.
12. Install intake camshaft bearing cap No. 2 through No. 5 with arrows pointing toward the crankshaft pulley. No. 1 bearing cap will be install later in this procedure.
13. Tighten intake camshaft bearing cap bolts to specifications in several steps in sequence shown in **Fig. 33.**
14. Remove pins from intake camshaft sub-gear.
15. Install No. 1 bearing cap. If No. 1 bearing cap does not fit properly, push the camshaft gear backward by prying apart the cylinder head and camshaft gear with a suitable pry tool.
16. Turn exhaust camshaft one revolution from TDC to TDC of No. 1 cylinder.
17. Ensure alignment marks on exhaust and intake gear align.
18. Install camshaft timing gear and secure camshaft and install timing gear bolt, **Fig. 19.**
19. Install timing belt as outlined under "Timing Belt & Camshaft Timing Pulley, Replace."
20. Install timing belt covers as outlined under "Timing Belt Cover, Replace."
21. Install cylinder head cover and connect battery ground cable.

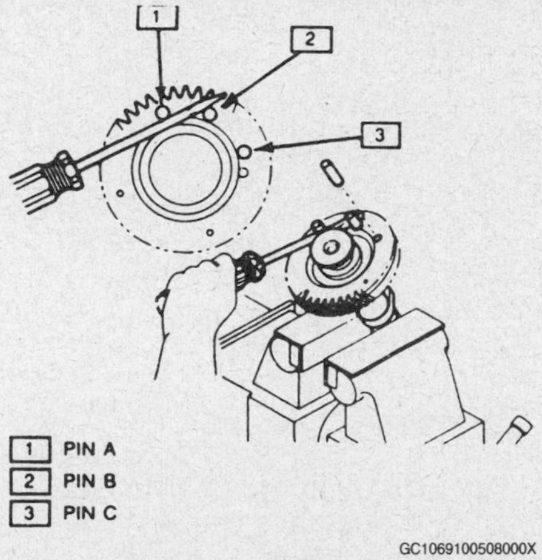
1
2
3
1 PIN A
2 PIN B
3 PIN C
GC1069100508000X

Fig. 31 Exploded view of intake camshaft. Except GSi models

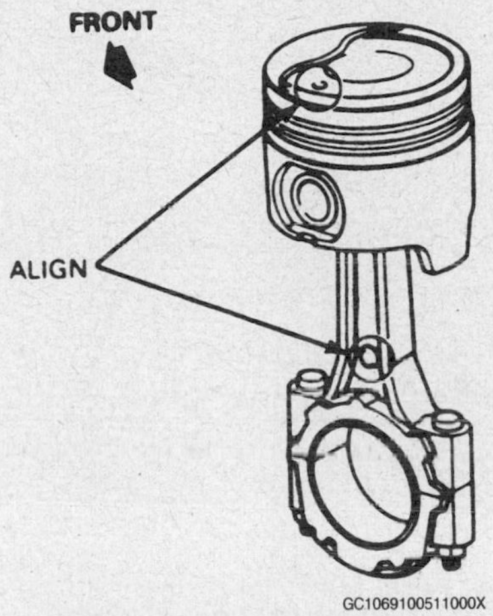
FRONT
ALIGN
GC1069100511000X

Fig. 34 Piston & rod assembly

PISTON & ROD ASSEMBLY

Assemble pistons to connecting rods as shown in **Fig. 34.**

MAIN & ROD BEARINGS

Main and rod service bearings are available in 5 standard sizes, marked 1 through 5. If replacing a bearing, replace with one having the same number. If the number of the bearing cannot be determined, select a bearing according to the numbers imprinted on the cylinder block and crankshaft then refer to Fig. 35 and 36 for proper bearing number.

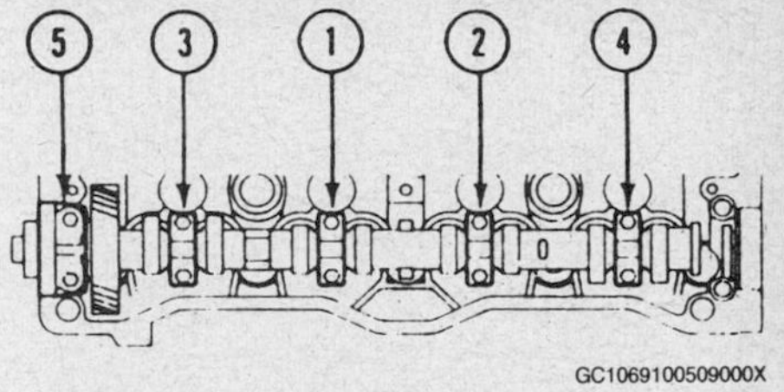
5
3
1
2
4
GC1069100509000X

Fig. 32 Exhaust camshaft tightening sequence. Except GSi models

Cylinder Block No.	1	2	3	1	2	3	1	2	3
Crankshaft No.	0	0	0	1	1	1	2	2	2
Bearing No.	1	2	3	2	3	4	3	4	5

GC1069100512000X

Fig. 35 Main & rod bearing identification. GSi models

BEARING SELECTION TABLE

Crankshaft Block Mark	1	2	3	1	2	3	1	2	3
Crankshaft Mark	0	0	0	1	1	1	2	2	2
Bearing Mark	1	2	3	3	2	4	3	4	5

GC1069100513000X

Fig. 36 Main & rod bearing identification. Except GSi models

CRANKSHAFT REAR OIL SEAL

REPLACE

1. Remove transaxle and flywheel assembly.
2. Remove rear end plate.
3. Remove rear main oil seal retainer.
4. Carefully knock out oil seal from retainer.
5. Replace old oil seal with a new one, then apply a suitable lubricant.
6. Assemble retainer, rear end plate onto engine, then insert and securely tighten attaching bolts.
7. Assemble flywheel assembly to engine, then install transaxle.

OIL PAN

REPLACE

GSi MODELS

1. Disconnect battery ground cable.
2. Raise and support vehicle.
3. Drain engine oil.
4. Remove righthand undercover.
5. Disconnect front exhaust pipe and bracket.
6. Remove oil pan bolts.
7. Remove oil pan.
8. Reverse procedure to install.

EXCEPT GSi MODELS

1. Disconnect battery ground cable.
2. Raise and support vehicle.
3. Drain engine oil.
4. Remove right and left stone covers.
5. Disconnect oxygen sensor connector.
6. Disconnect exhaust pipe from catalytic converter.
7. Disconnect exhaust pipe from exhaust manifold.
8. Remove oil pan bolts and pan.
9. Reverse procedure to install.

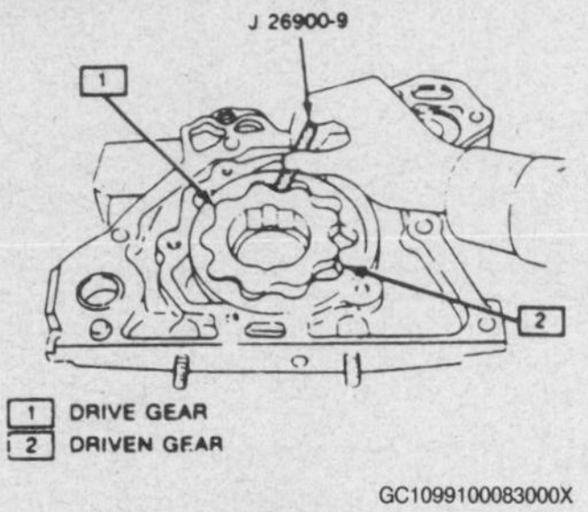
J 26900-9
1
2
1 DRIVE GEAR
2 DRIVEN GEAR
GC1099100083000X

Fig. 37 Oil pump gear to housing clearance check

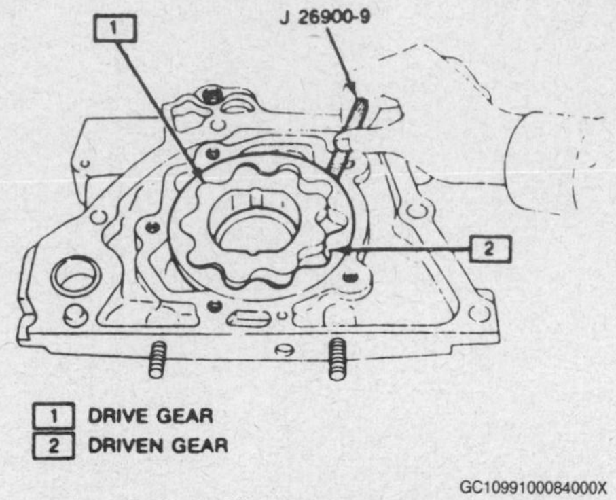
J 26900-9
1
2
1 DRIVE GEAR
2 DRIVEN GEAR
GC1099100084000X

Fig. 38 Oil pump gear to gear clearance check

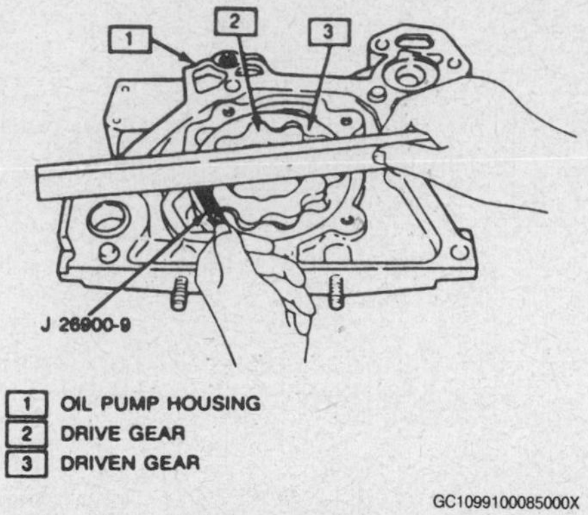
1
2
3
J 26900-9
1 OIL PUMP HOUSING
2 DRIVE GEAR
3 DRIVEN GEAR
GC1099100085000X

Fig. 39 Oil pump side clearance check

OIL PUMP

REPLACE

1. Disconnect battery ground cable.
2. Remove timing belt as outlined under "Timing Belt Cover, Replace" and "Timing Belt & Camshaft Timing Pulley, Replace."
3. Raise and support vehicle.
4. Remove crankshaft timing gear pulley.
5. Remove oil pan as outlined under "Oil Pan, Replace."
6. Remove oil pump bolts and oil pump assembly.
7. Reverse procedure to install, noting the following:
   a. Using feeler gauge, measure driven gear to housing clearance, **Fig. 37.** If clearance is greater than .0078 inch, replace the oil pump.
   b. Using feeler gauge, measure drive gear to driven gear clearance, **Fig. 38.** If clearance is greater than .0012 inch, replace the gear set.
   c. Using feeler gauge, measure oil pump body to gear clearance, **Fig. 39.** If clearance is greater than .004 inch replace the oil pump.

BELT TENSION DATA

Year	Engine Code	Belt	New Ft. Lbs.	Used Ft. Lbs.
1992	**5 & 6**	**A/C**	**140–180**	**80–120**
	5	**Alt.**	**170–180**	**95–135**
	6	**Alt.**	**140–180**	**110–150**
1993–94	**6 & 8**	**Alt.**	①②	—
	6 & 8	**A/C**	①③	—
	6 & 8	**P.S.**	①③	—
1995	**6 & 8**	**Alt.**	**141-182**	**111-152**
	6 & 8	**A/C**	①②	—
	6 & 8	**P.S.**	**100-121**	**55-88**

①—With 22 lbs. exerted.
②—Deflection of 0.24–0.35 inches.
③—Deflection of 0.20–0.32 inches.

COOLING SYSTEM BLEED

These engines do not require a specified bleed procedure. After filling cooling system, run engine to operating temperature with radiator/pressure cap off. Air will then be automatically bled through cap opening.

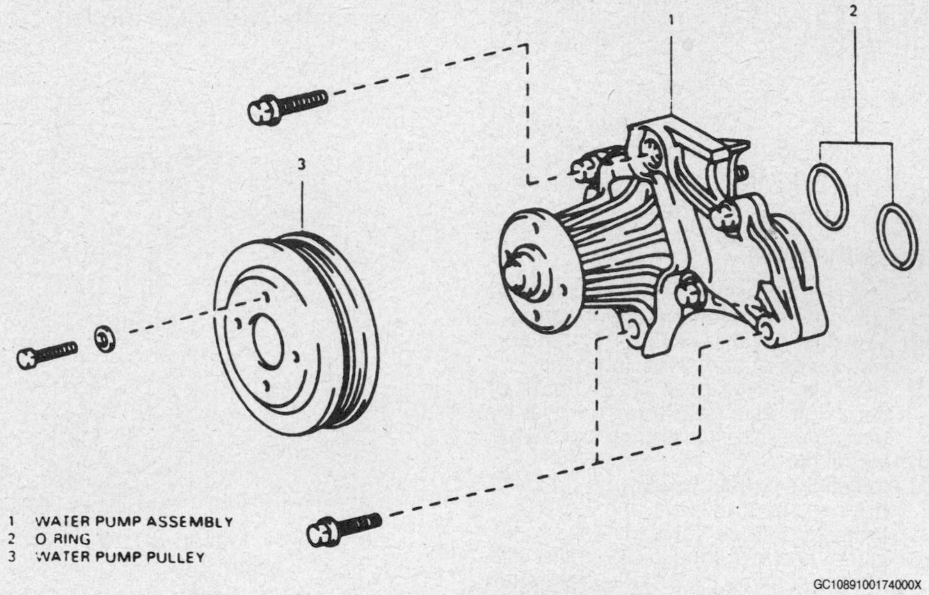
1
2
3
1 WATER PUMP ASSEMBLY
2 O RING
3 WATER PUMP PULLEY
GC1089100174000X

Fig. 40 Water pump removal

THERMOSTAT

REPLACE

1992

1. Drain coolant.
2. Remove water inlet housing and thermostat.
3. Thoroughly clean gasket surfaces.
4. Install thermostat with air bleed valve on top and aligned with protrusion on water inlet.
5. Install water inlet housing and new gasket, then **torque** bolts to 20 ft. lbs.
6. Fill radiator with coolant, then start engine and check for leaks.

1993–95

1. Drain engine coolant, then disconnect engine coolant switch electrical connector.
2. Remove thermostat housing attaching nuts, thermostat housing, then thermostat and gasket.
3. Reverse procedure to install, tighten thermostat housing to specifications.

WATER PUMP

REPLACE

1992

1. Drain cooling system.
2. Raise and support engine.
3. Remove nut for rear engine mount.
4. Lower vehicle.
5. Remove windshield washer reservoir, cruise control module and bracket.
6. Remove through bolt from right engine mount.
7. With a suitable jack, raise engine.
8. Loosen water pump pulley bolts.
9. Remove accessory drive belts.
10. Remove water pump pulley.
11. Lower engine into place.
12. Disconnect water inlet and bypass hoses from water inlet pipe.
13. Remove water inlet pipe and O-ring.
14. Remove and plug oil dipstick.
15. Remove upper timing belt cover as outlined under "Timing Belt Cover, Replace."
16. Remove water pump bolts and water pump, **Fig. 40.**
17. Reverse procedure to install.

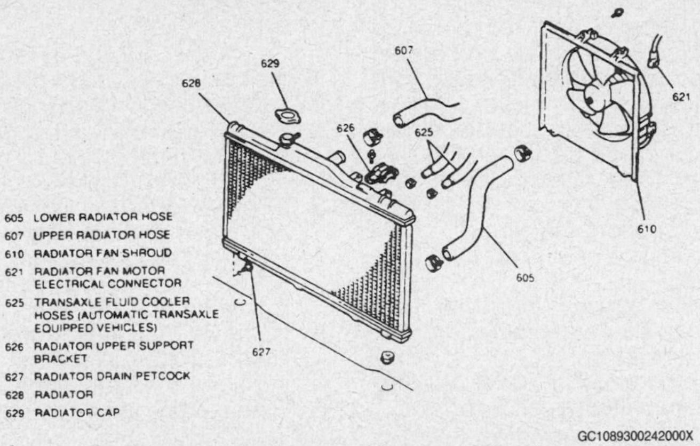
605 LOWER RADIATOR HOSE
607 UPPER RADIATOR HOSE
610 RADIATOR FAN SHROUD
621 RADIATOR FAN MOTOR ELECTRICAL CONNECTOR
625 TRANSAXLE FLUID COOLER HOSES (AUTOMATIC TRANSAXLE EQUIPPED VEHICLES)
626 RADIATOR UPPER SUPPORT BRACKET
627 RADIATOR DRAIN PETCOCK
628 RADIATOR
629 RADIATOR CAP
GC1089300242000X

Fig. 41 Radiator removal. 1993-95

1993–95

1. Disconnect battery ground cable, then drain cooling system.
2. Raise and support engine using tool No. J 28467-A or equivalent.
3. Remove right engine mount and insulator as outlined under "Engine Mount, Replace."
4. Remove timing covers, then on models equipped with power steering remove front transaxle mount from vehicle.
5. Remove radiator fan motor assembly, then engine wiring harness retainer clip from engine.
6. Remove oil level indicator from guide tube, guide tube mounting bolt, then guide tube.
7. Remove engine coolant temperature sending unit electrical connector, then two nut attaching engine coolant inlet pipe to cylinder block.
8. Loosen hose clamp, remove coolant inlet pipe from vehicle, then inlet hose from water pump.
9. Raise engine on vehicles equipped with power steering.
10. Remove water pump attaching bolts, water pump, then O-ring.
11. Reverse procedure to install.

RADIATOR
REPLACE

1992

1. Disconnect battery ground cable, then drain cooling system.
2. Remove coolant overflow reservoir.
3. Remove upper radiator hose at radiator.
4. Remove lower radiator hose at thermostat housing.
5. **On models with Automatic transaxle,** remove transaxle cooling lines.
6. **On all models,** remove upper radiator brackets.
7. Remove cooling fan electrical connector.
8. Remove cooling fan and shroud assembly.
9. Remove radiator.
10. Reverse procedure to install.

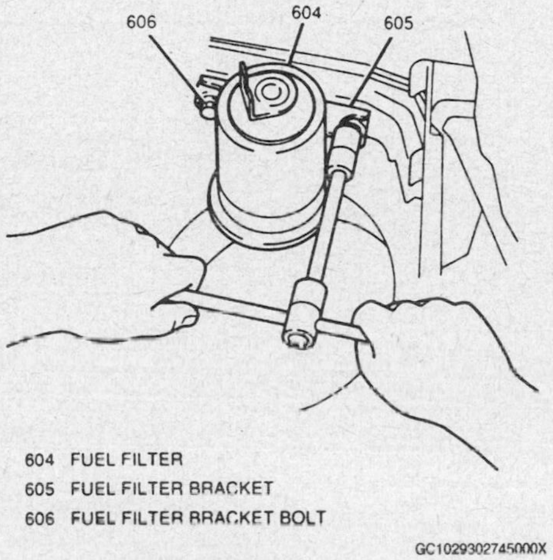
606
604
605
604 FUEL FILTER
605 FUEL FILTER BRACKET
606 FUEL FILTER BRACKET BOLT
GC1029302745000X

Fig. 43 Fuel filter replacement. 1993-95

1993–95

1. Disconnect battery ground cable, then drain cooling system.
2. Remove coolant recovery reservoir cap and hoses.
3. Remove upper radiator hose at radiator, **Fig. 41**.
4. Remove lower radiator hose at thermostat housing.
5. Unclip oxygen sensor electrical connector from fan shroud.
6. Raise and properly support vehicle.
7. Remove engine splash shield.
8. Remove lower radiator hose from vehicle.
9. **On models with automatic transaxle,** remove transaxle cooling lines.
10. **On all models,** remove cooling fan electrical connector.
11. Remove radiator fan assembly lower bolts.
12. Lower vehicle.
13. Remove radiator fan assembly upper bolts, then remove fan assembly from vehicle.
14. Remove radiator support bracket bolts.
15. Remove radiator from vehicle.
16. Reverse procedure to install.

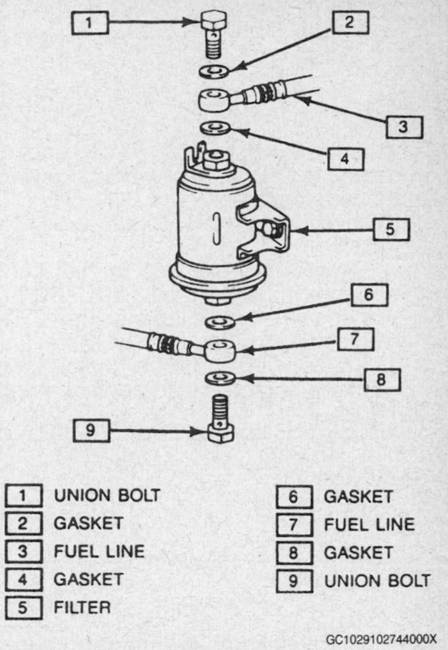
1 UNION BOLT
2 GASKET
3 FUEL LINE
4 GASKET
5 FILTER
6 GASKET
7 FUEL LINE
8 GASKET
9 UNION BOLT
GC1029102744000X

Fig. 42 Fuel filter replacement. 1992

FUEL PUMP
REPLACE

1992

1. Drain fuel tank.
2. Disconnect all fuel and electrical connections.
3. Raise and support vehicle.
4. Support fuel tank with a suitable jack.
5. Loosen and remove fuel tank support straps.
6. Lower fuel tank from vehicle.
7. Remove fuel tank bracket from fuel tank.
8. Remove fuel pump from fuel tank bracket.
9. Remove fuel pump filter from pump.
10. Reverse procedure to install, noting the following:
    a. **Torque** fuel tank bracket bolts to 30 inch lbs.
    b. **Torque** fuel tank flare nut to 22 ft. lbs.

1993–95

1. Release fuel system pressure as outlined under "Precautions."
2. Remove rear seat cushion, floor service hole cover attaching screws, then cover.
3. Disconnect fuel sender electrical connector, then fuel feed hose from sender assembly.
4. Remove fuel return hose from sender assembly, fuel sender attaching bolts, then fuel sender.
5. Remove fuel pump from fuel pump bracket by pulling off lower side of fuel pump from fuel pump bracket, then fuel pump electrical connector.
6. Remove rubber cushion from fuel pump, then fuel pump strainer from fuel pump.
7. Reverse procedure to install.

FUEL FILTER

REPLACE

1992

The fuel filter is located in the engine compartment, below the power brake vacuum booster assembly.

1. Relieve fuel system pressure as follows:
   a. Remove fuel filler cap, then disconnect circuit opening relay located under instrument panel near Engine Control Module (ECM).
   b. Start engine and allow to stall, then crank engine for an additional ten seconds.
   c. Slowly loosen and remove cold start injector valve line bolt at fuel rail. Cover lines to be removed with shop towel.
   d. Disconnect battery ground cable.
2. Remove air intake duct, then fuel line union bolt from filter outlet (upper connection), **Fig. 42.**
3. Raise and support vehicle.
4. Remove fuel line union bolt from filter lower fitting.
5. Loosen filter bracket retaining bolt, then remove filter and bracket assembly from vehicle.
6. Reverse procedure to install. **Torque** fuel line banjo fittings to 21 ft. lbs.

1993–95

1. Release fuel system pressure as outlined under "Precautions."
2. Remove intake air temperature sensor electrical connector, then loosen air cleaner (ACL) hose clamp bolt.
3. Remove four cap clips from ACL, then ACL hose and cap from vehicle.
4. Remove evaporative emission hose (EVAP) from EVAP canister, EVAP mounting bolt, EVAP canister.
5. Remove fuel feed outlet and outlet lines from fuel filter, fuel filter mounting bolts, then fuel filter, **Fig. 43.**
6. Reverse procedure to install.

TIGHTENING SPECIFICATIONS

Year	Component	Torque/Ft. Lbs.
1992	Camshaft Bearing Cap Bolts ② ③	115 ①
	Camshaft Timing Gear Bolt ②	43
	Camshaft Timing Pulley Bolt ③	34
	Cold Start Injector Pipe Union Bolt ②	13
	Connecting Rod Bearing Cap Nuts	36
	Crankshaft Pulley Bolt ②	105
	Crankshaft Pulley Bolt ③	87
	Cylinder Head Bolts	⑤
	Cylinder Head Cover Cap Nuts ②	15
	Engine Mount Support Bolts ③	35
	Engine Mount Through Bolt ③	64
	Engine Mount To Bracket Bolt ③	45
	Engine Mount To Engine Bracket Nuts ③	45
	Exhaust Manifold Nuts And Bolts ②	18
	Exhaust Manifold Nuts ③	18
	Exhaust Manifold Support Bolts ②	18
	Exhaust Manifold Insulator Bolts ②	18
	Exhaust Pipe To Exhaust Manifold Bolts ②	18
	Flywheel To Crankshaft Attaching Bolts (Automatic)	47
	Flywheel To Crankshaft Attaching Bolts (manual)	58
	Idler Pulley Bolt ③	27
	Intake Manifold Bolts ②	14
	Intake Manifold Bolts ③	20
	Intake Manifold Bracket Bolts ③	20
	Main Bearing Cap Bolts	44
	Oil Cooler Center Bolts ③	20
	Oil Pan Bolts ③	53 ①
	Oil Pan Nuts And Bolts ②	44 ①
	Oil Pump Bolts ②	16
	Oil Pump Bolts ③	89 ①
	Oil Pump Cover Screws	89 ①
	Oil Strainer/Pick Up Assembly Bolts And Nuts ②	89 ①
	Pressure Regulator Bolts ②	65
1992 —Cont'd	Rear End Plate Bolts ②	89 ①
	Rear Main Oil Seal Retainer Bolts ②	84 ①
	Rear Main Seal Retainer Bolts ③	89 ①
	Relief Valve Plug ③	27
	Right Engine Mount Through Bolt ②	64
	Spark Plugs	13
	Timing Belt Cover Bolt	44 ①
	Timing Belt Idler Pulley Bolt ②	27
	Transaxle Mount To Center Crossmember Nuts	45
	Transaxle Mount To Main Crossmember Nuts	45
1993–95	Accelerator Bracket Bolts	11
	A/C Compressor Flexible Hose Mounting Bolts	89 ①
	A/C Pipe Bracket Bolt	89 ①
	Actuator Bolt	19
	Air Cleaner (ACL) Lower Case Bolt	89 ①
	Air Intake Chamber Brace Bolt	21
	Air Intake Chamber Cover Nuts & Bolts	14
	Air Pipe Nut & Bolt	80 ①
	Alternator Bracket Bolts	23
	Camshaft Bearing Cap Bolts	115 ①
	Camshaft Timing Gear Bolt	43
	Center Support Bearing	45
	Connecting Rod Bearing Cap Nuts	22 ④
	Coolant Pump Bolts	124 ①
	Coolant Pump Pulley Bolts	18
	Coolant Reservoir Mounting Bolts	11
	Crankshaft Pulley Bolts	87
	Cruise Control Actuator Bracket Bolts	19
	Cylinder Head Bolts	⑤
	EGR Solenoid Valve Mounting Bolt	115 ①
	EGR Valve To EGR Pipe Nut & Bolts	43
	EGR Valve To Intake Manifold Nuts & Bolts	115 ①
	Engine Hanger Bolt	20

Continued

TIGHTENING SPECIFICATIONS-Continued

Year	Component	Torque/Ft. Lbs.
1993–95 —Cont'd	Engine Mount Bracket Mounting Nuts	38
	Engine Mount Through Nut & Bolts	47
	Engine Mount To Body Bolts	19
	Engine Mount To Cylinder Block Brake Bolts	38
	Engine Mount To Engine Bracket "A" Bolts	47
	Engine Mount To Engine Bracket "B" Bolts	18
	Engine Mount To Engine Bracket "C" Bolts	47
	Engine Oil Pan Nuts & Bolts	44①
	Exhaust Manifold Brace Bolts	29
	Exhaust Manifold Nuts	25
	Flywheel Bolts (Automatic Transaxles)	47
	Flywheel Bolts (Manual Transaxles)	58
	Front Pipe Hanger Bolts	14
	Front Pipe Support Bolts	14
	Front Pipe To Catalytic Converter	32
	Front Pipe To Exhaust Manifold Nuts & Bolts	46
	Fuel Feed Pipe Connector	22
	Fuel Inlet Hose Clamp Bolt	89①
	Fuel Rail Bolts	11
	Guide Tube Bolts	80①
	Idler Pulley Mounting Bolts	27
	Insulator Bolt	47
	Intake Manifold Brace Bolts	14
	Intake Manifold Nuts And Bolts	14
	Lower Engine Reinforcement Brace To Cylinder Block Bolts	47

Year	Component	Torque/Ft. Lbs.
1993–95 —Cont'd	Lower Engine Reinforcement Brace To Transaxle Bolts	47
	Lower Heat Insulator Bolts	80①
	Main Bearing Bolt Caps	44
	Mounting Bracket To Engine Mounting Bolt	47
	Mounting Bracket To Engine Mounting Nuts	38
	Oil Drain Plug	25
	Oil Pressure Switch	115①
	Oil Pump Bolts	16
	Oil Strainer Bolts	62①
	Power Steering Pump Bracket Bolts	32
	Rear End Plate Bolts	49①
	Rear Main Seal Bolts	89①
	Rotor Plate Screw	89①
	Splash Shield Bolts	89①
	Throttle Body Nuts & Bolts	17
	Timing Belt Cover Bolts	62①
	Transaxle To Engine Mounting Bolts	17
	Union Bolts	22
	Upper Heat Insulator Bolts	80①
	Wheelhousing Bolts	11
	Wheel Lug Nuts	76
	Wiring Harness Cover Bolts	53①

①—Inch lbs.
②—Except GSi models.
③—GSi models.
④—Plus an additional 90°.
⑤—Refer to text.

Clutch & Manual Transaxle

INDEX

ADJUSTMENTS

CLUTCH PEDAL

1. Check height as shown in **Fig. 1.**
2. If it is necessary to adjust pedal height, remove instrument lower finish panel and air duct.
3. Loosen locknut and turn stopper bolt until the height is correct, then tighten locknut.
4. Push in on clutch pedal until resistance is felt, then check pushrod and pedal freeplay. Pushrod play should be .039-.197 inch, while freeplay should be .20-.59 inch.

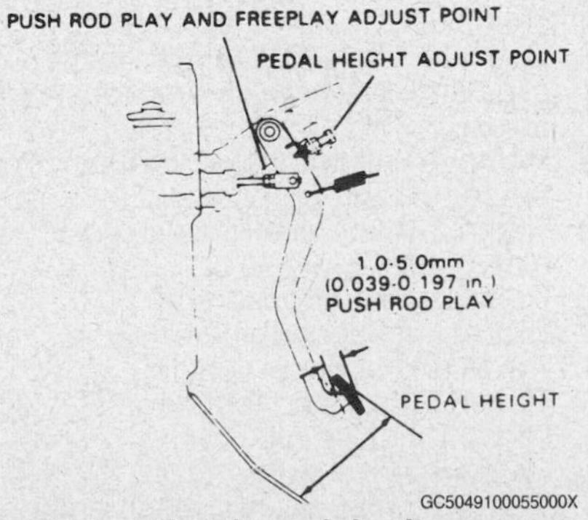

PUSH ROD PLAY AND FREEPLAY ADJUST POINT
PEDAL HEIGHT ADJUST POINT
1.0-5.0mm
(0.039-0.197 in.)
PUSH ROD PLAY
PEDAL HEIGHT
GC5049100055000X

Fig. 1 Clutch pedal adjustment

5. To adjust, loosen locknut and turn pushrod until freeplay and pushrod play are within specification, then tighten locknut.
6. Recheck pedal height and adjust as necessary.
7. Reinstall air duct and lower finish panel.

SHIFT LEVER FREEPLAY

Shift cables on these models are not adjustable. If cables are out of adjustment, replacement of the defective cable(s) will be required.

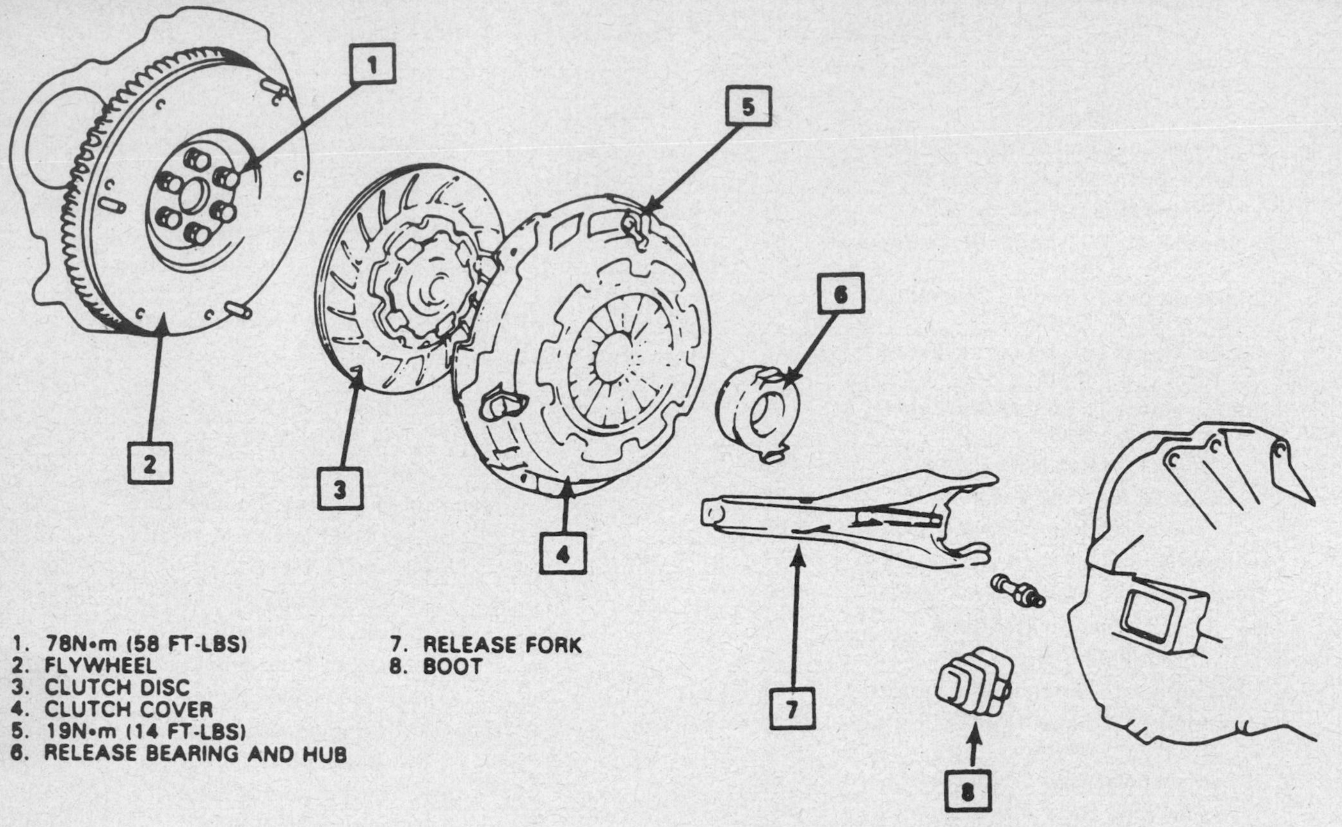
1
5
6
2
3
4
7
8
1. 78N•m (58 FT-LBS)
2. FLYWHEEL
3. CLUTCH DISC
4. CLUTCH COVER
5. 19N•m (14 FT-LBS)
6. RELEASE BEARING AND HUB
7. RELEASE FORK
8. BOOT
GC5049100056000X

Fig. 2 Clutch assembly

HYDRAULIC SYSTEM SERVICE

CLUTCH ACTUATOR, REPLACE

1. Disconnect negative battery cable.
2. Raise and support vehicle.
3. Disconnect clutch hydraulic line.
4. Remove two mounting bolts and actuator.
5. Reverse procedure to install. Bleed as follows:
   a. Clean top and sides of reservoir to ensure no foreign material enters system.
   b. Remove cap and fill reservoir with suitable brake fluid.
   c. Connect one end of a clear vinyl tube to bleeder screw and insert other end of tube into a half filled container of brake fluid.
   d. Slowly pump clutch pedal several times.
   e. While pumping clutch pedal, loosen bleeder screw until fluid starts to runout.
   f. Tighten bleeder screw.
   g. Repeat procedure until no air bubbles exist in escaping fluid.

CLUTCH

REPLACE

1. Remove transaxle assembly from vehicle.
2. Loosen each set bolt one turn at a time until spring tension is released.
3. Remove attaching bolts and pull off clutch assembly, **Fig. 2.**
4. Remove release bearing fork and boot from the transaxle.
5. Reverse procedure to install. Tighten bolts to specifications.

TRANSAXLE

REPLACE

1. Disconnect battery ground and positive cables.
2. Support engine using Engine Support Fixture tool No. J-28467-A, or equivalent.
3. Remove battery and battery tray.
4. Remove air cleaner assembly.
5. Disconnect back-up switch.
6. Disconnect ground cable at transaxle.
7. Remove two actuator mounting bolts.
8. Remove actuator line bracket.
9. Remove shift cable retainers, end clips and cables from bracket and lay aside.
10. Remove left transaxle mount cover, brace and through bolt.
11. Remove two upper transaxle to engine bolts.
12. Remove starter assembly.
13. Disconnect speedometer cable.
14. Raise and support vehicle.
15. Remove right and left stone shields.
16. Drain transaxle oil.
17. Remove drive axles.
18. Remove three center crossmember to radiator support bolts.
19. Remove front and center mount bolt shields.
20. Remove front, center and rear mount nuts.
21. Remove two center crossmember to main crossmember bolts.
22. Remove exhaust hangers.
23. Support main crossmember using a suitable jack.
24. Remove eight main crossmember to underbody bolts.
25. Remove two lower A-frame bracket to underbody bolts. **Lower main crossmember slowly while holding onto the center crossmember. Center crossmember will be free to fall at this time and could cause serious bodily injury.**
26. Remove front through bolt and mount.
27. Remove front mount bracket from transaxle.
28. Remove center mount from transaxle.
29. Remove transaxle inspection cover.
30. Remove two lower transaxle bracket to mount bolts.
31. Lower vehicle.
32. Remove remaining transaxle mount to bracket bolts.
33. Lower transaxle using Engine Support tool No. J-28467, or equivalent to gain clearance to remove transaxle.
34. Remove transaxle mount.
35. Raise and support vehicle.
36. Support transaxle using a suitable jack.
37. Remove front and rear lower transaxle to engine bolts.
38. Lower transaxle from vehicle.
39. Reverse procedure to install.

TIGHTENING SPECIFICATIONS

Year	Component	Torque/Ft. Lbs.
1992–94	Actuator Assembly Bolts	106 ①
	Back-Up Light Switch	30
	Bleeder Screw	97 ①
	Clutch Cover Bolts	14
	Clutch Line Tube	11
	Flywheel Bolts	58
	Master Cylinder Nuts	11
	Pedal Assembly Bracket To Instrument Panel Bolts	11
	Transaxle Case Cover Bolts	13
	Transaxle Case Bolts	22
1995	Actuator & Line Bracket	15
	Back-Up Light Switch	15
	Center Crossmember To Main Crossmember	45
	Center Crossmember To Radiator Support	45
	Center Mount To Transaxle	45
	Center & Rear Mounting	45
	Front Mount Bracket	45
	Front Mount	45
	Front Mount Through	64
	Left Mount Bracket	45
	Left Mount Cover	45
	Left Mount Through	64
	Lower A Frame To Underbody	94
	Main Crossmember To Underbody	152
	Oil Drain Plug	97 ①
	Oil Fill Plug	97 ①
	Starter Mounting	29
	Transaxle To Engine	64
	Vehicle Speed Sensor	97 ①

①—Inch lbs.

Rear Axle & Suspension

INDEX

HUB & BEARING
REPLACE

1992

1. Raise and support vehicle.
2. Support suspension using a suitable jack. Place jack under suspension supports, not the suspension arms.
3. Lower vehicle slightly so weight rests on jack.
4. Remove tire and wheel assembly.
5. **On except GSi models,** remove brake drum assembly.
6. **On GSi models,** remove rear disc brake assembly.
7. **On all models,** remove axle hub and rear suspension knuckle mounting bolts, **Fig. 1.**
8. Reverse procedure to install, using a new O-ring seal when installing.

1993–95

1. Raise and support vehicle. Place jack stand under suspension support, not suspension arms.
2. Lower vehicle, remove rear wheels, then rear drums.
3. Check hub bearing endplay using tools No. J 26900-13 or equivalent magnetic base and tool No. J 8001 or equivalent dial indicator. If endplay exceeds 0.020 inches replace axle hub bearing on vehicles without ABS or rear axle hub on vehicles with ABS.
4. Remove bolt attaching ABS speed sensor, if equipped.
5. Remove axle hub and rear suspension knuckle mounting bolts, then axle hub from vehicle.
6. Remove O-ring from backing plate.
7. Reverse procedure to install.

HUB & BEARING SERVICE

1. Remove rear axle hub as outlined under "Hub & Bearing, Replace."
2. Unstake wheel bearing locknut and remove.
3. Remove axle shaft from hub assembly using a Bearing Removal tool Nos. J-22912, J-38278 and J-8433, or equivalents, **Figs. 1 and 2.**
4. Remove bearing inner and outer race.
5. Remove oil seal from axle shaft using Seal Installer/Remover tool No. J-26941, or equivalent, and slide hammer.
6. Reverse procedure to install, using a new bearing locknut.

STRUT
REPLACE

Refer to "Coil Spring, Replace" for procedure.

STRUT ROD
REPLACE

1992

1. Raise and support vehicle.
2. Remove bolt and nut attaching strut rod to axle carrier.
3. Remove bolt and nut attaching strut rod to body, then the strut rod assembly from the vehicle.
4. Reverse procedure to install.

1993–95

1. Raise and support vehicle. Place jack

stand under suspension support, not suspension arms, remove two strut rod nut and bolts, then strut rod.
2. Remove resonator/intermediate pipe assembly from catalytic converter.
3. Remove resonator/intermediate pipe assembly from muffler/tail pipe assembly.
4. Remove muffler/tail pipe assembly attaching bolts, then muffler/tail pipe assembly from hanger.
5. Remove intermediate pipe heat shield, then six crossmember to body attaching bolts.
6. Remove front lateral link with the two bolts and four washers.
7. Reverse procedure to install, tighten nuts and bolts to specifications.

STRUT SERVICE

DISASSEMBLE

1. Remove strut assembly as outlined under "Coil Spring, Replace."
2. Mount strut assembly in Strut Holding/Spring Compression tool No. J-34013, or equivalent.
3. Remove strut piston rod to suspension support nut.
4. Remove suspension support, coil spring, insulator and bumper.

ASSEMBLE

1. Mount strut in Holding/Spring Compression tool No. J-34013, or equivalent.
2. Align coil spring end with lower seat hollow and install coil spring.
3. Install spring bumper and insulator.
4. Align suspension support with piston rod and install.
5. Align suspension support with strut lower bracket as shown in **Fig. 3.**
6. Compress spring slightly, install a new strut rod piston nut and tighten to specification.

COIL SPRING

REPLACE

1992

1. Raise and support vehicle.
2. Support suspension using a suitable jack. Place jack under suspension supports, not the suspension arms.
3. Lower vehicle slightly so weight rests on jack.
4. Remove tire and wheel assembly.
5. Disconnect brake hose from brake hose bracket.
6. Disconnect stabilizer bar link from strut assembly as outlined under "Stabilizer Bar, Replace."
7. Disconnect strut assembly mounting bolts from knuckle.
8. Remove seat back side cushion (sedan) or rear sill side panel (hatchback).
9. Disconnect strut assembly mounting nuts holding strut support.
10. Remove strut assembly from vehicle.
11. Reverse procedure to install.

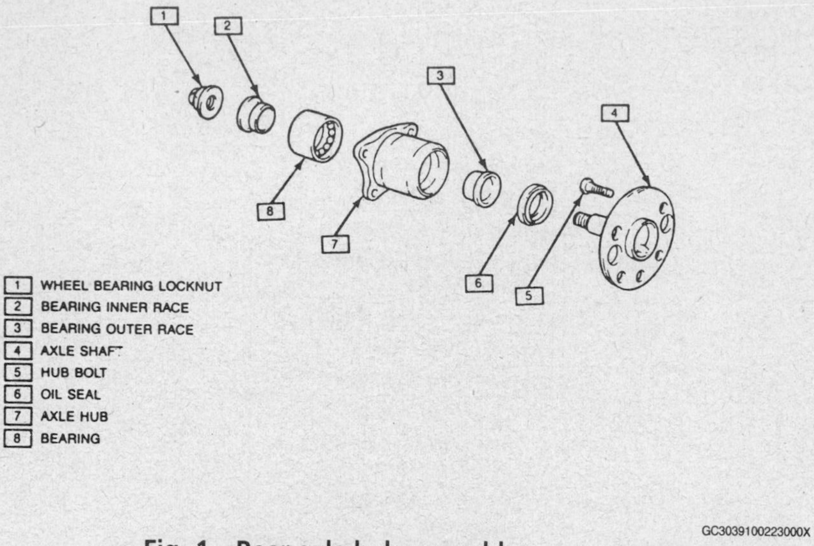

1
2
3
4
5
6
7
8
1 WHEEL BEARING LOCKNUT
2 BEARING INNER RACE
3 BEARING OUTER RACE
4 AXLE SHAFT
5 HUB BOLT
6 OIL SEAL
7 AXLE HUB
8 BEARING
GC3039100223000X

Fig. 1 Rear axle hub assembly

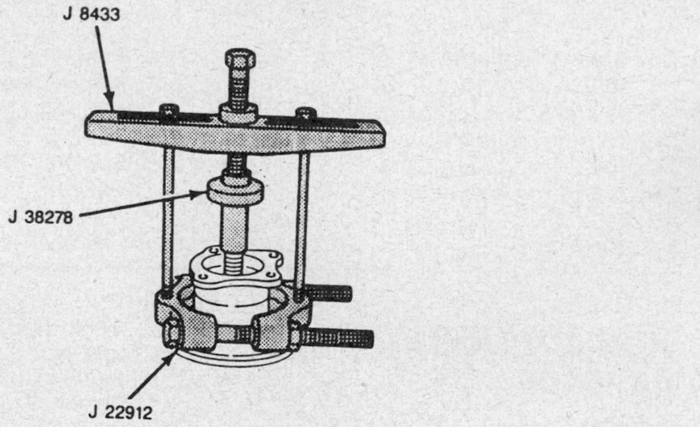

J 8433
J 38278
J 22912
GC3039100224000X

Fig. 2 Removing axle shaft from hub

1993–95

1. Raise and support vehicle. Place jack stand under suspension support, not suspension arms.
2. Remove rear wheels, brake lines from brake hoses and backing plate.
3. Remove brake clip from brake line, then brake hose from hose bracket.
4. Remove ABS wire harness attaching bolt, if equipped.
5. Remove stabilizer bar link attaching nut from strut assembly.
6. Remove strut assembly mounting bolts and nuts from rear suspension knuckle.
7. Remove strut top mounting nuts, then strut assembly from vehicle.
8. Reverse procedure to install.

CONTROL ARM

REPLACE

1992

Rear

1. Raise and support vehicle.
2. Remove bolt and nut attaching rear control arm to axle carrier.
3. Remove cam and bolt attaching rear control arm to body, then the rear suspension arm.
4. Note location of cam plate mark before removing bolt and cam.
5. Reverse procedure to install.

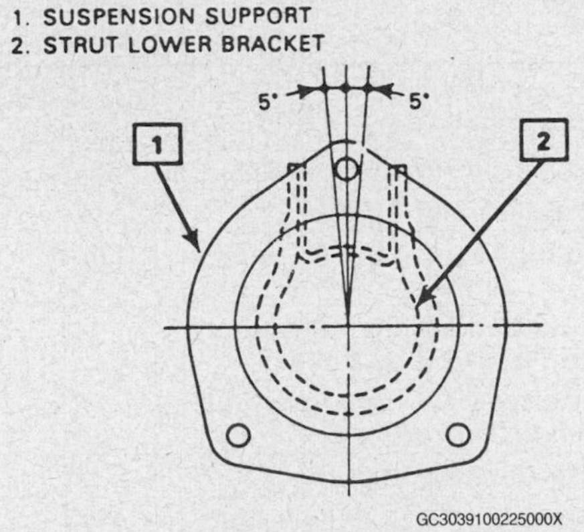
1. SUSPENSION SUPPORT
2. STRUT LOWER BRACKET
5°
5°
1
2
GC3039100225000X

Fig. 3 Aligning suspension support plate

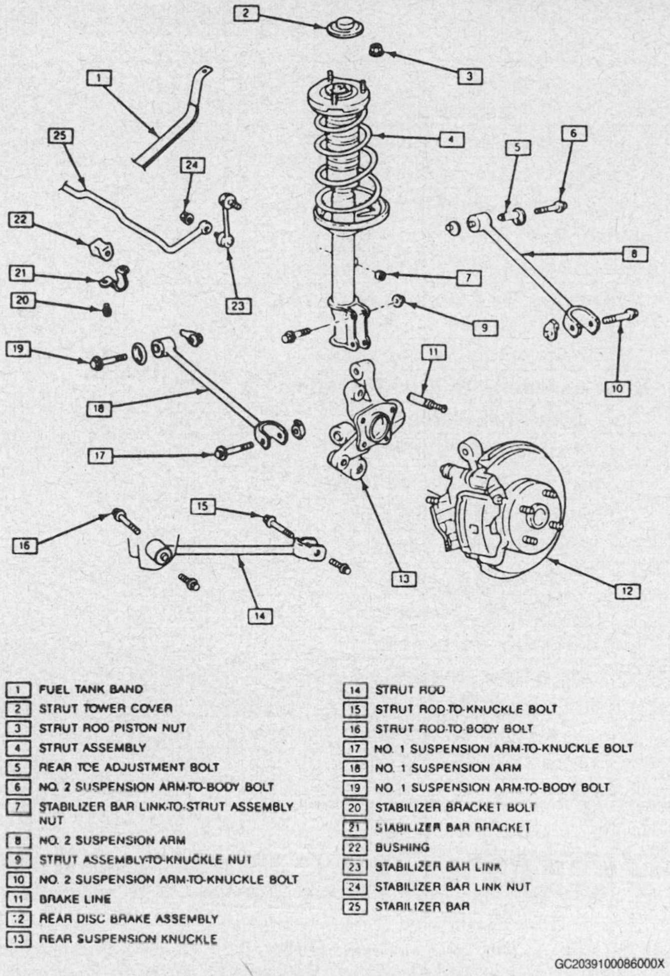
1 FUEL TANK BAND
2 STRUT TOWER COVER
3 STRUT ROD PISTON NUT
4 STRUT ASSEMBLY
5 REAR TOE ADJUSTMENT BOLT
6 NO. 2 SUSPENSION ARM-TO-BODY BOLT
7 STABILIZER BAR LINK-TO-STRUT ASSEMBLY NUT
8 NO. 2 SUSPENSION ARM
9 STRUT ASSEMBLY-TO-KNUCKLE NUT
10 NO. 2 SUSPENSION ARM-TO-KNUCKLE BOLT
11 BRAKE LINE
12 REAR DISC BRAKE ASSEMBLY
13 REAR SUSPENSION KNUCKLE
14 STRUT ROD
15 STRUT ROD-TO-KNUCKLE BOLT
16 STRUT ROD-TO-BODY BOLT
17 NO. 1 SUSPENSION ARM-TO-KNUCKLE BOLT
18 NO. 1 SUSPENSION ARM
19 NO. 1 SUSPENSION ARM-TO-BODY BOLT
20 STABILIZER BRACKET BOLT
21 STABILIZER BAR BRACKET
22 BUSHING
23 STABILIZER BAR LINK
24 STABILIZER BAR LINK NUT
25 STABILIZER BAR
GC2039100086000X

Fig. 4 Rear suspension assembly

Front

1. Raise and support vehicle.
2. Remove bolt and nut attaching front control arm to axle carrier.
3. Remove bolt and nut attaching front control arm to the body, then the front suspension arm.
4. Reverse procedure to install.

KNUCKLE

REPLACE

1992

1. Raise and support vehicle.
2. Support suspension using a suitable jack. Place jack under suspension supports, not the suspension arms.
3. Lower vehicle slightly so weight rests on jack.
4. Remove tire and wheel assembly.
5. **On except GSi models,** remove brake drum assembly.
6. **On GSi models**, remove rear disc brake assembly.
7. **On all models,** remove rear axle hub as outlined under "Hub & Bearing, Replace," **Fig. 4.**
8. **On except GSi models,** disconnect brake line from brake hose and backing plate.
9. **On GSi models,** disconnect brake hose from caliper assembly.
10. **On all models,** remove strut rod from knuckle as outlined under "Strut Rod, Replace."
11. Remove front and rear suspension arms from knuckle as outlined under "Control Arm, Replace."
12. Disconnect strut assembly as outlined under "Coil Spring, Replace."
13. Remove knuckle.
14. Reverse procedure to install, torquing attaching bolts to specifications.

1993–95

1. Remove rear hub as described under "Hub & Bearing, Replace."
2. Remove brake lines and hoses, then backing plate from rear suspension hub.
3. Remove nut, bolt, and strut rod from knuckle.
4. Remove nut, bolt, and both lateral links from knuckle.
5. Remove two nuts, bolts, and strut assembly from knuckle.
6. Remove rear suspension knuckle from vehicle.
7. Reverse procedure to install noting the following:
   a. When replacing rear suspension knuckle, tighten nuts and bolts to specifications.
   b. Bleed brakes, then check rear wheel alignment.

STABILIZER BAR

REPLACE

1992

1. Support fuel tank with a suitable jack.
2. Disconnect fuel tank straps.
3. Disconnect stabilizer bar links from strut assemblies, **Fig. 4.**
4. Disconnect stabilizer bar bracket mounting bolts.
5. Remove stabilizer bar from vehicle.
6. Reverse procedure to install.

1993–95

1. Raise and support vehicle. Place jack stand under suspension support, not suspension arms.
2. Remove rear wheels, then left and right stabilizer bar links.
3. Remove right and left stabilizer bar bushing retainers. Scribe marks between stabilizer bar bushings, stabilizer, and body.
4. Remove stabilizer bushings.
5. Remove resonator/intermediate pipe assembly from catalytic converter.
6. Remove resonator/intermediate pipe assembly from muffler/tail pipe assembly.
7. Remove muffler/tail pipe assembly attaching bolts, then muffler/tail pipe assembly from hanger.
8. Remove intermediate pipe heat shield, then right fuel tank band.
9. Support crossmember with jack, then remove six bolts attaching crossmember to body.
10. Remove stabilizer bar.
11. Reverse procedure to install, tighten all nuts and bolts to specifications.

TIGHTENING SPECIFICATIONS

Year	Component	Torque/Ft. Lbs.
1992	Axle Hub Mounting Bolts	59
	Brake Line To Backing Plate	11
	Stabilizer Bar Bracket Mounting Bolts	14
	Stabilizer Bar Link To Strut Assembly	26
	Stabilizer Bar Links To Strut Assembly	26
	Stabilizer Bar To Stabilizer Bar Links Nuts	26
	Strut Assembly To Body Nuts	29
	Strut Assembly To Knuckle Nuts	105
	Strut Rod Piston Nut	36
	Strut Rod To Body Nut	87
	Strut Rod To Knuckle Nuts	87
	Suspension Arm Bolts	87
	Wheel Bearing Locknut	90
	Wheel Lug Nuts	76
1993–95	ABS Speed Sensor Bolt	69①
	ABS Wire Harness Bolt	48①
	Axle Hub To Rear Knuckle Mounting Bolts	59
	Brake Line Fittings	11
	Fuel Tank Band Bolts	29

Year	Component	Torque/Ft. Lbs.
1993–95 -Cont'd	Intermediate Pipe Heat Shield Bolt	48①
	Lateral Link Nut & Bolts	87
	Muffler/Tail Pipe Assembly To Body Bolts	115①
	Resonator/Intermediate Pipe Assembly To Muffler/Tail Pipe Bolts	14
	Resonator/Intermediate Pipe Assembly To Catalytic Converter Bolts	32
	Stabilizer Bar Bushing Retainer Bolts	14
	Stabilizer Bar Link To Stabilizer Bar Bolts	26
	Stabilizer Bar Link To Strut Assembly Nut	32
	Stabilizer Assembly To Rear Suspension Knuckle Mounting Nuts & Bolts	105
	Stabilizer Assembly To Strut Support Mounting Nuts	29
	Strut Rod Nuts & Bolts	67
	Wheel Bearing Locknut	90
	Wheel Lug Nuts	76

①—Inch lbs.

Front Suspension & Steering

NOTE: On Air Bag Equipped Models, Refer To "Air Bag System Precautions" Located In The Front Of This Manual For System Disarming & Arming Procedures.

INDEX

PRECAUTIONS

AIR BAG SYSTEMS

Refer to "Air Bag System Precautions" in the front of this manual for system disarming and arming procedures.

DESCRIPTION

The front suspension, **Figs. 1 and 2,** on this vehicle is a McPherson strut design. The upper end of the strut is anchored to the body by a strut support. The strut and strut support are isolated by a rubber mount. The lower end of the strut is connected to the upper end of the steering knuckle. The lower end of the knuckle is attached to the ball joint, which is attached to the suspension control arm assembly. Movement of the steering wheel is transmitted to the tie-rod end and then to the knuckle, turning the wheel and tire assembly.

WHEEL HUB

REPLACE

1. Remove knuckle from vehicle and mount into a suitable vise.
2. Using a suitable screwdriver, remove dust deflector.
3. Using Seal Remover tool No. J-26941 or equivalent, remove inner grease seal from knuckle, **Fig. 3.**
4. Remove inner bearing snap ring and disc brake dust shield.
5. Push out hub using Hub Remover tool Nos. J-25287 and J-35378 or equivalents.
6. Using tools mentioned in step 5, remove outer bearing race from hub.
7. Using Seal Remover tool No. J-26941 or equivalent, remove outer grease seal.
8. Using Bearing Remover tool Nos. J-35399 and J-35379 or equivalents, remove bearing assembly.
9. Reverse procedure to install. Use Bearing Installation tool Nos. J-8092 and J-35411 to install hub bearing assembly. Use Seal Installation tool No. J-35737 to install outer grease seal. Install hub using tool Nos. J-8092 and J-35399. Use tool No. J-35737 to install inner grease seal. Use Ring In-

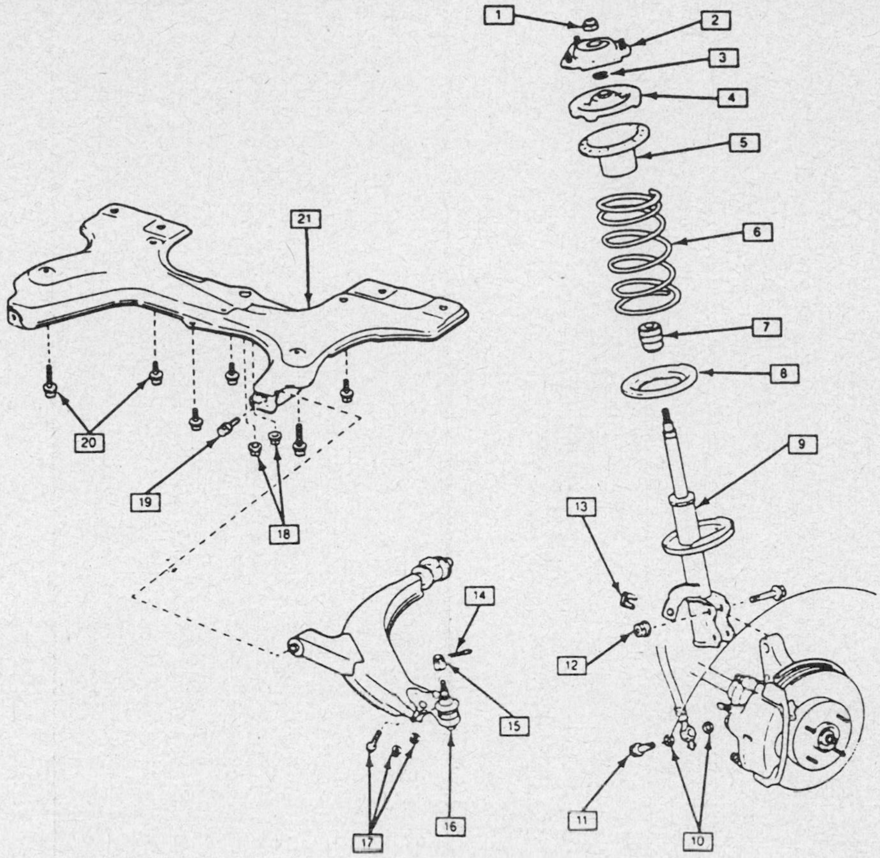

1 STRUT ROD PISTON NUT	12 STRUT MOUNTING NUT AND BOLT
2 SUSPENSION SUPPORT	13 BRAKE HOSE CLIP
3 DUST SEAL	14 COTTER PIN
4 SPRING SEAT	15 BALL JOINT CASTLE NUT
5 UPPER INSULATOR	16 BALL JOINT
6 COIL SPRING	17 BALL JOINT MOUNTING NUT AND BOLT
7 SPRING BUMPER	18 CROSSMEMBER MOUNTING NUTS
8 LOWER INSULATOR	19 CROSSMEMBER-TO-CONTROL-ARM BOLT
9 SHOCK ABSORBER	20 CROSSMEMBER MOUNTING BOLTS
10 BRAKE LINE GASKETS	21 SUSPENSION CROSSMEMBER
11 BRAKE LINE-TO-CALIPER BOLT	

GC2029100175000X

Fig. 1 Disassembled view of front suspension. Except GSi models

stallation tool No. J-35379 to install dust deflector ring. Ensure dust deflector ring faces down (open end down).

BALL JOINT
REPLACE

1. Raise and support vehicle.
2. Support suspension using a suitable jack. Place jack under suspension supports, not the control arm.
3. Lower vehicle slightly so weight rests on jack.
4. Loosen wheel lug nuts.
5. Remove tire and wheel assembly.
6. Install Inner Drive Joint Seal Protector tool No. J-34754, or equivalent. **Care must be taken not to allow tri-pot joints to over extend. Over extended tri-pot joints could result in separation of internal components and possible join failure.**
7. Using Ball Joint Removal tool No. J-35413 or equivalent, separate ball joint from knuckle assembly.
8. Remove two nuts and bolts attaching ball joint and control arm.
9. Remove ball joint.
10. Reverse procedure to install. Tighten knuckle to ball joint nut to specifications. During installation, always replace a self-locking nut with a new one.

COIL SPRING
REPLACE

Refer to "Strut, Replace" for coil spring replacement procedure.

STRUT
REPLACE

1. Raise and support vehicle.
2. Support suspension using a suitable jack. Place jack under suspension supports, not the control arm.
3. Lower vehicle slightly so weight rests on jack.
4. Install a Drive Joint Seal Protector tool No. J-34754, or equivalent.
5. Remove brake hose from disc brake caliper.
6. Remove clip from brake hose.
7. Remove brake hose from brake hose bracket.
8. Remove bolts and nuts attaching strut assembly to steering knuckle.
9. Remove strut assembly mounting nuts holding suspension support plate.
10. Remove strut assembly.
11. Reverse procedure to install.

COIL SPRING & STRUT SERVICE

1. Using Strut Holding/Spring Compression tool No. J-34013-A, or equivalent, compress spring slightly. **Ensure spring seat is secure and will not turn.**
2. Remove strut rod piston nut.
3. Remove suspension support, dust seal, spring seat and insulator and bumper.
4. Reverse procedure to assemble.

CONTROL ARM
REPLACE

1. Raise and support vehicle.
2. Remove lower control arm attaching nuts and bolts.
3. **On models with stabilizer bar,** disconnect stabilizer bar links.
4. **On all models,** remove the six bolts and two nuts and remove the suspension crossmember with control arms attached.
5. Remove control arm mounting bolts and nuts. Remove control arm from crossmember.
6. Reverse procedure to install. Tighten control arm to body front nuts and bolts to specifications.

CONTROL ARM BUSHING
REPLACE

1. Remove control arm as outlined under "Control Arm, Replace."
2. Using a suitable tool, remove lower control arm bushing from lower control arm.
3. Reverse procedure to install. Tighten bushing nut to specifications.

STEERING KNUCKLE
REPLACE

1. Remove locknut cap and bearing locknut.
2. Remove brake caliper and support with wire.
3. Remove disc brake rotor.
4. Separate tie rod from steering knuckle using Tie Rod Puller tool No. J-6627-A, or equivalent.
5. Remove lower ball joint bolt and nuts

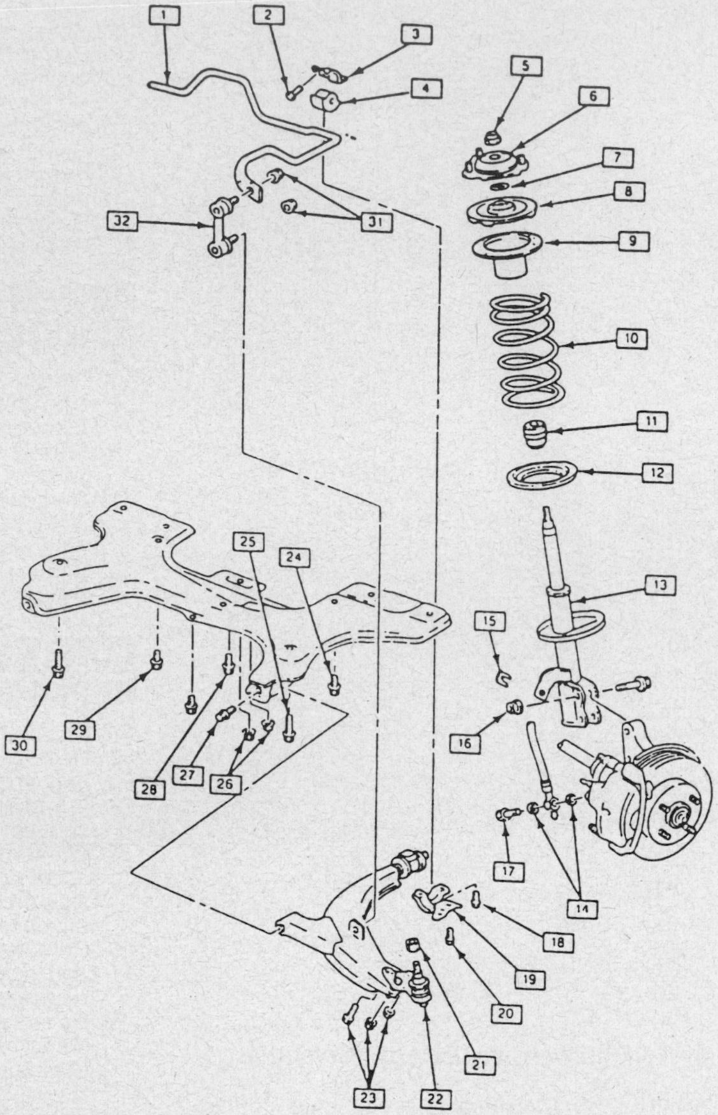
1
2
3
4
5
6
7
8
9
10
11
12
13
14
15
16
17
18
19
20
21
22
23
24
25
26
27
28
29
30
31
32

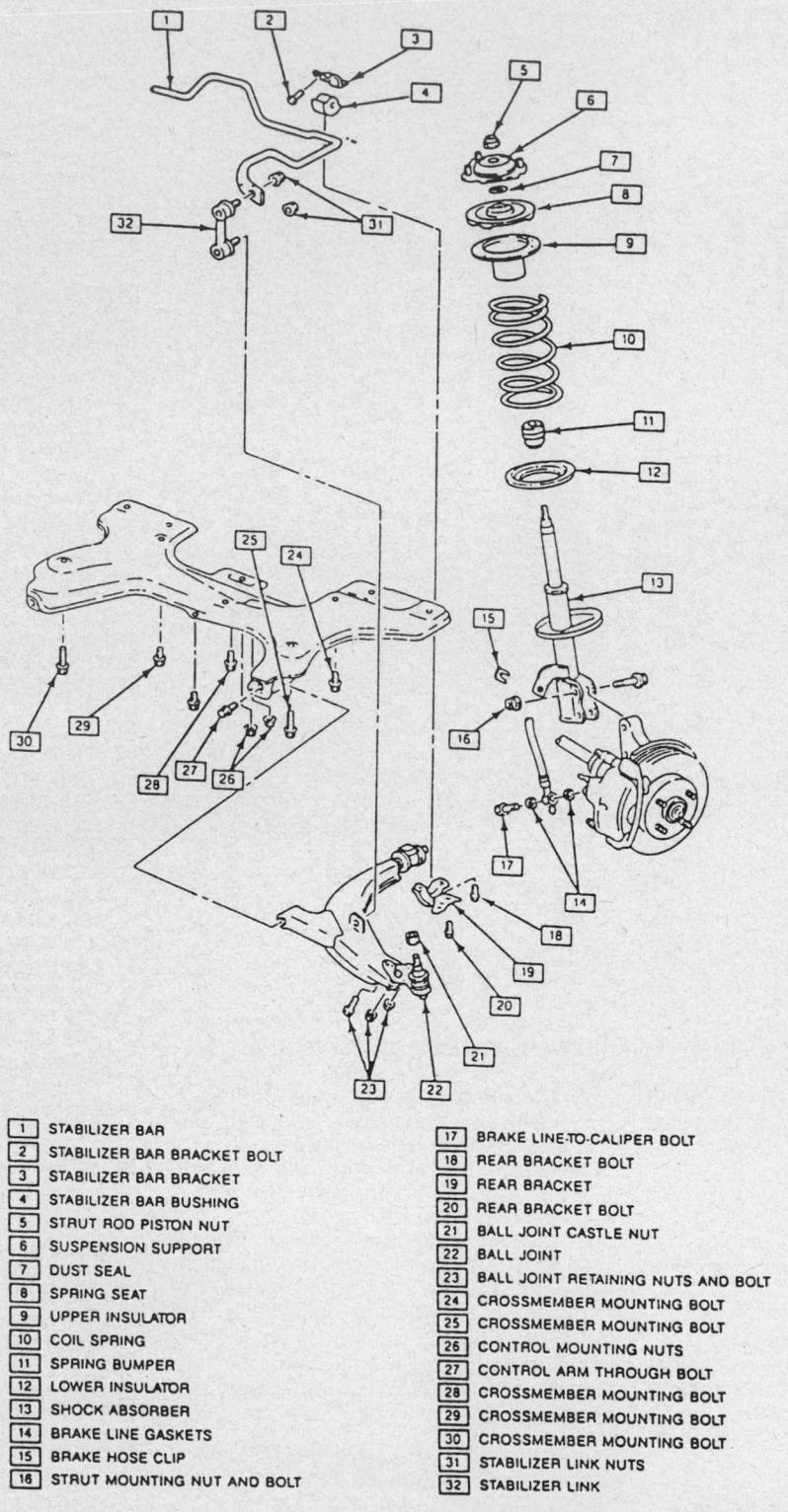

1	STABILIZER BAR
2	STABILIZER BAR BRACKET BOLT
3	STABILIZER BAR BRACKET
4	STABILIZER BAR BUSHING
5	STRUT ROD PISTON NUT
6	SUSPENSION SUPPORT
7	DUST SEAL
8	SPRING SEAT
9	UPPER INSULATOR
10	COIL SPRING
11	SPRING BUMPER
12	LOWER INSULATOR
13	SHOCK ABSORBER
14	BRAKE LINE GASKETS
15	BRAKE HOSE CLIP
16	STRUT MOUNTING NUT AND BOLT
17	BRAKE LINE-TO-CALIPER BOLT
18	REAR BRACKET BOLT
19	REAR BRACKET
20	REAR BRACKET BOLT
21	BALL JOINT CASTLE NUT
22	BALL JOINT
23	BALL JOINT RETAINING NUTS AND BOLT
24	CROSSMEMBER MOUNTING BOLT
25	CROSSMEMBER MOUNTING BOLT
26	CONTROL MOUNTING NUTS
27	CONTROL ARM THROUGH BOLT
28	CROSSMEMBER MOUNTING BOLT
29	CROSSMEMBER MOUNTING BOLT
30	CROSSMEMBER MOUNTING BOLT
31	STABILIZER LINK NUTS
32	STABILIZER LINK

GC2029100176000X

Fig. 2 Disassembled view of front suspension. GSi models

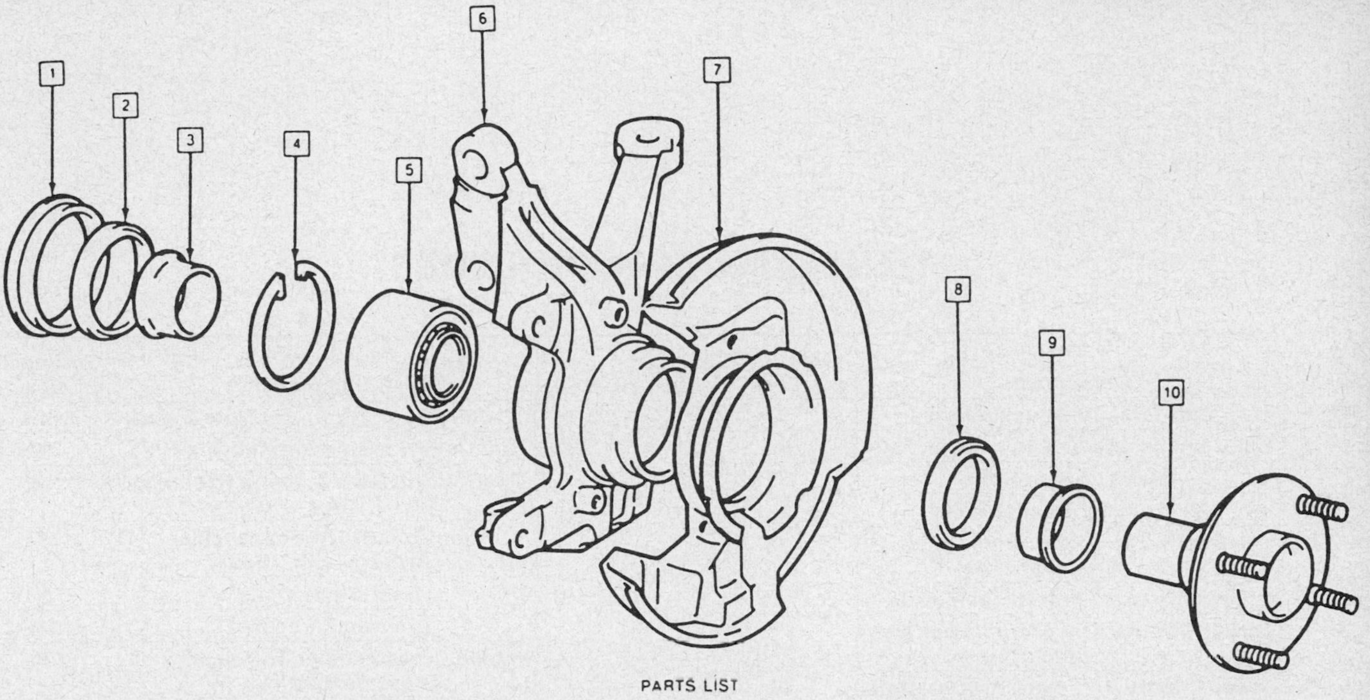
6
1
2
3
4
5
7
8
9
10
PARTS LIST
1 DEFLECTOR DUST
2 SEAL INNER GREASE
3 RACE INNER BEARING
4 RING SNAP
5 BEARING AXLE HUB
6 KNUCKLE STEERING FRONT
7 SHIELD DUST
8 SEAL OUTER GREASE
9 RACE OUTER BEARING
10 HUB DRIVE AXLE
GC3039100226000X

Fig. 3 Disassembled view of hub & bearing assembly

and separate it from lower control arm.

6. Remove two strut to steering knuckle nuts.
7. Install Drive Joint Protector tool No. J-34754, or equivalent.
8. Tap driveshaft with a plastic hammer and drive out driveshaft.
9. Remove two strut to steering knuckle bolts.
10. Remove steering knuckle assembly.
11. Reverse procedure to install.

STABILIZER BAR

REPLACE

1. Raise and support vehicle.
2. Disconnect stabilizer bar links from lower control arms.
3. Remove stabilizer bar brackets from body.
4. Disconnect exhaust pipe from manifold and/or catalytic converter.
5. Remove stabilizer bar from vehicle.
6. Reverse procedure to install.

POWER STEERING GEAR

REPLACE

1. Remove intermediate steering shaft protector.
2. Loosen upper, and remove lower intermediate shaft pinch bolts.
3. Open hood and place drain pan under gear assembly.
4. Loosen wheel lug nuts.
5. Raise and support vehicle.
6. Remove both front wheel and tire assemblies.
7. Using tie rod remover J-24319-01 or equivalent, remove both tie rod ends from knuckles.
8. Support transaxle with a suitable jack.
9. Remove rear center engine mounting member to body mounting bolts.
10. Remove rear engine mount to mount bracket attaching nut and bolt. Raise and lower rear of transaxle to gain access to steering gear to body attaching nuts and bolts.
11. Disconnect pressure and return lines at steering gear.
12. Remove four gear to body mounting nuts and bolts.
13. Remove gear through access opening.
14. Reverse procedure to install.

POWER STEERING PUMP

REPLACE

1. Remove air cleaner assembly.
2. Remove return hose clamp.
3. Disconnect and cap pressure and return lines from pump.
4. Loosen pump pulley and remove.
5. Remove adjusting bolt, pivot bolt and drive belt.
6. Remove pump assembly.
7. Reverse procedure to install.

MANUAL STEERING GEAR

REPLACE

1. Disconnect battery ground cable.
2. Remove intermediate shaft cover.
3. Loosen upper pinch bolt. Remove lower pinch bolt from pinion shaft.
4. Loosen wheel lug nuts.
5. Raise and support vehicle.
6. Remove both front wheel and tire assemblies.
7. Remove cotter pins from tie rod ends.
8. Disconnect both tie rod ends from steering knuckles. Using Tie Rod End Remover tool No. J-24319-01, or equivalent only, to separate tie rod joints.
9. Remove steering gear to body mounting nuts and bolts.
10. Remove steering assembly from vehicle.
11. Reverse procedure to install.

TIGHTENING SPECIFICATIONS

Year	Component	Torque/Ft. Lbs.
1992	Ball Joint To Knuckle Nuts	94
	Ball Joint To Lower Control Arm Nuts	105
	Brake Caliper Bolts	65
	Brake Line Bracket Bolts	22
	Control Arm Rear Bracket To Crossmember Nuts	14
	Lower Control Arm Bushing Nuts	101
	Lower Control Arm Front Lower Arm Bolt	152
	Lower Control Arm Rear Bracket Bolts	94
	Rear Bracket To Crossmember Bolt	14
	Stabilizer Bar Link Nuts	26
	Stabilizer Bar To Body Bolts	29
	Stabilizer Bracket Bolts	94
	Stabilizer Bracket Nuts & Bolts	94
	Strut Piston Nut	34
	Strut To Body Nuts	29
	Strut To Knuckle Nuts & Bolts	194
	Tie Rod To Knuckle Nuts	36
	Wheel Bearing Locknuts	137
	Wheel Lug Nuts	76
1993–95	ABS Hose Bolt	21
	ABS Speed Sensor Bolt	69①
	ABS Wire Harness Bolt	48①
	Brake Caliper To Steering Knuckle Set Bolt	65

Year	Component	Torque/Ft. Lbs.
1993–95 —Cont'd	Ball Joint To Control Arm Nuts & Bolts	105
	Ball Joint To Steering Knuckle Nut	87
	Control Arm Rear Bushing Retaining Nut	101
	Control Arm To Suspension Crossmember Bolt	161
	Dust Cover Bolts	73①
	Driveshaft Locknut	159
	Engine Crossmember To Suspension Crossmember Nut A	35
	Engine Crossmember To Suspension Crossmember Bolt B	45
	Engine Crossmember To Suspension Crossmember Nut C	35
	Left & Right Rear Control Arm Bushing Retaining Bracket Bolt A	108
	Left & Right Rear Control Arm Bushing Retaining Bracket Bolt	37
	Left & Right Rear Control Arm Bushing Retaining Bracket Nut C	14
	Steering Knuckle To Strut Assembly Nuts	203
	Strut Assembly Mounting Nuts	29
	Suspension Crossmember To Body Bolts	152
	Tie Rod End Nut	36
	Wheel Lug Nuts	76

①—Inch lbs.

Wheel Alignment

NOTE: On Air Bag Equipped Models, Refer To "Air Bag System Precautions" Located In The Front Of This Manual For System Disarming & Arming Procedures.

INDEX

GC2049100085000X

Fig. 1 Front toe adjustment

PRECAUTIONS

AIR BAG SYSTEMS

Refer to "Air Bag System Precautions" in the front of this manual for system disarming and arming procedures.

PRELIMINARY INSPECTION

Steering and vibration problems are not always the result of improper alignment. They may also be caused by wheel and tire imbalance, or other factors. To ensure correct alignment readings, the following inspections should be done and corrections made before checking caster, camber or toe:

1. Inspect all tires for proper inflation pressures and even tread wear.
2. Inspect wheel bearings for looseness.
3. Inspect ball joints and tie rod ends for excessive looseness.
4. Inspect steering gear operation and mountings.
5. Inspect operation of struts.
6. Inspect control arms.
7. Inspect hub and bearing assemblies for excessive wear

FRONT WHEEL ALIGNMENT

CASTER & CAMBER

Caster and camber cannot be adjusted. Should caster be found out of specification, locate cause first. If components are damaged, bent, loose, dented or worn, they should be replaced. To prevent an incorrect reading of camber or caster, jounce the bumper three times before checking.

TOE-IN

Toe-in is adjusted by changing tie rod length. Loosen boot clamps and slide from the boot assembly. Loosen right and left tie rod end locknuts, then turn right and left tie rods to align toe-in to specification. Right and left tie rods must be equal in length, **Fig. 1.**

After adjustment, install boot clamps, tighten nuts to specification and ensure rack boots are not twisted.

Tighten strut-to-knuckle nut to specifications, and **torque** tie rod locking nut to 41 ft. lbs.

REAR WHEEL ALIGNMENT

TOE

1992

Toe-in can be adjusted by rotating the cam located on the rear lower control arm. Loosen bolt and rotate nut to give the correct specification. Measure distance between left and right wheel discs and centerline of adjustment cam, **Fig. 2.**

1993–95

1. Loosen left and right lateral link locknuts.
2. Adjust total rear toe to 0.08-0.40° by turning lateral link adjusting tubes. One revolution of adjusting tube will adjust rear to approximately 1.2°.
3. Check difference between left and right lateral link length, the right link length must be less than 0.039 inches difference.
4. **Torque** lateral link locknuts to 41 ft. lbs.

CAMBER & CASTER

Rear caster and camber cannot be adjusted. Should camber be found out of specification, locate cause first. If components are damaged, bent loose, dented or worn, they should be replaced. To prevent an incorrect reading of camber, jounce the bumper three times before checking. If a tie rod or tie rod end is replaced, check toe and steering angle with turning radius gages. If steering angle is not correct, check right and left tie rods for equal length. If tie rod length is change to correct steering, reinspect toe.

REAR TOE ADJUSTMENT MECHANISM

Rear suspension arm No. 2 is equipped with toe adjustment cams.

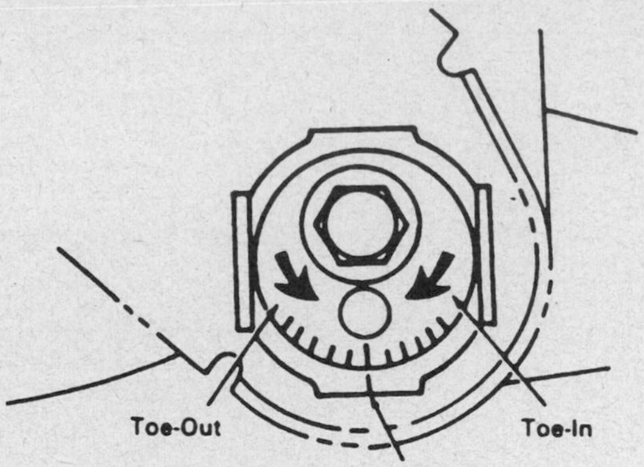
Toe-Out
Toe-In
Standard Center Line

Toe Adjustment

(1) Measure the distance and find the difference between the left and right disc wheels and the centerline of the adjustment cam. (If the difference is not within standard specifications, check each part for deformation.)

(2) Turn each cam an equal amount in the opposite direction. (Toe changes about 2 mm for each turn of the cam on each side.)

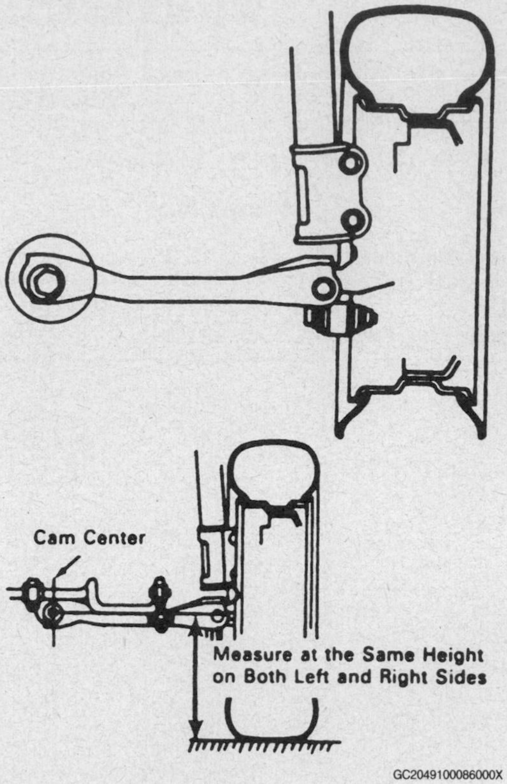
Cam Center
Measure at the Same Height
on Both Left and Right Sides
GC2049100086000X

Fig. 2 Rear toe adjustment

GEO METRO
(M Car)

NOTE: Refer To The Rear Of This Manual For Vehicle Manufacturer's Special Tool Suppliers.

INDEX OF SERVICE OPERATIONS

NOTE: For Service Operations Not Listed Below, Refer To The Table Of Contents In The Front Of This Manual.

Specifications

GENERAL ENGINE SPECIFICATIONS

Year	Engine Liter/CID	Engine VIN Code ①	Fuel System	Bore & Stroke Inches	Comp. Ratio	Net. H.P. @ RPM	Maximum Torque, Ft. Lbs. @ RPM	Normal Oil Pressure, psi
1992-95	1.0L/3-61	6	EFI	2.91 x 3.03	9.5	55 @ 5700	58 @ 3300	42.7-54②
1995	1.3L/4-79	9	EFI	2.91 x 3.03	9.5	70 @ 5500	74 @ 3500	46.9-61.1③

CID-Cubic Inch Displacement.
EFI—Electronic Port Fuel Injection.

①—The eighth digit of the VIN denotes engine code.

②—At 3000 RPM.
③—At 4000 RPM.

TUNE UP SPECIFICATIONS

Year & Engine/ VIN Code	Spark Plug Gap	Ignition Timing BTDC: Firing Order Fig.	Ignition Timing BTDC: Man. Trans.	Ignition Timing BTDC: Auto. Trans.	Ignition Timing BTDC: Mark Fig.	Curb Idle Speed, RPM: Man. Trans.	Curb Idle Speed, RPM: Auto. Trans.	Fast Idle Speed, RPM: Man. Trans.	Fast Idle Speed, RPM: Auto. Trans.	Fuel Pump Pressure, psi
1992-95										
1.0L/3-61	.041	A	①	①	C	750-850	800-900	③	③	②
1995										
1.3L/4-79	.041	B	①	①	C	750-850	800-900	③	③	②

BTDC: Before Top Dead Center.
①—When checking ignition timing, connect a jumper wire between diagnostic connector terminals D & E. The diagnostic connector is located next to LH strut tower. Refer to vehicle emission control information label for ignition timing setting.

②—At idle, 13-20 psi; ignition switch On, engine Off, 23-30 psi.
③—Controlled by an idle speed control motor.

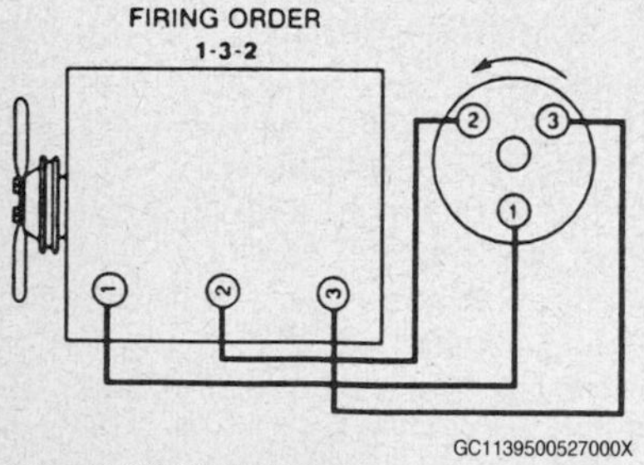
FIRING ORDER
1-3-2
GC1139500527000X

Fig. A

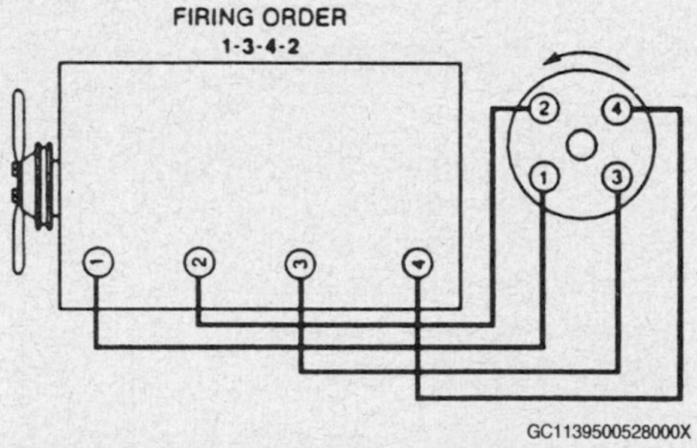
FIRING ORDER
1-3-4-2
GC1139500528000X

Fig. B

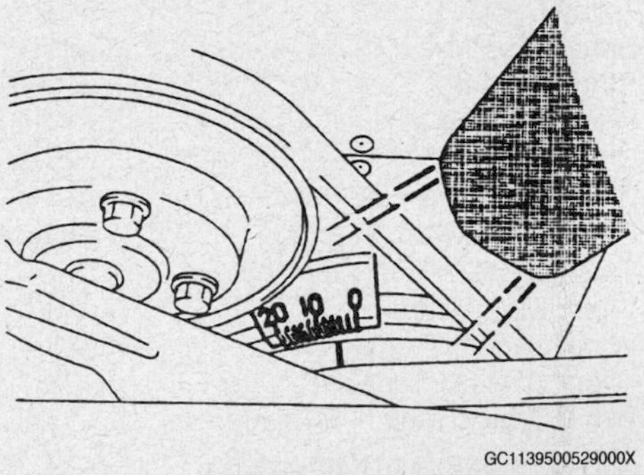
20 10 0
GC1139500529000X

Fig. C

FRONT WHEEL ALIGNMENT SPECIFICATIONS

Year	Models	Caster Angle, Degrees		Camber Angles, Degrees		Total Toe, Degrees	Turning Angle, Degrees	
		Limits	Desired	Limits	Desired		Inner Wheel	Outer Wheel
1992-95	All	+1 to +5	+3	-1 to +1	0	0 to .32	38	32

REAR WHEEL ALIGNMENT SPECIFICATIONS

Year	Camber Angles, Degrees				Total Toe, Degree
	Limits		Desired		
	Left	Right	Left	Right	
1992-95	-1 to +1	-1 to +1	0	0	.0 to .32

COOLING SYSTEM & CAPACITY DATA

Year	Engine	Coolant Capacity, Qts.		Radiator Cap Relief Pressure, psi	Thermostat Open Temp.°F	Fuel Tank Gals.	Engine Oil Qts.	Transaxle	
		Man. Trans.	Auto. Trans					Man. Pints	Auto. Pints ①
1992-95	1.0L/3-61	4.1	4.2	12.8	190	10.6	3.7②	5	③
1995	1.3L/4-79	4.2	5.2	12.8	190	10.6	3.3②	5.1	10.4

①—Make final check w/dipstick.
②—Additional oil may be required to bring oil level to full mark when changing oil filter.
③—Less TCC, 7.4; w/TCC, 10.4 pts.

LUBRICANT DATA

Year	Model	Lubricant Type			
		Transaxle			
		Manual	Automatic	Power Steering	Brake System
1992-95	All	SAE 75W90 (GL-4 Or GL-5)	Dexron II Or Dexron III	Dexron III	DOT 3 Or Delco Supreme II

Electrical

NOTE: On Air Bag Equipped Models, Refer To "Air Bag System Precautions" Located In The Front Of This Manual For System Disarming & Arming Procedures.

INDEX

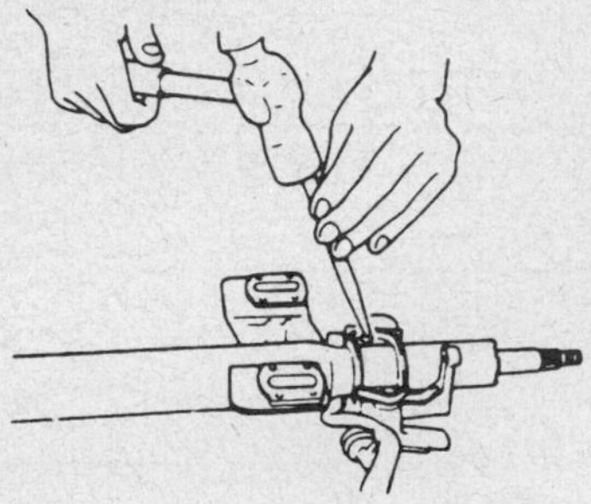

1 CENTER PUNCH (WITH SHARP POINT)
2 IGNITION SWITCH MOUNTING BOLTS
GC9129100029000X

Fig. 1 Ignition switch removal

PRECAUTIONS

AIR BAG SYSTEMS

Refer to "Air Bag System Precautions" in the front of this manual for system disarming and arming procedures.

FUSE PANEL & FLASHER LOCATION

The main fuse panel (alternator and ignition switch fuses and main fuse for junction fuse panel) is located in the engine compartment on the left hand fender apron. The junction fuse panel (fuses for other components) is located under the left hand side of the instrument panel. The air bag fuse panel, if equipped, is located behind the lefthand side of the instrument panel on the junction block support bracket.

The turn signal and hazard flasher is located under the left hand side of the instrument panel near the fuel panel.

RELAY CENTER LOCATION

The relay center is located at the left-hand side of the engine compartment, near the battery.

STARTER

REPLACE

1. Disconnect battery ground cable.
2. Disconnect solenoid lead and battery cable from starter terminals.
3. Remove two starter mounting bolts, then starter.
4. Reverse procedure to install. **Torque** starter mounting bolts to 17 ft. lbs.

DISTRIBUTOR

REPLACE

1. Remove negative battery cable.
2. Disconnect electrical connectors and vacuum lines.
3. Remove distributor cap, then mark rotor position on housing assembly.
4. Mark distributor housing assembly position on engine.
5. Remove distributor flange bolts, then remove distributor from engine.
6. Reverse procedure to install. Ensure alignment marks match.

IGNITION SWITCH

REPLACE

REMOVAL

1. Remove turn signal/dimmer switch as outlined under "Turn Signal Switch, Replace."
2. Disconnect ignition switch and key warning electrical connectors.
3. Lift up floor mat at steering shaft and remove steering column coupling cover.

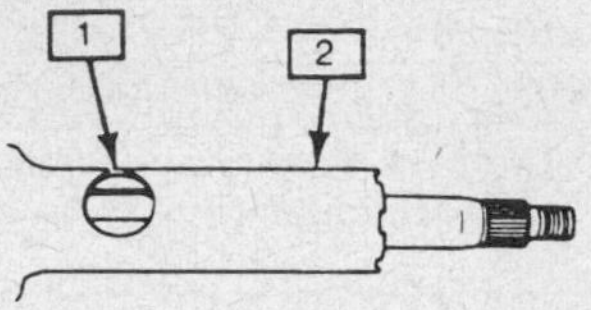

1
2
1 STEERING SHAFT
2 STEERING COLUMN
GC9129100030000X

Fig. 2 Aligning steering shaft & column

4. Remove upper steering shaft coupling bolt, then connect ignition switch and key warning electrical connectors.
5. Remove steering column attaching nuts, then remove column assembly.
6. Using a center punch, loosen and remove steering lock attaching bolts, **Fig. 1.**
7. Place ignition switch in ACC or ON position and remove from steering column.

INSTALLATION

1. Position oblong hole on steering shaft at center of hole in steering column, **Fig. 2.**
2. Place ignition switch in ACC or ON position.
3. Position ignition switch to steering column, then place switch in LOCK position.
4. Align ignition switch hub with oblong hole on steering shaft, then rotate steering shaft to ensure it locks.
5. Install replacement ignition switch attaching bolts. Tighten bolts until bolt head breaks off, **Fig. 3.**
6. Place ignition switch in ON or ACC and check for smooth steering shaft rotation. Also check steering shaft lock for proper operation.

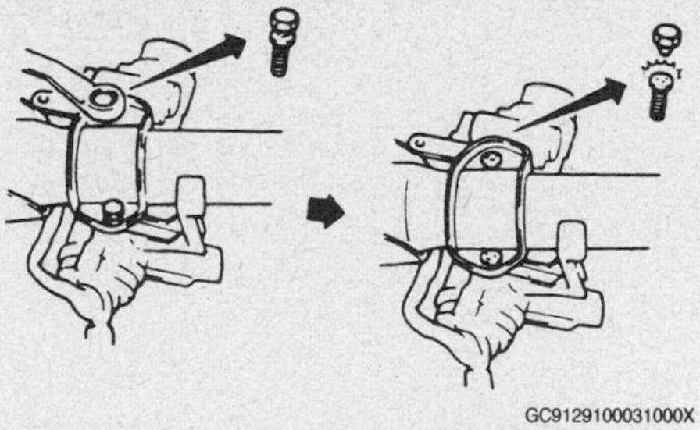
GC9129100031000X

Fig. 3 Ignition switch retaining bolt installation

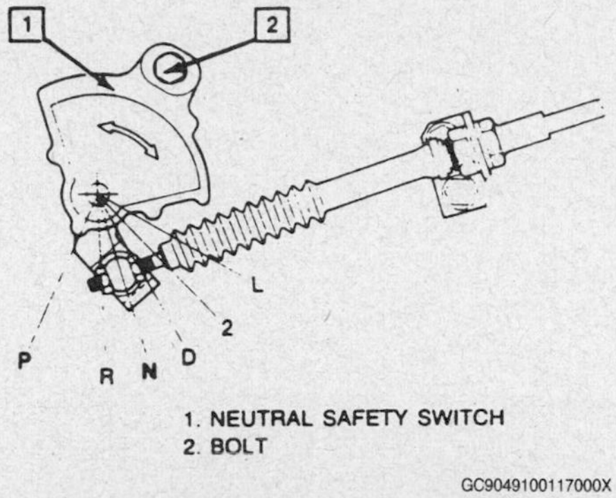
1
2
P
R
N
D
L
2
1. NEUTRAL SAFETY SWITCH
2. BOLT
GC9049100117000X

Fig. 6 Neutral safety switch to manual lever installation

7. Align ignition switch hub to steering shaft oblong hole, rotate shaft to ensure steering shaft is locked, **Fig. 4.**
8. Position steering column mounting brackets to mounting studs, then install and **torque** attaching nuts to 10 ft. lbs.
9. Install steering shaft coupling bolt and **torque** to 18 ft. lbs.
10. Install steering shaft coupling cover.
11. Install turn signal/dimmer switch as outlined under "Turn Signal Switch, Replace."

CLUTCH START SWITCH

ADJUST

1. Disconnect battery ground cable.
2. Disconnect electrical connector at clutch start switch.
3. Loosen switch locknut, then back off switch adjustment.
4. Connect an ohmmeter between switch terminals.
5. Position clutch pedal at approximately .6 to 1.2 inches from floor and hold.
6. Rotate switch into bracket until ohmmeter just indicates continuity, then tighten locknut. **Torque** locknut to 10 ft. lbs.
7. Connect switch electrical connector and battery ground cable.

NEUTRAL SAFETY SWITCH

REPLACE

1. Disconnect battery ground cable.
2. Remove attaching bolt, then remove neutral safety switch from transaxle.
3. Place shift lever in Neutral position.
4. Using a screwdriver, position neutral safety switch a shown in **Fig. 5.**

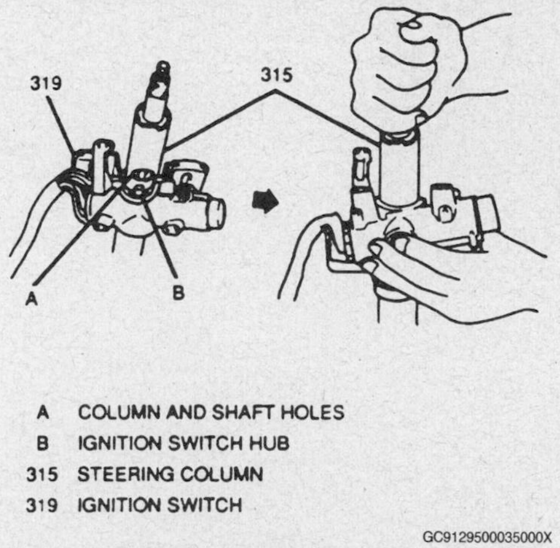
319
315
A
B
A COLUMN AND SHAFT HOLES
B IGNITION SWITCH HUB
315 STEERING COLUMN
319 IGNITION SWITCH
GC9129500035000X

Fig. 4 Ignition switch hub to steering shaft alignment

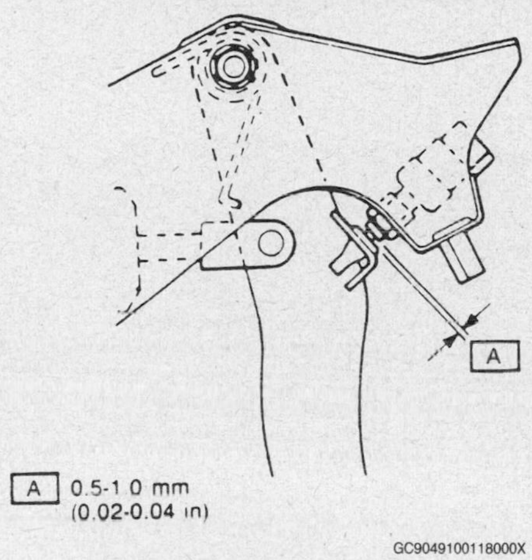
A
A 0.5-1.0 mm (0.02-0.04 in)
GC9049100118000X

Fig. 7 Stop lamp switch adjustment

Switch should click at this position.

5. Install neutral safety switch to manual shift shaft and loosely install attaching bolt.
6. Rotate switch slightly until a click is heard, then **torque** attaching bolt to 9.5-16.5 ft. lbs., **Fig. 6.**
7. Connect electrical connector to switch and battery ground cable to battery, then check switch for proper operation.

HEADLAMP SWITCH

REPLACE

1. Disconnect battery ground cable.
2. Remove steering column trim panel.
3. Lower steering column.
4. Remove instrument cluster bezel screws and pull bezel out.
5. Remove headlamp switch from bezel.
6. Remove cluster to instrument panel attaching screws.
7. Pull cluster rearward to reach and disconnect headlamp switch connector.
8. Remove headlamp switch.
9. Reverse procedure to install.

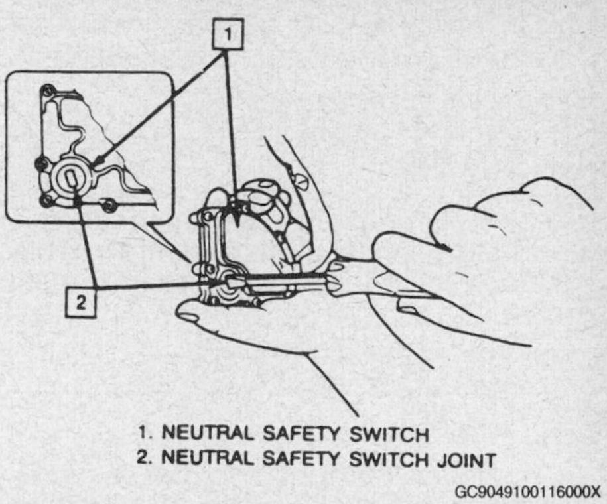
1
2
1. NEUTRAL SAFETY SWITCH
2. NEUTRAL SAFETY SWITCH JOINT
GC9049100116000X

Fig. 5 Positioning neutral safety switch

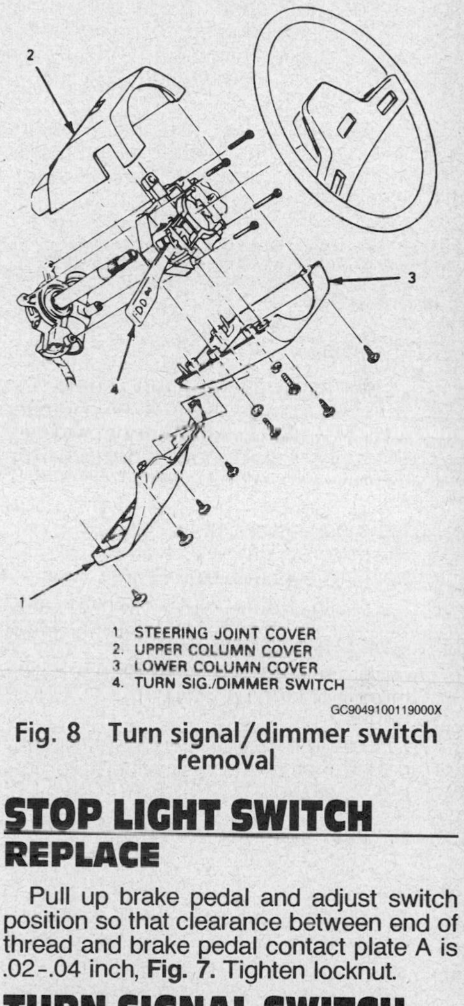
2
3
4
1
1. STEERING JOINT COVER
2. UPPER COLUMN COVER
3. LOWER COLUMN COVER
4. TURN SIG./DIMMER SWITCH
GC9049100119000X

Fig. 8 Turn signal/dimmer switch removal

STOP LIGHT SWITCH

REPLACE

Pull up brake pedal and adjust switch position so that clearance between end of thread and brake pedal contact plate A is .02-.04 inch, **Fig. 7.** Tighten locknut.

TURN SIGNAL SWITCH

REPLACE

1. **On models with air bag,** disarm air bag as outlined under "Precautions."
2. **On all models,** remove steering wheel, refer to "Steering Wheel, Replace."
3. Remove steering column covers, **Fig. 8.**
4. Disconnect turn signal/dimmer switch electrical connector.
5. Remove turn signal/dimmer switch attaching screws, then remove switch, **Fig. 8.**
6. Reverse procedure to install.

7. **On models with air bag,** rearm air bag as outlined under "Precautions."

DIMMER SWITCH

REPLACE

Replace dimmer switch as an assembly with the turn signal switch. Refer to "Turn Signal Switch, Replace" for replacement procedure.

STEERING WHEEL

REPLACE

1. Remove air bag inflator module as described in the "Passive Restraints" section.
2. **On all models,** remove steering wheel nut, then place alignment marks on steering shaft and wheel for use during installation.
3. Remove steering wheel using a suitable puller tool.
4. Reverse procedure to install. When installing steering wheel, align marks made during removal. **Torque** steering wheel nut to 24 ft. lbs.

INSTRUMENT CLUSTER

REPLACE

1992–94

1. Disconnect battery ground cable.
2. Remove four screws attaching cluster switch panel to instrument panel.
3. Disconnect electrical connectors from switches, then pull instrument cluster bezel and switch panel slightly outward as an assembly.
4. Remove six screws attaching cluster bezel to switch panel.
5. Remove front wiper switch and headlamp and hazard warning lamp switch from switch panel.
6. Remove four instrument cluster housing attaching screws from switch housing.
7. Disconnect instrument cluster electrical connectors and speedometer cable.
8. Remove instrument cluster, **Fig. 9.**
9. Reverse procedure to install.

1995

1. Disconnect battery ground cable.
2. Remove cluster lower cover two attaching screws and covers.
3. Remove gauge cluster bezel four attaching screws, then bezel.
4. Depress speedometer plastic tabs to disconnect cable.
5. Remove cluster four attaching screw.
6. Disconnect cluster electrical connectors, then remove cluster.
7. Reverse procedure to install.

RADIO

REPLACE

1992–94

1. Disconnect battery ground cable.
2. Remove three screws and center console bezel.

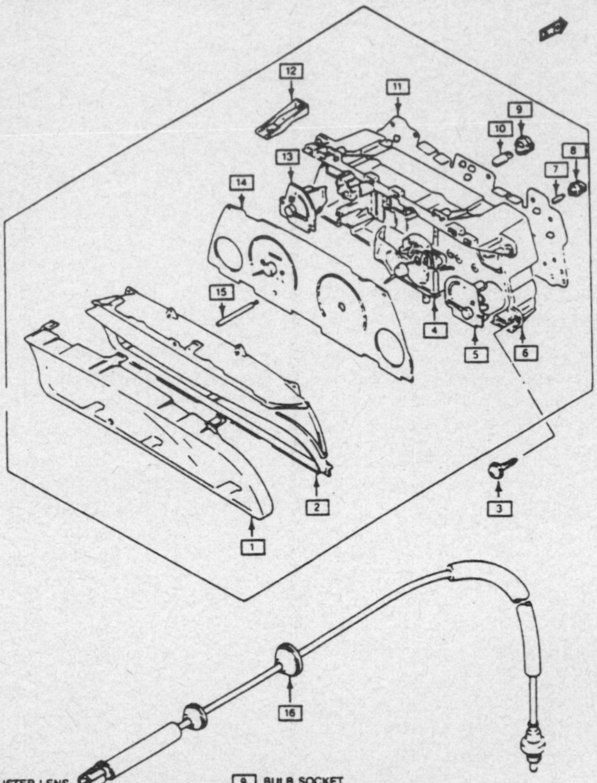

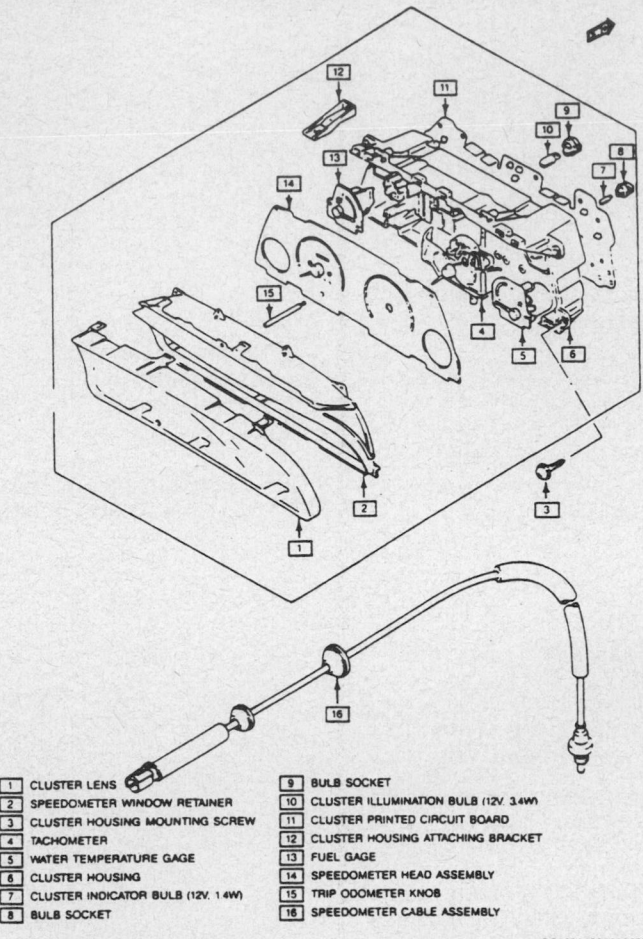

1 CLUSTER LENS	9 BULB SOCKET
2 SPEEDOMETER WINDOW RETAINER	10 CLUSTER ILLUMINATION BULB (12V, 3.4W)
3 CLUSTER HOUSING MOUNTING SCREW	11 CLUSTER PRINTED CIRCUIT BOARD
4 TACHOMETER	12 CLUSTER HOUSING ATTACHING BRACKET
5 WATER TEMPERATURE GAGE	13 FUEL GAGE
6 CLUSTER HOUSING	14 SPEEDOMETER HEAD ASSEMBLY
7 CLUSTER INDICATOR BULB (12V, 1.4W)	15 TRIP ODOMETER KNOB
8 BULB SOCKET	16 SPEEDOMETER CABLE ASSEMBLY

GC9099100239000X

Fig. 9 Instrument cluster assembly. 1992–94

3. Remove four screws from radio face.
4. Remove one bolt at rear of radio.
5. Pull radio out of instrument panel, then disconnect electrical and antenna connections before completely removing radio from vehicle.
6. Reverse procedure to install.

1995

1. Disconnect battery ground cable.
2. Through glove compartment, disconnect radio and antenna electrical connector.
3. Pull ashtray outward, push downward, then pull ashtray rearward to remove.
4. Remove instrument panel center trim bezel four attaching screws, then bezel.
5. Through instrument panel ashtray cutout, remove one cross recess screw below rear of radio.
6. Remove radio four attaching screws, then pull radio and mounting brackets rearward.
7. Remove radio mounting bracket to radio five attaching screws, if required, then radio.
8. Reverse procedure to install.

WIPER MOTOR

REPLACE

FRONT

1. Disconnect battery ground cable.
2. Disconnect connect electrical connector from wiper motor.
3. Remove three wiper motor attaching screws, then remove nut and washer attaching wiper linkage to motor, **Fig. 10.**
4. Remove wiper motor from vehicle.
5. Reverse procedure to install.

REAR

1992–94

1. Disconnect battery ground cable.
2. Remove left and right hand speaker grilles from rear lid, if equipped.
3. Disconnect electrical connector from rear speakers, then remove speakers, if equipped.
4. Remove nine push pins from lid access panel, then remove panel.
5. Disconnect wiper motor electrical connector.
6. Remove wiper motor ground screw, then remove wiper linkage arm to wiper motor attaching nut, **Fig. 11.**
7. Remove three wiper motor attaching screws, then remove wiper motor.
8. Reverse procedure to install.

1995

1. Disconnect battery ground cable.
2. Disconnect hatchback inner door trim panel clips, then remove panel.
3. Disconnect wiper motor electrical connector.

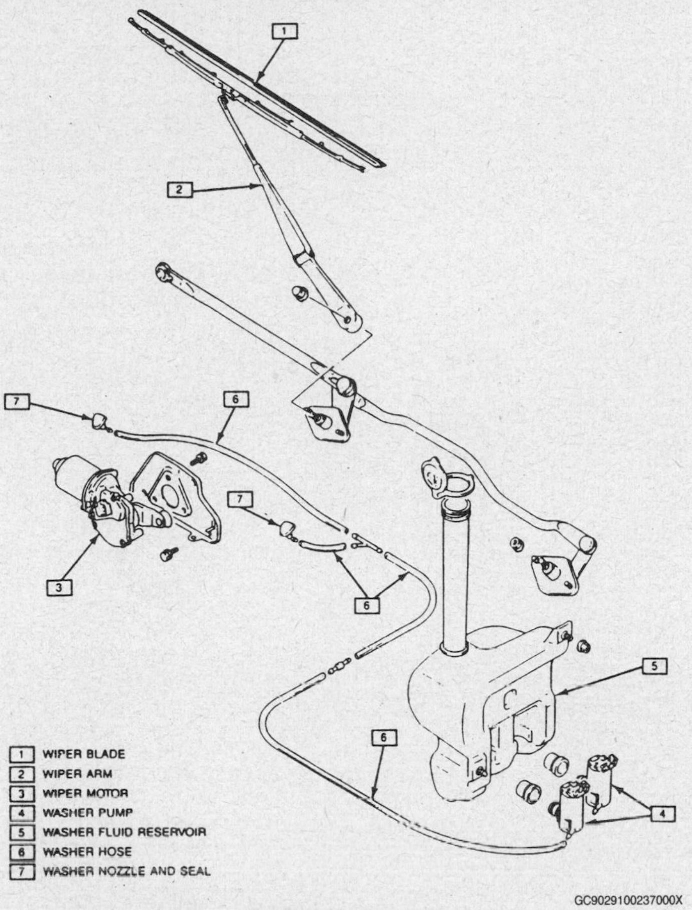
1 WIPER BLADE
2 WIPER ARM
3 WIPER MOTOR
4 WASHER PUMP
5 WASHER FLUID RESERVOIR
6 WASHER HOSE
7 WASHER NOZZLE AND SEAL
GC9029100237000X

Fig. 10 Front windshield wiper/washer motor & linkage assembly

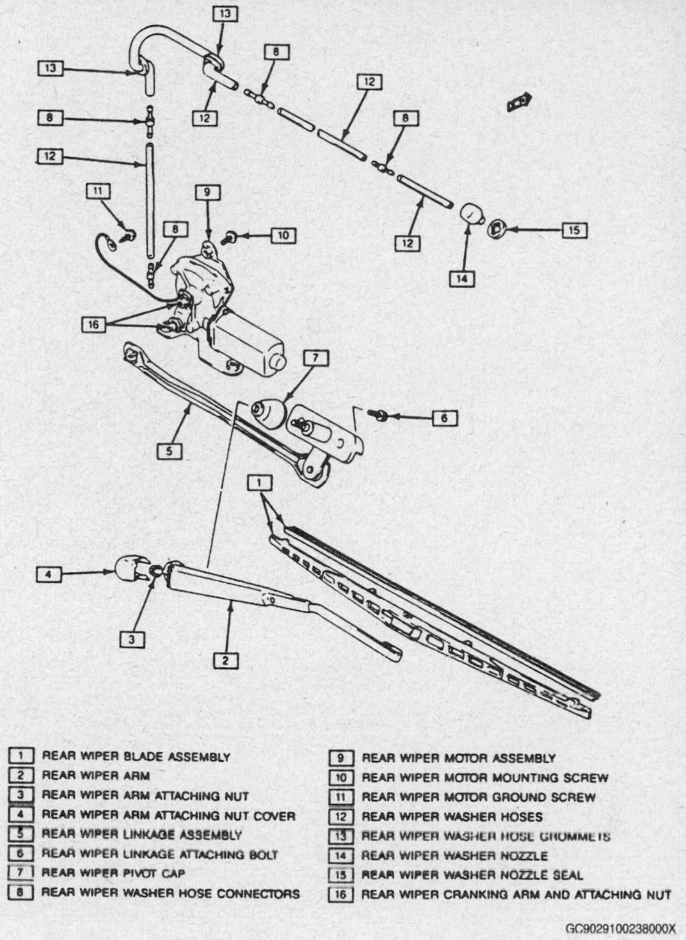
1 REAR WIPER BLADE ASSEMBLY
2 REAR WIPER ARM
3 REAR WIPER ARM ATTACHING NUT
4 REAR WIPER ARM ATTACHING NUT COVER
5 REAR WIPER LINKAGE ASSEMBLY
6 REAR WIPER LINKAGE ATTACHING BOLT
7 REAR WIPER PIVOT CAP
8 REAR WIPER WASHER HOSE CONNECTORS
9 REAR WIPER MOTOR ASSEMBLY
10 REAR WIPER MOTOR MOUNTING SCREW
11 REAR WIPER MOTOR GROUND SCREW
12 REAR WIPER WASHER HOSES
13 REAR WIPER WASHER HOSE GROMMETS
14 REAR WIPER WASHER NOZZLE
15 REAR WIPER WASHER NOZZLE SEAL
16 REAR WIPER CRANKING ARM AND ATTACHING NUT
GC9029100238000X

Fig. 11 Rear windshield wiper/washer motor & linkage assembly. 1992–94

4. Remove wiper motor ground screw, Fig. 12.
5. Remove three wiper motor attaching nuts.
6. Disconnect wiper linkage, then remove wiper motor.
7. Reverse procedure to install. **Torque** wiper motor attaching bolts 15 ft. lbs.

WIPER SWITCH
REPLACE
FRONT

1. Disconnect battery ground cable.
2. Remove steering column trim panel.
3. Lower steering column.
4. Remove instrument cluster bezel screws and pull bezel out.
5. Remove wiper switch from bezel.
6. Remove cluster to instrument panel attaching screws.
7. Pull cluster rearward to reach and disconnect wiper switch connector.
8. Remove wiper switch.
9. Reverse procedure to install.

REAR

1. Disconnect battery ground cable.
2. Remove lower steering column trim cover.
3. Remove both steering column mounting nuts and lower steering column.
4. Remove instrument panel cluster trim bezel.
5. Remove rear wiper switch from bezel.
6. Reverse procedure to install.

WIPER TRANSMISSION
REPLACE
FRONT
1992–94

1. Disconnect battery ground cable.
2. Remove both wiper arm and blade assemblies.
3. Remove five push pins and right hand cowl panel.
4. Remove three push pins and left hand cowl panel.
5. Remove front wiper motor from vehicle as outlined under "Wiper Motor, Replace."
6. Remove four nuts attaching wiper motor linkage, then remove wiper motor linkage through left hand cowl cover opening, **Fig. 10.**
7. Reverse procedure to install.

1995

1. Disconnect battery ground cable.
2. Inspect wiper arms, for proper installation location.
3. Remove wiper arm cover and attaching nut.
4. Disconnect 11 cowl vent grill plastic attaching clips, then remove grill.
5. Remove six wiper transmission to cowl attaching nuts.
6. Disconnect wiper motor electrical connector, then remove three motor attaching bolts, pull motor rearward from bulkhead.
7. Pry wiper transmission from motor crank arm, do not disconnect crank arm from motor.
8. Remove wiper motor assembly, then transmission.
9. Reverse procedure to install. **Torque** transmission attaching nuts to 11 ft. lbs.

REAR
1992–94

1. Disconnect battery ground cable.
2. Remove wiper blade and arm assembly, **Fig. 11.**
3. Remove rear wiper motor as outlined under "Wiper Motor, Replace."
4. Remove two nuts attaching wiper linkage to rear lid.
5. Remove linkage trough left hand side of rear lid.
6. Reverse procedure to install.

1995

1. Disconnect battery ground cable.
2. Inspect wiper arms, for proper installation location.

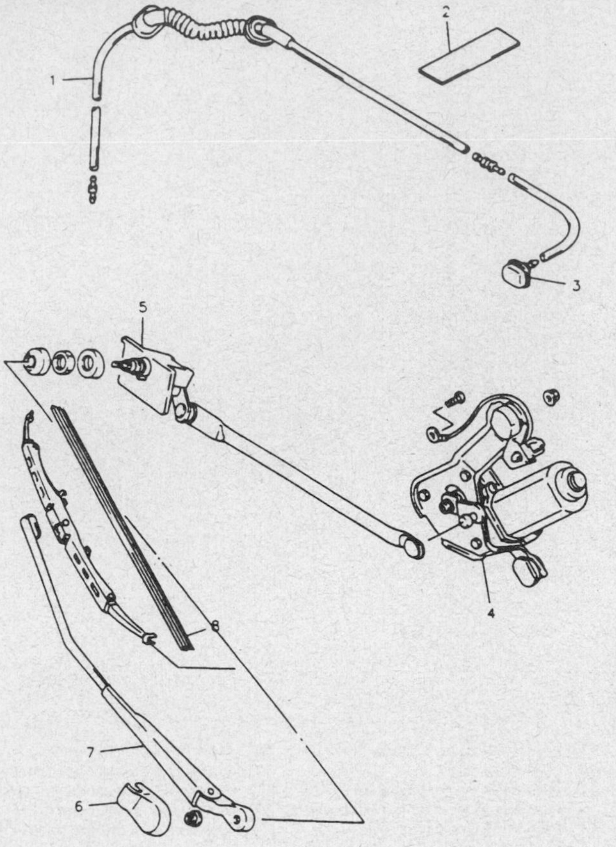
1
2
3
4
5
6
7
8

1 REAR WASHER HOSE
2 REAR WASHER HOSE COVER
3 REAR WASHER NOZZLE
4 REAR WIPER MOTOR
5 REAR WIPER LINKAGE
6 REAR WIPER NUT COVER
7 REAR WIPER ARM
8 REAR WIPER BLADE

GC9029500248000X

Fig. 12 Rear windshield wiper motor & linkage assembly. 1995

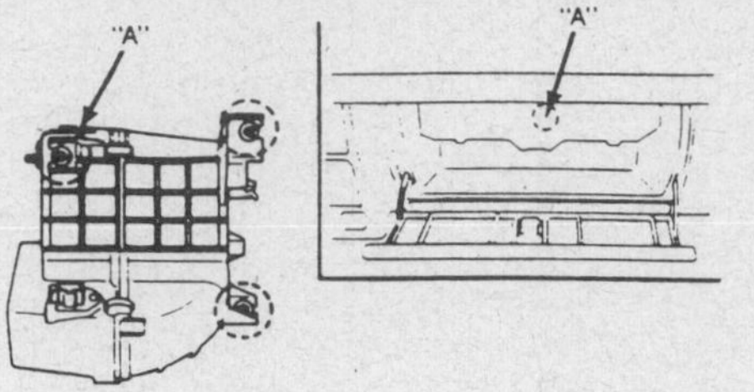
"A"
"A"

GC7029100068000X

Fig. 13 Blower motor case attaching screw locations

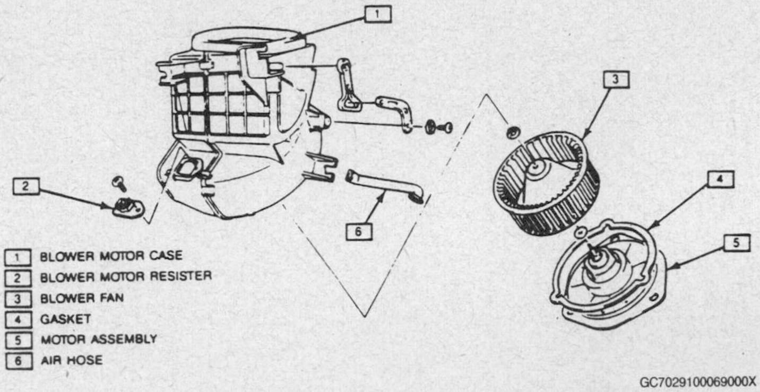
1 BLOWER MOTOR CASE
2 BLOWER MOTOR RESISTER
3 BLOWER FAN
4 GASKET
5 MOTOR ASSEMBLY
6 AIR HOSE

GC7029100069000X

Fig. 14 Blower motor & case assembly

3. Lift wiper arm nut plastic cover, then remove arm attaching nut, **Fig. 12.**
4. Remove wiper arm from transmission.
5. Remove hatchback door inner trim panel.
6. Disconnect wiper motor electrical connector.
7. Remove motor ground lead attaching screw.
8. Remove motor three attaching nuts, then separate motor from door.
9. Pry transmission from motor crank arm and wiper arm base, then slide transmission rearward to remove.
10. Remove wiper arm base from door, do not disconnect crank arm from motor.
11. Reverse procedure to install. **Torque** wiper arm nut to 15 ft. lbs.

BLOWER MOTOR
REPLACE

1. Disconnect battery ground cable.
2. **On 1992-94 models,** proceed as follows:
   a. Remove two screws attaching glove compartment striker to instrument panel.
   b. Remove one screw attaching rear of glove compartment upper panel, then remove upper panel.
3. **On 1995 models,** proceed as follows:
   a. Depress glove compartment stopper, then pull rearward.
   b. Remove glove compartment to instrument panel attaching screws, remove glove compartment.
   c. Remove ECM three attaching screws, disconnect electrical connectors, then remove ECM.
4. **On all models,** disconnect blower motor and blower resistor electrical connectors.
5. Disconnect fresh air control cable from blower motor housing.
6. Remove three blower motor housing attaching bolt, then remove blower motor housing, **Fig. 13.**
7. Remove air hose, then remove three attaching screws and separate blower motor from housing, **Fig. 14.**
8. Reverse procedure to install.

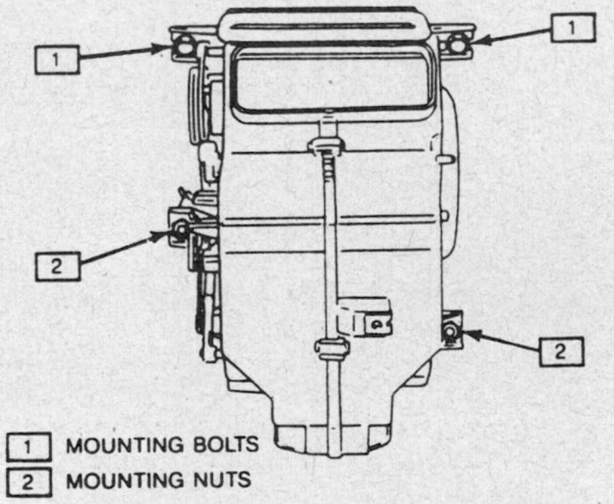
1
1
2
2
1 MOUNTING BOLTS
2 MOUNTING NUTS

GC7029100071000X

Fig. 15 Heater case attaching bolt & nut locations

HEATER CORE
REPLACE

1. Disconnect battery ground cable
2. Remove instrument panel as outlined under "Dash Panel Service"
3. Drain coolant into suitable container.
4. Remove heater core clamps and hoses, through engine compartment.
5. **On 1992-94 models,** disconnect temperature and mode control cables from heater case.
6. **On all models,** remove blower case to heater case air duct.
7. Remove heater case attaching nuts and bolts, **Fig. 15.** then remove case.

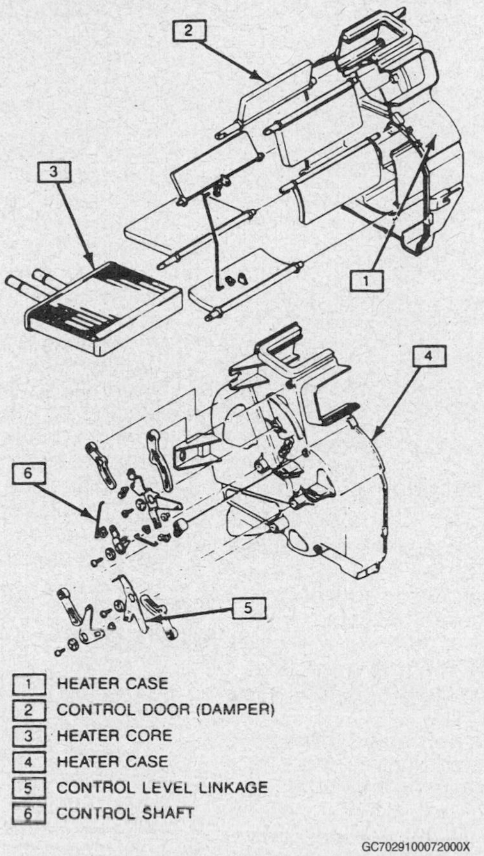
1 HEATER CASE
2 CONTROL DOOR (DAMPER)
3 HEATER CORE
4 HEATER CASE
5 CONTROL LEVEL LINKAGE
6 CONTROL SHAFT
GC7029100072000X

Fig. 16 Exploded view of heater case assembly

8. Remove heater case clip and two attaching screws, then separate case halves, **Fig. 16.**
9. Remove heater core from case.
10. Reverse procedure to install. **Torque** heater case attaching nuts and bolts to 89 inch lbs.

EVAPORATOR CORE
REPLACE

1. Disconnect battery ground cable.
2. Discharge and recover refrigerant as outlined under "Air Conditioning."
3. Remove blower motor case as outlined under "Blower Motor, Replace."
4. Disconnect A/C amplifier and evaporator thermistor electrical connectors.
5. Disconnect and cap evaporator case refrigerant inlet and outlet pipes.
6. Remove evaporator case drain hose.
7. Remove evaporator case two attaching bolts and one nut, then the case.
8. Depress A/C amplifier two lower locking tabs, then slide amplifier upward to remove.
9. Disengage evaporator case clips, to separate case halves.
10. Remove evaporator core from case.
11. Reverse procedure to install. **Torque** evaporator case bolts to 89 inch lbs., inlet pipe nut to 26 ft. lbs. and outlet pipe nut to 33 ft. lbs.

1.0L/3–61 Engine

NOTE: On Air Bag Equipped Models, Refer To "Air Bag System Precautions" Located In The Front Of This Manual For System Disarming & Arming Procedures.

INDEX

PRECAUTIONS
AIR BAG SYSTEMS

Refer to "Air Bag System Precautions" in the front of this manual for system disarming and arming procedures.

FUEL SYSTEM PRESSURE RELIEF

1. Loosen fuel filler cap to relieve fuel tank pressure
2. Remove fuel pump relay from relay box located at the lefthand front of the engine compartment, next to the battery,**Fig. 1.**
3. Crank engine and allow to stall. Crank engine for several seconds more to ensure relief of any remaining fuel.
4. Remove battery ground cable.

ENGINE MOUNT

REPLACE

FRONT

1. Disconnect battery ground cable.
2. Remove engine mount nut, then raise and support vehicle.
3. Support engine using an engine support fixture.
4. Remove engine mount and frame bracket, then remove mount from bracket.
5. Reverse procedure to install.

REAR

1. Disconnect battery ground cable.
2. Remove engine mount nut, then raise and support vehicle.
3. Remove nut retaining mount to body bracket.
4. Support engine using an engine support fixture.
5. Remove frame bracket, then remove mount.
6. Reverse procedure to install.

ENGINE

REPLACE

1. Relieve fuel system pressure as outlined under "Precautions".
2. Disconnect battery ground cable.
3. Disconnect windshield washer hose, then remove hood.
4. Remove air cleaner assembly.
5. Drain cooling system, then remove radiator and engine cooling fan.
6. Disconnect high tension lead from ignition coil.
7. Disconnect electrical connector from distributor.
8. Disconnect electrical connectors from coolant temperature sender, engine coolant temperature sensor, engine cooling fan switch and engine oil pressure sender.
9. Disconnect electrical connector from EGR vacuum switching valve.
10. Disconnect electrical connectors from idle speed control valve, throttle position switch, fuel injector and pressure sensor.
11. Disconnect electrical connectors and wiring from alternator and starter motor.
12. Disconnect electrical connector from oxygen sensor.
13. Disconnect battery ground cable from transaxle.
14. **On models with manual transaxle,** disconnect electrical connector from back-up lamp switch.
15. **On models with automatic transaxle,** disconnect electrical connectors from neutral safety switch, speed sensor and direct clutch and second brake solenoids.
16. **On all models,** disconnect intake manifold to power brake unit vacuum hose.
17. Disconnect evaporative emission canister hoses from intake manifold and tube connections.

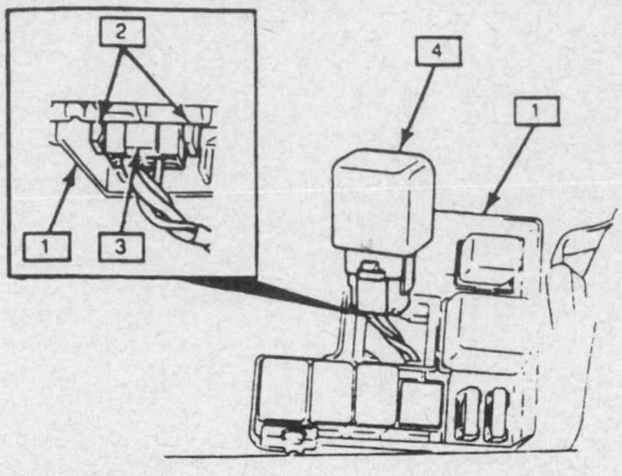

1
2
3
4

1 MAIN FUSE BOX
2 LOCK TABS
3 FUEL PUMP RELAY ELECTRICAL CONNECTOR
4 FUEL PUMP RELAY

GC1029102746000X

Fig. 1 Fuel pump relay location

18. Disconnect fuel hoses from throttle body.
19. Disconnect heater hoses from engine.
20. Disconnect accelerator cable from throttle body.
21. **On models with manual transaxle,** disconnect clutch cable from fork and housing.
22. **On models with automatic transaxle,** disconnect shift control and fluid pressure control cables from transaxle.
23. **On all models,** disconnect speedometer cable from transaxle.
24. Raise and support vehicle, then disconnect exhaust pipe from exhaust manifold.
25. Drain engine crankcase, then drain fluid from transaxle.
26. **On models with manual transaxle,** disconnect control shaft and extension rod from transaxle.
27. **On all models,** separate drive axles from transaxle. Support drive axles from chassis using wire.
28. **On models with automatic transaxle,** remove engine torque rod bracket from transaxle.
29. Lower vehicle and install an engine lifting fixture.
30. Remove engine and transaxle mounting bolts, then remove engine and transaxle assembly from vehicle.
31. Reverse procedure to install.

INTAKE MANIFOLD

REPLACE

1. Relieve fuel system pressure as outlined under "Precautions".
2. Disconnect battery ground cable.
3. Drain cooling system, then remove air cleaner assembly.
4. Disconnect electrical connectors from coolant temperature sender, engine and coolant temperature sensor.
5. Disconnect electrical connector from EGR vacuum switching valve.
6. Disconnect electrical connectors from idle speed control valve, throttle position switch and fuel injector.
7. Disconnect ground wires from intake manifold.
8. Disconnect fuel hoses from throttle body.
9. Disconnect coolant hoses from intake manifold.
10. Disconnect MAP sensor hose from intake manifold.
11. Disconnect evaporative emission hoses from intake manifold and tube.
12. Disconnect power brake unit vacuum hose from intake manifold.
13. Disconnect PCV valve hose from cylinder head cover.
14. Disconnect accelerator cable from throttle body.
15. Disconnect all other electrical connectors and hoses to permit intake manifold and throttle body removal.
16. Remove intake manifold to cylinder head attaching nuts and bolts, then remove intake manifold and throttle body as an assembly.
17. Reverse procedure to Install.

EXHAUST MANIFOLD

REPLACE

1. Disconnect battery ground cable.
2. Disconnect oxygen sensor electrical connector, then release wiring harness from clamps.
3. Disconnect exhaust pipe from exhaust manifold.
4. Remove exhaust manifold attaching bolts and nuts, then remove exhaust manifold from cylinder head.
5. Reverse procedure to install.

CYLINDER HEAD

REPLACE

1. Relieve fuel system pressure as outlined under "Precautions".
2. Disconnect battery ground cable.
3. Drain cooling system, then remove air cleaner assembly.
4. Disconnect coil wire from distributor cap.
5. Disconnect electrical connector from distributor.
6. Disconnect electrical connectors from coolant temperature sender, engine coolant temperature sensor and engine cooling fan switch.
7. Disconnect electrical connector from EGR vacuum switching valve.
8. Disconnect electrical connectors from idle speed control valve, throttle position switch and fuel injector.
9. Disconnect oxygen sensor electrical connector, then detach wiring harness from clamps.
10. Disconnect ground wires from intake manifold.
11. Disconnect heater hose from intake manifold and radiator hose from thermostat housing.
12. Disconnect fuel hoses from throttle body.
13. Disconnect MAP sensor hose from intake manifold.
14. Disconnect evaporative emission hoses from intake manifold and tube.
15. Disconnect power brake unit vacuum hose from intake manifold.

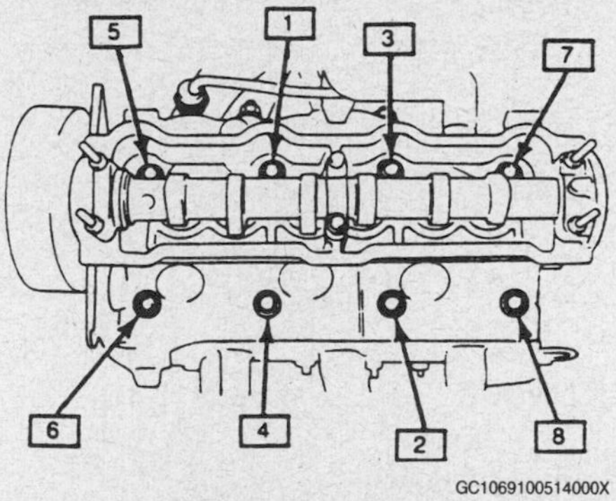
5
1
3
7
6
4
2
8
GC1069100514000X

Fig. 2 Cylinder head bolt tightening sequence

16. Disconnect accelerator cable from throttle body.
17. Raise and support vehicle, then disconnect exhaust pipe from exhaust manifold.
18. Lower vehicle, then remove cylinder head cover.
19. Remove cylinder head attaching bolts, then remove cylinder head.
20. Reverse procedure to install. Tighten cylinder head bolts to specifications in sequence shown in **Fig. 2.**

VALVE ARRANGEMENT

FRONT TO REAR

1.0L/3-61 .... I-E-I-E-I-E

VALVE ADJUSTMENT

These engines are equipped with hydraulic valve lash adjusters and no adjustment is required.

VALVE GUIDES

Valves and valve guides are available in standard size only. The Valve guide can be driven from cylinder bore using Valve Guide Remover tool No. J-37968-1 or equivalent. The valve guide should be driven from the combustion chamber side of the cylinder head out through the valve spring side.

The cylinder head valve guide bore should be reamed with an 11 mm reamer prior to valve guide installation. Heat cylinder head to 176 to 212°F, then drive valve guide into cylinder head bore using Valve Guide Remover tool No. J-37968-1 and Valve Guide Installer tool No. J-37968-2 or equivalent. Valve guide should be driven in until tool contacts cylinder head. Valve guide protrusion should be .45 inch from cylinder head surface. After installation, ream valve guide with a 5.5 mm reamer.

HYDRAULIC VALVE LASH ADJUSTER SERVICE

Hydraulic valve lash adjusters should not be disassembled.

1. Remove camshaft as outlined under "Camshaft, Replace."
2. Remove hydraulic valve lash adjusters from cylinder head, **Fig. 3.**

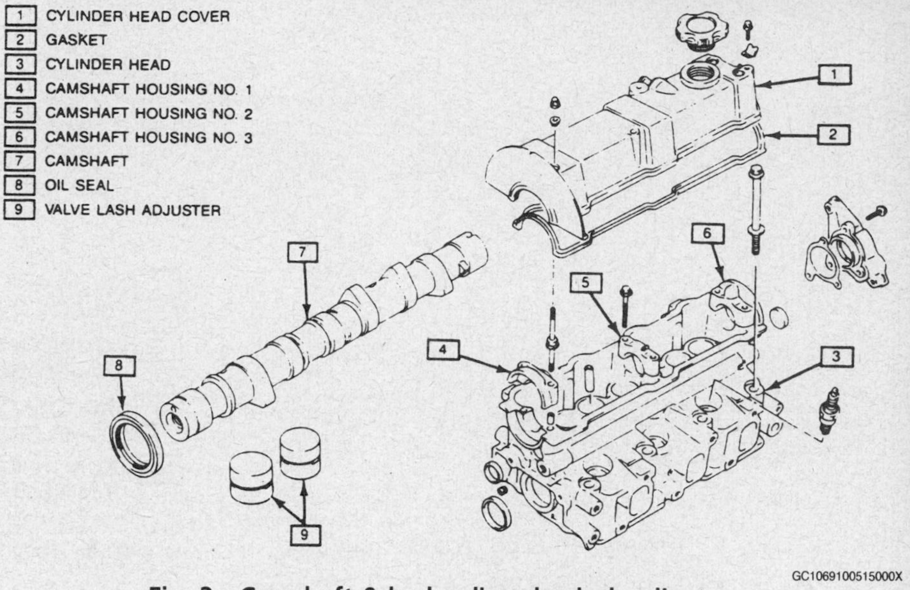
1 CYLINDER HEAD COVER
2 GASKET
3 CYLINDER HEAD
4 CAMSHAFT HOUSING NO. 1
5 CAMSHAFT HOUSING NO. 2
6 CAMSHAFT HOUSING NO. 3
7 CAMSHAFT
8 OIL SEAL
9 VALVE LASH ADJUSTER
GC1069100515000X

Fig. 3 Camshaft & hydraulic valve lash adjusters

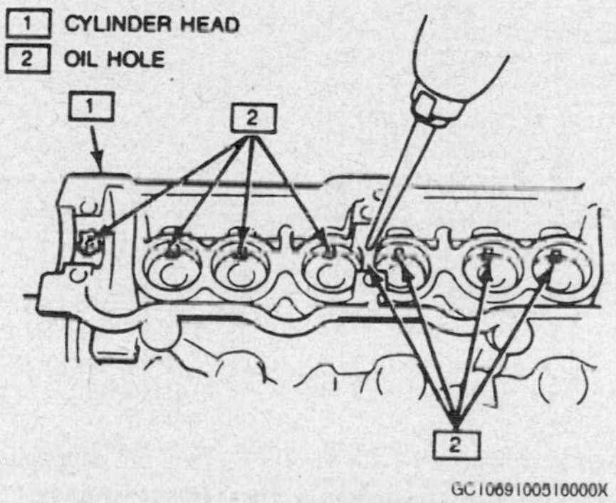
1 CYLINDER HEAD
2 OIL HOLE
GC1069100516000X

Fig. 4 Applying engine oil to camshaft oil holes

3. Check hydraulic valve lash adjusters for wear and damage and replace as necessary.
4. Using a micrometer, measure outside diameter of hydraulic valve lash adjuster. Outside diameter should be 1.2188 to 1.2194 inches.
5. Measure hydraulic valve lash adjuster bore in cylinder head. Bore diameter should be 1.2205 to 1.2214 inches.
6. To determine hydraulic valve lash adjuster to cylinder head bore clearance, subtract adjuster outside diameter from cylinder head adjuster bore diameter. Adjuster to bore clearance should be .0010 to .0025 inch. If clearance is greater than .0059 inch, replace adjuster or cylinder head as necessary.
7. Place valve lash adjuster in clean engine oil prior to installation. Also pour engine oil through camshaft journal oil holes, until oil is emitted from hydraulic valve lash adjuster oil holes, **Fig. 4.**
8. Apply engine oil to valve lash adjuster, then position adjuster in cylinder head bore and install camshaft.

TIMING BELT

REPLACE

REMOVAL

1. Disconnect battery ground cable, then raise and support vehicle.
2. Remove fender apron extension from right hand side of vehicle.
3. Remove water pump drive belt, then remove water pump pulley.
4. Remove four attaching bolts and crankshaft pulley.
5. Remove outer timing belt cover, **Fig. 5.**
6. Align camshaft and crankshaft timing marks, **Fig. 6.**
7. Remove timing belt tensioner, tensioner plate, spring and damper.
8. Remove timing belt.

INSPECTION

Check timing belt for wear and cracks and replace as necessary. Check timing belt tensioner for smoothness of rotation and replace as necessary.

INSTALLATION

1. Position lug on tensioner plate to hole in tensioner, **Fig. 7.**
2. Position tensioner and tensioner plate to engine, then install and hand tighten attaching bolt. Ensure that tensioner and tensioner plate move in the same direction, **Fig. 8.** If movement is not as indicated, remove tensioner and reinsert tensioner plate lug into tensioner.
3. Ensure camshaft and crankshaft timing marks are aligned, **Fig. 6.**
4. With tensioner plate pushed upward, install timing belt over camshaft and crankshaft pulleys. **Arrow on timing belt should face toward direction of crankshaft rotation. When installing timing belt, keep drive side of belt free of slack.**
5. Install tensioner spring and damper, then hand tighten tensioner stud.

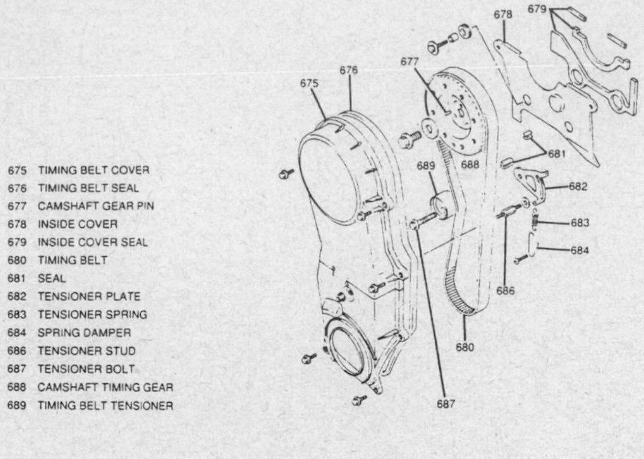
675 TIMING BELT COVER
676 TIMING BELT SEAL
677 CAMSHAFT GEAR PIN
678 INSIDE COVER
679 INSIDE COVER SEAL
680 TIMING BELT
681 SEAL
682 TENSIONER PLATE
683 TENSIONER SPRING
684 SPRING DAMPER
686 TENSIONER STUD
687 TENSIONER BOLT
688 CAMSHAFT TIMING GEAR
689 TIMING BELT TENSIONER

GC1069100517000X

Fig. 5 Timing belt & cover assembly

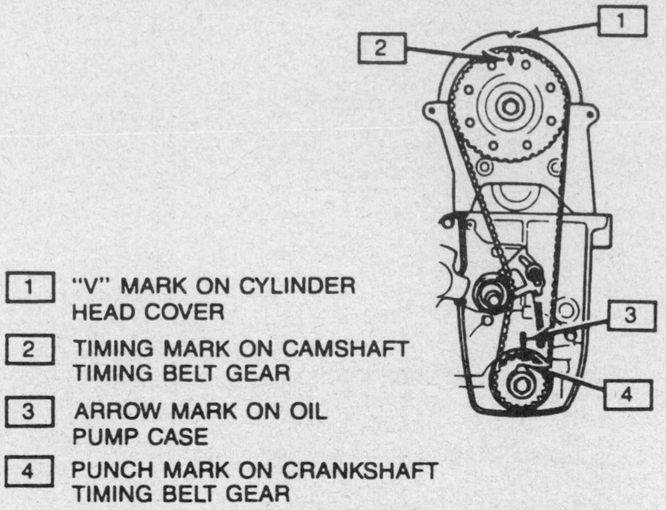
1 "V" MARK ON CYLINDER HEAD COVER
2 TIMING MARK ON CAMSHAFT TIMING BELT GEAR
3 ARROW MARK ON OIL PUMP CASE
4 PUNCH MARK ON CRANKSHAFT TIMING BELT GEAR

GC1069100518000X

Fig. 6 Aligning camshaft & crankshaft sprocket timing marks

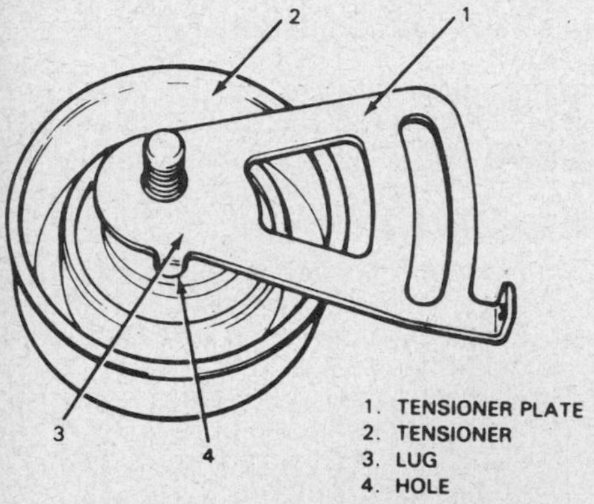
1. TENSIONER PLATE
2. TENSIONER
3. LUG
4. HOLE

GC1069100519000X

Fig. 7 Tensioner assembly

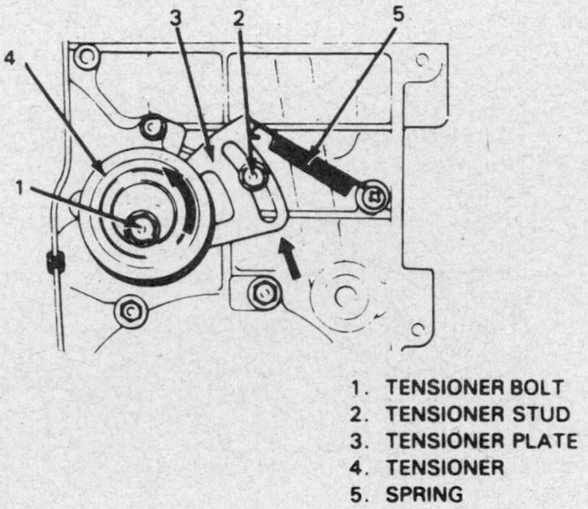
1. TENSIONER BOLT
2. TENSIONER STUD
3. TENSIONER PLATE
4. TENSIONER
5. SPRING

GC1069100520000X

Fig. 8 Checking tensioner plate movement

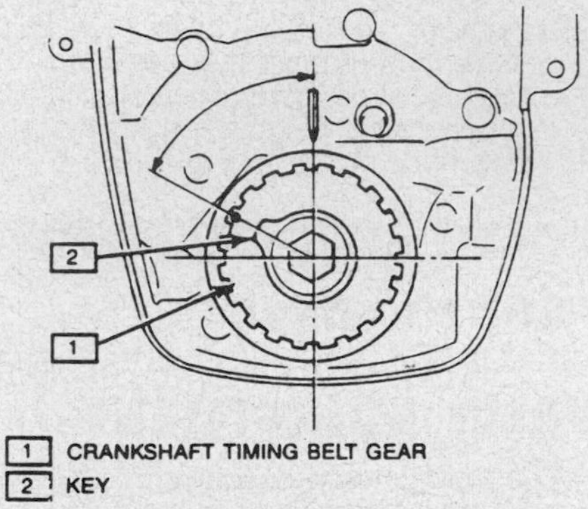
1 CRANKSHAFT TIMING BELT GEAR
2 KEY

GC1069100521000X

Fig. 9 Positioning crankshaft sprocket key

6. Rotate crankshaft two revolutions clockwise direction to remove slack from belt. **Ensure slack is removed from drive belt and that camshaft and crankshaft timing marks are aligned.**
7. Tighten tensioner stud, then tighten tensioner bolt to specifications.
8. Install timing belt outer cover and crankshaft pulley. **Ensure seal is between oil pump housing and water pump.**
9. Install water pump pulley and drive belt.
10. Install right hand side fender apron extension, then lower vehicle and connect battery ground cable.

CAMSHAFT

REPLACE

REMOVAL

1. Disconnect battery ground cable.
2. Remove air cleaner assembly, then remove cylinder head cover.
3. Remove distributor from cylinder head.
4. Remove timing belt as outlined under "Timing Belt, Replace."
5. After timing belt has been removed, position crankshaft sprocket key as shown in, **Fig. 9.**

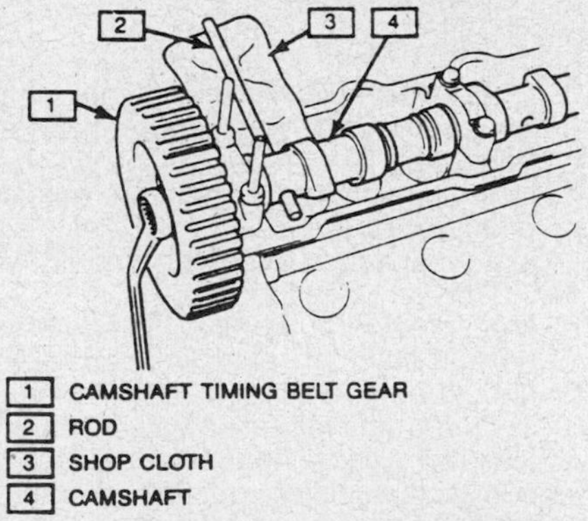
1 CAMSHAFT TIMING BELT GEAR
2 ROD
3 SHOP CLOTH
4 CAMSHAFT

GC1069100522000X

Fig. 10 Camshaft sprocket bolt removal & installation

6. Hold camshaft in position by inserting a rod into .39 inch hole in camshaft, then remove camshaft sprocket retaining bolt, **Fig. 10.** Place shop cloth under rod to prevent damage to cylinder head surface.
7. Remove camshaft housings to cylinder head attaching bolts and studs, **Fig. 3.**
8. Remove camshaft from cylinder head.

Hydraulic valve lash adjusters should also be removed and placed in engine oil until installation.

INSTALLATION

1. Pour engine oil into camshaft journal oil holes until oil is emitted from hydraulic valve lash adjuster holes, **Fig. 4.**
2. Lubricate valve lash adjusters with engine oil and install on cylinder head.
3. Lubricate camshaft with engine oil, then position on cylinder head with sprocket pin hole positioned as shown in **Fig. 11.**
4. Lubricate camshaft journal bores in camshaft housing with engine oil.
5. Apply sealant to cylinder head mating surface of camshaft housings No. 1 and No. 3, **Fig. 12.**
6. Position camshaft housings over camshaft and onto cylinder head mating surface. **Arrow on camshaft housing should face camshaft sprocket side of cylinder head.** Camshaft housings are numbered from 1 to 3. The housings are positioned on the cylinder head in numerical order, starting with No. 1 at camshaft sprocket side of cylinder head, **Fig. 13.**

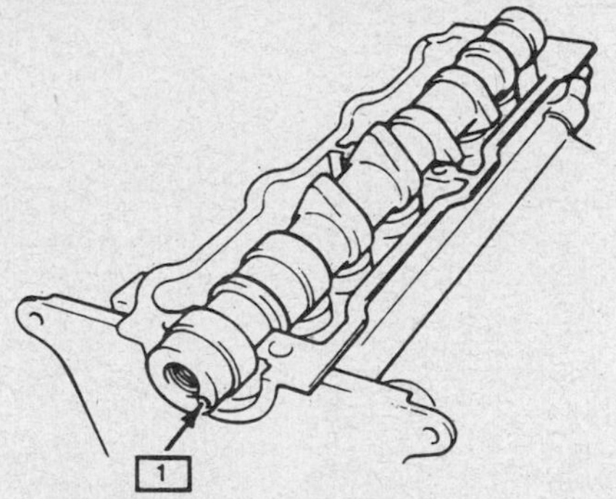
1

1 TIMING BELT GEAR PIN HOLE

GC1069100523000X

Fig. 11 Position camshaft sprocket pin hole

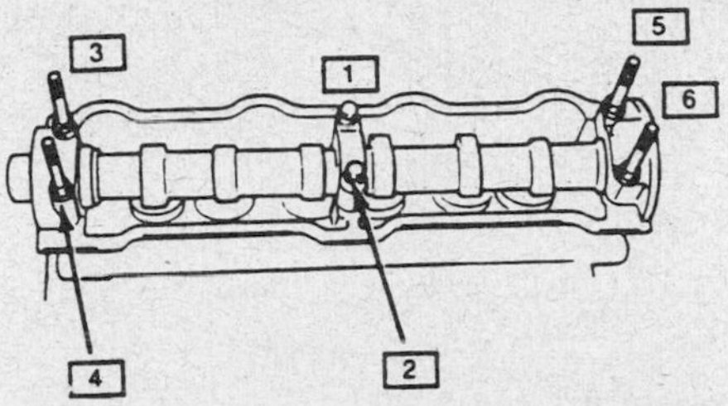
3
1
5
6
4
2

GC1069100526000X

Fig. 14 Camshaft housing bolt tightening sequence

7. Apply engine oil to camshaft housing attaching bolts and studs, then loosely install bolts and studs. Tighten bolts and studs in sequence shown in **Fig. 14.** to specifications.
8. Apply engine oil to camshaft oil seal lip, then install seal. Seal surface should be flush with housing surface.
9. Hold camshaft in position by inserting a rod into .39 inch hole in camshaft, then install and tighten camshaft sprocket retaining bolt, **Fig. 10.** Place shop cloth under rod to prevent damage to cylinder head surface.
10. Install cylinder head cover.
11. Install timing belt as outlined under "Timing Belt, Replace."
12. Install ignition distributor, then install air cleaner assembly.
13. Connect battery ground cable, then adjust ignition timing.

PISTON & ROD ASSEMBLY

Refer to **Fig. 15** when assembling piston and connecting rod. When installing piston and connecting rod, arrow on piston head should face front of engine and oil hole in connecting rod should face intake manifold. When installing connecting rod cap, arrow on cap should face front of engine.

Measure rod bearing side clearance using a feeler gauge. Connecting rod bearing side clearance should be .0039 to .0078 inch.

PISTONS, PINS & RINGS

Pistons and rings are available in standard size and oversizes of .010 and .020 inch. Piston pins are supplied with pistons in matched sets.

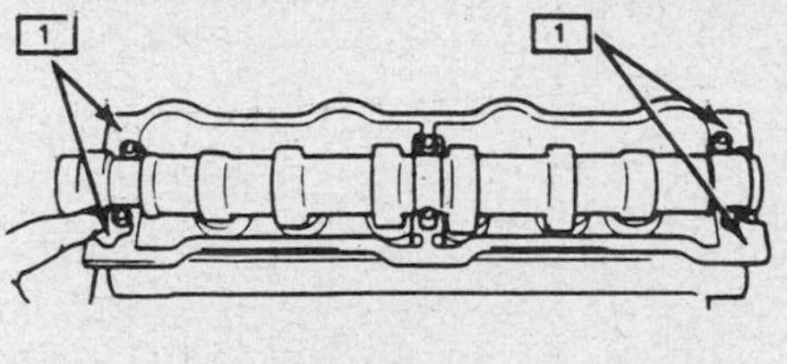
1
1

1 APPLY SEALANT

GC1069100524000X

Fig. 12 Camshaft housing to cylinder head surface sealant application

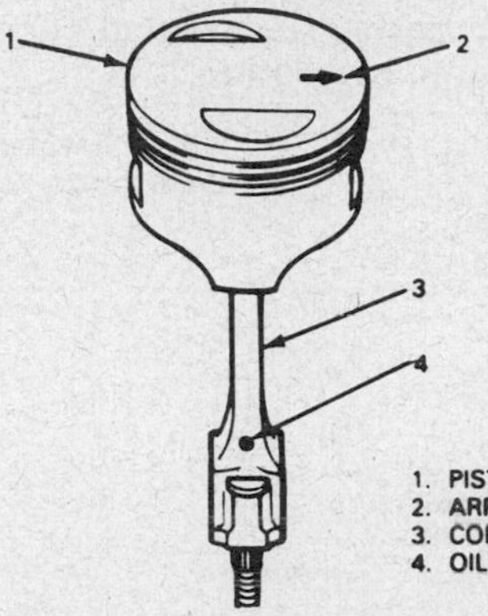
1
2
3
4

1. PISTON
2. ARROW MARK
3. CONNECTING ROD
4. OIL HOLE

GC1069100527000X

Fig. 15 Piston & connecting rod assembly

MAIN & ROD BEARINGS

Main and rod bearings are available in standard size and under size of .010 inch. Crankshaft thrust bearings are available in standard size and under size of .005 inch.

CRANKSHAFT REAR OIL SEAL

REPLACE

1. Remove transaxle as outlined under "Transaxle, Replace" in the "Automatic Transaxle" or "Clutch & Manual Transaxle" sections.
2. **On models with manual transaxle,** remove pressure plate and clutch disc.
3. **On all models,** remove flywheel.
4. Remove seal retainer, then remove seal from retainer.
5. Reverse procedure to install.

OIL PAN

REPLACE

1. Disconnect battery ground cable.
2. Raise and support vehicle.
3. Drain oil pan.
4. Remove flywheel dust cover.
5. Disconnect exhaust pipe at manifold.
6. Remove oil pan bolts and pan, **Fig. 16.**
7. Remove oil pump screen.
8. Reverse procedure to install. Apply continuous bead of silicon type sealer to oil pan flange inside bolt holes. When tightening oil pan attaching bolts, start at center and working outward. Tighten bolts to specifications.

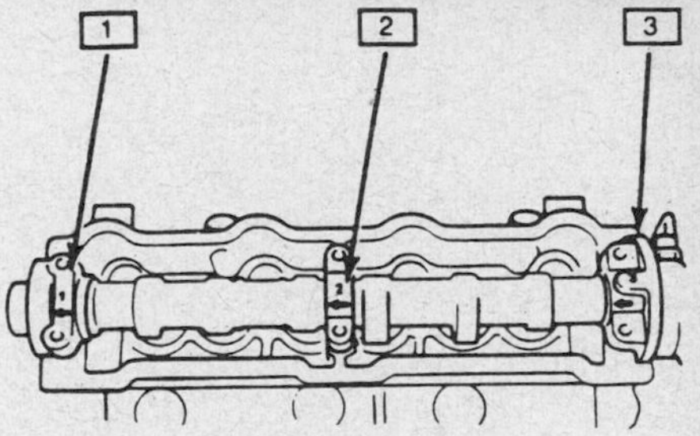
1
2
3

1 NO. 1 HOUSING
2 NO. 2 HOUSING
3 NO. 3 HOUSING

GC1069100525000X

Fig. 13 Camshaft housing locations

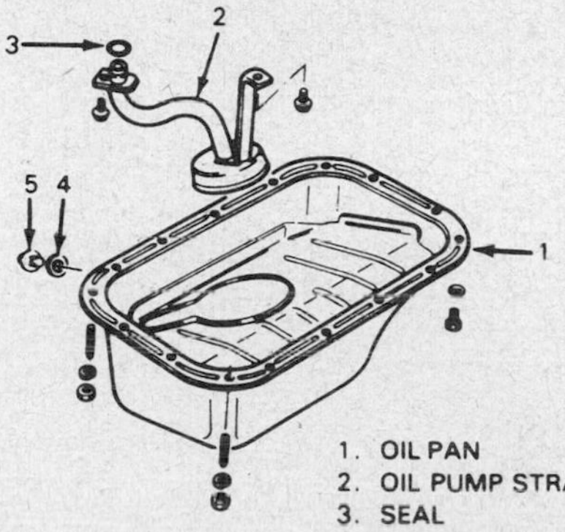
3
2
1
5 4
1

1. OIL PAN
2. OIL PUMP STRAINER
3. SEAL
4. DRAIN PLUG GASKET
5. DRAIN PLUG

GC1099100086000X

Fig. 16 Oil pan & pick-up tube

OIL PUMP

REPLACE

REMOVAL

1. Refer to "Timing Belt, Replace" procedure to remove timing belt.
2. Refer to "Oil Pan, Replace" procedure to remove oil pan.
3. Remove crankshaft timing belt sprocket.
4. Remove alternator mounting bracket, if necessary.
5. **On models with A/C,** remove compressor mounting bracket.
6. **On all models,** remove alternator adjusting bolt and upper cover bolt, if necessary.
7. Remove oil pump bolts and pump, **Fig. 17.**

INSTALLATION

1. Install oil pump pins and gasket on engine block.
2. Install Oil Seal Guide tool No. J-34853 or equivalent, onto crankshaft to prevent damage to oil seal lip, **Fig. 18.** Apply engine oil to your special tool.
3. Install oil pump onto crankshaft and engine block. Note location of mounting bolts, **Fig. 19. No. 1 bolts are shorter then No. 2 bolts in length.** Install bolts as shown in **Fig. 19**, then **tighten to specifications.**

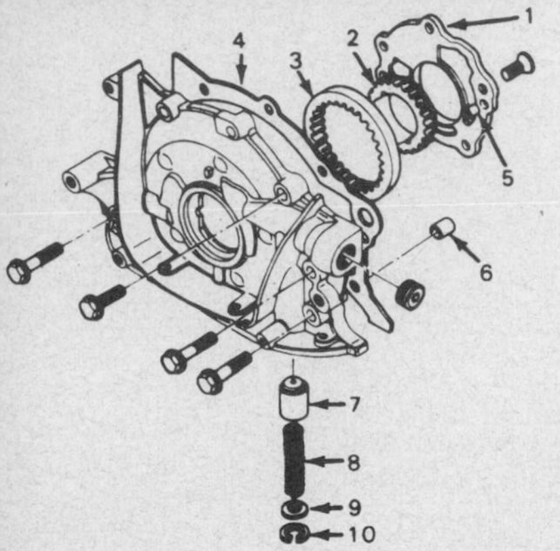
1
2
3
4
5
6
7
8
9
10

1. GEAR PLATE
2. INNER GEAR
3. OUTER GEAR
4. GASKET
5. PIN
6. PIN
7. RELIEF VALVE
8. SPRING
9. RETAINER
10. RETAINER RING

GC1099100087000X

Fig. 17 Rotor type (Trochoid) oil pump

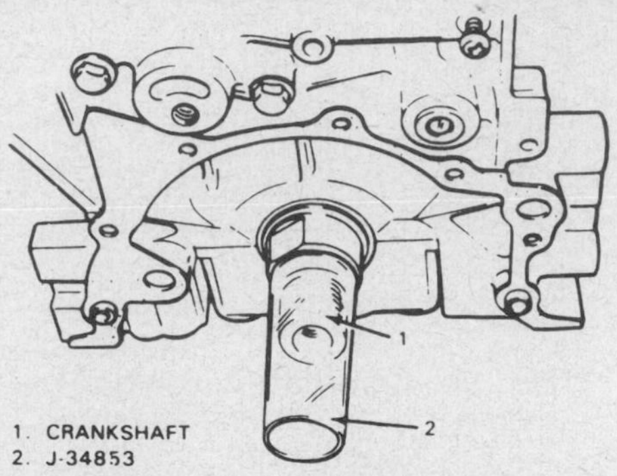
1
2
1. CRANKSHAFT
2. J-34853

GC1099100088000X

Fig. 18 Crankshaft oil seal guide tool installation

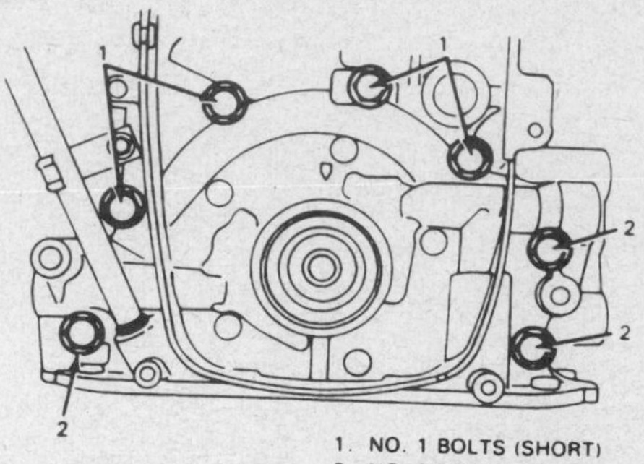
1
2

1. NO. 1 BOLTS (SHORT)
2. NO. 2 BOLTS (LONG)

GC1099100089000X

Fig. 19 Oil pump bolt location

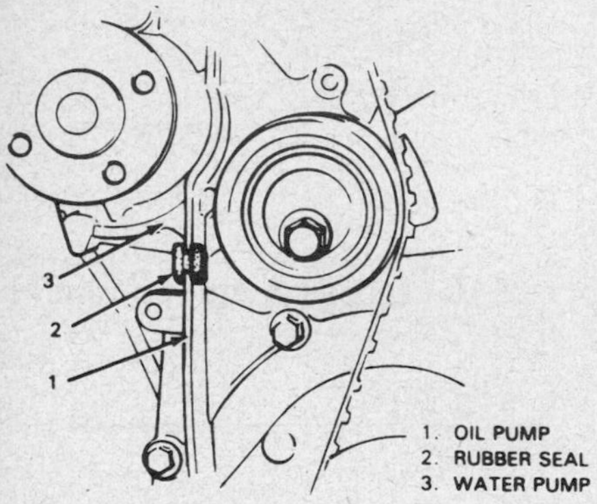
1
2
3
1. OIL PUMP
2. RUBBER SEAL
3. WATER PUMP

GC1099100090000X

Fig. 20 Rubber seal installation

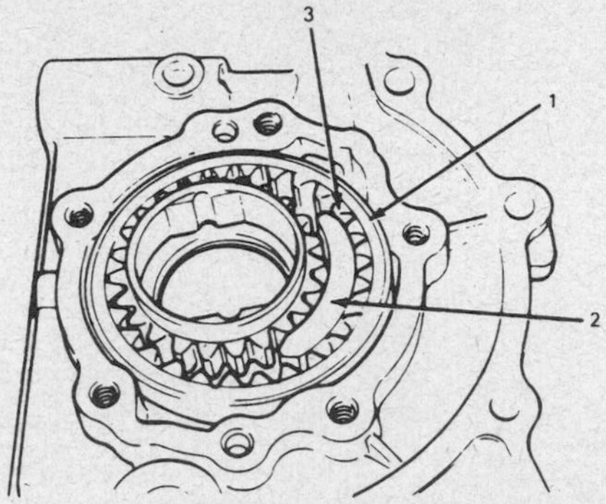
1
2
3

1. OUTER GAUGE
2. CRESCENT
3. CLEARANCE

GC1099100091000X

Fig. 21 Checking oil pump gear radial clearance. Rotor type similar

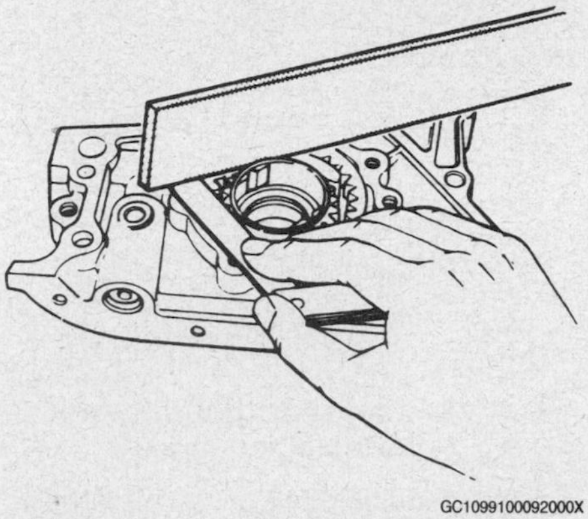

GC1099100092000X

Fig. 22 Checking oil pump gear side clearance. Rotor type similar

4. After installing oil pump, check that oil seal lip is not twisted, then remove tool.
5. Install rubber seal between oil pump and water pump, **Fig. 20.**
6. If necessary, trim edges of oil pump seal flush with oil pan mating surface.
7. Install timing belt guide, key and crankshaft timing sprocket. Note that timing belt guide must be installed so that curved side faces oil pump.
8. Install timing belt and tensioner components.
9. Adjust water pump belt tension.
10. Fill crankcase.
11. Connect battery ground cable.
12. Run engine to ensure oil pressure is correct.

OIL PUMP SERVICE

1. Remove dipstick tube from oil pump.
2. Remove gear/rotor plate screws and gear plate.
3. Remove outer and inner gears/rotors.
4. Inspect oil seal lip for damage and replace as necessary.
5. Inspect outer and inner gears/rotors, gear/rotor plate, and oil pump case for excessive wear or damage.
6. Using feeler gauge, check radial clearance between outer gear/rotor and crescent, **Fig. 21.** If clearance exceeds .0122 inch, replace outer gear/rotor.
7. Using straightedge and feeler gauge, measure side clearance which should not exceed .0059 inch, **Fig. 22.**
8. Wash, clean and dry all oil pump parts.
9. Apply light coat of engine oil to inner and outer gears/rotors, oil seal lip portion, and inside surfaces of oil pump case and plate.
10. Install outer and inner gears/rotors in pump case.
11. Install gear/rotor plate and tighten screws securely. Check that gears turn smoothly by hand.
12. Install O-ring in pump case, then dipstick tube.

BELT TENSION DATA

Belt & Year	Belt Deflection Inch ①
A/C Compressor	
1992-94	**.20-.25**
Alternator & Water Pump	
1992-94 New	**.20-.27**
1992-94 Used	**.24-.31**

①—With thumb pressure applied.

COOLING SYSTEM BLEED

These engines do not require a specified bleed procedure. After filling cooling system, run engine to operating temperature with radiator/pressure cap off. Air will then be automatically bled through cap opening.

THERMOSTAT

REPLACE

1. Disconnect battery ground cable.
2. Drain cooling system.
3. Remove radiator inlet hose at thermostat housing.
4. Remove thermostat housing and thermostat.
5. Clean both gasket surfaces thoroughly.
6. Reverse procedure to install.

WATER PUMP

REPLACE

1. Disconnect battery ground cable.
2. Drain cooling system.
3. Remove drive belt, water pump pulley, crankshaft pulley, timing belt outside cover, timing belt and timing belt tensioner.
4. Remove water pump mounting bolts and nuts, and water pump.
5. Install water pump on engine block.

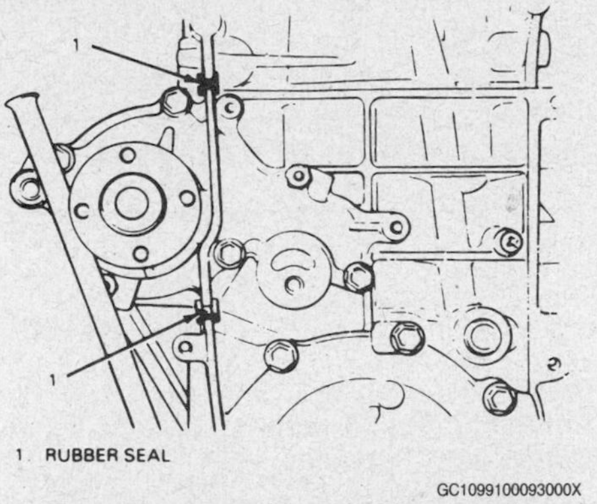
1
1
1. RUBBER SEAL
GC1099100093000X

Fig. 23 Installing rubber seals

6. Install rubber seals between water pump and oil pump, and between water pump and cylinder head, **Fig. 23.**
7. Install timing belt tensioner, timing belt, timing belt outside cover, crankshaft pulley, water pump pulley and drive belt.
8. Tighten drive belt so it deflects .25-.35 inch on span between water pump pulley and crankshaft pulley.
9. Install valve cover and air cleaner.
10. Fill cooling system.
11. Connect battery ground cable.

RADIATOR
REPLACE

1. Disconnect battery ground cable.
2. Drain cooling system.
3. Remove upper, lower, and overflow hoses from radiator.
4. Disconnect cooling fan electrical connector.
5. **On models with automatic transaxle,** disconnect transaxle cooling lines from bottom of radiator.
6. **On all models,** remove upper radiator/fan mounting bolts, then remove radiator/fan assembly from vehicle.
7. Reverse procedure to install.

FUEL PUMP
REPLACE

1. Relieve fuel system pressure as follows:
   a. Remove fuel pump relay from main fuse panel located in engine compartment, **Fig. 1.**
   b. Operate engine until it stalls, then crank engine several times in three second intervals.
   c. Remove fuel tank filler cap to release vapor pressure, then reinstall cap.
   d. Place ignition switch in off position, then install fuel pump relay.
2. Disconnect battery ground cable.
3. Remove rear seat cushion, then disconnect fuel pump and sending unit electrical connectors, then push harness through floor pan grommet.
4. Drain fuel tank, then disconnect inlet hose from fuel filter.
5. Disconnect fuel filler hose from fuel tank.
6. Disconnect vapor hoses and fuel feed and return hoses at fuel tank and pump.
7. Remove fuel tank mounting bolts, then lower fuel tank from vehicle.
8. Remove fuel pump to fuel tank attaching bolts, then remove fuel pump, **Fig. 24.**
9. Separate fuel pump from motor and sending unit as necessary.
10. Reverse procedure to install.

FUEL FILTER
REPLACE

The fuel filter is located at the lefthand front corner of the fuel tank assembly.

1. Relieve fuel system pressure as follows:
   a. Remove fuel pump relay from main fuse panel located in engine compartment, **Fig. 1.**
   b. Start engine and allow to run until it stalls, then crank engine several times in three second intervals.

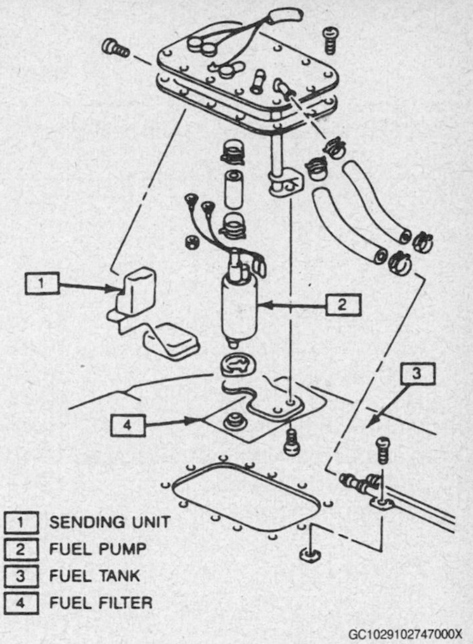
1
2
3
4
1 SENDING UNIT
2 FUEL PUMP
3 FUEL TANK
4 FUEL FILTER
GC1029102747000X

Fig. 24 Electric fuel pump & sending unit removal

   c. Remove fuel tank filler cap to release vapor pressure, then reinstall cap.
   d. Place ignition switch in off position, then install fuel pump relay.
2. Disconnect battery ground cable.
3. Raise and support vehicle, then place approved fuel holding container under fuel filter.
4. Disconnect fuel filter inlet hose clamp and hose from filter. **A small amount of fuel may be released after the fuel hose is disconnected. In order to reduce the chance of personal injury, cover the fittings with a shop towel.**
5. Disconnect fuel filter outlet hose clamp and hose from filter.
6. Remove mounting bracket and filter as an assembly.
7. Reverse procedure to install.

TIGHTENING SPECIFICATIONS

Tightening specifications are for clean and lightly lubricated threads only. Dry or dirty threads produce increased friction which prevents accurate measurement of tightness.

Component	Torque/Ft. Lbs.
Alternator Mounting Bolts & Nuts	17
Camshaft Housing To Cylinder Head	8
Camshaft Sprocket Bolt	44
Connecting Rod Cap Bolts	26
Crankshaft Pulley Bolts	8
Crankshaft Sprocket Bolt	81
Cylinder Head Bolts	54
Cylinder Head Cover	4
Exhaust Manifold To Cylinder Head	17
Flywheel To Crankshaft	45
Ignition Distributor To Cylinder Head	10
Intake Manifold To Cylinder Head	17
Main Bearing Cap Bolts	40

Component	Torque/Ft. Lbs.
Oil Pan Drain Plug	26
Oil Pan To Engine	8
Oil Pressure Switch	10
Oil Pump Pickup Tube Bolts	8
Oil Pump Rotor Plate Screws	8
Oil Pump To Engine	8
Spark Plug	18
Starter Mounting Bolts	17
Timing Belt Cover Nuts & Bolts	8
Timing Belt Tensioner Bolt	20
Timing Belt Tensioner Stud	8
Water Pump To Engine	7.5-9

1.3L/4–79 Engine

NOTE: On Air Bag Equipped Models, Refer To "Air Bag System Precautions" Located In The Front Of This Manual For System Disarming & Arming Procedures.

INDEX

PRECAUTIONS

AIR BAG SYSTEMS

Refer to "Air Bag System Precautions" in the front of this manual for system disarming and arming procedures.

FUEL SYSTEM PRESSURE RELIEF

1. Loosen fuel filler cap to relieve fuel tank pressure
2. Remove fuel pump relay from relay box located at the lefthand front of the engine compartment, next to the battery, **Fig. 1**.
3. Crank engine and allow to stall. Crank engine for several seconds more to ensure relief of any remaining fuel.
4. Remove battery ground cable.

ENGINE MOUNT

REPLACE

LEFT

1. Disconnect battery ground cable.
2. Remove engine mount nut, then raise and support vehicle.
3. Support engine using an engine support fixture.
4. Remove engine mount and frame bracket, then remove mount from bracket.
5. Reverse procedure to install.

RIGHT

1. Disconnect battery ground cable.
2. Remove engine mount nut, then raise and support vehicle.
3. Support engine using an engine support fixture.
4. Remove engine mount and frame bracket, then remove mount from bracket.
5. Reverse procedure to install.

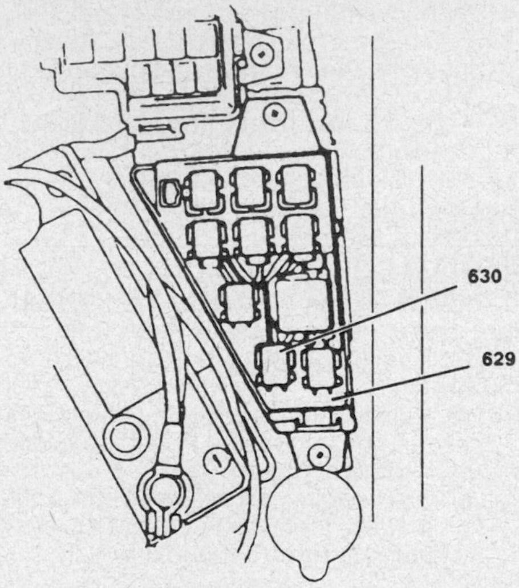

630
629

629 RELAY BOX

630 FUEL PUMP RELAY

GC1029503761000X

Fig. 1 Fuel pump relay location

REAR

1. Disconnect battery ground cable.
2. Remove engine mount nut, then raise and support vehicle.
3. Remove nut retaining mount to body bracket.
4. Support engine using an engine support fixture.
5. Remove frame bracket, then remove mount.
6. Reverse procedure to install.

TORQUE ROD

1. Disconnect battery ground cable.
2. Remove engine mount nut, then raise and support vehicle.
3. Remove nut retaining mount to body bracket.
4. Support engine using an engine support fixture.
5. Remove frame bracket, then remove mount.
6. Reverse procedure to install.

ENGINE

REPLACE

1. Relieve fuel system pressure as outlined under "Precautions".
2. Disconnect battery ground cable and remove battery
3. Disconnect windshield washer hose, then remove hood.
4. Remove air cleaner assembly.
5. Drain cooling system, then remove radiator and engine cooling fan.
6. Disconnect high tension lead from ignition coil.
7. Disconnect electrical connectors from body harness.
8. Disconnect battery ground cable from transaxle.
9. **On models with manual transaxle,** disconnect electrical connector from back-up lamp switch.
10. **On models with automatic transaxle,** disconnect electrical connectors from neutral safety switch and speed sensor.
11. **On all models,** disconnect intake manifold to power brake unit vacuum hose.
12. Disconnect evaporative emission canister hoses from intake manifold and tube connections.
13. Disconnect fuel hoses from throttle body.
14. Disconnect heater hoses from engine.
15. Disconnect accelerator cable from throttle body.
16. **On models with manual transaxle,** disconnect clutch cable from fork and housing.

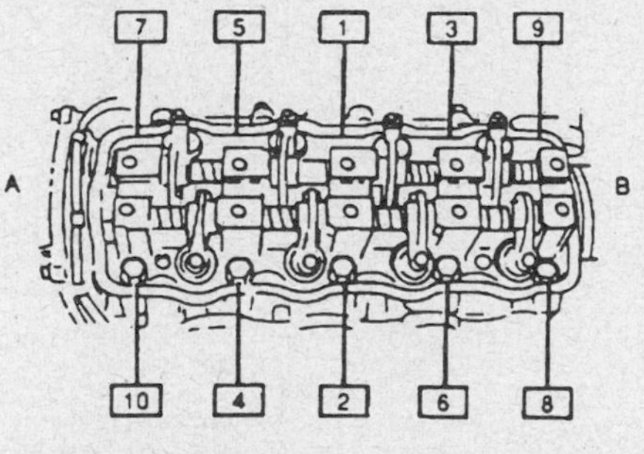
7
5
1
3
9
A
B
10
4
2
6
8

A CAMSHAFT PULLEY SIDE
B DISTRIBUTOR SIDE

GC1069500586000X

Fig. 2 Cylinder head tightening sequence

17. **On models with automatic transaxle,** disconnect shift control and fluid pressure control cables from transaxle.
18. **On all models,** disconnect speedometer cable from transaxle.
19. Raise and support vehicle, then disconnect exhaust pipe from exhaust manifold.
20. Drain engine crankcase, then drain fluid from transaxle.
21. **On models with manual transaxle,** disconnect control shaft and extension rod from transaxle.
22. **On all models,** separate drive axles from transaxle. Suspend drive axles from chassis using wire.
23. **On models with automatic transaxle,** remove engine torque rod bracket from transaxle.
24. Lower vehicle and install an engine lifting fixture.
25. Remove engine and transaxle mounting bolts, then remove engine and transaxle assembly from vehicle.
26. Reverse procedure to install.

INTAKE MANIFOLD
REPLACE

1. Relieve fuel system pressure as outlined under "Precautions".
2. Disconnect battery ground cable.
3. Drain cooling system, then remove air cleaner assembly.
4. Disconnect electrical connectors from coolant temperature sender, engine and coolant temperature sensor.
5. Disconnect electrical connector from EGR vacuum switching valve.
6. Disconnect electrical connectors from idle speed control valve, throttle position switch, oxygen sensor, and fuel injector.
7. Disconnect ground wires from intake manifold.
8. Disconnect fuel hoses from throttle body.
9. Disconnect coolant hoses from intake manifold.
10. Disconnect MAP sensor hose from intake manifold.
11. Disconnect evaporative emission hoses from intake manifold and tube.
12. Disconnect power brake unit vacuum hose from intake manifold.
13. Disconnect PCV valve hose from cylinder head cover.
14. Disconnect accelerator cable from throttle body.
15. Disconnect all other electrical connectors and hoses to permit intake manifold and throttle body removal.
16. Remove intake manifold to cylinder head attaching nuts and bolts, then remove intake manifold and throttle body as an assembly.
17. Reverse procedure to install, ensuring to install new gasket. Tighten fasteners to specifications.

EXHAUST MANIFOLD
REPLACE

1. Disconnect battery ground cable, then raise and support vehicle.
2. Disconnect catalytic converter from manifold, then lower vehicle.
3. Disconnect oxygen sensor electrical connector, then release wiring harness from clamps.
4. Remove heat shield and engine hanger.
5. Disconnect exhaust pipe from exhaust manifold.
6. Remove exhaust manifold attaching bolts and nuts, then remove exhaust manifold from cylinder head.
7. Reverse procedure to install, ensuring to install new gasket. Tighten fasteners to specifications.

CYLINDER HEAD
REPLACE

1. Relieve fuel system pressure as outlined under "Precautions".
2. Disconnect battery ground cable.
3. Drain cooling system, then remove air cleaner assembly.
4. Remove intake manifold as outlined under "Intake Manifold, Replace".
5. Remove timing belt and tensioner as outlined under "Timing Belt, Replace" .
6. Raise and support vehicle, then disconnect exhaust pipe from exhaust manifold.
7. Lower vehicle, then remove cylinder head cover.
8. Remove cylinder head attaching bolts, then remove cylinder head.
9. Reverse procedure to install. Tighten cylinder head bolts to specifications in sequence shown in **Fig. 2**.

VALVE ARRANGEMENT
FRONT TO REAR

1.3L/4-79 .... I-E-I-E-I-E-I-E

VALVE ADJUSTMENT

These engines are equipped with hydraulic valve lash adjusters and no adjustment is required.

VALVE GUIDES

Valves and valve guides are available in

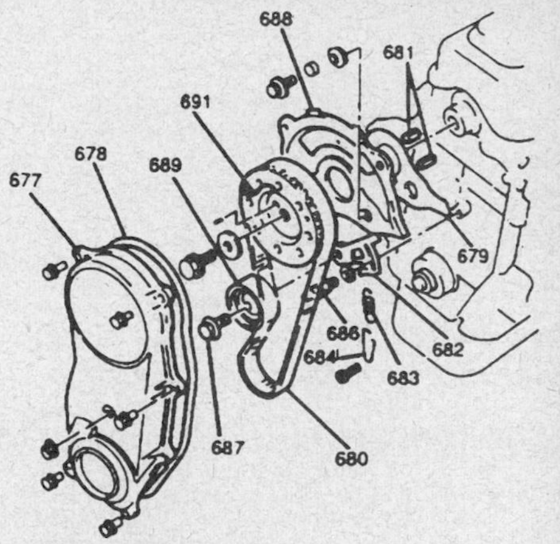
688
681
691
678
689
677
679
686
684
682
683
687
680

677 TIMING BELT COVER
678 OUTER TIMING BELT COVER GASKET
679 TIMING BELT INNER SEAL
680 TIMING BELT
681 SEAL
682 TENSIONER PLATE
683 TENSIONER SPRING
684 SPRING DAMPER
686 TENSIONER STUD
687 TENSIONER BOLT
688 TIMING BELT INNER COVER
689 TIMING BELT TENSIONER
691 CAMSHAFT TIMING GEAR SPROCKET

GC1069500587000X

Fig. 3 Timing belt assembly

standard size only. The valve guide can be driven from cylinder bore using valve guide remover/installer tool No. J-34834 or equivalent. The valve guide should be driven from the combustion chamber side of the cylinder head out through the valve spring side.

The cylinder head valve guide bore should be reamed with 14 mm reamer tool No. 34831, or equivalent, prior to valve guide installation. Drive valve guide into heated cylinder head bore using valve guide remover/installer tool No. J-34834 or equivalent. Valve guide should be driven in until tool contacts cylinder head. Valve guide protrusion should be .55 inch from cylinder head surface. After installation, ream valve guide with a 7 mm reamer tool No. J-34832, or equivalent.

TIMING BELT
REPLACE
REMOVAL

1. Disconnect battery ground cable, then raise and support vehicle.
2. Remove crankshaft timing pulley.
3. Remove timing belt cover, **Fig. 3**.
4. Align upper and lower timing marks, **Figs. 4 and 5**, by turning crankshaft.
5. Remove tensioner assembly and timing belt.

INSPECTION

Check timing belt for wear and cracks and replace as necessary. Check timing belt tensioner for smoothness of rotation and replace as necessary.

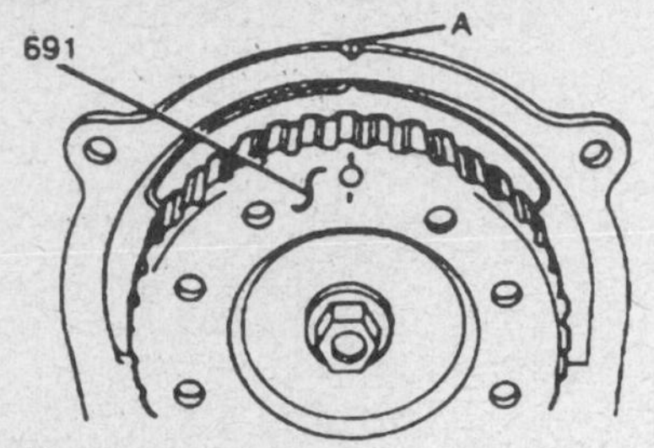
691
A

A "V" MARK
691 CAMSHAFT TIMING GEAR SPROCKET

GC1069500588000X

Fig. 4 Camshaft timing mark

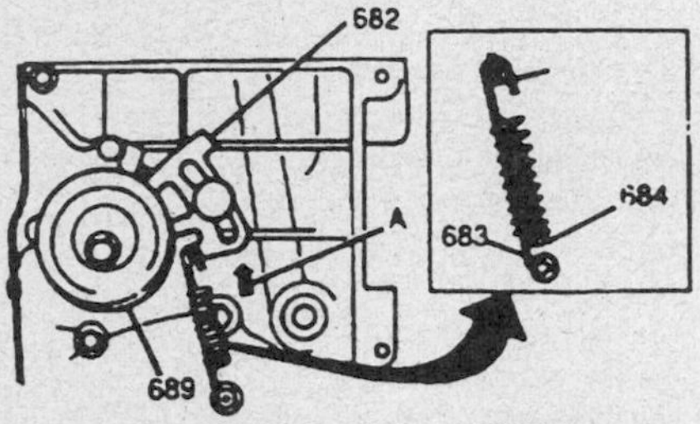
682
684
683
A
689

A DIRECTION OF TENSIONER MOVEMENT
682 TENSIONER PLATE
683 TENSIONER SPRING
684 SPRING DAMPER
689 TIMING BELT TENSIONER

GC1069500591000X

Fig. 7 Tensioner adjustment

INSTALLATION

1. Position lug on tensioner plate to hole in tensioner, **Fig. 6.**
2. Position tensioner and tensioner plate to engine, then install and hand tighten attaching bolt. Ensure that tensioner and tensioner plate move in the same direction, **Fig. 7.** If movement is not as indicated, remove tensioner and reinsert tensioner plate lug into tensioner.
3. Ensure camshaft and crankshaft timing marks are aligned,
4. Remove cylinder head cover and completely loosen all valve adjusting screws on intake and exhaust rocker arms. This will permit free rotation of camshaft and prevent damage to valves during timing belt adjustment.
5. With tensioner plate pushed upward, install timing belt over camshaft and crankshaft pulleys. **Arrow on timing belt should face toward direction of crankshaft rotation. When installing timing belt, keep drive side of belt free of slack.**
6. Install tensioner spring and damper, then hand tighten tensioner stud.
7. Rotate crankshaft two revolutions clockwise direction to remove slack from belt. **Ensure slack is removed from drive belt and that camshaft and crankshaft timing marks are aligned.**
8. Tighten tensioner stud, then tighten tensioner bolt to specifications.
9. Install timing belt outer cover and crankshaft pulley. **Ensure seal is between oil pump housing and water pump.**
10. Adjust valve lash and install cylinder head cover.
11. Lower vehicle and connect battery ground cable.

A
B
6021
674

A ARROW MARK ON OIL PUMP CASE
B PUNCH MARK ON CRANKSHAFT TIMING GEAR
674 CRANKSHAFT PULLEY TIMING GEAR BOLT
6021 CRANKSHAFT TIMING GEAR

GC1069500601000X

Fig. 5 Crankshaft timing mark

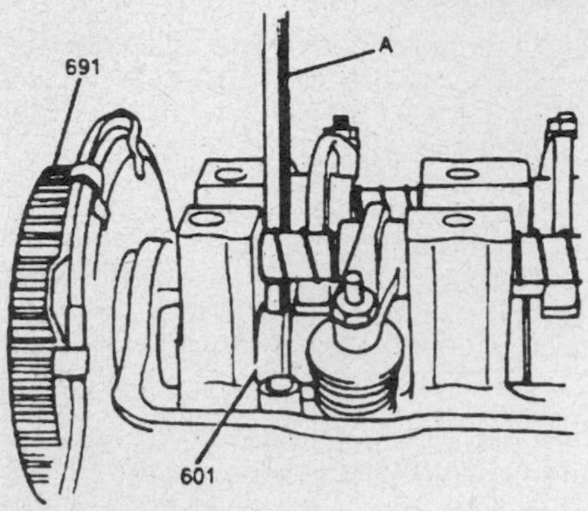
691
A
601

A 10 mm (0.39") ROD
601 CAMSHAFT
691 CAMSHAFT TIMING GEAR SPROCKET

GC1069500592000X

Fig. 8 Camshaft positioning

CAMSHAFT

REPLACE

REMOVAL

1. Disconnect battery ground cable.
2. **On models with A/C,** remove compressor and bracket.
3. **On all models,** remove air cleaner assembly, then remove cylinder head cover.
4. Remove distributor from cylinder head.
5. Remove rocker arm shafts, springs and rocker arms.
6. Remove timing belt as outlined under "Timing Belt, Replace."
7. Hold camshaft in position by inserting a rod into .39 inch hole in camshaft, then remove camshaft sprocket retaining bolt, **Fig. 8.** Place shop cloth under rod to prevent damage to cylinder head surface.
8. Remove camshaft housings to cylinder head attaching bolts and studs,
9. Remove camshaft from cylinder head.

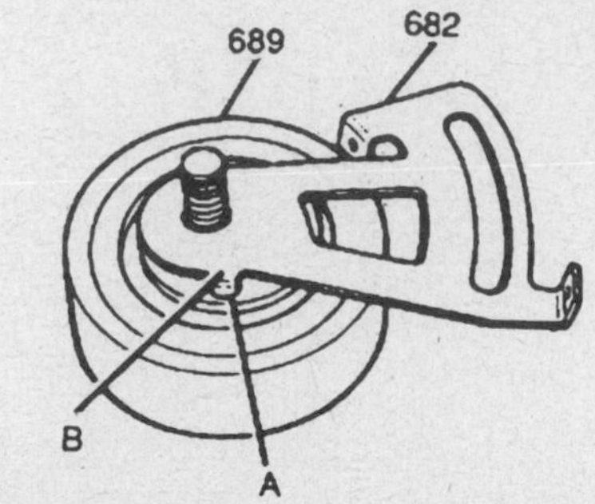
689
682
B
A

A TIMING BELT TENSIONER HOLE
B TENSIONER PLATE LUG
682 TENSIONER PLATE
689 TIMING BELT TENSIONER

GC1069500590000X

Fig. 6 Timing belt tensioner

INSTALLATION

1. Lubricate camshaft with engine oil, then position on cylinder head.
2. Rotate crankshaft clockwise and align the punch mark on the crankshaft timing belt gear with the arrow timing mark on the oil pump.
3. Lock camshaft in position by inserting a rod into .39 inch hole in camshaft.
4. Install camshaft timing sprocket to camshaft, ensuring pin on camshaft fits into slot on sprocket. Secure with bolt.
5. Install intake rocker arm shaft with stepped end toward distributor side.
6. Using rocker shaft assembly installer tool No. J-42388, or equivalent, install rocker arms, springs and rocker arm shafts, **Fig. 9.**
7. Tighten rocker shaft assembly in sequence shown in **Fig. 10.**
8. Install cylinder head cover.
9. Install timing belt as outlined under "Timing Belt, Replace."
10. Install ignition distributor, then install air cleaner assembly.
11. **On models with A/C,** install compressor and bracket.
12. **On all models,** connect battery ground cable.

PISTON & ROD ASSEMBLY

Refer to **Fig. 11** when assembling piston and connecting rod. When installing piston and connecting rod, arrow on piston head should face front of engine and oil hole in connecting rod should face intake manifold. When installing connecting rod cap, arrow on cap should face front of engine.

Measure rod bearing side clearance using a feeler gauge. Connecting rod bearing side clearance should be .0039 to .0078 inch.

PISTONS, PINS & RINGS

Pistons and rings are available in standard size and oversizes of .0098 and .0197 inch. Piston pins are supplied with pistons in matched sets.

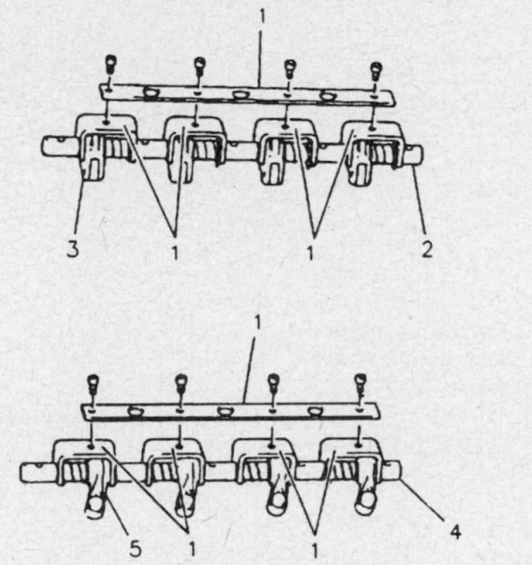
1
3
1
1
2
1
5
1
1
4

1 J 41388 ROCKER SHAFT ASSEMBLY INSTALLER
2 INTAKE ROCKER SHAFT
3 INTAKE ROCKER ARM
4 EXHAUST ROCKER SHAFT
5 EXHAUST ROCKER ARM

GC1069500593000X

Fig. 9 Rocker shaft installation

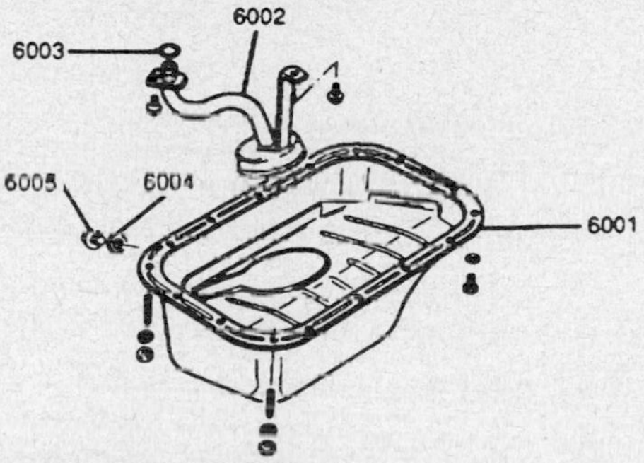
6002
6003
6005
6004
6001

6001 ENGINE OIL PAN
6002 OIL PUMP STRAINER
6003 OIL PUMP STRAINER SEAL
6004 ENGINE OIL DRAIN PLUG GASKET
6005 ENGINE OIL DRAIN PLUG

GC1099500106000X

Fig. 12 Oil pan assembly

MAIN & ROD BEARINGS

Main and rod bearings are available in standard size and under size of .010 inch.

CRANKSHAFT REAR OIL SEAL

REPLACE

1. Remove transaxle as outlined under "Transaxle, Replace" in the "Automatic Transaxle" or "Clutch & Manual Transaxle" sections.
2. **On models with manual transaxle,** remove pressure plate and clutch disc.
3. **On all models,** mark flywheel to engine position, then remove flywheel.
4. Remove seal retainer, then remove seal from retainer.
5. Reverse procedure to install, ensuring to install new seal.

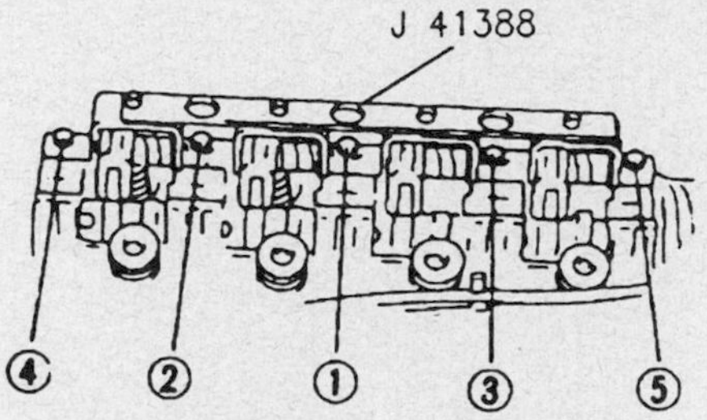
J 41388
④
②
①
③
⑤

GC1069500594000X

Fig. 10 Rocker shaft tightening sequence

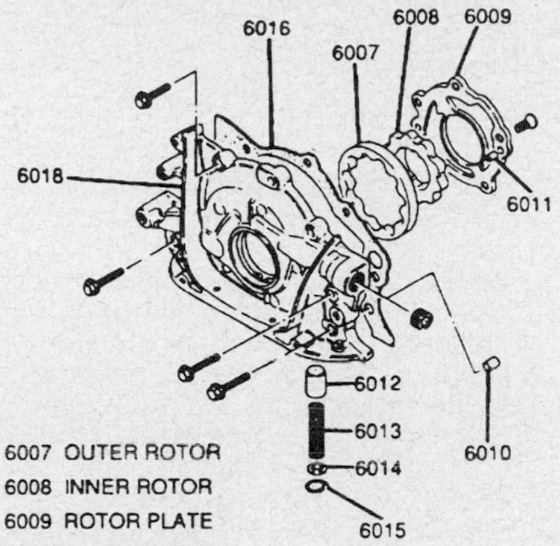
6016
6007
6008
6009
6018
6011
6012
6013
6014
6015
6010

6007 OUTER ROTOR
6008 INNER ROTOR
6009 ROTOR PLATE
6010 OIL PUMP PIN
6011 ROTOR PLATE PIN
6012 RELIEF VALVE
6013 SPRING
6014 RETAINER
6015 RETAINER RING
6016 OIL PUMP GASKET
6018 OIL PUMP BODY

GC1099500107000X

Fig. 13 Rotor type oil pump

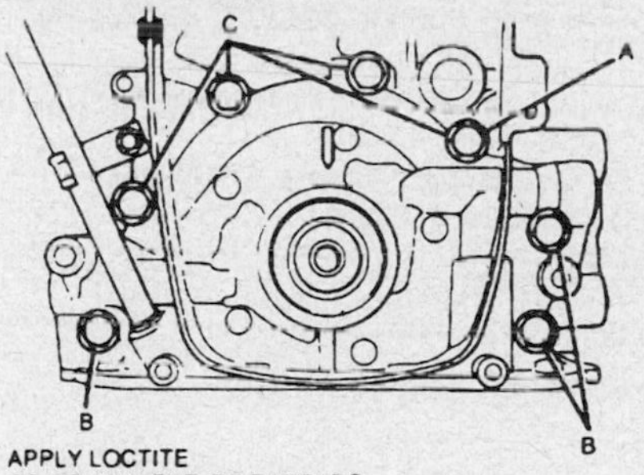
C
A
B
B

A APPLY LOCTITE OR EQUIVALENT, TO THREADS
B SHORT BOLTS
C LONG BOLTS

GC1099500109000X

Fig. 15 Oil pump bolt location

OIL PAN

REPLACE

1. Disconnect battery ground cable, then raise and support vehicle.
2. Drain oil pan.
3. Remove flywheel dust cover.
4. Disconnect exhaust pipe at manifold.
5. Remove oil pan bolts and pan, **Fig. 12.**
6. Remove oil pump screen.
7. Reverse procedure to install, ensuring to install new gasket. Apply continuous bead of silicon type sealer to oil pan flange inside bolt holes. When tightening oil pan attaching bolts, start at center and working outward. Tighten bolts to specifications.

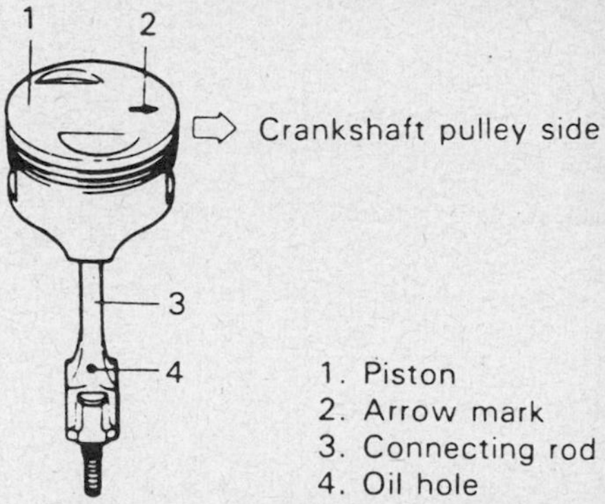
1
2
Crankshaft pulley side
3
4
1. Piston
2. Arrow mark
3. Connecting rod
4. Oil hole

GC1069500595000X

Fig. 11 Piston & connecting rod assembly

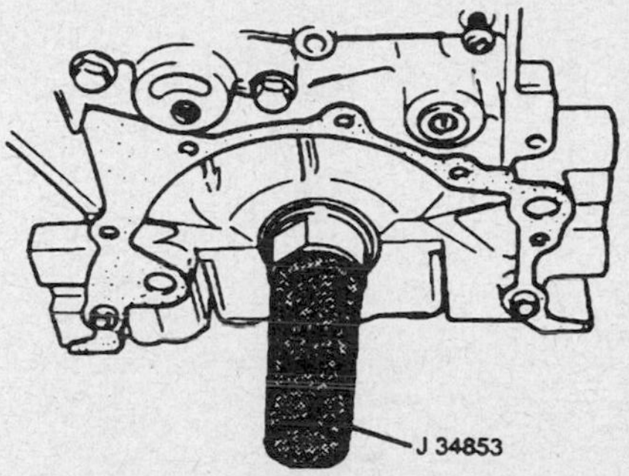
J 34853

GC1099500108000X

Fig. 14 Crankshaft oil seal guide tool

OIL PUMP

REPLACE

REMOVAL

1. Refer to "Timing Belt, Replace" procedure to remove timing belt.
2. Refer to "Oil Pan, Replace" procedure to remove oil pan.
3. Remove crankshaft timing belt sprocket.
4. Remove alternator mounting bracket, if necessary.
5. Remove A/C compressor mounting bracket, if so equipped.
6. Remove alternator adjusting bolt and upper cover bolt, if necessary.
7. Remove oil pump bolts and pump, **Fig. 13.**

INSTALLATION

1. Install oil pump pins and gasket on engine block.
2. Install Oil Seal Guide tool No. J-34853 or equivalent, onto crankshaft to prevent damage to oil seal lip, **Fig. 14.** Apply engine oil to special tool.
3. Install oil pump onto crankshaft and engine block. Note location of mounting bolts, **Fig. 15. No. 1 bolts are shorter than No. 2 bolts in length.** Install bolts as shown, then tighten to specifications.

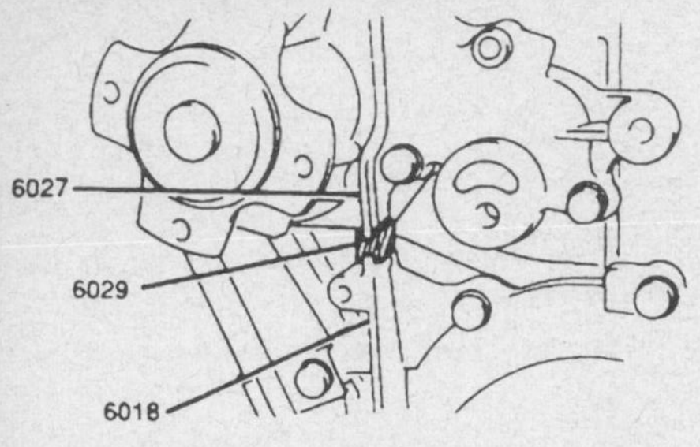
6027
6029
6018

6018 OIL PUMP BODY
6027 COOLANT PUMP
6029 RUBBER SEAL

GC1099500110000X

Fig. 16 Seal installation

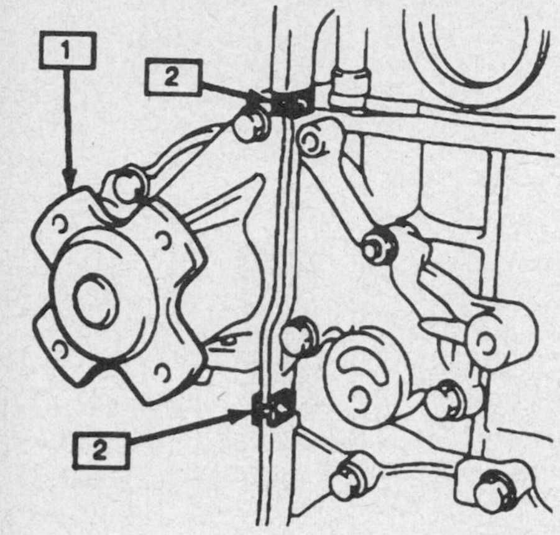
1
2
2

1 COOLANT PUMP
2 RUBBER SEALS

GC1089500243000X

Fig. 19 Water pump rubber seals

4. After installing oil pump, check that oil seal lip is not twisted, then remove tool.
5. Install rubber seal between oil pump and water pump, **Fig. 16**.
6. If necessary, trim edges of oil pump seal flush with oil pan mating surface.
7. Install timing belt guide, key and crankshaft timing sprocket. Note that timing belt guide must be installed so that curved side faces oil pump.
8. Install timing belt and tensioner components.
9. Adjust water pump belt tension.
10. Fill crankcase.
11. Connect battery ground cable.
12. Run engine and ensure oil pressure is correct.

OIL PUMP SERVICE

1. Drain oil, then remove dipstick tube from oil pump.
2. Remove rotor plate.
3. Remove outer and inner rotors.
4. Inspect oil seal lip for damage and replace as necessary.
5. Inspect outer and inner rotors, rotor plate, and oil pump case for excessive wear or damage.

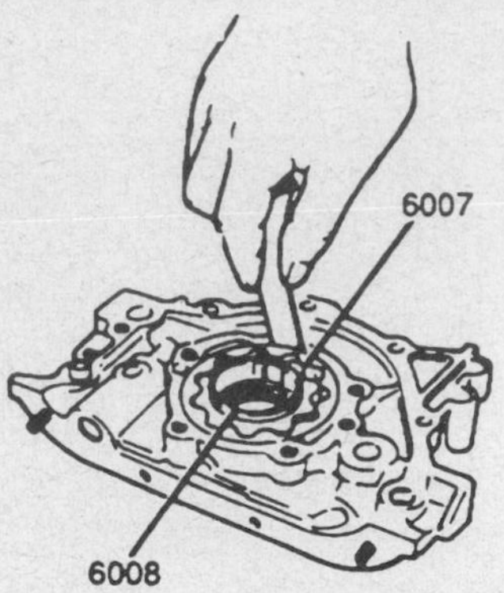
6007
6008

6007 OUTER ROTOR
6008 INNER ROTOR

GC1099500111000X

Fig. 17 Rotor radial clearance inspection

6. Using feeler gauge, check radial clearance between outer rotor and crescent, **Fig. 17.** If clearance exceeds .0122 inch, replace outer rotor.
7. Using straightedge and feeler gauge, measure side clearance which should not exceed .0059 inch, **Fig. 18.**
8. Wash, clean and dry all oil pump parts.
9. Apply light coat of engine oil to inner and outer rotors, oil seal lip portion, and inside surfaces of oil pump case and plate.
10. Install outer and inner rotors in pump case.
11. Install rotor plate and tighten screws securely. Check that gears turn smoothly by hand.
12. Install O-ring in pump case, then dipstick tube.

BELT TENSION DATA

Belt & Year	Belt Deflection Inch ①
A/C Compressor & Power Steering Pump	
1995	.30-.40
Water Pump & Alternator	
1995	.25-.32

①—With 22 lbs. pressure applied.

COOLING SYSTEM BLEED

These engines do not require a specified bleed procedure. After filling cooling system, run engine to operating temperature with radiator pressure cap off. Air will then be automatically bled through cap opening.

THERMOSTAT

REPLACE

1. Disconnect battery ground cable.
2. Drain cooling system.
3. Remove radiator inlet hose at thermostat housing.
4. Remove thermostat housing and thermostat.

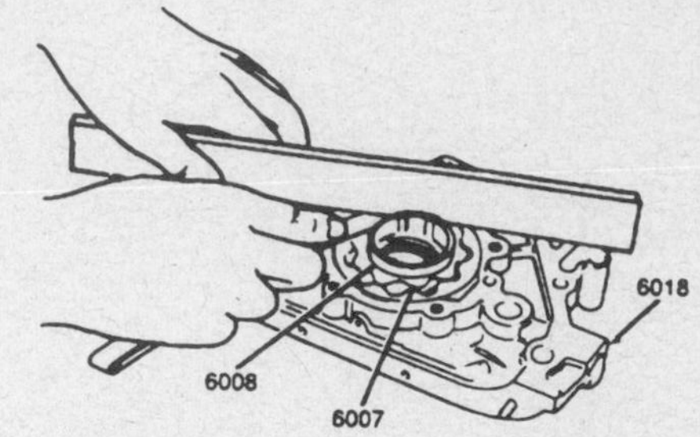
6018
6008
6007

6007 OUTER ROTOR
6008 INNER ROTOR
6018 OIL PUMP BODY

GC1099500112000X

Fig. 18 Rotor side clearance inspection

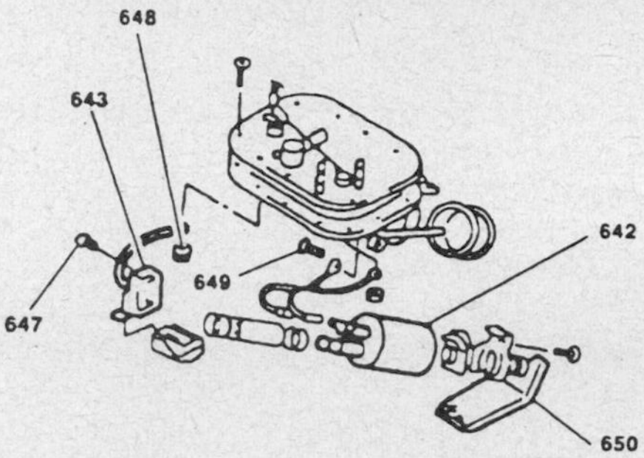
648
643
642
649
647
650

642 FUEL PUMP
643 FUEL GAGE SENDING UNIT
647 FUEL GAGE SENDING UNIT MOUNTING SCREW
648 FUEL GAGE SENDING UNIT LEAD WIRE NUT
649 FUEL PUMP MOUNTING SCREW
650 FUEL PUMP STRAINER

GC1029503762000X

Fig. 20 Fuel pump & sending unit removal

5. Clean both gasket surfaces thoroughly.
6. Reverse procedure to install, ensuring to use new gasket.

WATER PUMP

REPLACE

REMOVAL

1. Disconnect battery ground cable.
2. Drain cooling system.
3. Remove air cleaner assembly.
4. **On models with A/C,** remove compressor suction pipe bracket.
5. **On all models,** loosen, but do not remove, water pump bolts.
6. Raise and properly support vehicle.
7. Remove right lower splash shield.
8. **On models with A/C,** remove compressor drive belt.
9. Remove lower alternator cover plate, loosen alternator adjusting bolt, and remove water pump/alternator drive belt.
10. Remove crankshaft pulley and water pump pulley.
11. Remove dipstick tube.
12. Remove upper alternator adjusting bracket from water pump.

13. Remove rubber seals from water pump, **Fig. 19**.
14. Remove water pump mounting bolts and nuts, and water pump.

INSTALLATION

1. Install water pump on engine block, ensuring to use new gasket.
2. Install rubber seals between water pump and oil pump, and between water pump and cylinder head,
3. Install upper alternator adjusting bracket to water pump and tighten to specifications.
4. Install dipstick tube.
5. Install timing belt.
6. Install and hand tighten water pump pulley.
7. Install crankshaft pulley.
8. Install water pump/alternator drive belt and lower alternator cover plate.
9. **On models with A/C,** install compressor drive belt.
10. **On all models,** install right lower splash shield.
11. Lower vehicle.
12. **On models with A/C,** install compressor suction pipe bracket.
13. **On all models**, tighten upper alternator adjustment bolt to specifications.
14.
15. Tighten water pump/alternator drive belt to specifications listed in "Belt Tension Data".
16. Fill cooling system.
17. Connect battery ground cable.

RADIATOR

REPLACE

1. Disconnect battery ground cable.
2. Drain cooling system.
3. Remove upper, lower, and overflow hoses from radiator.
4. Disconnect cooling fan electrical connector.
5. **On models with automatic transaxle,** disconnect transaxle cooling lines from bottom of radiator.
6. **On all models,** remove upper radiator/fan mounting bolts, then remove radiator/fan assembly from vehicle.
7. Reverse procedure to install.

FUEL PUMP

REPLACE

1. Relieve fuel system pressure as outlined under "Precautions".
2. Disconnect battery ground cable.
3. Remove rear seat cushion, then disconnect fuel pump and sending unit electrical connectors, then push harness through floor pan grommet.
4. Drain fuel tank, then disconnect inlet hose from fuel filter.
5. Disconnect fuel filler hose from fuel tank.
6. Disconnect vapor hoses and fuel feed and return hoses at fuel tank and pump.
7. Remove fuel tank mounting bolts, then lower fuel tank from vehicle.
8. Remove fuel pump to fuel tank attaching bolts, then remove fuel pump, **Fig. 20.**
9. Separate fuel pump from sending unit as necessary.
10. Reverse procedure to install.

FUEL FILTER

REPLACE

The fuel filter is located at the lefthand front corner of the fuel tank assembly.

1. Relieve fuel system pressure as outlined under "Precautions".
2. Disconnect battery ground cable.
3. Raise and properly support vehicle, then place approved fuel holding container under fuel filter.
4. Remove parking brake cable bracket bolt and move cable aside
5. Disconnect fuel filter inlet hose clamp and hose from filter. **A small amount of fuel may be released after the fuel hose is disconnected. In order to reduce the chance of personal injury, cover the fittings with a shop towel.**
6. Disconnect fuel filter outlet hose clamp and hose from filter.
7. Remove mounting bracket and filter as an assembly.
8. Reverse procedure to install.

TIGHTENING SPECIFICATIONS

Tightening specifications are for clean and lightly lubricated threads only. Dry or dirty threads produce increased friction which prevents accurate measurement of tightness.

Component	Torque/Ft. Lbs.
Air Cleaner Assembly To Cylinder Head	89①
Alternator Cover	89①
Alternator Mounting	17
Alternator Upper Adjustment	41
Battery Cable To Battery Terminal	11
Connecting Rod Cap	26
Crankshaft Pulley	97①
Crankshaft Sprocket	79
Cylinder Head	54
Cylinder Head Cover	44
Exhaust Manifold To Cylinder Head	17
Engine Mounts	41
Flywheel To Crankshaft	45
Fuel Filter Mounting	11
Fuel Gauge Sending Unit	88①
Fuel Tank Mounting	18
Heat Shield	11
Ignition Distributor To Cylinder Head	11
Intake Manifold To Cylinder Head	17
Lower Rear Mounting Bracket	41
Main Bearing Cap	40

Component	Torque/Ft. Lbs.
Oil Pan Drain Plug	26
Oil Pan To Engine	97①
Oil Pressure Switch	10
Oil Pump Pickup Tube Bolts	97①
Oil Pump Rotor Plate Screws	97①
Oil Pump To Engine	97①
Radiator Lower Mounting	89①
Radiator Upper Mounting	89①
Rear Main Seal	106①
Rocker Arm Mounting	97①
Spark Plug	21
Starter Mounting	17
Thermostat Cap	15
Thermostat Housing	20
Timing Belt Cover	97①
Timing Belt Tensioner	20
Timing Belt Tensioner Stud	97①
Torque Rod Assembly	41
Water Pump To Engine	115①
Water Pump Pulley	18

①—Inch lbs.

Clutch & Manual Transaxle

INDEX

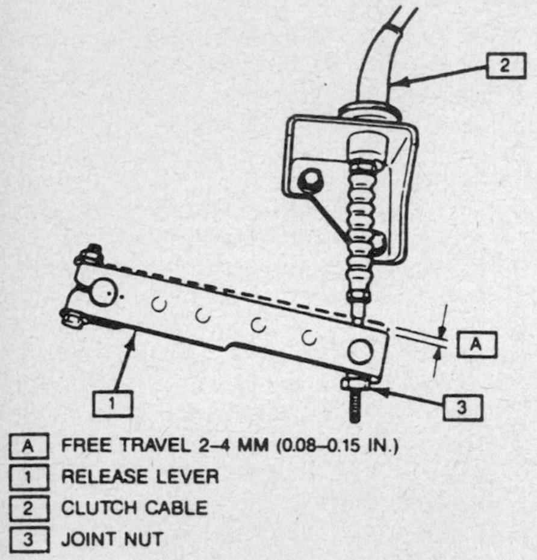

2
A
1
3
A FREE TRAVEL 2–4 MM (0.08–0.15 IN.)
1 RELEASE LEVER
2 CLUTCH CABLE
3 JOINT NUT
GC5049100057000X

Fig. 1 Clutch cable adjustment

ADJUSTMENTS

CLUTCH PEDAL HEIGHT

Clutch pedal height can be adjusted by turning the clutch pedal stop bolt located at the upper end of the clutch pedal lever, at the pedal bracket. Clutch pedal height should be the same as brake pedal height.

CLUTCH RELEASE ARM PLAY

1. Measure clutch pedal freeplay. Clutch pedal freeplay should be .6 to .8 inch.
2. If clutch pedal freeplay is not within specifications, adjust clutch cable joint nut to provide a free travel of .08 to .15 inch at release lever, **Fig. 1.**

SHIFT LINKAGE

Check gear shift control lever vertical endplay. Vertical endplay should be 0 to .007 inch. Check distance between instrument panel and gear shift control lever, with transaxle in neutral, **Fig. 2.** Distance should be approximately 8.5 inches, if not adjust.

CLUTCH

REPLACE

1. Refer to "Manual Transaxle, Replace" procedure to remove transaxle.
2. Install suitable tool into pilot bearing to support clutch assembly during removal.
3. Check for X mark or white painted letter on pressure plate and corresponding mark stamped on flywheel. If no markings are found, mark flywheel and pressure plate for assembly purposes.
4. Loosen pressure plate to flywheel mounting bolts 1 turn at a time until spring pressure is released, **Fig. 3.** It may be necessary to use Flywheel Holder tool No. J-35271 or equivalent to hold flywheel in position when loosening bolts.
5. Remove bolts, pressure plate and clutch disc.
6. Reverse procedure to install. Lubricate splines of transaxle input shaft and pilot bearing surface and release bearing with suitable lithium grease. **Torque** pressure plate cover bolts to 17 ft. lbs.

SHIFT CABLE

REPLACE

1. Disconnect battery ground cable at battery.
2. Remove clutch cable joint nut, then disconnect cable from release arm.
3. Remove clutch cable bracket bolts and bracket.
4. Remove cable retaining bolts at clutch pedal.
5. Remove clutch cable from vehicle.
6. Reverse procedure to install. Refer to "Adjustments" to adjust cable.

TRANSAXLE

REPLACE

1. Disconnect battery ground cable.
2. Disconnect clutch cable from release lever and bracket.
3. Disconnect electrical connectors from transaxle, then remove wiring harness to transaxle retaining brackets.
4. Disconnect speedometer cable from transaxle.
5. Remove upper transaxle attaching bolts.
6. Remove starter motor as outlined under "Starter, Replace."
7. Disconnect vacuum hose from pressure sensor.
8. Install an engine support fixture, then raise and support vehicle.
9. Drain lubricant from transaxle.
10. Disconnect gear shift control lever from gear shift shaft.
11. Remove extension rod nut, then remove extension rod with washers.
12. Remove attaching nuts and bolts, then remove exhaust pipe.
13. Remove clutch housing lower cover.
14. Remove left front wheel and tire assembly.
15. Disconnect left tie rod end and ball joint from steering knuckle.

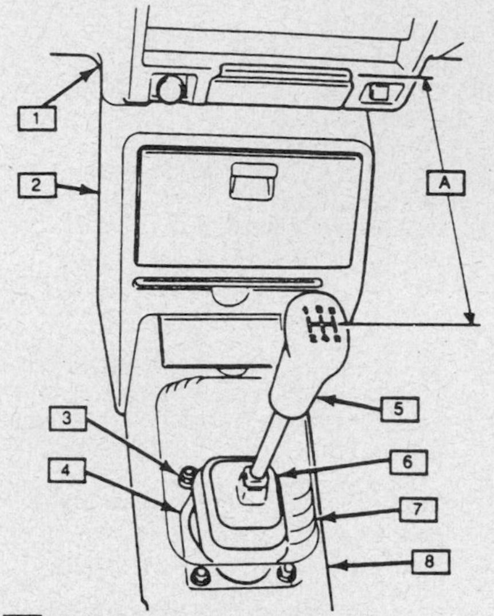

1
2
A
3
4
5
6
7
8
A CONTROL LEVER POSITION DISTANCE
1 INSTRUMENT PANEL
2 CONSOLE BOX
3 CONTROL LEVER HOUSING NUT
4 BOOT COVER
5 CONTROL LEVER KNOB
6 CONTROL LEVER BOOT
7 BOOT NO. 2
8 SHIFT CONTROL LEVER COVER
GC5049100058000X

Fig. 2 Gearshift control lever position

16. Separate drive axles from transaxle, **Fig. 4.** Support drive axles from chassis using wire.
17. Remove lower transaxle to engine attaching bolts and nuts.
18. Support transaxle using a suitable jack.
19. Remove two rear engine mounting nuts, then remove transaxle left hand mounting bracket attaching nuts and bolts and bracket.
20. Lower transaxle and engine assembly to disconnect assembly from stud bolts at rear engine mounting, then pull transaxle outward toward left hand side to disconnect input shaft from clutch assembly.
21. Lower transaxle, then remove from vehicle.
22. Reverse procedure to install. Lubricate splines of transaxle input shaft and pilot bearing surface and release bearing with suitable lithium grease. When installing transaxle, guide right drive axle into transaxle as it is raised into vehicle. Tighten to specifications.

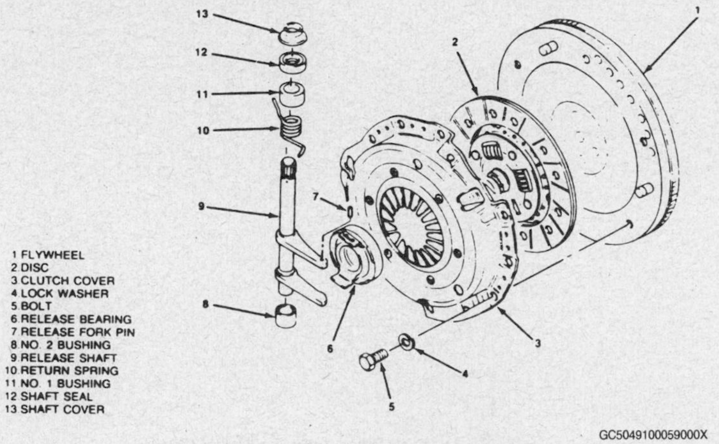
1 FLYWHEEL
2 DISC
3 CLUTCH COVER
4 LOCK WASHER
5 BOLT
6 RELEASE BEARING
7 RELEASE FORK PIN
8 NO. 2 BUSHING
9 RELEASE SHAFT
10 RETURN SPRING
11 NO. 1 BUSHING
12 SHAFT SEAL
13 SHAFT COVER
GC5049100059000X

Fig. 3 Clutch assembly

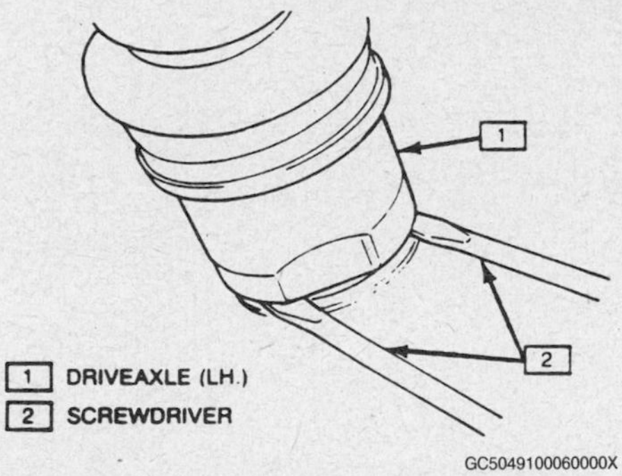
1 DRIVEAXLE (LH.)
2 SCREWDRIVER
GC5049100060000X

Fig. 4 Front drive axle snap ring removal

TIGHTENING SPECIFICATIONS

Component	Torque/Ft. Lbs.
Back-Up Lamp Switch	17
Battery Cable To Terminal	11
Cable Bracket	21
Clutch Cover	17
Clutch Pedal Shaft	15
Clutch Release Lever	12
Extension Rod Nut	29
Flywheel	①
Gear Shift Control Shaft Bolts And Nuts	15

Component	Torque/Ft. Lbs.
Starter	21
Switch Locknut	10
Transaxle Hanger	106①
Transaxle Mounts	44
Transaxle To Engine Bolts	44
Transaxle Oil Drain & Filler Plugs	15
Transaxle Side Cover	106①
Wheel Lug Nuts	44

①—1992-94 models, 45 ft. lbs.; 1995 models, 57.5 ft. lbs.

Rear Axle & Suspension

INDEX

HUB & BEARING

REPLACE

1. Raise and support rear of vehicle, then remove wheel and tire assembly.
2. Remove wheel bearing dust cap from brake drum.
3. Using a chisel, unstake wheel bearing nut, then remove wheel bearing nut and washer.
4. Loosen parking brake cable adjusting nuts, then remove plug from backing plate and back off drum brake adjustment.
5. Using a suitable puller, remove brake drum.
6. Using a brass drift, remove wheel bearings from brake drum.
7. Reverse procedure to install, noting the following:
   a. Fill Hub cavity (A), **Fig. 1,** with lithium wheel bearing grease.
   b. Install wheel bearings and spacer using Bearing and Hub Installer tool Nos. J-7079-2 and J-34842 or equivalents. **Wheel bearing should be installed with sealed side facing outward, Fig. 1.**
   c. Install brake drum on spindle. Tighten wheel bearing nut to specifications, then stake nut in position.
   d. After completing installation, adjust drum brake and parking brake.
   e. Bleed and check brake system for proper operation prior to moving vehicle.

STRUT

REPLACE

1. **On two door models,** open hatchback for access to upper strut mounting.
2. **On four door models,** open trunk for access to upper strut mounting.
3. **On all models,** raise and support rear of vehicle, then remove wheel and tire assembly.
4. Support suspension using a suitable jack.
5. Remove strut upper support nuts, then push downward on strut, **Fig. 2.**
6. Remove strut lower mounting bolt, **Fig. 3.**
7. Separate strut from rear suspension knuckle, by compressing strut. **If strut is difficult to remove, open slit on knuckle just enough to allow strut removal.**
8. Reverse procedure to install. When installing strut, align projection on strut with slit on rear suspension knuckle, **Fig. 4.**

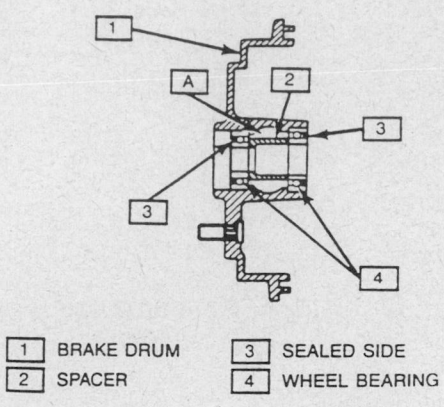

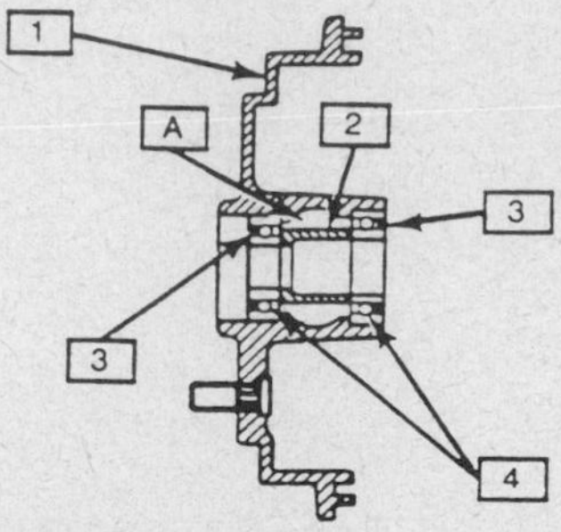
1
A
2
3
3
4
1 BRAKE DRUM
2 SPACER
3 SEALED SIDE
4 WHEEL BEARING
GC3039100227000X

Fig. 1 Wheel bearing installation

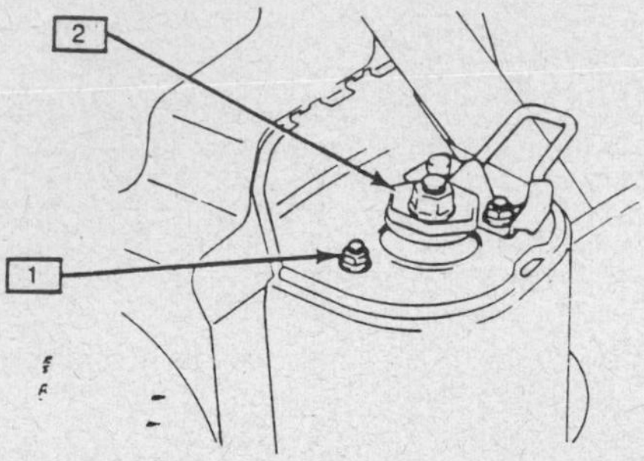
2
1
1 SUPPORT NUT
2 STRUT
GC2039100086000X

Fig. 2 Strut upper attaching nuts

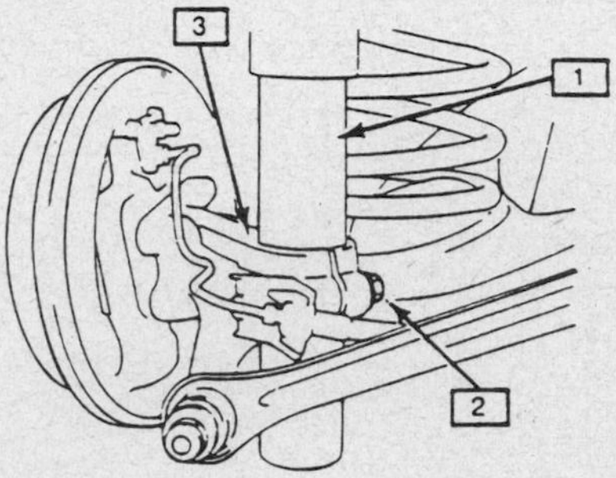
3
1
2
1 STRUT
2 MOUNT BOLT
3 KNUCKLE
GC2039100087000X

Fig. 3 Strut lower mounting bolt

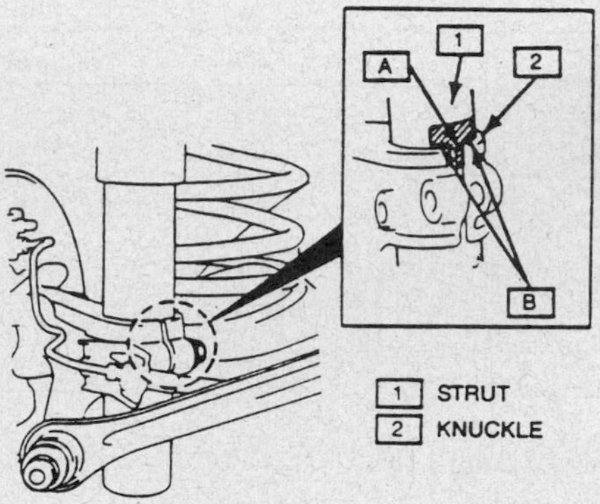
1
A
2
B
1 STRUT
2 KNUCKLE
GC2039100088000X

Fig. 4 Strut to rear suspension knuckle position

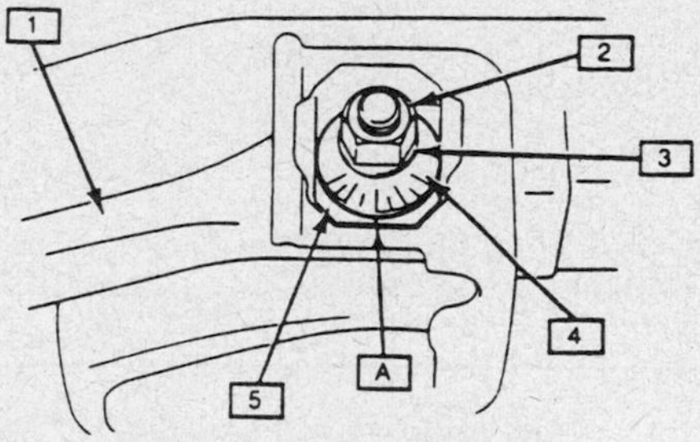
1
2
3
4
A
5
1 CONTROL ROD
2 INSIDE NUT
3 LOCK WASHER
4 WASHER
5 CAR BODY
GC2039100089000X

Fig. 5 Control rod inner bolt

COIL SPRING
REPLACE

1. Raise and support rear of vehicle, then remove wheel and tire assembly.
2. Place alignment marks on control rod and control rod washer (A), **Fig. 5,** for setting toe during installation.
3. Remove control rod to body attaching bolt, then separate control rod from bracket.
4. From wheel side of control rod, remove nut from rear suspension knuckle stud, then disconnect control rod.
5. Loosen, but do not remove suspension arm rear attaching nut.
6. Loosen rear suspension knuckle lower mounting nut. Position a suitable jack under suspension arm, then remove knuckle lower mounting nut.
7. Raise lower arm slightly to allow removal of rear suspension knuckle lower mounting bolt.
8. Disengage rear suspension knuckle from suspension arm, then carefully lower suspension arm and remove coil spring, **Fig. 6.**
9. Remove remaining suspension arm attaching bolts and nuts and remove suspension arm, if necessary.
10. Reverse procedure to install. When installing spring, position spring end to stepped portion of suspension arm, **Fig. 7.** When installing control rod to body bracket, align marks made on washer and control rod during removal. **Do not tighten control rod or suspension arm attaching nuts and bolts until after vehicle has been lowered.**

CONTROL ARM
REPLACE

1. Raise and support rear of vehicle, then remove wheel and tire assembly.
2. Remove E-ring, then detach brake hose from control rod.
3. Place alignment marks on control rod and control rod washer at body brack-

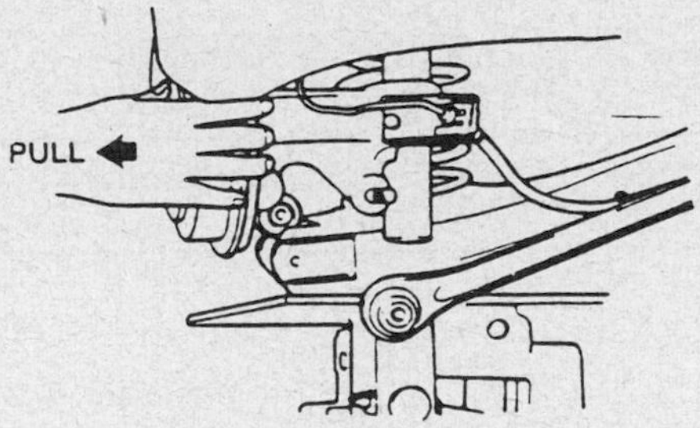
PULL

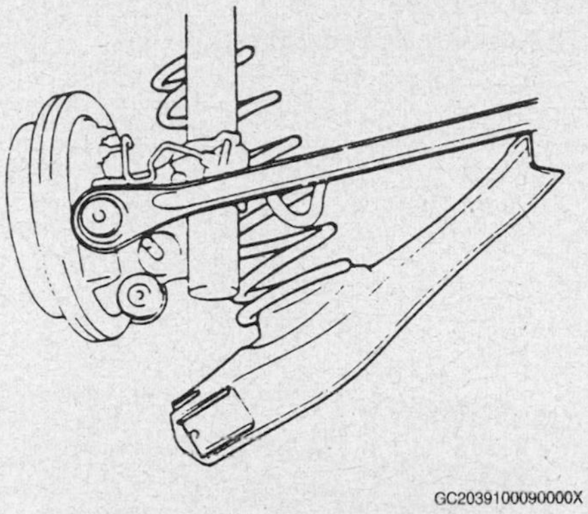
GC2039100090000X

Fig. 6 Coil spring removal

et for setting toe during installation, **Fig. 5.**

4. Remove control rod to rear suspension knuckle attaching nut, **Fig. 8.**
5. Remove control rod to body bracket bolt, then remove control rod.
6. Reverse procedure to install. Position control rod to vehicle as shown in **Fig. 9.** When installing control rod to body bracket, align marks made on washer and control rod during removal. **Do not tighten control rod attaching nuts and bolts until after vehicle has been lowered.**

KNUCKLE

REPLACE

1. Raise and support rear of vehicle, then remove wheel and tire assembly.

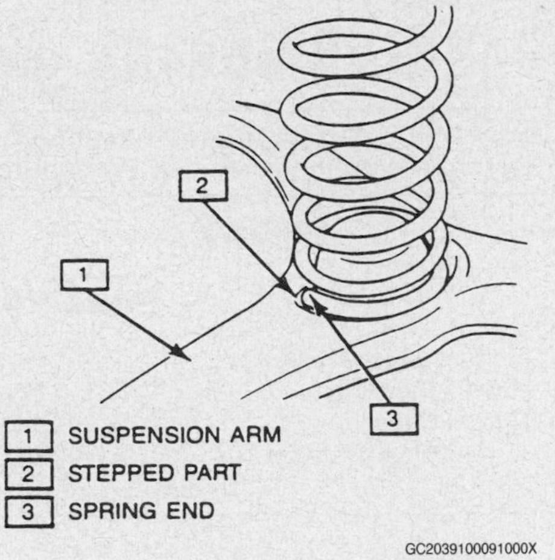
1
2
3
1 SUSPENSION ARM
2 STEPPED PART
3 SPRING END
GC2039100091000X

Fig. 7 Coil spring installation

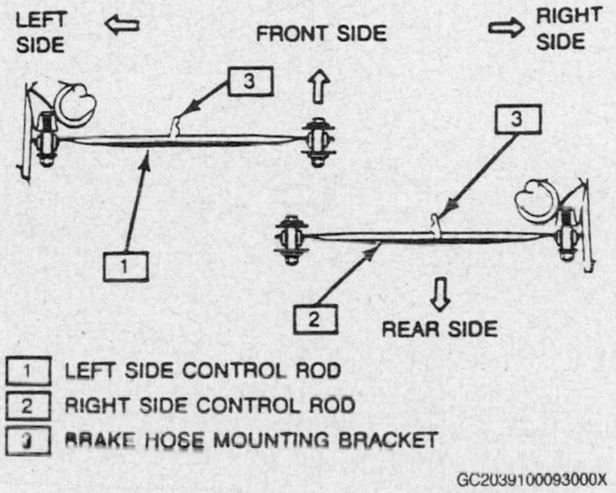
LEFT SIDE
FRONT SIDE
RIGHT SIDE
REAR SIDE
1 LEFT SIDE CONTROL ROD
2 RIGHT SIDE CONTROL ROD
3 BRAKE HOSE MOUNTING BRACKET
GC2039100093000X

Fig. 9 Control arm installation

2. Remove brake drum, then disconnect brake hose from rear suspension knuckle bracket.
3. Disconnect brake line from wheel cylinder. Cap brake line and wheel cylinder fitting bore.
4. Remove brake backing plate attaching bolts, then remove brake backing plate.
5. Position a suitable jack under suspension arm.
6. Place alignment marks on control rod and control rod washer at body bracket for setting toe during installation.

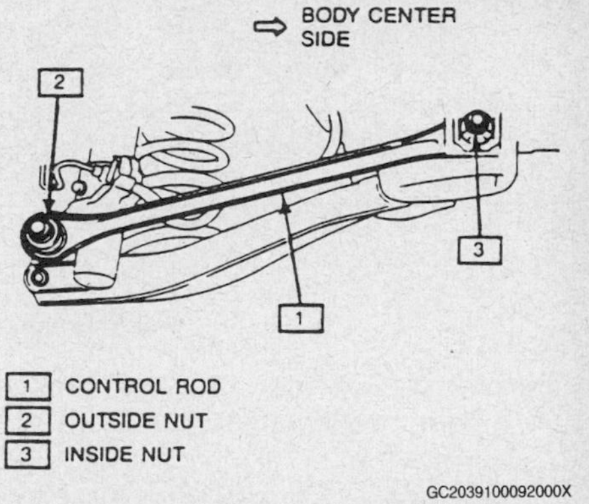
BODY CENTER SIDE
1 CONTROL ROD
2 OUTSIDE NUT
3 INSIDE NUT
GC2039100092000X

Fig. 8 Control arm installation

7. Remove control rod to body bracket attaching nut and washer.
8. Remove control rod to rear suspension knuckle stud nut, then remove control rod.
9. Remove strut to rear suspension knuckle attaching bolt.
10. Remove strut to suspension arm attaching bolt, then separate rear suspension knuckle from suspension arm and strut. **If strut is difficult to remove, open slit on knuckle just enough to allow strut removal.**
11. Reverse procedure to install. When installing control rod to body bracket, align marks made on washer and control rod during removal. **Do not tighten control rod or suspension arm attaching nuts and bolts until after vehicle has been lowered.** Prior to installation, apply sealer to mating surface of brake backing plate and rear suspension knuckle. When installing brake drum, tighten wheel bearing nut to specification listed at the end of this section, then stake nut in place using a suitable chisel. After completing installation, adjust and bleed brake system, then check for proper brake operation before moving vehicle.

TIGHTENING SPECIFICATIONS

Component	Torque/Ft. Lbs.
Brake Backing Plate Retaining Nuts	17
Brake Line Fitting To Wheel Cylinder	12
Brake Line Bracket	17
Control Rod Nuts	59
Rear Suspension Knuckle Arm Lower Mounting Nut	37
Spindle Nut	129
Suspension Arm Front Mounting	33
Suspension Arm To Knuckle	37
Suspension Arm Rear Nut	37

Component	Torque/Ft. Lbs.
Stabilizer Mounting	19
Stabilizer Link To Bar	38
Stabilizer Link To Control Arm	19
Strut Lower Mounting Bolt	44
Strut Support Nut	24
Strut Upper Nut	37
Wheel Bearing Retaining Nut	74①
Wheel Lug Nuts	44

①—Tighten nut, then stake in position.

Front Suspension & Steering

NOTE: On Air Bag Equipped Models, Refer To "Air Bag System Precautions" Located In The Front Of This Manual For System Disarming & Arming Procedures.

INDEX

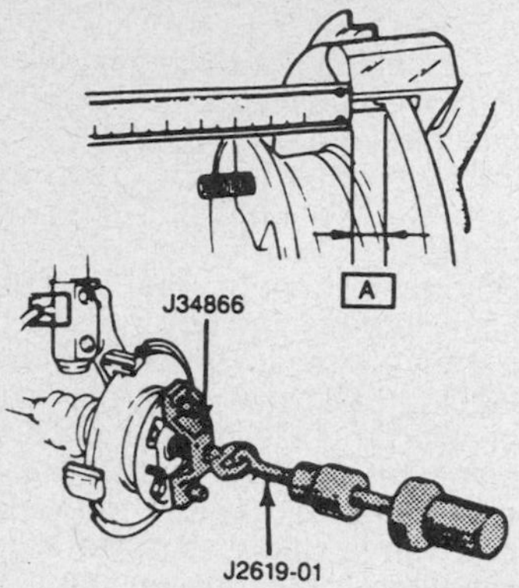

A
J34866
J2619-01

A NOTE DIMENSION "A" AS SHOWN BEFORE HUB REMOVAL AS AN AID IN INSTALLATION.

GC3039100228000X

Fig. 1 Hub dimension

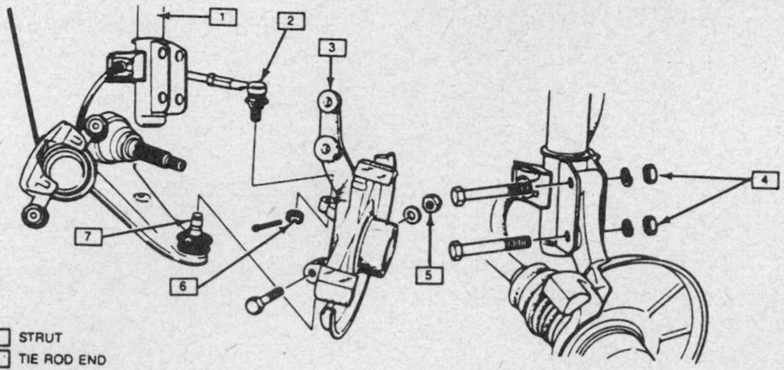

1
2
3
4
5
6
7

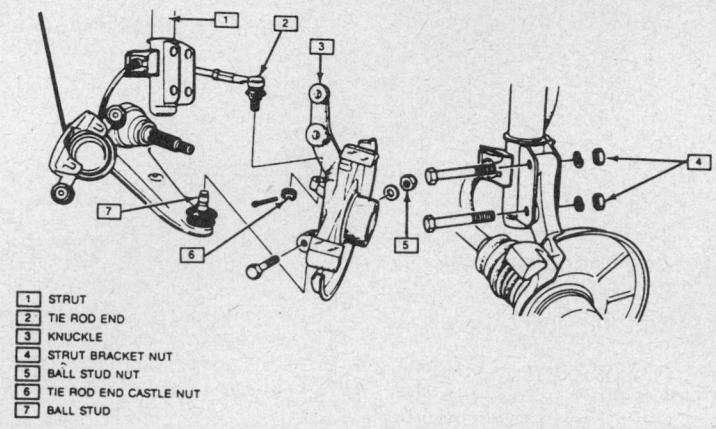

1 STRUT
2 TIE ROD END
3 KNUCKLE
4 STRUT BRACKET NUT
5 BALL STUD NUT
6 TIE ROD END CASTLE NUT
7 BALL STUD

GC2029100177000X

Fig. 2 Steering knuckle removal

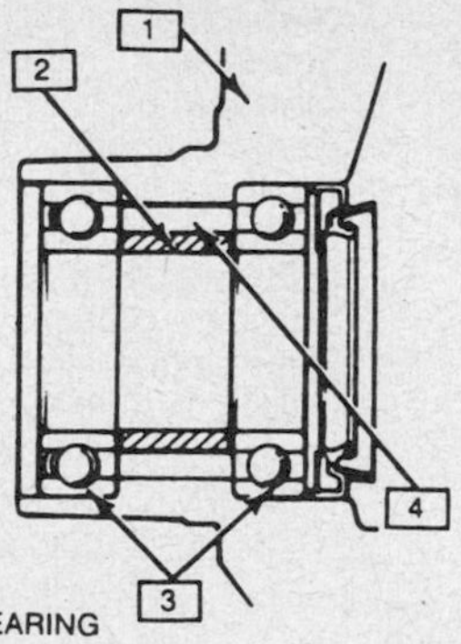

1
2
3
4

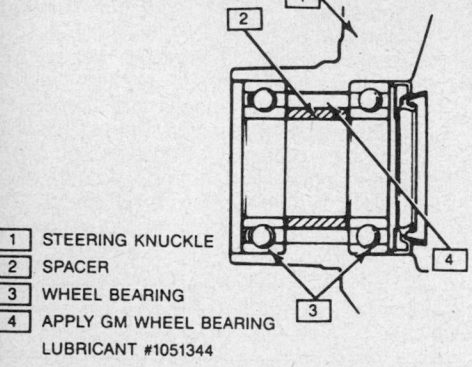

1 STEERING KNUCKLE
2 SPACER
3 WHEEL BEARING
4 APPLY GM WHEEL BEARING LUBRICANT #1051344

GC2029100178000X

Fig. 3 Steering knuckle hub bearings & seal

PRECAUTIONS

AIR BAG SYSTEMS

Refer to "Air Bag System Precautions" in the front of this manual for system disarming and arming procedures.

HUB & BEARING

REPLACE

When checking wheel bearings, raise and support front of vehicle, then rotate wheel and tire assembly to check bearing for smoothness of rotation and noise. Also check wheel bearing endplay with a dial indicator. Wheel bearing endplay should not exceed .016 inch.

REMOVAL

1. Raise and support vehicle, then remove front wheel and tire assembly.
2. Unstake, then remove hub retaining nut.
3. Remove caliper bolts, then caliper with brake line attached. Suspend caliper from chassis with wire.
4. Refer to **Fig. 1,** and measure dimension A for assembly reference. Pull hub out of knuckle.
5. Disconnect tie rod end from knuckle with Tie Rod End Remover tool No. J-21687-02 or equivalent.
6. Remove strut to knuckle bolts and then ball joint stud pinch bolt, **Fig. 2.**
7. Remove knuckle.
8. Using a drift, remove outer, then inner bearing from knuckle.

INSTALLATION

1. Apply suitable grease to balls and oil seal lips of wheel bearings. Fill area A, **Fig. 3**, to approximately 40 percent of capacity with suitable grease.
2. Install wheel bearings using Bearing Installer tool No. J-34856 or equivalent. **Install wheel bearings with sealed side facing outward. Also ensure spacer is spacer is snug and centered between inner and outer bearings.**

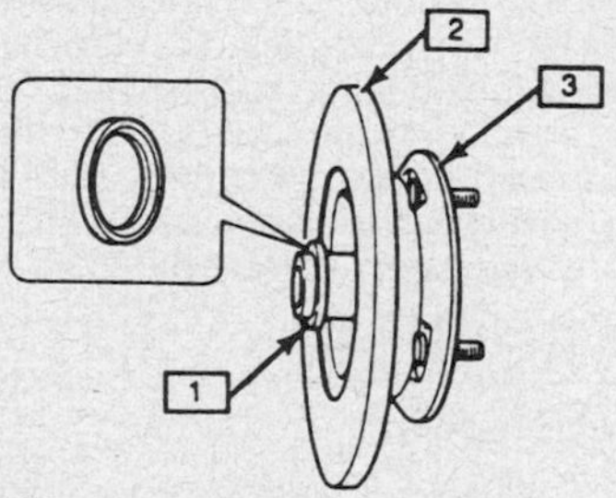

1
2
3

1 SPACER
2 BRAKE DISC
3 WHEEL HUB

GC2029100179000X

Fig. 4 Wheel hub spacer installation

3. Install wheel bearing seal (5), **Fig. 3,** using Seal Installer tool No. J-34881 or equivalent.
4. Install spacer on hub with bevel side first, **Fig. 4.**
5. Check that wheel bearing spacer bore is aligned with bearing bores. If not, move spacer until aligned.
6. Using plastic hammer, tap hub lightly into knuckle, taking care that alignment is maintained.
7. Using Wheel Hub Installer tool No. J-34856 and Handle tool No. J-7079-2 or equivalent, drive hub until dimension A, noted in step 4, is obtained.
8. Install brake caliper.
9. Tighten caliper bolts to specifications.
10. Tighten driveshaft castle nut to specifications

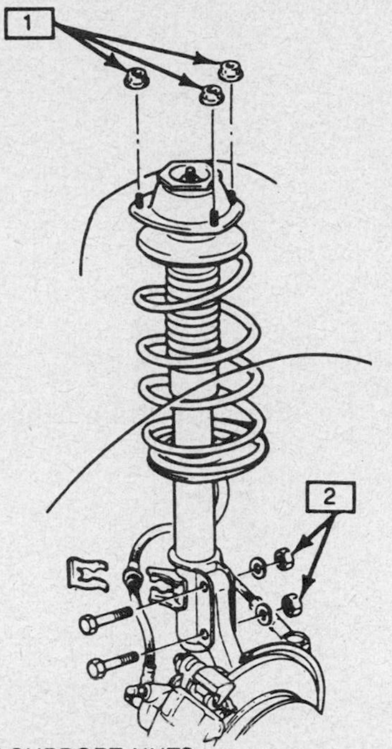
1
2
1 STRUT SUPPORT NUTS
2 STRUT BRACKET BOLTS
GC2029100184000X

Fig. 5 Strut attaching nut bolt locations

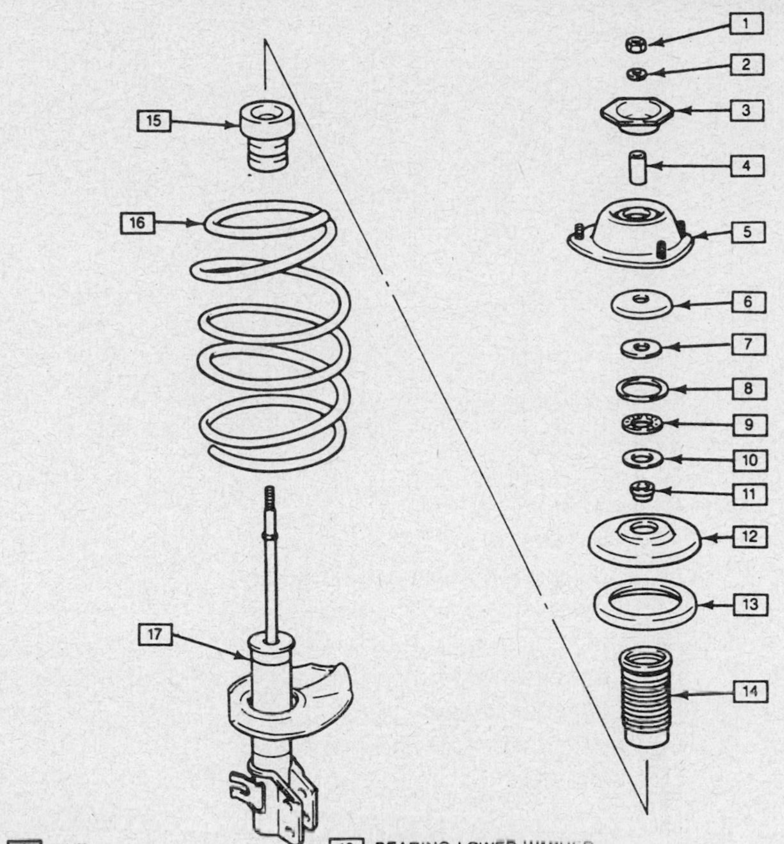
1
2
3
4
5
6
7
8
9
10
11
12
13
14
15
16
17
1 NUT
2 WASHER
3 STOPPER
4 INNER SPACER
5 SUPPORT COMP.
6 BEARING SEAT
7 BEARING UPPER WASHER
8 BEARING SEAL
9 BEARING
10 BEARING LOWER WASHER
11 BEARING SPACER
12 COIL SPRING UPPER SEAT
13 COIL SPRING SEAT
14 STRUT COVER
15 BUMP STOPPER
16 COIL SPRING
17 STRUT
GC2029100185000X

Fig. 6 Exploded view of strut assembly

11. Stake nut in position.
12. Install wheel and tire assembly, then lower vehiclo.

STRUT

REPLACE

1. Raise and support vehicle allowing front suspension to hang tree.
2. Remove front wheel and tire assembly.
3. Remove E-clip from brake hose and disengage hose from strut bracket, **Fig. 5.**
4. Support lower control arm and knuckle assembly, then remove strut to knuckle bolts.
5. Remove upper strut mount nuts, then remove strut from vehicle.
6. Reverse procedure to install.

STRUT SERVICE

1. Mount strut in a spring compressor.
2. Compress spring approximately 1/2 inch.
3. Remove nut from strut shaft and remove components, **Fig. 6.**
4. Reverse procedure to assemble. Compress spring so strut shaft protrudes through cap by about 1 inch. Tighten nut to specifications.

CONTROL ARM

REPLACE

1. Raise and support vehicle, then remove wheel and tire assembly.
2. Remove ball joint stud to steering knuckle pinch bolt, **Fig. 7.**
3. Remove control arm bracket nut, then remove bracket bolts.
4. Remove control arm and bracket.
5. If control arm bushing is to be replaced, proceed as follows:
   a. Remove lower control arm as outlined under "Lower Control Arm, Replace."
   b. Press rear bushing from control arm, **Fig. 7.**
   c. Cut flange off front bushing, then press front bushing from control arm, **Fig. 8.**
   d. Apply soap and water to outer surface of front bushing, then press front bushing into control arm until it is centered.
   e. Position rear bushing to control arm, then drive bushing into control arm, **Fig. 9 and 10.**
6. Reverse procedure to install.

MANUAL STEERING GEAR

REPLACE

1. Slide driver's seat rearward.
2. Pull back front part of floor mat on driver's side, then remove steering shaft joint cover.
3. Loosen steering shaft upper joint bolt without removing, **Fig. 11.**
4. Remove steering shaft lower joint bolt and disconnect lower joint from pinion.
5. Raise and properly support vehicle.
6. Remove front wheel and tire assemblies.
7. Remove cotter pins and castle nuts from tie rod ends.
8. Using tie rod end remover J-21687-02 or equivalent, disconnect tie rods from knuckles.
9. Remove steering gear housing mounting bolts, brackets and steering gear, **Fig. 12.**
10. Reverse procedure to install.

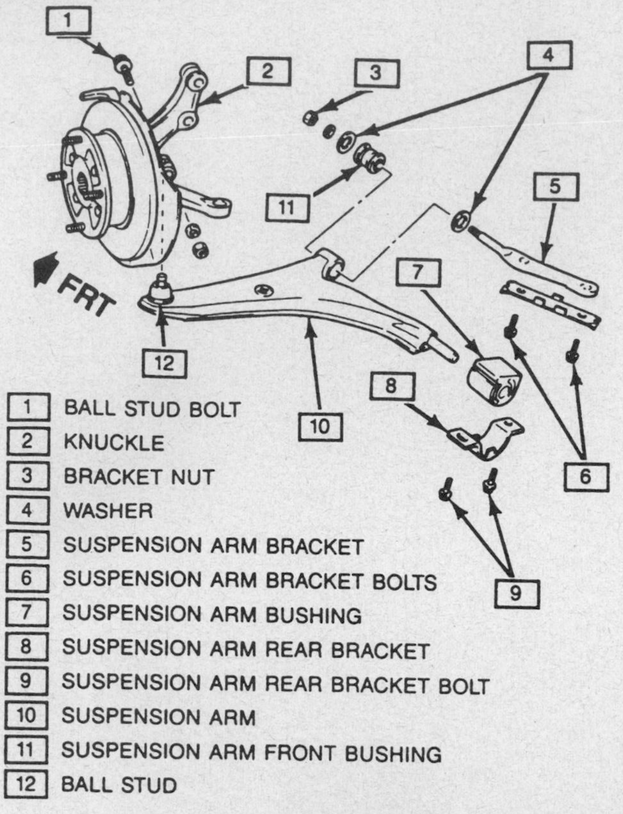
FRT
1 BALL STUD BOLT
2 KNUCKLE
3 BRACKET NUT
4 WASHER
5 SUSPENSION ARM BRACKET
6 SUSPENSION ARM BRACKET BOLTS
7 SUSPENSION ARM BUSHING
8 SUSPENSION ARM REAR BRACKET
9 SUSPENSION ARM REAR BRACKET BOLT
10 SUSPENSION ARM
11 SUSPENSION ARM FRONT BUSHING
12 BALL STUD
GC2029100180000X

Fig. 7 Lower control arm replacement

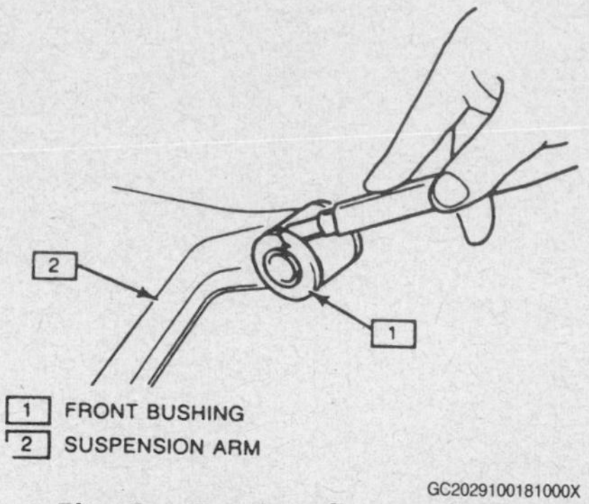
1 FRONT BUSHING
2 SUSPENSION ARM
GC2029100181000X

Fig. 8 Cutting flange from control arm front bushing

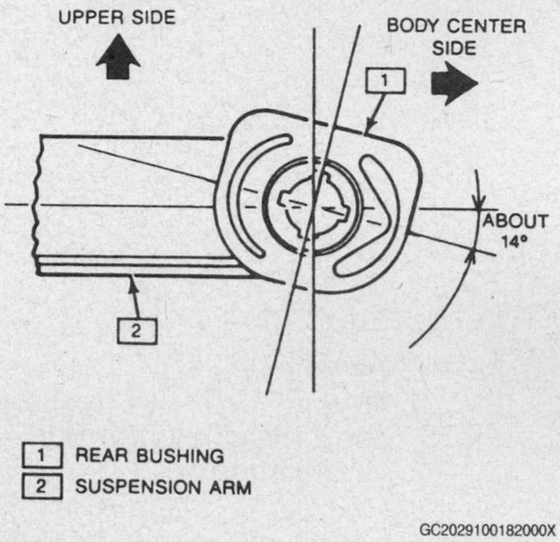
UPPER SIDE
BODY CENTER SIDE
ABOUT 14°
1 REAR BUSHING
2 SUSPENSION ARM
GC2029100182000X

Fig. 9 Rear bushing to control arm installation

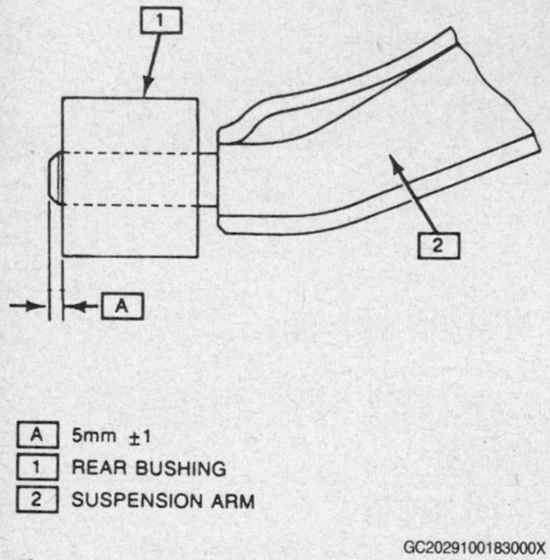
A 5mm ±1
1 REAR BUSHING
2 SUSPENSION ARM
GC2029100183000X

Fig. 10 Rear bushing positioning

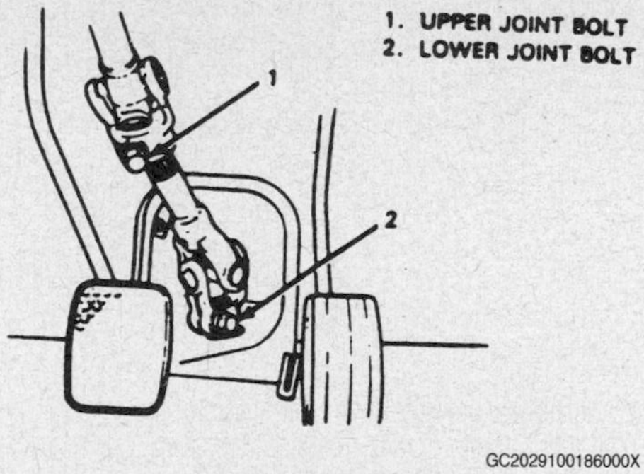
1. UPPER JOINT BOLT
2. LOWER JOINT BOLT
GC2029100186000X

Fig. 11 Steering shaft upper & lower joint bolts

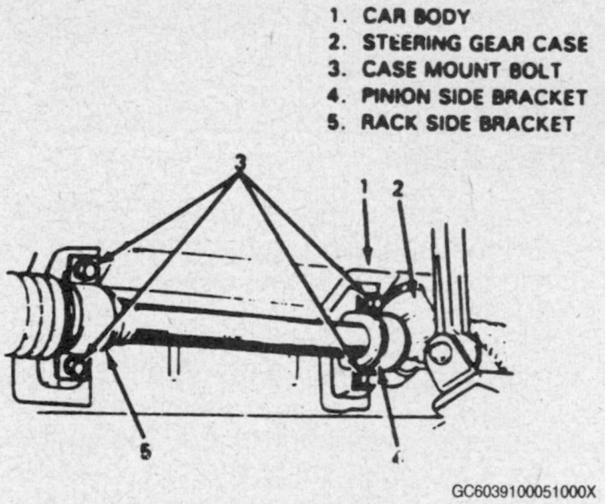
1. CAR BODY
2. STEERING GEAR CASE
3. CASE MOUNT BOLT
4. PINION SIDE BRACKET
5. RACK SIDE BRACKET
GC6039100051000X

Fig. 12 Steering gear attaching bolts & brackets

TIGHTENING SPECIFICATIONS

Component	Torque/Ft. Lbs.
Ball Joint Stud	44
Brake Caliper To Knuckle	20
Control Arm Front Bracket	66
Control Arm Rear Bracket	32
Front Control Arm Bracket	92
Hub Bearing	129①
Stabilizer Bar Link	20
Stabilizer Bar Mounting	20
Steering Gear Mounting Bracket	18

Component	Torque/Ft. Lbs.
Steering Shaft Coupling	18
Strut Bracket	59
Strut Nut	37
Strut Upper Mounting	20
Tie Rod Ball	63
Tie Rod End Castle	32
Tie Rod End Locknut	32
Wheel Lug Nuts	44

①—After tightening, stake nut in position.

Wheel Alignment

INDEX

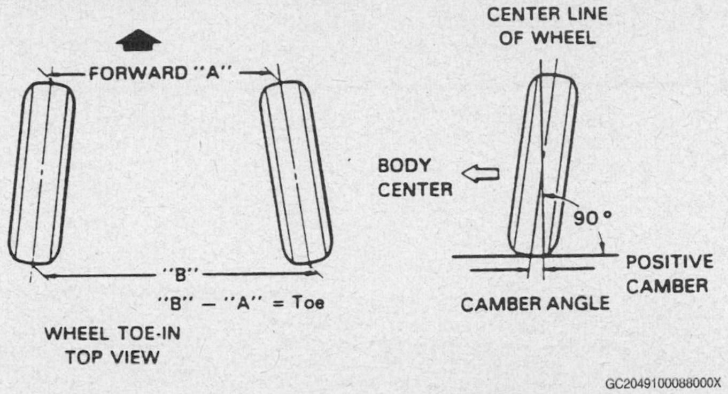
FORWARD "A"
"B"
"B" – "A" = Toe
WHEEL TOE-IN
TOP VIEW
CENTER LINE
OF WHEEL
BODY
CENTER
90°
POSITIVE
CAMBER
CAMBER ANGLE
GC2049100088000X

Fig. 1 Suspension geometry

DESCRIPTION

Wheel alignment, is the angular relationship between the wheels, suspension attaching parts and ground. The angle of the knuckle away from the vertical, pointing in or out of wheels, tilt of the wheels from vertical (when viewed from front of vehicle) and tilt of suspension members from vertical (when viewed from side of vehicle), all of these are involved in proper alignment, **Fig. 1.**

CASTER

Caster is tilting of the front steering axis either forward or backward from the vertical (when viewed from side of vehicle). A backward tilt is positive (+) and a forward tilt is negative (-). On short and long arm type suspensions you cannot see a caster angle without using a special instrument, but if you look straight down from the top of the upper control arm to the ground you would find that ball joints do not line up (fore and aft) when a caster angle other than 0° is present.

CAMBER

Camber is the tilting of front and rear wheels from the vertical when viewed from front of vehicle. When wheels tilt outward at top, camber is positive (+). When wheels tilt inward, camber is negative (MI). Amount of tilt is measured in degrees from the vertical and this is camber angle.

TOE

Toe is the turning in or out of wheels. The purpose of toe is to ensure parallel rolling of wheels. Excessive toe-in or toe-out may increase tire wear. Toe also serves to offset small deflections of the suspension which occurs when vehicle is moving.

PRELIMINARY INSPECTION

Steering and vibration problems are not always the result of alignment. An additional problem to be checked is tire lead due to worn or improperly manufactured tires. "Lead" is the deviation of the vehicle from a straight path on a level road without hand pressure on the steering wheel.

To insure correct alignment readings and alignment specifications, the following checks and inspections should be made.

1. Check tire for proper inflation and thread wear.
2. Check for loose ball joints and tie rod ends. If excessive looseness is noted, replace defective parts before adjusting toe.
3. Check for wheel and tire assembly runout.
4. Check trim heights. If not within specifications, correct before adjusting toe.
5. Check for loose control arms.
6. Check for loose or missing stabilizer bar components.
7. Consideration must be given to excess loads, such as tool boxes, kegs, etc. If excess load is normally carried in vehicle, it should remain during alignment checks.

FRONT WHEEL ALIGNMENT

CAMBER & CASTER

1. Position vehicle on an alignment fixture following manufacturer's instructions and check caster and camber angles. Bumper should be bounced three times before inspection, to prevent incorrect reading.
2. Camber and caster cannot be adjusted. Should either be found out of specification, locate the cause first.
3. If improper alignment is caused by damaged, worn or loose suspension parts, they should be replaced. If vehicle body or chassis is damaged, it should be repaired.

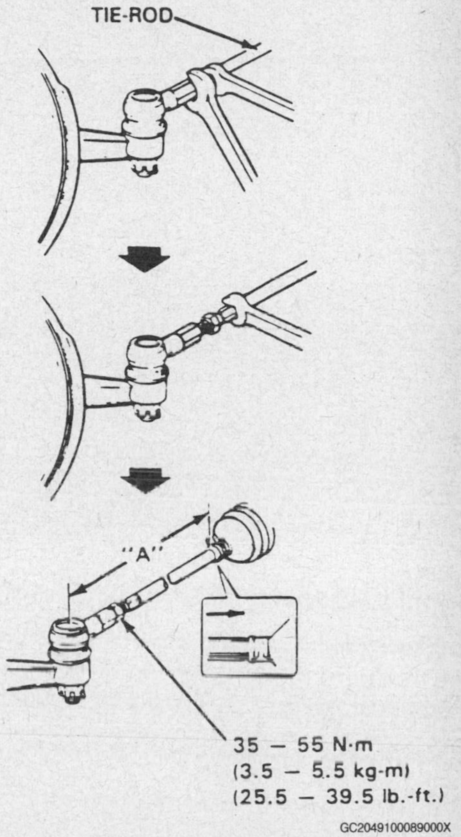
TIE-ROD
"A"
35 – 55 N·m
(3.5 – 5.5 kg-m)
(25.5 – 39.5 lb.-ft.)
GC2049100089000X

Fig. 2 Front wheel toe adjustment

TOE

1. Loosen right and left tie rod end locknuts, **Fig. 2.**
2. Apply grease between tie rods and rack boots.
3. Turn right and left tie rods by the same amount to align toe to specification. **Right and left tie rods should become equal in length.**
4. After adjustment, tighten locknuts and ensure rack boots are not twisted.

STEERING ANGLE

When a tie rod or tie rod end is replaced, check toe and steering angle with turning radius gages. If steering angle is not correct, check right and left tie rods for equal length.

REAR WHEEL ALIGNMENT

CAMBER

Camber cannot be adjusted. Should camber be found out of specification, locate the cause. If improper alignment is caused by damaged, worn or loose suspension parts, they should be replaced. If vehicle body or chassis is damaged, it should be repaired.

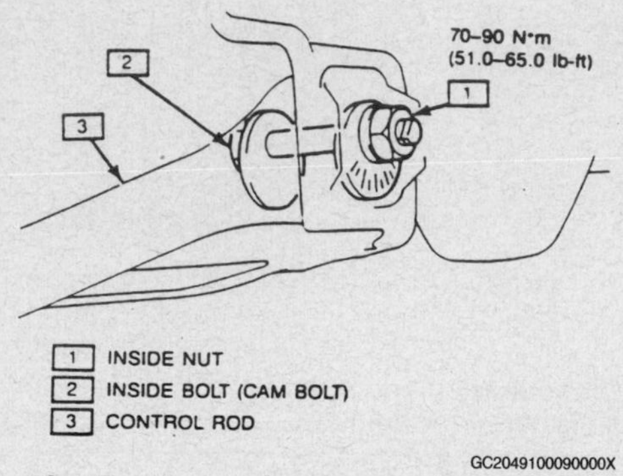
70–90 N·m
(51.0–65.0 lb-ft)
1
2
3
1 INSIDE NUT
2 INSIDE BOLT (CAM BOLT)
3 CONTROL ROD
GC2049100090000X

Fig. 3 Rear wheel toe adjustment.

TOE

The rear wheel toe is adjusted by the inner control arm cam bolt, **Fig. 3.** If toe is found to out of specification, loosen left and right inner control arm cam bolt nuts, then rotate cam bolts by equal amounts to correct toe setting. After completing adjustment, **torque** cam bolt nuts to 51 to 65 ft. lbs.

GEO STORM (R Car)

NOTE: Refer To The Rear Of This Manual For Vehicle Manufacturer's Special Tool Suppliers.

INDEX OF SERVICE OPERATIONS

NOTE: For Service Operations Not Listed Below, Refer To The Table Of Contents In The Front Of This Manual.

Specifications

GENERAL ENGINE SPECIFICATIONS

Year	Engine		Fuel System	Bore & Stroke	Comp. Ratio	Net HP @ RPM③	Maximum Torque Ft. Lbs. @ RPM	Normal Oil Pressure psi
	Liter/CID①	VIN Code ②						
1992–93	1.6L/4-97④	6	MFI	3.15 x 3.11	9.1	95 @ 5800	97 @ 4800	43.5–72.5⑥
	1.8L/4-110⑤	8	MFI	3.15 x 3.54	9.7	140 @ 6400	120 @ 4600	71⑥

①—CID: Cubic Inch Displacement.
②—The eighth digit of the VIN denotes engine code.
③—Ratings are net, as installed in vehicle.
④—Single overhead cam.
⑤—Double overhead cams.
⑥—At 3000 RPM.

TUNE UP SPECIFICATIONS

Year & Engine/ VIN Code ①	Spark Plug Gap	Ignition Timing BTDC				Curb Idle Speed ②		Fast Idle Speed		Fuel Pump Pressure psi
		Firing Order Fig. ③	Man. Trans.	Auto. Trans.	Mark Fig.	Man. Trans.	Auto. Trans.	Man. Trans.	Auto. Trans.	
1992										
1.6L/4-97(6) SOHC	.041	A	10⑥	10⑥	B	850④	940N④	④	④	⑤
1.8L/4-110(8) DOHC	.041	A	10⑥	10⑥	B	800④	800N④	④	④	⑤
1993										
1.6L/4-97(6) SOHC	.041	A	10⑥	10⑥	B	850④	940N④	④	④	30-46⑦
1.8L/4-110(8) DOHC	.041	A	10⑥	10⑥	B	800④	800N④	④	④	41-47⑦

BTDC—Before Top Dead Center.
DOHC—Dual Over Head Cams.
SOHC—Single Over Head Cam.
①—The eighth digit of the Vehicle Identification Number (VIN) denotes engine code.
②—N: Neutral.
③—Before disconnecting wires from distributor cap, determine location of No.1 wire in cap, as distributor position may have been altered from that shown at end of this chart.
④—Controlled by ECM, no adjustment.
⑤—Loosen fuel tank filler cap to relieve fuel vapor pressure. With shop towel wrapped around fuel pressure tap to prevent fuel spillage, connect a suitable fuel pressure gauge to fuel pressure tap. Check fuel pressure with engine idling. Fuel pressure should be 35 to 42 psi. with vacuum hose disconnected from fuel pressure regulator. Fuel pressure should be 25 to 30 psi. with vacuum hose connected to fuel pressure regulator.
⑥—Connect jumper wire between ALDL connector terminals 1 and 3. REfer to Fig. C for ALDL connector location.
⑦—Loosen fuel tank filler cap to relieve fuel vapor pressure. With shop towel wrapped around fuel pressure tap to prevent fuel spillage, connect a suitable fuel pressure gauge to fuel pressure tap. Check fuel pressure with engine idling.

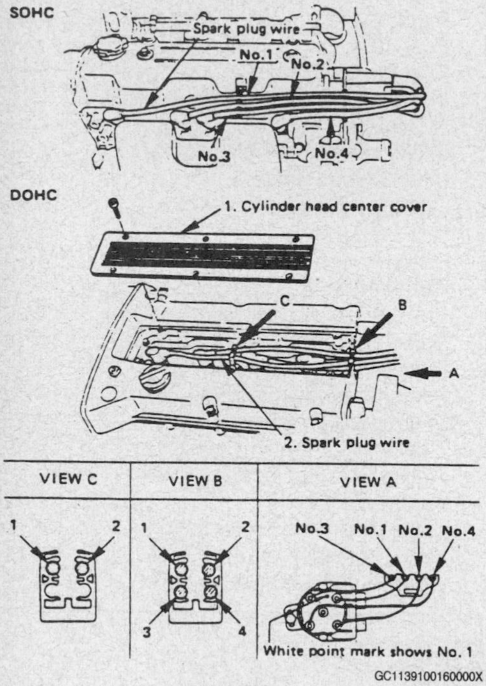
SOHC
Spark plug wire
No.1
No.2
No.3
No.4
DOHC
1. Cylinder head center cover
C
B
A
2. Spark plug wire
VIEW C
VIEW B
VIEW A
No.3 No.1 No.2 No.4
White point mark shows No. 1
GC1139100160000X

Fig. A

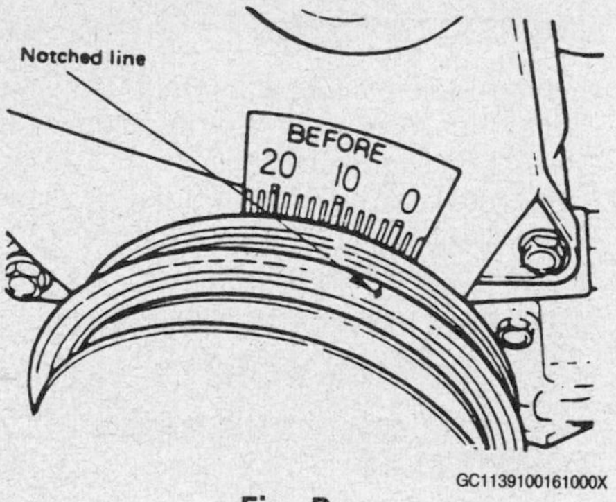
Notched line
BEFORE
20 10 0
GC1139100161000X

Fig. B

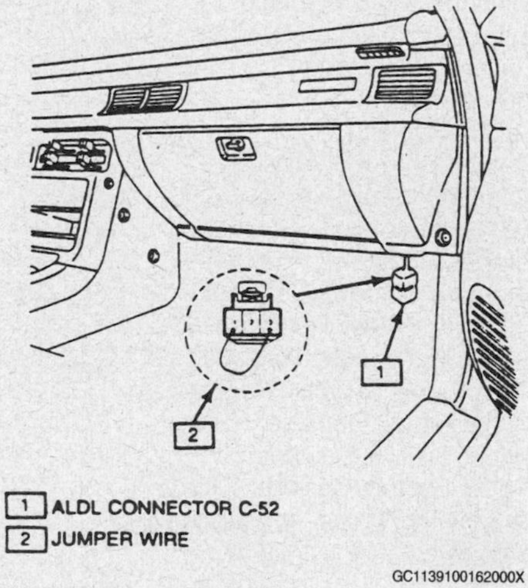
1
2
1 ALDL CONNECTOR C-52
2 JUMPER WIRE
GC1139100162000X

Fig. C

FRONT WHEEL ALIGNMENT SPECIFICATIONS

Year	Model	Caster Angle, Degrees		Camber Angle, Degrees		Toe In Inch
		Limits	Desired	Limits	Desired	
1992	Storm	+3.5 to +5.5	+4	-1.25 to +.25	-.5	-.039 to +.039
1993	Storm	+3.5 to +5.5	+4	-1.25 to +.25	-.5	-.08 to +.08

REAR WHEEL ALIGNMENT SPECIFICATIONS

Year	Model	Caster Angle, Degrees		Camber Angle, Degrees		Toe In Inch
		Limits	Desired	Limits	Desired	
1992	Storm	+4 to +6	+5	-1.25 to +.25	-.5	-.039 to +.118
1993	Storm	+4 to +6	+5	-1.25 to +.25	-.5	-.08 to +.24

COOLING SYSTEM & CAPACITY DATA

Year	Engine (VIN)	Coolant Capacity Qts.		Radiator Cap Relief Pressure, Lbs.	Thermo. Opening Temp. °F.	Fuel Tank Gals.	Engine Oil w/Filter Qts.③	Transaxle Oil	
		Automatic Transmission	Manual Transmission					Manual Transaxle, Pts.	Auto Transaxle, Qts.①
1992–93	1.6L/4-97 (6)	7.7	7.2	14.2	180°	12.4	3.2③	4	②
	1.8L/4-110 (8)	7.8	7.3	14.2	180°	12.4	4③	4	②

①—Approximate, make final check w/dipstick.

②—3 speed, 6.9 qts., 4 speed, 7 qts.

③—Includes filter.

LUBRICANT DATA

Year	Model	Lubricant Type			
		Transaxle		Power Steering	Brake System
		Manual	Automatic		
1992–93	All	Synchromesh Transmission Fluid①	Dexron II	Power Steering Fluid②	DOT 3

①—GM Part No. 12345349 or equivalent.

②—Meeting GM Specification No. 9985010

Electrical

NOTE: On Air Bag Equipped Models, Refer To "Air Bag System Precautions" Located In The Front Of This Manual For System Disarming & Arming Procedures.

INDEX

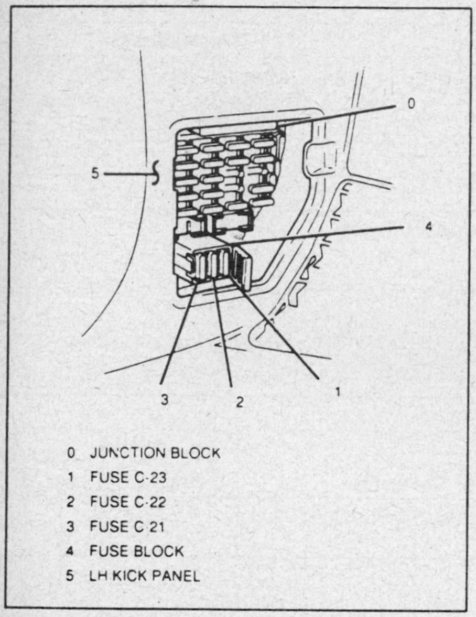
0
5
4
3
2
1
0 JUNCTION BLOCK
1 FUSE C-23
2 FUSE C-22
3 FUSE C 21
4 FUSE BLOCK
5 LH KICK PANEL

GC9049200127000X

Fig. 1 Fuse panel location

PRECAUTIONS

AIR BAG SYSTEMS

Refer to "Air Bag System Precautions" in the front of this manual for system disarming and arming procedures.

FUEL PRESSURE RELIEF

1. Loosen fuel filler cap to relieve fuel tank pressure.
2. Remove fuel pump relay from fuse and relay box.
3. Start engine and allow to stall.
4. Crank engine for an additional three seconds to assure relief of any remaining fuel pressure.
5. Disconnect battery ground cable to avoid possible fuel discharge if an attempt to start the vehicle is made.
6. Install fuel pump relay to fuse and relay box.
7. Tighten fuel filler cap.

FUSE PANEL & FLASHER LOCATION

The fuse panel is located behind lefthand side kick panel, **Fig. 1.**

Turn signal and hazard flasher is located above fuse panel, behind lefthand side of kick panel.

RELAY CENTER LOCATION

There are two relay boxes in the engine compartment, each being located on the left and right wheel wells.

STARTER

REPLACE

1. Disconnect battery ground cable, then battery positive cable from starter.
2. **On models with manual transaxle,** disconnect ignition switch lead from starter solenoid.
3. **On models with automatic transaxle,** disconnect ignition switch lead from starter solenoid pigtail.
4. **On all models,** remove two starter motor mounting bolts, then the motor.
5. Reverse procedure to install, **torque** starter attaching bolts to 29 ft. lbs. and battery positive cable nut to 26 ft. lbs.

DISTRIBUTOR

REPLACE

1. Remove all distributor electrical connections, then distributor cap.
2. Mark distributor housing position on engine, and the rotor position on distributor housing assembly.
3. Remove distributor mounting bolt, **Fig. 2,** then distributor from engine.
4. Remove O-ring from distributor shaft.
5. Reverse procedures to install, using new O-ring gaskets.

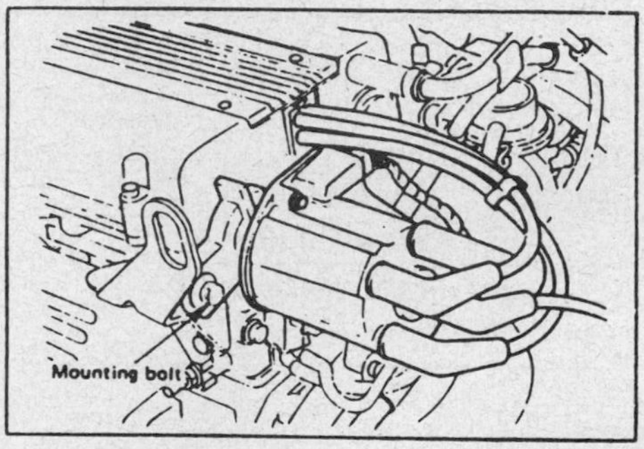
Mounting bolt

GC1129100059000X

Fig. 2 Distributor assembly

IGNITION LOCK

REPLACE

1. Remove steering wheel as described in "Steering Wheel, Replace."
2. Remove turn signal assembly as described in "Turn Signal/Dimmer Switch, Replace."
3. Turn key to Off position, depress retaining pin, then remove ignition lock cylinder from switch.
4. Reverse procedure to install.

IGNITION SWITCH

REPLACE

1. Remove steering wheel as described in "Steering Wheel, Replace."
2. Remove turn signal assembly as described in "Turn Signal/Dimmer Switch, Replace."
3. Remove ignition lock as described in "Ignition Lock, Replace."
4. Disconnect electrical connector from ignition switch, then remove snap ring and spacer collar from steering shaft, **Fig. 3.**
5. Disconnect back drive cable from ignition switch, then remove ignition switch retaining bolts and ignition switch from steering column.
6. Reverse procedure to install.

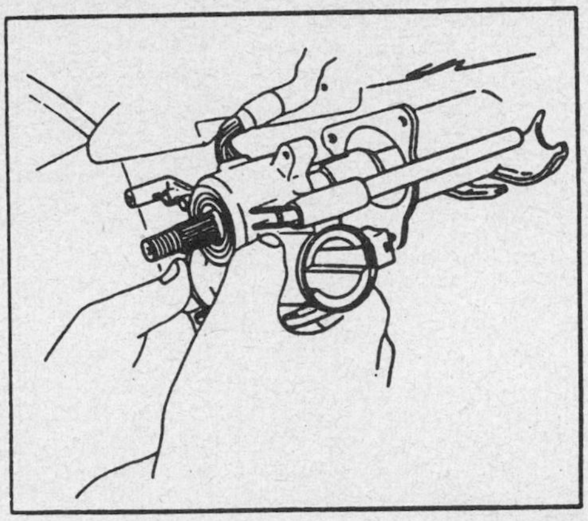

GC9049100120000X

Fig. 3 Ignition switch assembly

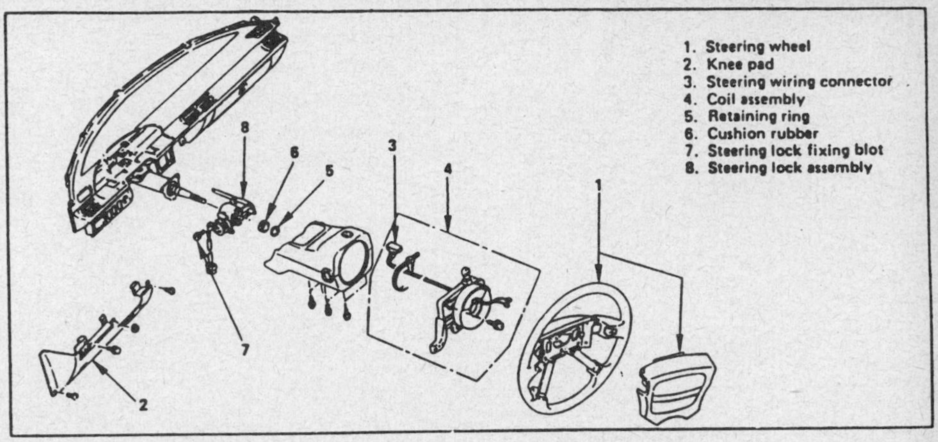
1. Steering wheel
2. Knee pad
3. Steering wiring connector
4. Coil assembly
5. Retaining ring
6. Cushion rubber
7. Steering lock fixing blot
8. Steering lock assembly

GC6049100146000X

Fig. 5 Steering column assembly

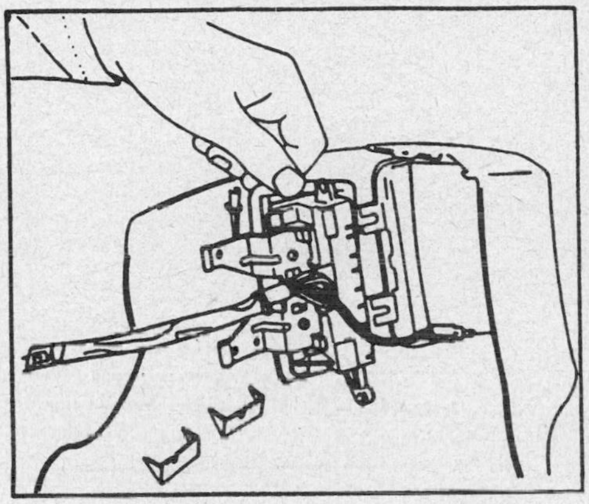

GC9049100121000X

Fig. 4 Headlamp control switch

GC8019100117000X

Fig. 6 SIR module removal

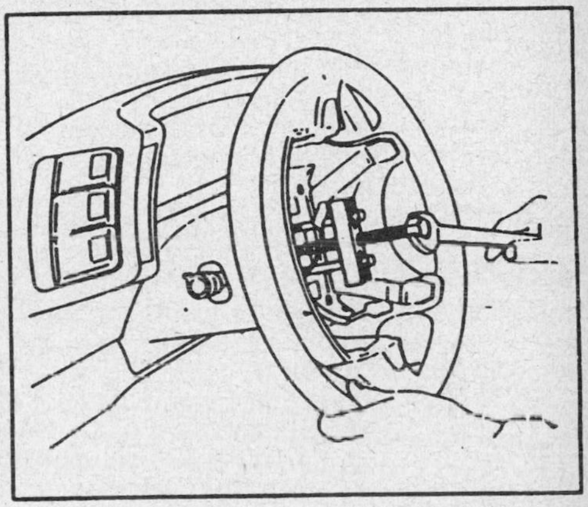

GC6049100147000X

Fig. 7 Steering wheel removal

CLUTCH START SWITCH
REPLACE

1. Disconnect electrical connector from clutch switch that is mounted above clutch pedal.
2. Remove front locknut, then the switch.
3. Remove rear locknut.
4. Reverse the procedure to install. Adjust clutch start switch as follows:
   a. Loosen clutch switch locknut, then rotate clutch switch until threaded portion bottoms on switch bracket, then tighten locknut.

HEADLAMP SWITCH
REPLACE

1. Refer to "Dash Panel Service" to remove meter hood.
2. Remove meter cluster from meter hood, then two clips attaching headlamp control harness.
3. Remove four headlamp control switch retaining screws, then the headlamp control switch with illumination box, **Fig. 4.**
4. Disconnect electrical connector, then two illumination box retaining screws and illumination box.
5. Reverse procedure to install.

STOP LIGHT SWITCH
REPLACE

1. Remove stop lamp switch locknut, then the stop lamp switch.
2. Reverse procedure to install. Adjust stop lamp switch as follows:
   a. Loosen stop lamp switch locknut. Thread stop lamp switch into bracket until tip of switch is gently resting on pedal arm. Carefully thread stop lamp switch inward, until freeplay between brake pedal and pushrod is eliminated, then tighten locknut.

TURN SIGNAL SWITCH
REPLACE

1. Remove steering wheel as described in "Steering Wheel, Replace."
2. Remove lower switch panel, dash lighter panel and hood release cable.
3. Remove lap air deflector attaching screws, then the lap air reflector.
4. Remove left lower dash trim panel attaching screws, then lower dash trim panel.
5. Remove upper steering column mounting bolts and lower column.
6. Remove two piece steering column cover attaching screws and cover.
7. Disconnect coil assembly wiring harness from turn signal switch, then remove four retaining screws and coil assembly, **Fig. 5.**
8. Remove turn signal switch retaining screws, then turn signal switch.
9. Reverse procedure to install.

DIMMER SWITCH
REPLACE

Refer to "Turn Signal Switch, Replace," for dimmer switch replacement.

STEERING WHEEL
REPLACE

1. Remove SIR module mounting screws and SIR module, **Fig. 6.**
2. Remove steering wheel retaining nut.
3. Using Steering Wheel Puller tool No. J-1859-03 or equivalent, remove steering wheel from column, **Fig. 7.**
4. Remove horn switch retaining screws and horn switch from steering wheel, **Fig. 8.**
5. Remove rear steering wheel cover attaching screws, then the cover.
6. Reverse procedure to install, **torque** steering wheel nut to 25 ft. lbs.

INSTRUMENT CLUSTER
REPLACE

1. Refer to "Dash Panel Service," then remove meter hood.
2. Remove four dash gauge retaining

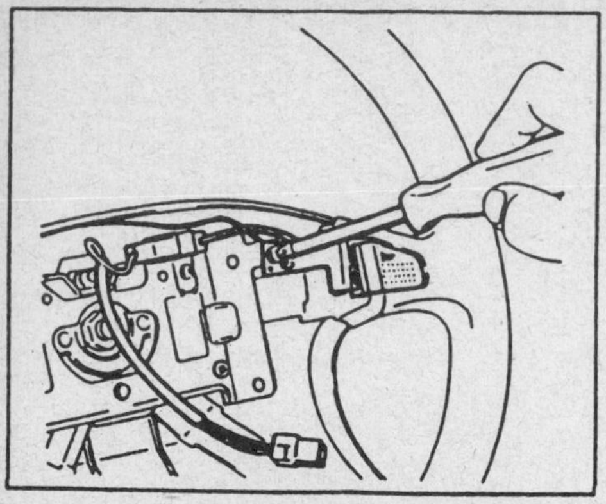
GC6049100148000X

Fig. 8 Horn switch removal

screws, then disconnect electrical connectors and speedometer cable, **Fig. 9.**

3. Remove dash gauge assembly, **Fig. 9.**
4. Reverse procedure to install, ensuring that all electrical connectors are securely connected.

RADIO

REPLACE

1. Remove four heater control knobs, then four radio bezel screws from radio bezel, **Fig. 9.**
2. Disconnect illumination lamp and harness from radio bezel.
3. Remove three righthand side panel retaining screws, then four radio bracket retaining screws.
4. Remove radio from I/P, then disconnect electrical and antenna connectors.
5. Reverse procedure to install.

WIPER MOTOR

REPLACE

FRONT

1. Remove cowl vent grille.
2. Disconnect front wiper motor electrical connector.
3. Disconnect wiper linkage from wiper motor arm.
4. Remove two retaining bolts from charcoal canister mounting bracket, allowing canister to slip down to gain access to wiper mounting bolt.
5. Remove four wiper motor mounting bolts.
6. Remove wiper motor.
7. Reverse procedure to install.

REAR

1. Remove wiper arm.
2. Remove rear hatchback trim panel.
3. Disconnect rear wiper motor electrical connector.
4. Remove mounting bolts. one locknut and wiper motor.
5. Reverse procedure to install.

WIPER SWITCH

REPLACE

FRONT

1. Remove meter hood as described in "Dash Panel Service."
2. Remove meter cluster, then the two attaching clips from wiper/washer switch harness.
3. Remove four switch attaching screws, then the switch with illumination bulb.
4. Reverse procedure to install.

REAR

1. Remove trim bezel.
2. Remove rear wiper switch, then disconnect electrical connector.

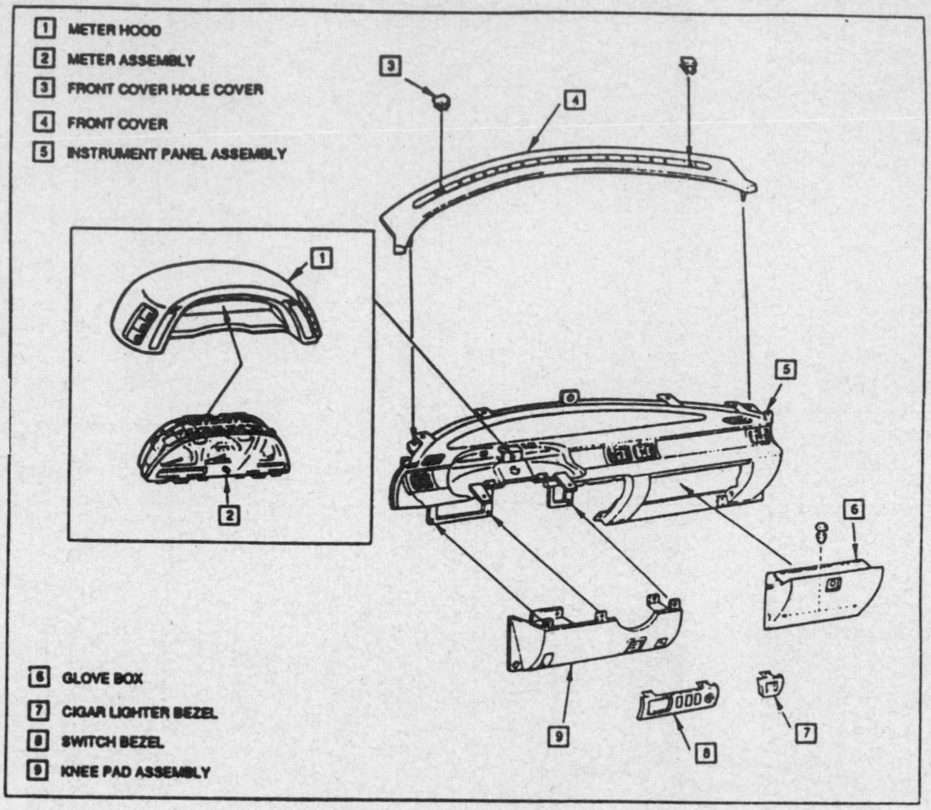
1 METER HOOD
2 METER ASSEMBLY
3 FRONT COVER HOLE COVER
4 FRONT COVER
5 INSTRUMENT PANEL ASSEMBLY
6 GLOVE BOX
7 CIGAR LIGHTER BEZEL
8 SWITCH BEZEL
9 KNEE PAD ASSEMBLY
GC9099100240000X

Fig. 9 Instrument panel

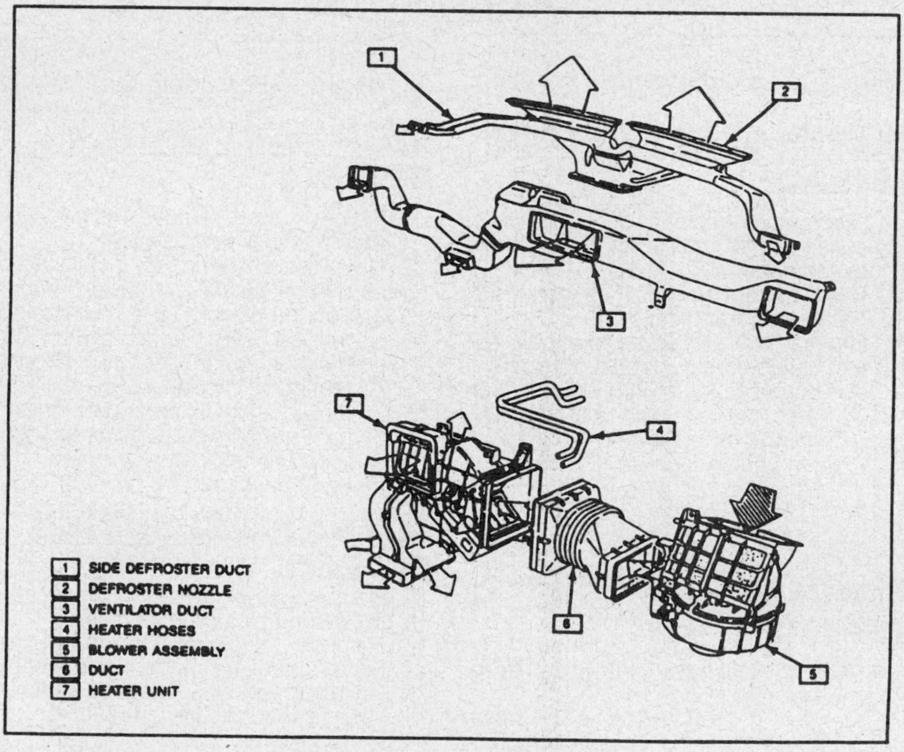
1 SIDE DEFROSTER DUCT
2 DEFROSTER NOZZLE
3 VENTILATOR DUCT
4 HEATER HOSES
5 BLOWER ASSEMBLY
6 DUCT
7 HEATER UNIT
GC7029100073000X

Fig. 10 Heater assembly

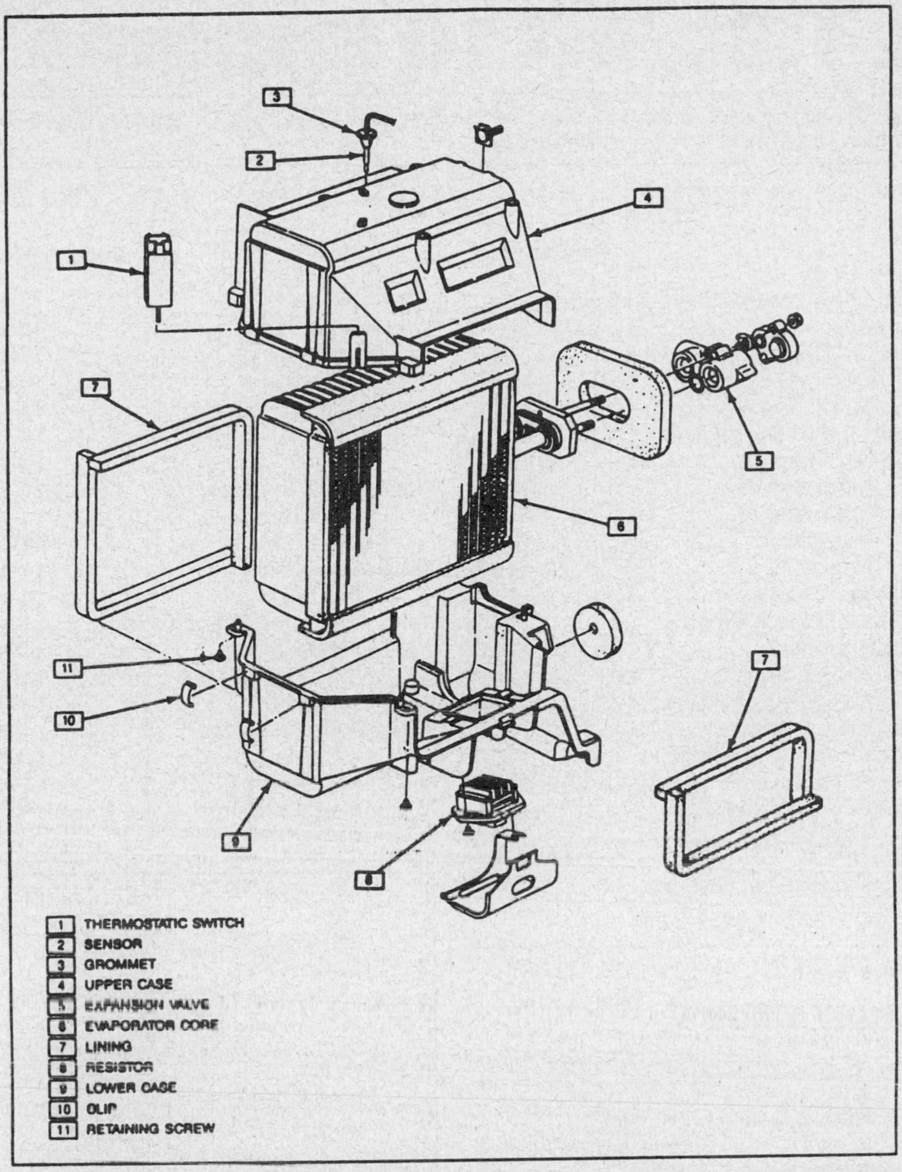
1
2
3
4
5
6
7
7
8
9
10
11
1 THERMOSTATIC SWITCH
2 SENSOR
3 GROMMET
4 UPPER CASE
5 EXPANSION VALVE
6 EVAPORATOR CORE
7 LINING
8 RESISTOR
9 LOWER CASE
10 CLIP
11 RETAINING SCREW

GC7029100074000X

Fig. 11 Evaporator assembly

3. Reverse procedure to install.

BLOWER MOTOR

REPLACE

1. Disconnect blower motor electrical connector.
2. Remove four blower motor attaching screws, then the blower motor, **Fig. 10.**
3. Reverse procedure to install.

HEATER CORE

REPLACE

1. Drain cooling system, then disconnect heater hoses at engine compartment.
2. Remove instrument panel assembly, referring to "Dash Panel Service" for procedure.
3. Remove evaporator assembly as described in "Evaporator Core, Replace.
4. Remove duct between blower assembly and heater unit, **Fig. 10,** then the center ventilation duct.
5. Remove four heater unit retaining nuts, then the heater unit.
6. Remove three duct mounting screws, then the five mode control to heater core case retaining screws.
7. Remove mode control case, but do not remove the link assembly at this time.
8. Remove five screws so that two halves of the heater core case may be separated, **Fig. 10.**
9. Remove heater core.
10. Reverse procedure to install.

EVAPORATOR CORE

REPLACE

1. Discharge A/C system as described in "Air Conditioning."
2. Remove A/C lines from expansion valve, capping all fittings immediately to keep moisture out of system.
3. Remove retaining clip and expansion valve from the evaporator.
4. Remove glove box assembly from I/P, then the lower dash reinforcement bracket.
5. Disconnect electrical connector from thermostat switch and blower motor resistor.
6. Remove air inlet cable from blend door, then retaining nuts from evaporator case.
7. Remove evaporator assembly from dash, then retaining clip from evaporator case.
8. Remove four case retaining screws, then separate case, **Fig. 11.**
9. Remove evaporator core and evaporator grommet from case.
10. Reverse procedure to install.

1.6L/4-97 & 1.8L/4-110 Engines

NOTE: On Air Bag Equipped Models, Refer To "Air Bag System Precautions" Located In The Front Of This Manual For System Disarming & Arming Procedures.

INDEX

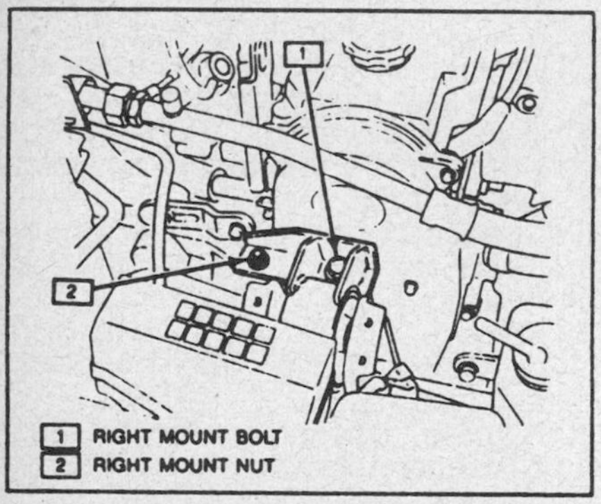
1
2
1 RIGHT MOUNT BOLT
2 RIGHT MOUNT NUT

GC1069100528000X

Fig. 1 Right engine mount

PRECAUTIONS

AIR BAG SYSTEMS

Refer to "Air Bag System Precautions" in the front of this manual for system disarming and arming procedures.

FUEL PRESSURE RELIEF

1. Loosen fuel filler cap to relieve fuel tank pressure.
2. Remove fuel pump relay from fuse and relay box.
3. Start engine and allow to stall.
4. Crank engine for an additional three seconds to assure relief of any remaining fuel pressure.
5. Disconnect battery ground cable to avoid possible fuel discharge if an attempt to start the vehicle is made.
6. Install fuel pump relay to fuse and relay box.
7. Tighten fuel filler cap.

ENGINE MOUNT

REPLACE

RIGHT MOUNT

1. Using Engine Support Fixture tool No. J28467-A or equivalent, support engine.
2. Raise and support vehicle.
3. Remove bolt and nut from mounting bridge bracket, **Fig. 1.**
4. Remove engine mount through bolt, then the engine mount.
5. Reverse procedure to install.

TORQUE ROD

1. Raise and support vehicle.
2. Remove torque rod bracket attaching nut and bolts, **Fig. 2.**
3. Remove torque rod center bolt and nut, then remove torque rod and bracket assembly.
4. Reverse procedure to install.

REAR MOUNT

1. Support engine using Engine Support Fixture tool No. J-28467-A or equivalent.
2. Raise and support vehicle.
3. Remove dampener weight from the engine mounting, then the bolt from transaxle case.
4. Remove center bolts from the center beam, then the rear engine mount.
5. Reverse procedure to install.

LEFT MOUNT

1
2
1 TORQUE ROD BRACKET
2 TORQUE ROD BOLT

GC1069100529000X

Fig. 2 Torque rod engine mount

1. Disconnect battery cables, then remove battery.
2. Remove cover plate, then the left engine mount bolts from transaxle case.
3. Remove left engine mount center bolt, then left engine mount.
4. Reverse procedure to install.

ENGINE

REPLACE

1. Disconnect battery cables, then remove battery, battery tray and hood.
2. Drain engine coolant, then remove accelerator cable from throttle valve.
3. Remove breather hose from intake air duct, then intake air duct from throttle valve.
4. Remove air cleaner assembly.
5. Disconnect MAP sensor hose from MAP sensor, then the brake booster vacuum hose and two canister hoses from pipes of the common chamber.

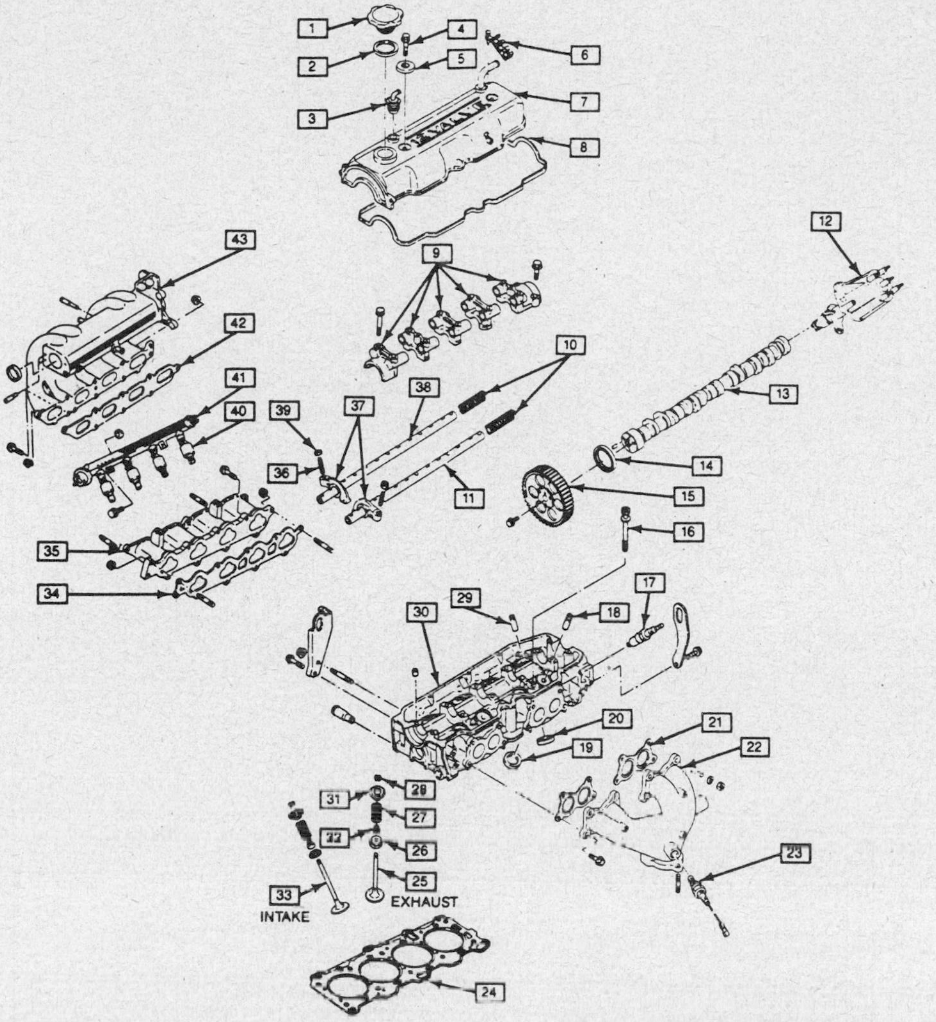
INTAKE
EXHAUST

1 OIL FILLER CAP
2 GASKET
3 POSITIVE CRANKCASE VENTILATION (PCV) VALVE
4 CYLINDER HEAD COVER BOLT
5 GASKET
6 CABLE CLIP
7 CYLINDER HEAD COVER
8 GASKET
9 ROCKER BRACKET
10 ROCKER SPRING
11 ROCKER SHAFT (EXHAUST)
12 DISTRIBUTOR
13 CAMSHAFT
14 CAMSHAFT OIL SEAL
15 TIMING PULLEY
16 CYLINDER HEAD BOLT
17 SPARK PLUG
18 VALVE GUIDE (EXHAUST)
19 SEAT INSERT (EXHAUST VALVE)
20 SEAT INSERT (INTAKE VALVE)
21 EXHAUST MANIFOLD GASKET
22 EXHAUST MANIFOLD
23 OXYGEN SENSOR (O2S)
24 CYLINDER HEAD GASKET
25 EXHAUST VALVE
26 LOWER SPRING SEAT
27 VALVE SPRING
28 SPLIT COLLAR
29 VALVE GUIDE (INTAKE)
30 CYLINDER HEAD
31 UPPER SPRING SEAT
32 VALVE STEM SEAL
33 INTAKE VALVE
34 INDUCTION PORT GASKET
35 INDUCTION PORT
36 ADJUSTING SCREW
37 ROCKER ARM
38 ROCKER SHAFT (INTAKE)
39 NUT
40 FUEL INJECTOR
41 FUEL RAIL
42 COMMON CHAMBER GASKET
43 COMMON CHAMBER

GC1069100530000X

Fig. 3 SOHC engine cylinder head components

6. Remove two cable harness connectors near LH shock tower.
7. Disconnect ignition coil electrical connectors, then the ignition coil and bracket as an assembly.
8. Disconnect engine harness ground cable from LH inner fender, then the chassis harness terminal from relay and fuse box.
9. Disconnect cooling fan and oxygen sensor harness connectors.
10. Disconnect ground cable terminal at rear of cylinder head cover and four connectors from automatic transaxle control system harness.
11. **On models with manual transaxle,** disconnect clutch cable by loosening two adjusting nuts.
12. Remove two transaxle shift cables by disconnecting cotter pin and removing clip from shift cable bracket.
13. **On models with automatic transaxle,** disconnect transaxle shift cable by removing cotter pin, then the joint from shift cable lever.
14. **On all models,** remove two heater hoses from engine, speedometer cable from transaxle and upper radiator hose from radiator.
15. Remove fuel feed pipe and fuel return hose near the filter, then the coolant recovery tank with bracket as an assembly.
16. Remove power steering belt, power steering pump and bracket.
17. Remove cooling fan and shroud, then raise and support vehicle.
18. Remove right and left undercovers, then the lower radiator hose.
19. Remove two transaxle oil cooler lines from transaxle.
20. Remove two air conditioning compressor bracket bolts from engine and set aside.
21. Remove front tire and wheel assemblies, then the drive axles.
22. Remove front exhaust pipe from exhaust manifold, then lower vehicle.
23. Lower vehicle and attach a suitable engine hoist to the lifting bracket, applying slight pressure.
24. Remove engine and transaxle mounts.
25. Remove engine and transaxle as an assembly.
26. Remove transaxle from engine.
27. Reverse procedure to install.

INTAKE MANIFOLD REPLACE

SOHC ENGINE

Refer to Figs. 3 through 5 for SOHC engine breakdown.

1. Remove ignition coil wires.
2. Remove accelerator cable from throttle valve and common chamber, then two cable harness connectors at left-hand shock tower.
3. Disconnect cable harness from intake air control valve, MAT and TPS sensors.
4. Remove breather hose from intake air duct, then intake air duct from throttle

valve and PCV hose from the cylinder head cover.
5. Remove EGR valve and canister vacuum hoses from throttle valve, then the EGR pipe from EGR valve and exhaust manifold.
6. Remove common chamber bracket and throttle valve assembly attaching bolts, then the throttle valve.
7. Remove coolant bypass pipe clip bolt and MAP sensor from common chamber.
8. Remove brake booster and canister vacuum hoses from common chamber and throttle valve.
9. Remove pressure regulator and EGR vacuum hoses from common chamber.
10. Remove engine hanger bolt, then the common chamber retaining nuts and bolts.
11. Remove common chamber from engine assembly.
12. Reverse procedure to install.

DOHC ENGINE

Refer to **Figs. 6 through 9,** when working on DOHC engines.

1. Remove accelerator cable clip and PCV hose from intake air duct, then the intake air duct from vehicle.
2. Remove accelerator cable from throttle valve, then MAP sensor hose from MAP sensor.
3. Remove vacuum hose from brake booster and two canister hoses from pipes on common chamber, then remove canister pipe bracket.
4. Remove fuel pressure regulator vacuum hose, then remove induction control valve vacuum hose.
5. Remove throttle valve from common chamber, then disconnect alternator harness clip and three fuel injector harness cable clips.
6. Loosen EGR pipe bracket at exhaust manifold and loosen EGR clip at thermostat housing.
7. Remove two common chamber bracket bolts on lefthand side of engine and engine hanger bolt on righthand side of common chamber.
8. Remove ten bolts and two nuts from common chamber induction control valve assembly, then the common chamber.
9. Reverse procedure to install.

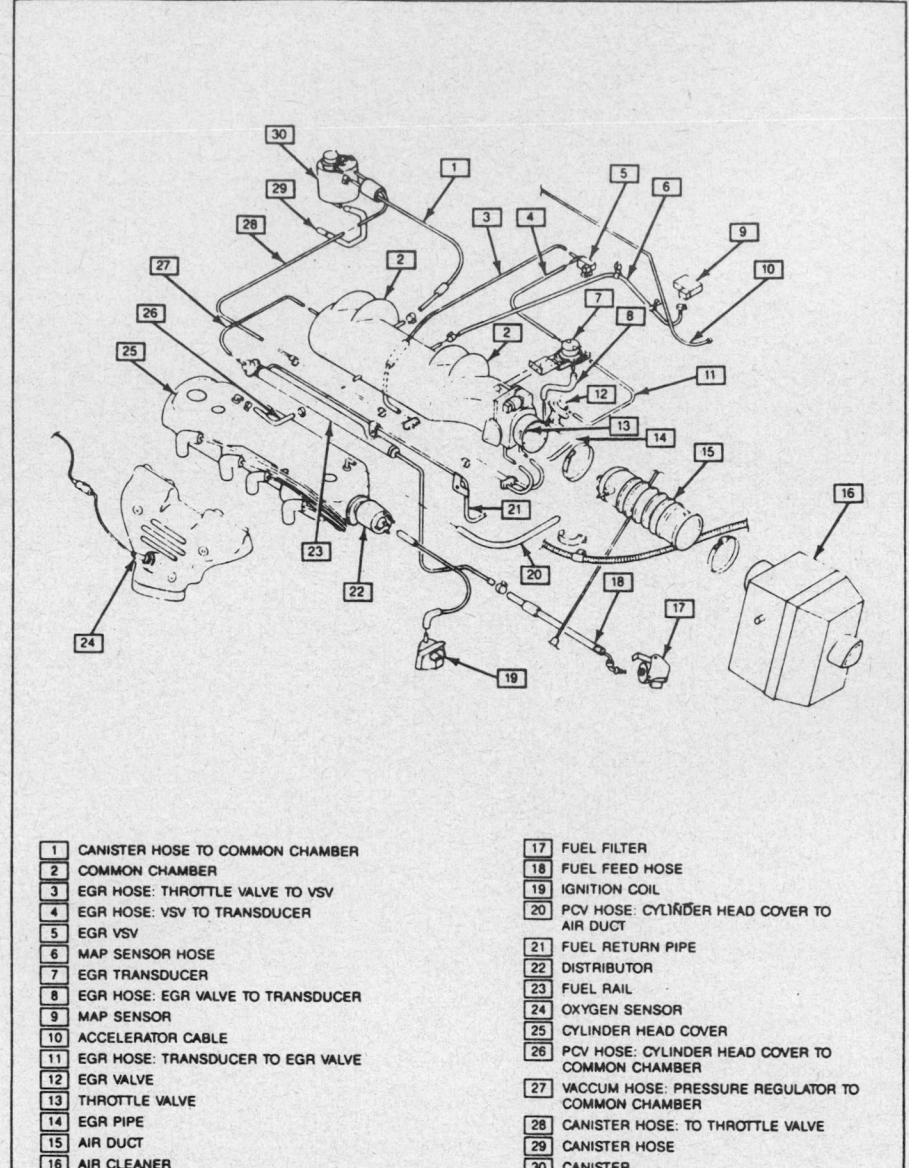

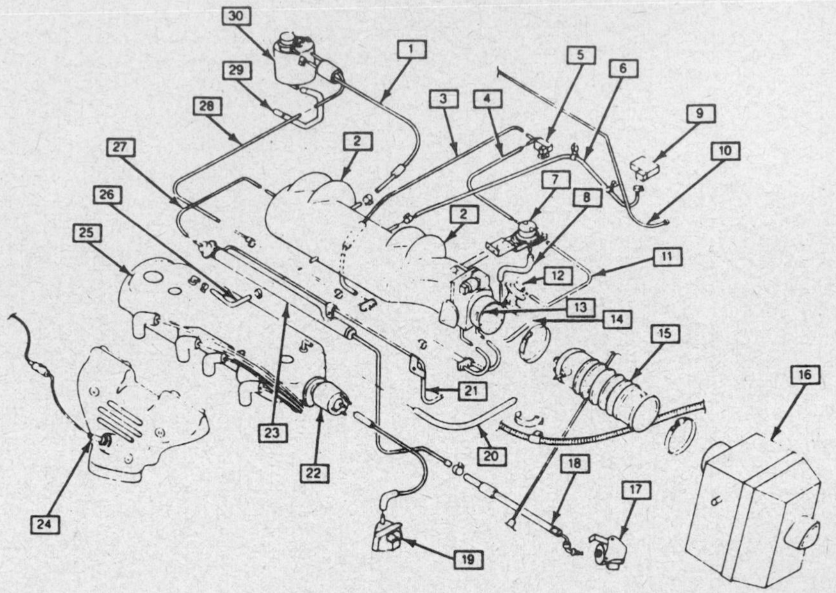
1 CANISTER HOSE TO COMMON CHAMBER
2 COMMON CHAMBER
3 EGR HOSE: THROTTLE VALVE TO VSV
4 EGR HOSE: VSV TO TRANSDUCER
5 EGR VSV
6 MAP SENSOR HOSE
7 EGR TRANSDUCER
8 EGR HOSE: EGR VALVE TO TRANSDUCER
9 MAP SENSOR
10 ACCELERATOR CABLE
11 EGR HOSE: TRANSDUCER TO EGR VALVE
12 EGR VALVE
13 THROTTLE VALVE
14 EGR PIPE
15 AIR DUCT
16 AIR CLEANER
17 FUEL FILTER
18 FUEL FEED HOSE
19 IGNITION COIL
20 PCV HOSE: CYLINDER HEAD COVER TO AIR DUCT
21 FUEL RETURN PIPE
22 DISTRIBUTOR
23 FUEL RAIL
24 OXYGEN SENSOR
25 CYLINDER HEAD COVER
26 PCV HOSE: CYLINDER HEAD COVER TO COMMON CHAMBER
27 VACCUM HOSE: PRESSURE REGULATOR TO COMMON CHAMBER
28 CANISTER HOSE: TO THROTTLE VALVE
29 CANISTER HOSE
30 CANISTER
GC1069100531000X

Fig. 4 SOHC engine air intake system

INDUCTION CONTROL VALVE ASSEMBLY
REPLACE

1. Disconnect ignition coil wires.
2. Remove common chamber as described in "Intake Manifold, Replace."
3. Remove two oil cooler pipe clip nuts from studs located under induction control valve.
4. Remove fuel feed pipe and return fuel hose, then two fuel rail retaining bolts.
5. Remove two fuel injector harness bracket retaining bolts, then the fuel injector harness and fuel rail with fuel injectors attached from injection control valve assembly.
6. Disconnect VSV harness connector from induction control valve.
7. Remove seven bolts and two nuts from induction control valve assembly, then the induction control assembly.
8. Reverse procedures to install, **torquing** induction control valve retaining bolts to 17 ft. lbs.

EXHAUST MANIFOLD
REPLACE

1. Remove heat protector, then disconnect oxygen sensor electrical connector.
2. Remove the EGR pipe from exhaust manifold and EGR valve, then the front exhaust pipe from exhaust manifold.
3. Remove exhaust manifold retaining nuts and bolts, then the exhaust manifold.
4. Reverse procedure to install.

CYLINDER HEAD
REPLACE

SOHC ENGINE

1. Drain coolant.
2. Disconnect accelerator cable from throttle valve.
3. Remove breather hose from intake air duct, then the intake air duct from the throttle valve.
4. Remove MAP sensor hose from MAP sensor, then the brake booster vacuum hose.
5. Remove two canister hoses and EGR vacuum hoses from common chamber.

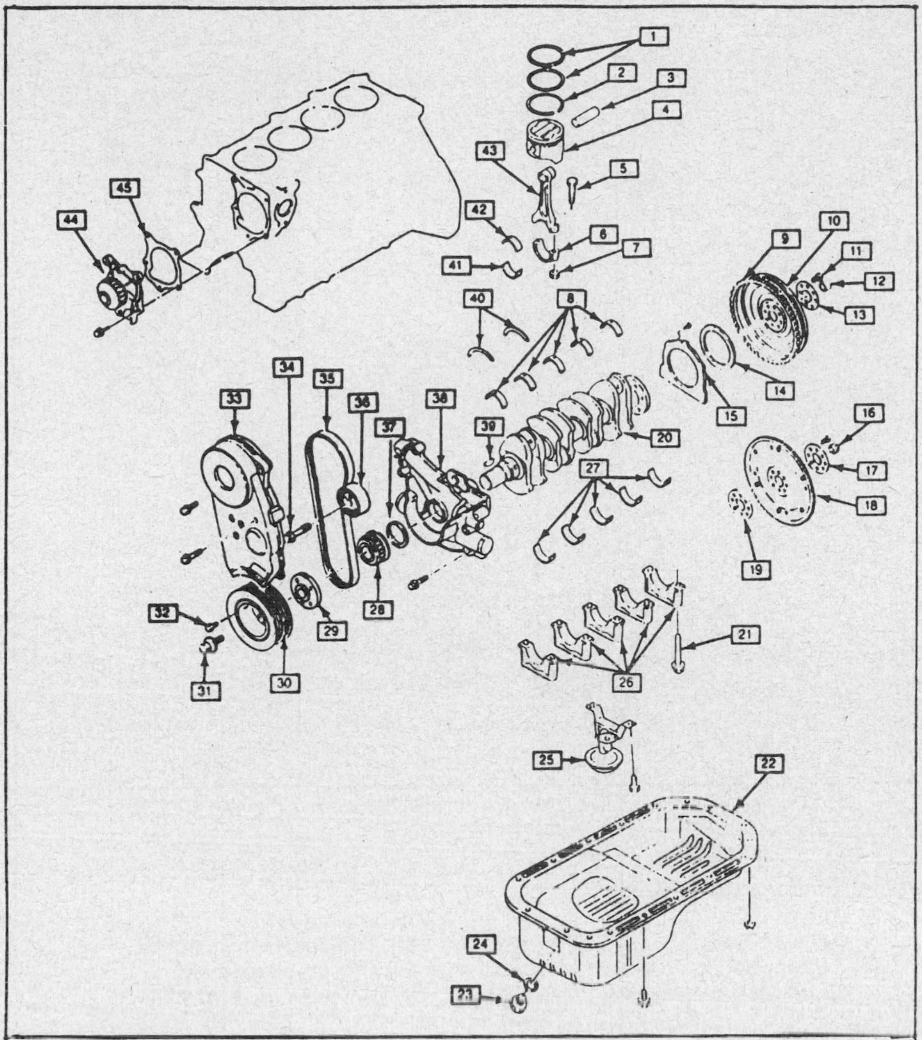

1	COMPRESSION RING	24	GASKET
2	OIL RING	25	OIL PIPE ASSEMBLY
3	PISTON PIN	26	BEARING CAP
4	PISTON	27	CRANKSHAFT LOWER BEARING
5	CONNECTING ROD BOLT	28	TIMING PULLEY
6	CONNECTING ROD CAP	29	PULLEY BOSS
7	CONNECTING ROD NUT	30	CRANK PULLEY
8	CRANKSHAFT UPPER BEARING	31	CRANKSHAFT BOLT
9	RING GEAR	32	PULLEY BOSS BOLT
10	FLYWHEEL	33	TIMING COVER
11	FLYWHEEL BOLT	34	TENSION PULLEY BOLT
12	SLEEVE (M/T)	35	TIMING BELT
13	WASHER (M/T)	36	TENSION PULLEY
14	OIL SEAL	37	OIL SEAL
15	REAR RETAINER	38	OIL PUMP ASSEMBLY
16	SLEEVE (A/T)	39	KEY
17	WASHER (A/T)	40	THRUST WASHER
18	RING GEAR ASSEMBLY	41	CONNECTING ROD LOWER BEARING
19	SPACER (A/T)	42	CONNECTING ROD UPPER BEARING
20	CRANKSHAFT	43	CONNECTING ROD
21	BEARING CAP BOLT	44	WATER PUMP ASSEMBLY
22	OIL PAN	45	GASKET
23	PLUG		

GC1069100532000X

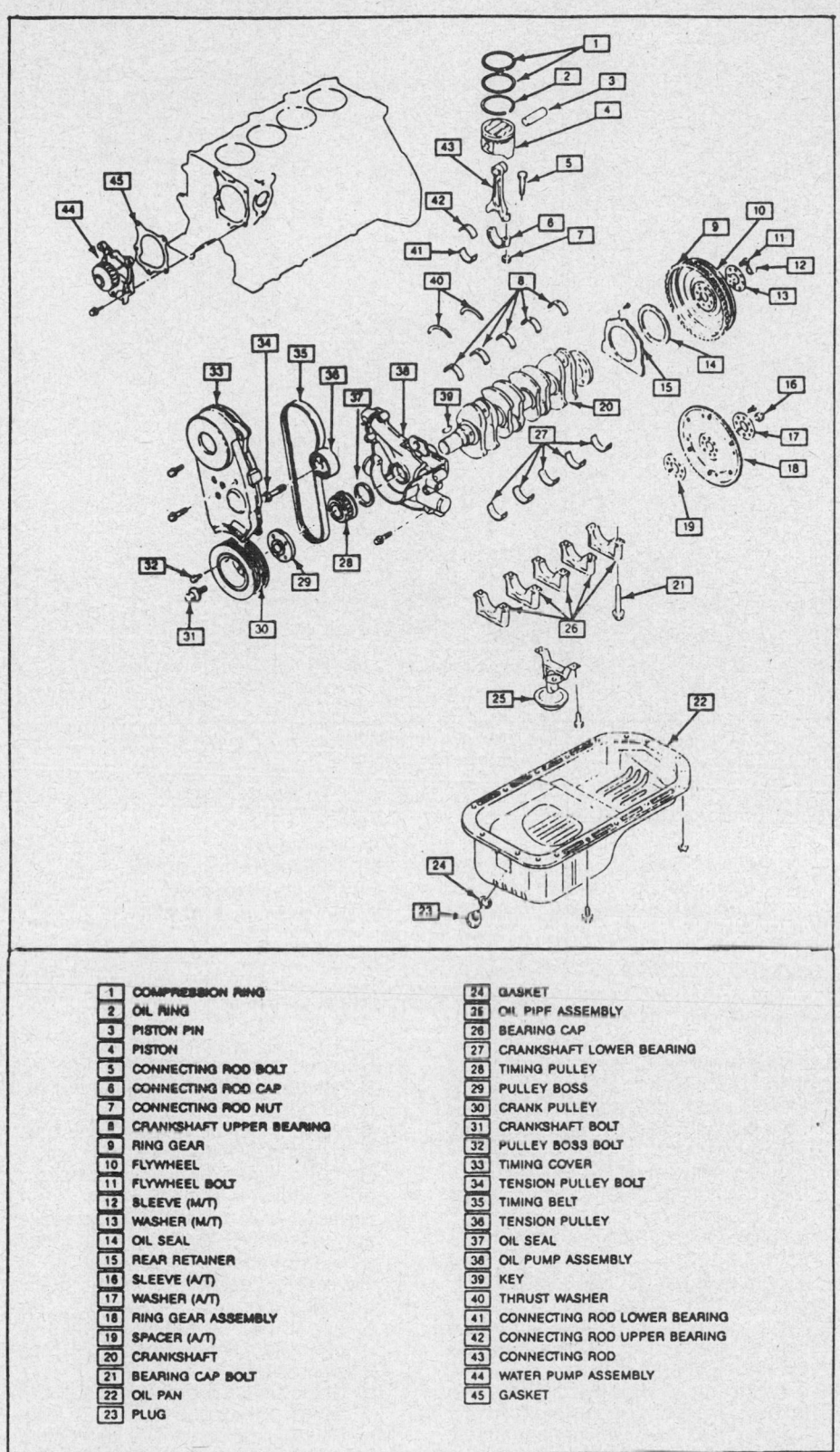

Fig. 5 SOHC cylinder block components

6. Disconnect oxygen sensor harness from oxygen sensor, ignition coil ground from thermostat housing flange and coolant temperature sensor from thermo unit harness.
7. Remove cable harness clip from bracket at coolant outlet pipe, then two cable harness connectors near lefthand strut tower.
8. Remove two heater hoses from engine and upper radiator hose from radiator.
9. Remove fuel feed hose and return hose, then raise and support vehicle.
10. Remove righthand undercover and exhaust pipe from exhaust manifold, then lower vehicle.
11. Remove right side engine mount, then the alternator and power steering belts.
12. Remove engine mounting bracket from timing cover, timing cover and timing belt.
13. Remove cylinder head center cover, cylinder head bolts, then the cylinder head.
14. Reverse procedure to install, noting the following:
    a. Using tightening sequence shown in **Fig. 10, torque** cylinder head bolts in two steps. First to 29 ft. lbs, then to 58 ft. lbs.
    b. Install timing belt as described in "Timing Belt Replace."

DOHC ENGINE

1. Drain coolant.
2. Disconnect accelerator cable from intake air duct, then accelerator cable clips from cylinder head cover and common chamber.
3. Disconnect accelerator cable from throttle valve and remove PCV hose from intake duct side.
4. Remove intake air duct from throttle valve, then MAP sensor hose from MAP sensor.
5. Remove brake booster vacuum hose from brake booster, then two canister hoses from pipes on common chambor.
6. Remove two canister pipes and MAP sensor pipe from common chamber, then canister pipe support bracket.
7. Disconnect oxygen sensor harness connector, ignition coil ground cable from thermostat housing flange, coolant temperature sensor and thermo unit harness connector at thermostat housing.
8. Disconnect two ground cable terminals from right side of common chamber, then ground cable from rear RH side of common chamber.
9. Disconnect starter and alternator cable clip.
10. Remove two heater hoses from engine, then upper radiator hose.
11. Remove throttle valve heating hose from coolant bypass pipe, then coolant bypass pipe bracket from cylinder head and fuel feed pipe and return fuel hose.
12. Raise and support vehicle, then remove righthand side undercover.
13. Remove front exhaust pipe from exhaust manifold, then lower vehicle.
14. Remove right side engine mount, then cylinder head center cover.
15. Remove spark plug wires from spark plugs and clips, then PCV hose from cylinder head cover.
16. Remove upper timing cover and cylinder head cover.

17. Remove timing belt, then cylinder head bolts as shown in **Fig. 11.**
18. Raise cylinder head and remove oil cooler pipe from oil cooler.
19. Remove cylinder head.
20. Reverse procedure to install, using tightening sequence shown in **Fig. 12, torque** cylinder head bolts in two steps. First to 29 ft. lbs., then to 58 ft. lbs.

CAMSHAFT LOBE LIFT SPECIFICATIONS

SOHC ENGINE

Year	Liter/CID	Intake & Exhaust
1992–93	1.6L/4-97	1.426①

①—Minimum height.

DOHC ENGINE

Year	Liter/CID	Intake & Exhaust
1992–93	1.8L/4-110	1.531①

①—Minimum height.

VALVE CLEARANCE SPECIFICATIONS

SOHC ENGINE

Year	Engine	Intake Inch	Exhaust Inch
1992–93	1.6L/4-97	.006	.010

DOHC ENGINE

Year	Engine	Intake, Inch	Exhaust, Inch
1992–93	1.8L/4-110	①	①

①—Equipped w/hydraulic valve lash adjusters.

VALVE ADJUSTMENT

SOHC ENGINE

1. Set number one cylinder at TDC on the compression stroke, then turn crankshaft pulley to align its notched line with the 0 mark on timing cover.
2. Ensure that valves on No. 1 cylinder have play and valves No. 4 cylinder do not. If not as specified, turn crankshaft pulley 360° and align the 0 mark on lower timing cover, **Fig. 13.**
3. Measure valve lash between rocker arm and valve stem as follows:
   a. Intake and exhaust valves on No. 1 cylinder.
   b. Intake valve on No. 2 cylinder.
   c. Exhaust valves on No. 3 cylinder.
4. Valve lash should be 0.006 inch on intake and 0.010 on exhaust valves.

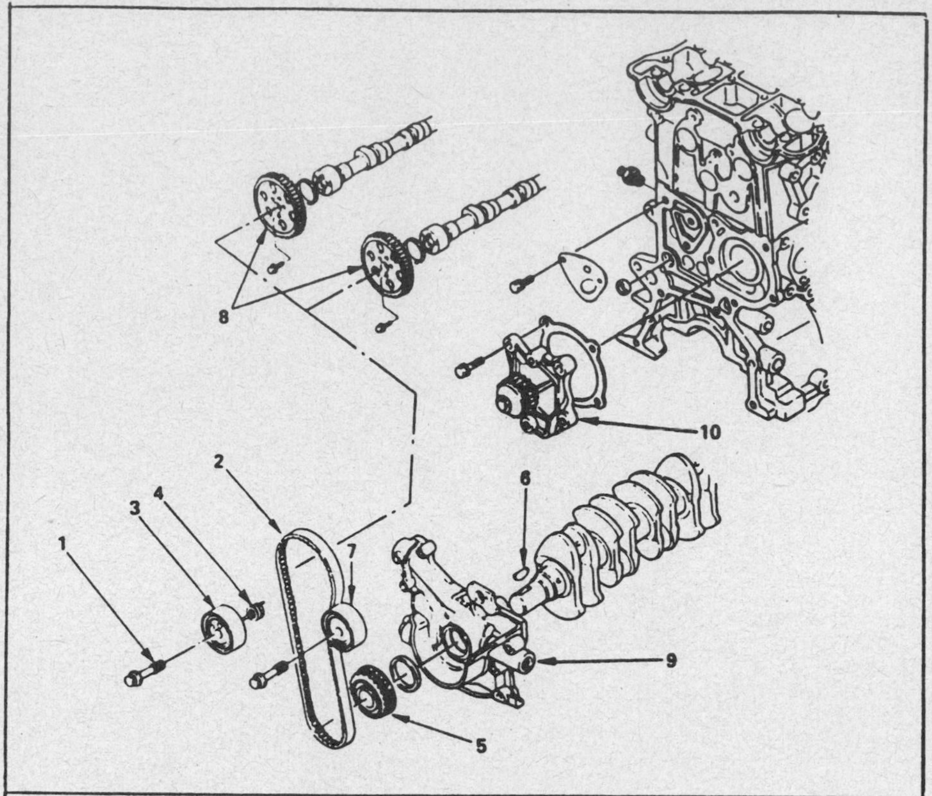

1
2
3
4
5
6
7
8
9
10

1. Tension pulley lock bolt
2. Timing belt
3. Tension pulley
4. Tension spring
5. Crankshaft timing pulley
6. Key
7. Idle pulley
8. Camshaft timing pulley
9. Oil pump assembly
10. Water pump assembly

GC1069100533000X

Fig. 6 DOHC engine

5. If lash is not as specified, adjust valve lash by loosening adjustment screw locknut and turn adjustment screw until lash is within specifications, **Fig. 14.**
6. Tighten adjustment locknut, then rotate crankshaft 360° and measure lash as follows:
   a. Intake and exhaust on No. 4 cylinder.
   b. Intake valves on No. 3 cylinder.
   c. Exhaust valves on No. 2 cylinder.
7. Valve lash measurement for intake valves should be 0.006 inch and 0.010 on exhaust valves.
8. If lash is not as specified, adjust valve lash by loosening adjustment screw locknut and turn adjustment screw until lash is within specifications.
9. Install cylinder head cover.

ROCKER ARMS

REPLACE

SOHC ENGINE

1. Remove PCV hoses and spark plug wires from the clip.
2. Remove two bolts from timing belt cover, then loosen lower timing belt cover bolts.
3. Remove cylinder head cover bolts, then cylinder head cover.
4. Remove rocker arm bracket bolts in order shown in **Fig. 15.**
5. Remove rocker arm shaft and rocker arm assembly, then remove rocker arms from shafts.
6. Reverse procedure to install, noting the following:
   a. Apply GM 1052942 sealant or equivalent to No. 1 and No. 5 rocker brackets.
   b. Using tightening sequence shown in **Fig. 16, torque** bolts to 22 ft. lbs.
   c. Make necessary valve lash adjustments.

VALVE GUIDES

Using Valve Guide Remover tool No. J-37985 or equivalent, drive valve guides from cylinder head with a hammer. Install valve guides using Installer tool No. J-38462 with Valve Guide Remover tool No. J-37985 or equivalents.

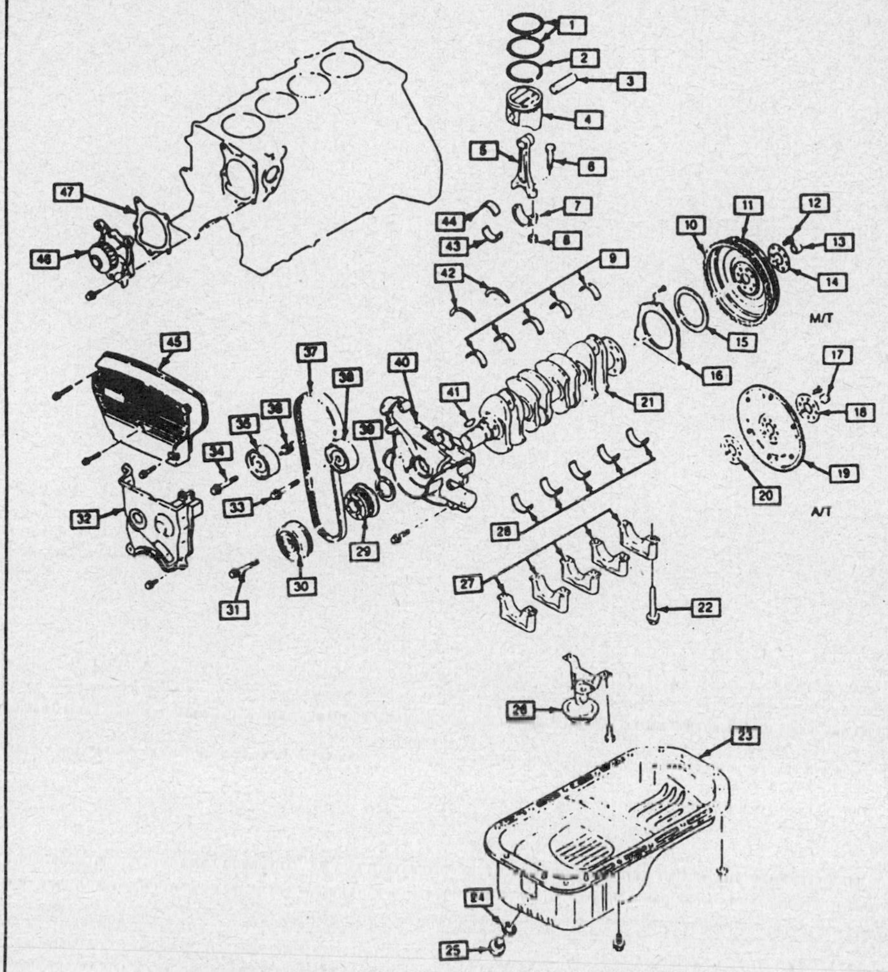
M/T
A/T

1. COMPRESSION RING
2. OIL RING
3. PISTON PIN
4. PISTON
5. CONNECTING ROD
6. CONNECTING ROD BOLT
7. CONNECTING ROD CAP
8. CONNECTING ROD NUT
9. UPPER BEARING (CRANKSHAFT)
10. RING GEAR (M/T)
11. FLYWHEEL (M/T)
12. FLYWHEEL BOLT
13. SLEEVE (M/T)
14. WASHER (M/T)
15. OIL SEAL
16. REAR RETAINING GASKET
17. SLEEVE (M/T)
18. WASHER (M/T)
19. REAR GEAR ASSEMBLY (A/T)
20. SPACER (A/T)
21. CRANKSHAFT
22. BEARING CAP BOLT
23. OIL PAN
24. GASKET
25. PLUG
26. OIL PIPE ASSEMBLY
27. BEARING CAP
28. LOWER BEARING (CRANKSHAFT)
29. CRANKSHAFT TIMING PULLEY
30. CRANKSHAFT PULLEY
31. CRANKSHAFT BOLT
32. LOWER TIMING COVER
33. IDLE PULLEY BOLT
34. TENSION PULLEY BOLT
35. TENSION PULLEY
36. TENSION SPRING
37. TIMING BELT
38. IDLE PULLEY
39. OIL SEAL
40. OIL PUMP ASSEMBLY
41. KEY
42. THRUST WASHER
43. LOWER BEARING (CONNECTING ROD)
44. UPPER BEARING (CONNECTING ROD)
45. UPPER TIMING COVER
46. WATER PUMP ASSEMBLY
47. GASKET

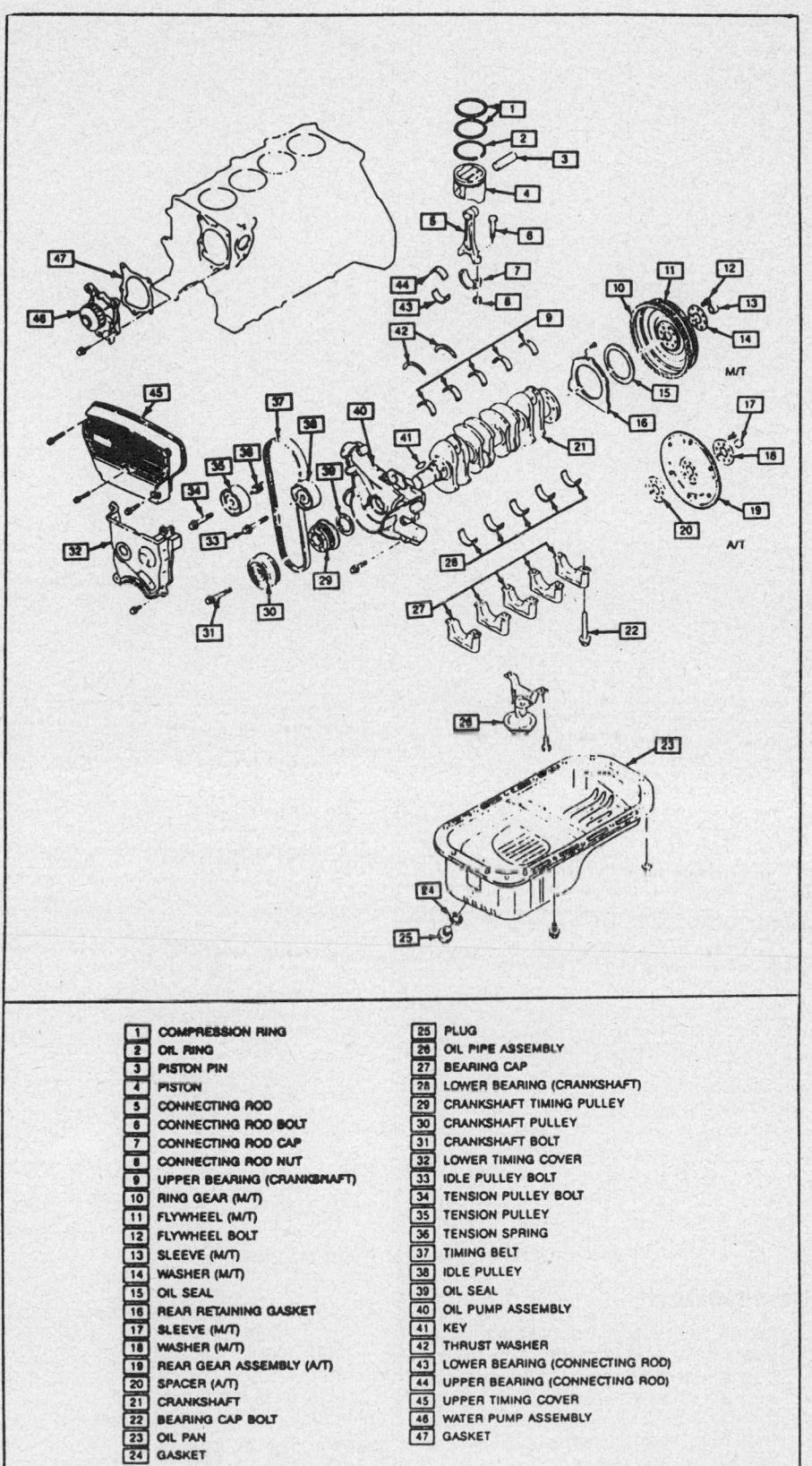

GC1069100534000X

Fig. 7 DOHC cylinder block components

TIMING BELT

REPLACE

SOHC ENGINE

Removal

1. Remove alternator and power steering belts, then support engine using Engine Support Fixture tool No. J-28467-A or equivalent.
2. Remove right side engine mount, then the timing belt cover.
3. Rotate crankshaft until No. 4 cylinder is at TDC compression stroke, then place camshaft pulley timing mark at the 9 o'clock position, **Fig. 17.**
4. Remove crankshaft pulley bolt, then raise and support vehicle.
5. Remove crankshaft pulley, then lower vehicle.
6. Loosen tension pulley retaining bolt 1/2 turn and remove timing belt.

Installation

1. Ensure camshaft pulley timing marks are aligned as shown in **Fig. 17.**
2. Install timing belt over, camshaft pulley, water pump pulley and tensioner pulley in order as shown in **Fig. 18.**
3. **Torque** timing belt tensioner to 31 ft. lbs., then rotate crankshaft two turns to ensure that crankshaft timing mark and camshaft pulley marks are correct.
4. Install timing belt cover, then raise and support vehicle.
5. **Torque** crankshaft pulley center bolt to 87 ft. lbs. and pulley side bolts to 89 inch lbs.
6. Lower vehicle, then install belts, right side engine mount and remove engine support fixture.

DOHC ENGINE

Removal

1. Support engine using Engine Support Fixture tool No. J-28467-A or equivalent, then remove right side engine mount.
2. Remove power steering and alternator drive belts, then upper timing belt cover.
3. Raise and support vehicle, then remove crankshaft pulley bolt and crankshaft pulley.
4. Lower vehicle and remove lower timing cover.
5. Align crankshaft pulley to TDC, then loosen tension pulley retaining bolt 1/2 turn and remove timing belt.

Installation

1. Align camshaft pulleys timing marks, **Fig. 19.**
2. Raise and support vehicle, then align crankshaft pulley to TDC.
3. Install timing belt over crankshaft pulley, then install crankshaft pulley, but do not tighten.
4. Lower vehicle, then install timing belt over crankshaft pulley, water pump pulley, idler pulley, exhaust camshaft pulley, intake camshaft pulley and then tensioner pulley as shown in **Fig. 20.**

5. **Torque** timing belt tensioner to 31 ft. lbs., then rotate crankshaft two turns to ensure that crankshaft timing pulley mark and camshaft pulley marks are correctly aligned.
6. Install lower timing cover
7. Raise and support vehicle, then **torque** crankshaft pulley bolt to 108 ft. lbs.
8. Lower vehicle and install upper timing cover.
9. Install alternator and power steering belts, then right side engine mount.
10. Remove engine support.

CAMSHAFT

REPLACE

SOHC ENGINE

Removal

1. Remove PCV hoses and spark plug wires from the clip.
2. Remove two bolts from the timing belt cover, then loosen lower timing belt cover bolts.
3. Remove cylinder head cover bolts, then cylinder head cover.
4. Rotate crankshaft to TDC on compression stroke by aligning the camshaft pulley timing marks, **Fig. 17.**
5. Loosen timing belt tensioner, then remove timing belt.
6. Remove distributor, camshaft bearing cap retaining bolts and covers.
7. Remove camshaft and camshaft seal.

Installation

1. Install camshaft in cylinder head with dowel pin in the upright position.
2. Install camshaft bearing caps, but do not tighten.
3. Apply GM 1052942 sealant or equivalent to No. 1 and No. 5 camshaft bearing caps.
4. **Torque** camshaft bearing caps to 89 inch lbs.
5. Install new camshaft oil seal using Seal Installation tool No. J-5268 or equivalent.
6. Install distributor, camshaft timing pulley and timing belt, referring to "Timing Belt Replace" for procedure.
7. Install cylinder head cover.

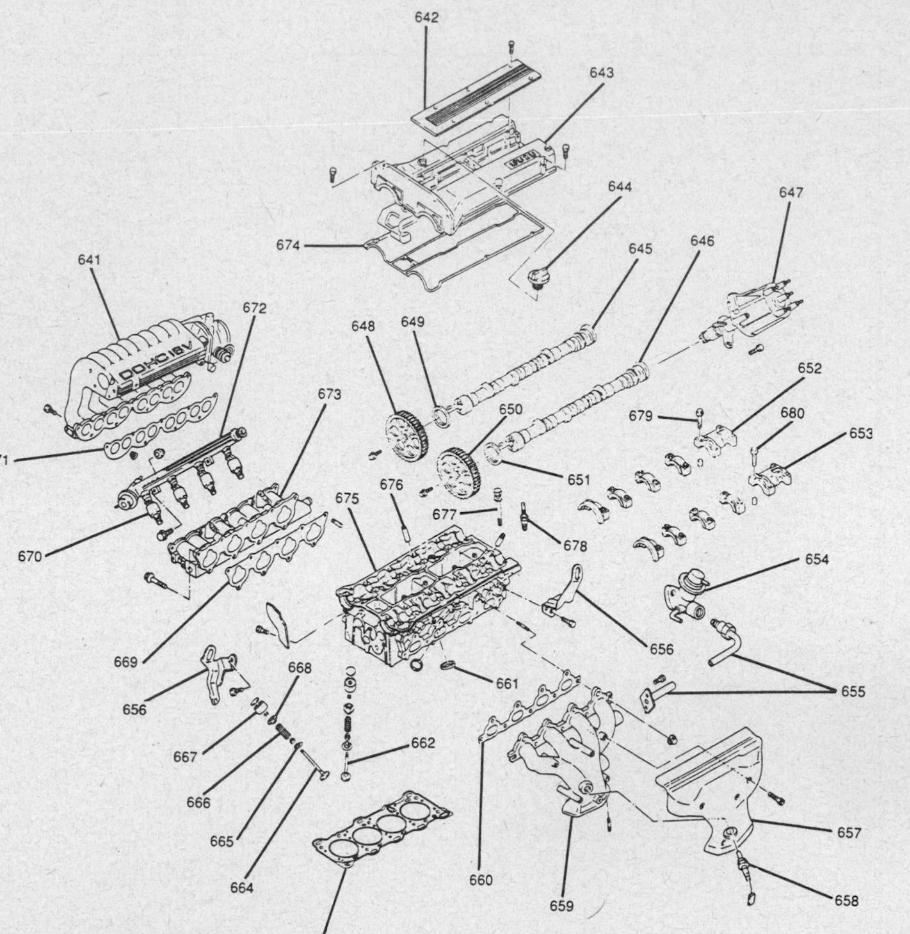
642
643
644
647
674
641
645
646
672
648
649
652
673
650
679
680
653
671
651
676
675
677
678
670
654
656
669
668
656
661
655
667
662
666
657
665
660
664
659
658
663

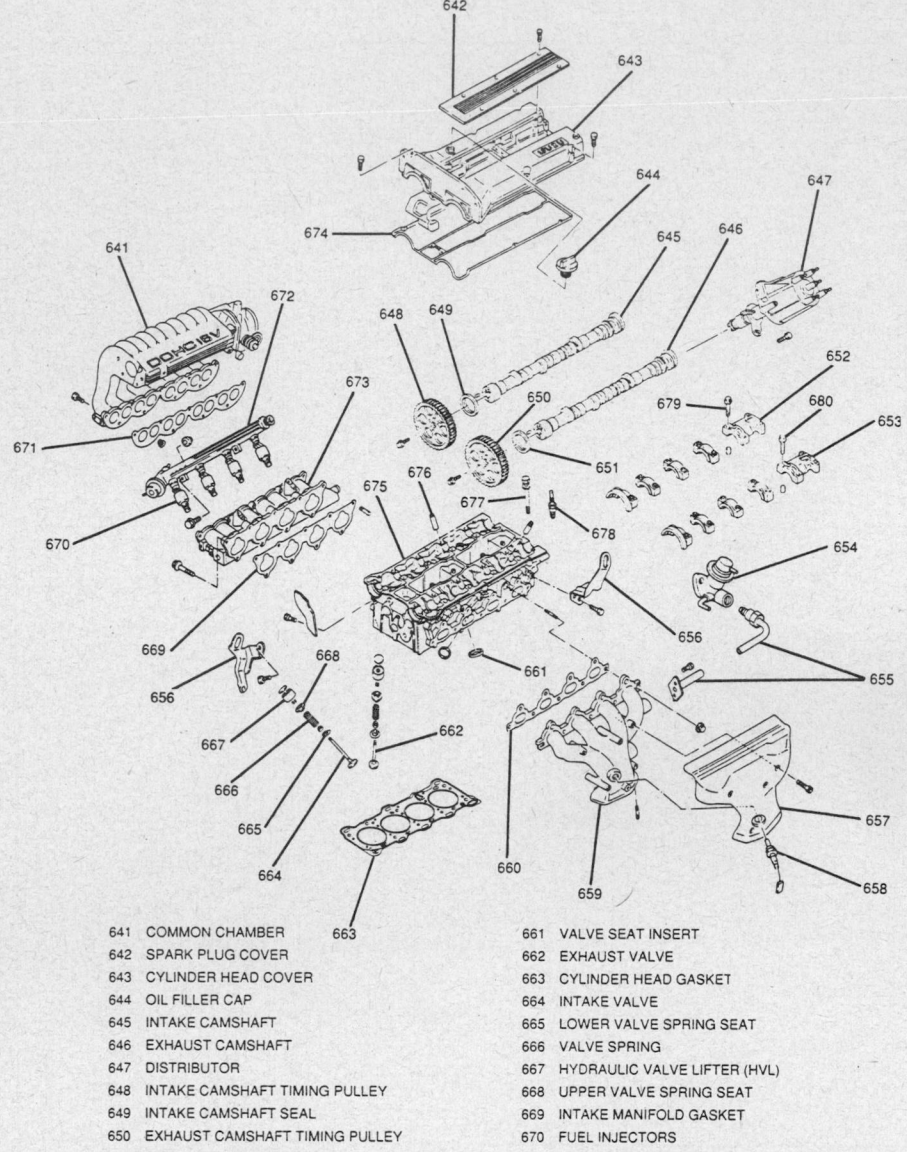

641	COMMON CHAMBER	661	VALVE SEAT INSERT
642	SPARK PLUG COVER	662	EXHAUST VALVE
643	CYLINDER HEAD COVER	663	CYLINDER HEAD GASKET
644	OIL FILLER CAP	664	INTAKE VALVE
645	INTAKE CAMSHAFT	665	LOWER VALVE SPRING SEAT
646	EXHAUST CAMSHAFT	666	VALVE SPRING
647	DISTRIBUTOR	667	HYDRAULIC VALVE LIFTER (HVL)
648	INTAKE CAMSHAFT TIMING PULLEY	668	UPPER VALVE SPRING SEAT
649	INTAKE CAMSHAFT SEAL	669	INTAKE MANIFOLD GASKET
650	EXHAUST CAMSHAFT TIMING PULLEY	670	FUEL INJECTORS
651	EXHAUST CAMSHAFT SEAL	671	COMMON CHAMBER GASKET
652	INTAKE CAMSHAFT BEARING CAPS	672	FUEL RAIL
653	EXHAUST CAMSHAFT BEARING CAPS	673	INTAKE MANIFOLD
654	EXHAUST GAS RECIRCULATION (EGR) VALVE	674	CYLINDER HEAD COVER GASKET
655	EGR PIPE	675	CYLINDER HEAD
656	ENGINE LIFT BRACKET	676	VALVE GUIDE
657	HEAT SHIELD	677	CYLINDER HEAD BOLT
658	OXYGEN SENSOR (O2S)	678	SPARK PLUG
659	EXHAUST MANIFOLD	679	INTAKE CAMSHAFT BEARING CAP BOLT
660	EXHAUST MANIFOLD GASKET	680	EXHAUST CAMSHAFT BEARING CAP BOLT

GC1069100535000X

Fig. 8 DOHC cylinder head components

DOHC ENGINE

Removal

1. Remove cylinder head cover, then rotate crankshaft to TDC by aligning camshaft pulley timing marks, **Fig. 19.**
2. Loosen timing belt tensioner, then remove camshaft pulleys from camshaft.
3. Remove distributor, then camshaft bearing caps bolts. **Bolts must be kept in the order they were taken out. To ensure that they will be installed into the same threaded hole.**
4. Remove the camshaft, then the camshaft seals.

Installation

1. Install camshaft into cylinder head, ensuring that dowel pin is in the up position and distributor drive slot is at end of exhaust camshaft, **Fig. 21.**
2. Install bearing caps and bolts in order that they were removed, but do not tighten at this time.
3. Apply GM 1052942 sealant or equivalent to No. 1 and No. 5 camshaft bearing caps, **Fig. 22.**
4. **Torque** camshaft bearing cap bolts to 89 inch lbs. using sequence shown in **Fig. 23.**
5. Install new camshaft oil seal using Oil Seal Installer tool No. J-35268 or equivalent.
6. Install distributor, camshaft timing pulleys, then the timing belt.
7. Install cylinder head cover.

PISTON & ROD ASSEMBLY

Align front marks on piston and rod assemblies, **Figs. 24 and 25.**. Ensure that mark is facing front of engine when installing into cylinder block.

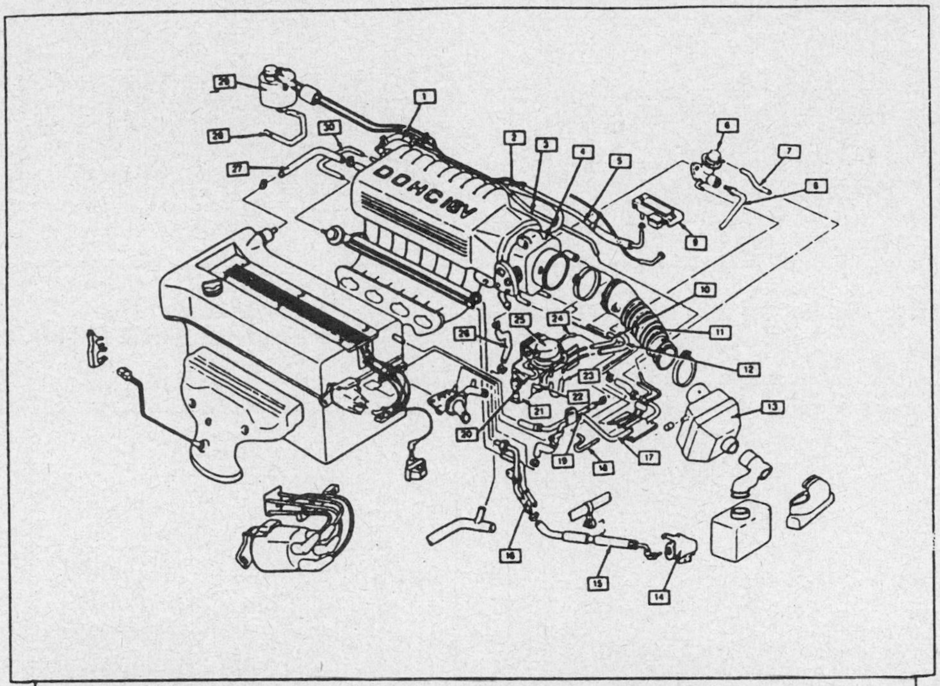

1 MAP SENSOR HOSE: CYLINDER HEAD COVER TO PIPE	17 THROTTLE VALVE HEATING HOSE: THERMOSTAT HSG TO T-VALVE
2 CANISTER HOSE: TO THROTTLE VALVE	18 CANISTER HOSE: PIPE TO THROTTLE VALVE
3 CANISTER HOSE: TO PIPE	19 PCV HOSE: CYLINDER HEAD COVER TO AIR DUCT
4 THROTTLE VALVE	20 EGR HOSE: VSV TO TRANSDUCER
5 MAP SENSOR HOSE: PIPE TO MAP SENSOR	21 VSV: EGR
6 EGR VALVE	22 EGR HOSE: PIPE TO VSV
7 EGR HOSE: PIPE TO EGR VALVE	23 EGR HOSE: EGR VALVE TO TRANSDUCER
8 EGR PIPE	24 EGR HOSE: TRANSDUCER TO PIPE
9 MAP SENSOR	25 EGR TRANSDUCER
10 EGR HOSE: THROTTLE VALVE TO PIPE	26 THROTTLE VALVE HEATING HOSE: T-VALVE TO BYPASS PIPE
11 AIR DUCT	27 PCV HOSE: CYLINDER HEAD COVER TO AIR DUCT
12 EGR HOSE: TRANSDUCER TO EGR VALVE	28 CANISTER HOSE
13 AIR CLEANER	29 CANISTER
14 FUEL FILTER	30 VACUUM HOSE: FUEL PRESSURE REGULATOR TO COMMON CHAMBER
15 FUEL FEED PIPE	
16 FUEL RETURN PIPE	

GC1059100091000X

Fig. 9 DOHC intake & exhaust components

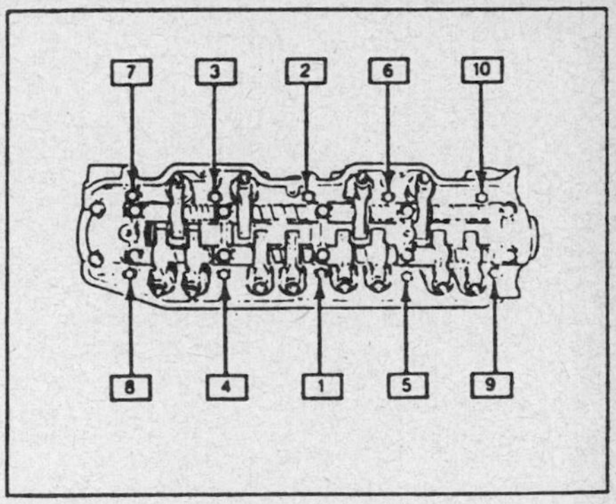

GC1069100536000X

Fig. 10 SOHC cylinder head tightening sequence

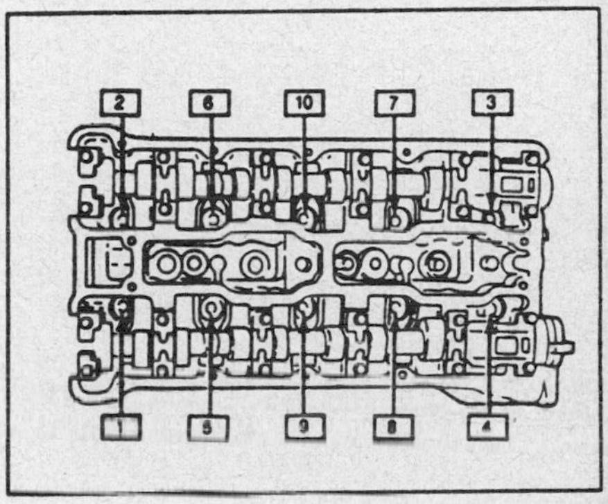

GC1069100537000X

Fig. 11 DOHC cylinder head bolt removal sequence

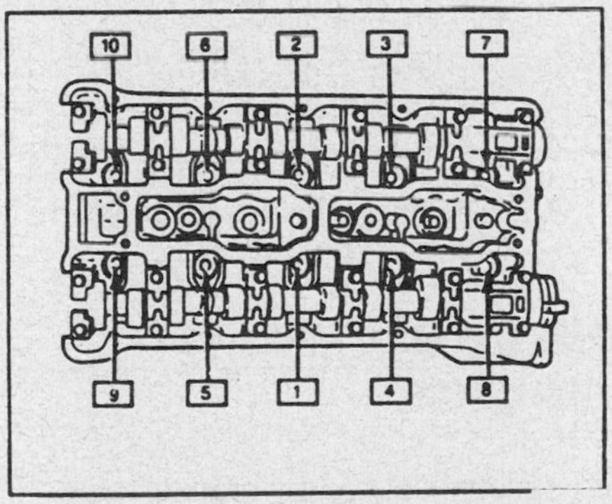

GC1069100538000X

Fig. 12 DOHC cylinder head tightening sequence

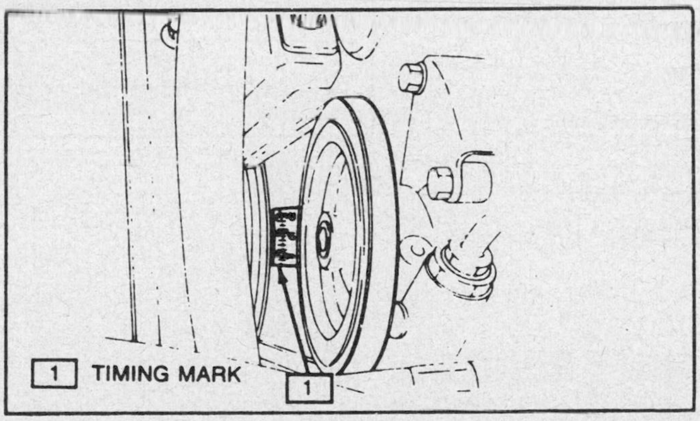
1 TIMING MARK
1

GC1069100539000X

Fig. 13 SOHC crankshaft pulley timing mark

PISTONS, PINS & RINGS

There are three standard size pistons and two oversized pistons. When installing piston rings, ensure that code marks are facing upwards. Install pin into piston and rod as shown in **Fig. 26.**

MAIN & ROD BEARINGS

Rod bearings come in three standard sizes and two oversize, 0.0098 inch and 0.0196 inch. If after replacing rod bearing, thrust clearance is still excessive, replace crankshaft.

When replacing a main bearing, always replace it with one that has the same number. If you can not read number, refer to **Figs. 27 and 28,** for sizes of main bearings. When servicing the crankshaft, inspect all journals for wear or damage. Install upper half of bearings into cylinder block, and the lower half into main bearing caps. If oil clearance can not be brought within specifications using a standard

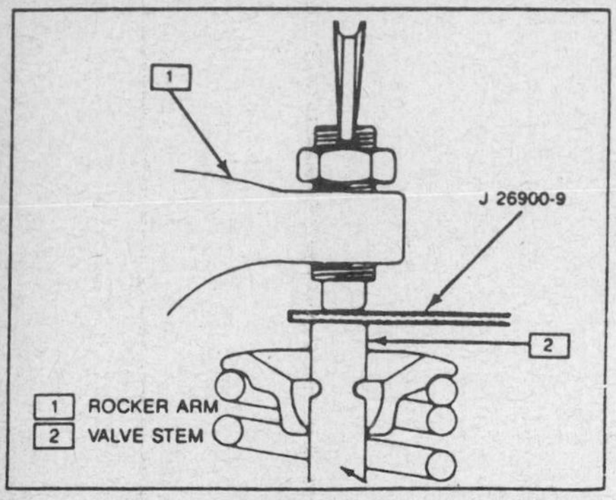
1
J 26900-9
2
1 ROCKER ARM
2 VALVE STEM

GC1069100540000X

Fig. 14 Valve clearance adjustment. SOHC engine

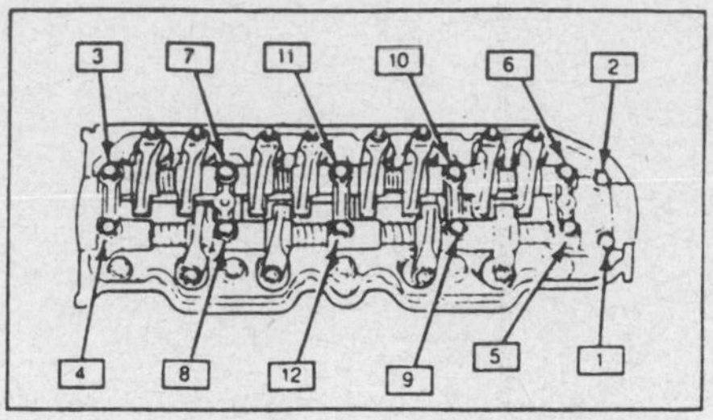
3 7 11 10 6 2
4 8 12 9 5 1

GC1069100544000X

Fig. 15 Rocker arm shaft removal. SOHC Engine

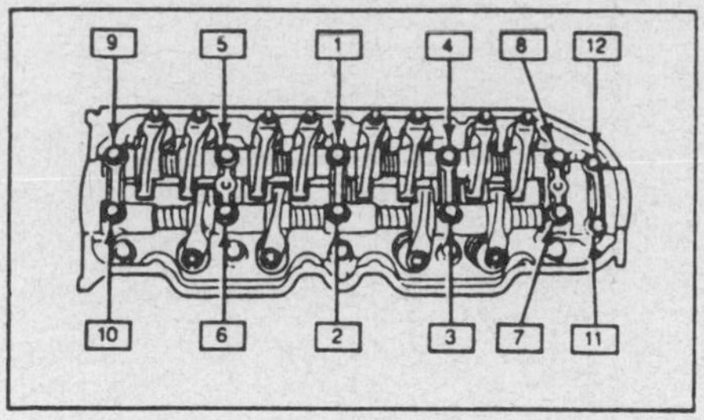
9 5 1 4 8 12
10 6 2 3 7 11

GC1069100545000X

Fig. 16 Rocker arm shaft tightening sequence. SOHC Engine

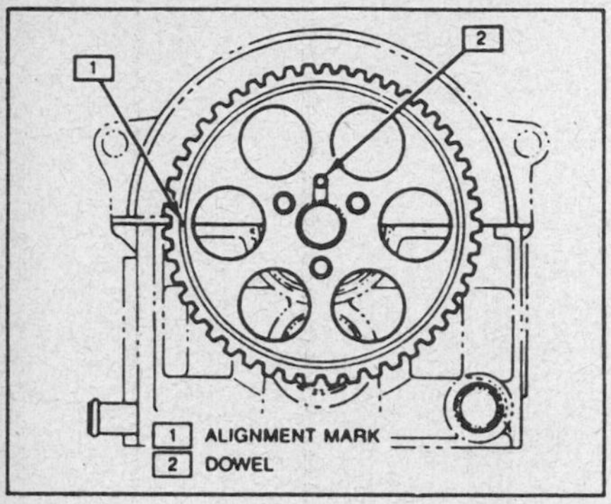
1
2
1 ALIGNMENT MARK
2 DOWEL

GC1069100546000X

Fig. 17 SOHC cam pulley timing mark

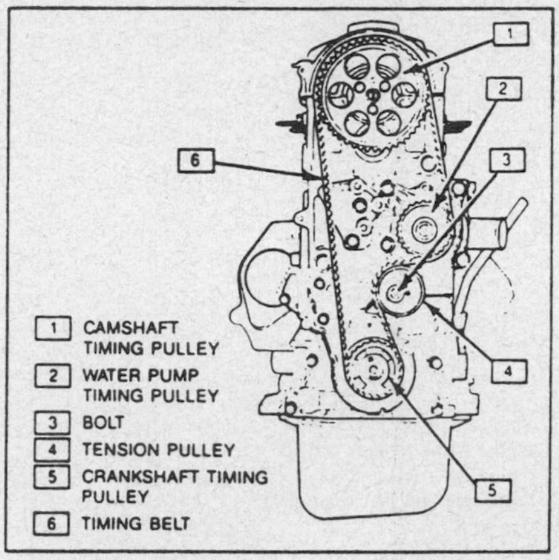
1
2
3
4
5
6
1 CAMSHAFT TIMING PULLEY
2 WATER PUMP TIMING PULLEY
3 BOLT
4 TENSION PULLEY
5 CRANKSHAFT TIMING PULLEY
6 TIMING BELT

GC1069100547000X

Fig. 18 SOHC timing belt

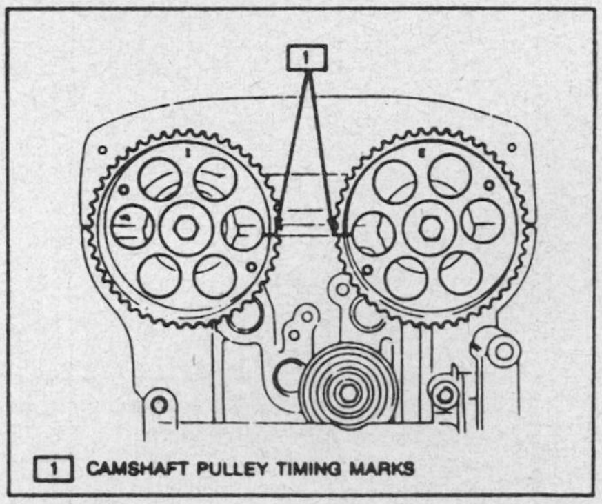
1
1 CAMSHAFT PULLEY TIMING MARKS

GC1069100548000X

Fig. 19 DOHC cam pulley timing mark

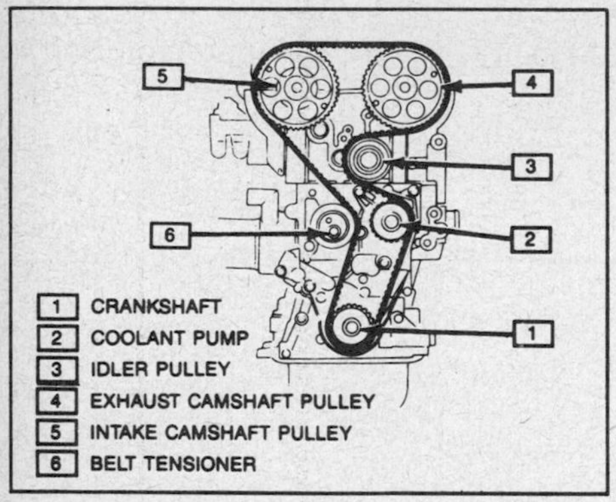
5
4
3
6
2
1
1 CRANKSHAFT
2 COOLANT PUMP
3 IDLER PULLEY
4 EXHAUST CAMSHAFT PULLEY
5 INTAKE CAMSHAFT PULLEY
6 BELT TENSIONER

GC1069100549000X

Fig. 20 DOHC timing belt

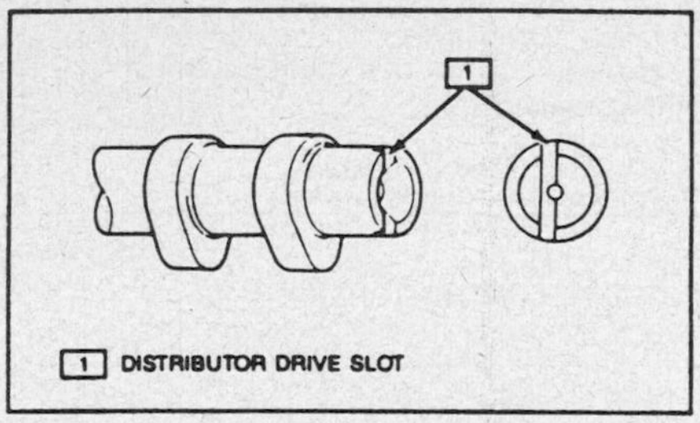
1
1 DISTRIBUTOR DRIVE SLOT

GC1069100550000X

Fig. 21 Distributor drive slot

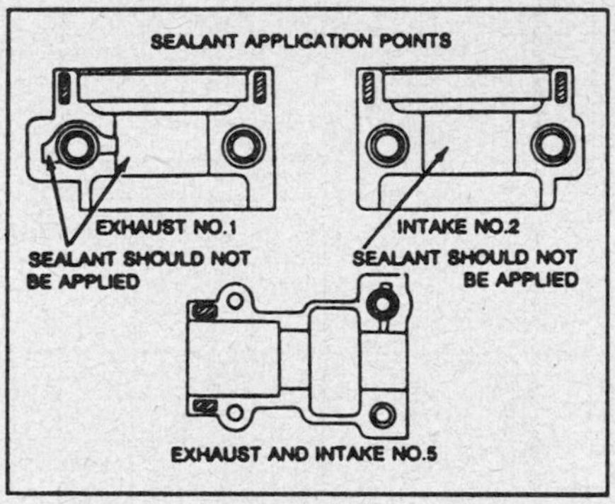
SEALANT APPLICATION POINTS
EXHAUST NO.1
SEALANT SHOULD NOT BE APPLIED
INTAKE NO.2
SEALANT SHOULD NOT BE APPLIED
EXHAUST AND INTAKE NO.5

GC1069100551000X

Fig. 22 Camshaft bearing cap sealant

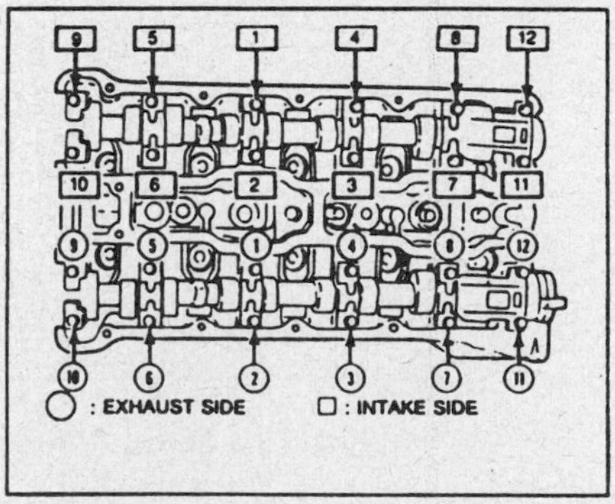
9 5 1 4 8 12
10 6 2 3 7 11
10 6 2 3 7 11
: EXHAUST SIDE
: INTAKE SIDE

GC1069100552000X

Fig. 23 Camshaft bearing cap tightening sequence

bearing, regrind crankshaft for next oversize bearing.

CRANKSHAFT REAR OIL SEAL

REPLACE

1. Disconnect battery ground cable, then raise and support vehicle.
2. Remove right and left undercovers, then the oil pan as described in "Oil Pan, Replace."
3. Remove transaxle as described in "Transaxle, Replace" in "Clutch & Manual Transaxle" section.
4. Mark flywheel and engine position for installation reference, then remove flywheel.
5. Remove flywheel spacer and rear main seal retainer.
6. Remove rear main seal from retainer, **Fig. 29.**
7. Reverse procedure to install.

OIL PAN

REPLACE

1. Disconnect battery ground cable.
2. Raise and support vehicle, then drain crankcase oil.
3. Remove righthand undercover, then exhaust pipe from exhaust manifold.
4. Remove torque rod and flywheel dust cover.
5. Remove stiffener from cylinder block, then oil pan.
6. Reverse procedure to install. Use new oil pan gasket, applying GM 1052942 sealant or equivalent to gasket surface. **Torque** stiffener bolts to 50 ft. lbs.

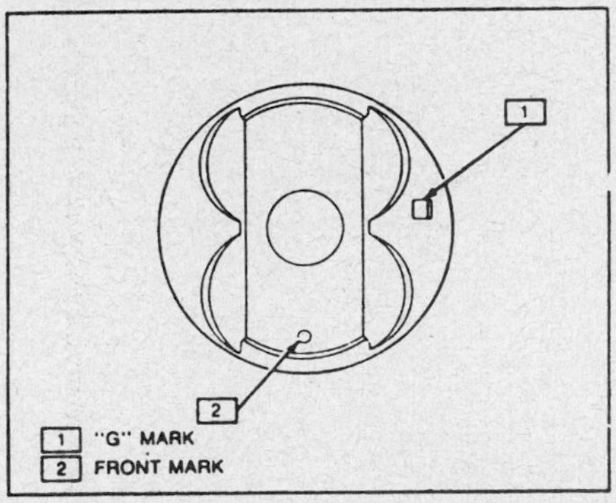
1
2
1 "G" MARK
2 FRONT MARK

GC1069100553000X

Fig. 24 Piston mark location. 1.6L/4-97 engine

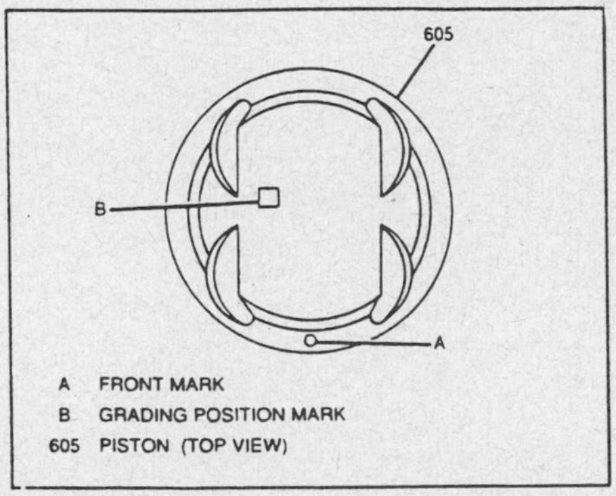
605
B
A
A FRONT MARK
B GRADING POSITION MARK
605 PISTON (TOP VIEW)

GC1069100554000X

Fig. 25 Piston mark location. 1.8L/4-110 engine

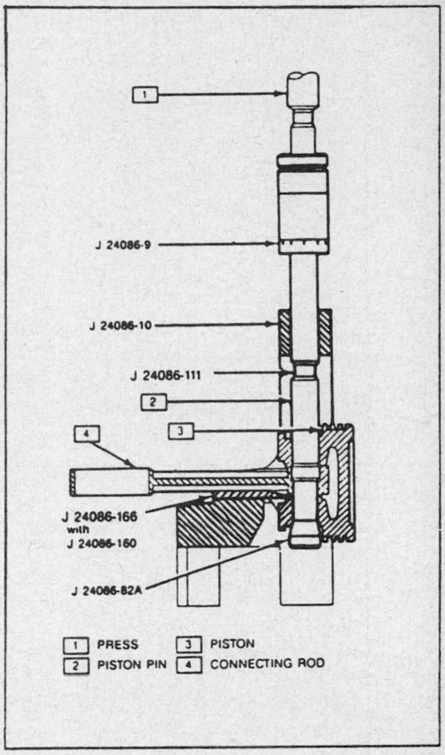
1
J 24086-9
J 24086-10
J 24086-111
2
3
4
J 24086-166 with J 24086-160
J 24086-82A
1 PRESS
2 PISTON PIN
3 PISTON
4 CONNECTING ROD

GC1069100555000X

Fig. 26 Piston pin installation

① Size mark	Main Bearing Bore Diameter (mm)	Crank Shaft Main Journal Diameter (mm)	② Size Mark	Crank Shaft Bearing Size Mark (Upper Side)	Crank Shaft Bearing Size Mark (Lower Side)	Oil Clearance (mm) (Reference)
1	55.992-56.000	51.918-51.928	– –	Blue	Blue	0.022-0.048
		51.929-51.938	–	Black	Black	0.020-0.046
2	55.984-55.991	51.918-51.928	– –			0.022-0.048
		51.929-51.938	–	Brown	Brown	0.020-0.046
3	55.976-55.983	51.918-51.928	– –			0.022-0.048
		51.929-51.938	–	Green	Green	0.020-0.046
Under Size 0.25	55.976-56.000	51.668-51.688		Stamp of Size	Stamp of Size	0.020-0.088
Under Size 0.50		51.418-51.438				

GC1069100556000X

Fig. 27 Main bearing selection table. 1.6L/4-97 engine

SIZE MARK	MAIN BEARING BORE DIAMETER (mm)	CRANKSHAFT MAIN JOURNAL DIAMETER (mm)	SIZE MARK	CRANKSHAFT BEARING SIZE MARK (UPPER SIDE)	CRANKSHAFT BEARING SIZE MARK (LOWER SIDE)	OIL CLEARANCE (mm) (REFERENCE)
1	55.992-56.000	51.918-51.928	– –	BLUE	BLUE	0.023-0.048
		51.929-51.938	–	BLACK	BLACK	0.020-0.046
2	55.984-55.991	51.918-51.928	– –			0.023-0.048
		51.929-51.938	–	BROWN	BROWN	0.020-0.046
3	55.976-55.983	51.918-51.928	– –			0.023-0.048
		51.929-51.938	–	GREEN	GREEN	0.020-0.046

GC1069100557000X

Fig. 28 Main bearing selection table. 1.8L/4-110 engine

OIL PUMP SERVICE

REMOVAL

1. Disconnect battery ground cable.
2. Remove timing belt cover, alternator and power steering belts, then raise and support vehicle.
3. Remove crankshaft pulley, then oil pump attaching bolts and oil pump, **Fig. 30.**

INSPECTION

1. Measure oil pump driven gear to housing clearance, **Fig. 31,** using suitable feeler gauge. If clearance is more than 0.078 inch, replace oil pump.
2. Measure oil pump drive gear to driven gear clearance, **Fig. 32.** If the clearance is more than 0.012 inch, replace the gear set.
3. Measure oil pump body to gear clearance, **Fig. 33,** using a feeler gauge and precision straightedge. If the clearance is more than 0.004 inch, replace oil pump.

INSTALLATION

1. Apply GM 1052942 sealant or equivalent to oil pump gasket surface.
2. Install oil pump, **torque** oil pump to block bolts to 89 inch lbs.
3. Install crankshaft pulley, then lower vehicle.
4. Install timing belt cover, then the power steering and alternator belts.
5. Connect battery ground cable.

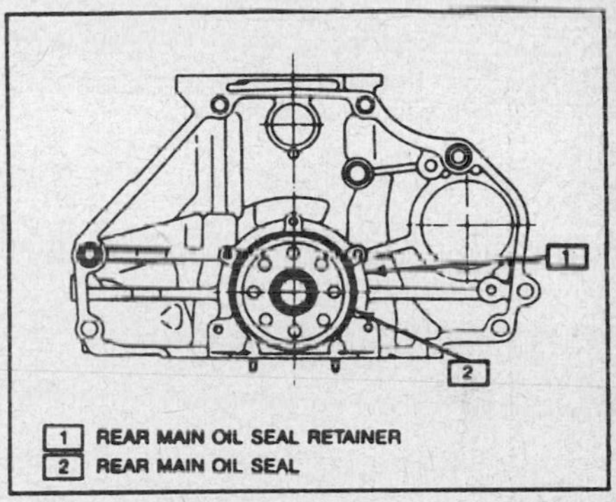
1
2
1 REAR MAIN OIL SEAL RETAINER
2 REAR MAIN OIL SEAL

GC1069100558000X

Fig. 29 Rear main oil seal retainer

SERPENTINE DRIVE BELT

REMOVAL

1. Rotate serpentine belt tensioner pulley clockwise to release tension from belt using a 3/8 drive socket wrench.
2. Remove serpentine belt from pulleys.

INSTALLATION

1. Route serpentine belt around all pulleys as shown in **Fig. 34.**
2. Rotate tensioner pulley away from drive belt and install drive belt to tensioner pulley.

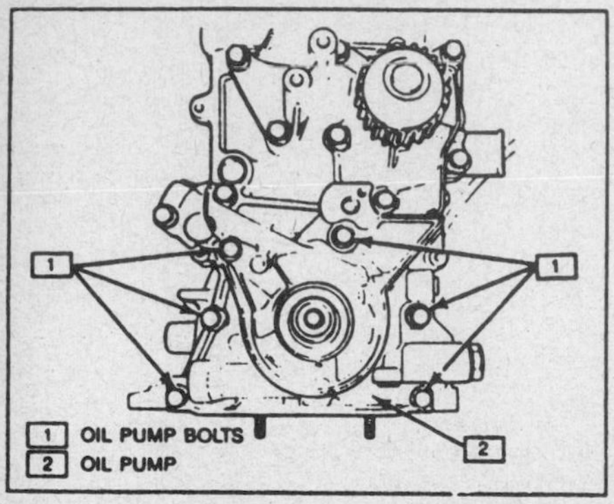
1
1
2
1 OIL PUMP BOLTS
2 OIL PUMP

GC1099100094000X

Fig. 30 Oil pump removal

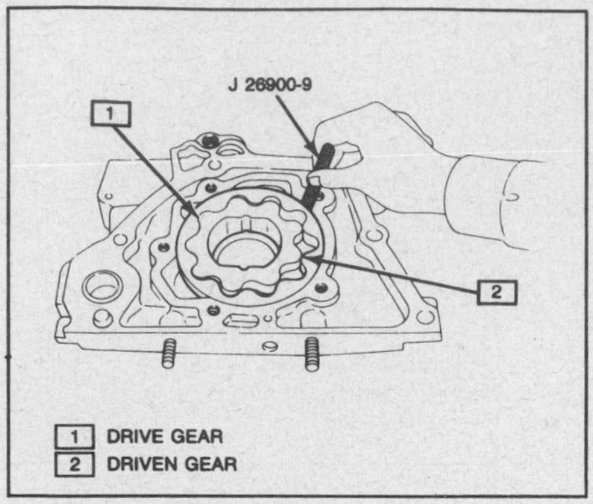
J 26900-9
1
2
1 DRIVE GEAR
2 DRIVEN GEAR

GC1099100095000X

Fig. 31 Oil pump driven gear to housing inspection

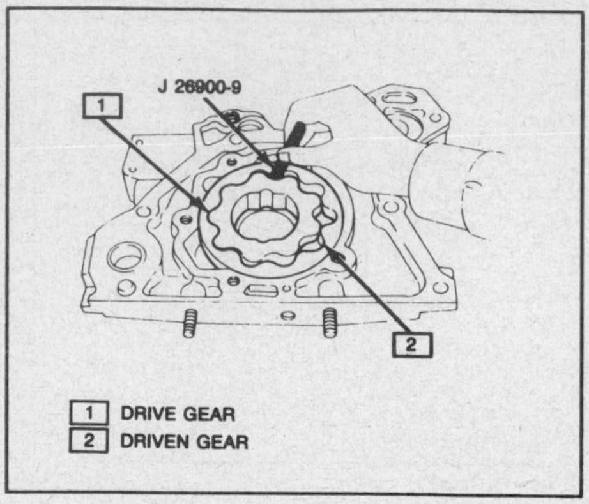
J 26900-9
1
2
1 DRIVE GEAR
2 DRIVEN GEAR

GC1099100096000X

Fig. 32 Oil pump drive to driven gear inspection

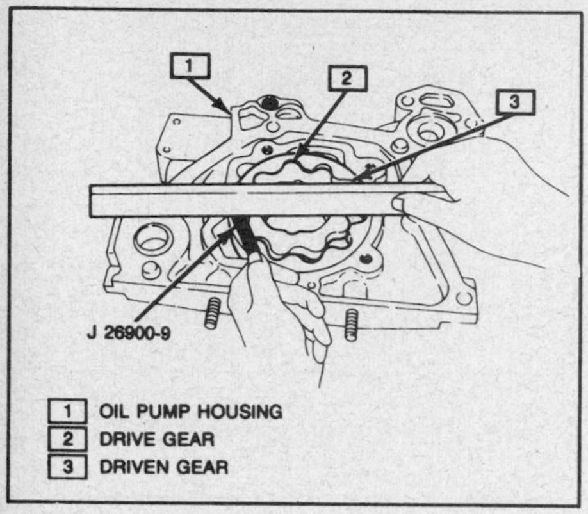
1
2
3
J 26900-9
1 OIL PUMP HOUSING
2 DRIVE GEAR
3 DRIVEN GEAR

GC1099100097000X

Fig. 33 Oil pump body to gear clearance inspection

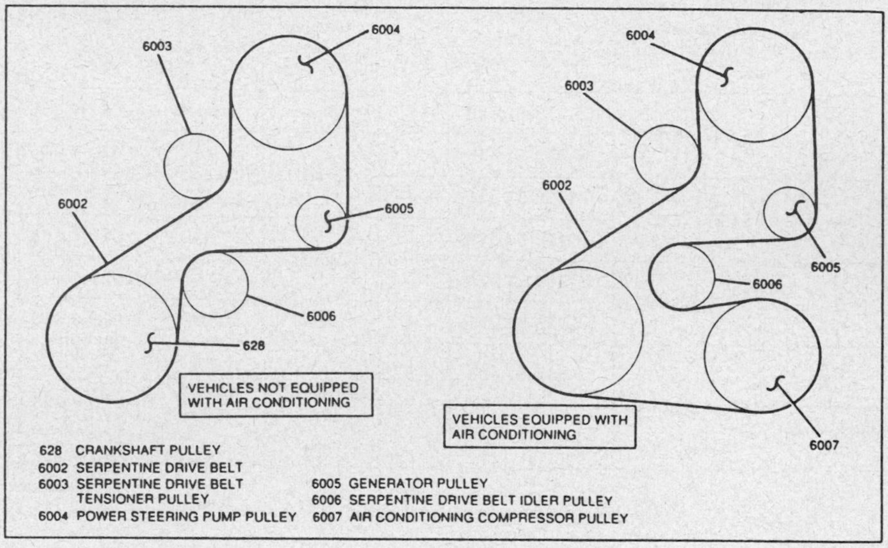
6003
6004
6002
6005
6006
628
VEHICLES NOT EQUIPPED WITH AIR CONDITIONING
6004
6003
6002
6005
6006
6007
VEHICLES EQUIPPED WITH AIR CONDITIONING
628 CRANKSHAFT PULLEY
6002 SERPENTINE DRIVE BELT
6003 SERPENTINE DRIVE BELT TENSIONER PULLEY
6004 POWER STEERING PUMP PULLEY
6005 GENERATOR PULLEY
6006 SERPENTINE DRIVE BELT IDLER PULLEY
6007 AIR CONDITIONING COMPRESSOR PULLEY

GC1069100559000X

Fig. 34 Serpentine belt routing

3. Return tensioner to its original position and remove socket wrench.

COOLING SYSTEM BLEED

These engines do not require a specified bleed procedure. After filling cooling system, run engine to operating temperature with radiator/pressure cap off. Air will then be automatically bled through cap opening.

THERMOSTAT

REPLACE

SOHC ENGINE

1. Drain cooling System.
2. Disconnect radiator hose from thermostat housing cap.
3. Remove thermostat housing cap and thermostat from thermostat housing.
4. Clean both gasket surfaces thoroughly.
5. Reverse procedure to install.

DOHC ENGINE

1. Disconnect battery ground cable.
2. Drain cooling system.
3. Disconnect ignition wire from ignition coil.
4. Remove distributor cap from distributor and set aside.
5. Disconnect lower radiator hose from thermostat housing cap.
6. Disconnect EGR pipe bracket from thermostat housing.
7. Disconnect EGR pipe from exhaust manifold.
8. Disconnect upper radiator hose from thermostat housing.
9. Remove thermostat housing cap and thermostat from thermostat housing.
10. Clean both gasket surfaces thoroughly.
11. Reverse procedure to install.

WATER PUMP

REPLACE

SOHC ENGINE

1. Disconnect battery ground cable, then drain coolant system.
2. Remove power steering belt, then timing belt cover and timing belt. See "Timing Belt Replace."
3. Remove water pump to block retaining bolts, then water pump.
4. Reverse procedure to install.

DOHC ENGINE

1. Disconnect battery ground cable, then drain cooling system.
2. Remove right front engine mount as outlined under "Engine Mount, Replace."
3. Remove engine mount bridge.
4. Remove upper timing belt cover assembly.
5. Remove power steering belt.
6. Remove lower timing belt cover assembly.
7. Loosen timing belt tensioner, then remove timing belt at water pump pulley.
8. Remove water pump attaching bolts, then remove water pump.
9. Reverse procedure to install.

RADIATOR

REPLACE

1. Drain coolant, into suitable container.
2. Disconnect upper radiator hose from radiator.
3. Remove two upper radiator fan shroud mounting bolts.

4. Raise and support vehicle.
5. Remove lower radiator fan shroud mounting bolts.
6. Disconnect lower radiator hose from radiator.
7. **On models equipped with automatic transaxle,** disconnect and cap fluid cooler hoses from lower radiator tank.
8. **On all models,** disconnect radiator fan and thermo switch electrical connectors.
9. Remove radiator fan assembly from vehicle.
10. Remove radiator core support bolts and support from vehicle.
11. Remove radiator from vehicle.
12. Remove fan thermo switch from radiator.
13. Reverse procedure to install.

FUEL PUMP

REPLACE

1. Disconnect battery ground cable, then loosen fuel filler cap to relieve tank vapor pressure.
2. Disconnect fuel fitting, wrapping a shop towel around fitting to prevent spraying.
3. Siphon or pump fuel into approved container.
4. Raise and support vehicle with suitable floor jacks.
5. Remove exhaust pipe from catalytic converter, then fuel filler neck hose from fuel tank.
6. Remove fuel overflow pipe hose from fuel tank.
7. Disconnect fuel gauge sending unit and fuel pump electrical connectors.
8. Remove fuel vapor, fuel supply and fuel return hose from the fuel tank.
9. Support fuel tank using a suitable transaxle jack or equivalent, then remove six tank retaining bolts and tank.
10. Remove eight fuel pump mounting screws, then fuel pump/bracket from fuel tank.
11. Remove fuel pump supply hose extension from bracket, gasket from pump bracket or tank and filter from pump pick-up tube.
12. Disconnect electrical connector wires from pump.
13. Remove pump from bracket, then outlet hose from pump.
14. Reverse procedure to install.

FUEL FILTER

REPLACE

The fuel filter is located in the engine compartment, below the power brake vacuum booster assembly.

1. Relieve fuel system pressure as follows:
   a. Remove fuel filler cap, then fuel pump relay from underhood relay center.
   b. Start engine and allow to run until it stalls, then crank engine for an additional ten seconds.
   c. Disconnect battery ground cable.
2. Remove air intake duct, then disconnect fuel line from filter outlet (upper connection).
3. Raise and support vehicle.
4. Disconnect fuel line lower fitting from filter, then cap the ends of the fuel line fittings.
5. Loosen filter bracket clamp bolt, then remove filter from bracket.
6. Reverse procedure to install, noting the following:
   a. Apply clean engine oil to sealing surface of fuel lines.
   b. **Torque** fuel line fittings to 25 ft. lbs.

TIGHTENING SPECIFICATIONS

1.6L/4-97 ENGINE

Year	Component	Torque/ Ft. Lbs.
1992–93	Accelerator Cable Bracket Bolts	89①
	Air Conditioning Compressor Mounting Bolts	30
	Air Conditioning Compressor Mounting Bracket Bolts	15
	Battery Cable To Battery Terminal Retainers	11
	Battery Retainer Bolt	44①
	Battery Retainer Nut	72①
	Camshaft Pulley Retaining Bolts	106①
	Common Chamber Bolts & Nuts	17
	Connecting Rod Bearing Cap Nuts	11②
	Crankshaft Pulley Center Bolt	87
	Crankshaft Pulley Side Bolts	17
	Cylinder Head Bolts	58
	Cylinder Head Cover Bolts	89①
	EGR Pipe Bolts	32
	Exhaust Manifold Bolts & Nuts	29
	Flywheel Bolts	22②
	Induction Port Retaining Bolt	17
	Left Engine Mount Center Bolt	50
	Left Engine Mount To Transaxle Case Bolts	35
	Main Bearing Cap Bolts (Three Passes)	44
	Mounting Bridge Bracket Bolt	29

Year	Component	Torque/ Ft. Lbs.
1992–93	Oil Drain Plug	20
	Oil Pan Bolts & Nuts	89①
	Oil Pump Bolts	89①
	Power Steering Pump Mounting Bolts	15
	Rear Crankshaft Seal Retaining Bolts	89①
	Rear Engine Mount Center Bolt	76
	Rear Engine Mount Transaxle Case Bolt	37
	Relief Valve Plug	27
	Right Engine Mount Bracket Nut & Bolt	30
	Right Engine Mount Through Bolt	50
	Rocker Arm Bracket Bolt	16
	Spark Plugs	21
	Starter Motor Nut & Bolt	29
	Suspension To Rear Engine Mount Brace Bolt & Nut	15
	Throttle Body Bolts	17
	Timing Belt Cover Bolts	89①
	Timing Belt Tensioner Pulley Bolt	31
	Torque Rod Center Bolt	50
	Torque Rod Bracket Bolts & Nuts	28

①—Inch lbs.
②—Plus 45–60°.

TIGHTENING SPECIFICATIONS-Continued

1.6L/4–110 ENGINE

Year	Component	Torque/ Ft. Lbs.
1992–93	Accelerator Cable Bracket Bolts	89①
	Air Conditioning Compressor Mounting Bolts	30
	Air Conditioning Compressor Mounting Bracket Bolts	15
	Battery Cable To Battery Terminal Retainers	11
	Battery Retainer Bolt	44①
	Battery Retainer Nut	72①
	Camshaft Bearing Cap Bolts	89①
	Center Crossmember Bolts	45
	Common Chamber Bolts & Nuts	17
	Connecting Rod Bearing Cap Nuts	18③
	Crankshaft Pulley Center Bolt	108
	Cylinder Head Bolts	58
	Cylinder Head Cover Bolts	53①
	EGR Pipe Nut	11
	EGR Pipe Bracket Bolt	89①
	EGR Pipe To Exhaust Manifold	11
	Engine Lift Bracket Bolts	18
	Engine Wiring Harness Conduit Bolt	53①
	Exhaust Camshaft Timing Pulley Bolt	44
	Exhaust Manifold Nuts	29
	Exhaust Manifold To Cylinder Block Brace Bolts	15
	Flywheel Bolts	22
	Forward Exhaust Pipe Nuts	46
	Fuel Pipe Bracket Bolt	89①
	Ground Cable Bolt	71①
	Guide Tube Bolt	11
	Heat Shield Bolts	11
	Hood Bolts	15
	Intake Camshaft Timing Pulley Bolt	44

Year	Component	Torque/ Ft. Lbs.
1992–93	Oil Cooler Center Bolt	32
	Oil Cooler Pipe Bolt	89①
	Oil Drain Plug	20
	Oil Pan Bolts & Nuts	89①
	Oil Pressure Switch	10
	Oil Pump Bolts	89①
	Main Bearing Cap Bolts (Three Passes)	65
	Power Steering Pump Mounting Bolts	15
	Power Steering Pump Fluid Pressure Pipe Union Bolt	15
	Rear Crankshaft Seal Retaining Bolts	89①
	Rear Engine Mount Through Bolt	37
	Rear Engine Mount To Cylinder Block Bolts	75
	Relief Valve Plug	27
	Right Engine Mount Bracket Nut & Bolt	30
	Right Engine Mount Bridge Bolt	37
	Right Engine Mount Through Bolt	50
	Right Side Intake Manifold Brace Nut & Bolt	15
	Serpentine Belt Idler Pulley Bolt	22
	Serpentine Belt Tensioner Center Bolt	30
	Spark Plugs	21
	Starter Motor Nut & Bolt	29
	Suspension To Rear Engine Mount Brace Bolt & Nut	15
	Torque Rod Bolts	14
	Torque Rod Nut	94
	Torque To Center Crossmember Through Bolt & Nut	51
	Timing Belt Cover Bolts	89①
	Timing Belt Tensioner Pulley Bolt	31
	Vacuum Switching Valve Bolts	89①

①—Inch lbs.
②—Refer to text.
③—Plus 100°.

Clutch & Manual Transaxle

INDEX

ADJUSTMENTS

CLUTCH CABLE

1. Measure clutch pedal freeplay, **Fig. 1**, to confirm adjustments are within specifications.
2. If freeplay is not within specifications, turn adjustment nut clockwise or counterclockwise to adjust cable.
3. Repeat step 2 so that play between clutch release arm and clutch cable is within

SHIFT CABLE

1. Place transaxle in "Neutral" position.
2. Turn adjusting nuts (2) until change lever (1) is at right angle to pivot case, as viewed from side of gear control, **Fig. 2.**
3. Turn adjusting nuts (4) until change lever (1) is at a right angle to pivot case as viewed from rear of gear control, **Fig. 3.**

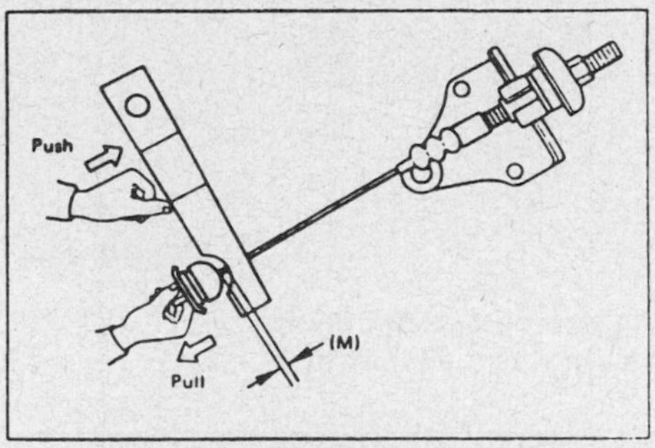
Push
Pull
(M)

Clutch lever free play (M)	2±1 (0.08±0.04)
Clutch pedal free play (L)	10±5 (0.39±0.20)

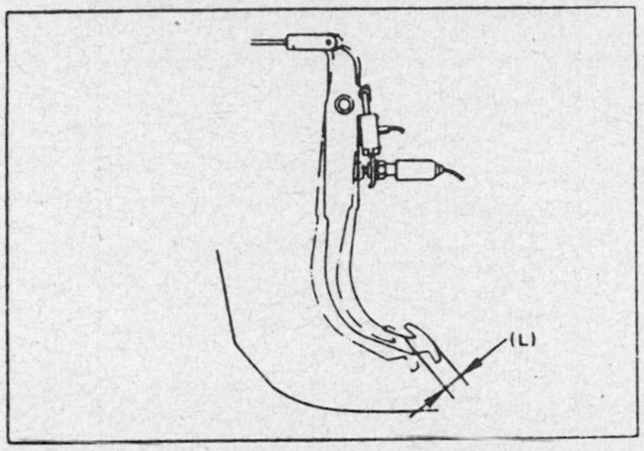
(L)

GC5049100061000X

Fig. 1 Clutch cable adjustment

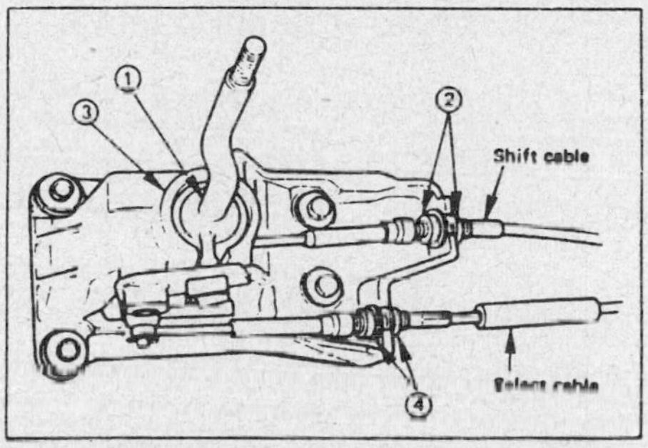
Shift cable

GC5049100062000X

Fig. 2 Shift cable adjustment

4. After making adjustments, tighten adjusting nuts (2) and (4).specifications shown in **Fig. 1.**

CLUTCH

REPLACE

1. Remove transaxle assembly as outlined under "Transaxle, Replace."
2. Mark clutch cover assembly position to flywheel for installation alignment.
3. Remove clutch cover bolts evenly, releasing spring tension.
4. Remove clutch cover and disc.
5. Reverse procedure to install, tighten-clutch cover bolts to specifications.

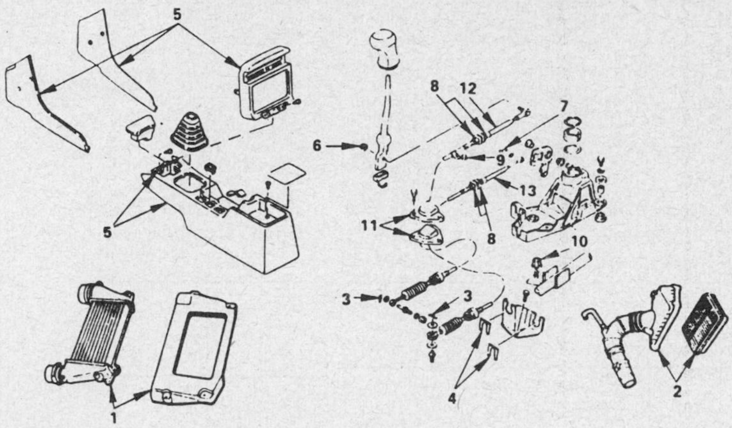

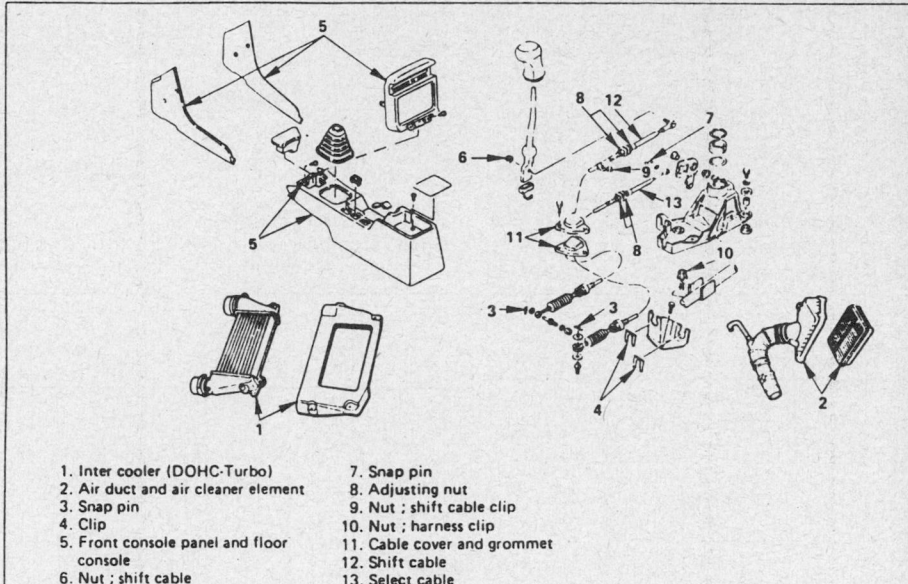

1. Inter cooler (DOHC-Turbo)
2. Air duct and air cleaner element
3. Snap pin
4. Clip
5. Front console panel and floor console
6. Nut ; shift cable
7. Snap pin
8. Adjusting nut
9. Nut ; shift cable clip
10. Nut ; harness clip
11. Cable cover and grommet
12. Shift cable
13. Select cable

GC5049100063000X

Fig. 3 Shift cable assembly

TRANSAXLE

REPLACE

REMOVAL

1. Disconnect battery cables, then remove battery and battery tray.
2. Drain transaxle fluid, then remove air cleaner assembly.
3. Disconnect wire connectors and ground cable.
4. Disconnect engine wiring harness clip, then remove ignition coil ground cable.
5. Remove battery bracket and ignition coil assembly.
6. Remove speedometer cable, clutch cable and shifter cable, **Fig. 3**, then using Engine Support Fixture tool No. J28467-A or equivalent, support engine assembly.
7. Raise and support vehicle, then remove wheel and tire assembly.
8. Remove front undercovers, then remove ball joints at steering knuckles.
9. Remove front drive axles, then remove front exhaust pipe.
10. Remove torque rod and bracket, then left transaxle mount.
11. Remove front transaxle through bolt, then center beam with rear transaxle mount.
12. Remove engine stiffener and flywheel dust cover.
13. Using suitable jacks, support transaxle, then remove transaxle attaching bolts.
14. Remove transaxle assembly.

INSTALLATION

1. Install transaxle assembly, then tighten attaching bolts to specifications.
2. Remove transaxle support, then install flywheel dust cover.
3. Install engine stiffener, then install center beam with rear transaxle mount, then install front and left transaxle mount through bolts.
4. Tighten bolts to specifications.
5. Install torque rod, bracket and front exhaust pipe.
6. Install right drive axle assemblies, then install ball joints.
7. Install front undercovers, then wheel and tire assembly, then lower vehicle.
8. Remove engine support fixture.
9. Install shift cable, clutch cable and speedometer cable.
10. Install battery bracket, ignition coil assembly and ignition coil ground cable.
11. Install engine electrical harness clamp, then connect ground cable.
12. Connect electrical connectors, battery, battery tray and battery cables.

TIGHTENING SPECIFICATIONS

Year	Component	Torque/ ft. lbs.
1992–93	Clutch Cover Bolts	13
	Clutch Flywheel Bolts	58
	Transaxle Center Crossmember Bolts	45
	Transaxle Filler Plug	20
	Transaxle Front Mount Bracket	45

Year	Component	Torque/ ft. lbs.
1992–93	Transaxle Front Retaining Nut	45
	Transaxle Left Axle Mount Bolts	29
	Transaxle Left Through Bolt	64
	Transaxle Rear Mount Bolt	29
	Transaxle To Engine Bolts	55

Rear Axle & Suspension

INDEX

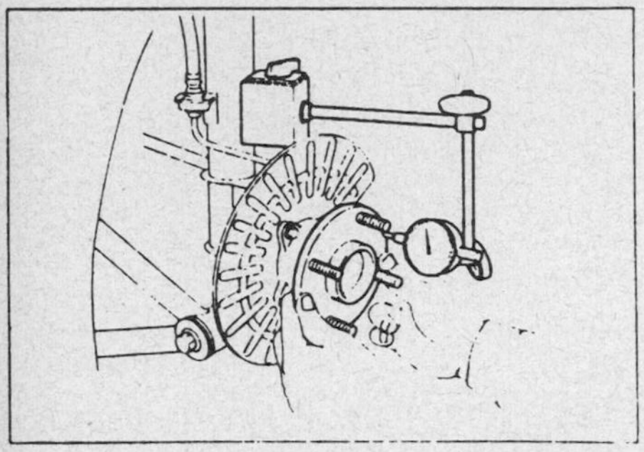

GC3039100229000X

Fig. 1 Measuring hub axial play

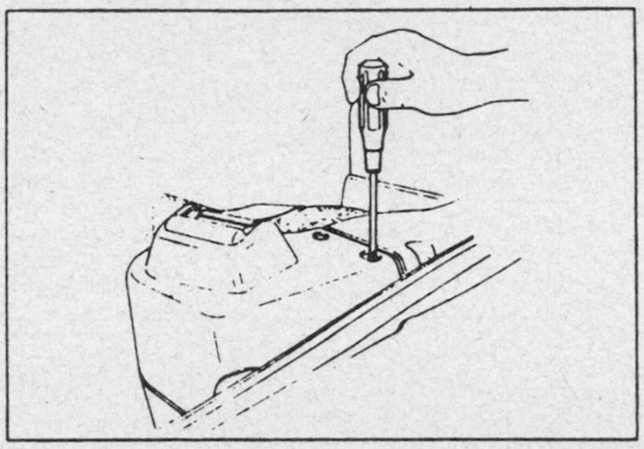

GC2039100096000X

Fig. 2 Strut tower cover removal

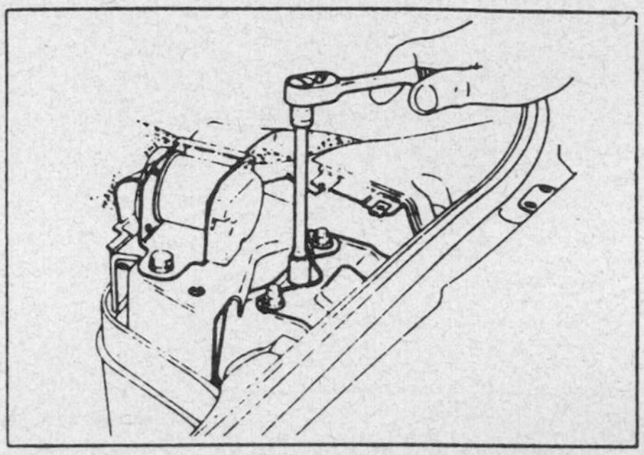

GC2039100097000X

Fig. 3 Upper strut nut removal

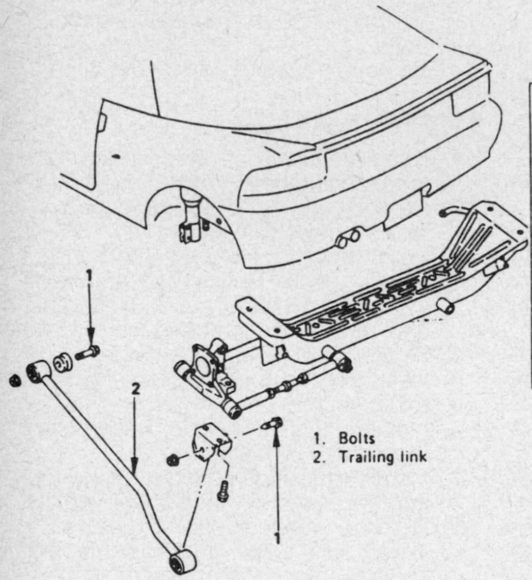
1
2
1
1. Bolts
2. Trailing link

GC2039100098000X

Fig. 4 Trailing link removal

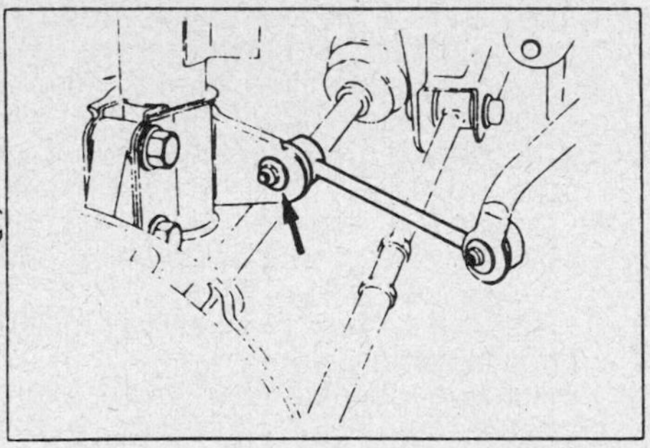

GC2039100099000X

Fig. 5 Stabilizer bar connection

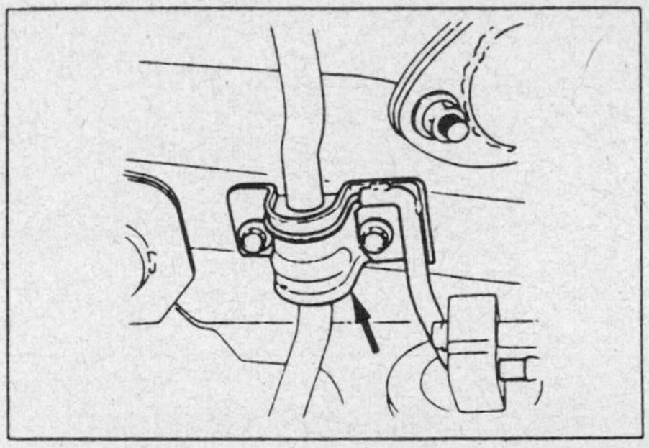

GC2039100100000X

Fig. 6 Stabilizer brackets

HUB & BEARING
REPLACE

1. Disconnect battery ground cable.
2. Raise and support vehicle, then remove wheel and tire assembly.
3. Using suitable jack stands, support rear suspension, then remove rear brake drum assembly.
4. Check hub axial play at hub flange, **Fig. 1,** using suitable dial indicator. If axial play is greater then 0.020 inch, replace hub assembly.
5. Remove four hub to knuckle bolts, then the hub assembly.
6. Reverse procedures to install.

STRUT
REPLACE

1. Place vehicle on level surface, then disconnect battery ground cable.
2. Raise and support vehicle, then remove tire and wheel assemblies.
3. Support suspension with jackstands, then lower vehicle slightly so weight rest on jackstands and not suspension arms.
4. Remove flexible brake hose and clip at strut.
5. Remove stabilizer bar link from strut, then strut to knuckle bolts.
6. Open rear hatch and remove strut tower cover, then loosen nuts for strut mount and remove strut assemblies, **Figs. 2 and 3.**
7. Reverse procedure to install.

KNUCKLE
REPLACE

1. Raise and support vehicle, then remove tire and wheel assemblies.
2. Place jack stands under suspension support, then lower vehicle slightly so that vehicle weight rests on support not on suspension arms.
3. Remove rear brake drum, then hub unit assembly as described in "Hub Assembly, Replace."
4. Remove backing plate with brake assembly and set aside.
5. Remove through bolt from lateral link at axial side.
6. Remove suspension knuckle from strut.
7. Reverse procedure to install.

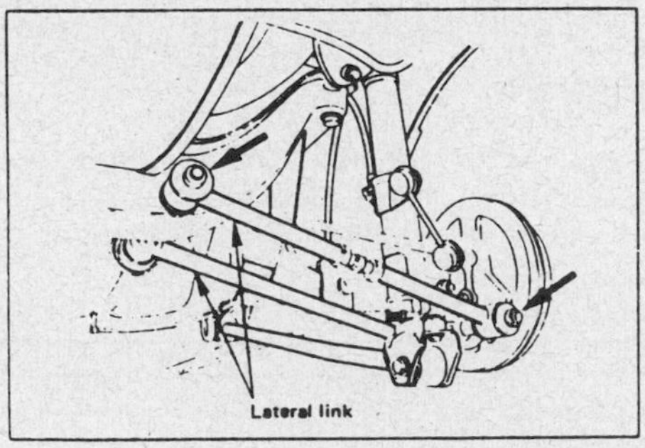
Lateral link

GC2039100094000X

Fig. 7 Lateral link adjustment

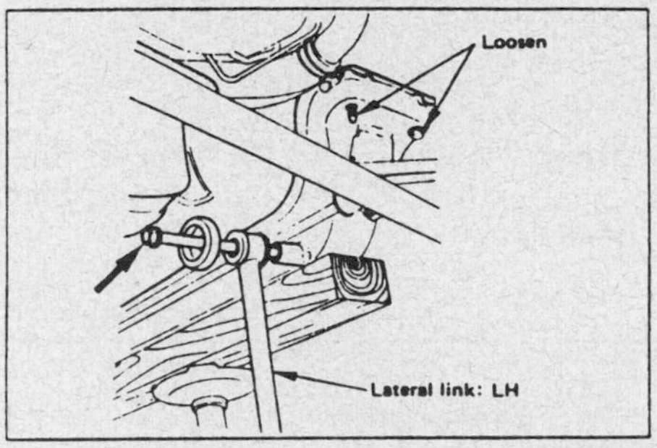
Loosen
Lateral link: LH

GC2039100095000X

Fig. 8 Lateral link replacement

TRAILING ARM

REPLACE

1. Place vehicle on level surface, then disconnect battery ground cable.
2. Raise and support vehicle, then remove tire and wheel assemblies.
3. Remove trailing link bolts, then trailing link, **Fig. 4.**
4. Reverse procedure to install, noting the following:
   a. It will be necessary to reset trim height before tightening trailing link bolts. Refer to "Vehicle Ride Height in "Wheel Alignment" section.
   b. Tighten trailing link bolts to specifications.

STABILIZER BAR

REPLACE

Refer to **Figs. 5 and 6** when replacing stabilizer bar.

1. Disconnect battery ground cable, then raise and support vehicle.
2. Place jack stands under suspension support, then lower vehicle slightly so that vehicle weight rests on support not on suspension arms.
3. Remove bracket with rubber bushing from body, then the stabilizer bar.
4. Reverse procedure to install.

LATERAL LINK

REPLACE

1. Place vehicle on level surface, then disconnect battery ground cable.
2. Raise and support vehicle, then remove tire and wheel assemblies. Refer to **Figs. 7 and 8** when servicing lateral links.
3. Remove lateral link bolt on lefthand side and push crossmember down to prevent interference with fuel tank.
4. Remove righthand side lateral link mounting bolts from rear crossmember and rear suspension knuckle.
5. Remove lateral links.
6. Reverse procedures to install.

TIGHTENING SPECIFICATIONS

Year	Component	Torque/ Ft. Lbs.
1992–93	Crossmember Bolts	94
	Hub Assembly	49
	Lateral Link Bolts	94
	Link Bolts	18
	Stabilizer Bar Brackets	71
	Stabilizer Bar Link	19
	Strut Rod Piston Nut	36
	Strut To Knuckle Bolts	116
	Strut Tower Nuts	50
	Trailing Link Bolts	94
	Wheel Lug Nuts	87

Front Suspension & Steering

INDEX

1 WHEEL STUD
2 ROTOR DISC
3 HUB NUT
4 AXLE HUB
5 DUST COVER
6 OUTER OIL SEAL
7 STEERING KNUCKLE
8 HUB BEARING
9 SNAP RING
10 INNER OIL SEAL

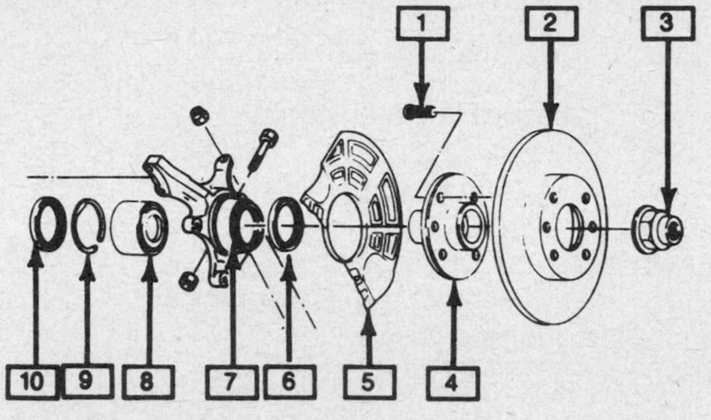
1
2
3
10
9
8
7
6
5
4
GC3039100230000X

Fig. 1 Wheel hub & steering knuckle assembly

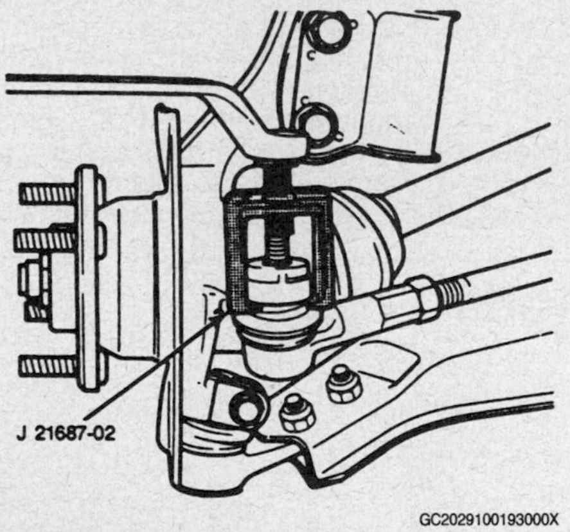
J 21687-02
GC2029100193000X

Fig. 2 Tie rod removal

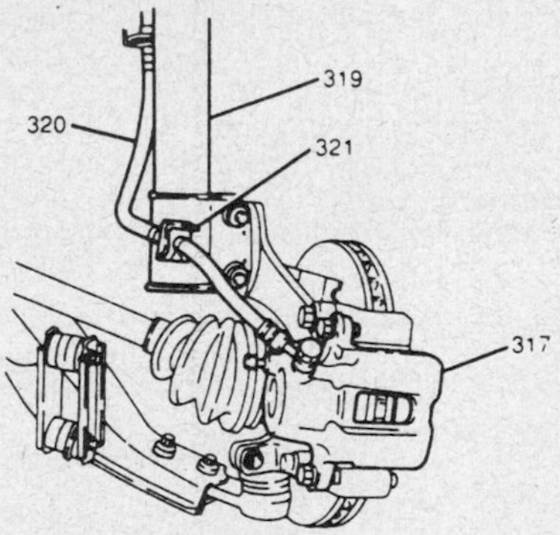
319
320
321
317

317 FRONT DISC BRAKE CALIPER
319 STRUT ASSEMBLY
320 BRAKE HOSE
321 BRAKE HOSE RETAINING CLIP

GC2029100187000X

Fig. 3 Front brake hose removal

PRECAUTIONS

AIR BAG SYSTEMS

Refer to "Air Bag System Precautions" in the front of this manual for system disarming and arming procedures.

HUB & BEARING

REPLACE

REMOVAL

1. Raise and support vehicle, then remove wheel and tire assembly.
2. Remove brake caliper attaching bolts, support caliper and position aside, **Fig. 1.**
3. Remove brake rotor assembly.
4. Using suitable gauge measure hub bearing endplay. If endplay exceeds .0002 inch, replace hub bearing.
5. Stake hub axle attaching nut, then remove hub axle attaching nut.
6. Using tool No. J-34866 and tool No. J-2619-01 or equivalents, remove hub assembly.
7. Using Tie Rod End Remover tool No. J-21687-02 or equivalent, remove tie rod, **Fig. 2.**
8. Remove lower ball joint assembly.
9. Remove lower strut to steering knuckle attaching nuts and bolts, then remove steering knuckle.

INSTALLATION

1. Install knuckle assembly into driveshaft and snug hub nuts. **Ensure that seals are not damaged when installing the shaft into the knuckle. If hub and knuckle assemblies are disassembled, seals, inter and outer must be replaced with new seals.**
2. Install ball joint of lower control arm to knuckle. Do not loosen boot on ball joint.
3. Install lower ball joint. Tighten to specifications
4. Install tie rod, tighten to specifications.
5. Install hub nut and tightento specifications, then stake hub nut.
6. Install rotor, then brake caliper, tighten caliper bolts to specifications.

STRUT

REPLACE

1. Raise and support vehicle, then remove wheel and tire assembly.
2. Using suitable jack stands, support front suspension.
3. Disconnect front caliper brake hose,

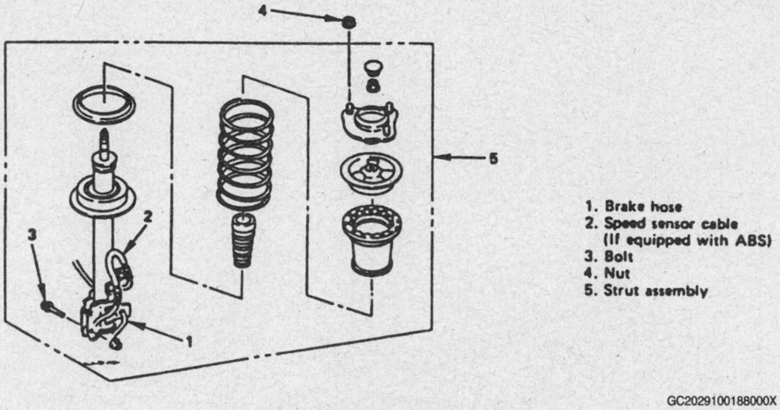

4
5
3
2
1
1. Brake hose
2. Speed sensor cable
(If equipped with ABS)
3. Bolt
4. Nut
5. Strut assembly
GC2029100188000X

Fig. 4 Front strut assembly

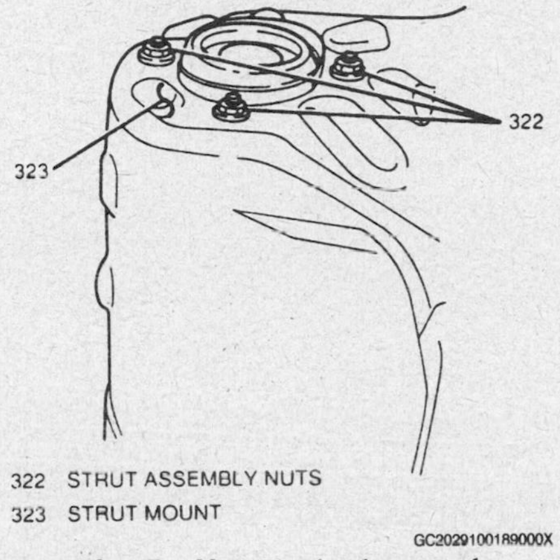

322
323
322 STRUT ASSEMBLY NUTS
323 STRUT MOUNT
GC2029100189000X

Fig. 5 Upper strut mount

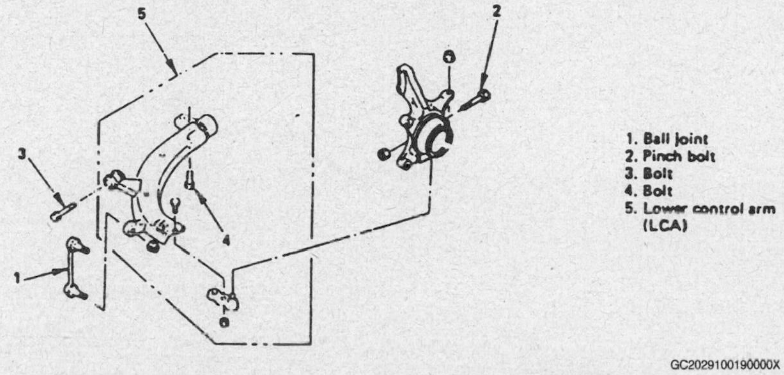

5
2
3
4
1
1. Ball joint
2. Pinch bolt
3. Bolt
4. Bolt
5. Lower control arm
(LCA)
GC2029100190000X

Fig. 6 Lower control arm assembly

clip and bracket, then drain brake fluid, **Fig. 3.**

4. Cap brake hose to prevent fluid leakage and dirt from entering system.
5. Remove strut assembly lower attaching bolts and nuts, **Fig. 4.**
6. Remove upper strut mount attaching nuts, **Fig. 5,** then remove strut assembly.
7. Reverse procedure to install. tightenattaching nuts and bolt to specifications.

CONTROL ARM
REPLACE
LOWER

1. Raise and support vehicle, then remove wheel and tire assembly.
2. Remove stabilizer bar link to control arm assembly.
3. Remove lower ball joint attaching nuts, **Fig. 6.**
4. Remove control arm front bushing attaching bolt.
5. Remove control arm rear bushing attaching bolts, then remove control arm assembly.
6. Reverse procedure to install, tightenattaching nuts and bolt to specifications.

STEERING KNUCKLE
REPLACE

Refer to "Hub & Bearing, Replace" for steering knuckle replacement.

STABILIZER BAR
REPLACE

1. Using Engine Support Fixture tool No. J28467-A or equivalent, support engine assembly.
2. Raise and support vehicle, then using suitable jack stands, support front suspension.
3. Remove wheel and tire assembly, then remove front exhaust pipe.
4. Disconnect power steering gear lines, **Fig. 7.**
5. Remove steering shaft and boot inside vehicle, **Fig. 8.**
6. Remove lower ball joint assemblies.
7. Using Tie Rod End Removal tool No. J-21687-02 or equivalent, remove tie rod at steering knuckle, **Fig. 2.**
8. Remove engine torque rod center beam attaching nut and bolt.
9. Remove rear engine mount.
10. Remove center beam attaching bolts, then remove crossmember attaching bolts.
11. Remove center beam, crossmember, steering gear and stabilizer bar assembly.
12. Remove steering gear assembly, then remove stabilizer bar.
13. Reverse procedure to install, tightenattaching nuts and bolts to specifications.

POWER STEERING GEAR
REPLACE

1. Remove intermediate steering shaft cover, then remove dust boot ring attaching nuts.
2. Raise and support vehicle, then remove wheel and tire assembly.
3. Remove dust boot from bulkhead, then position drain pan under vehicle.
4. Remove intermediate steering shaft pinch bolt.
5. Using Tie Rod End Remover tool No. J-21687-02 or equivalent, disconnect tie rod ends at steering knuckles.
6. Remove power steering fluid line hold-down bracket.
7. Disconnect power steering high pressure line, drain power steering fluid, then remove rack to crossmember attaching bolts.
8. Remove steering gear bracket attaching nut and bolt, then position steering gear from mounts.
9. Disconnect power steering return line, then disconnect intermediate shaft knuckle.
10. Remove steering gear through right side of vehicle.
11. Reverse procedure to install.

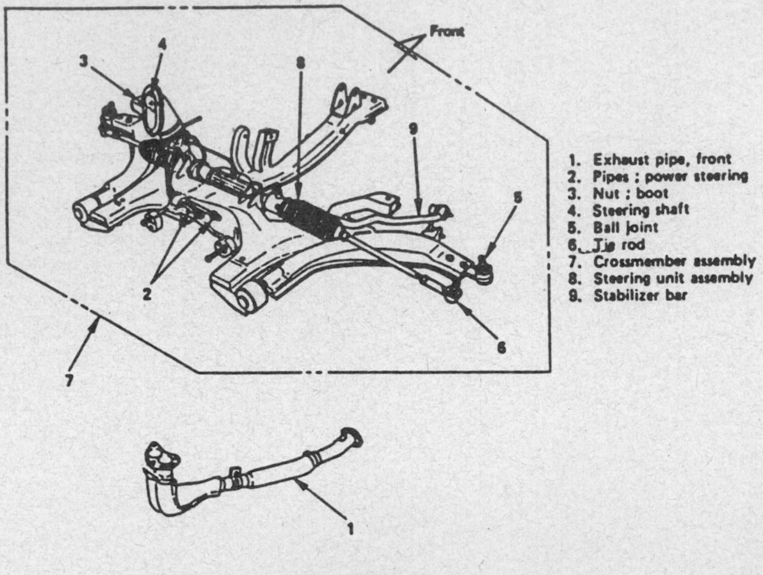
Front
1. Exhaust pipe, front
2. Pipes ; power steering
3. Nut ; boot
4. Steering shaft
5. Ball joint
6. Tie rod
7. Crossmember assembly
8. Steering unit assembly
9. Stabilizer bar
GC2029100191000X

Fig. 7 Front crossmember assembly

POWER STEERING PUMP

REPLACE

1. Raise and support vehicle, then place drain pan underneath vehicle.
2. Loosen power steering pump adjusting and pivot bolts, then remove drive belt.
3. Disconnect power steering pump high pressure and return lines, cap lines to prevent contamination.
4. Remove adjusting and pivot bolts, then remove power steering pump and bracket assembly.
5. Reverse procedure to install.

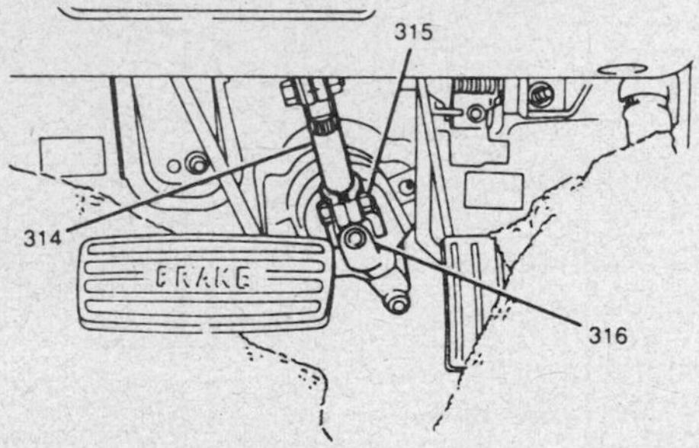
315
314
BRAKE
316
314 INTERMEDIATE SHAFT
315 INTERMEDIATE SHAFT-TO-STEERING JOINT PINCH BOLT
316 STEERING JOINT
GC2029100192000X

Fig. 8 Steering shaft

TIGHTENING SPECIFICATIONS

Year	Component	Torque/ Ft. Lbs.
1992–93	Ball Joint To Control Arm	115
	Ball Joint To Steering Knuckle	49
	Brake Caliper Bolt	72
	Control Arm To Crossmember	117
	Crossmember Assembly to Frame Bolt	137
	Engine Torque Rod To Center Beam Bolt	37
	Hub Assembly Nut	137
	Inner Tire Rod	65
	Knuckle To Strut Bolts	116
	Lower Control Arm Front Bushing	95
	Lower Control Arm Rear Bushing	51
	Lower Strut To Knuckle Bolt	115

Year	Component	Torque/ Ft. Lbs.
1992–93	Outer Tie Rod Nut To Steering Knuckle	40
	Pinch Bolt To Ball Joint Of Lower Control Arm	48
	Power Steering Pump Adjusting Bolt	15
	Power Steering Pump Pivot Bolt	15
	Stabilizer Bar To Control Arm	19
	Stabilizer Bar To Crossmember	12
	Stabilizer Link Bolt	19
	Steering Gear To Crossmember	41
	Strut Rod Piston Nut	34
	Tie Rod Nut To Lower Control Arm	19
	Upper Strut Mounting Nuts	50
	Wheel Lug Nuts	87

Wheel Alignment

INDEX

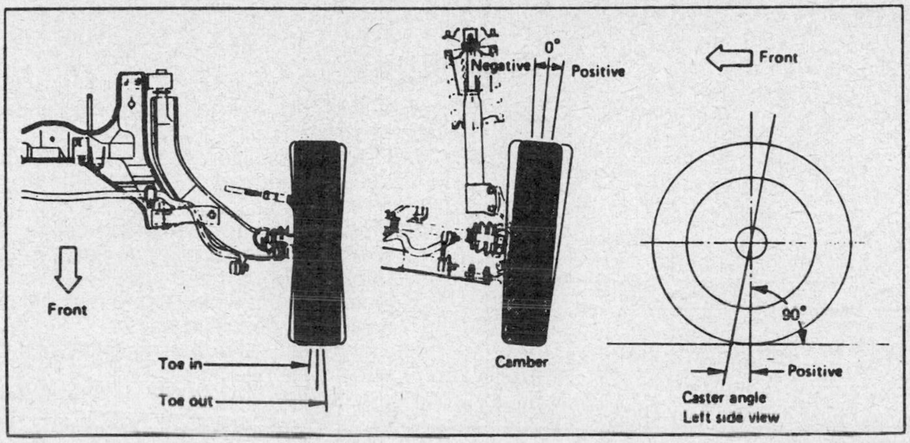

0°
Negative
Positive
Front
Front
Toe in
Toe out
Camber
90°
Positive
Caster angle
Left side view
GC2049100091000X

Fig. 1 Front alignment angles

PRECAUTIONS

AIR BAG SYSTEMS

Refer to "Air Bag System Precautions" in the front of this manual for system disarming and arming procedures.

DESCRIPTION

Wheel alignment is the angular relationship between the wheels, suspension attaching parts and ground, **Fig. 1.** The angle of the knuckle away from the vertical, pointing in or out of wheels, tilt of the wheels from vertical (when viewed from front of vehicle) and tilt of suspension members from vertical (when viewed from side of vehicle), all of these are involved in proper alignment.

CASTER

Caster is tilting of the steering axis either forward or backward from the vertical (when viewed from side of vehicle). A backward tilt is positive (+) and a forward tilt is negative (-). On short and long arm type suspension you cannot see a caster angle without using a special instrument, but if you look straight down from the top of the upper control arm to the ground, you would find that ball joints do not line up what a caster angle other than 0° is present.

CAMBER

Camber is the tilting of front and rear wheels from the vertical when viewed from front of vehicle. When wheels tilt outward at top, camber is positive(+). When wheels tilt inward, camber is negative (-). Amount of tilt is measured in degrees from the vertical and this is camber angle.

TOE

Toe is the turning in or out of wheels. The purpose of toe is to ensure parallel rolling of wheels. Excessive toe-in or toe-out may increase tire wear. Toe also serves to offset small deflections of the suspension which occurs when vehicle is moving.

PRELIMINARY INSPECTION

Steering and vibration problems are not always the results of poor alignment. An additional problem to be checked is tire lead due to worn or improperly manufactured tires. "Lead" is the deviation of the vehicle from a straight path on a level road without hand pressure on the steering wheel.

Refer to "Front Wheel Alignment Specifications" and "Rear Wheel Alignment Specifications" located in the front of this chapter, to insure correct specifications, if vehicle is within specification the following checks and inspections should be performed.

1. Check tires for proper inflation and tread wear.
2. Check for loose ball joints and tie rod ends. If excessive looseness is noted, replace defective parts before adjusting toe.
3. Check for wheel and tire assembly run-out.
4. Check trim heights. If not within specifications, correct before adjusting toe.
5. Check for loose control arms.
6. Check for loose or missing stabilizer bar components.
7. Consideration must be given to excess loads. If excess load is normally carried in vehicle, it should remain during alignment checks.

FRONT WHEEL ALIGNMENT

CAMBER & CASTER

Camber and caster are not adjustable. If during inspection, either is found to be out of specifications, locate the cause. Check for damaged, loose, bent or worn front suspension parts. Replace worn or damaged parts as needed. To prevent any incorrect reading during inspection, bounce front bumper three or more times.

TOE-IN

1. Loosen right and left tie rod end locknuts.
2. Apply grease between tie rods and rack boots.
3. Turn right and left tie rods by the same amount to align toe to specification. **Right and left tie rods should become equal in length.**
4. After adjustment, tighten locknuts and ensure rack boots are not twisted.

REAR WHEEL ALIGNMENT

CAMBER

Camber cannot be adjusted. Should camber be found out of specification, locate the cause and replace vehicle parts to correct the damage. If the body or chassis is found to be damaged, the damaged area must be corrected to provide proper alignment.

TOE

1. Loosen jam nuts on rear support rod.
2. Turn hex screw in center to obtain proper toe angle.
3. Tighten jam nuts. **Torque** jam nuts to 65 ft. lbs.

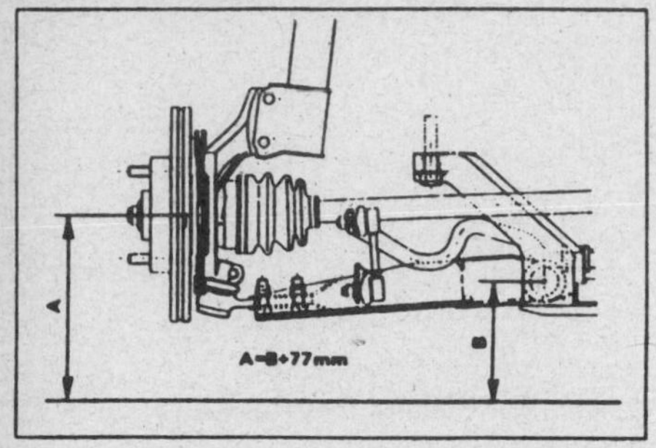
A
A=B+77mm
B

GC2049100092000X

Fig. 2 Vehicle ride height

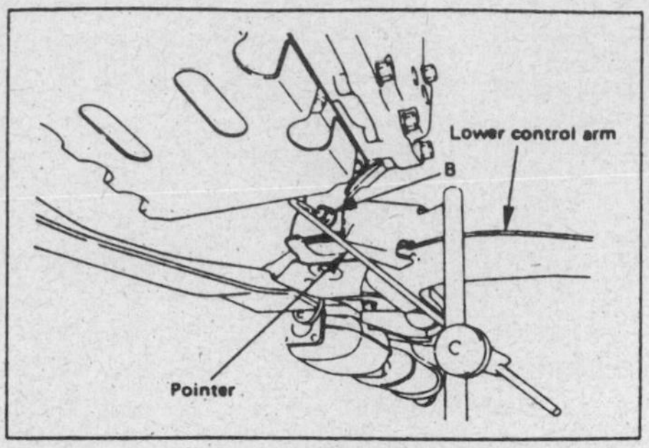
Lower control arm
B
C
Pointer

GC2049100093000X

Fig. 3 Vehicle ride height, bushing center

A

GC2049100094000X

Fig. 4 Vehicle ride height, wheel level

VEHICLE RIDE HEIGHT

FRONT

When reattaching the control arm, hold the position of wheel center to keep distance of 3 inches at bushing center (B) height, **Fig. 2.** Bushing will twist if the wheel center height is too high or low. If bushing does twist, bushing will suffer premature damage.

Measure height (B) at front bushing center and set point at height of (B) plus 3 inches, **Figs. 3 and 4.** Move front rotor assembly by using a suitable floor jack until reaching specification height (A), then tighten the bushing bolts at this time.

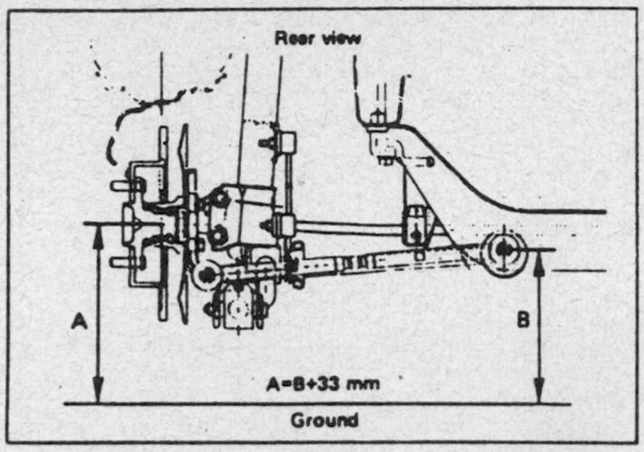
Rear view
A
B
A=B+33 mm
Ground

GC2049100095000X

Fig. 5 Vehicle ride height center

REAR

Refer to **Fig. 5** when adjusting vehicle ride height.

1. Hold the position of wheel center to keep distance of 1.3 inch height from rear bushing center of lateral link.
2. Measure height of bushing center at rear side of crossmember. Set point at height of B + 1.299 inch.
3. Raise up rear wheel using a jack until it reaches specified height.
4. Tighten lateral or trailing links bolts to specifications.

PONTIAC LEMANS (T Car)

NOTE: Refer To The Rear Of This Manual For Vehicle Manufacturer's Special Tool Suppliers.

INDEX OF SERVICE OPERATIONS

NOTE: For Service Operations Not Listed Below, Refer To The Table Of Contents In The Front Of This Manual.

Specifications

GENERAL ENGINE SPECIFICATIONS

Year	Engine Liter/CID①	Engine VIN Code②	Fuel System	Bore x Stroke Inches	Compression Ratio	Net HP @ RPM③	Maximum Torque Ft. Lbs. @ RPM	Oil Pressure, psi
1992–93	1.6L/4-98	6	TBI	3.11 x 3.21	8.5	74 @ 5600	90 @ 2800	4.35–21.75

①—CID: Cubic Inch Displacement.

②—The eighth digit of the VIN denotes engine code.

③—Ratings are net as installed in vehicle.

TUNE UP SPECIFICATIONS

Year & Engine/ VIN Code ①	Spark Plug Gap	Ignition Timing BTDC Firing Order ②	Man. Trans.	Auto. Trans.	Mark Fig.	Curb Idle Speed ③ Man. Trans.	Auto. Trans.	Fast Idle Speed Man. Trans.	Auto. Trans.	Fuel Pump Pressure psi
1992–93										
1.6L/4-98/6	.060	1-3-4-2	8④	8④	A	600⑤⑥	500⑤⑥	⑤	⑤	9–13⑦

BTDC—Before top dead center.
①—The eighth digit of the Vehicle Identification Number (VIN) denotes engine code.
②—Before disconnecting wires from distributor cap, determine location of No. 1 wire in cap, as distributor position may have been altered from that shown at the end of this chart.
③—N: Neutral.
④—Align notch on crankshaft pulley with pointer. Prior to checking ignition timing, connect a jumper wire between terminals A & B of ALDL diagnostic connector. The ALDL diagnostic connector is located under the righthand side of the instrument panel.
⑤—Idle speed is controlled by the Idle Air Control (IAC) assembly.
⑥—Minimum.
⑦—Remove fuel pump fuse from fuse panel, then start engine & operate until engine stops. Crank engine for approximately 3 seconds to relieve fuel pressure from lines. Disconnect fuel supply hose, then connect a suitable fuel pressure gauge between hose & tube. Operate engine at idle & note gauge reading.

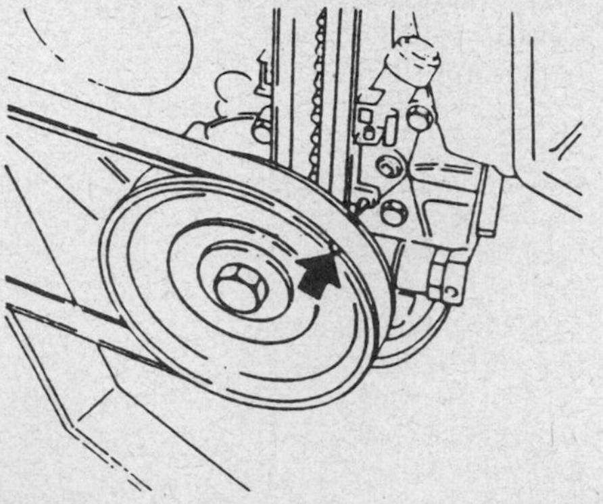
GC1139100163000X

Fig. A

FRONT WHEEL ALIGNMENT SPECIFICATIONS

Year	Model	Caster Angle, degrees Limits	Desired	Camber Angle, degrees Limits Left	Limits Right	Desired Left	Desired Right	Toe-In, degrees
1992–93	All	+.75 to +2.75	+1.75①	+.25 to -1.25	+.25 to -1.25	-.75	-.75	-.33 to 0

①—Deviation from left to right side of vehicle: 1° maximum.

REAR WHEEL ALIGNMENT SPECIFICATIONS

Year	Model	Camber Angle, degrees Limits	Desired	Toe-In, degrees
1992-93	All	-1.25 to -.75	-1①	-.67 to -.17

①—Variation from left to right side of vehicle: .25° maximum.

COOLING SYSTEM & CAPACITY DATA

Year	Engine (VIN)	Coolant Capacity Qts.		Radiator Cap Relief Pressure, psi.	Thermo. Opening Temp.	Fuel Tank Gals.	Engine Oil Refill Qts.	Transaxle Oil	
		Less A/C	With A/C					Man. Trans. Pts.	Auto. Trans. Qts. ①
1992–93	1.6L/4-98 (6)	8.1	8.1	15	195	13	4②	3.4	③

①—Approximate, make final check with dipstick.

②—Additional oil maybe required with filter change.

③—Oil pan only, 4 qts.; total capacity, 6 qts.

LUBRICANT DATA

Year	Model	Lubricant Type			
		Transaxle		Power Steering	Brake System
		Manual	Automatic		
1992–93	All	80W	Dexron IIE	GM Type Power Steering Fluid	DOT 3

Electrical

INDEX

FUSE PANEL & FLASHER LOCATION

The fuse panel is located under the lefthand side of the instrument panel.

The flasher is located on the fuse panel under the lefthand side of the instrument panel.

RELAY CENTER LOCATION

The relays are located at the fuse panel, under the lefthand side of the instrument panel.

STARTER

REPLACE

1. Disconnect battery ground cable.
2. Disconnect wiring at starter motor, then remove upper and lower starter attaching bolts.
3. Remove starter motor from vehicle.
4. Reverse procedure to install. **Torque** starter bolts to 33 ft. lbs.

DISTRIBUTOR

REPLACE

1. Disconnect battery ground cable.
2. Remove ignition coil and spark plug wires at distributor cap.
3. Disconnect coil and EST electrical connectors.
4. Remove distributor clamp attaching bolt.
5. Mark distributor tang drive and camshaft for correct assembly, then remove distributor.
6. Reverse procedure to install.

IGNITION LOCK

REPLACE

1. Disconnect battery ground cable.
2. Remove lower instrument cluster trim.
3. Remove turn signal and wiper switch cover attaching screws and the cover.
4. Turn ignition key to position "II."
5. Depress detent spring, **Fig. 1,** then slide lock cylinder out of steering column.
6. Reverse procedure to install.

IGNITION SWITCH

REPLACE

1. Disconnect battery ground cable.
2. Remove lower instrument cluster trim.
3. Remove turn signal and wiper switch cover attaching screws and the cover.
4. Disconnect electrical connector from ignition switch.
5. Remove ignition switch setscrew, then remove ignition switch, **Fig. 2.**
6. Reverse procedure to install.

NEUTRAL SAFETY SWITCH

REPLACE

1. Disconnect battery ground cable.
2. Disconnect shift linkage and electrical connector from switch, **Fig. 3.**
3. Remove switch attaching bolts and the switch.
4. Reverse procedure to install. Adjust switch prior to tightening attaching bolts, as follows:

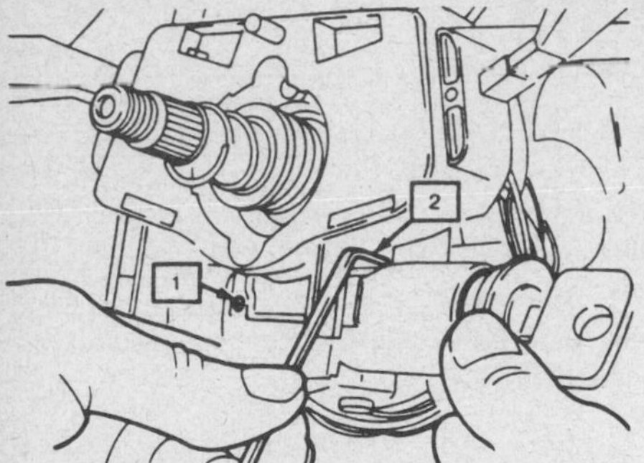
2
1

1. SET SCREW
2. DETENT SPRING

GC9129100033000X

Fig. 1 Ignition lock replacement

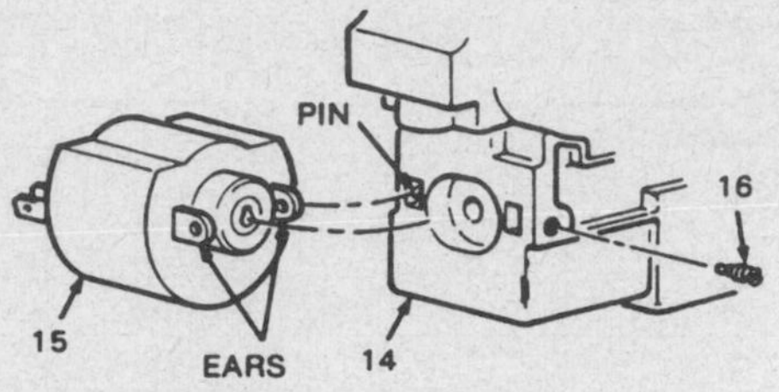
PIN
16
15
EARS
14

14- HOUSING ASM, IGN SWITCH
15- SWITCH ASM, IGNITION
16- SCREW, IGN SWITCH RETAINING

GC9049100122000X

Fig. 2 Ignition switch replacement

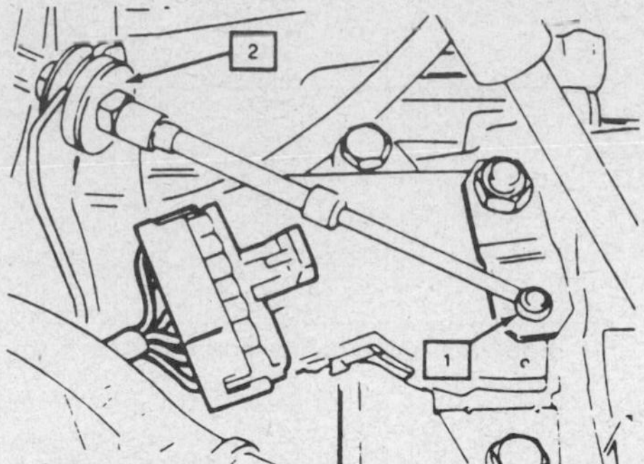
2
1

1 RETAINING RING
2. CABLE AT SUPPORT

GC9049100124000X

Fig. 3 Neutral start switch replacement

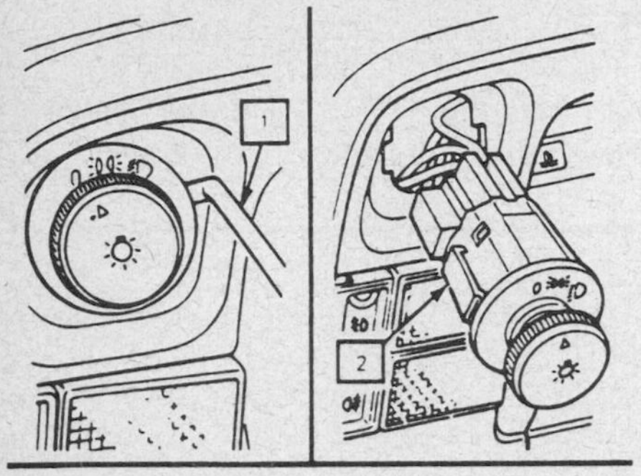
1
2

1 OFFSET SCREWDRIVER
2 RETAINER

GC9049100125000X

Fig. 4 Headlamp switch replacement

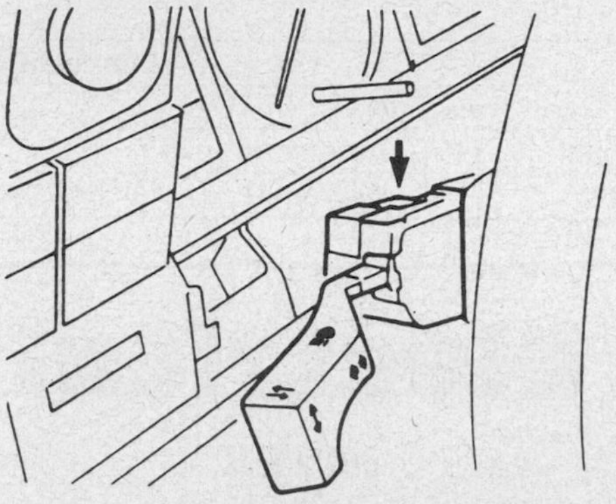

GC9049100123000X

Fig. 5 Turn signal & wiper switch replacement

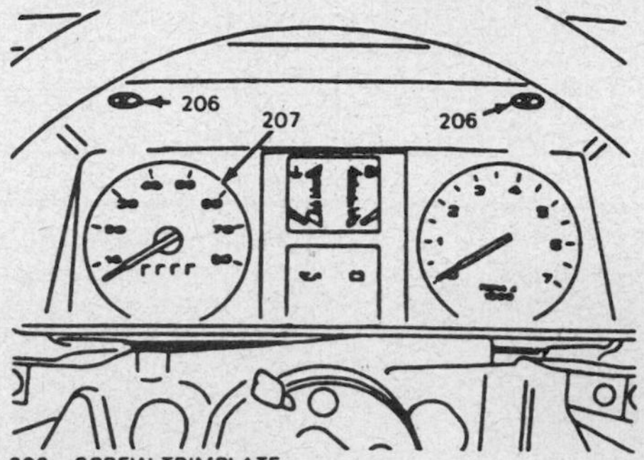
206
207
206

206 SCREW-TRIMPLATE
207 TRIMPLATE-INSTRUMENT PANEL

GC9099100241000X

Fig. 6 Instrument cluster trim plate screw locations

a. Shift transaxle into Neutral.
b. Loosen switch attaching bolts, then rotate switch on shift assembly to align adjustment hole with carrier tang hole. Insert a 3/32 drill bit into adjustment hole on switch to a depth of 3/8 inch.
c. **Torque** attaching bolts to 22 ft. lbs., then remove drill bit.

HEADLAMP SWITCH

REPLACE

1. Disconnect battery ground cable.
2. Depress switch retaining clips using a suitable screwdriver, **Fig. 4.**
3. Disconnect electrical connector and remove switch.
4. Reverse procedure to install.

TURN SIGNAL SWITCH

REPLACE

1. Disconnect battery ground cable.
2. Remove lower instrument cluster trim.
3. Remove screws from both sides of upper cover panel. Rotate steering wheel as necessary to gain access to all screws.
4. Remove three lower panel attaching screws, then pull handle from lock release lever and remove tilt lever, if equipped.
5. Depress switch release tabs, **Fig. 5,** then disconnect electrical connector and remove switch.
6. Reverse procedure to install.

STEERING WHEEL

REPLACE

1. Disconnect battery ground cable.
2. Remove steering wheel horn cap, then disconnect horn electrical leads.
3. Remove steering wheel retaining nut and retainer, then place alignment marks on steering wheel and steering shaft.
4. Remove steering wheel using Steering Wheel Puller tool No. J-36541 or equivalent.
5. Unclip steering wheel contact ring, if required.
6. Reverse procedure to install. When installing steering wheel, align marks placed on steering wheel and steering shaft. Also the turn signal cancelling cam on the steering wheel should be to the left. **Torque** steering wheel attaching nut to 13 ft. lbs.

INSTRUMENT CLUSTER

REPLACE

1. Disconnect battery ground cable.
2. Remove turn signal switch housing attaching screws and the housing. Rotate steering wheel as necessary to gain access to all screws.
3. Remove two instrument panel trim plate attaching screws and the trim plate, **Fig. 6.**
4. Depress speedometer cable retainer spring and disconnect cable from cluster.
5. Remove instrument cluster attaching screws.
6. Disconnect electrical connectors from cluster, then remove cluster from vehicle, **Fig. 7.**
7. Reverse procedure to install.

RADIO

REPLACE

1. Disconnect battery ground cable.
2. Place ignition switch in On position, then set transaxle selector lever in the 1 position.
3. Using a suitable pointed plastic tool, remove package panel, **Fig. 8.**
4. Remove front center console attaching screws from under ashtray and plastic cap, **Fig. 9.**
5. **On models with automatic transaxle,** remove selector lever, then pull indicator strap from cover. Remove retaining clips and trim cover.
6. **On models with manual transaxle,** remove shift knob, trim plate and boot.
7. **On all models,** remove front console.
8. Remove four console upper attaching screws, then slide console toward rear of vehicle.
9. Remove radio from instrument panel, **Fig. 10.**

WIPER MOTOR

REPLACE

1. Disconnect battery ground cable.
2. Remove cowl vent grille attaching screws and the grille.
3. Disconnect wiper motor electrical

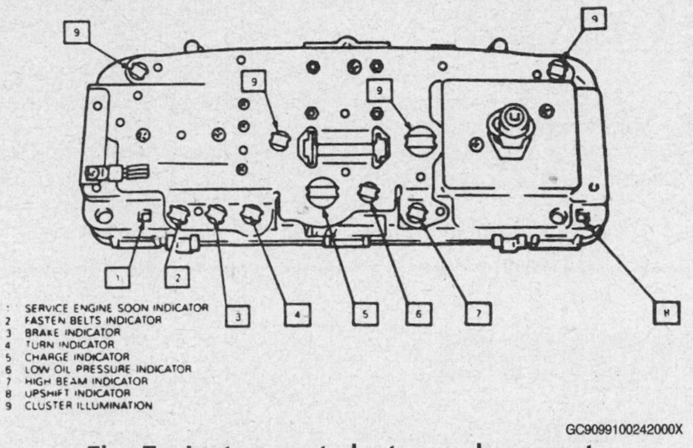

1 SERVICE ENGINE SOON INDICATOR
2 FASTEN BELTS INDICATOR
3 BRAKE INDICATOR
4 TURN INDICATOR
5 CHARGE INDICATOR
6 LOW OIL PRESSURE INDICATOR
7 HIGH BEAM INDICATOR
8 UPSHIFT INDICATOR
9 CLUSTER ILLUMINATION
GC9099100242000X

Fig. 7 Instrument cluster replacement

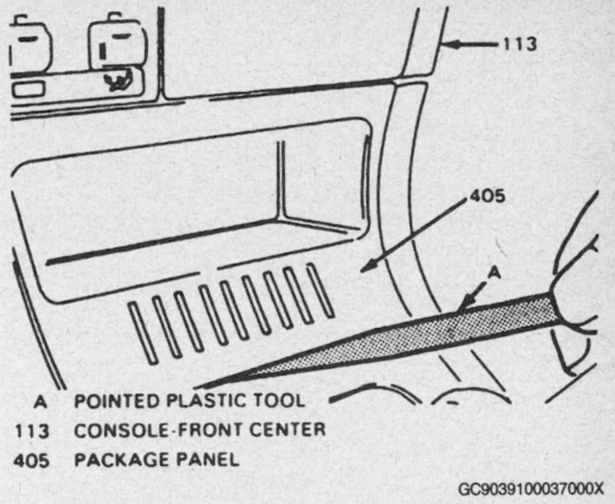

113
405
A
A POINTED PLASTIC TOOL
113 CONSOLE-FRONT CENTER
405 PACKAGE PANEL
GC9039100037000X

Fig. 8 Package panel removal

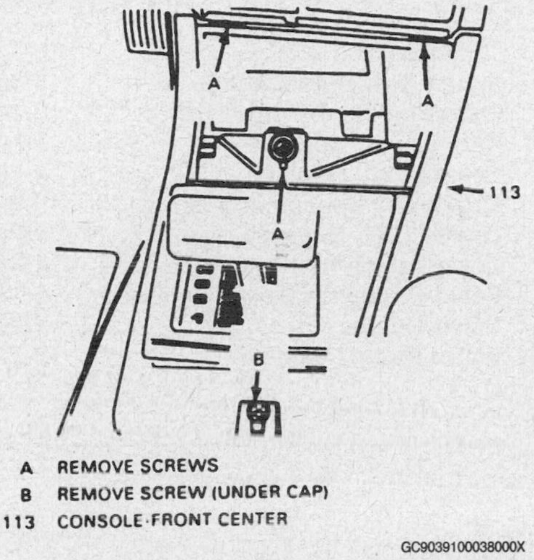

A
A
A
113
B
A REMOVE SCREWS
B REMOVE SCREW (UNDER CAP)
113 CONSOLE-FRONT CENTER
GC9039100038000X

Fig. 9 Front console attaching screw location

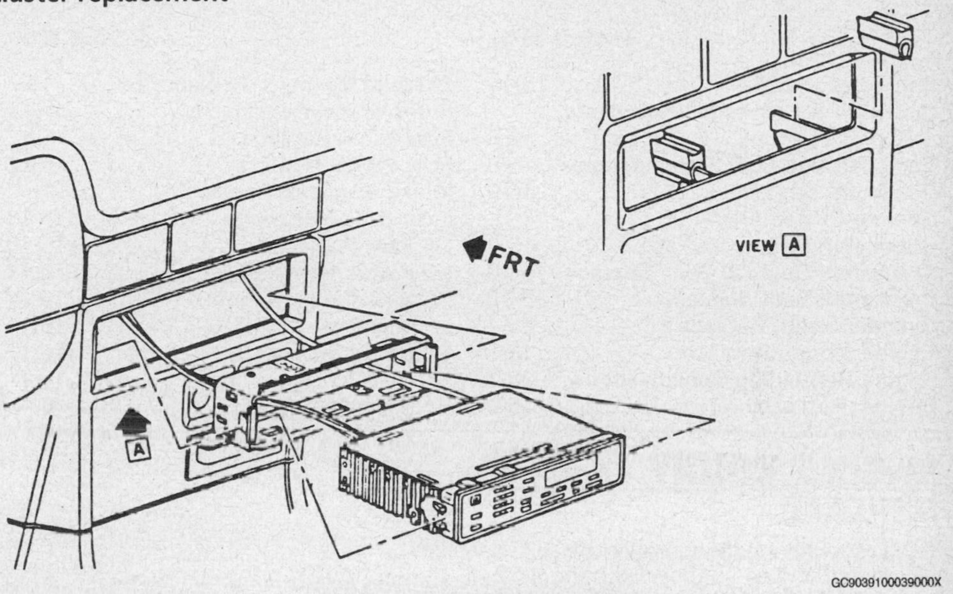

FRT
A
VIEW A
GC9039100039000X

Fig. 10 Radio replacement

connectors.
4. Remove crank arm to wiper motor attaching nut.
5. Remove wiper motor attaching bolts and the wiper motor.
6. Reverse procedure to install.

BLOWER MOTOR

REPLACE

LESS A/C

1. Disconnect battery ground cable.
2. Remove wiper arm attaching nuts, then slide arms off splined shafts.
3. Remove four wind deflector attaching screws and the deflector halves.
4. Remove washer nozzle hoses from washer nozzles.
5. Remove seal from dash panel and clip, then the right side wiper bearing attaching nut.
6. Remove water deflector, then disconnect electrical connector from blower motor housing.
7. Remove blower motor housing attaching screws and the housing.
8. Remove housing cover attaching cover screws and the cover.
9. Remove blower motor from housing.
10. Reverse procedure to install.

WITH A/C

1. Disconnect battery ground cable.
2. Disconnect blower motor electrical connectors.
3. Disconnect air hose from lower housing.
4. Remove blower motor to case attaching screws.
5. Remove blower motor and fan assembly from housing.
6. Remove blower fan retaining nut and the fan from motor.
7. Reverse procedure to install.

HEATER CORE

REPLACE

LESS A/C

1. Disconnect battery ground cable, then drain cooling system.
2. Block off heater hoses with spring clips, then mark hoses for installation reference.
3. Disconnect heater hoses from heater core.
4. Remove package panel, then move heater control levers to lowest position.
5. Disconnect temperature control cable from actuating lever and air distributor.
6. Remove kick panel from under glove box.
7. Disconnect temperature valve linkage from righthand air distributor.
8. Lift carpeting, then remove air distributor cover attaching screws and the cover.
9. Remove heater core attaching screws, then the heater core and bracket assembly. Move temperature valve as necessary to gain access to all screws.
10. Reverse procedure to install.

WITH A/C

1. Disconnect battery ground cable.
2. Block off heater hoses with spring clips, then disconnect the hoses from heater core.
3. Disconnect evaporator drain hose from heater case.
4. **On models equipped with manual transaxle,** remove gear shift boot.
5. **On all models,** remove package shelf, then the front floor console shift plate and front center console.
6. Remove glove box attaching screws and straps, then the glove box.
7. Remove hush panel retainers and the hush panel.
8. Remove outer heater case cover re-

tainers, then bend back tab and remove the cover.

9. Remove heater case cover retaining clips and the cover.
10. Remove heater core cover attaching screws and the cover.
11. Remove heater core clamps and the heater core.
12. Reverse procedure to install.

EVAPORATOR CORE
REPLACE

1. Disconnect battery ground cable.
2. Discharge air conditioning system.
3. Remove heater core as previously outlined.
4. Disconnect accumulator to evaporator pipe and orifice tube to evaporator at dash panel.
5. Remove evaporator cover attaching screws, then remove evaporator cover.
6. Remove evaporator bracket attaching screws, then remove pipe clamps.
7. Remove evaporator core.
8. Reverse procedure to install.

Engine

INDEX

ENGINE MOUNT
REPLACE

1. Disconnect battery ground cable.
2. Install engine support fixture tool No. J28467-A, with fixture adapters No. J28467-70, or equivalents. **Support tool must be positioned in center of cowl and properly tightened prior to supporting engine and transaxle assembly.**
3. Remove engine mount attaching bolts and the mount, **Fig. 1.**
4. Reverse procedure to install. Tighten mount attaching bolts to specifications.

ENGINE
REPLACE

1. Relieve fuel system pressure as follows:
   a. Remove fuel pump fuse from fuse panel.
   b. Start engine. After engine stalls, crank for ten seconds to relieve residual pressure from fuel system.
   c. Turn ignition off and install fuel pump fuse.
2. Disconnect battery cables and engine ground wire.
3. Disconnect lower radiator hose and drain cooling system into a suitable container.
4. Remove air cleaner assembly.
5. Disconnect upper radiator hose and heater hose from engine.
6. Disconnect cable from throttle body.
7. Label and disconnect the following

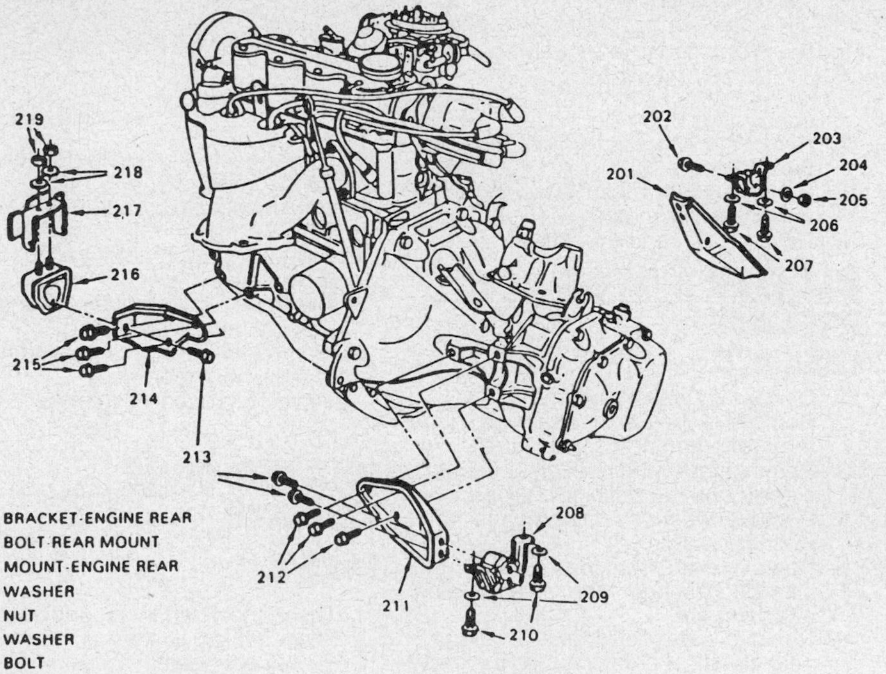

219
218
217
216
215
214
213
212
211
210
209
208
202
203
204
201
205
206
207

201 BRACKET-ENGINE REAR
202 BOLT-REAR MOUNT
203 MOUNT-ENGINE REAR
204 WASHER
205 NUT
206 WASHER
207 BOLT
208 MOUNT-ENGINE FRONT LEFT
209 WASHER
210 BOLT
211 BRACKET-ENGINE MOUNT FRONT LEFT
212 BOLT
213 BOLT
214 BRACKET-ENGINE MOUNT-FRONT RIGHT
215 BOLT
216 MOUNT-ENGINE FRONT RIGHT
217 SUPPORT-ENGINE FRONT MOUNT
218 WASHER
219 NUT

GC1069100056000X

Fig. 1 Engine mounts

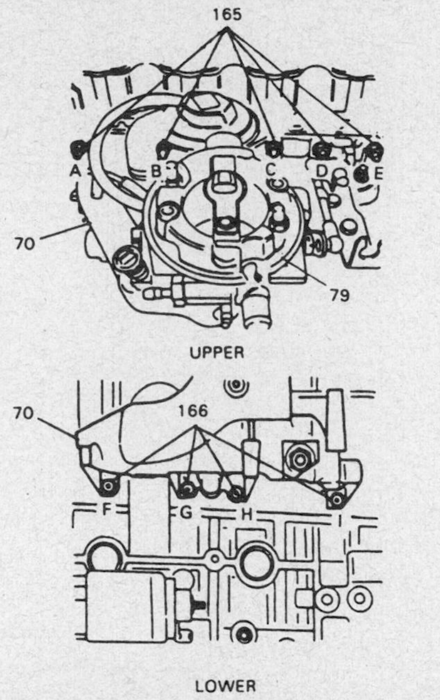
165
A
B
C
D
E
70
79
UPPER
70
166
F
G
H
I
LOWER

70 MANIFOLD-INTAKE
79 THROTTLE BODY INJECTION (TBI)
165 NUT-TORQUE TO 22 N•m (16 Lbs. Ft.)
166 BOLT-TORQUE TO 22 N•m (16 Lbs. Ft.)
LOOSENING SEQUENCE: C-G-B-H-D-F-E-I-A
TIGHTENING SEQUENCE: A-I-E-F-D-H-B-G-C

GC105910009200X

Fig. 2 Intake manifold tightening sequence

vacuum hoses; brake servo, vacuum sensor, intake manifold to vapor canister and throttle valve body to vapor canister.

8. **On models equipped with automatic transaxle,** disconnect transaxle shift cable from throttle body.
9. **On all models,** disconnect fuel lines from throttle body. **Place shop towel over fuel line and fitting when disconnecting.**
10. Disconnect electrical connectors from the following components: oxygen sensor, oil pressure switch, intake manifold temperature sensor, speed sensor, injector nozzle, back-up lamp switch, neutral start switch, throttle valve, idle air control motor and distributor.
11. Disconnect instrument panel harness connector, ground wires from camshaft housing and intake manifold and wiring harness retaining strap.
12. Remove ignition coil plugs and cable.
13. Disconnect bulkhead wiring harness connector.
14. **On models equipped with automatic transaxle,** disconnect torque converter clutch electrical connector.
15. **On all models,** raise and support vehicle.
16. Remove splash shield.
17. Remove exhaust pipe and catalytic converter.
18. Pull driveshaft out of transaxle, then remove closure plug from transaxle case.

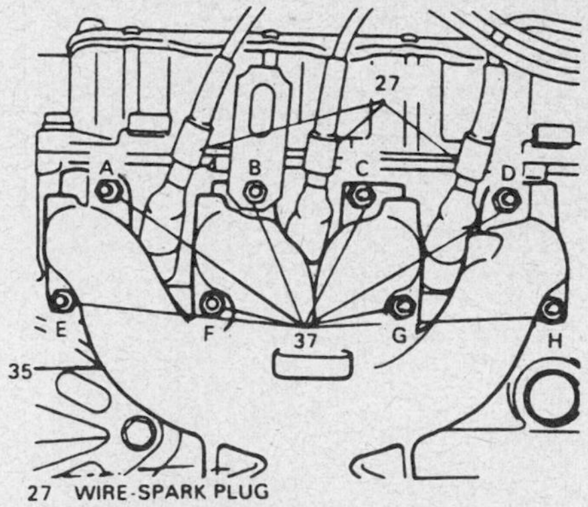
27
A
B
C
D
E
F
37
G
H
35

27 WIRE-SPARK PLUG
35 MANIFOLD-EXHAUST
37 NUTS-TORQUE TO 22 N•m (16 LBS. FT)
LOOSENING SEQUENCE: H-A-E-D-F-C-G-B
TIGHTENING SEQUENCE: B-G-C-F-D-E-A-H

GC107910002900OX

Fig. 3 Exhaust manifold tightening sequence

19. Disconnect interference suppression cable from transaxle.
20. Remove clutch cover plate, then remove clutch housing to engine block lower attaching bolts.
21. Lower vehicle, then attach suitable lifting equipment to engine lift hooks.
22. Support transaxle with a suitable jack, then remove right front and left front engine mount attaching bolts and the mount, then remove rear engine mount attaching bolts.
23. Remove clutch housing to engine block upper attaching bolts.
24. Separate engine from clutch housing, then carefully lift engine from vehicle.
25. Reverse procedure to install.

INTAKE MANIFOLD

REPLACE

1. Relieve fuel system pressure as follows:
   a. Remove fuel pump fuse from fuse panel.
   b. Start engine. After engine stalls, crank for ten seconds to relieve residual pressure from fuel system.
   c. Turn ignition off and install fuel pump fuse.
2. Disconnect battery ground cable.
3. Remove air cleaner assembly, then drain cooling system.
4. Unfasten alternator and position aside.
5. Disconnect throttle cable from intake manifold bracket.
6. Disconnect throttle and throttle valve cables from throttle body.
7. Disconnect electrical connectors from throttle body.
8. Disconnect fuel inlet and return lines, then the coolant hoses from intake manifold. **Place shop towel over fuel line and fitting when disconnecting.**
9. Remove manifold attaching bolts and the manifold, **Fig. 2.**
10. Reverse procedure to install. Clean manifold and cylinder head mating surfaces and install a new gasket prior to installation. Tighten intake manifold attaching nuts and bolts in sequence shown in **Fig. 2.**

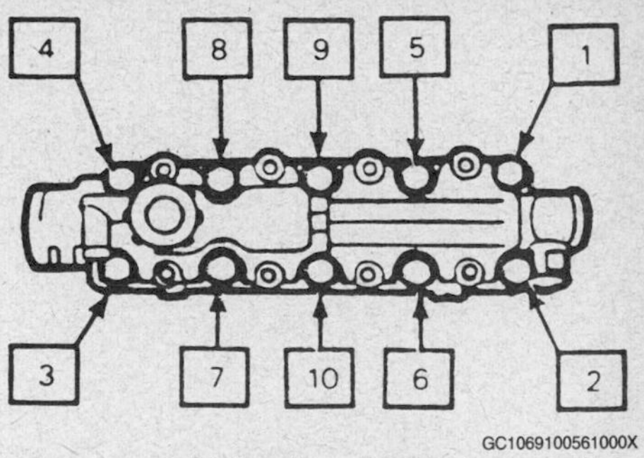
4
8
9
5
1
3
7
10
6
2

GC106910056100OX

Fig. 4 Cylinder head bolt loosening sequence

EXHAUST MANIFOLD

REPLACE

1. Remove air cleaner assembly.
2. Disconnect spark plug wires and the oxygen sensor electrical connector.
3. Remove pre-heater from exhaust manifold.
4. Disconnect exhaust pipe from manifold, then remove manifold attaching nuts and the manifold, **Fig. 3.**
5. Reverse procedure to install. Clean manifold and cylinder head mating surfaces and install a new gasket prior to installation. Tighten exhaust manifold attaching nuts to specifications and in sequence shown in **Fig. 3.**

CYLINDER HEAD

REPLACE

1. Relieve fuel system pressure as follows:
   a. Remove fuel pump fuse from fuse panel.
   b. Start engine. After engine stalls, crank for ten seconds to relieve residual pressure from fuel system.
   c. Turn ignition off and install fuel pump fuse.
2. Disconnect battery ground cable.
3. Remove air cleaner assembly, then drain cooling system.
4. Unfasten alternator and position aside.
5. Remove distributor and ignition wires.
6. Disconnect cables from intake manifold bracket, throttle body and downshift cable.
7. Disconnect ECM electrical connectors at the throttle body and intake manifold.
8. Disconnect fuel inlet and return lines, then the coolant and heater hoses from intake manifold and water outlet. **Place shop towel over fuel line and fitting when disconnecting.**
9. Disconnect breather and PCV hoses at camshaft carrier.
10. Remove upper radiator hose.
11. Disconnect exhaust pipe from manifold, then disconnect oxygen sensor electrical connector.
12. Disconnect engine wiring harness and the thermostat housing electrical connector.

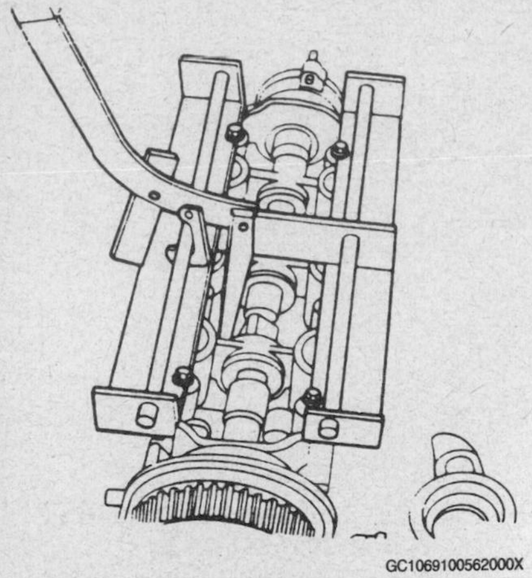
GC1069100562000X

Fig. 5 Valve spring compression

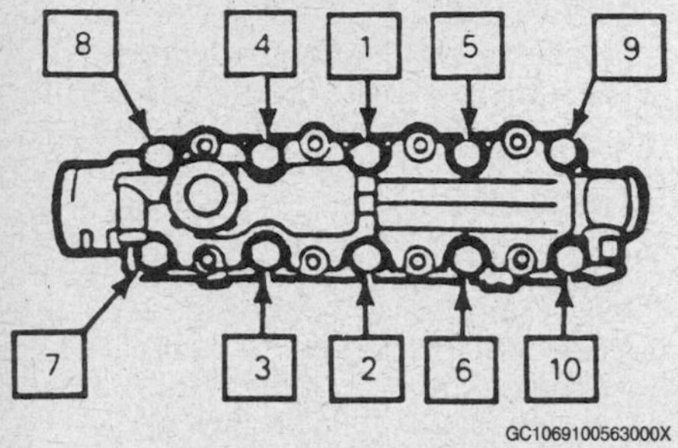
8
4
1
5
9
7
3
2
6
10
GC1069100563000X

Fig. 6 Cylinder head bolt tightening sequence

13. Remove timing belt as described under "Timing Belt, Replace."
14. Loosen cylinder head attaching bolts gradually in sequence, **Fig. 4**, until all bolts are removed.
15. Remove valve cover, then compress valve springs using a suitable tool, **Fig. 5**, and remove rocker arms and valve lash compensators. **Identify components for installation reference.**
16. Remove cylinder head as an assembly with intake and exhaust manifolds.
17. Reverse procedure to install, noting the following:
    a. Clean all cylinder head, valve cover and block mating surfaces.
    b. Apply a continuous bead (3 mm) of anerobic sealant to cam carrier sealing surface.
    c. Install new cylinder head gasket.
    d. Tighten cylinder head attaching bolts to specifications in sequence shown in **Fig. 6.**

CAMSHAFT LOBE LIFT SPECIFICATIONS

Engine	Year	Int. Inch	Exh. Inch
1.6L/4-98	All	.220	.241

VALVE CLEARANCE SPECIFICATIONS

This engine is equipped with hydraulic lash adjusters. If valve lash is present, check for worn rocker arm, stuck hydraulic valve lash adjuster plunger or defective valve lash adjuster.

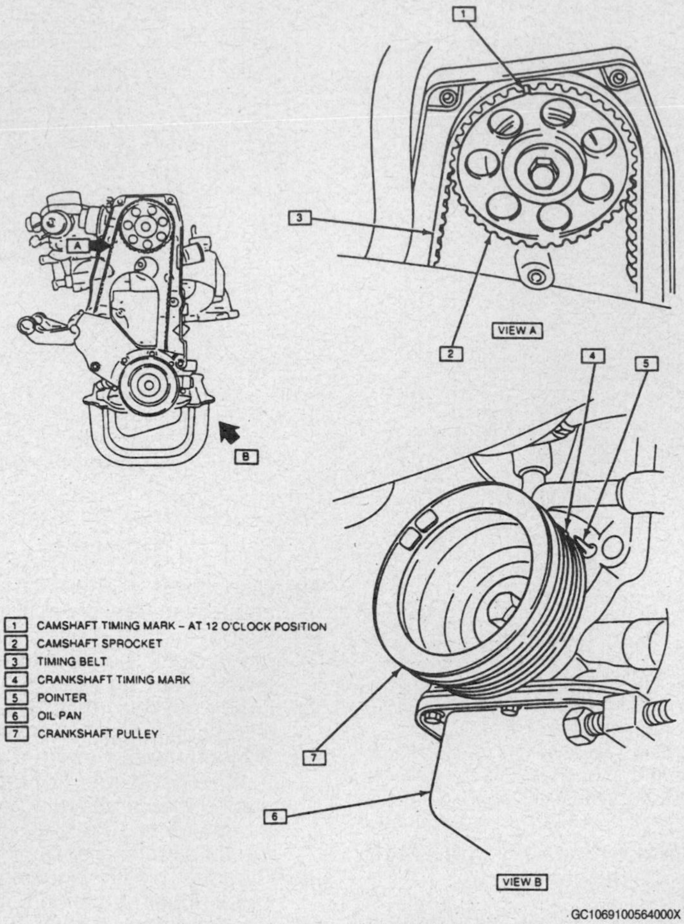
1
2
3
A
B
VIEW A
4
5
1 CAMSHAFT TIMING MARK – AT 12 O'CLOCK POSITION
2 CAMSHAFT SPROCKET
3 TIMING BELT
4 CRANKSHAFT TIMING MARK
5 POINTER
6 OIL PAN
7 CRANKSHAFT PULLEY
7
6
VIEW B
GC1069100564000X

Fig. 7 Timing mark alignment

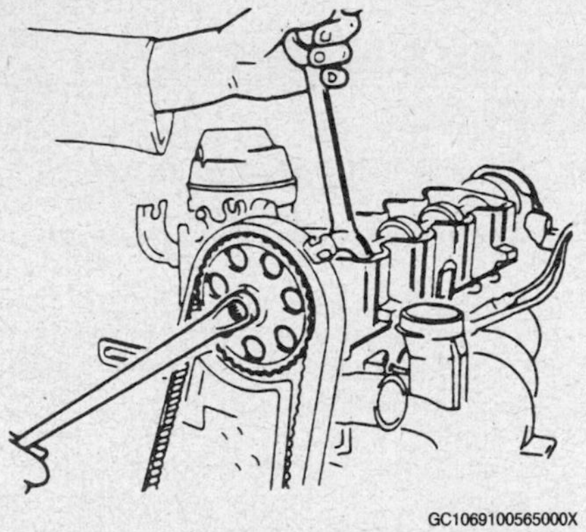
GC1069100565000X

Fig. 8 Camshaft gear removal

VALVE ADJUSTMENT

This vehicle has hydraulic lash adjusters and no adjustment is necessary.

VALVE GUIDES

Valve guides are an integral part of the cylinder head. If stem to guide clearance becomes excessive, the valve guide should be reamed to the next oversize and the appropriate oversize valve should be installed. Valve are available in oversizes of .003, .006 and .010 inch.

FRONT COVER

REPLACE

1. Disconnect battery ground cable.
2. Remove alternator and A/C compressor drive belts.
3. Remove power steering pump.
4. Unsnap upper to lower portions of cover, then remove cover from engine.
5. Reverse procedure to install. Snap lower portion of cover in first.

TIMING BELT

REPLACE

1. Remove front cover as outlined under "Front Cover, Replace."
2. Remove air cleaner assembly, then disconnect breather hoses from valve cover.
3. Remove valve cover attaching bolts and the cover.
4. Remove timing belt.
5. Align camshaft sprocket mark with rear timing belt cover mark, **Fig. 7.**
6. Reverse procedure to install.

CAMSHAFT & CRANKSHAFT SPROCKETS

REPLACE

1. Remove timing belt cover as previously described.

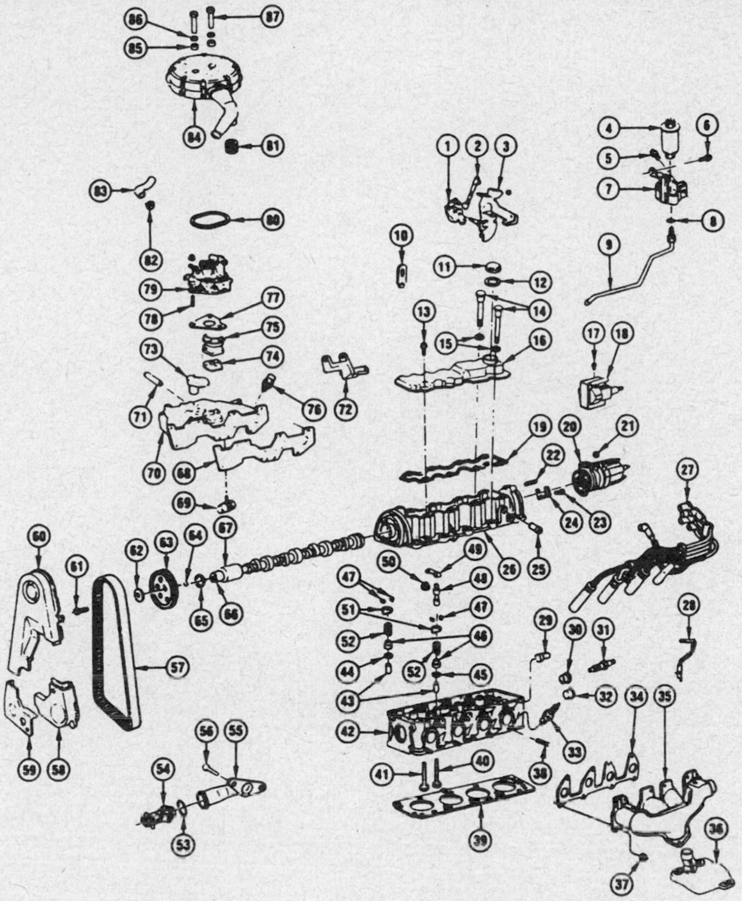

1 LEVER-ACCELERATOR CONTROL
2 ROD-THROTTLE CONTROL
3 BRACKET-ACCELERATOR CONTROL
4 FILTER-FUEL
5 BOLT
6 BOLT
7 BRACKET-FUEL FILTER
8 SEAL FUEL FEED LINE O-RING
9 PIPE-FUEL TANK TO FILTER
10 BRACKET-ENGINE LIFT
11 CAP-OIL
12 SEAL-OIL CAP
13 BOLT
14 BOLT-CAMSHAFT CARRIER HOUSING
15 WASHER
16 COVER-CAMSHAFT HOUSING
17 BOLT
18 COIL
19 GASKET CAMSHAFT CARRIER COVER
20 DISTRIBUTOR
21 NUT
22 BOLT
23 BOLT
24 PLATE-CAMSHAFT PRESS
25 TUBE-PCV
26 HOUSING-CAMSHAFT CARRIER
27 WIRE-SPARK PLUG
28 SUPPORT-SPARK PLUG WIRE
29 VALVE-CYLINDER HEAD BYPASS
30 ADAPTER
31 SENSOR-COOLANT TEMPERATURE
32 CAP
33 PLUG-SPARK
34 GASKET-EXHAUST MANIFOLD
35 MANIFOLD-EXHAUST
36 STOVE-EXHAUST MANIFOLD HEAT
37 NUT
38 STUD
39 GASKET-CYLINDER HEAD
40 VALVE-EXHAUST
41 VALVE-INTAKE
42 HEAD-CYLINDER
43 GUIDE
44 WASHER-INTAKE VALVE SPRING SEAT
45 ROTO CAP-EXHAUST VALVE
46 SEAL-VALVE
47 LOCK (COLLAR)-VALVE STEM
48 ADJUSTER-HYDRAULIC VALVE LASH
49 ARM-VALVE ROCKER
50 VALVE-THRUST PIECE
51 CAP-VALVE SPRING
52 SPRING-INTAKE AND EXHAUST VALVE
53 RING-SEAL
54 THERMOSTAT (92 DEGREE)
55 HOUSING-COOLING THERMOSTAT
56 BOLT-SPROCKET
57 BELT-TIMING
58 COVER-TIMING BELT LOWER REAR
59 COVER-TIMING BELT LOWER FRONT
60 COVER-TIMING BELT UPPER FRONT
61 BOLT
62 WASHER-TIMING GEAR
63 SPROCKET-CAMSHAFT TIMING
64 BALL
65 SEAL-CAMSHAFT OIL
66 PIN
67 CAMSHAFT
68 GASKET-INTAKE MANIFOLD
69 CONNECTOR-FUEL GAGE
70 MANIFOLD-INTAKE
71 CONNECTOR-INTAKE MANIFOLD
72 BRACKET-GENERAL MOUNTING
73 INSERT-INTAKE MANIFOLD TBI
74 GASKET-E.G.R.
75 VALVE-E.G.R.
76 SENSOR-INTAKE MANIFOLD COOLANT TEMPERATURE
77 GASKET-TBI
78 STUD
79 THROTTLE BODY INJECTOR (TBI)
80 GASKET-AIR CLEANER
81 HOSE-HEAT STOVE
82 CLAMP
83 HOSE-CYLINDER BLOCK VENT
84 AIR CLEANER
85 SEAL-AIR CLEANER CAP NUT
86 WASHER-AIR CLEANER CAP NUT
87 NUT-AIR CLEANER

GC1069100566000X

Fig. 9 Cylinder head & components

2. Remove air cleaner assembly, then disconnect breather hoses from valve cover.
3. Remove valve cover attaching bolts and the cover.
4. Remove timing belt.
5. Hold camshaft with a suitable wrench, then remove bolt, washer and camshaft sprocket, **Figs. 8 through 10.**
6. Remove retaining bolt and washer, then the crankshaft pulley and sprocket.
7. Reverse procedure to install, noting the following:
   a. Align mark on camshaft sprocket with mark on rear timing belt cover.
   b. Tighten camshaft gear attaching bolt and crankshaft sprocket retaining bolt to torque listed at the end of this section.

REAR COVER
REPLACE

1. Remove camshaft sprocket as previously described.
2. Remove rear cover attaching bolts and the cover. Guide cover over water pump rear cover.
3. Reverse procedure to install.

CRANKSHAFT PULLEY
REPLACE

1. Disconnect battery ground cable.
2. Loosen and remove alternator and A/C compressor drive belts.
3. Remove crankshaft pulley attaching bolt and the pulley.
4. Reverse procedure to install. Torque attaching bolt to specification listed at the end of this section.

CAMSHAFT
REPLACE

1. Remove air cleaner assembly, then disconnect breather hoses from valve cover.
2. Remove valve cover attaching bolts and the cover.
3. Apply compressed air to spark plug hole using a suitable adapter to hole valves in place.
4. Compress valve springs using a suitable tool, **Fig. 5,** then remove rocker arms and valve lash compensators. **Identify components for installation reference.**
5. Remove camshaft gear attaching bolt and the gear.
6. Remove distributor, then the camshaft thrust plate and camshaft.
7. Reverse procedure to install, noting following:
   a. Tighten camshaft thrust plate attaching bolts to torque listed at the end of this section.
   b. Ensure camshaft endplay measures .0035-.0083 inch.

PISTON & ROD ASSEMBLY

Assemble piston to rod, with notch on piston head toward front of engine, **Fig. 11.** Upon installation, measure rod bearing side clearance using a suitable feeler gauge. Rod bearing side clearance should be .0028-.0095 inch.

PISTONS, PINS & RINGS

Pistons and rings are available in standard size and oversize of .020 inch. Pistons and pins are supplied in matched sets.

MAIN & ROD BEARINGS

Main and rod bearings are available in standard sizes and undersizes of .010 and .020 inch.

CRANKSHAFT SEAL

REPLACE

1. Remove crankshaft gear as previously described.
2. Remove crankshaft key and rear thrust washer.
3. Remove timing belt rear cover, then pry front seal out of groove.
4. Lubricate, then install new seal using seal installer tool No. J36534, or equivalent, **Fig. 12.**

CRANKSHAFT REAR OIL SEAL

REPLACE

1. Remove transaxle assembly.
2. Remove flywheel attaching bolts and the flywheel.
3. **On models equipped with manual transaxle,** remove clutch pressure plate and disc.
4. **On all models,** pry rear seal out of groove.
5. Lubricate outer surface of new seal, then install the seal using seal installer tool No. J36792, or equivalent.

OIL PAN

REPLACE

1. Disconnect battery ground cable.
2. Raise and support vehicle.
3. Remove right splash shield.
4. Drain engine oil, then disconnect exhaust pipe from exhaust manifold.
5. **On models equipped with manual transaxle,** remove clutch cover plate attaching bolts, then remove clutch cover plate.
6. **On all models,** remove oil pan attaching bolts and the oil pan.
7. Reverse procedure to install. Apply suitable sealant to bolt threads and oil pan seams, **Fig. 13.**

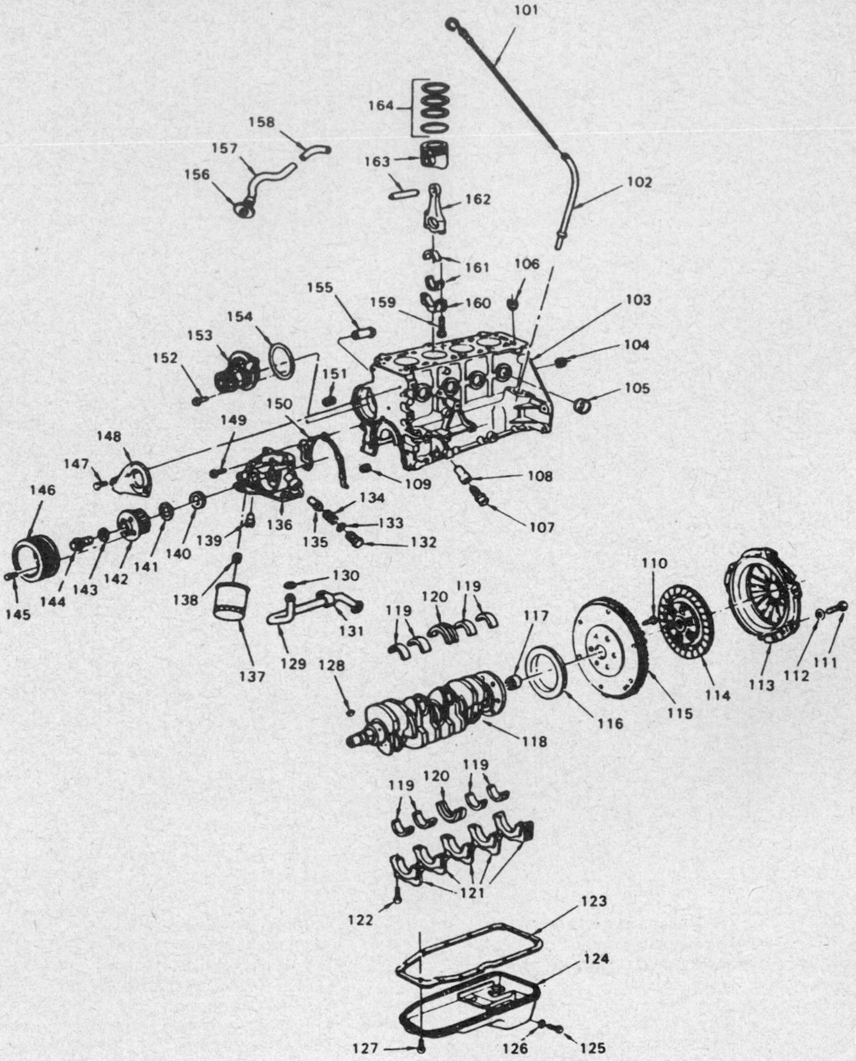

101	INDICATOR (ROD)-OIL LEVEL
102	TUBE-OIL
103	BLOCK-ENGINE CYLINDER
104	SLEEVE-TRANSMISSION
105	PLUG-CLIP TYPE
106	SLEEVE-CYLINDER TO CYLINDER BLOCK
107	PLUG-IGNITION TIMING BUSHING
108	BUSHING-IGNITION TIMING
109	SLEEVE-OIL PLUG
110	BOLT
111	BOLT
112	WASHER
113	COVER-CLUTCH PRESSURE WITH PLATE
114	PLATE (DISC)-CLUTCH DRIVEN (M/T)
115	FLYWHEEL
116	RING-REAR CRANKSHAFT OIL SEAL
117	BEARING
118	CRANKSHAFT
119	BEARING SET-CRANKSHAFT
120	BEARING-CRANKSHAFT MAIN
121	CAP-CRANKSHAFT MAIN BEARING
122	BOLT
123	GASKET-OIL PAN
124	PAN-OIL
125	BOLT-OIL PAN DRAIN
126	GASKET (RING)-OIL PAN DRAIN BOLT
127	BOLT
128	KEY-CRANKSHAFT
129	PIPE-OIL PUMP SUCTION
130	RING-OIL PUMP SUCTION PIPE
131	BRACKET
132	BOLT-OIL PUMP PRESSURE RELIEF VALVE
133	RING-OIL PUMP PRESSURE RELIEF VALVE
134	SPRING-OIL PUMP PRESSURE RELIEF VALVE
135	PLUNGER-OIL PUMP PRESSURE RELIEF VALVE
136	PUMP-OIL
137	FILTER-OIL
138	CONNECTOR-OIL FILTER
139	VALVE-OIL PUMP BYPASS
140	RING-OIL PUMP SEAL
141	WASHER
142	GEAR-CRANKSHAFT TIMING
143	WASHER-CRANKSHAFT PULLEY
144	BOLT-CRANKSHAFT TIMING GEAR
145	BOLT-CRANKSHAFT PULLEY
146	PULLEY-CRANKSHAFT
147	SCREW-REAR TIMING BELT COVER
148	COVER-TIMING BELT UPPER REAR
149	BOLT
150	GASKET-OIL PUMP
151	PLUG
152	BOLT-COOLANT PUMP
153	PUMP-COOLANT
154	RING-COOLANT PUMP SEAL
155	NECK-CYLINDER BLOCK COOLANT INLET
156	GASKET-CYLINDER BLOCK VENT PIPE
157	PIPE-CYLINDER BLOCK VENT
158	HOSE-CYLINDER BLOCK VENT
159	BOLT-CONNECTING ROD
160	CAP-CONNECTING ROD BEARING
161	BEARING SET-CONNECTING ROD
162	ROD-CONNECTING
163	PISTON WITH PIN
164	PISTON RINGS

GC1069100567000X

Fig. 10 Cylinder block & components

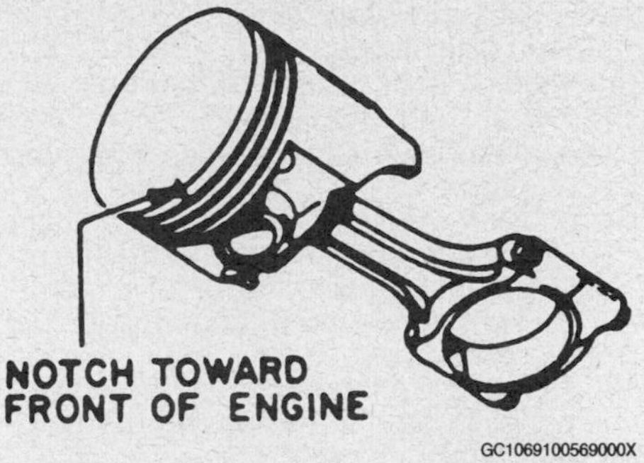
NOTCH TOWARD
FRONT OF ENGINE
GC1069100569000X

Fig. 11 Piston & rod assembly

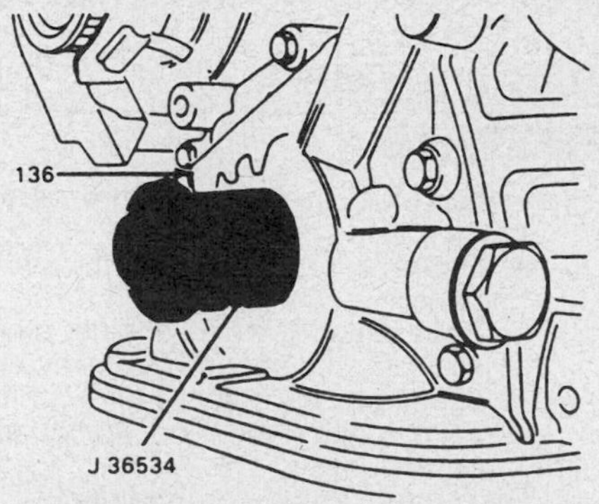
136
J 36534

136 PUMP-OIL

GC1069100568000X

Fig. 12 Crankshaft front seal installation

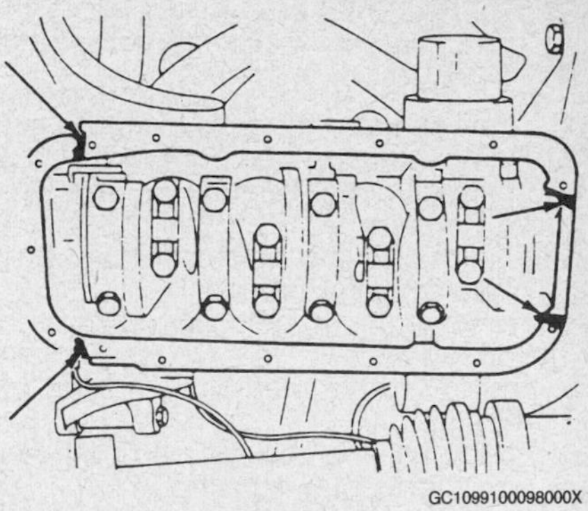
GC1099100098000X

Fig. 13 Oil pan sealant application

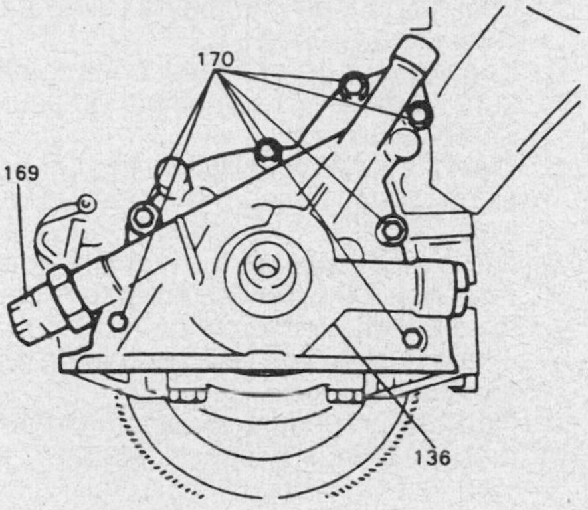
170
169
136

136 PUMP-OIL
169 SWITCH-OIL PRESSURE
170 BOLTS-OIL PUMP

GC1099100099000X

Fig. 14 Oil pump replacement

1. PUMP, OIL
2. PLUG
3. RING, SEAL
4. GEAR, OIL PUMP DRIVE
5. GEAR, OIL PUMP DRIVEN
6. COVER, OIL PUMP
7. BOLT (M6 x 1 x 16)
8. GASKET
9. SLEEVE
10. VALVE, BYPASS
11. BOLT, PRESS. REL. VLV.
12. RING, PRESS. REL. VLV.
13. SPRING PRESS. REL. VLV.
14. PLUNGER, PRESS. REL. VLV.
15. BOLT (6 x 1 x 25) WASHER

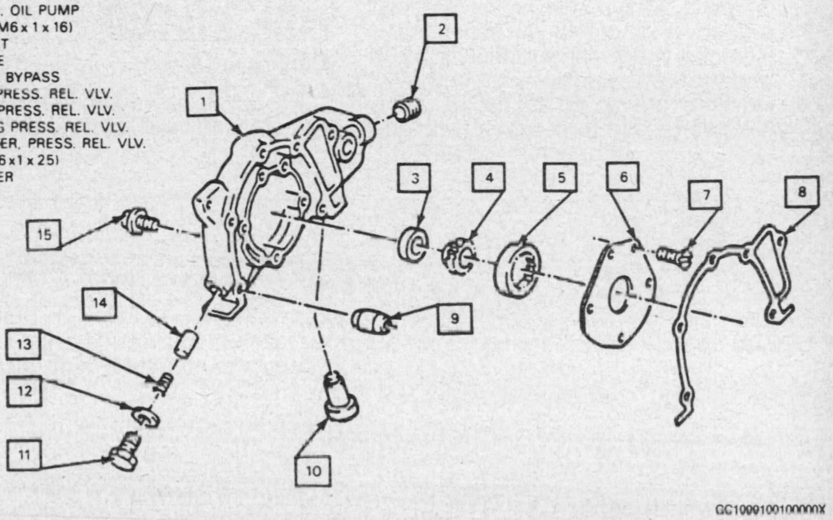
1
2
3
4
5
6
7
8
9
10
11
12
13
14
15
GC1099100100000X

Fig. 15 Exploded view of oil pump assembly

OIL PUMP

REPLACE

REMOVAL

1. Remove crankshaft gear and timing belt rear cover as previously described.
2. Disconnect electrical connector from oil pressure switch.
3. Remove oil pan as previously described.
4. Remove oil filter, then the pickup tube and oil pump, **Fig. 14.**
5. Remove crankshaft front oil seal.

INSTALLATION

1. Install oil pump using a new gasket.
2. Install pickup tube and support using a new O-ring.
3. Install oil pan, then a new front seal using Seal Installer tool No. J36534 or equivalent.
4. Install new oil filter, then reconnect oil pressure switch electrical connector.
5. Install rear timing belt cover and crankshaft gear.

OIL PUMP SERVICE

DISASSEMBLY

1. Drain oil from pump, then remove suction pipe and screen assembly.
2. Remove oil pump cover and gears, **Fig. 15.**
3. Carefully remove pressure regulator valve plug or cotter pin, then the valve spring and valve.

INSPECTION

1. Clean all pump components in suitable solvent.
2. Inspect pump housing and cover for damage or casting imperfections. Replace housing if necessary.
3. Inspect idler gear shaft fit in housing. If shaft fits loosely, replace pump or timing chain cover as needed.
4. Inspect pressure regulator valve for damaging or sticking. Small burrs may be removed with an oil stone.
5. Install pressure regulator valve spring for loss of tension or damage and replace as necessary.
6. Inspect suction pipe and screen for looseness or damage and replace as necessary.
7. Inspect gears for damage and replace as necessary.
8. Inspect driveshaft for looseness or excessive wear and replace as necessary.

ASSEMBLY

1. Lubricate all internal components with clean engine oil.
2. Pack all pump cavities with petroleum jelly, then install the gears. **Ensure mark on gears faces timing cover.**
3. Install cover and gasket, then the pressure regulator valve and spring.
4. Apply Loctite sealant to pressure regulator valve plug threads, then install the plug and torque to specifications listed at the end of this section.

BELT TENSION DATA

Year	Belt	Lbs. New	Lbs. Used
All	A/C	155	80
	Comp. Alt. & P/S	①	①

①—.5–.75 inch deflection.

COOLING SYSTEM BLEED

These engines do not require a specified bleed procedure. After filling cooling system, run engine to operating temperature with radiator/pressure cap off. Air will then be automatically bled through cap opening.

THERMOSTAT

REPLACE

1. Drain radiator through lower hose.
2. Remove timing belt front cover as described under "Timing Belt Front Cover, Replace."
3. Remove timing belt described under "Timing Belt, Replace."
4. Remove timing belt rear cover as described under " Rear Cover, Replace."
5. Remove thermostat housing and thermostat.
6. Clean sealing surfaces on both head and thermostat housing.
7. Reverse procedure to install.

WATER PUMP

REPLACE

1. Disconnect lower radiator hose and drain coolant into a suitable container.
2. Remove front cover, timing belt and rear cover as previously described.
3. Remove water pump attaching bolts and the water pump.
4. Reverse procedure to install. Apply silicone grease to pump sealing surface and new seal ring prior to installation.

FUEL PUMP

REPLACE

1. Relieve fuel system pressure as follows:
   a. Remove fuel pump fuse from fuse panel.
   b. Start engine. After engine stalls, crank for ten seconds to relieve residual pressure from fuel system.
   c. Turn ignition off and install fuel pump fuse.
2. Disconnect battery ground cable.
3. Raise rear seat, then remove cover from floor pan.
4. Disconnect electrical fuel pump connector and fuel line from fuel pump.
5. Remove fuel pump attaching bolts and the fuel pump.
6. Reverse procedure to install.

FUEL FILTER

REPLACE

The inline filters can be found on the rear crossmember of the vehicle. Always use a backup wrench anytime the filter is removed or installed.

1. Relieve fuel system pressure as follows:
   a. Remove fuel pump fuse from fuse panel.
   b. Start engine. After engine stalls, crank for ten seconds to relieve residual pressure from fuel system.
   c. Turn ignition off and install fuel pump fuse.
2. Remove fuel pump fuse from fuse panel located in the passenger compartment.
3. Crank engine, engine will start and run until fuel supply remaining in the fuel lines is consumed.
4. Engage starter for 3.0 seconds to ensure relief of any remaining pressure in the system.
5. Turn the ignition switch to the Off position, then replace the fuel pump fuse.
6. Raise and support the vehicle, then disconnect the front and rear fuel lines from the filter assembly.
7. Remove retaining bolt and clamp assembly.
8. Reverse procedure to install. Tighten fuel line fittings to specifications.

TIGHTENING SPECIFICATIONS

Torque specifications are for clean & lightly lubricated threads only. Dry or dirty threads increase friction which prevents accurate measurement of tightness.

Year	Component	Torque/ Ft. Lbs.
1992–93	A/C Compressor Nuts & Bolts	18
	Camshaft Carrier & Cylinder Head Bolts	18(1)
	Camshaft Carrier Cover Bolts	18
	Camshaft Sprocket Bolt	33
	Connecting Rod Cap Bolts	18(4)
	Crankshaft Pulley Bolt	41
	Crankshaft Sprocket Bolt	33
	Cylinder head bolts	18(6)
	Exhaust Manifold Heat Stove Bolts	89(2)
	Exhaust Manifold Nuts	16
	Exhaust Pipe Nuts	115(2)
	Fuel Line Fittings	22
	Flywheel Bolts	26(5)
	Generator Bolts	18
	Intake Manifold Nuts & Bolts	16
	Left Front Engine Mount	37
	Left Front Mounting Bracket To Block	30
	Left Front Mounting Bracket To Engine Mount	30
	Lower Timing Belt Front Cover Bolts	71(2)
	Main Bearing Cap Bolts	37(3)

Year	Component	Torque/ Ft. Lbs.
1992–93	Oil Pan Bolts	71(2)
—Cont'd	Oil Plug	33
	Oil Pump Bolts	62(2)
	Power Steering Pump Bolts	18
	Power Steering Pump Pulley Bolts	20
	Pressure Relief Valve Bolt	22
	Rear Engine Mount Bolts	37
	Rear Mounting Bracket Nut & Bolt	30
	Rear Thrust Plate Bolts	71(4)
	Right Front Engine Mount Nuts	37
	Right Front Mounting Bracket To Block Bolts	30
	Right Front Mounting Bracket To Engine Mount Bolt	30
	Timing Belt Rear Cover Bolts	89(2)
	Upper Timing Belt Front Cover Bolts	71(2)

(1)—Plus 2 turns of 60° each & 1 turn of 30°
(2)—Inch Lbs.
(3)—Plus 1 turn of 45° to 60°
(4)—Plus 1 turn of 30°
(5)—Plus 1 turn of 30° to 45°
(6)—Plus one turn of 60°, another turn of 60°, and finally a 30° turn in specified sequence.

Clutch & Manual Transaxle

INDEX

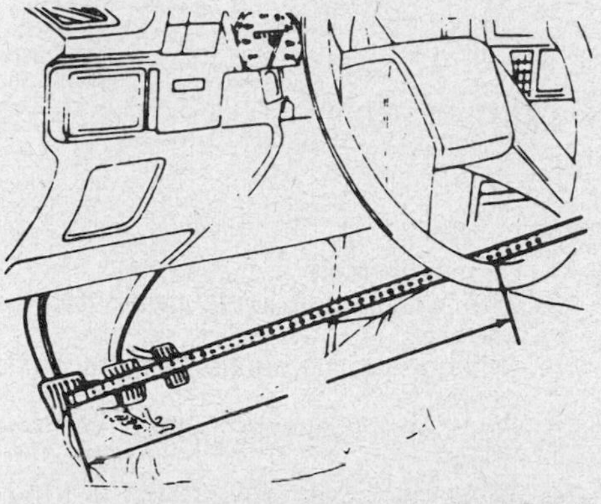

GC5049100064000X

Fig. 1 Clutch pedal adjustments

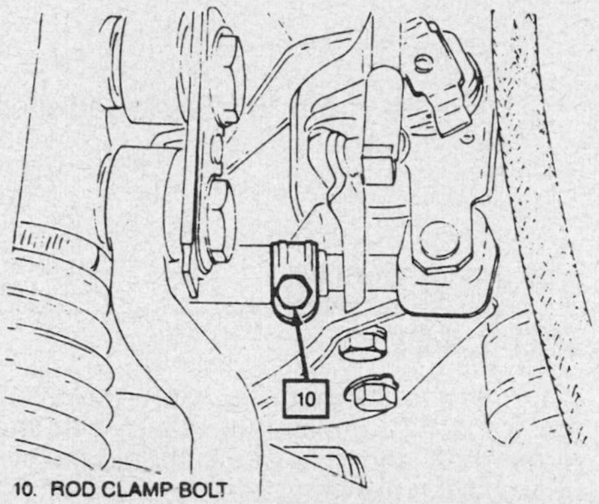
10

10. ROD CLAMP BOLT

GC5049100065000X

Fig. 2 Shift lever measurements

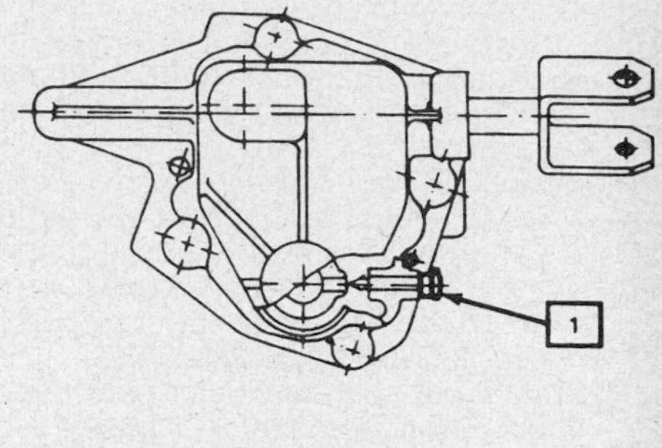
1

1. ADJUSTMENT HOLE PLUG

GC5049100066000X

Fig. 3 Shift rod clamp bolt

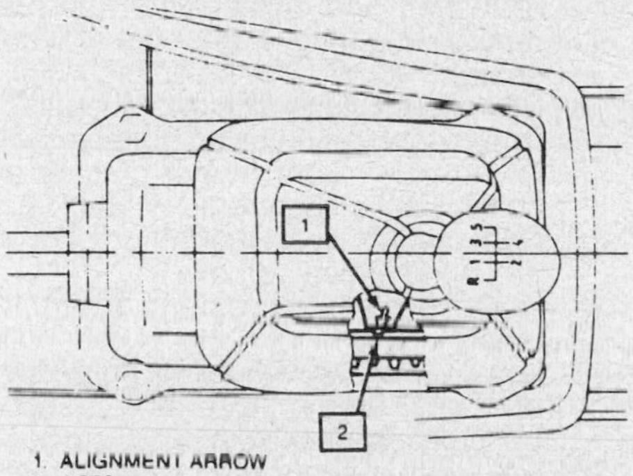
1
2

1. ALIGNMENT ARROW
2. NOTCH

GC5049100067000X

Fig. 4 Shift linkage adjustment hole plug

ADJUSTMENTS

CLUTCH PEDAL

1. Measure and record distance between outer edge of steering wheel and center of clutch pedal, **Fig. 1.**
2. Fully depress clutch pedal and repeat measurement made in previous step.
3. Determine clutch pedal travel by subtracting first measurement from second measurement.
4. If clutch pedal travel is not 5.43-5.71 inches, remove clip and adjust cable nut as necessary, then install clip.

SHIFT LINKAGE

1. Disconnect battery ground cable.
2. Place gearshift lever in Neutral position, then loosen rod clamp bolt, **Fig. 2.**
3. Remove adjustment hole plug from shift lever cover, **Fig. 3,** then turn shift rod to the left until a 3/16 inch gauge pin can be inserted into adjustment hole in intermediate shift lever.
4. Remove shift boot from console, then unfasten console and lift upward to gain access to shift control lever mechanism.
5. Move gearshift lever to 1st/2nd gear position while still in Neutral.
6. Ensure lever is against stop and arrow is aligned with notch, **Fig. 4,** then **torque** rod clamp bolt to 10 ft. lbs. plus an additional 90-180°.
7. Measure clearance between catch "A, **Fig. 5,** and stop "B" with lever in neutral position. Clearance should measure .12 inch.
8. Remove gauge pin and install plug.
9. Adjust dimension "C," **Fig. 5,** to .449-.465 inch by turning adjusting nut "D" as necessary. **Bend back two locking tabs at nut prior to adjustment.**
10. Install boot then the console assembly.
11. Reconnect battery ground cable.

CLUTCH

REPLACE

REMOVAL

1. Disconnect battery ground cable.
2. Remove clip and nut, then disconnect clutch cable from release lever. **Prior to disconnecting, measure threaded end of clutch cable at clutch release lever, so that cable may be set in the same position during installation.**
3. Raise and support vehicle.
4. Remove left front wheel and tire assembly.
5. Remove 17 mm plug from transaxle cover.

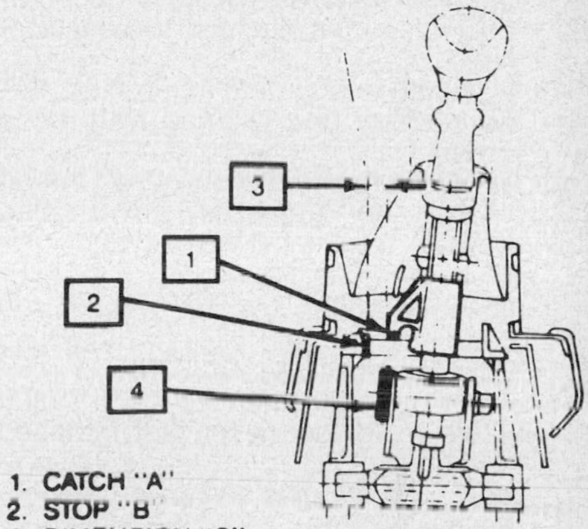
1
2
3
4

1. CATCH "A"
2. STOP "B"
3. DIMENSION "C"
4. ADJ. NUT "D"

GC5049100068000X

Fig. 5 Shift lever alignment

6. Mark relationship between input shaft and cluster gear, then remove snap ring from end of input shaft.
7. Remove screw at end of input shaft using Input Shaft Retaining Screw Remover & Installer tool No. J-36668 or equivalent.
8. Screw Input Shaft Remover & Installer tool No. J-36644 and Slide Hammer tool No. J-6125-B or equivalents into end of input shaft, then pull input shaft out of cluster gear.
9. Remove clutch cover attaching bolts and the cover.
10. Push back clutch release lever, then install Pressure Plate Spring Clamps tool No. J-36554 or equivalent on pressure plate.
11. Rotate flywheel 120° and install a second clamp, then rotate an additional 120° and install a third clamp. **Pressure plate and clutch disc cannot be removed without the three**

spring clamps properly installed.

12. Support pressure plate and remove attaching bolts, pressure plate and clutch disc, **Fig. 6.**

INSTALLATION

1. Position new pressure in a suitable press and apply enough pressure to install three spring clamps.
2. Install pressure plate and clutch disc, noting the following:
   a. Ensure long portion of clutch disc hub faces transaxle.
   b. Apply suitable grease to clutch disc spline and release bearing.
   c. Ensure reference marks on flywheel and pressure plate are properly aligned.
   d. Install two pressure plate bolts. Align clutch disc splines with input shaft splines and marks on input shaft with marks on cluster gear, then install remaining bolts and tighten all to specifications.
3. Seat input shaft in cluster gear using Input Shaft Remover & Installer tool No. J-36644 and Slide Hammer tool No. J-6125-B or equivalents.
4. Install screw at end of input shaft using Input Shaft Retaining Screw Remover & Installer tool No. J-36668 or equivalent, then tighten to specifications.
5. Install snap ring onto input shaft. **Ensure sharp end of snap ring faces cover.**
6. Apply suitable Teflon pipe thread sealant to transaxle cover plug threads, then install the plug and tighten to specifications.
7. Remove spring clamps, then install clutch cover and tighten attaching bolts to specifications.
8. Lower vehicle, then connect clutch cable to release lever. Set threaded portion of clutch to measurement noted during removal and adjust as necessary.

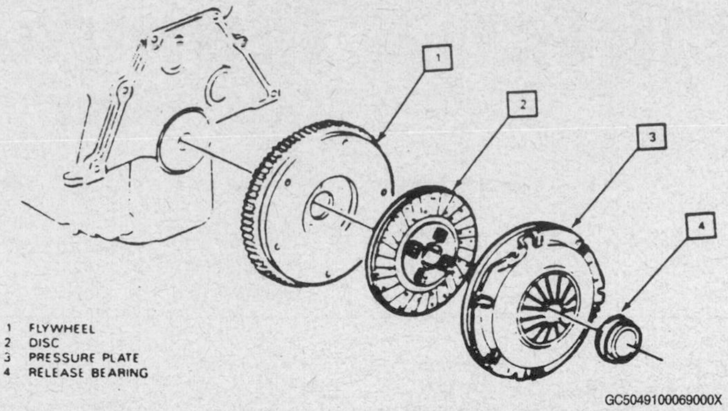
1
2
3
4
1 FLYWHEEL
2 DISC
3 PRESSURE PLATE
4 RELEASE BEARING
GC5049100069000X

Fig. 6 Exploded view of clutch assembly

TRANSAXLE

REPLACE

If only the transaxle is to be removed, the transaxle end shield along with the main shaft and driveshaft should be removed from the transaxle casing.

1. Disconnect battery ground cable.
2. Remove air cleaner.
3. Remove clutch cable at release lever attaching clip and nut.
4. Remove universal joint attaching clip and bolt.
5. Disconnect speedometer cable, speed sensor and back-up lamp electrical connectors.
6. Loosen shift rod clamp attaching bolt.
7. Remove upper transaxle to engine attaching bolts.
8. Install Engine Support Fixture tool No. J28467-A or equivalent.
9. Raise and support vehicle.
10. Remove front wheel and tire assemblies.
11. Remove splash shield.
12. Disconnect interference suppression capacitor cable at transaxle.
13. Press both ball joints from steering knuckle.
14. Disengage axle shafts from transaxle casing.
15. Remove transaxle cover at end shield.
16. Disengage both drive axles at transaxle using Drive Axle Remover tool No. J-36639 or equivalent.
17. Mark relationship between transaxle driveshaft and cluster gear, then remove snap ring from end of input shaft.
18. Pull out left drive axle and support.
19. Support transaxle using suitable jack.
20. Remove left front mount bracket attaching bolts, then remove bracket.
21. Remove left rear mount bracket to transaxle attaching bolts.
22. Remove lower transaxle to engine attaching bolts.
23. Lower jack while guiding right drive axle out of transaxle and remove transaxle from vehicle.
24. Reverse procedure to install. Tighten all attaching points to specifications.

TIGHTENING SPECIFICATIONS

Year	Component	Torque/ Ft. Lbs.
1992-93	Ball Joint Nut	50
	Clutch Cover Plug	36
	Clutch Fork To Release Lever Shaft Bolt	26
	Flywheel Bolts	26②
	Flywheel Cover Bolts	62①
	Front Mount Bracket To Mount	55
	Front Mount Bracket To Transaxle	48
	Input Shaft Attaching Screw	11
	Pressure Plate To Flywheel	11
	Rear Mount Bracket To Transaxle	55
	Release Bearing Guide Sleeve Bolts	45①
	Upper & Lower Transaxle To Engine	55
	Wheel Lug Nuts	66

①—Inch lbs.
②—Plus 1 turn of 30° to 45°.

Rear Axle & Suspension

INDEX

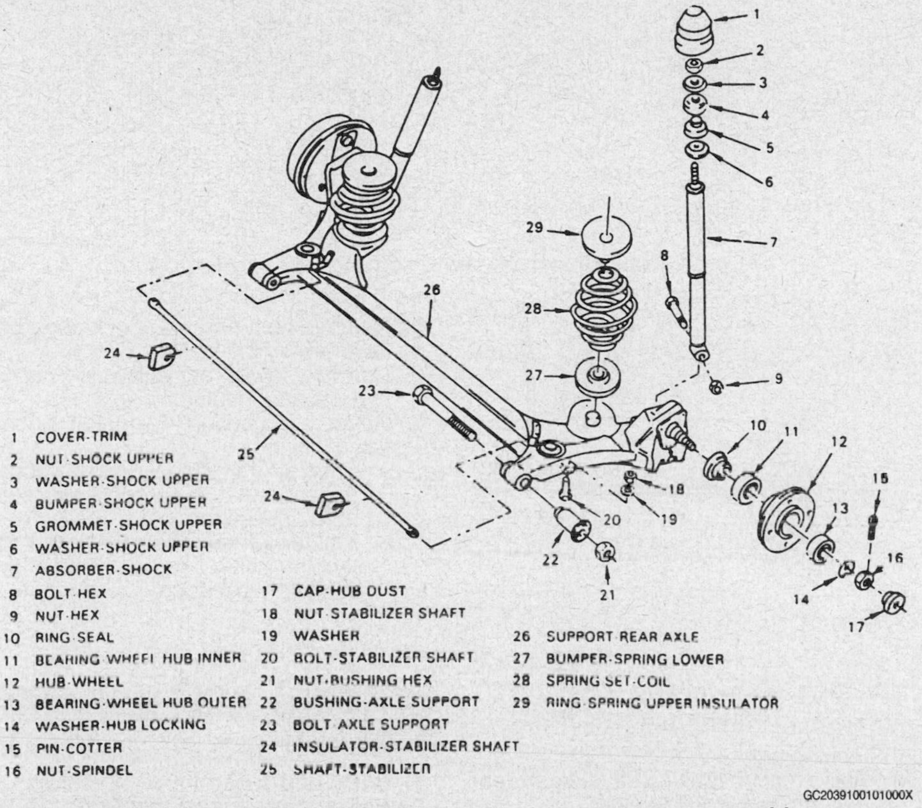

1 COVER-TRIM
2 NUT-SHOCK UPPER
3 WASHER-SHOCK UPPER
4 BUMPER-SHOCK UPPER
5 GROMMET-SHOCK UPPER
6 WASHER-SHOCK UPPER
7 ABSORBER-SHOCK
8 BOLT-HEX
9 NUT-HEX
10 RING-SEAL
11 BEARING-WHEEL HUB INNER
12 HUB-WHEEL
13 BEARING-WHEEL HUB OUTER
14 WASHER-HUB LOCKING
15 PIN-COTTER
16 NUT-SPINDEL
17 CAP-HUB DUST
18 NUT-STABILIZER SHAFT
19 WASHER
20 BOLT-STABILIZER SHAFT
21 NUT-BUSHING HEX
22 BUSHING-AXLE SUPPORT
23 BOLT-AXLE SUPPORT
24 INSULATOR-STABILIZER SHAFT
25 SHAFT-STABILIZER
26 SUPPORT-REAR AXLE
27 BUMPER-SPRING LOWER
28 SPRING SET-COIL
29 RING-SPRING UPPER INSULATOR
GC2039100101000X

Fig. 1 Exploded view of rear axle & suspension assembly

REAR AXLE

REPLACE

REMOVAL

1. Raise and support vehicle.
2. Remove rear wheel and tire assemblies.
3. Remove exhaust heat shield from vehicle underbody.
4. Measure and record length of thread on parking brake lever pushrod.
5. Remove self-locking nut from parking brake lever pushrod and the lock plate from brake cable compensation yoke.
6. Disconnect parking brake cable from brake cable compensation yoke.
7. Disconnect parking brake cable from guides on transaxle tunnel and plastic sleeves on fuel tank and position toward muffler.
8. Raise one rear axle arm using a suitable jack.
9. Disconnect brake lines from brake pressure hoses on rear axle bracket and remove lock clips. **Cap brake line fittings.**
10. Disconnect brake pressure hoses from bracket.
11. Remove shock absorbers as described under "Shock Absorber, Replace."
12. Remove rear axle arm attaching bolt, then lower the arm and remove coil spring. If necessary, depress rear axle arm using a pry bar positioned in shock absorber bracket.
13. Repeat step 12 on opposite side.
14. Support center of rear axle assembly using a suitable jack.
15. Remove rear axle attaching bolts and carefully lower axle assembly from vehicle, **Fig. 1.**
16. If rear axle assembly is to be replaced, proceed as follows:
    a. Remove brake drum setscrew and the drum.
    b. Remove dust cap from wheel hub.
    c. Remove wheel hub retaining nut and the wheel hub.
    d. Bend open brake line retaining clamps.
    e. Remove brake anchor plates and paper seal from rear axle arm.
    f. Remove stabilizer bar attaching bolts and the stabilizer bar.
    g. Disconnect parking brake cable from mounting.

INSTALLATION

1. If rear axle assembly is being replaced, proceed as follows:
    a. Attach stabilizer bar to rear axle and tighten attaching bolts to torque listed at the end of this section.
    b. Apply suitable sealant to brake anchor plate, then position new paper seals on plate.
    c. Apply suitable locking compound to anchor plate attaching bolts, then install the bolts and tighten to torque listed at the end of this section.
    d. Position brake lines in rear axle clamps and bend clamps closed.
    e. Apply suitable grease to wheel spindle, then install wheel hub and tighten attaching nut to specifications.
    f. Adjust wheel bearings as described under "Wheel Bearing, Adjust."
    g. Install brake drums and setscrew.
    h. Position parking brake cable over exhaust muffler.
2. Raise rear axle assembly and secure to vehicle underbody. Raise one rear axle arm slightly using a suitable jack.
3. Install coil spring, ensuring lower rubber damper is properly positioned in spring seat.
4. Raise axle arm and install shock absorber. Tighten attaching bolts to specifications.
5. Repeat steps 3 and 4 on opposite side.
6. Fasten brake pressure hoses to rear axle bracket and retaining clips.
7. Attach brake pressure lines to pressure hoses.
8. Install parking brake cable and adjust to dimension recorded at removal.
9. Install rear wheel and tire assemblies, then adjust wheel bearings as described under "Wheel Bearing, Adjust.
10. Tighten rear axle attaching bolts to torque listed at the end of this section, with weight of vehicle on wheels.
11. Bleed brake system, then adjust parking brake as necessary.

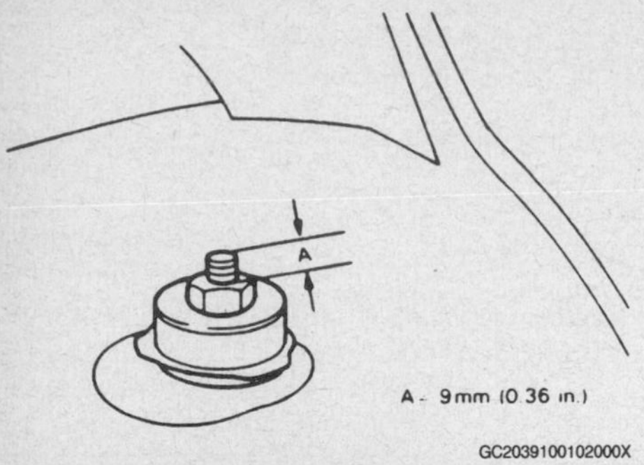
A
A - 9mm (0.36 in.)
GC2039100102000X

Fig. 2 Shock absorber upper nut installation

HUB & BEARING

REPLACE

1. Raise and support rear of vehicle.
2. Remove wheel and tire assembly.
3. Remove brake drum setscrew and the drum. If necessary, loosen parking brake cable and press parking brake lever in with a screwdriver.
4. Remove dust cap from hub, then the spindle nut cotter pin and nut.
5. Remove wheel hub and lockwasher.
6. Remove seal from wheel hub using a suitable screwdriver.
7. Remove inner tapered roller bearing from hub.
8. Drive inner and outer bearing outer races out of wheel hub using a suitable drift.
9. Reverse procedure to install, noting the following:
   a. Press bearing outer races into hub using Rear Hub Inner and Outer Bearing Race Installer tool No. J-6791 and Driver Handle tool No. J-8092 or equivalents.
   b. Pack wheel bearings, seal lip and wheel hub with suitable wheel bearing grease.
   c. Following completion of installation, adjust wheel bearings and parking brake as needed.

WHEEL BEARING

ADJUST

1. Raise and support rear of vehicle.
2. Remove hub dust cap, then the spindle nut cotter pin and nut.
3. Tighten spindle nut to specifications while turning wheel assembly forward by hand.
4. Back off spindle nut until just loose, then hand-tighten the nut.
5. Loosen spindle nut until either hole in spindle aligns with slot in nut, then install new cotter pin. **Do not loosen nut more than 1/2 turn.**
6. Ensure bearing endplay measures .001 to .005 inch, then install dust cap on hub.

SHOCK ABSORBER

REPLACE

1. Open deck lid and remove trim cover, if equipped.
2. Remove upper shock absorber attaching nut.
3. Raise rear of vehicle and support rear axle using a suitable jack.
4. Remove lower attaching bolt and nut and the shock absorber. **Do not remove both shock absorbers at the same time.**
5. Reverse procedure to install, noting the following:
   a. Tighten lower attaching bolt to torque listed at the end of this section.
   b. Tighten upper attaching nut until thread extends .36 inch above the nut, **Fig. 2.**

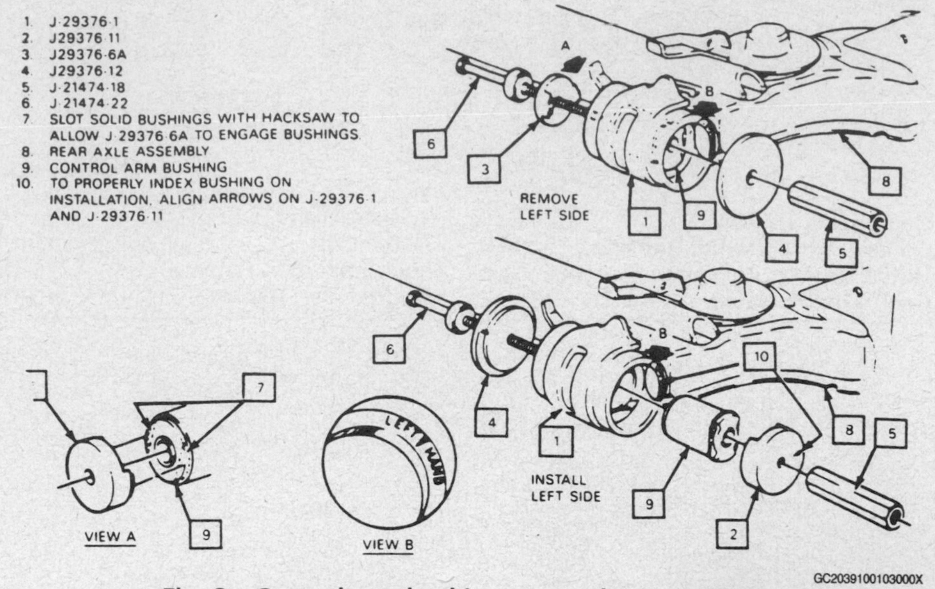
1. J-29376-1
2. J29376-11
3. J29376-6A
4. J29376-12
5. J-21474-18
6. J-21474-22
7. SLOT SOLID BUSHINGS WITH HACKSAW TO ALLOW J-29376-6A TO ENGAGE BUSHINGS.
8. REAR AXLE ASSEMBLY
9. CONTROL ARM BUSHING
10. TO PROPERLY INDEX BUSHING ON INSTALLATION, ALIGN ARROWS ON J-29376-1 AND J-29376-11
REMOVE LEFT SIDE
INSTALL LEFT SIDE
VIEW A
VIEW B
GC2039100103000X

Fig. 3 Control arm bushing removal & installation

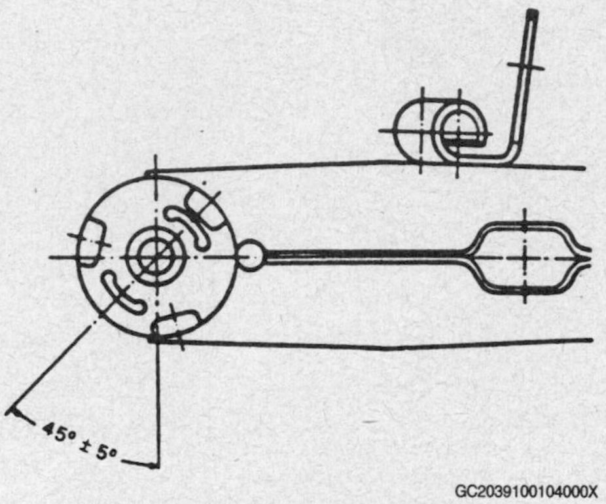
45° ± 5°
GC2039100104000X

Fig. 4 Control arm bushing alignment

COIL SPRING

REPLACE

1. Raise and support rear of vehicle. Support control arms with suitable jackstands.
2. Remove brake line clips from body bracket and allow brake line to hang free.
3. Disconnect parking brake cable at equalizer.
4. Disconnect brake hoses and cap fittings.
5. Remove right and left shock absorber lower attaching bolts.
6. Carefully lower rear axle and remove springs and insulators.
7. Reverse procedure to install, noting the following:
   a. Prior to installing springs, secure upper insulators to body with suitable adhesive.
   b. Tighten shock absorber lower attaching bolts to torque listed at the end of this section.

CONTROL ARM BUSHING

REPLACE

1. Raise and support rear of vehicle.
2. Raise one rear axle arm using a suitable jack and remove shock absorber lower attaching bolt.
3. Raise opposite rear axle arm and remove shock absorber lower attaching bolt.
4. Lower axle arm slightly and remove coil spring with rubber damper, then raise axle and install shock absorber lower attaching bolt.
5. Repeat step 4 on opposite side of axle.
6. Support center of rear axle assembly using a suitable jack.
7. Remove brake line retaining clips from vehicle underbody and position brake lines in underbody recess.
8. Remove rear axle attaching bolts, then lower axle slightly and support with Hangar tool No. J-29376-13 or equivalent.
9. Heat control arm bushings to 122-158°F, then remove the bushings using tools shown in **Fig. 3.**
10. Install new bushings as shown in **Fig. 3.**
11. Reverse remainder of removal procedure to complete installation. Ensure bushings are properly aligned, **Fig. 4.**

STABILIZER BAR
REPLACE

1. Raise and support rear of vehicle.
2. Remove one rear wheel and tire assembly.
3. Remove stabilizer bar attaching bolts and nuts from both sides of axle, then remove stabilizer bar toward side of vehicle less wheel.
4. Reverse procedure to install. Tighten stabilizer bar attaching bolts to torque listed at the end of this section.

TIGHTENING SPECIFICATIONS

Year	Component	Torque/ Ft. Lbs.
1992-93	Brake Anchor Plate Bolt To Rear Axle Arm	21
	Brake Pipe To Brake Hose Cap Screws	8
	Control Arm To Body Bracket Nut	70
	Rear Axle To Underbody Nut & Bolt	76
	Rear Axle To Underbody Nut & Bolt w/New Control Arm Bushing	70
	Rear Axle Wheel Spindle Nut	18
	Shock Absorber To Axle Bolt	51

Year	Component	Torque/ Ft. Lbs.
1992-93 —Cont'd	Shock Absorber To Body Mount	①
	Spindle Nut	18
	Stabilizer Shaft To Axle Nuts	59
	Wheel Hub Attaching Nuts	12
	Wheel Lug Nuts	66

①—Tighten until .36 inch of thread is exposed above top of nut.

Front Suspension & Steering

INDEX

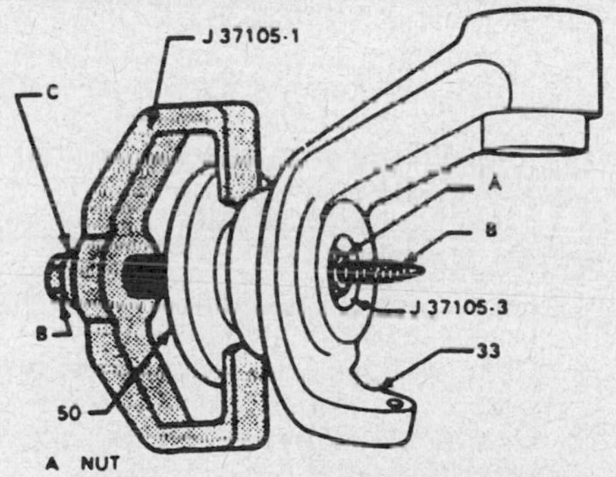

J 37105-1
C
A
B
J 37105-3
33
B
50
A NUT
B BOLT
C BEARING
33 KNUCKLE AND SUPPORT TUBE
50 HUB
GC2029100202000X

Fig. 1 Hub removal from steering knuckle

HUB & BEARING
REPLACE

1. Remove steering knuckle as outlined under "Steering Knuckle, Replace."
2. Remove hub from steering knuckle and wheel bearing using Drive Axle Separator tool No. J-37105-1 or Front Wheel Hub Remover tool No. J-37105-3 or equivalent, **Fig. 1.**
3. Using Inner Bearing Race Remover Legs tool No. J-22888-35 and Inner Bearing Race Remover Support Bracket tool No. J-22888-36 or equivalents, remove bearing race from hub, **Fig. 2.**
4. Remove snap rings retaining bearing to steering knuckle, then remove bearing using tool J-37105-1 or J-37105-3 or equivalent, **Fig. 3.**

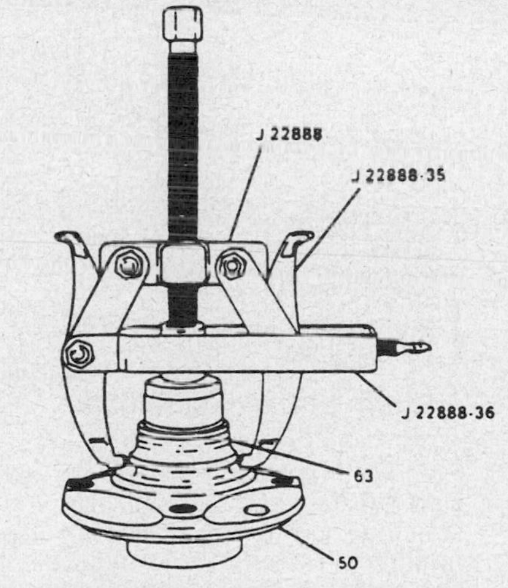

J 22888
J 22888-35
J 22888-36
63
50
50 HUB-FRONT WHEEL
63 INNER RACE
GC2029100203000X

Fig. 2 Bearing inner race removal

5. Position snap ring into steering knuckle bore, then install bearing using tool No. J-37105-1 or J-37105-3 or equivalent.
6. Using tool No. J-37105-1 or J-37105-3 or equivalent, pull hub onto bearing assembly and steering knuckle, then install snap ring.

BALL JOINT INSPECTION

1. Raise and support front of vehicle so that suspension is allowed to hang free.

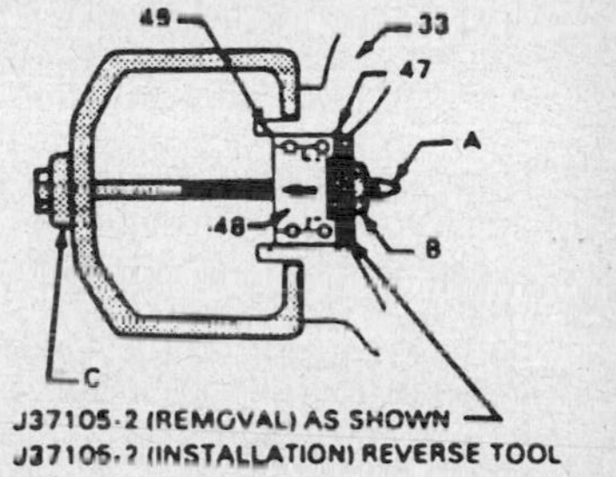

49
33
47
A
48
B
C
J37105-2 (REMOVAL) AS SHOWN
J37105-2 (INSTALLATION) REVERSE TOOL
A BOLT
B NUT
C BEARING
33 KNUCKLE AND SUPPORT TUBE
47 RING-SNAP-MUST BE REMOVED FOR BEARING REMOVAL. INSTALL AFTER HUB (50) INSTALLATION
48 BEARING-FRONT WHEEL
49 RING-SNAP-MUST BE INSTALLED FOR BEARING INSTALLATION AND REMOVED FOR BEARING REMOVAL.
GC2029100204000X

Fig. 3 Bearing removal from steering knuckle bore

2. Grasp wheel and tire assembly at 6 and 12 o'clock positions, then rock top of wheel and tire assembly inward and outward.
3. While rocking wheel and tire assembly, observe movement between steering knuckle and control arm. If any horizontal movement is present, replace ball joint.
4. If ball joint is disconnected from steering knuckle, use finger pressure to try to twist ball joint in its socket. If ball joint can be twisted in its socket, replace ball joint.

BALL JOINT
REPLACE

1. Remove control arm as previously described.
2. Drill heads off ball joint rivets, then punch out rivets using a suitable drift and remove ball joint.
3. Reverse procedure to install. Tighten ball joint retaining nuts from below the control arm to torque listed at the end of this section.

STRUT
REPLACE

Refer to "Steering Knuckle, Replace," for strut replacement procedure.

STRUT SERVICE

1. Secure strut assembly in Spring Compressor tool No. J-34013 with Adapter tool No. J-34013-87 or equivalents, **Fig. 4.**
2. Turn compressor forcing screw to compress spring slightly, then remove upper bearing dust cover.
3. Remove dampener shaft nut while using a suitable socket to prevent shaft from turning.
4. Guide dampener shaft out of strut assembly while loosening compressor screw.
5. Continue to loosen compressor screw, then remove strut dampener and spring.
6. Remove thrust washer, upper strut mount, raised edge washer and plastic mount from top of strut, **Fig. 5.**
7. Remove strut shield, upper spring insulator, spring, strut bumper and front brake shield.
8. Remove strut cartridge nut and the cartridge using Strut Cartridge Nut Wrench tool No. J-36804 or equivalent. **Exercise extreme caution as strut cartridge nut is under high torque pressure.**
9. Reverse procedure to assemble, noting the following:
   a. Install new strut cartridge nut and tighten to torque listed at the end of this section. Do not remove wax lubricant from nut.
   b. Apply suitable lubricant to upper strut bearings prior to assembly.
   c. Position spring as shown, **Fig. 6,** and move assembly upright in strut compressor before installing upper locking pin.
   d. Tighten dampener shaft nut to torque listed at the end of this section, while preventing nut from turning.

CONTROL ARM
REPLACE

1. Raise and support front of vehicle. Support vehicle on suitable jackstands placed under frame.
2. Remove wheel and tire assembly.
3. Disconnect stabilizer bar from control arm.
4. Install modified outer seal protector J-28712 or equivalent.

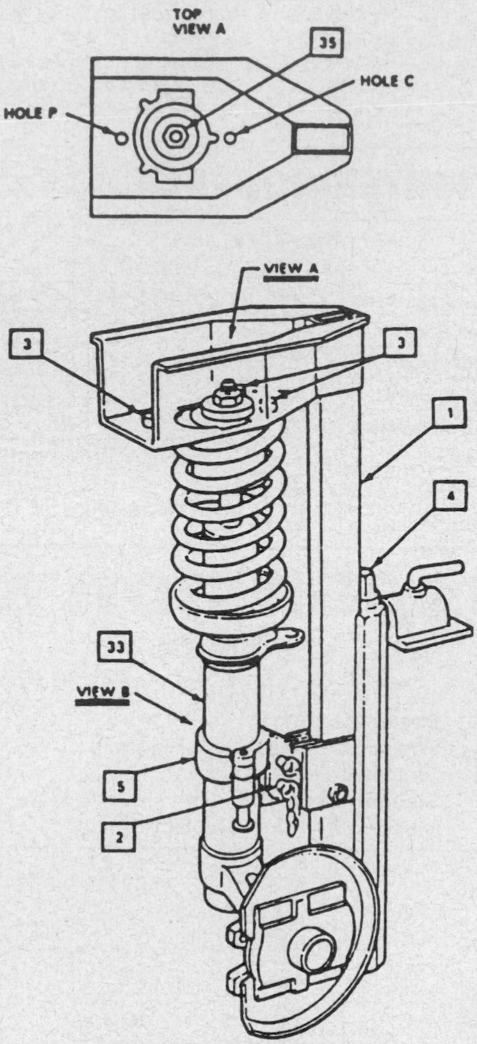
TOP
VIEW A
35
HOLE C
HOLE P
VIEW A
3
3
1
4
33
VIEW B
5
2

1. STRUT COMPRESSOR J 34013
2. INSTALL LOCKING PINS THROUGH STRUT ASSEMBLY
3. TIGHTEN NUTS TILL FLUSH WITH STRUT COMPRESSOR (SEE VIEW A)
4. COMPRESSOR FORCING SCREW
5. CLAMPING TOOL J 34013-87 (SEE VIEW B)
33. STRUT ASSEMBLY
35. NUT, PISTON ROD

GC2029100195000X

Fig. 4 Strut disassembly

5. Remove ball joint retaining clip and stud nut, then separate ball joint from steering knuckle using Ball Joint Separator tool No. J-36226 or equivalent. **Disregard "This Side Towards Wheel" marking on tool. Tool must be turned to opposite position when used on these vehicles.**
6. Remove control arm attaching bolts and the control arm.
7. If necessary, replace control arm bushings as shown in **Figs. 7 through 10.**
8. Reverse procedure to install. Tighten attachments to torque listed at the end of this section.

STEERING KNUCKLE
REPLACE

1. Loosen two upper strut to body attaching nuts, **Fig. 5.**
2. Loosen wheel lug nuts, then remove drive axle shaft retaining pin, nut and washer.
3. Raise and support front of vehicle. Support vehicle on suitable jackstands.
4. Remove wheel and tire assembly.
5. Install modified outer seal protector J-28712 or equivalent.
6. Remove brake caliper and position aside, leaving brake line attached.
7. Remove brake disc attaching screws and the disc.
8. Remove outer tie rod to steering arm attaching nuts, then separate tie rod from arm using Tie Rod Remover tool No. J-24319-01 or equivalent.
9. Remove lower ball joint retaining clip and stud nut, then separate ball joint from steering knuckle using Ball Joint Separator tool No. J-36226 or equivalent. **Disregard "This Side Towards Wheel" marking on tool. Tool must be turned to opposite position when used on these vehicles.**
10. Support drive axle, then separate the axle from front wheel hub using Drive Axle Separator tool No. J-37105 or equivalent and remove two strut to body attaching nuts and steering knuckle and strut assembly from vehicle.
11. Reverse procedure to install, noting the following:
    a. Tighten nuts and bolts to specifications.
    b. With weight of vehicle on wheels, **torque** new drive axle to hub nut to 74 ft. lbs., then back off nut and retorque to 15 ft. lbs. Tighten nut an additional 1/4 turn, then install cotter pin. If necessary, loosen nut slightly to align cotter pin holes.

STABILIZER BAR
REPLACE

1. Raise vehicle and support so that front suspension hangs free.
2. Remove front wheel and tire assemblies.
3. Disconnect stabilizer bar link assemblies from control arms, **Fig. 5.**
4. Remove stabilizer bar bracket attaching bolts, then the bushings, brackets and stabilizer bar.
5. Reverse procedure to install. Tighten stabilizer bar to body bolts to specifications and the stabilizer bar to control arm nuts to a length of 1 15/32 inch, **Fig. 11.**

STEERING GEAR
REPLACE

1. Disconnect battery ground cable.
2. **On models equipped with manual steering,** remove both pinch bolts from coupling assembly, then slide coupling up on steering spindle. Position steering wheel straight ahead as shown in **Fig. 12.**
3. **On all models,** remove air cleaner assembly.
4. Loosen both tie rods from center of steering gear housing, then pry lock plate in half, then remove both tie rod bolts from center of steering gear housing.

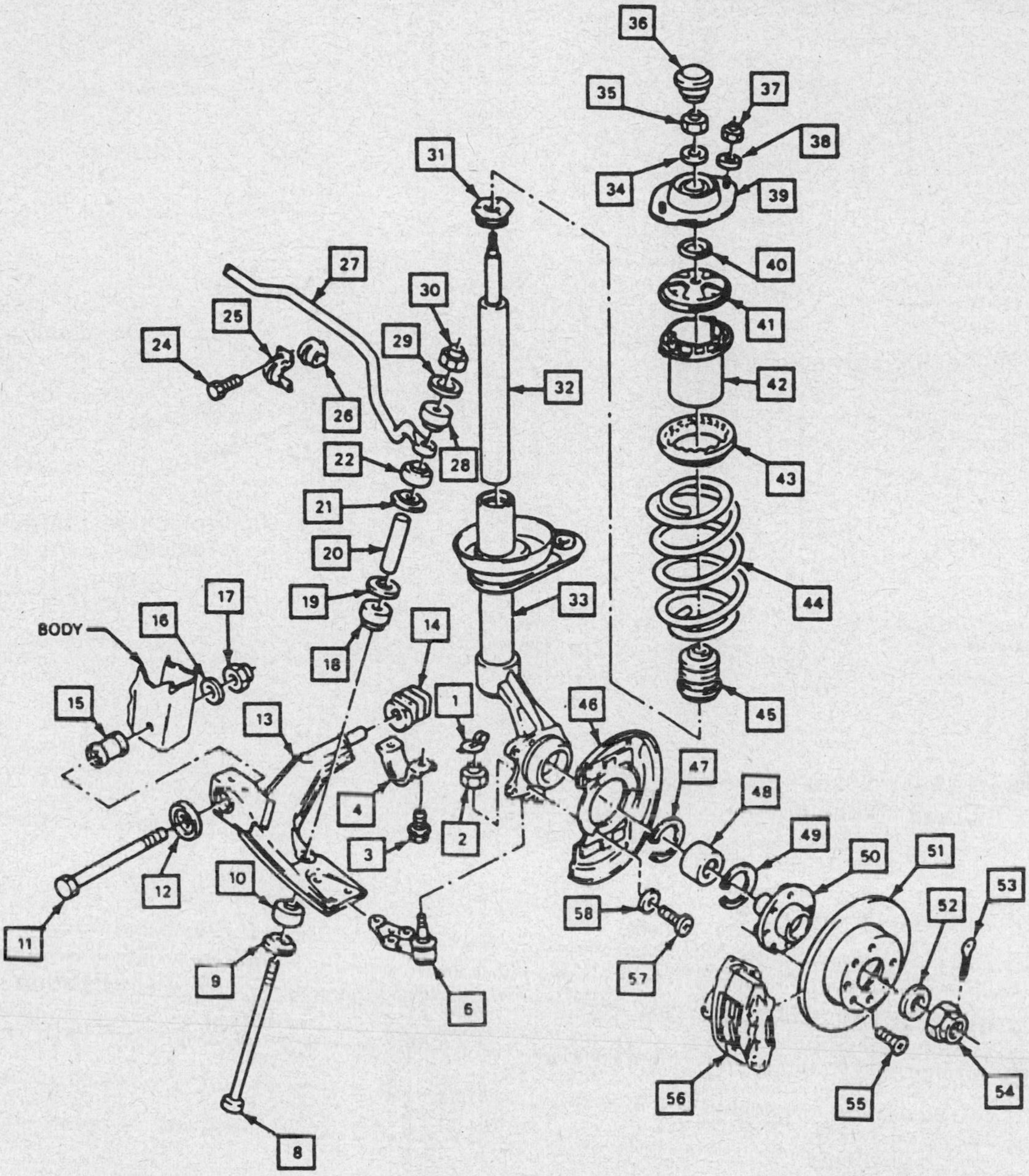
BODY
1
2
3
4
6
8
9
10
11
12
13
14
15
16
17
18
19
20
21
22
24
25
26
27
28
29
30
31
32
33
34
35
36
37
38
39
40
41
42
43
44
45
46
47
48
49
50
51
52
53
54
55
56
57
58

1. CLIP, RETAINING
2. NUT
3. BOLT
4. CLAMP, FRT STAB SHF
5.
6. BALL JOINT, LOWER CONT ARM
7.
8. BOLT
9. WASHER
10. GROMMET, STAB SHF LINK
11. BOLT
12. WASHER
13. ARM, LOWER CONTROL
14. BUSHING, LOWER CONTROL REAR
15. BUSHING, LOWER CONTROL FRONT
16. WASHER
17. NUT
18. GROMMET, STAB SHF LINK
19. WASHER
20. SPACER
21. WASHER
22. GROMMET, STAB SHF LINK
23.
24. BOLT
25. CLAMP
26. INSULATOR, STAB SHF
27. SHAFT, FRONT STAB
28. GROMMET, STAB SHF LINK
29. WASHER
30. NUT
31. NUT, STRUT CARTRIDGE CLOSURE
32. CARTRIDGE, STRUT
33. KNUCKLE/SUPT TUBE
34. WASHER, THRUST
35. NUT, PISTON ROD
36. COVER, UPPER BEARING DUST
37. NUT
38. WASHER
39. MOUNT (BEARING) UPPER STRUT
40. WASHER, RAISED EDGE
41. MOUNT (PLASTIC)
42. SHIELD, STRUT
43. INSULATOR, UPPER SPRING
44. SPRING
45. BUMPER, STRUT
46. SHIELD, FRONT BRAKE
47. RING, SNAP
48. BEARING, FRONT WHEEL
49. RING, SNAP
50. HUB, FRONT WHEEL
51. DISC, BRAKE
52. WASHER
53. PIN, COTTER
54. NUT, DRIVE SHAFT
55. SCREW, STOP
56. CALIPER, FRONT BRAKE
57. SCREW
58. WASHER

GC2029100194000X

Fig. 5 Exploded view of front suspension

5. Remove steering damper brackets and mounting clamps, then remove steering damper, then push flex coupling upward on steering spindle, as equipped.
6. **On models equipped with power steering gear,** disconnect fluid lines from gear.
7. **On models equipped with power steering,** remove steering gear and pinion flexible coupling clamp attaching bolts.

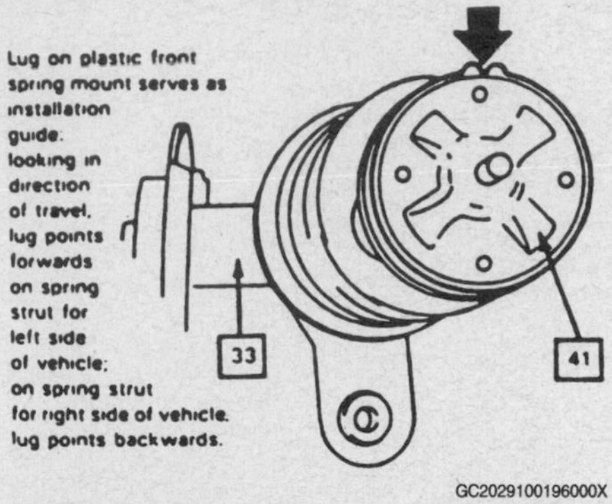

Lug on plastic front spring mount serves as installation guide: looking in direction of travel, lug points forwards on spring strut for left side of vehicle; on spring strut for right side of vehicle, lug points backwards.
33
41
GC2029100196000X

Fig. 6 Spring mount alignment

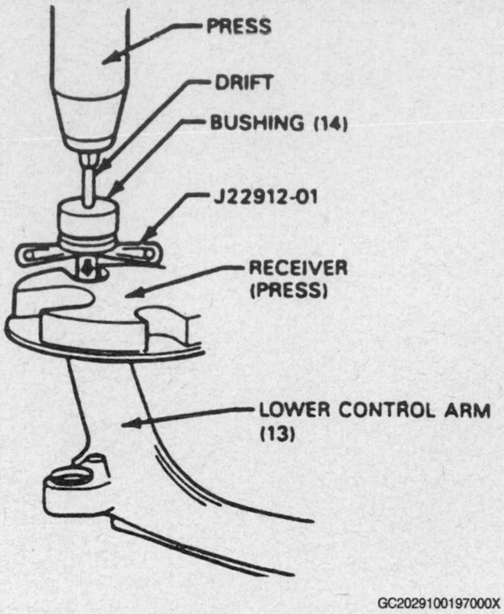

PRESS
DRIFT
BUSHING (14)
J22912-01
RECEIVER (PRESS)
LOWER CONTROL ARM (13)
GC2029100197000X

Fig. 7 Control arm rear bushing removal

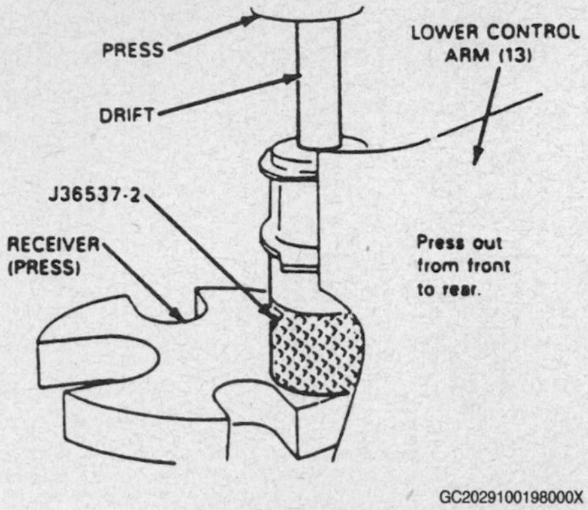

PRESS
DRIFT
LOWER CONTROL ARM (13)
J36537-2
RECEIVER (PRESS)
Press out from front to rear.
GC2029100198000X

Fig. 8 Control arm front bushing removal

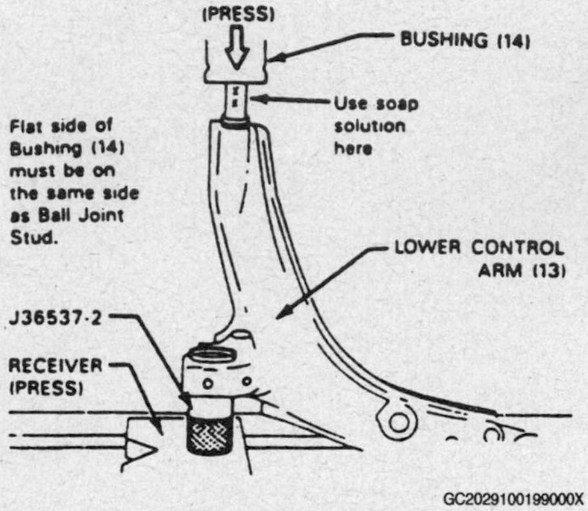

(PRESS)
BUSHING (14)
Use soap solution here
Flat side of Bushing (14) must be on the same side as Ball Joint Stud.
LOWER CONTROL ARM (13)
J36537-2
RECEIVER (PRESS)
GC2029100199000X

Fig. 9 Control arm rear bushing installation

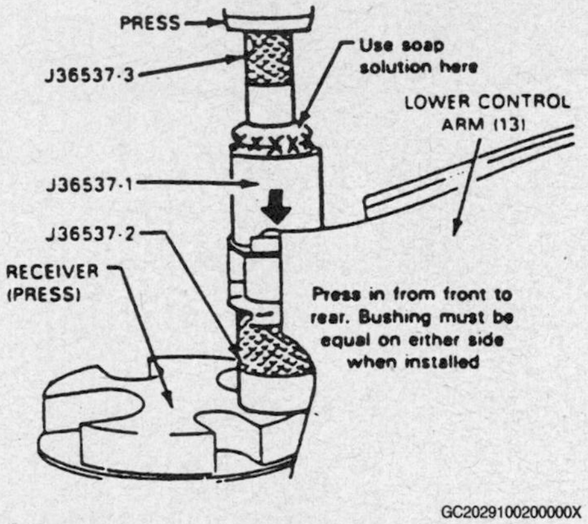

PRESS
J36537-3
Use soap solution here
LOWER CONTROL ARM (13)
J36537-1
J36537-2
RECEIVER (PRESS)
Press in from front to rear. Bushing must be equal on either side when installed
GC2029100200000X

Fig. 10 Control arm front bushing installation

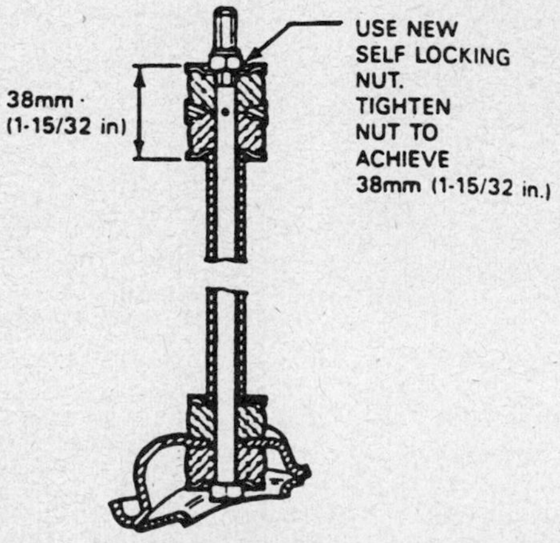

38mm (1-15/32 in)
USE NEW SELF LOCKING NUT. TIGHTEN NUT TO ACHIEVE 38mm (1-15/32 in.)
GC2029100201000X

Fig. 11 Stabilizer bar attaching nut installation

8. **On models equipped with manual steering,** remove left and right mounting clamp bolt and nut, then remove clamp.
9. **On all models,** Remove instrument panel seal from gear, then remove steering gear through righthand wheel opening.
10. Reverse procedure to install, noting the following:
    a. After second reuse of mounting clamp studs, thread locking kit No. 1052624 or equivalent must be used.
    b. Tighten mounting clamp attaching nuts to specifications.
    c. Tighten coupling to steering column attaching bolts to specifications.

POWER STEERING PUMP

REPLACE

1. Disconnect battery ground cable.
2. Remove power steering pump drive belt, then three attaching bolts and power steering pulley.
3. Disconnect fluid lines from pump.
4. Remove pump to upper timing belt cover attaching clips, then remove clips.
5. Remove power steering pump mounting bolts, then remove pump from vehicle.
6. Reverse procedure to install. After completing installation, bleed system by cycling steering wheel from side to side without contacting stops. Keep fluid at proper level during bleeding procedure.

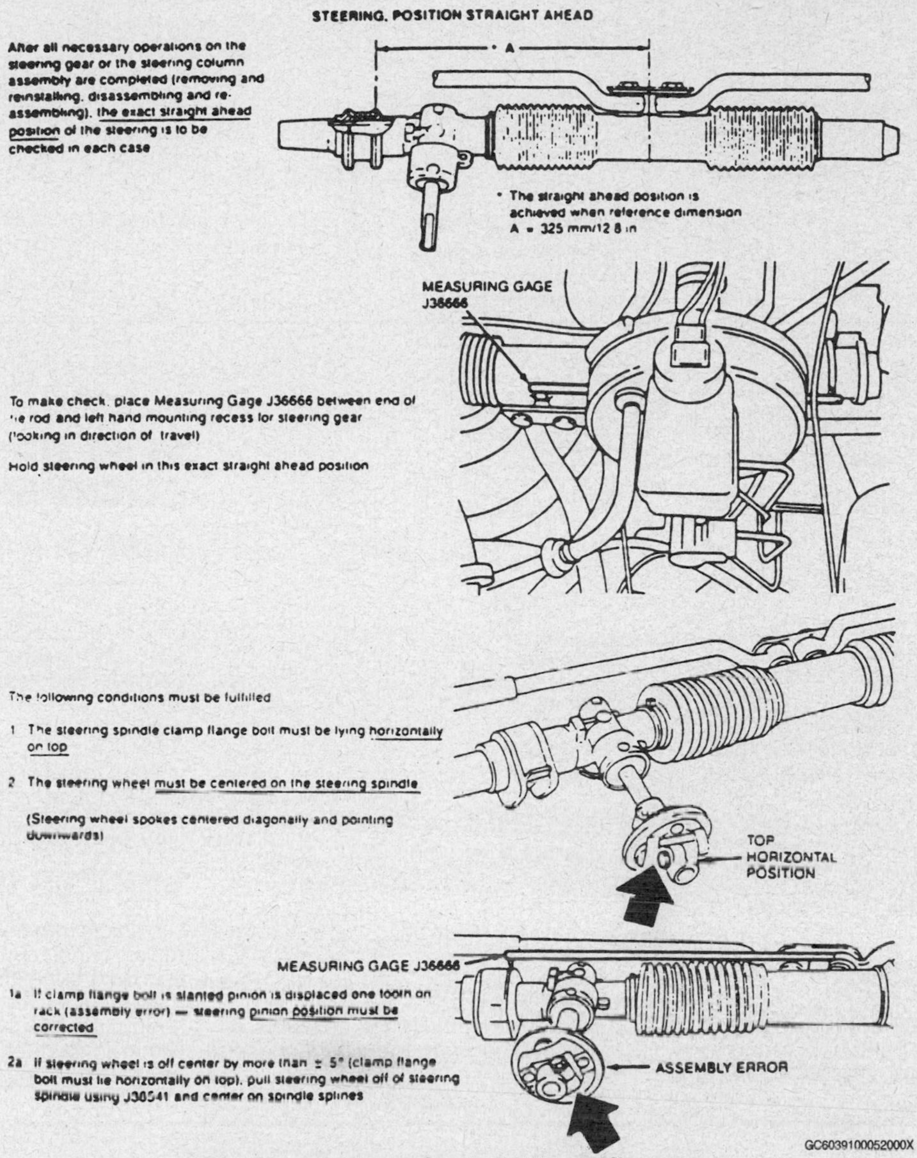
STEERING, POSITION STRAIGHT AHEAD
After all necessary operations on the steering gear or the steering column assembly are completed (removing and reinstalling, disassembling and re-assembling), the exact straight ahead position of the steering is to be checked in each case
A
* The straight ahead position is achieved when reference dimension A = 325 mm/12.8 in
MEASURING GAGE J36666
To make check, place Measuring Gage J36666 between end of tie rod and left hand mounting recess for steering gear (looking in direction of travel)
Hold steering wheel in this exact straight ahead position
The following conditions must be fulfilled
1 The steering spindle clamp flange bolt must be lying horizontally on top
2 The steering wheel must be centered on the steering spindle
(Steering wheel spokes centered diagonally and pointing downwards)
TOP HORIZONTAL POSITION
MEASURING GAGE J36666
1a If clamp flange bolt is slanted pinion is displaced one tooth on rack (assembly error) — steering pinion position must be corrected
2a If steering wheel is off center by more than ± 5° (clamp flange bolt must lie horizontally on top), pull steering wheel off of steering spindle using J36541 and center on spindle splines
ASSEMBLY ERROR
GC6039100052000X

Fig. 12 Steering wheel position adjustment

TIGHTENING SPECIFICATIONS

Year	Component	Torque/ Ft. Lbs.
1992-93	Ball Joint To Strut/Knuckle Assembly Nut	50
	Control Arm Front Mounting Bolts	100
	Control Arm Rear Mounting Bolts	50
	Disc Brake Rotor To Hub Screw	3
	Drive Axle Hub Nut	②
	Flex Coupling To Steering Shaft Clamp Bolt	16
	Flex Coupling To Stub Shaft Clamp Bolt	16
	Hub & Bearing Nut	①
	Inner Tie Rod To Steering Gear	66
	Power Steering Fluid Line Fittings	20
	Power Steering Pump Attaching Bolts	18
	Power Steering Pump Pulley Attaching Bolts	20
	Stabilizer Bar To Body Clamp Bolts	29
	Steering Damper Bracket To Steering Gear Bolts	16

Year	Component	Torque/ Ft. Lbs.
1992-93 —Cont'd	Steering Gear Mounting Clamp Bolts & Nuts	28
	Steering Gear Retaining Bracket Nuts	16
	Strut Cartridge Retaining Nut	145
	Strut Push Rod Nut	40
	Strut To Body Nuts	18
	Tie Rod End To Steering Knuckle Assembly Nut	45
	Tie Rod Pinch Bolts	16
	Wheel Lug Nuts	66

①—With weight of vehicle on wheels, torque new drive axle to hub nut to 74 ft. lbs., then back off nut and returque to 15 ft. lbs. Tighten nut an additional 1/4 turn, then install cotter pin. If required, loosen nut slightly to aling cotter pin holes.

②—Refer to text.

Wheel Alignment

INDEX

PRELIMINARY INSPECTION

1. Inspect tires for proper inflation and similar tread wear.
2. Inspect hub and bearing for excessive wear, repair as required.
3. Inspect ball joints.
4. Inspect tie rod ends for excessive looseness.
5. Check wheel and tire runout.
6. Inspect vehicle ride height.
7. Inspect rack and pinion for looseness at frame.
8. Ensure proper strut operation.
9. Check suspension and steering components for damage, replace as required.

FRONT WHEEL ALIGNMENT

CASTER & CAMBER

Front caster and camber angles are not adjustable. If caster or camber is found to be out of specifications, inspect suspension and related body components for damage and repair or replace as necessary.

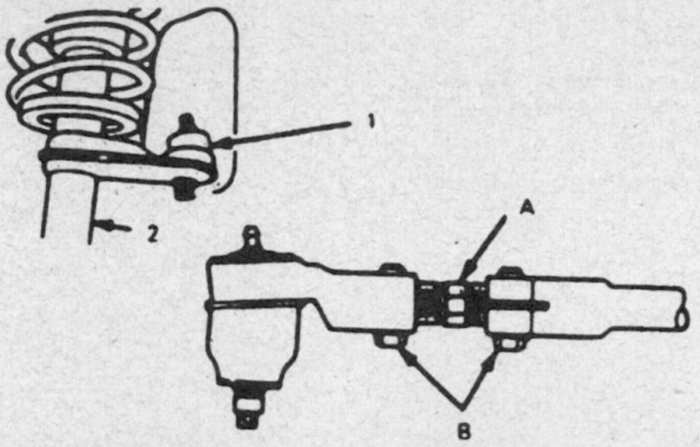
1
2
A
B
A ADJUST TOE SETTING HERE
B LOOSEN CLAMP BOLTS ADJUST TOE.
1 TIE ROD-OUTER
2 DAMPER-STRUT
GC2049100096000X

Fig. 1 Front toe adjustment

TOE

1. Loosen right and left tie rod end clamps, **Fig. 1.**
2. Turn right and left tie rod adjusters as necessary to bring toe within specifications.
3. Ensure right and left tie rods are equal in length, then **torque** clamp bolts to 15 ft. lbs.

REAR WHEEL ALIGNMENT

CASTER & CAMBER

Rear caster and camber angles are not adjustable. If caster or camber is found to be out of specifications, inspect suspension and related body components for damage and repair or replace as necessary.

TOE

Rear toe is not adjustable. If toe is found to be out of specifications, inspect rear axle assembly and wheel spindle for damage and correct as necessary.

VEHICLE RIDE HEIGHT

Vehicle trim height is measured from the rocker panel to ground. From rocker panel front to ground should be 7.7 inches. From rocker panel rear to ground, trim height should be 7.5 inches. If trim height is not within limits, check control arms, struts and ball joints for wear and damage.

AIR CONDITIONING

TABLE OF CONTENTS

System Testing

INDEX

PRECAUTIONS

R-12 SYSTEMS

The Freon refrigerant used is also known as R-12. It is colorless and odorless both as a gas and a liquid. Since it boils (vaporizes) at -21.7°F, it will usually be in a vapor state when being handled in a repair shop. But if a portion of the liquid coolant should come in contact with the hands or face, note that its temperature momentarily will be at least -22°F.

Protective goggles should be worn when opening any refrigerant lines. If liquid coolant does touch the eyes, bathe the eyes quickly in cold water, then apply a bland disinfectant oil to the eyes. See an eye doctor.

When checking a system for leaks with a torch type leak detector, do not breathe the vapors coming from the flame. Do not discharge refrigerant in the area of a live flame. A poisonous phosgene gas is produced when R-12 is burned. While the small amount of gas produced by a leak detector is not harmful unless inhaled directly at the flame, the quantity of refrigerant released into the air when a system is purged can be extremely dangerous if allowed to come into contact with an open flame.

Never allow the temperature of refrigerant drums to exceed 125°F. The excessive increase in temperature will cause a corresponding increase in pressure which may cause the safety plug to release or the drum to burst.

If it is necessary to heat a drum of refrigerant when charging a system, the drum should be placed in water no hotter than 125°F. Never use a blow torch or other open flame. If possible, a pressure release mechanism should be attached before the drum is heated.

When connecting and disconnecting service gauges on an A/C system, ensure that gauge hand valves are fully closed and that compressor service valves, if equipped, are in the back-seated (fully counterclockwise) position. Do not disconnect gauge hoses from service port adapters, if used, while gauges are connected to A/C system. To disconnect hoses, always remove adapter from service port. Do not disconnect hoses from gauge manifold while connected to A/C system, as refrigerant will be rapidly discharged.

After disconnecting gauge lines, check the valve areas to be sure service valves are correctly seated and Schraeder valves, if used, are not leaking.

R-134a SYSTEMS

R-134a refrigerant is a non toxic, nonflammable, clear colorless odorless liquified gas.

R-134a refrigerant is not compatible with R-12 refrigerant. Even small amounts of R-12 in a R-134a system will cause lubricant contamination, compressor failure or improper A/C performance. Never add R-12 to a R-134a system.

Avoid breathing R-134a refrigerant and lubricant vapor or mist. Exposure may irritate eyes, nose and throat. Use only approved service equipment to discharge R-134a systems.

TROUBLESHOOTING

SYMPTOM DIAGNOSIS CHARTS

Clutch Cycling Orifice Tube System

Refer to **Figs. 1 through 6**, for symptom troubleshooting charts.

Variable Displacement Orifice Tube System

Refer to **Figs. 7 through 13**, for symptom troubleshooting charts.

Thermal Expansion Valve System

Refer to **Figs. 14 through 21**, for symptom troubleshooting charts.

EXERCISE SYSTEM

An important fact most owners ignore is that A/C units must be used periodically. Manufacturers caution that when the air conditioner is not used regularly, particularly during the cold months, it should be turned on for a few minutes once every two or three weeks while the engine is running. This keeps the system in good operating condition.

Checking out the system for the effects of disuse before the onset of summer is one of the most important aspects of A/C servicing.

First clean out the condenser core, mounted in all cases at the front of the radiator. All obstructions, such as leaves, bugs or dirt, must be removed, as they will reduce heat transfer and impair the effi-

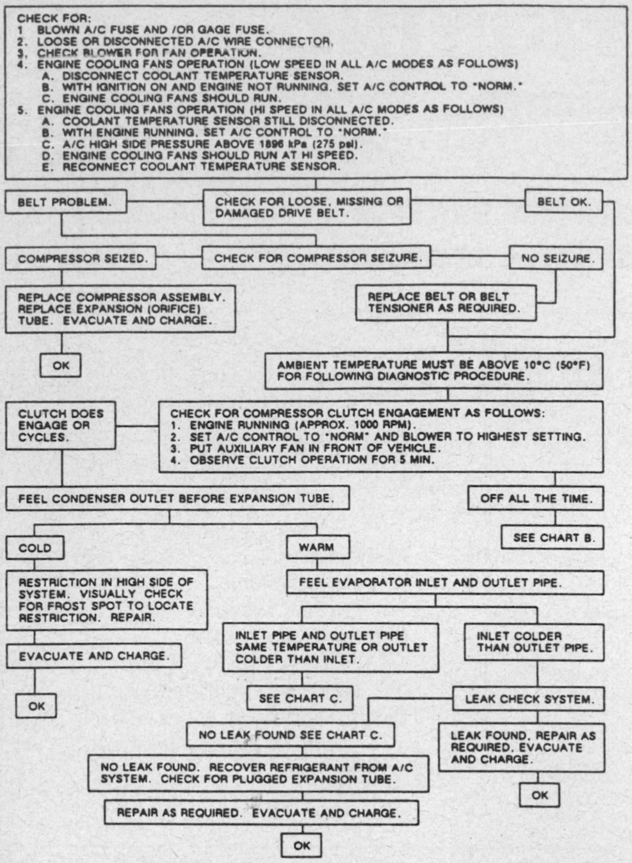

CHECK FOR:
1 BLOWN A/C FUSE AND /OR GAGE FUSE.
2. LOOSE OR DISCONNECTED A/C WIRE CONNECTOR.
3. CHECK BLOWER FOR FAN OPERATION.
4. ENGINE COOLING FANS OPERATION (LOW SPEED IN ALL A/C MODES AS FOLLOWS)
A. DISCONNECT COOLANT TEMPERATURE SENSOR.
B. WITH IGNITION ON AND ENGINE NOT RUNNING, SET A/C CONTROL TO "NORM."
C. ENGINE COOLING FANS SHOULD RUN.
5. ENGINE COOLING FANS OPERATION (HI SPEED IN ALL A/C MODES AS FOLLOWS)
A. COOLANT TEMPERATURE SENSOR STILL DISCONNECTED.
B. WITH ENGINE RUNNING, SET A/C CONTROL TO "NORM."
C. A/C HIGH SIDE PRESSURE ABOVE 1896 kPa (275 psi).
D. ENGINE COOLING FANS SHOULD RUN AT HI SPEED.
E. RECONNECT COOLANT TEMPERATURE SENSOR.
BELT PROBLEM.
CHECK FOR LOOSE, MISSING OR DAMAGED DRIVE BELT.
BELT OK.
COMPRESSOR SEIZED.
CHECK FOR COMPRESSOR SEIZURE.
NO SEIZURE.
REPLACE COMPRESSOR ASSEMBLY. REPLACE EXPANSION (ORIFICE) TUBE. EVACUATE AND CHARGE.
REPLACE BELT OR BELT TENSIONER AS REQUIRED.
OK
AMBIENT TEMPERATURE MUST BE ABOVE 10°C (50°F) FOR FOLLOWING DIAGNOSTIC PROCEDURE.
CLUTCH DOES ENGAGE OR CYCLES.
CHECK FOR COMPRESSOR CLUTCH ENGAGEMENT AS FOLLOWS:
1. ENGINE RUNNING (APPROX. 1000 RPM).
2. SET A/C CONTROL TO "NORM" AND BLOWER TO HIGHEST SETTING.
3. PUT AUXILIARY FAN IN FRONT OF VEHICLE.
4. OBSERVE CLUTCH OPERATION FOR 5 MIN.
FEEL CONDENSER OUTLET BEFORE EXPANSION TUBE.
OFF ALL THE TIME.
SEE CHART B.
COLD
WARM
RESTRICTION IN HIGH SIDE OF SYSTEM. VISUALLY CHECK FOR FROST SPOT TO LOCATE RESTRICTION. REPAIR.
FEEL EVAPORATOR INLET AND OUTLET PIPE.
INLET PIPE AND OUTLET PIPE SAME TEMPERATURE OR OUTLET COLDER THAN INLET.
INLET COLDER THAN OUTLET PIPE.
EVACUATE AND CHARGE.
OK
SEE CHART C.
LEAK CHECK SYSTEM.
NO LEAK FOUND SEE CHART C.
LEAK FOUND, REPAIR AS REQUIRED, EVACUATE AND CHARGE.
NO LEAK FOUND. RECOVER REFRIGERANT FROM A/C SYSTEM. CHECK FOR PLUGGED EXPANSION TUBE.
OK
REPAIR AS REQUIRED. EVACUATE AND CHARGE.
OK
GC7029100028000X

Fig. 1 Troubleshooting chart A. 1992–93 models w/clutch cycling orifice tube system

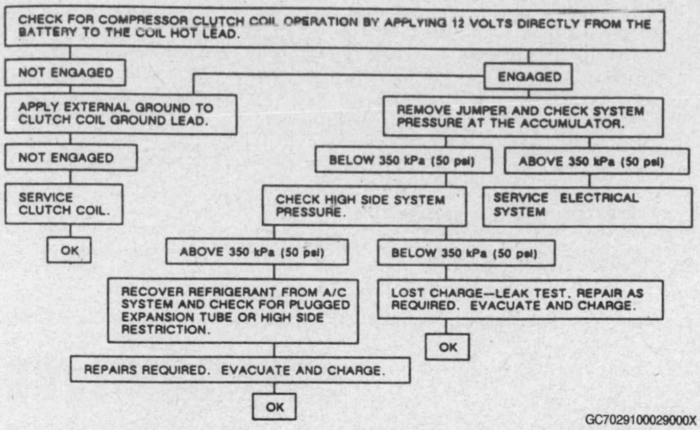

CHECK FOR COMPRESSOR CLUTCH COIL OPERATION BY APPLYING 12 VOLTS DIRECTLY FROM THE BATTERY TO THE COIL HOT LEAD.
NOT ENGAGED
ENGAGED
APPLY EXTERNAL GROUND TO CLUTCH COIL GROUND LEAD.
REMOVE JUMPER AND CHECK SYSTEM PRESSURE AT THE ACCUMULATOR.
NOT ENGAGED
BELOW 350 kPa (50 psi)
ABOVE 350 kPa (50 psi)
SERVICE CLUTCH COIL.
CHECK HIGH SIDE SYSTEM PRESSURE.
SERVICE ELECTRICAL SYSTEM
OK
ABOVE 350 kPa (50 psi)
BELOW 350 kPa (50 psi)
RECOVER REFRIGERANT FROM A/C SYSTEM AND CHECK FOR PLUGGED EXPANSION TUBE OR HIGH SIDE RESTRICTION.
LOST CHARGE—LEAK TEST, REPAIR AS REQUIRED. EVACUATE AND CHARGE.
OK
REPAIRS REQUIRED. EVACUATE AND CHARGE.
OK
GC7029100029000X

Fig. 2 Troubleshooting chart B. 1992–93 models w/clutch cycling orifice tube system

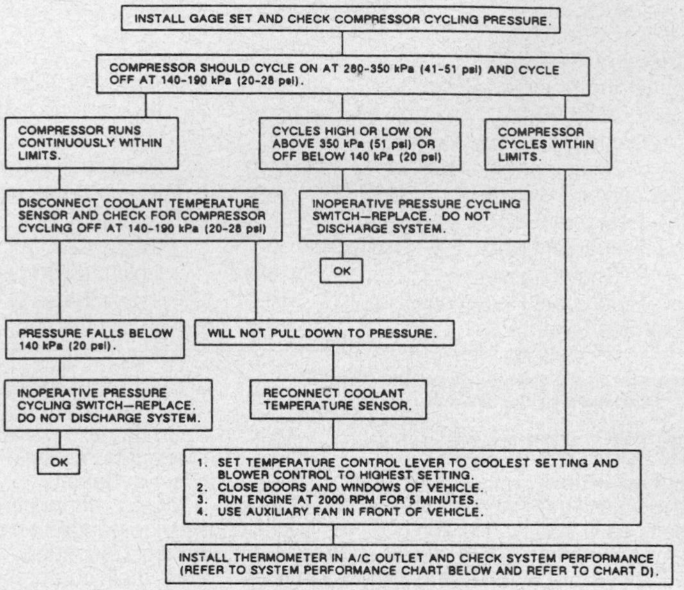

INSTALL GAGE SET AND CHECK COMPRESSOR CYCLING PRESSURE.
COMPRESSOR SHOULD CYCLE ON AT 280-350 kPa (41-51 psi) AND CYCLE OFF AT 140-190 kPa (20-28 psi).
COMPRESSOR RUNS CONTINUOUSLY WITHIN LIMITS.
CYCLES HIGH OR LOW ON ABOVE 350 kPa (51 psi) OR OFF BELOW 140 kPa (20 psi)
COMPRESSOR CYCLES WITHIN LIMITS.
DISCONNECT COOLANT TEMPERATURE SENSOR AND CHECK FOR COMPRESSOR CYCLING OFF AT 140-190 kPa (20-28 psi)
INOPERATIVE PRESSURE CYCLING SWITCH—REPLACE. DO NOT DISCHARGE SYSTEM.
OK
PRESSURE FALLS BELOW 140 kPa (20 psi).
WILL NOT PULL DOWN TO PRESSURE.
INOPERATIVE PRESSURE CYCLING SWITCH—REPLACE. DO NOT DISCHARGE SYSTEM.
RECONNECT COOLANT TEMPERATURE SENSOR.
OK
1. SET TEMPERATURE CONTROL LEVER TO COOLEST SETTING AND BLOWER CONTROL TO HIGHEST SETTING.
2. CLOSE DOORS AND WINDOWS OF VEHICLE.
3. RUN ENGINE AT 2000 RPM FOR 5 MINUTES.
4. USE AUXILIARY FAN IN FRONT OF VEHICLE.
INSTALL THERMOMETER IN A/C OUTLET AND CHECK SYSTEM PERFORMANCE (REFER TO SYSTEM PERFORMANCE CHART BELOW AND REFER TO CHART D).

PERFORMANCE CHART

TEMPERATURE OF AIR ENTERING CONDENSER	°F (°C)	70 (21)	80 (27)	90 (32)	100 (38)
COMPRESSOR HIGH PRESSURE	psi (kPa)	135-170 (950-1200)	165-200 (1150-1400)	200-245 (1400-1700)	245-300 (1700-2050)
ACCUMULATOR PRESSURE	psi kPa)	22-28 (150-193)	22-29 (150-200)	26-35 (180-240)	30-40 (205-275)
AVERAGE A/C AIR DISCHARGE	°F (°C)	36-43 (2.2-6.0)	36-43 (2.2-6.0)	36-43 (2.2-6.0)	42-48 (5.50-9.0)

GC7029100030000X

Fig. 3 Troubleshooting chart C. 1992–93 models w/clutch cycling orifice tube system

ciency of the system. Make sure the space between the condenser and the radiator also is free of foreign matter.

Make certain the evaporator water drain is open. The evaporator cools and dehumidifies the air before it enters the passenger compartment; there, the refrigerant is changed from a liquid to a vapor. As the core cools the air, moisture condenses on it but is prevented from collecting in the evaporator by the water drain.

PERFORMANCE TEST

The system should be operated for at least 15 minutes to allow sufficient time for all parts to become completely stabilized. Determine if the system is fully charged by the use of test gauges and sight glass if one is installed on system. Head pressure will read from 180 psi to 220 psi or higher, depending upon ambient temperature and the type of unit being tested. The sight glass should be free of bubbles. Low side pressures should read approximately 15-30 psi, depending on the ambient temperature and the unit being tested. The type of control and component installation used on a particular system will directly influence the pressure readings on the high and low sides, **Fig. 22**.

The high side pressure will be affected by the ambient or outside air temperature. A system that is operating normally will indicate a high side gauge reading between 150-170 psi with an 80°F ambient temperature. The same system will register 210-230 psi with an ambient temperature of 100°. No two systems will register exactly the same, therefore, allowance for variations in head pressures must be considered. Refer to **Fig. 23**for the most important normal readings likely to be encountered during the season.

RELATIVE TEMPERATURE OF HIGH & LOW SIDES

The high side of the system should be uniformly hot to the touch throughout. A difference in temperature will indicate a partial blockage of liquid or gas at this point.

The low side of the system should be uniformly cool to the touch with no excessive sweating of the suction line or low side service valve. Excessive sweating or frosting of the low side service valve usually indicates an expansion valve is allowing an excessive amount of refrigerant into the evaporator.

EVAPORATOR OUTPUT

At this point, provided all other inspection tests have been performed, and components have been found to operate as they should, a rapid cooling down of the interior of the vehicle should result. The use of a thermometer is not necessary to de-

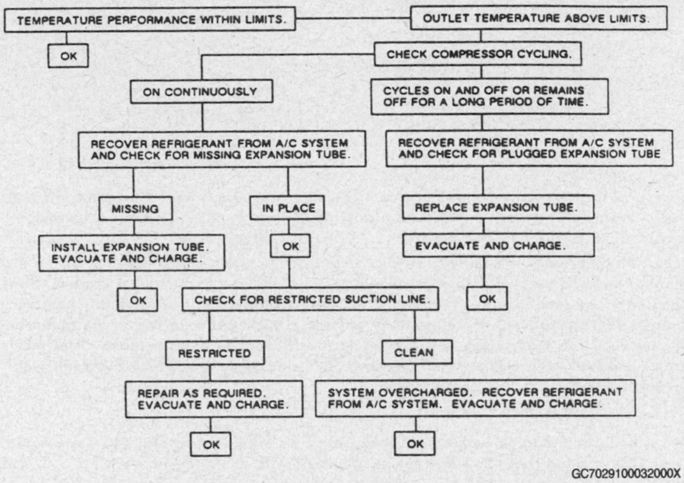
TEMPERATURE PERFORMANCE WITHIN LIMITS.
OUTLET TEMPERATURE ABOVE LIMITS.
OK
CHECK COMPRESSOR CYCLING.
ON CONTINUOUSLY
CYCLES ON AND OFF OR REMAINS OFF FOR A LONG PERIOD OF TIME.
RECOVER REFRIGERANT FROM A/C SYSTEM AND CHECK FOR MISSING EXPANSION TUBE.
RECOVER REFRIGERANT FROM A/C SYSTEM AND CHECK FOR PLUGGED EXPANSION TUBE
MISSING
IN PLACE
REPLACE EXPANSION TUBE.
INSTALL EXPANSION TUBE. EVACUATE AND CHARGE.
OK
EVACUATE AND CHARGE.
OK
CHECK FOR RESTRICTED SUCTION LINE.
OK
RESTRICTED
CLEAN
REPAIR AS REQUIRED. EVACUATE AND CHARGE.
SYSTEM OVERCHARGED. RECOVER REFRIGERANT FROM A/C SYSTEM. EVACUATE AND CHARGE.
OK
OK
GC7029100032000X

Fig. 4 Troubleshooting chart D. 1992–93 models w/clutch cycling orifice tube system

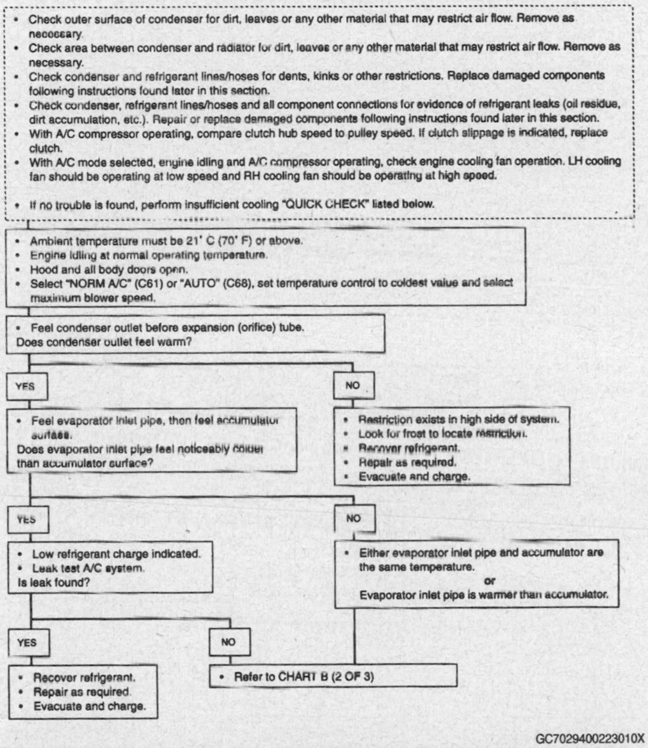
• Check outer surface of condenser for dirt, leaves or any other material that may restrict air flow. Remove as necessary.
• Check area between condenser and radiator for dirt, leaves or any other material that may restrict air flow. Remove as necessary.
• Check condenser and refrigerant lines/hoses for dents, kinks or other restrictions. Replace damaged components following instructions found later in this section.
• Check condenser, refrigerant lines/hoses and all component connections for evidence of refrigerant leaks (oil residue, dirt accumulation, etc.). Repair or replace damaged components following instructions found later in this section.
• With A/C compressor operating, compare clutch hub speed to pulley speed. If clutch slippage is indicated, replace clutch.
• With A/C mode selected, engine idling and A/C compressor operating, check engine cooling fan operation. LH cooling fan should be operating at low speed and RH cooling fan should be operating at high speed.
• If no trouble is found, perform insufficient cooling "QUICK CHECK" listed below.
• Ambient temperature must be 21° C (70° F) or above.
• Engine idling at normal operating temperature.
• Hood and all body doors open.
• Select "NORM A/C" (C61) or "AUTO" (C68), set temperature control to coldest value and select maximum blower speed.
• Feel condenser outlet before expansion (orifice) tube.
Does condenser outlet feel warm?
YES
NO
• Feel evaporator inlet pipe, then feel accumulator surface.
Does evaporator inlet pipe feel noticeably colder than accumulator surface?
• Restriction exists in high side of system.
• Look for frost to locate restriction.
• Recover refrigerant.
• Repair as required.
• Evacuate and charge.
YES
NO
• Low refrigerant charge indicated.
• Leak test A/C system.
Is leak found?
• Either evaporator inlet pipe and accumulator are the same temperature.
or
Evaporator inlet pipe is warmer than accumulator.
YES
NO
• Recover refrigerant.
• Repair as required.
• Evacuate and charge.
• Refer to CHART B (2 OF 3)
GC7029400223010X

Fig. 6 Troubleshooting chart B (Insufficient cooling, part 1 of 3). 1994 models w/clutch cycling orifice tube system

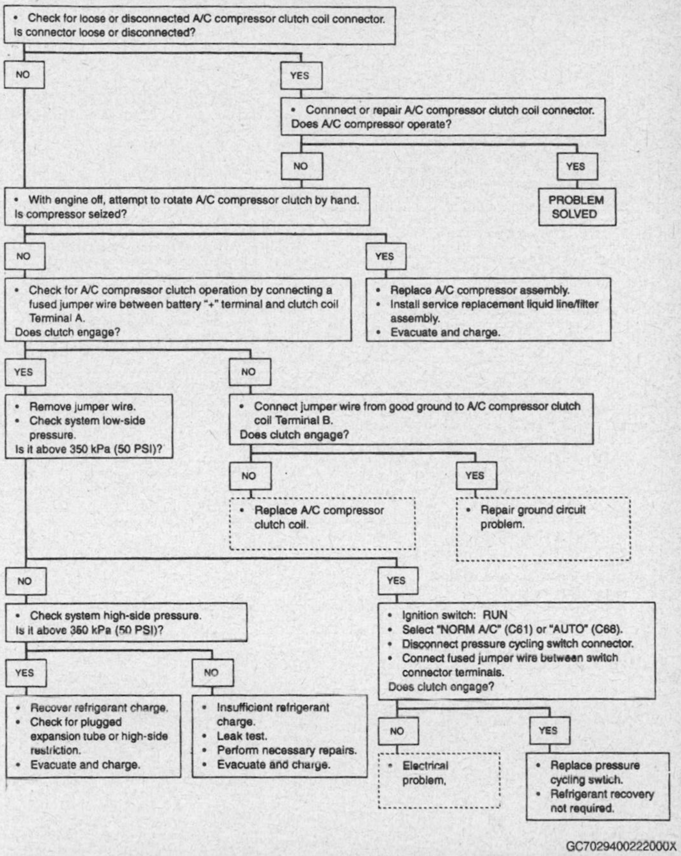
• Check for loose or disconnected A/C compressor clutch coil connector.
Is connector loose or disconnected?
NO
YES
• Connnect or repair A/C compressor clutch coil connector.
Does A/C compressor operate?
NO
YES
• With engine off, attempt to rotate A/C compressor clutch by hand.
Is compressor seized?
PROBLEM SOLVED
NO
YES
• Check for A/C compressor clutch operation by connecting a fused jumper wire between battery "+" terminal and clutch coil Terminal A.
Does clutch engage?
• Replace A/C compressor assembly.
• Install service replacement liquid line/filter assembly.
• Evacuate and charge.
YES
NO
• Remove jumper wire.
• Check system low-side pressure.
Is it above 350 kPa (50 PSI)?
• Connect jumper wire from good ground to A/C compressor clutch coil Terminal B.
Does clutch engage?
NO
YES
• Replace A/C compressor clutch coil.
• Repair ground circuit problem.
NO
YES
• Check system high-side pressure.
Is it above 350 kPa (50 PSI)?
• Ignition switch: RUN
• Select "NORM A/C" (C61) or "AUTO" (C68).
• Disconnect pressure cycling switch connector.
• Connect fused jumper wire between switch connector terminals.
Does clutch engage?
YES
NO
• Recover refrigerant charge.
• Check for plugged expansion tube or high-side restriction.
• Evacuate and charge.
• Insufficient refrigerant charge.
• Leak test.
• Perform necessary repairs.
• Evacuate and charge.
NO
YES
• Electrical problem.
• Replace pressure cycling switch.
• Refrigerant recovery not required.
GC7029400222000X

Fig. 5 Troubleshooting chart A (A/C compressor does not operate). 1994 models w/clutch cycling orifice tube system

termine evaporator output. Bringing all units to the correct operating specifications will insure that the evaporator performs as intended.

LEAK TEST

Testing the refrigerant system for leaks is one of the most important phases of troubleshooting. One or more of the methods outlined will prove useful in detecting leaks or checking connections if service work is performed. Before beginning any leak test, attach a manifold gauge set and note pressure. If little or no pressure is indicated, a partial charge must be installed. Check all connections, compressor head gasket, oil filler plug and compressor shaft seal for leaks.

ELECTRONIC LEAK DETECTORS

There are a number of electronic leak detectors available to perform leak tests. Current versions of the electronic leak detectors have three settings, one for R-12, one for R-134a and one for gross. The gross setting is for isolating very large leaks already found in one of the other two settings. Refer to operating instructions for the unit being used and observe these general procedures.

1. Move detector probe one inch per second in areas of suspected leaks.
2. Position probe below test point, as refrigerant gas is heavier than air.
3. Be sure to check service access gauge port valve fittings, particularly when valve caps are missing, as dirt accumulations can destroy the sealing area of valve core when manifold gauge set is attached. Replace missing valve caps after cleaning valve core area. **Valve caps should only be finger tightened. Using pliers to tighten valve caps may distort sealing surface of valve.**
4. Check for leaks in manifold gauge set and hoses, as well as the rest of the system.

FLAME-TYPE (HALIDE) LEAK DETECTORS

1. Adjust detector flame as low as possible to obtain maximum sensitivity. Be sure copper element is cherry red and not burned away. The flame will be almost colorless.
2. Slowly move detector along areas of suspected leaks. A slight leak will cause the flame to change to a bright yellow-green color. A significant leak will be indicated by a brilliant blue flame. Position flame under areas being tested as refrigerant gas is heavier than air. **The presence of dust in the pickup hose may cause a change**

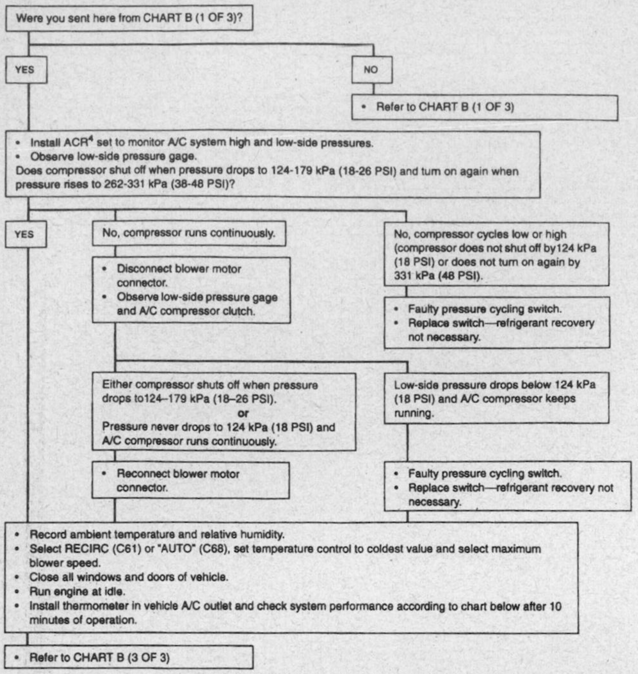
Were you sent here from CHART B (1 OF 3)?
YES
NO
• Refer to CHART B (1 OF 3)
• Install ACR4 set to monitor A/C system high and low-side pressures.
• Observe low-side pressure gage.
Does compressor shut off when pressure drops to 124-179 kPa (18-26 PSI) and turn on again when pressure rises to 262-331 kPa (38-48 PSI)?
YES
No, compressor runs continuously.
No, compressor cycles low or high (compressor does not shut off by 124 kPa (18 PSI) or does not turn on again by 331 kPa (48 PSI).
• Disconnect blower motor connector.
• Observe low-side pressure gage and A/C compressor clutch.
• Faulty pressure cycling switch.
• Replace switch—refrigerant recovery not necessary.
Either compressor shuts off when pressure drops to124–179 kPa (18–26 PSI).
or
Pressure never drops to 124 kPa (18 PSI) and A/C compressor runs continuously.
Low-side pressure drops below 124 kPa (18 PSI) and A/C compressor keeps running.
• Reconnect blower motor connector.
• Faulty pressure cycling switch.
• Replace switch—refrigerant recovery not necessary.
• Record ambient temperature and relative humidity.
• Select RECIRC (C61) or "AUTO" (C68), set temperature control to coldest value and select maximum blower speed.
• Close all windows and doors of vehicle.
• Run engine at idle.
• Install thermometer in vehicle A/C outlet and check system performance according to chart below after 10 minutes of operation.
• Refer to CHART B (3 OF 3)
GC7029400223020X

Fig. 6 Troubleshooting chart B (Insufficient cooling, part 2 of 3). 1994 models w/clutch cycling orifice tube system

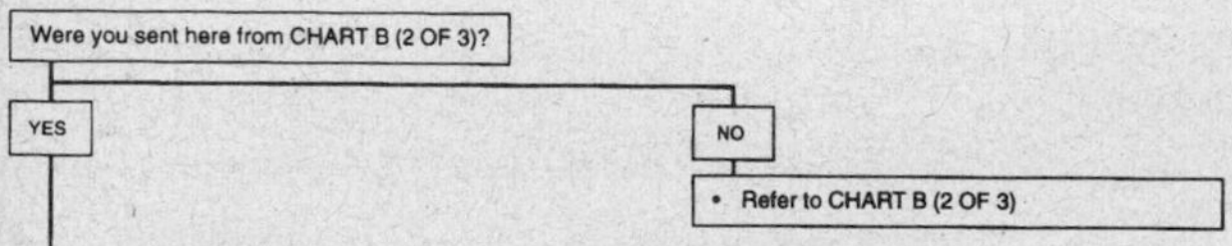
Were you sent here from CHART B (2 OF 3)?
YES
NO
• Refer to CHART B (2 OF 3)

SYSTEM PERFORMANCE CHART				
Temperature	Humidity	Low Side Service Port Pressure (in PSIG)	High Side Service Port Pressure (in PSIG)	A/C Discharge Temperature
21° C (70° F)	Low (≤50%)	25-30	140-190	6-9° C (43-48° F)
	High (>50%)	31-36	165-205	11-14° C (52-57° F)
27° C (80° F)	Low (≤50%)	26-32	150-200	7-11° C (45-51° F)
	High (>50%)	35-43	190-240	13-17° C (56-62° F)
32° C (90° F)	Low (≤40%)	31-37	170-220	10-13° C (50-56° F)
	High (>40%)	40-48	210-260	16-19° C (61-67° F)
38° C (100° F)	Low (≤20%)	35-43	195-245	12-16° C (54-50° F)
	High (>20%)	44-52	230-280	17-21° C (63-69° F)
43° C (110° F)	Low (≤20%)	40-48	235-285	14-18° C (58-64° F)
	High (>20%)	46-54	260-310	18-21° C (64-70° F)

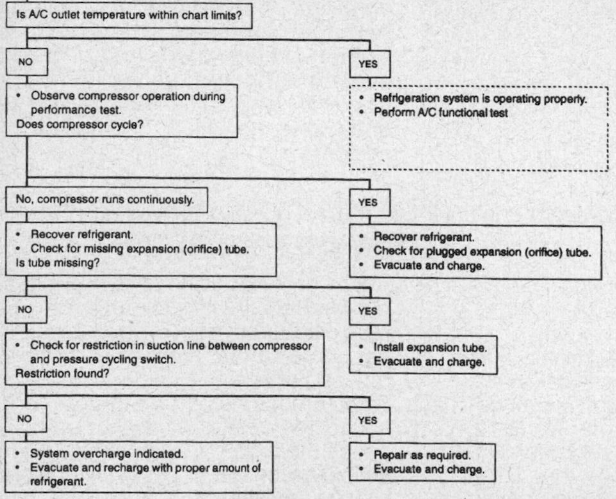
Is A/C outlet temperature within chart limits?
NO
YES
• Observe compressor operation during performance test.
Does compressor cycle?
• Refrigeration system is operating properly.
• Perform A/C functional test
No, compressor runs continuously.
YES
• Recover refrigerant.
• Check for missing expansion (orifice) tube.
Is tube missing?
• Recover refrigerant.
• Check for plugged expansion (orifice) tube.
• Evacuate and charge.
NO
YES
• Check for restriction in suction line between compressor and pressure cycling switch.
Restriction found?
• Install expansion tube.
• Evacuate and charge.
NO
YES
• System overcharge indicated.
• Evacuate and recharge with proper amount of refrigerant.
• Repair as required.
• Evacuate and charge.
GC7029400223030X

Fig. 6 Troubleshooting chart B (Insufficient cooling, part 3 of 3). 1994 models w/clutch cycling orifice tube system

Diagnostic Procedures
For
Variable Displacement Orifice Tube (VDOT)
Systems

The procedures in the following charts will help you diagnose V5 compressor and VDOT refrigerant system problems causing <u>insufficient cooling</u>. They must be used in conjunction with other appropriate manual information.

The V5 compressor is a variable displacement compressor which matches air conditioning demand by changing its stroke, instead of cycling its clutch. A control valve located in the rear head of the compressor senses compressor low side pressure and causes the compressor mechanism to change stroke. Because the V5 compressor always runs and the system does not cycle, these diagnostic procedures differ from those used for fixed displacement systems. By using these procedures, you will avoid needlessly replacing A/C components.

STEP 1--*Preliminary Checks*

Repair the following as necessary. If discharge air temperature with A/C on is normal after making the following repairs, the system is operating properly.

- A/C fuse
- A/C blower operation.
- Temperature door. Move temp. door lever rapidly from cold to hot. Listen for temp. door hitting at each end. Adjust as necessary. (Cable operated temp. door only.).
- Clutch coil and rear head switch(es) connections.
- Compressor belt. Adjust or replace if damaged or missing.
- Engine cooling fan operation.
- Condenser - Check for restricted air flow.

GC7029100031000X

Fig. 7 Troubleshooting step 1. Variable displacement orifice tube system

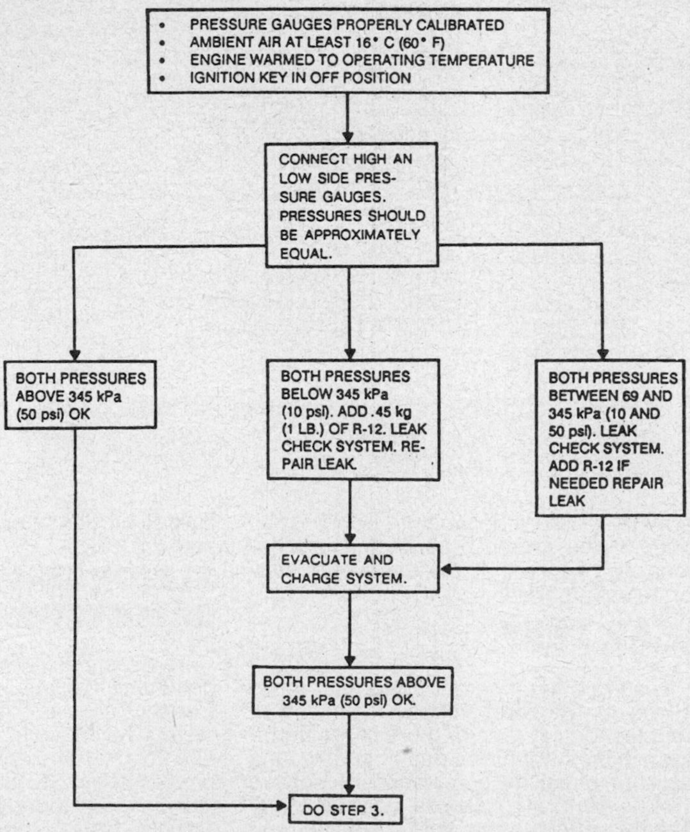
• PRESSURE GAUGES PROPERLY CALIBRATED
• AMBIENT AIR AT LEAST 16° C (60° F)
• ENGINE WARMED TO OPERATING TEMPERATURE
• IGNITION KEY IN OFF POSITION
CONNECT HIGH AN LOW SIDE PRESSURE GAUGES. PRESSURES SHOULD BE APPROXIMATELY EQUAL.
BOTH PRESSURES ABOVE 345 kPa (50 psi) OK
BOTH PRESSURES BELOW 345 kPa (10 psi). ADD .45 kg (1 LB.) OF R-12. LEAK CHECK SYSTEM. REPAIR LEAK.
BOTH PRESSURES BETWEEN 69 AND 345 kPa (10 AND 50 psi). LEAK CHECK SYSTEM. ADD R-12 IF NEEDED REPAIR LEAK
EVACUATE AND CHARGE SYSTEM.
BOTH PRESSURES ABOVE 345 kPa (50 psi) OK.
DO STEP 3.
GC7029100033000X

Fig. 8 Troubleshooting step 2. Variable displacement orifice tube system

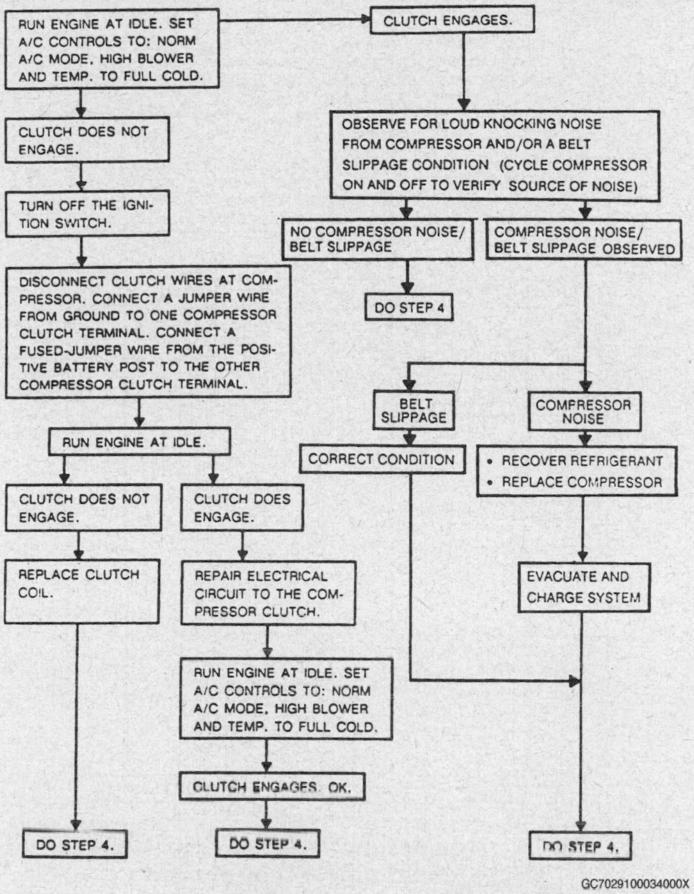
RUN ENGINE AT IDLE. SET A/C CONTROLS TO: NORM A/C MODE, HIGH BLOWER AND TEMP. TO FULL COLD.
CLUTCH ENGAGES.
CLUTCH DOES NOT ENGAGE.
TURN OFF THE IGNITION SWITCH.
DISCONNECT CLUTCH WIRES AT COMPRESSOR. CONNECT A JUMPER WIRE FROM GROUND TO ONE COMPRESSOR CLUTCH TERMINAL. CONNECT A FUSED-JUMPER WIRE FROM THE POSITIVE BATTERY POST TO THE OTHER COMPRESSOR CLUTCH TERMINAL.
RUN ENGINE AT IDLE.
CLUTCH DOES NOT ENGAGE.
CLUTCH DOES ENGAGE.
REPLACE CLUTCH COIL.
REPAIR ELECTRICAL CIRCUIT TO THE COMPRESSOR CLUTCH.
RUN ENGINE AT IDLE. SET A/C CONTROLS TO: NORM A/C MODE, HIGH BLOWER AND TEMP. TO FULL COLD.
CLUTCH ENGAGES. OK.
DO STEP 4.
DO STEP 4.
OBSERVE FOR LOUD KNOCKING NOISE FROM COMPRESSOR AND/OR A BELT SLIPPAGE CONDITION (CYCLE COMPRESSOR ON AND OFF TO VERIFY SOURCE OF NOISE)
NO COMPRESSOR NOISE/ BELT SLIPPAGE
COMPRESSOR NOISE/ BELT SLIPPAGE OBSERVED
DO STEP 4
BELT SLIPPAGE
COMPRESSOR NOISE
CORRECT CONDITION
• RECOVER REFRIGERANT
• REPLACE COMPRESSOR
EVACUATE AND CHARGE SYSTEM
DO STEP 4.
GC7029100034000X

Fig. 9 Troubleshooting step 3. Variable displacement orifice tube system

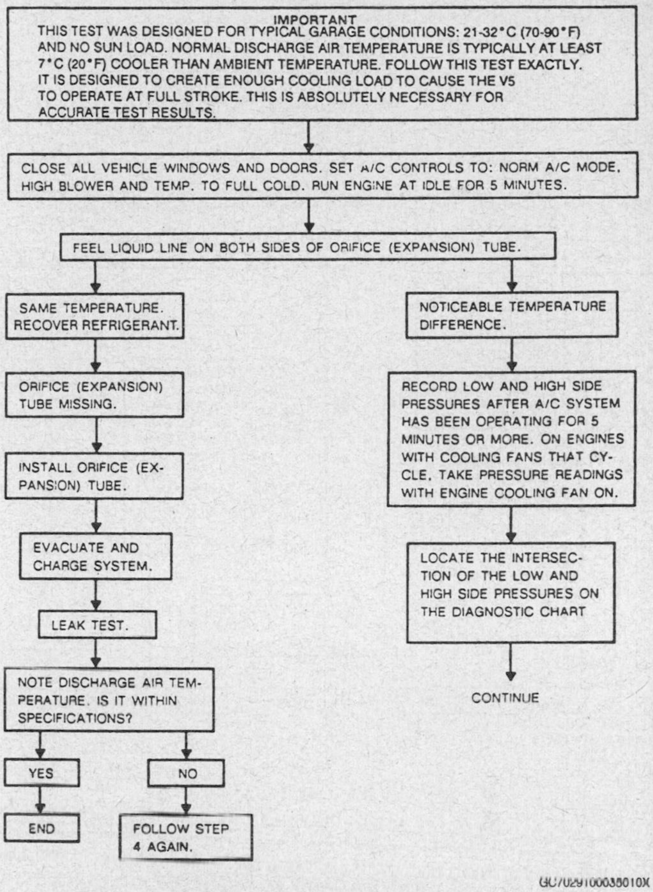
IMPORTANT
THIS TEST WAS DESIGNED FOR TYPICAL GARAGE CONDITIONS: 21-32°C (70-90°F) AND NO SUN LOAD. NORMAL DISCHARGE AIR TEMPERATURE IS TYPICALLY AT LEAST 7°C (20°F) COOLER THAN AMBIENT TEMPERATURE. FOLLOW THIS TEST EXACTLY. IT IS DESIGNED TO CREATE ENOUGH COOLING LOAD TO CAUSE THE V5 TO OPERATE AT FULL STROKE. THIS IS ABSOLUTELY NECESSARY FOR ACCURATE TEST RESULTS.
CLOSE ALL VEHICLE WINDOWS AND DOORS. SET A/C CONTROLS TO: NORM A/C MODE, HIGH BLOWER AND TEMP. TO FULL COLD. RUN ENGINE AT IDLE FOR 5 MINUTES.
FEEL LIQUID LINE ON BOTH SIDES OF ORIFICE (EXPANSION) TUBE.
SAME TEMPERATURE. RECOVER REFRIGERANT.
ORIFICE (EXPANSION) TUBE MISSING.
INSTALL ORIFICE (EXPANSION) TUBE.
EVACUATE AND CHARGE SYSTEM.
LEAK TEST.
NOTE DISCHARGE AIR TEMPERATURE. IS IT WITHIN SPECIFICATIONS?
YES
NO
END
FOLLOW STEP 4 AGAIN.
NOTICEABLE TEMPERATURE DIFFERENCE.
RECORD LOW AND HIGH SIDE PRESSURES AFTER A/C SYSTEM HAS BEEN OPERATING FOR 5 MINUTES OR MORE. ON ENGINES WITH COOLING FANS THAT CYCLE, TAKE PRESSURE READINGS WITH ENGINE COOLING FAN ON.
LOCATE THE INTERSECTION OF THE LOW AND HIGH SIDE PRESSURES ON THE DIAGNOSTIC CHART
CONTINUE
GC7029100035010X

Fig. 10 Troubleshooting step 4 (Part 1 of 2). Variable displacement orifice tube system

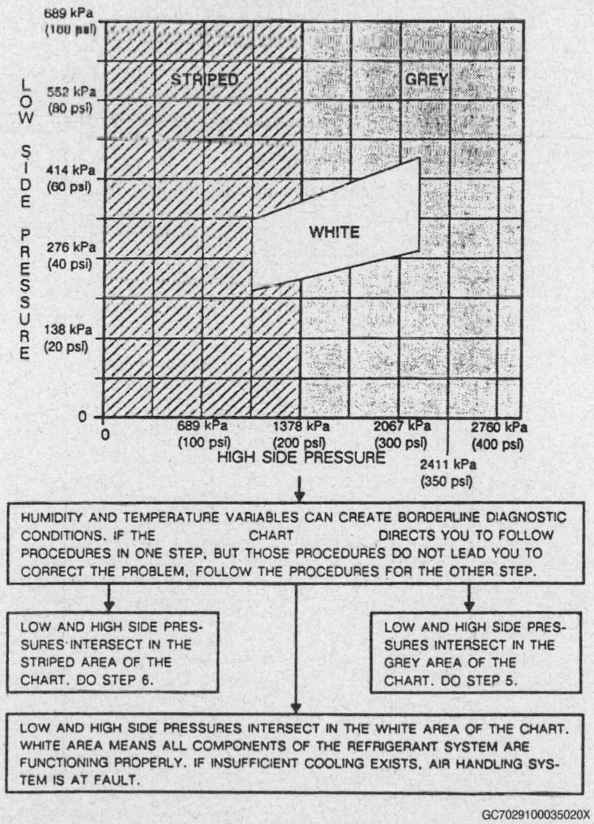
689 kPa (100 psi)
552 kPa (80 psi)
414 kPa (60 psi)
276 kPa (40 psi)
138 kPa (20 psi)
0
LOW SIDE PRESSURE
STRIPED
GREY
WHITE
0
689 kPa (100 psi)
1378 kPa (200 psi)
2067 kPa (300 psi)
2760 kPa (400 psi)
2411 kPa (350 psi)
HIGH SIDE PRESSURE
HUMIDITY AND TEMPERATURE VARIABLES CAN CREATE BORDERLINE DIAGNOSTIC CONDITIONS. IF THE CHART DIRECTS YOU TO FOLLOW PROCEDURES IN ONE STEP, BUT THOSE PROCEDURES DO NOT LEAD YOU TO CORRECT THE PROBLEM, FOLLOW THE PROCEDURES FOR THE OTHER STEP.
LOW AND HIGH SIDE PRESSURES INTERSECT IN THE STRIPED AREA OF THE CHART. DO STEP 6.
LOW AND HIGH SIDE PRESSURES INTERSECT IN THE GREY AREA OF THE CHART. DO STEP 5.
LOW AND HIGH SIDE PRESSURES INTERSECT IN THE WHITE AREA OF THE CHART. WHITE AREA MEANS ALL COMPONENTS OF THE REFRIGERANT SYSTEM ARE FUNCTIONING PROPERLY. IF INSUFFICIENT COOLING EXISTS, AIR HANDLING SYSTEM IS AT FAULT.
GC7029100035020X

Fig. 10 Troubleshooting step 4 (Part 2 of 2). Variable displacement orifice tube system

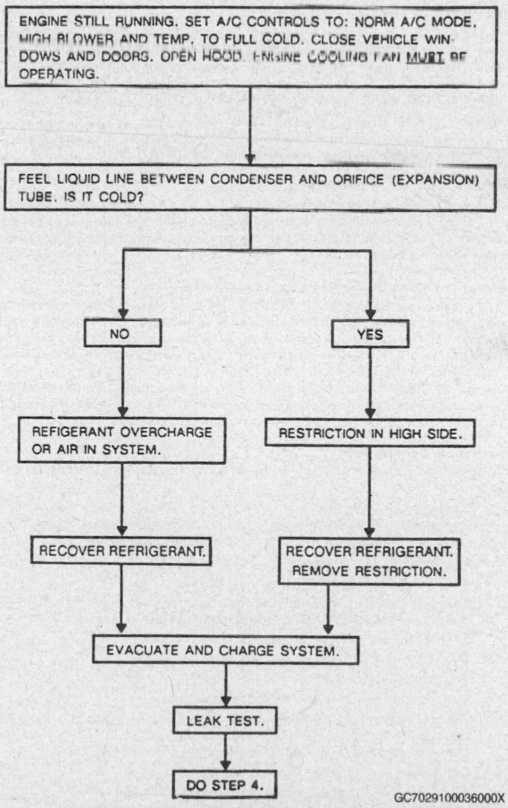
ENGINE STILL RUNNING. SET A/C CONTROLS TO: NORM A/C MODE, HIGH BLOWER AND TEMP. TO FULL COLD. CLOSE VEHICLE WINDOWS AND DOORS. OPEN HOOD. ENGINE COOLING FAN MUST BE OPERATING.
FEEL LIQUID LINE BETWEEN CONDENSER AND ORIFICE (EXPANSION) TUBE. IS IT COLD?
NO
YES
REFIGERANT OVERCHARGE OR AIR IN SYSTEM.
RESTRICTION IN HIGH SIDE.
RECOVER REFRIGERANT.
RECOVER REFRIGERANT. REMOVE RESTRICTION.
EVACUATE AND CHARGE SYSTEM.
LEAK TEST.
DO STEP 4.
GC7029100036000X

Fig. 11 Troubleshooting step 5. Variable displacement orifice tube system

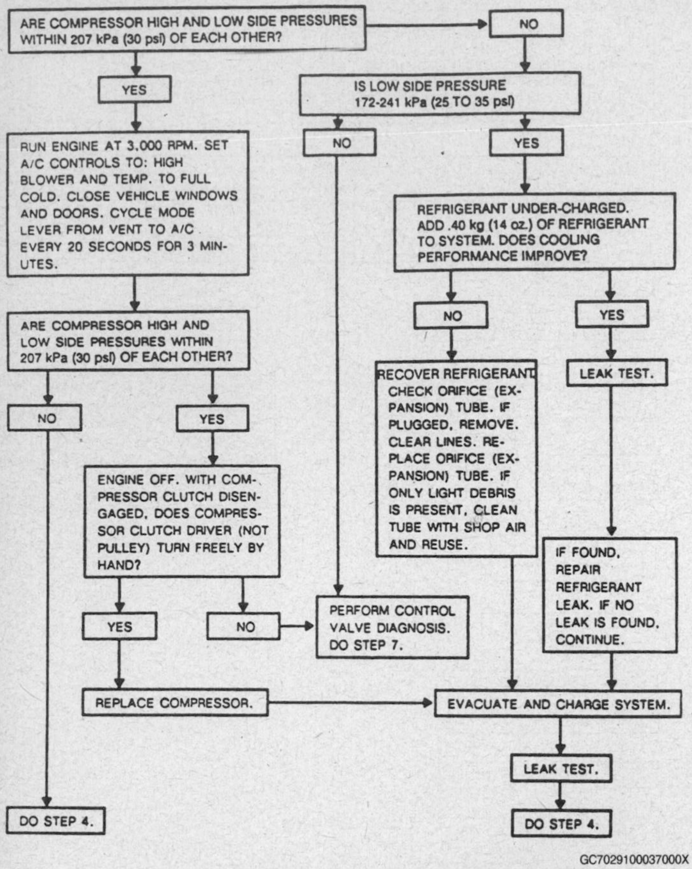
ARE COMPRESSOR HIGH AND LOW SIDE PRESSURES WITHIN 207 kPa (30 psi) OF EACH OTHER?
NO
YES
IS LOW SIDE PRESSURE 172-241 kPa (25 TO 35 psi)
RUN ENGINE AT 3,000 RPM. SET A/C CONTROLS TO: HIGH BLOWER AND TEMP. TO FULL COLD. CLOSE VEHICLE WINDOWS AND DOORS. CYCLE MODE LEVER FROM VENT TO A/C EVERY 20 SECONDS FOR 3 MINUTES.
NO
YES
REFRIGERANT UNDER-CHARGED. ADD .40 kg (14 oz.) OF REFRIGERANT TO SYSTEM. DOES COOLING PERFORMANCE IMPROVE?
ARE COMPRESSOR HIGH AND LOW SIDE PRESSURES WITHIN 207 kPa (30 psi) OF EACH OTHER?
NO
YES
RECOVER REFRIGERANT CHECK ORIFICE (EXPANSION) TUBE. IF PLUGGED, REMOVE. CLEAR LINES. REPLACE ORIFICE (EXPANSION) TUBE. IF ONLY LIGHT DEBRIS IS PRESENT, CLEAN TUBE WITH SHOP AIR AND REUSE.
LEAK TEST.
NO
YES
ENGINE OFF. WITH COMPRESSOR CLUTCH DISENGAGED, DOES COMPRESSOR CLUTCH DRIVER (NOT PULLEY) TURN FREELY BY HAND?
IF FOUND, REPAIR REFRIGERANT LEAK. IF NO LEAK IS FOUND, CONTINUE.
YES
NO
PERFORM CONTROL VALVE DIAGNOSIS. DO STEP 7.
REPLACE COMPRESSOR.
EVACUATE AND CHARGE SYSTEM.
LEAK TEST.
DO STEP 4.
DO STEP 4.
GC7029100037000X

Fig. 12 Troubleshooting step 6. Variable displacement orifice tube system

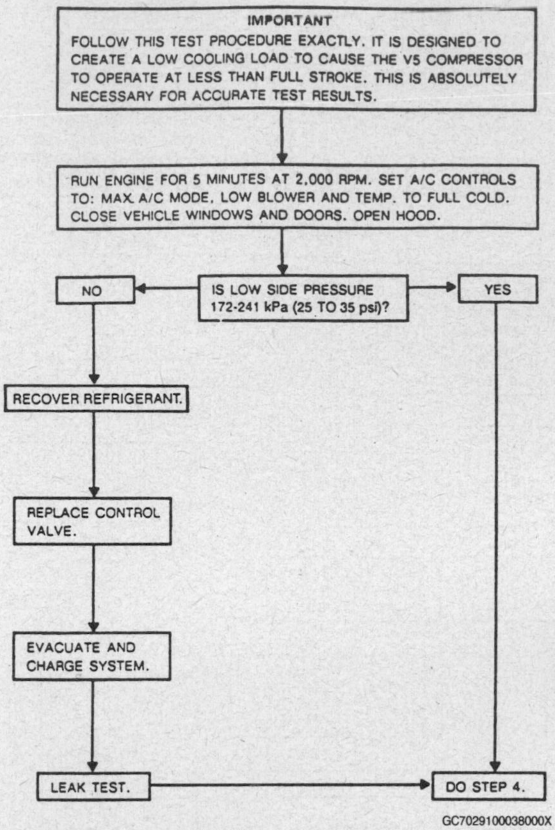
IMPORTANT
FOLLOW THIS TEST PROCEDURE EXACTLY. IT IS DESIGNED TO CREATE A LOW COOLING LOAD TO CAUSE THE V5 COMPRESSOR TO OPERATE AT LESS THAN FULL STROKE. THIS IS ABSOLUTELY NECESSARY FOR ACCURATE TEST RESULTS.
RUN ENGINE FOR 5 MINUTES AT 2,000 RPM. SET A/C CONTROLS TO: MAX. A/C MODE, LOW BLOWER AND TEMP. TO FULL COLD. CLOSE VEHICLE WINDOWS AND DOORS. OPEN HOOD.
NO
IS LOW SIDE PRESSURE 172-241 kPa (25 TO 35 psi)?
YES
RECOVER REFRIGERANT.
REPLACE CONTROL VALVE.
EVACUATE AND CHARGE SYSTEM.
LEAK TEST.
DO STEP 4.
GC7029100038000X

Fig. 13 Troubleshooting step 7. Variable displacement orifice tube system

V5/TXV SYSTEM DIAGNOSTICS

Diagnostic Flow Chart

This chart is the starting point for verifying and diagnosing all air conditioning and HVAC control related complaints. It represents the correct path to follow from a customer complaint or condition through delivery of the vehicle back to the customer.

Preliminary Checks

This step covers all physical and visual inspections of interior and underhood components. Many problems can be detected by a thorough inspection. Failure to perform this step could result in wasted time proceeding further down the flow chart.

Vehicle Set Up and Performance Test

To run an air conditioning performance test the vehicle must be set-up according to instructions. The instructions include manifold gauge set installation and controller settings. Improper vehicle set up will result in inaccurate pressure and temperature readings.

General and Specific System Condition Charts

These charts were developed in a wind tunnel by producing known system problems and recording pressures and temperatures at various ambient temperatures. The tests were then validated using the same vehicle set up in a service environment. To find your system problem, compare the performance test readings to the readings on the charts for your ambient temperature and humidity. When all pressure and temperature readings fall within the limits of a given chart, use that chart to repair the vehicle. There is some variance in readings between systems of different vehicles; however the target areas have been developed to accommodate these changes.

Compressor Control Test

This is designed to evaluate the compressor's ability to change displacement with varying heat loads.

Step 1 — *Preliminary Checks*

Repair the following as necessary. If discharge temperature with A/C on is normal after making the following repairs, the system is operating properly.

- A/C fuse
- A/C blower operation
- Temperature door. Move temperature door lever rapidly from cold to hot. Listen for temperature door hitting at each end. Adjust as necessary. (Cable operated door only)
- Clutch coil connection
- Transducer connection
- Compressor belt. Replace if damaged or missing
- Engine cooling fan operation (at idle, cooling fan must be on at any A/C mode) cooling fan must be operating in correct direction (drawing outside air through the condenser toward engine)
- Condenser — Check for restricted air flow
- Dealer technical bulletins for updates on A/C system

GC7029100039000X

Fig. 14 Troubleshooting step 1. Thermal expansion valve system

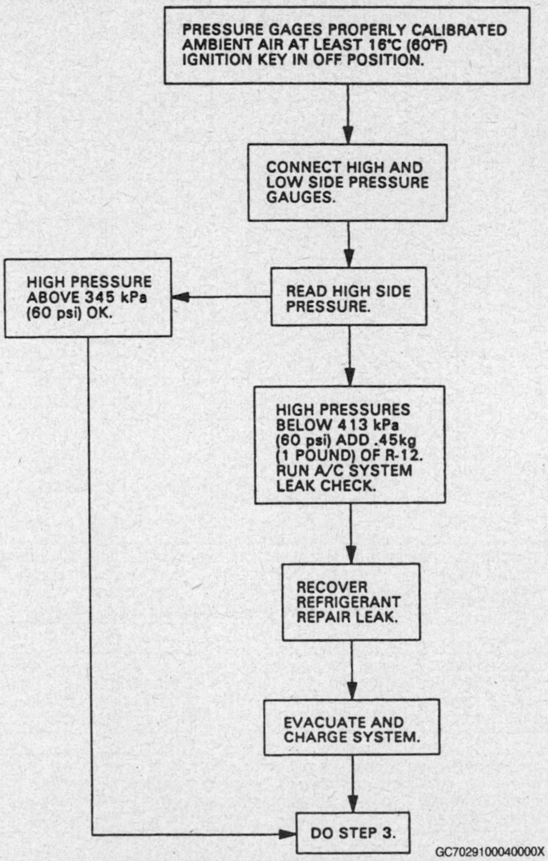
PRESSURE GAGES PROPERLY CALIBRATED AMBIENT AIR AT LEAST 16°C (60°F) IGNITION KEY IN OFF POSITION.
CONNECT HIGH AND LOW SIDE PRESSURE GAUGES.
HIGH PRESSURE ABOVE 345 kPa (60 psi) OK.
READ HIGH SIDE PRESSURE.
HIGH PRESSURES BELOW 413 kPa (60 psi) ADD .45kg (1 POUND) OF R-12. RUN A/C SYSTEM LEAK CHECK.
RECOVER REFRIGERANT REPAIR LEAK.
EVACUATE AND CHARGE SYSTEM.
DO STEP 3.
GC7029100040000X

Fig. 15 Troubleshooting step 2. Thermal expansion valve system

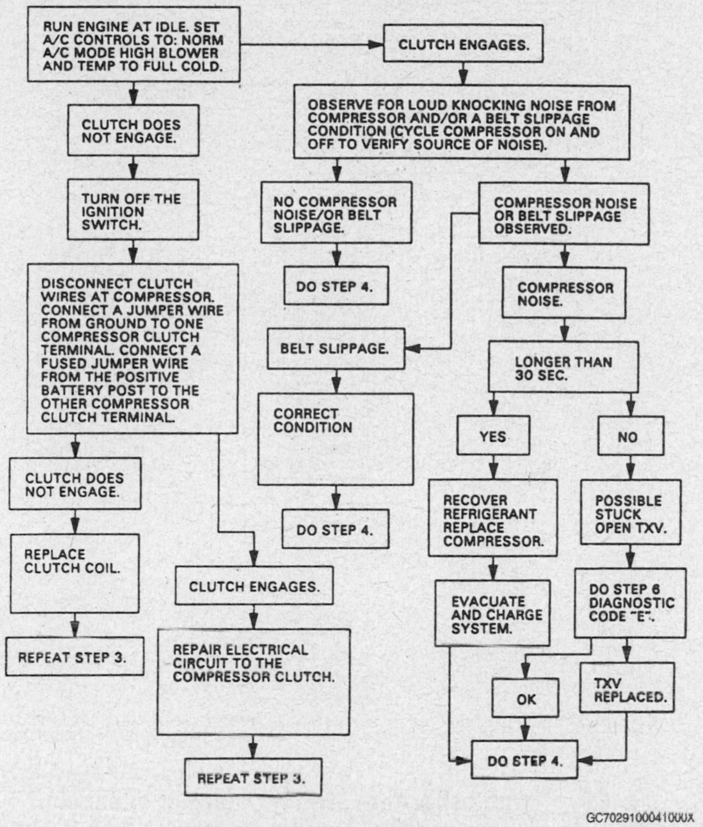

RUN ENGINE AT IDLE. SET A/C CONTROLS TO: NORM A/C MODE HIGH BLOWER AND TEMP TO FULL COLD.
CLUTCH ENGAGES.
CLUTCH DOES NOT ENGAGE.
OBSERVE FOR LOUD KNOCKING NOISE FROM COMPRESSOR AND/OR A BELT SLIPPAGE CONDITION (CYCLE COMPRESSOR ON AND OFF TO VERIFY SOURCE OF NOISE).
TURN OFF THE IGNITION SWITCH.
NO COMPRESSOR NOISE/OR BELT SLIPPAGE.
COMPRESSOR NOISE OR BELT SLIPPAGE OBSERVED.
DO STEP 4.
COMPRESSOR NOISE.
DISCONNECT CLUTCH WIRES AT COMPRESSOR. CONNECT A JUMPER WIRE FROM GROUND TO ONE COMPRESSOR CLUTCH TERMINAL. CONNECT A FUSED JUMPER WIRE FROM THE POSITIVE BATTERY POST TO THE OTHER COMPRESSOR CLUTCH TERMINAL.
BELT SLIPPAGE.
LONGER THAN 30 SEC.
CORRECT CONDITION
YES
NO
CLUTCH DOES NOT ENGAGE.
RECOVER REFRIGERANT REPLACE COMPRESSOR.
POSSIBLE STUCK OPEN TXV.
DO STEP 4.
REPLACE CLUTCH COIL.
CLUTCH ENGAGES.
EVACUATE AND CHARGE SYSTEM.
DO STEP 6 DIAGNOSTIC CODE "E".
REPEAT STEP 3.
REPAIR ELECTRICAL CIRCUIT TO THE COMPRESSOR CLUTCH.
OK
TXV REPLACED.
DO STEP 4.
REPEAT STEP 3.
GC702910004100X

Fig. 16 Troubleshooting step 3. Thermal expansion valve system

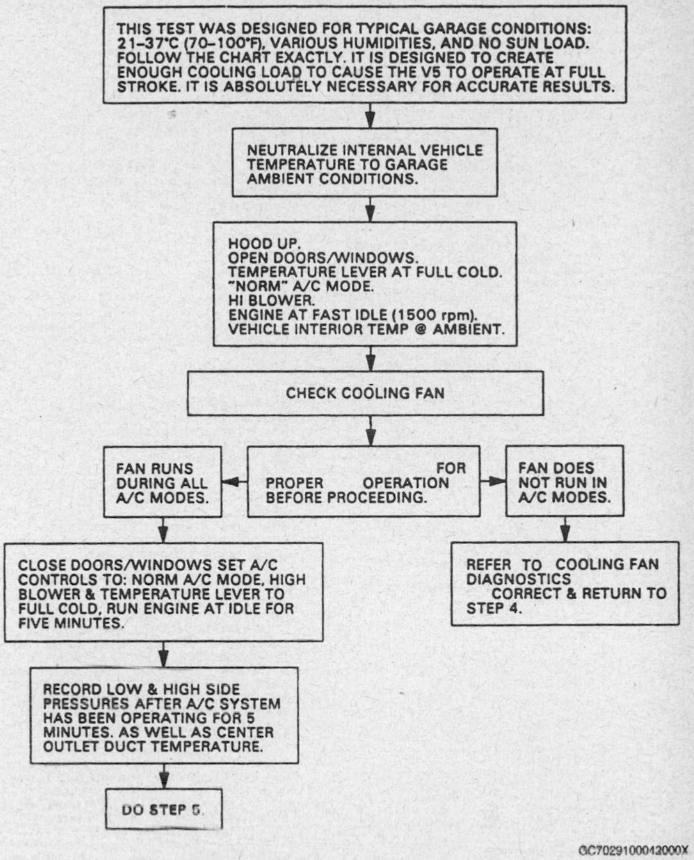

THIS TEST WAS DESIGNED FOR TYPICAL GARAGE CONDITIONS: 21–37°C (70–100°F), VARIOUS HUMIDITIES, AND NO SUN LOAD. FOLLOW THE CHART EXACTLY. IT IS DESIGNED TO CREATE ENOUGH COOLING LOAD TO CAUSE THE V5 TO OPERATE AT FULL STROKE. IT IS ABSOLUTELY NECESSARY FOR ACCURATE RESULTS.
NEUTRALIZE INTERNAL VEHICLE TEMPERATURE TO GARAGE AMBIENT CONDITIONS.
HOOD UP.
OPEN DOORS/WINDOWS.
TEMPERATURE LEVER AT FULL COLD.
"NORM" A/C MODE.
HI BLOWER.
ENGINE AT FAST IDLE (1500 rpm).
VEHICLE INTERIOR TEMP @ AMBIENT.
CHECK COOLING FAN
FAN RUNS DURING ALL A/C MODES.
FOR PROPER OPERATION BEFORE PROCEEDING.
FAN DOES NOT RUN IN A/C MODES.
CLOSE DOORS/WINDOWS SET A/C CONTROLS TO: NORM A/C MODE, HIGH BLOWER & TEMPERATURE LEVER TO FULL COLD, RUN ENGINE AT IDLE FOR FIVE MINUTES.
REFER TO COOLING FAN DIAGNOSTICS CORRECT & RETURN TO STEP 4.
RECORD LOW & HIGH SIDE PRESSURES AFTER A/C SYSTEM HAS BEEN OPERATING FOR 5 MINUTES. AS WELL AS CENTER OUTLET DUCT TEMPERATURE.
DO STEP 5.
GC7029100042000X

Fig. 17 Troubleshooting step 4. Thermal expansion valve system

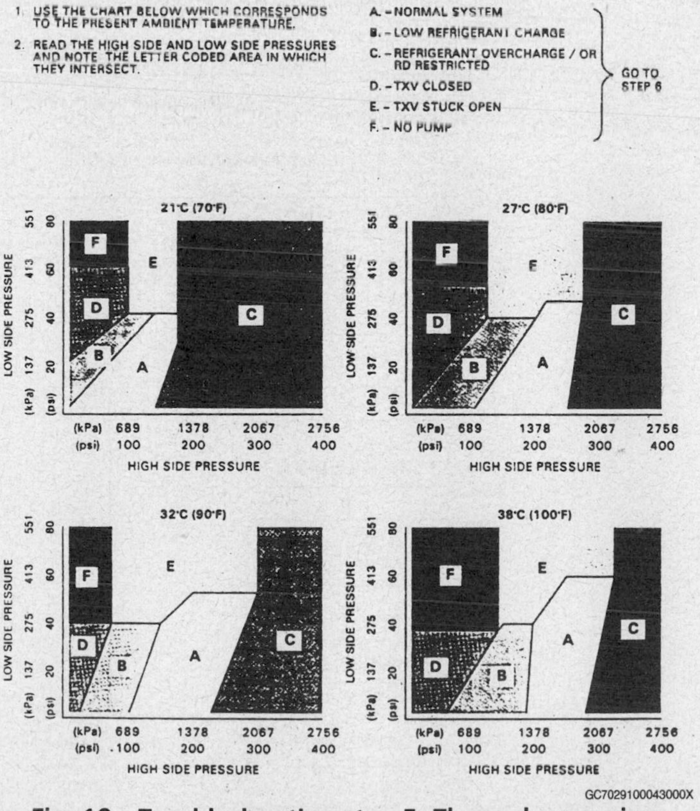

1. USE THE CHART BELOW WHICH CORRESPONDS TO THE PRESENT AMBIENT TEMPERATURE.
2. READ THE HIGH SIDE AND LOW SIDE PRESSURES AND NOTE THE LETTER CODED AREA IN WHICH THEY INTERSECT.
A. - NORMAL SYSTEM
B. - LOW REFRIGERANT CHARGE
C. - REFRIGERANT OVERCHARGE / OR RD RESTRICTED
D. - TXV CLOSED
E. - TXV STUCK OPEN
F. - NO PUMP
GO TO STEP 6
21°C (70°F)
27°C (80°F)
32°C (90°F)
38°C (100°F)
LOW SIDE PRESSURE
(kPa) 137 275 413 551
(psi) 20 40 60 80
HIGH SIDE PRESSURE
(kPa) 689 1378 2067 2756
(psi) 100 200 300 400
GC7029100043000X

Fig. 18 Troubleshooting step 5. Thermal expansion valve system

in the color of the flame. If not recognized, a false diagnosis could be made. Store leak detector in a clean place and ensure hose is free of dust before leak testing.

3. Check for leaks in the manifold gauge set and hoses, as well as the rest of the system.
4. Use a small fan to ventilate areas where the leak detector indicates refrigerant constantly. These areas are contaminated with refrigerant and must be ventilated before leak can be pinpointed.

FLUID LEAK DETECTORS

Apply leak detector solution around joints to be tested. A cluster of bubbles will form immediately if there is a leak. A white foam that forms after a short while will indicate an extremely small leak. In some confined areas such as sections of the evaporator and condenser, electronic leak detectors will be more useful.

FLUORESCENT LEAK DETECTORS

R-12 Refrigerant

To test for leaks with this method, add fluorescent leak detection additive J-36790 or equivalent to the refrigeration system following manufacturers instructions. Scan all accessible areas of refrigeration system with tester No. J-28428-D. The additive can remain in the refrigeration system as it is not harmful to system components.

Step 6 — *Diagnostic Code Procedures*

Refer to appropriate diagnostic code chart for ambient garage conditions. NOTE: High humidity is above 60% relative. (Obtain humidity level from local radio weather report.)

	Condition / Ambient temperature	Humidity	Outlet temp ranges	Additional indicators
A –	NORMAL SYSTEM PERFORMANCE — AMBIENT TEMPERATURE – OUTLET TEMP RANGES:			ADDITIONAL INDICATORS
	70	LOW HUMIDITY	45 – 50	SYSTEM WITHIN SPECS.
		HI HUMIDITY	51 – 56	
	80	LOW HUMIDITY	50 – 57	NOTE: IF LOW SIDE PRESSURE IS LESS THAN 172 kPa (25 psi), MAY INDICATE POSSIBLE CONTROL VALVE PROBLEM — GO TO STEP 8.
		HI HUMIDITY	58 – 65	
	90	LOW HUMIDITY	60 – 65	
		HI HUMIDITY	66 – 70	
	100	LOW HUMIDITY	67 – 75	
		HI HUMIDITY	76 – 80	
B –	LOW REFRIGERANT CHARGE — AMBIENT TEMPERATURE – OUTLET TEMP RANGES:			
	70	LOW HUMIDITY	63 – 70	SYSTEM SLIGHTLY COOLER THAN AMBIENT DEPENDING UPON REMAINING CHARGE.
		HI HUMIDITY	63 – 77	
	80	LOW HUMIDITY	64 – 75	
		HI HUMIDITY	74 – 81	
	90	LOW HUMIDITY	75 – 85	CONFIRM BY TOUCHING COMPRESSOR SUCTION/DISCHARGE PIPE. SUCTION PIPE WILL BE COOL TO WARM & DISCHARGE WARM TO HOT. LEAK CHECK, RECOVER REPAIR & RECHARGE. REPEAT STEP 4.
		HI HUMIDITY	81 – 88	
	100	LOW HUMIDITY	85 – 102	
		HI HUMIDITY	90 – 105	
C –	REFRIGERANT OVERCHARGE OR RESTRICTED RECEIVER/DRYER			CONFIRM BY TOUCHING R/D INLET/ OUTLET IF TEMP DIFFERENCE R&R RD & RETURN TO STEP 4.
	COMPLAINT WILL BE POOR OR INTERMEDIATE COOLING AT HIGH AMBIENTS (TRANSDUCER SHUTS SYSTEM DOWN BECAUSE OF EXCESSIVE HIGH SIDE SYSTEM PRESSURE)			CONFIRM BY TOUCHING COMPRESSOR SUCTION/DISCHARGE PIPE — IT WILL BE COOL & DISCHARGE PIPE WILL BE HOT.
D –	TXV STUCK CLOSED OUTLET TEMPERATURE COOL TO WARM			CONFIRM BY THOROUGH PHYSICAL INSPECTION OF ALL LINES AND COMPONENTS. PRIOR TO FRONT OF DASH. IF INLET LINE IS COOL AT FOD CHECK FOR RESTRICTION ON HIGH SIDE. (NOTICEABLE WARM/COLD TEMPERATURE DIFFERENCE AT GIVEN POINT ON LIQUID LINE OR RD) IF NO RESTRICTION FOUND, CONFIRM BY LISTENING FOR 'HISS' ON NORM A/C, LOW BLOWER. VERIFY BY RUNNING ENGINE AT 2000 rpm; IF PRESSURES DO NOT CHANGE BY MORE THAN 20 psi AND OUTLET AIR DOESN'T FEEL COOL, REPLACE TXV.
E –	TXV STUCK OPEN SYSTEM APPEARS TO PERFORM NORMALLY, BUT MAY GO WARM TEMPORARILY ON EXTENDED DRIVES AND RECORRECT ITSELF AFTER VEHICLE SHUT DOWN. MAY ALSO CAUSE COMPRESSOR "SLUGGING" — NOISE			RUN HI BLOWER, NORMAL A/C FAST IDLE FOR 2 MIN. ENGINE OFF FOR 3 MIN. RESTART ENGINE WITH A/C OFF. LET ENGINE RPM STABALIZE. ON LOW BLOWER RUN A/C AND LISTEN FOR SLUGGING. REPLACE TXV. HOOD SHOULD BE LOWERED FOR THIS PROCEDURE.
F –	COMPRESSOR NO PUMP OUTLET TEMPERATURE IS AMBIENT			CONFIRM BY FOLLOWING STEP 7.

NOTE: IF NONE OF THE ABOVE CONDITIONS CAN BE VERIFIED, RECOVER, EVACUATE AND RECHARGE WITH PROPER CHARGE AND PREFORM STEP 4 AGAIN.

GC7029100044000X

Fig. 19 Troubleshooting step 6. Thermal expansion valve system

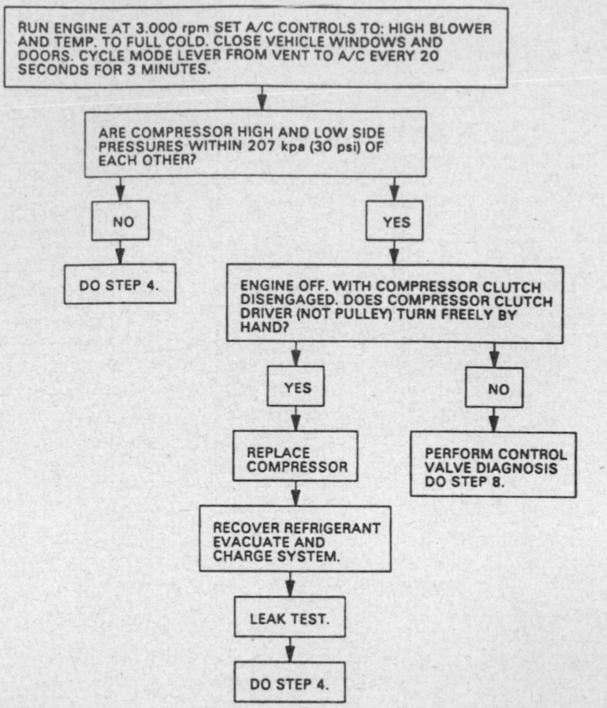
RUN ENGINE AT 3.000 rpm SET A/C CONTROLS TO: HIGH BLOWER AND TEMP. TO FULL COLD. CLOSE VEHICLE WINDOWS AND DOORS. CYCLE MODE LEVER FROM VENT TO A/C EVERY 20 SECONDS FOR 3 MINUTES.
ARE COMPRESSOR HIGH AND LOW SIDE PRESSURES WITHIN 207 kpa (30 psi) OF EACH OTHER?
NO
YES
DO STEP 4.
ENGINE OFF. WITH COMPRESSOR CLUTCH DISENGAGED. DOES COMPRESSOR CLUTCH DRIVER (NOT PULLEY) TURN FREELY BY HAND?
YES
NO
REPLACE COMPRESSOR
PERFORM CONTROL VALVE DIAGNOSIS DO STEP 8.
RECOVER REFRIGERANT EVACUATE AND CHARGE SYSTEM.
LEAK TEST.
DO STEP 4.

NOTE: FAILED TXV CAN CAUSE INTERNAL COMPRESSOR FAILURE. AFTER REPLACING FAILED COMPRESSOR, PAY PARTICULAR ATTENTION TO TXV OPERATION. IF PROBLEM INDICATED, PERFORM APPROPRIATE REPAIR PROCEDURE.

GC7029100045000X

Fig. 20 Troubleshooting step 7. Thermal expansion valve system

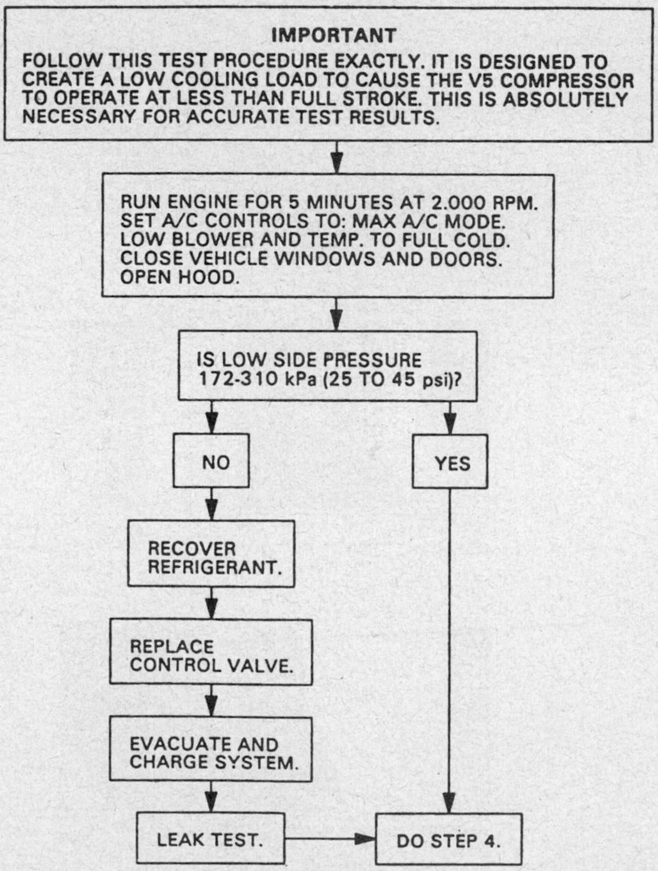
IMPORTANT
FOLLOW THIS TEST PROCEDURE EXACTLY. IT IS DESIGNED TO CREATE A LOW COOLING LOAD TO CAUSE THE V5 COMPRESSOR TO OPERATE AT LESS THAN FULL STROKE. THIS IS ABSOLUTELY NECESSARY FOR ACCURATE TEST RESULTS.
RUN ENGINE FOR 5 MINUTES AT 2.000 RPM. SET A/C CONTROLS TO: MAX A/C MODE. LOW BLOWER AND TEMP. TO FULL COLD. CLOSE VEHICLE WINDOWS AND DOORS. OPEN HOOD.
IS LOW SIDE PRESSURE 172-310 kPa (25 TO 45 psi)?
NO
YES
RECOVER REFRIGERANT.
REPLACE CONTROL VALVE.
EVACUATE AND CHARGE SYSTEM.
LEAK TEST.
DO STEP 4.

GC7029100046000X

Fig. 21 Troubleshooting step 8. Thermal expansion valve system

R-134a Refrigerant

No fluorescent detection additive is currently approved by General Motors for use in R-134a systems.

DISCHARGING SYSTEM

REFRIGERANT RECOVERY

The refrigerant system must be discharged using an air conditioning refrigerant recovery and recycling system J-38100-C. After completing any necessary repairs the refrigerant system can then be evacuated and charged using air conditioning service charging station J-23500-A or equivalent, or manifold gauge set J-23500-A or equivalent. Service fitting caps are color coded for easy reference. Red cap indicates high side port. Blue cap indicates low side port.

Failure to check for residual oil from previous recovery can result in adding extra oil to the current vehicle being serviced. This will result in reduced performance and possible compressor damage.

1. Start vehicle and run with the A/C On for two minutes, then attach manifold gauge set to the A/C system, **Fig. 24.** Attach recovery station inlet hose to center fitting of manifold gauge set.
2. Open both valves of manifold gauge

Evaporator Pressure Gauge Reading	Evaporator Temperature F°	High Pressure Gauge Reading	Ambient Temperature
0	-21°	45	20°
0.6	-20°	55	30°
2.4	-15°	72	40°
4.5	-10°	86	50°
6.8	- 5°	105	60°
9.2	0°	126	70°
11.8	5°	140	75°
14.7	10°	160	80°
17.1	15°	185	90°
21.1	20°	195	95°
22.5	22°	220	100°
23.9	24°	240	105°
25.4	26°	260	110°
26.9	28°	275	115°
28.5	30°	290	120°
37.0	40°	305	125°
46.7	50°	325	130°
57.7	60°		
70.1	70°		
84.1	80°		
99.6	90°		
116.9	100°		
136.0	110°		
157.1	120°		
179.0	130°		

GC7029100025000X

Fig. 22 Pressure-temperature relationship. Conditions equivalent to 30 mph or 1750 engine RPM

Ambient Temp.	High Side Pressure
80	150-170
90	175-195
95	185-205
100	210-230
105	230-250
110	250-270

Fig. 23 High side pressure specifications

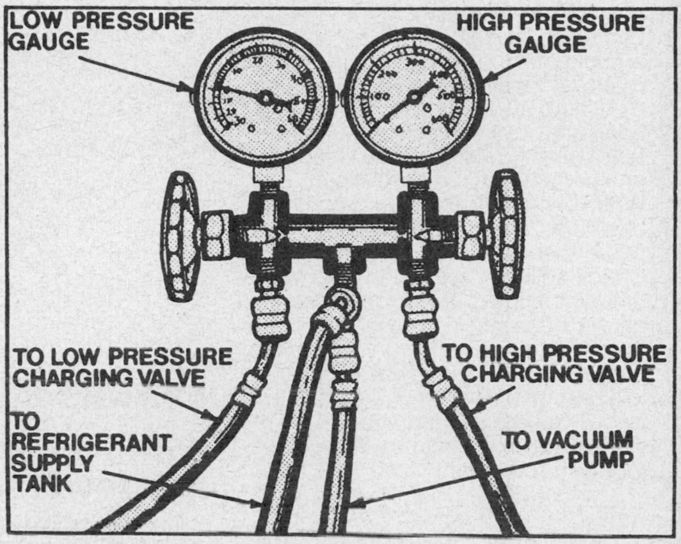
LOW PRESSURE GAUGE
HIGH PRESSURE GAUGE
TO LOW PRESSURE CHARGING VALVE
TO HIGH PRESSURE CHARGING VALVE
TO REFRIGERANT SUPPLY TANK
TO VACUUM PUMP

GC7029100026000X

Fig. 24 Manifold gauge set hose connections

set. Ensure refrigerant tank vapor valve and liquid valve are open.
3. Turn main power switch On.
4. Depress compressor start switch. The amber "Compressor On" light will come on and the compressor will start. The compressor will shutoff automatically when recovery is complete. Wait two minutes and check for pressure rise. If pressure rise occurs, depress compressor start switch to repeat recovery procedure.
5. To drain receiver dehydrator of A/C system oil, open receiver dehydrator pressurizing valve for 15 seconds to allow some compressor discharge pressure back into receiver dehydrator. Open oil drain valve slowly and drain receiver dehydrator. When oil stops draining, close oil drain valve. **Do not allow receiver dehydrator to completely depressurize.**

REFRIGERANT RECYCLING

1. Turn main power switch On.
2. Open both valves on recovery tank.
3. Turn "Recycle Start" switch On. The amber "Recycle On" light will come on and the refrigerant pump will start.
4. Refrigerant will be seen going through the "Moisture Indicator" at start up. If there is a sufficient supply of refrigerant, bubbles will clear after a few seconds. When bubbles clear from "Moisture Indicator," refrigerant pump is operating at maximum efficiency.
5. Allow station to operate until dot in center of "Moisture Indicator" turns green. "Moisture Indicator Dot" should change to a shade indicated on the reference decal. Always run recycling system a minimum of 30 minutes. If "Moisture Indicator" starts out yellow, it could take as long as two hours to turn green, depending on moisture content of refrigerant.
6. Turn Off station when recycling is complete.

REFRIGERANT RECOVERY & RECYCLING OPERATING HINTS

1. When using recovery station in conjunction with a charging station, attach center port hose of manifold gauge set to inlet port of recovery station, then follow normal operating procedures for recovery/recycling station.
2. When using recovery station in conjunction with an automatic charging station, attach exhaust hose to inlet of recovery station. On automatic A/C service stations, a hole has been added at rear of cabinet for access to exhaust hose. On older type stations, open front doors of cabinet to reach exhaust hose.
3. After attaching exhaust hose to recovery station, depress main power switch on automatic charging station. Depress exhaust switch. Then follow normal operating procedures for recovery station.
4. Air is automatically vented from recovery tank during recycling. This feature eliminated the need to purge hoses before recovering refrigerant.
5. Operating engine with A/C Off during recovery may reduce recovery time.
6. To help prevent escape of refrigerant to the atmosphere, the recovery station can be attached to a "Dial A Charge" cylinder top vent port when filling the cylinder.
7. Always check the recovery station for residual oil from previous recovery.

SYSTEM EVACUATION

WITH VACUUM PUMP

Vacuum pumps suitable for removing air and moisture from A/C systems are commercially available. A specification for system pump-down used here is 28-29½ inches vacuum. This reading can be attained at or near sea level only. For each 1000 feet of altitude this operation is being performed, the reading will be 1 inch vacuum lower. As an example, at 5000 feet elevation, only 23-24½ inch of vacuum can be obtained. **The system must be com-**

pletely discharged before it can be evacuated. Damage to vacuum pump may result if pressurized refrigerant is allowed to enter.

1. With hand gauges connected into system, remove cap from vacuum hose connector. Install hand gauge manifold center hose to vacuum pump connector. Open low side gauge manifold hand valve only.
2. Ensure low side gauge is calibrated correctly. It should be reading zero. If not, adjust calibration.
3. Evacuate system with the vacuum pump until the low pressure gauge reads at least 28 inches of vacuum. Continue evacuating system for an additional 15 minutes for routine system servicing or 20 to 30 minutes, if any parts have been replaced.
4. When system evacuation is complete, close low side gauge manifold hand valve, then turn vacuum pump off.
5. Check ability of system to hold vacuum. Watch low side gauge to see that gauge does not rise at a faster rate than 1 inch vacuum every 4 to 5 minutes. If low side gauge rises at too rapid a rate, install partial charge and leak test. Evacuate system again.
6. If system holds vacuum, charge system with refrigerant.

USING CHARGING STATION

A vacuum pump is built into the charging station and is constructed to withstand repeated and prolonged use without damage. Complete moisture removal from the system is possible only with a vacuum pump constructed for the purpose.

The system must be completely discharged before it can be evacuated. Damage to the vacuum pump may result if pressurized refrigerant is allowed to enter.

1. Connect hose to vacuum pump, if system was discharged through charging station.
2. Open low side gauge hand valve of charging station.
3. Connect station into 110 volt current.
4. Turn vacuum pump on according to instructions for specific station being used.
5. Evacuate system with the vacuum pump until the low pressure gauge reads at least 28 inches of vacuum. Continue evacuating system for an additional 15 minutes for routine system servicing or 20 to 30 minutes, if any parts have been replaced.
6. Close low side gauge hand valve, then turn vacuum pump off.
7. Check ability of system to hold vacuum. Watch low side gauge to see that gauge does not rise at a faster rate than 1 inch vacuum every 4 to 5 minutes. If low side gauge rises at too rapid a rate, install partial charge and leak test. Then evacuate system again.
8. If system holds vacuum, charge system with refrigerant.

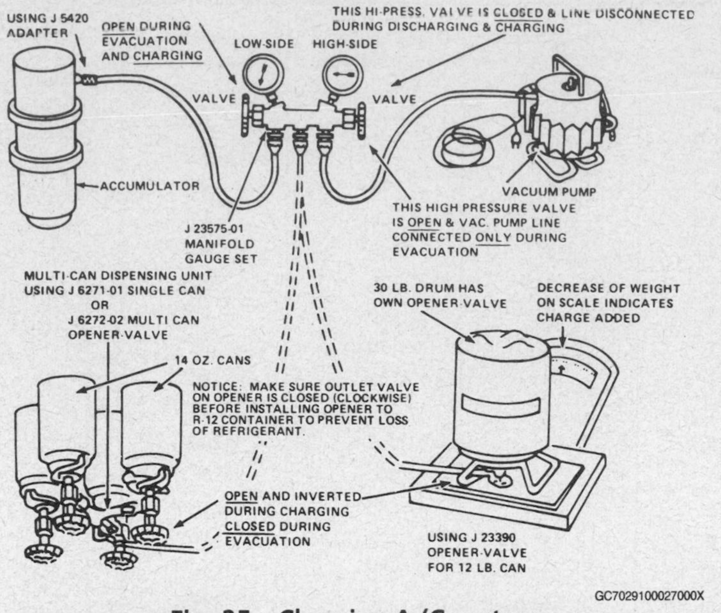
USING J 5420 ADAPTER
OPEN DURING EVACUATION AND CHARGING
LOW-SIDE
HIGH-SIDE
THIS HI-PRESS. VALVE IS CLOSED & LINE DISCONNECTED DURING DISCHARGING & CHARGING
VALVE
VALVE
ACCUMULATOR
VACUUM PUMP
THIS HIGH PRESSURE VALVE IS OPEN & VAC. PUMP LINE CONNECTED ONLY DURING EVACUATION
J 23575-01 MANIFOLD GAUGE SET
MULTI-CAN DISPENSING UNIT USING J 6271-01 SINGLE CAN OR J 6272-02 MULTI CAN OPENER-VALVE
30 LB. DRUM HAS OWN OPENER-VALVE
DECREASE OF WEIGHT ON SCALE INDICATES CHARGE ADDED
14 OZ. CANS
NOTICE: MAKE SURE OUTLET VALVE ON OPENER IS CLOSED (CLOCKWISE) BEFORE INSTALLING OPENER TO R-12 CONTAINER TO PREVENT LOSS OF REFRIGERANT.
OPEN AND INVERTED DURING CHARGING
CLOSED DURING EVACUATION
USING J 23390 OPENER-VALVE FOR 12 LB. CAN
GC7029100027000X

Fig. 25 Charging A/C system

CHARGING SYSTEM

USING CHARGING STATION J-23500-01

Use instructions provided with charging station with the following exceptions:

1. Do not connect high pressure line to A/C system.
2. Always keep high pressure valve closed on charging station.
3. Perform all evacuation and charging through accumulator low-side pressure service fitting.

Use of these procedures will prevent charging station from being accidentally exposed to high-side vehicle system pressure.

USING DISPOSABLE CANS OR REFRIGERANT DRUM

Never use these cans to charge into the high pressure side of the system (compressor discharge port) or into a system that is at high temperature, because the high system pressures could be transferred into the charging can causing it to explode.

If R-12 drum is used, place on scale and note total weight before charging. During charging, watch scale to determine amount of R-12 used.

If 14 ounce R-12 cans are used, close tapping valve, then attach cans following instructions included with manifold adapter.

Charging Of System

1. Start and run engine until normal operating temperature is reached and allow to warm up (choke off, normal idle). Set A/C control lever to OFF.
2. With R-12 drum or cans inverted, open R-12 supply valve and allow 1 lb. of liquid R-12 to flow into system through low-side service fitting on accumulator, **Fig. 25.**
3. **On all models except Cadillac w/display diagnosis,** when 1 lb. of refrigerant has entered system, engage compressor by setting A/C lever to NORM and blower switch to HI to draw in remainder of charge.
4. **On Cadillac models w/display diagnosis,** when 1 lb. of refrigerant has entered system, engage compressor by setting climate control panel to AUTO and blower switch to HI to draw in remainder of charge. If system switches to ECON when AUTO is pressed, low refrigerant is indicated, and the compressor will not operate. To obtain compressor operation, clear diagnostic trouble codes and select AUTO again.
5. **On all models,** cooling condenser with a large fan will speed up charging procedure by maintaining condenser temperature below charging cylinder temperature.
6. Close refrigerant supply valve and run engine for 30 seconds to clear lines and gauges.
7. With engine running, remove charging low side hose adapter from accumulator service fitting. Unscrew rapidly to avoid excessive refrigerant loss. **Do not remove a gauge line from its adapter when line is connected to A/C system. To disconnect line, always remove line adapter from service fitting. Do not remove charging hose at gauge set while attached to accumulator, as system will be discharged due to depressed Schraeder valve.**
8. Replace protective cap on accumulator fitting and turn engine off.
9. Check system for leaks.
10. Start engine and check for proper system pressures.

System Service

INDEX

OIL CHARGE

When replacing certain components of an air conditioning system a oil charge must be added to the system to keep the proper level of refrigerant oil in the system. Refer to "Oil Charge Data Table" for oil charge specifications.

If the refrigerant charge is abruptly lost due to a large refrigerant leak, approximately three ounces of refrigerant oil will be carried out of the system with the refrigerant. Upon replacement of a component which caused a large refrigerant leak, add three ounces of oil to the system plus the amount required for any component replaced as outlined under "Oil Charge Data Table." If possible, add oil directly to the replacement component.

OIL CHARGE DATA TABLE

Application			Oil Charge (Fl. Oz.) When replacing component				
Model	Year	Compressor Model	Compressor	Evaporator	Condenser	Accumulator	Receiver& Dehyrator
BUICK							
Century	1992-93	⑨	③	3	1	3.5	—
	1994	V-5①	③	3	1	④	—
LeSabre	1992-93	HR-6②	③	3	1	3.5	—
	1994	HD6/HR6-HE②	③	3	1	3.5	—
Park Avenue	1992-93	HR-6②	③	3	1	3.5	—
	1994	HD6/HR6-HE②	③	3	1	3.5	—
Regal	1992-93	⑬	③	3	1	3.5	—
	1994	V-5①	③	3	1	—	⑫
Riviera	1992-93	HR-6②	③	3	1	3.5	—
Roadmaster	1992	R-4②	③	3	1	3.5	—
	1993	HR100T/HR100-MD②	③	3	1	3.5	—
	1994	HD6/HR6-HE②	③	3	1	3.5	—
Skylark	1992-93	V-5①	⑨	3	1	3.5	—
	1994	V-5①	③	3	1	—	⑩
CADILLAC							
Brougham	1992	HR100T/HR110T②	⑪	3	1	⑤	—
DeVille	1992-93	HR-6HE②	③	3	1	④	—
	1994	HD6/HR6-HE②	③	3	1	3.5	—
Eldorado	1992-93	HR-6HE②	③	3	1	3.5	—
	1994	HD6/HR6-HE②	③	3	1	④	—
Fleetwood (FWD)	1992-93	HR-6HE②	③	3	1	3.5	—
Fleetwood (RWD)	1993	HR100T/HR110-MD②	③	3	1	3.5	—
	1994	HD6/HR6-HE②	③	3	1	3.5	—
Seville	1992-93	HR-6HE②	③	3	1	3.5	—
	1994	HD6/HR6-HE②	③	3	1	④	—
CHEVROLET							
Beretta	1992-93	V-5①	③	2	1	—	3.5
	1994	V-5①	③	3	1	—	3.5
Camaro	1992	R-4②	③	3	1	3.5	—
	1993-94	HD6/HR6-HE②	③	3	1	—	⑫
Caprice & Impala SS	1992	R-4②	③	3	1	3.5	—
	1993	HR100T/HR110T②	③	3	1	3.5	—
	1994	HD6/HR6-HE②	③	3	1	3.5	—
Cavalier	1992-94	V-5①	③	3	1	3.5	—
Corsica	1992-93	V-5①	③	2	1	—	3.5
	1994	V-5①	③	3	1	—	3.5

Continued

OIL CHARGE DATA TABLE-Continued

Application			Oil Charge (Fl. Oz.) When replacing component				
Model	Year	Compressor Model	Compressor	Evaporator	Condenser	Accumulator	Receiver& Dehyrator
Corvette	1992-94	10PA20②	⑥	3	1	3.5	—
	1992-94	10PA17⑭ ②	⑥	3	1	3.5	—
Lumina	1992-93	V-5①	③	3	1	3.5	—
	1994	V-5①	③	3	1	—	⑫
GEO							
Metro	1992-94	⑮	⑧	.7-1.0	.7-1.0	—	.4
Prizm	1992-94	—	③	3	⑦	—	3.5
Storm	1992-93	KC-50	⑩	1.7	1	—	1
OLDSMOBILE							
Achieva	1992-93	V-5①	③	3	1	—	3.5
	1994	V-5①	③	3	1	—	⑫
Custom Cruiser	1992	R-4②	③	3	1	3.5	—
Cutlass Ciera	1992	⑨	③	3	1	3.5	—
	1993	⑯	③	3	1	3.5	—
	1994	V-5①	③	3	1	④	—
Cutlass Cruiser	1992	⑨	③	3	1	3.5	—
	1993	⑯	③	3	1	3.5	—
	1994	V-5①	③	3	1	④	—
Cutlass Supreme	1992-93	V-5①	③	3	1	3.5	—
	1994	V-5①	③	3	1	—	⑫
Toronado	1992	HR-6②	③	3	1	3.5	—
Trofeo	1992	HR-6②	③	3	1	3.5	—
88 & 98	1992-93	HR-6②	③	3	1	3.5	—
	1994	HD6/HR6-HE②	③	3	1	3.5	—
PONTIAC							
Bonneville	1992-93	HR-6②	③	3	1	3.5	—
	1994	HD6/HR6-HE②	③	3	1	3.5	—
Firebird	1992	R-4②	③	3	1	3.5	—
	1993-94	HD6/HR6-HE②	③	3	1	—	⑫
Grand Am	1992-93	V-5①	③	3	1	3.5	—
	1994	V-5①	③	3	1	—	⑫
Grand Prix	1992-93	V-5①	③	3	1	3.5	—
	1994	V-5①	③	3	1	—	⑫
LeMans	1992-93	V-5①	③	3	1	3.5	—
Sunbird	1992-94	V-5①	③	3	1	3.5	—

①—Variable displacement compressor.

②—Fixed displacement compressor.

③—Drain oil from old compressor and measure, then drain new compressor. If more than one ounce is drained from old compressor, add same amount to new compressor. If less than one ounce is drained from compressor, add two ounces.

④—Drain oil from accumulator and measure. Add same amount of oil to new accumulator, plus one ounce. If no oil is drained, add two ounces to new accumulator.

⑤—Drain oil from accumulator and measure. Add same amount of oil to new accumulator, plus two ounces. If no oil is drained, add two ounces to new accumulator.

⑥—Drain oil from old compressor and measure, then drain new compressor. Add same amount to new compressor as drained from old compressor, plus one ounce.

⑦—Drain oil from old condenser and measure. If more than .5 ounce is drained from old condenser, add same amount to new condenser. If less than .5 ounce is drained from condenser, add .5 ounce.

⑧—Replacement compressors contain 2.7 ounces. Drain 1.4 ounces from new compressor before installing.

⑨—2.5L engine is equipped with V-5 compressors. 3.3L engine is equipped with HR-6 compressor.

⑩—Replacement compressors contain 5.1 ounces. Drain 2.4 ounces from new compressor before installing.

⑪—Drain oil from old compressor and measure, then drain new compressor. Amount drained from old compressor should not be more than five ounces. Add same amount of oil to new compressor as drained from old compressor, plus enough extra oil to equal a total of six ounces.

⑫—Drain oil from receiver and dehyrator assembly and measure. Add same amount of oil to new receiver and dehydrator assembly, plus one ounce.

⑬—3.1L engine is equipped with V-5 compressor. 3.8L engine is equipped with HR-6 compressor.

⑭—ZR-1 engine.

⑮—Nippondenso 10 cylinder compressor.

⑯—2.2L engine is equipped with V-5 compressors. 3.3L engine is equipped with HR-6 compressor.

OIL LEVEL CHECK

The oil level cannot be checked.

TECHNICAL SERVICE BULLETINS

NO A/C COOLING

1992 Bonneville

On these models, if a no A/C or no cooling condition exists, always check for a trouble code 66 first. Trouble code 66 is stored in the ECM to protect the compressor from engaging when the system is low on refrigerant. The ECM monitors the A/C request line (ckt 67) for a switching voltage controlled by the pressure cycling switch. If voltage is present at the ECM for less than 1.5 seconds, 10 successive times, trouble code 66 will set and the ECM will not provide a ground for the A/C relay for the rest of the ignition cycle.

If trouble code 66 is set three times, the ECM will never engage the A/C relay until the code is cleared from memory. Code 66 will not illuminate the service engine soon lamp and can only be detected with a scan tool or by disconnecting battery power to the ECM.

Trouble code 66 was designed to protect the compressor from damage by preventing its operation when the system was low on refrigerant. The ECM assumes the system is low on refrigerant if it sees the pressure cycling switch cycling more rapidly than normal, just like a system will do when it is low on refrigerant. Based on this rapid cycling, the ECM sets code 66 and will not provide a ground to the A/C clutch relay.

CAMS and TECH1 scan tools will also be unable to command the A/C clutch relay On when code 66 is stored. Do not replace the ECM if it fails to ground the A/C clutch relay. Ensure code 66 is not set first. The A/C compressor will start working when a new ECM is installed, as disconnecting the ECM clears all codes. However, the malfunction has not been found.

Air Conditioning Specifications

INDEX

Page No.

A/C SPECIFICATIONS

Model	Year	Refrigerant Capacity, Lbs.	Refrigerant Type	Refrigeration Oil: Viscosity	Refrigeration Oil: Total System Capacity, Ounces	Refrigeration Oil: Compressor Oil Level	Compressor Clutch Air Gap Inch
BUICK							
Century	1992-93	2.375	R-12	525	9	①	.020-.030
	1994	③	R-134a	④	8	①	.015-.020
LeSabre & Park Avenue	1992-93	2.42	R-12	525	8	①	.020-.030
	1994	2.42	R-134a	④	8	①	.020-.030
Regal	1992-93	②	R-12	525	9	①	.020-.030
	1994	2.00	R-134a	④	8	①	.015-.020
Riviera	1992-93	2.375	R-12	525	8	①	.020-.030
Roadmaster	1992-93	3.125	R-12	525	6	①	.020-.030
	1994	1.75	R-134a	④	8	①	.020-.030
Skylark	1992-93	2.65	R-12	525	8	①	.020-.030
	1994	2.25	R-134a	④	8	①	.015-.020
CADILLAC							
Brougham & Fleetwood RWD	1992-93	3.131	R-12	525	6	①	.020-.030
	1994	1.75	R-134a	④	6	①	.015-.020
DeVille & Fleetwood (FWD)	1992-93	2.42	R-12	525	8	①	.020-.030
	1994	1.75	R-134a	④	8	①	.015-.020
Eldorado & Seville	1992-93	2.40	R-12	525	8	①	.020-.030
	1994	1.75	R-134a	④	8	①	.015-.020
CHEVROLET							
Beretta & Corsica	1992-93	2.63	R-12	525	8	①	.020-.030
	1994	2.25	R-134a	④	9	①	.015-.020

Continued

A/C SPECIFICATIONS—Continued

Model	Year	Refrigerant Capacity, Lbs.	Refrigerant Type	Refrigeration Oil Viscosity	Refrigeration Oil Total System Capacity, Ounces	Refrigeration Oil Compressor Oil Level	Compressor Clutch Air Gap Inch
Camaro	1992	3.12	R-12	525	6	①	.020-.030
	1993-94	2.00	R-134a	④	8	①	.020-.030
Caprice & Impala SS	1992-93	3.12	R-12	525	6	①	.020-.030
	1994	1.75	R-134a	④	8	①	.020-.030
Cavalier	1992-94	2.25	R-12	525	8	①	.020-.030
Corvette	1992-93	2.25	R-12	500	8	①	.014-.026
	1994	2.00	R-134a	④	8	①	.014-.026
Lumina	1992-93	2.25	R-12	525	9	①	.020-.030
	1994	2.00	R-134a	④	8	①	.015-.020
GEO							
Metro	1992-93	1.10	R-12	525	2.7	①	.016-.028
	1994	1.10	R-134a	525	3.4	①	.016-.028
Prizm	1992-93	1.4-1.7	R-12	525	6	①	.014-.026
	1994	1.4-1.7	R-134a	525	6	①	.014-.026
Storm	1992-93	1.2-1.4	R-12	⑤	5.1	①	.010-.020
OLDSMOBILE							
Achieva	1992-93	2.65	R-12	525	8	①	.020-.030
	1994	2.25	R-134a	④	8	①	.015-.020
Custom Cruiser	1992	3.12	R-12	525	6	①	.020-.030
Cutlass Ciera & Cutlass Cruiser	1992-93	2.40	R-12	525	8	①	.020-.030
	1994	③	R-134a	④	9	①	.015-.020
Cutlass Supreme	1992-93	2.25	R-12	525	9	①	.020-.030
	1994	2.00	R-134a	④	8	①	.015-.020
Toronado & Trofeo	1992	2.40	R-12	525	8	①	.020-.030
88 & 98	1992-93	2.42	R-12	525	8	①	.020-.030
	1994	2.42	R-134a	④	8	①	.020-.030
PONTIAC							
Bonneville	1992-93	2.42	R-12	525	8	①	.020-.030
	1994	2.42	R-134a	④	8	①	.020-.030
Firebird	1992	3.12	R-12	525	6	①	.020-.030
	1993-94	2.00	R-134a	④	8	①	.020-.030
Grand Am	1992-93	2.65	R-12	525	8	①	.020-.030
	1994	2.25	R-134a	④	8	①	.015-.020
Grand Prix	1992-93	2.25	R-12	525	9	①	.020-.030
	1994	2.00	R-134a	④	8	①	.015-.020
LeMans	1992-93	2.20	R-12	525	8	①	.020-.030
Sunbird	1992-94	2.25	R-12	525	8	①	.020-.030

① —Note that "Oil Level" cannot be checked. Refer to total capacity in ounces.

② —Models less 3800 engine, 2.25 lbs., models w/3800 engine, 2.75 lbs.

③ —Models w/2.2L/4-134 engine, 1.75 lbs., models w/3.1L/V6-192 engine, 2.00 lbs.

④ —PAG (Polyalkine Glycol) synthetic refrigerant oil, GM part No. 12345923 or equivalent.

⑤ —Use D-220WX (GM part No. 12345762 or equivalent).

CHARGING VALVE LOCATION

The high pressure charging valve is located either on the high pressure line or the muffler, and the low pressure charging valve is located either on the accumulator or low pressure line.

BELT TENSION

Model	Engine	Year	Belt Tension
BUICK			
Century	2.2L/4-134	1993-94	50-70①
	2.5L/4-150	1992	50-70①
	3.1L/V6-189	1994	50-70①
	3.3L/V6-204	1992-93	67-80①
LeSabre	3800/V6-231	1992-94	50-70①
Park Avenue	3800/V6-231	1992-94	50-70①
Regal	3.1L/V6-192	1992-94	50-70①
	3800/V6-231	1992-94	50-70①
Riviera	3800/V6-231	1992-93	50-70①
Roadmaster	5.7L/V8-350	1992-94	105-125①
Skylark	2.3L/4-138	1992-94	50-70①
	3.3L/V6-204	1992-93	67-80①
CADILLAC			
Brougham	5.7L/V8-350	1992	105-125①
DeVille	4.9L/V8-300	1992-94	120①
Eldorado	4.6L/V8-279	1993-94	110①
	4.9L/V8-300	1992-93	120①
Fleetwood (FWD)	4.9L/V8-300	1992	120①
Fleetwood (RWD)	5.7L/V8-350	1993-94	105-125①
Seville	4.6L/V8-279	1993-94	110①
	4.9L/V8-300	1992-94	120①
CHEVROLET			
Beretta	2.2L/4-134	1992-94	63-77①
	2.3L/4-138	1992-94	50-70①
	3.1L/V6-192	1992-94	50-70①
Camaro	3.1/V6-191	1992	85-110①
	3.4L/V6-204	1993-94	50-70①
	5.0L/V8-305	1992	99-121①
	5.7L/V8-350	1993-94	105-125①
Caprice & Impala SS	4.3L/V6-262	1992-93	105-125①
	4.3L/V8-265	1994	105-125①
	5.0L/V8-305	1992-93	105-125①
	5.7L/V8-350	1992-94	105-125①
Cavalier	2.2L/4-134	1992-94	63-77①
	3.1L/V6-192	1992-94	50-70①
Corsica	2.2L/4-134	1992-94	63-77①
	2.3L/4-138	1992-94	50-70①
	3.1L/V6-192	1992-94	50-70①
Corvette	5.7L/V8-350	1992-94	60-90①
Lumina	2.2L/4-134	1993-94	63-77①
	2.5L/4-150	1992	50-70①
	3.1L/V6-192	1992-94	50-70①
	3.4L/V6-204	1992-94	50-70①
GEO			
Metro	1.0L/3-61	1992-94	.20-.25②
Prizm	1.6L/4-97	1992-94	.20-.32②
	1.8L/4-107.5	1993-94	.20-.32②
Storm	1.6L/4-97	1992-93	120-150①
	1.8L/4-110	1992-93	120-150①

Continued

BELT TENSION —Continued

Model	Engine	Year	Belt Tension
OLDSMOBILE			
Achieva	2.3L/4-138	1992-94	50-70 ①
	3.3L/V6-204	1992-93	67-80 ①
Custom Cruiser	5.0L/V8-305	1992	105-125 ①
	5.7L/V8-350	1992	105-125 ①
Cutlass Ciera & Cutlass Cruiser	2.2L/4-134	1993-94	50-70 ①
	2.5L/4-150	1992	50-70 ①
	3.1L/V6-189	1994	50-70 ①
	3.3L/V6-204	1992-93	67-80 ①
Cutlass Supreme	3.1L/V6-192	1992-94	50-70 ①
	3.4L/V6-204	1992-94	50-70 ①
Toronado	3800/V6-231	1992	50-70 ①
Trofeo	3800/V6-231	1992	50-70 ①
88 & 98	3800/V6-231	1992-94	50-70 ①
PONTIAC			
Bonneville	3800/V6-231	1992-94	50-70 ①
Firebird	3.0/V6-191	1992	85-110 ①
	3.4L/V6-204	1993-94	50-70 ①
	5.0L/V8-305	1992	99-121 ①
	5.7L/V8-350	1993-94	105-125 ①
Grand Am	2.3L/4-138	1992-94	50-70 ①
	3.3L/V6-204	1992-93	67-80 ①
Grand Prix	3.1L/V6-192	1992-94	50-70 ①
	3.4L/V6-204	1992-94	50-70 ①
LeMans	1.6L/4-98	1992-93	63-70 ①
Sunbird	2.0L/4-121	1992-94	63-77 ①
	3.1L/V6-192	1992-94	50-70 ①

①—Belt tension is controlled automatically by the belt tensioner. If belt tensioner has to operate out of its range to obtain adequate belt tension, replace belt.

②—Belt deflection measured in inches, using 22 lbs. of force.

COOLING FANS

TABLE OF CONTENTS

NOTE: On Air Bag Equipped Models, Refer To "Air Bag System Precautions" Located In The Front Of This Manual For System Disarming & Arming Procedures.

Variable Speed Fans

INDEX

FAN DRIVE
CLUTCH

GC1089100032000X

Fig. 1 Typical variable-speed cooling fan

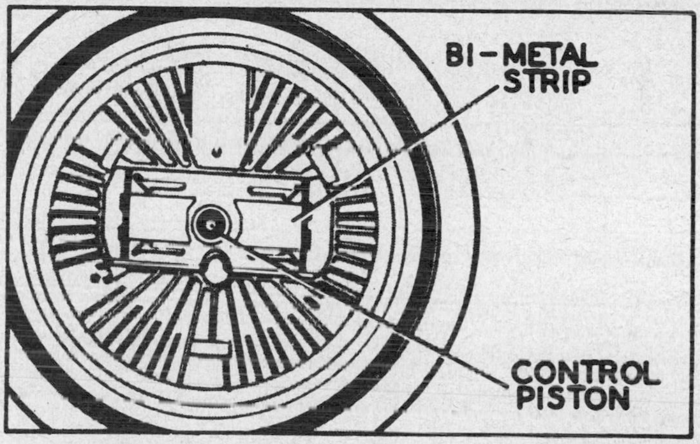
BI-METAL
STRIP
CONTROL
PISTON

GC1089100033000X

Fig. 2 Variable-speed fan w/flat bi-metal thermostatic spring

DESCRIPTION

The fan drive clutch, **Fig. 1**, is a fluid coupling containing silicone oil. Fan speed is regulated by the torque-carrying capacity of the silicone oil. The more silicone oil in the coupling, the greater the fan speed; the less silicone oil, the slower the fan speed.

Two types of fan drive clutches are in use. On one, **Fig. 2**, a bi-metallic strip and control piston on the front of the fluid coupling regulates the amount of silicone oil entering the coupling. The bi-metallic strip flexes outward with an increase in surrounding temperature and allows a piston to move outward. The piston opens a valve regulating the flow of silicone oil into the coupling from a reserve chamber. The silicone oil is returned to the reserve chamber through a bleed hole when the valve is closed.

On the other type of fan drive clutch, **Fig. 3**, a heat-sensitive, bi-metal spring connected to an opening plate brings about a similar result. Both units cause the fan speed to increase with a rise in temperature and to decrease as the temperature goes down.

In some cases a Flex-Fan is used instead of a Fan Drive Clutch. Flexible blades vary the volume of air being drawn through the radiator, automatically increasing the pitch at low engine speeds.

COMPONENT DIAGNOSIS & TESTING

FAN DRIVE CLUTCH TEST

Do not operate the engine until the fan has been checked for possible cracks and separations.

Run the engine at a fast idle speed (1000 RPM) until normal operating temperature is reached. This process can be expedited by blocking off the front of the radiator with a suitable piece of cardboard. Regardless of temperature, the unit must be operated for at least five minutes before being tested.

Stop the engine and, using a glove or a cloth, immediately check the effort required to turn the fan. If considerable effort is required, it can be assumed that the coupling is operating satisfactorily. If very little effort is required to turn the fan, it is an indication that the coupling is not operating properly and should be replaced.

If the clutch fan is the coiled bi-metal spring type, it may be tested while the vehicle is being driven. To check, disconnect the bi-metal spring, **Fig. 3**, and rotate the spring 90° counterclockwise. This disables the temperature-controlled freewheeling feature and the clutch performs like a conventional fan. If this cures the overheating condition, replace the fan clutch.

COMPONENT SERVICE

To prevent silicone fluid from draining into fan drive bearing, do not store or place drive unit on bench with rear of shaft pointing downward.

The removal procedure for either type of fan clutch assembly is similar for all vehicles. The unit must be unfastened from the water pump, then it may be lifted from the vehicle.

The type of unit shown in **Fig. 2** may be partially disassembled for inspection and cleaning as follows:

1. Remove capscrews holding assembly together and separate fan from drive clutch.
2. Remove metal strip on front of fan clutch by pushing one end toward fan clutch body to clear retaining bracket.
3. Push strip aside until its opposite end springs out of place, then remove small control piston.
4. Inspect piston for free movement in coupling device. If piston sticks, clean it with emery cloth. If bi-metal strip is damaged, replace entire unit. **These strips are not interchangeable.**
5. When reassembling, install control piston so that projection on end will contact metal strip, then install metal strip.
6. After reassembly, clean clutch drive with a solvent-soaked cloth. Avoid dipping clutch assembly in any type of liquid.
7. Install assembly in vehicle.

The coil spring type of fan clutch cannot be disassembled, serviced or repaired. If it does not function properly, it must be replaced with a new unit.

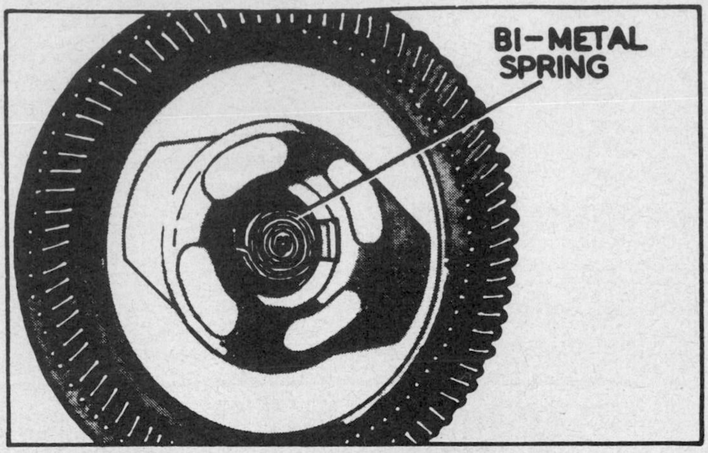
BI-METAL SPRING

Fig. 3 Variable-speed fan w/coiled bi-metal thermostatic spring

Electric Cooling Fans

NOTE: Wire Color Code Identification And Electrical Symbol Identification Located In The Front Of This Manual Can Be Used As An Aid When Using Wiring Circuits Found In This Section.

NOTE: On Air Bag Equipped Models, Refer To Air Bag System Precautions Located In The Front Of This Manual For System Disarming & Arming Procedures.

INDEX

INDEX–Continued

PRECAUTIONS

AIR BAG SYSTEMS

Refer to "Air Bag System Precautions" in the front of this manual for system disarming and arming procedures.

DESCRIPTION

METRO

Radiator Fan

When ignition switch is in On position, system voltage is applied through ignition fuse to radiator fan switch. Fan switch closes when engine coolant temperature reaches 208°F. With fan switch closed, voltage is applied to radiator fan motor. Since the fan motor is permanently grounded, fan operates as soon as voltage is applied. When temperature falls below 199°F, fan switch opens and voltage to fan motor is interrupted.

A/C Condenser Fan

When ignition switch is in On position, system voltage is applied to dual pressure switch through heater fuse on vehicles equipped w/automatic transaxle, or ignition fuse on vehicles equipped w/manual transaxle. Dual pressure switch remains closed as long as refrigerant pressure is between 30-383 psi **on 1992-1993 models** and 28-455 psi **on 1994 models.** With dual pressure switch closed, voltage is applied to A/C clutch relay. A/C clutch relay is energized when A/C amplifier grounds coil of relay. With A/C clutch relay energized, voltage is applied through A/C fuse and closed contacts of A/C clutch relay to coil of A/C condenser fan relay. Since A/C condenser fan relay is permanently grounded, relay energizes, contacts close, and voltage is applied to condenser fan. Since condenser fan is permanently grounded, an operates as soon voltage is applied.

BERETTA & CORSICA

1992–93

Voltage is available at all times through fusible link A to cooling fan relay contacts. With ignition switch in Run position, voltage is available through fuse 9 to cooling fan relay coil. When the ECM receives a signal from coolant temperature sensor, ground is provided for cooling fan relay by module's cooling fan terminal. Voltage is applied through fuse 9 to cooling fan relay coil. When ECM grounds the circuit, cooling fan relay contacts close and voltage is applied through cooling fan relay contacts to cooling fan and the fan runs.

When refrigerant pressure opens cooling fan pressure switch **on models equipped with 3.1L/V6-192 (VIN T) engine,** the ECM responds by energizing cooling fan relay which turns cooling fan on. **On models equipped with 2.3L/4-138 engine,** fan operation will begin with A/C clutch request. The PCM opens ground at vehicle speeds above 35 MPH and fan is turned off.

1994

2.2L/4–134 Engine

The electric cooling fan is controlled by the ECM based on inputs provided by the intake air temperature sensor, the A/C refrigerant pressure sensor and the vehicle speed sensor. When the engine coolant temperature is above 223°F or the A/C is requested, and the vehicle speed is less than 35 mph. The fan will be turned on if any diagnostic trouble codes (DTC 14 or 15) are set, A/C pressure is excessive, or engine coolant temperature is in excess of 239°F regardless of vehicle speed. The fan will remain on and may continue running for up to seven minutes after ignition switch is turned to Off position if engine coolant temperature is above 212°F and intake air temperature is in excess of 176°F. The cooling fan will also continue to run if engine coolant temperature is in excess of 233°F and air intake temperature is in excess of 100°F or if coolant temperature is in excess of 240°F. Fan operation is discontinued if vehicle speed exceeds 70 mph, engine coolant temperature drops below 243°F, or A/C refrigerant pressure is greater than 300 psi.

2.3L/4–138 Engine

The electric cooling fan is controlled by the ECM based on inputs provided by the intake air temperature sensor, the A/C refrigerant pressure sensor and the vehicle speed sensor. The fan will run when the engine coolant temperature is above 217° or when the A/C is turned on at a vehicle speed below 35 mph. The fan will also be turned on if any diagnostic trouble codes (DTC 14 or 15) are set, A/C pressure is excessive, or engine coolant temperature is in excess of 239°F, regardless of vehicle speed.

3.1L/V6–192 Engine

The electric cooling fan is controlled by the ECM based on inputs provided by the intake air temperature sensor, the A/C refrigerant pressure sensor and the vehicle speed sensor. The fan will run when the engine coolant temperature is above 226°F, A/C is turned on and the vehicle speed is less than 70 mph or ECM is in back-up mode. The fan will also run if any diagnostic trouble codes (DTC 14 ,15 or 70) are set, A/C pressure is greater than 187°F or engine coolant temperature is in excess of 239°F. Fan operation is discontinued 30 seconds after engine coolant temperature drops below 219°F and when vehicle speed exceeds 70 mph.

CENTURY, CUTLASS CIERA & CUTLASS CRUISER

2.2L/4-134 ENGINE

Primary Fan

The primary cooling fan is turned on and off by the ECM based on inputs from the ECT sensor, vehicle speed sensor and the A/C system. Battery voltage is applied at all times to terminal "A" of the cooling fan relay and when the ignition switch is in the Run position, battery voltage is applied to terminal "D" of the relay. The ECM energizes the cooling fan relay by grounding the dark green (535) wire. The relay energizes and battery voltage is applied to the cooling fan. The ECM opens circuit (535) to de-energize the relay and turn off the cooling fan. The ECM will turn the cooling fan on when the A/C is requested at any vehicle speed and when A/C is off and vehicle speed is less than 35 mph, coolant temperature is above 225°F (104°C) and vehicle speed is less than 35 mph, or the ECT sensor fails.

Auxiliary Fan

The auxiliary fan will operate when the engine coolant temperature sensor signal indicates a temperature greater than 253°F with A/C Off. The fan will also operate when A/C is requested and vehicle speed is less than 40 MPH. When A/C pressure sensor switch pressure is greater than 200 psi, then the fan will operate.

2.5L/4-151 ENGINE

The cooling fan is turned on and off by the ECM based on inputs from the coolant temperature sensor, vehicle speed sensor and the A/C system. Battery voltage is applied at all times to terminal E of the cooling fan relay and when the ignition switch is in Run position, battery voltage is applied to terminal C of the relay. The ECM energizes the cooling fan relay by grounding the circuit (335). The relay energizes and battery voltage is applied to the cooling fan. The ECM opens circuit 335 to deenergize the relay and turn off the cooling fan. The ECM will turn on the cooling fan when A/C is on and vehicle speed is less than 35 mph or when coolant temperature is above approximately 225°F and vehicle speed is less than 35 mph.

3.1L/V6-192 ENGINE

Primary Fan

This engine is equipped with primary and secondary cooling fans. The primary fan operates when engine temperature is greater than 223° F. When vehicle speed is less than 50 MPH and A/C is requested the fan will operate. The fan will turn On when A/C pressure exceeds 190 psi and A/C is requested.

Secondary Fan

The secondary cooling fan will operate when engine coolant temperature is greater than 223° F. When A/C is requested and the vehicle speed is less than 50 MPH, then the fan will turn On. The fan will operate when A/C refrigerant pressure is greater than 246 psi.

3.3L/V6-204 ENGINE

1992

Two types of cooling fans are used with this engine. The cooling fans are turned on and off either by the cooling fan relay, the cooling fan delay relay, the pusher cooling fan relay or the puller cooling fan relay depending on the specific application or engine requirement.

For operation without A/C, the cooling fan relay is controlled by the cooling fan switch or the ECM. For operation with A/C, the cooling fan relay is controlled by the cooling fan switch, the A/C high pressure switch and the ECM.

When one of these components grounds the coil of the cooling fan relay, the contacts close and the fan comes on.

The heavy duty coolant system, used on some models, consists of two cooling fans. The puller cooling fan is controlled by the puller cooling fan relay. This relay is controlled by the ECM, the puller contacts of the A/C dual pressure switch and the cooling fan switch. The pusher cooling fan is controlled by the pusher cooling fan relay. This relay is controlled by the cooling fan switch and the pusher contacts of the A/C high pressure switch. When any one of these components grounds the coil of one of the relays, that particular fan runs.

When a ground path is provided for the pusher cooling fan relay, the puller cooling fan relay also receives the ground path. When the pusher cooling fan runs, so does the puller cooling fan.

On all vehicles, the cooling fan delay relay operates the cooling fan(s) for a short period of time after the engine is turned off. A solid state timer relay removes the path to ground for the cooling fan delay relay coil to turn off the fan.

1993

The cooling fan is controlled by the cooling fan relay. The cooling fan relay is electrically operated by the ECM. The ECM receives input signals from the ECT sensor, the vehicle speed sensor and the A/C mode selector. The ECM will activate the cooling fan relay when the engine coolant temperature reaches 212°F (100°C), the A/C is turned on and vehicle speed is below 40 mph, or the ECT sensor fails. Any of these input signals causes the ECM to ground circuit (535). When circuit (535) is grounded, the cooling fan relay is energized and its contacts close, turning the cooling fan on.

CAMARO & FIREBIRD

3.1L/V6-192, 3.4L/V6-204 (VIN S), 5.0L/V8-305 (VIN F) & 5.7L/V8-350 (VIN 8) ENGINES

The cooling fan is controlled by the ECM. In the 6 cylinder, the cooling fan is also controlled by the redundant cooling fan switch. When the ECM grounds circuit 335, the cooling fan relay is energized and battery voltage is applied to the cooling fan. If the ECM fails on the 6 cylinder engine, the redundant cooling fan switch will ground the 335 circuit and energize the cooling fan relay. The ECM will ground the cooling fan relay when the coolant temperature sensor indicates the coolant temperature is greater than 222°F or when A/C control head pressure is greater than 233 psi and vehicle speed is less than 40 mph.

The auxiliary cooling fan, used on 8 cylinder engines, is controlled by the fan pressure switch and the auxiliary cooling fan switch. If one of these switches closes, the auxiliary cooling fan relay is turned on. When a switch is closed, terminal D11 of ECM connector C2 is grounded. This tells the ECM that the auxiliary cooling fan should be on.

5.0L/V8-305 (VIN E) ENGINE

The cooling fan is activated by the cooling fan switch. The switch closes when coolant temperature is over 238°F completing a path to ground through the cooling fan relay windings. The relay contacts then close and voltage is applied to the cooling fan. When the coolant temperature drops to 214°F, the switch opens and the cooling fan stops.

In A/C equipped vehicles, the A/C control head completes a path to ground for the cooling fan relay. Voltage is then applied to the cooling fan.

5.7L/V8-350 (VIN P) ENGINE

1993 & 1994 (Early Production)

The cooling fan is controlled by the ECM based on various inputs. Battery voltage is supplied to the primary fan relay on terminals D1 and F4 of the secondary fan relay. Ignition voltage is supplied to terminal D5 of the primary fan relay and F2 of the secondary fan relay. Grounding circuit 335 will energize the primary cooling fan relay and supply battery voltage to the secondary fan motor. Grounding circuit 473 will energize the secondary cooling fan relay and supply battery voltage to the secondary fan motor.

1994 (Late Production)

This engine is equipped with two cooling fans. When cooling fan relay No. 1 is energized the cooling fans are connected in series and operate at low speed. When all three relays are energized the fans are connected in parallel and operate together at high speed. When coolant temperature exceeds 226°F, then the ECM will command the low speed fan to operate. At a coolant temperature of 235°F, the high speed fans begin operation, When coolant temperature drops to 230°F the high speed fans are commanded Off. When certain diagnostic codes are set, then the ECM commands low speed fans On.

3.4L/V6-204 (VIN S) ENGINE

1994

This engine is equipped with an ECM controlled electric cooling fan. The fan begins operation when engine coolant temperature is above 228°F or A/C refrigerant pressure is greater than 20 psi. If diagnostic trouble codes (DTC 14 or 15) are set then the cooling fan will be in operation. If engine coolant temperature is above 235°F or A/C is requested and vehicle speed is less than 35 mph, then the fan will operate. The fan will also operate if A/C pressure is greater than 240 psi and remain On until vehicle speed exceeds 70 mph. Current flows to ground through the ECM energizing the fan relays.

BONNEVILLE

1992–93

Two cooling fans, wired in parallel, operate whenever cooling is required.

The powertrain control module (PCM) has two cooling fan control terminals, one for high speed and one for low speed. When the PCM's low speed control closes at connector C3, terminal C4, it grounds the low speed cooling fan relay coil. When the ignition switch is in the Run position and relay contacts close, voltage is supplied to the cooling fans. The cooling fan resistors drop the voltage to the lefthand cooling fan, causing it to run in low speed. The righthand cooling fan runs also, but at high speed because the cooling fan resistors are bypassed. The PCM's low speed output is turned on when coolant temperature reaches 212°F.

High speed operation is similar to low speed: when the coolant temperature reaches 226°F, the PCM's high speed control closes at connector C3, terminal C3, grounding the high speed coolant relay coil. The relay contacts close and both fans run at high speed since the PCM's low speed control remains closed. When A/C head pressure reaches 210 psi, the A/C pressure fan switch closes, grounding PCM connector C1, terminal D9. This also

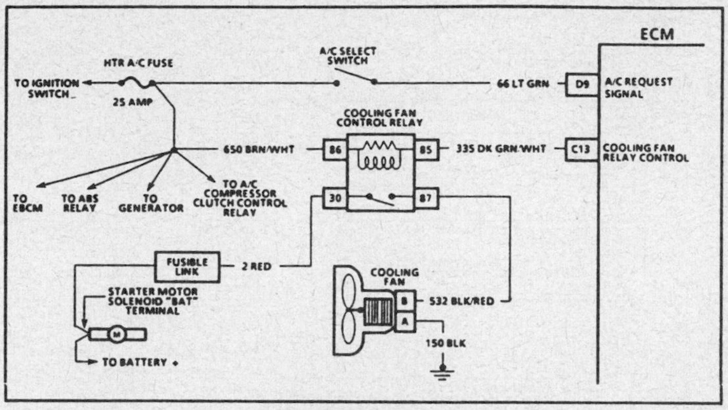
ECM
HTR A/C FUSE
A/C SELECT SWITCH
TO IGNITION SWITCH
25 AMP
66 LT GRN
D9
A/C REQUEST SIGNAL
COOLING FAN CONTROL RELAY
650 BRN/WHT
86
85
335 DK GRN/WHT
C13
COOLING FAN RELAY CONTROL
30
87
TO EBCM
TO ABS RELAY
TO GENERATOR
TO A/C COMPRESSOR CLUTCH CONTROL RELAY
FUSIBLE LINK
2 RED
STARTER MOTOR SOLENOID "BAT" TERMINAL
COOLING FAN
B
A
532 BLK/RED
150 BLK
TO BATTERY +

CHART C-12
COOLING FAN CONTROL
2.2L

Circuit Description:

Battery voltage to operate the cooling fan motor is supplied to relay by CKT 2. Ignition voltage to energize the relay is supplied to relay by CKT 650. When the ECM grounds CKT 335, the relay is energized and the cooling fan is turned "ON." When the engine is running, the ECM will turn the cooling fan "ON" if:

- A/C is "ON."

When the engine is running, the ECM will turn the engine cooling fan "ON" for any of the following reasons:

- Diagnostic Trouble Code (DTC) 14 is set.
- Engine coolant temperature is 106°C (223°F) or greater.
- A/C refrigerant pressure is 51 psi or greater with A/C selected and a Diagnostic Trouble Code (DTC) 66 is not set.

Once the cooling fan is enabled, the ECM will turn the fan "OFF" when:

- Engine is turned "OFF."
- Engine coolant temperature drops to 99°C (210°F) or less.
- A/C refrigerant pressure drops to 41 psi or less with A/C selected.

Diagnostic Aids:

If the owner complained of an overheating problem, it must be determined if the complaint was due to an actual boil over, or the hot light, or temperature gage indicated overheating.

If the gage or light indicates overheating, but no boil over is detected, the gage circuit should be checked. The gage accuracy can also be checked by checking the engine coolant temperature display using a scan tool and comparing its display with the instrument cluster gage.

If the engine is actually overheating and the gage indicates overheating, but the cooling fan is not coming "ON," the ECT sensor has probably shifted out of calibration and should be replaced.

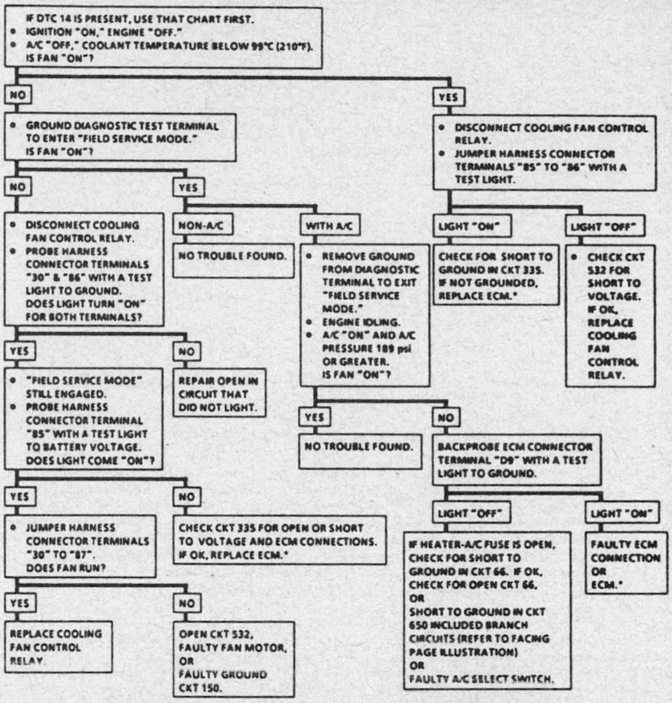
IF DTC 14 IS PRESENT, USE THAT CHART FIRST.
• IGNITION "ON," ENGINE "OFF."
• A/C "OFF," COOLANT TEMPERATURE BELOW 99°C (210°F). IS FAN "ON"?
NO
YES
• GROUND DIAGNOSTIC TEST TERMINAL TO ENTER "FIELD SERVICE MODE." IS FAN "ON"?
• DISCONNECT COOLING FAN CONTROL RELAY.
• JUMPER HARNESS CONNECTOR TERMINALS "85" TO "86" WITH A TEST LIGHT.
NO
YES
• DISCONNECT COOLING FAN CONTROL RELAY.
• PROBE HARNESS CONNECTOR TERMINALS "30" & "86" WITH A TEST LIGHT TO GROUND. DOES LIGHT TURN "ON" FOR BOTH TERMINALS?
NON-A/C
NO TROUBLE FOUND.
WITH A/C
• REMOVE GROUND FROM DIAGNOSTIC TERMINAL TO EXIT "FIELD SERVICE MODE."
• ENGINE IDLING.
• A/C "ON" AND A/C PRESSURE 189 psi OR GREATER. IS FAN "ON"?
LIGHT "ON"
CHECK FOR SHORT TO GROUND IN CKT 335. IF NOT GROUNDED, REPLACE ECM.*
LIGHT "OFF"
• CHECK CKT 532 FOR SHORT TO VOLTAGE. IF OK, REPLACE COOLING FAN CONTROL RELAY.
YES
NO
• "FIELD SERVICE MODE" STILL ENGAGED.
• PROBE HARNESS CONNECTOR TERMINAL "85" WITH A TEST LIGHT TO BATTERY VOLTAGE. DOES LIGHT COME "ON"?
REPAIR OPEN IN CIRCUIT THAT DID NOT LIGHT.
YES
NO TROUBLE FOUND.
NO
BACKPROBE ECM CONNECTOR TERMINAL "D9" WITH A TEST LIGHT TO GROUND.
YES
NO
• JUMPER HARNESS CONNECTOR TERMINALS "30" TO "87". DOES FAN RUN?
CHECK CKT 335 FOR OPEN OR SHORT TO VOLTAGE AND ECM CONNECTIONS. IF OK, REPLACE ECM.*
LIGHT "OFF"
IF HEATER-A/C FUSE IS OPEN, CHECK FOR SHORT TO GROUND IN CKT 66. IF OK, CHECK FOR OPEN CKT 66, OR SHORT TO GROUND IN CKT 650 INCLUDED BRANCH CIRCUITS (REFER TO FACING PAGE ILLUSTRATION) OR FAULTY A/C SELECT SWITCH.
LIGHT "ON"
FAULTY ECM CONNECTION OR ECM.*
YES
NO
REPLACE COOLING FAN CONTROL RELAY.
OPEN CKT 532, FAULTY FAN MOTOR, OR FAULTY GROUND CKT 150.

IF ECM IS FAULTY AND MUST BE REPLACED, THE NEW ECM MUST BE PROGRAMMED.

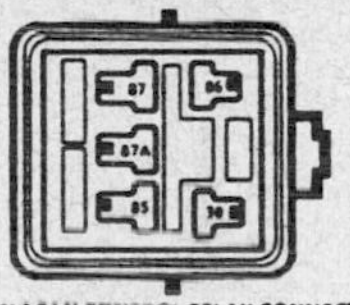
87
86
87A
85
30

COOLING FAN CONTROL RELAY CONNECTOR

GC1089200062000X

Fig. 1 Chart C-12, cooling fan diagnosis. 1992–93 Cavalier w/2.2L/4-134 engine

causes the PCM high speed control to close, and both cooling fans run at high speed.

1994

This engine uses two cooling fans, the lefthand fan has two speeds and the righthand fan one speed. When engine coolant temperature is reaches 212°F or when A/C is requested then the low speed cooling fan operates. The high speed fan begins operation at coolant temperatures in excess of 226°F or when A/C refrigerant pressure is above 210 psi. Power for the fan motors is supplied by the 40 amp Maxifuse at terminal 87 on cooling fan relays. The relays are energized when current flows to ground through the ECM.

CAVALIER

1992–93

Refer to "Circuit Description" in **Figs. 1 and 2** for cooling fan operation.

1994

2.2L/4-134 (VIN 4) Engine

The cooling fan is controlled by the ECM through the fan relay by inputs received from the engine coolant temperature sensor, intake air temperature sensors, A/C control switch, A/C pressure switch and the vehicle speed sensor. When the ECM grounds circuit 335 the cooling fan begins operation. When A/C is requested the cooling fan will run. When vehicle speed is below 35 MPH the fan will operate. At speeds above 35 MPH the ECM opens the ground circuit to the fan and discontinues fan operation. If A/C pressure or coolant temperature becomes excessive or diagnostic trouble codes (DTC 14 or 15) are set, the ECM will begin fan operation regardless of vehicle speed.

Fan run-on will occur up to seven minutes after vehicle ignition is turned Off under certain high temperature conditions. If engine coolant temperature is greater than 212°F and intake air temperature is greater than 176°F, then the cooling fan will run-on. If engine coolant temperature is greater than 234°F and air intake temperature is greater than 158°F then the cooling fan will run-on. If engine coolant temperature is greater than 240°F, then the cooling fan will run-on. The cooling fan will remain On up to seven minutes until these combinations of conditions no longer exist.

3.1L/V6-192 (VIN T) Engine

The cooling fan is controlled by the ECM through the fan relay by inputs received from the engine coolant temperature sensor, intake air temperature sensors, A/C control switch, A/C pressure switch and the vehicle speed sensor. When the ECM grounds circuit 335 the cooling fan begins operation. If engine coolant temperature is in excess of 228°F or when A/C is requested and the A/C pressure is above 200 psi, then the cooling fan will run. When vehicle speed is above 70 MPH the ECM opens the ground circuit to the fan and discontinues fan operation. If A/C head pressure or coolant temperature becomes excessive or diagnostic trouble codes (DTC 14 or 15) are set, the ECM will begin fan operation regardless of vehicle speed.

REGAL

3.1L/V6-192 ENGINE

1992–93

Refer to "Cutlass Supreme & Grand Prix in this section for a description of cooling fan system operation.

3.8L/V6-231 (VIN L) ENGINE

Low Speed Operation

When coolant temperature is greater than 212°F, ECM provides a ground signal to coil of fan relay No. 1. Relay energizes and voltage is applied to primary and secondary cooling fans, which are connected in series through normally closed contacts of relay No. 3. ECM will continue to energize fan relay No. 1 for two minutes when ignition is shut off if coolant temperature is above 230°F and inlet air temperature is above 104°F. Also, ECM will energize fan relay No. 1 if A/C is required.

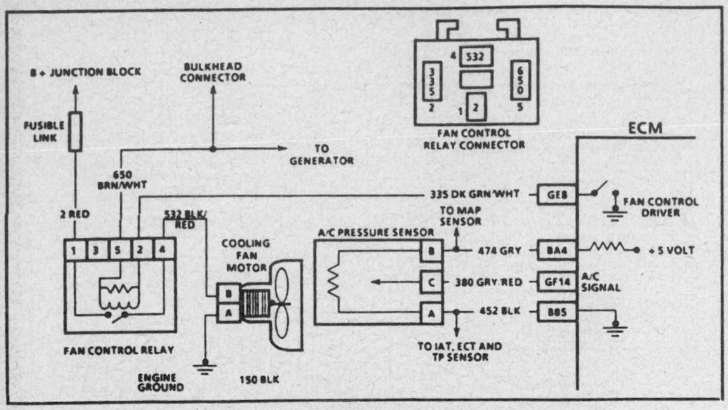
B + JUNCTION BLOCK
BULKHEAD CONNECTOR
FUSIBLE LINK
TO GENERATOR
650 BRN/WHT
2 RED
532 BLK/RED
335 DK GRN/WHT
FAN CONTROL RELAY CONNECTOR
ECM
GE8
FAN CONTROL DRIVER
TO MAP SENSOR
A/C PRESSURE SENSOR
COOLING FAN MOTOR
474 GRY
BA4
+5 VOLT
380 GRY/RED
GF14
A/C SIGNAL
452 BLK
BB5
TO IAT, ECT AND TP SENSOR
FAN CONTROL RELAY
ENGINE GROUND
150 BLK

CHART C-12
(Page 1 of 2)
COOLANT FAN CONTROL DIAGNOSIS

Circuit Description:

The electric cooling fan is controlled by the ECM based on inputs from the engine coolant temperature sensor, the A/C pressure sensor and vehicle speed. The ECM controls the fan by grounding CKT 335, which energizes the fan control relay. Battery voltage is then supplied to the fan motor.

The ECM grounds CKT 335 when engine coolant temperature is over about 109°C (228°F) or when A/C has been requested and the A/C pressure sensor indicates high A/C pressure, 200 psi (1380 kPa). Once the ECM turns the relay "ON," it will keep it "ON" for a minimum of 25 seconds or until vehicle speed exceeds 70 mph.

Also, if DTC 14 or 15 sets or the ECM is in back up, the fan will run at all times.

Test Description: Number(s) below refer to circled number(s) on the diagnostic chart.

1. With the diagnostic terminal grounded, the cooling fan control driver will close, which should energize the fan control relay.
2. If the A/C fan control switch or circuit is open, the fan would run whenever A/C is requested.
3. With A/C clutch engaged, the A/C fan control switch should open when A/C high pressure exceeds about 200 psi (1380 kPa). This signal should cause the ECM to energize the fan control relay.
4. Disconnecting the A/C pressure sensor will cause a DTC 66 to set. After finishing this step, be sure to clear DTC(s).

Diagnostic Aids:

If the owner complained of an overheating problem, it must be determined if the complaint was due to an actual boilover or the hot light (temperature gage) indicated over heating.

If the gage (light) indicates overheating but no boilover is detected, the gage circuit should be checked. The gage accuracy can also be checked by comparing the coolant sensor reading using a Tech 1 scan tool and comparing its reading with the gage reading.

If the engine is actually overheating and the gage indicates overheating but the cooling fan is not coming "ON," the ECT sensor has probably shifted out of calibration and should be replaced.

If the engine is overheating and the cooling fan is "ON," the cooling system should be checked.

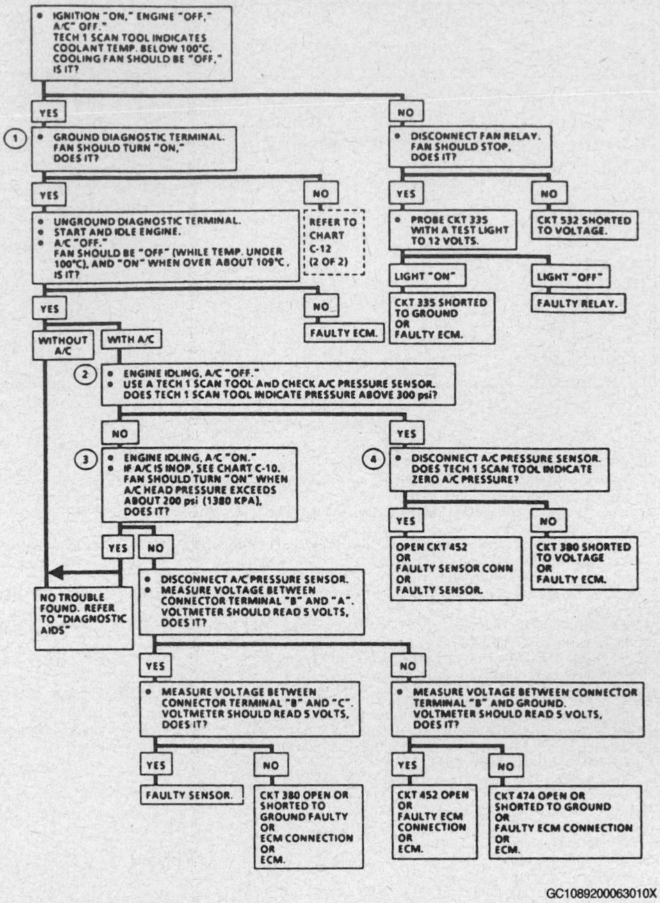
• IGNITION "ON," ENGINE "OFF," A/C" OFF." TECH 1 SCAN TOOL INDICATES COOLANT TEMP. BELOW 100°C. COOLING FAN SHOULD BE "OFF," IS IT?
YES
NO
1
• GROUND DIAGNOSTIC TERMINAL. FAN SHOULD TURN "ON," DOES IT?
• DISCONNECT FAN RELAY. FAN SHOULD STOP, DOES IT?
YES
NO
YES
NO
• UNGROUND DIAGNOSTIC TERMINAL.
• START AND IDLE ENGINE.
• A/C "OFF." FAN SHOULD BE "OFF" (WHILE TEMP. UNDER 100°C), AND "ON" WHEN OVER ABOUT 109°C. IS IT?
REFER TO CHART C-12 (2 OF 2)
• PROBE CKT 335 WITH A TEST LIGHT TO 12 VOLTS.
CKT 532 SHORTED TO VOLTAGE.
LIGHT "ON"
LIGHT "OFF"
CKT 335 SHORTED TO GROUND OR FAULTY ECM.
FAULTY RELAY.
YES
NO
FAULTY ECM.
WITHOUT A/C
WITH A/C
2
• ENGINE IDLING, A/C "OFF."
• USE A TECH 1 SCAN TOOL AND CHECK A/C PRESSURE SENSOR. DOES TECH 1 SCAN TOOL INDICATE PRESSURE ABOVE 300 psi?
NO
YES
3
• ENGINE IDLING, A/C "ON."
• IF A/C IS INOP, SEE CHART C-10. FAN SHOULD TURN "ON" WHEN A/C HEAD PRESSURE EXCEEDS ABOUT 200 psi (1380 KPA), DOES IT?
4
• DISCONNECT A/C PRESSURE SENSOR. DOES TECH 1 SCAN TOOL INDICATE ZERO A/C PRESSURE?
YES
NO
YES
NO
OPEN CKT 452 OR FAULTY SENSOR CONN OR FAULTY SENSOR.
CKT 380 SHORTED TO VOLTAGE OR FAULTY ECM.
NO TROUBLE FOUND. REFER TO "DIAGNOSTIC AIDS"
• DISCONNECT A/C PRESSURE SENSOR.
• MEASURE VOLTAGE BETWEEN CONNECTOR TERMINAL "B" AND "A". VOLTMETER SHOULD READ 5 VOLTS, DOES IT?
YES
NO
• MEASURE VOLTAGE BETWEEN CONNECTOR TERMINAL "B" AND "C". VOLTMETER SHOULD READ 5 VOLTS, DOES IT?
• MEASURE VOLTAGE BETWEEN CONNECTOR TERMINAL "B" AND GROUND. VOLTMETER SHOULD READ 5 VOLTS, DOES IT?
YES
NO
YES
NO
FAULTY SENSOR.
CKT 380 OPEN OR SHORTED TO GROUND FAULTY OR ECM CONNECTION OR ECM.
CKT 452 OPEN OR FAULTY ECM CONNECTION OR ECM.
CKT 474 OPEN OR SHORTED TO GROUND OR FAULTY ECM CONNECTION OR ECM.
GC1089200063010X

Fig. 2 Chart C-12, cooling fan diagnosis (Part 1 of 2). 1992–93 Cavalier w/3.1L/V6-192 (VIN T) engine

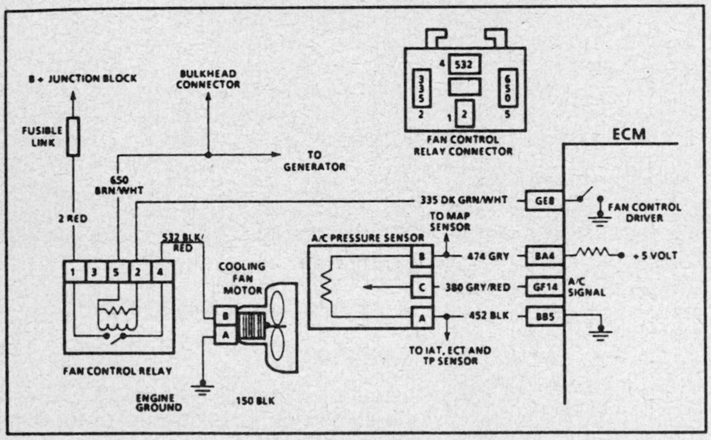
B + JUNCTION BLOCK
BULKHEAD CONNECTOR
FUSIBLE LINK
TO GENERATOR
650 BRN/WHT
2 RED
532 BLK/RED
335 DK GRN/WHT
FAN CONTROL RELAY CONNECTOR
ECM
GE8
FAN CONTROL DRIVER
TO MAP SENSOR
A/C PRESSURE SENSOR
COOLING FAN MOTOR
474 GRY
BA4
+5 VOLT
380 GRY/RED
GF14
A/C SIGNAL
452 BLK
BB5
TO IAT, ECT AND TP SENSOR
FAN CONTROL RELAY
ENGINE GROUND
150 BLK

CHART C-12
(Page 2 of 2)
COOLANT FAN CONTROL DIAGNOSIS

Test Description: Number(s) below refer to circled number(s) on the diagnostic chart.

1. 12 volts should be available to both terminal "2" and CKT 532 when the ignition is "ON."
2. This test checks the ability of the ECM to ground CKT 335.

The Malfunction Indicator Lamp (MIL) should also be flashing at this point.

3. If the fan does not turn "ON" at this point, CKT 532 or CKT 150 is open or the cooling fan motor is faulty.

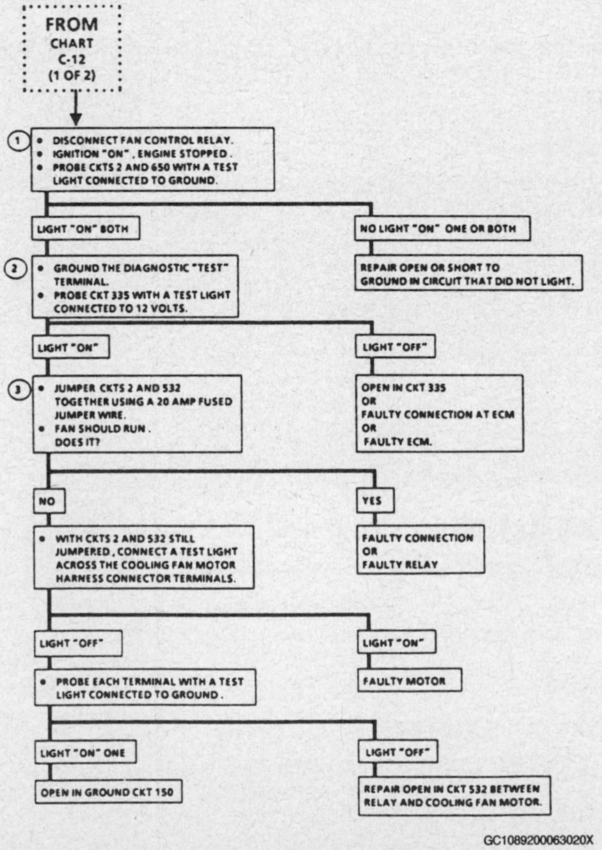
FROM CHART C-12 (1 OF 2)
1
• DISCONNECT FAN CONTROL RELAY.
• IGNITION "ON", ENGINE STOPPED.
• PROBE CKTS 2 AND 650 WITH A TEST LIGHT CONNECTED TO GROUND.
LIGHT "ON" BOTH
NO LIGHT "ON" ONE OR BOTH
2
• GROUND THE DIAGNOSTIC "TEST" TERMINAL.
• PROBE CKT 335 WITH A TEST LIGHT CONNECTED TO 12 VOLTS.
REPAIR OPEN OR SHORT TO GROUND IN CIRCUIT THAT DID NOT LIGHT.
LIGHT "ON"
LIGHT "OFF"
3
• JUMPER CKTS 2 AND 532 TOGETHER USING A 20 AMP FUSED JUMPER WIRE.
• FAN SHOULD RUN. DOES IT?
OPEN IN CKT 335 OR FAULTY CONNECTION AT ECM OR FAULTY ECM.
NO
YES
• WITH CKTS 2 AND 532 STILL JUMPERED, CONNECT A TEST LIGHT ACROSS THE COOLING FAN MOTOR HARNESS CONNECTOR TERMINALS.
FAULTY CONNECTION OR FAULTY RELAY
LIGHT "OFF"
LIGHT "ON"
• PROBE EACH TERMINAL WITH A TEST LIGHT CONNECTED TO GROUND.
FAULTY MOTOR
LIGHT "ON" ONE
LIGHT "OFF"
OPEN IN GROUND CKT 150
REPAIR OPEN IN CKT 532 BETWEEN RELAY AND COOLING FAN MOTOR.
GC1089200063020X

Fig. 2 Chart C-12, cooling fan diagnosis (Part 2 of 2). 1992–93 Cavalier w/3.1L/V6-192 (VIN T) engine

High Speed Operation

When coolant temperature is greater than 226°F, ECM provides a ground signal to fan relay No. 2 and 3. Relays energize and cooling fans are now connected in parallel and fans now run at high speed. Relays remain energized until coolant temperature drops below 225°F. ECM will also energize fan relays 2 and 3 if A/C is requested and fan A/C pressure switch closes.

If cooling fans are operating in low speed mode and vehicle is travelling at 50 mph or greater, ECM will de-energize fan relay No. 1. If cooling fans are operating in high speed mode, ECM will not de-energize relay.

CUTLASS SUPREME & GRAND PRIX

3.1L/V6—192 (VIN M) ENGINE

The primary cooling fan operates when engine coolant temperature is above 226°F with A/C Off or 223°F with A/C or Defrost functions requested and vehicle speed is less than 50 mph. When A/C refrigerant pressure is greater than 185 psi, then the cooling fans will run. When diagnostic trouble codes (DTC14 ,15, or 70) are set then cooling fans will operate. The ECM will discontinue primary fan operation when the ignition is turned Off, engine coolant temperature falls below 210°F or A/C pressure drops below 189 psi with A/C selected.

Secondary fan operation begins when engine coolant temperature reaches 235°F with A/C Off or On. The secondary fan will operate if A/C pressure is above 136 psi with A/C requested and vehicle speed is below 50 mph . The secondary fan will discontinue operation if engine coolant temperature drops below 228°F, refrigerant pressure drops to less than 185 psi or the ignition switch is turned to the Off position.

3.1L/V6—192 (VIN T) ENGINE

1992

The primary cooling fan operates when engine coolant temperature is above 226°F with A/C Off or 223°F with A/C or Defrost functions requested and vehicle speed is less than 70 mph. When A/C refrigerant pressure is greater than 200 psi, then the cooling fans will run. When diagnostic trouble codes (DTC14 or 15) are set then cooling fans will operate.

Secondary fan operation begins when engine coolant temperature reaches 227°F with A/C Off. The secondary fan will operate if A/C pressure is above 200 psi with A/C requested and vehicle speed is below 40 mph.

1993

The primary cooling fan operates when engine coolant temperature is above 223°F with A/C functions requested and vehicle speed is less than 70 mph. When A/C refrigerant pressure is greater than 200 psi, then the primary cooling fan will run. When diagnostic trouble codes (DTC14 or 15) are set then cooling fans will operate. The primary cooling fan will operate if ECM is in back-up mode.

Secondary fan operation begins when engine coolant temperature reaches 227°F with A/C requested. The secondary fan will operate if A/C pressure is above 200 psi with A/C requested and vehicle speed is below 40 mph.

3.4L/V6—204 (VIN X) ENGINE

This engine is equipped with two ECM controlled electric cooling fans. The lefthand fan, No. 1, begins operation when engine coolant temperature is above 223°F or A/C refrigerant pressure is greater than 240 psi. If diagnostic trouble codes (DTC PO117 or PO118) are set then the cooling fan will be in operation. The righthand fan, No. 2, is used for heavy duty cooling with A/C. If engine coolant temperature is above 235°F or A/C is requested and vehicle speed is less than 40 MPH then the fan will operate. The righthand fan will also operate if A/C pressure is greater than 240 psi. Power for both fans is supplied by a 60 amp maxifuse to the fan relays. Current flows to ground through the ECM energizing the fan relays

3.8L/V6-231 (VIN L) ENGINE

Each cooling fan is turned on and off by separate cooling fan relays.

The primary cooling fan relay coil is grounded through the ECM when vehicle speed is less than a speed determined by the ECM and engine coolant reaches 227°F with A/C off and 223°F with A/C on. The contacts close and voltage is applied through the primary cooling fan relay to the primary cooling fan. The primary cooling fan runs until the Ignition switch is turned off, or coolant temperature decreases to 220°F with A/C off or 216°F with A/C on.

The secondary cooling fan relay coil is grounded through the ECM when the coolant temperature reaches 245°F. The contacts close and voltage is applied to the cooling fan. The fan runs at high speed. The cooling fan will continue to run at high speed in Run position until coolant temperature lowers to 238°F.

LUMINA

2.5L/4—151 (VIN R) ENGINE

1992

This engine is equipped with two ECM controlled electric cooling fans. The lefthand fan, No. 1, begins operation when engine coolant temperature is above 223°F or A/C refrigerant pressure is greater than 250 psi and vehicle speed is below 30 mph. If diagnostic trouble codes (DTC 14 or 15) are set then the primary fan will be in operation. If the ECM is in back-up mode then the fan will operate. The righthand fan, No. 2, is used for heavy duty cooling with A/C. If engine coolant temperature is above 244°F or A/C is requested and vehicle speed is less than 40 MPH then the fan will operate. The righthand fan will also operate if A/C pressure is greater than 250 psi. Current flows to ground through the ECM energizing the fan relays

2.2L/4—134 (VIN 4) ENGINE

1993

This engine is equipped with two ECM controlled electric cooling fans. The primary fan, No. 1, begins operation when engine coolant temperature is above 223°F or A/C refrigerant head pressure is greater than 219 psi if diagnostic trouble code (DTC 66) is not set. If diagnostic trouble codes (DTC 14) is set or ECM is in backup mode, then the primary cooling fan will be in operation. The secondary fan, No. 2, is used for heavy duty cooling with A/C. If engine is running, coolant temperature is above 235°F, or A/C is requested, then the fan will operate. The secondary fan will also operate if the A/C compressor clutch is On. Current flows to ground through the ECM energizing the fan relays.

The cooling fans will cease operation when coolant temperature drops below 210°F or less, A/C pressure drops below 189 psi or less with A/C requested.

3.1L/V6—192 (VIN T) ENGINE

1992

Each cooling fan is controlled by individual cooling fan relays. The primary cooling fan relay coil is grounded through the ECM when vehicle speed is less than the speed set by the ECM and the coolant temperature reaches 227°F with the A/C off, and 223°F with A/C on. The primary cooling fan runs until the ignition switch is turned off, or coolant temperature decreases to 220°F with A/C off, or 216°F with A/C on.

The secondary cooling fan relay coil is grounded through the ECM when the coolant temperature reaches 245°F. The contacts close and voltage is applied to the secondary cooling fan, and **on models with the 3.1L/V6-192 VIN X engine,** the generator cooling fan. The fan runs at high speed and will continue with the ignition in Run position until the coolant temperature lowers to 238°F.

1993

Each cooling fan is turned on and off by a separate cooling fan relay.

The primary cooling fan relay coil is grounded by the ECM when vehicle speed is less than a speed determined by and engine coolant temperature reaches 227°F (108°C) with A/C off or 223°F (106°C) with A/C on. The relay contacts close and voltage is applied through the primary cooling fan relay to the primary cooling fan. The primary cooling fan will run until the ignition switch is turned off or engine coolant temperature decreases to 220°F (104°C) with A/C off 216°F (102°C) with A/C on.

The secondary cooling fan relay coil is grounded by the ECM when the engine coolant temperature reaches 245°F (118°C). The relay contacts close and voltage is applied to the secondary cooling fan. The fan runs at high speed until engine coolant temperature lowers to 238°F (114°C).

1994

The primary cooling fan operates when engine coolant temperature is above 223°F with A/C requested and vehicle speed is less than 70 mph. When A/C refrigerant pressure is greater than 200 psi, then the cooling fans will run. When diagnostic trouble codes (DTC 14 , or 15 are set) or the ECM is in back mode the cooling fans will operate. The ECM will discontinue primary fan operation when the vehicle speed exceeds 70 mph.

Secondary fan operation begins when engine coolant temperature reaches 223°F with A/C requested. The secondary fan will operate if A/C pressure is above 200 psi with A/C requested and vehicle speed is below 40 mph.

3.4L/V6—204 ENGINE

1992—93

This engine is equipped with two ECM controlled electric cooling fans. The primary fan, No.1, begins operation when engine coolant temperature is above 223°F or A/C is requested and refrigerant pressure is greater than 200 psi. If diagnostic trouble codes (DTC 14 or 15) are set or ECM is in back-up mode, then the cooling fan will be in operation. The secondary fan, No. 2, is used for heavy duty cooling with A/C. If engine coolant temperature is above 235°F or A/C is requested and vehicle speed is less than 40 mph then the fan will operate. The secondary fan will also operate if A/C pressure is greater than 240 psi. Current flows to ground through the ECM energizing the fan relays

1994

This engine is equipped with two ECM controlled electric cooling fans. The primary fan, No.1 lefthand fan, begins operation when engine coolant temperature is above 223°F or A/C is requested and refrigerant pressure is greater than 240 psi. If diagnostic trouble codes (DTC P0117 or P0118) are set or ECM is in back-up mode, then the cooling fan will be in operation. The secondary fan, No. 2 righthand fan, is used for heavy duty cooling with A/C. If engine coolant temperature is above 235°F or A/C is requested and vehicle speed is less than 40 mph then the fan will operate. The secondary fan will also operate if A/C pressure is greater than 240 psi. Current flows to ground through the ECM energizing the fan relays

CORVETTE

1992—93

VIN J

Operation is similar to the VIN P engine except the secondary cooling fan is operated by the A/C cooling fan switch instead of the A/C pressure sensor.

When the A/C cooling fan switch is open (above 240 psi), the switch removes ground to the A/C cooling fan switch input at the ECM. The ECM then grounds the secondary cooling fan relay coil, closing the relay contacts and turning on the secondary cooling fan motor.

If ECM codes are set or if the ECM is running in fuel-mode back-up, the fans will be On at all times.

VIN P

The primary and secondary cooling fans are turned on and off by the ECM based on inputs from the coolant temperature sensor, the vehicle speed sensor and the A/C pressure sensor, if equipped. Battery is applied at all times to terminal E of the cooling fan relay and when ignition switch is in Run position, battery voltage is applied to terminal D of the relays. The ECM energizes the cooling fan by grounding circuit 335. The relay energizes, and battery voltage is applied to the primary cooling fan motor.

The secondary coolant operates similar to the primary cooling fan. Voltage is supplied at all times to the secondary cooling fan relay contacts by fusible link E. Voltage is supplied to the secondary cooling fan relay coil when ignition switch is in the Run, Bulb Test or Start position.

If ECM codes are set or if the ECM is running in back-up mode, the fans will run.

1994

VIN J

Operation is similar to the VIN P engine except the secondary cooling fan is operated by the A/C cooling fan switch instead of the A/C pressure sensor.

When the A/C cooling fan switch is open (above 240 psi), the switch removes ground to the A/C cooling fan switch input at the ECM. The ECM then grounds the secondary cooling fan relay coil, closing the relay contacts and turning on the secondary cooling fan motor.

If ECM diagnostic trouble codes (DTC 14,15, 52, or 62 are set), engine oil temperature is too high or A/C head pressure is too high, then the fans will operate. The ECM will command primary fan On at an engine coolant temperature greater than 226°F and command fan Off at 217°F. The ECM will command secondary fan On at an engine coolant temperature greater than 234°F and command fan Off at 230°F.

VIN P

The primary and secondary cooling fans are turned on and off by the ECM based on inputs from the coolant temperature sensor, the vehicle speed sensor and the A/C pressure sensor, if equipped. Battery is applied at all times to terminal E of the cooling fan relay and when ignition switch is in Run position, battery voltage is applied to terminal D of the relays. The ECM energizes the cooling fan by grounding circuit 335. The relay energizes, and battery voltage is applied to the primary cooling fan motor. The primary fan operates when engine coolant temperature is above 219°F and when the A/C is requested. ECM will command fan Off at 208°F.

The secondary coolant operates similar to the primary cooling fan. Voltage is supplied at all times to the secondary cooling fan relay contacts by fusible link E. Voltage is supplied to the secondary cooling fan relay coil when ignition switch is in the Run, Bulb Test or Start position. The ECM commands secondary fan On at 228°F and commands fan Off at 217°F. If diagnostic codes are set or if the ECM is in back-up mode, the fans will operate.

DEVILLE, ELDORADO, SEVILLE & FLEETWOOD (FWD)

1992

The powertrain control module (PCM) controls both cooling fans by controlling three relays through two outputs. There are two modes of cooling fan operation, low speed and high speed. In the low speed mode the cooling fans are powered in series, cooling fan relay 1 is energized by the PCM and both cooling fans run at low speed. In the high speed mode the cooling fans are powered in parallel which allows the fans to run at high speed. Cooling fans operate only when the ignition is in run.

1993

This system uses two cooling fans wired in parallel. Both fans run whenever cooling is required.

The Powertrain Control Module (PCM) has two cooling fan outputs, one each for high and low speed. When PCM low speed output is turned on at connector C2 (terminal 11), it grounds the low speed cooling fan relay's coil. If ignition switch is in the Run position, the relay's contacts close, completing the circuit to the cooling fans. The cooling fan resistor lowers voltage to the left side cooling fan, which causes it to run at low speed. Since the right side cooling fan is wired in parallel, it also runs, but at high speed because the cooling fan resistor is bypassed. The PCM low speed output is turned on when coolant temperature reaches 208°F (98°C).

If coolant temperature reaches 226°F (106°C) or refrigerant temperature reaches 212°F (100°C), the PCM's high speed output at connector C2 (terminal B8) is turned on. This output grounds the coil of the high speed cooling fan relay, which causes the relay contacts to close and both fans run at high speed.

The PCM controls its outputs based on signals received from the Coolant Temperature Sensor (CTS) and Refrigerant High Side Temperature Sensor. The CTS is wired directly to the PCM and the refrigerant temperature sensor is wired to the BCM. The BCM processes the signal from the sensor and sends it to the PCM through a Serial Data Line.

1994

4.6L/V8—279 Northstar Engine

The ECM will turn on the cooling fans at an engine temperature in excess of 223°F, transaxle temperature greater than 239°F, when A/C is requested. A/C high side temperature in excess of 158°F and or A/C high side refrigerant temperature sensor fails. The ECM commands fans On if low coolant level is detected and engine coolant temperature is above 168°F. Under low coolant level conditions the fans will be commanded Off when engine coolant temperature drops below 168°F. With correct engine coolant level the fans are commanded Off at an engine coolant temperature below 215°F, transaxle temperature below 230°F and or A/C high side temperature below 138°F.

The ECM will command cooling fans on at high speed when engine temperature exceeds 230°F, engine coolant temperature sensor circuit fails, transaxle temperature is in excess of 248°F or when A/C is requested. Under low engine coolant level conditions the ECM commands high speed cooling fans On when engine coolant temperature exceeds 185°F and switches to low speed fan operation below 176°F.

4.9L/V8-300 Engine

This system uses two cooling fans operated in high and low speed modes. In the low speed mode the cooling fans are powered in series. When cooling fan relay No. 1 is energized both fans operate at low speed. In high speed mode both fans are wired in parallel which allows them to run at high speed. The cooling fans operate only when ignition is in On position. The ECM activates the low speed cooling fans when engine coolant temperature is greater than 226°F. The heater and A/C programmer will activate low speed fans when A/C high side pressure reaches temperature in excess of 140°F and vehicle speed is below 20 mph with outside air temperature greater than 45°F. The ECM will command fans Off when engine coolant temperature drops below 208°F, A/C high side temperature drops below 122°F.

The ECM activates fans at high speed when engine coolant temperature exceeds 226°F, engine coolant temperature circuit fails, A/C high side temperature sensor failure or refrigerant temperature exceeds 158°F. The heater and A/C programmer will request fans be switched to low speed when A/C high side temperature drops below 138°F.

CAPRICE, FLEETWOOD (RWD), IMPALA SS & ROADMASTER

1993

The primary and secondary cooling fans are turned on and off by the ECM based on inputs from A/C head pressure, engine coolant temperature, vehicle speed and A/C request signals.

The primary cooling fan is turned on when vehicle speed is below 35 mph, diagnostic trouble codes (DTC) 14 or 15 are set, coolant temperature is greater than 226°F or high A/C pressure is indicated.

The secondary cooling fan is controlled by the ECM through the engine coolant temperature sensor. The A/C cooling fan switch on the A/C high pressure line is grounded when head pressure exceeds 200-300 psi, enabling the secondary fan motor. The secondary fan is also turned on when DTC's 14 or 15 are set or coolant temperature is greater than 231°F.

1994

Base & V03 Extra Cooling Capacity

This two fan system is ECM controlled by inputs received from the engine coolant temperature sensor, vehicle speed sensor, and the A/C system. The ECM commands the primary cooling fan On when engine coolant temperature exceeds 225°F, A/C head pressure is above 189 psi and when certain diagnostic trouble codes are set. The primary fan is commanded Off when engine coolant temperature drops below 217°F, or A/C head pressure drops below 150 psi.

The secondary cooling fan is commanded On when the engine coolant temperature exceeds 232°F, A/C head pressure is above 240 psi or certain diagnostic trouble codes are set. The ECM commands the secondary fan Off when engine coolant temperature drops below 224°F, or A/C head pressure drops below 210 psi.

Heavy Duty Cooling

The primary engine cooling fan in this system is mechanical. Refer to "Variable Speed Fans" in this section.

The secondary cooling fan is an electric fan. Refer to "Diagnosis and Testing."

88 & 98

1992–93

Two cooling fans, wired in parallel, operate whenever cooling is required.

The powertrain control module (PCM) has two cooling fan control terminals: one for high speed and one for low speed. When the PCM's low speed control closes at connector C3, terminal C4, it grounds the low speed coolant relay coil. When the ignition switch is in the Run position and the relay contacts close, voltage is supplied to the cooling fans. The cooling fan resistors drop the voltage to the lefthand cooling fan, causing it to run in low speed. The righthand cooling fan also runs, but at high speed because the cooling fan resistors are bypassed. The PCM's low speed output is turned on when coolant temperature reaches 212°F.

High speed operation is similar to low speed. When coolant temperature reaches 226°F, the PCM's high speed control closes at connector C3, terminal C3, grounding the high speed coolant relay coil. The relay contacts close and both fans run at high speed since the PCM's low speed control remains closed. When A/C head pressure reaches 210 psi, the A/C pressure fan switch closes, grounding PCM input connector C1, terminal D9. This also causes the PCM high speed control to close, and both cooling fans run at high speed.

1994

Refer to "System Diagnosis & Testing."

ACHIEVA, GRAND AM, & SKYLARK

1992–93

The cooling fan is controlled by the cooling fan relay. The cooling fan relay is electrically operated by the ECM. The ECM receives input signals from the coolant temperature sensor, the vehicle speed sensor and the A/C mode selector. The ECM activates the cooling fan relay when the engine coolant, which is sensed by the coolant temperature sensor, is above 227°F, when the A/C is turned on or when the coolant temperature sensor fails. Any of these input signals causes the ECM to ground circuit 535 or 536 when vehicle speed is less than 35 mph. With circuit 535 or 536 grounded, the cooling fan relay is energized and its contacts close, turning the cooling fan on.

1994

2.3L/4-138 (VIN D, A & 3) Engine

The electric cooling fan is control by the ECM based on inputs from the engine coolant sensor, intake air temperature sensor , the A/C control switch, A/C refrigerant pressure sensor and the speed sensor. The fan normally operates when the engine coolant temperature exceeds 217°F, A/C is requested, and vehicle speed is greater than 35 mph. The cooling fan will also run if regardless of vehicle speed if coolant temperature exceeds 224°F, any diagnostic trouble code is set or A/C refrigerant pressure is high. If the ECM is in back-up mode then the cooling fan will run. **The cooling fan will run-on up to seven minutes after ignition switch is turned to Off position if engine coolant temperature is greater than 212°F and intake air temperature is greater than 176°F.**

3.1L/V6-192 (VIN M) Engine

The electric engine cooling fan is controlled by the ECM based on inputs from the engine coolant sensor, intake air temperature sensor , the A/C control switch, A/C refrigerant pressure sensor and the speed sensor. The fan normally operates when engine coolant temperature is above 226°F, A/C is requested and vehicle speed is below 70 mph. The fan will run if A/C refrigerant pressure sensor is open or pressure is greater than 187 psi. If diagnostic trouble codes (DTC 14, 15, or 70) are set then the cooling fan will run. The cooling fan will turn Off 30 seconds after coolant temperature drops below 219°F.

Skylark

The cooling fan is controlled by the cooling fan relay. The cooling fan relay is electrically operated by the ECM. The ECM receives input signals from the coolant temperature sensor, vehicle speed sensor and A/C mode selector. The ECM will activate the cooling fan relay when engine temperature is above 227°F, air conditioning is turned on, or the coolant temperature sensor fails. Any of these input signals causes the ECM to ground circuit 335 on 2.5L/4-151 VIN U engine, circuit 536 on 2.3L/4-138 VIN D and VIN 3 engines and circuit 535 on 3.3L/V6-204 VIN N engine, when vehicle speed is less than 35 mph. When circuits are grounded, the cooling fan relay is energized and its contacts close, turning the cooling fan on.

LEMANS

Less A/C

Cooling fan operation is controlled by an engine temperature switch. When engine temperature reaches 221°F, the switch closes and the fan is energized. As the engine cools, the engine temperature switch opens and the cooling fan stops.

With A/C

Operation of the two-speed cooling fan is controlled by high and low speed cooling fan relays. When the A/C system is turned on, voltage is supplied to the A/C compressor relay, the ECM grounds the compressor relay coil and the low speed fan relay is energized. Voltage is then transferred from fuse No. 14, through the cooling fan resistor and to the fan.

When the ECM determines that the engine should be cooled, it will ground the high speed fan relay to apply voltage directly from the fuse to the fan motor.

SUNBIRD

1992–93

The cooling fan is controlled by the cooling fan relay. The cooling fan relay is electrically operated by the ECM. The ECM receives input signal from the coolant temperature sensor, vehicle speed sensor and the A/C mode selector. The ECM activates the cooling fan relay when engine coolant, which is sensed by the coolant temperature sensor, is above 227°F, when A/C is turned on and when coolant temperature sensor fails. Any of these input signals causes the ECM to ground circuit 335. With circuit 335 grounded, the cooling fan relay is energized and its contacts close. The battery runs with battery voltage across its terminals.

1994

2.0L/4-121 (VIN H) Engine

The electric cooling fan will operate when the engine coolant temperature is above 223°F, A/C refrigerant pressure is above 51 psi or diagnostic trouble codes (DTC 14) has been set. A DTC 14 condition indicates a failed engine coolant temperature sensor, when this occurs the fan will receive an On command from the ECM and the cooling fan will run. **On vehicle equipped with air conditioning the fan will run when A/C is requested.** When engine coolant temperature drops below 211°F, then the ECM will command fan Off.

3.1L/V6-192 (VIN T) Engine

The electric cooling fan will operate when the engine coolant temperature is above 228°F and vehicle speed below 70 mph, A/C is requested or diagnostic trouble codes (DTC 14 or 15) have been set. A DTC 14 condition indicates a failed engine coolant temperature sensor, when this occurs the fan will receive an On command from the ECM and the cooling fan will run. On vehicle equipped with air conditioning the fan will run when engine cooling temperature exceeds 228°F and A/C refrigerant pressure exceeds 200 psi. When engine coolant temperature drops below 211°F, then the ECM will command fan Off.

PARK AVENUE & LESABRE

A two speed cooling fan is turned on and off by the low and high speed cooling fan relays.

For low speed operation, the low speed cooling fan relay coil is grounded through the ECM or the low speed contacts of the A/C dual pressure switch. The ECM grounds the coil when vehicle speed is less than 35 mph and the engine coolant is warmed up. The A/C dual pressure switch low speed contacts close with high refrigerant pressure above 260 psi.

With the low speed relay coil grounded, its contacts close. Voltage is applied through the cooling fan resistor to the cooling fan. The resistor reduces battery voltage supplied to the fan so that the fan runs at a low speed.

For high speed operation, the high speed cooling fan relay coil is grounded through the high speed contacts in the A/C dual pressure switch or by the temperature switch. The pressure switch high speed contacts close at a refrigerant pressure above 300 psi. The temperature switch closes when coolant temperature rises above 230°F.

With the high speed relay coil grounded, its contacts close. Battery voltage is applied to the cooling fan. The fan runs at high speed.

The heavy duty cooling fan is turned on and off by the heavy duty cooling fan relay. The heavy duty cooling fan relay is grounded through the high speed contacts in the A/C dual pressure switch or by the temperature switch. With the heavy duty relay coil grounded, its contacts close. Battery voltage is applied to the heavy duty cooling fan. The fan runs at high speed.

RIVIERA, TORONADO & TROFEO

The cooling fan system on these models consists of a fan located behind the radiator, and a fan mounted in front of the radiator.

The rear fan operates on two speeds, while the front fan operates only on high speed. Both fans are activated any time the cooling fans are in the high speed mode.

The fans will be activated by the ECM, when the engine coolant temperature sensor or the A/C high pressure sensor reach calibration points.

PRIZM

When the ignition switch is in either the Run or Start positions, system voltage is applied to the coils of the main engine relay and to fan relay 1. Because the main relay is grounded at G108, the relay is energized, its contacts close, and battery voltage is applied through the relay and the radiator fan fusible link to the contacts of fan relay 1.

When engine coolant temperature is below 194°F, the cooling fan temperature switch provides a ground for relay 1, the relay energizes and its contacts are pulled open.

Whenever engine coolant temperature reaches or exceeds 194°F, the cooling fan temperature switch opens, fan relay 1 is de-energized, its contacts close, and system voltage is applied through the relay to the cooling fan motor. Since the fan motor is grounded at G108, it start to operate as soon as voltage is applied.

When engine coolant temperature drops below 194°F, the cooling fan temperature switch closes to ground, fan relay 1 is energized the relay contacts are pulled open and system voltage is no longer applied to the fan motor.

STORM

With the engine running, the generator applies voltage to the restart relay. The voltage passes through the closed contacts of the restart relay to the condenser fan relay and the radiator fan relay. The triple switch closes when the refrigerant pressure is above 214 psi. When the triple switch closes, the condenser fan and radiator fan relays energize.

The condenser fan receives battery voltage from fuse E-4 through the closed contacts of the condenser fan relay. The radiator fan receives battery voltage from fusible link FL-4 through the radiator fan relay.

The thermo switch closes when the coolant temperature is above 179°F. When the thermo switch closes, the radiator fan and condenser fan operate in the same manner as when the triple switch closes.

When the ignition switch is turned to Start position, the restart relay is energized, the contacts are opened and the fans will not operate.

TROUBLESHOOTING

METRO

PRELIMINARY CHECK

1992–93

1. Using a suitable fuse tester, check A/C, IG and radiator fan fuses, also fusible link B.
2. Check engine coolant level.
3. Check A/C system for proper charge.
4. Ensure all system grounds are clean and tight.

1994

1. Check A/C fuse for open.
2. Check IG fuse for open.

3. Check fusible link "B"for open.
4. Check radiator fan fuse for open.
5. Check engine coolant level.
6. Check A/C system for proper refrigerant charge.
7. Check grounds G101, G104, and G201 are clean tight.

SYSTEM CHECK

1992–93

1. 1. Run engine until engine coolant temperature reaches 208°F. Cooling fan should run.
2. 2. Turn A/C switch to On position. A/C compressor clutch should engage and a/c condenser fan motor should run.
3. 3. Turn A/C switch to Off position. A/C compressor clutch should disengage and A/C condenser fan motor should stop.

BERETTA & CORSICA

1992–93

Preliminary Check

1. If cooling fan does not operate, check fuse No. 9 and Fuse Link A.
2. If cooling fan runs with ignition switch in the Off position, replace the cooling fan relay.
3. Ensure that ground G101 is clean and tight.

System Check

1. With engine cold and at idle speed, move A/C selector switch to the Norm position, cooling fan should come on. Move the A/C selector to the Off position, cooling fan should turn off.
2. Run engine at fast idle for several minutes, cooling fan should come on before coolant temperature indicator comes on or if equipped with temperature gauge before gauge reads H.
3. If cooling fan does not operate as described above refer to "Cooling Fan Does Not Run At All" or "Cooling Fan Does Not Turn Off With Ignition Switch In Run Position."

1994

Refer to "System Diagnosis & Testing."

CAPRICE, IMPALA SS, ROADMASTER & FLEETWOOD (RWD)

Refer to "System Diagnosis & Testing."

CENTURY

PRELIMINARY CHECK

1. **On 1992 models,** check FAN/ELECT fuse.
2. **On 1993-94 models,** check ENG/A/C fuse.
3. **On 1994 models,** check fusible link "F."
4. **On all models,** if cooling fan runs with ignition switch in Off position, inspect wiring and or replace the cooling fan relay.

SYSTEM CHECK

1992–93 Less Heavy Duty Cooling

1. With ambient temperature above 60°F, start car and set A/C mode selector to Max position. Cooling fan should turn on.
2. With engine coolant below operating temperature, move A/C mode selector to Off position. Cooling fan should turn off in a short time period.
3. Run engine at fast idle until engine coolant becomes hot. Cooling fan should come on and run before coolant temperature indicator comes on or the coolant temperature gage reads hot.

1992–93 w/Heavy Duty Cooling

1. With ambient temperature above 60°F, start car and set A/C mode selector to the Max position. Puller cooling fan should turn on.
2. With engine coolant below operating temperature, move A/C mode selector to Off position. Puller cooling fan should turn off in a short time period.
3. Run engine at fast idle until engine coolant becomes hot. Puller cooling fan should come on when coolant temperature reaches 202°F and the pusher cooling fan should come on when coolant temperature reaches 226°F.

1994

Refer to "System Diagnosis & Testing."

CUTLASS CIERA & CUTLASS CRUISER

PRELIMINARY CHECK

1. **On 1992 models,** check FAN/ALT fuse.
2. **On 1993 models,** check ENG/A/C fuse.
3. **On 1994 models,** check fusible link "F."
4. **On all models,** if cooling fan runs with ignition switch off, inspect wiring and or replace cooling fan relay.

SYSTEM CHECK

1992–93

1. With ambient air temperature above 60°F, start engine and set A/C mode selector, if equipped, to Max position. Cooling fan should turn on.
2. With engine coolant below operating temperature, move A/C mode selector to Off position. Cooling fan should turn off in a short period of time.
3. Run engine at fast idle until engine coolant becomes hot. The cooling fan should turn on before coolant temperature indicator comes on or coolant temperature gage needle reaches HOT.

1994

Refer to "System Diagnosis & Testing."

CAMARO & FIREBIRD

PRELIMINARY CHECK

1992–93

1. Check FAN/FP fuse if cooling fan does not run.
2. Check that ground G118 (3.1L/V6-192), G112 (5.0L/V8-305 VIN E), G104 (5.0L/V8-305 VIN F and 5.7L/V8-350 VIN 8) or G106 (3.4L/V6-204 and 5.7L/V8-350 VIN P) is clean and tight.
3. Check fusible link.
4. If cooling fan runs with ignition switch off, replace cooling fan relay.

SYSTEM CHECK

1992–93

1. With engine cold and idling, turn A/C selector, if equipped, to Norm position. On VIN E, cooling fan should turn on. On VINs T, F and 8, cooling fan, and auxiliary cooling fan if equipped, should turn on when A/C control head pressure exceeds 233 psi.
2. With engine coolant below operating temperature, move A/C selector to Off position. On VIN E, cooling fan should turn off. On VIN T, F and 8, cooling fan and auxiliary cooling fan (if equipped) should turn off when A/C control head pressure falls below 233 psi.
3. With engine warm, run engine at fast idle for several minutes. Ensure cooling fan turns on before coolant temperature indicator lights or before coolant temperature gage needle indicates hot.
4. Turn ignition switch to Off position. Cooling fan, and auxiliary cooling fan if equipped, should turn off.

1994

Refer to "System Diagnosis & Testing."

BONNEVILLE

PRELIMINARY CHECK

1992–93

1. Visually inspect fuse 16.
2. Visually inspect lefthand underhood fuse block fuse 4.
3. When only one cooling fan does not run check cooling fan motor for mechanical binding or wiring to suspect cooling fan. If satisfactory, replace cooling fan motor.
4. If either fan runs with ignition switch off, replace associated cooling fan relay.

1994

Refer to "System Diagnosis & Testing."

SYSTEM CHECK

1992–93

1. With ambient temperature above 60°F and engine cold and idling, set A/C mode selector in On position. Lefthand cooling fan should run at low speed and righthand cooling fan should run at high speed.

2. Set A/C mode selector to Off position. Cooling fans should turn off after about one minute.
3. Run engine at fast idle for several minutes. Lefthand cooling fan should run at low speed and righthand cooling fan should run at high speed.
4. Raise engine coolant temperature to 226°F, both cooling fans should operate at high speed.

1994

Refer to "System Diagnosis & Testing."

CAVALIER

PRELIMINARY CHECK

1. If cooling fan does not operate, check the following:
   a. **On 1992-93 models,** check fusible link C.
   b. **On all models,** check HTR/A/C fuse.
2. If cooling fan runs with ignition switch off, replace cooling fan relay.

SYSTEM CHECK

1992–93

1. With ambient temperature above 70°F, open all doors, start engine and set mode selector (if equipped) to Max position. Cooling fan should turn on.
2. With engine coolant below operating temperature, move mode selector to Off position. Cooling fan should turn off in a short period of time.
3. Run engine at fast idle for several minutes, cooling fan should turn on before coolant temperature indicator comes on or coolant temperature display shows H.
4. Turn ignition switch to Off position, cooling fan should turn off.

1994

Refer to "System Diagnosis & Testing."

CUTLASS SUPREME, GRAND PRIX & REGAL

1992–93

1. Visually inspect IGN fuses and fusible elements.
2. If cooling fan runs with ignition switch in Off position, check black/red (702 and 532) wires for a short to battery, or dark green/white (335) or dark blue/white (473) wires for short to ground. If wires are satisfactory, replace suspect cooling fan relay.

1994

Refer to "System Diagnosis & Testing."

CORVETTE

PRELIMINARY CHECK

1992–93

1. Check for an open Gauges fuse.
2. Check for an open fusible link D or E.
3. Check for corrosion on cooling fan and cooling fan relay terminals.
4. Ensure grounds are clean and tight.

1994

1. Check for open fan fuse.
2. Check for open primary or secondary fuse
3. Check for corrosion on the cooling fan and cooling fan relay.
4. Check for clean and tight ground G117.

SYSTEM CHECK

Refer to "System Diagnosis & Testing."

DEVILLE & FLEETWOOD (FWD)

If only one cooling fan fails to operate, check wires to that cooling fan. If wires are satisfactory, replace cooling fan.

SYSTEM CHECK

1992–93

1. Start engine and let idle. Left side cooling fans should run at low speed and right side fan should run at high speed after a few minutes.
2. With engine idling, restrict air flow through radiator by covering half of grill side of the radiator. Cooling fans should run at high speed after a few minutes.
3. Uncover radiator. Left side cooling fans should return to low speed and right side cooling fan should continue to run at high speed.

1994

Refer to "System Diagnosis & Testing."

ELDORADO & SEVILLE

SYSTEM CHECK

1992–93

1. If both cooling fans do not operate, check fusible link L by operating the horn.
2. If there is also a problem with A/C compressor clutch engagement, check cooling fan fuse 1 in the underhood relay center.
3. If both cooling fans operate in low speed with ignition switch in Off position, check for a short to battery voltage on circuit 532. If circuit is satisfactory, replace cooling fan relay B.
4. If both cooling fans operate in high speed but not in low speed, check the 533 circuit between cooling fan relay C and S161 for an open. Also check continuity of cooling fan relay C between terminals 1 and 3.
5. For a continuous low speed operation with ignition switch in Run position only, check circuit 535 for a short to ground. If circuit is satisfactory, problem is ECM related.
6. If puller fan runs continuously with ignition switch in On or Off position, check circuit 533 for a short to battery voltage If circuit is satisfactory, replace cooling fan relay D.
7. If puller fan run continuously with ignition switch in Run position only, check circuit 536 for a short to ground. If circuit is satisfactory, problem is ECM related.
8. If a no low speed, no high speed puller fan condition exists, check circuit 533 between S161 and puller fan for an open. Check circuit 804 between puller fan and S112 for and open. Check puller fan and terminal contacts.
9. If a no low speed or pusher fan runs in high speed when in system test ES08, check circuit 533 for a short to ground between pusher fan and cooling fan relay C. If circuit is satisfactory, replace cooling fan relay C.

1994

Refer to "System Diagnosis & Testing."

88, 98, LESABRE & PARK AVENUE

PRELIMINARY CHECK

1992–93

1. Visually inspect instrument panel fuse No. 16 and lefthand underhood fuse block fuse 4.
2. If only one cooling fan does not run, proceed as follows:
   a. Check fan for mechanical binding.
   b. Check wiring to suspect cooling fan.
   c. If wiring is satisfactory, replace cooling fan motor.
3. If cooling fan runs continuously with ignition switch off, remove both cooling fan relays one at a time. replace relay that caused fans to stop.

SYSTEM CHECK

1992–93

1. With ambient temperature above 60°F and engine cold and idling, set A/C mode selector to Norm position. Lefthand cooling fan should run at low speed. Righthand cooling fan should run at high speed.
2. With engine cold, move A/C mode selector to Off position. Cooling fans should turn off after about one minute.
3. Run engine at fast idle for several minutes. Lefthand cooling fan runs at low speed and righthand cooling fan runs at high speed.
4. Restrict air flow through radiator by covering half of grill side of radiator. After a few minutes both cooling fans should run at high speed.

1994

Refer to "System Diagnosis & Testing."

RIVIERA

Refer to "System Diagnosis & Testing."

GRAND AM

If cooling fan runs with ignition switch in Off position, replace cooling fan relay.

SYSTEM CHECK

1992–93

1. With ambient air temperature above 70°F, open all doors, start vehicle and set A/C mode selector, if equipped, to Max position. Cooling fan should turn on in a short period of time.

2. With engine coolant below operating temperature, move A/C selector to Off position. Cooling fan should turn off in a short period of time.
3. Run engine at fast idle for several minutes. Cooling fan should turn on before coolant temperature indicator comes on or coolant temperature gage needle reaches HOT.
4. Turn ignition switch to Off position. Cooling fan should turn off when engine temperature lowers.

1994

Refer to "System Diagnosis & Testing."

SKYLARK

If cooling fan runs with ignition switch Off, replace cooling fan relay.

SYSTEM CHECK

1. With ambient air temperature above 70°F, open all doors, start car and set A/C mode selector in Max position. Cooling fan should turn on.
2. With engine coolant below operating temperature, move A/C mode selector to Off position. Cooling fan should turn off in a short period of time.
3. Run engine at fast idle for several minutes. Cooling fan should come on before the coolant temperature indicator comes on or the coolant temperature display shows H.
4. Turn ignition switch Off. Cooling fan turns off when engine temperature lowers.

SUNBIRD

1992–93

Preliminary Check

1. If cooling fan does not operate, check fusible link C and HTR-A/C fuse.
2. If cooling fan runs with ignition switch in Off position, replace cooling fan relay.

System Check

1. With ambient temperature air temperature above 70°F, open all doors, start vehicle and set A/C mode selector to Max position. Cooling fan should turn on.
2. With engine coolant below operating temperature, move A/C mode selector to Off position. Cooling fan should turn off in a short time.
3. With engine warm, run engine at a fast idle for several minutes. Cooling fan should turn on before coolant temperature indicator shows H.
4. Turn ignition switch to Off position; cooling fan should also turn off.

1994

Refer to "System Diagnosis & Testing."

LEMANS

System Check

Refer to "System Diagnosis & Testing."

LUMINA

SYSTEM CHECK

1992

1. If cooling fan does not operate, check IGN fuse.
2. If cooling fan runs with ignition switch in the Off position, replace the cooling fan relay.

1993

1. Check IGN fuses and fusible elements "L" and "N."
2. If cooling fan runs with ignition switch in the Off position, check the following:
   a. Circuits (702) and (532) for a short to battery.
   b. Circuits (335) and (473) for a short to ground.
   c. Check for broken or partially broken wires inside of the insulation which could cause failure but prove good in a continuity/voltage check.
   d. Check for proper installation of aftermarket equipment.
   e. If circuits are satisfactory and equipment is installed correctly, replace cooling fan relay.

1994

Refer to "System Diagnosis & Testing."

ACHIEVA

PRELIMINARY CHECK

1992–93

If cooling fan continues to run with ignition switch in the Off position after engine coolant temperature lowers, replace cooling fan relay.

SYSTEM CHECK

1992–93

1. With ambient temperature above 70°F, start car, open all doors and set A/C mode selector to Max position. Cooling fan should turn on.
2. With engine coolant below operating temperature, move A/C mode selector to Off position. Cooling fan should turn off in a short time period.
3. Run engine at fast idle until engine coolant becomes hot. Cooling fan should come on and run before coolant temperature indicator comes on or the coolant temperature gage reads 280°F or temperature indicator light comes on.
4. Turn ignition switch to Off position. Cooling fan turns off when engine temperature lowers.

1994

Refer to "System Diagnosis & Testing."

PRIZM

1992–93

1. Check the IGN fuse by turning ignition switch to Run position and noting indicator lamp operation.
2. Check the ECM/IG fuse with a fuse tester.
3. Check the A/C fuse with a fuse tester.
4. Check all relays in junction blocks 2 and 5 are mounted securely.
5. Check radiator fan fusible link for an open.
6. Check, clean and tighten body grounds G102 and G203.

1994

Refer to "System Diagnosis & Testing."

STORM

1992–93

1. Check fuse C-21, C11 and E-4 using a fuse tester.
2. Be sure that grounds G102 and G103 are clean and tight.
3. Check that A/C system is properly charged.

TORONADO & TROFEO

Refer to "System Diagnosis & Testing."

SYSTEM DIAGNOSIS & TESTING

METRO

1992–93

Refer to **Figs. 3 and 4** when performing diagnostic procedures.

Engine Cooling Fan

1. Start and run engine, then ensure engine coolant temperature is below 199°F. If fan operates, proceed to step 3.
2. If fan motor operates, run engine until coolant temperature is above 208°F. If fan continues to operate, system is functioning properly. If fan does not operate, proceed to step 6.
3. Disconnect fan switch connector, if fan stops running, replace fan switch.
4. If fan continues to run, connect a suitable test lamp from fan switch connector cavity 2 to ground. If lamp lights, repair short to voltage in blue wire.
5. If lamp does not light, disconnect fan relay connector. If fan stops running, replace fan relay. If fan continues running, repair short to voltage in blue/red wire.
6. Disconnect fan relay connector and connect a fused jumper wire between cavities 2 and 4 on connector. If fan does not operate, proceed to step 11.
7. If fan operates, connect a suitable digital ohmmeter from fan relay connector cavity 3 to ground and measure resistance. If resistance is greater than 1.0 ohms (1992-93), repair black wire between fan relay and ground.
8. If resistance is less than .3 ohms, connect test lamp from fan relay connector cavity 1 to ground. If test lamp lights, replace fan relay.
9. If test lamp does not light, backprobe fan switch connector with test lamp from cavity 2 to ground. If test lamp lights, repair open in blue wire.

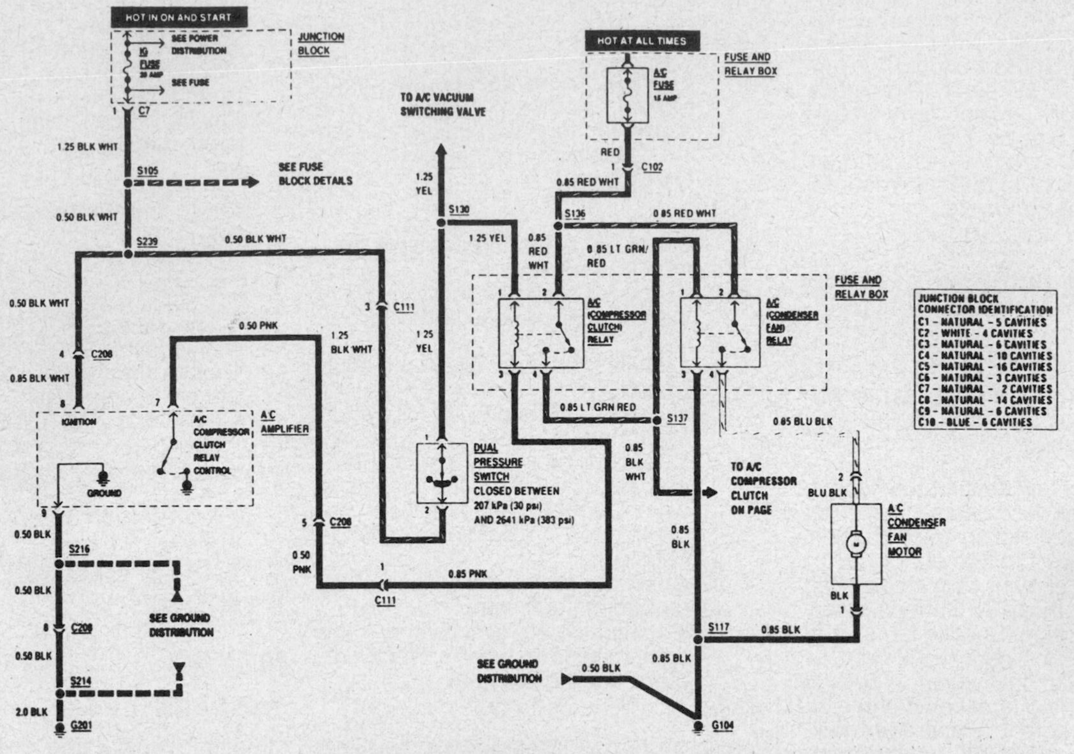
HOT IN ON AND START
SEE POWER DISTRIBUTION
IG FUSE 20 AMP
SEE FUSE
JUNCTION BLOCK
C7
1.25 BLK WHT
S105
SEE FUSE BLOCK DETAILS
0.50 BLK WHT
S239
0.50 BLK WHT
TO A/C VACUUM SWITCHING VALVE
1.25 YEL
S130
HOT AT ALL TIMES
A/C FUSE 15 AMP
FUSE AND RELAY BOX
RED
C102
0.85 RED WHT
S136
0.85 RED WHT
1.25 YEL
0.85 RED WHT
0.85 LT GRN/RED
FUSE AND RELAY BOX
A/C (COMPRESSOR CLUTCH) RELAY
A/C (CONDENSER FAN) RELAY
JUNCTION BLOCK CONNECTOR IDENTIFICATION
C1 - NATURAL - 5 CAVITIES
C2 - WHITE - 4 CAVITIES
C3 - NATURAL - 6 CAVITIES
C4 - NATURAL - 10 CAVITIES
C5 - NATURAL - 16 CAVITIES
C6 - NATURAL - 3 CAVITIES
C7 - NATURAL - 2 CAVITIES
C8 - NATURAL - 14 CAVITIES
C9 - NATURAL - 6 CAVITIES
C10 - BLUE - 6 CAVITIES
0.50 BLK WHT
C111
0.50 PNK
1.25 BLK WHT
1.25 YEL
C208
0.85 BLK WHT
IGNITION
A/C COMPRESSOR CLUTCH RELAY CONTROL
A/C AMPLIFIER
GROUND
0.85 LT GRN RED
S137
0.85 BLU BLK
DUAL PRESSURE SWITCH CLOSED BETWEEN 207 kPa (30 psi) AND 2641 kPa (383 psi)
0.85 BLK WHT
TO A/C COMPRESSOR CLUTCH ON PAGE
BLU BLK
A/C CONDENSER FAN MOTOR
0.50 BLK
S216
C208
0.50 PNK
0.85 PNK
C111
0.85 BLK
0.50 BLK
SEE GROUND DISTRIBUTION
BLK
0.50 BLK
S117
0.85 BLK
S214
SEE GROUND DISTRIBUTION
0.50 BLK
0.85 BLK
2.0 BLK
G201
G104

GC1089100036000X

Fig. 3 Cooling fan wiring circuit (A/C condenser fan). 1992–93 Metro

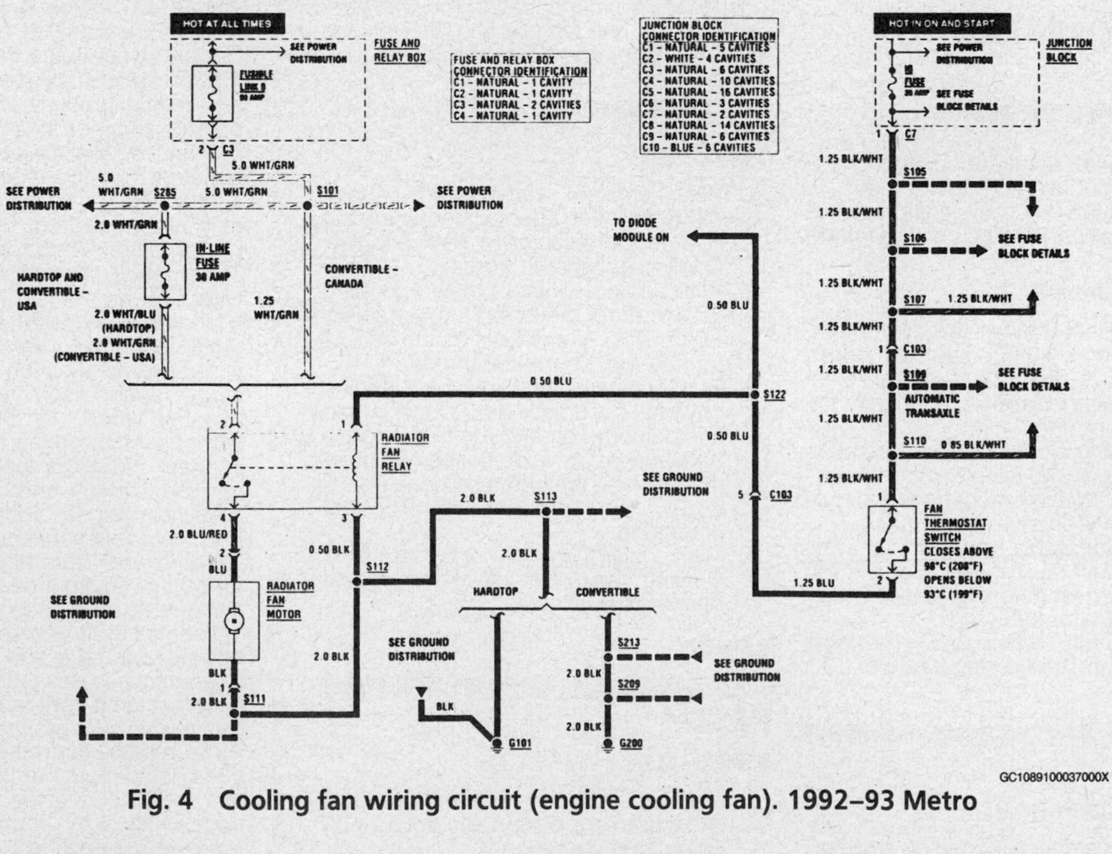
HOT AT ALL TIMES
SEE POWER DISTRIBUTION
FUSIBLE LINK B 50 AMP
FUSE AND RELAY BOX
FUSE AND RELAY BOX CONNECTOR IDENTIFICATION
C1 - NATURAL - 1 CAVITY
C2 - NATURAL - 1 CAVITY
C3 - NATURAL - 2 CAVITIES
C4 - NATURAL - 1 CAVITY
JUNCTION BLOCK CONNECTOR IDENTIFICATION
C1 - NATURAL - 5 CAVITIES
C2 - WHITE - 4 CAVITIES
C3 - NATURAL - 6 CAVITIES
C4 - NATURAL - 10 CAVITIES
C5 - NATURAL - 16 CAVITIES
C6 - NATURAL - 3 CAVITIES
C7 - NATURAL - 2 CAVITIES
C8 - NATURAL - 14 CAVITIES
C9 - NATURAL - 6 CAVITIES
C10 - BLUE - 6 CAVITIES
HOT IN ON AND START
SEE POWER DISTRIBUTION
HI FUSE 20 AMP
SEE FUSE BLOCK DETAILS
JUNCTION BLOCK
C3
5.0 WHT/GRN
SEE POWER DISTRIBUTION
5.0 WHT/GRN
S285
5.0 WHT/GRN
S101
SEE POWER DISTRIBUTION
2.0 WHT/GRN
IN-LINE FUSE 30 AMP
HARDTOP AND CONVERTIBLE - USA
CONVERTIBLE - CANADA
1.25 WHT/GRN
2.0 WHT/BLU (HARDTOP)
2.0 WHT/GRN (CONVERTIBLE - USA)
TO DIODE MODULE ON
C7
1.25 BLK/WHT
S105
1.25 BLK/WHT
S106
SEE FUSE BLOCK DETAILS
1.25 BLK/WHT
S107
1.25 BLK/WHT
1.25 BLK/WHT
C103
1.25 BLK/WHT
S109
SEE FUSE BLOCK DETAILS
AUTOMATIC TRANSAXLE
1.25 BLK/WHT
S110
0.85 BLK/WHT
1.25 BLK/WHT
0.50 BLU
0.50 BLU
S122
0.50 BLU
RADIATOR FAN RELAY
SEE GROUND DISTRIBUTION
C103
2.0 BLK
S113
2.0 BLU/RED
BLU
0.50 BLK
2.0 BLK
S112
HARDTOP
CONVERTIBLE
FAN THERMOSTAT SWITCH CLOSES ABOVE 98°C (208°F) OPENS BELOW 93°C (199°F)
1.25 BLU
SEE GROUND DISTRIBUTION
RADIATOR FAN MOTOR
2.0 BLK
SEE GROUND DISTRIBUTION
S213
SEE GROUND DISTRIBUTION
2.0 BLK
S209
BLK
2.0 BLK
S111
BLK
2.0 BLK
G101
G200

GC1089100037000X

Fig. 4 Cooling fan wiring circuit (engine cooling fan). 1992–93 Metro

10. If test lamp does not light, backprobe fan switch connector with test lamp from cavity 1 to ground. If test lamp lights, replace fan switch. If test lamp does not light, repair open in black/white wire between fan switch and junction block.
11. Connect test lamp from fan relay connector cavity 2 to ground. If test lamp does not light, repair open in white/green wire between fuse and relay box fan relay.
12. If lamp lights, reinstall relay and disconnect fan motor connector. Connect an ohmmeter from connector cavity 1 to ground and measure resistance. If resistance is greater than 1.0 ohms (1992-93), repair black wire between fan motor and ground G200 on 1992-93 convertible models or black wire between fan motor and ground G101 1992-93 hardtop models.
13. If resistance is less than 1.0 ohms (1992-93), connect test lamp from fan motor connector cavity 2 to ground. If lamp lights, replace fan motor. If lamp does not light, repair open in blue/red wire.

A/C Condenser Fan

1. Turn ignition switch to On position and press A/C switch. If condenser fan does not operate, proceed to step 3.
2. If fan operates, press A/C switch Off. If fan stops, system is functioning properly. If fan continues to operate, proceed to step 16.
3. Disconnect fan motor connector and connect a suitable test lamp between cavities 1 and 2. If lamp lights, replace condenser fan motor.
4. If lamp does not light, connect a suitable digital ohmmeter from fan motor connector cavity 1 to ground and measure resistance. If resistance is greater than 3 ohms, repair black wire between fan motor and ground G104.
5. If resistance is less than 3 ohms, backprobe fan relay connector with test lamp from cavity 4 to ground. If lamp lights, repair open in blue/black wire.
6. If lamp does not light, disconnect fan relay connector and connect test lamp from cavity 2 to ground. If lamp does not light, repair open in red wire.
7. If lamp lights, connect an ohmmeter from fan relay connector cavity 3 to ground and measure resistance. If resistance is greater than 1.0 ohms, repair black wire between fuse and relay box and G104.
8. If resistance is less than 1.0 ohms, connect test lamp from fan relay connector cavity 1 to ground. If lamp lights, replace fan relay.
9. If lamp does not light, backprobe A/C clutch relay with test lamp from cavity 4 to ground. If lamp lights, repair open in light green/red wire between clutch relay and fan relay.
10. If lamp does not light, disconnect clutch relay connector and connect a test lamp from cavity 3 to battery positive. If test lamp lights, replace condenser fan relay. If test lamp does not light, go to step 14.
11. Connect test lamp from A/C compressor clutch relay connector cavity 1 to chassis ground. If test lamp lights, replace A/C compressor clutch relay.
12. If lamp does not light, disconnect dual pressure switch connector. Connect test lamp from cavity 2 to ground. If lamp does not light, repair open in black/white wire between S105 and dual pressure switch.
13. If lamp lights, connect a fused jumper from dual pressure switch connector cavity 2 to cavity 1 and reconnect all relays. If condenser fan operates, replace dual pressure switch. If condenser fan does not operate, repair open in yellow wire between dual pressure switch and compressor clutch relay.
14. Disconnect A/C amplifier connector, then connect an ohmmeter from amplifier connector cavity 7 to clutch relay connector cavity 3 and measure resistance. If resistance is greater than 1.0 ohms, repair open in pink wire. If resistance is less than 1.0 ohms, problem is in A/C amplifier system.
15. Disconnect condenser fan relay connector, if fan continues to operate, repair short to voltage in blue/black wire.
16. If fan stops, connect test lamp from fan relay connector cavity 1 to ground. If lamp does not light, replace fan relay.
17. If lamp lights, disconnect clutch relay connector and connect test lamp from connector cavity 4 to ground. If lamp lights, repair short to voltage in light green/red wire between compressor clutch relay and condenser fan relay.
18. If lamp does not light, connect an ohmmeter from clutch relay connector cavity 3 to ground and measure resistance. Is resistance is infinite, replace clutch relay. If resistance is less than infinite, problem is in A/C amplifier system.

1994

Refer to **Figs. 5 and 6** when performing diagnostic procedures.

BERETTA & CORSICA

1992

Refer to **Figs. 7 and 8** when performing diagnostic procedures.

Cooling Fan Does Not Run At All

1. Connect a jumper wire between the Assembly Line Diagnostic Link (ALDL) connector terminal B and ground.
2. Turn ignition switch to the Run position. If cooling fan does not run, proceed to step 3. If cooling fan runs, problem is ECM related.
3. With ignition switch in Run position, connect a fused jumper wire between ECM connector terminal C3 and terminal E8 (VIN A & T) or terminal C1 and terminal C13 (VIN 4). If cooling fan does not run, proceed to step 4. If cooling fan runs, problem is ECM related.
4. With ECM connector terminal C3 and terminal E8 (VIN A & T) or terminal C1 and terminal C13 (VIN 4) grounded, disconnect cooling fan relay connector and connect a volt meter between terminal D (pink/black wire) and ground. If battery voltage is present, proceed to step 5. If battery voltage is not present, repair open in circuit 39.
5. With ECM connector terminal C3 and terminal E8 (VIN A & T) or terminal C1 and terminal C13 (VIN 4) grounded, disconnect cooling fan relay connector and connect a volt meter between terminal D (pink/black wire) and terminal F (dark green/white). If battery voltage is present, proceed to step 6. If battery voltage is not present, repair open in circuit 335.
6. Connect a volt meter to terminal A (red wire) and terminal E (black/red wire) of cooling fan relay connector. If battery voltage is not present, proceed to step 7. If battery voltage is present, repair open in circuit 2.
7. With cooling fan relay connector disconnected, connect a fused jumper wire between terminal A red wire and terminal E black/red wire. If cooling fan does not run, proceed to step 8. If cooling fan runs, replace cooling fan relay.
8. With ignition switch in Run position and jumper wire connected as in step 7, connect a volt meter between terminal B black/red wire and ground. If battery voltage is not present, repair open in circuit 702. If battery voltage is present proceed to step 9.
9. With ignition switch in Run position and jumper wire connected as in step 7, connect a volt meter between terminal B black/red wire and terminal A black wire of cooling fan connector. If battery voltage is not present, repair open in circuit 150. If battery voltage is present replace cooling fan motor.

Cooling Fan Does Not Turn Off With Ignition Switch In Run Position

1. Turn ignition switch to Run position, then disconnect cooling fan relay.
2. Connect a test lamp between terminals D (pink/black) and F (dark green/white) of cooling fan relay connector. If lamp does not light, replace cooling fan relay. If lamp lights, check circuit 335 for short to ground. If wire is satisfactory, problem is ECM related.

1993

For cooling fan system diagnosis on these models, refer to **Figs. 9 through 14.**

1994

Refer to **Figs. 15 through 20** when performing diagnostic procedures.

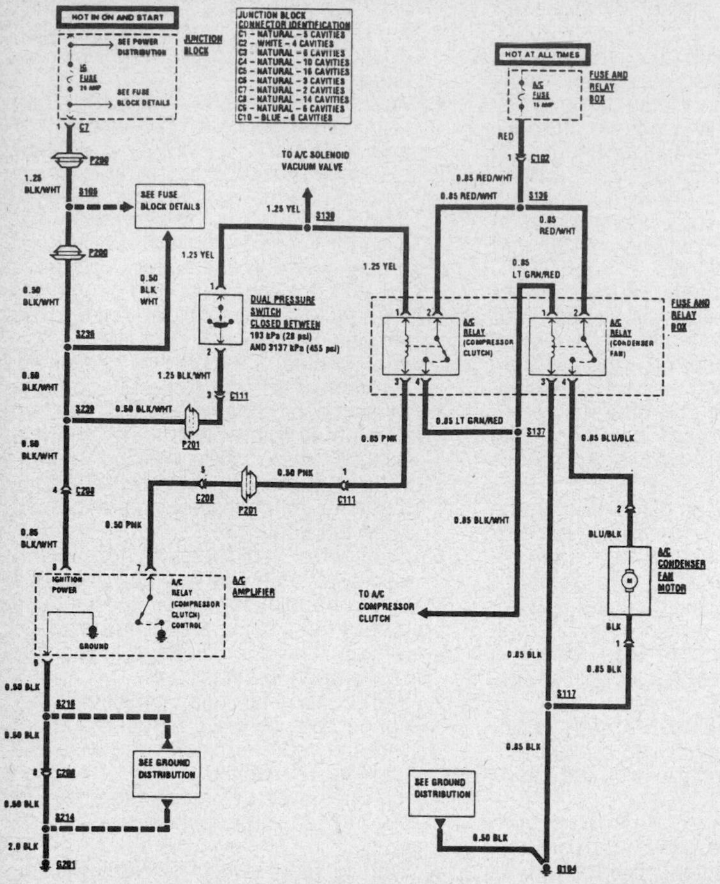
HOT IN ON AND START
JUNCTION BLOCK
HOT AT ALL TIMES
FUSE AND RELAY BOX
TO A/C SOLENOID VACUUM VALVE
SEE FUSE BLOCK DETAILS
DUAL PRESSURE SWITCH
A/C RELAY (COMPRESSOR CLUTCH)
A/C RELAY (CONDENSER FAN)
A/C CONDENSER FAN MOTOR
A/C AMPLIFIER
TO A/C COMPRESSOR CLUTCH
SEE GROUND DISTRIBUTION

GC1089400178000X

Fig. 5 Cooling fan wiring circuit (A/C condenser fan). 1994 Metro

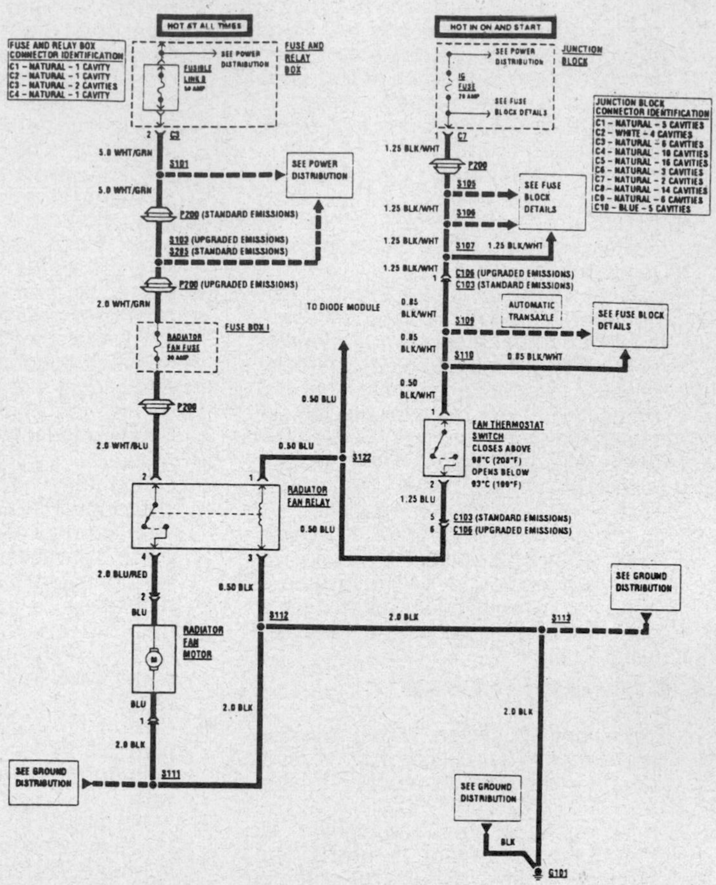
HOT AT ALL TIMES
FUSE AND RELAY BOX
HOT IN ON AND START
JUNCTION BLOCK
SEE POWER DISTRIBUTION
SEE FUSE BLOCK DETAILS
TO DIODE MODULE
AUTOMATIC TRANSAXLE
SEE FUSE BLOCK DETAILS
FUSE BOX I
FAN THERMOSTAT SWITCH
RADIATOR FAN RELAY
RADIATOR FAN MOTOR
SEE GROUND DISTRIBUTION

GC1089400179000X

Fig. 6 Cooling fan wiring circuit (engine cooling fan). 1994 Metro

CENTURY

1992

Refer to **Figs. 21 through 22** when performing the following diagnostic procedures.

Cooling Fan Does Not Turn On

1. With ignition switch in the Run position, ground terminal B white/black wire of the DLC (ALDL) connector. If cooling fan does not run, proceed to step 2. If cooling fan runs, problem is ECM related.
2. With ignition switch in the Run position, use a fused jumper wire and ground ECM terminal C1/21 (VIN R), or terminal C3/E38 (VIN N). If cooling fan does not run, proceed to step 3. If cooling fan runs, problem is ECM related.
3. Leaving fused jumper connected and ignition in the Run position, disconnect cooling fan relay connector.
4. Measure voltage from the brown/white wire of the cooling fan relay connector to ground. If voltage is equal to battery voltage, proceed to step 5. If there is no voltage indicated, check FAN/ELECT fuse, brown and brown/white wires for an open circuit.
5. Fused jumper still connected and ignition switch still in Run position, measure voltage as follows:
   a. **On 2.5L/4-151 engine,** measure between brown/white and dark green/white wires.
   b. **On 3.3L/V6-204 engine,** measure between brown/white and dark green wires.
6. If battery voltage is indicated, proceed to step 7. If no voltage is indicated, check dark green/white (2.5L/4-151), or dark green (3.3L/V6-204) wire, for an open circuit.
7. With cooling fan relay disconnected, measure voltage between terminal A (red wire) of the connector and ground. If battery voltage is indicated, proceed to step 8. If battery voltage is not indicated, check red wire or fusible link for an open.
8. Connect a fused jumper with a 20 amp fuse between terminals A and E at the cooling fan relay connector. If cooling fan does not run, proceed to step 9. If cooling fan runs, replace cooling fan relay.
9. Leaving fused jumper wire connected from step 8, disconnect connector from the cooling fan.
10. Measure voltage between terminal B of the connector and ground. If battery voltage is indicated, proceed to step 11. If battery voltage is not indicated, check for an open circuit in black/red (2.5L/4-151), or pink/black (3.3L/V6-204) wire.
11. Leaving fused jumper connected at the cooling fan relay connector, measure voltage between terminals A and B of the cooling fan connector. If battery voltage is indicated, replace cooling fan motor. If no voltage is indicated, check black wire for an open circuit.

Cooling Fan Does Not Turn Off With Engine Coolant Cool, A/C Off & Ignition Switch In Run

1. Turn ignition switch off, then disconnect cooling fan relay connector.
2. Connect a test lamp between terminals F and D of the cooling fan relay connector. If test lamp lights, proceed to step 3. If test lamp does not light, replace cooling fan relay.
3. Check wires for a short to ground as follows:
   a. **On 2.5L/4-151 engine,** check dark green/white wire.
   b. **On 3.3L/V6-204 engine,** check dark green wire.
4. If all wires are satisfactory, problem is ECM related.

Cooling Fan Does Not Turn On With A/C On

1. Turn ignition switch to run, put A/C mode selector in the Max position.
2. Measure voltage between terminal

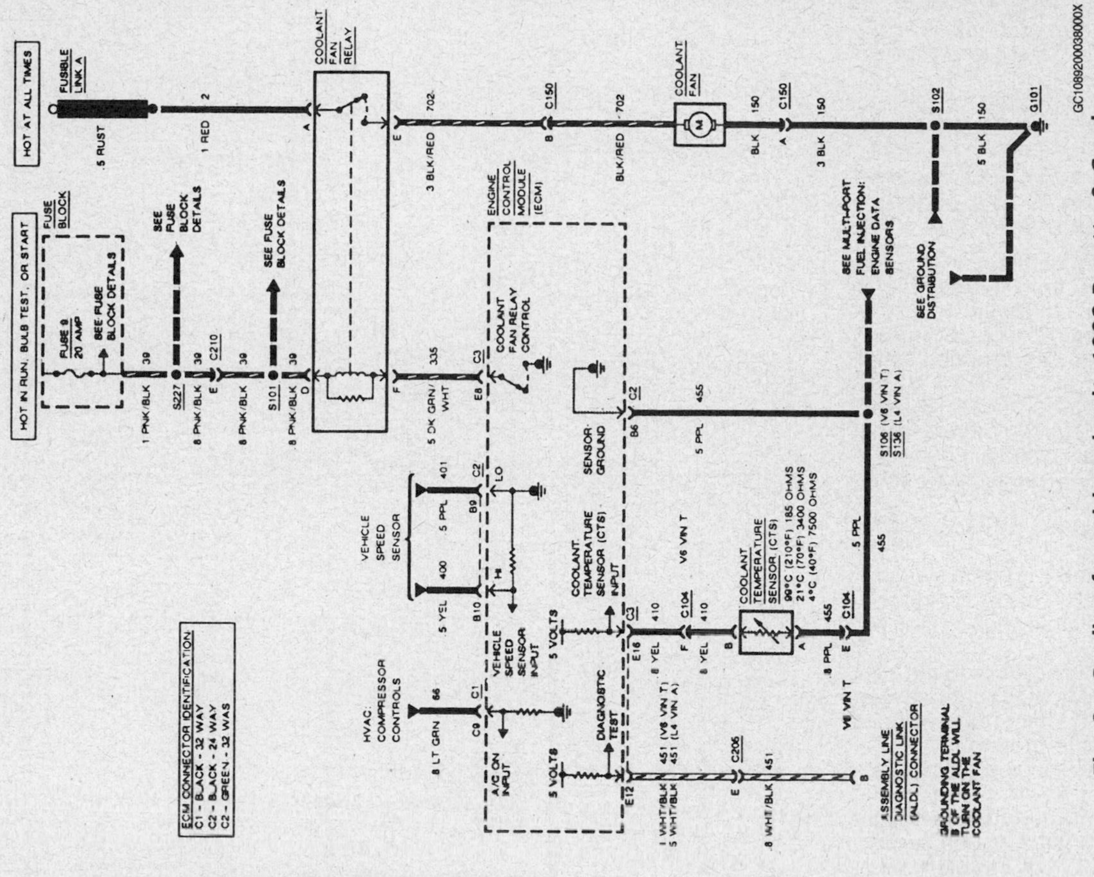
HOT AT ALL TIMES
FUSIBLE LINK A
.5 RUST
1 RED
HOT IN RUN, BULB TEST, OR START
FUSE BLOCK
FUSE 9 20 AMP
SEE FUSE BLOCK DETAILS
1 PNK/BLK
S227
8 PNK/BLK
C210
S101
COOLANT FAN RELAY
3 BLK/RED
5 DK GRN/WHT
ENGINE CONTROL MODULE (ECM)
COOLANT FAN RELAY CONTROL
C150
BLK/RED
COOLANT FAN
3 BLK
S102
5 BLK
G101
SEE MULTI-PORT FUEL INJECTION: ENGINE DATA SENSORS
SEE GROUND DISTRIBUTION
ECM CONNECTOR IDENTIFICATION
C1 - BLACK - 32 WAY
C2 - BLACK - 24 WAY
C2 - GREEN - 32 WAS
VEHICLE SPEED SENSOR
HVAC: COMPRESSOR CONTROLS
8 LT GRN
A/C ON INPUT
5 VOLTS
DIAGNOSTIC TEST
VEHICLE SPEED SENSOR INPUT
COOLANT TEMPERATURE SENSOR (CTS) INPUT
SENSOR GROUND
COOLANT TEMPERATURE SENSOR (CTS)
90°C (210°F) 185 OHMS
21°C (70°F) 3400 OHMS
4°C (40°F) 7500 OHMS
S106 (V6 VIN T)
S136 (L4 VIN A)
ASSEMBLY LINE DIAGNOSTIC LINK (ALDL) CONNECTOR
GROUNDING TERMINAL B OF THE ALDL WILL TURN ON THE COOLANT FAN
GC1089200038000X

Fig. 8 Cooling fan wiring circuit. 1992 Beretta & Corsica w/3.1L/V6-192 & 2.3L/4-138 engines

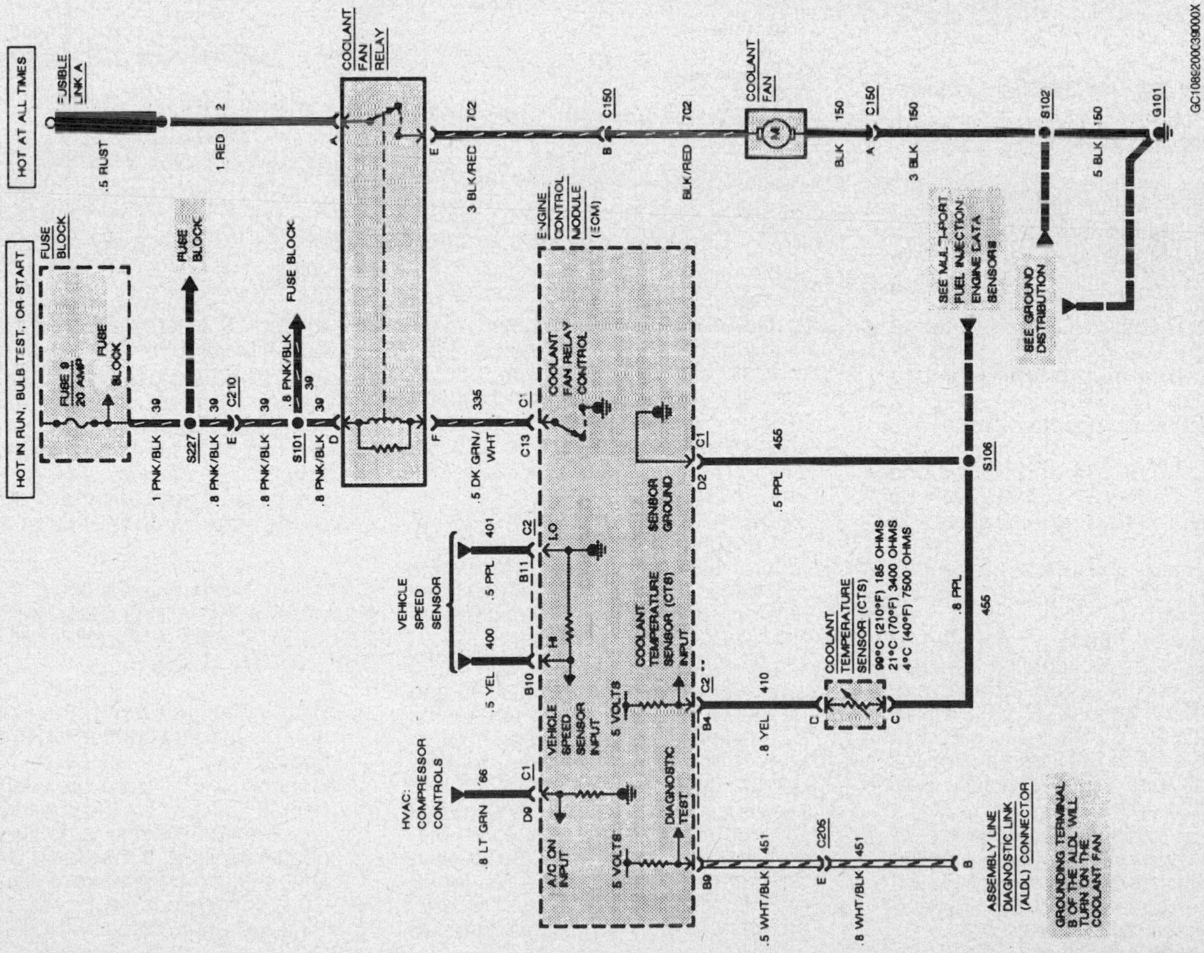
HOT AT ALL TIMES
FUSIBLE LINK A
.5 RUST
1 RED
HOT IN RUN, BULB TEST, OR START
FUSE BLOCK
FUSE 9 20 AMP
1 PNK/BLK
S227
.8 PNK/BLK
C210
S101
COOLANT FAN RELAY
3 BLK/RED
.5 DK GRN/WHT
ENGINE CONTROL MODULE (ECM)
COOLANT FAN RELAY CONTROL
C150
BLK/RED
COOLANT FAN
3 BLK
S102
5 BLK
G101
SEE MULTI-PORT FUEL INJECTION: ENGINE DATA SENSORS
SEE GROUND DISTRIBUTION
VEHICLE SPEED SENSOR
HVAC: COMPRESSOR CONTROLS
.8 LT GRN
A/C ON INPUT
5 VOLTS
DIAGNOSTIC TEST
VEHICLE SPEED SENSOR INPUT
COOLANT TEMPERATURE SENSOR (CTS) INPUT
SENSOR GROUND
COOLANT TEMPERATURE SENSOR (CTS)
90°C (210°F) 185 OHMS
21°C (70°F) 3400 OHMS
4°C (40°F) 7500 OHMS
S106
ASSEMBLY LINE DIAGNOSTIC LINK (ALDL) CONNECTOR
GROUNDING TERMINAL B OF THE ALDL WILL TURN ON THE COOLANT FAN
GC1089200C39000X

Fig. 7 Cooling fan wiring circuit. 1992 Beretta & Corsica w/2.2L/4-134 engine

C1/24 (2.5L/4-151) or C1/C9 (3.3L/V6-204) and ground.
3. If battery voltage is indicated, problem is ECM related.
4. If no voltage is indicated, check light blue/black wire or light blue wire for an open circuit.

Cooling Fan Does Not Turn On With A/C On & A/C Head Pressure Above 200 psi

1. Disconnect ECM connector C1, measure resistance from C1/D12 dark green/white wire to ground.
2. If resistance is zero, proceed to step 3. If resistance is infinite, proceed as follows:
   a. Check dark green/white wire for an open circuit, repair if necessary.
   b. If wire is satisfactory, check that cooling fan A/C pressure switch is closed.
   c. If switch is closed, problem is ECM related.
   d. If switch is open, replace switch.
3. Leaving ECM C1 connector disconnected, turn ignition switch to Run position.
4. Switch A/C mode selector to the Max position, measure voltage between terminal C1/C9 light green/white wire of the ECM to ground.
5. If battery voltage is indicated, problem is ECM related.
6. If no voltage is indicated, check light green/white wire for an open circuit.
7. If wire is satisfactory, problem is in A/C system.

1993

Refer to **Figs. 23 and 24** when performing diagnostic procedures.

Cooling Fan Does Not Turn On

1. Turn ignition switch to the Run position, then ground terminal "B" of the DLC. If cooling fan does not run, proceed to step 2. If cooling fan runs, problem is ECM related.
2. Ground terminal the following terminals:
   a. **On 2.2L/4-134 engine,** ground terminal "C1/D13" of the ECM with a fused jumper and proceed to step 3.
   b. **On 3.3L/V6-204 engine,** ground terminal "C3/E8" of the ECM with a fused jumper and proceed to step 3.
3. If cooling fan does not run, proceed to step 4. If cooling fan runs, problem is ECM related.
4. Leaving fused jumper connected at the ECM, disconnect cooling fan relay connector and measure voltage from brown wire to ground. If battery voltage is indicated, proceed to step 5. If battery voltage is not indicated, check ENG/A/C fuse and pink/black wire (639) for an open.
5. With fused jumper still grounded at the ECM, measure voltage as follows:
   a. **On 2.2L/4-134 engine,** measure between pink/black wire (639) and dark green/white wire (535).

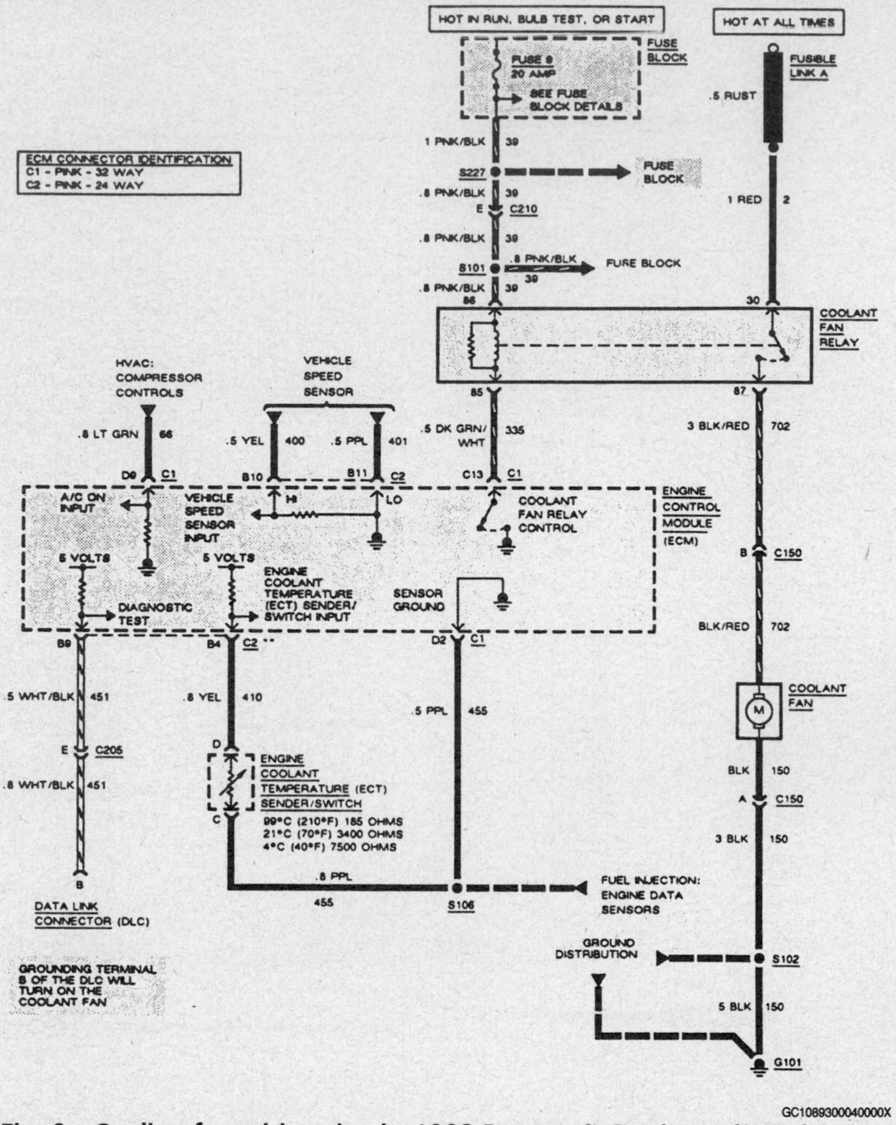

HOT IN RUN, BULB TEST, OR START
HOT AT ALL TIMES
FUSE BLOCK
FUSE 9 20 AMP
SEE FUSE BLOCK DETAILS
FUSIBLE LINK A
.5 RUST
ECM CONNECTOR IDENTIFICATION
C1 - PINK - 32 WAY
C2 - PINK - 24 WAY
1 PNK/BLK 39
S227
FUSE BLOCK
.8 PNK/BLK 39
C210
1 RED 2
.8 PNK/BLK 39
.8 PNK/BLK
S101
FUSE BLOCK
COOLANT FAN RELAY
HVAC: COMPRESSOR CONTROLS
VEHICLE SPEED SENSOR
.8 LT GRN 66
.5 YEL 400
.5 PPL 401
.5 DK GRN/WHT 335
3 BLK/RED 702
A/C ON INPUT
VEHICLE SPEED SENSOR INPUT
COOLANT FAN RELAY CONTROL
ENGINE CONTROL MODULE (ECM)
5 VOLTS
DIAGNOSTIC TEST
ENGINE COOLANT TEMPERATURE (ECT) SENDER/SWITCH INPUT
SENSOR GROUND
C150
BLK/RED 702
.5 WHT/BLK 451
.8 YEL 410
.5 PPL 455
COOLANT FAN
C205
.8 WHT/BLK 451
ENGINE COOLANT TEMPERATURE (ECT) SENDER/SWITCH
99°C (210°F) 185 OHMS
21°C (70°F) 3400 OHMS
4°C (40°F) 7500 OHMS
BLK 150
3 BLK 150
.8 PPL
455
S106
FUEL INJECTION: ENGINE DATA SENSORS
DATA LINK CONNECTOR (DLC)
GROUND DISTRIBUTION
S102
GROUNDING TERMINAL B OF THE DLC WILL TURN ON THE COOLANT FAN
5 BLK 150
G101
GC1089300040000X

Fig. 9 Cooling fan wiring circuit. 1993 Beretta & Corsica w/2.2L/4-134 engine

   b. **On 3.3L/V6-204 engine,** measure between pink/black wire (639) and dark green wire (535).
6. If battery voltage is indicated, proceed to step 7. If zero voltage is indicated, check dark green/white wire (2.2L/4-134) or dark green wire (3.3L/V6-204) for an open circuit.
7. Measure voltage from terminal "A" of the cooling fan relay connector to ground. If battery voltage is indicated, proceed to step 8. If zero voltage is indicated, check red wire (2) and fusible link for an open.
8. Connect a fused jumper with a 20 amp fuse between terminals "A" and "E" at the cooling fan relay connector. If cooling fan does not run, proceed to step 9. If cooling fan runs, replace cooling fan relay.
9. Leaving fused jumper connected at the cooling fan relay connector, disconnect connector from the cooling fan. Measure voltage between terminal "B" of the connector and ground. If battery voltage is indicated, proceed to step 10. If zero voltage is indicated, check black/pink wire for an open.
10. With fused jumper connected at the cooling fan relay connector, measure voltage between terminals "B" and "A" of the cooling fan connector. If battery voltage is indicated, replace cooling fan motor. If zero voltage is indicated, check black wire (150) for an open.

Cooling Fan Does Not Turn Off With Engine Coolant Cool, A/C Off & Ignition Switch In Run

1. With ignition switch in the Run position, disconnect cooling fan relay connector.
2. Connect a test lamp between terminals "F" and "D" of the cooling fan relay connector. If test lamp lights, proceed to step 3. If test lamp does not light, replace cooling fan relay.
3. Check dark green/white wire (2.2L/4-134) or dark green wire (3.3L/V6-

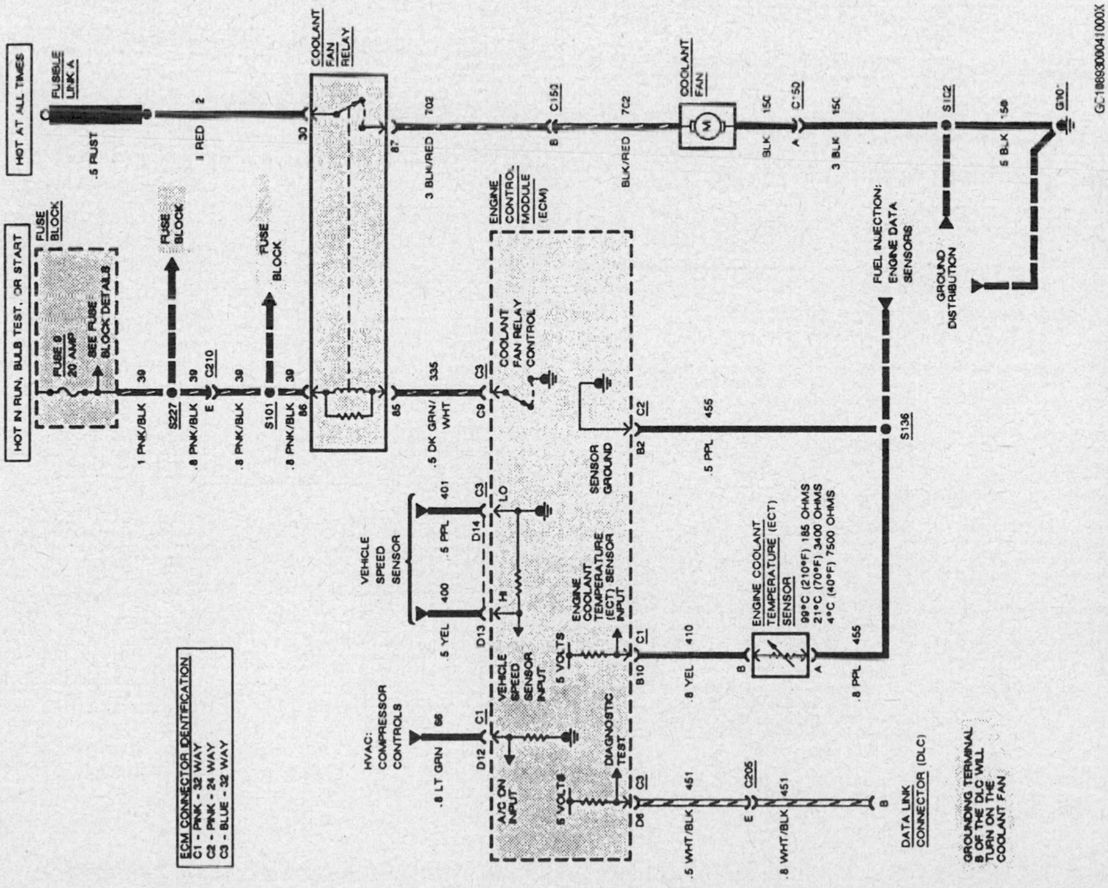
HOT IN RUN, BULB TEST, OR START
FUSE BLOCK
FUSE 9 20 AMP
SEE FUSE BLOCK DETAILS
HOT AT ALL TIMES
FUSIBLE LINK A
.5 RUST
1 RED
COOLANT FAN RELAY
ENGINE CONTROL MODULE (ECM)
COOLANT FAN RELAY CONTROL
COOLANT FAN
VEHICLE SPEED SENSOR
HVAC: COMPRESSOR CONTROLS
SENSOR GROUND
ENGINE COOLANT TEMPERATURE (ECT) SENSOR INPUT
VEHICLE SPEED SENSOR INPUT
DIAGNOSTIC TEST
A/C ON INPUT
5 VOLTS
ENGINE COOLANT TEMPERATURE (ECT) SENSOR
99°C (210°F) 185 OHMS
21°C (70°F) 3400 OHMS
4°C (40°F) 7500 OHMS
FUEL INJECTION: ENGINE DATA SENSORS
GROUND DISTRIBUTION
DATA LINK CONNECTOR (DLC)
GROUNDING TERMINAL B OF THE DLC WILL TURN ON THE COOLANT FAN
ECM CONNECTOR IDENTIFICATION
C1 - PINK - 32 WAY
C2 - PINK - 24 WAY
C3 - BLUE - 32 WAY
GC1089300041000X

Fig. 10 Cooling fan wiring circuit. 1993 Beretta & Corsica w/2.3L/4-138 engine

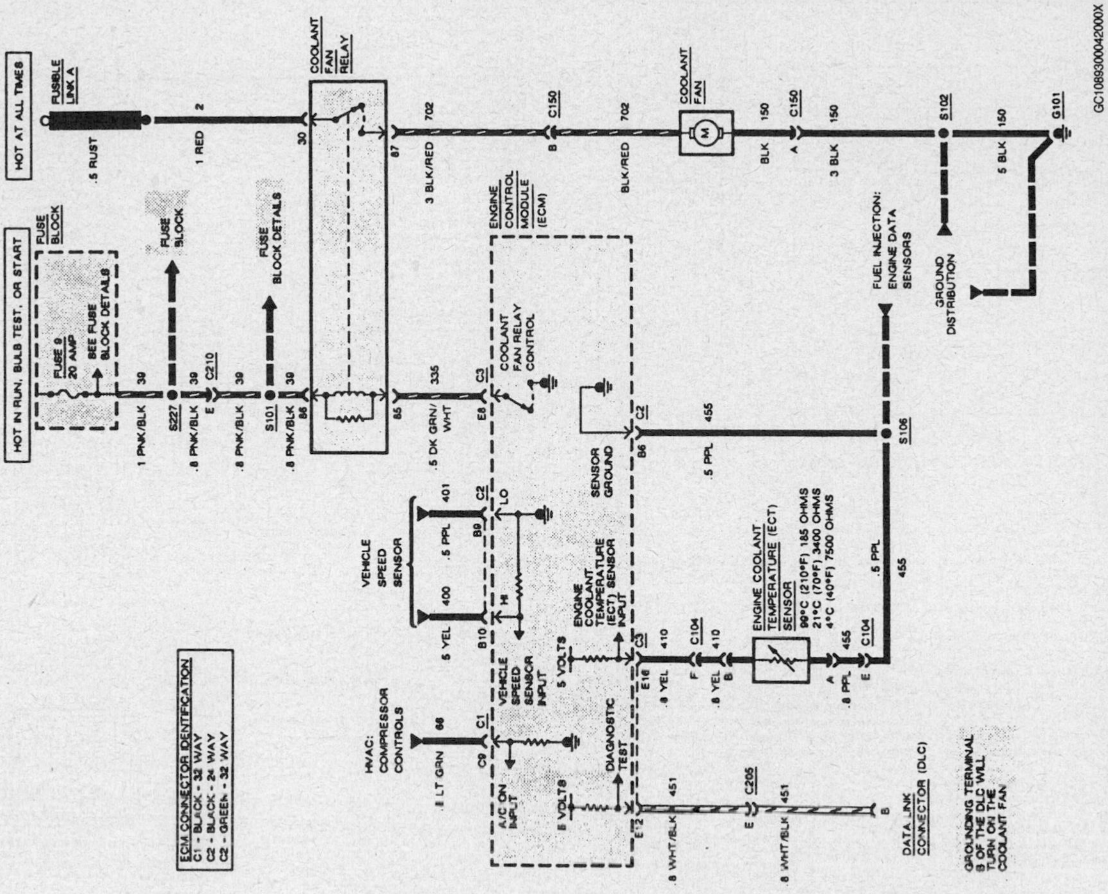
HOT IN RUN, BULB TEST, OR START
FUSE BLOCK
FUSE 9 20 AMP
SEE FUSE BLOCK DETAILS
HOT AT ALL TIMES
FUSIBLE LINK A
.5 RUST
1 RED
COOLANT FAN RELAY
ENGINE CONTROL MODULE (ECM)
COOLANT FAN RELAY CONTROL
COOLANT FAN
VEHICLE SPEED SENSOR
HVAC: COMPRESSOR CONTROLS
SENSOR GROUND
ENGINE COOLANT TEMPERATURE (ECT) SENSOR INPUT
VEHICLE SPEED SENSOR INPUT
DIAGNOSTIC TEST
A/C ON INPUT
5 VOLTS
ENGINE COOLANT TEMPERATURE (ECT) SENSOR
99°C (210°F) 185 OHMS
21°C (70°F) 3400 OHMS
4°C (40°F) 7500 OHMS
FUEL INJECTION: ENGINE DATA SENSORS
GROUND DISTRIBUTION
DATA LINK CONNECTOR (DLC)
GROUNDING TERMINAL B OF THE DLC WILL TURN ON THE COOLANT FAN
ECM CONNECTOR IDENTIFICATION
C1 - BLACK - 32 WAY
C2 - BLACK - 24 WAY
C2 - GREEN - 32 WAY
GC1089300042000X

Fig. 11 Cooling fan wiring circuit. 1993 Beretta & Corsica w/3.1L/V6-192 engine

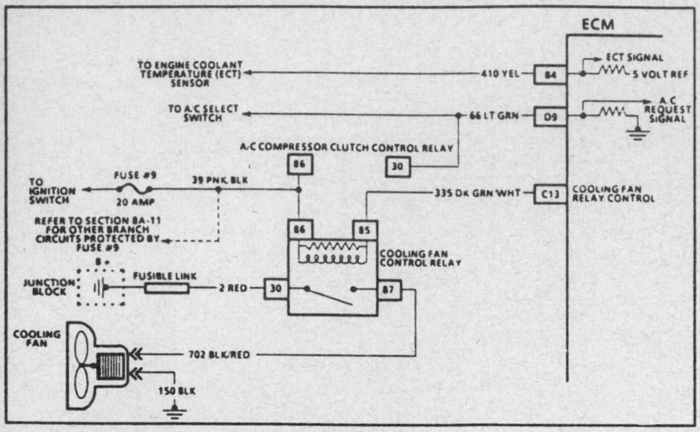
ECM
TO ENGINE COOLANT TEMPERATURE (ECT) SENSOR
410 YEL
B4
ECT SIGNAL
5 VOLT REF
TO A/C SELECT SWITCH
66 LT GRN
D9
A/C REQUEST SIGNAL
A/C COMPRESSOR CLUTCH CONTROL RELAY
86
30
TO IGNITION SWITCH
FUSE #9
20 AMP
39 PNK/BLK
335 DK GRN/WHT
C13
COOLING FAN RELAY CONTROL
REFER TO SECTION 8A-11 FOR OTHER BRANCH CIRCUITS PROTECTED BY FUSE #9
86
85
COOLING FAN CONTROL RELAY
B+
JUNCTION BLOCK
FUSIBLE LINK
2 RED
30
87
COOLING FAN
702 BLK/RED
150 BLK

CHART C-12

COOLING FAN CONTROL DIAGNOSIS 2.2L

Circuit Description:

Battery voltage to operate the cooling fan motor is supplied to relay by CKT 2. Ignition voltage to energize the cooling fan control is supplied by CKT 39. When the ECM grounds CKT 335, the relay is energized and the cooling fan is turned "ON."

When the engine is running, the ECM will turn the engine cooling fan "ON" for any of the following reasons:

- Diagnostic Trouble Code (DTC) 14 is set.
- Coolant temperature is 106°C (223°F) or greater.
- A/C refrigerant pressure is 189 psi or greater with A/C selected and a Diagnostic Trouble Code (DTC) 66 is not set.

Once the cooling fan is enabled, the ECM will turn the fan "OFF" when:

- Engine is turned "OFF."
- Coolant temperature drops to 99°C (203°F) or less.
- A/C refrigerant pressure drops to 38 psi or less with A/C selected.

Diagnostic Aids:

If the owner complained of an overheating problem, it must be determined if the complaint was due to an actual boil over, or the hot light, or temperature gage indicated overheating.

If the gage or light indicates overheating, but no boil over is detected, the gage circuit should be checked. The gage accuracy can also be checked by checking the engine coolant temperature reading using a scan tool and comparing its display with the instrument cluster gage.

If the engine is actually overheating and the gage indicates overheating, but the cooling fan is not coming "ON," the ECT sensor has probably shifted out of calibration and should be replaced.

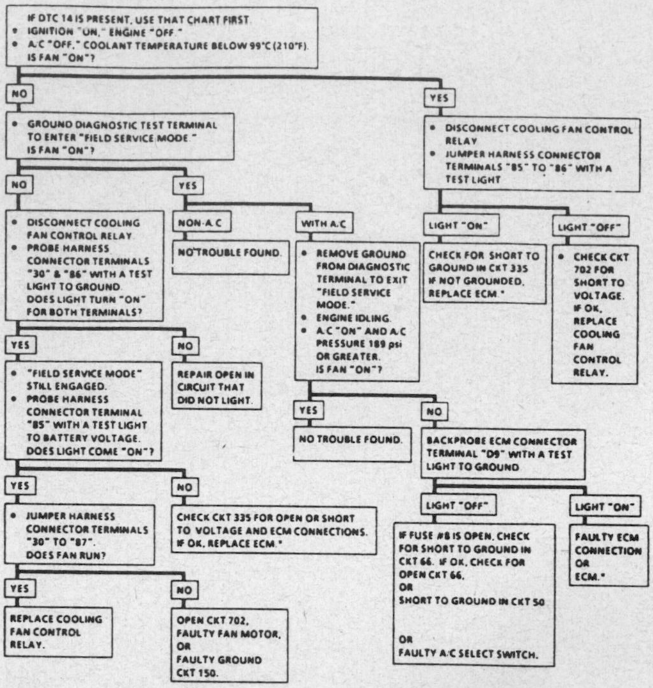
IF DTC 14 IS PRESENT, USE THAT CHART FIRST.
• IGNITION "ON," ENGINE "OFF."
• A/C "OFF," COOLANT TEMPERATURE BELOW 99°C (210°F). IS FAN "ON"?
NO
YES
• GROUND DIAGNOSTIC TEST TERMINAL TO ENTER "FIELD SERVICE MODE." IS FAN "ON"?
• DISCONNECT COOLING FAN CONTROL RELAY
• JUMPER HARNESS CONNECTOR TERMINALS "85" TO "86" WITH A TEST LIGHT
NO
YES
• DISCONNECT COOLING FAN CONTROL RELAY.
• PROBE HARNESS CONNECTOR TERMINALS "30" & "86" WITH A TEST LIGHT TO GROUND. DOES LIGHT TURN "ON" FOR BOTH TERMINALS?
NON-A/C
NO TROUBLE FOUND.
WITH A/C
• REMOVE GROUND FROM DIAGNOSTIC TERMINAL TO EXIT "FIELD SERVICE MODE."
• ENGINE IDLING.
• A/C "ON" AND A/C PRESSURE 189 psi OR GREATER. IS FAN "ON"?
LIGHT "ON"
CHECK FOR SHORT TO GROUND IN CKT 335. IF NOT GROUNDED, REPLACE ECM.*
LIGHT "OFF"
• CHECK CKT 702 FOR SHORT TO VOLTAGE. IF OK, REPLACE COOLING FAN CONTROL RELAY.
YES
NO
• "FIELD SERVICE MODE" STILL ENGAGED.
• PROBE HARNESS CONNECTOR TERMINAL "85" WITH A TEST LIGHT TO BATTERY VOLTAGE. DOES LIGHT COME "ON"?
REPAIR OPEN IN CIRCUIT THAT DID NOT LIGHT.
YES
NO TROUBLE FOUND.
NO
BACKPROBE ECM CONNECTOR TERMINAL "D9" WITH A TEST LIGHT TO GROUND
YES
NO
• JUMPER HARNESS CONNECTOR TERMINALS "30" TO "87". DOES FAN RUN?
CHECK CKT 335 FOR OPEN OR SHORT TO VOLTAGE AND ECM CONNECTIONS. IF OK, REPLACE ECM.*
LIGHT "OFF"
IF FUSE #8 IS OPEN, CHECK FOR SHORT TO GROUND IN CKT 66. IF OK, CHECK FOR OPEN CKT 66, OR SHORT TO GROUND IN CKT 50 OR FAULTY A/C SELECT SWITCH.
LIGHT "ON"
FAULTY ECM CONNECTION OR ECM.*
YES
REPLACE COOLING FAN CONTROL RELAY.
NO
OPEN CKT 702, FAULTY FAN MOTOR, OR FAULTY GROUND CKT 150.

IF ECM IS FAULTY AND MUST BE REPLACED, THE NEW ECM MUST BE PROGRAMMED.

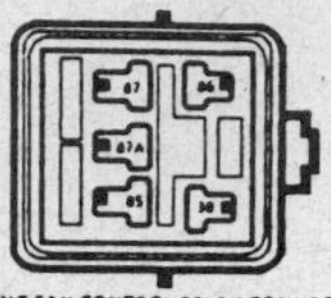
87
86
87A
85
30

COOLING FAN CONTROL RELAY CONNECTOR

GC1089300043000X

Fig. 12 Chart C-12, cooling fan diagnosis. 1993 Beretta & Corsica w/2.2L/4-134 engine

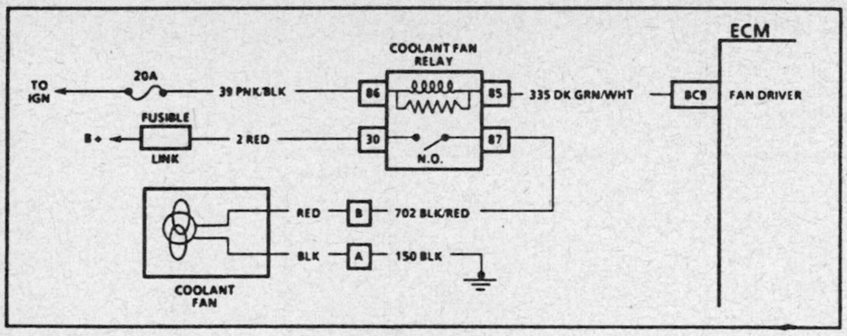
ECM
COOLANT FAN RELAY
TO IGN
20A
39 PNK/BLK
86
85
335 DK GRN/WHT
BC9
FAN DRIVER
FUSIBLE LINK
B+
2 RED
30
87
N.O.
RED
B
702 BLK/RED
BLK
A
150 BLK
COOLANT FAN

CHART C-12

COOLANT FAN FUNCTIONAL CHECK 2.3L (VIN A) "L" CARLINE

Circuit Description:

The electric coolant fan is controlled by the Engine Control Module (ECM) through the fan relay based on inputs from the engine coolant and intake air temperature sensors, the A/C control switch, A/C refrigerant pressure sensor and the vehicle speed sensor. The ECM controls the coolant fan by grounding CKT 335 which turns "ON" the fan relay.

The fan relay will be commanded "ON" when:

- Engine coolant temperature 103°C (217°F) - 106°C (223°F) or more.
- A/C clutch requested.
- Vehicle speed is less than 35 mph.

The fan relay will be commanded "ON" regardless of vehicle speed when:

- DTC 14 or 15 are set.
- Engine coolant temperature 115°C (239°F) - 118°C (224°F) or more.
- A/C refrigerant pressure is high.

The coolant fan may be commanded "ON" when the engine is not running under fan "Run-ON" conditions described previously in this section.

Test Description: Number(s) below refer to circled number(s) on the diagnostic chart.

1. With the field service mode activated, the coolant fan control driver should close, which should energize the fan control relay.
2. Test to see if fault is in wiring to the fan or the fan/relay connection.

Diagnostic Aids:

If the owner complained of an overheating problem, it must be determined if the complaint was due to an actual boil over, or the "Temp" light, or temperature gage indicated overheating.

If the gage, or light, indicates overheating, but no boil over is detected, the gage or light circuit should be checked. The gage accuracy can also be checked by comparing the coolant sensor reading using a scan tool with the gage reading.

If the engine is actually overheating, and the gage indicates overheating, but the coolant fan is not coming "ON," the Engine Coolant Temperature (ECT) sensor has probably shifted out of calibration and should be replaced.

If the engine is overheating, and the coolant fan is "ON," the cooling system should be checked.

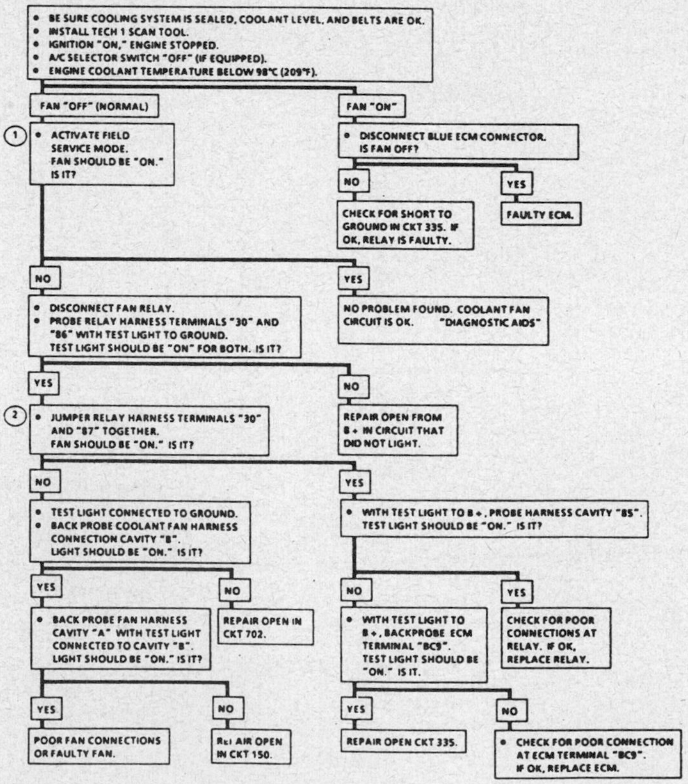
• BE SURE COOLING SYSTEM IS SEALED, COOLANT LEVEL, AND BELTS ARE OK.
• INSTALL TECH 1 SCAN TOOL.
• IGNITION "ON," ENGINE STOPPED.
• A/C SELECTOR SWITCH "OFF" (IF EQUIPPED).
• ENGINE COOLANT TEMPERATURE BELOW 98°C (209°F).
FAN "OFF" (NORMAL)
FAN "ON"
1
• ACTIVATE FIELD SERVICE MODE. FAN SHOULD BE "ON." IS IT?
• DISCONNECT BLUE ECM CONNECTOR. IS FAN OFF?
NO
YES
CHECK FOR SHORT TO GROUND IN CKT 335. IF OK, RELAY IS FAULTY.
FAULTY ECM.
NO
YES
• DISCONNECT FAN RELAY.
• PROBE RELAY HARNESS TERMINALS "30" AND "86" WITH TEST LIGHT TO GROUND. TEST LIGHT SHOULD BE "ON" FOR BOTH. IS IT?
NO PROBLEM FOUND. COOLANT FAN CIRCUIT IS OK. "DIAGNOSTIC AIDS"
YES
NO
2
• JUMPER RELAY HARNESS TERMINALS "30" AND "87" TOGETHER. FAN SHOULD BE "ON." IS IT?
REPAIR OPEN FROM B+ IN CIRCUIT THAT DID NOT LIGHT.
NO
YES
• TEST LIGHT CONNECTED TO GROUND.
• BACK PROBE COOLANT FAN HARNESS CONNECTION CAVITY "B". LIGHT SHOULD BE "ON." IS IT?
• WITH TEST LIGHT TO B+, PROBE HARNESS CAVITY "85". TEST LIGHT SHOULD BE "ON." IS IT?
YES
NO
NO
YES
• BACK PROBE FAN HARNESS CAVITY "A" WITH TEST LIGHT CONNECTED TO CAVITY "B". LIGHT SHOULD BE "ON." IS IT?
REPAIR OPEN IN CKT 702.
• WITH TEST LIGHT TO B+, BACKPROBE ECM TERMINAL "BC9". TEST LIGHT SHOULD BE "ON." IS IT.
CHECK FOR POOR CONNECTIONS AT RELAY. IF OK, REPLACE RELAY.
YES
NO
YES
NO
POOR FAN CONNECTIONS OR FAULTY FAN.
REPAIR OPEN IN CKT 150.
REPAIR OPEN CKT 335.
• CHECK FOR POOR CONNECTION AT ECM TERMINAL "BC9". IF OK, REPLACE ECM.

GC1089300044000X

Fig. 13 Chart C-12, cooling fan diagnosis. 1993 Beretta & Corsica w/2.3L/4-138 engine

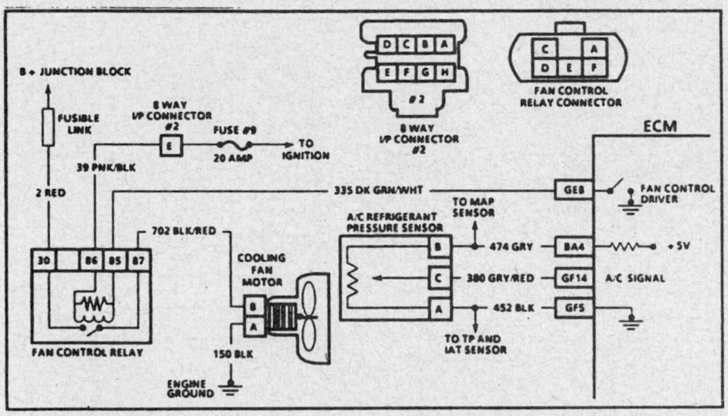
B + JUNCTION BLOCK
FUSIBLE LINK
8 WAY I/P CONNECTOR #2
FUSE #9
20 AMP
TO IGNITION
39 PNK/BLK
2 RED
E
D C B A
E F G H
#2
8 WAY I/P CONNECTOR #2
C A
D E F
FAN CONTROL RELAY CONNECTOR
ECM
335 DK GRN/WHT
GE8
FAN CONTROL DRIVER
TO MAP SENSOR
A/C REFRIGERANT PRESSURE SENSOR
702 BLK/RED
30 86 85 87
COOLING FAN MOTOR
474 GRY
BA4
+5V
380 GRY/RED
GF14
A/C SIGNAL
452 BLK
GF5
TO TP AND IAT SENSOR
FAN CONTROL RELAY
150 BLK
ENGINE GROUND

Circuit Description:

The electric cooling fan is controlled by the ECM, based on inputs from the engine coolant temperature sensor, the A/C refrigerant pressure sensor and vehicle speed. The ECM controls the fan by grounding CKT 335 which energizes the fan control relay. Battery voltage is then supplied to the fan motor.

The ECM grounds CKT 335 when coolant temperature is over about 109°C (228°F), or when A/C has been requested and the A/C refrigerant pressure sensor indicates high A/C pressure, 200 psi (1380 kPa). Once the ECM turns the relay "ON," it will keep it "ON" for a minimum of 25 seconds, or until vehicle speed exceeds 70 mph.

Also, if DTC 14 or 15 sets or the ECM is in back up, the fan will run at all times.

Test Description: Number(s) below refer to circled number(s) on the diagnostic chart.

1. With the diagnostic terminal grounded, the cooling fan control driver will close, which should energize the fan control relay.
2. If the A/C fan control switch or circuit is open, the fan would run whenever A/C is requested.
3. With A/C compressor clutch engaged, the A/C fan control switch should open when A/C refrigerant pressure exceeds about 200 psi (1380 kPa). This signal should cause the ECM to energize the fan control relay.
4. Disconnecting the A/C refrigerant pressure sensor will cause a DTC 66 to set. After finishing this step, be sure to clear DTC(s).

Diagnostic Aids:

If the owner complained of an overheating problem, it must be determined if the complaint was due to an actual boil over, or the hot light (temperature gage) indicated overheating.

If the gage (light) indicates overheating, but no boil over is detected, the gage circuit should be checked. The gage accuracy can also be checked by comparing the engine coolant temperature sensor reading using a scan tool and comparing its reading with the gage reading.

If the engine is actually overheating, and the gage indicates overheating, but the cooling fan is not coming "ON," the engine coolant temperature sensor has probably shifted out of calibration and should be replaced.

If the engine is overheating, and the cooling fan is "ON," the cooling system should be checked.

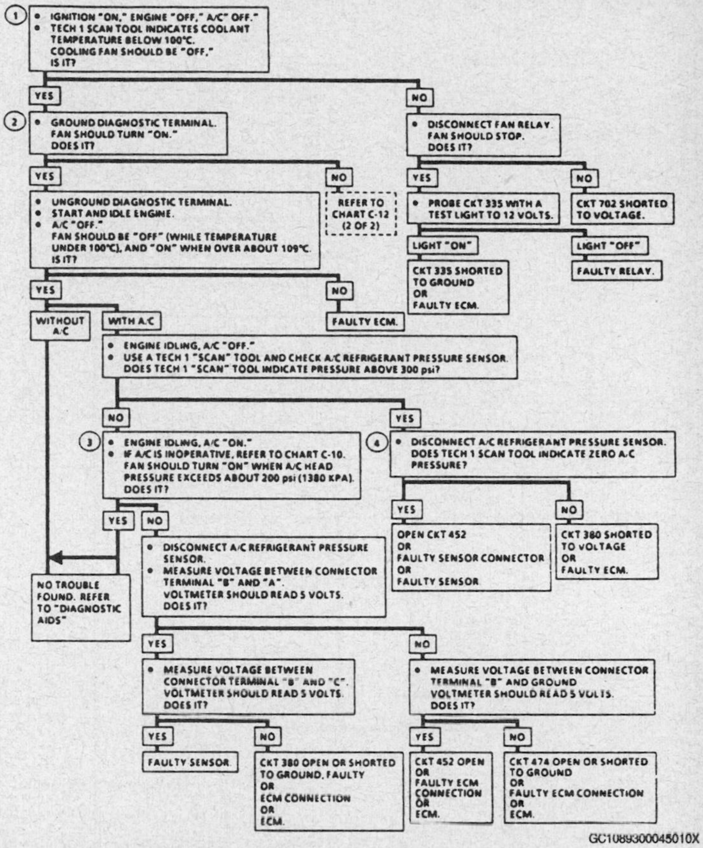
1
• IGNITION "ON," ENGINE "OFF," A/C" OFF."
• TECH 1 SCAN TOOL INDICATES COOLANT TEMPERATURE BELOW 100°C. COOLING FAN SHOULD BE "OFF," IS IT?
YES
2
• GROUND DIAGNOSTIC TERMINAL. FAN SHOULD TURN "ON." DOES IT?
YES
• UNGROUND DIAGNOSTIC TERMINAL.
• START AND IDLE ENGINE.
• A/C "OFF." FAN SHOULD BE "OFF" (WHILE TEMPERATURE UNDER 100°C), AND "ON" WHEN OVER ABOUT 109°C. IS IT?
YES
WITHOUT A/C
WITH A/C
• ENGINE IDLING, A/C "OFF."
• USE A TECH 1 "SCAN" TOOL AND CHECK A/C REFRIGERANT PRESSURE SENSOR. DOES TECH 1 "SCAN" TOOL INDICATE PRESSURE ABOVE 300 psi?
NO
3
• ENGINE IDLING, A/C "ON."
• IF A/C IS INOPERATIVE, REFER TO CHART C-10. FAN SHOULD TURN "ON" WHEN A/C HEAD PRESSURE EXCEEDS ABOUT 200 psi (1380 KPA). DOES IT?
YES
NO
NO TROUBLE FOUND. REFER TO "DIAGNOSTIC AIDS"
• DISCONNECT A/C REFRIGERANT PRESSURE SENSOR.
• MEASURE VOLTAGE BETWEEN CONNECTOR TERMINAL "B" AND "A". VOLTMETER SHOULD READ 5 VOLTS. DOES IT?
YES
• MEASURE VOLTAGE BETWEEN CONNECTOR TERMINAL "B" AND "C". VOLTMETER SHOULD READ 5 VOLTS. DOES IT?
YES
FAULTY SENSOR.
NO
CKT 380 OPEN OR SHORTED TO GROUND, FAULTY OR ECM CONNECTION OR ECM.
NO
• MEASURE VOLTAGE BETWEEN CONNECTOR TERMINAL "B" AND GROUND VOLTMETER SHOULD READ 5 VOLTS. DOES IT?
YES
CKT 452 OPEN OR FAULTY ECM CONNECTION OR ECM.
NO
CKT 474 OPEN OR SHORTED TO GROUND OR FAULTY ECM CONNECTION OR ECM.
YES
4
• DISCONNECT A/C REFRIGERANT PRESSURE SENSOR. DOES TECH 1 SCAN TOOL INDICATE ZERO A/C PRESSURE?
YES
OPEN CKT 452 OR FAULTY SENSOR CONNECTOR OR FAULTY SENSOR
NO
CKT 380 SHORTED TO VOLTAGE OR FAULTY ECM.
NO
FAULTY ECM.
NO
REFER TO CHART C-12 (2 OF 2)
NO
• DISCONNECT FAN RELAY. FAN SHOULD STOP. DOES IT?
YES
• PROBE CKT 335 WITH A TEST LIGHT TO 12 VOLTS.
LIGHT "ON"
CKT 335 SHORTED TO GROUND OR FAULTY ECM.
LIGHT "OFF"
FAULTY RELAY.
NO
CKT 702 SHORTED TO VOLTAGE.
GC1089300045010X

Fig. 14 Chart C-12, cooling fan diagnosis (Part 1 of 2). 1993 Beretta & Corsica w/3.1L/V6-192 engine

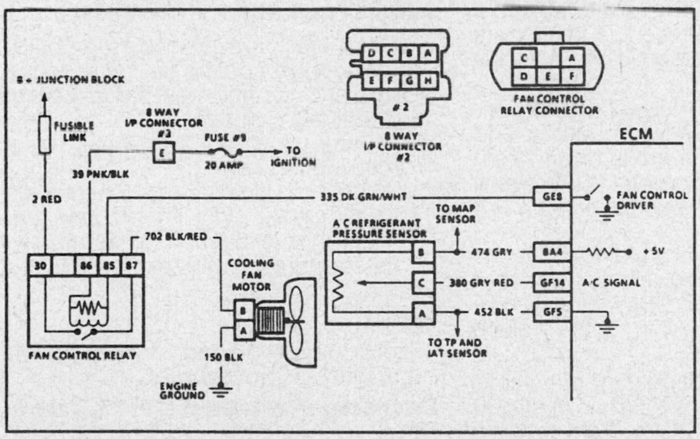
B + JUNCTION BLOCK
FUSIBLE LINK
8 WAY I/P CONNECTOR #2
FUSE #9
20 AMP
TO IGNITION
39 PNK/BLK
2 RED
E
D C B A
E F G H
#2
8 WAY I/P CONNECTOR #2
C A
D E F
FAN CONTROL RELAY CONNECTOR
ECM
335 DK GRN/WHT
GE8
FAN CONTROL DRIVER
TO MAP SENSOR
A/C REFRIGERANT PRESSURE SENSOR
702 BLK/RED
30 86 85 87
COOLING FAN MOTOR
474 GRY
BA4
+5V
380 GRY RED
GF14
A/C SIGNAL
452 BLK
GF5
TO TP AND IAT SENSOR
FAN CONTROL RELAY
150 BLK
ENGINE GROUND

Test Description: Number(s) below refer to circled number(s) on the diagnostic chart.

1. 12 volts should be available to both terminals "A" and "D" when the ignition is "ON."
2. This test checks the ability of the ECM to ground CKT 335. The MIL (Service Engine Soon) should also be flashing at this point
3. If the fan does not turn "ON" at this point, CKT 702 or CKT 150 is open or the cooling fan motor is faulty.

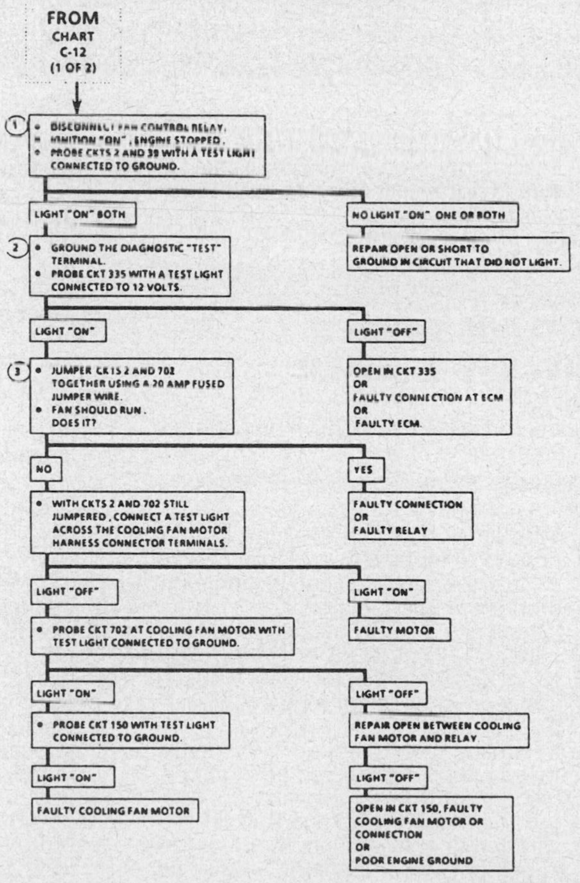
FROM CHART C-12 (1 OF 2)
1
• DISCONNECT FAN CONTROL RELAY.
• IGNITION "ON", ENGINE STOPPED.
• PROBE CKTS 2 AND 39 WITH A TEST LIGHT CONNECTED TO GROUND.
LIGHT "ON" BOTH
2
• GROUND THE DIAGNOSTIC "TEST" TERMINAL.
• PROBE CKT 335 WITH A TEST LIGHT CONNECTED TO 12 VOLTS.
LIGHT "ON"
3
• JUMPER CKTS 2 AND 702 TOGETHER USING A 20 AMP FUSED JUMPER WIRE.
• FAN SHOULD RUN. DOES IT?
NO
• WITH CKTS 2 AND 702 STILL JUMPERED, CONNECT A TEST LIGHT ACROSS THE COOLING FAN MOTOR HARNESS CONNECTOR TERMINALS.
LIGHT "OFF"
• PROBE CKT 702 AT COOLING FAN MOTOR WITH TEST LIGHT CONNECTED TO GROUND.
LIGHT "ON"
• PROBE CKT 150 WITH TEST LIGHT CONNECTED TO GROUND.
LIGHT "ON"
FAULTY COOLING FAN MOTOR
LIGHT "OFF"
OPEN IN CKT 150, FAULTY COOLING FAN MOTOR OR CONNECTION OR POOR ENGINE GROUND
LIGHT "OFF"
REPAIR OPEN BETWEEN COOLING FAN MOTOR AND RELAY.
LIGHT "ON"
FAULTY MOTOR
YES
FAULTY CONNECTION OR FAULTY RELAY
LIGHT "OFF"
OPEN IN CKT 335 OR FAULTY CONNECTION AT ECM OR FAULTY ECM.
NO LIGHT "ON" ONE OR BOTH
REPAIR OPEN OR SHORT TO GROUND IN CIRCUIT THAT DID NOT LIGHT.
GC1089300045020X

Fig. 14 Chart C-12, cooling fan diagnosis (Part 2 of 2). 1993 Beretta & Corsica w/3.1L/V6-192 engine

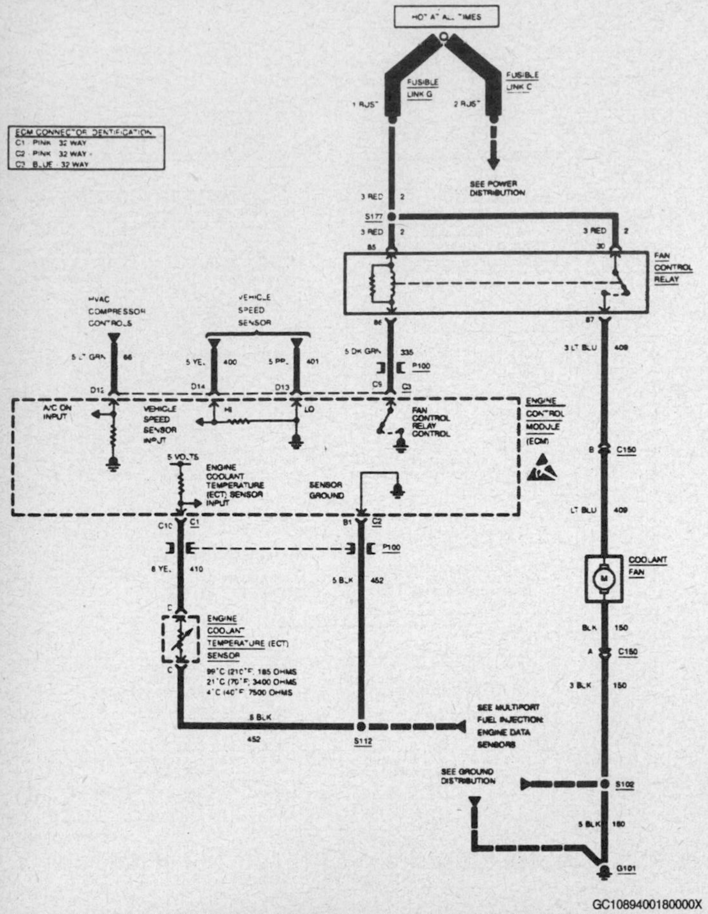
GC1089400180000X

Fig. 15 Cooling fan wiring circuit. 1994 Beretta & Corsica w/2.2L/4-134 engine

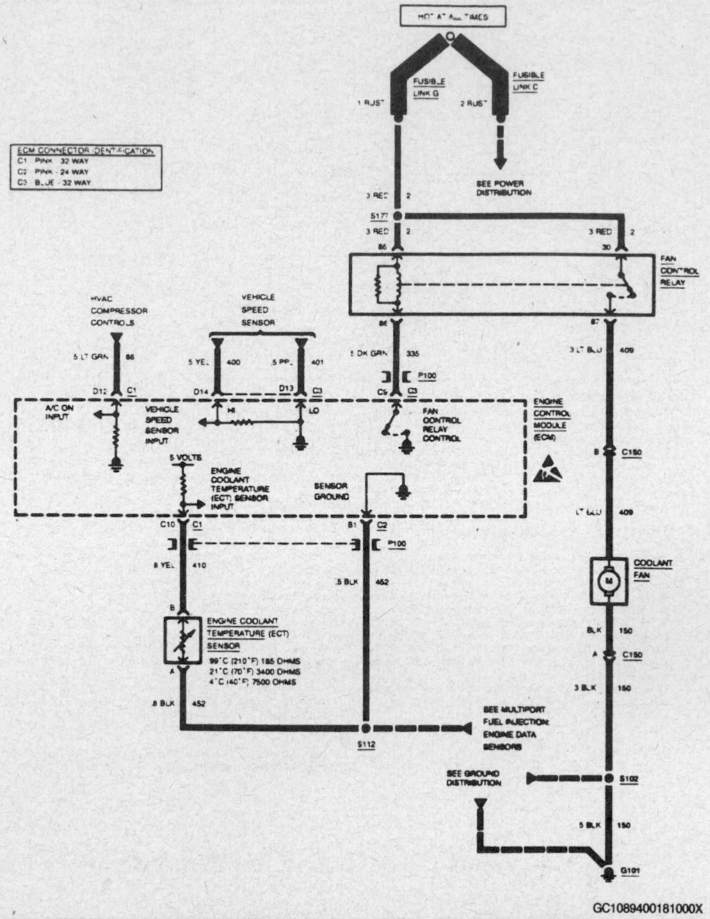
GC1089400181000X

Fig. 16 Cooling fan wiring circuit. 1994 Beretta & Corsica w/2.3L/4–138 engine

204) for a short to ground. If wire is satisfactory, problem is ECM related. If wire is not satisfactory, replace or repair as necessary.

1994

Refer to **Figs. 25 through 27** when performing diagnostic procedures.

CUTLASS CIERA & CUTLASS CRUISER

1992

Refer to **Figs. 28 and 29** when performing diagnostic procedures.

Cooling Fan Does Not Turn On

1. With ignition switch in Run position, ground terminal B (white/black) wire of ALDL connector. If cooling fan runs, problem is ECM related.
2. If cooling fan does not run, ground terminal C1/21 (VIN R) or C3/E8 (VIN N) of ECM connector with a fused jumper. If cooling fan runs, problem is ECM related.
3. If cooling fan does not run, leave fused jumper connected as in step 2, disconnect cooling fan relay connector and measure voltage from brown wire terminal to ground. If no voltage is present, check FAN/ALT fuse and brown wires for open.
4. If battery voltage is present, leave fused jumper connected as in step 2, measure voltage between brown and dark green (VIN N) or dark green/white (VIN R) wire terminals. If no voltage is present, check dark green or dark green/white wire for open.
5. If battery voltage is present, disconnect cooling fan relay connector and measure voltage from terminal A (red) wire to ground. If no voltage is present, check red wire and fusible link for open.
6. If battery voltage is present, connect a 20 amp fused jumper between terminals A and E of cooling fan relay connector. If cooling fan runs, replace cooling fan relay.
7. If cooling fan does not run, leave fused jumper connected as in step 6, disconnect connector from cooling fan and measure voltage between terminal B and ground. If no voltage is present, check black/red (VIN R) or black/pink (VIN N) wire for open.
8. If battery voltage is present, leave fused jumper connected as in step 6 and measure voltage between terminals B and A of cooling fan connector.
9. If no voltage is present, check black wire for open.
10. If battery voltage is present, replace cooling fan motor.

Cooling Fan Does Not Turn Off With Engine Coolant Cool, A/C Off & Ignition Switch In Run Position

1. Turn ignition switch to Run position, disconnect cooling fan relay connector and connect test lamp between terminals F and D .
2. If lamp does not illuminate, replace cooling fan relay.
3. If lamp illuminates, check dark green/white (VIN R) or dark green (VIN N) wire for short to ground. If wire is satisfactory, problem is ECM related.

1993

Refer to **Figs. 30 and 31** when performing diagnostic procedures.

Cooling Fan Does Not Turn On

1. Turn ignition switch to the Run position and ground terminal "B" of the DLC connector. If cooling fan does not run, refer to step 2. If cooling fan runs, check for possible ECM failure.
2. Using a fused jumper, ground ECM terminals (C1/D13) on 2.2L/4-134 engine or (C3/E8) on 3.3L/V6-204 engine. If cooling fan does not run, refer to step 3. If cooling fan runs, check for possible ECM failure.

Continued on page 17-32

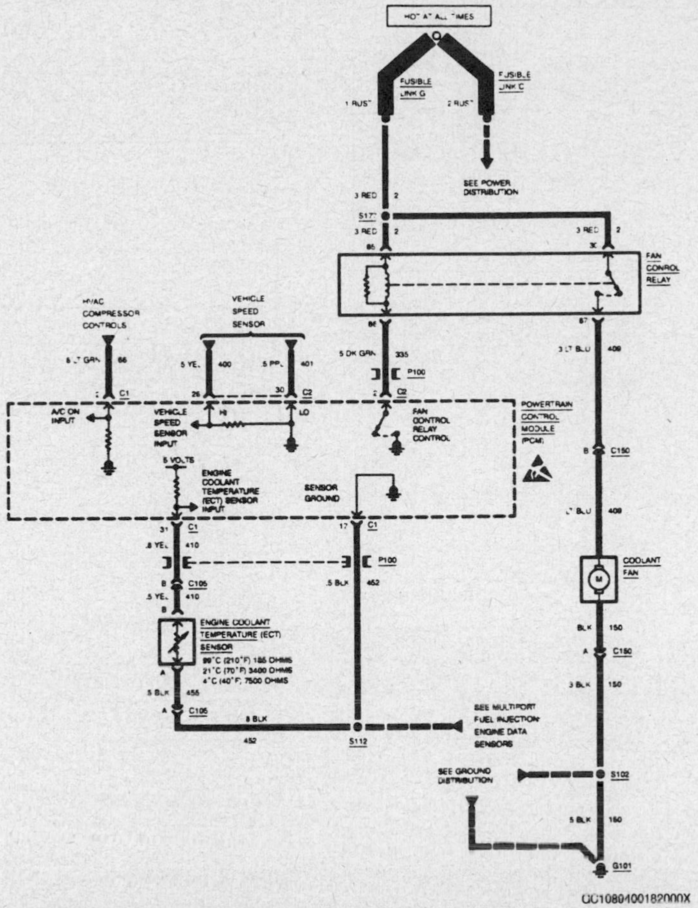

GC10804001820O0X

Fig. 17 Cooling fan wiring circuit. 1994 Beretta & Corsica w/3.1L/V6-192 engine

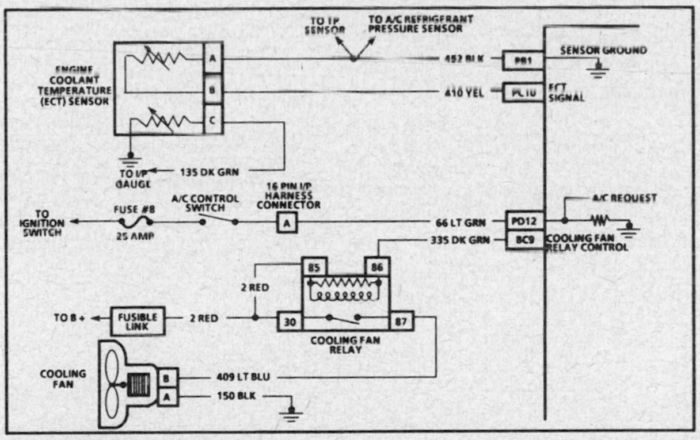

ENGINE COOLANT TEMPERATURE (ECT) SENSOR
TO I/P SENSOR
TO A/C REFRIGERANT PRESSURE SENSOR
452 BLK
PB1
SENSOR GROUND
410 YEL
PC10
ECT SIGNAL
TO I/P GAUGE
135 DK GRN
TO IGNITION SWITCH
FUSE #8
25 AMP
A/C CONTROL SWITCH
16 PIN I/P HARNESS CONNECTOR
66 LT GRN
PD12
A/C REQUEST
335 DK GRN
BC9
COOLING FAN RELAY CONTROL
2 RED
TO B+
FUSIBLE LINK
COOLING FAN RELAY
COOLING FAN
409 LT BLU
150 BLK

Circuit Description:

The electric cooling fan is controlled by the Powertrain Control Module (PCM) through the fan relay based on inputs from the engine coolant and intake air temperature sensors, the A/C control switch, A/C refrigerant pressure sensor and the vehicle speed sensor. The PCM controls the cooling fan by grounding CKT 335 which turns the fan relay "ON."

The fan relay will be commanded "ON" when:

- Engine coolant temperature is greater than 106°C (223°F).
- A/C clutch requested.
- Vehicle speed is less than 35 mph.
- A DTC is set.

Once the fan is enabled, the PCM will turn the fan "OFF" when:

- Engine coolant temperature drops below 120°C (243°F).
- A/C refrigerant pressure is greater than 300 psi.
- Vehicle speed is greater than 70 mph.

The cooling fan may be commanded "ON" when the engine is not running under fan "Run-ON" conditions described previously in this section.

Chart Test Description: Number(s) below refer to circled number(s) on the diagnostic chart.

1. With the field service mode activated, the coolant fan control driver should close, which should energize the fan relay control.
2. Test to see if fault is in the wiring to the fan or the fan relay connection.

Diagnostic Aids: If the owner complained of an overheating problem, it must be determined if the complaint was due to an actual boil over, or the "temp light," or temperature gage indicated overheating.

If the gage, or light, indicates overheating, but no boil over is detected, the gage or light circuit should be checked. The gage accuracy can also be checked by comparing the coolant sensor reading using a scan tool with the gage reading.

If the engine is actually overheating, and the gage indicates overheating, but the coolant fan is not coming "ON," the Engine Coolant Temperature (ECT) sensor has probably shifted out of calibration and should be replaced.

If the engine is overheating, and the coolant fan is "ON," the cooling system should be checked.

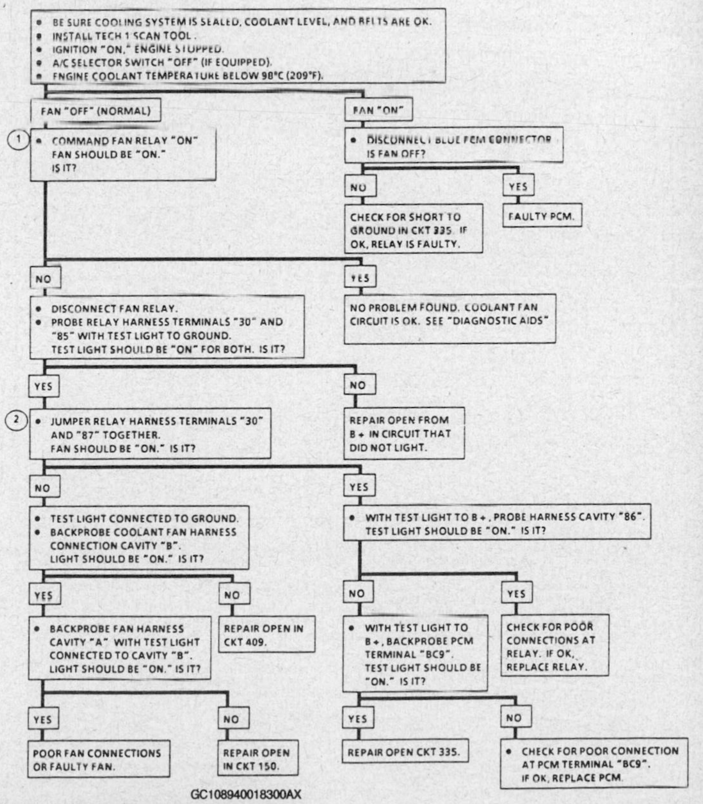

• BE SURE COOLING SYSTEM IS SEALED, COOLANT LEVEL, AND BELTS ARE OK.
• INSTALL TECH 1 SCAN TOOL.
• IGNITION "ON," ENGINE STOPPED.
• A/C SELECTOR SWITCH "OFF" (IF EQUIPPED).
• ENGINE COOLANT TEMPERATURE BELOW 98°C (209°F).
FAN "OFF" (NORMAL)
FAN "ON"
1
• COMMAND FAN RELAY "ON" FAN SHOULD BE "ON." IS IT?
• DISCONNECT BLUE PCM CONNECTOR IS FAN OFF?
NO
YES
CHECK FOR SHORT TO GROUND IN CKT 335. IF OK, RELAY IS FAULTY.
FAULTY PCM.
NO
YES
• DISCONNECT FAN RELAY.
• PROBE RELAY HARNESS TERMINALS "30" AND "85" WITH TEST LIGHT TO GROUND. TEST LIGHT SHOULD BE "ON" FOR BOTH. IS IT?
NO PROBLEM FOUND. COOLANT FAN CIRCUIT IS OK. SEE "DIAGNOSTIC AIDS"
YES
NO
2
• JUMPER RELAY HARNESS TERMINALS "30" AND "87" TOGETHER. FAN SHOULD BE "ON." IS IT?
REPAIR OPEN FROM B+ IN CIRCUIT THAT DID NOT LIGHT.
NO
YES
• TEST LIGHT CONNECTED TO GROUND.
• BACKPROBE COOLANT FAN HARNESS CONNECTION CAVITY "B". LIGHT SHOULD BE "ON." IS IT?
• WITH TEST LIGHT TO B+, PROBE HARNESS CAVITY "86". TEST LIGHT SHOULD BE "ON." IS IT?
YES
NO
NO
YES
• BACKPROBE FAN HARNESS CAVITY "A" WITH TEST LIGHT CONNECTED TO CAVITY "B". LIGHT SHOULD BE "ON." IS IT?
REPAIR OPEN IN CKT 409.
• WITH TEST LIGHT TO B+, BACKPROBE PCM TERMINAL "BC9". TEST LIGHT SHOULD BE "ON." IS IT?
CHECK FOR POOR CONNECTIONS AT RELAY. IF OK, REPLACE RELAY.
YES
NO
YES
NO
POOR FAN CONNECTIONS OR FAULTY FAN.
REPAIR OPEN IN CKT 150.
REPAIR OPEN CKT 335.
• CHECK FOR POOR CONNECTION AT PCM TERMINAL "BC9". IF OK, REPLACE PCM.

GC108940018300AX

Fig. 18 Chart C-12, cooling fan diagnosis. 1994 Beretta & Corsica w/2.2L/4-134 engine

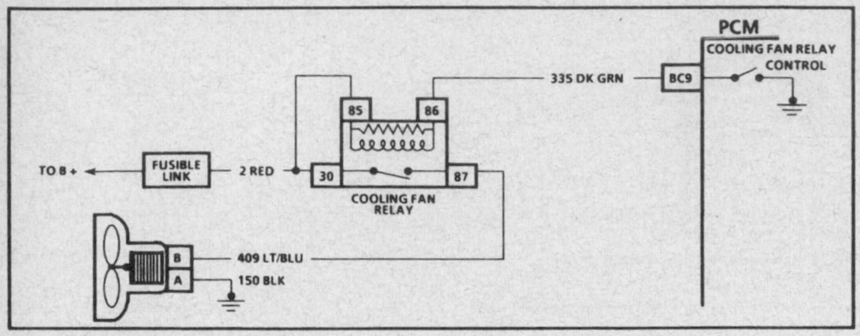
PCM
COOLING FAN RELAY CONTROL
335 DK GRN
BC9
85
86
TO B+
FUSIBLE LINK
2 RED
30
87
COOLING FAN RELAY
409 LT/BLU
B
A
150 BLK

Circuit Description:

The electric coolant fan is controlled by the Powertrain Control Module (PCM) through the fan relay based on inputs from the engine coolant and intake air temperature sensors, the A/C control switch, A/C refrigerant pressure sensor and the vehicle speed sensor. The PCM controls the coolant fan by grounding CKT 335 which turns "ON" the fan relay.

The fan relay will be commanded "ON" when:

- Engine coolant temperature reaches 103°C (217°F) - 106°C (223°F) or more.
- A/C clutch requested.
- Vehicle speed is less than 35 mph.

The fan relay will be commanded "ON" regardless of vehicle speed when:

- Any DTC is set.
- Engine coolant temperature 115°C (239°F) - 118°C (224°F) or more.
- A/C refrigerant pressure is high.

The coolant fan may be commanded "ON" when the engine is not running under fan "Run-ON" conditions described previously in this section.

Chart Test Description: Number(s) below refer to circled number(s) on the diagnostic chart.

1. With the fan relay commanded "ON," the coolant fan control driver should close, which should energize the fan control relay.
2. Tests to see if fault is in wiring to the fan or the fan/relay connection.

Diagnostic Aids: If the owner complained of an overheating problem, it must be determined if the complaint was due to an actual boil over, or the "Temp" light, or temperature gauge indicated overheating.

If the gauge, or light, indicates overheating, but no boil over is detected, the gauge or light circuit should be checked. The gauge accuracy can also be checked by comparing the coolant sensor reading using a scan tool with the gauge reading.

If the engine is actually overheating, and the gauge indicates overheating, but the coolant fan is not coming "ON," the Engine Coolant Temperature (ECT) sensor has probably shifted out of calibration and should be replaced.

If the engine is overheating, and the coolant fan is "ON," the cooling system should be checked.

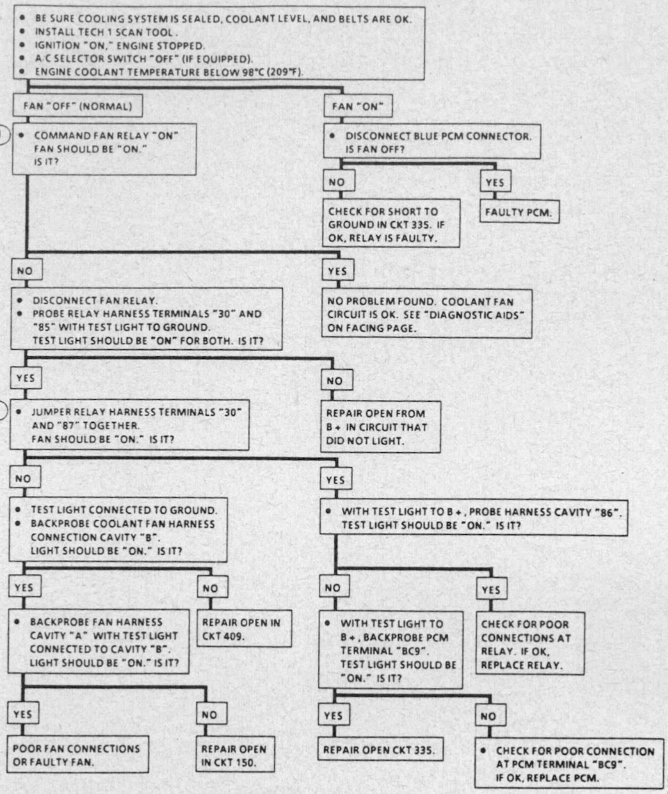
• BE SURE COOLING SYSTEM IS SEALED, COOLANT LEVEL, AND BELTS ARE OK.
• INSTALL TECH 1 SCAN TOOL.
• IGNITION "ON," ENGINE STOPPED.
• A/C SELECTOR SWITCH "OFF" (IF EQUIPPED).
• ENGINE COOLANT TEMPERATURE BELOW 98°C (209°F).
FAN "OFF" (NORMAL)
FAN "ON"
1
• COMMAND FAN RELAY "ON" FAN SHOULD BE "ON." IS IT?
• DISCONNECT BLUE PCM CONNECTOR. IS FAN OFF?
NO
YES
CHECK FOR SHORT TO GROUND IN CKT 335. IF OK, RELAY IS FAULTY.
FAULTY PCM.
NO
YES
• DISCONNECT FAN RELAY.
• PROBE RELAY HARNESS TERMINALS "30" AND "85" WITH TEST LIGHT TO GROUND. TEST LIGHT SHOULD BE "ON" FOR BOTH. IS IT?
NO PROBLEM FOUND. COOLANT FAN CIRCUIT IS OK. SEE "DIAGNOSTIC AIDS" ON FACING PAGE.
YES
NO
2
• JUMPER RELAY HARNESS TERMINALS "30" AND "87" TOGETHER. FAN SHOULD BE "ON." IS IT?
REPAIR OPEN FROM B+ IN CIRCUIT THAT DID NOT LIGHT.
NO
YES
• TEST LIGHT CONNECTED TO GROUND.
• BACKPROBE COOLANT FAN HARNESS CONNECTION CAVITY "B". LIGHT SHOULD BE "ON." IS IT?
• WITH TEST LIGHT TO B+, PROBE HARNESS CAVITY "86". TEST LIGHT SHOULD BE "ON." IS IT?
YES
NO
NO
YES
• BACKPROBE FAN HARNESS CAVITY "A" WITH TEST LIGHT CONNECTED TO CAVITY "B". LIGHT SHOULD BE "ON." IS IT?
REPAIR OPEN IN CKT 409.
• WITH TEST LIGHT TO B+, BACKPROBE PCM TERMINAL "BC9". TEST LIGHT SHOULD BE "ON." IS IT?
CHECK FOR POOR CONNECTIONS AT RELAY. IF OK, REPLACE RELAY.
YES
NO
YES
NO
POOR FAN CONNECTIONS OR FAULTY FAN.
REPAIR OPEN IN CKT 150.
REPAIR OPEN CKT 335.
• CHECK FOR POOR CONNECTION AT PCM TERMINAL "BC9". IF OK, REPLACE PCM.

GC108940018400AX

Fig. 19 Chart C-12, cooling fan diagnosis. 1994 Beretta & Corsica w/2.3L/4-138 engine

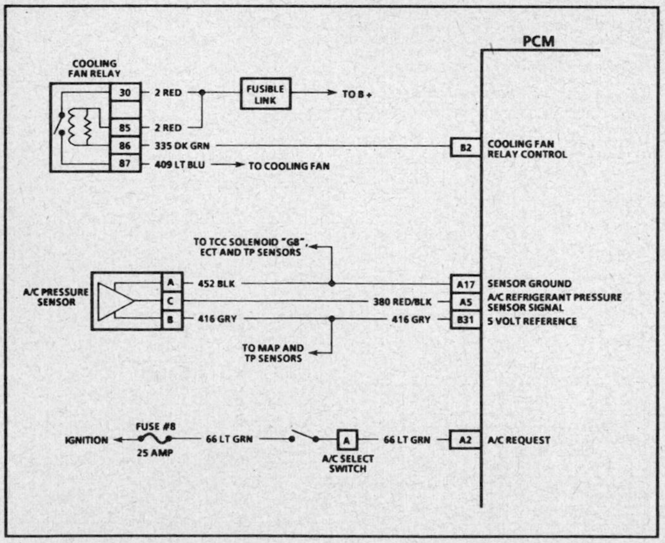
PCM
COOLING FAN RELAY
30
2 RED
FUSIBLE LINK
TO B+
85
2 RED
86
335 DK GRN
87
409 LT BLU
TO COOLING FAN
B2
COOLING FAN RELAY CONTROL
TO TCC SOLENOID "G8", ECT AND TP SENSORS
A/C PRESSURE SENSOR
A
452 BLK
C
380 RED/BLK
B
416 GRY
A17
SENSOR GROUND
A5
A/C REFRIGERANT PRESSURE SENSOR SIGNAL
B31
5 VOLT REFERENCE
TO MAP AND TP SENSORS
FUSE #8
IGNITION
25 AMP
66 LT GRN
A
A/C SELECT SWITCH
66 LT GRN
A2
A/C REQUEST

Circuit Description:

Battery voltage to operate the cooling fan is supplied to the cooling fan relay by CKT 2 on cooling fan relay cavities "30" and "85". When the PCM grounds CKT 335, the relay is energized and the cooling fan is turned "ON."

When the engine is running, the PCM will turn the cooling fan "ON" for any one of the following reasons:

- Diagnostic Trouble Code (DTC) 14, 15 or 70 is set.
- Vehicle speed is less than 70 mph (113 km/h).
- Engine coolant temperature is 108°C (226°F) or greater, with A/C "ON" or "OFF."
- A/C refrigerant pressure is greater than 187 psi (1289 kPa).
- PCM is in backup mode.

Chart Test Description: Number(s) below refer to circled number(s) on the diagnostic chart.

1. With the diagnostic terminal grounded, the cooling fan control driver will close, which should energize the fan control relay.
2. If the A/C pressure is above 300 psi (2069 kPa) or circuit is open, the fan would run whenever A/C is requested.
3. With A/C clutch engaged and the A/C pressure sensor is functioning properly, the fan should come "ON" when pressure exceeds about 200 psi (1380 kPa). This signal should cause the PCM to energize the fan control relay.
4. This will determine if the A/C pressure sensor is faulty or if the PCM or circuitry is faulty.

Diagnostic Aids: If the owner complained of an overheating problem, it must be determined if the complaint was due to an actual boilover, a hot light or temp. gage indicated over heating.

If the gage, or light, indicates overheating, but no boilover is detected, the gage circuit should be checked.

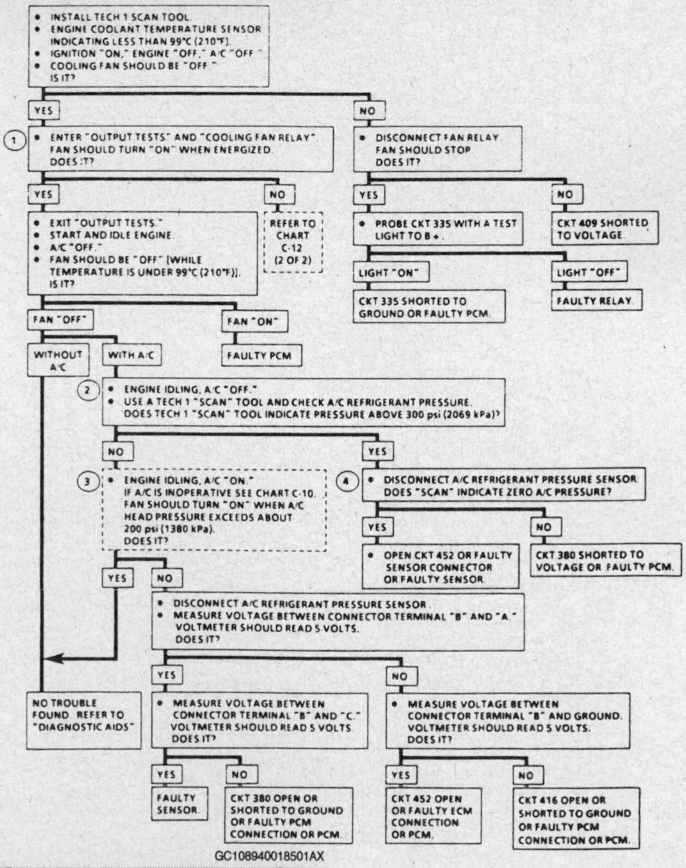
• INSTALL TECH 1 SCAN TOOL.
• ENGINE COOLANT TEMPERATURE SENSOR INDICATING LESS THAN 99°C (210°F).
• IGNITION "ON," ENGINE "OFF," A/C "OFF."
• COOLING FAN SHOULD BE "OFF." IS IT?
YES
NO
1
• ENTER "OUTPUT TESTS" AND "COOLING FAN RELAY". FAN SHOULD TURN "ON" WHEN ENERGIZED. DOES IT?
• DISCONNECT FAN RELAY. FAN SHOULD STOP. DOES IT?
YES
NO
YES
NO
• EXIT "OUTPUT TESTS."
• START AND IDLE ENGINE.
• A/C "OFF."
• FAN SHOULD BE "OFF" [WHILE TEMPERATURE IS UNDER 99°C (210°F)]. IS IT?
REFER TO CHART C-12 (2 OF 2)
• PROBE CKT 335 WITH A TEST LIGHT TO B+.
CKT 409 SHORTED TO VOLTAGE.
LIGHT "ON"
LIGHT "OFF"
CKT 335 SHORTED TO GROUND OR FAULTY PCM.
FAULTY RELAY.
FAN "OFF"
FAN "ON"
WITHOUT A/C
WITH A/C
FAULTY PCM
2
• ENGINE IDLING, A/C "OFF."
• USE A TECH 1 "SCAN" TOOL AND CHECK A/C REFRIGERANT PRESSURE. DOES TECH 1 "SCAN" TOOL INDICATE PRESSURE ABOVE 300 psi (2069 kPa)?
NO
YES
3
• ENGINE IDLING, A/C "ON." IF A/C IS INOPERATIVE SEE CHART C-10. FAN SHOULD TURN "ON" WHEN A/C HEAD PRESSURE EXCEEDS ABOUT 200 psi (1380 kPa). DOES IT?
4
• DISCONNECT A/C REFRIGERANT PRESSURE SENSOR. DOES "SCAN" INDICATE ZERO A/C PRESSURE?
YES
NO
• OPEN CKT 452 OR FAULTY SENSOR CONNECTOR OR FAULTY SENSOR.
CKT 380 SHORTED TO VOLTAGE OR FAULTY PCM.
YES
NO
• DISCONNECT A/C REFRIGERANT PRESSURE SENSOR.
• MEASURE VOLTAGE BETWEEN CONNECTOR TERMINAL "B" AND "A." VOLTMETER SHOULD READ 5 VOLTS. DOES IT?
YES
NO
NO TROUBLE FOUND. REFER TO "DIAGNOSTIC AIDS"
• MEASURE VOLTAGE BETWEEN CONNECTOR TERMINAL "B" AND "C." VOLTMETER SHOULD READ 5 VOLTS. DOES IT?
• MEASURE VOLTAGE BETWEEN CONNECTOR TERMINAL "B" AND GROUND. VOLTMETER SHOULD READ 5 VOLTS. DOES IT?
YES
NO
YES
NO
FAULTY SENSOR.
CKT 380 OPEN OR SHORTED TO GROUND OR FAULTY PCM CONNECTION OR PCM.
CKT 452 OPEN OR FAULTY ECM CONNECTION OR PCM.
CKT 416 OPEN OR SHORTED TO GROUND OR FAULTY PCM CONNECTION OR PCM.

GC108940018501AX

Fig. 20 Chart C-12, cooling fan diagnosis (Part 1 of 2). 1994 Beretta & Corsica w/3.1L/V6-192 engine

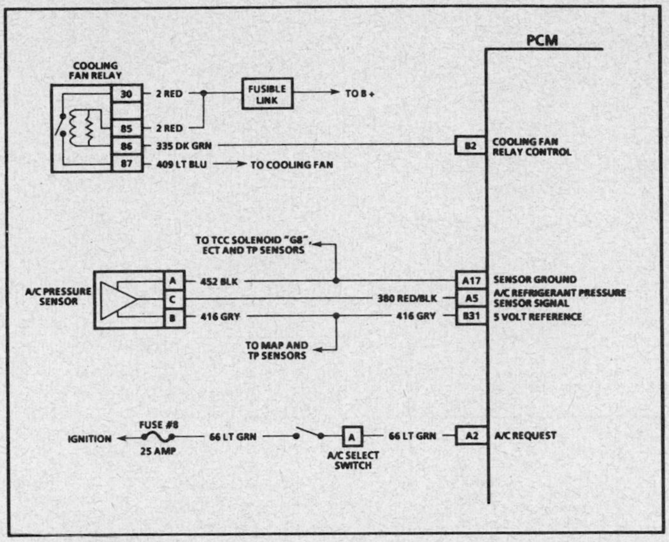

PCM
COOLING FAN RELAY
30
85
86
87
2 RED
FUSIBLE LINK
TO B+
2 RED
335 DK GRN
409 LT BLU
TO COOLING FAN
B2
COOLING FAN RELAY CONTROL
TO TCC SOLENOID "G8", ECT AND TP SENSORS
A/C PRESSURE SENSOR
A
C
B
452 BLK
380 RED/BLK
416 GRY
A17
A5
B31
SENSOR GROUND
A/C REFRIGERANT PRESSURE SENSOR SIGNAL
5 VOLT REFERENCE
TO MAP AND TP SENSORS
IGNITION
FUSE #8
25 AMP
66 LT GRN
A/C SELECT SWITCH
A2
A/C REQUEST

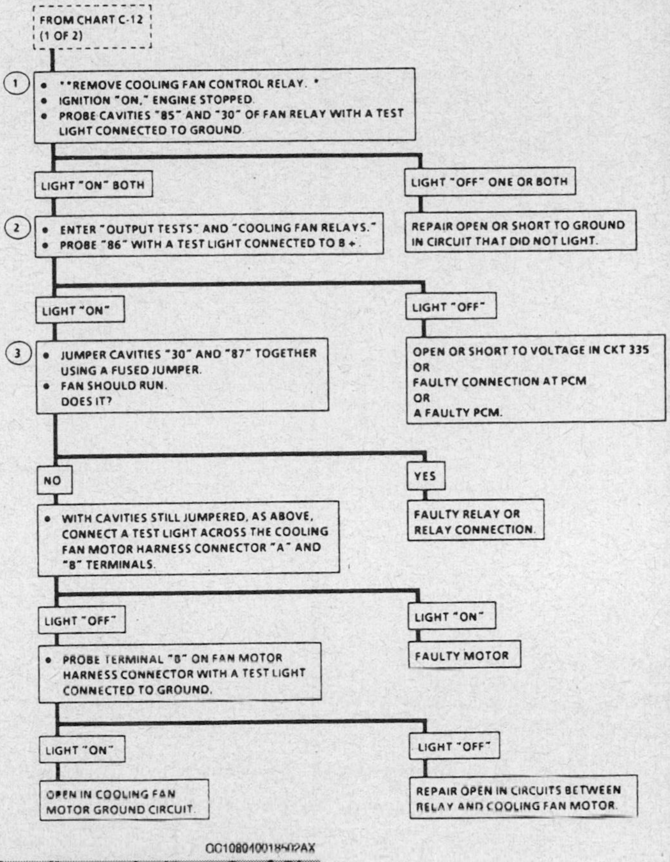

FROM CHART C-12 (1 OF 2)
1
• "REMOVE COOLING FAN CONTROL RELAY."
• IGNITION "ON," ENGINE STOPPED.
• PROBE CAVITIES "85" AND "30" OF FAN RELAY WITH A TEST LIGHT CONNECTED TO GROUND.
LIGHT "ON" BOTH
LIGHT "OFF" ONE OR BOTH
2
• ENTER "OUTPUT TESTS" AND "COOLING FAN RELAYS."
• PROBE "86" WITH A TEST LIGHT CONNECTED TO B+.
REPAIR OPEN OR SHORT TO GROUND IN CIRCUIT THAT DID NOT LIGHT.
LIGHT "ON"
LIGHT "OFF"
3
• JUMPER CAVITIES "30" AND "87" TOGETHER USING A FUSED JUMPER.
• FAN SHOULD RUN. DOES IT?
OPEN OR SHORT TO VOLTAGE IN CKT 335 OR FAULTY CONNECTION AT PCM OR A FAULTY PCM.
NO
YES
• WITH CAVITIES STILL JUMPERED, AS ABOVE, CONNECT A TEST LIGHT ACROSS THE COOLING FAN MOTOR HARNESS CONNECTOR "A" AND "B" TERMINALS.
FAULTY RELAY OR RELAY CONNECTION.
LIGHT "OFF"
LIGHT "ON"
• PROBE TERMINAL "B" ON FAN MOTOR HARNESS CONNECTOR WITH A TEST LIGHT CONNECTED TO GROUND.
FAULTY MOTOR
LIGHT "ON"
LIGHT "OFF"
OPEN IN COOLING FAN MOTOR GROUND CIRCUIT.
REPAIR OPEN IN CIRCUITS BETWEEN RELAY AND COOLING FAN MOTOR.
GC1089100189502AX

Circuit Description:

Battery voltage to operate the cooling fan is supplied to the cooling fan relay by CKT 2 on cooling fan relay cavities 30 and 85. When the PCM grounds CKT 335, the relay is energized and the cooling fan is turned "ON."

When the engine is running, the PCM will turn the cooling fan "ON," for any one of the following reasons:

- Engine Coolant Temperature (ECT) sensor indicating a temperature greater than 108°C (226°F) with A/C "ON" or "OFF."
- Vehicle speed is less than 70 mph (113 km/h).
- A/C refrigerant pressure sensor is greater than 187 psi (1289 kPa).
- Diagnostic Trouble Code (DTC) 14, 15 or 70 is set.
- PCM is in backup mode.

Chart Test Description: Number(s) below refer to circled number(s) on the diagnostic chart.

1. B+ should be available to cooling fan relay cavities "85" and "30".
2. This test checks the ability of the PCM to ground CKT 335
3. If the fan does not turn "ON" at this point, CKT 409 cooling fan motor ground circuit is open, or the cooling fan motor is faulty.

Fig. 20 Chart C-12, cooling fan diagnosis (Part 2 of 2). 1994 Beretta & Corsica w/3.1L/V6-192 engine

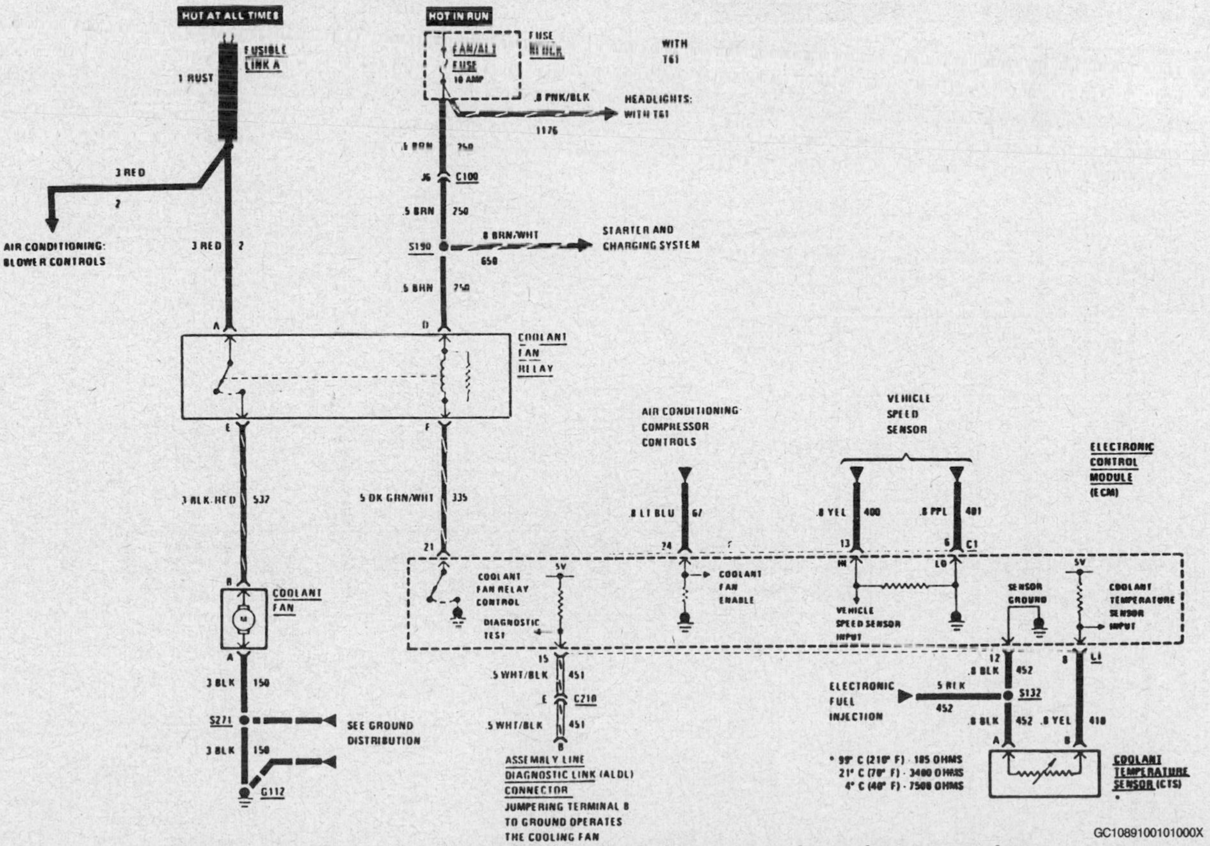

HOT AT ALL TIMES
FUSIBLE LINK A
1 RUST
3 RED
AIR CONDITIONING: BLOWER CONTROLS
HOT IN RUN
FUSE BLOCK
FAN/ALT FUSE 10 AMP
WITH T61
.8 PNK/BLK
HEADLIGHTS: WITH T61
STARTER AND CHARGING SYSTEM
COOLANT FAN RELAY
3 BLK-RED
537
5 DK GRN/WHT
335
COOLANT FAN
3 BLK
150
S271
SEE GROUND DISTRIBUTION
G112
AIR CONDITIONING COMPRESSOR CONTROLS
VEHICLE SPEED SENSOR
ELECTRONIC CONTROL MODULE (ECM)
COOLANT FAN RELAY CONTROL
DIAGNOSTIC TEST
COOLANT FAN ENABLE
VEHICLE SPEED SENSOR INPUT
SENSOR GROUND
COOLANT TEMPERATURE SENSOR INPUT
.5 WHT/BLK
451
C210
ASSEMBLY LINE DIAGNOSTIC LINK (ALDL) CONNECTOR
JUMPERING TERMINAL B TO GROUND OPERATES THE COOLING FAN
ELECTRONIC FUEL INJECTION
S132
.8 BLK
452
.8 YEL
410
COOLANT TEMPERATURE SENSOR (CTS)
GC1089100101000X

Fig. 21 Cooling fan wiring circuit. 1992 Century w/2.5L/4-151 engine

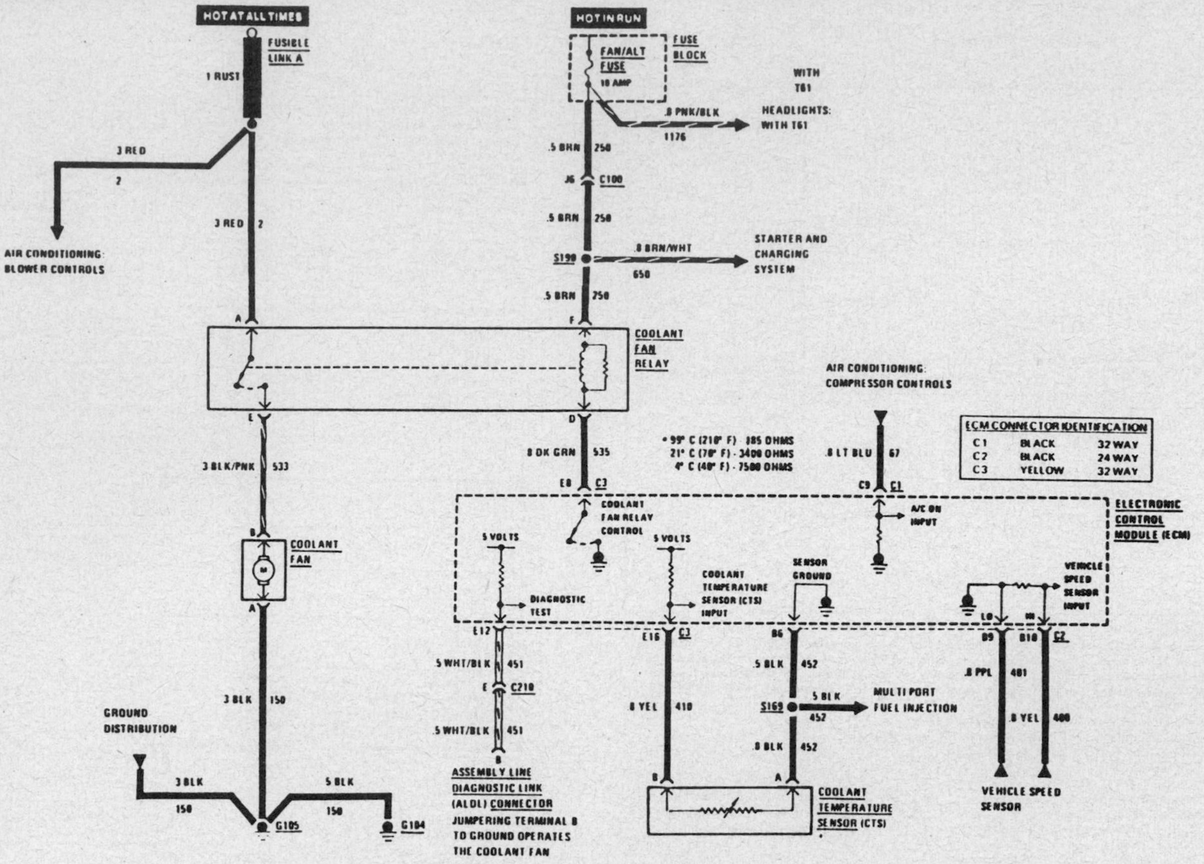
HOT AT ALL TIMES
FUSIBLE LINK A
1 RUST
3 RED
2
AIR CONDITIONING: BLOWER CONTROLS
3 RED 2
HOT IN RUN
FAN/ALT FUSE 10 AMP
FUSE BLOCK
WITH T61
.8 PNK/BLK
HEADLIGHTS: WITH T61
1176
.5 BRN 250
J6 C100
.5 BRN 250
STARTER AND CHARGING SYSTEM
S190
.8 BRN/WHT
650
.5 BRN 250
COOLANT FAN RELAY
AIR CONDITIONING: COMPRESSOR CONTROLS
3 BLK/PNK 533
.8 DK GRN 535
• 99° C (210° F) - 185 OHMS
21° C (70° F) - 3400 OHMS
4° C (40° F) - 7500 OHMS
.8 LT BLU 67
ECM CONNECTOR IDENTIFICATION
C1 BLACK 32 WAY
C2 BLACK 24 WAY
C3 YELLOW 32 WAY
COOLANT FAN
COOLANT FAN RELAY CONTROL
A/C ON INPUT
ELECTRONIC CONTROL MODULE (ECM)
5 VOLTS
DIAGNOSTIC TEST
COOLANT TEMPERATURE SENSOR (CTS) INPUT
SENSOR GROUND
VEHICLE SPEED SENSOR INPUT
.5 WHT/BLK 451
C210
.5 BLK 452
.8 PPL 401
3 BLK 150
GROUND DISTRIBUTION
.8 YEL 410
S169
.5 BLK
MULTI PORT FUEL INJECTION
452
.5 WHT/BLK 451
.8 BLK 452
.8 YEL 400
3 BLK 150
.5 BLK 150
G105
G104
ASSEMBLY LINE DIAGNOSTIC LINK (ALDL) CONNECTOR
JUMPERING TERMINAL B TO GROUND OPERATES THE COOLANT FAN
COOLANT TEMPERATURE SENSOR (CTS)
VEHICLE SPEED SENSOR
GC1089100102000X

Fig. 22 Cooling fan wiring circuit. 1992 Century w/3.3L/V6-204 engine

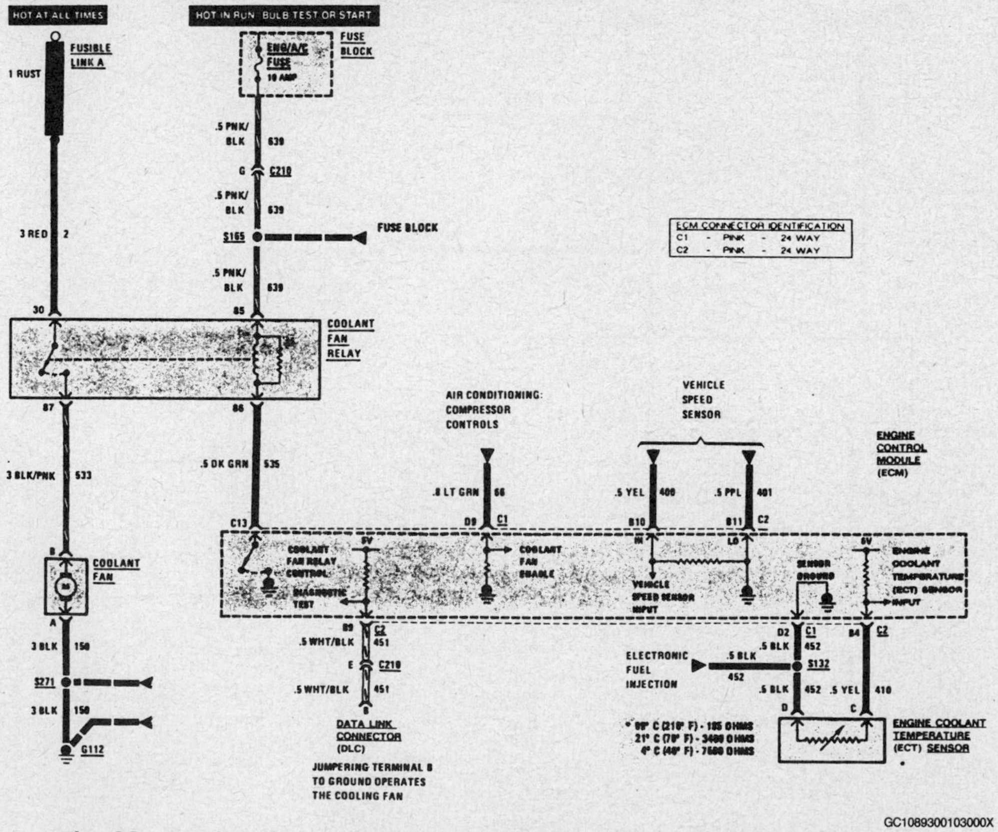
HOT AT ALL TIMES
FUSIBLE LINK A
1 RUST
HOT IN RUN, BULB TEST OR START
ENG/A/C FUSE 10 AMP
FUSE BLOCK
.5 PNK/BLK 639
G C210
.5 PNK/BLK 639
3 RED 2
S165
FUSE BLOCK
ECM CONNECTOR IDENTIFICATION
C1 - PINK - 24 WAY
C2 - PINK - 24 WAY
.5 PNK/BLK 639
COOLANT FAN RELAY
AIR CONDITIONING: COMPRESSOR CONTROLS
VEHICLE SPEED SENSOR
ENGINE CONTROL MODULE (ECM)
3 BLK/PNK 533
.5 DK GRN 535
.8 LT GRN 66
.5 YEL 400
.5 PPL 401
COOLANT FAN
COOLANT FAN RELAY CONTROL
DIAGNOSTIC TEST
COOLANT FAN ENABLE
VEHICLE SPEED SENSOR INPUT
SENSOR GROUND
ENGINE COOLANT TEMPERATURE (ECT) SENSOR INPUT
3 BLK 150
.5 WHT/BLK 451
C210
S271
ELECTRONIC FUEL INJECTION
.5 BLK 452
S132
452
.5 WHT/BLK 451
.5 BLK 452
.5 YEL 410
3 BLK 150
G112
DATA LINK CONNECTOR (DLC)
JUMPERING TERMINAL B TO GROUND OPERATES THE COOLING FAN
• 99° C (210° F) - 185 OHMS
21° C (70° F) - 3400 OHMS
4° C (40° F) - 7500 OHMS
ENGINE COOLANT TEMPERATURE (ECT) SENSOR
GC1089300103000X

Fig. 23 Cooling fan wiring circuit. 1993 Century w/2.2L/4-134 engine

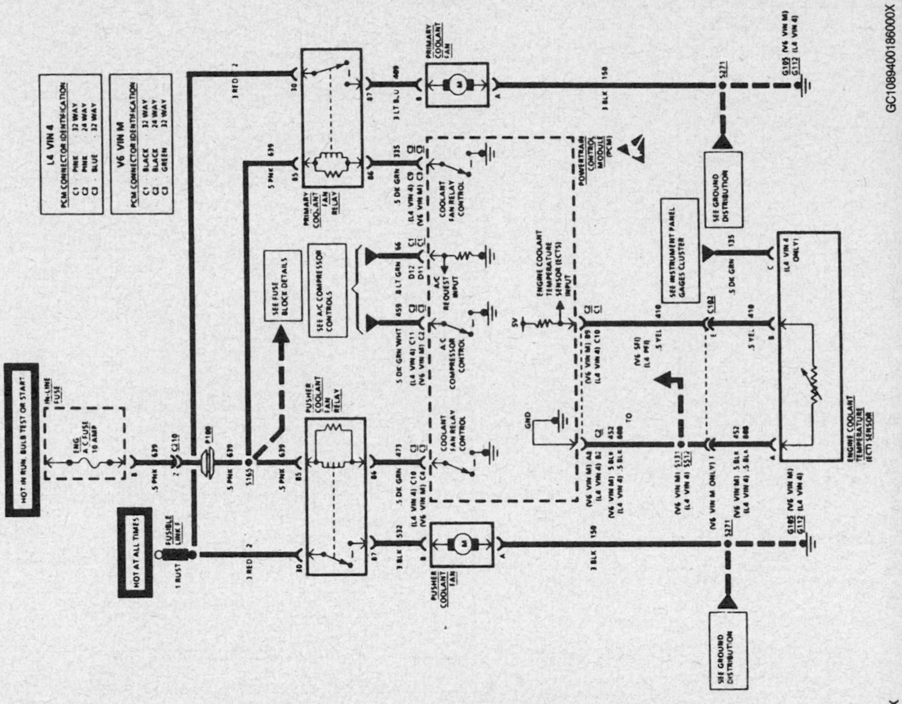
HOT IN RUN, BULB TEST OR START
HOT AT ALL TIMES
PUSHER COOLANT FAN RELAY
PRIMARY COOLANT FAN RELAY
PUSHER COOLANT FAN
PRIMARY COOLANT FAN
POWERTRAIN CONTROL MODULE (PCM)
ENGINE COOLANT TEMPERATURE (ECT) SENSOR
SEE GROUND DISTRIBUTION
SEE INSTRUMENT PANEL GAGES CLUSTER
SEE FUSE BLOCK DETAILS
SEE A/C COMPRESSOR CONTROLS

GC10894001860000X

Fig. 25 Cooling fan wiring circuit. 1994 Century, Cutlass Ciera & Cutlass Cruiser w/2.2L/4-134 and 3.1L/V6-192 engines

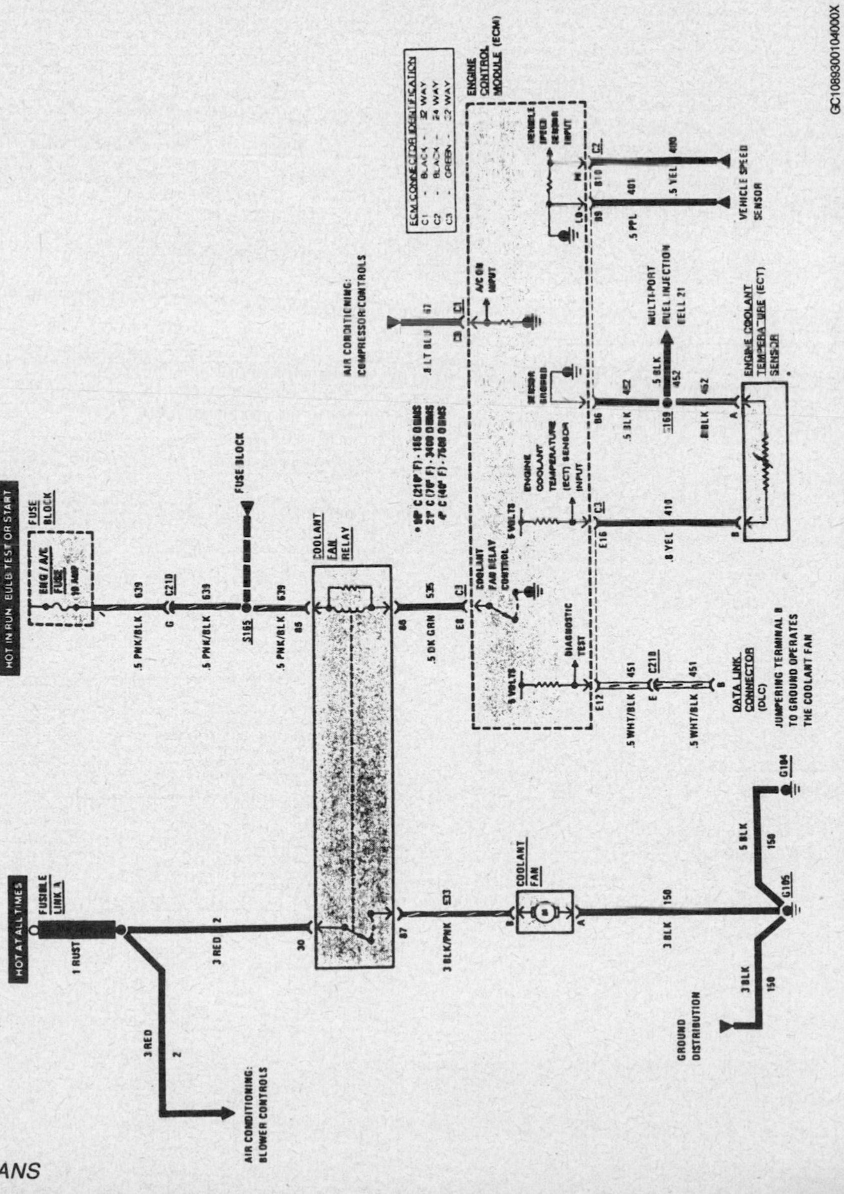
HOT AT ALL TIMES
FUSIBLE LINK A
HOT IN RUN, BULB TEST OR START
FUSE BLOCK
COOLANT FAN RELAY
COOLANT FAN
ENGINE CONTROL MODULE (ECM)
ECM CONNECTOR IDENTIFICATION
C1 - BLACK - 32 WAY
C2 - BLACK - 24 WAY
C3 - GREEN - 32 WAY
AIR CONDITIONING: COMPRESSOR CONTROLS
AIR CONDITIONING: BLOWER CONTROLS
GROUND DISTRIBUTION
DATA LINK CONNECTOR (DLC)
JUMPERING TERMINAL B TO GROUND OPERATES THE COOLANT FAN
ENGINE COOLANT TEMPERATURE (ECT) SENSOR
MULTI-PORT FUEL INJECTION CELL 21
VEHICLE SPEED SENSOR

GC10893001040000X

Fig. 24 Cooling fan wiring circuit. 1993 Century w/3.3L/V6-204 engine

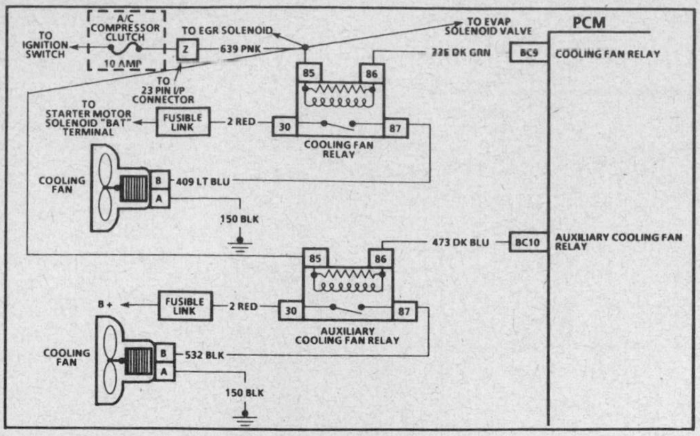

A/C COMPRESSOR CLUTCH
TO IGNITION SWITCH
10 AMP
TO EGR SOLENOID
TO EVAP SOLENOID VALVE
PCM
Z
639 PNK
335 DK GRN
BC9
COOLING FAN RELAY
TO 23 PIN I/P CONNECTOR
TO STARTER MOTOR SOLENOID "BAT" TERMINAL
FUSIBLE LINK
2 RED
85
86
30
87
COOLING FAN RELAY
COOLING FAN
B
A
409 LT BLU
150 BLK
473 DK BLU
BC10
AUXILIARY COOLING FAN RELAY
B+
AUXILIARY COOLING FAN RELAY
532 BLK

CHART C-12

(Page 1 of 2)
COOLING FAN CONTROL DIAGNOSIS
2.2L (VIN 4) "A" CARLINE

Circuit Description:

The primary and auxiliary electric cooling fan(s) are controlled by the PCM based on inputs from the Engine Coolant Temperature (ECT) sensor, the A/C control switches, vehicle speed and state of the A/C refrigerant pressure sensor. The PCM controls the fan(s) by grounding CKT 335 and CKT 473, which energizes the fan control relay. Battery voltage is then supplied to the fan motor.

The PCM grounds CKT 335 and/or CKT 473, when engine coolant temperature is over about 108°C (226°F), or when A/C has been requested and the A/C pressure is about 1380 kPa (200 psi). Once the PCM turns the relay "ON," it will keep it "ON" for a minimum of 30 seconds or until vehicle speed exceeds 70 mph (40 mph for auxiliary fan).

Also, if DTC is set, or the PCM is in backup, the primary fan will run at all times.

Chart Test Description: Number(s) below refer to circled number(s) on the diagnostic chart.

1. When cooling fans are commanded "ON," the cooling fan control driver(s) will close, which should energize the fan control relay(s).
2. If the A/C pressure is above 300 psi (2069 kPa) or the circuit is open, the fan would run whenever A/C is requested.
3. With A/C clutch engaged and the A/C refrigerant pressure sensor functioning properly, the fan should come "ON" when pressure exceeds about 1380 kPa (200 psi). This signal should cause the PCM to energize the fan control relay(s).
4. This will determine if the A/C refrigerant pressure sensor is faulty or if the PCM or circuitry is faulty.

Diagnostic Aids: If the owner complained of an overheating problem, it must be determined if the complaint was due to an actual boil over, a "temp" light, or temperature gage indicated overheating.

If the gage or light indicates overheating, but no boil over is detected, the gage circuit should be checked. The gage accuracy can also be checked by comparing the engine coolant temperature sensor reading using a Tech 1 scan tool and comparing its reading with the gage reading. If the engine is actually overheating, and the gage indicates overheating but the cooling fan is not coming "ON," the coolant sensor has probably shifted out of calibration and should be replaced.

If the engine is overheating, and the cooling fan is "ON," the cooling system should be checked.

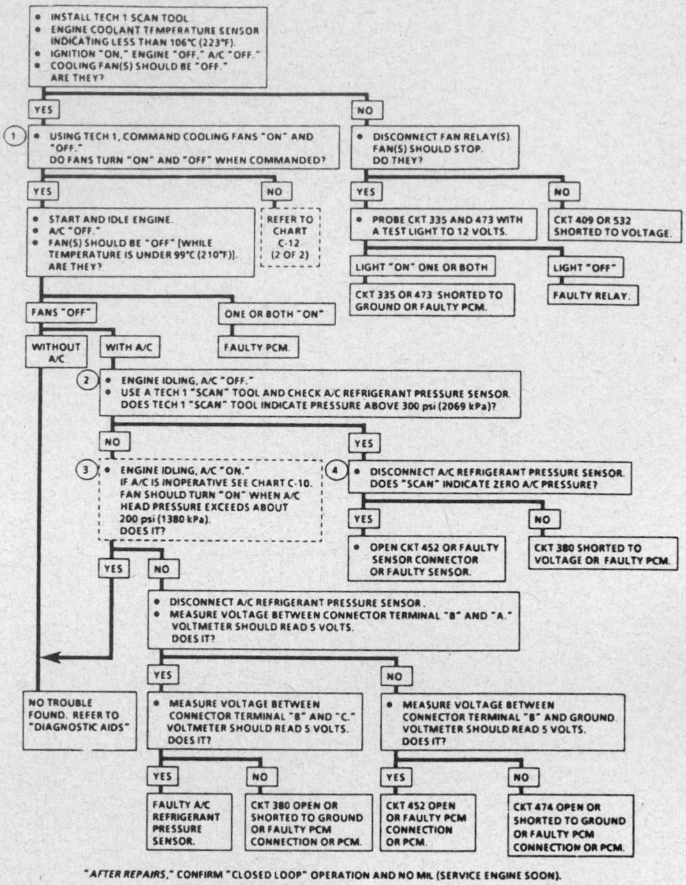

• INSTALL TECH 1 SCAN TOOL
• ENGINE COOLANT TEMPERATURE SENSOR INDICATING LESS THAN 106°C (223°F).
• IGNITION "ON," ENGINE "OFF," A/C "OFF."
• COOLING FAN(S) SHOULD BE "OFF."
ARE THEY?
YES
NO
1
• USING TECH 1, COMMAND COOLING FANS "ON" AND "OFF."
DO FANS TURN "ON" AND "OFF" WHEN COMMANDED?
• DISCONNECT FAN RELAY(S).
FAN(S) SHOULD STOP.
DO THEY?
YES
NO
YES
NO
• START AND IDLE ENGINE.
• A/C "OFF."
• FAN(S) SHOULD BE "OFF" (WHILE TEMPERATURE IS UNDER 99°C (210°F)).
ARE THEY?
REFER TO CHART C-12 (2 OF 2)
• PROBE CKT 335 AND 473 WITH A TEST LIGHT TO 12 VOLTS.
CKT 409 OR 532 SHORTED TO VOLTAGE.
LIGHT "ON" ONE OR BOTH
LIGHT "OFF"
CKT 335 OR 473 SHORTED TO GROUND OR FAULTY PCM.
FAULTY RELAY.
FANS "OFF"
ONE OR BOTH "ON"
WITHOUT A/C
WITH A/C
FAULTY PCM.
2
• ENGINE IDLING, A/C "OFF."
• USE A TECH 1 "SCAN" TOOL AND CHECK A/C REFRIGERANT PRESSURE SENSOR.
DOES TECH 1 "SCAN" TOOL INDICATE PRESSURE ABOVE 300 psi (2069 kPa)?
NO
YES
3
• ENGINE IDLING, A/C "ON."
IF A/C IS INOPERATIVE SEE CHART C-10.
FAN SHOULD TURN "ON" WHEN A/C HEAD PRESSURE EXCEEDS ABOUT 200 psi (1380 kPa).
DOES IT?
4
• DISCONNECT A/C REFRIGERANT PRESSURE SENSOR.
DOES "SCAN" INDICATE ZERO A/C PRESSURE?
YES
NO
• OPEN CKT 452 OR FAULTY SENSOR CONNECTOR OR FAULTY SENSOR.
CKT 380 SHORTED TO VOLTAGE OR FAULTY PCM.
YES
NO
• DISCONNECT A/C REFRIGERANT PRESSURE SENSOR.
• MEASURE VOLTAGE BETWEEN CONNECTOR TERMINAL "B" AND "A."
VOLTMETER SHOULD READ 5 VOLTS.
DOES IT?
YES
NO
NO TROUBLE FOUND. REFER TO "DIAGNOSTIC AIDS"
• MEASURE VOLTAGE BETWEEN CONNECTOR TERMINAL "B" AND "C."
VOLTMETER SHOULD READ 5 VOLTS.
DOES IT?
• MEASURE VOLTAGE BETWEEN CONNECTOR TERMINAL "B" AND GROUND.
VOLTMETER SHOULD READ 5 VOLTS.
DOES IT?
YES
NO
YES
NO
FAULTY A/C REFRIGERANT PRESSURE SENSOR.
CKT 380 OPEN OR SHORTED TO GROUND OR FAULTY PCM CONNECTION OR PCM.
CKT 452 OPEN OR FAULTY PCM CONNECTION OR PCM.
CKT 474 OPEN OR SHORTED TO GROUND OR FAULTY PCM CONNECTION OR PCM.
"AFTER REPAIRS," CONFIRM "CLOSED LOOP" OPERATION AND NO MIL (SERVICE ENGINE SOON).

GC108940018701AX

Fig. 26 Chart C-12, cooling fan diagnosis (Part 1 of 2). 1994 Century, Cutlass Ciera & Cutlass Cruiser w/2.2L/4-134 engine

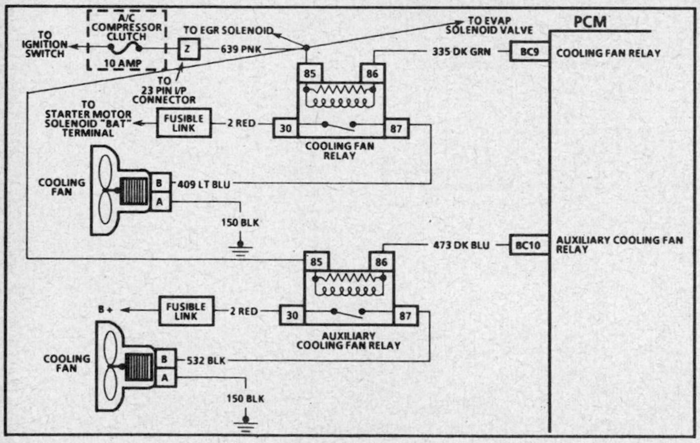

A/C COMPRESSOR CLUTCH
TO IGNITION SWITCH
10 AMP
TO EGR SOLENOID
TO EVAP SOLENOID VALVE
PCM
Z
639 PNK
335 DK GRN
BC9
COOLING FAN RELAY
TO 23 PIN I/P CONNECTOR
TO STARTER MOTOR SOLENOID "BAT" TERMINAL
FUSIBLE LINK
2 RED
85
86
30
87
COOLING FAN RELAY
COOLING FAN
B
A
409 LT BLU
150 BLK
473 DK BLU
BC10
AUXILIARY COOLING FAN RELAY
B+
AUXILIARY COOLING FAN RELAY
532 BLK

CHART C-12

(Page 2 of 2)
COOLING FAN CONTROL DIAGNOSIS
2.2L (VIN 4) "A" CARLINE

Chart Test Description: Number(s) below refer to circled number(s) on the diagnostic chart.

1. 12 volts should be available to CKT 639 on each relay when the ignition is "ON."
2. This test checks the ability of the PCM to ground CKT 335 and CKT 473.
3. If the fan does not turn "ON" at this point, CKT 409, CKT 532 or CKT 150 is open, or the cooling fan motor(s) are faulty.

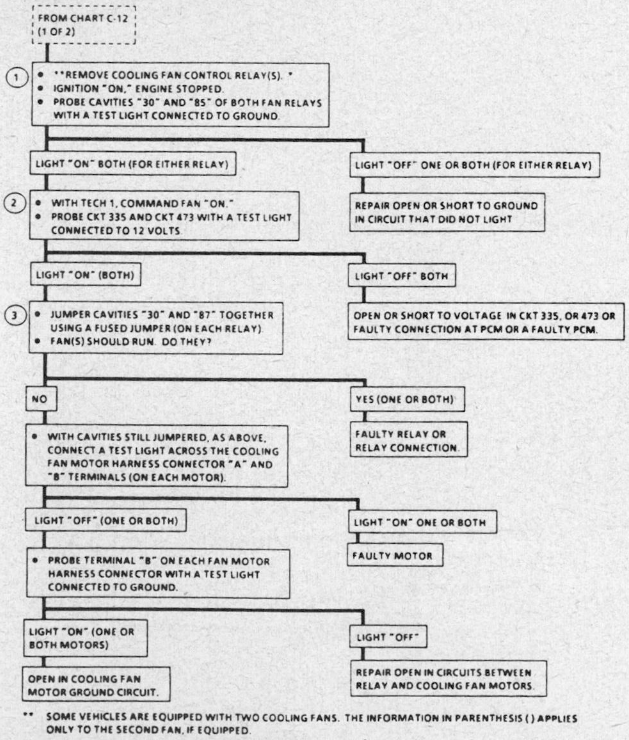

FROM CHART C-12 (1 OF 2)
1
• **REMOVE COOLING FAN CONTROL RELAY(S). *
• IGNITION "ON," ENGINE STOPPED.
• PROBE CAVITIES "30" AND "85" OF BOTH FAN RELAYS WITH A TEST LIGHT CONNECTED TO GROUND.
LIGHT "ON" BOTH (FOR EITHER RELAY)
LIGHT "OFF" ONE OR BOTH (FOR EITHER RELAY)
2
• WITH TECH 1, COMMAND FAN "ON."
• PROBE CKT 335 AND CKT 473 WITH A TEST LIGHT CONNECTED TO 12 VOLTS.
REPAIR OPEN OR SHORT TO GROUND IN CIRCUIT THAT DID NOT LIGHT
LIGHT "ON" (BOTH)
LIGHT "OFF" BOTH
3
• JUMPER CAVITIES "30" AND "87" TOGETHER USING A FUSED JUMPER (ON EACH RELAY).
• FAN(S) SHOULD RUN. DO THEY?
OPEN OR SHORT TO VOLTAGE IN CKT 335, OR 473 OR FAULTY CONNECTION AT PCM OR A FAULTY PCM.
NO
YES (ONE OR BOTH)
• WITH CAVITIES STILL JUMPERED, AS ABOVE, CONNECT A TEST LIGHT ACROSS THE COOLING FAN MOTOR HARNESS CONNECTOR "A" AND "B" TERMINALS (ON EACH MOTOR).
FAULTY RELAY OR RELAY CONNECTION.
LIGHT "OFF" (ONE OR BOTH)
LIGHT "ON" ONE OR BOTH
• PROBE TERMINAL "B" ON EACH FAN MOTOR HARNESS CONNECTOR WITH A TEST LIGHT CONNECTED TO GROUND.
FAULTY MOTOR
LIGHT "ON" (ONE OR BOTH MOTORS)
LIGHT "OFF"
OPEN IN COOLING FAN MOTOR GROUND CIRCUIT.
REPAIR OPEN IN CIRCUITS BETWEEN RELAY AND COOLING FAN MOTORS.
** SOME VEHICLES ARE EQUIPPED WITH TWO COOLING FANS. THE INFORMATION IN PARENTHESIS ( ) APPLIES ONLY TO THE SECOND FAN, IF EQUIPPED.

GC108940018702AX

Fig. 26 Chart C-12, cooling fan diagnosis (Part 2 of 2). 1994 Century, Cutlass Ciera & Cutlass Cruiser w/2.2L/4-134 engine

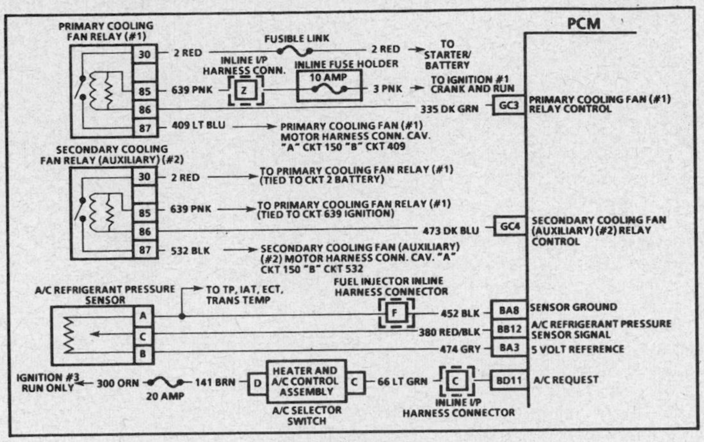
PRIMARY COOLING FAN RELAY (#1)
FUSIBLE LINK
2 RED
INLINE I/P HARNESS CONN.
INLINE FUSE HOLDER
10 AMP
TO STARTER/ BATTERY
TO IGNITION #1 CRANK AND RUN
3 PNK
639 PNK
335 DK GRN
GC3
PRIMARY COOLING FAN (#1) RELAY CONTROL
PCM
409 LT BLU
PRIMARY COOLING FAN (#1) MOTOR HARNESS CONN. CAV. "A" CKT 150 "B" CKT 409
SECONDARY COOLING FAN RELAY (AUXILIARY) (#2)
TO PRIMARY COOLING FAN RELAY (#1) (TIED TO CKT 2 BATTERY)
TO PRIMARY COOLING FAN RELAY (#1) (TIED TO CKT 639 IGNITION)
473 DK BLU
GC4
SECONDARY COOLING FAN (AUXILIARY) (#2) RELAY CONTROL
532 BLK
SECONDARY COOLING FAN (AUXILIARY) (#2) MOTOR HARNESS CONN. CAV. "A" CKT 150 "B" CKT 532
A/C REFRIGERANT PRESSURE SENSOR
TO TP, IAT, ECT, TRANS TEMP
FUEL INJECTOR INLINE HARNESS CONNECTOR
452 BLK
BA8
SENSOR GROUND
380 RED/BLK
BB12
A/C REFRIGERANT PRESSURE SENSOR SIGNAL
474 GRY
BA3
5 VOLT REFERENCE
IGNITION #3 RUN ONLY
300 ORN
20 AMP
141 BRN
HEATER AND A/C CONTROL ASSEMBLY
66 LT GRN
BD11
A/C REQUEST
A/C SELECTOR SWITCH
INLINE I/P HARNESS CONNECTOR

CHART C-12

(Page 1 of 2)

COOLING FAN CONTROL CIRCUIT DIAGNOSIS

3100 (VIN M) "A" CARLINE (SFI) (MAF)

Circuit Description:

The primary and secondary electric cooling fan(s) are controlled by the PCM, based on inputs from the Engine Coolant Temperature (ECT) sensor, the A/C control switch, vehicle speed, and state of the A/C pressure sensor. The PCM controls the fan(s) by grounding CKT 335 and/or CKT 473, which energizes the fan control relay, battery voltage is then supplied to the fan motor.

Chart Test Description: Number(s) below refer to circled number(s) on the diagnostic chart.

1. Using the Tech 1 scan tool, commanding both relays "ON," the cooling fan control driver(s) will close, which should energize the fan control relay(s).
2. If the A/C pressure is above 246 psi, both fans should be energized whenever A/C is requested.
3. With A/C clutch engaged and the A/C pressure sensor functioning properly, the primary fan should come "ON" when pressure exceeds about 190 psi). This signal should cause the PCM to energize the fan control relay(s).
4. This will determine if the A/C pressure sensor is faulty, or if the PCM or circuitry is faulty.

Diagnostic Aids: If the owner comments about an overheating problem, it must be determined whether the comment was due to an actual boil over, or the hot light, or temperature gage indicated overheating.

If the gage or light indicates overheating, but no boil over is detected, the gage circuit should be checked. The gage accuracy can also be checked by comparing the engine coolant temperature reading using a scan tool and comparing its display with the gage reading.

If the engine is actually overheating and the gage indicates overheating, but the cooling fan is not coming "ON," the Engine Coolant Temperature (ECT) sensor has probably shifted out of calibration and should be replaced.

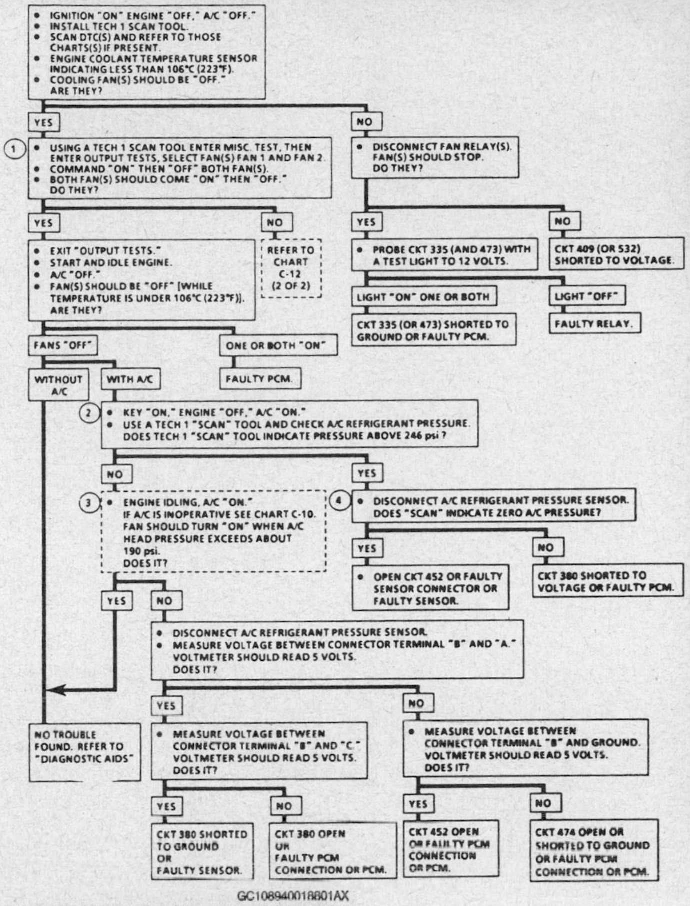
• IGNITION "ON" ENGINE "OFF," A/C "OFF."
• INSTALL TECH 1 SCAN TOOL.
• SCAN DTC(S) AND REFER TO THOSE CHARTS(S) IF PRESENT.
• ENGINE COOLANT TEMPERATURE SENSOR INDICATING LESS THAN 106°C (223°F).
• COOLING FAN(S) SHOULD BE "OFF." ARE THEY?
YES
NO
1
• USING A TECH 1 SCAN TOOL ENTER MISC. TEST, THEN ENTER OUTPUT TESTS, SELECT FAN(S) FAN 1 AND FAN 2.
• COMMAND "ON" THEN "OFF" BOTH FAN(S).
• BOTH FAN(S) SHOULD COME "ON" THEN "OFF." DO THEY?
• DISCONNECT FAN RELAY(S). FAN(S) SHOULD STOP. DO THEY?
YES
NO
YES
NO
• EXIT "OUTPUT TESTS."
• START AND IDLE ENGINE.
• A/C "OFF."
• FAN(S) SHOULD BE "OFF" (WHILE TEMPERATURE IS UNDER 106°C (223°F)). ARE THEY?
REFER TO CHART C-12 (2 OF 2)
• PROBE CKT 335 (AND 473) WITH A TEST LIGHT TO 12 VOLTS.
CKT 409 (OR 532) SHORTED TO VOLTAGE.
LIGHT "ON" ONE OR BOTH
LIGHT "OFF"
CKT 335 (OR 473) SHORTED TO GROUND OR FAULTY PCM.
FAULTY RELAY.
FANS "OFF"
ONE OR BOTH "ON"
WITHOUT A/C
WITH A/C
FAULTY PCM.
2
• KEY "ON," ENGINE "OFF," A/C "ON."
• USE A TECH 1 "SCAN" TOOL AND CHECK A/C REFRIGERANT PRESSURE. DOES TECH 1 "SCAN" TOOL INDICATE PRESSURE ABOVE 246 psi ?
NO
YES
3
• ENGINE IDLING, A/C "ON." IF A/C IS INOPERATIVE SEE CHART C-10. FAN SHOULD TURN "ON" WHEN A/C HEAD PRESSURE EXCEEDS ABOUT 190 psi. DOES IT?
4
• DISCONNECT A/C REFRIGERANT PRESSURE SENSOR. DOES "SCAN" INDICATE ZERO A/C PRESSURE?
YES
NO
• OPEN CKT 452 OR FAULTY SENSOR CONNECTOR OR FAULTY SENSOR.
CKT 380 SHORTED TO VOLTAGE OR FAULTY PCM.
YES
NO
• DISCONNECT A/C REFRIGERANT PRESSURE SENSOR.
• MEASURE VOLTAGE BETWEEN CONNECTOR TERMINAL "B" AND "A." VOLTMETER SHOULD READ 5 VOLTS. DOES IT?
YES
NO
NO TROUBLE FOUND. REFER TO "DIAGNOSTIC AIDS"
• MEASURE VOLTAGE BETWEEN CONNECTOR TERMINAL "B" AND "C." VOLTMETER SHOULD READ 5 VOLTS. DOES IT?
• MEASURE VOLTAGE BETWEEN CONNECTOR TERMINAL "B" AND GROUND. VOLTMETER SHOULD READ 5 VOLTS. DOES IT?
YES
NO
YES
NO
CKT 380 SHORTED TO GROUND OR FAULTY SENSOR.
CKT 380 OPEN OR FAULTY PCM CONNECTION OR PCM.
CKT 452 OPEN OR FAULTY PCM CONNECTION OR PCM.
CKT 474 OPEN OR SHORTED TO GROUND OR FAULTY PCM CONNECTION OR PCM.
GC108940018801AX

Fig. 27 Chart C-12, cooling fan diagnosis (Part 1 of 2). 1994 Century, Cutlass Ciera & Cutlass Cruiser w/3.1L/V6–192 engine

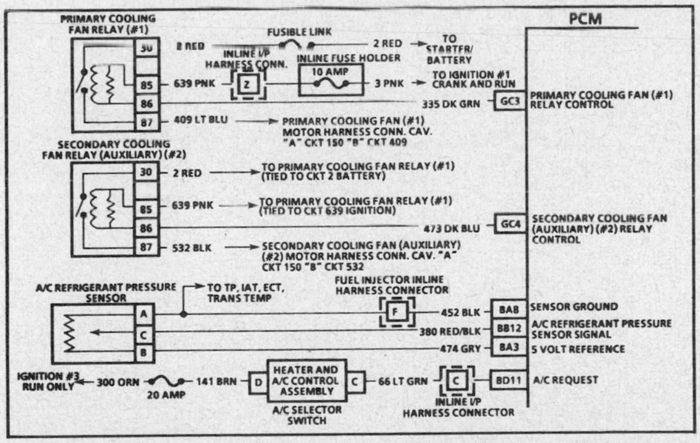
PRIMARY COOLING FAN RELAY (#1)
FUSIBLE LINK
2 RED
INLINE I/P HARNESS CONN.
INLINE FUSE HOLDER
10 AMP
TO STARTER/ BATTERY
TO IGNITION #1 CRANK AND RUN
3 PNK
639 PNK
335 DK GRN
GC3
PRIMARY COOLING FAN (#1) RELAY CONTROL
PCM
409 LT BLU
PRIMARY COOLING FAN (#1) MOTOR HARNESS CONN. CAV. "A" CKT 150 "B" CKT 409
SECONDARY COOLING FAN RELAY (AUXILIARY) (#2)
TO PRIMARY COOLING FAN RELAY (#1) (TIED TO CKT 2 BATTERY)
TO PRIMARY COOLING FAN RELAY (#1) (TIED TO CKT 639 IGNITION)
473 DK BLU
GC4
SECONDARY COOLING FAN (AUXILIARY) (#2) RELAY CONTROL
532 BLK
SECONDARY COOLING FAN (AUXILIARY) (#2) MOTOR HARNESS CONN. CAV. "A" CKT 150 "B" CKT 532
A/C REFRIGERANT PRESSURE SENSOR
TO TP, IAT, ECT, TRANS TEMP
FUEL INJECTOR INLINE HARNESS CONNECTOR
452 BLK
BA8
SENSOR GROUND
380 RED/BLK
BB12
A/C REFRIGERANT PRESSURE SENSOR SIGNAL
474 GRY
BA3
5 VOLT REFERENCE
IGNITION #3 RUN ONLY
300 ORN
20 AMP
141 BRN
HEATER AND A/C CONTROL ASSEMBLY
66 LT GRN
BD11
A/C REQUEST
A/C SELECTOR SWITCH
INLINE I/P HARNESS CONNECTOR

Chart Test Description: Number(s) below refer to circled number(s) on the diagnostic chart.

1. 12 volts should be available to CKT 639 and CKT2 on each relay when the ignition is "ON."
2. This test checks the ability of the PCM to ground CKT 335 (CKT 473).
3. If the fan does not turn "ON" at this point, CKT 409, 532 or 150 is open, or the cooling fan motor(s) are at fault.

Diagnostic Aids: If the owner comments about an overheating problem, it must be determined whether the comment was due to an actual boil over, or the hot light, or temperature gage indicated overheating.

If the gage or light indicates overheating, but no boil over is detected, the gage circuit should be checked. The gage accuracy can also be checked by comparing the engine coolant temperature reading using a scan tool and comparing its display with the gage reading.

If the engine is actually overheating and the gage indicates overheating, but the cooling fan is not coming "ON," the Engine Coolant Temperature (ECT) sensor has probably shifted out of calibration and should be replaced.

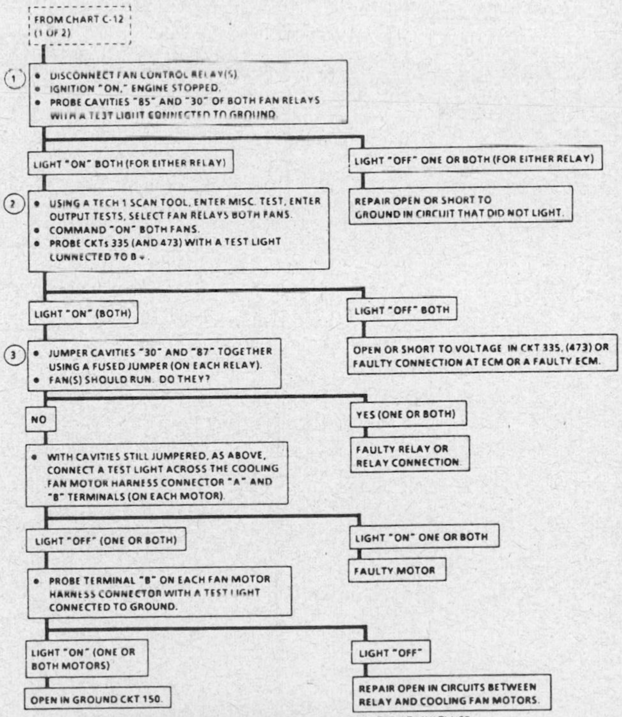
FROM CHART C-12 (1 OF 2)
1
• DISCONNECT FAN CONTROL RELAY(S).
• IGNITION "ON," ENGINE STOPPED.
• PROBE CAVITIES "85" AND "30" OF BOTH FAN RELAYS WITH A TEST LIGHT CONNECTED TO GROUND.
LIGHT "ON" BOTH (FOR EITHER RELAY)
LIGHT "OFF" ONE OR BOTH (FOR EITHER RELAY)
2
• USING A TECH 1 SCAN TOOL, ENTER MISC. TEST, ENTER OUTPUT TESTS, SELECT FAN RELAYS BOTH FANS.
• COMMAND "ON" BOTH FANS.
• PROBE CKTs 335 (AND 473) WITH A TEST LIGHT CONNECTED TO B+.
REPAIR OPEN OR SHORT TO GROUND IN CIRCUIT THAT DID NOT LIGHT.
LIGHT "ON" (BOTH)
LIGHT "OFF" BOTH
3
• JUMPER CAVITIES "30" AND "87" TOGETHER USING A FUSED JUMPER (ON EACH RELAY).
• FAN(S) SHOULD RUN. DO THEY?
OPEN OR SHORT TO VOLTAGE IN CKT 335, (473) OR FAULTY CONNECTION AT ECM OR A FAULTY ECM.
NO
YES (ONE OR BOTH)
FAULTY RELAY OR RELAY CONNECTION.
• WITH CAVITIES STILL JUMPERED, AS ABOVE, CONNECT A TEST LIGHT ACROSS THE COOLING FAN MOTOR HARNESS CONNECTOR "A" AND "B" TERMINALS (ON EACH MOTOR).
LIGHT "OFF" (ONE OR BOTH)
LIGHT "ON" ONE OR BOTH
FAULTY MOTOR
• PROBE TERMINAL "B" ON EACH FAN MOTOR HARNESS CONNECTOR WITH A TEST LIGHT CONNECTED TO GROUND.
LIGHT "ON" (ONE OR BOTH MOTORS)
LIGHT "OFF"
OPEN IN GROUND CKT 150.
REPAIR OPEN IN CIRCUITS BETWEEN RELAY AND COOLING FAN MOTORS.

SECONDARY COOLING FAN (AUXILIARY (#2) RELAY. LOCATED AT MULTI-USE RELAY BRACKET MOUNTED UNDERHOOD RIGHT SIDE FRONT OF VEHICLE.

Fig. 27 Chart C-12, cooling fan diagnosis (Part 2 of 2). 1994 Century, Cutlass Ciera & Cutlass Cruiser w/3.1L/V6–192 engine

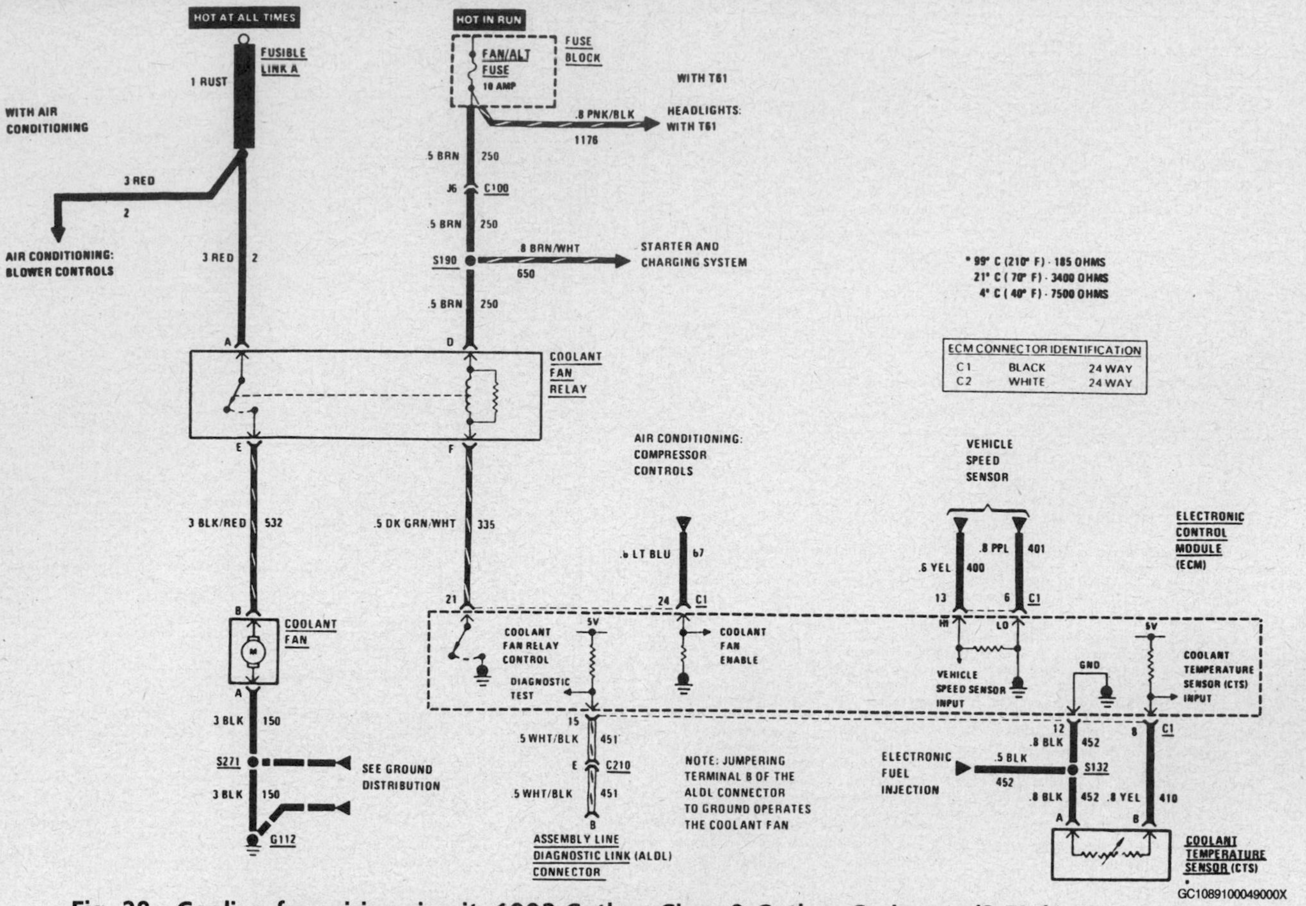
HOT AT ALL TIMES
FUSIBLE LINK A
1 RUST
WITH AIR CONDITIONING
3 RED
2
AIR CONDITIONING: BLOWER CONTROLS
3 RED 2
HOT IN RUN
FAN/ALT FUSE 10 AMP
FUSE BLOCK
WITH T61
.8 PNK/BLK
HEADLIGHTS: WITH T61
1176
.5 BRN 250
J6 C100
.5 BRN 250
.8 BRN/WHT
S190
650
STARTER AND CHARGING SYSTEM
.5 BRN 250
* 99° C (210° F) - 185 OHMS
21° C (70° F) - 3400 OHMS
4° C (40° F) - 7500 OHMS
ECM CONNECTOR IDENTIFICATION
C1 BLACK 24 WAY
C2 WHITE 24 WAY
COOLANT FAN RELAY
AIR CONDITIONING: COMPRESSOR CONTROLS
VEHICLE SPEED SENSOR
ELECTRONIC CONTROL MODULE (ECM)
3 BLK/RED 532
.5 DK GRN/WHT 335
.6 LT BLU 67
.8 PPL 401
.6 YEL 400
COOLANT FAN
COOLANT FAN RELAY CONTROL
5V
COOLANT FAN ENABLE
DIAGNOSTIC TEST
VEHICLE SPEED SENSOR INPUT
GND
COOLANT TEMPERATURE SENSOR (CTS) INPUT
3 BLK 150
S271
SEE GROUND DISTRIBUTION
3 BLK 150
G112
.5 WHT/BLK 451
C210
.5 WHT/BLK 451
ASSEMBLY LINE DIAGNOSTIC LINK (ALDL) CONNECTOR
NOTE: JUMPERING TERMINAL B OF THE ALDL CONNECTOR TO GROUND OPERATES THE COOLANT FAN
ELECTRONIC FUEL INJECTION
.5 BLK
452
S132
.8 BLK 452
.8 BLK 452 .8 YEL 410
COOLANT TEMPERATURE SENSOR (CTS)
GC1089100049000X

Fig. 28 Cooling fan wiring circuit. 1992 Cutlass Ciera & Cutlass Cruiser w/2.5L/4-151 engine

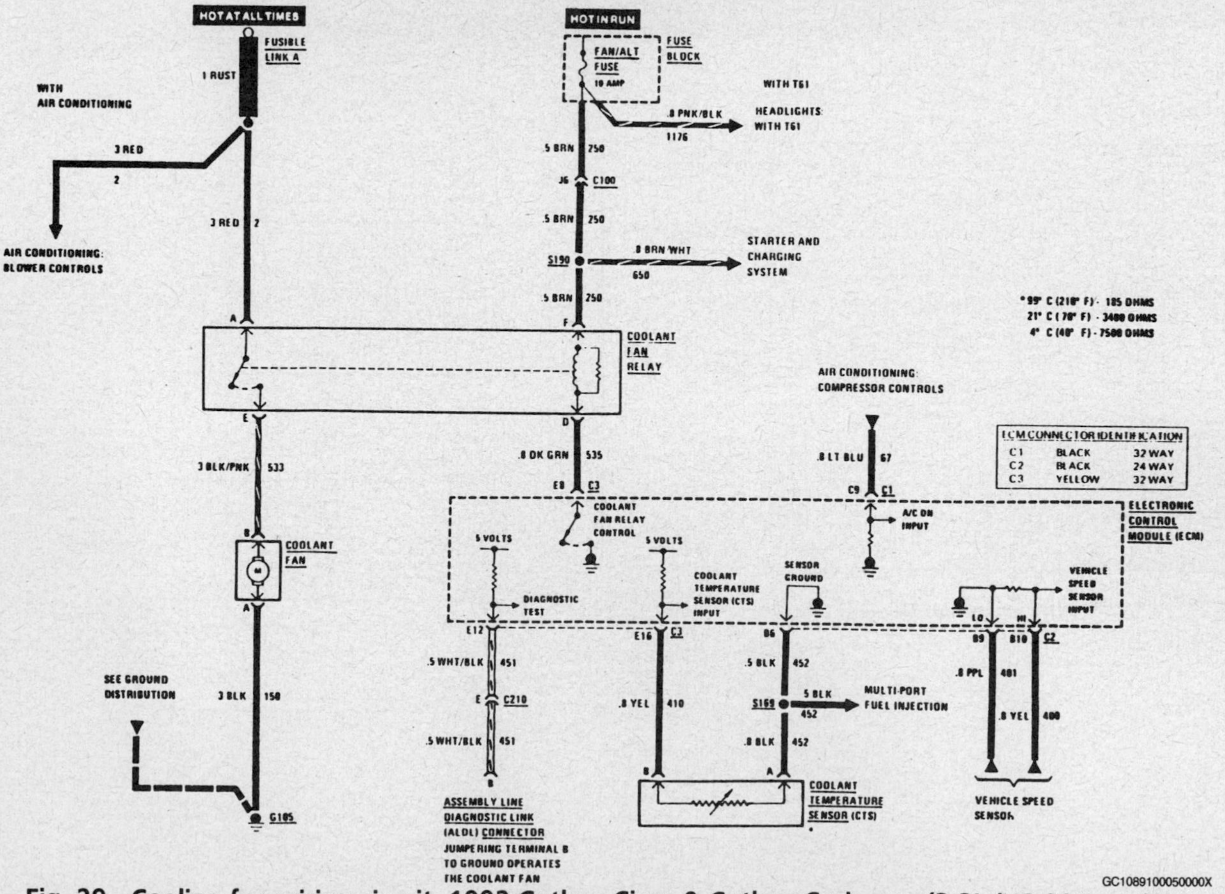
HOT AT ALL TIMES
FUSIBLE LINK A
1 RUST
WITH AIR CONDITIONING
3 RED
2
AIR CONDITIONING: BLOWER CONTROLS
3 RED 2
HOT IN RUN
FAN/ALT FUSE 10 AMP
FUSE BLOCK
WITH T61
.8 PNK/BLK
HEADLIGHTS: WITH T61
1176
.5 BRN 250
J6 C100
.5 BRN 250
.8 BRN/WHT
S190
650
STARTER AND CHARGING SYSTEM
.5 BRN 250
* 99° C (210° F) - 185 OHMS
21° C (70° F) - 3400 OHMS
4° C (40° F) - 7500 OHMS
COOLANT FAN RELAY
AIR CONDITIONING: COMPRESSOR CONTROLS
ECM CONNECTOR IDENTIFICATION
C1 BLACK 32 WAY
C2 BLACK 24 WAY
C3 YELLOW 32 WAY
3 BLK/PNK 533
.8 DK GRN 535
.8 LT BLU 67
COOLANT FAN RELAY CONTROL
A/C ON INPUT
ELECTRONIC CONTROL MODULE (ECM)
COOLANT FAN
5 VOLTS
DIAGNOSTIC TEST
COOLANT TEMPERATURE SENSOR (CTS) INPUT
SENSOR GROUND
VEHICLE SPEED SENSOR INPUT
.5 WHT/BLK 451
C210
.5 WHT/BLK 451
.8 YEL 410
.5 BLK 452
S169
.5 BLK
MULTI-PORT FUEL INJECTION
.8 BLK 452
.8 PPL 401
.8 YEL 400
SEE GROUND DISTRIBUTION
3 BLK 150
G105
ASSEMBLY LINE DIAGNOSTIC LINK (ALDL) CONNECTOR
JUMPERING TERMINAL B TO GROUND OPERATES THE COOLANT FAN
COOLANT TEMPERATURE SENSOR (CTS)
VEHICLE SPEED SENSOR
GC1089100050000X

Fig. 29 Cooling fan wiring circuit. 1992 Cutlass Ciera & Cutlass Cruiser w/3.3L/V6-204 engine

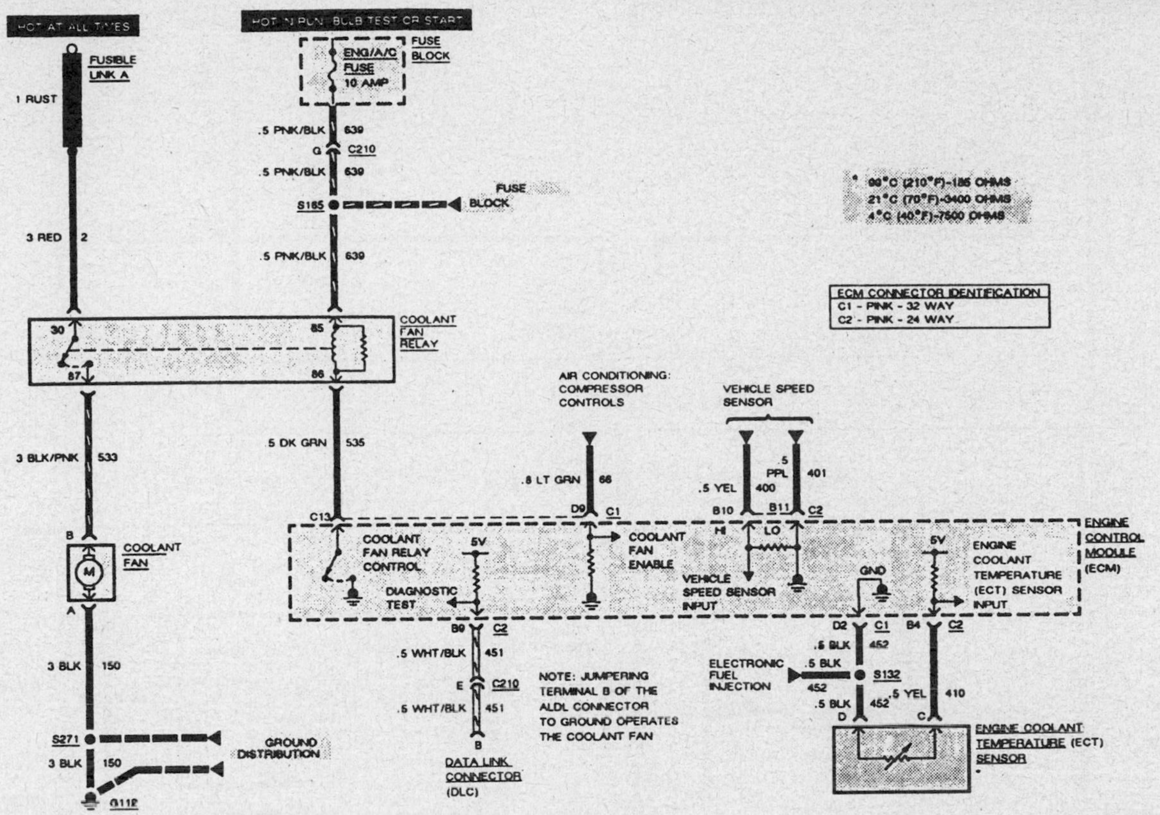
HOT AT ALL TIMES
HOT IN RUN, BULB TEST OR START
FUSIBLE LINK A
1 RUST
ENG/A/C FUSE 10 AMP
FUSE BLOCK
.5 PNK/BLK 639
G C210
S165
FUSE BLOCK
3 RED 2
COOLANT FAN RELAY
30
85
87
86
3 BLK/PNK 533
.5 DK GRN 535
COOLANT FAN
B
A
3 BLK 150
S271
GROUND DISTRIBUTION
G112
* 99°C (210°F)-185 OHMS
21°C (70°F)-3400 OHMS
4°C (40°F)-7500 OHMS
ECM CONNECTOR IDENTIFICATION
C1 - PINK - 32 WAY
C2 - PINK - 24 WAY
AIR CONDITIONING: COMPRESSOR CONTROLS
VEHICLE SPEED SENSOR
.8 LT GRN 66
.5 YEL 400
.5 PPL 401
D9 C1
B10 B11 C2
C13
COOLANT FAN RELAY CONTROL
5V
DIAGNOSTIC TEST
COOLANT FAN ENABLE
HI LO
VEHICLE SPEED SENSOR INPUT
GND
ENGINE COOLANT TEMPERATURE (ECT) SENSOR INPUT
ENGINE CONTROL MODULE (ECM)
B9 C2
.5 WHT/BLK 451
E C210
B
DATA LINK CONNECTOR (DLC)
NOTE: JUMPERING TERMINAL B OF THE ALDL CONNECTOR TO GROUND OPERATES THE COOLANT FAN
D2 C1 B4 C2
.5 BLK 452
ELECTRONIC FUEL INJECTION
S132
.5 YEL 410
D C
ENGINE COOLANT TEMPERATURE (ECT) SENSOR
GC1089300051000X

Fig. 30 Cooling fan wiring circuit. 1993 Cutlass Ciera & Cutlass Cruiser w/2.2L/4-134 engine

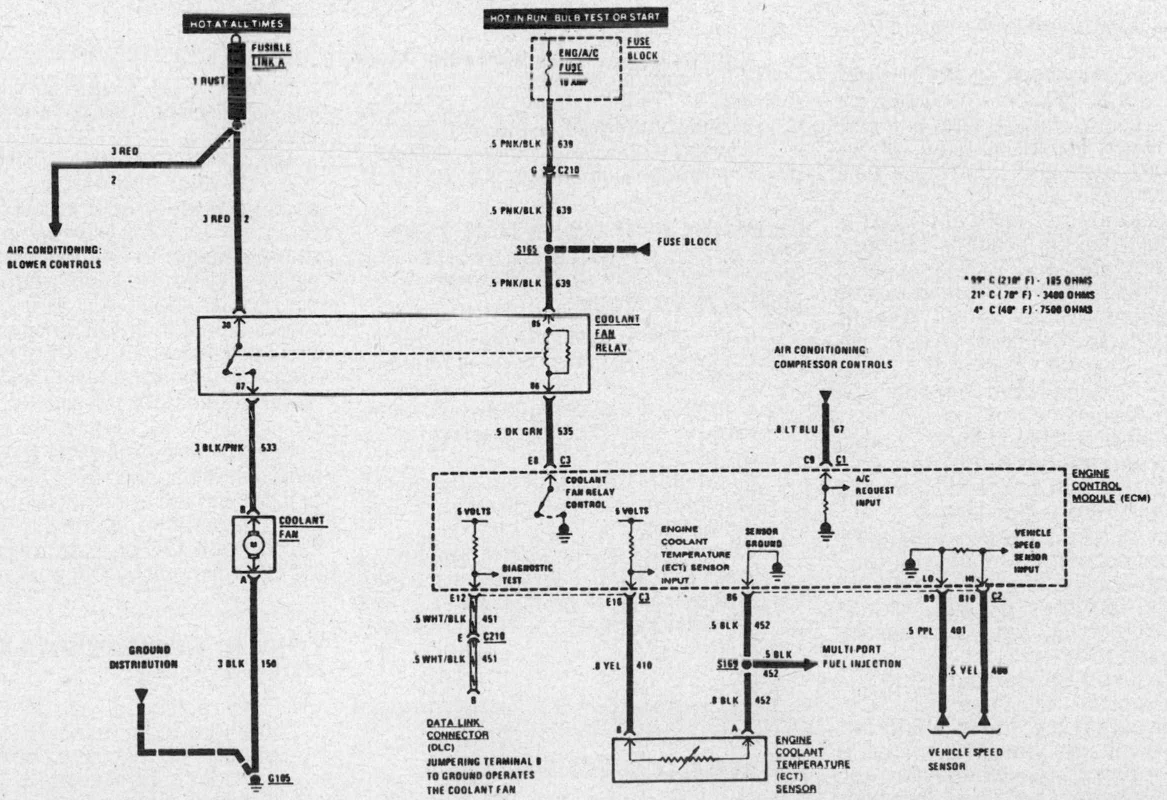
HOT AT ALL TIMES
FUSIBLE LINK A
1 RUST
3 RED
2
AIR CONDITIONING: BLOWER CONTROLS
HOT IN RUN, BULB TEST OR START
ENG/A/C FUSE 10 AMP
FUSE BLOCK
.5 PNK/BLK 639
G C210
S165
FUSE BLOCK
* 99° C (210° F) - 185 OHMS
21° C (70° F) - 3400 OHMS
4° C (40° F) - 7500 OHMS
COOLANT FAN RELAY
30
86
87
3 BLK/PNK 533
.5 DK GRN 535
AIR CONDITIONING: COMPRESSOR CONTROLS
.8 LT BLU 67
E8 C3
C9 C1
COOLANT FAN RELAY CONTROL
A/C REQUEST INPUT
ENGINE CONTROL MODULE (ECM)
COOLANT FAN
5 VOLTS
DIAGNOSTIC TEST
ENGINE COOLANT TEMPERATURE (ECT) SENSOR INPUT
SENSOR GROUND
VEHICLE SPEED SENSOR INPUT
LO HI
E12
E16 C3
B6
B9 B10 C2
.5 WHT/BLK 451
E C210
GROUND DISTRIBUTION
3 BLK 150
.8 YEL 410
.5 BLK 452
S169
MULTI PORT FUEL INJECTION
.5 PPL 401
.5 YEL 400
DATA LINK CONNECTOR (DLC)
JUMPERING TERMINAL B TO GROUND OPERATES THE COOLANT FAN
G105
ENGINE COOLANT TEMPERATURE (ECT) SENSOR
VEHICLE SPEED SENSOR
GC1089300052000X

Fig. 31 Cooling fan wiring circuit. 1993 Cutlass Ciera & Cutlass Cruiser w/3.3L/V6-204 engine

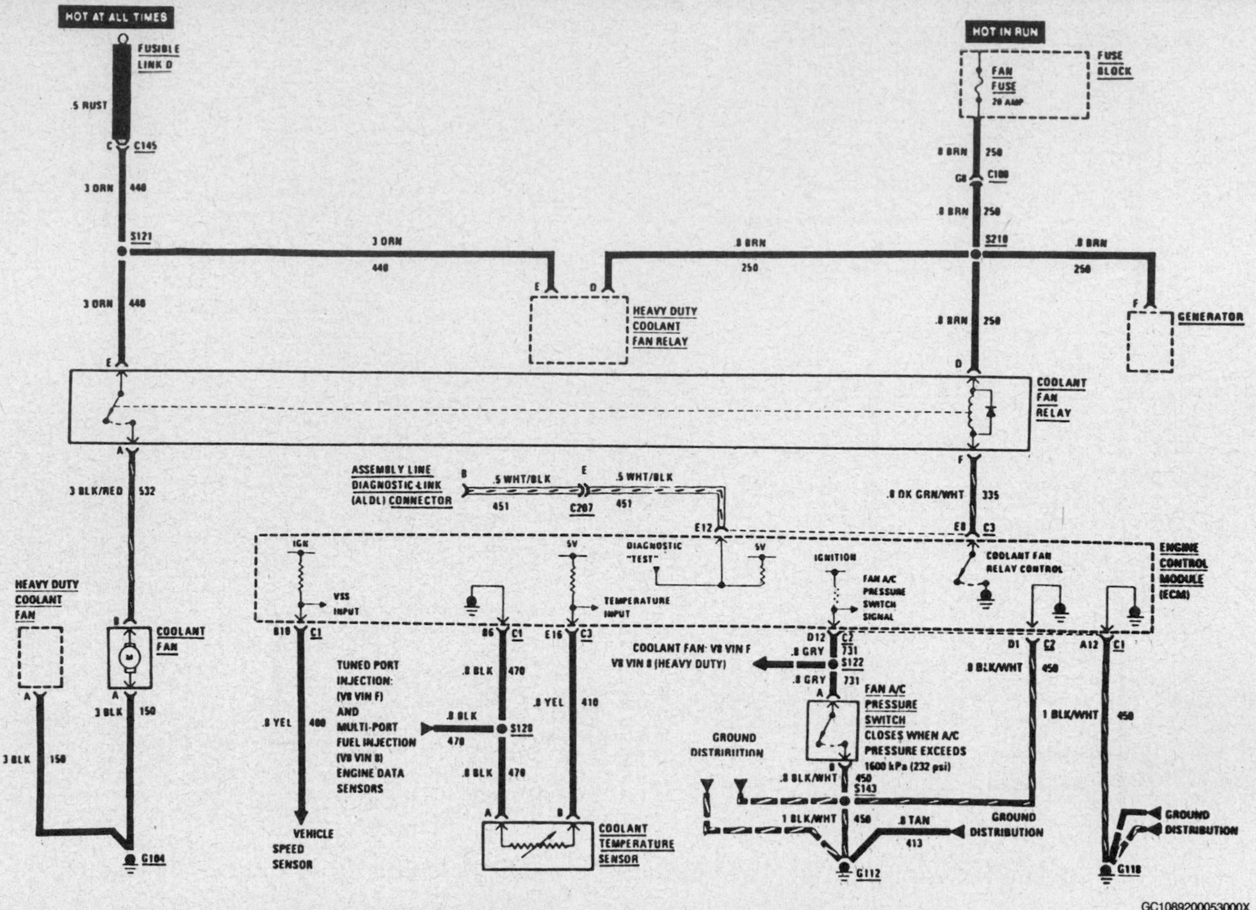

HOT AT ALL TIMES
FUSIBLE LINK D
HOT IN RUN
FUSE BLOCK
FAN FUSE 20 AMP
HEAVY DUTY COOLANT FAN RELAY
GENERATOR
COOLANT FAN RELAY
ASSEMBLY LINE DIAGNOSTIC LINK (ALDL) CONNECTOR
ENGINE CONTROL MODULE (ECM)
HEAVY DUTY COOLANT FAN
COOLANT FAN
COOLANT FAN: V8 VIN F V8 VIN 8 (HEAVY DUTY)
TUNED PORT INJECTION: (V8 VIN F) AND MULTI-PORT FUEL INJECTION (V8 VIN 8) ENGINE DATA SENSORS
FAN A/C PRESSURE SWITCH CLOSES WHEN A/C PRESSURE EXCEEDS 1600 kPa (232 psi)
GROUND DISTRIBUTION
VEHICLE SPEED SENSOR
COOLANT TEMPERATURE SENSOR
GC1089200053000X

Fig. 32 Cooling fan wiring circuit (less auxiliary cooling fan). 1992 Camaro & Firebird w/5.0L/V8-305 (VIN F) & 5.7L/V8-350 (VIN 8) engines

3. Leaving fused jumper grounded at ECM, disconnect cooling fan relay connector. Measure voltage from brown wire to ground. If battery voltage is present, refer to step 4. If battery voltage is not present, check ENG/A/C fuse and pink/black wire for an open circuit.
4. With fused jumper still connected at the ECM, measure voltage between pink/black and dark green wires. If battery voltage is present, refer to step 5. If battery voltage is not present, check dark green wire for an open circuit.
5. Measure voltage from terminal "A" (red) to ground at cooling fan relay connector. If battery voltage is present, proceed to step 6. If battery voltage is not present, check red wire and fusible link for an open circuit.
6. Connect a fused jumper with a 20 amp fuse between terminals "A" and "E" of the cooling fan relay connector. If cooling fan does not run, refer to step 7. If cooling fan runs, replace cooling fan relay.
7. Leaving fused jumper connected at the cooling fan relay connector, disconnect connector from cooling fan. Measure voltage between terminal "B of the cooling fan connector and ground. If battery voltage is present, refer to step 8. If battery voltage is not present, check black/pink wire for an open circuit.
8. Leaving fused jumper connected at the cooling fan relay connector. Measure voltage between terminals "B" and "A" of the cooling fan connector. If battery voltage is present, replace cooling fan motor. If battery voltage is not present, check black wire for an open circuit.

Cooling Fan Does Not Turn Off With Engine Coolant Cool, A/C Off & Ignition Switch In Run

1. Turn ignition switch to the Run position and disconnect cooling fan relay connector.
2. Connect a test lamp between terminals "F" and "D" of the cooling fan relay connector.
3. If test lamp lights, proceed to step 4. If test lamp does not light, replace cooling fan relay.
4. Check dark green wire of relay for a short to ground. If wire is satisfactory, problem is ECM related. If wire is not satisfactory, repair or replace as required.

1994

Refer to "Century" in this section when performing diagnostic procedures.

CAMARO & FIREBIRD

1992

Refer to **Figs. 32 through 35** for cooling fan wiring diagrams.

1993

Refer to **Figs. 36 and 37** when performing diagnostic procedures, **Figs. 38 and39.**

On 5.0L/V8-305 (VIN F) and 5.7L/V8-350 engines, perform test A if cooling fan does not turn on. If cooling fan does not turn off with engine cool, A/C mode selector in Off position and ignition switch in Run position, perform test B. If cooling fan does not turn on with A/C mode selector in On position and head pressure above 233 psi, but does run with engine hot, perform test C and, if only auxiliary coolant does not turn on, perform test D.

On 5.0L/V8-305 (VIN E) engine, perform test E if cooling fan does not run at all or if cooling fan does not run with high engine temperature. If cooling fan does not turn On with A/C on, perform test F. If cooling fan will not turn Off, perform test G.

Test A: Cooling Fan Does Not Turn On

1. Turn ignition switch to On position, then ground terminal B (white/black) of ALDL connector. If cooling fan runs, problem is ECM related.
2. If cooling fan does not run, ground terminal C3/E8 (dark green/white) of ECM with a fused jumper wire. If cooling fan runs, problem is ECM related.

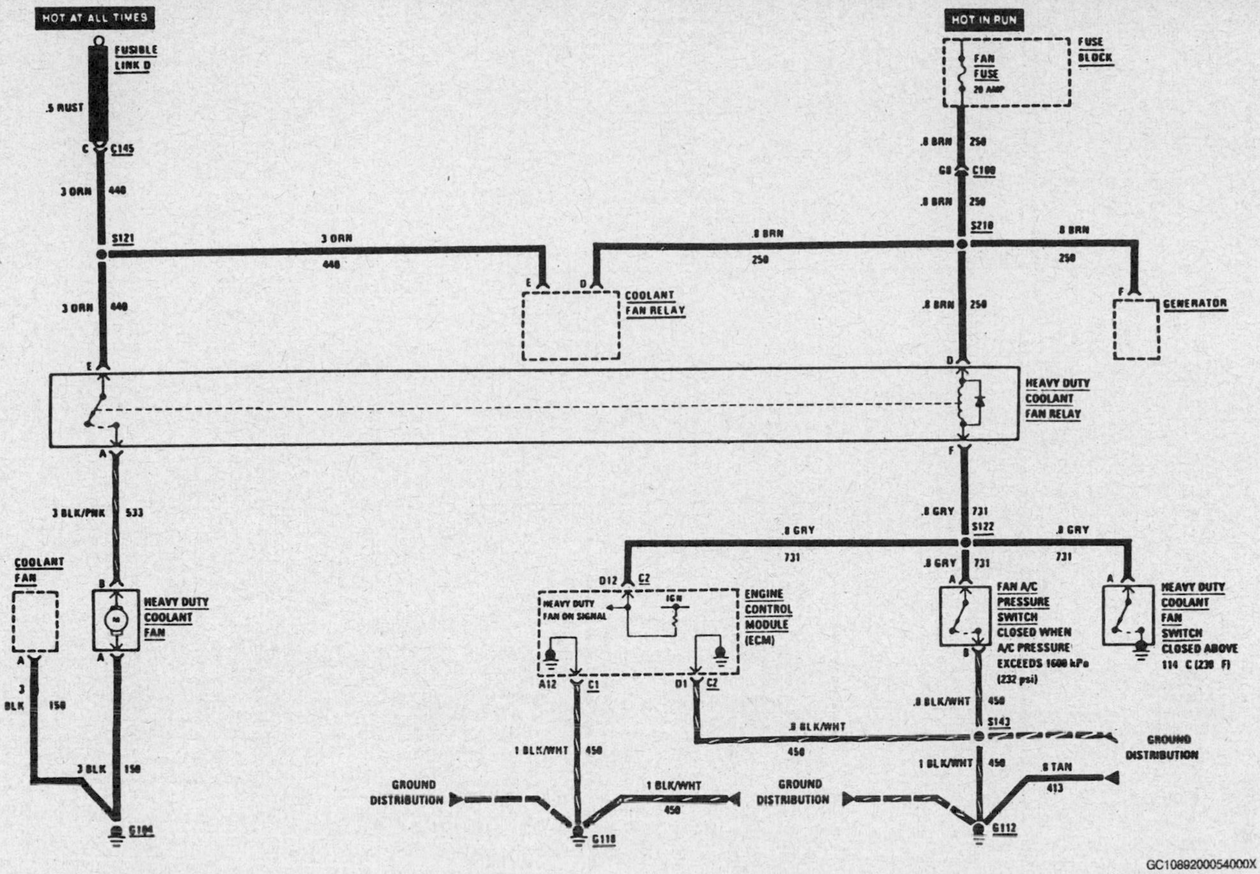
HOT AT ALL TIMES
FUSIBLE LINK D
.5 RUST
C145
3 ORN 440
S121
3 ORN
440
E
D
COOLANT FAN RELAY
HOT IN RUN
FAN FUSE 20 AMP
FUSE BLOCK
.8 BRN 250
C100
S210
.8 BRN
250
F
GENERATOR
D
HEAVY DUTY COOLANT FAN RELAY
A
F
3 BLK/PNK 533
.8 GRY 731
S122
COOLANT FAN
HEAVY DUTY COOLANT FAN
D12 C2
HEAVY DUTY FAN ON SIGNAL
IGN
ENGINE CONTROL MODULE (ECM)
A12 C1
D1 C2
FAN A/C PRESSURE SWITCH CLOSED WHEN A/C PRESSURE EXCEEDS 1600 kPa (232 psi)
HEAVY DUTY COOLANT FAN SWITCH CLOSED ABOVE 114 C (238 F)
3 BLK 150
.8 BLK/WHT 450
S142
GROUND DISTRIBUTION
1 BLK/WHT 450
.8 TAN 413
G104
G110
G112
GC1089200054000X

Fig. 33 Cooling fan wiring circuit (auxiliary cooling fan). 1992 Camaro & Firebird w/5.0L/V8-305 (VIN F) & 5.7L/V8-350 (VIN 8) engines

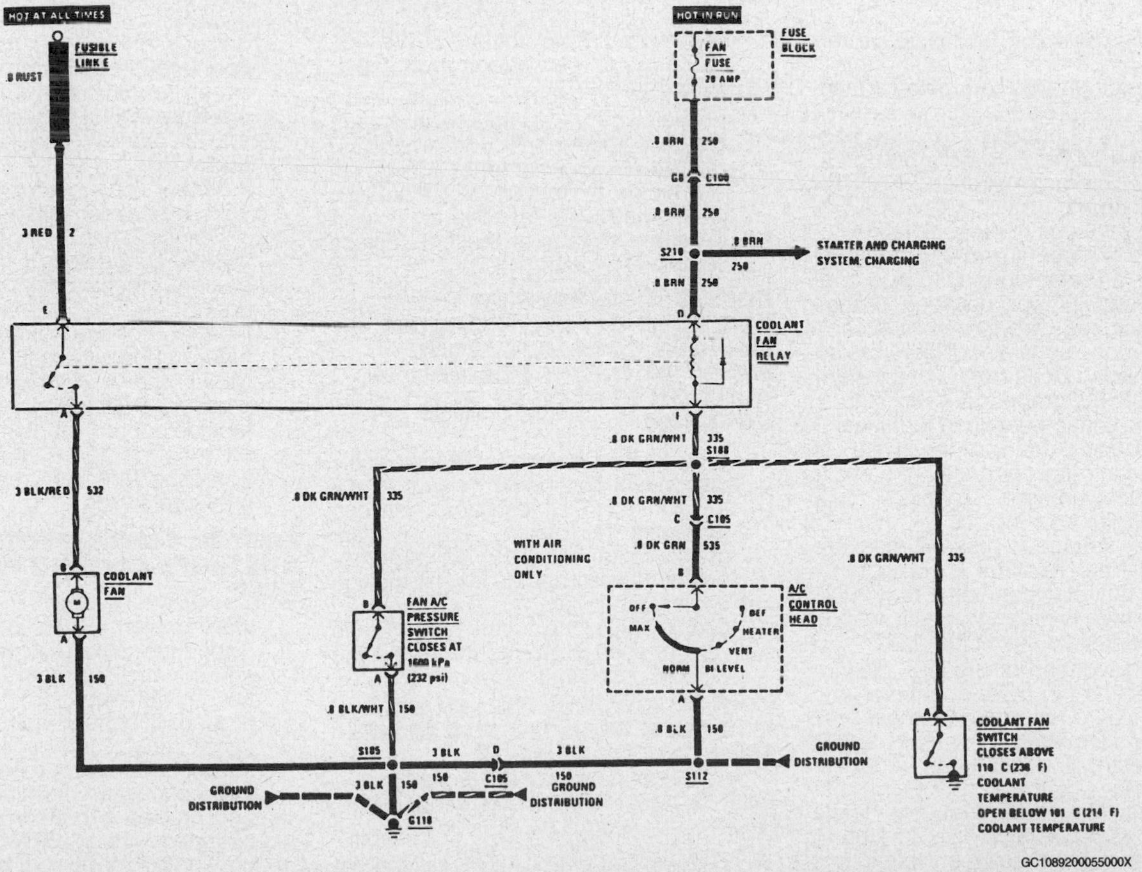
HOT AT ALL TIMES
FUSIBLE LINK E
.8 RUST
3 RED 2
E
HOT IN RUN
FAN FUSE 20 AMP
FUSE BLOCK
.8 BRN 250
C100
S210
STARTER AND CHARGING SYSTEM: CHARGING
D
COOLANT FAN RELAY
A
I
.8 DK GRN/WHT 335
S188
3 BLK/RED 532
C105
WITH AIR CONDITIONING ONLY
.8 DK GRN 535
COOLANT FAN
FAN A/C PRESSURE SWITCH CLOSES AT 1600 kPa (232 psi)
OFF
MAX
DEF
HEATER
VENT
NORM
BI LEVEL
A/C CONTROL HEAD
COOLANT FAN SWITCH CLOSES ABOVE 110 C (230 F) COOLANT TEMPERATURE OPEN BELOW 101 C (214 F) COOLANT TEMPERATURE
3 BLK 150
.8 BLK/WHT 150
.8 BLK 150
S105
S112
GROUND DISTRIBUTION
G110
GC1089200055000X

Fig. 34 Cooling fan wiring circuit. 1992 Camaro & Firebird w/5.0L/V8-305 (VIN E) engine

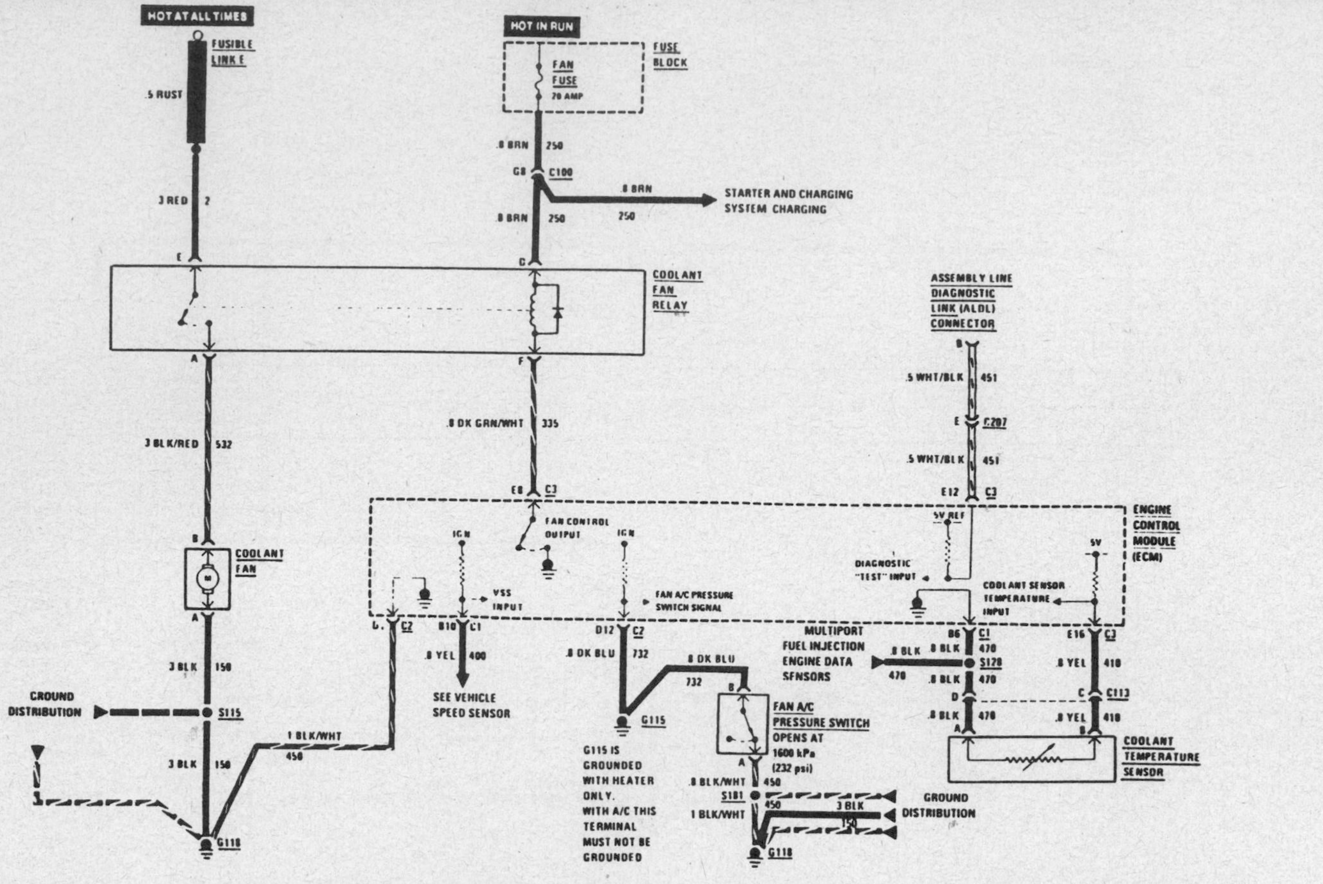
HOT AT ALL TIMES
FUSIBLE LINK E
.5 RUST
3 RED 2
HOT IN RUN
FAN FUSE 20 AMP
FUSE BLOCK
.8 BRN 250
G8 C100
.8 BRN
STARTER AND CHARGING SYSTEM CHARGING
COOLANT FAN RELAY
.8 DK GRN/WHT 335
3 BLK/RED 532
COOLANT FAN
3 BLK 150
GROUND DISTRIBUTION
S115
1 BLK/WHT 450
G118
ASSEMBLY LINE DIAGNOSTIC LINK (ALDL) CONNECTOR
.5 WHT/BLK 451
C207
ENGINE CONTROL MODULE (ECM)
FAN CONTROL OUTPUT
VSS INPUT
FAN A/C PRESSURE SWITCH SIGNAL
DIAGNOSTIC "TEST" INPUT
COOLANT SENSOR TEMPERATURE INPUT
.8 YEL 400
SEE VEHICLE SPEED SENSOR
.8 DK BLU 732
G115
G115 IS GROUNDED WITH HEATER ONLY. WITH A/C THIS TERMINAL MUST NOT BE GROUNDED
MULTIPORT FUEL INJECTION ENGINE DATA SENSORS
FAN A/C PRESSURE SWITCH OPENS AT 1600 kPa (232 psi)
.8 BLK 470
S128
.8 YEL 410
C113
COOLANT TEMPERATURE SENSOR
S181
GROUND DISTRIBUTION
GC1089200056000X

Fig. 35 Cooling fan wiring circuit. 1992 Camaro & Firebird w/3.1L/V6-192 (VIN T) engine

3. If cooling fan does not run, leave terminal C3/E8 grounded as in step 2. Disconnect cooling fan relay connector and measure voltage from terminal D (brown) of cooling fan relay connector to ground. If no voltage is present, check brown wire and FAN/FP fuse for open.
4. If battery voltage is present, lamp illuminates in steps a and b, disconnect cooling fan relay connector and connect fused jumper between orange and black/red wire terminals. If cooling fan runs, replace cooling fan relay.
5. If cooling fan does not run, leave terminal C3/E8 grounded as in step 2. Measure voltage between terminals D (brown) and F (dark green/white) of cooling fan relay connector. If no voltage is present, check dark green/white wire for open.
6. If battery voltage is present, measure voltage from terminal E (orange) of cooling fan relay connector to ground. If no voltage is present, check orange wire and fusible link D for open.
7. If battery voltage is present, disconnect cooling fan relay connector and connect a 20 amp fused jumper wire between terminals E (orange) and A (red/black). If cooling fan runs, replace relay.
8. If cooling fan does not run, leave jumper wire connected as in step 7. Measure voltage between terminal B (black/red) of cooling fan connector and ground. If no voltage is present, check black/red wire for open.
9. If battery voltage is present, leave jumper wire connected as in step 7. Measure voltage between terminals B (black/red) and A (red) of cooling fan connector. If no voltage is present, check black wire for open.
10. If battery voltage is present, replace cooling fan motor.

Test B: Cooling Fan Does Not Turn Off With Engine Coolant Cool, A/C Mode Selector In Off Position & Ignition Switch In Run Position

1. With ignition switch in Run position, disconnect cooling fan relay connector and connect test lamp between terminals D (brown) and F (dark green/white) of cooling fan relay connector. If lamp does not light, replace cooling fan relay.
2. If lamp lights, check dark green/white wire for short to ground. If wire is satisfactory, problem is ECM related.

Test C: Cooling Fan Does Not Turn On With A/C Mode Selector On & Head Pressure Above 233 psi, But Does Run With Engine Hot

1. Turn ignition switch to On position, set A/C mode selector to Max position, disconnect fan A/C pressure switch connector, then measure voltage between terminal B (gray) Of fan A/C pressure switch and ground. If no voltage is present, check gray wire for open.
2. If battery voltage is present, measure voltage between terminal B (gray) and A (black/white) of A/C pressure switch connector. If no voltage is present, check black/white wire for open.
3. If battery voltage is present, connect a fused jumper wire between terminal B (gray) and A (black/white) of A/C pressure switch connector. If cooling fans do not run, problem is ECM related.
4. If cooling fans run, replace fan A/C pressure switch.

Test D: Cooling Fan & Auxiliary Cooling Fan Open Test

1. With ignition switch in Run position, disconnect auxiliary cooling fan relay and connect a suitable voltmeter between terminal E (orange) and ground. If battery voltage is not obtained, check fusible link D and orange wire for open, then connect voltmeter between terminal D (brown) and ground. If battery voltage is not obtained, check FAN/FP fuse and brown wire for open. If battery voltage was obtained, proceed to step 2.

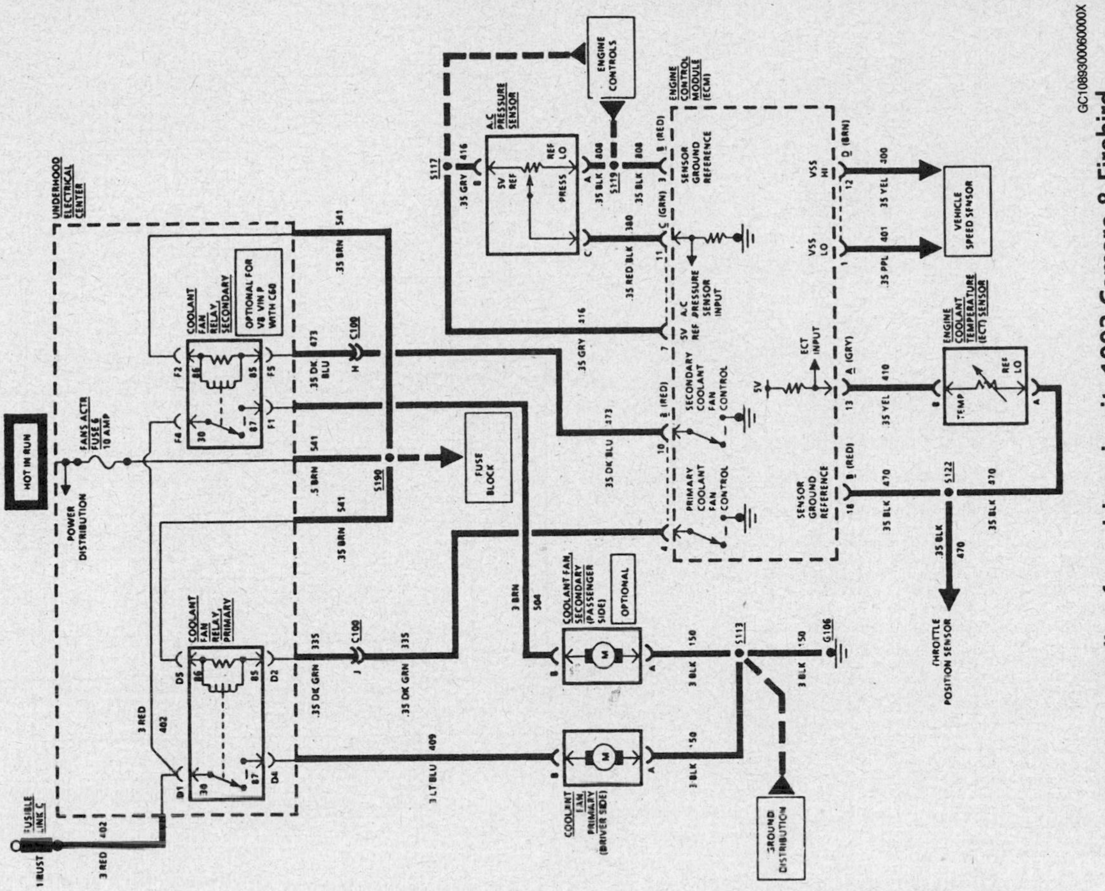

GC108930006000X

Fig. 37 Cooling fan wiring circuit. 1993 Camaro & Firebird w/5.7L/V8-350 (VIN P) engine

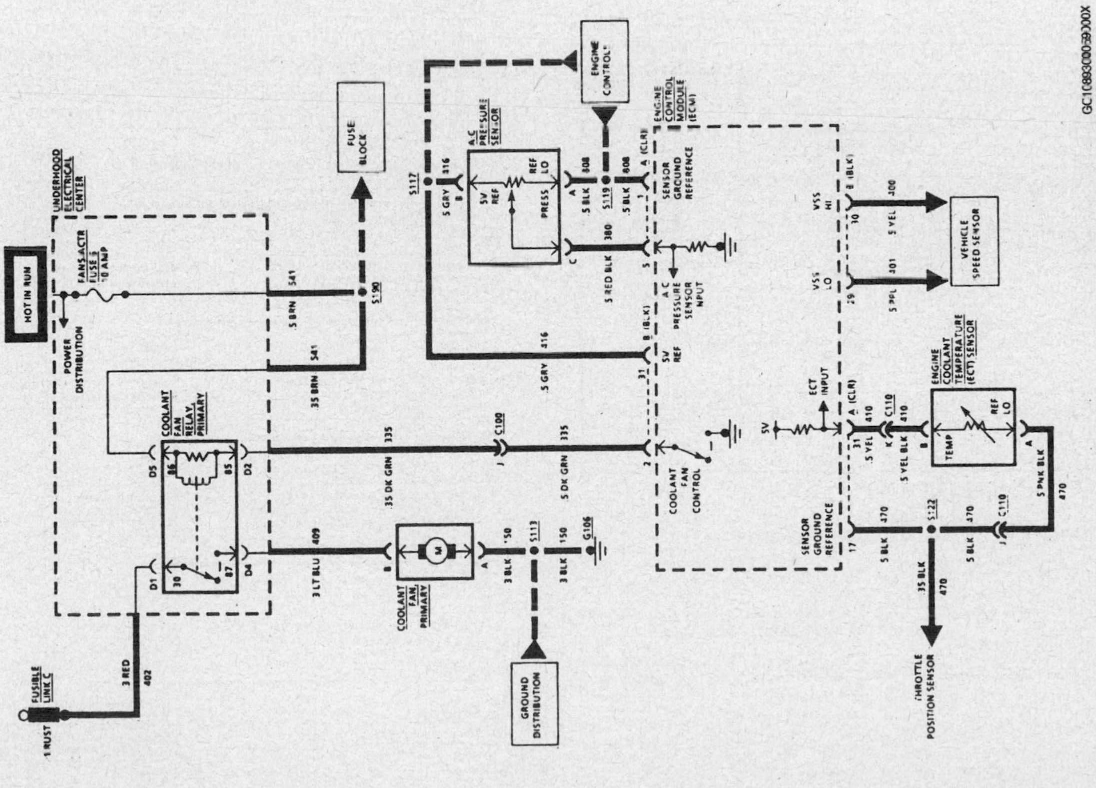

GC108930005900X

Fig. 36 Cooling fan wiring circuit. 1993 Camaro & Firebird w/3.4L/V6-204 (VIN S) engine

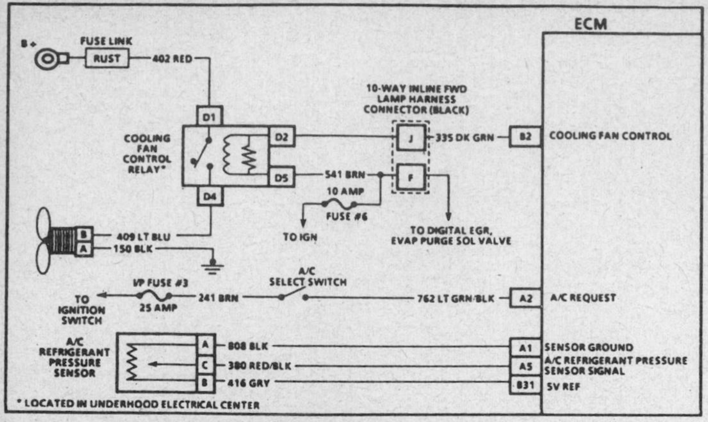

ECM
B+
FUSE LINK
RUST
402 RED
10-WAY INLINE FWD LAMP HARNESS CONNECTOR (BLACK)
D1
COOLING FAN CONTROL RELAY*
D2
D5
D4
J
F
335 DK GRN
B2
COOLING FAN CONTROL
541 BRN
10 AMP
FUSE #6
TO IGN
TO DIGITAL EGR, EVAP PURGE SOL VALVE
B
A
409 LT BLU
150 BLK
I/P FUSE #3
TO IGNITION SWITCH
25 AMP
241 BRN
A/C SELECT SWITCH
762 LT GRN/BLK
A2
A/C REQUEST
A/C REFRIGERANT PRESSURE SENSOR
A
C
B
808 BLK
380 RED/BLK
416 GRY
A1
A5
B31
SENSOR GROUND
A/C REFRIGERANT PRESSURE SENSOR SIGNAL
5V REF
* LOCATED IN UNDERHOOD ELECTRICAL CENTER

CHART C-12
(Page 1 of 2)
COOLING FAN CONTROL CIRCUIT DIAGNOSIS

Circuit Description:

The electric cooling fan is controlled by the ECM, based on inputs from the Engine Coolant Temperature (ECT) sensor, the A/C control switches, vehicle speed, and state of the A/C refrigerant pressure sensor. The ECM controls the fan by grounding CKT 335 which energizes the fan control relay. Battery voltage is then supplied to the fan motor.

The ECM grounds CKT 335 when engine coolant temperature is over about 109°C (228°F), or when A/C has been requested and the A/C refrigerant pressure is about 1655 kPa (240 psi). Once the ECM turns the relay "ON," it will keep it "ON" for a minimum of 30 seconds, or until vehicle speed exceeds 113 km/h (70 mph).

Also, if DTC 14 or 15 sets or the ECM is in back up, the primary fan will run at all time.

Test Description: Number(s) below refer to circled number(s) on the diagnostic chart.

1. With the diagnostic terminal grounded, the cooling fan control driver(s) will close, which should energize the fan control relay(s).
2. If the A/C pressure is above 240 psi (1655 kPa) or circuit is open, the fan would run whenever A/C is requested.
3. With A/C clutch engaged and the A/C refrigerant pressure sensor is functioning properly, the fan should come "ON" when pressure exceeds about 20 psi. Under very cold ambient conditions, the fan will remain "OFF." This signal should cause the ECM to energize the cooling fan control relay.
4. This will determine if the A/C refrigerant pressure sensor is faulty or if the ECM or circuitry is faulty.

Diagnostic Aids:

If the owner complained of an overheating problem, it must be determined if the complaint was due to an actual boilover, a hot light or temp. gage indicated over heating.

If the gage or light indicates overheating, but no boilover is detected, the gage circuit should be checked.

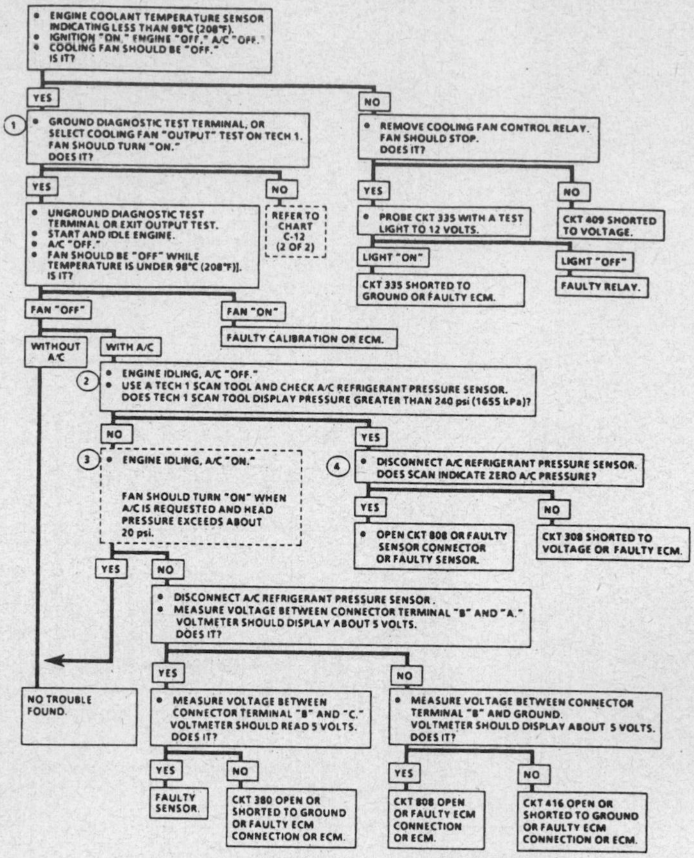

• ENGINE COOLANT TEMPERATURE SENSOR INDICATING LESS THAN 98°C (208°F).
• IGNITION "ON," ENGINE "OFF," A/C "OFF."
• COOLING FAN SHOULD BE "OFF." IS IT?
YES
NO
1
• GROUND DIAGNOSTIC TEST TERMINAL, OR SELECT COOLING FAN "OUTPUT" TEST ON TECH 1. FAN SHOULD TURN "ON." DOES IT?
• REMOVE COOLING FAN CONTROL RELAY. FAN SHOULD STOP. DOES IT?
YES
NO
• UNGROUND DIAGNOSTIC TEST TERMINAL OR EXIT OUTPUT TEST.
• START AND IDLE ENGINE.
• A/C "OFF."
• FAN SHOULD BE "OFF" WHILE TEMPERATURE IS UNDER 98°C (208°F)]. IS IT?
REFER TO CHART C-12 (2 OF 2)
YES
NO
• PROBE CKT 335 WITH A TEST LIGHT TO 12 VOLTS.
CKT 409 SHORTED TO VOLTAGE.
LIGHT "ON"
LIGHT "OFF"
CKT 335 SHORTED TO GROUND OR FAULTY ECM.
FAULTY RELAY.
FAN "OFF"
FAN "ON"
FAULTY CALIBRATION OR ECM.
WITHOUT A/C
WITH A/C
2
• ENGINE IDLING, A/C "OFF."
• USE A TECH 1 SCAN TOOL AND CHECK A/C REFRIGERANT PRESSURE SENSOR. DOES TECH 1 SCAN TOOL DISPLAY PRESSURE GREATER THAN 240 psi (1655 kPa)?
NO
YES
3
• ENGINE IDLING, A/C "ON."
FAN SHOULD TURN "ON" WHEN A/C IS REQUESTED AND HEAD PRESSURE EXCEEDS ABOUT 20 psi.
4
• DISCONNECT A/C REFRIGERANT PRESSURE SENSOR. DOES SCAN INDICATE ZERO A/C PRESSURE?
YES
NO
• OPEN CKT 808 OR FAULTY SENSOR CONNECTOR OR FAULTY SENSOR.
CKT 308 SHORTED TO VOLTAGE OR FAULTY ECM.
YES
NO
• DISCONNECT A/C REFRIGERANT PRESSURE SENSOR.
• MEASURE VOLTAGE BETWEEN CONNECTOR TERMINAL "B" AND "A." VOLTMETER SHOULD DISPLAY ABOUT 5 VOLTS. DOES IT?
YES
NO
NO TROUBLE FOUND.
• MEASURE VOLTAGE BETWEEN CONNECTOR TERMINAL "B" AND "C." VOLTMETER SHOULD READ 5 VOLTS. DOES IT?
• MEASURE VOLTAGE BETWEEN CONNECTOR TERMINAL "B" AND GROUND. VOLTMETER SHOULD DISPLAY ABOUT 5 VOLTS. DOES IT?
YES
NO
YES
NO
FAULTY SENSOR.
CKT 380 OPEN OR SHORTED TO GROUND OR FAULTY ECM CONNECTION OR ECM.
CKT 808 OPEN OR FAULTY ECM CONNECTION OR ECM.
CKT 416 OPEN OR SHORTED TO GROUND OR FAULTY ECM CONNECTION OR ECM.

GC1089300057010X

Fig. 38 Chart C-12, cooling fan diagnosis (Part 1 of 2). 1993 Camaro & Firebird w/3.4L/V6-204 (VIN S) engine

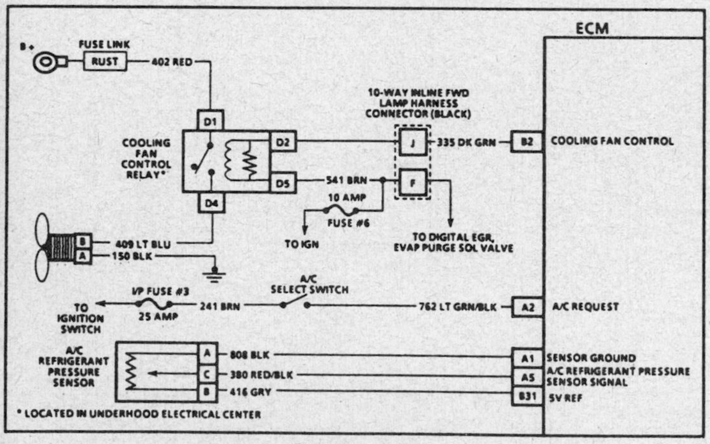

ECM
B+
FUSE LINK
RUST
402 RED
10-WAY INLINE FWD LAMP HARNESS CONNECTOR (BLACK)
D1
COOLING FAN CONTROL RELAY*
D2
D5
D4
J
F
335 DK GRN
B2
COOLING FAN CONTROL
541 BRN
10 AMP
FUSE #6
TO IGN
TO DIGITAL EGR, EVAP PURGE SOL VALVE
B
A
409 LT BLU
150 BLK
I/P FUSE #3
TO IGNITION SWITCH
25 AMP
241 BRN
A/C SELECT SWITCH
762 LT GRN/BLK
A2
A/C REQUEST
A/C REFRIGERANT PRESSURE SENSOR
A
C
B
808 BLK
380 RED/BLK
416 GRY
A1
A5
B31
SENSOR GROUND
A/C REFRIGERANT PRESSURE SENSOR SIGNAL
5V REF
* LOCATED IN UNDERHOOD ELECTRICAL CENTER

CHART C-12
(Page 2 of 2)
COOLING FAN CONTROL CIRCUIT DIAGNOSIS

Test Description: Number(s) below refer to circled number(s) on the diagnostic chart.

1. 12 volts should be available to CKT 541 and CKT 402 of the relay when the ignition is "ON."
2. This test checks the ability of the ECM to ground CKT 335.

The Malfunction Indicator Lamp (MIL) "Service Engine Soon" should also be flashing at this point.

3. If the fan does not turn "ON" at this point, CKT 409 or CKT 150 is open, or the cooling fan motor is faulty.

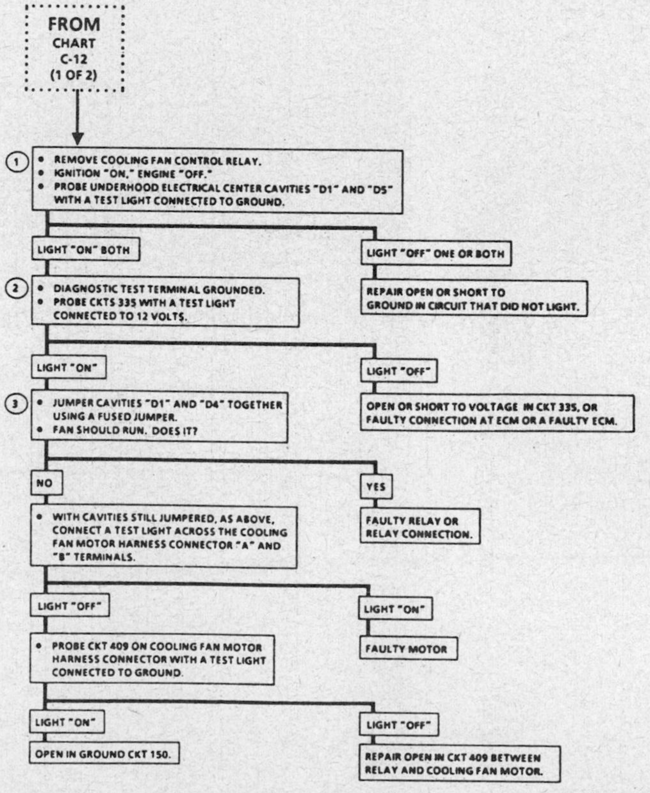

FROM CHART C-12 (1 OF 2)
1
• REMOVE COOLING FAN CONTROL RELAY.
• IGNITION "ON," ENGINE "OFF."
• PROBE UNDERHOOD ELECTRICAL CENTER CAVITIES "D1" AND "D5" WITH A TEST LIGHT CONNECTED TO GROUND.
LIGHT "ON" BOTH
LIGHT "OFF" ONE OR BOTH
2
• DIAGNOSTIC TEST TERMINAL GROUNDED.
• PROBE CKTS 335 WITH A TEST LIGHT CONNECTED TO 12 VOLTS.
REPAIR OPEN OR SHORT TO GROUND IN CIRCUIT THAT DID NOT LIGHT.
LIGHT "ON"
LIGHT "OFF"
3
• JUMPER CAVITIES "D1" AND "D4" TOGETHER USING A FUSED JUMPER.
• FAN SHOULD RUN. DOES IT?
OPEN OR SHORT TO VOLTAGE IN CKT 335, OR FAULTY CONNECTION AT ECM OR A FAULTY ECM.
NO
YES
• WITH CAVITIES STILL JUMPERED, AS ABOVE, CONNECT A TEST LIGHT ACROSS THE COOLING FAN MOTOR HARNESS CONNECTOR "A" AND "B" TERMINALS.
FAULTY RELAY OR RELAY CONNECTION.
LIGHT "OFF"
LIGHT "ON"
• PROBE CKT 409 ON COOLING FAN MOTOR HARNESS CONNECTOR WITH A TEST LIGHT CONNECTED TO GROUND.
FAULTY MOTOR
LIGHT "ON"
LIGHT "OFF"
OPEN IN GROUND CKT 150.
REPAIR OPEN IN CKT 409 BETWEEN RELAY AND COOLING FAN MOTOR.

GC1089300057020X

Fig. 38 Chart C-12, cooling fan diagnosis (Part 2 of 2). 1993 Camaro & Firebird w/3.4L/V6-204 (VIN S) engine

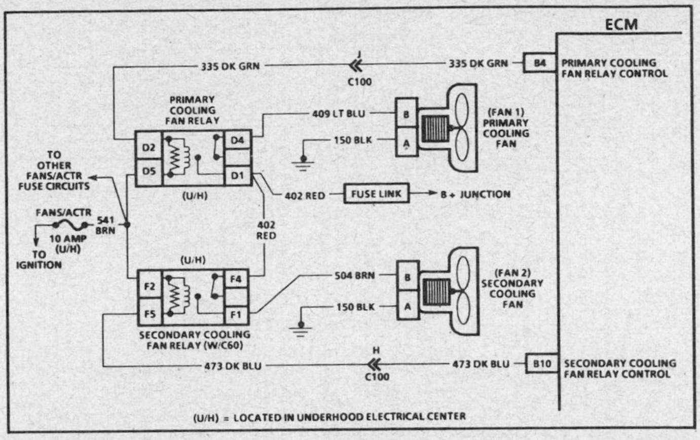
ECM
335 DK GRN
J
C100
335 DK GRN
B4
PRIMARY COOLING FAN RELAY CONTROL
PRIMARY COOLING FAN RELAY
409 LT BLU
150 BLK
(FAN 1) PRIMARY COOLING FAN
TO OTHER FANS/ACTR FUSE CIRCUITS
D2
D4
D5
D1
(U/H)
402 RED
FUSE LINK
B+ JUNCTION
FANS/ACTR
541 BRN
10 AMP (U/H)
TO IGNITION
402 RED
(U/H)
504 BRN
150 BLK
(FAN 2) SECONDARY COOLING FAN
F2
F4
F5
F1
SECONDARY COOLING FAN RELAY (W/C60)
H
473 DK BLU
C100
473 DK BLU
B10
SECONDARY COOLING FAN RELAY CONTROL
(U/H) = LOCATED IN UNDERHOOD ELECTRICAL CENTER

Circuit Description:

The cooling fans are controlled by the ECM based on various inputs. Battery voltage is supplied to the primary fan relay on terminals "D1" and "F4" of the secondary fan relay. Ignition voltage is supplied to terminal "D5" of the primary fan relay and "F2" of the secondary fan relay. Grounding CKT 335 (relay terminal "D2") will energize the primary cooling fan relay (Fan 1) and supply battery voltage to the primary cooling fan motor. Grounding CKT 473 (relay terminal "F5") will energize the secondary cooling fan relay (Fan 2) and supply battery voltage to the secondary fan motor.

When certain Diagnostic Trouble Codes (DTCs) are set, the ECM will enable the cooling fans.

Test Description: Number(s) below refer to circled number(s) on the diagnostic chart.

1. With the diagnostic "test" terminal grounded, the cooling fan control driver(s) will close, which should energize the fan control relay(s).
2. The cooling fans should come "ON" anytime A/C system is operating.
3. Comparing Tech 1 pressure and manifold gage set pressure will determine if the A/C refrigerant pressure sensor is out of range. An out of range A/C refrigerant pressure sensor can cause the cooling fans to operate at the wrong times.

Diagnostic Aids:

If the owner complained of an overheating problem, it must be determined if the complaint was due to an actual boil over, or the warning indicator light, or engine coolant temperature gage indicated overheating.

The gage accuracy can also be checked by comparing the Engine Coolant Temperature (ECT) sensor reading using a Tech 1 and comparing its reading with the gage reading.

If the engine is actually overheating and the gage indicated overheating, but the cooling fan is not coming "ON," the Engine Coolant Temperature (ECT) sensor has probably shifted out of calibration and should be replaced.

If the engine is overheating and the cooling fans are "ON," the cooling system should be checked.

The ECM will command fan 1 "ON" at 108°C (226°F) and "OFF" at 105°C (221°F) and, fan 2 "ON" at 113°C (235°F) and "OFF" at 110°C (230°F).

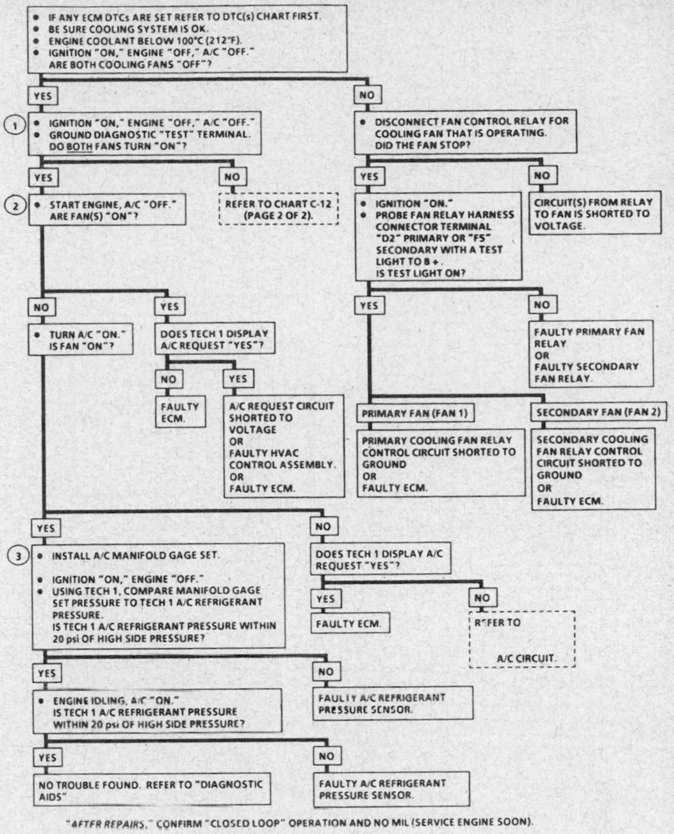
• IF ANY ECM DTCs ARE SET REFER TO DTC(s) CHART FIRST.
• BE SURE COOLING SYSTEM IS OK.
• ENGINE COOLANT BELOW 100°C (212°F).
• IGNITION "ON," ENGINE "OFF," A/C "OFF." ARE BOTH COOLING FANS "OFF"?
YES
NO
1
• IGNITION "ON," ENGINE "OFF," A/C "OFF."
• GROUND DIAGNOSTIC "TEST" TERMINAL. DO BOTH FANS TURN "ON"?
• DISCONNECT FAN CONTROL RELAY FOR COOLING FAN THAT IS OPERATING. DID THE FAN STOP?
YES
NO
YES
NO
2
• START ENGINE, A/C "OFF." ARE FAN(S) "ON"?
REFER TO CHART C-12 (PAGE 2 OF 2).
• IGNITION "ON."
• PROBE FAN RELAY HARNESS CONNECTOR TERMINAL "D2" PRIMARY OR "F5" SECONDARY WITH A TEST LIGHT TO B+. IS TEST LIGHT ON?
CIRCUIT(S) FROM RELAY TO FAN IS SHORTED TO VOLTAGE.
NO
YES
YES
NO
• TURN A/C "ON." IS FAN "ON"?
DOES TECH 1 DISPLAY A/C REQUEST "YES"?
FAULTY PRIMARY FAN RELAY OR FAULTY SECONDARY FAN RELAY.
NO
YES
FAULTY ECM.
A/C REQUEST CIRCUIT SHORTED TO VOLTAGE OR FAULTY HVAC CONTROL ASSEMBLY. OR FAULTY ECM.
PRIMARY FAN (FAN 1)
SECONDARY FAN (FAN 2)
PRIMARY COOLING FAN RELAY CONTROL CIRCUIT SHORTED TO GROUND OR FAULTY ECM.
SECONDARY COOLING FAN RELAY CONTROL CIRCUIT SHORTED TO GROUND OR FAULTY ECM.
YES
NO
3
• INSTALL A/C MANIFOLD GAGE SET.
• IGNITION "ON," ENGINE "OFF."
• USING TECH 1, COMPARE MANIFOLD GAGE SET PRESSURE TO TECH 1 A/C REFRIGERANT PRESSURE. IS TECH 1 A/C REFRIGERANT PRESSURE WITHIN 20 psi OF HIGH SIDE PRESSURE?
DOES TECH 1 DISPLAY A/C REQUEST "YES"?
YES
NO
FAULTY ECM.
REFER TO A/C CIRCUIT.
YES
NO
• ENGINE IDLING, A/C "ON." IS TECH 1 A/C REFRIGERANT PRESSURE WITHIN 20 psi OF HIGH SIDE PRESSURE?
FAULTY A/C REFRIGERANT PRESSURE SENSOR.
YES
NO
NO TROUBLE FOUND. REFER TO "DIAGNOSTIC AIDS"
FAULTY A/C REFRIGERANT PRESSURE SENSOR.
"AFTER REPAIRS," CONFIRM "CLOSED LOOP" OPERATION AND NO MIL (SERVICE ENGINE SOON).

GC1089300058010X

Fig. 39 Chart C-12, cooling fan diagnosis (Part 1 of 2). 1993 Camaro & Firebird w/5.7L/V8-350 (VIN P) engine

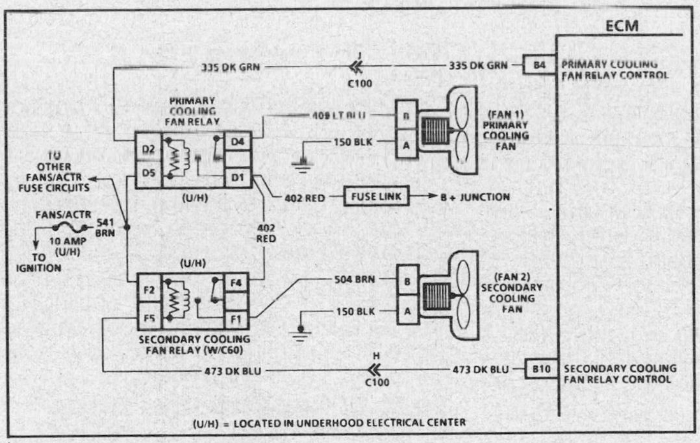
ECM
335 DK GRN
J
C100
335 DK GRN
B4
PRIMARY COOLING FAN RELAY CONTROL
PRIMARY COOLING FAN RELAY
150 BLK
(FAN 1) PRIMARY COOLING FAN
TO OTHER FANS/ACTR FUSE CIRCUITS
D2
D4
D5
D1
(U/H)
402 RED
FUSE LINK
B+ JUNCTION
FANS/ACTR
541 BRN
10 AMP (U/H)
TO IGNITION
402 RED
(U/H)
504 BRN
150 BLK
(FAN 2) SECONDARY COOLING FAN
F2
F4
F5
F1
SECONDARY COOLING FAN RELAY (W/C60)
H
473 DK BLU
C100
473 DK BLU
B10
SECONDARY COOLING FAN RELAY CONTROL
(U/H) = LOCATED IN UNDERHOOD ELECTRICAL CENTER

Circuit Description:

The cooling fans are controlled by the ECM based on various inputs. Battery voltage is supplied to the primary fan relay on terminals "D1" and "F4" of the secondary fan relay. Ignition voltage is supplied to terminal "D5" of the primary fan relay and "F2" of the secondary fan relay. Grounding CKT 335 (relay terminal "D2") will energize the primary cooling fan relay (Fan 1) and supply battery voltage to the primary cooling fan motor. Grounding CKT 473 (relay terminal "F5") will energize the secondary cooling fan relay (Fan 2) and supply battery voltage to the secondary fan motor.

The ECM will enable the cooling fans, when certain Diagnostic Trouble Codes (DTCs) are set.

Diagnostic Aids:

If the owner complained of an overheating problem, it must be determined if the complaint was due to an actual boil over, the warning indicator light, or engine coolant temperature gage indicated overheating.

The gage accuracy can also be checked by comparing the Engine Coolant Temperature (ECT) sensor reading using a Tech 1 and comparing its reading with the gage reading.

If the engine is actually overheating and the gage indicated overheating, but the cooling fan is not coming "ON," the Engine Coolant Temperature (ECT) sensor has probably shifted out of calibration and should be replaced.

If the engine is overheating and the cooling fans are "ON," the cooling system should be checked.

The ECM will command fan 1 "ON" at 108°C (226°F) and "OFF" at 105°C (221°F) and an 2 "ON" at 113°C (235°F) and "OFF" at 110°C (230°F).

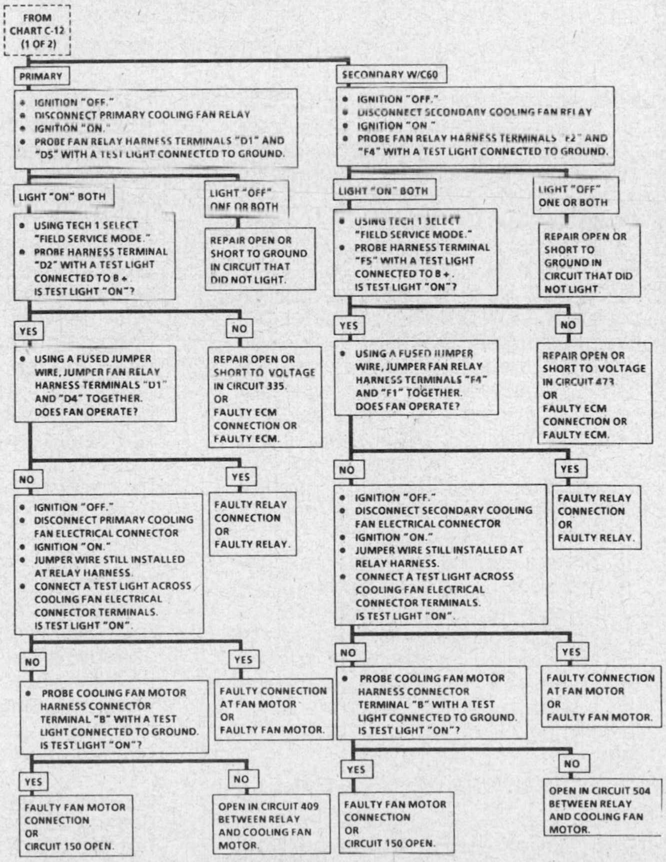
FROM CHART C-12 (1 OF 2)
PRIMARY
SECONDARY W/C60
• IGNITION "OFF."
• DISCONNECT PRIMARY COOLING FAN RELAY
• IGNITION "ON."
• PROBE FAN RELAY HARNESS TERMINALS "D1" AND "D5" WITH A TEST LIGHT CONNECTED TO GROUND.
• IGNITION "OFF."
• DISCONNECT SECONDARY COOLING FAN RELAY
• IGNITION "ON."
• PROBE FAN RELAY HARNESS TERMINALS "F2" AND "F4" WITH A TEST LIGHT CONNECTED TO GROUND.
LIGHT "ON" BOTH
LIGHT "OFF" ONE OR BOTH
LIGHT "ON" BOTH
LIGHT "OFF" ONE OR BOTH
• USING TECH 1 SELECT "FIELD SERVICE MODE."
• PROBE HARNESS TERMINAL "D2" WITH A TEST LIGHT CONNECTED TO B+. IS TEST LIGHT "ON"?
REPAIR OPEN OR SHORT TO GROUND IN CIRCUIT THAT DID NOT LIGHT.
• USING TECH 1 SELECT "FIELD SERVICE MODE."
• PROBE HARNESS TERMINAL "F5" WITH A TEST LIGHT CONNECTED TO B+. IS TEST LIGHT "ON"?
REPAIR OPEN OR SHORT TO GROUND IN CIRCUIT THAT DID NOT LIGHT
YES
NO
YES
NO
• USING A FUSED JUMPER WIRE, JUMPER FAN RELAY HARNESS TERMINALS "D1" AND "D4" TOGETHER. DOES FAN OPERATE?
REPAIR OPEN OR SHORT TO VOLTAGE IN CIRCUIT 335. OR FAULTY ECM CONNECTION OR FAULTY ECM.
• USING A FUSED JUMPER WIRE, JUMPER FAN RELAY HARNESS TERMINALS "F4" AND "F1" TOGETHER. DOES FAN OPERATE?
REPAIR OPEN OR SHORT TO VOLTAGE IN CIRCUIT 473. OR FAULTY ECM CONNECTION OR FAULTY ECM.
NO
YES
NO
YES
• IGNITION "OFF."
• DISCONNECT PRIMARY COOLING FAN ELECTRICAL CONNECTOR
• IGNITION "ON."
• JUMPER WIRE STILL INSTALLED AT RELAY HARNESS.
• CONNECT A TEST LIGHT ACROSS COOLING FAN ELECTRICAL CONNECTOR TERMINALS. IS TEST LIGHT "ON".
FAULTY RELAY CONNECTION OR FAULTY RELAY.
• IGNITION "OFF."
• DISCONNECT SECONDARY COOLING FAN ELECTRICAL CONNECTOR
• IGNITION "ON."
• JUMPER WIRE STILL INSTALLED AT RELAY HARNESS.
• CONNECT A TEST LIGHT ACROSS COOLING FAN ELECTRICAL CONNECTOR TERMINALS. IS TEST LIGHT "ON".
FAULTY RELAY CONNECTION OR FAULTY RELAY.
NO
YES
NO
YES
• PROBE COOLING FAN MOTOR HARNESS CONNECTOR TERMINAL "B" WITH A TEST LIGHT CONNECTED TO GROUND. IS TEST LIGHT "ON"?
FAULTY CONNECTION AT FAN MOTOR OR FAULTY FAN MOTOR.
• PROBE COOLING FAN MOTOR HARNESS CONNECTOR TERMINAL "B" WITH A TEST LIGHT CONNECTED TO GROUND. IS TEST LIGHT "ON"?
FAULTY CONNECTION AT FAN MOTOR OR FAULTY FAN MOTOR.
YES
NO
YES
NO
FAULTY FAN MOTOR CONNECTION OR CIRCUIT 150 OPEN.
OPEN IN CIRCUIT 409 BETWEEN RELAY AND COOLING FAN MOTOR.
FAULTY FAN MOTOR CONNECTION OR CIRCUIT 150 OPEN.
OPEN IN CIRCUIT 504 BETWEEN RELAY AND COOLING FAN MOTOR.

GC1089300058020X

Fig. 39 Chart C-12, cooling fan diagnosis (Part 2 of 2). 1993 Camaro & Firebird w/5.7L/V8-350 (VIN P) engine

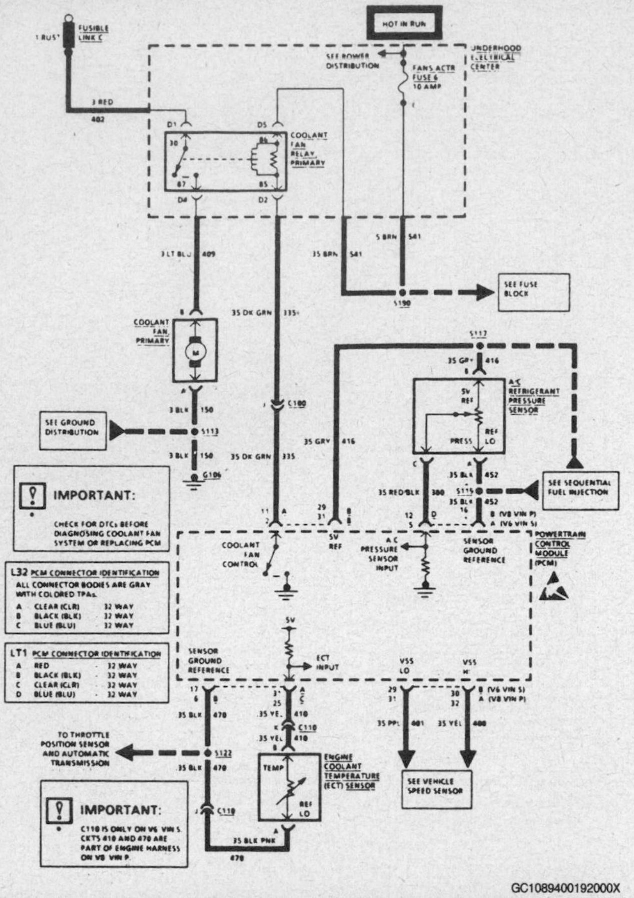
HOT IN RUN
FUSIBLE LINK C
COOLANT FAN RELAY PRIMARY
SEE FUSE BLOCK
SEE GROUND DISTRIBUTION
IMPORTANT:
CHECK FOR DTCs BEFORE DIAGNOSING COOLANT FAN SYSTEM OR REPLACING PCM
SEE SEQUENTIAL FUEL INJECTION
POWERTRAIN CONTROL MODULE (PCM)
TO THROTTLE POSITION SENSOR AND AUTOMATIC TRANSMISSION
SEE VEHICLE SPEED SENSOR
GC1089400192000X

Fig. 40 Cooling fan wiring circuit. 1994 Camaro & Firebird w/3.4L/V6-204 (VIN S) and 5.7L/V8-350 (VIN P) engines & C41

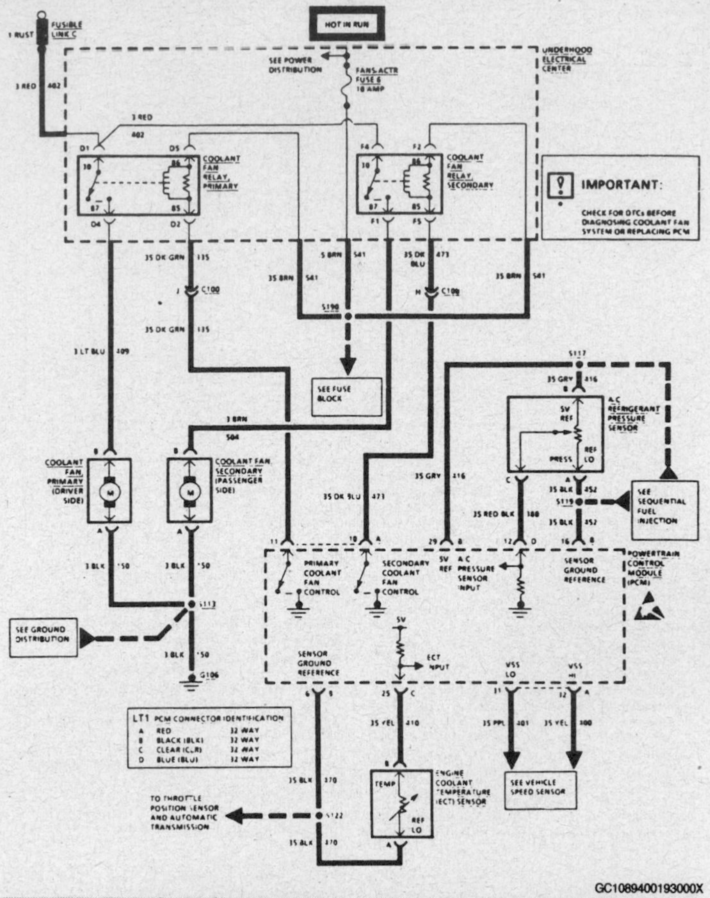
HOT IN RUN
FUSIBLE LINK C
COOLANT FAN RELAY PRIMARY
COOLANT FAN RELAY SECONDARY
IMPORTANT:
CHECK FOR DTCs BEFORE DIAGNOSING COOLANT FAN SYSTEM OR REPLACING PCM
SEE FUSE BLOCK
SEE GROUND DISTRIBUTION
POWERTRAIN CONTROL MODULE (PCM)
TO THROTTLE POSITION SENSOR AND AUTOMATIC TRANSMISSION
SEE VEHICLE SPEED SENSOR
GC1089400193000X

Fig. 41 Cooling fan wiring circuit, early production. 1994 Camaro w/5.7L/V8-350 engine (VIN P) & C60

2. With auxiliary cooling fan relay connector disconnected, connect a 20 amp fused jumper wire between terminals E (orange) and A (black/pink). If cooling fan runs, proceed to last step. If cooling fan does not run, leave jumper in place and proceed to next step.
3. Disconnect auxiliary cooling fan connector, then connect a voltmeter between terminal D (black/pink) and ground. If battery voltage is not obtained, check black/pink wire for open, then connect voltmeter between terminals B (black/pink) and A (black). If battery voltage is not obtained, check black wire for open. If battery voltage was obtained, repair or replace cooling fan.
4. Reconnect cooling fan relay and connect a fused jumper wire from auxiliary cooling fan switch connector to ground. If cooling fan runs, check or replace cooling fan switch. If cooling fan does not run, check gray and black wires for open. If wires are satisfactory, check or replace cooling fan relay.

Test E: Cooling Fan Open Test

1. Turn ignition switch to On position, then disconnect cooling fan relay connector and connect a suitable voltmeter between terminal E (red) and ground. If battery voltage is not obtained, check fusible link E and red wire for open, then connect voltmeter between terminal D (brown) and ground. If battery voltage is not obtained, check FAN/FP fuse and brown wire for open. If battery voltage was obtained, proceed to step 2.
2. With cooling fan relay disconnected, connect a 20 amp fused jumper wire between terminals E (red) and A (black/red). If cooling fan runs, proceed to step 4. If cooling fan does not run, leave jumper in place and proceed to step 3.
3. Disconnect cooling fan connector, then connect voltmeter between terminal B (black/red) and ground. If battery voltage is not obtained, check black/red wire for open, then connect voltmeter between terminals B (black/red) and A (black). If battery voltage is not obtained, check black wire for open. If battery voltage was obtained, repair or replace cooling fan.
4. Reconnect cooling fan relay, then connect fused jumper from cooling fan switch connector to ground. If cooling fan runs, check or replace cooling fan switch. If cooling fan does not run, check dark green/white wires for open. If wires are satisfactory, check or replace cooling fan relay.

Test F: Cooling Fan A/C Open

1. Turn ignition switch to On position, then disconnect A/C control head connector and connect fused jumper wire between terminal B (dark green) and ground. If cooling fan does not run, check dark green/white and dark green wires for open, then connect jumper between terminals B (dark green) and A (black). If cooling fan does not run, check black wire for open. If cooling fan runs, repair or replace A/C control head.

Test G: Cooling Fan Does Not Turn Off

1. If cooling fan runs with ignition in Off position, replace cooling fan relay.
2. With ignition in Run position and A/C Off, disconnect cooling fan switch. If cooling fan turns Off, check or replace cooling fan switch. If cooling fan continues to run, check dark green/white and dark green wires and A/C control head for short to ground.

1994

Refer to **Figs. 40 through 45** when performing the following diagnostic procedures.

BONNEVILLE

1992–93

Refer to **Fig. 46** when performing diagnostic procedures.

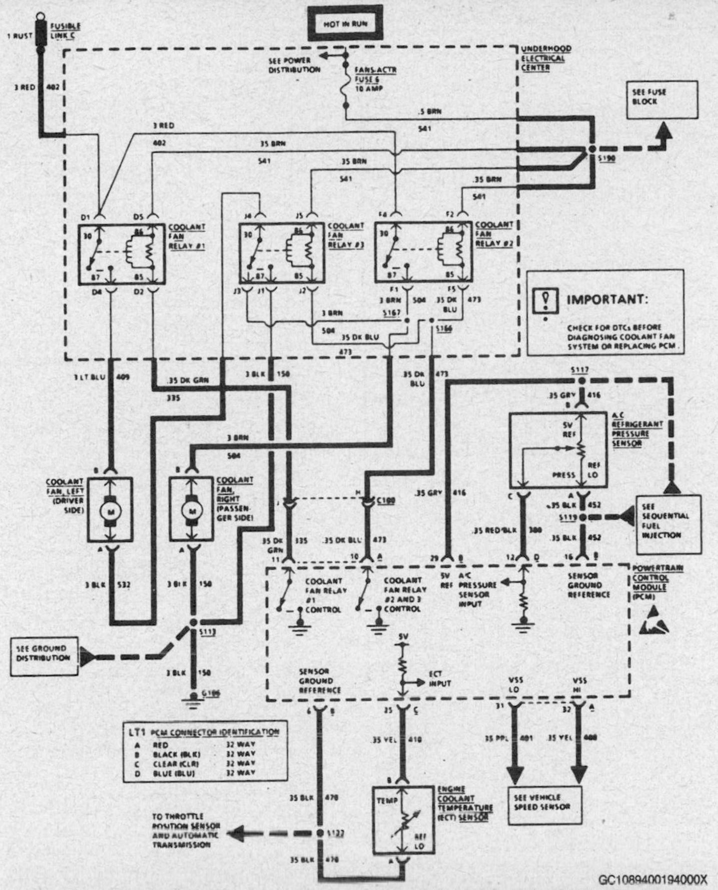

Fig. 42 Cooling fan wiring circuit. 1994 Camaro & Firebird w/5.7L/V8-350 (VIN P) engine & C60

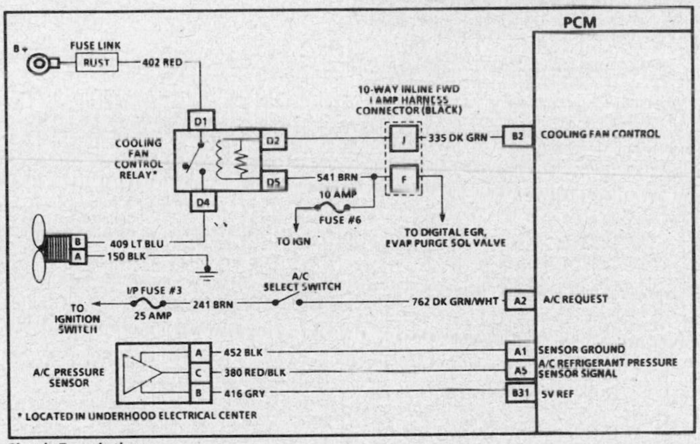

PCM
B+
FUSE LINK
RUST
402 RED
COOLING FAN CONTROL RELAY*
D1
D2
D5
D4
10-WAY INLINE FWD 1 AMP HARNESS CONNECTOR (BLACK)
335 DK GRN
B2
COOLING FAN CONTROL
541 BRN
10 AMP
FUSE #6
TO IGN
TO DIGITAL EGR, EVAP PURGE SOL VALVE
409 LT BLU
150 BLK
I/P FUSE #3
25 AMP
TO IGNITION SWITCH
241 BRN
A/C SELECT SWITCH
762 DK GRN/WHT
A2
A/C REQUEST
A/C PRESSURE SENSOR
452 BLK
380 RED/BLK
416 GRY
A1
A5
B31
SENSOR GROUND
A/C REFRIGERANT PRESSURE SENSOR SIGNAL
5V REF
* LOCATED IN UNDERHOOD ELECTRICAL CENTER

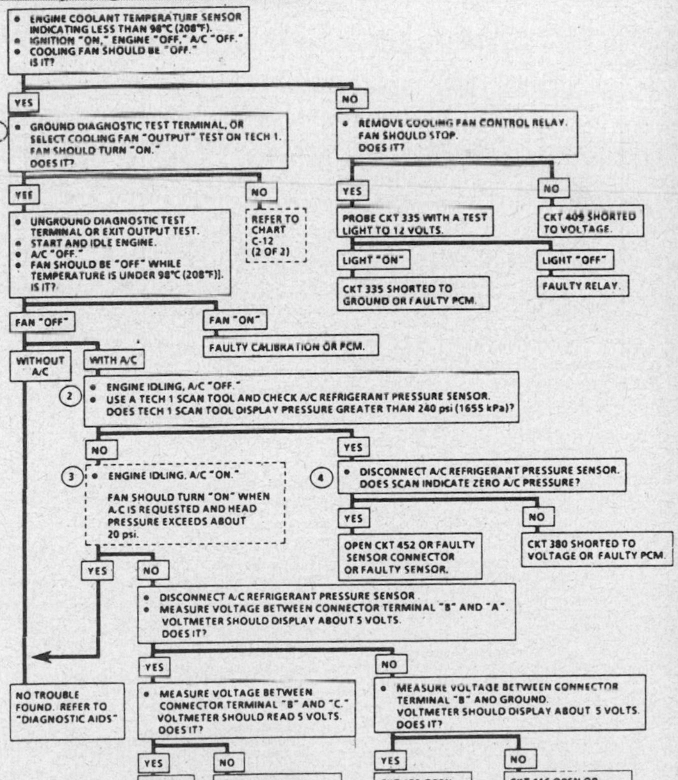

• ENGINE COOLANT TEMPERATURE SENSOR INDICATING LESS THAN 98°C (208°F).
• IGNITION "ON," ENGINE "OFF," A/C "OFF."
• COOLING FAN SHOULD BE "OFF."
IS IT?
YES
NO
1
• GROUND DIAGNOSTIC TEST TERMINAL, OR SELECT COOLING FAN "OUTPUT" TEST ON TECH 1. FAN SHOULD TURN "ON." DOES IT?
• REMOVE COOLING FAN CONTROL RELAY. FAN SHOULD STOP. DOES IT?
YES
NO
REFER TO CHART C-12 (2 OF 2)
PROBE CKT 335 WITH A TEST LIGHT TO 12 VOLTS.
CKT 409 SHORTED TO VOLTAGE.
LIGHT "ON"
LIGHT "OFF"
CKT 335 SHORTED TO GROUND OR FAULTY PCM.
FAULTY RELAY.
• UNGROUND DIAGNOSTIC TEST TERMINAL OR EXIT OUTPUT TEST.
• START AND IDLE ENGINE.
• A/C "OFF."
• FAN SHOULD BE "OFF" WHILE TEMPERATURE IS UNDER 98°C (208°F)].
IS IT?
FAN "OFF"
FAN "ON"
FAULTY CALIBRATION OR PCM.
WITHOUT A/C
WITH A/C
2
• ENGINE IDLING, A/C "OFF."
• USE A TECH 1 SCAN TOOL AND CHECK A/C REFRIGERANT PRESSURE SENSOR. DOES TECH 1 SCAN TOOL DISPLAY PRESSURE GREATER THAN 240 psi (1655 kPa)?
NO
YES
3
• ENGINE IDLING, A/C "ON."
FAN SHOULD TURN "ON" WHEN A/C IS REQUESTED AND HEAD PRESSURE EXCEEDS ABOUT 20 psi.
4
• DISCONNECT A/C REFRIGERANT PRESSURE SENSOR. DOES SCAN INDICATE ZERO A/C PRESSURE?
YES
NO
OPEN CKT 452 OR FAULTY SENSOR CONNECTOR OR FAULTY SENSOR.
CKT 380 SHORTED TO VOLTAGE OR FAULTY PCM.
YES
NO
• DISCONNECT A/C REFRIGERANT PRESSURE SENSOR.
• MEASURE VOLTAGE BETWEEN CONNECTOR TERMINAL "B" AND "A". VOLTMETER SHOULD DISPLAY ABOUT 5 VOLTS. DOES IT?
YES
NO
NO TROUBLE FOUND. REFER TO "DIAGNOSTIC AIDS"
• MEASURE VOLTAGE BETWEEN CONNECTOR TERMINAL "B" AND "C." VOLTMETER SHOULD READ 5 VOLTS. DOES IT?
• MEASURE VOLTAGE BETWEEN CONNECTOR TERMINAL "B" AND GROUND. VOLTMETER SHOULD DISPLAY ABOUT 5 VOLTS. DOES IT?
YES
NO
YES
NO
FAULTY SENSOR.
CKT 380 OPEN OR SHORTED TO GROUND OR FAULTY PCM CONNECTION OR PCM.
CKT 452 OPEN OR FAULTY PCM CONNECTION OR PCM.
CKT 416 OPEN OR SHORTED TO GROUND OR FAULTY PCM CONNECTION OR PCM.
GC108940018901AX

Circuit Description:

The electric cooling fan is controlled by the PCM, based on inputs from the Engine Coolant Temperature (ECT) sensor, the A/C control switches, vehicle speed, and state of the A/C refrigerant pressure sensor. The PCM controls the fan by grounding CKT 335 which energizes the fan control relay. Battery voltage is then supplied to the fan motor.

The PCM grounds CKT 335 when engine coolant temperature is over about 109°C (228°F), or when A/C has been requested and the A/C refrigerant pressure is about 1655 kPa (240 psi). Once the PCM turns the relay "ON," it will keep it "ON" for a minimum of 30 seconds, or until vehicle speed exceeds 113 km/h (70 mph).

Also, if DTC 14 or 15 sets or the PCM is in backup, the primary fan will run at all time.

Chart Test Description: Number(s) below refer to circled number(s) on the diagnostic chart.

1. With the diagnostic terminal grounded, the cooling fan control driver(s) will close, which should energize the fan control relay(s).
2. If the A/C pressure is above 240 psi (1655 kPa) or circuit is open, the fan would run whenever A/C is requested.
3. With A/C clutch engaged and the A/C refrigerant pressure sensor is functioning properly, the fan should come "ON" when pressure exceeds about 20 psi. Under very cold ambient conditions, the fan will remain "OFF." This signal should cause the PCM to energize the cooling fan control relay.
4. This will determine if the A/C refrigerant pressure sensor is faulty or if the PCM or circuitry is faulty.

Diagnostic Aids: If the owner complained of an overheating problem, it must be determined if the complaint was due to an actual boilover, a hot light or temp. gage indicated over heating.

If the gage or light indicates overheating, but no boilover is detected, the gage circuit should be checked.

Fig. 43 Chart C-12A, cooling fan diagnosis (Part 1 of 2). 1994 Camaro & Firebird w/3.4L/V6-204 (VIN S) engine

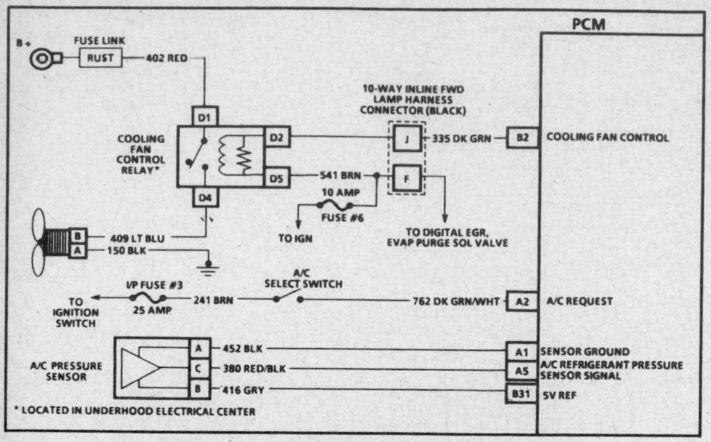
PCM
B+
FUSE LINK
RUST
402 RED
10-WAY INLINE FWD LAMP HARNESS CONNECTOR (BLACK)
COOLING FAN CONTROL RELAY*
D1
D2
D5
D4
335 DK GRN
B2
COOLING FAN CONTROL
541 BRN
10 AMP
FUSE #6
TO IGN
TO DIGITAL EGR, EVAP PURGE SOL VALVE
409 LT BLU
150 BLK
A/C SELECT SWITCH
I/P FUSE #3
TO IGNITION SWITCH
25 AMP
241 BRN
762 DK GRN/WHT
A2
A/C REQUEST
A/C PRESSURE SENSOR
452 BLK
380 RED/BLK
416 GRY
A1
SENSOR GROUND
A5
A/C REFRIGERANT PRESSURE SENSOR SIGNAL
B31
5V REF
* LOCATED IN UNDERHOOD ELECTRICAL CENTER

CHART C-12

(Page 2 of 2)
COOLING FAN CONTROL CIRCUIT DIAGNOSIS
3.4L (VIN S) "F" CARLINE (SFI)

Chart Test Description: Number(s) below refer to circled number(s) on the diagnostic chart.

1. 12 volts should be available to CKT 541 and CKT 402 of the relay when the ignition is "ON."
2. This test checks the ability of the PCM to ground CKT 335.

The Malfunction Indicator Lamp (MIL) "Service Engine Soon" should also be flashing at this point. If it isn't flashing, refer to CHART A-2.

3. If the fan does not turn "ON" at this point, CKT 409 or CKT 150 is open, or the cooling fan motor is faulty.

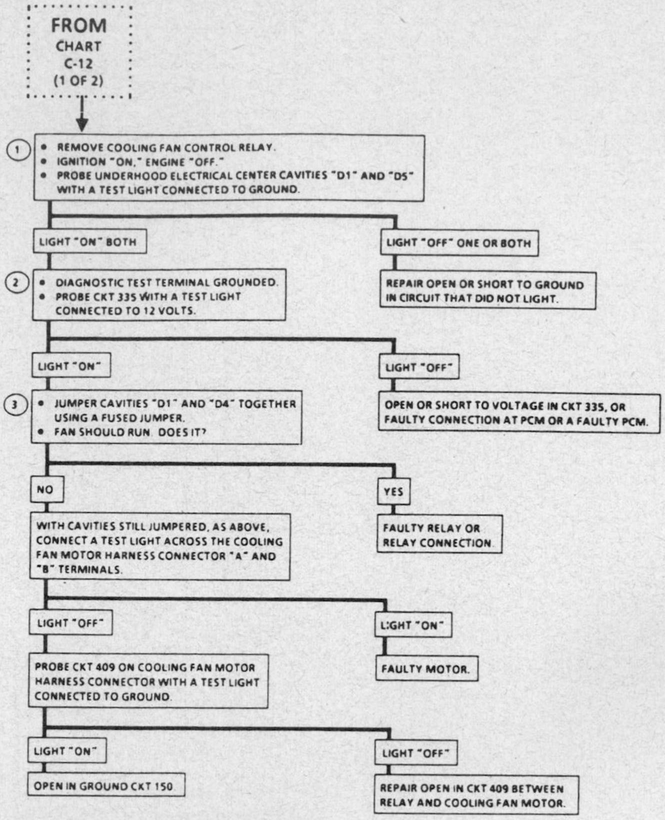
FROM CHART C-12 (1 OF 2)
1
• REMOVE COOLING FAN CONTROL RELAY.
• IGNITION "ON," ENGINE "OFF."
• PROBE UNDERHOOD ELECTRICAL CENTER CAVITIES "D1" AND "D5" WITH A TEST LIGHT CONNECTED TO GROUND.
LIGHT "ON" BOTH
LIGHT "OFF" ONE OR BOTH
REPAIR OPEN OR SHORT TO GROUND IN CIRCUIT THAT DID NOT LIGHT.
2
• DIAGNOSTIC TEST TERMINAL GROUNDED.
• PROBE CKT 335 WITH A TEST LIGHT CONNECTED TO 12 VOLTS.
LIGHT "ON"
LIGHT "OFF"
OPEN OR SHORT TO VOLTAGE IN CKT 335, OR FAULTY CONNECTION AT PCM OR A FAULTY PCM.
3
• JUMPER CAVITIES "D1" AND "D4" TOGETHER USING A FUSED JUMPER.
• FAN SHOULD RUN. DOES IT?
NO
YES
FAULTY RELAY OR RELAY CONNECTION.
WITH CAVITIES STILL JUMPERED, AS ABOVE, CONNECT A TEST LIGHT ACROSS THE COOLING FAN MOTOR HARNESS CONNECTOR "A" AND "B" TERMINALS.
LIGHT "OFF"
LIGHT "ON"
FAULTY MOTOR.
PROBE CKT 409 ON COOLING FAN MOTOR HARNESS CONNECTOR WITH A TEST LIGHT CONNECTED TO GROUND.
LIGHT "ON"
LIGHT "OFF"
OPEN IN GROUND CKT 150.
REPAIR OPEN IN CKT 409 BETWEEN RELAY AND COOLING FAN MOTOR.

GC108940018902AX

Fig. 43 Chart C-12A, cooling fan diagnosis (Part 2 of 2). 1994 Camaro & Firebird w/3.4L/V6-204 (VIN S) engine

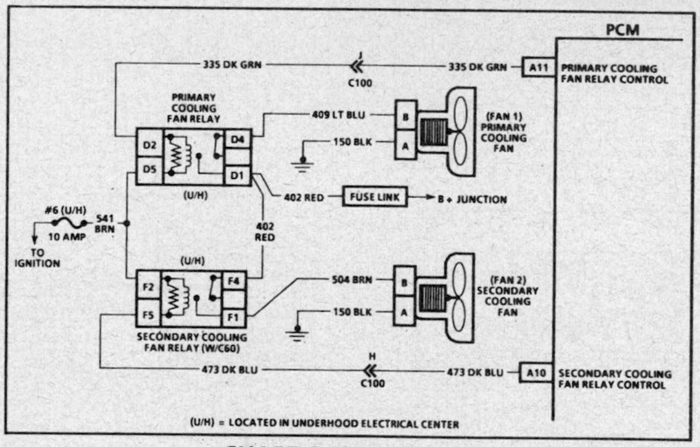
PCM
335 DK GRN
C100
A11
PRIMARY COOLING FAN RELAY CONTROL
PRIMARY COOLING FAN RELAY
409 LT BLU
150 BLK
(FAN 1) PRIMARY COOLING FAN
D2
D4
D5
D1
(U/H)
402 RED
FUSE LINK
B+ JUNCTION
#6 (U/H)
10 AMP
541 BRN
TO IGNITION
402 RED
F2
F4
F5
F1
504 BRN
150 BLK
(FAN 2) SECONDARY COOLING FAN
SECONDARY COOLING FAN RELAY (W/C60)
473 DK BLU
A10
SECONDARY COOLING FAN RELAY CONTROL
(U/H) = LOCATED IN UNDERHOOD ELECTRICAL CENTER

CHART C-12A (Page 1 of 2)

ELECTRIC COOLING FAN CONTROL CIRCUIT DIAGNOSIS
(NON A/C AND EARLY PRODUCTION A/C)
5.7L (VIN P) "F" CARLINE (SFI)

Circuit Description:

The cooling fans are controlled by the PCM based on various inputs. Battery voltage is supplied to the primary fan relay on terminal "D1" and on "F4" of the secondary fan relay. Ignition voltage is supplied to terminal "D5" of the primary fan relay and "F2" of the secondary fan relay. Grounding CKT 335 (relay terminal "D2") will energize the primary cooling fan relay (Fan 1) and supply battery voltage to the primary cooling fan motor. Grounding CKT 473 (relay terminal "F5") will energize the secondary cooling fan relay (Fan 2) and supply battery voltage to the secondary fan motor.

When certain Diagnostic Trouble Codes (DTCs) are set, the PCM will enable the cooling fans.

Chart Test Description: Number(s) below refer to circled number(s) on the diagnostic chart.

1. With the output/field service enable terminal grounded, the cooling fan control driver(s) will close, which should energize the fan control relay(s).
   If vehicle is equipped with one cooling fan (non A/C) and cooling fan operation is OK, refer to diagnostic aids below for further diagnosis of cooling system.
2. Engine coolant temperature must be below 100°C (212°F) to perform this step. The cooling fans should come "ON" anytime A/C system is operating.
3. Comparing Tech 1 pressure and manifold gage set pressure will determine if the A/C refrigerant pressure sensor is out of range. An out of range A/C refrigerant pressure sensor can cause the cooling fans to operate at the wrong times.

Diagnostic Aids: If the owner complained of an overheating problem, it must be determined if the complaint was due to an actual boil over, or the warning indicator light, or engine coolant temperature gage indicated overheating.

The gage accuracy can also be checked by comparing the Engine Coolant Temperature (ECT) sensor reading using a Tech 1 and comparing its reading with the gage reading.

If the engine is actually overheating and the gage indicated overheating, but the cooling fan is not coming "ON," the Engine Coolant Temperature (ECT) sensor has probably shifted out of calibration and should be replaced.

If the engine is overheating and the cooling fans are "ON," the cooling system should be checked.

The PCM will command fan 1 "ON" at 108°C (226°F) and "OFF" at 105°C (221°F) and, fan 2 "ON" at 113°C (235°F) and "OFF" at 110°C (230°F).

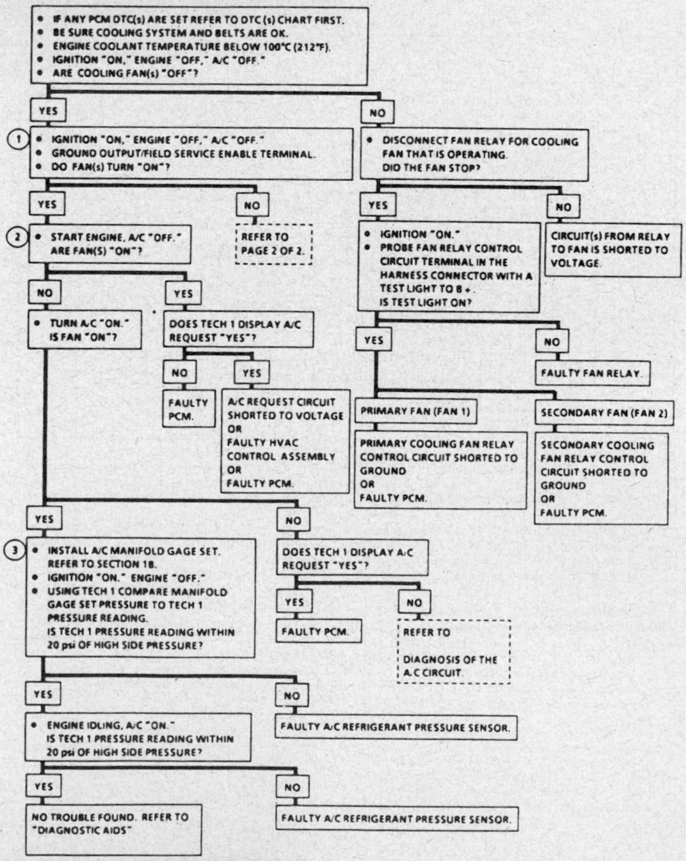
• IF ANY PCM DTC(s) ARE SET REFER TO DTC(s) CHART FIRST.
• BE SURE COOLING SYSTEM AND BELTS ARE OK.
• ENGINE COOLANT TEMPERATURE BELOW 100°C (212°F).
• IGNITION "ON," ENGINE "OFF," A/C "OFF."
• ARE COOLING FAN(s) "OFF"?
YES
NO
1
• IGNITION "ON," ENGINE "OFF," A/C "OFF."
• GROUND OUTPUT/FIELD SERVICE ENABLE TERMINAL.
• DO FAN(s) TURN "ON"?
• DISCONNECT FAN RELAY FOR COOLING FAN THAT IS OPERATING. DID THE FAN STOP?
YES
NO
YES
NO
2
• START ENGINE, A/C "OFF."
ARE FAN(S) "ON"?
REFER TO PAGE 2 OF 2.
• IGNITION "ON."
• PROBE FAN RELAY CONTROL CIRCUIT TERMINAL IN THE HARNESS CONNECTOR WITH A TEST LIGHT TO B+.
IS TEST LIGHT ON?
CIRCUIT(S) FROM RELAY TO FAN IS SHORTED TO VOLTAGE.
NO
YES
• TURN A/C "ON."
IS FAN "ON"?
DOES TECH 1 DISPLAY A/C REQUEST "YES"?
YES
NO
NO
YES
FAULTY FAN RELAY.
FAULTY PCM.
A/C REQUEST CIRCUIT SHORTED TO VOLTAGE OR FAULTY HVAC CONTROL ASSEMBLY OR FAULTY PCM.
PRIMARY FAN (FAN 1)
SECONDARY FAN (FAN 2)
PRIMARY COOLING FAN RELAY CONTROL CIRCUIT SHORTED TO GROUND OR FAULTY PCM.
SECONDARY COOLING FAN RELAY CONTROL CIRCUIT SHORTED TO GROUND OR FAULTY PCM.
YES
NO
3
• INSTALL A/C MANIFOLD GAGE SET. REFER TO SECTION 1B.
• IGNITION "ON," ENGINE "OFF."
• USING TECH 1 COMPARE MANIFOLD GAGE SET PRESSURE TO TECH 1 PRESSURE READING.
IS TECH 1 PRESSURE READING WITHIN 20 psi OF HIGH SIDE PRESSURE?
DOES TECH 1 DISPLAY A/C REQUEST "YES"?
YES
NO
FAULTY PCM.
REFER TO DIAGNOSIS OF THE A/C CIRCUIT.
YES
NO
• ENGINE IDLING, A/C "ON."
IS TECH 1 PRESSURE READING WITHIN 20 psi OF HIGH SIDE PRESSURE?
FAULTY A/C REFRIGERANT PRESSURE SENSOR.
YES
NO
NO TROUBLE FOUND. REFER TO "DIAGNOSTIC AIDS"
FAULTY A/C REFRIGERANT PRESSURE SENSOR.

GC108940019001AX

Fig. 44 Chart C-12B, cooling fan diagnosis, non A/C and early production A/C (Part 1 of 2). 1994 Camaro & Firebird w/5.7L/V8-350 (VIN P) engine

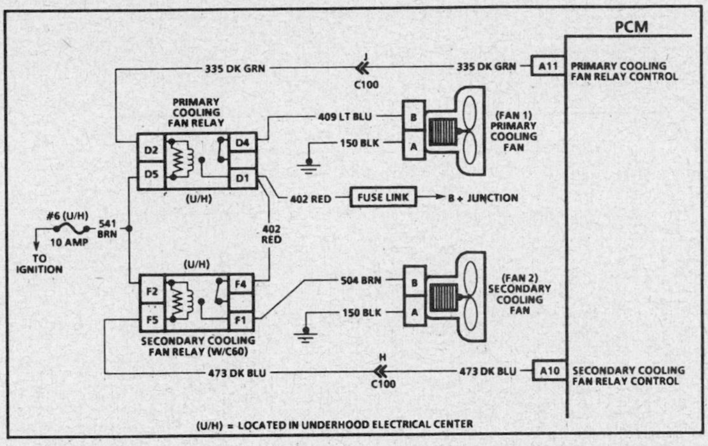
PCM
335 DK GRN
C100
335 DK GRN
A11
PRIMARY COOLING FAN RELAY CONTROL
PRIMARY COOLING FAN RELAY
409 LT BLU
(FAN 1) PRIMARY COOLING FAN
150 BLK
D2
D4
D5
D1
(U/H)
402 RED
FUSE LINK
B+ JUNCTION
#6 (U/H)
10 AMP
541 BRN
TO IGNITION
402 RED
(U/H)
504 BRN
(FAN 2) SECONDARY COOLING FAN
F2
F4
F5
F1
150 BLK
SECONDARY COOLING FAN RELAY (W/C60)
473 DK BLU
C100
473 DK BLU
A10
SECONDARY COOLING FAN RELAY CONTROL
(U/H) = LOCATED IN UNDERHOOD ELECTRICAL CENTER

Circuit Description:

The cooling fans are controlled by the PCM based on various inputs. Battery voltage is supplied to the primary fan relay on terminals "D1" and "F4" of the secondary fan relay. Ignition voltage is supplied to terminal "D5" of the primary fan relay and "F2" of the secondary fan relay. Grounding CKT 335 (relay terminal "D2") will energize the primary cooling fan relay (Fan 1) and supply battery voltage to the primary cooling fan motor. Grounding CKT 473 (relay terminal "F5") will energize the secondary cooling fan relay (Fan 2) and supply battery voltage to the secondary fan motor.

The PCM will enable the cooling fans, when certain Diagnostic Trouble Codes (DTCs) are set.

Diagnostic Aids: If the owner complained of an overheating problem, it must be determined if the complaint was due to an actual boil over, the warning indicator light, or engine coolant temperature gage indicated overheating.

The gage accuracy can also be checked by comparing the Engine Coolant Temperature (ECT) sensor reading using a Tech 1 and comparing its reading with the gage reading.

If the engine is actually overheating and the gage indicated overheating, but the cooling fan is not coming "ON," the Engine Coolant Temperature (ECT) sensor has probably shifted out of calibration and should be replaced.

If the engine is overheating and the cooling fans are "ON," the cooling system should be checked, refer to SECTION 6B.

The PCM will command fan 1 "ON" at 108°C (226°F) and "OFF" at 105°C (221°F) and an 2 "ON" at 113°C (235°F) and "OFF" at 110°C (230°F).

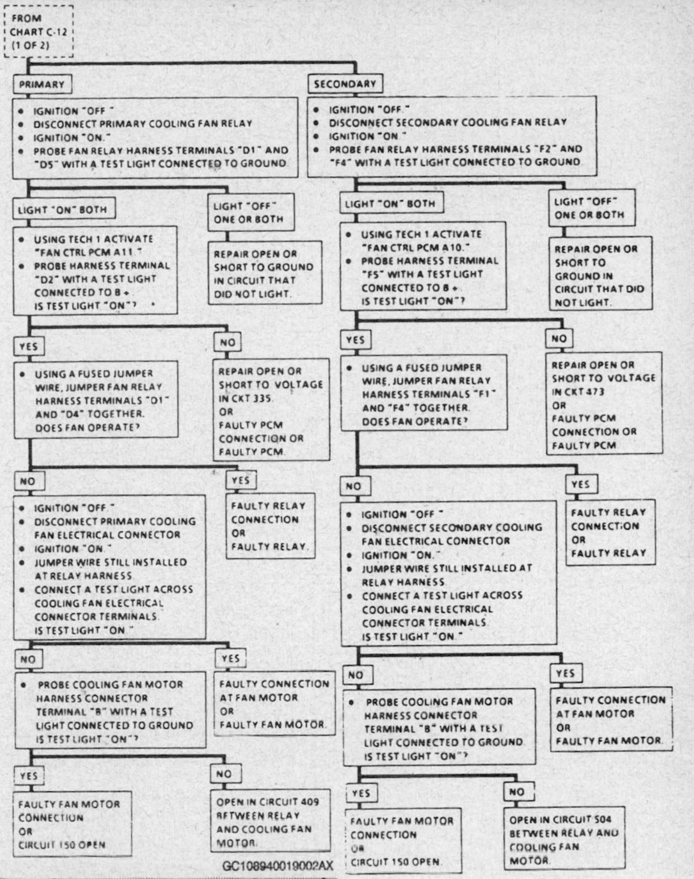
FROM CHART C-12 (1 OF 2)
PRIMARY
• IGNITION "OFF."
• DISCONNECT PRIMARY COOLING FAN RELAY
• IGNITION "ON."
• PROBE FAN RELAY HARNESS TERMINALS "D1" AND "D5" WITH A TEST LIGHT CONNECTED TO GROUND.
LIGHT "ON" BOTH
LIGHT "OFF" ONE OR BOTH
• USING TECH 1 ACTIVATE "FAN CTRL PCM A11."
• PROBE HARNESS TERMINAL "D2" WITH A TEST LIGHT CONNECTED TO B+.
IS TEST LIGHT "ON"?
REPAIR OPEN OR SHORT TO GROUND IN CIRCUIT THAT DID NOT LIGHT.
YES
NO
• USING A FUSED JUMPER WIRE, JUMPER FAN RELAY HARNESS TERMINALS "D1" AND "D4" TOGETHER.
DOES FAN OPERATE?
REPAIR OPEN OR SHORT TO VOLTAGE IN CKT 335.
OR
FAULTY PCM CONNECTION OR FAULTY PCM.
NO
YES
• IGNITION "OFF."
• DISCONNECT PRIMARY COOLING FAN ELECTRICAL CONNECTOR
• IGNITION "ON."
• JUMPER WIRE STILL INSTALLED AT RELAY HARNESS.
• CONNECT A TEST LIGHT ACROSS COOLING FAN ELECTRICAL CONNECTOR TERMINALS.
IS TEST LIGHT "ON."
FAULTY RELAY CONNECTION OR FAULTY RELAY.
NO
YES
• PROBE COOLING FAN MOTOR HARNESS CONNECTOR TERMINAL "B" WITH A TEST LIGHT CONNECTED TO GROUND.
IS TEST LIGHT "ON"?
FAULTY CONNECTION AT FAN MOTOR OR FAULTY FAN MOTOR.
YES
NO
FAULTY FAN MOTOR CONNECTION OR CIRCUIT 150 OPEN.
OPEN IN CIRCUIT 409 BETWEEN RELAY AND COOLING FAN MOTOR.
SECONDARY
• IGNITION "OFF."
• DISCONNECT SECONDARY COOLING FAN RELAY
• IGNITION "ON."
• PROBE FAN RELAY HARNESS TERMINALS "F2" AND "F4" WITH A TEST LIGHT CONNECTED TO GROUND.
LIGHT "ON" BOTH
LIGHT "OFF" ONE OR BOTH
• USING TECH 1 ACTIVATE "FAN CTRL PCM A10."
• PROBE HARNESS TERMINAL "F5" WITH A TEST LIGHT CONNECTED TO B+.
IS TEST LIGHT "ON"?
REPAIR OPEN OR SHORT TO GROUND IN CIRCUIT THAT DID NOT LIGHT.
YES
NO
• USING A FUSED JUMPER WIRE, JUMPER FAN RELAY HARNESS TERMINALS "F1" AND "F4" TOGETHER.
DOES FAN OPERATE?
REPAIR OPEN OR SHORT TO VOLTAGE IN CKT 473
OR
FAULTY PCM CONNECTION OR FAULTY PCM.
NO
YES
• IGNITION "OFF."
• DISCONNECT SECONDARY COOLING FAN ELECTRICAL CONNECTOR
• IGNITION "ON."
• JUMPER WIRE STILL INSTALLED AT RELAY HARNESS.
• CONNECT A TEST LIGHT ACROSS COOLING FAN ELECTRICAL CONNECTOR TERMINALS.
IS TEST LIGHT "ON."
FAULTY RELAY CONNECTION OR FAULTY RELAY
NO
YES
• PROBE COOLING FAN MOTOR HARNESS CONNECTOR TERMINAL "B" WITH A TEST LIGHT CONNECTED TO GROUND.
IS TEST LIGHT "ON"?
FAULTY CONNECTION AT FAN MOTOR OR FAULTY FAN MOTOR.
YES
NO
FAULTY FAN MOTOR CONNECTION OR CIRCUIT 150 OPEN.
OPEN IN CIRCUIT 504 BETWEEN RELAY AND COOLING FAN MOTOR.
GC108940019002AX

Fig. 44 Chart C-12B, cooling fan diagnosis, non A/C and early production A/C (Part 2 of 2). 1994 Camaro & Firebird w/5.7L/V8-350 (VIN P) engine

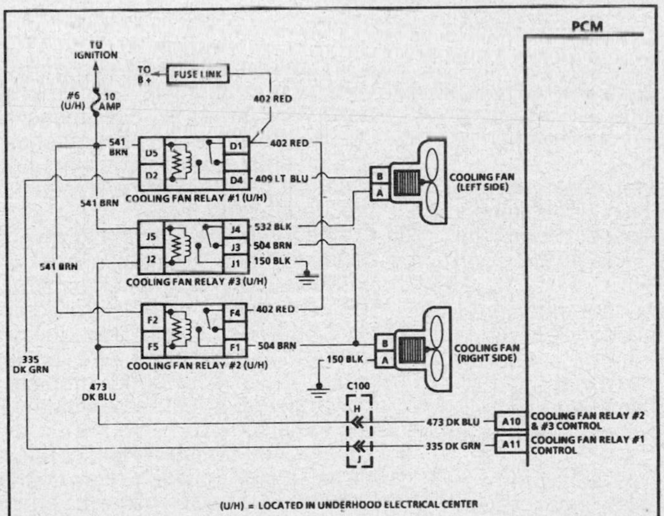
PCM
TO IGNITION
TO B+
FUSE LINK
#6 (U/H)
10 AMP
402 RED
541 BRN
D5
D1
402 RED
D2
D4
409 LT BLU
COOLING FAN (LEFT SIDE)
541 BRN
COOLING FAN RELAY #1 (U/H)
J5
J4
532 BLK
J3
504 BRN
J2
J1
150 BLK
541 BRN
COOLING FAN RELAY #3 (U/H)
F2
F4
402 RED
F5
F1
504 BRN
COOLING FAN (RIGHT SIDE)
150 BLK
335 DK GRN
COOLING FAN RELAY #2 (U/H)
C100
473 DK BLU
473 DK BLU
A10
COOLING FAN RELAY #2 & #3 CONTROL
335 DK GRN
A11
COOLING FAN RELAY #1 CONTROL
(U/H) = LOCATED IN UNDERHOOD ELECTRICAL CENTER

Circuit Description:

The cooling fans are controlled by the PCM based on various inputs. Ignition voltage is supplied to all three cooling fan relay coils on CKT 541. The PCM controls cooling fan relay #1 by providing the ground path through CKT 335. The PCM controls cooling fan relays #2 and #3 together by providing the ground path through CKT 473. When cooling fan relay #1 is energized the cooling fans are connected in series and operate together at low speed. When all three relays are energized the fans are connected in parallel and operate together at high speed. When certain DTCs are set, the PCM will enable cooling fans.

Chart Test Description: Number(s) below refer to circled number(s) on the diagnostic chart.

1. The cooling fans should come "ON" anytime A/C system is operating.
2. Comparing Tech 1 pressure and manifold gage set pressure will determine if the A/C refrigerant pressure sensor is out of range. An out of range A/C refrigerant pressure sensor can cause the cooling fans to operate at the wrong times.

Diagnostic Aids: If the owner complained of an overheating problem, it must be determined if the complaint was due to an actual boil over, the warning indicator light, or engine coolant temperature gage indicated overheating.

If the engine is overheating and the cooling fans are "ON," the cooling system should be checked, refer to SECTION 6B.

The PCM will command low speed fans "ON" at 108°C (226°F) and "OFF" at 105° C (221°F) and, high speed fans "ON" at 113°C (235°F) and "OFF" at 110°C (230°F).

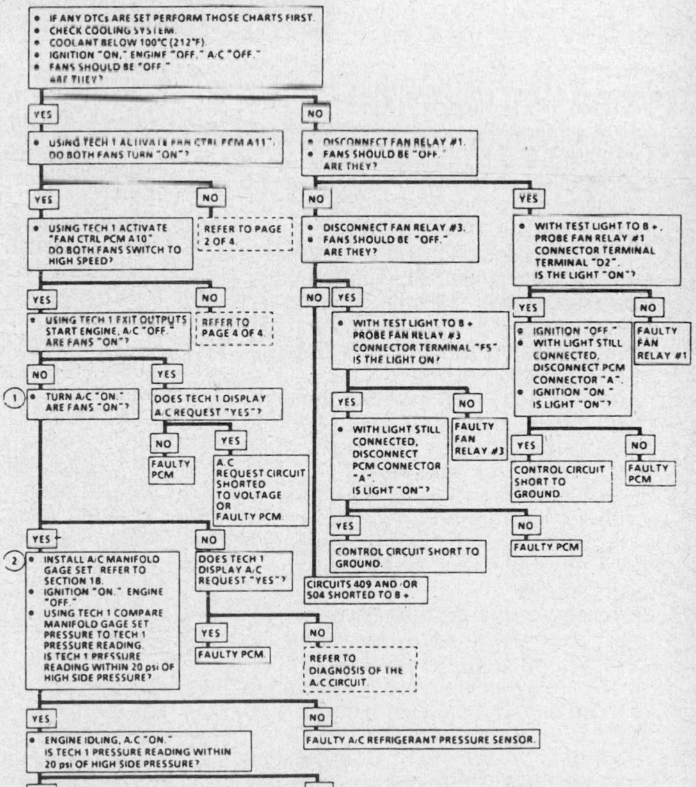
• IF ANY DTCs ARE SET PERFORM THOSE CHARTS FIRST.
• CHECK COOLING SYSTEM.
• COOLANT BELOW 100°C (212°F).
• IGNITION "ON," ENGINE "OFF," A/C "OFF."
• FANS SHOULD BE "OFF."
ARE THEY?
YES
NO
• USING TECH 1 ACTIVATE FAN CTRL PCM A11".
DO BOTH FANS TURN "ON"?
• DISCONNECT FAN RELAY #1.
• FANS SHOULD BE "OFF."
ARE THEY?
YES
NO
• USING TECH 1 ACTIVATE "FAN CTRL PCM A10".
DO BOTH FANS SWITCH TO HIGH SPEED?
REFER TO PAGE 2 OF 4.
NO
YES
• DISCONNECT FAN RELAY #3.
• FANS SHOULD BE "OFF."
ARE THEY?
• WITH TEST LIGHT TO B+, PROBE FAN RELAY #1 CONNECTOR TERMINAL "D2".
IS THE LIGHT "ON"?
YES
NO
• USING TECH 1 EXIT OUTPUTS START ENGINE, A/C "OFF."
ARE FANS "ON"?
REFER TO PAGE 4 OF 4.
NO
YES
• WITH TEST LIGHT TO B+ PROBE FAN RELAY #3 CONNECTOR TERMINAL "F5".
IS THE LIGHT ON?
YES
NO
• IGNITION "OFF."
• WITH LIGHT STILL CONNECTED, DISCONNECT PCM CONNECTOR "A".
• IGNITION "ON."
IS LIGHT "ON"?
FAULTY FAN RELAY #1
NO
YES
1
• TURN A/C "ON."
ARE FANS "ON"?
DOES TECH 1 DISPLAY A/C REQUEST "YES"?
YES
NO
• WITH LIGHT STILL CONNECTED, DISCONNECT PCM CONNECTOR "A".
IS LIGHT "ON"?
FAULTY FAN RELAY #3
YES
NO
CONTROL CIRCUIT SHORT TO GROUND.
FAULTY PCM
NO
YES
FAULTY PCM
A/C REQUEST CIRCUIT SHORTED TO VOLTAGE OR FAULTY PCM.
YES
NO
CONTROL CIRCUIT SHORT TO GROUND.
NO
FAULTY PCM
YES
NO
2
• INSTALL A/C MANIFOLD GAGE SET. REFER TO SECTION 1B.
• IGNITION "ON." ENGINE "OFF."
• USING TECH 1 COMPARE MANIFOLD GAGE SET PRESSURE TO TECH 1 PRESSURE READING.
IS TECH 1 PRESSURE READING WITHIN 20 psi OF HIGH SIDE PRESSURE?
DOES TECH 1 DISPLAY A/C REQUEST "YES"?
CIRCUITS 409 AND/OR 504 SHORTED TO B+.
YES
NO
FAULTY PCM.
REFER TO DIAGNOSIS OF THE A/C CIRCUIT.
YES
NO
• ENGINE IDLING, A/C "ON."
IS TECH 1 PRESSURE READING WITHIN 20 psi OF HIGH SIDE PRESSURE?
FAULTY A/C REFRIGERANT PRESSURE SENSOR.
YES
NO
NO TROUBLE FOUND. REFER TO "DIAGNOSTIC AIDS"
FAULTY A/C REFRIGERANT PRESSURE SENSOR.
GC108940019101AX

Fig. 45 Chart C-12B, cooling fan diagnosis, late production A/C (Part 1 of 4). 1994 Camaro & Firebird w/5.7L/V8-350 (VIN P) engine

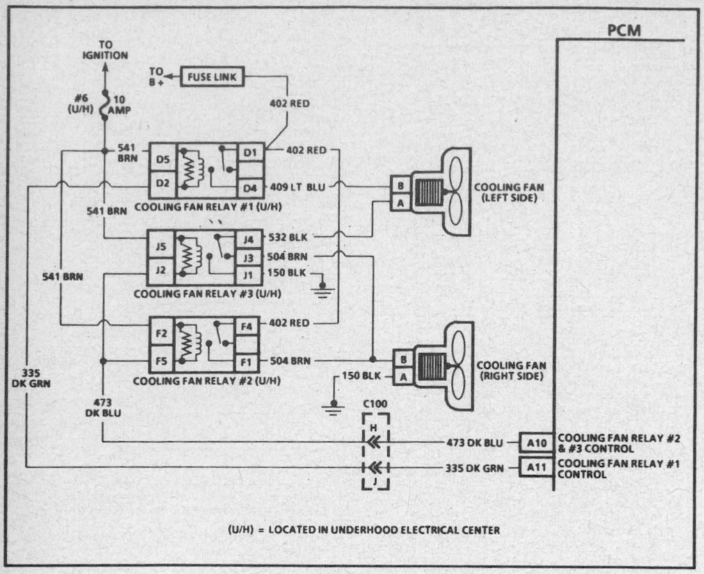
PCM
TO IGNITION
TO B+
FUSE LINK
#6 (U/H)
10 AMP
402 RED
541 BRN
D5
D2
D1
D4
402 RED
409 LT BLU
COOLING FAN RELAY #1 (U/H)
541 BRN
COOLING FAN (LEFT SIDE)
J5
J2
J4
J3
J1
532 BLK
504 BRN
150 BLK
541 BRN
COOLING FAN RELAY #3 (U/H)
F2
F5
F4
F1
402 RED
504 BRN
335 DK GRN
COOLING FAN RELAY #2 (U/H)
150 BLK
COOLING FAN (RIGHT SIDE)
473 DK BLU
C100
473 DK BLU
A10
COOLING FAN RELAY #2 & #3 CONTROL
335 DK GRN
A11
COOLING FAN RELAY #1 CONTROL
(U/H) = LOCATED IN UNDERHOOD ELECTRICAL CENTER

CHART C-12B (Page 2 of 4)

ELECTRIC COOLING FAN CONTROL CIRCUIT DIAGNOSIS
(LATE PRODUCTION A/C)
5.7 (VIN P) "F" CARLINE (SFI)

Circuit Description:
The cooling fans are controlled by the PCM based on various inputs. Ignition voltage is supplied to all three cooling fan relay coils on CKT 541. The PCM controls cooling fan relay #1 by providing the ground path through CKT 335. The PCM controls cooling fan relays #2 and #3 together by providing the ground path through CKT 473. When cooling fan relay #1 is energerized the cooling fans are connected in series and operate together at low speed. When all three relays are energized the fans are connected in parallel and operate together at high speed. When certain DTCs are set, the PCM will enable cooling fans.

Diagnostic Aids: If the owner complained of an overheating problem, it must be determined if the complaint was due to an actual boil over, or the warning indicator light, or engine coolant temperature gage indicated overheating.

If the engine is overheating and the cooling fans are "ON," the cooling system should be checked

The PCM will command low speed fans "ON" at 108°C (226°F) and "OFF" at 105° C (221°F) and, high speed fans "ON" at 113°C (235°F) and "OFF" at 110°C (230°F).

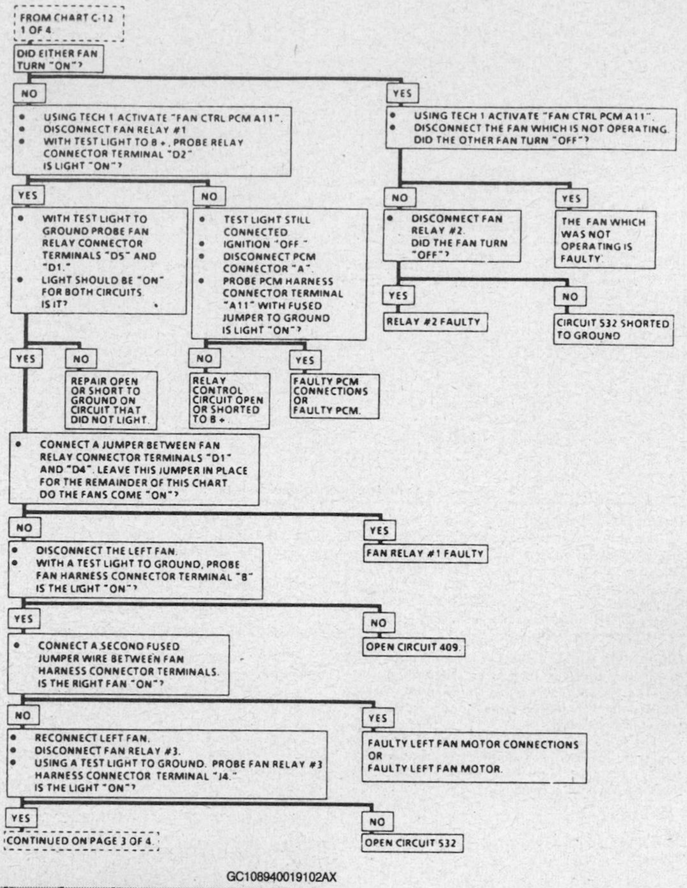
FROM CHART C-12 1 OF 4
DID EITHER FAN TURN "ON"?
NO
YES
• USING TECH 1 ACTIVATE "FAN CTRL PCM A11". • DISCONNECT FAN RELAY #1 • WITH TEST LIGHT TO B+, PROBE RELAY CONNECTOR TERMINAL "D2" IS LIGHT "ON"?
• USING TECH 1 ACTIVATE "FAN CTRL PCM A11". • DISCONNECT THE FAN WHICH IS NOT OPERATING. DID THE OTHER FAN TURN "OFF"?
• WITH TEST LIGHT TO GROUND PROBE FAN RELAY CONNECTOR TERMINALS "D5" AND "D1." • LIGHT SHOULD BE "ON" FOR BOTH CIRCUITS. IS IT?
• TEST LIGHT STILL CONNECTED • IGNITION "OFF" • DISCONNECT PCM CONNECTOR "A". • PROBE PCM HARNESS CONNECTOR TERMINAL "A11" WITH FUSED JUMPER TO GROUND IS LIGHT "ON"?
• DISCONNECT FAN RELAY #2. DID THE FAN TURN "OFF"?
THE FAN WHICH WAS NOT OPERATING IS FAULTY.
RELAY #2 FAULTY
CIRCUIT 532 SHORTED TO GROUND
REPAIR OPEN OR SHORT TO GROUND ON CIRCUIT THAT DID NOT LIGHT.
RELAY CONTROL CIRCUIT OPEN OR SHORTED TO B+.
FAULTY PCM CONNECTIONS OR FAULTY PCM.
• CONNECT A JUMPER BETWEEN FAN RELAY CONNECTOR TERMINALS "D1" AND "D4". LEAVE THIS JUMPER IN PLACE FOR THE REMAINDER OF THIS CHART DO THE FANS COME "ON"?
FAN RELAY #1 FAULTY
• DISCONNECT THE LEFT FAN. • WITH A TEST LIGHT TO GROUND, PROBE FAN HARNESS CONNECTOR TERMINAL "B" IS THE LIGHT "ON"?
OPEN CIRCUIT 409.
• CONNECT A SECOND FUSED JUMPER WIRE BETWEEN FAN HARNESS CONNECTOR TERMINALS. IS THE RIGHT FAN "ON"?
FAULTY LEFT FAN MOTOR CONNECTIONS OR FAULTY LEFT FAN MOTOR.
• RECONNECT LEFT FAN. • DISCONNECT FAN RELAY #3. • USING A TEST LIGHT TO GROUND. PROBE FAN RELAY #3 HARNESS CONNECTOR TERMINAL "J4." IS THE LIGHT "ON"?
CONTINUED ON PAGE 3 OF 4.
OPEN CIRCUIT 532
GC108940019102AX

Fig. 45 Chart C-12B, cooling fan diagnosis, late production A/C (Part 2 of 4). 1994 Camaro & Firebird w/5.7L/V8-350 (VIN P) engine

Cooling Fan Input Test

1. Turn ignition to run, then connect terminals B and A of ALDL connector. If cooling fan does not turn On, proceed to step 2. If cooling fan turns On, problem is PCM related.
2. Turn ignition switch off and remove jumper wire from ALDL connector, then disconnect righthand cooling fan motor connector and measure resistance between connector C123 terminal A and ground.
3. If resistance is less than 50 ohms, repair black/red wire for short to ground, and inspect low speed cooling fan relay for damage.
4. If resistance is more than 50 ohms, reconnect righthand cooling fan motor connector and measure resistance between connector C123 terminal B and ground.
5. If resistance is less than 50 ohms, repair pink/black wire for short to ground and inspect high speed cooling fan relay for damage. If resistance is more than 50 ohms, proceed to step 6.
6. Turn ignition switch to Run position and reconnect terminals A and B of ALDL connector. Measure voltage from connector C123 terminal A to ground.
7. If battery voltage is not measured, perform "Low Speed Cooling Fan Test." If battery voltage is measured, keep ALDL terminals connected and measure voltage from connector C123 terminal B to ground.
8. If battery voltage is not measured, turn ignition switch off, disconnect jumper wire from ALDL, reconnect connector C123 and perform "High Speed Cooling Fan Input Test."
9. If battery voltage is not measured, keep ALDL terminals connected and measure voltage from connector C123 terminal B to terminal C. If battery voltage is not measured, turn ignition switch off and check black wire for and open.
10. If battery voltage is measured, turn ignition switch off and check wiring within cooling fan assembly. If wiring is good, replace cooling fan motor.

Low Speed Cooling Fan Input Test

1. Disconnect low speed cooling fan relay and turn ignition switch to run, then measure voltage from relay connector terminal 2 to ground. If battery voltage is not measured, check brown wire for an open or short to ground and replace fuses where necessary. If battery voltage is measured, proceed to step 2.
2. Turn ignition switch off and measure voltage from terminal 1 to ground. If battery voltage is not measured, check red wire for an open or short to ground and replace fuses where necessary. If battery voltage is measured proceed to step 3.
3. Connect terminals A and B of ALDL connector and connect a test lamp between relay connector terminal 1 and terminal 5, then turn ignition switch to Run. If test light does not light check gray/black wire for open circuit. If wiring is good, problem is PCM related. If test lamp lights, proceed to step 4.
4. Turn ignition switch off and connect a fused jumper between relay connector terminal 1 and terminal 4. Lefthand cooling fan should run at low speed and righthand cooling fan should run at high speed.
5. If fan does not run as specified, check black/red wire and cooling fan resistor for an open. If fan does run as specified, replace low speed cooling fan relay.

High Speed Cooling Fan Input Test

1. Disconnect high speed cooling fan relay and turn ignition switch to run.

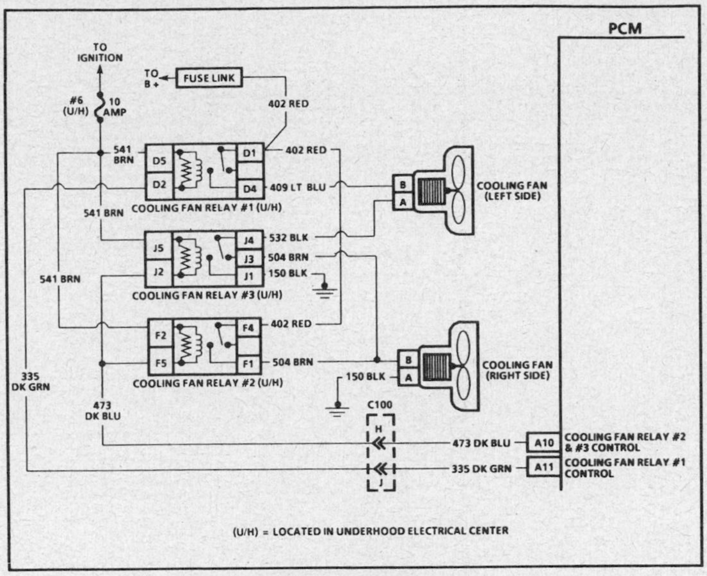
PCM
TO IGNITION
TO B+
FUSE LINK
#6 (U/H)
10 AMP
402 RED
541 BRN
D5
D2
D1
D4
402 RED
409 LT BLU
COOLING FAN RELAY #1 (U/H)
541 BRN
J5
J2
J4
J3
J1
532 BLK
504 BRN
150 BLK
COOLING FAN RELAY #3 (U/H)
541 BRN
F2
F5
F4
F1
402 RED
504 BRN
COOLING FAN RELAY #2 (U/H)
335 DK GRN
473 DK BLU
150 BLK
C100
H
J
COOLING FAN (LEFT SIDE)
COOLING FAN (RIGHT SIDE)
473 DK BLU
A10
COOLING FAN RELAY #2 & #3 CONTROL
335 DK GRN
A11
COOLING FAN RELAY #1 CONTROL
(U/H) = LOCATED IN UNDERHOOD ELECTRICAL CENTER

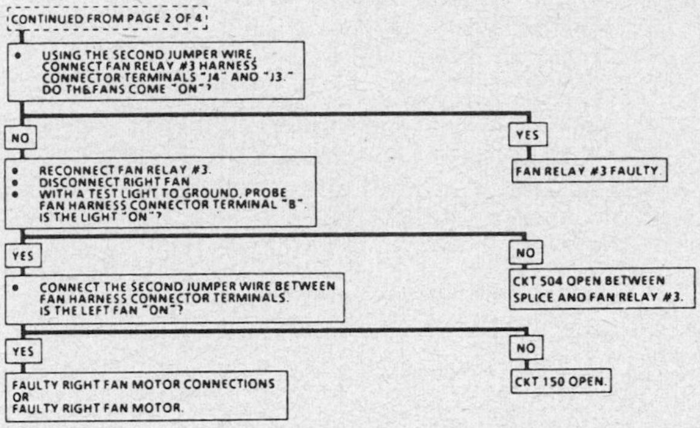
CONTINUED FROM PAGE 2 OF 4
• USING THE SECOND JUMPER WIRE, CONNECT FAN RELAY #3 HARNESS CONNECTOR TERMINALS "J4" AND "J3." DO THE FANS COME "ON"?
NO
YES
FAN RELAY #3 FAULTY.
• RECONNECT FAN RELAY #3.
• DISCONNECT RIGHT FAN
• WITH A TEST LIGHT TO GROUND, PROBE FAN HARNESS CONNECTOR TERMINAL "B". IS THE LIGHT "ON"?
YES
NO
CKT 504 OPEN BETWEEN SPLICE AND FAN RELAY #3.
• CONNECT THE SECOND JUMPER WIRE BETWEEN FAN HARNESS CONNECTOR TERMINALS. IS THE LEFT FAN "ON"?
YES
NO
FAULTY RIGHT FAN MOTOR CONNECTIONS OR FAULTY RIGHT FAN MOTOR.
CKT 150 OPEN.

CHART C-12B (Page 3 of 4)

ELECTRIC COOLING FAN CONTROL CIRCUIT DIAGNOSIS
(LATE PRODUCTION A/C)
5.7 (VIN P) "F" CARLINE (SFI)

Circuit Description:

The cooling fans are controlled by the PCM based on various inputs. Ignition voltage is supplied to all three cooling fan relay coils on CKT 541. The PCM controls cooling fan relay #1 by providing the ground path through CKT 335. The PCM controls cooling fan relays #2 and #3 together by providing the ground path through CKT 473. When cooling fan relay #1 is energerized the cooling fans are connected in series and operate together at low speed. When all three relays are energized the fans are connected in parallel and operate together at high speed. When certain DTCs are set, the PCM will enable cooling fans.

Diagnostic Aids: If the owner complained of an overheating problem, it must be determined if the complaint was due to an actual boil over, or the warning indicator light, or engine coolant temperature gage indicated overheating

If the engine is overheating and the cooling fans are "ON," the cooling system should be checked

The PCM will command low speed fans "ON" at 108°C (220°F) and "OFF" at 105° C (221°F) and, high speed fans "ON" at 113°C (235°F) and "OFF" at 110°C (230°F).

GC108940019103AX

Fig. 45 Chart C-12B, cooling fan diagnosis, late production A/C (Part 3 of 4). 1994 Camaro & Firebird w/5.7L/V8-350 (VIN P) engine

Measure voltage from terminal 2 to ground. If battery voltage is not present, check brown wire for an open or short to ground and replace fuses where necessary. If battery voltage is present, proceed to step 2.

2. Turn ignition switch off and measure voltage from relay connector terminal 1 to ground. If battery voltage is not present, check red wire for open or short to ground and replace fuses where necessary. If battery voltage is present, proceed to step 3.
3. Connect terminals A and B of ALDL connector and connect a test lamp between relay connector terminal 1 and terminal 5, then turn ignition to run. If test lamp does not light, check dark green/white wire for an open. If satisfactory, problem is PCM related. If test lamp lights, proceed to step 4.
4. Turn ignition switch to Off position and connect a fused jumper between relay connector terminal 1 and terminal 4, then turn ignition switch back to Run position. If cooling fan runs at high speed, replace high speed cooling fan relay. If cooling fan does not run at high speed, check black/pink wire and cooling fan resistor for an open.

LH Cooling Fan Runs Continuously In Low Speed w/Ignition Switch At Run, Engine Coolant Cool & A/C Off

1. Turn ignition switch off and disconnect low speed cooling fan relay, then measure resistance between relay connector terminal 5 and ground.
2. If infinite ohms resistance is measured, replace low speed cooling fan relay.
3. If infinite ohms resistance is not measured, check gray/black wire for short to ground. If satisfactory, problem is PCM related.

LH Cooling Fan Runs Continuously In High Speed w/Ignition Switch At Run, Engine Coolant Cool & A/C Off

1. Turn ignition switch off and disconnect high speed cooling fan relay, then measure resistance between relay connector terminal 5 and ground.
2. If resistance is present, check dark green/white wire for short to ground. If satisfactory, problem is PCM related. If resistance is not present, proceed to step 3.
3. Measure resistance between high speed cooling fan relay terminals 1 and 4. If resistance is present, replace high speed cooling fan relay. If resistance is not present, proceed to step 4.
4. Disconnect A/C pressure fan switch and measure continuity between connector terminal A and ground. If continuity does not exist, replace A/C pressure fan switch. If continuity does exist proceed to step 5.
5. Check dark green/white wire for a short to ground. If satisfactory, problem is PCM related.

LH Cooling Fan Does Not Operate In High Speed with A/C Head Pressure Above 210 psi

1. Turn ignition switch off and disconnect A/C pressure fan switch connector, then measure resistance from terminal B to ground. If more than 2 ohms was measured, check black/white wire for an open. If less than 2 ohms was measured, proceed to step 2.
2. Connect a jumper wire between terminal A and terminal B of switch connector, then turn ignition switch to

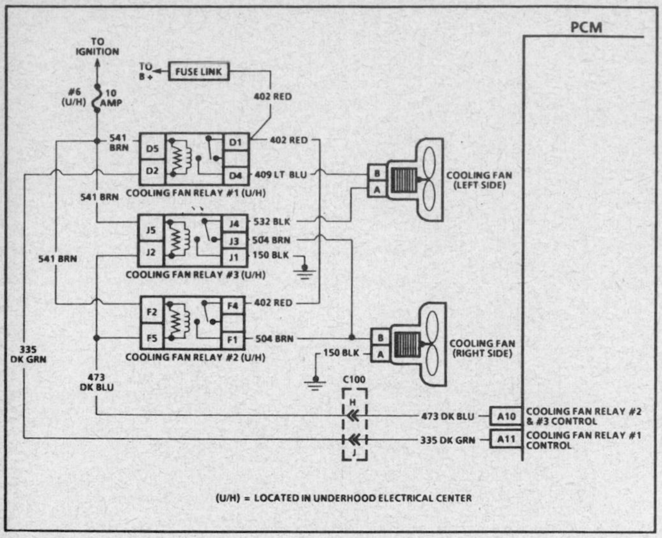
PCM
TO IGNITION
TO B+
FUSE LINK
#6 (U/H)
10 AMP
402 RED
541 BRN
D5
D1
D2
D4
402 RED
409 LT BLU
541 BRN
COOLING FAN RELAY #1 (U/H)
B
A
COOLING FAN (LEFT SIDE)
J5
J4
J3
J2
J1
532 BLK
504 BRN
150 BLK
541 BRN
COOLING FAN RELAY #3 (U/H)
F2
F4
F5
F1
402 RED
504 BRN
150 BLK
COOLING FAN (RIGHT SIDE)
335 DK GRN
COOLING FAN RELAY #2 (U/H)
473 DK BLU
C100
H
J
473 DK BLU
A10
COOLING FAN RELAY #2 & #3 CONTROL
335 DK GRN
A11
COOLING FAN RELAY #1 CONTROL
(U/H) = LOCATED IN UNDERHOOD ELECTRICAL CENTER

Circuit Description:

The cooling fans are controlled by the PCM based on various inputs. Ignition voltage is supplied to all three cooling fan relay coils on CKT 541. The PCM controls cooling fan relay #1 by providing the ground path through CKT 335. The PCM controls cooling fan relays #2 and #3 together by providing the ground path through CKT 473. When cooling fan relay #1 is energized the cooling fans are connected in series and operate together at low speed. When all three relays are energized the fans are connected in parallel and operate together at high speed. When certain DTCs are set, the PCM will enable cooling fans.

Chart Test Description: Number(s) below refer to circled number(s) on the diagnostic chart.

1. It may be necessary to raise the vehicle and observe the cooling fans from underneath during this test. Both fans should operate at low speed when "FAN CTRL PCM A11" is activated. Both fans should operate at high speed when "FAN CTRL PCM A10" is activated.

Diagnostic Aids: If the owner complained of an overheating problem, it must be determined if the complaint was due to an actual boil over, or the warning indicator light, or engine coolant temperature gage indicated overheating.

If the engine is overheating and the cooling fans are "ON," the cooling system should be checked

The PCM will command low speed fans "ON" at 108°C (226°F) and "OFF" at 105° C (221°F) and, high speed fans "ON" at 113°C (235°F) and "OFF" at 110°C (230°F).

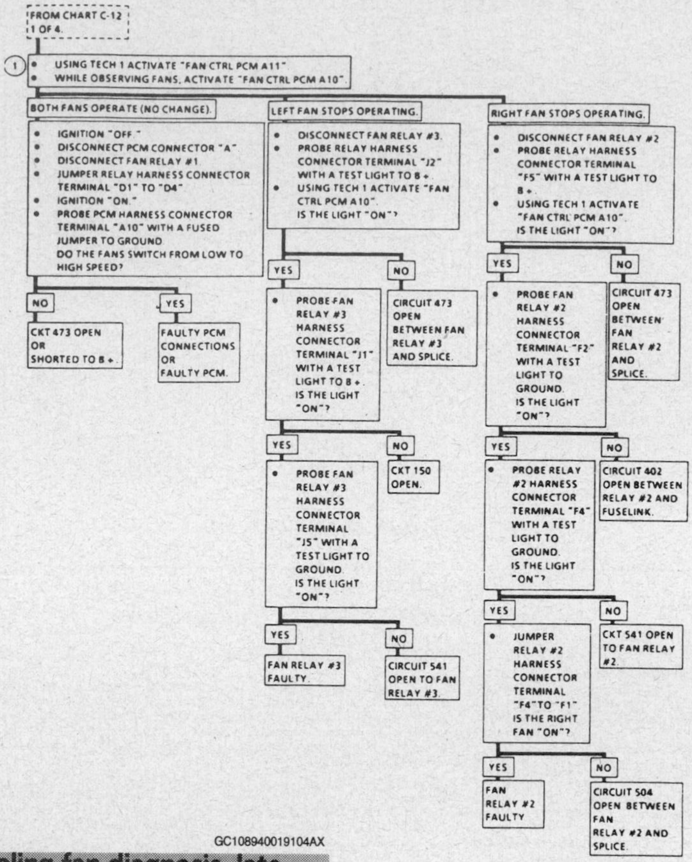
FROM CHART C-12
1 OF 4.
1
• USING TECH 1 ACTIVATE "FAN CTRL PCM A11"
• WHILE OBSERVING FANS, ACTIVATE "FAN CTRL PCM A10".
BOTH FANS OPERATE (NO CHANGE).
• IGNITION "OFF."
• DISCONNECT PCM CONNECTOR "A"
• DISCONNECT FAN RELAY #1
• JUMPER RELAY HARNESS CONNECTOR TERMINAL "D1" TO "D4"
• IGNITION "ON."
• PROBE PCM HARNESS CONNECTOR TERMINAL "A10" WITH A FUSED JUMPER TO GROUND.
DO THE FANS SWITCH FROM LOW TO HIGH SPEED?
NO
YES
CKT 473 OPEN OR SHORTED TO B+.
FAULTY PCM CONNECTIONS OR FAULTY PCM.
LEFT FAN STOPS OPERATING.
• DISCONNECT FAN RELAY #3.
• PROBE RELAY HARNESS CONNECTOR TERMINAL "J2" WITH A TEST LIGHT TO B+.
• USING TECH 1 ACTIVATE "FAN CTRL PCM A10". IS THE LIGHT "ON"?
YES
NO
• PROBE FAN RELAY #3 HARNESS CONNECTOR TERMINAL "J1" WITH A TEST LIGHT TO B+. IS THE LIGHT "ON"?
CIRCUIT 473 OPEN BETWEEN FAN RELAY #3 AND SPLICE.
YES
NO
• PROBE FAN RELAY #3 HARNESS CONNECTOR TERMINAL "J5" WITH A TEST LIGHT TO GROUND. IS THE LIGHT "ON"?
CKT 150 OPEN.
YES
NO
FAN RELAY #3 FAULTY.
CIRCUIT 541 OPEN TO FAN RELAY #3.
RIGHT FAN STOPS OPERATING.
• DISCONNECT FAN RELAY #2
• PROBE RELAY HARNESS CONNECTOR TERMINAL "F5" WITH A TEST LIGHT TO B+.
• USING TECH 1 ACTIVATE "FAN CTRL PCM A10". IS THE LIGHT "ON"?
YES
NO
• PROBE FAN RELAY #2 HARNESS CONNECTOR TERMINAL "F2" WITH A TEST LIGHT TO GROUND. IS THE LIGHT "ON"?
CIRCUIT 473 OPEN BETWEEN FAN RELAY #2 AND SPLICE.
YES
NO
• PROBE RELAY #2 HARNESS CONNECTOR TERMINAL "F4" WITH A TEST LIGHT TO GROUND. IS THE LIGHT "ON"?
CIRCUIT 402 OPEN BETWEEN RELAY #2 AND FUSELINK.
YES
NO
• JUMPER RELAY #2 HARNESS CONNECTOR TERMINAL "F4" TO "F1". IS THE RIGHT FAN "ON"?
CKT 541 OPEN TO FAN RELAY #2.
YES
NO
FAN RELAY #2 FAULTY.
CIRCUIT 504 OPEN BETWEEN FAN RELAY #2 AND SPLICE.
GC108940019104AX

Fig. 45 Chart C-12B, cooling fan diagnosis, late production A/C (Part 4 of 4). 1994 Camaro & Firebird w/5.7L/V8-350 (VIN P) engine

Run position. If cooling fan does not run at high speed, check dark green/white wire for an open If satisfactory, problem is PCM related. If cooling fan does run at high speed, proceed to step 3.

3. Reconnect A/C pressure fan switch connector and install pressure gauge set, then perform "System Check" while monitoring A/C head pressure.
4. If pressure does not rise above 210 psi, repair A/C system. If pressure does rise above 210 psi, replace A/C pressure fan switch.

1994

Refer to Fig. 47 when performing diagnostic procedures, Figs. 48 through 51.

CAVALIER

1992–93

Refer to **Figs. 52 through 53** for cooling fan circuit diagrams.

1994

To perform diagnosis and testing procedures on these systems, refer to wiring diagrams and diagnostic charts, Figs. 54 through 57.

CUTLASS SUPREME, GRAND PRIX & REGAL

1992 EXCEPT REGAL W/3.8L/V6–231 (VIN L) ENGINE

Refer to **Figs. 58 through 61** when performing diagnostic procedures.

Primary Cooling Fan Does Not Run

1. With ignition switch in Run position, ground terminal B (white/black) of ALDL connector. If primary cooling fan runs, problem is ECM related.
2. If primary cooling fan does not run, turn ignition switch to Run position and ground terminal A9 (dark green/white) at ECM with fused jumper. If primary cooling fan runs, problem is ECM related.
3. If primary cooling fan does not run, turn ignition switch to Run position, leave fused jumper connected as in step 2, disconnect primary cooling fan relay connector and measure voltage from terminal 3 (red) to ground. If no voltage is present, check for open in red wire.
4. If battery voltage is present, turn ignition switch to Run position, leave fused jumper connected as in step 2 and measure voltage between terminals 3 (red) and 1 (dark green/white). If no voltage is present, check dark green/white wire for an open.
5. If battery voltage is present, disconnect primary cooling fan relay connector and measure voltage from terminal 2 (red on VINs D & X, brown/white on all VIN T except early production Regal or pink/black on early production regal VIN T) to ground at RS electrical center. If no voltage is present, check brown/white, red or pink/black wire for open.
6. If battery voltage is present, disconnect primary cooling fan relay connector and connect a 20 amp fused jumper between terminals 3 (red) and 5 (black/red) at RS electrical center. If primary cooling fan runs, check for satisfactory contact between primary cooling fan relay and RS electrical center. If satisfactory, replace primary cooling fan relay.
7. If primary cooling fan does not run, leave fused jumper connected as in step 6, disconnect primary cooling fan connector and measure voltage from terminal B (black/red) to ground. If no voltage is present, check black/red wire for open.
8. If battery voltage is present, leave fused jumper in place as in step 6 and measure voltage between terminals B (black/red) and A (black).
9. If no voltage is present, check black wire for open.

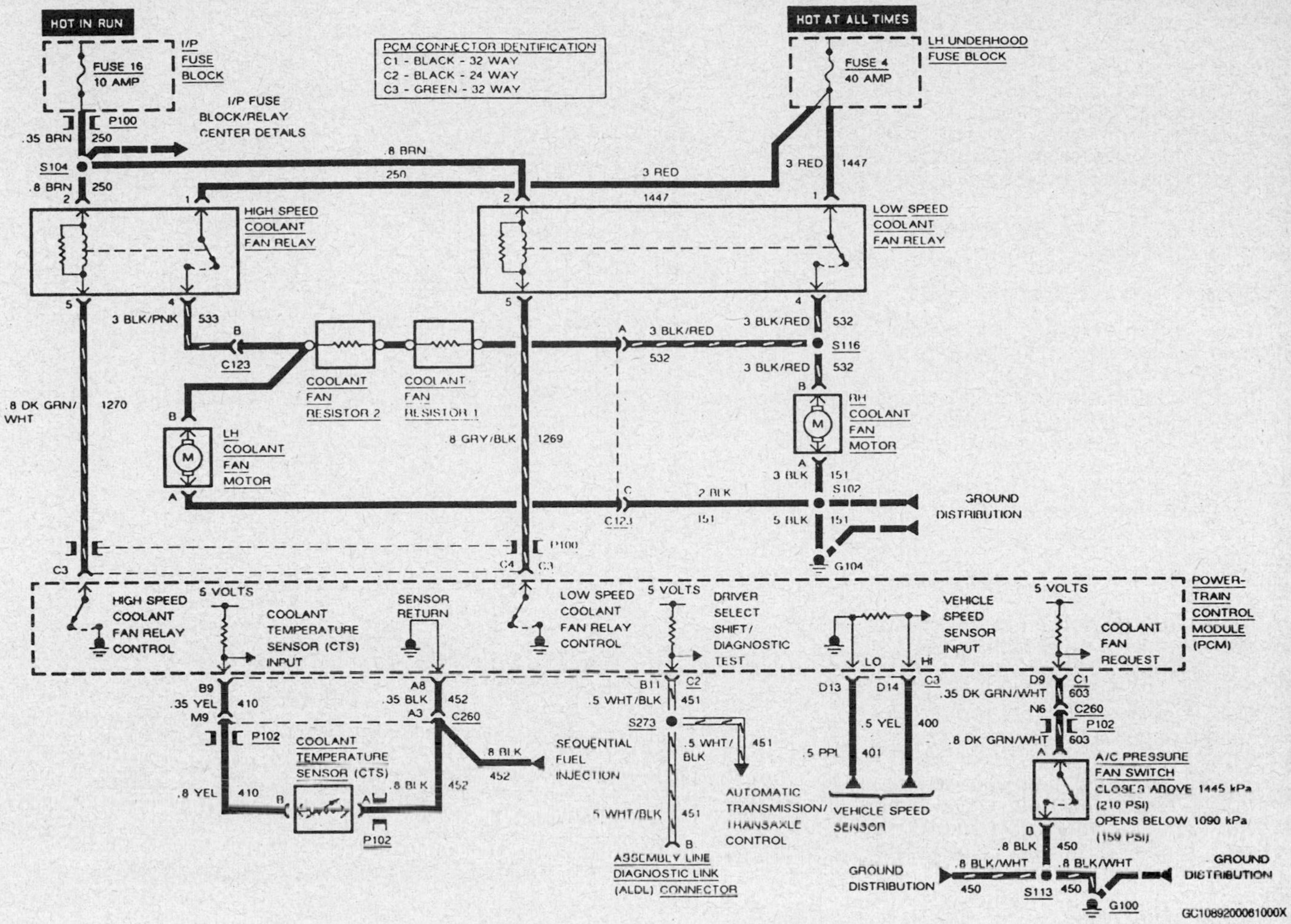

Fig. 46 Cooling fan wiring circuit. 1992–93 Bonneville

10. If battery voltage is present, check primary cooling fan connector terminals for cleanness and tightness and, if satisfactory, replace primary cooling fan.

Secondary Cooling Fan And/Or Generator Cooling Fan (VIN X) Does Not Run

1. With ignition switch in Run position, ground terminal A3 (dark blue/white) at ECM with fused jumper. If cooling fan runs, problem is ECM related.
2. If cooling fan does not run, leave fused jumper connected as in step 1, disconnect secondary cooling fan relay connector, turn ignition switch to Run position and measure voltage at RS electrical center terminal 2 (brown) or (pink/black early production Regal VIN T) to ground. If no voltage is present, check brown or pink/black wire for open.
3. If battery voltage is present, leave fused jumper connected as in step 1, turn ignition switch to Run position and measure voltage between terminals 2 (brown on all models except early production Regal VIN T or pink/black on early production Regal VIN T) and 1 (dark blue/white). If no voltage is present, check dark blue/white wire for open.
4. If battery voltage is present, measure voltage between terminal 3 (red) and ground. If no voltage is present, check red wire for open.
5. If battery voltage is present, disconnect secondary cooling fan relay connector and connect 20 amp fused jumper between terminals 3 (red) and 5 (black/red) at RS electrical center.
6. If secondary and/or generator cooling fan (VIN X) runs, check secondary cooling fan relay connector terminal contact at RS electrical center. If satisfactory, replace secondary cooling fan relay.
7. If secondary and/or generator cooling fan (VIN X) does not run, leave fused jumper connected as in step 5, then disconnect secondary and/or generator cooling fan connector (VIN X) and measure voltage between terminal B (except VIN X) or terminal A (VIN X) (black/red) and ground. If no voltage is present, check black/red wire for open.
8. If battery voltage is present, leave fused jumper connected as in step 5 and measure voltage between terminals B (black/red) and A (black) or terminals A (black/red) and B (black) (VIN X). If no voltage is present, check black wire for open.
9. If battery voltage is present, check suspect cooling fan connector and ensure terminals are clean and tight. If satisfactory, replace suspect cooling fan.

Primary Cooling Fan Runs Continuously With Engine Coolant Cool & A/C Mode Selector Off

1. Disconnect primary cooling fan relay at RS electrical center, turn ignition switch to Run position and connect test lamp between terminals 3 (red) and 1 (dark green/white).
2. If lamp does not illuminate, replace primary cooling fan relay.
3. If lamp illuminates, check dark green/white wire for short to ground. If wire is satisfactory, problem is ECM related.

Secondary Cooling Fan And/Or Generator Cooling Fan Runs Continuously With Engine Coolant Cool & A/C Mode Selector Off

1. Disconnect secondary cooling fan relay at RS electrical center, turn ignition

switch to Run position and connect test lamp between terminals 3 (red) and 1 (dark blue/white).
2. If lamp does not illuminate, replace secondary cooling fan relay.
3. If lamp illuminates, check dark blue/white wire for short to ground. If wire is satisfactory, problem is ECM related.

1992 REGAL W/3.8L/V6-231 (VIN L) ENGINE

Cooling Fan Isolation Test

1. Turn ignition switch to Run position, then connect a fused jumper wire between terminal B of ALDL connector and ground. If both cooling fans run at low speed for several seconds and then at high speed, problem is ECM related.
2. If both cooling fans do not run at low speed for several seconds and then at high speed, observe if both fans run at low speed.
3. If both fans run at low speed, proceed to step 7.
4. If both fans do not run at low speed, observe if they run at high speed.
5. If both fans run at high speed, refer to "Cooling Fans Run At High Speed Only." If both fans do not run at high speed, observe if either fan runs at high speed.
6. If secondary (righthand) does not run, refer to "Secondary Cooling Fan Does Not Run." If primary (lefthand) does not run, refer to "Primary Cooling Fan Does Not Run."
7. If both fans run at low speed, observe if they run at high speed.
8. If both fans run at high speed, system is operating normally.
9. If both fans do not run at high speed, observe if either fan runs at high speed.
10. If neither fan runs, refer to "No Cooling Fans Operate At High Speed." If secondary (righthand) does not run, refer to "Secondary Cooling Fan Does Not Run At High Speed." If primary (lefthand) does not run, refer to "Primary Cooling Fan Does Not Run At High Speed."

Cooling Fan Runs At High Speed Only

1. Disconnect fan relay No. 3, then connect a fused jumper wire at RS electrical center from terminal 3 to 4. Ground terminal A8 at ECM connector with a fused jumper, then observe if both cooling fans run at low speed.
2. If both cooling fans do not run at low speed, check black/red wire for open.
3. If both cooling fans run at low speed, replace fan relay No. 3.

Secondary Cooling Fan Does Not Run

1. Disconnect fan relay No. 1, then connect a fused jumper wire at RS electrical center from terminal 3 to 5. Observe if primary (lefthand) cooling fan runs.
2. If primary cooling fan runs, check black/red wires for short to ground.

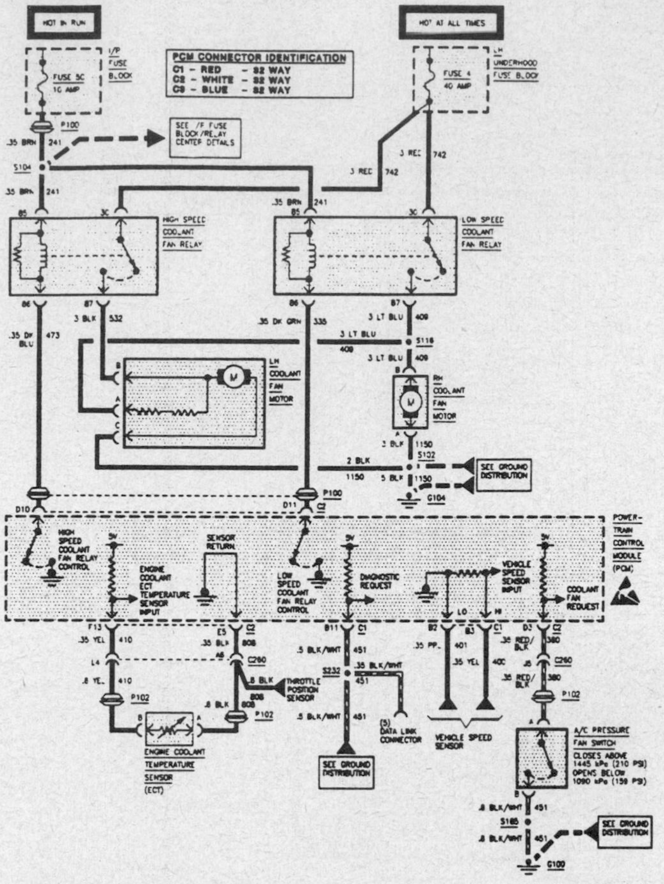

GC1089400195000X

Fig. 47 Cooling fan wiring circuit. 1994 Bonneville

3. If primary cooling fan does not run, leave jumper connected as in step 1 and disconnect fan relay No. 3. Connect a fused jumper from terminal 3 to terminal 4 and observe if secondary (righthand) cooling fan runs.
4. If secondary cooling fan runs, replace fan relay No. 3.
5. If secondary cooling fan does not run, leave jumper connected as in step 1 and disconnect secondary cooling fan connector. Connect test lamp from terminal B to ground. If lamp does not light, check black/red wire for open.
6. If lamp lights, leave jumper connected as in step 1 and connect test lamp between terminals B and A. If lamp does not light, check black wire for open.
7. If lamp lights, replace secondary cooling fan.

Primary Cooling Fan Does Not Run

1. Disconnect fan relay No. 1, then turn ignition switch to Run position and connect a test lamp at RS electrical center from terminal 2 to ground. If lamp does not light, check fan fuse and orange wire.
2. If lamp lights, set heater and A/C control selector to Norm position and connect test lamp from terminals 2 to 1 of fan relay No. 1. If lamp does not light, check dark green wire for open. If wire is satisfactory, problem Is ECM related.
3. If lamp lights, connect test lamp from terminal 3 of fan relay No. 1 to ground. If lamp does not light, check fusible link N and red wire for open.
4. If lamp lights, connect fused jumper between terminals 3 and 5 of fan relay No. 1 and observe if both cooling fans run.
5. If both cooling fans run, replace fan relay No. 1.
6. If both cooling fans do not run, leave jumper connected as in step 4 and disconnect primary cooling fan connector. Connect test lamp from terminal B to ground. If lamp does not light, check black/red wire for an open.
7. If lamp lights, leave jumper connected as in step 4 and connect test lamp between terminals B and A. If lamp lights, replace primary cooling fan.
8. If lamp does not light, reconnect primary cooling fan connector and disconnect fan relay No. 3. Leave jumper connected as in step 4 and connect fused jumper from terminal 3 of fan relay No. 3 to ground. If primary cooling fan runs at high speed, replace fan relay No. 3.
9. If primary cooling fan does not run at high speed, check black/pink wire for open.

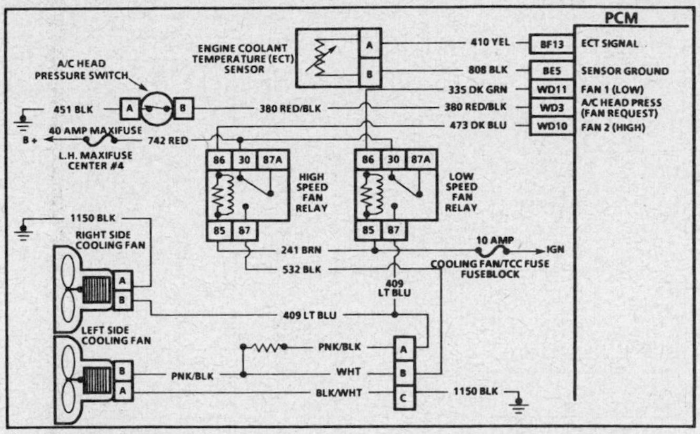
PCM
ENGINE COOLANT TEMPERATURE (ECT) SENSOR
A
B
410 YEL
BF13
ECT SIGNAL
808 BLK
BE5
SENSOR GROUND
335 DK GRN
WD11
FAN 1 (LOW)
380 RED/BLK
WD3
A/C HEAD PRESS (FAN REQUEST)
473 DK BLU
WD10
FAN 2 (HIGH)
A/C HEAD PRESSURE SWITCH
451 BLK
380 RED/BLK
40 AMP MAXIFUSE
B+
742 RED
L.H. MAXIFUSE CENTER #4
86
30
87A
85
87
HIGH SPEED FAN RELAY
LOW SPEED FAN RELAY
1150 BLK
RIGHT SIDE COOLING FAN
241 BRN
532 BLK
10 AMP
IGN
COOLING FAN/TCC FUSE FUSEBLOCK
409 LT BLU
LEFT SIDE COOLING FAN
PNK/BLK
WHT
BLK/WHT
C

Circuit Description:

Power for the fan motors comes from a 40A maxifuse element to terminal "87" on the relays. The relays are energized when current flows to ground through the PCM Quad-Driver #4. The left fan has two speeds and the right fan is a single speed fan.

Low Speed (Fan 1) Relay - The PCM energizes the relay through terminal "WD11" when engine coolant temperature reaches 100°C (212°F) or when A/C is requested.

High Speed (Fan 2) Relay - The high speed relay is energized by the PCM if the A/C head pressure switch opens, indicating refrigerant pressure above 210 psi (1448 kPa), or engine coolant temperature reaches 108°C (226°F).

Chart Test Description: Number(s) below refer to circled number(s) on the diagnostic chart.

1. Using the Tech 1 "Misc. Tests," Fan 1 control will cause the PCM to ground CKT 335 and the cooling fans should run at low speed.
2. Selecting Fan 2 with the Tech 1 allows control of CKT 473 and the high speed (Fan 2) relay.
3. Disconnecting the A/C head pressure switch harness connector will cause the PCM to energize the high speed (Fan 2) relay.

Diagnostic Aids: An intermittent may be caused by a poor connection, rubbed through wire insulation, or a wire broken inside the insulation.

Check for:

- Poor connection or damaged harness - Inspect PCM harness connectors for backed out terminals "WD10" or "WD11", improper mating, broken locks, improperly formed or damaged terminals, poor terminal to wire connection, and damaged harness.
- Intermittent test - If connections and harness check OK, a digital voltmeter connected from affected terminal to ground while moving related connectors and wiring harness. If the failure is induced, the voltage reading will change.
- Mis-Scaled Engine Coolant Temperature (ECT) sensor - See "Engine Coolant Temperature Sensor
- Basic cooling system problem for engine cooling and radiator diagnosis.

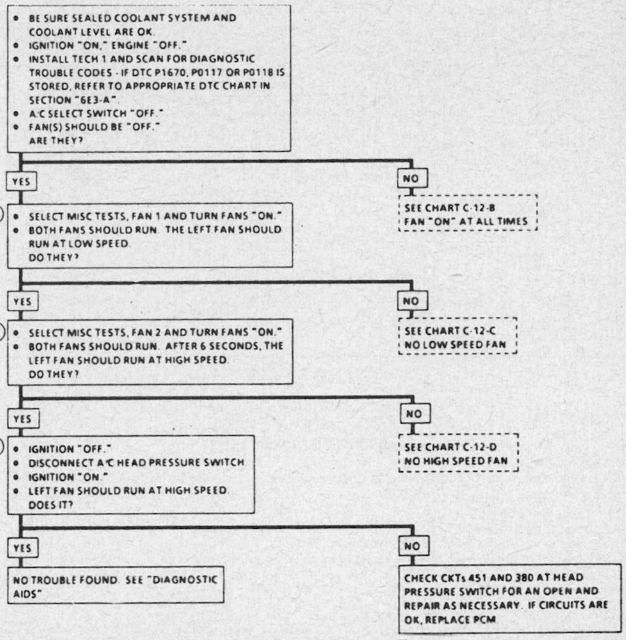
• BE SURE SEALED COOLANT SYSTEM AND COOLANT LEVEL ARE OK.
• IGNITION "ON," ENGINE "OFF."
• INSTALL TECH 1 AND SCAN FOR DIAGNOSTIC TROUBLE CODES - IF DTC P1670, P0117 OR P0118 IS STORED, REFER TO APPROPRIATE DTC CHART IN SECTION "6E3-A".
• A/C SELECT SWITCH "OFF."
• FAN(S) SHOULD BE "OFF."
ARE THEY?
YES
NO
SEE CHART C-12-B FAN "ON" AT ALL TIMES
1
• SELECT MISC TESTS, FAN 1 AND TURN FANS "ON."
• BOTH FANS SHOULD RUN. THE LEFT FAN SHOULD RUN AT LOW SPEED.
DO THEY?
YES
NO
SEE CHART C-12-C NO LOW SPEED FAN
2
• SELECT MISC TESTS, FAN 2 AND TURN FANS "ON."
• BOTH FANS SHOULD RUN. AFTER 6 SECONDS, THE LEFT FAN SHOULD RUN AT HIGH SPEED.
DO THEY?
YES
NO
SEE CHART C-12-D NO HIGH SPEED FAN
3
• IGNITION "OFF."
• DISCONNECT A/C HEAD PRESSURE SWITCH.
• IGNITION "ON."
• LEFT FAN SHOULD RUN AT HIGH SPEED.
DOES IT?
YES
NO
NO TROUBLE FOUND. SEE "DIAGNOSTIC AIDS"
CHECK CKTs 451 AND 380 AT HEAD PRESSURE SWITCH FOR AN OPEN AND REPAIR AS NECESSARY. IF CIRCUITS ARE OK, REPLACE PCM.

GC108940019600AX

Fig. 48 Chart C-12A, cooling fan diagnosis. 1994 Bonneville w/3.8L/V6-231 (VIN 1 & L) engine

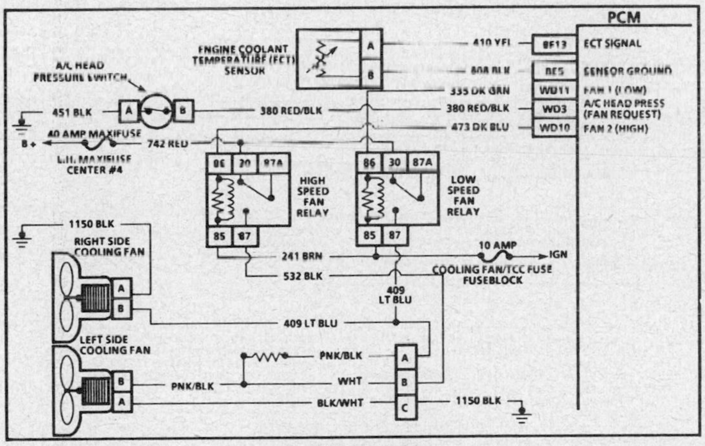
PCM
ENGINE COOLANT TEMPERATURE (ECT) SENSOR
A
B
410 YEL
BF13
ECT SIGNAL
808 BLK
BE5
SENSOR GROUND
335 DK GRN
WD11
FAN 1 (LOW)
380 RED/BLK
WD3
A/C HEAD PRESS (FAN REQUEST)
473 DK BLU
WD10
FAN 2 (HIGH)
A/C HEAD PRESSURE SWITCH
451 BLK
380 RED/BLK
40 AMP MAXIFUSE
B+
742 RED
L.H. MAXIFUSE CENTER #4
86
30
87A
85
87
HIGH SPEED FAN RELAY
LOW SPEED FAN RELAY
1150 BLK
RIGHT SIDE COOLING FAN
241 BRN
532 BLK
10 AMP
IGN
COOLING FAN/TCC FUSE FUSEBLOCK
409 LT BLU
LEFT SIDE COOLING FAN
PNK/BLK
WHT
BLK/WHT
C

CHART C-12B

FAN(S) "ON" AT ALL TIMES
COOLING FAN CHECK
3800 (VIN 1, L) (SFI)

Circuit Description:

Power for the fan motors comes from a 40A maxifuse element to terminal "87" on the relays. The relays are energized when current flows to ground through the PCM Quad-Driver #4. The left fan has two speeds and the right fan is a single speed fan.

Low Speed (Fan 1) Relay - The PCM energizes the relay through terminal "WD11" when engine coolant temperature reaches 100°C (212°F) or when A/C is requested.

High Speed (Fan 2) Relay - The high speed relay is energized by the PCM if the A/C head pressure switch opens, indicating refrigerant pressure above 210 psi (1448 kPa), or engine coolant temperature reaches 108°C (226°F).

Chart Test Description: Number(s) below refer to circled number(s) on the diagnostic chart.

1. Checks to see if CKT 335 is shorted to ground, which would keep the relay closed at all times.
2. Checks to see if CKT 473 is shorted to ground. A light indicates the wire is shorted to ground, the following steps will isolate the short.
3. If the test light is "OFF" after disconnecting the PCM, be sure CKT 335 is not shorted to B+. If not shorted to B+, the PCM is shorted internally.
4. If the test light is "OFF" after disconnecting the PCM, be sure CKT 473 is not shorted to B+. If not shorted to B+, the PCM is shorted internally.

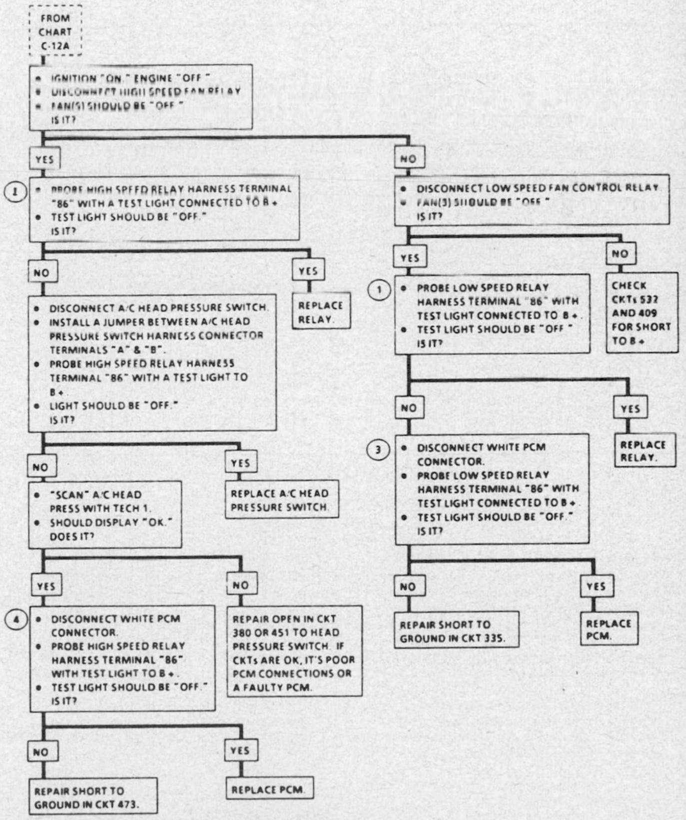
FROM CHART C-12A
• IGNITION "ON," ENGINE "OFF."
• DISCONNECT HIGH SPEED FAN RELAY
• FAN(S) SHOULD BE "OFF."
IS IT?
YES
NO
1
• PROBE HIGH SPEED RELAY HARNESS TERMINAL "86" WITH A TEST LIGHT CONNECTED TO B+
• TEST LIGHT SHOULD BE "OFF."
IS IT?
NO
YES
REPLACE RELAY.
• DISCONNECT A/C HEAD PRESSURE SWITCH.
• INSTALL A JUMPER BETWEEN A/C HEAD PRESSURE SWITCH HARNESS CONNECTOR TERMINALS "A" & "B".
• PROBE HIGH SPEED RELAY HARNESS TERMINAL "86" WITH A TEST LIGHT TO B+.
• LIGHT SHOULD BE "OFF."
IS IT?
NO
YES
• "SCAN" A/C HEAD PRESS WITH TECH 1.
• SHOULD DISPLAY "OK."
DOES IT?
REPLACE A/C HEAD PRESSURE SWITCH.
YES
NO
4
• DISCONNECT WHITE PCM CONNECTOR.
• PROBE HIGH SPEED RELAY HARNESS TERMINAL "86" WITH TEST LIGHT TO B+.
• TEST LIGHT SHOULD BE "OFF."
IS IT?
REPAIR OPEN IN CKT 380 OR 451 TO HEAD PRESSURE SWITCH. IF CKTs ARE OK, IT'S POOR PCM CONNECTIONS OR A FAULTY PCM.
NO
YES
REPAIR SHORT TO GROUND IN CKT 473.
REPLACE PCM.
• DISCONNECT LOW SPEED FAN CONTROL RELAY
• FAN(S) SHOULD BE "OFF."
IS IT?
YES
NO
1
• PROBE LOW SPEED RELAY HARNESS TERMINAL "86" WITH TEST LIGHT CONNECTED TO B+.
• TEST LIGHT SHOULD BE "OFF."
IS IT?
CHECK CKTs 532 AND 409 FOR SHORT TO B+
NO
YES
3
• DISCONNECT WHITE PCM CONNECTOR.
• PROBE LOW SPEED RELAY HARNESS TERMINAL "86" WITH TEST LIGHT CONNECTED TO B+.
• TEST LIGHT SHOULD BE "OFF."
IS IT?
REPLACE RELAY.
NO
YES
REPAIR SHORT TO GROUND IN CKT 335.
REPLACE PCM.

GC108940019700AX

Fig. 49 Chart C-12B, cooling fan diagnosis. 1994 Bonneville w/3.8L/V6-231 (VIN 1 & L) engine

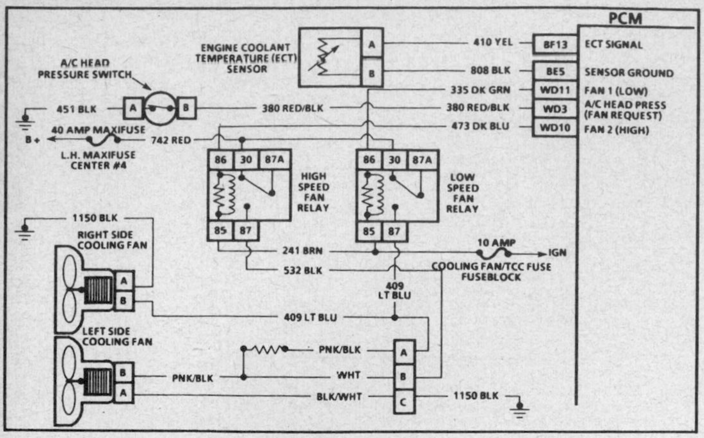
PCM
ENGINE COOLANT TEMPERATURE (ECT) SENSOR
A/C HEAD PRESSURE SWITCH
410 YEL
BF13
ECT SIGNAL
808 BLK
BE5
SENSOR GROUND
335 DK GRN
WD11
FAN 1 (LOW)
451 BLK
380 RED/BLK
WD3
A/C HEAD PRESS (FAN REQUEST)
40 AMP MAXIFUSE
473 DK BLU
WD10
FAN 2 (HIGH)
B+
742 RED
L.H. MAXIFUSE CENTER #4
86
30
87A
HIGH SPEED FAN RELAY
LOW SPEED FAN RELAY
85
87
1150 BLK
RIGHT SIDE COOLING FAN
241 BRN
10 AMP
IGN
532 BLK
COOLING FAN/TCC FUSE FUSEBLOCK
409 LT BLU
LEFT SIDE COOLING FAN
PNK/BLK
WHT
BLK/WHT

CHART C-12C

NO LOW SPEED FAN COOLING FAN CHECK 3800 (VIN 1, L) (SFI)

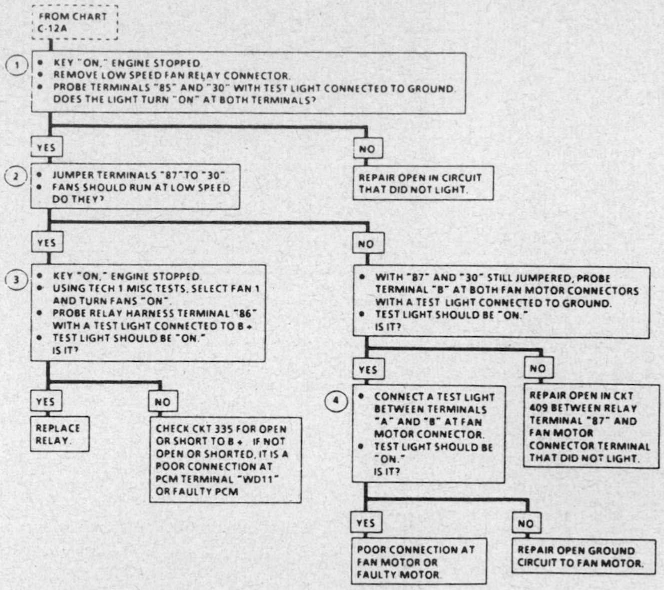
FROM CHART C-12A
1
• KEY "ON," ENGINE STOPPED.
• REMOVE LOW SPEED FAN RELAY CONNECTOR.
• PROBE TERMINALS "85" AND "30" WITH TEST LIGHT CONNECTED TO GROUND.
DOES THE LIGHT TURN "ON" AT BOTH TERMINALS?
YES
NO
REPAIR OPEN IN CIRCUIT THAT DID NOT LIGHT.
2
• JUMPER TERMINALS "87" TO "30".
• FANS SHOULD RUN AT LOW SPEED.
DO THEY?
YES
NO
3
• KEY "ON," ENGINE STOPPED.
• USING TECH 1 MISC TESTS, SELECT FAN 1 AND TURN FANS "ON".
• PROBE RELAY HARNESS TERMINAL "86" WITH A TEST LIGHT CONNECTED TO B+.
• TEST LIGHT SHOULD BE "ON."
IS IT?
• WITH "87" AND "30" STILL JUMPERED, PROBE TERMINAL "B" AT BOTH FAN MOTOR CONNECTORS WITH A TEST LIGHT CONNECTED TO GROUND.
• TEST LIGHT SHOULD BE "ON."
IS IT?
YES
NO
REPLACE RELAY.
CHECK CKT 335 FOR OPEN OR SHORT TO B+. IF NOT OPEN OR SHORTED, IT IS A POOR CONNECTION AT PCM TERMINAL "WD11" OR FAULTY PCM.
YES
NO
4
• CONNECT A TEST LIGHT BETWEEN TERMINALS "A" AND "B" AT FAN MOTOR CONNECTOR.
• TEST LIGHT SHOULD BE "ON."
IS IT?
REPAIR OPEN IN CKT 409 BETWEEN RELAY TERMINAL "87" AND FAN MOTOR CONNECTOR TERMINAL THAT DID NOT LIGHT.
YES
NO
POOR CONNECTION AT FAN MOTOR OR FAULTY MOTOR.
REPAIR OPEN GROUND CIRCUIT TO FAN MOTOR.

Circuit Description:

Power for the fan motors comes from a 40A maxifuse element to terminal "87" on the relays. The relays are energized when current flows to ground through the PCM Quad-Driver #4. The left fan has two speeds and the right fan is a single speed fan.

Low Speed (Fan 1) Relay - The PCM energizes the relay through terminal "WD11" when engine coolant temperature reaches 100°C (212°F) or when A/C is requested.

High Speed (Fan 2) Relay - The high speed relay is energized by the PCM if the A/C head pressure switch opens, indicating refrigerant pressure above 210 psi (1448 kPa), or engine coolant temperature reaches 108°C (226°F).

Chart Test Description: Number(s) below refer to circled number(s) on the diagnostic chart.

1. Checks for B+ at relay harness connector.
2. Jumpering terminals "87" to "30" bypasses the relay, which should cause the fans to run if fan motors and wiring are OK.
3. Selecting Fan 1 with Tech 1 misc. tests and turning fans "ON" should cause the PCM to ground CKT 335. At this point, the test light should light, if the PCM is functioning and CKT 335 isn't open.
4. This checks for B+ and ground to the fan motor. A test light "ON" at this point indicates a faulty fan motor connection or motor.

GC108940019800AX

Fig. 50 Chart C-12C, cooling fan diagnosis. 1994 Bonneville w/3.8L/V6-231 (VIN 1 & L) engine

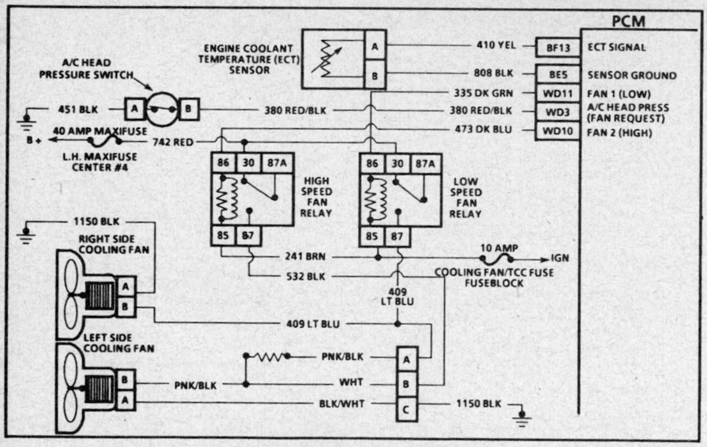
PCM
ENGINE COOLANT TEMPERATURE (ECT) SENSOR
A/C HEAD PRESSURE SWITCH
410 YEL
BF13
ECT SIGNAL
808 BLK
BE5
SENSOR GROUND
335 DK GRN
WD11
FAN 1 (LOW)
451 BLK
380 RED/BLK
WD3
A/C HEAD PRESS (FAN REQUEST)
40 AMP MAXIFUSE
473 DK BLU
WD10
FAN 2 (HIGH)
B+
742 RED
L.H. MAXIFUSE CENTER #4
86
30
87A
HIGH SPEED FAN RELAY
LOW SPEED FAN RELAY
85
87
1150 BLK
RIGHT SIDE COOLING FAN
241 BRN
10 AMP
IGN
532 BLK
COOLING FAN/TCC FUSE FUSEBLOCK
409 LT BLU
LEFT SIDE COOLING FAN
PNK/BLK
WHT
BLK/WHT

CHART C-12D

NO HIGH SPEED FAN COOLING FAN CHECK 3800 (VIN 1, L) (SFI)

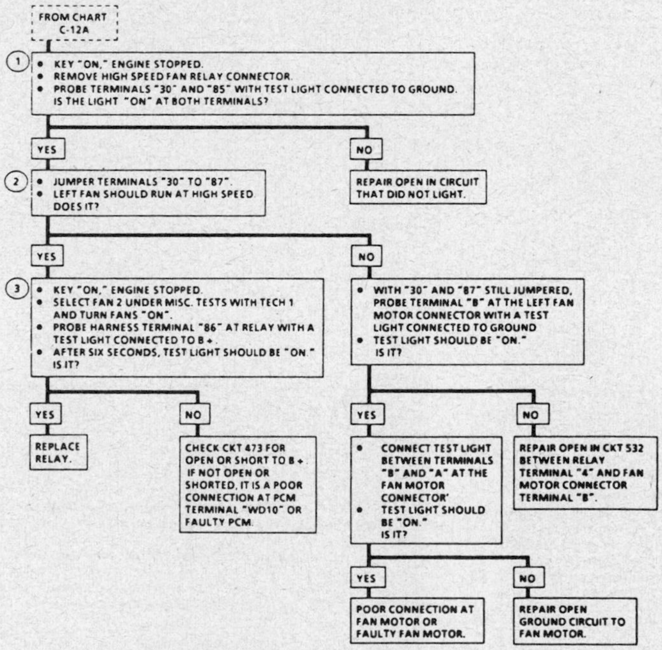
FROM CHART C-12A
1
• KEY "ON," ENGINE STOPPED.
• REMOVE HIGH SPEED FAN RELAY CONNECTOR.
• PROBE TERMINALS "30" AND "85" WITH TEST LIGHT CONNECTED TO GROUND.
IS THE LIGHT "ON" AT BOTH TERMINALS?
YES
NO
REPAIR OPEN IN CIRCUIT THAT DID NOT LIGHT.
2
• JUMPER TERMINALS "30" TO "87".
• LEFT FAN SHOULD RUN AT HIGH SPEED.
DOES IT?
YES
NO
3
• KEY "ON," ENGINE STOPPED.
• SELECT FAN 2 UNDER MISC. TESTS WITH TECH 1 AND TURN FANS "ON".
• PROBE HARNESS TERMINAL "86" AT RELAY WITH A TEST LIGHT CONNECTED TO B+.
• AFTER SIX SECONDS, TEST LIGHT SHOULD BE "ON."
IS IT?
• WITH "30" AND "87" STILL JUMPERED, PROBE TERMINAL "B" AT THE LEFT FAN MOTOR CONNECTOR WITH A TEST LIGHT CONNECTED TO GROUND.
• TEST LIGHT SHOULD BE "ON."
IS IT?
YES
NO
REPLACE RELAY.
CHECK CKT 473 FOR OPEN OR SHORT TO B+. IF NOT OPEN OR SHORTED, IT IS A POOR CONNECTION AT PCM TERMINAL "WD10" OR FAULTY PCM.
YES
NO
• CONNECT TEST LIGHT BETWEEN TERMINALS "B" AND "A" AT THE FAN MOTOR CONNECTOR.
• TEST LIGHT SHOULD BE "ON."
IS IT?
REPAIR OPEN IN CKT 532 BETWEEN RELAY TERMINAL "4" AND FAN MOTOR CONNECTOR TERMINAL "B".
YES
NO
POOR CONNECTION AT FAN MOTOR OR FAULTY FAN MOTOR.
REPAIR OPEN GROUND CIRCUIT TO FAN MOTOR.

Circuit Description:

Power for the fan motor comes from a 40A maxifuse element to terminal "87" on the relays. The relays are energized when current flows to ground through the PCM Quad-Driver #4. The left fan has two speeds and the right fan is a single speed fan.

Low Speed (Fan 1) Relay - The PCM energizes the relay through terminal "WD11" when engine coolant temperature reaches 100°C (212°F) or when A/C is requested.

High Speed (Fan 2) Relay - The high speed relay is energized by the PCM if the A/C head pressure switch opens, indicating refrigerant above 210 psi (1448 kPa), or engine coolant temperature reaches 108°C (226°F).

Chart Test Description: Number(s) below refer to circled number(s) on the diagnostic chart.

1. Test light should be "ON" because harness terminal "85" has B+ with ignition switch turned "ON."
2. Jumpering harness terminals "30" and "87" bypasses the relay. If fan runs, the relay is faulty.
3. Checks CKT 473 back to the PCM. If CKT 473 is OK, it's a bad relay.

GC108940019900AX

Fig. 51 Chart C-12D, cooling fan diagnosis. 1994 Bonneville w/3.8L/V6-231 (VIN 1 & L) engine

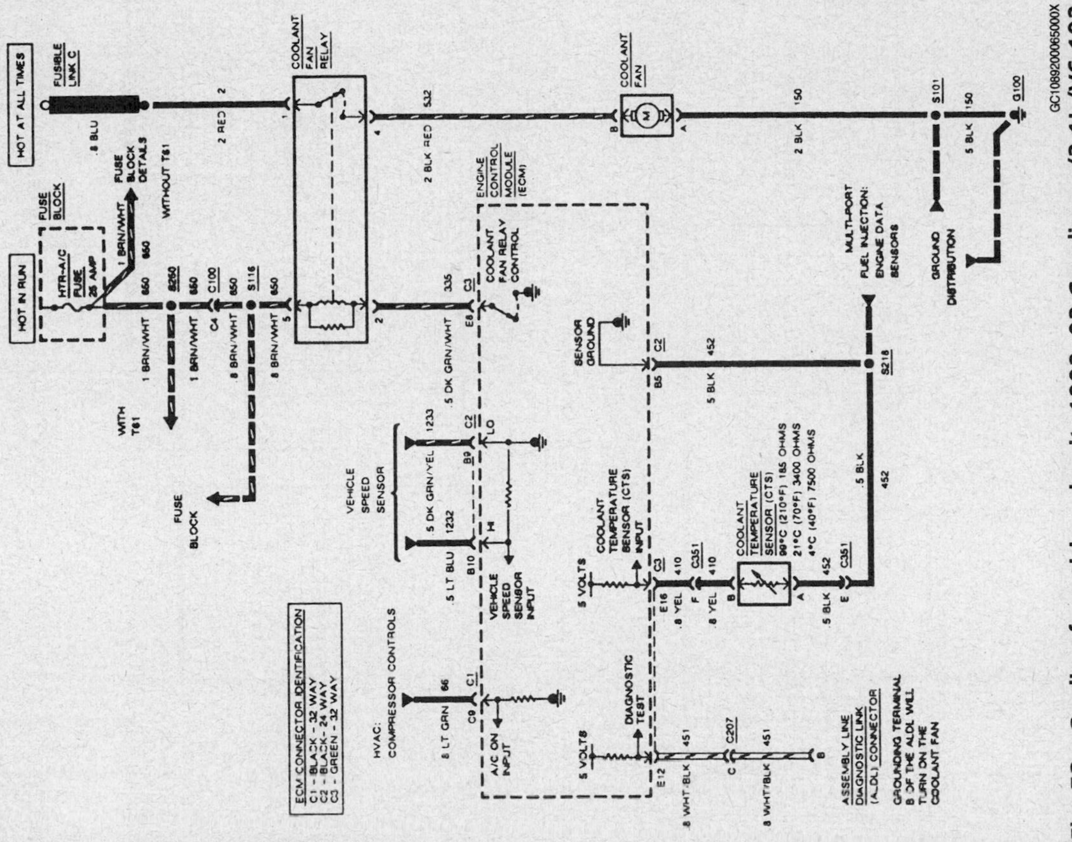
HOT AT ALL TIMES
FUSIBLE LINK C
HOT IN RUN
FUSE BLOCK
HTR-A/C FUSE 25 AMP
FUSE BLOCK DETAILS
WITHOUT T61
WITH T61
FUSE BLOCK
COOLANT FAN RELAY
COOLANT FAN
ENGINE CONTROL MODULE (ECM)
COOLANT FAN RELAY CONTROL
VEHICLE SPEED SENSOR
VEHICLE SPEED SENSOR INPUT
SENSOR GROUND
COOLANT TEMPERATURE SENSOR (CTS) INPUT
COOLANT TEMPERATURE SENSOR (CTS)
99°C (210°F) 185 OHMS
21°C (70°F) 3400 OHMS
4°C (40°F) 7500 OHMS
ECM CONNECTOR IDENTIFICATION
C1 - BLACK - 32 WAY
C2 - BLACK - 24 WAY
C3 - GREEN - 32 WAY
HVAC: COMPRESSOR CONTROLS
A/C ON INPUT
5 VOLTS
DIAGNOSTIC TEST
ASSEMBLY LINE DIAGNOSTIC LINK (ALDL) CONNECTOR
GROUNDING TERMINAL B OF THE ALDL WILL TURN ON THE COOLANT FAN
MULTI-PORT FUEL INJECTION: ENGINE DATA SENSORS
GROUND DISTRIBUTION
GC1089200065000X

Fig. 53 Cooling fan wiring circuit. 1992–93 Cavalier w/3.1L/V6-192 engine

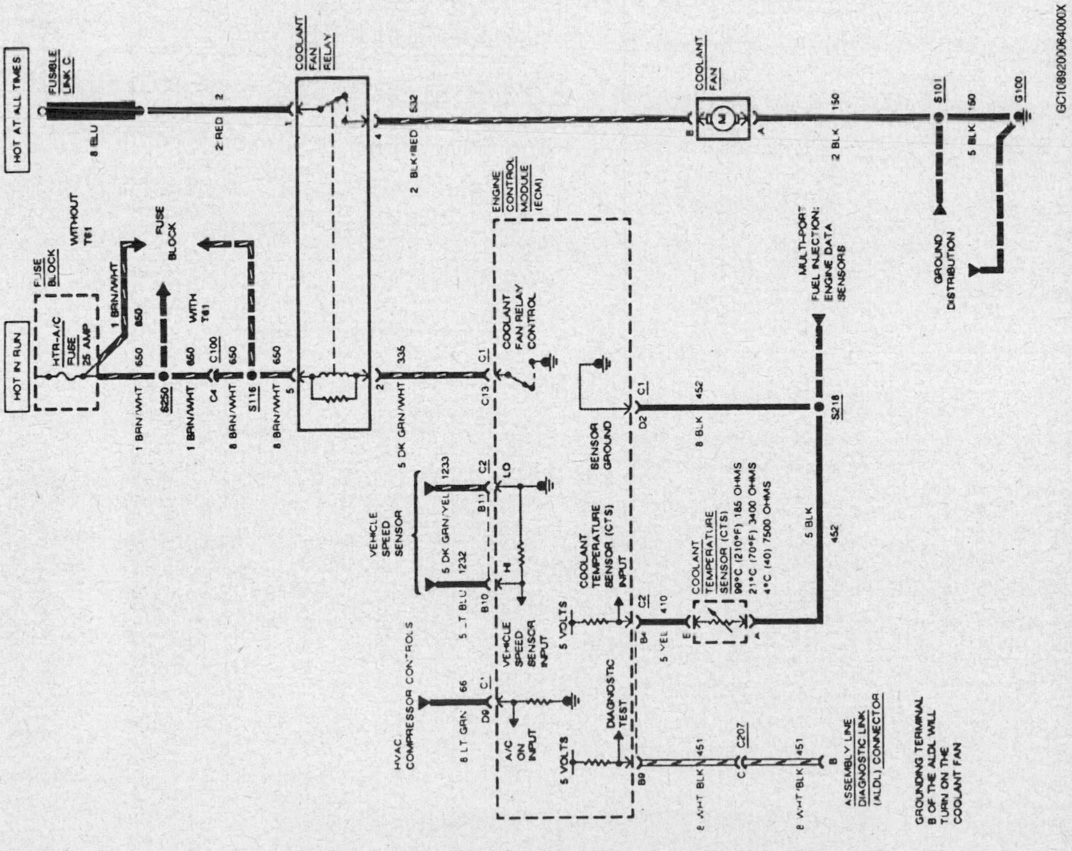
HOT AT ALL TIMES
FUSIBLE LINK C
HOT IN RUN
FUSE BLOCK
HTR-A/C FUSE 25 AMP
WITHOUT T61
WITH T61
FUSE BLOCK
COOLANT FAN RELAY
COOLANT FAN
ENGINE CONTROL MODULE (ECM)
COOLANT FAN RELAY CONTROL
VEHICLE SPEED SENSOR
VEHICLE SPEED SENSOR INPUT
SENSOR GROUND
COOLANT TEMPERATURE SENSOR (CTS) INPUT
COOLANT TEMPERATURE SENSOR (CTS)
99°C (210°F) 185 OHMS
21°C (70°F) 3400 OHMS
4°C (40) 7500 OHMS
HVAC COMPRESSOR CONTROLS
A/C ON INPUT
5 VOLTS
DIAGNOSTIC TEST
ASSEMBLY LINE DIAGNOSTIC LINK (ALDL) CONNECTOR
GROUNDING TERMINAL B OF THE ALDL WILL TURN ON THE COOLANT FAN
MULTI-PORT FUEL INJECTION: ENGINE DATA SENSORS
GROUND DISTRIBUTION
GC1089200064000X

Fig. 52 Cooling fan wiring circuit. 1992–93 Cavalier w/2.2L/4-134 engine

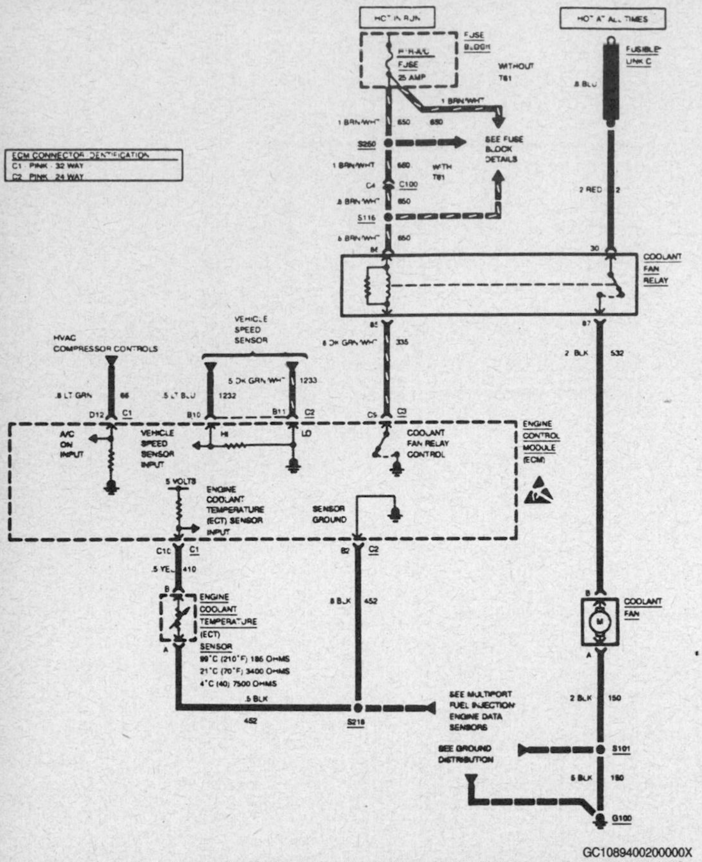
HOT IN RUN
HOT AT ALL TIMES
FUSIBLE LINK C
COOLANT FAN RELAY
ENGINE CONTROL MODULE (ECM)
COOLANT FAN
G100

GC1089400200000X

Fig. 54 Cooling fan wiring circuit. 1994 Cavalier w/2.2L/4-134 engine

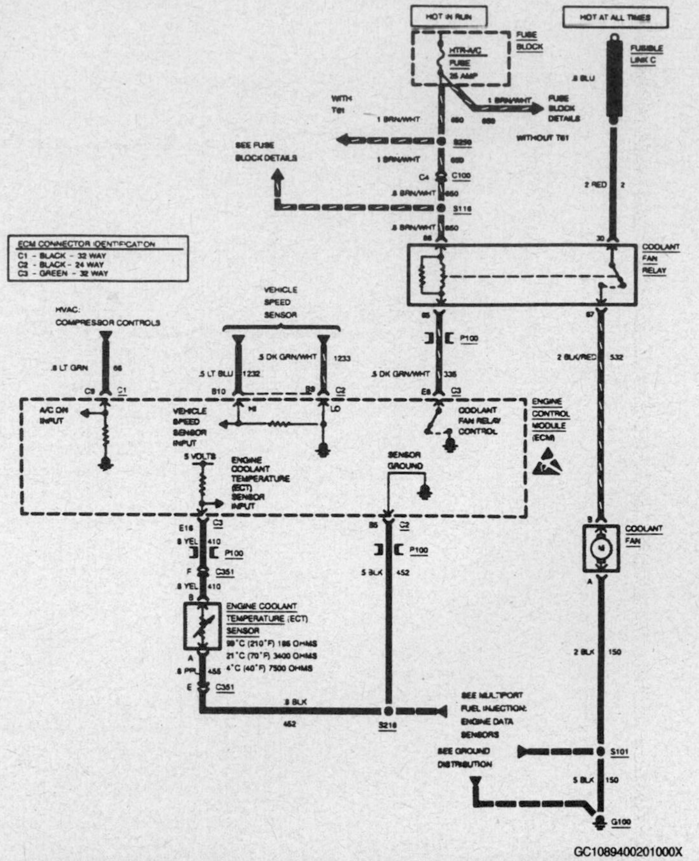
HOT IN RUN
HOT AT ALL TIMES
FUSIBLE LINK C
COOLANT FAN RELAY
ENGINE CONTROL MODULE (ECM)
COOLANT FAN
G100

GC1089400201000X

Fig. 55 Cooling fan wiring circuit. 1994 Cavalier w/3.1L/V6-192 engine

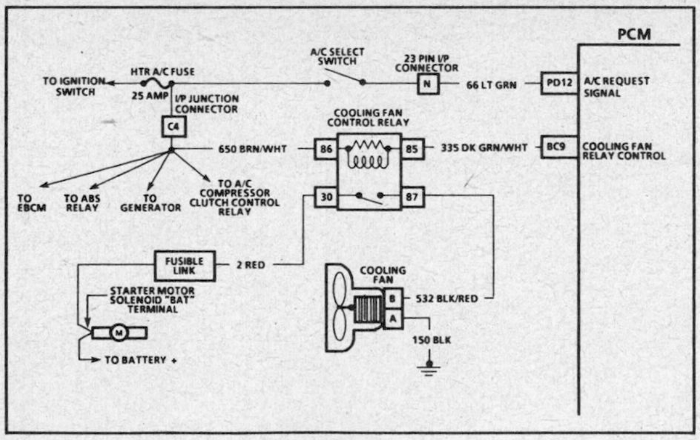
PCM
TO IGNITION SWITCH
HTR A/C FUSE
25 AMP
I/P JUNCTION CONNECTOR
C4
A/C SELECT SWITCH
23 PIN I/P CONNECTOR
N
66 LT GRN
PD12
A/C REQUEST SIGNAL
COOLING FAN CONTROL RELAY
650 BRN/WHT
86
85
335 DK GRN/WHT
BC9
COOLING FAN RELAY CONTROL
30
87
TO EBCM
TO ABS RELAY
TO GENERATOR
TO A/C COMPRESSOR CLUTCH CONTROL RELAY
FUSIBLE LINK
2 RED
STARTER MOTOR SOLENOID "BAT" TERMINAL
TO BATTERY +
COOLING FAN
532 BLK/RED
150 BLK

CHART C-12

COOLING FAN FUNCTIONAL CHECK 2.2L (VIN 4) "J" CARLINE

Circuit Description:

The electric cooling fan is controlled by the Powertrain Control Module (PCM) through the fan relay based on inputs from the engine coolant and intake air temperature sensors, the A/C control switch, A/C refrigerant pressure sensor and the vehicle speed sensor. The PCM controls the cooling fan by grounding CKT 335 which turns the fan relay "ON."

The fan relay will be commanded "ON" when:

- Engine coolant temperature is greater than 106°C.
- A/C clutch requested.
- Vehicle speed is less than 35 mph.
- A DTC is set.

Once the fan is enabled, the PCM will turn the fan "OFF" when:

- Engine coolant temperature drops below 120°C
- A/C refrigerant pressure is high.

The cooling fan may be commanded "ON" when the engine is not running under fan "Run-ON" conditions described previously in this section.

Chart Test Description: Number(s) below refer to circled number(s) on the diagnostic chart.

1. With the field service mode activated, the coolant fan control driver should close, which should energize the fan relay control.
2. Test to see if fault is in the wiring to the fan or the fan relay connection.

Diagnostic Aids: If the owner complained of an overheating problem, it must be determined if the complaint was due to an actual boil over, or the "temp light," or temperature gage indicated overheating.

If the gage, or light, indicates overheating, but no boil over is detected, the gage or light circuit should be checked. The gage accuracy can also be checked by comparing the coolant sensor reading using a scan tool with the gage reading.

If the engine is actually overheating, and the gage indicates overheating, but the coolant fan is not coming "ON," the Engine Coolant Temperature (ECT) sensor has probably shifted out of calibration and should be replaced. See DTC 15 chart for a temperature to resistance chart.

If the engine is overheating, and the coolant fan is "ON," the cooling system should be checked.

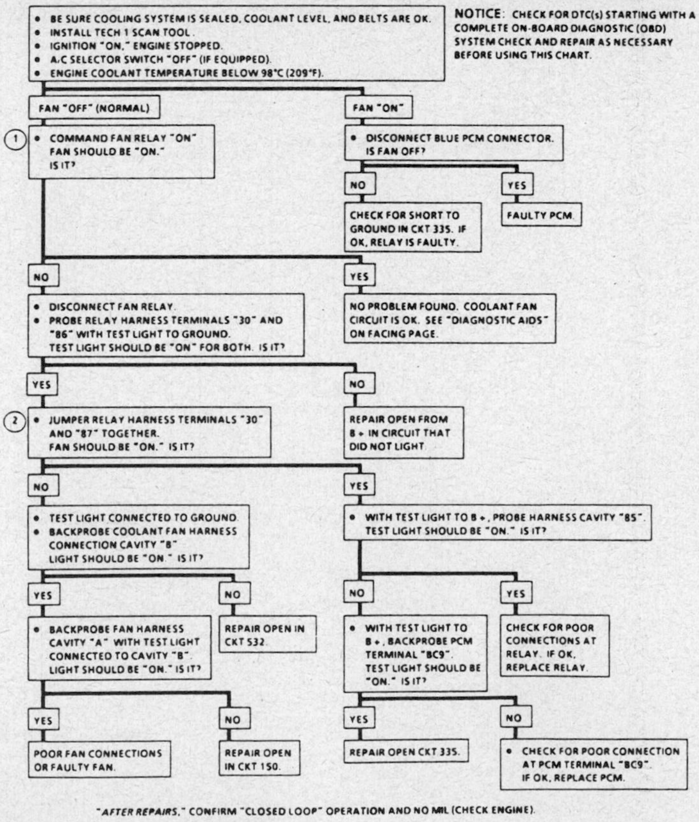
• BE SURE COOLING SYSTEM IS SEALED, COOLANT LEVEL, AND BELTS ARE OK.
• INSTALL TECH 1 SCAN TOOL.
• IGNITION "ON," ENGINE STOPPED.
• A/C SELECTOR SWITCH "OFF" (IF EQUIPPED).
• ENGINE COOLANT TEMPERATURE BELOW 98°C (209°F).
NOTICE: CHECK FOR DTC(s) STARTING WITH A COMPLETE ON-BOARD DIAGNOSTIC (OBD) SYSTEM CHECK AND REPAIR AS NECESSARY BEFORE USING THIS CHART.
FAN "OFF" (NORMAL)
FAN "ON"
1
• COMMAND FAN RELAY "ON" FAN SHOULD BE "ON." IS IT?
• DISCONNECT BLUE PCM CONNECTOR. IS FAN OFF?
NO
YES
CHECK FOR SHORT TO GROUND IN CKT 335. IF OK, RELAY IS FAULTY.
FAULTY PCM.
NO
YES
• DISCONNECT FAN RELAY.
• PROBE RELAY HARNESS TERMINALS "30" AND "86" WITH TEST LIGHT TO GROUND. TEST LIGHT SHOULD BE "ON" FOR BOTH. IS IT?
NO PROBLEM FOUND. COOLANT FAN CIRCUIT IS OK. SEE "DIAGNOSTIC AIDS" ON FACING PAGE.
YES
NO
2
• JUMPER RELAY HARNESS TERMINALS "30" AND "87" TOGETHER. FAN SHOULD BE "ON." IS IT?
REPAIR OPEN FROM B+ IN CIRCUIT THAT DID NOT LIGHT.
NO
YES
• TEST LIGHT CONNECTED TO GROUND.
• BACKPROBE COOLANT FAN HARNESS CONNECTION CAVITY "B". LIGHT SHOULD BE "ON." IS IT?
• WITH TEST LIGHT TO B+, PROBE HARNESS CAVITY "85". TEST LIGHT SHOULD BE "ON." IS IT?
YES
NO
NO
YES
• BACKPROBE FAN HARNESS CAVITY "A" WITH TEST LIGHT CONNECTED TO CAVITY "B". LIGHT SHOULD BE "ON." IS IT?
REPAIR OPEN IN CKT 532.
• WITH TEST LIGHT TO B+, BACKPROBE PCM TERMINAL "BC9". TEST LIGHT SHOULD BE "ON." IS IT?
CHECK FOR POOR CONNECTIONS AT RELAY. IF OK, REPLACE RELAY.
YES
NO
YES
NO
POOR FAN CONNECTIONS OR FAULTY FAN.
REPAIR OPEN IN CKT 150.
REPAIR OPEN CKT 335.
• CHECK FOR POOR CONNECTION AT PCM TERMINAL "BC9". IF OK, REPLACE PCM.
"AFTER REPAIRS," CONFIRM "CLOSED LOOP" OPERATION AND NO MIL (CHECK ENGINE).

GC108940020200AX

Fig. 56 Chart C-12 cooling fan diagnosis. 1994 Cavalier w/2.2L/4-134 engine

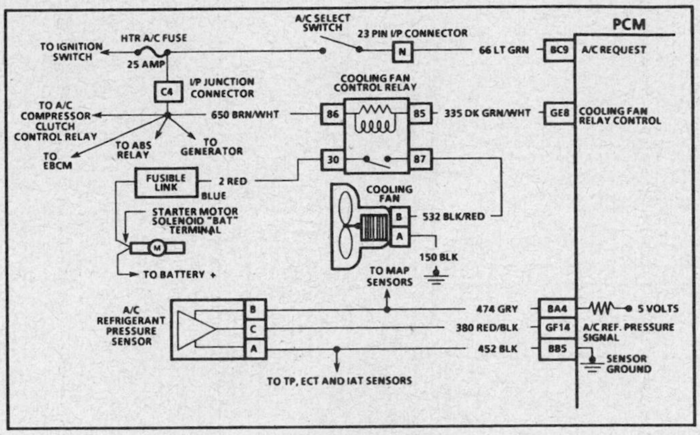

A/C SELECT SWITCH
23 PIN I/P CONNECTOR
PCM
TO IGNITION SWITCH
HTR A/C FUSE
25 AMP
N
66 LT GRN
BC9
A/C REQUEST
C4
I/P JUNCTION CONNECTOR
COOLING FAN CONTROL RELAY
TO A/C COMPRESSOR CLUTCH CONTROL RELAY
650 BRN/WHT
86
85
335 DK GRN/WHT
GE8
COOLING FAN RELAY CONTROL
TO ABS RELAY
TO GENERATOR
TO EBCM
30
87
FUSIBLE LINK
2 RED
BLUE
STARTER MOTOR SOLENOID "BAT" TERMINAL
COOLING FAN
B
532 BLK/RED
A
TO BATTERY +
150 BLK
TO MAP SENSORS
A/C REFRIGERANT PRESSURE SENSOR
B
C
A
474 GRY
BA4
5 VOLTS
380 RED/BLK
GF14
A/C REF. PRESSURE SIGNAL
452 BLK
BB5
SENSOR GROUND
TO TP, ECT AND IAT SENSORS

CHART C-12

(Page 1 of 2)
COOLING FAN CONTROL DIAGNOSIS
3.1L (VIN T) "J" CARLINE (MFI)

Circuit Description:

The electric cooling fan is controlled by the PCM based on inputs from the engine coolant temperature sensor, the A/C pressure sensor and vehicle speed. The PCM controls the fan by grounding CKT 335, which energizes the fan control relay. Battery voltage is then supplied to the fan motor.

The PCM grounds CKT 335 when engine coolant temperature is over about 109°C (228°F) or when A/C has been requested and the A/C pressure sensor indicates high A/C pressure, 200 psi (1380 kPa). Once the PCM turns the relay "ON," it will keep it "ON" for a minimum of 25 seconds or until vehicle speed exceeds 70 mph.

Also, if DTC 14 or 15 sets or the PCM is in backup, the fan will run at all times.

Chart Test Description: Number(s) below refer to circled number(s) on the diagnostic chart.

1. With the diagnostic terminal grounded, the cooling fan control driver will close, which should energize the fan control relay.
2. If the A/C fan control switch or circuit is open, the fan would run whenever A/C is requested.
3. With A/C clutch engaged, the A/C fan control switch should open when A/C high pressure exceeds about 200 psi (1380 kPa). This signal should cause the PCM to energize the fan control relay.
4. Disconnecting the A/C pressure sensor will cause a DTC 66 to set. After finishing this step, be sure to clear DTC(s).

Diagnostic Aids: If the owner complained of an overheating problem, it must be determined if the complaint was due to an actual boilover or the hot light (temperature gage) indicated over heating.

If the gage (light) indicates overheating but no boilover is detected, the gage circuit should be checked. The gage accuracy can also be checked by comparing the coolant sensor reading using a Tech 1 scan tool and comparing its reading with the gage reading.

If the engine is actually overheating and the gage indicates overheating but the cooling fan is not coming "ON," the ECT sensor has probably shifted out of calibration and should be replaced.

If the engine is overheating and the cooling fan is "ON," the cooling system should be checked.

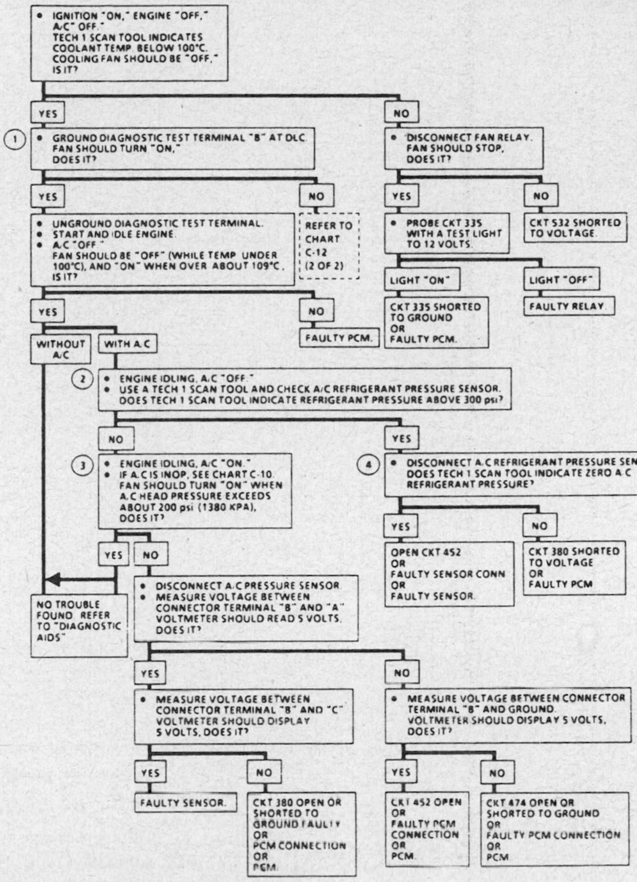

• IGNITION "ON," ENGINE "OFF," A/C" OFF." TECH 1 SCAN TOOL INDICATES COOLANT TEMP. BELOW 100°C. COOLING FAN SHOULD BE "OFF," IS IT?
YES
NO
1
• GROUND DIAGNOSTIC TEST TERMINAL "B" AT DLC. FAN SHOULD TURN "ON," DOES IT?
• DISCONNECT FAN RELAY. FAN SHOULD STOP, DOES IT?
YES
NO
YES
NO
• UNGROUND DIAGNOSTIC TEST TERMINAL. • START AND IDLE ENGINE. • A/C "OFF." FAN SHOULD BE "OFF" (WHILE TEMP. UNDER 100°C), AND "ON" WHEN OVER ABOUT 109°C. IS IT?
REFER TO CHART C-12 (2 OF 2)
• PROBE CKT 335 WITH A TEST LIGHT TO 12 VOLTS.
CKT 532 SHORTED TO VOLTAGE.
LIGHT "ON"
LIGHT "OFF"
YES
NO
CKT 335 SHORTED TO GROUND OR FAULTY PCM.
FAULTY RELAY.
WITHOUT A/C
WITH A/C
FAULTY PCM.
2
• ENGINE IDLING, A/C "OFF." • USE A TECH 1 SCAN TOOL AND CHECK A/C REFRIGERANT PRESSURE SENSOR. DOES TECH 1 SCAN TOOL INDICATE REFRIGERANT PRESSURE ABOVE 300 psi?
NO
YES
3
• ENGINE IDLING, A/C "ON." • IF A/C IS INOP, SEE CHART C-10. FAN SHOULD TURN "ON" WHEN A/C HEAD PRESSURE EXCEEDS ABOUT 200 psi (1380 KPA), DOES IT?
4
• DISCONNECT A/C REFRIGERANT PRESSURE SENSOR. DOES TECH 1 SCAN TOOL INDICATE ZERO A/C REFRIGERANT PRESSURE?
YES
NO
YES
NO
OPEN CKT 452 OR FAULTY SENSOR CONN OR FAULTY SENSOR.
CKT 380 SHORTED TO VOLTAGE OR FAULTY PCM
NO TROUBLE FOUND. REFER TO "DIAGNOSTIC AIDS"
• DISCONNECT A/C PRESSURE SENSOR. • MEASURE VOLTAGE BETWEEN CONNECTOR TERMINAL "B" AND "A" VOLTMETER SHOULD READ 5 VOLTS. DOES IT?
YES
NO
• MEASURE VOLTAGE BETWEEN CONNECTOR TERMINAL "B" AND "C" VOLTMETER SHOULD DISPLAY 5 VOLTS, DOES IT?
• MEASURE VOLTAGE BETWEEN CONNECTOR TERMINAL "B" AND GROUND. VOLTMETER SHOULD DISPLAY 5 VOLTS, DOES IT?
YES
NO
YES
NO
FAULTY SENSOR.
CKT 380 OPEN OR SHORTED TO GROUND FAULTY OR PCM CONNECTION OR PCM.
CKT 452 OPEN OR FAULTY PCM CONNECTION OR PCM.
CKT 474 OPEN OR SHORTED TO GROUND OR FAULTY PCM CONNECTION OR PCM

GC108940020301AX

Fig. 57 Chart C-12 cooling fan diagnosis (Part 1 of 2). 1994 Cavalier w/3.1L/V6– 192 engine

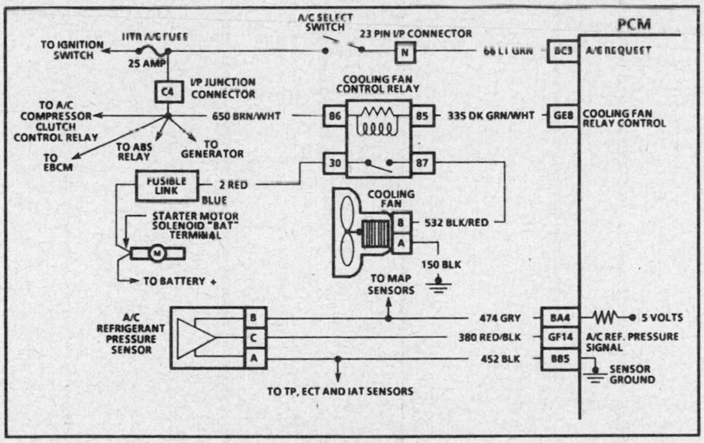

A/C SELECT SWITCH
23 PIN I/P CONNECTOR
PCM
TO IGNITION SWITCH
HTR A/C FUSE
25 AMP
N
66 LT GRN
BC9
A/C REQUEST
C4
I/P JUNCTION CONNECTOR
COOLING FAN CONTROL RELAY
TO A/C COMPRESSOR CLUTCH CONTROL RELAY
650 BRN/WHT
86
85
335 DK GRN/WHT
GE8
COOLING FAN RELAY CONTROL
TO ABS RELAY
TO GENERATOR
TO EBCM
30
87
FUSIBLE LINK
2 RED
BLUE
STARTER MOTOR SOLENOID "BAT" TERMINAL
COOLING FAN
B
532 BLK/RED
A
TO BATTERY +
150 BLK
TO MAP SENSORS
A/C REFRIGERANT PRESSURE SENSOR
B
C
A
474 GRY
BA4
5 VOLTS
380 RED/BLK
GF14
A/C REF. PRESSURE SIGNAL
452 BLK
BB5
SENSOR GROUND
TO TP, ECT AND IAT SENSORS

CHART C-12

(Page 2 of 2)
COOLING FAN CONTROL DIAGNOSIS
3.1L (VIN T) "J" CARLINE (MFI)

Chart Test Description: Number(s) below refer to circled number(s) on the diagnostic chart.

1. 12 volts should be available to both terminals "30" (CKT 2) and "87" (CKT 532) when the ignition is "ON."
2. This test checks the ability of the PCM to ground CKT 335.

The Malfunction Indicator Lamp (MIL) should also be flashing at this point. If it isn't flashing, see CHART A-2.

3. If the fan does not turn "ON" at this point, CKT 532 or CKT 150 is open or the cooling fan motor is faulty.

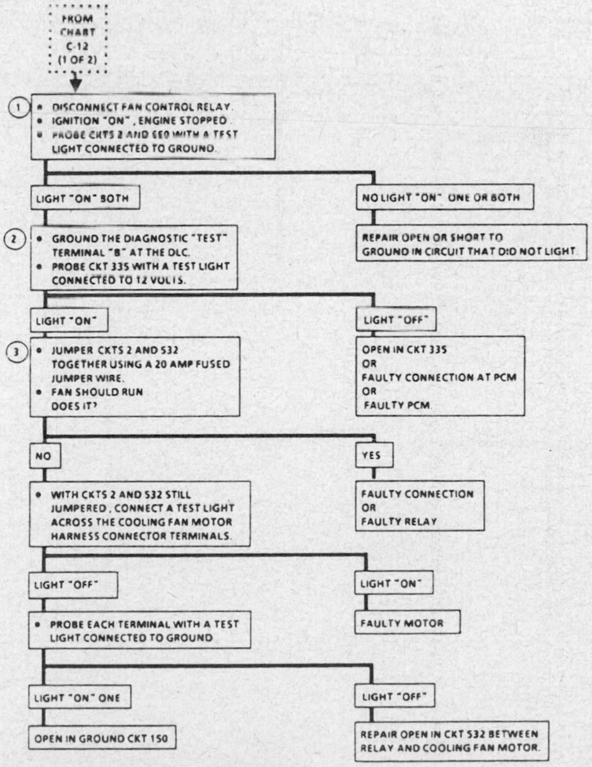

FROM CHART C-12 (1 OF 2)
1
• DISCONNECT FAN CONTROL RELAY. • IGNITION "ON", ENGINE STOPPED. • PROBE CKTS 2 AND 532 WITH A TEST LIGHT CONNECTED TO GROUND.
LIGHT "ON" BOTH
NO LIGHT "ON" ONE OR BOTH
2
• GROUND THE DIAGNOSTIC "TEST" TERMINAL "B" AT THE DLC. • PROBE CKT 335 WITH A TEST LIGHT CONNECTED TO 12 VOLTS.
REPAIR OPEN OR SHORT TO GROUND IN CIRCUIT THAT DID NOT LIGHT.
LIGHT "ON"
LIGHT "OFF"
3
• JUMPER CKTS 2 AND 532 TOGETHER USING A 20 AMP FUSED JUMPER WIRE. • FAN SHOULD RUN DOES IT?
OPEN IN CKT 335 OR FAULTY CONNECTION AT PCM OR FAULTY PCM.
NO
YES
• WITH CKTS 2 AND 532 STILL JUMPERED, CONNECT A TEST LIGHT ACROSS THE COOLING FAN MOTOR HARNESS CONNECTOR TERMINALS.
FAULTY CONNECTION OR FAULTY RELAY
LIGHT "OFF"
LIGHT "ON"
• PROBE EACH TERMINAL WITH A TEST LIGHT CONNECTED TO GROUND.
FAULTY MOTOR
LIGHT "ON" ONE
LIGHT "OFF"
OPEN IN GROUND CKT 150
REPAIR OPEN IN CKT 532 BETWEEN RELAY AND COOLING FAN MOTOR.

GC108940020302AX

Fig. 57 Chart C-12 cooling fan diagnosis (Part 2 of 2). 1994 Cavalier w/3.1L/V6– 192 engine

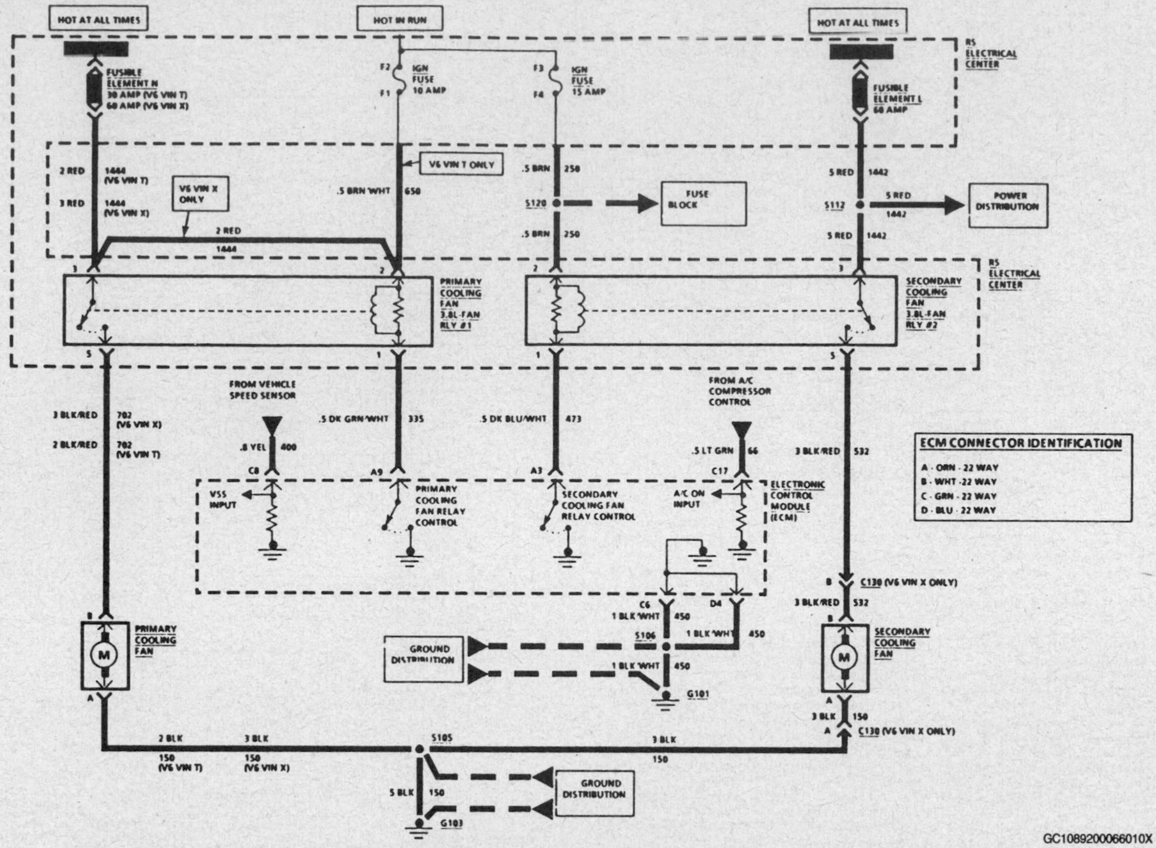

HOT AT ALL TIMES
HOT IN RUN
HOT AT ALL TIMES
RS ELECTRICAL CENTER
FUSIBLE ELEMENT N 30 AMP (V6 VIN T) 60 AMP (V6 VIN X)
F2 IGN FUSE 10 AMP F1
F3 IGN FUSE 15 AMP F4
FUSIBLE ELEMENT L 60 AMP
2 RED 1444 (V6 VIN T)
3 RED 1444 (V6 VIN X)
V6 VIN X ONLY
2 RED 1444
V6 VIN T ONLY
.5 BRN WHT 650
.5 BRN 250
S120
FUSE BLOCK
.5 BRN 250
5 RED 1442
S112
5 RED 1442
POWER DISTRIBUTION
5 RED 1442
PRIMARY COOLING FAN 3.8L-FAN RLY #1
SECONDARY COOLING FAN 3.8L-FAN RLY #2
RS ELECTRICAL CENTER
FROM VEHICLE SPEED SENSOR
3 BLK/RED 702 (V6 VIN X)
2 BLK/RED 702 (V6 VIN T)
.8 YEL 400
.5 DK GRN/WHT 335
.5 DK BLU/WHT 473
FROM A/C COMPRESSOR CONTROL
.5 LT GRN 66
3 BLK/RED 532
C8
A9
A3
C17
VSS INPUT
PRIMARY COOLING FAN RELAY CONTROL
SECONDARY COOLING FAN RELAY CONTROL
A/C ON INPUT
ELECTRONIC CONTROL MODULE (ECM)
ECM CONNECTOR IDENTIFICATION
A - ORN - 22 WAY
B - WHT - 22 WAY
C - GRN - 22 WAY
D - BLU - 22 WAY
C130 (V6 VIN X ONLY)
3 BLK/RED 532
C6
D4
1 BLK/WHT 450
S106
1 BLK/WHT 450
GROUND DISTRIBUTION
1 BLK/WHT 450
G101
PRIMARY COOLING FAN
SECONDARY COOLING FAN
3 BLK 150
C130 (V6 VIN X ONLY)
2 BLK 150 (V6 VIN T)
3 BLK 150 (V6 VIN X)
S105
3 BLK 150
5 BLK 150
GROUND DISTRIBUTION
G103
GC1089200066010X

Fig. 58 Cooling fan wiring circuit (Part 1 of 2). 1992 Cutlass Supreme & Grand Prix

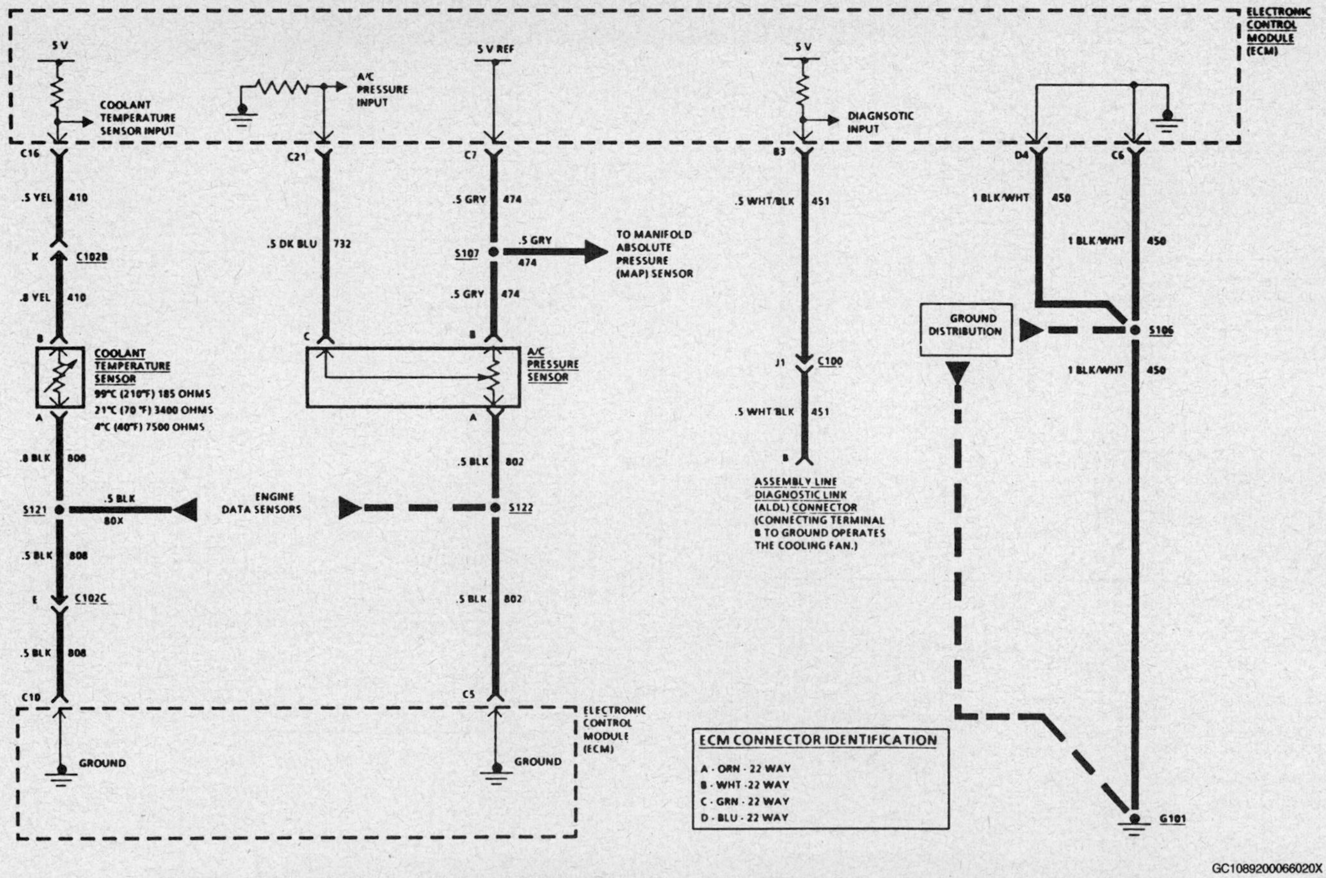

ELECTRONIC CONTROL MODULE (ECM)
5 V
COOLANT TEMPERATURE SENSOR INPUT
A/C PRESSURE INPUT
5 V REF
5 V
DIAGNSOTIC INPUT
C16
C21
C7
B3
D4
C6
.5 YEL 410
.5 GRY 474
.5 WHT/BLK 451
1 BLK/WHT 450
K C102B
.5 DK BLU 732
S107
.5 GRY 474
TO MANIFOLD ABSOLUTE PRESSURE (MAP) SENSOR
1 BLK/WHT 450
.8 YEL 410
.5 GRY 474
GROUND DISTRIBUTION
S106
COOLANT TEMPERATURE SENSOR
99°C (210°F) 185 OHMS
21°C (70 °F) 3400 OHMS
4°C (40°F) 7500 OHMS
A/C PRESSURE SENSOR
J1 C100
1 BLK/WHT 450
.5 WHT/BLK 451
.8 BLK 808
.5 BLK 802
S121
.5 BLK 80X
ENGINE DATA SENSORS
S122
ASSEMBLY LINE DIAGNOSTIC LINK (ALDL) CONNECTOR (CONNECTING TERMINAL B TO GROUND OPERATES THE COOLING FAN.)
.5 BLK 808
E C102C
.5 BLK 802
.5 BLK 808
C10
C5
ELECTRONIC CONTROL MODULE (ECM)
GROUND
GROUND
ECM CONNECTOR IDENTIFICATION
A - ORN - 22 WAY
B - WHT - 22 WAY
C - GRN - 22 WAY
D - BLU - 22 WAY
G101
GC1089200066020X

Fig. 58 Cooling fan wiring circuit (Part 2 of 2). 1992 Cutlass Supreme & Grand Prix

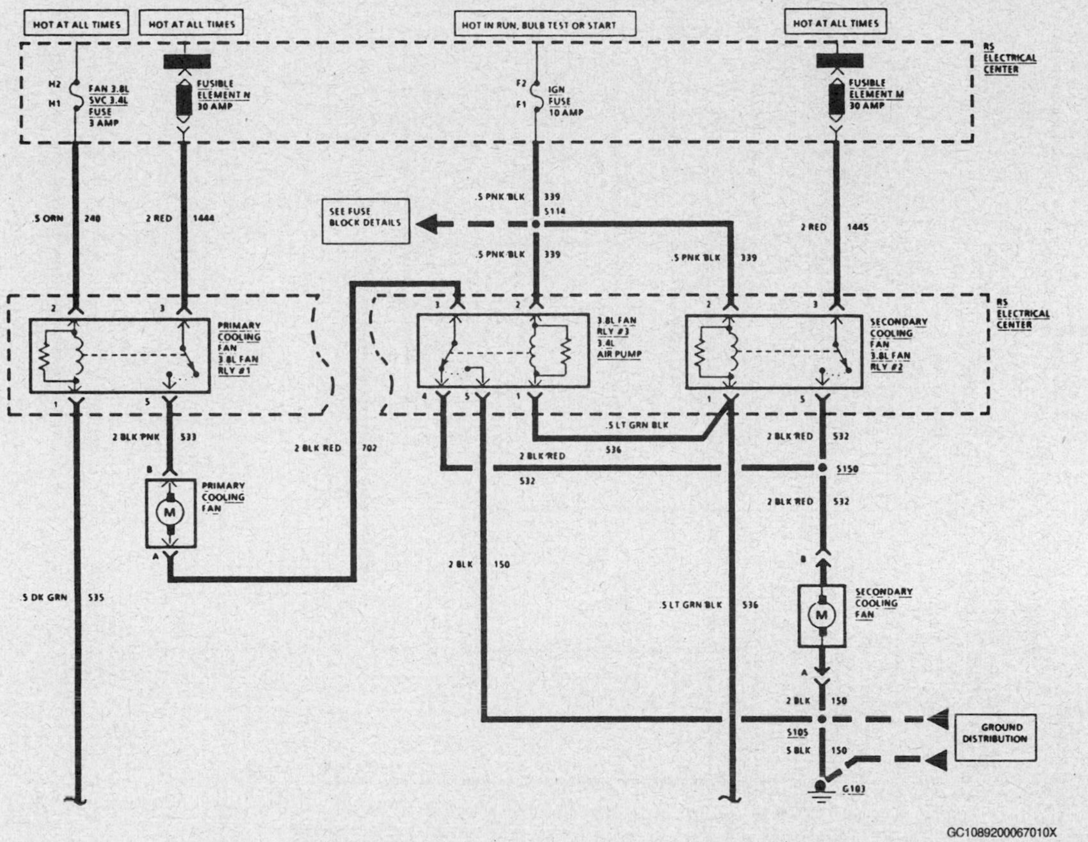
HOT AT ALL TIMES
HOT AT ALL TIMES
HOT IN RUN, BULB TEST OR START
HOT AT ALL TIMES
RS ELECTRICAL CENTER
FAN 3.8L SVC 3.4L FUSE 3 AMP
FUSIBLE ELEMENT N 30 AMP
IGN FUSE 10 AMP
FUSIBLE ELEMENT M 30 AMP
SEE FUSE BLOCK DETAILS
.5 ORN 240
2 RED 1444
.5 PNK/BLK 339
S114
2 RED 1445
PRIMARY COOLING FAN 3.8L FAN RLY #1
3.8L FAN RLY #3 3.4L AIR PUMP
SECONDARY COOLING FAN 3.8L FAN RLY #2
2 BLK/PNK 533
2 BLK/RED 702
.5 LT GRN/BLK 536
2 BLK/RED 532
S150
PRIMARY COOLING FAN
SECONDARY COOLING FAN
2 BLK 150
.5 DK GRN 535
S105
GROUND DISTRIBUTION
G103
GC1089200067010X

Fig. 59 Cooling fan wiring circuit (Part 1 of 2). 1992 Regal

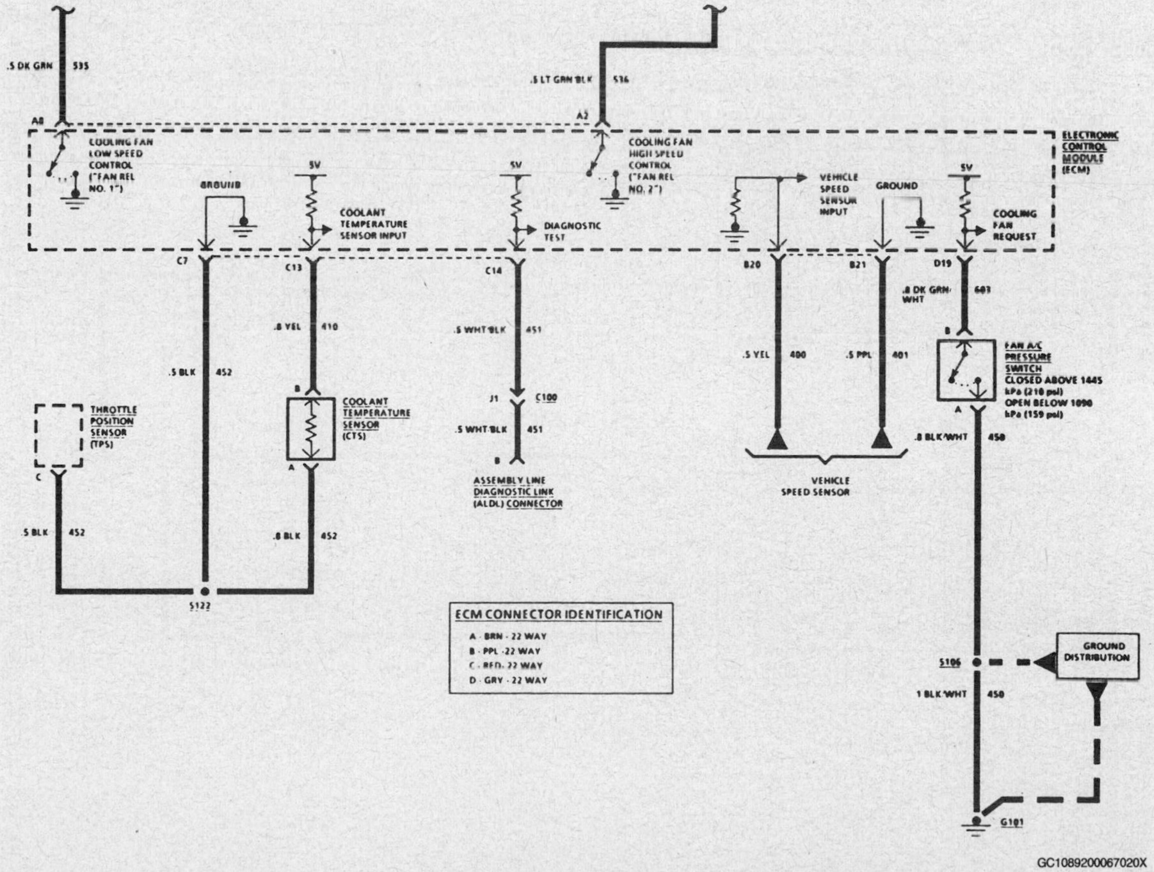
.5 DK GRN 535
.5 LT GRN/BLK 536
COOLING FAN LOW SPEED CONTROL ("FAN REL NO. 1")
COOLING FAN HIGH SPEED CONTROL ("FAN REL NO. 2")
ELECTRONIC CONTROL MODULE (ECM)
GROUND
5V
COOLANT TEMPERATURE SENSOR INPUT
DIAGNOSTIC TEST
VEHICLE SPEED SENSOR INPUT
COOLING FAN REQUEST
.8 YEL 410
.5 WHT/BLK 451
.8 DK GRN/WHT 603
.5 BLK 452
.5 YEL 400
.5 PPL 401
FAN A/C PRESSURE SWITCH CLOSED ABOVE 1445 kPa (210 psi) OPEN BELOW 1090 kPa (159 psi)
THROTTLE POSITION SENSOR (TPS)
COOLANT TEMPERATURE SENSOR (CTS)
C100
ASSEMBLY LINE DIAGNOSTIC LINK (ALDL) CONNECTOR
VEHICLE SPEED SENSOR
.8 BLK/WHT 450
.8 BLK 452
S122
ECM CONNECTOR IDENTIFICATION
A - BRN - 22 WAY
B - PPL - 22 WAY
C - RED - 22 WAY
D - GRY - 22 WAY
S106
GROUND DISTRIBUTION
1 BLK/WHT 450
G101
GC1089200067020X

Fig. 59 Cooling fan wiring circuit (Part 2 of 2). 1992 Regal

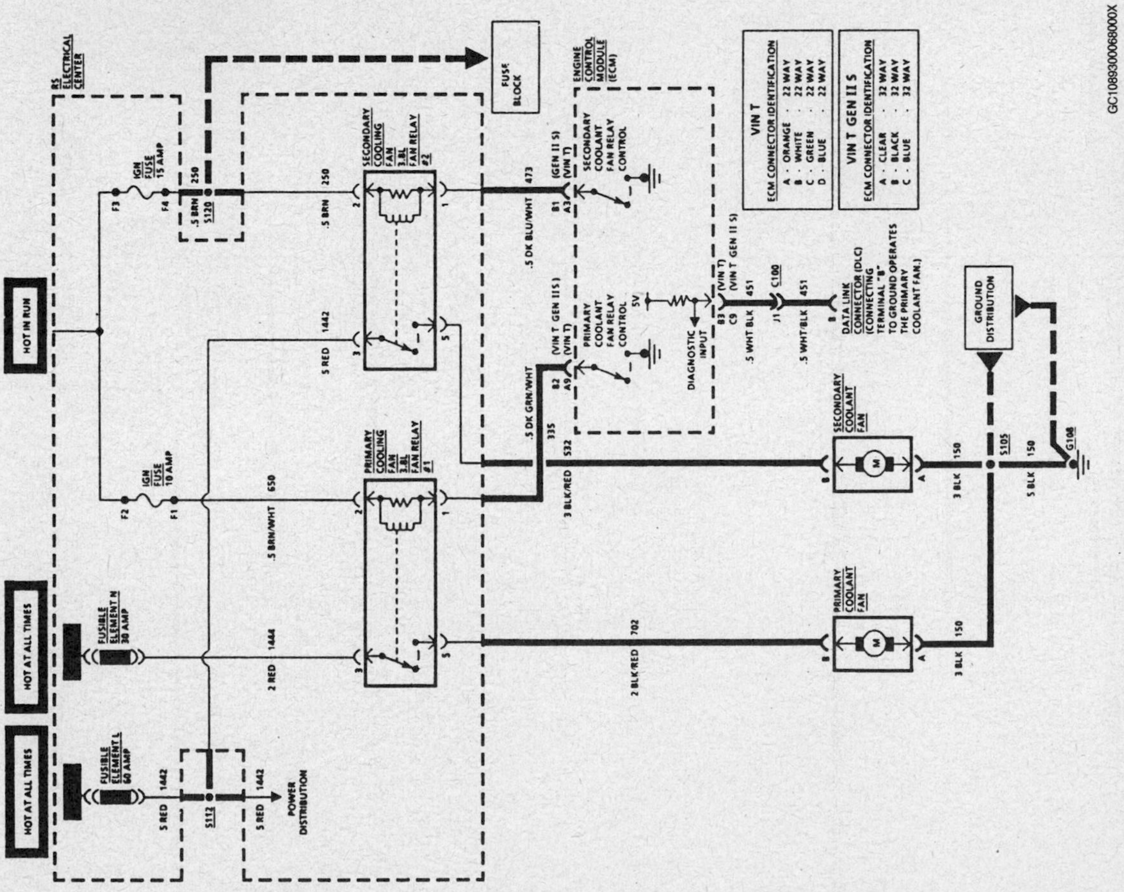
HOT AT ALL TIMES
FUSIBLE ELEMENT L 60 AMP
HOT AT ALL TIMES
FUSIBLE ELEMENT N 30 AMP
HOT IN RUN
IGN FUSE 10 AMP
IGN FUSE 15 AMP
POWER DISTRIBUTION
R5 ELECTRICAL CENTER
PRIMARY COOLING FAN 3.8L FAN RELAY #1
SECONDARY COOLING FAN 3.8L FAN RELAY #2
FUSE BLOCK
ENGINE CONTROL MODULE (ECM)
PRIMARY COOLANT FAN RELAY CONTROL
SECONDARY COOLANT FAN RELAY CONTROL
DIAGNOSTIC INPUT
DATA LINK CONNECTOR (DLC) (CONNECTING TERMINAL "B" TO GROUND OPERATES THE PRIMARY COOLANT FAN.)
PRIMARY COOLANT FAN
SECONDARY COOLANT FAN
GROUND DISTRIBUTION
VIN T ECM CONNECTOR IDENTIFICATION
A - ORANGE - 22 WAY
B - WHITE - 22 WAY
C - GREEN - 22 WAY
D - BLUE - 22 WAY
VIN T GEN II S ECM CONNECTOR IDENTIFICATION
A - CLEAR - 32 WAY
B - BLACK - 32 WAY
C - BLUE - 32 WAY
GC1089300068000X

Fig. 60 Cooling fan wiring circuit. 1993 Cutlass Supreme, Grand Prix & Regal except w/3.8L/V6-231 engine

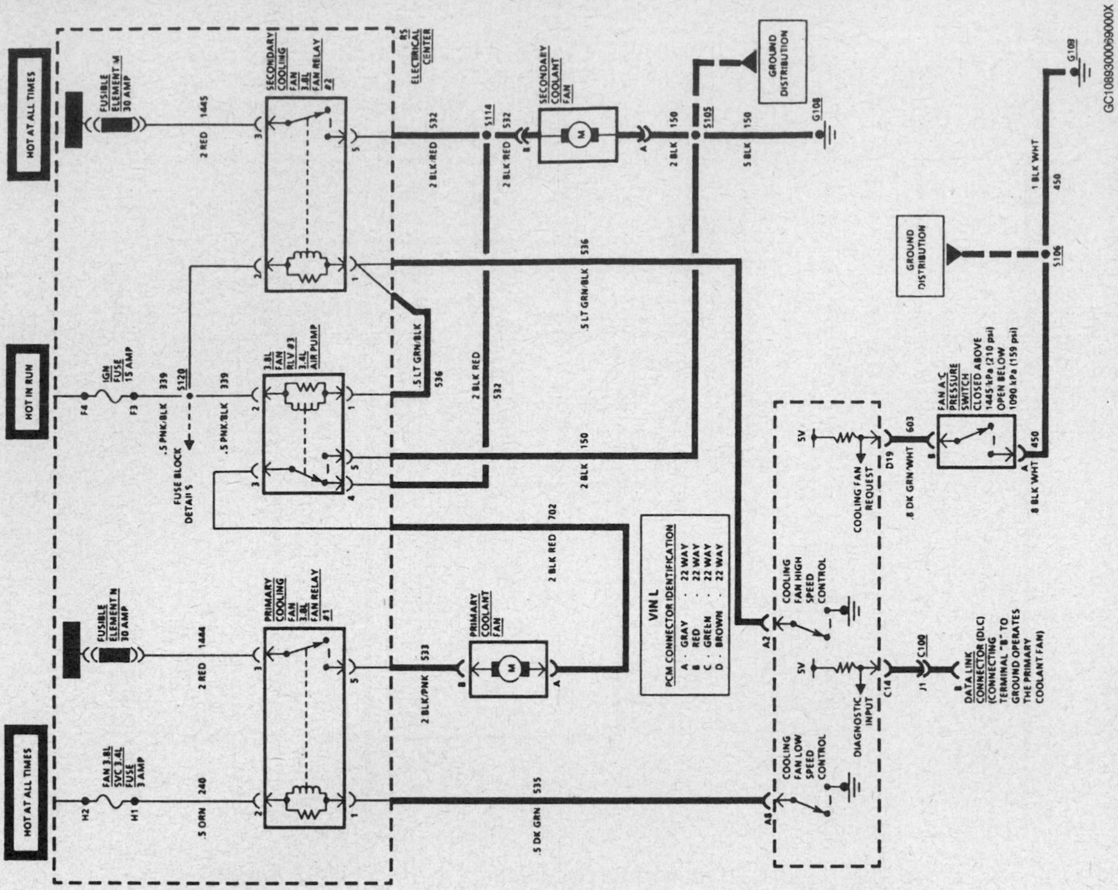
HOT AT ALL TIMES
FAN 3.8L SVC 3.4L FUSE 3 AMP
FUSIBLE ELEMENT N 30 AMP
HOT IN RUN
IGN FUSE 15 AMP
FUSE BLOCK DETAIL 5
HOT AT ALL TIMES
FUSIBLE ELEMENT M 30 AMP
R5 ELECTRICAL CENTER
PRIMARY COOLING FAN 3.8L FAN RELAY #1
3.8L FAN RLY #3 3.4L AIR PUMP
SECONDARY COOLING FAN 3.8L FAN RELAY #2
PRIMARY COOLANT FAN
SECONDARY COOLANT FAN
GROUND DISTRIBUTION
VIN L PCM CONNECTOR IDENTIFICATION
A - GRAY - 22 WAY
B - RED - 22 WAY
C - GREEN - 22 WAY
D - BROWN - 22 WAY
COOLING FAN LOW SPEED CONTROL
DIAGNOSTIC INPUT
COOLING FAN HIGH SPEED CONTROL
COOLING FAN REQUEST
DATA LINK CONNECTOR (DLC) (CONNECTING TERMINAL "B" TO GROUND OPERATES THE PRIMARY COOLANT FAN)
FAN A/C PRESSURE SWITCH CLOSED ABOVE 1445 kPa (210 psi) OPEN BELOW 1090 kPa (159 psi)
GROUND DISTRIBUTION
GC1089300069000X

Fig. 61 Cooling fan wiring circuit. 1993 Regal w/3.8L/V6-231 engine

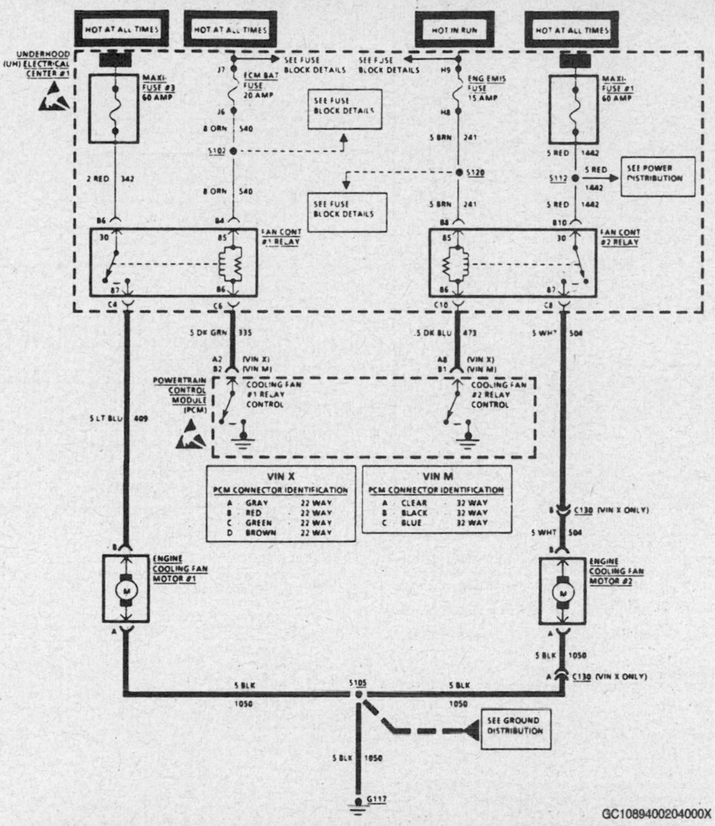

GC1089400204000X

Fig. 62 Cooling fan wiring circuit. 1994 Cutlass Supreme, Grand Prix & Regal w/3.1L/V6-192 & 3.4L/V6-204 engines

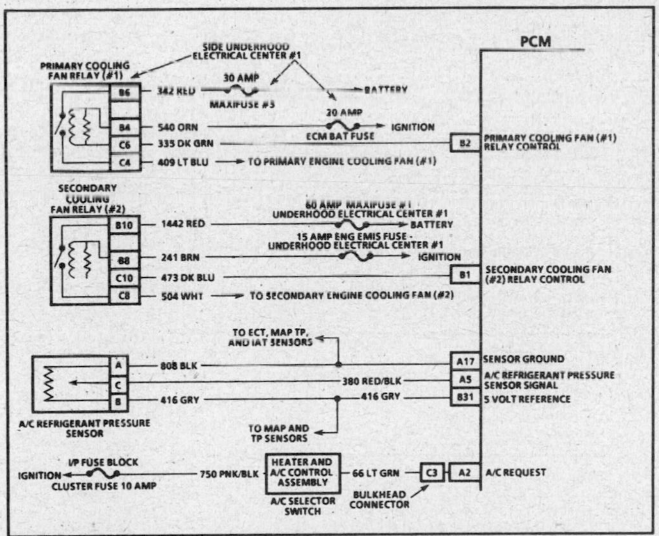

PCM
SIDE UNDERHOOD ELECTRICAL CENTER #1
PRIMARY COOLING FAN RELAY (#1)
30 AMP
MAXIFUSE #5
BATTERY
342 RED
20 AMP
540 ORN
IGNITION
ECM BAT FUSE
335 DK GRN
409 LT BLU
TO PRIMARY ENGINE COOLING FAN (#1)
B2
PRIMARY COOLING FAN (#1) RELAY CONTROL
SECONDARY COOLING FAN RELAY (#2)
60 AMP MAXIFUSE #1 UNDERHOOD ELECTRICAL CENTER #1
1442 RED
15 AMP ENG EMIS FUSE - UNDERHOOD ELECTRICAL CENTER #1
241 BRN
473 DK BLU
504 WHT
TO SECONDARY ENGINE COOLING FAN (#2)
B1
SECONDARY COOLING FAN (#2) RELAY CONTROL
TO ECT, MAP TP, AND IAT SENSORS
808 BLK
A17
SENSOR GROUND
380 RED/BLK
A5
A/C REFRIGERANT PRESSURE SENSOR SIGNAL
416 GRY
B31
5 VOLT REFERENCE
A/C REFRIGERANT PRESSURE SENSOR
TO MAP AND TP SENSORS
I/P FUSE BLOCK
IGNITION
CLUSTER FUSE 10 AMP
750 PNK/BLK
HEATER AND A/C CONTROL ASSEMBLY
A/C SELECTOR SWITCH
66 LT GRN
C3
A2
A/C REQUEST
BULKHEAD CONNECTOR

Circuit Description:

Battery voltage to operate the primary cooling fan is supplied to the primary cooling fan (#1) relay by CKT 342. Ignition voltage to energize the primary cooling fan (#1) relay is supplied by CKT 540. When the PCM grounds CKT 335, the relay is energized and the primary cooling fan (#1) is turned "ON."

When the engine is running, the PCM will turn the primary cooling fan (#1) "ON" for any one of the following reasons:

- Diagnostic Trouble Code (DTC) 14, 15 or 70 is set.
- A/C is requested and vehicle speed is less than 50 mph (81 km/h).
- Engine coolant temperature is 108°C (226°F) or greater, with A/C "OFF." [106°C (223°F) with A/C "ON."]
- A/C refrigerant pressure is greater than 1275 kPa (185 psi).

Once the primary cooling fan (#1) is enabled, the PCM will turn the primary cooling fan (#1) "OFF" when:

- Engine is turned "OFF."
- Engine coolant temperature drops to 104°C (210°F) or less.
- A/C refrigerant pressure drops to 189 psi or less with A/C selected.

Diagnostic Aids: If the owner comments about an overheating problem, it must be determined whether the comment was due to an actual boil over, or the hot light, or temperature gage indicated overheating.

If the gage or light indicates overheating, but no boil over is detected, the gage circuit should be checked. The gage accuracy can also be checked by comparing the engine coolant temperature reading using a scan tool and comparing its display with the gage reading.

If the engine is actually overheating and the gage indicates overheating, but the cooling fan is not coming "ON," the Engine Coolant Temperature (ECT) sensor has probably shifted out of calibration and should be replaced.

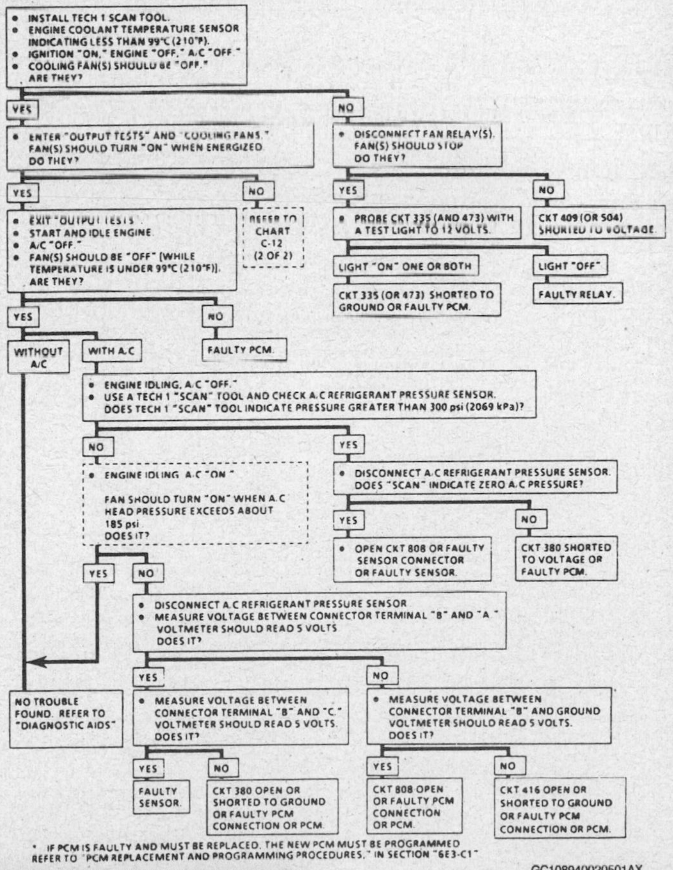

• INSTALL TECH 1 SCAN TOOL.
• ENGINE COOLANT TEMPERATURE SENSOR INDICATING LESS THAN 99°C (210°F).
• IGNITION "ON," ENGINE "OFF," A/C "OFF."
• COOLING FAN(S) SHOULD BE "OFF." ARE THEY?
YES
NO
• ENTER "OUTPUT TESTS" AND "COOLING FANS." FAN(S) SHOULD TURN "ON" WHEN ENERGIZED DO THEY?
• DISCONNECT FAN RELAY(S). FAN(S) SHOULD STOP DO THEY?
YES
NO
• EXIT "OUTPUT TESTS".
• START AND IDLE ENGINE.
• A/C "OFF."
• FAN(S) SHOULD BE "OFF" (WHILE TEMPERATURE IS UNDER 99°C (210°F)). ARE THEY?
REFER TO CHART C-12 (2 OF 2)
• PROBE CKT 335 (AND 473) WITH A TEST LIGHT TO 12 VOLTS.
CKT 409 (OR 504) SHORTED TO VOLTAGE.
LIGHT "ON" ONE OR BOTH
LIGHT "OFF"
CKT 335 (OR 473) SHORTED TO GROUND OR FAULTY PCM.
FAULTY RELAY.
WITHOUT A/C
WITH A/C
FAULTY PCM.
• ENGINE IDLING, A/C "OFF."
• USE A TECH 1 "SCAN" TOOL AND CHECK A/C REFRIGERANT PRESSURE SENSOR. DOES TECH 1 "SCAN" TOOL INDICATE PRESSURE GREATER THAN 300 psi (2069 kPa)?
• ENGINE IDLING A/C "ON."
FAN SHOULD TURN "ON" WHEN A/C HEAD PRESSURE EXCEEDS ABOUT 185 psi DOES IT?
• DISCONNECT A/C REFRIGERANT PRESSURE SENSOR. DOES "SCAN" INDICATE ZERO A/C PRESSURE?
• OPEN CKT 808 OR FAULTY SENSOR CONNECTOR OR FAULTY SENSOR.
CKT 380 SHORTED TO VOLTAGE OR FAULTY PCM.
• DISCONNECT A/C REFRIGERANT PRESSURE SENSOR
• MEASURE VOLTAGE BETWEEN CONNECTOR TERMINAL "B" AND "A." VOLTMETER SHOULD READ 5 VOLTS DOES IT?
NO TROUBLE FOUND. REFER TO "DIAGNOSTIC AIDS"
• MEASURE VOLTAGE BETWEEN CONNECTOR TERMINAL "B" AND "C." VOLTMETER SHOULD READ 5 VOLTS. DOES IT?
• MEASURE VOLTAGE BETWEEN CONNECTOR TERMINAL "B" AND GROUND VOLTMETER SHOULD READ 5 VOLTS. DOES IT?
FAULTY SENSOR.
CKT 380 OPEN OR SHORTED TO GROUND OR FAULTY PCM CONNECTION OR PCM.
CKT 808 OPEN OR FAULTY PCM CONNECTION OR PCM.
CKT 416 OPEN OR SHORTED TO GROUND OR FAULTY PCM CONNECTION OR PCM.
* IF PCM IS FAULTY AND MUST BE REPLACED. THE NEW PCM MUST BE PROGRAMMED REFER TO "PCM REPLACEMENT AND PROGRAMMING PROCEDURES," IN SECTION "6E3-C1"

GC108940020501AX

Fig. 63 Chart C-12, cooling fan diagnosis (Part 1 of 2). 1994 Cutlass Supreme, Grand Prix & Regal w/3.1L/V6-192 engine

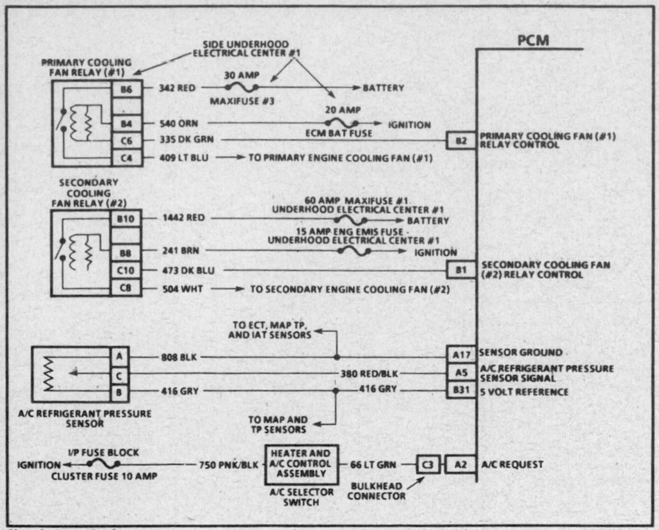
PCM
SIDE UNDERHOOD ELECTRICAL CENTER #1
PRIMARY COOLING FAN RELAY (#1)
B6
342 RED
30 AMP
MAXIFUSE #3
BATTERY
B4
540 ORN
20 AMP
ECM BAT FUSE
IGNITION
C6
335 DK GRN
B2
PRIMARY COOLING FAN (#1) RELAY CONTROL
C4
409 LT BLU
TO PRIMARY ENGINE COOLING FAN (#1)
SECONDARY COOLING FAN RELAY (#2)
B10
1442 RED
60 AMP MAXIFUSE #1 UNDERHOOD ELECTRICAL CENTER #1
BATTERY
B8
241 BRN
15 AMP ENG EMIS FUSE - UNDERHOOD ELECTRICAL CENTER #1
IGNITION
C10
473 DK BLU
B1
SECONDARY COOLING FAN (#2) RELAY CONTROL
C8
504 WHT
TO SECONDARY ENGINE COOLING FAN (#2)
TO ECT, MAP TP, AND IAT SENSORS
808 BLK
A17
SENSOR GROUND
380 RED/BLK
A5
A/C REFRIGERANT PRESSURE SENSOR SIGNAL
416 GRY
B31
5 VOLT REFERENCE
A/C REFRIGERANT PRESSURE SENSOR
TO MAP AND TP SENSORS
I/P FUSE BLOCK
IGNITION
CLUSTER FUSE 10 AMP
750 PNK/BLK
HEATER AND A/C CONTROL ASSEMBLY
A/C SELECTOR SWITCH
66 LT GRN
C3
A2
A/C REQUEST
BULKHEAD CONNECTOR

Circuit Description:

Battery voltage to operate secondary cooling fan (#2) motor is supplied to secondary cooling fan (#2) relay by CKT 1442. Ignition voltage to energize secondary cooling fan (#2) relay is supplied by CKT 241. When the A/C compressor clutch is energized by selecting "A/C" or "Defrost," the relay is energized and the secondary cooling fan (#2) is turned "ON."

When the engine is running, the PCM will turn the secondary cooling fan (#2) "ON," for any one of the following reasons:

- Engine Coolant Temperature (ECT) sensor indicating a temperature greater than 113°C (235°F) with A/C "OFF" or "ON."
- A/C is requested and vehicle speed is less than 50 mph (81 km/h).
- A/C refrigerant pressure sensor is open (pressure greater than 136 psi [938 kPa]).

Once the secondary cooling fan (#2) is enabled, the PCM will turn the secondary cooling fan (#2) "OFF" when:

- Engine is turned "OFF."
  OR
- When the Engine Coolant Temperature (ECT) sensor indicates the coolant temperature has dropped to 109°C (228°F) or less.
  OR
- When the A/C refrigerant pressure drops to 185 psi or less.

Diagnostic Aids: If the owner comments about poor A/C cooling, it must be determined whether a low A/C refrigerant charge is the cause, or DTC 66 or 70 is set, or the secondary cooling fan (#2) is faulty.

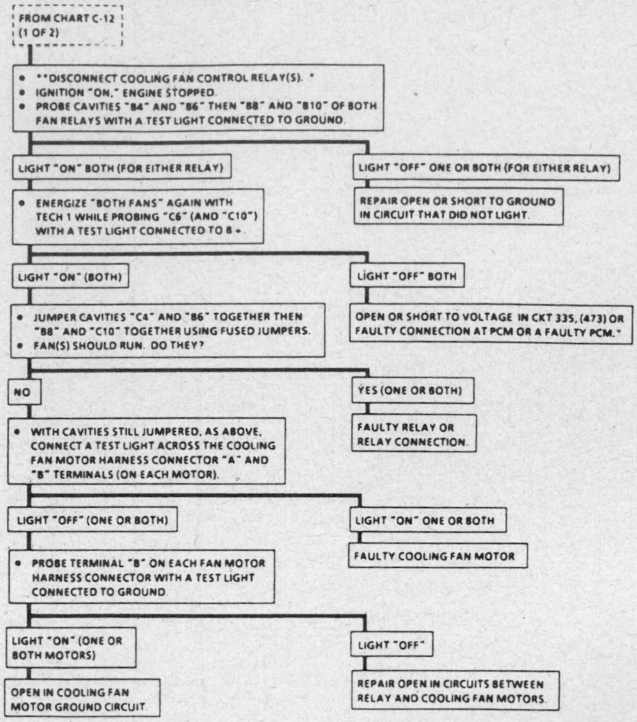
FROM CHART C-12 (1 OF 2)
• **DISCONNECT COOLING FAN CONTROL RELAY(S). *
• IGNITION "ON," ENGINE STOPPED.
• PROBE CAVITIES "B4" AND "B6" THEN "B8" AND "B10" OF BOTH FAN RELAYS WITH A TEST LIGHT CONNECTED TO GROUND.
LIGHT "ON" BOTH (FOR EITHER RELAY)
LIGHT "OFF" ONE OR BOTH (FOR EITHER RELAY)
REPAIR OPEN OR SHORT TO GROUND IN CIRCUIT THAT DID NOT LIGHT.
• ENERGIZE "BOTH FANS" AGAIN WITH TECH 1 WHILE PROBING "C6" (AND "C10") WITH A TEST LIGHT CONNECTED TO B+.
LIGHT "ON" (BOTH)
LIGHT "OFF" BOTH
OPEN OR SHORT TO VOLTAGE IN CKT 335, (473) OR FAULTY CONNECTION AT PCM OR A FAULTY PCM.*
• JUMPER CAVITIES "C4" AND "B6" TOGETHER THEN "B8" AND "C10" TOGETHER USING FUSED JUMPERS.
• FAN(S) SHOULD RUN. DO THEY?
NO
YES (ONE OR BOTH)
FAULTY RELAY OR RELAY CONNECTION.
• WITH CAVITIES STILL JUMPERED, AS ABOVE, CONNECT A TEST LIGHT ACROSS THE COOLING FAN MOTOR HARNESS CONNECTOR "A" AND "B" TERMINALS (ON EACH MOTOR).
LIGHT "OFF" (ONE OR BOTH)
LIGHT "ON" ONE OR BOTH
FAULTY COOLING FAN MOTOR
• PROBE TERMINAL "B" ON EACH FAN MOTOR HARNESS CONNECTOR WITH A TEST LIGHT CONNECTED TO GROUND.
LIGHT "ON" (ONE OR BOTH MOTORS)
LIGHT "OFF"
OPEN IN COOLING FAN MOTOR GROUND CIRCUIT.
REPAIR OPEN IN CIRCUITS BETWEEN RELAY AND COOLING FAN MOTORS.

GC108940020502AX

Fig. 63 Chart C-12, cooling fan diagnosis (Part 2 of 2). 1994 Cutlass Supreme, Grand Prix & Regal w/3.1L/V6-192 engine

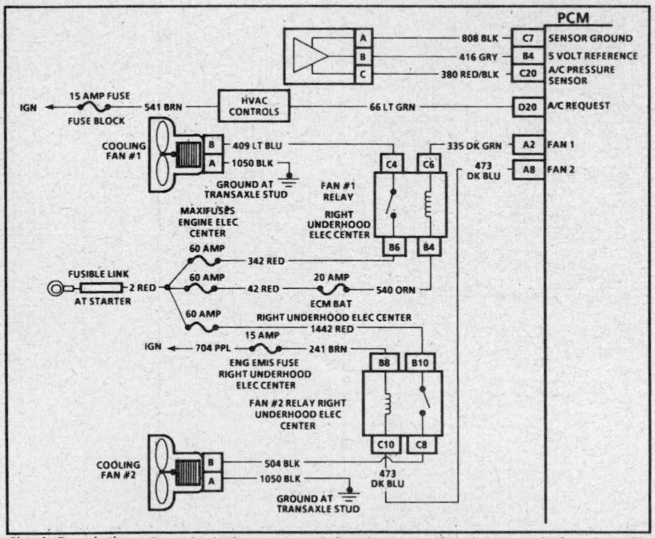
PCM
A
808 BLK
C7
SENSOR GROUND
B
416 GRY
B4
5 VOLT REFERENCE
C
380 RED/BLK
C20
A/C PRESSURE SENSOR
15 AMP FUSE
IGN
541 BRN
FUSE BLOCK
HVAC CONTROLS
66 LT GRN
D20
A/C REQUEST
COOLING FAN #1
409 LT BLU
1050 BLK
GROUND AT TRANSAXLE STUD
335 DK GRN
A2
FAN 1
473 DK BLU
A8
FAN 2
C4
C6
FAN #1 RELAY
RIGHT UNDERHOOD ELEC CENTER
B6
B4
MAXIFUSES ENGINE ELEC CENTER
60 AMP
342 RED
FUSIBLE LINK
2 RED
AT STARTER
60 AMP
42 RED
20 AMP
540 ORN
ECM BAT
60 AMP
RIGHT UNDERHOOD ELEC CENTER
1442 RED
15 AMP
IGN
704 PPL
241 BRN
ENG EMIS FUSE RIGHT UNDERHOOD ELEC CENTER
B8
B10
FAN #2 RELAY RIGHT UNDERHOOD ELEC CENTER
C10
C8
COOLING FAN #2
504 BLK
1050 BLK
473 DK BLU
GROUND AT TRANSAXLE STUD

Circuit Description: Power for the fan motors comes from 60 amp maxifuse elements to the fan relays. The relays are energized when current flows to ground through the PCM (Quad-Driver).

Fan 1 relay - The PCM energizes the relay through terminal "A2" when the engine coolant temperature reaches 106°C (223°F) or when A/C is requested.

Fan 2 relay - The fan 2 relay is energized by the PCM if the A/C refrigerant pressure reaches 240 psi or the engine coolant temperature reaches 113°C (235°F).

Chart Test Description: Number(s) below refer to circled number(s) on the diagnostic chart.

1. Using the Tech 1 misc. tests, "Fan 1" control will cause the PCM to ground CKT 335, energizing the Fan 1 relay.
2. Selecting "Fan 2" with the Tech 1 allows control of CKT 473 and the Fan 2 relay.

Diagnostic Aids: An intermittent may be caused by a poor connection, rubbed through wire insulation, or a wire broken inside the insulation.

Check for:

- Poor connection or damaged harness · Inspect PCM harness connectors for backed out terminals "A2" or "A8", improper mating, broken locks, improperly formed or damaged terminals, poor terminal to wire connection, and damaged harness.
- Intermittent test - If connections and harness check OK, a digital voltmeter connected from affected terminal to ground while moving related connectors and wiring harness. If the failure is induced, the voltage reading will change.
- Mis-scaled Engine Coolant Temperature (ECT) sensor - See "Engine Coolant Temperature Sensor Temperature vs. Resistance Values" table on DTC P0117 chart
- Basic cooling system problem - Refer to engine cooling and radiator diagnosis.

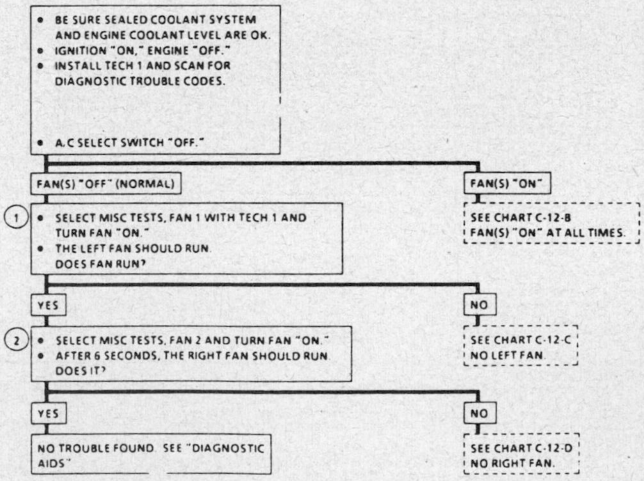
• BE SURE SEALED COOLANT SYSTEM AND ENGINE COOLANT LEVEL ARE OK.
• IGNITION "ON," ENGINE "OFF."
• INSTALL TECH 1 AND SCAN FOR DIAGNOSTIC TROUBLE CODES.
• A/C SELECT SWITCH "OFF."
FAN(S) "OFF" (NORMAL)
FAN(S) "ON"
1
• SELECT MISC TESTS, FAN 1 WITH TECH 1 AND TURN FAN "ON."
• THE LEFT FAN SHOULD RUN. DOES FAN RUN?
SEE CHART C-12-B FAN(S) "ON" AT ALL TIMES.
YES
NO
2
• SELECT MISC TESTS, FAN 2 AND TURN FAN "ON."
• AFTER 6 SECONDS, THE RIGHT FAN SHOULD RUN. DOES IT?
SEE CHART C-12-C NO LEFT FAN.
YES
NO
NO TROUBLE FOUND. SEE "DIAGNOSTIC AIDS"
SEE CHART C-12-D NO RIGHT FAN.

GC108940020600AX

Fig. 64 Chart C-12A, cooling fan diagnosis. 1994 Cutlass Supreme & Grand Prix w/3.4L/V6-204 engine

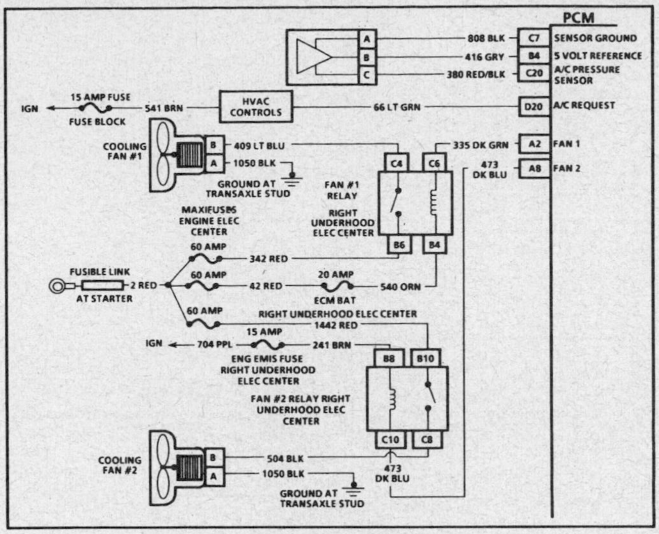

PCM
808 BLK
C7
SENSOR GROUND
416 GRY
B4
5 VOLT REFERENCE
380 RED/BLK
C20
A/C PRESSURE SENSOR
D20
A/C REQUEST
IGN
15 AMP FUSE
541 BRN
FUSE BLOCK
HVAC CONTROLS
66 LT GRN
COOLING FAN #1
409 LT BLU
1050 BLK
GROUND AT TRANSAXLE STUD
335 DK GRN
A2
FAN 1
473 DK BLU
A8
FAN 2
FAN #1 RELAY
RIGHT UNDERHOOD ELEC CENTER
MAXIFUSES ENGINE ELEC CENTER
60 AMP
342 RED
FUSIBLE LINK
2 RED
AT STARTER
60 AMP
42 RED
20 AMP
540 ORN
ECM BAT
60 AMP
RIGHT UNDERHOOD ELEC CENTER
1442 RED
15 AMP
IGN
704 PPL
241 BRN
ENG EMIS FUSE RIGHT UNDERHOOD ELEC CENTER
FAN #2 RELAY RIGHT UNDERHOOD ELEC CENTER
COOLING FAN #2
504 BLK
1050 BLK
473 DK BLU
GROUND AT TRANSAXLE STUD

CHART C-12B

FAN(S) "ON" AT ALL TIMES COOLING FAN CHECK 3.4L (VIN X) (SFI)

Circuit Description:

Power for the fan motors comes from 60 amp maxifuse elements to the fan relays. The relays are energized when current flows to ground through the PCM (Quad-Driver).

Fan 1 relay - The PCM energizes the relay through terminal "A2" when the engine coolant temperature reaches 106°C (223°F) or when A/C is requested.

Fan 2 relay - The fan 2 relay is energized by the PCM if the A/C refrigerant pressure sensor reaches 240 psi or the engine coolant temperature reaches 113°C (235°F).

Chart Test Description: Number(s) below refer to circled number(s) on the diagnostic chart.

1. Checks to see if CKT 473 is grounded all the time. A light indicates the wire is shorted to ground, the following steps will isolate the problem.
2. Checks to see if CKT 335 is grounded all the time, which would keep the relay closed at all times.
3. If the test light is "OFF" after disconnecting the PCM, be sure CKT 335 is not shorted to B+. If not shorted to B+, the PCM is shorted internally.
4. If the test light is "OFF" after disconnecting the PCM, be sure CKT 473 is not shorted to B+. If not shorted to B+, the PCM is shorted internally.

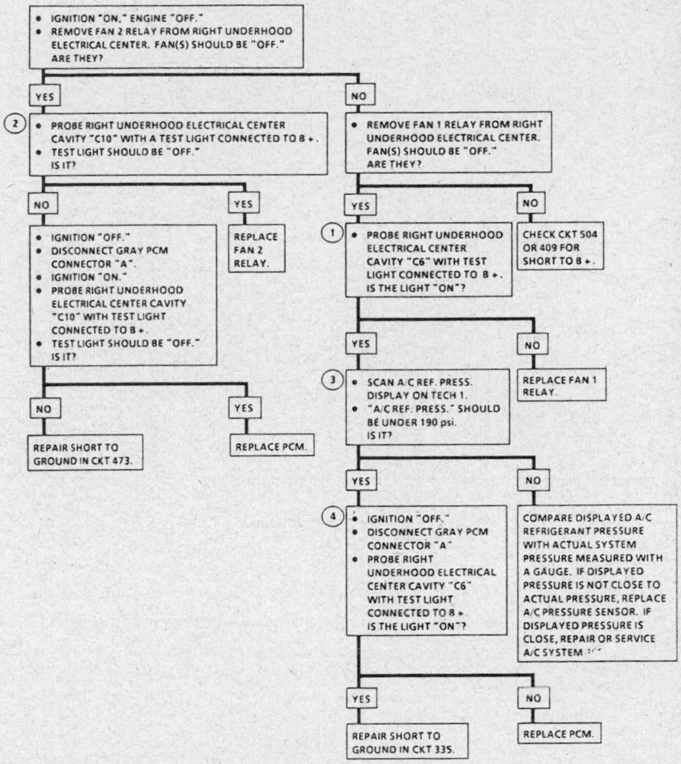

• IGNITION "ON," ENGINE "OFF."
• REMOVE FAN 2 RELAY FROM RIGHT UNDERHOOD ELECTRICAL CENTER. FAN(S) SHOULD BE "OFF." ARE THEY?
YES
NO
2
• PROBE RIGHT UNDERHOOD ELECTRICAL CENTER CAVITY "C10" WITH A TEST LIGHT CONNECTED TO B+.
• TEST LIGHT SHOULD BE "OFF." IS IT?
• REMOVE FAN 1 RELAY FROM RIGHT UNDERHOOD ELECTRICAL CENTER. FAN(S) SHOULD BE "OFF." ARE THEY?
NO
YES
YES
NO
• IGNITION "OFF."
• DISCONNECT GRAY PCM CONNECTOR "A".
• IGNITION "ON."
• PROBE RIGHT UNDERHOOD ELECTRICAL CENTER CAVITY "C10" WITH TEST LIGHT CONNECTED TO B+.
• TEST LIGHT SHOULD BE "OFF." IS IT?
REPLACE FAN 2 RELAY.
1
• PROBE RIGHT UNDERHOOD ELECTRICAL CENTER CAVITY "C6" WITH TEST LIGHT CONNECTED TO B+. IS THE LIGHT "ON"?
CHECK CKT 504 OR 409 FOR SHORT TO B+.
YES
NO
NO
YES
3
• SCAN A/C REF. PRESS. DISPLAY ON TECH 1.
• "A/C REF. PRESS." SHOULD BE UNDER 190 psi. IS IT?
REPLACE FAN 1 RELAY.
REPAIR SHORT TO GROUND IN CKT 473.
REPLACE PCM.
YES
NO
4
• IGNITION "OFF."
• DISCONNECT GRAY PCM CONNECTOR "A"
• PROBE RIGHT UNDERHOOD ELECTRICAL CENTER CAVITY "C6" WITH TEST LIGHT CONNECTED TO B+.
IS THE LIGHT "ON"?
COMPARE DISPLAYED A/C REFRIGERANT PRESSURE WITH ACTUAL SYSTEM PRESSURE MEASURED WITH A GAUGE. IF DISPLAYED PRESSURE IS NOT CLOSE TO ACTUAL PRESSURE, REPLACE A/C PRESSURE SENSOR. IF DISPLAYED PRESSURE IS CLOSE, REPAIR OR SERVICE A/C SYSTEM
YES
NO
REPAIR SHORT TO GROUND IN CKT 335.
REPLACE PCM.

GC108940020700AX

Fig. 65 Chart C-12B, cooling fan diagnosis. 1994 Cutlass Supreme & Grand Prix w/3.4L/V6-204 engine

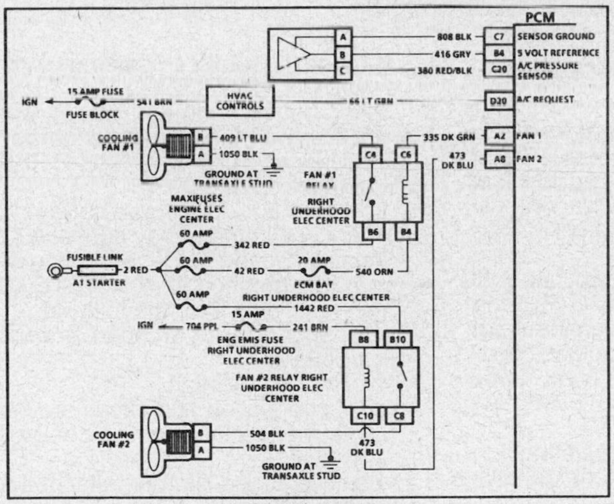

PCM
808 BLK
C7
SENSOR GROUND
416 GRY
B4
5 VOLT REFERENCE
380 RED/BLK
C20
A/C PRESSURE SENSOR
D20
A/C REQUEST
IGN
15 AMP FUSE
FUSE BLOCK
HVAC CONTROLS
COOLING FAN #1
409 LT BLU
1050 BLK
GROUND AT
335 DK GRN
A2
FAN 1
473 DK BLU
A8
FAN 2
FAN #1
RIGHT UNDERHOOD ELEC CENTER
MAXIFUSES
CENTER
60 AMP
342 RED
FUSIBLE LINK
2 RED
AT STARTER
60 AMP
42 RED
20 AMP
540 ORN
ECM BAT
60 AMP
RIGHT UNDERHOOD ELEC CENTER
1442 RED
15 AMP
IGN
704 PPL
241 BRN
ENG EMIS FUSE RIGHT UNDERHOOD ELEC CENTER
FAN #2 RELAY RIGHT UNDERHOOD ELEC CENTER
COOLING FAN #2
504 BLK
1050 BLK
473 DK BLU
GROUND AT TRANSAXLE STUD

CHART C-12C

NO FAN 1 (LEFT SIDE) COOLING FAN CHECK 3.4L (VIN X) (SFI)

Circuit Description:

Power for the fan motors comes from 60 amp maxifuse elements to the fan relays. The relays are energized when current flows to ground through the PCM (Quad-Driver).

Fan 1 relay - The PCM energizes the relay through terminal "A2" when the engine coolant temperature reaches 106°C (223°F) or when A/C is requested.

Fan 2 relay - The fan 2 relay is energized by the PCM if the A/C refrigerant pressure sensor reaches 240 psi or the engine coolant temperature reaches 113°C (235°F).

Chart Test Description: Number(s) below refer to circled number(s) on the diagnostic chart.

1. Checks for power feed to relay at right side underhood electrical center terminals "B4" and "B6".
2. Jumpering terminals "B6" to "C4" bypasses the relay, which should cause the left fan to run if fan motor and wiring are OK.
3. Turning fan 1 "ON" with the Tech 1 should cause the PCM to ground CKT 335. At this point, the test light should light, provided the PCM is OK and CKT 335 isn't open.
4. This checks for B+ and ground to the left fan motor. A test light "ON" at this point indicates a faulty motor connection, fan 1 or motor.

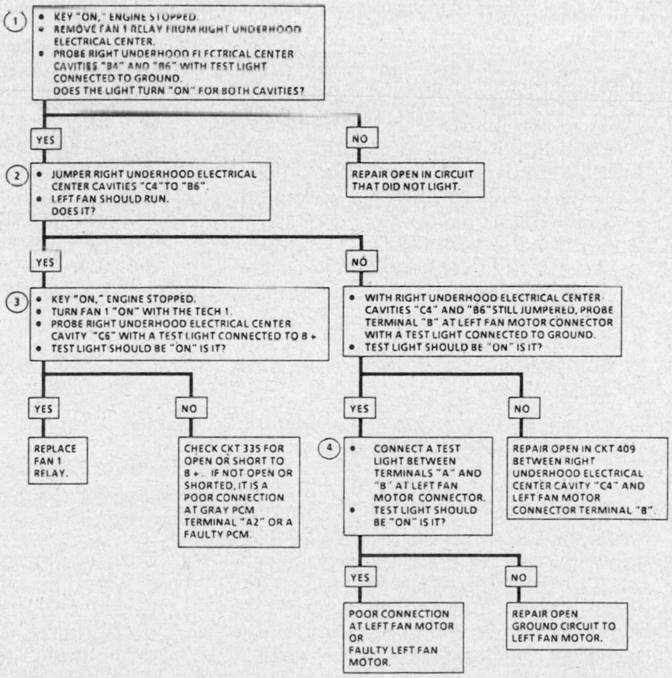

1
• KEY "ON," ENGINE STOPPED.
• REMOVE FAN 1 RELAY FROM RIGHT UNDERHOOD ELECTRICAL CENTER.
• PROBE RIGHT UNDERHOOD ELECTRICAL CENTER CAVITIES "B4" AND "B6" WITH TEST LIGHT CONNECTED TO GROUND.
DOES THE LIGHT TURN "ON" FOR BOTH CAVITIES?
YES
NO
2
• JUMPER RIGHT UNDERHOOD ELECTRICAL CENTER CAVITIES "C4" TO "B6".
• LEFT FAN SHOULD RUN.
DOES IT?
REPAIR OPEN IN CIRCUIT THAT DID NOT LIGHT.
YES
NO
3
• KEY "ON," ENGINE STOPPED.
• TURN FAN 1 "ON" WITH THE TECH 1.
• PROBE RIGHT UNDERHOOD ELECTRICAL CENTER CAVITY "C6" WITH A TEST LIGHT CONNECTED TO B+
• TEST LIGHT SHOULD BE "ON" IS IT?
• WITH RIGHT UNDERHOOD ELECTRICAL CENTER CAVITIES "C4" AND "B6" STILL JUMPERED, PROBE TERMINAL "B" AT LEFT FAN MOTOR CONNECTOR WITH A TEST LIGHT CONNECTED TO GROUND.
• TEST LIGHT SHOULD BE "ON" IS IT?
YES
NO
YES
NO
REPLACE FAN 1 RELAY.
CHECK CKT 335 FOR OPEN OR SHORT TO B+. IF NOT OPEN OR SHORTED, IT IS A POOR CONNECTION AT GRAY PCM TERMINAL "A2" OR A FAULTY PCM.
4
• CONNECT A TEST LIGHT BETWEEN TERMINALS "A" AND "B" AT LEFT FAN MOTOR CONNECTOR.
• TEST LIGHT SHOULD BE "ON" IS IT?
REPAIR OPEN IN CKT 409 BETWEEN RIGHT UNDERHOOD ELECTRICAL CENTER CAVITY "C4" AND LEFT FAN MOTOR CONNECTOR TERMINAL "B".
YES
NO
POOR CONNECTION AT LEFT FAN MOTOR OR FAULTY LEFT FAN MOTOR.
REPAIR OPEN GROUND CIRCUIT TO LEFT FAN MOTOR.

GC108940020800AX

Fig. 66 Chart C-12C, cooling fan diagnosis. 1994 Cutlass Supreme & Grand Prix w/3.4L/V6-204 engine

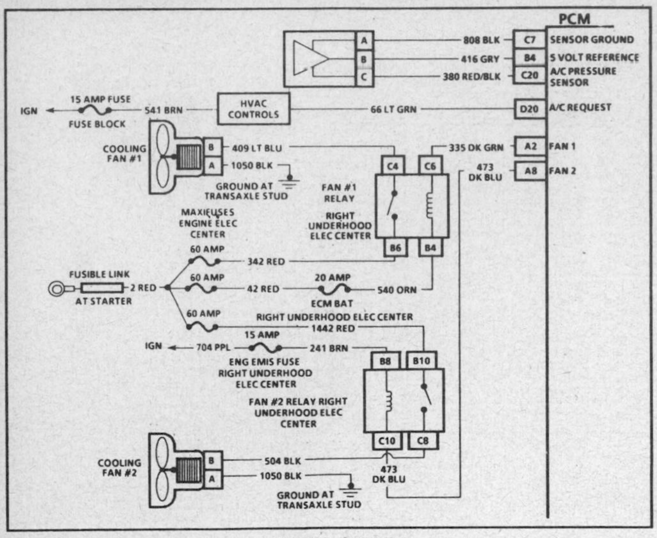
PCM
808 BLK
416 GRY
380 RED/BLK
C7 SENSOR GROUND
B4 5 VOLT REFERENCE
C20 A/C PRESSURE SENSOR
IGN
15 AMP FUSE
FUSE BLOCK
541 BRN
HVAC CONTROLS
66 LT GRN
D20 A/C REQUEST
COOLING FAN #1
409 LT BLU
1050 BLK
GROUND AT TRANSAXLE STUD
335 DK GRN
A2 FAN 1
473 DK BLU
A8 FAN 2
FAN #1 RELAY
RIGHT UNDERHOOD ELEC CENTER
MAXIFUSES ENGINE ELEC CENTER
60 AMP
342 RED
FUSIBLE LINK
2 RED
AT STARTER
42 RED
20 AMP
540 ORN
ECM BAT
RIGHT UNDERHOOD ELEC CENTER
1442 RED
15 AMP
704 PPL
241 BRN
ENG EMIS FUSE RIGHT UNDERHOOD ELEC CENTER
FAN #2 RELAY RIGHT UNDERHOOD ELEC CENTER
COOLING FAN #2
504 BLK
1050 BLK
GROUND AT TRANSAXLE STUD

CHART C-12D

NO FAN 2 (RIGHT SIDE) COOLING FAN CHECK 3.4L (VIN X) (SFI)

Circuit Description:

Power for the fan motors comes from 60 amp maxifuse elements to the fan relays. The relays are energized when current flows to ground through the PCM (Quad-Driver).

Fan 1 relay - The PCM energizes the relay through terminal "A2" when the engine coolant temperature reaches 106°C (223°F) or when A/C is requested.

Fan 2 relay - The fan 2 relay is energized by the PCM if the A/C refrigerant pressure sensor reaches 240 psi or the engine coolant temperature reaches 108°C (226°F).

Chart Test Description: Number(s) below refer to circled number(s) on the diagnostic chart.

1. Verifies power feed to fan 2 relay at right side underhood electrical center terminals "B8" and "B10".
2. Jumpering terminals "B10" and "C8" bypasses the fan 2 relay. If right side fan runs, the relay is faulty.
3. Checks CKT 473 back to the PCM. If CKT 473 is OK, it's a bad fan 2 relay.
4. Checks wiring to the fan 2 (right side) motor. If OK, problem is connections, open ground circuit or faulty fan 2 (right side) fan motor.

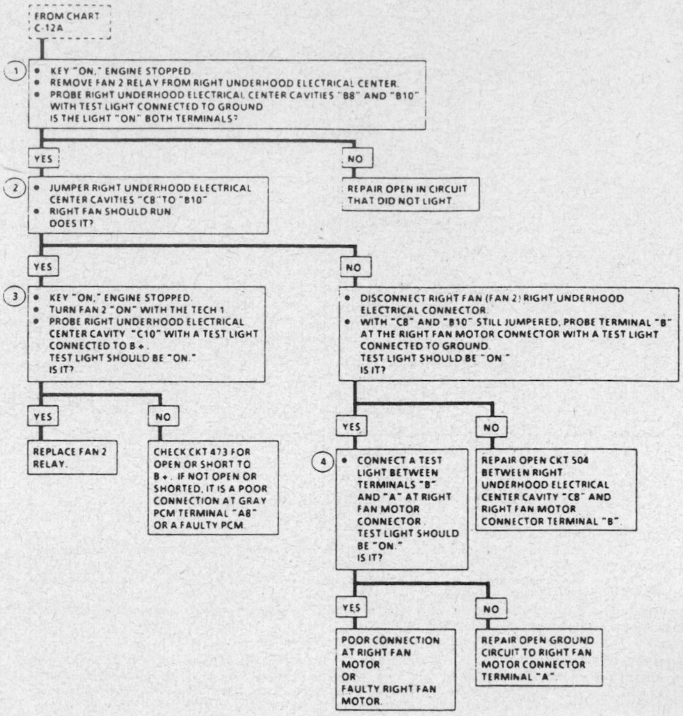
FROM CHART C-12A
1
• KEY "ON," ENGINE STOPPED.
• REMOVE FAN 2 RELAY FROM RIGHT UNDERHOOD ELECTRICAL CENTER.
• PROBE RIGHT UNDERHOOD ELECTRICAL CENTER CAVITIES "B8" AND "B10" WITH TEST LIGHT CONNECTED TO GROUND IS THE LIGHT "ON" BOTH TERMINALS?
YES
NO
REPAIR OPEN IN CIRCUIT THAT DID NOT LIGHT.
2
• JUMPER RIGHT UNDERHOOD ELECTRICAL CENTER CAVITIES "C8" TO "B10"
• RIGHT FAN SHOULD RUN. DOES IT?
YES
NO
3
• KEY "ON," ENGINE STOPPED.
• TURN FAN 2 "ON" WITH THE TECH 1
• PROBE RIGHT UNDERHOOD ELECTRICAL CENTER CAVITY "C10" WITH A TEST LIGHT CONNECTED TO B+. TEST LIGHT SHOULD BE "ON." IS IT?
• DISCONNECT RIGHT FAN (FAN 2) RIGHT UNDERHOOD ELECTRICAL CONNECTOR.
• WITH "C8" AND "B10" STILL JUMPERED, PROBE TERMINAL "B" AT THE RIGHT FAN MOTOR CONNECTOR WITH A TEST LIGHT CONNECTED TO GROUND. TEST LIGHT SHOULD BE "ON." IS IT?
YES
NO
REPLACE FAN 2 RELAY.
CHECK CKT 473 FOR OPEN OR SHORT TO B+. IF NOT OPEN OR SHORTED, IT IS A POOR CONNECTION AT GRAY PCM TERMINAL "A8" OR A FAULTY PCM.
YES
NO
4
• CONNECT A TEST LIGHT BETWEEN TERMINALS "B" AND "A" AT RIGHT FAN MOTOR CONNECTOR. TEST LIGHT SHOULD BE "ON." IS IT?
REPAIR OPEN CKT 504 BETWEEN RIGHT UNDERHOOD ELECTRICAL CENTER CAVITY "C8" AND RIGHT FAN MOTOR CONNECTOR TERMINAL "B".
YES
NO
POOR CONNECTION AT RIGHT FAN MOTOR OR FAULTY RIGHT FAN MOTOR.
REPAIR OPEN GROUND CIRCUIT TO RIGHT FAN MOTOR CONNECTOR TERMINAL "A".

GC108940020900AX

Fig. 67 Chart C-12D, cooling fan diagnosis. 1994 Cutlass Supreme and Grand Prix w/3.4L/V6-204 engine

Secondary Cooling Fan Does Not Run At High Speed

1. Disconnect fan relay No. 2, then turn ignition switch to Run position and connect two test lamps from terminals 2 and 3 of fan relay to ground. If one or both lamps do not light, check fusible link M and red wire or IGN fuse and pink/black for open.
2. If lamps light, connect fused jumper between terminals 3 and 5 of fan relay No. 2. If secondary cooling fan runs at high speed, replace fan relay No. 2.
3. If secondary cooling fan does not run at high speed, check black/red wire for open circuit.

Primary Cooling Fan Does Not Run At High Speed

1. Disconnect fan relay No. 3, then turn ignition switch to Run position and connect test lamp from terminal 2 of fan relay to ground. If lamp does not light, check pink/black wire for open.
2. If lamp lights, connect test lamp between terminals 2 and 5. If lamp does not light, check black wire for open.
3. If lamp lights, connect terminal B of ALDL to ground and wait 10 seconds. Connect test lamp between terminals 2 and 1. If lamp does not light, check light green/black wire for open.
4. If lamp lights, replace fan relay No. 3.

No Cooling Fans Operate At High Speed

1. Disconnect fan relay No. 2, then turn ignition switch to Run position and connect test lamp from terminal 2 of fan relay to ground. If lamp does not light, check IGN fuse and pink/black wire for open.
2. If lamp lights, connect terminal B of ALDL to ground and wait 10 seconds. Connect test lamp between terminals 2 and 1. If lamp does not light, check light green/black wire for open. If wire is satisfactory, problem is ECM related.
3. If lamp lights, system is operating normally. Check for intermittent faults.

1993

Refer to **Figs. 60 through 61**

Primary Cooling Fan Does Not Run

1. Turn ignition switch to the Run position and connect a fused jumper between DLC connector terminal "B" and ground. If cooling fan does not run, proceed to step 2. If cooling fan runs, problem is ECM related.
2. Remove primary cooling fan relay and connect a test light between primary cooling fan relay connector terminal "3" and ground. Then connect the test light between terminal "2" and ground. If test light comes on in both cases, proceed to step 3. If test light does not come in both cases, check for faulty connection. If connection is satisfactory, check circuits 650 and 1444 for an open.
3. Connect a fused jumper between primary cooling fan relay connector terminals "3" and "5." If cooling fan does not run, proceed to step 4. If cooling fan runs, check for the following:
   a. Circuit 335 for an open or short to battery.
   b. Poor connection.
   c. If connection and circuit are satisfactory, replace primary cooling fan relay.
4. Leaving fused jumper attached between terminals "3" and "5," disconnect primary cooling fan relay connector and connect a test light between cooling fan connector terminal "B" and ground. If test light comes on, proceed to step 5. If test light does not come on, check for poor connection or an open in circuit (702).
5. Leave fused jumper attached between terminals "3" and "5." Connect a test light between primary cooling fan connector terminals "A" and "B," then proceed as follows:
   a. If test lamp comes on, check for poor connection. If connection is satisfactory, replace primary cooling fan motor.

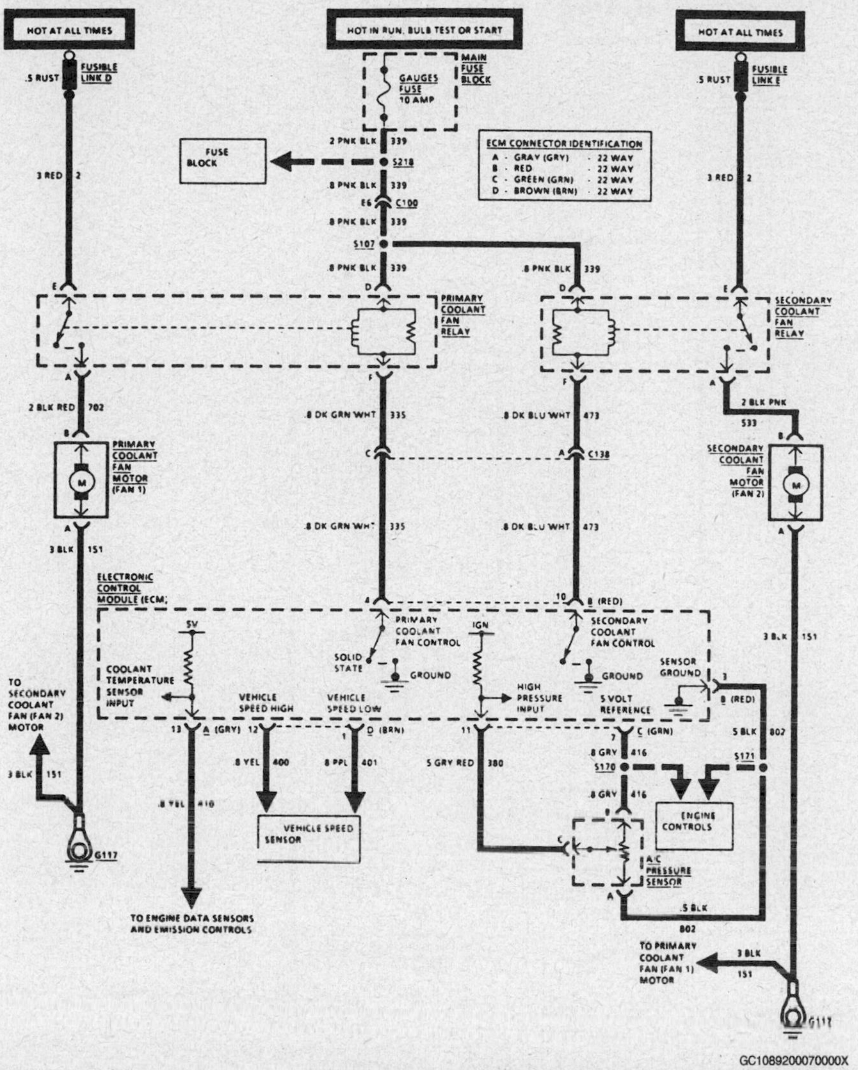
HOT AT ALL TIMES
HOT IN RUN, BULB TEST OR START
HOT AT ALL TIMES
FUSIBLE LINK D
FUSIBLE LINK E
MAIN FUSE BLOCK
GAUGES FUSE 10 AMP
FUSE BLOCK
ECM CONNECTOR IDENTIFICATION
A - GRAY (GRY) - 22 WAY
B - RED - 22 WAY
C - GREEN (GRN) - 22 WAY
D - BROWN (BRN) - 22 WAY
PRIMARY COOLANT FAN RELAY
SECONDARY COOLANT FAN RELAY
PRIMARY COOLANT FAN MOTOR (FAN 1)
SECONDARY COOLANT FAN MOTOR (FAN 2)
ELECTRONIC CONTROL MODULE (ECM)
PRIMARY COOLANT FAN CONTROL
SECONDARY COOLANT FAN CONTROL
COOLANT TEMPERATURE SENSOR INPUT
VEHICLE SPEED HIGH
VEHICLE SPEED LOW
HIGH PRESSURE INPUT
5 VOLT REFERENCE
SENSOR GROUND
TO SECONDARY COOLANT FAN (FAN 2) MOTOR
VEHICLE SPEED SENSOR
ENGINE CONTROLS
A/C PRESSURE SENSOR
TO ENGINE DATA SENSORS AND EMISSION CONTROLS
TO PRIMARY COOLANT FAN (FAN 1) MOTOR
G117
GC1089200070000X

Fig. 68 Cooling fan wiring circuit. 1992 Corvette w/5.7L/V8-350 (VIN P) engine

b. If test lamp does not come on, check for poor connection or an open circuit 150 between primary cooling fan and splice (S105).

Secondary Cooling Fan Does Not Run

1. Attach a fused jumper between secondary cooling fan relay terminal "1" and ground, then turn ignition switch to Run position. If cooling fan does not run, proceed to step 2. If cooling fan runs, check for an open in circuit (473) or poor connection at ECM. If circuit and connection are satisfactory, problem is ECM related.
2. Remove fused jumper and secondary cooling fan relay. Connect a test light between secondary cooling fan relay connector terminal "3" and ground, then between terminal "2" and ground. If test light comes on in both cases, proceed to step 3. If test light does not come on in both cases, check for a poor connection. If connection is satisfactory, check for an open in circuits (250) and (1442) on all engines except 3.8L/V6-231 or circuit (1445) on 3.8L/V6-231.
3. Connect a fused jumper between secondary cooling fan relay connector terminals "3" and "5." If secondary cooling fan does not run, proceed to step 4. If secondary cooling fan runs, check circuit (473) for an open or short to battery. If circuit is satisfactory, replace cooling fan relay.
4. Leave fused jumper attached between terminals "3" and "5." Disconnect secondary cooling fan connector, then connect a test light between secondary cooling fan connector terminal "B" and ground. If test lamp lights, proceed to step 5. If test lamp does not light, check for a poor connection or open in circuit (532).
5. Connect a test lamp between secondary cooling fan connector terminals "A and "B." If test lamp lights, check for poor connection. If connection is satisfactory, replace secondary cooling fan motor. If test lamp does not light, check for poor connection or open in circuit (150).

Primary Cooling Fan Runs Continuously With Engine Coolant Cool & A/C Mode Selector Off

1. Disconnect primary cooling fan relay number "1." If cooling fan stops running, proceed to step 2. If cooling fan continues to run, check circuit (702) for a short to battery.
2. Turn ignition switch to the Run position and connect a test lamp between primary cooling fan relay terminals "1 and "3." If test lamp lights, check circuit (335) for a short to ground. If circuit (335) is satisfactory, problem is ECM related. If test lamp does not light, replace primary cooling fan relay.

Secondary Cooling Fan Runs Continuously With Engine Coolant Cool & A/C Mode Selector Off

1. Disconnect secondary cooling fan relay number "2." If cooling fan stops running, proceed to step 2. If cooling fan continues to run, check circuit (532) for a short to battery.
2. Turn ignition switch to the Run position and connect a test lamp between secondary cooling fan relay terminals "1" and "3." If test lamp lights, check circuit (473) for a short to ground. If circuit (473) is satisfactory, problem is ECM related. If test lamp does not light, replace secondary cooling fan relay.

1994

Refer to Figs. 62 through 67 when performing diagnostic procedures on these systems.

CORVETTE

Refer to wiring diagrams, **Figs. 68 through 73**, when performing diagnostic procedures on these systems.

1992

Refer to **Figs. 74 and 75** for system diagnostic charts.

1993

Refer to **Figs. 76 and 77** for system diagnostic charts.

1994

Refer toFigs. 78 and 79 for system diagnostic charts.

DEVILLE & FLEETWOOD (FWD)

1992–93

Refer to **Fig. 80** when performing diagnostic procedures.

Cooling Fans Do Not Operate

1. Enter diagnostics and turn cooling fans on using PCM override. If cooling fans turn on, proceed to step 2. If cooling fans do not turn on, proceed to step 3.

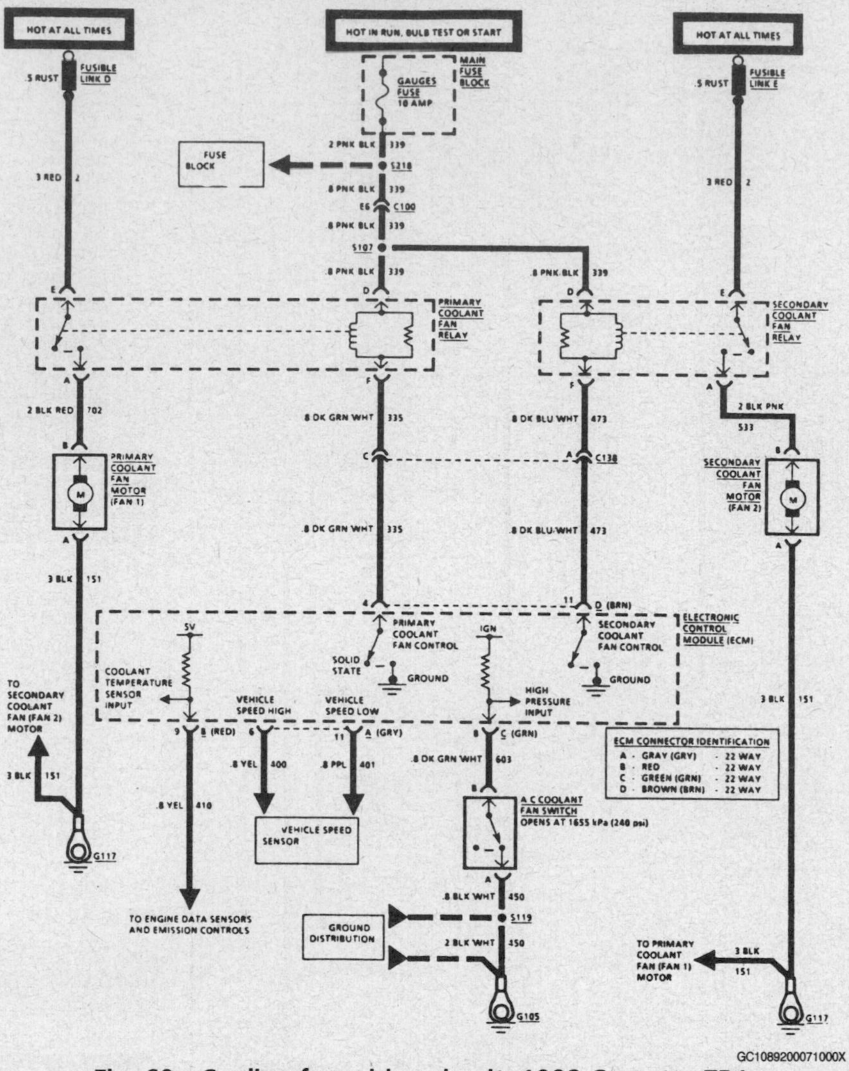
HOT AT ALL TIMES
HOT IN RUN, BULB TEST OR START
HOT AT ALL TIMES
FUSIBLE LINK D
FUSIBLE LINK E
MAIN FUSE BLOCK
GAUGES FUSE 10 AMP
FUSE BLOCK
PRIMARY COOLANT FAN RELAY
SECONDARY COOLANT FAN RELAY
PRIMARY COOLANT FAN MOTOR (FAN 1)
SECONDARY COOLANT FAN MOTOR (FAN 2)
ELECTRONIC CONTROL MODULE (ECM)
PRIMARY COOLANT FAN CONTROL
SECONDARY COOLANT FAN CONTROL
COOLANT TEMPERATURE SENSOR INPUT
VEHICLE SPEED HIGH
VEHICLE SPEED LOW
HIGH PRESSURE INPUT
GROUND
VEHICLE SPEED SENSOR
A C COOLANT FAN SWITCH OPENS AT 1655 kPa (240 psi)
ECM CONNECTOR IDENTIFICATION
A - GRAY (GRY) - 22 WAY
B - RED - 22 WAY
C - GREEN (GRN) - 22 WAY
D - BROWN (BRN) - 22 WAY
TO SECONDARY COOLANT FAN (FAN 2) MOTOR
TO PRIMARY COOLANT FAN (FAN 1) MOTOR
TO ENGINE DATA SENSORS AND EMISSION CONTROLS
GROUND DISTRIBUTION
G117
G105
GC1089200071000X

Fig. 69 Cooling fan wiring circuit. 1992 Corvette ZR1 w/5.7L/V8-350 (VIN J) engine

2. Start engine, turn on A/C and idle engine for a few minutes. Read PCM Data-Coolant Temperature Sensor (CTS) and read BCM Data-Refrigerant Temperature Sensor. If both readings are above ambient and rising parameters, replace PCM. If readings are not above ambient and rising parameters, check wiring to suspect sensor. If wiring is satisfactory, replace sensor.
3. Disconnect high speed cooling fan relay and measure voltage between relay terminal No. 1 (red) and ground. If battery voltage is indicated, proceed to step 4. If battery voltage is not indicated, check red wire from relay connector to left side underhood fuse block for an open circuit.
4. Turn ignition switch to the Run position, measure voltage between high speed relay terminal No. 2 (brown) and ground. If battery voltage is indicated, repair open circuit in cooling fan ground (black) wire. If battery voltage is not indicated, check brown wire from relay connector to instrument panel fuse block for an open circuit.

Cooling Fans Do Not Operate At Low Speed

The right side cooling fan runs at high speed when activated.

1. Enter diagnostics and turn cooling fans on low speed using PCM override. If cooling fans turn on, proceed to step 2. If cooling fans do not turn on, proceed to step 3.
2. Start engine, turn on A/C and idle engine for a few minutes. Read PCM Data-Coolant Temperature Sensor (CTS) and read BCM Data-Refrigerant Temperature Sensor. If both readings are above ambient and rising, replace PCM. If readings are not above ambient and rising, check wiring to suspect sensor, if wiring is satisfactory, replace sensor.
3. Leave PCM connected and turn ignition to the Run position, connect a fused jumper between PCM connector C2 (terminal A11, gray/black) and ground. If cooling fans run, replace PCM. If cooling fans do not run, proceed to step 4.
4. Leaving fused jumper in place at the PCM connector, check voltages at low speed cooling fan relay as follows:
   a. From terminal No. 1 (red) to ground. If battery voltage is indicated proceed to step b. If battery voltage is not indicated, repair open circuit in red wire.
   b. From terminal No. 1 (red) to terminal 5 (gray/black). If battery voltage is indicated, proceed to step c. If battery voltage is not indicated, repair open circuit in gray/black wire.
   c. From terminal No. 2 (brown) to ground. If battery voltage is indicated, proceed to step 5. If battery voltage is not indicated, repair open circuit in brown wire.
5. Connect a fused jumper between low speed cooling fan relay terminal No. 2 (brown) and terminal No. 4 (black/red). If cooling fans do not run, check red/black wire for an open circuit, if wire is satisfactory, check cooling fan resistors and wiring. If cooling fans run, replace low speed cooling fan relay.

Continued on page 17-66

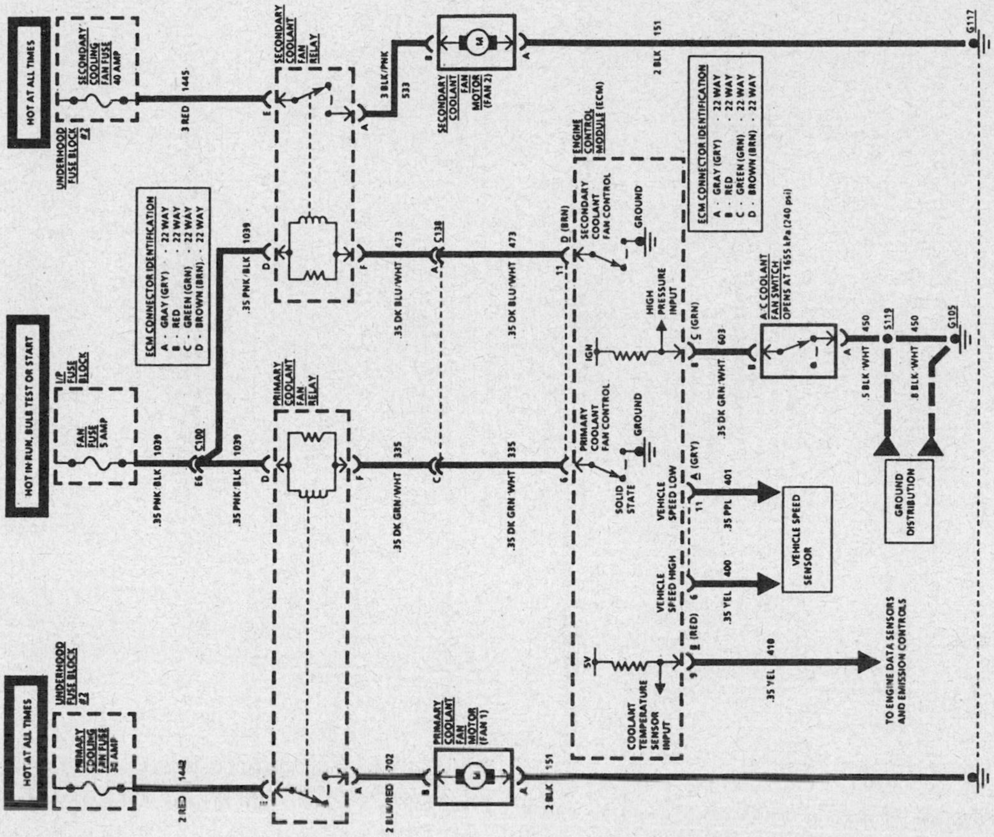

Fig. 71 Cooling fan wiring circuit. 1993 Corvette ZR1 w/5.7L/V8-350 (VIN J) engine

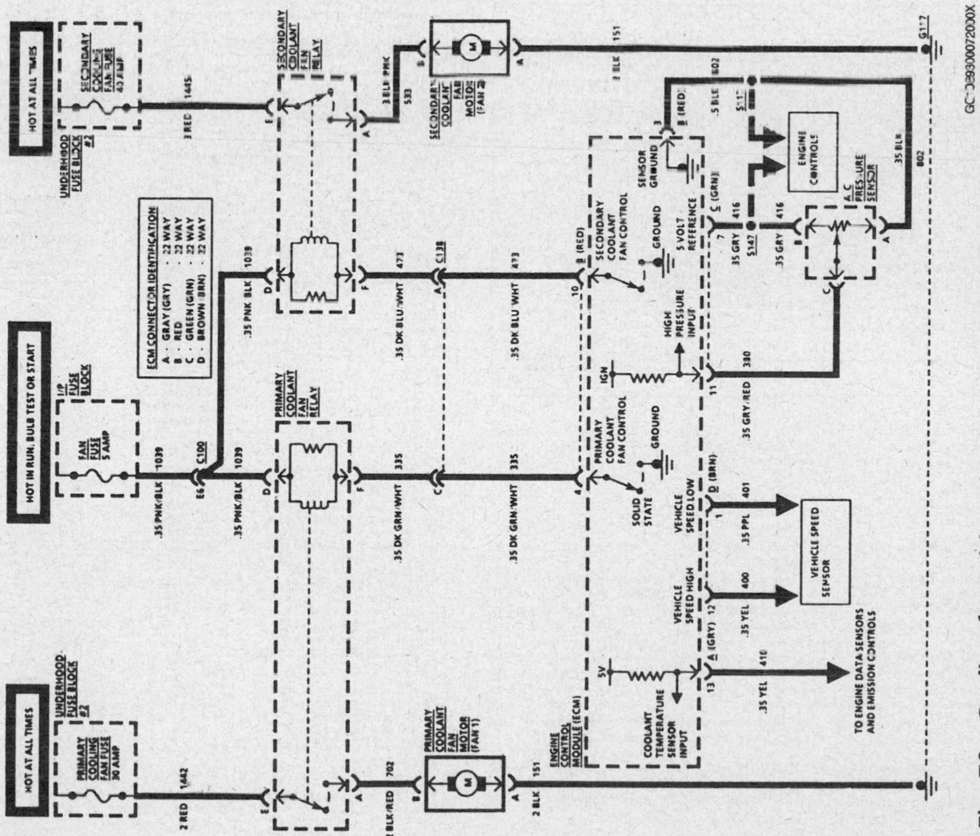

Fig. 70 Cooling fan wiring circuit. 1993 Corvette w/5.7L/V8-350 (VIN P) engine

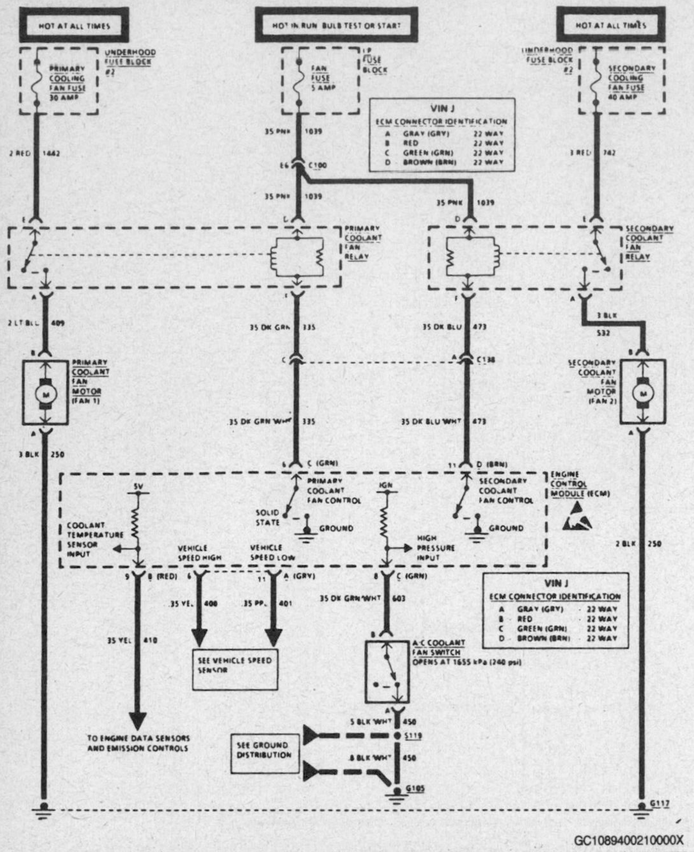

GC1089400210000X

Fig. 72 Cooling fan wiring circuit. 1994 Corvette ZR1 w/5.7L/V8-350 (VIN J) engine

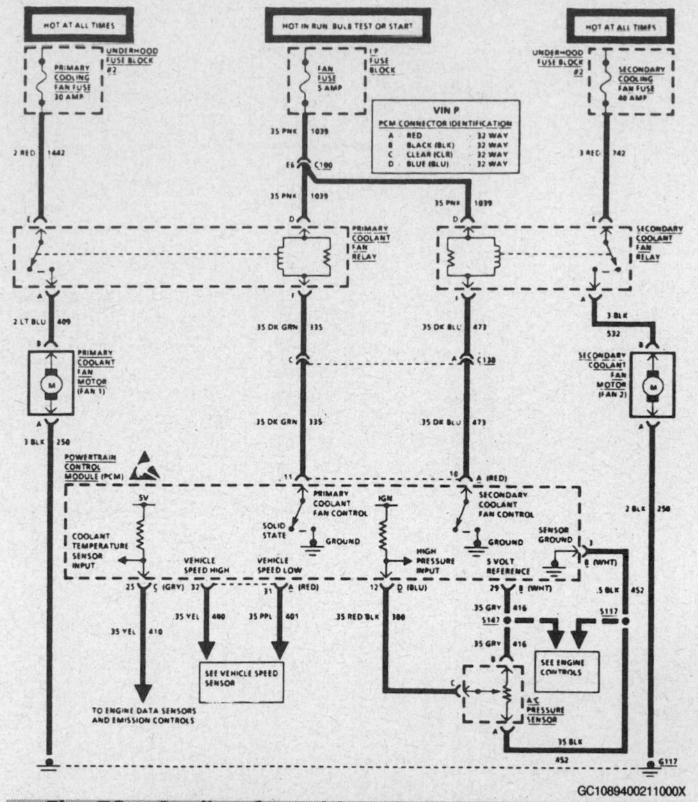

GC1089400211000X

Fig. 73 Cooling fan wiring circuit. 1994 Corvette w/5.7L/V8-350 (VIN P) engine

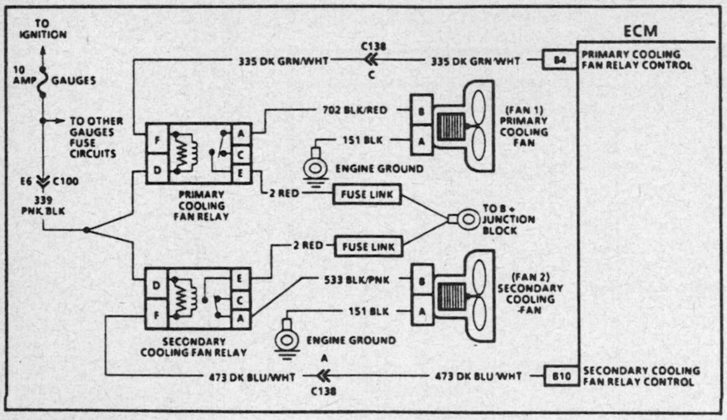

TO IGNITION
10 AMP GAUGES
TO OTHER GAUGES FUSE CIRCUITS
E6 C100
339 PNK BLK
ECM
C138
335 DK GRN/WHT
335 DK GRN WHT
C
B4
PRIMARY COOLING FAN RELAY CONTROL
702 BLK/RED
151 BLK
(FAN 1) PRIMARY COOLING FAN
ENGINE GROUND
PRIMARY COOLING FAN RELAY
2 RED
FUSE LINK
TO B+ JUNCTION BLOCK
533 BLK/PNK
(FAN 2) SECONDARY COOLING FAN
SECONDARY COOLING FAN RELAY
473 DK BLU/WHT
473 DK BLU WHT
B10
SECONDARY COOLING FAN RELAY CONTROL

Circuit Description:

The cooling fans are controlled by the ECM based on various inputs. Battery voltage is supplied to the fan relays on terminal "E" and ignition voltage to terminal "D". Grounding CKT 409 (relay terminal "F") will energize the primary cooling fan relay (Fan 1) and supply battery voltage to the primary cooling fan motor. Grounding CKT 473 (relay terminal "F") will energize the secondary cooling fan relay (Fan 2) and supply battery voltage to the secondary fan motor.

If any ECM codes are set or the ECM is operating in the fuel back-up mode, the ECM will turn "ON" the cooling fans.

Test Description:

Number(s) below refer to circled number(s) on the diagnostic chart.

1. With the diagnostic "test" terminal grounded, the cooling fan control driver(s) will close, which should energize the fan control relay(s).
2. The cooling fans should come "ON" anytime A/C system is operating.
3. Comparing Tech 1 pressure and manifold gage set pressure will determine if the A/C pressure sensor is out of range. An out of range A/C pressure sensor can cause the cooling fans to operate at the wrong times.

Diagnostic Aids:

If the owner complained of an overheating problem, it must be determined if the complaint was due to an actual boil over, or the warning indicator light, or engine coolant temperature gage indicated overheating.

The gage accuracy can also be checked by comparing the Coolant Temperature Sensor (CTS) reading using a Tech 1 and comparing its reading with the gage reading.

If the engine is actually overheating and the gage indicated overheating, but the cooling fan is not coming "ON," the Coolant Temperature Sensor (CTS) has probably shifted out of calibration and should be replaced.

If the engine is overheating and the cooling fans are "ON," the cooling system should be checked.

The ECM will command Fan 1 "ON" at 108°C (226°F) and "OFF" at 105°C (221°F) and, Fan 2 "ON" at 113°C (235°F) and "OFF" at 108°C (226°F).

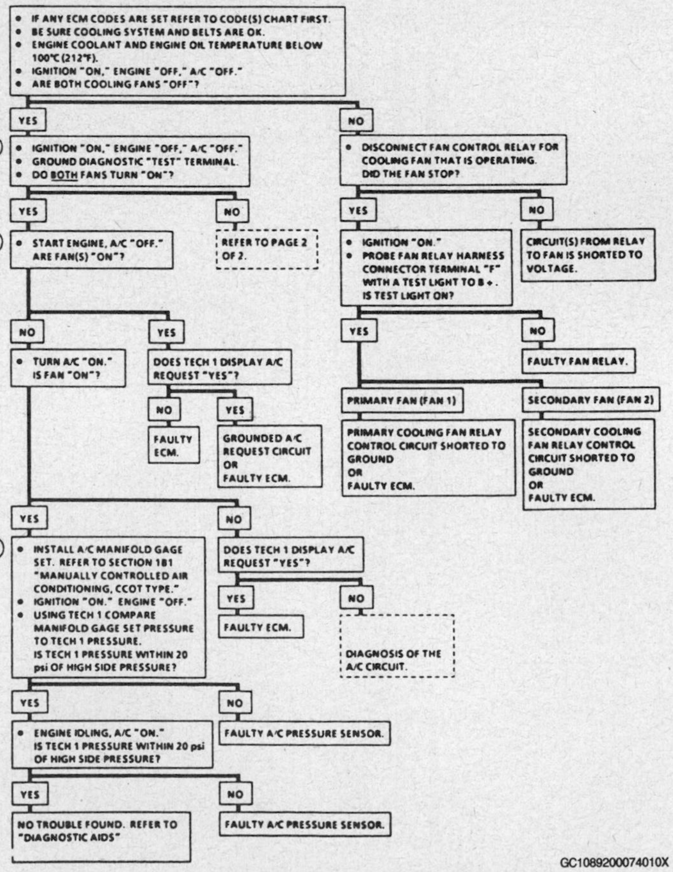

• IF ANY ECM CODES ARE SET REFER TO CODE(S) CHART FIRST.
• BE SURE COOLING SYSTEM AND BELTS ARE OK.
• ENGINE COOLANT AND ENGINE OIL TEMPERATURE BELOW 100°C (212°F).
• IGNITION "ON," ENGINE "OFF," A/C "OFF."
• ARE BOTH COOLING FANS "OFF"?
YES
NO
1
• IGNITION "ON," ENGINE "OFF," A/C "OFF."
• GROUND DIAGNOSTIC "TEST" TERMINAL.
• DO BOTH FANS TURN "ON"?
• DISCONNECT FAN CONTROL RELAY FOR COOLING FAN THAT IS OPERATING. DID THE FAN STOP?
2
• START ENGINE, A/C "OFF." ARE FAN(S) "ON"?
REFER TO PAGE 2 OF 2.
• IGNITION "ON."
• PROBE FAN RELAY HARNESS CONNECTOR TERMINAL "F" WITH A TEST LIGHT TO B+. IS TEST LIGHT ON?
CIRCUIT(S) FROM RELAY TO FAN IS SHORTED TO VOLTAGE.
FAULTY FAN RELAY.
• TURN A/C "ON." IS FAN "ON"?
DOES TECH 1 DISPLAY A/C REQUEST "YES"?
FAULTY ECM.
GROUNDED A/C REQUEST CIRCUIT OR FAULTY ECM.
PRIMARY FAN (FAN 1)
SECONDARY FAN (FAN 2)
PRIMARY COOLING FAN RELAY CONTROL CIRCUIT SHORTED TO GROUND OR FAULTY ECM.
SECONDARY COOLING FAN RELAY CONTROL CIRCUIT SHORTED TO GROUND OR FAULTY ECM.
3
• INSTALL A/C MANIFOLD GAGE SET. REFER TO SECTION 1B1 "MANUALLY CONTROLLED AIR CONDITIONING, CCOT TYPE."
• IGNITION "ON," ENGINE "OFF."
• USING TECH 1 COMPARE MANIFOLD GAGE SET PRESSURE TO TECH 1 PRESSURE. IS TECH 1 PRESSURE WITHIN 20 psi OF HIGH SIDE PRESSURE?
DOES TECH 1 DISPLAY A/C REQUEST "YES"?
FAULTY ECM.
DIAGNOSIS OF THE A/C CIRCUIT.
• ENGINE IDLING, A/C "ON." IS TECH 1 PRESSURE WITHIN 20 psi OF HIGH SIDE PRESSURE?
FAULTY A/C PRESSURE SENSOR.
NO TROUBLE FOUND. REFER TO "DIAGNOSTIC AIDS"
FAULTY A/C PRESSURE SENSOR.

GC1089200074010X

Fig. 74 Chart C-12, cooling fan diagnosis (Part 1 of 2). 1992 Corvette w/5.7L/V8-350 (VIN P) engine

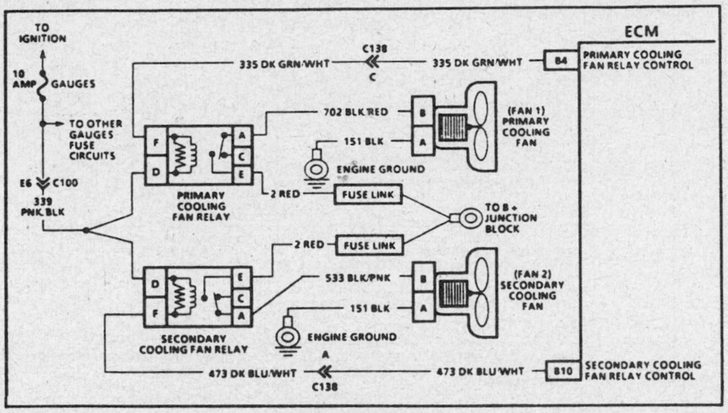

TO IGNITION
10 AMP GAUGES
TO OTHER GAUGES FUSE CIRCUITS
E6 C100
339 PNK/BLK
C138
335 DK GRN/WHT
ECM
B4
PRIMARY COOLING FAN RELAY CONTROL
702 BLK/RED
151 BLK
(FAN 1) PRIMARY COOLING FAN
ENGINE GROUND
PRIMARY COOLING FAN RELAY
2 RED
FUSE LINK
TO B+ JUNCTION BLOCK
533 BLK/PNK
(FAN 2) SECONDARY COOLING FAN
SECONDARY COOLING FAN RELAY
473 DK BLU/WHT
B10
SECONDARY COOLING FAN RELAY CONTROL

CHART C-12

(Page 2 of 2)

ELECTRIC COOLING FAN CONTROL CIRCUIT DIAGNOSIS

5.7L "Y" CARLINE (PORT)

Circuit Description:

The cooling fans are controlled by the ECM based on various inputs. Battery voltage is supplied to the fan relays on terminal "E" and ignition voltage to terminal "D". Grounding CKT 409 (relay terminal "F") will energize the primary cooling fan relay (Fan 1) and supply battery voltage to the primary cooling fan motor. Grounding CKT 473 (relay terminal "F") will energize the secondary cooling fan relay (Fan 2) and supply battery voltage to the secondary fan motor.

If any ECM codes are set or the ECM is operating in the fuel back-up mode, the ECM will turn "ON" the cooling fans.

Diagnostic Aids:

If the owner complained of an overheating problem, it must be determined if the complaint was due to an actual boil over, or the warning indicator light, or engine coolant temperature gage indicated overheating.

The gage accuracy can also be checked by comparing the Coolant Temperature Sensor (CTS) reading using a Tech 1 and comparing its reading with the gage reading.

If the engine is actually overheating and the gage indicated overheating, but the cooling fan is not coming "ON," the Coolant Temperature Sensor (CTS) has probably shifted out of calibration and should be replaced.

If the engine is overheating and the cooling fans are "ON," the cooling system should be checked

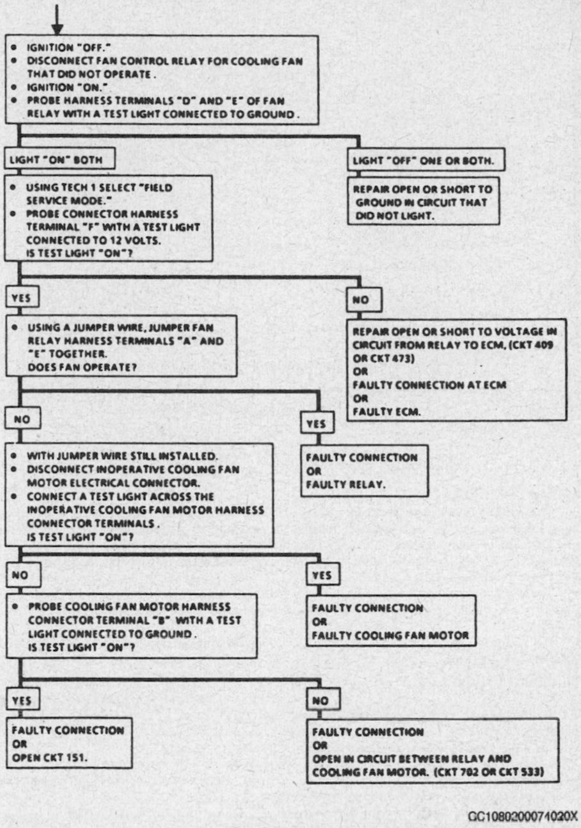

• IGNITION "OFF."
• DISCONNECT FAN CONTROL RELAY FOR COOLING FAN THAT DID NOT OPERATE.
• IGNITION "ON."
• PROBE HARNESS TERMINALS "D" AND "E" OF FAN RELAY WITH A TEST LIGHT CONNECTED TO GROUND.
LIGHT "ON" BOTH
LIGHT "OFF" ONE OR BOTH.
REPAIR OPEN OR SHORT TO GROUND IN CIRCUIT THAT DID NOT LIGHT.
• USING TECH 1 SELECT "FIELD SERVICE MODE."
• PROBE CONNECTOR HARNESS TERMINAL "F" WITH A TEST LIGHT CONNECTED TO 12 VOLTS. IS TEST LIGHT "ON"?
YES
NO
REPAIR OPEN OR SHORT TO VOLTAGE IN CIRCUIT FROM RELAY TO ECM. (CKT 409 OR CKT 473) OR FAULTY CONNECTION AT ECM OR FAULTY ECM.
• USING A JUMPER WIRE, JUMPER FAN RELAY HARNESS TERMINALS "A" AND "E" TOGETHER. DOES FAN OPERATE?
NO
YES
FAULTY CONNECTION OR FAULTY RELAY.
• WITH JUMPER WIRE STILL INSTALLED.
• DISCONNECT INOPERATIVE COOLING FAN MOTOR ELECTRICAL CONNECTOR.
• CONNECT A TEST LIGHT ACROSS THE INOPERATIVE COOLING FAN MOTOR HARNESS CONNECTOR TERMINALS. IS TEST LIGHT "ON"?
NO
YES
FAULTY CONNECTION OR FAULTY COOLING FAN MOTOR
• PROBE COOLING FAN MOTOR HARNESS CONNECTOR TERMINAL "B" WITH A TEST LIGHT CONNECTED TO GROUND. IS TEST LIGHT "ON"?
YES
NO
FAULTY CONNECTION OR OPEN CKT 151.
FAULTY CONNECTION OR OPEN IN CIRCUIT BETWEEN RELAY AND COOLING FAN MOTOR. (CKT 702 OR CKT 533)
GC1080200074020X

Fig. 74 Chart C-12, cooling fan diagnosis (Part 2 of 2). 1992 Corvette w/5.7L/V8-350 (VIN P) engine

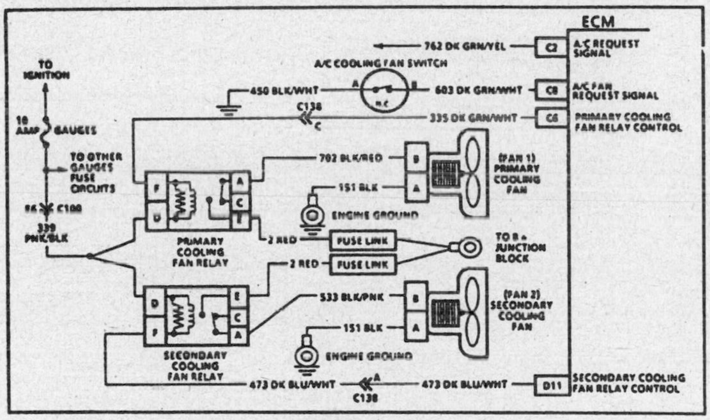

ECM
762 DK GRN/YEL
C2
A/C REQUEST SIGNAL
A/C COOLING FAN SWITCH
TO IGNITION
450 BLK/WHT
603 DK GRN/WHT
C8
A/C FAN REQUEST SIGNAL
C136
335 DK GRN/WHT
C6
PRIMARY COOLING FAN RELAY CONTROL
10 AMP GAUGES
TO OTHER GAUGES FUSE CIRCUITS
C100
339 PNK/BLK
702 BLK/RED
151 BLK
(FAN 1) PRIMARY COOLING FAN
ENGINE GROUND
PRIMARY COOLING FAN RELAY
2 RED
FUSE LINK
TO B+ JUNCTION BLOCK
533 BLK/PNK
(FAN 2) SECONDARY COOLING FAN
SECONDARY COOLING FAN RELAY
473 DK BLU/WHT
C138
D11
SECONDARY COOLING FAN RELAY CONTROL

CHART C-12

(Page 1 of 2)

ELECTRIC COOLING FAN CONTROL CIRCUIT DIAGNOSIS

5.7L "Y" CARLINE (PORT)

Circuit Description:

The cooling fans are controlled by the ECM based on various inputs. Battery voltage is supplied to the fan relays on terminal "E" and ignition voltage to terminal "D". Grounding CKT 335 (relay terminal "F") will energize the primary cooling fan relay (Fan 1) and supply battery voltage to the primary cooling fan motor. Grounding CKT 473 (relay terminal "F") will energize the secondary cooling fan relay (Fan 2) and supply battery voltage to the secondary fan motor.

The A/C cooling fan switch, mounted in the A/C high pressure line, will open when head pressure is approximately 1655 kPa (240 psi) and this input will cause the ECM to ground CKT 473 or CKT 335 if other criteria are met.

If a Codes 14, 15, 52 or 62 are set or the ECM is operating in the fuel back-up mode, the ECM will turn "ON" both the cooling fans.

Diagnostic Aids:

If the owner complained of an overheating problem it must be determined if the complaint was due to an actual boil over, or the warning indicator light, or engine coolant temperature gage indicated overheating.

The gage accuracy can also be checked by comparing the Coolant Temperature Sensor (CTS) reading using a "Scan" tool and comparing its reading with the gage reading.

If the engine is actually overheating and the gage indicates overheating, but the cooling fan is not coming "ON," the Coolant Temperature Sensor (CTS) has probably shifted out of calibration and should be replaced.

If the engine is overheating and the cooling fans are "ON," the cooling system should be checked

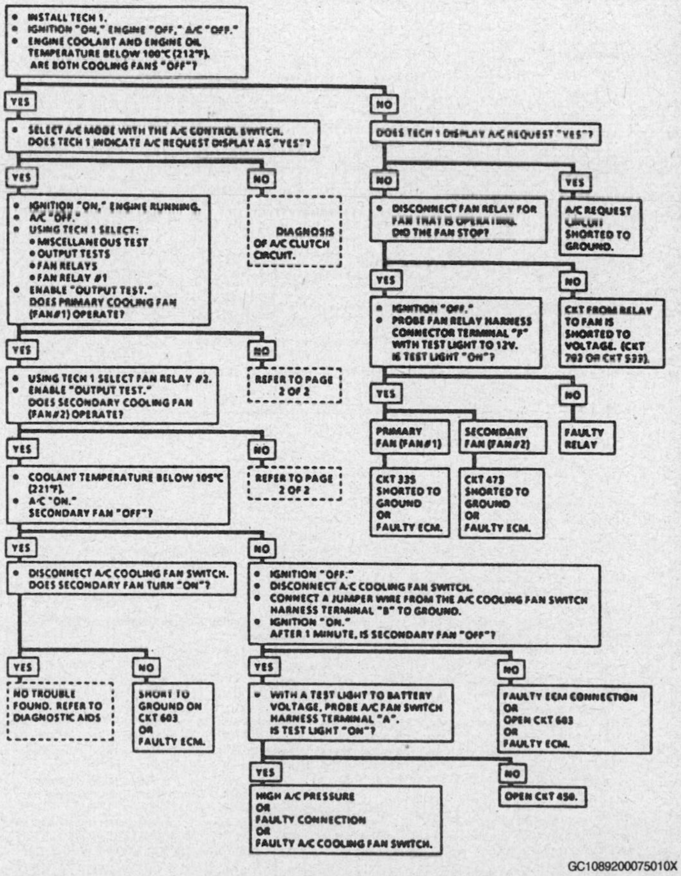

• INSTALL TECH 1.
• IGNITION "ON," ENGINE "OFF," A/C "OFF."
• ENGINE COOLANT AND ENGINE OIL TEMPERATURE BELOW 100°C (212°F). ARE BOTH COOLING FANS "OFF"?
YES
NO
• SELECT A/C MODE WITH THE A/C CONTROL SWITCH. DOES TECH 1 INDICATE A/C REQUEST DISPLAY AS "YES"?
DOES TECH 1 DISPLAY A/C REQUEST "YES"?
• IGNITION "ON," ENGINE RUNNING.
• A/C "OFF."
• USING TECH 1 SELECT:
• MISCELLANEOUS TEST
• OUTPUT TESTS
• FAN RELAYS
• FAN RELAY #1
• ENABLE "OUTPUT TEST." DOES PRIMARY COOLING FAN (FAN#1) OPERATE?
DIAGNOSIS OF A/C CLUTCH CIRCUIT.
• DISCONNECT FAN RELAY FOR FAN THAT IS OPERATING. DID THE FAN STOP?
A/C REQUEST CIRCUIT SHORTED TO GROUND.
• USING TECH 1 SELECT FAN RELAY #2.
• ENABLE "OUTPUT TEST." DOES SECONDARY COOLING FAN (FAN#2) OPERATE?
REFER TO PAGE 2 OF 2
• IGNITION "OFF."
• PROBE FAN RELAY HARNESS CONNECTOR TERMINAL "F" WITH TEST LIGHT TO 12V. IS TEST LIGHT "ON"?
CKT FROM RELAY TO FAN IS SHORTED TO VOLTAGE. (CKT 702 OR CKT 533).
PRIMARY FAN (FAN#1)
SECONDARY FAN (FAN#2)
FAULTY RELAY
CKT 335 SHORTED TO GROUND OR FAULTY ECM.
CKT 473 SHORTED TO GROUND OR FAULTY ECM.
• COOLANT TEMPERATURE BELOW 105°C (221°F).
• A/C "ON." SECONDARY FAN "OFF"?
REFER TO PAGE 2 OF 2
• DISCONNECT A/C COOLING FAN SWITCH. DOES SECONDARY FAN TURN "ON"?
• IGNITION "OFF."
• DISCONNECT A/C COOLING FAN SWITCH.
• CONNECT A JUMPER WIRE FROM THE A/C COOLING FAN SWITCH HARNESS TERMINAL "B" TO GROUND.
• IGNITION "ON." AFTER 1 MINUTE, IS SECONDARY FAN "OFF"?
NO TROUBLE FOUND. REFER TO DIAGNOSTIC AIDS
SHORT TO GROUND ON CKT 603 OR FAULTY ECM.
• WITH A TEST LIGHT TO BATTERY VOLTAGE, PROBE A/C FAN SWITCH HARNESS TERMINAL "A". IS TEST LIGHT "ON"?
FAULTY ECM CONNECTION OR OPEN CKT 603 OR FAULTY ECM.
HIGH A/C PRESSURE OR FAULTY CONNECTION OR FAULTY A/C COOLING FAN SWITCH.
OPEN CKT 450.
GC1089200075010X

Fig. 75 Chart C-12, cooling fan diagnosis (Part 1 of 2). 1992 Corvette ZR1 w/5.7L/V8-350 (VIN J) engine

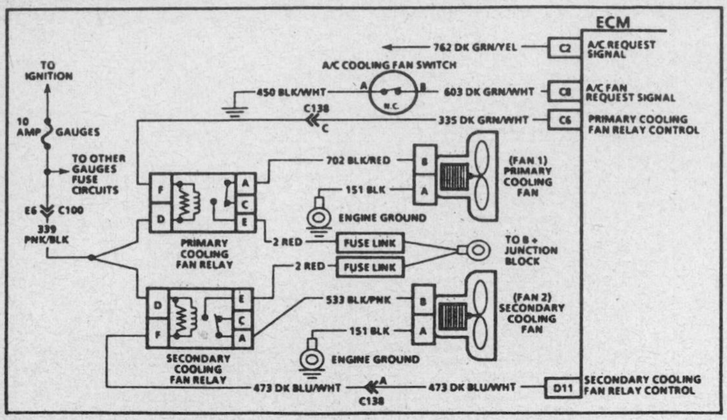

ECM
762 DK GRN/YEL
C2
A/C REQUEST SIGNAL
A/C COOLING FAN SWITCH
TO IGNITION
450 BLK/WHT
603 DK GRN/WHT
C8
A/C FAN REQUEST SIGNAL
C138
335 DK GRN/WHT
C6
PRIMARY COOLING FAN RELAY CONTROL
10 AMP GAUGES
TO OTHER GAUGES FUSE CIRCUITS
E6 C100
339 PNK/BLK
702 BLK/RED
151 BLK
(FAN 1) PRIMARY COOLING FAN
ENGINE GROUND
PRIMARY COOLING FAN RELAY
2 RED
FUSE LINK
TO B+ JUNCTION BLOCK
533 BLK/PNK
(FAN 2) SECONDARY COOLING FAN
SECONDARY COOLING FAN RELAY
473 DK BLU/WHT
D11
SECONDARY COOLING FAN RELAY CONTROL

CHART C-12

(Page 2 of 2)
ELECTRIC COOLING FAN CONTROL CIRCUIT DIAGNOSIS
5.7L "Y" CARLINE (PORT)

Circuit Description:

The cooling fans are controlled by the ECM based on various inputs. Battery voltage is supplied to the fan relays on terminal "E" and ignition voltage to terminal "D". Grounding CKT 335 (relay terminal "F") will energize the primary cooling fan relay (Fan 1) and supply battery voltage to the primary cooling fan motor. Grounding CKT 473 (relay terminal "F") will energize the secondary cooling fan relay (Fan 2) and supply battery voltage to the secondary fan motor.

The A/C cooling fan switch, mounted in the A/C high pressure line, will open when head pressure is approximately 1655 kPa (240 psi). This input will cause the ECM to ground CKT 473 or CKT 335 if other criteria are met.

If a Codes 14, 15, 52 or 62 are set or the ECM is operating in the fuel back-up mode, the ECM will turn "ON" both the cooling fans.

Diagnostic Aids:

If the owner complained of an overheating problem, it must be determined if the complaint was due to an actual boil over or the warning indicator light or engine coolant temperature gage indicated overheating.

The gage accuracy can also be checked by comparing the Coolant Temperature Sensor (CTS) reading using a "Scan" tool and comparing its reading with the gage reading.

If the engine is actually overheating and the gage indicates overheating, but the cooling fan is not coming "ON," the Coolant Temperature Sensor (CTS) has probably shifted out of calibration and should be replaced.

If the engine is overheating and the cooling fans are "ON," the cooling system should be checked

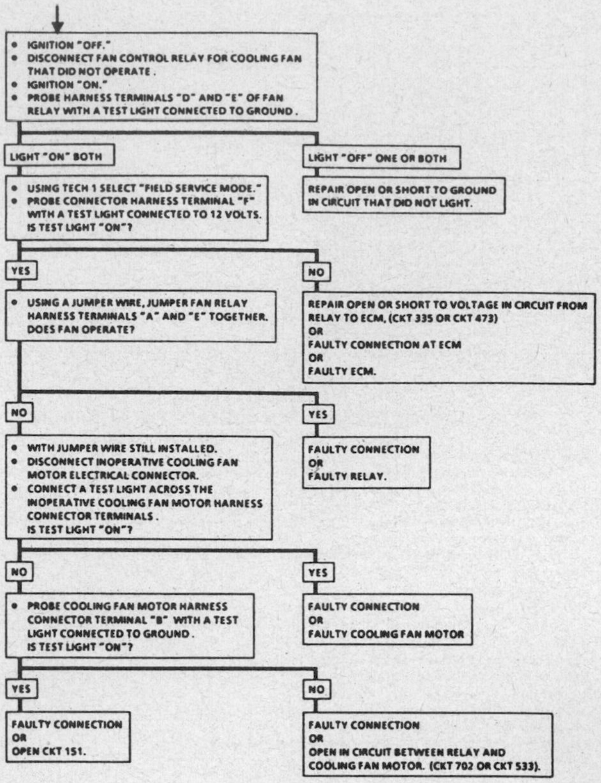

• IGNITION "OFF."
• DISCONNECT FAN CONTROL RELAY FOR COOLING FAN THAT DID NOT OPERATE.
• IGNITION "ON."
• PROBE HARNESS TERMINALS "D" AND "E" OF FAN RELAY WITH A TEST LIGHT CONNECTED TO GROUND.
LIGHT "ON" BOTH
LIGHT "OFF" ONE OR BOTH
REPAIR OPEN OR SHORT TO GROUND IN CIRCUIT THAT DID NOT LIGHT.
• USING TECH 1 SELECT "FIELD SERVICE MODE."
• PROBE CONNECTOR HARNESS TERMINAL "F" WITH A TEST LIGHT CONNECTED TO 12 VOLTS. IS TEST LIGHT "ON"?
YES
NO
• USING A JUMPER WIRE, JUMPER FAN RELAY HARNESS TERMINALS "A" AND "E" TOGETHER. DOES FAN OPERATE?
REPAIR OPEN OR SHORT TO VOLTAGE IN CIRCUIT FROM RELAY TO ECM, (CKT 335 OR CKT 473) OR FAULTY CONNECTION AT ECM OR FAULTY ECM.
NO
YES
• WITH JUMPER WIRE STILL INSTALLED.
• DISCONNECT INOPERATIVE COOLING FAN MOTOR ELECTRICAL CONNECTOR.
• CONNECT A TEST LIGHT ACROSS THE INOPERATIVE COOLING FAN MOTOR HARNESS CONNECTOR TERMINALS. IS TEST LIGHT "ON"?
FAULTY CONNECTION OR FAULTY RELAY.
NO
YES
• PROBE COOLING FAN MOTOR HARNESS CONNECTOR TERMINAL "B" WITH A TEST LIGHT CONNECTED TO GROUND. IS TEST LIGHT "ON"?
FAULTY CONNECTION OR FAULTY COOLING FAN MOTOR
YES
NO
FAULTY CONNECTION OR OPEN CKT 151.
FAULTY CONNECTION OR OPEN IN CIRCUIT BETWEEN RELAY AND COOLING FAN MOTOR. (CKT 702 OR CKT 533).

GC1089200075020X

Fig. 75 Chart C-12, cooling fan diagnosis (Part 2 of 2). 1992 Corvette ZR1 w/5.7L/V8-350 (VIN J) engine

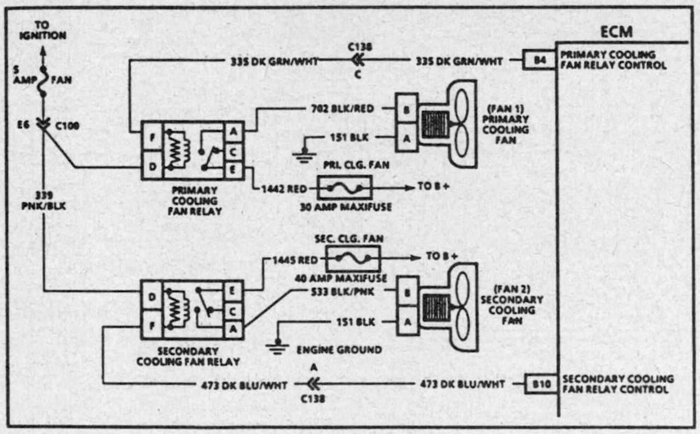

TO IGNITION
ECM
C138
335 DK GRN/WHT
B4
PRIMARY COOLING FAN RELAY CONTROL
5 AMP FAN
E6 C100
702 BLK/RED
151 BLK
(FAN 1) PRIMARY COOLING FAN
PRI. CLG. FAN
1442 RED
TO B+
30 AMP MAXIFUSE
339 PNK/BLK
PRIMARY COOLING FAN RELAY
SEC. CLG. FAN
1445 RED
40 AMP MAXIFUSE
533 BLK/PNK
(FAN 2) SECONDARY COOLING FAN
SECONDARY COOLING FAN RELAY
ENGINE GROUND
473 DK BLU/WHT
B10
SECONDARY COOLING FAN RELAY CONTROL

CHART C-12

(Page 1 of 2)
ELECTRIC COOLING FAN CONTROL CIRCUIT DIAGNOSIS
5.7L (VIN P) "Y" CARLINE (MFI)

Circuit Description:

The cooling fans are controlled by the ECM based on various inputs. Battery voltage is supplied to the fan relays on terminal "E" and ignition voltage to terminal "D". Grounding CKT 335 (relay terminal "F") will energize the primary cooling fan relay (Fan 1) and supply battery voltage to the primary cooling fan motor. Grounding CKT 473 (relay terminal "F") will energize the secondary cooling fan relay (Fan 2) and supply battery voltage to the secondary fan motor.

If any ECM DTC(s) are set or the ECM is operating in the fuel back-up mode, the ECM will turn "ON" the cooling fans.

Test Description: Number(s) below refer to circled number(s) on the diagnostic chart.

1. With the diagnostic "test" terminal grounded, the cooling fan control driver(s) will close, which should energize the fan control relay(s).
2. The cooling fans should come "ON" anytime A/C system is operating.
3. Comparing Tech 1 pressure and manifold gage set pressure will determine if the A/C refrigerant pressure sensor is out of range. An out of range A/C refrigerant pressure sensor can cause the cooling fans to operate at the wrong times.

Diagnostic Aids:

If the owner complained of an overheating problem, it must be determined if the complaint was due to an actual boil over, or the warning indicator light, or engine coolant temperature gage indicated overheating.

The gage accuracy can also be checked by comparing the Engine Coolant Temperature (ECT) sensor reading using a Tech 1 and comparing its reading with the gage reading.

If the engine is actually overheating and the gage indicated overheating, but the cooling fan is not coming "ON," the Engine Coolant Temperature (ECT) sensor has probably shifted out of calibration and should be replaced.

If the engine is overheating and the cooling fans are "ON," the cooling system should be checked,

The ECM will command fan 1 "ON" at 108°C (226°F) and "OFF" at 105°C (221°F) and, fan 2 "ON" at 113°C (235°F) and "OFF" at 108°C (226°F).

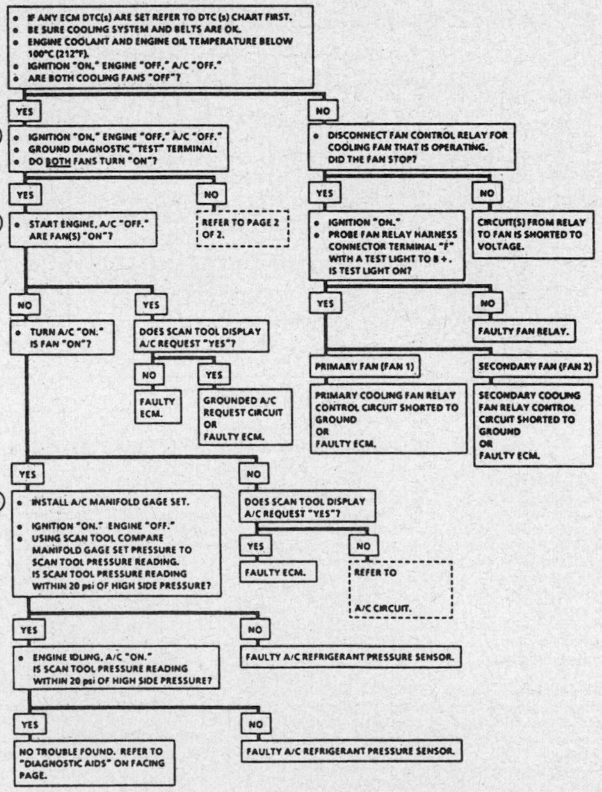

• IF ANY ECM DTC(s) ARE SET REFER TO DTC (s) CHART FIRST.
• BE SURE COOLING SYSTEM AND BELTS ARE OK.
• ENGINE COOLANT AND ENGINE OIL TEMPERATURE BELOW 100°C (212°F).
• IGNITION "ON," ENGINE "OFF," A/C "OFF."
• ARE BOTH COOLING FANS "OFF"?
YES
NO
1
• IGNITION "ON," ENGINE "OFF," A/C "OFF."
• GROUND DIAGNOSTIC "TEST" TERMINAL.
• DO BOTH FANS TURN "ON"?
• DISCONNECT FAN CONTROL RELAY FOR COOLING FAN THAT IS OPERATING. DID THE FAN STOP?
YES
NO
YES
NO
2
• START ENGINE, A/C "OFF." ARE FAN(S) "ON"?
REFER TO PAGE 2 OF 2.
• IGNITION "ON."
• PROBE FAN RELAY HARNESS CONNECTOR TERMINAL "F" WITH A TEST LIGHT TO B+. IS TEST LIGHT ON?
CIRCUIT(S) FROM RELAY TO FAN IS SHORTED TO VOLTAGE.
NO
YES
YES
NO
• TURN A/C "ON." IS FAN "ON"?
DOES SCAN TOOL DISPLAY A/C REQUEST "YES"?
FAULTY FAN RELAY.
NO
YES
PRIMARY FAN (FAN 1)
SECONDARY FAN (FAN 2)
FAULTY ECM.
GROUNDED A/C REQUEST CIRCUIT OR FAULTY ECM.
PRIMARY COOLING FAN RELAY CONTROL CIRCUIT SHORTED TO GROUND OR FAULTY ECM.
SECONDARY COOLING FAN RELAY CONTROL CIRCUIT SHORTED TO GROUND OR FAULTY ECM.
YES
NO
3
• INSTALL A/C MANIFOLD GAGE SET.
• IGNITION "ON." ENGINE "OFF."
• USING SCAN TOOL COMPARE MANIFOLD GAGE SET PRESSURE TO SCAN TOOL PRESSURE READING. IS SCAN TOOL PRESSURE READING WITHIN 20 psi OF HIGH SIDE PRESSURE?
DOES SCAN TOOL DISPLAY A/C REQUEST "YES"?
YES
NO
FAULTY ECM.
REFER TO A/C CIRCUIT.
YES
NO
• ENGINE IDLING, A/C "ON." IS SCAN TOOL PRESSURE READING WITHIN 20 psi OF HIGH SIDE PRESSURE?
FAULTY A/C REFRIGERANT PRESSURE SENSOR.
YES
NO
NO TROUBLE FOUND. REFER TO "DIAGNOSTIC AIDS" ON FACING PAGE.
FAULTY A/C REFRIGERANT PRESSURE SENSOR.

GC1089300076010X

Fig. 76 Chart C-12, cooling fan diagnosis (Part 1 of 2). 1993 Corvette w/5.7L/V8-350 (VIN P) engine

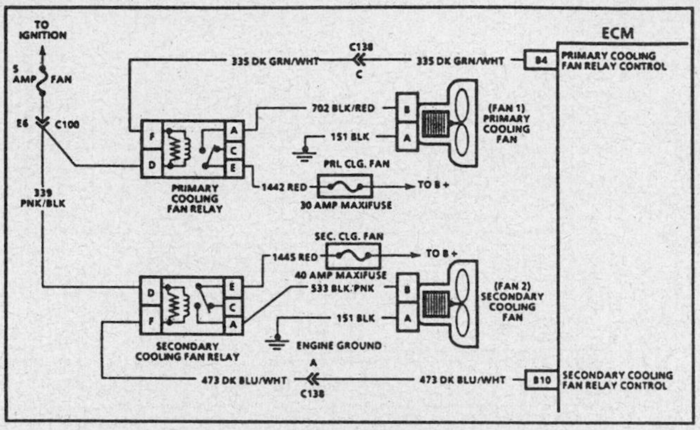
TO IGNITION
5 AMP
FAN
E6
C100
339 PNK/BLK
C138
335 DK GRN/WHT
C
335 DK GRN/WHT
ECM
B4
PRIMARY COOLING FAN RELAY CONTROL
702 BLK/RED
151 BLK
(FAN 1) PRIMARY COOLING FAN
PRIMARY COOLING FAN RELAY
PRL CLG. FAN
1442 RED
TO B +
30 AMP MAXIFUSE
SEC. CLG. FAN
1445 RED
TO B +
40 AMP MAXIFUSE
533 BLK/PNK
151 BLK
(FAN 2) SECONDARY COOLING FAN
SECONDARY COOLING FAN RELAY
ENGINE GROUND
A
473 DK BLU/WHT
C138
473 DK BLU/WHT
B10
SECONDARY COOLING FAN RELAY CONTROL

CHART C-12

(Page 2 of 2)
ELECTRIC COOLING FAN CONTROL CIRCUIT DIAGNOSIS
5.7L (VIN P) "Y" CARLINE (MFI)

Circuit Description:

The cooling fans are controlled by the ECM based on various inputs. Battery voltage is supplied to the fan relays on terminal "E" and ignition voltage to terminal "D". Grounding CKT 335 (relay terminal "F") will energize the primary cooling fan relay (Fan 1) and supply battery voltage to the primary cooling fan motor. Grounding CKT 473 (relay terminal "F") will energize the secondary cooling fan relay (Fan 2) and supply battery voltage to the secondary fan motor.

If any ECM DTC(s) are set or the ECM is operating in the fuel back-up mode, the ECM will turn "ON" the cooling fans.

Diagnostic Aids:

If the owner complained of an overheating problem, it must be determined if the complaint was due to an actual boil over, the warning indicator light, or engine coolant temperature gage indicated overheating.

The gage accuracy can also be checked by comparing the Engine Coolant Temperature (ECT) sensor reading using a Tech 1 and comparing its reading with the gage reading.

If the engine is actually overheating and the gage indicated overheating, but the cooling fan is not coming "ON," the Engine Coolant Temperature (ECT) sensor has probably shifted out of calibration and should be replaced.

If the engine is overheating and the cooling fans are "ON," the cooling system should be checked,

The ECM will command fan 1 "ON" at 108°C (226°F) and "OFF" at 105°C (221°F) and, fan 2 "ON" at 113°C (235°F) and "OFF" at 108°C (226°F).

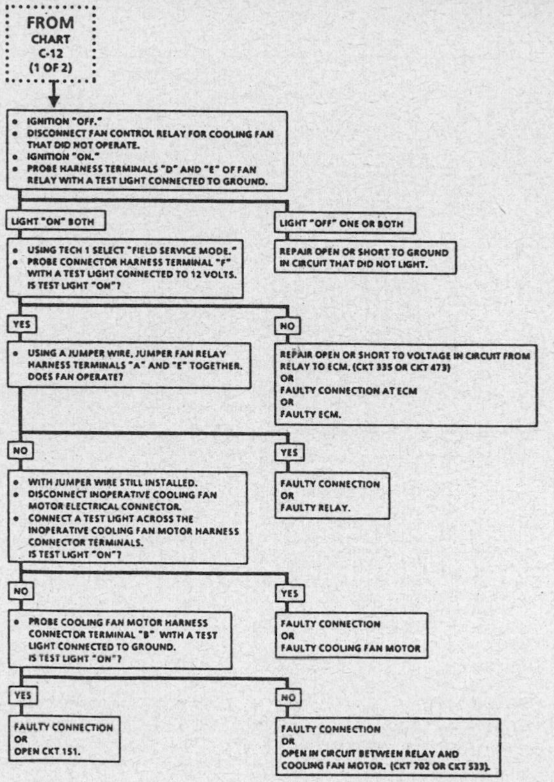
FROM CHART C-12 (1 OF 2)
• IGNITION "OFF."
• DISCONNECT FAN CONTROL RELAY FOR COOLING FAN THAT DID NOT OPERATE.
• IGNITION "ON."
• PROBE HARNESS TERMINALS "D" AND "E" OF FAN RELAY WITH A TEST LIGHT CONNECTED TO GROUND.
LIGHT "ON" BOTH
LIGHT "OFF" ONE OR BOTH
• USING TECH 1 SELECT "FIELD SERVICE MODE."
• PROBE CONNECTOR HARNESS TERMINAL "F" WITH A TEST LIGHT CONNECTED TO 12 VOLTS. IS TEST LIGHT "ON"?
REPAIR OPEN OR SHORT TO GROUND IN CIRCUIT THAT DID NOT LIGHT.
YES
NO
• USING A JUMPER WIRE, JUMPER FAN RELAY HARNESS TERMINALS "A" AND "E" TOGETHER. DOES FAN OPERATE?
REPAIR OPEN OR SHORT TO VOLTAGE IN CIRCUIT FROM RELAY TO ECM. (CKT 335 OR CKT 473) OR FAULTY CONNECTION AT ECM OR FAULTY ECM.
NO
YES
• WITH JUMPER WIRE STILL INSTALLED.
• DISCONNECT INOPERATIVE COOLING FAN MOTOR ELECTRICAL CONNECTOR.
• CONNECT A TEST LIGHT ACROSS THE INOPERATIVE COOLING FAN MOTOR HARNESS CONNECTOR TERMINALS. IS TEST LIGHT "ON"?
FAULTY CONNECTION OR FAULTY RELAY.
NO
YES
• PROBE COOLING FAN MOTOR HARNESS CONNECTOR TERMINAL "B" WITH A TEST LIGHT CONNECTED TO GROUND. IS TEST LIGHT "ON"?
FAULTY CONNECTION OR FAULTY COOLING FAN MOTOR
YES
NO
FAULTY CONNECTION OR OPEN CKT 151.
FAULTY CONNECTION OR OPEN IN CIRCUIT BETWEEN RELAY AND COOLING FAN MOTOR. (CKT 702 OR CKT 533).
GC1089300076020X

Fig. 76 Chart C-12, cooling fan diagnosis (Part 2 of 2). 1993 Corvette w/5.7L/V8-350 (VIN P) engine

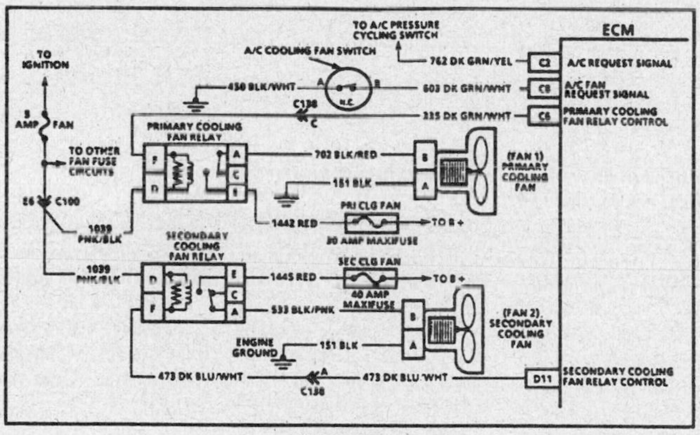
TO A/C PRESSURE CYCLING SWITCH
A/C COOLING FAN SWITCH
ECM
TO IGNITION
762 DK GRN/YEL
C2
A/C REQUEST SIGNAL
450 BLK/WHT
A
B
N.C.
603 DK GRN/WHT
C8
A/C FAN REQUEST SIGNAL
C138
C
C6
PRIMARY COOLING FAN RELAY CONTROL
5 AMP
FAN
PRIMARY COOLING FAN RELAY
TO OTHER FAN FUSE CIRCUITS
702 BLK/RED
(FAN 1) PRIMARY COOLING FAN
151 BLK
E6
C100
PRI CLG FAN
1039 PNK/BLK
1442 RED
TO B +
30 AMP MAXIFUSE
SECONDARY COOLING FAN RELAY
SEC CLG FAN
1039 PNK/BLK
1445 RED
TO B +
40 AMP MAXIFUSE
533 BLK/PNK
(FAN 2) SECONDARY COOLING FAN
ENGINE GROUND
151 BLK
473 DK BLU/WHT
A
C138
473 DK BLU/WHT
D11
SECONDARY COOLING FAN RELAY CONTROL

CHART C-12

(Page 1 of 2)
ELECTRIC COOLING FAN CONTROL CIRCUIT DIAGNOSIS
5.7L (VIN J) "Y" CARLINE (SFI)

Circuit Description:

The cooling fans are controlled by the ECM based on various inputs. Battery voltage is supplied to the fan relays on terminal "E" and ignition voltage to terminal "D". Grounding CKT 335 (relay terminal "F") will energize the primary cooling fan relay (Fan 1) and supply battery voltage to the primary cooling fan motor. Grounding CKT 473 (relay terminal "F") will energize the secondary cooling fan relay (Fan 2) and supply battery voltage to the secondary fan motor.

The A/C cooling fan switch, mounted in the A/C high pressure line, will open when head pressure is approximately 1655 kPa (240 psi) and this input will cause the ECM to ground CKT 473 or CKT 335 if other criteria are met.

If DTCs 14, 15, 52 or 62 are set or the ECM is operating in the fuel back-up mode, the ECM will turn "ON" both the cooling fans.

Diagnostic Aids:

If the owner complained of an overheating problem it must be determined if the complaint was due to an actual boil over, or the warning indicator light, or engine coolant temperature gage indicated overheating.

The gage accuracy can also be checked by comparing the Engine Coolant Temperature (ECT) sensor reading using a scan tool and comparing its reading with the gage reading.

If the engine is actually overheating and the gage indicates overheating, but the cooling fan is not coming "ON," the Engine Coolant Temperature (ECT) sensor has probably shifted out of calibration and should be replaced.

If the engine is overheating and the cooling fans are "ON," the cooling system should be checked,

The ECM will command Fan 1 "ON" when coolant temperature is greater than 108°C (226°F) and "OFF" at 103°C (217°F) and, Fan 2 "ON" at 112°C (234°F) and "OFF" at 110°C (230°F). The ECM will also enable the cooling fans when ECM DTCs 14, 15, 52 and 62 are set, engine oil temperature is too high or A/C head pressure is too high.

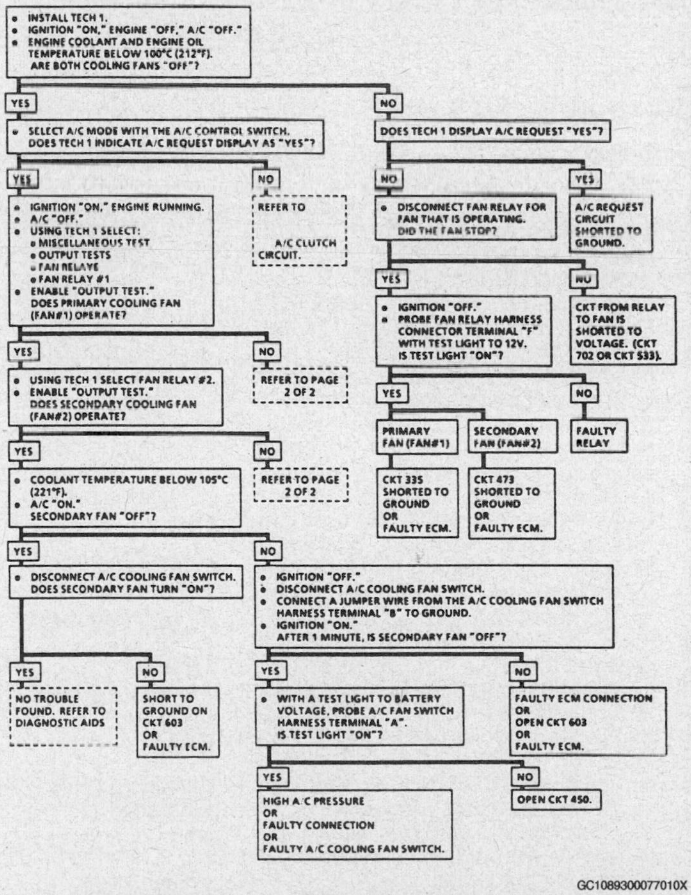
• INSTALL TECH 1.
• IGNITION "ON," ENGINE "OFF," A/C "OFF."
• ENGINE COOLANT AND ENGINE OIL TEMPERATURE BELOW 100°C (212°F). ARE BOTH COOLING FANS "OFF"?
YES
NO
• SELECT A/C MODE WITH THE A/C CONTROL SWITCH. DOES TECH 1 INDICATE A/C REQUEST DISPLAY AS "YES"?
DOES TECH 1 DISPLAY A/C REQUEST "YES"?
YES
NO
NO
YES
• IGNITION "ON," ENGINE RUNNING.
• A/C "OFF."
• USING TECH 1 SELECT:
• MISCELLANEOUS TEST
• OUTPUT TESTS
• FAN RELAYS
• FAN RELAY #1
• ENABLE "OUTPUT TEST." DOES PRIMARY COOLING FAN (FAN#1) OPERATE?
REFER TO A/C CLUTCH CIRCUIT.
• DISCONNECT FAN RELAY FOR FAN THAT IS OPERATING. DID THE FAN STOP?
A/C REQUEST CIRCUIT SHORTED TO GROUND.
YES
NO
• IGNITION "OFF."
• PROBE FAN RELAY HARNESS CONNECTOR TERMINAL "F" WITH TEST LIGHT TO 12V. IS TEST LIGHT "ON"?
CKT FROM RELAY TO FAN IS SHORTED TO VOLTAGE. (CKT 702 OR CKT 533).
YES
NO
• USING TECH 1 SELECT FAN RELAY #2.
• ENABLE "OUTPUT TEST." DOES SECONDARY COOLING FAN (FAN#2) OPERATE?
REFER TO PAGE 2 OF 2
YES
NO
PRIMARY FAN (FAN#1)
SECONDARY FAN (FAN#2)
FAULTY RELAY
CKT 335 SHORTED TO GROUND OR FAULTY ECM.
CKT 473 SHORTED TO GROUND OR FAULTY ECM.
YES
NO
• COOLANT TEMPERATURE BELOW 105°C (221°F).
• A/C "ON." SECONDARY FAN "OFF"?
REFER TO PAGE 2 OF 2
YES
NO
• DISCONNECT A/C COOLING FAN SWITCH. DOES SECONDARY FAN TURN "ON"?
• IGNITION "OFF."
• DISCONNECT A/C COOLING FAN SWITCH.
• CONNECT A JUMPER WIRE FROM THE A/C COOLING FAN SWITCH HARNESS TERMINAL "B" TO GROUND.
• IGNITION "ON." AFTER 1 MINUTE, IS SECONDARY FAN "OFF"?
YES
NO
YES
NO
NO TROUBLE FOUND. REFER TO DIAGNOSTIC AIDS
SHORT TO GROUND ON CKT 603 OR FAULTY ECM.
• WITH A TEST LIGHT TO BATTERY VOLTAGE, PROBE A/C FAN SWITCH HARNESS TERMINAL "A". IS TEST LIGHT "ON"?
FAULTY ECM CONNECTION OR OPEN CKT 603 OR FAULTY ECM.
YES
NO
HIGH A/C PRESSURE OR FAULTY CONNECTION OR FAULTY A/C COOLING FAN SWITCH.
OPEN CKT 450.
GC1089300077010X

Fig. 77 Chart C-12, cooling fan diagnosis (Part 1 of 2). 1993 Corvette ZR1 w/5.7L/V8-350 (VIN J) engine

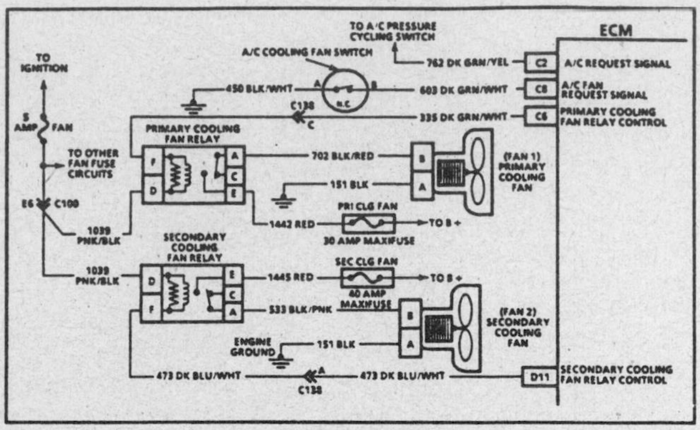
TO A/C PRESSURE CYCLING SWITCH
ECM
A/C COOLING FAN SWITCH
TO IGNITION
762 DK GRN/YEL
C2
A/C REQUEST SIGNAL
450 BLK/WHT
A
B
N.C
603 DK GRN/WHT
C8
A/C FAN REQUEST SIGNAL
C138
C
335 DK GRN/WHT
C6
PRIMARY COOLING FAN RELAY CONTROL
5 AMP
FAN
PRIMARY COOLING FAN RELAY
TO OTHER FAN FUSE CIRCUITS
702 BLK/RED
(FAN 1) PRIMARY COOLING FAN
151 BLK
E6
C100
1442 RED
PRI CLG FAN
TO B+
30 AMP MAXIFUSE
1039 PNK/BLK
SECONDARY COOLING FAN RELAY
SEC CLG FAN
1445 RED
TO B+
40 AMP MAXIFUSE
533 BLK/PNK
(FAN 2) SECONDARY COOLING FAN
ENGINE GROUND
151 BLK
473 DK BLU/WHT
473 DK BLU/WHT
D11
SECONDARY COOLING FAN RELAY CONTROL
C138

CHART C-12

(Page 2 of 2)
ELECTRIC COOLING FAN CONTROL CIRCUIT DIAGNOSIS
5.7L (VIN J) "Y" CARLINE (SFI)

Circuit Description:

The cooling fans are controlled by the ECM based on various inputs. Battery voltage is supplied to the fan relays on terminal "E" and ignition voltage to terminal "D". Grounding CKT 335 (relay terminal "F") will energize the primary cooling fan relay (Fan 1) and supply battery voltage to the primary cooling fan motor. Grounding CKT 473 (relay terminal "F") will energize the secondary cooling fan relay (Fan 2) and supply battery voltage to the secondary fan motor.

The A/C cooling fan switch, mounted in the A/C high pressure line, will open when head pressure is approximately 1655 kPa (240 psi). This input will cause the ECM to ground CKT 473 or CKT 335 if other criteria are met.

If DTCs 14, 15, 52 or 62 are set or the ECM is operating in the fuel back-up mode, the ECM will turn "ON" both the cooling fans.

Diagnostic Aids:

If the owner complained of an overheating problem, it must be determined if the complaint was due to an actual boil over or the warning indicator light or engine coolant temperature gage indicated overheating.

The gage accuracy can also be checked by comparing the Engine Coolant Temperature (ECT) sensor reading using a scan tool and comparing its reading with the gage reading.

If the engine is actually overheating and the gage indicates overheating, but the cooling fan is not coming "ON," the Engine Coolant Temperature (ECT) sensor has probably shifted out of calibration and should be replaced.

If the engine is overheating and the cooling fans are "ON," the cooling system should be checked.

The ECM will command Fan 1 "ON" when coolant temperature is greater than 108°C (226°F) and "OFF" at 103°C (217°F) and, Fan 2 "ON" at 112°C (234°F) and "OFF" at 110°C (230°F). The ECM will also enable the cooling fans when ECM DTCs 14, 15, 52 and 62 are set, engine oil temperature is too high or A/C head pressure is too high.

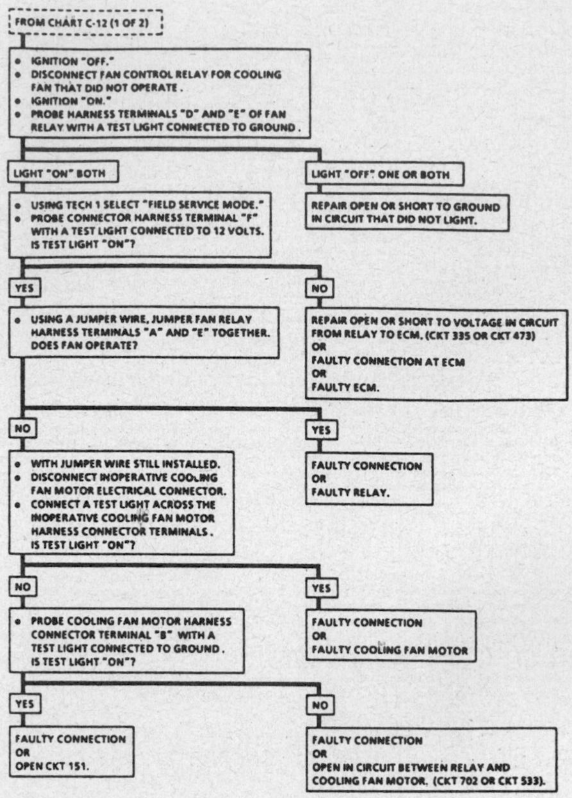
FROM CHART C-12 (1 OF 2)
• IGNITION "OFF."
• DISCONNECT FAN CONTROL RELAY FOR COOLING FAN THAT DID NOT OPERATE.
• IGNITION "ON."
• PROBE HARNESS TERMINALS "D" AND "E" OF FAN RELAY WITH A TEST LIGHT CONNECTED TO GROUND.
LIGHT "ON" BOTH
LIGHT "OFF" ONE OR BOTH
• USING TECH 1 SELECT "FIELD SERVICE MODE."
• PROBE CONNECTOR HARNESS TERMINAL "F" WITH A TEST LIGHT CONNECTED TO 12 VOLTS. IS TEST LIGHT "ON"?
REPAIR OPEN OR SHORT TO GROUND IN CIRCUIT THAT DID NOT LIGHT.
YES
NO
• USING A JUMPER WIRE, JUMPER FAN RELAY HARNESS TERMINALS "A" AND "E" TOGETHER. DOES FAN OPERATE?
REPAIR OPEN OR SHORT TO VOLTAGE IN CIRCUIT FROM RELAY TO ECM. (CKT 335 OR CKT 473) OR FAULTY CONNECTION AT ECM OR FAULTY ECM.
NO
YES
• WITH JUMPER WIRE STILL INSTALLED.
• DISCONNECT INOPERATIVE COOLING FAN MOTOR ELECTRICAL CONNECTOR.
• CONNECT A TEST LIGHT ACROSS THE INOPERATIVE COOLING FAN MOTOR HARNESS CONNECTOR TERMINALS. IS TEST LIGHT "ON"?
FAULTY CONNECTION OR FAULTY RELAY.
NO
YES
• PROBE COOLING FAN MOTOR HARNESS CONNECTOR TERMINAL "B" WITH A TEST LIGHT CONNECTED TO GROUND. IS TEST LIGHT "ON"?
FAULTY CONNECTION OR FAULTY COOLING FAN MOTOR
YES
NO
FAULTY CONNECTION OR OPEN CKT 151.
FAULTY CONNECTION OR OPEN IN CIRCUIT BETWEEN RELAY AND COOLING FAN MOTOR. (CKT 702 OR CKT 533).

GC1089300077020X

Fig. 77 Chart C-12, cooling fan diagnosis (Part 2 of 2). 1993 Corvette ZR1 w/5.7L/V8-350 (VIN J) engine

1. Enter diagnostics and turn cooling fans on high speed using PCM override. If cooling fans turn on, proceed to step 2. If cooling fans do not turn on, proceed to step 3.
2. Start engine, turn on A/C and idle engine for a few minutes. Read PCM Data-Coolant Temperature Sensor (CTS) and read BCM Data-Refrigerant Temperature Sensor. If both readings are above ambient and rising, replace PCM. If readings are not above ambient and rising, check wiring to suspect sensor, if wiring is satisfactory, replace sensor.
3. Leave PCM connected and turn ignition to the Run position, connect a fused jumper between PCM connector C2 (terminal B8, dark green/white) and ground. If cooling fans run, replace PCM. If cooling fans do not run, proceed to step 4.
4. Leaving fused jumper in place at the PCM connector, check voltages at high speed cooling fan relay as follows:
   a. From terminal No. 1 (red) to ground. If battery voltage is indicated proceed to step b. If battery voltage is not indicated, repair open circuit in red wire.
   b. From terminal No. 1 (red) to terminal 5 (dark green/white). If battery voltage is indicated, proceed to step c. If battery voltage is not indicated, repair open circuit in gray/black wire.
   c. From terminal No. 2 (brown) to ground. If battery voltage is indicated, proceed to step 5. If battery voltage is not indicated, repair open circuit in brown wire.
5. Connect a fused jumper between high speed cooling fan relay terminal No. 2 (brown) and terminal No. 4 (black/pink). If cooling fans do not run, check black/pink wire for an open circuit. If cooling fans run, replace low speed cooling fan relay.

1994

Refer to **Fig. 81.** when performing diagnostic procedures.

FLEETWOOD (RWD)

1993

Refer to **Figs. 82 through 83** for system diagnosis.

1994

Refer to **Figs. 84 through 86** for system diagnosis.

ELDORADO & SEVILLE

1992–93

Refer to **Figs. 88 through 90** when performing diagnostic procedures.

Low Speed Conditions

On models with 4.6L/V8-279 engine, the PCM will turn on the cooling fans at low speed when engine coolant temperature exceeds 222°F. The cooling fans will be turned off when the coolant temperature drops below 215°F. The PCM monitors engine coolant temperature using the coolant temperature sensor at terminal "1B5" through circuit (585).

The PCM will also activate low speed operation if the transaxle temperature exceeds 239°F. The cooling fans will be turned off when the transaxle temperature falls below 230°F. The PCM monitors transaxle temperature using the transaxle temperature sensor input at terminal "1B14" through circuit (585).

The heater and A/C programmer will request the PCM to turn on the cooling fans at low speed through the UART data line. The PCM will turn on the cooling fans at low speed if a low coolant level is detected and the engine coolant temperature exceeds 176°F. The cooling fans will be turned off when the coolant temperature drops below 113°F. The PCM monitors coolant level using the coolant level switch input at terminal "1B16" through circuit (1478).

On models with 4.9L/V8-300 engine, the PCM will turn on the cooling fans at

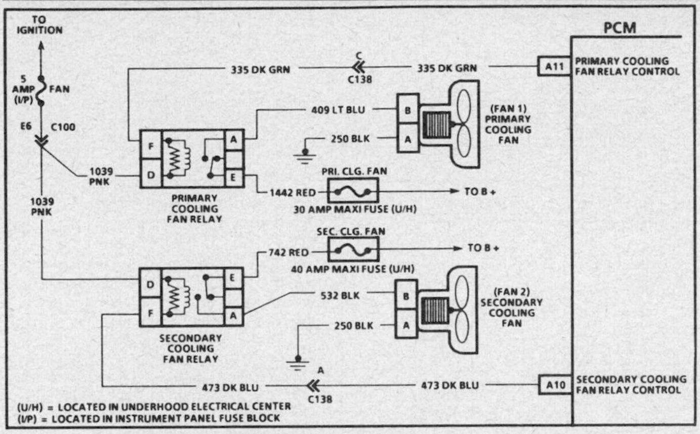
TO IGNITION
PCM
5 AMP (I/P) FAN
E6
C100
335 DK GRN
C138
335 DK GRN
A11
PRIMARY COOLING FAN RELAY CONTROL
409 LT BLU
(FAN 1) PRIMARY COOLING FAN
250 BLK
1039 PNK
1039 PNK
PRIMARY COOLING FAN RELAY
PRI. CLG. FAN
1442 RED
TO B+
30 AMP MAXI FUSE (U/H)
SEC. CLG. FAN
742 RED
TO B+
40 AMP MAXI FUSE (U/H)
532 BLK
(FAN 2) SECONDARY COOLING FAN
250 BLK
SECONDARY COOLING FAN RELAY
473 DK BLU
C138
473 DK BLU
A10
SECONDARY COOLING FAN RELAY CONTROL
(U/H) = LOCATED IN UNDERHOOD ELECTRICAL CENTER
(I/P) = LOCATED IN INSTRUMENT PANEL FUSE BLOCK

CHART C-12 (Page 1 of 2)

ELECTRIC COOLING FAN CONTROL CIRCUIT DIAGNOSIS 5.7L (VIN P) "Y" CARLINE (SFI)

Circuit Description:

The cooling fans are controlled by the PCM based on various inputs. Battery voltage is supplied to the primary and secondary fan relays on terminal "E". Ignition voltage is supplied to terminal "D" of the primary and secondary fan relays. Grounding CKT 335 (relay terminal "F") will energize the primary cooling fan relay (Fan 1) and supply battery voltage to the primary cooling fan motor. Grounding CKT 473 (relay terminal "F") will energize the secondary cooling fan relay (Fan 2) and supply battery voltage to the secondary fan motor.

When certain Diagnostic Trouble Codes (DTCs) are set, the PCM will enable the cooling fans.

Chart Test Description: Number(s) below refer to circled number(s) on the diagnostic chart.

1. With the output/field service enable terminal grounded at DLC, the cooling fan control driver(s) will close, which should energize the fan control relay(s).
2. The cooling fans should come "ON" anytime A/C system is operating.
3. Comparing Tech 1 pressure and manifold gage set pressure will determine if the A/C refrigerant pressure sensor is out of range. An out of range A/C refrigerant pressure sensor can cause the cooling fans to operate at the wrong times.

Diagnostic Aids: If the owner complained of an overheating problem, it must be determined if the complaint was due to an actual boil over, or the warning indicator light, or engine coolant temperature gage indicated overheating.

The gage accuracy can also be checked by comparing the Engine Coolant Temperature (ECT) sensor reading using a Tech 1 and comparing its reading with the gage reading.

If the engine is actually overheating and the gage indicated overheating, but the cooling fan is not coming "ON," the Engine Coolant Temperature (ECT) sensor has probably shifted out of calibration and should be replaced.

If the engine is overheating and the cooling fans are "ON," the cooling system should be checked

The PCM will command fan 1 "ON" at 104°C (219°F) and "OFF" at 98°C (208°F) and, fan 2 "ON" at 109°C (228°F) and "OFF" at 103°C (217°F).

GC108940021201AX

Fig. 78 Chart C-12, cooling fan diagnosis (Part 1 of 2). 1994 Corvette w/5.7L/V8-350 (VIN P) engine

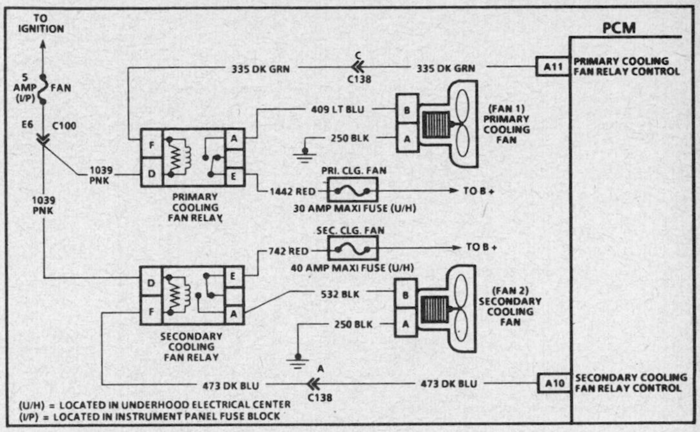
TO IGNITION
PCM
5 AMP (I/P) FAN
E6
C100
335 DK GRN
C138
335 DK GRN
A11
PRIMARY COOLING FAN RELAY CONTROL
409 LT BLU
(FAN 1) PRIMARY COOLING FAN
250 BLK
1039 PNK
1039 PNK
PRIMARY COOLING FAN RELAY
PRI. CLG. FAN
1442 RED
TO B+
30 AMP MAXI FUSE (U/H)
SEC. CLG. FAN
742 RED
TO B+
40 AMP MAXI FUSE (U/H)
532 BLK
(FAN 2) SECONDARY COOLING FAN
250 BLK
SECONDARY COOLING FAN RELAY
473 DK BLU
C138
473 DK BLU
A10
SECONDARY COOLING FAN RELAY CONTROL
(U/H) = LOCATED IN UNDERHOOD ELECTRICAL CENTER
(I/P) = LOCATED IN INSTRUMENT PANEL FUSE BLOCK

CHART C-12

(Page 2 of 2)

ELECTRIC COOLING FAN CONTROL CIRCUIT DIAGNOSIS 5.7L (VIN P) "Y" CARLINE (SFI)

Circuit Description:

The cooling fans are controlled by the PCM based on various inputs. Battery voltage is supplied to the primary and secondary fan relays on terminal "E". Ignition voltage is supplied to terminal "D" of the primary and secondary fan relays. Grounding CKT 335 (relay terminal "F") will energize the primary cooling fan relay (Fan 1) and supply battery voltage to the primary cooling fan motor. Grounding CKT 473 (relay terminal "F") will energize the secondary cooling fan relay (Fan 2) and supply battery voltage to the secondary fan motor.

The PCM will enable the cooling fans, when certain Diagnostic Trouble Codes (DTCs) are set.

Diagnostic Aids: If the owner complained of an overheating problem, it must be determined if the complaint was due to an actual boil over, the warning indicator light, or engine coolant temperature gage indicated overheating.

The gage accuracy can also be checked by comparing the Engine Coolant Temperature (ECT) sensor reading using a Tech 1 and comparing its reading with the gage reading.

If the engine is actually overheating and the gage indicated overheating, but the cooling fan is not coming "ON," the Engine Coolant Temperature (ECT) sensor has probably shifted out of calibration and should be replaced.

If the engine is overheating and the cooling fans are "ON," the cooling system should be checked

The PCM will command fan 1 "ON" at 104°C (219°F) and "OFF" at 103°C (217°F) and an 2 "ON" at 109°C (228°F) and "OFF" at 103°C (217°F).

GC108940021202AX

Fig. 78 Chart C-12, cooling fan diagnosis (Part 2 of 2). 1994 Corvette w/5.7L/V8-350 (VIN P) engine

low speed when the engine coolant temperature exceeds 223°F. The cooling fans will be turned off when the coolant temperature drops below 208°F. The PCM monitors engine coolant temperature using the coolant temperature sensor at terminal 3E16 through circuit 410.

The heater and A/C (HVAC) programmer will request the PCM to turn on the cooling fans at low speed through the UART data line when the A/C high side refrigerant temperature exceeds 140°F. The HVAC programmer will request that the cooling fans be turned off once the A/C high side refrigerant temperature falls below 122°F.

The HVAC programmer also will request low cooling fan speed operation when all of the following conditions are met:

1. Vehicle speed is below 20 mph.
2. A/C compressor clutch engagement is possible.
3. Outside air temperature is greater than 45°F.

Low Speed Operation

On models with 4.6L/V8-279 engine, low speed cooling fan operation will occur when the PCM grounds cooling fan relay No. 1. The PCM grounds the relay through circuit (1269) at terminal "3F8." When cooling fan relay No. 1 is energized, voltage is applied to both left and right fans. The voltage path to the fans is through relay No. 1 contacts, circuits (532) and (533), and cooling fan relay No. 2 contacts. The two fans are connected to each other through a series circuit. This causes the voltage that is applied through fuse 6 to be divided between the two fans. The division of voltage causes the fans to operate at a lower speed. In the series mode the fans are grounded through circuit (804) and ground (G107).

On models with 4.9L/V8-300 engine, low speed cooling fan operation will occur when the PCM grounds cooling fan relay number 1's coil through circuit 1269 at terminal 2A11. With only cooling fan relay 1 energized, voltage is applied to both pusher and puller cooling fans. The voltage path to the fans is through cooling fan number 1's contacts, circuits 532 and 533, and the cooling fan relay number 2's contacts. The two fans are connected to each other through a series circuit. This causes the voltage being applied by fuse 6 to be divided between the two fans. The division of voltage causes the fans to operate at a lower speed. In the series mode the fans are grounded through circuit 804 and ground G104.

High Speed Conditions

On models with 4.6L/V8-279 engine, the PCM will turn on the cooling fans at high speed when the coolant temperature exceeds 230°F or if the coolant temperature sensor circuit has failed. The PCM will switch the cooling fans to low speed operation when the coolant level temperature falls below 221°F.

The PCM will request high speed operation if the transaxle temperature exceeds 248°F. The PCM will switch to low speed operation once the transaxle temperature falls below 239°F. The PCM will turn on the cooling fans at high speed if a low coolant level is detected and coolant temperature exceeds 185°F. The PCM will switch to low speed operation once the coolant temperature drops below 176°F.

The heater and A/C programmer can request the PCM to turn on the cooling fans at high speed through the UART data line.

On models with 4.9L/V8-300 engine, the PCM will turn on the cooling fans at high speed when the engine coolant temperature exceeds 226°F or if the coolant temperature sensor circuit has failed. The PCM will switch the cooling fans to low speed operation when the coolant temperature falls below 223°F.

The HVAC programmer will request the PCM to turn on the cooling fans at high speed through the UART data line if the A/C high side refrigerant temperature exceeds 158°F or an A/C high side temperature sensor circuit failure occurs. The HVAC programmer will request that the cooling fans be switched to low speed operation when the high side refrigerant temperature falls below 138°F.

High Speed Operation

On models with 4.6L/V8-279 engine, the cooling fans run at high speed when

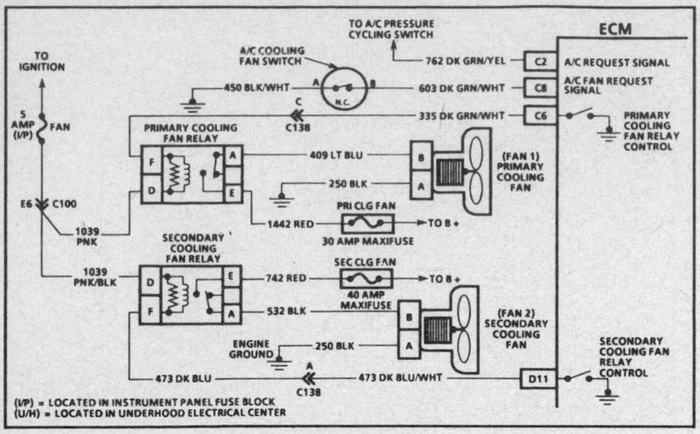
TO A/C PRESSURE CYCLING SWITCH
ECM
TO IGNITION
A/C COOLING FAN SWITCH
762 DK GRN/YEL
C2
A/C REQUEST SIGNAL
450 BLK/WHT
A
B
N.C.
603 DK GRN/WHT
C8
A/C FAN REQUEST SIGNAL
C
5 AMP (I/P)
FAN
335 DK GRN/WHT
C6
C138
PRIMARY COOLING FAN RELAY
PRIMARY COOLING FAN RELAY CONTROL
F
D
A
E
409 LT BLU
250 BLK
(FAN 1) PRIMARY COOLING FAN
E6
C100
PRI CLG FAN
1442 RED
TO B+
30 AMP MAXIFUSE
1039 PNK
SECONDARY COOLING FAN RELAY
SEC CLG FAN
1039 PNK/BLK
742 RED
40 AMP MAXIFUSE
532 BLK
(FAN 2) SECONDARY COOLING FAN
ENGINE GROUND
250 BLK
SECONDARY COOLING FAN RELAY CONTROL
473 DK BLU
473 DK BLU/WHT
C138
D11
(I/P) = LOCATED IN INSTRUMENT PANEL FUSE BLOCK
(U/H) = LOCATED IN UNDERHOOD ELECTRICAL CENTER

CHART C-12

(Page 1 of 2)
ELECTRIC COOLING FAN CONTROL CIRCUIT DIAGNOSIS
5.7L (VIN J) "Y" CARLINE (SFI)

Circuit Description:

The cooling fans are controlled by the ECM based on various inputs. Battery voltage is supplied to the fan relays on terminal "E" and ignition voltage to terminal "D". Grounding CKT 335 (relay terminal "F") will energize the primary cooling fan relay (Fan 1) and supply battery voltage to the primary cooling fan motor. Grounding CKT 473 (relay terminal "F") will energize the secondary cooling fan relay (Fan 2) and supply battery voltage to the secondary fan motor.

The A/C cooling fan switch, mounted in the A/C high pressure line, will open when head pressure is approximately 1655 kPa (240 psi) and this input will cause the ECM to ground CKT 473 or CKT 335 if other criteria are met.

If DTCs 14, 15, 52 or 62 are set or the ECM is operating in the fuel back-up mode, the ECM will turn "ON" both the cooling fans.

Diagnostic Aids:

If the owner complained of an overheating problem it must be determined if the complaint was due to an actual boil over, or the warning indicator light, or engine coolant temperature gage indicated overheating.

The gage accuracy can also be checked by comparing the Engine Coolant Temperature (ECT) sensor reading using a scan tool and comparing its reading with the gage reading.

If the engine is actually overheating and the gage indicates overheating, but the cooling fan is not coming "ON," the Engine Coolant Temperature (ECT) sensor has probably shifted out of calibration and should be replaced.

If the engine is overheating and the cooling fans are "ON," the cooling system should be checked

The ECM will command the primary cooling fan "ON" when coolant temperature is greater than 108°C (226°F) and "OFF" at 103°C (217°F) and, secondary cooling fan "ON" at 112°C (234°F) and "OFF" at 110°C (230°F). The ECM will also enable the cooling fans when ECM DTCs 14, 15, 52 and 62 are set, engine oil temperature is too high or A/C head pressure is too high.

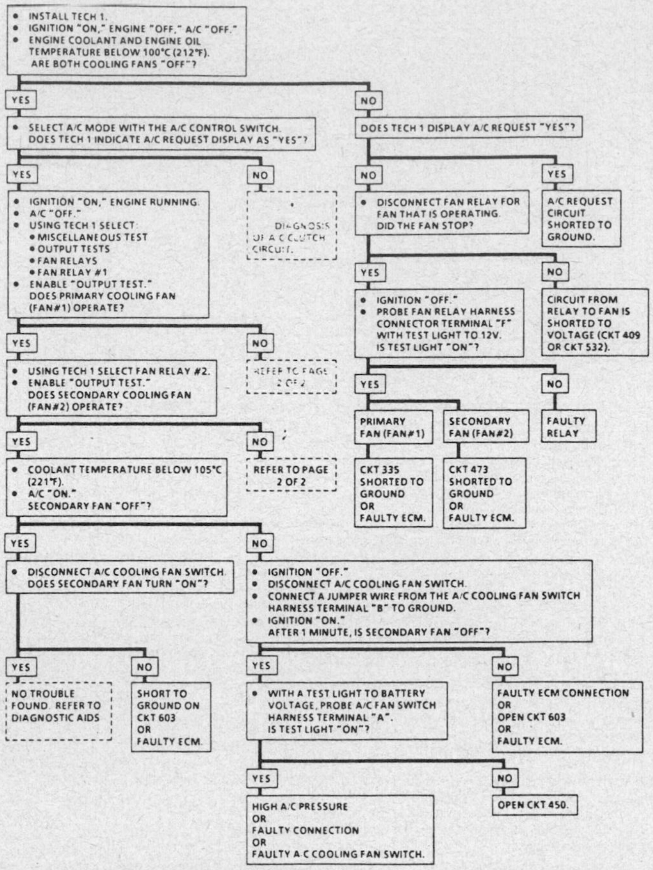
• INSTALL TECH 1.
• IGNITION "ON," ENGINE "OFF," A/C "OFF."
• ENGINE COOLANT AND ENGINE OIL TEMPERATURE BELOW 100°C (212°F). ARE BOTH COOLING FANS "OFF"?
YES
NO
• SELECT A/C MODE WITH THE A/C CONTROL SWITCH. DOES TECH 1 INDICATE A/C REQUEST DISPLAY AS "YES"?
DOES TECH 1 DISPLAY A/C REQUEST "YES"?
YES
NO
NO
YES
• IGNITION "ON," ENGINE RUNNING.
• A/C "OFF."
• USING TECH 1 SELECT:
• MISCELLANEOUS TEST
• OUTPUT TESTS
• FAN RELAYS
• FAN RELAY #1
• ENABLE "OUTPUT TEST." DOES PRIMARY COOLING FAN (FAN#1) OPERATE?
• DISCONNECT FAN RELAY FOR FAN THAT IS OPERATING. DID THE FAN STOP?
A/C REQUEST CIRCUIT SHORTED TO GROUND.
YES
NO
• IGNITION "OFF."
• PROBE FAN RELAY HARNESS CONNECTOR TERMINAL "F" WITH TEST LIGHT TO 12V. IS TEST LIGHT "ON"?
CIRCUIT FROM RELAY TO FAN IS SHORTED TO VOLTAGE (CKT 409 OR CKT 532).
YES
NO
• USING TECH 1 SELECT FAN RELAY #2.
• ENABLE "OUTPUT TEST." DOES SECONDARY COOLING FAN (FAN#2) OPERATE?
YES
NO
PRIMARY FAN (FAN#1)
SECONDARY FAN (FAN#2)
FAULTY RELAY
• COOLANT TEMPERATURE BELOW 105°C (221°F).
• A/C "ON." SECONDARY FAN "OFF"?
REFER TO PAGE 2 OF 2
CKT 335 SHORTED TO GROUND OR FAULTY ECM.
CKT 473 SHORTED TO GROUND OR FAULTY ECM.
• DISCONNECT A/C COOLING FAN SWITCH. DOES SECONDARY FAN TURN "ON"?
• IGNITION "OFF."
• DISCONNECT A/C COOLING FAN SWITCH.
• CONNECT A JUMPER WIRE FROM THE A/C COOLING FAN SWITCH HARNESS TERMINAL "B" TO GROUND.
• IGNITION "ON." AFTER 1 MINUTE, IS SECONDARY FAN "OFF"?
NO TROUBLE FOUND. REFER TO DIAGNOSTIC AIDS
SHORT TO GROUND ON CKT 603 OR FAULTY ECM.
• WITH A TEST LIGHT TO BATTERY VOLTAGE, PROBE A/C FAN SWITCH HARNESS TERMINAL "A". IS TEST LIGHT "ON"?
FAULTY ECM CONNECTION OR OPEN CKT 603 OR FAULTY ECM.
HIGH A/C PRESSURE OR FAULTY CONNECTION OR FAULTY A/C COOLING FAN SWITCH.
OPEN CKT 450.
GC108940021301AX

Fig. 79 Chart C-12, cooling fan diagnosis (Part 1 of 2). 1994 Corvette w/5.7L/V8-350 (VIN J) engine

cooling fan relays 1, 2 and 3 are grounded by PCM terminals "3F8" and "3F7" through circuits (1269) and (1270). With cooling fan relay No. 1 energized, battery voltage is applied to the left cooling fan motor through the relay contacts. The left cooling fan runs at high speed because the fan is grounded directly through the contacts of cooling fan relay No. 2, circuit (150) and ground (G109).

Since cooling fan relay No. 3 is also energized during high speed operation, battery voltage is applied directly to the right cooling fan through the closed contacts of the relay. The fan will run at high speed since it is no longer in series with the left cooling fan.

On models with 4.9L/V8-300 engine, the cooling fans run at high speed when cooling fan relays 1, 2 and 3 are grounded by PCM terminals 2B8 and 2A11 through circuits 1269 and 1270. With cooling fan relay number 1 energized, battery voltage is applied to the pusher fan through the relay contacts. The pusher fan runs at high speed because now the fan is grounded directly through the contacts of cooling fan relay number 2.

Since cooling fan relay number 3 is also energized during high speed operation, battery voltage is applied directly to the puller cooling fan through the closed contacts of the relay. The fan will run at high speed since it is no longer in series with the pusher fan.

1994

Refer to **Fig. 91** when performing diagnostic procedures on these systems.

LE SABRE, PARK AVENUE, 88 & 98

1992–93

Refer to **Figs. 92 through 100** when performing diagnostic procedures.

Both Cooling Fans Do Not Run

1. Turn ignition switch to Run position, connect a fused jumper between ALDL terminals A and B. If cooling fans run, problem is PCM related. If cooling fans do not run, proceed to next step.
2. Leave jumper connected as in step 1 and disconnect connector (C123). Measure voltage between terminal A (black/red) and ground. If battery voltage is not present, refer to "Lefthand Cooling Fan Does Not Operate In Low Speed." If battery voltage is present, proceed to step 3.
3. With jumper still connected, measure voltage between terminal B (black/pink) and ground. If battery voltage is not present, refer to "Lefthand Cooling Fan Does Not Operate In High Speed." If battery voltage is present, proceed to step 4.
4. Jumper still connected to ALDL, measure voltage from terminal B (black/pink) to terminal C (black). If battery voltage is not present, check black wire for an open circuit. If battery voltage is present, check wiring within cooling fan assembly. If wiring is satisfactory, replace fan motor.

Lefthand Cooling Fan Does Not Operate In Low Speed

1. Disconnect low speed cooling fan relay and turn ignition switch to Run position. Measure voltage from relay connector terminal No. 2 (brown) to ground. If battery voltage is not present, check brown wire for an open circuit. If battery voltage is present, proceed to step 2.
2. Measure voltage from terminal No. 1 (red) to ground. If battery voltage is not present, check red wire for an open circuit. If battery voltage is present, proceed to step 3.
3. Connect a test lamp between relay connector terminal Nos. 1 (red) and 5 (gray/black), then connect a jumper between ALDL terminals A and B. If test lamp does not light, check

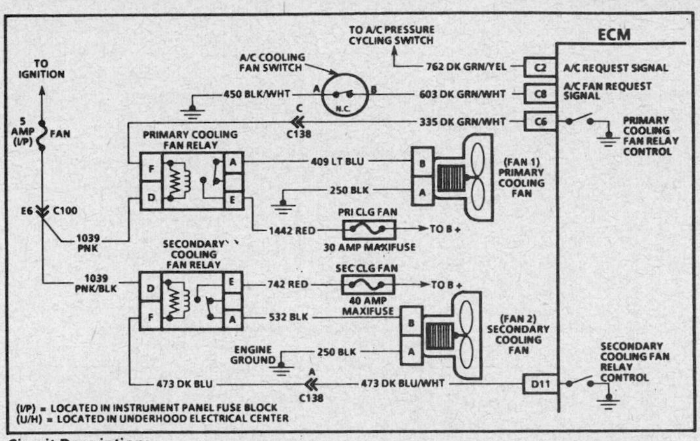

TO A/C PRESSURE CYCLING SWITCH
ECM
TO IGNITION
A/C COOLING FAN SWITCH
762 DK GRN/YEL
C2
A/C REQUEST SIGNAL
450 BLK/WHT
603 DK GRN/WHT
C8
A/C FAN REQUEST SIGNAL
335 DK GRN/WHT
C6
PRIMARY COOLING FAN RELAY CONTROL
5 AMP (I/P) FAN
PRIMARY COOLING FAN RELAY
C138
409 LT BLU
(FAN 1) PRIMARY COOLING FAN
250 BLK
E6 C100
PRI CLG FAN
1442 RED
TO B+
1039 PNK
30 AMP MAXIFUSE
SECONDARY COOLING FAN RELAY
SEC CLG FAN
1039 PNK/BLK
742 RED
TO B+
40 AMP MAXIFUSE
532 BLK
(FAN 2) SECONDARY COOLING FAN
ENGINE GROUND
250 BLK
SECONDARY COOLING FAN RELAY CONTROL
473 DK BLU
473 DK BLU/WHT
D11
C138
(I/P) = LOCATED IN INSTRUMENT PANEL FUSE BLOCK
(U/H) = LOCATED IN UNDERHOOD ELECTRICAL CENTER

Circuit Description:

The cooling fans are controlled by the ECM based on various inputs. Battery voltage is supplied to the fan relays on terminal "E" and ignition voltage to terminal "D". Grounding CKT 335 (relay terminal "F") will energize the primary cooling fan relay (Fan 1) and supply battery voltage to the primary cooling fan motor. Grounding CKT 473 (relay terminal "F") will energize the secondary cooling fan relay (Fan 2) and supply battery voltage to the secondary fan motor.

The A/C cooling fan switch, mounted in the A/C high pressure line, will open when head pressure is approximately 1655 kPa (240 psi). This input will cause the ECM to ground CKT 473 or CKT 335 if other criteria are met.

If DTCs 14, 15, 52 or 62 are set or the ECM is operating in the fuel back-up mode, the ECM will turn "ON" both the cooling fans.

Diagnostic Aids:

If the owner complained of an overheating problem, it must be determined if the complaint was due to an actual boil over or the warning indicator light or engine coolant temperature gage indicated overheating.

The gage accuracy can also be checked by comparing the Engine Coolant Temperature (ECT) sensor reading using a scan tool and comparing its reading with the gage reading.

If the engine is actually overheating and the gage indicates overheating, but the cooling fan is not coming "ON," the Engine Coolant Temperature (ECT) sensor has probably shifted out of calibration and should be replaced.

If the engine is overheating and the cooling fans are "ON," the cooling system should be checked.

The ECM will command the primary cooling fan "ON" when coolant temperature is greater than 108°C (226°F) and "OFF" at 103°C (217°F) and, secondary cooling fan "ON" at 112°C (234°F) and "OFF" at 110°C (230°F). The ECM will also enable the cooling fans when ECM DTCs 14, 15, 52 and 62 are set, engine oil temperature is too high or A/C head pressure is too high.

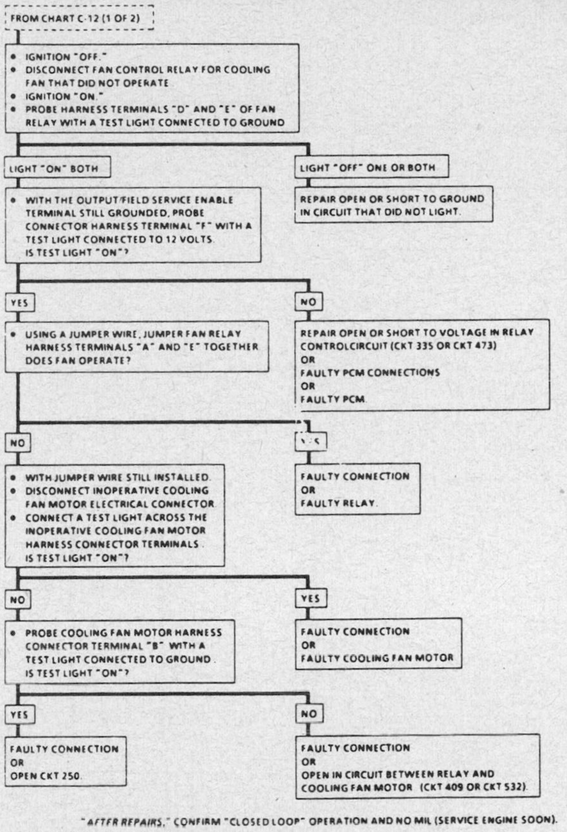

FROM CHART C-12 (1 OF 2)
• IGNITION "OFF."
• DISCONNECT FAN CONTROL RELAY FOR COOLING FAN THAT DID NOT OPERATE.
• IGNITION "ON."
• PROBE HARNESS TERMINALS "D" AND "E" OF FAN RELAY WITH A TEST LIGHT CONNECTED TO GROUND.
LIGHT "ON" BOTH
LIGHT "OFF" ONE OR BOTH
• WITH THE OUTPUT/FIELD SERVICE ENABLE TERMINAL STILL GROUNDED, PROBE CONNECTOR HARNESS TERMINAL "F" WITH A TEST LIGHT CONNECTED TO 12 VOLTS. IS TEST LIGHT "ON"?
REPAIR OPEN OR SHORT TO GROUND IN CIRCUIT THAT DID NOT LIGHT.
YES
NO
• USING A JUMPER WIRE, JUMPER FAN RELAY HARNESS TERMINALS "A" AND "E" TOGETHER. DOES FAN OPERATE?
REPAIR OPEN OR SHORT TO VOLTAGE IN RELAY CONTROL CIRCUIT (CKT 335 OR CKT 473) OR FAULTY PCM CONNECTIONS OR FAULTY PCM.
NO
YES
• WITH JUMPER WIRE STILL INSTALLED.
• DISCONNECT INOPERATIVE COOLING FAN MOTOR ELECTRICAL CONNECTOR.
• CONNECT A TEST LIGHT ACROSS THE INOPERATIVE COOLING FAN MOTOR HARNESS CONNECTOR TERMINALS. IS TEST LIGHT "ON"?
FAULTY CONNECTION OR FAULTY RELAY.
NO
YES
• PROBE COOLING FAN MOTOR HARNESS CONNECTOR TERMINAL "B" WITH A TEST LIGHT CONNECTED TO GROUND. IS TEST LIGHT "ON"?
FAULTY CONNECTION OR FAULTY COOLING FAN MOTOR
YES
NO
FAULTY CONNECTION OR OPEN CKT 250.
FAULTY CONNECTION OR OPEN IN CIRCUIT BETWEEN RELAY AND COOLING FAN MOTOR (CKT 409 OR CKT 532).
"AFTER REPAIRS," CONFIRM "CLOSED LOOP" OPERATION AND NO MIL (SERVICE ENGINE SOON).

GC108940021302AX

Fig. 79 Chart C-12, cooling fan diagnosis (Part 2 of 2). 1994 Corvette w/5.7L/V8-350 (VIN J) engine

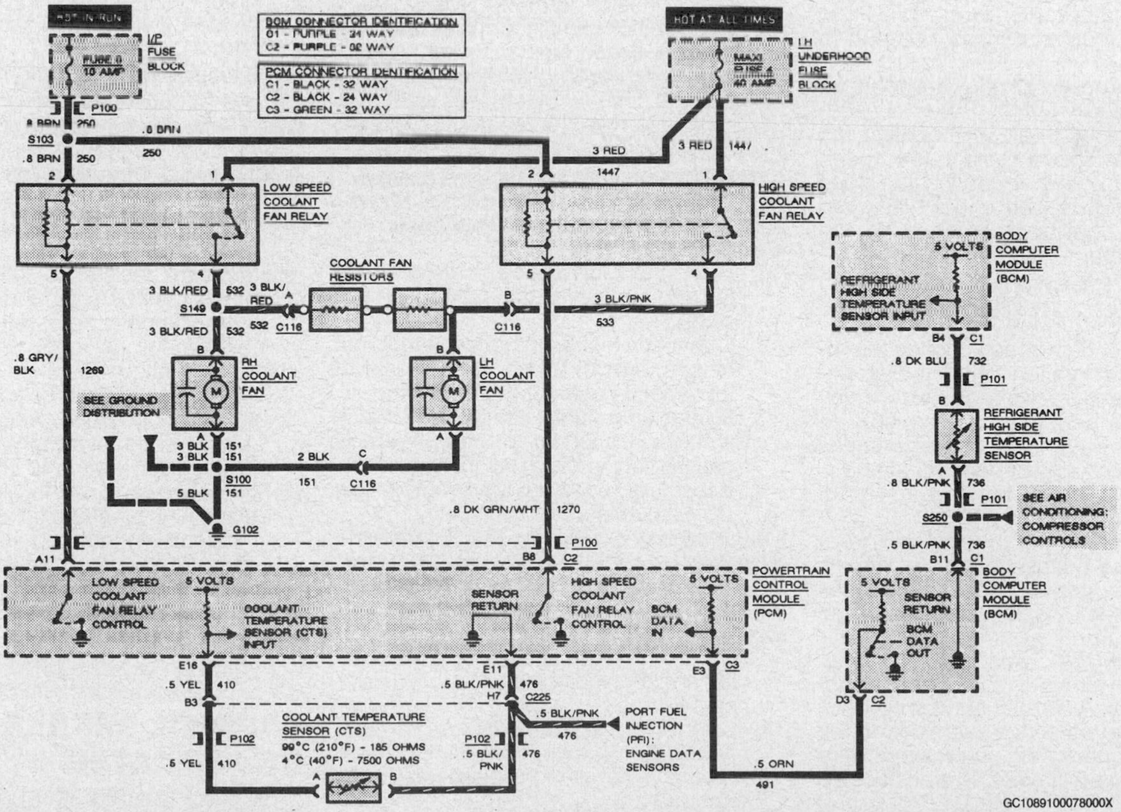

BCM CONNECTOR IDENTIFICATION
C1 - PURPLE - 24 WAY
C2 - PURPLE - 32 WAY
PCM CONNECTOR IDENTIFICATION
C1 - BLACK - 32 WAY
C2 - BLACK - 24 WAY
C3 - GREEN - 32 WAY
HOT AT ALL TIMES
I/P FUSE BLOCK
LH UNDERHOOD FUSE BLOCK
MAXI FUSE 4 40 AMP
LOW SPEED COOLANT FAN RELAY
HIGH SPEED COOLANT FAN RELAY
COOLANT FAN RESISTORS
BODY COMPUTER MODULE (BCM)
REFRIGERANT HIGH SIDE TEMPERATURE SENSOR INPUT
RH COOLANT FAN
LH COOLANT FAN
SEE GROUND DISTRIBUTION
REFRIGERANT HIGH SIDE TEMPERATURE SENSOR
SEE AIR CONDITIONING: COMPRESSOR CONTROLS
LOW SPEED COOLANT FAN RELAY CONTROL
COOLANT TEMPERATURE SENSOR (CTS) INPUT
SENSOR RETURN
HIGH SPEED COOLANT FAN RELAY CONTROL
BCM DATA IN
POWERTRAIN CONTROL MODULE (PCM)
BCM DATA OUT
COOLANT TEMPERATURE SENSOR (CTS)
99°C (210°F) - 185 OHMS
4°C (40°F) - 7500 OHMS
PORT FUEL INJECTION (PFI): ENGINE DATA SENSORS

GC1089100078000X

Fig. 80 Cooling fan wiring circuit. 1992–93 DeVille & 1992 Fleetwood (FWD)

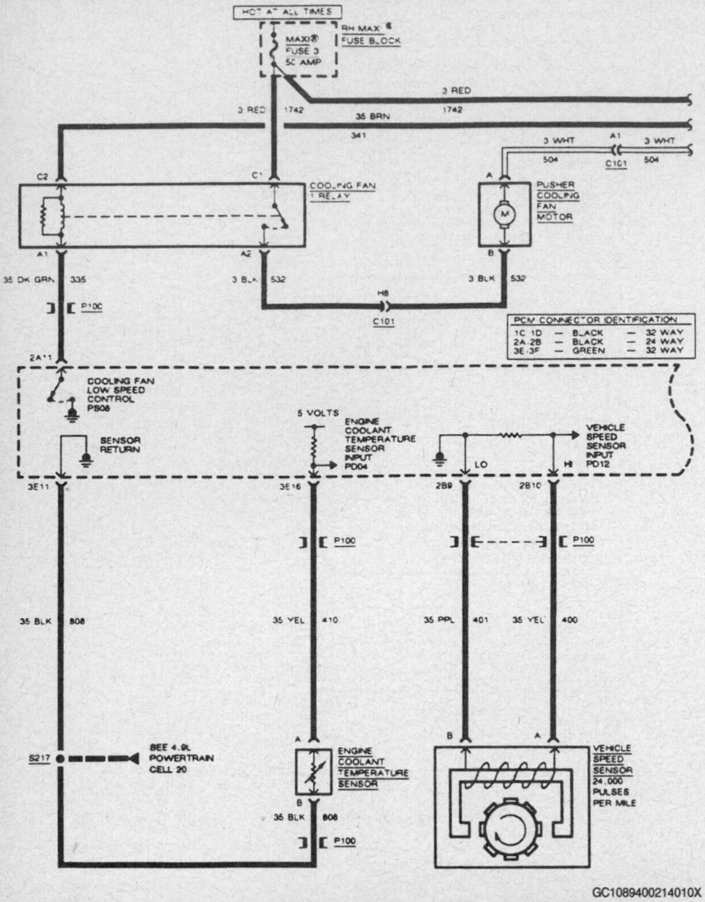
HOT AT ALL TIMES
MAXI® FUSE 3 50 AMP
RH MAXI FUSE BLOCK
COOLING FAN 1 RELAY
PUSHER COOLING FAN MOTOR
PCM CONNECTOR IDENTIFICATION
1C 1D — BLACK — 32 WAY
2A 2B — BLACK — 24 WAY
3E 3F — GREEN — 32 WAY
COOLING FAN LOW SPEED CONTROL P508
SENSOR RETURN
5 VOLTS
ENGINE COOLANT TEMPERATURE SENSOR INPUT PD04
VEHICLE SPEED SENSOR INPUT PD12
SEE 4.9L POWERTRAIN CELL 20
ENGINE COOLANT TEMPERATURE SENSOR
VEHICLE SPEED SENSOR 24,000 PULSES PER MILE
GC1089400214010X

Fig. 81 Cooling fan wiring circuit (Part 1 of 2). 1994 DeVille w/4.9L/V8-300 engine

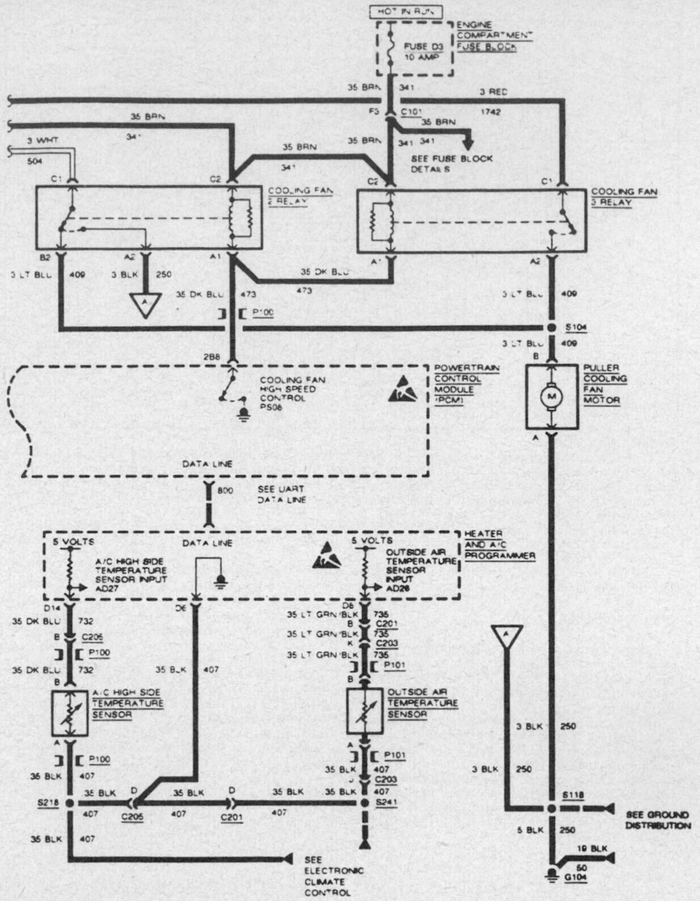
HOT IN RUN
FUSE D3 10 AMP
ENGINE COMPARTMENT FUSE BLOCK
SEE FUSE BLOCK DETAILS
COOLING FAN 2 RELAY
COOLING FAN 3 RELAY
COOLING FAN HIGH SPEED CONTROL P508
POWERTRAIN CONTROL MODULE (PCM)
PULLER COOLING FAN MOTOR
DATA LINE
SEE UART DATA LINE
A/C HIGH SIDE TEMPERATURE SENSOR INPUT AD27
OUTSIDE AIR TEMPERATURE SENSOR INPUT AD26
HEATER AND A/C PROGRAMMER
A/C HIGH SIDE TEMPERATURE SENSOR
OUTSIDE AIR TEMPERATURE SENSOR
SEE GROUND DISTRIBUTION
SEE ELECTRONIC CLIMATE CONTROL
GC1089400214020X

Fig. 81 Cooling fan wiring circuit (Part 2 of 2). 1994 DeVille w/4.9L/V8-300 engine

gray/black wire for an open circuit. If circuit is satisfactory, problem is PCM related. If test lamp lights, proceed to step 4.

4. Connect a fused jumper between relay connector terminal Nos. 1 (red) and 4 (black). If lefthand cooling fan runs in low speed, replace low speed cooling fan relay. If cooling fan does not run in low speed, check black/red wire and cooling fan resistor for an open circuit.

Lefthand Cooling Fan Does Not Operate In High Speed

1. Disconnect high speed cooling fan relay and turn ignition switch to Run position. Measure voltage from relay connector terminal 2 (brown) to ground. If battery voltage is present, proceed to step 2. If battery voltage is not present, check brown wire for an open circuit.
2. Measure voltage from terminal 1 (red) to ground. If battery voltage is present, proceed to step 3. If battery voltage is not present, check red wire for an open circuit.
3. Connect a test lamp between relay connector terminal Nos. 1 (red) and 5 (dark green/white). If test lamp lights, proceed to step 4. If test lamp does not light, check dark green/white wire for an open. If wire is satisfactory, problem is PCM related.
4. Connect a fused jumper between relay connector terminal Nos. 1 (red) and 4 (black/pink). If cooling fan runs in high speed, replace high speed cooling fan relay. If cooling fan does not run, check black/red wire and cooling fan resistor for an open circuit.

Lefthand Cooling Fan Runs Continuously In Low Speed With Ignition Switch In Run Position, Engine Coolant Cool & A/C Off

1. Disconnect low speed cooling fan relay and turn ignition switch to Run position.
2. Connect a test lamp between terminal Nos. 2 (brown) and 5 (gray/black) at low speed cooling fan connector.
3. If test lamp lights, check gray/black wire for a short to ground. If wire is satisfactory, problem is PCM related.
4. If test lamp does not light, replace low speed cooling fan relay.

Lefthand Cooling Fan Runs Continuously In High Speed With Ignition Switch In Run Position, Engine Coolant Cool & A/C Off

1. Disconnect high speed cooling fan relay and turn ignition switch to Run position.
2. Connect a test lamp between terminal Nos. 2 (brown) and 5 (dark green/white) at high speed relay connector.
3. If test lamp lights, check dark green/white wire for a short to ground. If wire is satisfactory, problem is PCM related.
4. If test lamp does not light, replace high speed cooling fan relay.

Cooling Fans Do Not Operate In High Speed With A/C Head Pressure Above 210 psi

1. Disconnect A/C pressure fan switch connector.
2. Measure resistance from terminal B (black/white) to ground.
3. If resistance is zero, refer to step 4. If resistance is not zero, check black/white wire for an open circuit.
4. Connect a jumper between terminals A (dark green/white) and B (black/white) of switch connector and turn ignition switch to Run position.
5. If cooling fans run in high speed, replace A/C pressure fan switch. If cooling fans do not run in high speed, check dark green/white wire for an open circuit. If wire is satisfactory, problem is PCM related.

1994

Refer to **Figs. 101 through 105** when performing diagnostic procedures.

CAPRICE, IMPALA SS & ROADMASTER

Refer to **Figs. 106 through 108** for system diagnosis.

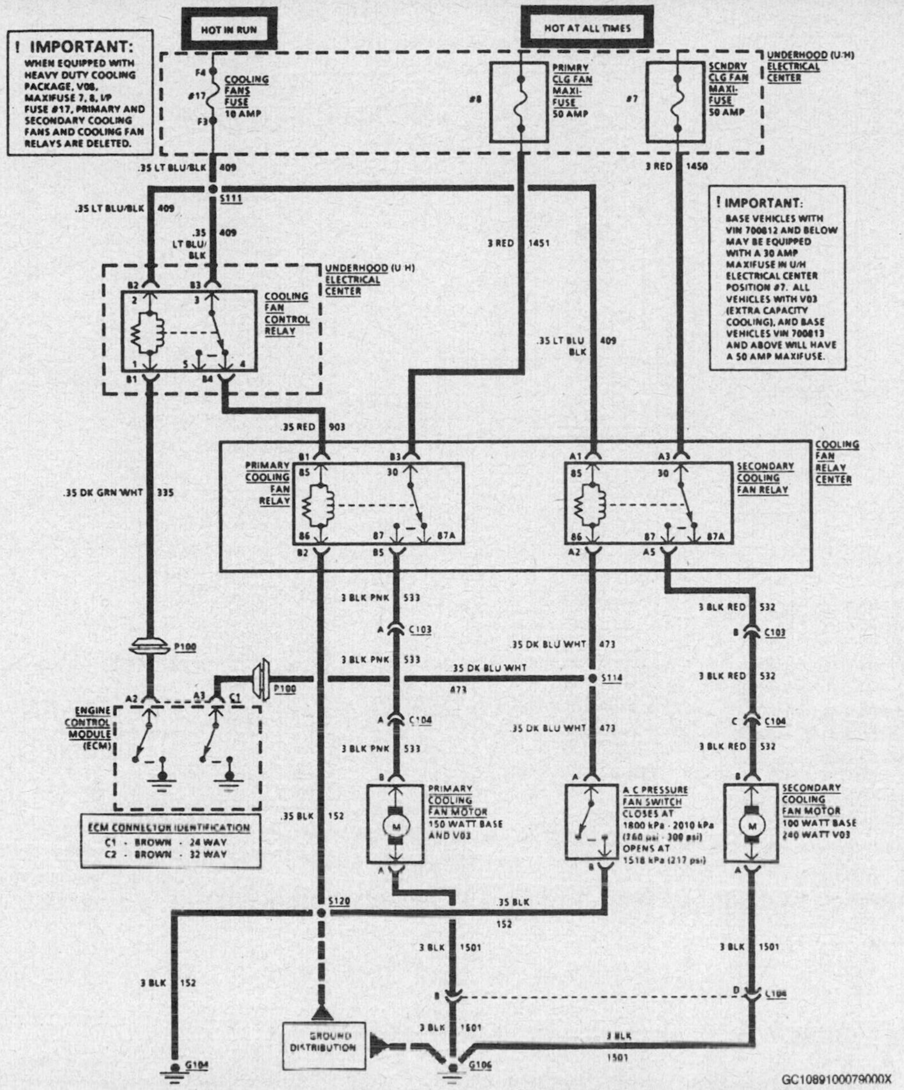
HOT IN RUN
HOT AT ALL TIMES
! IMPORTANT:
WHEN EQUIPPED WITH HEAVY DUTY COOLING PACKAGE, V08, MAXIFUSE 7, 8, I/P FUSE #17, PRIMARY AND SECONDARY COOLING FANS AND COOLING FAN RELAYS ARE DELETED.
COOLING FANS FUSE 10 AMP
PRIMRY CLG FAN MAXI-FUSE 50 AMP
SCNDRY CLG FAN MAXI-FUSE 50 AMP
UNDERHOOD (U/H) ELECTRICAL CENTER
! IMPORTANT:
BASE VEHICLES WITH VIN 700812 AND BELOW MAY BE EQUIPPED WITH A 30 AMP MAXIFUSE IN U/H ELECTRICAL CENTER POSITION #7. ALL VEHICLES WITH V03 (EXTRA CAPACITY COOLING), AND BASE VEHICLES VIN 700813 AND ABOVE WILL HAVE A 50 AMP MAXIFUSE.
COOLING FAN CONTROL RELAY
PRIMARY COOLING FAN RELAY
SECONDARY COOLING FAN RELAY
COOLING FAN RELAY CENTER
ENGINE CONTROL MODULE (ECM)
ECM CONNECTOR IDENTIFICATION
C1 - BROWN - 24 WAY
C2 - BROWN - 32 WAY
PRIMARY COOLING FAN MOTOR 150 WATT BASE AND V03
A/C PRESSURE FAN SWITCH CLOSES AT 1800 kPa - 2010 kPa (260 psi - 300 psi) OPENS AT 1518 kPa (217 psi)
SECONDARY COOLING FAN MOTOR 100 WATT BASE 240 WATT V03
GROUND DISTRIBUTION
GC1089100079000X

Fig. 82 Cooling fan wiring circuit. 1993 Fleetwood (RWD)

ACHIEVA, GRAND AM & SKYLARK

1992–93

Refer to **Figs. 109 through 111** when performing diagnostic procedures on these systems.

Cooling Fan Does Not Turn On

1. With ignition switch in Run position, ground terminal B of ALDL connector. If cooling fan runs, problem is ECM related.
2. If cooling fan does not run, turn ignition switch to Run position and jump ECM C3, terminal E8 to ground with a fused jumper. If cooling fan runs, problem is ECM related.
3. If cooling fan does not run, leave fused jumper connected as in step 2, turn ignition switch to Run position, disconnect cooling fan relay connector and measure voltage from terminal 2 (red) wire terminal to ground. If battery voltage is not present, repair open in circuit 2.
4. If battery voltage is present, leave fused jumper connected as in step 2, turn ignition switch to Run position, disconnect cooling fan relay connector and measure voltage between terminal 2 (red) and terminal 5 (dark green or light green/black) wire terminals of cooling fan relay connector. If battery voltage is not present, repair open in circuit 535 or 536.
5. If battery voltage is present, disconnect cooling fan relay connector and measure voltage from red (1) wire terminal to ground. If battery voltage is not present, repair open in circuit 2.
6. If battery voltage is present, disconnect cooling fan relay connector and connect fused jumper with 20 amp fuse between terminals 1 (red) and 4 (black/red) wire terminals. If cooling fan runs, replace cooling fan relay.
7. If cooling fan does not run, leave fused jumper connected as in step 6, disconnect cooling fan connector and measure voltage between terminal B (black/red) wire terminal and ground. If battery voltage is not present, repair open in circuit 532.
8. If battery voltage is present, leave fused jumper connected as in step 6, and measure voltage between terminals B (black/red) and A (black) wire terminals of cooling fan connector.
9. If battery voltage is not present, repair open in circuit 151.
10. If battery voltage is present, replace cooling fan motor.

Cooling Fan Does Not Turn Off With Engine Cool, A/C Mode Selector Off & Ignition Switch In Run Position

1. Turn ignition switch to Run position, disconnect cooling fan relay connector and connect test lamp between terminals 2 (red) and 5 (dark green or light green/black) wire terminals. If lamp does not illuminate, replace cooling fan relay.
2. If lamp illuminates, check circuit 535 or 536 for a short to ground. If wire is satisfactory, problem is ECM related.

1994

Refer to **Figs. 112 through 114** when performing diagnostic procedures.

LEMANS

Refer to **Figs. 115 and 116** when performing diagnostic procedures on this system.

LESS A/C

Cooling Fan Does Not Run

1. Check fuses 11 and 12, replace as necessary.
2. Connect a fused jumper wire between terminal B of the Assembly Line Diagnostic Link Connector (ALDL) and ground, then turn the ignition switch to the Run position. If cooling fan does not run, proceed to step 3. If cooling fan runs, problem is ECM related.
3. Disconnect ECM C2 connector, then connect a fused jumper wire between C1 green/white connector and ground. Turn ignition switch to Run position, If cooling fan does not run, proceed to step 4. If cooling fan runs, problem is ECM related.
4. Leaving jumper wire connected from the previous step, disconnect cooling fan relay connector. Turn ignition switch to Run position; then, using a test lamp, proceed as follows:
   a. Connect test lamp between terminal 1 (brown) wire and ground. If test lamp lights, proceed to step b. If test lamp does not light, locate and repair open in brown wire.
   b. Connect test lamp between terminal 3 (red/yellow) wire and ground. If test lamp lights, proceed to step c. If test lamp does not light, locate and repair open in red/yellow wire.
   c. Connect test lamp between terminal 1 (brown) and terminal 4 (green/white) wires. If test lamp lights, proceed to step d. If test lamp does not light, locate and repair open in green/white wire.
   d. Connect test lamp between terminal 1 (brown) and terminal 2 (red/white) wires. If test lamp lights, replace high speed cooling fan relay. If test lamp does not light, proceed to step 5.
5. With cooling fan relay connector disconnected, connect fused jumper wire between terminal 2 (red/white) and

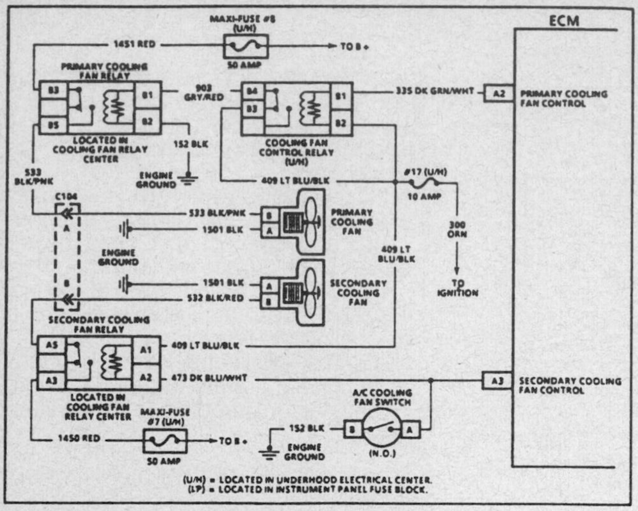
MAXI-FUSE #8 (U/H)
1451 RED
TO B+
50 AMP
ECM
PRIMARY COOLING FAN RELAY
903 GRY/RED
335 DK GRN/WHT
A2
PRIMARY COOLING FAN CONTROL
LOCATED IN COOLING FAN RELAY CENTER
152 BLK
COOLING FAN CONTROL RELAY (U/H)
533 BLK/PNK
ENGINE GROUND
409 LT BLU/BLK
#17 (U/H) 10 AMP
C104
533 BLK/PNK
1501 BLK
PRIMARY COOLING FAN
300 ORN
ENGINE GROUND
409 LT BLU/BLK
TO IGNITION
1501 BLK
532 BLK/RED
SECONDARY COOLING FAN
SECONDARY COOLING FAN RELAY
409 LT BLU/BLK
473 DK BLU/WHT
A3
SECONDARY COOLING FAN CONTROL
LOCATED IN COOLING FAN RELAY CENTER
MAXI-FUSE #7 (U/H)
A/C COOLING FAN SWITCH
1450 RED
TO B+
152 BLK
ENGINE GROUND
50 AMP
(N.O.)
(U/H) = LOCATED IN UNDERHOOD ELECTRICAL CENTER.
(I/P) = LOCATED IN INSTRUMENT PANEL FUSE BLOCK.

CHART C-12 (Page 1 of 3)

ELECTRIC COOLING FAN CONTROL CIRCUIT DIAGNOSIS

Circuit Description:

The cooling fans are controlled by the ECM based on various inputs. The primary cooling fan relay is energized by the cooling fan control relay when the cooling fan control relay is de-energized. The primary fan relay will be energized and supply battery voltage to the primary cooling fan motor. Grounding CKT 473 (relay terminal "2") will energize the secondary cooling fan relay (Fan 2) and supply battery voltage to the secondary fan motor.

The A/C cooling fan switch, mounted in the A/C high pressure line, will be grounded when head pressure exceeds 1800 kPa-2070 kPa (200-300 psi) and enable the secondary cooling fan motor.

If a DTC 14, or 15 sets or the ECM is operating in the fuel back-up mode, the ECM will turn "ON" the cooling fans.

Diagnostic Aids:

If the owner complained of an overheating problem, it must be determined if the complaint was due to an actual boil over, or the warning indicator light, or engine coolant temperature gage indicated overheating.

The gage accuracy can also be checked by comparing the Engine Coolant Temperature (ECT) sensor reading using a Tech 1 and comparing its reading with the gage reading. If the engine is actually overheating and the gage indicated overheating, but the cooling fan is not coming "ON," the Engine Coolant Temperature (ECT) sensor has probably shifted out of calibration and should be replaced.

If the engine is overheating and the cooling fans are "ON," the cooling system should be checked.

The ECM will command Fan 1 "ON" at 108°C (226°F) and "OFF" at 105°C (221°F) and, Fan 2 "ON" at 111°C (231°F) and "OFF" at 107°C (225°F).

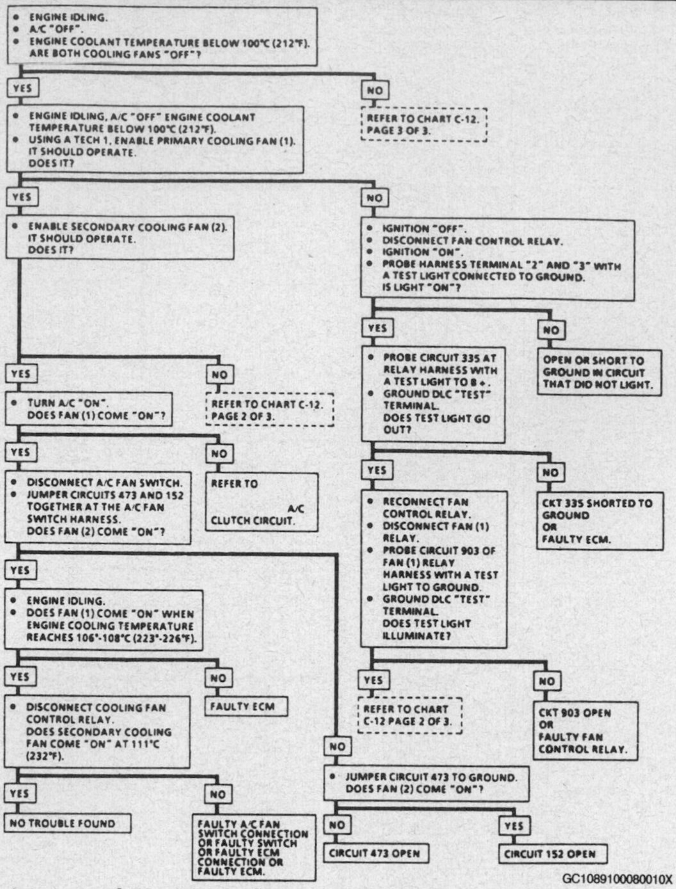
• ENGINE IDLING.
• A/C "OFF".
• ENGINE COOLANT TEMPERATURE BELOW 100°C (212°F). ARE BOTH COOLING FANS "OFF"?
YES
NO
REFER TO CHART C-12. PAGE 3 OF 3.
• ENGINE IDLING, A/C "OFF" ENGINE COOLANT TEMPERATURE BELOW 100°C (212°F).
• USING A TECH 1, ENABLE PRIMARY COOLING FAN (1). IT SHOULD OPERATE. DOES IT?
YES
NO
• ENABLE SECONDARY COOLING FAN (2). IT SHOULD OPERATE. DOES IT?
• IGNITION "OFF".
• DISCONNECT FAN CONTROL RELAY.
• IGNITION "ON".
• PROBE HARNESS TERMINAL "2" AND "3" WITH A TEST LIGHT CONNECTED TO GROUND. IS LIGHT "ON"?
YES
NO
OPEN OR SHORT TO GROUND IN CIRCUIT THAT DID NOT LIGHT.
• PROBE CIRCUIT 335 AT RELAY HARNESS WITH A TEST LIGHT TO B+.
• GROUND DLC "TEST" TERMINAL. DOES TEST LIGHT GO OUT?
YES
NO
• TURN A/C "ON". DOES FAN (1) COME "ON"?
REFER TO CHART C-12. PAGE 2 OF 3.
YES
NO
• DISCONNECT A/C FAN SWITCH.
• JUMPER CIRCUITS 473 AND 152 TOGETHER AT THE A/C FAN SWITCH HARNESS. DOES FAN (2) COME "ON"?
REFER TO A/C CLUTCH CIRCUIT.
YES
NO
• RECONNECT FAN CONTROL RELAY.
• DISCONNECT FAN (1) RELAY.
• PROBE CIRCUIT 903 OF FAN (1) RELAY HARNESS WITH A TEST LIGHT TO GROUND.
• GROUND DLC "TEST" TERMINAL. DOES TEST LIGHT ILLUMINATE?
CKT 335 SHORTED TO GROUND OR FAULTY ECM.
YES
• ENGINE IDLING.
• DOES FAN (1) COME "ON" WHEN ENGINE COOLING TEMPERATURE REACHES 106°-108°C (223°-226°F).
YES
NO
FAULTY ECM
• DISCONNECT COOLING FAN CONTROL RELAY. DOES SECONDARY COOLING FAN COME "ON" AT 111°C (232°F).
YES
NO
REFER TO CHART C-12 PAGE 2 OF 3.
CKT 903 OPEN OR FAULTY FAN CONTROL RELAY.
NO
• JUMPER CIRCUIT 473 TO GROUND. DOES FAN (2) COME "ON"?
YES
NO
NO TROUBLE FOUND
FAULTY A/C FAN SWITCH CONNECTION OR FAULTY SWITCH OR FAULTY ECM CONNECTION OR FAULTY ECM.
NO
YES
CIRCUIT 473 OPEN
CIRCUIT 152 OPEN

GC1089100080010X

Fig. 83 Chart C-12, cooling fan diagnosis (Part 1 of 3). 1993 Fleetwood (RWD)

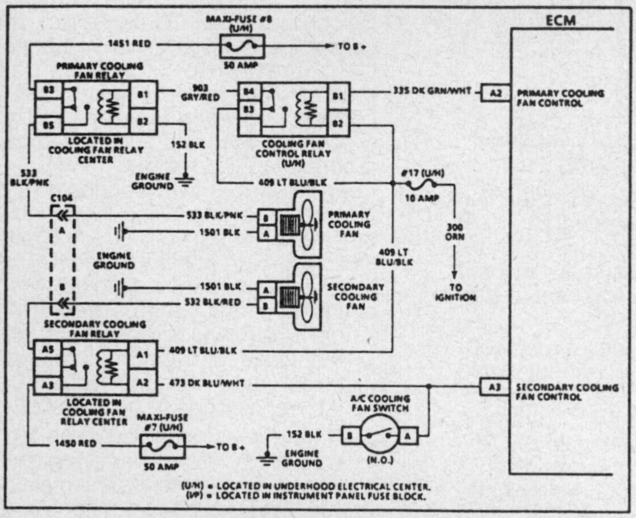
MAXI-FUSE #8 (U/H)
1451 RED
TO B+
50 AMP
ECM
PRIMARY COOLING FAN RELAY
903 GRY/RED
335 DK GRN/WHT
A2
PRIMARY COOLING FAN CONTROL
LOCATED IN COOLING FAN RELAY CENTER
152 BLK
COOLING FAN CONTROL RELAY (U/H)
533 BLK/PNK
ENGINE GROUND
409 LT BLU/BLK
#17 (U/H) 10 AMP
C104
533 BLK/PNK
1501 BLK
PRIMARY COOLING FAN
300 ORN
ENGINE GROUND
409 LT BLU/BLK
TO IGNITION
1501 BLK
532 BLK/RED
SECONDARY COOLING FAN
SECONDARY COOLING FAN RELAY
409 LT BLU/BLK
473 DK BLU/WHT
A3
SECONDARY COOLING FAN CONTROL
LOCATED IN COOLING FAN RELAY CENTER
MAXI-FUSE #7 (U/H)
A/C COOLING FAN SWITCH
1450 RED
TO B+
152 BLK
ENGINE GROUND
50 AMP
(N.O.)
(U/H) = LOCATED IN UNDERHOOD ELECTRICAL CENTER.
(I/P) = LOCATED IN INSTRUMENT PANEL FUSE BLOCK.

CHART C-12 (Page 2 of 3)

ELECTRIC COOLING FAN CONTROL CIRCUIT DIAGNOSIS

Circuit Description:

The cooling fans are controlled by the ECM based on various inputs. The primary cooling fan relay is energized by the cooling fan control relay when the cooling fan control relay is de-energized. The primary fan relay will be energized and supply battery voltage to the primary cooling fan motor. Grounding CKT 473 (relay terminal "2") will energize the secondary cooling fan relay (Fan 2) and supply battery voltage to the secondary fan motor.

The A/C cooling fan switch, mounted in the A/C high pressure line, will be grounded when head pressure exceeds 1800 kPa-2070 kPa (200-300 psi) and enable the secondary cooling fan motor.

If a DTC 14, or 15 sets or the ECM is operating in the fuel back-up mode, the ECM will turn "ON" the cooling fans.

Diagnostic Aids:

If the owner complained of an overheating problem, it must be determined if the complaint was due to an actual boil over, or the warning indicator light, or engine coolant temperature gage indicated overheating.

The gage accuracy can also be checked by comparing the Engine Coolant Temperature (ECT) sensor reading using a Tech 1 and comparing its reading with the gage reading. If the engine is actually overheating and the gage indicated overheating, but the cooling fan is not coming "ON," the Engine Coolant Temperature (ECT) sensor has probably shifted out of calibration and should be replaced.

If the engine is overheating and the cooling fans are "ON," the cooling system should be checked.

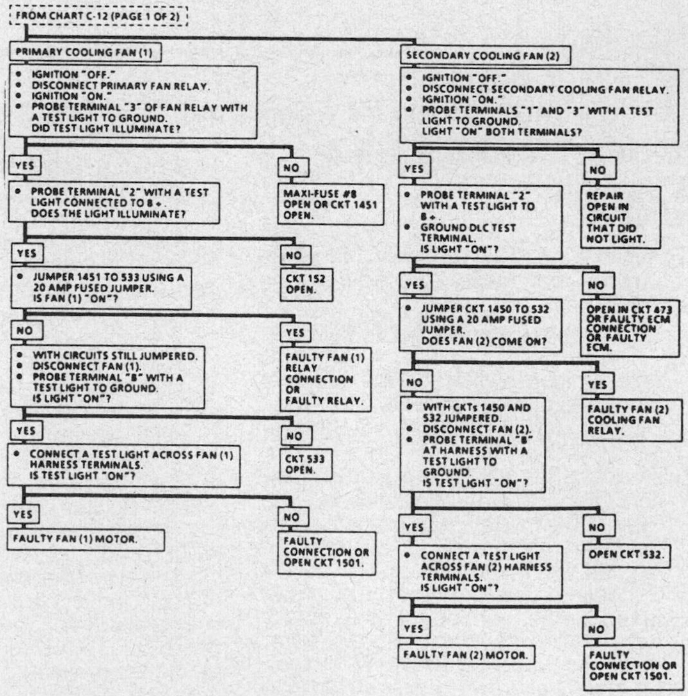
FROM CHART C-12 (PAGE 1 OF 2)
PRIMARY COOLING FAN (1)
• IGNITION "OFF."
• DISCONNECT PRIMARY FAN RELAY.
• IGNITION "ON."
• PROBE TERMINAL "3" OF FAN RELAY WITH A TEST LIGHT TO GROUND. DID TEST LIGHT ILLUMINATE?
YES
NO
• PROBE TERMINAL "2" WITH A TEST LIGHT CONNECTED TO B+. DOES THE LIGHT ILLUMINATE?
MAXI-FUSE #8 OPEN OR CKT 1451 OPEN.
YES
NO
• JUMPER 1451 TO 533 USING A 20 AMP FUSED JUMPER. IS FAN (1) "ON"?
CKT 152 OPEN.
NO
YES
• WITH CIRCUITS STILL JUMPERED.
• DISCONNECT FAN (1).
• PROBE TERMINAL "B" WITH A TEST LIGHT TO GROUND. IS LIGHT "ON"?
FAULTY FAN (1) RELAY CONNECTION OR FAULTY RELAY.
YES
NO
• CONNECT A TEST LIGHT ACROSS FAN (1) HARNESS TERMINALS. IS TEST LIGHT "ON"?
CKT 533 OPEN.
YES
NO
FAULTY FAN (1) MOTOR.
FAULTY CONNECTION OR OPEN CKT 1501.
SECONDARY COOLING FAN (2)
• IGNITION "OFF."
• DISCONNECT SECONDARY COOLING FAN RELAY.
• IGNITION "ON."
• PROBE TERMINALS "1" AND "3" WITH A TEST LIGHT TO GROUND. LIGHT "ON" BOTH TERMINALS?
YES
NO
• PROBE TERMINAL "2" WITH A TEST LIGHT TO B+.
• GROUND DLC TEST TERMINAL. IS LIGHT "ON"?
REPAIR OPEN IN CIRCUIT THAT DID NOT LIGHT.
YES
NO
• JUMPER CKT 1450 TO 532 USING A 20 AMP FUSED JUMPER. DOES FAN (2) COME ON?
OPEN IN CKT 473 OR FAULTY ECM CONNECTION OR FAULTY ECM.
NO
YES
• WITH CKTs 1450 AND 532 JUMPERED.
• DISCONNECT FAN (2).
• PROBE TERMINAL "B" AT HARNESS WITH A TEST LIGHT TO GROUND. IS TEST LIGHT "ON"?
FAULTY FAN (2) COOLING FAN RELAY.
YES
NO
• CONNECT A TEST LIGHT ACROSS FAN (2) HARNESS TERMINALS. IS LIGHT "ON"?
OPEN CKT 532.
YES
NO
FAULTY FAN (2) MOTOR.
FAULTY CONNECTION OR OPEN CKT 1501.

GC1089100080020X

Fig. 83 Chart C-12, cooling fan diagnosis (Part 2 of 3). 1993 Fleetwood (RWD)

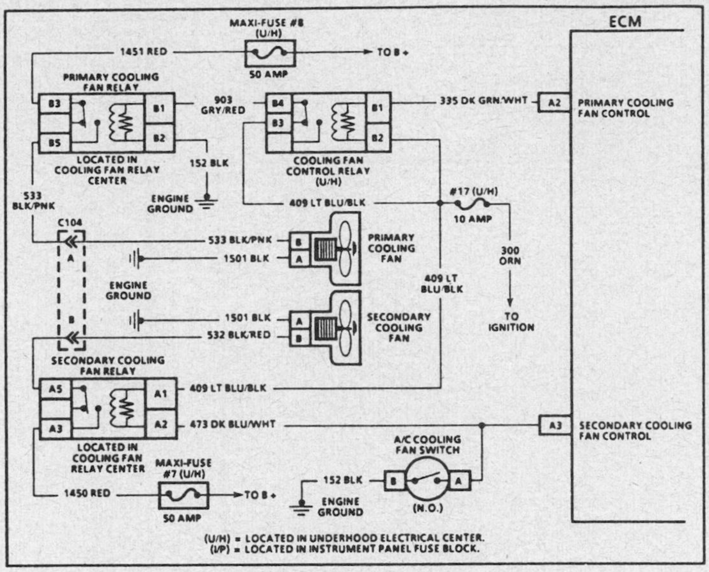
MAXI-FUSE #8
(U/H)
1451 RED
TO B+
50 AMP
ECM
PRIMARY COOLING FAN RELAY
903 GRY/RED
335 DK GRN/WHT
A2
PRIMARY COOLING FAN CONTROL
LOCATED IN COOLING FAN RELAY CENTER
152 BLK
COOLING FAN CONTROL RELAY (U/H)
533 BLK/PNK
ENGINE GROUND
409 LT BLU/BLK
#17 (U/H)
10 AMP
C104
533 BLK/PNK
1501 BLK
PRIMARY COOLING FAN
300 ORN
409 LT BLU/BLK
ENGINE GROUND
1501 BLK
532 BLK/RED
SECONDARY COOLING FAN
TO IGNITION
SECONDARY COOLING FAN RELAY
409 LT BLU/BLK
473 DK BLU/WHT
A3
SECONDARY COOLING FAN CONTROL
LOCATED IN COOLING FAN RELAY CENTER
MAXI-FUSE #7 (U/H)
A/C COOLING FAN SWITCH
152 BLK
1450 RED
TO B+
ENGINE GROUND
(N.O.)
50 AMP
(U/H) = LOCATED IN UNDERHOOD ELECTRICAL CENTER.
(I/P) = LOCATED IN INSTRUMENT PANEL FUSE BLOCK.

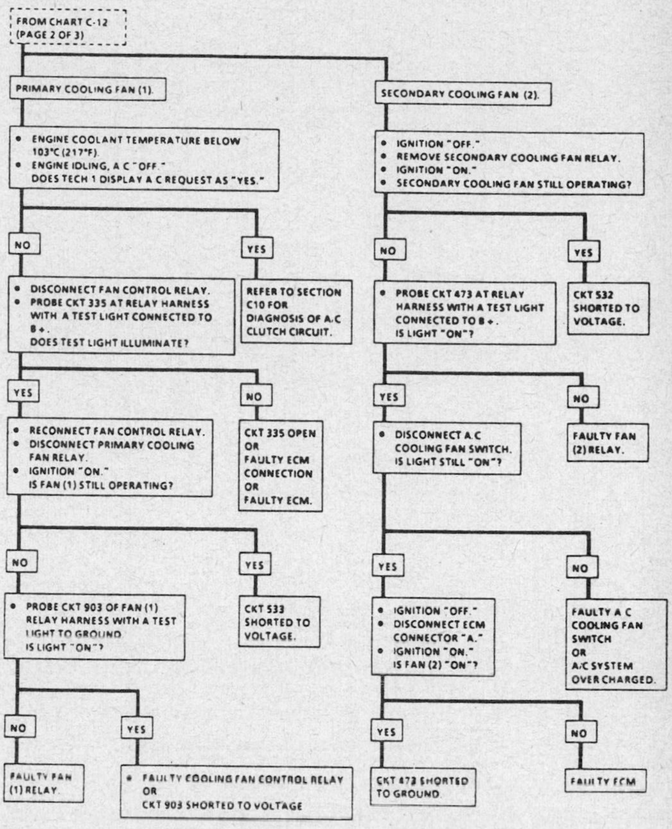
FROM CHART C-12 (PAGE 2 OF 3)
PRIMARY COOLING FAN (1).
SECONDARY COOLING FAN (2).
• ENGINE COOLANT TEMPERATURE BELOW 103°C (217°F).
• ENGINE IDLING, A/C "OFF."
DOES TECH 1 DISPLAY A/C REQUEST AS "YES."
• IGNITION "OFF."
• REMOVE SECONDARY COOLING FAN RELAY.
• IGNITION "ON."
• SECONDARY COOLING FAN STILL OPERATING?
NO
YES
NO
YES
• DISCONNECT FAN CONTROL RELAY.
• PROBE CKT 335 AT RELAY HARNESS WITH A TEST LIGHT CONNECTED TO B+.
DOES TEST LIGHT ILLUMINATE?
REFER TO SECTION C10 FOR DIAGNOSIS OF A/C CLUTCH CIRCUIT.
• PROBE CKT 473 AT RELAY HARNESS WITH A TEST LIGHT CONNECTED TO B+.
IS LIGHT "ON"?
CKT 532 SHORTED TO VOLTAGE.
YES
NO
YES
NO
• RECONNECT FAN CONTROL RELAY.
• DISCONNECT PRIMARY COOLING FAN RELAY.
• IGNITION "ON."
IS FAN (1) STILL OPERATING?
CKT 335 OPEN OR FAULTY ECM CONNECTION OR FAULTY ECM.
• DISCONNECT A/C COOLING FAN SWITCH.
IS LIGHT STILL "ON"?
FAULTY FAN (2) RELAY.
NO
YES
YES
NO
• PROBE CKT 903 OF FAN (1) RELAY HARNESS WITH A TEST LIGHT TO GROUND.
IS LIGHT "ON"?
CKT 533 SHORTED TO VOLTAGE.
• IGNITION "OFF."
• DISCONNECT ECM CONNECTOR "A."
• IGNITION "ON."
IS FAN (2) "ON"?
FAULTY A/C COOLING FAN SWITCH OR A/C SYSTEM OVERCHARGED.
NO
YES
YES
NO
FAULTY FAN (1) RELAY.
• FAULTY COOLING FAN CONTROL RELAY OR CKT 903 SHORTED TO VOLTAGE
CKT 473 SHORTED TO GROUND.
FAULTY ECM.

CHART C-12 (Page 3 of 3)

ELECTRIC COOLING FAN CONTROL CIRCUIT DIAGNOSIS

Circuit Description:

The cooling fans are controlled by the ECM based on various inputs. The primary cooling fan relay is energized by the cooling fan control relay when the cooling fan control relay is de-energized. The primary fan relay will be energized and supply battery voltage to the primary cooling fan motor. Grounding CKT 473 (relay terminal "2") will energize the secondary cooling fan relay (Fan 2) and supply battery voltage to the secondary fan motor.

The A/C cooling fan switch, mounted in the A/C high pressure line, will be grounded when head pressure exceeds 1800 kPa-2070 kPa (200-300 psi) and enable the secondary cooling fan motor.

If a DTC 14, or 15 sets or the ECM is operating in the fuel back-up mode, the ECM will turn "ON" the cooling fans.

Diagnostic Aids:

If the owner complained of an overheating problem, it must be determined if the complaint was due to an actual boil over, or the warning indicator light, or engine coolant temperature gage indicated overheating.

The gage accuracy can also be checked by comparing the Engine Coolant Temperature (ECT) sensor reading using a Tech 1 and comparing its reading with the gage reading. If the engine is actually overheating and the gage indicated overheating, but the cooling fan is not coming "ON," the Engine Coolant Temperature (ECT) sensor has probably shifted out of calibration and should be replaced.

If the engine is overheating and the cooling fans are "ON," the cooling system should be checked.

The ECM will command Fan 1 "ON" at 108°C (226°F) and "OFF" at 105°C (221°F) and, Fan 2 "ON" at 111°C (231°F) and "OFF" at 107°C (225°F).

GC1089100080030X

Fig. 83 Chart C-12, cooling fan diagnosis (Part 3 of 3). 1993 Fleetwood (RWD)

terminal 3 (red/yellow).

6. Check voltage between red/white terminal and ground. If battery voltage is indicated, proceed to step 7. If battery voltage is not indicated, locate and repair open circuit in red/white wire.
7. Check voltage between red/white and black wires. If battery voltage is indicated, replace cooling fan. If battery voltage is not indicated, locate and repair open circuit in black wire.

Cooling Fan Runs Constantly When Ignition Switch Is In Run Position

1. Disconnect ECM connector C2, then turn ignition switch to Run position.
2. If cooling fan is off, problem is ECM related.
3. If cooling fan is on, locate and repair short to ground in green/white wire.

Cooling Fan Does Not Run At Low Speed

1. Disconnect Connector C1 from ECM, then turn ignition switch to the Run position.
2. Connect a fused jumper wire between terminal A4 (blue) wire and ground. If cooling fan does not run, proceed to step 3. If cooling fan runs, problem is ECM related.
3. With ignition switch in Run position and jumper wire connected as in step 2. Disconnect low speed cooling fan relay connector and proceed as follows:
   a. Connect a test lamp between connector terminal 1 (red/yellow) and ground. If test lamp lights, proceed to step b. If test lamp does not light, locate and repair open in red/yellow wire.
   b. Connect a test lamp between connector terminals 1 (red/yellow) and 4 (black). If test lamp lights, replace low cooling fan relay. If test lamp does not light, locate and repair open in black wire.

With A/C

Refer to **Fig. 117** when performing diagnostic procedures on this system.

SUNBIRD

1992–93

Refer to **Figs. 118 through 119** when performing diagnostic procedures on these systems.

1994

Refer to **Figs. 120 through 123** when performing diagnostic procedures on these systems.

RIVIERA, TORONADO & TROFEO

1992–93

Refer to **Figs. 124 through 130** for system diagnosis.

LUMINA

Refer to **Figs. 131 through 132** when performing diagnostic procedures.

1992
Primary Cooling Fan Does Not Run

1. With ignition switch in Run position, ground terminal B (WHT/BLK) of the ALDL connector. If cooling fan runs, problem is ECM related.
2. If cooling fan does not run, ground terminal A9 (DK GRN/WHT) at the ECM with a fused jumper. If cooling fan runs, problem is ECM related.
3. If cooling fan does not run, ignition switch in Run position, leave jumper from step 2 installed and disconnect cooling fan relay connector. Measure voltage between terminal 3 (RED) and ground. If no voltage is present, check red wire for an open.
4. If battery voltage is present, ensure ignition switch in Run position, measure voltage between terminal 3 (RED)

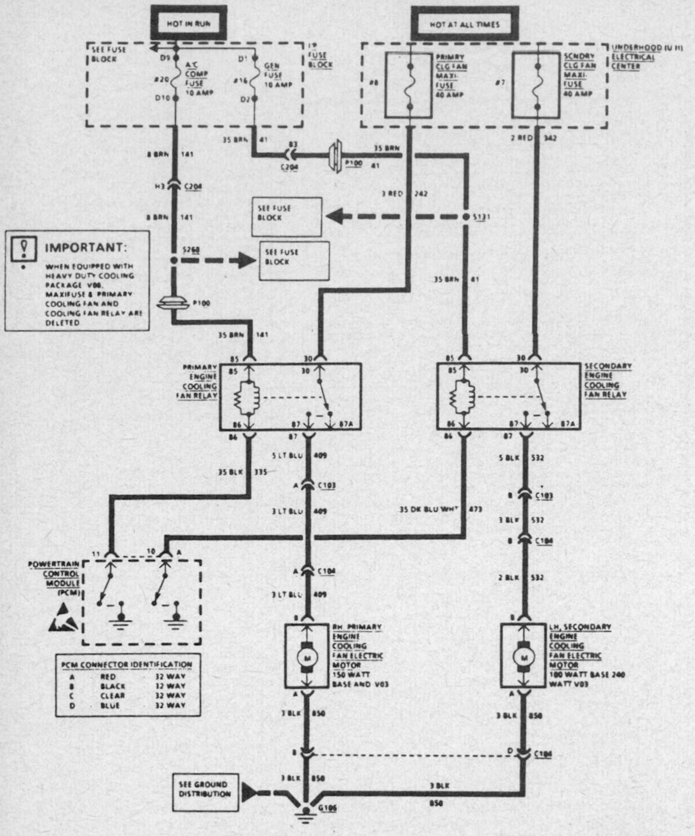

GC1089400215000X

Fig. 84 Cooling fan wiring circuit. 1994 Fleetwood (RWD) w/base & extra cooling

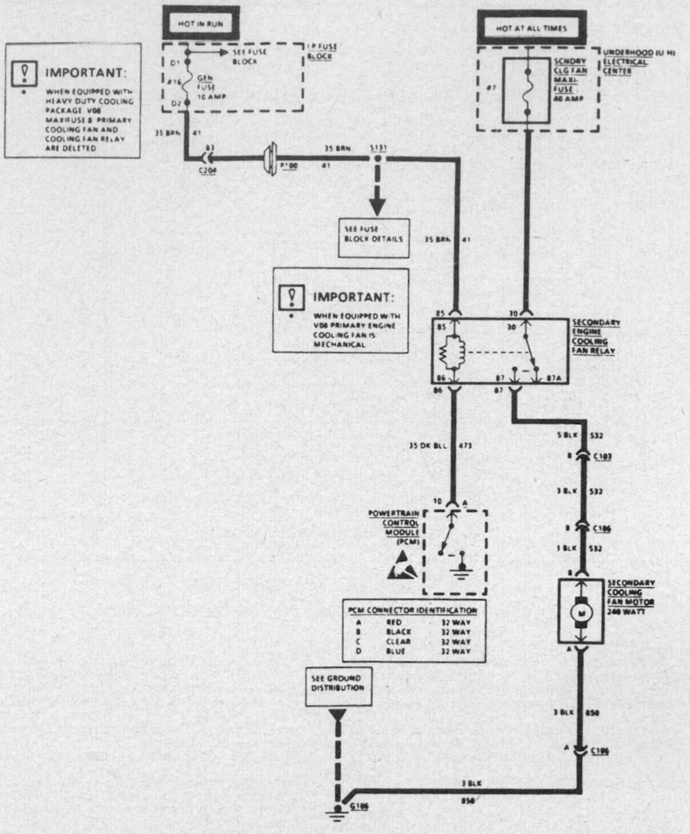

GC1089400216000X

Fig. 85 Cooling fan wiring circuit. 1994 Fleetwood (RWD) w/V08 heavy cooling

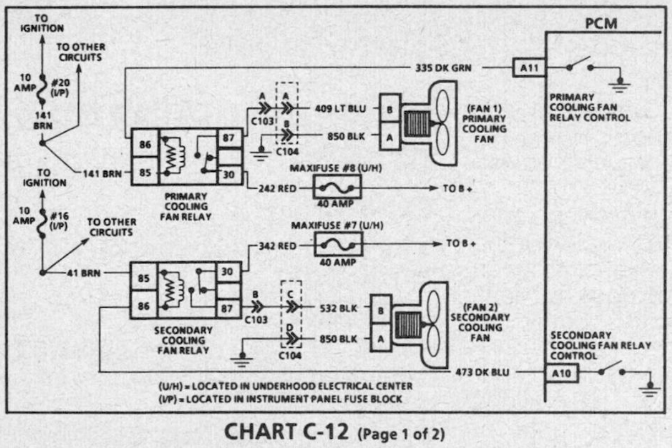

TO IGNITION
TO OTHER CIRCUITS
PCM
335 DK GRN
PRIMARY COOLING FAN RELAY CONTROL
409 LT BLU
850 BLK
(FAN 1) PRIMARY COOLING FAN
PRIMARY COOLING FAN RELAY
MAXIFUSE #8 (U/H)
242 RED
40 AMP
TO B+
MAXIFUSE #7 (U/H)
342 RED
532 BLK
(FAN 2) SECONDARY COOLING FAN
SECONDARY COOLING FAN RELAY
SECONDARY COOLING FAN RELAY CONTROL
473 DK BLU
(U/H) = LOCATED IN UNDERHOOD ELECTRICAL CENTER
(I/P) = LOCATED IN INSTRUMENT PANEL FUSE BLOCK

CHART C-12 (Page 1 of 2)

ELECTRIC COOLING FAN CONTROL CIRCUIT DIAGNOSIS 5.7L (VIN P) "D" CARLINE (SFI)

Circuit Description:

The cooling fans are controlled by the PCM based on various inputs. Battery voltage is supplied to the primary and secondary fan relays on terminal "30". Ignition voltage is supplied to terminal "85" of the primary and secondary fan relays. Grounding CKT 335 (relay terminal "86") will energize the primary cooling fan relay (Fan 1) and supply battery voltage to the primary cooling fan motor. Grounding CKT 473 (relay terminal "86") will energize the secondary cooling fan relay (Fan 2) and supply battery voltage to the secondary fan motor.

When certain Diagnostic Trouble Codes (DTCs) are set, the PCM will enable the cooling fans.

Chart Test Description: Number(s) below refer to circled number(s) on the diagnostic chart.

1. With the output/field service enable terminal grounded at DLC, the cooling fan control driver(s) will close, which should energize the fan control relay(s).
2. The cooling fans should come "ON" anytime A/C system is operating.
3. Comparing Tech 1 pressure and manifold gage set pressure will determine if the A/C refrigerant pressure sensor is out of range. An out of range A/C refrigerant pressure sensor can cause the cooling fans to operate at the wrong times.

Diagnostic Aids: If the owner complained of an overheating problem, it must be determined if the complaint was due to an actual boil over, or the warning indicator light, or engine coolant temperature gage indicated overheating.

The gage accuracy can also be checked by comparing the Engine Coolant Temperature (ECT) sensor reading using a Tech 1 and comparing its reading with the gage reading.

If the engine is actually overheating and the gage indicated overheating, but the cooling fan is not coming "ON," the Engine Coolant Temperature (ECT) sensor has probably shifted out of calibration and should be replaced.

If the engine is overheating and the cooling fans are "ON," the cooling system should be checked.

The PCM will command fan 1 "ON" at 107°C (225°F) and "OFF" at 103°C (217°F) and, fan 2 "ON" at 111°C (232°F) and "OFF" at 107°C (224°F).

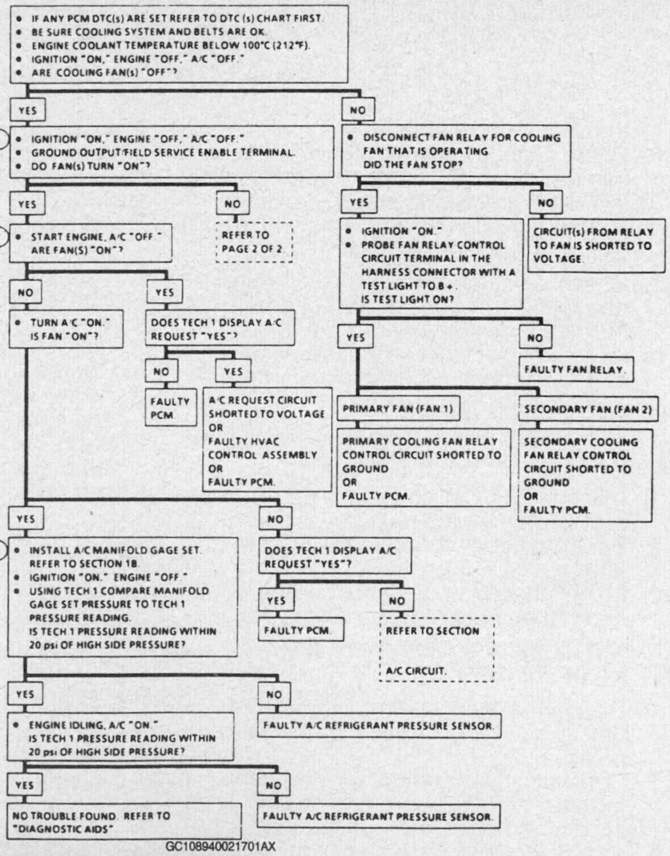

• IF ANY PCM DTC(s) ARE SET REFER TO DTC(s) CHART FIRST.
• BE SURE COOLING SYSTEM AND BELTS ARE OK.
• ENGINE COOLANT TEMPERATURE BELOW 100°C (212°F).
• IGNITION "ON," ENGINE "OFF," A/C "OFF."
• ARE COOLING FAN(s) "OFF"?
YES
NO
1 • IGNITION "ON," ENGINE "OFF," A/C "OFF."
• GROUND OUTPUT/FIELD SERVICE ENABLE TERMINAL.
• DO FAN(s) TURN "ON"?
• DISCONNECT FAN RELAY FOR COOLING FAN THAT IS OPERATING. DID THE FAN STOP?
YES
NO
YES
NO
2 • START ENGINE, A/C "OFF." ARE FAN(S) "ON"?
REFER TO PAGE 2 OF 2.
• IGNITION "ON."
• PROBE FAN RELAY CONTROL CIRCUIT TERMINAL IN THE HARNESS CONNECTOR WITH A TEST LIGHT TO B+. IS TEST LIGHT ON?
CIRCUIT(s) FROM RELAY TO FAN IS SHORTED TO VOLTAGE.
NO
YES
• TURN A/C "ON." IS FAN "ON"?
DOES TECH 1 DISPLAY A/C REQUEST "YES"?
YES
NO
NO
YES
FAULTY FAN RELAY.
FAULTY PCM.
A/C REQUEST CIRCUIT SHORTED TO VOLTAGE OR FAULTY HVAC CONTROL ASSEMBLY OR FAULTY PCM.
PRIMARY FAN (FAN 1)
SECONDARY FAN (FAN 2)
PRIMARY COOLING FAN RELAY CONTROL CIRCUIT SHORTED TO GROUND OR FAULTY PCM.
SECONDARY COOLING FAN RELAY CONTROL CIRCUIT SHORTED TO GROUND OR FAULTY PCM.
YES
NO
3 • INSTALL A/C MANIFOLD GAGE SET. REFER TO SECTION 1B.
• IGNITION "ON," ENGINE "OFF."
• USING TECH 1 COMPARE MANIFOLD GAGE SET PRESSURE TO TECH 1 PRESSURE READING. IS TECH 1 PRESSURE READING WITHIN 20 psi OF HIGH SIDE PRESSURE?
DOES TECH 1 DISPLAY A/C REQUEST "YES"?
YES
NO
FAULTY PCM.
REFER TO SECTION A/C CIRCUIT.
YES
NO
• ENGINE IDLING, A/C "ON." IS TECH 1 PRESSURE READING WITHIN 20 psi OF HIGH SIDE PRESSURE?
FAULTY A/C REFRIGERANT PRESSURE SENSOR.
YES
NO
NO TROUBLE FOUND. REFER TO "DIAGNOSTIC AIDS"
FAULTY A/C REFRIGERANT PRESSURE SENSOR.

GC108940021701AX

Fig. 86 Chart C-12, cooling fan diagnosis (Part 1 of 2). 1994 Fleetwood (RWD) w/5.7L/V8-350 engine

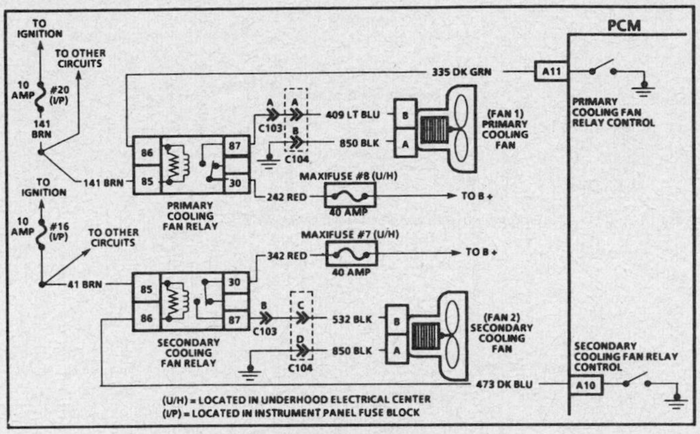
TO IGNITION
TO OTHER CIRCUITS
10 AMP
#20 (I/P)
141 BRN
PCM
335 DK GRN
A11
409 LT BLU
850 BLK
(FAN 1) PRIMARY COOLING FAN
PRIMARY COOLING FAN RELAY CONTROL
C103
C104
86
87
85
30
141 BRN
PRIMARY COOLING FAN RELAY
MAXIFUSE #8 (U/H)
242 RED
40 AMP
TO B+
#16 (I/P)
TO OTHER CIRCUITS
MAXIFUSE #7 (U/H)
342 RED
40 AMP
TO B+
41 BRN
532 BLK
850 BLK
(FAN 2) SECONDARY COOLING FAN
SECONDARY COOLING FAN RELAY
SECONDARY COOLING FAN RELAY CONTROL
473 DK BLU
A10
(U/H) = LOCATED IN UNDERHOOD ELECTRICAL CENTER
(I/P) = LOCATED IN INSTRUMENT PANEL FUSE BLOCK

CHART C-12

(Page 2 of 2)

ELECTRIC COOLING FAN CONTROL CIRCUIT DIAGNOSIS

5.7L (VIN P) "D" CARLINE (SFI)

Circuit Description:

The cooling fans are controlled by the PCM based on various inputs. Battery voltage is supplied to the primary and secondary fan relays on terminal "30". Ignition voltage is supplied to terminal "85" of the primary and secondary fan relays. Grounding CKT 335 (relay terminal "86") will energize the primary cooling fan relay (Fan 1) and supply battery voltage to the primary cooling fan motor. Grounding CKT 473 (relay terminal "85") will energize the secondary cooling fan relay (Fan 2) and supply battery voltage to the secondary fan motor.

The PCM will enable the cooling fans, when certain Diagnostic Trouble Codes (DTCs) are set.

Diagnostic Aids: If the owner complained of an overheating problem, it must be determined if the complaint was due to an actual boil over, the warning indicator light, or engine coolant temperature gage indicated overheating.

The gage accuracy can also be checked by comparing the Engine Coolant Temperature (ECT) sensor reading using a Tech 1 and comparing its reading with the gage reading.

If the engine is actually overheating and the gage indicated overheating, but the cooling fan is not coming "ON," the Engine Coolant Temperature (ECT) sensor has probably shifted out of calibration and should be replaced.

If the engine is overheating and the cooling fans are "ON," the cooling system should be checked, refer to SECTION 6B.

The PCM will command fan 1 "ON" at 107°C (225°F) and "OFF" at 103°C (217°F) and an 2 "ON" at 111°C (232°F) and "OFF" at 107°C (224°F).

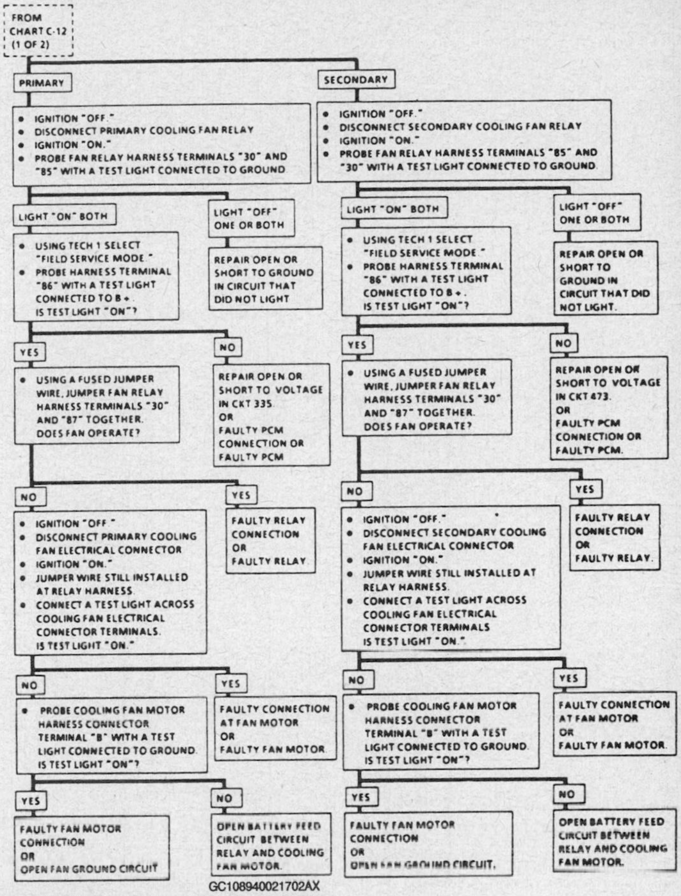
FROM CHART C-12 (1 OF 2)
PRIMARY
SECONDARY
• IGNITION "OFF." • DISCONNECT PRIMARY COOLING FAN RELAY • IGNITION "ON." • PROBE FAN RELAY HARNESS TERMINALS "30" AND "85" WITH A TEST LIGHT CONNECTED TO GROUND
• IGNITION "OFF." • DISCONNECT SECONDARY COOLING FAN RELAY • IGNITION "ON." • PROBE FAN RELAY HARNESS TERMINALS "85" AND "30" WITH A TEST LIGHT CONNECTED TO GROUND.
LIGHT "ON" BOTH
LIGHT "OFF" ONE OR BOTH
• USING TECH 1 SELECT "FIELD SERVICE MODE." • PROBE HARNESS TERMINAL "86" WITH A TEST LIGHT CONNECTED TO B+. IS TEST LIGHT "ON"?
REPAIR OPEN OR SHORT TO GROUND IN CIRCUIT THAT DID NOT LIGHT
REPAIR OPEN OR SHORT TO GROUND IN CIRCUIT THAT DID NOT LIGHT.
YES
NO
• USING A FUSED JUMPER WIRE, JUMPER FAN RELAY HARNESS TERMINALS "30" AND "87" TOGETHER. DOES FAN OPERATE?
REPAIR OPEN OR SHORT TO VOLTAGE IN CKT 335. OR FAULTY PCM CONNECTION OR FAULTY PCM
REPAIR OPEN OR SHORT TO VOLTAGE IN CKT 473. OR FAULTY PCM CONNECTION OR FAULTY PCM.
FAULTY RELAY CONNECTION OR FAULTY RELAY
• IGNITION "OFF." • DISCONNECT PRIMARY COOLING FAN ELECTRICAL CONNECTOR • IGNITION "ON." • JUMPER WIRE STILL INSTALLED AT RELAY HARNESS. • CONNECT A TEST LIGHT ACROSS COOLING FAN ELECTRICAL CONNECTOR TERMINALS. IS TEST LIGHT "ON."
• IGNITION "OFF." • DISCONNECT SECONDARY COOLING FAN ELECTRICAL CONNECTOR • IGNITION "ON." • JUMPER WIRE STILL INSTALLED AT RELAY HARNESS. • CONNECT A TEST LIGHT ACROSS COOLING FAN ELECTRICAL CONNECTOR TERMINALS IS TEST LIGHT "ON."
• PROBE COOLING FAN MOTOR HARNESS CONNECTOR TERMINAL "B" WITH A TEST LIGHT CONNECTED TO GROUND. IS TEST LIGHT "ON"?
FAULTY CONNECTION AT FAN MOTOR OR FAULTY FAN MOTOR
FAULTY FAN MOTOR CONNECTION OR OPEN FAN GROUND CIRCUIT
OPEN BATTERY FEED CIRCUIT BETWEEN RELAY AND COOLING FAN MOTOR.
GC108940021702AX

Fig. 87 Chart C-12, cooling fan diagnosis (Part 2 of 2). 1994 Fleetwood (RWD) w/5.7L/V8-350 engine

and terminal 1 (DK GRN/WHT). If no voltage is present, check 335 (DK GRN/WHT) wire for an open.

5. If battery voltage is present, disconnect primary cooling fan relay then measure voltage from terminal 2 (RED) (VIN X, VIN T) or 2 (BRN/WHT) (VIN R) to ground at RS electrical center. If no voltage is present, check 650 (BRN/WHT) or 1444 (RED) for open.
6. If battery voltage is present, with primary cooling fan relay disconnected connect a fused jumper with 20 amp fuse between terminals 3 (RED) and 5 (BLK/RED) at RS electrical center. If cooling fan runs, check terminal contact between primary cooling fan relay and RH electrical center, if good, replace primary cooling fan relay.
7. If primary cooling fan does not run, leave jumper installed from step 6 then disconnect the primary cooling fan connector and measure voltage between terminal B (BLK/RED) and ground. If no voltage is present, check 702 (BLK/RED) wire for an open.
8. If battery voltage is present, measure voltage between terminals B (BLK/RED) and A (BLK). If no voltage is present, check 150 (BLK) wire for an open.
9. If battery voltage is present, check primary cooling fan connector, if good, replace primary cooling fan.

Secondary Cooling Fan Does Not Run

1. Turn ignition switch to Run position, ground terminal A3 (DK BLU/WHT) at ECM with fused jumper. If cooling fan runs, problem is ECM related.
2. If cooling fan does not run, disconnect secondary cooling fan relay, leave fused jumper at ECM, ensure ignition switch in Run position, then measure voltage at RH electrical center terminal 2 (BRN) to ground. If no voltage, check 250 (BRN) wire for open.
3. If battery voltage is present, leave ignition switch in Run position and fused jumper at ECM, then measure voltage between terminals 2 (BRN) and 1 (DK BLU/WHT). If no voltage, check 473 (DK BLU/WHT) wire for open.
4. If battery voltage is present, measure voltage between terminal 3 (RED) and ground. If no voltage, check 1442 (RED) wire for open.
5. If battery voltage is present, disconnect secondary cooling fan relay, then connect fused jumper between terminals 3 (RED and 5 (BLK/RED) at RH electrical center. If secondary cooling and generator run, check secondary cooling fan relay terminals, if good, replace secondary cooling fan relay.
6. If secondary cooling and generator fan do not run, ensure fused jumper in place, measure voltage from secondary cooling fan relay terminal B (BLK/RED) to ground or generator cooling fan relay terminal A (BLK/RED) to ground. If no voltage, check 532 (BLK/RED) wire for open.
7. If battery voltage is present, ensure fused jumper in place, then measure voltage between secondary cooling fan relay terminals B (BLK/RED) and A (BLK) or generator cooling fan connector terminals a (BLK/RED) and B (BLK). If no voltage, check 150 (BLK) wire for open.
8. If battery voltage is present, check cooling fan connector terminals, if good replace cooling fan.

Primary Cooling Fan Runs Continuously w/Engine Coolant Cool & A/C Mode Selector Off

1. Disconnect primary fan relay at RH electrical center, turn ignition switch to Run position, then connect test lamp between terminals 3 (RED) and 1 (DK GRN/WHT). If test lamp does not light, replace primary cooling fan relay.
2. If test lamp lights, check 335 (DK GRN/WHT) wire for short to ground, if good, problem is ECM related.

Continued on page 17-102

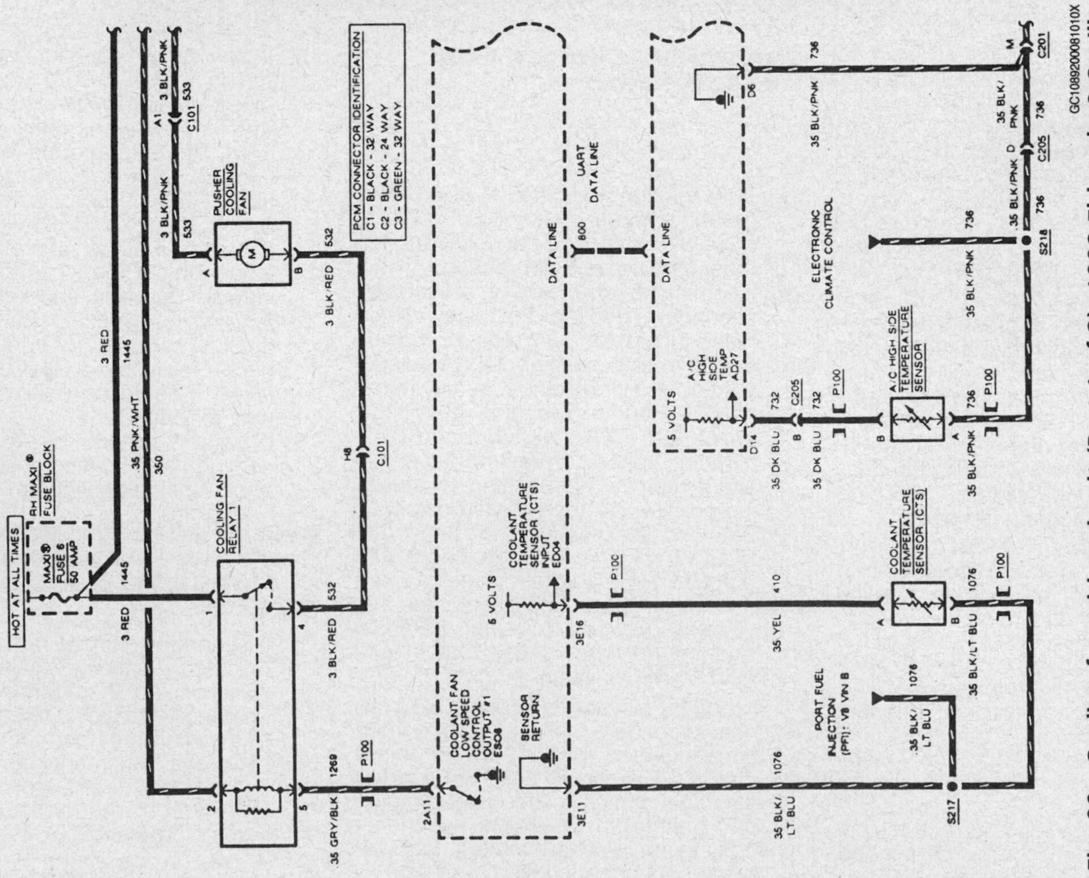
HOT AT ALL TIMES
RH MAXI FUSE BLOCK
MAXI FUSE 6 50 AMP
COOLING FAN RELAY 1
PUSHER COOLING FAN
PCM CONNECTOR IDENTIFICATION
C1 - BLACK - 32 WAY
C2 - BLACK - 24 WAY
C3 - GREEN - 32 WAY
COOLANT FAN LOW SPEED CONTROL OUTPUT #1 ES06
SENSOR RETURN
COOLANT TEMPERATURE SENSOR (CTS) INPUT ED04
5 VOLTS
DATA LINE
UART DATA LINE
ELECTRONIC CLIMATE CONTROL
A/C HIGH SIDE TEMP AD27
A/C HIGH SIDE TEMPERATURE SENSOR
COOLANT TEMPERATURE SENSOR (CTS)
PORT FUEL INJECTION (PFI): V8 VIN B
GC108920081010X
Fig. 88 Cooling fan wiring circuit (Part 1 of 2). 1992 Eldorado & Seville

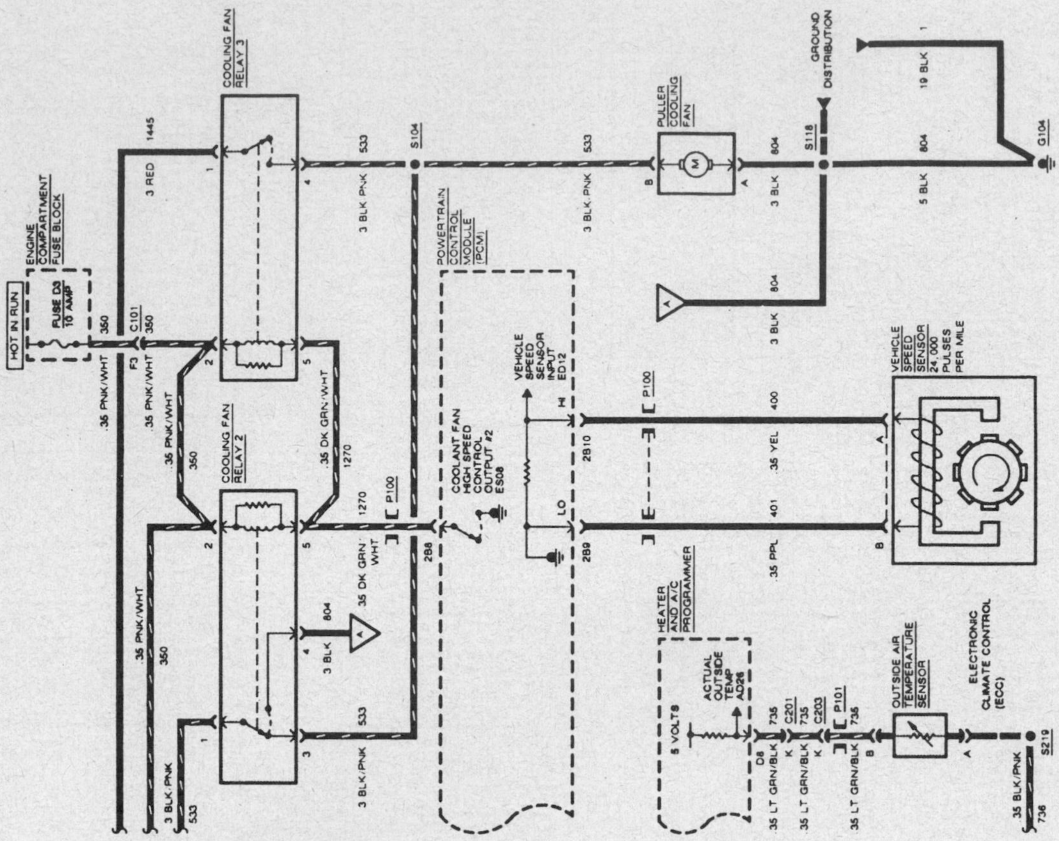
HOT IN RUN
ENGINE COMPARTMENT FUSE BLOCK
FUSE D3 10 AMP
COOLING FAN RELAY 3
COOLING FAN RELAY 2
POWERTRAIN CONTROL MODULE (PCM)
COOLANT FAN HIGH SPEED CONTROL OUTPUT #2 ES08
VEHICLE SPEED SENSOR INPUT ED12
PULLER COOLING FAN
GROUND DISTRIBUTION
HEATER AND A/C PROGRAMMER
ACTUAL OUTSIDE TEMP AD26
5 VOLTS
OUTSIDE AIR TEMPERATURE SENSOR
ELECTRONIC CLIMATE CONTROL (ECC)
VEHICLE SPEED SENSOR 24,000 PULSES PER MILE
GC108920081020X
Fig. 88 Cooling fan wiring circuit (Part 2 of 2). 1992 Eldorado & Seville

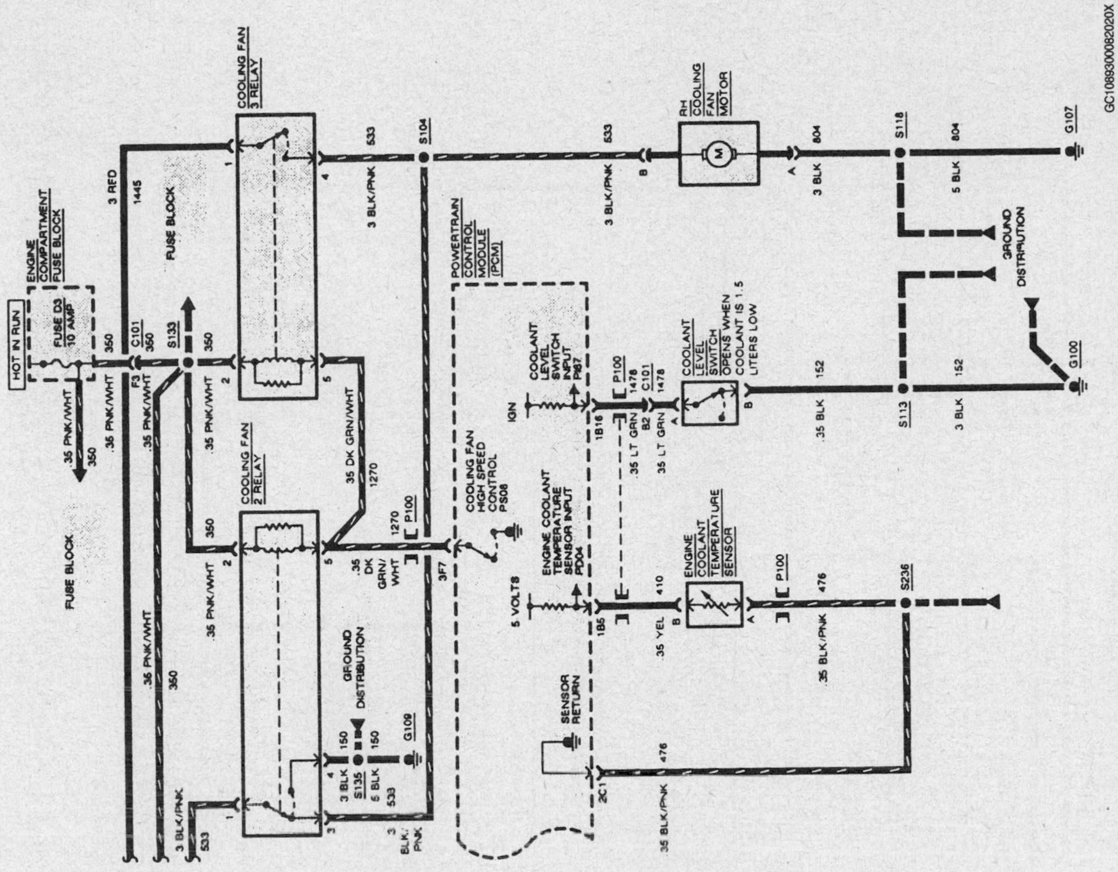

GC1089300082020X

Fig. 89 Cooling fan wiring circuit (Part 2 of 2). 1993 Eldorado & Seville w/4.6L/V8-279 engine

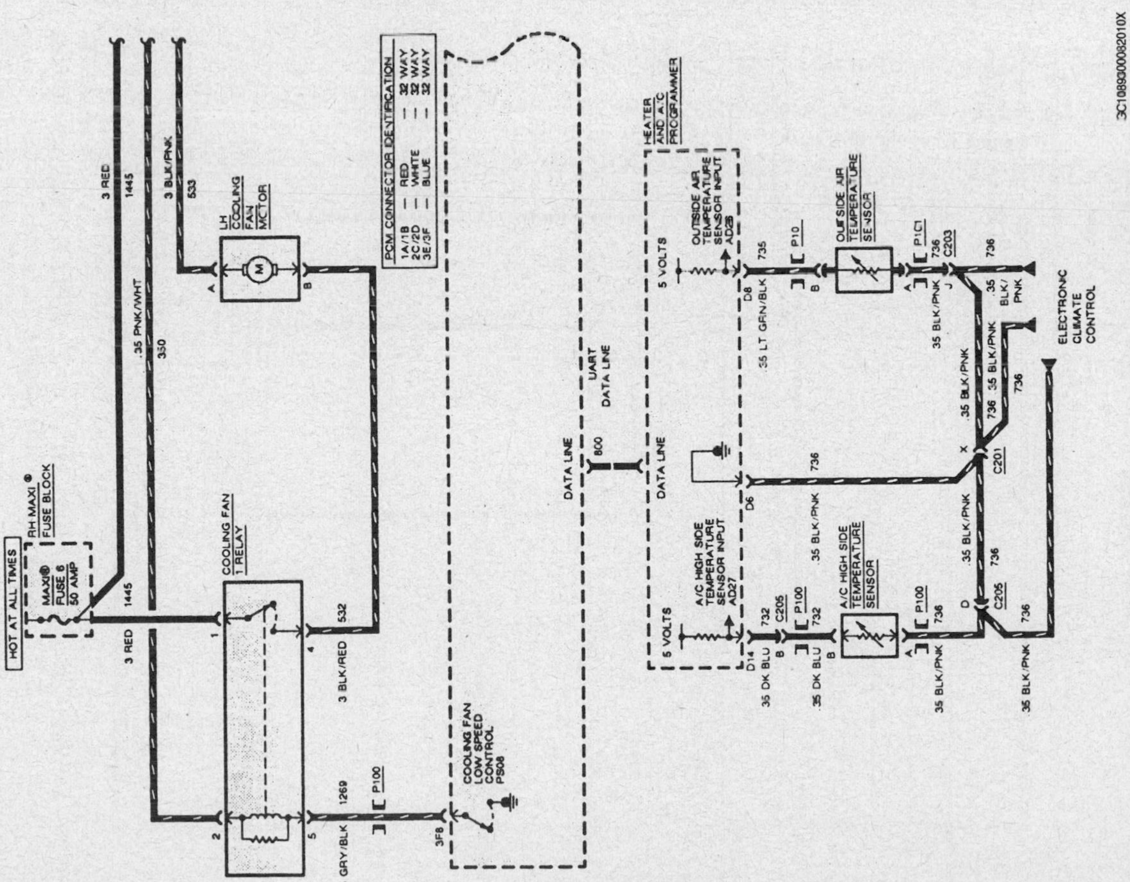

GC1089300082010X

Fig. 89 Cooling fan wiring circuit (Part 1 of 2). 1993 Eldorado & Seville w/4.6L/V8-279 engine

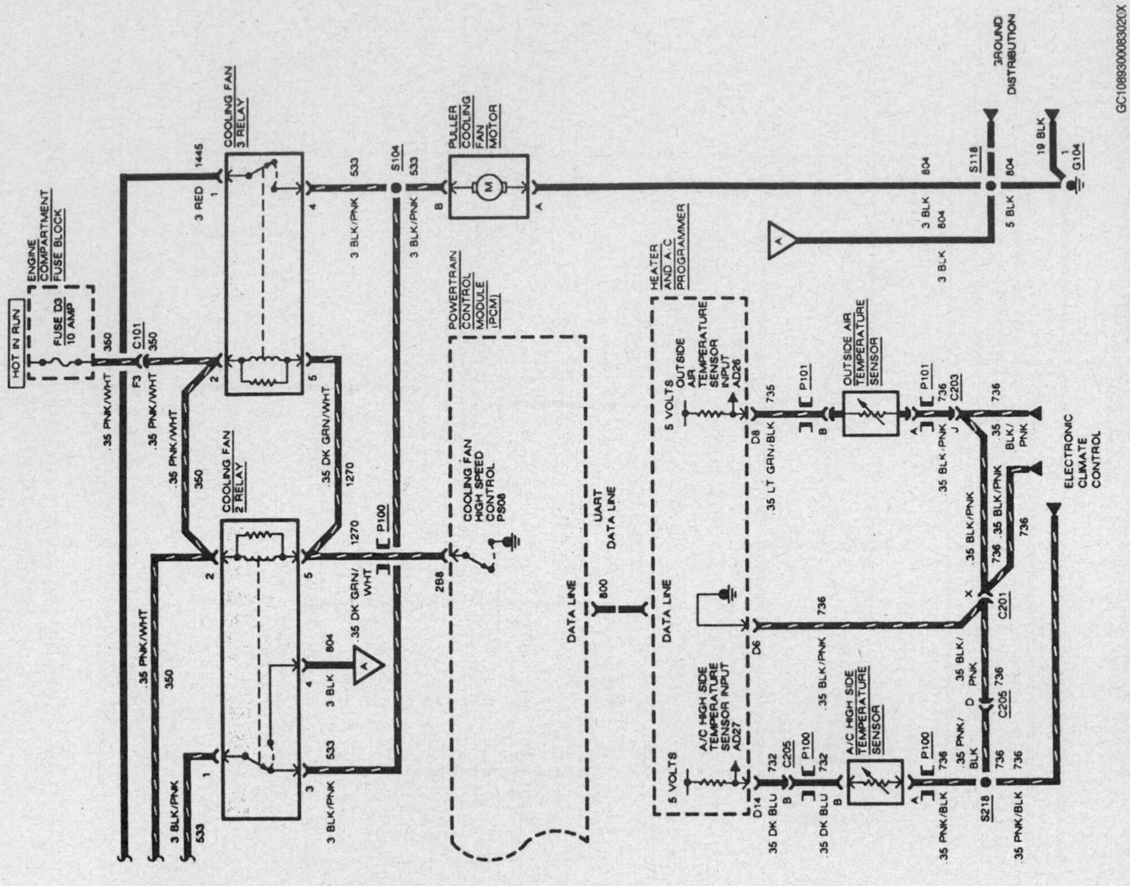
COOLING FAN 3 RELAY
ENGINE COMPARTMENT FUSE BLOCK
HOT IN RUN
FUSE D3 10 AMP
PULLER COOLING FAN MOTOR
COOLING FAN 2 RELAY
POWERTRAIN CONTROL MODULE (PCM)
COOLING FAN HIGH SPEED CONTROL P508
DATA LINE
UART DATA LINE
HEATER AND A/C PROGRAMMER
OUTSIDE AIR TEMPERATURE SENSOR INPUT AD26
A/C HIGH SIDE TEMPERATURE SENSOR INPUT AD27
OUTSIDE AIR TEMPERATURE SENSOR
A/C HIGH SIDE TEMPERATURE SENSOR
ELECTRONIC CLIMATE CONTROL
GROUND DISTRIBUTION
GC1089300083020X

Fig. 90 Cooling fan wiring circuit (Part 2 of 2). 1993 Eldorado & Seville w/4.9L/V8-300 engine

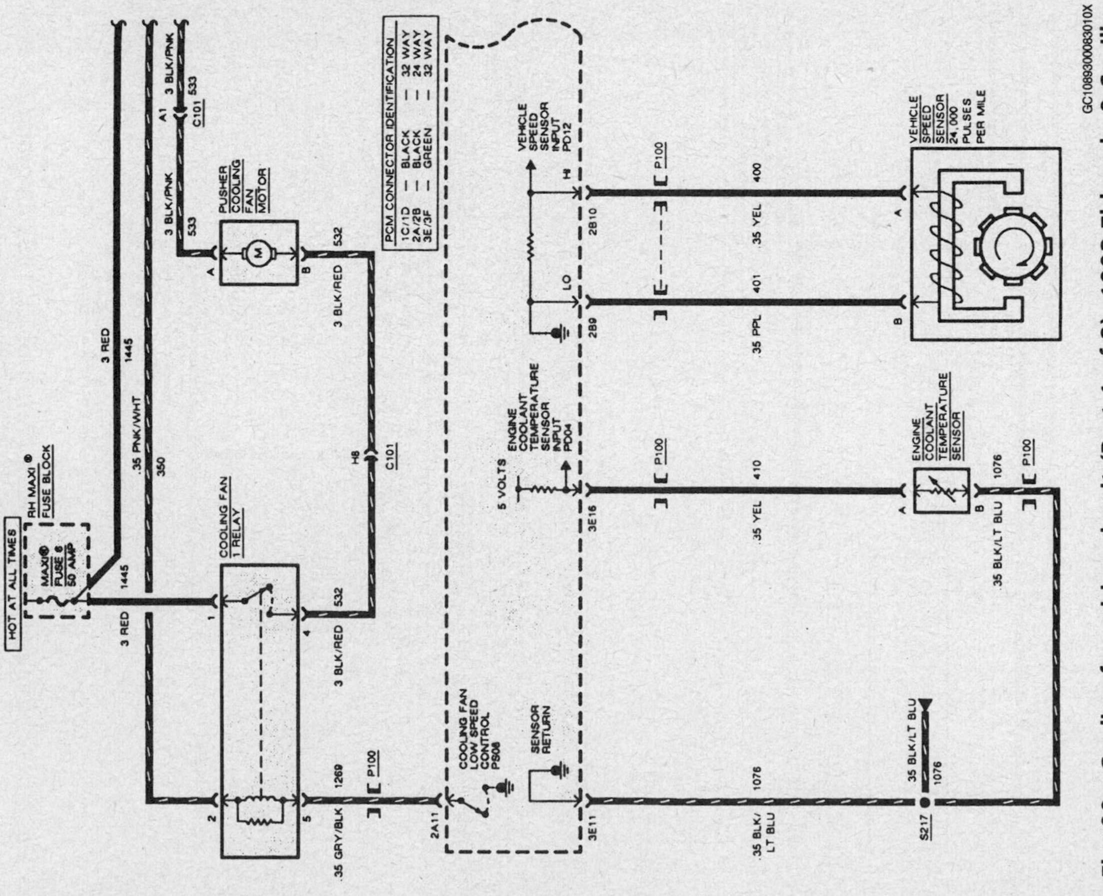
HOT AT ALL TIMES
RH MAXI FUSE BLOCK
MAXI FUSE 6 50 AMP
COOLING FAN 1 RELAY
PUSHER COOLING FAN MOTOR
PCM CONNECTOR IDENTIFICATION
1C/1D — BLACK — 32 WAY
2A/2B — BLACK — 24 WAY
3E/3F — GREEN — 32 WAY
COOLING FAN LOW SPEED CONTROL P508
SENSOR RETURN
ENGINE COOLANT TEMPERATURE SENSOR INPUT PD04
VEHICLE SPEED SENSOR INPUT PD12
ENGINE COOLANT TEMPERATURE SENSOR
VEHICLE SPEED SENSOR 24,000 PULSES PER MILE
GC1089300083010X

Fig. 90 Cooling fan wiring circuit (Part 1 of 2). 1993 Eldorado & Seville w/4.9L/V8-300 engine

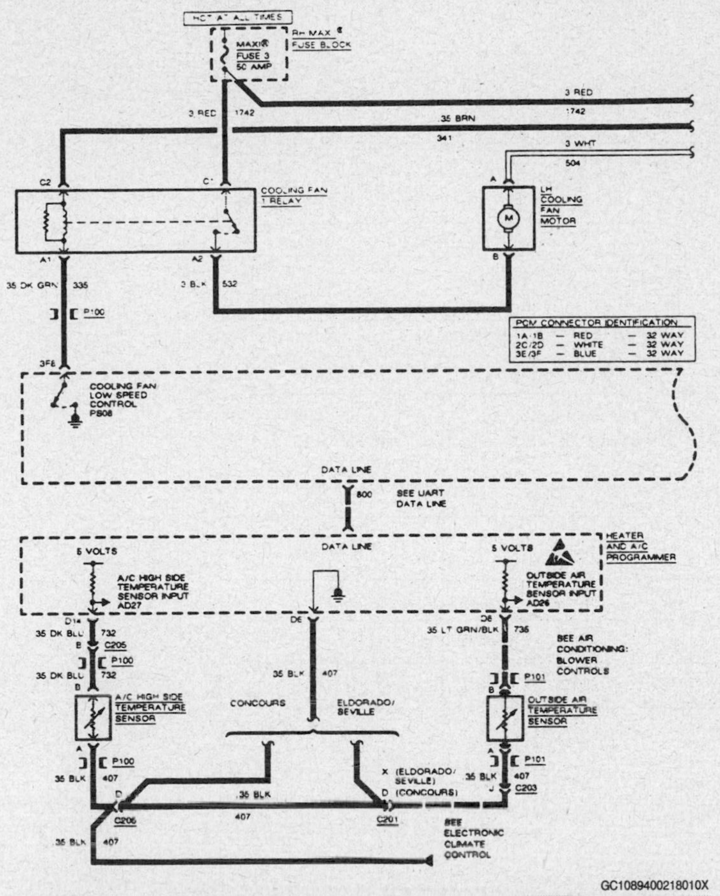
HOT AT ALL TIMES
RH MAXI FUSE BLOCK
MAXI FUSE 3 50 AMP
COOLING FAN 1 RELAY
LH COOLING FAN MOTOR
PCM CONNECTOR IDENTIFICATION
1A/1B — RED — 32 WAY
2C/2D — WHITE — 32 WAY
3E/3F — BLUE — 32 WAY
COOLING FAN LOW SPEED CONTROL PS08
DATA LINE
SEE UART DATA LINE
HEATER AND A/C PROGRAMMER
A/C HIGH SIDE TEMPERATURE SENSOR INPUT AD27
OUTSIDE AIR TEMPERATURE SENSOR INPUT AD26
SEE AIR CONDITIONING: BLOWER CONTROLS
A/C HIGH SIDE TEMPERATURE SENSOR
OUTSIDE AIR TEMPERATURE SENSOR
CONCOURS
ELDORADO/ SEVILLE
SEE ELECTRONIC CLIMATE CONTROL
GC1089400218010X

Fig. 91 Cooling fan wiring circuit (Part 1 of 2). 1994 Eldorado & Seville w/4.6L/V8-279 Northstar engine

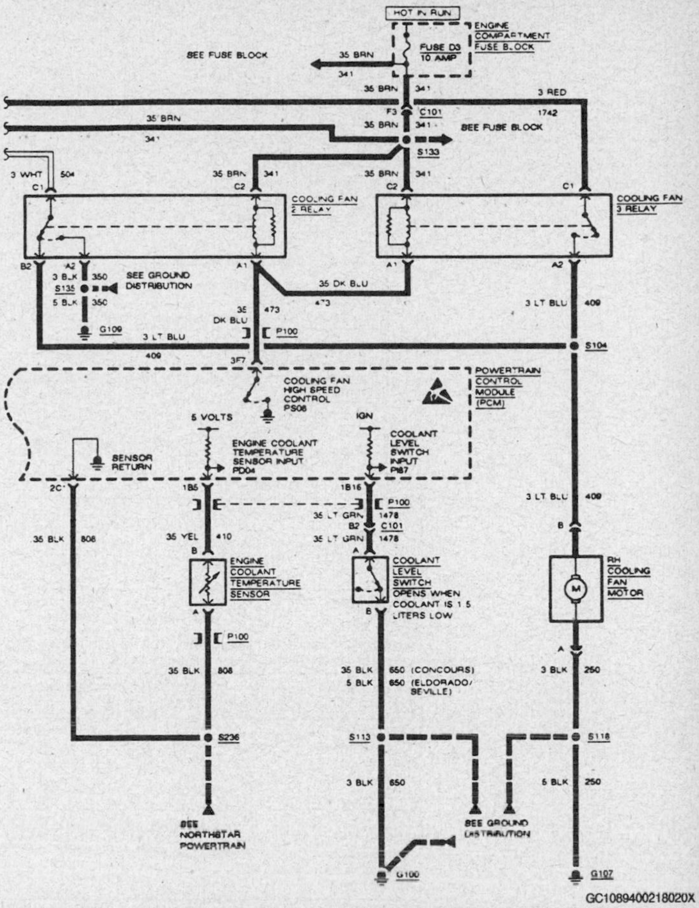
HOT IN RUN
ENGINE COMPARTMENT FUSE BLOCK
FUSE D3 10 AMP
SEE FUSE BLOCK
COOLING FAN 2 RELAY
COOLING FAN 3 RELAY
SEE GROUND DISTRIBUTION
COOLING FAN HIGH SPEED CONTROL PS06
POWERTRAIN CONTROL MODULE (PCM)
SENSOR RETURN
ENGINE COOLANT TEMPERATURE SENSOR INPUT PD04
COOLANT LEVEL SWITCH INPUT PB7
ENGINE COOLANT TEMPERATURE SENSOR
COOLANT LEVEL SWITCH OPENS WHEN COOLANT IS 1.5 LITERS LOW
RH COOLING FAN MOTOR
SEE NORTHSTAR POWERTRAIN
SEE GROUND DISTRIBUTION
GC1089400218020X

Fig. 91 Cooling fan wiring circuit (Part 2 of 2). 1994 Eldorado & Seville w/4.6L/V8-279 Northstar engine

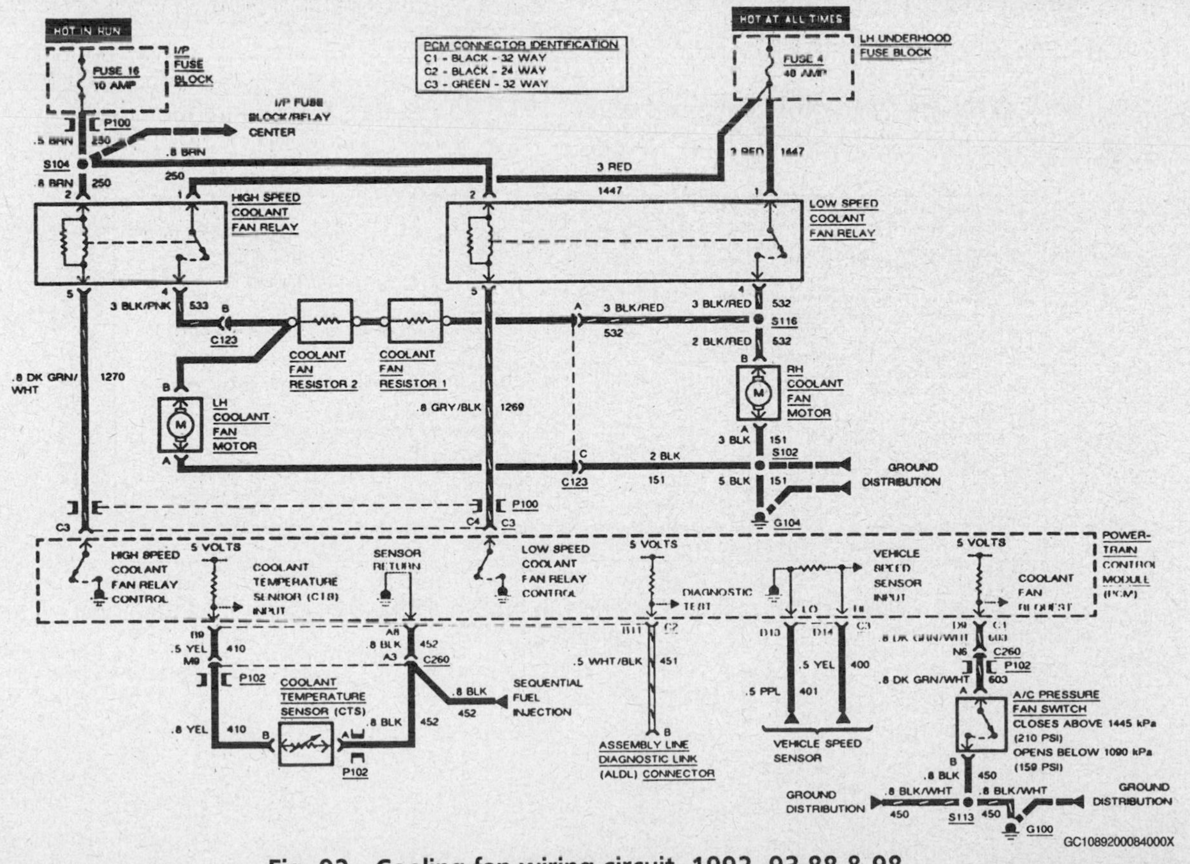
HOT IN RUN
I/P FUSE BLOCK
FUSE 16 10 AMP
I/P FUSE BLOCK/RELAY CENTER
PCM CONNECTOR IDENTIFICATION
C1 - BLACK - 32 WAY
C2 - BLACK - 24 WAY
C3 - GREEN - 32 WAY
HOT AT ALL TIMES
LH UNDERHOOD FUSE BLOCK
FUSE 4 40 AMP
HIGH SPEED COOLANT FAN RELAY
LOW SPEED COOLANT FAN RELAY
COOLANT FAN RESISTOR 2
COOLANT FAN RESISTOR 1
LH COOLANT FAN MOTOR
RH COOLANT FAN MOTOR
GROUND DISTRIBUTION
HIGH SPEED COOLANT FAN RELAY CONTROL
COOLANT TEMPERATURE SENSOR (CTS) INPUT
SENSOR RETURN
LOW SPEED COOLANT FAN RELAY CONTROL
DIAGNOSTIC TEST
VEHICLE SPEED SENSOR INPUT
COOLANT FAN REQUEST
POWERTRAIN CONTROL MODULE (PCM)
COOLANT TEMPERATURE SENSOR (CTS)
SEQUENTIAL FUEL INJECTION
ASSEMBLY LINE DIAGNOSTIC LINK (ALDL) CONNECTOR
VEHICLE SPEED SENSOR
A/C PRESSURE FAN SWITCH
CLOSES ABOVE 1445 kPa (210 PSI)
OPENS BELOW 1090 kPa (159 PSI)
GROUND DISTRIBUTION
GC1089200084000X

Fig. 92 Cooling fan wiring circuit. 1992–93 88 & 98

SYSTEM CHECK - NORMAL OPERATION

CONDITIONS:
- Ignition switch: RUN (engine idling)
- Engine: cold (below normal operating temperature)
- Ambient temperature: above 16°C (60°F)

ACTION	NORMAL RESULT
Set heater and A/C control assembly to A/C mode.	LH coolant fan runs in low speed; RH coolant fan runs in high speed.
Set heater and A/C control assembly to OFF.	Coolant fans turn off after about a minute.
Run engine at fast idle for several minutes.	LH coolant fan runs in low speed; RH coolant fan runs in high speed.
Restrict air flow through radiator by covering half of grille side of radiator.	Both coolant fans runs at high speed after a few minutes.

GC1089100092000X

Fig. 93 System check. Park Avenue & 1992–93 LeSabre

SYMPTOM	DIAGNOSIS		
	• Do 1st	• Do 2nd	• Do 3rd
Both coolant fans do not run.	Check I/P fuse block fuse 16 by visual inspection.	Check LH underhood fuse block fuse 4 by visual inspection.	Do Coolant Fan Input Test A.
LH coolant fan does not operate in low speed.	Do Low Speed Coolant Fan Input Test C.		
LH coolant fan does not operate in high speed.	Do High Speed Coolant Fan Input Test B.		
LH coolant fan runs continuously in low speed with ignition switch at RUN, engine coolant cool, and A/C off.	Do LH Coolant Fan Runs Continuously in Low Speed Test E.		
LH coolant fan runs continuously in high speed with ignition switch at RUN, engine coolant cool, and A/C off.	Do LH Coolant Fan Runs Continuously in High Speed Test D.		
LH coolant fan does not operate at high speed with A/C head pressure above 1445 kPa (210 psi).	Do A/C Pressure Signal Test F.		
Only one coolant fan does not run.	Check coolant fan and motor for mechanical bindings.	Check wiring to suspect coolant fan; check coolant fan connector for proper terminal contact.	Replace coolant fan motor, see ③ or ④.

GC1089200094000X

Fig. 94 Symptom diagnosis guide. 1992–93 LeSabre & Park Avenue

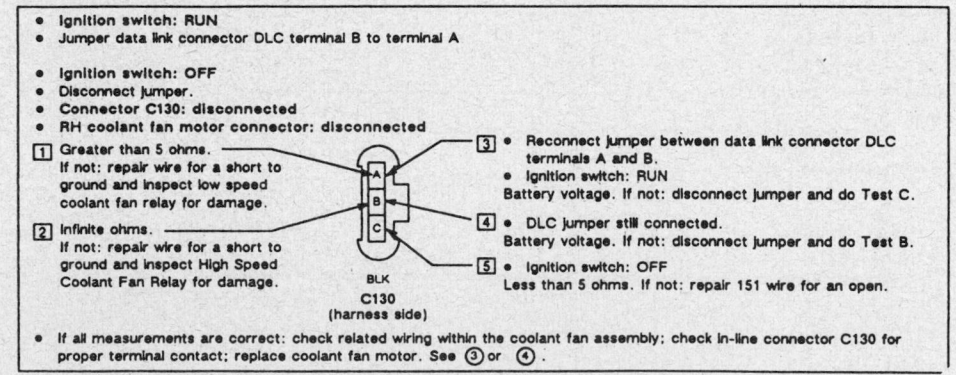

- Ignition switch: RUN
- Jumper data link connector DLC terminal B to terminal A

- Ignition switch: OFF
- Disconnect jumper.
- Connector C130: disconnected
- RH coolant fan motor connector: disconnected

1 Greater than 5 ohms.
If not: repair wire for a short to ground and inspect low speed coolant fan relay for damage.

2 Infinite ohms.
If not: repair wire for a short to ground and inspect High Speed Coolant Fan Relay for damage.

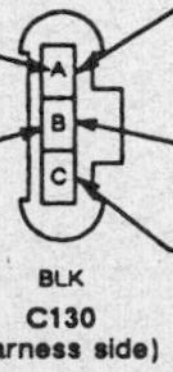
A
B
C
BLK
C130
(harness side)

3 • Reconnect jumper between data link connector DLC terminals A and B.
• Ignition switch: RUN
Battery voltage. If not: disconnect jumper and do Test C.

4 • DLC jumper still connected.
Battery voltage. If not: disconnect jumper and do Test B.

5 • Ignition switch: OFF
Less than 5 ohms. If not: repair 151 wire for an open.

- If all measurements are correct: check related wiring within the coolant fan assembly; check in-line connector C130 for proper terminal contact; replace coolant fan motor. See ③ or ④.

GC1089200095000X

Fig. 95 Cooling fan test A (Cooling fan input). 1992–93 LeSabre & Park Avenue

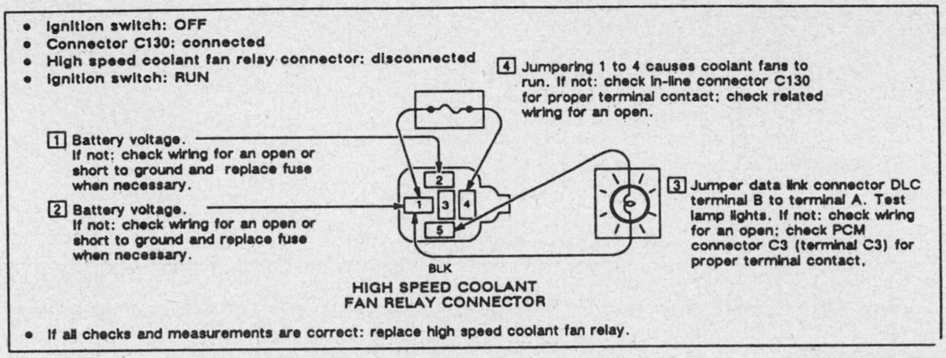
• Ignition switch: OFF
• Connector C130: connected
• High speed coolant fan relay connector: disconnected
• Ignition switch: RUN
4 Jumpering 1 to 4 causes coolant fans to run. If not: check in-line connector C130 for proper terminal contact; check related wiring for an open.
1 Battery voltage. If not: check wiring for an open or short to ground and replace fuse when necessary.
2 Battery voltage. If not: check wiring for an open or short to ground and replace fuse when necessary.
3 Jumper data link connector DLC terminal B to terminal A. Test lamp lights. If not: check wiring for an open; check PCM connector C3 (terminal C3) for proper terminal contact.
BLK
HIGH SPEED COOLANT FAN RELAY CONNECTOR
• If all checks and measurements are correct: replace high speed coolant fan relay.

GC1089200096000X

Fig. 96 Cooling fan test B (High speed cooling fan input). 1992–93 LeSabre & Park Avenue

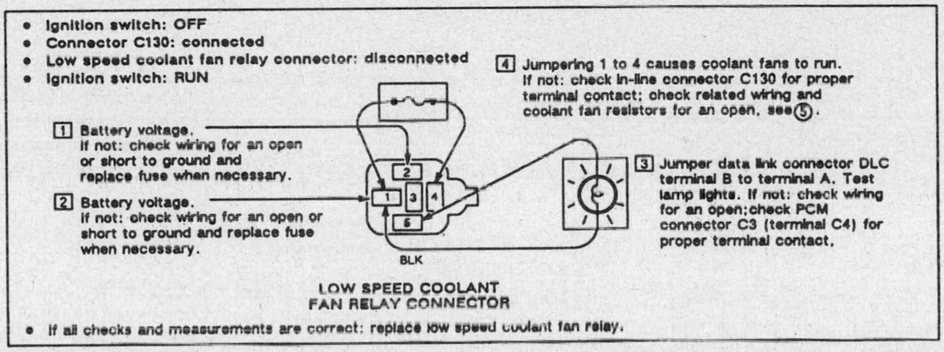
• Ignition switch: OFF
• Connector C130: connected
• Low speed coolant fan relay connector: disconnected
• Ignition switch: RUN
4 Jumpering 1 to 4 causes coolant fans to run. If not: check in-line connector C130 for proper terminal contact; check related wiring and coolant fan resistors for an open, see 5.
1 Battery voltage. If not: check wiring for an open or short to ground and replace fuse when necessary.
2 Battery voltage. If not: check wiring for an open or short to ground and replace fuse when necessary.
3 Jumper data link connector DLC terminal B to terminal A. Test lamp lights. If not: check wiring for an open;check PCM connector C3 (terminal C4) for proper terminal contact.
BLK
LOW SPEED COOLANT FAN RELAY CONNECTOR
• If all checks and measurements are correct: replace low speed coolant fan relay.

GC1089200097000X

Fig. 97 Cooling fan test C (Low speed cooling fan input). 1992–93 LeSabre & Park Avenue

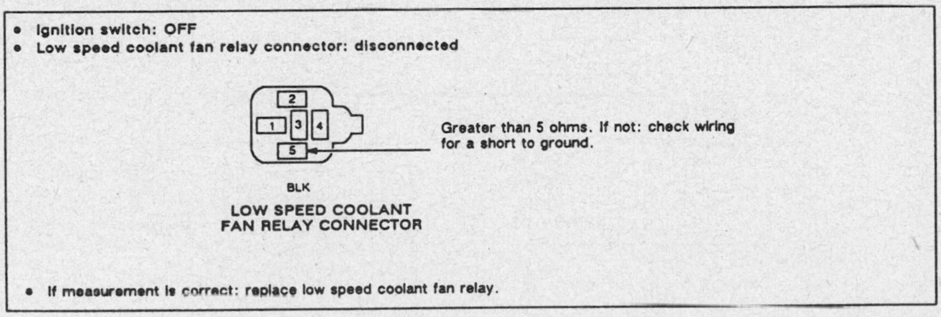
• Ignition switch: OFF
• Low speed coolant fan relay connector: disconnected
Greater than 5 ohms. If not: check wiring for a short to ground.
BLK
LOW SPEED COOLANT FAN RELAY CONNECTOR
• If measurement is correct: replace low speed coolant fan relay.

GC1089200099000X

Fig. 98 Cooling fan test D (Lefthand cooling fan runs continuously in high speed). 1992–93 LeSabre & Park Avenue

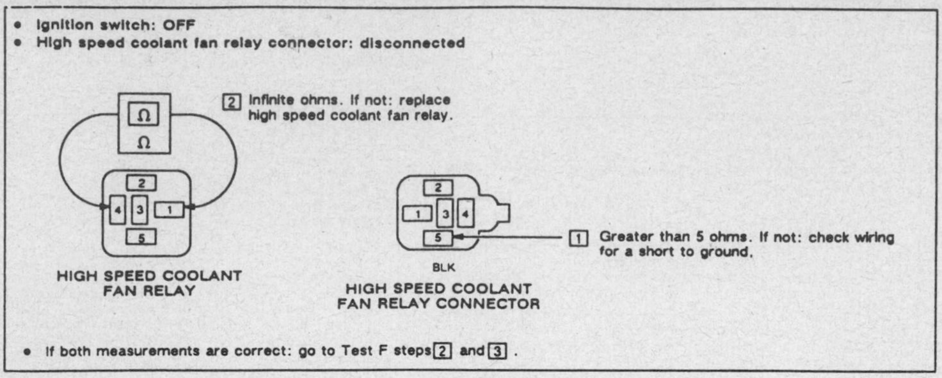
• Ignition switch: OFF
• High speed coolant fan relay connector: disconnected
2 Infinite ohms. If not: replace high speed coolant fan relay.
Ω
Ω
2
4 3 1
5
HIGH SPEED COOLANT FAN RELAY
2
1 3 4
5
BLK
HIGH SPEED COOLANT FAN RELAY CONNECTOR
1 Greater than 5 ohms. If not: check wiring for a short to ground.
• If both measurements are correct: go to Test F steps 2 and 3 .

GC1089200098000X

Fig. 99 Cooling fan test E (Lefthand cooling fan runs continuously in low speed). 1992–93 LeSabre & Park Avenue

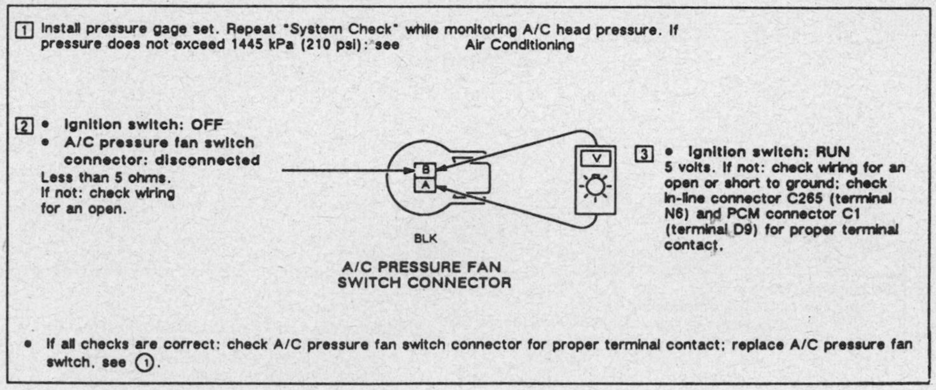
1 Install pressure gage set. Repeat "System Check" while monitoring A/C head pressure. If pressure does not exceed 1445 kPa (210 psi): see Air Conditioning
2 • Ignition switch: OFF
• A/C pressure fan switch connector: disconnected
Less than 5 ohms.
If not: check wiring for an open.
B
A
V
BLK
A/C PRESSURE FAN SWITCH CONNECTOR
3 • Ignition switch: RUN
5 volts. If not: check wiring for an open or short to ground; check in-line connector C265 (terminal N6) and PCM connector C1 (terminal D9) for proper terminal contact.
• If all checks are correct: check A/C pressure fan switch connector for proper terminal contact; replace A/C pressure fan switch, see ①.

GC1089200100000X

Fig. 100 Cooling fan test F (A/C pressure signal). 1992–93 LeSabre & Park Avenue

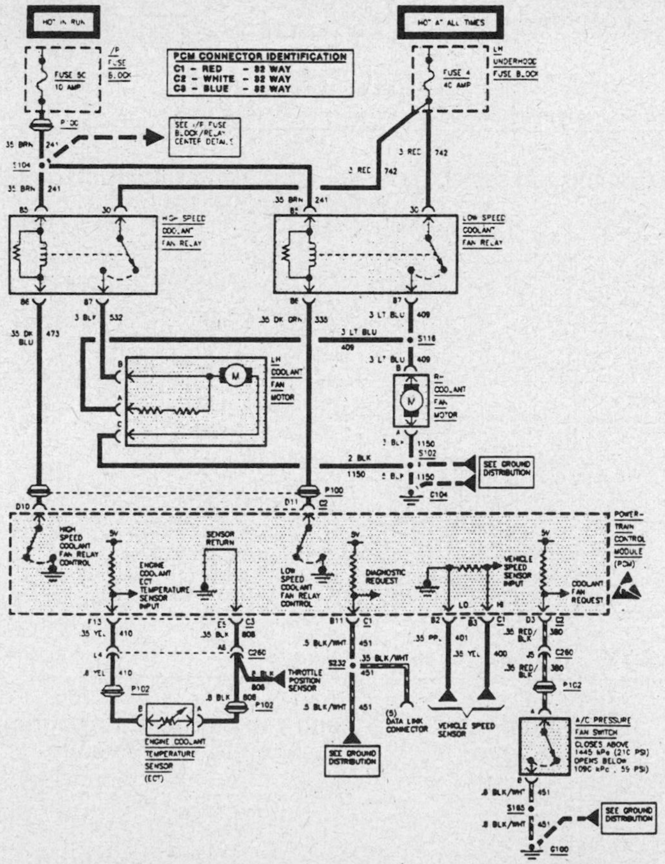
PCM CONNECTOR IDENTIFICATION
C1 - RED - 32 WAY
C2 - WHITE - 32 WAY
C3 - BLUE - 32 WAY
SEE GROUND DISTRIBUTION
A/C PRESSURE FAN SWITCH

GC1089400219000X

Fig. 101 Cooling fan wiring circuit. 1994 88 & 98

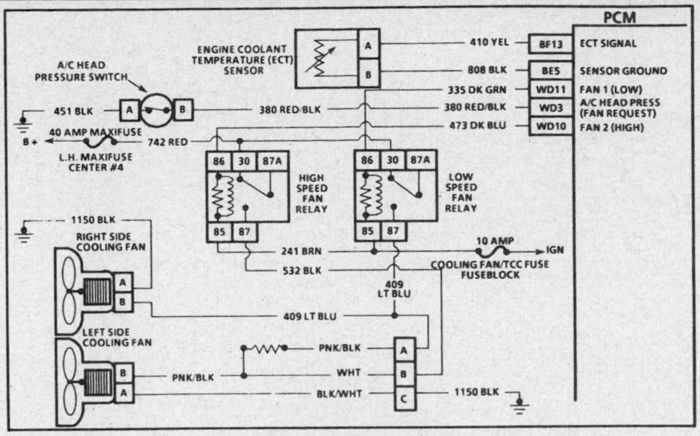
PCM
ENGINE COOLANT TEMPERATURE (ECT) SENSOR
A/C HEAD PRESSURE SWITCH
451 BLK
380 RED/BLK
40 AMP MAXIFUSE
742 RED
L.H. MAXIFUSE CENTER #4
410 YEL
BF13
ECT SIGNAL
808 BLK
BE5
SENSOR GROUND
335 DK GRN
WD11
FAN 1 (LOW)
380 RED/BLK
WD3
A/C HEAD PRESS (FAN REQUEST)
473 DK BLU
WD10
FAN 2 (HIGH)
HIGH SPEED FAN RELAY
LOW SPEED FAN RELAY
1150 BLK
RIGHT SIDE COOLING FAN
241 BRN
532 BLK
10 AMP
IGN
COOLING FAN/TCC FUSE FUSEBLOCK
409 LT BLU
LEFT SIDE COOLING FAN
PNK/BLK
WHT
BLK/WHT
1150 BLK

CHART C-12A

COOLING FAN CHECK
3800 (VIN 1, L) (SFI)

Circuit Description:

Power for the fan motors comes from a 40A maxifuse element to terminal "87" on the relays. The relays are energized when current flows to ground through the PCM Quad-Driver #4. The left fan has two speeds and the right fan is a single speed fan.

Low Speed (Fan 1) Relay - The PCM energizes the relay through terminal "WD11" when engine coolant temperature reaches 100°C (212°F) or when A/C is requested.

High Speed (Fan 2) Relay - The high speed relay is energized by the PCM if the A/C head pressure switch opens, indicating refrigerant pressure above 210 psi (1448 kPa), or engine coolant temperature reaches 108°C (226°F).

Chart Test Description: Number(s) below refer to circled number(s) on the diagnostic chart.

1. Using the Tech 1 "Misc. Tests," Fan 1 control will cause the PCM to ground CKT 335 and the cooling fans should run at low speed.
2. Selecting Fan 2 with the Tech 1 allows control of CKT 473 and the high speed (Fan 2) relay.
3. Disconnecting the A/C head pressure switch harness connector will cause the PCM to energize the high speed (Fan 2) relay.

Diagnostic Aids: An intermittent may be caused by a poor connection, rubbed through wire insulation, or a wire broken inside the insulation.

Check for:

- Poor connection or damaged harness - Inspect PCM harness connectors for backed out terminals "WD10" or "WD11", improper mating, broken locks, improperly formed or damaged terminals, poor terminal to wire connection, and damaged harness.
- Intermittent test - If connections and harness check OK, a digital voltmeter connected from affected terminal to ground while moving related connectors and wiring harness. If the failure is induced, the voltage reading will change.
- Mis-Scaled Engine Coolant Temperature (ECT) sensor - See "Engine Coolant Temperature Sensor Temperature vs. Resistance Values" table on DTC P0118 chart
- Basic cooling system problem - Refer to engine cooling and radiator diagnosis

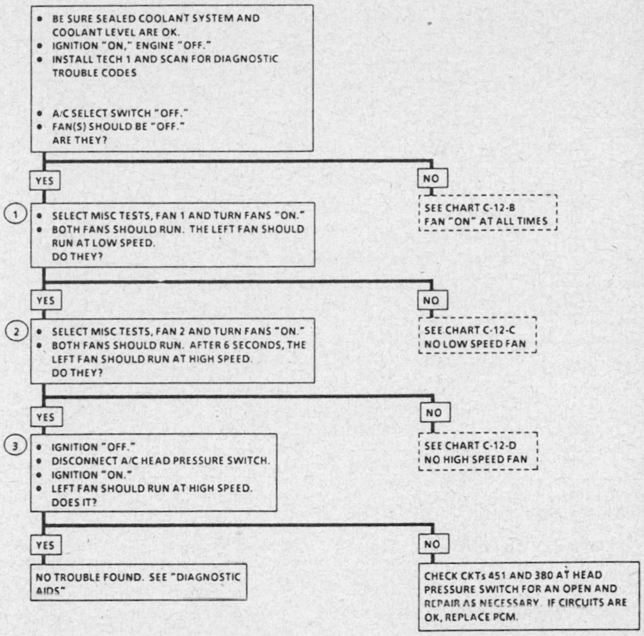
• BE SURE SEALED COOLANT SYSTEM AND COOLANT LEVEL ARE OK.
• IGNITION "ON," ENGINE "OFF."
• INSTALL TECH 1 AND SCAN FOR DIAGNOSTIC TROUBLE CODES
• A/C SELECT SWITCH "OFF."
• FAN(S) SHOULD BE "OFF."
ARE THEY?
YES
NO
SEE CHART C-12-B FAN "ON" AT ALL TIMES
1
• SELECT MISC TESTS, FAN 1 AND TURN FANS "ON."
• BOTH FANS SHOULD RUN. THE LEFT FAN SHOULD RUN AT LOW SPEED.
DO THEY?
YES
NO
SEE CHART C-12-C NO LOW SPEED FAN
2
• SELECT MISC TESTS, FAN 2 AND TURN FANS "ON."
• BOTH FANS SHOULD RUN. AFTER 6 SECONDS, THE LEFT FAN SHOULD RUN AT HIGH SPEED.
DO THEY?
YES
NO
SEE CHART C-12-D NO HIGH SPEED FAN
3
• IGNITION "OFF."
• DISCONNECT A/C HEAD PRESSURE SWITCH.
• IGNITION "ON."
• LEFT FAN SHOULD RUN AT HIGH SPEED.
DOES IT?
YES
NO
NO TROUBLE FOUND. SEE "DIAGNOSTIC AIDS"
CHECK CKTs 451 AND 380 AT HEAD PRESSURE SWITCH FOR AN OPEN AND REPAIR AS NECESSARY. IF CIRCUITS ARE OK, REPLACE PCM.

GC108940022000AX

Fig. 102 Chart C-12A, cooling fan diagnosis. 1994 88, 98, Le Sabre & Park Avenue

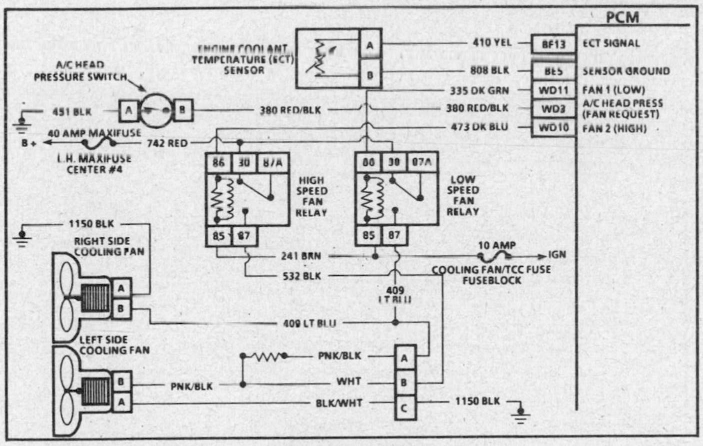
PCM
ENGINE COOLANT TEMPERATURE (ECT) SENSOR
A/C HEAD PRESSURE SWITCH
451 BLK
380 RED/BLK
40 AMP MAXIFUSE
742 RED
L.H. MAXIFUSE CENTER #4
410 YEL
BF13
ECT SIGNAL
808 BLK
BE5
SENSOR GROUND
335 DK GRN
WD11
FAN 1 (LOW)
380 RED/BLK
WD3
A/C HEAD PRESS (FAN REQUEST)
473 DK BLU
WD10
FAN 2 (HIGH)
HIGH SPEED FAN RELAY
LOW SPEED FAN RELAY
1150 BLK
RIGHT SIDE COOLING FAN
241 BRN
532 BLK
10 AMP
IGN
COOLING FAN/TCC FUSE FUSEBLOCK
409 LT BLU
LEFT SIDE COOLING FAN
PNK/BLK
WHT
BLK/WHT
1150 BLK

CHART C-12B

FAN(S) "ON" AT ALL TIMES
COOLING FAN CHECK
3800 (VIN 1, L) (SFI)

Circuit Description:

Power for the fan motors comes from a 40A maxifuse element to terminal "87" on the relays. The relays are energized when current flows to ground through the PCM Quad-Driver #4. The left fan has two speeds and the right fan is a single speed fan.

Low Speed (Fan 1) Relay - The PCM energizes the relay through terminal "WD11" when engine coolant temperature reaches 100°C (212°F) or when A/C is requested.

High Speed (Fan 2) Relay - The high speed relay is energized by the PCM if the A/C head pressure switch opens, indicating refrigerant pressure above 210 psi (1448 kPa), or engine coolant temperature reaches 108°C (226°F).

Chart Test Description: Number(s) below refer to circled number(s) on the diagnostic chart.

1. Checks to see if CKT 335 is shorted to ground, which would keep the relay closed at all times.
2. Checks to see if CKT 473 is shorted to ground. A light indicates the wire is shorted to ground, the following steps will isolate the short.
3. If the test light is "OFF" after disconnecting the PCM, be sure CKT 335 is not shorted to B+. If not shorted to B+, the PCM is shorted internally.
4. If the test light is "OFF" after disconnecting the PCM, be sure CKT 473 is not shorted to B+. If not shorted to B+, the PCM is shorted internally.

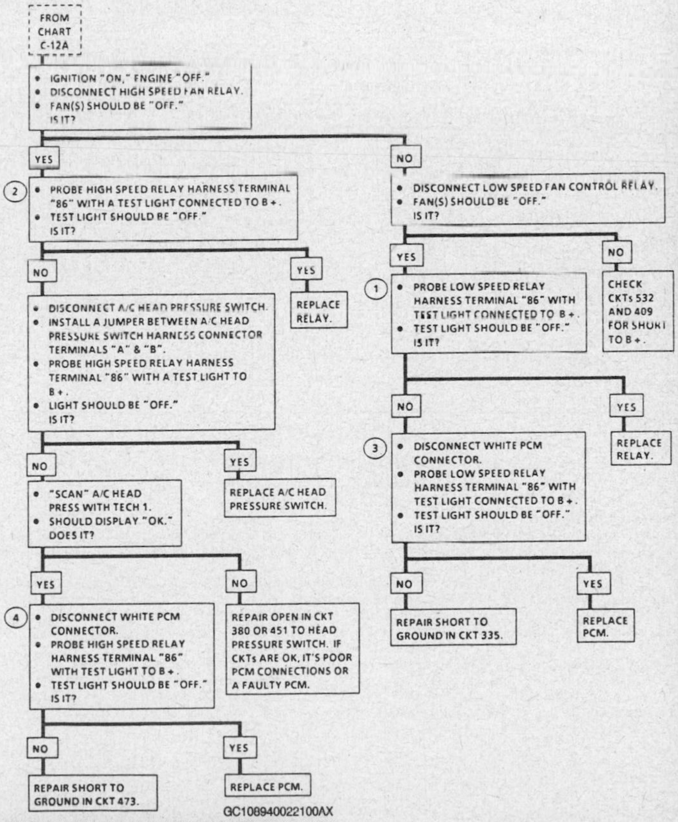
FROM CHART C-12A
• IGNITION "ON," ENGINE "OFF."
• DISCONNECT HIGH SPEED FAN RELAY.
• FAN(S) SHOULD BE "OFF."
IS IT?
YES
NO
2
• PROBE HIGH SPEED RELAY HARNESS TERMINAL "86" WITH A TEST LIGHT CONNECTED TO B+.
• TEST LIGHT SHOULD BE "OFF."
IS IT?
• DISCONNECT LOW SPEED FAN CONTROL RELAY.
• FAN(S) SHOULD BE "OFF."
IS IT?
NO
YES
REPLACE RELAY.
• DISCONNECT A/C HEAD PRESSURE SWITCH.
• INSTALL A JUMPER BETWEEN A/C HEAD PRESSURE SWITCH HARNESS CONNECTOR TERMINALS "A" & "B".
• PROBE HIGH SPEED RELAY HARNESS TERMINAL "86" WITH A TEST LIGHT TO B+.
• LIGHT SHOULD BE "OFF."
IS IT?
YES
NO
1
• PROBE LOW SPEED RELAY HARNESS TERMINAL "86" WITH TEST LIGHT CONNECTED TO B+.
• TEST LIGHT SHOULD BE "OFF."
IS IT?
CHECK CKTs 532 AND 409 FOR SHORT TO B+.
NO
YES
REPLACE A/C HEAD PRESSURE SWITCH.
• "SCAN" A/C HEAD PRESS WITH TECH 1.
• SHOULD DISPLAY "OK."
DOES IT?
3
• DISCONNECT WHITE PCM CONNECTOR.
• PROBE LOW SPEED RELAY HARNESS TERMINAL "86" WITH TEST LIGHT CONNECTED TO B+.
• TEST LIGHT SHOULD BE "OFF."
IS IT?
REPLACE RELAY.
YES
NO
4
• DISCONNECT WHITE PCM CONNECTOR.
• PROBE HIGH SPEED RELAY HARNESS TERMINAL "86" WITH TEST LIGHT TO B+.
• TEST LIGHT SHOULD BE "OFF."
IS IT?
REPAIR OPEN IN CKT 380 OR 451 TO HEAD PRESSURE SWITCH. IF CKTs ARE OK, IT'S POOR PCM CONNECTIONS OR A FAULTY PCM.
NO
YES
REPAIR SHORT TO GROUND IN CKT 335.
REPLACE PCM.
NO
YES
REPAIR SHORT TO GROUND IN CKT 473.
REPLACE PCM.

GC108940022100AX

Fig. 103 Chart C-12B, cooling fan diagnosis. 1994 88, 98, Le Sabre & Park Avenue

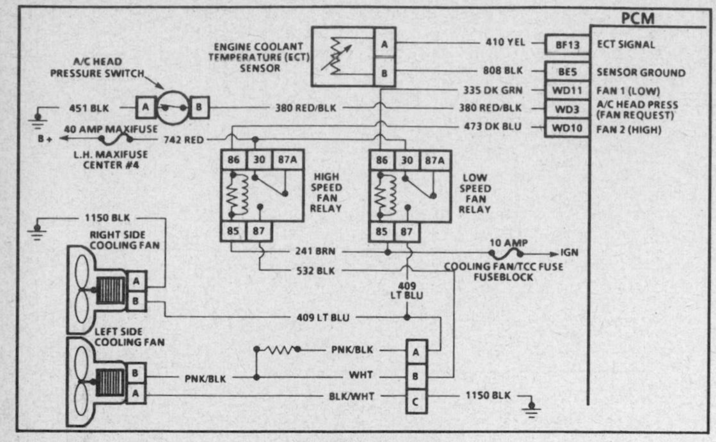
PCM
ENGINE COOLANT TEMPERATURE (ECT) SENSOR
A
B
410 YEL
BF13
ECT SIGNAL
808 BLK
BE5
SENSOR GROUND
335 DK GRN
WD11
FAN 1 (LOW)
380 RED/BLK
WD3
A/C HEAD PRESS (FAN REQUEST)
473 DK BLU
WD10
FAN 2 (HIGH)
A/C HEAD PRESSURE SWITCH
451 BLK
380 RED/BLK
40 AMP MAXIFUSE
B+
742 RED
L.H. MAXIFUSE CENTER #4
86
30
87A
85
87
HIGH SPEED FAN RELAY
LOW SPEED FAN RELAY
1150 BLK
RIGHT SIDE COOLING FAN
241 BRN
532 BLK
10 AMP
IGN
COOLING FAN/TCC FUSE
FUSEBLOCK
409 LT BLU
LEFT SIDE COOLING FAN
PNK/BLK
WHT
BLK/WHT
C
1150 BLK

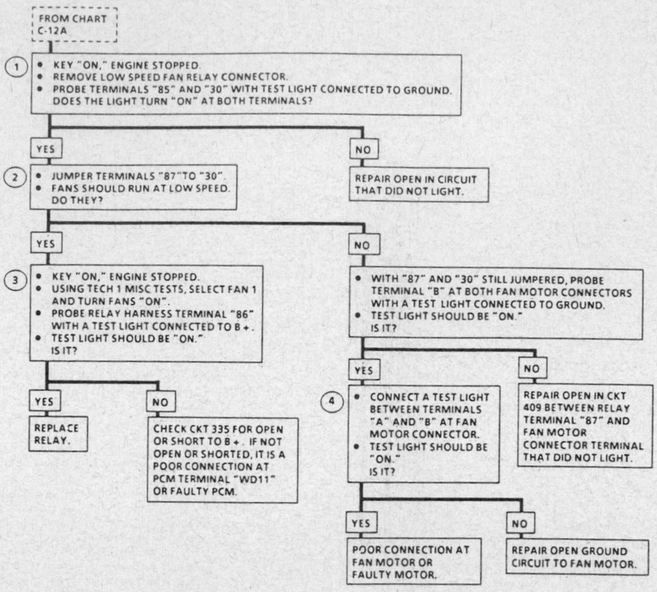
FROM CHART C-12A
1
• KEY "ON," ENGINE STOPPED.
• REMOVE LOW SPEED FAN RELAY CONNECTOR.
• PROBE TERMINALS "85" AND "30" WITH TEST LIGHT CONNECTED TO GROUND. DOES THE LIGHT TURN "ON" AT BOTH TERMINALS?
YES
NO
REPAIR OPEN IN CIRCUIT THAT DID NOT LIGHT.
2
• JUMPER TERMINALS "87" TO "30".
• FANS SHOULD RUN AT LOW SPEED. DO THEY?
YES
NO
3
• KEY "ON," ENGINE STOPPED.
• USING TECH 1 MISC TESTS, SELECT FAN 1 AND TURN FANS "ON".
• PROBE RELAY HARNESS TERMINAL "86" WITH A TEST LIGHT CONNECTED TO B+.
• TEST LIGHT SHOULD BE "ON." IS IT?
• WITH "87" AND "30" STILL JUMPERED, PROBE TERMINAL "B" AT BOTH FAN MOTOR CONNECTORS WITH A TEST LIGHT CONNECTED TO GROUND.
• TEST LIGHT SHOULD BE "ON." IS IT?
YES
NO
REPLACE RELAY.
CHECK CKT 335 FOR OPEN OR SHORT TO B+. IF NOT OPEN OR SHORTED, IT IS A POOR CONNECTION AT PCM TERMINAL "WD11" OR FAULTY PCM.
4
• CONNECT A TEST LIGHT BETWEEN TERMINALS "A" AND "B" AT FAN MOTOR CONNECTOR.
• TEST LIGHT SHOULD BE "ON." IS IT?
REPAIR OPEN IN CKT 409 BETWEEN RELAY TERMINAL "87" AND FAN MOTOR CONNECTOR TERMINAL THAT DID NOT LIGHT.
POOR CONNECTION AT FAN MOTOR OR FAULTY MOTOR.
REPAIR OPEN GROUND CIRCUIT TO FAN MOTOR.

CHART C-12C

NO LOW SPEED FAN COOLING FAN CHECK 3800 (VIN 1, L) (SFI)

Circuit Description:

Power for the fan motors comes from a 40A maxifuse element to terminal "87" on the relays. The relays are energized when current flows to ground through the PCM Quad-Driver #4. The left fan has two speeds and the right fan is a single speed fan.

Low Speed (Fan 1) Relay - The PCM energizes the relay through terminal "WD11" when engine coolant temperature reaches 100°C (212°F) or when A/C is requested.

High Speed (Fan 2) Relay - The high speed relay is energized by the PCM if the A/C head pressure switch opens, indicating refrigerant pressure above 210 psi (1448 kPa), or engine coolant temperature reaches 108°C (226°F).

Chart Test Description: Number(s) below refer to circled number(s) on the diagnostic chart.

1. Checks for B+ at relay harness connector.
2. Jumpering terminals "87" to "30" bypasses the relay, which should cause the fans to run if fan motors and wiring are OK.
3. Selecting Fan 1 with Tech 1 misc. tests and turning fans "ON" should cause the PCM to ground CKT 335. At this point, the test light should light, if the PCM is functioning and CKT 335 isn't open.
4. This checks for B+ and ground to the fan motor. A test light "ON" at this point indicates a faulty fan motor connection or motor.

GC108940022200AX

Fig. 104 Chart C-12C, cooling fan diagnosis. 1994 88, 98, Le Sabre & Park Avenue

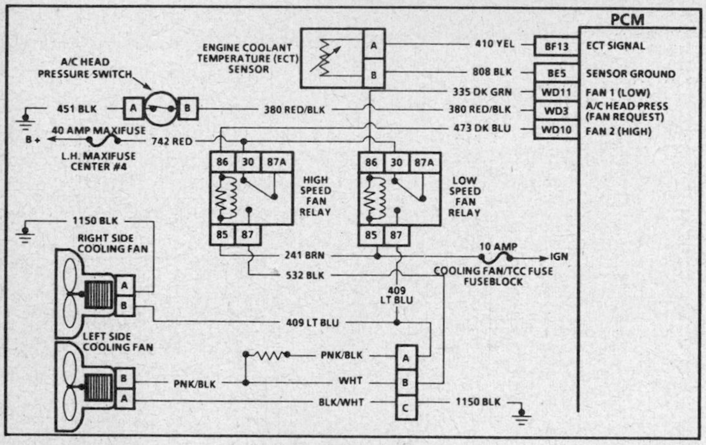
PCM
ENGINE COOLANT TEMPERATURE (ECT) SENSOR
A
B
410 YEL
BF13
ECT SIGNAL
808 BLK
BE5
SENSOR GROUND
335 DK GRN
WD11
FAN 1 (LOW)
380 RED/BLK
WD3
A/C HEAD PRESS (FAN REQUEST)
473 DK BLU
WD10
FAN 2 (HIGH)
A/C HEAD PRESSURE SWITCH
451 BLK
380 RED/BLK
40 AMP MAXIFUSE
B+
742 RED
L.H. MAXIFUSE CENTER #4
86
30
87A
85
87
HIGH SPEED FAN RELAY
LOW SPEED FAN RELAY
1150 BLK
RIGHT SIDE COOLING FAN
241 BRN
532 BLK
10 AMP
IGN
COOLING FAN/TCC FUSE
FUSEBLOCK
409 LT BLU
LEFT SIDE COOLING FAN
PNK/BLK
WHT
BLK/WHT
C
1150 BLK

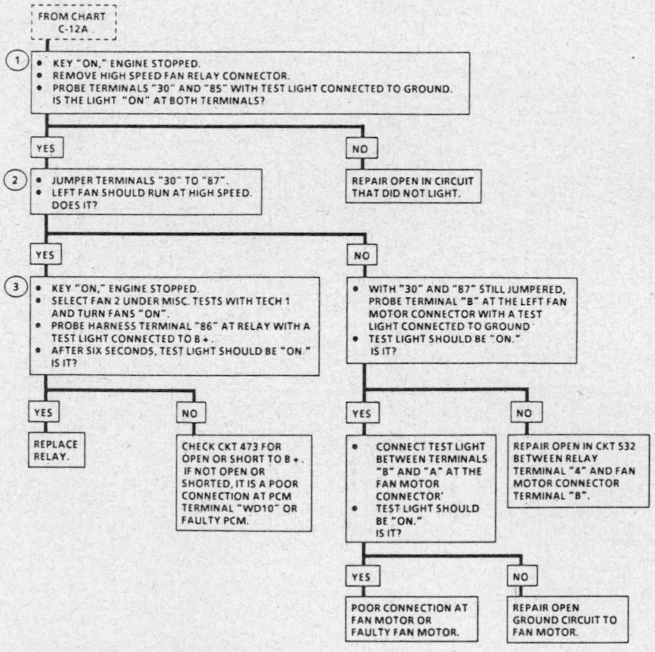
FROM CHART C-12A
1
• KEY "ON," ENGINE STOPPED.
• REMOVE HIGH SPEED FAN RELAY CONNECTOR.
• PROBE TERMINALS "30" AND "85" WITH TEST LIGHT CONNECTED TO GROUND. IS THE LIGHT "ON" AT BOTH TERMINALS?
YES
NO
REPAIR OPEN IN CIRCUIT THAT DID NOT LIGHT.
2
• JUMPER TERMINALS "30" TO "87".
• LEFT FAN SHOULD RUN AT HIGH SPEED. DOES IT?
YES
NO
3
• KEY "ON," ENGINE STOPPED.
• SELECT FAN 2 UNDER MISC. TESTS WITH TECH 1 AND TURN FANS "ON".
• PROBE HARNESS TERMINAL "86" AT RELAY WITH A TEST LIGHT CONNECTED TO B+.
• AFTER SIX SECONDS, TEST LIGHT SHOULD BE "ON." IS IT?
• WITH "30" AND "87" STILL JUMPERED, PROBE TERMINAL "B" AT THE LEFT FAN MOTOR CONNECTOR WITH A TEST LIGHT CONNECTED TO GROUND
• TEST LIGHT SHOULD BE "ON." IS IT?
YES
NO
REPLACE RELAY.
CHECK CKT 473 FOR OPEN OR SHORT TO B+. IF NOT OPEN OR SHORTED, IT IS A POOR CONNECTION AT PCM TERMINAL "WD10" OR FAULTY PCM.
• CONNECT TEST LIGHT BETWEEN TERMINALS "B" AND "A" AT THE FAN MOTOR CONNECTOR'
• TEST LIGHT SHOULD BE "ON." IS IT?
REPAIR OPEN IN CKT 532 BETWEEN RELAY TERMINAL "4" AND FAN MOTOR CONNECTOR TERMINAL "B".
POOR CONNECTION AT FAN MOTOR OR FAULTY FAN MOTOR.
REPAIR OPEN GROUND CIRCUIT TO FAN MOTOR.

CHART C-12D

NO HIGH SPEED FAN COOLING FAN CHECK 3800 (VIN 1, L) (SFI)

Circuit Description:

Power for the fan motor comes from a 40A maxifuse element to terminal "87" on the relays. The relays are energized when current flows to ground through the PCM Quad-Driver #4. The left fan has two speeds and the right fan is a single speed fan.

Low Speed (Fan 1) Relay - The PCM energizes the relay through terminal "WD11" when engine coolant temperature reaches 100°C (212°F) or when A/C is requested.

High Speed (Fan 2) Relay - The high speed relay is energized by the PCM if the A/C head pressure switch opens, indicating refrigerant above 210 psi (1448 kPa), or engine coolant temperature reaches 108°C (226°F).

Chart Test Description: Number(s) below refer to circled number(s) on the diagnostic chart.

1. Test light should be "ON" because harness terminal "85" has B+ with ignition switch turned "ON."
2. Jumpering harness terminals "30" and "87" bypasses the relay. If fan runs, the relay is faulty.
3. Checks CKT 473 back to the PCM. If CKT 473 is OK, it's a bad relay.

GC108940022300AX

Fig. 105 Chart C-12D, cooling fan diagnosis. 1994 88, 98, Le Sabre & Park Avenue

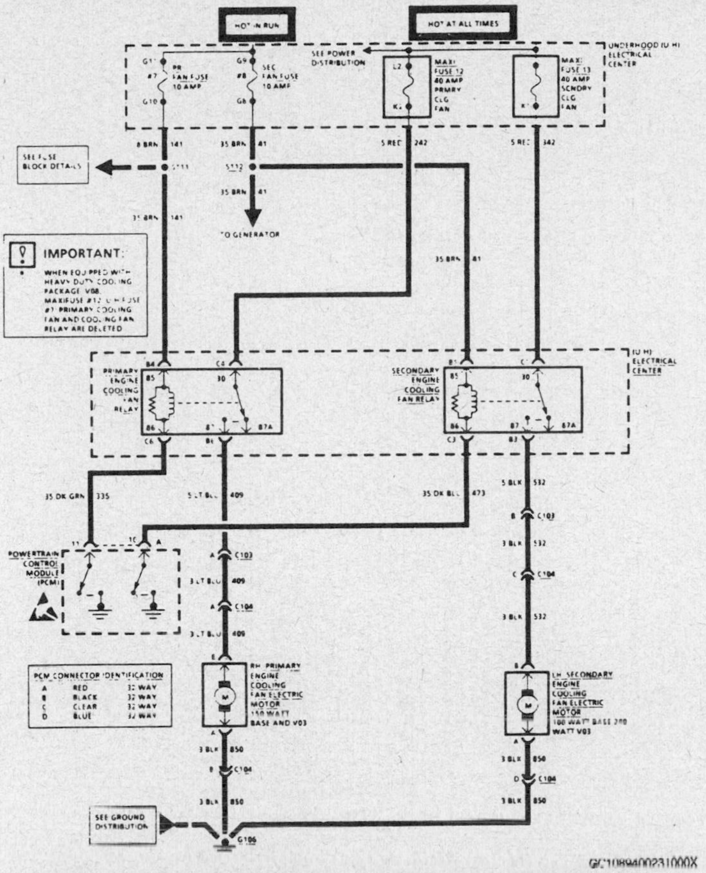
HOT IN RUN
HOT AT ALL TIMES
IMPORTANT:
PRIMARY ENGINE COOLING FAN RELAY
SECONDARY ENGINE COOLING FAN RELAY
POWERTRAIN CONTROL MODULE (PCM)
PCM CONNECTOR IDENTIFICATION
RH PRIMARY ENGINE COOLING FAN ELECTRIC MOTOR
LH SECONDARY ENGINE COOLING FAN ELECTRIC MOTOR
SEE GROUND DISTRIBUTION
G106
GC1089400231000X

Fig. 106 Cooling fan wiring circuit. 1994 Caprice, Impala SS & Roadmaster w/base & V03 extra cooling capacity

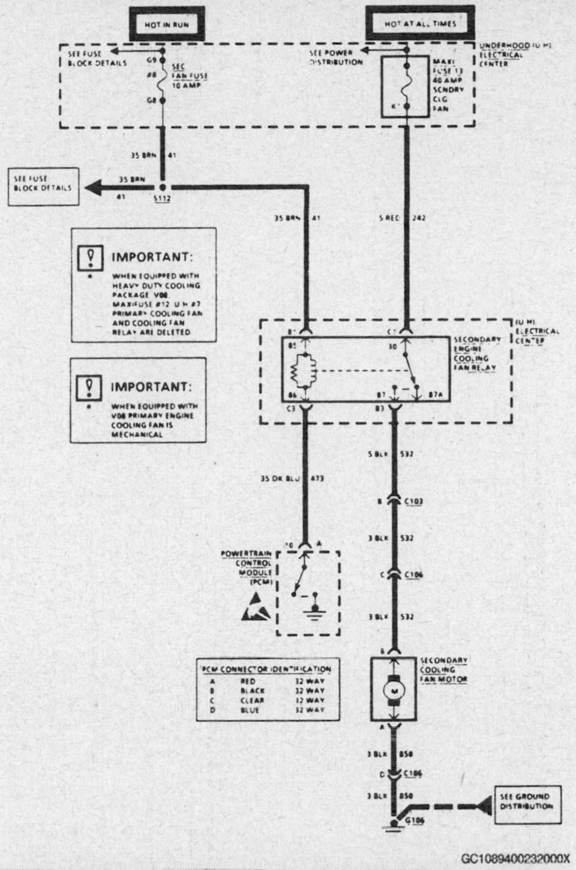
HOT IN RUN
HOT AT ALL TIMES
IMPORTANT:
WHEN EQUIPPED WITH HEAVY DUTY COOLING PACKAGE V08 MAXIFUSE #12 (U/H) #7 PRIMARY COOLING FAN AND COOLING FAN RELAY ARE DELETED
IMPORTANT:
WHEN EQUIPPED WITH V08 PRIMARY ENGINE COOLING FAN IS MECHANICAL
SECONDARY ENGINE COOLING FAN RELAY
POWERTRAIN CONTROL MODULE (PCM)
PCM CONNECTOR IDENTIFICATION
SECONDARY COOLING FAN MOTOR
SEE GROUND DISTRIBUTION
G106
GC1089400232000X

Fig. 107 Cooling fan wiring circuit. 1994 Caprice, Impala SS & Roadmaster w/V08 heavy duty cooling capacity

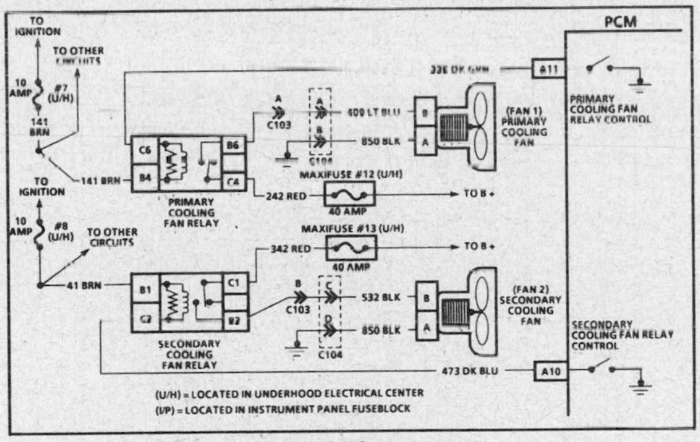
TO IGNITION
TO OTHER CIRCUITS
PCM
PRIMARY COOLING FAN RELAY
MAXIFUSE #12 (U/H)
40 AMP
TO B+
MAXIFUSE #13 (U/H)
40 AMP
TO B+
(FAN 1) PRIMARY COOLING FAN
PRIMARY COOLING FAN RELAY CONTROL
(FAN 2) SECONDARY COOLING FAN
SECONDARY COOLING FAN RELAY CONTROL
SECONDARY COOLING FAN RELAY
335 DK GRN
409 LT BLU
850 BLK
242 RED
342 RED
532 BLK
473 DK BLU
(U/H) = LOCATED IN UNDERHOOD ELECTRICAL CENTER
(I/P) = LOCATED IN INSTRUMENT PANEL FUSEBLOCK

CHART C-12 (Page 1 of 2)

ELECTRIC COOLING FAN CONTROL CIRCUIT DIAGNOSIS "B" CARLINE (SFI)

Circuit Description:

The cooling fans are controlled by the PCM based on various inputs. Battery voltage is supplied to the primary fan relay on terminal "C4", and secondary fan relay on terminal "C1". Ignition voltage is supplied to terminal "B4" of the primary and "B1" of the secondary fan relay. Grounding CKT 335 (relay terminal "C6") will energize the primary cooling fan relay (Fan 1) and supply battery voltage to the primary cooling fan motor. Grounding CKT 473 (relay terminal "C3") will energize the secondary cooling fan relay (Fan 2) and supply battery voltage to the secondary fan motor.

When certain Diagnostic Trouble Codes (DTCs) are set, the PCM will enable the cooling fans.

Chart Test Description: Number(s) below refer to circled number(s) on the diagnostic chart.

1. With the output/field service enable terminal grounded at DLC, the cooling fan control driver(s) will close, which should energize the fan control relay(s).
2. The cooling fans should come "ON" anytime A/C system is operating. Engine coolant temperature must be below 100°C (212°F) when performing this step.
3. Comparing Tech 1 pressure and manifold gage set pressure will determine if the A/C refrigerant pressure sensor is out of range. An out of range A/C refrigerant pressure sensor can cause the cooling fans to operate at the wrong times.

Diagnostic Aids: For detailed underhood electrical center relay cavity identification

If the owner complained of an overheating problem, it must be determined if the complaint was due to an actual boil over, or the warning indicator light, or engine coolant temperature gage indicated overheating.

The gage accuracy can also be checked by comparing the Engine Coolant Temperature (ECT) sensor reading using a Tech 1 and comparing its reading with the gage reading.

If the engine is actually overheating and the gage indicated overheating, but the cooling fan is not coming "ON," the Engine Coolant Temperature (ECT) sensor has probably shifted out of calibration and should be replaced.

If the engine is overheating and the cooling fans are "ON," the cooling system should be checked.

The PCM will command fan 1 "ON" at 107°C (225°F) and "OFF" at 103°C (217°F) and, fan 2 "ON" at 111°C (232°F) and "OFF" at 107°C (224°F).

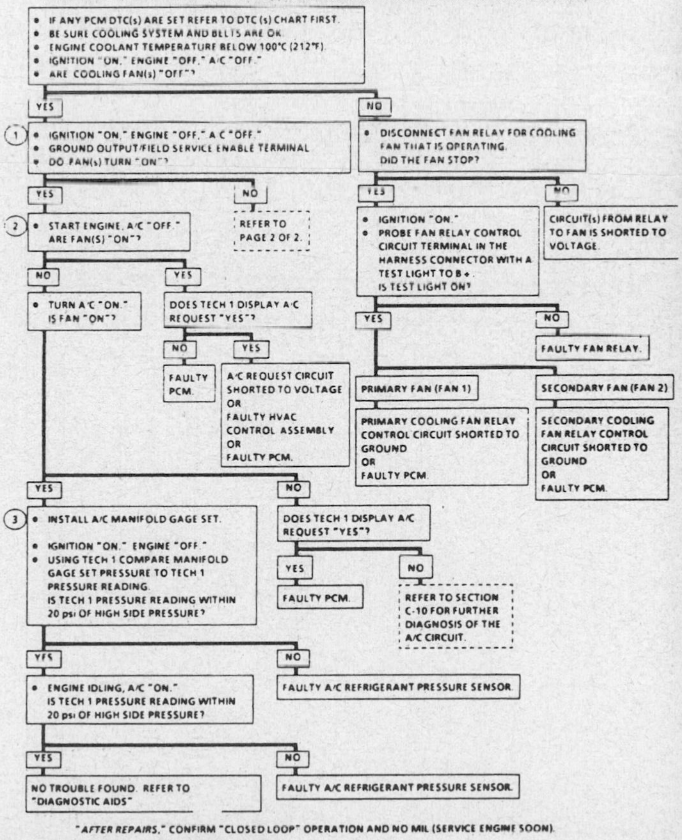
• IF ANY PCM DTC(s) ARE SET REFER TO DTC(s) CHART FIRST.
• BE SURE COOLING SYSTEM AND BELTS ARE OK.
• ENGINE COOLANT TEMPERATURE BELOW 100°C (212°F).
• IGNITION "ON," ENGINE "OFF," A/C "OFF."
• ARE COOLING FAN(s) "OFF"?
YES
NO
1 • IGNITION "ON," ENGINE "OFF," A/C "OFF."
• GROUND OUTPUT/FIELD SERVICE ENABLE TERMINAL
• DO FAN(s) TURN "ON"?
• DISCONNECT FAN RELAY FOR COOLING FAN THAT IS OPERATING.
DID THE FAN STOP?
REFER TO PAGE 2 OF 2.
2 • START ENGINE, A/C "OFF."
ARE FAN(S) "ON"?
• IGNITION "ON."
• PROBE FAN RELAY CONTROL CIRCUIT TERMINAL IN THE HARNESS CONNECTOR WITH A TEST LIGHT TO B+.
IS TEST LIGHT ON?
CIRCUIT(s) FROM RELAY TO FAN IS SHORTED TO VOLTAGE.
• TURN A/C "ON."
IS FAN "ON"?
DOES TECH 1 DISPLAY A/C REQUEST "YES"?
FAULTY FAN RELAY.
FAULTY PCM.
A/C REQUEST CIRCUIT SHORTED TO VOLTAGE OR FAULTY HVAC CONTROL ASSEMBLY OR FAULTY PCM.
PRIMARY FAN (FAN 1)
SECONDARY FAN (FAN 2)
PRIMARY COOLING FAN RELAY CONTROL CIRCUIT SHORTED TO GROUND OR FAULTY PCM.
SECONDARY COOLING FAN RELAY CONTROL CIRCUIT SHORTED TO GROUND OR FAULTY PCM.
3 • INSTALL A/C MANIFOLD GAGE SET.
• IGNITION "ON," ENGINE "OFF."
• USING TECH 1 COMPARE MANIFOLD GAGE SET PRESSURE TO TECH 1 PRESSURE READING.
IS TECH 1 PRESSURE READING WITHIN 20 psi OF HIGH SIDE PRESSURE?
DOES TECH 1 DISPLAY A/C REQUEST "YES"?
FAULTY PCM.
REFER TO SECTION C-10 FOR FURTHER DIAGNOSIS OF THE A/C CIRCUIT.
• ENGINE IDLING, A/C "ON."
IS TECH 1 PRESSURE READING WITHIN 20 psi OF HIGH SIDE PRESSURE?
FAULTY A/C REFRIGERANT PRESSURE SENSOR.
NO TROUBLE FOUND. REFER TO "DIAGNOSTIC AIDS"
FAULTY A/C REFRIGERANT PRESSURE SENSOR.
"AFTER REPAIRS," CONFIRM "CLOSED LOOP" OPERATION AND NO MIL (SERVICE ENGINE SOON).
GC1089400233O1AX

Fig. 108 Chart C-12, cooling fan diagnosis (Part 1 of 2). 1994 Caprice, Impala SS & Roadmaster

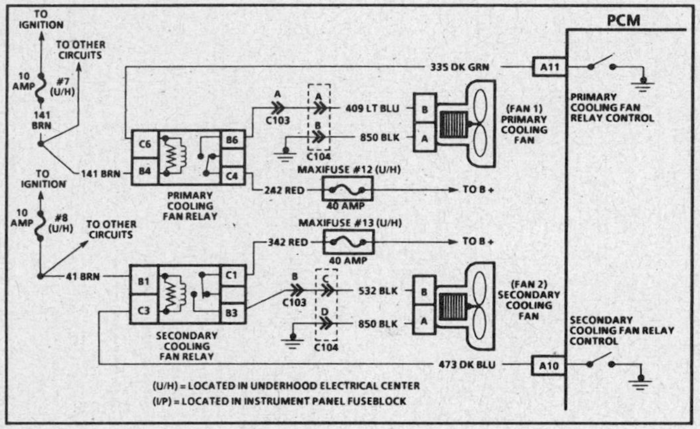
TO IGNITION
TO OTHER CIRCUITS
10 AMP
#7 (U/H)
141 BRN
141 BRN
C6
B4
B6
C4
PRIMARY COOLING FAN RELAY
TO IGNITION
10 AMP
#8 (U/H)
TO OTHER CIRCUITS
41 BRN
B1
C3
C1
B3
SECONDARY COOLING FAN RELAY
C103
C104
409 LT BLU
850 BLK
MAXIFUSE #12 (U/H)
242 RED
40 AMP
TO B+
MAXIFUSE #13 (U/H)
342 RED
40 AMP
TO B+
532 BLK
850 BLK
335 DK GRN
473 DK BLU
(FAN 1) PRIMARY COOLING FAN
(FAN 2) SECONDARY COOLING FAN
A11
A10
PCM
PRIMARY COOLING FAN RELAY CONTROL
SECONDARY COOLING FAN RELAY CONTROL
(U/H) = LOCATED IN UNDERHOOD ELECTRICAL CENTER
(I/P) = LOCATED IN INSTRUMENT PANEL FUSEBLOCK

CHART C-12

(Page 2 of 2)

ELECTRIC COOLING FAN CONTROL CIRCUIT DIAGNOSIS "B" CARLINE (SFI)

Circuit Description:

The cooling fans are controlled by the PCM based on various inputs. Battery voltage is supplied to the primary fan relay on terminal "C4", and secondary fan relay on terminal "C1". Ignition voltage is supplied to terminal "B4" of the primary and "B1" of the secondary fan relay. Grounding CKT 335 (relay terminal "C6") will energize the primary cooling fan relay (Fan 1) and supply battery voltage to the primary cooling fan motor. Grounding CKT 473 (relay terminal "C3") will energize the secondary cooling fan relay (Fan 2) and supply battery voltage to the secondary fan motor.

When certain Diagnostic Trouble Codes (DTCs) are set, the PCM will enable the cooling fans.

Diagnostic Aids: For detailed underhood electrical center relay cavity identification

If the owner complained of an overheating problem, it must be determined if the complaint was due to an actual boil over, the warning indicator light, or engine coolant temperature gage indicated overheating.

The gage accuracy can also be checked by comparing the Engine Coolant Temperature (ECT) sensor reading using a Tech 1 and comparing its reading with the gage reading.

If the engine is actually overheating and the gage indicated overheating, but the cooling fan is not coming "ON," the Engine Coolant Temperature (ECT) sensor has probably shifted out of calibration and should be replaced.

If the engine is overheating and the cooling fans are "ON," the cooling system should be checked.

The PCM will command fan 1 "ON" at 107°C (225°F) and "OFF" at 103°C (217°F) and an 2 "ON" at 111°C (232°F) and "OFF" at 107°C (224°F).

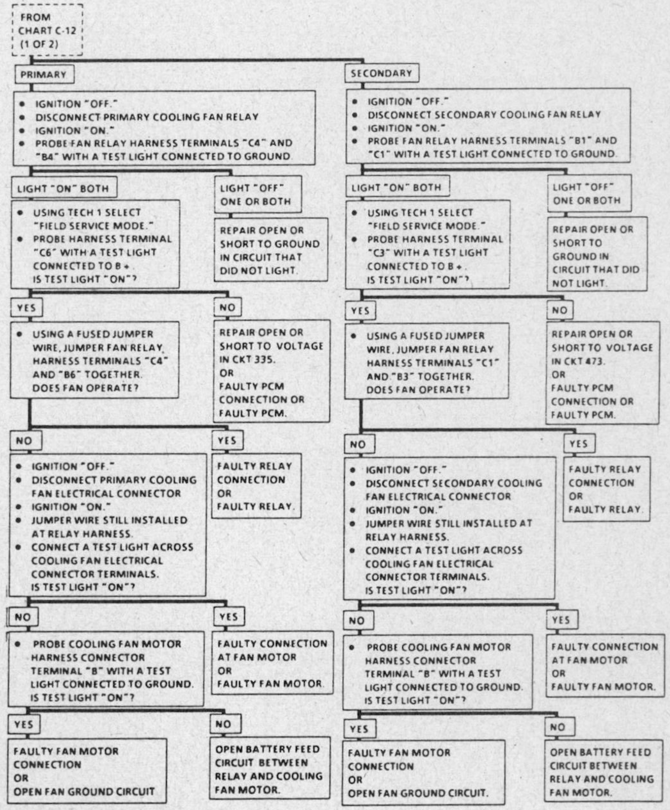
FROM CHART C-12 (1 OF 2)
PRIMARY
• IGNITION "OFF." • DISCONNECT PRIMARY COOLING FAN RELAY • IGNITION "ON." • PROBE FAN RELAY HARNESS TERMINALS "C4" AND "B4" WITH A TEST LIGHT CONNECTED TO GROUND.
LIGHT "ON" BOTH
• USING TECH 1 SELECT "FIELD SERVICE MODE." • PROBE HARNESS TERMINAL "C6" WITH A TEST LIGHT CONNECTED TO B+. IS TEST LIGHT "ON"?
LIGHT "OFF" ONE OR BOTH
REPAIR OPEN OR SHORT TO GROUND IN CIRCUIT THAT DID NOT LIGHT.
YES
• USING A FUSED JUMPER WIRE, JUMPER FAN RELAY HARNESS TERMINALS "C4" AND "B6" TOGETHER. DOES FAN OPERATE?
NO
REPAIR OPEN OR SHORT TO VOLTAGE IN CKT 335. OR FAULTY PCM CONNECTION OR FAULTY PCM.
NO
• IGNITION "OFF." • DISCONNECT PRIMARY COOLING FAN ELECTRICAL CONNECTOR • IGNITION "ON." • JUMPER WIRE STILL INSTALLED AT RELAY HARNESS. • CONNECT A TEST LIGHT ACROSS COOLING FAN ELECTRICAL CONNECTOR TERMINALS. IS TEST LIGHT "ON"?
YES
FAULTY RELAY CONNECTION OR FAULTY RELAY.
NO
• PROBE COOLING FAN MOTOR HARNESS CONNECTOR TERMINAL "B" WITH A TEST LIGHT CONNECTED TO GROUND. IS TEST LIGHT "ON"?
YES
FAULTY CONNECTION AT FAN MOTOR OR FAULTY FAN MOTOR.
YES
FAULTY FAN MOTOR CONNECTION OR OPEN FAN GROUND CIRCUIT
NO
OPEN BATTERY FEED CIRCUIT BETWEEN RELAY AND COOLING FAN MOTOR.
SECONDARY
• IGNITION "OFF." • DISCONNECT SECONDARY COOLING FAN RELAY • IGNITION "ON." • PROBE FAN RELAY HARNESS TERMINALS "B1" AND "C1" WITH A TEST LIGHT CONNECTED TO GROUND.
LIGHT "ON" BOTH
• USING TECH 1 SELECT "FIELD SERVICE MODE." • PROBE HARNESS TERMINAL "C3" WITH A TEST LIGHT CONNECTED TO B+. IS TEST LIGHT "ON"?
LIGHT "OFF" ONE OR BOTH
REPAIR OPEN OR SHORT TO GROUND IN CIRCUIT THAT DID NOT LIGHT.
YES
• USING A FUSED JUMPER WIRE, JUMPER FAN RELAY HARNESS TERMINALS "C1" AND "B3" TOGETHER. DOES FAN OPERATE?
NO
REPAIR OPEN OR SHORT TO VOLTAGE IN CKT 473. OR FAULTY PCM CONNECTION OR FAULTY PCM.
NO
• IGNITION "OFF." • DISCONNECT SECONDARY COOLING FAN ELECTRICAL CONNECTOR • IGNITION "ON." • JUMPER WIRE STILL INSTALLED AT RELAY HARNESS. • CONNECT A TEST LIGHT ACROSS COOLING FAN ELECTRICAL CONNECTOR TERMINALS. IS TEST LIGHT "ON"?
YES
FAULTY RELAY CONNECTION OR FAULTY RELAY.
NO
• PROBE COOLING FAN MOTOR HARNESS CONNECTOR TERMINAL "B" WITH A TEST LIGHT CONNECTED TO GROUND. IS TEST LIGHT "ON"?
YES
FAULTY CONNECTION AT FAN MOTOR OR FAULTY FAN MOTOR.
YES
FAULTY FAN MOTOR CONNECTION OR OPEN FAN GROUND CIRCUIT.
NO
OPEN BATTERY FEED CIRCUIT BETWEEN RELAY AND COOLING FAN MOTOR.

GC108940023302AX

Fig. 108 Chart C-12, cooling fan diagnosis (Part 2 of 2). 1994 Caprice, Impala SS & Roadmaster

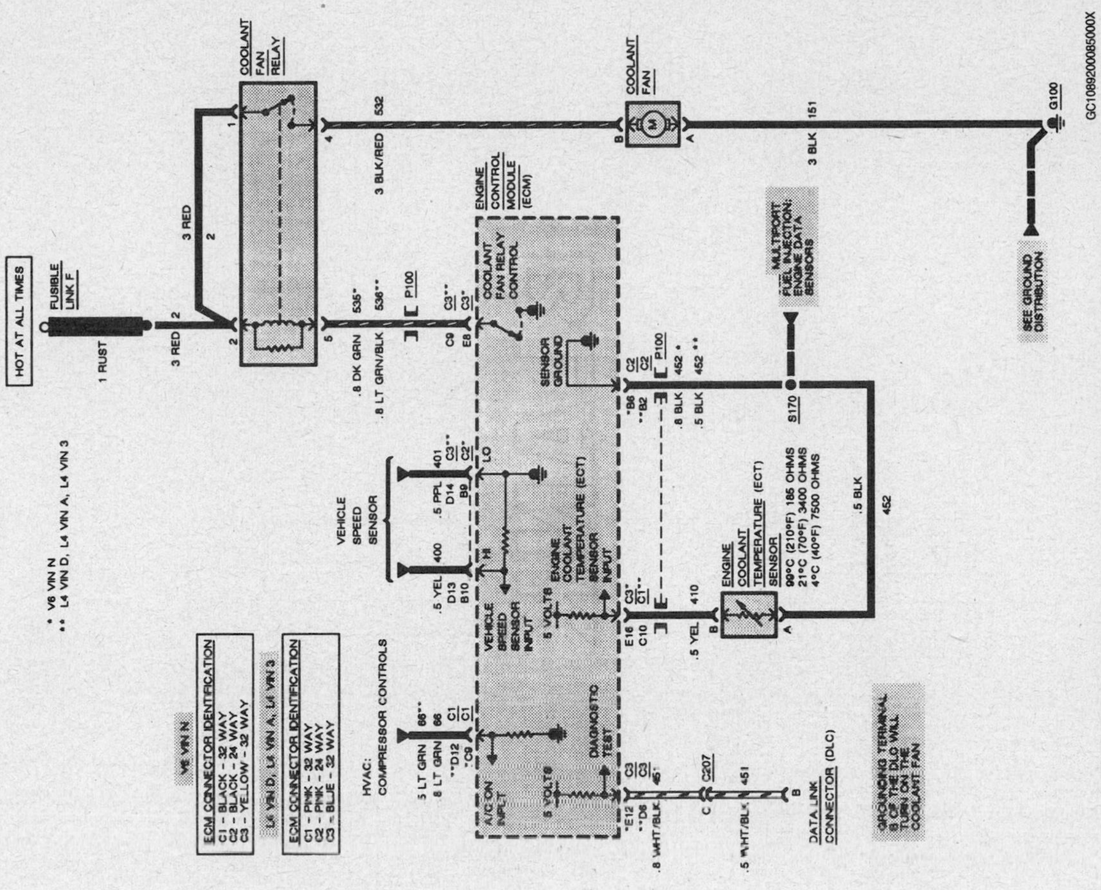

Fig. 110 Cooling fan wiring circuit. 1992–93 Grand Am

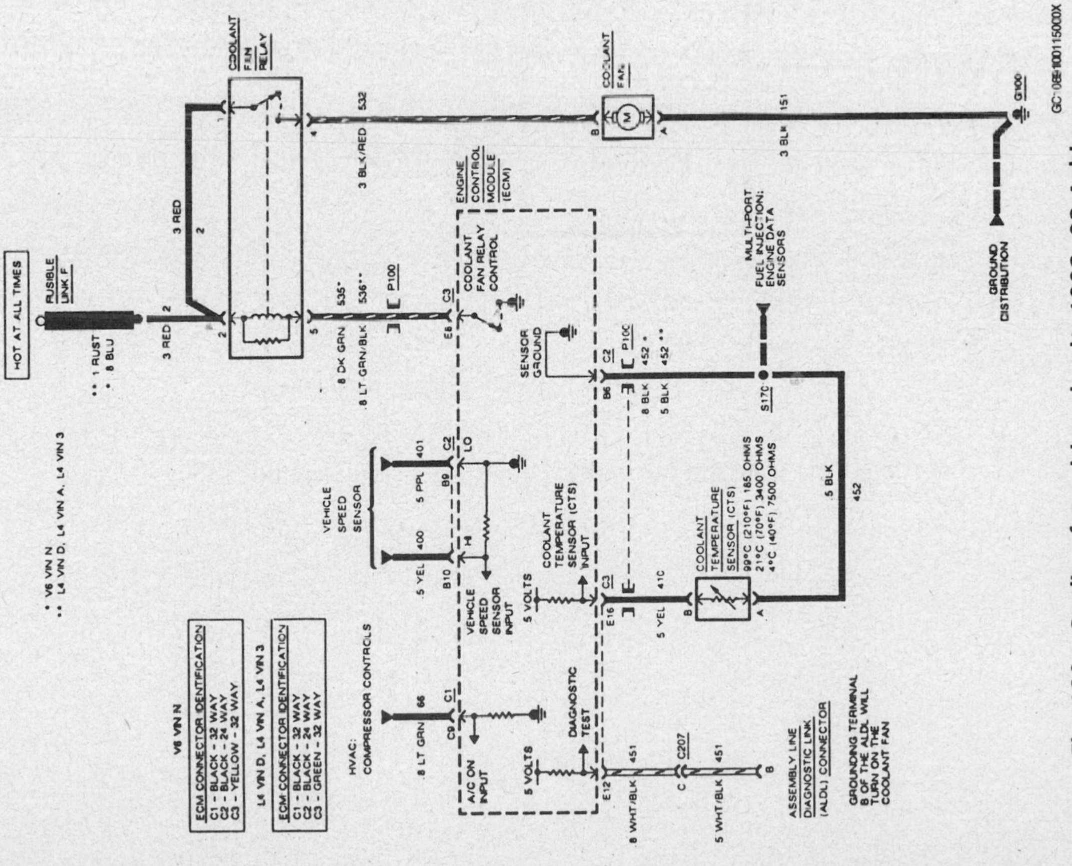

Fig. 109 Cooling fan wiring circuit. 1992–93 Achieva

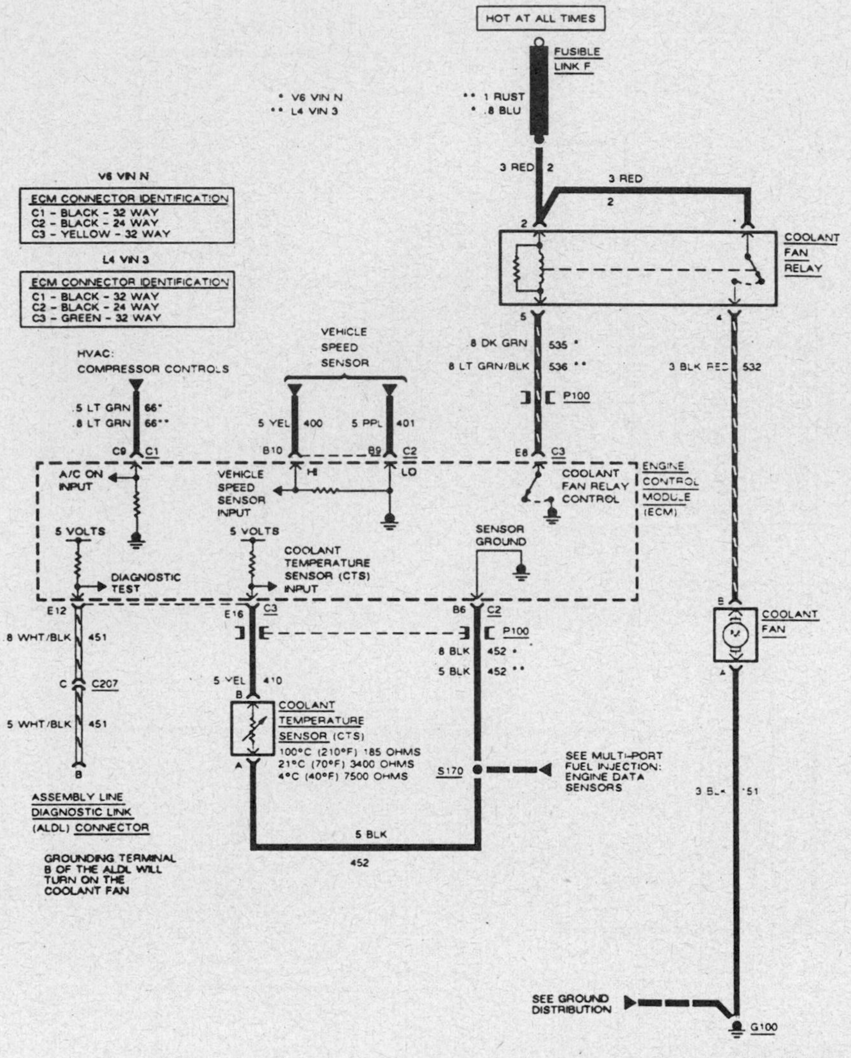
HOT AT ALL TIMES
FUSIBLE LINK F
* V6 VIN N
** L4 VIN 3
** 1 RUST
* .8 BLU
3 RED 2
3 RED
2
V6 VIN N
ECM CONNECTOR IDENTIFICATION
C1 - BLACK - 32 WAY
C2 - BLACK - 24 WAY
C3 - YELLOW - 32 WAY
L4 VIN 3
ECM CONNECTOR IDENTIFICATION
C1 - BLACK - 32 WAY
C2 - BLACK - 24 WAY
C3 - GREEN - 32 WAY
COOLANT FAN RELAY
.8 DK GRN 535 *
.8 LT GRN/BLK 536 **
3 BLK RED 532
P100
VEHICLE SPEED SENSOR
HVAC: COMPRESSOR CONTROLS
.5 LT GRN 66*
.8 LT GRN 66**
5 YEL 400
5 PPL 401
C9 C1
B10
B9 C2
E8 C3
A/C ON INPUT
VEHICLE SPEED SENSOR INPUT
HI
LO
COOLANT FAN RELAY CONTROL
ENGINE CONTROL MODULE (ECM)
5 VOLTS
5 VOLTS
SENSOR GROUND
COOLANT TEMPERATURE SENSOR (CTS) INPUT
DIAGNOSTIC TEST
E12
E16 C3
B6 C2
COOLANT FAN
.8 WHT/BLK 451
P100
.8 BLK 452 *
.5 BLK 452 **
C C207
5 YEL 410
.5 WHT/BLK 451
COOLANT TEMPERATURE SENSOR (CTS)
100°C (210°F) 185 OHMS
21°C (70°F) 3400 OHMS
4°C (40°F) 7500 OHMS
S170
SEE MULTI-PORT FUEL INJECTION: ENGINE DATA SENSORS
ASSEMBLY LINE DIAGNOSTIC LINK (ALDL) CONNECTOR
GROUNDING TERMINAL B OF THE ALDL WILL TURN ON THE COOLANT FAN
.5 BLK
452
SEE GROUND DISTRIBUTION
G100
GC1089200089000X

Fig. 111 Cooling fan wiring circuit. 1992–93 Skylark

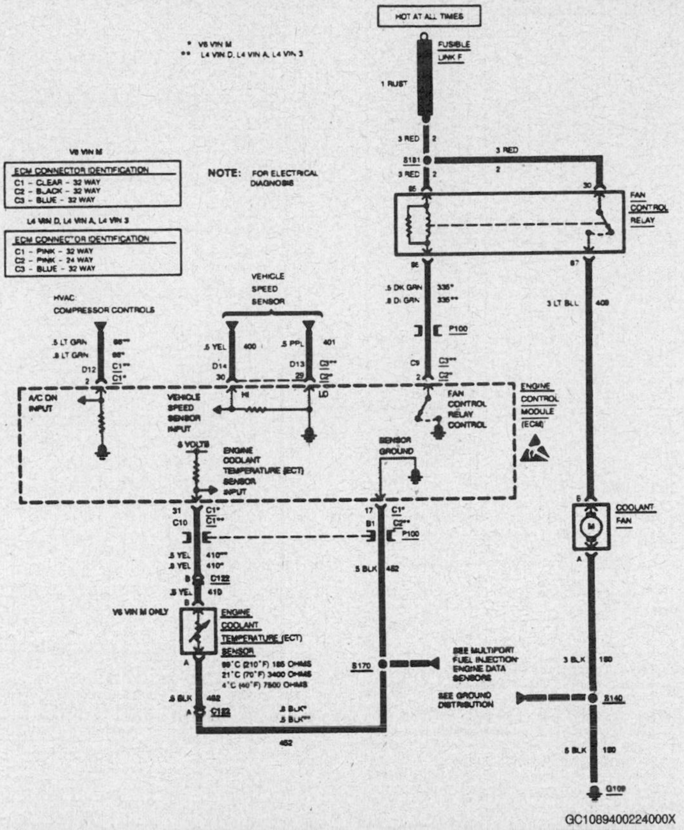
HOT AT ALL TIMES
FUSIBLE LINK F
FAN CONTROL RELAY
ENGINE CONTROL MODULE (ECM)
COOLANT FAN
ENGINE COOLANT TEMPERATURE (ECT) SENSOR
NOTE: FOR ELECTRICAL DIAGNOSIS
GC1089400224000X

Fig. 112 Cooling fan wiring circuit. 1994 Achieva, Grand Am & Skylark

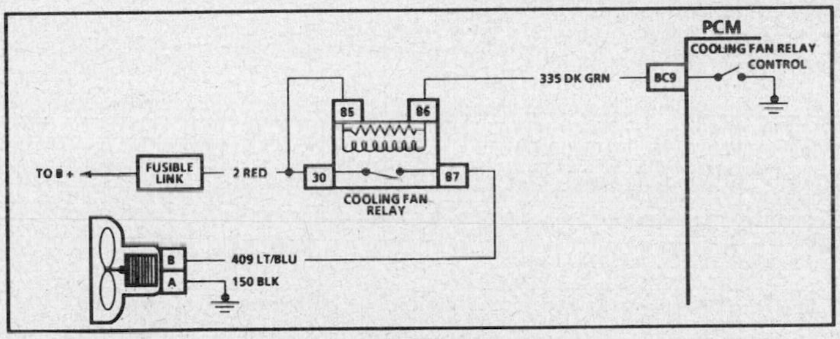
PCM
COOLING FAN RELAY CONTROL
335 DK GRN
BC9
TO B+
FUSIBLE LINK
2 RED
85
86
30
87
COOLING FAN RELAY
409 LT/BLU
150 BLK
B
A

CHART C-12

COOLANT FAN FUNCTIONAL CHECK 2.3L (VIN D, A & 3) "N" CARLINE

Circuit Description:

The electric coolant fan is controlled by the Powertrain Control Module (PCM) through the fan relay based on inputs from the engine coolant and intake air temperature sensors, the A/C control switch, A/C refrigerant pressure sensor and the vehicle speed sensor. The PCM controls the coolant fan by grounding CKT 335 which turns "ON" the fan relay.

The fan relay will be commanded "ON" when:

- Engine coolant temperature reaches 103°C (217°F) - 106°C (223°F) or more.
- A/C clutch requested.
- Vehicle speed is less than 35 mph.

The fan relay will be commanded "ON" regardless of vehicle speed when:

- Any DTC is set.
- Engine coolant temperature 115°C (239°F) - 118°C (224°F) or more.
- A/C refrigerant pressure is high.

The coolant fan may be commanded "ON" when the engine is not running under fan "Run-ON" conditions described previously in this section.

Chart Test Description: Number(s) below refer to circled number(s) on the diagnostic chart.

1. With the fan relay commanded "ON," the coolant fan control driver should close, which should energize the fan control relay.
2. Test to see if fault is in wiring to the fan or the fan/relay connection.

Diagnostic Aids: If the owner complained of an overheating problem, it must be determined if the complaint was due to an actual boil over, or the "Temp Light," or temperature gauge indicated overheating.

If the gauge, or light, indicates overheating, but no boil over is detected, the gauge or light circuit should be checked. The gauge accuracy can also be checked by comparing the coolant sensor reading using a scan tool with the gauge reading.

If the engine is actually overheating, and the gauge indicates overheating, but the coolant fan is not coming "ON," the Engine Coolant Temperature (ECT) sensor has probably shifted out of calibration and should be replaced. See DTC 15 chart for "Temperature vs. Resistance" chart.

If the engine is overheating, and the coolant fan is "ON," the cooling system should be checked.

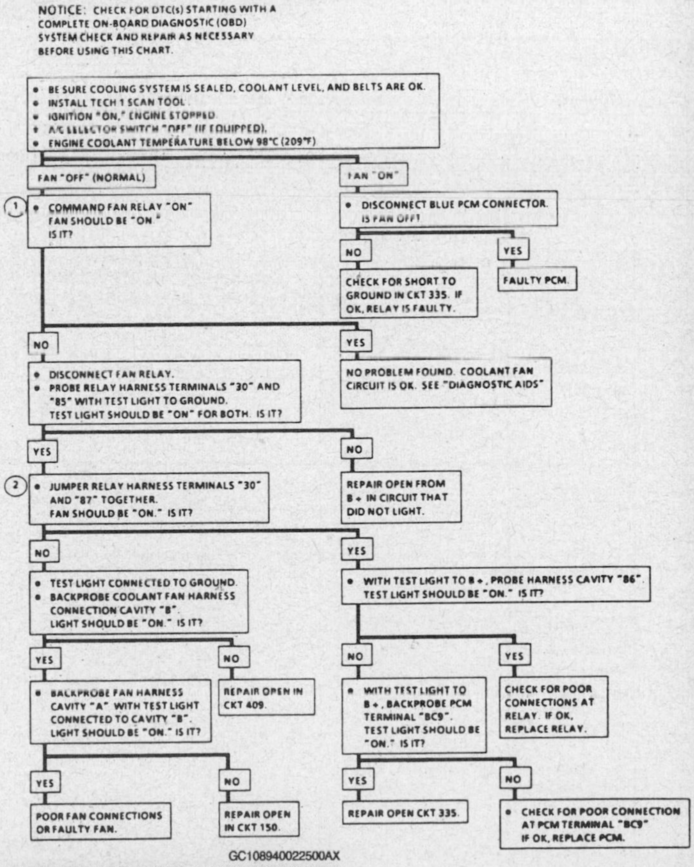
NOTICE: CHECK FOR DTC(s) STARTING WITH A COMPLETE ON-BOARD DIAGNOSTIC (OBD) SYSTEM CHECK AND REPAIR AS NECESSARY BEFORE USING THIS CHART.
• BE SURE COOLING SYSTEM IS SEALED, COOLANT LEVEL, AND BELTS ARE OK.
• INSTALL TECH 1 SCAN TOOL.
• IGNITION "ON," ENGINE STOPPED.
• A/C SELECTOR SWITCH "OFF" (IF EQUIPPED).
• ENGINE COOLANT TEMPERATURE BELOW 98°C (209°F)
FAN "OFF" (NORMAL)
FAN "ON"
1
• COMMAND FAN RELAY "ON" FAN SHOULD BE "ON." IS IT?
• DISCONNECT BLUE PCM CONNECTOR. IS FAN OFF?
NO
YES
CHECK FOR SHORT TO GROUND IN CKT 335. IF OK, RELAY IS FAULTY.
FAULTY PCM.
NO
YES
• DISCONNECT FAN RELAY.
• PROBE RELAY HARNESS TERMINALS "30" AND "85" WITH TEST LIGHT TO GROUND. TEST LIGHT SHOULD BE "ON" FOR BOTH. IS IT?
NO PROBLEM FOUND. COOLANT FAN CIRCUIT IS OK. SEE "DIAGNOSTIC AIDS"
YES
NO
2
• JUMPER RELAY HARNESS TERMINALS "30" AND "87" TOGETHER. FAN SHOULD BE "ON." IS IT?
REPAIR OPEN FROM B+ IN CIRCUIT THAT DID NOT LIGHT.
NO
YES
• TEST LIGHT CONNECTED TO GROUND.
• BACKPROBE COOLANT FAN HARNESS CONNECTION CAVITY "B". LIGHT SHOULD BE "ON." IS IT?
• WITH TEST LIGHT TO B+, PROBE HARNESS CAVITY "86". TEST LIGHT SHOULD BE "ON." IS IT?
YES
NO
NO
YES
• BACKPROBE FAN HARNESS CAVITY "A" WITH TEST LIGHT CONNECTED TO CAVITY "B". LIGHT SHOULD BE "ON." IS IT?
REPAIR OPEN IN CKT 409.
• WITH TEST LIGHT TO B+, BACKPROBE PCM TERMINAL "BC9". TEST LIGHT SHOULD BE "ON." IS IT?
CHECK FOR POOR CONNECTIONS AT RELAY. IF OK, REPLACE RELAY.
YES
NO
YES
NO
POOR FAN CONNECTIONS OR FAULTY FAN.
REPAIR OPEN IN CKT 150.
REPAIR OPEN CKT 335.
• CHECK FOR POOR CONNECTION AT PCM TERMINAL "BC9" IF OK, REPLACE PCM.
GC108940022500AX

Fig. 113 Chart C-12, cooling fan diagnosis. 1994 Achieva, Grand Am & Skylark w/2.3L/4–138 engine

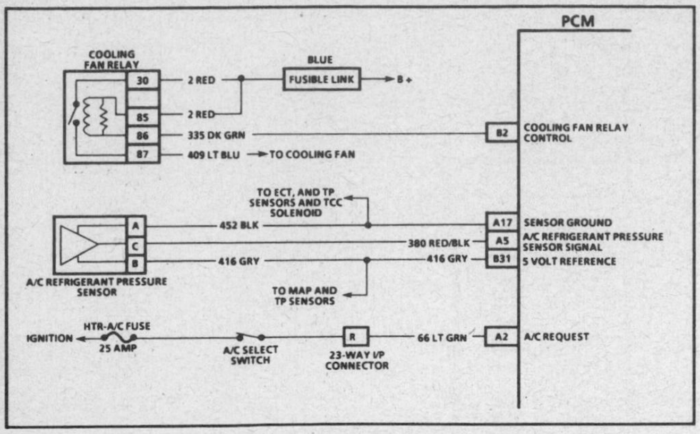
PCM
COOLING FAN RELAY
30
85
86
87
2 RED
2 RED
335 DK GRN
409 LT BLU
TO COOLING FAN
BLUE
FUSIBLE LINK
B+
B2
COOLING FAN RELAY CONTROL
TO ECT, AND TP SENSORS AND TCC SOLENOID
A
C
B
452 BLK
380 RED/BLK
416 GRY
416 GRY
A17
A5
B31
SENSOR GROUND
A/C REFRIGERANT PRESSURE SENSOR SIGNAL
5 VOLT REFERENCE
A/C REFRIGERANT PRESSURE SENSOR
TO MAP AND TP SENSORS
HTR-A/C FUSE
IGNITION
25 AMP
A/C SELECT SWITCH
R
23-WAY I/P CONNECTOR
66 LT GRN
A2
A/C REQUEST

CHART C-12

(Page 1 of 2)

COOLING FAN CONTROL DIAGNOSIS
3100 (VIN M) "N" CARLINE (SFI)

Circuit Description:

Battery voltage to operate the cooling fan is supplied to the cooling fan relay by CKT 2 on cooling fan relay cavities "30" and "85". When the PCM grounds CKT 335, the relay is energized and the cooling fan is turned "ON."

When the engine is running, the PCM will turn the cooling fan "ON" for any one of the following reasons:

- Diagnostic Trouble Code (DTC) 14, 15 or 70 is set.
- Vehicle speed is less than 70 mph (113 km/h).
- Engine coolant temperature is 108°C (226°F) or greater, with A/C "ON" or "OFF."
- A/C refrigerant pressure is greater than 187 psi (1289 kPa).
- PCM is in backup mode.

Chart Test Description: Number(s) below refer to circled number(s) on the diagnostic chart.

1. With the diagnostic terminal grounded, the cooling fan control driver will close, which should energize the fan control relay.
2. If the A/C pressure is above 300 psi (2069 kPa) or circuit is open, the fan would run whenever A/C is requested.
3. With A/C clutch engaged and the pressure sensor is functioning properly, the fan should come "ON" when pressure exceeds about 200 psi (1380 kPa). This signal should cause the PCM to energize the fan control relay(s).
4. This will determine if the A/C refrigerant pressure sensor is faulty or if the PCM or circuitry is faulty.

Diagnostic Aids: If the owner complained of an overheating problem, it must be determined if the complaint was due to an actual boilover, a hot light or temperature gage indicated over heating.

If the gage, or light, indicates overheating, but no boilover is detected, the gage circuit should be checked.

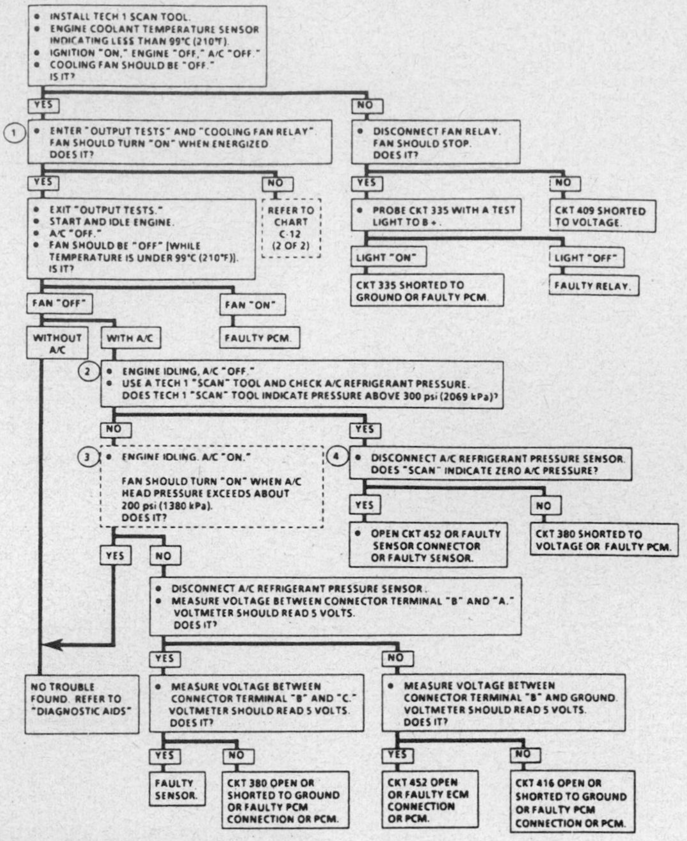
• INSTALL TECH 1 SCAN TOOL.
• ENGINE COOLANT TEMPERATURE SENSOR INDICATING LESS THAN 99°C (210°F).
• IGNITION "ON," ENGINE "OFF," A/C "OFF."
• COOLING FAN SHOULD BE "OFF."
IS IT?
YES
NO
1
• ENTER "OUTPUT TESTS" AND "COOLING FAN RELAY". FAN SHOULD TURN "ON" WHEN ENERGIZED DOES IT?
• DISCONNECT FAN RELAY. FAN SHOULD STOP. DOES IT?
YES
NO
YES
NO
• EXIT "OUTPUT TESTS."
• START AND IDLE ENGINE.
• A/C "OFF."
• FAN SHOULD BE "OFF" [WHILE TEMPERATURE IS UNDER 99°C (210°F)]. IS IT?
REFER TO CHART C-12 (2 OF 2)
• PROBE CKT 335 WITH A TEST LIGHT TO B+.
CKT 409 SHORTED TO VOLTAGE.
LIGHT "ON"
LIGHT "OFF"
CKT 335 SHORTED TO GROUND OR FAULTY PCM.
FAULTY RELAY.
FAN "OFF"
FAN "ON"
WITHOUT A/C
WITH A/C
FAULTY PCM.
2
• ENGINE IDLING, A/C "OFF."
• USE A TECH 1 "SCAN" TOOL AND CHECK A/C REFRIGERANT PRESSURE.
DOES TECH 1 "SCAN" TOOL INDICATE PRESSURE ABOVE 300 psi (2069 kPa)?
NO
YES
3
• ENGINE IDLING. A/C "ON."
FAN SHOULD TURN "ON" WHEN A/C HEAD PRESSURE EXCEEDS ABOUT 200 psi (1380 kPa). DOES IT?
4
• DISCONNECT A/C REFRIGERANT PRESSURE SENSOR. DOES "SCAN" INDICATE ZERO A/C PRESSURE?
YES
NO
• OPEN CKT 452 OR FAULTY SENSOR CONNECTOR OR FAULTY SENSOR.
CKT 380 SHORTED TO VOLTAGE OR FAULTY PCM.
YES
NO
• DISCONNECT A/C REFRIGERANT PRESSURE SENSOR.
• MEASURE VOLTAGE BETWEEN CONNECTOR TERMINAL "B" AND "A." VOLTMETER SHOULD READ 5 VOLTS. DOES IT?
YES
NO
NO TROUBLE FOUND. REFER TO "DIAGNOSTIC AIDS"
• MEASURE VOLTAGE BETWEEN CONNECTOR TERMINAL "B" AND "C." VOLTMETER SHOULD READ 5 VOLTS. DOES IT?
• MEASURE VOLTAGE BETWEEN CONNECTOR TERMINAL "B" AND GROUND. VOLTMETER SHOULD READ 5 VOLTS. DOES IT?
YES
NO
YES
NO
FAULTY SENSOR.
CKT 380 OPEN OR SHORTED TO GROUND OR FAULTY PCM CONNECTION OR PCM.
CKT 452 OPEN OR FAULTY ECM CONNECTION OR PCM.
CKT 416 OPEN OR SHORTED TO GROUND OR FAULTY PCM CONNECTION OR PCM.
GC108940022601AX

Fig. 114 Chart C-12, cooling fan diagnosis (Part 1 of 2). 1994 Achieva, Grand Am & Skylark w/3.1L/V6–192 engine

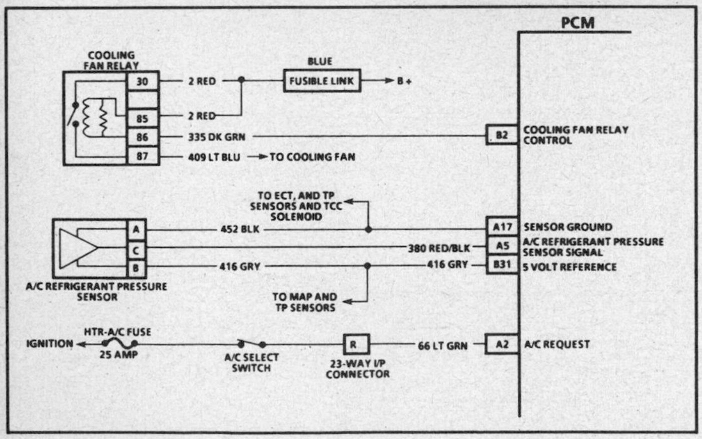
PCM
COOLING FAN RELAY
30
85
86
87
2 RED
2 RED
335 DK GRN
409 LT BLU
TO COOLING FAN
BLUE
FUSIBLE LINK
B+
B2
COOLING FAN RELAY CONTROL
TO ECT, AND TP SENSORS AND TCC SOLENOID
A
C
B
452 BLK
380 RED/BLK
416 GRY
416 GRY
A17
A5
B31
SENSOR GROUND
A/C REFRIGERANT PRESSURE SENSOR SIGNAL
5 VOLT REFERENCE
A/C REFRIGERANT PRESSURE SENSOR
TO MAP AND TP SENSORS
HTR-A/C FUSE
IGNITION
25 AMP
A/C SELECT SWITCH
R
23-WAY I/P CONNECTOR
66 LT GRN
A2
A/C REQUEST

Circuit Description:

Battery voltage to operate the cooling fan motor is supplied to the cooling fan relay by CKT 2, on cooling for relay cavities "30" and "85". When the PCM grounds CKT 335, the relay is energized and the cooling fan is turned "ON."

When the engine is running, the PCM will turn the cooling fan "ON," for any one of the following reasons:

- Diagnostic Trouble Code (DTC) 14, 15 or 70 is set.
- Engine Coolant Temperature (ECT) sensor indicating a temperature greater than 108°C (226°F) with A/C "ON" or "OFF."
- Vehicle speed is less than 70 mph (113 km/h).
- A/C refrigerant pressure is greater than 187 psi (1289 kPa).
- PCM is in backup mode.

Chart Test Description: Number(s) below refer to circled number(s) on the diagnostic chart.

1. B+ should be availble to the cooling fan relay cavities "B30" and "B85".
2. This test checks the ability of the PCM to ground CKT 335.
3. If the fan does not turn "ON" at this point, CKT 409 or the cooling fan ground circuit is open, or the cooling fan motor is faulty.

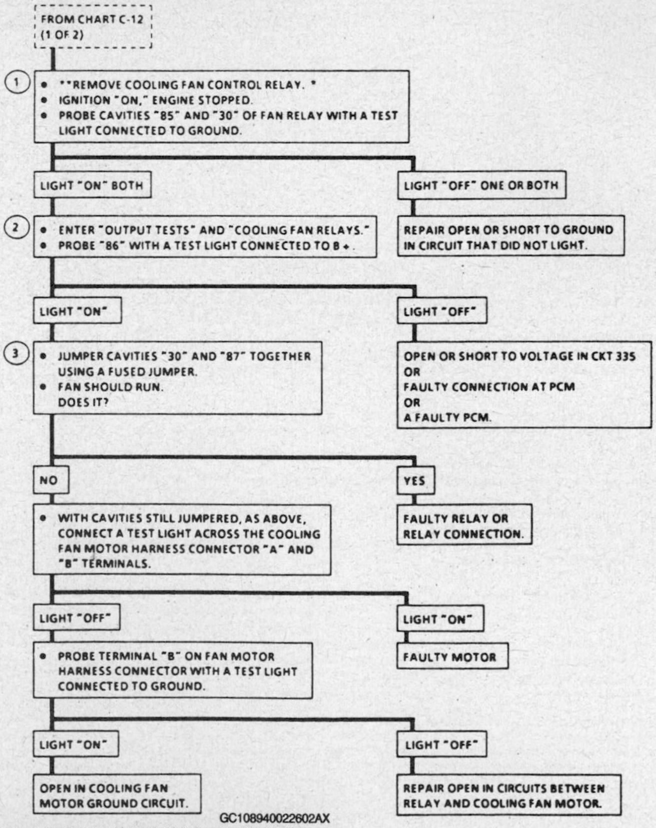
FROM CHART C-12 (1 OF 2)
1
• **REMOVE COOLING FAN CONTROL RELAY. *
• IGNITION "ON," ENGINE STOPPED.
• PROBE CAVITIES "85" AND "30" OF FAN RELAY WITH A TEST LIGHT CONNECTED TO GROUND.
LIGHT "ON" BOTH
LIGHT "OFF" ONE OR BOTH
2
• ENTER "OUTPUT TESTS" AND "COOLING FAN RELAYS."
• PROBE "86" WITH A TEST LIGHT CONNECTED TO B+.
REPAIR OPEN OR SHORT TO GROUND IN CIRCUIT THAT DID NOT LIGHT.
LIGHT "ON"
LIGHT "OFF"
3
• JUMPER CAVITIES "30" AND "87" TOGETHER USING A FUSED JUMPER.
• FAN SHOULD RUN. DOES IT?
OPEN OR SHORT TO VOLTAGE IN CKT 335 OR FAULTY CONNECTION AT PCM OR A FAULTY PCM.
NO
YES
• WITH CAVITIES STILL JUMPERED, AS ABOVE, CONNECT A TEST LIGHT ACROSS THE COOLING FAN MOTOR HARNESS CONNECTOR "A" AND "B" TERMINALS.
FAULTY RELAY OR RELAY CONNECTION.
LIGHT "OFF"
LIGHT "ON"
• PROBE TERMINAL "B" ON FAN MOTOR HARNESS CONNECTOR WITH A TEST LIGHT CONNECTED TO GROUND.
FAULTY MOTOR
LIGHT "ON"
LIGHT "OFF"
OPEN IN COOLING FAN MOTOR GROUND CIRCUIT.
REPAIR OPEN IN CIRCUITS BETWEEN RELAY AND COOLING FAN MOTOR.
GC108940022602AX

Fig. 114 Chart C-12, cooling fan diagnosis (Part 2 of 2). 1994 Achieva, Grand Am & Skylark w/3.1L/V6–192 engine

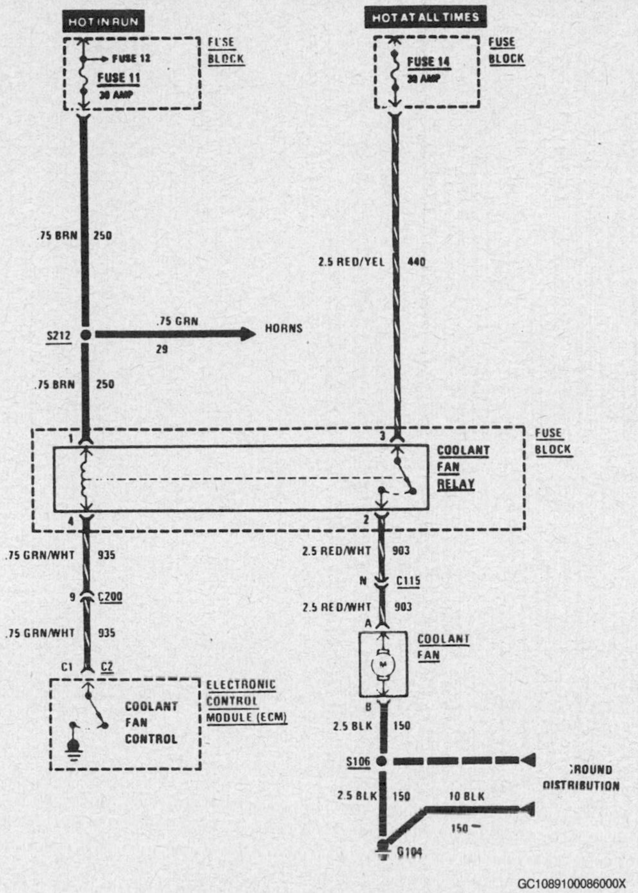
HOT IN RUN
HOT AT ALL TIMES
FUSE 12
FUSE 11
30 AMP
FUSE BLOCK
FUSE 14
30 AMP
FUSE BLOCK
.75 BRN 250
2.5 RED/YEL 440
S212
.75 GRN
29
HORNS
.75 BRN 250
COOLANT FAN RELAY
FUSE BLOCK
.75 GRN/WHT 935
2.5 RED/WHT 903
C115
C200
2.5 RED/WHT 903
.75 GRN/WHT 935
COOLANT FAN
C1 C2
ELECTRONIC CONTROL MODULE (ECM)
COOLANT FAN CONTROL
2.5 BLK 150
S106
GROUND DISTRIBUTION
2.5 BLK 150
10 BLK
G104
GC1089100086000X

Fig. 115 Cooling fan wiring circuit. LeMans less A/C

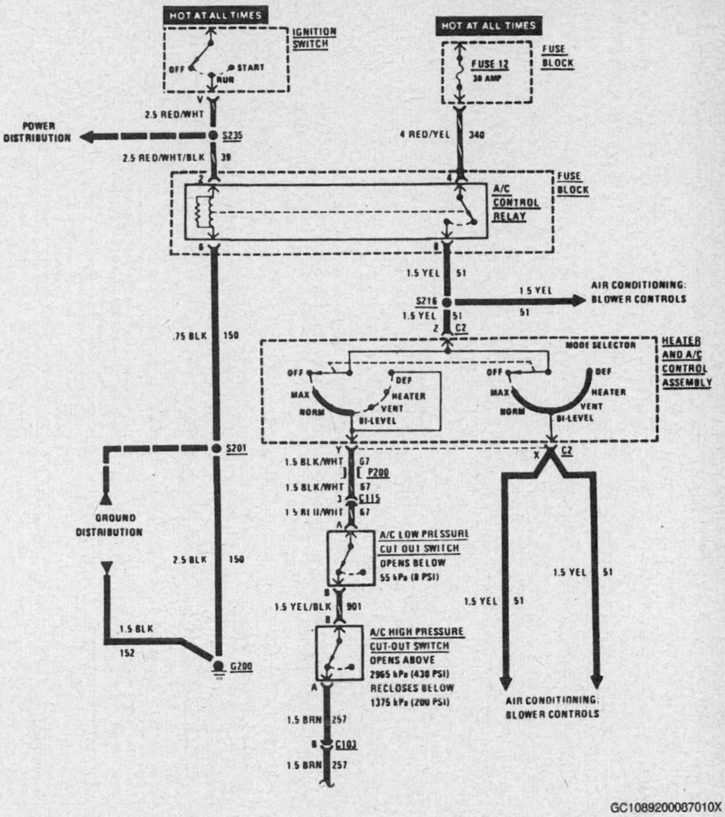
HOT AT ALL TIMES
IGNITION SWITCH
OFF
START
RUN
HOT AT ALL TIMES
FUSE 12
30 AMP
FUSE BLOCK
2.5 RED/WHT
POWER DISTRIBUTION
S235
2.5 RED/WHT/BLK 39
4 RED/YEL 340
A/C CONTROL RELAY
FUSE BLOCK
1.5 YEL 51
S216
1.5 YEL 51
AIR CONDITIONING BLOWER CONTROLS
.75 BLK 150
MODE SELECTOR
HEATER AND A/C CONTROL ASSEMBLY
OFF
DEF
MAX
HEATER
NORM
VENT
BI-LEVEL
S201
GROUND DISTRIBUTION
1.5 BLK/WHT 67
P200
C115
A/C LOW PRESSURE CUT OUT SWITCH
OPENS BELOW 55 kPa (8 PSI)
2.5 BLK 150
1.5 YEL/BLK 901
A/C HIGH PRESSURE CUT-OUT SWITCH
OPENS ABOVE 2965 kPa (430 PSI)
RECLOSES BELOW 1375 kPa (200 PSI)
1.5 BLK
152
G200
1.5 YEL 51
1.5 BRN 257
C103
1.5 BRN 257
AIR CONDITIONING BLOWER CONTROLS
GC1089200087010X

Fig. 116 Cooling fan wiring circuit (Part 1 of 2). LeMans w/A/C

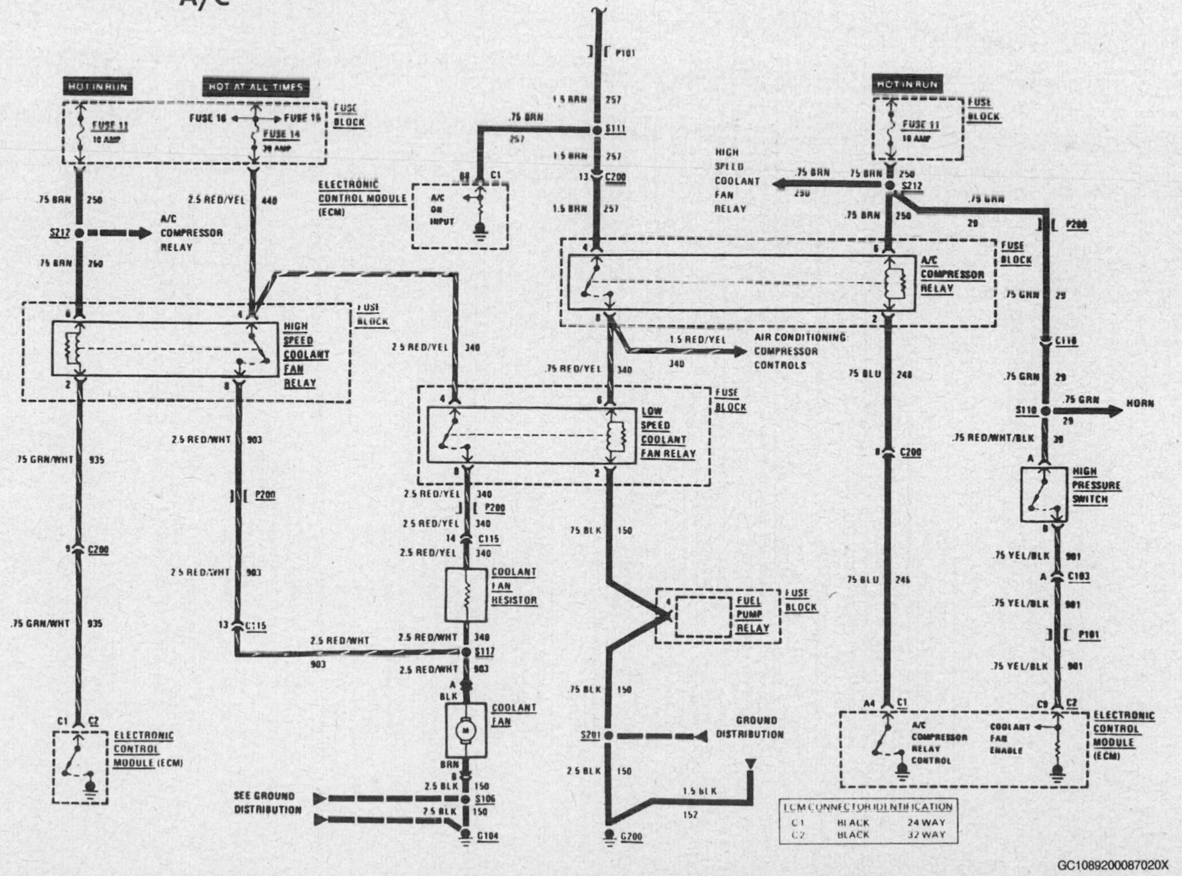
P101
HOT IN RUN
HOT AT ALL TIMES
FUSE 11
FUSE 16
FUSE 15
FUSE 14
FUSE BLOCK
.75 BRN 250
2.5 RED/YEL 440
ELECTRONIC CONTROL MODULE (ECM)
A/C ON INPUT
S217
A/C COMPRESSOR RELAY
HIGH SPEED COOLANT FAN RELAY
FUSE BLOCK
2.5 RED/YEL 340
.75 GRN/WHT 935
2.5 RED/WHT 903
LOW SPEED COOLANT FAN RELAY
FUSE BLOCK
P200
C200
C115
C115
COOLANT FAN RESISTOR
S117
COOLANT FAN
ELECTRONIC CONTROL MODULE (ECM)
SEE GROUND DISTRIBUTION
S106
G104
S111
C200
HIGH SPEED COOLANT FAN RELAY
S212
A/C COMPRESSOR RELAY
FUSE BLOCK
1.5 RED/YEL
AIR CONDITIONING COMPRESSOR CONTROLS
C118
S118
HORN
HIGH PRESSURE SWITCH
C200
FUEL PUMP RELAY
FUSE BLOCK
C103
P101
S201
GROUND DISTRIBUTION
G200
A/C COMPRESSOR RELAY CONTROL
COOLANT FAN ENABLE
ELECTRONIC CONTROL MODULE (ECM)
ECM CONNECTOR IDENTIFICATION
C1 BLACK 24 WAY
C2 BLACK 32 WAY
GC1089200087020X

Fig. 116 Cooling fan wiring circuit (Part 2 of 2). LeMans w/A/C

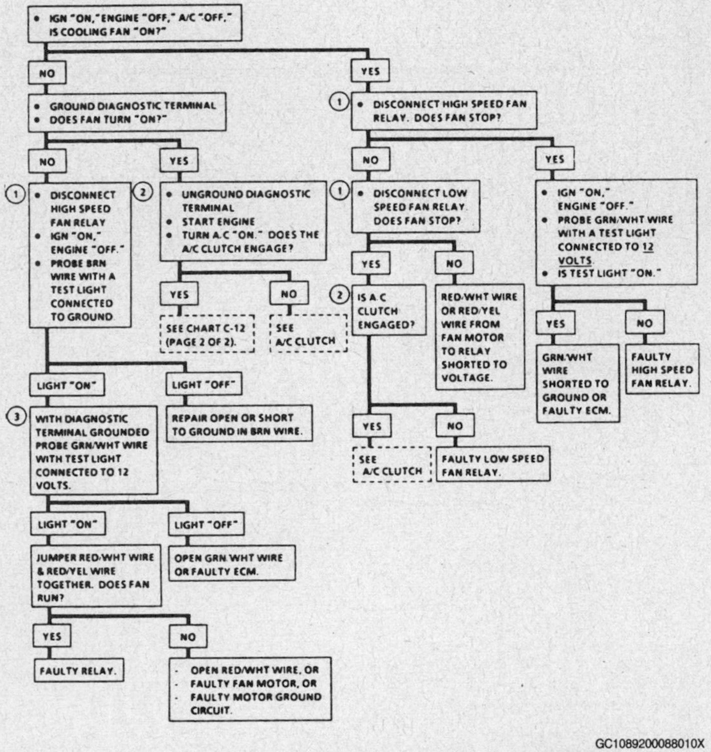

• IGN "ON," ENGINE "OFF," A/C "OFF." IS COOLING FAN "ON?"
NO
YES
• GROUND DIAGNOSTIC TERMINAL • DOES FAN TURN "ON?"
1 • DISCONNECT HIGH SPEED FAN RELAY. DOES FAN STOP?
NO
YES
1 • DISCONNECT HIGH SPEED FAN RELAY • IGN "ON," ENGINE "OFF." • PROBE BRN WIRE WITH A TEST LIGHT CONNECTED TO GROUND
2 • UNGROUND DIAGNOSTIC TERMINAL • START ENGINE • TURN A/C "ON." DOES THE A/C CLUTCH ENGAGE?
YES
NO
SEE CHART C-12 (PAGE 2 OF 2).
SEE A/C CLUTCH
1 • DISCONNECT LOW SPEED FAN RELAY. DOES FAN STOP?
YES
NO
2 IS A/C CLUTCH ENGAGED?
RED/WHT WIRE OR RED/YEL WIRE FROM FAN MOTOR TO RELAY SHORTED TO VOLTAGE.
YES
NO
SEE A/C CLUTCH
FAULTY LOW SPEED FAN RELAY.
• IGN "ON," ENGINE "OFF." • PROBE GRN/WHT WIRE WITH A TEST LIGHT CONNECTED TO 12 VOLTS. • IS TEST LIGHT "ON."
YES
NO
GRN/WHT WIRE SHORTED TO GROUND OR FAULTY ECM.
FAULTY HIGH SPEED FAN RELAY.
LIGHT "ON"
LIGHT "OFF"
3 WITH DIAGNOSTIC TERMINAL GROUNDED PROBE GRN/WHT WIRE WITH TEST LIGHT CONNECTED TO 12 VOLTS.
REPAIR OPEN OR SHORT TO GROUND IN BRN WIRE.
LIGHT "ON"
LIGHT "OFF"
JUMPER RED/WHT WIRE & RED/YEL WIRE TOGETHER. DOES FAN RUN?
OPEN GRN/WHT WIRE OR FAULTY ECM.
YES
NO
FAULTY RELAY.
· OPEN RED/WHT WIRE, OR · FAULTY FAN MOTOR, OR · FAULTY MOTOR GROUND CIRCUIT.
GC1089200088010X

Fig. 117 Chart C-12, cooling fan diagnosis chart (cooling fan circuit check) (Part 1 Of 2). LeMans w/A/C

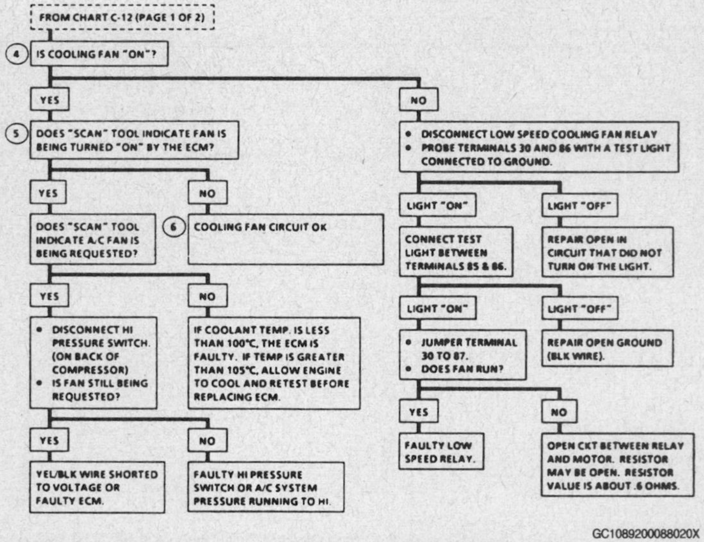

FROM CHART C-12 (PAGE 1 OF 2)
4 IS COOLING FAN "ON"?
YES
NO
5 DOES "SCAN" TOOL INDICATE FAN IS BEING TURNED "ON" BY THE ECM?
YES
NO
DOES "SCAN" TOOL INDICATE A/C FAN IS BEING REQUESTED?
6 COOLING FAN CIRCUIT OK
YES
NO
• DISCONNECT HI PRESSURE SWITCH. (ON BACK OF COMPRESSOR) • IS FAN STILL BEING REQUESTED?
IF COOLANT TEMP. IS LESS THAN 100°C, THE ECM IS FAULTY. IF TEMP IS GREATER THAN 105°C, ALLOW ENGINE TO COOL AND RETEST BEFORE REPLACING ECM.
YES
NO
YEL/BLK WIRE SHORTED TO VOLTAGE OR FAULTY ECM.
FAULTY HI PRESSURE SWITCH OR A/C SYSTEM PRESSURE RUNNING TO HI.
• DISCONNECT LOW SPEED COOLING FAN RELAY • PROBE TERMINALS 30 AND 86 WITH A TEST LIGHT CONNECTED TO GROUND.
LIGHT "ON"
LIGHT "OFF"
CONNECT TEST LIGHT BETWEEN TERMINALS 85 & 86.
REPAIR OPEN IN CIRCUIT THAT DID NOT TURN ON THE LIGHT.
LIGHT "ON"
LIGHT "OFF"
• JUMPER TERMINAL 30 TO 87. • DOES FAN RUN?
REPAIR OPEN GROUND (BLK WIRE).
YES
NO
FAULTY LOW SPEED RELAY.
OPEN CKT BETWEEN RELAY AND MOTOR. RESISTOR MAY BE OPEN. RESISTOR VALUE IS ABOUT .6 OHMS.
GC1089200088020X

Fig. 117 Chart C-12, cooling fan diagnosis chart (cooling fan circuit check) (Part 2 Of 2). LeMans w/A/C

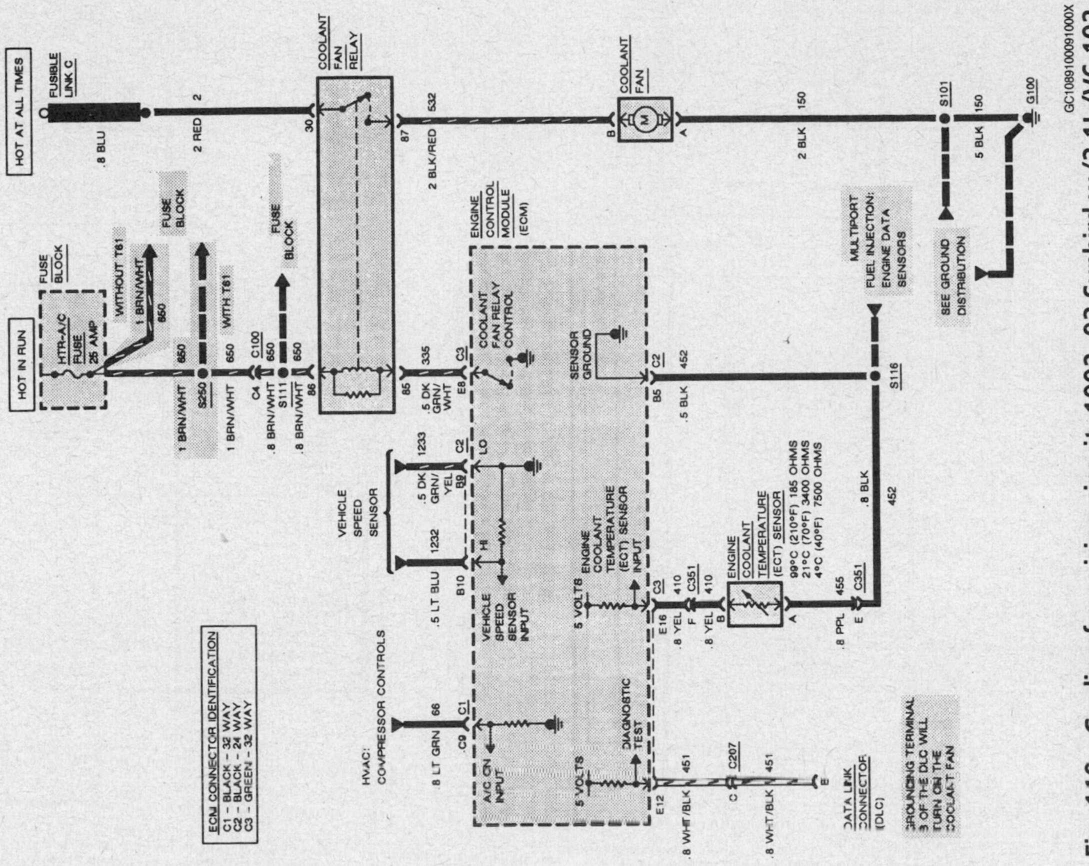
HOT AT ALL TIMES
FUSIBLE LINK C
.8 BLU
2 RED
COOLANT FAN RELAY
HOT IN RUN
FUSE BLOCK
HTR-A/C FUSE 25 AMP
WITHOUT T61
WITH T61
1 BRN/WHT
S250
C100
S111
.8 BRN/WHT
2 BLK/RED
532
COOLANT FAN
2 BLK
150
S101
5 BLK
G100
ENGINE CONTROL MODULE (ECM)
COOLANT FAN RELAY CONTROL
SENSOR GROUND
.5 DK GRN/WHT
335
452
.5 BLK
S116
MULTIPORT FUEL INJECTION: ENGINE DATA SENSORS
SEE GROUND DISTRIBUTION
VEHICLE SPEED SENSOR
.5 DK GRN/YEL
1233
1232
.5 LT BLU
VEHICLE SPEED SENSOR INPUT
ENGINE COOLANT TEMPERATURE (ECT) SENSOR INPUT
5 VOLTS
C351
410
.8 YEL
ENGINE COOLANT TEMPERATURE (ECT) SENSOR
99°C (210°F) 185 OHMS
21°C (70°F) 3400 OHMS
4°C (40°F) 7500 OHMS
.8 BLK
455
.8 PPL
ECM CONNECTOR IDENTIFICATION
C1 - BLACK - 32 WAY
C2 - BLACK - 24 WAY
C3 - GREEN - 32 WAY
HVAC: COMPRESSOR CONTROLS
.8 LT GRN
66
A/C ON INPUT
DIAGNOSTIC TEST
451
C207
.8 WHT/BLK
DATA LINK CONNECTOR (DLC)
GROUNDING TERMINAL B OF THE DLC WILL TURN ON THE COOLANT FAN
GC1089100091000X

Fig. 119 Cooling fan wiring circuit. 1992–93 Sunbird w/3.1L/V6-192 (VIN T) engine

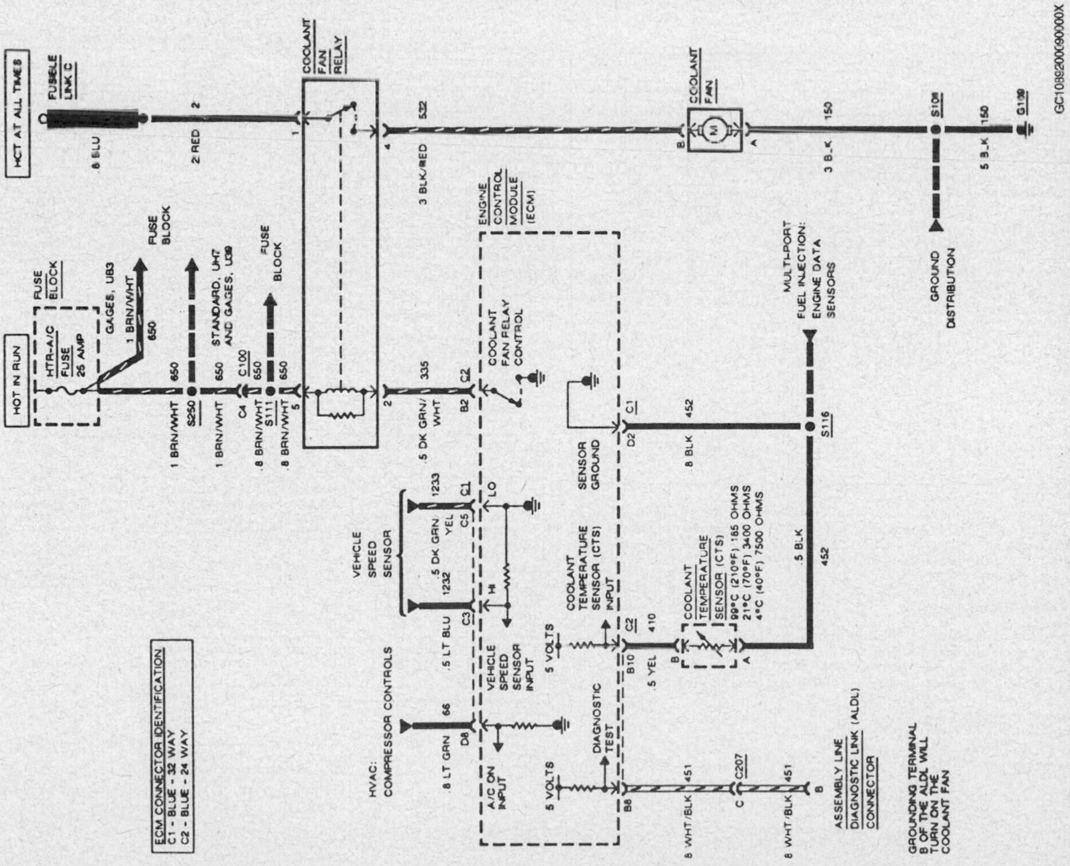
HOT AT ALL TIMES
FUSIBLE LINK C
.8 BLU
2 RED
COOLANT FAN RELAY
HOT IN RUN
FUSE BLOCK
HTR-A/C FUSE 25 AMP
GAGES, UB3
STANDARD, UH7 AND GAGES, UB3
1 BRN/WHT
S250
C100
S111
.8 BRN/WHT
3 BLK/RED
532
COOLANT FAN
3 BLK
150
S108
5 BLK
G109
ENGINE CONTROL MODULE (ECM)
COOLANT FAN RELAY CONTROL
SENSOR GROUND
.5 DK GRN/WHT
335
452
.8 BLK
S116
MULTI-PORT FUEL INJECTION: ENGINE DATA SENSORS
GROUND DISTRIBUTION
VEHICLE SPEED SENSOR
.5 DK GRN YEL
1233
1232
.5 LT BLU
VEHICLE SPEED SENSOR INPUT
COOLANT TEMPERATURE SENSOR (CTS) INPUT
5 VOLTS
410
.5 YEL
COOLANT TEMPERATURE SENSOR (CTS)
99°C (210°F) 185 OHMS
21°C (70°F) 3400 OHMS
4°C (40°F) 7500 OHMS
.5 BLK
452
ECM CONNECTOR IDENTIFICATION
C1 - BLUE - 32 WAY
C2 - BLUE - 24 WAY
HVAC: COMPRESSOR CONTROLS
.8 LT GRN
66
A/C ON INPUT
DIAGNOSTIC TEST
451
C207
.8 WHT/BLK
ASSEMBLY LINE DIAGNOSTIC LINK (ALDL) CONNECTOR
GROUNDING TERMINAL B OF THE ALDL WILL TURN ON THE COOLANT FAN
GC1088200090000X

Fig. 118 Cooling fan wiring circuit. 1992–93 Sunbird w/2.0L/4-121 (VIN H) engine

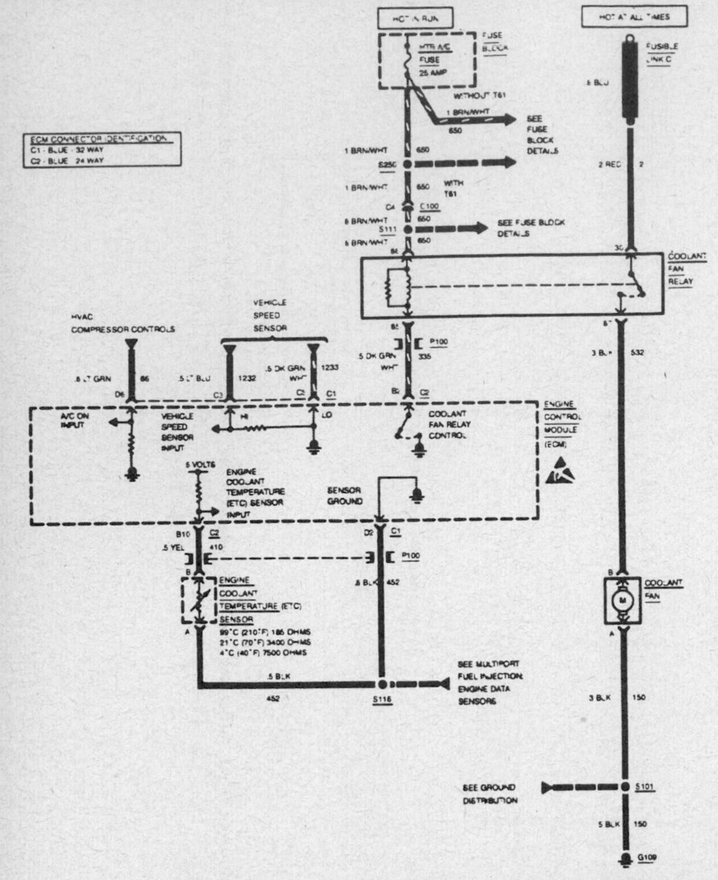

GC1089400227000X

Fig. 120 Cooling fan wiring circuit. 1994 Sunbird w/2.0L/4-121 (VIN H) engine

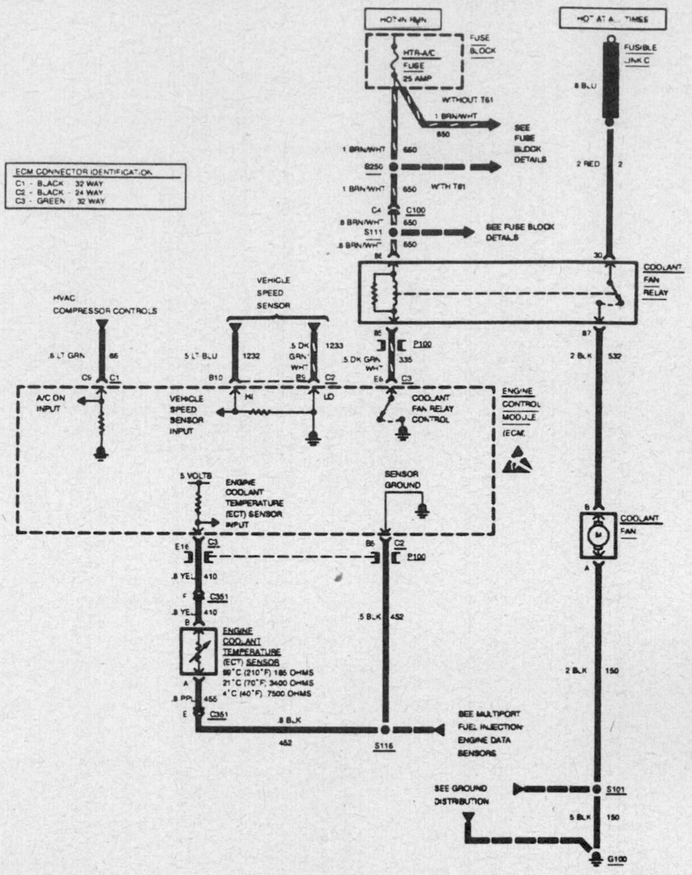

GC1089400228000X

Fig. 121 Cooling fan wiring circuit. 1994 Sunbird w/3.1L/V6-192 (VIN T) engine

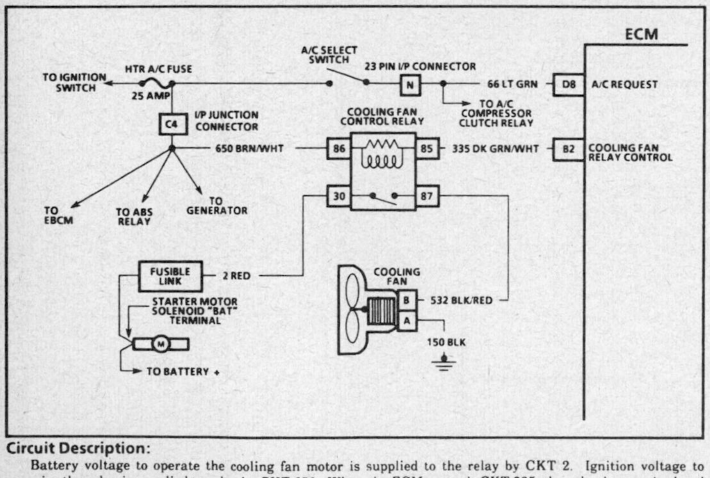

ECM
TO IGNITION SWITCH
HTR A/C FUSE
25 AMP
A/C SELECT SWITCH
23 PIN I/P CONNECTOR
N
66 LT GRN
D8
A/C REQUEST
TO A/C COMPRESSOR CLUTCH RELAY
C4
I/P JUNCTION CONNECTOR
COOLING FAN CONTROL RELAY
650 BRN/WHT
86
85
335 DK GRN/WHT
B2
COOLING FAN RELAY CONTROL
30
87
TO EBCM
TO ABS RELAY
TO GENERATOR
FUSIBLE LINK
2 RED
STARTER MOTOR SOLENOID "BAT" TERMINAL
TO BATTERY +
COOLING FAN
B
A
532 BLK/RED
150 BLK

Circuit Description:

Battery voltage to operate the cooling fan motor is supplied to the relay by CKT 2. Ignition voltage to energize the relay is supplied to relay by CKT 650. When the ECM grounds CKT 335, the relay is energized and the cooling fan is turned "ON." When the engine is running, the ECM will energize the cooling fan control relay if a coolant temperature sensor (DTC 14) has been set, or under the following conditions:

- Coolant temperature is greater than 106°C (223°F).

OR

- A/C refrigerant pressure is greater than 51 psi.

Diagnostic Aids: If the vehicle has an overheating problem, it must be determined if the complaint was due to an actual boil over, the coolant temperature warning light, or the temperature gauge indicated overheating.

If the gauge or light indicates overheating but no boil over is detected, the gauge circuit should be checked. The gauge accuracy can be checked by comparing it to the coolant temperature sensor reading using a Tech 1 scan tool.

If the engine is actually overheating and the gauge indicates overheating, but the cooling fan is not turning "ON," the coolant temperature sensor has probably shifted out of calibration and should be replaced.

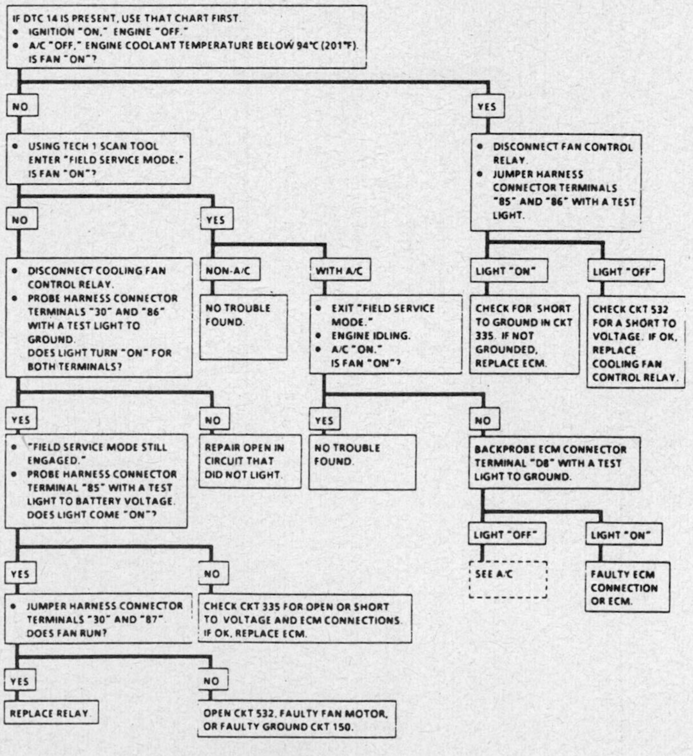

IF DTC 14 IS PRESENT, USE THAT CHART FIRST.
• IGNITION "ON," ENGINE "OFF."
• A/C "OFF," ENGINE COOLANT TEMPERATURE BELOW 94°C (201°F). IS FAN "ON"?
NO
YES
• USING TECH 1 SCAN TOOL ENTER "FIELD SERVICE MODE." IS FAN "ON"?
• DISCONNECT FAN CONTROL RELAY.
• JUMPER HARNESS CONNECTOR TERMINALS "85" AND "86" WITH A TEST LIGHT.
NO
YES
• DISCONNECT COOLING FAN CONTROL RELAY.
• PROBE HARNESS CONNECTOR TERMINALS "30" AND "86" WITH A TEST LIGHT TO GROUND. DOES LIGHT TURN "ON" FOR BOTH TERMINALS?
NON-A/C
NO TROUBLE FOUND.
WITH A/C
• EXIT "FIELD SERVICE MODE."
• ENGINE IDLING.
• A/C "ON." IS FAN "ON"?
LIGHT "ON"
CHECK FOR SHORT TO GROUND IN CKT 335. IF NOT GROUNDED, REPLACE ECM.
LIGHT "OFF"
CHECK CKT 532 FOR A SHORT TO VOLTAGE. IF OK, REPLACE COOLING FAN CONTROL RELAY.
YES
NO
YES
NO
• "FIELD SERVICE MODE STILL ENGAGED."
• PROBE HARNESS CONNECTOR TERMINAL "85" WITH A TEST LIGHT TO BATTERY VOLTAGE. DOES LIGHT COME "ON"?
REPAIR OPEN IN CIRCUIT THAT DID NOT LIGHT.
NO TROUBLE FOUND.
BACKPROBE ECM CONNECTOR TERMINAL "D8" WITH A TEST LIGHT TO GROUND.
LIGHT "OFF"
LIGHT "ON"
SEE A/C
FAULTY ECM CONNECTION OR ECM.
YES
NO
• JUMPER HARNESS CONNECTOR TERMINALS "30" AND "87". DOES FAN RUN?
CHECK CKT 335 FOR OPEN OR SHORT TO VOLTAGE AND ECM CONNECTIONS. IF OK, REPLACE ECM.
YES
NO
REPLACE RELAY.
OPEN CKT 532, FAULTY FAN MOTOR, OR FAULTY GROUND CKT 150.

GC108940022900AX

Fig. 122 Chart C-12, cooling fan diagnosis. 1994 Sunbird w/2.0L/4-121 (VIN H) engine

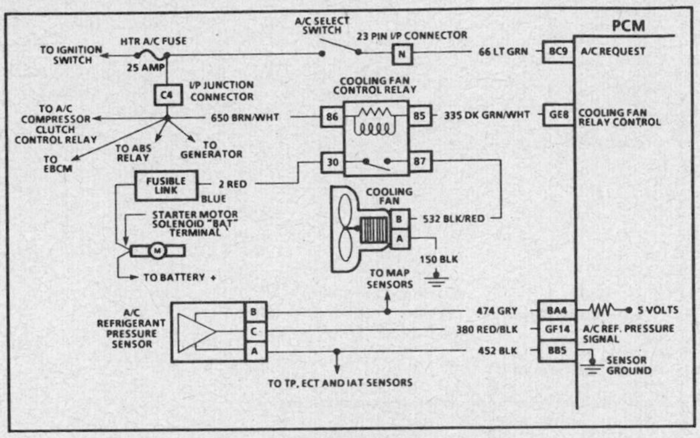
PCM
A/C SELECT SWITCH
23 PIN I/P CONNECTOR
HTR A/C FUSE
TO IGNITION SWITCH
25 AMP
66 LT GRN
BC9
A/C REQUEST
I/P JUNCTION CONNECTOR
C4
COOLING FAN CONTROL RELAY
TO A/C COMPRESSOR CLUTCH CONTROL RELAY
650 BRN/WHT
86
85
335 DK GRN/WHT
GE8
COOLING FAN RELAY CONTROL
TO ABS RELAY
TO GENERATOR
TO EBCM
30
87
FUSIBLE LINK
2 RED
BLUE
STARTER MOTOR SOLENOID "BAT" TERMINAL
COOLING FAN
532 BLK/RED
150 BLK
TO BATTERY +
TO MAP SENSORS
A/C REFRIGERANT PRESSURE SENSOR
474 GRY
BA4
5 VOLTS
380 RED/BLK
GF14
A/C REF. PRESSURE SIGNAL
452 BLK
BB5
SENSOR GROUND
TO TP, ECT AND IAT SENSORS

CHART C-12

(Page 1 of 2)
COOLING FAN CONTROL DIAGNOSIS
3.1L (VIN T) "J" CARLINE (MFI)

Circuit Description:

The electric cooling fan is controlled by the PCM based on inputs from the engine coolant temperature sensor, the A/C pressure sensor and vehicle speed. The PCM controls the fan by grounding CKT 335, which energizes the fan control relay. Battery voltage is then supplied to the fan motor.

The PCM grounds CKT 335 when engine coolant temperature is over about 109°C (228°F) or when A/C has been requested and the A/C pressure sensor indicates high A/C pressure, 200 psi (1380 kPa). Once the PCM turns the relay "ON," it will keep it "ON" for a minimum of 25 seconds or until vehicle speed exceeds 70 mph.

Also, if DTC 14 or 15 sets or the PCM is in backup, the fan will run at all times.

Chart Test Description: Number(s) below refer to circled number(s) on the diagnostic chart.

1. With the diagnostic terminal grounded, the cooling fan control driver will close, which should energize the fan control relay.
2. If the A/C fan control switch or circuit is open, the fan would run whenever A/C is requested.
3. With A/C clutch engaged, the A/C fan control switch should open when A/C high pressure exceeds about 200 psi (1380 kPa). This signal should cause the PCM to energize the fan control relay.
4. Disconnecting the A/C pressure sensor will cause a DTC 66 to set. After finishing this step, be sure to clear DTC(s).

Diagnostic Aids: If the owner complained of an overheating problem, it must be determined if the complaint was due to an actual boilover or the hot light (temperature gage) indicated over heating.

If the gage (light) indicates overheating but no boilover is detected, the gage circuit should be checked. The gage accuracy can also be checked by comparing the coolant sensor reading using a Tech 1 scan tool and comparing its reading with the gage reading.

If the engine is actually overheating and the gage indicates overheating but the cooling fan is not coming "ON," the ECT sensor has probably shifted out of calibration and should be replaced.

If the engine is overheating and the cooling fan is "ON," the cooling system should be checked.

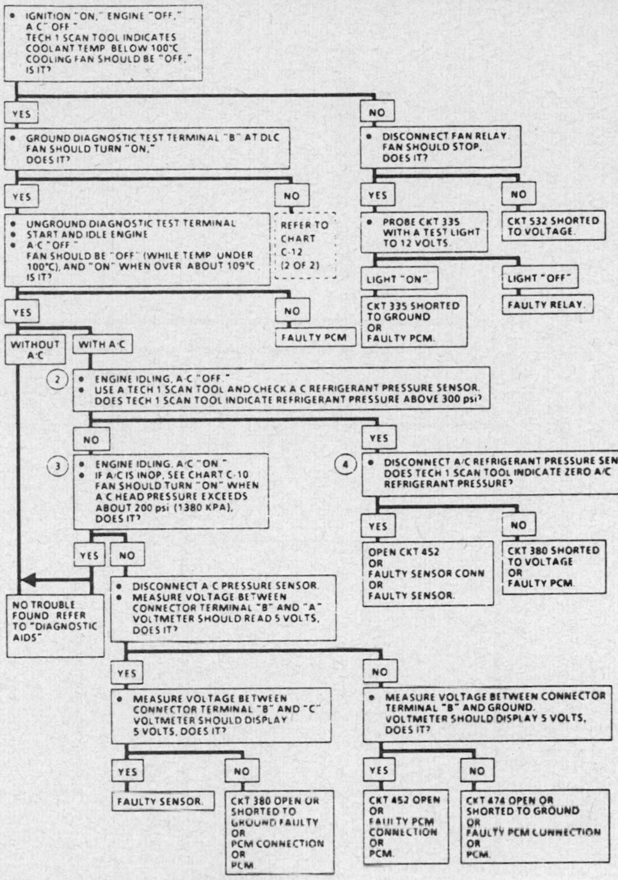
• IGNITION "ON," ENGINE "OFF," A/C "OFF." TECH 1 SCAN TOOL INDICATES COOLANT TEMP. BELOW 100°C. COOLING FAN SHOULD BE "OFF." IS IT?
YES
NO
① • GROUND DIAGNOSTIC TEST TERMINAL "B" AT DLC FAN SHOULD TURN "ON." DOES IT?
• DISCONNECT FAN RELAY. FAN SHOULD STOP. DOES IT?
YES
NO
YES
NO
• UNGROUND DIAGNOSTIC TEST TERMINAL • START AND IDLE ENGINE • A/C "OFF" FAN SHOULD BE "OFF" (WHILE TEMP. UNDER 100°C), AND "ON" WHEN OVER ABOUT 109°C. IS IT?
REFER TO CHART C-12 (2 OF 2)
• PROBE CKT 335 WITH A TEST LIGHT TO 12 VOLTS.
CKT 532 SHORTED TO VOLTAGE.
LIGHT "ON"
LIGHT "OFF"
YES
NO
FAULTY PCM
CKT 335 SHORTED TO GROUND OR FAULTY PCM.
FAULTY RELAY.
WITHOUT A/C
WITH A/C
② • ENGINE IDLING, A/C "OFF." • USE A TECH 1 SCAN TOOL AND CHECK A/C REFRIGERANT PRESSURE SENSOR. DOES TECH 1 SCAN TOOL INDICATE REFRIGERANT PRESSURE ABOVE 300 psi?
NO
YES
③ • ENGINE IDLING, A/C "ON." • IF A/C IS INOP, SEE CHART C-10 FAN SHOULD TURN "ON" WHEN A/C HEAD PRESSURE EXCEEDS ABOUT 200 psi (1380 KPA). DOES IT?
④ • DISCONNECT A/C REFRIGERANT PRESSURE SENSOR. DOES TECH 1 SCAN TOOL INDICATE ZERO A/C REFRIGERANT PRESSURE?
YES
NO
YES
NO
OPEN CKT 452 OR FAULTY SENSOR CONN OR FAULTY SENSOR.
CKT 380 SHORTED TO VOLTAGE OR FAULTY PCM.
NO TROUBLE FOUND. REFER TO "DIAGNOSTIC AIDS"
• DISCONNECT A/C PRESSURE SENSOR. • MEASURE VOLTAGE BETWEEN CONNECTOR TERMINAL "B" AND "A" VOLTMETER SHOULD READ 5 VOLTS. DOES IT?
YES
NO
• MEASURE VOLTAGE BETWEEN CONNECTOR TERMINAL "B" AND "C" VOLTMETER SHOULD DISPLAY 5 VOLTS. DOES IT?
• MEASURE VOLTAGE BETWEEN CONNECTOR TERMINAL "B" AND GROUND. VOLTMETER SHOULD DISPLAY 5 VOLTS. DOES IT?
YES
NO
YES
NO
FAULTY SENSOR.
CKT 380 OPEN OR SHORTED TO GROUND FAULTY OR PCM CONNECTION OR PCM.
CKT 452 OPEN OR FAULTY PCM CONNECTION OR PCM.
CKT 474 OPEN OR SHORTED TO GROUND OR FAULTY PCM CONNECTION OR PCM.
GC108940023001AX

Fig. 123 Chart C-12, cooling fan diagnosis (Part 1 of 2). 1994 Sunbird w/3.1L/V6-192 (VIN T) engine

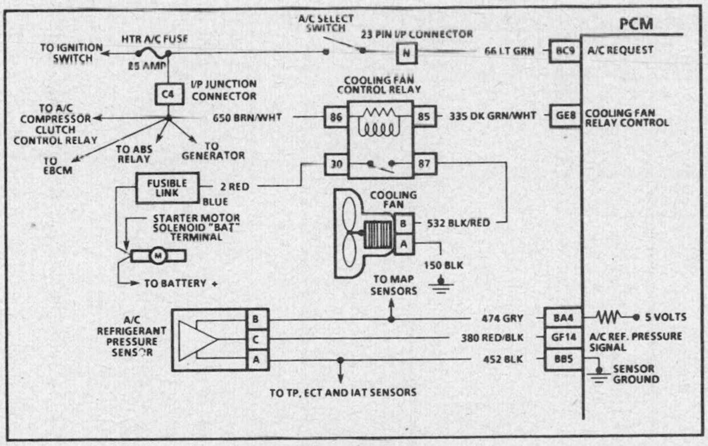
PCM
A/C SELECT SWITCH
23 PIN I/P CONNECTOR
HTR A/C FUSE
TO IGNITION SWITCH
25 AMP
66 LT GRN
BC9
A/C REQUEST
I/P JUNCTION CONNECTOR
C4
COOLING FAN CONTROL RELAY
TO A/C COMPRESSOR CLUTCH CONTROL RELAY
650 BRN/WHT
86
85
335 DK GRN/WHT
GE8
COOLING FAN RELAY CONTROL
TO ABS RELAY
TO GENERATOR
TO EBCM
30
87
FUSIBLE LINK
2 RED
BLUE
STARTER MOTOR SOLENOID "BAT" TERMINAL
COOLING FAN
532 BLK/RED
150 BLK
TO BATTERY +
TO MAP SENSORS
A/C REFRIGERANT PRESSURE SENSOR
474 GRY
BA4
5 VOLTS
380 RED/BLK
GF14
A/C REF. PRESSURE SIGNAL
452 BLK
BB5
SENSOR GROUND
TO TP, ECT AND IAT SENSORS

CHART C-12

(Page 2 of 2)
COOLING FAN CONTROL DIAGNOSIS
3.1L (VIN T) "J" CARLINE (MFI)

Chart Test Description: Number(s) below refer to circled number(s) on the diagnostic chart.

1. 12 volts should be available to both terminals "30" (CKT 2) and "87" (CKT 532) when the ignition is "ON."
2. This test checks the ability of the PCM to ground CKT 335.

The Malfunction Indicator Lamp (MIL) should also be flashing at this point.

3. If the fan does not turn "ON" at this point, CKT 532 or CKT 150 is open or the cooling fan motor is faulty.

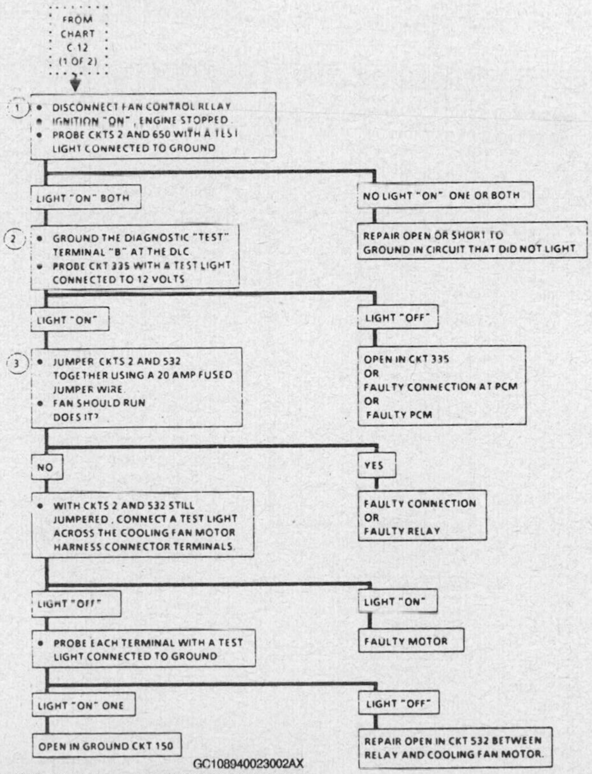
FROM CHART C-12 (1 OF 2)
① • DISCONNECT FAN CONTROL RELAY • IGNITION "ON", ENGINE STOPPED • PROBE CKTS 2 AND 650 WITH A TEST LIGHT CONNECTED TO GROUND
LIGHT "ON" BOTH
NO LIGHT "ON" ONE OR BOTH
REPAIR OPEN OR SHORT TO GROUND IN CIRCUIT THAT DID NOT LIGHT
② • GROUND THE DIAGNOSTIC "TEST" TERMINAL "B" AT THE DLC • PROBE CKT 335 WITH A TEST LIGHT CONNECTED TO 12 VOLTS
LIGHT "ON"
LIGHT "OFF"
③ • JUMPER CKTS 2 AND 532 TOGETHER USING A 20 AMP FUSED JUMPER WIRE. • FAN SHOULD RUN DOES IT?
OPEN IN CKT 335 OR FAULTY CONNECTION AT PCM OR FAULTY PCM
NO
YES
• WITH CKTS 2 AND 532 STILL JUMPERED, CONNECT A TEST LIGHT ACROSS THE COOLING FAN MOTOR HARNESS CONNECTOR TERMINALS.
FAULTY CONNECTION OR FAULTY RELAY
LIGHT "OFF"
LIGHT "ON"
• PROBE EACH TERMINAL WITH A TEST LIGHT CONNECTED TO GROUND
FAULTY MOTOR
LIGHT "ON" ONE
LIGHT "OFF"
OPEN IN GROUND CKT 150
REPAIR OPEN IN CKT 532 BETWEEN RELAY AND COOLING FAN MOTOR.
GC108940023002AX

Fig. 123 Chart C-12, cooling fan diagnosis (Part 2 of 2). 1994 Sunbird w/3.1L/V6-192 (VIN T) engine

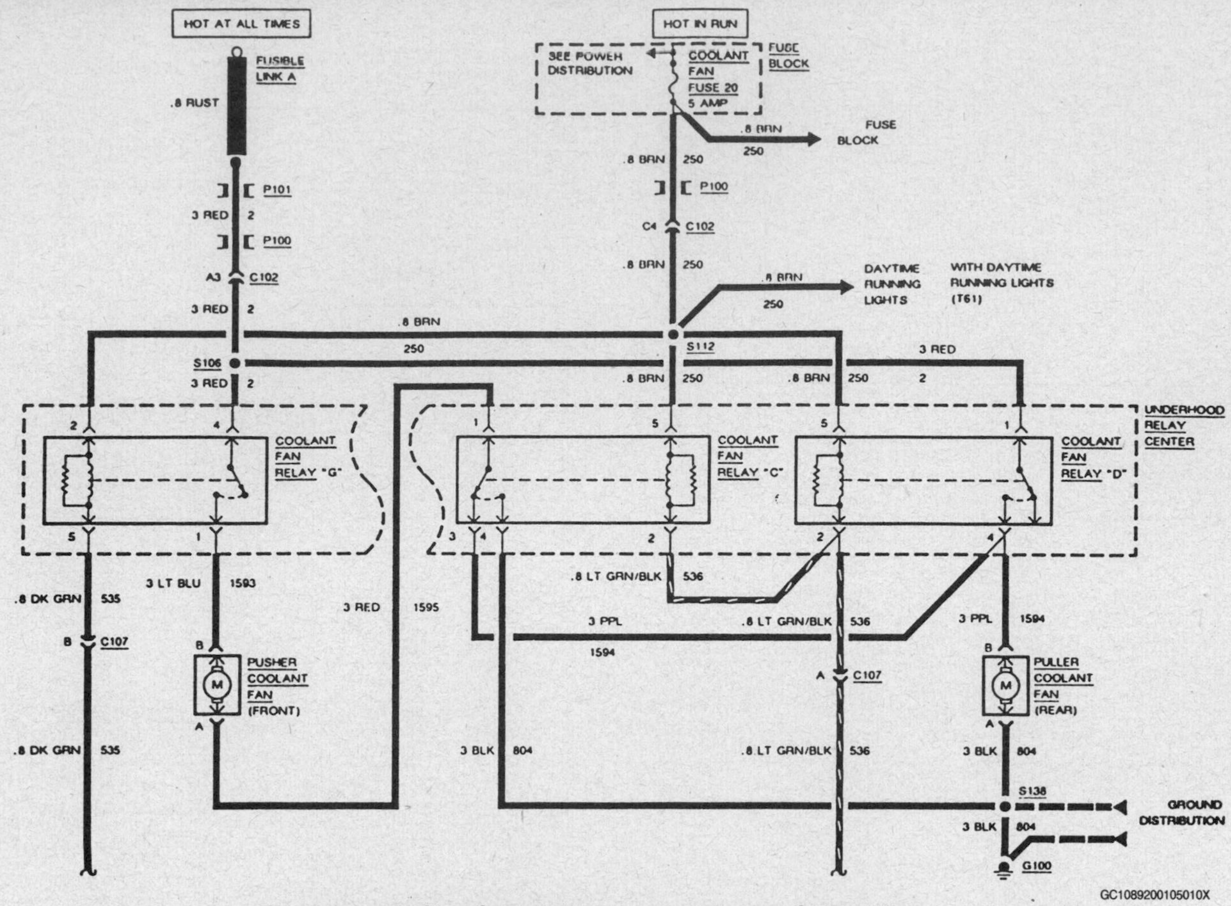
HOT AT ALL TIMES
HOT IN RUN
FUSIBLE LINK A
SEE POWER DISTRIBUTION
COOLANT FAN FUSE 20 5 AMP
FUSE BLOCK
DAYTIME RUNNING LIGHTS
WITH DAYTIME RUNNING LIGHTS (T61)
UNDERHOOD RELAY CENTER
COOLANT FAN RELAY "G"
COOLANT FAN RELAY "C"
COOLANT FAN RELAY "D"
PUSHER COOLANT FAN (FRONT)
PULLER COOLANT FAN (REAR)
GROUND DISTRIBUTION
G100
GC1089200105010X

Fig. 124 Cooling fan wiring circuit (Part 1 of 2). Riviera

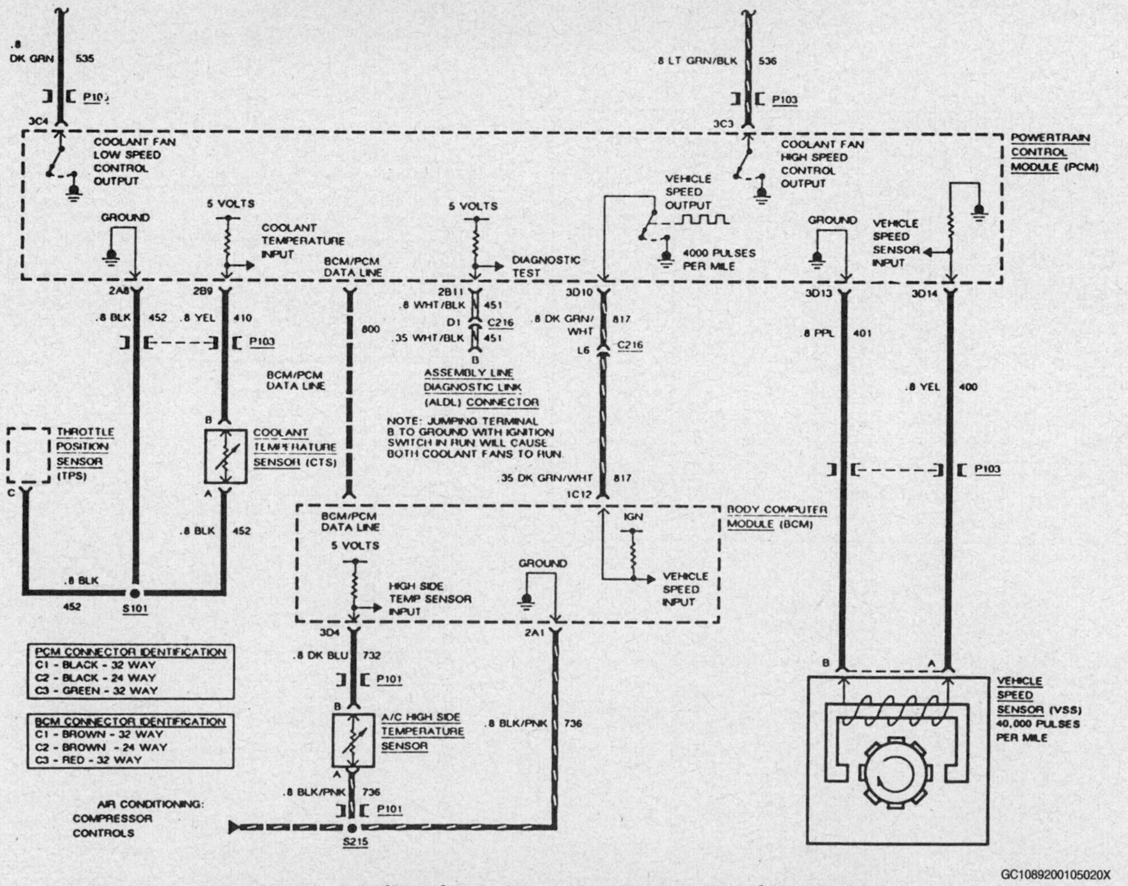
POWERTRAIN CONTROL MODULE (PCM)
COOLANT FAN LOW SPEED CONTROL OUTPUT
COOLANT FAN HIGH SPEED CONTROL OUTPUT
VEHICLE SPEED OUTPUT
4000 PULSES PER MILE
VEHICLE SPEED SENSOR INPUT
COOLANT TEMPERATURE INPUT
BCM/PCM DATA LINE
DIAGNOSTIC TEST
ASSEMBLY LINE DIAGNOSTIC LINK (ALDL) CONNECTOR
NOTE: JUMPING TERMINAL B TO GROUND WITH IGNITION SWITCH IN RUN WILL CAUSE BOTH COOLANT FANS TO RUN.
THROTTLE POSITION SENSOR (TPS)
COOLANT TEMPERATURE SENSOR (CTS)
BODY COMPUTER MODULE (BCM)
HIGH SIDE TEMP SENSOR INPUT
VEHICLE SPEED INPUT
PCM CONNECTOR IDENTIFICATION
C1 - BLACK - 32 WAY
C2 - BLACK - 24 WAY
C3 - GREEN - 32 WAY
BCM CONNECTOR IDENTIFICATION
C1 - BROWN - 32 WAY
C2 - BROWN - 24 WAY
C3 - RED - 32 WAY
A/C HIGH SIDE TEMPERATURE SENSOR
AIR CONDITIONING: COMPRESSOR CONTROLS
VEHICLE SPEED SENSOR (VSS) 40,000 PULSES PER MILE
GC1089200105020X

Fig. 124 Cooling fan wiring circuit (Part 2 of 2). Riviera

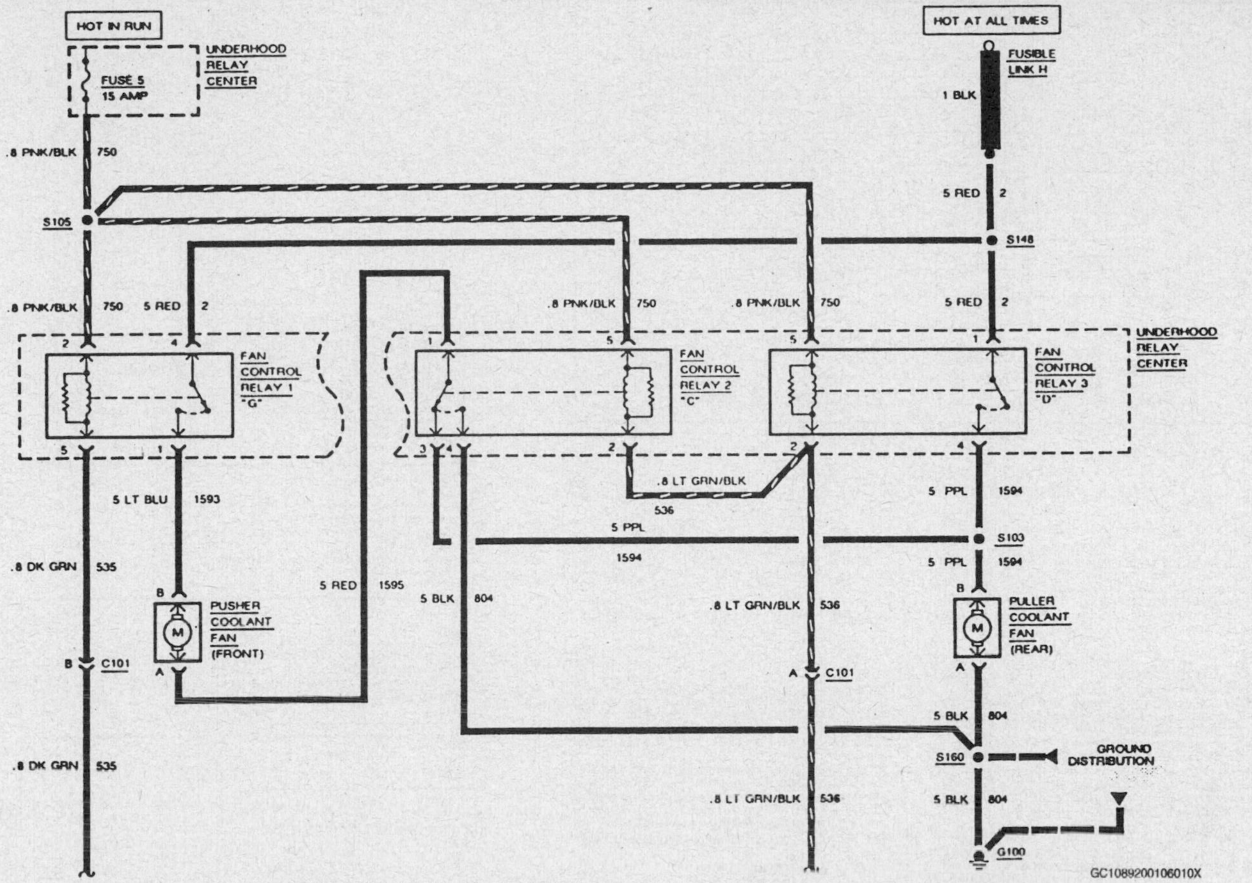
HOT IN RUN
UNDERHOOD RELAY CENTER
FUSE 5 15 AMP
HOT AT ALL TIMES
FUSIBLE LINK H
1 BLK
.8 PNK/BLK 750
5 RED 2
S105
S148
5 RED 2
FAN CONTROL RELAY 1 "G"
FAN CONTROL RELAY 2 "C"
FAN CONTROL RELAY 3 "D"
UNDERHOOD RELAY CENTER
5 LT BLU 1593
.8 LT GRN/BLK 536
5 PPL 1594
S103
.8 DK GRN 535
5 RED 1595
5 BLK 804
PUSHER COOLANT FAN (FRONT)
PULLER COOLANT FAN (REAR)
C101
S160
GROUND DISTRIBUTION
G100
GC1089200106010X

Fig. 125 Cooling fan wiring circuit (Part 1 of 2). 1992 Toronado & Trofeo

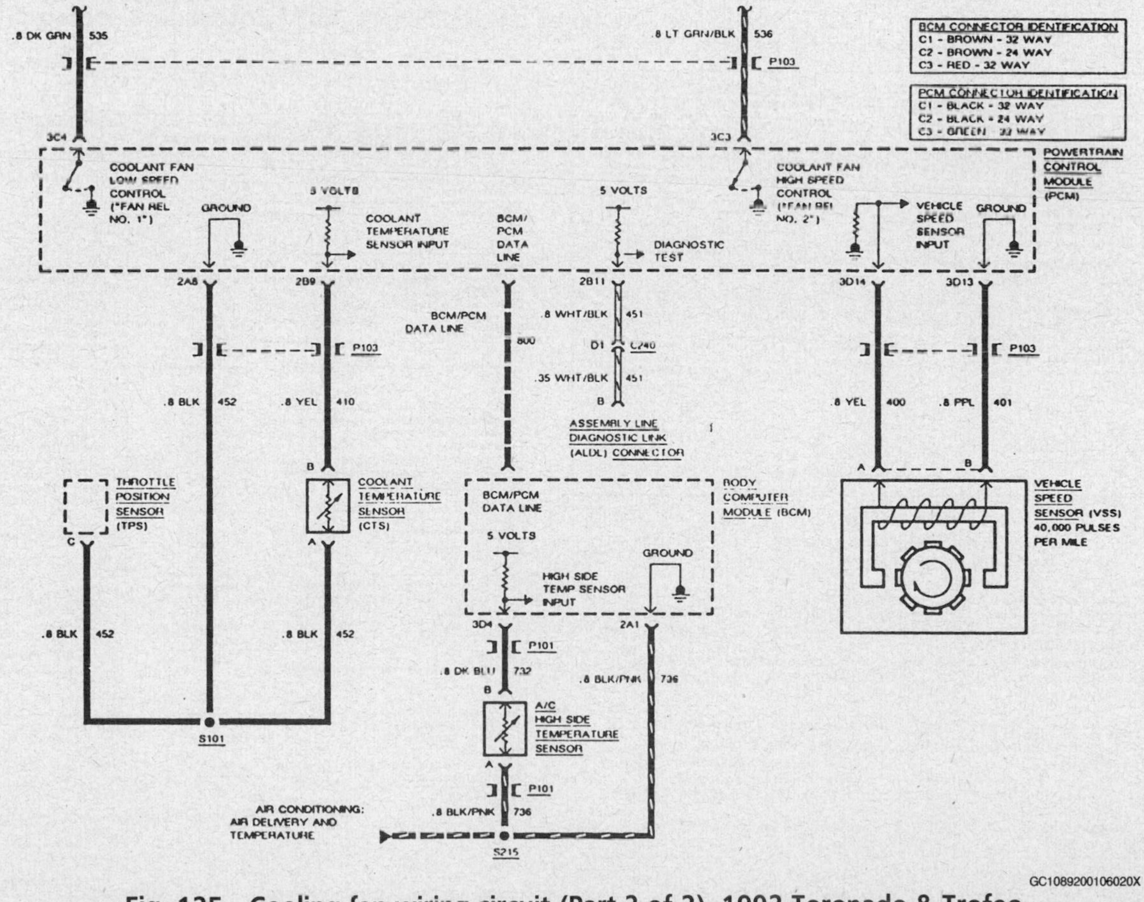
.8 DK GRN 535
.8 LT GRN/BLK 536
P103
BCM CONNECTOR IDENTIFICATION
C1 - BROWN - 32 WAY
C2 - BROWN - 24 WAY
C3 - RED - 32 WAY
PCM CONNECTOR IDENTIFICATION
C1 - BLACK - 32 WAY
C2 - BLACK - 24 WAY
C3 - GREEN - 32 WAY
POWERTRAIN CONTROL MODULE (PCM)
COOLANT FAN LOW SPEED CONTROL ("FAN REL NO. 1")
GROUND
5 VOLTS
COOLANT TEMPERATURE SENSOR INPUT
BCM/ PCM DATA LINE
DIAGNOSTIC TEST
COOLANT FAN HIGH SPEED CONTROL ("FAN REL NO. 2")
VEHICLE SPEED SENSOR INPUT
.8 BLK 452
.8 YEL 410
BCM/PCM DATA LINE 800
.8 WHT/BLK 451
C240
.35 WHT/BLK 451
ASSEMBLY LINE DIAGNOSTIC LINK (ALDL) CONNECTOR
.8 YEL 400
.8 PPL 401
THROTTLE POSITION SENSOR (TPS)
COOLANT TEMPERATURE SENSOR (CTS)
BODY COMPUTER MODULE (BCM)
HIGH SIDE TEMP SENSOR INPUT
VEHICLE SPEED SENSOR (VSS) 40,000 PULSES PER MILE
P101
.8 DK BLU 732
.8 BLK/PNK 736
A/C HIGH SIDE TEMPERATURE SENSOR
S101
AIR CONDITIONING: AIR DELIVERY AND TEMPERATURE
S215
GC1089200106020X

Fig. 125 Cooling fan wiring circuit (Part 2 of 2). 1992 Toronado & Trofeo

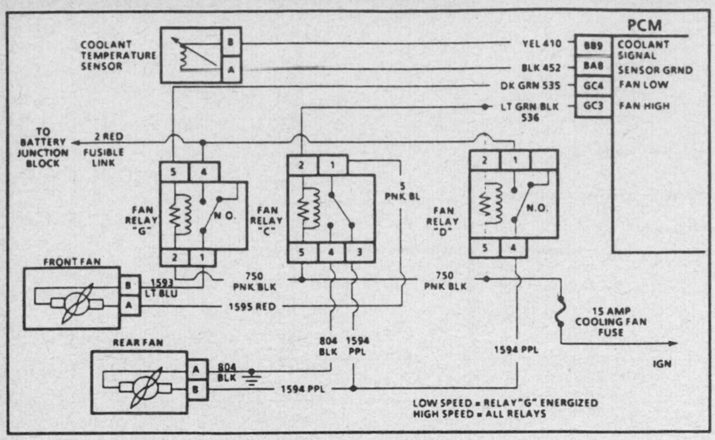
PCM
COOLANT TEMPERATURE SENSOR
YEL 410
BB9 COOLANT SIGNAL
BLK 452
BA8 SENSOR GRND
DK GRN 535
GC4 FAN LOW
LT GRN BLK 536
GC3 FAN HIGH
TO BATTERY JUNCTION BLOCK
2 RED
FUSIBLE LINK
FAN RELAY "G"
FAN RELAY "C"
FAN RELAY "D"
N.O.
5 PNK BL
FRONT FAN
1593 LT BLU
750 PNK BLK
1595 RED
15 AMP COOLING FAN FUSE
REAR FAN
804 BLK
1594 PPL
IGN
LOW SPEED = RELAY "G" ENERGIZED
HIGH SPEED = ALL RELAYS

CHART C–12A

COOLING FAN FUNCTIONAL CHECK
3800 (VIN L) "E" CARLINE (TPI)

Circuit Description:

The PCM and three relays are used to control the two cooling fans.

LO Speed Fans Operation- Low speed of both fans are controlled by the PCM The PCM energizes cooling fan relay "G" through terminal "GC4" when the coolant temperature exceeds 101°C (214°F) or when A/C high side refrigerant temperature exceeds 50°C (122°F).

High Speed Fans Operation- High speed of both fans are controlled by the PCM The PCM energizes all three relays when coolant temperature exceeds 108°C (226°F) or when A/C high side refrigerant temperature exceeds 65°C (149°F).

Test Description: Number(s) below refer to circled number(s) on the diagnostic chart.

1. Codes 14 or 15 could mean coolant system or sensor operation is not normal so fan(s) operation can't be checked correctly.
2. Selecting output tests, Fan 1 with the Tech 1 grounds fan relay "G" through the PCM fans should cycle "ON" and run at low speed.
3. Selecting output tests Fan 2 should cause the PCM to energize fan relays "G", "C", and "D". Both fans should run at high speed.

Diagnostic Aids:

An intermittent may be caused by a poor connection, rubbed through wire insulation, or a wire broken inside the insulation.

Check For:

- Poor Connection or Damaged Harness Inspect PCM harness connectors for backed out terminals "GC4" or "GC3", improper mating, broken locks, improperly formed or damaged terminals, poor terminal to wire connection, and damaged harness.
- Intermittent Test If connections and harness check OK, a digital voltmeter connected from affected terminal to ground while moving related connectors and wiring harness. If the failure is induced, the voltage reading will change.
- Mis-Scaled Coolant Temperature Sensor (CTS)
- Basic Cooling System Problem

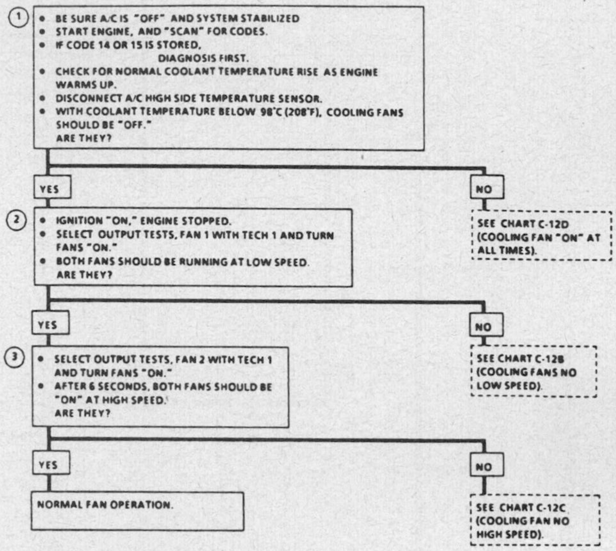
1
BE SURE A/C IS "OFF" AND SYSTEM STABILIZED
START ENGINE, AND "SCAN" FOR CODES.
IF CODE 14 OR 15 IS STORED, DIAGNOSIS FIRST.
CHECK FOR NORMAL COOLANT TEMPERATURE RISE AS ENGINE WARMS UP.
DISCONNECT A/C HIGH SIDE TEMPERATURE SENSOR.
WITH COOLANT TEMPERATURE BELOW 98°C (208°F), COOLING FANS SHOULD BE "OFF."
ARE THEY?
YES
NO
SEE CHART C-12D (COOLING FAN "ON" AT ALL TIMES).
2
IGNITION "ON," ENGINE STOPPED.
SELECT OUTPUT TESTS, FAN 1 WITH TECH 1 AND TURN FANS "ON."
BOTH FANS SHOULD BE RUNNING AT LOW SPEED.
ARE THEY?
YES
NO
SEE CHART C-12B (COOLING FANS NO LOW SPEED).
3
SELECT OUTPUT TESTS, FAN 2 WITH TECH 1 AND TURN FANS "ON."
AFTER 6 SECONDS, BOTH FANS SHOULD BE "ON" AT HIGH SPEED.
ARE THEY?
YES
NO
NORMAL FAN OPERATION.
SEE CHART C-12C (COOLING FAN NO HIGH SPEED).

GC1089100107000X

Fig. 126 Chart C-12A (Cooling fan functional check). Riviera, 1992 Toronado & Trofeo

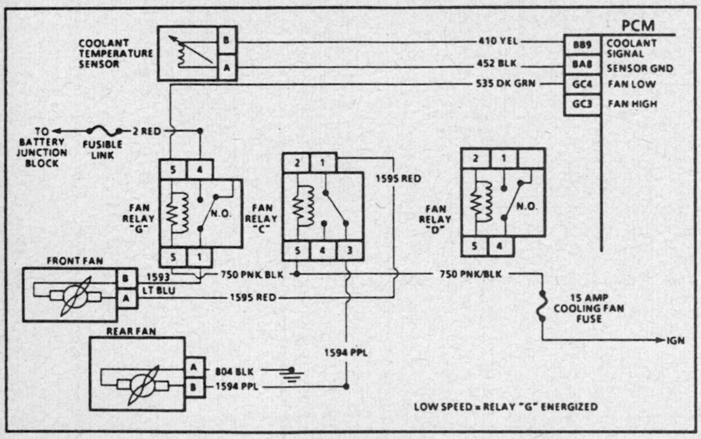
PCM
COOLANT TEMPERATURE SENSOR
410 YEL
BB9 COOLANT SIGNAL
452 BLK
BA8 SENSOR GND
535 DK GRN
GC4 FAN LOW
GC3 FAN HIGH
TO BATTERY JUNCTION BLOCK
FUSIBLE LINK
2 RED
1595 RED
FAN RELAY "G"
FAN RELAY "C"
FAN RELAY "D"
N.O.
FRONT FAN
1593 LT BLU
750 PNK BLK
750 PNK/BLK
1595 RED
15 AMP COOLING FAN FUSE
IGN
REAR FAN
1594 PPL
804 BLK
LOW SPEED = RELAY "G" ENERGIZED

CHART C-12B

COOLING FAN NO LOW SPEED
3800 (VIN L) "E" CARLINE (TPI)

Circuit Description:

The PCM and three relays are used to control the two cooling fans.

LO Speed Fans Operation - Low speed of both fans are controlled by the PCM. The PCM energizes cooling fan relay "G" through terminal "GC4" when the coolant temperature exceeds 101°C (214°F) or when A/C high side refrigerant temperature exceeds 50°C (122°F).

High Speed Fans Operation - High speed of both fans are controlled by the PCM. The PCM energizes all three relays, when coolant temperature exceeds 108°C (226°F) or when A/C high side refrigerant temperature exceeds 65°C (149°F).

NOTICE: Mechanization drawing above reflects only those circuits used for low speed fans.

Test Description: Number(s) below refer to circled number(s) on the diagnostic chart.

1. Test light should be "ON" because harness terminal "2" has B+ with ignition switch turned "ON." Terminal "4" has B+ all the time.
2. Test light "ON" validates relay "C", CKTs 1593, 1594, 1595 and 804.
3. Jumpering "1" to "4" of relay "G", removing relay "C" and touching a test light to terminal "1" validates the circuit up to relay "C". If light is "OFF," it is CKT 1593 or CKT 1595 to the front fan.
4. Test light "ON" validates CKTs 804 and 1594 to rear fan.

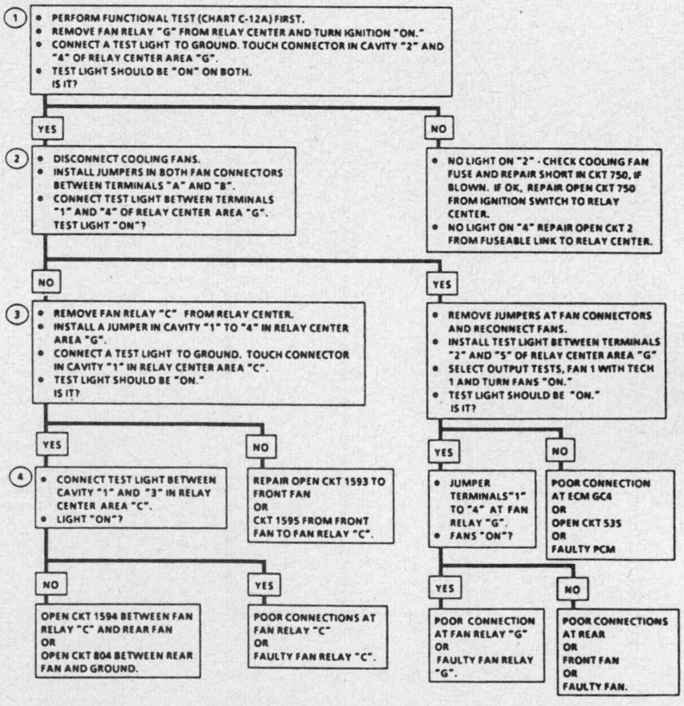
1
PERFORM FUNCTIONAL TEST (CHART C-12A) FIRST.
REMOVE FAN RELAY "G" FROM RELAY CENTER AND TURN IGNITION "ON."
CONNECT A TEST LIGHT TO GROUND. TOUCH CONNECTOR IN CAVITY "2" AND "4" OF RELAY CENTER AREA "G".
TEST LIGHT SHOULD BE "ON" ON BOTH.
IS IT?
YES
NO
2
DISCONNECT COOLING FANS.
INSTALL JUMPERS IN BOTH FAN CONNECTORS BETWEEN TERMINALS "A" AND "B".
CONNECT TEST LIGHT BETWEEN TERMINALS "1" AND "4" OF RELAY CENTER AREA "G".
TEST LIGHT "ON"?
NO LIGHT ON "2" - CHECK COOLING FAN FUSE AND REPAIR SHORT IN CKT 750, IF BLOWN. IF OK, REPAIR OPEN CKT 750 FROM IGNITION SWITCH TO RELAY CENTER.
NO LIGHT ON "4" REPAIR OPEN CKT 2 FROM FUSEABLE LINK TO RELAY CENTER.
NO
YES
3
REMOVE FAN RELAY "C" FROM RELAY CENTER.
INSTALL A JUMPER IN CAVITY "1" TO "4" IN RELAY CENTER AREA "G".
CONNECT A TEST LIGHT TO GROUND. TOUCH CONNECTOR IN CAVITY "1" IN RELAY CENTER AREA "C".
TEST LIGHT SHOULD BE "ON."
IS IT?
REMOVE JUMPERS AT FAN CONNECTORS AND RECONNECT FANS.
INSTALL TEST LIGHT BETWEEN TERMINALS "2" AND "5" OF RELAY CENTER AREA "G"
SELECT OUTPUT TESTS, FAN 1 WITH TECH 1 AND TURN FANS "ON."
TEST LIGHT SHOULD BE "ON."
IS IT?
YES
NO
YES
NO
4
CONNECT TEST LIGHT BETWEEN CAVITY "1" AND "3" IN RELAY CENTER AREA "C".
LIGHT "ON"?
REPAIR OPEN CKT 1593 TO FRONT FAN
OR
CKT 1595 FROM FRONT FAN TO FAN RELAY "C".
JUMPER TERMINALS "1" TO "4" AT FAN RELAY "G".
FANS "ON"?
POOR CONNECTION AT ECM GC4
OR
OPEN CKT 535
OR
FAULTY PCM
NO
YES
YES
NO
OPEN CKT 1594 BETWEEN FAN RELAY "C" AND REAR FAN
OR
OPEN CKT 804 BETWEEN REAR FAN AND GROUND.
POOR CONNECTIONS AT FAN RELAY "C"
OR
FAULTY FAN RELAY "C".
POOR CONNECTION AT FAN RELAY "G"
OR
FAULTY FAN RELAY "G".
POOR CONNECTIONS AT REAR
OR
FRONT FAN
OR
FAULTY FAN.

GC1089100108000X

Fig. 127 Chart C-12B (Cooling fan no low speed). Riviera, 1992 Toronado & Trofeo

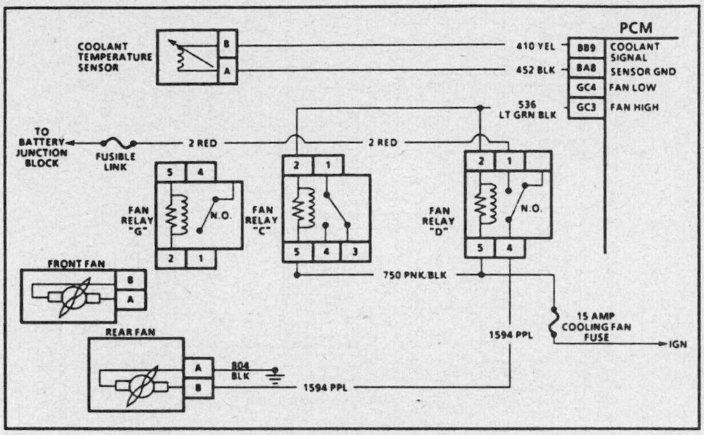

PCM
COOLANT TEMPERATURE SENSOR
B
A
410 YEL
452 BLK
BB9
BA8
GC4
GC3
COOLANT SIGNAL
SENSOR GND
FAN LOW
FAN HIGH
536 LT GRN BLK
TO BATTERY JUNCTION BLOCK
FUSIBLE LINK
2 RED
FAN RELAY "G"
FAN RELAY "C"
FAN RELAY "D"
N.O.
FRONT FAN
750 PNK/BLK
15 AMP COOLING FAN FUSE
1594 PPL
IGN
REAR FAN
804 BLK

CHART C-12C-A

COOLING FAN NO HIGH SPEED REAR FAN
3800 (VIN L) "E" CARLINE (TPI)

Circuit Description:

The PCM and three relays are used to control the two cooling fans.

LO Speed Fans Operation - Low speed of both fans are controlled by the PCM. The PCM energizes cooling fan relay "G" through terminal "GC4" when the coolant temperature exceeds 101°C (214°F) or when A/C high side refrigerant temperature exceeds 50°C (122°F).

High Speed Fans Operation - High speed of both fans are controlled by the PCM. The PCM energizes all three relays when coolant temperature exceeds 108°C (226°F) or when A/C high side refrigerant temperature exceeds 65°C (149°F).

Test Description: Number(s) below refer to circled number(s) on the diagnostic chart.

1. Test light should be "ON" because harness terminal "5" has B+ with ignition switch turned "ON." Terminal "1" has B+ all the time.
2. Test light should be "ON" with output tests, Fan 2 selected and cycled "ON" with the Tech 1.
3. Jumpering harness terminals "1" and "4" bypasses the relay. If fan runs, the relay is faulty.
4. Test light "ON" proves CKTs 1594 and 804 are OK, so fan motor is faulty.

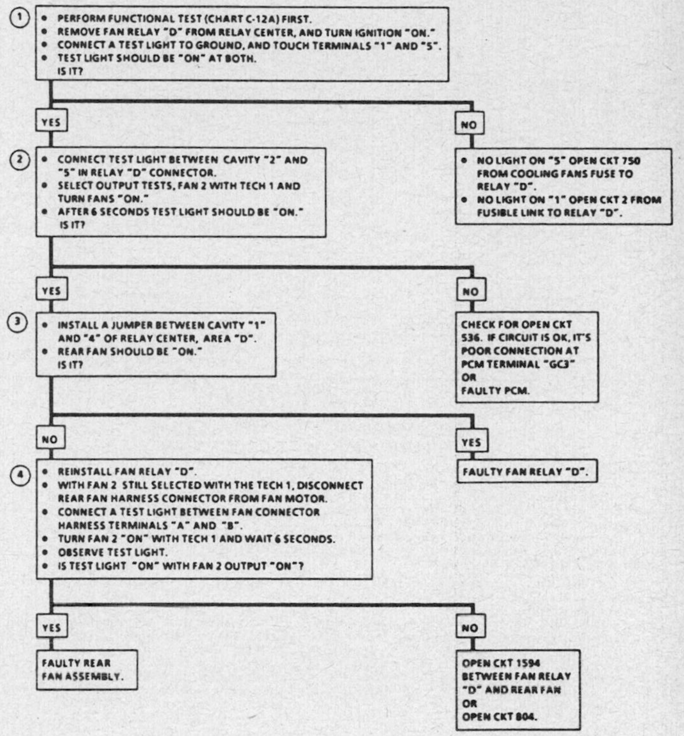

1
PERFORM FUNCTIONAL TEST (CHART C-12A) FIRST.
REMOVE FAN RELAY "D" FROM RELAY CENTER, AND TURN IGNITION "ON."
CONNECT A TEST LIGHT TO GROUND, AND TOUCH TERMINALS "1" AND "5".
TEST LIGHT SHOULD BE "ON" AT BOTH.
IS IT?
YES
NO
2
CONNECT TEST LIGHT BETWEEN CAVITY "2" AND "5" IN RELAY "D" CONNECTOR.
SELECT OUTPUT TESTS, FAN 2 WITH TECH 1 AND TURN FANS "ON."
AFTER 6 SECONDS TEST LIGHT SHOULD BE "ON."
IS IT?
NO LIGHT ON "5" OPEN CKT 750 FROM COOLING FANS FUSE TO RELAY "D".
NO LIGHT ON "1" OPEN CKT 2 FROM FUSIBLE LINK TO RELAY "D".
YES
NO
3
INSTALL A JUMPER BETWEEN CAVITY "1" AND "4" OF RELAY CENTER, AREA "D".
REAR FAN SHOULD BE "ON."
IS IT?
CHECK FOR OPEN CKT 536. IF CIRCUIT IS OK, IT'S POOR CONNECTION AT PCM TERMINAL "GC3" OR FAULTY PCM.
NO
YES
4
REINSTALL FAN RELAY "D".
WITH FAN 2 STILL SELECTED WITH THE TECH 1, DISCONNECT REAR FAN HARNESS CONNECTOR FROM FAN MOTOR.
CONNECT A TEST LIGHT BETWEEN FAN CONNECTOR HARNESS TERMINALS "A" AND "B".
TURN FAN 2 "ON" WITH TECH 1 AND WAIT 6 SECONDS.
OBSERVE TEST LIGHT.
IS TEST LIGHT "ON" WITH FAN 2 OUTPUT "ON"?
FAULTY FAN RELAY "D".
YES
NO
FAULTY REAR FAN ASSEMBLY.
OPEN CKT 1594 BETWEEN FAN RELAY "D" AND REAR FAN OR OPEN CKT 804.

GC1089100109000X

Fig. 128 Chart C-12C-A (Cooling fan no high speed rear fan). RIviera, 1992 Toronado & Trofeo

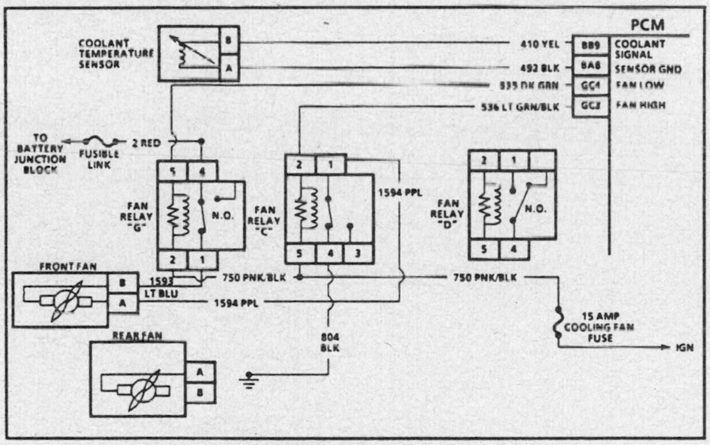

PCM
COOLANT TEMPERATURE SENSOR
B
A
410 YEL
492 BLK
335 DK GRN
536 LT GRN/BLK
BB9
BA8
GC4
GC3
COOLANT SIGNAL
SENSOR GND
FAN LOW
FAN HIGH
TO BATTERY JUNCTION BLOCK
FUSIBLE LINK
2 RED
FAN RELAY "G"
FAN RELAY "C"
FAN RELAY "D"
N.O.
1594 PPL
FRONT FAN
1593 LT BLU
750 PNK/BLK
15 AMP COOLING FAN FUSE
IGN
REAR FAN
804 BLK

CHART C-12C-B

COOLING FAN NO HIGH SPEED FRONT FAN
3800 (VIN L) "E" CARLINE (TPI)

Circuit Description:

The PCM and three relays are used to control the two cooling fans.

LO Speed Fans Operation - Low speed of both fans are controlled by the PCM. The PCM energizes cooling fan relay "G" through terminal "GC4" when the coolant temperature exceeds 101°C (214°F) or when A/C high side refrigerant temperature exceeds 50°C (122°F).

High Speed Fans Operation - High speed of both fans are controlled by the PCM. The PCM energizes all three relays when coolant temperature exceeds 108°C (226°F) or when A/C high side refrigerant temperature exceeds 65°C (149°F).

Test Description: Numbers below refer to circled numbers on the diagnostic chart.

1. Test light should be "ON" because harness terminal "5" has B+ with ignition switch turned "ON."
2. Test light "ON" validates circuit 536 from PCM to relay "C".
3. Jumpering "1" to "4" of relay "C" bypasses fan relay.
4. Test light "ON" validates all circuits. If light is "ON," front fan motor is faulty. If light is "OFF," it is a problem with the ground CKT 804.

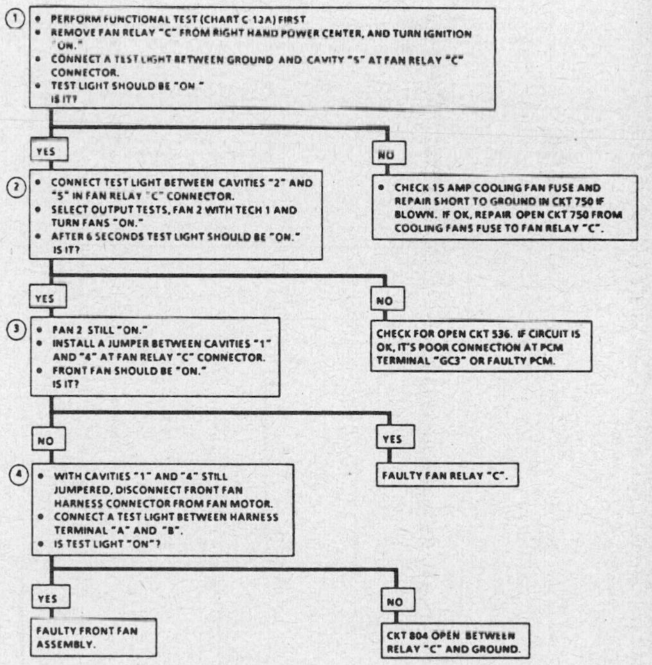

1
PERFORM FUNCTIONAL TEST (CHART C-13A) FIRST
REMOVE FAN RELAY "C" FROM RIGHT HAND POWER CENTER, AND TURN IGNITION "ON."
CONNECT A TEST LIGHT BETWEEN GROUND AND CAVITY "5" AT FAN RELAY "C" CONNECTOR.
TEST LIGHT SHOULD BE "ON."
IS IT?
YES
NO
2
CONNECT TEST LIGHT BETWEEN CAVITIES "2" AND "5" IN FAN RELAY "C" CONNECTOR.
SELECT OUTPUT TESTS, FAN 2 WITH TECH 1 AND TURN FANS "ON."
AFTER 6 SECONDS TEST LIGHT SHOULD BE "ON."
IS IT?
CHECK 15 AMP COOLING FAN FUSE AND REPAIR SHORT TO GROUND IN CKT 750 IF BLOWN. IF OK, REPAIR OPEN CKT 750 FROM COOLING FANS FUSE TO FAN RELAY "C".
YES
NO
3
FAN 2 STILL "ON."
INSTALL A JUMPER BETWEEN CAVITIES "1" AND "4" AT FAN RELAY "C" CONNECTOR.
FRONT FAN SHOULD BE "ON."
IS IT?
CHECK FOR OPEN CKT 536. IF CIRCUIT IS OK, IT'S POOR CONNECTION AT PCM TERMINAL "GC3" OR FAULTY PCM.
NO
YES
4
WITH CAVITIES "1" AND "4" STILL JUMPERED, DISCONNECT FRONT FAN HARNESS CONNECTOR FROM FAN MOTOR.
CONNECT A TEST LIGHT BETWEEN HARNESS TERMINAL "A" AND "B".
IS TEST LIGHT "ON"?
FAULTY FAN RELAY "C".
YES
NO
FAULTY FRONT FAN ASSEMBLY.
CKT 804 OPEN BETWEEN RELAY "C" AND GROUND.

GC1089100110000X

Fig. 129 Chart C-12C-B (Cooling fan no high speed front fan). Riviera, 1992 Toronado & Trofeo

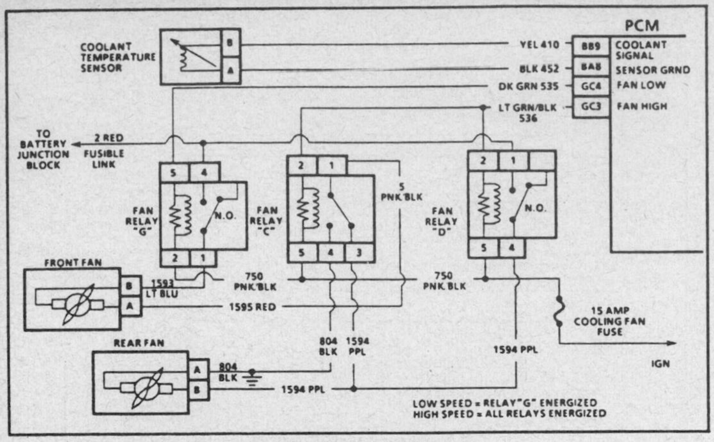
PCM
COOLANT TEMPERATURE SENSOR
B
A
YEL 410
BB9
COOLANT SIGNAL
BLK 452
BA8
SENSOR GRND
DK GRN 535
GC4
FAN LOW
LT GRN/BLK 536
GC3
FAN HIGH
TO BATTERY JUNCTION BLOCK
2 RED
FUSIBLE LINK
FAN RELAY "G"
N.O.
FAN RELAY "C"
5 PNK/BLK
FAN RELAY "D"
N.O.
FRONT FAN
1593 LT BLU
750 PNK/BLK
750 PNK/BLK
1595 RED
15 AMP COOLING FAN FUSE
REAR FAN
804 BLK
1594 PPL
804 BLK
1594 PPL
1594 PPL
IGN
LOW SPEED = RELAY "G" ENERGIZED
HIGH SPEED = ALL RELAYS ENERGIZED

CHART C-12D

COOLING FAN(S) "ON" AT ALL TIMES
3800 (VIN L) "E" CARLINE (TPI)

Circuit Description:

The PCM and three relays are used to control the two cooling fans.

LO Speed Fans Operation - Low speed of both fans are controlled by the PCM. The PCM energizes cooling fan relay "G" through terminal "GC4" when the coolant temperature exceeds 101°C (214°F) or when A/C high side refrigerant temperature exceeds 50°C (122°F).

High Speed Fans Operation - High speed of both fans are controlled by the PCM. The PCM energizes all three relays when coolant temperature exceeds 108°C (226°F) or when A/C high side refrigerant temperature exceeds 65°C (149°F).

Test Description: Number(s) below refer to circled number(s) on the diagnostic chart.

1. Fans run when key is "OFF."
2. Fans should not run when engine coolant temperature is below 101°C (214°F).
3. Disconnecting the A/C high side temperature sensor will disable the BCM to PCM request due to the A/C high side temperature.
4. Defines fan operation based on coolant temperature only.

Diagnostic Aids:

Cooling fans should be "OFF" if:

1. Coolant temperature is less than 98°C (208°F).
2. A/C high side temperature is less than 50°C (122°F).

NOTE: On-board diagnostics may assist in diagnosing; monitor the following parameters: ED04 and BD21 are coolant temperature.

BD27 is A/C high side temperature sensor.

Disconnecting the A/C high side temperature sensor should result in BD27 reading less than -30°C (-30°F)

Disconnecting the coolant temperature sensor should cause BD21 to read less than -30°C (-30°F) also. If not, see Code 14 or 15

BD27 should read about 50°C (122°F) when A/C system high side pressure is approximately 160 psi. Comparing these might isolate a bad sensor.

NOTE: Normal cooling fan operation requires low speed if:
Engine is running, vehicle speed is less than 45 mph and coolant temperature exceeds 101°C (214°F) or A/C high side temperature is greater than 50°C (122°F).

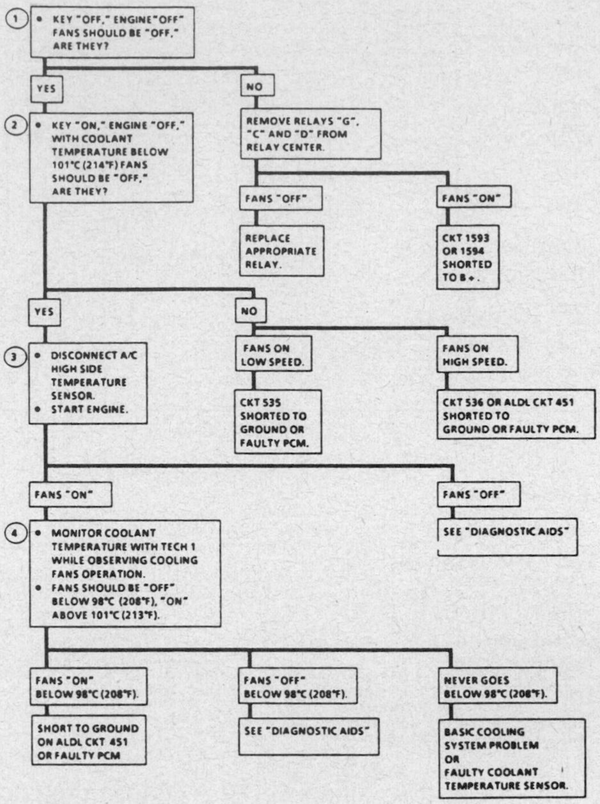
1
KEY "OFF," ENGINE "OFF" FANS SHOULD BE "OFF," ARE THEY?
YES
NO
2
KEY "ON," ENGINE "OFF," WITH COOLANT TEMPERATURE BELOW 101°C (214°F) FANS SHOULD BE "OFF," ARE THEY?
REMOVE RELAYS "G", "C" AND "D" FROM RELAY CENTER.
FANS "OFF"
FANS "ON"
REPLACE APPROPRIATE RELAY.
CKT 1593 OR 1594 SHORTED TO B+.
YES
NO
3
DISCONNECT A/C HIGH SIDE TEMPERATURE SENSOR.
START ENGINE.
FANS ON LOW SPEED.
FANS ON HIGH SPEED.
CKT 535 SHORTED TO GROUND OR FAULTY PCM.
CKT 536 OR ALDL CKT 451 SHORTED TO GROUND OR FAULTY PCM.
FANS "ON"
FANS "OFF"
SEE "DIAGNOSTIC AIDS"
4
MONITOR COOLANT TEMPERATURE WITH TECH 1 WHILE OBSERVING COOLING FANS OPERATION.
FANS SHOULD BE "OFF" BELOW 98°C (208°F), "ON" ABOVE 101°C (213°F).
FANS "ON" BELOW 98°C (208°F).
FANS "OFF" BELOW 98°C (208°F).
NEVER GOES BELOW 98°C (208°F).
SHORT TO GROUND ON ALDL CKT 451 OR FAULTY PCM
SEE "DIAGNOSTIC AIDS"
BASIC COOLING SYSTEM PROBLEM OR FAULTY COOLANT TEMPERATURE SENSOR.

GC1089100111000X

Fig. 130 Chart C-12D (Cooling fan/fans on at all times). Riviera, 1992 Toronado & Trofeo

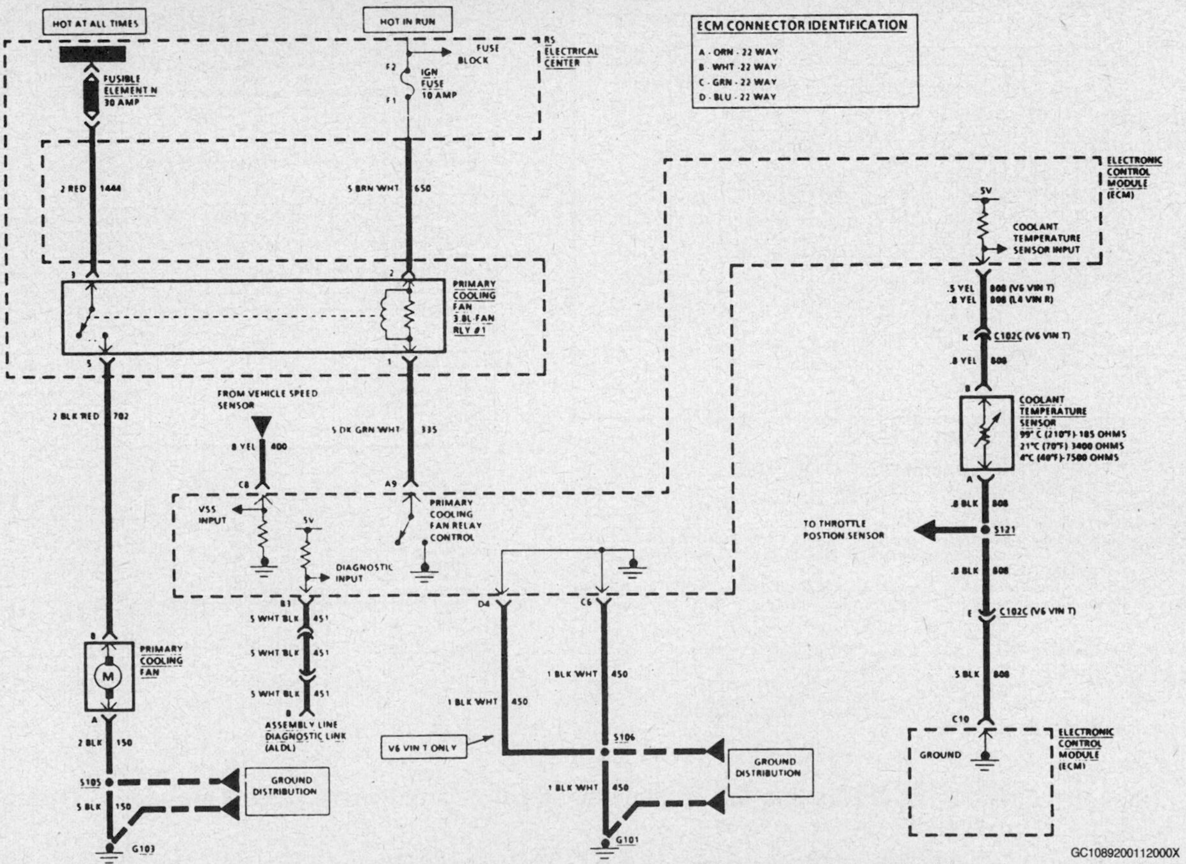
HOT AT ALL TIMES
HOT IN RUN
FUSIBLE ELEMENT N 30 AMP
FUSE BLOCK
F2
IGN FUSE 10 AMP
F1
RS ELECTRICAL CENTER
ECM CONNECTOR IDENTIFICATION
A - ORN - 22 WAY
B - WHT - 22 WAY
C - GRN - 22 WAY
D - BLU - 22 WAY
2 RED
1444
5 BRN WHT
650
3
2
PRIMARY COOLING FAN 3.8L FAN RLY #1
5
1
2 BLK RED
702
FROM VEHICLE SPEED SENSOR
8 YEL
400
5 DK GRN WHT
335
C8
A9
VSS INPUT
5V
PRIMARY COOLING FAN RELAY CONTROL
DIAGNOSTIC INPUT
B3
D4
C6
5 WHT BLK
451
5 WHT BLK
451
5 WHT BLK
451
B
ASSEMBLY LINE DIAGNOSTIC LINK (ALDL)
B
PRIMARY COOLING FAN
A
2 BLK
150
S105
GROUND DISTRIBUTION
5 BLK
150
G103
1 BLK WHT
450
1 BLK WHT
450
V6 VIN T ONLY
S106
GROUND DISTRIBUTION
1 BLK WHT
450
G101
ELECTRONIC CONTROL MODULE (ECM)
5V
COOLANT TEMPERATURE SENSOR INPUT
.5 YEL
808 (V6 VIN T)
.8 YEL
808 (L4 VIN R)
K
C102C (V6 VIN T)
.8 YEL
808
B
COOLANT TEMPERATURE SENSOR
99° C (210°F)-185 OHMS
21°C (70°F) 3400 OHMS
4°C (40°F)-7500 OHMS
A
.8 BLK
808
TO THROTTLE POSTION SENSOR
S121
.8 BLK
808
E
C102C (V6 VIN T)
5 BLK
808
C10
GROUND
ELECTRONIC CONTROL MODULE (ECM)

GC1089200112000X

Fig. 131 Cooling fan wiring circuit. 1992 Lumina less A/C

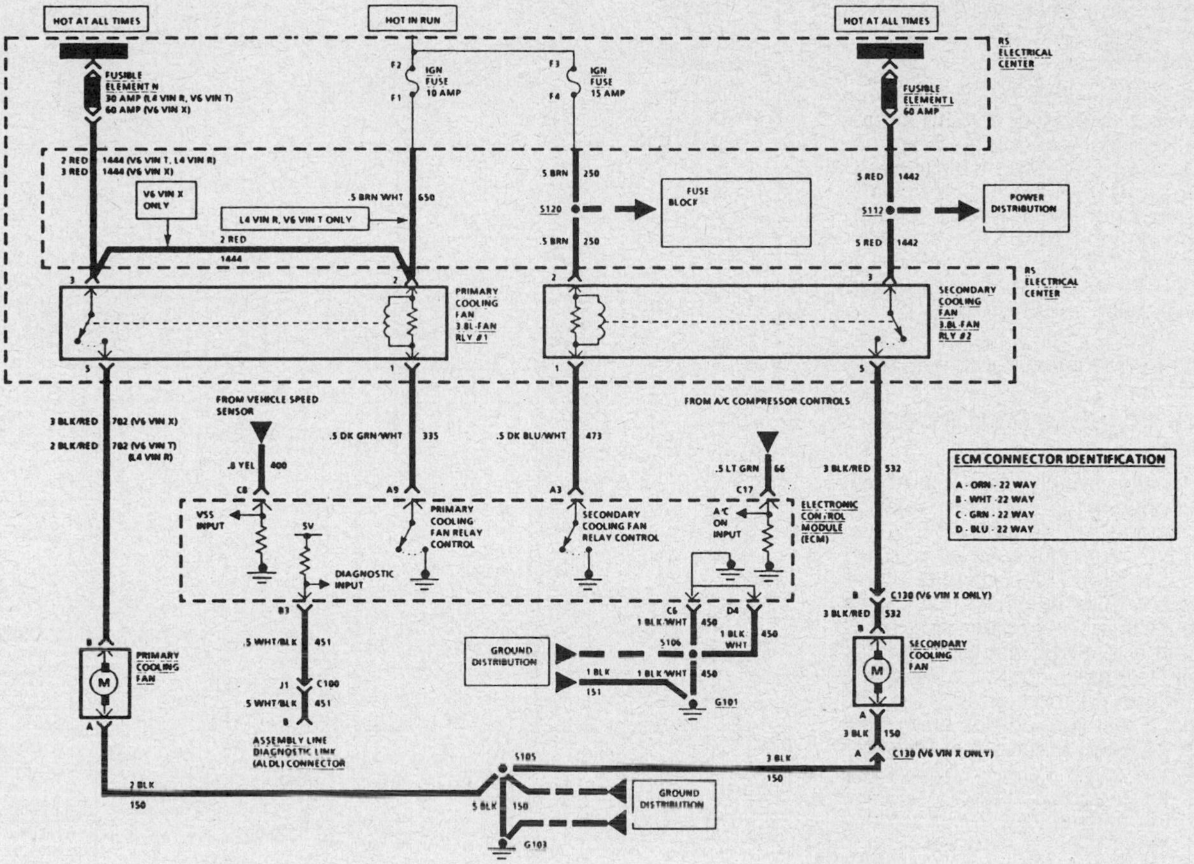

HOT AT ALL TIMES
HOT IN RUN
HOT AT ALL TIMES
FUSIBLE ELEMENT N
30 AMP (L4 VIN R, V6 VIN T)
60 AMP (V6 VIN X)
IGN FUSE 10 AMP
IGN FUSE 15 AMP
FUSIBLE ELEMENT L 60 AMP
RS ELECTRICAL CENTER
V6 VIN X ONLY
L4 VIN R, V6 VIN T ONLY
FUSE BLOCK
POWER DISTRIBUTION
PRIMARY COOLING FAN 3.8L-FAN RLY #1
SECONDARY COOLING FAN 3.8L-FAN RLY #2
FROM VEHICLE SPEED SENSOR
FROM A/C COMPRESSOR CONTROLS
VSS INPUT
DIAGNOSTIC INPUT
PRIMARY COOLING FAN RELAY CONTROL
SECONDARY COOLING FAN RELAY CONTROL
A/C ON INPUT
ELECTRONIC CONTROL MODULE (ECM)
ECM CONNECTOR IDENTIFICATION
A - ORN - 22 WAY
B - WHT - 22 WAY
C - GRN - 22 WAY
D - BLU - 22 WAY
PRIMARY COOLING FAN
SECONDARY COOLING FAN
GROUND DISTRIBUTION
ASSEMBLY LINE DIAGNOSTIC LINK (ALDL) CONNECTOR
G101
G103

GC1089200113010X

Fig. 132 Cooling fan wiring circuit (Part 1 Of 2). 1992 Lumina w/A/C

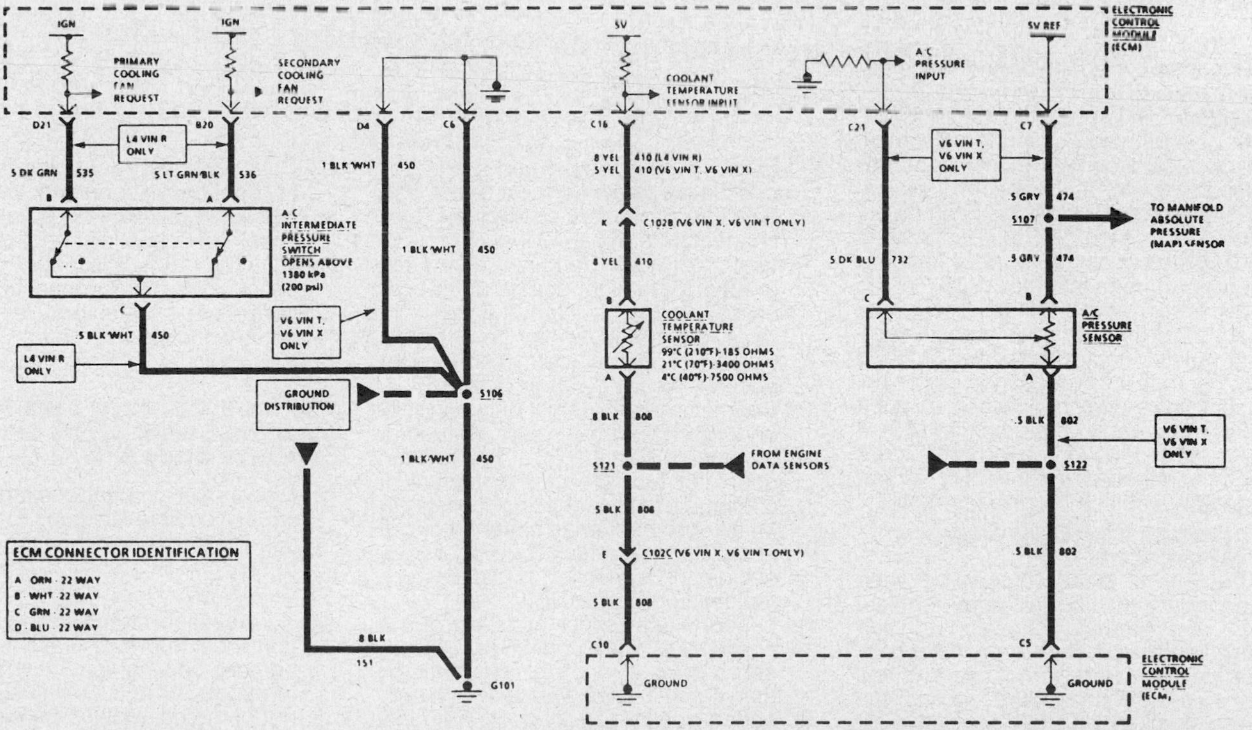

ELECTRONIC CONTROL MODULE (ECM)
PRIMARY COOLING FAN REQUEST
SECONDARY COOLING FAN REQUEST
COOLANT TEMPERATURE SENSOR INPUT
A/C PRESSURE INPUT
L4 VIN R ONLY
A/C INTERMEDIATE PRESSURE SWITCH OPENS ABOVE 1380 kPa (200 psi)
V6 VIN T, V6 VIN X ONLY
GROUND DISTRIBUTION
COOLANT TEMPERATURE SENSOR
99°C (210°F)-185 OHMS
21°C (70°F)-3400 OHMS
4°C (40°F)-7500 OHMS
TO MANIFOLD ABSOLUTE PRESSURE (MAP) SENSOR
A/C PRESSURE SENSOR
FROM ENGINE DATA SENSORS
ECM CONNECTOR IDENTIFICATION
A ORN 22 WAY
B WHT 22 WAY
C GRN 22 WAY
D BLU 22 WAY
G101
GROUND

GC1089200113020X

Fig. 132 Cooling fan wiring circuit (Part 2 Of 2). 1992 Lumina w/A/C

Secondary Cooling Or Generator Fan Runs Continuously w/Engine Coolant Cool & A/C Mode Selector Off

1. Turn ignition switch to Run position, disconnect secondary cooling fan relay at RH electrical center, then connect test lamp between terminals 3 (RED) and 1 (DK BLU/WHT). If test lamp does not light, replace secondary cooling fan relay.
2. If test lamp lights, check 473 (DK BLU/WHT) wire for short to ground, if good, problem is ECM related.

1993

Refer to **Fig. 133** when performing diagnostic procedures.

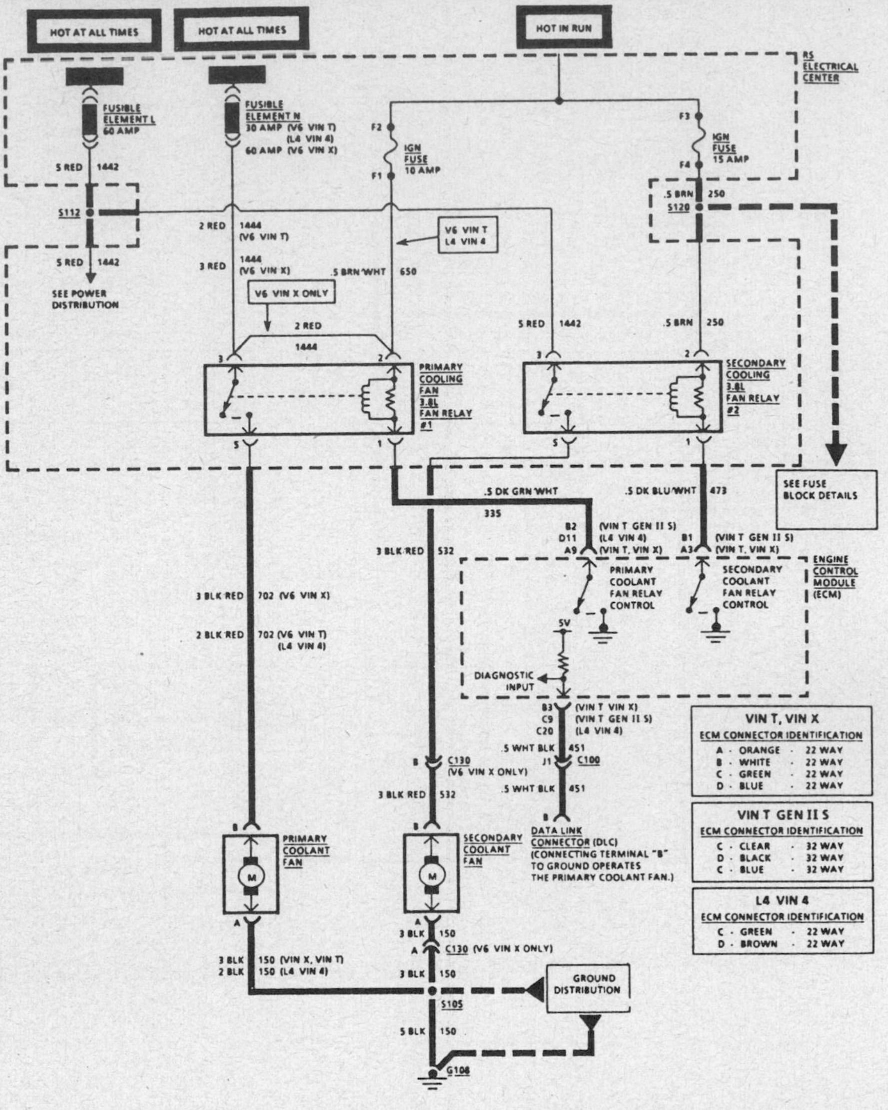

HOT AT ALL TIMES
HOT AT ALL TIMES
HOT IN RUN
RH ELECTRICAL CENTER
FUSIBLE ELEMENT L 60 AMP
FUSIBLE ELEMENT N 30 AMP (V6 VIN T) (L4 VIN 4) 60 AMP (V6 VIN X)
IGN FUSE 10 AMP
IGN FUSE 15 AMP
SEE POWER DISTRIBUTION
V6 VIN T L4 VIN 4
V6 VIN X ONLY
PRIMARY COOLING FAN 3.8L FAN RELAY #1
SECONDARY COOLING 3.8L FAN RELAY #2
SEE FUSE BLOCK DETAILS
ENGINE CONTROL MODULE (ECM)
PRIMARY COOLANT FAN RELAY CONTROL
SECONDARY COOLANT FAN RELAY CONTROL
DIAGNOSTIC INPUT
PRIMARY COOLANT FAN
SECONDARY COOLANT FAN
DATA LINK CONNECTOR (DLC) (CONNECTING TERMINAL "B" TO GROUND OPERATES THE PRIMARY COOLANT FAN.)
GROUND DISTRIBUTION
VIN T, VIN X
ECM CONNECTOR IDENTIFICATION
A - ORANGE - 22 WAY
B - WHITE - 22 WAY
C - GREEN - 22 WAY
D - BLUE - 22 WAY
VIN T GEN II S
ECM CONNECTOR IDENTIFICATION
C - CLEAR - 32 WAY
D - BLACK - 32 WAY
C - BLUE - 32 WAY
L4 VIN 4
ECM CONNECTOR IDENTIFICATION
C - GREEN - 22 WAY
D - BROWN - 22 WAY

GC1089300114000X

Fig. 133 Cooling fan wiring circuit. 1993 Lumina

Primary Cooling Fan Does Not Run

1. With ignition switch in the Run position, connect a fused jumper between DLC connector terminal "B" and ground. If cooling fan does not run, proceed to step 2. If cooling fan runs, problem is ECM related.
2. Remove primary cooling fan relay. Connect a test light between primary cooling fan relay connector terminal "3" and ground, then terminal "2" and ground. If test light comes on in both cases, proceed to step 3. If test light does not come on in both cases, check for a poor connection. If connection is satisfactory, check circuits (650) and (1444) for an open.
3. Connect a fused jumper between cooling fan relay connector terminals "3" and "5." If primary cooling fan does not run, proceed to step 4. If cooling fan runs, check circuit (335) for an open or short to battery. If circuit (335) is satisfactory, check for a poor connection. If connection is satisfactory, replace cooling fan relay.
4. Leave fused jumper attached and disconnect primary cooling fan electrical connector. Connect a test light between cooling fan connector terminal "B" and ground. If test light comes on, proceed to step 5. If test lamp does not come on, check for poor connection or an open in circuit (702).
5. With fused jumper still attached, connect a test light between primary cooling fan connector terminals "A" and "B." If test light does not come on, check for a poor connection or open in primary cooling fan circuit (150). If test light does come on, check for poor connection. If connection is satisfactory, replace cooling fan motor.

Secondary Cooling Fan Does Not Run

1. Attached a fused jumper between secondary cooling fan relay terminal "1" and ground, then turn ignition switch to the Run position. If secondary cooling fan does not run, proceed to step 2. If secondary cooling fan runs, check for an open in circuit (473) or a poor connection at ECM connector "A" terminal "3." If circuit and connection are satisfactory, problem is ECM related.
2. Remove fused jumper and secondary cooling fan relay. Connect a test light between secondary cooling fan relay connector terminal "3" and ground, then between terminal "2" and ground. If test light comes on in both cases, proceed to step 3. If test light does not come on in both cases. Check for a poor connection or an open in circuits (250) or (1442).
3. Connect a fused jumper between secondary cooling fan relay connector terminals "3" and "5." If cooling fan does not run, proceed to step 4. If cooling fan runs, check circuit (473) for an open or short to battery. If circuit is satisfactory, check for a poor connection. If connection is satisfactory, replace cooling fan relay.
4. Leave fused jumper attached at the cooling fan relay connector. Disconnect secondary cooling fan connector, then connect a test light between secondary cooling fan connector terminal "B" and ground. If test light comes on, proceed to step 5. If test light does not come on, check for a poor connection or an open in circuit (532).
5. Connect a test light between secondary cooling fan connector terminals "A and "B." If test light does not come on, check for a poor connection or open in circuit (150). If test light comes on, check for a poor connection. If connection is satisfactory, replace secondary cooling fan motor.

Primary Cooling Fan Runs Continuously With Engine Coolant Cool & A/C Off

1. Disconnect primary cooling fan relay No. 1. If cooling fan stops running, proceed to step 2. If cooling fan continues to run, check circuit (702) for a short to battery.
2. Turn ignition switch to the Run position, then connect a test light between primary cooling fan relay connector terminals "1" and "3." If test light does not come on, replace primary cooling fan relay. If test light comes on, check circuit (335) for a short to ground. If circuit is satisfactory, problem is ECM related.

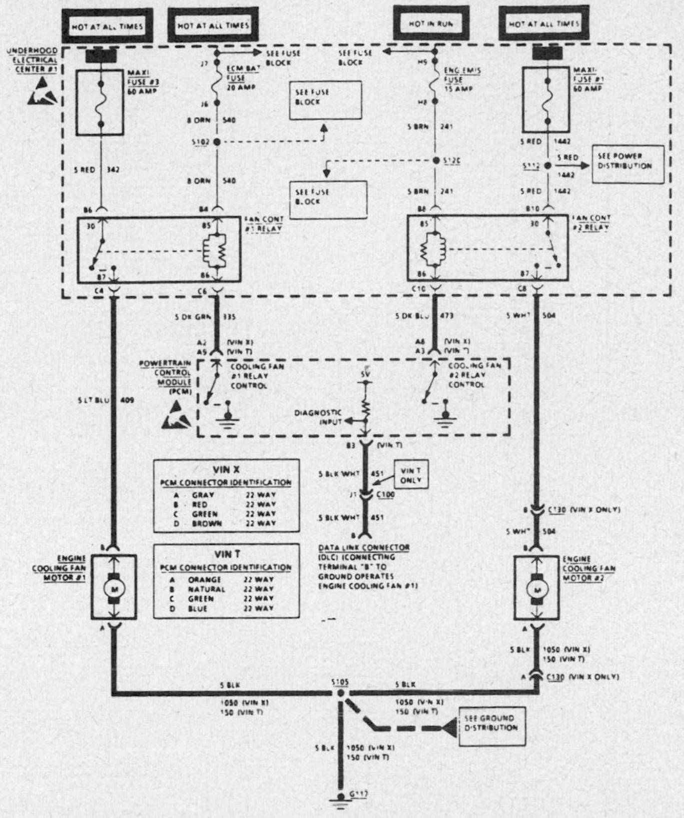
HOT AT ALL TIMES
HOT AT ALL TIMES
HOT IN RUN
HOT AT ALL TIMES
VIN X
VIN T

GC1089400234000X

Fig. 134 Cooling fan wiring circuit. 1994 Lumina

Secondary Cooling Fan Runs Continuously With Engine Coolant Cool & A/C Off

1. Disconnect secondary cooling fan relay No. 2. If cooling fan stops running, proceed to step 2. If cooling fan continues to run, check circuit (532) for a short to battery.
2. Turn ignition switch to the Run position, then connect a test light between secondary cooling fan relay connector terminals "1" and "3." If test light does not come on, replace secondary cooling fan relay. If test light does come on, check circuit (473) for a short to ground. If circuit is satisfactory, problem is ECM related.

1994

Refer to **Figs. 134 through 139** when performing diagnostic procedures.

PRIZM

1992

Refer to **Figs. 140 through 143** when performing diagnostic procedures.

1993

Refer to **Figs. 144 through 148** when performing diagnostic procedures on this system.

1994

Refer to **Figs. 149 and 150** when performing diagnostic procedures.

STORM

Refer to **Figs. 151 and 152** to perform diagnostic procedures on this system.

COMPONENT REPLACEMENT

Cooling Fan

METRO

1. Disconnect battery ground cable.
2. Drain cooling system and disconnect upper radiator hose from radiator.
3. Disconnect fan motor electrical connector.
4. Raise and support vehicle, then remove one lower mounting bolt from fan shroud.
5. Lower vehicle and remove two upper cooling fan mounting bolts, then remove fan from vehicle.
6. Reverse procedure to install.

BERETTA & CORSICA

1992–93

2.3L/4-138 Engine

1. Disconnect battery ground cable.
2. Disconnect electrical connectors from motor and fan frame.
3. Remove fan assembly from radiator.
4. Reverse procedure to install. **Torque** attaching bolts to 7 ft. lbs.

2.2L/4-134 & 3.1L/V6-192 Engines

1. Disconnect battery ground cable.
2. Remove air cleaner, intake ductwork and bracket.
3. Disconnect electrical connectors, then remove upper and lower mounting bolts.
4. Remove fan assembly.
5. Reverse procedure to install. **Torque** mounting bolts to 8 ft. lbs.

1994

2.2L/4–134 & 2.3L/4-138 Engines

1. Disconnect battery ground cable.
2. Disconnect electrical wiring from motor and fan frame.
3. Remove fan assembly from radiator.
4. Reverse procedure to install. **Torque** attaching bolts to 7 ft. lbs.

3.1L/V6-192 Engine

1. Disconnect battery ground cable.
2. Drain cooling system.
3. Remove cooling fan mounting bolt.
4. Disconnect electrical connector from fan.
5. Remove inlet hose from radiator.
6. Remove radiator mounting bolt.
7. Disconnect windshield washer fill tube from bottle.
8. Remove vacuum tank and bracket.
9. Remove cooling fan.
10. Reverse procedure to install.

CENTURY, CUTLASS CIERA & CUTLASS CRUISER

1992–93

1. Disconnect battery ground cable.
2. Remove engine strut brace bolts from upper tie bar and rotate strut and brace rearward. **To prevent shearing of rubber bushing(s) loosen bolt(s) on strut before rotating.**
3. Disconnect wiring harness from motor and the fan frame.
4. Remove fan frame attaching bolts, then the fan assembly.
5. Reverse procedure to install.

1994

2.2L/4–134 Engine

1. Remove air cleaner and resonator assembly.
2. Disconnect cooing fan electrical connector.
3. Remove cooling fan mounting bolts and the fan.

3.1L/V6–192 Engine

1. To replace primary fan, proceed as follows:
   a. Remove air cleaner and resonator assembly.
   b. Cooling fan electrical connector.
   c. Cooling fan mounting bolts and fan.
   d. Reverse procedure to install.
2. To replace auxiliary fan, proceed as follows:
   a. Disconnect battery ground cable.
   b. Remove grille.
   c. Disconnect electrical connector from fan.
   d. Remove front end support upper bolts.

Continued on page 17-119

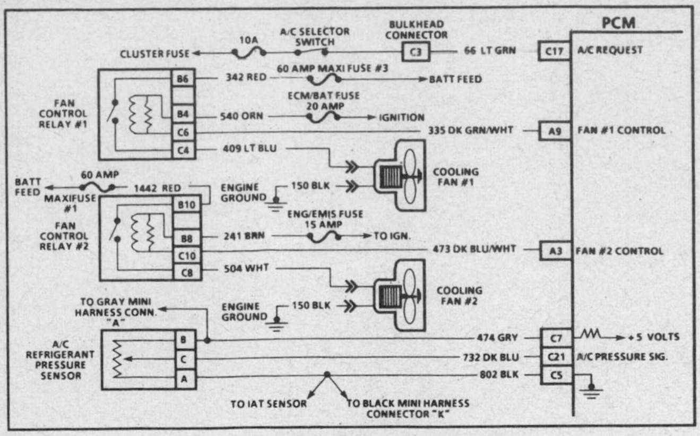

PCM
CLUSTER FUSE
10A
A/C SELECTOR SWITCH
BULKHEAD CONNECTOR
C3
66 LT GRN
C17
A/C REQUEST
B6
342 RED
60 AMP MAXI FUSE #3
BATT FEED
FAN CONTROL RELAY #1
B4
540 ORN
ECM/BAT FUSE 20 AMP
IGNITION
C6
335 DK GRN/WHT
A9
FAN #1 CONTROL
C4
409 LT BLU
COOLING FAN #1
BATT FEED
60 AMP
MAXIFUSE #1
1442 RED
ENGINE GROUND
150 BLK
B10
ENG/EMIS FUSE 15 AMP
FAN CONTROL RELAY #2
B8
241 BRN
TO IGN.
C10
473 DK BLU/WHT
A3
FAN #2 CONTROL
C8
504 WHT
COOLING FAN #2
TO GRAY MINI HARNESS CONN. "A"
ENGINE GROUND
150 BLK
A/C REFRIGERANT PRESSURE SENSOR
B
474 GRY
C7
+5 VOLTS
C
732 DK BLU
C21
A/C PRESSURE SIG.
A
802 BLK
C5
TO IAT SENSOR
TO BLACK MINI HARNESS CONNECTOR "K"

CHART C-12

(Page 1 of 2)

COOLING FAN CONTROL DIAGNOSIS 3.1L (VIN T) "W" CARLINE (MFI)

Circuit Description:

The primary and secondary electric cooling fan(s) are controlled by the PCM, based on inputs from the Engine Coolant Temperature (ECT) sensor, the A/C control switches, vehicle speed and state of the A/C pressure sensor. The PCM controls the fan(s) by grounding CKT 335 and/or CKT 473, which energizes the fan control relay. Battery voltage is then supplied to the fan motor.

The PCM grounds CKT 335 and/or CKT 473 when engine coolant temperature is over about 106°C (223°F), or when A/C has been requested and the A/C pressure is about 1380 kPa (200 psi). Once the PCM turns the relay "ON," it will keep it "ON" for a minimum of 30 seconds, or until vehicle speed exceeds 70 mph (40 mph for secondary fan).

Also, if DTC 14 or 15 sets or the PCM is in back up, the primary fan will run at all time.

Chart Test Description: Number(s) below refer to circled number(s) on the diagnostic chart.

1. With the diagnostic terminal grounded, the cooling fan control driver(s) will close, which should energize the fan control relay(s).
2. If the A/C pressure is above 300 psi (2069 kPa) or circuit is open, the fan would run whenever A/C is requested.
3. With A/C clutch engaged and the A/C refrigerant pressure sensor is functioning properly, the fan should come "ON" when pressure exceeds about 1380 kPa (200 psi). This signal should cause the PCM to energize the fan control relay(s).
4. This will determine if the A/C pressure sensor is faulty or if the PCM or circuitry is faulty.

Diagnostic Aids: If the owner complained of an overheating problem, it must be determined if the complaint was due to an actual boilover, a hot light or temp. gage indicated over heating.

If the gage or light indicates overheating, but no boilover is detected, the gage circuit should be checked. The gage accuracy can also be checked by comparing the coolant sensor reading using a Tech 1 scan tool and comparing its reading with the gage reading. If the engine is actually overheating and the gage indicates overheating but the cooling fan is not coming "ON," the coolant sensor has probably shifted out of calibration and should be replaced.

If the engine is overheating, and the cooling fan is "ON," the cooling system should be checked.

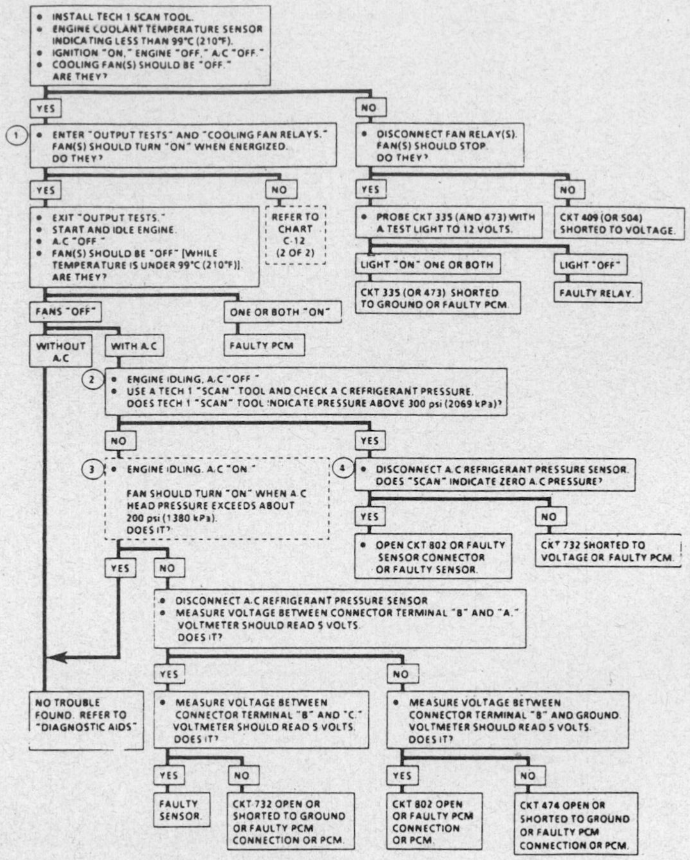

• INSTALL TECH 1 SCAN TOOL.
• ENGINE COOLANT TEMPERATURE SENSOR INDICATING LESS THAN 99°C (210°F).
• IGNITION "ON," ENGINE "OFF," A/C "OFF."
• COOLING FAN(S) SHOULD BE "OFF." ARE THEY?
YES
NO
1
• ENTER "OUTPUT TESTS" AND "COOLING FAN RELAYS." FAN(S) SHOULD TURN "ON" WHEN ENERGIZED. DO THEY?
• DISCONNECT FAN RELAY(S). FAN(S) SHOULD STOP. DO THEY?
YES
NO
YES
NO
• EXIT "OUTPUT TESTS."
• START AND IDLE ENGINE.
• A/C "OFF."
• FAN(S) SHOULD BE "OFF" (WHILE TEMPERATURE IS UNDER 99°C (210°F)). ARE THEY?
REFER TO CHART C-12 (2 OF 2)
• PROBE CKT 335 (AND 473) WITH A TEST LIGHT TO 12 VOLTS.
CKT 409 (OR 504) SHORTED TO VOLTAGE.
LIGHT "ON" ONE OR BOTH
LIGHT "OFF"
CKT 335 (OR 473) SHORTED TO GROUND OR FAULTY PCM.
FAULTY RELAY.
FANS "OFF"
ONE OR BOTH "ON"
WITHOUT A/C
WITH A/C
FAULTY PCM
2
• ENGINE IDLING, A/C "OFF."
• USE A TECH 1 "SCAN" TOOL AND CHECK A/C REFRIGERANT PRESSURE. DOES TECH 1 "SCAN" TOOL INDICATE PRESSURE ABOVE 300 psi (2069 kPa)?
NO
YES
3
• ENGINE IDLING, A/C "ON."
FAN SHOULD TURN "ON" WHEN A/C HEAD PRESSURE EXCEEDS ABOUT 200 psi (1380 kPa). DOES IT?
4
• DISCONNECT A/C REFRIGERANT PRESSURE SENSOR. DOES "SCAN" INDICATE ZERO A/C PRESSURE?
YES
NO
• OPEN CKT 802 OR FAULTY SENSOR CONNECTOR OR FAULTY SENSOR.
CKT 732 SHORTED TO VOLTAGE OR FAULTY PCM.
YES
NO
• DISCONNECT A/C REFRIGERANT PRESSURE SENSOR
• MEASURE VOLTAGE BETWEEN CONNECTOR TERMINAL "B" AND "A." VOLTMETER SHOULD READ 5 VOLTS. DOES IT?
YES
NO
NO TROUBLE FOUND. REFER TO "DIAGNOSTIC AIDS"
• MEASURE VOLTAGE BETWEEN CONNECTOR TERMINAL "B" AND "C." VOLTMETER SHOULD READ 5 VOLTS. DOES IT?
• MEASURE VOLTAGE BETWEEN CONNECTOR TERMINAL "B" AND GROUND. VOLTMETER SHOULD READ 5 VOLTS. DOES IT?
YES
NO
YES
NO
FAULTY SENSOR.
CKT 732 OPEN OR SHORTED TO GROUND OR FAULTY PCM CONNECTION OR PCM.
CKT 802 OPEN OR FAULTY PCM CONNECTION OR PCM.
CKT 474 OPEN OR SHORTED TO GROUND OR FAULTY PCM CONNECTION OR PCM.

GC108940023501AX

Fig. 135 Chart C-12, cooling fan diagnosis (Part 1 of 2). 1994 Lumina w/3.1L/V6–192 (VIN T) engine

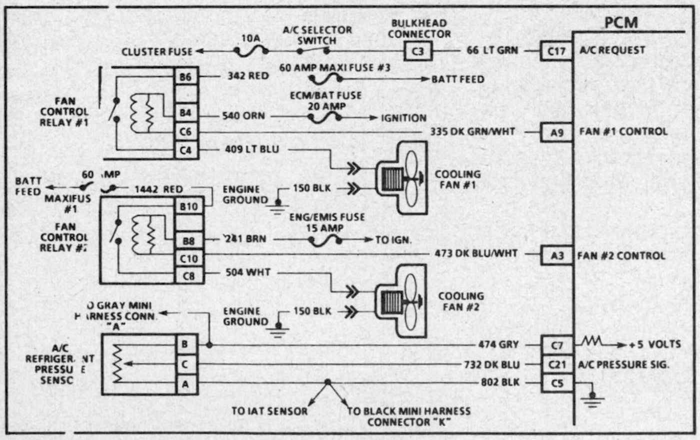

PCM
CLUSTER FUSE
10A
A/C SELECTOR SWITCH
BULKHEAD CONNECTOR
C3
66 LT GRN
C17
A/C REQUEST
B6
342 RED
60 AMP MAXI FUSE #3
BATT FEED
FAN CONTROL RELAY #1
B4
540 ORN
ECM/BAT FUSE 20 AMP
IGNITION
C6
335 DK GRN/WHT
A9
FAN #1 CONTROL
C4
409 LT BLU
COOLING FAN #1
BATT FEED
1442 RED
ENGINE GROUND
150 BLK
B10
ENG/EMIS FUSE 15 AMP
B8
241 BRN
TO IGN.
C10
473 DK BLU/WHT
A3
FAN #2 CONTROL
C8
504 WHT
COOLING FAN #2
ENGINE GROUND
150 BLK
B
474 GRY
C7
+5 VOLTS
C
732 DK BLU
C21
A/C PRESSURE SIG.
A
802 BLK
C5
TO IAT SENSOR
TO BLACK MINI HARNESS CONNECTOR "K"

CHART C-12

(Page 2 of 2)

COOLING FAN CONTROL DIAGNOSIS 3.1L (VIN T) "W" CARLINE (MFI)

Chart Test Description: Number(s) below refer to circled number(s) on the diagnostic chart.

1. 12 volts should be available to CKT 250 and CKT 2 on each relay when the ignition is "ON."
2. This test checks the ability of the PCM to ground CKT 335 (CKT 473).

The MIL (Service Engine Soon) should also be flashing at this point. If it isn't flashing, refer to CHART A-2.

3. If the fan does not turn "ON" at this point, CKT 702 (535) or CKT 150 is open, or the cooling fan motor(s) are faulty.

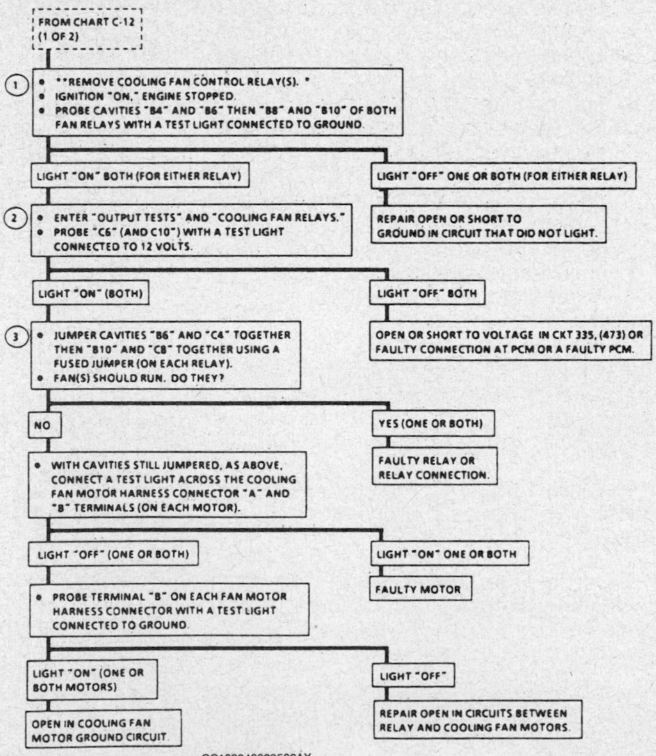

FROM CHART C-12 (1 OF 2)
1
• **REMOVE COOLING FAN CONTROL RELAY(S).**
• IGNITION "ON," ENGINE STOPPED.
• PROBE CAVITIES "B4" AND "B6" THEN "B8" AND "B10" OF BOTH FAN RELAYS WITH A TEST LIGHT CONNECTED TO GROUND.
LIGHT "ON" BOTH (FOR EITHER RELAY)
LIGHT "OFF" ONE OR BOTH (FOR EITHER RELAY)
2
• ENTER "OUTPUT TESTS" AND "COOLING FAN RELAYS."
• PROBE "C6" (AND C10") WITH A TEST LIGHT CONNECTED TO 12 VOLTS.
REPAIR OPEN OR SHORT TO GROUND IN CIRCUIT THAT DID NOT LIGHT.
LIGHT "ON" (BOTH)
LIGHT "OFF" BOTH
3
• JUMPER CAVITIES "B6" AND "C4" TOGETHER THEN "B10" AND "C8" TOGETHER USING A FUSED JUMPER (ON EACH RELAY).
• FAN(S) SHOULD RUN. DO THEY?
OPEN OR SHORT TO VOLTAGE IN CKT 335, (473) OR FAULTY CONNECTION AT PCM OR A FAULTY PCM.
NO
YES (ONE OR BOTH)
FAULTY RELAY OR RELAY CONNECTION.
• WITH CAVITIES STILL JUMPERED, AS ABOVE, CONNECT A TEST LIGHT ACROSS THE COOLING FAN MOTOR HARNESS CONNECTOR "A" AND "B" TERMINALS (ON EACH MOTOR).
LIGHT "OFF" (ONE OR BOTH)
LIGHT "ON" ONE OR BOTH
FAULTY MOTOR
• PROBE TERMINAL "B" ON EACH FAN MOTOR HARNESS CONNECTOR WITH A TEST LIGHT CONNECTED TO GROUND.
LIGHT "ON" (ONE OR BOTH MOTORS)
LIGHT "OFF"
OPEN IN COOLING FAN MOTOR GROUND CIRCUIT.
REPAIR OPEN IN CIRCUITS BETWEEN RELAY AND COOLING FAN MOTORS.

GC108940023502AX

Fig. 135 Chart C-12A, cooling fan diagnosis (Part 2 of 2). 1994 Lumina w/3.1L/V6–192 (VIN T) engine

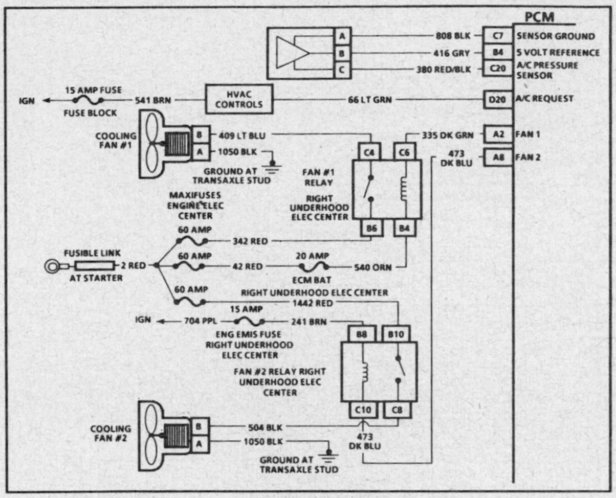
PCM
808 BLK
C7
SENSOR GROUND
416 GRY
B4
5 VOLT REFERENCE
380 RED/BLK
C20
A/C PRESSURE SENSOR
15 AMP FUSE
IGN
541 BRN
HVAC CONTROLS
66 LT GRN
D20
A/C REQUEST
FUSE BLOCK
COOLING FAN #1
409 LT BLU
1050 BLK
335 DK GRN
A2
FAN 1
473 DK BLU
A8
FAN 2
GROUND AT TRANSAXLE STUD
FAN #1 RELAY
RIGHT UNDERHOOD ELEC CENTER
MAXIFUSES ENGINE ELEC CENTER
60 AMP
342 RED
FUSIBLE LINK
2 RED
AT STARTER
42 RED
20 AMP
540 ORN
ECM BAT
RIGHT UNDERHOOD ELEC CENTER
1442 RED
15 AMP
704 PPL
241 BRN
ENG EMIS FUSE RIGHT UNDERHOOD ELEC CENTER
FAN #2 RELAY RIGHT UNDERHOOD ELEC CENTER
COOLING FAN #2
504 BLK
1050 BLK
GROUND AT TRANSAXLE STUD

CHART C-12A

COOLING FAN(S) CHECK 3.4L (VIN X) (SFI)

Circuit Description: Power for the fan motors comes from 60 amp maxifuse elements to the fan relays. The relays are energized when current flows to ground through the PCM (Quad-Driver).

Fan 1 relay - The PCM energizes the relay through terminal "A2" when the engine coolant temperature reaches 106°C (223°F) or when A/C is requested.

Fan 2 relay - The fan 2 relay is energized by the PCM if the A/C refrigerant pressure reaches 240 psi or the engine coolant temperature reaches 113°C (235°F).

Chart Test Description: Number(s) below refer to circled number(s) on the diagnostic chart.

1. Using the Tech 1 misc. tests, "Fan 1" control will cause the PCM to ground CKT 335, energizing the Fan 1 relay.
2. Selecting "Fan 2" with the Tech 1 allows control of CKT 473 and the Fan 2 relay.

Diagnostic Aids: An intermittent may be caused by a poor connection, rubbed through wire insulation, or a wire broken inside the insulation.

Check for:

- Poor connection or damaged harness - Inspect PCM harness connectors for backed out terminals "A2" or "A8", improper mating, broken locks, improperly formed or damaged terminals, poor terminal to wire connection, and damaged harness.
- Intermittent test - If connections and harness check OK, a digital voltmeter connected from affected terminal to ground while moving related connectors and wiring harness. If the failure is induced, the voltage reading will change.
- Mis-scaled Engine Coolant Temperature (ECT) sensor - See "Engine Coolant Temperature Sensor Temperature vs. Resistance Values" table on DTC P0117 chart
- Basic cooling system problem - Refer to engine cooling and radiator diagnosis.

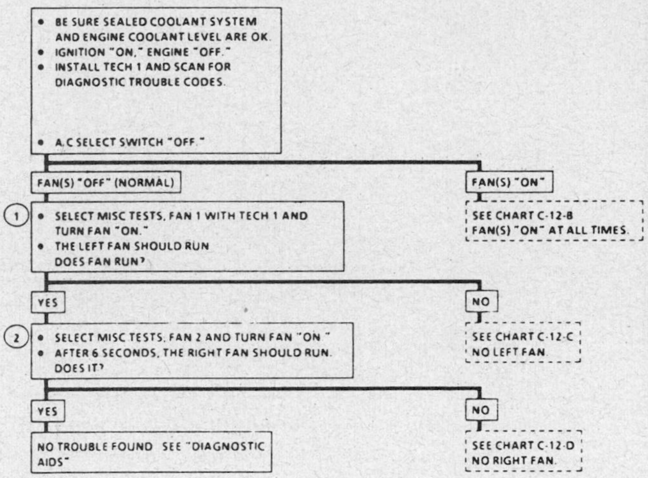
BE SURE SEALED COOLANT SYSTEM AND ENGINE COOLANT LEVEL ARE OK.
IGNITION "ON," ENGINE "OFF."
INSTALL TECH 1 AND SCAN FOR DIAGNOSTIC TROUBLE CODES.
A/C SELECT SWITCH "OFF."
FAN(S) "OFF" (NORMAL)
FAN(S) "ON"
SEE CHART C-12-B FAN(S) "ON" AT ALL TIMES.
1
SELECT MISC TESTS, FAN 1 WITH TECH 1 AND TURN FAN "ON."
THE LEFT FAN SHOULD RUN DOES FAN RUN?
YES
NO
SEE CHART C-12-C NO LEFT FAN
2
SELECT MISC TESTS, FAN 2 AND TURN FAN "ON."
AFTER 6 SECONDS, THE RIGHT FAN SHOULD RUN. DOES IT?
YES
NO
NO TROUBLE FOUND SEE "DIAGNOSTIC AIDS"
SEE CHART C-12-D NO RIGHT FAN.

GC108940023600AX

Fig. 136 Chart C-12A, cooling fan diagnosis. 1994 Lumina w/3.4L/V6-204 (VIN X) engine

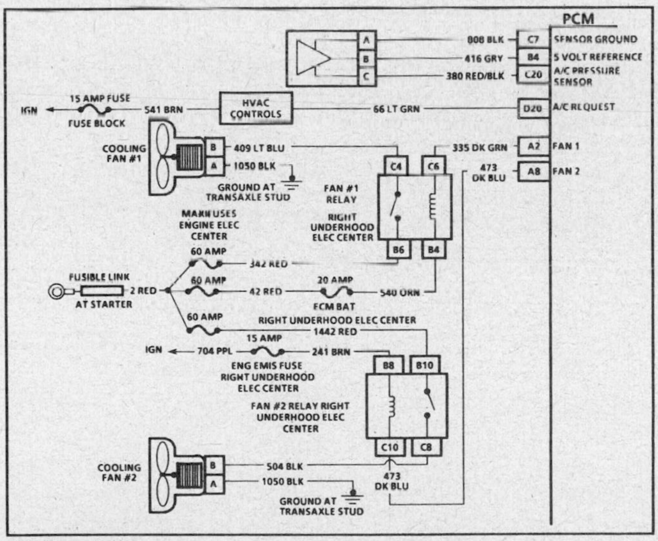
PCM
808 BLK
C7
SENSOR GROUND
416 GRY
B4
5 VOLT REFERENCE
380 RED/BLK
C20
A/C PRESSURE SENSOR
15 AMP FUSE
IGN
541 BRN
HVAC CONTROLS
66 LT GRN
D20
A/C REQUEST
FUSE BLOCK
COOLING FAN #1
409 LT BLU
1050 BLK
335 DK GRN
A2
FAN 1
473 DK BLU
A8
FAN 2
GROUND AT TRANSAXLE STUD
FAN #1 RELAY
RIGHT UNDERHOOD ELEC CENTER
ENGINE ELEC CENTER
60 AMP
342 RED
FUSIBLE LINK
2 RED
AT STARTER
42 RED
20 AMP
540 ORN
ECM BAT
RIGHT UNDERHOOD ELEC CENTER
1442 RED
15 AMP
704 PPL
241 BRN
ENG EMIS FUSE RIGHT UNDERHOOD ELEC CENTER
FAN #2 RELAY RIGHT UNDERHOOD ELEC CENTER
COOLING FAN #2
504 BLK
1050 BLK
GROUND AT TRANSAXLE STUD

Circuit Description:

Power for the fan motors comes from 60 amp maxifuse elements to the fan relays. The relays are energized when current flows to ground through the PCM (Quad-Driver).

Fan 1 relay - The PCM energizes the relay through terminal "A2" when the engine coolant temperature reaches 106°C (223°F) or when A/C is requested.

Fan 2 relay - The fan 2 relay is energized by the PCM if the A/C refrigerant pressure sensor reaches 240 psi or the engine coolant temperature reaches 113°C (235°F).

Chart Test Description: Number(s) below refer to circled number(s) on the diagnostic chart.

1. Checks to see if CKT 473 is grounded all the time. A light indicates the wire is shorted to ground; the following steps will isolate the problem.
2. Checks to see if CKT 335 is grounded all the time, which would keep the relay closed at all times.
3. If the test light is "OFF" after disconnecting the PCM, be sure CKT 335 is not shorted to B+. If not shorted to B+, the PCM is shorted internally.
4. If the test light is "OFF" after disconnecting the PCM, be sure CKT 473 is not shorted to B+. If not shorted to B+, the PCM is shorted internally.

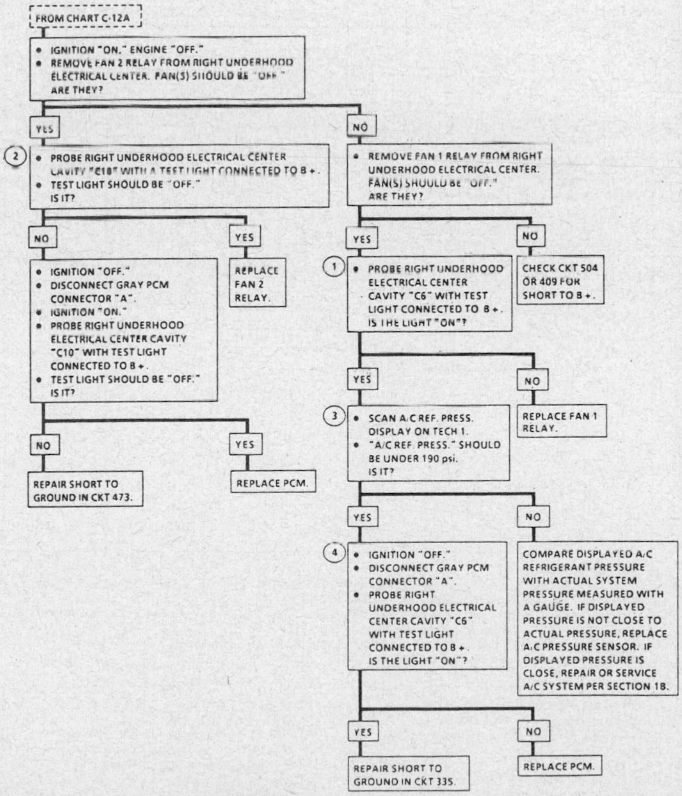
FROM CHART C-12A
IGNITION "ON," ENGINE "OFF."
REMOVE FAN 2 RELAY FROM RIGHT UNDERHOOD ELECTRICAL CENTER. FAN(S) SHOULD BE "OFF." ARE THEY?
YES
NO
2
PROBE RIGHT UNDERHOOD ELECTRICAL CENTER CAVITY "C10" WITH A TEST LIGHT CONNECTED TO B+.
TEST LIGHT SHOULD BE "OFF." IS IT?
REMOVE FAN 1 RELAY FROM RIGHT UNDERHOOD ELECTRICAL CENTER. FAN(S) SHOULD BE "OFF." ARE THEY?
NO
YES
IGNITION "OFF."
DISCONNECT GRAY PCM CONNECTOR "A".
IGNITION "ON."
PROBE RIGHT UNDERHOOD ELECTRICAL CENTER CAVITY "C10" WITH TEST LIGHT CONNECTED TO B+.
TEST LIGHT SHOULD BE "OFF." IS IT?
REPLACE FAN 2 RELAY.
1
PROBE RIGHT UNDERHOOD ELECTRICAL CENTER CAVITY "C6" WITH TEST LIGHT CONNECTED TO B+. IS THE LIGHT "ON"?
CHECK CKT 504 OR 409 FOR SHORT TO B+.
REPAIR SHORT TO GROUND IN CKT 473.
REPLACE PCM.
3
SCAN A/C REF. PRESS. DISPLAY ON TECH 1.
"A/C REF. PRESS." SHOULD BE UNDER 190 psi. IS IT?
REPLACE FAN 1 RELAY.
4
IGNITION "OFF."
DISCONNECT GRAY PCM CONNECTOR "A".
PROBE RIGHT UNDERHOOD ELECTRICAL CENTER CAVITY "C6" WITH TEST LIGHT CONNECTED TO B+. IS THE LIGHT "ON"?
COMPARE DISPLAYED A/C REFRIGERANT PRESSURE WITH ACTUAL SYSTEM PRESSURE MEASURED WITH A GAUGE. IF DISPLAYED PRESSURE IS NOT CLOSE TO ACTUAL PRESSURE, REPLACE A/C PRESSURE SENSOR. IF DISPLAYED PRESSURE IS CLOSE, REPAIR OR SERVICE A/C SYSTEM PER SECTION 1B.
REPAIR SHORT TO GROUND IN CKT 335.
REPLACE PCM.

GC108940023700AX

Fig. 137 Chart C-12B, cooling fan diagnosis. 1994 Lumina w/3.4L/V6-204 (VIN X) engine

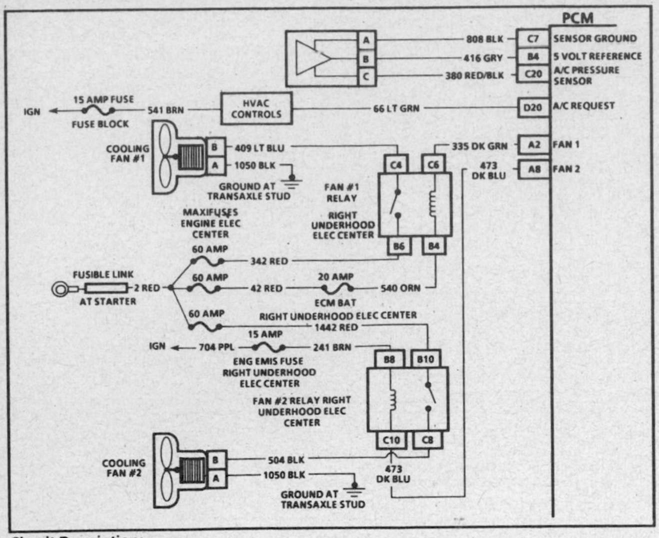

PCM
808 BLK
416 GRY
380 RED/BLK
C7 SENSOR GROUND
B4 5 VOLT REFERENCE
C20 A/C PRESSURE SENSOR
IGN
15 AMP FUSE
FUSE BLOCK
541 BRN
HVAC CONTROLS
66 LT GRN
D20 A/C REQUEST
COOLING FAN #1
409 LT BLU
1050 BLK
GROUND AT TRANSAXLE STUD
335 DK GRN
A2 FAN 1
473 DK BLU
A8 FAN 2
FAN #1 RELAY
RIGHT UNDERHOOD ELEC CENTER
MAXIFUSES ENGINE ELEC CENTER
60 AMP
342 RED
FUSIBLE LINK AT STARTER
2 RED
42 RED
20 AMP
540 ORN
ECM BAT
RIGHT UNDERHOOD ELEC CENTER
1442 RED
15 AMP
704 PPL
241 BRN
ENG EMIS FUSE RIGHT UNDERHOOD ELEC CENTER
FAN #2 RELAY RIGHT UNDERHOOD ELEC CENTER
COOLING FAN #2
504 BLK
1050 BLK
GROUND AT TRANSAXLE STUD

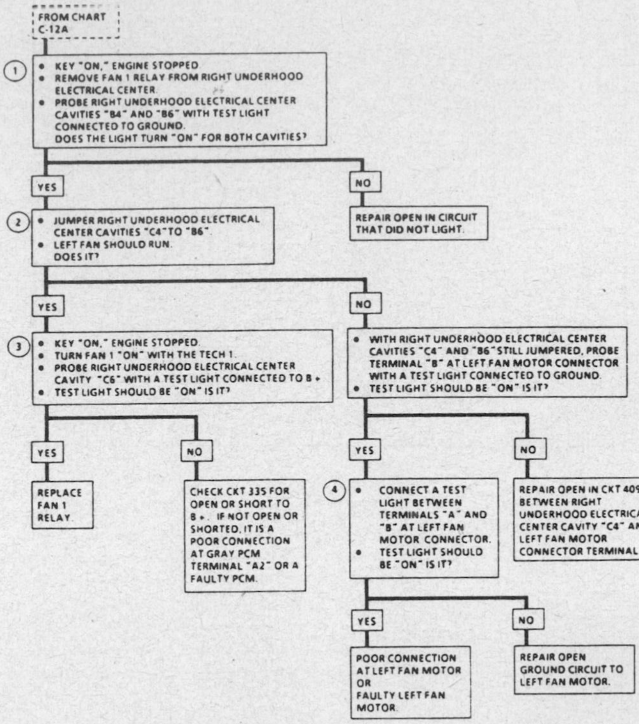

FROM CHART C-12A
1 • KEY "ON," ENGINE STOPPED • REMOVE FAN 1 RELAY FROM RIGHT UNDERHOOD ELECTRICAL CENTER. • PROBE RIGHT UNDERHOOD ELECTRICAL CENTER CAVITIES "B4" AND "B6" WITH TEST LIGHT CONNECTED TO GROUND. DOES THE LIGHT TURN "ON" FOR BOTH CAVITIES?
YES
NO
REPAIR OPEN IN CIRCUIT THAT DID NOT LIGHT.
2 • JUMPER RIGHT UNDERHOOD ELECTRICAL CENTER CAVITIES "C4" TO "B6". • LEFT FAN SHOULD RUN. DOES IT?
YES
NO
3 • KEY "ON," ENGINE STOPPED. • TURN FAN 1 "ON" WITH THE TECH 1. • PROBE RIGHT UNDERHOOD ELECTRICAL CENTER CAVITY "C6" WITH A TEST LIGHT CONNECTED TO B+. • TEST LIGHT SHOULD BE "ON" IS IT?
• WITH RIGHT UNDERHOOD ELECTRICAL CENTER CAVITIES "C4" AND "B6" STILL JUMPERED, PROBE TERMINAL "B" AT LEFT FAN MOTOR CONNECTOR WITH A TEST LIGHT CONNECTED TO GROUND. • TEST LIGHT SHOULD BE "ON" IS IT?
YES
NO
YES
NO
REPLACE FAN 1 RELAY.
CHECK CKT 335 FOR OPEN OR SHORT TO B+. IF NOT OPEN OR SHORTED, IT IS A POOR CONNECTION AT GRAY PCM TERMINAL "A2" OR A FAULTY PCM.
4 • CONNECT A TEST LIGHT BETWEEN TERMINALS "A" AND "B" AT LEFT FAN MOTOR CONNECTOR. • TEST LIGHT SHOULD BE "ON" IS IT?
REPAIR OPEN IN CKT 409 BETWEEN RIGHT UNDERHOOD ELECTRICAL CENTER CAVITY "C4" AND LEFT FAN MOTOR CONNECTOR TERMINAL "B".
YES
NO
POOR CONNECTION AT LEFT FAN MOTOR OR FAULTY LEFT FAN MOTOR.
REPAIR OPEN GROUND CIRCUIT TO LEFT FAN MOTOR.

Circuit Description:

Power for the fan motors comes from 60 amp maxifuse elements to the fan relays. The relays are energized when current flows to ground through the PCM (Quad-Driver).

Fan 1 relay - The PCM energizes the relay through terminal "A2" when the engine coolant temperature reaches 106°C (223°F) or when A/C is requested.

Fan 2 relay - The fan 2 relay is energized by the PCM if the A/C refrigerant pressure sensor reaches 240 psi or the engine coolant temperature reaches 113°C (235°F).

Chart Test Description: Number(s) below refer to circled number(s) on the diagnostic chart.

1. Checks for power feed to relay at right side underhood electrical center terminals "B4" and "B6".
2. Jumpering terminals "B6" to "C4" bypasses the relay, which should cause the left fan to run if fan motor and wiring are OK.
3. Turning fan 1 "ON" with the Tech 1 should cause the PCM to ground CKT 335. At this point, the test light should light, provided the PCM is OK and CKT 335 isn't open.
4. This checks for B+ and ground to the left fan motor. A test light "ON" at this point indicates a faulty motor connection, fan 1 or motor.

GC108940023800AX

Fig. 138 Chart C-12C, cooling fan diagnosis. 1994 Lumina w/3.4L/V6–204 (VIN X) engine

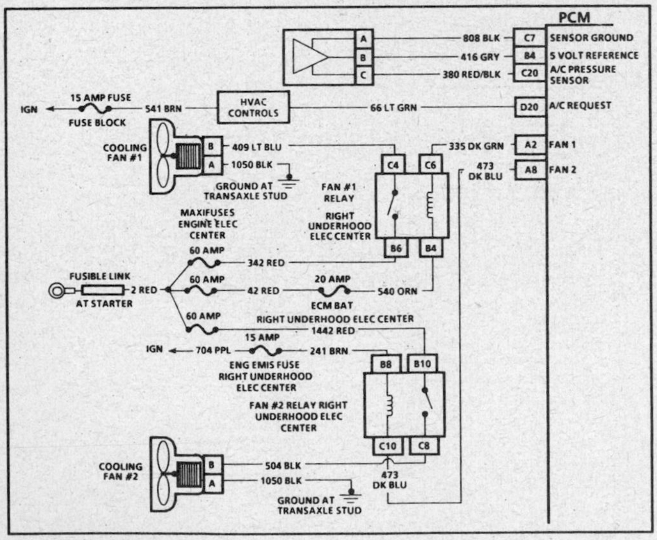

PCM
808 BLK
416 GRY
380 RED/BLK
C7 SENSOR GROUND
B4 5 VOLT REFERENCE
C20 A/C PRESSURE SENSOR
IGN
15 AMP FUSE
FUSE BLOCK
541 BRN
HVAC CONTROLS
66 LT GRN
D20 A/C REQUEST
COOLING FAN #1
409 LT BLU
1050 BLK
GROUND AT TRANSAXLE STUD
335 DK GRN
A2 FAN 1
473 DK BLU
A8 FAN 2
FAN #1 RELAY
RIGHT UNDERHOOD ELEC CENTER
MAXIFUSES ENGINE ELEC CENTER
60 AMP
342 RED
FUSIBLE LINK AT STARTER
2 RED
42 RED
20 AMP
540 ORN
ECM BAT
RIGHT UNDERHOOD ELEC CENTER
1442 RED
15 AMP
704 PPL
241 BRN
ENG EMIS FUSE RIGHT UNDERHOOD ELEC CENTER
FAN #2 RELAY RIGHT UNDERHOOD ELEC CENTER
COOLING FAN #2
504 BLK
1050 BLK
GROUND AT TRANSAXLE STUD

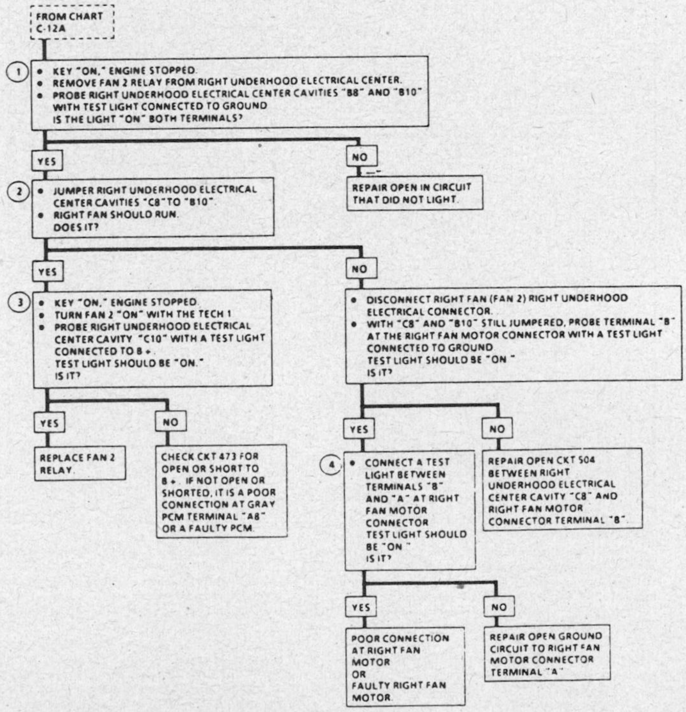

FROM CHART C-12A
1 • KEY "ON," ENGINE STOPPED. • REMOVE FAN 2 RELAY FROM RIGHT UNDERHOOD ELECTRICAL CENTER. • PROBE RIGHT UNDERHOOD ELECTRICAL CENTER CAVITIES "B8" AND "B10" WITH TEST LIGHT CONNECTED TO GROUND. IS THE LIGHT "ON" BOTH TERMINALS?
YES
NO
REPAIR OPEN IN CIRCUIT THAT DID NOT LIGHT.
2 • JUMPER RIGHT UNDERHOOD ELECTRICAL CENTER CAVITIES "C8" TO "B10". • RIGHT FAN SHOULD RUN. DOES IT?
YES
NO
3 • KEY "ON," ENGINE STOPPED. • TURN FAN 2 "ON" WITH THE TECH 1 • PROBE RIGHT UNDERHOOD ELECTRICAL CENTER CAVITY "C10" WITH A TEST LIGHT CONNECTED TO B+. TEST LIGHT SHOULD BE "ON." IS IT?
• DISCONNECT RIGHT FAN (FAN 2) RIGHT UNDERHOOD ELECTRICAL CONNECTOR. • WITH "C8" AND "B10" STILL JUMPERED, PROBE TERMINAL "B" AT THE RIGHT FAN MOTOR CONNECTOR WITH A TEST LIGHT CONNECTED TO GROUND. TEST LIGHT SHOULD BE "ON". IS IT?
YES
NO
YES
NO
REPLACE FAN 2 RELAY.
CHECK CKT 473 FOR OPEN OR SHORT TO B+. IF NOT OPEN OR SHORTED, IT IS A POOR CONNECTION AT GRAY PCM TERMINAL "A8" OR A FAULTY PCM.
4 • CONNECT A TEST LIGHT BETWEEN TERMINALS "B" AND "A" AT RIGHT FAN MOTOR CONNECTOR. TEST LIGHT SHOULD BE "ON" IS IT?
REPAIR OPEN CKT 504 BETWEEN RIGHT UNDERHOOD ELECTRICAL CENTER CAVITY "C8" AND RIGHT FAN MOTOR CONNECTOR TERMINAL "B".
YES
NO
POOR CONNECTION AT RIGHT FAN MOTOR OR FAULTY RIGHT FAN MOTOR.
REPAIR OPEN GROUND CIRCUIT TO RIGHT FAN MOTOR CONNECTOR TERMINAL "A".

Circuit Description:

Power for the fan motors comes from 60 amp maxifuse elements to the fan relays. The relays are energized when current flows to ground through the PCM (Quad-Driver).

Fan 1 relay - The PCM energizes the relay through terminal "A2" when the engine coolant temperature reaches 106°C (223°F) or when A/C is requested.

Fan 2 relay - The fan 2 relay is energized by the PCM if the A/C refrigerant pressure sensor reaches 240 psi or the engine coolant temperature reaches 108°C (226°F).

Chart Test Description: Number(s) below refer to circled number(s) on the diagnostic chart.

1. Verifies power feed to fan 2 relay at right side underhood electrical center terminals "B8" and "B10".
2. Jumpering terminals "B10" and "C8" bypasses the fan 2 relay. If right side fan runs, the relay is faulty.
3. Checks CKT 473 back to the PCM. If CKT 473 is OK, it's a bad fan 2 relay.
4. Checks wiring to the fan 2 (right side) motor. If OK, problem is connections, open ground circuit or faulty fan 2 (right side) fan motor.

GC108940023900AX

Fig. 139 Chart C-12D, cooling fan diagnosis. 1994 Lumina w/3.4L/V6–204 (VIN X) engine

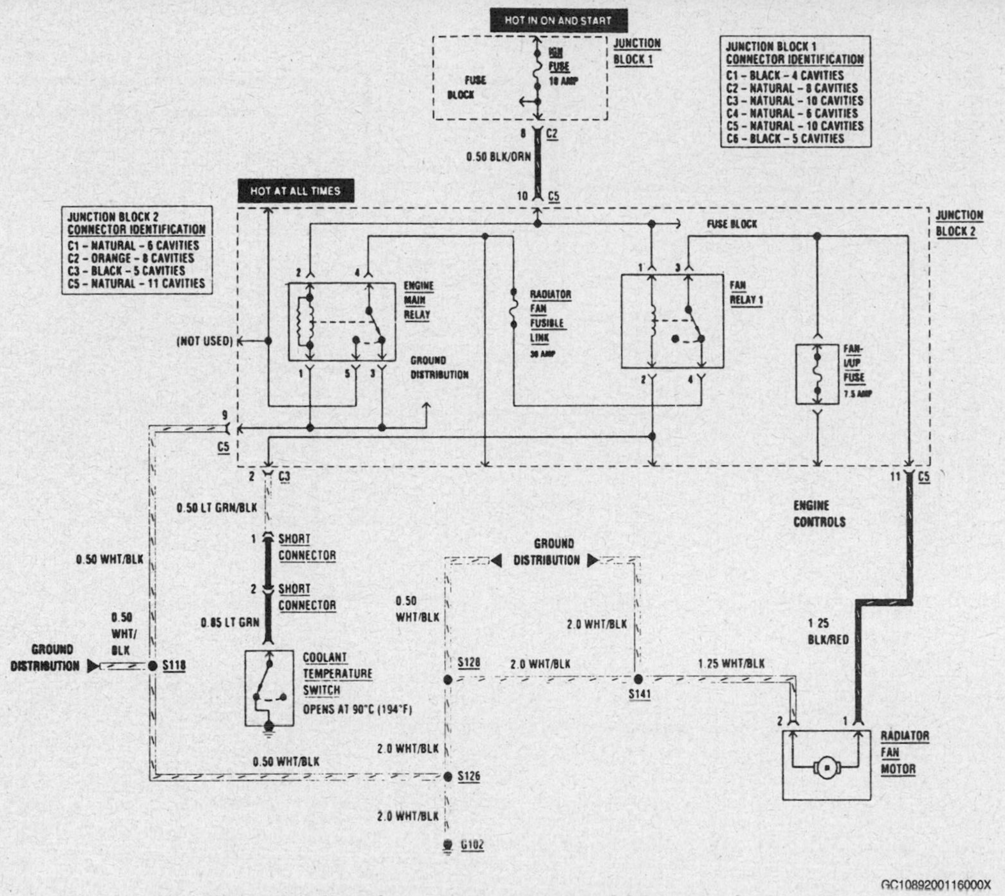
HOT IN ON AND START
JUNCTION BLOCK 1
IGN FUSE 10 AMP
FUSE BLOCK
JUNCTION BLOCK 1 CONNECTOR IDENTIFICATION
C1 - BLACK - 4 CAVITIES
C2 - NATURAL - 8 CAVITIES
C3 - NATURAL - 10 CAVITIES
C4 - NATURAL - 6 CAVITIES
C5 - NATURAL - 10 CAVITIES
C6 - BLACK - 5 CAVITIES
0.50 BLK/ORN
HOT AT ALL TIMES
JUNCTION BLOCK 2 CONNECTOR IDENTIFICATION
C1 - NATURAL - 6 CAVITIES
C2 - ORANGE - 8 CAVITIES
C3 - BLACK - 5 CAVITIES
C5 - NATURAL - 11 CAVITIES
JUNCTION BLOCK 2
ENGINE MAIN RELAY
RADIATOR FAN FUSIBLE LINK 30 AMP
FAN RELAY 1
FAN-I/UP FUSE 7.5 AMP
(NOT USED)
GROUND DISTRIBUTION
0.50 LT GRN/BLK
SHORT CONNECTOR
0.50 WHT/BLK
0.85 LT GRN
COOLANT TEMPERATURE SWITCH
OPENS AT 90°C (194°F)
S118
S128
S141
S126
G102
2.0 WHT/BLK
1.25 WHT/BLK
1.25 BLK/RED
ENGINE CONTROLS
RADIATOR FAN MOTOR
GC1089200116000X

Fig. 140 Cooling fan wiring circuit. 1992 Prizm less A/C

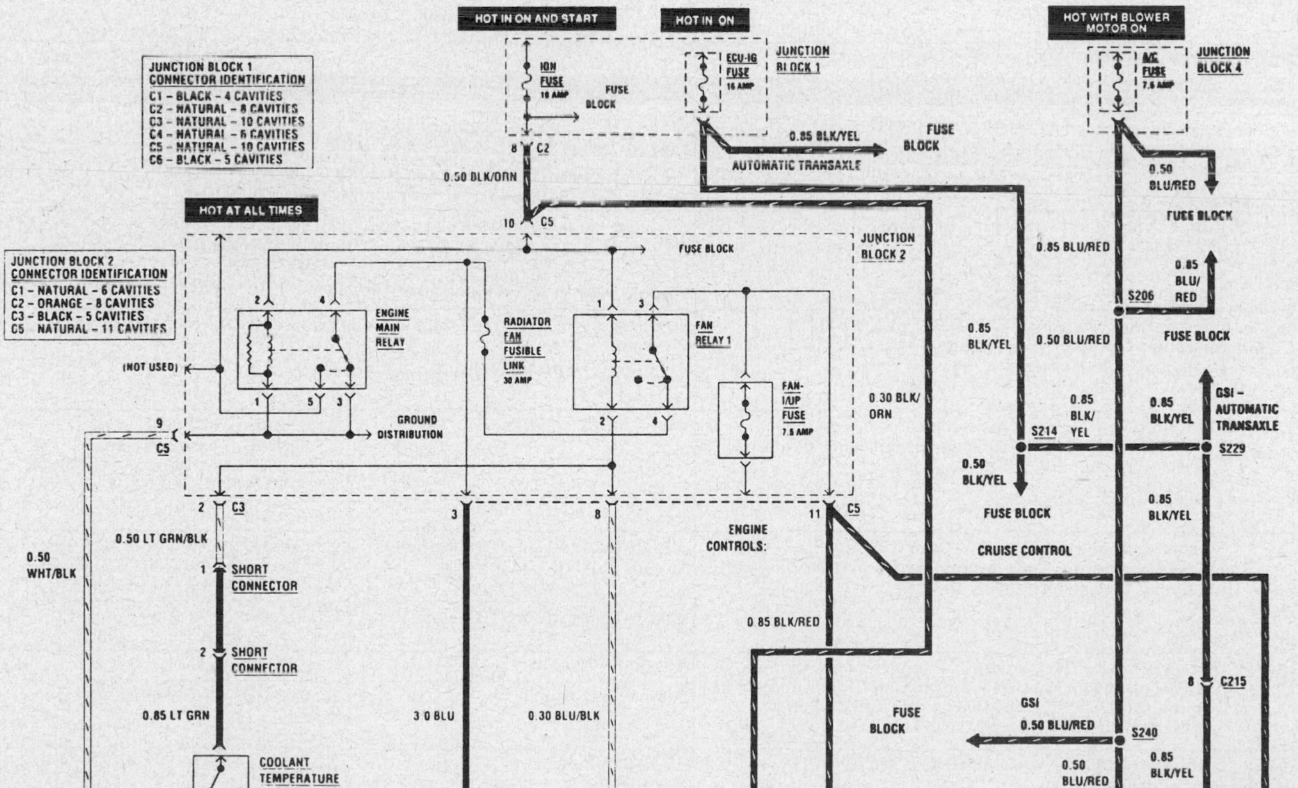
HOT IN ON AND START
HOT IN ON
HOT WITH BLOWER MOTOR ON
JUNCTION BLOCK 1 CONNECTOR IDENTIFICATION
C1 - BLACK - 4 CAVITIES
C2 - NATURAL - 8 CAVITIES
C3 - NATURAL - 10 CAVITIES
C4 - NATURAL - 6 CAVITIES
C5 - NATURAL - 10 CAVITIES
C6 - BLACK - 5 CAVITIES
IGN FUSE 10 AMP
ECU-IG FUSE 15 AMP
A/C FUSE 7.5 AMP
JUNCTION BLOCK 4
0.85 BLK/YEL
AUTOMATIC TRANSAXLE
FUSE BLOCK
0.50 BLK/ORN
HOT AT ALL TIMES
JUNCTION BLOCK 2 CONNECTOR IDENTIFICATION
C1 - NATURAL - 6 CAVITIES
C2 - ORANGE - 8 CAVITIES
C3 - BLACK - 5 CAVITIES
C5 NATURAL - 11 CAVITIES
ENGINE MAIN RELAY
RADIATOR FAN FUSIBLE LINK 30 AMP
FAN RELAY 1
FAN-I/UP FUSE 7.5 AMP
GROUND DISTRIBUTION
(NOT USED)
0.50 BLU/RED
0.85 BLU/RED
S206
S214
S229
GSI - AUTOMATIC TRANSAXLE
0.30 BLK/ORN
0.50 LT GRN/BLK
0.50 WHT/BLK
SHORT CONNECTOR
ENGINE CONTROLS
CRUISE CONTROL
0.85 BLK/RED
0.85 LT GRN
3.0 BLU
0.30 BLU/BLK
COOLANT TEMPERATURE SWITCH
OPENS AT 90°C (194°F)
GSI
S240
C215
1.25 BLK/RED
GC1089200118010X

Fig. 141 Cooling fan wiring circuit (Part 1 Of 2). 1992 Prizm w/A/C

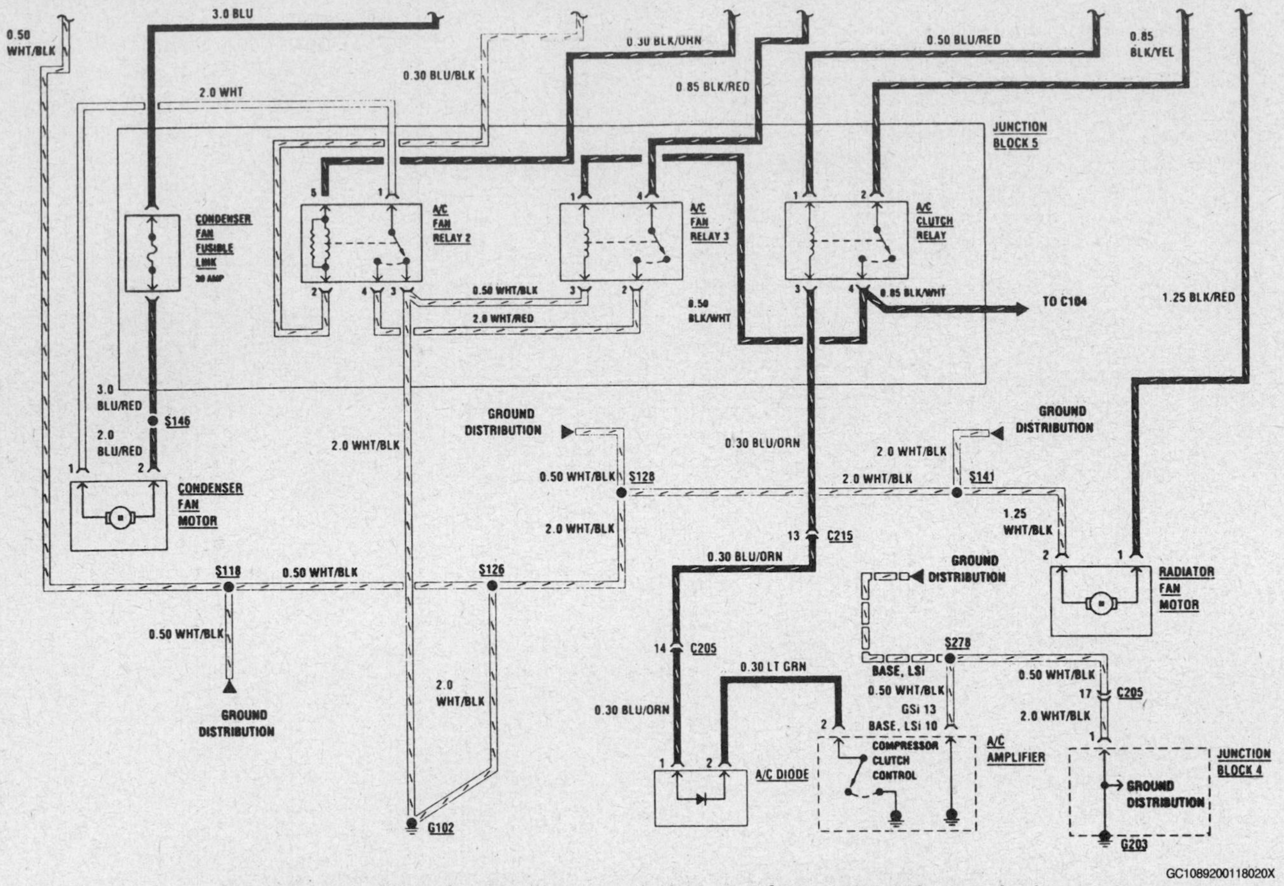

3.0 BLU
0.50 WHT/BLK
0.30 BLU/BLK
0.30 BLK/ORN
0.85 BLK/RED
0.50 BLU/RED
0.85 BLK/YEL
2.0 WHT
JUNCTION BLOCK 5
CONDENSER FAN FUSIBLE LINK 30 AMP
A/C FAN RELAY 2
A/C FAN RELAY 3
A/C CLUTCH RELAY
0.50 WHT/BLK
2.0 WHT/RED
0.50 BLK/WHT
0.85 BLK/WHT
TO C104
1.25 BLK/RED
3.0 BLU/RED
S146
2.0 BLU/RED
CONDENSER FAN MOTOR
2.0 WHT/BLK
GROUND DISTRIBUTION
0.50 WHT/BLK
S128
0.30 BLU/ORN
2.0 WHT/BLK
S141
1.25 WHT/BLK
C215
RADIATOR FAN MOTOR
S118
S126
C205
0.30 LT GRN
S278
BASE, LSi
GSi 13
BASE, LSi 10
COMPRESSOR CLUTCH CONTROL
A/C AMPLIFIER
A/C DIODE
JUNCTION BLOCK 4
G102
G203
GC1089200118020X

Fig. 141 Cooling fan wiring circuit (Part 2 Of 2). 1992 Prizm w/A/C

COOLANT FANS: WITHOUT AIR CONDITIONING — **DIAGNOSTIC CHART A**

TEST		RESULT	ACTION
A1.	Start and run the engine. Make certain that engine coolant temperature is below 90 °C (194 °F).	RADIATOR FAN MOTOR does not operate.	GO TO **A2.**
		RADIATOR FAN MOTOR operates below 90°C (194°F).	GO TO **A3.**
A2.	Run the engine until operating temperature reaches 90°C (194°F).	Radiator fan motor operates at 90°C (194°F) and above.	All systems diagnosed are functioning normally.
		Radiator fan motor does not operate at 90°C (194°F) or above.	GO TO **A7.**
A3.	Remove the COOLANT TEMPERATURE SWITCH connector. Connect a fused jumper between the connector cavity and chassis ground.	RADIATOR FAN MOTOR stops running.	Replace COOLANT TEMPERATURE SWITCH.
		RADIATOR FAN MOTOR continues to run.	GO TO **A4.**
A4.	Turn ignition switch to "OFF." Backprobe JUNCTION BLOCK 2 connector C3 with a digital multimeter from cavity 2 to chassis ground. Measure resistance.	More than 1.0 ohm.	Repair open in LT GRN wire or LT GRN/BLK wire between JUNCTION BLOCK 2 and COOLANT TEMPERATURE SWITCH.
		Less than 1.0 ohm.	GO TO **A5.**
A5.	Remove jumper. Reconnect COOLANT TEMPERATURE SWITCH connector. Turn ignition switch to "ON." Remove Fan Relay 1 from JUNCTION BLOCK 2.	RADIATOR FAN MOTOR continues to run.	Repair short to voltage in BLK/RED wire between JUNCTION BLOCK 2 and RADIATOR FAN MOTOR.
		RADIATOR FAN MOTOR stops running.	GO TO **A6.**
A6.	Disconnect JUNCTION BLOCK 2 connector C3. Connect a digital multimeter from JUNCTION BLOCK 2 connector C3 terminal 2 (JUNCTION BLOCK 2 side) to Fan Relay 1 connector cavity 2. Measure resistance.	Less than 1.0 ohm.	Replace Fan Relay 1.
		More than 1.0 ohm.	Replace JUNCTION BLOCK 2.
A7.	Disconnect COOLANT TEMPERATURE SWITCH connector.	RADIATOR FAN MOTOR starts running.	Replace COOLANT TEMPERATURE SWITCH.
		RADIATOR FAN MOTOR does not operate.	GO TO **A8.**

GC1089200117010X

Fig. 142 System diagnosis chart (Part 1 of 2). 1992 Prizm less A/C

COOLANT FANS: WITHOUT AIR CONDITIONING			DIAGNOSTIC CHART A (CONT'D)
	TEST	RESULT	ACTION
A8.	Disconnect JUNCTION BLOCK 2 connector C3. Connect a digital multimeter from cavity 2 to chassis ground. Measure resistance.	Less than infinite.	Repair short to ground in LT GRN or LT GRN/BLK wire between JUNCTION BLOCK 2 and COOLANT TEMPERATURE SWITCH.
		Infinite.	GO TO **A9.**
A9.	Disconnect Fan Relay 1 connector. Connect a digital multimeter from connector cavity 2 to chassis ground. Measure resistance.	Less than infinite.	Replace JUNCTION BLOCK 2.
		Infinite.	GO TO **A10.**
A10.	Connect a test lamp from Fan Relay 1 connector cavity 1 to chassis ground.	Test lamp does not light.	Replace JUNCTION BLOCK 2.
		Test lamp lights.	GO TO **A11.**
A11.	Connect a test lamp from Fan Relay 1 connector cavity 4 to chassis ground.	Test lamp does not light.	Check Radiator Fan Fusible Link if good, replace JUNCTION BLOCK 2.
		Test lamp lights.	GO TO **A12.**
A12.	Reconnect COOLANT TEMPERATURE SWITCH, Fan Relay 1 and JUNCTION BLOCK 2 connector C3. Backprobe Fan Relay 1 connector with a test lamp from cavity 3 to chassis ground.	Test lamp does not light.	Replace Fan Relay 1.
		Test lamp lights.	GO TO **A13.**
A13.	Backprobe JUNCTION BLOCK 2 connector C5 with a test lamp from cavity 11 to chassis ground.	Test lamp does not light.	Replace JUNCTION BLOCK 2.
		Test lamp lights.	GO TO **A14.**
A14.	Disconnect RADIATOR FAN MOTOR connector. Connect a test lamp from connector cavity 1 to chassis ground.	Test lamp does not light.	Repair open in BLK/RED wire.
		Test lamp lights.	GO TO **A15.**
A15.	Connect a digital multimeter from RADIATOR FAN MOTOR connector cavity 2 to chassis ground. Measure resistance.	More than 3.0 ohms.	Repair WHT/BLK ground wire between RADIATOR FAN MOTOR and G102.
		Less than 3.0 ohms.	Replace RADIATOR FAN MOTOR.

GC1089200117020X

Fig. 142 System diagnosis chart (Part 2 of 2). 1992 Prizm less A/C

COOLANT FANS: WITH AIR CONDITIONING			DIAGNOSTIC CHART B
	TEST	RESULT	ACTION
B1.	Start and run the engine. Make certain that engine coolant temperature is below 90°C (194°F).	RADIATOR FAN MOTOR and CONDENSER FAN MOTOR do not operate.	GO TO **B2.**
		RADIATOR FAN MOTOR operates at full speed.	GO TO **B4.**
		CONDENSER FAN MOTOR operates at full speed.	GO TO **B7.**
		RADIATOR FAN MOTOR and CONDENSER FAN MOTOR operate at half speed.	GO TO **B11.**
		RADIATOR FAN MOTOR and CONDENSER FAN MOTOR operate at full speed.	GO TO **B29.**
B2.	Press A/C switch to ON. Move blower switch to any position except "OFF."	RADIATOR FAN MOTOR and CONDENSER FAN MOTOR operate at half speed.	GO TO **B3.**
		RADIATOR FAN MOTOR and CONDENSER FAN MOTOR do not operate.	GO TO **B12.**
B3.	Run the engine until operating temperature reaches 90°C (194°F). Press A/C switch to OFF. Move blower switch to "OFF."	RADIATOR FAN MOTOR and CONDENSER FAN MOTOR operate at full speed.	All systems diagnosed are functioning normally.
		RADIATOR FAN MOTOR and CONDENSER FAN MOTOR do not operate at full speed.	GO TO **B27.**
		RADIATOR FAN MOTOR does not operate.	GO TO **B31.**
		CONDENSER FAN MOTOR does not operate.	GO TO **B37.**
B4.	Disconnect Fan Relay 1 connector. Connect a digital multimeter from cavity 2 to chassis ground. Measure resistance.	More than 1.0 ohm.	Replace JUNCTION BLOCK 2.
		Less than 1.0 ohm.	GO TO **B5.**

GC1089200119010X

Fig. 143 System diagnosis chart (Part 1 of 6). 1992 Prizm w/A/C

COOLANT FANS: WITH AIR CONDITIONING		DIAGNOSTIC CHART B (CONT'D)
TEST	**RESULT**	**ACTION**
B5. Connect a test lamp from Fan Relay 1 connector cavity 3 to chassis ground.	Test lamp does not light.	Replace Fan Relay 1.
	Test lamp lights.	GO TO **B6.**
B6. Disconnect JUNCTION BLOCK 2 connector C5. Connect a test lamp from cavity 11 to chassis ground.	Test lamp lights.	Repair short to voltage in BLK/RED wire.
	Test lamp does not light.	Replace JUNCTION BLOCK 2.
B7. Disconnect A/C Fan Relay 2 connector. Connect a digital multimeter from cavity 2 to chassis ground. Measure resistance.	More than 1.0 ohm.	GO TO **B8.**
	Less than 1.0 ohm.	GO TO **B9.**
B8. Backprobe JUNCTION BLOCK 2 connector C5 with a digital multimeter from cavity 8 to chassis ground. Measure resistance.	Less than 1.0 ohm.	Repair open in BLU/BLK wire.
	More than 1.0 ohm.	Replace JUNCTION BLOCK 2.
B9. Connect a test lamp from A/C Fan Relay 2 connector cavity 6 to chassis ground.	Test lamp does not light.	Repair open in BLK/ORN wire.
	Test lamp lights.	GO TO **B10.**
B10. Connect a test lamp from A/C Fan Relay 2 connector cavity 1 to chassis ground.	Test lamp lights.	Repair short to voltage in WHT wire.
	Test lamp does not light.	Replace A/C Fan Relay 2.
B11. Disconnect A/C Fan Relay 3 connector. Connect a test lamp from cavity 1 to chassis ground.	Test lamp lights.	Repair short to voltage in BLK/WHT wire.
	Test lamp does not light.	Replace A/C Fan Relay 3.
B12. Disconnect COOLANT TEMPERATURE SWITCH connector. Connect a fused jumper from connector cavity to chassis ground. Disconnect RADIATOR FAN MOTOR connector. Connect a digital multimeter from cavity 2 to chassis ground. Measure resistance.	More than 3.0 ohms.	Repair WHT/BLK ground wire between RADIATOR FAN MOTOR and G102.
	Less than 3.0 ohms.	GO TO **B13.**
B13. Connect a fused jumper from RADIATOR FAN MOTOR connector cavity 1 to chassis ground.	CONDENSER FAN MOTOR operates at full speed.	Replace RADIATOR FAN MOTOR.
	CONDENSER FAN MOTOR does not operate.	GO TO **B14.**

GC1089200119020X

Fig. 143 System diagnosis chart (Part 2 of 6). 1992 Prizm w/A/C

COOLANT FANS: WITH AIR CONDITIONING		DIAGNOSTIC CHART B (CONT'D)
TEST	**RESULT**	**ACTION**
B14. Backprobe A/C Fan Relay 3 connector with a fused jumper from cavity 4 to chassis ground.	CONDENSER FAN MOTOR operates at full speed.	Repair open in BLK/RED wire between A/C Fan Relay 3 and Junction Block 2.
	CONDENSER FAN MOTOR does not operate.	GO TO **B15.**
B15. Disconnect A/C FAN RELAY 3 connector. Connect a test lamp from cavity 1 to chassis ground.	Test lamp does not light.	Repair open in BLK/WHT wire.
	Test lamp lights.	GO TO **B16.**
B16. Connect a digital multimeter from A/C FAN RELAY 3 connector cavity 3 to chassis ground. Measure resistance.	More than 1.0 ohm.	Repair WHT/BLK ground wire between A/C Fan Relay 3 and G102.
	Less than 1.0 ohm.	GO TO **B17.**
B17. Connect a fused jumper from A/C Fan Relay 3 connector cavity 2 to chassis ground.	CONDENSER FAN MOTOR operates at full speed.	Replace A/C Fan Relay 3.
	CONDENSER FAN MOTOR does not operate.	GO TO **B18.**
B18. Backprobe A/C Fan Relay 2 connector with a fused jumper from cavity 4 to chassis ground.	CONDENSER FAN MOTOR operates at full speed.	Repair open in WHT/RED wire.
	CONDENSER FAN MOTOR does not operate.	GO TO **B19.**
B19. Disconnect A/C Fan Relay 2 connector. Connect a test lamp from cavity 6 to chassis ground.	Test lamp does not light.	Repair open in BLK/ORN wire.
	Test lamp lights.	GO TO **B20.**
B20. Connect a digital multimeter from A/C Fan Relay 2 connector cavity 2 to chassis ground. Measure resistance.	More than 1.0 ohm.	GO TO **B21.**
	Less than 1.0 ohm.	GO TO **B23.**
B21. Backprobe JUNCTION BLOCK 2 connector C5 with a digital multimeter from cavity 8 to chassis ground. Measure resistance.	Less than 1.0 ohm.	Repair open in BLU/BLK wire.
	More than 1.0 ohm.	GO TO **B22.**
B22. Backprobe JUNCTION BLOCK 2 connector C3 with a digital multimeter from cavity 2 to chassis ground. Measure resistance.	Less than 1.0 ohm.	Replace JUNCTION BLOCK 2.
	More than 1.0 ohm.	Repair open in LT GRN or LT GRN/BLK wire.

GC1089200119030X

Fig. 143 System diagnosis chart (Part 3 of 6). 1992 Prizm w/A/C

COOLANT FANS: WITH AIR CONDITIONING		DIAGNOSTIC CHART B (CONT'D)
TEST	**RESULT**	**ACTION**
B23. Connect a fused jumper from A/C Fan Relay 2 connector cavity 1 to chassis ground.	CONDENSER FAN MOTOR operates at full speed.	Replace A/C Fan Relay 2.
	CONDENSER FAN MOTOR does not operate.	GO TO **B24.**
B24. Backprobe CONDENSER FAN MOTOR connector with a fused jumper from cavity 1 to chassis ground.	CONDENSER FAN MOTOR operates at full speed.	Repair open in WHT wire.
	CONDENSER FAN MOTOR does not operate.	GO TO **B25.**
B25. Backprobe CONDENSER FAN MOTOR connector with a test lamp from cavity 2 to chassis ground.	Test lamp lights.	Replace CONDENSER FAN MOTOR.
	Test lamp does not light.	GO TO **B26.**
B26. Backprobe JUNCTION BLOCK 2 connector C5 with a test lamp from cavity 3 to chassis ground.	Test lamp lights.	Repair open in BLU/RED or BLU wire between JUNCTION BLOCK 2 and CONDENSOR FAN MOTOR, JUNCTION BLOCK 5 or Condenser Fan Fusible Link.
	Test lamp does not light.	Replace JUNCTION BLOCK 5.
B27. Disconnect COOLANT TEMPERATURE SWITCH connector.	RADIATOR FAN MOTOR begins to operate.	Replace COOLANT TEMPERATURE SWITCH.
	RADIATOR FAN MOTOR and CONDENSER FAN MOTOR do not operate at full speed.	GO TO **B28.**
B28. Disconnect JUNCTION BLOCK 2 connector C3.	RADIATOR FAN MOTOR and CONDENSER FAN MOTOR operate at full speed.	Repair short to ground in LT GRN/BLK or LT GRN wire.
	RADIATOR FAN MOTOR and CONDENSER FAN MOTOR do not operate at full speed.	Replace JUNCTION BLOCK 2.
B29. Disconnect COOLANT TEMPERATURE SWITCH connector. Connect a fused jumper from connector cavity to chassis ground.	RADIATOR FAN and CONDENSER FAN MOTOR stop operating.	Replace COOLANT TEMPERATURE SWITCH.
	RADIATOR FAN and CONDENSER FAN MOTOR continue to operate.	GO TO **B30.**

GC1089200119040X

Fig. 143 System diagnosis chart (Part 4 of 6). 1992 Prizm w/A/C

COOLANT FANS: WITH AIR CONDITIONING		DIAGNOSTIC CHART B (CONT'D)
TEST	**RESULT**	**ACTION**
B30. Backprobe JUNCTION BLOCK 2 connector C3 with a fused jumper from cavity 2 to chassis ground.	RADIATOR FAN MOTOR and CONDENSER FAN MOTOR stop operating.	Repair open in LT GRN or LT GRN/BLK wire.
	RADIATOR FAN MOTOR and CONDENSER FAN MOTOR continue to operate.	Replace JUNCTION BLOCK 2.
B31. Disconnect RADIATOR FAN MOTOR connector. Connect a digital multimeter from cavity 2 to chassis ground. Measure resistance.	More than 3.0 ohms.	Repair WHT/BLK ground wire between RADIATOR FAN MOTOR and G102.
	Less than 3.0 ohms.	GO TO **B32.**
B32. Connect a test lamp from RADIATOR FAN MOTOR connector cavity 1 to chassis ground.	Test lamp lights.	Replace RADIATOR FAN MOTOR.
	Test lamp does not light.	GO TO **B33.**
B33. Backprobe JUNCTION BLOCK 2 connector C5 with a test lamp from cavity 11 to chassis ground.	Test lamp lights.	Repair open in BLK/RED wire between JUNCTION BLOCK 2 and RADIATOR FAN MOTOR.
	Test lamp does not light.	GO TO **B34.**
B34. Backprobe Fan Relay 1 with a test lamp from cavity 3 to chassis ground.	Test lamp lights.	Replace JUNCTION BLOCK 2.
	Test lamp does not light.	GO TO **B35.**
B35. Disconnect Fan Relay 1 connector. Connect a digital multimeter from cavity 2 to chassis ground. Measure resistance.	Less than 1.0 ohm.	Replace JUNCTION BLOCK 2.
	More than 1.0 ohm.	GO TO **B36.**
B36. Connect a test lamp from Fan Relay 1 connector cavity 4 to chassis ground.	Test lamp does not light.	Check Radiator Fan Fusible Link. If good, replace JUNCTION BLOCK 2.
	Test lamp lights.	Replace Fan Relay 1.
B37. Disconnect CONDENSER FAN MOTOR connector. Connect a test lamp from cavity 1 to cavity 2.	Test lamp lights.	Replace CONDENSER FAN MOTOR.
	Test lamp does not light.	GO TO **B38.**
B38. Connect a test lamp from CONDENSER FAN MOTOR connector cavity 2 to chassis ground.	Test lamp does not light.	GO TO **B39.**
	Test lamp lights.	GO TO **B40.**

GC1089200119050X

Fig. 143 System diagnosis chart (Part 5 of 6). 1992 Prizm w/A/C

COOLANT FANS: WITH AIR CONDITIONING		DIAGNOSTIC CHART B (CONT'D)
TEST	**RESULT**	**ACTION**
B39. Backprobe JUNCTION BLOCK 2 connector C5 with a test lamp from cavity 3 to chassis ground.	Test lamp lights.	Repair open in BLU wire between JUNCTION BLOCK 2 and CONDENSER FAN MOTOR or BLU/RED wire or Condenser Fan Fusible Link.
	Test lamp does not light.	Replace JUNCTION BLOCK 2.
B40. Backprobe A/C Fan Relay 2 with a digital multimeter from cavity 1 to chassis ground. Measure resistance.	Less than 3.0 ohms.	Repair open in WHT wire.
	More than 3.0 ohms.	GO TO **B41.**
B41. Disconnect A/C Fan Relay 2 connector. Connect a digital multimeter from cavity 3 to chassis ground. Measure resistance.	More than 1.0 ohm.	Repair open in WHT/BLK wire between A/C Fan Relay 2 and G102.
	Less than 1.0 ohm.	GO TO **B42.**
B42. Connect a digital multimeter from A/C Fan Relay 2 cavity 2 to chassis ground. Measure resistance.	More than 1.0 ohm.	GO TO **B43.**
	Less than 1.0 ohm.	Replace A/C Fan Relay 2.
B43. Backprobe JUNCTION BLOCK 2 connector C5 with a digital multimeter from cavity 8 to chassis ground. Measure resistance.	Less than 1.0 ohm.	Repair open in BLU/BLK wire.
	More than 1.0 ohm.	Replace JUNCTION BLOCK 2.

GC1089200119060X

Fig. 143 System diagnosis chart (Part 6 of 6). 1992 Prizm w/A/C

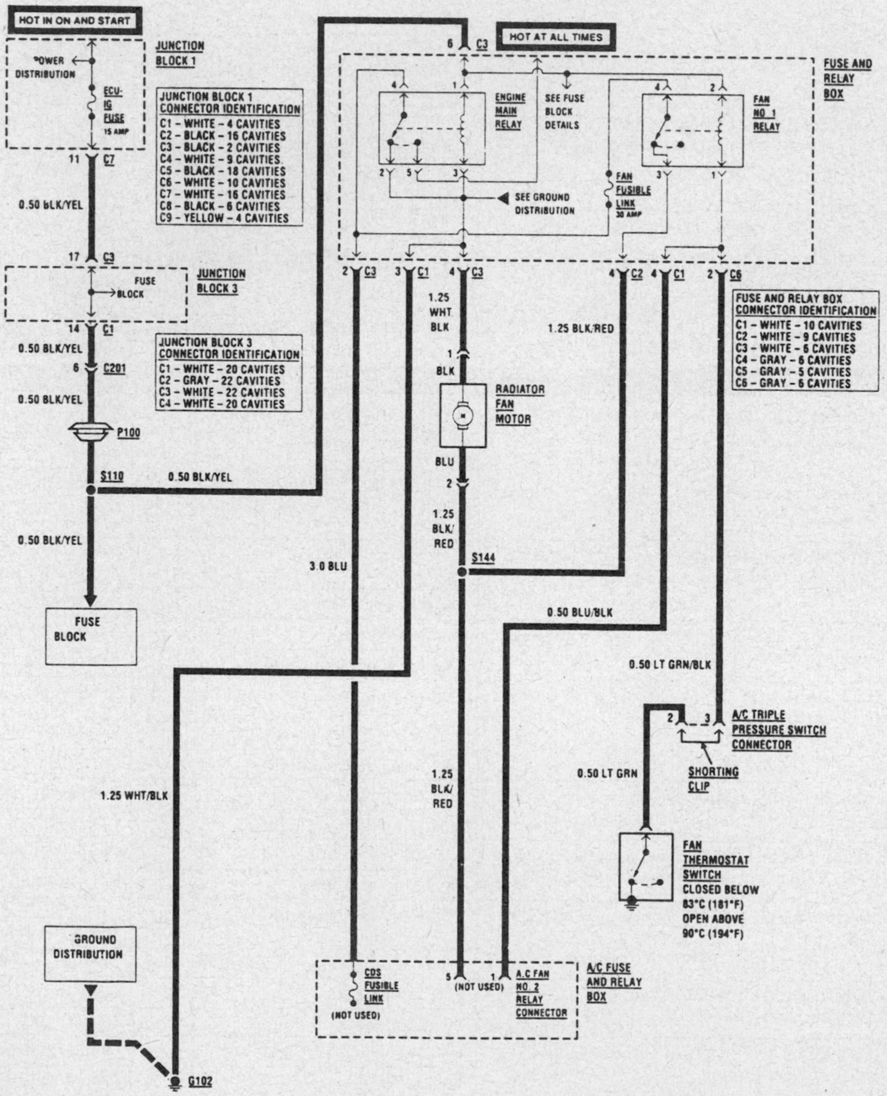
HOT IN ON AND START
JUNCTION BLOCK 1
POWER DISTRIBUTION
ECU-IG FUSE 15 AMP
JUNCTION BLOCK 1 CONNECTOR IDENTIFICATION
C1 - WHITE - 4 CAVITIES
C2 - BLACK - 16 CAVITIES
C3 - BLACK - 2 CAVITIES
C4 - WHITE - 9 CAVITIES
C5 - BLACK - 18 CAVITIES
C6 - WHITE - 10 CAVITIES
C7 - WHITE - 16 CAVITIES
C8 - BLACK - 6 CAVITIES
C9 - YELLOW - 4 CAVITIES
11 C7
0.50 BLK/YEL
17 C3
FUSE BLOCK
JUNCTION BLOCK 3
14 C1
0.50 BLK/YEL
6 C201
0.50 BLK/YEL
JUNCTION BLOCK 3 CONNECTOR IDENTIFICATION
C1 - WHITE - 20 CAVITIES
C2 - GRAY - 22 CAVITIES
C3 - WHITE - 22 CAVITIES
C4 - WHITE - 20 CAVITIES
P100
S110
0.50 BLK/YEL
0.50 BLK/YEL
FUSE BLOCK
GROUND DISTRIBUTION
G102
1.25 WHT/BLK
3.0 BLU
6 C3
HOT AT ALL TIMES
FUSE AND RELAY BOX
ENGINE MAIN RELAY
SEE FUSE BLOCK DETAILS
FAN NO 1 RELAY
SEE GROUND DISTRIBUTION
FAN FUSIBLE LINK 30 AMP
2 C3
3 C1
4 C3
4 C2
4 C1
2 C6
FUSE AND RELAY BOX CONNECTOR IDENTIFICATION
C1 - WHITE - 10 CAVITIES
C2 - WHITE - 9 CAVITIES
C3 - WHITE - 6 CAVITIES
C4 - GRAY - 6 CAVITIES
C5 - GRAY - 5 CAVITIES
C6 - GRAY - 6 CAVITIES
1.25 WHT BLK
1.25 BLK/RED
BLK
RADIATOR FAN MOTOR
BLU
1.25 BLK/ RED
S144
0.50 BLU/BLK
0.50 LT GRN/BLK
A/C TRIPLE PRESSURE SWITCH CONNECTOR
SHORTING CLIP
0.50 LT GRN
1.25 BLK/ RED
FAN THERMOSTAT SWITCH
CLOSED BELOW 83°C (181°F)
OPEN ABOVE 90°C (194°F)
CDS FUSIBLE LINK
(NOT USED)
(NOT USED)
A.C FAN NO. 2 RELAY CONNECTOR
A/C FUSE AND RELAY BOX

GC1089300120000X

Fig. 144 Cooling fan wiring circuit. 1993 Prizm less A/C

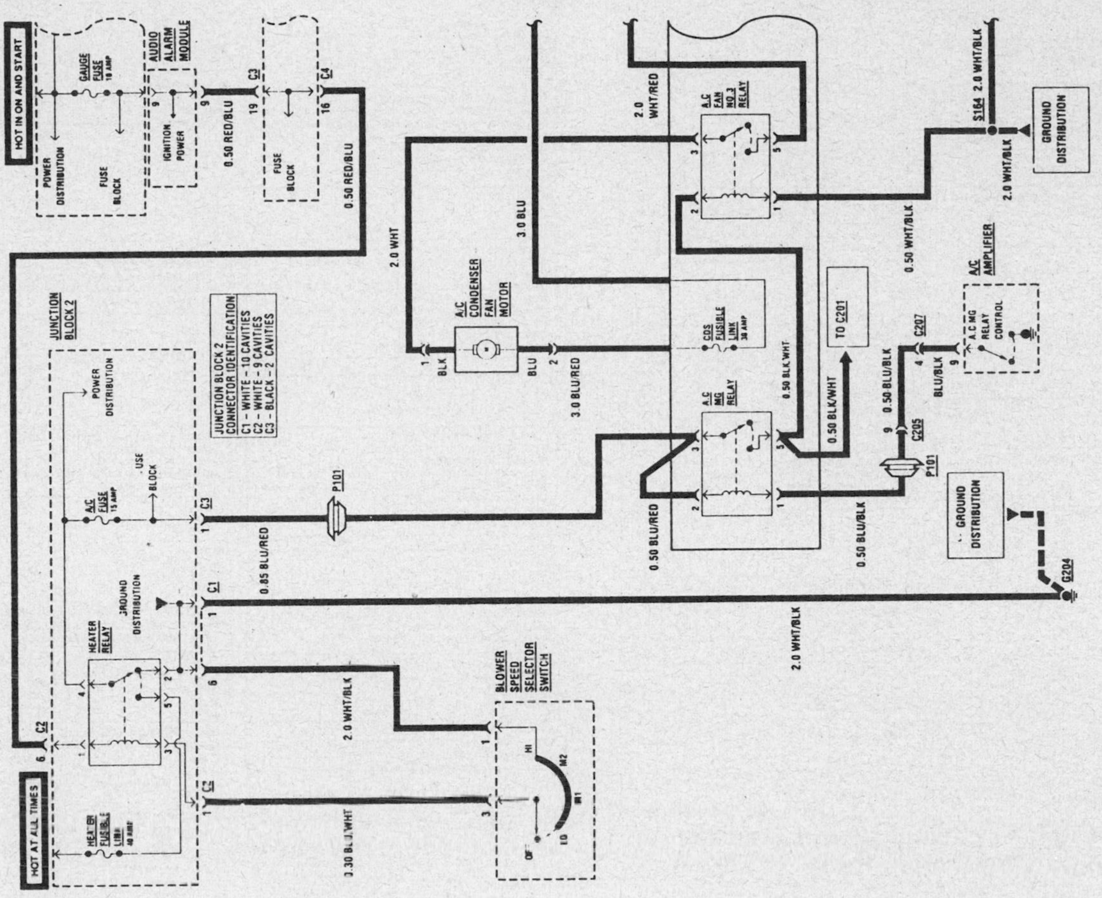
GC1089300121020X
HOT IN ON AND START
HOT AT ALL TIMES
JUNCTION BLOCK 2
A/C CONDENSER FAN MOTOR
A/C FAN NO. 3 RELAY
A/C MG RELAY
A/C AMPLIFIER
BLOWER SPEED SELECTOR SWITCH
HEATER RELAY
GROUND DISTRIBUTION
AUDIO ALARM MODULE
FUSE BLOCK
TO C201
G204
P101

Fig. 145 Cooling fan wiring circuit (Part 2 of 2). 1993 Prizm w/A/C

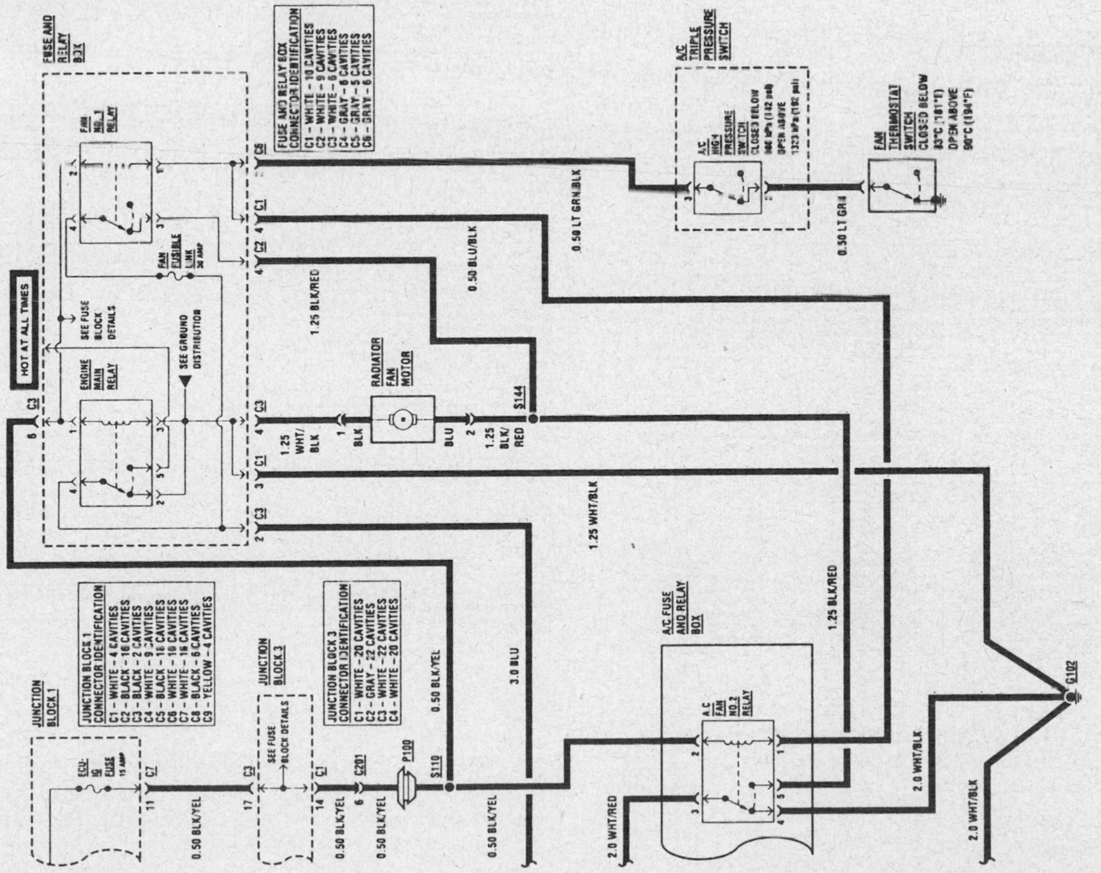
GC1089300121010X
HOT AT ALL TIMES
FUSE AND RELAY BOX
ENGINE MAIN RELAY
FAN NO. 1 RELAY
RADIATOR FAN MOTOR
A/C TRIPLE PRESSURE SWITCH
FAN THERMOSTAT SWITCH
A/C FUSE AND RELAY BOX
A/C FAN NO. 2 RELAY
JUNCTION BLOCK 1
JUNCTION BLOCK 3
G102
S110
S144
P100

Fig. 145 Cooling fan wiring circuit (Part 1 of 2). 1993 Prizm w/A/C

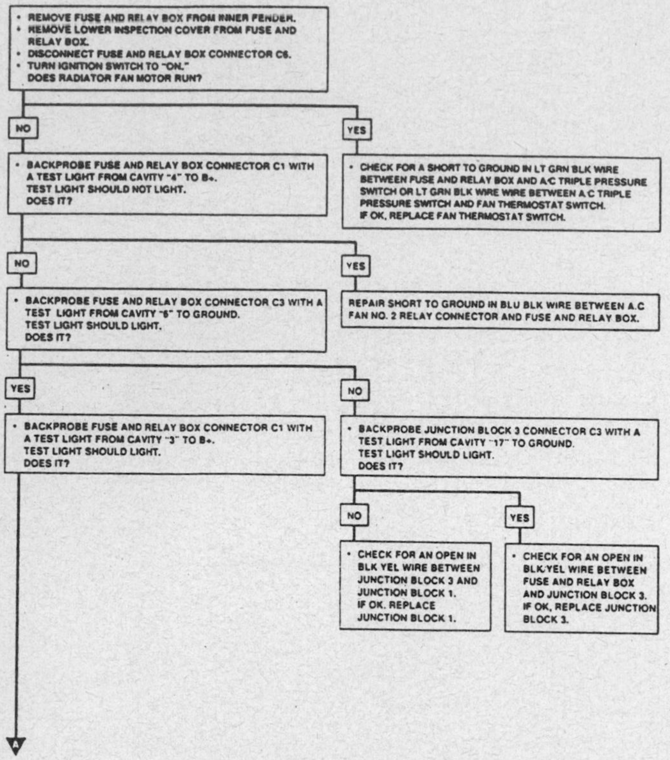
• REMOVE FUSE AND RELAY BOX FROM INNER FENDER.
• REMOVE LOWER INSPECTION COVER FROM FUSE AND RELAY BOX.
• DISCONNECT FUSE AND RELAY BOX CONNECTOR C6.
• TURN IGNITION SWITCH TO "ON."
DOES RADIATOR FAN MOTOR RUN?
NO
YES
• BACKPROBE FUSE AND RELAY BOX CONNECTOR C1 WITH A TEST LIGHT FROM CAVITY "4" TO B+.
TEST LIGHT SHOULD NOT LIGHT.
DOES IT?
• CHECK FOR A SHORT TO GROUND IN LT GRN BLK WIRE BETWEEN FUSE AND RELAY BOX AND A/C TRIPLE PRESSURE SWITCH OR LT GRN BLK WIRE WIRE BETWEEN A/C TRIPLE PRESSURE SWITCH AND FAN THERMOSTAT SWITCH.
IF OK, REPLACE FAN THERMOSTAT SWITCH.
NO
YES
• BACKPROBE FUSE AND RELAY BOX CONNECTOR C3 WITH A TEST LIGHT FROM CAVITY "6" TO GROUND.
TEST LIGHT SHOULD LIGHT.
DOES IT?
REPAIR SHORT TO GROUND IN BLU BLK WIRE BETWEEN A/C FAN NO. 2 RELAY CONNECTOR AND FUSE AND RELAY BOX.
YES
NO
• BACKPROBE FUSE AND RELAY BOX CONNECTOR C1 WITH A TEST LIGHT FROM CAVITY "3" TO B+.
TEST LIGHT SHOULD LIGHT.
DOES IT?
• BACKPROBE JUNCTION BLOCK 3 CONNECTOR C3 WITH A TEST LIGHT FROM CAVITY "17" TO GROUND.
TEST LIGHT SHOULD LIGHT.
DOES IT?
NO
YES
• CHECK FOR AN OPEN IN BLK YEL WIRE BETWEEN JUNCTION BLOCK 3 AND JUNCTION BLOCK 1.
IF OK, REPLACE JUNCTION BLOCK 1.
• CHECK FOR AN OPEN IN BLK/YEL WIRE BETWEEN FUSE AND RELAY BOX AND JUNCTION BLOCK 3.
IF OK, REPLACE JUNCTION BLOCK 3.
A
GC1089300122010X

Fig. 146 Cooling fan system diagnosis (Radiator fan motor does not run) (Part 1 of 2). 1993 Prizm

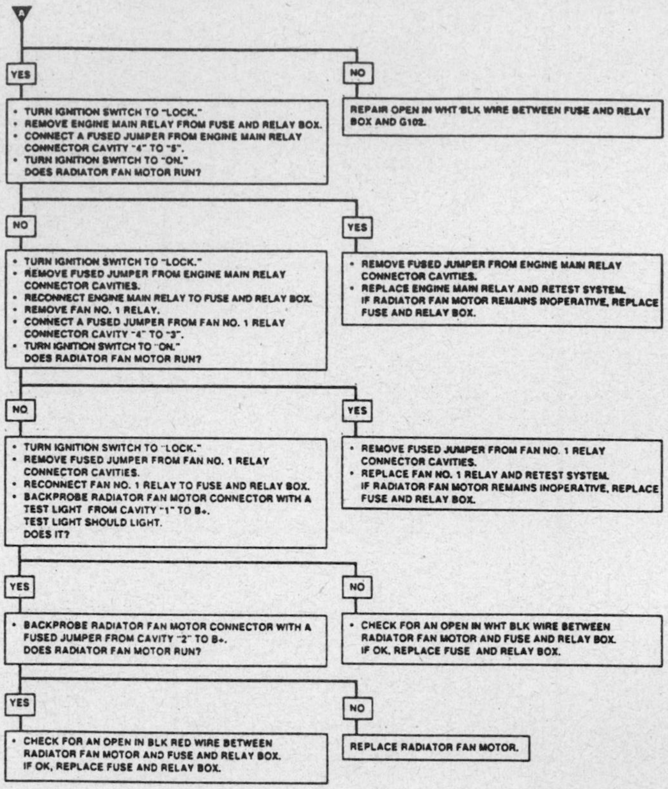
A
YES
NO
• TURN IGNITION SWITCH TO "LOCK."
• REMOVE ENGINE MAIN RELAY FROM FUSE AND RELAY BOX.
• CONNECT A FUSED JUMPER FROM ENGINE MAIN RELAY CONNECTOR CAVITY "4" TO "5".
• TURN IGNITION SWITCH TO "ON."
DOES RADIATOR FAN MOTOR RUN?
REPAIR OPEN IN WHT BLK WIRE BETWEEN FUSE AND RELAY BOX AND G102.
NO
YES
• TURN IGNITION SWITCH TO "LOCK."
• REMOVE FUSED JUMPER FROM ENGINE MAIN RELAY CONNECTOR CAVITIES.
• RECONNECT ENGINE MAIN RELAY TO FUSE AND RELAY BOX.
• REMOVE FAN NO. 1 RELAY.
• CONNECT A FUSED JUMPER FROM FAN NO. 1 RELAY CONNECTOR CAVITY "4" TO "3".
• TURN IGNITION SWITCH TO "ON."
DOES RADIATOR FAN MOTOR RUN?
• REMOVE FUSED JUMPER FROM ENGINE MAIN RELAY CONNECTOR CAVITIES.
• REPLACE ENGINE MAIN RELAY AND RETEST SYSTEM.
IF RADIATOR FAN MOTOR REMAINS INOPERATIVE, REPLACE FUSE AND RELAY BOX.
NO
YES
• TURN IGNITION SWITCH TO "LOCK."
• REMOVE FUSED JUMPER FROM FAN NO. 1 RELAY CONNECTOR CAVITIES.
• RECONNECT FAN NO. 1 RELAY TO FUSE AND RELAY BOX.
• BACKPROBE RADIATOR FAN MOTOR CONNECTOR WITH A TEST LIGHT FROM CAVITY "1" TO B+.
TEST LIGHT SHOULD LIGHT.
DOES IT?
• REMOVE FUSED JUMPER FROM FAN NO. 1 RELAY CONNECTOR CAVITIES.
• REPLACE FAN NO. 1 RELAY AND RETEST SYSTEM.
IF RADIATOR FAN MOTOR REMAINS INOPERATIVE, REPLACE FUSE AND RELAY BOX.
YES
NO
• BACKPROBE RADIATOR FAN MOTOR CONNECTOR WITH A FUSED JUMPER FROM CAVITY "2" TO B+.
DOES RADIATOR FAN MOTOR RUN?
• CHECK FOR AN OPEN IN WHT BLK WIRE BETWEEN RADIATOR FAN MOTOR AND FUSE AND RELAY BOX.
IF OK, REPLACE FUSE AND RELAY BOX.
YES
NO
• CHECK FOR AN OPEN IN BLK RED WIRE BETWEEN RADIATOR FAN MOTOR AND FUSE AND RELAY BOX.
IF OK, REPLACE FUSE AND RELAY BOX.
REPLACE RADIATOR FAN MOTOR.
GC1089300122020X

Fig. 146 Cooling fan system diagnosis (Radiator fan motor does not run) (Part 2 of 2). 1993 Prizm

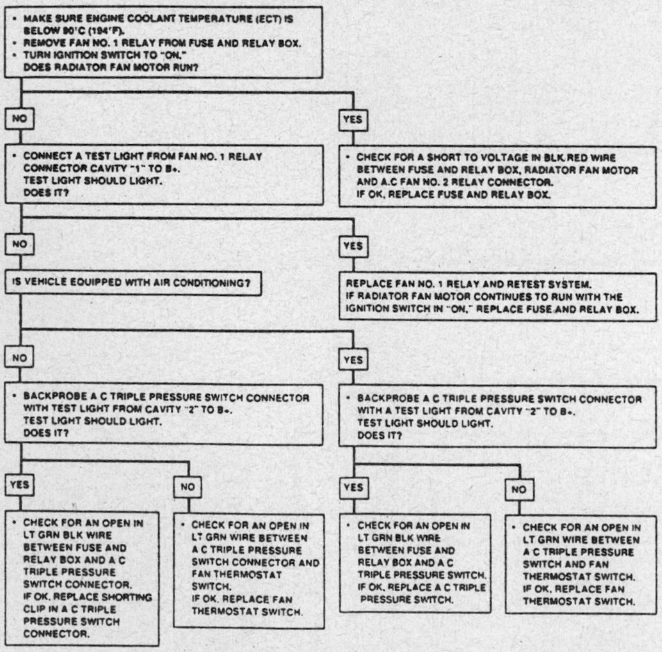
• MAKE SURE ENGINE COOLANT TEMPERATURE (ECT) IS BELOW 90°C (194°F).
• REMOVE FAN NO. 1 RELAY FROM FUSE AND RELAY BOX.
• TURN IGNITION SWITCH TO "ON."
DOES RADIATOR FAN MOTOR RUN?
NO
YES
• CONNECT A TEST LIGHT FROM FAN NO. 1 RELAY CONNECTOR CAVITY "1" TO B+.
TEST LIGHT SHOULD LIGHT.
DOES IT?
• CHECK FOR A SHORT TO VOLTAGE IN BLK RED WIRE BETWEEN FUSE AND RELAY BOX, RADIATOR FAN MOTOR AND A.C FAN NO. 2 RELAY CONNECTOR.
IF OK, REPLACE FUSE AND RELAY BOX.
NO
YES
IS VEHICLE EQUIPPED WITH AIR CONDITIONING?
REPLACE FAN NO. 1 RELAY AND RETEST SYSTEM.
IF RADIATOR FAN MOTOR CONTINUES TO RUN WITH THE IGNITION SWITCH IN "ON," REPLACE FUSE AND RELAY BOX.
NO
YES
• BACKPROBE A C TRIPLE PRESSURE SWITCH CONNECTOR WITH TEST LIGHT FROM CAVITY "2" TO B+.
TEST LIGHT SHOULD LIGHT.
DOES IT?
• BACKPROBE A C TRIPLE PRESSURE SWITCH CONNECTOR WITH A TEST LIGHT FROM CAVITY "2" TO B+.
TEST LIGHT SHOULD LIGHT.
DOES IT?
YES
NO
YES
NO
• CHECK FOR AN OPEN IN LT GRN BLK WIRE BETWEEN FUSE AND RELAY BOX AND A C TRIPLE PRESSURE SWITCH CONNECTOR.
IF OK, REPLACE SHORTING CLIP IN A C TRIPLE PRESSURE SWITCH CONNECTOR.
• CHECK FOR AN OPEN IN LT GRN WIRE BETWEEN A C TRIPLE PRESSURE SWITCH CONNECTOR AND FAN THERMOSTAT SWITCH.
IF OK, REPLACE FAN THERMOSTAT SWITCH.
• CHECK FOR AN OPEN IN LT GRN BLK WIRE BETWEEN FUSE AND RELAY BOX AND A C TRIPLE PRESSURE SWITCH.
IF OK, REPLACE A C TRIPLE PRESSURE SWITCH.
• CHECK FOR AN OPEN IN LT GRN WIRE BETWEEN A C TRIPLE PRESSURE SWITCH AND FAN THERMOSTAT SWITCH.
IF OK, REPLACE FAN THERMOSTAT SWITCH.
GC1089300123000X

Fig. 147 Cooling fan system diagnosis (Radiator fan motor runs continuously with ignition switch on). 1993 Prizm

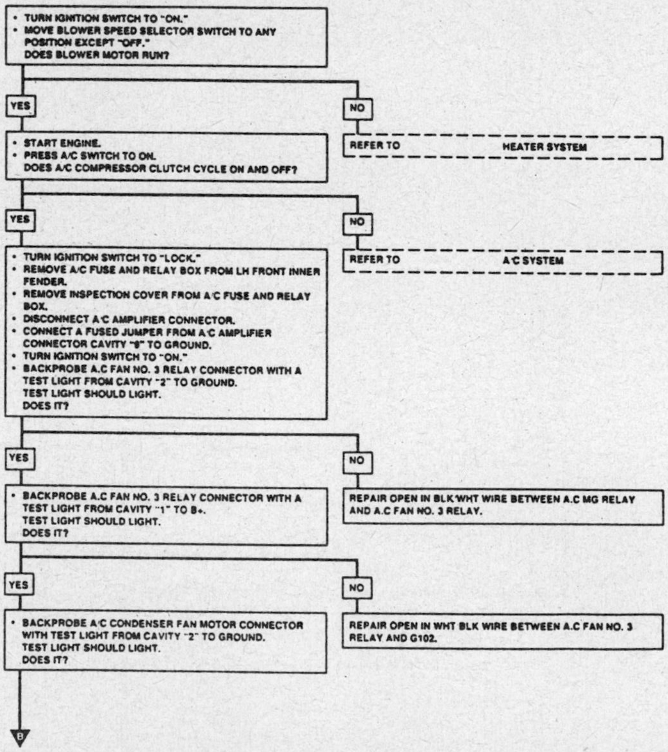
• TURN IGNITION SWITCH TO "ON."
• MOVE BLOWER SPEED SELECTOR SWITCH TO ANY POSITION EXCEPT "OFF."
DOES BLOWER MOTOR RUN?
YES
NO
• START ENGINE.
• PRESS A/C SWITCH TO ON.
DOES A/C COMPRESSOR CLUTCH CYCLE ON AND OFF?
REFER TO HEATER SYSTEM
YES
NO
• TURN IGNITION SWITCH TO "LOCK."
• REMOVE A/C FUSE AND RELAY BOX FROM LH FRONT INNER FENDER.
• REMOVE INSPECTION COVER FROM A/C FUSE AND RELAY BOX.
• DISCONNECT A/C AMPLIFIER CONNECTOR.
• CONNECT A FUSED JUMPER FROM A/C AMPLIFIER CONNECTOR CAVITY "8" TO GROUND.
• TURN IGNITION SWITCH TO "ON."
• BACKPROBE A.C FAN NO. 3 RELAY CONNECTOR WITH A TEST LIGHT FROM CAVITY "2" TO GROUND.
TEST LIGHT SHOULD LIGHT.
DOES IT?
REFER TO A/C SYSTEM
YES
NO
• BACKPROBE A.C FAN NO. 3 RELAY CONNECTOR WITH A TEST LIGHT FROM CAVITY "1" TO B+.
TEST LIGHT SHOULD LIGHT.
DOES IT?
REPAIR OPEN IN BLK WHT WIRE BETWEEN A.C MG RELAY AND A.C FAN NO. 3 RELAY.
YES
NO
• BACKPROBE A/C CONDENSER FAN MOTOR CONNECTOR WITH TEST LIGHT FROM CAVITY "2" TO GROUND.
TEST LIGHT SHOULD LIGHT.
DOES IT?
REPAIR OPEN IN WHT BLK WIRE BETWEEN A.C FAN NO. 3 RELAY AND G102.
B
GC1089300124010X

Fig. 148 Cooling fan system diagnosis (Radiator fan motor & A/C condenser fan motor do not run at half speed during A/C system operation) (Part 1 of 2). 1993 Prizm

B

YES

- BACKPROBE A/C FAN NO. 2 RELAY CONNECTOR WITH A TEST LIGHT FROM CAVITY "1" TO B+. TEST LIGHT SHOULD LIGHT. DOES IT?

NO

- CHECK FOR AN OPEN IN BLU RED WIRE BETWEEN A/C CONDENSER FAN MOTOR AND A/C FUSE AND RELAY BOX OR IN BLU WIRE BETWEEN A/C FUSE AND RELAY BOX AND FUSE AND RELAY BOX. IF OK, REPLACE FUSE AND RELAY BOX.

YES

- BACKPROBE A/C FAN NO. 2 RELAY CONNECTOR WITH A TEST LIGHT FROM CAVITY "2" TO GROUND. TEST LIGHT SHOULD LIGHT. DOES IT?

NO

- CHECK FOR AN OPEN IN BLU BLK WIRE BETWEEN A/C FAN NO. 2 RELAY AND FUSE AND RELAY BOX. IF OK, REPLACE FUSE AND RELAY BOX.

YES

- BACKPROBE A/C FAN NO. 3 RELAY CONNECTOR WITH A DIGITAL MULTIMETER FROM CAVITY "3" TO GROUND.
- MEASURE VOLTAGE.

NO

REPAIR OPEN BLK YEL WIRE BETWEEN S110 AND A/C FAN NO. 2 RELAY.

MORE THAN 10.0 VOLTS

- BACKPROBE A/C FAN NO. 2 RELAY CONNECTOR WITH A DIGITAL MULTIMETER FROM CAVITY "3" TO GROUND.
- MEASURE VOLTAGE.

LESS THAN 10.0 VOLTS

- CHECK FOR AN OPEN IN WHT WIRE BETWEEN A/C CONDENSER FAN MOTOR AND A/C FAN NO. 3 RELAY. IF OK, REPLACE A/C CONDENSER FAN MOTOR.

MORE THAN 10.0 VOLTS

- CHECK FOR AN OPEN IN BLK RED WIRE BETWEEN S144 AND A/C FAN NO. 2 RELAY. IF OK, REPLACE A/C FAN NO. 2 RELAY.

LESS THAN 10.0 VOLTS

- CHECK FOR AN OPEN IN WHT RED WIRE BETWEEN A/C FAN NO. 2 RELAY AND A/C FAN NO. 3 RELAY. IF OK, REPLACE A/C FAN NO. 3 RELAY.

GC1089300124020X

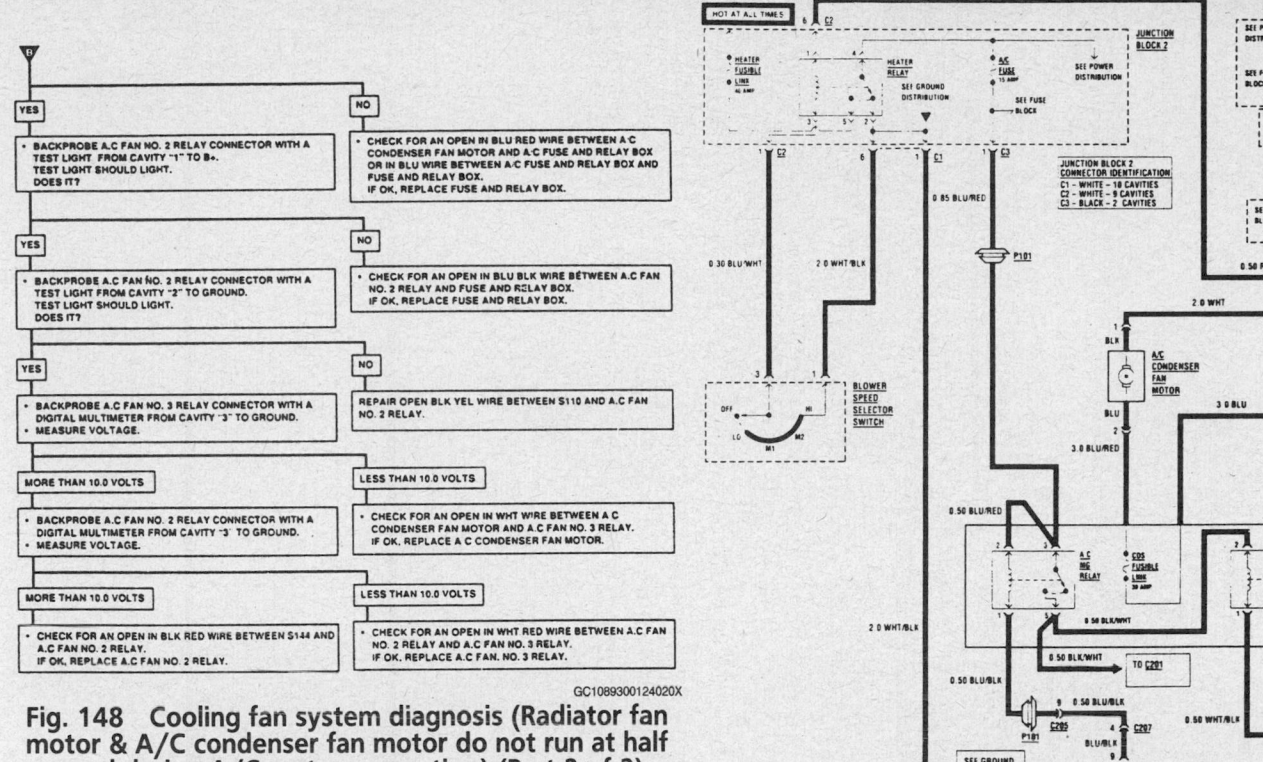

Fig. 148 Cooling fan system diagnosis (Radiator fan motor & A/C condenser fan motor do not run at half speed during A/C system operation) (Part 2 of 2). 1993 Prizm

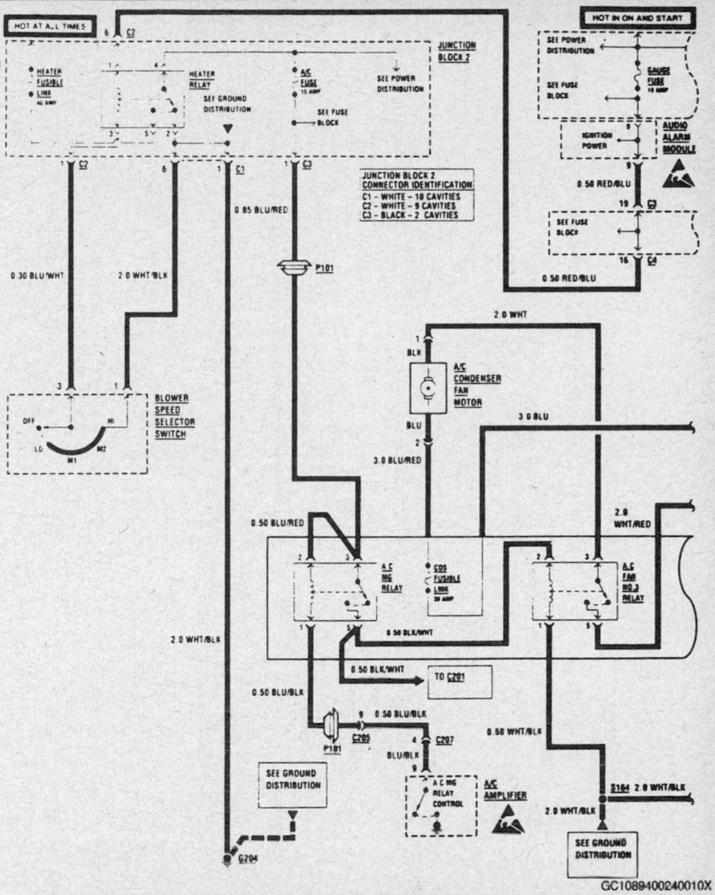
HOT AT ALL TIMES
HOT IN ON AND START
JUNCTION BLOCK 2
JUNCTION BLOCK 2 CONNECTOR IDENTIFICATION
C1 - WHITE - 10 CAVITIES
C2 - WHITE - 9 CAVITIES
C3 - BLACK - 2 CAVITIES
BLOWER SPEED SELECTOR SWITCH
A/C CONDENSER FAN MOTOR
A/C AMPLIFIER
SEE GROUND DISTRIBUTION
GC1089400240010X

Fig. 149 Cooling fan wiring circuit (Part 1 of 2). 1994 Prizm with A/C

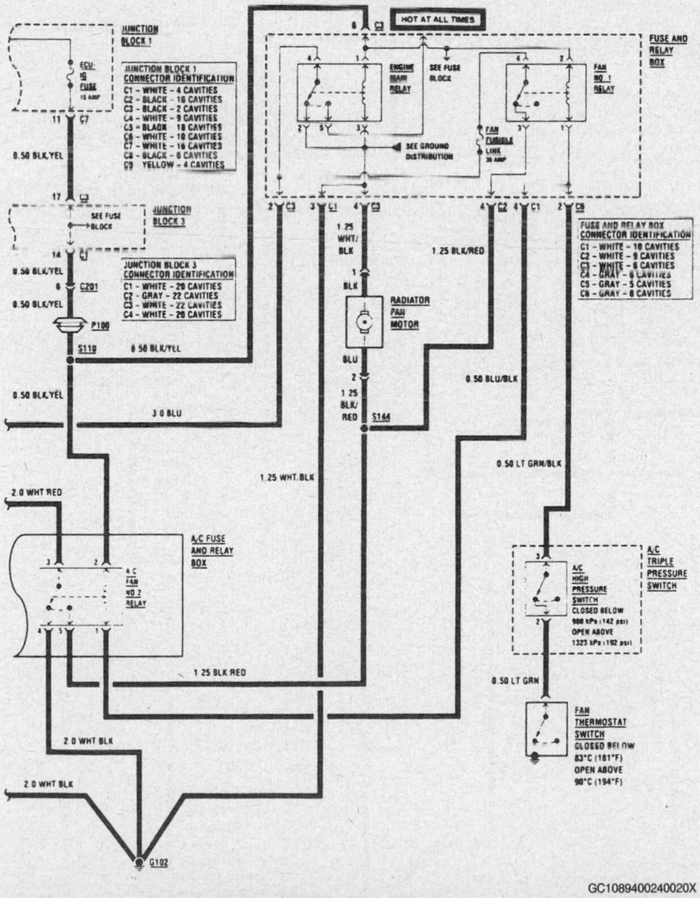
JUNCTION BLOCK 1
HOT AT ALL TIMES
FUSE AND RELAY BOX
JUNCTION BLOCK 3
RADIATOR FAN MOTOR
A/C FUSE AND RELAY BOX
A/C TRIPLE PRESSURE SWITCH
FAN THERMOSTAT SWITCH
G102
GC1089400240020X

Fig. 149 Cooling fan wiring circuit (Part 2 of 2). 1994 Prizm with A/C

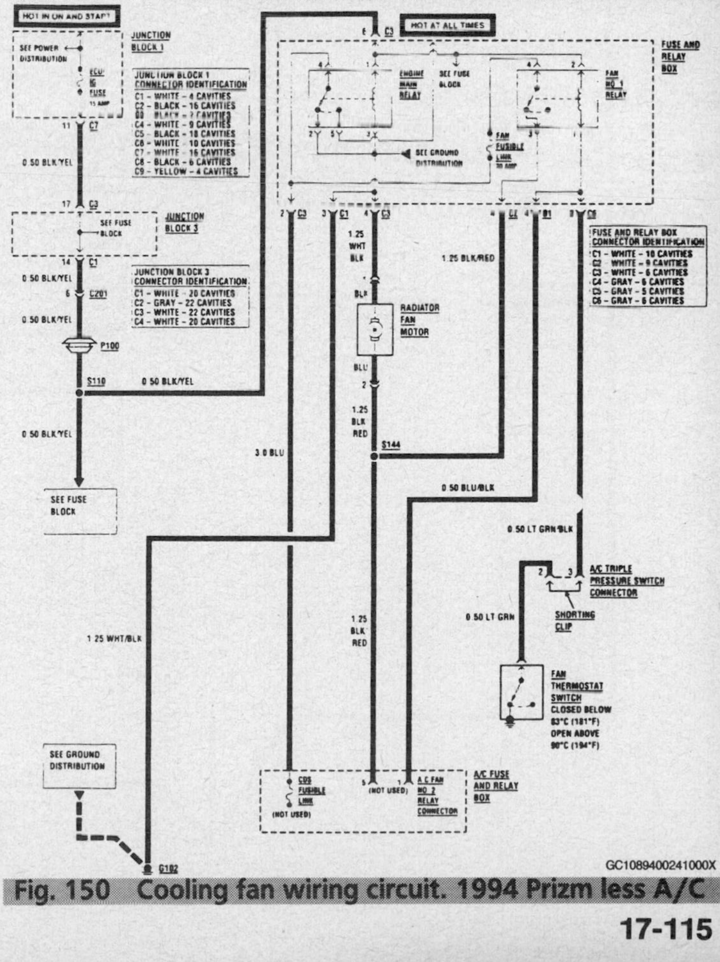
HOT IN ON AND START
HOT AT ALL TIMES
JUNCTION BLOCK 1
JUNCTION BLOCK 3
FUSE AND RELAY BOX
RADIATOR FAN MOTOR
A/C TRIPLE PRESSURE SWITCH CONNECTOR
SHORTING CLIP
FAN THERMOSTAT SWITCH
SEE GROUND DISTRIBUTION
A/C FUSE AND RELAY BOX
G102
GC1089400241000X

Fig. 150 Cooling fan wiring circuit. 1994 Prizm less A/C

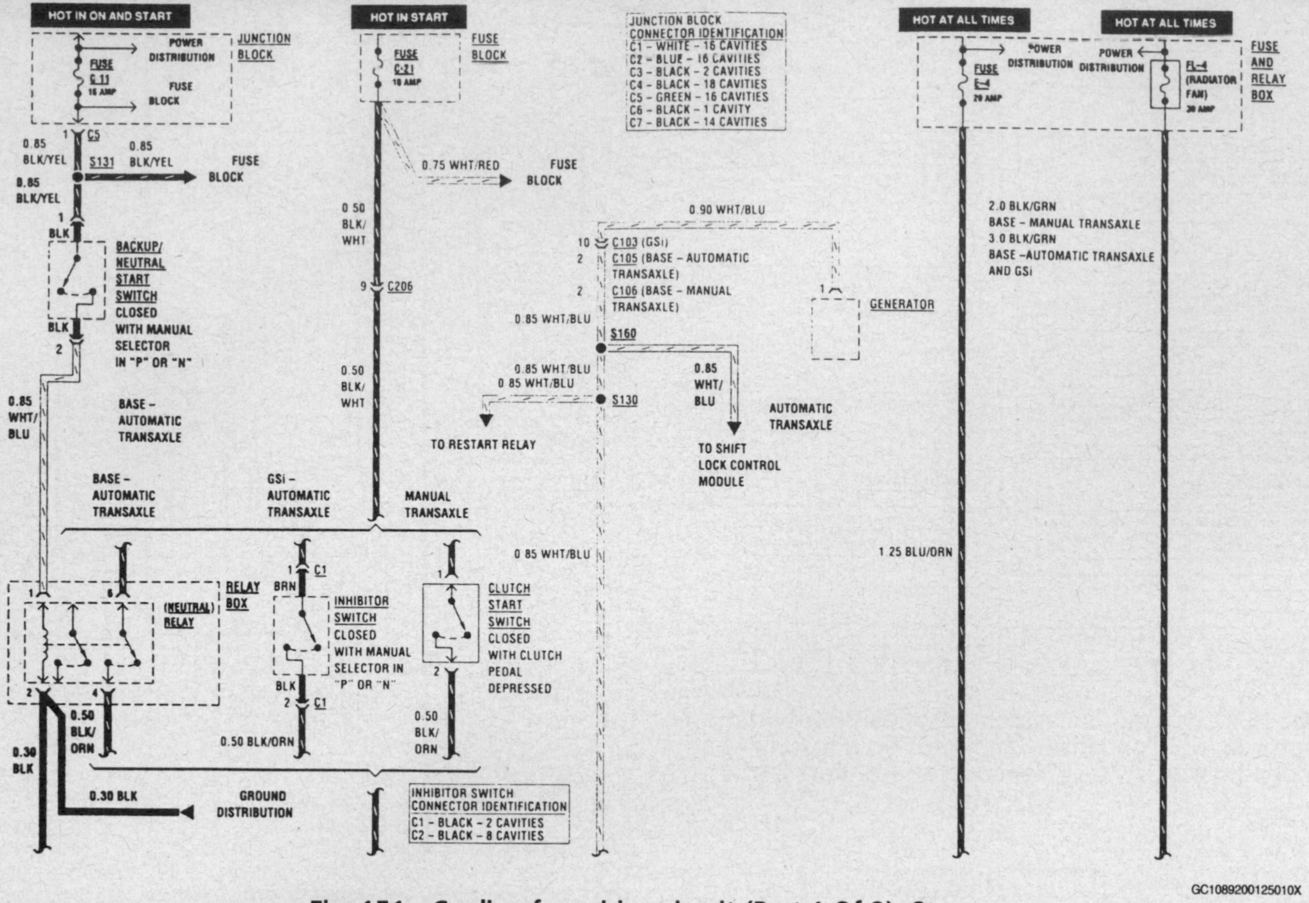
HOT IN ON AND START
POWER DISTRIBUTION
JUNCTION BLOCK
FUSE C-11 15 AMP
FUSE BLOCK
C5
0.85 BLK/YEL
S131
FUSE BLOCK
BACKUP/ NEUTRAL START SWITCH CLOSED WITH MANUAL SELECTOR IN "P" OR "N"
BLK
0.85 WHT/ BLU
BASE - AUTOMATIC TRANSAXLE
HOT IN START
FUSE C-21 10 AMP
FUSE BLOCK
0.75 WHT/RED
0.50 BLK/ WHT
C206
JUNCTION BLOCK CONNECTOR IDENTIFICATION
C1 - WHITE - 16 CAVITIES
C2 - BLUE - 16 CAVITIES
C3 - BLACK - 2 CAVITIES
C4 - BLACK - 18 CAVITIES
C5 - GREEN - 16 CAVITIES
C6 - BLACK - 1 CAVITY
C7 - BLACK - 14 CAVITIES
0.90 WHT/BLU
C103 (GSi)
C105 (BASE - AUTOMATIC TRANSAXLE)
C106 (BASE - MANUAL TRANSAXLE)
GENERATOR
0.85 WHT/BLU
S160
S130
0.85 WHT/ BLU
AUTOMATIC TRANSAXLE
TO RESTART RELAY
TO SHIFT LOCK CONTROL MODULE
HOT AT ALL TIMES
POWER DISTRIBUTION
FUSE E-4 20 AMP
FL-4 (RADIATOR FAN) 30 AMP
FUSE AND RELAY BOX
2.0 BLK/GRN BASE - MANUAL TRANSAXLE
3.0 BLK/GRN BASE - AUTOMATIC TRANSAXLE AND GSi
1.25 BLU/ORN
BASE - AUTOMATIC TRANSAXLE
GSi - AUTOMATIC TRANSAXLE
MANUAL TRANSAXLE
RELAY BOX
(NEUTRAL) RELAY
C1
BRN
INHIBITOR SWITCH CLOSED WITH MANUAL SELECTOR IN "P" OR "N"
CLUTCH START SWITCH CLOSED WITH CLUTCH PEDAL DEPRESSED
0.50 BLK/ ORN
0.30 BLK
0.50 BLK/ORN
0.50 BLK/ ORN
GROUND DISTRIBUTION
INHIBITOR SWITCH CONNECTOR IDENTIFICATION
C1 - BLACK - 2 CAVITIES
C2 - BLACK - 8 CAVITIES
GC1089200125010X

Fig. 151 Cooling fan wiring circuit (Part 1 Of 2). Storm

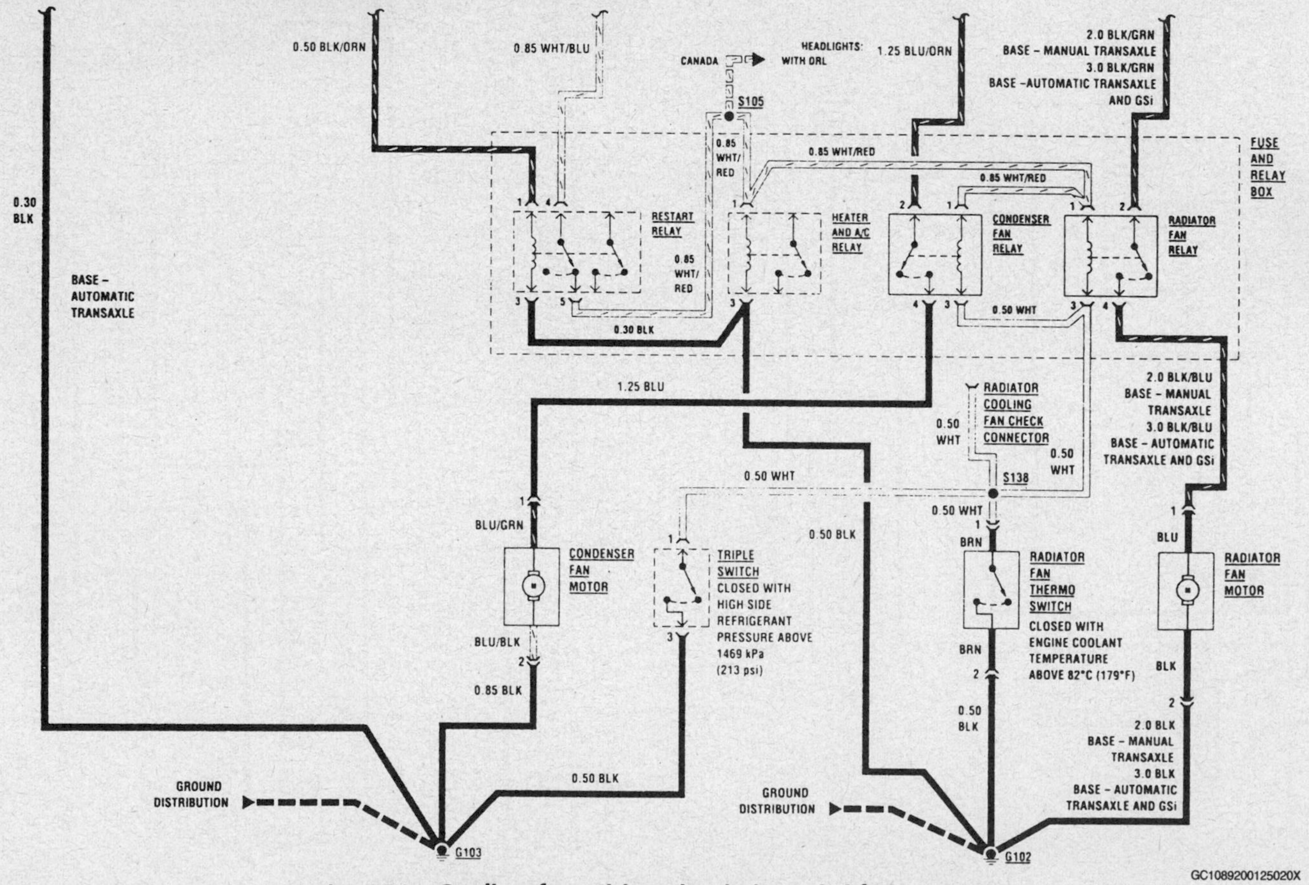
0.50 BLK/ORN
0.85 WHT/BLU
CANADA
HEADLIGHTS: WITH DRL
1.25 BLU/ORN
2.0 BLK/GRN BASE - MANUAL TRANSAXLE
3.0 BLK/GRN BASE - AUTOMATIC TRANSAXLE AND GSi
S105
FUSE AND RELAY BOX
0.85 WHT/RED
0.30 BLK
BASE - AUTOMATIC TRANSAXLE
RESTART RELAY
HEATER AND A/C RELAY
CONDENSER FAN RELAY
RADIATOR FAN RELAY
0.50 WHT
1.25 BLU
RADIATOR COOLING FAN CHECK CONNECTOR
S138
2.0 BLK/BLU BASE - MANUAL TRANSAXLE
3.0 BLK/BLU BASE - AUTOMATIC TRANSAXLE AND GSi
BLU/GRN
CONDENSER FAN MOTOR
TRIPLE SWITCH CLOSED WITH HIGH SIDE REFRIGERANT PRESSURE ABOVE 1469 kPa (213 psi)
0.50 BLK
BRN
RADIATOR FAN THERMO SWITCH CLOSED WITH ENGINE COOLANT TEMPERATURE ABOVE 82°C (179°F)
BLU
RADIATOR FAN MOTOR
BLU/BLK
0.85 BLK
BLK
2.0 BLK BASE - MANUAL TRANSAXLE
3.0 BLK BASE - AUTOMATIC TRANSAXLE AND GSi
GROUND DISTRIBUTION
G103
G102
GC1089200125020X

Fig. 151 Cooling fan wiring circuit (Part 2 Of 2). Storm

COOLANT FANS	DIAGNOSTIC CHART A	
TEST	**RESULT**	**ACTION**
A1. Start and run engine until coolant temperature reaches 82°C (179°F).	RADIATOR FAN MOTOR and CONDENSER FAN MOTOR operate.	GO TO **A2.**
	Neither fan operates.	GO TO **A4.**
	RADIATOR FAN MOTOR only operates.	GO TO **A7.**
	CONDENSER FAN MOTOR only operates.	GO TO **A13.**
A2. Shut off engine. Disconnect RADIATOR FAN THERMO SWITCH connector. Start engine. Operate air conditioning for five minutes.	RADIATOR FAN MOTOR and CONDENSER FAN MOTOR both operate at least once during the five minute test.	GO TO **A3.**
	Neither fan operates at all during the five minute test.	GO TO **A17.**
A3. Turn ignition switch to "OFF."	Both fans stop operating.	All systems diagnosed are functioning normally.
	Both fans continue to operate.	GO TO **A24.**
	CONDENSER FAN MOTOR continues to operate.	GO TO **A25.**
	RADIATOR FAN MOTOR continues to operate.	GO TO **A26.**
A4. Connect a fused jumper from RADIATOR COOLING FAN CHECK CONNECTOR to chassis ground.	Both fans operate.	GO TO **A5.**
	Neither fan operates.	GO TO **A19.**
A5. Shut off engine. Disconnect RADIATOR FAN THERMO SWITCH connector. Connect a fused jumper between terminals 1 and 2. Start engine.	Both fans operate.	Replace RADIATOR FAN THERMO SWITCH.
	Neither fan operates.	GO TO **A6.**
A6. Shut off engine. Remove jumper from RADIATOR FAN THERMO SWITCH. Connect a digital multimeter from connector terminal 2 to chassis ground. Measure resistance.	More than 0.4 ohms.	Repair BLK ground wire between RADIATOR FAN THERMO SWITCH and G102.
	Less than 0.4 ohms.	Repair open in WHT wire between RADIATOR FAN THERMO SWITCH and S138.

GC1089200126010X

Fig. 152 System diagnosis chart (Part 1 of 4). Storm

COOLANT FANS	DIAGNOSTIC CHART A (CONT'D)	
TEST	**RESULT**	**ACTION**
A7. Shut off engine. Remove Condenser Fan Relay and Radiator Fan Relay from FUSE AND RELAY BOX. Connect a digital multimeter from Condenser Fan Relay connector cavity 3 to chassis ground. Measure resistance	More than 2.0 ohms.	Repair open in WHT wire between Radiator Fan Relay and Condenser Fan Relay.
	Less than 2.0 ohms.	Reinstall Radiator Fan Relay and GO TO **A8.**
A8. Connect a test lamp from Condenser Fan Relay connector cavity 1 to chassis ground. Start engine.	Test lamp does not light.	Repair open in WHT/RED wire between Condenser Fan Relay and Radiator Fan Relay.
	Test lamp lights.	GO TO **A9.**
A9. Connect a test lamp from Condenser Fan Relay connector cavity 2 to chassis ground.	Test lamp does not light.	Repair open in BLU/ORN wire between Fuse E-4 and Condenser Fan Relay.
	Test lamp lights.	GO TO **A10.**
A10. Shut off engine. Disconnect CONDENSER FAN MOTOR connector. Connect a digital multimeter from Condenser Fan Relay connector cavity 4 to CONDENSER FAN MOTOR connector cavity 1. Measure resistance.	Less than 2.0 ohms.	Reconnect CONDENSER FAN MOTOR connector and GO TO **A11.**
	More than 2.0 ohms.	Repair open in BLU wire between CONDENSER FAN MOTOR and FUSE AND RELAY BOX.
A11. Reinstall Condenser Fan Relay. Backprobe CONDENSER FAN MOTOR with a test lamp from connector cavity 1 to chassis ground.	Test lamp does not light.	Replace Condenser Fan Relay.
	Test lamp lights.	GO TO **A12.**
A12. Disconnect CONDENSER FAN MOTOR connector. Connect a digital multimeter from cavity 2 to chassis ground. Measure resistance.	Less than 3.0 ohms.	Replace CONDENSER FAN MOTOR.
	More than 3.0 ohms.	Repair BLK ground wire between CONDENSER FAN MOTOR and G103.
A13. Shut off engine. Remove Radiator Fan Relay from FUSE AND RELAY BOX. Connect a test lamp from connector cavity 2 to chassis ground. Start engine.	Test lamp does not light.	Repair open in BLK/GRN wire between FL-4 and Radiator Fan Relay.
	Test lamp lights.	GO TO **A14.**
A14. Shut off engine. Disconnect RADIATOR FAN MOTOR connector. Remove Radiator Fan Relay from FUSE AND RELAY BOX. Connect a digital multimeter from connector cavity 4 to RADIATOR FAN MOTOR connector cavity 1. Measure resistance.	Less than 3.0 ohms.	Reconnect RADIATOR FAN MOTOR connector. GO TO **A15.**
	More than 3.0 ohms.	Repair open in BLK/BLU wire between RADIATOR FAN MOTOR and FUSE AND RELAY BOX.

GC1089200126020X

Fig. 152 System diagnosis chart (Part 2 of 4). Storm

COOLANT FANS	DIAGNOSTIC CHART A (CONT'D)		
	TEST	**RESULT**	**ACTION**
A15.	Reinstall Radiator Fan Relay. Backprobe RADIATOR FAN MOTOR connector cavity 1 with a test lamp to chassis ground. Start engine.	Test lamp does not light.	Replace Radiator Fan Relay.
		Test lamp lights.	GO TO **A16.**
A16.	Shut off engine. Disconnect RADIATOR FAN MOTOR connector. Connect a digital multimeter from connector terminal 2 to chassis ground. Measure resistance.	Less than 3.0 ohms.	Replace RADIATOR FAN MOTOR.
		More than 3.0 ohms.	Repair BLK ground wire between RADIATOR FAN MOTOR and G102.
A17.	Shut off engine. Disconnect TRIPLE SWITCH connector and remove Condenser Fan Relay from FUSE AND RELAY BOX. Connect a digital multimeter from TRIPLE SWITCH connector cavity 1 to Condenser Fan Relay connector cavity 3. Measure resistance.	More than 2.0 ohms.	Repair open in WHT wire between S138 and TRIPLE SWITCH.
		Less than 2.0 ohms.	GO TO **A18.**
A18.	Connect a digital multimeter from TRIPLE SWITCH connector terminal 3 to chassis ground. Measure resistance.	More than 2.0 ohms.	Repair BLK ground wire between TRIPLE SWITCH and G103.
		Less than 2.0 ohms.	Check for poor connection at TRIPLE SWITCH. If OK, replace TRIPLE SWITCH. IMPORTANT: Receiver/Dryer Assembly must be replaced as a unit in order to replace TRIPLE SWITCH.
A19.	Shut off engine. Remove Condenser Fan Relay and Radiator Fan Relay from FUSE AND RELAY BOX. Connect a digital multimeter from Radiator Fan Relay connector cavity 3 to RADIATOR FAN THERMO SWITCH connector terminal 1. Measure resistance.	More than 2.0 ohms.	Repair open in WHT wire between FUSE AND RELAY BOX and S138.
		Less than 2.0 ohms.	GO TO **A20.**
A20.	Backprobe GENERATOR connector with a test lamp from cavity 1 to chassis ground.	Test lamp does not light.	A fault exists within the GENERATOR or related circuitry. Refer to Starter and Charging System Diagnosis
		Test lamp lights.	GO TO **A21.**
A21.	Shut off engine. Remove Restart Relay from FUSE AND RELAY BOX. Connect a test lamp from connector cavity 4 to chassis ground. Start engine.	Test lamp does not light.	Repair open in WHT/BLU wire between GENERATOR and FUSE AND RELAY BOX.
		Test lamp lights.	GO TO **A22.**

GC1089200126030X

Fig. 152 System diagnosis chart (Part 3 of 4). Storm

COOLANT FANS	DIAGNOSTIC CHART A (CONT'D)		
	TEST	**RESULT**	**ACTION**
A22.	Shut off engine. Remove Heater and A/C Relay from FUSE AND RELAY BOX. Connect a digital multimeter from connector cavity 1 to Restart Relay connector cavity 5. Measure resistance.	Less than 2.0 ohms.	Reinstall Restart Relay. GO TO **A23.**
		More than 2.0 ohms.	Repair open in WHT/RED wire between Restart Relay and Heater and A/C Relay.
A23.	Connect a test lamp from Heater and A/C Relay connector cavity 1 to chassis ground. Start engine.	Test lamp does not light.	Replace Restart Relay.
		Test lamp lights.	Repair open in WHT/RED wire between Heater and A/C Relay and Radiator Fan Relay.
A24.	Remove Restart Relay from FUSE AND RELAY BOX.	Fans stop operating.	Repair short to voltage in WHT/BLU wire between GENERATOR and FUSE AND RELAY BOX.
		Fans continue to operate.	Repair short to voltage in WHT/RED wire between Restart Relay and Condenser Fan Relay.
A25.	Remove Condenser Fan Relay from FUSE AND RELAY BOX.	CONDENSER FAN MOTOR stops operating.	Replace Condenser Fan Relay.
		CONDENSER FAN MOTOR continues to operate.	Repair short to voltage in BLU wire between FUSE AND RELAY BOX and CONDENSER FAN MOTOR.
A26.	Remove Radiator Fan Relay from FUSE AND RELAY BOX.	RADIATOR FAN MOTOR stops operating.	Replace Radiator Fan Relay.
		RADIATOR FAN MOTOR continues to operate.	Repair short to voltage in BLK/BLU wire between FUSE AND RELAY BOX and RADIATOR FAN MOTOR.

GC1089200126040X

Fig. 152 System diagnosis chart (Part 4 of 4). Storm

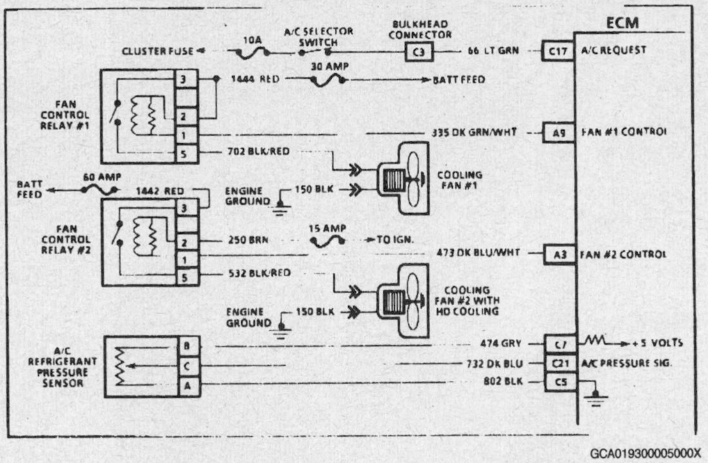
ECM
A/C SELECTOR SWITCH
BULKHEAD CONNECTOR
10A
CLUSTER FUSE
C3
66 LT GRN
C17
A/C REQUEST
30 AMP
1444 RED
BATT FEED
FAN CONTROL RELAY #1
335 DK GRN/WHT
A9
FAN #1 CONTROL
702 BLK/RED
COOLING FAN #1
BATT FEED
60 AMP
1442 RED
ENGINE GROUND
150 BLK
FAN CONTROL RELAY #2
15 AMP
250 BRN
TO IGN.
473 DK BLU/WHT
A3
FAN #2 CONTROL
532 BLK/RED
COOLING FAN #2 WITH HD COOLING
ENGINE GROUND
150 BLK
A/C REFRIGERANT PRESSURE SENSOR
474 GRY
C7
+5 VOLTS
732 DK BLU
C21
A/C PRESSURE SIG.
802 BLK
C5
GCA019300005000X

Fig. 153 Cooling fan relay circuit. 1993 Grand Prix w/3.4L/V6-204 (VIN X) engine

e. Remove upper fan mounting bolts.
f. Raise and support vehicle.
g. Remove front support lower bolts.
h. Remove lower fan mounting bolts and fan.
i. Reverse procedure to install.

CAMARO & FIREBIRD

1. Disconnect battery ground cable, then remove air cleaner top.
2. Disconnect wire harness.
3. Remove cooling fan to radiator support bolts.
4. Remove cooling fan assembly.
5. Reverse procedure to install.

BONNEVILLE

1. Disconnect battery ground cable.
2. Remove harness from fan motor and fan frame.
3. Remove fan guard and hose support if necessary, then frame to radiator support attaching bolts.
4. Remove fan and frame assembly.
5. Reverse procedure to install.

CAVALIER

2.2L/4-134 Engine

1. Disconnect battery ground cable.
2. Remove air cleaner duct, then disconnect wiring harness from motor and fan frame.
3. Remove fan assembly from radiator support.
4. Reverse procedure to install.

3.1L/V6-192 Engine

1. Disconnect battery ground cable.
2. Remove air cleaner duct, then air cleaner assembly.
3. Mark latch position for reassembly, then remove primary hood latch.
4. Drain engine coolant to a level below radiator inlet hose, then disconnect radiator inlet hose at radiator and position aside.
5. **On models with automatic transmission,** disconnect transaxle cooler lines and position aside.
6. **On all models,** disconnect wiring harness connector at cooling fan, then remove fan assembly from radiator support.
7. Reverse procedure to install.

SUNBIRD

1992–93

1. Disconnect battery ground cable.
2. Remove air cleaner duct and air cleaner assembly.
3. **On models with 4 cylinder engine,** remove wiring harness from motor and fan frame, then remove fan assembly from radiator support.
4. **On models with V6 engine**, remove primary hood latch.
5. Drain engine coolant, then disconnect upper radiator hose at radiator and position aside.
6. Disconnect transaxle cooler lines at radiator and position aside, then disconnect wiring harness connector at cooling fan and remove fan assembly from radiator support.
7. **On all models,** reverse procedure to install.

1994

2.0L/4-121 (VIN H)

1. Disconnect battery ground cable.
2. Remove air cleaner duct assembly.
3. Disconnect wiring harness from fan motor and frame.
4. Remove fan assembly.
5. Reverse procedure to install.

3.1L/V6–192 (VIN T)

1. Disconnect battery ground cable.
2. Remove air cleaner duct assembly.
3. Mark latch position for reassembly, then remove primary latch.
4. Drain cooling system below upper radiator hose level.
5. Disconnect upper radiator hose from radiator.
6. **On vehicles equipped with automatic transaxle,** disconnect transaxle cooler lines from radiator.
7. **On all vehicles models,** disconnect electrical connector from cooling fan.
8. Remove fan assembly from radiator support.
9. Reverse procedure to install.

CUTLASS SUPREME, GRAND PRIX & REGAL

1992–93

1. Disconnect battery ground cable, then remove air cleaner assembly.
2. **On VIN A & VIN D models,** remove lower bolt from engine strut to body brace.
3. **On all models,** remove engine strut brace bolts from upper tie bar and rotate strut(s) and brace(s) rearward. **To prevent shearing of rubber bushing(s), loosen bolt(s) on engine strut(s) before rotating.**
4. Remove coolant bottle.
5. Disconnect harness from fan motor and fan frame.
6. Remove fan frame to radiator support attaching bolts.
7. Remove fan and frame assembly.
8. Reverse procedure to install.

1994

1. Disconnect battery ground cable.
2. Remove air cleaner assembly.
3. Remove wiring harness from fan motor(s) and fan frame(s).
4. Remove fan frame mounting bolts.
5. Remove fan assembly.

CORVETTE

5.7L/V8-350 (VIN J) ENGINE

Primary (Left) Fan

1. Disconnect battery ground cable, then remove radiator pressure cap and drain coolant.
2. Remove air intake duct, then clamps and hoses from coolant outlets, radiator inlet and inlet pipe.
3. Remove hose and inlet pipe assembly from vehicle, then disconnect electrical connector from fan motor.
4. Remove screws retaining fan motor to motor support, then bolt retaining A/C discharge line clamp to crossmember.
5. Remove bolts retaining fan assembly to fan shroud, then end cap from power steering pulley.
6. Remove fan assembly from vehicle.
7. Reverse procedure to install.

Secondary (Right) Fan

1. Disconnect battery ground cable, then remove upper righthand bolt retaining fan assembly to fan shroud.
2. Raise and support vehicle, then disconnect electrical connector from fan motor.
3. Remove remaining bolts retaining fan assembly to fan shroud, then the fan assembly from vehicle.
4. Reverse procedure to install.

5.7L/V8-350 (VIN P) ENGINE

Primary (Left) Fan

1. Disconnect battery ground cable and remove air intake duct.
2. Disconnect electrical connector from fan motor.
3. Remove screws retaining fan assembly to fan shroud, then remove fan assembly from vehicle.
4. Reverse procedure to install.

Secondary (Right) Fan

1. Disconnect battery ground cable, then remove upper right bolt retaining fan assembly to fan shroud.
2. Raise and support vehicle.
3. Disconnect electrical connector from fan motor.
4. Remove screws retaining fan assembly to fan shroud, then remove fan assembly from vehicle.
5. Reverse procedure to install.

DEVILLE & FLEETWOOD (FWD)

1. Disconnect battery ground cable.
2. Raise and support vehicle.
3. Disconnect fan electrical connectors.
4. Remove fan to lower cradle attaching screws.
5. Lower vehicle.
6. For right fan, remove A/C accumulator from bracket and position out of the way.
7. Remove air cleaner intake duct.
8. Remove fan to upper radiator mounting panel attaching screws.
9. Remove upper radiator mounting panel.
10. Remove cooling fan(s).
11. Reverse procedure to install.

CAPRICE, IMPALA SS & ROADMASTER

1994

With Base Cooling System

The base cooling system 150 watt mounts on the righthand side. The 100 watt fan mounts on the lefthand side. Lefthand and righthand fans must be installed in their correct locations or inadequate cooling may result. Note and mark location prior to removal and installation.

1. Disconnect battery ground cable.
2. Disconnect fan electrical connectors.
3. Mark each fan location and slot location in radiator support for assembly reference.
4. Remove fan mounting bolts and the fan.
5. Reverse procedure to install.

With V03 & V08 Heavy Duty Cooling Capacity

The V03 and V08 cooling systems are equipped with a 240 watt fan mounted on the lefthand side. The 150 watt fan is mounted on the righthand side. Lefthand and righthand fans must be installed in their correct locations or inadequate cooling may result. Note and mark location prior to removal and installation.

1. Disconnect battery ground cable.
2. Remove air intake duct and resonator assembly.
3. Disconnect fan electrical connectors.
4. Mark each fan location and slot location in radiator support for assembly reference.
5. Remove fan mounting bolts and the fan.
6. Reverse procedure to install.

FLEETWOOD (RWD)

1993

Less Heavy Duty Cooling System

1. With ignition switch in off position, disconnect battery ground cable.
2. Disconnect cooling fan electrical connectors.
3. Remove fan assembly attaching bolts, then lift fan upward from radiator support slot.
4. Remove motor to fan attaching nuts.
5. Reverse procedure to install.

With Heavy Duty Cooling System

1. Disconnect battery ground cable.
2. Remove radiator fan shroud attaching bolts, then the upper fan shroud.
3. Remove fan blade assembly attaching nuts, then the fan blade and clutch assembly.
4. Remove clutch to fan blade attaching bolts, then the clutch from fan blade. **Place clutch in a upright position to prevent fluid leakage.**
5. Reverse procedure to install.

1994

Less Heavy Duty Cooling System

1. With ignition switch in off position, disconnect battery ground cable.
2. Disconnect cooling fan electrical connectors.
3. Remove fan assembly attaching bolts, then lift fan upward from radiator support slot.
4. Remove motor to fan attaching nuts.
5. Reverse procedure to install.

With Heavy Duty Cooling System

1. Disconnect battery ground cable.
2. Remove air intake duct and resonator assembly.
3. Disconnect fan electrical connectors.
4. Remove upper fan shroud bolts.
5. Remove fan assembly.
6. Reverse procedure to install.

ELDORADO & SEVILLE

1. Disconnect battery ground cable.
2. **On front cooling fan,** proceed as follows:
   a. Remove plastic radiator cover.
   b. Disconnect fan electrical connector.
   c. Remove right headlamp bracket.
   d. Remove three bolts and cooling fan from vehicle.
3. **On rear cooling fan,** proceed as follows:
   a. Remove upper engine to radiator support torque strut.
   b. Disconnect fan electrical connector.
   c. Disconnect oil cooler bracket from fan.
   d. Remove two upper and lower bolts and fan from vehicle.
4. **On both fans,** reverse procedure to install.

88 & 98

1. Disconnect battery ground cable.
2. Remove wiring harness from fan motor and fan frame.
3. Remove fan guard and hose support as necessary.
4. Remove fan assembly from radiator support.
5. Reverse procedure to install.

ACHIEVA, GRAND AM & SKYLARK

1992–93

2.3L/4-138 (VIN A, D & 3) Engine

1. Disconnect battery ground cable and remove air intake duct assembly.
2. Remove cooling fan mounting bolt and disconnect electrical connector from fan motor.
3. Remove cooling fan assembly out through bottom.
4. Reverse procedure to install.

2.5L/4-151 (VIN U) Engine

1. Disconnect battery ground cable.
2. Remove wiring harness from fan motor and fan frame.
3. Remove fan guard and hose support as necessary.
4. Remove fan assembly from radiator support.
5. Reverse procedure to install.

3.3L/V6-204 Engine

1. Disconnect battery ground cable and remove air intake duct assembly.
2. Partially drain cooling system and disconnect upper radiator hose from radiator.

3. Disconnect wiring harness from cooling fan motor and fan frame.
4. Remove fan guard and hose support if necessary.
5. Remove fan assembly from radiator support.
6. Reverse procedure to install.

1994

2.3L/4-138 (VIN A)

1. Disconnect battery ground cable.
2. Disconnect electrical connector and wiring harness from fan motor and fan frame.
3. Remove cooling fan mounting bolt and the fan.
4. Reverse procedure to install.

2.3L/4-138 (VIN 3 & D)

1. Disconnect battery ground cable.
2. Raise and support vehicle.
3. Remove right front wheel.
4. Remove bolt from lower torque axis mount.
5. Remove fan mounting bolt.
6. Disconnect electrical connector from cooling fan.
7. Tilt engine rearward and remove fan assembly.
8. Reverse procedure to install.

3.1L/V6-192

1. Disconnect battery ground cable.
2. Drain cooling system.
3. Remove cooling fan mounting bolt.
4. Disconnect electrical connector from cooling fan.
5. Remove inlet hose from radiator.
6. Remove radiator mounting bolt.
7. Disconnect windshield washer fill tube from bottle.
8. Remove vacuum tank and bracket.
9. Remove cooling fan.
10. Reverse procedure to install.

LEMANS

1. Disconnect battery ground cable.
2. Disconnect fan motor electrical connectors.
3. Remove oxygen sensor plug from air shroud.
4. Remove fan frame-to-radiator support attaching bolts, then the fan and frame assembly. **A bent or damaged fan assembly must be replaced.**
5. Reverse procedure to install.

PARK AVENUE & LESABRE

1. Disconnect battery ground cable.
2. Disconnect electrical connector from fan motor and frame.
3. Remove frame to radiator support attaching bolts.
4. Remove fan assembly.
5. Reverse procedure to install.

RIVIERA, TORONADO & TROFEO

1. Disconnect battery ground cable.
2. Remove wiring harness from fan motor and fan frame.
3. Remove fan assembly.
4. Reverse procedure to install.

LUMINA

1992-93

1. Disconnect battery ground cable.
2. Remove air cleaner assembly.
3. Remove coolant reservoir.
4. Remove engine strut brace bolts from upper tie bar and rotate strut(s) and brace(s) rearward. **Loosen strut retaining bolts on both ends to prevent damage to strut(s).**
5. Disconnect wiring harness from fan motor(s) and fan frame(s).
6. Remove fan frame attaching bolts.
7. Remove fan assembly.
8. Reverse procedure to install.

1994

1. Remove air cleaner assembly.
2. Disconnect wiring harness from fan motor and fan frame.
3. Remove fan mounting bolts and fan assembly.
4. Reverse procedure to install

PRIZM

1992-93

1. Disconnect battery ground cable.
2. Disconnect cooling fan electrical harness.
3. Remove cooling fan from vehicle.
4. Reverse procedure to install.

1994

1. Disconnect battery ground cable.
2. Drain engine coolant from radiator.
3. Disconnect oxygen sensor electrical connector.
4. Remove engine coolant recovery reservoir cap and hoses, then remove tank.
5. Remove upper radiator hose at radiator.
6. Remove cooling fan mounting bolts, then remove fan assembly from vehicle.
7. Reverse procedure to install.

STORM

1. Disconnect battery ground cable.
2. Drain coolant from radiator.
3. Remove upper radiator hose.
4. Disconnect electrical connections from cooling fan motor.
5. Disconnect cable form thermo switch.
6. Remove cooling fan assembly from vehicle.
7. Reverse procedure to install.

Thermo Switch

METRO

1. Disconnect battery ground cable, then drain cooling system.
2. Remove air cleaner and air inlet tube.
3. Disconnect switch electrical lead, then remove switch from thermostat cap.
4. Reverse procedure to install, wrapping switch threads with sealing tape before installation.

TECHNICAL SERVICE BULLETINS

COOLING FAN RELAY WIRING DIAGRAM CORRECTION

1993 Grand Prix w/3.4L/V6-204 (VIN X) Engine

The primary cooling fan control relay No. 1, terminals No. 2 and No. 3 circuit 1444 (Red), should be spliced together as shown in **Fig. 153.**

INTERMITTENT ELECTRICAL CONNECTIONS

1992-93 Grand Am

1992-93 GRAND AM

Intermittent Electrical Conditions

Improper relay wiring routing may cause chafing if relay wiring has been routed too closely to the transmission fluid indicator (models w/V6 engine) or the brake booster. Wire chafing may cause the following conditions:

Stalls or will not start
Cooling fan inoperative/engine overheats
Cooling fan always on/will not turn off
ABS indicator light on
DRL inoperative
Engine vent heater inoperative
Air conditioning inoperative
rear window defogger inoperative
Power seats inoperative
Horns inoperative
Instrument panel malfunctions/does not light
Cigar lighter inoperative
Remote keyless entry inoperative
Transaxle converter clutch inoperative
Power mirrors inoperative

To repair a chafed wiring condition, cover all chafed wiring with additional conduit and tape, then reroute electrical harness away from brake booster and/or transmission fluid indicator to avoid further contact.

COOLING FAN DISCHARGES BATTERY

Bonneville, Century, Cutlass Ciera, Cutlass Cruiser, LeSabre, Park Avenue, 88 & 98

If this problem occurs and the cooling fan relay is found to have failed because of its' contact points sticking together, the cause of the problem may either be the air conditioning system or the cooling fan temperature switch.

If the cooling fan motor is operating within acceptable current draw limits (20 amps on low speed or 35 amps on high speed), check A/C high side pressure with system operating. High side pressure should be stable. If high speed pressure shows a rapidly vibrating needle on the gauge, this will cause the A/C cooling fan pressure switch to cycle on and off as rapidly as the gauge needle is moving. This will cause the relay terminals to arc and eventually weld themselves together, which will leave the fan in operation with ignition key turned off. Check the fan pressure switch or check the A/C system for an internal failure.

The other cause of this condition may be the cooling fan temperature switch. To check the switch, touch one end of a test light to the positive battery terminal and the other end to the temperature switch located on the intake manifold. With the engine running, if the test light flickers on and off rapidly, the temperature switch may cause the cooling fan relay to fail in a similar manner as described above.

In either case, after the problem has been corrected, replace the cooling fan relay.

DASH GAUGES

NOTE: On Air Bag Equipped Models, Refer To "Air Bag System Precautions" Located In The Front Of This Manual For System Disarming & Arming Procedures.

INDEX

PRECAUTIONS

AIR BAG SYSTEMS

Refer to "Air Bag System Precautions" in the front of this manual for system disarming and arming procedures.

TROUBLESHOOTING

Gauge failures are often caused by defective wiring or grounds. The first step in locating a trouble should be a thorough inspection of all wiring, terminals and printed circuits. If wiring is secured by clamps, check to see whether the insulation has been severed thereby grounding the wire. In the case of a fuel gauge installation, rust may cause failure by corrosion at the ground connection of the tank unit.

GAUGES

VARIABLE VOLTAGE GAUGES

The variable voltage type dash gauge consists of two magnetic coils to which battery voltage is applied. The coils act on the gauge pointer and pull in opposite directions. One coil is grounded directly to the chassis, while the other coil is grounded through a variable resistor within the sending unit. Resistance through the sending unit determines current flow through its coil, and therefore pointer position.

When resistance is high in the sending unit, less current is allowed to flow through its coil, causing the gauge pointer to move toward the directly grounded coil. When resistance in the sending unit decreases, more current is allowed to pass through its coil, increasing the magnetic field. The gauge pointer is then attracted toward the coil which is grounded through the sending unit.

A special tester is required to diagnose this type gauge. Follow manufacturers instructions included with the tester.

VOLTMETER

The voltmeter is a gauge which measures the electrical flow from the battery to indicate whether the battery output is within tolerances. The voltmeter reading can range from 13.5-14.0 volts under normal operating conditions. If an undercharge or overcharge condition is indicated for an extended period, the battery and charging system should be checked.

Troubleshooting

To check voltmeter, turn key and headlights on with engine off. Pointer should move to 12.5 volts. If no needle movement is observed, check connections from battery to circuit breaker. If connections are tight and meter shows no movement, check wire continuity. If wire continuity is satisfactory, the meter is inoperative and must be replaced.

ELECTRICAL COOLANT TEMPERATURE GAUGES

This temperature indicating system consists of a sending unit, located on the cylinder head, electrical temperature gauge and an instrument voltage regulator. As engine temperature increases or decreases, the resistance of the sending unit changes, in turn controlling current flow through the gauge. When engine temperature is low sending unit resistance is high, current flow through the gauge is restricted, and the gauge pointer remains against the stop or moves very little. As engine temperature increases sending unit resistance decreases and current flow through the gauge increases, resulting in increased pointer movement.

Troubleshooting

Troubleshooting for the electrical temperature indicating system is the same as for the electrical oil pressure indicating system.

ELECTRICAL OIL TEMPERATURE GAUGES

CORVETTE

The operation of the oil temperature gauge is identical to the operation of the coolant temperature gauge. One of the coils of the gauge is grounded through the oil temperature sensor. The variable resistance of the sensor operates the same as the coolant temperature sensor.

Troubleshooting

Check for a defective wire inside the insulation which could cause system malfunction but prove "GOOD" in a continuity/voltage check with the system disconnected. These circuits may be intermittent or resistive when loaded, and if possible, should be checked by monitoring for a voltage drop with the system operational.

ELECTRICAL OIL PRESSURE GAUGES

This oil pressure indicating system incorporates an instrument voltage regulator, electrical oil pressure gauge and a sending unit which are connected in series. The sending unit consists of a diaphragm, contact and a variable resistor. As oil pressure increases or decreases, the diaphragm actuated the contact on the variable resistor, in turn controlling current flow through the gauge. When oil pressure is low, the resistance of the variable resistor is high, restricting current flow to the gauge, in turn indicating low oil pressure. As oil pressure increases, the resistance of the variable resistor is lowered, permitting an increased current flow to the gauge, resulting in an increased gauge reading.

Troubleshooting

Disconnect the oil pressure gauge lead from the sending unit, connect a 12 volt test lamp between the gauge lead and the ground and turn ignition on. If test lamp flashes, the instrument voltage regulator is functioning properly and the gauge circuit is not broken. If the test lamp remains lit, the instrument voltage regulator is defective and must be replaced. If the test lamp does not light, check the instrument voltage regulator for proper ground or an open circuit. Also, check for an open in the instrument voltage regulator to oil pressure gauge wire or in the gauge itself. **If test lamp flashes and gauge is not accurate, the gauge may be out of calibration, requiring replacement.**

FUEL GAUGES

The fuel gauge system consists of a sending unit, instrument voltage regulator and an electric fuel gauge. The sending unit is a variable resistor that is controlled by a float. Corresponding to actual fuel level, the float will rise or fall. When the ignition is turned to the On position, voltage is applied to the gauge through the voltage regulator, completing the gauge ground circuit through the sending unit.

When the tank is full and the float is raised, maximum resistance (approximately 90 ohms) is produced by the sending unit, current flow through the gauge is decreased, and the gauge pointer moves slightly. As the tank empties and the float drops resistance in the sending unit decreases, current flow through the gauge increases and the gauge pointer moves toward empty.

Most analog fuel gauges are of the free floating type, which means that the gauge pointer does not remain against the full stop when the ignition is off. Rather, the pointer floats to a mid-position when no voltage is applied to the gauge.

TROUBLESHOOTING

Gauge Reads Empty When Tank Is Full

This condition is generally caused by a short in the fuel tank unit circuit.

1. Disconnect electrical connector to sending unit, then turn ignition switch to ON position.
2. If gauge reads past full, test gauge with tester tool No. BT-6508, or equivalent. If gauge reads empty, disconnect main body harness connector, near the fuse block.
3. If gauge still shows empty, check for short in printed circuit or defective gauge. If gauge reads beyond full, reconnect front body harness connector and disconnect rear body harness connector (in left wheel house).
4. If gauge shows empty, locate and repair grounded wire in harness between front and rear body harness connectors. If gauge reads beyond full, check for short between rear body harness connector, damaged float or defective sending unit.

Gauge Reads Full Or Beyond At All Times

This condition is generally caused by an open in the tank unit circuit.

1. Check tank unit ground for proper contact with body or chassis and repair as needed.
2. If tank unit ground is satisfactory, disconnect electrical connector to tank unit and connect harness side of connector to suitable ground with jumper wire, then turn on ignition.
3. If gauge reads empty, remove fuel tank and inspect wiring to sending unit. If wiring and connections are satisfactory, replace tank unit.
4. If gauge still shows full, disconnect front body harness connector and ground fuel gauge wire terminal in instrument panel side of connector.
5. If gauge still reads full, check for loose connection in cluster, open (crack) in printed circuit or defective gauge. If gauge reads empty, locate and repair open or poor connection between front body connector and tank unit connector.

Fuel Gauge Inaccurate

Tester BT-6508 or equivalent must be used to diagnose dash gauge malfunction.

1. Ensure battery is fully charged, disconnect electrical connector to tank unit and connect tester to between harness connector and suitable ground following manufacturer's instructions.
2. Set tester on empty then turn on ignition. Gauge should read empty or below.
3. Set tester on full. Gauge should read full or above.
4. If gauge does not respond to tester input, replace dash gauge. If gauge responds correctly, check for poor connections at tank unit, poor tank unit ground or defective tank unit.

FUEL USAGE GAUGE

BUICK & CADILLAC

Operation

This system consists of green and amber indicator lights located on the fuel gauge or telltale lamp cluster, a switch mounted on the instrument panel behind the gauges and an interconnecting vacuum hose and tee. The system operates on engine vacuum through a dual contact vacuum sensing switch. When the accelerator is operated slowly and smoothly, engine vacuum remains high and the switch passes current to the green indicator light which indicates economical fuel consumption. When the accelerator pedal is depressed rapidly, vacuum decreases and the switch passes current to the amber indicator light, which indicates high fuel consumption. The amber indicator light will glow when the ignition switch is in the On position with the engine stopped.

Functional Test

1. With ignition switch in the on position, ground each terminal at the economy switch. Both green and amber indicator lights should glow. If not check for burned out bulbs.
2. With ignition switch in On position, amber indicator light should glow. If not, check for loose or disconnected wires at fuel economy switch or for poor ground. If amber indicator light still does not glow replace switch.
3. Start engine and allow to idle, the green indicator light should glow. If not, check for leaking, plugged or kinked vacuum hose between vacuum source and fuel economy switch. Check for loose or disconnected wires at economy switch or poor ground. If green indicator lamp still does not glow, replace switch.

WARNING LAMPS

ALTERNATOR INDICATOR LAMP

DELCOTRON CHARGING SYSTEM

The CS generator uses a new type of regulator which has a built in fault detection. The CS generator does not have a diode trio or test hole. This generator uses only two connections, battery positive and an "L" terminal to the charge indicator bulb. Use of "P," "F" and "S" terminals is optional. The "P" terminal is connected to the stator and may be connected to a tachometer or other device. The "F" terminal is connected internally to field positive and is used in service diagnostics. The "S" terminal may be connected externally to a voltage source, such as battery voltage.

Troubleshooting

If charge indicator light works abnormally, perform the following test procedure:

1. Visually check belt and wiring.
2. With engine control switch ON and engine stopped, charge indicator lamp should be on. If lamp is not on, detach wiring harness at generator and ground "L" terminal. If lamp lights, generator is faulty. If lamp does not light, locate open circuit between grounding lead and ignition switch and check for a faulty bulb.
3. With engine control switch ON and engine running at a moderate speed, charge indicator lamp should be off. If lamp is not off, detach wiring harness at generator. If lamp goes off, generator is faulty. If lamp stays on, check for grounded "L" terminal in wire harness.

OIL PRESSURE INDICATOR LAMP

Many cars utilize a warning light on the instrument panel in place of the conventional dash indicating gauge to warn the driver when the oil pressure is dangerously low. The warning light is wired in series with the ignition switch and the engine unit, which is an oil pressure switch.

The oil pressure switch contains a diaphragm and a set of contacts. When the ignition switch is turned on, the warning light circuit is energized and the circuit is completed through the closed contacts in the pressure switch. When the engine is started, build-up of oil pressure compresses the diaphragm, opening the contacts, thereby breaking the circuit and putting out the light.

Troubleshooting

On some models, the oil pressure indicator light also serves as the electric choke defect indicator. If Oil or engine indicator light does not light, check to ensure electric choke is not disconnected at carburetor. Also check for defect in electric choke heater, blown gauge fuse or defect in lamp or wiring circuit. If indicator light stays on with engine running possible causes are: oil pressure is low, switch to indicator light wiring has an open circuit, oil pressure switch wire connector has disconnected or on some models, gauge or radio fuse has blown.

The oil pressure warning light should go on when the ignition is turned on. If it does not light, disconnect the wire from the engine unit and ground the wire to the frame or cylinder block. Then if the warning light still does not go on with the ignition switch on, replace the bulb.

If the warning light goes on when the wire is grounded to the frame or cylinder block, the engine unit should be checked for being loose or poorly grounded. If the unit is found to be tight and properly grounded, it should be removed and a new one installed. The presence of sealing compound on the threads of the engine unit will cause a poor ground.

If the warning light remains lit when it normally should be out, replace the engine unit before proceeding to determine the cause for a low pressure indication.

The warning light sometimes will light up or will flicker when the engine is idling, even though the oil pressure is adequate. However, the light should go out when the engine speed is increased. There is no cause for alarm in such cases; it simply means that the pressure switch is not calibrated precisely correct.

TEMPERATURE INDICATOR LAMP

Troubleshooting

If the red light is not lit when the engine is being cranked, check for a burned out bulb, an open in the light circuit, or a defective ignition switch.

If the red light is lit when the engine is running, check the wiring between light and switch for a ground, temperature switch defective, or overheated cooling system. **As a test circuit to check whether the red bulb is functioning properly, a wire which is connected to the ground terminal of the ignition switch is tapped into its circuit. When the ignition is in the start engine cranking position, the ground terminal is grounded inside the switch and the red bulb will be lit. When the engine is started and the ignition switch is in the on position, the test circuit is opened and the bulb is then controlled by the temperature switch.**

WARNING SYSTEM

FIBER OPTIC MONITORING SYSTEM

Fiber optics are non-electric light conductors made up of coated strands which, when exposed to a light source at one end, will reflect the light through their entire length, thereby illuminating a monitoring lens on the instrument panel or fender without the use of a bulb when the exterior lights are turned on.

LOW FUEL WARNING SYSTEM

The switch type consists of an indicator light and a low fuel warning switch located on the instrument panel.

The warning switch contacts are closed by the difference in voltage potential between the fuel gauge terminals. This voltage differential will activate the warning switch when the fuel tank is less than 1/4 full and, in turn, cause the indicator to light.

Troubleshooting

This system incorporates an indicator light. With ignition switch turned to on, the indicator should light. If not, check bulb and all electrical connections. Replace warning switch if bulb and connections prove satisfactory.

"LOW TRAC" INDICATOR LAMP (MODELS W/ASR OR TCS SYSTEMS)

On models equipped with Accelerated Slip Reduction (ASR) or Traction Control Systems (TCS), the "LOW TRAC" indicator lamp comes on to indicate that the system is active and is limiting wheel slip.

The "LOW TRAC" lamp will turn on during ABS initialization, an ABS stop or a TCS event. It will remain on for approximately three seconds, then turn off. The "LOW TRAC" indicator lamp also comes on when ABS is adjusting brake pressure to help avoid a skip.

LOW WASHER FLUID INDICATOR

There are two types of low washer fluid indicating systems. They are the mechanical type and electrically controlled type. The mechanical type consists of a float and rod assembly, sending unit and a fiber optic. The electrically controlled type consists of a float, magnet, contact points and a resistor.

On the mechanical type, the upper end of the rod extends into the sending unit and has colored red and green portions. When the windshield wipers are activated, a lamp bulb in the sending unit lights either the red or green sections of the rod. The colored light is then picked up by the fiber optic and is transmitted through it to the telltale lens. The lens will show red or green depending upon washer fluid level.

The electrically controlled indicator is activated when the windshield wipers are engaged. A slight amount of current flows from the wiper motor to the washer bottle float unit. This current will either pass through the contact points or the resistor which is in parallel with the points. When the washer fluid level is high, the magnet holds the contact points open. The current will now flow through the resistor where it is reduced so the indicator will not light. When the washer fluid level is low, the float drops and the magnet will separate from the cap assembly allowing the current to pass through the contact points and activate the indicator light.

Troubleshooting

On the mechanical indicating system, if the telltale lens fails to glow when the windshield wipers are activated, check lamp bulb in sending unit and see that fiber optic is not broken.

On the electrically controlled system, the first item to check is the indicator bulb. With the windshield wipers On, connect a jumper wire between the two terminals on the washer bottle cap. The indicator should then light. If not, replace bulb. If the bulb is found to be satisfactory, remove cap and float assembly from washer bottle. Float should be able to move to the bottom of the stem and the magnet should separate from the cap. If not, replace float and cap assembly.

LOW COOLANT LEVEL INDICATOR

Some vehicles use a buzzer or indicator lamp to indicate a low coolant level condition. The buzzer or lamp is activated by a sensor, located in the radiator, when the coolant level becomes one quart or more low.

UPSHIFT INDICATOR

Description

This lamp is used on most models equipped with manual transmission. The Upshift lamp is illuminated to inform the driver of ideal shift points, with improved fuel economy as the specific objective. When the light is illuminated, the transmission should be shifted to the next highest gear, if driving conditions permit such an action.

Troubleshooting

If Upshift indicator is not working properly, perform the following test. It is necessary to refer to wiring diagrams located in MOTOR's "Vacuum & Wiring Diagram Manual" for the specific year and model being serviced.

1. Disconnect ECM connector C1.
2. Place ignition switch in run.
3. Measure voltage at terminal A2 of ECM connector.
4. If battery voltage is present, further ECM diagnosis is necessary.
5. If battery voltage is not present, repair open circuit in brown/black wire, circuit 456.

DRIVER REMINDER PACKAGE

Cutlass, Toronado, 88 & 98

The driver reminder package incorporates several warning and reminder features into one system. The system uses three distinct sounds, and warning and reminder lights on the center instrument cluster.

If engine coolant level is three quarts or more low, a red LOW COOLANT warning light will illuminate and a fast pulsed tone will be heard. The light will remain lit and the tone will be heard until coolant is added to the cooling system. The light will also illuminate during engine starting as a bulb check.

When the headlight switch is in the On position and the ignition is off, a red LIGHTS ON warning light will illuminate and a fast-pulsed tone will be heard. Turning the headlight switch to the right will dim the instrument panel lights and shutoff the tone.

When there is less than approximately three gallons of fuel in the tank, an amber LOW FUEL warning light will illuminate and a steady five second tone will be heard, however the lamp may not light until fuel level is diminished to as low as a 1/2 gallon. The light will remain lit until fuel is added to the tank. This warning light will also illuminate during engine starting as a bulb check.

The amber LOW WASH FLUID reminder light will illuminate while the windshield wipers are operated if the washer fluid reservoir is less than approximately 1/3 full. This light will remain lit during wiper operation until fluid is added.

Additional tones used to warn operator of potential problems are: engine overheating, fast pulsed tone; malfunction in the charging system, fast-pulsed tone; seat belt reminder, slow pulsed tone; key reminder, steady tone.

SPEEDOMETERS

The following information covers only that service on speedometers which can be performed by the average service man. Repairs on the units themselves are not included as they require special equipment and extreme care when making repairs and adjustments and only an experienced speedometer mechanic should attempt such servicing.

The speedometer has two main parts: the indicator head and the speedometer drive cable. When the speedometer fails to indicate speed or mileage, the cable or housing is probably broken.

SPEEDOMETER CABLE

Most cables are broken due to lack of lubrication or a sharp bend or kink in the housing.

Cable can break because the speedometer head mechanism binds. If such is the case, the speedometer head should be repaired or replaced before a new cable or housing is installed.

A jumpy pointer condition, together with a sort of scraping noise, is due, in most instances, to a dry or kinked speedometer cable. The kinked cable rubs on the housing and winds up, slowing down the pointer. The cable then unwinds and the pointer jumps.

To check for kinks, remove the cable, lay it on a flat surface and twist one end with the fingers. If it turns over smoothly the cable is not kinked. But if part of the cable flops over as it is twisted, the cable is kinked and should be replaced.

Lubrication

The speedometer cable should be lubricated with special cable lubricant every 10,000 miles.

Fill the ferrule on the upper end of the housing with the cable lubricant. Insert the cable in the housing, starting at the upper end. Turn the cable around carefully while feeding it into the housing. Repeat filling the ferrule except for the last six inches of cable. Too much lubricant at this point may cause the lubricant to work into the indicating hand.

Installation

During installation, if the cable sticks when inserted in the housing and will not go through, the housing is damaged inside or kinked. Be sure to check the housing from one end to the other. Straighten any sharp bends by relocating clamps or elbows. Replace housing if it is badly kinked or broken. Position the cable and housing so that they lead into the head as straight as possible.

Check the new cable for kinks before installing it. Use wide, sweeping, gradual curves when the cable comes out of the transmission and connects to the head so the cable will not be damaged during its installation.

If inspection indicates that the cable and housing are in good condition, yet pointer action is erratic, check the speedometer head for possible binding.

The speedometer drive pinion should also be checked. If the pinion is dry or its teeth are stripped, the speedometer may not register properly.

The transmission mainshaft nut must be tight or the speedometer drive gear may slip on the mainshaft and cause slow speed readings.

ELECTRONIC SPEEDOMETER

The vehicle speed sensor (VSS) generates a signal that indicates the vehicle speed. The signal is processed by the power control module (PCM) to supply inputs to the speedometer and odometer.

The VSS is mounted in the transaxle and generates an AC voltage signal with a frequency proportional to vehicle speed. The PCM takes the voltage pulses from the sensor and uses them to close a solid state output switch. The output terminal is switched to ground at a rate proportional to vehicle speed. The speedometer and odometer are switched at the same frequency that the sensor generates. The speedometer and odometer are operated by a circuit board in the instrument cluster that converts pulses received from the PCM into a control signal for the vacuum fluorescent display.

Troubleshooting

Check for a broken, or partially broken, wire inside the insulation which could cause system malfunction but prove "GOOD" in a continuity/voltage check with a system disconnected. These circuits may be intermittent or resistive when loaded, and if possible, should be checked by monitoring for a voltage drop with the system operational.

STARTER MOTORS

TABLE OF CONTENTS

AC Delco Starters

INDEX

APPLICATION CHART

Year	Engine	VIN①	Model No.
BUICK CENTURY & OLDSMOBILE CUTLASS CIERA & CUTLASS CRUISER			
1992	2.5L/4-151	R	10455017
	3.3L/V6-204	N	10455024
1993	2.2L/4-134	4	10455053
	3.3L/V6-204	N	10455053
1994	2.2/L4-134	4	10455053
	3.1L/V6-191	M	10455053
BUICK LESABRE & PARK AVE.; CADILLAC CONCOURS, DEVILLE & FLEETWOOD (FWD); OLDSMOBILE 88, 98 & PONTIAC BONNEVILLE			
1992-93	3.8L/V6-231	L, 1	10455024
	4.9L/V8-300	B	10455045
1994	3.8L/V6-231	L, 1	10455024
	4.6L/V8-279	Y	9000775
	4.9L/V8-300	B	10455046
BUICK REGAL; CHEVROLET LUMINA; OLDSMOBILE CUTLASS SUPREME & PONTIAC GRAND PRIX			
1992	2.5L/4-151	R	10455026
	3.1L/V6-192	T	10455048
	3.4L/V6-204	X	10455047
	3.8L/V6-231	L	10455023
1993–94	2.2L/4-134	4	10455053
	3.1L/V6-191	T	10455060
	3.4L/V6-204	X	10455061
	3.8L/V6-231	L	10455023
1994	3.1L/V6-191	M	10455060
BUICK RIVIERA: CADILLAC ELDORADO & SEVILLE; OLDSMOBILE TORONADO & TROFEO			
1992-93	4.9L/V8-300	B	10455046
1992-94	3.8L/V6-231	L	10455024
BUICK ROADMASTER; CADILLAC BROUGHAM, FLEETWOOD (RWD); CHEVROLET CAPRICE & OLDSMOBILE CUSTOM CRUISER			
1992-93	4.3L/V6-262	Z	10455012
	5.0L/V8-305	E	10455012
	5.7L/V8-350	7	10455301
1993	5.7L/V8-350	P	10465143

Continued

APPLICATION CHART—Continued

Year	Engine	VIN①	Model No.
CHEVROLET BERETTA & CORSICA			
1994	4.3L/V8-265	W	10455012
BUICK SKYLARK; OLDSMOBILE ACHIEVA & PONTIAC GRAND AM			
1992-93	3.3L/V6-204	N	10455024
1992-94	2.3L/4-138	A, D, 3	10455049
1994	3.1L/V6-191	M	10455053
CHEVROLET BERETTA & CORSICA			
1992	2.2L/4-134	4	10455048
	2.3L/4-138	A	10455049
	3.1L/V6-192	T	10455048
1993-94	2.2L/4-134	4	10455053
	2.3L/4-138	A	10455049
	3.1L/V6-192	T	10455053
CHEVROLET CAMARO & PONTIAC FIREBIRD			
1992	3.1L/V6-191	T	10455011
	5.0L/V8-305	E	10455012
	5.0L/V8-305	F	10455011
	5.7L/V8-350	8	10455300
1993	5.7L/V8-350	P	10465143
1993-94	3.4L/V6-204	S	10455054
CHEVROLET CAVALIER & PONTIAC SUNBIRD			
1992-94	2.0L/4-121	H	10455021
	2.2L/4-134	4	10455053
	3.1L/V6-192	T	10455053
CHEVROLET CORVETTE			
1992-94	5.7L/V8-350	P	10455709
PONTIAC LEMANS			
1992	1.6L/4-98	6	1998525
1993	1.6L/4-98	6	10465022

①—The eighth digit of VIN denotes engine code.

DESCRIPTION

The AC Delco starter, **Fig. 1**, has the solenoid shift lever mechanism and the solenoid plunger enclosed in the drive housing to protect them from exposure to road dirt, icing conditions and splash. They have an extruded field frame and an overrunning clutch type drive. The overrunning clutch is operated by a solenoid switch mounted to a flange on the drive housing.

The solenoid is attached to the drive end housing by two screws. The cover can be removed to inspect the contacts and contact disc, but the switch is serviced as assembly only.

Most motors of this type have graphite and oil impregnated bronze bearings which ordinarily require no added lubrication except at time of overhaul when a few drops of light engine oil should be placed on each bearing before reassembly.

TROUBLESHOOTING

SLOW OR NOT CRANKING

When trouble develops in the starter motor circuit, and the starter cranks the engine slowly or not at all, several preliminary checks can be made to determine whether the trouble lies in the battery, in the starter, in the wiring between them, or elsewhere. Many conditions besides defects in the starter itself can result in poor cranking performance.

To make a quick check of the starter system, turn on the headlights. They should burn with normal brilliance. If they do not, the battery may be run down.

If the battery is in a charged condition so that lights burn brightly, operate the starter motor. Any one of three things will happen to the lights: (1) They will go out, (2) dim considerably or (3) stay bright without any cranking action taking place.

If Lights Go Out

If the lights go out as the starter switch is closed, it indicates that there is a poor connection between the battery and starter motor. This poor connection will most often be found at the battery terminals. Correction is made by removing the cable clamps from the terminals, cleaning the terminals and clamps, replacing the clamps and tightening them securely. A coating of corrosion inhibitor (petroleum jelly will do) may be applied to the clamps and terminals to retard the formation of corrosion.

If Lights Dim

If the lights dim considerably as the starter switch is closed and the starter operates slowly or not at all, the battery may be run down, or there may be some mechanical condition in the engine or starter motor that is throwing a heavy burden on the starter motor. This imposes a high discharge rate on the battery which causes noticeable dimming of the lights.

Check the battery state of charge. If it is charged, the trouble probably lies in either the engine or starter motor itself. In the engine, tight bearings or pistons or heavy oil place an added burden on the starter motor. Low temperatures also hamper starter motor performance since it thickens engine oil and makes the engine considerably harder to crank and start. Also, a battery is less efficient at low temperatures.

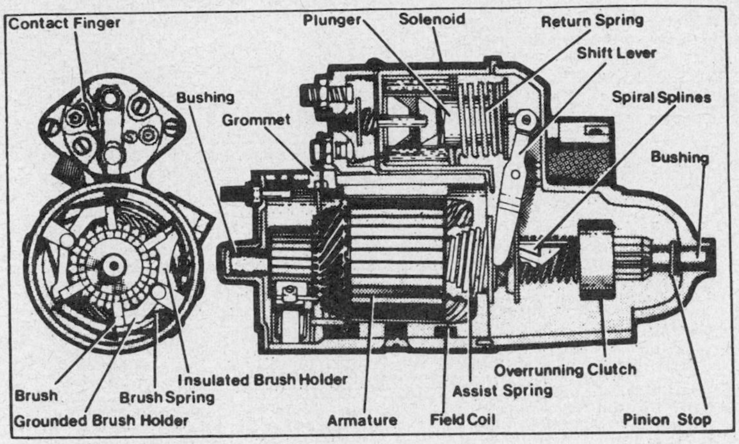
Contact Finger
Plunger
Solenoid
Return Spring
Shift Lever
Bushing
Grommet
Spiral Splines
Bushing
Insulated Brush Holder
Overrunning Clutch
Assist Spring
Brush
Brush Spring
Grounded Brush Holder
Armature
Field Coil
Pinion Stop
GC1129100028000X

Fig. 1 AC Delco starter motor

In the starter motor, a bent armature, loose pole shoe screws or worn bearings, any of which may allow the armature to drag, will reduce cranking performance and increase current draw.

In addition, more serious internal damage is sometimes found. Thrown armature windings or commutator bars, which sometimes occur on overrunning clutch drive starter motors, are usually caused by excessive overrunning after starter. This is the result of such conditions as the driver keeping the starter switch closed too long after the engine has started, the driver opening the throttle too wide in starting, or improper carburetor fast idle adjustment. Any of these subject the overrunning clutch to extra strain so it tends to seize, spinning the armature at high speed with resulting armature damage.

Another cause may be engine backfire during cranking which may result, among other things, from ignition timing being too far advanced.

To avoid such failures, the driver should pause a few seconds after a false start to make sure the engine has come completely to rest before another start is attempted. In addition, the ignition timing should be checked if engine backfiring has caused the trouble.

Lights Stay Bright; No Cranking Action

This condition indicates an open circuit at some point, either in the starter itself, the starter switch or control circuit. The solenoid control circuit can be eliminated momentarily by placing a heavy jumper lead across the solenoid main terminals to see if the starter will operate. This connects the starter directly to the battery and, if it operates, it indicates that the control circuit is not functioning normally. The wiring and control units must be checked to locate the trouble.

If the starter does not operate with the jumper attached, it will probably have to be removed from the engine so it can be examined in detail.

STARTER DRIVE PROBLEMS

Starter drive troubles are easy to diagnose and they usually cannot be confused with ordinary starter difficulties. If the starter does not turn over at all or if it drags, look for trouble in the starter or electrical supply system. Concentrate on the starter drive or ring gear if the starter is noisy, if it turns but does not engage the engine, or if the starter won't disengage after the engine is started. After the starter is removed, the trouble can usually be located quickly.

Worn or chipped ring gear or starter pinion are the usual causes of noisy operation. Before replacing either or both of these parts try to find out what caused the damage. With the Bendix type drive, incomplete engagement of the pinion with the ring gear is a common cause of tooth damage. The wrong pinion clearance on starter drives of the overrunning clutch type leads to poor meshing of the pinion and ring gear and too rapid tooth wear.

A less common cause of noise with either type of drive is a bent starter armature shaft. When this shaft is bent, the pinion gear alternately binds and then only partly meshes with the ring gear. Most manufacturers specify a maximum of .003 inch radial runout on the armature shaft.

Drive Clutch Failure

The overrunning clutch type drive seldom becomes so worn that it fails to engage since it is directly activated by a fork and lever. The only thing that is likely to happen is that, once engaged, it will not turn the engine because the clutch itself is worn out. A much more frequent difficulty and one that rapidly wears ring gear and teeth is partial engagement. Proper meshing of the pinion is controlled by the end clearance between the pinion gear and the starter housing or pinion stop, if used.

On some starters, the solenoids are completely enclosed in the starter housing and the pinion clearance is not adjustable. If the clearance is not correct, the starter must be disassembled and checked for excessive wear of solenoid linkage, shift lever mechanism, or improper assembly of parts.

Failure of the overrunning clutch drive to disengage is usually caused by binding between the armature shaft and the drive. If the drive, particularly the clutch, shows signs of overheating it indicates that it is not disengaging immediately after the engine starts. If the clutch is forced to overrun too long, it overheats and turns a bluish color. For the cause of the binding, look for rust or gum between the armature shaft and the drive, or for burred splines. Excess oil on the drive will lead to gumming, and inadequate air circulation in the flywheel housing will cause rust.

Overrunning clutch drives cannot be overhauled in the field so they must be replaced. In cleaning, never soak them in a solvent because the solvent may enter the clutch and dissolve the sealed-in lubricant. Wipe them off lightly with kerosene and lubricate them sparingly with SAE 10 or 10W oil.

Drive Failure

When a Bendix type drive doesn't engage the cause usually is one of three things: either the drive spring is broken, one of the drive spring bolts has sheared off, or the screw shaft threads won't allow the pinion to travel toward the flywheel. In the first two cases, remove the drive by unscrewing the setscrew under the last coil of the drive spring and replace the broken parts. Gummed or rusty screw shaft threads are fairly common causes of Bendix drive failure and are easily cleaned with a little kerosene or steel wool, depending on the trouble. Here again, as in the case of overrunning clutch drives, use light oil sparingly, and be sure the flywheel housing has adequate ventilation. There is usually a breather hole in the bottom of the flywheel housing which should be open.

The failure of a Bendix drive to disengage or to mesh properly is most often caused by gummed or rusty screw shaft threads. When this is not true, look for mechanical failure within the drive itself.

SOLENOID SWITCHES

The solenoid switch on a cranking motor not only closes the circuit between the battery and the cranking motor but also shifts the drive pinion into mesh with the engine flywheel ring gear. This is done by means of a linkage between the solenoid switch plunger and the shift lever on the cranking motor.

There are two windings in the solenoid; a pull-in winding and a hold-in winding. Both windings are energized when the external control switch is closed. They produce a magnetic field which pulls the plunger in so that the drive pinion is shifted into mesh, and the main contacts in the solenoid switch are closed to connect the battery directly to the cranking motor. Closing the main switch contacts shorts out the pull-in winding since this winding is connected across the main contacts. The magnetism produced by the hold-in winding is sufficient to hold the plunger in, and shorting out the pull-in winding reduces drain on the battery. When the control switch is opened, it disconnects the hold-in winding from the battery. When the hold-in winding is disconnected from the battery, the shift lever spring withdraws the plunger from the solenoid, opening the solenoid switch contacts and at the same time withdrawing the drive pinion from

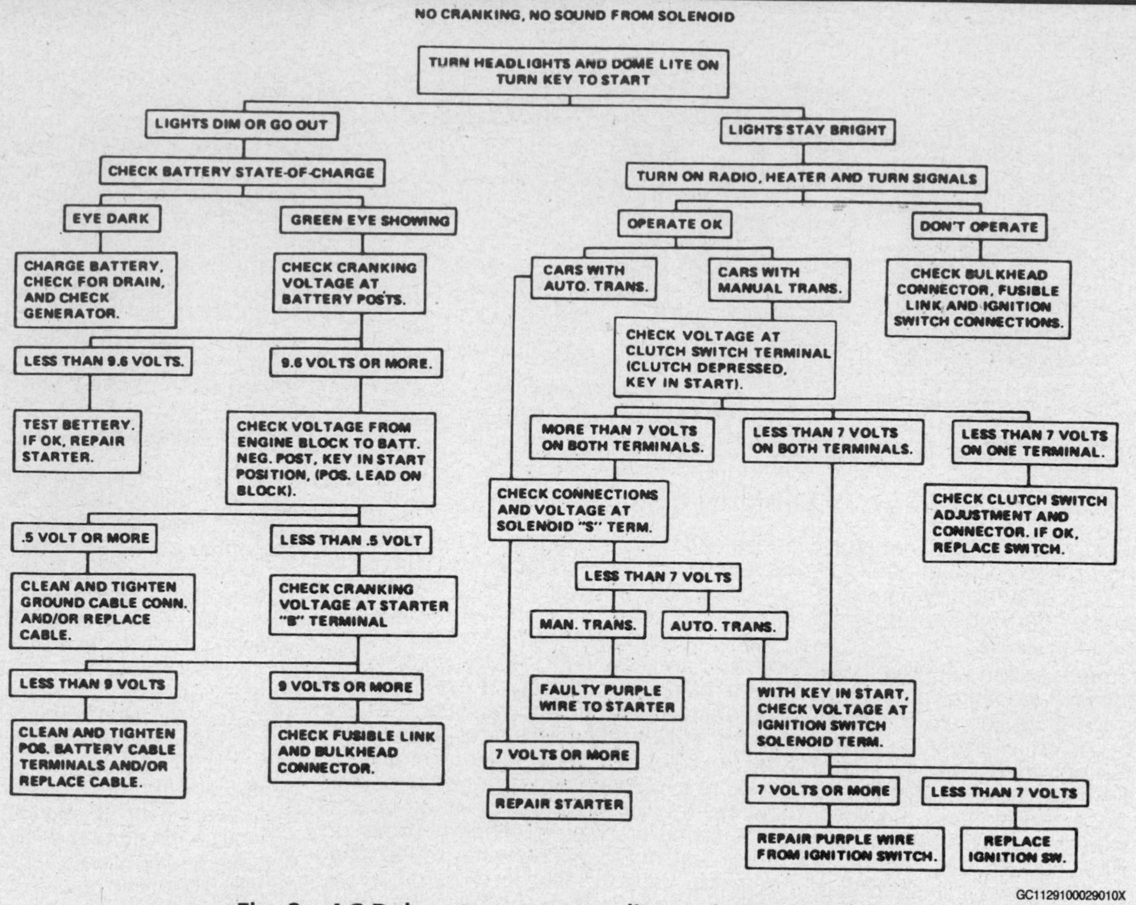
NO CRANKING, NO SOUND FROM SOLENOID
TURN HEADLIGHTS AND DOME LITE ON TURN KEY TO START
LIGHTS DIM OR GO OUT
LIGHTS STAY BRIGHT
CHECK BATTERY STATE-OF-CHARGE
TURN ON RADIO, HEATER AND TURN SIGNALS
EYE DARK
GREEN EYE SHOWING
OPERATE OK
DON'T OPERATE
CHARGE BATTERY, CHECK FOR DRAIN, AND CHECK GENERATOR.
CHECK CRANKING VOLTAGE AT BATTERY POSTS.
CARS WITH AUTO. TRANS.
CARS WITH MANUAL TRANS.
CHECK BULKHEAD CONNECTOR, FUSIBLE LINK AND IGNITION SWITCH CONNECTIONS.
CHECK VOLTAGE AT CLUTCH SWITCH TERMINAL (CLUTCH DEPRESSED, KEY IN START).
LESS THAN 9.6 VOLTS.
9.6 VOLTS OR MORE.
TEST BETTERY. IF OK, REPAIR STARTER.
CHECK VOLTAGE FROM ENGINE BLOCK TO BATT. NEG. POST, KEY IN START POSITION, (POS. LEAD ON BLOCK).
MORE THAN 7 VOLTS ON BOTH TERMINALS.
LESS THAN 7 VOLTS ON BOTH TERMINALS.
LESS THAN 7 VOLTS ON ONE TERMINAL.
CHECK CONNECTIONS AND VOLTAGE AT SOLENOID "S" TERM.
CHECK CLUTCH SWITCH ADJUSTMENT AND CONNECTOR. IF OK, REPLACE SWITCH.
.5 VOLT OR MORE
LESS THAN .5 VOLT
LESS THAN 7 VOLTS
CLEAN AND TIGHTEN GROUND CABLE CONN. AND/OR REPLACE CABLE.
CHECK CRANKING VOLTAGE AT STARTER "B" TERMINAL
MAN. TRANS.
AUTO. TRANS.
LESS THAN 9 VOLTS
9 VOLTS OR MORE
FAULTY PURPLE WIRE TO STARTER
WITH KEY IN START, CHECK VOLTAGE AT IGNITION SWITCH SOLENOID TERM.
CLEAN AND TIGHTEN POS. BATTERY CABLE TERMINALS AND/OR REPLACE CABLE.
CHECK FUSIBLE LINK AND BULKHEAD CONNECTOR.
7 VOLTS OR MORE
REPAIR STARTER
7 VOLTS OR MORE
LESS THAN 7 VOLTS
REPAIR PURPLE WIRE FROM IGNITION SWITCH.
REPLACE IGNITION SW.
GC1129100029010X

Fig. 2 AC Delco starter motor diagnosis (Part 1 of 2)

mesh. Proper operation of the switch depends on maintaining a definite balance between the magnetic strength of the pull-in and hold-in windings.

This balance is established in the design by the size of the wire and the number of turns specified. An open circuit in the hold-in winding or attempts to crank with a discharged battery will cause the switch to chatter.

DIAGNOSIS & TESTING

When diagnosing AC Delco starters, refer to **Fig. 2**.

CHECKING CIRCUIT w/VOLTMETER

Excessive resistance in the circuit between the battery and starter will reduce cranking performance. The resistance can be checked by using a voltmeter to measure voltage drop in the circuits while the starter is operated. There are three checks to be made:

1. Voltage drop between car frame and grounded battery terminal post.
2. Voltage drop between car frame and starter motor field frame.
3. Voltage drop between insulated battery terminal post and starter motor terminal stud, or the battery terminal stud of the solenoid.

Each of these should show no more than one-tenth (0.1) volt drop when the starter motor is cranking the engine. Do not use the starter for more than 30 sec-

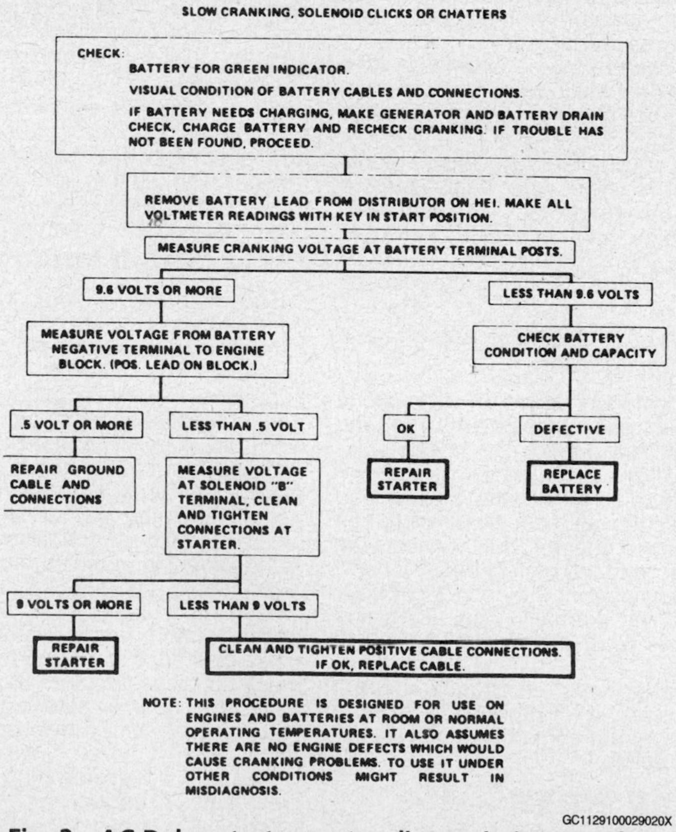
SLOW CRANKING, SOLENOID CLICKS OR CHATTERS
CHECK:
BATTERY FOR GREEN INDICATOR.
VISUAL CONDITION OF BATTERY CABLES AND CONNECTIONS.
IF BATTERY NEEDS CHARGING, MAKE GENERATOR AND BATTERY DRAIN CHECK, CHARGE BATTERY AND RECHECK CRANKING. IF TROUBLE HAS NOT BEEN FOUND, PROCEED.
REMOVE BATTERY LEAD FROM DISTRIBUTOR ON HEI. MAKE ALL VOLTMETER READINGS WITH KEY IN START POSITION.
MEASURE CRANKING VOLTAGE AT BATTERY TERMINAL POSTS.
9.6 VOLTS OR MORE
LESS THAN 9.6 VOLTS
MEASURE VOLTAGE FROM BATTERY NEGATIVE TERMINAL TO ENGINE BLOCK. (POS. LEAD ON BLOCK.)
CHECK BATTERY CONDITION AND CAPACITY
.5 VOLT OR MORE
LESS THAN .5 VOLT
OK
DEFECTIVE
REPAIR GROUND CABLE AND CONNECTIONS
MEASURE VOLTAGE AT SOLENOID "B" TERMINAL, CLEAN AND TIGHTEN CONNECTIONS AT STARTER.
REPAIR STARTER
REPLACE BATTERY
9 VOLTS OR MORE
LESS THAN 9 VOLTS
REPAIR STARTER
CLEAN AND TIGHTEN POSITIVE CABLE CONNECTIONS. IF OK, REPLACE CABLE.
NOTE: THIS PROCEDURE IS DESIGNED FOR USE ON ENGINES AND BATTERIES AT ROOM OR NORMAL OPERATING TEMPERATURES. IT ALSO ASSUMES THERE ARE NO ENGINE DEFECTS WHICH WOULD CAUSE CRANKING PROBLEMS. TO USE IT UNDER OTHER CONDITIONS MIGHT RESULT IN MISDIAGNOSIS.
GC1129100029020X

Fig. 2 AC Delco starter motor diagnosis (Part 2 of 2)

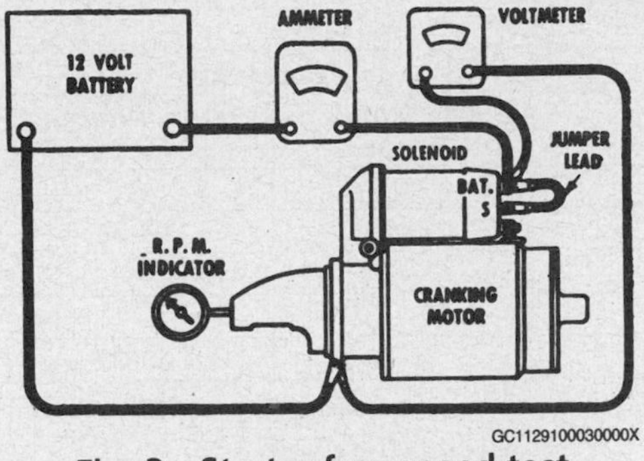
12 VOLT BATTERY
AMMETER
VOLTMETER
SOLENOID
JUMPER LEAD
BAT.
S
R.P.M. INDICATOR
CRANKING MOTOR
GC1129100030000X

Fig. 3 Starter free speed test connections

onds at a time to avoid overheating it.

If excessive voltage drop is found in any of these circuits, make correction by disconnecting the cables, cleaning the connections carefully, and then reconnecting the cables firmly in place. A coating of petroleum jelly on the battery cables and terminal clamps will retard corrosion.

On some cars, extra long battery cables may be required due to the location of the battery and starter. This may result in somewhat higher voltage drop than the above recommended 0.1 volt. The only means of determining the normal voltage drop in such cases is to check several of these vehicles. Then when the voltage drop is well above the normal figure for all cars checked, abnormal resistance will be indicated and correction can be made as already explained.

FREE SPEED TEST

With the circuit connected as shown in **Fig. 3**, use a tachometer to measure armature revolutions per minute. Failure of the motor to perform to specifications may be due to tight or dry bearings, or high resistance connections.

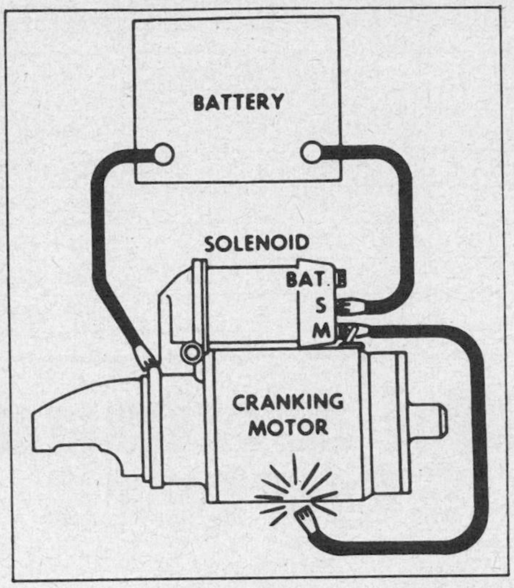
BATTERY
SOLENOID
BAT.
S
M
CRANKING MOTOR
GC1129100031000X

Fig. 4 Starter pinion clearance test connections

PINION CLEARANCE

There is no provision for adjusting pinion clearance on this type motor. When the shift lever mechanism is correctly assembled, the pinion clearance should fall within the limits of .010 to .140 inch. When the clearance is not within these limits, it may indicate excessive wear of the solenoid linkage or shift lever yoke buttons.

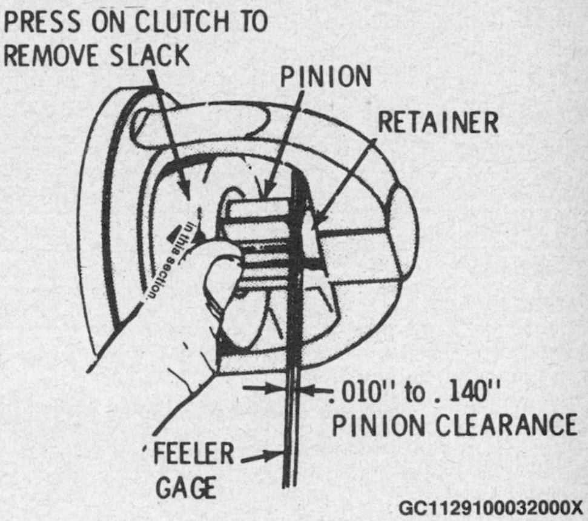
PRESS ON CLUTCH TO REMOVE SLACK
PINION
RETAINER
.010" to .140" PINION CLEARANCE
FEELER GAGE
GC1129100032000X

Fig. 5 Pinion clearance checking

Pinion clearance should be checked after the motor has been disassembled and reassembled. To check, disconnect motor field coil connector from solenoid terminal and insulate end. Connect one battery lead to solenoid switch terminal and the other lead to the solenoid frame, **Fig. 4.** Using a jumper lead connected to the solenoid motor terminal, momentarily flash the lead to the solenoid frame. This will shift the pinion into the cranking position until the battery is disconnected.

After energizing the solenoid with the clutch shifted toward the pinion stop retainer, push the pinion back toward the commutator end as far as possible to take up any slack movement; then check the clearance with feeler gauge, **Fig. 5.**

STARTER SPECIFICATIONS

	Free Speed Test			Solenoid	
Starter Ident. No	**Amps**	**Volts**	**RPM**	**Hold-In Windings, Amps**	**Pull-In Windings, Amps**
10455011	50-75	10	6500-11000	—	—
10455012	45-75	10	6500-11000	—	—
10455017	50-75	10	6000-11900	—	—
10455021	55-85	10	6000-12000	—	—
10455022	55-85	10	6000-12000	—	—
10455023	45-75	10	8600-13000	—	—
10455024	45-74	10	6000-11900	13-19	23-30
10455025	50-75	10	6000-12000	—	—
10455026	50-75	10	6000-11900	—	—
10455045	50-62	10	8500-12700	13-19	64-76
10455046	50-62	10	8500-12700	13-19	64-76
10455047	50-75	10	7000-11000	—	—
10455048	50-75	10	6000-11900	—	—
10455049	52-76	10	6000-12000	—	—
10455053	45-75	10	6000-11000	—	—
10455054	45-75	10	6000-11000	—	—
10455055	50-75	10	6000-12000	—	—
10455060	45-75	10	6000-11000	—	—
10455061	45-75	10	6000-11000	—	—

Continued

STARTER SPECIFICATIONS-Continued

Starter Ident. No	Free Speed Test			Solenoid	
	Amps	Volts	RPM	Hold-In Windings, Amps	Pull-In Windings, Amps
10455300	70-110	10	6500-10700	—	—
10455301	70-100	10	6500-10700	10-20	60-80
10455709	45-75	10	8600-12900	—	—
10465143	65-95	10	2750-3250	—	—
1998525	55-85	10	6000-12000	13-19	23-30

Mitsubishi & Nippondenso Starters

INDEX

APPLICATION CHART

Year	Engine	VIN①	Ident. No.
BUICK ROADMASTER, CADILLAC FLEETWOOD FWD, & CHEVROLET CAPRICE & IMPALA SS			
1994	5.7L/V8-350	P	9000773
			9000798
CADILLAC			
1993-94	4.6L/V8-279	9, Y	9000775
CHEVROLET CAMRO & PONTIAC FIREBIRD			
1994	5.7L/V8-350	P	9000773
			9000798
CHEVROLET CORVETTE			
1992-94	5.7L/V8-350	J	10455704
GEO PRIZM			
1992	1.6L/4-97	6	94844633
	1.8L/4-107.5	8	94844633
1993–94	1.6L/4-97	6	94854717
	1.8L/4-107.5	8	94854717
GEO METRO			
1992-94	1.0L/3-61②	6	④
	1.0L/3-61③	6	⑤
GEO STORM			
1992	1.6L/4-97③	6	128000-7400
	1.6L/4-97②	6	128000-7120
	1.8L/4-110③	8	128000-6990
	1.8L/4-110②	8	128000-7002
1993	1.6L/4-97	6	–
	1.8L/4-110③	8	—

①—The eighth digit of VIN denotes engine code.
②—Auto. trans.
③—Man. trans.
④—Mitsubishi starter. VIN 2, Country of origin Canada. The first digit of the VIN denotes countrry of origin.
⑤—Nippondenso satrter. VIN J, Country of origin Japan. The first digit of the VIN denotes countrry of origin.

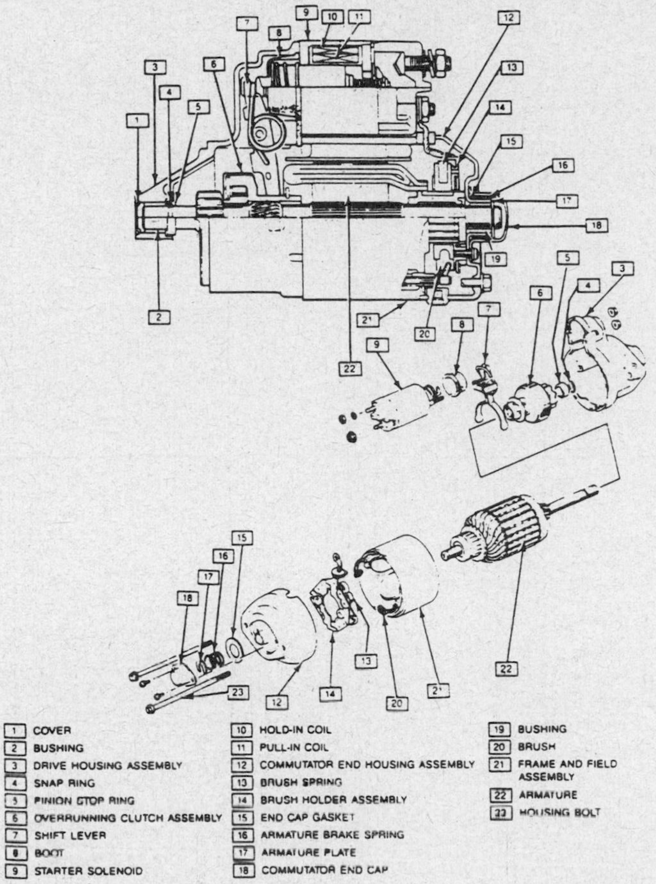
1 COVER
2 BUSHING
3 DRIVE HOUSING ASSEMBLY
4 SNAP RING
5 PINION STOP RING
6 OVERRUNNING CLUTCH ASSEMBLY
7 SHIFT LEVER
8 BOOT
9 STARTER SOLENOID
10 HOLD-IN COIL
11 PULL-IN COIL
12 COMMUTATOR END HOUSING ASSEMBLY
13 BRUSH SPRING
14 BRUSH HOLDER ASSEMBLY
15 END CAP GASKET
16 ARMATURE BRAKE SPRING
17 ARMATURE PLATE
18 COMMUTATOR END CAP
19 BUSHING
20 BRUSH
21 FRAME AND FIELD ASSEMBLY
22 ARMATURE
23 HOUSING BOLT
GC1129100033000X

Fig. 1 Exploded view of starter motor. Conventional w/manual trans

DESCRIPTION

Nippondenso starters, **Figs. 1 and 2**, are either a conventional type or reduction gear types. The conventional type used on manual transmissions consists of a frame and field assembly, an armature assembly, an overrunning clutch assembly, a starter solenoid assembly, a commutator end housing, a brush holder and a shift lever. The reduction gear type starters used on automatic transmissions which use all of the above components along with a reduction gear and shock absorber assembly.

When the ignition switch is turned to start and the clutch start/neutral safety switch is closed, the solenoid windings are energized, resulting in plunger and shift lever movement. This causes the pinion to engage the engine flywheel ring gear and the starter solenoid contacts to close. With the contacts closed, the starter solenoid provides a closed circuit between the battery positive terminal and the starter motor. The starter motor is grounded to the engine block, therefore the circuit is complete and engine cranking may occur.

Once the engine starts, the pinion is designed to overrun and protect the armature from excessive speeds until the ignition switch is released from the start position. When the ignition switch is released, a return spring in the solenoid assembly opens the starter solenoid contacts, breaking the circuit and disengaging the pinion.

TROUBLESHOOTING

SLOW OR NOT CRANKING

When trouble develops in the starter motor circuit, and the starter cranks the engine slowly or not at all, several preliminary checks can be made to determine whether the trouble lies in the battery, in the starter, in the wiring between them, or elsewhere. Many conditions besides defects in the starter itself can result in poor cranking performance.

To make a quick check of the starter system, turn on the headlights. They should burn with normal brilliance. If they do not, the battery may be run down.

If the battery is in a charged condition so that lights burn brightly, operate the starter motor. Any one of three things will happen to the lights: (1) They will go out, (2) dim considerably or (3) stay bright without any cranking action taking place.

If Lights Go Out

If the lights go out as the starter switch is closed, it indicates that there is a poor connection between the battery and starter motor. This poor connection will most often be found at the battery terminals. Correction is made by removing the cable clamps from the terminals, cleaning the terminals and clamps, replacing the clamps and tightening them securely. A coating of corrosion inhibitor (petroleum jelly will do) may be applied to the clamps and terminals to retard the formation of corrosion.

If Lights Dim

If the lights dim considerably as the starter switch is closed and the starter operates slowly or not at all, the battery may be run down, or there may be some mechanical condition in the engine or starter motor that is throwing a heavy burden on the starter motor. This imposes a high discharge rate on the battery which causes noticeable dimming of the lights.

Check the battery state of charge. If it is charged, the trouble probably lies in either the engine or starter motor itself. In the engine, tight bearings or pistons or heavy oil place an added burden on the starter motor. Low temperatures also hamper starter motor performance since it thickens engine oil and makes the engine considerably harder to crank and start. Also, a battery is less efficient at low temperatures.

In the starter motor, a bent armature, loose pole shoe screws or worn bearings, any of which may allow the armature to drag, will reduce cranking performance and increase current draw.

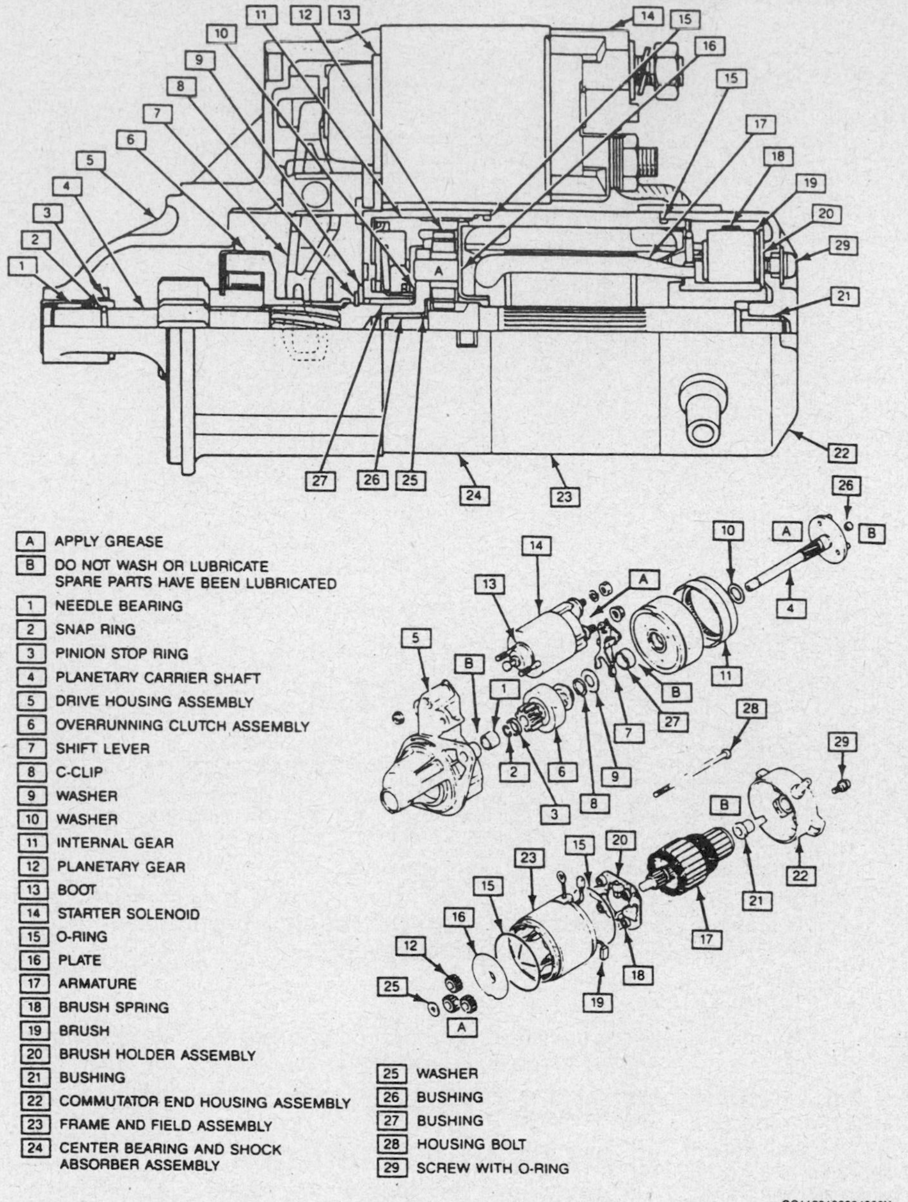
A APPLY GREASE
B DO NOT WASH OR LUBRICATE SPARE PARTS HAVE BEEN LUBRICATED
1 NEEDLE BEARING
2 SNAP RING
3 PINION STOP RING
4 PLANETARY CARRIER SHAFT
5 DRIVE HOUSING ASSEMBLY
6 OVERRUNNING CLUTCH ASSEMBLY
7 SHIFT LEVER
8 C-CLIP
9 WASHER
10 WASHER
11 INTERNAL GEAR
12 PLANETARY GEAR
13 BOOT
14 STARTER SOLENOID
15 O-RING
16 PLATE
17 ARMATURE
18 BRUSH SPRING
19 BRUSH
20 BRUSH HOLDER ASSEMBLY
21 BUSHING
22 COMMUTATOR END HOUSING ASSEMBLY
23 FRAME AND FIELD ASSEMBLY
24 CENTER BEARING AND SHOCK ABSORBER ASSEMBLY
25 WASHER
26 BUSHING
27 BUSHING
28 HOUSING BOLT
29 SCREW WITH O-RING
GC1129100034000X

Fig. 2 Exploded view of starter motor. Reduction w/automatic trans

In addition, more serious internal damage is sometimes found. Thrown armature windings or commutator bars, which sometimes occur on overrunning clutch drive starter motors, are usually caused by excessive overrunning after starter. This is the result of such conditions as the driver keeping the starter switch closed too long after the engine has started, the driver opening the throttle too wide in starting, or improper carburetor fast idle adjustment. Any of these subject the overrunning clutch to extra strain so it tends to seize, spinning the armature at high speed with resulting armature damage.

Another cause may be engine backfire during cranking which may result, among other things, from ignition timing being too far advanced.

To avoid such failures, the driver should pause a few seconds after a false start to make sure the engine has come completely to rest before another start is attempted. In addition, the ignition timing should be checked if engine backfiring has caused the trouble.

Lights Stay Bright; No Cranking Action

This condition indicates an open circuit at some point, either in the starter itself, the starter switch or control circuit. The solenoid control circuit can be eliminated momentarily by placing a heavy jumper lead across the solenoid main terminals to see if the starter will operate. This connects the starter directly to the battery and, if it operates, it indicates that the control circuit is not functioning normally. The wiring and control units must be checked to locate the trouble.

If the starter does not operate with the jumper attached, it will probably have to be removed from the engine so it can be examined in detail.

STARTER DRIVE PROBLEMS

Starter drive troubles are easy to diagnose and they usually cannot be confused with ordinary starter difficulties. If the starter does not turn over at all or if it drags, look for trouble in the starter or electrical supply system. Concentrate on the starter drive or ring gear if the starter is noisy, if it turns but does not engage the engine, or if the starter won't disengage after the engine is started. After the starter is removed, the trouble can usually be located quickly.

Worn or chipped ring gear or starter pinion are the usual causes of noisy operation. Before replacing either or both of these parts try to find out what caused the damage. With the Bendix type drive, incomplete engagement of the pinion with the ring gear is a common cause of tooth damage. The wrong pinion clearance on starter drives of the overrunning clutch

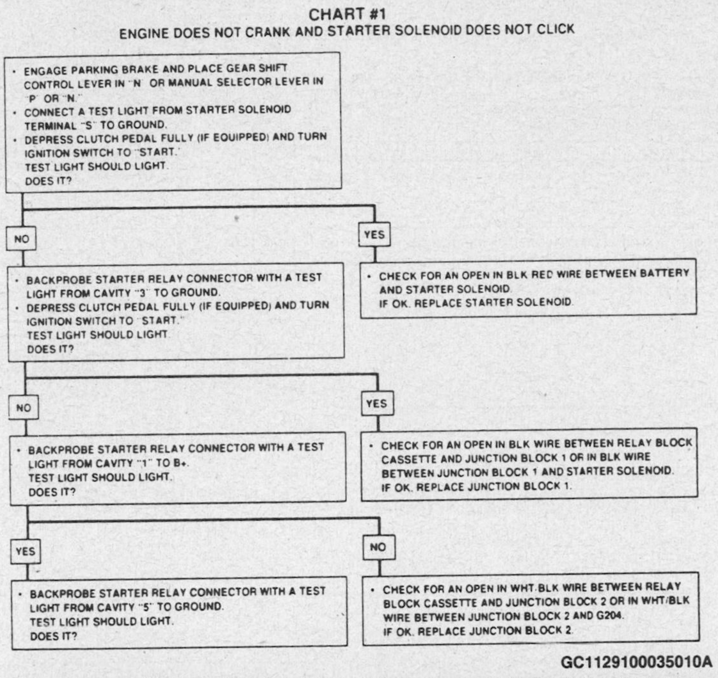
CHART #1
ENGINE DOES NOT CRANK AND STARTER SOLENOID DOES NOT CLICK
• ENGAGE PARKING BRAKE AND PLACE GEAR SHIFT CONTROL LEVER IN "N" OR MANUAL SELECTOR LEVER IN "P" OR "N."
• CONNECT A TEST LIGHT FROM STARTER SOLENOID TERMINAL "S" TO GROUND.
• DEPRESS CLUTCH PEDAL FULLY (IF EQUIPPED) AND TURN IGNITION SWITCH TO "START." TEST LIGHT SHOULD LIGHT. DOES IT?
NO
YES
• BACKPROBE STARTER RELAY CONNECTOR WITH A TEST LIGHT FROM CAVITY "3" TO GROUND.
• DEPRESS CLUTCH PEDAL FULLY (IF EQUIPPED) AND TURN IGNITION SWITCH TO "START." TEST LIGHT SHOULD LIGHT. DOES IT?
• CHECK FOR AN OPEN IN BLK/RED WIRE BETWEEN BATTERY AND STARTER SOLENOID. IF OK, REPLACE STARTER SOLENOID.
NO
YES
• BACKPROBE STARTER RELAY CONNECTOR WITH A TEST LIGHT FROM CAVITY "1" TO B+. TEST LIGHT SHOULD LIGHT. DOES IT?
• CHECK FOR AN OPEN IN BLK WIRE BETWEEN RELAY BLOCK CASSETTE AND JUNCTION BLOCK 1 OR IN BLK WIRE BETWEEN JUNCTION BLOCK 1 AND STARTER SOLENOID. IF OK, REPLACE JUNCTION BLOCK 1.
YES
NO
• BACKPROBE STARTER RELAY CONNECTOR WITH A TEST LIGHT FROM CAVITY "5" TO GROUND. TEST LIGHT SHOULD LIGHT. DOES IT?
• CHECK FOR AN OPEN IN WHT/BLK WIRE BETWEEN RELAY BLOCK CASSETTE AND JUNCTION BLOCK 2 OR IN WHT/BLK WIRE BETWEEN JUNCTION BLOCK 2 AND G204. IF OK, REPLACE JUNCTION BLOCK 2.
GC1129100035010A

Fig. 3 Diagnosis chart (Part 1 of 4)

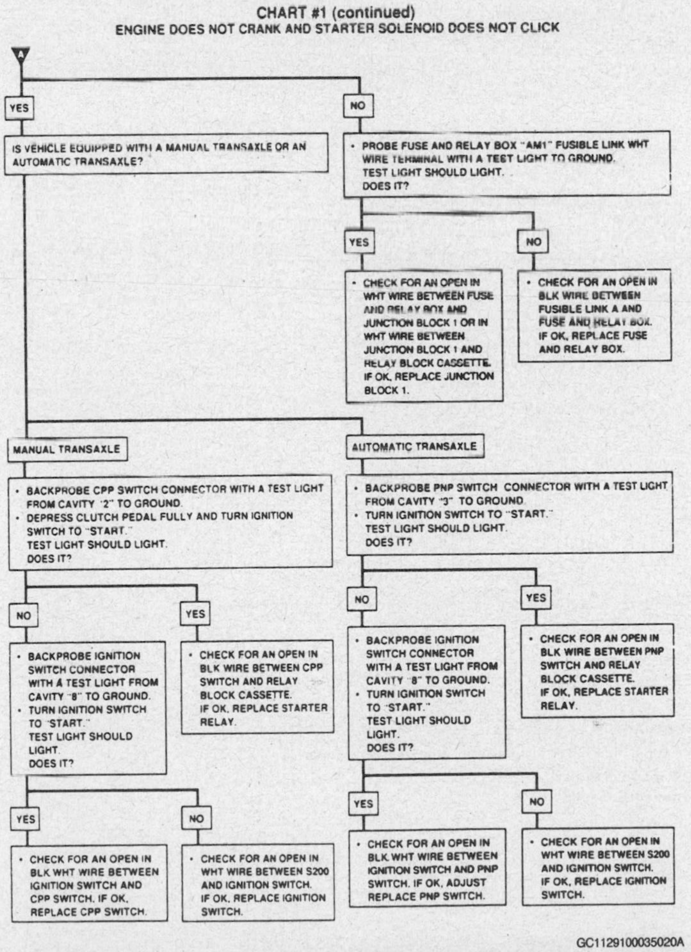
CHART #1 (continued)
ENGINE DOES NOT CRANK AND STARTER SOLENOID DOES NOT CLICK
A
YES
NO
IS VEHICLE EQUIPPED WITH A MANUAL TRANSAXLE OR AN AUTOMATIC TRANSAXLE?
• PROBE FUSE AND RELAY BOX "AM1" FUSIBLE LINK WHT WIRE TERMINAL WITH A TEST LIGHT TO GROUND. TEST LIGHT SHOULD LIGHT. DOES IT?
YES
NO
• CHECK FOR AN OPEN IN WHT WIRE BETWEEN FUSE AND RELAY BOX AND JUNCTION BLOCK 1 OR IN WHT WIRE BETWEEN JUNCTION BLOCK 1 AND RELAY BLOCK CASSETTE. IF OK, REPLACE JUNCTION BLOCK 1.
• CHECK FOR AN OPEN IN BLK WIRE BETWEEN FUSIBLE LINK A AND FUSE AND RELAY BOX. IF OK, REPLACE FUSE AND RELAY BOX.
MANUAL TRANSAXLE
AUTOMATIC TRANSAXLE
• BACKPROBE CPP SWITCH CONNECTOR WITH A TEST LIGHT FROM CAVITY "2" TO GROUND.
• DEPRESS CLUTCH PEDAL FULLY AND TURN IGNITION SWITCH TO "START." TEST LIGHT SHOULD LIGHT. DOES IT?
• BACKPROBE PNP SWITCH CONNECTOR WITH A TEST LIGHT FROM CAVITY "3" TO GROUND.
• TURN IGNITION SWITCH TO "START." TEST LIGHT SHOULD LIGHT. DOES IT?
NO
YES
NO
YES
• BACKPROBE IGNITION SWITCH CONNECTOR WITH A TEST LIGHT FROM CAVITY "8" TO GROUND.
• TURN IGNITION SWITCH TO "START." TEST LIGHT SHOULD LIGHT. DOES IT?
• CHECK FOR AN OPEN IN BLK WIRE BETWEEN CPP SWITCH AND RELAY BLOCK CASSETTE. IF OK, REPLACE STARTER RELAY.
• BACKPROBE IGNITION SWITCH CONNECTOR WITH A TEST LIGHT FROM CAVITY "8" TO GROUND.
• TURN IGNITION SWITCH TO "START." TEST LIGHT SHOULD LIGHT. DOES IT?
• CHECK FOR AN OPEN IN BLK WIRE BETWEEN PNP SWITCH AND RELAY BLOCK CASSETTE. IF OK, REPLACE STARTER RELAY.
YES
NO
YES
NO
• CHECK FOR AN OPEN IN BLK/WHT WIRE BETWEEN IGNITION SWITCH AND CPP SWITCH. IF OK, REPLACE CPP SWITCH.
• CHECK FOR AN OPEN IN WHT WIRE BETWEEN S200 AND IGNITION SWITCH. IF OK, REPLACE IGNITION SWITCH.
• CHECK FOR AN OPEN IN BLK/WHT WIRE BETWEEN IGNITION SWITCH AND PNP SWITCH. IF OK, ADJUST REPLACE PNP SWITCH.
• CHECK FOR AN OPEN IN WHT WIRE BETWEEN S200 AND IGNITION SWITCH. IF OK, REPLACE IGNITION SWITCH.
GC1129100035020A

Fig. 3 Diagnosis chart (Part 2 of 4)

type leads to poor meshing of the pinion and ring gear and too rapid tooth wear.

A less common cause of noise with either type of drive is a bent starter armature shaft. When this shaft is bent, the pinion gear alternately binds and then only partly meshes with the ring gear. Most manufacturers specify a maximum of .003 inch radial runout on the armature shaft.

Drive Clutch Failure

The overrunning clutch type drive seldom becomes so worn that it fails to engage since it is directly activated by a fork and lever. The only thing that is likely to happen is that, once engaged, it will not turn the engine because the clutch itself is worn out. A much more frequent difficulty and one that rapidly wears ring gear and teeth is partial engagement. Proper meshing of the pinion is controlled by the end clearance between the pinion gear and the starter housing or pinion stop, if used.

On some starters, the solenoids are completely enclosed in the starter housing and the pinion clearance is not adjustable. If the clearance is not correct, the starter must be disassembled and checked for excessive wear of solenoid linkage, shift lever mechanism, or improper assembly of parts.

Failure of the overrunning clutch drive to disengage is usually caused by binding between the armature shaft and the drive. If the drive, particularly the clutch, shows signs of overheating it indicates that it is not disengaging immediately after the engine starts. If the clutch is forced to overrun too long, it overheats and turns a bluish color. For the cause of the binding, look for rust or gum between the armature shaft and the drive, or for burred splines. Excess oil on the drive will lead to gumming, and inadequate air circulation in the flywheel housing will cause rust.

CHART #2
ENGINE DOES NOT CRANK OR CRANKS SLOWLY AND STARTER SOLENOID CLICKS

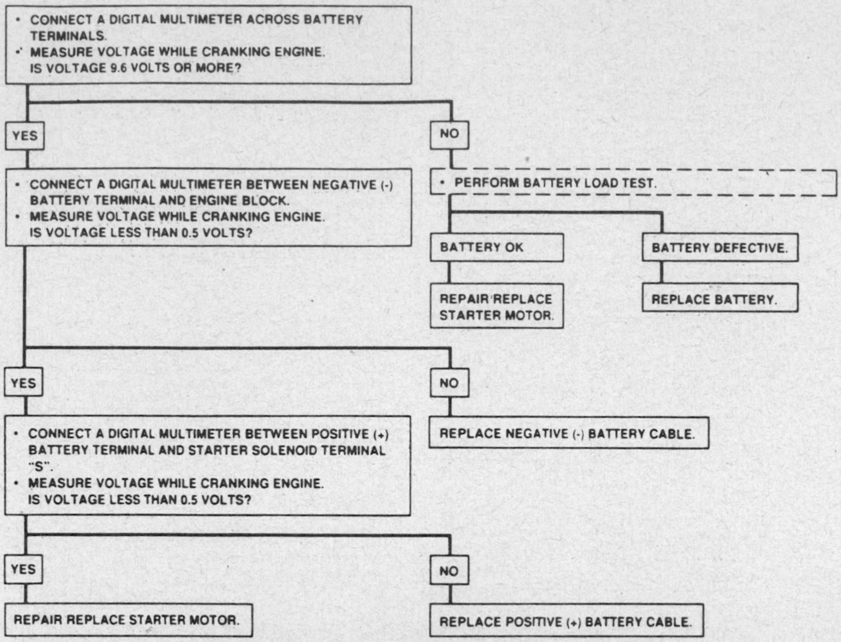
• CONNECT A DIGITAL MULTIMETER ACROSS BATTERY TERMINALS.
• MEASURE VOLTAGE WHILE CRANKING ENGINE. IS VOLTAGE 9.6 VOLTS OR MORE?
YES
NO
• CONNECT A DIGITAL MULTIMETER BETWEEN NEGATIVE (-) BATTERY TERMINAL AND ENGINE BLOCK.
• MEASURE VOLTAGE WHILE CRANKING ENGINE. IS VOLTAGE LESS THAN 0.5 VOLTS?
• PERFORM BATTERY LOAD TEST.
BATTERY OK
BATTERY DEFECTIVE.
REPAIR/REPLACE STARTER MOTOR.
REPLACE BATTERY.
YES
NO
• CONNECT A DIGITAL MULTIMETER BETWEEN POSITIVE (+) BATTERY TERMINAL AND STARTER SOLENOID TERMINAL "S".
• MEASURE VOLTAGE WHILE CRANKING ENGINE. IS VOLTAGE LESS THAN 0.5 VOLTS?
REPLACE NEGATIVE (-) BATTERY CABLE.
YES
NO
REPAIR/REPLACE STARTER MOTOR.
REPLACE POSITIVE (+) BATTERY CABLE.

GC1129100035030A

Fig. 3 Diagnosis chart (Part 3 of 4)

CHART #3
CHARGE INDICATOR DOES NOT LIGHT WITH IGNITION SWITCH IN "ON"

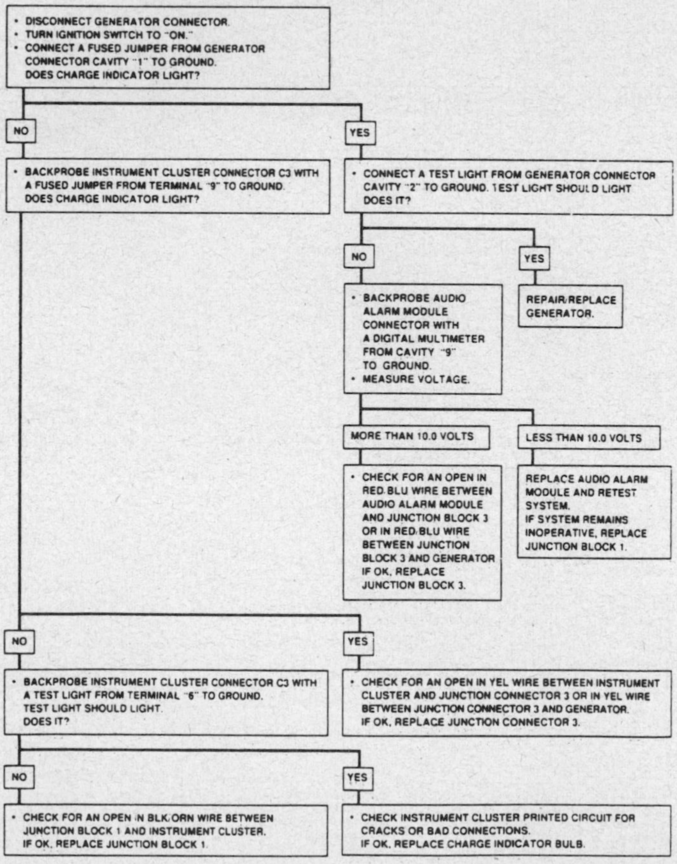
• DISCONNECT GENERATOR CONNECTOR.
• TURN IGNITION SWITCH TO "ON."
• CONNECT A FUSED JUMPER FROM GENERATOR CONNECTOR CAVITY "1" TO GROUND. DOES CHARGE INDICATOR LIGHT?
NO
YES
• BACKPROBE INSTRUMENT CLUSTER CONNECTOR C3 WITH A FUSED JUMPER FROM TERMINAL "9" TO GROUND. DOES CHARGE INDICATOR LIGHT?
• CONNECT A TEST LIGHT FROM GENERATOR CONNECTOR CAVITY "2" TO GROUND. TEST LIGHT SHOULD LIGHT DOES IT?
NO
YES
• BACKPROBE AUDIO ALARM MODULE CONNECTOR WITH A DIGITAL MULTIMETER FROM CAVITY "9" TO GROUND.
• MEASURE VOLTAGE.
REPAIR/REPLACE GENERATOR.
MORE THAN 10.0 VOLTS
LESS THAN 10.0 VOLTS
• CHECK FOR AN OPEN IN RED/BLU WIRE BETWEEN AUDIO ALARM MODULE AND JUNCTION BLOCK 3 OR IN RED/BLU WIRE BETWEEN JUNCTION BLOCK 3 AND GENERATOR IF OK, REPLACE JUNCTION BLOCK 3.
REPLACE AUDIO ALARM MODULE AND RETEST SYSTEM. IF SYSTEM REMAINS INOPERATIVE, REPLACE JUNCTION BLOCK 1.
NO
YES
• BACKPROBE INSTRUMENT CLUSTER CONNECTOR C3 WITH A TEST LIGHT FROM TERMINAL "6" TO GROUND. TEST LIGHT SHOULD LIGHT. DOES IT?
• CHECK FOR AN OPEN IN YEL WIRE BETWEEN INSTRUMENT CLUSTER AND JUNCTION CONNECTOR 3 OR IN YEL WIRE BETWEEN JUNCTION CONNECTOR 3 AND GENERATOR. IF OK, REPLACE JUNCTION CONNECTOR 3.
NO
YES
• CHECK FOR AN OPEN IN BLK/ORN WIRE BETWEEN JUNCTION BLOCK 1 AND INSTRUMENT CLUSTER. IF OK, REPLACE JUNCTION BLOCK 1.
• CHECK INSTRUMENT CLUSTER PRINTED CIRCUIT FOR CRACKS OR BAD CONNECTIONS. IF OK, REPLACE CHARGE INDICATOR BULB.

GC1129100035040A

Fig. 3 Diagnosis chart (Part 4 of 4)

Overrunning clutch drives cannot be overhauled in the field so they must be replaced. In cleaning, never soak them in a solvent because the solvent may enter the clutch and dissolve the sealed-in lubricant. Wipe them off lightly with kerosene and lubricate them sparingly with SAE 10 or 10W oil.

Drive Failure

When a Bendix type drive doesn't engage the cause usually is one of three things: either the drive spring is broken, one of the drive spring bolts has sheared off, or the screw shaft threads won't allow the pinion to travel toward the flywheel. In the first two cases, remove the drive by unscrewing the setscrew under the last coil of the drive spring and replace the broken parts. Gummed or rusty screw shaft threads are fairly common causes of Bendix drive failure and are easily cleaned with a little kerosene or steel wool, depending on the trouble. Here again, as in the case of overrunning clutch drives, use light oil sparingly, and be sure the flywheel housing has adequate ventilation. There is usually a breather hole in the bottom of the flywheel housing which should be open.

The failure of a Bendix drive to disengage or to mesh properly is most often caused by gummed or rusty screw shaft threads. When this is not true, look for mechanical failure within the drive itself.

SOLENOID SWITCHES

The solenoid switch on a cranking motor not only closes the circuit between the battery and the cranking motor but also shifts the drive pinion into mesh with the engine flywheel ring gear. This is done by means of a linkage between the solenoid switch plunger and the shift lever on the cranking motor.

There are two windings in the solenoid; a pull-in winding and a hold-in winding. Both windings are energized when the external control switch is closed. They produce a magnetic field which pulls the plunger in so that the drive pinion is shifted into mesh, and the main contacts in the solenoid switch are closed to connect the battery directly to the cranking motor. Closing the main switch contacts shorts out the pull-in winding since this winding is connected across the main contacts. The magnetism produced by the hold-in winding is sufficient to hold the plunger in, and shorting out the pull-in winding reduces drain on the battery. When the control switch is opened, it disconnects the hold-in winding from the battery. When the hold-in winding is disconnected from the battery, the shift lever spring withdraws the plunger from the solenoid, opening the solenoid switch contacts and at the same time withdrawing the drive pinion from mesh. Proper operation of the switch depends on maintaining a definite balance between the magnetic strength of the pull-in and hold-in windings.

This balance is established in the design by the size of the wire and the number of turns specified. An open circuit in the hold-in winding or attempts to crank with a discharged battery will cause the switch to chatter.

DIAGNOSIS & TESTING

Refer to **Fig. 3** when troubleshooting these starter motors.

CHECKING CIRCUIT W/VOLTMETER

Excessive resistance in the circuit between the battery and starter will reduce cranking performance. The resistance can be checked by using a voltmeter to measure voltage drop in the circuits while the starter is operated. There are three checks to be made:

1. Voltage drop between car frame and grounded battery terminal post.
2. Voltage drop between car frame and starter motor field frame.
3. Voltage drop between insulated battery terminal post and starter motor terminal stud, or the battery terminal stud of the solenoid.

Each of these should show no more than one-tenth (0.1) volt drop when the starter motor is cranking the engine. Do not use the starter for more than 30 seconds at a time to avoid overheating it.

If excessive voltage drop is found in any of these circuits, make correction by disconnecting the cables, cleaning the connections carefully, and then reconnecting the cables firmly in place. A coating of petroleum jelly on the battery cables and terminal clamps will retard corrosion.

On some cars, extra long battery cables may be required due to the location of the battery and starter. This may result in somewhat higher voltage drop than the above recommended 0.1 volt. The only means of determining the normal voltage drop in such cases is to check several of these vehicles. Then when the voltage drop is well above the normal figure for all cars checked, abnormal resistance will be indicated and correction can be made as already explained.

STARTER SPECIFICATIONS

Starter Ident. No.	Free Speed Test			Solenoid	
	Amps	Volts	RPM	Hold-In Windings, Amps	Pull-In Windings, Amps
① ②	60	11	—	—	—
① ③	75	11	—	—	—
② ⑤	42.5	11	—	—	—
③ ⑤	75	11	—	—	—
④ ②	35-90	11.5	1200-3000	—	—
④ ③	60-90	11.5	3000-5950	—	—
10455704	45-90	10	3500-5000	—	—
30005563 ③	75-230	11.5	—	—	—
30005925 ③	75	11	—	—	—
30005226 ②	60	11	—	—	—
9000773	65-95	10	2750-3250	10-20	60-85
9000775	55-90	10	2600-3200	10-20	60-85
9000798	65-95	10	2750-3250	10-20	60-85
94844633	60-90	11.5	5800-9000	—	—
94854717	60-90	11.5	5800-9000	—	—

①—Mitsubishi starter. VIN 2, Country of origin Canada. The first digit of the VIN denotes countrry of origin.
②—Manual transmission.
③—Automatic transmission.
④—Geo Storm.
⑤—Nippondenso starter. VIN J, country of origin Japan. The first digit of VIN denotes country of origin.

ALTERNATORS

TABLE OF CONTENTS

Mitsubishi & Nippondenso Alternators

INDEX

APPLICATION CHART

Model	Year	Manufacturer	Rated Hot Output Amps.
Metro	1992-94	Mitsubishi①	55
	1992-94	Nippondenso②	50
Prizm	1992-94	Nippondenso	70
Storm	1992-93	Nippondenso③	75
	1992-93	Nippondenso④	85

①—VIN 2, country of origin, Canada. The first digit of the VIN denotes country of origin

②—VIN J, country of origin, Japan. The first digit of the VIN denotes country of origin

③—1.6L engine. Alternator model 100211-7950

④—1.8L engine. Alternator model 100211-8350

PRECAUTIONS

1. Be certain that battery polarity is correct when servicing units. Reversed battery polarity will damage rectifiers and regulators.
2. If booster battery is used for starting, be sure to use correct polarity in hook up.
3. When a fast charger is used to charge a vehicle battery, the vchicle battery cables should be disconnected unless the fast charger is equipped with a special Alternator Protector, in which case the vehicle battery cables need not be disconnected. Also the fast charger should never be used to start a vehicle as damage to rectifiers will result.
4. Unless the system includes a load relay or field relay, grounding the alternator output terminal will damage the alternator and/or circuits. This is true even when the system is not in operation since no circuit breaker is used and the battery is applied to the alternator output terminal at all times. The field or load relay acts as a circuit breaker in that it is controlled by the ignition switch.
5. Before making any on vehicle tests of the alternator or regulator, the battery should be checked and the circuit inspected for faulty wiring or insulation. loose or corroded connections and poor ground circuits.
6. Check alternator belt tension to be sure the belt is tight enough to prevent slipping under load.
7. The ignition switch should be off and the battery ground cable disconnected before making any test connections to prevent damage to the system.
8. The vehicle battery must be fully charged or a fully charged battery may be installed for test purposes.

GENERAL INFORMATION

Alternators are composed of the same functional parts as the conventional D.C. generator but they operate differently. The field is called a rotor and is the turning portion of the unit. The generating part, called a stator, is the stationary member, comparable to the armature in a D.C. generator. The regulator, similar to those used in a D.C. system, regulates the output of the alternator-rectifier system.

The power source of the system is the alternator. Current is transmitted from the field terminal of the regulator through a slip ring to the field coil and back to ground through another slip ring. The strength of the field regulates the output of the alternating current. This alternating current is then transmitted from the alternator to the rectifier where it is converted to direct current.

These alternators employ a three-phase stator winding in which the phase windings are electrically 120° apart. The rotor consists of a field coil encased between interleaved sections producing. When the rotor is energized, a magnetic field with alternate north and south poles is created. By rotating the rotor inside the stator the alternating current is induced in the stator windings. This alternating current is rectified (changed to D.C.) by silicon diodes and brought out to the output terminal of the alternator.

DIODE RECTIFIERS

Six silicon diode rectifiers are used and act as electrical one-way valves. Three of the diodes have ground polarity and are pressed or screwed into a heat sink which is grounded. The other three diodes (ungrounded) are pressed or screwed into and insulated from the end head; these diodes are connected to the alternator output terminal.

Since the diodes have a high resistance to the flow of current in one direction and a low resistance in the opposite direction, they may be connected in a manner which allows current to flow from the alternator to the battery in the low resistance direction. The high resistance in the opposite direction prevents the flow of current from the battery to the alternator. Because of this feature no circuit breaker is required between the alternator and battery.

DESCRIPTION

This alternator has an IC integral solid state regulator. **Fig. 1.** All regulator components are enclosed into a solid mold and are attached to the slip ring end frame along with the brush holder assembly. The alternator voltage setting cannot be adjusted.

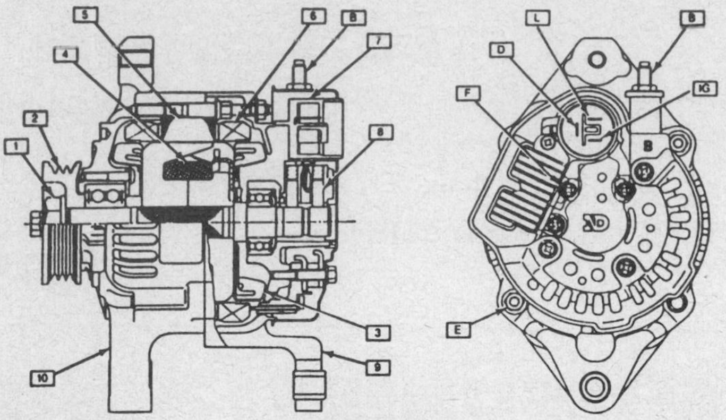

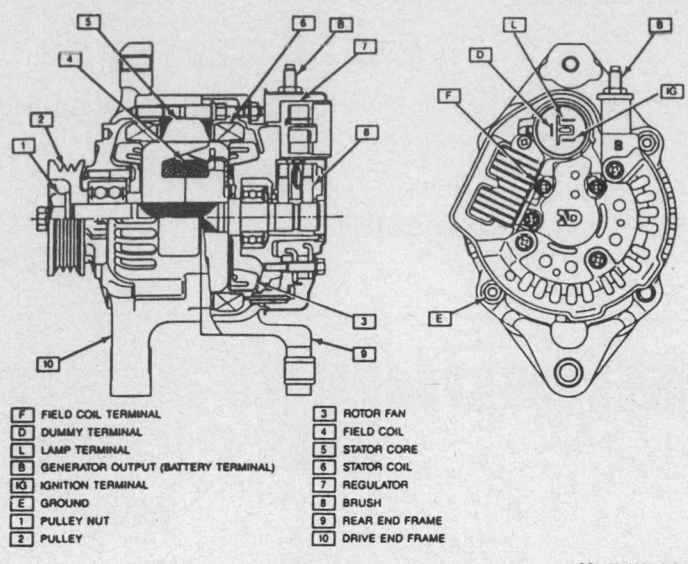

F FIELD COIL TERMINAL
D DUMMY TERMINAL
L LAMP TERMINAL
B GENERATOR OUTPUT (BATTERY TERMINAL)
IG IGNITION TERMINAL
E GROUND
1 PULLEY NUT
2 PULLEY
3 ROTOR FAN
4 FIELD COIL
5 STATOR CORE
6 STATOR COIL
7 REGULATOR
8 BRUSH
9 REAR END FRAME
10 DRIVE END FRAME

GC1129100036000X

Fig. 1 Nippondenso alternator

The alternator rotor bearing contain enough grease to eliminate the need for periodic lubrication. Two brushes carry current through the two slip rings to the field coil mounted on the rotor.

The stator windings are assembled on the inside of a laminated core that form part of the alternator frame. The rectifier bridge contains six diodes which electrically change stator A.C. voltage into D.C. voltage. The neutral diodes serve to convert the voltage fluctuation at the neutral point to direct current for increasing generator output.

DIAGNOSIS & TESTING

SYSTEM TEST

1. Connect a voltmeter across the battery.
2. Start engine and allow to run at 2,000 RPM, then check reading of voltmeter. Voltmeter should read at least 13.5 volts.
3. If voltage reading is not as specified, disconnect battery ground cable.
4. Disconnect alternator B terminal wire.
5. Connect ammeter red lead to alternator B terminal and black lead to disconnected B terminal wire.
6. Connect a voltmeter between altenator B terminal and chassis ground.
7. Connect battery ground cable, then start engine and turn On all accessories.
8. Operate engine at sufficent RPM (approximately 2000 RPM) to obtain maximum alternator current output.
9. If current reading is noth with in 10 amps of maximum rated output or voltage reading is not 13.5 to 16 volts, repair alternator.

REGULATOR TEST

1. Connect a voltmeter and fast charger to battery.
2. Turn ignition switch On and slowly increase charge rate. Indicator lamp in vehicle will begin to dim when voltage setting is reached.
3. Observe voltmeter, light should dim at 13.5 -16.0 volts.
4. If no voltage is present, replace voltage regulator.

ALTERNATOR SPECIFICATIONS

Model	Year	Alternator Manufacturer	Rated Hot Output Amps	Regulated Voltage
Metro	1992-94	Mitsubishi ①	55	14.7-15
	1992-94	Nippondenso ②	50	14.2-14.8
Prizm	1992-94	Nippondenso	70	13.5-15
Storm	1992-93	Nippondenso ③	75	—
	1992-93	Nippondensor ④	85	—

①—VIN 2, country of origin, Canada. The first digit of the VIN denotes country of origin

②—VIN J, country of origin, Japan. The first digit of the VIN denotes country of origin

③—1.6L engine. Alternator model 100211-7950

④—1.8L engine. Alternator model 100211-8350

AC-Delco CS Type Charging Alternators

INDEX

APPLICATION CHART

Model	Year	Alternator
BUICK		
Century	1992-94	CS-130
LeSabre & Park Avenue	1992	CS-130
		CS-144
	1993	CS-130
	1994	CS-130
		CS-130 DIF
Regal	1992-94	CS-130
Riviera	1992-93	CS-144 GEN II
Roadmaster	1992-93	CS-130
	1994	CS-130
		CS-144
Skylark	1992-94	CS-130
CADILLAC		
Brougham & Fleetwood (RWD)	1992	CS-130
		CS-144
	1993-94	CS-144
DeVille & Fleetwood (FWD)	1992-93	CS-144
	1993-94	CS-130
		CS-144 GEN II
Eldorado & Seville	1992-94	CS-144 GEN II
CHEVROLET & GEO		
Beretta & Corsica	1992-94	CS-130
Camaro	1992-94	CS-130
	1993-94	CS-144
Caprice & Impala SS	1992-94	CS-121
		CS-144
Cavalier	1992-93	CS-121
		CS-130
	1994	CS-130
Corvette	1992-94	CS-144
Lumina	1993-94	CS-130
Geo Prizm	1992-94	CS-121
OLDSMOBILE		
Achieva	1992-94	CS-130
Cutlass Ciera & Cutlass Cruiser	1992-94	Cs-130
Cutlass Supreme	1993-94	CS-130

Continued

APPLICATION CHART—Continued

Model	Year	Alternator
OLDSMOBILE -Continued		
88 & 98	1992	CS-130
		CS-144
	1993	CS-130
	1994	CS-130
		CS-130 DIF
PONTIAC		
Bonneville	1992	CS-130
		CS-144
	1993	CS-130
	1994	CS-130
		CS-130 DIF
Firebird	1992-94	CS-130
		CS-144
Grand Am	1992-94	CS-130
Grand Prix	1992-94	CS-130
LeMans	1992-93	CS-121
Sunbird	1992-94	CS-121
		CS-130

PRECAUTIONS

Refer to "General Information" at the front of this section.

DESCRIPTION

The CS alternator is available in three sizes: CS121, CS130 and CS144. The numerals denote the outer diameter of the stator laminations and the letters CS stand for charging system. The CS144 can be serviced. The CS121 and CS130 are serviced as an assembly only.

The CS alternators uses a new type regulator and a diode trio is not used. A delta stator, rectifier bridge, and rotor with slip rings and brushes are electrically similar to earlier alternators. A conventional fan mounted next to the pulley pulls air through the assembly for cooling. An internal fan mounted on the rotor pulls air through the slip ring end frame to cool rectifier, bridge and regulator. Air is expelled through openings in the end frame. No periodic maintenance is required.

SYSTEM OPERATION

CS130 and CS144 alternators may be used with only two connections. The battery positive BAT terminal must be connected to a battery during operation. The second required connection is through the indicator light, or a suitable external resistor to L terminal of the regulator which serves to turn unit On at start up. Three other regulator terminals are available for optional use in vehicle systems. The P terminal is connected to the stator, and may be connected to a tachometer or other device. The F terminal is connected internally to field positive, and may be used as a fault indicator. The S terminal may be connected externally to a voltage, such as battery voltage, to sense voltage to be controlled.

The regulator voltage setting varies with temperature, and limits system voltage by controlling rotor field current. Unlike others regulators, this regulator switches field current On and Off at a fixed frequency about 400 cycles per second. By varying On-Off time, correct average field current is obtained to provide proper system voltage. At high speeds, the On time may be 10% and Off time 90%. At low speeds with high electrical loads, On-Off time may be 90% and 10% respectively.

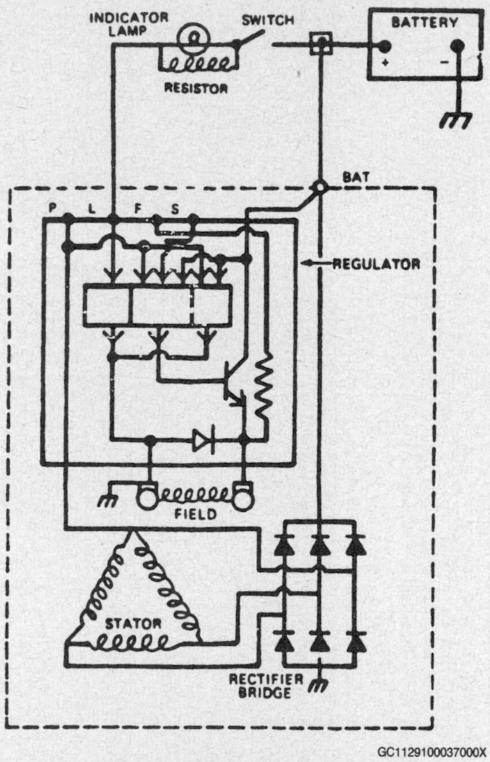
INDICATOR LAMP
SWITCH
BATTERY
RESISTOR
BAT
P
L
F
S
REGULATOR
FIELD
STATOR
RECTIFIER BRIDGE
GC1129100037000X

Fig. 1 CS charging system wiring diagram

Alternator systems on some applications are controlled by a Body Control Module (BCM). If cause of a system malfunction cannot be determined using the following test procedure, a problem in the electronic control system is indicated. For complete system diagnosis, refer to MOTOR's Auto Engine Tune Up and Electronics Manual.

DIAGNOSIS & TESTING

CHARGING SYSTEM

When the charging system is operating

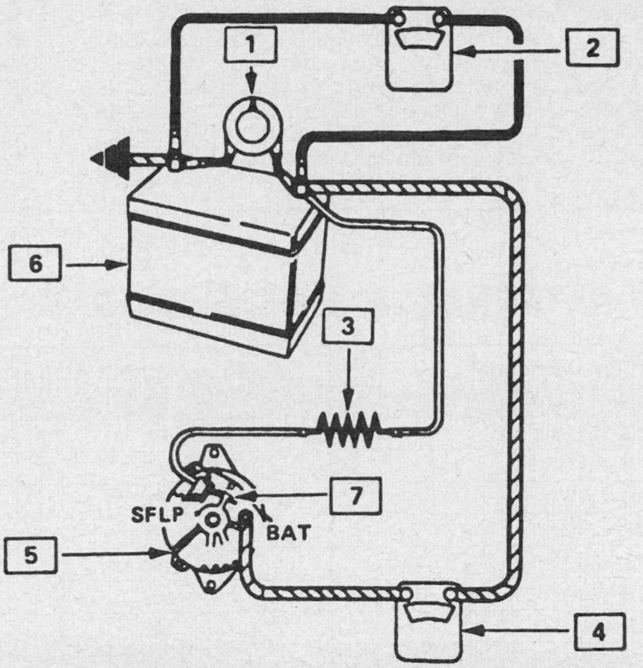
1
2
6
3
7
SFLP
BAT
5
4

1—CARBON PILE
2—VOLTMETER
3—RESISTOR
4—TESTAMMETER
5—GENERATOR
6—BATTERY
7—CONNECT RESISTOR TO "L" TERMINAL

GC1129100038000X

Fig. 2 CS alternator bench check

normally, the indicator lamp will come On when ignition switch is turned On and will go out when the engine starts. If the lamp operates abnormally, or if an undercharge or overcharge battery condition occurs, the following may be used to diagnose the charging system.

1. An undercharged battery is often caused by accessories being left On extended periods of time, or if an accessory lamp stays On.
2. Noise from an alternator may be caused by a loose drive pulley, loose mounting bolts, worn or dirty bearings, defective diodes or a defective stator.
3. To avoid damage to electrical equipment, refer to charging circuit wiring diagram, **Fig. 1** and proceed as follows:
   a. Do not reverse connections to the alternator.
   b. Do not short across or ground any of the terminals in charging system.
   c. Never disconnect output terminal while alternator is running.
4. Trouble in the charging system will appear as follows:
   a. Faulty indicator lamp operation.
   b. Undercharge battery, as evidenced by slow cranking or dark hydrometer.
   c. Overcharge battery, as evidenced by spewing of electrolyte from the vents.

IN-VEHICLE TESTING

1. Visually check belt and wiring and make any necessary repairs.
2. **On models equipped with charge indicator light,** turn ignition switch to On position (engine stopped), lamp should be on. If not, disconnect harness from alternator, and ground L terminal.
   a. If lamp lights, replace alternator.
   b. If lamp does not light, locate open circuit between grounding lead and ignition switch and check for defective indicator light bulb.
3. With ignition switch on and engine running at a moderate speed, lamp should be off. If not, disconnect wiring harness from alternator.
   a. If lamp goes off, replace alternator.
   b. If lamp stays on, check for grounded L terminal in wiring harness.
4. **On all models,** check for battery over-charging or under-charging as follows:
   a. Disconnect wiring harness connector from alternator.
   b. With ignition switch on and engine not running, connect voltmeter from ground to L terminal.
   c. Zero reading indicates open circuit between terminal and battery. Correct as required.
   d. Reconnect harness connector to alternator.
   e. Measure voltage across battery terminals with engine running at approximately 2000 RPM. If voltage is above 16 volts, replace alternator.
   f. Turn on accessories and load battery with carbon pile to obtain maximum amperage. Maintain voltage at 13 volts or less. If alternator is within 15 amps of rated output, it is acceptable.

ON-VEHICLE OUTPUT TEST

1. Connect ammeter in series at alternator output BAT terminal, then connect voltmeter and carbon pile across battery terminal. Ensure battery is fully charged.
2. Operate engine at moderate speed. With carbon pile turned Off, check voltage across battery terminals.
3. If voltmeter reads above 16 volts, repair (CS-144) only or replace alternator.
4. If voltmeter reads below 16 volts, proceed as follows:
   a. With engine still running at moderate speed turn accessories On and load battery with carbon pile to obtain maximum amperage output. Maintain voltage above 13 volts.
   b. If output is within 15 amps of rated output, alternator is satisfactory.
   c. If output is not within 15 amps of rated output, alternator is defective and requires repair (CS-144 only) or replace alternator.

BENCH TESTING

1. Make connections as shown in **Fig. 2,** however leave the carbon pile disconnected. The ground polarity of the alternator and battery must be the same. The battery must be fully

charged. Use a 30-500 ohm resistor between battery and L terminal.

2. Slowly increase alternator speed and observe voltage.
3. If voltage is uncontrolled and increases above 16 volts, the rotor field is shorted, the regulator is defective or both. A shorted rotor field can cause the regulator to become defective. **Battery must be fully charged when making this test.**
4. If voltage is below 16 volts, increase speed and adjust carbon pile obtain maximum amperage output. Maintain voltage above 13 volts.
5. If output is within 15 amps of rated output, alternator is satisfactory.
6. If output is not within 15 amps of rated output, alternator is defective and requires repair.

ALTERNATOR SPECIFICATIONS

Alternator Model	Rated Hot Output Amps
CS-121①	60
CS-121②	72
CS-121③	70
CS-121④	77
CS-121⑤	80
CS-130⑥	100
CS-130⑦	105
CS-130 DIF	105
CS-144	124
CS 144 GEN II	140

①—LeMans less A/C.
②—LeMans with A/C.
③—Geo Prizm models with man. trans.
④—Geo Prizm models with auto. trans.
⑤—Exc. Geo Prizm & LeMans.
⑥— Service part identification code K60 (100 amp. alternator). Refer to the service parts identification label located on the deck lid or the spare tire cover.
⑦— Service part identification code K68 (105 amp. alternator). Refer to the service parts identification label located on the deck lid or the spare tire cover.

SPEED CONTROL SYSTEMS

NOTE: On Air Bag Equipped Models, Refer To "Air Bag System Precautions" Located In The Front Of This Manual For System Disarming & Arming Procedures.

NOTE: Electrical Symbol & Wire Color Code Identification Located In The Front Of This Manual Can Be Used As An Aid When Using Wiring Circuits Found In This Section.

TABLE OF CONTENTS

Application Chart

Model	Year	Type	Page No.
BUICK			
Century	1992-94	2	21-35
LeSabre	1992-94	3	21-67
Park Avenue	1992-94	3	21-67
Regal	1992-94	2	21-35
Riviera	1992-93	3	21-67
Roadmaster	1992	2	21-35
	1993-94	5	21-112
Skylark	1992-94	2	21-35
CADILLAC			
Brougham	1992	1	21-2
DeVille	1992-94	1	21-2
Eldorado	1992-94	1	21-2
Fleetwood (FWD)	1992	1	21-2
Fleetwood (RWD)	1993-94	5	21-112
Seville	1992-94	1	21-2
CHEVROLET			
Beretta	1992-94	2	21-35
Camaro	1992	2	21-35
	1993-94	5	21-112
Caprice	1992	2	21-35
	1993-94	5	21-112
Cavalier	1992-94	2	21-35
Corsica	1992-94	2	21-35
CHEVROLET			
Corvette	1992-94	2	21-35
Impala SS	1994	5	21-112
Lumina	1992-94	2	21-35
GEO			
Prizm	1992-94	4	21-82
OLDSMOBILE			
Achieva	1992-94	2	21-35
Custom Cruiser	1992	2	21-35
Cutlass Ciera	1992-94	2	21-35
Cutlass Cruiser	1992-94	2	21-35
Cutlass Supreme	1992-94	2	21-35
Toronado & Trofeo	1992	3	21-67
88	1992-94	3	21-67
98	1992-94	3	21-67
PONTIAC			
Bonneville	1992-94	3	21-67
Firebird	1992	2	21-35
	1993-94	5	21-112
Grand Am	1992-94	2	21-35
Grand Prix	1992-94	2	21-35
Sunbird	1992-94	2	21-35

Type 1

NOTE: On Air Bag Equipped Models, Refer To Air Bag System Precautions Located In The Front Of This Manual For System Disarming & Arming Procedures.

NOTE: Electrical Symbol & Wire Color Code Identification Located In The Front Of This Manual Can Be Used As An Aid When Using Wiring Circuits Found In This Section.

INDEX

DESCRIPTION

This Cruise Control System utilizes vacuum to activate the throttle servo. Throttle position is changed when the servo unit diaphragm receives varying levels of vacuum, controlled by a solenoid valve. The solenoid valve modulates the vacuum signal to the servo in response to commands from the electronic controller. The electronic controller monitors signals from the engagement and electric brake release switch, and the speed sensor. The speed sensor, signals vehicle speed to the controller. These signals are used by the controller to activate the solenoid valve, regulating the level of vacuum to the servo diaphragm. This system uses two brake release switches. An electric brake release, mounted on the brake pedal support, turns the system Off and vents the servo diaphragm to the atmosphere through the solenoid valve. A second brake release switch, a vacuum release valve also located on the brake pedal support, vents the servo unit to the atmosphere.

ELECTRONIC CONTROLLER

The ECM or PCM receives input signals from the cruise control engagement switches, brake release switch, drive switch and speed sensor.

On models equipped with DFI or PFI, the ECM or PCM also receives engine control signals. The ECM then processes these signals and transmits a command signal to the solenoid valve, regulating vacuum to the servo unit diaphragm.

This is a test of the insert key.

CRUISE CONTROL MODULE

Brougham

The cruise control module (CCM) receives signals from the cruise engagement, instrument panel, and electric brake release switches, and servo position and speed sensors. The CCM then process this information and transmits signals to the vacuum and vent valves in the servo to control vehicle speed.

SPEED SENSOR

Except Brougham

On front wheel drive vehicles the speed sensor is mounted in the transaxle. A magnet rotates near a coil, producing voltage pulses in the coil. As speed increases, so do the number of voltage pulses per second.

The speed sensor buffer takes the sensor/voltage pulses from the sensor and uses them to close two solid state output switches. Each output terminal is switched to ground at a rate that is proportional to the speed of the car. The speedometer and the ECM are switched at 4000 pulses per mile. **The output switches in the speed sensor are solid state. Self-powered test lights or ohmmeters should not be used to test them. Do not measure the resistance at the outputs of the buffer.**

Brougham

The Vehicle Speed Sensor (VSS) is located at the rear of the transmission. The VSS is a permanent magnet generator consisting of a field coil and permanent magnet stator that produces AC voltage. When the vehicle is in motion a impulse is sent to the vehicle speed buffer. The information is then sent to the speedometer, engine control module, cruise control module, and passive restraint module at a rate of 4004 or 2002 pulses per minute.

VACUUM CONTROL VALVE

The vacuum control valve operates in response to a signal from the PCM, ECM or electronic controller and opens when the system is engaged. When the valve is opened, vacuum is available to the servo unit solenoid valve to regulate the servo unit. When the cruise control is disengaged, the vacuum control valve is closed.

SERVO UNIT SOLENOID VALVE

The solenoid valve modulates the vacuum signal to the servo unit in response to commands from the BCM, ECM or electronic controller in order for the throttle to be in proper position for desired cruise speed.

SERVO UNIT

The servo unit is essentially a vacuum activated variable diaphragm. It positions the throttle when the system is in operation through a bead chain actuator, combination chain and cable actuator or rod actuator depending on model of vehicle.

To operate the servo unit, a controlled vacuum provided by the servo unit solenoid valve is applied to the servo diaphragm, drawing the diaphragm inward, pulling the actuator to operate the throttle.

BRAKE RELEASE SWITCHES

The Cruise Control system utilizes an electrical brake release switch and a vacuum release valve.

The electric brake release switch cuts off the voltage supplied through the cruise control switch to the electronic controller when the brake pedal is depressed. The vacuum release valve operates after the electric release switch disengages. It serves as a back-up release system and opens a port that vents the servo unit to atmospheric pressure, allowing the throttle to return to the idle position.

ENGAGEMENT SWITCH OPERATION, CRUISE MODE

The turn signal lever mounted engagement switch has several modes of operation. With the switch in the On-Auto position, the engagement switch operates as follows:

Switch In Fully Released Position

1. System not operational.
2. System has been engaged previously. The electronic controller is supplying control voltage to the servo unit solenoid valve. The servo unit solenoid valve regulates vacuum to the servo unit which maintains throttle position for desired speed.

Push Button Depressed & Held

After using accelerator pedal to obtain desired speed, the operator can then momentarily depress the push button switch. The electronic controller will provide a control voltage to the servo unit solenoid valve and apply the required vacuum to the servo unit to maintain set speed. When a decrease in speed is desired, the operator may depress and hold the push button with no accelerator pedal pressure. The electronic controller then signals the servo unit solenoid valve to vent the servo unit to atmosphere, closing the throttle. When push button is released, vehicle will cruise at new desired speed.

Slide Lever Actuation

This switch allows the operator to resume a previously set speed after braking or accelerating. Depressing and releasing the slide switch above 25 mph, will accelerate vehicle until previously set speed is reached. If operator desires to advance speed from set speed, actuating and holding slide switch will accelerate vehicle until slide switch is released. Vehicle will now maintain new set speed.

SET/COAST BUTTON SWITCH

This switch has two positions, Normal and Depressed.

Set Position

With vehicle speed above approximately 25 mph and cruise control switch in On position, pressing and releasing set/coast button will cause the cruise speed to be set at speed vehicle was travelling at when button was released, ± 1 mph. The system will cruise until either the cruise control switch is moved to Off position, the ignition switch is turned off and/or the set/coast button is pushed in fully and held. Depressing the brake pedal releases the cruise, but not the resume capability.

Coast (Trim) Position

Cruise speed can be changed with the set/coast switch fully depressed. Cruise speed can be increased by accelerating to desired cruise speed, then fully depressing and releasing switch. When switch is released, a new cruise speed is set. To decrease cruise speed, fully depress and hold switch, then decelerate to desired cruise speed and release switch.

Tap Down Position

The cruise speed can be decreased in 1 mph increments by tapping the set/coast switch. With cruise control engaged and operating, quickly depress and release or tap switch. Each tap of switch will decrease cruise speed 1 mph to a maximum 10 mph decrease in cruise speed. This feature can be used to lower the cruise speed below the 25 mph minimum setting to as low as 16 mph.

RESUME/ACCEL SWITCH

This switch has two positions. When switch is **momentarily** moved toward the R/A position after braking, cruise control operation will be returned to last set speed.

If switch is held in R/A position for more than 1 second, the system reverts to the Accel mode. To accelerate vehicle, move switch to R/A position and hold until vehicle reaches desired increased speed. When switch is released, speed vehicle has accelerated to becomes new cruise speed. In order to use Accel mode, the cruise control switch must be in On position and vehicle speed must be above 25 mph.

Tap Up Position

This feature allows the cruise speed to be increased in 1 mph increments up to 10 mph by quickly pressing switch toward R/A position and quickly releasing switch.

LASH LEARN

4.6L/V8-279 Northstar Engine

The cruise control system utilizes a lash learn system to compensate for any minor misadjustments in the servo linkage due to tolerance stack-up or build error. The leash learn term is generally calculated when the PCM receives a cruise set command and the throttle is fully relaxed. The PCM calculates the servo position movement to offset the throttle position movement. The PCM uses this value to subsequent servo position commands.

To perform lash learn, perform the following procedure:

1. Drive vehicle to approximately 50 mph.
2. Take foot off accelerator for three seconds.
3. Engage cruise SET/COATS button.

PRECAUTIONS

AIR BAG SYSTEMS

Refer to "Air Bag System Precautions" in the front of this manual for system disarming and arming procedures.

TROUBLESHOOTING

PRELIMINARY CHECKS

Brougham

1. Check cruise control fuse.
2. Check cruise control servo linkage adjustment, and vacuum hose routing.
3. Check vacuum hoses for leaks, kinks, or restrictions.

DeVille & Fleetwood (FWD)

1. Check cruise control servo linkage adjustment, and vacuum hose routing.
2. Check vacuum hoses for leaks, kinks, or restrictions.
3. Check for sticking, leaking, or plugged vacuum release valve.

Eldorado & Seville

1. Check cruise fuse 8 for proper operation by observing the battery no charge indicator, with ignition switch in run and engine off
2. Check transaxle position switch by observing the PRNDL display.
3. Check vacuum hoses for leaks, kinks, and other restrictions.
4. Check cruise control servo linkage. If necessary to adjust, refer to **Fig. 1** for procedure.

ROAD TEST

Perform the following road test and note system operation. If a cause for the observed malfunction cannot be determined by following troubleshooting procedures, proceed to "System Diagnosis & Testing."

DeVille & Fleetwood (FWD)

Refer to **Fig. 2**, when performing vehicle road test.

Brougham

Perform road test with cruise control switch on and vehicle speed above 25 mph.

1. Place engagement switch in Set/Coast position, then release it. Cruise engage indicator should light and vehicle should maintain speed.
2. Hold engage switch in Set/Coast position with foot off accelerator. Vehicle should coast at a slower speed.
3. Release Set/Coast switch. Cruise control should engage and hold a slower speed above 25 mph.
4. Place engage switch in Resume/Accel position and hold it there. Vehicle should accelerate.
5. Release engage switch. Vehicle should hold new faster speed.
6. Tap brake pedal. Vehicle should coast slower.

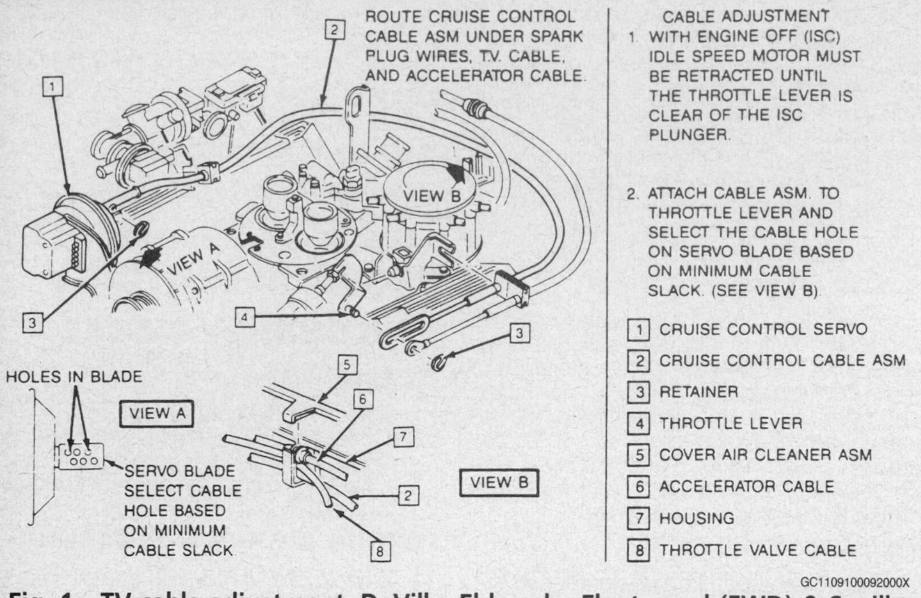
2
ROUTE CRUISE CONTROL CABLE ASM UNDER SPARK PLUG WIRES, T.V. CABLE, AND ACCELERATOR CABLE.
1
VIEW B
VIEW A
3
4
3
HOLES IN BLADE
5
VIEW A
6
7
SERVO BLADE SELECT CABLE HOLE BASED ON MINIMUM CABLE SLACK
2
VIEW B
8
CABLE ADJUSTMENT
1. WITH ENGINE OFF (ISC) IDLE SPEED MOTOR MUST BE RETRACTED UNTIL THE THROTTLE LEVER IS CLEAR OF THE ISC PLUNGER.
2. ATTACH CABLE ASM. TO THROTTLE LEVER AND SELECT THE CABLE HOLE ON SERVO BLADE BASED ON MINIMUM CABLE SLACK. (SEE VIEW B)
1 CRUISE CONTROL SERVO
2 CRUISE CONTROL CABLE ASM
3 RETAINER
4 THROTTLE LEVER
5 COVER AIR CLEANER ASM
6 ACCELERATOR CABLE
7 HOUSING
8 THROTTLE VALVE CABLE
GC1109100092000X

Fig. 1 TV cable adjustment. DeVille, Eldorado, Fleetwood (FWD) & Seville

7. Place engage switch in Resume/Accel position momentarily. Vehicle should accelerate to former set speed.
8. While cruising, accelerate, then remove foot from accelerator pedal. Vehicle should coast back to set speed.
9. While cruising, tap engage switch to Resume/Accel position. Vehicle speed should increase with each tap 1 mph.
10. While cruising, tap engage switch to Set/Coast position. Vehicle speed should decrease 1 mph for each tap down to 25 mph.
11. Place cruise control switch in Off position. Cruise control should turn off.

Eldorado & Seville

Perform road test with cruise switch in On position and vehicle speed above 25 mph.

1. Momentarily depress set/coast switch in steering wheel pad and ensure vehicle maintains speed.
2. Hold set/coast switch in with foot off accelerator and ensure vehicle coasts down to a lower speed.
3. Release set/coast switch and ensure cruise control engages and holds slower speed if speed is greater than 25 mph.
4. Slide and hold resume/accelerate switch in and ensure vehicle accelerates.
5. Release resume/accelerate switch and ensure vehicle holds new, faster speed.
6. Tap brake pedal and ensure vehicle coasts.
7. Slide resume/accelerate switch and ensure vehicle accelerates to speed set before tapping of brake pedal.
8. Tap set/coast switch and ensure vehicle speed decreases 1 mph for each tap.
9. Tap resume/accelerate switch and ensure vehicle speed increases 1 mph for each tap.
10. Slide cruise switch in righthand switch assembly to Off position and ensure cruise control releases to manual operation.

ADJUSTMENTS

CABLE OR ROD

DeVille, Eldorado, Fleetwood (FWD) & Seville

A cable is used in this system. The servo unit positions the throttle linkage through the use of a cable. To adjust this cable turn engine to the "Off" position. Retract idle speed control (ISC) motor plunger, **throttle lever must not touch ISC plunger.** Connect cruise control cable to servo hole blade, **Fig. 1**, that allows minimum slack.

BRAKE RELEASE SWITCH

With brake pedal depressed, push cruise control/stoplight switch fully into retainer, then pull brake pedal fully back to rest position. Switch will back out of retainer and adjust automatically. **On vehicles equipped with anti-lock brakes,** release brake pedal and allow to come to rest. Brake release switch contacts should open at 1/8-1/2 inch pedal travel, measured at centerline of brake pedal pad. Actuation of stop lamp contact is 3/16 after cruise control contact opens.

VACUUM RELEASE VALVE

With brake pedal depressed, push vacuum valve switch all the way into the retaining clip. Pull the brake pedal to the stop to automatically adjust the valve. On vehicle equipped with anti-lock brakes, release pedal and allow to come to rest. Vacuum dump valve assembly should open at 1-15/16 inch pedal travel, measured at centerline of brake pedal pad.

SYSTEM DIAGNOSIS & TESTING

Refer to **Figs. 3 through 5** for wiring diagrams.

ACTION	NORMAL RESULT
Drive vehicle faster than 25 mph Press Cruise Switch to ON Momentarily depress Set/Coast Switch	Vehicle maintains speed CRUISE Indicator lights when the switch is released and the system is engaged
Hold Set/Coast switch in, foot off accelerator	Vehicle coasts to a slower speed
Release Set/Coast Switch	Cruise Control engages and holds the slower speed, if the new speed remains above 25 mph
Depress and hold Resume/Accel Switch in	Vehicle accelerates
Release Resume/Accel Switch	Vehicle holds new faster speed
Tap Brake Pedal	Vehicle coasts
Depress and release Resume/Accel Switch	Vehicle accelerates to speed set prior to Brake Pedal tap
Tap Set/Coast Switch	Vehicle speed decreases 1 mph for each tap (can be tapped down to 25 mph)
Tap Resume/Accel Switch	Vehicle speed increases 1 mph for each tap
Move Cruise Switch to OFF	Cruise Control releases to manual operation

GC1109100093000X

Fig. 2 Road test system check. DeVille & Fleetwood (FWD)

DEVILLE & FLEETWOOD (FWD)

ACCESSING SELF-DIAGNOSTIC TROUBLE MODE

In the process of controlling the various subsystems, the ECM and PCM continually monitors operating conditions for possible malfunctions. By comparing system conditions against standard operating limits it certain circuits and component malfunctions scan be detected. A two digit numerical code is stored in the computer memory when a problem is detected by this self-diagnostic system.

If the ECM diagnostics detect a fault, the cruise control system will be inhibited for the entire ignition cycle. The faults that may inhibit the cruise control system are as follows:

1. Fault with vehicle speed sensor or throttle position sensor circuit.
2. Cruise control requested above 90 mph.
3. A rapid rise in RPM's.

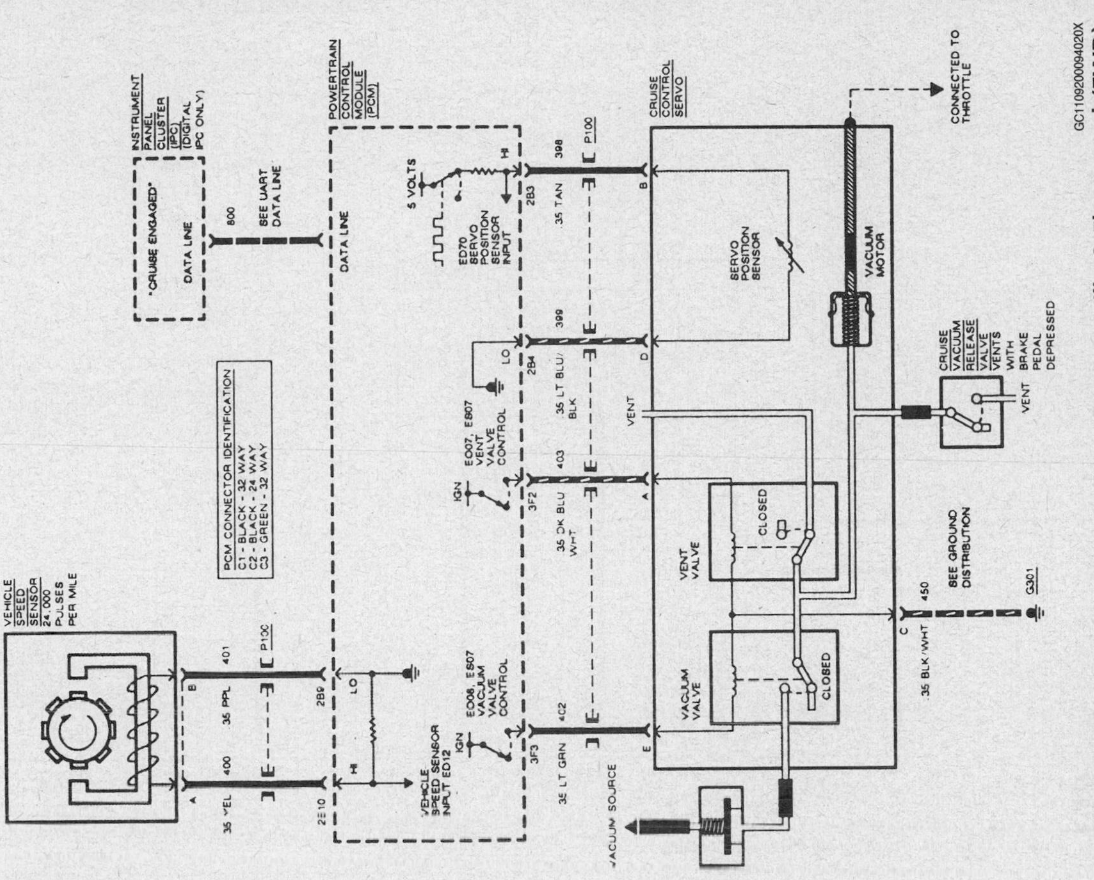

GC1109200094020X

Fig. 3 Wiring diagram (Part 2 of 2). 1992 DeVille & Fleetwood (FWD)

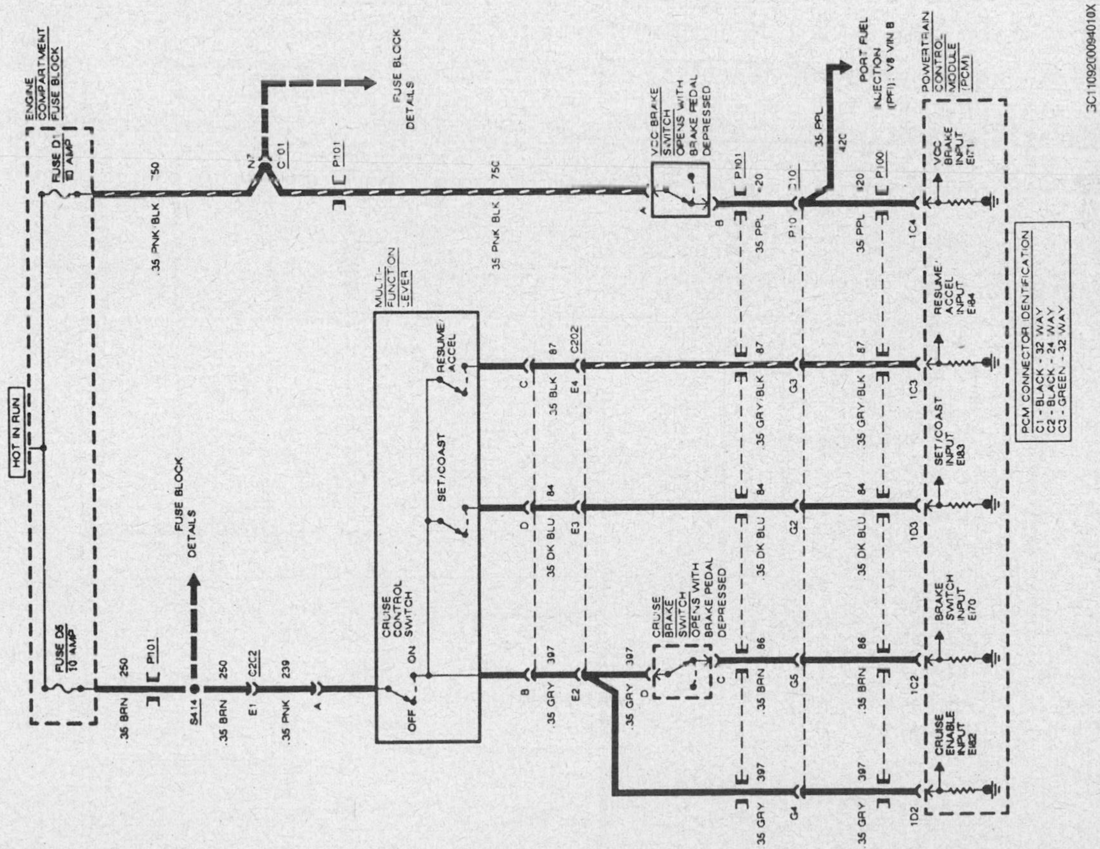

GC1109200094010X

Fig. 3 Wiring diagram (Part 1 of 2). 1992 DeVille & Fleetwood (FWD)

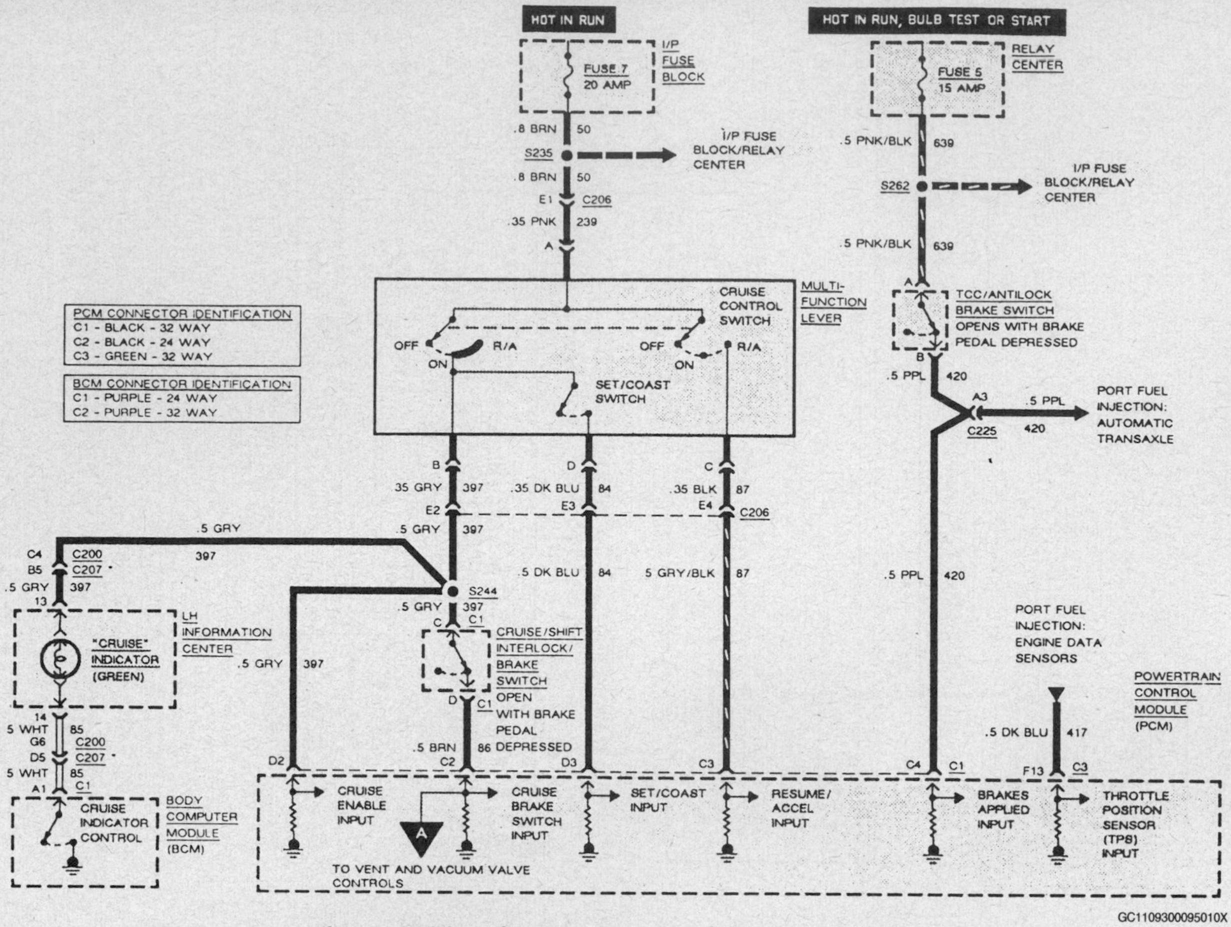
HOT IN RUN
HOT IN RUN, BULB TEST OR START
FUSE 7
20 AMP
I/P FUSE BLOCK
FUSE 5
15 AMP
RELAY CENTER
.8 BRN 50
S235
I/P FUSE BLOCK/RELAY CENTER
.8 BRN 50
E1 C206
.35 PNK 239
.5 PNK/BLK 639
S262
I/P FUSE BLOCK/RELAY CENTER
.5 PNK/BLK 639
PCM CONNECTOR IDENTIFICATION
C1 - BLACK - 32 WAY
C2 - BLACK - 24 WAY
C3 - GREEN - 32 WAY
BCM CONNECTOR IDENTIFICATION
C1 - PURPLE - 24 WAY
C2 - PURPLE - 32 WAY
CRUISE CONTROL SWITCH
MULTI-FUNCTION LEVER
OFF
R/A
ON
SET/COAST SWITCH
TCC/ANTILOCK BRAKE SWITCH OPENS WITH BRAKE PEDAL DEPRESSED
.5 PPL 420
A3
C225
.5 PPL
420
PORT FUEL INJECTION: AUTOMATIC TRANSAXLE
.35 GRY 397
.35 DK BLU 84
.35 BLK 87
E2
E3
E4
C206
.5 GRY
397
C4 C200
B5 C207
.5 GRY 397
S244
.5 DK BLU 84
.5 GRY/BLK 87
.5 PPL 420
LH INFORMATION CENTER
"CRUISE" INDICATOR (GREEN)
.5 GRY 397
CRUISE/SHIFT INTERLOCK/ BRAKE SWITCH OPEN WITH BRAKE PEDAL DEPRESSED
.5 BRN 86
PORT FUEL INJECTION: ENGINE DATA SENSORS
POWERTRAIN CONTROL MODULE (PCM)
.5 DK BLU 417
5 WHT 85
G6 C200
D5 C207
5 WHT 85
A1 C1
CRUISE INDICATOR CONTROL
BODY COMPUTER MODULE (BCM)
D2
C2
D3
C3
C4 C1
F13 C3
CRUISE ENABLE INPUT
CRUISE BRAKE SWITCH INPUT
SET/COAST INPUT
RESUME/ ACCEL INPUT
BRAKES APPLIED INPUT
THROTTLE POSITION SENSOR (TPS) INPUT
TO VENT AND VACUUM VALVE CONTROLS
GC1109300095010X

Fig. 4 Wiring diagram (Part 1 of 2). 1993 DeVille

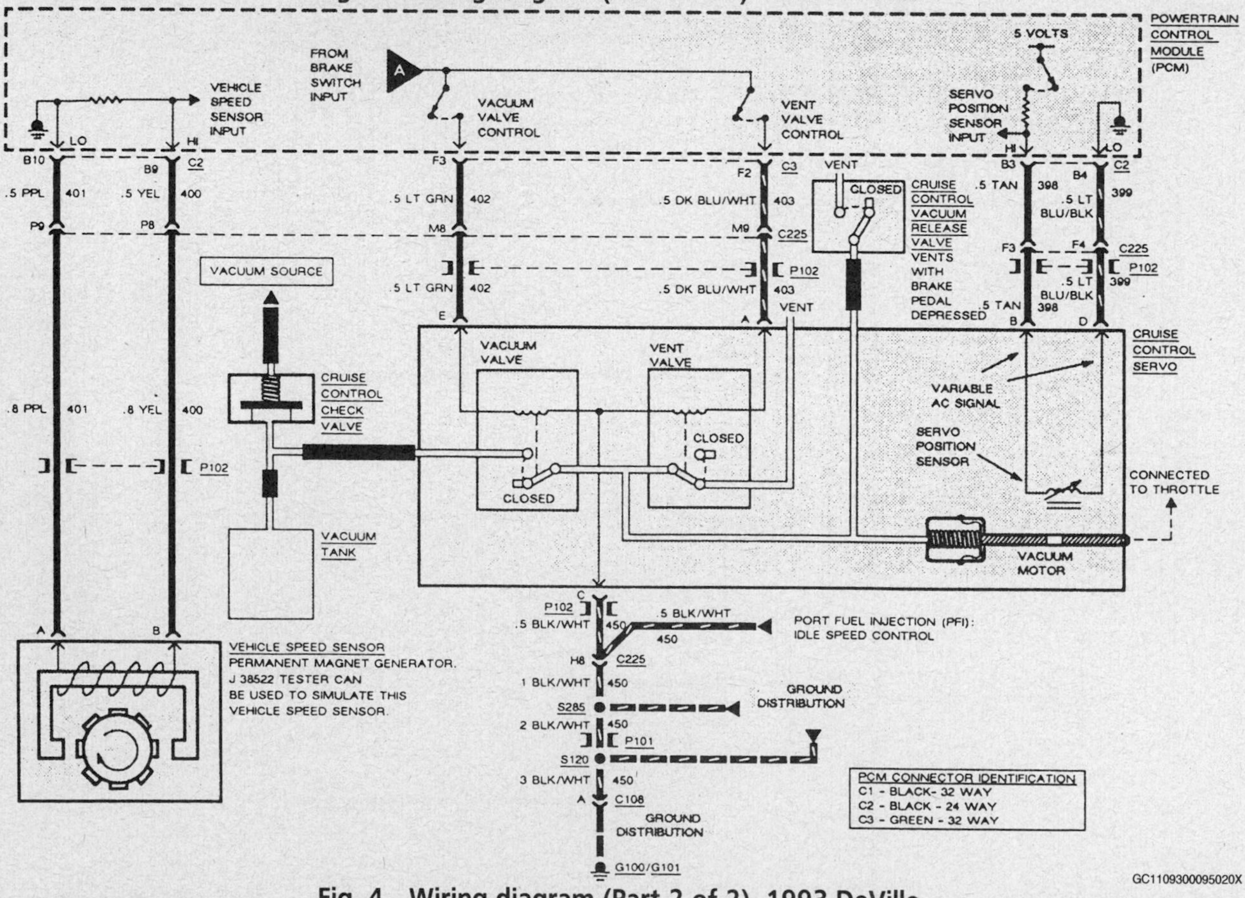
POWERTRAIN CONTROL MODULE (PCM)
5 VOLTS
FROM BRAKE SWITCH INPUT
VEHICLE SPEED SENSOR INPUT
VACUUM VALVE CONTROL
VENT VALVE CONTROL
SERVO POSITION SENSOR INPUT
LO
HI
B10
B9 C2
F3
F2 C3
B3
B4 C2
.5 PPL 401
.5 YEL 400
.5 LT GRN 402
.5 DK BLU/WHT 403
VENT
CLOSED
CRUISE CONTROL VACUUM RELEASE VALVE VENTS WITH BRAKE PEDAL DEPRESSED
.5 TAN 398
.5 LT BLU/BLK 399
P9
P8
M8
M9 C225
F3
F4 C225
P102
VACUUM SOURCE
.5 LT GRN 402
.5 DK BLU/WHT 403
.5 TAN 398
.5 LT BLU/BLK 399
VACUUM VALVE
VENT VALVE
CRUISE CONTROL SERVO
CRUISE CONTROL CHECK VALVE
.8 PPL 401
.8 YEL 400
P102
CLOSED
VARIABLE AC SIGNAL
SERVO POSITION SENSOR
CONNECTED TO THROTTLE
VACUUM TANK
VACUUM MOTOR
P102
.5 BLK/WHT 450
.5 BLK/WHT
450
PORT FUEL INJECTION (PFI): IDLE SPEED CONTROL
H8 C225
1 BLK/WHT 450
S285
GROUND DISTRIBUTION
2 BLK/WHT 450
P101
S120
3 BLK/WHT 450
C108
GROUND DISTRIBUTION
G100/G101
VEHICLE SPEED SENSOR
PERMANENT MAGNET GENERATOR.
J 38522 TESTER CAN BE USED TO SIMULATE THIS VEHICLE SPEED SENSOR.
PCM CONNECTOR IDENTIFICATION
C1 - BLACK- 32 WAY
C2 - BLACK - 24 WAY
C3 - GREEN - 32 WAY
GC1109300095020X

Fig. 4 Wiring diagram (Part 2 of 2). 1993 DeVille

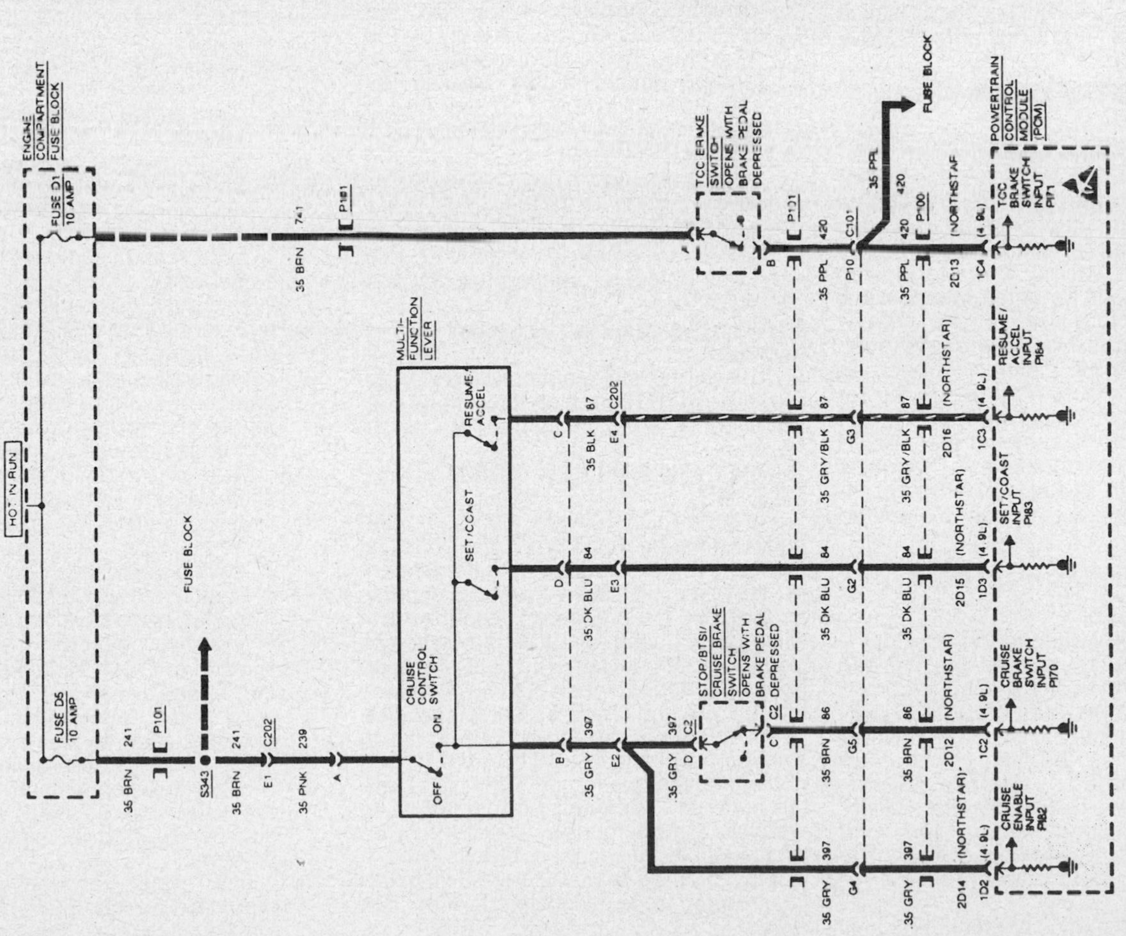

GC1109400317010X

Fig. 5 Wiring diagram (Part 1 of 2). 1994 DeVille

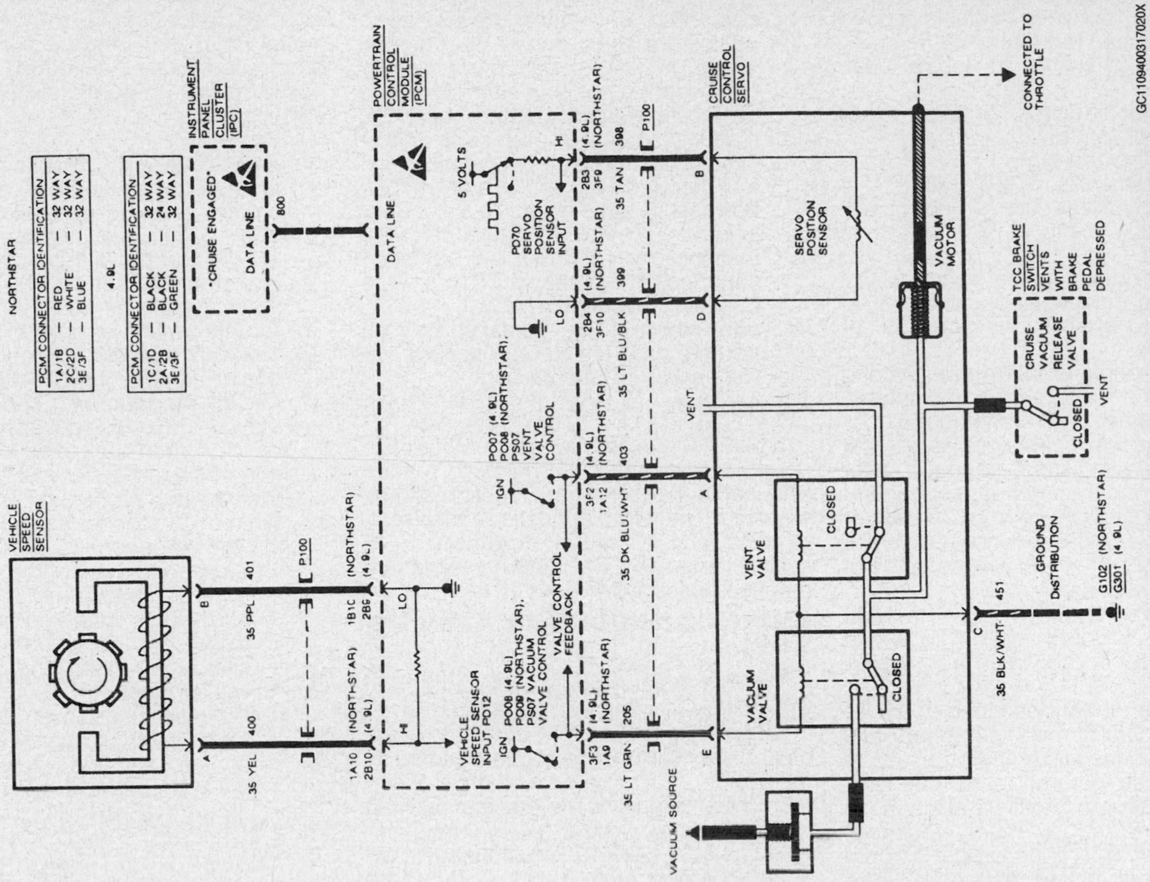

GC1109400317020X

Fig. 5 Wiring diagram (Part 2 of 2). 1994 DeVille

4. Difference between vehicle speed and set speed too high.
5. Transaxle is shifted to neutral position.
6. ECM detects battery voltage either too high or too low.
7. Acceleration too high.
8. Coolant temperature too high.
9. **On 1992 models,** cruise control servo position sensor is shorted or grounded.
10. **On all models,** cruise switch is On, brake is not depressed and the PCM output is HI when it should be LOW, or vise-versa.
11. A throttle angle greater than 20° and the servo position sensor indicates a stroke greater than commanded.
12. Servo position sensor indicates that the servo is stilled engaged after cruise control has been disengaged.
13. Vehicle speed cycles from 30 mph or greater to 0 mph with no VCC brake switch input, the PCM will record 10 of these consecutively.
14. Park neutral switch is closed when vehicle is in fourth gear with speed between 23 and 35 mph fro 10 seconds.

Codes other than described may be stored in the control models memory and displayed when the system is accessed to diagnose cruise control malfunctions. It may be necessary to identify and diagnose the failures caused by these additional codes in order to ensure proper system operation. For complete diagnosis of the system, refer to the "Fuel Injection Section in the MOTOR's Auto Engine Tune Up & Electronic Manual.

Intermittent Problem Diagnosis

Diagnostic trouble codes displayed during the first pass of ECM diagnostic codes, and not the second pass, are considered intermittent. Intermittent diagnostic trouble codes are those that the ECM previously determined to be faulty but later tested good. If the code is intermittent, most charts will refer to a specific note. **Do not bypass the charts when checking intermittent conditions.** Failure to check an intermittent condition may result in replacement of good components.

Many intermittent problems are caused by poor electrical connections. Diagnosis should start with visual and physical inspection of connectors which are related with the code.

Entering Self-Diagnosis Mode

1. Turn ignition switch to On position.
2. Simultaneously depress the Off and warmer buttons on the climate control panel and hold buttons until display panel segments are illuminated which indicates the beginning of the diagnostic readout. The purpose of illuminating the two display panels is to ensure that all segments are working. **If any segments are inoperative, the affected display panel must be replaced.**
3. After the display segment check is completed, any stored trouble code will be displayed on the data center. These two-digit codes will be displayed with a prefix of either E or F to designate which computer sensed the malfunction. If a trouble code is displayed, or if the self-diagnostics system cannot be accessed, a defect has been sensed in the vehicle's electronic control system. To diagnose these malfunctions, refer to the "Fuel Injection Section" in the MOTOR's Auto Engine & Electronic manual.
4. After all codes are displayed or if no trouble codes are stored, the code .7.0 will appear on the display.

Code .7.0

Code .7.0 is a decision point. When this code is displayed, the diagnostic feature relevant to the current malfunction can be selected. The two diagnostic modes relevant to cruise control diagnosis, ECM switch tests and ECM output cycling, are detailed as follows.

Clearing Diagnostic Trouble Codes

The diagnostic trouble codes stored in the system memory can be cleared to aid in diagnosing intermittent conditions. The clear diagnostic trouble codes, proceed as follows:

1. Enter diagnostic modes as outlined previously.
2. The clear ECM codes, simultaneously depress the HI and LO buttons on the climate control panel and hold buttons until the code E.0.0 is displayed.
3. The clear body control module (BCM) codes, simultaneously depress the Off and LO buttons on the climate control panel and hold until the code F.0.0 is displayed.
4. After E.0.0 and F.0.0 are displayed, the code .7.0 will be displayed. With this code displayed, turn off ignition and leave ignition off for at least 10 seconds before re-entering the diagnostic mode.

Exiting Self-Diagnosis Mode

To exit the self-diagnostic mode, depress the AUTO button on the climate control panel or turn of ignition for at least 10 seconds.

ECM/PCM SWITCH TEST SERIES

To perform the switch test series, the engine must be running and the code .7.0 must be displayed on the data center panel. To begin the test sequence, depress and release the brake pedal, and the test will begin as soon as the display changes from code .7.0 to code E.7.1. If the code does not change, check brake switch feed to the ECM and check for defective ECM.

The ECM will display a code for each switch, in sequence, and if the switch does not operate properly, the ECM will store the code as a diagnostic trouble code. In addition, the appropriate switch must be cycled within 10 seconds after its code is displayed or the ECM will store a diagnostic trouble code associated with that switch.

When performing the following tests, refer to **Figs. 3 through 7** for wiring diagrams and **Figs. 8 through 19** for diagnostic tests. Perform switch tests as follows:

1. With code E.7.1 displayed, depress and release brake pedal again to test cruise control brake switch circuit.
2. With code E.7.2 displayed, depress accelerator pedal from idle position to open throttle, then slowly release pedal. As throttle is moved the ECM tests throttle switch for proper operation.
3. **On 1992 models,** with code E.7.3 displayed, is not a valid test.
4. **On all models,** with code E.7.5 displayed, turn cruise control switch from off to on, then back to off to test operation of switch. Refer to **Fig. 8** for further testing procedure. For intermittent codes proceed as follows:
   a. The amber cruise-on indicator can be used to monitor the cruise dash switch status. Turn dash switch on and wiggle wiring and connectors. If switch or circuit from the fuse to switch are open, the amber light will blink out.
   b. If cruise fuse blows intermittently, turn switch on, then wiggle wiring, connectors and cruise steering column switch. If circuit becomes grounded, fuse will blow.
5. With code E.7.6 displayed and with instrument panel cruise control switch on, depress and release set/coast button to test set/coast button operation. Refer to **Fig. 9** for further testing procedure. For intermittent codes proceed as follows:
   a. Turn cruise dash switch to on and backprobe ECM B4 with a voltmeter to ground. B4 should show 12 volts with set/coast depressed and 0 volts with switch released. While observing meter, cycle switch and wiggle wiring and connectors.
6. With code E.7.7 displayed and with instrument panel cruise control switch on, depress and release resume/acceleration switch to test operation of switch. Refer to **Fig. 10** for further testing procedure. For intermittent codes proceed as follows:
   a. Turn cruise dash switch to on and backprobe ECM B6 with a voltmeter to ground. B6 should show 12 volts with resume/acceleration switch depressed and 0 volts with switch released. While observing meter, cycle switch and wiggle wiring and connectors.
7. With code E.7.8 displayed, turn steering wheel to full lock in both directions, then return wheel to straight ahead position to test power steering pressure switch operation.
8. When the switch tests are completed, the ECM will go back and display codes for switches which did not test properly.
9. Check circuit between each switch that failed and the ECM, test switches individually, repair as needed, then

CIRCUIT DESCRIPTION	CIRCUIT NUMBER	PCM (2A/B) BLACK (B / A)	CIRCUIT NUMBER	CIRCUIT DESCRIPTION
BATTERY	480	1	435	EGR SOLENOID
N/C		2	776	TRANS PRNDL INPUT PARITY
C/C SERVO POSITION SENSOR	398	3		N/C
C/C SERVO POSITION SENSOR	399	4		N/C
N/C		5	476	MAP/MAT SENSOR GROUND
LEFT O_2 SENSOR LO	413	6	1276	IGNITION
LEFT O_2 SENSOR HI	1589	7	427	THROTTLE SWITCH
HIGH SPEED COOLING FAN RLY	1270	8	800	UART SERIAL DATA
SPEED SENSOR INPUT LO	401	9	800	UART SERIAL DATA
SPEED SENSOR INPUT HI	400	10	419	'SERVICE ENGINE SOON' LIGHT
4K SPEED OUTPUT TO IPC	818	11	1269	LOW SPEED COOLING FAN RLY
4K SPEED OUTPUT TO CCR	817	12	450	PCM GROUND

GC1109200096010X

Fig. 6 PCM connector (Part 1 of 3). 1992 DeVille & Fleetwood (FWD)

CIRCUIT DESCRIPTION	CIRCUIT NUMBER	PCM (1C/D) BLACK (D / C)	CIRCUIT NUMBER	CIRCUIT DESCRIPTION
PCM GROUND	450	1	1586	OVERSPEED ALARM (EXP)
C/C ON-OFF	397	2	86	C/C BRAKE SWITCH
C/C SET/COAST	84	3	87	C/C RESUME
N/C		4	420	VCC BRAKE SWITCH
N/C		5	633	CAM SENSOR INPUT
PCM GROUND	450	6		N/C
PCM GROUND	450	7	424	EST BYPASS
EST REFERENCE PULSE HI	430	8	423	EST OUTPUT
EST REFERENCE/CAM LO	453	9	816	POWER STEERING SW
N/C		10	772	TRANS PRNDL INPUT B
N/C		11	841	INJECTOR 1
HEATED W S REQUEST	637	12	878	INJECTOR 8
INJECTOR 2	842	13	846	INJECTOR 6
INJECTOR 7	877	14	474	5V REFERENCE
INJECTOR 5	845	15	844	INJECTOR 4
INJECTOR 3	843	16	480	BATTERY

GC1109200096020X

Fig. 6 PCM connector (Part 2 of 3). 1992 DeVille & Fleetwood (FWD)

CIRCUIT DESCRIPTION	CIRCUIT NUMBER	PCM (3E/F) GREEN (F / E)	CIRCUIT NUMBER	CIRCUIT DESCRIPTION
FUEL PUMP RELAY	465	1	425	ISC HI
C/C VENT SOLENOID	403	2	426	ISC LO
C/C VAC SOLENOID	402	3		N/C
A/C CLUTCH RELAY	762	4	1223	SHIFT B SOLENOID
VCC MOD	446	5		N/C
VCC SOLENOID	422	6	1490	CCR LIFT/DIVE OUTPUT
TRANS PRNDL INPUT C	773	7	428	CANISTER PURGE SOLND
TRANS PRNDL INPUT A	771	8		N/C
N/C		9		N/C
PASS-KEY FUEL ENABLE	229	10	1222	SHIFT A SOLENOID
N/C		11	1076	CTS/TPS SENSOR GROUND
N/C		12	462	FIXED SPARK/SET TIMING
TPS SIGNAL	417	13	120	FUEL PUMP FEEDBACK
N/C		14	412	RIGHT O_2 SENSOR HI
MAP SIGNAL	432	15	413	RIGHT O_2 SENSOR LO
MAT SIGNAL	472	16	410	COOLANT TEMP SIGNAL

GC1109200096030X

Fig. 6 PCM connector (Part 3 of 3). 1992 DeVille & Fleetwood (FWD)

CIRCUIT DESCRIPTION	CIRCUIT NUMBER	PCM (1C/D) BLACK (D / C)	CIRCUIT NUMBER	CIRCUIT DESCRIPTION
PCM GROUND	450	1		N/C
C/C ON-OFF	397	2	86	C/C ENABLE
C/C SET/COAST	84	3	87	C/C RESUME
N/C		4	420	VCC BRAKE
N/C		5	633	CAM HI
PCM GROUND	450	6		N/C
PCM GROUND	450	7	424	BYPASS
EST REFERENCE PULSE HI	430	8	423	EST
EST REFERENCE/CAM LO	453	9	495	POWER STEERING SW.
N/C		10	772	TRANS INPUT B
N/C		11	841	INJECTOR 1
HEATED W/S	637	12	878	INJECTOR 8
INJECTOR 2	842	13	846	INJECTOR 6
INJECTOR 7	877	14	474	5V REFERENCE
INJECTOR 5	845	15	844	INJECTOR 4
INJECTOR 3	843	16	480	BATTERY

SINGLE CAVITY METRI PAK CONNECTOR

GC1109300097010X

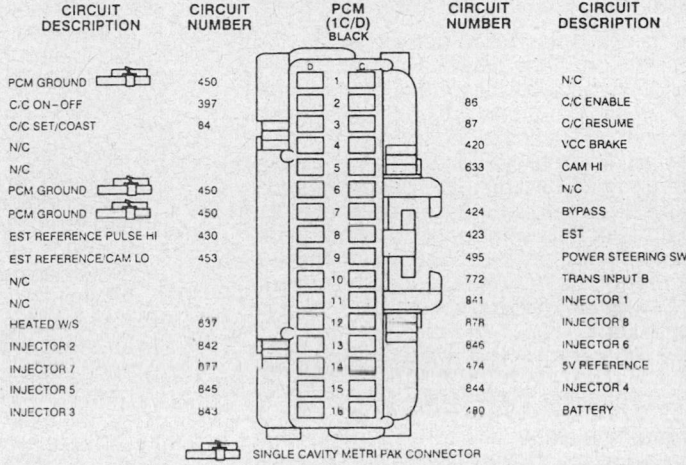

Fig. 7 PCM connector (Part 1 of 3). 1993–94 DeVille

NOTE: THE TPA STRAIN RELIEVERS IN THIS CONNECTOR WILL BE MARKED AS C AND D

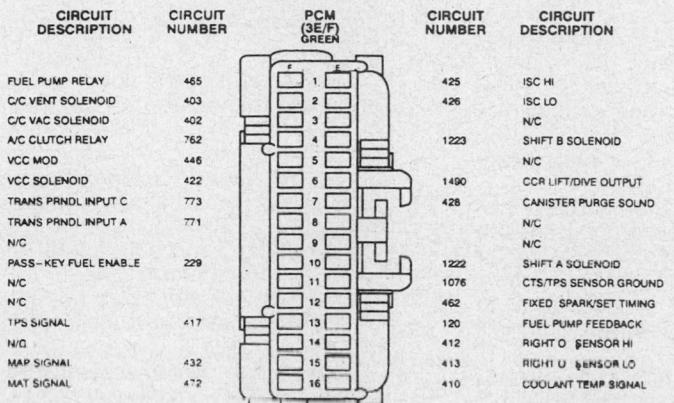

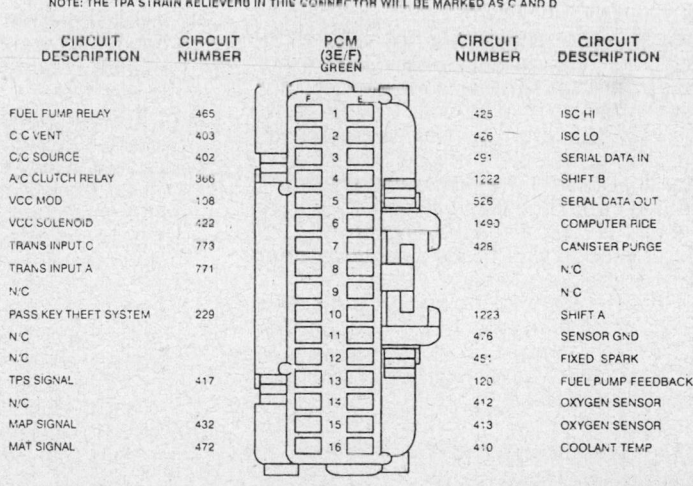

CIRCUIT DESCRIPTION	CIRCUIT NUMBER	PCM (2A/B) BLACK (B / A)	CIRCUIT NUMBER	CIRCUIT DESCRIPTION
BATTERY	480	1	435	EGR SOLENOID
N/C		2	776	TRANS INPUT P
C/C POSITION HI	398	3		
C/C POSITION LO	399	4		N/C
N/C		5	469	SENSOR GROUND
N/C		6	439	IGNITION
N/C		7	427	THROTTLE SWITCH
COOLING FAN RELAY #2	1270	8	800	UART SERIAL DATA
SPEED SENSOR INPUT LO	400	9	800	UART SERIAL DATA
SPEED SENSOR INPUT HI	401	10	419	CHECK ENGINE SIGNAL
4000 PULSE SPEED OUTPUT #1	389	11	1269	COOLING FAN RELAY #1
4000 PULSE SPEED OUTPUT #2	917	12	450	PCM GROUND

SINGLE CAVITY METRI PAK CONNECTOR

GC1109300097020X

Fig. 7 PCM connector (Part 2 of 3). 1993–94 DeVille

CIRCUIT DESCRIPTION	CIRCUIT NUMBER	PCM (3E/F) GREEN (F / E)	CIRCUIT NUMBER	CIRCUIT DESCRIPTION
FUEL PUMP RELAY	465	1	425	ISC HI
C/C VENT	403	2	426	ISC LO
C/C SOURCE	402	3	491	SERIAL DATA IN
A/C CLUTCH RELAY	366	4	1222	SHIFT B
VCC MOD	108	5	526	SERAL DATA OUT
VCC SOLENOID	422	6	1490	COMPUTER RIDE
TRANS INPUT C	773	7	428	CANISTER PURGE
TRANS INPUT A	771	8		N/C
N/C		9		N/C
PASS KEY THEFT SYSTEM	229	10	1223	SHIFT A
N/C		11	476	SENSOR GND
N/C		12	451	FIXED SPARK
TPS SIGNAL	417	13	120	FUEL PUMP FEEDBACK
N/C		14	412	OXYGEN SENSOR
MAP SIGNAL	432	15	413	OXYGEN SENSOR
MAT SIGNAL	472	16	410	COOLANT TEMP

GC1109300097030X

Fig. 7 PCM connector (Part 3 of 3). 1993–94 DeVille

clear diagnostic trouble codes and retest system.

10. If malfunction persists, refer to "Fuel Injection Section" in the MOTOR Auto Engine Tune Up & Electronics manual.

ECM OUTPUT CYCLING

ECM output cycling can be tested after code E.9.5 is displayed on the data center. Code E.9.5 can be reached by depressing the HI button on the climate control panel when code .7.0 is displayed. The ECM output cycling mode, code E.9.6, will then cycle ECM outputs on and off. To enter output cycling mode, proceed as follows:

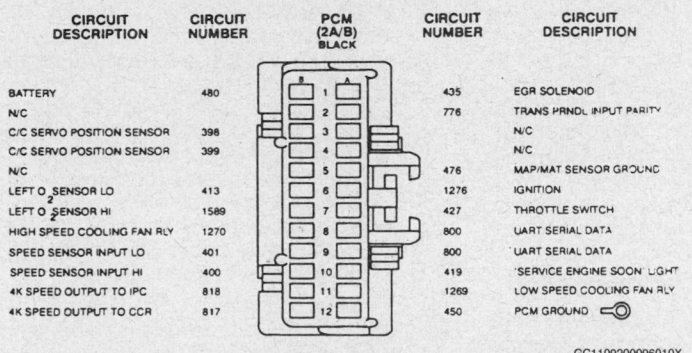

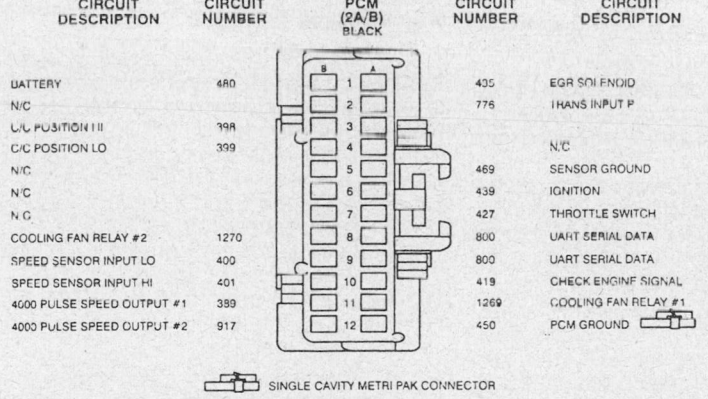

1. With engine running, turn instrument panel cruise control switch to ON position to allow cruise control outputs to cycle.
2. Turn ignition off, then within 2 seconds turn ignition back on.
3. Enter self-diagnostic mode and obtain code E.9.5 as outlined above.
4. Every 3 seconds devices will be cycled.
5. Depress HI button on climate control panel to advance device testing and depress LO button to return to E0.0 (cycle none).
6. If the system fails to operate as outlined, check wiring between effected component and ECM, test compo-

nents individually, repair as needed, then clear diagnostic trouble codes and repeat test. If malfunction persists, refer to "Fuel Injection Section" in the MOTOR's Auto Engine Tune Up & Electronics Manual.

ELDORADO & SEVILLE

Self-Diagnosis System

In the process of controlling the various subsystems, the ECM and BCM continually monitor operating conditions for possible malfunctions. By comparing system conditions against standard operating limits certain circuits and component malfunctions can be detected. A three digit numerical code is stored in the computer memory when a problem is detected by this self diagnostic system.

Entering Self-Diagnosis Mode

To enter diagnostic service mode, turn ignition on, then depress Off and Warm buttons on the climate control panel (CCP). Hold buttons until all display panel segments illuminate, indicating the beginning of diagnostic readout. The two display panels must be illuminated, except for turn signal lights, to ensure all segments are operating. **Do not attempt diagnosis unless all segments appear, as an improper diagnosis may result.** If any segments are inoperative, the display panel must be replaced.

ACCESSING DIAGNOSTIC TROUBLE CODES

After the diagnostic service mode is entered, any diagnostic trouble codes stored in the computer memory will be displayed, **Fig. 20.** ECM codes will be displayed first, then BCM codes. Codes will also be accompanied by Current or History. History indicates the failure was not present the last time the code was tested. Current indicates the fault still exists. At any time during the display of diagnostic trouble codes the Low button on the CCP is depressed, the display of codes will be bypassed. At any time during the display of diagnostic trouble codes the Reset/Recall button on the DIC is depressed, the system will exit diagnostic service mode and go back to normal vehicle operation.

Refer to **Figs. 21 through 50** for diagnostic trouble codes EO/PO60 through EO/PO69 and EO/PO99, **Figs. 51 through 54** for ECM/PCM input test diagnostics and **Figs. 55 and 56** for wiring diagrams.

DIAGNOSTIC TEST PROCEDURES

After diagnostic trouble codes have been displayed, the diagnostic service mode can be used to further test the speed control system. To do so, refer to **Fig. 20** and proceed as follows:

1. Following the display of diagnostic trouble codes, the first available system level will be displayed, which is the ECM system.
2. Depress Hi button on the CCP. This will display "Data," the first available test type.
3. Press Lo button on the CCP to display "Input," the test type level for speed control system testing.
4. Depress Hi button on the CCP. This will displayed the first test type. At this point, press Hi button until the correct test type appears as listed below under the applicable model year.
5. To display the previous test, press Lo button. To return to previous test type, press Off.

Cruise Control Inoperative

If cruise control is inoperative, enter ECM "input" tests and perform the following, referring to wiring diagrams and connector points, **Figs. 58 and 59,** and ECM replacement check. If cruise system does function, but indicator does not light, proceed to step 13.

1. With ignition switch in Run position, select ECM input test E182.
2. If ECM does not display LO with cruise control switch off, or does not display Hi with cruise control switch on, refer to **Fig. 52.** For intermittent codes, proceed as follows:
   a. The amber cruise on indicator can be used to monitor cruise dash switch status. Turn dash switch on and wiggle wiring and connectors. If switch or circuit from fuse to switch are open, amber light will blink out.
   b. If cruise 3A fuse blows intermittently, turn switch on, wiggle wiring, connectors, cruise steering column switch. If circuit becomes grounded, the fuse will blow.
3. If ECM displays LO with cruise switch on and displays HI with cruise switch on, select input test E170, on all models, turn ignition switch to Run position and cruise switch on.
4. If ECM does not display LO with brake pedal depressed, or does not display HI with brake pedal depressed, refer to **Fig. 51.**
5. If ECM displays LO with brake pedal depressed and HI with brake pedal released, select ECM input test E184, on all models turn ignition switch to Run position and cruise control on.
6. If ECM does not display HI with Resume/Accelerate switch depressed, or does not display LO with resume/accelerate switch released, refer to **Fig. 54.** For intermittent codes proceed as follows:
   a. Turn cruise dash switch to on and backprobe ECM B6 with a voltmeter to ground, B6 should show 12 volts with Resume/Accelerate depressed and 0 volts with Resume/Accelerate released. Cycle switch while observing the meter, wiggle wiring and connectors.
7. If ECM displays HI with resume/accelerate switch depressed and displays LO with resume accelerate switch released, select ECM input test E183, on all models, turn ignition switch to Run position and cruise switch on.
8. If ECM does not display HI with resume/accelerate switch depressed, or does not display LO with resume/accelerate switch released, refer to **Fig. 53.** For intermittent codes proceed as follows:
   a. Turn cruise dash switch to on and backprobe ECM B4 with a voltmeter to ground. B4 should show 12 volts with resume/accelerate depressed and 0 volts with resume/accelerate released. Cycle switch while observing meter, wiggle wiring and connectors.
9. If ECM displays HI when resume/accelerate switch is depressed and displays LO when resume/accelerate switch is released, run engine for 2 minutes, then turn engine off and select ECM override test ES04.
10. Vary override from 0 to 99, then to 0 again.
11. If cruise control servo does not pull fully in and then release, check vacuum source and hoses for leaks, kinks or restrictions and check servo linkage for mechanical binding, then replace cruise control servo as necessary.
12. If cruise control servo pulls fully in and then releases, replace ECM.
13. If cruise On indicator does not light, but cruise system does function, proceed as follows:
    a. Remove right switch assembly and connect test lamp between connector terminals B4 and BC1.
    b. If lamp does not illuminate, check flex circuit 804, repairing as necessary.

CLEARING DIAGNOSTIC TROUBLE CODES

The diagnostic trouble codes stored in the system memory can be cleared to aid in diagnosing intermittent conditions. To clear codes, proceed as follows:

1. Enter diagnostic service mode as outlined.
2. Follow steps 1 and 2 under "Diagnostic Test Procedures."
3. Depress LO button on the CCP until clear codes is displayed.
4. Depress HI button on the CCP, this will start the erasing process. **Note the following.**
   a. Selection of the clear codes test type will result in the message clear codes being displayed along with the selected system name.
   b. This message will appear for 3 seconds to indicate that all stored diagnostic trouble codes have been erased from that system's memory. After 3 seconds the display will automatically return to the next available test type for the selected system.

EXITING DIAGNOSTIC TROUBLE CODES MODE

To exit the diagnostic service mode, depress the Reset/Recall button on the DIC or turn the ignition switch off.

BROUGHAM

Refer to **Figs. 60 and 61** for test procedures.

When performing diagnostic tests, refer to **Fig. 62** for wiring diagrams, and **Fig. 63** for connector pin identification.

ELECTRICAL TESTING

Before proceeding with electrical tests on, ensure all test equipment such as test lights and voltmeters are in good working order, inspect cruise control fuse and replace as necessary, inspect all vacuum hoses for leaks and check for adequate system vacuum.

ELECTRIC BRAKE RELEASE SWITCH

On Vehicle

1. Turn ignition to On position and the cruise switch to On-Auto position.
2. Connect test light to suitable ground.
3. Probe brown wire at brake switch connector. Lamp should illuminate.
4. With probe still attached to brown wire, check switch adjustment. Light should go out when brake pedal is depressed 1/8-1/2 inch.
5. If lamp did not illuminate in step 3, probe wire in adjacent connector cavity.
6. If lamp illuminates, adjust or replace switch as necessary.
7. If lamp does not illuminate, repair wiring to switch.

Off Vehicle

Using self powered test lamp, lamp should be off with switch plunger extended, and should illuminate with switch plunger fully depressed.

INSTRUMENT PANEL & ENGAGEMENT SWITCHES

1. Turn ignition switch to On position.
2. Connect test light to ground.
3. Probe three terminals of turn signal lever cruise harness connector with cruise switch in both Off and On-Auto positions. With switch in Off position, there should be no power at any terminal. With switch in On-Auto position, test lamp should illuminate at B cavity. and amber indicator should light.
4. Probe cavity D and depress Set/Coast switch. Lamp should illuminate.
5. Probe cavity C and depress Resume/Accel switch. Lamp should illuminate.
6. If results are satisfactory in step 3, but lamp does not illuminate in step 4 or 5, replace turn signal lever engagement switch.

AMBER ON LAMP INOPERATIVE OR MALFUNCTIONING

1. Turn ignition switch to On position.
2. Place cruise control switch in On-Auto position.
3. If amber On switch does not illuminate, check for burned out lamp, open ground wire, open connector, inoperative switch, blown fuse or printed circuit.
4. Place cruise control switch in Off position.
5. If amber On light illuminates, check for shorted leads or inoperative switch.

GREEN CRUISE LAMP INOPERATIVE OR MALFUNCTIONING

1. If road test indicates that system controls speed, but green indicator light is not illuminated, check for burned out lamp or open in pink wire of cavity B between switch connector and controller connector.
2. Turn ignition switch to On position and place cruise control switch in On-Auto position, then ground cavity B in controller connector. If green lamp illuminates, replace controller.
3. If green indicator remains on when system is not controlling speed, check for short in harness between switch and controller connector and, if there is no short, replace controller.
4. Ensure amber light is illuminated to confirm power supply.

ENGAGE SWITCH & HARNESS

1. Disconnect turn lever engage switch from harness.
2. Using ohmmeter, test turn lever engage switch as follows:
   a. Place engage switch in released position. There should be no continuity between any two terminals.
   b. Depress engage switch slide. There should be continuity only between yellow and green wire terminals.
   c. Depress engage switch push button. There should be continuity only between green and red wire terminals.
3. If results are not correct in steps a, b or c, replace engagement switch and harness.
4. Connect one lead of ohmmeter to steering column mounting bracket and check each terminal. If any terminal indicates continuity, replace lever and harness.

DIAGNOSTIC CHART INDEX

Test/Code	Description	Year	Page No.	Fig. No.
BROUGHAM				
Test A	Isolation Test	1992	21-29	60
Tes B	Cruise Control Servo & Servo Actuation	1992	21-30	61
Tes C	Cruise Control Servo & Servo Actuation	1992	21-30	61
1992 DEVILLE & FLEETWOOD (FWD)				
Test E.7.5	ECM/PCM Input Test	1992	21-13	8
Test E.7.6	ECM/PCM Input Test.	1992	21-13	9
Test E.7.7	ECM/PCM Input Test.	1992	21-14	10
1992 DEVILLE				
Code EO60	PRNDL Switch Failure	1992	21-14	11
Code EO61	Diagnostic Test	1992	21-14	12
Code EO62	Diagnostic Test	1992	21-14	13
Code EO63	Diagnostic Test	1992	21-14	14
Code EO64	Diagnostic Test	1992	21-15	15

Continued

DIAGNOSTIC CHART INDEX –Continued

Test/Code	Description	Year	Page No.	Fig. No.
1992 DEVILLE				
Code EO65	Diagnostic Test	1992	21-15	16
Code EO66	Diagnostic Test	1992	21-15	17
Code EO67	Diagnostic Test	1992	21-15	18
Code EO68	Diagnostic Test	1992	21-15	19
ELDORADO & SEVILLE & 1993-94 DEVILLE				
Test A	Isolation Test	1992	21-16	21
Test A	Isolation Test	1993–94	21-17	24
Test B	Cruise Control Output	1992	21-16	22
Test B	Cruise Control Outpu Test	1993–94	21-17	25
Test C	Cruise Control Servo Test	1992	21-16	23
Test C	Cruise Control Servo Test	1993–94	21-17	26
Test E182	PCM Input Test	1992	21-23	51
Test E170	PCM Input Test	1992	21-23	52
Test E183	PCM Input Test	1992	21-23	53
Test E184	PCM Input Test	1992	21-23	54
ELDORADO w/ 4.9L/V8-300 ENGINE				
Code PO60	Diagnostic Test	1992-94	21-17	27
Code PO61	Diagnostic Test	1992	21-18	29
Code PO61	Diagnostic Test	1993-94	21-18	30
Code PO62	Diagnostic Test	1992-94	21-19	32
Code PO63	Diagnostic Test	1992-94	21-19	34
Code PO64	Diagnostic Test	1992	21-20	36
Code PO64	Diagnostic Test	1993–94	21-20	37
Code PO65	Diagnostic Test	1992	21-20	39
Code PO65	Diagnostic Test	1993–94	21-20	40
Code PO66	Diagnostic Test	1992-94	21-21	42
Code PO67	Diagnostic Test	1992	21-21	44
Code PO67	Diagnostic Test	1993–94	21-21	45
Code PO68	Diagnostic Test	1992	21-22	47
Code PO68	Diagnostic Test	1993–94	21-22	48
ELDORADO w/4.6L/V8-279 ENGINE				
Code PO60	Diagnostic Test	1992-94	21-18	28
Code PO61	Diagnostic Test	1992-94	21-18	31
Code PO62	Diagnostic Test	1992-94	21-19	33
Code PO63	Diagnostic Test	1992-94	21-19	35
Code PO64	Diagnostic Test	1992-94	21-20	38
Code PO65	Diagnostic Test	1992-94	21-21	41
Code PO66	Diagnostic Test	1992-94	21-21	43
Code PO67	Diagnostic Test	1992-94	21-22	46
Code PO68	Diagnostic Test	1992-94	21-22	49
Code PO69	Diagnostic Test	1992-94	21-23	50

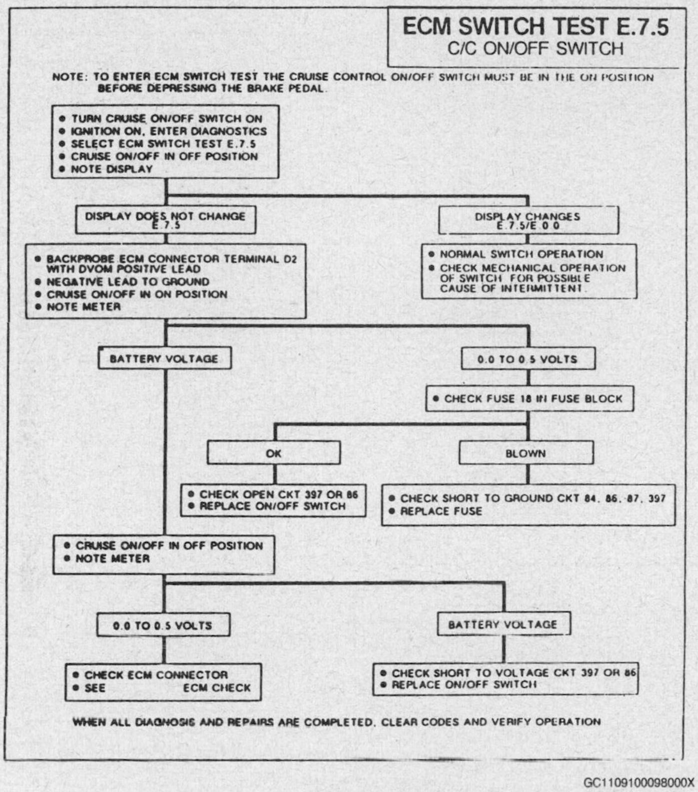
ECM SWITCH TEST E.7.5
C/C ON/OFF SWITCH
NOTE: TO ENTER ECM SWITCH TEST THE CRUISE CONTROL ON/OFF SWITCH MUST BE IN THE ON POSITION BEFORE DEPRESSING THE BRAKE PEDAL.
• TURN CRUISE ON/OFF SWITCH ON • IGNITION ON, ENTER DIAGNOSTICS • SELECT ECM SWITCH TEST E.7.5 • CRUISE ON/OFF IN OFF POSITION • NOTE DISPLAY
DISPLAY DOES NOT CHANGE E.7.5
DISPLAY CHANGES E.7.5/E.0.0
• BACKPROBE ECM CONNECTOR TERMINAL D2 WITH DVOM POSITIVE LEAD • NEGATIVE LEAD TO GROUND • CRUISE ON/OFF IN ON POSITION • NOTE METER
• NORMAL SWITCH OPERATION • CHECK MECHANICAL OPERATION OF SWITCH FOR POSSIBLE CAUSE OF INTERMITTENT
BATTERY VOLTAGE
0.0 TO 0.5 VOLTS
• CHECK FUSE 18 IN FUSE BLOCK
OK
BLOWN
• CHECK OPEN CKT 397 OR 86 • REPLACE ON/OFF SWITCH
• CHECK SHORT TO GROUND CKT 84, 86, 87, 397 • REPLACE FUSE
• CRUISE ON/OFF IN OFF POSITION • NOTE METER
0.0 TO 0.5 VOLTS
BATTERY VOLTAGE
• CHECK ECM CONNECTOR • SEE ECM CHECK
• CHECK SHORT TO VOLTAGE CKT 397 OR 86 • REPLACE ON/OFF SWITCH
WHEN ALL DIAGNOSIS AND REPAIRS ARE COMPLETED, CLEAR CODES AND VERIFY OPERATION
GC1109100098000X

Fig. 8 Test E.7.5: ECM/PCM Input Test. DeVille & Fleetwood (FWD)

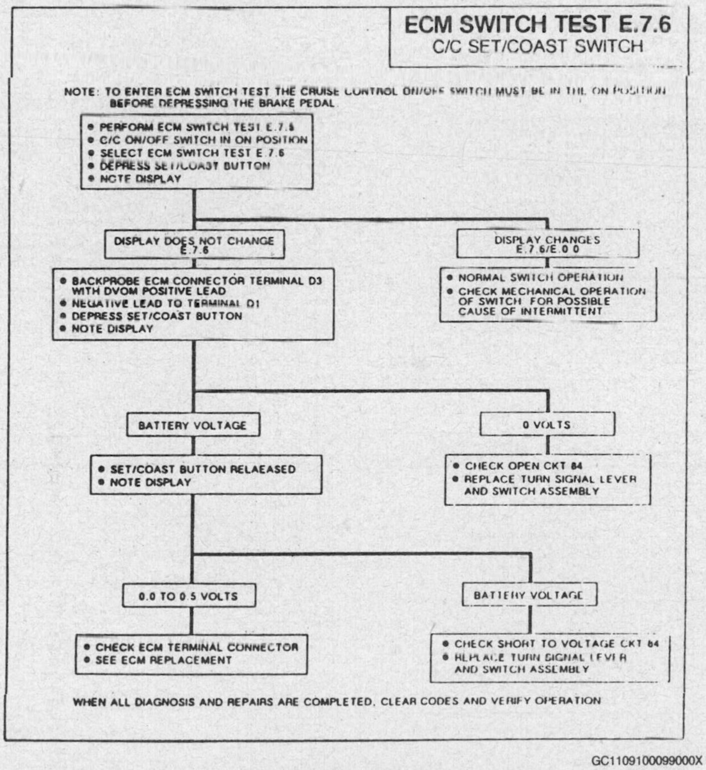
ECM SWITCH TEST E.7.6
C/C SET/COAST SWITCH
NOTE: TO ENTER ECM SWITCH TEST THE CRUISE CONTROL ON/OFF SWITCH MUST BE IN THE ON POSITION BEFORE DEPRESSING THE BRAKE PEDAL.
• PERFORM ECM SWITCH TEST E.7.5 • C/C ON/OFF SWITCH IN ON POSITION • SELECT ECM SWITCH TEST E.7.6 • DEPRESS SET/COAST BUTTON • NOTE DISPLAY
DISPLAY DOES NOT CHANGE E.7.6
DISPLAY CHANGES E.7.6/E.0.0
• BACKPROBE ECM CONNECTOR TERMINAL D3 WITH DVOM POSITIVE LEAD • NEGATIVE LEAD TO TERMINAL D1 • DEPRESS SET/COAST BUTTON • NOTE DISPLAY
• NORMAL SWITCH OPERATION • CHECK MECHANICAL OPERATION OF SWITCH FOR POSSIBLE CAUSE OF INTERMITTENT
BATTERY VOLTAGE
0 VOLTS
• SET/COAST BUTTON RELAEASED • NOTE DISPLAY
• CHECK OPEN CKT 84 • REPLACE TURN SIGNAL LEVER AND SWITCH ASSEMBLY
0.0 TO 0.5 VOLTS
BATTERY VOLTAGE
• CHECK ECM TERMINAL CONNECTOR • SEE ECM REPLACEMENT
• CHECK SHORT TO VOLTAGE CKT 84 • REPLACE TURN SIGNAL LEVER AND SWITCH ASSEMBLY
WHEN ALL DIAGNOSIS AND REPAIRS ARE COMPLETED, CLEAR CODES AND VERIFY OPERATION
GC1109100099000X

Fig. 9 Test E.7.6: ECM/PCM Input Test. DeVille & Fleetwood (FWD)

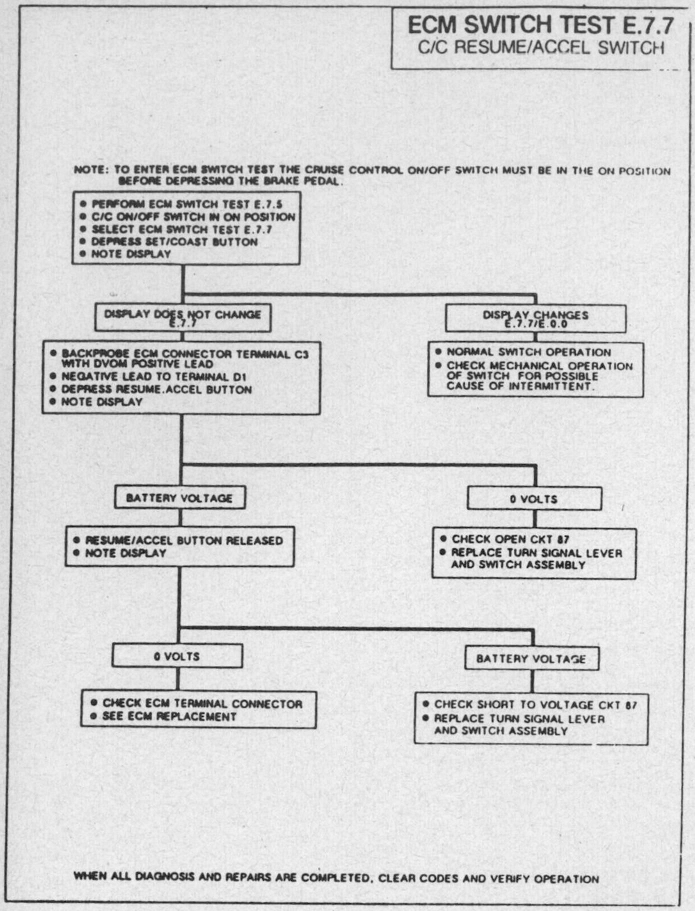
ECM SWITCH TEST E.7.7
C/C RESUME/ACCEL SWITCH
NOTE: TO ENTER ECM SWITCH TEST THE CRUISE CONTROL ON/OFF SWITCH MUST BE IN THE ON POSITION BEFORE DEPRESSING THE BRAKE PEDAL.
• PERFORM ECM SWITCH TEST E.7.5
• C/C ON/OFF SWITCH IN ON POSITION
• SELECT ECM SWITCH TEST E.7.7
• DEPRESS SET/COAST BUTTON
• NOTE DISPLAY
DISPLAY DOES NOT CHANGE E.7.7
DISPLAY CHANGES E.7.7/E.0.0
• BACKPROBE ECM CONNECTOR TERMINAL C3 WITH DVOM POSITIVE LEAD
• NEGATIVE LEAD TO TERMINAL D1
• DEPRESS RESUME.ACCEL BUTTON
• NOTE DISPLAY
• NORMAL SWITCH OPERATION
• CHECK MECHANICAL OPERATION OF SWITCH FOR POSSIBLE CAUSE OF INTERMITTENT.
BATTERY VOLTAGE
0 VOLTS
• RESUME/ACCEL BUTTON RELEASED
• NOTE DISPLAY
• CHECK OPEN CKT 87
• REPLACE TURN SIGNAL LEVER AND SWITCH ASSEMBLY
0 VOLTS
BATTERY VOLTAGE
• CHECK ECM TERMINAL CONNECTOR
• SEE ECM REPLACEMENT
• CHECK SHORT TO VOLTAGE CKT 87
• REPLACE TURN SIGNAL LEVER AND SWITCH ASSEMBLY
WHEN ALL DIAGNOSIS AND REPAIRS ARE COMPLETED, CLEAR CODES AND VERIFY OPERATION

GC1109100100000X

Fig. 10 Test E.7.7: ECM/PCM Input Test. DeVille & Fleetwood (FWD)

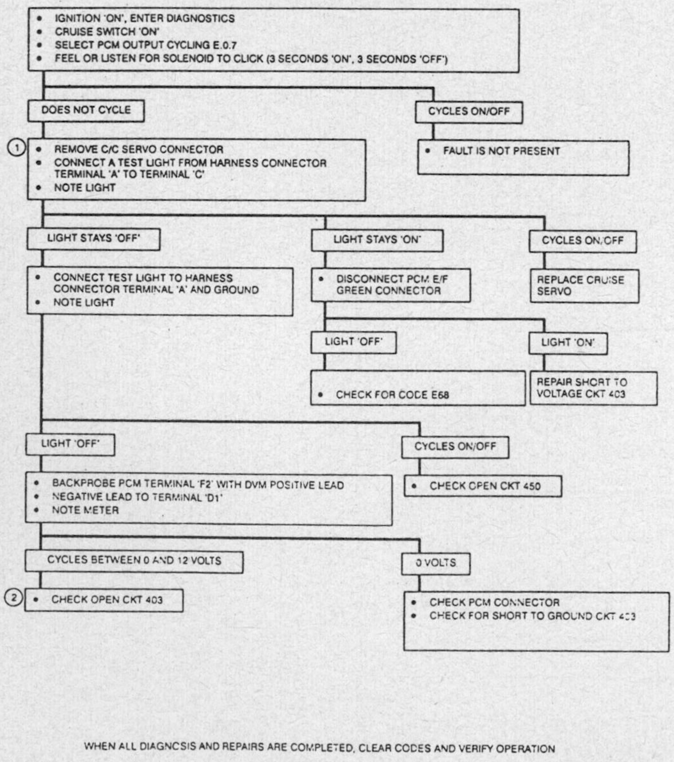
• IGNITION 'ON', ENTER DIAGNOSTICS
• CRUISE SWITCH 'ON'
• SELECT PCM OUTPUT CYCLING E.0.7
• FEEL OR LISTEN FOR SOLENOID TO CLICK (3 SECONDS 'ON', 3 SECONDS 'OFF')
DOES NOT CYCLE
CYCLES ON/OFF
1
• REMOVE C/C SERVO CONNECTOR
• CONNECT A TEST LIGHT FROM HARNESS CONNECTOR TERMINAL 'A' TO TERMINAL 'C'
• NOTE LIGHT
• FAULT IS NOT PRESENT
LIGHT STAYS 'OFF'
LIGHT STAYS 'ON'
CYCLES ON/OFF
• CONNECT TEST LIGHT TO HARNESS CONNECTOR TERMINAL 'A' AND GROUND
• NOTE LIGHT
• DISCONNECT PCM E/F GREEN CONNECTOR
REPLACE CRUISE SERVO
LIGHT 'OFF'
LIGHT 'ON'
• CHECK FOR CODE E68
REPAIR SHORT TO VOLTAGE CKT 403
LIGHT 'OFF'
CYCLES ON/OFF
• BACKPROBE PCM TERMINAL 'F2' WITH DVM POSITIVE LEAD
• NEGATIVE LEAD TO TERMINAL 'D1'
• NOTE METER
• CHECK OPEN CKT 450
CYCLES BETWEEN 0 AND 12 VOLTS
0 VOLTS
2
• CHECK OPEN CKT 403
• CHECK PCM CONNECTOR
• CHECK FOR SHORT TO GROUND CKT 403
WHEN ALL DIAGNOSIS AND REPAIRS ARE COMPLETED, CLEAR CODES AND VERIFY OPERATION

GC1109100102000X

Fig. 12 Code E061: Diagnostic Test. DeVille

- THE PRIMARY PURPOSE OF THIS CODE IS TO DETECT AN ACTION OF THE DRIVER THAT COULD CAUSE AN UNSAFE CONDITION OR DAMAGE TO THE VEHICLE.
- THIS CODE CAN BE DRIVER INDUCED BY SHIFTING THE GEAR SELECTOR INTO NEUTRAL WHEN THE CRUISE CONTROL IS ENGAGED.
- A FAILURE OF THE PRNDL SWITCH MAY CAUSE THE CODE TO SET.
- CHECK FOR CODE E91.

GC1109300101000X

Fig. 11 Code E060: PRNDL Switch Failure. DeVille

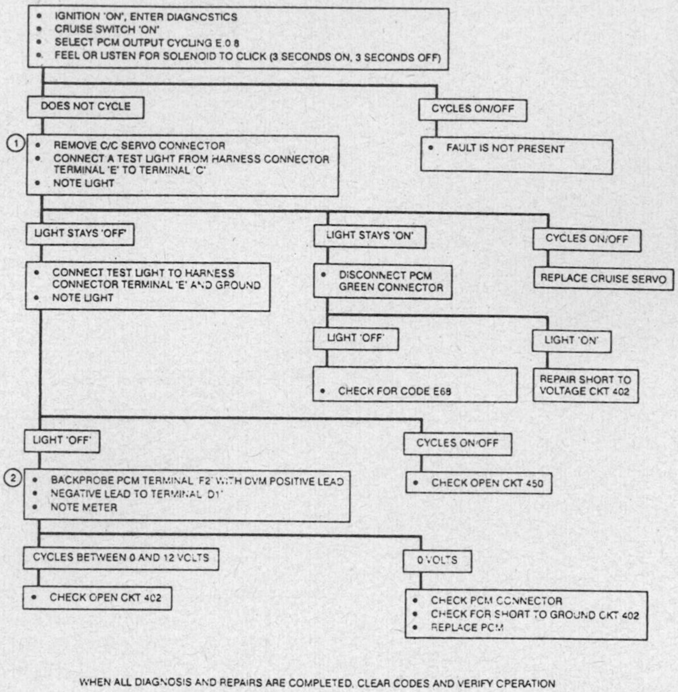
• IGNITION 'ON', ENTER DIAGNOSTICS
• CRUISE SWITCH 'ON'
• SELECT PCM OUTPUT CYCLING E.0.8
• FEEL OR LISTEN FOR SOLENOID TO CLICK (3 SECONDS ON, 3 SECONDS OFF)
DOES NOT CYCLE
CYCLES ON/OFF
1
• REMOVE C/C SERVO CONNECTOR
• CONNECT A TEST LIGHT FROM HARNESS CONNECTOR TERMINAL 'E' TO TERMINAL 'C'
• NOTE LIGHT
• FAULT IS NOT PRESENT
LIGHT STAYS 'OFF'
LIGHT STAYS 'ON'
CYCLES ON/OFF
• CONNECT TEST LIGHT TO HARNESS CONNECTOR TERMINAL 'E' AND GROUND
• NOTE LIGHT
• DISCONNECT PCM GREEN CONNECTOR
REPLACE CRUISE SERVO
LIGHT 'OFF'
LIGHT 'ON'
• CHECK FOR CODE E68
REPAIR SHORT TO VOLTAGE CKT 402
LIGHT 'OFF'
CYCLES ON/OFF
2
• BACKPROBE PCM TERMINAL 'F2' WITH DVM POSITIVE LEAD
• NEGATIVE LEAD TO TERMINAL 'D1'
• NOTE METER
• CHECK OPEN CKT 450
CYCLES BETWEEN 0 AND 12 VOLTS
0 VOLTS
• CHECK OPEN CKT 402
• CHECK PCM CONNECTOR
• CHECK FOR SHORT TO GROUND CKT 402
• REPLACE PCM
WHEN ALL DIAGNOSIS AND REPAIRS ARE COMPLETED, CLEAR CODES AND VERIFY OPERATION

GC1109300103000X

Fig. 13 Code E062: Diagnostic Test. DeVille

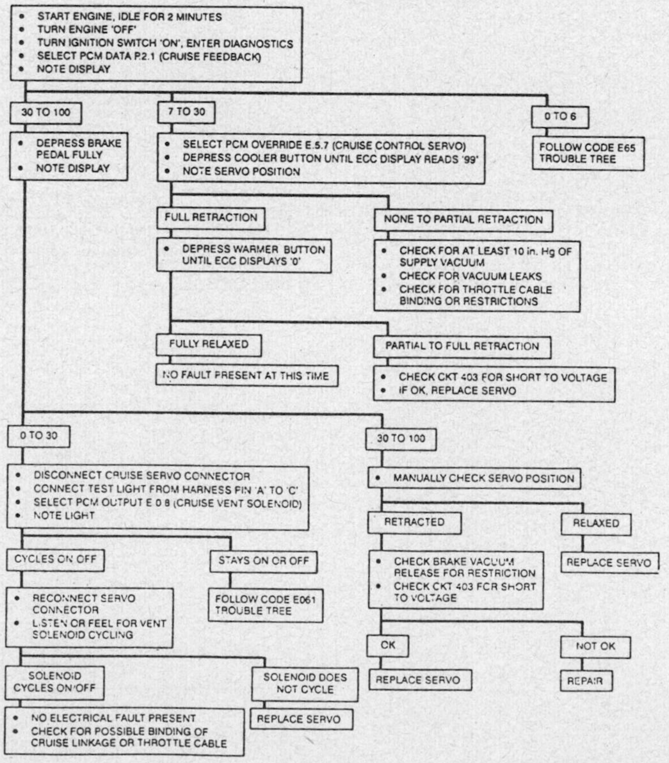
• START ENGINE, IDLE FOR 2 MINUTES
• TURN ENGINE 'OFF'
• TURN IGNITION SWITCH 'ON', ENTER DIAGNOSTICS
• SELECT PCM DATA P.2.1 (CRUISE FEEDBACK)
• NOTE DISPLAY
30 TO 100
7 TO 30
0 TO 6
• DEPRESS BRAKE PEDAL FULLY
• NOTE DISPLAY
• SELECT PCM OVERRIDE E.5.7 (CRUISE CONTROL SERVO)
• DEPRESS COOLER BUTTON UNTIL ECC DISPLAY READS '99'
• NOTE SERVO POSITION
FOLLOW CODE E65 TROUBLE TREE
FULL RETRACTION
NONE TO PARTIAL RETRACTION
• DEPRESS WARMER BUTTON UNTIL ECC DISPLAYS '0'
• CHECK FOR AT LEAST 10 in. Hg OF SUPPLY VACUUM
• CHECK FOR VACUUM LEAKS
• CHECK FOR THROTTLE CABLE BINDING OR RESTRICTIONS
FULLY RELAXED
PARTIAL TO FULL RETRACTION
NO FAULT PRESENT AT THIS TIME
• CHECK CKT 403 FOR SHORT TO VOLTAGE
• IF OK, REPLACE SERVO
0 TO 30
30 TO 100
• DISCONNECT CRUISE SERVO CONNECTOR
• CONNECT TEST LIGHT FROM HARNESS PIN 'A' TO 'C'
• SELECT PCM OUTPUT E.0.8 (CRUISE VENT SOLENOID)
• NOTE LIGHT
• MANUALLY CHECK SERVO POSITION
RETRACTED
RELAXED
CYCLES ON OFF
STAYS ON OR OFF
REPLACE SERVO
• CHECK BRAKE VACUUM RELEASE FOR RESTRICTION
• CHECK CKT 403 FOR SHORT TO VOLTAGE
• RECONNECT SERVO CONNECTOR
• LISTEN OR FEEL FOR VENT SOLENOID CYCLING
FOLLOW CODE E061 TROUBLE TREE
OK
NOT OK
SOLENOID CYCLES ON/OFF
SOLENOID DOES NOT CYCLE
REPLACE SERVO
REPAIR
• NO ELECTRICAL FAULT PRESENT
• CHECK FOR POSSIBLE BINDING OF CRUISE LINKAGE OR THROTTLE CABLE
REPLACE SERVO

GC1109300104000X

Fig. 14 Code E063: Diagnostic Test. DeVille

- Code E64 sets when the vehicle speed increases greater that 16 MPH in one second with the cruise engaged (4 mph in .25 second)
- If code E64 is set, cruise control will disengage and Code E64 is stored in memory.
- Most occurrences of Code E64 are caused by wheelspin due to icy or wet conditions
- If Code E64 is found and no other cruise control faults exists, clear codes and road test vehicle.

WHEN ALL DIAGNOSIS AND REPAIRS ARE COMPLETED, CLEAR CODES AND VERIFY OPERATION

GC1109300105000X

Fig. 15 Code E064: Diagnostic Test. DeVille

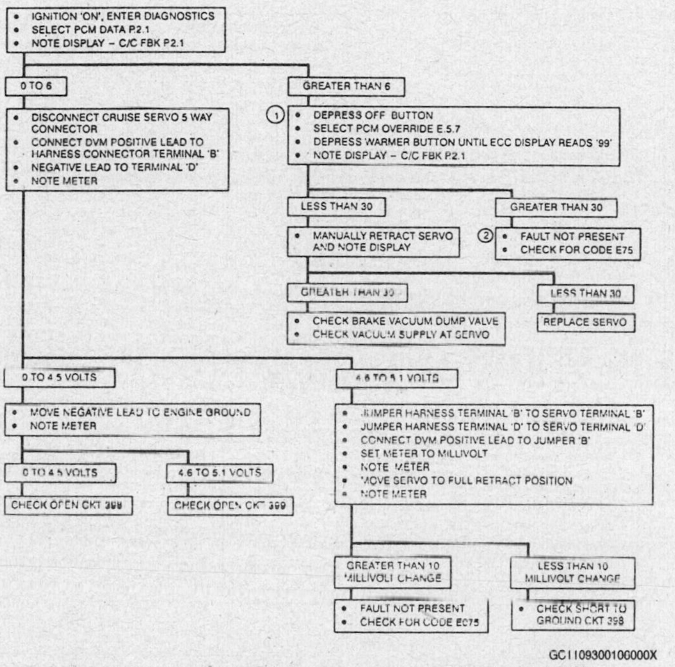
IGNITION 'ON', ENTER DIAGNOSTICS
SELECT PCM DATA P2.1
NOTE DISPLAY – C/C FBK P2.1
0 TO 6
GREATER THAN 6
DISCONNECT CRUISE SERVO 5 WAY CONNECTOR
CONNECT DVM POSITIVE LEAD TO HARNESS CONNECTOR TERMINAL 'B'
NEGATIVE LEAD TO TERMINAL 'D'
NOTE METER
DEPRESS OFF BUTTON
SELECT PCM OVERRIDE E.5.7
DEPRESS WARMER BUTTON UNTIL ECC DISPLAY READS '99'
NOTE DISPLAY – C/C FBK P2.1
LESS THAN 30
GREATER THAN 30
MANUALLY RETRACT SERVO AND NOTE DISPLAY
FAULT NOT PRESENT
CHECK FOR CODE E75
GREATER THAN 30
LESS THAN 30
CHECK BRAKE VACUUM DUMP VALVE
CHECK VACUUM SUPPLY AT SERVO
REPLACE SERVO
0 TO 4.5 VOLTS
4.6 TO 5.1 VOLTS
MOVE NEGATIVE LEAD TO ENGINE GROUND
NOTE METER
JUMPER HARNESS TERMINAL 'B' TO SERVO TERMINAL 'B'
JUMPER HARNESS TERMINAL 'D' TO SERVO TERMINAL 'D'
CONNECT DVM POSITIVE LEAD TO JUMPER 'B'
SET METER TO MILLIVOLT
NOTE METER
MOVE SERVO TO FULL RETRACT POSITION
NOTE METER
0 TO 4.5 VOLTS
4.6 TO 5.1 VOLTS
CHECK OPEN CKT 398
CHECK OPEN CKT 399
GREATER THAN 10 MILLIVOLT CHANGE
LESS THAN 10 MILLIVOLT CHANGE
FAULT NOT PRESENT
CHECK FOR CODE E075
CHECK SHORT TO GROUND CKT 398
GC1109300106000X

Fig. 16 Code E065: Diagnostic Test. DeVille

THIS CODE WILL SET IF ENGINE RPM EXCEEDS 4800 RPM. THIS MAY OCCUR ON SLIPPERY PAVEMENT, EXTENDED WIDE OPEN THROTTLE ACCELERATION, OR FOR SOME MECHANICAL PROBLEMS (SUCH AS TRANSMISSION SLIPPAGE). UNDER THESE CONDITIONS, CODE E066 WILL SET AND SHOULD BE CONSIDERED NORMAL. THE DRIVER SHOULD BE CONSIDERED NORMAL. THE DRIVER SHOULD BE ADVISED WHY THE CRUISE DISENGAGED. CLEAR THE CODE AND ROAD TEST VEHICLE TO VERIFY NORMAL OPERATION.

WHEN ALL DIAGNOSIS AND REPAIRS ARE COMPLETED, CLEAR CODES AND VERIFY OPERATION

GC1109300107000X

Fig. 17 Code E066: Diagnostic Test. DeVille

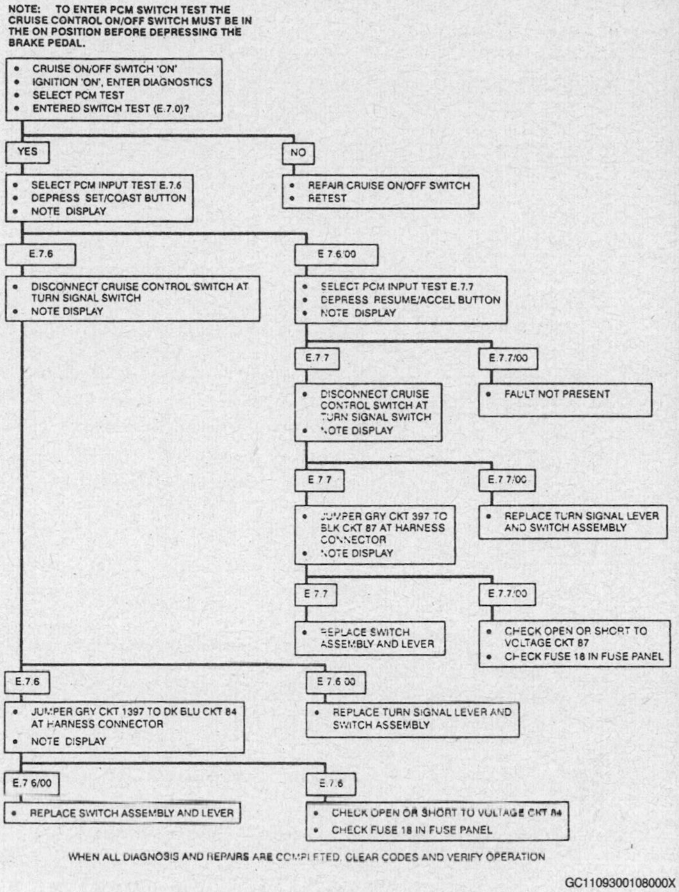
NOTE: TO ENTER PCM SWITCH TEST THE CRUISE CONTROL ON/OFF SWITCH MUST BE IN THE ON POSITION BEFORE DEPRESSING THE BRAKE PEDAL.
CRUISE ON/OFF SWITCH 'ON'
IGNITION 'ON', ENTER DIAGNOSTICS
SELECT PCM TEST
ENTERED SWITCH TEST (E.7.0)?
YES
NO
SELECT PCM INPUT TEST E.7.6
DEPRESS SET/COAST BUTTON
NOTE DISPLAY
REPAIR CRUISE ON/OFF SWITCH
RETEST
E.7.6
E.7.6/00
DISCONNECT CRUISE CONTROL SWITCH AT TURN SIGNAL SWITCH
NOTE DISPLAY
SELECT PCM INPUT TEST E.7.7
DEPRESS RESUME/ACCEL BUTTON
NOTE DISPLAY
E.7.7
E.7.7/00
DISCONNECT CRUISE CONTROL SWITCH AT TURN SIGNAL SWITCH
NOTE DISPLAY
FAULT NOT PRESENT
E.7.7
E.7.7/00
JUMPER GRY CKT 397 TO BLK CKT 87 AT HARNESS CONNECTOR
NOTE DISPLAY
REPLACE TURN SIGNAL LEVER AND SWITCH ASSEMBLY
E.7.7
E.7.7/00
REPLACE SWITCH ASSEMBLY AND LEVER
CHECK OPEN OR SHORT TO VOLTAGE CKT 87
CHECK FUSE 18 IN FUSE PANEL
E.7.6
E.7.6/00
JUMPER GRY CKT 1397 TO DK BLU CKT 84 AT HARNESS CONNECTOR
NOTE DISPLAY
REPLACE TURN SIGNAL LEVER AND SWITCH ASSEMBLY
E.7.6/00
E.7.6
REPLACE SWITCH ASSEMBLY AND LEVER
CHECK OPEN OR SHORT TO VOLTAGE CKT 84
CHECK FUSE 18 IN FUSE PANEL
WHEN ALL DIAGNOSIS AND REPAIRS ARE COMPLETED, CLEAR CODES AND VERIFY OPERATION
GC1109300108000X

Fig. 18 Code E067: Diagnostic Test. DeVille

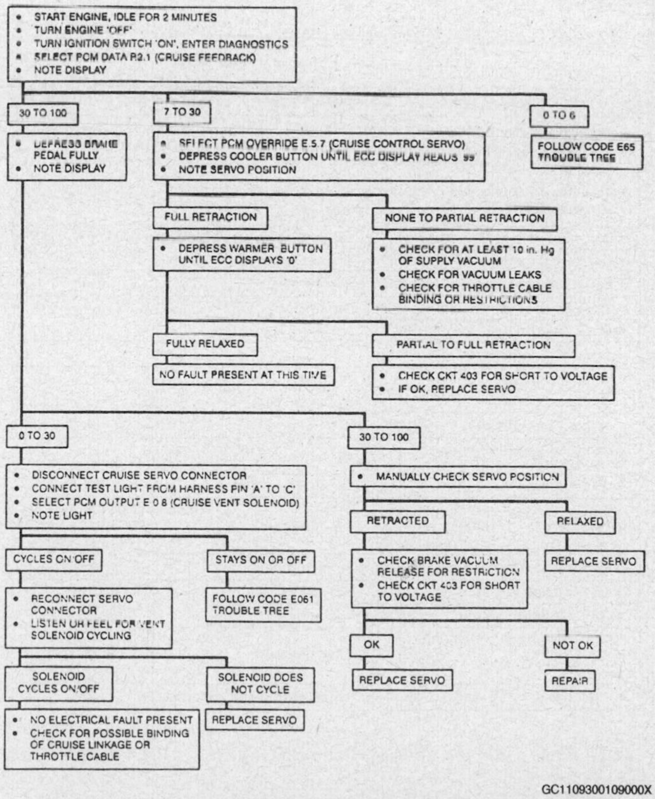
START ENGINE, IDLE FOR 2 MINUTES
TURN ENGINE 'OFF'
TURN IGNITION SWITCH 'ON', ENTER DIAGNOSTICS
SELECT PCM DATA P2.1 (CRUISE FEEDBACK)
NOTE DISPLAY
30 TO 100
7 TO 30
0 TO 6
DEPRESS BRAKE PEDAL FULLY
NOTE DISPLAY
SELECT PCM OVERRIDE E.5.7 (CRUISE CONTROL SERVO)
DEPRESS COOLER BUTTON UNTIL ECC DISPLAY READS 99
NOTE SERVO POSITION
FOLLOW CODE E65 TROUBLE TREE
FULL RETRACTION
NONE TO PARTIAL RETRACTION
DEPRESS WARMER BUTTON UNTIL ECC DISPLAYS '0'
CHECK FOR AT LEAST 10 in. Hg OF SUPPLY VACUUM
CHECK FOR VACUUM LEAKS
CHECK FOR THROTTLE CABLE BINDING OR RESTRICTIONS
FULLY RELAXED
PARTIAL TO FULL RETRACTION
NO FAULT PRESENT AT THIS TIME
CHECK CKT 403 FOR SHORT TO VOLTAGE
IF OK, REPLACE SERVO
0 TO 30
30 TO 100
DISCONNECT CRUISE SERVO CONNECTOR
CONNECT TEST LIGHT FROM HARNESS PIN 'A' TO 'C'
SELECT PCM OUTPUT E.0.8 (CRUISE VENT SOLENOID)
NOTE LIGHT
MANUALLY CHECK SERVO POSITION
RETRACTED
RELAXED
CYCLES ON/OFF
STAYS ON OR OFF
CHECK BRAKE VACUUM RELEASE FOR RESTRICTION
CHECK CKT 403 FOR SHORT TO VOLTAGE
REPLACE SERVO
RECONNECT SERVO CONNECTOR
LISTEN OR FEEL FOR VENT SOLENOID CYCLING
FOLLOW CODE E061 TROUBLE TREE
OK
NOT OK
SOLENOID CYCLES ON/OFF
SOLENOID DOES NOT CYCLE
REPLACE SERVO
REPAIR
NO ELECTRICAL FAULT PRESENT
CHECK FOR POSSIBLE BINDING OF CRUISE LINKAGE OR THROTTLE CABLE
REPLACE SERVO
GC1109300109000X

Fig. 19 Code E068: Diagnostic Test. DeVille

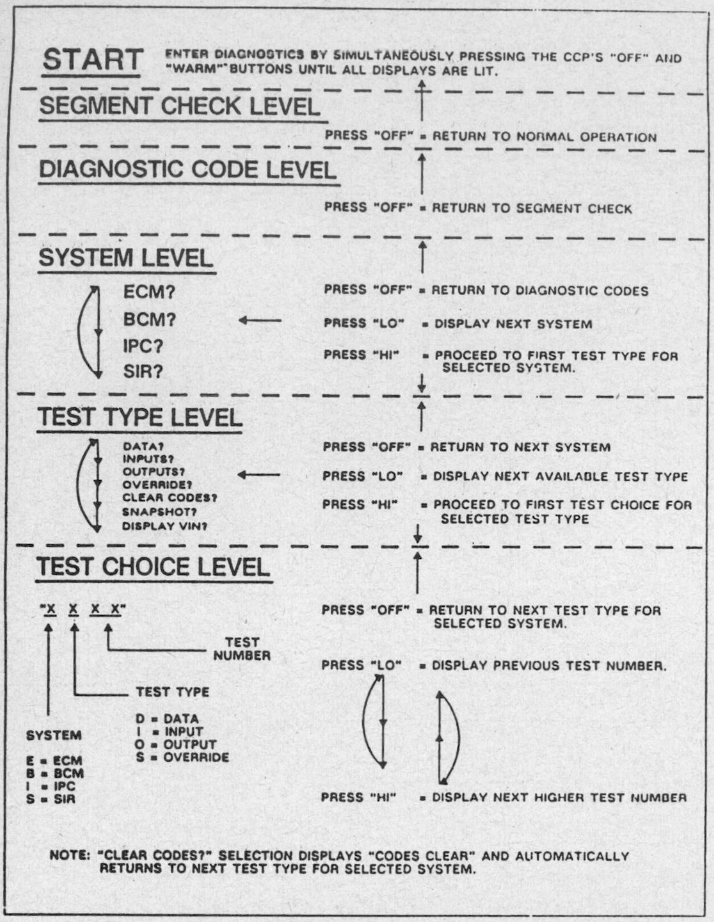
START
ENTER DIAGNOSTICS BY SIMULTANEOUSLY PRESSING THE CCP'S "OFF" AND "WARM" BUTTONS UNTIL ALL DISPLAYS ARE LIT.
SEGMENT CHECK LEVEL
PRESS "OFF" = RETURN TO NORMAL OPERATION
DIAGNOSTIC CODE LEVEL
PRESS "OFF" = RETURN TO SEGMENT CHECK
SYSTEM LEVEL
ECM?
BCM?
IPC?
SIR?
PRESS "OFF" = RETURN TO DIAGNOSTIC CODES
PRESS "LO" = DISPLAY NEXT SYSTEM
PRESS "HI" = PROCEED TO FIRST TEST TYPE FOR SELECTED SYSTEM.
TEST TYPE LEVEL
DATA?
INPUTS?
OUTPUTS?
OVERRIDE?
CLEAR CODES?
SNAPSHOT?
DISPLAY VIN?
PRESS "OFF" = RETURN TO NEXT SYSTEM
PRESS "LO" = DISPLAY NEXT AVAILABLE TEST TYPE
PRESS "HI" = PROCEED TO FIRST TEST CHOICE FOR SELECTED TEST TYPE
TEST CHOICE LEVEL
"X X X X"
TEST NUMBER
TEST TYPE
D = DATA
I = INPUT
O = OUTPUT
S = OVERRIDE
SYSTEM
E = ECM
B = BCM
I = IPC
S = SIR
PRESS "OFF" = RETURN TO NEXT TEST TYPE FOR SELECTED SYSTEM.
PRESS "LO" = DISPLAY PREVIOUS TEST NUMBER.
PRESS "HI" = DISPLAY NEXT HIGHER TEST NUMBER
NOTE: "CLEAR CODES?" SELECTION DISPLAYS "CODES CLEAR" AND AUTOMATICALLY RETURNS TO NEXT TEST TYPE FOR SELECTED SYSTEM.

GC1109100110000X

Fig. 20 Operating service mode. Eldorado & Seville

ACTION	NORMAL RESULT	FOR DIAGNOSIS
• PERFORM SELF-DIAGNOSTIC SYSTEM CHECK AND RECORD AND DIAGNOSE ANY STORED CODES		
• INSPECT CRUISE CONTROL SERVO THROTTLE ACTUATING CABLE, CRUISE BRAKE SWITCH AND VCC BRAKE SWITCH FOR PROPER ADJUSTMENT (A MISADJUSTED CABLE WILL CAUSE SURGING AND BINDING).		
• INSPECT VACUUM LINES FOR KINKS, RESTRICTIONS, AND DETERIORATION		
• ENTER DIAGNOSTICS AND SELECT ECM INPUT E182		
CRUISE SWITCH OFF	E182 DISPLAYS LO	REFER TO INPUT TEST E182
CRUISE SWITCH ON	E182 DISPLAYS HI	
• LEAVE CRUISE SWITCH ON AND SELECT ECM INPUT E170		
DEPRESS BRAKE PEDAL	E170 DISPLAYS LO	REFER TO INPUT TEST E170
RELEASE BRAKE PEDAL	E170 DISPLAYS HI	
• SELECT ECM INPUT E171		
DEPRESS BRAKE PEDAL	E171 DISPLAYS LO	REFER TO INPUT TEST E171
RELEASE BRAKE PEDAL	E171 DISPLAYS HI	
• SELECT ECM INPUT E184		
SLIDE CRUISE SWITCH TO RESUME/ ACCEL POSITION	E184 DISPLAYS HI	REFER TO INPUT TEST E184
RELEASE CRUISE SWITCH	E184 DISPLAYS LO	
DEPRESS SET/COAST SWITCH	E184 DISPLAYS LO	CHECK CKTS 84 AND 87 FOR A WIRE TO WIRE SHORT. IF OK, REPLACE MULTI-FUNCTION LEVER
• SELECT ECM INPUT TEST E183 (LEAVE CRUISE SWITCH ON)		
DEPRESS SET/COAST SWITCH	E183 DISPLAYS HI	REFER TO INPUT TEST E183
RELEASE SET/COAST SWITCH	E183 DISPLAYS LO	
SLIDE CRUISE SWITCH TO RESUME/ ACCEL POSITION	E183 DISPLAYS LO	CHECK CKTS 84 AND 87 FOR A WIRE TO WIRE SHORT. IF OK, REPLACE MULTI-FUNCTION LEVER
• IF ALL RESULTS ARE NORMAL, GO TO TEST B: CRUISE CONTROL OUTPUT TEST		

GC1109200111000X

Fig. 21 Test A: Isolation Test. 1992 Eldorado & Seville

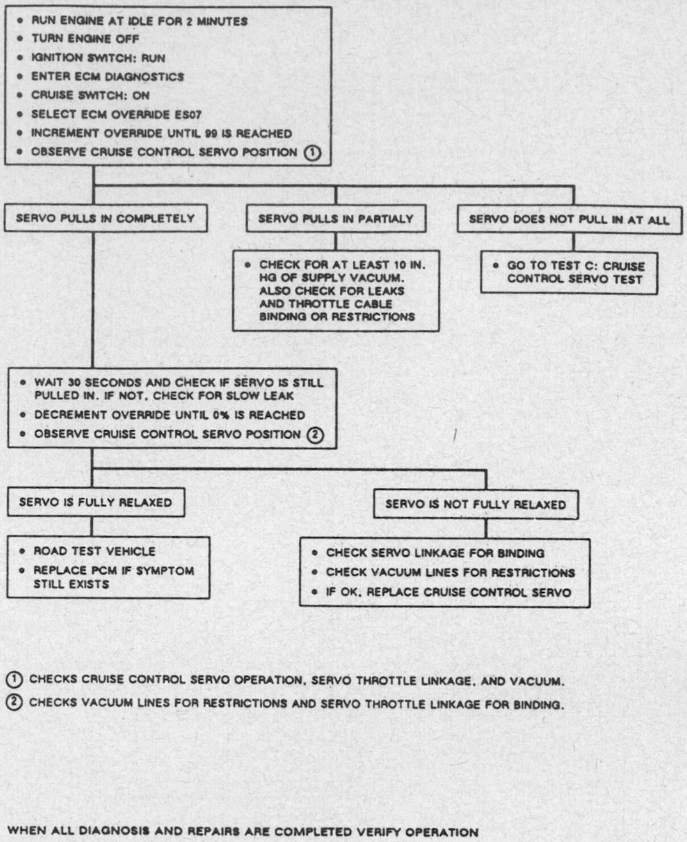
• RUN ENGINE AT IDLE FOR 2 MINUTES
• TURN ENGINE OFF
• IGNITION SWITCH: RUN
• ENTER ECM DIAGNOSTICS
• CRUISE SWITCH: ON
• SELECT ECM OVERRIDE ES07
• INCREMENT OVERRIDE UNTIL 99 IS REACHED
• OBSERVE CRUISE CONTROL SERVO POSITION ①
SERVO PULLS IN COMPLETELY
SERVO PULLS IN PARTIALY
SERVO DOES NOT PULL IN AT ALL
• CHECK FOR AT LEAST 10 IN. HG OF SUPPLY VACUUM. ALSO CHECK FOR LEAKS AND THROTTLE CABLE BINDING OR RESTRICTIONS
• GO TO TEST C: CRUISE CONTROL SERVO TEST
• WAIT 30 SECONDS AND CHECK IF SERVO IS STILL PULLED IN. IF NOT, CHECK FOR SLOW LEAK
• DECREMENT OVERRIDE UNTIL 0% IS REACHED
• OBSERVE CRUISE CONTROL SERVO POSITION ②
SERVO IS FULLY RELAXED
SERVO IS NOT FULLY RELAXED
• ROAD TEST VEHICLE
• REPLACE PCM IF SYMPTOM STILL EXISTS
• CHECK SERVO LINKAGE FOR BINDING
• CHECK VACUUM LINES FOR RESTRICTIONS
• IF OK, REPLACE CRUISE CONTROL SERVO
① CHECKS CRUISE CONTROL SERVO OPERATION, SERVO THROTTLE LINKAGE, AND VACUUM.
② CHECKS VACUUM LINES FOR RESTRICTIONS AND SERVO THROTTLE LINKAGE FOR BINDING.
WHEN ALL DIAGNOSIS AND REPAIRS ARE COMPLETED VERIFY OPERATION

GC1109200112000X

Fig. 22 Test B: Cruise Control Output. 1992 Eldorado & Seville

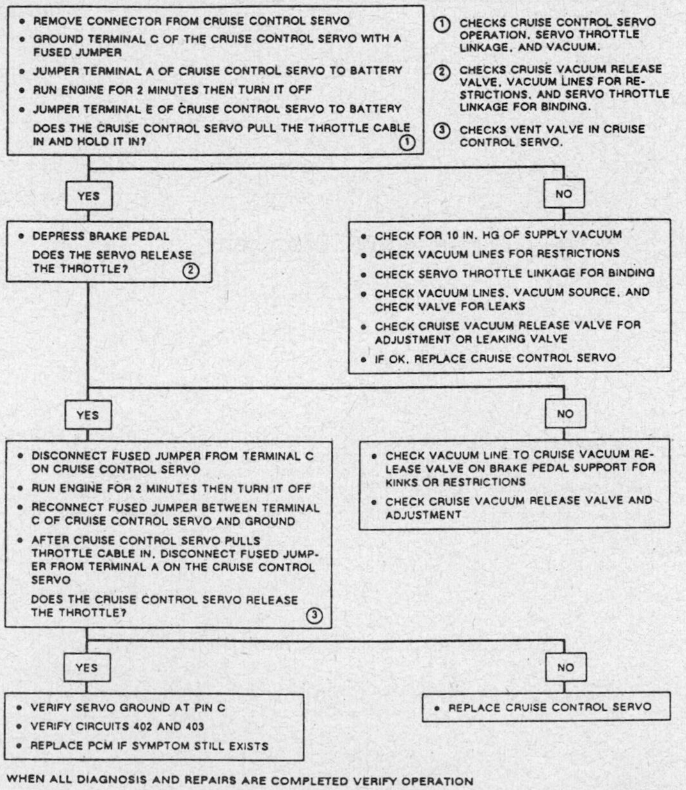
• REMOVE CONNECTOR FROM CRUISE CONTROL SERVO
• GROUND TERMINAL C OF THE CRUISE CONTROL SERVO WITH A FUSED JUMPER
• JUMPER TERMINAL A OF CRUISE CONTROL SERVO TO BATTERY
• RUN ENGINE FOR 2 MINUTES THEN TURN IT OFF
• JUMPER TERMINAL E OF CRUISE CONTROL SERVO TO BATTERY
DOES THE CRUISE CONTROL SERVO PULL THE THROTTLE CABLE IN AND HOLD IT IN? ①
① CHECKS CRUISE CONTROL SERVO OPERATION, SERVO THROTTLE LINKAGE, AND VACUUM.
② CHECKS CRUISE VACUUM RELEASE VALVE, VACUUM LINES FOR RESTRICTIONS, AND SERVO THROTTLE LINKAGE FOR BINDING.
③ CHECKS VENT VALVE IN CRUISE CONTROL SERVO.
YES
NO
• DEPRESS BRAKE PEDAL
DOES THE SERVO RELEASE THE THROTTLE? ②
• CHECK FOR 10 IN. HG OF SUPPLY VACUUM
• CHECK VACUUM LINES FOR RESTRICTIONS
• CHECK SERVO THROTTLE LINKAGE FOR BINDING
• CHECK VACUUM LINES, VACUUM SOURCE, AND CHECK VALVE FOR LEAKS
• CHECK CRUISE VACUUM RELEASE VALVE FOR ADJUSTMENT OR LEAKING VALVE
• IF OK, REPLACE CRUISE CONTROL SERVO
YES
NO
• DISCONNECT FUSED JUMPER FROM TERMINAL C ON CRUISE CONTROL SERVO
• RUN ENGINE FOR 2 MINUTES THEN TURN IT OFF
• RECONNECT FUSED JUMPER BETWEEN TERMINAL C OF CRUISE CONTROL SERVO AND GROUND
• AFTER CRUISE CONTROL SERVO PULLS THROTTLE CABLE IN, DISCONNECT FUSED JUMPER FROM TERMINAL A ON THE CRUISE CONTROL SERVO
DOES THE CRUISE CONTROL SERVO RELEASE THE THROTTLE? ③
• CHECK VACUUM LINE TO CRUISE VACUUM RELEASE VALVE ON BRAKE PEDAL SUPPORT FOR KINKS OR RESTRICTIONS
• CHECK CRUISE VACUUM RELEASE VALVE AND ADJUSTMENT
YES
NO
• VERIFY SERVO GROUND AT PIN C
• VERIFY CIRCUITS 402 AND 403
• REPLACE PCM IF SYMPTOM STILL EXISTS
• REPLACE CRUISE CONTROL SERVO
WHEN ALL DIAGNOSIS AND REPAIRS ARE COMPLETED VERIFY OPERATION

GC1109200113000X

Fig. 23 Test C: Cruise Control Servo Test. 1992 Eldorado & Seville

ACTION	NORMAL RESULT	FOR DIAGNOSIS
• PERFORM SELF-DIAGNOSTIC SYSTEM CHECK AND RECORD AND DIAGNOSE ANY STORED CODES • INSPECT CRUISE CONTROL SERVO THROTTLE ACTUATING CABLE, STOP/BTSI/CRUISE BRAKE SWITCH AND TCC BRAKE SWITCH FOR PROPER ADJUSTMENT (A MISADJUSTED CABLE WILL CAUSE SURGING AND BINDING). • INSPECT VACUUM LINES FOR KINKS, RESTRICTIONS, AND DETERIORATION • ENTER DIAGNOSTICS AND SELECT PCM INPUT PI82		
CRUISE SWITCH OFF	PI82 DISPLAYS LO	SEE ①
CRUISE SWITCH ON	PI82 DISPLAYS HI	SEE ②
• LEAVE CRUISE SWITCH ON AND SELECT PCM INPUT PI70		
DEPRESS BRAKE PEDAL	PI70 DISPLAYS LO	SEE ③
RELEASE BRAKE PEDAL	PI70 DISPLAYS HI	SEE ④
• SELECT PCM INPUT PI71		
DEPRESS BRAKE PEDAL	PI71 DISPLAYS LO	SEE ⑤
RELEASE BRAKE PEDAL	PI71 DISPLAYS HI	SEE ⑤
• SELECT PCM INPUT PI84		
SLIDE CRUISE SWITCH TO RESUME/ ACCEL POSITION	PI84 DISPLAYS HI	SEE ⑥
RELEASE CRUISE SWITCH	PI84 DISPLAYS LO	SEE ⑦
DEPRESS SET/COAST SWITCH	PI84 DISPLAYS LO	CHECK CKTS 84 AND 87 FOR A WIRE TO WIRE SHORT. IF OK, REPLACE MULTI-FUNCTION LEVER
• SELECT PCM INPUT TEST PI83 (LEAVE CRUISE SWITCH ON)		
DEPRESS SET/COAST SWITCH	PI83 DISPLAYS HI	SEE ⑧
RELEASE SET/COAST SWITCH	PI83 DISPLAYS LO	SEE ⑨
SLIDE CRUISE SWITCH TO RESUME/ ACCEL POSITION	PI83 DISPLAYS LO	CHECK CKTS 84 AND 87 FOR A WIRE TO WIRE SHORT. IF OK, REPLACE MULTI-FUNCTION LEVER
• IF ALL RESULTS ARE NORMAL, GO TO TEST B: CRUISE CONTROL OUTPUT TEST		

① SHORT TO VOLTAGE IN CKTS 397 OR 86. SHORTED CRUISE CONTROL SWITCH

② FUSE D5, CRUISE CONTROL SWITCH OR CKTS 250, 397 OPEN. CKT 250, 397 OR 86 SHORTED TO GROUND

③ STOP/BTSI/ CRUISE BRAKE SWITCH MISADJUSTED OR DEFECTIVE. SHORT TO VOLTAGE IN CKT 86

④ STOP/BTSI/CRUISE BRAKE SWITCH OPEN OR MIS-ADJUSTED. OPEN IN CKTS 397 OR 86

⑤ REFER TO CODE P090 DIAGNOSIS

⑥ OPEN RESUME/ACCEL SWITCH OR CKT 87

⑦ SHORTED RESUME/ACCEL SWITCH. SHORT TO VOLTAGE IN CKT 87

⑧ OPEN SET/COAST SWITCH OR CKT 84

⑨ SHORTED SET/COAST SWITCH. SHORT TO VOLTAGE IN CKT 84

• IF ALL CHECKS AND TERMINAL CONTACT ARE OK, REPLACE PCM

GC1109300114000X

Fig. 24 Test A: Isolation Test. 1993–94 DeVille, Eldorado & Seville

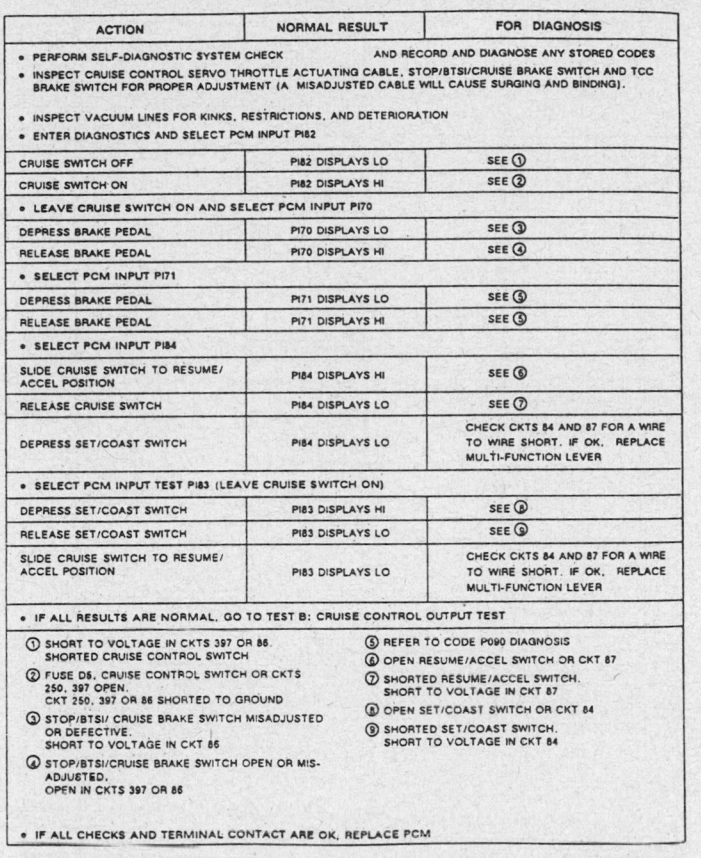

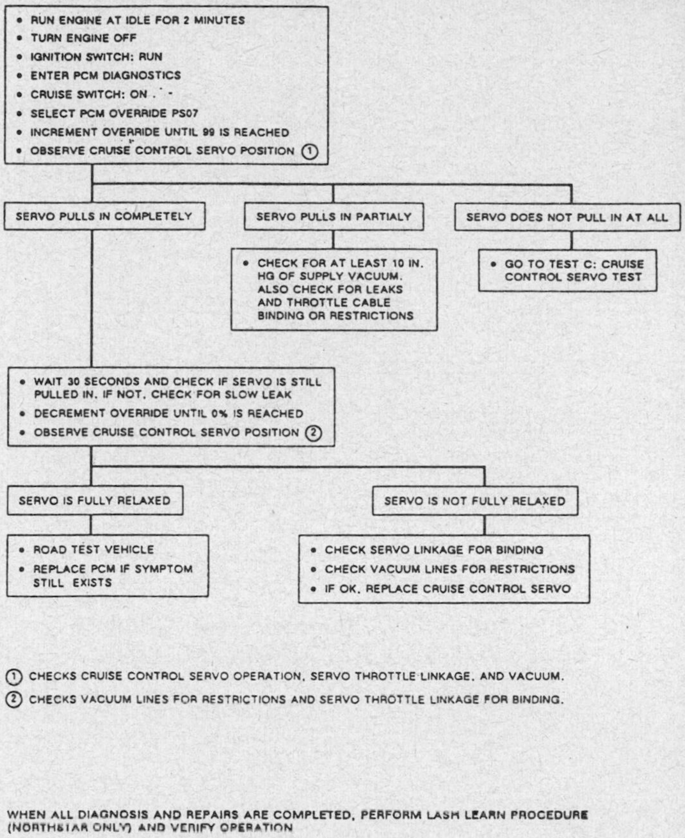
• RUN ENGINE AT IDLE FOR 2 MINUTES
• TURN ENGINE OFF
• IGNITION SWITCH: RUN
• ENTER PCM DIAGNOSTICS
• CRUISE SWITCH: ON
• SELECT PCM OVERRIDE PS07
• INCREMENT OVERRIDE UNTIL 99 IS REACHED
• OBSERVE CRUISE CONTROL SERVO POSITION ①
SERVO PULLS IN COMPLETELY
SERVO PULLS IN PARTIALY
SERVO DOES NOT PULL IN AT ALL
• CHECK FOR AT LEAST 10 IN. HG OF SUPPLY VACUUM. ALSO CHECK FOR LEAKS AND THROTTLE CABLE BINDING OR RESTRICTIONS
• GO TO TEST C: CRUISE CONTROL SERVO TEST
• WAIT 30 SECONDS AND CHECK IF SERVO IS STILL PULLED IN. IF NOT, CHECK FOR SLOW LEAK
• DECREMENT OVERRIDE UNTIL 0% IS REACHED
• OBSERVE CRUISE CONTROL SERVO POSITION ②
SERVO IS FULLY RELAXED
SERVO IS NOT FULLY RELAXED
• ROAD TEST VEHICLE
• REPLACE PCM IF SYMPTOM STILL EXISTS
• CHECK SERVO LINKAGE FOR BINDING
• CHECK VACUUM LINES FOR RESTRICTIONS
• IF OK, REPLACE CRUISE CONTROL SERVO
① CHECKS CRUISE CONTROL SERVO OPERATION, SERVO THROTTLE LINKAGE, AND VACUUM.
② CHECKS VACUUM LINES FOR RESTRICTIONS AND SERVO THROTTLE LINKAGE FOR BINDING.
WHEN ALL DIAGNOSIS AND REPAIRS ARE COMPLETED, PERFORM LASH LEARN PROCEDURE (NORTHSTAR ONLY) AND VERIFY OPERATION

GC1109300115000X

Fig. 25 Test B: Cruise control output test. 1993–94 DeVille, Eldorado & Seville

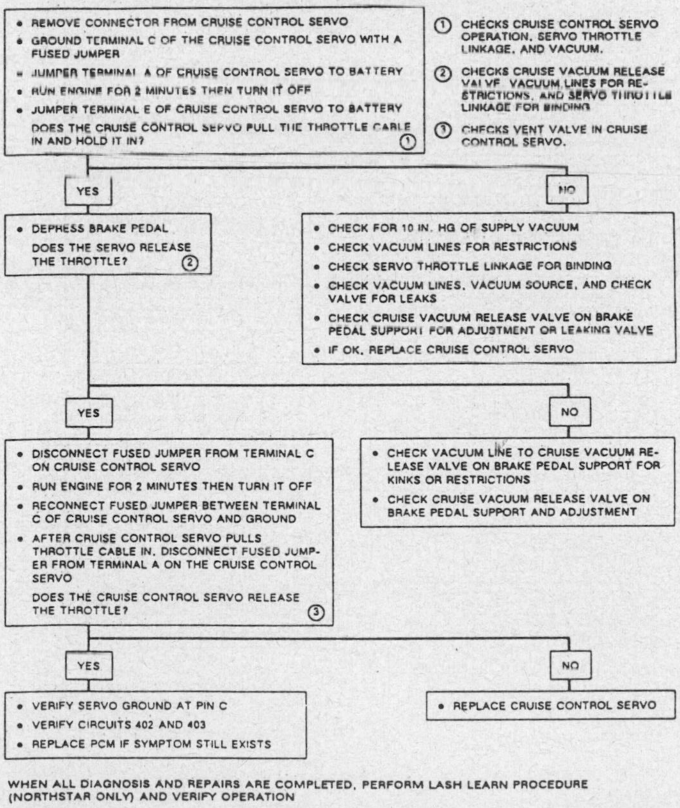
• REMOVE CONNECTOR FROM CRUISE CONTROL SERVO
• GROUND TERMINAL C OF THE CRUISE CONTROL SERVO WITH A FUSED JUMPER
• JUMPER TERMINAL A OF CRUISE CONTROL SERVO TO BATTERY
• RUN ENGINE FOR 2 MINUTES THEN TURN IT OFF
• JUMPER TERMINAL E OF CRUISE CONTROL SERVO TO BATTERY
DOES THE CRUISE CONTROL SERVO PULL THE THROTTLE CABLE IN AND HOLD IT IN? ①
① CHECKS CRUISE CONTROL SERVO OPERATION, SERVO THROTTLE LINKAGE, AND VACUUM.
② CHECKS CRUISE VACUUM RELEASE VALVE, VACUUM LINES FOR RESTRICTIONS, AND SERVO THROTTLE LINKAGE FOR BINDING
③ CHECKS VENT VALVE IN CRUISE CONTROL SERVO.
YES
NO
• DEPRESS BRAKE PEDAL
DOES THE SERVO RELEASE THE THROTTLE? ②
• CHECK FOR 10 IN. HG OF SUPPLY VACUUM
• CHECK VACUUM LINES FOR RESTRICTIONS
• CHECK SERVO THROTTLE LINKAGE FOR BINDING
• CHECK VACUUM LINES, VACUUM SOURCE, AND CHECK VALVE FOR LEAKS
• CHECK CRUISE VACUUM RELEASE VALVE ON BRAKE PEDAL SUPPORT FOR ADJUSTMENT OR LEAKING VALVE
• IF OK, REPLACE CRUISE CONTROL SERVO
YES
NO
• DISCONNECT FUSED JUMPER FROM TERMINAL C ON CRUISE CONTROL SERVO
• RUN ENGINE FOR 2 MINUTES THEN TURN IT OFF
• RECONNECT FUSED JUMPER BETWEEN TERMINAL C OF CRUISE CONTROL SERVO AND GROUND
• AFTER CRUISE CONTROL SERVO PULLS THROTTLE CABLE IN, DISCONNECT FUSED JUMPER FROM TERMINAL A ON THE CRUISE CONTROL SERVO
DOES THE CRUISE CONTROL SERVO RELEASE THE THROTTLE? ③
• CHECK VACUUM LINE TO CRUISE VACUUM RELEASE VALVE ON BRAKE PEDAL SUPPORT FOR KINKS OR RESTRICTIONS
• CHECK CRUISE VACUUM RELEASE VALVE ON BRAKE PEDAL SUPPORT AND ADJUSTMENT
YES
NO
• VERIFY SERVO GROUND AT PIN C
• VERIFY CIRCUITS 402 AND 403
• REPLACE PCM IF SYMPTOM STILL EXISTS
• REPLACE CRUISE CONTROL SERVO
WHEN ALL DIAGNOSIS AND REPAIRS ARE COMPLETED, PERFORM LASH LEARN PROCEDURE (NORTHSTAR ONLY) AND VERIFY OPERATION

GC1109300116000X

Fig. 26 Test C: Cruise Control Servo Test. 1993–94 DeVille, Eldorado & Seville

PCM CODE E060

CRUISE–TRANSAXLE NOT IN DRIVE

- **THE PRIMARY PURPOSE OF THIS CODE IS TO DETECT AN ACTION OF THE DRIVE THAT COULD CAUSE AN UNSAFE CONDITION OR DAMAGE TO THE VEHICLE.**
- **THIS CODE CAN BE DRIVER INDUCED BY SHIFTING THE GEAR SELECTOR INTO NEUTRAL WHEN THE CRUISE CONTROL IS ENGAGED.**
- **A FAILURE OF THE PRNDL SWITCH MAY CAUSE THE CODE TO SET.**
- **CHECK FOR CODE E091.**

GC1109100117000X

Fig. 27 Code PO60: Diagnostic Test. Eldorado & Seville w/4.9L/V8-300 engine

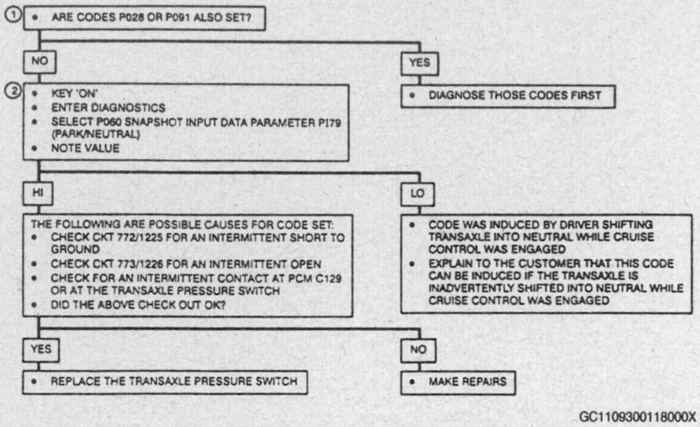
1 • ARE CODES P028 OR P091 ALSO SET?
NO
YES
• DIAGNOSE THOSE CODES FIRST
2 • KEY 'ON'
• ENTER DIAGNOSTICS
• SELECT P060 SNAPSHOT INPUT DATA PARAMETER P179 (PARK/NEUTRAL)
• NOTE VALUE
HI
LO
THE FOLLOWING ARE POSSIBLE CAUSES FOR CODE SET:
• CHECK CKT 772/1225 FOR AN INTERMITTENT SHORT TO GROUND
• CHECK CKT 773/1226 FOR AN INTERMITTENT OPEN
• CHECK FOR AN INTERMITTENT CONTACT AT PCM C129 OR AT THE TRANSAXLE PRESSURE SWITCH
• DID THE ABOVE CHECK OUT OK?
• CODE WAS INDUCED BY DRIVER SHIFTING TRANSAXLE INTO NEUTRAL WHILE CRUISE CONTROL WAS ENGAGED
• EXPLAIN TO THE CUSTOMER THAT THIS CODE CAN BE INDUCED IF THE TRANSAXLE IS INADVERTENTLY SHIFTED INTO NEUTRAL WHILE CRUISE CONTROL WAS ENGAGED
YES
NO
• REPLACE THE TRANSAXLE PRESSURE SWITCH
• MAKE REPAIRS
GC1109300118000X

Fig. 28 Code PO60: Diagnostic Test. Eldorado & Seville w/4.6L/V8-279 Northstar engine

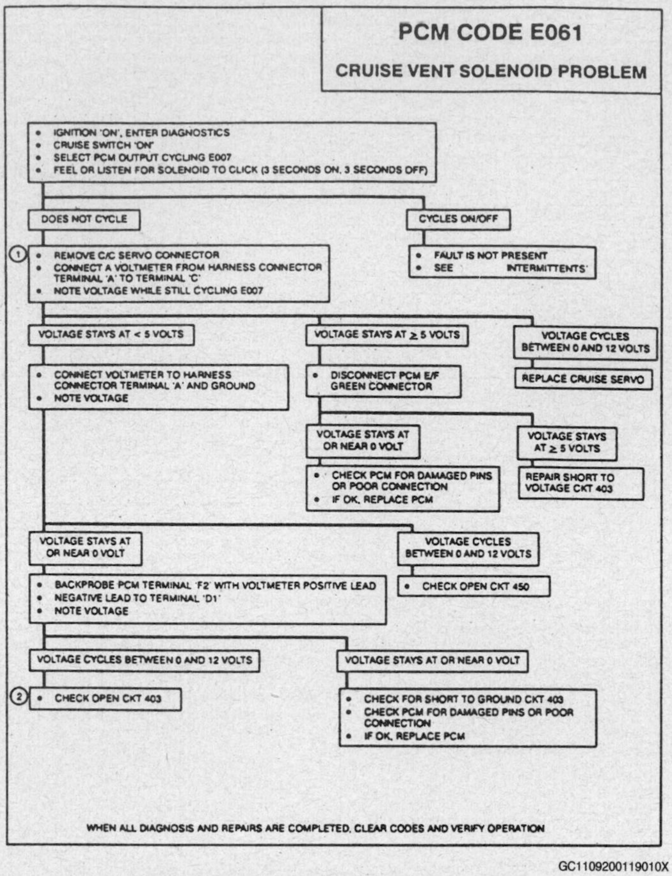
PCM CODE E061
CRUISE VENT SOLENOID PROBLEM
• IGNITION 'ON', ENTER DIAGNOSTICS
• CRUISE SWITCH 'ON'
• SELECT PCM OUTPUT CYCLING E007
• FEEL OR LISTEN FOR SOLENOID TO CLICK (3 SECONDS ON, 3 SECONDS OFF)
DOES NOT CYCLE
CYCLES ON/OFF
1 • REMOVE C/C SERVO CONNECTOR
• CONNECT A VOLTMETER FROM HARNESS CONNECTOR TERMINAL 'A' TO TERMINAL 'C'
• NOTE VOLTAGE WHILE STILL CYCLING E007
• FAULT IS NOT PRESENT
• SEE INTERMITTENTS'
VOLTAGE STAYS AT < 5 VOLTS
VOLTAGE STAYS AT ≥ 5 VOLTS
VOLTAGE CYCLES BETWEEN 0 AND 12 VOLTS
• CONNECT VOLTMETER TO HARNESS CONNECTOR TERMINAL 'A' AND GROUND
• NOTE VOLTAGE
• DISCONNECT PCM E/F GREEN CONNECTOR
REPLACE CRUISE SERVO
VOLTAGE STAYS AT OR NEAR 0 VOLT
VOLTAGE STAYS AT ≥ 5 VOLTS
• CHECK PCM FOR DAMAGED PINS OR POOR CONNECTION
• IF OK, REPLACE PCM
REPAIR SHORT TO VOLTAGE CKT 403
VOLTAGE STAYS AT OR NEAR 0 VOLT
VOLTAGE CYCLES BETWEEN 0 AND 12 VOLTS
• BACKPROBE PCM TERMINAL 'F2' WITH VOLTMETER POSITIVE LEAD
• NEGATIVE LEAD TO TERMINAL 'D1'
• NOTE VOLTAGE
• CHECK OPEN CKT 450
VOLTAGE CYCLES BETWEEN 0 AND 12 VOLTS
VOLTAGE STAYS AT OR NEAR 0 VOLT
2 • CHECK OPEN CKT 403
• CHECK FOR SHORT TO GROUND CKT 403
• CHECK PCM FOR DAMAGED PINS OR POOR CONNECTION
• IF OK, REPLACE PCM
WHEN ALL DIAGNOSIS AND REPAIRS ARE COMPLETED, CLEAR CODES AND VERIFY OPERATION
GC1109200119010X

Fig. 29 Code P061: Diagnostic Test. 1992 Eldorado & Seville w/4.9L/V8-300 engine

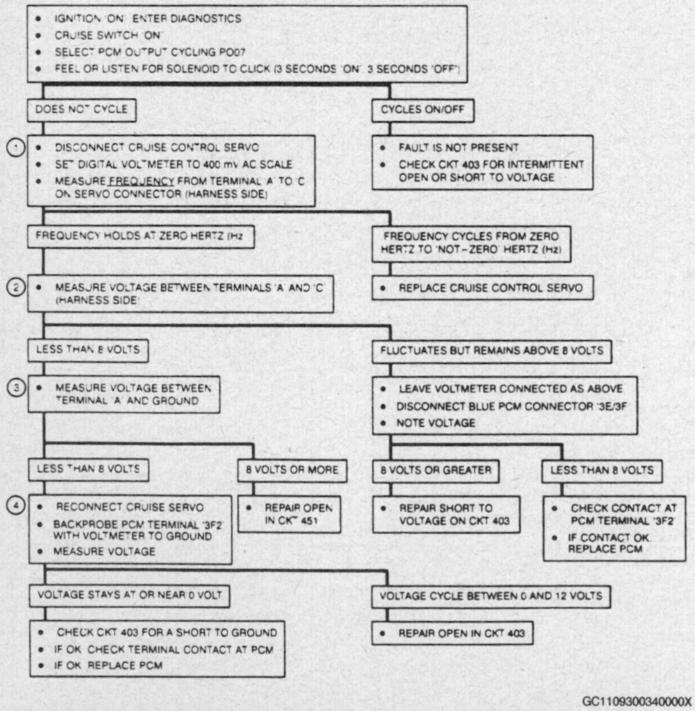
• IGNITION 'ON' ENTER DIAGNOSTICS
• CRUISE SWITCH 'ON'
• SELECT PCM OUTPUT CYCLING PO07
• FEEL OR LISTEN FOR SOLENOID TO CLICK (3 SECONDS 'ON' 3 SECONDS 'OFF')
DOES NOT CYCLE
CYCLES ON/OFF
1 • DISCONNECT CRUISE CONTROL SERVO
• SET DIGITAL VOLTMETER TO 400 mV AC SCALE
• MEASURE FREQUENCY FROM TERMINAL 'A' TO 'C' ON SERVO CONNECTOR (HARNESS SIDE)
• FAULT IS NOT PRESENT
• CHECK CKT 403 FOR INTERMITTENT OPEN OR SHORT TO VOLTAGE
FREQUENCY HOLDS AT ZERO HERTZ (Hz
FREQUENCY CYCLES FROM ZERO HERTZ TO 'NOT-ZERO' HERTZ (Hz)
2 • MEASURE VOLTAGE BETWEEN TERMINALS 'A' AND 'C' (HARNESS SIDE
• REPLACE CRUISE CONTROL SERVO
LESS THAN 8 VOLTS
FLUCTUATES BUT REMAINS ABOVE 8 VOLTS
3 • MEASURE VOLTAGE BETWEEN TERMINAL 'A' AND GROUND
• LEAVE VOLTMETER CONNECTED AS ABOVE
• DISCONNECT BLUE PCM CONNECTOR '3E/3F
• NOTE VOLTAGE
LESS THAN 8 VOLTS
8 VOLTS OR MORE
8 VOLTS OR GREATER
LESS THAN 8 VOLTS
4 • RECONNECT CRUISE SERVO
• BACKPROBE PCM TERMINAL '3F2' WITH VOLTMETER TO GROUND
• MEASURE VOLTAGE
• REPAIR OPEN IN CKT 451
• REPAIR SHORT TO VOLTAGE ON CKT 403
• CHECK CONTACT AT PCM TERMINAL '3F2'
• IF CONTACT OK, REPLACE PCM
VOLTAGE STAYS AT OR NEAR 0 VOLT
VOLTAGE CYCLE BETWEEN 0 AND 12 VOLTS
• CHECK CKT 403 FOR A SHORT TO GROUND
• IF OK CHECK TERMINAL CONTACT AT PCM
• IF OK REPLACE PCM
• REPAIR OPEN IN CKT 403
GC1109300340000X

Fig. 30 Code P061: Diagnostic Test. 1993–94 Eldorado & Seville w/4.9L/V8-300 engine

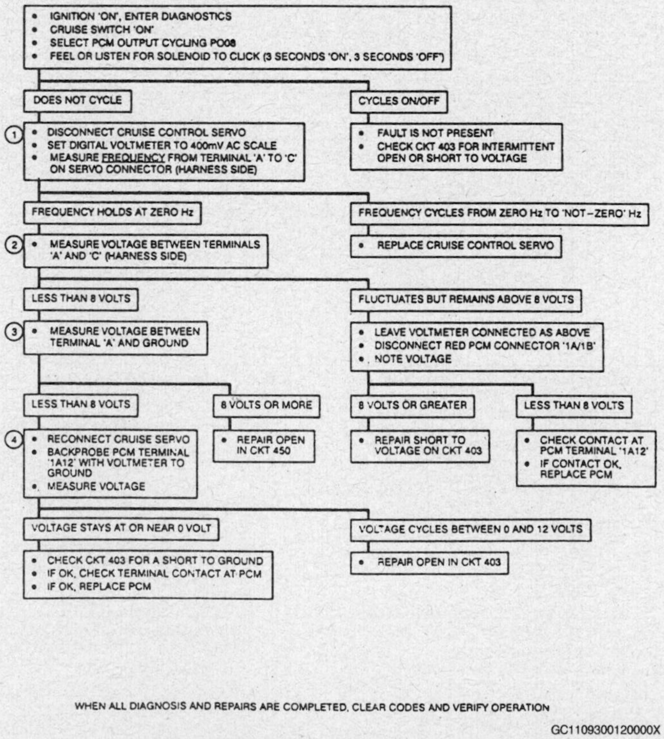
• IGNITION 'ON', ENTER DIAGNOSTICS
• CRUISE SWITCH 'ON'
• SELECT PCM OUTPUT CYCLING PO08
• FEEL OR LISTEN FOR SOLENOID TO CLICK (3 SECONDS 'ON', 3 SECONDS 'OFF')
DOES NOT CYCLE
CYCLES ON/OFF
1 • DISCONNECT CRUISE CONTROL SERVO
• SET DIGITAL VOLTMETER TO 400mV AC SCALE
• MEASURE FREQUENCY FROM TERMINAL 'A' TO 'C' ON SERVO CONNECTOR (HARNESS SIDE)
• FAULT IS NOT PRESENT
• CHECK CKT 403 FOR INTERMITTENT OPEN OR SHORT TO VOLTAGE
FREQUENCY HOLDS AT ZERO Hz
FREQUENCY CYCLES FROM ZERO Hz TO 'NOT-ZERO' Hz
2 • MEASURE VOLTAGE BETWEEN TERMINALS 'A' AND 'C' (HARNESS SIDE)
• REPLACE CRUISE CONTROL SERVO
LESS THAN 8 VOLTS
FLUCTUATES BUT REMAINS ABOVE 8 VOLTS
3 • MEASURE VOLTAGE BETWEEN TERMINAL 'A' AND GROUND
• LEAVE VOLTMETER CONNECTED AS ABOVE
• DISCONNECT RED PCM CONNECTOR '1A/1B'
• NOTE VOLTAGE
LESS THAN 8 VOLTS
8 VOLTS OR MORE
8 VOLTS OR GREATER
LESS THAN 8 VOLTS
4 • RECONNECT CRUISE SERVO
• BACKPROBE PCM TERMINAL '1A12' WITH VOLTMETER TO GROUND
• MEASURE VOLTAGE
• REPAIR OPEN IN CKT 450
• REPAIR SHORT TO VOLTAGE ON CKT 403
• CHECK CONTACT AT PCM TERMINAL '1A12'
• IF CONTACT OK, REPLACE PCM
VOLTAGE STAYS AT OR NEAR 0 VOLT
VOLTAGE CYCLES BETWEEN 0 AND 12 VOLTS
• CHECK CKT 403 FOR A SHORT TO GROUND
• IF OK, CHECK TERMINAL CONTACT AT PCM
• IF OK, REPLACE PCM
• REPAIR OPEN IN CKT 403
WHEN ALL DIAGNOSIS AND REPAIRS ARE COMPLETED, CLEAR CODES AND VERIFY OPERATION
GC1109300120000X

Fig. 31 Code P061: Diagnostic Test. Eldorado & Seville w/4.6L/V8-279 Northstar engine

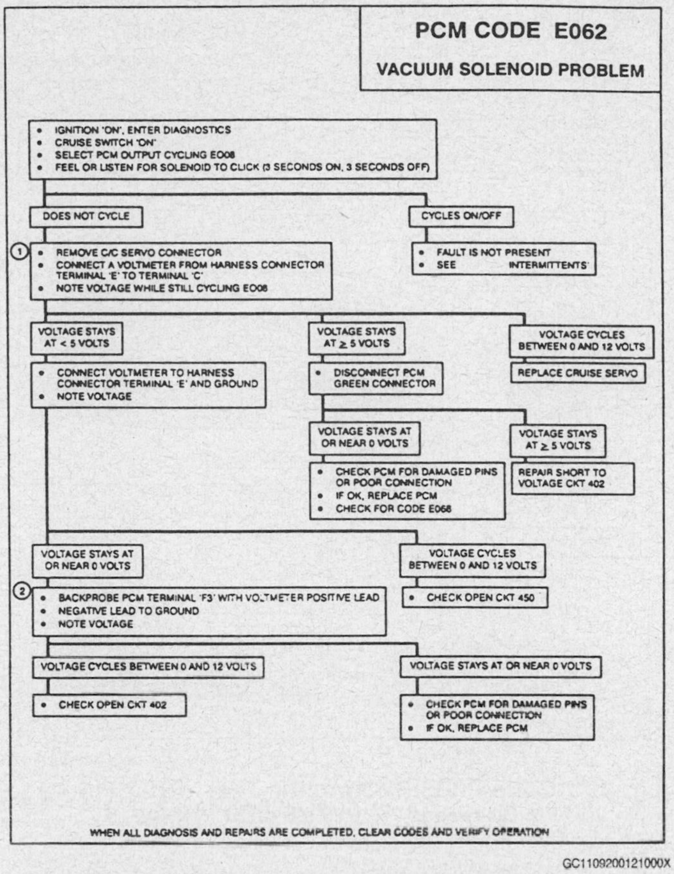
PCM CODE E062
VACUUM SOLENOID PROBLEM
• IGNITION 'ON', ENTER DIAGNOSTICS
• CRUISE SWITCH 'ON'
• SELECT PCM OUTPUT CYCLING E008
• FEEL OR LISTEN FOR SOLENOID TO CLICK (3 SECONDS ON, 3 SECONDS OFF)
DOES NOT CYCLE
CYCLES ON/OFF
1
• REMOVE C/C SERVO CONNECTOR
• CONNECT A VOLTMETER FROM HARNESS CONNECTOR TERMINAL 'E' TO TERMINAL 'C'
• NOTE VOLTAGE WHILE STILL CYCLING E008
• FAULT IS NOT PRESENT
• SEE 'INTERMITTENTS'
VOLTAGE STAYS AT < 5 VOLTS
VOLTAGE STAYS AT ≥ 5 VOLTS
VOLTAGE CYCLES BETWEEN 0 AND 12 VOLTS
• CONNECT VOLTMETER TO HARNESS CONNECTOR TERMINAL 'E' AND GROUND
• NOTE VOLTAGE
• DISCONNECT PCM GREEN CONNECTOR
REPLACE CRUISE SERVO
VOLTAGE STAYS AT OR NEAR 0 VOLTS
VOLTAGE STAYS AT ≥ 5 VOLTS
• CHECK PCM FOR DAMAGED PINS OR POOR CONNECTION
• IF OK, REPLACE PCM
• CHECK FOR CODE E068
REPAIR SHORT TO VOLTAGE CKT 402
VOLTAGE STAYS AT OR NEAR 0 VOLTS
VOLTAGE CYCLES BETWEEN 0 AND 12 VOLTS
2
• BACKPROBE PCM TERMINAL 'F3' WITH VOLTMETER POSITIVE LEAD
• NEGATIVE LEAD TO GROUND
• NOTE VOLTAGE
• CHECK OPEN CKT 450
VOLTAGE CYCLES BETWEEN 0 AND 12 VOLTS
VOLTAGE STAYS AT OR NEAR 0 VOLTS
• CHECK OPEN CKT 402
• CHECK PCM FOR DAMAGED PINS OR POOR CONNECTION
• IF OK, REPLACE PCM
WHEN ALL DIAGNOSIS AND REPAIRS ARE COMPLETED, CLEAR CODES AND VERIFY OPERATION
GC1109200121000X

Fig. 32 Code P062: Diagnostic Test. Eldorado & Seville w/4.9L/V8-300 engine

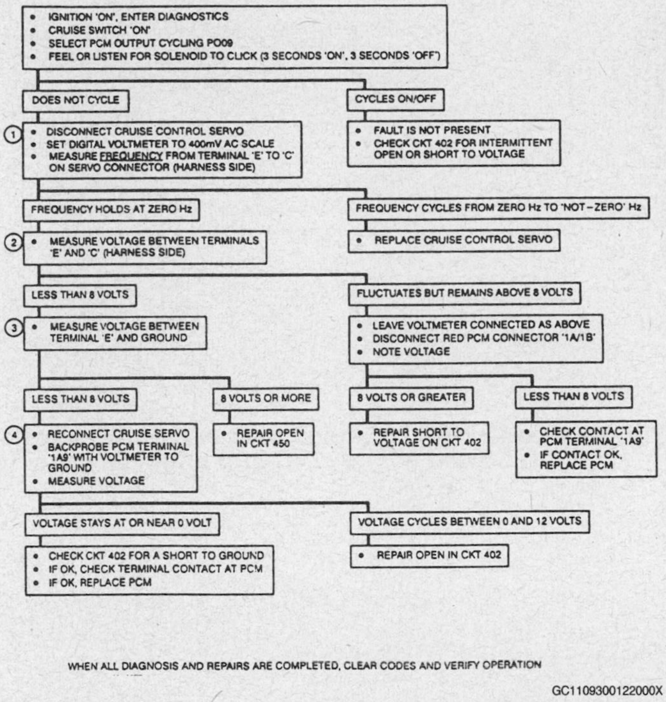
• IGNITION 'ON', ENTER DIAGNOSTICS
• CRUISE SWITCH 'ON'
• SELECT PCM OUTPUT CYCLING P009
• FEEL OR LISTEN FOR SOLENOID TO CLICK (3 SECONDS 'ON', 3 SECONDS 'OFF')
DOES NOT CYCLE
CYCLES ON/OFF
1
• DISCONNECT CRUISE CONTROL SERVO
• SET DIGITAL VOLTMETER TO 400mV AC SCALE
• MEASURE FREQUENCY FROM TERMINAL 'E' TO 'C' ON SERVO CONNECTOR (HARNESS SIDE)
• FAULT IS NOT PRESENT
• CHECK CKT 402 FOR INTERMITTENT OPEN OR SHORT TO VOLTAGE
FREQUENCY HOLDS AT ZERO Hz
FREQUENCY CYCLES FROM ZERO Hz TO 'NOT-ZERO' Hz
2
• MEASURE VOLTAGE BETWEEN TERMINALS 'E' AND 'C' (HARNESS SIDE)
• REPLACE CRUISE CONTROL SERVO
LESS THAN 8 VOLTS
FLUCTUATES BUT REMAINS ABOVE 8 VOLTS
3
• MEASURE VOLTAGE BETWEEN TERMINAL 'E' AND GROUND
• LEAVE VOLTMETER CONNECTED AS ABOVE
• DISCONNECT RED PCM CONNECTOR '1A/1B'
• NOTE VOLTAGE
LESS THAN 8 VOLTS
8 VOLTS OR MORE
8 VOLTS OR GREATER
LESS THAN 8 VOLTS
4
• RECONNECT CRUISE SERVO
• BACKPROBE PCM TERMINAL '1A9' WITH VOLTMETER TO GROUND
• MEASURE VOLTAGE
• REPAIR OPEN IN CKT 450
• REPAIR SHORT TO VOLTAGE ON CKT 402
• CHECK CONTACT AT PCM TERMINAL '1A9'
• IF CONTACT OK, REPLACE PCM
VOLTAGE STAYS AT OR NEAR 0 VOLT
VOLTAGE CYCLES BETWEEN 0 AND 12 VOLTS
• CHECK CKT 402 FOR A SHORT TO GROUND
• IF OK, CHECK TERMINAL CONTACT AT PCM
• IF OK, REPLACE PCM
• REPAIR OPEN IN CKT 402
WHEN ALL DIAGNOSIS AND REPAIRS ARE COMPLETED, CLEAR CODES AND VERIFY OPERATION
GC1109300122000X

Fig. 33 Code P062: Diagnostic Test. Eldorado & Seville w/4.6L/V8-279 Northstar engine

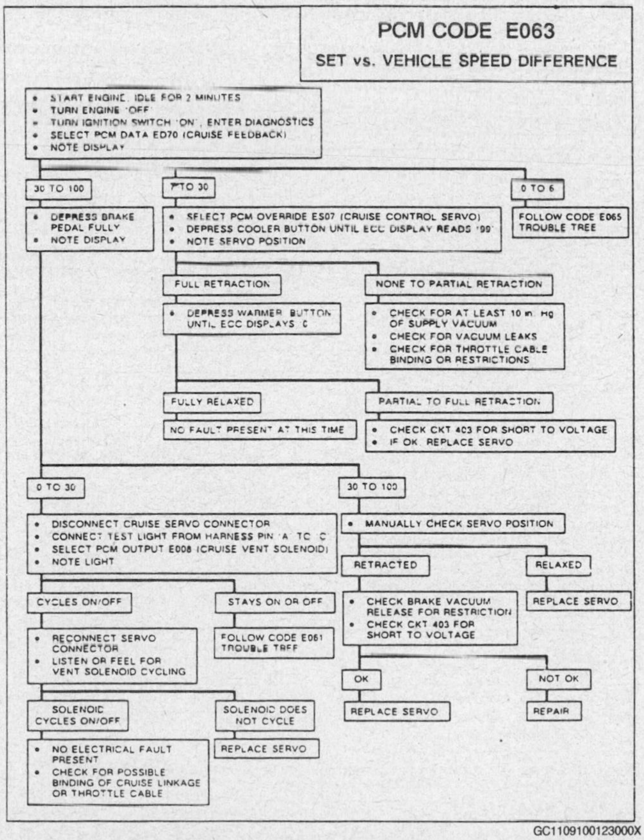
PCM CODE E063
SET vs. VEHICLE SPEED DIFFERENCE
• START ENGINE, IDLE FOR 2 MINUTES
• TURN ENGINE 'OFF'
• TURN IGNITION SWITCH 'ON', ENTER DIAGNOSTICS
• SELECT PCM DATA ED70 (CRUISE FEEDBACK)
• NOTE DISPLAY
30 TO 100
7 TO 30
0 TO 6
• DEPRESS BRAKE PEDAL FULLY
• NOTE DISPLAY
• SELECT PCM OVERRIDE ES07 (CRUISE CONTROL SERVO)
• DEPRESS COOLER BUTTON UNTIL ECC DISPLAY READS '99'
• NOTE SERVO POSITION
FOLLOW CODE E065 TROUBLE TREE
FULL RETRACTION
NONE TO PARTIAL RETRACTION
• DEPRESS WARMER BUTTON UNTIL ECC DISPLAYS '0'
• CHECK FOR AT LEAST 10 in. Hg OF SUPPLY VACUUM
• CHECK FOR VACUUM LEAKS
• CHECK FOR THROTTLE CABLE BINDING OR RESTRICTIONS
FULLY RELAXED
PARTIAL TO FULL RETRACTION
NO FAULT PRESENT AT THIS TIME
• CHECK CKT 403 FOR SHORT TO VOLTAGE
• IF OK, REPLACE SERVO
0 TO 30
30 TO 100
• DISCONNECT CRUISE SERVO CONNECTOR
• CONNECT TEST LIGHT FROM HARNESS PIN 'A' TO 'C'
• SELECT PCM OUTPUT E008 (CRUISE VENT SOLENOID)
• NOTE LIGHT
• MANUALLY CHECK SERVO POSITION
RETRACTED
RELAXED
CYCLES ON/OFF
STAYS ON OR OFF
• CHECK BRAKE VACUUM RELEASE FOR RESTRICTION
• CHECK CKT 403 FOR SHORT TO VOLTAGE
REPLACE SERVO
• RECONNECT SERVO CONNECTOR
• LISTEN OR FEEL FOR VENT SOLENOID CYCLING
FOLLOW CODE E061 TROUBLE TREE
OK
NOT OK
SOLENOID CYCLES ON/OFF
SOLENOID DOES NOT CYCLE
REPLACE SERVO
REPAIR
• NO ELECTRICAL FAULT PRESENT
• CHECK FOR POSSIBLE BINDING OF CRUISE LINKAGE OR THROTTLE CABLE
REPLACE SERVO
GC1109100123000X

Fig. 34 Code P063: Diagnostic Test. Eldorado & Seville w/4.9L/V8-300 engine

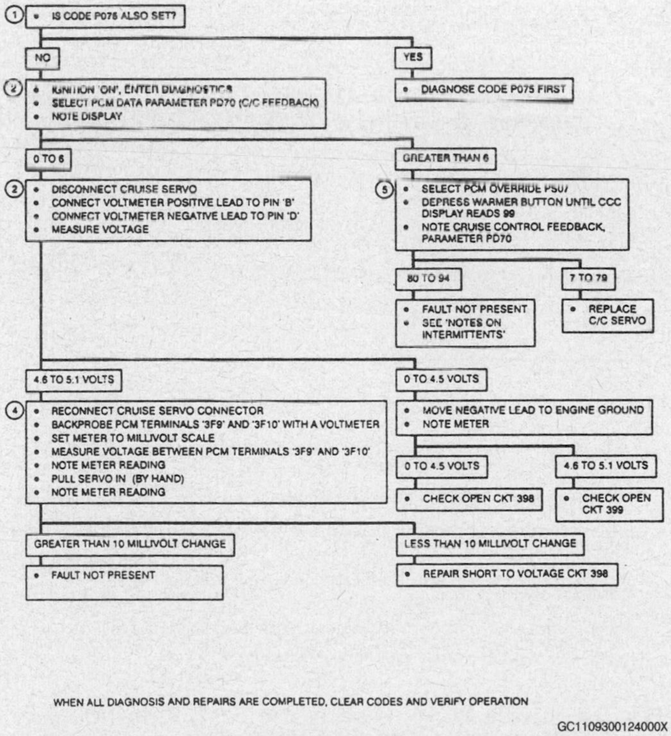
1
• IS CODE P075 ALSO SET?
NO
YES
2
• IGNITION 'ON', ENTER DIAGNOSTICS
• SELECT PCM DATA PARAMETER PD70 (C/C FEEDBACK)
• NOTE DISPLAY
• DIAGNOSE CODE P075 FIRST
0 TO 6
GREATER THAN 6
2
• DISCONNECT CRUISE SERVO
• CONNECT VOLTMETER POSITIVE LEAD TO PIN 'B'
• CONNECT VOLTMETER NEGATIVE LEAD TO PIN 'D'
• MEASURE VOLTAGE
5
• SELECT PCM OVERRIDE PS07
• DEPRESS WARMER BUTTON UNTIL CCC DISPLAY READS 99
• NOTE CRUISE CONTROL FEEDBACK, PARAMETER PD70
80 TO 94
7 TO 79
• FAULT NOT PRESENT
• SEE 'NOTES ON INTERMITTENTS'
• REPLACE C/C SERVO
4.6 TO 5.1 VOLTS
0 TO 4.5 VOLTS
4
• RECONNECT CRUISE SERVO CONNECTOR
• BACKPROBE PCM TERMINALS '3F9' AND '3F10' WITH A VOLTMETER
• SET METER TO MILLIVOLT SCALE
• MEASURE VOLTAGE BETWEEN PCM TERMINALS '3F9' AND '3F10'
• NOTE METER READING
• PULL SERVO IN (BY HAND)
• NOTE METER READING
• MOVE NEGATIVE LEAD TO ENGINE GROUND
• NOTE METER
0 TO 4.5 VOLTS
4.6 TO 5.1 VOLTS
• CHECK OPEN CKT 398
• CHECK OPEN CKT 399
GREATER THAN 10 MILLIVOLT CHANGE
LESS THAN 10 MILLIVOLT CHANGE
• FAULT NOT PRESENT
• REPAIR SHORT TO VOLTAGE CKT 398
WHEN ALL DIAGNOSIS AND REPAIRS ARE COMPLETED, CLEAR CODES AND VERIFY OPERATION
GC1109300124000X

Fig. 35 Code P063: Diagnostic Test. Eldorado & Seville w/4.6L/V8-279 Northstar engine

PCM CODE E064

VEHICLE ACCELERATION OUT OF RANGE

- Code E064 sets when the vehicle speed increases greater that 16 mph in one second with the cruise engaged (4 mph in .25 second)
- If code E064 is set, cruise control will disengage and Code E064 is stored in memory.
- Most occurrences of Code E064 are caused by wheelspin due to icy or wet conditions
- If Code E064 is found and no other cruise control faults exists, clear codes and road test vehicle.

WHEN ALL DIAGNOSIS AND REPAIRS ARE COMPLETED, CLEAR CODES AND VERIFY OPERATION

GC1109100125010X

Fig. 36 Code P064: Diagnostic Test. 1992 Eldorado & Seville w/4.9L/V8-300 engine

- CODE P064 SETS WHEN THE VEHICLE SPEED INCREASES GREATER THAN 16 MPH IN ONE SECOND WITH THE CRUISE ENGAGED.
- IF CODE P064 IS SET, CRUISE CONTROL WILL DISENGAGE.
- MOST OCCURRENCES OF CODE P064 ARE CAUSED BY WHEELSPIN DUE TO ICY, WET OR SLIPPERY CONDITIONS.
- IF CODE P064 IS FOUND AND NO OTHER CRUISE CONTROL FAULTS EXISTS, CLEAR CODES AND ROAD TEST VEHICLE.
- IF CODE P075 IS ALSO SET, LOOK FOR SOURCES OF ELECTROMAGNETIC INTERFERENCE (EMI). SUCH AS VSS WIRES RUN ALONG SIDE SPARK PLUG WIRES OR HIGH POWER TRANSMITTERS (LIKE MOBILE RADIOS) OPERATING IN THE VICINITY.

GC1109400344000X

Fig. 37 Code P064: Diagnostic Test. 1993–94 Eldorado & Seville w/4.9L/V8-300 engine

- CODE P064 SETS WHEN THE VEHICLE SPEED INCREASES GREATER THAN 16 MPH IN ONE SECOND WITH THE CRUISE ENGAGED.
- IF CODE P064 IS SET, CRUISE CONTROL WILL DISENGAGE.
- MOST OCCURRENCES OF CODE P064 ARE CAUSED BY WHEELSPIN DUE TO ICY, WET OR SLIPPERY CONDITIONS.
- IF CODE P064 IS FOUND AND NO OTHER CRUISE CONTROL FAULTS EXISTS, CLEAR CODES AND ROAD TEST VEHICLE.
- IF CODE P075 IS ALSO SET, LOOK FOR SOURCES OF ELECTROMAGNETIC INTERFERENCE (EMI), SUCH AS VSS WIRES RUN ALONG SIDE SPARK PLUG WIRES OR HIGH POWER TRANSMITTERS (LIKE MOBILE RADIOS) OPERATING IN THE VICINITY.

GC1109300126000X

Fig. 38 Code P064: Diagnostic Test. Eldorado & Seville w/4.6L/V8-279 Northstar engine

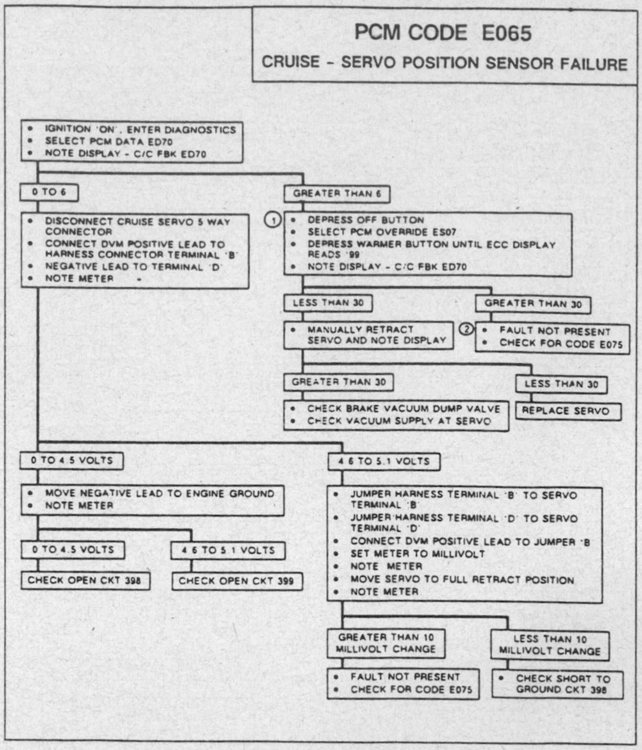
PCM CODE E065
CRUISE - SERVO POSITION SENSOR FAILURE
• IGNITION 'ON', ENTER DIAGNOSTICS • SELECT PCM DATA ED70 • NOTE DISPLAY - C/C FBK ED70
0 TO 6
• DISCONNECT CRUISE SERVO 5 WAY CONNECTOR • CONNECT DVM POSITIVE LEAD TO HARNESS CONNECTOR TERMINAL 'B' • NEGATIVE LEAD TO TERMINAL 'D' • NOTE METER
GREATER THAN 6
1
• DEPRESS OFF BUTTON • SELECT PCM OVERRIDE ES07 • DEPRESS WARMER BUTTON UNTIL ECC DISPLAY READS '99' • NOTE DISPLAY - C/C FBK ED70
LESS THAN 30
• MANUALLY RETRACT SERVO AND NOTE DISPLAY
GREATER THAN 30
2
• FAULT NOT PRESENT • CHECK FOR CODE E075
GREATER THAN 30
• CHECK BRAKE VACUUM DUMP VALVE • CHECK VACUUM SUPPLY AT SERVO
LESS THAN 30
REPLACE SERVO
0 TO 4.5 VOLTS
• MOVE NEGATIVE LEAD TO ENGINE GROUND • NOTE METER
0 TO 4.5 VOLTS
CHECK OPEN CKT 398
4.6 TO 5.1 VOLTS
CHECK OPEN CKT 399
4.6 TO 5.1 VOLTS
• JUMPER HARNESS TERMINAL 'B' TO SERVO TERMINAL 'B' • JUMPER HARNESS TERMINAL 'D' TO SERVO TERMINAL 'D' • CONNECT DVM POSITIVE LEAD TO JUMPER 'B' • SET METER TO MILLIVOLT • NOTE METER • MOVE SERVO TO FULL RETRACT POSITION • NOTE METER
GREATER THAN 10 MILLIVOLT CHANGE
• FAULT NOT PRESENT • CHECK FOR CODE E075
LESS THAN 10 MILLIVOLT CHANGE
• CHECK SHORT TO GROUND CKT 398

GC1109100127010X

Fig. 39 Code P065: Diagnostic Test. 1992 Eldorado & Seville w/4.9L/V8-300 engine

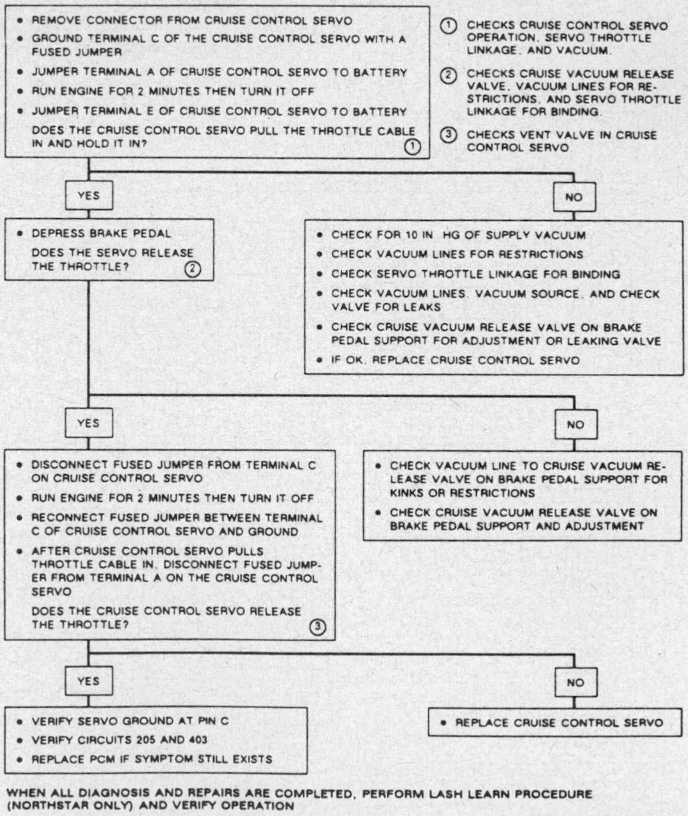
• REMOVE CONNECTOR FROM CRUISE CONTROL SERVO • GROUND TERMINAL C OF THE CRUISE CONTROL SERVO WITH A FUSED JUMPER • JUMPER TERMINAL A OF CRUISE CONTROL SERVO TO BATTERY • RUN ENGINE FOR 2 MINUTES THEN TURN IT OFF • JUMPER TERMINAL E OF CRUISE CONTROL SERVO TO BATTERY
DOES THE CRUISE CONTROL SERVO PULL THE THROTTLE CABLE IN AND HOLD IT IN? 1
1 CHECKS CRUISE CONTROL SERVO OPERATION, SERVO THROTTLE LINKAGE, AND VACUUM.
2 CHECKS CRUISE VACUUM RELEASE VALVE, VACUUM LINES FOR RESTRICTIONS, AND SERVO THROTTLE LINKAGE FOR BINDING.
3 CHECKS VENT VALVE IN CRUISE CONTROL SERVO
YES
• DEPRESS BRAKE PEDAL
DOES THE SERVO RELEASE THE THROTTLE? 2
NO
• CHECK FOR 10 IN. HG OF SUPPLY VACUUM • CHECK VACUUM LINES FOR RESTRICTIONS • CHECK SERVO THROTTLE LINKAGE FOR BINDING • CHECK VACUUM LINES, VACUUM SOURCE, AND CHECK VALVE FOR LEAKS • CHECK CRUISE VACUUM RELEASE VALVE ON BRAKE PEDAL SUPPORT FOR ADJUSTMENT OR LEAKING VALVE • IF OK, REPLACE CRUISE CONTROL SERVO
YES
• DISCONNECT FUSED JUMPER FROM TERMINAL C ON CRUISE CONTROL SERVO • RUN ENGINE FOR 2 MINUTES THEN TURN IT OFF • RECONNECT FUSED JUMPER BETWEEN TERMINAL C OF CRUISE CONTROL SERVO AND GROUND • AFTER CRUISE CONTROL SERVO PULLS THROTTLE CABLE IN, DISCONNECT FUSED JUMPER FROM TERMINAL A ON THE CRUISE CONTROL SERVO
DOES THE CRUISE CONTROL SERVO RELEASE THE THROTTLE? 3
NO
• CHECK VACUUM LINE TO CRUISE VACUUM RELEASE VALVE ON BRAKE PEDAL SUPPORT FOR KINKS OR RESTRICTIONS • CHECK CRUISE VACUUM RELEASE VALVE ON BRAKE PEDAL SUPPORT AND ADJUSTMENT
YES
• VERIFY SERVO GROUND AT PIN C • VERIFY CIRCUITS 205 AND 403 • REPLACE PCM IF SYMPTOM STILL EXISTS
NO
• REPLACE CRUISE CONTROL SERVO
WHEN ALL DIAGNOSIS AND REPAIRS ARE COMPLETED, PERFORM LASH LEARN PROCEDURE (NORTHSTAR ONLY) AND VERIFY OPERATION

GC1109400339000X

Fig. 40 Code P065: Diagnostic Test. 1993–94 Eldorado & Seville w/4.9L/V8-300 engine

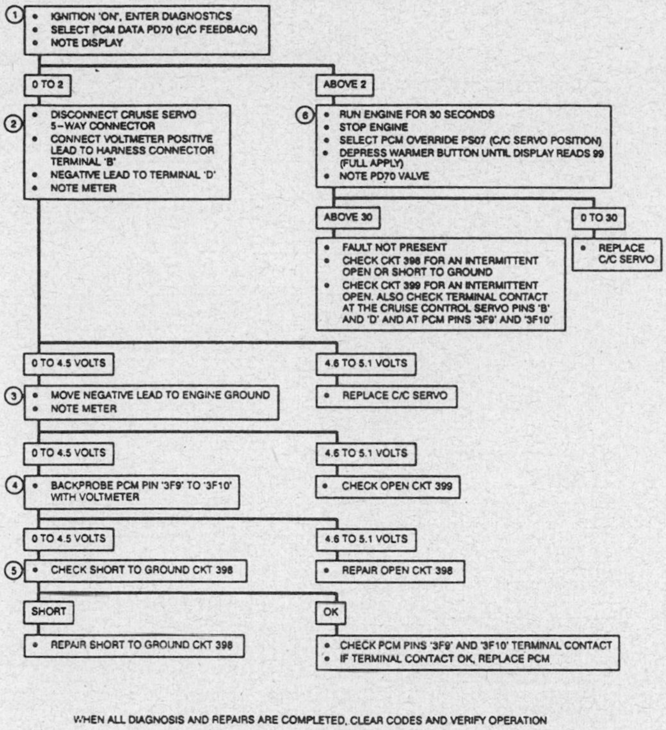
1
• IGNITION 'ON', ENTER DIAGNOSTICS
• SELECT PCM DATA PD70 (C/C FEEDBACK)
• NOTE DISPLAY
0 TO 2
ABOVE 2
2
• DISCONNECT CRUISE SERVO 5-WAY CONNECTOR
• CONNECT VOLTMETER POSITIVE LEAD TO HARNESS CONNECTOR TERMINAL 'B'
• NEGATIVE LEAD TO TERMINAL 'D'
• NOTE METER
6
• RUN ENGINE FOR 30 SECONDS
• STOP ENGINE
• SELECT PCM OVERRIDE PS07 (C/C SERVO POSITION)
• DEPRESS WARMER BUTTON UNTIL DISPLAY READS 99 (FULL APPLY)
• NOTE PD70 VALVE
ABOVE 30
0 TO 30
• FAULT NOT PRESENT
• CHECK CKT 398 FOR AN INTERMITTENT OPEN OR SHORT TO GROUND
• CHECK CKT 399 FOR AN INTERMITTENT OPEN. ALSO CHECK TERMINAL CONTACT AT THE CRUISE CONTROL SERVO PINS 'B' AND 'D' AND AT PCM PINS '3F9' AND '3F10'
• REPLACE C/C SERVO
0 TO 4.5 VOLTS
4.6 TO 5.1 VOLTS
3
• MOVE NEGATIVE LEAD TO ENGINE GROUND
• NOTE METER
• REPLACE C/C SERVO
0 TO 4.5 VOLTS
4.6 TO 5.1 VOLTS
4
• BACKPROBE PCM PIN '3F9' TO '3F10' WITH VOLTMETER
• CHECK OPEN CKT 399
0 TO 4.5 VOLTS
4.6 TO 5.1 VOLTS
5
• CHECK SHORT TO GROUND CKT 398
• REPAIR OPEN CKT 398
SHORT
OK
• REPAIR SHORT TO GROUND CKT 398
• CHECK PCM PINS '3F9' AND '3F10' TERMINAL CONTACT
• IF TERMINAL CONTACT OK, REPLACE PCM
WHEN ALL DIAGNOSIS AND REPAIRS ARE COMPLETED, CLEAR CODES AND VERIFY OPERATION

Fig. 41 Code P065: Diagnostic Test. Eldorado & Seville w/4.6L/V8-279 Northstar engine

PCM CODE E066

CRUISE-ENGINE RPM TOO HIGH

THIS CODE WILL SET IF ENGINE RPM EXCEEDS 4800 RPM. THIS MAY OCCUR ON SLIPPERY PAVEMENT, EXTENDED WIDE OPEN THROTTLE ACCELERATION, OR FOR SOME MECHANICAL PROBLEMS (SUCH AS TRANSMISSION SLIPPAGE). UNDER THESE CONDITIONS, CODE E066 WILL SET AND SHOULD BE CONSIDERED NORMAL. THE DRIVER SHOULD BE CONSIDERED NORMAL. THE DRIVER SHOULD BE ADVISED WHY THE CRUISE DISENGAGED. CLEAR THE CODE AND ROAD TEST VEHICLE TO VERIFY NORMAL OPERATION.

WHEN ALL DIAGNOSIS AND REPAIRS ARE COMPLETED CLEAR CODES AND VERIFY OPERATION

GC1109300129000X

Fig. 42 Code P066: Diagnostic Test. Eldorado & Seville w/4.9L/V8-300 engine

THIS CODE WILL SET IF ENGINE RPM EXCEEDS 5975 RPM WITH CRUISE CONTROL ENGAGED. THIS MAY OCCUR ON ICY, WET, OR SLIPPERY PAVEMENT, EXTENDED WIDE OPEN THROTTLE ACCELERATION, OR FOR SOME MECHANICAL PROBLEMS (SUCH AS TRANSAXLE SLIPPAGE). UNDER THESE CONDITIONS, CODE P066 WILL SET AND SHOULD BE CONSIDERED NORMAL. THE DRIVER SHOULD BE ADVISED WHY THE CRUISE DISENGAGED. CLEAR THE CODE AND ROAD TEST VEHICLE TO VERIFY NORMAL OPERATION.

GC1109300130000X

Fig. 43 Code P066: Diagnostic Test. Eldorado & Seville w/4.6L/V8-279 Northstar engine

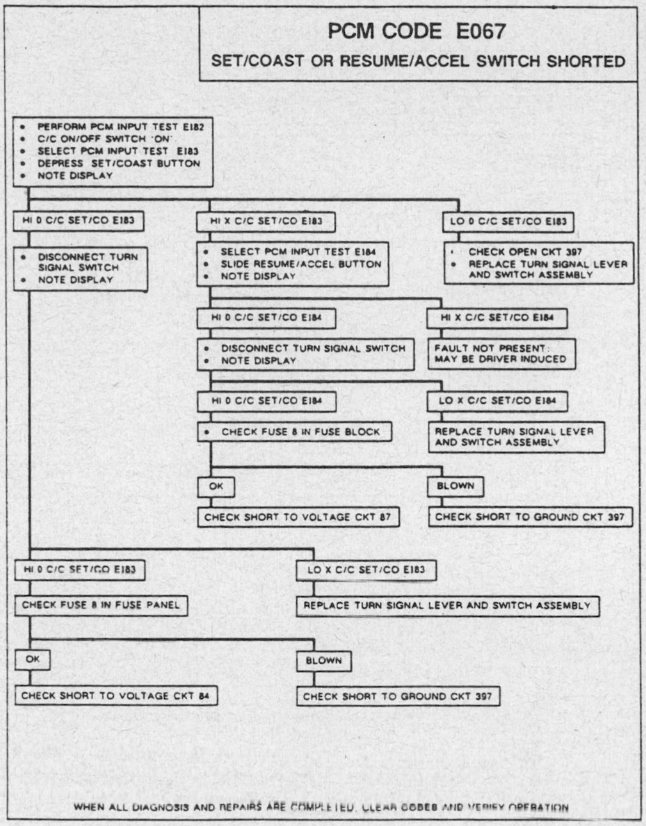
PCM CODE E067
SET/COAST OR RESUME/ACCEL SWITCH SHORTED
• PERFORM PCM INPUT TEST E182
• C/C ON/OFF SWITCH "ON"
• SELECT PCM INPUT TEST E183
• DEPRESS SET/COAST BUTTON
• NOTE DISPLAY
HI 0 C/C SET/CO E183
HI X C/C SET/CO E183
LO 0 C/C SET/CO E183
• DISCONNECT TURN SIGNAL SWITCH
• NOTE DISPLAY
• SELECT PCM INPUT TEST E184
• SLIDE RESUME/ACCEL BUTTON
• NOTE DISPLAY
• CHECK OPEN CKT 397
• REPLACE TURN SIGNAL LEVER AND SWITCH ASSEMBLY
HI 0 C/C SET/CO E184
HI X C/C SET/CO E184
• DISCONNECT TURN SIGNAL SWITCH
• NOTE DISPLAY
FAULT NOT PRESENT: MAY BE DRIVER INDUCED
HI 0 C/C SET/CO E184
LO X C/C SET/CO E184
• CHECK FUSE 8 IN FUSE BLOCK
REPLACE TURN SIGNAL LEVER AND SWITCH ASSEMBLY
OK
BLOWN
CHECK SHORT TO VOLTAGE CKT 87
CHECK SHORT TO GROUND CKT 397
HI 0 C/C SET/CO E183
LO X C/C SET/CO E183
CHECK FUSE 8 IN FUSE PANEL
REPLACE TURN SIGNAL LEVER AND SWITCH ASSEMBLY
OK
BLOWN
CHECK SHORT TO VOLTAGE CKT 84
CHECK SHORT TO GROUND CKT 397
WHEN ALL DIAGNOSIS AND REPAIRS ARE COMPLETED, CLEAR CODES AND VERIFY OPERATION

GC1109100131010X

Fig. 44 Code P067: Diagnostic Test. 1992 Eldorado & Seville w/4.9L/V8-300 engine

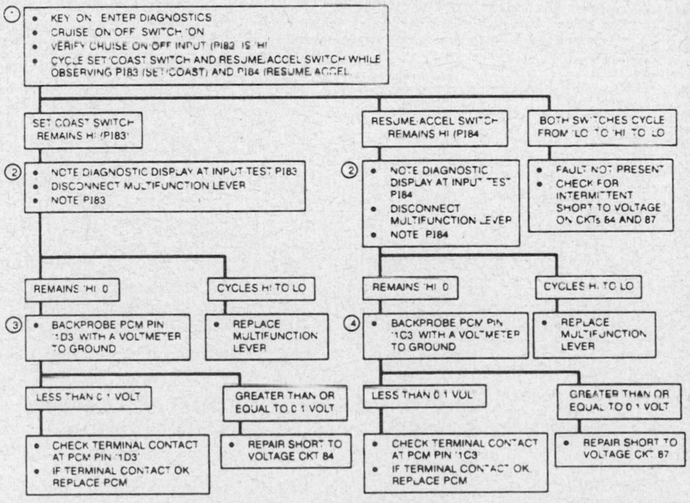
• KEY ON ENTER DIAGNOSTICS
• CRUISE ON OFF SWITCH 'ON
• VERIFY CRUISE ON OFF INPUT (P182 IS 'HI
• CYCLE SET COAST SWITCH AND RESUME ACCEL SWITCH WHILE OBSERVING P183 (SET/COAST) AND P184 (RESUME ACCEL
SET COAST SWITCH REMAINS HI (P183)
RESUME ACCEL SWITCH REMAINS HI (P184
BOTH SWITCHES CYCLE FROM 'LO TO 'HI TO LO
2
• NOTE DIAGNOSTIC DISPLAY AT INPUT TEST P183
• DISCONNECT MULTIFUNCTION LEVER
• NOTE P183
2
• NOTE DIAGNOSTIC DISPLAY AT INPUT TEST P184
• DISCONNECT MULTIFUNCTION LEVER
• NOTE P184
• FAULT NOT PRESENT
• CHECK FOR INTERMITTENT SHORT TO VOLTAGE ON CKTs 84 AND 87
REMAINS 'HI 0
CYCLES HI TO LO
REMAINS 'HI 0
CYCLES HI TO LO
3
• BACKPROBE PCM PIN '1D3' WITH A VOLTMETER TO GROUND
• REPLACE MULTIFUNCTION LEVER
4
• BACKPROBE PCM PIN '1C3 WITH A VOLTMETER TO GROUND
• REPLACE MULTIFUNCTION LEVER
LESS THAN 0.1 VOLT
GREATER THAN OR EQUAL TO 0.1 VOLT
LESS THAN 0.1 VOLT
GREATER THAN OR EQUAL TO 0.1 VOLT
• CHECK TERMINAL CONTACT AT PCM PIN '1D3'
• IF TERMINAL CONTACT OK REPLACE PCM
• REPAIR SHORT TO VOLTAGE CKT 84
• CHECK TERMINAL CONTACT AT PCM PIN '1C3'
• IF TERMINAL CONTACT OK, REPLACE PCM
• REPAIR SHORT TO VOLTAGE CKT 87

GC1109400345000X

Fig. 45 Code P067: Diagnostic Test. 1993–94 Eldorado & Seville w/4.9L/V8-300 engine

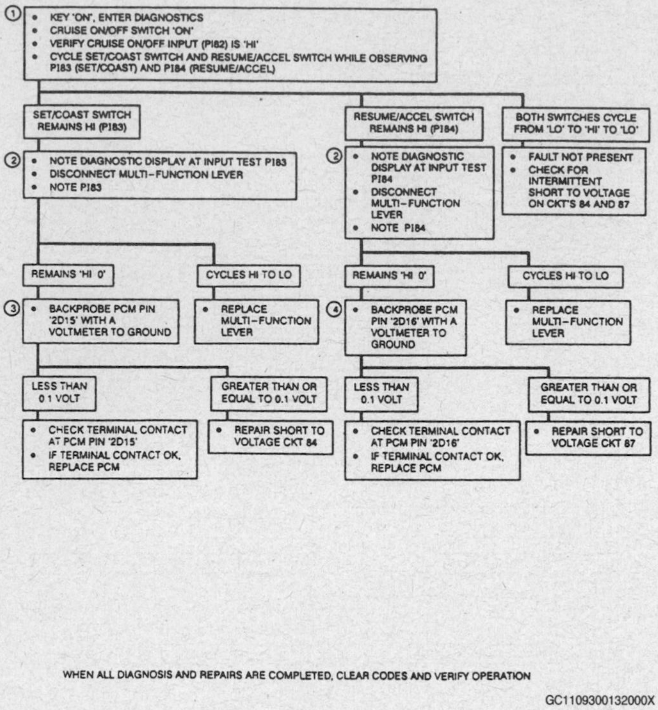

① • KEY 'ON', ENTER DIAGNOSTICS • CRUISE ON/OFF SWITCH 'ON' • VERIFY CRUISE ON/OFF INPUT (P182) IS 'HI' • CYCLE SET/COAST SWITCH AND RESUME/ACCEL SWITCH WHILE OBSERVING P183 (SET/COAST) AND P184 (RESUME/ACCEL)
SET/COAST SWITCH REMAINS HI (P183)
RESUME/ACCEL SWITCH REMAINS HI (P184)
BOTH SWITCHES CYCLE FROM 'LO' TO 'HI' TO 'LO'
② • NOTE DIAGNOSTIC DISPLAY AT INPUT TEST P183 • DISCONNECT MULTI-FUNCTION LEVER • NOTE P183
② • NOTE DIAGNOSTIC DISPLAY AT INPUT TEST P184 • DISCONNECT MULTI-FUNCTION LEVER • NOTE P184
• FAULT NOT PRESENT • CHECK FOR INTERMITTENT SHORT TO VOLTAGE ON CKT'S 84 AND 87
REMAINS 'HI 0'
CYCLES HI TO LO
REMAINS 'HI 0'
CYCLES HI TO LO
③ • BACKPROBE PCM PIN '2D15' WITH A VOLTMETER TO GROUND
• REPLACE MULTI-FUNCTION LEVER
④ • BACKPROBE PCM PIN '2D16' WITH A VOLTMETER TO GROUND
• REPLACE MULTI-FUNCTION LEVER
LESS THAN 0.1 VOLT
GREATER THAN OR EQUAL TO 0.1 VOLT
LESS THAN 0.1 VOLT
GREATER THAN OR EQUAL TO 0.1 VOLT
• CHECK TERMINAL CONTACT AT PCM PIN '2D15' • IF TERMINAL CONTACT OK, REPLACE PCM
• REPAIR SHORT TO VOLTAGE CKT 84
• CHECK TERMINAL CONTACT AT PCM PIN '2D16' • IF TERMINAL CONTACT OK, REPLACE PCM
• REPAIR SHORT TO VOLTAGE CKT 87
WHEN ALL DIAGNOSIS AND REPAIRS ARE COMPLETED, CLEAR CODES AND VERIFY OPERATION
GC1109300132000X

Fig. 46 Code P067: Diagnostic Test. Eldorado & Seville w/4.6L/V8-279 Northstar engine

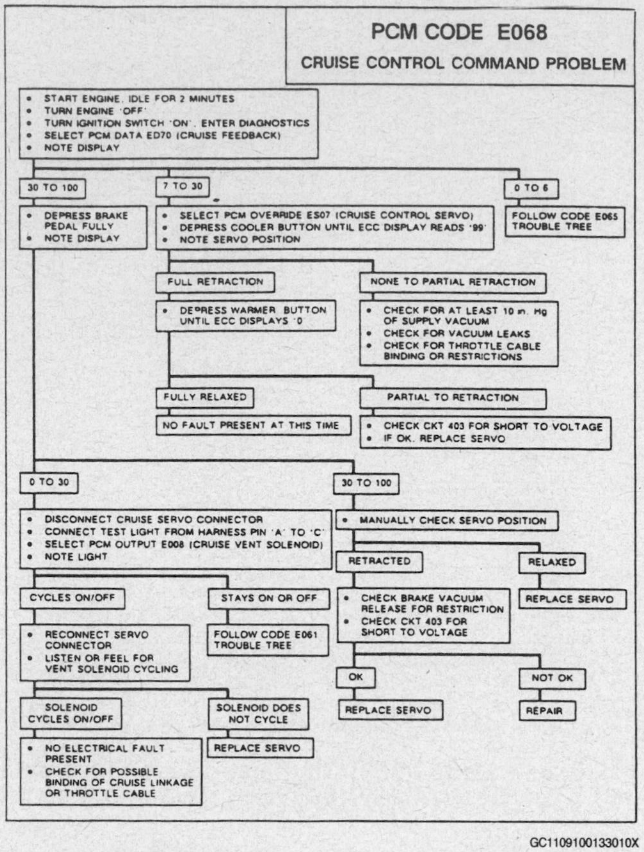

PCM CODE E068
CRUISE CONTROL COMMAND PROBLEM
• START ENGINE, IDLE FOR 2 MINUTES • TURN ENGINE 'OFF' • TURN IGNITION SWITCH 'ON', ENTER DIAGNOSTICS • SELECT PCM DATA ED70 (CRUISE FEEDBACK) • NOTE DISPLAY
30 TO 100
7 TO 30
0 TO 6
• DEPRESS BRAKE PEDAL FULLY • NOTE DISPLAY
• SELECT PCM OVERRIDE ES07 (CRUISE CONTROL SERVO) • DEPRESS COOLER BUTTON UNTIL ECC DISPLAY READS '99' • NOTE SERVO POSITION
FOLLOW CODE E065 TROUBLE TREE
FULL RETRACTION
NONE TO PARTIAL RETRACTION
• DEPRESS WARMER BUTTON UNTIL ECC DISPLAYS '0'
• CHECK FOR AT LEAST 10 in. Hg OF SUPPLY VACUUM • CHECK FOR VACUUM LEAKS • CHECK FOR THROTTLE CABLE BINDING OR RESTRICTIONS
FULLY RELAXED
PARTIAL TO RETRACTION
NO FAULT PRESENT AT THIS TIME
• CHECK CKT 403 FOR SHORT TO VOLTAGE • IF OK, REPLACE SERVO
0 TO 30
30 TO 100
• DISCONNECT CRUISE SERVO CONNECTOR • CONNECT TEST LIGHT FROM HARNESS PIN 'A' TO 'C' • SELECT PCM OUTPUT E008 (CRUISE VENT SOLENOID) • NOTE LIGHT
• MANUALLY CHECK SERVO POSITION
RETRACTED
RELAXED
CYCLES ON/OFF
STAYS ON OR OFF
• CHECK BRAKE VACUUM RELEASE FOR RESTRICTION • CHECK CKT 403 FOR SHORT TO VOLTAGE
REPLACE SERVO
• RECONNECT SERVO CONNECTOR • LISTEN OR FEEL FOR VENT SOLENOID CYCLING
FOLLOW CODE E061 TROUBLE TREE
OK
NOT OK
REPLACE SERVO
REPAIR
SOLENOID CYCLES ON/OFF
SOLENOID DOES NOT CYCLE
• NO ELECTRICAL FAULT PRESENT • CHECK FOR POSSIBLE BINDING OF CRUISE LINKAGE OR THROTTLE CABLE
REPLACE SERVO
GC1109100133010X

Fig. 47 Code P068: Diagnostic Test. 1992 Eldorado & Seville w/4.9L/V8-300 engine

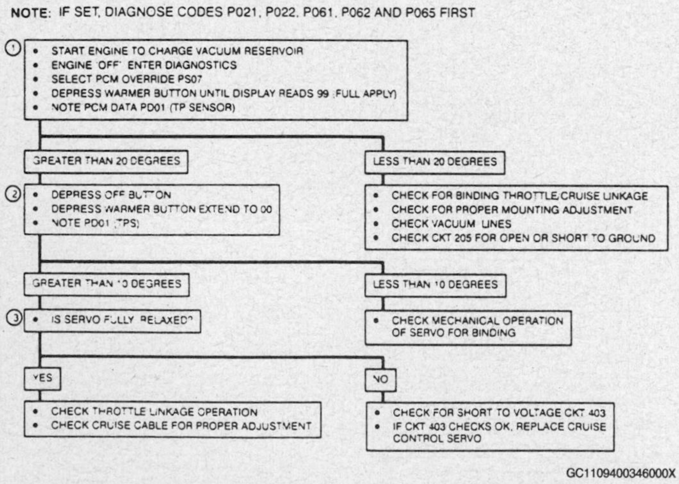

NOTE: IF SET, DIAGNOSE CODES P021, P022, P061, P062 AND P065 FIRST
① • START ENGINE TO CHARGE VACUUM RESERVOIR • ENGINE 'OFF' ENTER DIAGNOSTICS • SELECT PCM OVERRIDE PS07 • DEPRESS WARMER BUTTON UNTIL DISPLAY READS 99 (FULL APPLY) • NOTE PCM DATA PD01 (TP SENSOR)
GREATER THAN 20 DEGREES
LESS THAN 20 DEGREES
② • DEPRESS OFF BUTTON • DEPRESS WARMER BUTTON EXTEND TO 00 • NOTE PD01 (TPS)
• CHECK FOR BINDING THROTTLE/CRUISE LINKAGE • CHECK FOR PROPER MOUNTING ADJUSTMENT • CHECK VACUUM LINES • CHECK CKT 205 FOR OPEN OR SHORT TO GROUND
GREATER THAN 10 DEGREES
LESS THAN 10 DEGREES
③ • IS SERVO FULLY RELAXED?
• CHECK MECHANICAL OPERATION OF SERVO FOR BINDING
YES
NO
• CHECK THROTTLE LINKAGE OPERATION • CHECK CRUISE CABLE FOR PROPER ADJUSTMENT
• CHECK FOR SHORT TO VOLTAGE CKT 403 • IF CKT 403 CHECKS OK, REPLACE CRUISE CONTROL SERVO
GC1109400346000X

Fig. 48 Code P068: Diagnostic Test. 1993–94 Eldorado & Seville w/4.9L/V8-300 engine

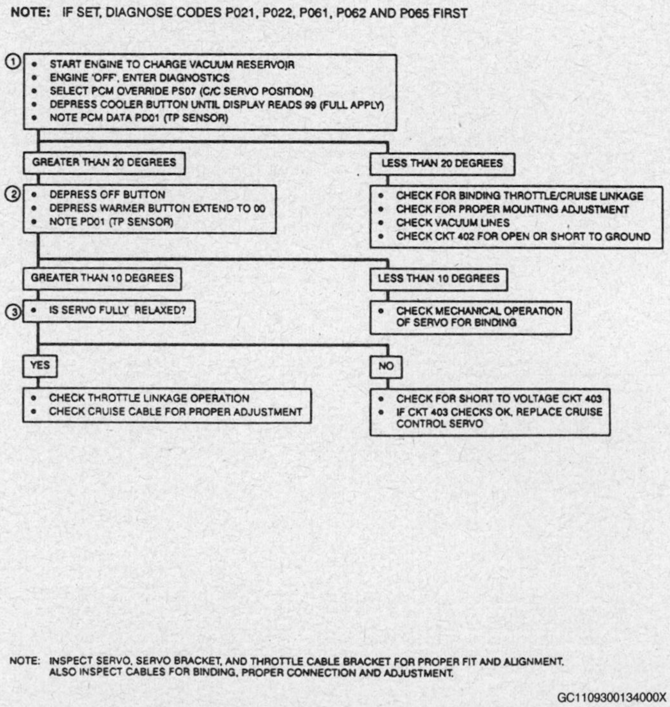

NOTE: IF SET, DIAGNOSE CODES P021, P022, P061, P062 AND P065 FIRST
① • START ENGINE TO CHARGE VACUUM RESERVOIR • ENGINE 'OFF', ENTER DIAGNOSTICS • SELECT PCM OVERRIDE PS07 (C/C SERVO POSITION) • DEPRESS COOLER BUTTON UNTIL DISPLAY READS 99 (FULL APPLY) • NOTE PCM DATA PD01 (TP SENSOR)
GREATER THAN 20 DEGREES
LESS THAN 20 DEGREES
② • DEPRESS OFF BUTTON • DEPRESS WARMER BUTTON EXTEND TO 00 • NOTE PD01 (TP SENSOR)
• CHECK FOR BINDING THROTTLE/CRUISE LINKAGE • CHECK FOR PROPER MOUNTING ADJUSTMENT • CHECK VACUUM LINES • CHECK CKT 402 FOR OPEN OR SHORT TO GROUND
GREATER THAN 10 DEGREES
LESS THAN 10 DEGREES
③ • IS SERVO FULLY RELAXED?
• CHECK MECHANICAL OPERATION OF SERVO FOR BINDING
YES
NO
• CHECK THROTTLE LINKAGE OPERATION • CHECK CRUISE CABLE FOR PROPER ADJUSTMENT
• CHECK FOR SHORT TO VOLTAGE CKT 403 • IF CKT 403 CHECKS OK, REPLACE CRUISE CONTROL SERVO
NOTE: INSPECT SERVO, SERVO BRACKET, AND THROTTLE CABLE BRACKET FOR PROPER FIT AND ALIGNMENT. ALSO INSPECT CABLES FOR BINDING, PROPER CONNECTION AND ADJUSTMENT.
GC1109300134000X

Fig. 49 Code P068: Diagnostic Test. Eldorado & Seville w/4.6L/V8-279 Northstar engine

- THIS DIAGNOSTIC TROUBLE CODE SETS WHEN TRACTION CONTROL AND CRUISE CONTROL ARE ACTIVE AT THE SAME TIME.
- IF DIAGNOSTIC TROUBLE CODE P069 SETS, CRUISE CONTROL WILL BE DISENGAGED
- CHECK FOR TRACTION CONTROL CODES.
- MOST CASES OF DIAGNOSTIC TROUBLE CODE P069 ARE CAUSED BY WHEEL SPIN UNDER ICY, WET, OR SLIPPERY CONDITIONS WHILE CRUISE ACTIVE.
- IF NO OTHER CRUISE CONTROL OR TRACTION CONTROL FAULTS EXIST, CLEAR CODES AND VERIFY CORRECT CRUISE AND TRACTION CONTROL OPERATION.

WHEN ALL DIAGNOSIS AND REPAIRS ARE COMPLETED, CLEAR CODES AND VERIFY OPERATION

GC1109100135000X

Fig. 50 Code P069: Diagnostic Test. Eldorado & Seville w/4.6L/V8-279 Northstar engine

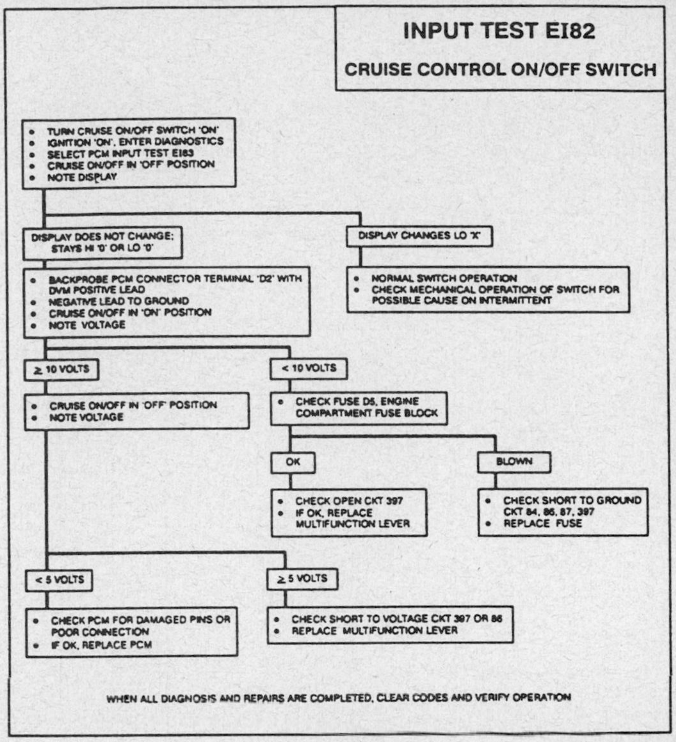
INPUT TEST EI82
CRUISE CONTROL ON/OFF SWITCH
TURN CRUISE ON/OFF SWITCH 'ON'
IGNITION 'ON', ENTER DIAGNOSTICS
SELECT PCM INPUT TEST EI83
CRUISE ON/OFF IN 'OFF' POSITION
NOTE DISPLAY
DISPLAY DOES NOT CHANGE: STAYS HI '0' OR LO '0'
DISPLAY CHANGES LO 'X'
BACKPROBE PCM CONNECTOR TERMINAL 'D2' WITH DVM POSITIVE LEAD
NEGATIVE LEAD TO GROUND
CRUISE ON/OFF IN 'ON' POSITION
NOTE VOLTAGE
NORMAL SWITCH OPERATION
CHECK MECHANICAL OPERATION OF SWITCH FOR POSSIBLE CAUSE ON INTERMITTENT
≥ 10 VOLTS
< 10 VOLTS
CRUISE ON/OFF IN 'OFF' POSITION
NOTE VOLTAGE
CHECK FUSE D5, ENGINE COMPARTMENT FUSE BLOCK
OK
BLOWN
CHECK OPEN CKT 397
IF OK, REPLACE MULTIFUNCTION LEVER
CHECK SHORT TO GROUND CKT 84, 86, 87, 397
REPLACE FUSE
< 5 VOLTS
≥ 5 VOLTS
CHECK PCM FOR DAMAGED PINS OR POOR CONNECTION
IF OK, REPLACE PCM
CHECK SHORT TO VOLTAGE CKT 397 OR 86
REPLACE MULTIFUNCTION LEVER
WHEN ALL DIAGNOSIS AND REPAIRS ARE COMPLETED, CLEAR CODES AND VERIFY OPERATION

GC1109200136000X

Fig. 52 Test E182: PCM Input Test. 1992 Eldorado & Seville

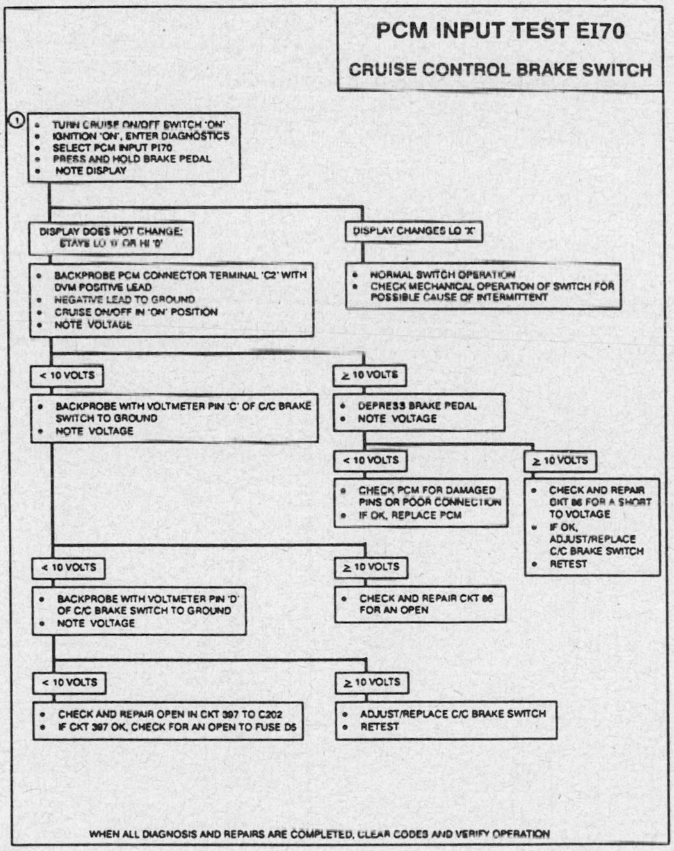
PCM INPUT TEST EI70
CRUISE CONTROL BRAKE SWITCH
TURN CRUISE ON/OFF SWITCH 'ON'
IGNITION 'ON', ENTER DIAGNOSTICS
SELECT PCM INPUT P170
PRESS AND HOLD BRAKE PEDAL
NOTE DISPLAY
DISPLAY DOES NOT CHANGE: STAYS LO '0' OR HI '0'
DISPLAY CHANGES LO 'X'
BACKPROBE PCM CONNECTOR TERMINAL 'C2' WITH DVM POSITIVE LEAD
NEGATIVE LEAD TO GROUND
CRUISE ON/OFF IN 'ON' POSITION
NOTE VOLTAGE
NORMAL SWITCH OPERATION
CHECK MECHANICAL OPERATION OF SWITCH FOR POSSIBLE CAUSE OF INTERMITTENT
< 10 VOLTS
≥ 10 VOLTS
BACKPROBE WITH VOLTMETER PIN 'C' OF C/C BRAKE SWITCH TO GROUND
NOTE VOLTAGE
DEPRESS BRAKE PEDAL
NOTE VOLTAGE
< 10 VOLTS
≥ 10 VOLTS
CHECK PCM FOR DAMAGED PINS OR POOR CONNECTION
IF OK, REPLACE PCM
CHECK AND REPAIR CKT 86 FOR A SHORT TO VOLTAGE
IF OK, ADJUST/REPLACE C/C BRAKE SWITCH
RETEST
< 10 VOLTS
≥ 10 VOLTS
BACKPROBE WITH VOLTMETER PIN 'D' OF C/C BRAKE SWITCH TO GROUND
NOTE VOLTAGE
CHECK AND REPAIR CKT 86 FOR AN OPEN
< 10 VOLTS
≥ 10 VOLTS
CHECK AND REPAIR OPEN IN CKT 397 TO C202
IF CKT 397 OK, CHECK FOR AN OPEN TO FUSE D5
ADJUST/REPLACE C/C BRAKE SWITCH
RETEST
WHEN ALL DIAGNOSIS AND REPAIRS ARE COMPLETED, CLEAR CODES AND VERIFY OPERATION

GC1109200137000X

Fig. 51 Test E170: PCM Input Test. 1992 Eldorado & Seville

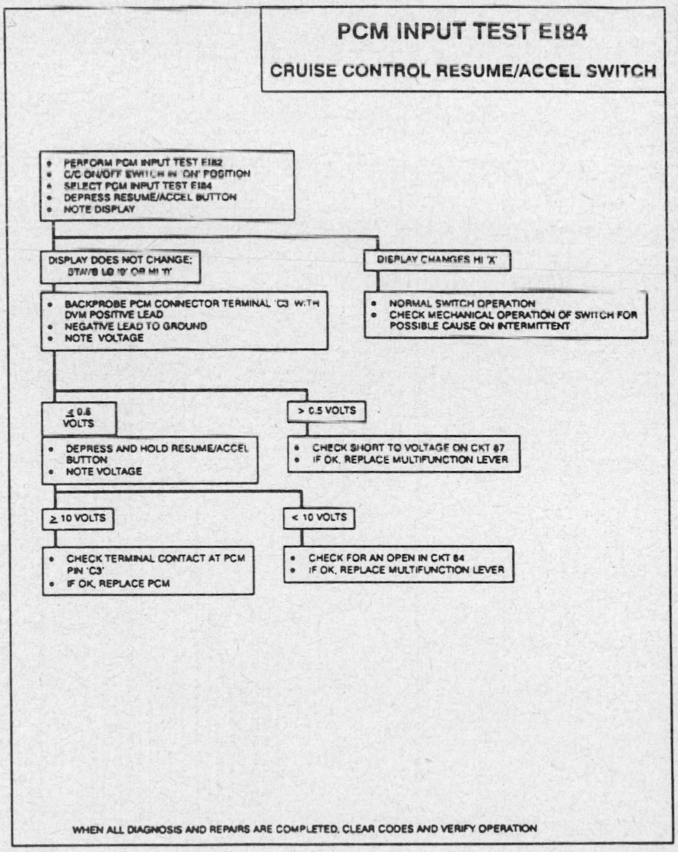
PCM INPUT TEST EI84
CRUISE CONTROL RESUME/ACCEL SWITCH
PERFORM PCM INPUT TEST EI82
C/C ON/OFF SWITCH IN 'ON' POSITION
SELECT PCM INPUT TEST EI84
DEPRESS RESUME/ACCEL BUTTON
NOTE DISPLAY
DISPLAY DOES NOT CHANGE: STAYS LO '0' OR HI '0'
DISPLAY CHANGES HI 'X'
BACKPROBE PCM CONNECTOR TERMINAL 'C3' WITH DVM POSITIVE LEAD
NEGATIVE LEAD TO GROUND
NOTE VOLTAGE
NORMAL SWITCH OPERATION
CHECK MECHANICAL OPERATION OF SWITCH FOR POSSIBLE CAUSE ON INTERMITTENT
≤ 0.5 VOLTS
> 0.5 VOLTS
DEPRESS AND HOLD RESUME/ACCEL BUTTON
NOTE VOLTAGE
CHECK SHORT TO VOLTAGE ON CKT 87
IF OK, REPLACE MULTIFUNCTION LEVER
≥ 10 VOLTS
< 10 VOLTS
CHECK TERMINAL CONTACT AT PCM PIN 'C3'
IF OK, REPLACE PCM
CHECK FOR AN OPEN IN CKT 84
IF OK, REPLACE MULTIFUNCTION LEVER
WHEN ALL DIAGNOSIS AND REPAIRS ARE COMPLETED, CLEAR CODES AND VERIFY OPERATION

GC1109200138000X

Fig. 53 Test E183: PCM Input Test. 1992 Eldorado & Seville

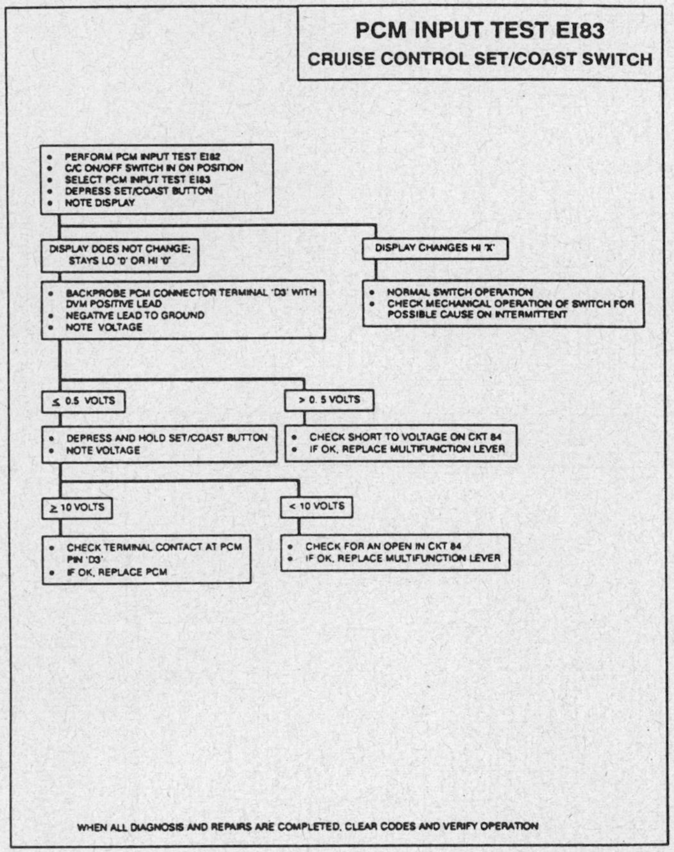
PCM INPUT TEST EI83
CRUISE CONTROL SET/COAST SWITCH
• PERFORM PCM INPUT TEST EI82
• C/C ON/OFF SWITCH IN ON POSITION
• SELECT PCM INPUT TEST EI83
• DEPRESS SET/COAST BUTTON
• NOTE DISPLAY
DISPLAY DOES NOT CHANGE; STAYS LO '0' OR HI '0'
DISPLAY CHANGES HI 'X'
• BACKPROBE PCM CONNECTOR TERMINAL 'D3' WITH DVM POSITIVE LEAD
• NEGATIVE LEAD TO GROUND
• NOTE VOLTAGE
• NORMAL SWITCH OPERATION
• CHECK MECHANICAL OPERATION OF SWITCH FOR POSSIBLE CAUSE ON INTERMITTENT
≤ 0.5 VOLTS
> 0.5 VOLTS
• DEPRESS AND HOLD SET/COAST BUTTON
• NOTE VOLTAGE
• CHECK SHORT TO VOLTAGE ON CKT 84
• IF OK, REPLACE MULTIFUNCTION LEVER
≥ 10 VOLTS
< 10 VOLTS
• CHECK TERMINAL CONTACT AT PCM PIN 'D3'
• IF OK, REPLACE PCM
• CHECK FOR AN OPEN IN CKT 84
• IF OK, REPLACE MULTIFUNCTION LEVER
WHEN ALL DIAGNOSIS AND REPAIRS ARE COMPLETED, CLEAR CODES AND VERIFY OPERATION
GC1109200139000X

Fig. 54 Test E184: PCM Input Test. 1992 Eldorado & Seville

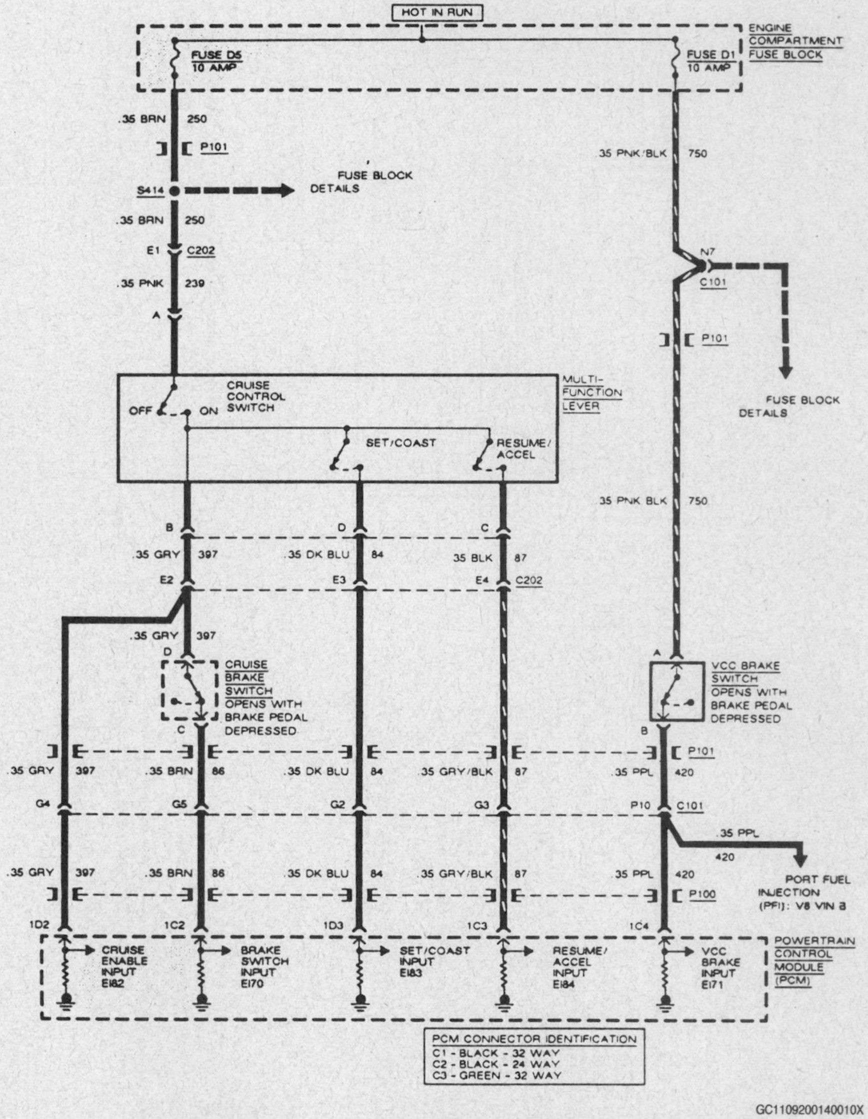
HOT IN RUN
FUSE D5 10 AMP
FUSE D1 10 AMP
ENGINE COMPARTMENT FUSE BLOCK
.35 BRN 250
P101
S414
FUSE BLOCK DETAILS
E1 C202
.35 PNK 239
.35 PNK/BLK 750
N7
C101
CRUISE CONTROL SWITCH
OFF ON
SET/COAST
RESUME/ ACCEL
MULTI-FUNCTION LEVER
.35 GRY 397
.35 DK BLU 84
.35 BLK 87
CRUISE BRAKE SWITCH OPENS WITH BRAKE PEDAL DEPRESSED
VCC BRAKE SWITCH OPENS WITH BRAKE PEDAL DEPRESSED
.35 BRN 86
.35 GRY/BLK 87
.35 PPL 420
PORT FUEL INJECTION (PFI): V8 VIN B
P100
CRUISE ENABLE INPUT EI82
BRAKE SWITCH INPUT EI70
SET/COAST INPUT EI83
RESUME/ ACCEL INPUT EI84
VCC BRAKE INPUT EI71
POWERTRAIN CONTROL MODULE (PCM)
PCM CONNECTOR IDENTIFICATION
C1 - BLACK - 32 WAY
C2 - BLACK - 24 WAY
C3 - GREEN - 32 WAY
GC1109200140010X

Fig. 55 Wiring diagram (Part 1 of 2). 1992 Eldorado & Seville

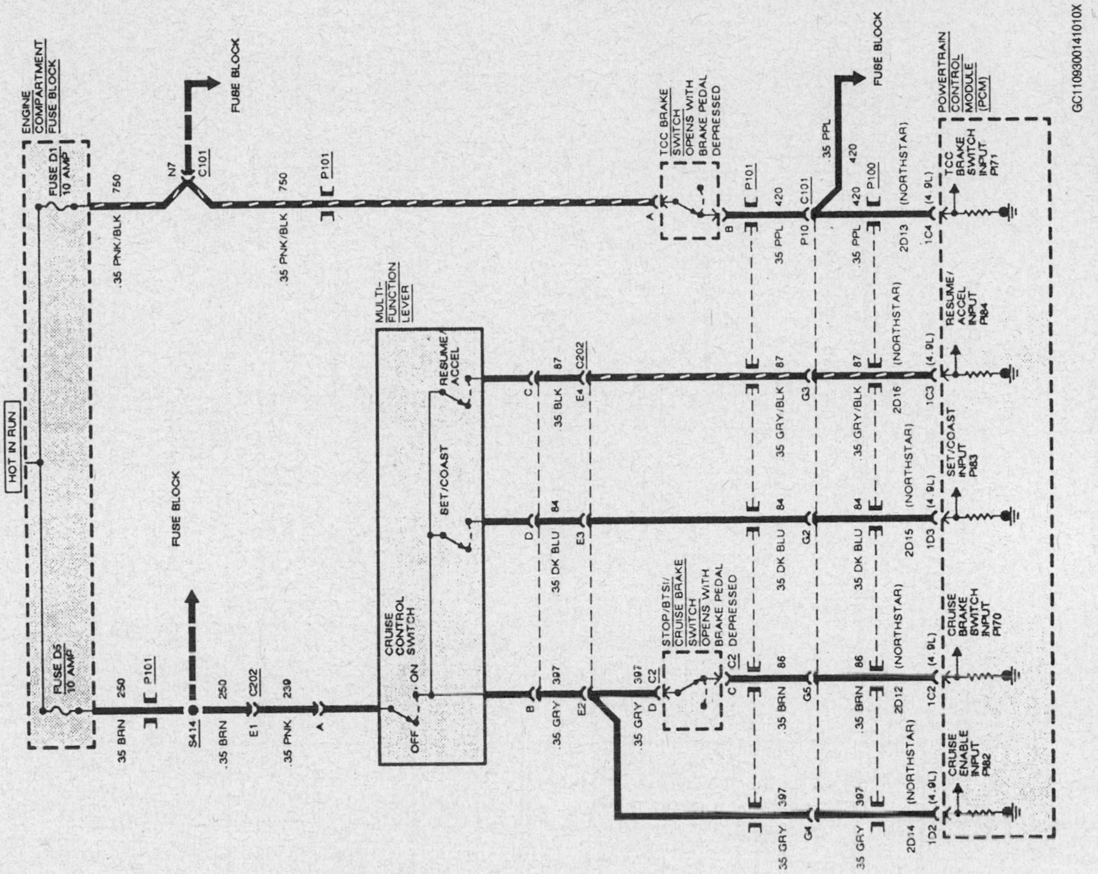
HOT IN RUN
ENGINE COMPARTMENT FUSE BLOCK
FUSE D1 10 AMP
FUSE D5 10 AMP
FUSE BLOCK
MULTI-FUNCTION LEVER
CRUISE CONTROL SWITCH
OFF
ON
SET/COAST
RESUME/ACCEL
TCC BRAKE SWITCH OPENS WITH BRAKE PEDAL DEPRESSED
STOP/BTSI/CRUISE BRAKE SWITCH OPENS WITH BRAKE PEDAL DEPRESSED
POWERTRAIN CONTROL MODULE (PCM)
CRUISE ENABLE INPUT P182
CRUISE BRAKE SWITCH INPUT P170
SET/COAST INPUT P183
RESUME/ACCEL INPUT P184
TCC BRAKE SWITCH INPUT P171
(NORTHSTAR)
(4.9L)
GC1109300141010X

Fig. 56 Wiring diagram (Part 1 of 2). 1993 Eldorado & Seville

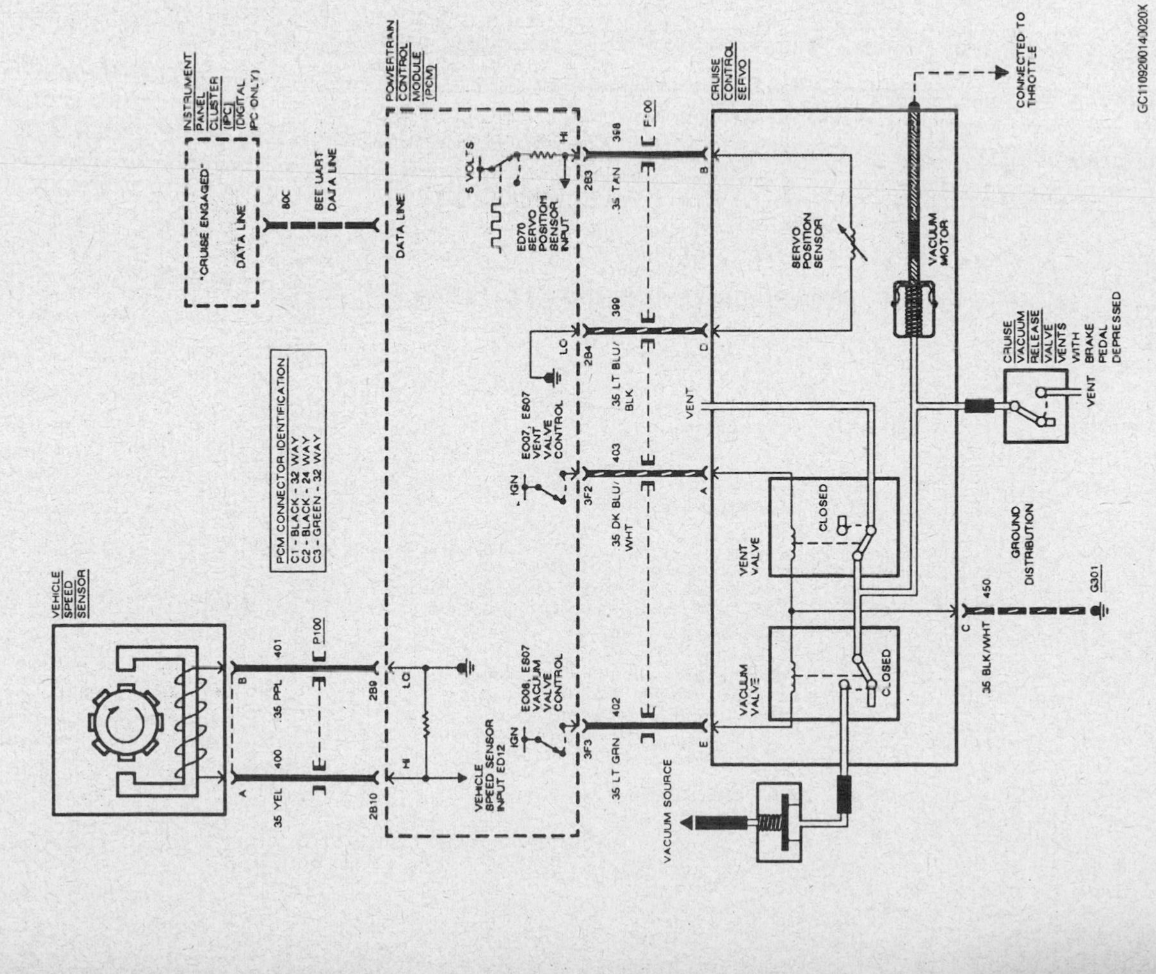
VEHICLE SPEED SENSOR
INSTRUMENT PANEL CLUSTER (IPC) (DIGITAL IPC ONLY)
"CRUISE ENGAGED"
DATA LINE
SEE UART DATA LINE
POWERTRAIN CONTROL MODULE (PCM)
PCM CONNECTOR IDENTIFICATION
C1 - BLACK - 32 WAY
C2 - BLACK - 24 WAY
C3 - GREEN - 32 WAY
VEHICLE SPEED SENSOR INPUT ED12
E008, E607 VACUUM VALVE CONTROL
E007, E607 VENT VALVE CONTROL
E070 SERVO POSITION SENSOR INPUT
5 VOLTS
CRUISE CONTROL SERVO
SERVO POSITION SENSOR
VACUUM MOTOR
VENT VALVE
VACUUM VALVE
CLOSED
CRUISE VACUUM RELEASE VALVE VENTS WITH BRAKE PEDAL DEPRESSED
GROUND DISTRIBUTION
VACUUM SOURCE
CONNECTED TO THROTTLE
GC1109200140020X

Fig. 55 Wiring diagram (Part 2 of 2). 1992 Eldorado & Seville

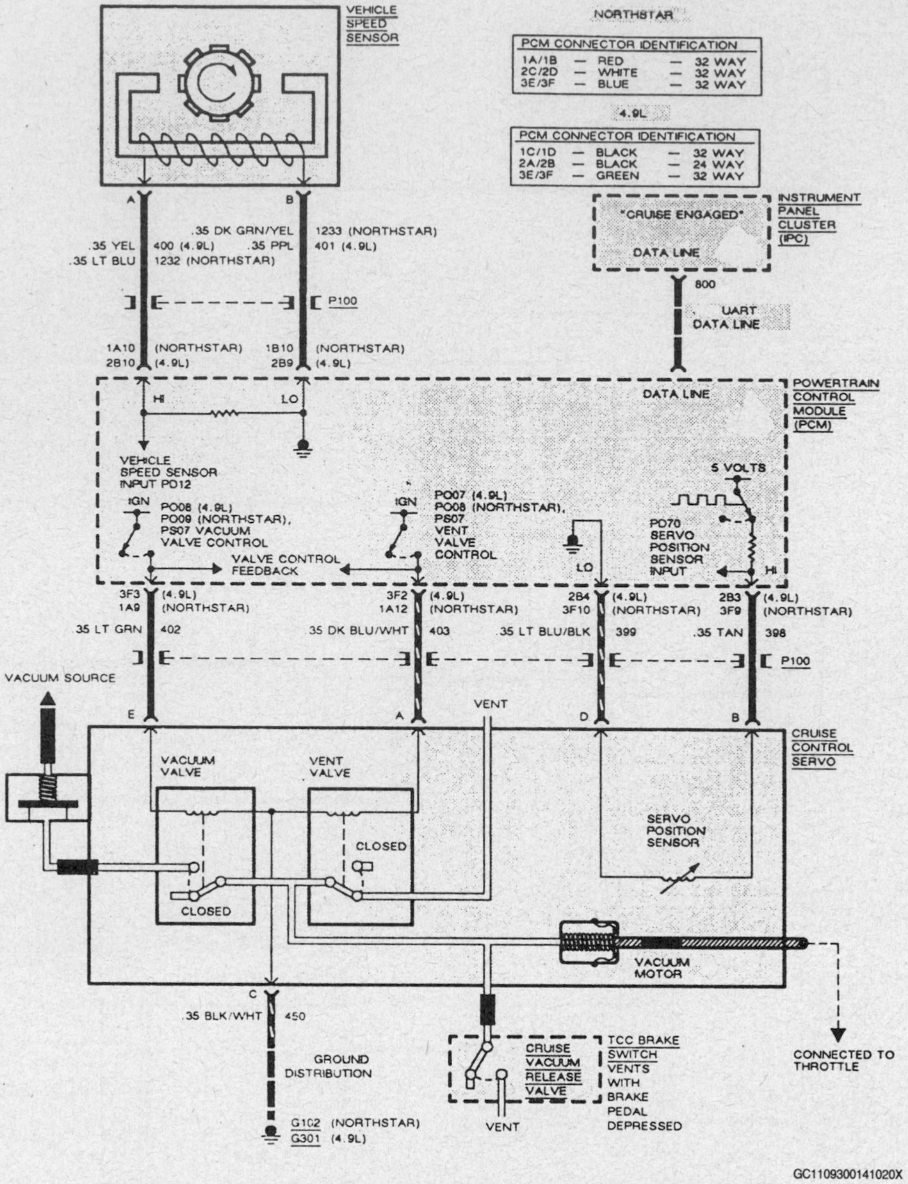
VEHICLE SPEED SENSOR
NORTHSTAR
PCM CONNECTOR IDENTIFICATION
1A/1B — RED — 32 WAY
2C/2D — WHITE — 32 WAY
3E/3F — BLUE — 32 WAY
4.9L
PCM CONNECTOR IDENTIFICATION
1C/1D — BLACK — 32 WAY
2A/2B — BLACK — 24 WAY
3E/3F — GREEN — 32 WAY
INSTRUMENT PANEL CLUSTER (IPC)
"CRUISE ENGAGED"
DATA LINE
800
UART DATA LINE
A
B
.35 YEL 400 (4.9L)
.35 LT BLU 1232 (NORTHSTAR)
.35 DK GRN/YEL 1233 (NORTHSTAR)
.35 PPL 401 (4.9L)
P100
1A10 (NORTHSTAR)
2B10 (4.9L)
1B10 (NORTHSTAR)
2B9 (4.9L)
POWERTRAIN CONTROL MODULE (PCM)
HI
LO
DATA LINE
VEHICLE SPEED SENSOR INPUT P012
5 VOLTS
IGN
P008 (4.9L)
P009 (NORTHSTAR),
PS07 VACUUM VALVE CONTROL
IGN
P007 (4.9L)
P008 (NORTHSTAR),
PS07 VENT VALVE CONTROL
P070 SERVO POSITION SENSOR INPUT
VALVE CONTROL FEEDBACK
LO
HI
3F3 (4.9L)
1A9 (NORTHSTAR)
3F2 (4.9L)
1A12 (NORTHSTAR)
2B4 (4.9L)
3F10 (NORTHSTAR)
2B3 (4.9L)
3F9 (NORTHSTAR)
.35 LT GRN 402
.35 DK BLU/WHT 403
.35 LT BLU/BLK 399
.35 TAN 398
P100
VACUUM SOURCE
VENT
E
A
D
B
CRUISE CONTROL SERVO
VACUUM VALVE
VENT VALVE
CLOSED
CLOSED
SERVO POSITION SENSOR
VACUUM MOTOR
C
.35 BLK/WHT 450
GROUND DISTRIBUTION
G102 (NORTHSTAR)
G301 (4.9L)
CRUISE VACUUM RELEASE VALVE
TCC BRAKE SWITCH
VENTS WITH BRAKE PEDAL DEPRESSED
VENT
CONNECTED TO THROTTLE
GC1109300141020X

Fig. 56 Wiring diagram (Part 2 of 2). 1993 Eldorado & Seville

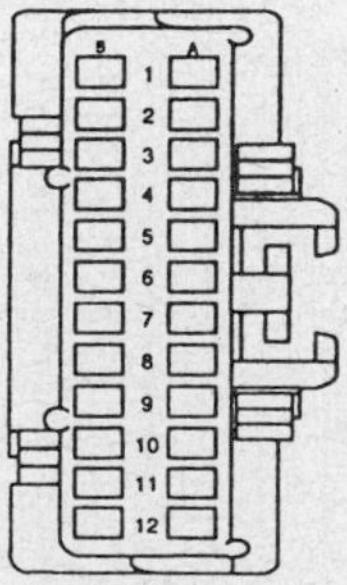

CIRCUIT DESCRIPTION	CIRCUIT NUMBER	PCM (2A/B) BLACK	CIRCUIT NUMBER	CIRCUIT DESCRIPTION
BATTERY	480	1	435	EGR SOLENOID
N/C	—	2	776	TRANS PRNDL INPUT PARITY
C/C SERVO POSITION SENSOR	398	3		N/C
C/C SERVO POSITION SENSOR	399	4		N/C
N/C		5	476	MAP/MAT SENSOR GROUND
LEFT O_2 SENSOR LO	413	6	1276	IGNITION
LEFT O_2 SENSOR HI	1589	7	427	THROTTLE SWITCH
HIGH SPEED COOLING FAN RLY	1270	8	800	UART SERIAL DATA
SPEED SENSOR INPUT LO	401	9	800	UART SERIAL DATA
SPEED SENSOR INPUT HI	400	10	419	'SERVICE ENGINE SOON' LIGHT
4K SPEED OUTPUT TO IPC	818	11	1269	LOW SPEED COOLING FAN RLY
4K SPEED OUTPUT TO CCR	817	12	450	PCM GROUND

GC1109200142010X

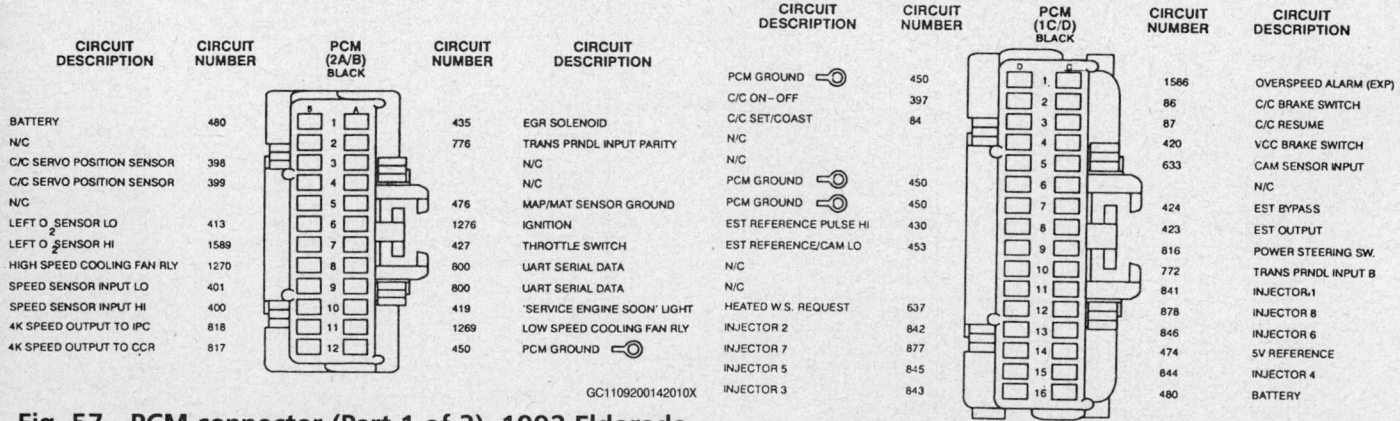

Fig. 57 PCM connector (Part 1 of 3). 1992 Eldorado & Seville

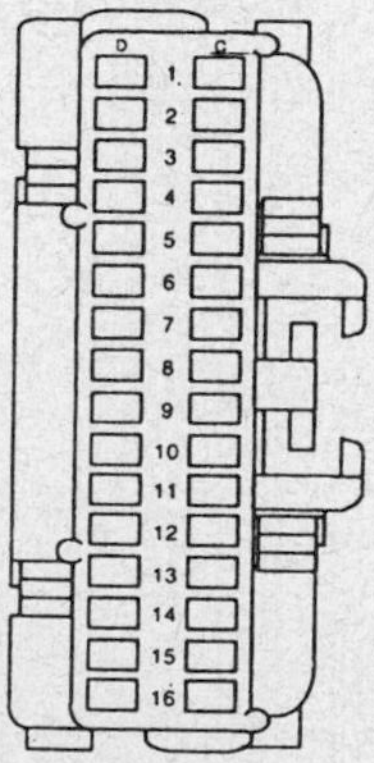

CIRCUIT DESCRIPTION	CIRCUIT NUMBER	PCM (1C/D) BLACK	CIRCUIT NUMBER	CIRCUIT DESCRIPTION
PCM GROUND	450	1	1586	OVERSPEED ALARM (EXP)
C/C ON-OFF	397	2	86	C/C BRAKE SWITCH
C/C SET/COAST	84	3	87	C/C RESUME
N/C		4	420	VCC BRAKE SWITCH
N/C		5	633	CAM SENSOR INPUT
PCM GROUND	450	6		N/C
PCM GROUND	450	7	424	EST BYPASS
EST REFERENCE PULSE HI	430	8	423	EST OUTPUT
EST REFERENCE/CAM LO	453	9	816	POWER STEERING SW.
N/C		10	772	TRANS PRNDL INPUT B
N/C		11	841	INJECTOR 1
HEATED W.S. REQUEST	637	12	878	INJECTOR 8
INJECTOR 2	842	13	846	INJECTOR 6
INJECTOR 7	877	14	474	5V REFERENCE
INJECTOR 5	845	15	844	INJECTOR 4
INJECTOR 3	843	16	480	BATTERY

GC1109200142020X

Fig. 57 PCM connector (Part 2 of 3). 1992 Eldorado & Seville

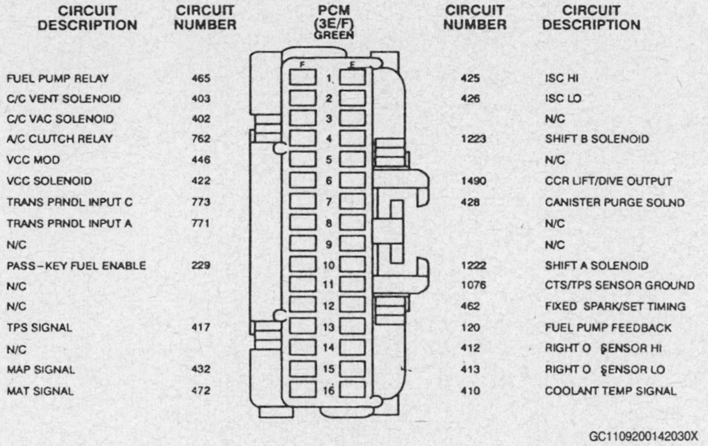
CIRCUIT DESCRIPTION
CIRCUIT NUMBER
PCM (3E/F) GREEN
CIRCUIT NUMBER
CIRCUIT DESCRIPTION
FUEL PUMP RELAY 465 1 425 ISC HI
C/C VENT SOLENOID 403 2 426 ISC LO
C/C VAC SOLENOID 402 3 N/C
A/C CLUTCH RELAY 762 4 1223 SHIFT B SOLENOID
VCC MOD 446 5 N/C
VCC SOLENOID 422 6 1490 CCR LIFT/DIVE OUTPUT
TRANS PRNDL INPUT C 773 7 428 CANISTER PURGE SOLND
TRANS PRNDL INPUT A 771 8 N/C
N/C 9 N/C
PASS-KEY FUEL ENABLE 229 10 1222 SHIFT A SOLENOID
N/C 11 1076 CTS/TPS SENSOR GROUND
N/C 12 462 FIXED SPARK/SET TIMING
TPS SIGNAL 417 13 120 FUEL PUMP FEEDBACK
N/C 14 412 RIGHT O SENSOR HI
MAP SIGNAL 432 15 413 RIGHT O SENSOR LO
MAT SIGNAL 472 16 410 COOLANT TEMP SIGNAL
GC1109200142030X

Fig. 57 PCM connector (Part 3 of 3). 1992 Eldorado & Seville

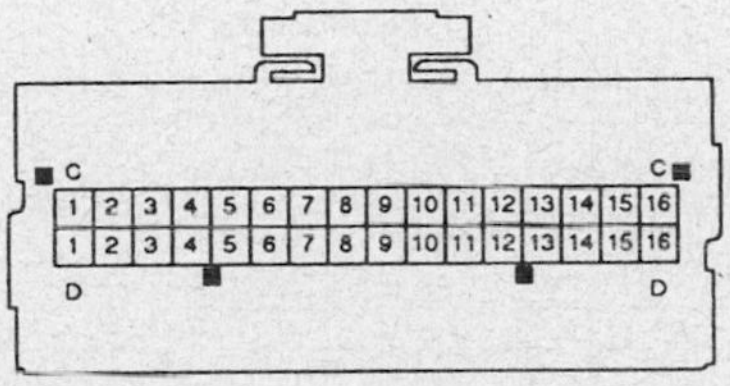
C
C
D
D

BLACK

Micro-Pack 100

POWERTRAIN CONTROL MODULE (PCM)-1C/1D

CAVITY	WIRE COLOR	CIRCUIT NUMBER	DESCRIPTION
1C1	BRN/WHT	1500	Vehicle Speed Output (2,000 PPM) (with Leaded Fuel System NM8)
1C2	BRN	86	Cruise Brake Switch Input
1C3	GRY/BLK	87	Cruise Resume/Accel Input
1C4	PPL	420	TCC Brake Switch Input
1C5	BRN/WHT	630	Cam HI Input
1C6	—	—	NOT USED
1C7	TAN/BLK	424	Bypass Spark Output
1C8	WHT	423	Ignition Control
1C9	DK BLU/WHT	816	Power Steering Pressure Input
1C10	YEL	772	Transaxle Range Switch Input B
1C11	BLK	841	Injector 1 Control
1C12	DK BLU/WHT	878	Injector 8 Control
1C13	BLK/YEL	846	Injector 6 Control
1C14	GRY	474	5 Volt Reference
1C15	BLK/LT BLU	844	Injector 4 Control
1C16	ORN	480	Battery
1D1	BLK/WHT	450	Ground
1D2	GRY	397	Cruise Enable Input
1D3	DK BLU	84	Cruise Set/Coast Input
1D4	—	—	NOT USED
1D5	—	—	NOT USED
1D6	BLK/WHT	450	Ground
1D7	BLK/WHT	450	Ground
1D8	PPL/WHT	430	Dist Reference HI Input (Engine RPM)
1D9	BLK/RED	453	Cam Reference Lo Input
1D10	—	—	NOT USED
1D11	—	—	NOT USED
1D12	WHT	637	Fast Idle Request Input
1D13	BLK/LT GRN	842	Injector 2 Control
1D14	RED/BLK	877	Injector 7 Control
1D15	BLK/WHT	845	Injector 5 Control
1D16	BLK/PNK	843	Injector 3 Control

GC1109300143010X

Fig. 58 PCM connector (Part 1 of 2). 1993–94 Eldorado & Seville w/4.9L/V8-300 engine

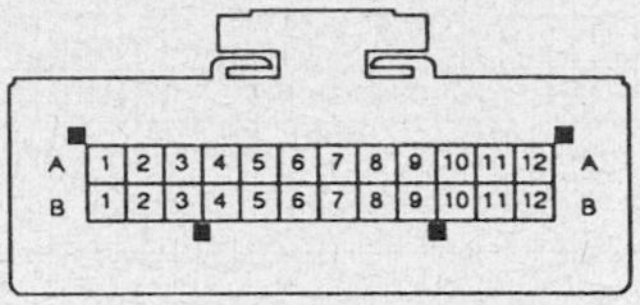
A
B
A
B

BLACK

Micro-Pack 100

POWERTRAIN CONTROL MODULE (PCM)-2A/2B

CAVITY	WIRE COLOR	CIRCUIT NUMBER	DESCRIPTION
2A1	GRY	435	EGR Solenoid Control*
2A2	WHT	776	Transaxle Range Switch Input Parity
2A3	—	—	NOT USED
2A4	—	—	NOT USED
2A5	BLK/PNK	476	IAT & MAP Sensor Return
2A6	PNK/WHT	1276	Ignition 1
2A7	PNK	427	Throttle Switch Input
2A8	TAN	800	UART Data Line
2A9	TAN	800	UART Data Line
2A10	BRN/WHT	419	SERVICE ENGINE SOON Indicator Control
2A11	GRY/BLK	1269	Cooling Fan Low Speed Control
2A12	BLK/WHT	450	Ground
2B1	ORN	480	Battery
2B2	—	—	NOT USED
2B3	TAN	398	Cruise Servo Position Sensor Input HI
2B4	LT BLU/BLK	399	Cruise Servo Position Sensor Input LO
2B5	—	—	NOT USED
2B6	TAN	413	Front Oxygen Sensor LO*
2B7	PPL	1589	Front Oxygen Sensor HI*
2B8	DK GRN/WHT	1270	Cooling Fan High Speed Control
2B9	PPL	401	Vehicle Speed Sensor Input LO
2B10	YEL	400	Vehicle Speed Sensor Input HI
2B11	RED/WHT	818	Vehicle Speed Output (4,000 PPM)
2B12	DK GRN/WHT	817	Vehicle Speed Output (4,000 PPM)

* WIRING IS PRESENT WITH UNLEADED FUEL SYSTEMS NA5, NB2 OR NN5

GC1109300143020X

Fig. 58 PCM connector (Part 2 of 2). 1993–94 Eldorado & Seville w/4.9L/V8-300 engine

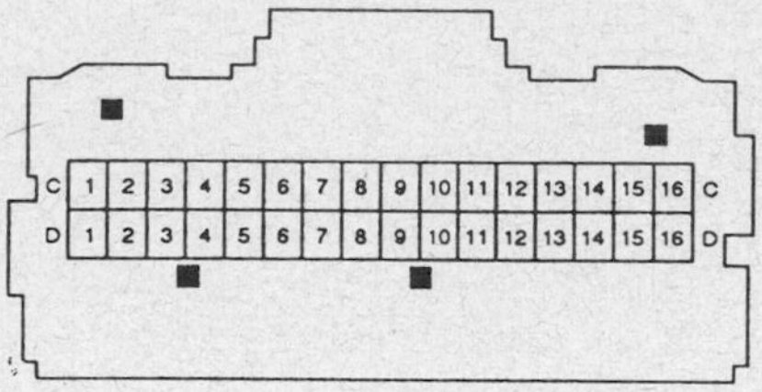
C 1 2 3 4 5 6 7 8 9 10 11 12 13 14 15 16 C
D 1 2 3 4 5 6 7 8 9 10 11 12 13 14 15 16 D

WHITE

Micro-Pack 100

POWERTRAIN CONTROL MODULE (PCM)-2C/2D

CAVITY	WIRE COLOR	CIRCUIT NUMBER	DESCRIPTION
2C1	BLK/PNK	476	Sensor Return
2C2	BLK/WHT	450	Ground
2C3	BLK/WHT	450	Ground
2C4	ORN	480	Battery
2C5	PNK/BLK	750	Ignition 3
2C6	GRY	1714	Desired Torque Input
2C7	ORN	1725	Extended Travel Brake Switch Input
2C8	DK BLU	229	Cranking Fuel Enable
2C9	BRN	1456	EGR Valve Feedback
2C10	—	—	NOT USED
2C11	TAN	472	IAT Sensor Input
2C12	TAN	800	UART Data Line
2C13	TAN	800	UART Data Line
2C14	RED	225	Generator Control/Feedback
2C15	LT BLU/WHT	1229	Transaxle Pressure Control Solenoid Enable
2C16	RED/BLK	1228	Transaxle Pressure Solenoid Control
2D1	BLK/ORN	469	Sensor Return
2D2	BLK/WHT	450	Ground
2D3	BLK/WHT	450	Ground
2D4	ORN	480	Battery
2D5	PPL/WHT	1276	Ignition 1
2D6	PNK	114	Oil Level Switch Input
2D7	WHT	637	Fast Idle Request Input
2D8	PNK	427	Throttle Position Switch Input
2D9	ORN/BLK	434	Park/Neutral Input
2D10	YEL	1726	Brake Booster Vacuum Sensor Input
2D11	—	—	NOT USED
2D12	BRN	86	Cruise Brake Switch Input
2D13	PPL	420	TCC Brake Switch Input
2D14	GRY	397	Cruise Enable Input
2D15	DK BLU	84	Set/Coast Input
2D16	GRY/BLK	87	Resume/Accel Input

GC1109300144010X

Fig. 59 PCM connector (Part 1 of 2). Eldorado & Seville w/4.6L/V8-279 Northstar engine

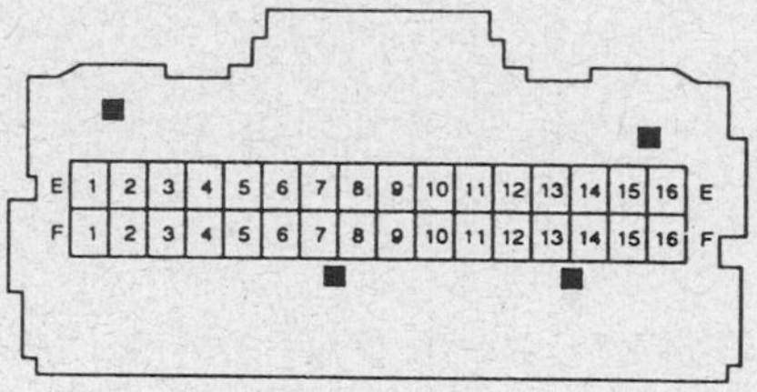
E 1 2 3 4 5 6 7 8 9 10 11 12 13 14 15 16 E
F 1 2 3 4 5 6 7 8 9 10 11 12 13 14 15 16 F

BLUE

Micro-Pack 100

POWERTRAIN CONTROL MODULE (PCM)-3E/3F

CAVITY	WIRE COLOR	CIRCUIT NUMBER	DESCRIPTION
3E1	BLK/RED	453	REF LO Input
3E2	PPL/WHT	430	4X REF HI Input
3E3	—	—	NOT USED
3E4	LT GRN	1222	Transaxle Shift A Solenoid Control
3E5	YEL/BLK	1223	Transaxle Shift B Solenoid Control
3E6	DK GRN	1433	Starter Inhibit Output
3E7	—	—	NOT USED
3E8	—	—	NOT USED
3E9	DK BLU	426	ISC Motor Control
3E10	LT BLU	425	ISC Motor Control
3E11	LT BLU	1715	Delivered Torque Output
3E12	DK GRN/YEL	428	Evaporative Emission Solenoid Control
3E13	TAN/BLK	422	Torque Converter Clutch Solenoid Control
3E14	—	—	NOT USED
3E15	DK GRN/YEL	762	A/C Compressor Clutch Relay Control
3E16	GRY	474	5 Volt Reference
3F1	LT BLU/BLK	647	24X REF HI Input
3F2	BRN/WHT	633	Cam HI Input
3F3	WHT	423	Ignition Control
3F4	TAN/BLK	424	Bypass Spark Output
3F5	BRN/WHT	419	SERVICE ENGINE SOON Indicator Control
3F6	—	—	NOT USED
3F7	DK GRN/WHT	1270	Cooling Fan High Speed Control
3F8	GRY/BLK	1269	Cooling Fan Low Speed Control
3F9	TAN	398	Servo Position Sensor Input (HI)
3F10	LT BLU/BLK	399	Servo Position Sensor Input (LO)
3F11	PPL	1490	Lift/Dive Signal Output
3F12	—	—	NOT USED
3F13	TAN	413	Front Heated Oxygen Sensor Input (LO)
3F14	PPL	412	Front Heated Oxygen Sensor Input (HI)
3F15	TAN	413	Rear Heated Oxygen Sensor Input (LO)
3F16	PPL	1589	Rear Heated Oxygen Sensor Input (HI)

GC1109300144020X

Fig. 59 PCM connector (Part 2 of 2). Eldorado & Seville w/4.6L/V8-279 Northstar engine

Connect: QUICK CHECKER (J34185, SPECMO QC-3 OR EQUIVALENT) or DIGITAL MULTIMETER

At: CRUISE CONTROL MODULE CONNECTOR (Disconnected)

Conditions:

- Ignore status of lights not mentioned in Quick Checker column steps.
- Ignition Switch: RUN
- When making any resistance measurements throughout this test, turn the Ignition Switch to OFF. Failure to do so could cause incorrect results and misdiagnosis.

Step	Condition	With Quick Checker, Correct Response	Without Quick Checker, Using Digital Multimeter			For Different Response:
			Meter Range	Connector Terminals	Correct Response	
1	Cruise Switch OFF	—	200 ohms	J & Ground	0 ohms	Check BLK ground wire for an open
	Cruise Switch OFF	All lights off	20 VDC	A & J, L & J, M & J, G & J	0 volts	See 3, 2
2	Cruise Switch ON	ON/OFF Light On	20 VDC	A & J	Battery voltage	See 1, 6, 2
		BRK Light On	20 VDC	G & J	Battery voltage	See 1, 4
		LAMP light On	20 VDC	B & J	Battery voltage	See 1, 2
		VENT Light On	200 ohms	C & J	30 to 55 ohms	See 1, 6, 5
		VAC Light On	200 ohms	K & J	30 to 55 ohms	See 1, 6, 5
		SPS Light On	200 ohms	F & H	15 to 20 ohms	See 1, 6, 5
		RA Light Off	20 VDC	M & J	0 volts	See 3, 7
		SC Light Off	20 VDC	L & J	0 volts	See 3, 7

GC1109100145010X

Fig. 60 Test A: Isolation Test (Part 1 of 3). Brougham

3	Cruise Switch ON, Set Switch pressed	SC Light On	20 VDC	L & J	Battery voltage	See 1, 8
		VAC & SHORT Lights OFF	—	—	—	Check CKT 402 for a short to ground. If OK see 5.
		R A Light Off	20 VDC	M & J	0 volts	See 9, 7
4	Cruise Switch in R A	R A Light On	20 VDC	M & J	Battery voltage	See 1, 8
		VENT & SHORT Lights OFF	—	—	—	Check CKT 403 for a short to ground. If OK see 5.
		SC Light Off	20 VDC	L & J	0 volts	See 10, 7
5	Cruise Switch ON, drive wheels turned by hand	VSS Light flashes On and Off	20 VDC	A & D	Pulses between approximately battery voltage and less than 2 volts	See 1, 6, 11.
6	Quick Checker not connected	—	200 ohms	F & J	Open in circuit (infinite resistance)	See 12
7	Quick Checker not connected	—	200 ohms	F & C	Open in circuit (infinite resistance)	See 13
8	Quick Checker not connected	—	200 ohms	F & K	Open in circuit (infinite resistance)	
9	Quick Checker not connected	—	200 ohms	H & C	Open in circuit (infinite resistance)	

GC1109100145020X

Fig. 60 Test A: Isolation Test (Part 2 of 3). Brougham

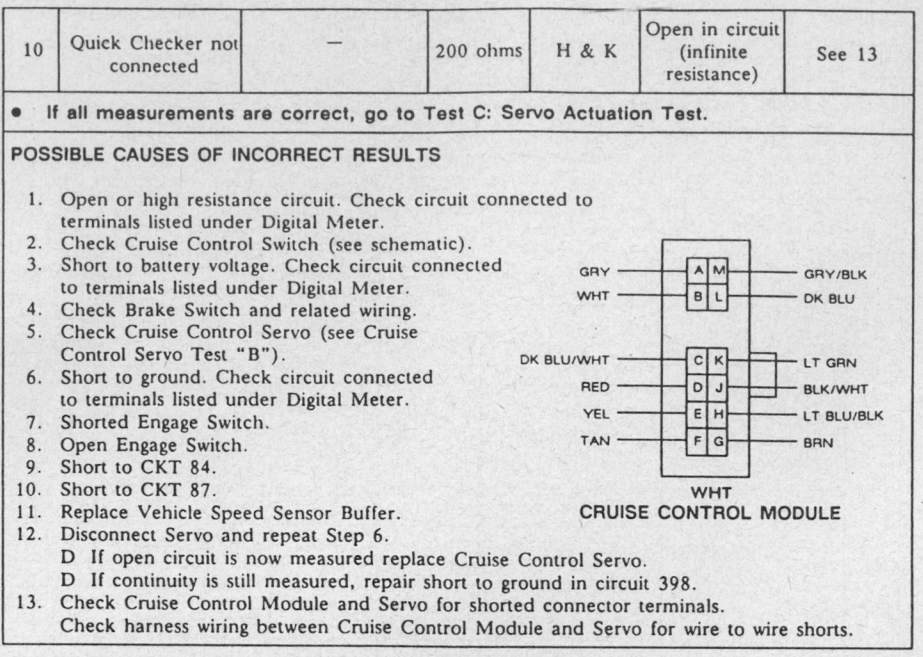

10	Quick Checker not connected	—	200 ohms	H & K	Open in circuit (infinite resistance)	See 13

- If all measurements are correct, go to Test C: Servo Actuation Test.

POSSIBLE CAUSES OF INCORRECT RESULTS

1. Open or high resistance circuit. Check circuit connected to terminals listed under Digital Meter.
2. Check Cruise Control Switch (see schematic).
3. Short to battery voltage. Check circuit connected to terminals listed under Digital Meter.
4. Check Brake Switch and related wiring.
5. Check Cruise Control Servo (see Cruise Control Servo Test "B").
6. Short to ground. Check circuit connected to terminals listed under Digital Meter.
7. Shorted Engage Switch.
8. Open Engage Switch.
9. Short to CKT 84.
10. Short to CKT 87.
11. Replace Vehicle Speed Sensor Buffer.
12. Disconnect Servo and repeat Step 6.
    D If open circuit is now measured replace Cruise Control Servo.
    D If continuity is still measured, repair short to ground in circuit 398.
13. Check Cruise Control Module and Servo for shorted connector terminals.
    Check harness wiring between Cruise Control Module and Servo for wire to wire shorts.

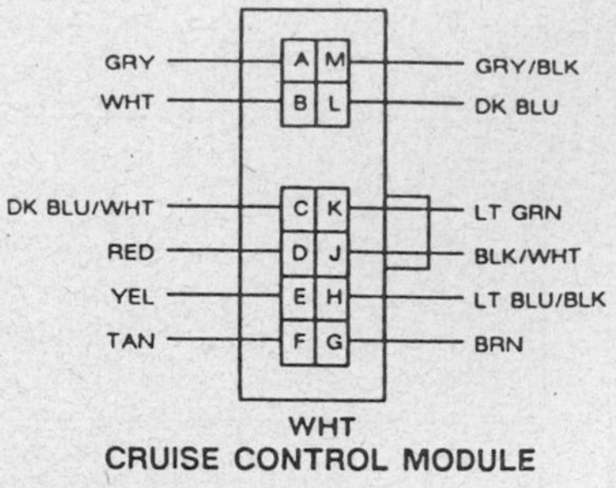
GRY
WHT
A M
B L
GRY/BLK
DK BLU
DK BLU/WHT
RED
YEL
TAN
C K
D J
E H
F G
LT GRN
BLK/WHT
LT BLU/BLK
BRN
WHT
CRUISE CONTROL MODULE

GC1109100145030X

Fig. 60 Test A: Isolation Test (Part 3 of 3). Brougham

B: CRUISE CONTROL SERVO TEST

- Disconnect Cruise Control Servo.
- Measure resistance between Cruise Control Servo terminals indicated.

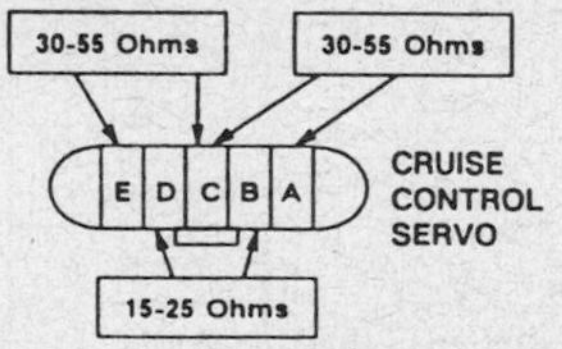
30-55 Ohms
30-55 Ohms
E D C B A
CRUISE CONTROL SERVO
15-25 Ohms

- If any measurements are incorrect, replace Cruise Control Servo.

C: SERVO ACTUATION TEST

- Remove connector from Cruise Control Servo
- Ground terminal C of the Cruise Control Servo with a fused jumper
- Jumper terminal A of Cruise Control Servo to Battery positive voltage.
- Run engine for two minutes then turn it off.
- Jumper terminal E of Cruise Control Servo to Battery positive voltage.
- Observe Cruise Control Servo position

Servo does not pull in at all

- Check for at least 10 in. HG of supply vacuum. Also check for leaks and throttle cable binding or restrictions

- Disconnect Vacuum Release hose from Cruise Control Servo
- Plug Vacuum Release port
- Retry first step in troubletree

Servo does not pull in at all

- Verify Servo ground at terminal C
- Replace Cruise Control Servo

Servo pulls in completely

- Repair/Check Vacuum Release valve (at brake pedal) or hose

Servo pulls in partially

- Check for at least 10 in. HG of supply vacuum. Also check for leaks and throttle cable binding or restrictions

Servo pulls in completely

- Wait 30 seconds and check if Servo is still pulled in. If not, check for slow leak.

- Remove fused jumpers from Servo
- Observe Cruise Control Servo position

Servo is fully retracted

- Check/repair linkage for binding

Servo is fully relaxed

- Connect Servo connector
- Lift the drive wheels
- Start engine (allow vacuum to build)
- Place gear selector in Drive
- Accelerate to a speed above 25 MPH
- Engage Cruise Control and observe the CRUISE CONTROL ENGAGED indicator

A

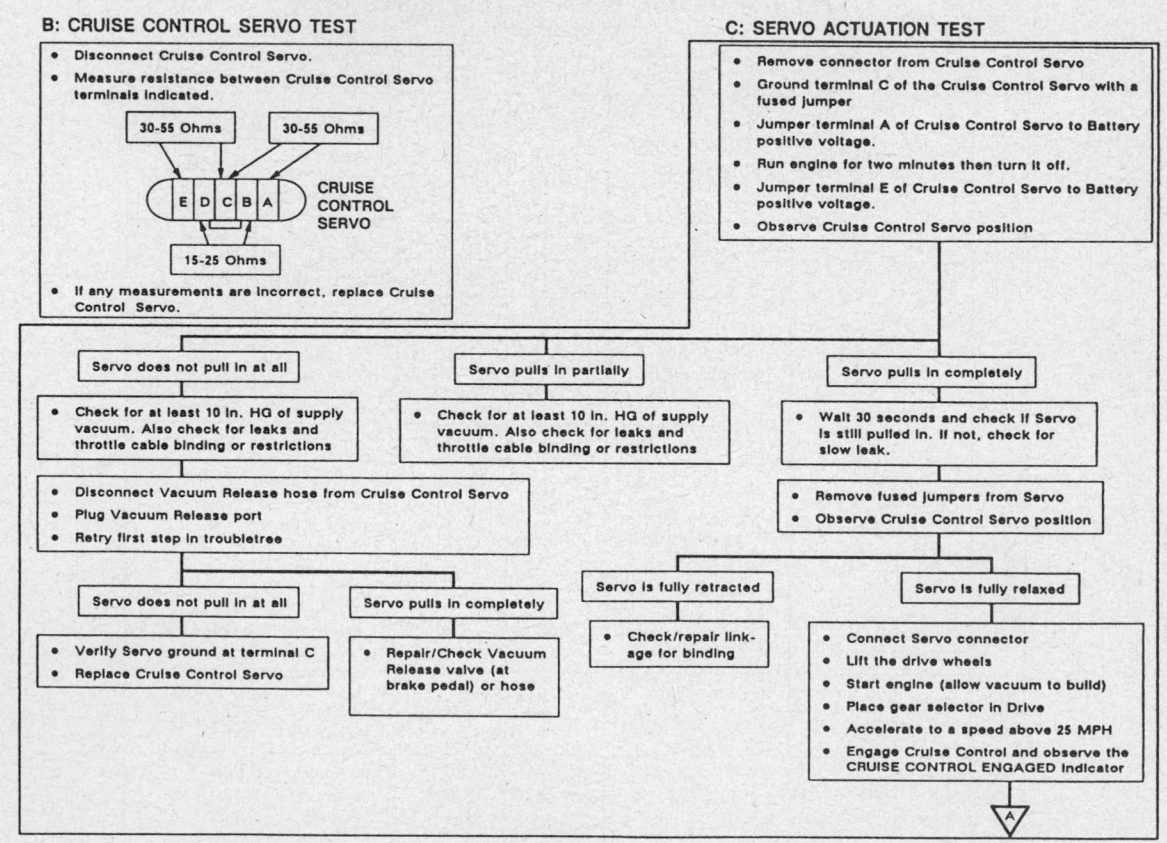

GC1109100146010X

Fig. 61 Test B & C: Cruise Control Servo & Servo Actuation (Part 1 of 2). Brougham

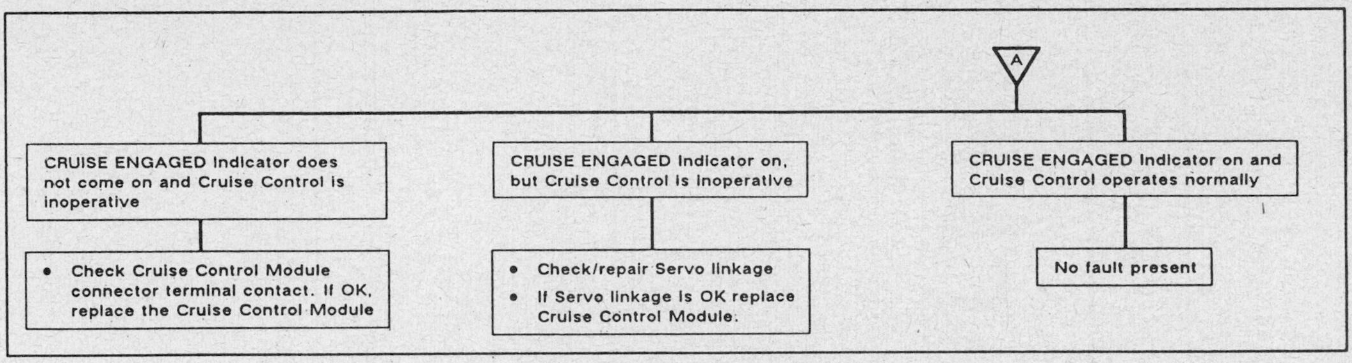
A
CRUISE ENGAGED Indicator does not come on and Cruise Control is inoperative
• Check Cruise Control Module connector terminal contact. If OK, replace the Cruise Control Module
CRUISE ENGAGED Indicator on, but Cruise Control is inoperative
• Check/repair Servo linkage
• If Servo linkage is OK replace Cruise Control Module.
CRUISE ENGAGED Indicator on and Cruise Control operates normally
No fault present

GC1109100146020X

Fig. 61 Test B & C: Cruise Control Servo & Servo Actuation (Part 2 of 2). Brougham

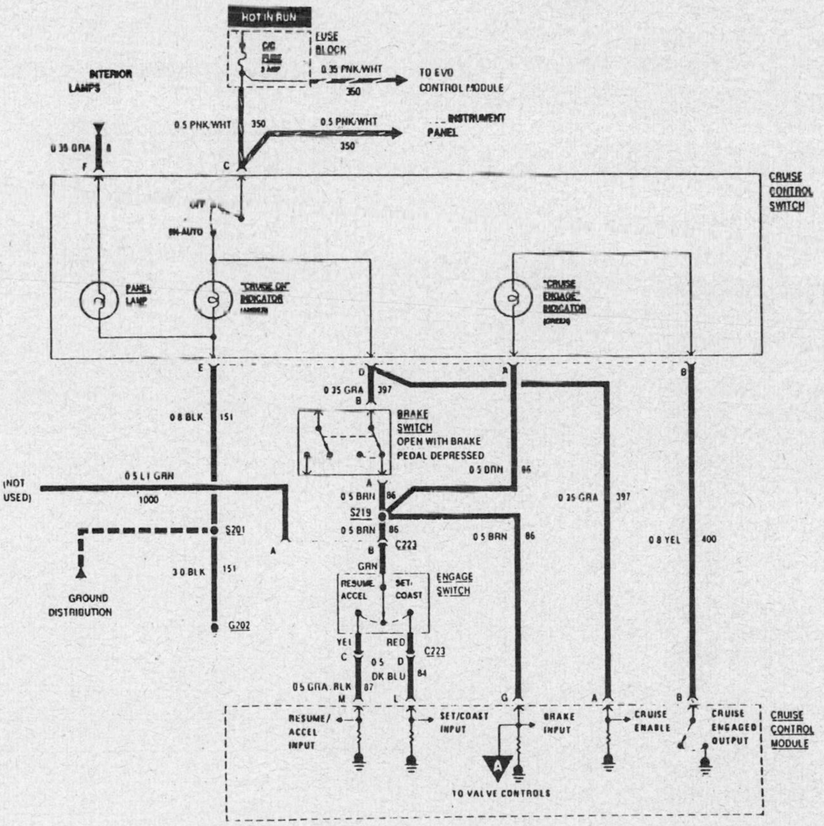
HOT IN RUN
FUSE BLOCK
0.35 PNK/WHT
350
TO EVO CONTROL MODULE
INTERIOR LAMPS
0.5 PNK/WHT
INSTRUMENT PANEL
CRUISE CONTROL SWITCH
PANEL LAMP
"CRUISE ON" INDICATOR
"CRUISE ENGAGE" INDICATOR
0.8 BLK
151
0.35 GRA
397
BRAKE SWITCH
OPEN WITH BRAKE PEDAL DEPRESSED
0.5 BRN
86
(NOT USED)
0.5 LT GRN
1000
S219
S201
C223
GROUND DISTRIBUTION
3.0 BLK
G202
ENGAGE SWITCH
RESUME ACCEL
SET COAST
YEL
RED
0.5 DK BLU
0.5 GRA/BLK
0.8 YEL
400
RESUME/ACCEL INPUT
SET/COAST INPUT
BRAKE INPUT
CRUISE ENABLE
CRUISE ENGAGED OUTPUT
CRUISE CONTROL MODULE
TO VALVE CONTROLS

GC1109100147010X

Fig. 62 Wiring diagram (Part 1 of 2). Brougham

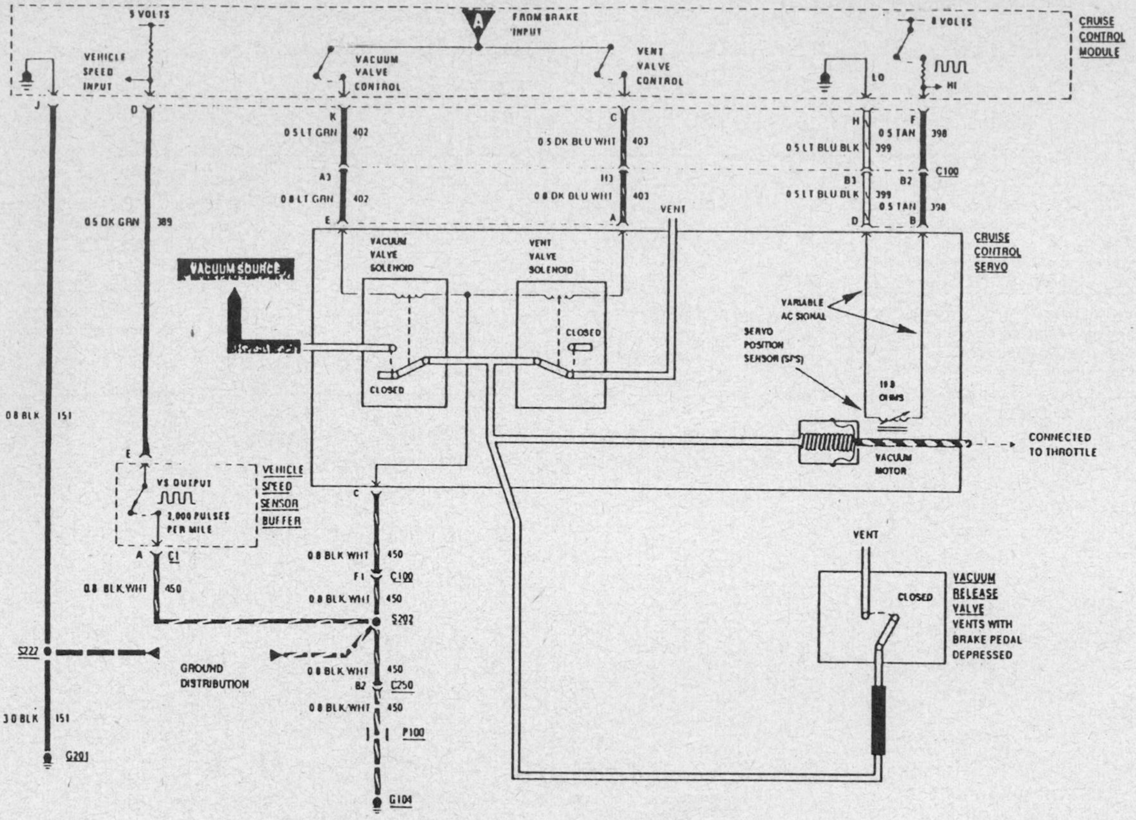
5 VOLTS
FROM BRAKE INPUT
8 VOLTS
CRUISE CONTROL MODULE
VEHICLE SPEED INPUT
VACUUM VALVE CONTROL
VENT VALVE CONTROL
LO
HI
0.5 LT GRN 402
0.5 DK BLU/WHT 403
0.5 TAN 398
0.5 LT BLU/BLK 399
C100
0.8 LT GRN 402
0.8 DK BLU/WHT 403
VENT
0.5 DK GRN 389
CRUISE CONTROL SERVO
VACUUM SOURCE
VACUUM VALVE SOLENOID
VENT VALVE SOLENOID
CLOSED
VARIABLE AC SIGNAL
SERVO POSITION SENSOR (SPS)
0.8 BLK 151
CONNECTED TO THROTTLE
VACUUM MOTOR
VS OUTPUT
2,000 PULSES PER MILE
VEHICLE SPEED SENSOR BUFFER
0.8 BLK/WHT 450
C100
S202
S222
GROUND DISTRIBUTION
C250
P100
G104
3.0 BLK 151
G201
VACUUM RELEASE VALVE
VENTS WITH BRAKE PEDAL DEPRESSED

GC1109100147020X

Fig. 62 Wiring diagram (Part 2 of 2). Brougham

COMPONENT REPLACEMENT

CRUISE CONTROL CABLE

DeVille & Fleetwood (FWD)

Refer to **Fig. 64** when performing the procedure.

1. Remove air cleaner housing lid and throttle body intake ductwork.
2. Remove retainer at servo, then remove cable from rear bracket by releasing lock tangs.
3. Remove accelerator cable, clip and cruise control cable from air cleaner housing.
4. Remove accelerator cable and cruise control cable from front bracket by releasing locking tang.
5. Disconnect cruise control cable from throttle lever, then remove cable.
6. Reverse procedure to install, adjusting cable as outlined.

SERVO UNIT

Brougham

1. Disconnect electrical connector and vacuum hoses.
2. Disconnect throttle cable, throttle actuating chain or actuating rod from servo unit.
3. Remove screws securing servo unit and servo unit solenoid valve assembly to mounting bracket.
4. Reverse procedure to install. **Torque** servo unit mounting bracket screws 10-15 inch lbs.

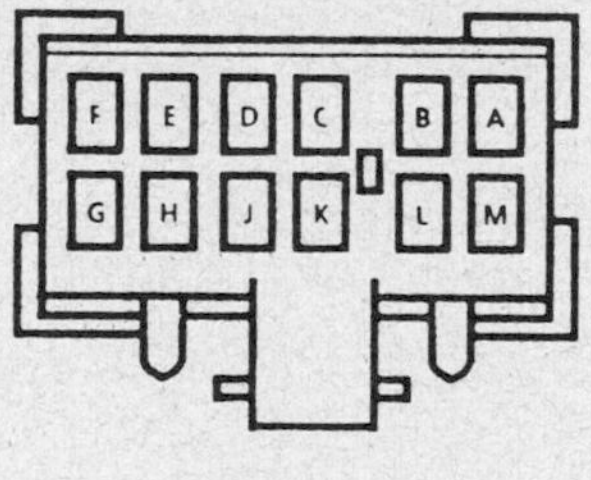
F
E
D
C
B
A
G
H
J
K
L
M

WHITE

Printed Circuit (Edgeboard-ECM)

CRUISE CONTROL MODULE

CAVITY	WIRE COLOR SOCKET HALF	CIRCUIT NUMBER
A	GRA	397
B	YEL	400
C	DK BLU/WHT	403
D	DK GRN	389
E	—	—
F	TAN	398
G	BRN	86
H	LT BLU/BLK	399
J	BLK	151
K	LT GRN	402
L	DK BLU	84
M	GRA/BLK	87

GC1109100148000X

Fig. 63 Control module connector pin locations. Brougham

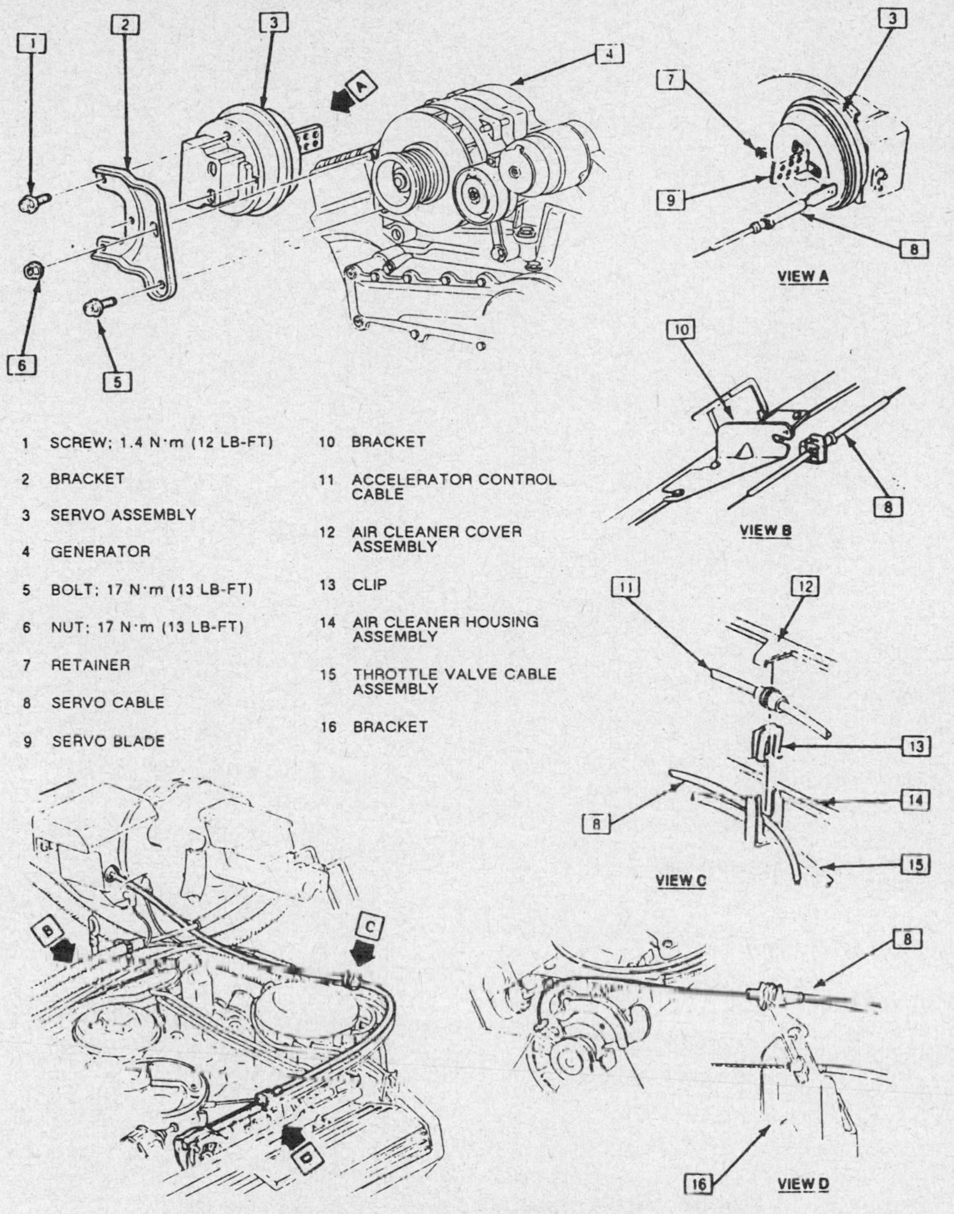
VIEW A
VIEW B
VIEW C
VIEW D
1 SCREW; 1.4 N·m (12 LB-FT)
2 BRACKET
3 SERVO ASSEMBLY
4 GENERATOR
5 BOLT; 17 N·m (13 LB-FT)
6 NUT; 17 N·m (13 LB-FT)
7 RETAINER
8 SERVO CABLE
9 SERVO BLADE
10 BRACKET
11 ACCELERATOR CONTROL CABLE
12 AIR CLEANER COVER ASSEMBLY
13 CLIP
14 AIR CLEANER HOUSING ASSEMBLY
15 THROTTLE VALVE CABLE ASSEMBLY
16 BRACKET
GC1109200149000X

Fig. 64 Cruise control replacement. DeVille & Fleetwood (FWD)

1992 DeVille & Fleetwood (FWD)

Refer to **Fig. 65** for replacement procedure.

1993–94 DeVille

1. Disconnect cruise control cable at retainer.
2. Disconnect vacuum hoses and electrical connector.
3. Remove mounting bracket and nut, then servo and bracket assembly.
4. Remove servo retaining screws, then servo.
5. Reverse procedure to install, noting the following:
   a. **Torque** servo to bracket screws to 12 inch lbs.
   b. **Torque** mounting bracket nut and bolt to 13 ft. lbs.
   c. Adjust cruise control cable as outlined.

Eldorado & Seville

1. Disconnect electrical connector from servo unit.
2. Remove vacuum hoses from servo unit.
3. Disconnect throttle cable or throttle actuator rod from servo unit.
4. Remove screws securing servo unit to mounting bracket.
5. Reverse procedure to install. **Torque** servo unit mounting bracket screws 11-15 inch lbs.

ELECTRIC BRAKE RELEASE SWITCH & VACUUM DUMP VALVE

An inoperative switch must be replaced. Install new switch and adjust as described under "Adjustments."

Vacuum Dump Valve

An inoperative switch must be replaced. Install new switch and adjust as described under "Adjustments."

ENGAGEMENT SWITCH

The engagement switch cannot be serviced. The complete turn signal lever must be replaced as an assembly.

1. Disconnect battery ground cable.
2. Remove steering column lower cover and remove tape securing wire to column.
3. Disconnect cruise control switch connector and attach a suitable piece of wire to switch connector.
4. Remove turn signal lever by pulling it out of the detent retaining clip inside the steering column. **On some models, it may be necessary to remove steering wheel.**
5. Pull harness up gently so guide wire can be used to install new unit.
6. Reverse procedure to install.

SPEED SENSOR & HARNESS

Access to the speed sensor and harness assembly is gained by partially removing the speedometer cluster and disconnecting the electrical connector at the cluster and electronic controller ends of the harness. Refer to "Instrument Cluster, Replace" in appropriate chassis section, for partial removal of the speedometer cluster.

BUFFER AMPLIFIER

Brougham

1. Disconnect battery ground cable.
2. Remove RH hush panel, then two screws from ECM bracket.
3. Disconnect electrical connector, then buffer amplifier.
4. Reverse procedure to install.

CONTROLLER

Brougham

1. Remove radio.
2. Disconnect cruise module electrical connectors.
3. Remove control module attaching screws to right of steering column, then remove module.
4. Reverse procedure to install.

DeVille & Fleetwood (FWD)

1. Remove steering column lower cover.
2. Disconnect electrical connectors from controller.
3. Remove screws securing controller to steering column lower cover.
4. Reverse procedure to install.

Eldorado & Seville

1. Disconnect battery ground cable.
2. Remove lower instrument panel cover.
3. Unclip relay panel from twilight sentinel amplifier and cruise control controller mounting bracket, located to the left of the steering column.
4. Remove screws securing controller mounting bracket to instrument panel assembly.
5. Lower mounting bracket and disconnect electrical connectors from cruise control controller.
6. Remove screws securing controller to mounting bracket and remove controller.
7. Reverse procedure to install.

SERVO UNIT SOLENOID VALVE

1. Remove screw securing solenoid valve to servo unit.
2. Disconnect vacuum hose and electrical connector and pull solenoid valve away from the servo unit.
3. Reverse procedure to install.

VACUUM CONTROL SOLENOID VALVE

1. Disconnect one electrical connector and two vacuum hoses from valve.
2. Remove screw securing valve to servo unit mounting bracket on front of dash bracket.
3. Reverse procedure to install.

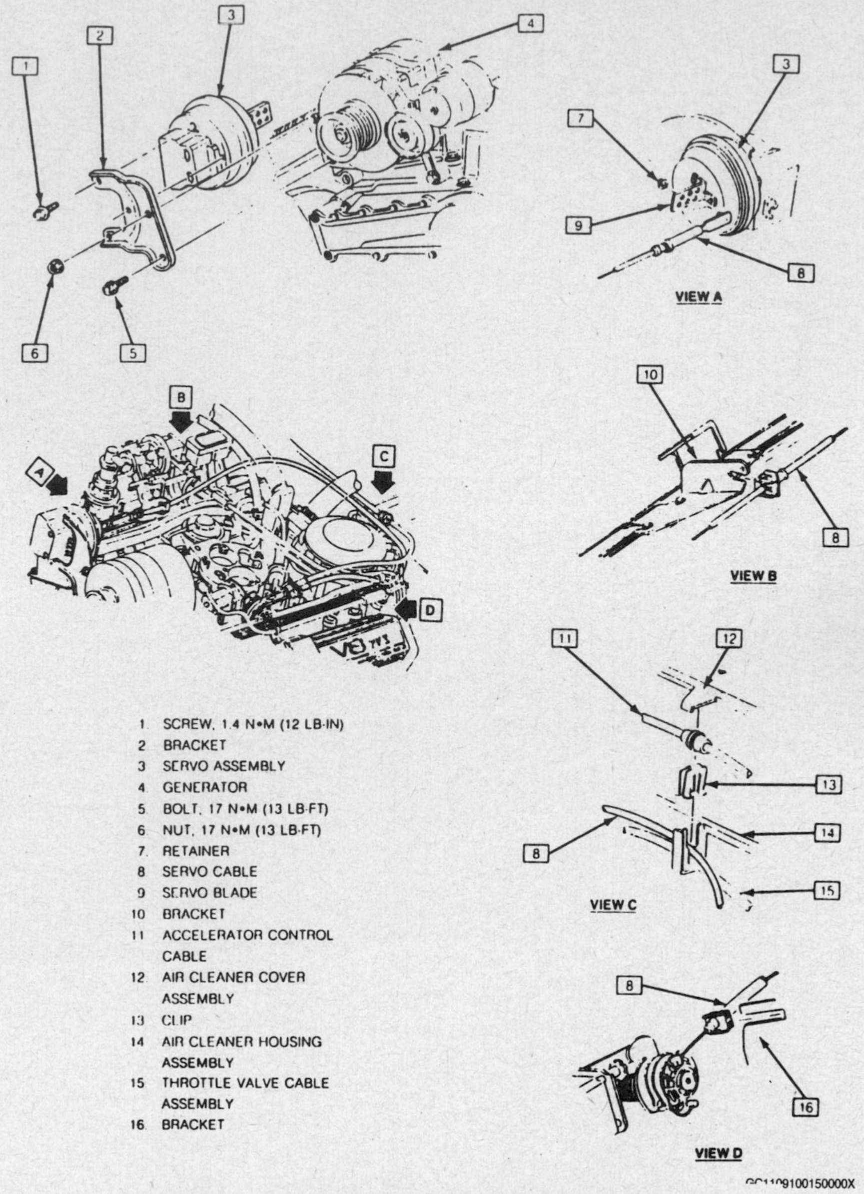
VIEW A
VIEW B
VIEW C
VIEW D
1 SCREW, 1.4 N•M (12 LB-IN)
2 BRACKET
3 SERVO ASSEMBLY
4 GENERATOR
5 BOLT, 17 N•M (13 LB-FT)
6 NUT, 17 N•M (13 LB-FT)
7 RETAINER
8 SERVO CABLE
9 SERVO BLADE
10 BRACKET
11 ACCELERATOR CONTROL CABLE
12 AIR CLEANER COVER ASSEMBLY
13 CLIP
14 AIR CLEANER HOUSING ASSEMBLY
15 THROTTLE VALVE CABLE ASSEMBLY
16 BRACKET

Fig. 65 Cruise control servo. 1992 DeVille & Fleetwood (FWD)

Type 2

NOTE: On Air Bag Equipped Models, Refer To Air Bag System Precautions Located In The Front Of This Manual For System Disarming & Arming Procedures.

NOTE: Electrical Symbol & Wire Color Code Identification Located In The Front Of This Manual Can Be Used As An Aid When Using Wiring Circuits Found In This Section.

INDEX

DESCRIPTION

This system consists of a mode control assembly, electronic controller (module), Vehicle Speed Sensor (VSS) buffer amplifier, servo unit, and release switches and valves. The servo unit maintains vehicle speed (throttle position) by trapping vacuum in its diaphragm chamber at servo positions determined by the control module. The module monitors mode control switch position, signals from the VSS buffer amplifier, servo position and release switch operation, then operates vacuum valves within the servo unit to control servo operation and vehicle speed. The module also contains a speed limiting function which prevents system operation at speeds below approximately 25 mph.

The mode control assembly consists of a 3 position slide-type switch and a set/coast switch button. To operate the system, the slide switch must be in on position and vehicle speed must be above 25 mph. The system is engaged at the desired speed by fully depressing, then releasing the set/coast button. Cruise speed can be increased from the set position by accelerating vehicle to desired speed, then pressing and releasing button. In order to decrease speed, the set/coast button is held in the fully-depressed position (disengaging system), then released when the desired speed is reached. The system can be disengaged at any time by depressing the brake or clutch pedal, or by moving the slide switch to off position.

If the system is disengaged by depressing the brake or clutch pedal, the last set speed will be retained in the module memory until the slide switch or ignition switch is moved to off position. Momentarily moving the slide switch to the resume/accel. position will cause the vehicle to accelerate to the last set speed and maintain that speed. If the slide switch is held in the resume/accel. position, the vehicle will continue to accelerate until the switch is released. When the switch is released, the speed that the vehicle accelerated to becomes the new set speed.

The slide switch also allows a tap-up function to increase cruise set speed in 1 mph increments. With the cruise control engaged and operating, tapping-up is done by pressing the slide switch to the resume position, then quickly releasing it. This procedure can be repeated 10 times before the system must be reset to a new speed in the conventional manner.

SYSTEM COMPONENTS

SPEED SENSOR

On models with conventional instrument panels, a speedometer frame mounted optic head is used to pick up light reflected by a speedometer cable mounted blade. The reflected light is produced by a light emitting diode (LED). As the speedometer cable mounted blade enters the LED light beam, the light is reflected into the optic head. From there, the light enters a photocell in the optic head and produces a low power speed signal. This signal is sent to a buffer for amplification and conditioning, then to the controller.

On models with electronic speedometers or electronic instrumentation, a transmission mounted speed sensor is used. This sensor utilizes a permanent magnet (PM) to generate vehicle speed information to the controller. Some models use a buffer amplifier to modify the sensor output.

CRUISE CONTROL MODULE

The module will interpret the position of the servo, the position of the control switches and the output of the speed sensor. In response to these inputs, the module electrically signals the opening or closing of the vent and vacuum solenoid valves in the servo.

The module is mounted on the dash support bracket at the right side of the steering column, but is integral with the ECM on some models with certain engines.

VACUUM RELEASE VALVE

The vacuum release valve provides an additional vent to atmosphere for the servo unit when the brake pedal is held in the depressed position. The venting is spring actuated and occurs within the free travel of the brake pedal arm.

COMBINATION VACUUM RELEASE VALVE/CONVERTER CLUTCH SWITCH

This combination valve and switch is used on vehicles equipped with a lock-up torque converter. The vacuum release valve portion operates identically to the release valve previously described. At the same time, the converter clutch switch contacts open and the locking clutch mechanism in the transmission is disengaged.

COMBINATION CRUISE/STOP LIGHT SWITCH

A separately mounted vacuum release valve is used with this combination switch. When the brake pedal is depressed, the switch resets the cruise function to a non-cruise condition and illuminates the brake lights. Two sets of electrical contacts are used in the switch: one to operate the stop lights, and the other to operate the cruise release function.

CLUTCH SWITCH

The clutch switch is used on vehicles equipped with manual transmission. When the clutch pedal is depressed, the cruise function is disconnected and will remain so after the pedal is released.

SERVO UNIT

The servo unit, **Fig. 1,** operates the throttle in response to signals from the electronic controller.

During a steady speed cruise condition, both vacuum and vent valves are closed or sealed. The servo holds a constant vacuum on the diaphragm and places no flow requirements on the vacuum source.

During vehicle deceleration, the vacuum solenoid is energized by the controller to open vacuum valve to vacuum source. Throttle angle is increased by increased vacuum level in the servo, and the vent remains closed.

During vehicle acceleration, the vent solenoid is de-energized by the controller to open the vent valve to atmosphere. This reduces vacuum in the servo and allows throttle return spring to decrease throttle angle while the vacuum valve remains closed.

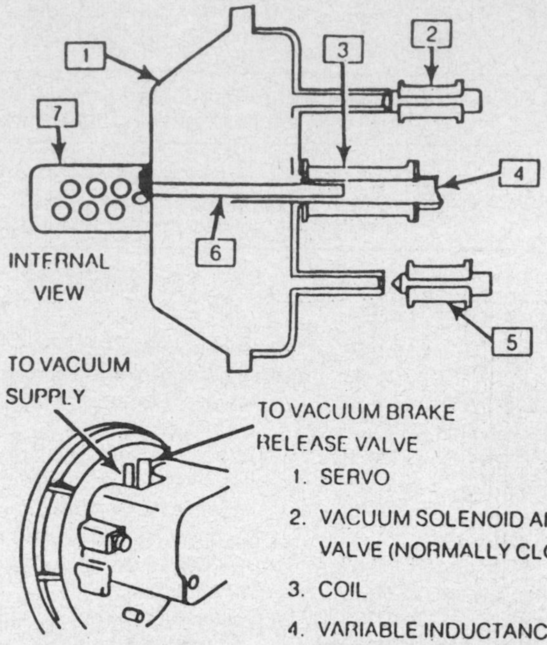
1
2
3
4
5
6
7
INTERNAL VIEW
TO VACUUM SUPPLY
TO VACUUM BRAKE RELEASE VALVE

1. SERVO
2. VACUUM SOLENOID AND VALVE (NORMALLY CLOSED)
3. COIL
4. VARIABLE INDUCTANCE POSITION SENSOR
5. VENT SOLENOID AIR VALVE (NORMALLY OPEN)
6. STEEL CORE
7. SERVO BLADE

GC1109100151000X

Fig. 1 Servo unit

PRECAUTIONS

AIR BAG SYSTEMS

Refer to "Air Bag System Precautions" in the front of this manual for system disarming and arming procedures.

ANTI-LOCK BRAKE SYSTEMS

On vehicles equipped with ABS brake system, the hydraulic accumulator, when fully charged contains brake fluid at high pressure. Before disconnecting any lines, hoses or fittings, ensure accumulator is full depressurized. Failure to do so may result in personal injury.

To depressurize the hydraulic accumulator, turn the ignition to the Off position or disconnect negative battery cable, pump brake pedal a minimum of 40 times at approximately 50 lbs. of force. A noticeable change in pedal feel will occur when accumulator is fully discharged.

ADJUSTMENTS

CABLE

1. Ensure cable assembly in cable and servo bracket.
2. Pull servo assembly cable and toward servo without moving throttle body lever.
3. If one of the holes in the servo tab aligns with cable pin, connect pin to tab with retainer.
4. If tab hole does not align with pin, move cable from servo assembly until next closest tab hole lines up, then connect pin to tab with retainer. **Do not stretch cable to make adjustment, as the engine will not be able to return to idle.**

SERVO ROD

1. Ensure engine high idle speed is properly adjusted, turn off engine, the set carburetor choke to hot idle position.
2. Remove servo rod retainer, then adjust rod and install retainer in hole which provides some clearance between retainer and servo bushing. Clearance must not exceed width of one hole.

ELECTRIC & VACUUM RELEASE SWITCHES

1. With brake pedal fully depressed, insert switch into retainer until valve seats fully.
2. **On vehicles equipped with ABS,** release brake pedal and allow to come to rest.
3. **On models less ABS,** pull brake pedal rearward against pedal stop until clicking sounds are no longer heard.
4. **On all models,** release brake pedal, then repeat and ensure clicking is not present.

ELECTRIC BRAKE RELEASE SWITCH & VACUUM RELEASE VALVE

The switch assembly and valve assembly cannot be adjusted until brake booster pushrod is assembled to brake pedal assembly. Adjustment is as follows:

1. Depress brake pedal and switch assembly and valve assembly into their proper retaining clips until fully seated.
2. **On vehicles equipped with ABS,** release brake pedal and allow to come to rest.
3. **On models less ABS,** slowly pull pedal back to its fully retracted position. The switch assembly and valve assembly will move within their retainers to their adjusted position.
4. **On all models,** the following brake pedal travel distances may be used to check for a properly adjusted cruise control and stop lamp switch assembly and vacuum release valve assembly.
   a. Cruise control switch contacts must open at $1/8$–$1/2$ inch pedal travel, measured at centerline of brake pedal pad. **Nominal actuation of stop lamp contacts is $3/16$ inch after cruise control contacts open.**

b. Vacuum release valve assembly must open at 1 1/16–1 5/16 inches pedal travel, measured at centerline of brake pedal pad.

CLUTCH ELECTRIC RELEASE SWITCH

1. Ensure clutch release switch is fully seated in retainer.
2. Pull clutch pedal pad upward. **Do not exert an upward force on the clutch pedal of more than 20 lbs.,**

Continued on page 21-42

Connect: QUICK CHECKER (J34185, SPECMO QC-3 OR EQUIVALENT) or DIGITAL MULTI-METER
At: CRUISE CONTROL MODULE CONNECTOR (Disconnected)
Conditions:
- Ignition Switch: RUN
- When making any resistance measurements throughout this test, turn the Ignition Switch to OFF. Failure to do so could cause incorrect results and misdiagnosis

Step	Action	With Quick Checker, Correct Response	Without Quick Checker, Using a Digital Multi-Meter			For Different Result, Do Test
			Meter Range	Connector Terminals	Correct Response	
1	Cruise Switch OFF	–	200 ohms	J & Ground	0 ohms	Check BLK wire for an open
		All the lights off	20 VDC	A & J	0 volts	E
			20 VDC	M & J	0 volts	
2	Cruise Switch ON	ON/OFF Light on	20 VDC	A & J	Battery voltage	F
		BRK Light on	20 VDC	G & J	Battery voltage	G
		VENT Light on	200 ohms	C & J	30 to 55 ohms	H
		VAC Light on	200 ohms	K & J	30 to 55 ohms	I
		SPS Light on	200 ohms	F & H	15 to 25 ohms	J
		RA Light off	20 VDC	M & J	0 volts	E
		SC Light off	20 VDC	L & J	0 volts	E
3	Cruise Switch ON, Set/Coast Switch pressed	SC Light on	20 VDC	L & J	Battery voltage	K
		VAC & SHORT Lights off	–	–	–	L
4	Resume/Accel/Switch pressed	ON/OFF Light on	–	–	–	F
		RA Light on	20 VDC	M & J	Battery voltage	M
		VENT & SHORT Lights off	–	–	–	N

GC1109100157010X

Fig. 2 Cruise control system diagnosis chart (Part 1 of 2). 1992 Except Bonneville, Camaro, Caprice, Firebird, Roadmaster & 1992 Achieva, Beretta, Corsica, Grand Am & Skylark

Step	Action	With Quick Checker, Correct Response	Without Quick Checker, Using a Digital Multi-Meter			For Different Result, Do Test
			Meter Range	Connector Terminals	Correct Response	
5	Cruise Switch ON, drive wheels turned by hand	VSS Light flashes on and off	20 VDC	A & D	Pulses between approximately battery voltage and less than 7 volts	O, P
6	Quick Checker not connected	–	200 ohms	F & J	Open circuit (infinite resistance)	Q
7	Quick Checker not connected	–	200 ohms	F & C	Open circuit (infinite resistance)	
8	Quick Checker not connected	–	200 ohms	F & K	Open circuit (infinite resistance)	
9	Quick Checker not connected	–	200 ohms	H & C	Open circuit (infinite resistance)	R
10	Quick Checker not connected	–	200 ohms	H & K	Open circuit (infinite resistance)	

- If all measurements are correct, go to Test S: Servo Actuation Test

GC1109100157020X

Fig. 2 Cruise control system diagnosis chart (Part 2 of 2). 1992 Except Bonneville, Camaro, Caprice, Firebird, Roadmaster & 1992 Achieva, Beretta, Corsica, Grand Am & Skylark

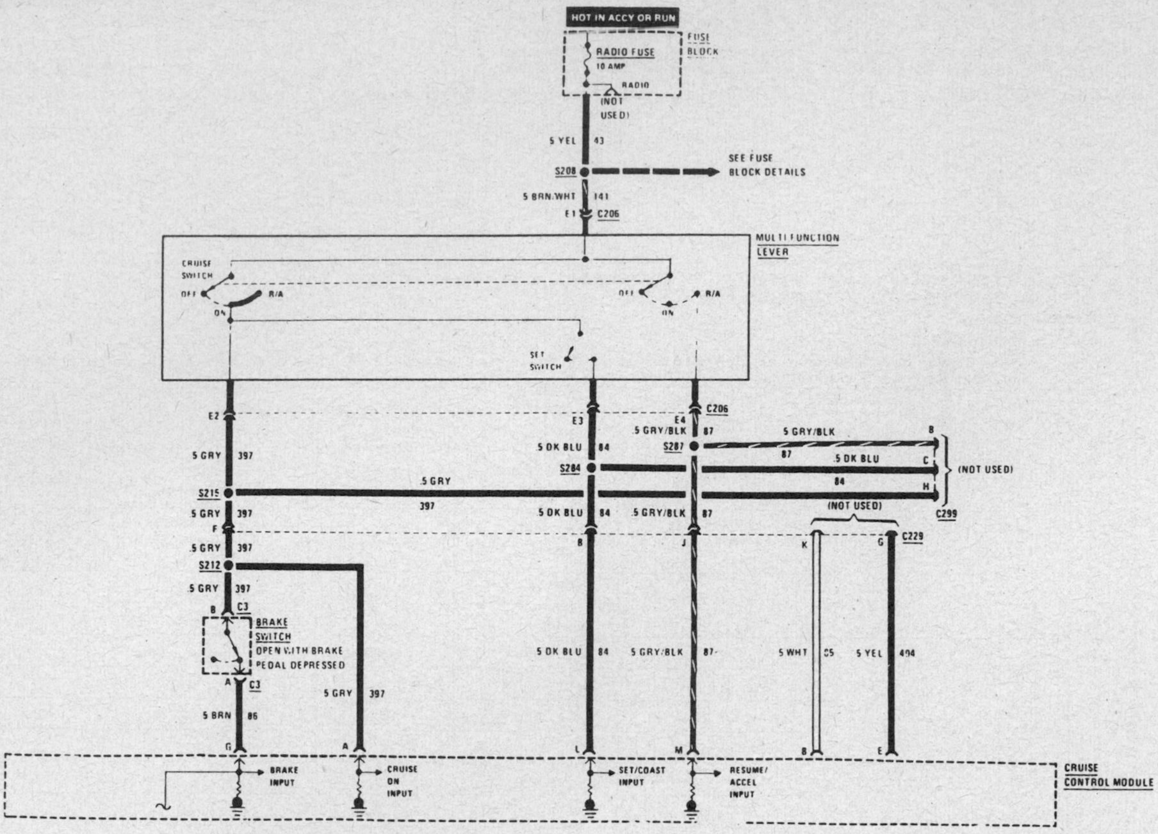
HOT IN ACCY OR RUN
FUSE BLOCK
RADIO FUSE
10 AMP
RADIO
(NOT USED)
5 YEL 43
S208
SEE FUSE BLOCK DETAILS
5 BRN/WHT 141
E1 C206
MULTIFUNCTION LEVER
CRUISE SWITCH
OFF
R/A
ON
SET SWITCH
E2
E3
E4
C206
5 GRY 397
5 DK BLU 84
5 GRY/BLK 87
S287
S284
S215
5 GRY/BLK
(NOT USED)
C299
S212
BRAKE SWITCH
OPEN WITH BRAKE PEDAL DEPRESSED
C3
5 BRN 86
5 WHT 05
5 YEL 404
C229
BRAKE INPUT
CRUISE ON INPUT
SET/COAST INPUT
RESUME/ ACCEL INPUT
CRUISE CONTROL MODULE
GC1109100158010X

Fig. 3 Wiring diagram (Part 1 of 2). 1992 Century, Cutlass Ciera & Cutlass Cruiser

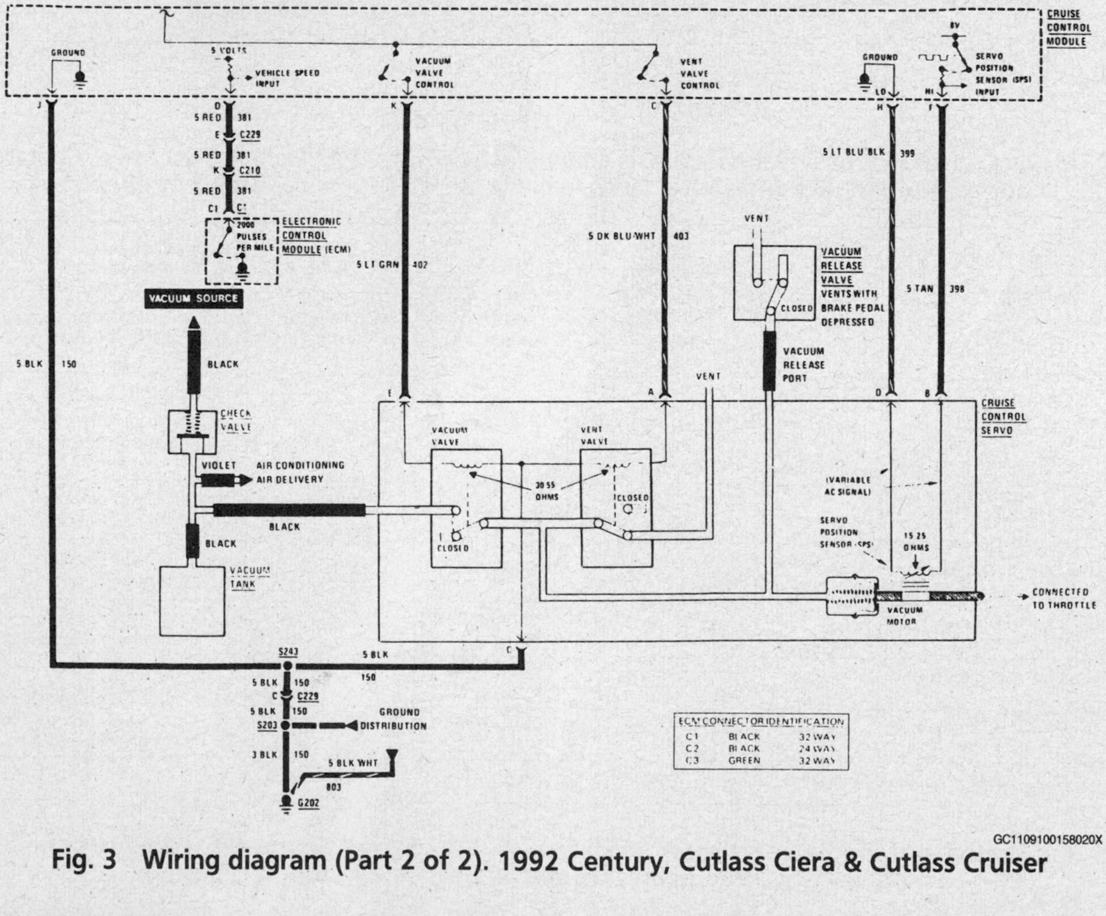
CRUISE CONTROL MODULE
GROUND
5 VOLTS
VEHICLE SPEED INPUT
VACUUM VALVE CONTROL
VENT VALVE CONTROL
SERVO POSITION SENSOR (SPS) INPUT
5 RED 381
C229
C210
ELECTRONIC CONTROL MODULE (ECM)
2000 PULSES PER MILE
VACUUM SOURCE
5 LT GRN 402
5 DK BLU/WHT 403
5 LT BLU/BLK 399
5 TAN 398
5 BLK 150
BLACK
CHECK VALVE
VIOLET
AIR CONDITIONING AIR DELIVERY
VACUUM TANK
VENT
VACUUM RELEASE VALVE VENTS WITH BRAKE PEDAL DEPRESSED
CLOSED
VACUUM RELEASE PORT
VACUUM VALVE
VENT VALVE
30-55 OHMS
(VARIABLE AC SIGNAL)
SERVO POSITION SENSOR (SPS)
15-25 OHMS
VACUUM MOTOR
CRUISE CONTROL SERVO
CONNECTED TO THROTTLE
S243
S203
GROUND DISTRIBUTION
5 BLK/WHT 803
G202
ECM CONNECTOR IDENTIFICATION
C1 BLACK 32 WAY
C2 BLACK 24 WAY
C3 GREEN 32 WAY
GC1109100158020X

Fig. 3 Wiring diagram (Part 2 of 2). 1992 Century, Cutlass Ciera & Cutlass Cruiser

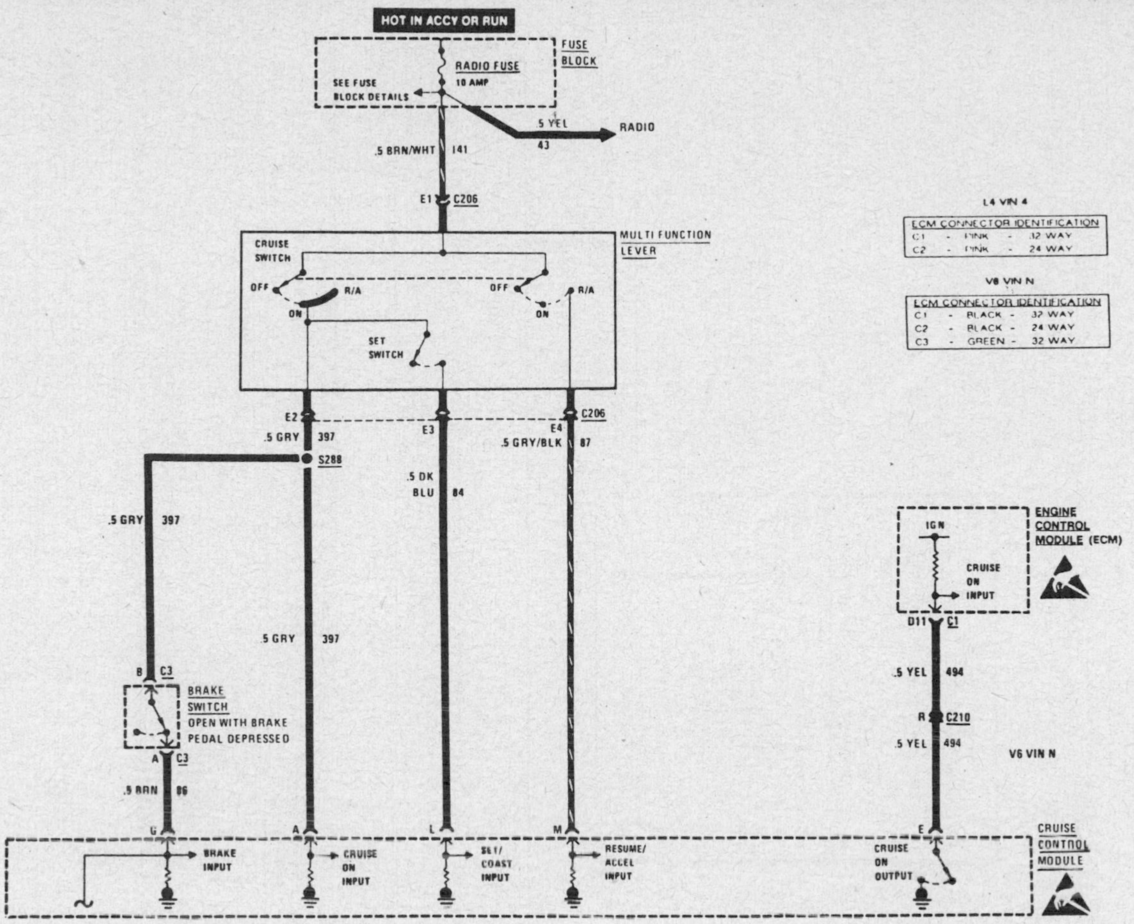
HOT IN ACCY OR RUN
FUSE BLOCK
RADIO FUSE 10 AMP
SEE FUSE BLOCK DETAILS
.5 YEL 43
RADIO
.5 BRN/WHT 141
E1 C206
CRUISE SWITCH
MULTI FUNCTION LEVER
OFF
R/A
ON
SET SWITCH
E2
E3
E4
C206
.5 GRY 397
S288
.5 GRY/BLK 87
.5 DK BLU 84
B C3
BRAKE SWITCH
OPEN WITH BRAKE PEDAL DEPRESSED
A C3
.5 BRN 86
BRAKE INPUT
CRUISE ON INPUT
SET/ COAST INPUT
RESUME/ ACCEL INPUT
CRUISE ON OUTPUT
CRUISE CONTROL MODULE
L4 VIN 4
ECM CONNECTOR IDENTIFICATION
C1 - PINK - 32 WAY
C2 - PINK - 24 WAY
V8 VIN N
ECM CONNECTOR IDENTIFICATION
C1 - BLACK - 32 WAY
C2 - BLACK - 24 WAY
C3 - GREEN - 32 WAY
IGN
ENGINE CONTROL MODULE (ECM)
CRUISE ON INPUT
D11 C1
.5 YEL 494
R C210
V6 VIN N

GC1109300348010X

Fig. 4 Wiring diagram (Part 1 of 2). 1993 Century, Cutlass Ciera & Cutlass Cruiser

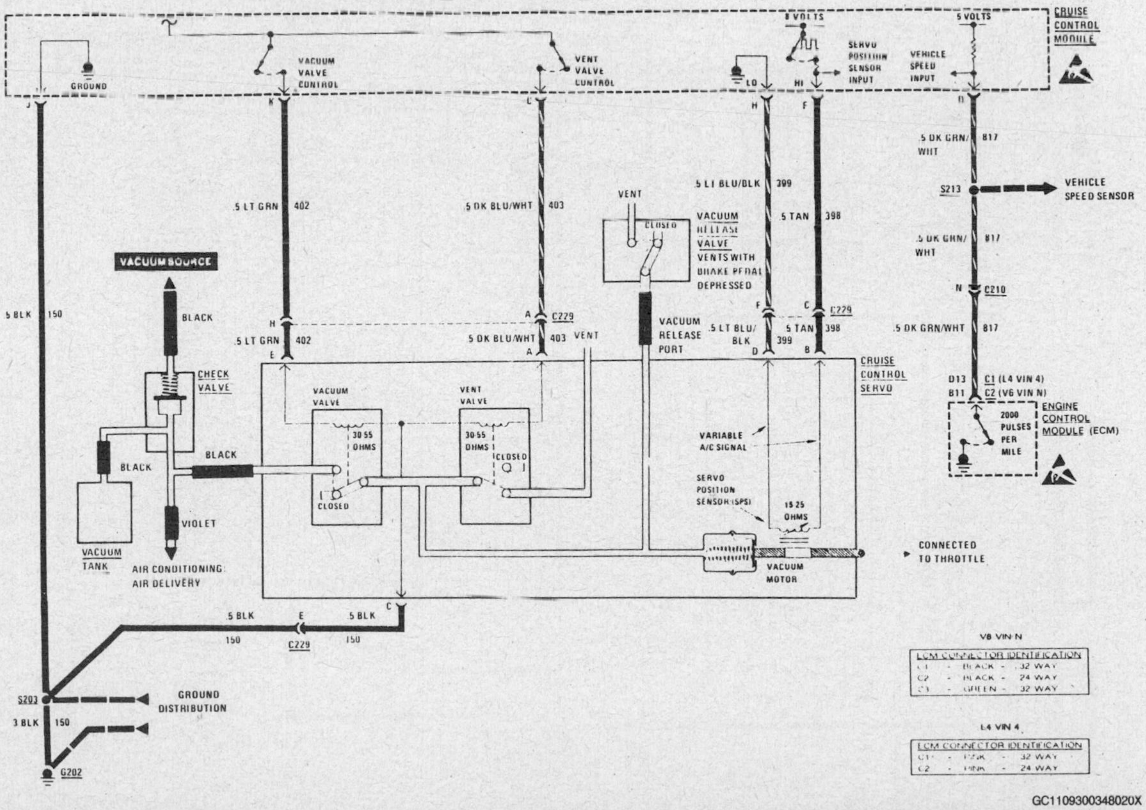
CRUISE CONTROL MODULE
GROUND
VACUUM VALVE CONTROL
VENT VALVE CONTROL
8 VOLTS
5 VOLTS
SERVO POSITION SENSOR INPUT
VEHICLE SPEED INPUT
.5 LT GRN 402
.5 DK BLU/WHT 403
.5 LT BLU/BLK 399
.5 TAN 398
.5 DK GRN/WHT 817
S213
VEHICLE SPEED SENSOR
VENT
VACUUM RELEASE VALVE
VENTS WITH BRAKE PEDAL DEPRESSED
VACUUM SOURCE
BLACK
CHECK VALVE
VACUUM RELEASE PORT
C229
N C210
CRUISE CONTROL SERVO
VACUUM VALVE
VENT VALVE
30-55 OHMS
CLOSED
VARIABLE A/C SIGNAL
SERVO POSITION SENSOR (SPS)
15-25 OHMS
VACUUM MOTOR
CONNECTED TO THROTTLE
VIOLET
VACUUM TANK
AIR CONDITIONING AIR DELIVERY
D13 C1 (L4 VIN 4)
B11 C2 (V6 VIN N)
2000 PULSES PER MILE
ENGINE CONTROL MODULE (ECM)
.5 BLK 150
S203
GROUND DISTRIBUTION
3 BLK 150
G202
V8 VIN N
ECM CONNECTOR IDENTIFICATION
C1 - BLACK - 32 WAY
C2 - BLACK - 24 WAY
C3 - GREEN - 32 WAY
L4 VIN 4
ECM CONNECTOR IDENTIFICATION
C1 - PINK - 32 WAY
C2 - PINK - 24 WAY

GC1109300348020X

Fig. 4 Wiring diagram (Part 2 of 2). 1993 Century, Cutlass Ciera & Cutlass Cruiser

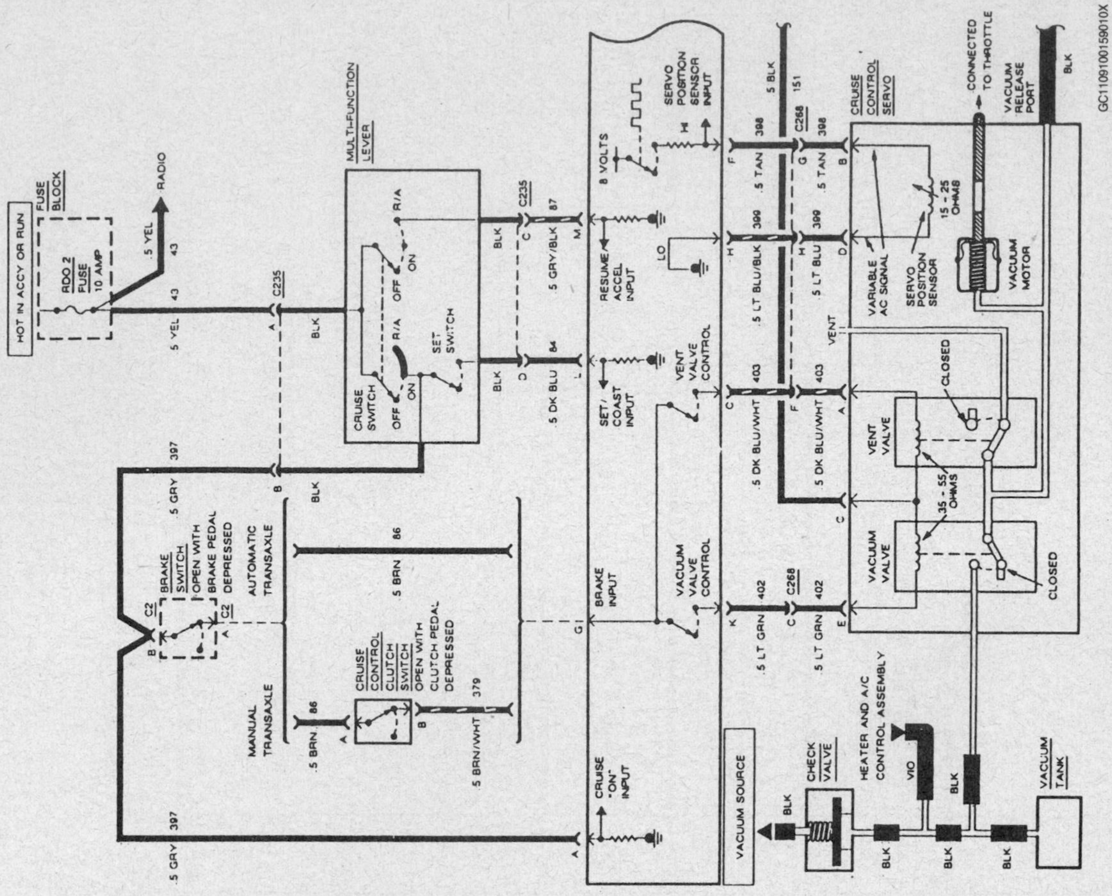
HOT IN ACCY OR RUN
FUSE BLOCK
RDO 2 FUSE 10 AMP
RADIO
MULTI-FUNCTION LEVER
CRUISE SWITCH
SET SWITCH
BRAKE SWITCH OPEN WITH BRAKE PEDAL DEPRESSED
AUTOMATIC TRANSAXLE
MANUAL TRANSAXLE
CRUISE CONTROL CLUTCH SWITCH OPEN WITH CLUTCH PEDAL DEPRESSED
CRUISE "ON" INPUT
BRAKE INPUT
VACUUM VALVE CONTROL
SET/COAST INPUT
VENT VALVE CONTROL
RESUME ACCEL INPUT
SERVO POSITION SENSOR INPUT
8 VOLTS
VACUUM SOURCE
CHECK VALVE
HEATER AND A/C CONTROL ASSEMBLY
VACUUM TANK
VACUUM VALVE
VENT VALVE
CLOSED
VARIABLE AC SIGNAL
SERVO POSITION SENSOR
VACUUM MOTOR
CRUISE CONTROL SERVO
CONNECTED TO THROTTLE
VACUUM RELEASE PORT
GC1109100159010X

Fig. 6 Wiring diagram (Part 1 of 2). 1992 Cavalier & Sunbird

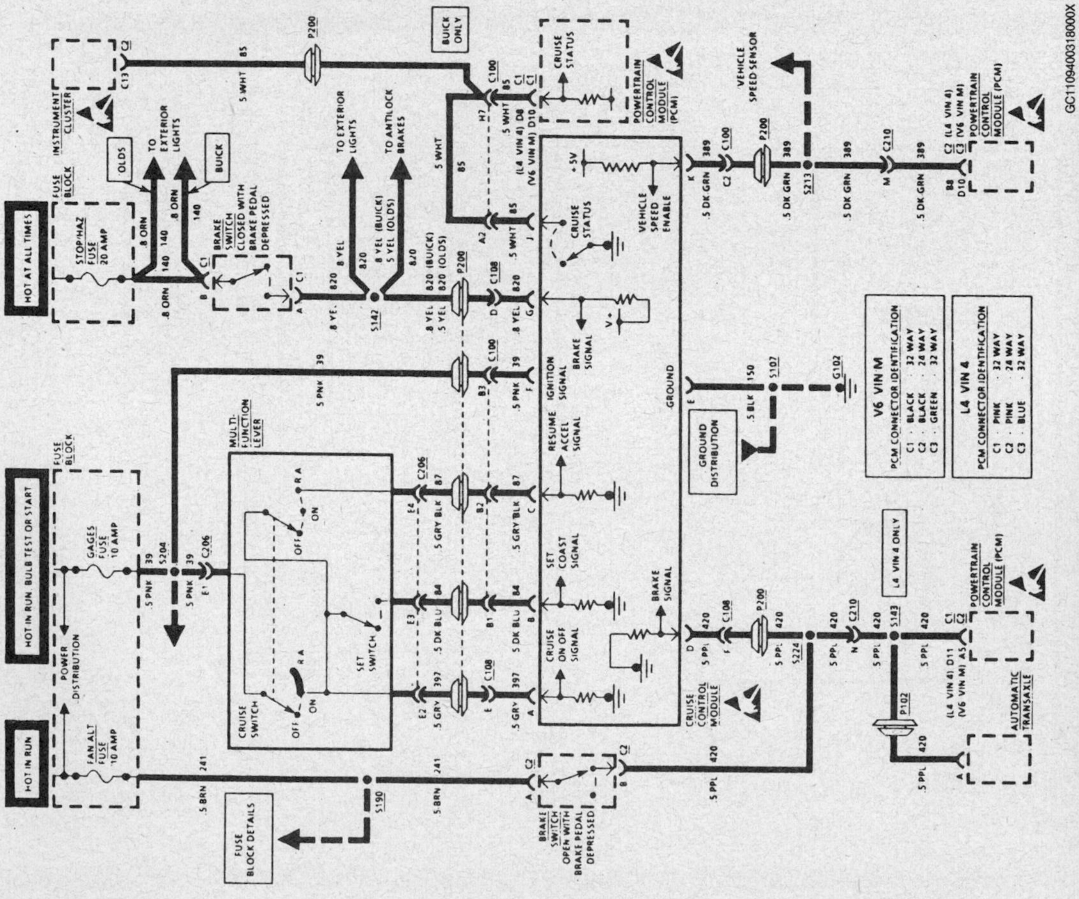
HOT IN RUN
HOT IN RUN, BULB TEST OR START
HOT AT ALL TIMES
FUSE BLOCK
FAN/ALT FUSE 10 AMP
GAGES FUSE 10 AMP
STOP/HAZ FUSE 20 AMP
POWER DISTRIBUTION
INSTRUMENT CLUSTER
TO EXTERIOR LIGHTS
TO ANTILOCK BRAKES
OLDS
BUICK
BUICK ONLY
FUSE BLOCK DETAILS
BRAKE SWITCH OPEN WITH BRAKE PEDAL DEPRESSED
BRAKE SWITCH CLOSED WITH BRAKE PEDAL DEPRESSED
MULTI-FUNCTION LEVER
CRUISE SWITCH
SET SWITCH
CRUISE CONTROL MODULE
GROUND DISTRIBUTION
POWERTRAIN CONTROL MODULE (PCM)
VEHICLE SPEED SENSOR
AUTOMATIC TRANSAXLE
L4 VIN 4 ONLY
V6 VIN M
L4 VIN 4
GC1109400318000X

Fig. 5 Wiring diagram. 1994 Century, Cutlass Ciera & Cutlass Cruiser

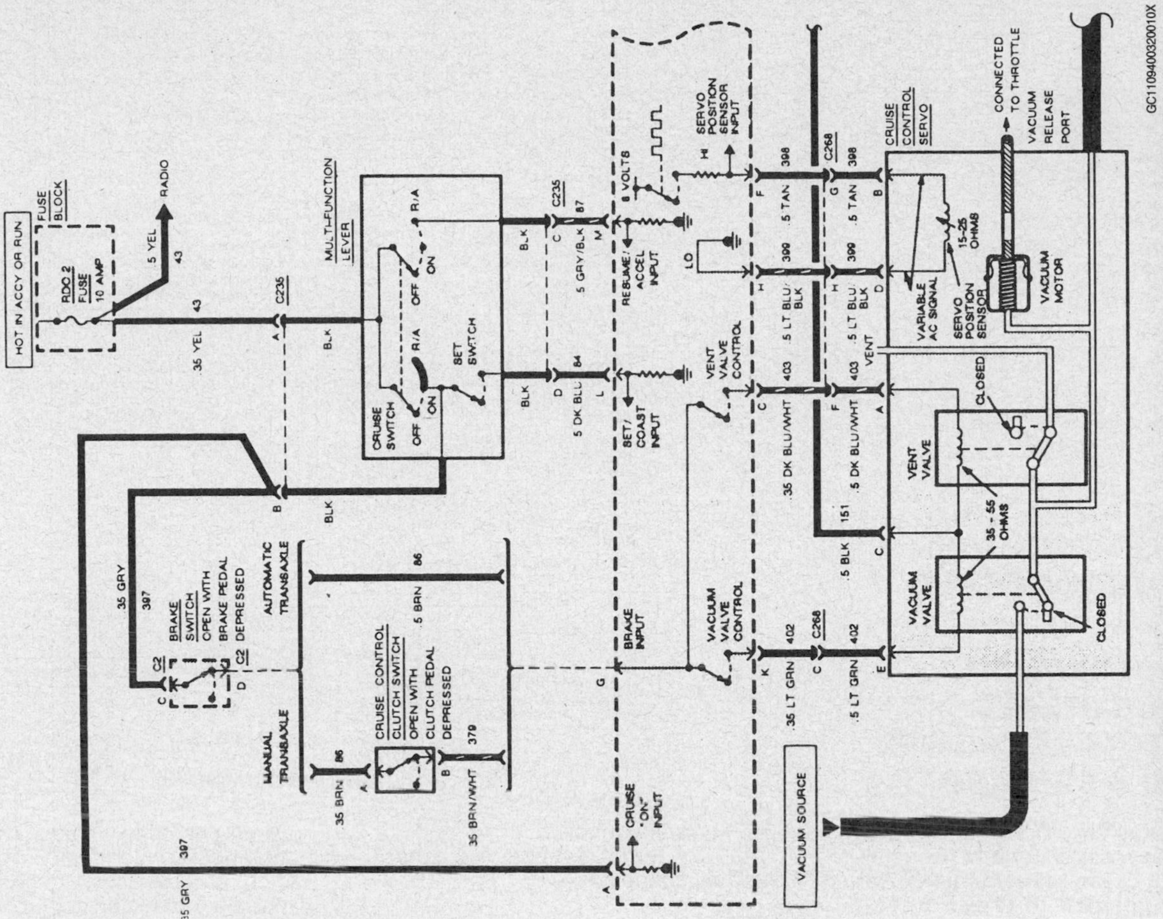

Fig. 7 Wiring diagram (Part 1 of 2). 1993–94 Cavalier & Sunbird

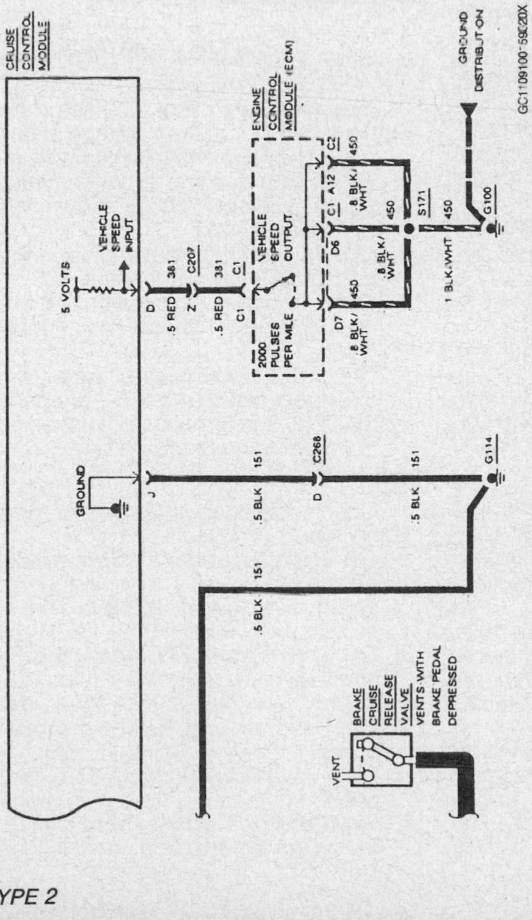

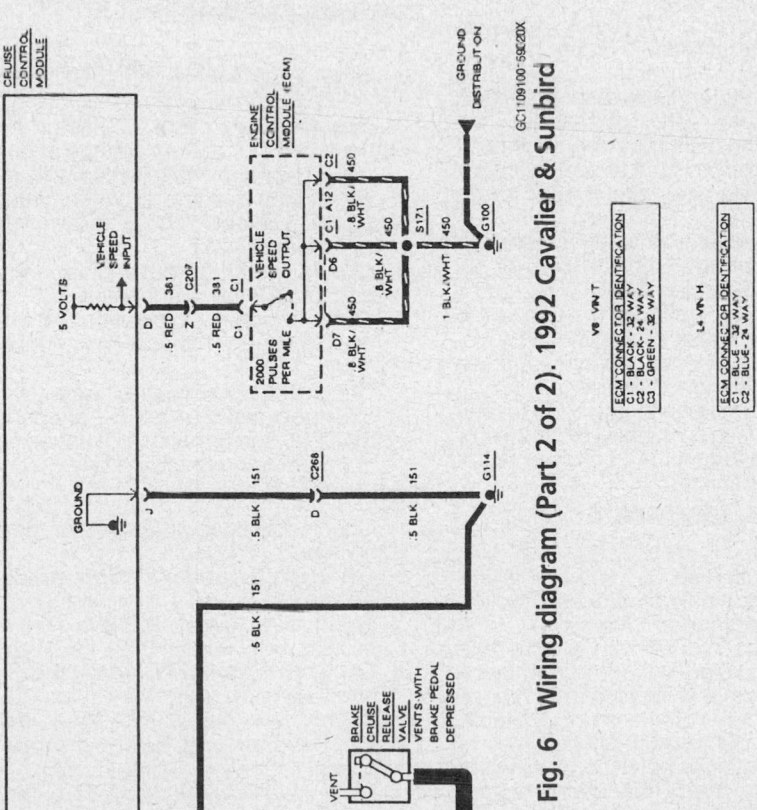

Fig. 6 Wiring diagram (Part 2 of 2). 1992 Cavalier & Sunbird

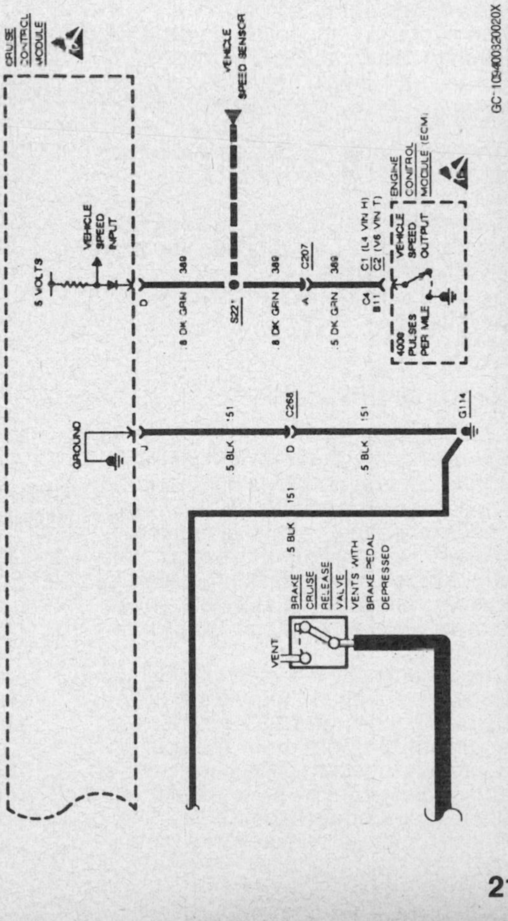

Fig. 7 Wiring diagram (Part 2 of 2). 1993–94 Cavalier & Sunbird

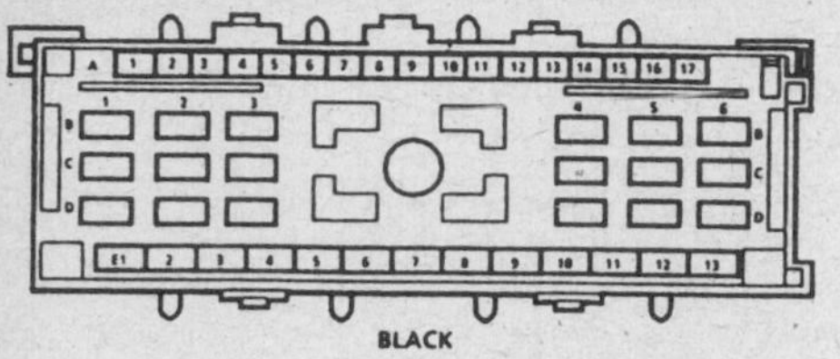
BLACK

GC1109100160000X

Fig. 8 Cruise control module connector C206 pin location. Century, Cutlass Ciera & Cutlass Cruiser

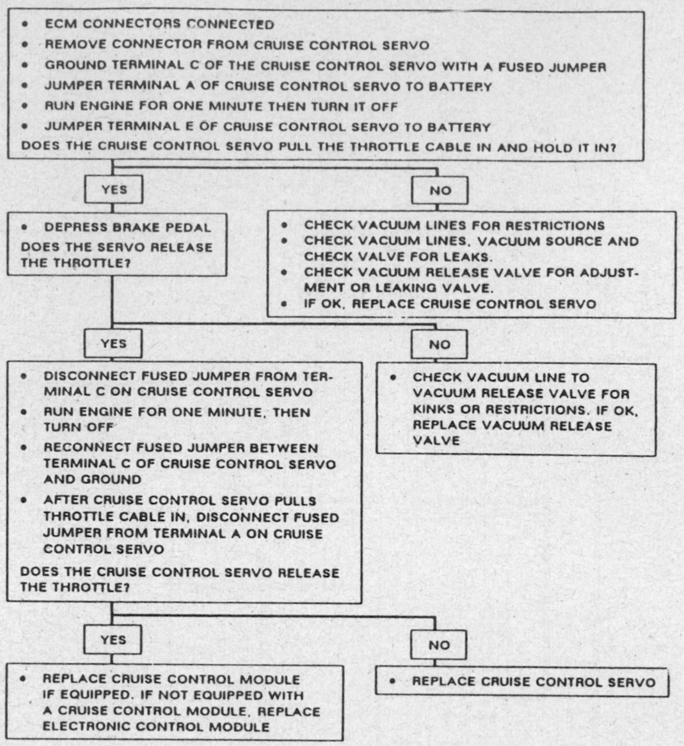
• ECM CONNECTORS CONNECTED
• REMOVE CONNECTOR FROM CRUISE CONTROL SERVO
• GROUND TERMINAL C OF THE CRUISE CONTROL SERVO WITH A FUSED JUMPER
• JUMPER TERMINAL A OF CRUISE CONTROL SERVO TO BATTERY
• RUN ENGINE FOR ONE MINUTE THEN TURN IT OFF
• JUMPER TERMINAL E OF CRUISE CONTROL SERVO TO BATTERY
DOES THE CRUISE CONTROL SERVO PULL THE THROTTLE CABLE IN AND HOLD IT IN?
YES
NO
• DEPRESS BRAKE PEDAL
DOES THE SERVO RELEASE THE THROTTLE?
• CHECK VACUUM LINES FOR RESTRICTIONS
• CHECK VACUUM LINES, VACUUM SOURCE AND CHECK VALVE FOR LEAKS.
• CHECK VACUUM RELEASE VALVE FOR ADJUSTMENT OR LEAKING VALVE.
• IF OK, REPLACE CRUISE CONTROL SERVO
YES
NO
• DISCONNECT FUSED JUMPER FROM TERMINAL C ON CRUISE CONTROL SERVO
• RUN ENGINE FOR ONE MINUTE, THEN TURN OFF
• RECONNECT FUSED JUMPER BETWEEN TERMINAL C OF CRUISE CONTROL SERVO AND GROUND
• AFTER CRUISE CONTROL SERVO PULLS THROTTLE CABLE IN, DISCONNECT FUSED JUMPER FROM TERMINAL A ON CRUISE CONTROL SERVO
DOES THE CRUISE CONTROL SERVO RELEASE THE THROTTLE?
• CHECK VACUUM LINE TO VACUUM RELEASE VALVE FOR KINKS OR RESTRICTIONS. IF OK, REPLACE VACUUM RELEASE VALVE
YES
NO
• REPLACE CRUISE CONTROL MODULE IF EQUIPPED. IF NOT EQUIPPED WITH A CRUISE CONTROL MODULE, REPLACE ELECTRONIC CONTROL MODULE
• REPLACE CRUISE CONTROL SERVO

GC1109300161000X

Fig. 9 Servo actuation test S

or damage to clutch master cylinder retaining ring may result.

SYSTEM DIAGNOSIS & TESTING

CAMARO, CAVALIER, CENTURY, CUTLASS CIERA, CUTLASS CRUISER, FIREBIRD & SUNBIRD

Perform test as shown, **Fig. 2.** If results are other than specified, perform designated test. **Do not press set switch and Resume/Accel position of cruise switch at same time while engine is running. If quick checker displays a short light, release switches immediately.**

When performing the following tests refer to wiring diagrams **Figs. 3 through 7** and control module pin connectors **Fig. 8.**

TEST E

1. Check for shorts to voltage in wires to terminals A, G, L and M of cruise control module.
2. If wires are satisfactory, check multi-function lever and cruise control switch for a short.
3. If switch is satisfactory, replace multi-function lever.

TEST F

Beretta & Corsica

1. Check fuse No. 14.
2. Ensure terminal J (black wire) of cruise control module is grounded.
3. Disconnect connector C235 and check for battery voltage at terminal A (brown/white wire) of harness half with ignition switch in Run position. If battery voltage is not available, check brown/white wire (circuit 141) for an open.
4. Check continuity between terminals A (brown wire) and C (gray wire) of pin half of connector C235 with cruise switch in On position. If there is no continuity, check multi-function lever and cruise control switches for an open, replacing as necessary.
5. Check for an open in gray wire (circuit 397) between terminal A of connector C235 and terminal A of cruise control module connector.

Cavalier

1. Check cruise fuse.
2. Ensure terminal J (black wire) of cruise control module is grounded.
3. Disconnect connector C235 and check for battery voltage at terminal A (brown/white wire) of harness half with ignition switch in Run position. If battery voltage is not available, check brown/white wire (circuit 141) for an open.
4. Check continuity between terminals A (black wire) and B (black wire) of pin half of connector C235 with cruise switch in On position. If there is no continuity, check multi-function lever and cruise control switches for an open, replacing as necessary.
5. Check for an open in gray wire (circuit 397) between terminal D of connector C235 and terminal A of cruise control module connector.

Grand Am, Skylark & Sunbird

1. Check radio fuse.
2. Ensure terminal J of cruise control module is grounded.
3. Disconnect connector C235 and check for battery voltage at terminal A (yellow wire) with ignition in Run position. If battery voltage is not available, check yellow wire (circuit 43).
4. Check continuity between terminals A (black wire) and B (black wire) of connector C235 with cruise switch in On position. If there is no continuity, replace multi-function lever.
5. Check for open in gray wire (circuit 397) between terminal B of connector C235 and terminal A of cruise control module connector.

Century, Cutlass Ciera & Cutlass Cruiser

1. Check radio fuse.
2. Ensure terminal J of cruise control module is grounded.
3. Disconnect row E of connector C206 and check for battery voltage at terminal E1 (brown/white wire) with ignition in Run position. If battery voltage is not available, check brown/white wire (circuit 141).
4. Check continuity between terminals E1 and E2 of connector C206 with cruise switch in On position. If there is no continuity, replace multi-function lever.
5. Check for open in gray wire (circuit 397) between terminal E2 of connector C206 and terminal A of cruise control module connector.

TEST G

1. Check for open in brake or clutch switch.
2. **On Beretta and Corsica models,** check brown wire (circuit 86), dark green wire (circuit 986), brown and brown/white (circuit 379), for an open.
3. **On Grand Am and Skylark models,** check brown/white wire (circuit 86), or gray wire (circuit 986), for an open.
4. **On Cavalier and Sunbird models,** check brown (circuit 86), or brown/white wire (circuit 379), for an open.
5. **On Century, Cutlass Ciera and Cutlass Cruiser models,** check for an

open in brown wire (circuit 86) and gray wire (circuit 397) to the brake switch.

TEST H

1. If measurement is less than 30 ohms, proceed to test N. Otherwise, remove connector from cruise control servo and measure resistance between terminals A and C of servo.
2. If resistance is greater than 55 ohms, replace cruise control servo.
3. If resistance is less than 55 ohms, check for open in dark blue or dark blue/white wire (circuit 403) between terminal C of cruise control module and terminal A of cruise control servo. Ensure terminal C of servo connector is grounded.

TEST I

1. If measurement was less than 30 ohms, proceed to test L. Otherwise, remove connector from cruise control servo and measure resistance between terminals E and C of servo.
2. If resistance is greater than 55 ohms, replace cruise control servo.
3. If resistance is less than 55 ohms, check for open in light green wire (circuit 402) between terminal K of cruise control module and terminal E of cruise control servo. Ensure terminal C of servo connector Is grounded.

TEST J

1. If measurement was less than 15 ohms, proceed to test Q. Otherwise, remove connector from cruise control servo and measure resistance between terminals B and D of servo.
2. If resistance is greater than 25 ohms, replace cruise control servo.
3. If resistance is less than 25 ohms, check for open in light blue/black or light blue wire (circuit 399) between terminal H of cruise control module and terminal D of cruise control servo. Also, check for open in tan wire (circuit 398) between terminal F of module and terminal B of servo.

TEST K

1. Disconnect connector C235 and check switch continuity between terminals B (black wire) and D (black wire) with set switch pressed.
2. If there is no continuity, replace multi-function lever.
3. If there is continuity, check for open in dark blue wire (circuit 84) between terminal D and terminal L of cruise control module.

Century, Cutlass Ciera & Cutlass Cruiser

1. Disconnect row E of connector C206 and check switch continuity between terminals E2 and E3 with set switch pressed.
2. If there is no continuity, replace multi-function lever.
3. If there is continuity, check for open in dark blue wire (circuit 84) between terminal E2 of connector C206 and terminal L of cruise control module.

TEST L

1. Remove connector from servo and measure resistance between terminals C and E of servo.
2. If resistance is less than 30 ohms, replace cruise control servo.
3. If resistance is 30 ohms or greater, check for short to ground in light green wire (circuit 402) from terminal K of cruise control module to terminal E of cruise control servo.

TEST M

1. Disconnect connector C235 and check switch continuity between terminals A and C with cruise switch in Resume/Accel position.
2. If there is no continuity, replace multi-function lever.
3. If there is continuity, check for open in gray/black wire (circuit 87) between terminal C and terminal M of cruise control module.

Century, Cutlass Ciera & Cutlass Cruiser

1. Disconnect row E of connector C206 and check switch continuity between terminals E1 and E4 with cruise switch in Resume/Accel position.
2. If there is no continuity, replace multi-function lever.
3. If there is continuity, check for open in gray/black wire (circuit 87) between terminal E4 of connector C206 and terminal M of cruise control module.

TEST N

1. Remove connector from cruise control servo and measure resistance between terminals A and C of servo.
2. If resistance is less than 30 ohms, replace cruise control servo.
3. If resistance is 30 ohms or greater, check for short to ground in dark blue/white wire or dark blue wire (circuit 403) from terminal C of cruise control module to terminal A of cruise control servo.

TEST O

Cavalier & Sunbird

If VSS light does not illuminate, or voltage between terminals A and D remains less than 7 volts check for open in red wire (circuit 381) from the engine control module .

Century, Cutlass Ciera & Cutlass Cruiser

If VSS light does not illuminate, or voltage between terminals A and D remains less than 7 volts check for open in red wire (circuit 381).

TEST P

2. If resistance is now over range, replace cruise control servo.
3. If resistance is still low repair short in tan wire (circuit 398) from terminal F of cruise control module to terminal B of cruise control servo.

TEST R

1. Disconnect cruise control servo connector and repeat test 7, 8, 9 and 10 **Fig. 2.** Perform test on the cruise control servo (male side).
2. If circuit is now open check cruise control servo connector and cruise control module connector for corrosion. Repair wire if connector is OK.
3. If resistance is still low, check cruise control servo terminals for corrosion. Replace cruise control servo if connectors are OK.

TEST S

When performing servo actuation test S refer to **Fig. 9.**

Cavalier & Sunbird

If VSS light does not go off or battery voltage remains between terminals A and D, check for short to ground on red wire (circuit 381) from the engine control module.

Century, Cutlass Ciera & Cutlass Cruiser

If VSS light does not go off, or battery voltage remains between terminals A and D remains less than 7 volts check for short to ground in red wire (circuit 381).

TEST Q

1. Disconnect cruise control servo connector and repeat test 6, **Fig. 2.**

ACHIEVA, BERETTA, CORSICA, GRAND AM & SKYLARK

Perform tests in isolation chart, **Fig. 10.** If results are incorrect perform tests in diagnostic charts, **Figs. 11 through 24. Do not press both the set switch and Resume/Accel position of cruise switch at same time with engine running. If quick checker displays a short light, release switches immediately.**

When performing the following tests, refer to **Figs. 25 through 29,** for wiring diagrams.

CAPRICE, CUSTOM CRUISER & ROADMASTER

When diagnosing and testing system refer to **Figs. 30 through 33** for diagnostic charts, and **Figs. 34 through 3** for wiring diagrams.

CORVETTE

Troubleshooting

1. Check for open cruise fuse.
2. Check for vacuum leaks in cruise control servo vacuum lines.
3. Check cruise control cable for looseness, binding, and connection at throttle body.
4. Ensure proper terminal mating at connectors, then check for corrosion or bent terminals.

System Diagnosis

When diagnosing and testing system refer to **Figs. 36 and 37** for wiring diagrams.

Refer to **Figs. 38 through 44** for symptom and system diagnosis.

CUTLASS SUPREME, GRAND PRIX, LUMINA & REGAL

TROUBLESHOOTING

1. Check vacuum hoses for leaks, kinks and/or restrictions.
2. Check cruise control servo linkage for proper slack.
3. If system works except for tap-up and tap-down functions, replace cruise control module.

ROAD TEST

1. Drive vehicle at speed greater than 25 mph, place cruise switch in On position and depress set button at end of multi-function lever. Cruise indicator should illuminate and vehicle should maintain speed.
2. With foot off accelerator, hold set button in. Vehicle should coast at a slower speed.
3. Release set button. If new speed is greater than 25 mph, cruise control should engage and hold slower speed.
4. Slide cruise switch to Resume/Accel position and hold it there. Vehicle should accelerate.
5. Release cruise switch back to On position. Vehicle should hold new, faster speed.
6. Tap brake pedal. Vehicle should coast slower and cruise indicator should go out.
7. Slide cruise control switch momentarily to Resume/Accel position. Cruise indicator should illuminate and vehicle should accelerate to former set speed.
8. While cruising, accelerate, then remove foot from accelerator pedal. Vehicle should coast back to set speed.
9. While cruising, tap cruise switch to Resume/Accel position. Vehicle speed should increase 1 mph for each tap up to ten.
10. While cruising, tap set button. Vehicle speed should decrease 1 mph for each tap down to 25 mph.
11. Slide cruise control switch to Off position. Cruise control should turn off and cruise indicator should go out.

SYSTEM DIAGNOSIS

Perform tests in diagnostic charts, **Figs. 45 through 48.** If results are incorrect perform designated test. **Do not press both the set switch and Resume/Accel position of cruise switch at same time with engine running. If quick checker displays a short light, release switches immediately. Refer to Figs. 49 through 52 for wiring diagrams.**

TEST A

1. Check for shorts to voltage in wires to terminals A, G, M, and L terminals of cruise control module.
2. If wires are satisfactory, replace multi-function lever.

TEST B

1. Check instrument cluster fuse.
2. Ensure terminal J of cruise control module connector is grounded.
3. Disconnect connector C202 and check for battery voltage at terminal E12 (pink/black wire) of female half with ignition switch in Run position. If battery voltage is not available, check pink/black wire (circuit 750).
4. Check continuity between terminals E1 (gray wire) and E12 (pink/black wire) of male half of connector C202 with cruise switch in On position. If there is no continuity, replace multi-function lever.
5. Check for open in gray/white wire (circuit 397) between terminal E1 of connector C202 and terminal A of cruise control module connector.

TEST D

1. If measurement was less than 30 ohms, proceed to test J. Otherwise, remove connector from cruise control servo and measure resistance between terminals A and C of servo.
2. If resistance is greater than 55 ohms, replace cruise control servo.
3. If resistance is less than 55 ohms, check for open in dark blue/white wire (circuit 403, Lumina) or dark blue wire (circuit 403, Grand Prix and Regal) or light/green wire between terminal C of cruise control module and terminal A of cruise control servo. Ensure terminal C of cruise control servo connector is grounded.

TEST E

1. If measurement is less than 30 ohms, proceed to test H. Otherwise, remove connector from cruise control servo and measure resistance between terminals E and C of cruise control servo.
2. If resistance is greater than 55 ohms, replace cruise control servo.
3. If resistance is less than 55 ohms, check for open in light green wire (circuit 402) between terminal K of cruise control module and terminal E of cruise control servo. Ensure terminal C of cruise control servo connector is grounded.

TEST F

1. If measurement is less than 15 ohms, remove connector from cruise control servo and measure resistance between terminals B and D of cruise control servo.
2. If resistance is greater than 25 ohms, replace cruise control servo.
3. If resistance is less than 25 ohms, check for open in light blue/black wire (circuit 399) between terminal H of cruise control module and terminal D of cruise control servo. Also, check for open in tan wire (circuit 398) between terminal F of cruise control module and terminal B of cruise control servo.

TEST G

1. Check for shorts to voltage in wires to terminals A, G, M, and L terminals of cruise control module.
2. If wires are satisfactory, replace multi-function lever.

TEST H

1. Remove connector from cruise control servo and measure resistance between terminals C and E of cruise

control servo connector.
2. If resistance is less than 30 ohms, replace cruise control servo.
3. If resistance is 30 ohms or greater, check for short to ground in light green wire (circuit 402) between terminal K of cruise control module and terminal E of cruise control servo.

TEST I

Cutlass Supreme, Grand Prix, Lumina & Regal

1. Disconnect connector C202 and check cruise switch continuity between terminals E12 and E13 of male half of connector C202 with cruise switch in Resume/Accel position.
2. If there is no continuity, replace multifunction lever.
3. If there is continuity, check for open in gray/black wire (circuit 87) between terminal E13 of connector C202 and terminal M of cruise control module.

TEST J

1. Remove connector from cruise control servo and measure resistance between terminals A and C of cruise control servo.
2. If resistance is less than 30 ohms, replace cruise control servo.

TEST M

1. Disconnect the cruise control servo connector and repeat test 6 of the isolation test **Fig. 48.**
2. If resistance is now open, replace cruise control test.
3. If resistance is still low, repair short in wire from terminal H of the cruise control module to terminal D of the cruise control servo.

TEST N

Except Cutlass Supreme, Grand Prix, Lumina & Regal

1. Disconnect cruise control servo connector and repeat test 7.
2. If resistance is now over range, replace cruise control servo.
3. If resistance is still low, check for short in tan wire (circuit 398) from terminal F of cruise control module to terminal B of cruise control servo.

Cutlass Supreme, Grand Prix, Lumina & Regal

1. Disconnect cruise control servo connector and repeat test 7, 8, 9 and 10 **Fig. 48.**
2. If resistance is now open, check the cruise control servo connector and cruise control module connector for corrosion between terminals. If OK, repair shorted wire.
3. If resistance is still low, check servo terminals for corrosion.

COMPONENT DIAGNOSIS & TESTING

ELECTRIC BRAKE RELEASE SWITCH

1. Turn ignition switch to On position.
2. Connect test light to ground.
3. Probe brown wire at brake switch connector. Lamp should illuminate.
4. Check switch adjustment, with probe still at brown wire, depressing brake pedal 1/8-1/2 inch. Light should go out.
5. If lamp did not illuminate in step 3, probe wire in adjacent connector cavity. If lamp illuminates, adjust or replace switch as necessary. If light does not illuminate, check wiring to switch.

DIAGNOSTIC CHART INDEX

Test/Code	Description	Page No.	Fig. No.
ACHIEVA, BERETTA, CORSCIA, GRAND AM & SKYLARK			
Test 1	Isolation Test	21-46	10
Test 2	Cruise Switch Short Test	21-46	11
Test 3	Power Circuit Open Test	21-46	12
Test 4	Brake Circuit Open Test	21-46	13
Test 5	Vent Circuit Open Test	21-46	14
Test 6	Vacuum Circuit Open Test	21-47	15
Test 7	SPS Circuit Open Test	21-47	16
Test 8	SC Circuit Open Test	21-47	17
Test 9	Vacuum Circuit Short Test	21-47	18
Test 10	R/A Circuit Open Test	21-47	19
Test 11	Vent Circuit Short Test	21-47	20
Test 12	VSS Circuit Open/Short Test	21-47	21
Test 13	R/A Circuit Open Test	21-47	22
Test 14	Servo Test	21-47	23
Test 15	Servo Actuation Test	21-47	24
CAPRICE, CUSTOM CRUISER &ROADMASTER			
Test 1	Cruise Control Will Not Engage	21-51	30
Test 2	Cruise Control Will Not Resume, Accelerate, Tap-Up Or Tap-Down	21-54	31
Test 3	Cruise Indicator Inoperative	21-54	32
Test 4	Cruise Indicator On At All Times	21-54	33
1992 CORVETTE			
Test 1	Cruise Control System Diagnosis	21-58	39
Test 2	Cruise Control System Diagnosis	21-58	40
Test 3	Cruise Control System Diagnosis	21-58	41

Continued

DIAGNOSTIC CHART INDEX—Continued

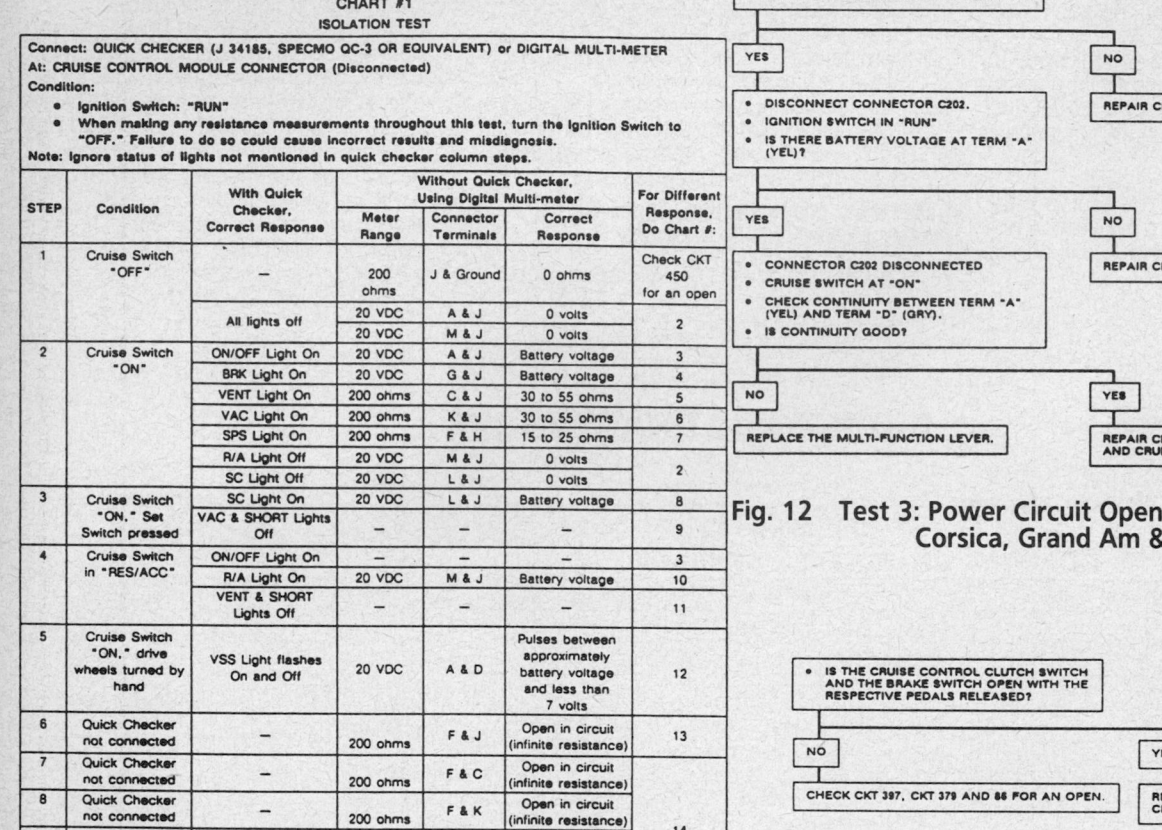

CHART #1
ISOLATION TEST

Connect: QUICK CHECKER (J 34185, SPECMO QC-3 OR EQUIVALENT) or DIGITAL MULTI-METER
At: CRUISE CONTROL MODULE CONNECTOR (Disconnected)
Condition:

- Ignition Switch: "RUN"
- When making any resistance measurements throughout this test, turn the Ignition Switch to "OFF." Failure to do so could cause incorrect results and misdiagnosis.

Note: Ignore status of lights not mentioned in quick checker column steps.

STEP	Condition	With Quick Checker, Correct Response	Without Quick Checker, Using Digital Multi-meter			For Different Response, Do Chart #:
			Meter Range	Connector Terminals	Correct Response	
1	Cruise Switch "OFF"	—	200 ohms	J & Ground	0 ohms	Check CKT 450 for an open
		All lights off	20 VDC	A & J	0 volts	2
			20 VDC	M & J	0 volts	
2	Cruise Switch "ON"	ON/OFF Light On	20 VDC	A & J	Battery voltage	3
		BRK Light On	20 VDC	G & J	Battery voltage	4
		VENT Light On	200 ohms	C & J	30 to 55 ohms	5
		VAC Light On	200 ohms	K & J	30 to 55 ohms	6
		SPS Light On	200 ohms	F & H	15 to 25 ohms	7
		R/A Light Off	20 VDC	M & J	0 volts	2
		SC Light Off	20 VDC	L & J	0 volts	
3	Cruise Switch "ON," Set Switch pressed	SC Light On	20 VDC	L & J	Battery voltage	8
		VAC & SHORT Lights Off	—	—	—	9
4	Cruise Switch in "RES/ACC"	ON/OFF Light On	—	—	—	3
		R/A Light On	20 VDC	M & J	Battery voltage	10
		VENT & SHORT Lights Off	—	—	—	11
5	Cruise Switch "ON," drive wheels turned by hand	VSS Light flashes On and Off	20 VDC	A & D	Pulses between approximately battery voltage and less than 7 volts	12
6	Quick Checker not connected	—	200 ohms	F & J	Open in circuit (infinite resistance)	13
7	Quick Checker not connected	—	200 ohms	F & C	Open in circuit (infinite resistance)	14
8	Quick Checker not connected	—	200 ohms	F & K	Open in circuit (infinite resistance)	
9	Quick Checker not connected	—	200 ohms	H & C	Open in circuit (infinite resistance)	
10	Quick Checker not connected	—	200 ohms	H & K	Open in circuit (infinite resistance)	

D If all measurements are correct, go to Chart #15: Servo Actuation Test.

GC1109300162000X

Fig. 10 Test 1: Isolation Test. Achieva, Beretta, Corsica, Grand Am & Skylark

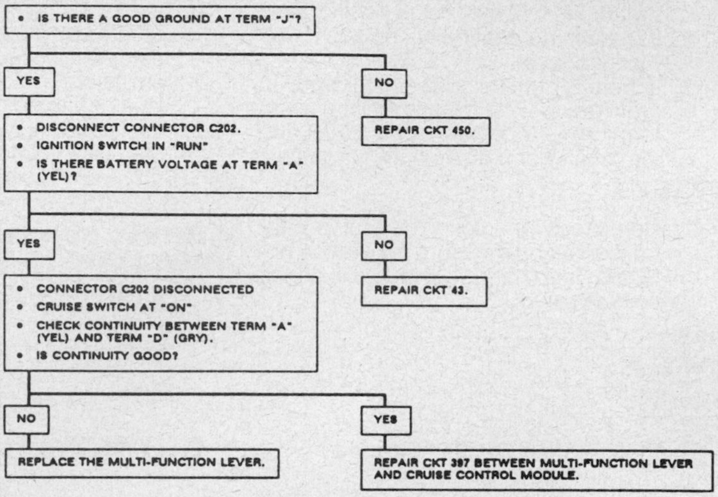

• IS THERE A GOOD GROUND AT TERM "J"?
YES
NO
REPAIR CKT 450.
• DISCONNECT CONNECTOR C202.
• IGNITION SWITCH IN "RUN"
• IS THERE BATTERY VOLTAGE AT TERM "A" (YEL)?
YES
NO
REPAIR CKT 43.
• CONNECTOR C202 DISCONNECTED
• CRUISE SWITCH AT "ON"
• CHECK CONTINUITY BETWEEN TERM "A" (YEL) AND TERM "D" (GRY).
• IS CONTINUITY GOOD?
NO
YES
REPLACE THE MULTI-FUNCTION LEVER.
REPAIR CKT 397 BETWEEN MULTI-FUNCTION LEVER AND CRUISE CONTROL MODULE.

GC1109200164000X

Fig. 12 Test 3: Power Circuit Open Test. Achieva, Beretta, Corsica, Grand Am & Skylark

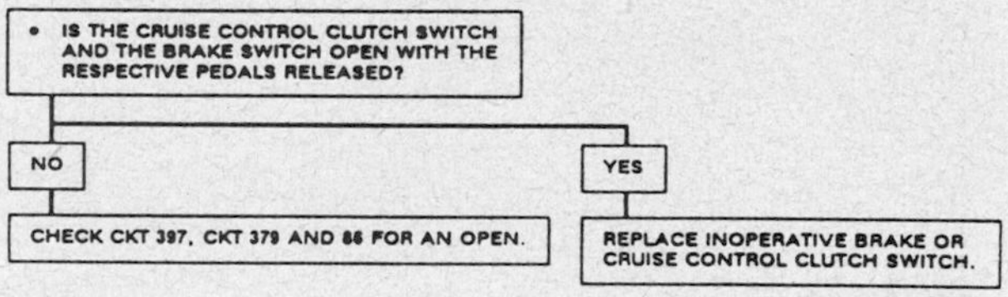

• IS THE CRUISE CONTROL CLUTCH SWITCH AND THE BRAKE SWITCH OPEN WITH THE RESPECTIVE PEDALS RELEASED?
NO
YES
CHECK CKT 397, CKT 379 AND 86 FOR AN OPEN.
REPLACE INOPERATIVE BRAKE OR CRUISE CONTROL CLUTCH SWITCH.

GC1109200165000X

Fig. 13 Test 4: Brake Circuit Open Test. Achieva, Beretta, Corsica, Grand Am & Skylark

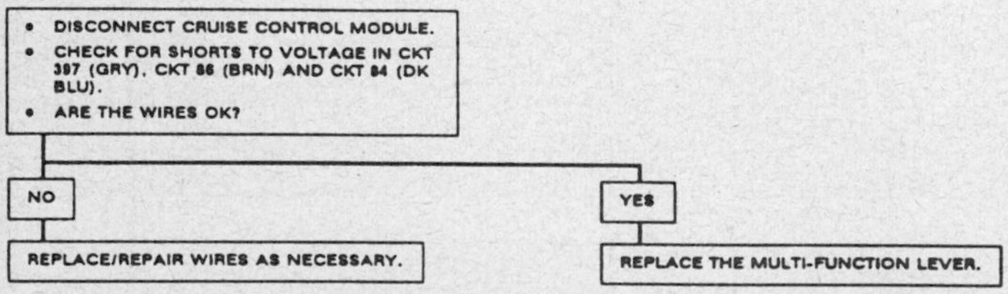

• DISCONNECT CRUISE CONTROL MODULE.
• CHECK FOR SHORTS TO VOLTAGE IN CKT 397 (GRY), CKT 86 (BRN) AND CKT 84 (DK BLU).
• ARE THE WIRES OK?
NO
YES
REPLACE/REPAIR WIRES AS NECESSARY.
REPLACE THE MULTI-FUNCTION LEVER.

GC1109200163000X

Fig. 11 Test 2: Cruise Switch Short Test. Achieva, Beretta, Corsica, Grand Am & Skylark

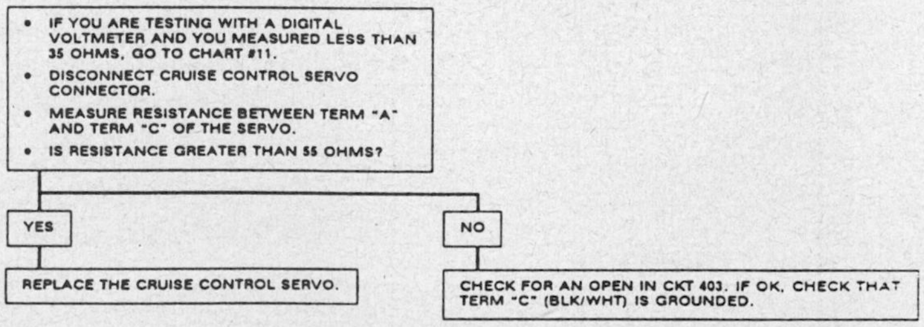

• IF YOU ARE TESTING WITH A DIGITAL VOLTMETER AND YOU MEASURED LESS THAN 35 OHMS, GO TO CHART #11.
• DISCONNECT CRUISE CONTROL SERVO CONNECTOR.
• MEASURE RESISTANCE BETWEEN TERM "A" AND TERM "C" OF THE SERVO.
• IS RESISTANCE GREATER THAN 55 OHMS?
YES
NO
REPLACE THE CRUISE CONTROL SERVO.
CHECK FOR AN OPEN IN CKT 403. IF OK, CHECK THAT TERM "C" (BLK/WHT) IS GROUNDED.

GC1109200166000X

Fig. 14 Test 5: Vent Circuit Open Test. Achieva, Beretta, Corsica, Grand Am & Skylark

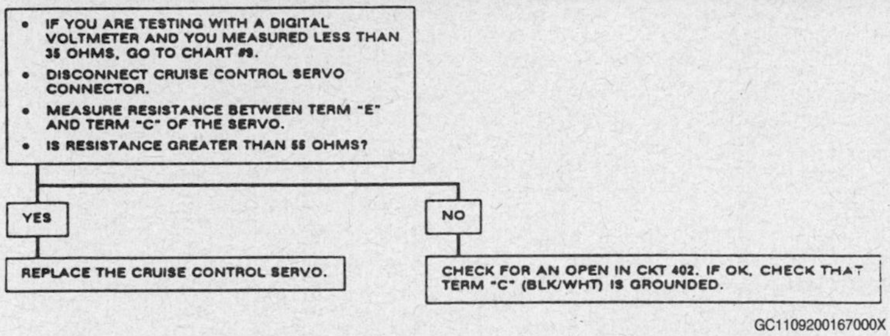
IF YOU ARE TESTING WITH A DIGITAL VOLTMETER AND YOU MEASURED LESS THAN 35 OHMS, GO TO CHART #9.
DISCONNECT CRUISE CONTROL SERVO CONNECTOR.
MEASURE RESISTANCE BETWEEN TERM "E" AND TERM "C" OF THE SERVO.
IS RESISTANCE GREATER THAN 55 OHMS?
YES
NO
REPLACE THE CRUISE CONTROL SERVO.
CHECK FOR AN OPEN IN CKT 402. IF OK, CHECK THAT TERM "C" (BLK/WHT) IS GROUNDED.
GC1109200167000X

Fig. 15 Test 6: Vacuum Circuit Open Test. Achieva, Beretta, Corsica, Grand Am & Skylark

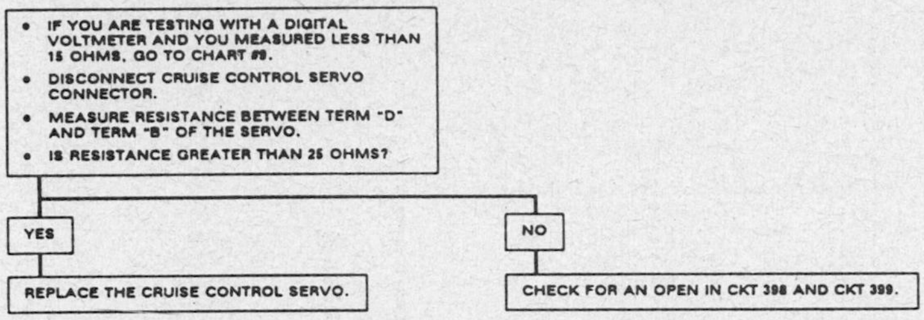
IF YOU ARE TESTING WITH A DIGITAL VOLTMETER AND YOU MEASURED LESS THAN 15 OHMS, GO TO CHART #9.
DISCONNECT CRUISE CONTROL SERVO CONNECTOR.
MEASURE RESISTANCE BETWEEN TERM "D" AND TERM "B" OF THE SERVO.
IS RESISTANCE GREATER THAN 25 OHMS?
YES
NO
REPLACE THE CRUISE CONTROL SERVO.
CHECK FOR AN OPEN IN CKT 398 AND CKT 399.
GC1109200168000X

Fig. 16 Test 7: SPS Circuit Open Test. Achieva, Beretta, Corsica, Grand Am & Skylark

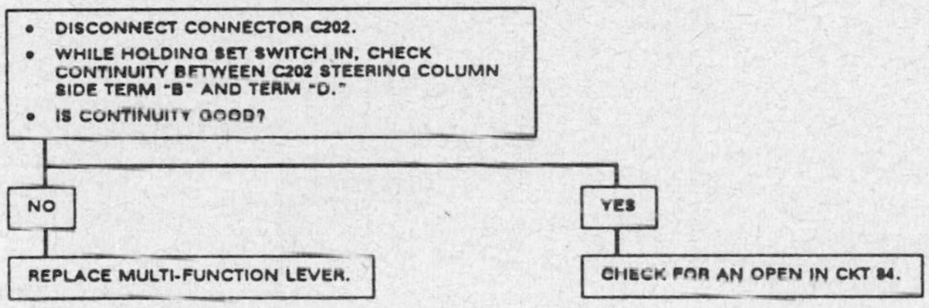
DISCONNECT CONNECTOR C202.
WHILE HOLDING SET SWITCH IN, CHECK CONTINUITY BETWEEN C202 STEERING COLUMN SIDE TERM "B" AND TERM "D."
IS CONTINUITY GOOD?
NO
YES
REPLACE MULTI-FUNCTION LEVER.
CHECK FOR AN OPEN IN CKT 84.
GC1109200169000X

Fig. 17 Test 8: SC Circuit Open Test. Achieva, Beretta, Corsica, Grand Am & Skylark

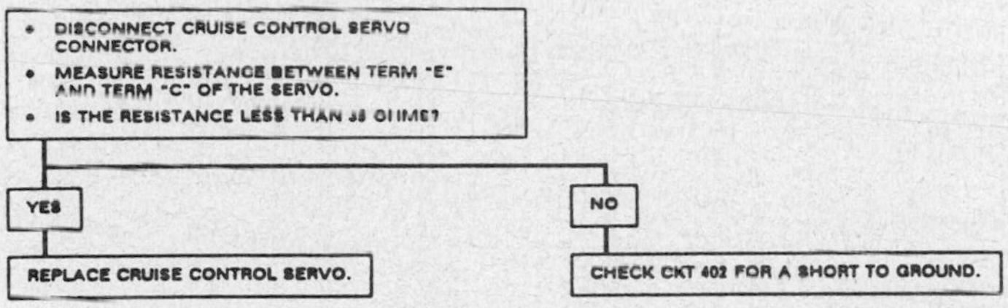
DISCONNECT CRUISE CONTROL SERVO CONNECTOR.
MEASURE RESISTANCE BETWEEN TERM "E" AND TERM "C" OF THE SERVO.
IS THE RESISTANCE LESS THAN
YES
NO
REPLACE CRUISE CONTROL SERVO.
CHECK CKT 402 FOR A SHORT TO GROUND.
GC1109200170000X

Fig. 18 Test 9: Vacuum Circuit Short Test. Achieva, Beretta, Corsica, Grand Am & Skylark

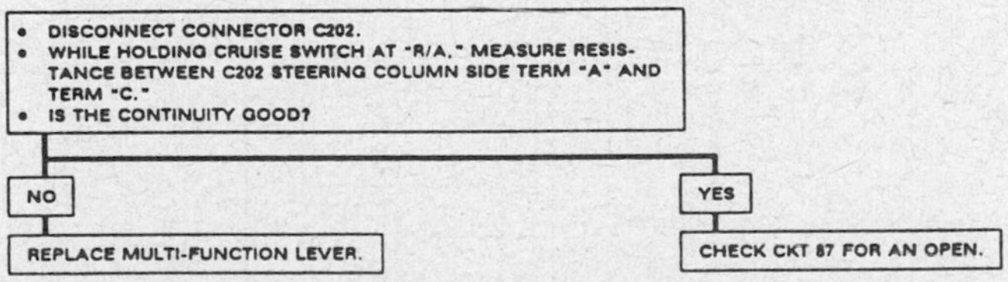
DISCONNECT CONNECTOR C202.
WHILE HOLDING CRUISE SWITCH AT "R/A," MEASURE RESISTANCE BETWEEN C202 STEERING COLUMN SIDE TERM "A" AND TERM "C."
IS THE CONTINUITY GOOD?
NO
YES
REPLACE MULTI-FUNCTION LEVER.
CHECK CKT 87 FOR AN OPEN.
GC1109200171000X

Fig. 19 Test 10: R/A Circuit Open Test. Achieva, Beretta, Corsica, Grand Am & Skylark

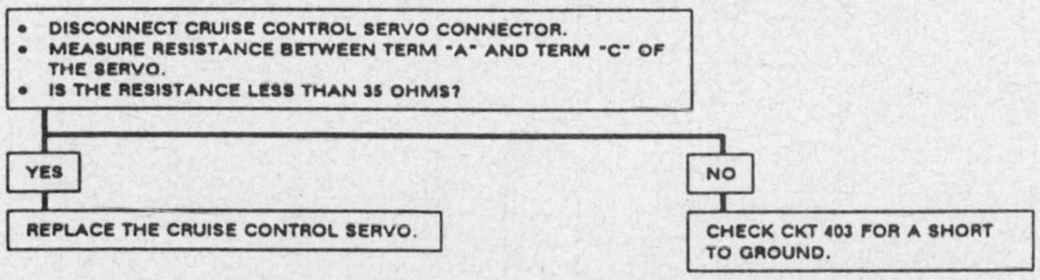
DISCONNECT CRUISE CONTROL SERVO CONNECTOR.
MEASURE RESISTANCE BETWEEN TERM "A" AND TERM "C" OF THE SERVO.
IS THE RESISTANCE LESS THAN 35 OHMS?
YES
NO
REPLACE THE CRUISE CONTROL SERVO.
CHECK CKT 403 FOR A SHORT TO GROUND.
GC1109200172000X

Fig. 20 Test 11: Vent Circuit Short Test. Achieva, Beretta, Corsica, Grand Am & Skylark

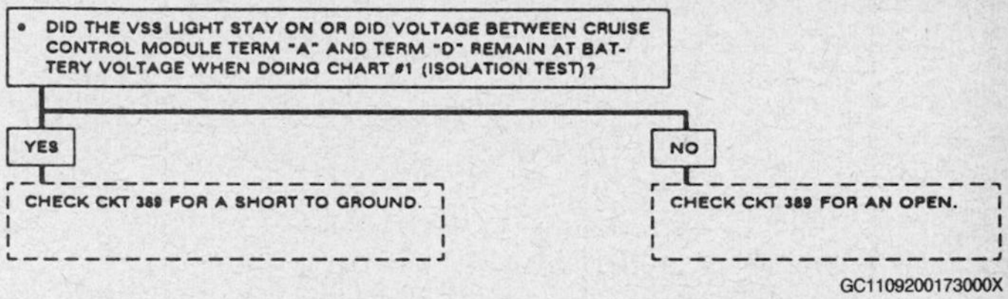
DID THE VSS LIGHT STAY ON OR DID VOLTAGE BETWEEN CRUISE CONTROL MODULE TERM "A" AND TERM "D" REMAIN AT BATTERY VOLTAGE WHEN DOING CHART #1 (ISOLATION TEST)?
YES
NO
CHECK CKT 389 FOR A SHORT TO GROUND.
CHECK CKT 389 FOR AN OPEN.
GC1109200173000X

Fig. 21 Test 12: VSS Circuit Open/Short Test. Achieva, Beretta, Corsica, Grand Am & Skylark

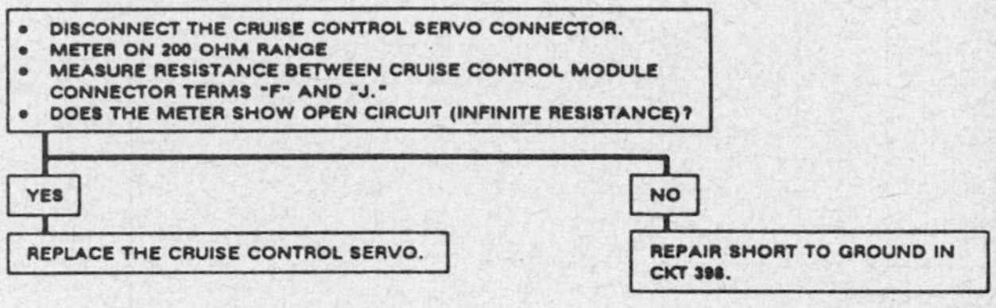
DISCONNECT THE CRUISE CONTROL SERVO CONNECTOR.
METER ON 200 OHM RANGE
MEASURE RESISTANCE BETWEEN CRUISE CONTROL MODULE CONNECTOR TERMS "F" AND "J."
DOES THE METER SHOW OPEN CIRCUIT (INFINITE RESISTANCE)?
YES
NO
REPLACE THE CRUISE CONTROL SERVO.
REPAIR SHORT TO GROUND IN CKT 398.
GC1109200174000X

Fig. 22 Test 13: R/A Circuit Open Test. Achieva, Beretta, Corsica, Grand Am & Skylark

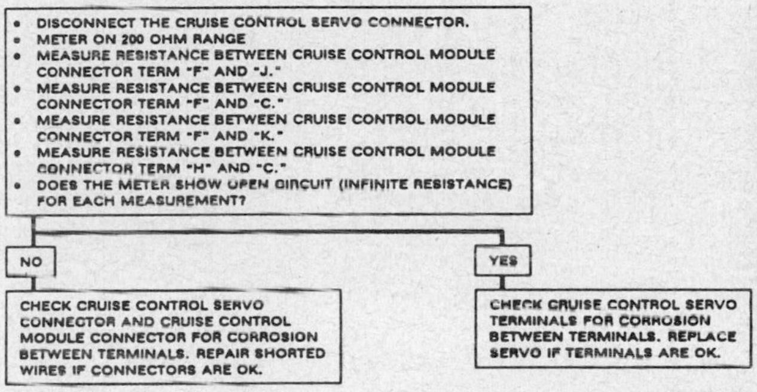
DISCONNECT THE CRUISE CONTROL SERVO CONNECTOR.
METER ON 200 OHM RANGE
MEASURE RESISTANCE BETWEEN CRUISE CONTROL MODULE CONNECTOR TERM "F" AND "J."
MEASURE RESISTANCE BETWEEN CRUISE CONTROL MODULE CONNECTOR TERM "F" AND "C."
MEASURE RESISTANCE BETWEEN CRUISE CONTROL MODULE CONNECTOR TERM "F" AND "K."
MEASURE RESISTANCE BETWEEN CRUISE CONTROL MODULE CONNECTOR TERM "H" AND "C."
DOES THE METER SHOW OPEN CIRCUIT (INFINITE RESISTANCE) FOR EACH MEASUREMENT?
NO
YES
CHECK CRUISE CONTROL SERVO CONNECTOR AND CRUISE CONTROL MODULE CONNECTOR FOR CORROSION BETWEEN TERMINALS. REPAIR SHORTED WIRES IF CONNECTORS ARE OK.
CHECK CRUISE CONTROL SERVO TERMINALS FOR CORROSION BETWEEN TERMINALS. REPLACE SERVO IF TERMINALS ARE OK.
GC1109200175000X

Fig. 23 Test 14: Servo Test. Achieva, Beretta, Corsica, Grand Am & Skylark

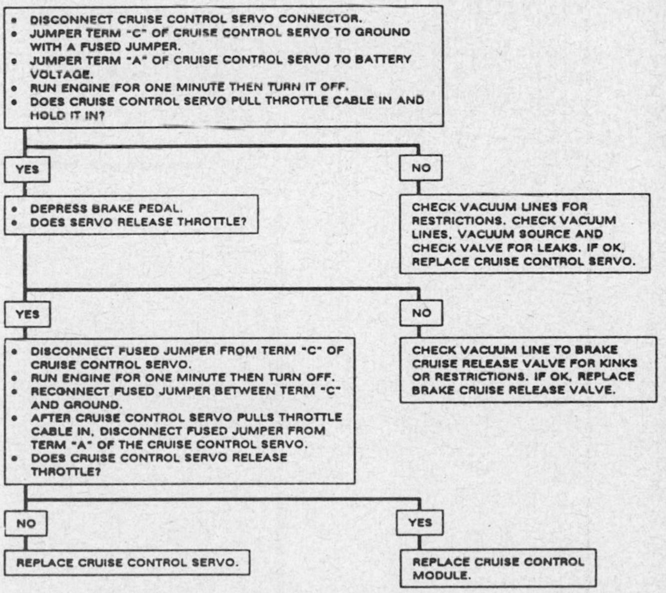
DISCONNECT CRUISE CONTROL SERVO CONNECTOR.
JUMPER TERM "C" OF CRUISE CONTROL SERVO TO GROUND WITH A FUSED JUMPER.
JUMPER TERM "A" OF CRUISE CONTROL SERVO TO BATTERY VOLTAGE.
RUN ENGINE FOR ONE MINUTE THEN TURN IT OFF.
DOES CRUISE CONTROL SERVO PULL THROTTLE CABLE IN AND HOLD IT IN?
YES
NO
DEPRESS BRAKE PEDAL.
DOES SERVO RELEASE THROTTLE?
CHECK VACUUM LINES FOR RESTRICTIONS. CHECK VACUUM LINES, VACUUM SOURCE AND CHECK VALVE FOR LEAKS. IF OK, REPLACE CRUISE CONTROL SERVO.
YES
NO
DISCONNECT FUSED JUMPER FROM TERM "C" OF CRUISE CONTROL SERVO.
RUN ENGINE FOR ONE MINUTE THEN TURN OFF.
RECONNECT FUSED JUMPER BETWEEN TERM "C" AND GROUND.
AFTER CRUISE CONTROL SERVO PULLS THROTTLE CABLE IN, DISCONNECT FUSED JUMPER FROM TERM "A" OF THE CRUISE CONTROL SERVO.
DOES CRUISE CONTROL SERVO RELEASE THROTTLE?
CHECK VACUUM LINE TO BRAKE CRUISE RELEASE VALVE FOR KINKS OR RESTRICTIONS. IF OK, REPLACE BRAKE CRUISE RELEASE VALVE.
NO
YES
REPLACE CRUISE CONTROL SERVO.
REPLACE CRUISE CONTROL MODULE.
GC1109200176000X

Fig. 24 Test 15: Servo Actuation Test. Achieva, Beretta, Corsica, Grand Am & Skylark

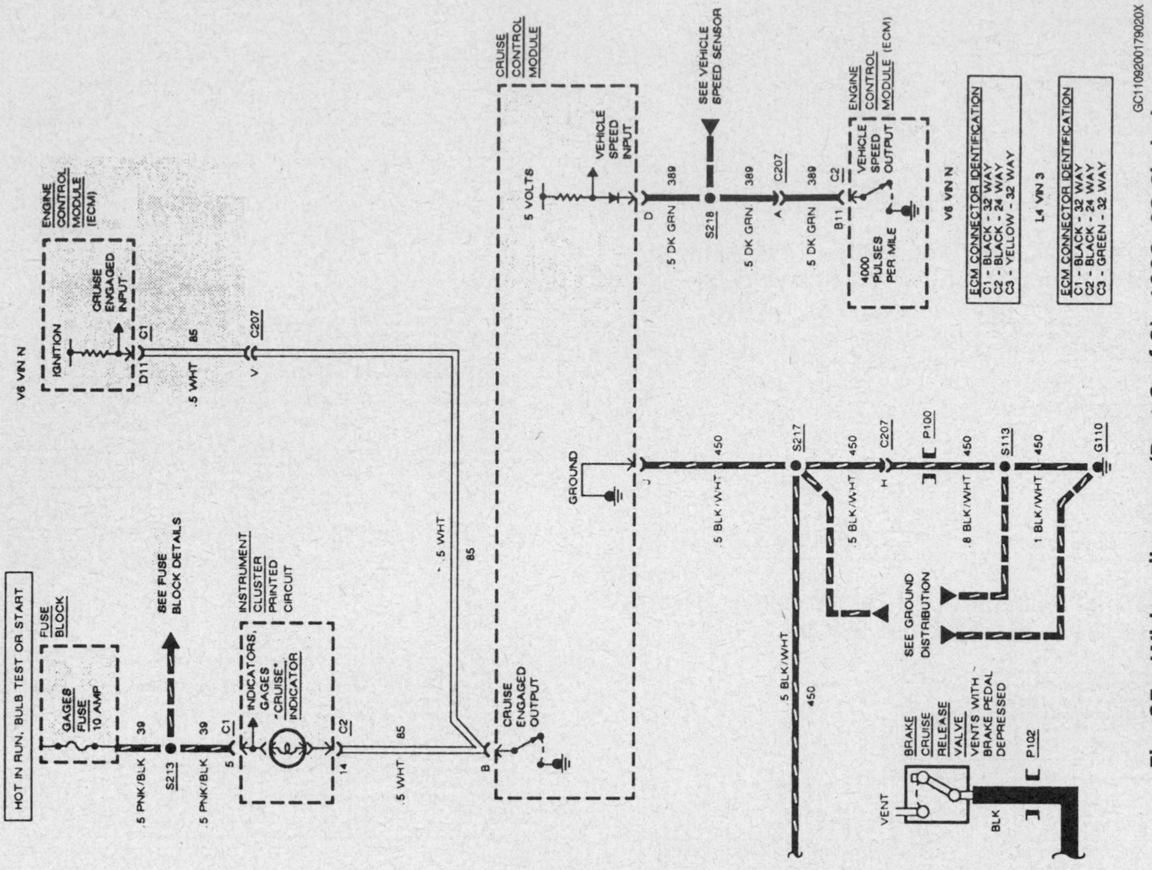
HOT IN RUN, BULB TEST OR START
FUSE BLOCK
GAGES FUSE 10 AMP
SEE FUSE BLOCK DETAILS
INSTRUMENT CLUSTER PRINTED CIRCUIT
INDICATORS, GAGES "CRUISE" INDICATOR
.5 PNK/BLK
S213
.5 WHT
V6 VIN N
ENGINE CONTROL MODULE (ECM)
IGNITION
CRUISE ENGAGED INPUT
C207
CRUISE CONTROL MODULE
CRUISE ENGAGED OUTPUT
GROUND
5 VOLTS
VEHICLE SPEED INPUT
SEE VEHICLE SPEED SENSOR
.5 DK GRN
S218
VEHICLE SPEED OUTPUT
4000 PULSES PER MILE
.5 BLK/WHT
S217
P100
S113
G110
.8 BLK/WHT
1 BLK/WHT
SEE GROUND DISTRIBUTION
BRAKE CRUISE RELEASE VALVE
VENTS WITH BRAKE PEDAL DEPRESSED
VENT
BLK
P102
ECM CONNECTOR IDENTIFICATION
C1 - BLACK - 32 WAY
C2 - BLACK - 24 WAY
C3 - YELLOW - 32 WAY
L4 VIN 3
ECM CONNECTOR IDENTIFICATION
C1 - BLACK - 32 WAY
C2 - BLACK - 24 WAY
C3 - GREEN - 32 WAY
GC1109200179020X

Fig. 25 Wiring diagram (Part 2 of 2). 1992–93 Skylark

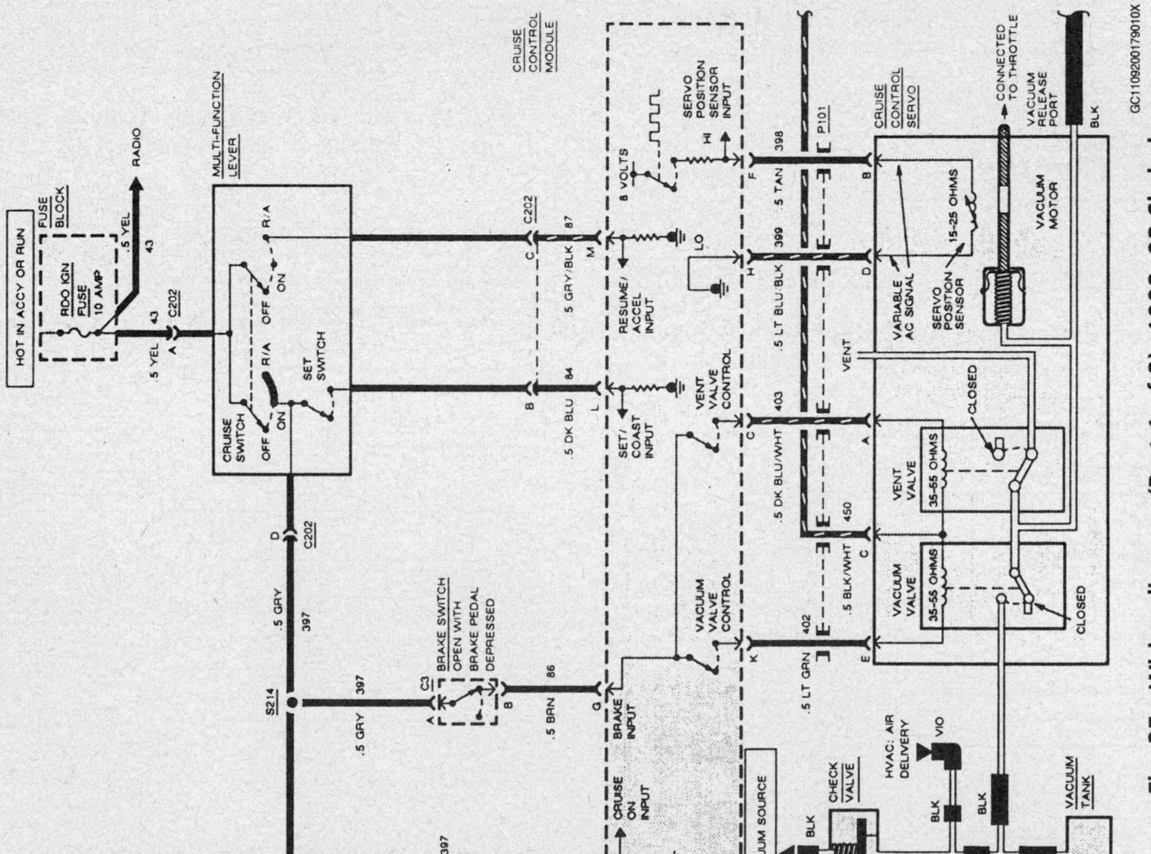
HOT IN ACCY OR RUN
FUSE BLOCK
RDO IGN FUSE 10 AMP
.5 YEL
RADIO
C202
MULTI-FUNCTION LEVER
CRUISE SWITCH
OFF ON R/A
SET SWITCH
.5 GRY
S214
BRAKE SWITCH OPEN WITH BRAKE PEDAL DEPRESSED
.5 BRN
.5 DK BLU
.5 GRY/BLK
CRUISE CONTROL MODULE
CRUISE ON INPUT
BRAKE INPUT
SET/ COAST INPUT
RESUME/ ACCEL INPUT
8 VOLTS
SERVO POSITION SENSOR INPUT
VACUUM VALVE CONTROL
VENT VALVE CONTROL
.5 LT GRN
.5 BLK/WHT
.5 DK BLU/WHT
.5 LT BLU/BLK
.5 TAN
P101
CRUISE CONTROL SERVO
VACUUM VALVE 35-55 OHMS
VENT VALVE 35-55 OHMS
CLOSED
VENT
VARIABLE AC SIGNAL
SERVO POSITION SENSOR
15-25 OHMS
VACUUM MOTOR
CONNECTED TO THROTTLE
VACUUM RELEASE PORT
VACUUM SOURCE
CHECK VALVE
HVAC: AIR DELIVERY
VIO
BLK
VACUUM TANK
GC1109200179010X

Fig. 25 Wiring diagram (Part 1 of 2). 1992–93 Skylark

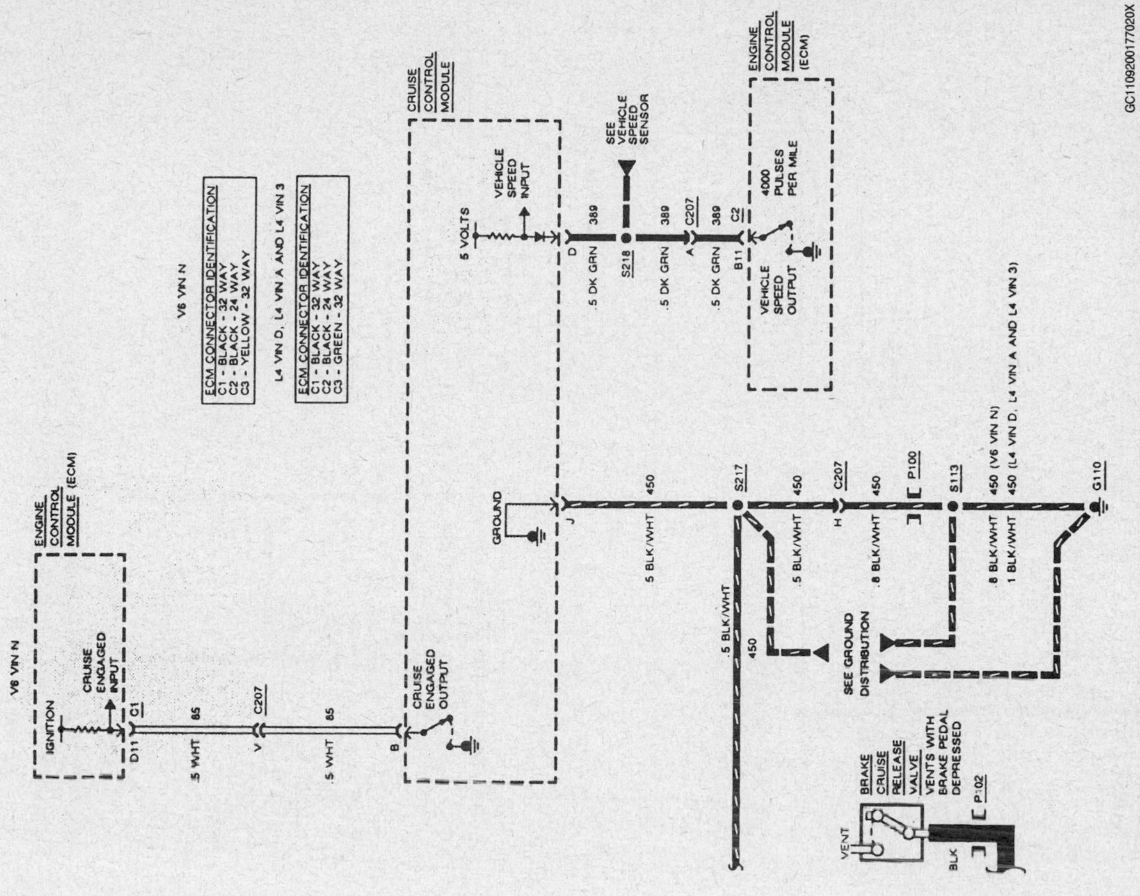

ENGINE CONTROL MODULE (ECM)
V6 VIN N
IGNITION
CRUISE ENGAGED INPUT
D11
C1
.5 WHT
85
C207
V
B
CRUISE ENGAGED OUTPUT
CRUISE CONTROL MODULE
GROUND
J
.5 BLK/WHT
450
S217
H
.8 BLK/WHT
P100
S113
.8 BLK/WHT
1 BLK/WHT
450 (V6 VIN N)
450 (L4 VIN D, L4 VIN A AND L4 VIN 3)
G110
SEE GROUND DISTRIBUTION
BRAKE CRUISE RELEASE VALVE
VENTS WITH BRAKE PEDAL DEPRESSED
VENT
BLK
P102
ECM CONNECTOR IDENTIFICATION
C1 - BLACK - 32 WAY
C2 - BLACK - 24 WAY
C3 - YELLOW - 32 WAY
L4 VIN D, L4 VIN A AND L4 VIN 3
C3 - GREEN - 32 WAY
5 VOLTS
VEHICLE SPEED INPUT
389
.5 DK GRN
S218
SEE VEHICLE SPEED SENSOR
B11
C2
VEHICLE SPEED OUTPUT
4000 PULSES PER MILE
ENGINE CONTROL MODULE (ECM)
GC1109200177020X

Fig. 26 Wiring diagram (Part 2 of 2). 1992–93 Achieva & Grand Am

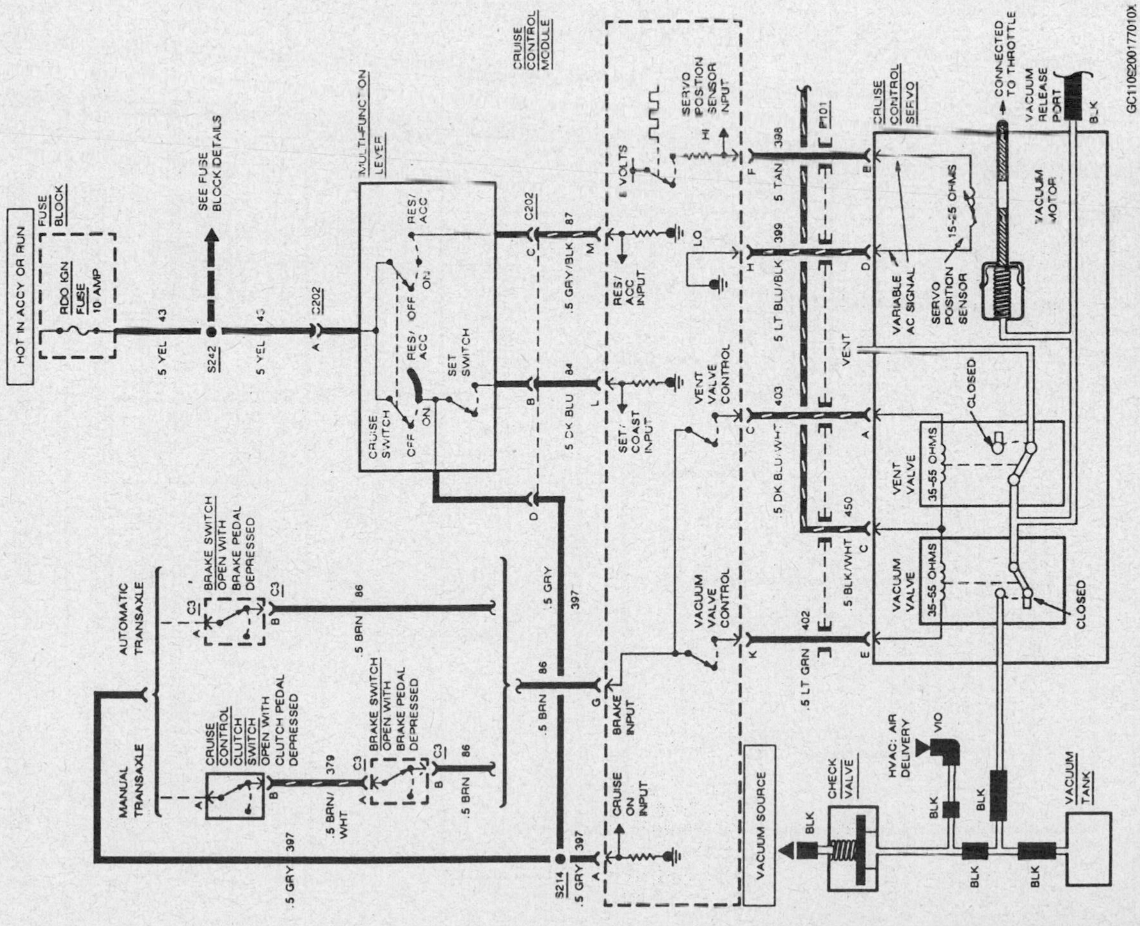

HOT IN ACCY OR RUN
RDO IGN FUSE 10 AMP
FUSE BLOCK
SEE FUSE BLOCK DETAILS
.5 YEL
43
S242
C202
MULTI-FUNCTION LEVER
CRUISE SWITCH
OFF
ON
RES/ACC
SET SWITCH
.5 DK BLU
84
.5 GRY/BLK
87
SET/COAST INPUT
RES/ACC INPUT
5 VOLTS
SERVO POSITION SENSOR INPUT
CRUISE CONTROL MODULE
MANUAL TRANSAXLE
AUTOMATIC TRANSAXLE
CRUISE CONTROL CLUTCH SWITCH
OPEN WITH CLUTCH PEDAL DEPRESSED
BRAKE SWITCH
OPEN WITH BRAKE PEDAL DEPRESSED
379
.5 BRN/WHT
86
.5 BRN
.5 GRY
397
S214
CRUISE ON INPUT
BRAKE INPUT
VACUUM VALVE CONTROL
VENT VALVE CONTROL
402
.5 LT GRN
.5 BLK/WHT
450
403
.5 DK BLU/WHT
399
.5 LT BLU/BLK
398
.5 TAN
P101
VACUUM SOURCE
VACUUM VALVE
35-55 OHMS
CLOSED
VENT VALVE
VARIABLE AC SIGNAL
SERVO POSITION SENSOR
15-25 OHMS
VACUUM MOTOR
CRUISE CONTROL SERVO
CONNECTED TO THROTTLE
VACUUM RELEASE PORT
CHECK VALVE
HVAC: AIR DELIVERY
VIO
BLK
VACUUM TANK
GC1109200177010X

Fig. 26 Wiring diagram (Part 1 of 2). 1992–93 Achieva & Grand Am

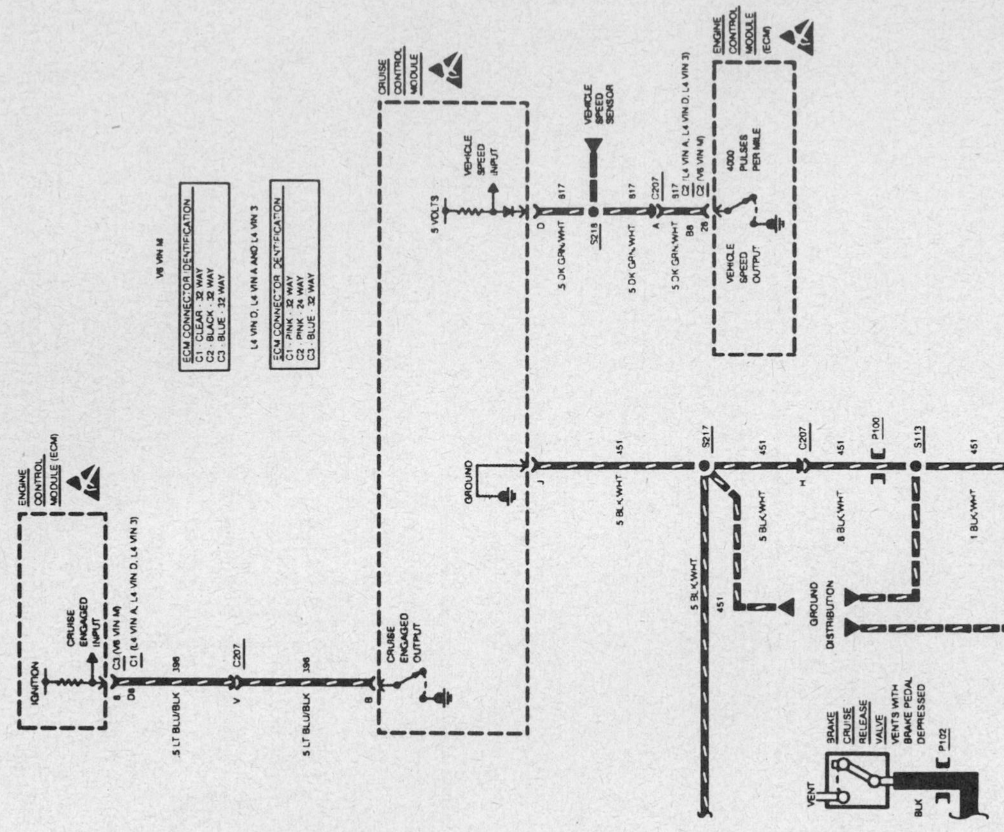
CRUISE CONTROL MODULE
ENGINE CONTROL MODULE (ECM)
ECM CONNECTOR IDENTIFICATION
C1 - CLEAR - 32 WAY
C2 - BLACK - 32 WAY
C3 - BLUE - 32 WAY
ECM CONNECTOR IDENTIFICATION
C1 - PINK - 32 WAY
C2 - PINK - 24 WAY
C3 - BLUE - 32 WAY
VEHICLE SPEED INPUT
VEHICLE SPEED SENSOR
VEHICLE SPEED OUTPUT
4000 PULSES PER MILE
CRUISE ENGAGED INPUT
CRUISE ENGAGED OUTPUT
GROUND
GROUND DISTRIBUTION
BRAKE CRUISE RELEASE VALVE VENTS WITH BRAKE PEDAL DEPRESSED
VENT
BLK
GC1109400319020X

Fig. 27 Wiring diagram (Part 2 of 2). 1994 Achieva, Grand Am & Skylark

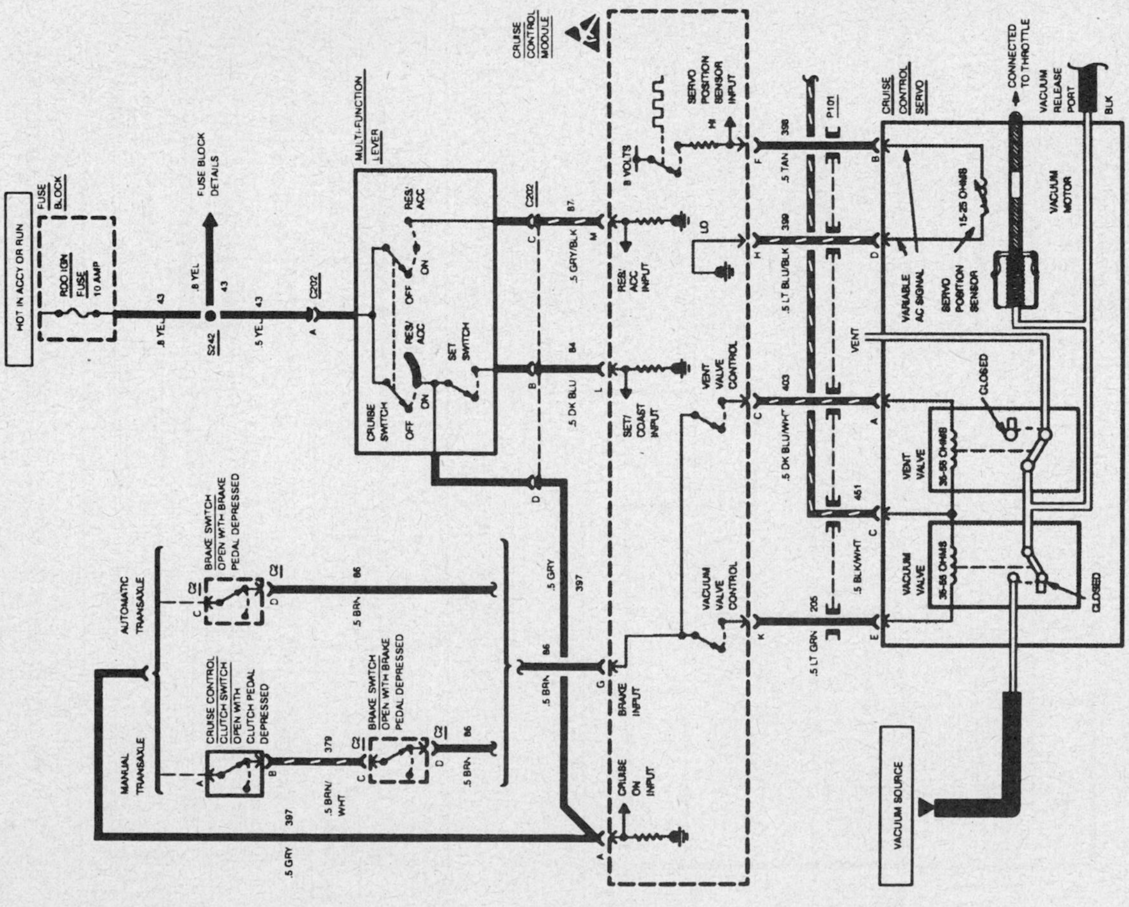
HOT IN ACCY OR RUN
FUSE BLOCK
ROO IGN FUSE 10 AMP
FUSE BLOCK DETAILS
MULTI-FUNCTION LEVER
CRUISE SWITCH
SET SWITCH
MANUAL TRANSAXLE
AUTOMATIC TRANSAXLE
CRUISE CONTROL CLUTCH SWITCH OPEN WITH CLUTCH PEDAL DEPRESSED
BRAKE SWITCH OPEN WITH BRAKE PEDAL DEPRESSED
CRUISE CONTROL MODULE
CRUISE ON INPUT
BRAKE INPUT
SET/ COAST INPUT
RES/ ACC INPUT
SERVO POSITION SENSOR INPUT
VACUUM VALVE CONTROL
VENT VALVE CONTROL
CRUISE CONTROL SERVO
VARIABLE AC SIGNAL
SERVO POSITION SENSOR
VACUUM MOTOR
VENT VALVE
VACUUM VALVE
CLOSED
CONNECTED TO THROTTLE
VACUUM RELEASE PORT
VACUUM SOURCE
BLK
GC1109400319010X

Fig. 27 Wiring diagram (Part 1 of 2). 1994 Achieva, Grand Am & Skylark

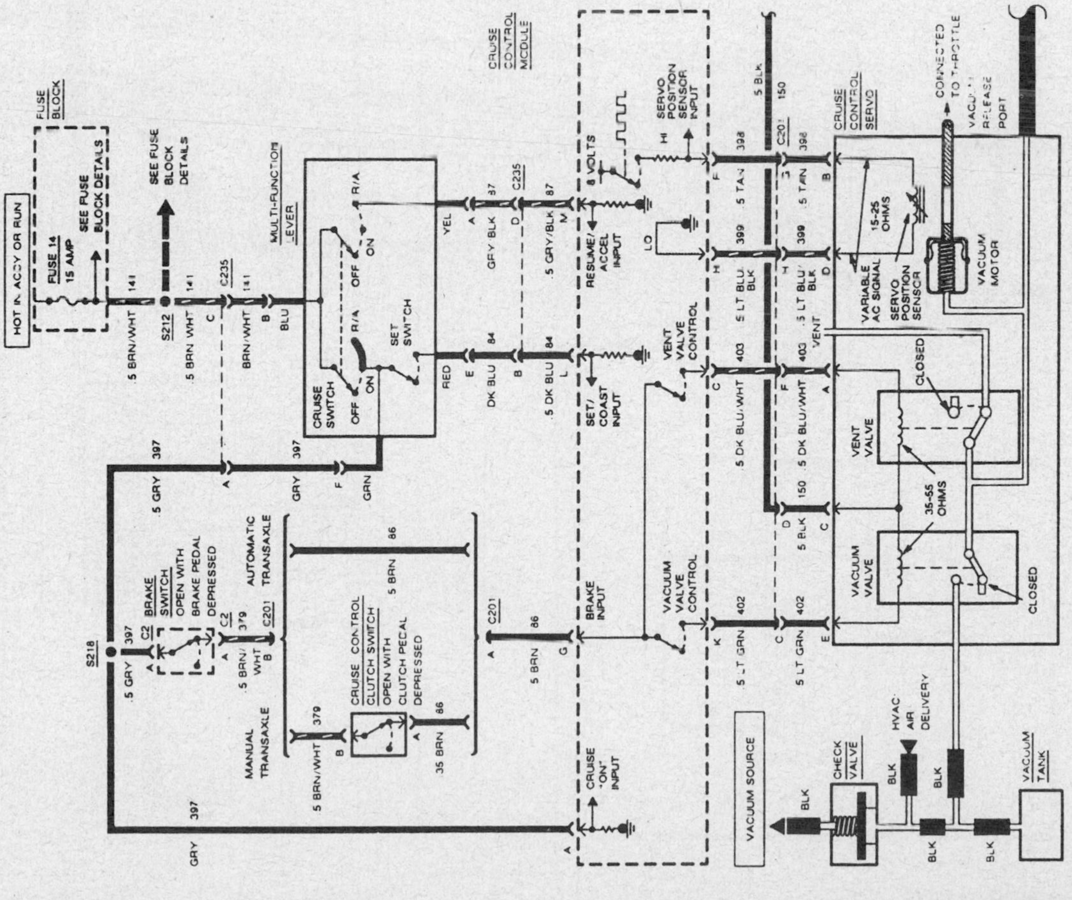

HOT IN ACCY OR RUN
FUSE BLOCK
FUSE 14 15 AMP
SEE FUSE BLOCK DETAILS
S212
S218
C235
C201
C235
MULTI-FUNCTION LEVER
CRUISE SWITCH
SET SWITCH
BRAKE SWITCH OPEN WITH BRAKE PEDAL DEPRESSED
CRUISE CONTROL CLUTCH SWITCH OPEN WITH CLUTCH PEDAL DEPRESSED
MANUAL TRANSAXLE
AUTOMATIC TRANSAXLE
CRUISE CONTROL MODULE
CRUISE "ON" INPUT
BRAKE INPUT
SET/ COAST INPUT
RESUME/ ACCEL INPUT
VENT VALVE CONTROL
VACUUM VALVE CONTROL
SERVO POSITION SENSOR INPUT
8 VOLTS
CRUISE CONTROL SERVO
VACUUM VALVE
VENT VALVE
35-55 OHMS
15-25 OHMS
CLOSED
VARIABLE AC SIGNAL
SERVO POSITION SENSOR
VACUUM MOTOR
CONNECTED TO THROTTLE
VACUUM RELEASE PORT
VACUUM SOURCE
CHECK VALVE
HVAC AIR DELIVERY
VACUUM TANK

Fig. 28 Wiring diagram (Part 1 of 2). 1992–93 Beretta & Corsica

GC1109200178010X

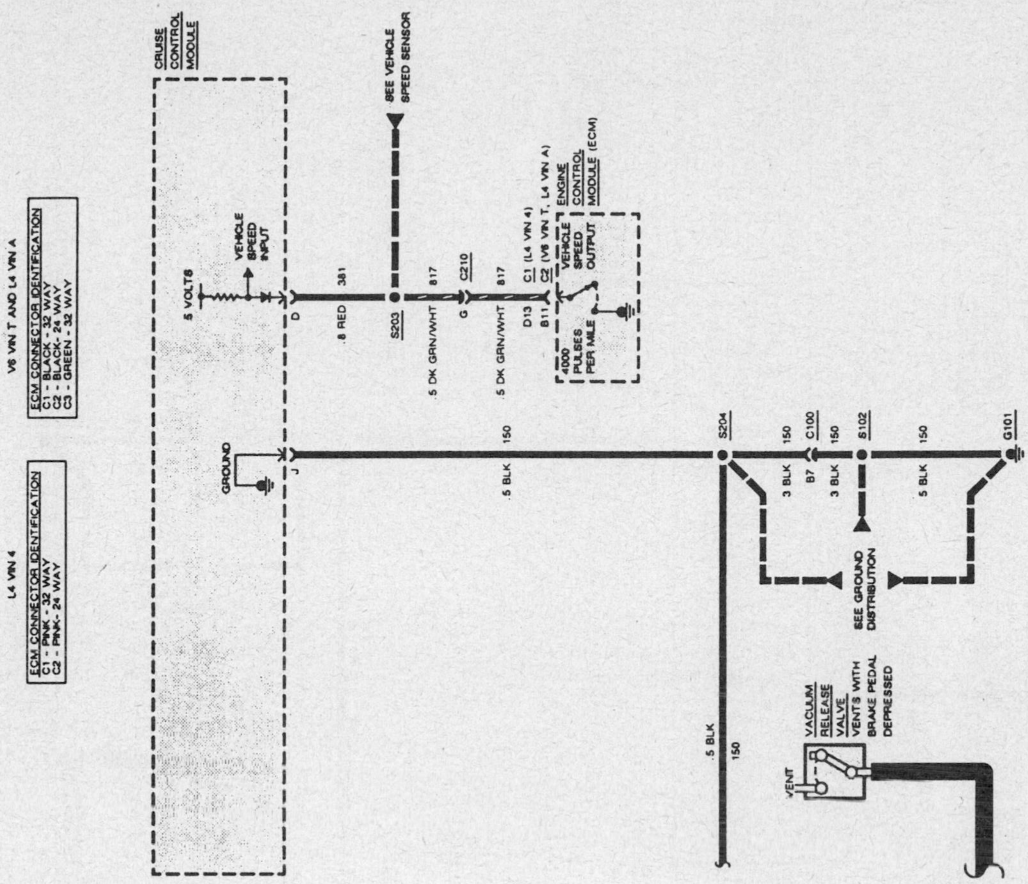

L4 VIN 4
ECM CONNECTOR IDENTIFICATION
C1 - PINK - 32 WAY
C2 - PINK - 24 WAY
V6 VIN T AND L4 VIN A
ECM CONNECTOR IDENTIFICATION
C1 - BLACK - 32 WAY
C2 - BLACK - 24 WAY
C3 - GREEN - 32 WAY
CRUISE CONTROL MODULE
GROUND
5 VOLTS
VEHICLE SPEED INPUT
SEE VEHICLE SPEED SENSOR
S203
C210
VEHICLE SPEED OUTPUT
4000 PULSES PER MILE
ENGINE CONTROL MODULE (ECM)
S204
C100
S102
G101
SEE GROUND DISTRIBUTION
VACUUM RELEASE VALVE VENTS WITH BRAKE PEDAL DEPRESSED
VENT

Fig. 28 Wiring diagram (Part 2 of 2). 1992–93 Beretta & Corsica

GC1109200178020X

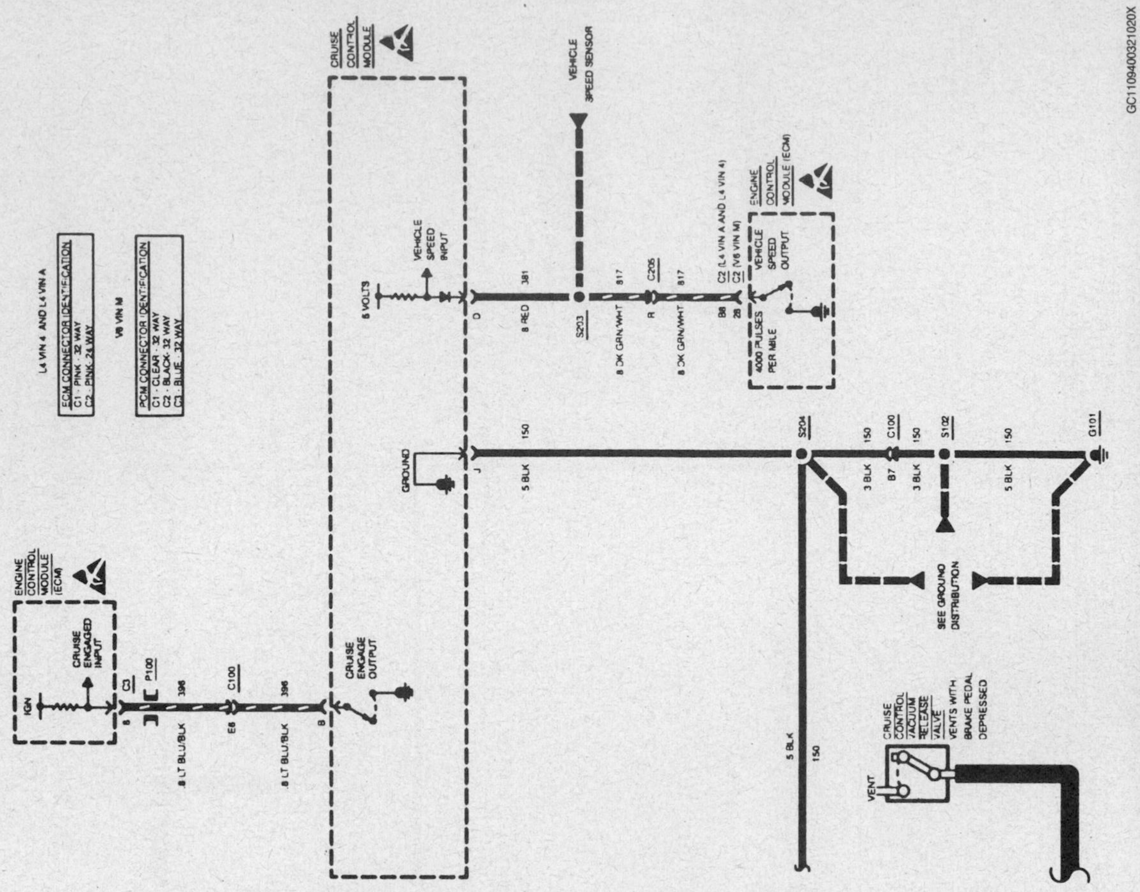

Fig. 29 Wiring diagram (Part 2 of 2). 1994 Corsica & Beretta

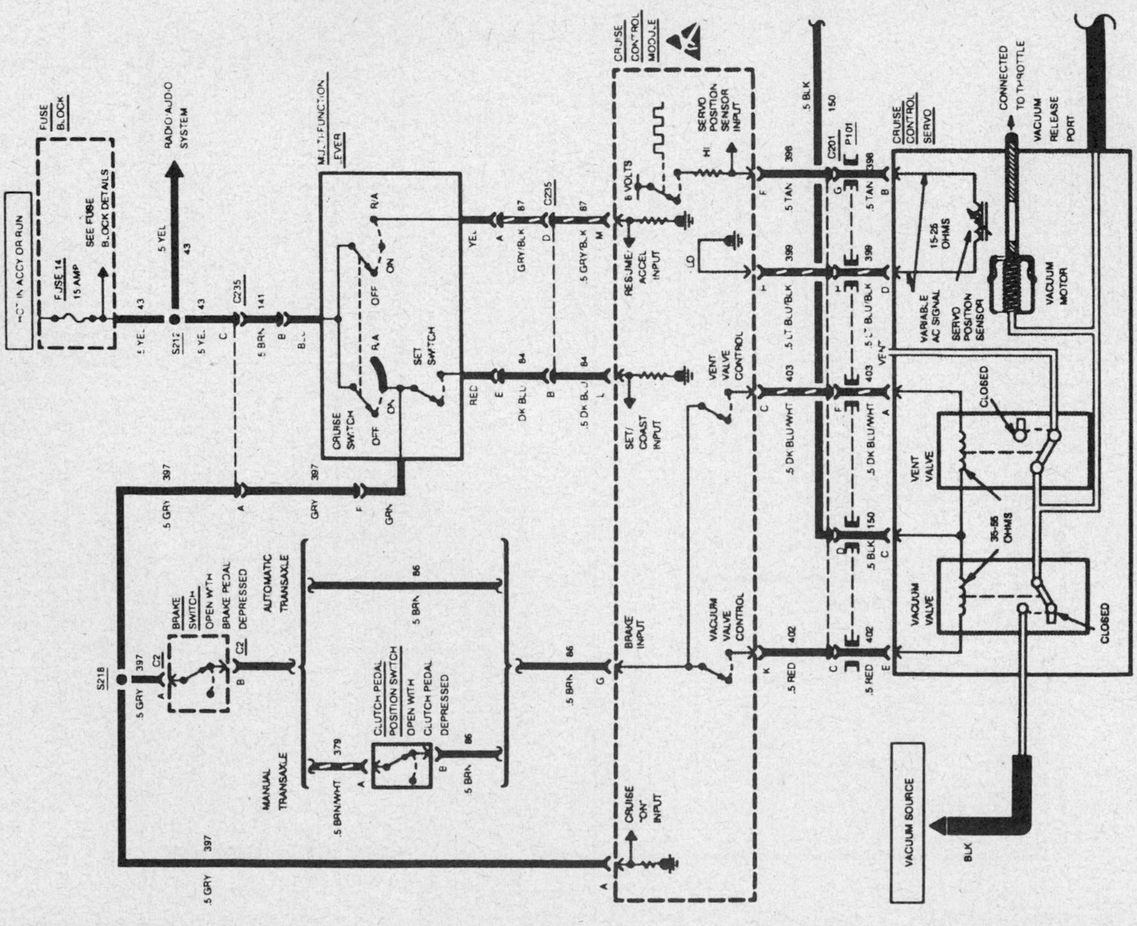

Fig. 29 Wiring diagram (Part 1 of 2). 1994 Corsica & Beretta

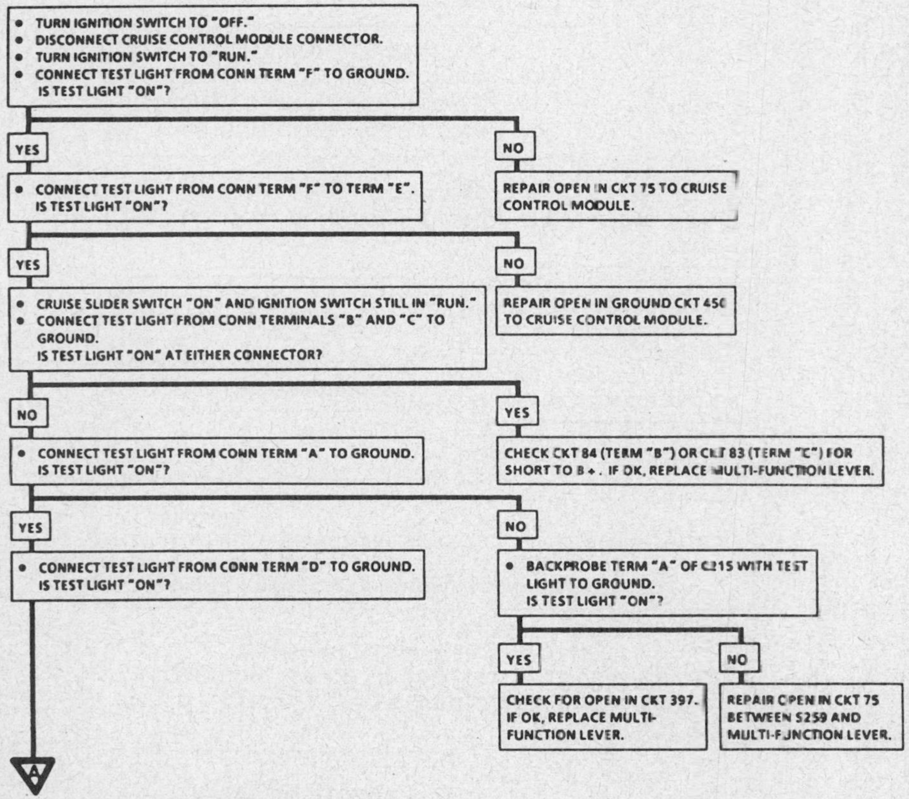
TURN IGNITION SWITCH TO "OFF."
DISCONNECT CRUISE CONTROL MODULE CONNECTOR.
TURN IGNITION SWITCH TO "RUN."
CONNECT TEST LIGHT FROM CONN TERM "F" TO GROUND. IS TEST LIGHT "ON"?
YES
NO
CONNECT TEST LIGHT FROM CONN TERM "F" TO TERM "E". IS TEST LIGHT "ON"?
REPAIR OPEN IN CKT 75 TO CRUISE CONTROL MODULE.
CRUISE SLIDER SWITCH "ON" AND IGNITION SWITCH STILL IN "RUN."
CONNECT TEST LIGHT FROM CONN TERMINALS "B" AND "C" TO GROUND. IS TEST LIGHT "ON" AT EITHER CONNECTOR?
REPAIR OPEN IN GROUND CKT 450 TO CRUISE CONTROL MODULE.
CONNECT TEST LIGHT FROM CONN TERM "A" TO GROUND. IS TEST LIGHT "ON"?
CHECK CKT 84 (TERM "B") OR CKT 83 (TERM "C") FOR SHORT TO B+. IF OK, REPLACE MULTI-FUNCTION LEVER.
CONNECT TEST LIGHT FROM CONN TERM "D" TO GROUND. IS TEST LIGHT "ON"?
BACKPROBE TERM "A" OF C215 WITH TEST LIGHT TO GROUND. IS TEST LIGHT "ON"?
CHECK FOR OPEN IN CKT 397. IF OK, REPLACE MULTI-FUNCTION LEVER.
REPAIR OPEN IN CKT 75 BETWEEN S259 AND MULTI-FUNCTION LEVER.
A

GC1109200180010X

Fig. 30 Test 1: Cruise Control Will Not Engage (Part 1 of 2). 1992 Caprice, Custom Cruiser & Roadmaster

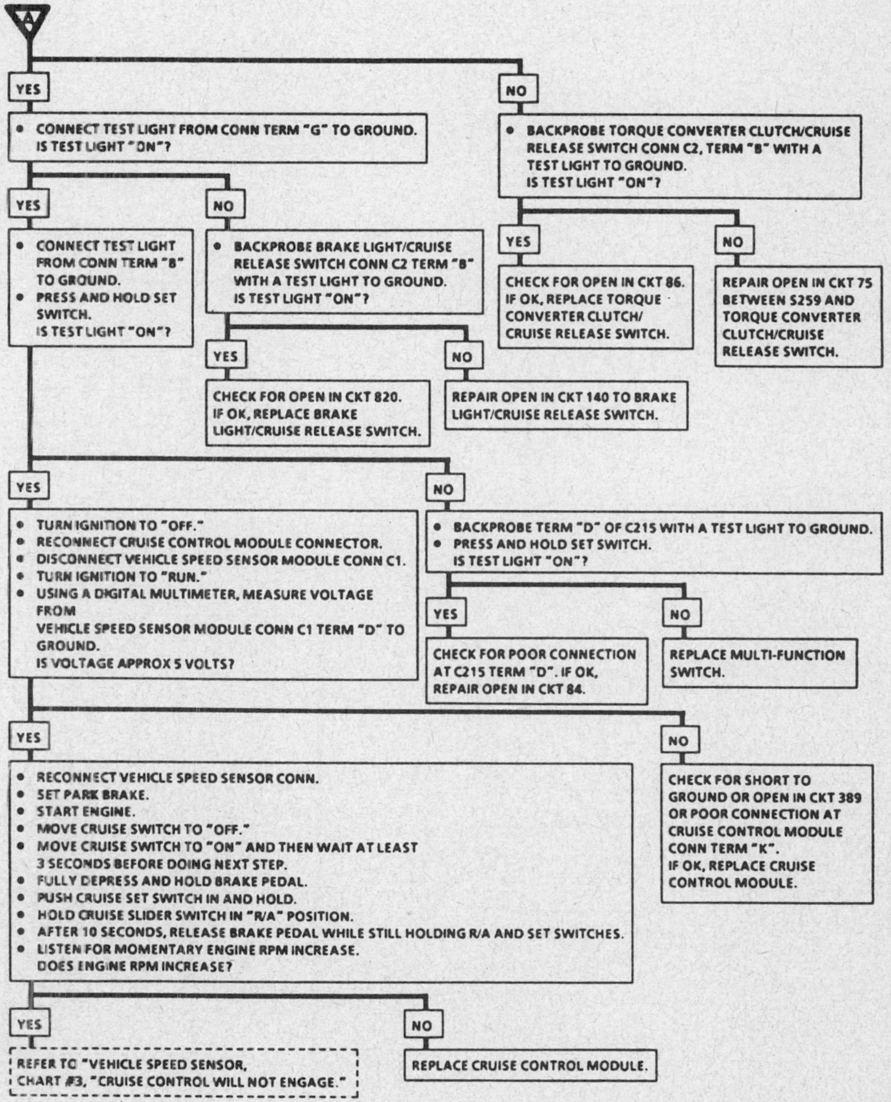
A
YES
NO
CONNECT TEST LIGHT FROM CONN TERM "G" TO GROUND. IS TEST LIGHT "ON"?
BACKPROBE TORQUE CONVERTER CLUTCH/CRUISE RELEASE SWITCH CONN C2, TERM "B" WITH A TEST LIGHT TO GROUND. IS TEST LIGHT "ON"?
CONNECT TEST LIGHT FROM CONN TERM "B" TO GROUND.
PRESS AND HOLD SET SWITCH. IS TEST LIGHT "ON"?
BACKPROBE BRAKE LIGHT/CRUISE RELEASE SWITCH CONN C2 TERM "B" WITH A TEST LIGHT TO GROUND. IS TEST LIGHT "ON"?
CHECK FOR OPEN IN CKT 86. IF OK, REPLACE TORQUE CONVERTER CLUTCH/ CRUISE RELEASE SWITCH.
REPAIR OPEN IN CKT 75 BETWEEN S259 AND TORQUE CONVERTER CLUTCH/CRUISE RELEASE SWITCH.
CHECK FOR OPEN IN CKT 820. IF OK, REPLACE BRAKE LIGHT/CRUISE RELEASE SWITCH.
REPAIR OPEN IN CKT 140 TO BRAKE LIGHT/CRUISE RELEASE SWITCH.
TURN IGNITION TO "OFF."
RECONNECT CRUISE CONTROL MODULE CONNECTOR.
DISCONNECT VEHICLE SPEED SENSOR MODULE CONN C1.
TURN IGNITION TO "RUN."
USING A DIGITAL MULTIMETER, MEASURE VOLTAGE FROM VEHICLE SPEED SENSOR MODULE CONN C1 TERM "D" TO GROUND. IS VOLTAGE APPROX 5 VOLTS?
BACKPROBE TERM "D" OF C215 WITH A TEST LIGHT TO GROUND.
PRESS AND HOLD SET SWITCH. IS TEST LIGHT "ON"?
CHECK FOR POOR CONNECTION AT C215 TERM "D". IF OK, REPAIR OPEN IN CKT 84.
REPLACE MULTI-FUNCTION SWITCH.
RECONNECT VEHICLE SPEED SENSOR CONN.
SET PARK BRAKE.
START ENGINE.
MOVE CRUISE SWITCH TO "OFF."
MOVE CRUISE SWITCH TO "ON" AND THEN WAIT AT LEAST 3 SECONDS BEFORE DOING NEXT STEP.
FULLY DEPRESS AND HOLD BRAKE PEDAL.
PUSH CRUISE SET SWITCH IN AND HOLD.
HOLD CRUISE SLIDER SWITCH IN "R/A" POSITION.
AFTER 10 SECONDS, RELEASE BRAKE PEDAL WHILE STILL HOLDING R/A AND SET SWITCHES.
LISTEN FOR MOMENTARY ENGINE RPM INCREASE. DOES ENGINE RPM INCREASE?
CHECK FOR SHORT TO GROUND OR OPEN IN CKT 389 OR POOR CONNECTION AT CRUISE CONTROL MODULE CONN TERM "K". IF OK, REPLACE CRUISE CONTROL MODULE.
REFER TO "VEHICLE SPEED SENSOR, CHART #3, "CRUISE CONTROL WILL NOT ENGAGE."
REPLACE CRUISE CONTROL MODULE.

GC1109200180020X

Fig. 30 Test 1: Cruise Control Will Not Engage (Part 2 of 2). 1992 Caprice, Custom Cruiser & Roadmaster

- TURN IGNITION SWITCH TO "RUN."
- CRUISE CONTROL SWITCH TO "ON."
- BACKPROBE C215 WITH A TEST LIGHT FROM TERM "C" TO GROUND.
- PRESS RESUME/ACCEL SWITCH.
  IS TEST LIGHT ON?

YES → CHECK FOR OPEN IN CKT 83. ALSO CHECK FOR POOR CONNECTION AT CRUISE CONTROL MODULE TERM "C". IF OK, REPLACE CRUISE CONTROL MODULE.

NO → REPLACE MULTI-FUNCTION LEVER.

GC1109200181000X

Fig. 31 Test 2: Cruise Control Will Not Resume, Accelerate, Tap-Up Or Tap-Down. 1992 Caprice, Custom Cruiser & Roadmaster

- DISCONNECT CRUISE CONTROL MODULE CONNECTOR.
- TURN IGNITION SWITCH TO "RUN."
- MEASURE VOLTAGE FROM CRUISE CONTROL MODULE CONN TERM "J" TO GROUND.

B+ → CHECK FOR POOR CONNECTION AT CRUISE CONTROL MODULE CONN TERM "J". IF OK, REPLACE CRUISE CONTROL MODULE.

0 VOLT → CHECK FOR POOR CONNECTION AT C200 TERM "C1", INSTRUMENT CLUSTER CONN C2 TERM "B6" OR "CRUISE" INDICATOR LAMP, OR OPEN IN CKT 1677.

GC1109200182000X

Fig. 32 Test 3: Cruise Indicator Inoperative. 1992 Roadmaster

- TURN IGNITION SWITCH TO "RUN."
- CRUISE CONTROL SWITCH "OFF."
- DISCONNECT CRUISE CONTROL MODULE.
  IS "CRUISE" INDICATOR ON?

YES → CHECK FOR SHORT TO GROUND ON CKT 1677. IF OK, SERVICE INSTRUMENT CLUSTER.

NO → REPLACE CRUISE CONTROL MODULE.

GC1109200183000X

Fig. 33 Test 4: Cruise Indicator On At All Times. 1992 Roadmaster

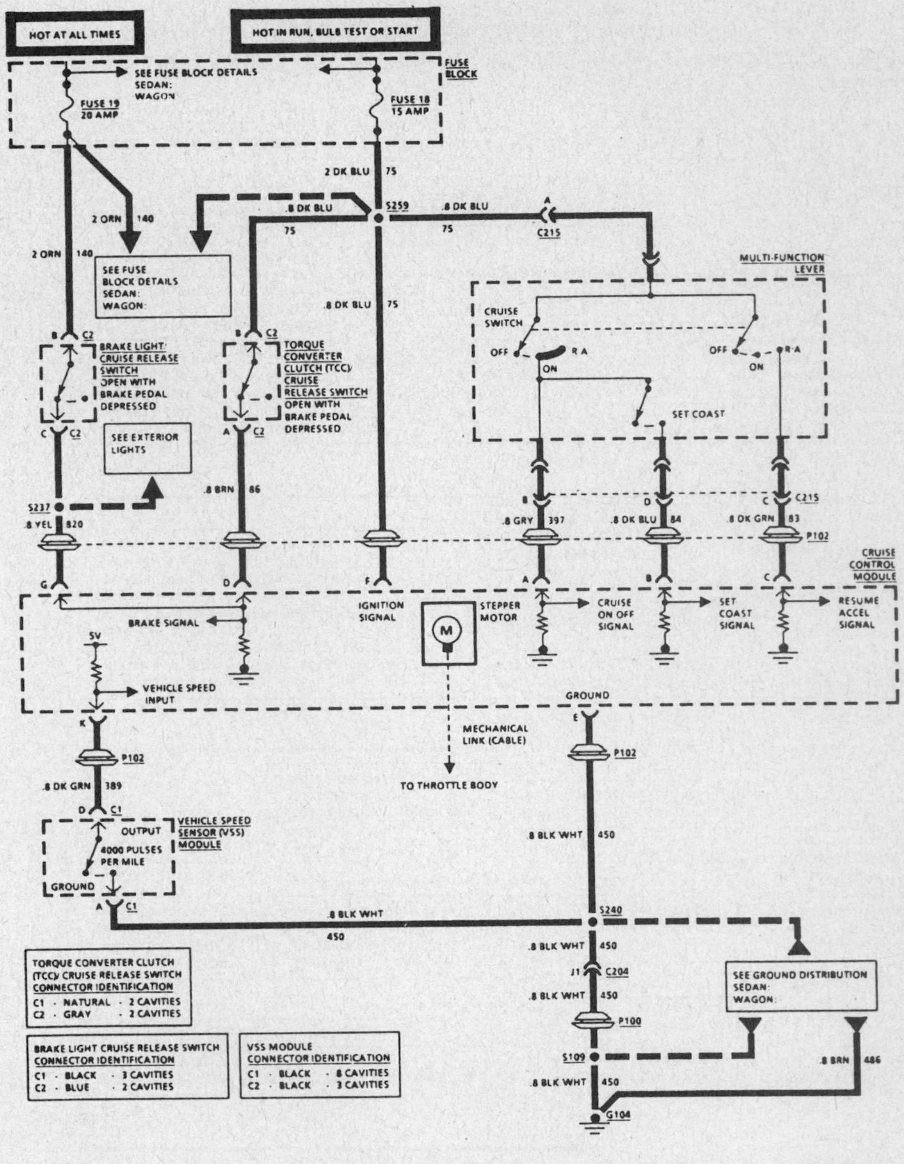
HOT AT ALL TIMES
HOT IN RUN, BULB TEST OR START
FUSE BLOCK
SEE FUSE BLOCK DETAILS SEDAN: WAGON:
FUSE 19 20 AMP
FUSE 18 15 AMP
MULTI-FUNCTION LEVER
CRUISE SWITCH
SET COAST
BRAKE LIGHT/ CRUISE RELEASE SWITCH OPEN WITH BRAKE PEDAL DEPRESSED
TORQUE CONVERTER CLUTCH (TCC)/ CRUISE RELEASE SWITCH OPEN WITH BRAKE PEDAL DEPRESSED
SEE EXTERIOR LIGHTS
CRUISE CONTROL MODULE
BRAKE SIGNAL
IGNITION SIGNAL
STEPPER MOTOR
CRUISE ON OFF SIGNAL
SET COAST SIGNAL
RESUME ACCEL SIGNAL
VEHICLE SPEED INPUT
GROUND
MECHANICAL LINK (CABLE)
TO THROTTLE BODY
VEHICLE SPEED SENSOR (VSS) MODULE
OUTPUT
4000 PULSES PER MILE
SEE GROUND DISTRIBUTION SEDAN: WAGON:
TORQUE CONVERTER CLUTCH (TCC) CRUISE RELEASE SWITCH CONNECTOR IDENTIFICATION
C1 - NATURAL - 2 CAVITIES
C2 - GRAY - 2 CAVITIES
BRAKE LIGHT CRUISE RELEASE SWITCH CONNECTOR IDENTIFICATION
C1 - BLACK - 3 CAVITIES
C2 - BLUE - 2 CAVITIES
VSS MODULE CONNECTOR IDENTIFICATION
C1 - BLACK - 8 CAVITIES
C2 - BLACK - 3 CAVITIES

GC1109200184000X

Fig. 34 Wiring diagram . 1992 Caprice & Custom Cruiser

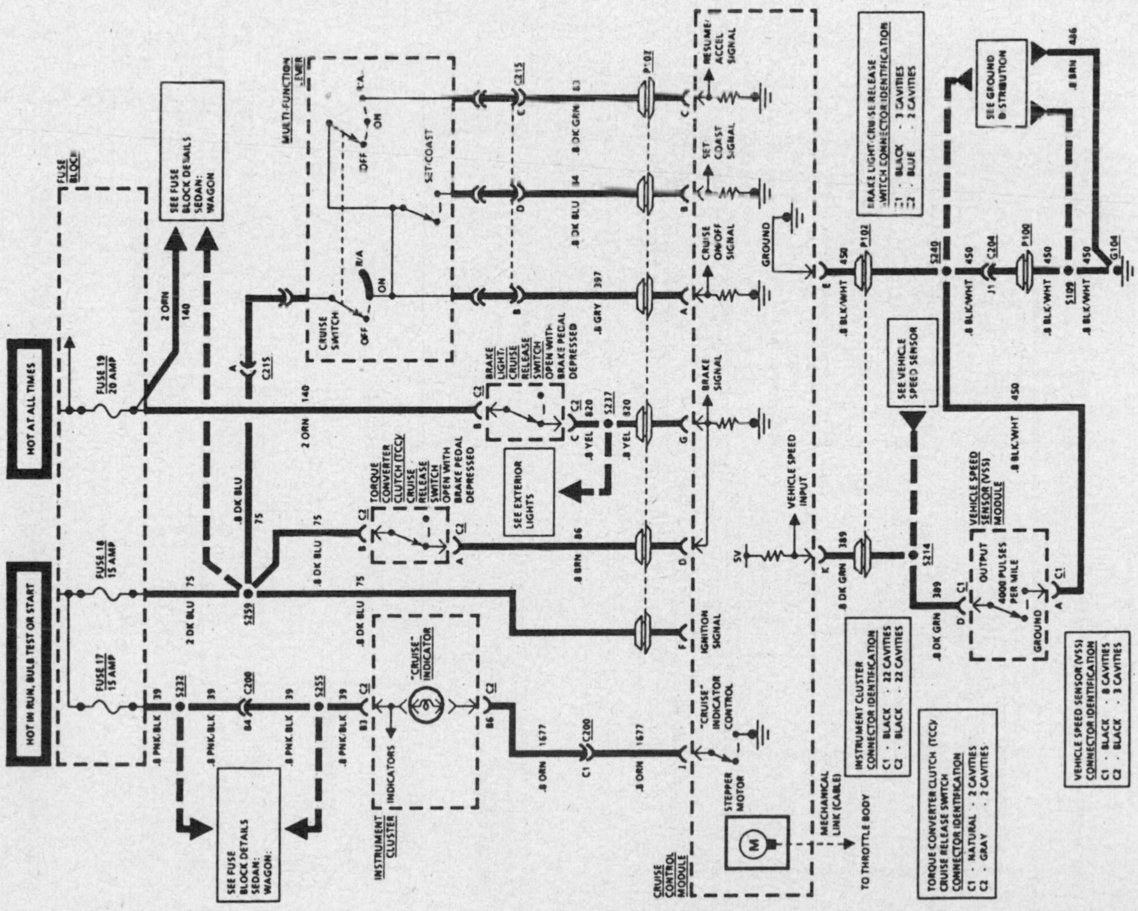
HOT IN RUN, BULB TEST OR START
HOT AT ALL TIMES
FUSE BLOCK
FUSE 17 15 AMP
FUSE 18 15 AMP
FUSE 19 20 AMP
SEE FUSE BLOCK DETAILS SEDAN: WAGON:
INSTRUMENT CLUSTER
"CRUISE" INDICATOR
INDICATORS
TORQUE CONVERTER CLUTCH (TCC) CRUISE RELEASE SWITCH OPEN WITH BRAKE PEDAL DEPRESSED
BRAKE LIGHT/ CRUISE RELEASE SWITCH OPEN WITH BRAKE PEDAL DEPRESSED
SEE EXTERIOR LIGHTS
MULTI-FUNCTION LEVER
CRUISE SWITCH
SET/COAST
CRUISE CONTROL MODULE
STEPPER MOTOR
MECHANICAL LINK (CABLE)
TO THROTTLE BODY
"CRUISE" INDICATOR CONTROL
IGNITION SIGNAL
VEHICLE SPEED INPUT
BRAKE SIGNAL
CRUISE ON/OFF SIGNAL
SET COAST SIGNAL
RESUME/ ACCEL SIGNAL
GROUND
SEE VEHICLE SPEED SENSOR
VEHICLE SPEED SENSOR (VSS) MODULE
4000 PULSES PER MILE
OUTPUT
SEE GROUND DISTRIBUTION
INSTRUMENT CLUSTER CONNECTOR IDENTIFICATION
C1 : BLACK : 22 CAVITIES
C2 : BLACK : 22 CAVITIES
TORQUE CONVERTER CLUTCH (TCC) CRUISE RELEASE SWITCH CONNECTOR IDENTIFICATION
C1 : NATURAL : 2 CAVITIES
C2 : GRAY : 2 CAVITIES
BRAKE LIGHT/CRUISE RELEASE SWITCH CONNECTOR IDENTIFICATION
C1 : BLACK : 3 CAVITIES
C2 : BLUE : 2 CAVITIES
VEHICLE SPEED SENSOR (VSS) CONNECTOR IDENTIFICATION
C1 : BLACK : 8 CAVITIES
C2 : BLACK : 3 CAVITIES
GC1109200185000X

Fig. 35 Wiring diagram. 1992 Roadmaster

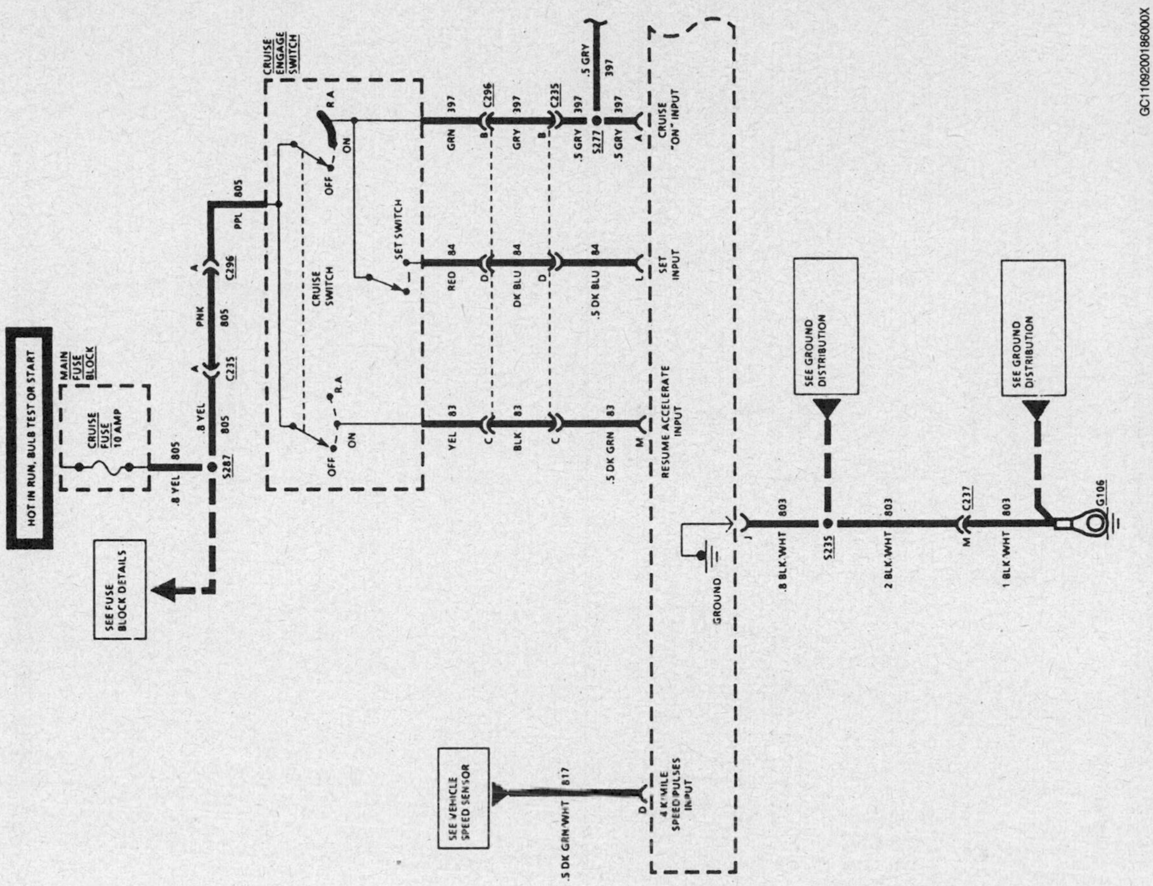
HOT IN RUN, BULB TEST OR START
MAIN FUSE BLOCK
CRUISE FUSE 10 AMP
SEE FUSE BLOCK DETAILS
CRUISE ENGAGE SWITCH
CRUISE SWITCH
SET SWITCH
SEE VEHICLE SPEED SENSOR
4 K/MILE SPEED PULSES INPUT
RESUME ACCELERATE INPUT
SET INPUT
CRUISE "ON" INPUT
GROUND
SEE GROUND DISTRIBUTION
GC1109200186000X

Fig. 36 Cruise control wiring diagram, (Part 1 of 2). 1992–93 Corvette

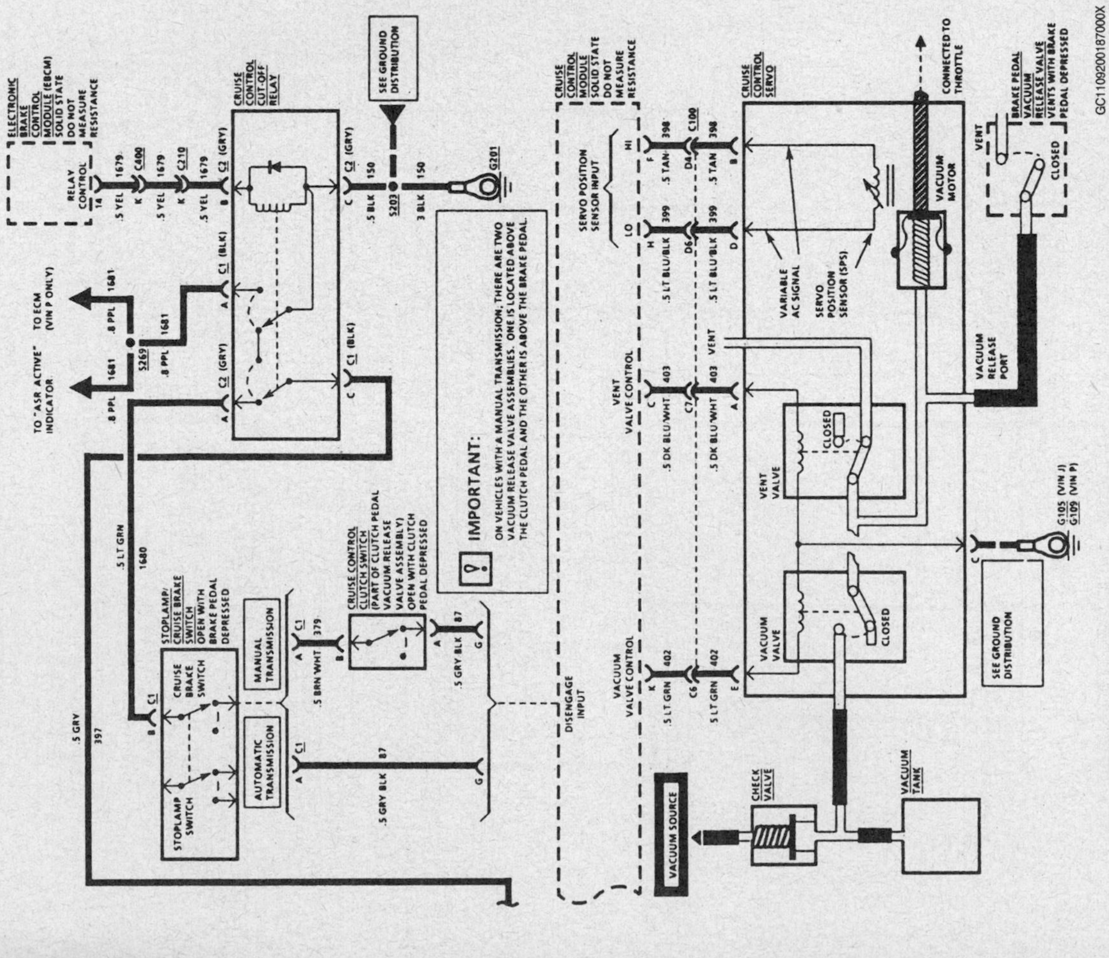
STOPLAMP SWITCH
STOPLAMP/CRUISE BRAKE SWITCH OPEN WITH BRAKE PEDAL DEPRESSED
AUTOMATIC TRANSMISSION
MANUAL TRANSMISSION
CRUISE CONTROL CLUTCH SWITCH (PART OF CLUTCH PEDAL VACUUM RELEASE VALVE ASSEMBLY) OPEN WITH CLUTCH PEDAL DEPRESSED
IMPORTANT:
ON VEHICLES WITH A MANUAL TRANSMISSION, THERE ARE TWO VACUUM RELEASE VALVE ASSEMBLIES. ONE IS LOCATED ABOVE THE CLUTCH PEDAL AND THE OTHER IS ABOVE THE BRAKE PEDAL.
TO "ASR ACTIVE" INDICATOR
TO ECM (VIN P ONLY)
CRUISE CONTROL CUT-OFF RELAY
ELECTRONIC BRAKE CONTROL MODULE (EBCM) SOLID STATE DO NOT MEASURE RESISTANCE
RELAY CONTROL
SEE GROUND DISTRIBUTION
CRUISE CONTROL MODULE SOLID STATE DO NOT MEASURE RESISTANCE
DISENGAGE INPUT
VACUUM VALVE CONTROL
VENT VALVE CONTROL
SERVO POSITION SENSOR INPUT
CRUISE CONTROL SERVO
VARIABLE AC SIGNAL
SERVO POSITION SENSOR (SPS)
VACUUM MOTOR
CONNECTED TO THROTTLE
VACUUM RELEASE PORT
BRAKE PEDAL VACUUM RELEASE VALVE VENTS WITH BRAKE PEDAL DEPRESSED
VENT VALVE
VACUUM VALVE
CLOSED
VACUUM SOURCE
CHECK VALVE
VACUUM TANK
G105 (VIN J)
G109 (VIN P)

GC1109200187000X

Fig. 36 Cruise control wiring diagram, (Part 2 of 2). 1992–93 Corvette

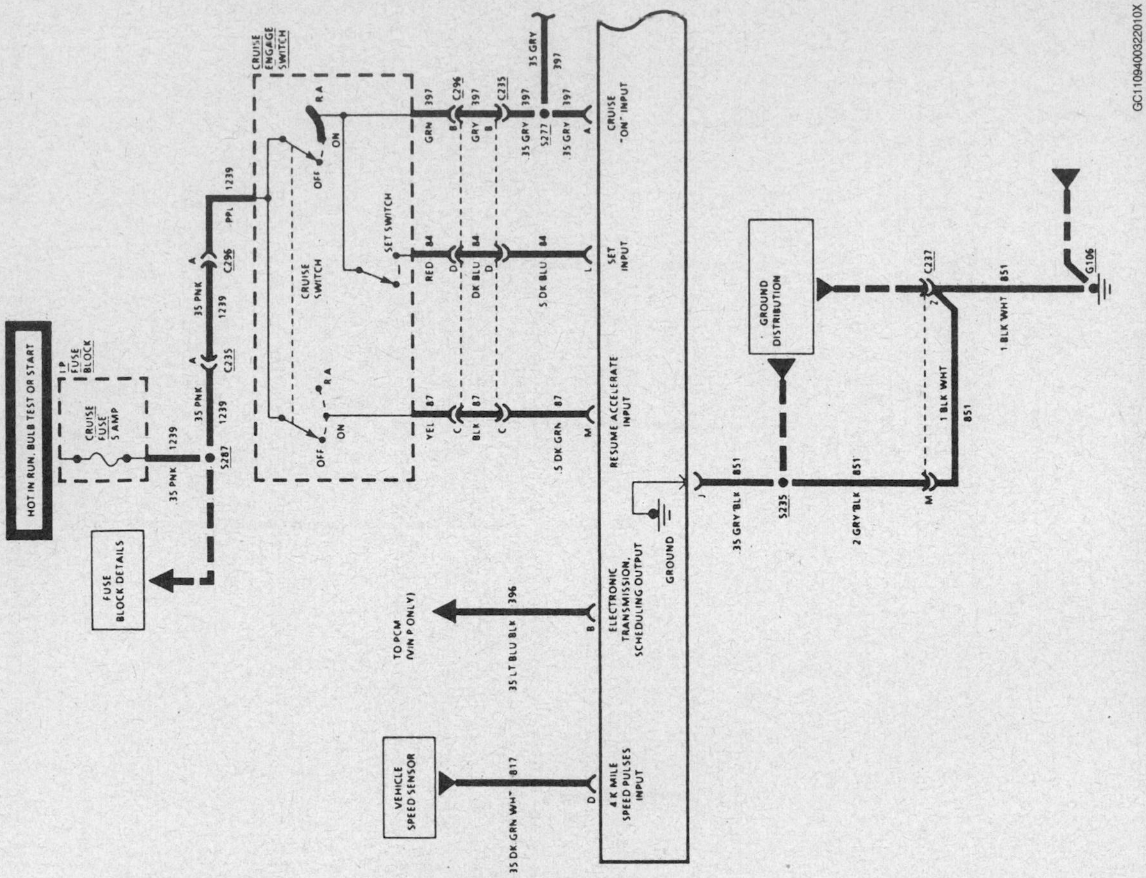
HOT IN RUN, BULB TEST OR START
I/P FUSE BLOCK
CRUISE FUSE 5 AMP
FUSE BLOCK DETAILS
CRUISE ENGAGE SWITCH
CRUISE SWITCH
SET SWITCH
VEHICLE SPEED SENSOR
TO PCM (VIN P ONLY)
4K MILE SPEED PULSES INPUT
ELECTRONIC TRANSMISSION SCHEDULING OUTPUT
GROUND
RESUME ACCELERATE INPUT
SET INPUT
CRUISE "ON" INPUT
GROUND DISTRIBUTION

GC1109400322010X

Fig. 37 Wiring diagram (Part 1 of 2). 1994 Corvette

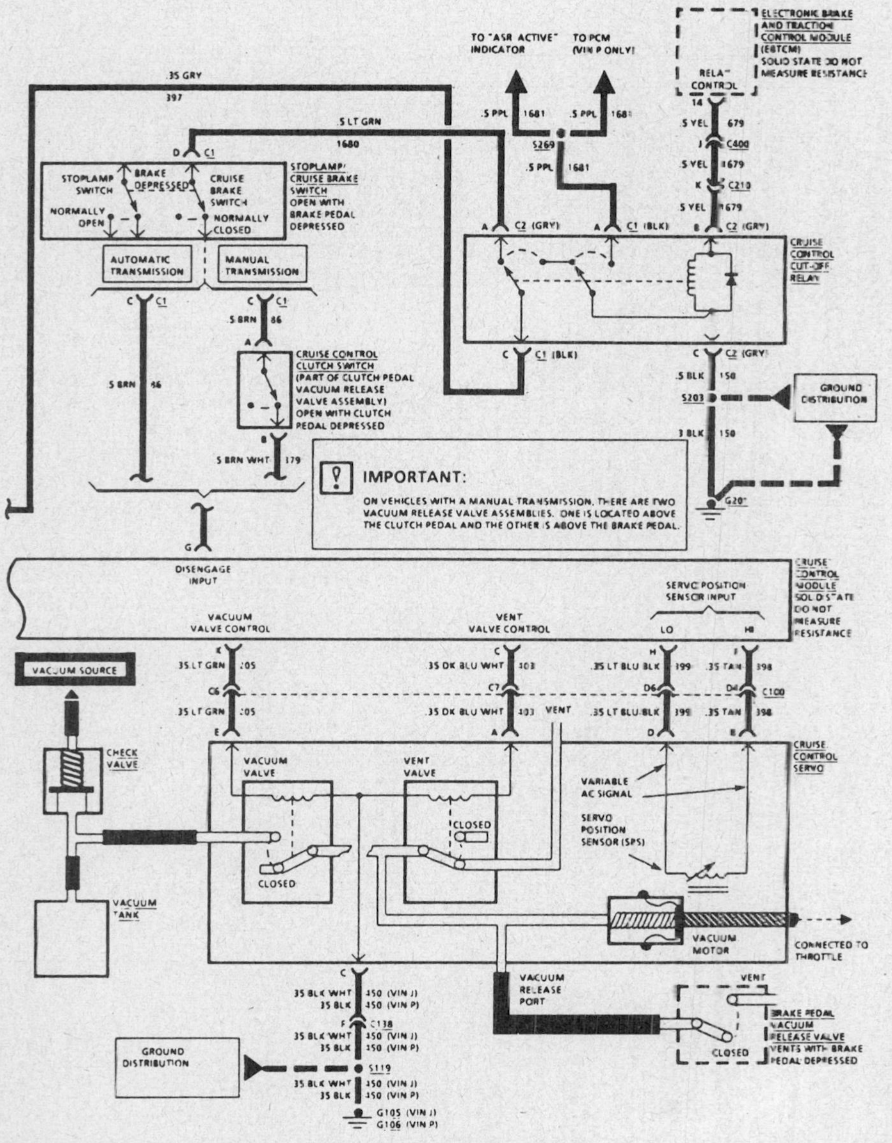
TO "ASR ACTIVE" INDICATOR
TO PCM (VIN P ONLY)
ELECTRONIC BRAKE AND TRACTION CONTROL MODULE (EBTCM) SOLID STATE DO NOT MEASURE RESISTANCE
RELAY CONTROL
STOPLAMP SWITCH
NORMALLY OPEN
BRAKE DEPRESSED
CRUISE BRAKE SWITCH
NORMALLY CLOSED
STOPLAMP/ CRUISE BRAKE SWITCH OPEN WITH BRAKE PEDAL DEPRESSED
AUTOMATIC TRANSMISSION
MANUAL TRANSMISSION
CRUISE CONTROL CLUTCH SWITCH (PART OF CLUTCH PEDAL VACUUM RELEASE VALVE ASSEMBLY) OPEN WITH CLUTCH PEDAL DEPRESSED
CRUISE CONTROL CUT-OFF RELAY
GROUND DISTRIBUTION
IMPORTANT:
ON VEHICLES WITH A MANUAL TRANSMISSION, THERE ARE TWO VACUUM RELEASE VALVE ASSEMBLIES. ONE IS LOCATED ABOVE THE CLUTCH PEDAL AND THE OTHER IS ABOVE THE BRAKE PEDAL.
DISENGAGE INPUT
VACUUM VALVE CONTROL
VENT VALVE CONTROL
SERVO POSITION SENSOR INPUT
LO
HI
CRUISE CONTROL MODULE SOLID STATE DO NOT MEASURE RESISTANCE
VACUUM SOURCE
CHECK VALVE
VACUUM TANK
VACUUM VALVE
VENT VALVE
CLOSED
VARIABLE AC SIGNAL
SERVO POSITION SENSOR (SPS)
VACUUM MOTOR
CRUISE CONTROL SERVO
CONNECTED TO THROTTLE
VACUUM RELEASE PORT
VENT
BRAKE PEDAL VACUUM RELEASE VALVE VENTS WITH BRAKE PEDAL DEPRESSED

GC1109400322020X

Fig. 37 Wiring diagram (Part 2 of 2). 1994 Corvette

SYMPTOM	PROCEDURE
Cruise will,not engage.	Chart #1
Cruise will not maintain set speed or cruise surges.	Chart #2
Does not resume, accelerate or tap up	Chart #3

GC1109100188000X

Fig. 38 Cruise control symptom chart. Corvette

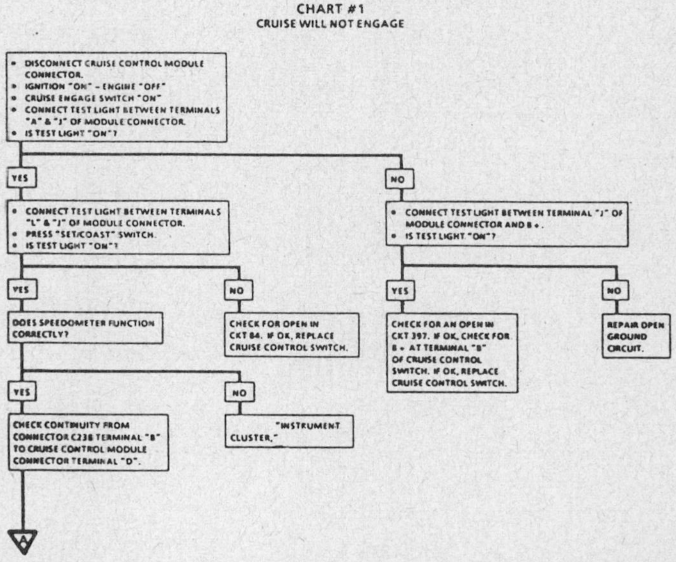
CHART #1
CRUISE WILL NOT ENGAGE
• DISCONNECT CRUISE CONTROL MODULE CONNECTOR.
• IGNITION "ON" - ENGINE "OFF"
• CRUISE ENGAGE SWITCH "ON"
• CONNECT TEST LIGHT BETWEEN TERMINALS "A" & "J" OF MODULE CONNECTOR.
• IS TEST LIGHT "ON"?
YES
NO
• CONNECT TEST LIGHT BETWEEN TERMINALS "L" & "J" OF MODULE CONNECTOR.
• PRESS "SET/COAST" SWITCH.
• IS TEST LIGHT "ON"?
• CONNECT TEST LIGHT BETWEEN TERMINAL "J" OF MODULE CONNECTOR AND B+.
• IS TEST LIGHT "ON"?
DOES SPEEDOMETER FUNCTION CORRECTLY?
CHECK FOR OPEN IN CKT 84. IF OK, REPLACE CRUISE CONTROL SWITCH.
CHECK FOR AN OPEN IN CKT 397. IF OK, CHECK FOR B+ AT TERMINAL "B" OF CRUISE CONTROL SWITCH. IF OK, REPLACE CRUISE CONTROL SWITCH.
REPAIR OPEN GROUND CIRCUIT.
CHECK CONTINUITY FROM CONNECTOR C238 TERMINAL "B" TO CRUISE CONTROL MODULE CONNECTOR TERMINAL "D".
"INSTRUMENT CLUSTER,"
A

GC1109100189010X

Fig. 39 Test 1: Cruise Control System Diagnosis (Part 1 Of 3). 1992 Corvette

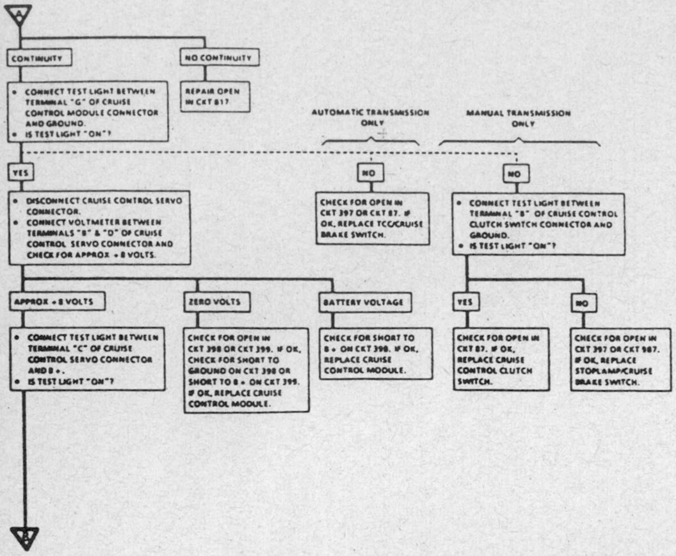
A
CONTINUITY
NO CONTINUITY
• CONNECT TEST LIGHT BETWEEN TERMINAL "G" OF CRUISE CONTROL MODULE CONNECTOR AND GROUND.
• IS TEST LIGHT "ON"?
REPAIR OPEN IN CKT 81?
AUTOMATIC TRANSMISSION ONLY
MANUAL TRANSMISSION ONLY
YES
NO
NO
• DISCONNECT CRUISE CONTROL SERVO CONNECTOR.
• CONNECT VOLTMETER BETWEEN TERMINALS "B" & "D" OF CRUISE CONTROL SERVO CONNECTOR AND CHECK FOR APPROX +8 VOLTS.
CHECK FOR OPEN IN CKT 397 OR CKT 87. IF OK, REPLACE TCC/CRUISE BRAKE SWITCH.
• CONNECT TEST LIGHT BETWEEN TERMINAL "B" OF CRUISE CONTROL CLUTCH SWITCH CONNECTOR AND GROUND.
• IS TEST LIGHT "ON"?
APPROX +8 VOLTS
ZERO VOLTS
BATTERY VOLTAGE
YES
NO
• CONNECT TEST LIGHT BETWEEN TERMINAL "C" OF CRUISE CONTROL SERVO CONNECTOR AND B+.
• IS TEST LIGHT "ON"?
CHECK FOR OPEN IN CKT 398 OR CKT 399. IF OK, CHECK FOR SHORT TO GROUND ON CKT 398 OR SHORT TO B+ ON CKT 399. IF OK, REPLACE CRUISE CONTROL MODULE.
CHECK FOR SHORT TO B+ ON CKT 398. IF OK, REPLACE CRUISE CONTROL MODULE.
CHECK FOR OPEN IN CKT 87. IF OK, REPLACE CRUISE CONTROL CLUTCH SWITCH.
CHECK FOR OPEN IN CKT 397 OR CKT 987. IF OK, REPLACE STOPLAMP/CRUISE BRAKE SWITCH.
B

GC1109100189020X

Fig. 39 Test 1: Cruise Control System Diagnosis (Part 2 Of 3). 1992 Corvette

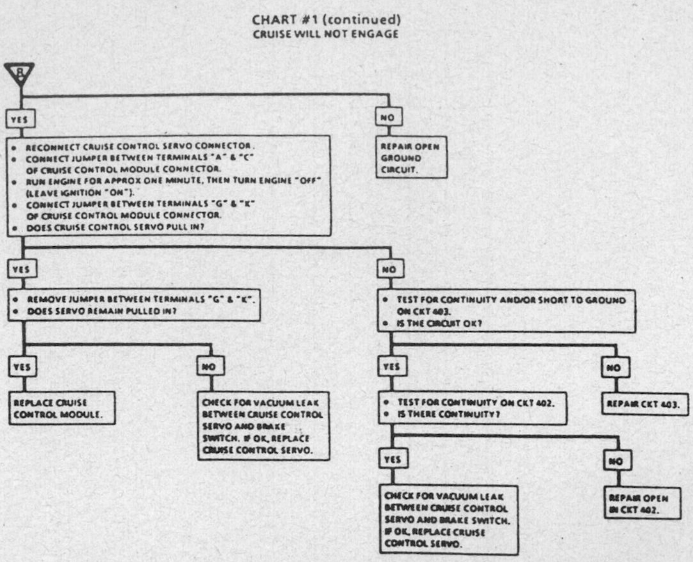
CHART #1 (continued)
CRUISE WILL NOT ENGAGE
B
YES
NO
• RECONNECT CRUISE CONTROL SERVO CONNECTOR.
• CONNECT JUMPER BETWEEN TERMINALS "A" & "C" OF CRUISE CONTROL MODULE CONNECTOR.
• RUN ENGINE FOR APPROX ONE MINUTE, THEN TURN ENGINE "OFF" (LEAVE IGNITION "ON").
• CONNECT JUMPER BETWEEN TERMINALS "G" & "K" OF CRUISE CONTROL MODULE CONNECTOR.
• DOES CRUISE CONTROL SERVO PULL IN?
REPAIR OPEN GROUND CIRCUIT.
YES
NO
• REMOVE JUMPER BETWEEN TERMINALS "G" & "K".
• DOES SERVO REMAIN PULLED IN?
• TEST FOR CONTINUITY AND/OR SHORT TO GROUND ON CKT 403.
• IS THE CIRCUIT OK?
YES
NO
YES
NO
REPLACE CRUISE CONTROL MODULE.
CHECK FOR VACUUM LEAK BETWEEN CRUISE CONTROL SERVO AND BRAKE SWITCH. IF OK, REPLACE CRUISE CONTROL SERVO.
• TEST FOR CONTINUITY ON CKT 402.
• IS THERE CONTINUITY?
REPAIR CKT 403.
YES
NO
CHECK FOR VACUUM LEAK BETWEEN CRUISE CONTROL SERVO AND BRAKE SWITCH. IF OK, REPLACE CRUISE CONTROL SERVO.
REPAIR OPEN IN CKT 402.

GC1109100189030X

Fig. 39 Test 1: Cruise Control System Diagnosis (Part 3 Of 3). 1992 Corvette

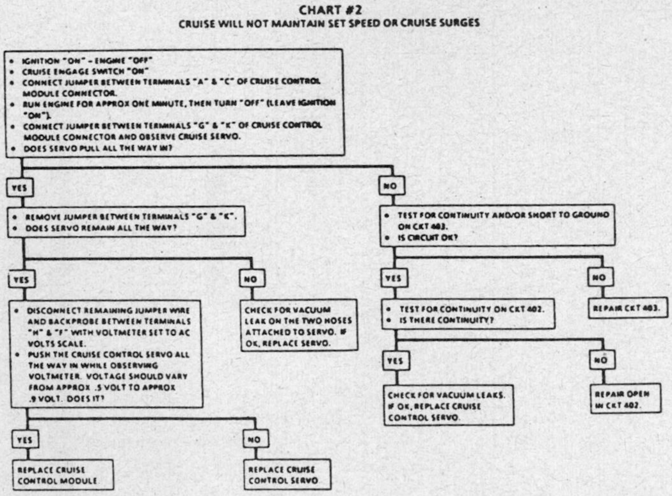
CHART #2
CRUISE WILL NOT MAINTAIN SET SPEED OR CRUISE SURGES
• IGNITION "ON" – ENGINE "OFF"
• CRUISE ENGAGE SWITCH "ON"
• CONNECT JUMPER BETWEEN TERMINALS "A" & "C" OF CRUISE CONTROL MODULE CONNECTOR.
• RUN ENGINE FOR APPROX ONE MINUTE, THEN TURN "OFF" (LEAVE IGNITION "ON").
• CONNECT JUMPER BETWEEN TERMINALS "G" & "K" OF CRUISE CONTROL MODULE CONNECTOR AND OBSERVE CRUISE SERVO.
• DOES SERVO PULL ALL THE WAY IN?
YES
NO
• REMOVE JUMPER BETWEEN TERMINALS "G" & "K".
• DOES SERVO REMAIN ALL THE WAY?
• TEST FOR CONTINUITY AND/OR SHORT TO GROUND ON CKT 403.
• IS CIRCUIT OK?
YES
NO
YES
NO
• DISCONNECT REMAINING JUMPER WIRE AND BACKPROBE BETWEEN TERMINALS "H" & "F" WITH VOLTMETER SET TO AC VOLTS SCALE.
• PUSH THE CRUISE CONTROL SERVO ALL THE WAY IN WHILE OBSERVING VOLTMETER. VOLTAGE SHOULD VARY FROM APPROX .5 VOLT TO APPROX .9 VOLT. DOES IT?
CHECK FOR VACUUM LEAK ON THE TWO HOSES ATTACHED TO SERVO. IF OK, REPLACE SERVO.
• TEST FOR CONTINUITY ON CKT 402.
• IS THERE CONTINUITY?
REPAIR CKT 403.
YES
NO
CHECK FOR VACUUM LEAKS. IF OK, REPLACE CRUISE CONTROL SERVO.
REPAIR OPEN IN CKT 402.
YES
NO
REPLACE CRUISE CONTROL MODULE
REPLACE CRUISE CONTROL SERVO

GC1109100190000X

Fig. 40 Test 2: Cruise Control System Diagnosis. 1992 Corvette

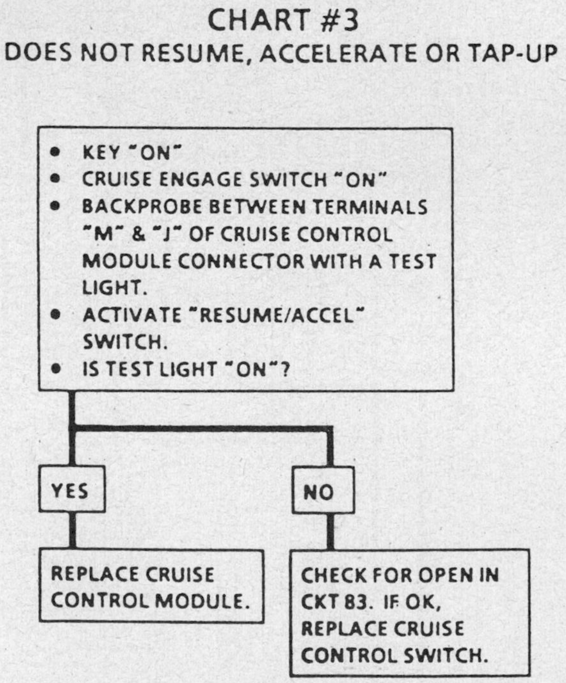
CHART #3
DOES NOT RESUME, ACCELERATE OR TAP-UP
• KEY "ON"
• CRUISE ENGAGE SWITCH "ON"
• BACKPROBE BETWEEN TERMINALS "M" & "J" OF CRUISE CONTROL MODULE CONNECTOR WITH A TEST LIGHT.
• ACTIVATE "RESUME/ACCEL" SWITCH.
• IS TEST LIGHT "ON"?
YES
NO
REPLACE CRUISE CONTROL MODULE.
CHECK FOR OPEN IN CKT 83. IF OK, REPLACE CRUISE CONTROL SWITCH.

GC1109100191000X

Fig. 41 Test 3: Cruise Control System Diagnosis. 1992 Corvette

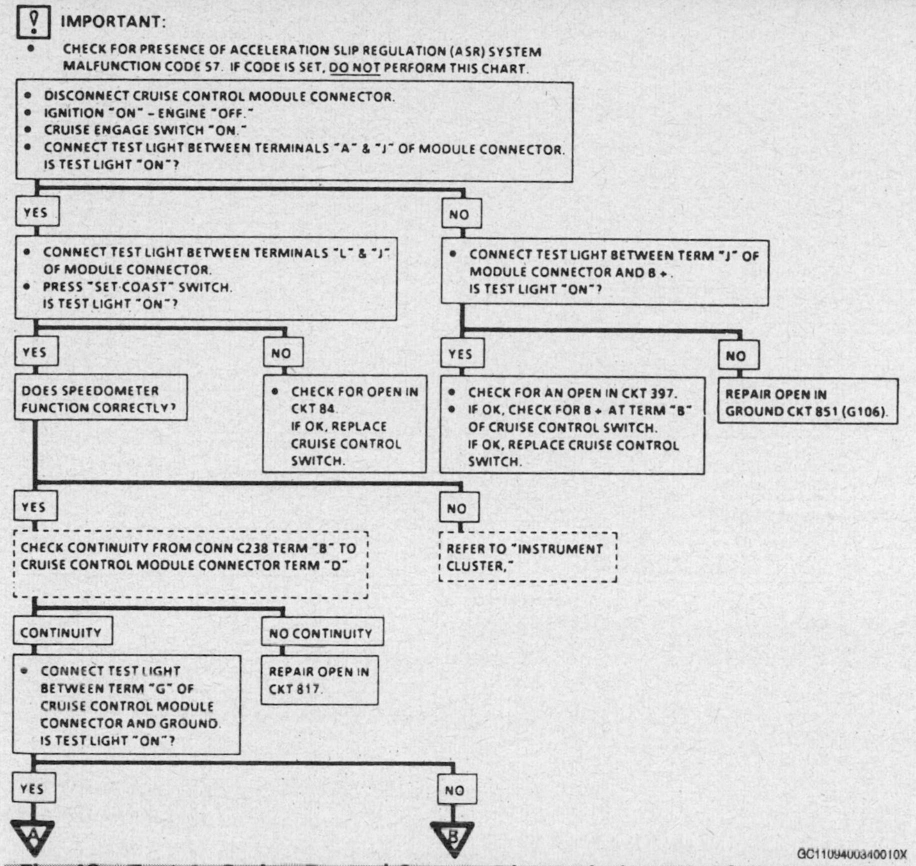
IMPORTANT:
CHECK FOR PRESENCE OF ACCELERATION SLIP REGULATION (ASR) SYSTEM MALFUNCTION CODE 57. IF CODE IS SET, DO NOT PERFORM THIS CHART.
DISCONNECT CRUISE CONTROL MODULE CONNECTOR. IGNITION "ON" – ENGINE "OFF." CRUISE ENGAGE SWITCH "ON." CONNECT TEST LIGHT BETWEEN TERMINALS "A" & "J" OF MODULE CONNECTOR. IS TEST LIGHT "ON"?
YES
NO
CONNECT TEST LIGHT BETWEEN TERMINALS "L" & "J" OF MODULE CONNECTOR. PRESS "SET COAST" SWITCH. IS TEST LIGHT "ON"?
CONNECT TEST LIGHT BETWEEN TERM "J" OF MODULE CONNECTOR AND B+. IS TEST LIGHT "ON"?
YES
NO
YES
NO
DOES SPEEDOMETER FUNCTION CORRECTLY?
CHECK FOR OPEN IN CKT 84. IF OK, REPLACE CRUISE CONTROL SWITCH.
CHECK FOR AN OPEN IN CKT 397. IF OK, CHECK FOR B+ AT TERM "B" OF CRUISE CONTROL SWITCH. IF OK, REPLACE CRUISE CONTROL SWITCH.
REPAIR OPEN IN GROUND CKT 851 (G106).
YES
NO
CHECK CONTINUITY FROM CONN C238 TERM "B" TO CRUISE CONTROL MODULE CONNECTOR TERM "D"
REFER TO "INSTRUMENT CLUSTER."
CONTINUITY
NO CONTINUITY
CONNECT TEST LIGHT BETWEEN TERM "G" OF CRUISE CONTROL MODULE CONNECTOR AND GROUND. IS TEST LIGHT "ON"?
REPAIR OPEN IN CKT 817.
YES
NO
A
B
GC1109400340010X

Fig. 42 Test 1: Cruise Control System Diagnosis (Part 1 Of 3). 1993–94 Corvette

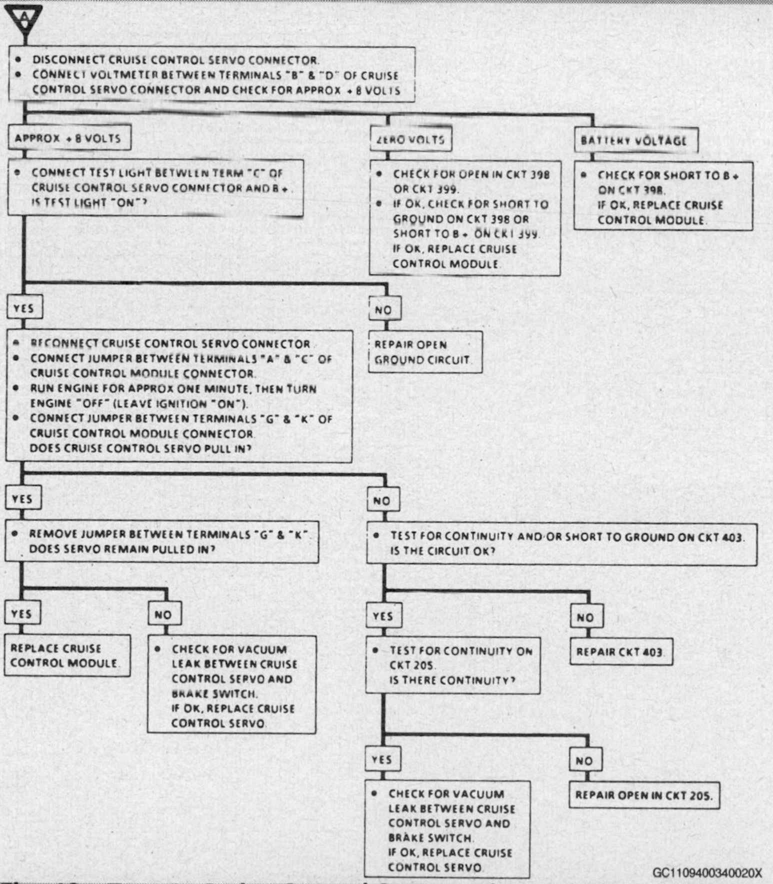
A
DISCONNECT CRUISE CONTROL SERVO CONNECTOR. CONNECT VOLTMETER BETWEEN TERMINALS "B" & "D" OF CRUISE CONTROL SERVO CONNECTOR AND CHECK FOR APPROX +8 VOLTS
APPROX +8 VOLTS
ZERO VOLTS
BATTERY VOLTAGE
CONNECT TEST LIGHT BETWEEN TERM "C" OF CRUISE CONTROL SERVO CONNECTOR AND B+. IS TEST LIGHT "ON"?
CHECK FOR OPEN IN CKT 398 OR CKT 399. IF OK, CHECK FOR SHORT TO GROUND ON CKT 398 OR SHORT TO B+ ON CKT 399. IF OK, REPLACE CRUISE CONTROL MODULE.
CHECK FOR SHORT TO B+ ON CKT 398. IF OK, REPLACE CRUISE CONTROL MODULE.
YES
NO
RECONNECT CRUISE CONTROL SERVO CONNECTOR. CONNECT JUMPER BETWEEN TERMINALS "A" & "C" OF CRUISE CONTROL MODULE CONNECTOR. RUN ENGINE FOR APPROX ONE MINUTE, THEN TURN ENGINE "OFF" (LEAVE IGNITION "ON"). CONNECT JUMPER BETWEEN TERMINALS "G" & "K" OF CRUISE CONTROL MODULE CONNECTOR. DOES CRUISE CONTROL SERVO PULL IN?
REPAIR OPEN GROUND CIRCUIT.
YES
NO
REMOVE JUMPER BETWEEN TERMINALS "G" & "K". DOES SERVO REMAIN PULLED IN?
TEST FOR CONTINUITY AND/OR SHORT TO GROUND ON CKT 403. IS THE CIRCUIT OK?
YES
NO
YES
NO
REPLACE CRUISE CONTROL MODULE.
CHECK FOR VACUUM LEAK BETWEEN CRUISE CONTROL SERVO AND BRAKE SWITCH. IF OK, REPLACE CRUISE CONTROL SERVO.
TEST FOR CONTINUITY ON CKT 205. IS THERE CONTINUITY?
REPAIR CKT 403.
YES
NO
CHECK FOR VACUUM LEAK BETWEEN CRUISE CONTROL SERVO AND BRAKE SWITCH. IF OK, REPLACE CRUISE CONTROL SERVO.
REPAIR OPEN IN CKT 205.
GC1109400340020X

Fig. 42 Test 1: Cruise Control System Diagnosis (Part 2 Of 3). 1993–94 Corvette

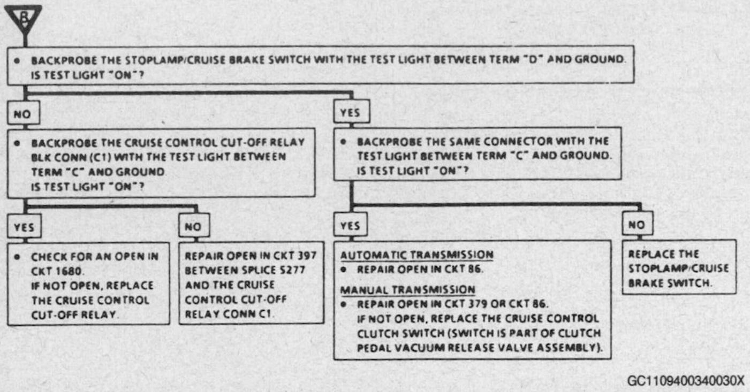
B
• BACKPROBE THE STOPLAMP/CRUISE BRAKE SWITCH WITH THE TEST LIGHT BETWEEN TERM "D" AND GROUND. IS TEST LIGHT "ON"?
NO
YES
• BACKPROBE THE CRUISE CONTROL CUT-OFF RELAY BLK CONN (C1) WITH THE TEST LIGHT BETWEEN TERM "C" AND GROUND. IS TEST LIGHT "ON"?
• BACKPROBE THE SAME CONNECTOR WITH THE TEST LIGHT BETWEEN TERM "C" AND GROUND. IS TEST LIGHT "ON"?
YES
NO
YES
NO
• CHECK FOR AN OPEN IN CKT 1680. IF NOT OPEN, REPLACE THE CRUISE CONTROL CUT-OFF RELAY.
REPAIR OPEN IN CKT 397 BETWEEN SPLICE S277 AND THE CRUISE CONTROL CUT-OFF RELAY CONN C1.
AUTOMATIC TRANSMISSION
• REPAIR OPEN IN CKT 86.
MANUAL TRANSMISSION
• REPAIR OPEN IN CKT 379 OR CKT 86. IF NOT OPEN, REPLACE THE CRUISE CONTROL CLUTCH SWITCH (SWITCH IS PART OF CLUTCH PEDAL VACUUM RELEASE VALVE ASSEMBLY).
REPLACE THE STOPLAMP/CRUISE BRAKE SWITCH.
GC1109400340030X

Fig. 42 Test 1: Cruise Control System Diagnosis (Part 3 Of 3). 1993–94 Corvette

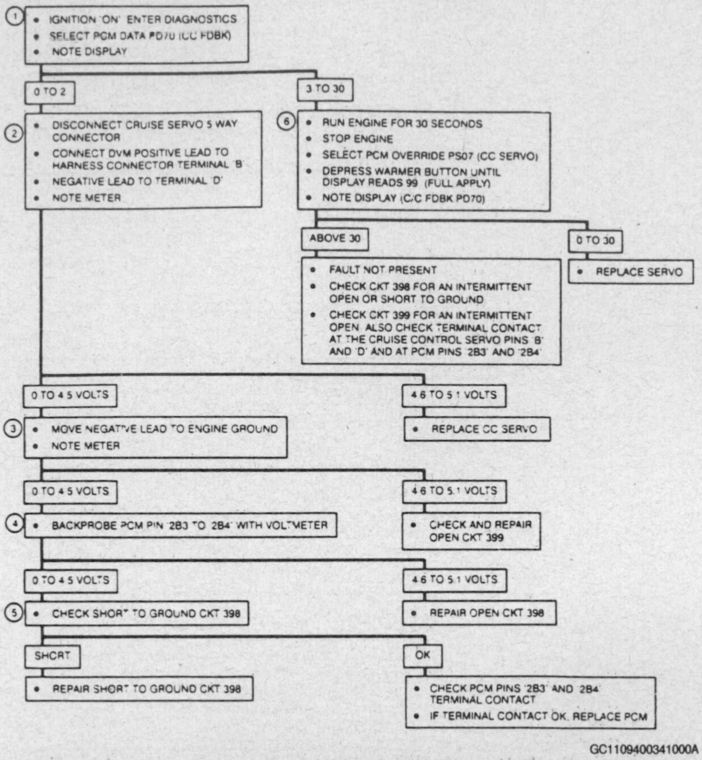
1
• IGNITION 'ON' ENTER DIAGNOSTICS
• SELECT PCM DATA PD70 (CC FDBK)
• NOTE DISPLAY
0 TO 2
3 TO 30
2
• DISCONNECT CRUISE SERVO 5 WAY CONNECTOR
• CONNECT DVM POSITIVE LEAD TO HARNESS CONNECTOR TERMINAL 'B'
• NEGATIVE LEAD TO TERMINAL 'D'
• NOTE METER
6
• RUN ENGINE FOR 30 SECONDS
• STOP ENGINE
• SELECT PCM OVERRIDE PS07 (CC SERVO)
• DEPRESS WARMER BUTTON UNTIL DISPLAY READS 99 (FULL APPLY)
• NOTE DISPLAY (C/C FDBK PD70)
ABOVE 30
0 TO 30
• FAULT NOT PRESENT
• CHECK CKT 398 FOR AN INTERMITTENT OPEN OR SHORT TO GROUND
• CHECK CKT 399 FOR AN INTERMITTENT OPEN. ALSO CHECK TERMINAL CONTACT AT THE CRUISE CONTROL SERVO PINS 'B' AND 'D' AND AT PCM PINS '2B3' AND '2B4'
• REPLACE SERVO
0 TO 4.5 VOLTS
4.6 TO 5.1 VOLTS
3
• MOVE NEGATIVE LEAD TO ENGINE GROUND
• NOTE METER
• REPLACE CC SERVO
0 TO 4.5 VOLTS
4.6 TO 5.1 VOLTS
4
• BACKPROBE PCM PIN '2B3' TO '2B4' WITH VOLTMETER
• CHECK AND REPAIR OPEN CKT 399
0 TO 4.5 VOLTS
4.6 TO 5.1 VOLTS
5
• CHECK SHORT TO GROUND CKT 398
• REPAIR OPEN CKT 398
SHORT
OK
• REPAIR SHORT TO GROUND CKT 398
• CHECK PCM PINS '2B3' AND '2B4' TERMINAL CONTACT
• IF TERMINAL CONTACT OK, REPLACE PCM
GC1109400341000A

Fig. 43 Test 2: Cruise Control System Diagnosis. 1993–94 Corvette

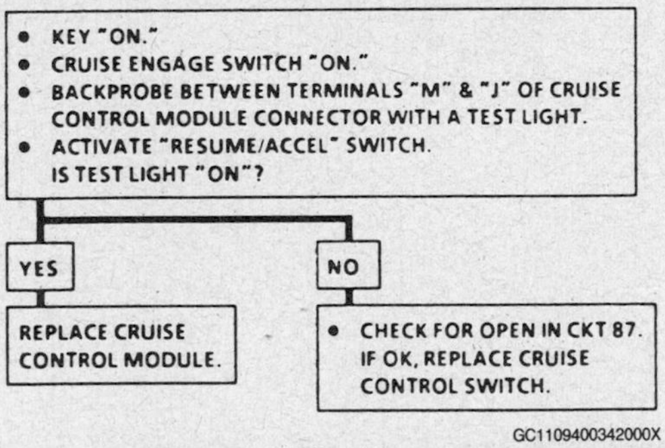
• KEY "ON."
• CRUISE ENGAGE SWITCH "ON."
• BACKPROBE BETWEEN TERMINALS "M" & "J" OF CRUISE CONTROL MODULE CONNECTOR WITH A TEST LIGHT.
• ACTIVATE "RESUME/ACCEL" SWITCH. IS TEST LIGHT "ON"?
YES
NO
REPLACE CRUISE CONTROL MODULE.
• CHECK FOR OPEN IN CKT 87. IF OK, REPLACE CRUISE CONTROL SWITCH.
GC1109400342000X

Fig. 44 Test 3: Cruise Control System Diagnosis. 1993–94 Corvette

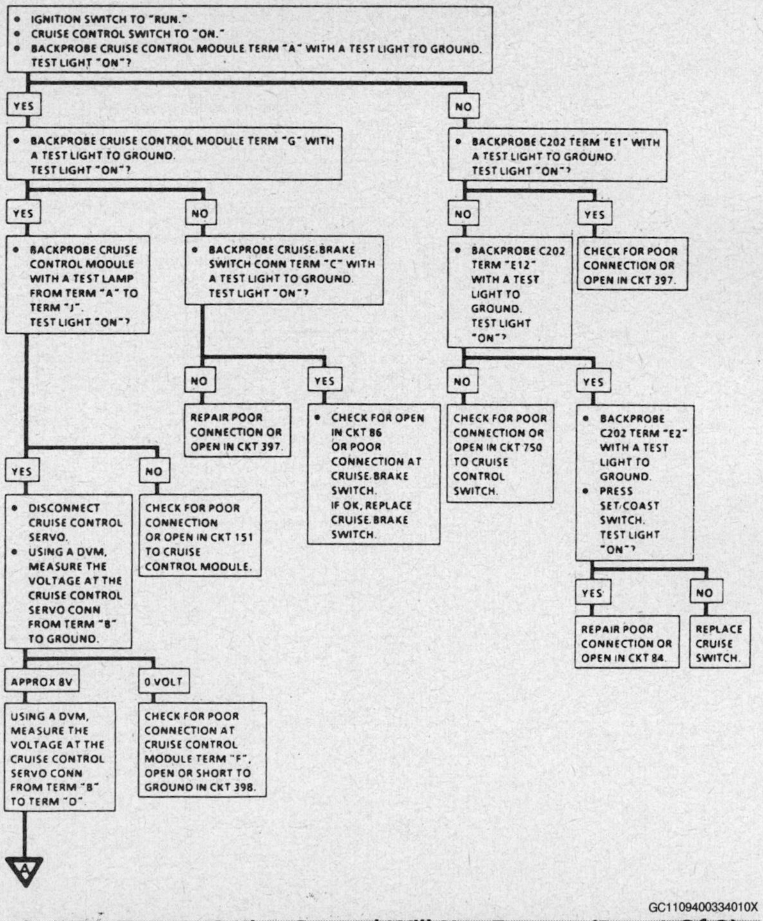
• IGNITION SWITCH TO "RUN."
• CRUISE CONTROL SWITCH TO "ON."
• BACKPROBE CRUISE CONTROL MODULE TERM "A" WITH A TEST LIGHT TO GROUND. TEST LIGHT "ON"?
YES
NO
• BACKPROBE CRUISE CONTROL MODULE TERM "G" WITH A TEST LIGHT TO GROUND. TEST LIGHT "ON"?
• BACKPROBE C202 TERM "E1" WITH A TEST LIGHT TO GROUND. TEST LIGHT "ON"?
YES
NO
NO
YES
• BACKPROBE CRUISE CONTROL MODULE WITH A TEST LAMP FROM TERM "A" TO TERM "J". TEST LIGHT "ON"?
• BACKPROBE CRUISE/BRAKE SWITCH CONN TERM "C" WITH A TEST LIGHT TO GROUND. TEST LIGHT "ON"?
• BACKPROBE C202 TERM "E12" WITH A TEST LIGHT TO GROUND. TEST LIGHT "ON"?
CHECK FOR POOR CONNECTION OR OPEN IN CKT 397.
NO
YES
NO
YES
REPAIR POOR CONNECTION OR OPEN IN CKT 397.
• CHECK FOR OPEN IN CKT 86 OR POOR CONNECTION AT CRUISE/BRAKE SWITCH. IF OK, REPLACE CRUISE/BRAKE SWITCH.
CHECK FOR POOR CONNECTION OR OPEN IN CKT 750 TO CRUISE CONTROL SWITCH.
• BACKPROBE C202 TERM "E2" WITH A TEST LIGHT TO GROUND.
• PRESS SET/COAST SWITCH. TEST LIGHT "ON"?
YES
NO
• DISCONNECT CRUISE CONTROL SERVO.
• USING A DVM, MEASURE THE VOLTAGE AT THE CRUISE CONTROL SERVO CONN FROM TERM "B" TO GROUND.
CHECK FOR POOR CONNECTION OR OPEN IN CKT 151 TO CRUISE CONTROL MODULE.
YES
NO
REPAIR POOR CONNECTION OR OPEN IN CKT 84.
REPLACE CRUISE SWITCH.
APPROX 8V
0 VOLT
USING A DVM, MEASURE THE VOLTAGE AT THE CRUISE CONTROL SERVO CONN FROM TERM "B" TO TERM "D".
CHECK FOR POOR CONNECTION AT CRUISE CONTROL MODULE TERM "F", OPEN OR SHORT TO GROUND IN CKT 398.
A
GC1109400334010X

Fig. 45 Test 1: Cruise Control Will Not Engage (Part 1 Of 2). 1992–94 Cutlass Supreme, Grand Prix, Lumina & Regal

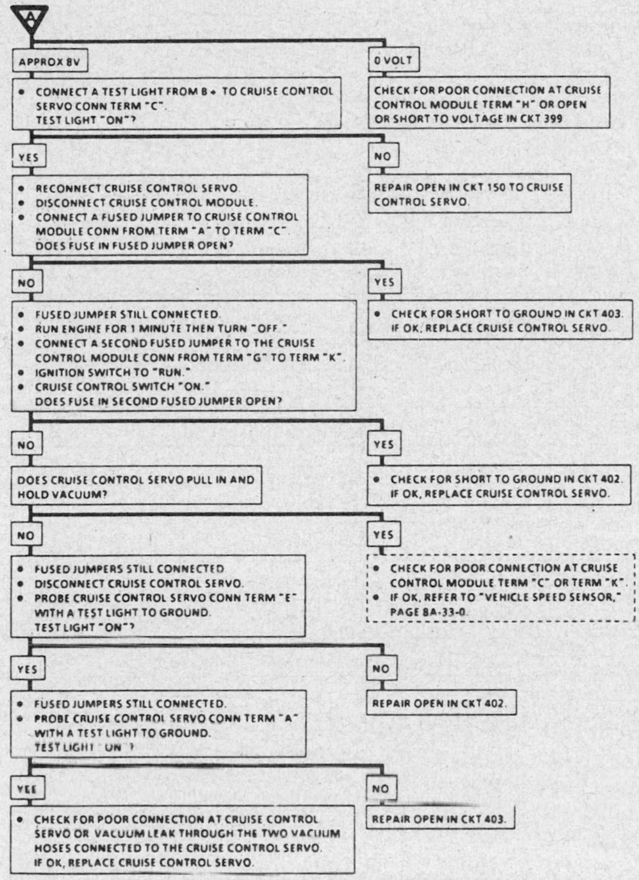
A
APPROX 8V
0 VOLT
• CONNECT A TEST LIGHT FROM B+ TO CRUISE CONTROL SERVO CONN TERM "C". TEST LIGHT "ON"?
CHECK FOR POOR CONNECTION AT CRUISE CONTROL MODULE TERM "H" OR OPEN OR SHORT TO VOLTAGE IN CKT 399
YES
NO
• RECONNECT CRUISE CONTROL SERVO. • DISCONNECT CRUISE CONTROL MODULE. • CONNECT A FUSED JUMPER TO CRUISE CONTROL MODULE CONN FROM TERM "A" TO TERM "C". DOES FUSE IN FUSED JUMPER OPEN?
REPAIR OPEN IN CKT 150 TO CRUISE CONTROL SERVO.
NO
YES
• FUSED JUMPER STILL CONNECTED. • RUN ENGINE FOR 1 MINUTE THEN TURN "OFF." • CONNECT A SECOND FUSED JUMPER TO THE CRUISE CONTROL MODULE CONN FROM TERM "G" TO TERM "K". • IGNITION SWITCH TO "RUN." • CRUISE CONTROL SWITCH "ON." DOES FUSE IN SECOND FUSED JUMPER OPEN?
• CHECK FOR SHORT TO GROUND IN CKT 403. IF OK, REPLACE CRUISE CONTROL SERVO.
NO
YES
DOES CRUISE CONTROL SERVO PULL IN AND HOLD VACUUM?
• CHECK FOR SHORT TO GROUND IN CKT 402. IF OK, REPLACE CRUISE CONTROL SERVO.
NO
YES
• FUSED JUMPERS STILL CONNECTED. • DISCONNECT CRUISE CONTROL SERVO. • PROBE CRUISE CONTROL SERVO CONN TERM "E" WITH A TEST LIGHT TO GROUND. TEST LIGHT "ON"?
• CHECK FOR POOR CONNECTION AT CRUISE CONTROL MODULE TERM "C" OR TERM "K". • IF OK, REFER TO "VEHICLE SPEED SENSOR," PAGE 8A-33-0.
YES
NO
• FUSED JUMPERS STILL CONNECTED. • PROBE CRUISE CONTROL SERVO CONN TERM "A" WITH A TEST LIGHT TO GROUND. TEST LIGHT "ON"?
REPAIR OPEN IN CKT 402.
YES
NO
• CHECK FOR POOR CONNECTION AT CRUISE CONTROL SERVO OR VACUUM LEAK THROUGH THE TWO VACUUM HOSES CONNECTED TO THE CRUISE CONTROL SERVO. IF OK, REPLACE CRUISE CONTROL SERVO.
REPAIR OPEN IN CKT 403.

GC1109400334020X

Fig. 45 Test 1: Cruise Control Will Not Engage (Part 2 of 2). Cutlass Supreme, Grand Prix, Lumina & Regal

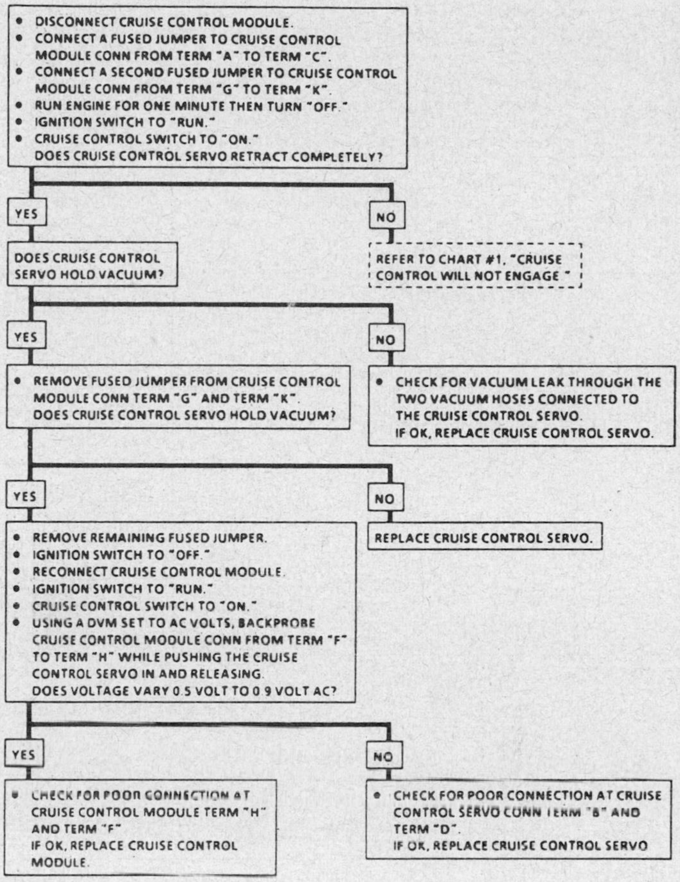
• DISCONNECT CRUISE CONTROL MODULE. • CONNECT A FUSED JUMPER TO CRUISE CONTROL MODULE CONN FROM TERM "A" TO TERM "C". • CONNECT A SECOND FUSED JUMPER TO CRUISE CONTROL MODULE CONN FROM TERM "G" TO TERM "K". • RUN ENGINE FOR ONE MINUTE THEN TURN "OFF." • IGNITION SWITCH TO "RUN." • CRUISE CONTROL SWITCH TO "ON." DOES CRUISE CONTROL SERVO RETRACT COMPLETELY?
YES
NO
DOES CRUISE CONTROL SERVO HOLD VACUUM?
REFER TO CHART #1, "CRUISE CONTROL WILL NOT ENGAGE."
YES
NO
• REMOVE FUSED JUMPER FROM CRUISE CONTROL MODULE CONN TERM "G" AND TERM "K". DOES CRUISE CONTROL SERVO HOLD VACUUM?
• CHECK FOR VACUUM LEAK THROUGH THE TWO VACUUM HOSES CONNECTED TO THE CRUISE CONTROL SERVO. IF OK, REPLACE CRUISE CONTROL SERVO.
YES
NO
• REMOVE REMAINING FUSED JUMPER. • IGNITION SWITCH TO "OFF." • RECONNECT CRUISE CONTROL MODULE. • IGNITION SWITCH TO "RUN." • CRUISE CONTROL SWITCH TO "ON." • USING A DVM SET TO AC VOLTS, BACKPROBE CRUISE CONTROL MODULE CONN FROM TERM "F" TO TERM "H" WHILE PUSHING THE CRUISE CONTROL SERVO IN AND RELEASING. DOES VOLTAGE VARY 0.5 VOLT TO 0.9 VOLT AC?
REPLACE CRUISE CONTROL SERVO.
YES
NO
• CHECK FOR POOR CONNECTION AT CRUISE CONTROL MODULE TERM "H" AND TERM "F". IF OK, REPLACE CRUISE CONTROL MODULE.
• CHECK FOR POOR CONNECTION AT CRUISE CONTROL SERVO CONN TERM "B" AND TERM "D". IF OK, REPLACE CRUISE CONTROL SERVO.

GC1109400335000X

Fig. 46 Test 2: Cruise Will Not Maintain Speed. Cutlass Supreme, Grand Prix, Lumina & Regal

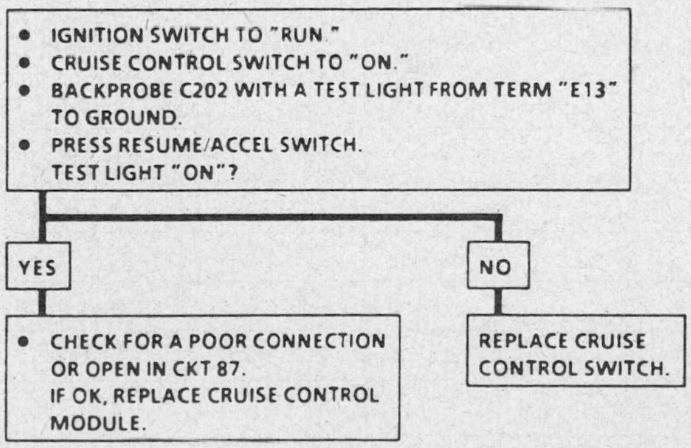
• IGNITION SWITCH TO "RUN." • CRUISE CONTROL SWITCH TO "ON." • BACKPROBE C202 WITH A TEST LIGHT FROM TERM "E13" TO GROUND. • PRESS RESUME/ACCEL SWITCH. TEST LIGHT "ON"?
YES
NO
• CHECK FOR A POOR CONNECTION OR OPEN IN CKT 87. IF OK, REPLACE CRUISE CONTROL MODULE.
REPLACE CRUISE CONTROL SWITCH.

GC1109400336000X

Fig. 47 Test 3: Cruise Will Not Resume, Accelerate Or Tap-Up. Cutlass Supreme, Grand Prix, Lumina & Regal

Connect: QUICK CHECKER (J-34185, SPECMO QC-3 OR EQUIVALENT) or VOLT-OHMETER
At: CRUISE CONTROL MODULE CONNECTOR (Disconnected)
Conditions:

- Ignition Switch: RUN
- When making resistance measurements throughout this text, turn Ignition Switch to off. Failure to do so could cause incorrect results and misdiagnosis.
- Test with quick checker (J-34185 or equivalent) or digital meter

Test	Condition	With quick checker, Correct Response	Without quick checker, Using a Digital Meter			For Different Response, do Test:
			Meter Range	Connector Terminals	Connector Response	
1	Cruise Switch OFF	–	200 ohms	J & Ground	0 ohms	B
		All lights Off	20 VDC	A & J	0 volts	A
			20 VDC	M & J	0 volts	
2	Cruise Switch ON	ON/OFF Light on	20 VDC	A & J	Battery voltage	B
		BRK Light on	20 VDC	G & J	Battery voltage	C
		VENT Light on	200 ohms	C & J	30 to 55 ohms	D
		VAC Light on	200 ohms	K & J	30 to 55 ohms	E
		SPS Light on	200 ohms	F & H	15 to 25 ohms	F
		RA Light off	20 VDC	M & J	0 volts	A
		SC Light off	20 VDC	L & J	0 volts	A

GC1109100192010X

Fig. 48 Cruise control system isolation test (Part 1 of 2)

Test	Condition	With quick checker Correct Response	Without quick checker Using a Digital Meter			For Different Response, do Test:
			Meter Range	Connector Terminals	Connector Response	
3	Cruise Switch ON, Set Switch pressed	SC Light on	20 VDC	L & J	Battery voltage	G
		VAC & SHORT Lights off	not applicable	not applicable	not applicable	H
4	Cruise Switch in R/A	ON/OFF Light on	not applicable	not applicable	not applicable	B
		RA Light on	20 VDC	M & J	Battery voltage	I
		VENT & SHORT Lights off	not applicable	not applicable	not applicable	J
5	Cruise Switch ON, drive wheels turned by hand	VSS Light flashes on and off	20 VDC	A & D	Pulses between approximately battery voltage and less than 7 volts	K, L
6	Quick checker not connected	–	200 ohms	H & J	Open Circuit (infinite resistance)	M
7	Quick checker not connected	–	200 ohms	F & C	Open Circuit (infinite resistance)	N
8	Quick checker not connected	–	200 ohms	F & K	Open Circuit (infinite resistance)	N
9	Quick checker not connected	–	200 ohms	H & C	Open Circuit (infinite resistance)	N
10	Quick checker not connected	–	200 ohms	H & K	Open Circuit (infinite resistance)	N

- If all responses were correct, go to Test O: Servo Actuation Test

GC1109100192020X

Fig. 48 Cruise control system isolation test (Part 2 of 2)

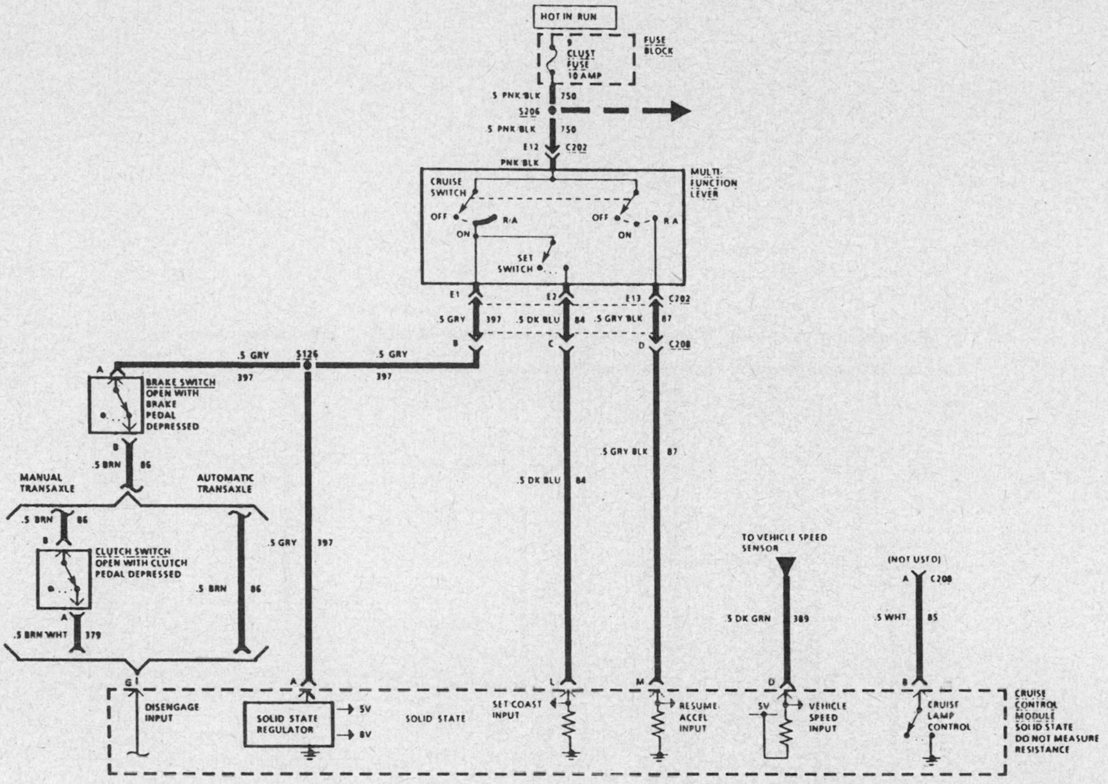
HOT IN RUN
CLUST FUSE 10 AMP
FUSE BLOCK
.5 PNK/BLK 750
S206
.5 PNK/BLK 750
E12 C202
PNK/BLK
CRUISE SWITCH
MULTI-FUNCTION LEVER
OFF
R/A
ON
SET SWITCH
E1
E2
E13
C202
.5 GRY 397
.5 DK BLU 84
.5 GRY/BLK 87
C208
.5 GRY 397
S126
BRAKE SWITCH OPEN WITH BRAKE PEDAL DEPRESSED
.5 BRN 86
MANUAL TRANSAXLE
AUTOMATIC TRANSAXLE
CLUTCH SWITCH OPEN WITH CLUTCH PEDAL DEPRESSED
.5 BRN/WHT 379
.5 GRY/BLK 87
.5 DK BLU 84
TO VEHICLE SPEED SENSOR
(NOT USED)
.5 DK GRN 389
.5 WHT 85
DISENGAGE INPUT
SOLID STATE REGULATOR
5V
8V
SOLID STATE
SET/COAST INPUT
RESUME/ACCEL INPUT
VEHICLE SPEED INPUT
CRUISE LAMP CONTROL
CRUISE CONTROL MODULE
SOLID STATE
DO NOT MEASURE RESISTANCE

GC1109100194010X

Fig. 49 Cruise control wiring diagram (Part 1 of 2). 1992–93 Cutlass Supreme & Grand Prix

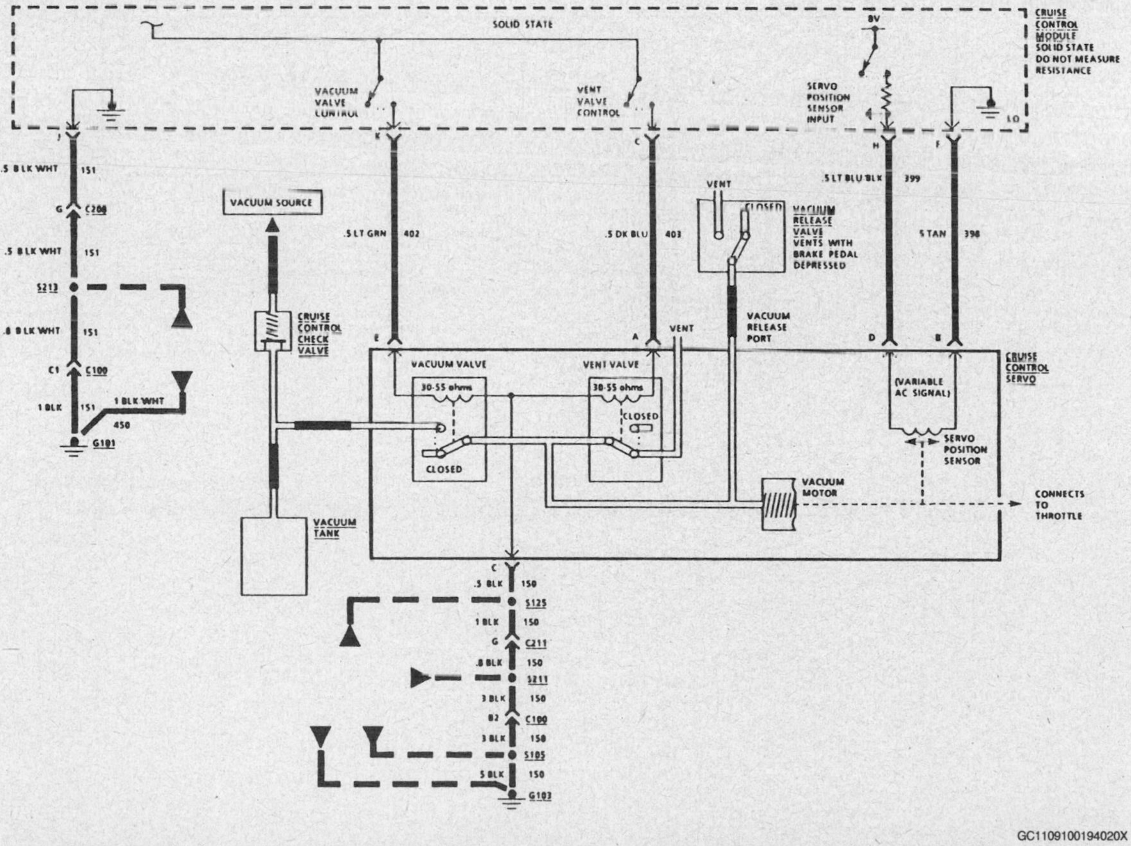
SOLID STATE
8V
CRUISE CONTROL MODULE
SOLID STATE
DO NOT MEASURE RESISTANCE
VACUUM VALVE CONTROL
VENT VALVE CONTROL
SERVO POSITION SENSOR INPUT
.5 BLK/WHT 151
C208
.5 BLK/WHT 151
S213
.8 BLK/WHT 151
C100
1 BLK 151
1 BLK/WHT 450
G101
VACUUM SOURCE
CRUISE CONTROL CHECK VALVE
.5 LT GRN 402
.5 DK BLU 403
VENT
CLOSED
VACUUM RELEASE VALVE VENTS WITH BRAKE PEDAL DEPRESSED
.5 LT BLU/BLK 399
.5 TAN 398
VACUUM RELEASE PORT
VACUUM VALVE
VENT VALVE
30-55 ohms
CLOSED
(VARIABLE AC SIGNAL)
SERVO POSITION SENSOR
CRUISE CONTROL SERVO
VACUUM MOTOR
CONNECTS TO THROTTLE
VACUUM TANK
.5 BLK 150
S125
1 BLK 150
C211
.8 BLK 150
S211
3 BLK 150
C100
3 BLK 150
S105
5 BLK 150
G103

GC1109100194020X

Fig. 49 Cruise control wiring diagram (Part 2 of 2). 1992–93 Cutlass Supreme & Grand Prix

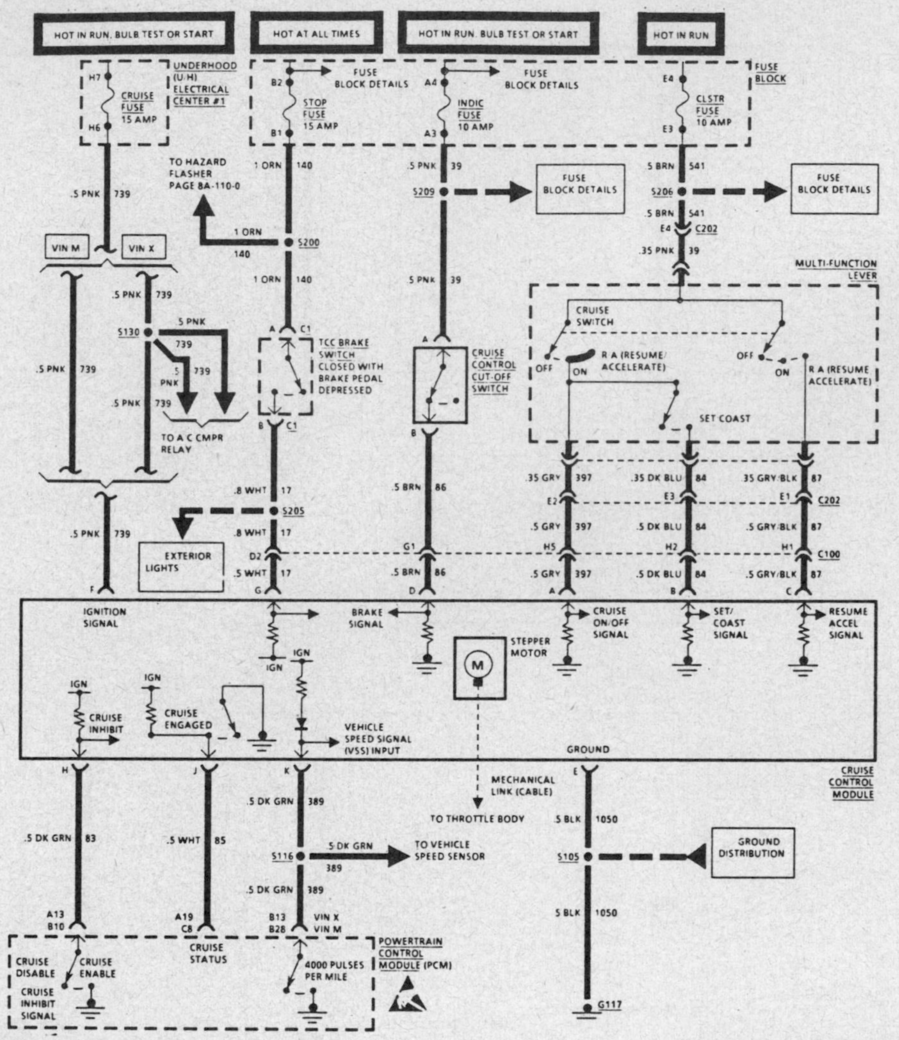

HOT IN RUN, BULB TEST OR START
HOT AT ALL TIMES
HOT IN RUN, BULB TEST OR START
HOT IN RUN
UNDERHOOD (U/H) ELECTRICAL CENTER #1
CRUISE FUSE 15 AMP
FUSE BLOCK DETAILS
STOP FUSE 15 AMP
INDIC FUSE 10 AMP
CLSTR FUSE 10 AMP
FUSE BLOCK
TO HAZARD FLASHER PAGE 8A-110-0
VIN M
VIN X
S130
S200
S209
S206
C202
MULTI-FUNCTION LEVER
CRUISE SWITCH
R A (RESUME/ ACCELERATE)
OFF
ON
SET COAST
TCC BRAKE SWITCH CLOSED WITH BRAKE PEDAL DEPRESSED
CRUISE CONTROL CUT-OFF SWITCH
TO A C CMPR RELAY
S205
EXTERIOR LIGHTS
C100
IGNITION SIGNAL
BRAKE SIGNAL
STEPPER MOTOR
CRUISE ON/OFF SIGNAL
SET/ COAST SIGNAL
RESUME ACCEL SIGNAL
CRUISE INHIBIT
CRUISE ENGAGED
VEHICLE SPEED SIGNAL (VSS) INPUT
GROUND
CRUISE CONTROL MODULE
MECHANICAL LINK (CABLE)
TO THROTTLE BODY
S116
TO VEHICLE SPEED SENSOR
S105
GROUND DISTRIBUTION
CRUISE DISABLE
CRUISE ENABLE
CRUISE INHIBIT SIGNAL
CRUISE STATUS
4000 PULSES PER MILE
POWERTRAIN CONTROL MODULE (PCM)
G117

GC1109400337000X

Fig. 50 Wiring diagram. 1994 Cutlass Supreme & Grand Prix

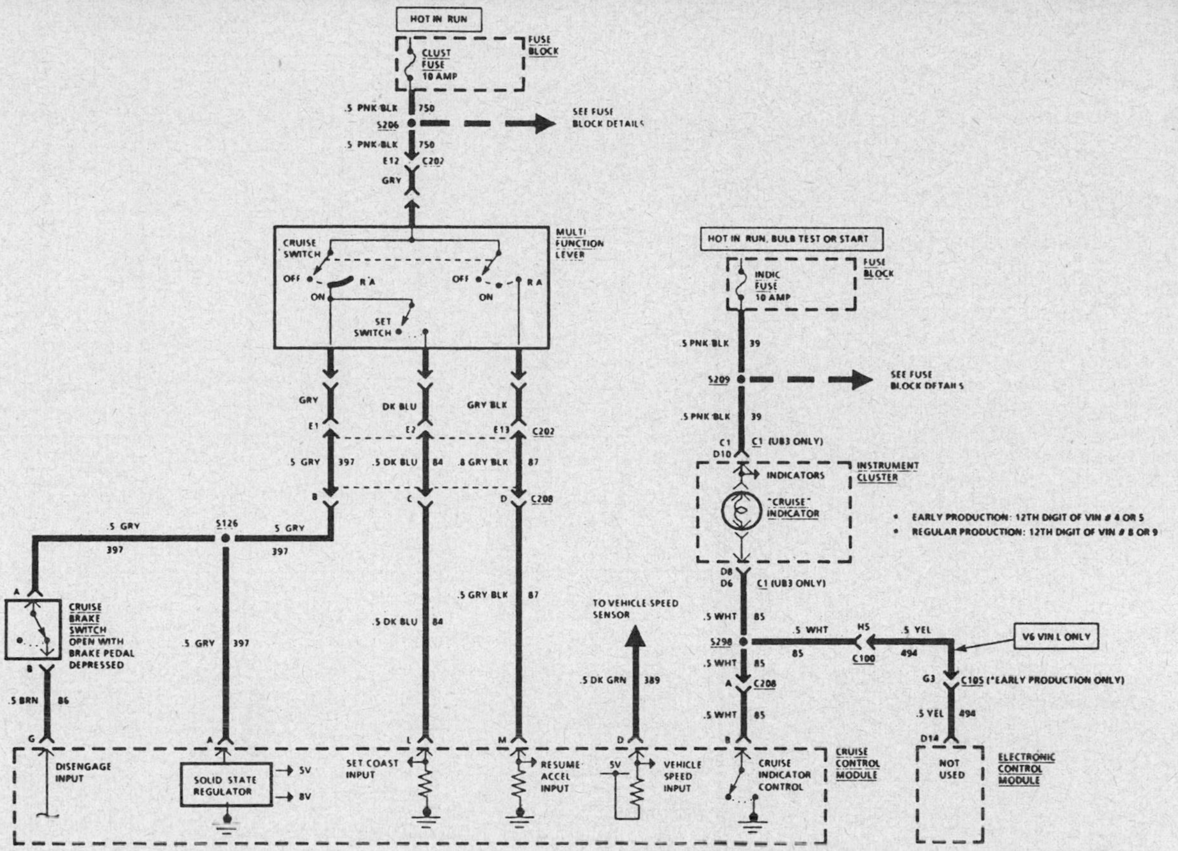

HOT IN RUN
CLUST FUSE 10 AMP
FUSE BLOCK
.5 PNK-BLK 750
S206
SEE FUSE BLOCK DETAILS
E12 C202
GRY
CRUISE SWITCH
MULTI FUNCTION LEVER
OFF
ON
R/A
SET SWITCH
GRY
DK BLU
GRY-BLK
E1
E2
E13 C202
.5 GRY 397
.5 DK BLU 84
.8 GRY BLK 87
C208
.5 GRY
S126
397
CRUISE BRAKE SWITCH OPEN WITH BRAKE PEDAL DEPRESSED
.5 BRN 86
.5 GRY-BLK 87
.5 DK BLU 84
TO VEHICLE SPEED SENSOR
.5 DK GRN 389
HOT IN RUN, BULB TEST OR START
INDIC FUSE 10 AMP
.5 PNK-BLK 39
S209
C1 (UB3 ONLY)
D10
INDICATORS
"CRUISE" INDICATOR
INSTRUMENT CLUSTER
• EARLY PRODUCTION: 12TH DIGIT OF VIN # 4 OR 5
• REGULAR PRODUCTION: 12TH DIGIT OF VIN # 8 OR 9
D8
D6
.5 WHT 85
S298
H5
.5 YEL
494
C100
V6 VIN L ONLY
G3
C105 (*EARLY PRODUCTION ONLY)
DISENGAGE INPUT
SOLID STATE REGULATOR
5V
8V
SET COAST INPUT
RESUME ACCEL INPUT
VEHICLE SPEED INPUT
CRUISE INDICATOR CONTROL
CRUISE CONTROL MODULE
NOT USED
ELECTRONIC CONTROL MODULE

GC1109100195010X

Fig. 51 Cruise control wiring diagram (Part 1 of 2). 1992–93 Lumina & Regal

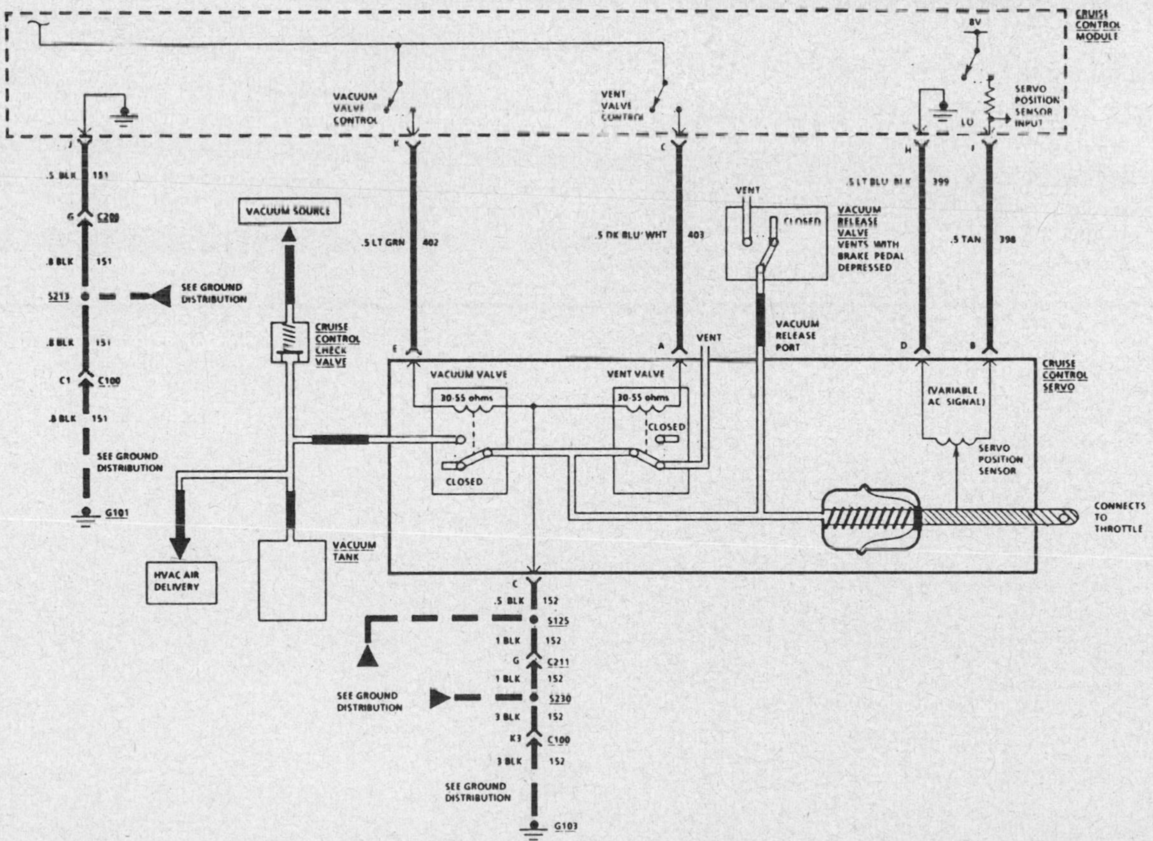

CRUISE CONTROL MODULE
8V
VACUUM VALVE CONTROL
VENT VALVE CONTROL
SERVO POSITION SENSOR INPUT
LO
.5 BLK 151
C208
.8 BLK 151
S213
SEE GROUND DISTRIBUTION
C100
G101
VACUUM SOURCE
.5 LT GRN 402
.5 DK BLU/WHT 403
VENT
CLOSED
VACUUM RELEASE VALVE VENTS WITH BRAKE PEDAL DEPRESSED
.5 LT BLU-BLK 399
.5 TAN 398
CRUISE CONTROL CHECK VALVE
VACUUM RELEASE PORT
VACUUM VALVE
VENT VALVE
30-55 ohms
CLOSED
(VARIABLE AC SIGNAL)
SERVO POSITION SENSOR
CRUISE CONTROL SERVO
CONNECTS TO THROTTLE
HVAC AIR DELIVERY
VACUUM TANK
.5 BLK 152
S125
1 BLK 152
C211
S230
3 BLK 152
K3
C100
G103

GC1109100195020X

Fig. 51 Cruise control wiring diagram (Part 2 of 2). 1992–93 Lumina & Regal

COMPONENT REPLACEMENT

SERVO UNIT

1. Disconnect servo assembly electrical connector.
2. Disconnect vacuum hoses.
3. Disconnect actuating chain, cable or rod from servo assembly.
4. Remove servo assembly and servo unit solenoid valve assembly to mounting bracket attaching screws, then remove servo assembly.
5. Reverse procedure to install. **Torque** servo assembly to bracket attaching screws to 14-18 inch lbs.

ENGAGEMENT SWITCH

Refer to appropriate "Electrical" section for multi-function switch replacement procedures.

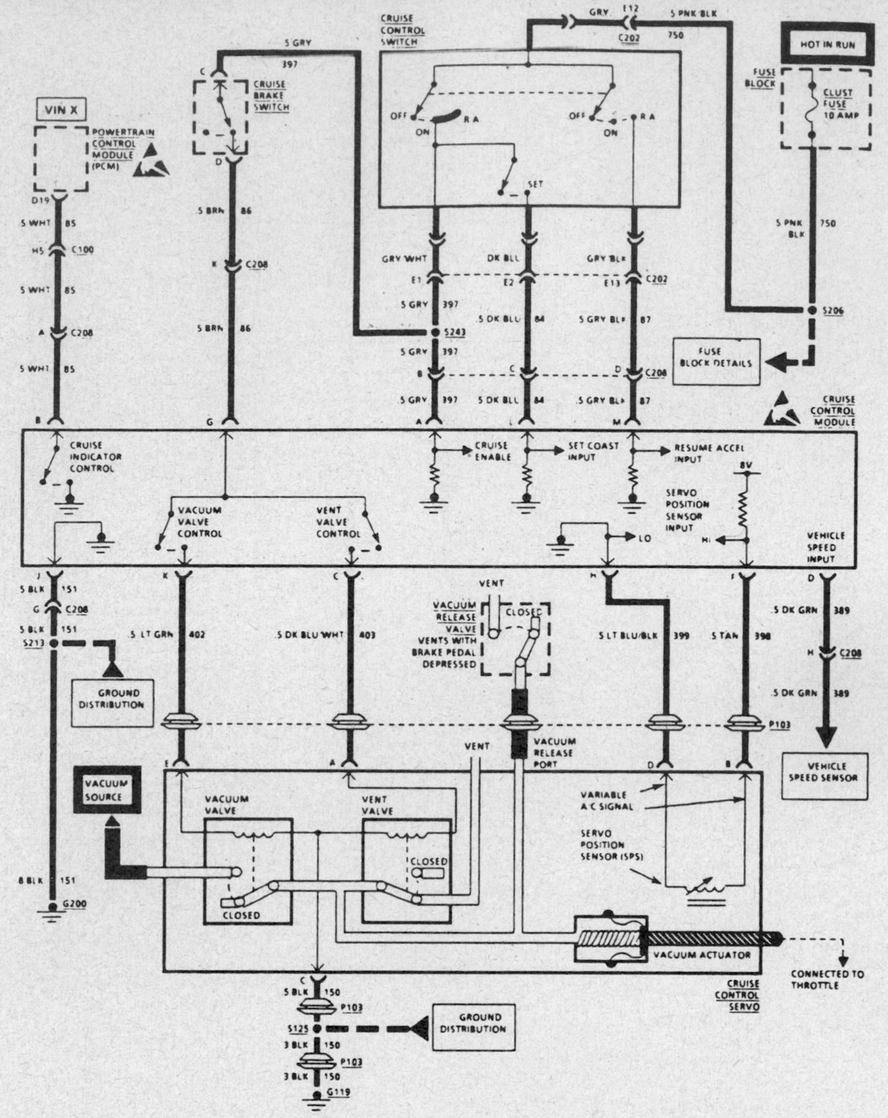
CRUISE CONTROL SWITCH
HOT IN RUN
FUSE BLOCK
CLUST FUSE 10 AMP
CRUISE BRAKE SWITCH
VIN X
POWERTRAIN CONTROL MODULE (PCM)
FUSE BLOCK DETAILS
CRUISE CONTROL MODULE
CRUISE INDICATOR CONTROL
CRUISE ENABLE
SET COAST INPUT
RESUME ACCEL INPUT
SERVO POSITION SENSOR INPUT
VEHICLE SPEED INPUT
VACUUM VALVE CONTROL
VENT VALVE CONTROL
GROUND DISTRIBUTION
VACUUM RELEASE VALVE VENTS WITH BRAKE PEDAL DEPRESSED
VACUUM RELEASE PORT
VEHICLE SPEED SENSOR
VACUUM SOURCE
VACUUM VALVE
VENT VALVE
CLOSED
VARIABLE A C SIGNAL
SERVO POSITION SENSOR (SPS)
VACUUM ACTUATOR
CONNECTED TO THROTTLE
CRUISE CONTROL SERVO
GROUND DISTRIBUTION

GC1109400324000X

Fig. 52 Wiring diagram. 1994 Lumina & Regal

Type 3

NOTE: On Air Bag Equipped Models, Refer To "Air Bag System Precautions" Located In The Front Of This Manual For System Disarming & Arming Procedures.

NOTE: Electrical Symbol & Wire Color Code Identification Located In The Front Of This Manual Can Be Used As An Aid When Using Wiring Circuits Found In This Section.

INDEX

DESCRIPTION

This system is basically the same as Type 2, excepting the fact that on this type the function of the cruise control module is performed by the PCM. The main parts of the cruise control system are the mode control switches, PCM, servo unit, vehicle speed sensor, vacuum supply, electrical and vacuum release switches, and electrical harness. The cruise system uses vacuum to operate a throttle servo. The PCM monitors vehicle speed and servo position to operate the servo vacuum and vent valves to maintain desired speed.

PRECAUTIONS

AIR BAG SYSTEMS

Refer to "Air Bag System Precautions" in the front of this manual for system disarming and arming procedures.

ANTI-LOCK BRAKE SYSTEMS

On vehicles equipped with ABS brake system, the hydraulic accumulator, when fully charged contains brake fluid at high pressure. Before disconnecting any lines, hoses or fittings, ensure accumulator is full depressurized. Failure to do so may result in personal injury.

To depressurize the hydraulic accumulator, turn the ignition to the Off position or disconnect negative battery cable, pump brake pedal a minimum of 40 times at approximately 50 lbs. of force. A noticeable change in pedal feel will occur when accumulator is fully discharged.

ADJUSTMENTS

CRUISE CONTROL CABLE

Adjust cruise control cable to minimum slack as follows:

1. Ensure throttle lever is in idle position with engine off.
2. Pull servo assembly end of cable toward servo blade.
3. If hole in servo blade is aligned with cable pin, install pin in that hole and install retainer.
4. If hole does not align with pin, install pin in next hole away from servo assembly. **Do not stretch cable.**

ELECTRIC BRAKE RELEASE SWITCH & VACUUM RELEASE/VCC SWITCH

The switch assembly and valve assembly cannot be adjusted until brake booster pushrod is assembled to brake pedal assembly. Adjustment is as follows:

1. Depress brake pedal and install switch assembly and valve assembly into their proper retaining clips until fully seated.
2. **On vehicles equipped with ABS,** release brake pedal and allow to come to rest.
3. **On vehicles less ABS brakes,** slowly pull pedal back to its fully retracted position. The switch assembly and valve assembly will move within their retainers to their adjusted position.
4. **On all models,** the following brake pedal travel distances may be used to check for a properly adjusted cruise control and stop lamp switch assembly and vacuum release valve assembly.
   a. Cruise control switch contacts must open at .88-1.2 inch pedal travel, measured at centerline of brake pedal pad. **Nominal actuation of stop lamp contacts is .4 inch after cruise control contacts open.**
   b. Vacuum release valve assembly must open at 1 1/16-1 5/16 inches pedal travel, measured at centerline of brake pedal pad.

SYSTEM DIAGNOSIS & TESTING

The operation of the cruise control system is integral with the Body Control Module (BCM) or Power Control Module (PCM). The BCM or PCM monitors the cruise control system and other systems by comparing the actual operating conditions to standard values stored in memory. When certain system malfunctions are detected, a three digit diagnostic trouble code is stored in the BCM memory. These diagnostic trouble codes can be displayed to aid in system diagnosis. In this manner, the speed control system can be diagnosed by accessing fault codes, if they exist, that pertain to the speed control system.

Codes other than those described below may be stored in the BCM memory and displayed when the system is accessed to diagnose cruise control malfunctions. It may be necessary to diagnose these codes and identify the non-speed control related failure in order to ensure proper speed control system operation. For further diagnosis of other systems related to the BCM, refer to MOTOR's "Auto Engine Tune Up & Electronic Manual."

ENTERING DIAGNOSTIC SERVICE MODE

BONNEVILLE, LESABRE, PARK AVENUE, RIVIERA, TORONADO, TROFEO, 88 & 98

Connect TECH 1 Diagnostic Scan tool or equivalent to DLC (ALDL) connector, **Figs. 1 and 2,** which is located under the

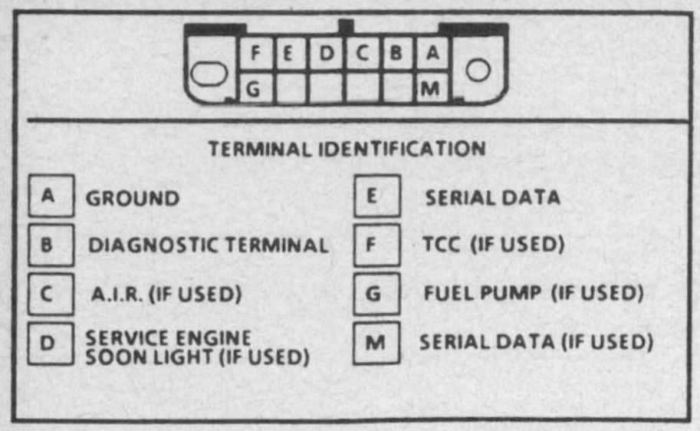
F E D C B A
G M
TERMINAL IDENTIFICATION
A GROUND
B DIAGNOSTIC TERMINAL
C A.I.R. (IF USED)
D SERVICE ENGINE SOON LIGHT (IF USED)
E SERIAL DATA
F TCC (IF USED)
G FUEL PUMP (IF USED)
M SERIAL DATA (IF USED)

GC1109100196000X

Fig. 1 DLC (ALDL) connector. 1992

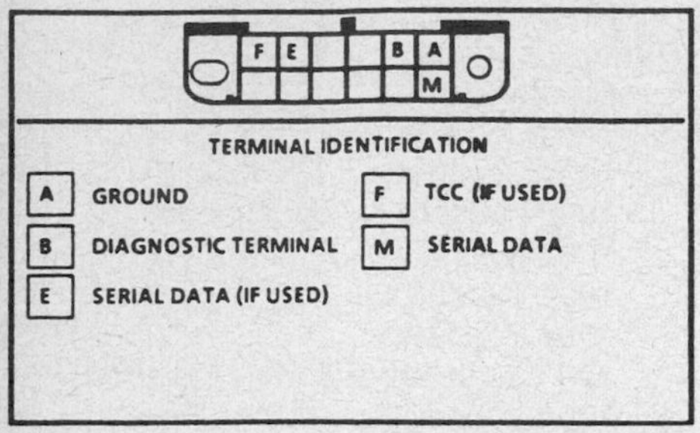
F E B A
M
TERMINAL IDENTIFICATION
A GROUND
B DIAGNOSTIC TERMINAL
E SERIAL DATA (IF USED)
F TCC (IF USED)
M SERIAL DATA

GC1109300197000X

Fig. 2 DLC connector. 1993–94

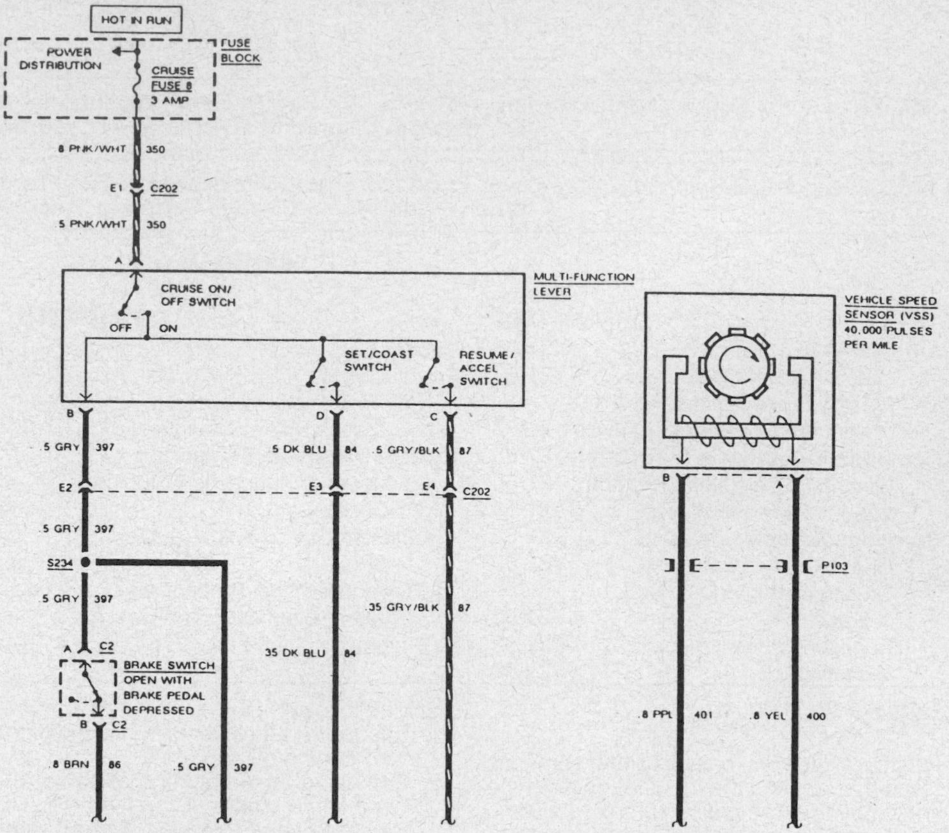
HOT IN RUN
POWER DISTRIBUTION
FUSE BLOCK
CRUISE FUSE 8 3 AMP
8 PNK/WHT 350
E1 C202
5 PNK/WHT 350
CRUISE ON/ OFF SWITCH
OFF ON
MULTI-FUNCTION LEVER
SET/COAST SWITCH
RESUME/ ACCEL SWITCH
VEHICLE SPEED SENSOR (VSS) 40,000 PULSES PER MILE
.5 GRY 397
.5 DK BLU 84
.5 GRY/BLK 87
E2 E3 E4 C202
S234
C2
BRAKE SWITCH OPEN WITH BRAKE PEDAL DEPRESSED
.35 GRY/BLK 87
.35 DK BLU 84
P103
.8 PPL 401
.8 YEL 400
.8 BRN 86
.5 GRY 397

GC1109100198010X

Fig. 3 Wiring diagram (Part 1 of 2). Riviera

instrument panel and is sometimes covered by a plastic cover.

ACCESSING DIAGNOSTIC TROUBLE CODES

Terminal B of the connector is the diagnostic terminal and is grounded by connecting it to terminal A (internal ECM/PCM/VCM/ ground). Once terminals A and B have been connected, the ignition switch must be moved to the On position with the engine not running. The Service Engine Soon light should flash Diagnostic Trouble Code (DTC) 12 three times consecutively. The flash sequence should be as follows: flash, pause, flash-flash, long pause, flash, pause, flash-flash, long pause, flash, pause, flash-flash. DTC 12 indicates that the system is operating properly. If DTC 12 is not indicated, a problem is present within the diagnostic system itself.

Following the output of DTC 12, the Service Engine Soon light will indicate a diagnostic trouble code three times, if present, or it will continue to output DTC 12. If more than one code is present, the codes will be output in lowest number to highest with each code being output three times.

DIAGNOSTIC TEST PROCEDURES

When diagnosing and testing system, refer to **Figs. 3 through 11,** for wiring diagrams and **Figs. 12 through 25** for cruise control system check and diagnostic trouble code charts.

CLEARING DIAGNOSTIC TROUBLE CODES

To clear code the ECM must power feed must be disconnected for at least 30 seconds. Depending how vehicle is equipped, the power feed can be disconnected at the ECM fuse in the fuse box, the inline fuse holder at the battery, or the positive battery terminal pigtail connector.

ROAD TEST

1. Drive vehicle at speed greater than 25 mph, place cruise switch in On position and depress set button at end of multi-function lever. Cruise indicator should illuminate and vehicle should maintain speed.
2. With foot off accelerator, hold set button in. Vehicle should coast at a slower speed.
3. Release set button. If new speed is greater than 25 mph, cruise control should engage and hold slower speed.
4. Slide cruise switch to Resume/Accel position and hold it there. Vehicle should accelerate.
5. Release cruise switch back to On position. Vehicle should hold new, faster speed.
6. Tap brake pedal. Vehicle should coast slower and cruise indicator should go out.
7. Slide cruise control switch momentarily to Resume/Accel position. Cruise indicator should illuminate and vehicle should accelerate to former set speed.
8. While cruising, accelerate, then remove foot from accelerator pedal. Vehicle should coast back to set speed.
9. While cruising, tap cruise switch to Resume/Accel position. Vehicle speed should increase 1 mph for each tap up to ten.
10. While cruising, tap set button. Vehicle speed should decrease 1 mph for each tap down to 25 mph.
11. Slide cruise control switch to Off position. Cruise control should turn off and cruise indicator should go out.

COMPONENT DIAGNOSIS & TESTING

ELECTRIC BRAKE RELEASE SWITCH

1. Turn ignition switch to On position.
2. Connect test light to ground.
3. Probe brown wire at brake switch connector. Lamp should illuminate.
4. Check switch adjustment, with probe still at brown wire, depressing brake pedal 1/8-1/2 inch. Light should go out.
5. If light did not illuminate in step 3, probe wire in adjacent connector cavity. If lamp illuminates, adjust or replace switch as necessary. If light does not illuminate, check wiring to switch.

VACUUM RELEASE VALVES

An inoperative valve must be replaced. Ensure vacuum hose to switch is firmly connected and that it is not cracked or deteriorated. Vacuum source and hoses should be checked for improper routing, leaks, kinks or restrictions.

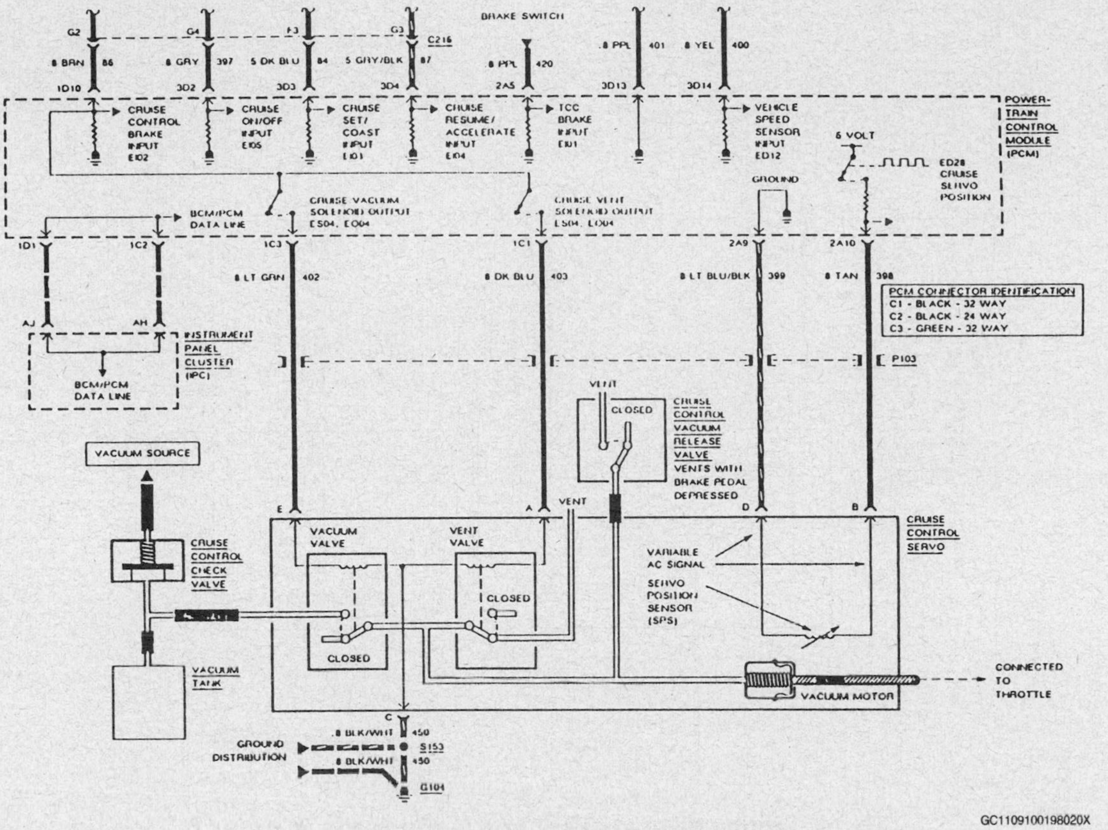

BRAKE SWITCH
C216
CRUISE CONTROL BRAKE INPUT E102
CRUISE ON/OFF INPUT E105
CRUISE SET/COAST INPUT E101
CRUISE RESUME/ACCELERATE INPUT E104
TCC BRAKE INPUT E101
VEHICLE SPEED SENSOR INPUT ED12
5 VOLT
CRUISE SERVO POSITION
GROUND
POWER-TRAIN CONTROL MODULE (PCM)
BCM/PCM DATA LINE
CRUISE VACUUM SOLENOID OUTPUT
CRUISE VENT SOLENOID OUTPUT
INSTRUMENT PANEL CLUSTER (IPC)
PCM CONNECTOR IDENTIFICATION
C1 - BLACK - 32 WAY
C2 - BLACK - 24 WAY
C3 - GREEN - 32 WAY
P103
VACUUM SOURCE
CRUISE CONTROL CHECK VALVE
VACUUM TANK
VENT
CLOSED
CRUISE CONTROL VACUUM RELEASE VALVE VENTS WITH BRAKE PEDAL DEPRESSED
VACUUM VALVE
VENT VALVE
VARIABLE AC SIGNAL
SERVO POSITION SENSOR (SPS)
CRUISE CONTROL SERVO
VACUUM MOTOR
CONNECTED TO THROTTLE
GROUND DISTRIBUTION
S153
G104

GC1109100198020X

Fig. 3 Wiring diagram (Part 2 of 2). Riviera

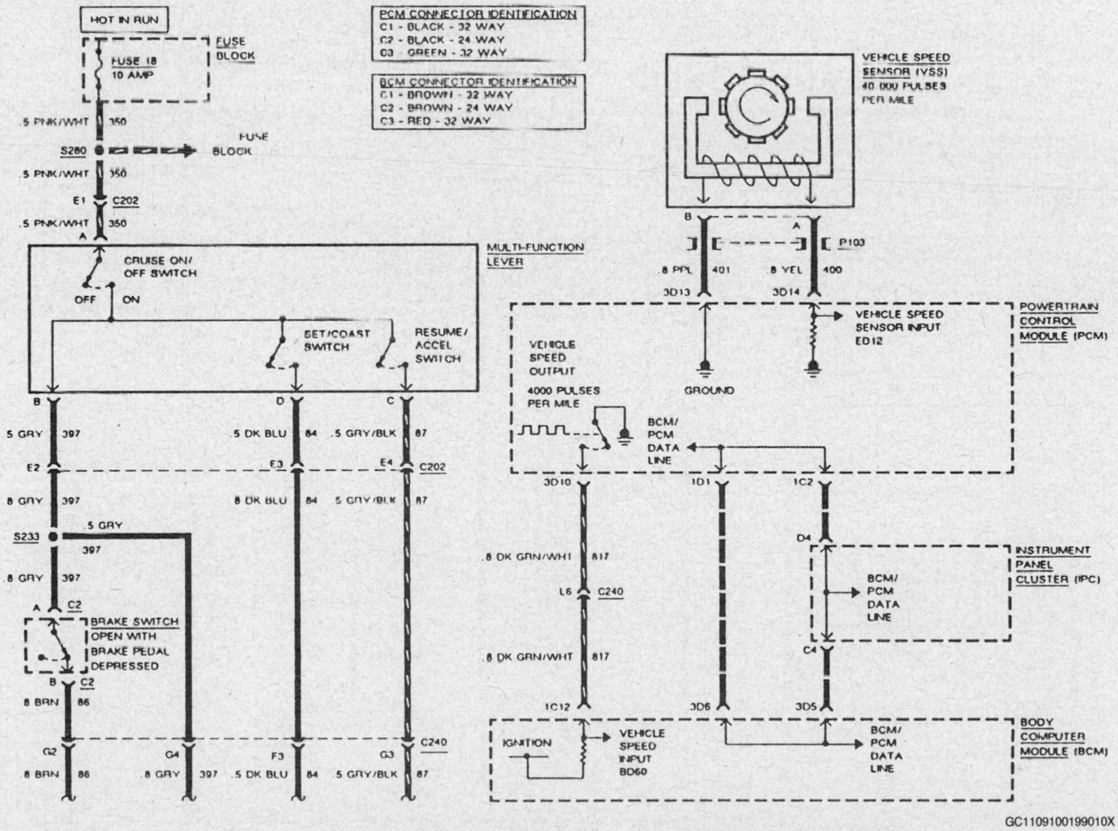

HOT IN RUN
FUSE 18 10 AMP
FUSE BLOCK
PCM CONNECTOR IDENTIFICATION
C1 - BLACK - 32 WAY
C2 - BLACK - 24 WAY
C3 - GREEN - 32 WAY
BCM CONNECTOR IDENTIFICATION
C1 - BROWN - 32 WAY
C2 - BROWN - 24 WAY
C3 - RED - 32 WAY
VEHICLE SPEED SENSOR (VSS) 40 000 PULSES PER MILE
S280
C202
MULTI-FUNCTION LEVER
CRUISE ON/OFF SWITCH
OFF
ON
SET/COAST SWITCH
RESUME/ACCEL SWITCH
P103
VEHICLE SPEED SENSOR INPUT ED12
POWERTRAIN CONTROL MODULE (PCM)
VEHICLE SPEED OUTPUT
4000 PULSES PER MILE
GROUND
BCM/PCM DATA LINE
S233
BRAKE SWITCH OPEN WITH BRAKE PEDAL DEPRESSED
C240
INSTRUMENT PANEL CLUSTER (IPC)
IGNITION
VEHICLE SPEED INPUT BD60
BODY COMPUTER MODULE (BCM)

GC1109100199010X

Fig. 4 Wiring diagram (Part 1 of 2). Toronado & Trofeo

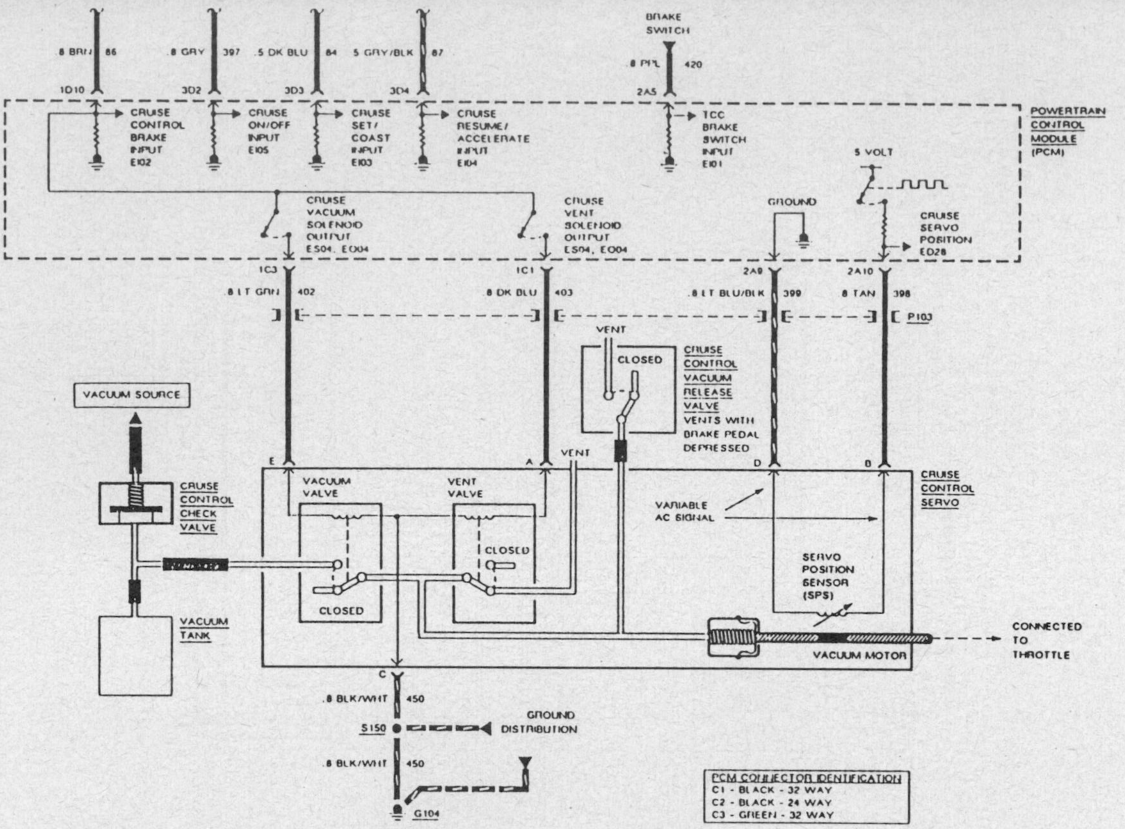
BRAKE SWITCH
CRUISE CONTROL BRAKE INPUT E102
CRUISE ON/OFF INPUT E105
CRUISE SET/ COAST INPUT E103
CRUISE RESUME/ ACCELERATE INPUT E104
TCC BRAKE SWITCH INPUT E101
POWERTRAIN CONTROL MODULE (PCM)
5 VOLT
GROUND
CRUISE VACUUM SOLENOID OUTPUT ES04, E004
CRUISE VENT SOLENOID OUTPUT ES04, E004
CRUISE SERVO POSITION ED28
P103
VENT
CLOSED
CRUISE CONTROL VACUUM RELEASE VALVE VENTS WITH BRAKE PEDAL DEPRESSED
VACUUM SOURCE
CRUISE CONTROL CHECK VALVE
VACUUM TANK
VACUUM VALVE
VENT VALVE
VARIABLE AC SIGNAL
SERVO POSITION SENSOR (SPS)
CRUISE CONTROL SERVO
VACUUM MOTOR
CONNECTED TO THROTTLE
GROUND DISTRIBUTION
S150
G104
PCM CONNECTOR IDENTIFICATION
C1 - BLACK - 32 WAY
C2 - BLACK - 24 WAY
C3 - GREEN - 32 WAY
GC1109100199020X

Fig. 4 Wiring diagram (Part 2 of 2). Toronado & Trofeo

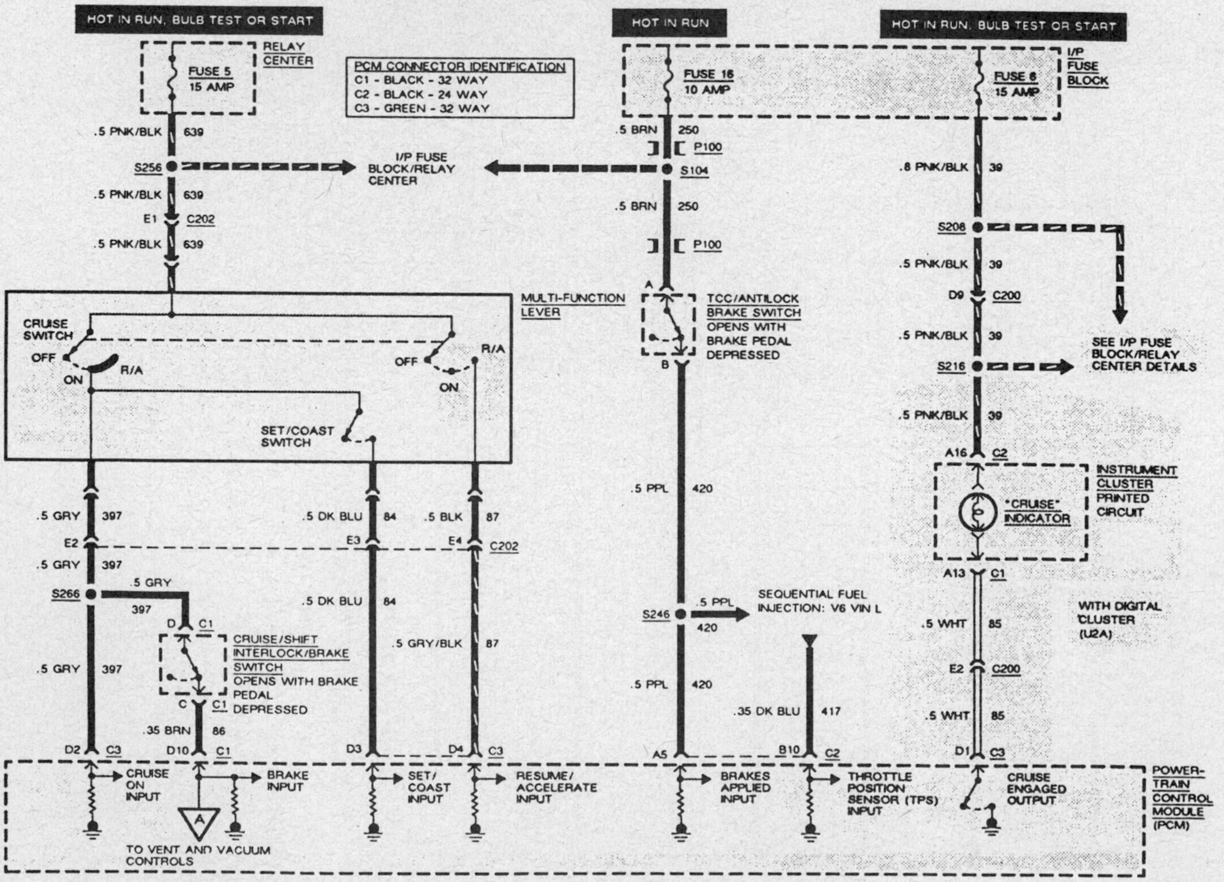
HOT IN RUN, BULB TEST OR START
HOT IN RUN
HOT IN RUN, BULB TEST OR START
RELAY CENTER
FUSE 5 15 AMP
PCM CONNECTOR IDENTIFICATION
C1 - BLACK - 32 WAY
C2 - BLACK - 24 WAY
C3 - GREEN - 32 WAY
FUSE 16 10 AMP
FUSE 6 15 AMP
I/P FUSE BLOCK
I/P FUSE BLOCK/RELAY CENTER
S256
S104
P100
C202
S206
C200
S216
SEE I/P FUSE BLOCK/RELAY CENTER DETAILS
MULTI-FUNCTION LEVER
CRUISE SWITCH
OFF
ON
R/A
SET/COAST SWITCH
TCC/ANTILOCK BRAKE SWITCH OPENS WITH BRAKE PEDAL DEPRESSED
INSTRUMENT CLUSTER PRINTED CIRCUIT
"CRUISE" INDICATOR
WITH DIGITAL CLUSTER (U2A)
S266
CRUISE/SHIFT INTERLOCK/BRAKE SWITCH OPENS WITH BRAKE PEDAL DEPRESSED
S246
SEQUENTIAL FUEL INJECTION: V6 VIN L
CRUISE ON INPUT
BRAKE INPUT
SET/ COAST INPUT
RESUME/ ACCELERATE INPUT
BRAKES APPLIED INPUT
THROTTLE POSITION SENSOR (TPS) INPUT
CRUISE ENGAGED OUTPUT
POWER-TRAIN CONTROL MODULE (PCM)
TO VENT AND VACUUM CONTROLS
GC1109200200010X

Fig. 5 Wiring diagram (Part 1 of 2). 1992 88

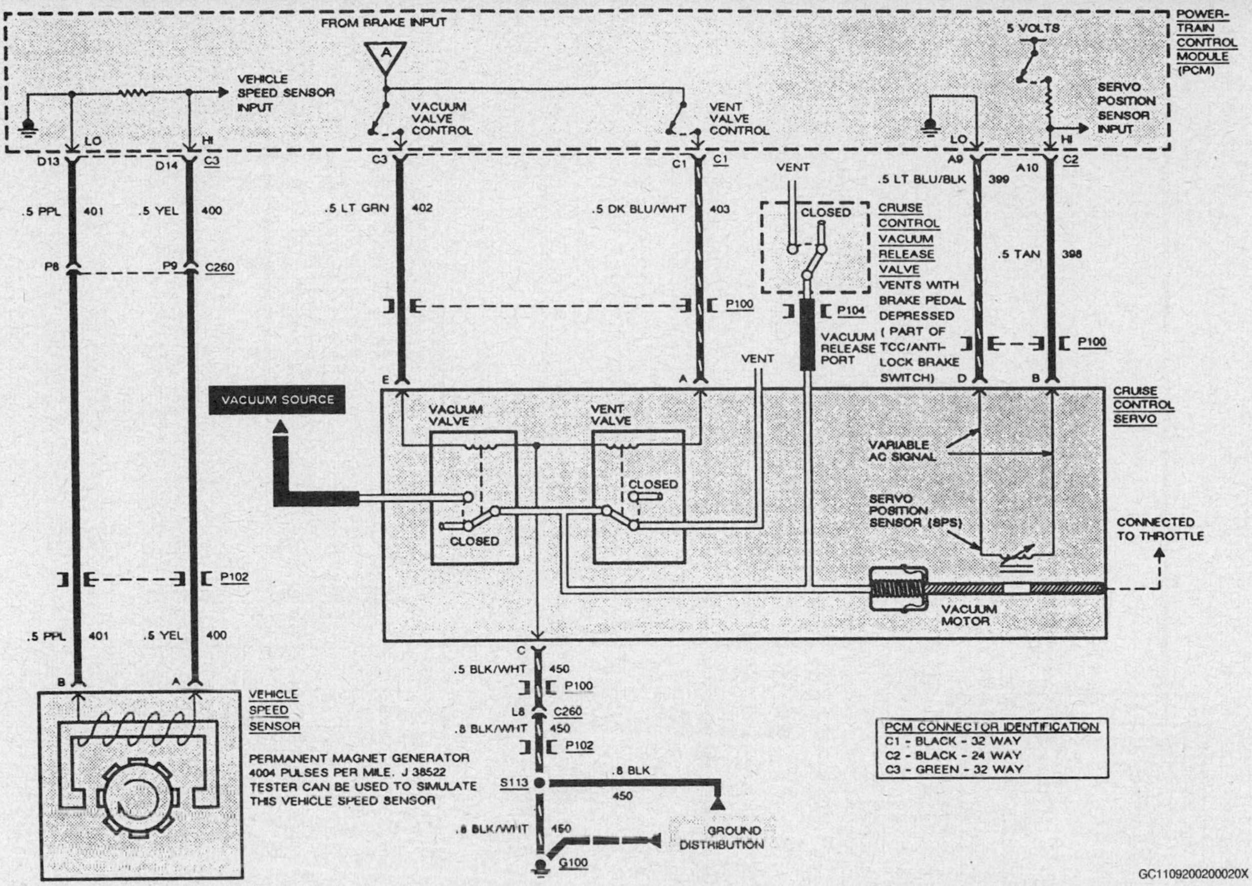
FROM BRAKE INPUT
5 VOLTS
POWER-TRAIN CONTROL MODULE (PCM)
VEHICLE SPEED SENSOR INPUT
VACUUM VALVE CONTROL
VENT VALVE CONTROL
SERVO POSITION SENSOR INPUT
LO
HI
D13
D14
C3
C1
A9
A10
C2
.5 PPL 401
.5 YEL 400
.5 LT GRN 402
.5 DK BLU/WHT 403
VENT
CLOSED
CRUISE CONTROL VACUUM RELEASE VALVE VENTS WITH BRAKE PEDAL DEPRESSED (PART OF TCC/ANTI-LOCK BRAKE SWITCH)
.5 LT BLU/BLK 399
.5 TAN 398
P8
P9
C260
P100
P104
VACUUM RELEASE PORT
VACUUM SOURCE
VACUUM VALVE
VENT VALVE
CLOSED
VARIABLE AC SIGNAL
SERVO POSITION SENSOR (SPS)
CRUISE CONTROL SERVO
CONNECTED TO THROTTLE
VACUUM MOTOR
P102
.5 BLK/WHT 450
L8
.8 BLK/WHT 450
S113
.8 BLK
GROUND DISTRIBUTION
G100
VEHICLE SPEED SENSOR
PERMANENT MAGNET GENERATOR 4004 PULSES PER MILE. J 38522 TESTER CAN BE USED TO SIMULATE THIS VEHICLE SPEED SENSOR
PCM CONNECTOR IDENTIFICATION
C1 - BLACK - 32 WAY
C2 - BLACK - 24 WAY
C3 - GREEN - 32 WAY
GC1109200200020X

Fig. 5 Wiring diagram (Part 2 of 2). 1992 88

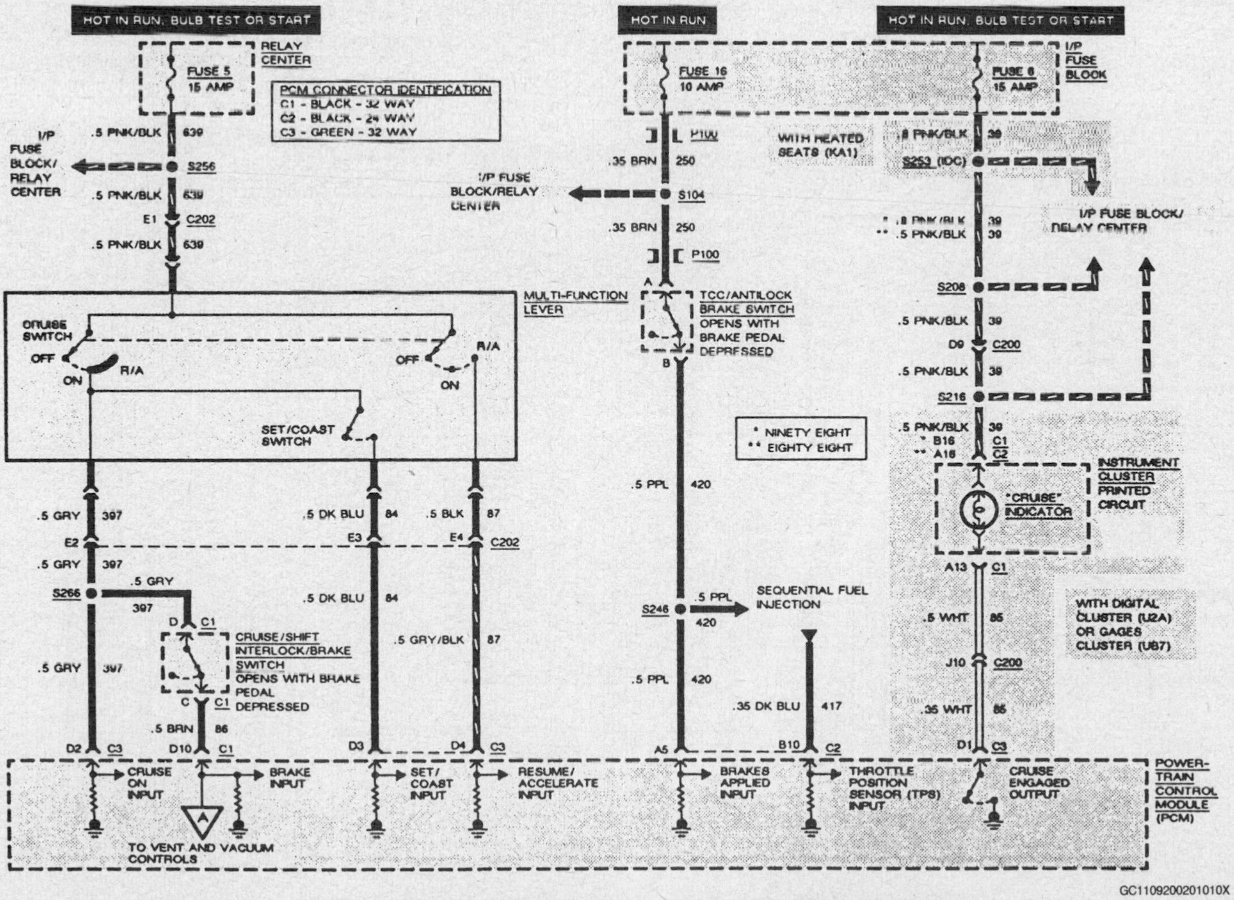
HOT IN RUN, BULB TEST OR START
HOT IN RUN
HOT IN RUN, BULB TEST OR START
RELAY CENTER
FUSE 5 15 AMP
FUSE 16 10 AMP
FUSE 6 15 AMP
I/P FUSE BLOCK
PCM CONNECTOR IDENTIFICATION
C1 - BLACK - 32 WAY
C2 - BLACK - 24 WAY
C3 - GREEN - 32 WAY
.5 PNK/BLK 639
I/P FUSE BLOCK/ RELAY CENTER
S256
C202
.35 BRN 250
S104
WITH HEATED SEATS (KA1)
S253 (IDC)
I/P FUSE BLOCK/ RELAY CENTER
S208
MULTI-FUNCTION LEVER
TCC/ANTILOCK BRAKE SWITCH OPENS WITH BRAKE PEDAL DEPRESSED
CRUISE SWITCH
OFF
ON
R/A
SET/COAST SWITCH
C200
S216
* NINETY EIGHT
** EIGHTY EIGHT
INSTRUMENT CLUSTER PRINTED CIRCUIT
"CRUISE" INDICATOR
.5 GRY 397
.5 DK BLU 84
.5 BLK 87
.5 PPL 420
S266
S246
SEQUENTIAL FUEL INJECTION
CRUISE/SHIFT INTERLOCK/BRAKE SWITCH OPENS WITH BRAKE PEDAL DEPRESSED
.5 GRY/BLK 87
.5 WHT 85
WITH DIGITAL CLUSTER (U2A) OR GAGES CLUSTER (UB7)
.35 DK BLU 417
.35 WHT 85
.5 BRN 86
CRUISE ON INPUT
BRAKE INPUT
SET/ COAST INPUT
RESUME/ ACCELERATE INPUT
BRAKES APPLIED INPUT
THROTTLE POSITION SENSOR (TPS) INPUT
CRUISE ENGAGED OUTPUT
POWER-TRAIN CONTROL MODULE (PCM)
TO VENT AND VACUUM CONTROLS
GC1109200201010X

Fig. 6 Wiring diagram (Part 1 of 2). 1992–93 88 & 98

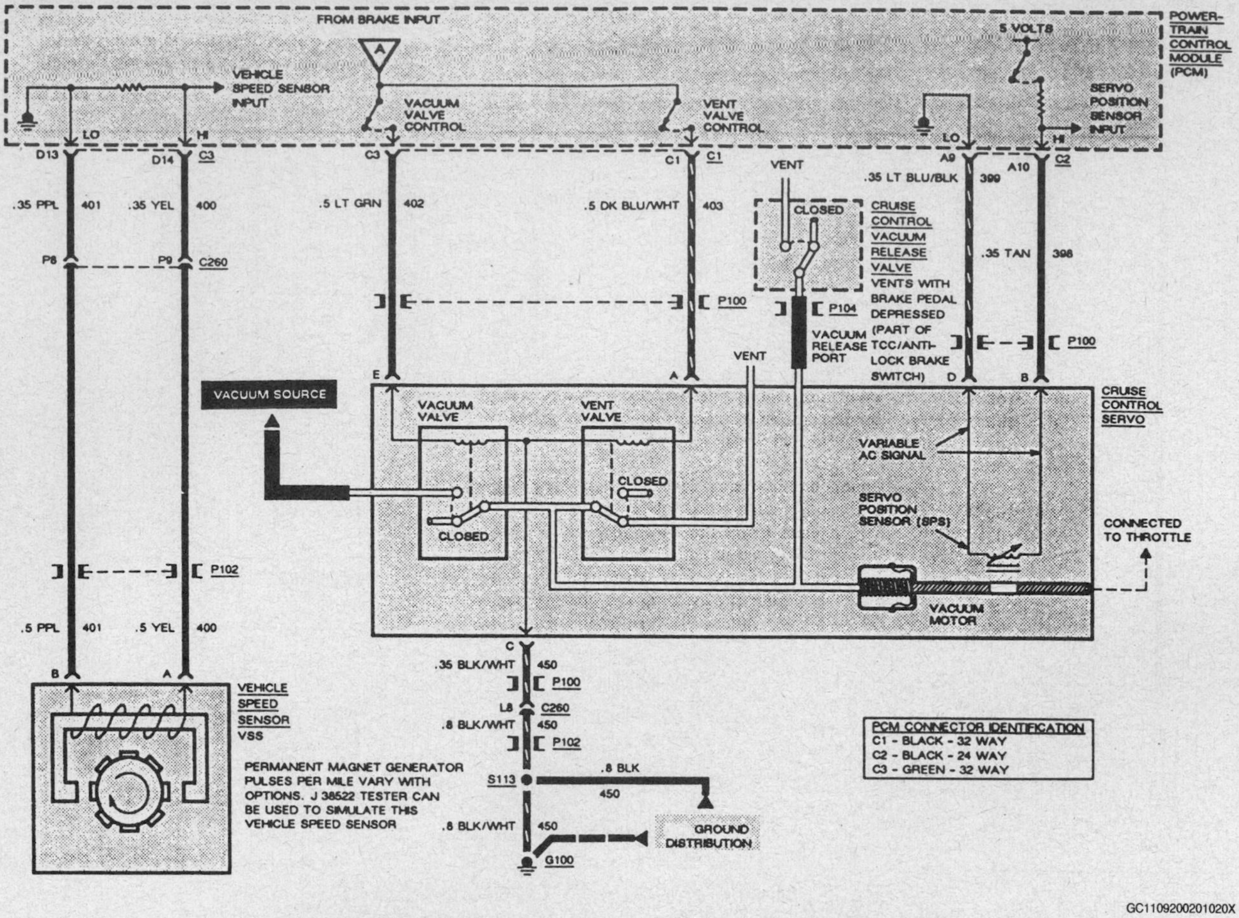
FROM BRAKE INPUT
5 VOLTS
POWER-TRAIN CONTROL MODULE (PCM)
VEHICLE SPEED SENSOR INPUT
VACUUM VALVE CONTROL
VENT VALVE CONTROL
SERVO POSITION SENSOR INPUT
LO
HI
D13
D14
C3
C1
A9
A10
C2
.35 PPL 401
.35 YEL 400
.5 LT GRN 402
.5 DK BLU/WHT 403
.35 LT BLU/BLK 399
.35 TAN 398
VENT
CLOSED
CRUISE CONTROL VACUUM RELEASE VALVE VENTS WITH BRAKE PEDAL DEPRESSED (PART OF TCC/ANTI-LOCK BRAKE SWITCH)
P104
VACUUM RELEASE PORT
P8
P9
C260
P100
VACUUM SOURCE
VACUUM VALVE
VENT VALVE
CLOSED
CRUISE CONTROL SERVO
VARIABLE AC SIGNAL
SERVO POSITION SENSOR (SPS)
CONNECTED TO THROTTLE
VACUUM MOTOR
P102
.5 PPL 401
.5 YEL 400
.35 BLK/WHT 450
L8
.8 BLK/WHT 450
S113
.8 BLK 450
GROUND DISTRIBUTION
G100
VEHICLE SPEED SENSOR VSS
PERMANENT MAGNET GENERATOR PULSES PER MILE VARY WITH OPTIONS. J 38522 TESTER CAN BE USED TO SIMULATE THIS VEHICLE SPEED SENSOR
PCM CONNECTOR IDENTIFICATION
C1 - BLACK - 32 WAY
C2 - BLACK - 24 WAY
C3 - GREEN - 32 WAY
GC1109200201020X

Fig. 6 Wiring diagram (Part 2 of 2). 1992–93 88 & 98

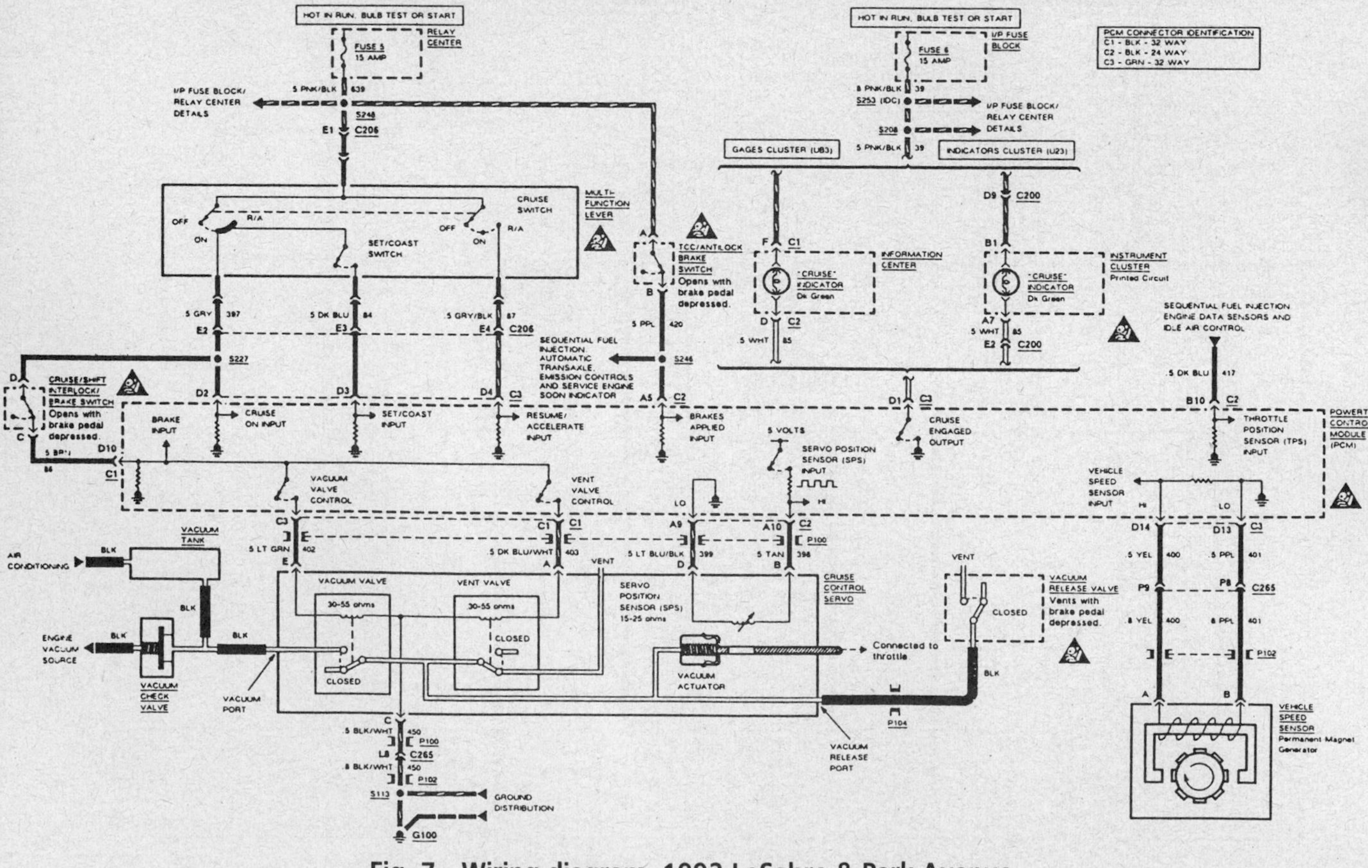
HOT IN RUN, BULB TEST OR START
FUSE 5 15 AMP
RELAY CENTER
FUSE 6 15 AMP
I/P FUSE BLOCK
I/P FUSE BLOCK/ RELAY CENTER DETAILS
PCM CONNECTOR IDENTIFICATION
C1 - BLK - 32 WAY
C2 - BLK - 24 WAY
C3 - GRN - 32 WAY
GAGES CLUSTER (U83)
INDICATORS CLUSTER (U23)
CRUISE SWITCH
MULTI-FUNCTION LEVER
SET/COAST SWITCH
TCC/ANTI-LOCK BRAKE SWITCH Opens with brake pedal depressed.
"CRUISE" INDICATOR
INFORMATION CENTER
INSTRUMENT CLUSTER Printed Circuit
SEQUENTIAL FUEL INJECTION ENGINE DATA SENSORS AND IDLE AIR CONTROL
SEQUENTIAL FUEL INJECTION, AUTOMATIC TRANSAXLE, EMISSION CONTROLS AND SERVICE ENGINE SOON INDICATOR
CRUISE/SHIFT INTERLOCK/ BRAKE SWITCH Opens with brake pedal depressed.
BRAKE INPUT
CRUISE ON INPUT
SET/COAST INPUT
RESUME/ ACCELERATE INPUT
BRAKES APPLIED INPUT
CRUISE ENGAGED OUTPUT
THROTTLE POSITION SENSOR (TPS) INPUT
POWERTRAIN CONTROL MODULE (PCM)
5 VOLTS
SERVO POSITION SENSOR (SPS) INPUT
VACUUM VALVE CONTROL
VENT VALVE CONTROL
VEHICLE SPEED SENSOR INPUT
VACUUM TANK
AIR CONDITIONING
ENGINE VACUUM SOURCE
VACUUM CHECK VALVE
VACUUM PORT
VACUUM VALVE
VENT VALVE
30-55 ohms
CLOSED
SERVO POSITION SENSOR (SPS) 15-25 ohms
CRUISE CONTROL SERVO
VACUUM ACTUATOR
Connected to throttle
VACUUM RELEASE VALVE Vents with brake pedal depressed.
VACUUM RELEASE PORT
P104
GROUND DISTRIBUTION
G100
S113
VEHICLE SPEED SENSOR Permanent Magnet Generator

Fig. 7 Wiring diagram. 1992 LeSabre & Park Avenue

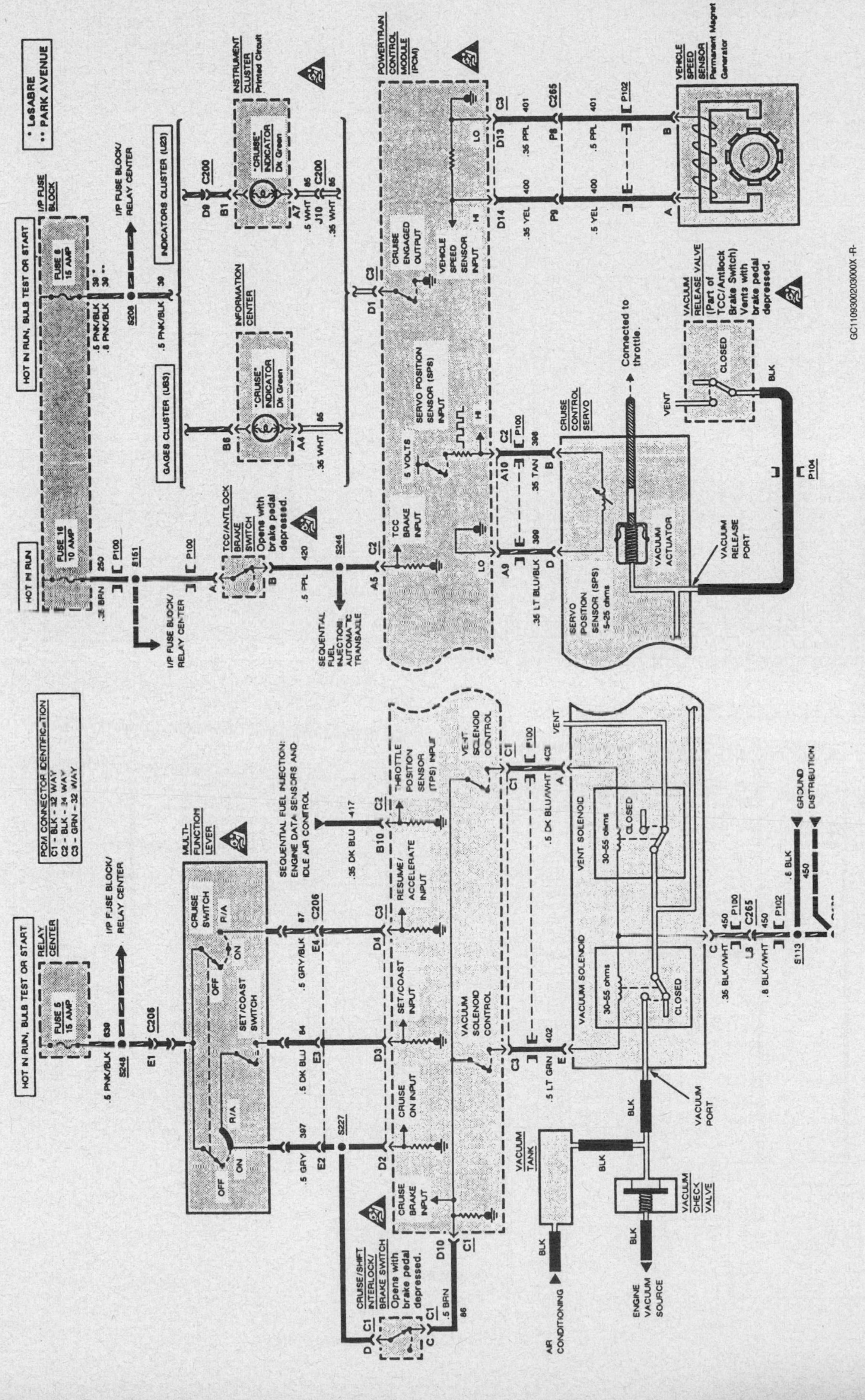
HOT IN RUN, BULB TEST OR START
RELAY CENTER
FUSE 5 15 AMP
I/P FUSE BLOCK/ RELAY CENTER
PCM CONNECTOR IDENTIFICATION
C1 - BLK - 32 WAY
C2 - BLK - 24 WAY
C3 - GRN - 32 WAY
MULTI-FUNCTION LEVER
CRUISE SWITCH
SET/COAST SWITCH
SEQUENTIAL FUEL INJECTION: ENGINE DATA SENSORS AND IDLE AIR CONTROL
CRUISE/SHIFT INTERLOCK/ BRAKE SWITCH
Opens with brake pedal depressed.
CRUISE BRAKE INPUT
CRUISE ON INPUT
SET/COAST INPUT
RESUME/ ACCELERATE INPUT
THROTTLE POSITION SENSOR (TPS) INPUT
VACUUM SOLENOID CONTROL
VENT SOLENOID CONTROL
VACUUM SOLENOID
VENT SOLENOID
30-55 ohms
CLOSED
VENT
VACUUM PORT
VACUUM TANK
VACUUM CHECK VALVE
AIR CONDITIONING
ENGINE VACUUM SOURCE
GROUND DISTRIBUTION
HOT IN RUN
FUSE 16 10 AMP
TCC/ANTILOCK BRAKE SWITCH
Opens with brake pedal depressed.
SEQUENTIAL FUEL INJECTION/ AUTOMATIC TRANSAXLE
TCC BRAKE INPUT
HOT IN RUN, BULB TEST OR START
I/P FUSE BLOCK
FUSE 6 15 AMP
* LeSABRE
** PARK AVENUE
GAGES CLUSTER (U83)
INDICATORS CLUSTER (U23)
INFORMATION CENTER
INSTRUMENT CLUSTER
Printed Circuit
"CRUISE" INDICATOR
Dk Green
POWERTRAIN CONTROL MODULE (PCM)
CRUISE ENGAGED OUTPUT
VEHICLE SPEED SENSOR INPUT
SERVO POSITION SENSOR (SPS) INPUT
5 VOLTS
CRUISE CONTROL SERVO
SERVO POSITION SENSOR (SPS) 5-25 ohms
VACUUM ACTUATOR
VACUUM RELEASE PORT
Connected to throttle.
VACUUM RELEASE VALVE (Part of TCC/Antilock Brake Switch) Vents with brake pedal depressed.
VEHICLE SPEED SENSOR
Permanent Magnet Generator
GC1109300203000X -R-

Fig. 8 Wiring diagram. 1993–94 LeSabre & Park Avenue

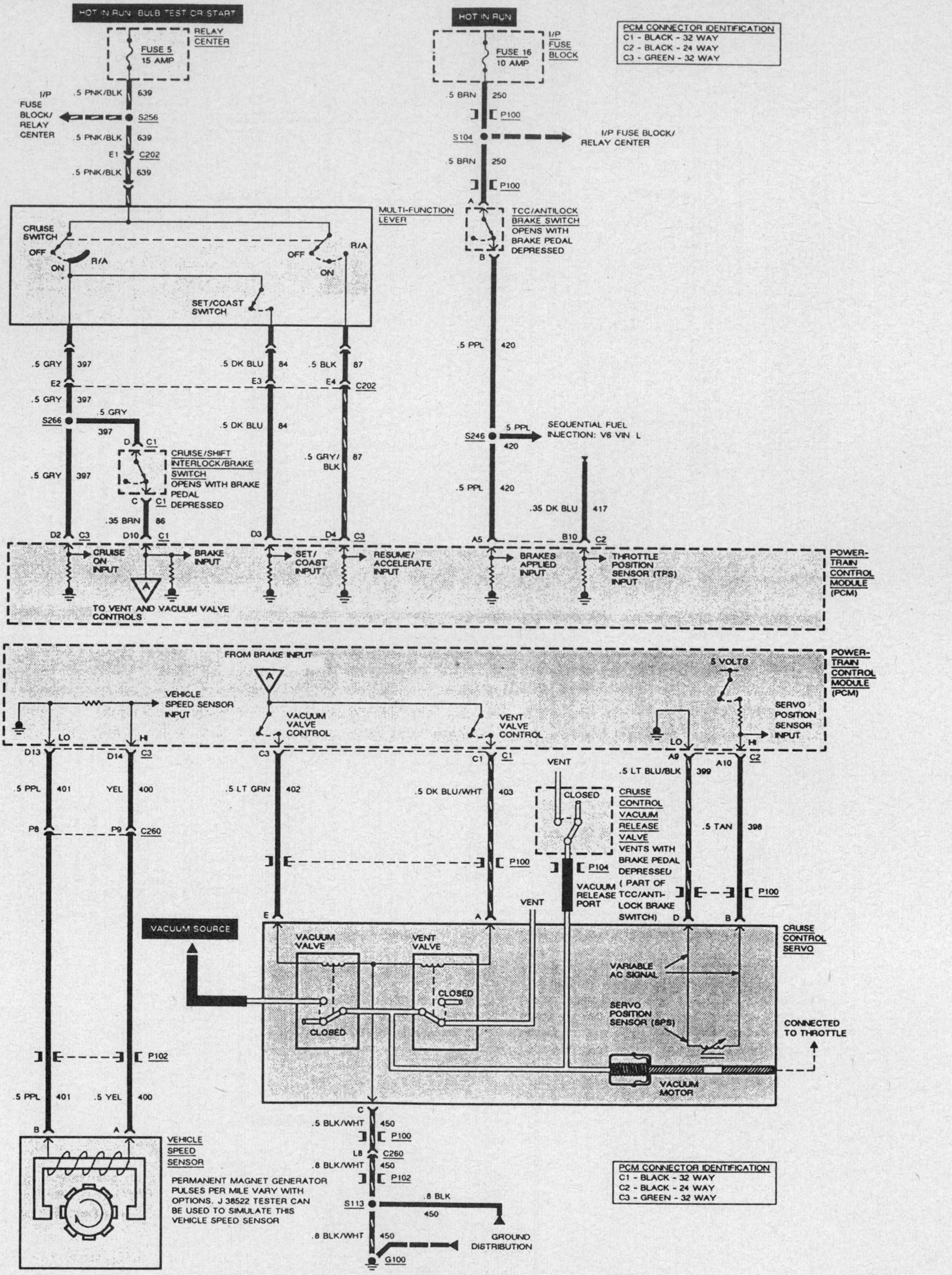

HOT IN RUN, BULB TEST OR START
RELAY CENTER
FUSE 5 15 AMP
I/P FUSE BLOCK/ RELAY CENTER
.5 PNK/BLK 639
S256
E1 C202
HOT IN RUN
FUSE 16 10 AMP
I/P FUSE BLOCK
.5 BRN 250
P100
S104
I/P FUSE BLOCK/ RELAY CENTER
PCM CONNECTOR IDENTIFICATION
C1 - BLACK - 32 WAY
C2 - BLACK - 24 WAY
C3 - GREEN - 32 WAY
MULTI-FUNCTION LEVER
CRUISE SWITCH
OFF
ON
R/A
SET/COAST SWITCH
TCC/ANTILOCK BRAKE SWITCH OPENS WITH BRAKE PEDAL DEPRESSED
.5 GRY 397
.5 DK BLU 84
.5 BLK 87
E2
E3
E4
C202
.5 PPL 420
S266
.5 GRY
CRUISE/SHIFT INTERLOCK/BRAKE SWITCH OPENS WITH BRAKE PEDAL DEPRESSED
.5 GRY/ BLK 87
.35 BRN 86
S246
SEQUENTIAL FUEL INJECTION: V6 VIN L
.35 DK BLU 417
D2 C3
D10 C1
D3
D4 C3
A5
B10 C2
CRUISE ON INPUT
BRAKE INPUT
SET/ COAST INPUT
RESUME/ ACCELERATE INPUT
BRAKES APPLIED INPUT
THROTTLE POSITION SENSOR (TPS) INPUT
POWER-TRAIN CONTROL MODULE (PCM)
TO VENT AND VACUUM VALVE CONTROLS
FROM BRAKE INPUT
5 VOLTS
VEHICLE SPEED SENSOR INPUT
VACUUM VALVE CONTROL
VENT VALVE CONTROL
SERVO POSITION SENSOR INPUT
LO
HI
D13
D14 C3
C3
C1 C1
A9
A10 C2
.5 PPL 401
YEL 400
.5 LT GRN 402
.5 DK BLU/WHT 403
.5 LT BLU/BLK 399
.5 TAN 398
VENT
CLOSED
CRUISE CONTROL VACUUM RELEASE VALVE VENTS WITH BRAKE PEDAL DEPRESSED (PART OF TCC/ANTI-LOCK BRAKE SWITCH)
P8
P9 C260
P100
P104
VACUUM RELEASE PORT
VACUUM SOURCE
CRUISE CONTROL SERVO
VACUUM VALVE
VENT VALVE
VARIABLE AC SIGNAL
SERVO POSITION SENSOR (SPS)
CONNECTED TO THROTTLE
VACUUM MOTOR
P102
.5 YEL 400
VEHICLE SPEED SENSOR
PERMANENT MAGNET GENERATOR PULSES PER MILE VARY WITH OPTIONS. J 38522 TESTER CAN BE USED TO SIMULATE THIS VEHICLE SPEED SENSOR
.5 BLK/WHT 450
L8 C260
.8 BLK/WHT 450
S113
.8 BLK 450
GROUND DISTRIBUTION
G100
GC1109200204000X

Fig. 9 Wiring diagram. 1992 Bonneville

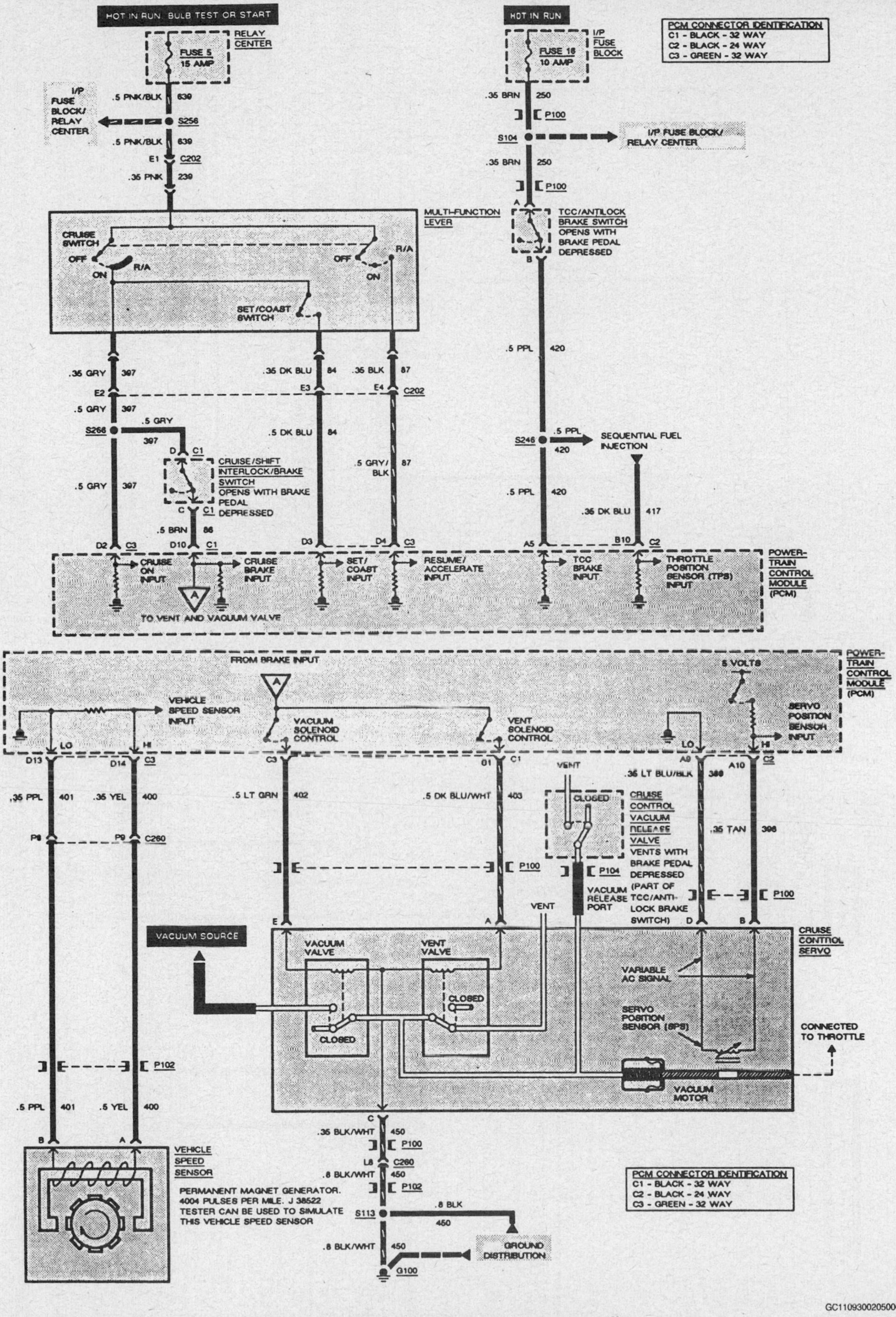
HOT IN RUN, BULB TEST OR START
RELAY CENTER
FUSE 5 15 AMP
I/P FUSE BLOCK/ RELAY CENTER
HOT IN RUN
FUSE 16 10 AMP
I/P FUSE BLOCK
PCM CONNECTOR IDENTIFICATION
C1 - BLACK - 32 WAY
C2 - BLACK - 24 WAY
C3 - GREEN - 32 WAY
I/P FUSE BLOCK/ RELAY CENTER
MULTI-FUNCTION LEVER
TCC/ANTILOCK BRAKE SWITCH OPENS WITH BRAKE PEDAL DEPRESSED
CRUISE SWITCH
SET/COAST SWITCH
CRUISE/SHIFT INTERLOCK/BRAKE SWITCH OPENS WITH BRAKE PEDAL DEPRESSED
SEQUENTIAL FUEL INJECTION
CRUISE ON INPUT
CRUISE BRAKE INPUT
SET/ COAST INPUT
RESUME/ ACCELERATE INPUT
TCC BRAKE INPUT
THROTTLE POSITION SENSOR (TPS) INPUT
POWER-TRAIN CONTROL MODULE (PCM)
TO VENT AND VACUUM VALVE
FROM BRAKE INPUT
VEHICLE SPEED SENSOR INPUT
VACUUM SOLENOID CONTROL
VENT SOLENOID CONTROL
5 VOLTS
SERVO POSITION SENSOR INPUT
CRUISE CONTROL VACUUM RELEASE VALVE VENTS WITH BRAKE PEDAL DEPRESSED (PART OF TCC/ANTI-LOCK BRAKE SWITCH)
VACUUM RELEASE PORT
VACUUM SOURCE
VACUUM VALVE
VENT VALVE
CLOSED
VARIABLE AC SIGNAL
SERVO POSITION SENSOR (SPS)
VACUUM MOTOR
CRUISE CONTROL SERVO
CONNECTED TO THROTTLE
VEHICLE SPEED SENSOR
PERMANENT MAGNET GENERATOR. 4004 PULSES PER MILE. J 38522 TESTER CAN BE USED TO SIMULATE THIS VEHICLE SPEED SENSOR
GROUND DISTRIBUTION
PCM CONNECTOR IDENTIFICATION
C1 - BLACK - 32 WAY
C2 - BLACK - 24 WAY
C3 - GREEN - 32 WAY
GC1109300205000X

Fig. 10 Wiring diagram. 1993 Bonneville

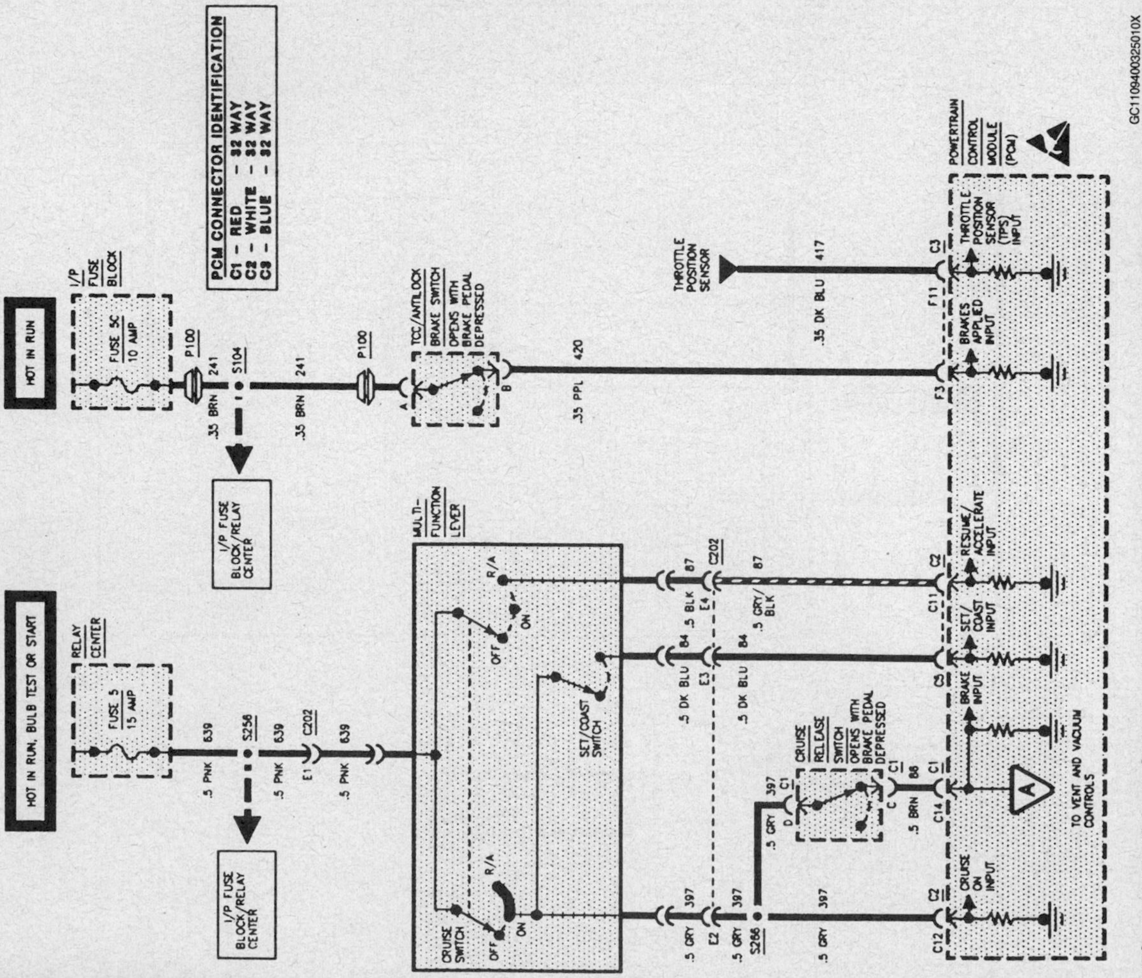
HOT IN RUN, BULB TEST OR START
RELAY CENTER
FUSE 5 15 AMP
I/P FUSE BLOCK/RELAY CENTER
HOT IN RUN
I/P FUSE BLOCK
FUSE 5C 10 AMP
TCC/ANTILOCK BRAKE SWITCH
OPENS WITH BRAKE PEDAL DEPRESSED
PCM CONNECTOR IDENTIFICATION
C1 - RED - 32 WAY
C2 - WHITE - 32 WAY
C3 - BLUE - 32 WAY
MULTI-FUNCTION LEVER
CRUISE SWITCH
SET/COAST SWITCH
CRUISE RELEASE SWITCH
OPENS WITH BRAKE PEDAL DEPRESSED
THROTTLE POSITION SENSOR
POWERTRAIN CONTROL MODULE (PCM)
TO VENT AND VACUUM CONTROLS
GC109400325010X

Fig. 11 Wiring diagram (Part 1 of 2). 1994 Bonneville, LeSabre, Park Avenue, 88 & 98

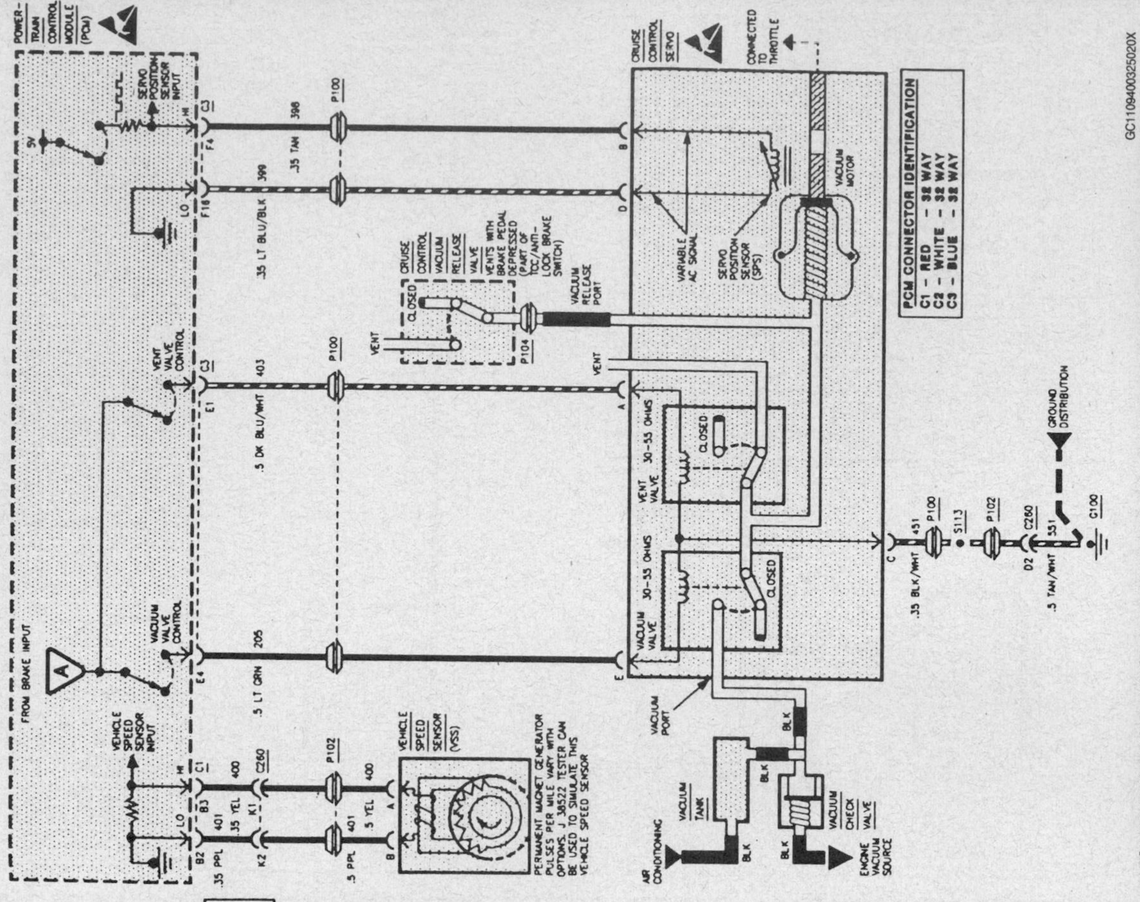
POWER-TRAIN CONTROL MODULE (PCM)
SERVO POSITION SENSOR INPUT
VENT VALVE CONTROL
VACUUM VALVE CONTROL
FROM BRAKE INPUT
VEHICLE SPEED SENSOR INPUT
VEHICLE SPEED SENSOR (VSS)
CRUISE CONTROL VACUUM RELEASE VALVE
CRUISE CONTROL SERVO
VACUUM MOTOR
VENT VALVE
VACUUM VALVE
VACUUM TANK
VACUUM CHECK VALVE
ENGINE VACUUM SOURCE
AIR CONDITIONING
GROUND DISTRIBUTION
PCM CONNECTOR IDENTIFICATION
C1 - RED - 32 WAY
C2 - WHITE - 32 WAY
C3 - BLUE - 32 WAY
GC1094003250 20X

Fig. 11 Wiring diagram (Part 2 of 2). 1994 Bonneville, LeSabre, Park Avenue, 88 & 98

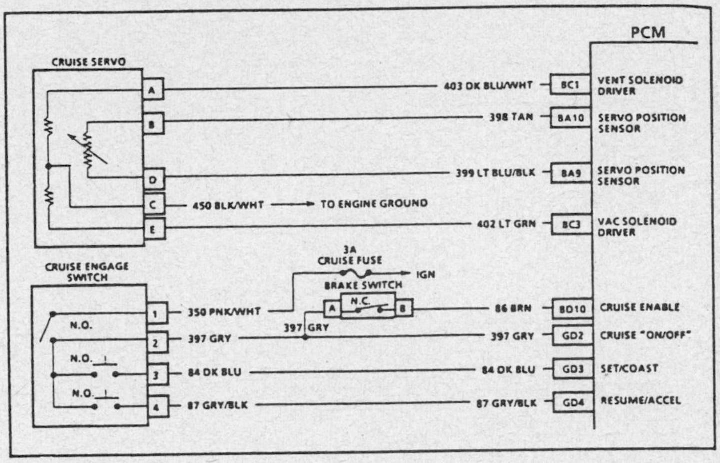
PCM
CRUISE SERVO
A
B
D
C
E
403 DK BLU/WHT
BC1
VENT SOLENOID DRIVER
398 TAN
BA10
SERVO POSITION SENSOR
399 LT BLU/BLK
BA9
SERVO POSITION SENSOR
450 BLK/WHT
TO ENGINE GROUND
402 LT GRN
BC3
VAC SOLENOID DRIVER
CRUISE ENGAGE SWITCH
3A CRUISE FUSE
IGN
BRAKE SWITCH
N.C.
N.O.
350 PNK/WHT
397 GRY
84 DK BLU
87 GRY/BLK
86 BRN
BD10
CRUISE ENABLE
GD2
CRUISE "ON/OFF"
GD3
SET/COAST
GD4
RESUME/ACCEL

GC1109100206000X

Fig. 12 Cruise control system check & diagnostic trouble code wiring diagram. 1992

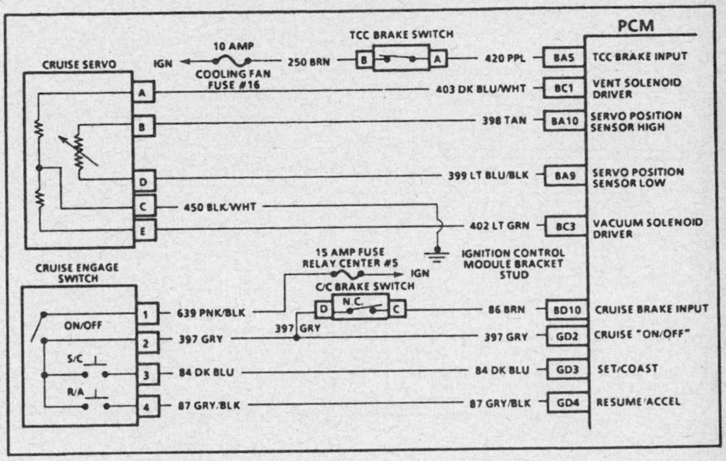
PCM
CRUISE SERVO
IGN
10 AMP
COOLING FAN FUSE #16
250 BRN
TCC BRAKE SWITCH
420 PPL
BA5
TCC BRAKE INPUT
403 DK BLU/WHT
BC1
VENT SOLENOID DRIVER
398 TAN
BA10
SERVO POSITION SENSOR HIGH
399 LT BLU/BLK
BA9
SERVO POSITION SENSOR LOW
450 BLK/WHT
402 LT GRN
BC3
VACUUM SOLENOID DRIVER
IGNITION CONTROL MODULE BRACKET STUD
CRUISE ENGAGE SWITCH
15 AMP FUSE RELAY CENTER #5
C/C BRAKE SWITCH
ON/OFF
S/C
R/A
639 PNK/BLK
397 GRY
84 DK BLU
87 GRY/BLK
86 BRN
BD10
CRUISE BRAKE INPUT
GD2
CRUISE "ON/OFF"
GD3
SET/COAST
GD4
RESUME/ACCEL

GC1109300207000X

Fig. 13 Cruise control system check & diagnostic trouble code wiring diagram. 1993–94 except Riviera

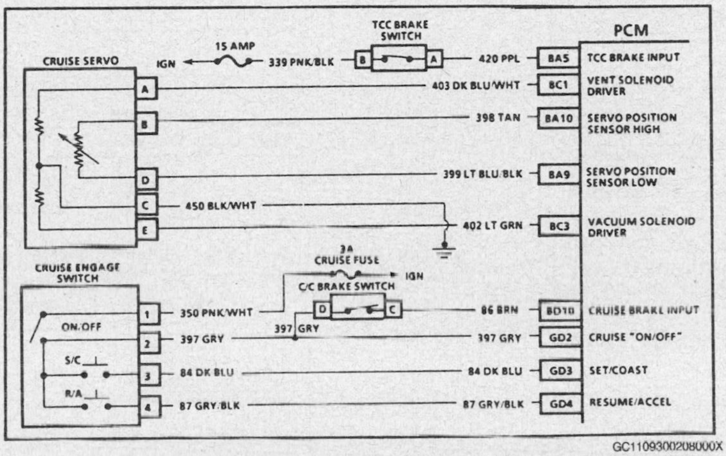
PCM
CRUISE SERVO
IGN
15 AMP
339 PNK/BLK
TCC BRAKE SWITCH
420 PPL
BA5
TCC BRAKE INPUT
403 DK BLU/WHT
BC1
VENT SOLENOID DRIVER
398 TAN
BA10
SERVO POSITION SENSOR HIGH
399 LT BLU/BLK
BA9
SERVO POSITION SENSOR LOW
450 BLK/WHT
402 LT GRN
BC3
VACUUM SOLENOID DRIVER
CRUISE ENGAGE SWITCH
3A CRUISE FUSE
C/C BRAKE SWITCH
ON/OFF
S/C
R/A
350 PNK/WHT
397 GRY
84 DK BLU
87 GRY/BLK
86 BRN
BD10
CRUISE BRAKE INPUT
GD2
CRUISE "ON/OFF"
GD3
SET/COAST
GD4
RESUME/ACCEL

GC1109300208000X

Fig. 14 Cruise control system check & diagnostic trouble code wiring diagram. 1993 Riviera

DIAGNOSTIC CHART INDEX

Test/Code	Description	Year	Page No.	Fig. No.
BONNEVILLE, LESABRE, PARK AVENUE, TORONADO, TROFEO, 88 & 98				
Test C-17	Cruise Control System Check	1992	21-78	15
Test C-17	Cruise Control System Check	1993–94	21-78	16
Code 38	TCC Brake Input Circuit	1993–94	21-79	18
Code 61	Cruise Vent Solenoid Circuit	1992	21-80	20
Code 62	Cruise Vacuum Solenoid Circuit	1992	21-80	21
Code 65	Cruise Servo Position Circuit	1992	21-80	22
Code 65	Cruise Servo Position Sensor Circuit	1993–94	21-80	23
Code 67	Cruise Switches Circuits	1992	21-81	24
Code 68	Cruise System Problem	1992	21-81	25
RIVIERA				
Test C-17	Cruise Control System Check	1992	21-78	15
Test C-17	Cruise Control System Check	1993	21-79	17
Code 38	Brake Input Circuit	1993	21-79	19
Code 61	Cruise Vent Solenoid Circuit	1992	21-80	20
Code 62	Cruise Vacuum Solenoid Circuit	1992	21-80	21
Code 65	Cruise Servo Position Circuit	1992	21-80	22
Code 65	Cruise Servo Position Sensor Circuit	1993	21-80	23
Code 67	Cruise Switches Circuits	1992	21-81	24
Code 68	Cruise System Problem	1992	21-81	25

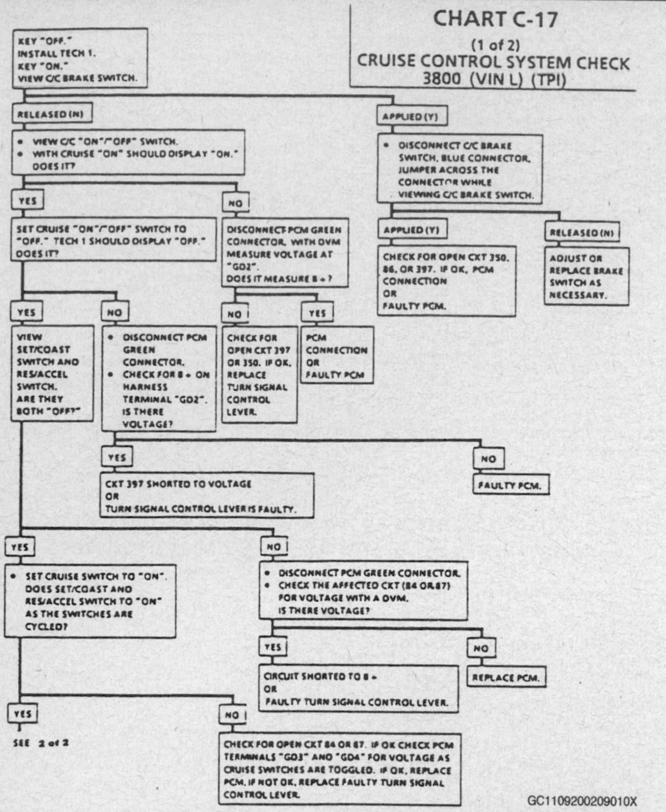
CHART C-17
(1 of 2)
CRUISE CONTROL SYSTEM CHECK
3800 (VIN L) (TPI)
KEY "OFF." INSTALL TECH 1. KEY "ON." VIEW C/C BRAKE SWITCH.
RELEASED (N)
APPLIED (Y)
• VIEW C/C "ON"/"OFF" SWITCH. • WITH CRUISE "ON" SHOULD DISPLAY "ON." DOES IT?
• DISCONNECT C/C BRAKE SWITCH, BLUE CONNECTOR, JUMPER ACROSS THE CONNECTOR WHILE VIEWING C/C BRAKE SWITCH.
YES
NO
SET CRUISE "ON"/"OFF" SWITCH TO "OFF." TECH 1 SHOULD DISPLAY "OFF." DOES IT?
DISCONNECT PCM GREEN CONNECTOR, WITH DVM MEASURE VOLTAGE AT "GD2". DOES IT MEASURE B + ?
APPLIED (Y)
RELEASED (N)
CHECK FOR OPEN CKT 350, 86, OR 397. IF OK, PCM CONNECTION OR FAULTY PCM.
ADJUST OR REPLACE BRAKE SWITCH AS NECESSARY.
VIEW SET/COAST SWITCH AND RES/ACCEL SWITCH. ARE THEY BOTH "OFF?"
• DISCONNECT PCM GREEN CONNECTOR. • CHECK FOR B + ON HARNESS TERMINAL "GD2". IS THERE VOLTAGE?
CHECK FOR OPEN CKT 397 OR 350. IF OK, REPLACE TURN SIGNAL CONTROL LEVER.
PCM CONNECTION OR FAULTY PCM
CKT 397 SHORTED TO VOLTAGE OR TURN SIGNAL CONTROL LEVER IS FAULTY.
FAULTY PCM.
• SET CRUISE SWITCH TO "ON". DOES SET/COAST AND RES/ACCEL SWITCH TO "ON" AS THE SWITCHES ARE CYCLED?
• DISCONNECT PCM GREEN CONNECTOR. • CHECK THE AFFECTED CKT (84 OR 87) FOR VOLTAGE WITH A DVM. IS THERE VOLTAGE?
CIRCUIT SHORTED TO B + OR FAULTY TURN SIGNAL CONTROL LEVER.
REPLACE PCM.
SEE 2 of 2
CHECK FOR OPEN CKT 84 OR 87. IF OK CHECK PCM TERMINALS "GD3" AND "GD4" FOR VOLTAGE AS CRUISE SWITCHES ARE TOGGLED. IF OK, REPLACE PCM. IF NOT OK, REPLACE FAULTY TURN SIGNAL CONTROL LEVER.
GC1109200209010X

Fig. 15 Test C-17: Cruise Control System Check (Part 1 of 2). 1992 Bonneville, LeSabre, Park Avenue, Riviera, Toronado, Trofeo, 88 & 98

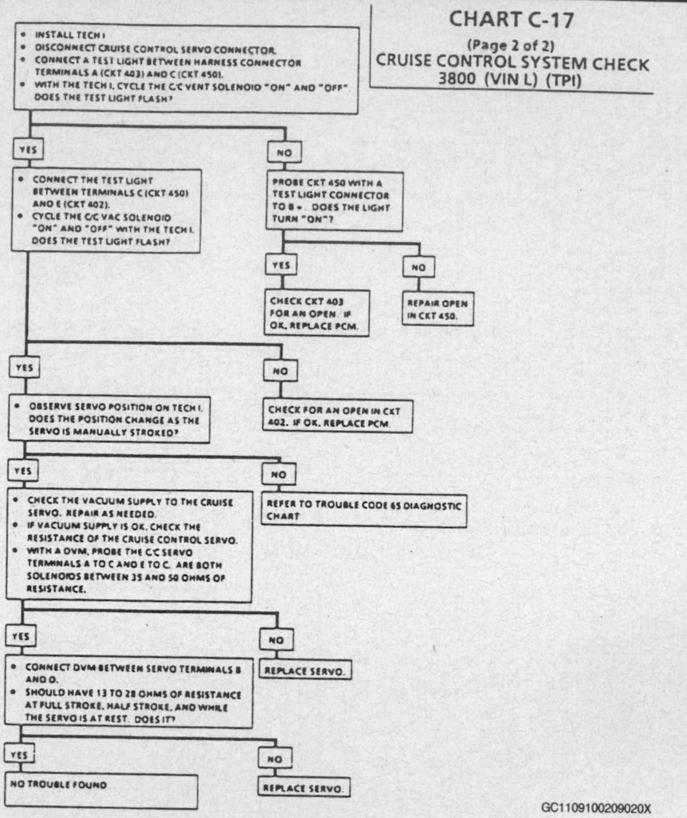
CHART C-17
(Page 2 of 2)
CRUISE CONTROL SYSTEM CHECK
3800 (VIN L) (TPI)
• INSTALL TECH I • DISCONNECT CRUISE CONTROL SERVO CONNECTOR. • CONNECT A TEST LIGHT BETWEEN HARNESS CONNECTOR TERMINALS A (CKT 403) AND C (CKT 450). • WITH THE TECH I, CYCLE THE C/C VENT SOLENOID "ON" AND "OFF" DOES THE TEST LIGHT FLASH?
YES
NO
• CONNECT THE TEST LIGHT BETWEEN TERMINALS C (CKT 450) AND E (CKT 402). • CYCLE THE C/C VAC SOLENOID "ON" AND "OFF" WITH THE TECH I. DOES THE TEST LIGHT FLASH?
PROBE CKT 450 WITH A TEST LIGHT CONNECTOR TO B +. DOES THE LIGHT TURN "ON"?
CHECK CKT 403 FOR AN OPEN. IF OK, REPLACE PCM.
REPAIR OPEN IN CKT 450.
• OBSERVE SERVO POSITION ON TECH I. DOES THE POSITION CHANGE AS THE SERVO IS MANUALLY STROKED?
CHECK FOR AN OPEN IN CKT 402. IF OK, REPLACE PCM.
• CHECK THE VACUUM SUPPLY TO THE CRUISE SERVO. REPAIR AS NEEDED. • IF VACUUM SUPPLY IS OK, CHECK THE RESISTANCE OF THE CRUISE CONTROL SERVO. • WITH A DVM, PROBE THE C/C SERVO TERMINALS A TO C AND E TO C. ARE BOTH SOLENOIDS BETWEEN 35 AND 50 OHMS OF RESISTANCE.
REFER TO TROUBLE CODE 65 DIAGNOSTIC CHART
• CONNECT DVM BETWEEN SERVO TERMINALS B AND D. • SHOULD HAVE 13 TO 28 OHMS OF RESISTANCE AT FULL STROKE, HALF STROKE, AND WHILE THE SERVO IS AT REST. DOES IT?
REPLACE SERVO.
NO TROUBLE FOUND
REPLACE SERVO.
GC1109100209020X

Fig. 15 Test C-17: Cruise Control System Check (Part 2 of 2). 1992 Bonneville, LeSabre, Park Avenue, Riviera, Toronado, Trofeo, 88 & 98

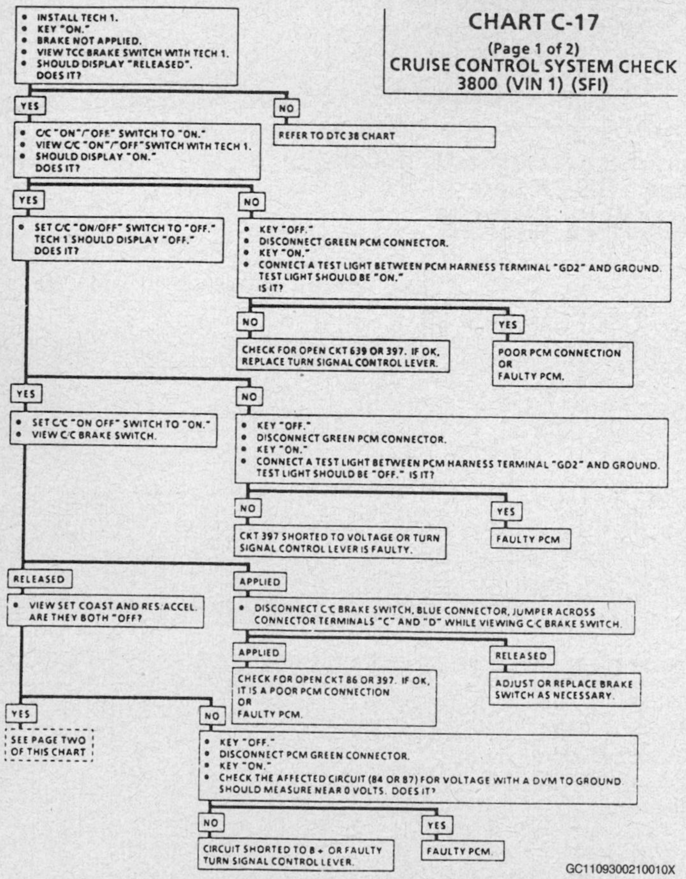
CHART C-17
(Page 1 of 2)
CRUISE CONTROL SYSTEM CHECK
3800 (VIN 1) (SFI)
• INSTALL TECH 1. • KEY "ON." • BRAKE NOT APPLIED. • VIEW TCC BRAKE SWITCH WITH TECH 1. • SHOULD DISPLAY "RELEASED". DOES IT?
YES
NO
REFER TO DTC 38 CHART
• C/C "ON"/"OFF" SWITCH TO "ON." • VIEW C/C "ON"/"OFF" SWITCH WITH TECH 1. • SHOULD DISPLAY "ON." DOES IT?
• SET C/C "ON/OFF" SWITCH TO "OFF." TECH 1 SHOULD DISPLAY "OFF." DOES IT?
• KEY "OFF." • DISCONNECT GREEN PCM CONNECTOR. • KEY "ON." • CONNECT A TEST LIGHT BETWEEN PCM HARNESS TERMINAL "GD2" AND GROUND. TEST LIGHT SHOULD BE "ON." IS IT?
CHECK FOR OPEN CKT 639 OR 397. IF OK, REPLACE TURN SIGNAL CONTROL LEVER.
POOR PCM CONNECTION OR FAULTY PCM.
• SET C/C "ON OFF" SWITCH TO "ON." • VIEW C/C BRAKE SWITCH.
• KEY "OFF." • DISCONNECT GREEN PCM CONNECTOR. • KEY "ON." • CONNECT A TEST LIGHT BETWEEN PCM HARNESS TERMINAL "GD2" AND GROUND. TEST LIGHT SHOULD BE "OFF." IS IT?
CKT 397 SHORTED TO VOLTAGE OR TURN SIGNAL CONTROL LEVER IS FAULTY.
FAULTY PCM
RELEASED
APPLIED
• VIEW SET COAST AND RES ACCEL. ARE THEY BOTH "OFF"?
• DISCONNECT C/C BRAKE SWITCH, BLUE CONNECTOR, JUMPER ACROSS CONNECTOR TERMINALS "C" AND "D" WHILE VIEWING C/C BRAKE SWITCH.
CHECK FOR OPEN CKT 86 OR 397. IF OK, IT IS A POOR PCM CONNECTION OR FAULTY PCM.
ADJUST OR REPLACE BRAKE SWITCH AS NECESSARY.
SEE PAGE TWO OF THIS CHART
• KEY "OFF." • DISCONNECT PCM GREEN CONNECTOR. • KEY "ON." • CHECK THE AFFECTED CIRCUIT (84 OR 87) FOR VOLTAGE WITH A DVM TO GROUND. SHOULD MEASURE NEAR 0 VOLTS. DOES IT?
CIRCUIT SHORTED TO B + OR FAULTY TURN SIGNAL CONTROL LEVER.
FAULTY PCM.
GC1109300210010X

Fig. 16 Test C-17: Cruise Control System Check (Part 1 of 2). 1993–94 Bonneville, LeSabre, Park Avenue, Riviera, 88 & 98

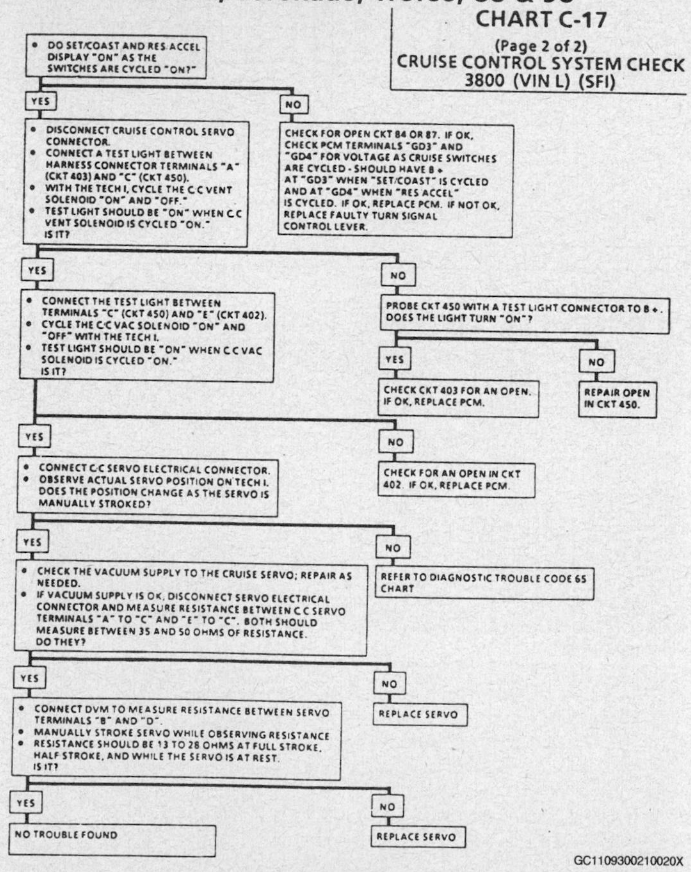
CHART C-17
(Page 2 of 2)
CRUISE CONTROL SYSTEM CHECK
3800 (VIN L) (SFI)
• DO SET/COAST AND RES ACCEL DISPLAY "ON" AS THE SWITCHES ARE CYCLED "ON?"
YES
NO
• DISCONNECT CRUISE CONTROL SERVO CONNECTOR. • CONNECT A TEST LIGHT BETWEEN HARNESS CONNECTOR TERMINALS "A" (CKT 403) AND "C" (CKT 450). • WITH THE TECH I, CYCLE THE C/C VENT SOLENOID "ON" AND "OFF." • TEST LIGHT SHOULD BE "ON" WHEN C/C VENT SOLENOID IS CYCLED "ON." IS IT?
CHECK FOR OPEN CKT 84 OR 87. IF OK, CHECK PCM TERMINALS "GD3" AND "GD4" FOR VOLTAGE AS CRUISE SWITCHES ARE CYCLED - SHOULD HAVE B + AT "GD3" WHEN "SET/COAST" IS CYCLED AND AT "GD4" WHEN "RES ACCEL" IS CYCLED. IF OK, REPLACE PCM. IF NOT OK, REPLACE FAULTY TURN SIGNAL CONTROL LEVER.
• CONNECT THE TEST LIGHT BETWEEN TERMINALS "C" (CKT 450) AND "E" (CKT 402). • CYCLE THE C/C VAC SOLENOID "ON" AND "OFF" WITH THE TECH I. • TEST LIGHT SHOULD BE "ON" WHEN C/C VAC SOLENOID IS CYCLED "ON." IS IT?
PROBE CKT 450 WITH A TEST LIGHT CONNECTOR TO B +. DOES THE LIGHT TURN "ON"?
CHECK CKT 403 FOR AN OPEN. IF OK, REPLACE PCM.
REPAIR OPEN IN CKT 450.
• CONNECT C/C SERVO ELECTRICAL CONNECTOR. • OBSERVE ACTUAL SERVO POSITION ON TECH I. DOES THE POSITION CHANGE AS THE SERVO IS MANUALLY STROKED?
CHECK FOR AN OPEN IN CKT 402. IF OK, REPLACE PCM.
• CHECK THE VACUUM SUPPLY TO THE CRUISE SERVO; REPAIR AS NEEDED. • IF VACUUM SUPPLY IS OK, DISCONNECT SERVO ELECTRICAL CONNECTOR AND MEASURE RESISTANCE BETWEEN C/C SERVO TERMINALS "A" TO "C" AND "E" TO "C". BOTH SHOULD MEASURE BETWEEN 35 AND 50 OHMS OF RESISTANCE. DO THEY?
REFER TO DIAGNOSTIC TROUBLE CODE 65 CHART
• CONNECT DVM TO MEASURE RESISTANCE BETWEEN SERVO TERMINALS "B" AND "D". • MANUALLY STROKE SERVO WHILE OBSERVING RESISTANCE • RESISTANCE SHOULD BE 13 TO 28 OHMS AT FULL STROKE, HALF STROKE, AND WHILE THE SERVO IS AT REST. IS IT?
REPLACE SERVO
NO TROUBLE FOUND
REPLACE SERVO
GC1109300210020X

Fig. 16 Test C-17: Cruise Control System Check (Part 2 of 2). 1993–94 Bonneville, LeSabre, Park Avenue, Riviera, 88 & 98

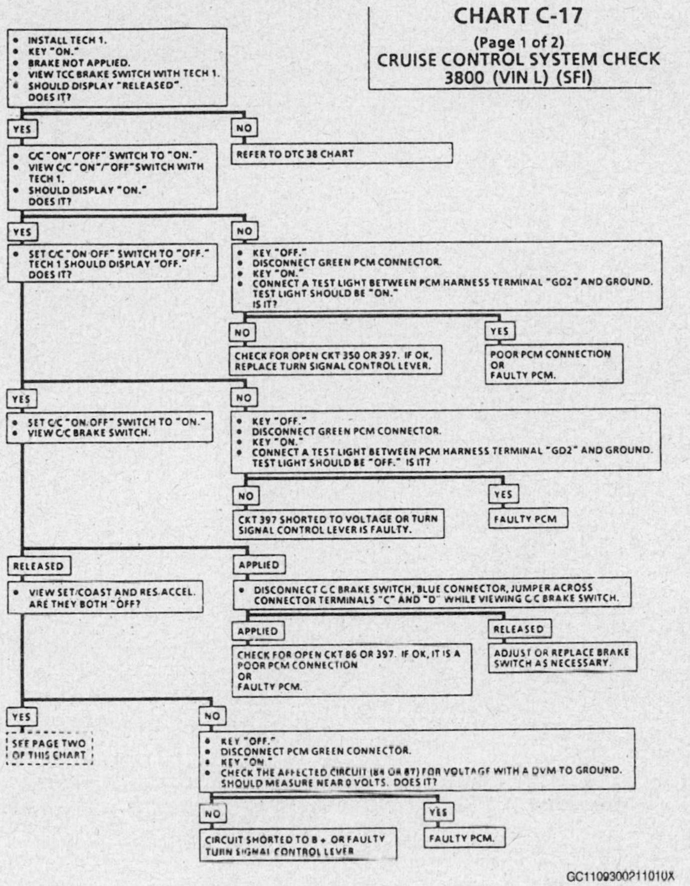
CHART C-17
(Page 1 of 2)
CRUISE CONTROL SYSTEM CHECK
3800 (VIN L) (SFI)
• INSTALL TECH 1. • KEY "ON." • BRAKE NOT APPLIED. • VIEW TCC BRAKE SWITCH WITH TECH 1. • SHOULD DISPLAY "RELEASED". DOES IT?
YES
NO
REFER TO DTC 38 CHART
• C/C "ON"/"OFF" SWITCH TO "ON." • VIEW C/C "ON"/"OFF" SWITCH WITH TECH 1. • SHOULD DISPLAY "ON." DOES IT?
YES
NO
• SET C/C "ON OFF" SWITCH TO "OFF." TECH 1 SHOULD DISPLAY "OFF." DOES IT?
• KEY "OFF." • DISCONNECT GREEN PCM CONNECTOR. • KEY "ON." • CONNECT A TEST LIGHT BETWEEN PCM HARNESS TERMINAL "GD2" AND GROUND. TEST LIGHT SHOULD BE "ON." IS IT?
NO
YES
CHECK FOR OPEN CKT 350 OR 397. IF OK, REPLACE TURN SIGNAL CONTROL LEVER.
POOR PCM CONNECTION OR FAULTY PCM.
YES
NO
• SET C/C "ON.OFF" SWITCH TO "ON." • VIEW C/C BRAKE SWITCH.
• KEY "OFF." • DISCONNECT GREEN PCM CONNECTOR. • KEY "ON." • CONNECT A TEST LIGHT BETWEEN PCM HARNESS TERMINAL "GD2" AND GROUND. TEST LIGHT SHOULD BE "OFF." IS IT?
NO
YES
CKT 397 SHORTED TO VOLTAGE OR TURN SIGNAL CONTROL LEVER IS FAULTY.
FAULTY PCM
RELEASED
APPLIED
• VIEW SET/COAST AND RES.ACCEL. ARE THEY BOTH "OFF?
• DISCONNECT C.C BRAKE SWITCH, BLUE CONNECTOR, JUMPER ACROSS CONNECTOR TERMINALS "C" AND "D" WHILE VIEWING C.C BRAKE SWITCH.
APPLIED
RELEASED
CHECK FOR OPEN CKT 86 OR 397. IF OK, IT IS A POOR PCM CONNECTION OR FAULTY PCM.
ADJUST OR REPLACE BRAKE SWITCH AS NECESSARY.
YES
NO
SEE PAGE TWO OF THIS CHART
• KEY "OFF." • DISCONNECT PCM GREEN CONNECTOR. • KEY "ON." • CHECK THE AFFECTED CIRCUIT (84 OR 87) FOR VOLTAGE WITH A DVM TO GROUND. SHOULD MEASURE NEAR 0 VOLTS. DOES IT?
NO
YES
CIRCUIT SHORTED TO B + OR FAULTY TURN SIGNAL CONTROL LEVER
FAULTY PCM.
GC1109300211010X

Fig. 17 Test C-17: Cruise Control System Check (Part 1 of 2). 1993 Riviera

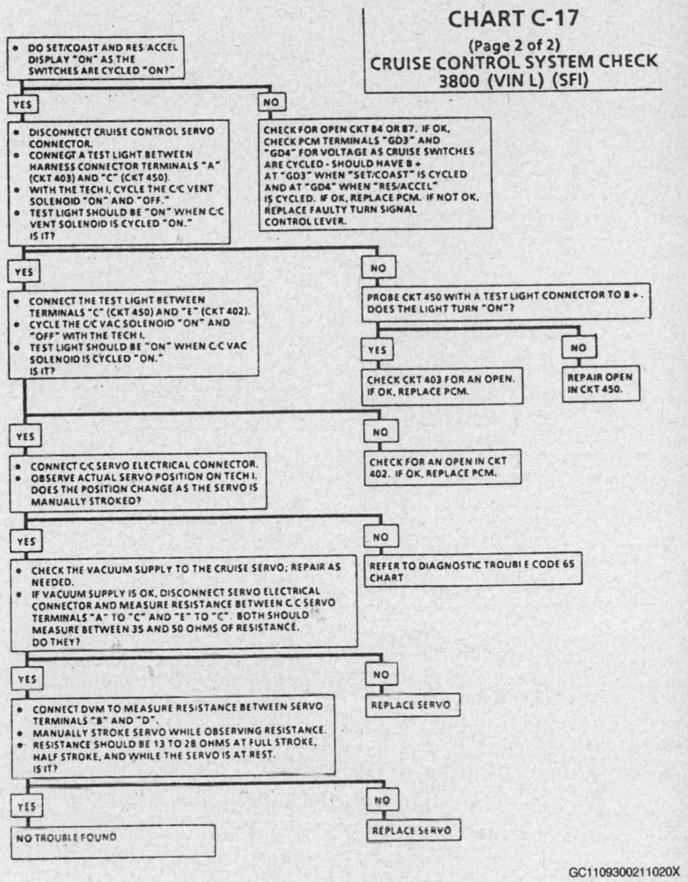
CHART C-17
(Page 2 of 2)
CRUISE CONTROL SYSTEM CHECK
3800 (VIN L) (SFI)
• DO SET/COAST AND RES/ACCEL DISPLAY "ON" AS THE SWITCHES ARE CYCLED "ON?"
YES
NO
• DISCONNECT CRUISE CONTROL SERVO CONNECTOR. • CONNECT A TEST LIGHT BETWEEN HARNESS CONNECTOR TERMINALS "A" (CKT 403) AND "C" (CKT 450). • WITH THE TECH I, CYCLE THE C/C VENT SOLENOID "ON" AND "OFF." • TEST LIGHT SHOULD BE "ON" WHEN C/C VENT SOLENOID IS CYCLED "ON." IS IT?
CHECK FOR OPEN CKT 84 OR 87. IF OK, CHECK PCM TERMINALS "GD3" AND "GD4" FOR VOLTAGE AS CRUISE SWITCHES ARE CYCLED - SHOULD HAVE B + AT "GD3" WHEN "SET/COAST" IS CYCLED AND AT "GD4" WHEN "RES/ACCEL" IS CYCLED. IF OK, REPLACE PCM. IF NOT OK, REPLACE FAULTY TURN SIGNAL CONTROL LEVER.
YES
NO
• CONNECT THE TEST LIGHT BETWEEN TERMINALS "C" (CKT 450) AND "E" (CKT 402). • CYCLE THE C/C VAC SOLENOID "ON" AND "OFF" WITH THE TECH I. • TEST LIGHT SHOULD BE "ON" WHEN C.C VAC SOLENOID IS CYCLED "ON." IS IT?
PROBE CKT 450 WITH A TEST LIGHT CONNECTOR TO B +. DOES THE LIGHT TURN "ON"?
YES
NO
CHECK CKT 403 FOR AN OPEN. IF OK, REPLACE PCM.
REPAIR OPEN IN CKT 450.
YES
NO
• CONNECT C/C SERVO ELECTRICAL CONNECTOR. • OBSERVE ACTUAL SERVO POSITION ON TECH I. DOES THE POSITION CHANGE AS THE SERVO IS MANUALLY STROKED?
CHECK FOR AN OPEN IN CKT 402. IF OK, REPLACE PCM.
YES
NO
• CHECK THE VACUUM SUPPLY TO THE CRUISE SERVO; REPAIR AS NEEDED. • IF VACUUM SUPPLY IS OK, DISCONNECT SERVO ELECTRICAL CONNECTOR AND MEASURE RESISTANCE BETWEEN C.C SERVO TERMINALS "A" TO "C" AND "E" TO "C". BOTH SHOULD MEASURE BETWEEN 35 AND 50 OHMS OF RESISTANCE. DO THEY?
REFER TO DIAGNOSTIC TROUBLE CODE 65 CHART
YES
NO
• CONNECT DVM TO MEASURE RESISTANCE BETWEEN SERVO TERMINALS "B" AND "D". • MANUALLY STROKE SERVO WHILE OBSERVING RESISTANCE. • RESISTANCE SHOULD BE 13 TO 28 OHMS AT FULL STROKE, HALF STROKE, AND WHILE THE SERVO IS AT REST. IS IT?
REPLACE SERVO
YES
NO
NO TROUBLE FOUND
REPLACE SERVO
GC1109300211020X

Fig. 17 Test C-17: Cruise Control System Check (Part 2 of 2). 1993 Riviera

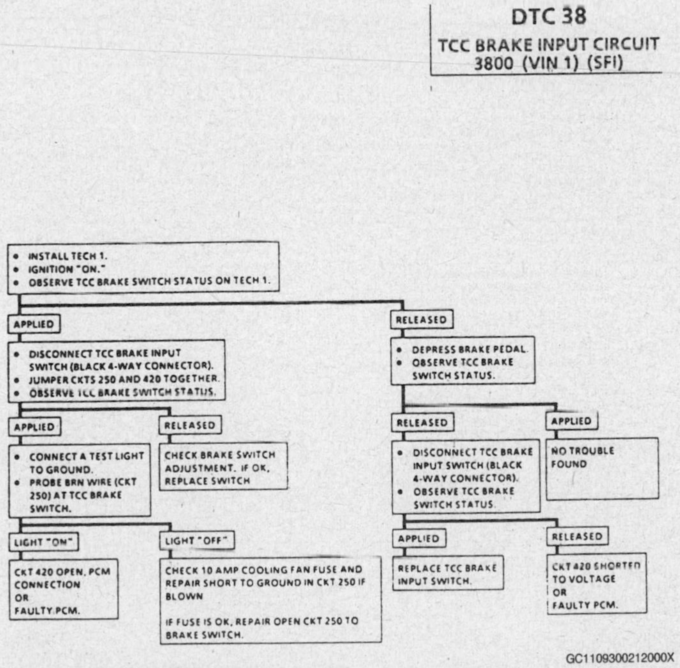
DTC 38
TCC BRAKE INPUT CIRCUIT
3800 (VIN 1) (SFI)
• INSTALL TECH 1. • IGNITION "ON." • OBSERVE TCC BRAKE SWITCH STATUS ON TECH 1.
APPLIED
RELEASED
• DISCONNECT TCC BRAKE INPUT SWITCH (BLACK 4-WAY CONNECTOR). • JUMPER CKTS 250 AND 420 TOGETHER. • OBSERVE TCC BRAKE SWITCH STATUS.
• DEPRESS BRAKE PEDAL. • OBSERVE TCC BRAKE SWITCH STATUS.
APPLIED
RELEASED
RELEASED
APPLIED
• CONNECT A TEST LIGHT TO GROUND. • PROBE BRN WIRE (CKT 250) AT TCC BRAKE SWITCH.
CHECK BRAKE SWITCH ADJUSTMENT. IF OK, REPLACE SWITCH
• DISCONNECT TCC BRAKE INPUT SWITCH (BLACK 4-WAY CONNECTOR). • OBSERVE TCC BRAKE SWITCH STATUS.
NO TROUBLE FOUND
LIGHT "ON"
LIGHT "OFF"
APPLIED
RELEASED
CKT 420 OPEN, PCM CONNECTION OR FAULTY PCM.
CHECK 10 AMP COOLING FAN FUSE AND REPAIR SHORT TO GROUND IN CKT 250 IF BLOWN
IF FUSE IS OK, REPAIR OPEN CKT 250 TO BRAKE SWITCH.
REPLACE TCC BRAKE INPUT SWITCH.
CKT 420 SHORTED TO VOLTAGE OR FAULTY PCM.
GC1109300212000X

Fig. 18 Code 38: TCC Brake Input Circuit. 1993—94 Bonneville, LeSabre, Park Avenue, Riviera, 88 & 98

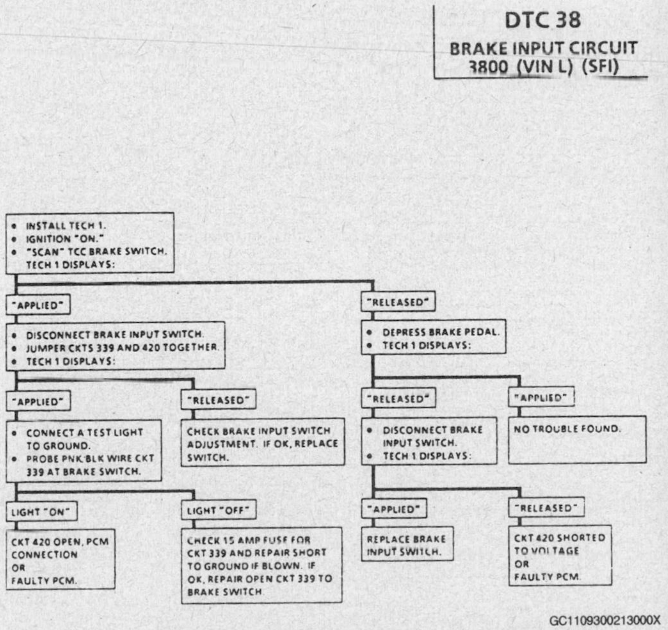
DTC 38
BRAKE INPUT CIRCUIT
3800 (VIN L) (SFI)
• INSTALL TECH 1. • IGNITION "ON." • "SCAN" TCC BRAKE SWITCH. TECH 1 DISPLAYS:
"APPLIED"
"RELEASED"
• DISCONNECT BRAKE INPUT SWITCH. • JUMPER CKTS 339 AND 420 TOGETHER. • TECH 1 DISPLAYS:
• DEPRESS BRAKE PEDAL. • TECH 1 DISPLAYS:
"APPLIED"
"RELEASED"
"RELEASED"
"APPLIED"
• CONNECT A TEST LIGHT TO GROUND. • PROBE PNK/BLK WIRE CKT 339 AT BRAKE SWITCH.
CHECK BRAKE INPUT SWITCH ADJUSTMENT. IF OK, REPLACE SWITCH.
• DISCONNECT BRAKE INPUT SWITCH. • TECH 1 DISPLAYS:
NO TROUBLE FOUND.
LIGHT "ON"
LIGHT "OFF"
"APPLIED"
"RELEASED"
CKT 420 OPEN, PCM CONNECTION OR FAULTY PCM.
CHECK 15 AMP FUSE FOR CKT 339 AND REPAIR SHORT TO GROUND IF BLOWN. IF OK, REPAIR OPEN CKT 339 TO BRAKE SWITCH.
REPLACE BRAKE INPUT SWITCH.
CKT 420 SHORTED TO VOLTAGE OR FAULTY PCM.
GC1109300213000X

Fig. 19 Code 38: Brake Input Circuit. 1993 Riviera

CODE 61

CRUISE VENT SOLENOID CIRCUIT
3800 (VIN L) (TPI)

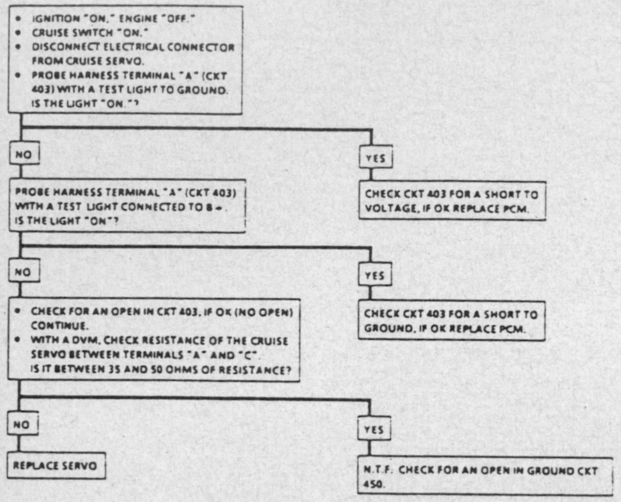
IGNITION "ON," ENGINE "OFF."
CRUISE SWITCH "ON."
DISCONNECT ELECTRICAL CONNECTOR FROM CRUISE SERVO.
PROBE HARNESS TERMINAL "A" (CKT 403) WITH A TEST LIGHT TO GROUND. IS THE LIGHT "ON"?
NO
YES
PROBE HARNESS TERMINAL "A" (CKT 403) WITH A TEST LIGHT CONNECTED TO B+. IS THE LIGHT "ON"?
CHECK CKT 403 FOR A SHORT TO VOLTAGE. IF OK REPLACE PCM.
NO
YES
CHECK FOR AN OPEN IN CKT 403. IF OK (NO OPEN) CONTINUE.
WITH A DVM, CHECK RESISTANCE OF THE CRUISE SERVO BETWEEN TERMINALS "A" AND "C". IS IT BETWEEN 35 AND 50 OHMS OF RESISTANCE?
CHECK CKT 403 FOR A SHORT TO GROUND. IF OK REPLACE PCM.
NO
YES
REPLACE SERVO
N.T.F. CHECK FOR AN OPEN IN GROUND CKT 450.

GC1109100214000X

Fig. 20 Code 61: Cruise Vent Solenoid Circuit. 1992 Bonneville, LeSabre, Park Avenue, Riviera, Toronado, Trofeo, 88 & 98

CODE 62

CRUISE VAC SOLENOID CIRCUIT
3800 (VIN L) (TPI)

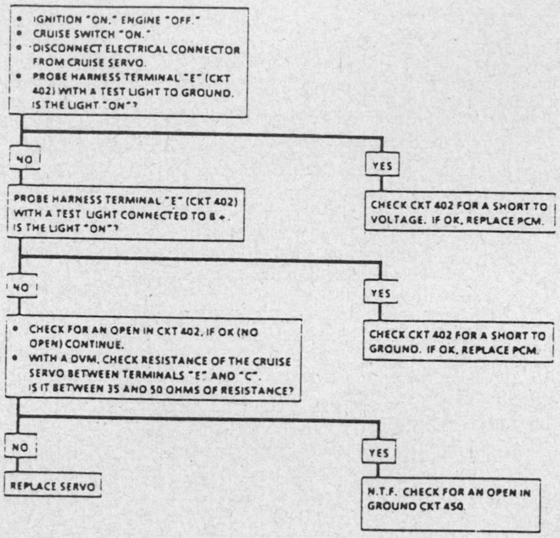
IGNITION "ON," ENGINE "OFF."
CRUISE SWITCH "ON."
DISCONNECT ELECTRICAL CONNECTOR FROM CRUISE SERVO.
PROBE HARNESS TERMINAL "E" (CKT 402) WITH A TEST LIGHT TO GROUND. IS THE LIGHT "ON"?
NO
YES
PROBE HARNESS TERMINAL "E" (CKT 402) WITH A TEST LIGHT CONNECTED TO B+. IS THE LIGHT "ON"?
CHECK CKT 402 FOR A SHORT TO VOLTAGE. IF OK, REPLACE PCM.
NO
YES
CHECK FOR AN OPEN IN CKT 402. IF OK (NO OPEN) CONTINUE.
WITH A DVM, CHECK RESISTANCE OF THE CRUISE SERVO BETWEEN TERMINALS "E" AND "C". IS IT BETWEEN 35 AND 50 OHMS OF RESISTANCE?
CHECK CKT 402 FOR A SHORT TO GROUND. IF OK, REPLACE PCM.
NO
YES
REPLACE SERVO
N.T.F. CHECK FOR AN OPEN IN GROUND CKT 450.

GC1109100215000X

Fig. 21 Code 62: Cruise Vacuum Circuit. 1992 Bonneville, LeSabre, Park Avenue, Riviera, Toronado, Trofeo, 88 & 98

CODE 65

CRUISE SERVO POSITION CIRCUIT
3800 (VIN L) (TPI)

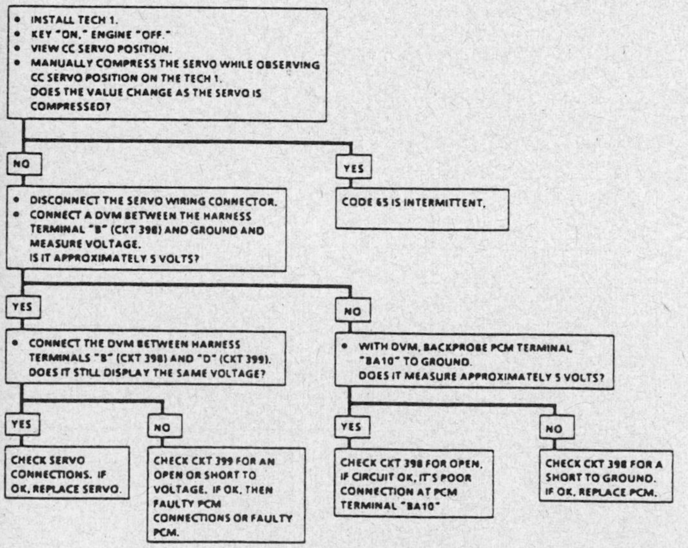
INSTALL TECH 1.
KEY "ON," ENGINE "OFF."
VIEW CC SERVO POSITION.
MANUALLY COMPRESS THE SERVO WHILE OBSERVING CC SERVO POSITION ON THE TECH 1. DOES THE VALUE CHANGE AS THE SERVO IS COMPRESSED?
NO
YES
DISCONNECT THE SERVO WIRING CONNECTOR.
CONNECT A DVM BETWEEN THE HARNESS TERMINAL "B" (CKT 398) AND GROUND AND MEASURE VOLTAGE. IS IT APPROXIMATELY 5 VOLTS?
CODE 65 IS INTERMITTENT.
YES
NO
CONNECT THE DVM BETWEEN HARNESS TERMINALS "B" (CKT 398) AND "D" (CKT 399). DOES IT STILL DISPLAY THE SAME VOLTAGE?
WITH DVM, BACKPROBE PCM TERMINAL "BA10" TO GROUND. DOES IT MEASURE APPROXIMATELY 5 VOLTS?
YES
NO
YES
NO
CHECK SERVO CONNECTIONS. IF OK, REPLACE SERVO.
CHECK CKT 399 FOR AN OPEN OR SHORT TO VOLTAGE. IF OK, THEN FAULTY PCM CONNECTIONS OR FAULTY PCM.
CHECK CKT 398 FOR OPEN. IF CIRCUIT OK, IT'S POOR CONNECTION AT PCM TERMINAL "BA10"
CHECK CKT 398 FOR A SHORT TO GROUND. IF OK, REPLACE PCM.

GC1109100216000X

Fig. 22 Code 65: Cruise Servo Position Circuit. 1992 Bonneville, LeSabre, Park Avenue, Riviera, Toronado, Trofeo, 88 & 98

DTC 65

CRUISE SERVO POSITION SENSOR CIRCUIT
3800 (VIN 1) (SFI)

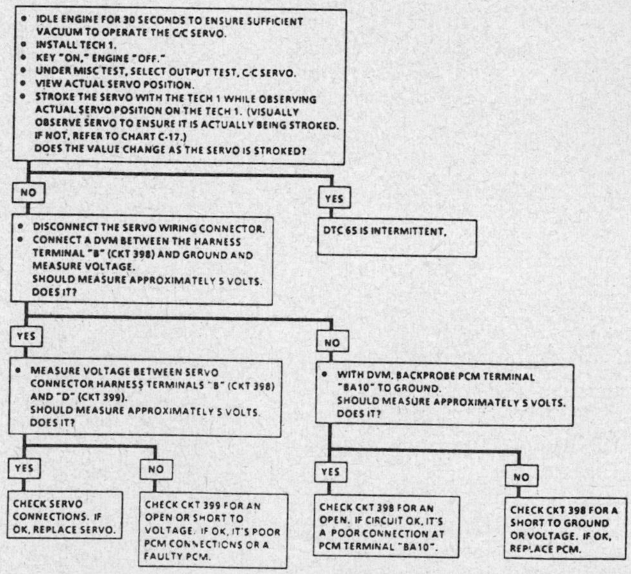
IDLE ENGINE FOR 30 SECONDS TO ENSURE SUFFICIENT VACUUM TO OPERATE THE C/C SERVO.
INSTALL TECH 1.
KEY "ON," ENGINE "OFF."
UNDER MISC TEST, SELECT OUTPUT TEST, C/C SERVO.
VIEW ACTUAL SERVO POSITION.
STROKE THE SERVO WITH THE TECH 1 WHILE OBSERVING ACTUAL SERVO POSITION ON THE TECH 1. (VISUALLY OBSERVE SERVO TO ENSURE IT IS ACTUALLY BEING STROKED. IF NOT, REFER TO CHART C-17.) DOES THE VALUE CHANGE AS THE SERVO IS STROKED?
NO
YES
DISCONNECT THE SERVO WIRING CONNECTOR.
CONNECT A DVM BETWEEN THE HARNESS TERMINAL "B" (CKT 398) AND GROUND AND MEASURE VOLTAGE. SHOULD MEASURE APPROXIMATELY 5 VOLTS. DOES IT?
DTC 65 IS INTERMITTENT.
YES
NO
MEASURE VOLTAGE BETWEEN SERVO CONNECTOR HARNESS TERMINALS "B" (CKT 398) AND "D" (CKT 399). SHOULD MEASURE APPROXIMATELY 5 VOLTS. DOES IT?
WITH DVM, BACKPROBE PCM TERMINAL "BA10" TO GROUND. SHOULD MEASURE APPROXIMATELY 5 VOLTS. DOES IT?
YES
NO
YES
NO
CHECK SERVO CONNECTIONS. IF OK, REPLACE SERVO.
CHECK CKT 399 FOR AN OPEN OR SHORT TO VOLTAGE. IF OK, IT'S POOR PCM CONNECTIONS OR A FAULTY PCM.
CHECK CKT 398 FOR AN OPEN. IF CIRCUIT OK, IT'S A POOR CONNECTION AT PCM TERMINAL "BA10".
CHECK CKT 398 FOR A SHORT TO GROUND OR VOLTAGE. IF OK, REPLACE PCM.

GC1109300217000X

Fig. 23 Code 65: Cruise Servo Position Circuit. 1993–94 Bonneville, LeSabre, Park Avenue, Riviera, 88 & 98

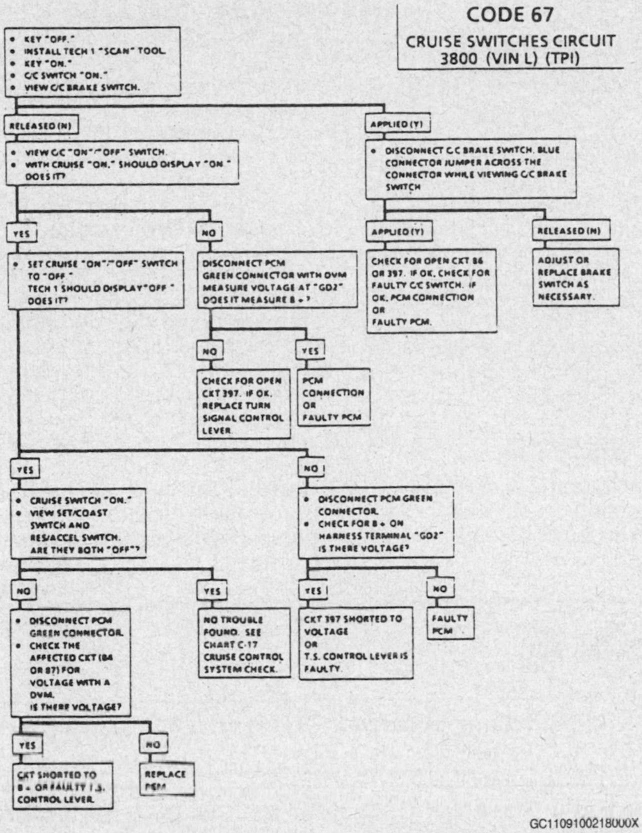
CODE 67
CRUISE SWITCHES CIRCUIT
3800 (VIN L) (TPI)
• KEY "OFF."
• INSTALL TECH 1 "SCAN" TOOL.
• KEY "ON."
• C/C SWITCH "ON."
• VIEW C/C BRAKE SWITCH.
RELEASED (N)
APPLIED (Y)
• VIEW C/C "ON"/"OFF" SWITCH.
• WITH CRUISE "ON," SHOULD DISPLAY "ON." DOES IT?
• DISCONNECT C/C BRAKE SWITCH. BLUE CONNECTOR JUMPER ACROSS THE CONNECTOR WHILE VIEWING C/C BRAKE SWITCH
YES
NO
APPLIED (Y)
RELEASED (N)
• SET CRUISE "ON"/"OFF" SWITCH TO "OFF." TECH 1 SHOULD DISPLAY "OFF." DOES IT?
DISCONNECT PCM GREEN CONNECTOR WITH DVM MEASURE VOLTAGE AT "GD2" DOES IT MEASURE B+?
CHECK FOR OPEN CKT 86 OR 397. IF OK, CHECK FOR FAULTY C/C SWITCH. IF OK, PCM CONNECTION OR FAULTY PCM.
ADJUST OR REPLACE BRAKE SWITCH AS NECESSARY.
NO
YES
CHECK FOR OPEN CKT 397. IF OK, REPLACE TURN SIGNAL CONTROL LEVER.
PCM CONNECTION OR FAULTY PCM
YES
NO
• CRUISE SWITCH "ON."
• VIEW SET/COAST SWITCH AND RES/ACCEL SWITCH. ARE THEY BOTH "OFF"?
• DISCONNECT PCM GREEN CONNECTOR.
• CHECK FOR B+ ON HARNESS TERMINAL "GD2" IS THERE VOLTAGE?
NO
YES
YES
NO
• DISCONNECT PCM GREEN CONNECTOR.
• CHECK THE AFFECTED CKT (84 OR 87) FOR VOLTAGE WITH A DVM. IS THERE VOLTAGE?
NO TROUBLE FOUND. SEE CHART C-17 CRUISE CONTROL SYSTEM CHECK.
CKT 397 SHORTED TO VOLTAGE OR T.S. CONTROL LEVER IS FAULTY.
FAULTY PCM
YES
NO
CKT SHORTED TO B+ OR FAULTY T.S. CONTROL LEVER.
REPLACE PCM
GC1109100218000X

Fig. 24 Code 67: Cruise Switches Circuit. 1992 Bonneville, LeSabre, Park Avenue, Riviera, Toronado, Trofeo, 88 & 98

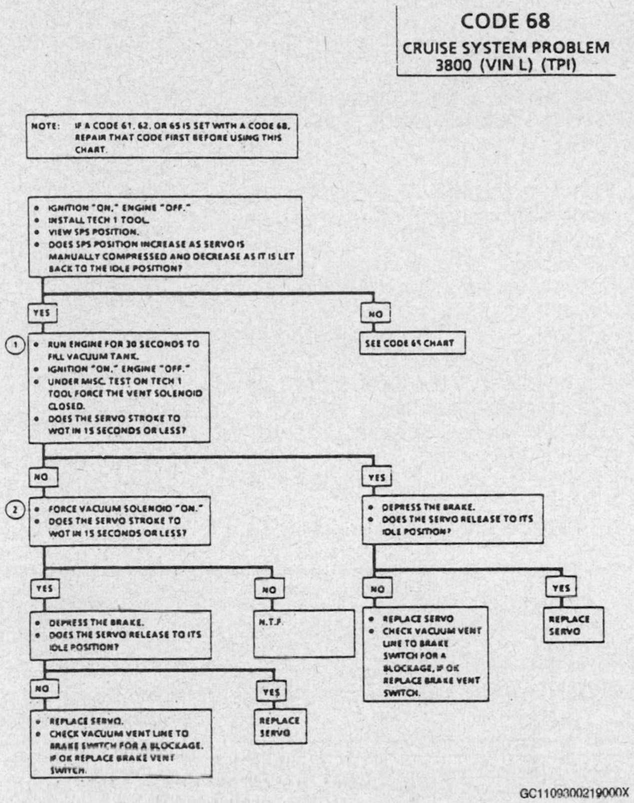
CODE 68
CRUISE SYSTEM PROBLEM
3800 (VIN L) (TPI)
NOTE: IF A CODE 61, 62, OR 65 IS SET WITH A CODE 68, REPAIR THAT CODE FIRST BEFORE USING THIS CHART.
• IGNITION "ON," ENGINE "OFF."
• INSTALL TECH 1 TOOL.
• VIEW SPS POSITION.
• DOES SPS POSITION INCREASE AS SERVO IS MANUALLY COMPRESSED AND DECREASE AS IT IS LET BACK TO THE IDLE POSITION?
YES
NO
SEE CODE 65 CHART
1
• RUN ENGINE FOR 30 SECONDS TO FILL VACUUM TANK.
• IGNITION "ON," ENGINE "OFF."
• UNDER MISC. TEST ON TECH 1 TOOL FORCE THE VENT SOLENOID CLOSED.
• DOES THE SERVO STROKE TO WOT IN 15 SECONDS OR LESS?
NO
YES
2
• FORCE VACUUM SOLENOID "ON."
• DOES THE SERVO STROKE TO WOT IN 15 SECONDS OR LESS?
• DEPRESS THE BRAKE.
• DOES THE SERVO RELEASE TO ITS IDLE POSITION?
YES
NO
NO
YES
• DEPRESS THE BRAKE.
• DOES THE SERVO RELEASE TO ITS IDLE POSITION?
N.T.F.
• REPLACE SERVO
• CHECK VACUUM VENT LINE TO BRAKE SWITCH FOR A BLOCKAGE, IF OK REPLACE BRAKE VENT SWITCH.
REPLACE SERVO
NO
YES
• REPLACE SERVO.
• CHECK VACUUM VENT LINE TO BRAKE SWITCH FOR A BLOCKAGE. IF OK REPLACE BRAKE VENT SWITCH.
REPLACE SERVO
GC1109300219000X

Fig. 25 Code 68: Cruise System Problem. 1992 Bonneville, LeSabre, Park Avenue, Riviera, Toronado, Trofeo, 88 & 98

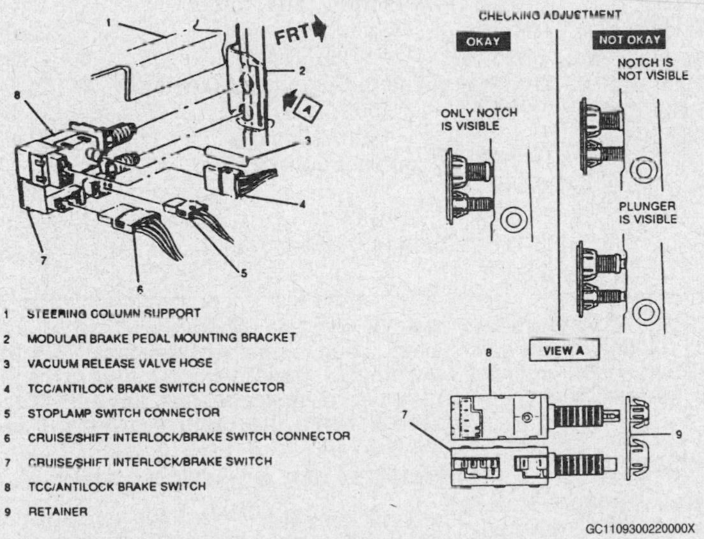
FRT
A
CHECKING ADJUSTMENT
OKAY
NOT OKAY
NOTCH IS NOT VISIBLE
ONLY NOTCH IS VISIBLE
PLUNGER IS VISIBLE
VIEW A
1 STEERING COLUMN SUPPORT
2 MODULAR BRAKE PEDAL MOUNTING BRACKET
3 VACUUM RELEASE VALVE HOSE
4 TCC/ANTILOCK BRAKE SWITCH CONNECTOR
5 STOPLAMP SWITCH CONNECTOR
6 CRUISE/SHIFT INTERLOCK/BRAKE SWITCH CONNECTOR
7 CRUISE/SHIFT INTERLOCK/BRAKE SWITCH
8 TCC/ANTILOCK BRAKE SWITCH
9 RETAINER
GC1109300220000X

Fig. 26 Cruise/shift interlock/brake switch disassebly. 1993–94 Bonneville, LeSabre, Park Avenue, Riviera, 88 & 98

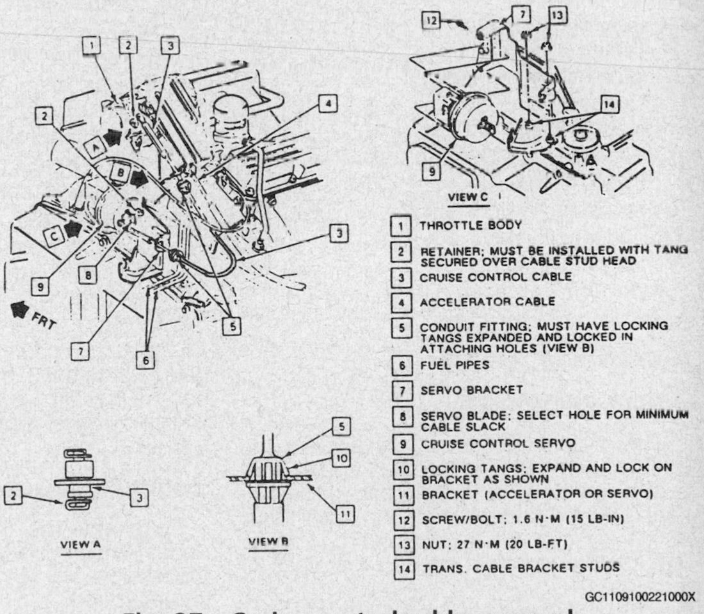
FRT
VIEW A
VIEW B
VIEW C
1 THROTTLE BODY
2 RETAINER; MUST BE INSTALLED WITH TANG SECURED OVER CABLE STUD HEAD
3 CRUISE CONTROL CABLE
4 ACCELERATOR CABLE
5 CONDUIT FITTING; MUST HAVE LOCKING TANGS EXPANDED AND LOCKED IN ATTACHING HOLES (VIEW B)
6 FUEL PIPES
7 SERVO BRACKET
8 SERVO BLADE; SELECT HOLE FOR MINIMUM CABLE SLACK
9 CRUISE CONTROL SERVO
10 LOCKING TANGS; EXPAND AND LOCK ON BRACKET AS SHOWN
11 BRACKET (ACCELERATOR OR SERVO)
12 SCREW/BOLT; 1.6 N·M (15 LB-IN)
13 NUT; 27 N·M (20 LB-FT)
14 TRANS. CABLE BRACKET STUDS
GC1109100221000X

Fig. 27 Cruise control cable removal

COMPONENT REPLACEMENT

SERVO UNIT

Bonneville, LeSabre, Park Avenue, Toronado, Trofeo, 88 & 89

1. Remove throttle body intake ductwork, then disconnect retainer at servo blade.
2. Disconnect cruise control cable at from servo bracket by release locking tangs.
3. Disconnect vacuum hoses and electrical connector.
4. Remove servo bracket nuts, servo and bracket assembly.
5. Remove bolts retaining servo to bracket, then servo.
6. Reverse procedure to install noting the following:
   a. **Torque** servo to bracket bolts to 14 ft. lbs.
   b. **Torque** servo bracket nuts to 20 ft. lbs.
   c. **Retainer must be installed with tang secured over cable stud head.**

Riviera

1. Disconnect electrical connector and vacuum hoses.
2. Disconnect throttle actuating chain, cable or rod from servo unit.
3. Remove 3 screws retaining servo unit and servo unit solenoid valve assembly to mounting bracket and remove servo.
4. Reverse procedure to install. **Torque** servo unit to mounting bracket attaching screws to 10-15 inch lbs.

ENGAGEMENT SWITCH

The cruise control engagement switch is part of the multi-function lever, which must be replaced as an assembly. Refer to individual car chapter.

CRUISE/SHIFT INTERLOCK/BRAKE SWITCH

1. Remove sound insulator, then electrical connectors.
2. Disconnect vacuum hose, then remove switch by carefully pulling switch rearward.
3. Disassemble brake switches, **Fig. 26.**
4. Reverse procedure to install.

CRUISE CONTROL CABLE

1. Disconnect cruise control cable from throttle lever by removing retainer.
2. Remove retainer at servo blade.
3. Disconnect cable from servo bracket by releasing lock tangs, **Fig. 27.**
4. Remove cable.
5. Reverse procedure to install noting the following:
   a. **Conduit fittings at both ends must have locking tangs expanded and locked in attaching holes.**

Type 4

NOTE: On Air Bag Equipped Models, Refer To Air Bag System Precautions Located In The Front Of This Manual For System Disarming & Arming Procedures.

NOTE: Electrical Symbol & Wire Color Code Identification Located In The Front Of This Manual Can Be Used As An Aid When Using Wiring Circuits Found In This Section.

INDEX

DESCRIPTION

1992 MODELS

This system automatically adjusts the opening of the engine throttle valve so that a selected vehicle speed can be maintained during favorable driving conditions. When system is engaged, the vehicle maintains a constant speed regardless of terrain.

OPERATION

Setting Desired Speed

Turn main switch to On position. The indicator lamp will illuminate. Depress accelerator pedal to obtain desired speed above 25 mph. Turn control switch downward toward Set (Coast), then release it. This will set the system at the speed the vehicle was moving at when the switch was released.

Temporary Acceleration

Accelerate by depressing accelerator pedal. When accelerator pedal is released, the vehicle will automatically slow to the preset speed.

Resetting At A Higher Speed

Turn control switch upward toward Resume (Accel). The vehicle speed will keep increasing until the control switch is released. Release control switch when desired speed is reached. **On vehicles with automatic transmission, overdrive is released during acceleration and is restored when the control switch is released.**

Resetting At Lower Speed

Turn control switch downward toward Set (Coast). The vehicle speed will continue decreasing until control switch is released. Release control switch at desired speed.

Cancelling Preset Speed

Once the preset speed has been set, it may be cancelled by doing any of the following:

1. Depress brake pedal.
2. Depress clutch pedal (vehicles with manual transmission).
3. Place shift lever at Neutral position (vehicles with automatic transmission).
4. Slightly pull the parking brake lever.
5. Turn main switch to Off position.

Resuming Preset Speed

Automatic cruising is only temporarily cancelled by steps 1 through 4 under "Cancelling The Preset Speed" if vehicle has not decelerated to below 25 mph. The preset speed will be resumed when the control switch is turned upward toward Resume (Accel).

1993–94 MODELS

The cruise control system maintains a selected speed under normal driving conditions. Steep grades up or down may cause variations in the selected speeds. This cruise control system has the ability to cruise, coast, resume speed, accelerate and -tap-up- or -tap-down.-

The main system components of the cruise control system are the cruise control module (CCM), the actuator, cruise control switch and vehicle speed sensor (VSS).

The CCM and actuator are the two main components that allow the system to control and maintain desired vehicle speed. The CCM monitors vehicle speed and provides cruise control actuator with the necessary command to maintain and change vehicle speed in response to inputs from the cruise control switch. Cruise control operation is disengaged when the CCM receives a cancel signal from the parking brake switch, stoplamp switch, brake fluid level switch, cruise control switch, park/neutral (PNP) switch (automatic transaxles) or clutch pedal position (CPP) interrupt switch (manual transaxles).

SYSTEM COMPONENTS

Cruise Control Module (CCM)

The cruise control module is mounted on the center console under the radio. The main function of the CCM is to monitor and act upon input signals from the cruise control switch and VSS. There are four different kinds of input signals received by the CCM: ON/OFF, speed control, throttle position and cancel. The ON/OFF signal is provided by the cruise control switch and activates and deactivates the cruise control system. The speed control input signal to the CCM is provided by the cruise control switch and VSS. Speed control input signals from the cruise control switch are the RES/ACC (resume/accelerate) signal and the SET/COAST signal; these signals are also used to initiate the -tap-up- and -tap-down- functions. The CCM uses these signals in addition to the signal from the VSS to determine and maintain or alter vehicle speed in accordance with the driver's commands. The throttle position signals to the CCM are provided by the actuator and the idle switch inside the Throttle Position (TP) Sensor. These signals allow the CCM to constantly monitor throttle position during cruise control operation. The cancel signals are provided by the cruise control switch CANCEL signal, the parking brake switch, stoplamp switch, brake fluid level switch, Park/Neutral (PNP) Switch (automatic transaxles) or Clutch Pedal Position (CPP) interrupt switch (manual transaxles).

Cruise Control Actuator

The actuator is mounted to the right inner fender. The actuator consists of a DC servo motor, a worm gear, a throttle angle sensor (potentiometer) and a magnetic clutch.

Vehicle Speed Sensor (VSS)

The Vehicle Speed Sensor (VSS) is an electronic relay that is mounted on the transaxle. As the transaxle's output shaft turns, the VSS provides the speedometer with vehicle speed input (voltage pulses).

Clutch Pedal Position (CPP) Interrupt Switch (Manual Transaxles)

The Clutch Pedal Position (CPP) interrupt switch is mounted directly above the clutch pedal. Whenever the clutch pedal is depressed, the CPP interrupt switch closes and provides a ground to the CCM. The CCM disengages cruise control operation when this ground signal is sensed.

Park/Neutral Position (PNP) Switch (Automatic Transaxles)

The park/neutral position (PNP) switch is mounted to the transaxle. Whenever the manual selector lever is placed in Park or Neutral, the PNP closes and provides a ground to the CCM. The CCM disengages cruise control operation when this ground signal is sensed.

Brake Fluid Level Switch

The brake fluid level switch is mounted inside the brake fluid reservoir. Whenever the brake fluid level drops below a specified level, the brake fluid level switch closes and provides a ground to the CCM. The CCM disengages cruise control operation when this ground signal is sensed.

Parking Brake Switch

The parking brake switch is located in the center console directly under the parking brake. Whenever the parking brake is engaged, the switch closes and provides a ground to the CCM. The CCM disengages cruise control operation when this ground signal is sensed.

Stoplamp Switch

The stoplamp switch is located under the instrument panel directly above the brake pedal. Whenever the brake pedal is depressed, one set of stoplamp switches close and provide a ground to the CCM. The CCM disengages cruise control operation when this ground signal is sensed. When the brake pedal is depressed, another set of stoplamp switch contacts open, and the voltage circuit from the CCM to the magnetic clutch inside the actuator is interrupted. With voltage removed from the magnetic clutch, the actuator's DC servo motor is disengaged from the worm gear and the throttle is permitted to return to the idle position. This feature is provided to ensure cancellation of the cruise control system operation during vehicle braking.

Throttle Position Sensor (TP)

The Throttle Position (TP) sensor is located on the throttle body. Whenever the throttle is in the idle position, the idle switch contacts within the TP sensor close and provide a ground to the CCM.

Powertrain Control Module (PCM)

On vehicles equipped with four-speed automatic transaxles, the CCM receives a shift solenoid number 2 signal. This signal informs the CCM that the transaxle is in second or third gear and is out of the OVERDRIVE mode.

Cruise On-Off Switch

The On-Off switch is a temporary contact type button located on the end of the cruise control switch. The purpose of the switch is turn the cruise control system on and off.

RES/ACC Switch

The RES/ACC (resume/accelerate) switch returns cruise control operation to the last speed setting after a cancel signal is received by the CCM. If acceleration during cruise speed is desired, move cruise control switch upward into RES/ACC position and hold it there until desired speed is attained.

The RES/ACC switch can also be used to "tap-up" vehicle speed. Tapping-up is accomplished by quickly moving cruise control switch up into RES/ACC position and releasing it. Tapping-up will increase vehicle speed in 1 mph increments.

SET/COAST Switch

The SET/COAST witch is activated when the cruise control switch is moved downward. The vehicle will cruise at the speed when the switch was activated. By moving the switch downward and holding it there, the cruise control system will disengage and the throttle will return to idle position. The SET/COAST switch can also be used to -tap-down- vehicle speed. -Tapping-down- is performed by quickly moving and releasing the SET/COAST switch. This will decrease vehicle speed in 1 mph increments.

PRECAUTIONS

AIR BAG SYSTEMS

Refer to "Air Bag System Precautions" in the front of this manual for system disarming and arming procedures.

Symptom	Read	Result	Circuits
• Cruise control switch indicator blinks five times or • Cruise control system does not set or • Cruise control system does not operate.	Type B Codes	11	• Actuator • Cruise Control Module
		21	• Speed Sensor • Cruise Control Module
		23	• Check speedometer cable operation • Actuator • Speed Sensor • Vacuum Pump and Hose • Vacuum Switch • Cruise Control Module
		31	• Engage Switch • Cruise Control Module
		33	• Engage Switch • Cruise Control Module
	Type A Code 5	No Code	• Speed Sensor • Cruise Control Module
		OK	• Cruise Control Switch • Engage Switch • Stoplamp Switch • Clutch or Neutral Start Switch • Parking Brake Switch • Check speedometer cable operation • Actuator • Cruise Control Module • Vacuum Hose and Brake Fluid
Setting speed deviated on high or low speed.	Type A Code 3	OK	• Check speedometer cable operation • Speed Sensor • Vacuum Pump • Vacuum Switch • Actuator • Cruise Control Module
		No Code	• Speed Sensor
Vehicle speed fluctuates when control switch is turned to "SET/COAST."			• Speed Sensor • Check speedometer cable operation • Actuator • Cruise Control Module
Setting speed does not cancel when the brake pedal is depressed.	Type A Code 4	OK	• Actuator • Stoplamp Switch • Cruise Control Module
		No Code	• Stoplamp Switch • Cruise Control Module
Setting speed does not cancel when the parking brake is applied.	Type A Code 4	OK	• Actuator • Cruise Control Module
		No Code	• Parking Brake Switch • Cruise Control Module

GC1109100222010X

Fig. 1 Cruise control system troubleshooting chart (Part 1 of 2)

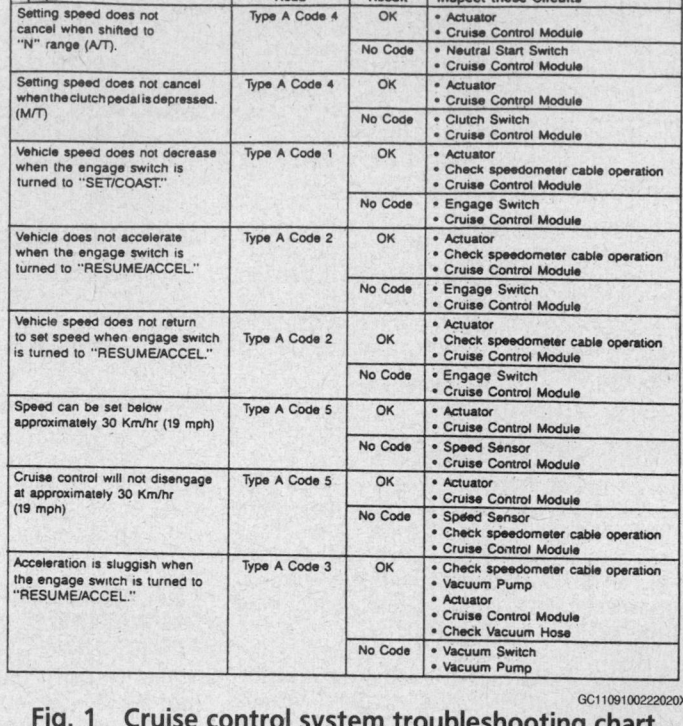

Symptom	Read	Result	Inspect these Circuits
Setting speed does not cancel when shifted to "N" range (A/T).	Type A Code 4	OK	• Actuator • Cruise Control Module
		No Code	• Neutral Start Switch • Cruise Control Module
Setting speed does not cancel when the clutch pedal is depressed. (M/T)	Type A Code 4	OK	• Actuator • Cruise Control Module
		No Code	• Clutch Switch • Cruise Control Module
Vehicle speed does not decrease when the engage switch is turned to "SET/COAST."	Type A Code 1	OK	• Actuator • Check speedometer cable operation • Cruise Control Module
		No Code	• Engage Switch • Cruise Control Module
Vehicle does not accelerate when the engage switch is turned to "RESUME/ACCEL."	Type A Code 2	OK	• Actuator • Check speedometer cable operation • Cruise Control Module
		No Code	• Engage Switch • Cruise Control Module
Vehicle speed does not return to set speed when engage switch is turned to "RESUME/ACCEL."	Type A Code 2	OK	• Actuator • Check speedometer cable operation • Cruise Control Module
		No Code	• Engage Switch • Cruise Control Module
Speed can be set below approximately 30 Km/hr (19 mph)	Type A Code 5	OK	• Actuator • Cruise Control Module
		No Code	• Speed Sensor • Cruise Control Module
Cruise control will not disengage at approximately 30 Km/hr (19 mph)	Type A Code 5	OK	• Actuator • Cruise Control Module
		No Code	• Speed Sensor • Check speedometer cable operation • Cruise Control Module
Acceleration is sluggish when the engage switch is turned to "RESUME/ACCEL."	Type A Code 3	OK	• Check speedometer cable operation • Vacuum Pump • Actuator • Cruise Control Module • Check Vacuum Hose
		No Code	• Vacuum Switch • Vacuum Pump

GC1109100222020X

Fig. 1 Cruise control system troubleshooting chart (Part 2 of 2)

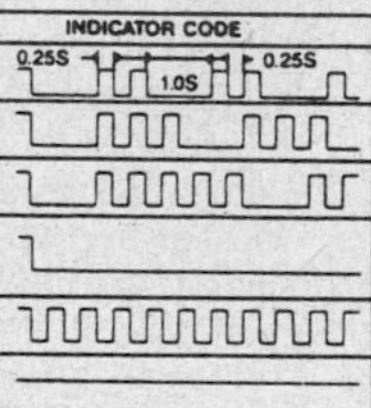
0.25S
1.0S
0.25S

NO.	CONDITIONS	INDICATOR CODE	DIAGNOSIS
1	"SET/COAST" on	ON / OFF	"SET/COAST" circuit is normal.
2	"RESUME/ACCEL" on	ON / OFF	"RESUME/ACCEL" circuit is normal.
3	Vacuum switch on	ON / OFF	Vacuum switch circuit is normal.
4	Each cancel switch on (Stoplamp switch, Parking brake switch, Clutch switch, Neutral start switch)	ON / OFF	Each cancel switch circuit is normal.
5	Drive 40 km/h (25 mph) or over	ON / OFF	Speed sensor circuit is normal.
6	Drive 30 km/h (19 mph) or below	ON / OFF	Speed sensor circuit is normal

GC1109100223000X

Fig. 2 Type A code chart

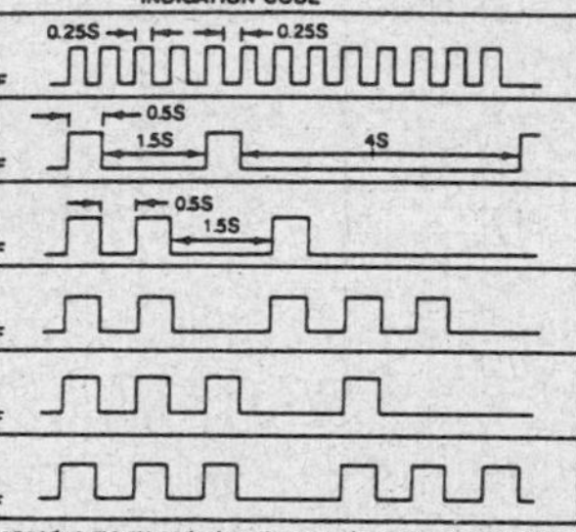
0.25S
0.25S
0.5S
1.5S
4S
0.5S
1.5S

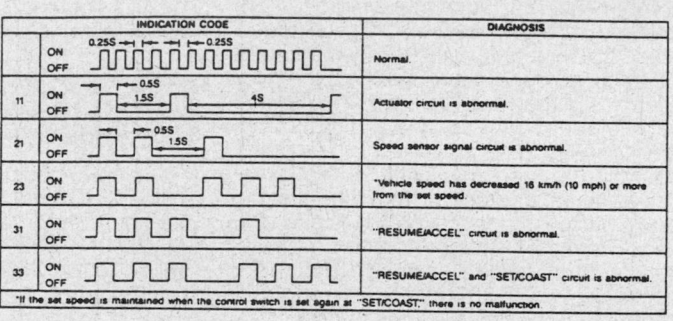

INDICATION CODE		DIAGNOSIS
	ON / OFF	Normal.
11	ON / OFF	Actuator circuit is abnormal.
21	ON / OFF	Speed sensor signal circuit is abnormal.
23	ON / OFF	*Vehicle speed has decreased 16 km/h (10 mph) or more from the set speed.
31	ON / OFF	"RESUME/ACCEL" circuit is abnormal.
33	ON / OFF	"RESUME/ACCEL" and "SET/COAST" circuit is abnormal.

*If the set speed is maintained when the control switch is set again at "SET/COAST," there is no malfunction.

GC1109100224000X

Fig. 3 Type B code chart

TROUBLESHOOTING

1992

1. Refer to **Fig. 1** for troubleshooting chart.
2. If instructed to read a type A code, refer to **Fig. 2** and proceed as follows:
   a. Turn ignition switch on.
   b. Turn set/coast switch on.
   c. Push main switch on.
   d. Turn set/coast switch off.
   e. Meet conditions listed in chart. **Checking of No. 4 code is done with front of vehicle raised and supported and with engine idling.**
   f. Read diagnostic code on main switch indicator. If there is no indication code, refer to Diagnosis.
3. If instructed to read type B codes, refer to **Fig. 3** and proceed as follows:
   a. If, while driving with cruise control on, the system is cancelled by a malfunction in either the actuator or the speed sensor, the main switch indicator will blink 5 times.
   b. While driving at a speed of no more than 10 mph, press set/coast switch three times within two seconds. **In order to save diagnostic code(s) when a malfunction has occurred, always inspect with ignition and main switches on. Should the power be cut, the diagnostic code(s) will be erased from the computer memory. If there is no indication code, refer to Diagnosis.**

1993–94

Refer to **Fig. 4** for cruise module connector location, **Fig. 5** for wiring diagram and **Figs. 6 and 7** for diagnostic trouble code interpretation and CCM connector idientification.

ADJUSTMENTS

ACTUATOR CABLE

1992

This system utilizes the actuator cable for adjustment. Check that the cables are properly installed. Measure the cable stroke to where the throttle valve begins to open. If the cable stroke is not approximately .39 inches with a slight amount of freeplay, adjustment is required. Loosen cable tightening nut and carefully position cable forward until specification is met. **Do not stretch cable.**

SYSTEM DIAGNOSIS & TESTING

1992

Refer to **Figs. 8 through 17** when diagnosing system, **Figs. 18 and 19** for wiring diagram and terminal idientification.

1993–94

Refer to **Figs. 20 through 37** when diagnosing system, **Figs. 38 through 40** for wiring diagram and terminal idientification.

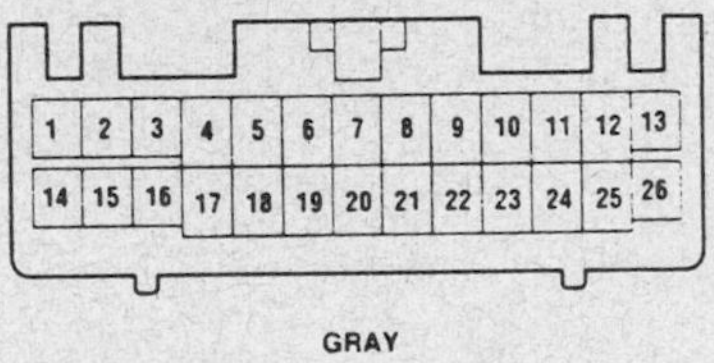
1 2 3 4 5 6 7 8 9 10 11 12 13
14 15 16 17 18 19 20 21 22 23 24 25 26
GRAY

WIRING DETAIL LEGEND

CAVITY	WIRE	COLOR CIRCUIT
1	RED/WHT	BATTERY POWER
2	BLK	CLUTCH PEDAL DEPRESSED SIGNAL (MANUAL TRANSAXLE)
	BLK	"P" OR "N" SIGNAL (VIN 6 – AUTOMATIC TRANSAXLE)
	BLK/WHT	"P" OR "N" SIGNAL (VIN 8 – AUTOMATIC TRANSAXLE)
3	RED/BLK	PARKING BRAKE SWITCH/BRAKE FLUID LEVEL SWITCH SIGNAL
4	WHT/BLU	CRUISE "ON" – "OFF" SIGNAL
5	GRN/RED	"CRUISE" INDICATOR CONTROL
6	—	NOT USED
7	—	NOT USED
8	PPL	DIAGNOSTIC REQUEST SIGNAL
9	RED	O/D CUT CONTROL (VIN 8 – AUTOMATIC TRANSAXLE)
10	GRN/BLK	MAGNETIC CLUTCH CONTROL
11	RED/BLK	DC SERVO MOTOR CONTROL – CLOSE
12	RED/GRN	DC SERVO MOTOR CONTROL – OPEN
13	WHT/BLK	GROUND – G204
14	BLK/YEL	IGNITION POWER
15	RED/GRN	MEMORY POWER
16	GRN/WHT	BRAKE SIGNAL
17	—	NOT USED
18	GRN/BLK	RES/ACC, SET/COAST, CANCEL SIGNAL
19	—	NOT USED
20	PPL/WHT	VEHICLE SPEED INPUT
21	—	NOT USED
22	BRN/WHT	SHIFT SOLENOID NO.2 SIGNAL (VIN 8 – AUTOMATIC TRANSAXLE)
23	BLU	IDLE SWITCH SIGNAL
24	BLU/ORN	REFERENCE VOLTAGE (THROTTLE ANGLE SENSOR)
25	LT GRN	THROTTLE ANGLE SENSOR INPUT
26	BLU/RED	THROTTLE ANGLE SENSOR GROUND

GC1109400328000X

Fig. 4 Cruise control module connector

COMPONENT DIAGNOSIS & TESTING

CRUISE CONTROL MODULE

Refer to **Fig. 41** to test cruise control module.

CRUISE CONTROL SWITCH

To test control switch, refer to **Fig. 42**.

CLUTCH SWITCH

1. Disconnect clutch switch electrical connector.
2. Connect digital multimeter, J34029-A, or equivalent, to clutch switch terminals 1 and 2.
3. With clutch pedal depressed, ensure continuity.
4. With clutch pedal released, ensure no continuity.
5. If results are not as indicated, replace clutch switch.

SPEED SENSOR

Refer to **Fig. 14,** to test speed sensor.

STOPLAMP SWITCH

Refer to **Fig. 43** to test stoplamp switch.

PARKING BRAKE SWITCH

1. Disconnect parking brake switch electrical connectors.
2. Ensure continuity between terminals with parking brake engaged.
3. No continuity should be indicated between terminals with parking brake returned.
4. If results are not as indicated, replace parking brake switch.

ACTUATOR

1. Ensure control cable freeplay is less than .39 inch, **Fig. 44,** adjusting as necessary.
2. Using a digital multimeter, J 43029-A, or equivalent, measure resistance values between terminals 2 and 3, then measure resistance between terminals 1 and 3.
3. If resistance is not approximately 30 ohms between terminals 2 and 3, and approximately 68 ohms between terminals 1 and 3, replace actuator.
4. Disconnect actuator electrical connector.
5. Connect positive lead from battery to terminals 1 and 2 and the negative lead to terminal 3.
6. Using a hand held vacuum pump, J 23738-A, or equivalent, slowly apply vacuum from 0 to 11.8 inches Hg, ensuring control cable can be pulled smoothly.
7. Disconnect terminal 1 and 2, then check control cable returns to original position, and vacuum returns to 0 inches Hg.
8. If results are not as indicated, replace actuator.

VACUUM PUMP

1. Connect a hand held vacuum pump, J 23738-A, or equivalent, to actuator side of vacuum pump.
2. Connect positive battery terminal to terminal 1 of vacuum pump.
3. Connect negative battery lead to terminal 2.
4. Ensure vacuum of 7.87 inches Hg or above.
5. If results are not as indicated, replace vacuum pump.

VACUUM SWITCH

1. Ensure no continuity between vacuum switch terminal 1 and 2 with vacuum of 6.30 to 7.08 inches Hg applied.
2. Ensure no continuity between terminals with no vacuum applied.
3. If results are not as indicated, replace switch.

NEUTRAL SAFETY SWITCH

1. Disconnect neutral safety switch electrical connector.
2. Connect a digital multimeter, J 34029-A, or equivalent, to neutral safety switch terminals 1 and 2, then test continuity with switch in "P" and "N" position.
3. Ensure continuity between terminals 3 and 4 with switch in "R" position.
4. If results are not as indicated, replace neutral safety switch.

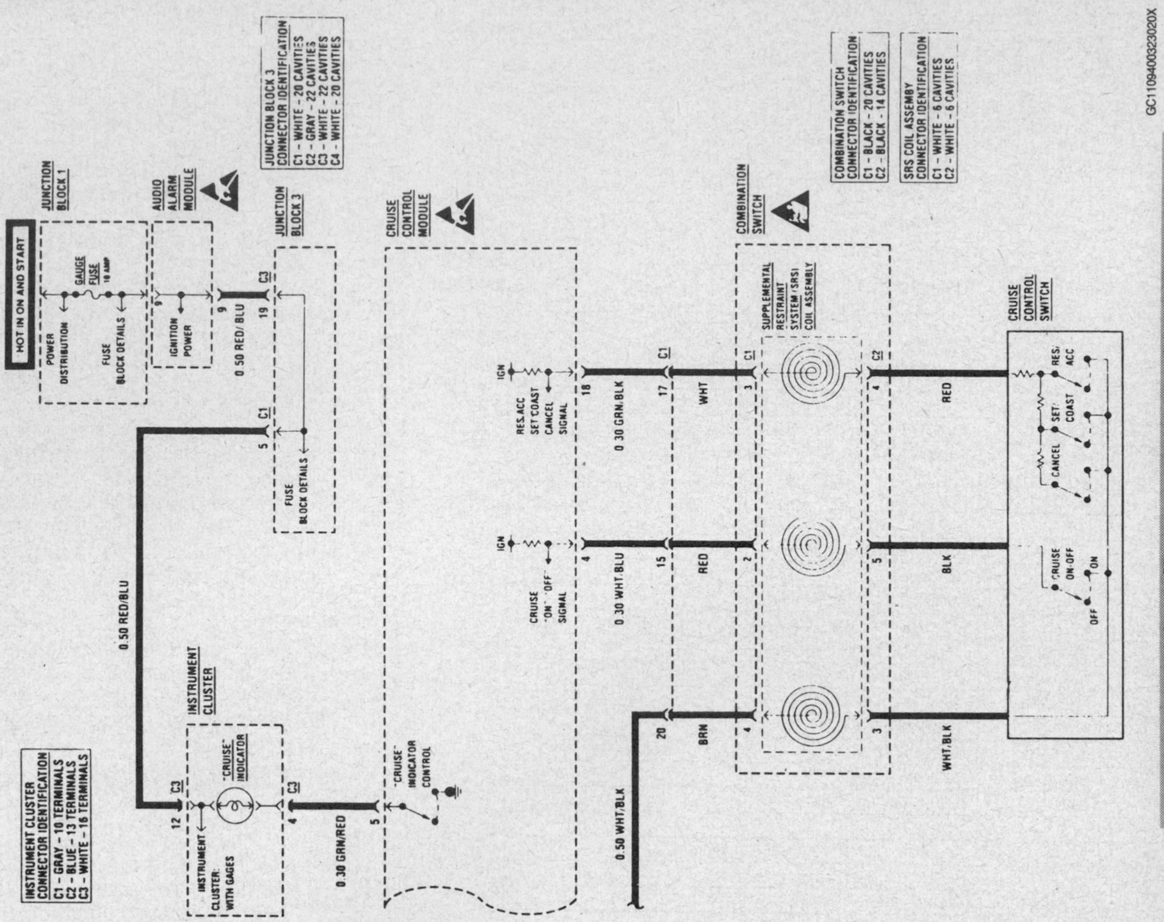
HOT IN ON AND START
JUNCTION BLOCK 1
POWER DISTRIBUTION
GAUGE FUSE 10 AMP
FUSE BLOCK DETAILS
AUDIO ALARM MODULE
IGNITION POWER
0.50 RED/BLU
JUNCTION BLOCK 3
JUNCTION BLOCK 3 CONNECTOR IDENTIFICATION
C1 - WHITE - 20 CAVITIES
C2 - GRAY - 22 CAVITIES
C3 - WHITE - 22 CAVITIES
C4 - WHITE - 20 CAVITIES
INSTRUMENT CLUSTER
INSTRUMENT CLUSTER CONNECTOR IDENTIFICATION
C1 - GRAY - 10 TERMINALS
C2 - BLUE - 13 TERMINALS
C3 - WHITE - 16 TERMINALS
"CRUISE" INDICATOR
INSTRUMENT CLUSTER: WITH GAGES
0.30 GRN/RED
CRUISE CONTROL MODULE
"CRUISE" INDICATOR CONTROL
RES/ACC SET COAST CANCEL SIGNAL
CRUISE "ON" "OFF" SIGNAL
0.30 GRN/BLK
0.30 WHT/BLU
0.50 WHT/BLK
COMBINATION SWITCH
SUPPLEMENTAL RESTRAINT SYSTEM (SRS) COIL ASSEMBLY
WHT
RED
BRN
BLK
WHT/BLK
CRUISE CONTROL SWITCH
RES/ACC
SET/COAST
CANCEL
CRUISE ON-OFF
OFF
ON
COMBINATION SWITCH CONNECTOR IDENTIFICATION
C1 - BLACK - 20 CAVITIES
C2 - BLACK - 14 CAVITIES
SRS COIL ASSEMBLY CONNECTOR IDENTIFICATION
C1 - WHITE - 6 CAVITIES
C2 - WHITE - 6 CAVITIES
GC1109400323020X

Fig. 5 Wiring diagram (Part 2 of 7). 1993–94

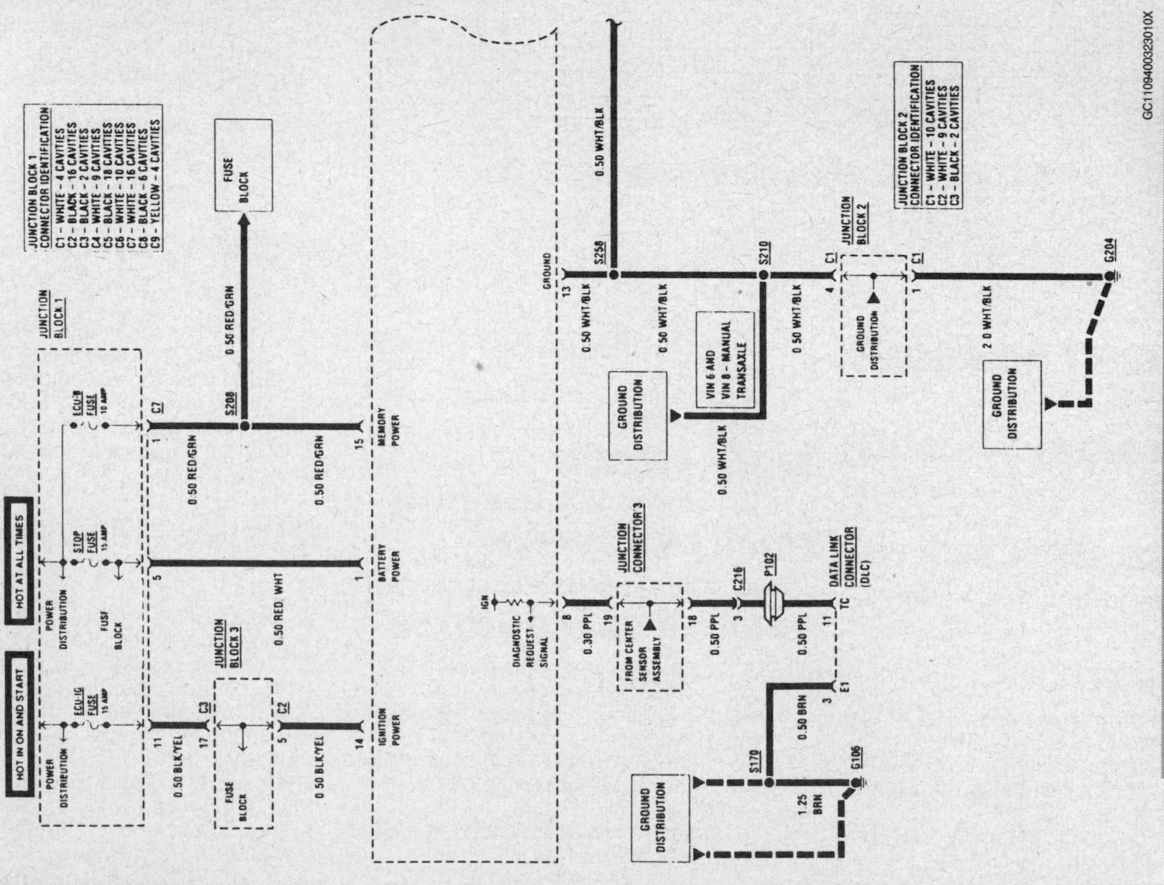
HOT IN ON AND START
HOT AT ALL TIMES
POWER DISTRIBUTION
ECU-IG FUSE 15 AMP
STOP FUSE 15 AMP
ECU-B FUSE 10 AMP
FUSE BLOCK
JUNCTION BLOCK 1
JUNCTION BLOCK 1 CONNECTOR IDENTIFICATION
C1 - WHITE - 4 CAVITIES
C2 - BLACK - 16 CAVITIES
C3 - BLACK - 2 CAVITIES
C4 - WHITE - 9 CAVITIES
C5 - BLACK - 18 CAVITIES
C6 - WHITE - 10 CAVITIES
C7 - WHITE - 16 CAVITIES
C8 - BLACK - 6 CAVITIES
C9 - YELLOW - 4 CAVITIES
JUNCTION BLOCK 3
0.50 BLK/YEL
0.50 RED/WHT
0.50 RED/GRN
IGNITION POWER
BATTERY POWER
MEMORY POWER
DIAGNOSTIC REQUEST SIGNAL
0.30 PPL
0.50 PPL
FROM CENTER SENSOR ASSEMBLY
JUNCTION CONNECTOR 3
DATA LINK CONNECTOR (DLC)
0.50 BRN
1.25 BRN
GROUND DISTRIBUTION
0.50 WHT/BLK
2.0 WHT/BLK
VIN 6 AND VIN 8 - MANUAL TRANSAXLE
JUNCTION BLOCK 2
JUNCTION BLOCK 2 CONNECTOR IDENTIFICATION
C1 - WHITE - 10 CAVITIES
C2 - WHITE - 9 CAVITIES
C3 - BLACK - 2 CAVITIES
GC1109400323010X

Fig. 5 Wiring diagram (Part 1 of 7). 1993–94

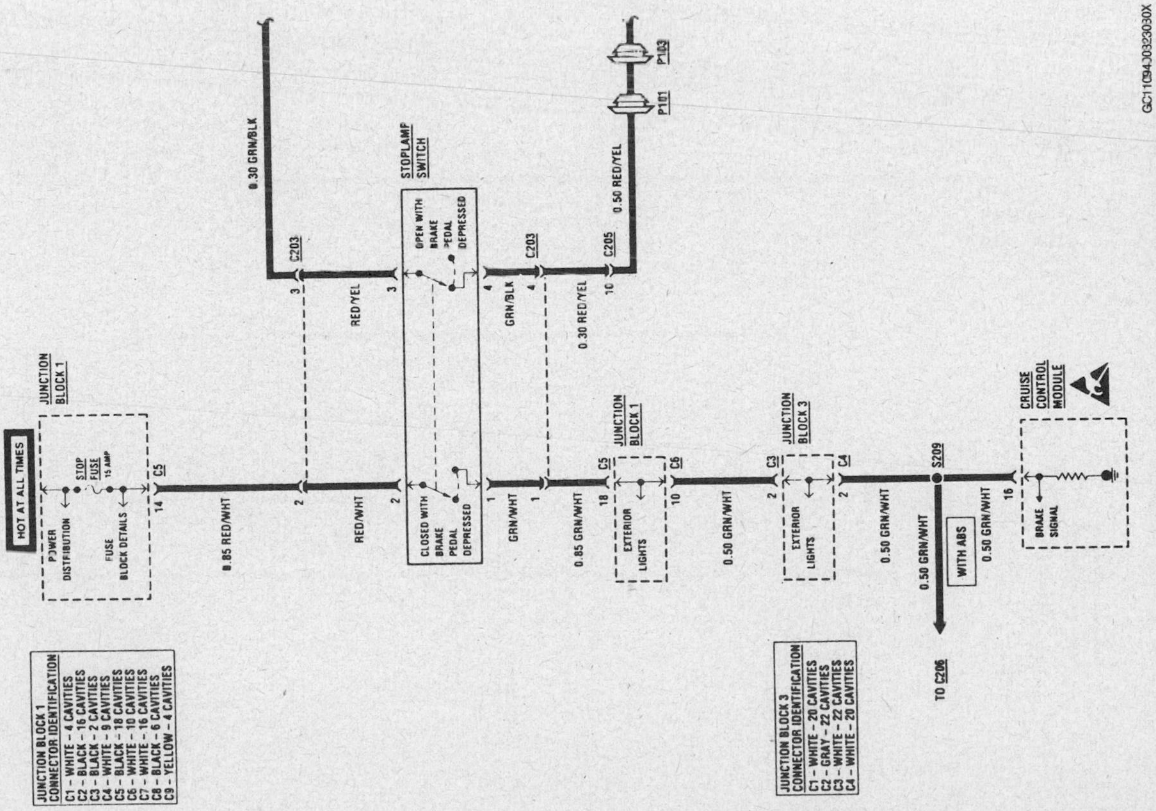

HOT AT ALL TIMES
JUNCTION BLOCK 1
POWER DISTRIBUTION
STOP FUSE 15 AMP
FUSE BLOCK DETAILS
C5
0.85 RED/WHT
STOPLAMP SWITCH
CLOSED WITH BRAKE PEDAL DEPRESSED
OPEN WITH BRAKE PEDAL DEPRESSED
RED/WHT
RED/YEL
GRN/WHT
GRN/BLK
C203
0.30 GRN/BLK
C205
0.50 RED/YEL
0.30 RED/YEL
P101
P103
0.85 GRN/WHT
EXTERIOR LIGHTS
C6
0.50 GRN/WHT
JUNCTION BLOCK 3
C3
C4
S209
WITH ABS
TO C206
CRUISE CONTROL MODULE
BRAKE SIGNAL
JUNCTION BLOCK 1 CONNECTOR IDENTIFICATION
C1 - WHITE - 4 CAVITIES
C2 - BLACK - 16 CAVITIES
C3 - BLACK - 2 CAVITIES
C4 - WHITE - 8 CAVITIES
C5 - BLACK - 18 CAVITIES
C6 - WHITE - 10 CAVITIES
C7 - WHITE - 16 CAVITIES
C8 - BLACK - 6 CAVITIES
C9 - YELLOW - 4 CAVITIES
JUNCTION BLOCK 3 CONNECTOR IDENTIFICATION
C1 - WHITE - 20 CAVITIES
C2 - GRAY - 22 CAVITIES
C3 - WHITE - 22 CAVITIES
C4 - WHITE - 20 CAVITIES
GC1109400323030X

Fig. 5 Wiring diagram (Part 3 of 7). 1993–94

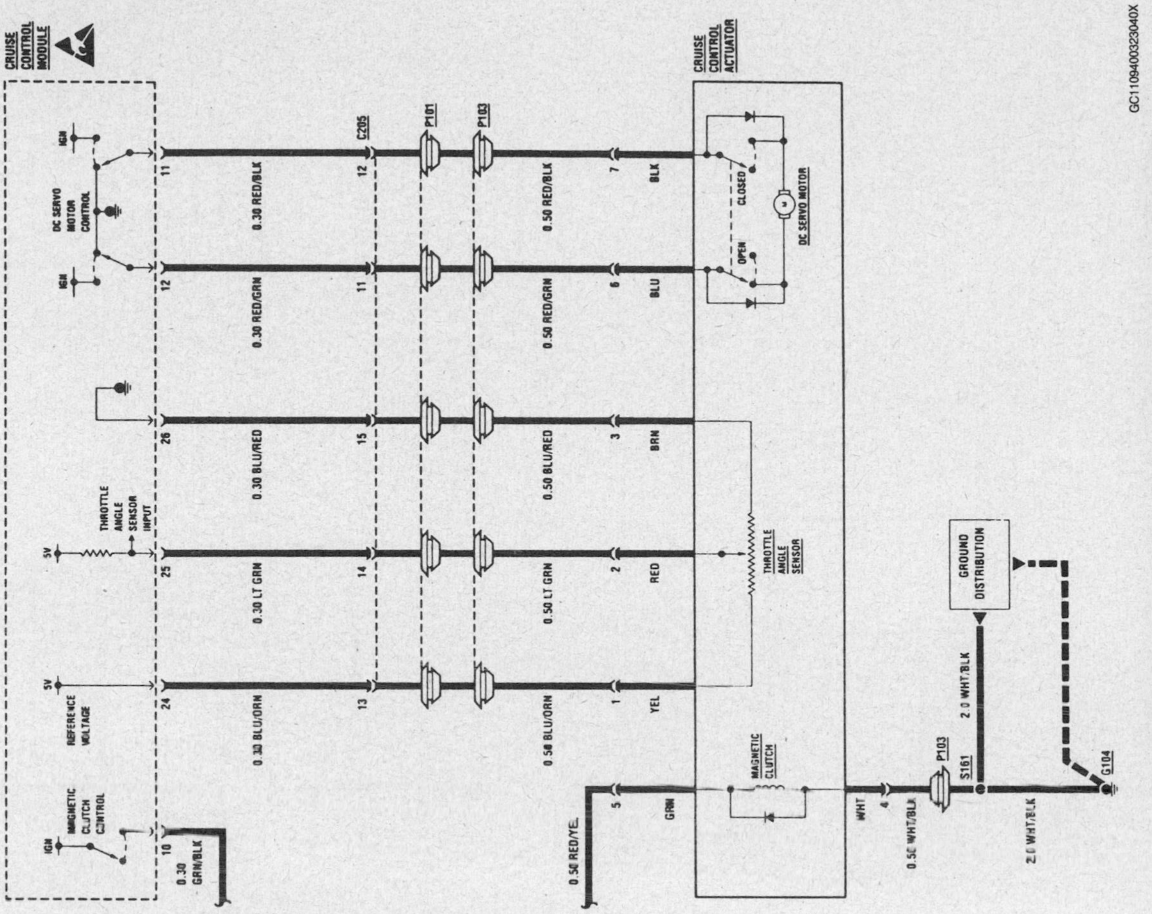

CRUISE CONTROL MODULE
IGN
MAGNETIC CLUTCH CONTROL
REFERENCE VOLTAGE
5V
THROTTLE ANGLE SENSOR INPUT
DC SERVO MOTOR CONTROL
0.30 GRN/BLK
0.30 BLU/ORN
0.30 LT GRN
0.30 BLU/RED
0.30 RED/GRN
0.30 RED/BLK
C205
P101
P103
0.50 RED/YEL
0.50 BLU/ORN
0.50 LT GRN
0.50 BLU/RED
0.50 RED/GRN
0.50 RED/BLK
GRN
YEL
RED
BRN
BLU
BLK
WHT
CRUISE CONTROL ACTUATOR
MAGNETIC CLUTCH
THROTTLE ANGLE SENSOR
OPEN
CLOSED
DC SERVO MOTOR
0.50 WHT/BLK
S161
2.0 WHT/BLK
G104
GROUND DISTRIBUTION
GC1109400323040X

Fig. 5 Wiring diagram (Part 4 of 7). 1993–94

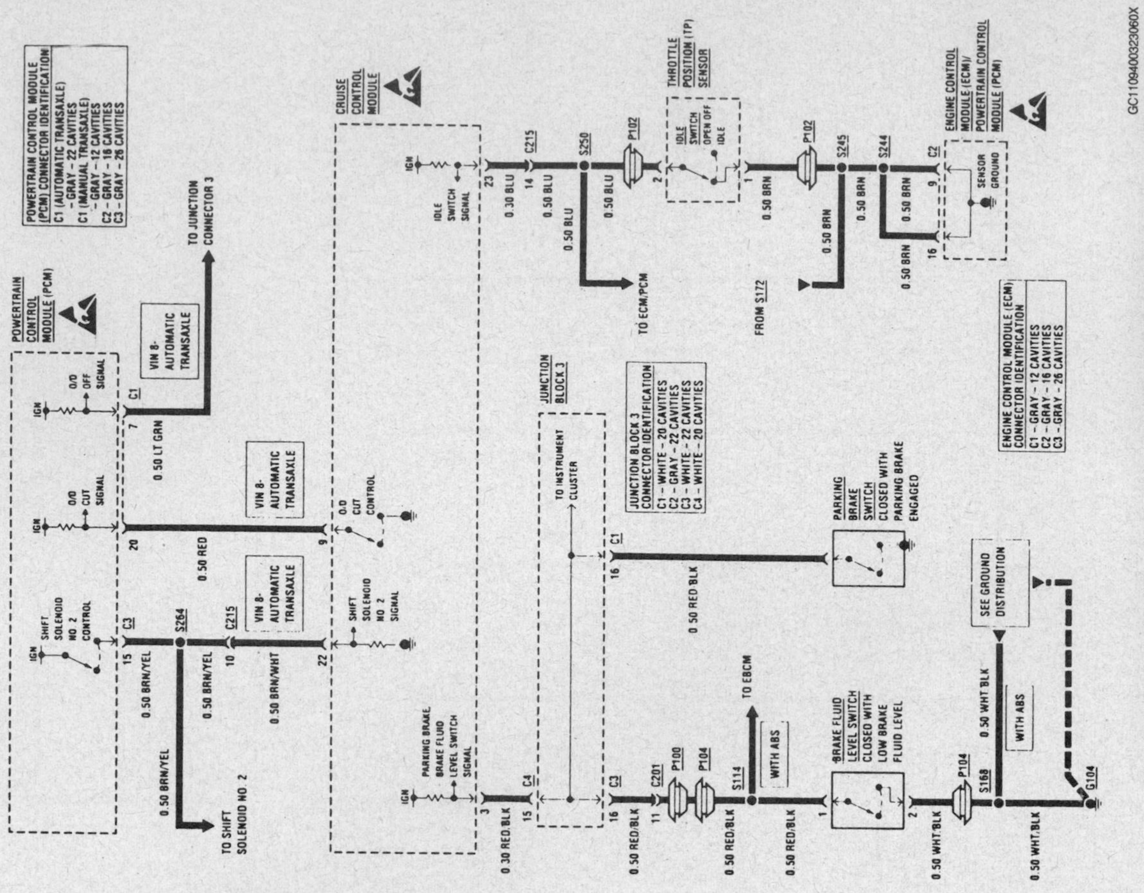
GC1109400323060X
POWERTRAIN CONTROL MODULE (PCM)
CRUISE CONTROL MODULE
JUNCTION BLOCK 3
THROTTLE POSITION (TP) SENSOR
ENGINE CONTROL MODULE (ECM)/ POWERTRAIN CONTROL MODULE (PCM)
PARKING BRAKE SWITCH
BRAKE FLUID LEVEL SWITCH
TO SHIFT SOLENOID NO 2
TO JUNCTION CONNECTOR 3
TO ECM/PCM
TO EBCM
WITH ABS
SEE GROUND DISTRIBUTION
VIN 8- AUTOMATIC TRANSAXLE
JUNCTION BLOCK 3 CONNECTOR IDENTIFICATION
C1 - WHITE - 20 CAVITIES
C2 - GRAY - 22 CAVITIES
C3 - WHITE - 22 CAVITIES
C4 - WHITE - 20 CAVITIES
ENGINE CONTROL MODULE (ECM) CONNECTOR IDENTIFICATION
C1 - GRAY - 12 CAVITIES
C2 - GRAY - 16 CAVITIES
C3 - GRAY - 26 CAVITIES
Fig. 5 Wiring diagram (Part 6 of 7). 1993–94

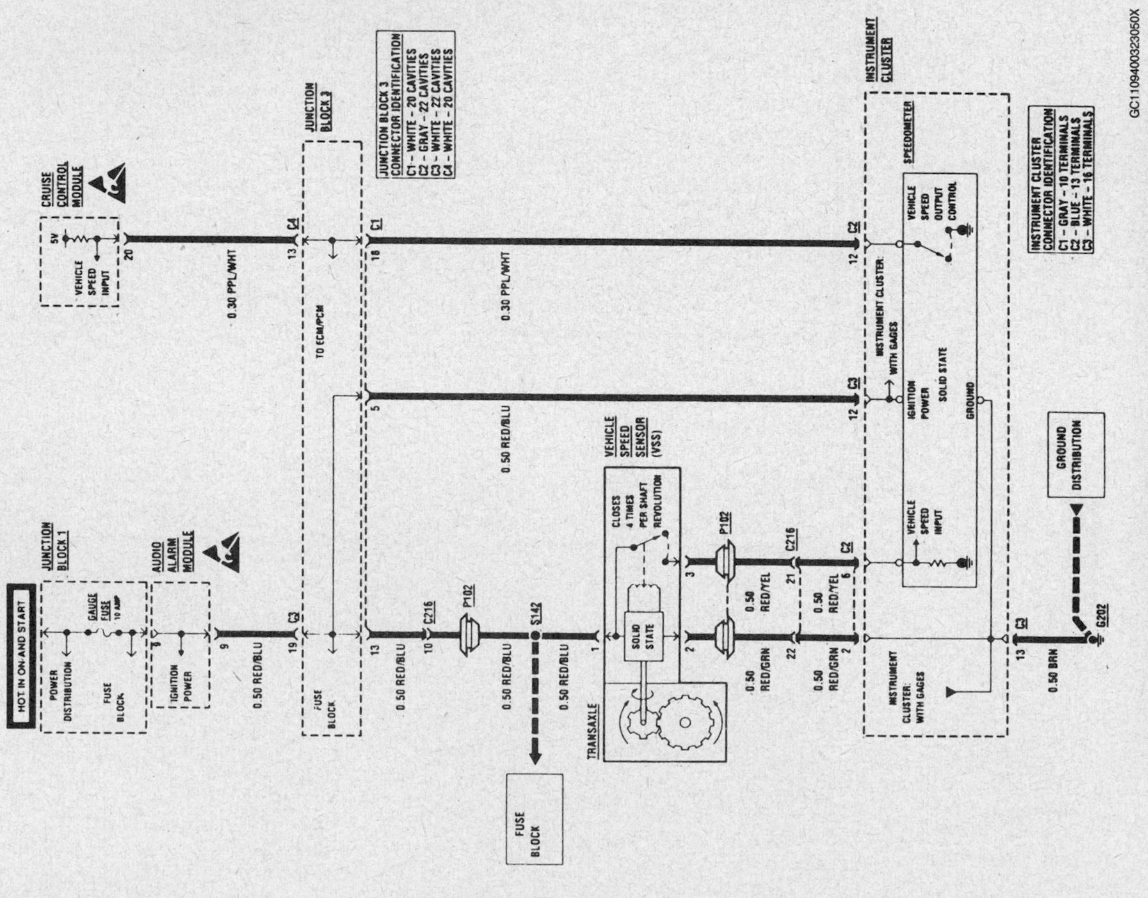
GC1109400323050X
HOT IN ON AND START
JUNCTION BLOCK 1
AUDIO ALARM MODULE
CRUISE CONTROL MODULE
JUNCTION BLOCK 3
VEHICLE SPEED SENSOR (VSS)
TRANSAXLE
INSTRUMENT CLUSTER
SPEEDOMETER
GROUND DISTRIBUTION
FUSE BLOCK
JUNCTION BLOCK 3 CONNECTOR IDENTIFICATION
C1 - WHITE - 20 CAVITIES
C2 - GRAY - 22 CAVITIES
C3 - WHITE - 22 CAVITIES
C4 - WHITE - 20 CAVITIES
INSTRUMENT CLUSTER CONNECTOR IDENTIFICATION
C1 - GRAY - 10 TERMINALS
C2 - BLUE - 13 TERMINALS
C3 - WHITE - 16 TERMINALS
Fig. 5 Wiring diagram (Part 5 of 7). 1993–94

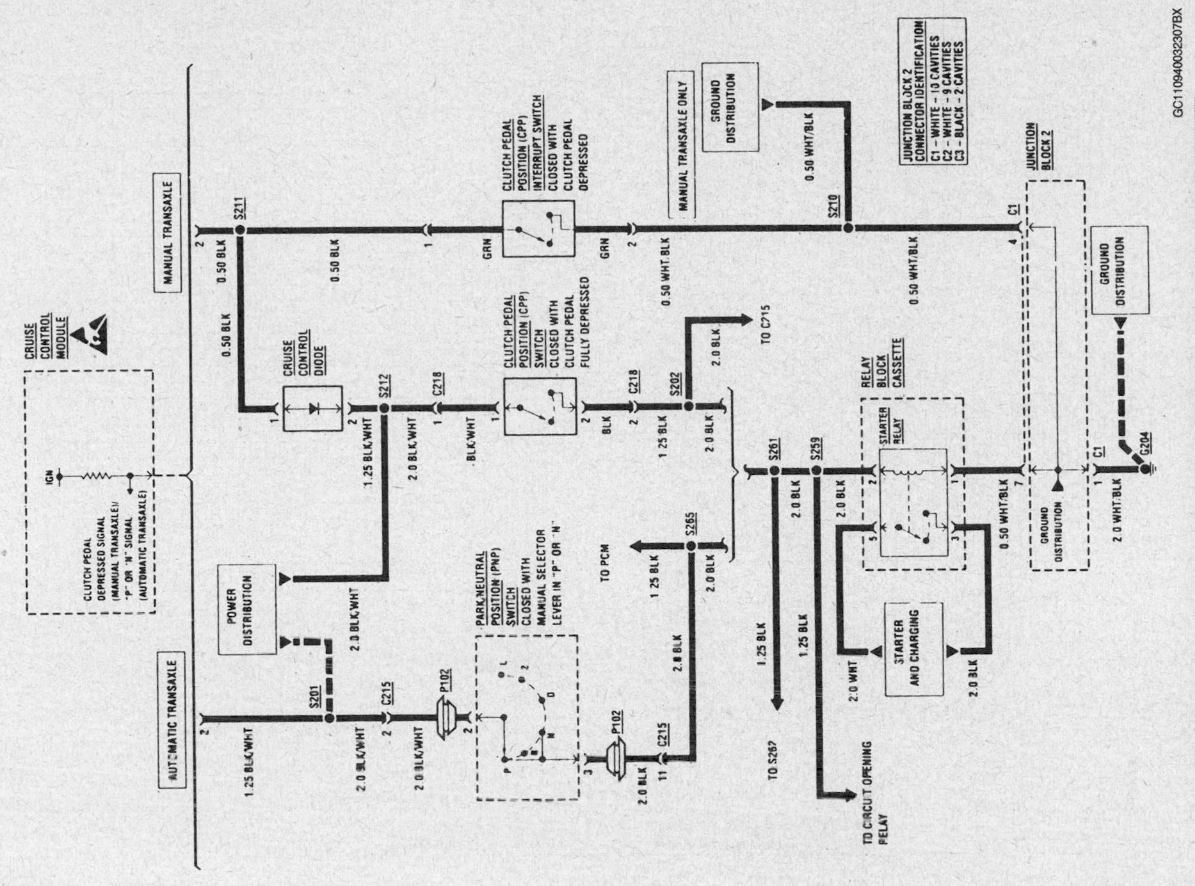

CRUISE CONTROL MODULE
CLUTCH PEDAL DEPRESSED SIGNAL (MANUAL TRANSAXLE)/ "P" OR "N" SIGNAL (AUTOMATIC TRANSAXLE)
IGN
MANUAL TRANSAXLE
AUTOMATIC TRANSAXLE
CRUISE CONTROL DIODE
CLUTCH PEDAL POSITION (CPP) SWITCH CLOSED WITH CLUTCH PEDAL FULLY DEPRESSED
CLUTCH PEDAL POSITION (CPP) INTERRUPT SWITCH CLOSED WITH CLUTCH PEDAL DEPRESSED
MANUAL TRANSAXLE ONLY
GROUND DISTRIBUTION
POWER DISTRIBUTION
PARK/NEUTRAL POSITION (PNP) SWITCH CLOSED WITH MANUAL SELECTOR LEVER IN "P" OR "N"
TO C715
TO PCM
TO S262
TO CIRCUIT OPENING RELAY
RELAY BLOCK CASSETTE
STARTER RELAY
STARTER AND CHARGING
JUNCTION BLOCK 2
JUNCTION BLOCK 2 CONNECTOR IDENTIFICATION
C1 - WHITE - 10 CAVITIES
C2 - WHITE - 9 CAVITIES
C3 - BLACK - 2 CAVITIES
GC110940032307BX

Fig. 5 Wiring diagram (Part 7 of 7). 1993–94 w/1.8L/4-108 engine

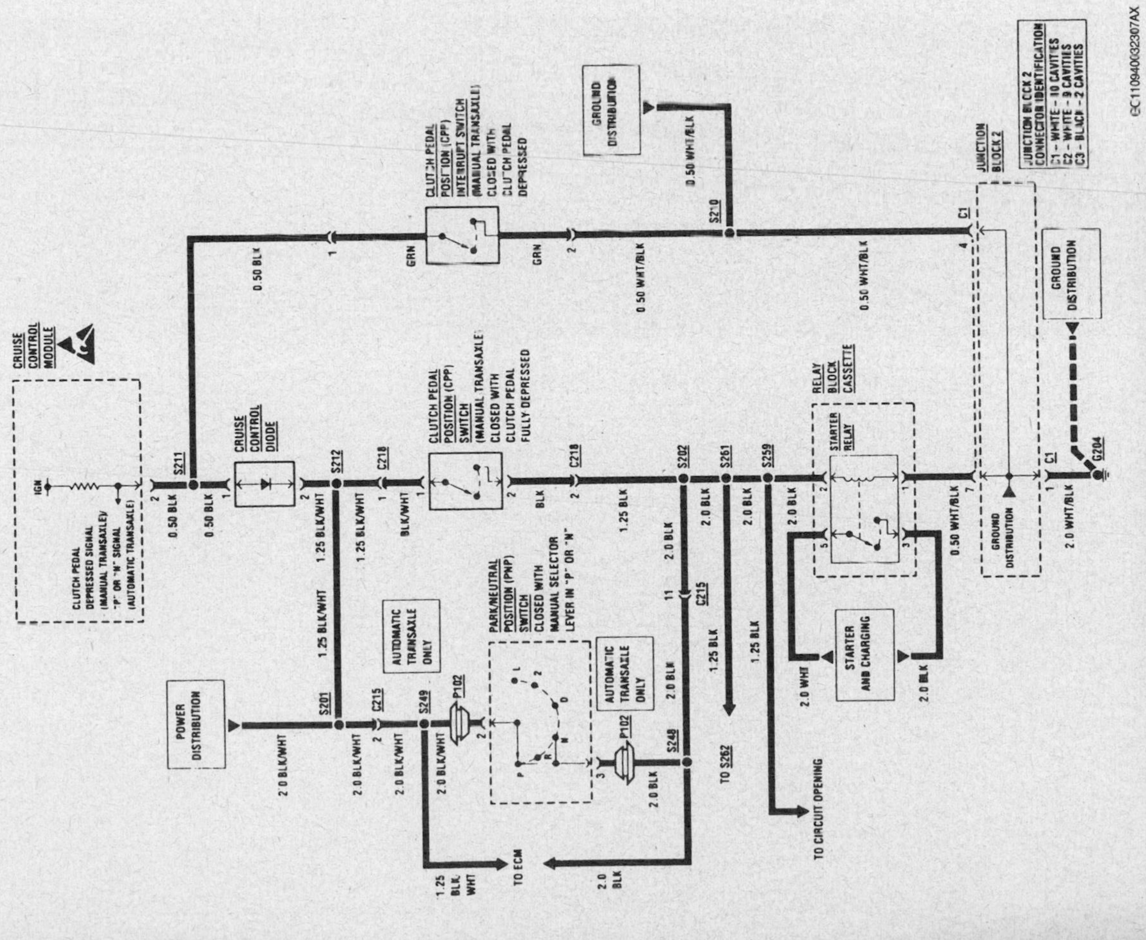

CRUISE CONTROL MODULE
CLUTCH PEDAL DEPRESSED SIGNAL (MANUAL TRANSAXLE)/ "P" OR "N" SIGNAL (AUTOMATIC TRANSAXLE)
IGN
CRUISE CONTROL DIODE
CLUTCH PEDAL POSITION (CPP) SWITCH (MANUAL TRANSAXLE) CLOSED WITH CLUTCH PEDAL FULLY DEPRESSED
CLUTCH PEDAL POSITION (CPP) INTERRUPT SWITCH (MANUAL TRANSAXLE) CLOSED WITH CLUTCH PEDAL DEPRESSED
GROUND DISTRIBUTION
POWER DISTRIBUTION
AUTOMATIC TRANSAXLE ONLY
PARK/NEUTRAL POSITION (PNP) SWITCH CLOSED WITH MANUAL SELECTOR LEVER IN "P" OR "N"
TO ECM
TO S262
TO CIRCUIT OPENING
RELAY BLOCK CASSETTE
STARTER RELAY
STARTER AND CHARGING
JUNCTION BLOCK 2
JUNCTION BLOCK 2 CONNECTOR IDENTIFICATION
C1 - WHITE - 10 CAVITIES
C2 - WHITE - 9 CAVITIES
C3 - BLACK - 2 CAVITIES
GC110940032307AX

Fig. 5 Wiring diagram (Part 7 of 7). 1993–94 w/1.6L/4-97 engine

EXAMPLE: Vehicle Speed Sensor (VSS) (DTC 21)

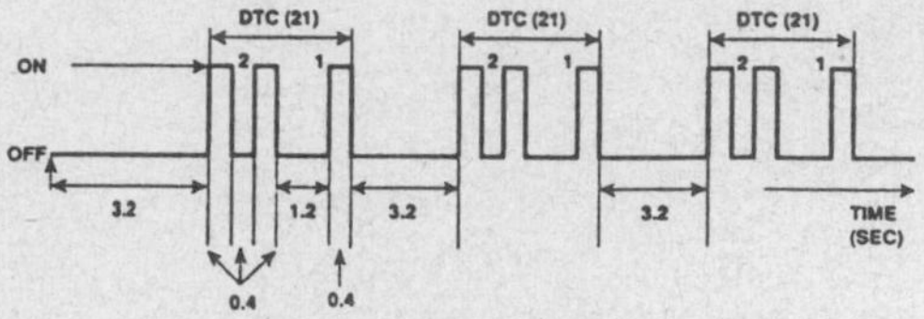
DTC (21)
DTC (21)
DTC (21)
ON
OFF
2
1
2
1
2
1
3.2
1.2
3.2
3.2
TIME
(SEC)
0.4
0.4

CODE	DIAGNOSTIC AREA	MODE	FAILURE
—	Normal*	ON OFF	—
11	Actuator DC Servo Motor		Short
12	Actuator Magnetic Clutch		Short
13	Actuator		Open
21	Vehicle Speed Sensor (VSS)		Open or Short
23	Vehicle Speed Sensor (VSS)		Vehicle Speed Input 16 km/h (10 mph) lower than Set Speed
32	Cruise Control Switch		Short
34	Cruise Control Switch		Incorrect Voltage

* FAILURE WITHIN ELECTRONIC CIRCUIT IF FLASHED ON-OFF 5 TIMES ONLY

GC1109300225000X

Fig. 6 Cruise control module diagnostic trouble code chart

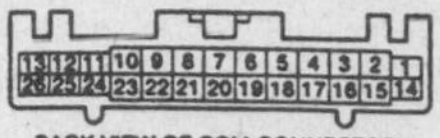
13 12 11 10 9 8 7 6 5 4 3 2 1
26 25 24 23 22 21 20 19 18 17 16 15 14

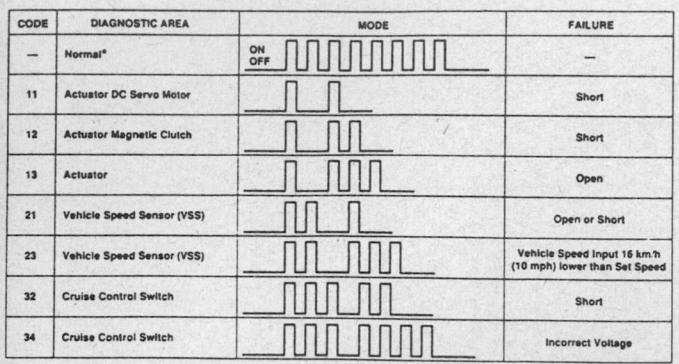

BACK VIEW OF CCM CONNECTOR

CAVITY	WIRE COLOR	CIRCUIT	VOLTAGE
1	RED/WHT	BATTERY POWER	12V
2	BLK (VIN 6 AND VIN 8 – M/T) BLK/WHT (VIN 8 – A/T)	CLUTCH PEDAL DEPRESSED SIGNAL (M/T) "P" OR "N" SIGNAL (A/T)	12V ①
3	RED/BLK	PARKING BRAKE AND BRAKE FLUID LEVEL SWITCH SIGNAL	12V ②
4	WHT/BLU	CRUISE "ON-OFF" SIGNAL	12V ③
5	GRN/RED	"CRUISE" INDICATOR CONTROL	12V ④
6	—	NOT USED	—
7	—	NOT USED	—
8	PPL	DIAGNOSTIC REQUEST SIGNAL	12V
9	RED	O/D CUT CONTROL (VIN 8 – A/T)	12V ⑤
10	GRN/BLK	MAGNETIC CLUTCH CONTROL	0V* ⑥
11	RED/BLK	DC SERVO MOTOR – CLOSE	0V ⑦
12	RED/GRN	DC SERVO MOTOR – OPEN	0V* ⑧
13	WHT/BLK	GROUND	0V*
14	BLK/YEL	IGNITION POWER	12V
15	RED/GRN	MEMORY POWER	12V
16	GRN/WHT	BRAKE SIGNAL	0V* ⑨
17	—	NOT USED	—
18	GRN/BLK	RES/ACC, SET/COAST AND CANCEL SWITCH SIGNAL	12V ⑩
19	—	NOT USED	—
20	PPL/WHT	VEHICLE SPEED INPUT	⑪
21	—	NOT USED	—
22	BRN/WHT	SHIFT SOLENOID NUMBER 2 SIGNAL (VIN 8 – A/T)	0V* ⑫
23	BLU	IDLE SWITCH SIGNAL	0V* ⑬
24	BLU/ORN	REFERENCE VOLTAGE (THROTTLE ANGLE SENSOR)	5V
25	LT GRN	THROTTLE ANGLE INPUT	⑭
26	BLU/RED	THROTTLE ANGLE SENSOR GROUND	0V*

* LESS THAN 1.0 VOLTS
① 0V WITH PNP OR CPP INTERRUPT SWITCH CLOSED
② 0V WITH PARKING BRAKE OR BRAKE FLUID LEVEL SWITCH CLOSED
③ MOMENTARY 0V WITH BUTTON PRESSED
④ 0V WITH "CRUISE" INDICATOR LIT
⑤ 0V WITH "OVERDRIVE" AND CRUISE CONTROL ENGAGED AND ENGINE UNDER A HEAVY LOAD
⑥ 12V WITH CRUISE CONTROL ENGAGED
⑦ 12V WITH DC SERVO MOTOR
⑧ 12V WITH DC SERVO MOTOR OPEN SIDE ENERGIZED
⑨ 12V WITH BRAKE PEDAL DEPRESSED
⑩ 0.7–2.5V WITH CRUISE CONTROL SWITCH IN RES/ACC POSITION
2.4–4.6V WITH CRUISE CONTROL SWITCH IN SET/COAST POSITION
4.1–7.2V WITH CRUISE CONTROL SWITCH IN CANCEL POSITION
⑪ VARIES WITH VEHICLE SPEED 0–5V
⑫ 12V WITH TRANSAXLE IN 2ND OR 3RD GEAR
⑬ 12V WITH IDLE SWITCH OPEN
⑭ VOLTAGE VARIES WITH THROTTLE POSITION

GC1109300226000X

Fig. 7 Cruise control connector identification chart

DIAGNOSTIC CHART INDEX

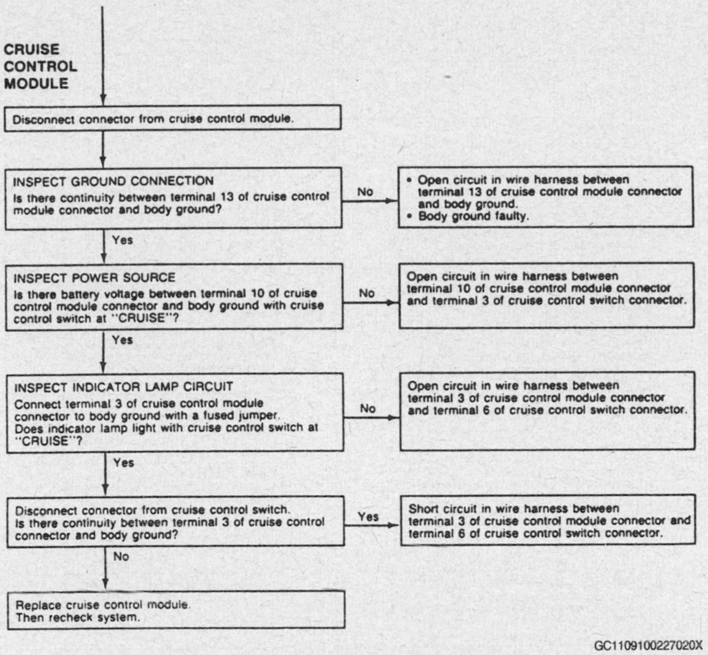
CRUISE
CONTROL
MODULE
Disconnect connector from cruise control module.
INSPECT GROUND CONNECTION
Is there continuity between terminal 13 of cruise control module connector and body ground?
No
• Open circuit in wire harness between terminal 13 of cruise control module connector and body ground.
• Body ground faulty.
Yes
INSPECT POWER SOURCE
Is there battery voltage between terminal 10 of cruise control module connector and body ground with cruise control switch at "CRUISE"?
No
Open circuit in wire harness between terminal 10 of cruise control module connector and terminal 3 of cruise control switch connector.
Yes
INSPECT INDICATOR LAMP CIRCUIT
Connect terminal 3 of cruise control module connector to body ground with a fused jumper. Does indicator lamp light with cruise control switch at "CRUISE"?
No
Open circuit in wire harness between terminal 3 of cruise control module connector and terminal 6 of cruise control switch connector.
Yes
Disconnect connector from cruise control switch. Is there continuity between terminal 3 of cruise control connector and body ground?
Yes
Short circuit in wire harness between terminal 3 of cruise control module connector and terminal 6 of cruise control switch connector.
No
Replace cruise control module. Then recheck system.
GC1109100227020X

Fig. 8 Test 1: Cruise Control Switch Circuit Diagnosis (Part 1 of 2). 1992

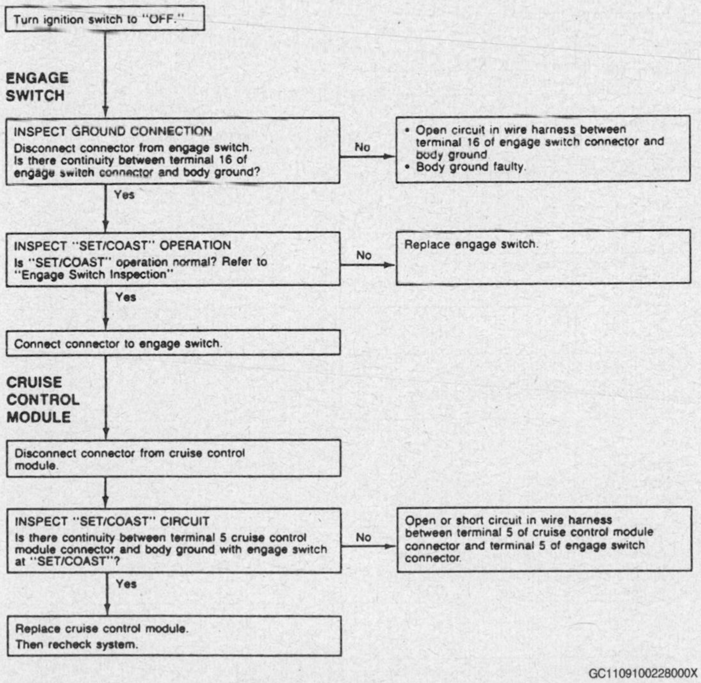
Turn ignition switch to "OFF."
ENGAGE
SWITCH
INSPECT GROUND CONNECTION
Disconnect connector from engage switch. Is there continuity between terminal 16 of engage switch connector and body ground?
No
• Open circuit in wire harness between terminal 16 of engage switch connector and body ground
• Body ground faulty.
Yes
INSPECT "SET/COAST" OPERATION
Is "SET/COAST" operation normal? Refer to "Engage Switch Inspection"
No
Replace engage switch.
Yes
Connect connector to engage switch.
CRUISE
CONTROL
MODULE
Disconnect connector from cruise control module.
INSPECT "SET/COAST" CIRCUIT
Is there continuity between terminal 5 cruise control module connector and body ground with engage switch at "SET/COAST"?
No
Open or short circuit in wire harness between terminal 5 of cruise control module connector and terminal 5 of engage switch connector.
Yes
Replace cruise control module. Then recheck system.
GC1109100228000X

Fig. 9 Test 2: Engage Switch "Set/Coast" Circuit Diagnosis. 1992

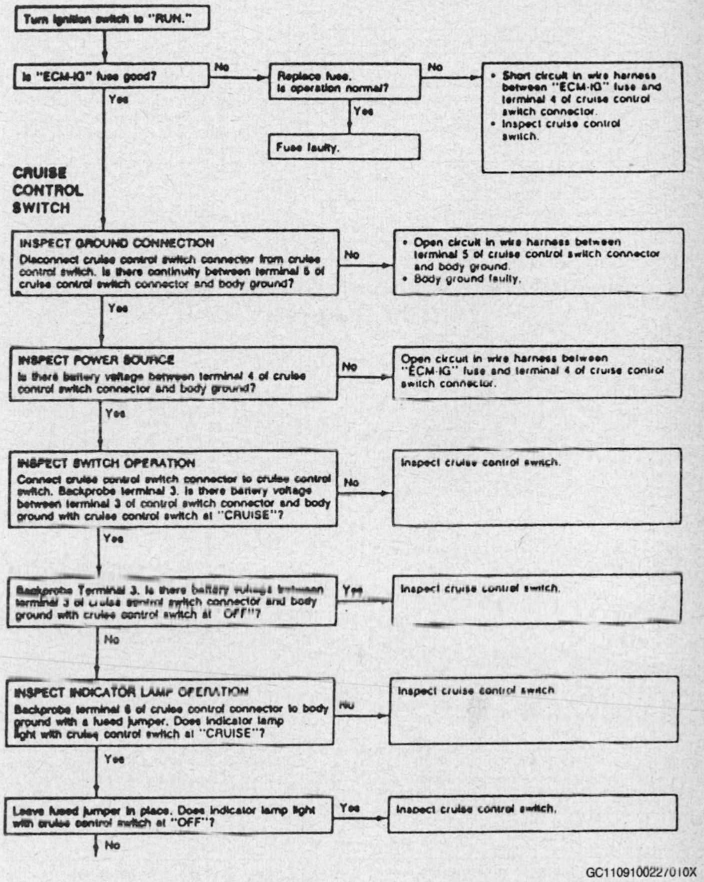
Turn ignition switch to "RUN."
Is "ECM-IG" fuse good?
No
Replace fuse. Is operation normal?
No
• Short circuit in wire harness between "ECM-IG" fuse and terminal 4 of cruise control switch connector.
• Inspect cruise control switch.
Yes
Fuse faulty.
Yes
CRUISE
CONTROL
SWITCH
INSPECT GROUND CONNECTION
Disconnect cruise control switch connector from cruise control switch. Is there continuity between terminal 5 of cruise control switch connector and body ground?
No
• Open circuit in wire harness between terminal 5 of cruise control switch connector and body ground.
• Body ground faulty.
Yes
INSPECT POWER SOURCE
Is there battery voltage between terminal 4 of cruise control switch connector and body ground?
No
Open circuit in wire harness between "ECM-IG" fuse and terminal 4 of cruise control switch connector.
Yes
INSPECT SWITCH OPERATION
Connect cruise control switch connector to cruise control switch. Backprobe terminal 3. Is there battery voltage between terminal 3 of control switch connector and body ground with cruise control switch at "CRUISE"?
No
Inspect cruise control switch.
Yes
Backprobe Terminal 3. Is there battery voltage between terminal 3 of cruise control switch connector and body ground with cruise control switch at "OFF"?
Yes
Inspect cruise control switch.
No
INSPECT INDICATOR LAMP OPERATION
Backprobe terminal 6 of cruise control connector to body ground with a fused jumper. Does indicator lamp light with cruise control switch at "CRUISE"?
No
Inspect cruise control switch
Yes
Leave fused jumper in place. Does indicator lamp light with cruise control switch at "OFF"?
Yes
Inspect cruise control switch.
No
GC1109100227010X

Fig. 8 Test 1: Cruise Control Switch Circuit Diagnosis (Part 2 of 2). 1992

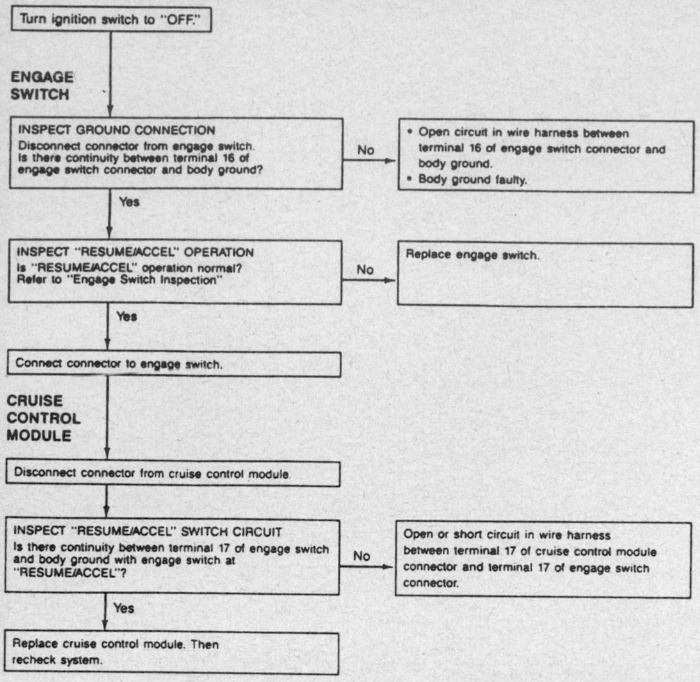
Turn ignition switch to "OFF."
ENGAGE SWITCH
INSPECT GROUND CONNECTION
Disconnect connector from engage switch. Is there continuity between terminal 16 of engage switch connector and body ground?
No
• Open circuit in wire harness between terminal 16 of engage switch connector and body ground.
• Body ground faulty.
Yes
INSPECT "RESUME/ACCEL" OPERATION
Is "RESUME/ACCEL" operation normal? Refer to "Engage Switch Inspection"
No
Replace engage switch.
Yes
Connect connector to engage switch.
CRUISE CONTROL MODULE
Disconnect connector from cruise control module.
INSPECT "RESUME/ACCEL" SWITCH CIRCUIT
Is there continuity between terminal 17 of engage switch and body ground with engage switch at "RESUME/ACCEL"?
No
Open or short circuit in wire harness between terminal 17 of cruise control module connector and terminal 17 of engage switch connector.
Yes
Replace cruise control module. Then recheck system.

GC1109100229000X

Fig. 10 Test 3: Engage Switch "Resume/Accel" Circuit Diagnosis. 1992

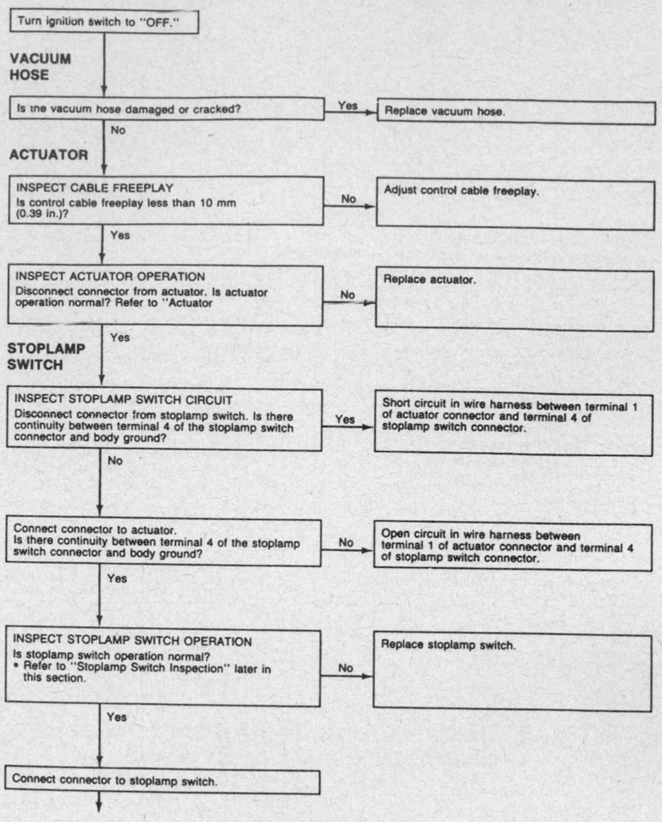
Turn ignition switch to "OFF."
VACUUM HOSE
Is the vacuum hose damaged or cracked?
Yes
Replace vacuum hose.
No
ACTUATOR
INSPECT CABLE FREEPLAY
Is control cable freeplay less than 10 mm (0.39 in.)?
No
Adjust control cable freeplay.
Yes
INSPECT ACTUATOR OPERATION
Disconnect connector from actuator. Is actuator operation normal? Refer to "Actuator
No
Replace actuator.
Yes
STOPLAMP SWITCH
INSPECT STOPLAMP SWITCH CIRCUIT
Disconnect connector from stoplamp switch. Is there continuity between terminal 4 of the stoplamp switch connector and body ground?
Yes
Short circuit in wire harness between terminal 1 of actuator connector and terminal 4 of stoplamp switch connector.
No
Connect connector to actuator.
Is there continuity between terminal 4 of the stoplamp switch connector and body ground?
No
Open circuit in wire harness between terminal 1 of actuator connector and terminal 4 of stoplamp switch connector.
Yes
INSPECT STOPLAMP SWITCH OPERATION
Is stoplamp switch operation normal?
• Refer to "Stoplamp Switch Inspection" later in this section.
No
Replace stoplamp switch.
Yes
Connect connector to stoplamp switch.

GC1109100230010X

Fig. 11 Test 4: Actuator Circuit Diagnosis (Part 1 of 2). 1992

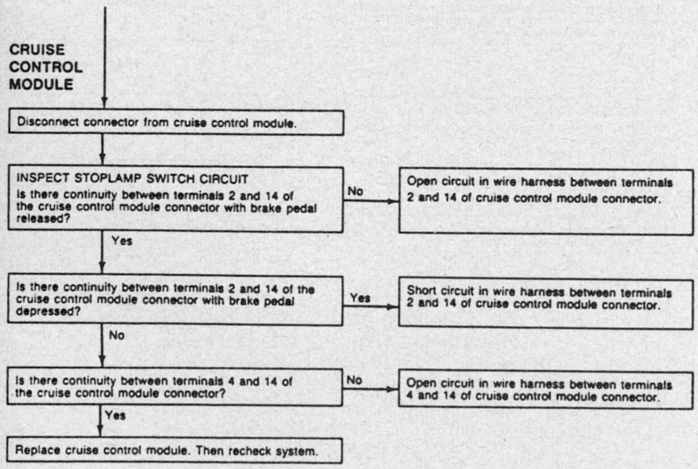
CRUISE CONTROL MODULE
Disconnect connector from cruise control module.
INSPECT STOPLAMP SWITCH CIRCUIT
Is there continuity between terminals 2 and 14 of the cruise control module connector with brake pedal released?
No
Open circuit in wire harness between terminals 2 and 14 of cruise control module connector.
Yes
Is there continuity between terminals 2 and 14 of the cruise control module connector with brake pedal depressed?
Yes
Short circuit in wire harness between terminals 2 and 14 of cruise control module connector.
No
Is there continuity between terminals 4 and 14 of the cruise control module connector?
No
Open circuit in wire harness between terminals 4 and 14 of cruise control module connector.
Yes
Replace cruise control module. Then recheck system.

GC1109100230020X

Fig. 11 Test 4: Actuator Circuit Diagnosis (Part 2 of 2). 1992

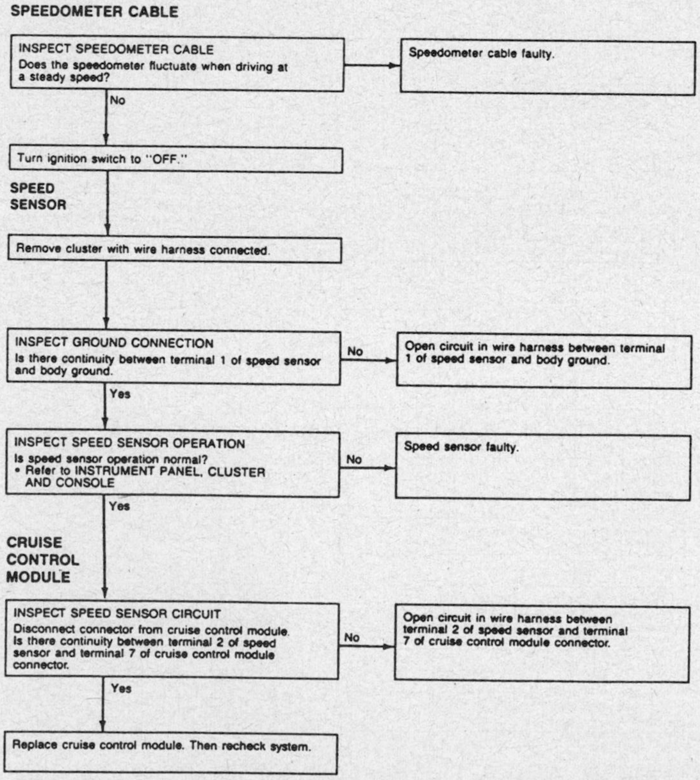
SPEEDOMETER CABLE
INSPECT SPEEDOMETER CABLE
Does the speedometer fluctuate when driving at a steady speed?
Speedometer cable faulty.
No
Turn ignition switch to "OFF."
SPEED SENSOR
Remove cluster with wire harness connected.
INSPECT GROUND CONNECTION
Is there continuity between terminal 1 of speed sensor and body ground.
No
Open circuit in wire harness between terminal 1 of speed sensor and body ground.
Yes
INSPECT SPEED SENSOR OPERATION
Is speed sensor operation normal?
• Refer to INSTRUMENT PANEL, CLUSTER AND CONSOLE
No
Speed sensor faulty.
Yes
CRUISE CONTROL MODULE
INSPECT SPEED SENSOR CIRCUIT
Disconnect connector from cruise control module. Is there continuity between terminal 2 of speed sensor and terminal 7 of cruise control module connector.
No
Open circuit in wire harness between terminal 2 of speed sensor and terminal 7 of cruise control module connector.
Yes
Replace cruise control module. Then recheck system.

GC1109100231000X

Fig. 12 Test 5: Speed Sensor Circuit Diagnosis. 1992

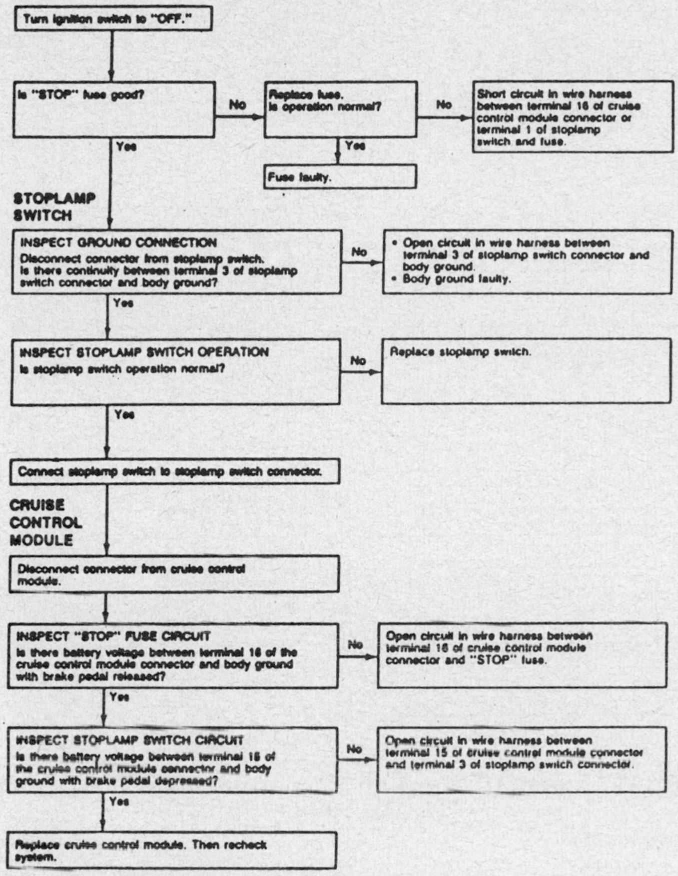
Turn ignition switch to "OFF."
Is "STOP" fuse good?
No
Replace fuse. Is operation normal?
No
Short circuit in wire harness between terminal 16 of cruise control module connector or terminal 1 of stoplamp switch and fuse.
Yes
Fuse faulty.
Yes
STOPLAMP SWITCH
INSPECT GROUND CONNECTION
Disconnect connector from stoplamp switch. Is there continuity between terminal 3 of stoplamp switch connector and body ground?
No
• Open circuit in wire harness between terminal 3 of stoplamp switch connector and body ground.
• Body ground faulty.
Yes
INSPECT STOPLAMP SWITCH OPERATION
Is stoplamp switch operation normal?
No
Replace stoplamp switch.
Yes
Connect stoplamp switch to stoplamp switch connector.
CRUISE CONTROL MODULE
Disconnect connector from cruise control module.
INSPECT "STOP" FUSE CIRCUIT
Is there battery voltage between terminal 16 of the cruise control module connector and body ground with brake pedal released?
No
Open circuit in wire harness between terminal 16 of cruise control module connector and "STOP" fuse.
Yes
INSPECT STOPLAMP SWITCH CIRCUIT
Is there battery voltage between terminal 15 of the cruise control module connector and body ground with brake pedal depressed?
No
Open circuit in wire harness between terminal 15 of cruise control module connector and terminal 3 of stoplamp switch connector.
Yes
Replace cruise control module. Then recheck system.
GC1109100232000X

Fig. 13 Test 6: Stoplamp Switch Circuit Diagnosis. 1992

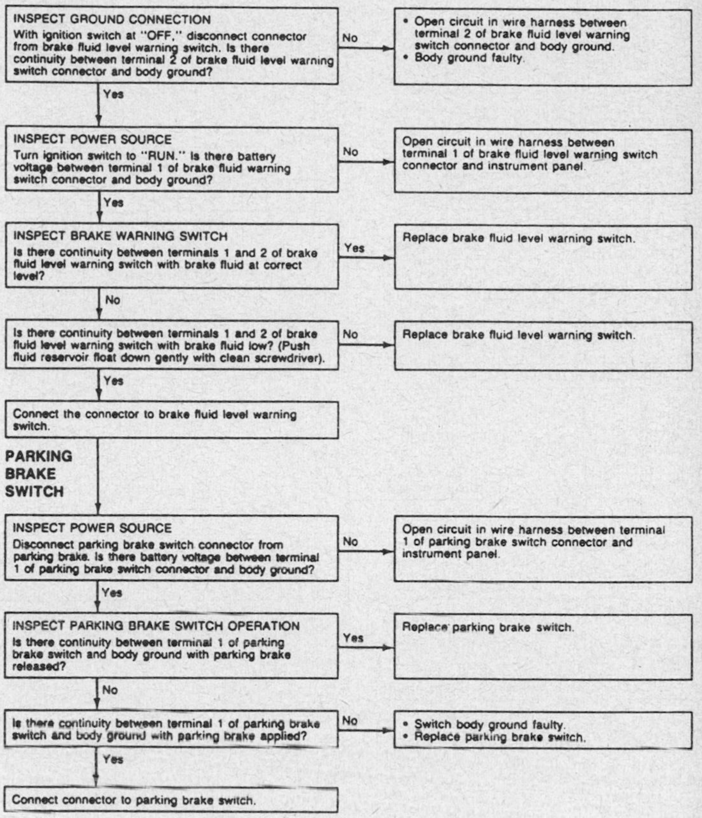
BRAKE FLUID LEVEL WARNING SWITCH
INSPECT GROUND CONNECTION
With ignition switch at "OFF," disconnect connector from brake fluid level warning switch. Is there continuity between terminal 2 of brake fluid level warning switch connector and body ground?
No
• Open circuit in wire harness between terminal 2 of brake fluid level warning switch connector and body ground.
• Body ground faulty.
Yes
INSPECT POWER SOURCE
Turn ignition switch to "RUN." Is there battery voltage between terminal 1 of brake fluid warning switch connector and body ground?
No
Open circuit in wire harness between terminal 1 of brake fluid level warning switch connector and instrument panel.
Yes
INSPECT BRAKE WARNING SWITCH
Is there continuity between terminals 1 and 2 of brake fluid level warning switch with brake fluid at correct level?
Yes
Replace brake fluid level warning switch.
No
Is there continuity between terminals 1 and 2 of brake fluid level warning switch with brake fluid low? (Push fluid reservoir float down gently with clean screwdriver).
No
Replace brake fluid level warning switch.
Yes
Connect the connector to brake fluid level warning switch.
PARKING BRAKE SWITCH
INSPECT POWER SOURCE
Disconnect parking brake switch connector from parking brake. Is there battery voltage between terminal 1 of parking brake switch connector and body ground?
No
Open circuit in wire harness between terminal 1 of parking brake switch connector and instrument panel.
Yes
INSPECT PARKING BRAKE SWITCH OPERATION
Is there continuity between terminal 1 of parking brake switch and body ground with parking brake released?
Yes
Replace parking brake switch.
No
Is there continuity between terminal 1 of parking brake switch and body ground with parking brake applied?
No
• Switch body ground faulty.
• Replace parking brake switch.
Yes
Connect connector to parking brake switch.
GC1109100233010X

Fig. 14 Test 7: Parking Brake Switch Circuit Diagnosis (Part 1 of 2). 1992

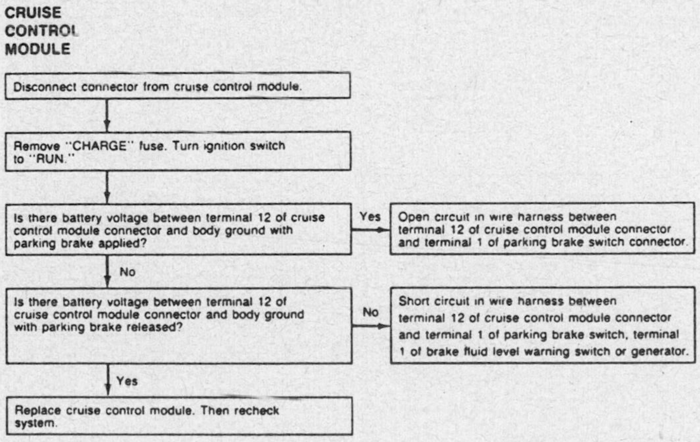
CRUISE CONTROL MODULE
Disconnect connector from cruise control module.
Remove "CHARGE" fuse. Turn ignition switch to "RUN."
Is there battery voltage between terminal 12 of cruise control module connector and body ground with parking brake applied?
Yes
Open circuit in wire harness between terminal 12 of cruise control module connector and terminal 1 of parking brake switch connector.
No
Is there battery voltage between terminal 12 of cruise control module connector and body ground with parking brake released?
No
Short circuit in wire harness between terminal 12 of cruise control module connector and terminal 1 of parking brake switch, terminal 1 of brake fluid level warning switch or generator.
Yes
Replace cruise control module. Then recheck system.
GC1109100233020X

Fig. 14 Test 7: Parking Brake Switch Circuit Diagnosis (Part 2 of 2). 1992

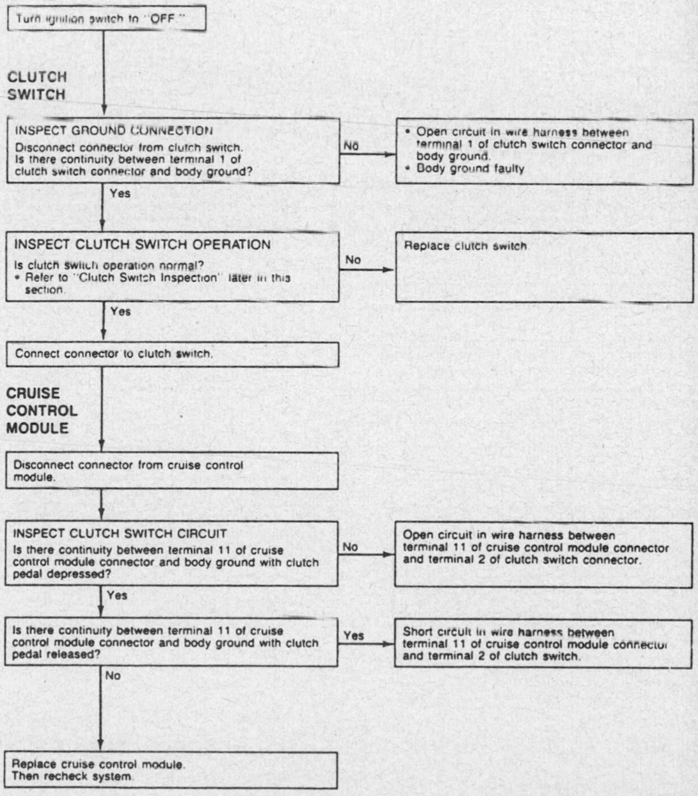
Turn ignition switch to "OFF."
CLUTCH SWITCH
INSPECT GROUND CONNECTION
Disconnect connector from clutch switch. Is there continuity between terminal 1 of clutch switch connector and body ground?
No
• Open circuit in wire harness between terminal 1 of clutch switch connector and body ground.
• Body ground faulty
Yes
INSPECT CLUTCH SWITCH OPERATION
Is clutch switch operation normal?
• Refer to "Clutch Switch Inspection" later in this section.
No
Replace clutch switch
Yes
Connect connector to clutch switch.
CRUISE CONTROL MODULE
Disconnect connector from cruise control module.
INSPECT CLUTCH SWITCH CIRCUIT
Is there continuity between terminal 11 of cruise control module connector and body ground with clutch pedal depressed?
No
Open circuit in wire harness between terminal 11 of cruise control module connector and terminal 2 of clutch switch connector.
Yes
Is there continuity between terminal 11 of cruise control module connector and body ground with clutch pedal released?
Yes
Short circuit in wire harness between terminal 11 of cruise control module connector and terminal 2 of clutch switch.
No
Replace cruise control module. Then recheck system.
GC1109100234000X

Fig. 15 Test 8: Clutch Switch Circuit Diagnosis. 1992

Turn ignition switch to "OFF."

NEUTRAL SAFETY SWITCH

INSPECT GROUND CONNECTION
Disconnect connector from neutral safety switch.
Is there continuity between terminal 1 of neutral safety switch connector and body ground?
- No → Open circuit in wire harness between terminal 1 of neutral safety switch connector and body ground.
- Yes ↓

INSPECT NEUTRAL SAFETY SWITCH OPERATION
Is neutral safety switch operation normal?
• Refer to "Neutral Safety Switch
- No → Replace neutral safety switch.
- Yes ↓

Connect connector to neutral safety switch.

CRUISE CONTROL MODULE

Disconnect connector from cruise control module.

INSPECT NEUTRAL SAFETY SWITCH CIRCUIT
Is there continuity between terminal 11 of cruise control module connector and body ground when shift lever is moved to "N" and "P" range?
- No → Open circuit in wire harness between terminal 11 of cruise control module connector and terminal 2 of neutral safety switch connector.
- Yes ↓

Replace cruise control module, then recheck system.

GC1109100235000X

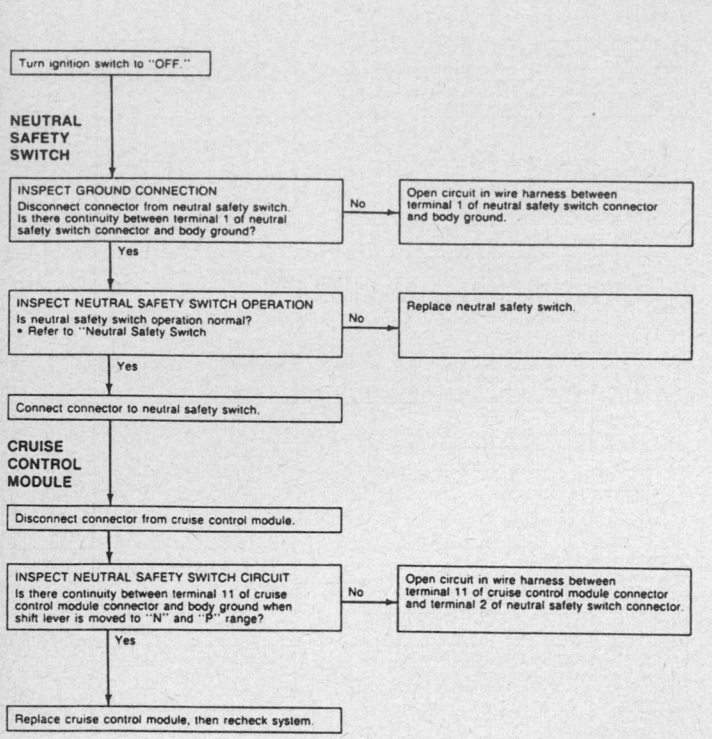

Fig. 16 Test 9: Neutral Safety Switch Circuit Diagnosis. 1992

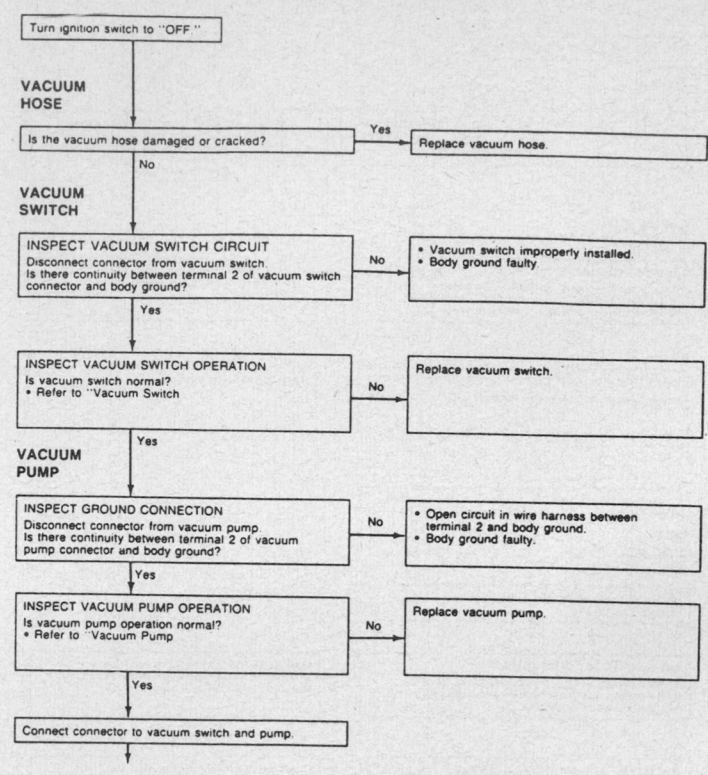

Turn ignition switch to "OFF."

VACUUM HOSE

Is the vacuum hose damaged or cracked?
- Yes → Replace vacuum hose.
- No ↓

VACUUM SWITCH

INSPECT VACUUM SWITCH CIRCUIT
Disconnect connector from vacuum switch.
Is there continuity between terminal 2 of vacuum switch connector and body ground?
- No → • Vacuum switch improperly installed. • Body ground faulty.
- Yes ↓

INSPECT VACUUM SWITCH OPERATION
Is vacuum switch normal?
• Refer to "Vacuum Switch
- No → Replace vacuum switch.
- Yes ↓

VACUUM PUMP

INSPECT GROUND CONNECTION
Disconnect connector from vacuum pump.
Is there continuity between terminal 2 of vacuum pump connector and body ground?
- No → • Open circuit in wire harness between terminal 2 and body ground. • Body ground faulty.
- Yes ↓

INSPECT VACUUM PUMP OPERATION
Is vacuum pump operation normal?
• Refer to "Vacuum Pump
- No → Replace vacuum pump.
- Yes ↓

Connect connector to vacuum switch and pump.

GC1109100236010X

Fig. 17 Test 10: Vacuum Circuit Diagnosis (Part 1 of 2). 1992

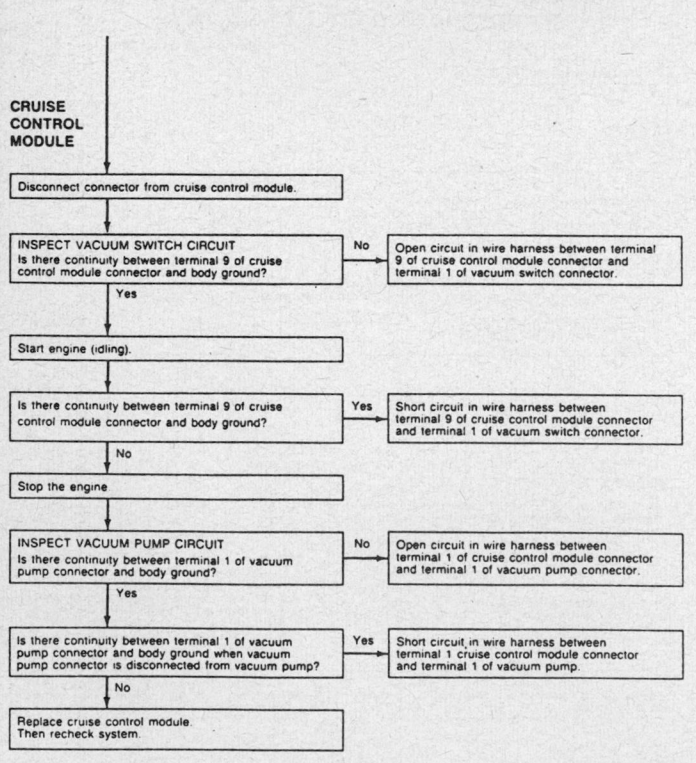

CRUISE CONTROL MODULE

Disconnect connector from cruise control module.

INSPECT VACUUM SWITCH CIRCUIT
Is there continuity between terminal 9 of cruise control module connector and body ground?
- No → Open circuit in wire harness between terminal 9 of cruise control module connector and terminal 1 of vacuum switch connector.
- Yes ↓

Start engine (idling).

Is there continuity between terminal 9 of cruise control module connector and body ground?
- Yes → Short circuit in wire harness between terminal 9 of cruise control module connector and terminal 1 of vacuum switch connector.
- No ↓

Stop the engine

INSPECT VACUUM PUMP CIRCUIT
Is there continuity between terminal 1 of vacuum pump connector and body ground?
- No → Open circuit in wire harness between terminal 1 of cruise control module connector and terminal 1 of vacuum pump connector.
- Yes ↓

Is there continuity between terminal 1 of vacuum pump connector and body ground when vacuum pump connector is disconnected from vacuum pump?
- Yes → Short circuit in wire harness between terminal 1 cruise control module connector and terminal 1 of vacuum pump.
- No ↓

Replace cruise control module. Then recheck system.

GC1109100236020X

Fig. 17 Test 10: Vacuum Circuit Diagnosis (Part 2 of 2). 1992

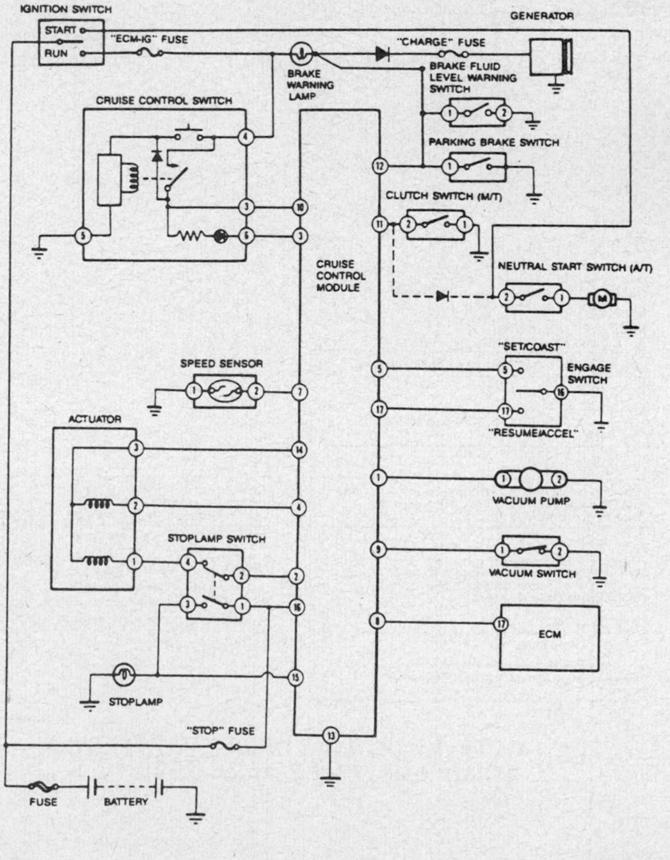
IGNITION SWITCH
START
RUN
"ECM-IG" FUSE
BRAKE WARNING LAMP
"CHARGE" FUSE
GENERATOR
BRAKE FLUID LEVEL WARNING SWITCH
CRUISE CONTROL SWITCH
PARKING BRAKE SWITCH
CLUTCH SWITCH (M/T)
CRUISE CONTROL MODULE
NEUTRAL START SWITCH (A/T)
SPEED SENSOR
"SET/COAST"
ENGAGE SWITCH
"RESUME/ACCEL"
ACTUATOR
VACUUM PUMP
STOPLAMP SWITCH
VACUUM SWITCH
ECM
STOPLAMP
"STOP" FUSE
FUSE
BATTERY

GC1109100237000X

Fig. 18 Cruise control system wiring diagram. 1992

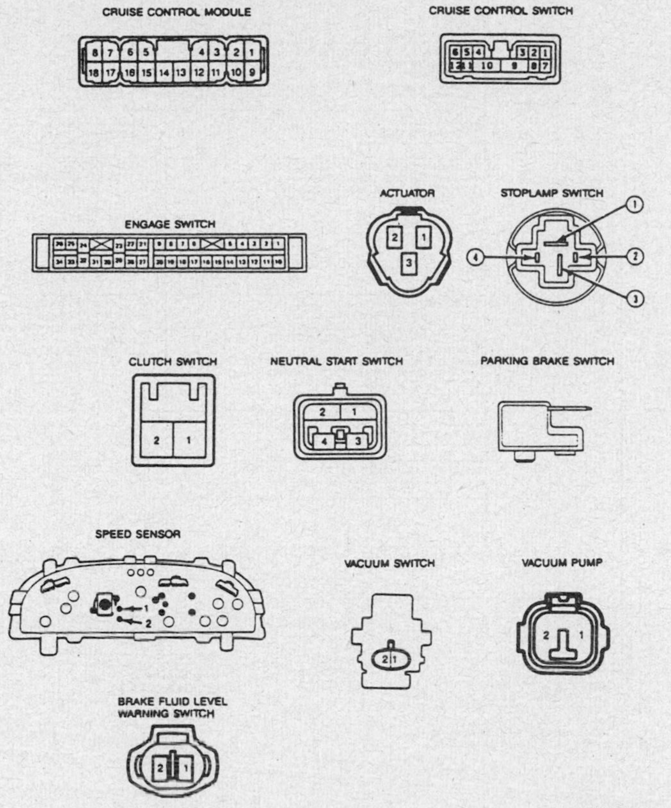
CRUISE CONTROL MODULE
CRUISE CONTROL SWITCH
ENGAGE SWITCH
ACTUATOR
STOPLAMP SWITCH
CLUTCH SWITCH
NEUTRAL START SWITCH
PARKING BRAKE SWITCH
SPEED SENSOR
VACUUM SWITCH
VACUUM PUMP
BRAKE FLUID LEVEL WARNING SWITCH
GC1109100238000X

Fig. 19 Cruise control system connector terminal identification. 1992

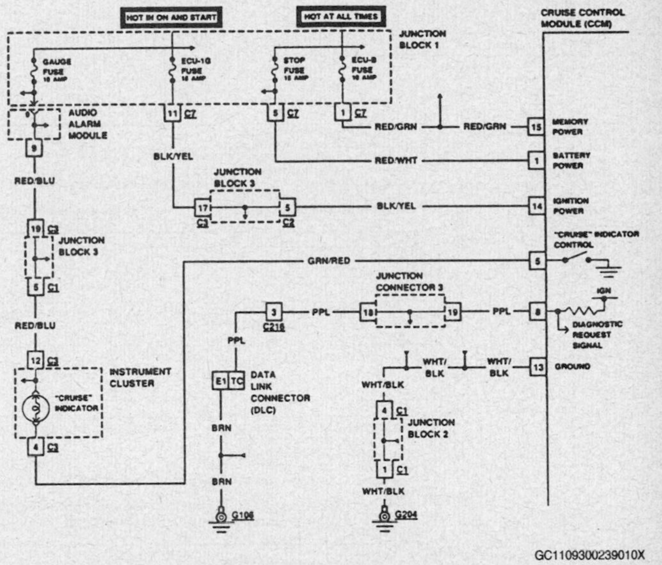
HOT IN ON AND START
HOT AT ALL TIMES
JUNCTION BLOCK 1
CRUISE CONTROL MODULE (CCM)
GAUGE FUSE 10 AMP
ECU-IG FUSE 10 AMP
STOP FUSE 15 AMP
ECU-B FUSE 15 AMP
AUDIO ALARM MODULE
RED/GRN
MEMORY POWER
BATTERY POWER
RED/WHT
BLK/YEL
JUNCTION BLOCK 3
IGNITION POWER
RED/BLU
"CRUISE" INDICATOR CONTROL
GRN/RED
JUNCTION CONNECTOR 3
PPL
DIAGNOSTIC REQUEST SIGNAL
WHT/BLK
GROUND
INSTRUMENT CLUSTER
"CRUISE" INDICATOR
DATA LINK CONNECTOR (DLC)
BRN
JUNCTION BLOCK 2
G106
G204
GC1109300239010X

Fig. 20 Cruise control module on-board diagnostic (OBD) system check (Part 1 of 5). 1993–94

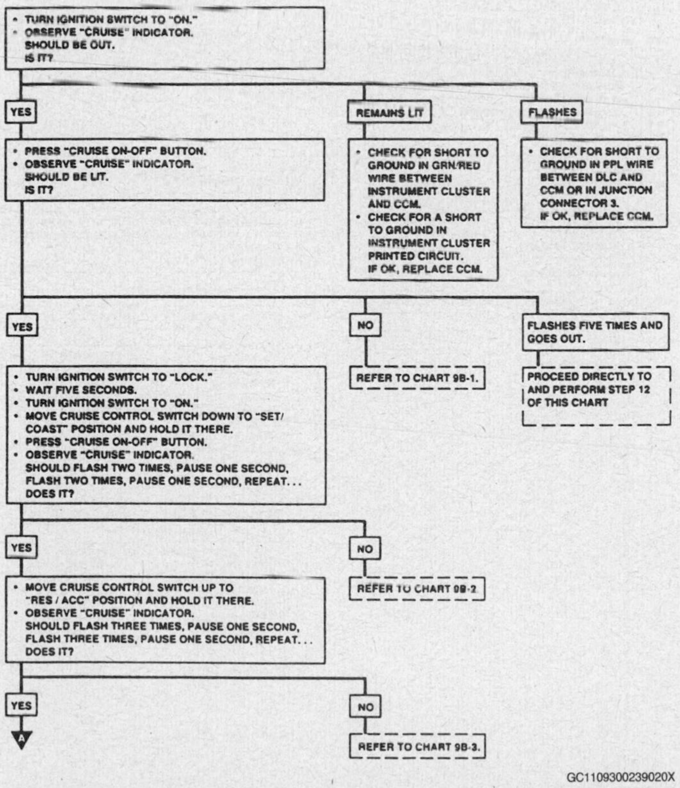
• TURN IGNITION SWITCH TO "ON."
• OBSERVE "CRUISE" INDICATOR. SHOULD BE OUT. IS IT?
YES
REMAINS LIT
FLASHES
• PRESS "CRUISE ON-OFF" BUTTON.
• OBSERVE "CRUISE" INDICATOR. SHOULD BE LIT. IS IT?
• CHECK FOR SHORT TO GROUND IN GRN/RED WIRE BETWEEN INSTRUMENT CLUSTER AND CCM.
• CHECK FOR A SHORT TO GROUND IN INSTRUMENT CLUSTER PRINTED CIRCUIT. IF OK, REPLACE CCM.
• CHECK FOR SHORT TO GROUND IN PPL WIRE BETWEEN DLC AND CCM OR IN JUNCTION CONNECTOR 3. IF OK, REPLACE CCM.
YES
NO
FLASHES FIVE TIMES AND GOES OUT.
• TURN IGNITION SWITCH TO "LOCK."
• WAIT FIVE SECONDS.
• TURN IGNITION SWITCH TO "ON."
• MOVE CRUISE CONTROL SWITCH DOWN TO "SET/COAST" POSITION AND HOLD IT THERE.
• PRESS "CRUISE ON-OFF" BUTTON.
• OBSERVE "CRUISE" INDICATOR. SHOULD FLASH TWO TIMES, PAUSE ONE SECOND, FLASH TWO TIMES, PAUSE ONE SECOND, REPEAT... DOES IT?
REFER TO CHART 9B-1.
PROCEED DIRECTLY TO AND PERFORM STEP 12 OF THIS CHART
YES
NO
REFER TO CHART 9B-2
• MOVE CRUISE CONTROL SWITCH UP TO "RES / ACC" POSITION AND HOLD IT THERE.
• OBSERVE "CRUISE" INDICATOR. SHOULD FLASH THREE TIMES, PAUSE ONE SECOND, FLASH THREE TIMES, PAUSE ONE SECOND, REPEAT... DOES IT?
YES
NO
REFER TO CHART 9B-3.
GC1109300239020X

Fig. 20 Cruise control module on-board diagnostic (OBD) system check (Part 2 of 5). 1993–94

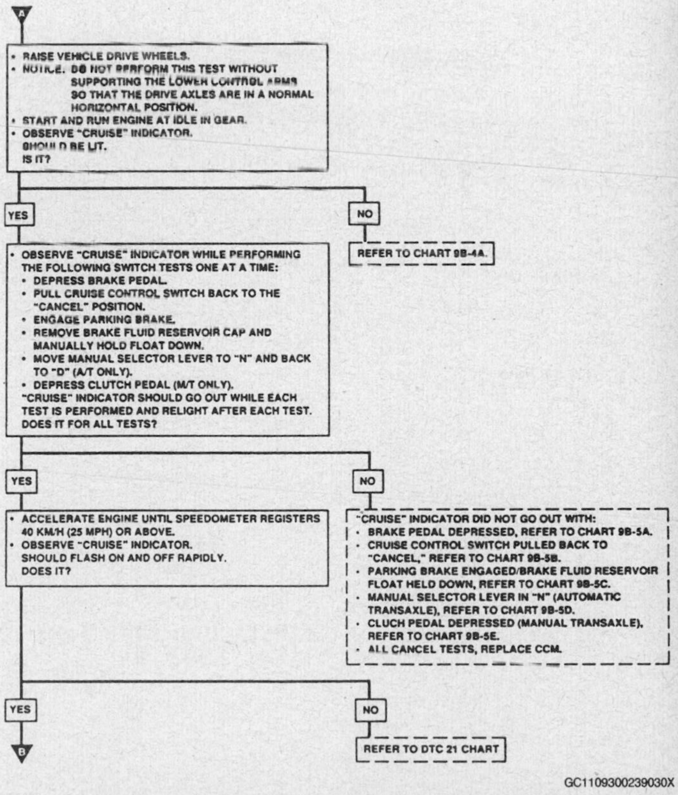
• RAISE VEHICLE DRIVE WHEELS.
• NOTICE: DO NOT PERFORM THIS TEST WITHOUT SUPPORTING THE LOWER CONTROL ARMS SO THAT THE DRIVE AXLES ARE IN A NORMAL HORIZONTAL POSITION.
• START AND RUN ENGINE AT IDLE IN GEAR.
• OBSERVE "CRUISE" INDICATOR. SHOULD BE LIT. IS IT?
YES
NO
REFER TO CHART 9B-4A.
• OBSERVE "CRUISE" INDICATOR WHILE PERFORMING THE FOLLOWING SWITCH TESTS ONE AT A TIME:
• DEPRESS BRAKE PEDAL.
• PULL CRUISE CONTROL SWITCH BACK TO THE "CANCEL" POSITION.
• ENGAGE PARKING BRAKE.
• REMOVE BRAKE FLUID RESERVOIR CAP AND MANUALLY HOLD FLOAT DOWN.
• MOVE MANUAL SELECTOR LEVER TO "N" AND BACK TO "D" (A/T ONLY).
• DEPRESS CLUTCH PEDAL (M/T ONLY).
"CRUISE" INDICATOR SHOULD GO OUT WHILE EACH TEST IS PERFORMED AND RELIGHT AFTER EACH TEST. DOES IT FOR ALL TESTS?
YES
NO
• ACCELERATE ENGINE UNTIL SPEEDOMETER REGISTERS 40 KM/H (25 MPH) OR ABOVE.
• OBSERVE "CRUISE" INDICATOR. SHOULD FLASH ON AND OFF RAPIDLY. DOES IT?
"CRUISE" INDICATOR DID NOT GO OUT WITH:
• BRAKE PEDAL DEPRESSED, REFER TO CHART 9B-5A.
• CRUISE CONTROL SWITCH PULLED BACK TO "CANCEL," REFER TO CHART 9B-5B.
• PARKING BRAKE ENGAGED/BRAKE FLUID RESERVOIR FLOAT HELD DOWN, REFER TO CHART 9B-5C.
• MANUAL SELECTOR LEVER IN "N" (AUTOMATIC TRANSAXLE), REFER TO CHART 9B-5D.
• CLUCH PEDAL DEPRESSED (MANUAL TRANSAXLE), REFER TO CHART 9B-5E.
• ALL CANCEL TESTS, REPLACE CCM.
YES
NO
REFER TO DTC 21 CHART
GC1109300239030X

Fig. 20 Cruise control module on-board diagnostic (OBD) system check (Part 3 of 5). 1993–94

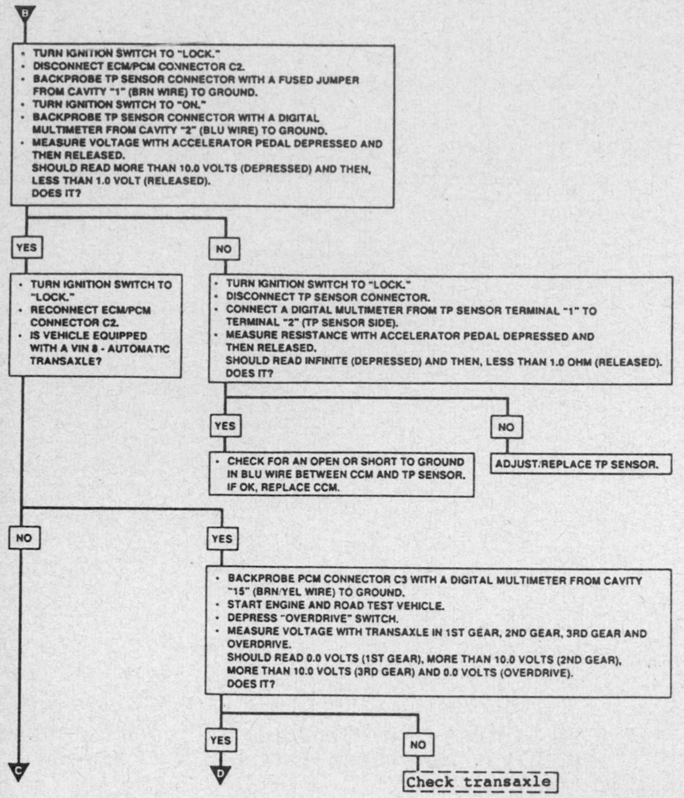
B
• TURN IGNITION SWITCH TO "LOCK."
• DISCONNECT ECM/PCM CONNECTOR C2.
• BACKPROBE TP SENSOR CONNECTOR WITH A FUSED JUMPER FROM CAVITY "1" (BRN WIRE) TO GROUND.
• TURN IGNITION SWITCH TO "ON."
• BACKPROBE TP SENSOR CONNECTOR WITH A DIGITAL MULTIMETER FROM CAVITY "2" (BLU WIRE) TO GROUND.
• MEASURE VOLTAGE WITH ACCELERATOR PEDAL DEPRESSED AND THEN RELEASED.
SHOULD READ MORE THAN 10.0 VOLTS (DEPRESSED) AND THEN, LESS THAN 1.0 VOLT (RELEASED).
DOES IT?
YES
NO
• TURN IGNITION SWITCH TO "LOCK."
• RECONNECT ECM/PCM CONNECTOR C2.
• IS VEHICLE EQUIPPED WITH A VIN 8 - AUTOMATIC TRANSAXLE?
• TURN IGNITION SWITCH TO "LOCK."
• DISCONNECT TP SENSOR CONNECTOR.
• CONNECT A DIGITAL MULTIMETER FROM TP SENSOR TERMINAL "1" TO TERMINAL "2" (TP SENSOR SIDE).
• MEASURE RESISTANCE WITH ACCELERATOR PEDAL DEPRESSED AND THEN RELEASED.
SHOULD READ INFINITE (DEPRESSED) AND THEN, LESS THAN 1.0 OHM (RELEASED).
DOES IT?
YES
NO
• CHECK FOR AN OPEN OR SHORT TO GROUND IN BLU WIRE BETWEEN CCM AND TP SENSOR. IF OK, REPLACE CCM.
ADJUST/REPLACE TP SENSOR.
NO
YES
• BACKPROBE PCM CONNECTOR C3 WITH A DIGITAL MULTIMETER FROM CAVITY "15" (BRN/YEL WIRE) TO GROUND.
• START ENGINE AND ROAD TEST VEHICLE.
• DEPRESS "OVERDRIVE" SWITCH.
• MEASURE VOLTAGE WITH TRANSAXLE IN 1ST GEAR, 2ND GEAR, 3RD GEAR AND OVERDRIVE.
SHOULD READ 0.0 VOLTS (1ST GEAR), MORE THAN 10.0 VOLTS (2ND GEAR), MORE THAN 10.0 VOLTS (3RD GEAR) AND 0.0 VOLTS (OVERDRIVE).
DOES IT?
YES
NO
C
D
Check transaxle
GC1109300239040X

Fig. 20 Cruise control module on-board diagnostic (OBD) system check (Part 4 of 5). 1993–94

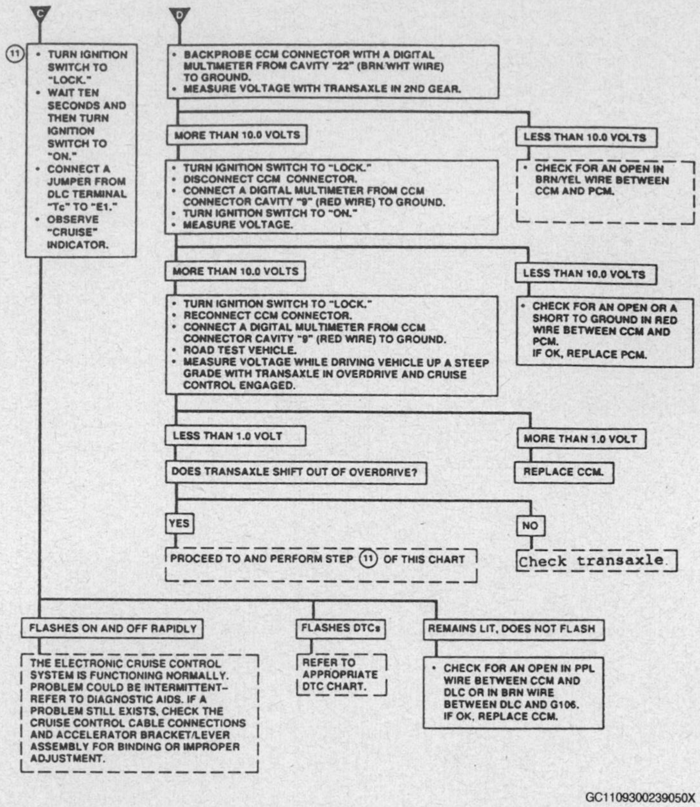
C
D
11
• TURN IGNITION SWITCH TO "LOCK."
• WAIT TEN SECONDS AND THEN TURN IGNITION SWITCH TO "ON."
• CONNECT A JUMPER FROM DLC TERMINAL "Tc" TO "E1."
• OBSERVE "CRUISE" INDICATOR.
• BACKPROBE CCM CONNECTOR WITH A DIGITAL MULTIMETER FROM CAVITY "22" (BRN/WHT WIRE) TO GROUND.
• MEASURE VOLTAGE WITH TRANSAXLE IN 2ND GEAR.
MORE THAN 10.0 VOLTS
LESS THAN 10.0 VOLTS
• TURN IGNITION SWITCH TO "LOCK."
• DISCONNECT CCM CONNECTOR.
• CONNECT A DIGITAL MULTIMETER FROM CCM CONNECTOR CAVITY "9" (RED WIRE) TO GROUND.
• TURN IGNITION SWITCH TO "ON."
• MEASURE VOLTAGE.
• CHECK FOR AN OPEN IN BRN/YEL WIRE BETWEEN CCM AND PCM.
MORE THAN 10.0 VOLTS
LESS THAN 10.0 VOLTS
• TURN IGNITION SWITCH TO "LOCK."
• RECONNECT CCM CONNECTOR.
• CONNECT A DIGITAL MULTIMETER FROM CCM CONNECTOR CAVITY "9" (RED WIRE) TO GROUND.
• ROAD TEST VEHICLE.
• MEASURE VOLTAGE WHILE DRIVING VEHICLE UP A STEEP GRADE WITH TRANSAXLE IN OVERDRIVE AND CRUISE CONTROL ENGAGED.
• CHECK FOR AN OPEN OR A SHORT TO GROUND IN RED WIRE BETWEEN CCM AND PCM.
IF OK, REPLACE PCM.
LESS THAN 1.0 VOLT
MORE THAN 1.0 VOLT
DOES TRANSAXLE SHIFT OUT OF OVERDRIVE?
REPLACE CCM.
YES
NO
PROCEED TO AND PERFORM STEP 11 OF THIS CHART
Check transaxle.
FLASHES ON AND OFF RAPIDLY
FLASHES DTCs
REMAINS LIT, DOES NOT FLASH
THE ELECTRONIC CRUISE CONTROL SYSTEM IS FUNCTIONING NORMALLY. PROBLEM COULD BE INTERMITTENT–REFER TO DIAGNOSTIC AIDS. IF A PROBLEM STILL EXISTS, CHECK THE CRUISE CONTROL CABLE CONNECTIONS AND ACCELERATOR BRACKET/LEVER ASSEMBLY FOR BINDING OR IMPROPER ADJUSTMENT.
REFER TO APPROPRIATE DTC CHART.
• CHECK FOR AN OPEN IN PPL WIRE BETWEEN CCM AND DLC OR IN BRN WIRE BETWEEN DLC AND G106.
IF OK, REPLACE CCM.
GC1109300239050X

Fig. 20 Cruise control module on-board diagnostic (OBD) system check (Part 5 of 5). 1993–94

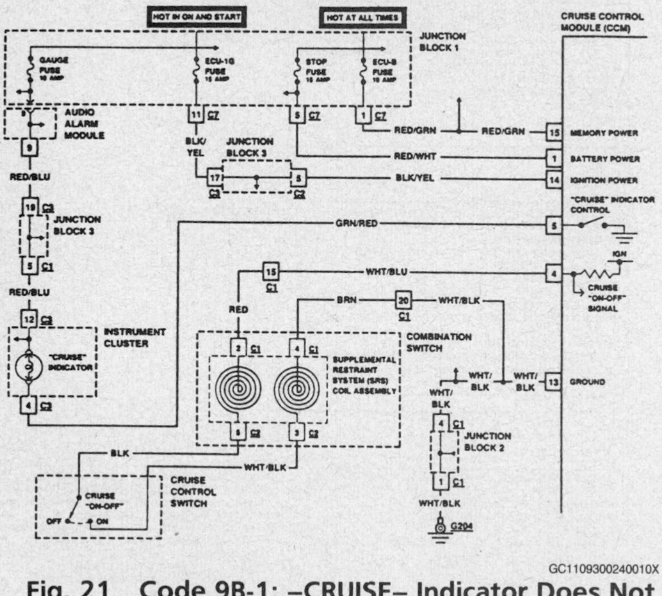
HOT IN ON AND START
HOT AT ALL TIMES
JUNCTION BLOCK 1
CRUISE CONTROL MODULE (CCM)
GAUGE FUSE 10 AMP
ECU-IG FUSE 15 AMP
STOP FUSE 15 AMP
ECU-B FUSE 15 AMP
AUDIO ALARM MODULE
11 C7
5 C7
1 C7
RED/GRN
RED/GRN
15
MEMORY POWER
BLK/YEL
JUNCTION BLOCK 3
RED/WHT
1
BATTERY POWER
BLK/YEL
14
IGNITION POWER
RED/BLU
17 C3
5 C2
"CRUISE" INDICATOR CONTROL
GRN/RED
5
WHT/BLU
4
IGN
CRUISE "ON-OFF" SIGNAL
15 C1
RED
BRN
20 C1
WHT/BLK
INSTRUMENT CLUSTER
"CRUISE" INDICATOR
COMBINATION SWITCH
SUPPLEMENTAL RESTRAINT SYSTEM (SRS) COIL ASSEMBLY
WHT/BLK
13
GROUND
JUNCTION BLOCK 2
BLK
WHT/BLK
CRUISE CONTROL SWITCH
CRUISE "ON-OFF"
OFF
ON
G204
GC1109300240010X

Fig. 21 Code 9B-1: –CRUISE– Indicator Does Not Light (Part 1 of 4). 1993–94

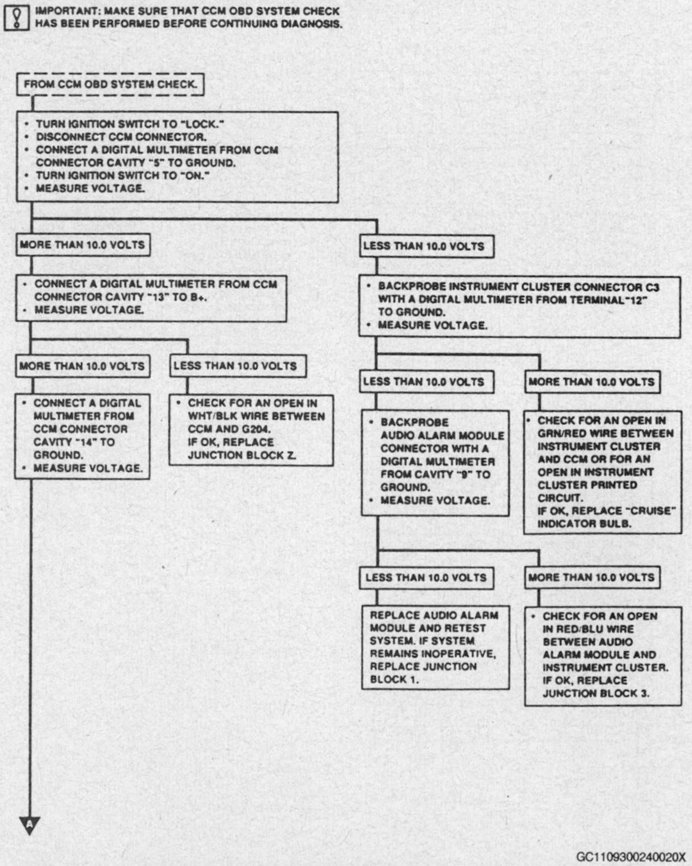
IMPORTANT: MAKE SURE THAT CCM OBD SYSTEM CHECK HAS BEEN PERFORMED BEFORE CONTINUING DIAGNOSIS.
FROM CCM OBD SYSTEM CHECK.
• TURN IGNITION SWITCH TO "LOCK."
• DISCONNECT CCM CONNECTOR.
• CONNECT A DIGITAL MULTIMETER FROM CCM CONNECTOR CAVITY "5" TO GROUND.
• TURN IGNITION SWITCH TO "ON."
• MEASURE VOLTAGE.
MORE THAN 10.0 VOLTS
LESS THAN 10.0 VOLTS
• CONNECT A DIGITAL MULTIMETER FROM CCM CONNECTOR CAVITY "13" TO B+.
• MEASURE VOLTAGE.
• BACKPROBE INSTRUMENT CLUSTER CONNECTOR C3 WITH A DIGITAL MULTIMETER FROM TERMINAL "12" TO GROUND.
• MEASURE VOLTAGE.
MORE THAN 10.0 VOLTS
LESS THAN 10.0 VOLTS
LESS THAN 10.0 VOLTS
MORE THAN 10.0 VOLTS
• CONNECT A DIGITAL MULTIMETER FROM CCM CONNECTOR CAVITY "14" TO GROUND.
• MEASURE VOLTAGE.
• CHECK FOR AN OPEN IN WHT/BLK WIRE BETWEEN CCM AND G204.
IF OK, REPLACE JUNCTION BLOCK 2.
• BACKPROBE AUDIO ALARM MODULE CONNECTOR WITH A DIGITAL MULTIMETER FROM CAVITY "9" TO GROUND.
• MEASURE VOLTAGE.
• CHECK FOR AN OPEN IN GRN/RED WIRE BETWEEN INSTRUMENT CLUSTER AND CCM OR FOR AN OPEN IN INSTRUMENT CLUSTER PRINTED CIRCUIT.
IF OK, REPLACE "CRUISE" INDICATOR BULB.
LESS THAN 10.0 VOLTS
MORE THAN 10.0 VOLTS
REPLACE AUDIO ALARM MODULE AND RETEST SYSTEM. IF SYSTEM REMAINS INOPERATIVE, REPLACE JUNCTION BLOCK 1.
• CHECK FOR AN OPEN IN RED/BLU WIRE BETWEEN AUDIO ALARM MODULE AND INSTRUMENT CLUSTER.
IF OK, REPLACE JUNCTION BLOCK 3.
A
GC1109300240020X

Fig. 21 Code 9B-1: –CRUISE– Indicator Does Not Light (Part 2 of 4). 1993–94

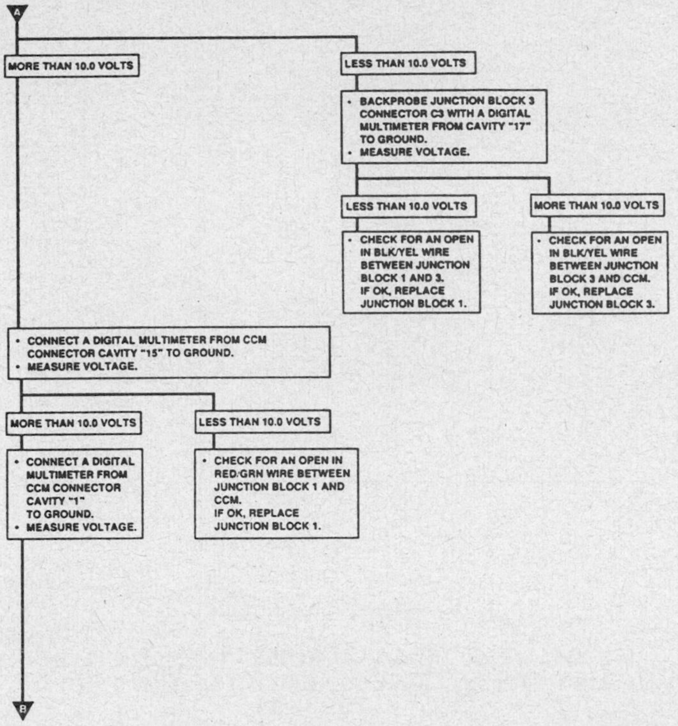

A
MORE THAN 10.0 VOLTS
LESS THAN 10.0 VOLTS
• BACKPROBE JUNCTION BLOCK 3 CONNECTOR C3 WITH A DIGITAL MULTIMETER FROM CAVITY "17" TO GROUND.
• MEASURE VOLTAGE.
LESS THAN 10.0 VOLTS
MORE THAN 10.0 VOLTS
• CHECK FOR AN OPEN IN BLK/YEL WIRE BETWEEN JUNCTION BLOCK 1 AND 3. IF OK, REPLACE JUNCTION BLOCK 1.
• CHECK FOR AN OPEN IN BLK/YEL WIRE BETWEEN JUNCTION BLOCK 3 AND CCM. IF OK, REPLACE JUNCTION BLOCK 3.
• CONNECT A DIGITAL MULTIMETER FROM CCM CONNECTOR CAVITY "15" TO GROUND.
• MEASURE VOLTAGE.
MORE THAN 10.0 VOLTS
LESS THAN 10.0 VOLTS
• CONNECT A DIGITAL MULTIMETER FROM CCM CONNECTOR CAVITY "1" TO GROUND.
• MEASURE VOLTAGE.
• CHECK FOR AN OPEN IN RED/GRN WIRE BETWEEN JUNCTION BLOCK 1 AND CCM. IF OK, REPLACE JUNCTION BLOCK 1.
B
GC1109300240030X

Fig. 21 Code 9B-1: –CRUISE– Indicator Does Not Light (Part 3 of 4). 1993–94

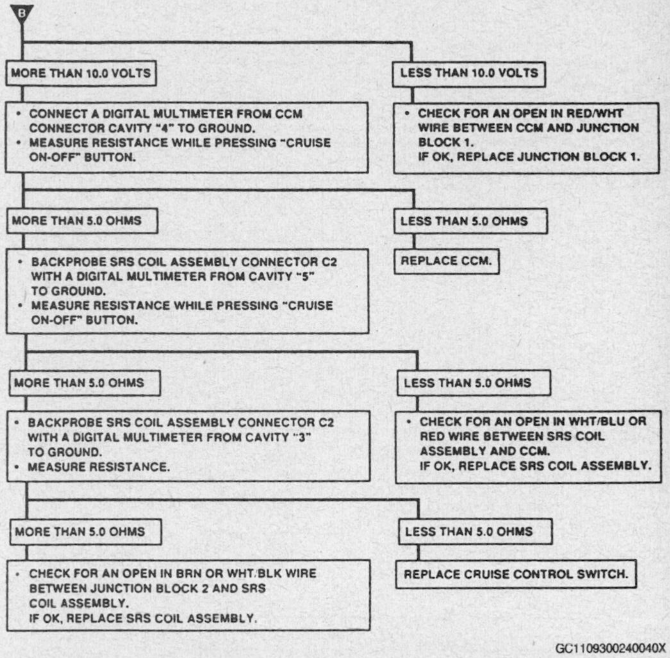

B
MORE THAN 10.0 VOLTS
LESS THAN 10.0 VOLTS
• CONNECT A DIGITAL MULTIMETER FROM CCM CONNECTOR CAVITY "4" TO GROUND.
• MEASURE RESISTANCE WHILE PRESSING "CRUISE ON-OFF" BUTTON.
• CHECK FOR AN OPEN IN RED/WHT WIRE BETWEEN CCM AND JUNCTION BLOCK 1. IF OK, REPLACE JUNCTION BLOCK 1.
MORE THAN 5.0 OHMS
LESS THAN 5.0 OHMS
• BACKPROBE SRS COIL ASSEMBLY CONNECTOR C2 WITH A DIGITAL MULTIMETER FROM CAVITY "5" TO GROUND.
• MEASURE RESISTANCE WHILE PRESSING "CRUISE ON-OFF" BUTTON.
REPLACE CCM.
MORE THAN 5.0 OHMS
LESS THAN 5.0 OHMS
• BACKPROBE SRS COIL ASSEMBLY CONNECTOR C2 WITH A DIGITAL MULTIMETER FROM CAVITY "3" TO GROUND.
• MEASURE RESISTANCE.
• CHECK FOR AN OPEN IN WHT/BLU OR RED WIRE BETWEEN SRS COIL ASSEMBLY AND CCM. IF OK, REPLACE SRS COIL ASSEMBLY.
MORE THAN 5.0 OHMS
LESS THAN 5.0 OHMS
• CHECK FOR AN OPEN IN BRN OR WHT/BLK WIRE BETWEEN JUNCTION BLOCK 2 AND SRS COIL ASSEMBLY. IF OK, REPLACE SRS COIL ASSEMBLY.
REPLACE CRUISE CONTROL SWITCH.
GC1109300240040X

Fig. 21 Code 9B-1: –CRUISE– Indicator Does Not Light (Part 4 of 4). 1993–94

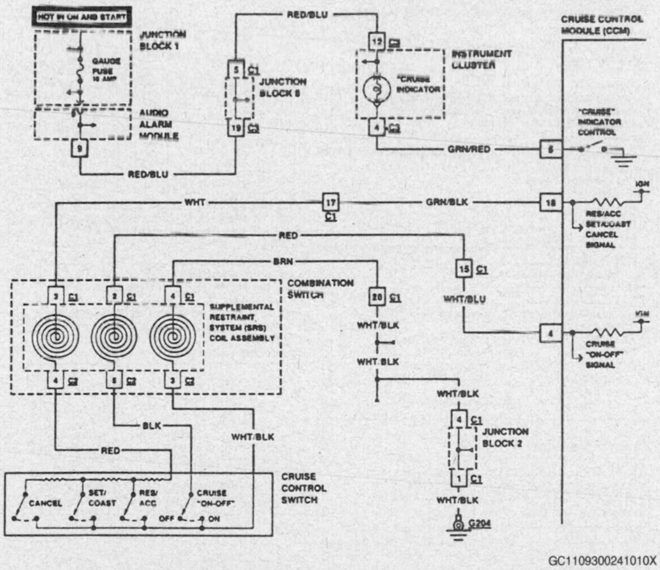

HOT IN ON AND START
JUNCTION BLOCK 1
GAUGE FUSE 10 AMP
AUDIO ALARM MODULE
RED/BLU
JUNCTION BLOCK 8
INSTRUMENT CLUSTER
"CRUISE" INDICATOR
CRUISE CONTROL MODULE (CCM)
"CRUISE" INDICATOR CONTROL
GRN/RED
WHT
GRN/BLK
IGN
RES/ACC SET/COAST CANCEL SIGNAL
RED
BRN
COMBINATION SWITCH
SUPPLEMENTAL RESTRAINT SYSTEM (SRS) COIL ASSEMBLY
WHT/BLU
WHT/BLK
CRUISE "ON-OFF" SIGNAL
BLK
JUNCTION BLOCK 2
CRUISE CONTROL SWITCH
CANCEL
SET/ COAST
RES/ ACC
CRUISE "ON-OFF"
OFF
ON
G204
GC1109300241010X

Fig. 22 Code 9B-2: –CRUISE– Indicator Does Not Flash SET/COAST Test (Part 1 of 3). 1993–94

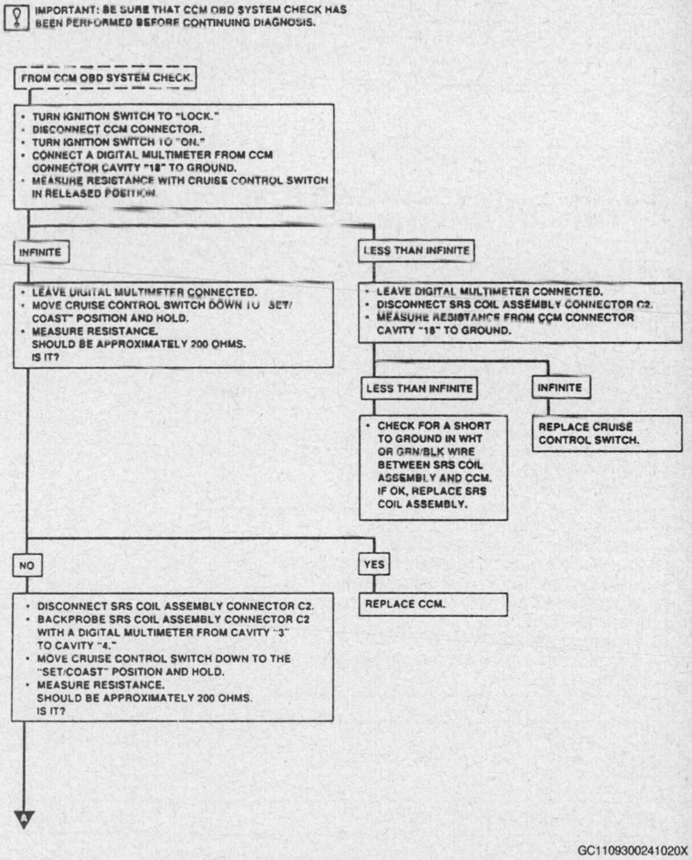

IMPORTANT: BE SURE THAT CCM OBD SYSTEM CHECK HAS BEEN PERFORMED BEFORE CONTINUING DIAGNOSIS.
FROM CCM OBD SYSTEM CHECK.
• TURN IGNITION SWITCH TO "LOCK."
• DISCONNECT CCM CONNECTOR.
• TURN IGNITION SWITCH TO "ON."
• CONNECT A DIGITAL MULTIMETER FROM CCM CONNECTOR CAVITY "18" TO GROUND.
• MEASURE RESISTANCE WITH CRUISE CONTROL SWITCH IN RELEASED POSITION.
INFINITE
LESS THAN INFINITE
• LEAVE DIGITAL MULTIMETER CONNECTED.
• MOVE CRUISE CONTROL SWITCH DOWN TO "SET/COAST" POSITION AND HOLD.
• MEASURE RESISTANCE. SHOULD BE APPROXIMATELY 200 OHMS. IS IT?
• LEAVE DIGITAL MULTIMETER CONNECTED.
• DISCONNECT SRS COIL ASSEMBLY CONNECTOR C2.
• MEASURE RESISTANCE FROM CCM CONNECTOR CAVITY "18" TO GROUND.
LESS THAN INFINITE
INFINITE
• CHECK FOR A SHORT TO GROUND IN WHT OR GRN/BLK WIRE BETWEEN SRS COIL ASSEMBLY AND CCM. IF OK, REPLACE SRS COIL ASSEMBLY.
REPLACE CRUISE CONTROL SWITCH.
NO
YES
• DISCONNECT SRS COIL ASSEMBLY CONNECTOR C2.
• BACKPROBE SRS COIL ASSEMBLY CONNECTOR C2 WITH A DIGITAL MULTIMETER FROM CAVITY "3" TO CAVITY "4."
• MOVE CRUISE CONTROL SWITCH DOWN TO THE "SET/COAST" POSITION AND HOLD.
• MEASURE RESISTANCE. SHOULD BE APPROXIMATELY 200 OHMS. IS IT?
REPLACE CCM.
A
GC1109300241020X

Fig. 22 Code 9B-2: –CRUISE– Indicator Does Not Flash SET/COAST Test (Part 2 of 3). 1993–94

A

YES

- CHECK FOR AN OPEN IN WHT OR GRN/BLK WIRE BETWEEN SRS COIL ASSEMBLY AND CCM. IF OK, REPLACE SRS COIL ASSEMBLY.

NO

REPLACE CRUISE CONTROL SWITCH.

GC1109300241030X

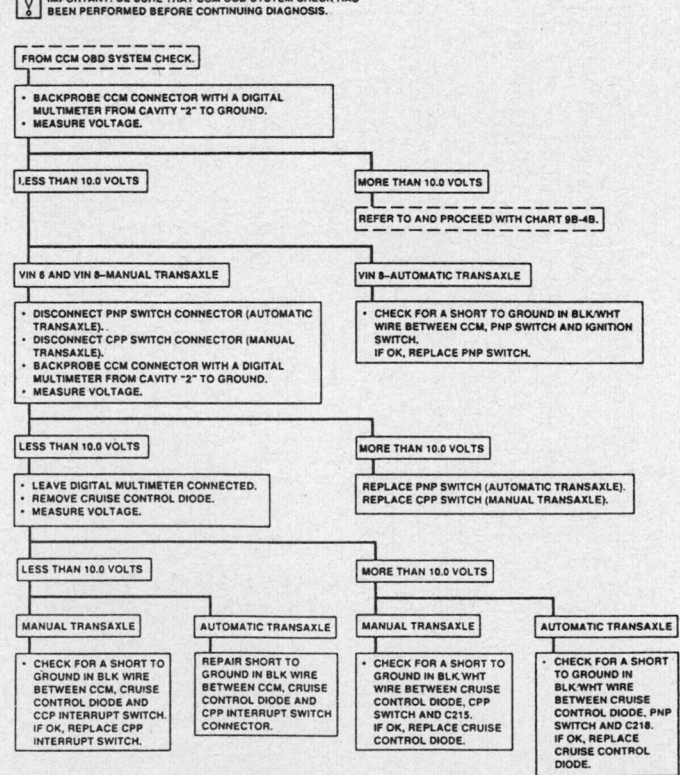

Fig. 22 Code 9B-2: –CRUISE– Indicator Does Not Flash SET/COAST Test (Part 3 of 3). 1993–94

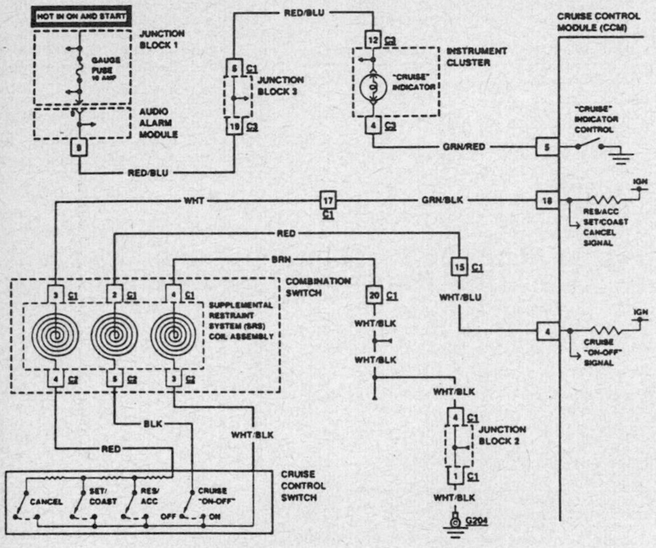
HOT IN ON AND START
JUNCTION BLOCK 1
GAUGE FUSE 10 AMP
AUDIO ALARM MODULE
RED/BLU
JUNCTION BLOCK 3
INSTRUMENT CLUSTER
"CRUISE" INDICATOR
CRUISE CONTROL MODULE (CCM)
"CRUISE" INDICATOR CONTROL
GRN/RED
WHT
GRN/BLK
IGN
RES/ACC SET/COAST CANCEL SIGNAL
RED
BRN
COMBINATION SWITCH
SUPPLEMENTAL RESTRAINT SYSTEM (SRS) COIL ASSEMBLY
WHT/BLU
WHT/BLK
CRUISE "ON-OFF" SIGNAL
JUNCTION BLOCK 2
BLK
CRUISE CONTROL SWITCH
CANCEL
SET/ COAST
RES/ ACC
CRUISE "ON-OFF"
OFF
ON
G204

GC1109300242010X

Fig. 23 Code 9B-3: –CRUISE– Indicator Does Not Flash RES/ACC Test (Part 1 of 2). 1993–94

IMPORTANT: BE SURE THAT CCM OBD SYSTEM CHECK HAS BEEN PERFORMED BEFORE CONTINUING DIAGNOSIS.

FROM CCM OBD SYSTEM CHECK.

- TURN IGNITION SWITCH TO "LOCK."
- DISCONNECT CCM CONNECTOR.
- CONNECT A DIGITAL MULTIMETER FROM CCM CONNECTOR CAVITY "18" TO GROUND.
- MOVE CRUISE CONTROL SWITCH UP TO "RES / ACC" POSITION AND HOLD.
- MEASURE RESISTANCE. SHOULD BE APPROXIMATELY 70 OHMS. IS IT?

NO

REPLACE CRUISE CONTROL SWITCH.

YES

REPLACE CCM.

GC1109300242020X

Fig. 23 Code 9B-3: –CRUISE– Indicator Does Not Flash RES/ACC Test (Part 2 of 2). 1993–94

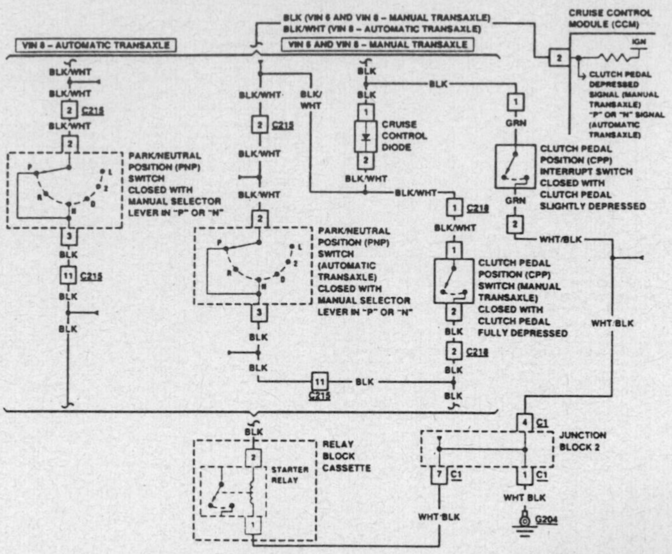
BLK (VIN 6 AND VIN 8 – MANUAL TRANSAXLE)
BLK/WHT (VIN 8 – AUTOMATIC TRANSAXLE)
CRUISE CONTROL MODULE (CCM)
VIN 8 – AUTOMATIC TRANSAXLE
VIN 6 AND VIN 8 – MANUAL TRANSAXLE
IGN
CLUTCH PEDAL DEPRESSED SIGNAL (MANUAL TRANSAXLE) "P" OR "N" SIGNAL (AUTOMATIC TRANSAXLE)
BLK/WHT
C215
PARK/NEUTRAL POSITION (PNP) SWITCH CLOSED WITH MANUAL SELECTOR LEVER IN "P" OR "N"
CRUISE CONTROL DIODE
GRN
CLUTCH PEDAL POSITION (CPP) INTERRUPT SWITCH CLOSED WITH CLUTCH PEDAL SLIGHTLY DEPRESSED
C218
PARK/NEUTRAL POSITION (PNP) SWITCH (AUTOMATIC TRANSAXLE) CLOSED WITH MANUAL SELECTOR LEVER IN "P" OR "N"
WHT/BLK
CLUTCH PEDAL POSITION (CPP) SWITCH (MANUAL TRANSAXLE) CLOSED WITH CLUTCH PEDAL FULLY DEPRESSED
BLK
RELAY BLOCK CASSETTE
STARTER RELAY
JUNCTION BLOCK 2
G204

GC1109300243010X

Fig. 24 Code 9B-4A: –CRUISE– Indicator Does Not Light During CANCEL Switch Test (Part 1 of 2). 1993–94

IMPORTANT: BE SURE THAT CCM OBD SYSTEM CHECK HAS BEEN PERFORMED BEFORE CONTINUING DIAGNOSIS.

FROM CCM OBD SYSTEM CHECK.

- BACKPROBE CCM CONNECTOR WITH A DIGITAL MULTIMETER FROM CAVITY "2" TO GROUND.
- MEASURE VOLTAGE.

LESS THAN 10.0 VOLTS

MORE THAN 10.0 VOLTS

REFER TO AND PROCEED WITH CHART 9B-4B.

VIN 6 AND VIN 8–MANUAL TRANSAXLE

- DISCONNECT PNP SWITCH CONNECTOR (AUTOMATIC TRANSAXLE).
- DISCONNECT CPP SWITCH CONNECTOR (MANUAL TRANSAXLE).
- BACKPROBE CCM CONNECTOR WITH A DIGITAL MULTIMETER FROM CAVITY "2" TO GROUND.
- MEASURE VOLTAGE.

VIN 8–AUTOMATIC TRANSAXLE

- CHECK FOR A SHORT TO GROUND IN BLK/WHT WIRE BETWEEN CCM, PNP SWITCH AND IGNITION SWITCH. IF OK, REPLACE PNP SWITCH.

LESS THAN 10.0 VOLTS

- LEAVE DIGITAL MULTIMETER CONNECTED.
- REMOVE CRUISE CONTROL DIODE.
- MEASURE VOLTAGE.

MORE THAN 10.0 VOLTS

REPLACE PNP SWITCH (AUTOMATIC TRANSAXLE). REPLACE CPP SWITCH (MANUAL TRANSAXLE).

LESS THAN 10.0 VOLTS

MANUAL TRANSAXLE

- CHECK FOR A SHORT TO GROUND IN BLK WIRE BETWEEN CCM, CRUISE CONTROL DIODE AND CCP INTERRUPT SWITCH. IF OK, REPLACE CPP INTERRUPT SWITCH.

AUTOMATIC TRANSAXLE

REPAIR SHORT TO GROUND IN BLK WIRE BETWEEN CCM, CRUISE CONTROL DIODE AND CPP INTERRUPT SWITCH CONNECTOR.

MORE THAN 10.0 VOLTS

MANUAL TRANSAXLE

- CHECK FOR A SHORT TO GROUND IN BLK/WHT WIRE BETWEEN CRUISE CONTROL DIODE, CPP SWITCH AND C215. IF OK, REPLACE CRUISE CONTROL DIODE.

AUTOMATIC TRANSAXLE

- CHECK FOR A SHORT TO GROUND IN BLK/WHT WIRE BETWEEN CRUISE CONTROL DIODE, PNP SWITCH AND C218. IF OK, REPLACE CRUISE CONTROL DIODE.

GC1109300243020X

Fig. 24 Code 9B-4A: –CRUISE– Indicator Does Not Light During CANCEL Switch Test (Part 2 of 2). 1993–94

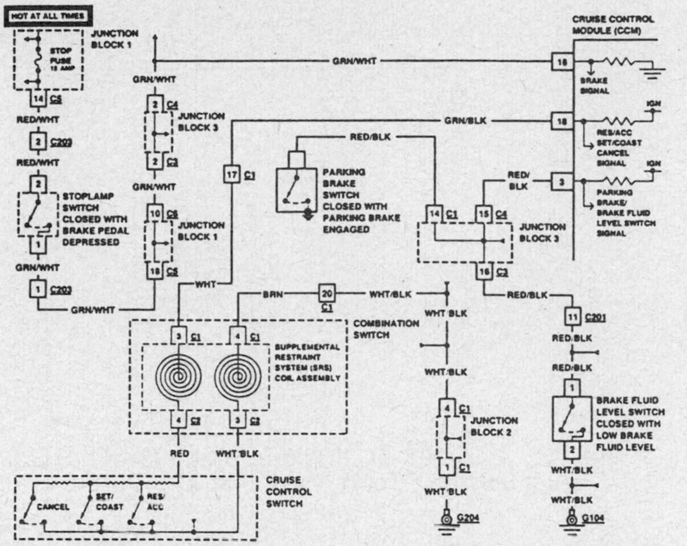
HOT AT ALL TIMES
JUNCTION BLOCK 1
STOP FUSE 15 AMP
CRUISE CONTROL MODULE (CCM)
GRN/WHT
BRAKE SIGNAL
RED/WHT
JUNCTION BLOCK 3
GRN/BLK
RES/ACC SET/COAST CANCEL SIGNAL
RED/BLK
PARKING BRAKE SWITCH CLOSED WITH PARKING BRAKE ENGAGED
STOPLAMP SWITCH CLOSED WITH BRAKE PEDAL DEPRESSED
PARKING BRAKE/ BRAKE FLUID LEVEL SWITCH SIGNAL
JUNCTION BLOCK 1
WHT
BRN
WHT/BLK
COMBINATION SWITCH
SUPPLEMENTAL RESTRAINT SYSTEM (SRS) COIL ASSEMBLY
RED/BLK
JUNCTION BLOCK 2
BRAKE FLUID LEVEL SWITCH CLOSED WITH LOW BRAKE FLUID LEVEL
RED
CRUISE CONTROL SWITCH
CANCEL
SET/ COAST
RES/ ACC
G204
G104
GC1109300244010X

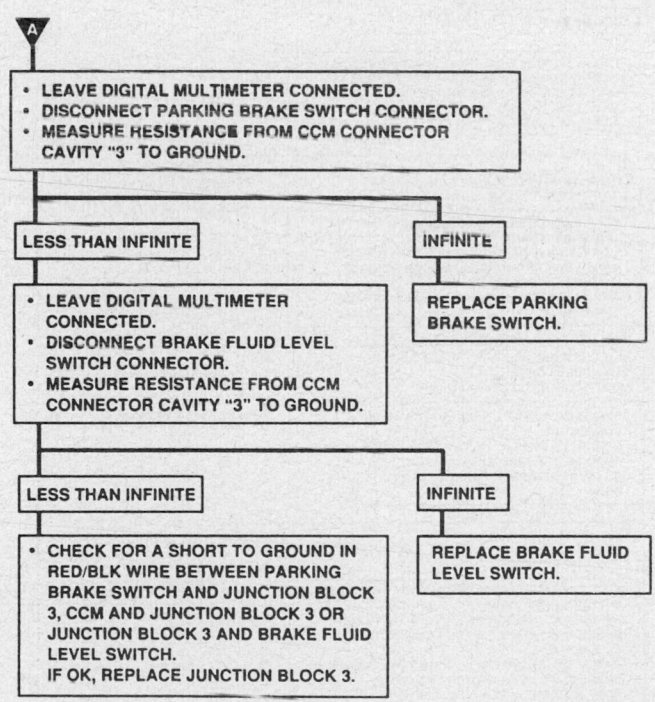

Fig. 25 Code 9B-4B: –CRUISE– Indicator Does Not Light During CANCEL Switch Test (Part 1 of 3). 1993–94

IMPORTANT: BE SURE THAT CCM OBD SYSTEM CHECK AND CHART 9B-4A HAVE BEEN PERFORMED BEFORE CONTINUING DIAGNOSIS.

FROM CHART 9B-4A.

- PLACE TRANSAXLE IN PARK.
- TURN IGNITION SWITCH TO "LOCK."
- DISCONNECT CCM CONNECTOR.
- CONNECT A DIGITAL MULTIMETER FROM CCM CONNECTOR CAVITY "16" TO GROUND.
- TURN IGNITION SWITCH TO "ON."
- MEASURE VOLTAGE.

LESS THAN 1.0 VOLT

- CONNECT A DIGITAL MULTIMETER FROM CCM CONNECTOR CAVITY "3" TO GROUND.
- MEASURE RESISTANCE.

LESS THAN INFINITE → A

INFINITE

- CONNECT A DIGITAL MULTIMETER FROM CCM CONNECTOR CAVITY "18" TO GROUND.
- MEASURE RESISTANCE.

LESS THAN INFINITE

REPLACE CRUISE CONTROL SWITCH.

INFINITE

PROBLEM IS NOT IN CANCEL SWITCH CIRCUITRY.

MORE THAN 1.0 VOLT

Check stoplamp circuit

GC1109300244020X

Fig. 25 Code 9B-4B: –CRUISE– Indicator Does Not Light During CANCEL Switch Test (Part 2 of 3). 1993–94

A

- LEAVE DIGITAL MULTIMETER CONNECTED.
- DISCONNECT PARKING BRAKE SWITCH CONNECTOR.
- MEASURE RESISTANCE FROM CCM CONNECTOR CAVITY "3" TO GROUND.

LESS THAN INFINITE

- LEAVE DIGITAL MULTIMETER CONNECTED.
- DISCONNECT BRAKE FLUID LEVEL SWITCH CONNECTOR.
- MEASURE RESISTANCE FROM CCM CONNECTOR CAVITY "3" TO GROUND.

LESS THAN INFINITE

- CHECK FOR A SHORT TO GROUND IN RED/BLK WIRE BETWEEN PARKING BRAKE SWITCH AND JUNCTION BLOCK 3, CCM AND JUNCTION BLOCK 3 OR JUNCTION BLOCK 3 AND BRAKE FLUID LEVEL SWITCH.
  IF OK, REPLACE JUNCTION BLOCK 3.

INFINITE

REPLACE BRAKE FLUID LEVEL SWITCH.

INFINITE

REPLACE PARKING BRAKE SWITCH.

GC1109300244030X

Fig. 25 Code 9B-4B: –CRUISE– Indicator Does Not Light During CANCEL Switch Test (Part 3 of 3). 1993–94

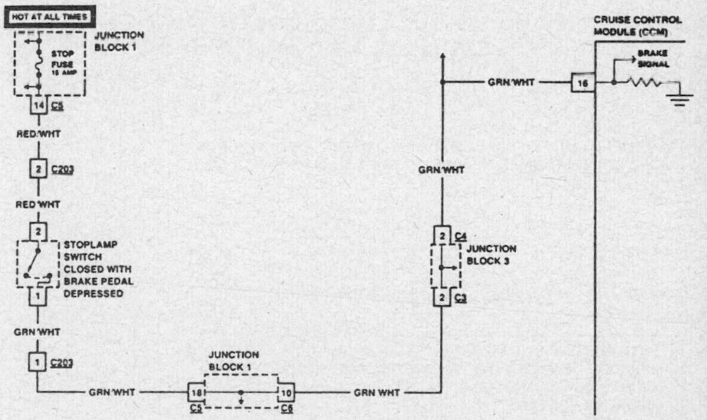
HOT AT ALL TIMES
JUNCTION BLOCK 1
STOP FUSE 15 AMP
CRUISE CONTROL MODULE (CCM)
BRAKE SIGNAL
GRN/WHT
RED/WHT
STOPLAMP SWITCH CLOSED WITH BRAKE PEDAL DEPRESSED
JUNCTION BLOCK 3
JUNCTION BLOCK 1
GC1109300245010X

Fig. 26 Code 9B-5A: Stoplamp Switch Circuit (Part 1 of 2). 1993–94

IMPORTANT: BE SURE THAT CCM OBD SYSTEM CHECK HAS BEEN PERFORMED BEFORE CONTINUING DIAGNOSIS.

FROM CCM OBD SYSTEM CHECK.

DO THE STOPLAMPS WORK PROPERLY?

YES

- TURN IGNITION SWITCH TO "ON."
- BACKPROBE CCM CONNECTOR WITH A DIGITAL MULTIMETER FROM CAVITY "16" TO GROUND.
- MEASURE VOLTAGE WHILE DEPRESSING BRAKE PEDAL.

LESS THAN 10.0 VOLTS

- BACKPROBE JUNCTION BLOCK 1 CONNECTOR C6 WITH A DIGITAL MULTIMETER FROM CAVITY "10" TO GROUND.
- MEASURE VOLTAGE WHILE DEPRESSING BRAKE PEDAL.

MORE THAN 10.0 VOLTS

- CHECK FOR AN OPEN IN GRN/WHT WIRE BETWEEN JUNCTION BLOCK 1 AND JUNCTION BLOCK 3 OR JUNCTION BLOCK 3 AND CCM. IF OK, REPLACE JUNCTION BLOCK 3.

LESS THAN 10.0 VOLTS

REPLACE JUNCTION BLOCK 1.

MORE THAN 10.0 VOLTS

REPLACE CCM.

NO

Check stoplamp circuit

GC1109300245020X

Fig. 26 Code 9B-5A: Stoplamp Switch Circuit (Part 2 of 2). 1993–94

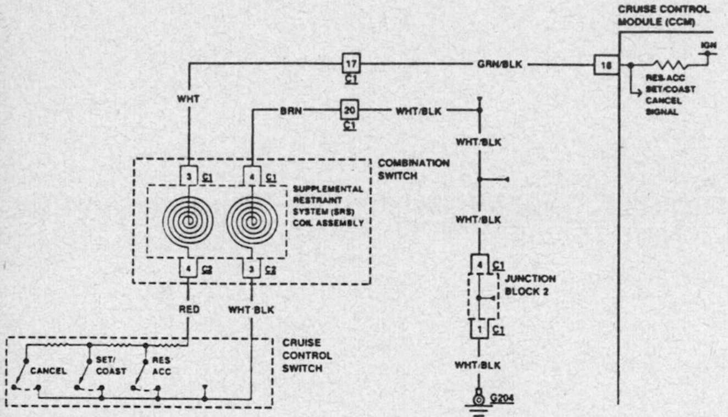
CRUISE CONTROL MODULE (CCM)
IGN
GRN/BLK
17
C1
18
RES-ACC SET/COAST CANCEL SIGNAL
WHT
BRN
20
C1
WHT/BLK
WHT/BLK
COMBINATION SWITCH
3 C1
4 C1
SUPPLEMENTAL RESTRAINT SYSTEM (SRS) COIL ASSEMBLY
4 C2
3 C2
WHT/BLK
4 C1
JUNCTION BLOCK 2
1 C1
RED
WHT/BLK
CRUISE CONTROL SWITCH
CANCEL
SET/ COAST
RES ACC
WHT/BLK
G204

GC1109300246010X

Fig. 27 Code 9B-5B: Cruise Control CANCEL Switch Circuit (Part 1 of 2). 1993–94

IMPORTANT: BE SURE THAT CCM OBD SYSTEM CHECK HAS BEEN PERFORMED BEFORE CONTINUING DIAGNOSIS.

FROM CCM OBD SYSTEM CHECK.

- WITH IGNITION SWITCH IN "ON," BACKPROBE CCM CONNECTOR WITH A DIGITAL MULTIMETER FROM CAVITY "18" TO GROUND.
- MEASURE VOLTAGE.

MORE THAN 10.0 VOLTS

REPLACE CRUISE CONTROL SWITCH.

LESS THAN 10.0 VOLTS

REPLACE CCM.

GC1109300246020X

Fig. 27 Code 9B-5B: Cruise Control CANCEL Switch Circuit (Part 2 of 2). 1993–94

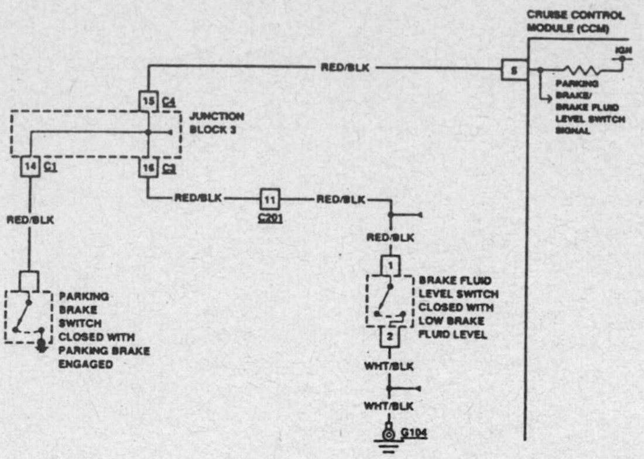
CRUISE CONTROL MODULE (CCM)
IGN
RED/BLK
5
PARKING BRAKE/ BRAKE FLUID LEVEL SWITCH SIGNAL
15 C4
JUNCTION BLOCK 3
14 C1
16 C3
RED/BLK
11
C201
RED/BLK
RED/BLK
RED/BLK
1
PARKING BRAKE SWITCH CLOSED WITH PARKING BRAKE ENGAGED
BRAKE FLUID LEVEL SWITCH CLOSED WITH LOW BRAKE FLUID LEVEL
2
WHT/BLK
WHT/BLK
G104

GC1109300247010X

Fig. 28 Code 9B-5C: Parking Brake/Brake Fluid Level Switch Circuit (Part 1 of 2). 1993–94

IMPORTANT: BE SURE THAT THE CCM OBD SYSTEM CHECK HAS BEEN PERFORMED BEFORE CONTINUING DIAGNOSIS.

FROM CCM OBD SYSTEM CHECK.

- REMOVE GAUGE FUSE FROM JUNCTION BLOCK 1.
- WITH IGNITION SWITCH IN "ON" BACKPROBE CCM CONNECTOR WITH A DIGITAL MULTIMETER FROM CAVITY "5" TO GROUND.
- MEASURE VOLTAGE.

MORE THAN 10.0 VOLTS

- TURN IGNITION SWITCH TO "LOCK."
- DISCONNECT PARKING BRAKE SWITCH CONNECTOR.
- CONNECT A DIGITAL MULTIMETER FROM PARKING BRAKE SWITCH TERMINAL (SWITCH SIDE) TO GROUND.
- MEASURE RESISTANCE WITH PARKING BRAKE ENGAGED.

LESS THAN 1.0 OHM

- DISCONNECT BRAKE FLUID LEVEL SWITCH CONNECTOR.
- CONNECT A DIGITAL MULTIMETER ACROSS BRAKE FLUID SWITCH TERMINALS (SWITCH SIDE).
- MEASURE RESISTANCE WHILE HOLDING FLOAT DOWN.

LESS THAN 1.0 OHM

- CHECK FOR AN OPEN IN RED BLK WIRE BETWEEN CCM AND JUNCTION BLOCK 3, PARKING BRAKE SWITCH AND JUNCTION BLOCK 3 OR BETWEEN BRAKE FLUID LEVEL SWITCH AND JUNCTION BLOCK 3.
- CHECK FOR AN OPEN IN WHT/BLK WIRE BETWEEN BRAKE FLUID LEVEL SWITCH AND G104. IF OK, REPLACE JUNCTION BLOCK 3.

MORE THAN 1.0 OHM

REPLACE BRAKE FLUID LEVEL SWITCH.

MORE THAN 1.0 OHM

REPLACE PARKING BRAKE SWITCH.

LESS THAN 10.0 VOLTS

REPLACE CCM.

GC1109300247020X

Fig. 28 Code 9B-5C: Parking Brake/Brake Fluid Level Switch Circuit (Part 2 of 2). 1993–94

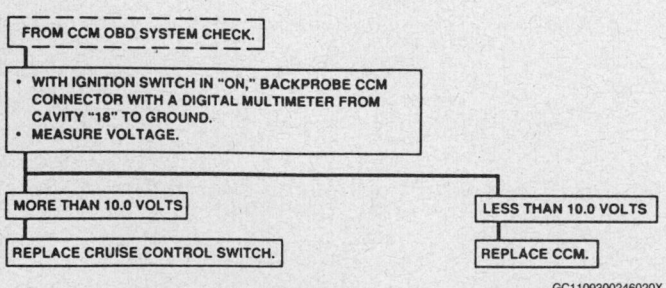

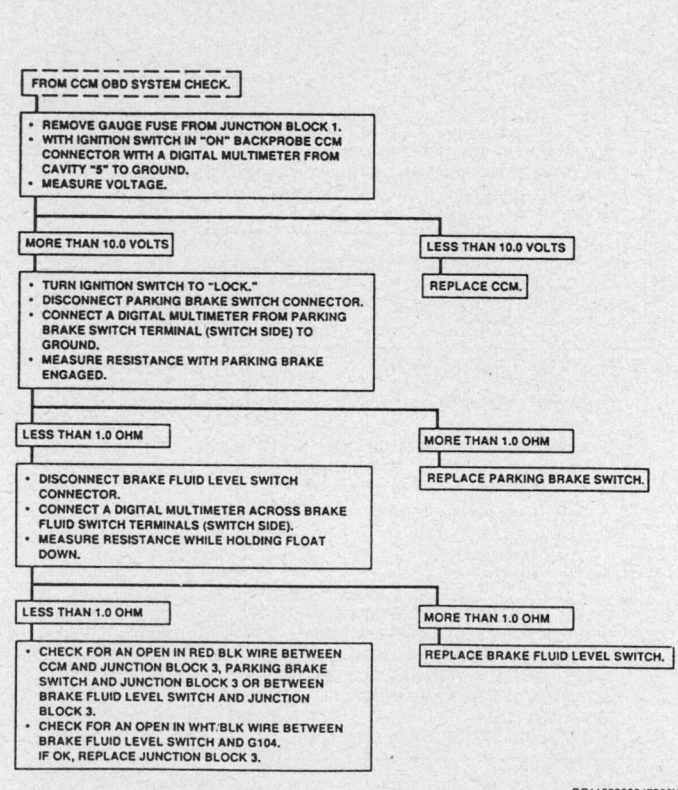

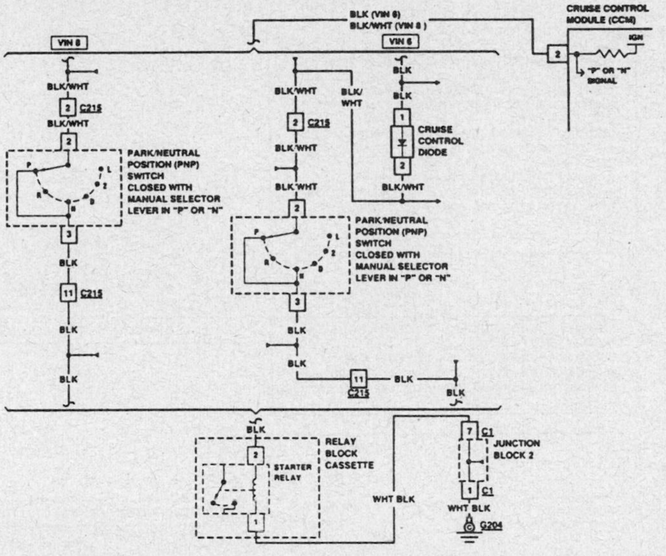
CRUISE CONTROL MODULE (CCM)
BLK (VIN 6)
BLK/WHT (VIN 8)
VIN 8
VIN 6
"P" OR "N" SIGNAL
PARK/NEUTRAL POSITION (PNP) SWITCH CLOSED WITH MANUAL SELECTOR LEVER IN "P" OR "N"
CRUISE CONTROL DIODE
RELAY BLOCK CASSETTE
STARTER RELAY
JUNCTION BLOCK 2
G204
GC1109300248010X

Fig. 29 Code 9B-5D: PNP Switch Circuit (Part 1 of 2). 1993–94 Models w/Auto Trans

IMPORTANT: BE SURE THAT CCM OBD SYSTEM CHECK HAS BEEN PERFORMED BEFORE CONTINUING DIAGNOSIS.

FROM CCM OBD SYSTEM CHECK.

DOES STARTER MOTOR FUNCTION NORMALLY WITH PARK/NEUTRAL POSITION (PNP) SWITCH IN "P" AND "N"?

- **NO**
  - Check starter circuit
- **YES**
  - DISCONNECT ECM CONNECTOR C3 (VIN 6) OR PCM CONNECTOR C1 (VIN 8).
  - TURN IGNITION SWITCH TO "ON."
  - BACKPROBE CCM CONNECTOR WITH A DIGITAL MULTIMETER FROM CAVITY "2" TO GROUND.
  - MOVE MANUAL SELECTOR LEVER TO ANY POSITION EXCEPT "P" OR "N".
  - MEASURE VOLTAGE.
    - **LESS THAN 10.0 VOLTS**
      - REPLACE CCM.
    - **MORE THAN 10.0 VOLTS**
      - **VIN 8**
        - REPAIR OPEN IN BLK/WHT WIRE BETWEEN CCM AND PNP SWITCH.
      - **VIN 6**
        - BACKPROBE CRUISE CONTROL DIODE WITH A DIGITAL MULTIMETER FROM CAVITY "1" TO GROUND.
        - MEASURE VOLTAGE.
          - **MORE THAN 10.0 VOLTS**
            - CHECK FOR AN OPEN IN BLK/WHT WIRE BETWEEN CRUISE CONTROL DIODE AND PNP SWITCH. IF OK, REPLACE CRUISE CONTROL DIODE.
          - **LESS THAN 10.0 VOLTS**
            - REPAIR OPEN IN BLK WIRE BETWEEN CRUISE CONTROL DIODE AND CCM.

GC1109300240020X

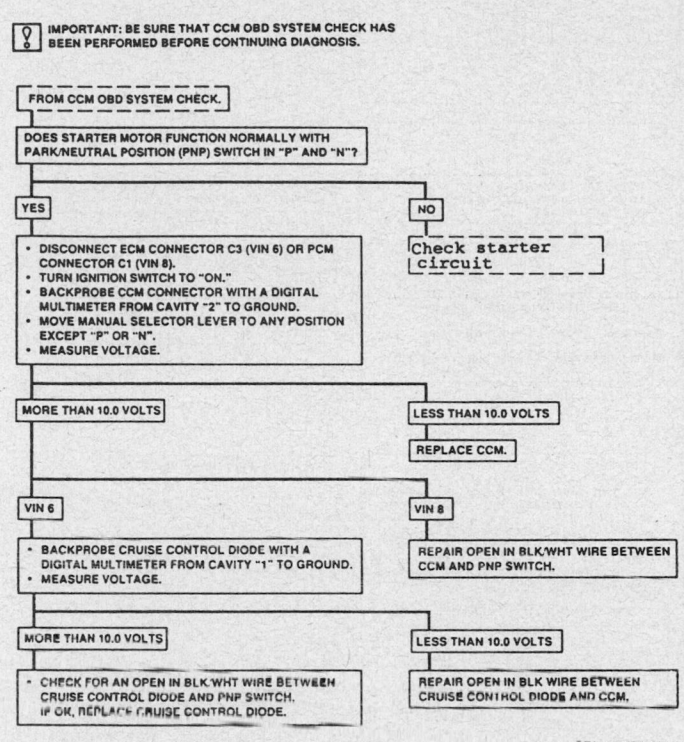

Fig. 29 Code 9B-5D: PNP Switch Circuit (Part 2 of 2). 1993–94 Models w/Auto Trans

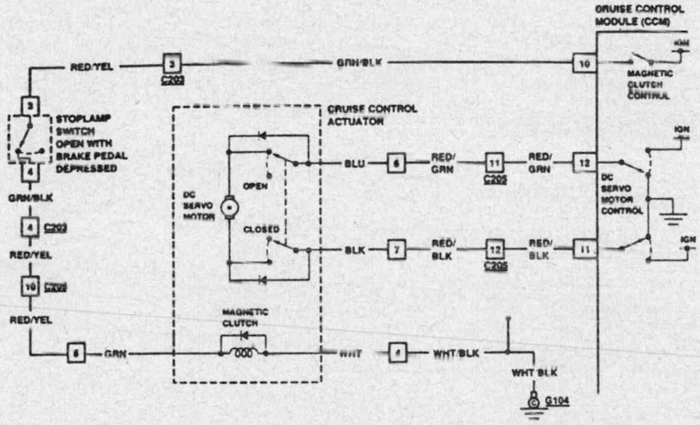
CRUISE CONTROL MODULE (CCM)
RED/YEL
GRN/BLK
STOPLAMP SWITCH OPEN WITH BRAKE PEDAL DEPRESSED
CRUISE CONTROL ACTUATOR
DC SERVO MOTOR
OPEN
CLOSED
MAGNETIC CLUTCH
MAGNETIC CLUTCH CONTROL
DC SERVO MOTOR CONTROL
BLU
BLK
RED/GRN
RED/BLK
WHT/BLK
G104
GC1109300250010X

Fig. 30 Code 9B-5E: PNP Switch Circuit (Part 1 of 2). 1993–94 Models w/Man Trans

IMPORTANT: BE SURE THAT CCM OBD SYSTEM CHECK HAS BEEN PERFORMED BEFORE CONTINUING DIAGNOSIS.

FROM CCM OBD SYSTEM CHECK.

- TURN IGNITION SWITCH TO "LOCK."
- DISCONNECT CCM CONNECTOR.
- CONNECT A DIGITAL MULTIMETER FROM CCM CONNECTOR CAVITY "2" TO GROUND.
- MEASURE RESISTANCE WITH CLUTCH PEDAL DEPRESSED SLIGHTLY (DO NOT DEPRESS FULLY).
  - **LESS THAN 1.0 OHM**
    - REPLACE CCM.
  - **MORE THAN 1.0 OHM**
    - BACKPROBE CPP INTERRUPT SWITCH CONNECTOR WITH A DIGITAL MULTIMETER FROM CAVITY "2" TO GROUND.
    - MEASURE RESISTANCE.
      - **MORE THAN 1.0 OHM**
        - CHECK FOR AN OPEN IN WHT/BLK WIRE BETWEEN CPP INTERRUPT SWITCH AND JUNCTION BLOCK 2. IF OK, REPLACE JUNCTION BLOCK 2.
      - **LESS THAN 1.0 OHM**
        - CHECK FOR AN OPEN IN BLK WIRE BETWEEN CCM AND CPP INTERRUPT SWITCH AND CONDITION OF CRUISE CONTROL DIODE. IF OK, REPLACE CPP INTERRUPT SWITCH.

GC1109300249020X

Fig. 30 Code 9B-5E: PNP Switch Circuit (Part 2 of 2). 1993–94 Models w/Man Trans

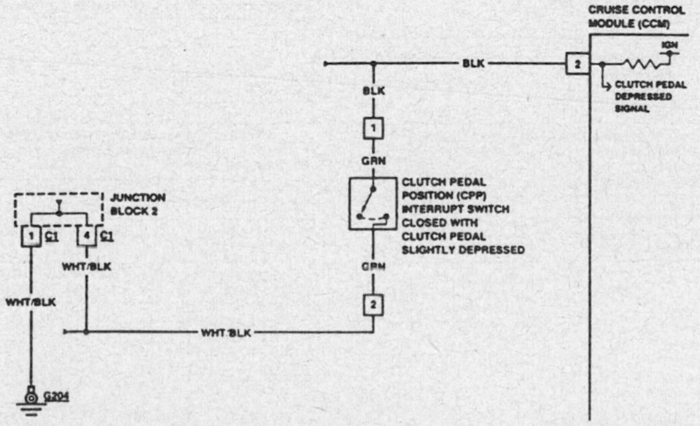
CRUISE CONTROL MODULE (CCM)
CLUTCH PEDAL DEPRESSED SIGNAL
JUNCTION BLOCK 2
CLUTCH PEDAL POSITION (CPP) INTERRUPT SWITCH CLOSED WITH CLUTCH PEDAL SLIGHTLY DEPRESSED
WHT/BLK
G204
GC1109300249010X

Fig. 31 Code 11: Overvoltage On Motor Open Circuit (Part 1 of 3). 1993–94

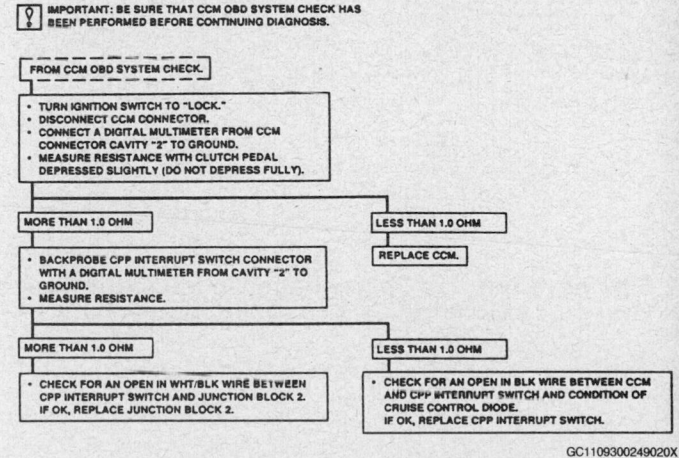

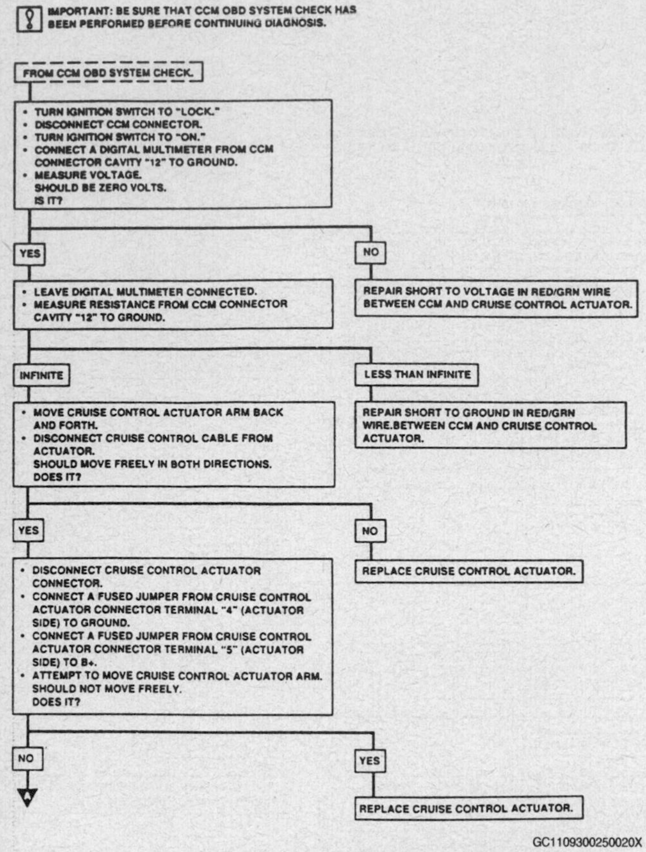
IMPORTANT: BE SURE THAT CCM OBD SYSTEM CHECK HAS BEEN PERFORMED BEFORE CONTINUING DIAGNOSIS.
FROM CCM OBD SYSTEM CHECK.
• TURN IGNITION SWITCH TO "LOCK." • DISCONNECT CCM CONNECTOR. • TURN IGNITION SWITCH TO "ON." • CONNECT A DIGITAL MULTIMETER FROM CCM CONNECTOR CAVITY "12" TO GROUND. • MEASURE VOLTAGE. SHOULD BE ZERO VOLTS. IS IT?
YES
NO
• LEAVE DIGITAL MULTIMETER CONNECTED. • MEASURE RESISTANCE FROM CCM CONNECTOR CAVITY "12" TO GROUND.
REPAIR SHORT TO VOLTAGE IN RED/GRN WIRE BETWEEN CCM AND CRUISE CONTROL ACTUATOR.
INFINITE
LESS THAN INFINITE
• MOVE CRUISE CONTROL ACTUATOR ARM BACK AND FORTH. • DISCONNECT CRUISE CONTROL CABLE FROM ACTUATOR. SHOULD MOVE FREELY IN BOTH DIRECTIONS. DOES IT?
REPAIR SHORT TO GROUND IN RED/GRN WIRE.BETWEEN CCM AND CRUISE CONTROL ACTUATOR.
YES
NO
• DISCONNECT CRUISE CONTROL ACTUATOR CONNECTOR. • CONNECT A FUSED JUMPER FROM CRUISE CONTROL ACTUATOR CONNECTOR TERMINAL "4" (ACTUATOR SIDE) TO GROUND. • CONNECT A FUSED JUMPER FROM CRUISE CONTROL ACTUATOR CONNECTOR TERMINAL "5" (ACTUATOR SIDE) TO B+. • ATTEMPT TO MOVE CRUISE CONTROL ACTUATOR ARM. SHOULD NOT MOVE FREELY. DOES IT?
REPLACE CRUISE CONTROL ACTUATOR.
NO
YES
A
REPLACE CRUISE CONTROL ACTUATOR.
GC1109300250020X

Fig. 31 Code 11: Overvoltage On Motor Open Circuit (Part 2 of 3). 1993–94

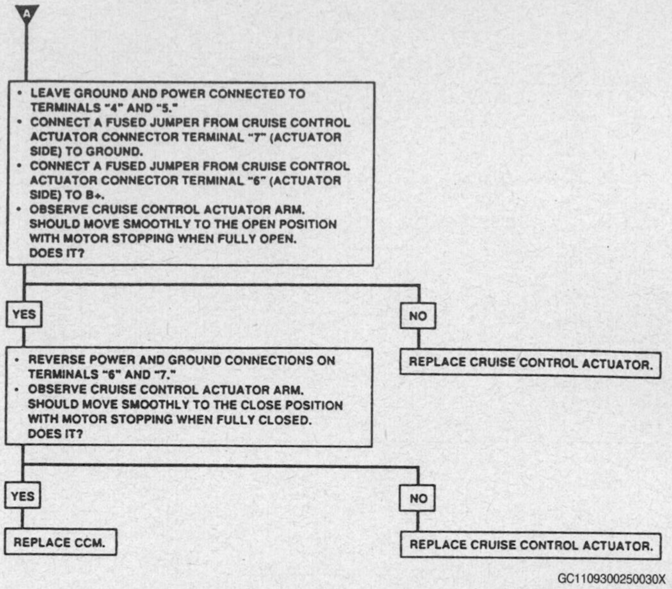
A
• LEAVE GROUND AND POWER CONNECTED TO TERMINALS "4" AND "5." • CONNECT A FUSED JUMPER FROM CRUISE CONTROL ACTUATOR CONNECTOR TERMINAL "7" (ACTUATOR SIDE) TO GROUND. • CONNECT A FUSED JUMPER FROM CRUISE CONTROL ACTUATOR CONNECTOR TERMINAL "6" (ACTUATOR SIDE) TO B+. • OBSERVE CRUISE CONTROL ACTUATOR ARM. SHOULD MOVE SMOOTHLY TO THE OPEN POSITION WITH MOTOR STOPPING WHEN FULLY OPEN. DOES IT?
YES
NO
• REVERSE POWER AND GROUND CONNECTIONS ON TERMINALS "6" AND "7." • OBSERVE CRUISE CONTROL ACTUATOR ARM. SHOULD MOVE SMOOTHLY TO THE CLOSE POSITION WITH MOTOR STOPPING WHEN FULLY CLOSED. DOES IT?
REPLACE CRUISE CONTROL ACTUATOR.
YES
NO
REPLACE CCM.
REPLACE CRUISE CONTROL ACTUATOR.
GC1109300250030X

Fig. 31 Code 11: Overvoltage On Motor Open Circuit (Part 3 of 3). 1993–94

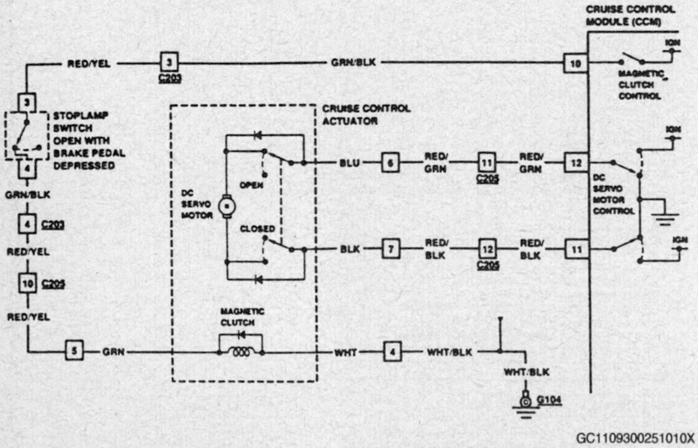
CRUISE CONTROL MODULE (CCM)
RED/YEL
3
C203
GRN/BLK
10
IGN
MAGNETIC CLUTCH CONTROL
3
STOPLAMP SWITCH OPEN WITH BRAKE PEDAL DEPRESSED
4
GRN/BLK
4 C203
RED/YEL
10 C205
RED/YEL
CRUISE CONTROL ACTUATOR
OPEN
DC SERVO MOTOR
CLOSED
BLU
6
RED/ GRN
11
C205
RED/ GRN
12
IGN
DC SERVO MOTOR CONTROL
BLK
7
RED/ BLK
12
C205
RED/ BLK
11
IGN
MAGNETIC CLUTCH
5
GRN
WHT
4
WHT/BLK
WHT/BLK
G104
GC1109300251010X

Fig. 32 Code 12: Overvoltage On Magnetic Clutch Circuit (Part 1 of 3). 1993–94

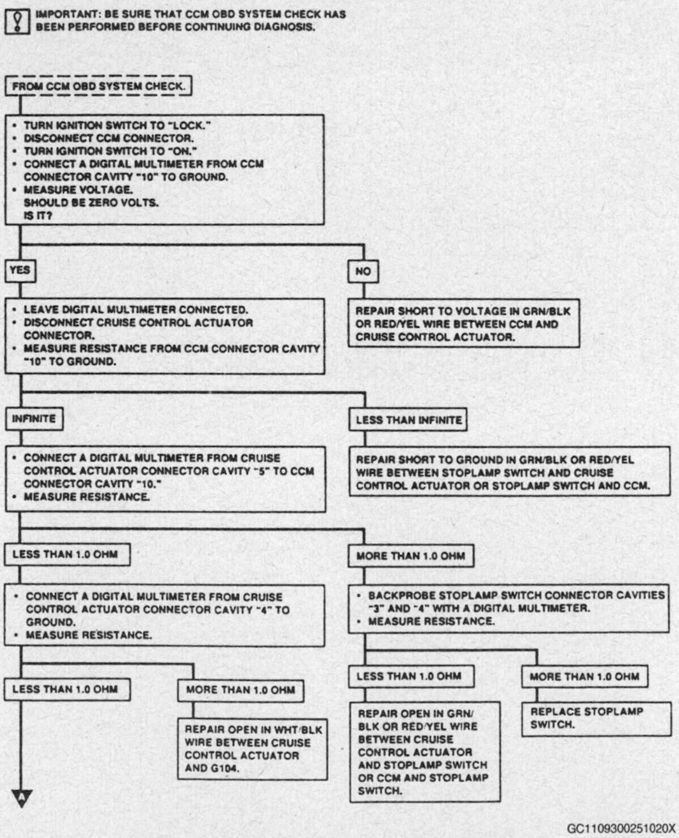
IMPORTANT: BE SURE THAT CCM OBD SYSTEM CHECK HAS BEEN PERFORMED BEFORE CONTINUING DIAGNOSIS.
FROM CCM OBD SYSTEM CHECK.
• TURN IGNITION SWITCH TO "LOCK." • DISCONNECT CCM CONNECTOR. • TURN IGNITION SWITCH TO "ON." • CONNECT A DIGITAL MULTIMETER FROM CCM CONNECTOR CAVITY "10" TO GROUND. • MEASURE VOLTAGE. SHOULD BE ZERO VOLTS. IS IT?
YES
NO
• LEAVE DIGITAL MULTIMETER CONNECTED. • DISCONNECT CRUISE CONTROL ACTUATOR CONNECTOR. • MEASURE RESISTANCE FROM CCM CONNECTOR CAVITY "10" TO GROUND.
REPAIR SHORT TO VOLTAGE IN GRN/BLK OR RED/YEL WIRE BETWEEN CCM AND CRUISE CONTROL ACTUATOR.
INFINITE
LESS THAN INFINITE
• CONNECT A DIGITAL MULTIMETER FROM CRUISE CONTROL ACTUATOR CONNECTOR CAVITY "5" TO CCM CONNECTOR CAVITY "10." • MEASURE RESISTANCE.
REPAIR SHORT TO GROUND IN GRN/BLK OR RED/YEL WIRE BETWEEN STOPLAMP SWITCH AND CRUISE CONTROL ACTUATOR OR STOPLAMP SWITCH AND CCM.
LESS THAN 1.0 OHM
MORE THAN 1.0 OHM
• CONNECT A DIGITAL MULTIMETER FROM CRUISE CONTROL ACTUATOR CONNECTOR CAVITY "4" TO GROUND. • MEASURE RESISTANCE.
• BACKPROBE STOPLAMP SWITCH CONNECTOR CAVITIES "3" AND "4" WITH A DIGITAL MULTIMETER. • MEASURE RESISTANCE.
LESS THAN 1.0 OHM
MORE THAN 1.0 OHM
LESS THAN 1.0 OHM
MORE THAN 1.0 OHM
REPAIR OPEN IN WHT/BLK WIRE BETWEEN CRUISE CONTROL ACTUATOR AND G104.
REPAIR OPEN IN GRN/ BLK OR RED/YEL WIRE BETWEEN CRUISE CONTROL ACTUATOR AND STOPLAMP SWITCH OR CCM AND STOPLAMP SWITCH.
REPLACE STOPLAMP SWITCH.
A
GC1109300251020X

Fig. 32 Code 12: Overvoltage On Magnetic Clutch Circuit (Part 2 of 3). 1993–94

A

- MOVE CRUISE CONTROL ACTUATOR ARM BACK AND FORTH. SHOULD MOVE FREELY. DOES IT?

YES

- CONNECT A FUSED JUMPER FROM CRUISE CONTROL ACTUATOR CONNECTOR TERMINAL "4" (ACTUATOR SIDE) TO GROUND.
- CONNECT A FUSED JUMPER FROM CRUISE CONTROL ACTUATOR CONNECTOR TERMINAL "5" (ACTUATOR SIDE) TO B+.
- ATTEMPT TO MOVE CRUISE CONTROL ACTUATOR ARM. SHOULD NOT MOVE FREELY. DOES IT?

YES

REPLACE CRUISE CONTROL ACTUATOR.

NO

REPLACE CCM.

NO

REPLACE CRUISE CONTROL ACTUATOR.

GC1109300251030X

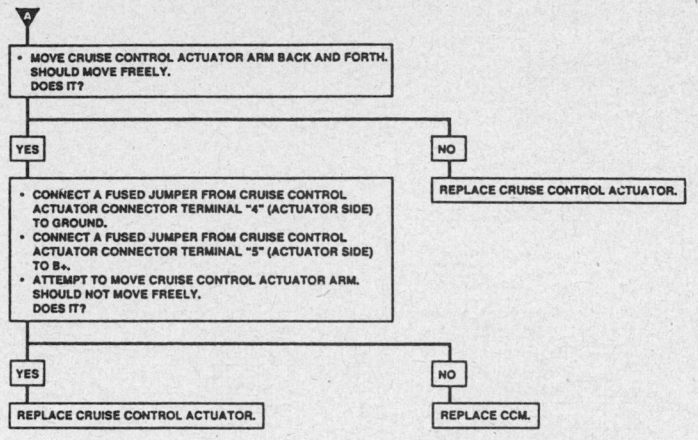

Fig. 32 Code 12: Overvoltage On Magnetic Clutch Circuit (Part 3 of 3). 1993–94

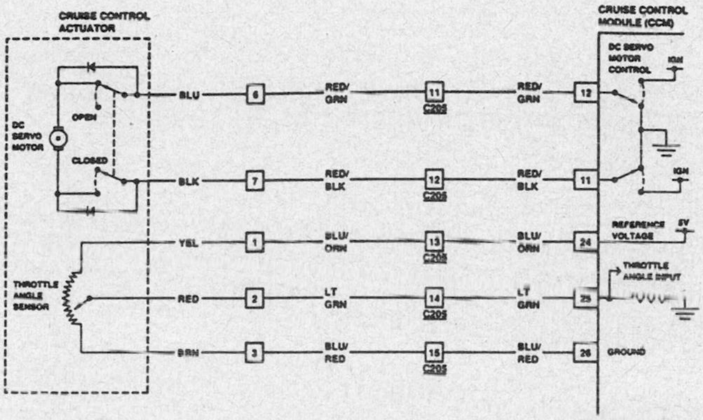

CRUISE CONTROL ACTUATOR
CRUISE CONTROL MODULE (CCM)
DC SERVO MOTOR CONTROL
IGN
OPEN
DC SERVO MOTOR
CLOSED
BLU
6
RED/ GRN
11
C205
RED/ GRN
12
BLK
7
RED/ BLK
12
C205
RED/ BLK
11
IGN
REFERENCE VOLTAGE
5V
YEL
1
BLU/ ORN
13
C205
BLU/ ORN
24
THROTTLE ANGLE INPUT
THROTTLE ANGLE SENSOR
RED
2
LT GRN
14
C205
LT GRN
25
BRN
3
BLU/ RED
15
C205
BLU/ RED
26
GROUND

GC1109300252010X

Fig. 33 Code 13: Open Motor Circuit Or Abnormal Throttle Angle Sensor Signal (Part 1 of 5). 1993–94

IMPORTANT, BE SURE THAT CCM OBD SYSTEM CHECK HAS BEEN PERFORMED BEFORE CONTINUING DIAGNOSIS.

FROM CCM OBD SYSTEM CHECK.

- TURN IGNITION SWITCH TO "LOCK."
- DISCONNECT CCM CONNECTOR.
- DISCONNECT CRUISE CONTROL ACTUATOR CONNECTOR.
- CONNECT A DIGITAL MULTIMETER FROM CCM CONNECTOR CAVITY "12" TO GROUND.
- MEASURE RESISTANCE.

INFINITE

- CONNECT A DIGITAL MULTIMETER FROM CCM CONNECTOR CAVITY "11" TO GROUND.
- MEASURE RESISTANCE.

INFINITE

- CONNECT A DIGITAL MULTIMETER FROM CCM CONNECTOR CAVITY "24" TO GROUND.
- MEASURE RESISTANCE.

INFINITE

- CONNECT A DIGITAL MULTIMETER FROM CCM CONNECTOR CAVITY "25" TO GROUND.
- MEASURE RESISTANCE.

INFINITE

A

LESS THAN INFINITE

REPAIR SHORT TO GROUND IN RED/GRN WIRE BETWEEN CCM AND CRUISE CONTROL ACTUATOR.

LESS THAN INFINITE

REPAIR SHORT TO GROUND IN RED/BLK WIRE BETWEEN CCM AND CRUISE CONTROL ACTUATOR.

LESS THAN INFINITE

REPAIR SHORT TO GROUND IN BLU/ORN WIRE BETWEEN CCM AND CRUISE CONTROL ACTUATOR.

LESS THAN INFINITE

REPAIR SHORT TO GROUND IN LT GRN WIRE BETWEEN CCM AND CRUISE CONTROL ACTUATOR.

GC1109300252020X

Fig. 33 Code 13: Open Motor Circuit Or Abnormal Throttle Angle Sensor Signal (Part 2 of 5). 1993–94

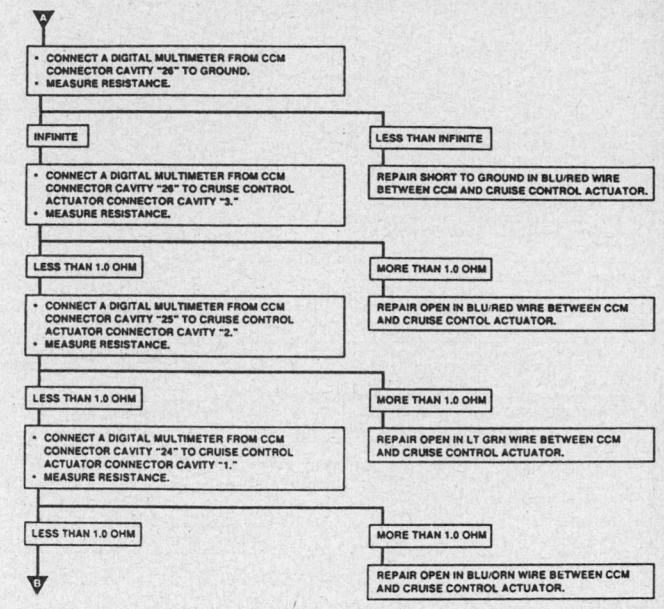

A

- CONNECT A DIGITAL MULTIMETER FROM CCM CONNECTOR CAVITY "26" TO GROUND.
- MEASURE RESISTANCE.

INFINITE

- CONNECT A DIGITAL MULTIMETER FROM CCM CONNECTOR CAVITY "26" TO CRUISE CONTROL ACTUATOR CONNECTOR CAVITY "3."
- MEASURE RESISTANCE.

LESS THAN 1.0 OHM

- CONNECT A DIGITAL MULTIMETER FROM CCM CONNECTOR CAVITY "25" TO CRUISE CONTROL ACTUATOR CONNECTOR CAVITY "2."
- MEASURE RESISTANCE.

LESS THAN 1.0 OHM

- CONNECT A DIGITAL MULTIMETER FROM CCM CONNECTOR CAVITY "24" TO CRUISE CONTROL ACTUATOR CONNECTOR CAVITY "1."
- MEASURE RESISTANCE.

LESS THAN 1.0 OHM

B

LESS THAN INFINITE

REPAIR SHORT TO GROUND IN BLU/RED WIRE BETWEEN CCM AND CRUISE CONTROL ACTUATOR.

MORE THAN 1.0 OHM

REPAIR OPEN IN BLU/RED WIRE BETWEEN CCM AND CRUISE CONTOL ACTUATOR.

MORE THAN 1.0 OHM

REPAIR OPEN IN LT GRN WIRE BETWEEN CCM AND CRUISE CONTROL ACTUATOR.

MORE THAN 1.0 OHM

REPAIR OPEN IN BLU/ORN WIRE BETWEEN CCM AND CRUISE CONTROL ACTUATOR.

GC1109300252030X

Fig. 33 Code 13: Open Motor Circuit Or Abnormal Throttle Angle Sensor Signal (Part 3 of 5). 1993–94

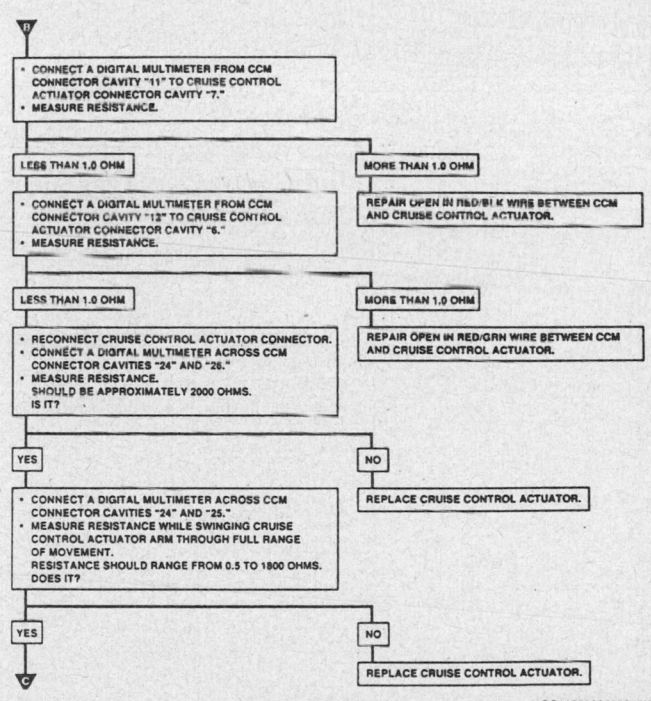

B

- CONNECT A DIGITAL MULTIMETER FROM CCM CONNECTOR CAVITY "11" TO CRUISE CONTROL ACTUATOR CONNECTOR CAVITY "7."
- MEASURE RESISTANCE.

LESS THAN 1.0 OHM

- CONNECT A DIGITAL MULTIMETER FROM CCM CONNECTOR CAVITY "12" TO CRUISE CONTROL ACTUATOR CONNECTOR CAVITY "6."
- MEASURE RESISTANCE.

LESS THAN 1.0 OHM

- RECONNECT CRUISE CONTROL ACTUATOR CONNECTOR.
- CONNECT A DIGITAL MULTIMETER ACROSS CCM CONNECTOR CAVITIES "24" AND "26."
- MEASURE RESISTANCE. SHOULD BE APPROXIMATELY 2000 OHMS. IS IT?

YES

- CONNECT A DIGITAL MULTIMETER ACROSS CCM CONNECTOR CAVITIES "24" AND "25."
- MEASURE RESISTANCE WHILE SWINGING CRUISE CONTROL ACTUATOR ARM THROUGH FULL RANGE OF MOVEMENT. RESISTANCE SHOULD RANGE FROM 0.5 TO 1800 OHMS. DOES IT?

YES

C

NO

REPLACE CRUISE CONTROL ACTUATOR.

MORE THAN 1.0 OHM

REPAIR OPEN IN RED/BLK WIRE BETWEEN CCM AND CRUISE CONTROL ACTUATOR.

MORE THAN 1.0 OHM

REPAIR OPEN IN RED/GRN WIRE BETWEEN CCM AND CRUISE CONTROL ACTUATOR.

NO

REPLACE CRUISE CONTROL ACTUATOR.

GC1109300252040X

Fig. 33 Code 13: Open Motor Circuit Or Abnormal Throttle Angle Sensor Signal (Part 4 of 5). 1993–94

C

- CONNECT A FUSED JUMPER FROM CCM CONNECTOR CAVITY "12" TO B+.
- CONNECT A FUSED JUMPER FROM CCM CONNECTOR CAVITY "11" TO GROUND.
- OBSERVE CRUISE CONTROL ACTUATOR ARM. SHOULD MOVE SMOOTHLY TO THE OPEN POSITION WITH MOTOR STOPPING WHEN FULLY OPEN. DOES IT?

NO → REPLACE CRUISE CONTROL ACTUATOR.

YES →

- REVERSE POWER AND GROUND CONNECTIONS ON CCM CONNECTOR CAVITIES "11" AND "12."
- OBSERVE CRUISE CONTROL ACTUATOR ARM. SHOULD MOVE SMOOTHLY TO THE CLOSE POSITION WITH MOTOR STOPPING WHEN FULLY CLOSED. DOES IT?

YES → REPLACE CCM.

NO → REPLACE CRUISE CONTROL ACTUATOR.

GC1109300252050X

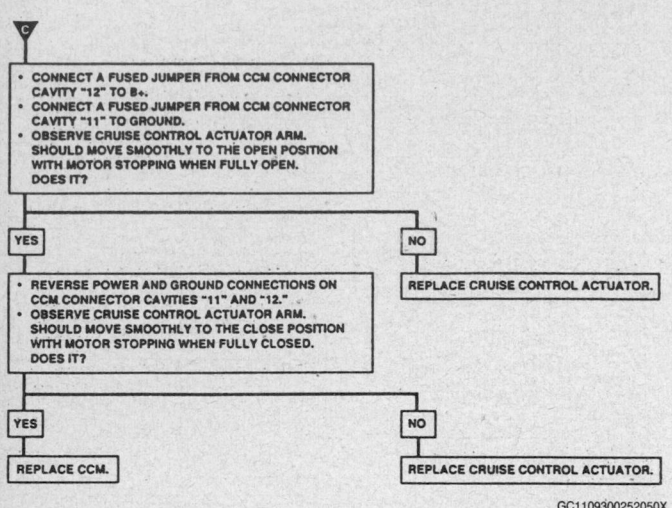

Fig. 33 Code 13: Open Motor Circuit Or Abnormal Throttle Angle Sensor Signal (Part 5 of 5). 1993–94

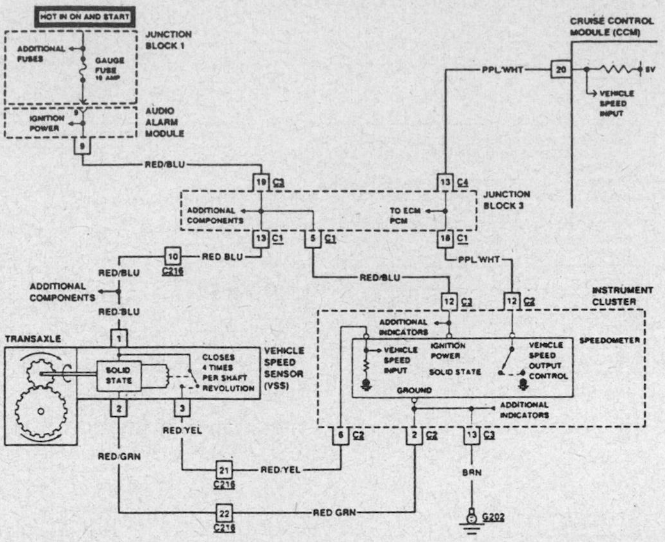

HOT IN ON AND START
JUNCTION BLOCK 1
ADDITIONAL FUSES
GAUGE FUSE 10 AMP
IGNITION POWER
AUDIO ALARM MODULE
9
RED/BLU
19 C3
13 C4
PPL/WHT
20
CRUISE CONTROL MODULE (CCM)
5V
VEHICLE SPEED INPUT
JUNCTION BLOCK 3
ADDITIONAL COMPONENTS
TO ECM PCM
13 C1
5 C1
18 C1
10
C216
RED BLU
RED/BLU
ADDITIONAL COMPONENTS
PPL WHT
12 C3
12 C2
INSTRUMENT CLUSTER
TRANSAXLE
1
SOLID STATE
CLOSES 4 TIMES PER SHAFT REVOLUTION
VEHICLE SPEED SENSOR (VSS)
ADDITIONAL INDICATORS
SPEEDOMETER
VEHICLE SPEED INPUT
IGNITION POWER
SOLID STATE
VEHICLE SPEED OUTPUT CONTROL
GROUND
2
3
RED/YEL
RED/GRN
6 C2
2 C2
13 C3
21
C216
22
RED GRN
BRN
G202
GC1109300253010X

Fig. 34 Code 21: Open/Shorted Vehicle Speed Sensor Circuit (Part 1 of 3). 1993–94

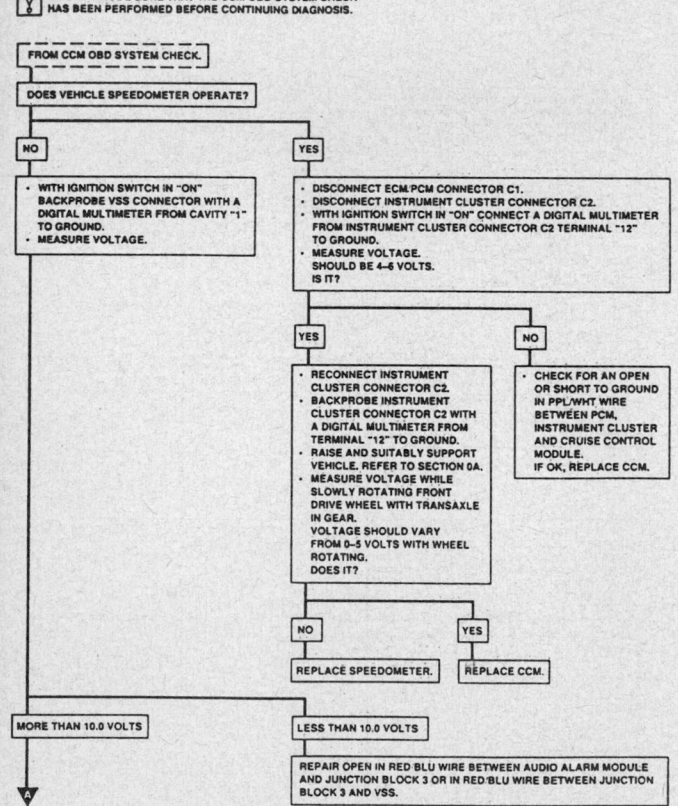

IMPORTANT: BE SURE THAT THE CCM OBD SYSTEM CHECK HAS BEEN PERFORMED BEFORE CONTINUING DIAGNOSIS.

FROM CCM OBD SYSTEM CHECK.

DOES VEHICLE SPEEDOMETER OPERATE?

NO →

- WITH IGNITION SWITCH IN "ON" BACKPROBE VSS CONNECTOR WITH A DIGITAL MULTIMETER FROM CAVITY "1" TO GROUND.
- MEASURE VOLTAGE.

MORE THAN 10.0 VOLTS → A

LESS THAN 10.0 VOLTS → REPAIR OPEN IN RED/BLU WIRE BETWEEN AUDIO ALARM MODULE AND JUNCTION BLOCK 3 OR IN RED/BLU WIRE BETWEEN JUNCTION BLOCK 3 AND VSS.

YES →

- DISCONNECT ECM/PCM CONNECTOR C1.
- DISCONNECT INSTRUMENT CLUSTER CONNECTOR C2.
- WITH IGNITION SWITCH IN "ON" CONNECT A DIGITAL MULTIMETER FROM INSTRUMENT CLUSTER CONNECTOR C2 TERMINAL "12" TO GROUND.
- MEASURE VOLTAGE. SHOULD BE 4–6 VOLTS. IS IT?

NO →

- CHECK FOR AN OPEN OR SHORT TO GROUND IN PPL/WHT WIRE BETWEEN PCM, INSTRUMENT CLUSTER AND CRUISE CONTROL MODULE. IF OK, REPLACE CCM.

YES →

- RECONNECT INSTRUMENT CLUSTER CONNECTOR C2.
- BACKPROBE INSTRUMENT CLUSTER CONNECTOR C2 WITH A DIGITAL MULTIMETER FROM TERMINAL "12" TO GROUND.
- RAISE AND SUITABLY SUPPORT VEHICLE. REFER TO SECTION 0A.
- MEASURE VOLTAGE WHILE SLOWLY ROTATING FRONT DRIVE WHEEL WITH TRANSAXLE IN GEAR. VOLTAGE SHOULD VARY FROM 0–5 VOLTS WITH WHEEL ROTATING. DOES IT?

NO → REPLACE SPEEDOMETER.

YES → REPLACE CCM.

GC1109300253020X

Fig. 34 Code 21: Open/Shorted Vehicle Speed Sensor Circuit (Part 2 of 3). 1993–94

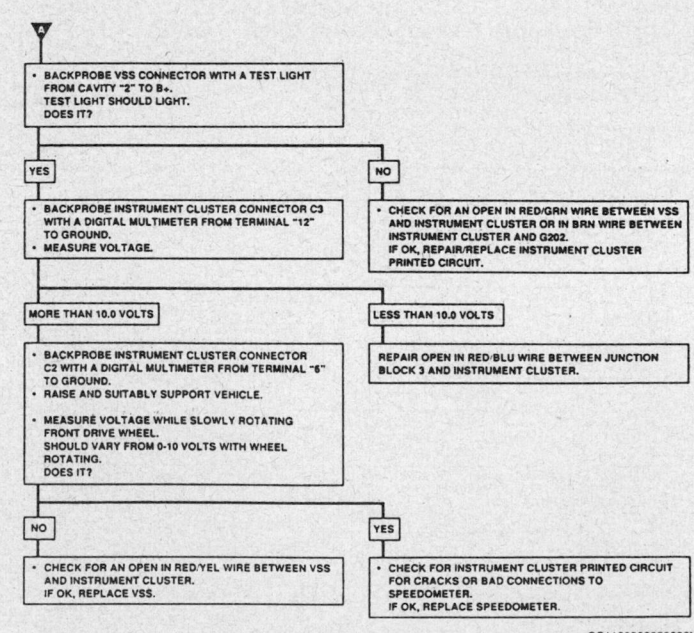

A

- BACKPROBE VSS CONNECTOR WITH A TEST LIGHT FROM CAVITY "2" TO B+. TEST LIGHT SHOULD LIGHT. DOES IT?

NO →

- CHECK FOR AN OPEN IN RED/GRN WIRE BETWEEN VSS AND INSTRUMENT CLUSTER OR IN BRN WIRE BETWEEN INSTRUMENT CLUSTER AND G202. IF OK, REPAIR/REPLACE INSTRUMENT CLUSTER PRINTED CIRCUIT.

YES →

- BACKPROBE INSTRUMENT CLUSTER CONNECTOR C3 WITH A DIGITAL MULTIMETER FROM TERMINAL "12" TO GROUND.
- MEASURE VOLTAGE.

LESS THAN 10.0 VOLTS → REPAIR OPEN IN RED/BLU WIRE BETWEEN JUNCTION BLOCK 3 AND INSTRUMENT CLUSTER.

MORE THAN 10.0 VOLTS →

- BACKPROBE INSTRUMENT CLUSTER CONNECTOR C2 WITH A DIGITAL MULTIMETER FROM TERMINAL "6" TO GROUND.
- RAISE AND SUITABLY SUPPORT VEHICLE.
- MEASURE VOLTAGE WHILE SLOWLY ROTATING FRONT DRIVE WHEEL. SHOULD VARY FROM 0-10 VOLTS WITH WHEEL ROTATING. DOES IT?

NO →

- CHECK FOR AN OPEN IN RED/YEL WIRE BETWEEN VSS AND INSTRUMENT CLUSTER. IF OK, REPLACE VSS.

YES →

- CHECK FOR INSTRUMENT CLUSTER PRINTED CIRCUIT FOR CRACKS OR BAD CONNECTIONS TO SPEEDOMETER. IF OK, REPLACE SPEEDOMETER.

GC1109300253030X

Fig. 34 Code 21: Open/Shorted Vehicle Speed Sensor Circuit (Part 3 of 3). 1993–94

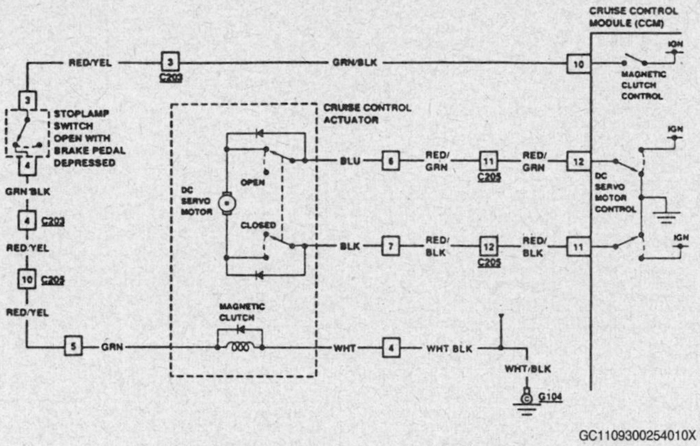
CRUISE CONTROL MODULE (CCM)
RED/YEL
3
C203
GRN/BLK
10
IGN
MAGNETIC CLUTCH CONTROL
3
STOPLAMP SWITCH OPEN WITH BRAKE PEDAL DEPRESSED
4
GRN/BLK
4 C203
RED/YEL
10 C205
RED/YEL
CRUISE CONTROL ACTUATOR
DC SERVO MOTOR
OPEN
CLOSED
BLU
6
RED/ GRN
11
C205
RED/ GRN
12
IGN
DC SERVO MOTOR CONTROL
BLK
7
RED/ BLK
12
C205
RED/ BLK
11
IGN
MAGNETIC CLUTCH
5
GRN
WHT
4
WHT BLK
WHT/BLK
G104

GC1109300254010X

Fig. 35 Code 23: Vehicle Speed Drops More Than 10 mph Under Set Speed (Part 1 of 4). 1993–94

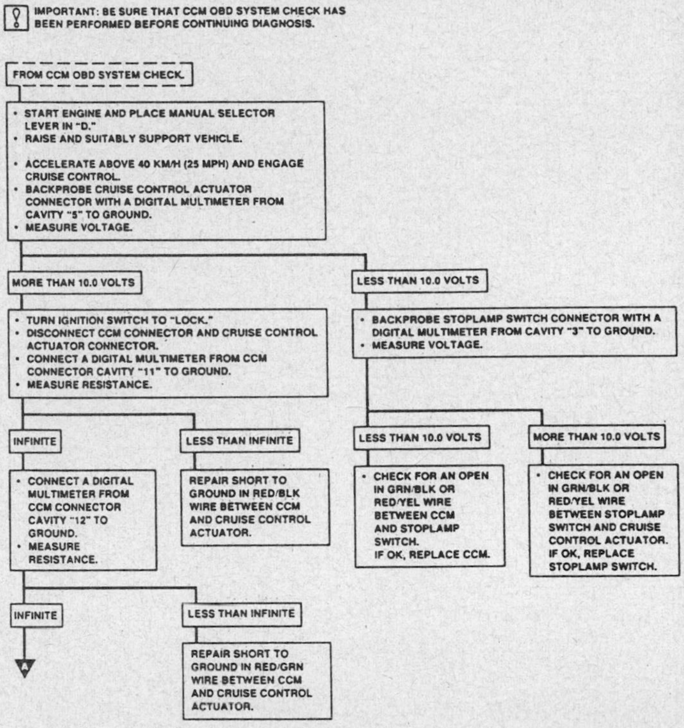
IMPORTANT: BE SURE THAT CCM OBD SYSTEM CHECK HAS BEEN PERFORMED BEFORE CONTINUING DIAGNOSIS.
FROM CCM OBD SYSTEM CHECK.
• START ENGINE AND PLACE MANUAL SELECTOR LEVER IN "D."
• RAISE AND SUITABLY SUPPORT VEHICLE.
• ACCELERATE ABOVE 40 KM/H (25 MPH) AND ENGAGE CRUISE CONTROL.
• BACKPROBE CRUISE CONTROL ACTUATOR CONNECTOR WITH A DIGITAL MULTIMETER FROM CAVITY "5" TO GROUND.
• MEASURE VOLTAGE.
MORE THAN 10.0 VOLTS
LESS THAN 10.0 VOLTS
• TURN IGNITION SWITCH TO "LOCK."
• DISCONNECT CCM CONNECTOR AND CRUISE CONTROL ACTUATOR CONNECTOR.
• CONNECT A DIGITAL MULTIMETER FROM CCM CONNECTOR CAVITY "11" TO GROUND.
• MEASURE RESISTANCE.
• BACKPROBE STOPLAMP SWITCH CONNECTOR WITH A DIGITAL MULTIMETER FROM CAVITY "3" TO GROUND.
• MEASURE VOLTAGE.
INFINITE
LESS THAN INFINITE
LESS THAN 10.0 VOLTS
MORE THAN 10.0 VOLTS
• CONNECT A DIGITAL MULTIMETER FROM CCM CONNECTOR CAVITY "12" TO GROUND.
• MEASURE RESISTANCE.
REPAIR SHORT TO GROUND IN RED/BLK WIRE BETWEEN CCM AND CRUISE CONTROL ACTUATOR.
• CHECK FOR AN OPEN IN GRN/BLK OR RED/YEL WIRE BETWEEN CCM AND STOPLAMP SWITCH. IF OK, REPLACE CCM.
• CHECK FOR AN OPEN IN GRN/BLK OR RED/YEL WIRE BETWEEN STOPLAMP SWITCH AND CRUISE CONTROL ACTUATOR. IF OK, REPLACE STOPLAMP SWITCH.
INFINITE
LESS THAN INFINITE
A
REPAIR SHORT TO GROUND IN RED/GRN WIRE BETWEEN CCM AND CRUISE CONTROL ACTUATOR.

GC1109300254020X

Fig. 35 Code 23: Vehicle Speed Drops More Than 10 mph Under Set Speed (Part 2 of 4). 1993–94

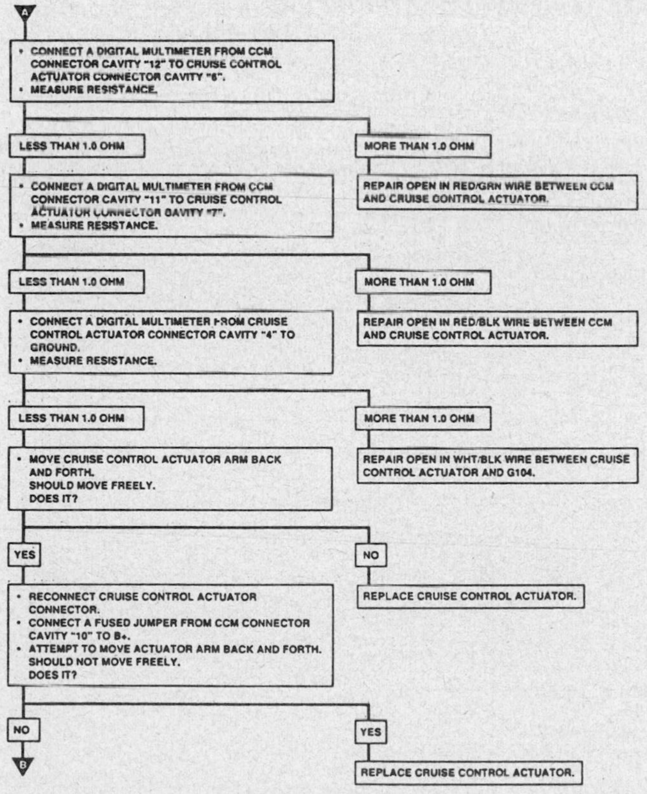
A
• CONNECT A DIGITAL MULTIMETER FROM CCM CONNECTOR CAVITY "12" TO CRUISE CONTROL ACTUATOR CONNECTOR CAVITY "6".
• MEASURE RESISTANCE.
LESS THAN 1.0 OHM
MORE THAN 1.0 OHM
• CONNECT A DIGITAL MULTIMETER FROM CCM CONNECTOR CAVITY "11" TO CRUISE CONTROL ACTUATOR CONNECTOR CAVITY "7".
• MEASURE RESISTANCE.
REPAIR OPEN IN RED/GRN WIRE BETWEEN CCM AND CRUISE CONTROL ACTUATOR.
LESS THAN 1.0 OHM
MORE THAN 1.0 OHM
• CONNECT A DIGITAL MULTIMETER FROM CRUISE CONTROL ACTUATOR CONNECTOR CAVITY "4" TO GROUND.
• MEASURE RESISTANCE.
REPAIR OPEN IN RED/BLK WIRE BETWEEN CCM AND CRUISE CONTROL ACTUATOR.
LESS THAN 1.0 OHM
MORE THAN 1.0 OHM
• MOVE CRUISE CONTROL ACTUATOR ARM BACK AND FORTH. SHOULD MOVE FREELY. DOES IT?
REPAIR OPEN IN WHT/BLK WIRE BETWEEN CRUISE CONTROL ACTUATOR AND G104.
YES
NO
• RECONNECT CRUISE CONTROL ACTUATOR CONNECTOR.
• CONNECT A FUSED JUMPER FROM CCM CONNECTOR CAVITY "10" TO B+.
• ATTEMPT TO MOVE ACTUATOR ARM BACK AND FORTH. SHOULD NOT MOVE FREELY. DOES IT?
REPLACE CRUISE CONTROL ACTUATOR.
NO
YES
B
REPLACE CRUISE CONTROL ACTUATOR.

GC1109300254030X

Fig. 35 Code 23: Vehicle Speed Drops More Than 10 mph Under Set Speed (Part 3 of 4). 1993–94

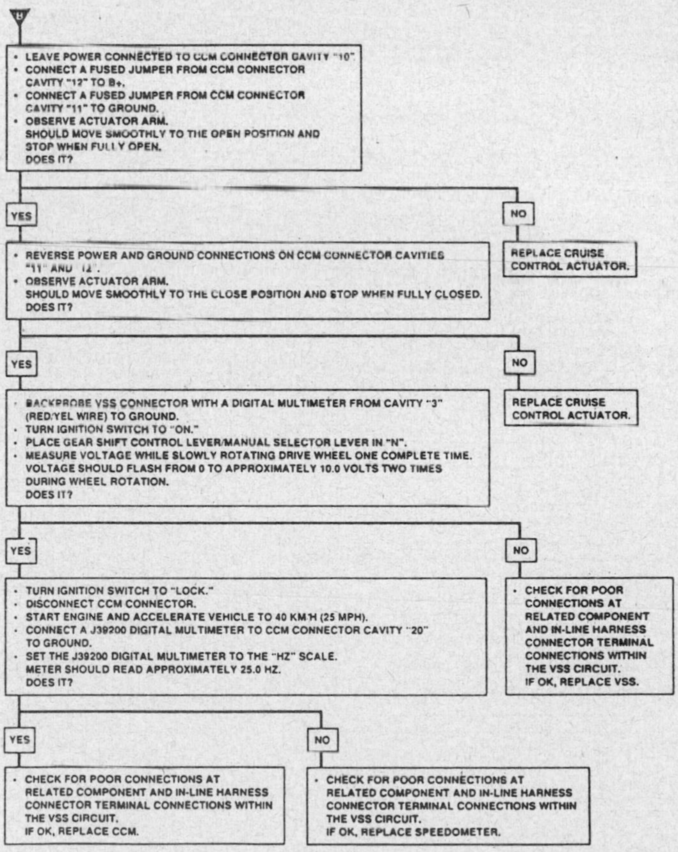
B
• LEAVE POWER CONNECTED TO CCM CONNECTOR CAVITY "10".
• CONNECT A FUSED JUMPER FROM CCM CONNECTOR CAVITY "12" TO B+.
• CONNECT A FUSED JUMPER FROM CCM CONNECTOR CAVITY "11" TO GROUND.
• OBSERVE ACTUATOR ARM. SHOULD MOVE SMOOTHLY TO THE OPEN POSITION AND STOP WHEN FULLY OPEN. DOES IT?
YES
NO
• REVERSE POWER AND GROUND CONNECTIONS ON CCM CONNECTOR CAVITIES "11" AND "12".
• OBSERVE ACTUATOR ARM. SHOULD MOVE SMOOTHLY TO THE CLOSE POSITION AND STOP WHEN FULLY CLOSED. DOES IT?
REPLACE CRUISE CONTROL ACTUATOR.
YES
NO
• BACKPROBE VSS CONNECTOR WITH A DIGITAL MULTIMETER FROM CAVITY "3" (RED/YEL WIRE) TO GROUND.
• TURN IGNITION SWITCH TO "ON."
• PLACE GEAR SHIFT CONTROL LEVER/MANUAL SELECTOR LEVER IN "N".
• MEASURE VOLTAGE WHILE SLOWLY ROTATING DRIVE WHEEL ONE COMPLETE TIME. VOLTAGE SHOULD FLASH FROM 0 TO APPROXIMATELY 10.0 VOLTS TWO TIMES DURING WHEEL ROTATION. DOES IT?
REPLACE CRUISE CONTROL ACTUATOR.
YES
NO
• TURN IGNITION SWITCH TO "LOCK."
• DISCONNECT CCM CONNECTOR.
• START ENGINE AND ACCELERATE VEHICLE TO 40 KM/H (25 MPH).
• CONNECT A J39200 DIGITAL MULTIMETER TO CCM CONNECTOR CAVITY "20" TO GROUND.
• SET THE J39200 DIGITAL MULTIMETER TO THE "HZ" SCALE. METER SHOULD READ APPROXIMATELY 25.0 HZ. DOES IT?
• CHECK FOR POOR CONNECTIONS AT RELATED COMPONENT AND IN-LINE HARNESS CONNECTOR TERMINAL CONNECTIONS WITHIN THE VSS CIRCUIT. IF OK, REPLACE VSS.
YES
NO
• CHECK FOR POOR CONNECTIONS AT RELATED COMPONENT AND IN-LINE HARNESS CONNECTOR TERMINAL CONNECTIONS WITHIN THE VSS CIRCUIT. IF OK, REPLACE CCM.
• CHECK FOR POOR CONNECTIONS AT RELATED COMPONENT AND IN-LINE HARNESS CONNECTOR TERMINAL CONNECTIONS WITHIN THE VSS CIRCUIT. IF OK, REPLACE SPEEDOMETER.

GC1109300254040X

Fig. 35 Code 23: Vehicle Speed Drops More Than 10 mph Under Set Speed (Part 4 of 4). 1993–94

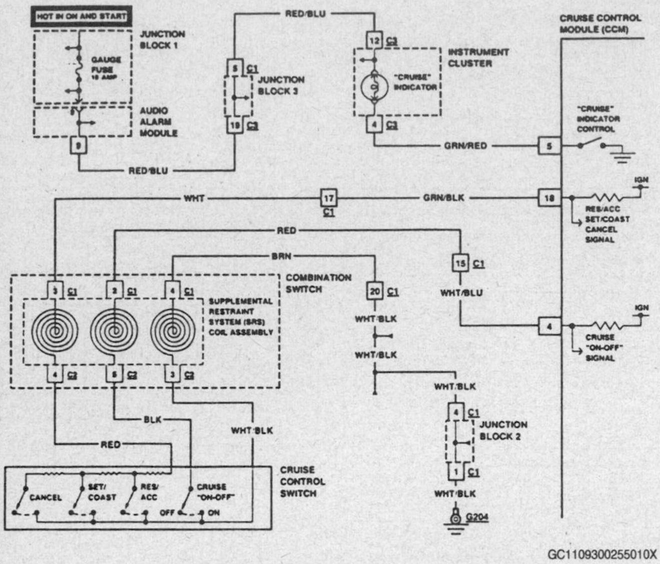
HOT IN ON AND START
JUNCTION BLOCK 1
GAUGE FUSE 10 AMP
AUDIO ALARM MODULE
RED/BLU
JUNCTION BLOCK 3
INSTRUMENT CLUSTER
"CRUISE" INDICATOR
CRUISE CONTROL MODULE (CCM)
"CRUISE" INDICATOR CONTROL
GRN/RED
WHT
GRN/BLK
IGN
RES/ACC SET/COAST CANCEL SIGNAL
RED
BRN
COMBINATION SWITCH
SUPPLEMENTAL RESTRAINT SYSTEM (SRS) COIL ASSEMBLY
WHT/BLU
WHT/BLK
CRUISE "ON-OFF" SIGNAL
BLK
JUNCTION BLOCK 2
CRUISE CONTROL SWITCH
CANCEL
SET/ COAST
RES/ ACC
CRUISE "ON-OFF"
OFF
ON
G204
GC1109300255010X

Fig. 36 Code 32: Cruise Control Switch Shorted (Part 1 of 3). 1993–94

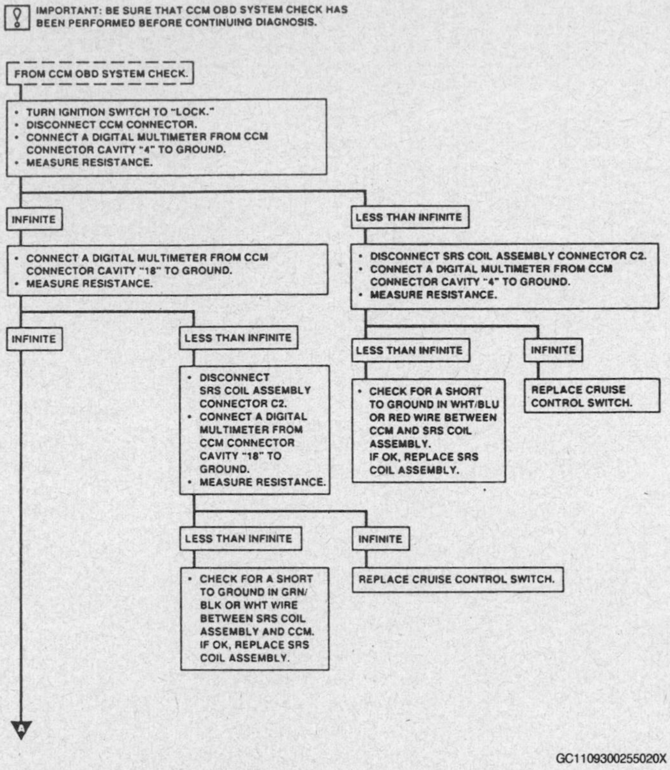
IMPORTANT: BE SURE THAT CCM OBD SYSTEM CHECK HAS BEEN PERFORMED BEFORE CONTINUING DIAGNOSIS.
FROM CCM OBD SYSTEM CHECK.
• TURN IGNITION SWITCH TO "LOCK."
• DISCONNECT CCM CONNECTOR.
• CONNECT A DIGITAL MULTIMETER FROM CCM CONNECTOR CAVITY "4" TO GROUND.
• MEASURE RESISTANCE.
INFINITE
LESS THAN INFINITE
• CONNECT A DIGITAL MULTIMETER FROM CCM CONNECTOR CAVITY "18" TO GROUND.
• MEASURE RESISTANCE.
• DISCONNECT SRS COIL ASSEMBLY CONNECTOR C2.
• CONNECT A DIGITAL MULTIMETER FROM CCM CONNECTOR CAVITY "4" TO GROUND.
• MEASURE RESISTANCE.
INFINITE
LESS THAN INFINITE
• DISCONNECT SRS COIL ASSEMBLY CONNECTOR C2.
• CONNECT A DIGITAL MULTIMETER FROM CCM CONNECTOR CAVITY "18" TO GROUND.
• MEASURE RESISTANCE.
LESS THAN INFINITE
INFINITE
• CHECK FOR A SHORT TO GROUND IN WHT/BLU OR RED WIRE BETWEEN CCM AND SRS COIL ASSEMBLY. IF OK, REPLACE SRS COIL ASSEMBLY.
REPLACE CRUISE CONTROL SWITCH.
LESS THAN INFINITE
INFINITE
• CHECK FOR A SHORT TO GROUND IN GRN/BLK OR WHT WIRE BETWEEN SRS COIL ASSEMBLY AND CCM. IF OK, REPLACE SRS COIL ASSEMBLY.
REPLACE CRUISE CONTROL SWITCH.
A
GC1109300255020X

Fig. 36 Code 32: Cruise Control Switch Shorted (Part 2 of 3). 1993–94

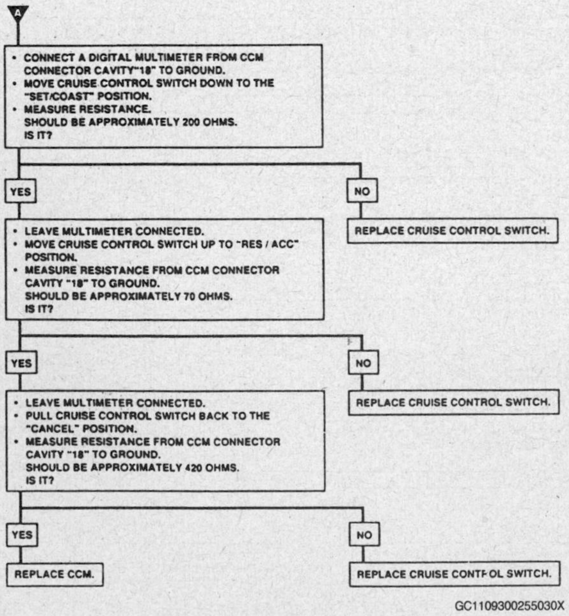
A
• CONNECT A DIGITAL MULTIMETER FROM CCM CONNECTOR CAVITY"18" TO GROUND.
• MOVE CRUISE CONTROL SWITCH DOWN TO THE "SET/COAST" POSITION.
• MEASURE RESISTANCE. SHOULD BE APPROXIMATELY 200 OHMS. IS IT?
YES
NO
REPLACE CRUISE CONTROL SWITCH.
• LEAVE MULTIMETER CONNECTED.
• MOVE CRUISE CONTROL SWITCH UP TO "RES / ACC" POSITION.
• MEASURE RESISTANCE FROM CCM CONNECTOR CAVITY "18" TO GROUND. SHOULD BE APPROXIMATELY 70 OHMS. IS IT?
YES
NO
REPLACE CRUISE CONTROL SWITCH.
• LEAVE MULTIMETER CONNECTED.
• PULL CRUISE CONTROL SWITCH BACK TO THE "CANCEL" POSITION.
• MEASURE RESISTANCE FROM CCM CONNECTOR CAVITY "18" TO GROUND. SHOULD BE APPROXIMATELY 420 OHMS. IS IT?
YES
NO
REPLACE CCM.
REPLACE CRUISE CONTROL SWITCH.
GC1109300255030X

Fig. 36 Code 32: Cruise Control Switch Shorted (Part 3 of 3). 1993–94

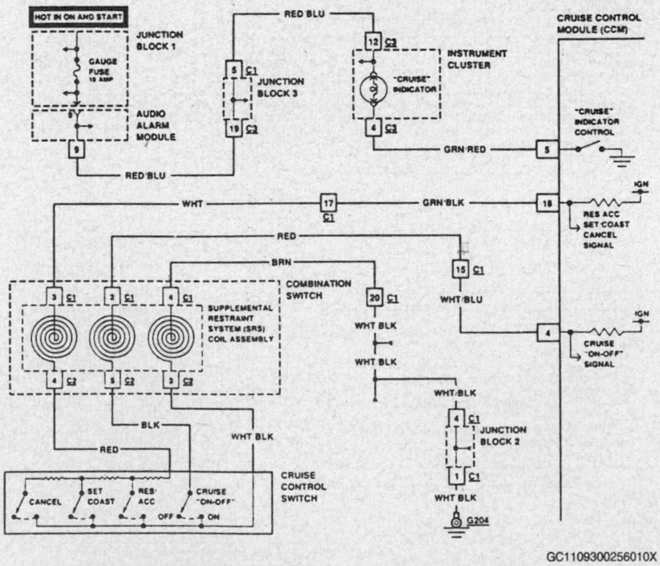
HOT IN ON AND START
JUNCTION BLOCK 1
GAUGE FUSE 10 AMP
AUDIO ALARM MODULE
RED BLU
JUNCTION BLOCK 3
INSTRUMENT CLUSTER
"CRUISE" INDICATOR
CRUISE CONTROL MODULE (CCM)
"CRUISE" INDICATOR CONTROL
GRN RED
WHT
GRN BLK
IGN
RES ACC SET COAST CANCEL SIGNAL
RED
BRN
COMBINATION SWITCH
SUPPLEMENTAL RESTRAINT SYSTEM (SRS) COIL ASSEMBLY
WHT/BLU
WHT BLK
CRUISE "ON-OFF" SIGNAL
BLK
JUNCTION BLOCK 2
CRUISE CONTROL SWITCH
CANCEL
SET COAST
RES ACC
CRUISE "ON-OFF"
OFF
ON
G204
GC1109300256010X

Fig. 37 Code 34: Abnormal Signal From Cruise Control Switch (Part 1 of 3). 1993–94

IMPORTANT: BE SURE THAT CCM OBD SYSTEM CHECK HAS BEEN PERFORMED BEFORE CONTINUING DIAGNOSIS.

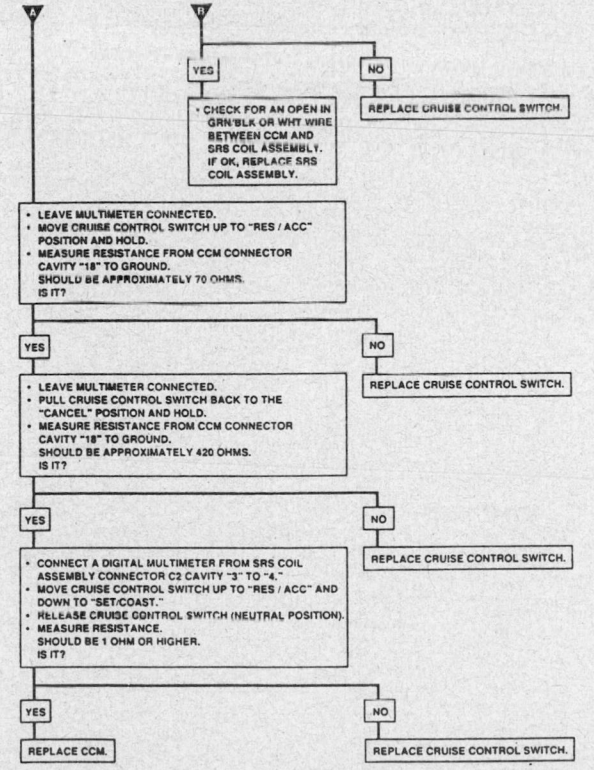

FROM CCM OBD SYSTEM CHECK.

- TURN IGNITION SWITCH TO "LOCK."
- DISCONNECT CCM CONNECTOR.
- CONNECT A DIGITAL MULTIMETER FROM CCM CONNECTOR CAVITY "4" TO GROUND.
- PRESS "CRUISE ON-OFF" BUTTON AND HOLD.
- MEASURE RESISTANCE.

LESS THAN 5.0 OHMS

- RELEASE "CRUISE ON-OFF" BUTTON.
- CONNECT A DIGITAL MULTIMETER FROM CCM CONNECTOR CAVITY "18" TO GROUND.
- MOVE CRUISE CONTROL SWITCH DOWN TO "SET/COAST" POSITION AND HOLD.
- MEASURE RESISTANCE. SHOULD BE APPROXIMATELY 200 OHMS. IS IT?

YES → A

NO

- DISCONNECT SRS COIL ASSEMBLY CONNECTOR C2.
- CONNECT A DIGITAL MULTIMETER FROM SRS COIL ASSEMBLY CONNECTOR C2 CAVITY "3" TO "4".
- MEASURE RESISTANCE WITH CRUISE CONTROL SWITCH HELD DOWN IN THE "SET/COAST" POSITION. SHOULD BE APPROXIMATELY 200 OHMS. IS IT?

→ B

MORE THAN 5.0 OHMS

- BACKPROBE JUNCTION BLOCK 2 CONNECTOR C1 WITH A DIGITAL MULTIMETER FROM CAVITY "4" TO GROUND.
- MEASURE RESISTANCE.

LESS THAN 5.0 OHMS

- BACKPROBE SRS COIL ASSEMBLY CONNECTOR C2 WITH A DIGITAL MULTIMETER FROM CAVITY "3" TO GROUND.
- MEASURE RESISTANCE.

MORE THAN 5.0 OHMS

- CHECK FOR AN OPEN IN WHT/BLK WIRE BETWEEN G204 AND JUNCTION BLOCK 2. IF OK, REPLACE JUNCTION BLOCK 2.

LESS THAN 5.0 OHMS

- BACKPROBE SRS COIL ASSEMBLY CONNECTOR C2 WITH A DIGITAL MULTIMETER FROM CAVITY "5" TO GROUND.
- PRESS AND HOLD "CRUISE ON-OFF" BUTTON.
- MEASURE RESISTANCE.

MORE THAN 5.0 OHMS

- CHECK FOR AN OPEN IN BRN OR WHT/BLK WIRE BETWEEN JUNCTION BLOCK 2 AND SRS COIL ASSEMBLY. IF OK, REPLACE SRS COIL ASSEMBLY.

LESS THAN 5.0 OHMS

- CHECK FOR AN OPEN IN WHT/BLU OR RED WIRE BETWEEN CCM AND SRS COIL ASSEMBLY. IF OK, REPLACE SRS COIL ASSEMBLY.

MORE THAN 5.0 OHMS

REPLACE CRUISE CONTROL SWITCH.

GC1109300256020X

Fig. 37 Code 34: Abnormal Signal From Cruise Control Switch (Part 2 of 3). 1993–94

A

B

YES

- CHECK FOR AN OPEN IN GRN/BLK OR WHT WIRE BETWEEN CCM AND SRS COIL ASSEMBLY. IF OK, REPLACE SRS COIL ASSEMBLY.

NO

REPLACE CRUISE CONTROL SWITCH.

- LEAVE MULTIMETER CONNECTED.
- MOVE CRUISE CONTROL SWITCH UP TO "RES / ACC" POSITION AND HOLD.
- MEASURE RESISTANCE FROM CCM CONNECTOR CAVITY "18" TO GROUND. SHOULD BE APPROXIMATELY 70 OHMS. IS IT?

NO

REPLACE CRUISE CONTROL SWITCH.

YES

- LEAVE MULTIMETER CONNECTED.
- PULL CRUISE CONTROL SWITCH BACK TO THE "CANCEL" POSITION AND HOLD.
- MEASURE RESISTANCE FROM CCM CONNECTOR CAVITY "18" TO GROUND. SHOULD BE APPROXIMATELY 420 OHMS. IS IT?

NO

REPLACE CRUISE CONTROL SWITCH.

YES

- CONNECT A DIGITAL MULTIMETER FROM SRS COIL ASSEMBLY CONNECTOR C2 CAVITY "3" TO "4."
- MOVE CRUISE CONTROL SWITCH UP TO "RES / ACC" AND DOWN TO "SET/COAST."
- RELEASE CRUISE CONTROL SWITCH (NEUTRAL POSITION).
- MEASURE RESISTANCE. SHOULD BE 1 OHM OR HIGHER. IS IT?

YES

REPLACE CCM.

NO

REPLACE CRUISE CONTROL SWITCH.

GC1109300256030X

Fig. 37 Code 34: Abnormal Signal From Cruise Control Switch (Part 3 of 3). 1993–94

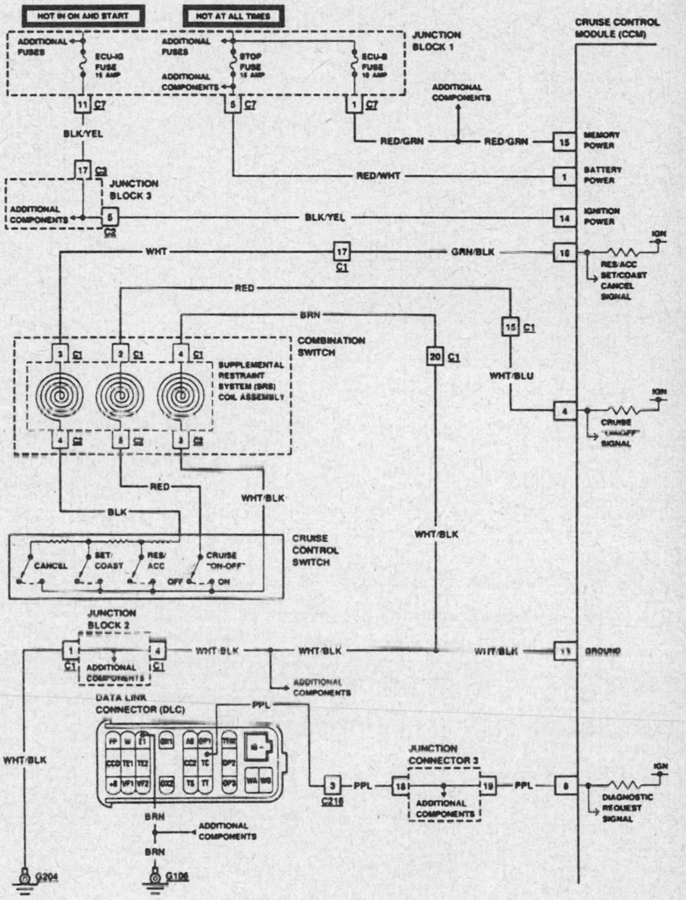
HOT IN ON AND START
HOT AT ALL TIMES
JUNCTION BLOCK 1
CRUISE CONTROL MODULE (CCM)
MEMORY POWER
BATTERY POWER
IGNITION POWER
COMBINATION SWITCH
CRUISE CONTROL SWITCH
JUNCTION BLOCK 2
JUNCTION BLOCK 3
DATA LINK CONNECTOR (DLC)
JUNCTION CONNECTOR 3
GROUND
G204
G106

GC1109300257010X

Fig. 38 Cruise control module wiring diagram (Part 1 of 5). 1993–94

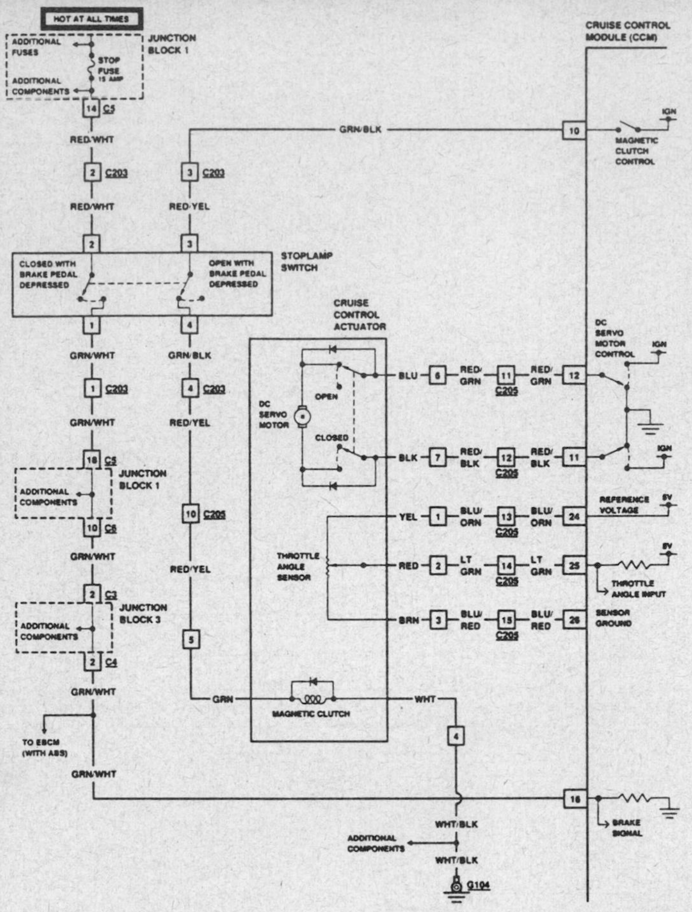
HOT AT ALL TIMES
JUNCTION BLOCK 1
STOP FUSE 15 AMP
CRUISE CONTROL MODULE (CCM)
MAGNETIC CLUTCH CONTROL
STOPLAMP SWITCH
CLOSED WITH BRAKE PEDAL DEPRESSED
OPEN WITH BRAKE PEDAL DEPRESSED
CRUISE CONTROL ACTUATOR
DC SERVO MOTOR
DC SERVO MOTOR CONTROL
REFERENCE VOLTAGE
THROTTLE ANGLE SENSOR
THROTTLE ANGLE INPUT
SENSOR GROUND
MAGNETIC CLUTCH
JUNCTION BLOCK 3
TO EBCM (WITH ABS)
BRAKE SIGNAL
ADDITIONAL COMPONENTS
G104

GC1109300257020X

Fig. 38 Cruise control module wiring diagram (Part 2 of 5). 1993–94

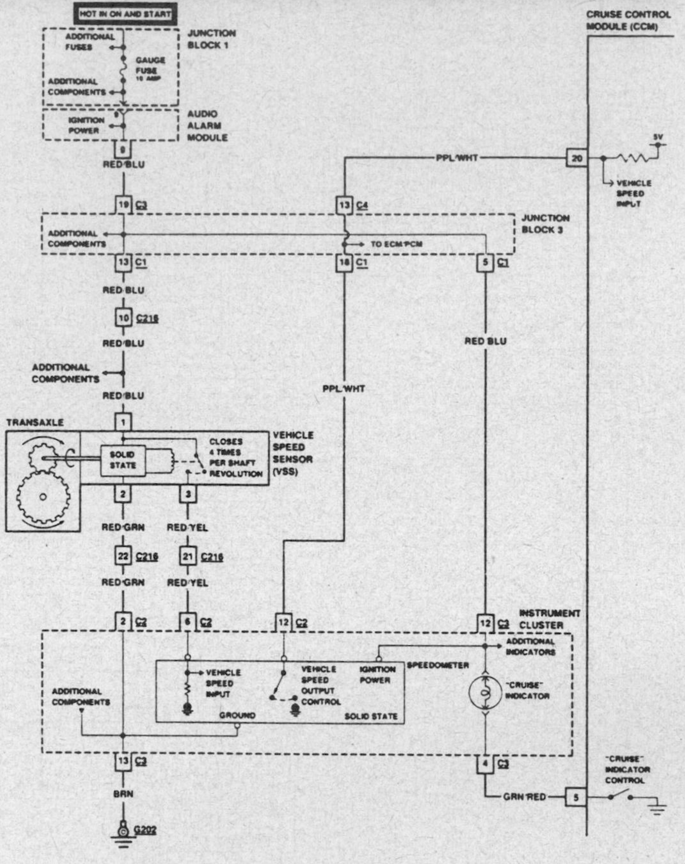
HOT IN ON AND START
JUNCTION BLOCK 1
GAUGE FUSE 10 AMP
AUDIO ALARM MODULE
CRUISE CONTROL MODULE (CCM)
VEHICLE SPEED INPUT
JUNCTION BLOCK 3
TO ECM/PCM
TRANSAXLE
VEHICLE SPEED SENSOR (VSS)
SOLID STATE
CLOSES 4 TIMES PER SHAFT REVOLUTION
INSTRUMENT CLUSTER
SPEEDOMETER
"CRUISE" INDICATOR
"CRUISE" INDICATOR CONTROL
G202

GC1109300257030X

Fig. 38 Cruise control module wiring diagram (Part 3 of 5). 1993–94

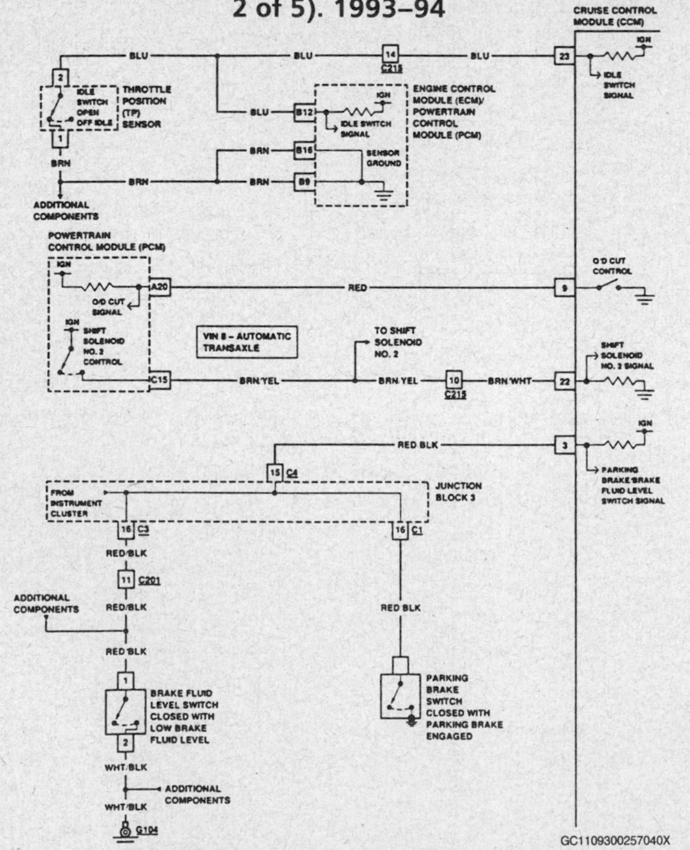
CRUISE CONTROL MODULE (CCM)
THROTTLE POSITION (TP) SENSOR
IDLE SWITCH SIGNAL
ENGINE CONTROL MODULE (ECM)/ POWERTRAIN CONTROL MODULE (PCM)
SENSOR GROUND
POWERTRAIN CONTROL MODULE (PCM)
O/D CUT CONTROL
VIN 8 – AUTOMATIC TRANSAXLE
TO SHIFT SOLENOID NO. 2
SHIFT SOLENOID NO. 2 SIGNAL
PARKING BRAKE/BRAKE FLUID LEVEL SWITCH SIGNAL
JUNCTION BLOCK 3
FROM INSTRUMENT CLUSTER
BRAKE FLUID LEVEL SWITCH CLOSED WITH LOW BRAKE FLUID LEVEL
PARKING BRAKE SWITCH CLOSED WITH PARKING BRAKE ENGAGED
ADDITIONAL COMPONENTS
G104

GC1109300257040X

Fig. 38 Cruise control module wiring diagram (Part 4 of 5). 1993–94

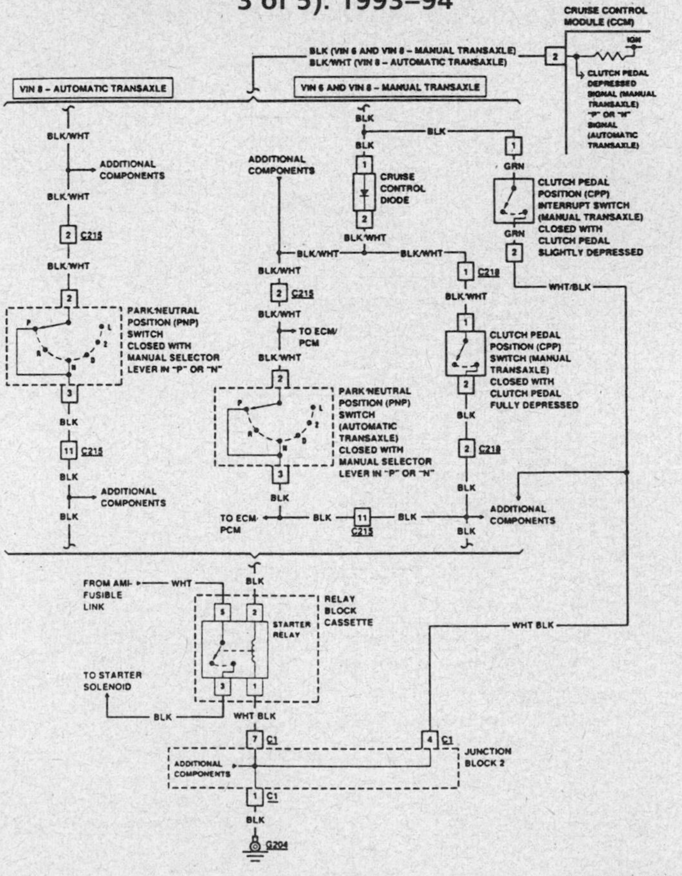
CRUISE CONTROL MODULE (CCM)
BLK (VIN 6 AND VIN 8 – MANUAL TRANSAXLE)
BLK/WHT (VIN 8 – AUTOMATIC TRANSAXLE)
VIN 8 – AUTOMATIC TRANSAXLE
VIN 6 AND VIN 8 – MANUAL TRANSAXLE
CRUISE CONTROL DIODE
CLUTCH PEDAL POSITION (CPP) INTERRUPT SWITCH (MANUAL TRANSAXLE) CLOSED WITH CLUTCH PEDAL SLIGHTLY DEPRESSED
PARK/NEUTRAL POSITION (PNP) SWITCH CLOSED WITH MANUAL SELECTOR LEVER IN "P" OR "N"
CLUTCH PEDAL POSITION (CPP) SWITCH (MANUAL TRANSAXLE) CLOSED WITH CLUTCH PEDAL FULLY DEPRESSED
PARK/NEUTRAL POSITION (PNP) SWITCH (AUTOMATIC TRANSAXLE) CLOSED WITH MANUAL SELECTOR LEVER IN "P" OR "N"
TO ECM/PCM
FROM AMI FUSIBLE LINK
RELAY BLOCK CASSETTE
STARTER RELAY
TO STARTER SOLENOID
JUNCTION BLOCK 2
ADDITIONAL COMPONENTS
G204

GC1109300257050X

Fig. 38 Cruise control module wiring diagram (Part 5 of 5). 1993–94

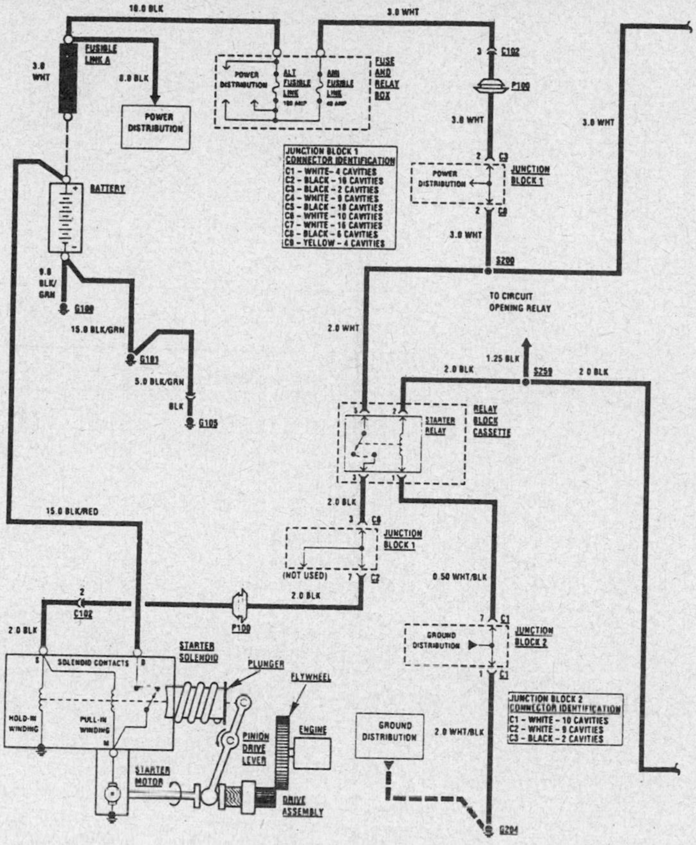
FUSIBLE LINK A
POWER DISTRIBUTION
BATTERY
FUSE AND RELAY BOX
JUNCTION BLOCK 1
TO CIRCUIT OPENING RELAY
STARTER RELAY
RELAY BLOCK CASSETTE
STARTER SOLENOID
PLUNGER
FLYWHEEL
PINION DRIVE LEVER
ENGINE
STARTER MOTOR
DRIVE ASSEMBLY
JUNCTION BLOCK 2
GROUND DISTRIBUTION

GC1109300250010X

Fig. 39 Starter wiring diagram (Part 1 of 2). 1993–94

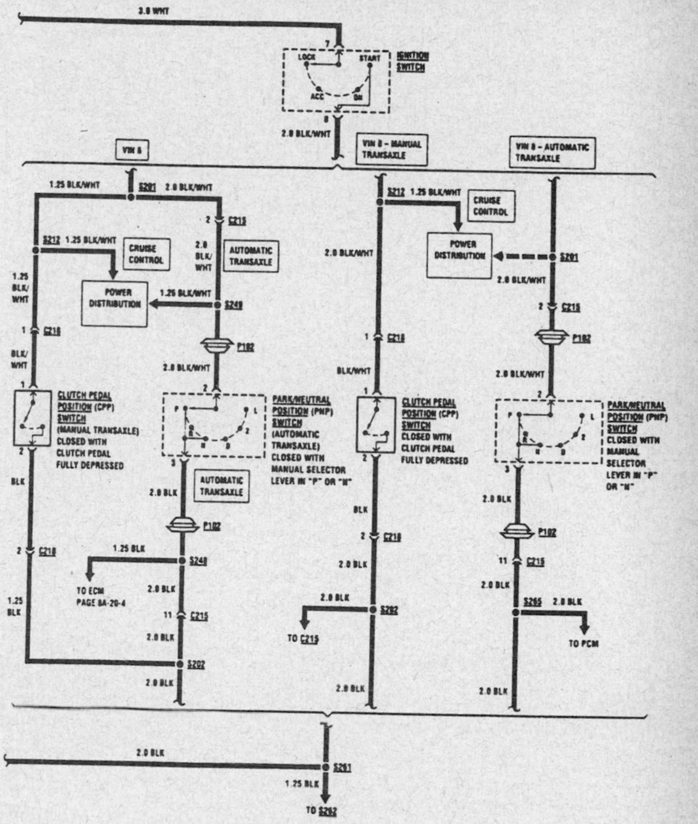
IGNITION SWITCH
CRUISE CONTROL
POWER DISTRIBUTION
AUTOMATIC TRANSAXLE
CLUTCH PEDAL POSITION (CPP) SWITCH
PARK/NEUTRAL POSITION (PNP) SWITCH
TO ECM
TO PCM

GC1109300250020X

Fig. 39 Starter wiring diagram (Part 2 of 2). 1993–94

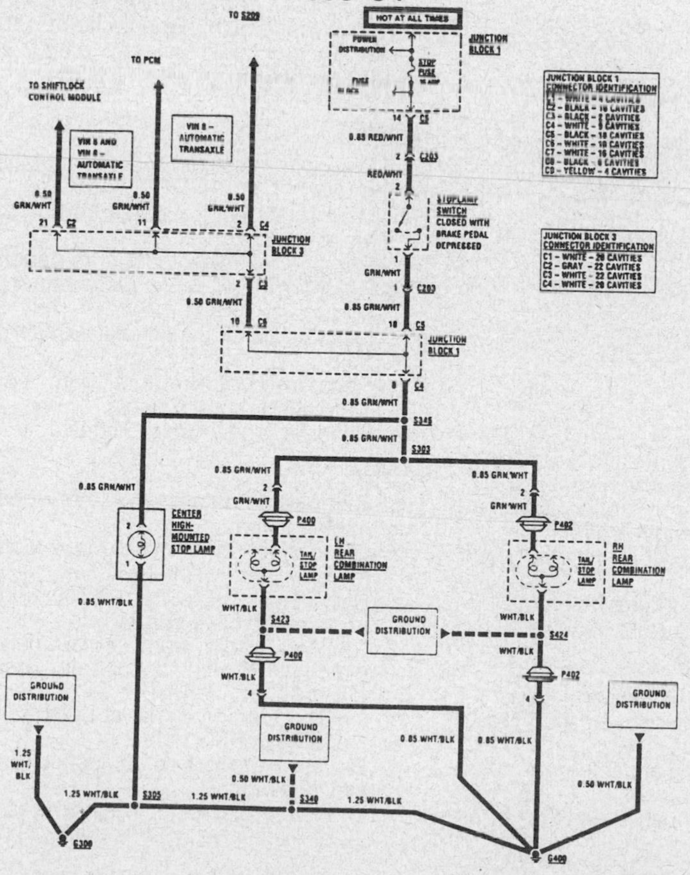
HOT AT ALL TIMES
JUNCTION BLOCK 1
TO SHIFTLOCK CONTROL MODULE
TO PCM
STOPLAMP SWITCH
JUNCTION BLOCK 3
CENTER HIGH-MOUNTED STOP LAMP
LH REAR COMBINATION LAMP
RH REAR COMBINATION LAMP
GROUND DISTRIBUTION

GC1109300259000X

Fig. 40 Stoplamp wiring diagram. 1993–94

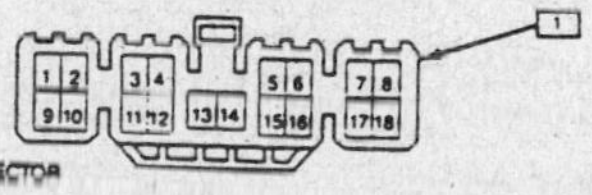

1 CRUISE CONTROL MODULE CONNECTOR (WIRE HARNESS SIDE)

Connection or measure item	Check for	Tester connection	Condition	Specified value
"STOP" Fuse	Voltage	16–Body ground	–	Battery voltage
Stoplamp Switch	Voltage	15–16	Brake pedal depressed	No voltage
			Brake pedal released	Battery voltage
Stoplamp Switch (Release Valve)	Resistance	2–14	Brake pedal released	Approx. 68 ohms
Control Valve	Resistance	4–14	–	Approx. 30 ohms
Cruise Control Switch	Voltage	10–Body ground	Turn ignition switch to "RUN" and cruise control switch to "CRUISE"	Battery voltage
			Turn ignition switch to "RUN" and cruise control switch to "OFF"	No voltage
Cruise Control Switch (indicator circuit)	Voltage	3–Body ground	Turn ignition switch to "RUN" and cruise control switch to "CRUISE"	Battery voltage
			Turn ignition switch to "RUN" and cruise control switch to "OFF"	No voltage
Engage Switch "SET/COAST"	Continuity	5–Body ground	Turn "SET/COAST" on	Continuity
			Turn "SET/COAST" off	No continuity
Engage Switch "RESUME/ACCEL"	Continuity	17–Body ground	Turn "RESUME/ACCEL" on	Continuity
			Turn "RESUME/ACCEL" off	No continuity
Speed Sensor	Continuity	7–Body ground	Vehicle moving slowly	1 pulse each 40 cm (15.75 in.)
Clutch Switch (M/T) or Neutral Start Switch (A/T)	Continuity	11–Body ground	Clutch pedal depressed or shifted into "N" range	Continuity
			Clutch pedal released or shifted into any range except "N" and "P" range	No continuity
Parking Brake Switch	Voltage	12–Body ground	Remove "CHARGE" fuse. Turn ignition switch to "RUN" with parking brake applied.	No voltage
			Remove "CHARGE" fuse and turn ignition switch to "RUN" with parking brake lever released.	Battery voltage
Vacuum Switch	Continuity	9–Body ground	Apply vacuum approx.170 mmHg (6.69 in. Hg. 22.7 kPa)	No continuity
			No vacuum	Continuity
Vacuum Pump	Continuity	1–Body ground	–	Continuity
Body Ground	Continuity	13–Body ground	–	Continuity

GC1109100260000X

Fig. 41 Cruise control module test chart. 1992

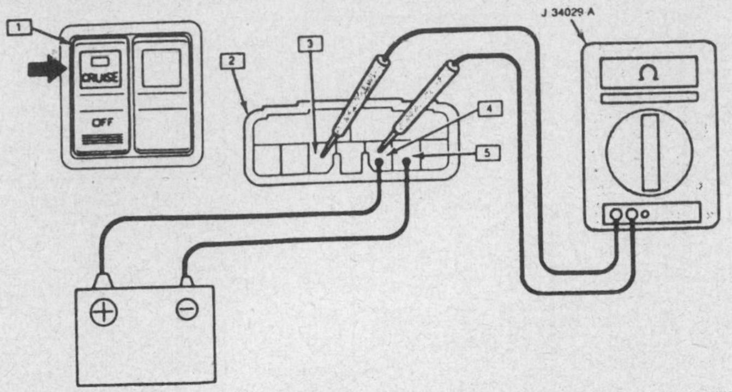
J 34029 A
CRUISE
OFF
1
2
3
4
5

GC1109100261000X

Fig. 42 Testing cruise control switch. 1992

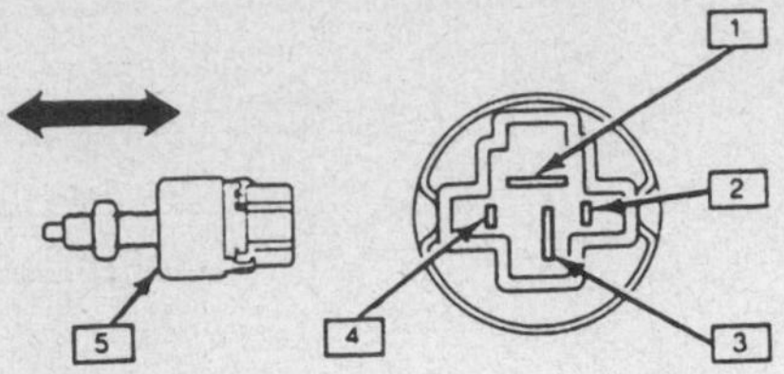
1
2
3
4
5

Terminals / Switch Position	1	2	3	4
Switch free (Brake pedal depressed)	o—	—	o	
Switch pin pushed in (Brake pedal released)		o—	—	o

1 TERMINAL 1
2 TERMINAL 2
3 TERMINAL 3
4 TERMINAL 4
5 STOPLAMP SWITCH

GC1109100262000X

Fig. 43 Testing stop light switch. 1992

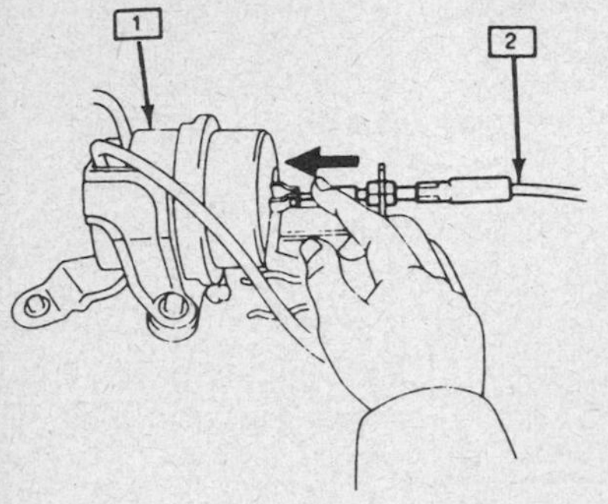
1
2

1 ACTUATOR
2 CONTROL CABLE

GC1109100263000X

Fig. 44 Checking control cable freeplay. 1992

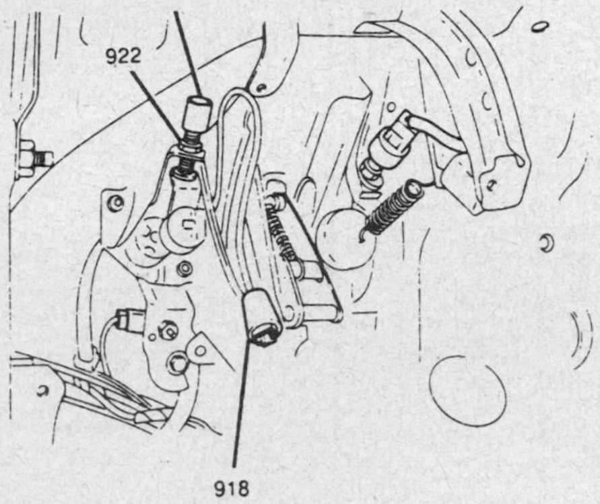
922
918

904 CLUTCH PEDAL POSITION (CPP) INTERRUPT SWITCH
918 ELECTRICAL CONNECTOR
922 CPP INTERRUPT SWITCH LOCKNUT

GC1109300264000X

Fig. 45 Clutch pedal position (CPP) interrupt switch location. 1993–94

COMPONENT REPLACEMENT

CLUTCH PEDAL POSITION (CPP) INTERRUPT SWITCH (MANUAL TRANSAXLES)

1993–94

1. Disconnect battery ground cable.
2. Remove two cover plates from knee bolster.
3. Disconnect hood release cable from hood release lever and bracket.
4. Remove four bolts and knee bolster from instrument panel.
5. Disconnect electrical connector from ABS data link connector (DLC), if equipped.
6. Remove one screw and left side ventilation from left side duct outlet.
7. Disconnect CPP interrupt switch electrical connector from CPP interrupt switch, **Fig. 45,** then loosen CPP interrupt switch locknut.
8. Remove CPP interrupt switch locknut and switch by turning counterclockwise.
9. Reverse procedure to install noting the following:
   a. **Torque** CPP interrupt switch locknut to 89 inch lbs.
   b. **Torque** knee bolster bolts to 89 inch lbs.
   c. **Torque** battery ground cable to 11 ft. lbs.

CRUISE CONTROL ACTUATOR

1992

1. Remove actuator electrical connector, then remove vacuum hose.
2. Remove actuator cover attaching screws, then remove cover.
3. Remove control cable as outlined previously.
4. Remove actuator attaching nuts.
5. Reverse procedure to install.

1993–94

1. Disconnect battery ground cable.
2. Remove actuator cover, then loosen cable locknuts.
3. Disconnect control cable from actuator lever and bracket.
4. Disconnect actuator electrical connector.
5. Remove three bolts from actuator, then actuator and brackets.
6. Reverse procedure to install noting the following:
   a. **Torque** actuator bolts to 89 inch lbs.
   b. Inspect cable for excessive wear or loose fit, replace as necessary.
   c. **Torque** cable locknuts to 44 ft. lbs.

CRUISE CONTROL CABLE

1992

1. Remove actuator cover attaching screws.
2. Disconnect control cable from actuator assembly.
3. Remove left lower dash trim panel.
4. Remove inner cable plate attaching nuts.
5. Remove outer cable plate attaching bolt.
6. Remove control cable from cable plate, then remove cable.
7. Reverse procedure to install.

1993–94

1. Remove actuator cover, then loosen cable locknuts.
2. Disconnect control cable from actuator lever and bracket.
3. Disconnect cable from three underhood guide clips, **Fig. 45.**
4. Remove cable from cruise control bellcrank above accelerator pedal, **Fig. 46.**
5. Unclip cable grommet at bulkhead.
6. Remove control cable.
7. Reverse procedure to install noting the following:
   a. Inspect cable for fraying, loose fit or excessive wear, replace as necessary.
   b. **Torque** cable locknuts to 44 inch lbs.

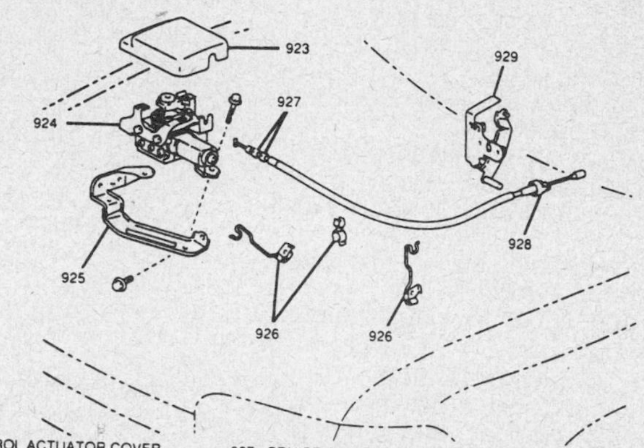
923
924
925
926
926
927
928
929

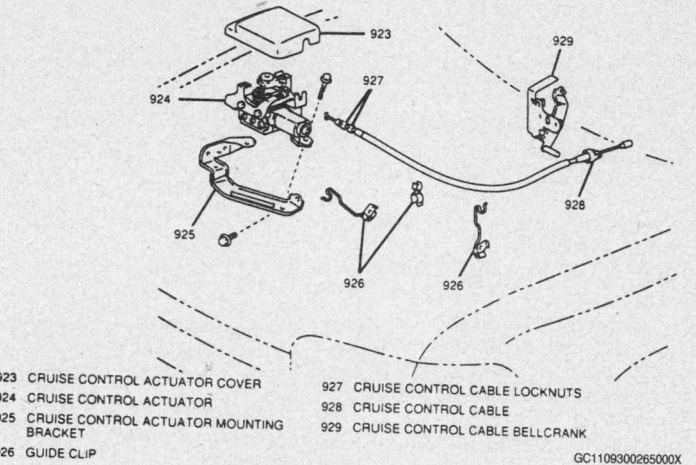

923 CRUISE CONTROL ACTUATOR COVER
924 CRUISE CONTROL ACTUATOR
925 CRUISE CONTROL ACTUATOR MOUNTING BRACKET
926 GUIDE CLIP
927 CRUISE CONTROL CABLE LOCKNUTS
928 CRUISE CONTROL CABLE
929 CRUISE CONTROL CABLE BELLCRANK

GC1109300265000X

Fig. 46 Cruise control actuator components. 1993–94

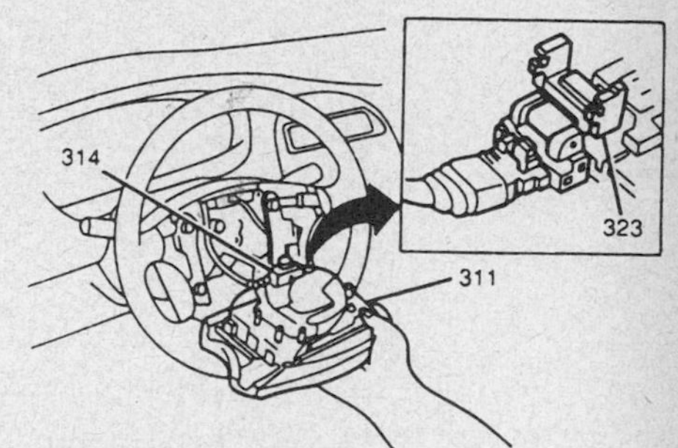
314
323
311

311 INFLATOR MODULE
314 UPPER STEERING COLUMN CONNECTOR
323 CONNECTOR POSITION ASSURANCE (CPA)

GC1109300266000X

Fig. 47 Inflator module removal. 1993–94

CRUISE CONTROL MODULE (CCM)

1993–94

1. Disconnect battery ground cable.
2. **On automatic transaxles,** move shifter to -L- (Low) position.
3. **On models equipped with manual transaxles,** remove gear shift knob and boot from lever, then move shifter to 4th gear.
4. **On all models,** remove center console trim bezel, then disconnect electrical connectors from rear defogger switch, hazard switch and cigar lighter at rear of center console trim bezel.
5. Remove center console tray, then four screws and radio.
6. Disconnect electrical connectors and antenna lead from rear of radio.
7. Remove five screws and rear console from vehicle.
8. **On models equipped with automatic transaxles,** remove shifter trim bezel from center console.
9. **On all models,** Remove two screws and center console from vehicle.
10. Disconnect CCM electrical connector, then remove two bolts and CCM from vehicle.
11. Reverse procedure to install noting the following:
    a. **Torque** CCM bolts to 89 inch lbs.
    b. **Torque** battery ground cable to 11 ft. lbs.

CRUISE CONTROL SWITCH

1993–94

1. Remove inflator module from steering wheel as follows:
    a. Place front wheels in straight ahead position.
    b. Remove side trim covers from steering wheel.
    c. Remove two Torx head screws, release connector position assurance (CPA) and disconnect upper steering column connector, **Fig. 47.**
    d. Remove inflator module from

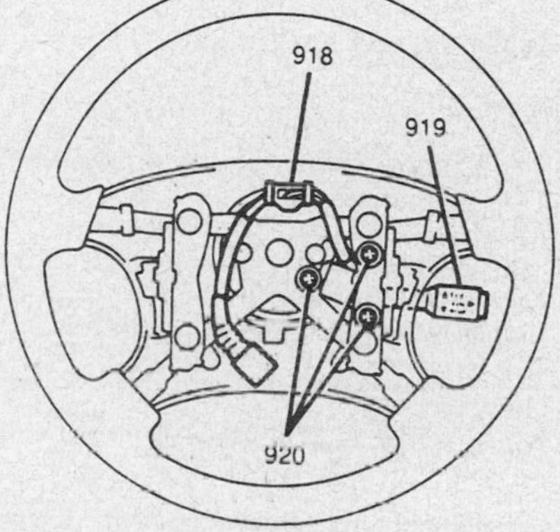
918
919
920

918 ELECTRICAL CONNECTOR
919 CRUISE CONTROL SWITCH
920 CRUISE CONTROL SWITCH SCREWS

GC1109300267000X

Fig 48 Cruise control switch location. 1993–94

steering wheel.
2. Disconnect cruise control switch electrical connector from air bag coil assembly, **Fig. 48.**
3. Open terminal position assurance (TPA) on top of cruise control switch electrical connector using a terminal remove from J 38125-A terminal repair kit or equivalent.

ENGAGEMENT SWITCH

1992

The cruise control engagement switch is part of the multi-function lever, which must be replaced as an assembly. Refer to individual car chapter.

PARK/NEUTRAL POSITION (PNP) SWITCH (AUTOMATIC TRANSAXLES)

1993–94

1. Disconnect battery ground cable, then place shifter in Neutral position.
2. Raise and support vehicle.
3. Remove six splash shield bolts and splash shield.
4. Remove one nut, one lock washer and shift select cable from manual lever.
5. Disconnect PNP electrical connector.
6. Remove one nut, one lock washer and manual lever from manual shaft. Unstake lock plate behind manual shaft nut.
7. Remove manual shaft nut and lock plate from PNP switch, then PNP switch bolts and switch.
8. Reverse procedure to install noting the following:
    a. **Torque** manual shaft nut to 61 inch lbs.
    b. Adjust PNP switch by aligning neutral basic line scribed in PNP switch with groove in PNP switch sleeve, **Fig. 51.**
    c. **Torque** PNP switch to 48 inch lbs.
    d. **Torque** manual lever nut to 106 inch lbs.
    e. Adjust shift select cable by rotating manual lever counterclockwise until it reaches Park position. Rotate manual lever clockwise two detent positions until manual lever is in Neutral position. Install shift select cable into manual lever and secure with cable nut. Pull cable taut making sure no deflection exists.
    f. **Torque** shift select cable to 115 inch lbs.
    g. **Torque** left splash shield bolts to 44 inch lbs.
    h. **Torque** battery ground cable to 11 ft. lbs.
9. **Ensure proper operation of PNP switch by performing the following steps:**
    a. Apply parking brake and block wheels.
    b. With shifter in Park, turn start engine and verify starter operation, then stop engine and turn engine Off with key in On position.
    c. Move shifter to Neutral, turn start engine and verify starter operation.
    d. Verify that starter does not operate in Drive, 2nd, Low or Reverse.

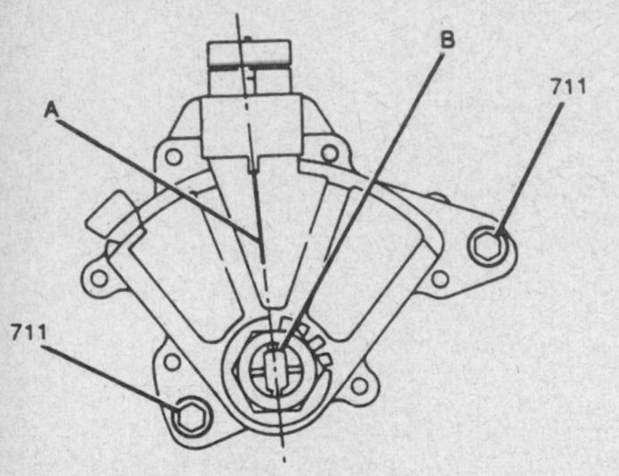
B
711
A
711

A NEUTRAL BASIC LINE
B PNP SWITCH SLEEVE GROOVE
711 PNP SWITCH BOLTS

GC1109300268000X

Fig. 49 Park/neutral position (PNP) switch adjustment. 1993–94

STOPLAMP SWITCH

1993–94

1. Disconnect battery ground cable, then slide hood latch release cable sideways to release from holder.
2. Disconnect hood release cable from hood latch release lever.
3. Remove two screws and hood latch release lever from knee bolster.
4. Remove two cover plates, two screws, four bolts and knee bolster from instrument panel.
5. Remove left side ventilation duct from left side duct outlet.
6. Disconnect stoplamp electrical connector from stoplamp switch, then loosen stoplamp switch locknut, **Fig. 50.**
7. Remove stoplamp switch locknut, then stoplamp switch.
8. Reverse procedure to install noting the following:
   a. Adjust stoplamp switch. Turn switch until distance between end of switch plunger and end of threaded portion of switch is within .02-.09 inch.
   b. **Torque** stoplamp switch locknut to 89 inch lbs.
   c. **Torque** knee bolster bolts to 124 inch lbs.
   d. **Torque** battery ground cable to 11 ft. lbs.

VACUUM PUMP

1992

1. Disconnect vacuum pump electrical connector.
2. Disconnect vacuum hoses.
3. Remove vacuum pump attaching bolts, then remove vacuum pump.
4. Reverse procedure to install.

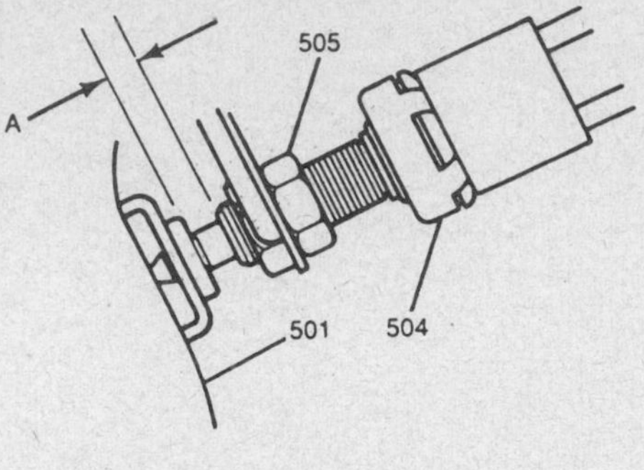
505
A
501
504

A STOPLAMP SWITCH CLEARANCE 0.5 – 2.4 mm (0.02 – 0.09")
501 BRAKE PEDAL
504 STOPLAMP SWITCH
505 STOPLAMP SWITCH LOCKNUT

GC1109300269000X

Fig. 50 Stoplamp switch clearance. 1993–94

VACUUM SWITCH

1992

1. Disconnect vacuum switch electrical connector.
2. Disconnect vacuum switch vacuum hose.
3. Unscrew vacuum switch, then remove vacuum switch.
4. Reverse procedure to install.

Type 5

NOTE: On Air Bag Equipped Models, Refer To "Air Bag System Precautions" Located In The Front Of This Manual For System Disarming & Arming Procedures.

NOTE: Electrical Symbol & Wire Color Code Identification Located In The Front Of This Manual Can Be Used As An Aid When Using Wiring Circuits Found In This Section.

INDEX

DESCRIPTION

The main parts of the cruise control system are the functional control switches, cruise control module assembly, vehicle speed sensor assembly and cruise control release switch, stop lamp and Torque Converter Clutch (TCC) switch, and clutch on 5.7L/V8-350 engines (Camaro and Firebird) or clutch anticipate switch assemblies on 3.4L/V6-204 engines (Camaro and Firebird).

The cruise control system uses a cruise control module assembly to obtain the desired vehicle cruise speed. Two important components in the module assembly assist in this. The first is electronic controller and second is an electric stepper motor. The controller monitors vehicle speed and operates the electric stepper motor. The motor moves a ribbon and throttle linkage, in response to the controller, to maintain the desired cruise speed. The cruise control module assembly contains a low speed limit which will prevent the system from operation during speeds below 25 mph. The operation of the controller is controlled by functional switches located on the turn signal and headlamp switch and cruise control actuator and windshield wiper/washer lever assembly.

Cruise control release switch, stop lamp and clutch or clutch anticipate switch assemblies are provided to disengage the cruise system. The switch assemblies are mounted on the brake and accelerator and

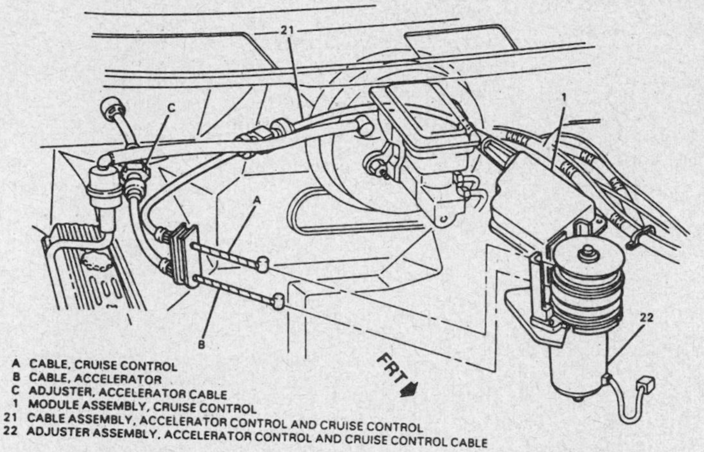
21
C
1
A
B
22
FRT
A CABLE, CRUISE CONTROL
B CABLE, ACCELERATOR
C ADJUSTER, ACCELERATOR CABLE
1 MODULE ASSEMBLY, CRUISE CONTROL
21 CABLE ASSEMBLY, ACCELERATOR CONTROL AND CRUISE CONTROL
22 ADJUSTER ASSEMBLY, ACCELERATOR CONTROL AND CRUISE CONTROL CABLE

GC1109300304000X

Fig. 1 Accelerator control and cruise control cable assembly. Fleetwood (RWD) less V4U Coachbuilder Equipment Option

clutch pedal bracket. When the brake pedal or clutch pedal is depressed, the cruise control system is electrically disengaged and the throttle is returned to idle position.

SYSTEM COMPONENTS

SPEED SENSOR

Camaro & Firebird

The vehicle speed sensor is mounted to the automatic transmission and produces and alternating current (AC) signal. The frequency of this signal is proportional to the speed in which the transmission output shaft rotates, which is proportional to the speed of the vehicle.

The AC signal produced by the sensor is supplied to the engine control module (ECM), cruise control module and instrument cluster. The signal is transmitted at a rate of 4000 pulses per mile. The ECM, cruise control module and speedometer internally convert the number of pulses per miles per second to determine vehicle speed.

SPEED SENSOR BUFFER

Caprice, Fleetwood (RWD), Impala SS & Roadmaster

The Vehicle Speed Sensor (VSS) buffer receives a signal from the VSS (permanent magnet generator) indicating vehicle speed. The buffer processes the signal which is then sent to the Engine Control Module (ECM), cruise control module and speedometer.

CRUISE CONTROL MODULE

Camaro, Caprice, Firebird, Fleetwood (RWD), Impala SS & Roadmaster

On Camaro and Firebird models, the module is mounted on the left engine compartment inner side rail. On Caprice, Fleetwood (RWD) and Roadmaster models, the module is mounted on the left wheelhouse panel near the master cylinder. The module has an electronic controller and an electric stepper motor to vary the throttle with each different cruise mode. The module is not serviceable and must be replaced as an assembly.

PRECAUTIONS

AIR BAG SYSTEMS

Refer to "Air Bag System Precautions" in the front of this manual for system disarming and arming procedures.

ADJUSTMENTS

CRUISE CONTROL CABLE

Camaro & Firebird

With throttle closed, lock cable conduit by pressing down on lock tab. When cable is in unlocked position and throttle is closed, cable adjustment spring removes appropriate amount of slack. Lock button must be fully extended to allow proper adjustment spring operation prior to locking.

Caprice, Fleetwood (RWD), Impala SS w/V4U Coachbuilder Option Equipment & Roadmaster

1. Remove air cleaner and resonator.
2. Unlock cable conduit at support bracket.
3. With throttle closed, lock cable conduit by pressing down on lock tab.
4. When cable is in unlocked position and throttle is closed, cable adjustment spring removes appropriate amount of slack.
5. Lock button must be fully extended to allow proper adjustment spring operation prior to locking.
6. Install air cleaner and resonator.

ACCELERATOR CABLE

Fleetwood (RWD) Less V4U Coachbuilder Option Equipment

The accelerator control and cruise control assembly is serviced as an assembly. The cruise control cable is a non-adjustable but the accelerator cable requires adjustment after installation.

1. Press accelerator cable adjuster button and hold.
2. Position accelerator cable adjuster in non-adjusted position, **Fig. 1.** Pull cable casing away from adjuster so that casing will be at its longest position.
3. Release accelerator cable adjuster button.
4. Using moderate foot pressure (approximately 50 ft. lbs. of force), press accelerator pedal down to wide open throttle position; several clicks of the accelerator cable should be heard.

CRUISE CONTROL SWTICH & STOP LAMP ASSEMBLIES

Camaro & Firebird

The release switch assembly must be adjusted at the same time the stop lamp and torque converter clutch (TCC) switch is adjusted. The clutch switch assembly or clutch anticipate switch assembly cannot be adjusted until clutch pedal assembly is installed. **Proper stop lamp switch adjustment is essential. Improper adjustment will cause brake drag and excessive brake lining wear.** Refer to **Fig. 2** when performing this procedure.

1. Depress brake pedal or clutch pedal and insert release switch assembly, stop lamp and TCC switch assembly and clutch switch or clutch anticipate switch assembly into pedal assembly with bracket until retainer on release switch, stop lamp and TCC switch assembly and clutch switch or clutch anticipate switch assembly is fully seated.
2. **Ensure proper amount of force is applied to brake pedal assembly during adjustment. Excessive force could damage vacuum booster, too little force could result in dragging brakes.**
3. Slowly pull brake or clutch pedal rearward with 50 pounds of force until click sounds can no longer be heard. Release switch assembly, stop lamp and TCC switch assembly and clutch switch or clutch anticipate switch will have moved retainers to their original positions.
4. Release switch and stop lamp and TCC switch contacts should be open at 1 inch or less of pedal travel and occur at same time or before beginning of braking. The brake pedal can travel up to 1 inch before cruise control disengages.

Caprice, Impala SS & Roadmaster

The release switch and stop lamp switch cannot be adjusted until after the brake booster pushrod is assembled to brake pedal assembly. Refer to **Fig. 3** when performing this procedure.

1. Depress brake pedal and insert release switch and stop lamp switch assembly into retainers until fully seated.
2. Slowly release brake pedal back to its original position. Release switch and stop lamp switch assemblies will move within retainers to their adjusted position.

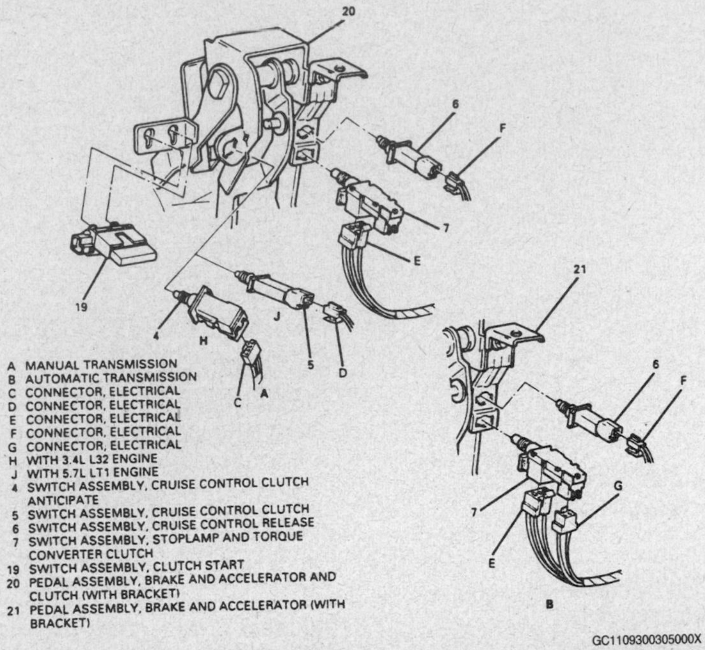
A MANUAL TRANSMISSION
B AUTOMATIC TRANSMISSION
C CONNECTOR, ELECTRICAL
D CONNECTOR, ELECTRICAL
E CONNECTOR, ELECTRICAL
F CONNECTOR, ELECTRICAL
G CONNECTOR, ELECTRICAL
H WITH 3.4L L32 ENGINE
J WITH 5.7L LT1 ENGINE
4 SWITCH ASSEMBLY, CRUISE CONTROL CLUTCH ANTICIPATE
5 SWITCH ASSEMBLY, CRUISE CONTROL CLUTCH
6 SWITCH ASSEMBLY, CRUISE CONTROL RELEASE
7 SWITCH ASSEMBLY, STOPLAMP AND TORQUE CONVERTER CLUTCH
19 SWITCH ASSEMBLY, CLUTCH START
20 PEDAL ASSEMBLY, BRAKE AND ACCELERATOR AND CLUTCH (WITH BRACKET)
21 PEDAL ASSEMBLY, BRAKE AND ACCELERATOR (WITH BRACKET)
GC1109300305000X

Fig. 2 Exploded view of cruise control switch assembly. Camaro & Firebird

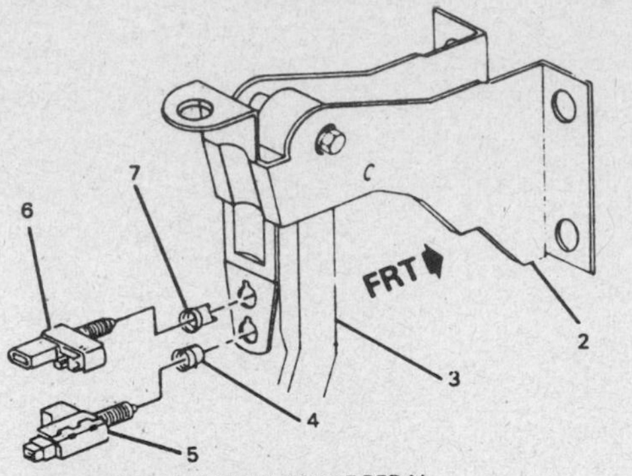
FRT
2 BRACKET ASSEMBLY, BRAKE PEDAL
3 PEDAL ASSEMBLY, BRAKE
4 RETAINER, STOPLAMP SWITCH
5 SWITCH ASSEMBLY, STOPLAMP
6 SWITCH ASSEMBLY, CRUISE CONTROL RELEASE
7 RETAINER, CRUISE CONTROL RELEASE SWITCH
GC1109300306000X

Fig. 3 Cruise control release switch & stop lamp switch assemblies. Caprice, Impala SS & Roadmaster

3. The following brake pedal travel distances can be used to check for properly adjusted release switch and stop lamp switch assemblies:
   a. Release switch and stop lamp switch assemblies contacts must be open at 1/8–1/2 inch brake pedal travel, measured at centerline of brake pedal pad.
   b. Nominal actuation of stop lamp switch contacts is about 3/16 inch after cruise switch control contacts close.

TV CABLE

Fleetwood (RWD) Less V4U Coachbuilder Option Equipment

The TV cable setting synchronizes the TV cable assembly and the throttle body. If unset, shifting problems and premature transmission wear may result. This procedure sets the accelerator cable from the throttle body and TV cable from adjuster to automatic transmission. The TV cable requires no periodic adjustment.

1. Stop engine, then remove cover, shield and inner cover, **Fig. 4.**
2. Put accelerator control cable from adjuster to throttle body in non-adjusted position by pressing button and slide out to fully stretched position, then releasing button.
3. Put TV cable from adjuster to automatic transmission in non-adjusted position by flipping toggle switch up.
4. Insert 1/8 inch drill bit, grooved side up, through cams. If bit goes down further, it will hit gear and bind adjuster assembly.
5. Set torque wrench to 35 inch lbs. Insert torque wrench with 1/4 inch drive extension through round hole in top of first pulley and into square hole in second pulley. **Torque** relaxer cams to 35 inch lbs. Once relaxer cams are tightened, maintain torque with wrench until after toggle switch on TV cable is flipped down to lock setting.
6. Remove torque wrench with extension and drill bit, then install inner cover, shield and cover.
7. Install TECH 1 with mass storage cartridge to vehicle.
8. Fully depress accelerator pedal while monitoring throttle angle on TECH 1. Throttle angle must be 90 percent or above. If throttle angle is below 90 percent, repeat cable setting as outlined.

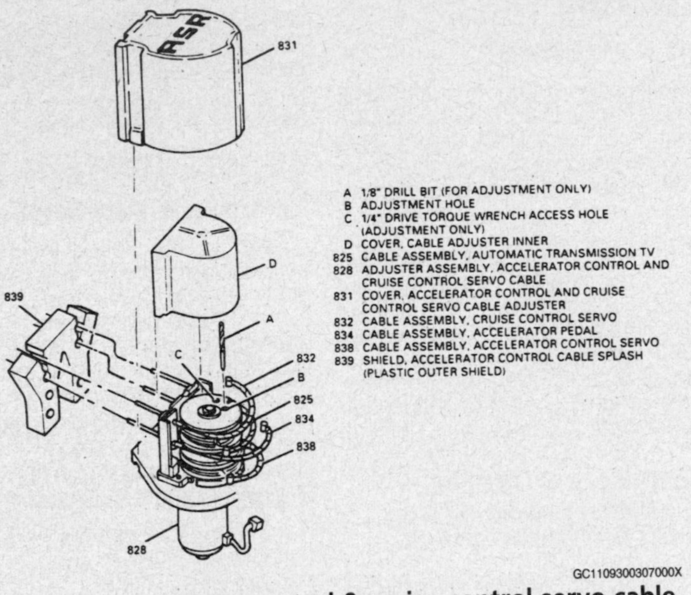
RSR
831
D
A
C
839
832
B
825
834
838
828
A 1/8" DRILL BIT (FOR ADJUSTMENT ONLY)
B ADJUSTMENT HOLE
C 1/4" DRIVE TORQUE WRENCH ACCESS HOLE (ADJUSTMENT ONLY)
D COVER, CABLE ADJUSTER INNER
825 CABLE ASSEMBLY, AUTOMATIC TRANSMISSION TV
828 ADJUSTER ASSEMBLY, ACCELERATOR CONTROL AND CRUISE CONTROL SERVO CABLE
831 COVER, ACCELERATOR CONTROL AND CRUISE CONTROL SERVO CABLE ADJUSTER
832 CABLE ASSEMBLY, CRUISE CONTROL SERVO
834 CABLE ASSEMBLY, ACCELERATOR PEDAL
838 CABLE ASSEMBLY, ACCELERATOR CONTROL SERVO
839 SHIELD, ACCELERATOR CONTROL CABLE SPLASH (PLASTIC OUTER SHIELD)
GC1109300307000X

Fig. 4 Accelerator control & cruise control servo cable adjuster. Fleetwood (RWD) less V4U Coachbuilder Equipment Option

Fleetwood (RWD) w/V4U Coachbuilder Option Equipment

Setting of the cable must be done by rotating throttle body injector throttle lever at the throttle body. Do not use accelerator pedal to rotate throttle body injector throttle lever.

1. Stop engine, then remove air cleaner.
2. Depress and hold down readjust button at engine end of TV cable assembly.
3. Move slider **Fig. 5** rearward until it stops.

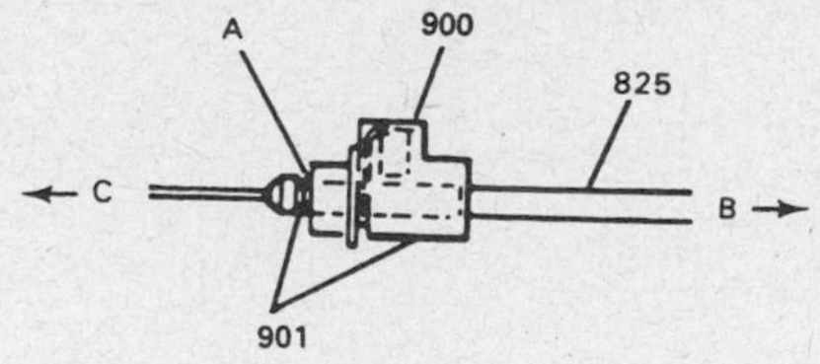
A
900
825
C
B
901

A SLIDER AGAINST FITTING (ZERO OR RESET POSITION)
B TO TRANSMISSION
C TO THROTTLE BODY
825 CABLE ASSEMBLY, AUTOMATIC TRANSMISSION TV
900 TAB, AUTOMATIC TRANSMISSION TV CABLE RESET
901 SLIDER, AUTOMATIC TRANSMISSION TV CABLE

GC1109300308000X

Fig. 5 Automatic transmission TV cable readjustment. Fleetwood (RWD) w/V4U Coachbuilder Equipment Option

4. Release adjust button, then rotate throttle body injector throttle lever to its full-travel position.
5. Slider must move toward throttle body injector lever assembly when injector throttle lever is rotated to its full-travel position.
6. Install air cleaner, then ensure cable moves freely after engine has been warmed up.

SYSTEM DIAGNOSIS & TESTING

Refer to **Figs. 6 through 45** for cruise control and vehicle speed sensor wiring diagrams, cruise module pin location, diagnosis and troubleshooting. After service, verify operation system operation as follows:

1. Set parking brake, then start engine.
2. Move cruise switch to Off, then move cruise switch to On and wait at least three seconds before proceeding.
3. Fully depress and hold brake pedal, then push cruise switch in and hold.
4. Hold cruise slider switch in R/A position, then after ten seconds, release brake pedal while holding R/A and Set switches.
5. Engine RPM should increase momentarily then return to normal.

COMPONENT REPLACEMENT

CRUISE CONTROL CABLE

Camaro, Caprice, Firebird, Fleetwood (RWD), Impala SS w/V4U Coachbuilder Option Equipment & Roadmaster

The cable is connected between the cruise control module and throttle body lever.

1. **On Caprice, Impala SS, Fleetwood (RWD) and Roadmaster models,** remove air cleaner and resonator.
2. **On all models,** remove cable and conduit from engine bracket, **Fig. 46.**
3. Remove cable end fitting from throttle body lever stud.
4. Remove cruise control retainer at module.
5. Remove cable from module as follows:
   a. Compress conduit tangs, **Fig. 47,** and pull out of module housing.
   b. Disconnect cable bead from cruise motor band end fitting on module, **Fig. 47.**
   c. Note routing and remove cable.
6. Reverse procedure to install noting the following:
   a. **Ribbon must not be twisted;** slide cable conduit fitting over ribbon and snap into module housing ensuring both tangs are engaged.
   b. Adjust cable as outlined.

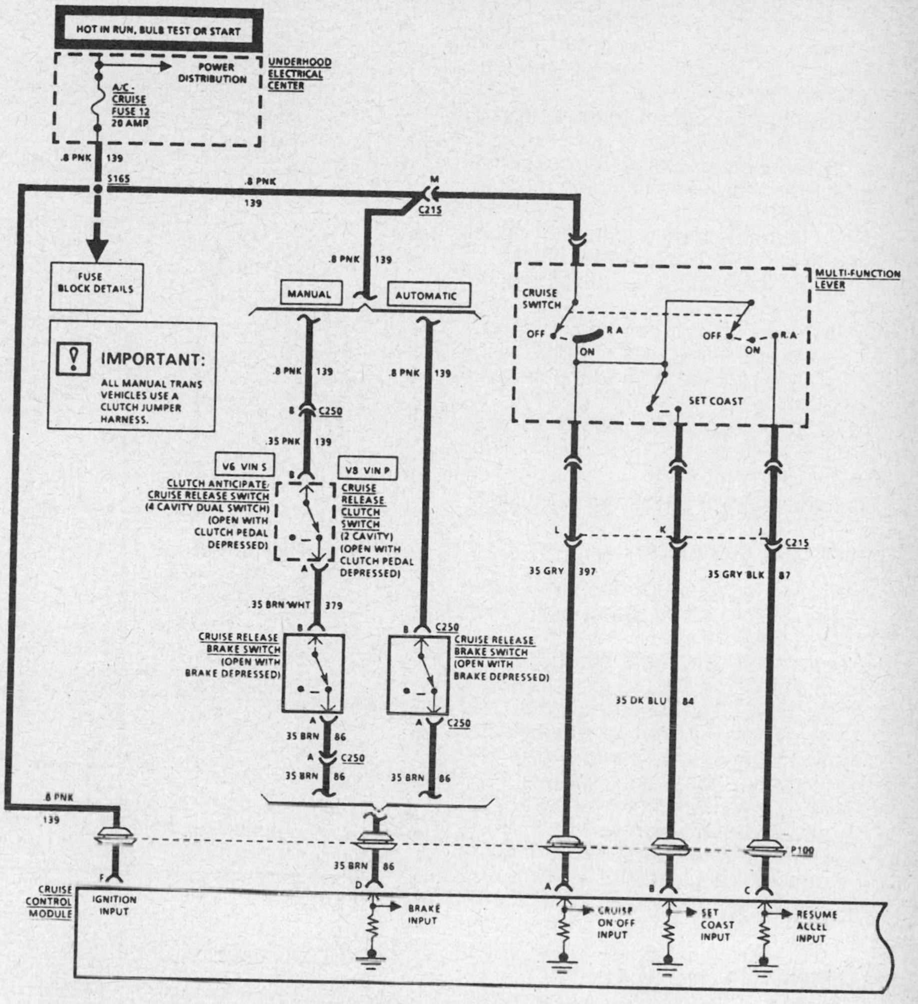
HOT IN RUN, BULB TEST OR START
POWER DISTRIBUTION
UNDERHOOD ELECTRICAL CENTER
A/C-CRUISE FUSE 12 20 AMP
.8 PNK 139
S165
M
C215
FUSE BLOCK DETAILS
IMPORTANT:
ALL MANUAL TRANS VEHICLES USE A CLUTCH JUMPER HARNESS.
MANUAL
AUTOMATIC
CRUISE SWITCH
MULTI-FUNCTION LEVER
OFF
ON
R A
SET COAST
C250
.35 PNK 139
V6 VIN S
V8 VIN P
CLUTCH ANTICIPATE/ CRUISE RELEASE SWITCH (4 CAVITY DUAL SWITCH) (OPEN WITH CLUTCH PEDAL DEPRESSED)
CRUISE RELEASE CLUTCH SWITCH (2 CAVITY) (OPEN WITH CLUTCH PEDAL DEPRESSED)
.35 GRY 397
.35 GRY BLK 87
.35 BRN/WHT 379
CRUISE RELEASE BRAKE SWITCH (OPEN WITH BRAKE DEPRESSED)
.35 DK BLU 84
.35 BRN 86
P100
CRUISE CONTROL MODULE
IGNITION INPUT
BRAKE INPUT
CRUISE ON/OFF INPUT
SET COAST INPUT
RESUME ACCEL INPUT

GC1109300270010X

Fig. 6 Cruise control wiring diagram (Part 1 of 2). 1993 Camaro & Firebird

ACCELERATOR & CRUISE CONTROL CABLE ADJUSTER

Fleetwood (RWD)

1. Remove cover and shield from adjuster, then squeeze tabs on side of cover to remove, **Fig. 48.**
2. Remove accelerator control and cruise control cable as outlined.
3. Remove accelerator control and automatic transmission TV as outlined.
4. Disconnect electrical connector, then loosen bolts/screws and reposition module.
5. Remove adjuster and bracket assembly from vehicle.
6. Remove bracket nuts, then bracket from adjuster.
7. Remove bracket from adjuster, then retainers and bolts/screws.
8. Reverse procedure to install noting the following:
   a. **Torque** bracket nuts to 71 inch lbs.
   b. **Torque** module bolts/screws to 71 inch lbs.
   c. Adjust automatic transmission TV cable as outlined.
   d. Adjust accelerator cable (without V4U Coachbuilder Equipment Option) as outlined.

ACCELERATOR CONTROL & CRUISE CONTROL CABLE

Fleetwood (RWD) Less V4U Coachbuilder Equipment Option

1. Remove cover and shield from adjuster, then clip from cable and cover from adjuster, **Fig. 49.**
2. Using a small flat-bladed tool, release lock tab on cable assembly while slid-

ing cable casing out of adjuster.

3. Remove beads of cable from slots in adjuster, then cable from cruise control module as follows:
   a. Compress conduit tangs and pull out of module.
   b. Disconnect cable bead from cruise motor ribbon end fitting on module, **Fig. 50.**
4. Remove cable from accelerator pedal and body, then cable from vehicle.
5. Reverse procedure to install noting the following:
   a. **Ribbon must not be twisted.** Slide end fitting over ribbon and install in module until tangs snap in place.
   b. Adjust accelerator cable as outlined (less V4U Coachbuilder Equipment Option).

CRUISE CONTROL MODULE

Camaro & Firebird

1. Remove accelerator control cable splash shield screws and bolts, then splash shield.
2. Remove left hand front bumper fascia lower deflector, **Fig. 51** as follows:
   a. Remove retainer, then bolts and screws from front lower deflector and wheelhouse panel liner.
   b. Remove bolts and screws from front lower deflector and radiator air lower deflector.
   c. Remove retainers from front lower deflector and radiator lower baffle.
   d. Remove front lower deflector by sliding outward from radiator lower deflector and wheelhouse panel liner.
3. Remove cruise control cover to access connectors, then disconnect electrical connector from cruise control module.
4. Disconnect cruise control cable from module, then remove bolts and screws.
5. Remove module with bracket, **Fig. 51**, then module from bracket.
6. Reverse procedure to install noting the following:
   a. **Torque** cruise control module to bracket screws and bolts to 53 ft. lbs.
   b. **Torque** cruise control module to left engine compartment inner side rail screws and bolts to 89 ft. lbs.
   c. **Torque** radiator air lower deflector and front lower deflector screws and bolts to 49 ft. lbs.
   d. **Torque** accelerator cable splash shield screws and bolts to 17 ft. lbs.

Caprice, Impala SS & Roadmaster

1. Disconnect battery ground cable.
2. Disconnect electrical connector from module, **Fig. 52.**
3. Disconnect cruise control cable from module, then remove bolts and screws.
4. Remove module and plugs.
5. Remove plugs from module if a new module is being installed.
6. Reverse procedure to install noting the following:

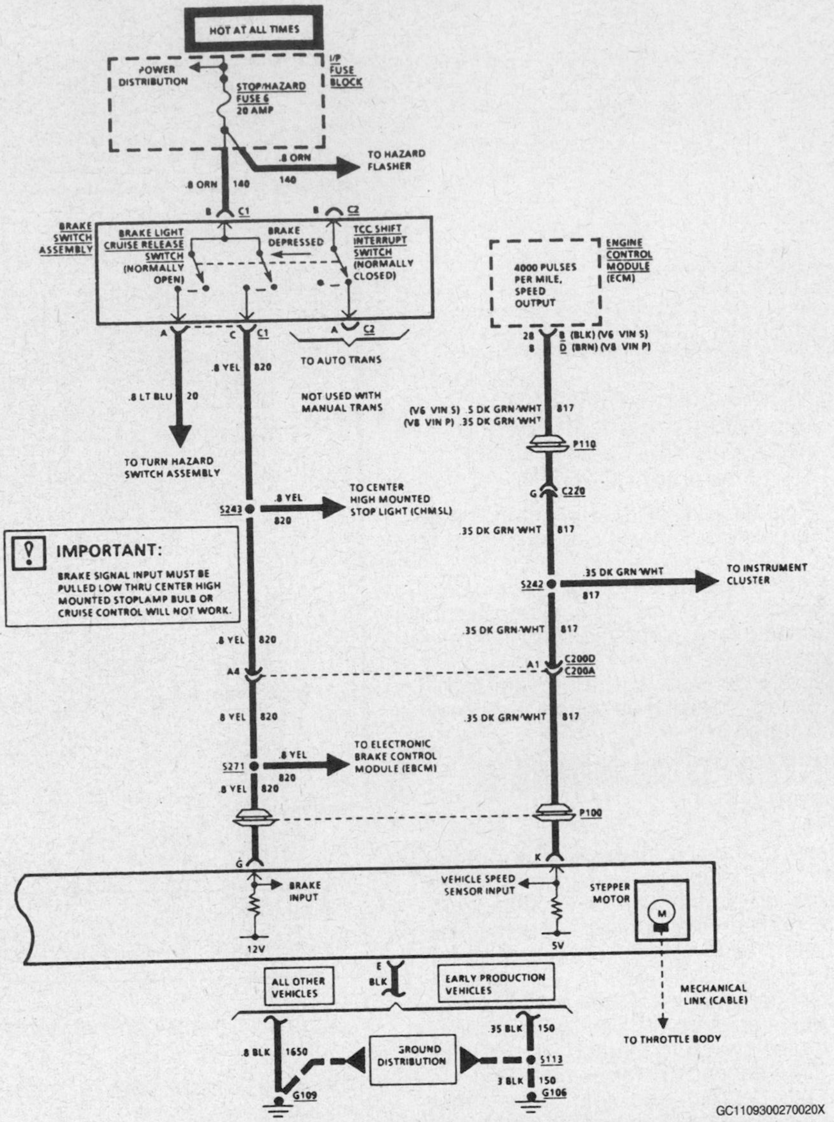
HOT AT ALL TIMES
POWER DISTRIBUTION
STOP/HAZARD FUSE 6 20 AMP
I/P FUSE BLOCK
TO HAZARD FLASHER
BRAKE SWITCH ASSEMBLY
BRAKE LIGHT CRUISE RELEASE SWITCH (NORMALLY OPEN)
BRAKE DEPRESSED
TCC SHIFT INTERRUPT SWITCH (NORMALLY CLOSED)
ENGINE CONTROL MODULE (ECM)
4000 PULSES PER MILE, SPEED OUTPUT
TO AUTO TRANS
NOT USED WITH MANUAL TRANS
TO TURN HAZARD SWITCH ASSEMBLY
TO CENTER HIGH MOUNTED STOP LIGHT (CHMSL)
IMPORTANT:
BRAKE SIGNAL INPUT MUST BE PULLED LOW THRU CENTER HIGH MOUNTED STOPLAMP BULB OR CRUISE CONTROL WILL NOT WORK.
TO INSTRUMENT CLUSTER
TO ELECTRONIC BRAKE CONTROL MODULE (EBCM)
BRAKE INPUT
VEHICLE SPEED SENSOR INPUT
STEPPER MOTOR
MECHANICAL LINK (CABLE)
TO THROTTLE BODY
ALL OTHER VEHICLES
EARLY PRODUCTION VEHICLES
GROUND DISTRIBUTION
GC1109300270020X

Fig. 6 Cruise control wiring diagram (Part 2 of 2). 1993 Camaro & Firebird

   a. Align holes in accelerator and cruise control adjuster bracket to holes in wheelhouse panel and position module on wheelhouse panel.
   b. **Torque** module bolts and screws to 71 ft. lbs.
   c. Adjust cable, if necessary, as outlined.

CRUISE CONTROL SWITCH ASSEMBLIES

Camaro & Firebird

1. Remove left hand instrument panel sound insulator, then disconnect electrical connectors.
2. Remove release switch assembly, stop lamp and TCC switch assembly and clutch switch or clutch anticipate switch, if equipped from pedal with bracket, **Fig. 2.**
3. Reverse procedure to install. Adjust as outlined.

ENGAGEMENT SWITCH

The engagement switch is not serviceable. The complete turn signal, headlamp dimmer switch, cruise control actuator and windshield wiper/washer must be replaced as an assembly.

1. Disconnect battery ground cable.
2. Remove steering column access cover, then disconnect electrical connector. **Ensure windshield wiper switch is in Off position.**
3. Remove lever assembly by pulling straight out.
4. Reverse procedure to install.

RELEASE SWITCH & STOP LAMP SWITCH

Caprice, Impala SS & Roadmaster

1. Disconnect electrical connectors, then remove release switch and stop lamp switch assemblies from retainers, **Fig. 3.**
2. Remove retainers from bracket.
3. Reverse procedure to install. Adjust as outlined.

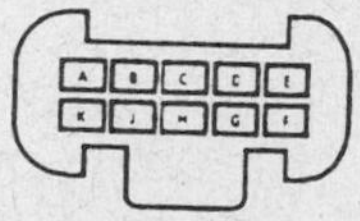

12065425
10-WAY F METRI-PACK 150 SERIES
BLK
CRUISE CONTROL MODULE

**CAVITIES NOT LISTED ARE NOT USED

CAVITY	WIRE COLOR	CKT	DESCRIPTION	PAGE
A	GRY	397	CRUISE CONTROL SWITCH - ON	8A-34-0
B	DK BLU	84	CRUISE CONTROL SWITCH - SET COAST	8A-34-0
C	GRY BLK	87	CRUISE CONTROL SWITCH - RESUME ACCEL	8A-34-0
D	BRN	86	CRUISE RELEASE/BRAKE SWITCH OUTPUT	8A-34-0
E	BLK	1650	GROUND	8A-14-0, 2
F	PNK	139	POWER FEED FROM A/C-CRUISE FUSE #12	8A-34-0
G	YEL	820	BRAKE DEPRESSED INPUT	8A-34-1
K	DK GRN WHT	817	VEHICLE SPEED SIGNAL	8A-34-1

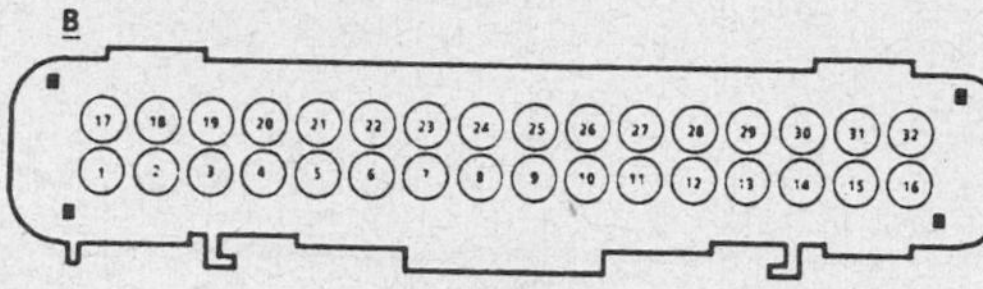
B

12129025
32-WAY F MICRO-PACK 100 SERIES
NAT
POWERTRAIN CONTROL MODULE
(V6 VIN S) AND (V8 VIN P)

V6 VIN S	
CONNECTOR ASSEMBLY BREAKDOWN	
TPA	12129021 (BLK)
SEAL	12146093
STRAIN RELIEF	12129010
CONNECTOR	12129025

V8 VIN P	
CONNECTOR ASSEMBLY BREAKDOWN	
TPA	12129021 (BLK)
SEAL	12146093
STRAIN RELIEF	12129020
CONNECTOR	12129025

GC1109400329000X

Fig. 7 Cruise control module pin location. Camaro & Firebird

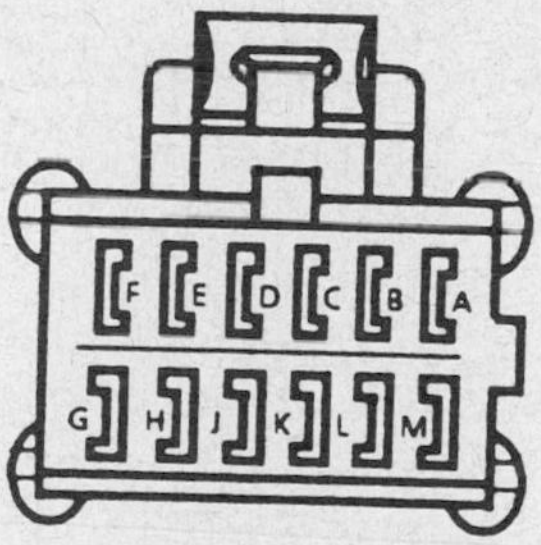
F
E
D
C
B
A
G
H
J
K
L
M

12065666
12-WAY PC EDGEBOARD
BLK
CRUISE CONTROL MODULE

GC1109400347000X

Fig. 8 Cruise control module pin location. Caprice, Fleetwood (RWD), Impala SS & Roadmaster

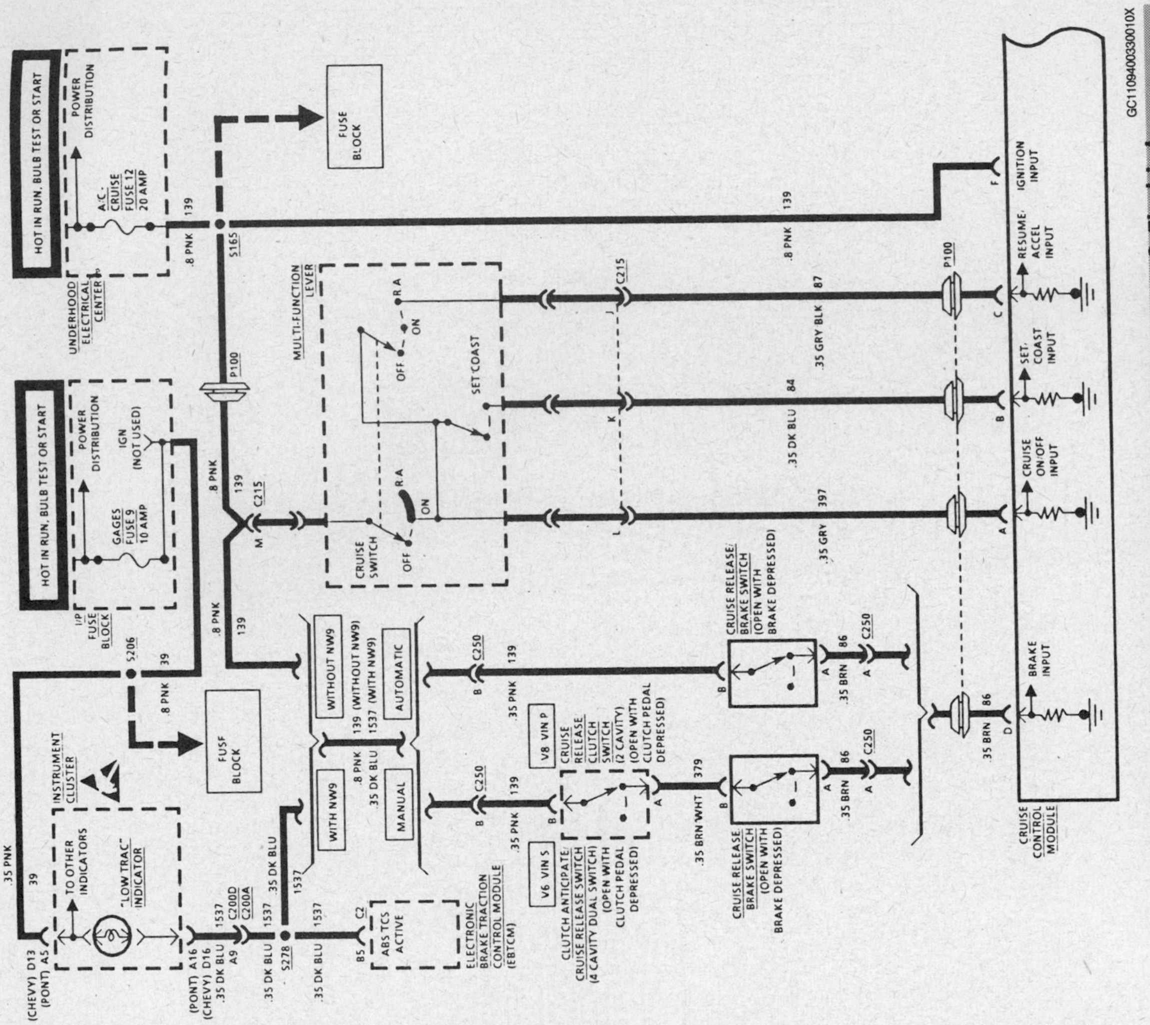
HOT IN RUN, BULB TEST OR START
POWER DISTRIBUTION
A/C-CRUISE FUSE 12 20 AMP
UNDERHOOD ELECTRICAL CENTER
GAGES FUSE 9 10 AMP
IGN (NOT USED)
I/P FUSE BLOCK
FUSE BLOCK
INSTRUMENT CLUSTER
TO OTHER INDICATORS
"LOW TRAC" INDICATOR
ABS TCS ACTIVE
ELECTRONIC BRAKE TRACTION CONTROL MODULE (EBTCM)
MULTI-FUNCTION LEVER
CRUISE SWITCH
SET COAST
WITHOUT NW9
WITH NW9
AUTOMATIC
MANUAL
CRUISE RELEASE BRAKE SWITCH (OPEN WITH BRAKE DEPRESSED)
CRUISE RELEASE CLUTCH SWITCH (2 CAVITY) (OPEN WITH CLUTCH PEDAL DEPRESSED)
CLUTCH ANTICIPATE/ CRUISE RELEASE SWITCH (4 CAVITY DUAL SWITCH) (OPEN WITH CLUTCH PEDAL DEPRESSED)
V6 VIN S
V8 VIN P
CRUISE CONTROL MODULE
BRAKE INPUT
CRUISE ON/OFF INPUT
SET/ COAST INPUT
RESUME/ ACCEL INPUT
IGNITION INPUT
GC1109400330010X

Fig. 9 Wiring diagram (Part 1 of 2). 1994 Camaro & Firebird

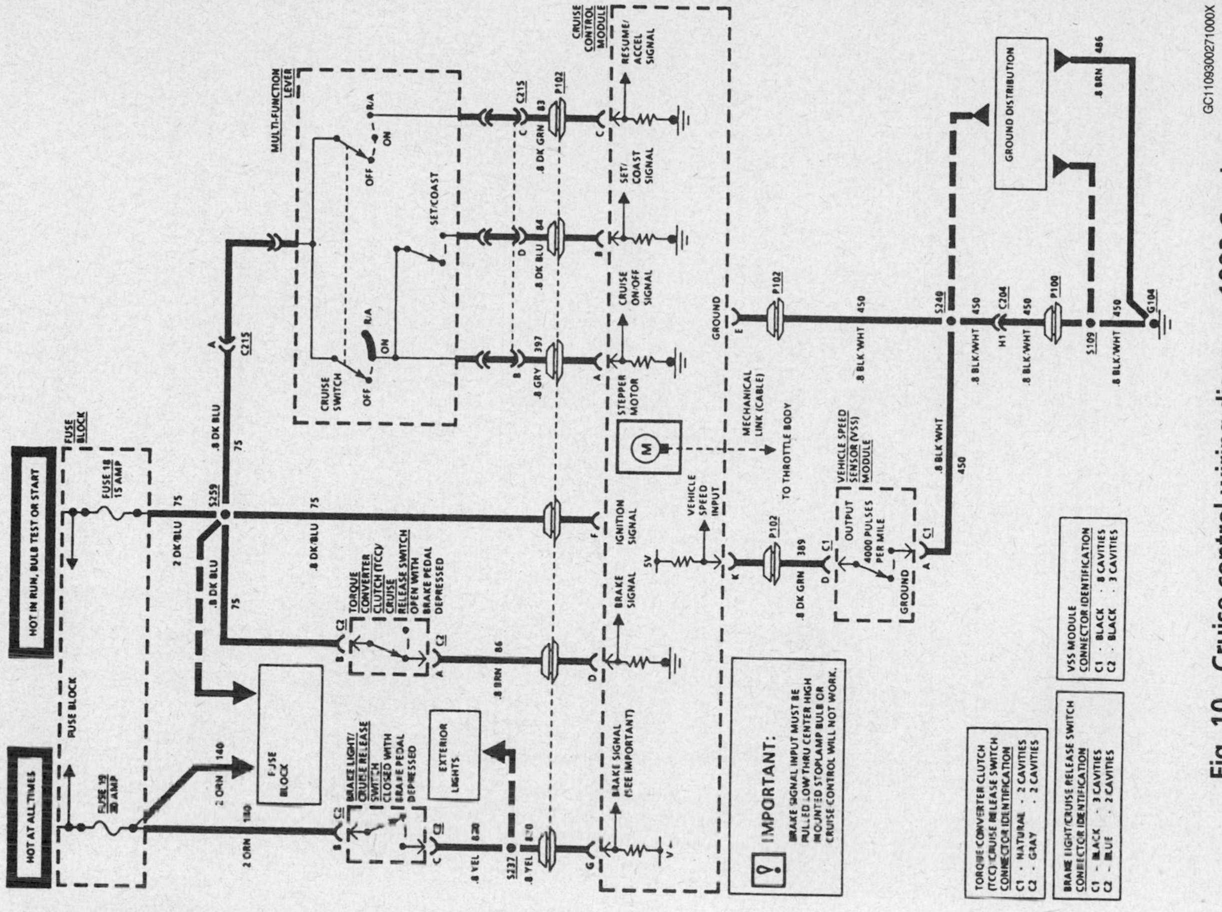
HOT IN RUN, BULB TEST OR START
HOT AT ALL TIMES
FUSE BLOCK
MULTI-FUNCTION LEVER
CRUISE CONTROL MODULE
GROUND DISTRIBUTION
IMPORTANT:
BRAKE SIGNAL INPUT MUST BE PULLED LOW THRU CENTER HIGH MOUNTED STOPLAMP BULB OR CRUISE CONTROL WILL NOT WORK.
GC1109300271000X

Fig. 10 Cruise control wiring diagram. 1993 Caprice

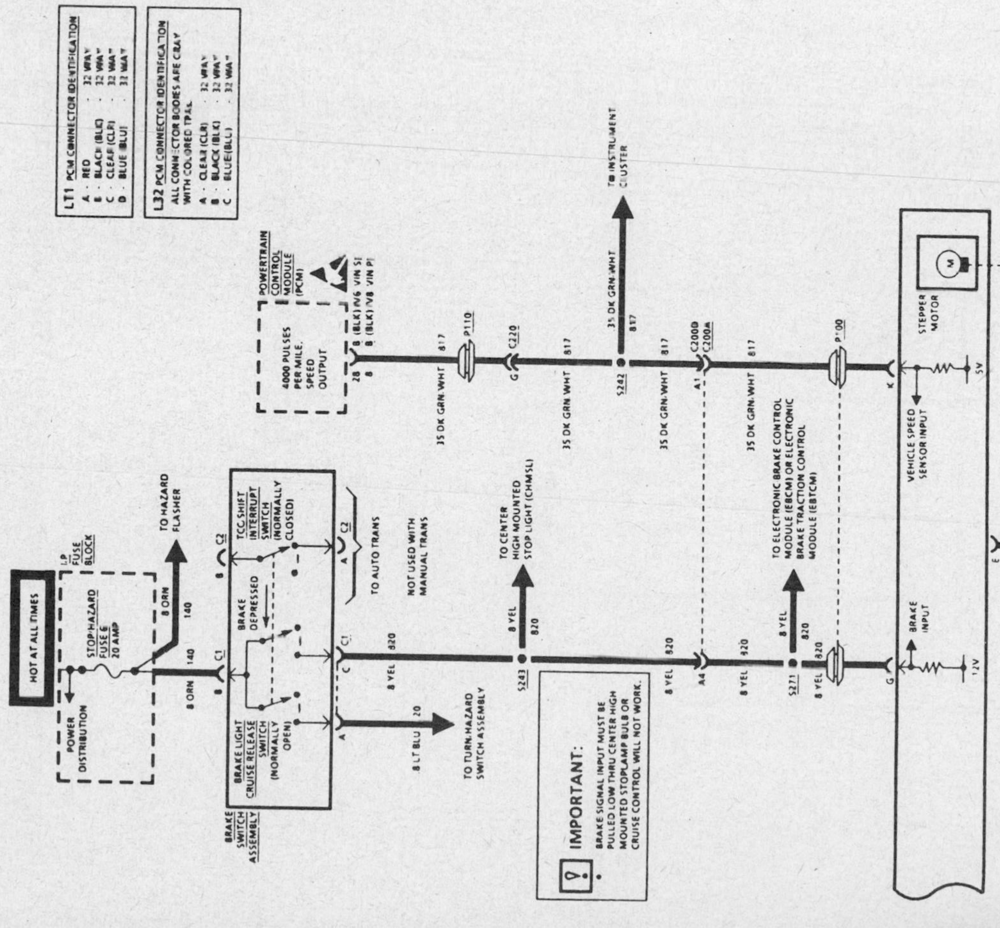
HOT AT ALL TIMES
POWERTRAIN CONTROL MODULE (PCM)
TO INSTRUMENT CLUSTER
GROUND DISTRIBUTION
TO THROTTLE BODY
IMPORTANT:
BRAKE SIGNAL INPUT MUST BE PULLED LOW THRU CENTER HIGH MOUNTED STOPLAMP BULB OR CRUISE CONTROL WILL NOT WORK.
GC1109400330020X

Fig. 9 Wiring diagram (Part 2 of 2). 1994 Camaro & Firebird

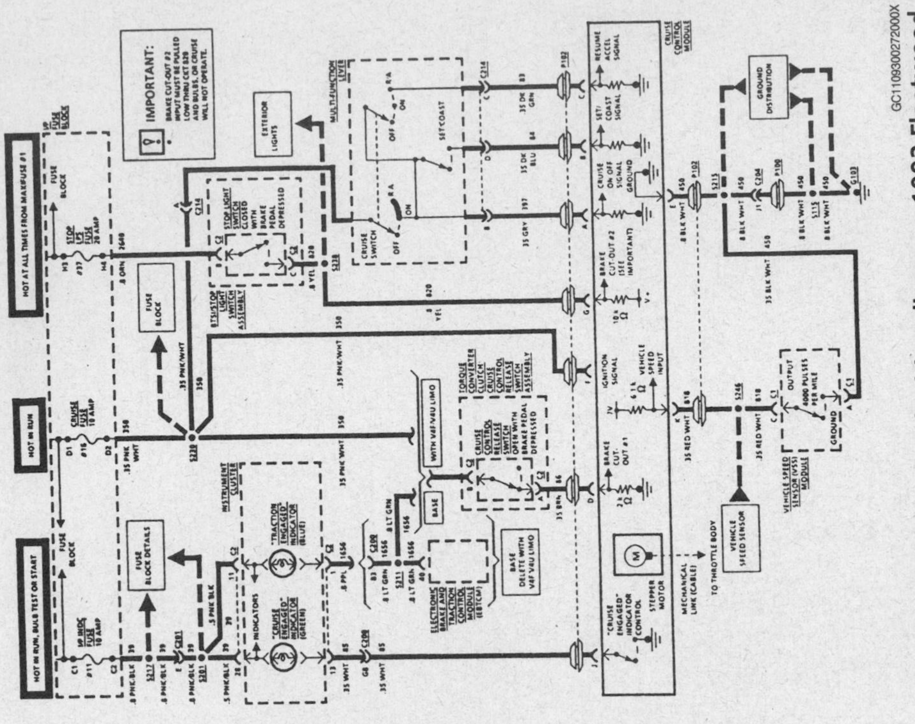
GC1109300272000X
HOT IN RUN, BULB TEST OR START
HOT IN RUN
HOT AT ALL TIMES FROM MAXIFUSE #1
FUSE BLOCK
IMPORTANT:
EXTERIOR LIGHTS
MULTI-FUNCTION LEVER
CRUISE SWITCH
SET COAST
INSTRUMENT CLUSTER
STEPPER MOTOR
MECHANICAL LINK (CABLE)
TO THROTTLE BODY
VEHICLE SPEED SENSOR
GROUND DISTRIBUTION
CRUISE CONTROL MODULE

Fig. 12 Cruise control wiring diagram. 1993 Fleetwood (RWD)

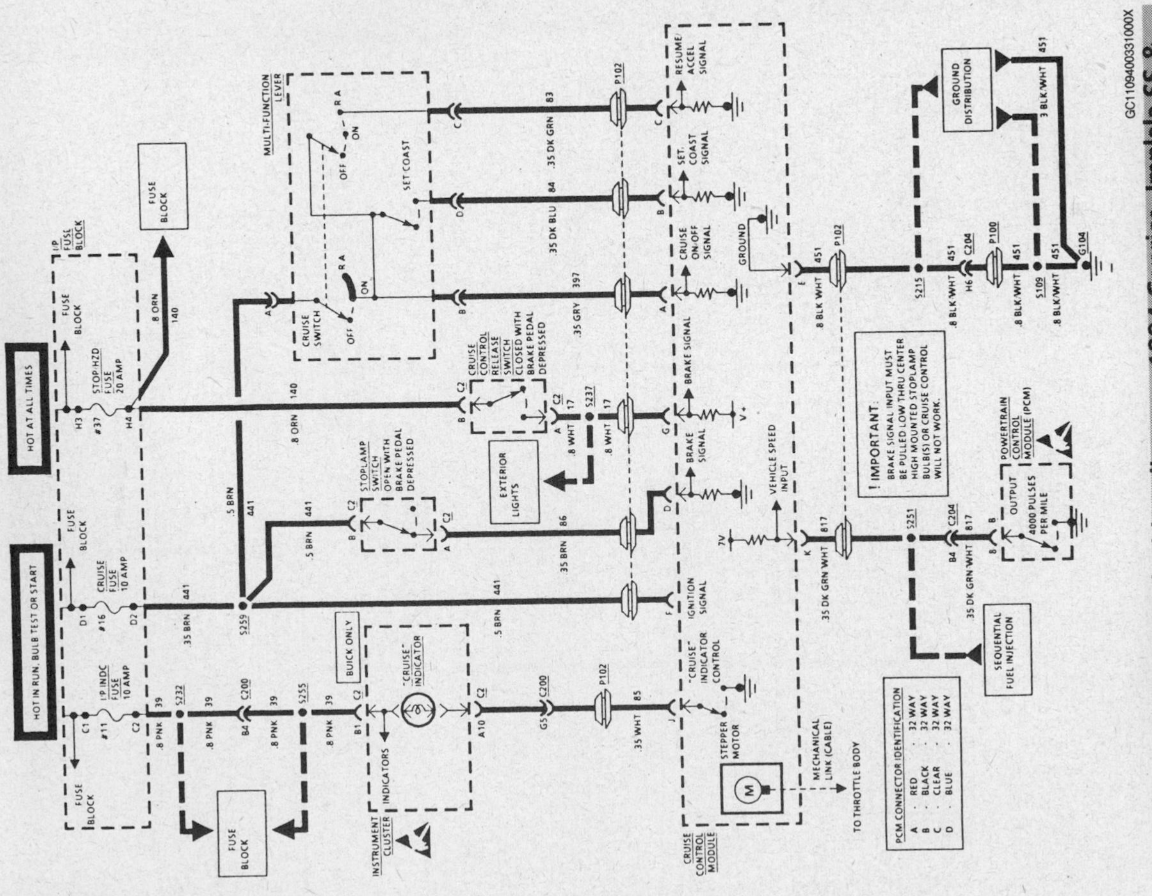
GC1109400331000X
HOT IN RUN, BULB TEST OR START
HOT AT ALL TIMES
FUSE BLOCK
I/P FUSE BLOCK
CRUISE FUSE 10 AMP
STOP-HZD FUSE 20 AMP
BUICK ONLY
"CRUISE" INDICATOR
INSTRUMENT CLUSTER
INDICATORS
STOPLAMP SWITCH OPEN WITH BRAKE PEDAL DEPRESSED
CRUISE CONTROL RELEASE SWITCH CLOSED WITH BRAKE PEDAL DEPRESSED
EXTERIOR LIGHTS
CRUISE SWITCH
MULTI-FUNCTION LEVER
SET COAST
"CRUISE" INDICATOR CONTROL
IGNITION SIGNAL
BRAKE SIGNAL
VEHICLE SPEED INPUT
CRUISE ON/OFF SIGNAL
SET/COAST SIGNAL
RESUME/ACCEL SIGNAL
GROUND
STEPPER MOTOR
MECHANICAL LINK (CABLE)
TO THROTTLE BODY
CRUISE CONTROL MODULE
! IMPORTANT:
BRAKE SIGNAL INPUT MUST BE PULLED LOW THRU CENTER HIGH MOUNTED STOPLAMP BULB(S) OR CRUISE CONTROL WILL NOT WORK.
POWERTRAIN CONTROL MODULE (PCM)
OUTPUT 4000 PULSES PER MILE
SEQUENTIAL FUEL INJECTION
GROUND DISTRIBUTION
PCM CONNECTOR IDENTIFICATION
A : RED : 32 WAY
B : BLACK : 32 WAY
C : CLEAR : 32 WAY
D : BLUE : 32 WAY

Fig. 11 Cruise control wiring diagram. 1994 Caprice, Implala SS & Roadmaster

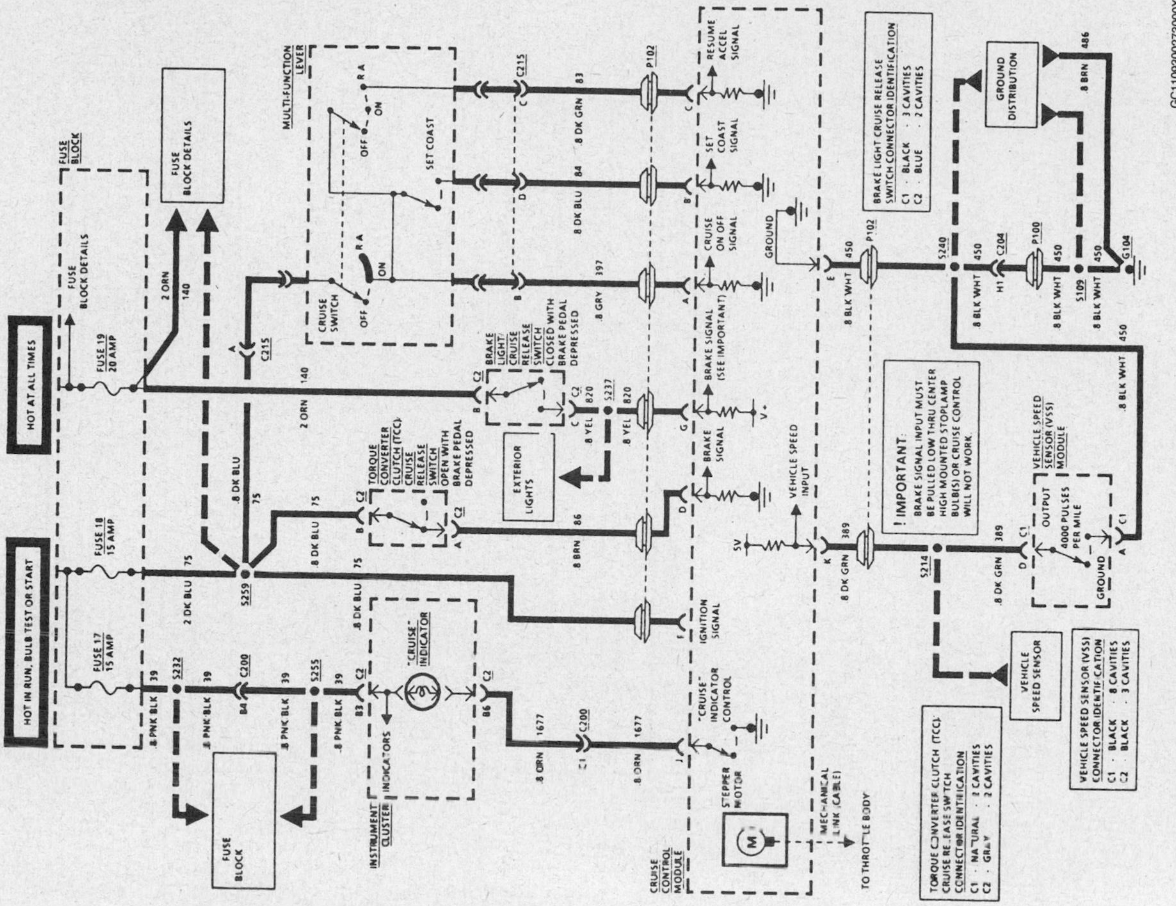
HOT AT ALL TIMES
HOT IN RUN, BULB TEST OR START
FUSE BLOCK
FUSE BLOCK DETAILS
FUSE 19 20 AMP
FUSE 18 15 AMP
FUSE 17 15 AMP
MULTI-FUNCTION LEVER
CRUISE SWITCH
SET COAST
BRAKE LIGHT/ CRUISE RELEASE SWITCH CLOSED WITH BRAKE PEDAL DEPRESSED
TORQUE CONVERTER CLUTCH (TCC)/ CRUISE RELEASE SWITCH OPEN WITH BRAKE PEDAL DEPRESSED
EXTERIOR LIGHTS
INSTRUMENT CLUSTER
"CRUISE" INDICATOR
INDICATORS
CRUISE CONTROL MODULE
STEPPER MOTOR
MECHANICAL LINK (CABLE)
TO THROTTLE BODY
RESUME ACCEL SIGNAL
SET COAST SIGNAL
CRUISE ON OFF SIGNAL
GROUND
BRAKE SIGNAL (SEE IMPORTANT)
BRAKE SIGNAL
VEHICLE SPEED INPUT
IGNITION SIGNAL
"CRUISE" INDICATOR CONTROL
IMPORTANT
BRAKE SIGNAL INPUT MUST BE PULLED LOW THRU CENTER HIGH MOUNTED STOPLAMP BULB(S) OR CRUISE CONTROL WILL NOT WORK.
BRAKE LIGHT CRUISE RELEASE SWITCH CONNECTOR IDENTIFICATION
C1 : BLACK : 3 CAVITIES
C2 : BLUE : 2 CAVITIES
GROUND DISTRIBUTION
VEHICLE SPEED SENSOR (VSS) MODULE
OUTPUT
4000 PULSES PER MILE
VEHICLE SPEED SENSOR
VEHICLE SPEED SENSOR (VSS) CONNECTOR IDENTIFICATION
C1 : BLACK : 8 CAVITIES
C2 : BLACK : 3 CAVITIES
TORQUE CONVERTER CLUTCH (TCC) CRUISE RELEASE SWITCH CONNECTOR IDENTIFICATION
C1 : NATURAL : 3 CAVITIES
C2 : GRAY : 2 CAVITIES
GC1109300273000X

Fig. 14 Cruise control wiring diagram. 1993 Roadmaster

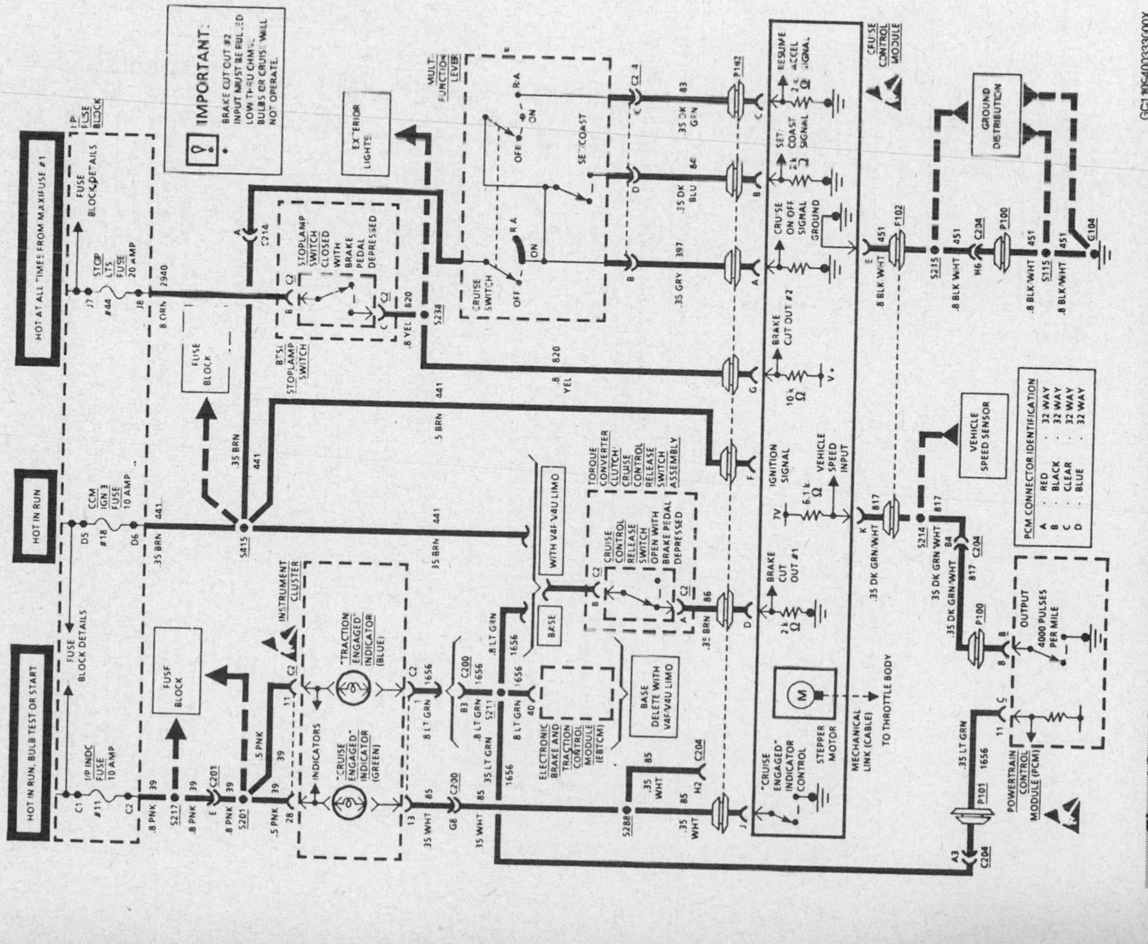
HOT IN RUN, BULB TEST OR START
HOT IN RUN
HOT AT ALL TIMES FROM MAXIFUSE #1
I/P INDC FUSE 10 AMP
CCM IGN 3 FUSE 10 AMP
STOP LTS FUSE 20 AMP
FUSE BLOCK DETAILS
I/P FUSE BLOCK
FUSE BLOCK
IMPORTANT
BRAKE CUT OUT #2 INPUT MUST BE PULLED LOW THRU CHMSL BULBS OR CRUISE WILL NOT OPERATE.
EXTERIOR LIGHTS
MULTI-FUNCTION LEVER
CRUISE SWITCH
SET/COAST
STOPLAMP SWITCH CLOSED WITH BRAKE PEDAL DEPRESSED
BTSI STOPLAMP SWITCH
INSTRUMENT CLUSTER
"TRACTION ENGAGED" INDICATOR (BLUE)
"CRUISE ENGAGED" INDICATOR (GREEN)
INDICATORS
ELECTRONIC BRAKE AND TRACTION CONTROL MODULE (EBTCM)
BASE DELETE WITH V4F/V4U LIMO
BASE
WITH V4F/V4U LIMO
TORQUE CONVERTER CLUTCH/ CRUISE CONTROL RELEASE SWITCH ASSEMBLY
CRUISE CONTROL RELEASE SWITCH OPEN WITH BRAKE PEDAL DEPRESSED
CRUISE CONTROL MODULE
RESUME ACCEL SIGNAL
SET COAST SIGNAL
CRUISE ON OFF SIGNAL
GROUND
BRAKE CUT OUT #2
IGNITION SIGNAL
VEHICLE SPEED INPUT
BRAKE CUT OUT #1
"CRUISE ENGAGED" INDICATOR CONTROL
STEPPER MOTOR
MECHANICAL LINK (CABLE)
TO THROTTLE BODY
GROUND DISTRIBUTION
VEHICLE SPEED SENSOR
PCM CONNECTOR IDENTIFICATION
A : RED : 32 WAY
B : BLACK : 32 WAY
C : CLEAR : 32 WAY
D : BLUE : 32 WAY
OUTPUT
4000 PULSES PER MILE
POWERTRAIN CONTROL MODULE (PCM)
GC1105400333000X

Fig. 13 Cruise control wiring diagram. 1994 Fleetwood (RWD)

ACTION	NORMAL RESULTS
[1] • Drive vehicle above 25 mph. • Cruise Switch to "ON." • Depress Set Switch once and release. • Remove foot from accelerator pedal.	Vehicle maintains set speed.
[2] • Depress and hold Set Switch until vehicle speed decreases by 4 to 5 mph. • Release Set Switch.	Vehicle decelerates and maintains a new lower set speed, if speed is above 25 mph.
[3] • Depress and hold R/A Switch until vehicle speed increases by 4 to 5 mph. • Release R/A Switch.	Vehicle accelerates and maintains a new higher set speed.
[4] • Depress brake pedal slightly.	Cruise Control disengages. Memory unchanged.
[5] • Depress R/A Switch once and release.	Vehicle accelerates to and maintains previous set speed.
[6] • Depress R/A Switch once and release (less than 3/4 of a second).	Vehicle speed increases by 1 mph and maintains new set speed.

GC1109100274010X

Fig. 15 Cruise control system check (Part 1 of 2)

ACTION	NORMAL RESULTS
[7] • Depress Set Switch once and release (less than 3/8 of a second).	Vehicle speed decreases by 1 mph and maintains new set speed.
[8] • Depress Set and R/A Switches simultaneously.	Vehicle put in Non-Cruise mode with memory unchanged.
[9] • Depress R/A Switch once and release.	Vehicle accelerates to and maintains previous set speed.
[10] • Cruise Switch to "OFF."	Cruise Control disengages. Memory is lost.

GC1109100274020X

Fig. 15 Cruise control system check (Part 2 of 2)

SYMPTOM	PROCEDURE
Cruise Control will not engage. Speedometer operates normally.	Chart #1
Cruise Control will not resume, accelerate, tap-up or tap-down.	Chart #2

GC1109300275000X

Fig. 16 Cruise control symptom table. Camaro & Firebird

SYMPTOM	PROCEDURE
Cruise Control will not engage.	Chart #1
Cruise Control will not resume, accelerate, tap-up or tap-down.	Chart #2

GC1109300276000X

Fig. 17 Cruise control symptom table. Caprice, Impala SS & Roadmaster

SYMPTOM	PROCEDURE
Cruise Control will not engage.	Chart #1
Cruise Control will not resume, accelerate, tap-up or tap-down.	Chart #2
"CRUISE ENGAGED" Indicator inoperative.	Chart #3
"CRUISE ENGAGED" Indicator on at all times.	Chart #4

GC1109300277000X

Fig. 18 Cruise control symptom table. Fleetwood (RWD)

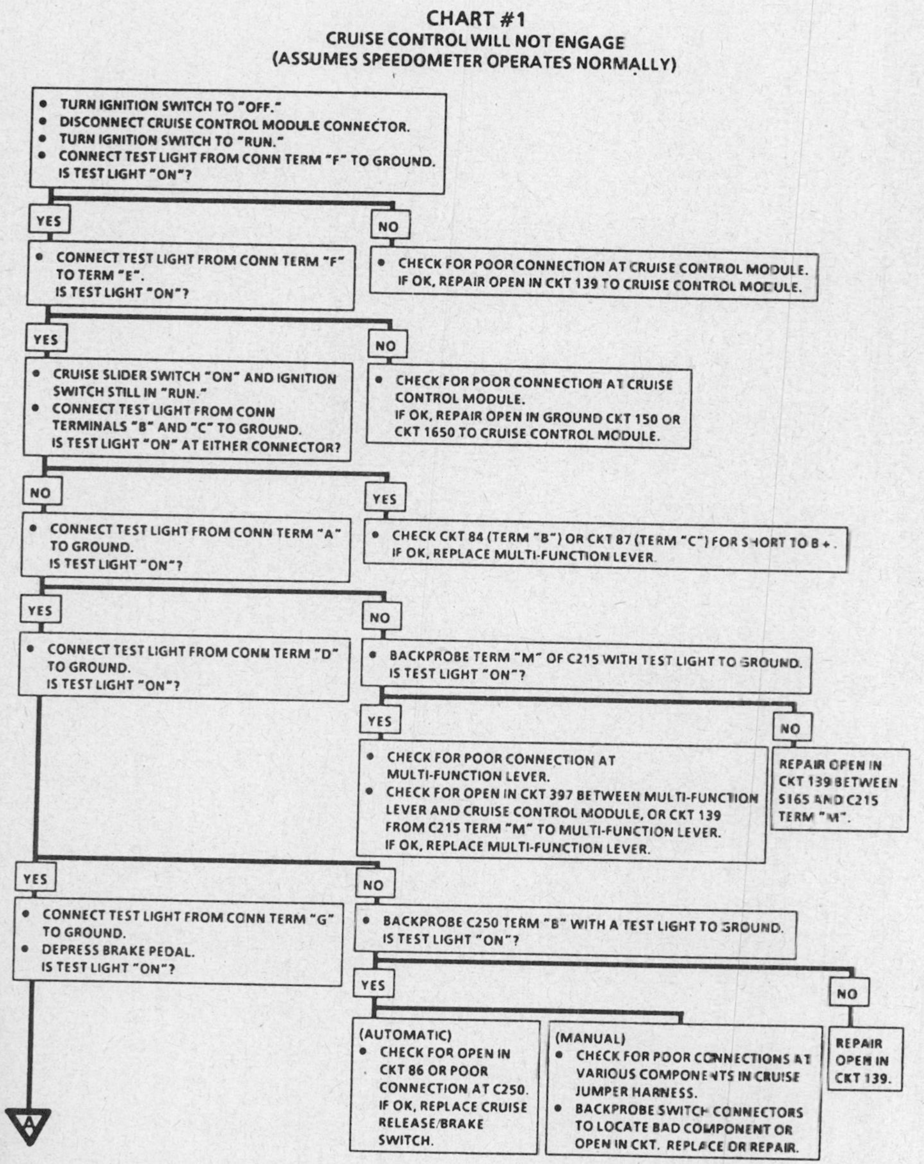
CHART #1
CRUISE CONTROL WILL NOT ENGAGE
(ASSUMES SPEEDOMETER OPERATES NORMALLY)
• TURN IGNITION SWITCH TO "OFF."
• DISCONNECT CRUISE CONTROL MODULE CONNECTOR.
• TURN IGNITION SWITCH TO "RUN."
• CONNECT TEST LIGHT FROM CONN TERM "F" TO GROUND.
IS TEST LIGHT "ON"?
YES
NO
• CONNECT TEST LIGHT FROM CONN TERM "F" TO TERM "E".
IS TEST LIGHT "ON"?
• CHECK FOR POOR CONNECTION AT CRUISE CONTROL MODULE.
IF OK, REPAIR OPEN IN CKT 139 TO CRUISE CONTROL MODULE.
YES
NO
• CRUISE SLIDER SWITCH "ON" AND IGNITION SWITCH STILL IN "RUN."
• CONNECT TEST LIGHT FROM CONN TERMINALS "B" AND "C" TO GROUND.
IS TEST LIGHT "ON" AT EITHER CONNECTOR?
• CHECK FOR POOR CONNECTION AT CRUISE CONTROL MODULE.
IF OK, REPAIR OPEN IN GROUND CKT 150 OR CKT 1650 TO CRUISE CONTROL MODULE.
NO
YES
• CONNECT TEST LIGHT FROM CONN TERM "A" TO GROUND.
IS TEST LIGHT "ON"?
• CHECK CKT 84 (TERM "B") OR CKT 87 (TERM "C") FOR SHORT TO B+.
IF OK, REPLACE MULTI-FUNCTION LEVER.
YES
NO
• CONNECT TEST LIGHT FROM CONN TERM "D" TO GROUND.
IS TEST LIGHT "ON"?
• BACKPROBE TERM "M" OF C215 WITH TEST LIGHT TO GROUND.
IS TEST LIGHT "ON"?
YES
NO
• CHECK FOR POOR CONNECTION AT MULTI-FUNCTION LEVER.
• CHECK FOR OPEN IN CKT 397 BETWEEN MULTI-FUNCTION LEVER AND CRUISE CONTROL MODULE, OR CKT 139 FROM C215 TERM "M" TO MULTI-FUNCTION LEVER.
IF OK, REPLACE MULTI-FUNCTION LEVER.
REPAIR OPEN IN CKT 139 BETWEEN S165 AND C215 TERM "M".
YES
NO
• CONNECT TEST LIGHT FROM CONN TERM "G" TO GROUND.
• DEPRESS BRAKE PEDAL.
IS TEST LIGHT "ON"?
• BACKPROBE C250 TERM "B" WITH A TEST LIGHT TO GROUND.
IS TEST LIGHT "ON"?
YES
NO
(AUTOMATIC)
• CHECK FOR OPEN IN CKT 86 OR POOR CONNECTION AT C250.
IF OK, REPLACE CRUISE RELEASE/BRAKE SWITCH.
(MANUAL)
• CHECK FOR POOR CONNECTIONS AT VARIOUS COMPONENTS IN CRUISE JUMPER HARNESS.
• BACKPROBE SWITCH CONNECTORS TO LOCATE BAD COMPONENT OR OPEN IN CKT. REPLACE OR REPAIR.
REPAIR OPEN IN CKT 139.
A
GC1109300027801CX

Fig. 19 Cruise control troubleshooting chart No. 1 (Part 1 of 2). Camaro & Firebird

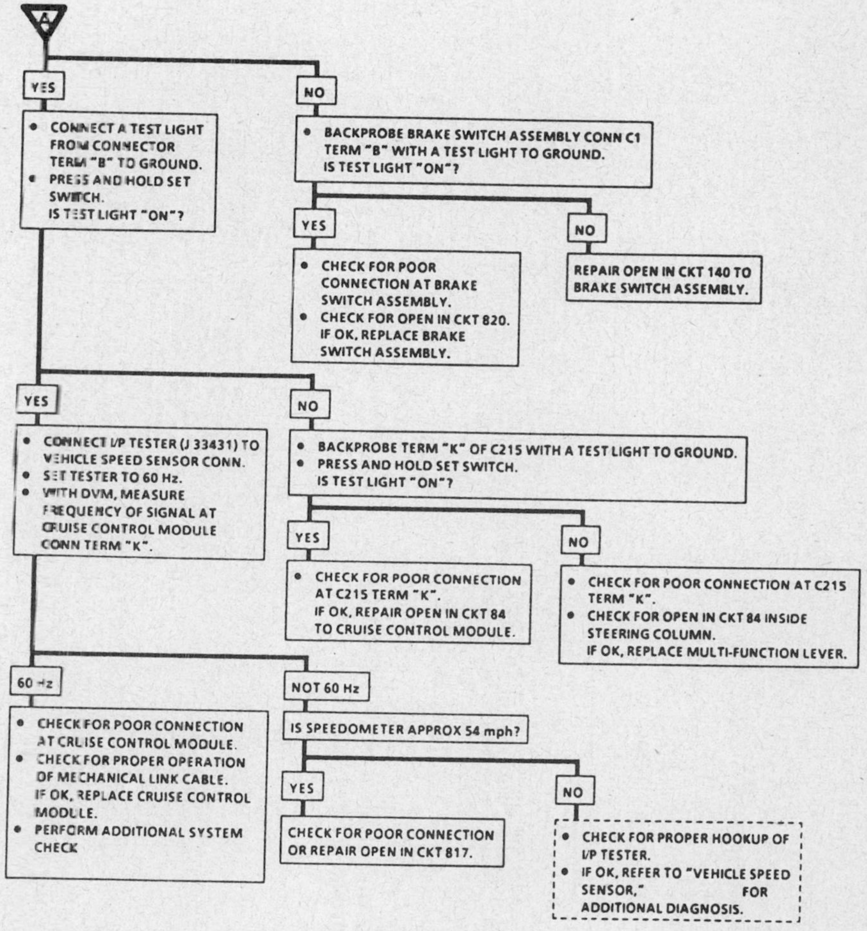
A
YES
NO
• CONNECT A TEST LIGHT FROM CONNECTOR TERM "B" TO GROUND.
• PRESS AND HOLD SET SWITCH.
IS TEST LIGHT "ON"?
• BACKPROBE BRAKE SWITCH ASSEMBLY CONN C1 TERM "B" WITH A TEST LIGHT TO GROUND.
IS TEST LIGHT "ON"?
YES
NO
• CHECK FOR POOR CONNECTION AT BRAKE SWITCH ASSEMBLY.
• CHECK FOR OPEN IN CKT 820.
IF OK, REPLACE BRAKE SWITCH ASSEMBLY.
REPAIR OPEN IN CKT 140 TO BRAKE SWITCH ASSEMBLY.
YES
NO
• CONNECT I/P TESTER (J 33431) TO VEHICLE SPEED SENSOR CONN.
• SET TESTER TO 60 Hz.
• WITH DVM, MEASURE FREQUENCY OF SIGNAL AT CRUISE CONTROL MODULE CONN TERM "K".
• BACKPROBE TERM "K" OF C215 WITH A TEST LIGHT TO GROUND.
• PRESS AND HOLD SET SWITCH.
IS TEST LIGHT "ON"?
YES
NO
• CHECK FOR POOR CONNECTION AT C215 TERM "K".
IF OK, REPAIR OPEN IN CKT 84 TO CRUISE CONTROL MODULE.
• CHECK FOR POOR CONNECTION AT C215 TERM "K".
• CHECK FOR OPEN IN CKT 84 INSIDE STEERING COLUMN.
IF OK, REPLACE MULTI-FUNCTION LEVER.
60 Hz
NOT 60 Hz
• CHECK FOR POOR CONNECTION AT CRUISE CONTROL MODULE.
• CHECK FOR PROPER OPERATION OF MECHANICAL LINK CABLE.
IF OK, REPLACE CRUISE CONTROL MODULE.
• PERFORM ADDITIONAL SYSTEM CHECK
IS SPEEDOMETER APPROX 54 mph?
YES
NO
CHECK FOR POOR CONNECTION OR REPAIR OPEN IN CKT 817.
• CHECK FOR PROPER HOOKUP OF I/P TESTER.
• IF OK, REFER TO "VEHICLE SPEED SENSOR," FOR ADDITIONAL DIAGNOSIS.
GC1109300278020X

Fig. 19 Cruise control troubleshooting chart No. 1 (Part 2 of 2). Camaro & Firebird

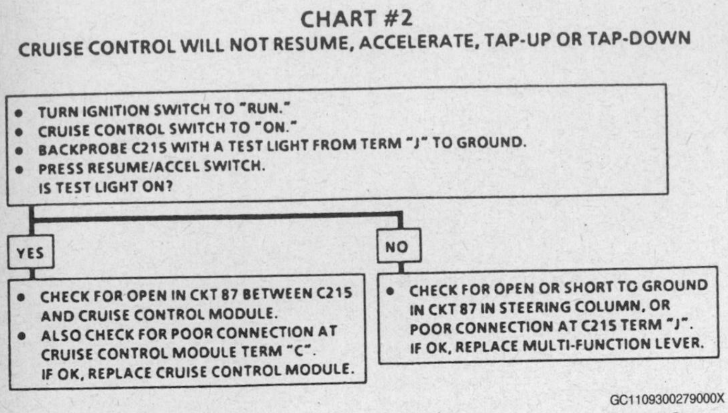
CHART #2
CRUISE CONTROL WILL NOT RESUME, ACCELERATE, TAP-UP OR TAP-DOWN
• TURN IGNITION SWITCH TO "RUN."
• CRUISE CONTROL SWITCH TO "ON."
• BACKPROBE C215 WITH A TEST LIGHT FROM TERM "J" TO GROUND.
• PRESS RESUME/ACCEL SWITCH.
IS TEST LIGHT ON?
YES
NO
• CHECK FOR OPEN IN CKT 87 BETWEEN C215 AND CRUISE CONTROL MODULE.
• ALSO CHECK FOR POOR CONNECTION AT CRUISE CONTROL MODULE TERM "C".
IF OK, REPLACE CRUISE CONTROL MODULE.
• CHECK FOR OPEN OR SHORT TO GROUND IN CKT 87 IN STEERING COLUMN, OR POOR CONNECTION AT C215 TERM "J".
IF OK, REPLACE MULTI-FUNCTION LEVER.
GC1109300279000X

Fig. 20 Cruise control troubleshooting chart No. 2. Camaro & Firebird

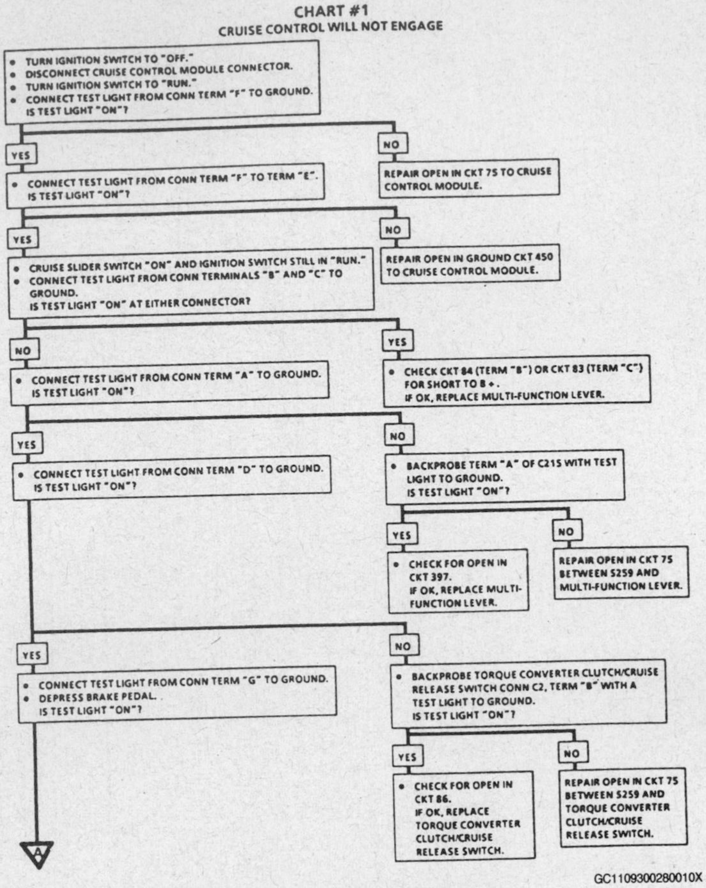
CHART #1
CRUISE CONTROL WILL NOT ENGAGE
• TURN IGNITION SWITCH TO "OFF."
• DISCONNECT CRUISE CONTROL MODULE CONNECTOR.
• TURN IGNITION SWITCH TO "RUN."
• CONNECT TEST LIGHT FROM CONN TERM "F" TO GROUND.
IS TEST LIGHT "ON"?
YES
NO
REPAIR OPEN IN CKT 75 TO CRUISE CONTROL MODULE.
• CONNECT TEST LIGHT FROM CONN TERM "F" TO TERM "E".
IS TEST LIGHT "ON"?
YES
NO
REPAIR OPEN IN GROUND CKT 450 TO CRUISE CONTROL MODULE.
• CRUISE SLIDER SWITCH "ON" AND IGNITION SWITCH STILL IN "RUN."
• CONNECT TEST LIGHT FROM CONN TERMINALS "B" AND "C" TO GROUND.
IS TEST LIGHT "ON" AT EITHER CONNECTOR?
NO
YES
• CHECK CKT 84 (TERM "B") OR CKT 83 (TERM "C") FOR SHORT TO B+.
IF OK, REPLACE MULTI-FUNCTION LEVER.
• CONNECT TEST LIGHT FROM CONN TERM "A" TO GROUND.
IS TEST LIGHT "ON"?
YES
NO
• BACKPROBE TERM "A" OF C215 WITH TEST LIGHT TO GROUND.
IS TEST LIGHT "ON"?
YES
NO
• CHECK FOR OPEN IN CKT 397.
IF OK, REPLACE MULTI-FUNCTION LEVER.
REPAIR OPEN IN CKT 75 BETWEEN S259 AND MULTI-FUNCTION LEVER.
• CONNECT TEST LIGHT FROM CONN TERM "D" TO GROUND.
IS TEST LIGHT "ON"?
YES
NO
• BACKPROBE TORQUE CONVERTER CLUTCH/CRUISE RELEASE SWITCH CONN C2, TERM "B" WITH A TEST LIGHT TO GROUND.
IS TEST LIGHT "ON"?
YES
NO
• CHECK FOR OPEN IN CKT 86.
IF OK, REPLACE TORQUE CONVERTER CLUTCH/CRUISE RELEASE SWITCH.
REPAIR OPEN IN CKT 75 BETWEEN S259 AND TORQUE CONVERTER CLUTCH/CRUISE RELEASE SWITCH.
• CONNECT TEST LIGHT FROM CONN TERM "G" TO GROUND.
• DEPRESS BRAKE PEDAL.
IS TEST LIGHT "ON"?
A
GC1109300280010X

Fig. 21 Cruise control troubleshooting chart No. 1 (Part 1 of 2). Caprice, Impala SS & Roadmaster

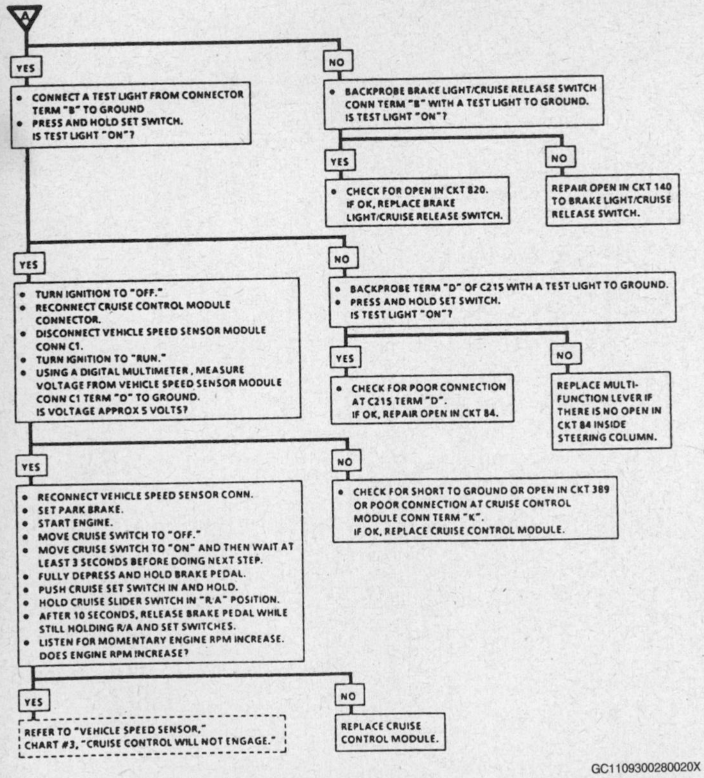
A
YES
NO
• CONNECT A TEST LIGHT FROM CONNECTOR TERM "B" TO GROUND
• PRESS AND HOLD SET SWITCH.
IS TEST LIGHT "ON"?
• BACKPROBE BRAKE LIGHT/CRUISE RELEASE SWITCH CONN TERM "B" WITH A TEST LIGHT TO GROUND.
IS TEST LIGHT "ON"?
YES
NO
• CHECK FOR OPEN IN CKT 820.
IF OK, REPLACE BRAKE LIGHT/CRUISE RELEASE SWITCH.
REPAIR OPEN IN CKT 140 TO BRAKE LIGHT/CRUISE RELEASE SWITCH.
YES
NO
• TURN IGNITION TO "OFF."
• RECONNECT CRUISE CONTROL MODULE CONNECTOR.
• DISCONNECT VEHICLE SPEED SENSOR MODULE CONN C1.
• TURN IGNITION TO "RUN."
• USING A DIGITAL MULTIMETER, MEASURE VOLTAGE FROM VEHICLE SPEED SENSOR MODULE CONN C1 TERM "D" TO GROUND.
IS VOLTAGE APPROX 5 VOLTS?
• BACKPROBE TERM "D" OF C215 WITH A TEST LIGHT TO GROUND.
• PRESS AND HOLD SET SWITCH.
IS TEST LIGHT "ON"?
YES
NO
• CHECK FOR POOR CONNECTION AT C215 TERM "D".
IF OK, REPAIR OPEN IN CKT 84.
REPLACE MULTI-FUNCTION LEVER IF THERE IS NO OPEN IN CKT 84 INSIDE STEERING COLUMN.
YES
NO
• RECONNECT VEHICLE SPEED SENSOR CONN.
• SET PARK BRAKE.
• START ENGINE.
• MOVE CRUISE SWITCH TO "OFF."
• MOVE CRUISE SWITCH TO "ON" AND THEN WAIT AT LEAST 3 SECONDS BEFORE DOING NEXT STEP.
• FULLY DEPRESS AND HOLD BRAKE PEDAL.
• PUSH CRUISE SET SWITCH IN AND HOLD.
• HOLD CRUISE SLIDER SWITCH IN "R/A" POSITION.
• AFTER 10 SECONDS, RELEASE BRAKE PEDAL WHILE STILL HOLDING R/A AND SET SWITCHES.
• LISTEN FOR MOMENTARY ENGINE RPM INCREASE.
DOES ENGINE RPM INCREASE?
• CHECK FOR SHORT TO GROUND OR OPEN IN CKT 389 OR POOR CONNECTION AT CRUISE CONTROL MODULE CONN TERM "K".
IF OK, REPLACE CRUISE CONTROL MODULE.
YES
NO
REFER TO "VEHICLE SPEED SENSOR," CHART #3, "CRUISE CONTROL WILL NOT ENGAGE."
REPLACE CRUISE CONTROL MODULE.
GC1109300280020X

Fig. 21 Cruise control troubleshooting chart No. 1 (Part 2 of 2). Caprice, Impala SS & Roadmaster

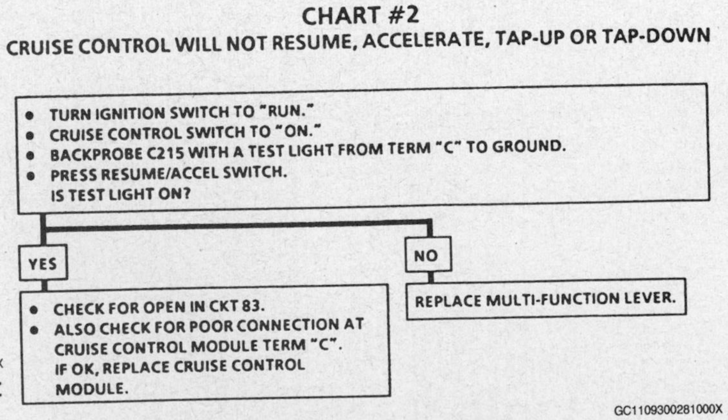
CHART #2
CRUISE CONTROL WILL NOT RESUME, ACCELERATE, TAP-UP OR TAP-DOWN
• TURN IGNITION SWITCH TO "RUN."
• CRUISE CONTROL SWITCH TO "ON."
• BACKPROBE C215 WITH A TEST LIGHT FROM TERM "C" TO GROUND.
• PRESS RESUME/ACCEL SWITCH.
IS TEST LIGHT ON?
YES
NO
• CHECK FOR OPEN IN CKT 83.
• ALSO CHECK FOR POOR CONNECTION AT CRUISE CONTROL MODULE TERM "C".
IF OK, REPLACE CRUISE CONTROL MODULE.
REPLACE MULTI-FUNCTION LEVER.
GC1109300281000X

Fig. 22 Cruise control troubleshooting chart No. 2. Caprice, Impala SS & Roadmaster

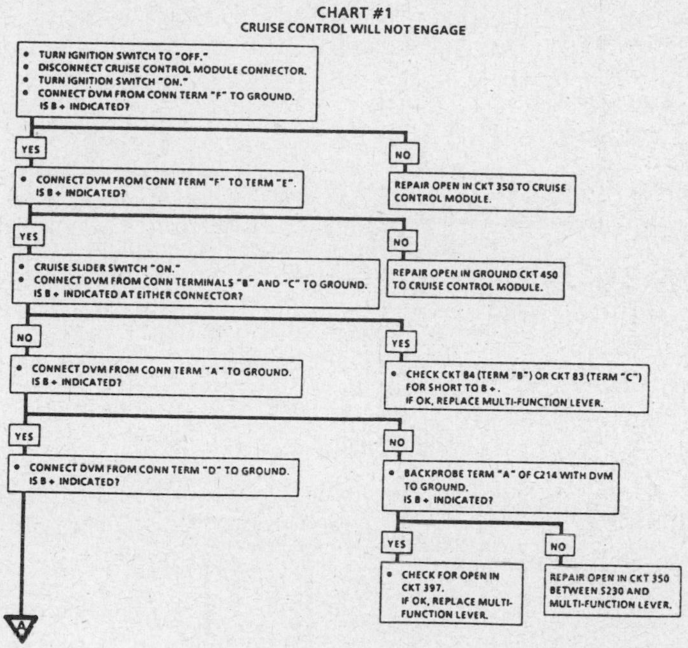
CHART #1
CRUISE CONTROL WILL NOT ENGAGE
• TURN IGNITION SWITCH TO "OFF." • DISCONNECT CRUISE CONTROL MODULE CONNECTOR. • TURN IGNITION SWITCH "ON." • CONNECT DVM FROM CONN TERM "F" TO GROUND. IS B + INDICATED?
YES
NO
• CONNECT DVM FROM CONN TERM "F" TO TERM "E". IS B + INDICATED?
REPAIR OPEN IN CKT 350 TO CRUISE CONTROL MODULE.
YES
NO
• CRUISE SLIDER SWITCH "ON." • CONNECT DVM FROM CONN TERMINALS "B" AND "C" TO GROUND. IS B + INDICATED AT EITHER CONNECTOR?
REPAIR OPEN IN GROUND CKT 450 TO CRUISE CONTROL MODULE.
NO
YES
• CONNECT DVM FROM CONN TERM "A" TO GROUND. IS B + INDICATED?
• CHECK CKT 84 (TERM "B") OR CKT 83 (TERM "C") FOR SHORT TO B +. IF OK, REPLACE MULTI-FUNCTION LEVER.
YES
NO
• CONNECT DVM FROM CONN TERM "D" TO GROUND. IS B + INDICATED?
• BACKPROBE TERM "A" OF C214 WITH DVM TO GROUND. IS B + INDICATED?
YES
NO
• CHECK FOR OPEN IN CKT 397. IF OK, REPLACE MULTI-FUNCTION LEVER.
REPAIR OPEN IN CKT 350 BETWEEN S230 AND MULTI-FUNCTION LEVER.
A

GC1109300282010X

Fig. 23 Cruise control troubleshooting chart No. 1 (Part 1 of 2). Fleetwood (RWD)

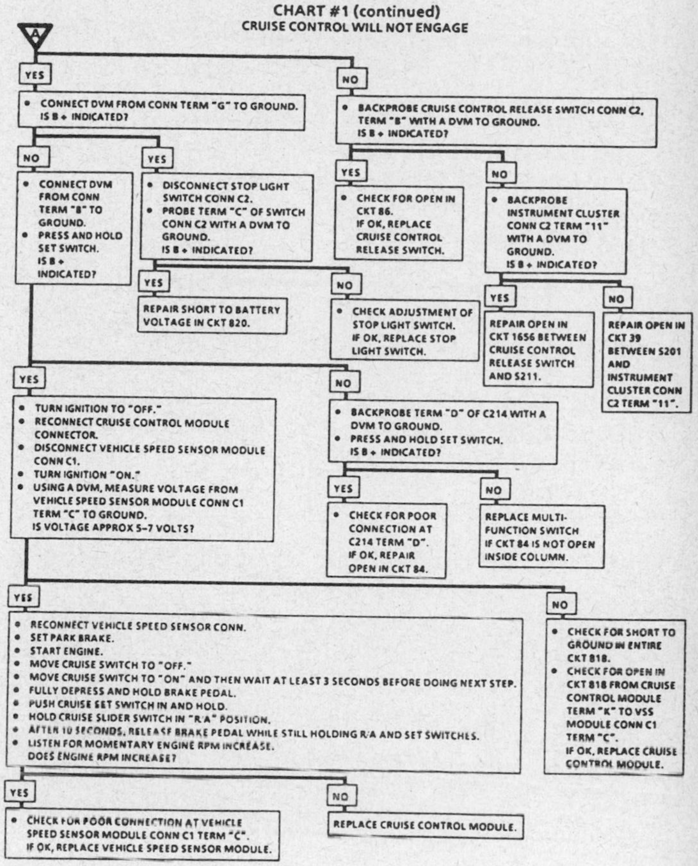
CHART #1 (continued)
CRUISE CONTROL WILL NOT ENGAGE
A
YES
NO
• CONNECT DVM FROM CONN TERM "G" TO GROUND. IS B + INDICATED?
• BACKPROBE CRUISE CONTROL RELEASE SWITCH CONN C2, TERM "B" WITH A DVM TO GROUND. IS B + INDICATED?
NO
YES
• CONNECT DVM FROM CONN TERM "B" TO GROUND. • PRESS AND HOLD SET SWITCH. IS B + INDICATED?
• DISCONNECT STOP LIGHT SWITCH CONN C2. • PROBE TERM "C" OF SWITCH CONN C2 WITH A DVM TO GROUND. IS B + INDICATED?
YES
NO
• CHECK FOR OPEN IN CKT 86. IF OK, REPLACE CRUISE CONTROL RELEASE SWITCH.
• BACKPROBE INSTRUMENT CLUSTER CONN C2 TERM "11" WITH A DVM TO GROUND. IS B + INDICATED?
YES
REPAIR SHORT TO BATTERY VOLTAGE IN CKT 820.
NO
• CHECK ADJUSTMENT OF STOP LIGHT SWITCH. IF OK, REPLACE STOP LIGHT SWITCH.
YES
NO
REPAIR OPEN IN CKT 1656 BETWEEN CRUISE CONTROL RELEASE SWITCH AND S211.
REPAIR OPEN IN CKT 39 BETWEEN S201 AND INSTRUMENT CLUSTER CONN C2 TERM "11".
YES
NO
• TURN IGNITION TO "OFF." • RECONNECT CRUISE CONTROL MODULE CONNECTOR. • DISCONNECT VEHICLE SPEED SENSOR MODULE CONN C1. • TURN IGNITION "ON." • USING A DVM, MEASURE VOLTAGE FROM VEHICLE SPEED SENSOR MODULE CONN C1 TERM "C" TO GROUND. IS VOLTAGE APPROX 5–7 VOLTS?
• BACKPROBE TERM "D" OF C214 WITH A DVM TO GROUND. • PRESS AND HOLD SET SWITCH. IS B + INDICATED?
YES
NO
• CHECK FOR POOR CONNECTION AT C214 TERM "D". IF OK, REPAIR OPEN IN CKT 84.
REPLACE MULTI-FUNCTION SWITCH IF CKT 84 IS NOT OPEN INSIDE COLUMN.
YES
NO
• RECONNECT VEHICLE SPEED SENSOR CONN. • SET PARK BRAKE. • START ENGINE. • MOVE CRUISE SWITCH TO "OFF." • MOVE CRUISE SWITCH TO "ON" AND THEN WAIT AT LEAST 3 SECONDS BEFORE DOING NEXT STEP. • FULLY DEPRESS AND HOLD BRAKE PEDAL. • PUSH CRUISE SET SWITCH IN AND HOLD. • HOLD CRUISE SLIDER SWITCH IN "R/A" POSITION. • AFTER 10 SECONDS, RELEASE BRAKE PEDAL WHILE STILL HOLDING R/A AND SET SWITCHES. • LISTEN FOR MOMENTARY ENGINE RPM INCREASE. DOES ENGINE RPM INCREASE?
• CHECK FOR SHORT TO GROUND IN ENTIRE CKT 818. • CHECK FOR OPEN IN CKT 818 FROM CRUISE CONTROL MODULE TERM "K" TO VSS MODULE CONN C1 TERM "C". IF OK, REPLACE CRUISE CONTROL MODULE.
YES
NO
• CHECK FOR POOR CONNECTION AT VEHICLE SPEED SENSOR MODULE CONN C1 TERM "C". IF OK, REPLACE VEHICLE SPEED SENSOR MODULE.
REPLACE CRUISE CONTROL MODULE.

GC1109300282020X

Fig. 23 Cruise control troubleshooting chart No. 1 (Part 2 of 2). Fleetwood (RWD)

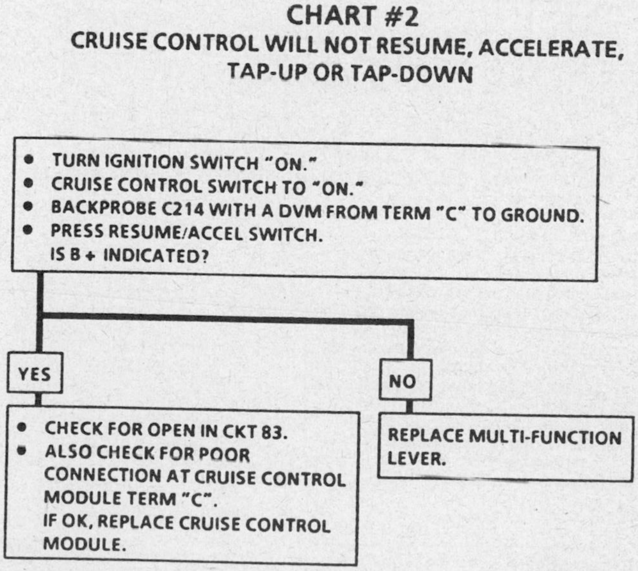
CHART #2
CRUISE CONTROL WILL NOT RESUME, ACCELERATE, TAP-UP OR TAP-DOWN
• TURN IGNITION SWITCH "ON." • CRUISE CONTROL SWITCH TO "ON." • BACKPROBE C214 WITH A DVM FROM TERM "C" TO GROUND. • PRESS RESUME/ACCEL SWITCH. IS B + INDICATED?
YES
NO
• CHECK FOR OPEN IN CKT 83. • ALSO CHECK FOR POOR CONNECTION AT CRUISE CONTROL MODULE TERM "C". IF OK, REPLACE CRUISE CONTROL MODULE.
REPLACE MULTI-FUNCTION LEVER.

GC1109300283000X

Fig. 24 Cruise control troubleshooting chart No. 2. Fleetwood (RWD)

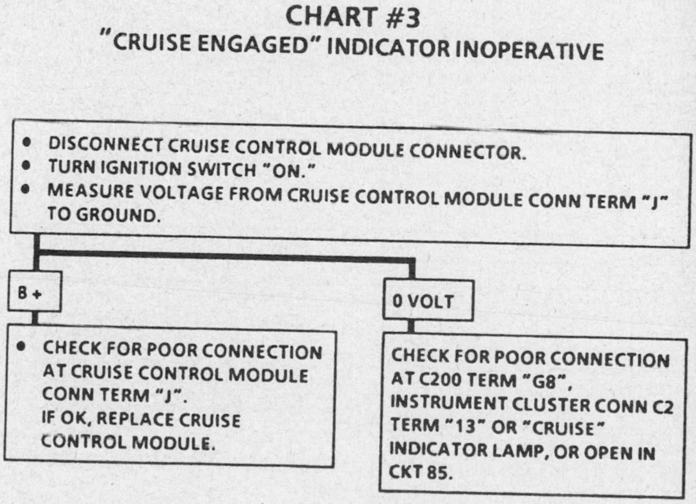
CHART #3
"CRUISE ENGAGED" INDICATOR INOPERATIVE
• DISCONNECT CRUISE CONTROL MODULE CONNECTOR. • TURN IGNITION SWITCH "ON." • MEASURE VOLTAGE FROM CRUISE CONTROL MODULE CONN TERM "J" TO GROUND.
B +
0 VOLT
• CHECK FOR POOR CONNECTION AT CRUISE CONTROL MODULE CONN TERM "J". IF OK, REPLACE CRUISE CONTROL MODULE.
CHECK FOR POOR CONNECTION AT C200 TERM "G8", INSTRUMENT CLUSTER CONN C2 TERM "13" OR "CRUISE" INDICATOR LAMP, OR OPEN IN CKT 85.

GC1109300284000X

Fig. 25 Cruise control troubleshooting chart No. 3. Fleetwood (RWD)

CHART #4
"CRUISE ENGAGED" INDICATOR ON AT ALL TIMES

- TURN IGNITION SWITCH "ON."
- CRUISE CONTROL SWITCH "OFF."
- DISCONNECT CRUISE CONTROL MODULE.
  IS "CRUISE" INDICATOR ON?

YES

- CHECK FOR SHORT TO GROUND ON CKT 85.
  IF OK, SERVICE INSTRUMENT CLUSTER.

NO

REPLACE CRUISE CONTROL MODULE.

GC1109300285000X

Fig. 26 Cruise control troubleshooting chart No. 4. Fleetwood (RWD)

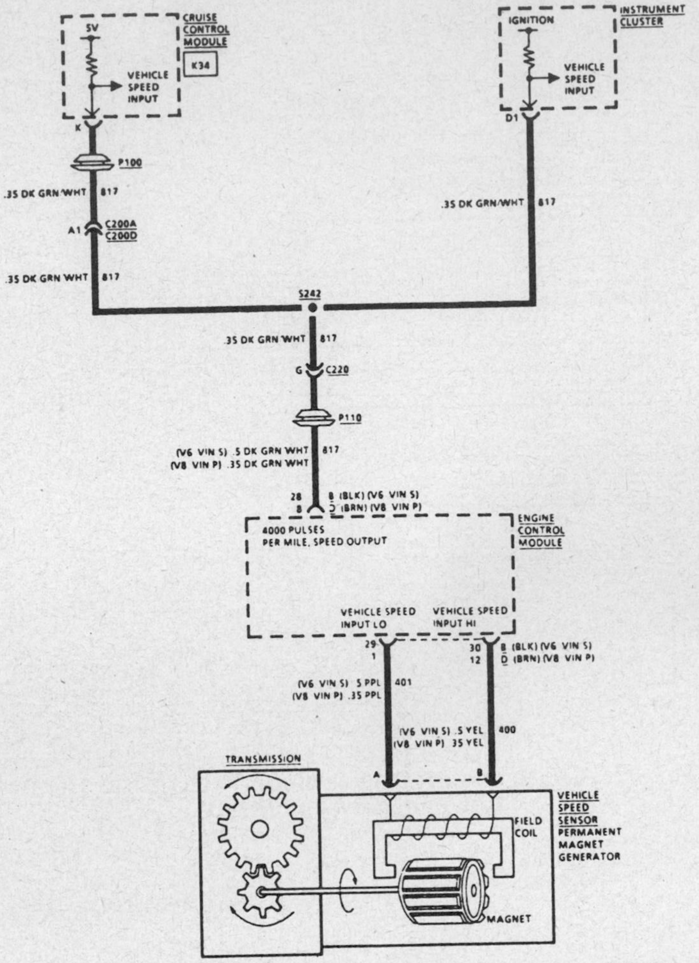
CRUISE
CONTROL
MODULE
K34
5V
VEHICLE
SPEED
INPUT
K
P100
.35 DK GRN/WHT 817
A1
C200A
C200D
.35 DK GRN WHT 817
INSTRUMENT
CLUSTER
IGNITION
VEHICLE
SPEED
INPUT
D1
.35 DK GRN/WHT 817
S242
.35 DK GRN WHT 817
G
C220
P110
(V6 VIN S) .5 DK GRN WHT 817
(V8 VIN P) .35 DK GRN WHT
28
8
B (BLK) (V6 VIN S)
D (BRN) (V8 VIN P)
ENGINE
CONTROL
MODULE
4000 PULSES
PER MILE, SPEED OUTPUT
VEHICLE SPEED
INPUT LO
VEHICLE SPEED
INPUT HI
29
1
30
12
B (BLK) (V6 VIN S)
D (BRN) (V8 VIN P)
(V6 VIN S) .5 PPL 401
(V8 VIN P) .35 PPL
(V6 VIN S) .5 YEL 400
(V8 VIN P) 35 YEL
TRANSMISSION
A
B
VEHICLE
SPEED
SENSOR
PERMANENT
MAGNET
GENERATOR
FIELD
COIL
MAGNET

GC1109300286000X

Fig. 27 Vehicle speed sensor wiring diagram. Camaro & Firebird

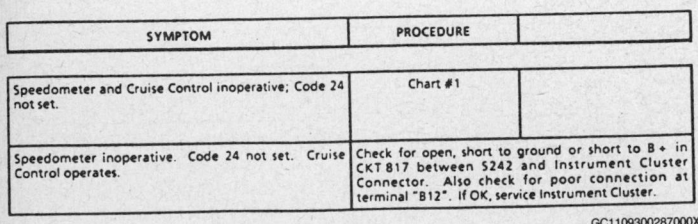

SYMPTOM	PROCEDURE	
Speedometer and Cruise Control inoperative; Code 24 not set.	Chart #1	
Speedometer inoperative. Code 24 not set. Cruise Control operates.	Check for open, short to ground or short to B+ in CKT 817 between S242 and Instrument Cluster Connector. Also check for poor connection at terminal "B12". If OK, service Instrument Cluster.	

GC1109300287000X

Fig. 28 Vehicle speed sensor symptom table. Camaro & Firebird

CHART #1
SPEEDOMETER AND CRUISE CONTROL INOPERATIVE; CODE 24 NOT SET

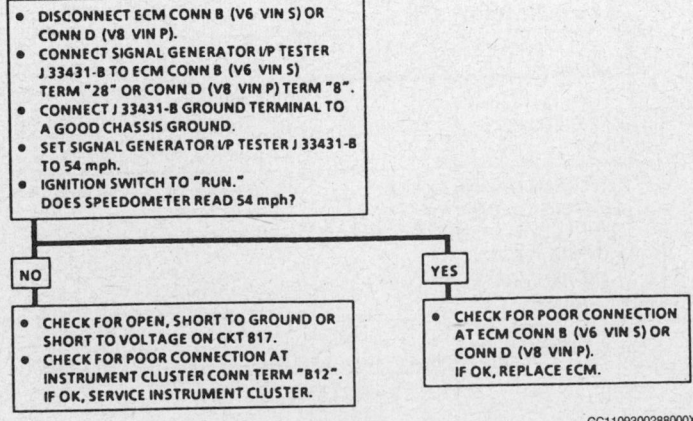

- DISCONNECT ECM CONN B (V6 VIN S) OR CONN D (V8 VIN P).
- CONNECT SIGNAL GENERATOR I/P TESTER J 33431-B TO ECM CONN B (V6 VIN S) TERM "28" OR CONN D (V8 VIN P) TERM "8".
- CONNECT J 33431-B GROUND TERMINAL TO A GOOD CHASSIS GROUND.
- SET SIGNAL GENERATOR I/P TESTER J 33431-B TO 54 mph.
- IGNITION SWITCH TO "RUN."
  DOES SPEEDOMETER READ 54 mph?

NO

- CHECK FOR OPEN, SHORT TO GROUND OR SHORT TO VOLTAGE ON CKT 817.
- CHECK FOR POOR CONNECTION AT INSTRUMENT CLUSTER CONN TERM "B12".
  IF OK, SERVICE INSTRUMENT CLUSTER.

YES

- CHECK FOR POOR CONNECTION AT ECM CONN B (V6 VIN S) OR CONN D (V8 VIN P).
  IF OK, REPLACE ECM.

GC1109300288000X

Fig. 29 Code 24: Vehicle Speed Sensor. Camaro & Firebird

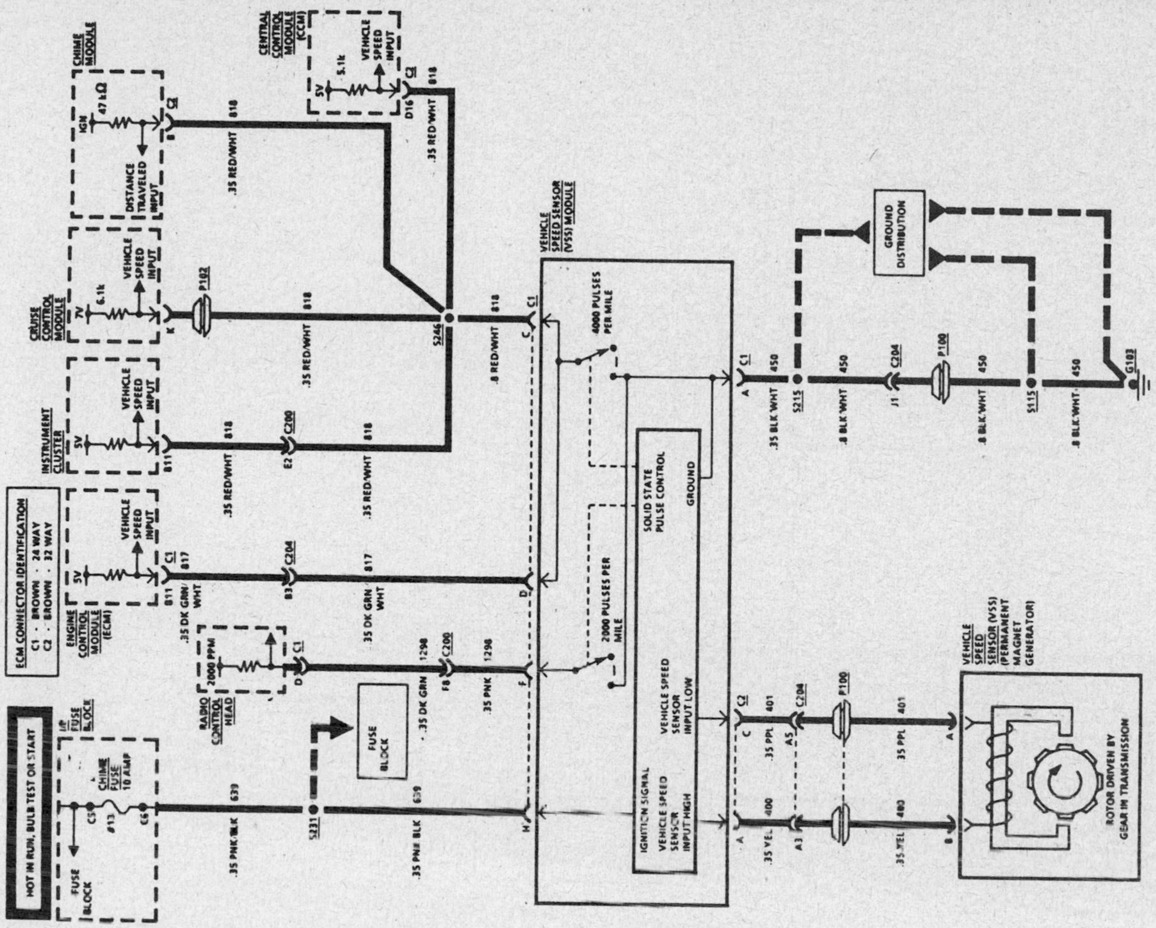
CHIME MODULE
DISTANCE TRAVELED INPUT
CRUISE CONTROL MODULE
VEHICLE SPEED INPUT
INSTRUMENT CLUSTER
ENGINE CONTROL MODULE (ECM)
ECM CONNECTOR IDENTIFICATION
C1 · BROWN · 24 WAY
C2 · BROWN · 32 WAY
CENTRAL CONTROL MODULE (CCM)
HOT IN RUN, BULB TEST OR START
I/P FUSE BLOCK
CHIME FUSE 10 AMP
RADIO CONTROL HEAD
2000 PPM
FUSE BLOCK
VEHICLE SPEED SENSOR (VSS) MODULE
4000 PULSES PER MILE
2000 PULSES PER MILE
SOLID STATE PULSE CONTROL
GROUND
IGNITION SIGNAL
VEHICLE SPEED SENSOR INPUT HIGH
VEHICLE SPEED SENSOR INPUT LOW
GROUND DISTRIBUTION
VEHICLE SPEED SENSOR (VSS) (PERMANENT MAGNET GENERATOR)
ROTOR DRIVEN BY GEAR IN TRANSMISSION

GC1093002900000X

Fig. 31 Vehicle speed sensor wiring diagram. Fleetwood (RWD)

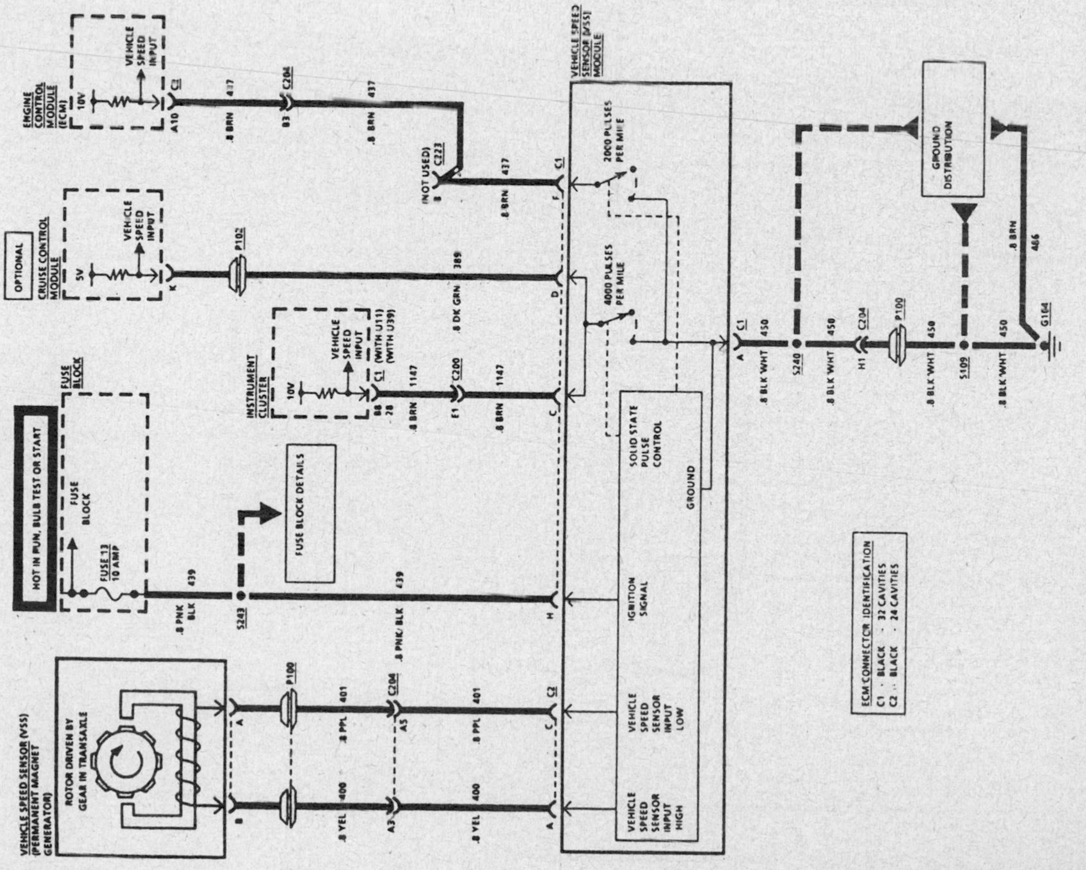
VEHICLE SPEED SENSOR (VSS) (PERMANENT MAGNET GENERATOR)
ROTOR DRIVEN BY GEAR IN TRANSAXLE
HOT IN RUN, BULB TEST OR START
FUSE BLOCK
FUSE 13 10 AMP
FUSE BLOCK DETAILS
INSTRUMENT CLUSTER
VEHICLE SPEED INPUT
OPTIONAL
CRUISE CONTROL MODULE
ENGINE CONTROL MODULE (ECM)
VEHICLE SPEED SENSOR (VSS) MODULE
2000 PULSES PER MILE
4000 PULSES PER MILE
SOLID STATE PULSE CONTROL
GROUND
IGNITION SIGNAL
VEHICLE SPEED SENSOR INPUT LOW
VEHICLE SPEED SENSOR INPUT HIGH
GROUND DISTRIBUTION
ECM CONNECTOR IDENTIFICATION
C1 · BLACK · 32 CAVITIES
C2 · BLACK · 24 CAVITIES

Fig. 30 Vehicle speed sensor wiring diagram. Caprice & Impala SS

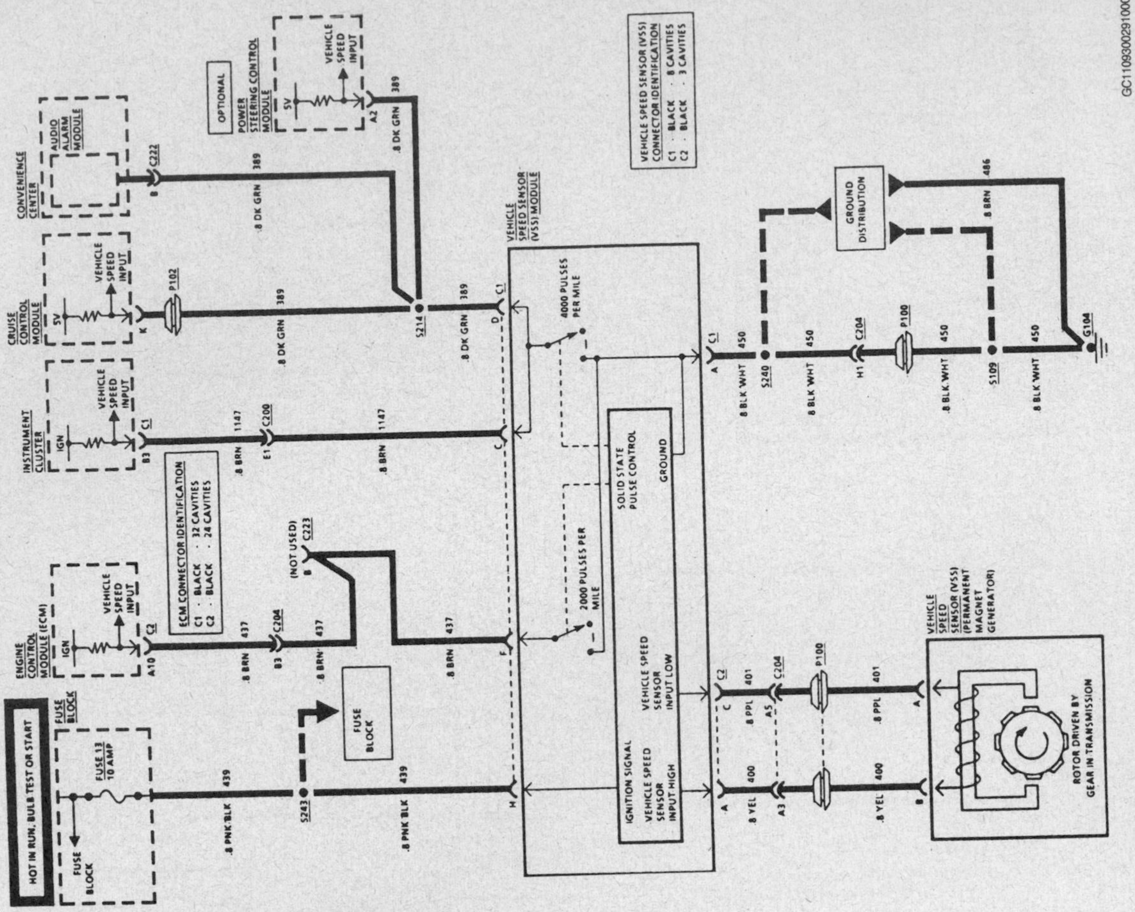
HOT IN RUN, BULB TEST OR START
FUSE BLOCK
FUSE 13 10 AMP
ENGINE CONTROL MODULE (ECM)
VEHICLE SPEED INPUT
ECM CONNECTOR IDENTIFICATION
C1 : BLACK : 32 CAVITIES
C2 : BLACK : 24 CAVITIES
INSTRUMENT CLUSTER
CRUISE CONTROL MODULE
CONVENIENCE CENTER
AUDIO ALARM MODULE
OPTIONAL POWER STEERING CONTROL MODULE
VEHICLE SPEED SENSOR (VSS) MODULE
4000 PULSES PER MILE
2000 PULSES PER MILE
(NOT USED)
SOLID STATE PULSE CONTROL
GROUND
IGNITION SIGNAL
VEHICLE SPEED SENSOR INPUT HIGH
VEHICLE SPEED SENSOR INPUT LOW
VEHICLE SPEED SENSOR (VSS) CONNECTOR IDENTIFICATION
C1 : BLACK : 8 CAVITIES
C2 : BLACK : 3 CAVITIES
GROUND DISTRIBUTION
VEHICLE SPEED SENSOR (VSS) (PERMANENT MAGNET GENERATOR)
ROTOR DRIVEN BY GEAR IN TRANSMISSION
GC1093002910000X

Fig. 33 Vehicle speed sensor wiring diagram. Roadmaster Sedan

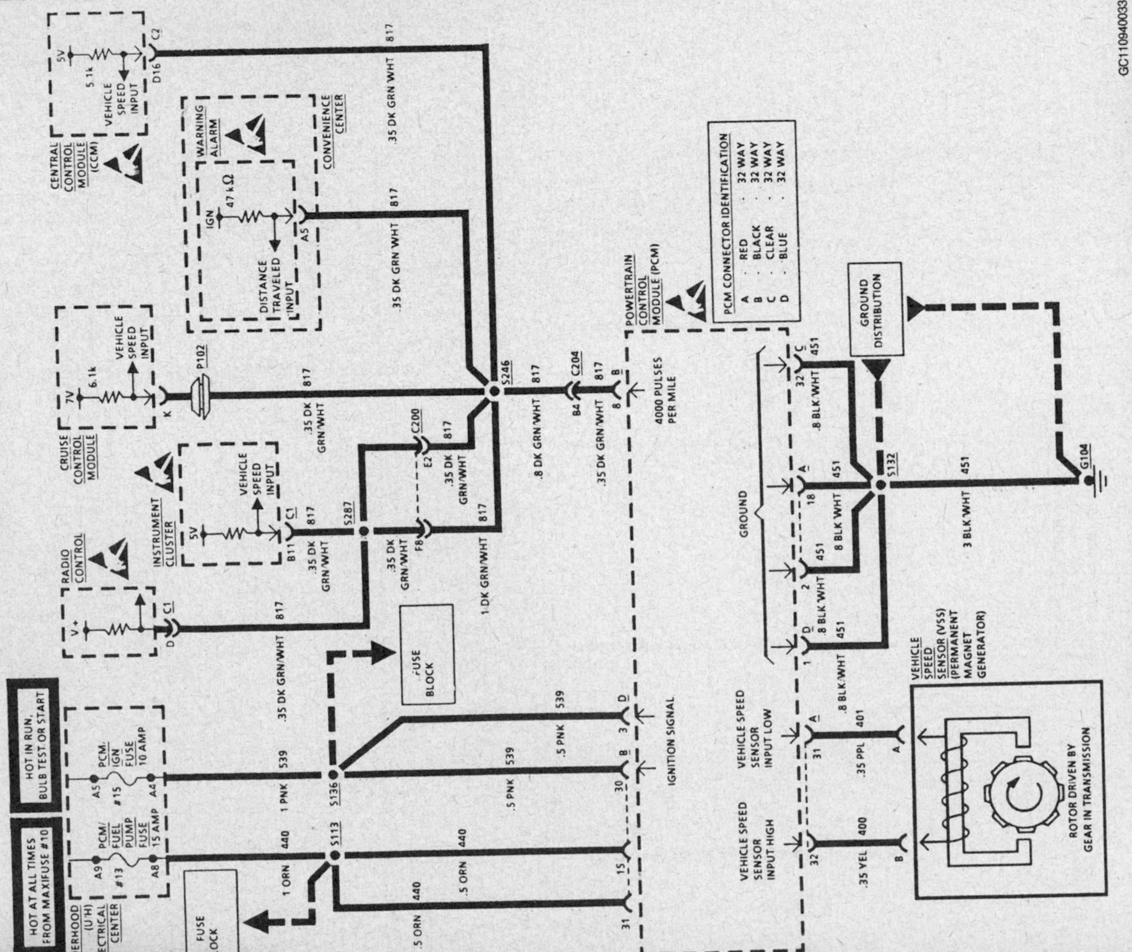
UNDERHOOD (U/H) ELECTRICAL CENTER
HOT AT ALL TIMES FROM MAXIFUSE #10
HOT IN RUN, BULB TEST OR START
PCM/FUEL PUMP FUSE 15 AMP
PCM/IGN FUSE 10 AMP
FUSE BLOCK
RADIO CONTROL
INSTRUMENT CLUSTER
CRUISE CONTROL MODULE
VEHICLE SPEED INPUT
WARNING ALARM
DISTANCE TRAVELED INPUT
CONVENIENCE CENTER
CENTRAL CONTROL MODULE (CCM)
POWERTRAIN CONTROL MODULE (PCM)
4000 PULSES PER MILE
PCM CONNECTOR IDENTIFICATION
A : RED : 32 WAY
B : BLACK : 32 WAY
C : CLEAR : 32 WAY
D : BLUE : 32 WAY
IGNITION SIGNAL
VEHICLE SPEED SENSOR INPUT HIGH
VEHICLE SPEED SENSOR INPUT LOW
GROUND
GROUND DISTRIBUTION
VEHICLE SPEED SENSOR (VSS) (PERMANENT MAGNET GENERATOR)
ROTOR DRIVEN BY GEAR IN TRANSMISSION
GC1109400332000X

Fig. 32 Vehicle speed sensor wiring diagram. 1994 Fleetwood (RWD)

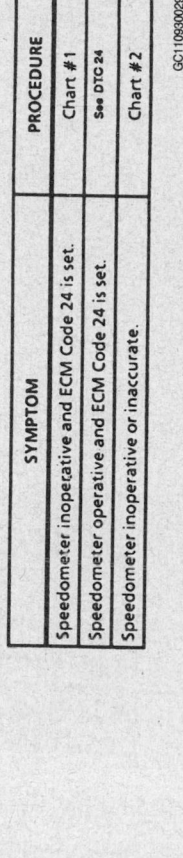

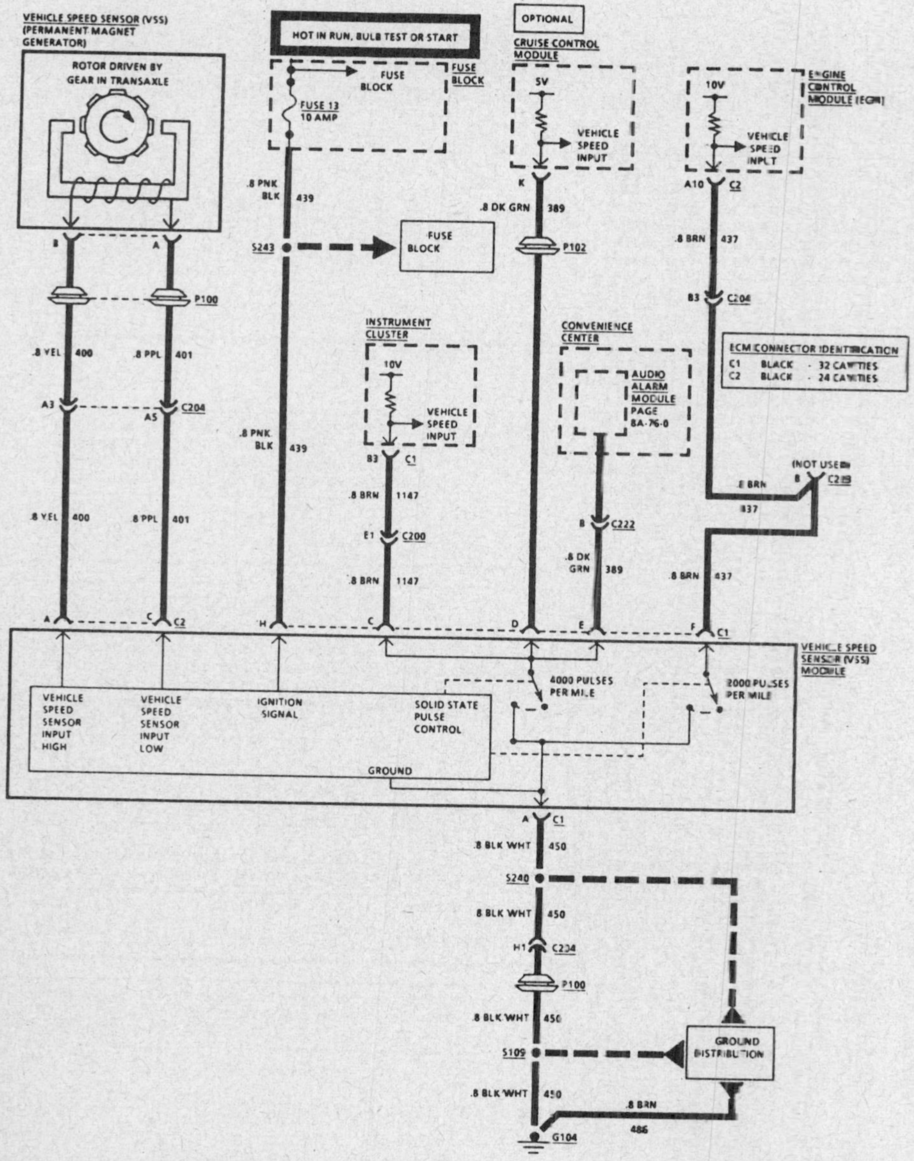
VEHICLE SPEED SENSOR (VSS) (PERMANENT MAGNET GENERATOR)
ROTOR DRIVEN BY GEAR IN TRANSAXLE
HOT IN RUN, BULB TEST OR START
FUSE BLOCK
FUSE 13 10 AMP
OPTIONAL
CRUISE CONTROL MODULE
5V
VEHICLE SPEED INPUT
10V
ENGINE CONTROL MODULE (ECM)
S243
P100
P102
C204
C200
C222
INSTRUMENT CLUSTER
CONVENIENCE CENTER
AUDIO ALARM MODULE PAGE 8A-76-0
ECM CONNECTOR IDENTIFICATION
C1 BLACK - 32 CAVITIES
C2 BLACK - 24 CAVITIES
(NOT USED)
.8 YEL 400
.8 PPL 401
.8 PNK BLK 439
.8 DK GRN 389
.8 BRN 437
.8 BRN 1147
VEHICLE SPEED SENSOR (VSS) MODULE
4000 PULSES PER MILE
2000 PULSES PER MILE
VEHICLE SPEED SENSOR INPUT HIGH
VEHICLE SPEED SENSOR INPUT LOW
IGNITION SIGNAL
SOLID STATE PULSE CONTROL
GROUND
.8 BLK WHT 450
S240
C224
S109
GROUND DISTRIBUTION
.8 BRN 486
G104
GC1109300292000X

Fig. 34 Vehicle speed sensor wiring diagram. Roadmaster Wagon

SYMPTOM	PROCEDURE
Speedometer inoperative and ECM Code 24 is set.	Chart #1
Speedometer operative and ECM Code 24 is set .	See DTC 24
Speedometer inoperative or inaccurate.	Chart #2
Cruise Control does not engage.	Chart #3

GC1109300293000X

Fig. 35 Vehicle speed sensor symptom table. Caprice, Impala SS & Roadmaster

SYMPTOM	PROCEDURE
Speedometer inoperative and ECM Code 24 is set.	Chart #1
Speedometer operative and ECM Code 24 is set.	See DTC 24
Speedometer inoperative or inaccurate.	Chart #2

GC1109300294000X

Fig. 36 Vehicle speed sensor symptom table. Fleetwood (RWD)

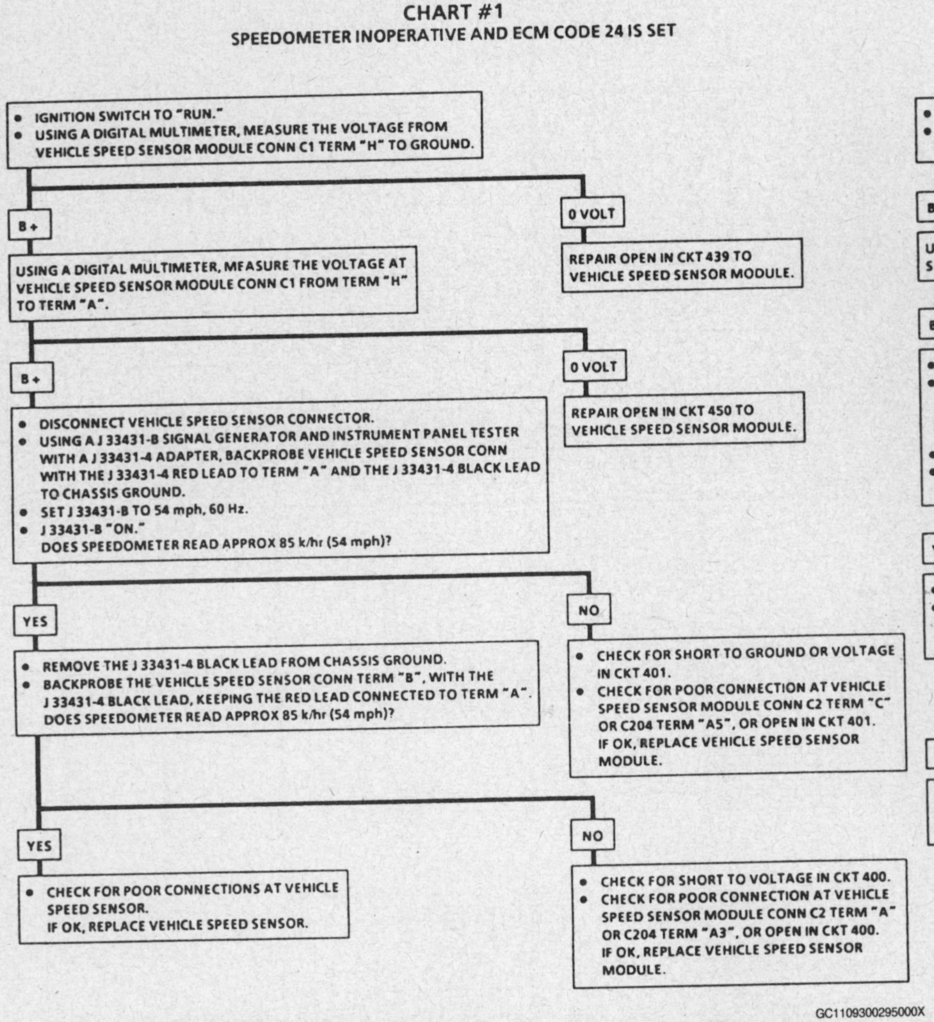
CHART #1
SPEEDOMETER INOPERATIVE AND ECM CODE 24 IS SET
• IGNITION SWITCH TO "RUN."
• USING A DIGITAL MULTIMETER, MEASURE THE VOLTAGE FROM VEHICLE SPEED SENSOR MODULE CONN C1 TERM "H" TO GROUND.
B+
0 VOLT
REPAIR OPEN IN CKT 439 TO VEHICLE SPEED SENSOR MODULE.
USING A DIGITAL MULTIMETER, MEASURE THE VOLTAGE AT VEHICLE SPEED SENSOR MODULE CONN C1 FROM TERM "H" TO TERM "A".
B+
0 VOLT
REPAIR OPEN IN CKT 450 TO VEHICLE SPEED SENSOR MODULE.
• DISCONNECT VEHICLE SPEED SENSOR CONNECTOR.
• USING A J 33431-B SIGNAL GENERATOR AND INSTRUMENT PANEL TESTER WITH A J 33431-4 ADAPTER, BACKPROBE VEHICLE SPEED SENSOR CONN WITH THE J 33431-4 RED LEAD TO TERM "A" AND THE J 33431-4 BLACK LEAD TO CHASSIS GROUND.
• SET J 33431-B TO 54 mph, 60 Hz.
• J 33431-B "ON."
DOES SPEEDOMETER READ APPROX 85 k/hr (54 mph)?
YES
NO
• CHECK FOR SHORT TO GROUND OR VOLTAGE IN CKT 401.
• CHECK FOR POOR CONNECTION AT VEHICLE SPEED SENSOR MODULE CONN C2 TERM "C" OR C204 TERM "A5", OR OPEN IN CKT 401.
IF OK, REPLACE VEHICLE SPEED SENSOR MODULE.
• REMOVE THE J 33431-4 BLACK LEAD FROM CHASSIS GROUND.
• BACKPROBE THE VEHICLE SPEED SENSOR CONN TERM "B", WITH THE J 33431-4 BLACK LEAD, KEEPING THE RED LEAD CONNECTED TO TERM "A".
DOES SPEEDOMETER READ APPROX 85 k/hr (54 mph)?
YES
NO
• CHECK FOR POOR CONNECTIONS AT VEHICLE SPEED SENSOR.
IF OK, REPLACE VEHICLE SPEED SENSOR.
• CHECK FOR SHORT TO VOLTAGE IN CKT 400.
• CHECK FOR POOR CONNECTION AT VEHICLE SPEED SENSOR MODULE CONN C2 TERM "A" OR C204 TERM "A3", OR OPEN IN CKT 400.
IF OK, REPLACE VEHICLE SPEED SENSOR MODULE.
GC1109300295000X

Fig. 37 Vehicle speed sensor troubleshooting chart No. 1. Caprice, Impala SS & Roadmaster

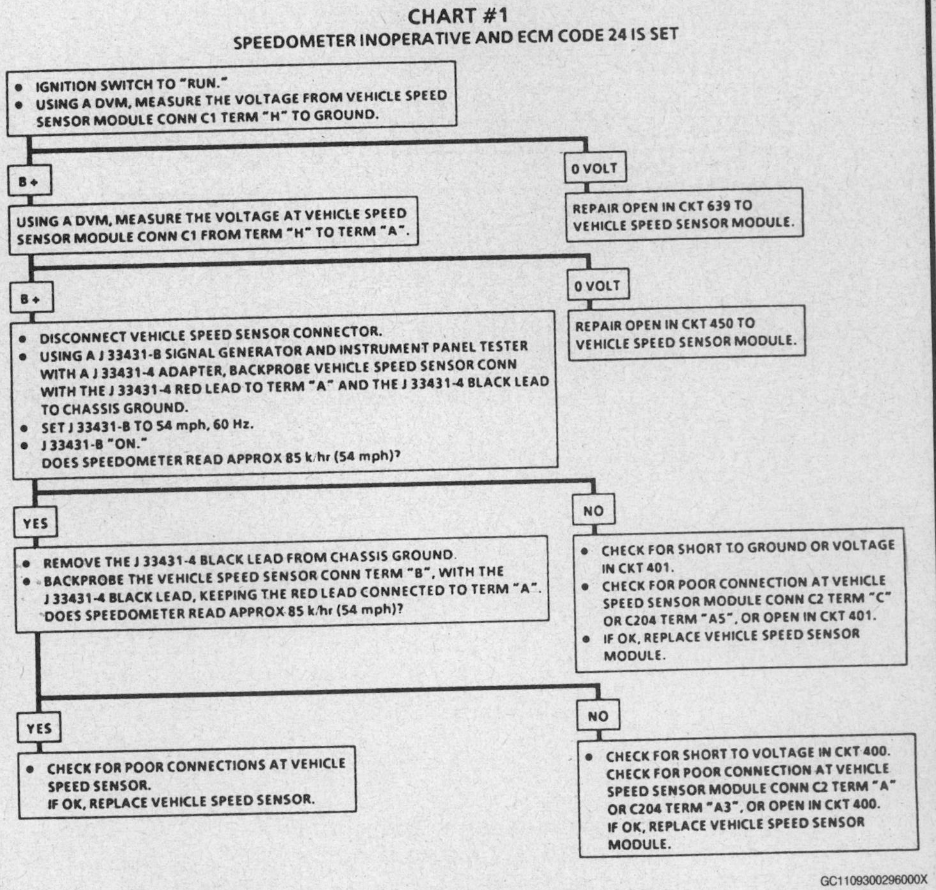
CHART #1
SPEEDOMETER INOPERATIVE AND ECM CODE 24 IS SET
• IGNITION SWITCH TO "RUN."
• USING A DVM, MEASURE THE VOLTAGE FROM VEHICLE SPEED SENSOR MODULE CONN C1 TERM "H" TO GROUND.
B+
0 VOLT
REPAIR OPEN IN CKT 639 TO VEHICLE SPEED SENSOR MODULE.
USING A DVM, MEASURE THE VOLTAGE AT VEHICLE SPEED SENSOR MODULE CONN C1 FROM TERM "H" TO TERM "A".
B+
0 VOLT
REPAIR OPEN IN CKT 450 TO VEHICLE SPEED SENSOR MODULE.
• DISCONNECT VEHICLE SPEED SENSOR CONNECTOR.
• USING A J 33431-B SIGNAL GENERATOR AND INSTRUMENT PANEL TESTER WITH A J 33431-4 ADAPTER, BACKPROBE VEHICLE SPEED SENSOR CONN WITH THE J 33431-4 RED LEAD TO TERM "A" AND THE J 33431-4 BLACK LEAD TO CHASSIS GROUND.
• SET J 33431-B TO 54 mph, 60 Hz.
• J 33431-B "ON."
DOES SPEEDOMETER READ APPROX 85 k/hr (54 mph)?
YES
NO
• CHECK FOR SHORT TO GROUND OR VOLTAGE IN CKT 401.
• CHECK FOR POOR CONNECTION AT VEHICLE SPEED SENSOR MODULE CONN C2 TERM "C" OR C204 TERM "A5", OR OPEN IN CKT 401.
• IF OK, REPLACE VEHICLE SPEED SENSOR MODULE.
• REMOVE THE J 33431-4 BLACK LEAD FROM CHASSIS GROUND.
• BACKPROBE THE VEHICLE SPEED SENSOR CONN TERM "B", WITH THE J 33431-4 BLACK LEAD, KEEPING THE RED LEAD CONNECTED TO TERM "A".
DOES SPEEDOMETER READ APPROX 85 k/hr (54 mph)?
YES
NO
• CHECK FOR POOR CONNECTIONS AT VEHICLE SPEED SENSOR.
IF OK, REPLACE VEHICLE SPEED SENSOR.
• CHECK FOR SHORT TO VOLTAGE IN CKT 400.
CHECK FOR POOR CONNECTION AT VEHICLE SPEED SENSOR MODULE CONN C2 TERM "A" OR C204 TERM "A3", OR OPEN IN CKT 400.
IF OK, REPLACE VEHICLE SPEED SENSOR MODULE.
GC1109300296000X

Fig. 38 Vehicle speed sensor troubleshooting chart No. 1. Fleetwood (RWD)

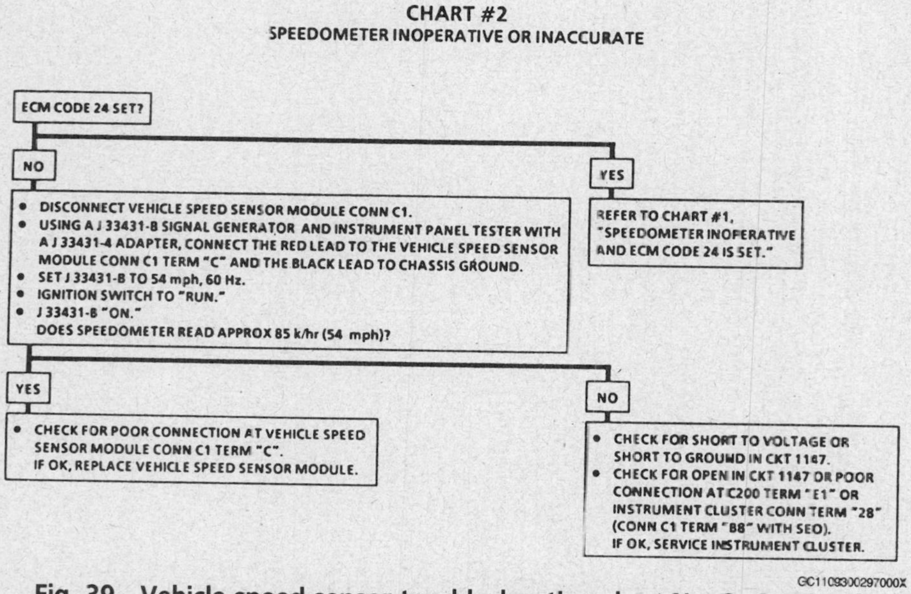
CHART #2
SPEEDOMETER INOPERATIVE OR INACCURATE
ECM CODE 24 SET?
NO
• DISCONNECT VEHICLE SPEED SENSOR MODULE CONN C1.
• USING A J 33431-B SIGNAL GENERATOR AND INSTRUMENT PANEL TESTER WITH A J 33431-4 ADAPTER, CONNECT THE RED LEAD TO THE VEHICLE SPEED SENSOR MODULE CONN C1 TERM "C" AND THE BLACK LEAD TO CHASSIS GROUND.
• SET J 33431-B TO 54 mph, 60 Hz.
• IGNITION SWITCH TO "RUN."
• J 33431-B "ON."
DOES SPEEDOMETER READ APPROX 85 k/hr (54 mph)?
YES
REFER TO CHART #1, "SPEEDOMETER INOPERATIVE AND ECM CODE 24 IS SET."
YES
• CHECK FOR POOR CONNECTION AT VEHICLE SPEED SENSOR MODULE CONN C1 TERM "C".
IF OK, REPLACE VEHICLE SPEED SENSOR MODULE.
NO
• CHECK FOR SHORT TO VOLTAGE OR SHORT TO GROUND IN CKT 1147.
• CHECK FOR OPEN IN CKT 1147 OR POOR CONNECTION AT C200 TERM "E1" OR INSTRUMENT CLUSTER CONN TERM "28" (CONN C1 TERM "B8" WITH SEO).
IF OK, SERVICE INSTRUMENT CLUSTER.
GC1109300297000X

Fig. 39 Vehicle speed sensor troubleshooting chart No. 2. Caprice & Impala SS

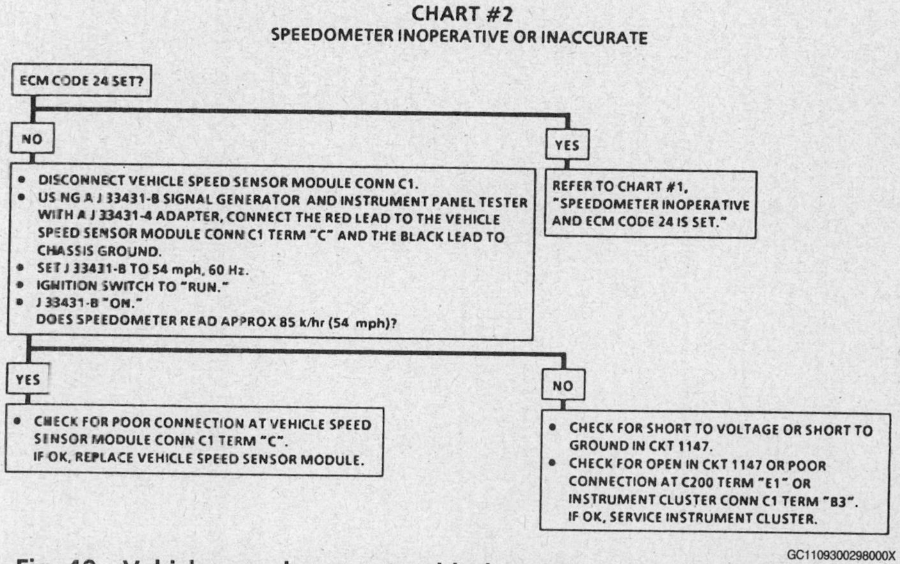
CHART #2
SPEEDOMETER INOPERATIVE OR INACCURATE
ECM CODE 24 SET?
NO
• DISCONNECT VEHICLE SPEED SENSOR MODULE CONN C1.
• USING A J 33431-B SIGNAL GENERATOR AND INSTRUMENT PANEL TESTER WITH A J 33431-4 ADAPTER, CONNECT THE RED LEAD TO THE VEHICLE SPEED SENSOR MODULE CONN C1 TERM "C" AND THE BLACK LEAD TO CHASSIS GROUND.
• SET J 33431-B TO 54 mph, 60 Hz.
• IGNITION SWITCH TO "RUN."
• J 33431-B "ON."
DOES SPEEDOMETER READ APPROX 85 k/hr (54 mph)?
YES
REFER TO CHART #1, "SPEEDOMETER INOPERATIVE AND ECM CODE 24 IS SET."
YES
• CHECK FOR POOR CONNECTION AT VEHICLE SPEED SENSOR MODULE CONN C1 TERM "C".
IF OK, REPLACE VEHICLE SPEED SENSOR MODULE.
NO
• CHECK FOR SHORT TO VOLTAGE OR SHORT TO GROUND IN CKT 1147.
• CHECK FOR OPEN IN CKT 1147 OR POOR CONNECTION AT C200 TERM "E1" OR INSTRUMENT CLUSTER CONN C1 TERM "B3".
IF OK, SERVICE INSTRUMENT CLUSTER.
GC1109300298000X

Fig. 40 Vehicle speed sensor troubleshooting chart No. 2. Roadmaster

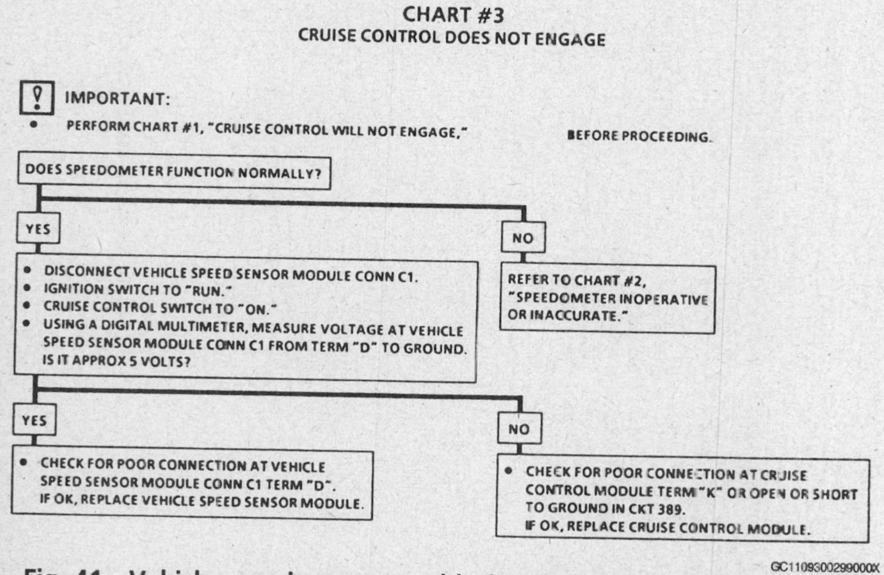
CHART #3
CRUISE CONTROL DOES NOT ENGAGE
IMPORTANT:
• PERFORM CHART #1, "CRUISE CONTROL WILL NOT ENGAGE," BEFORE PROCEEDING.
DOES SPEEDOMETER FUNCTION NORMALLY?
YES
• DISCONNECT VEHICLE SPEED SENSOR MODULE CONN C1.
• IGNITION SWITCH TO "RUN."
• CRUISE CONTROL SWITCH TO "ON."
• USING A DIGITAL MULTIMETER, MEASURE VOLTAGE AT VEHICLE SPEED SENSOR MODULE CONN C1 FROM TERM "D" TO GROUND. IS IT APPROX 5 VOLTS?
NO
REFER TO CHART #2, "SPEEDOMETER INOPERATIVE OR INACCURATE."
YES
• CHECK FOR POOR CONNECTION AT VEHICLE SPEED SENSOR MODULE CONN C1 TERM "D".
IF OK, REPLACE VEHICLE SPEED SENSOR MODULE.
NO
• CHECK FOR POOR CONNECTION AT CRUISE CONTROL MODULE TERM "K" OR OPEN OR SHORT TO GROUND IN CKT 389.
IF OK, REPLACE CRUISE CONTROL MODULE.
GC1109300299000X

Fig. 41 Vehicle speed sensor troubleshooting chart No. 3. Caprice & Impala SS

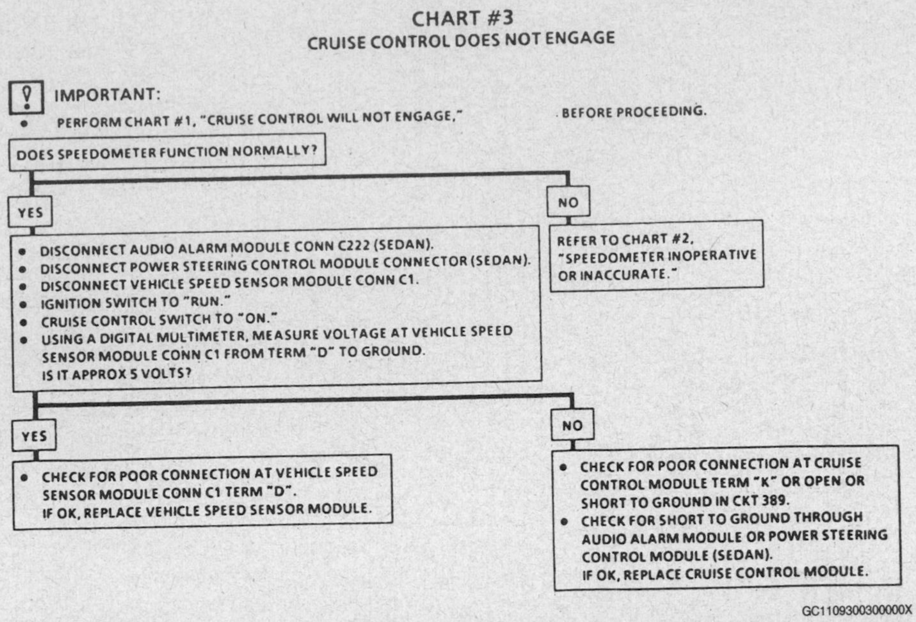
CHART #3
CRUISE CONTROL DOES NOT ENGAGE
IMPORTANT:
• PERFORM CHART #1, "CRUISE CONTROL WILL NOT ENGAGE," BEFORE PROCEEDING.
DOES SPEEDOMETER FUNCTION NORMALLY?
YES
NO
REFER TO CHART #2, "SPEEDOMETER INOPERATIVE OR INACCURATE."
• DISCONNECT AUDIO ALARM MODULE CONN C222 (SEDAN).
• DISCONNECT POWER STEERING CONTROL MODULE CONNECTOR (SEDAN).
• DISCONNECT VEHICLE SPEED SENSOR MODULE CONN C1.
• IGNITION SWITCH TO "RUN."
• CRUISE CONTROL SWITCH TO "ON."
• USING A DIGITAL MULTIMETER, MEASURE VOLTAGE AT VEHICLE SPEED SENSOR MODULE CONN C1 FROM TERM "D" TO GROUND. IS IT APPROX 5 VOLTS?
YES
NO
• CHECK FOR POOR CONNECTION AT VEHICLE SPEED SENSOR MODULE CONN C1 TERM "D". IF OK, REPLACE VEHICLE SPEED SENSOR MODULE.
• CHECK FOR POOR CONNECTION AT CRUISE CONTROL MODULE TERM "K" OR OPEN OR SHORT TO GROUND IN CKT 389.
• CHECK FOR SHORT TO GROUND THROUGH AUDIO ALARM MODULE OR POWER STEERING CONTROL MODULE (SEDAN). IF OK, REPLACE CRUISE CONTROL MODULE.
GC1109300300000X

Fig. 42 Vehicle speed sensor troubleshooting chart No. 3. Roadmaster

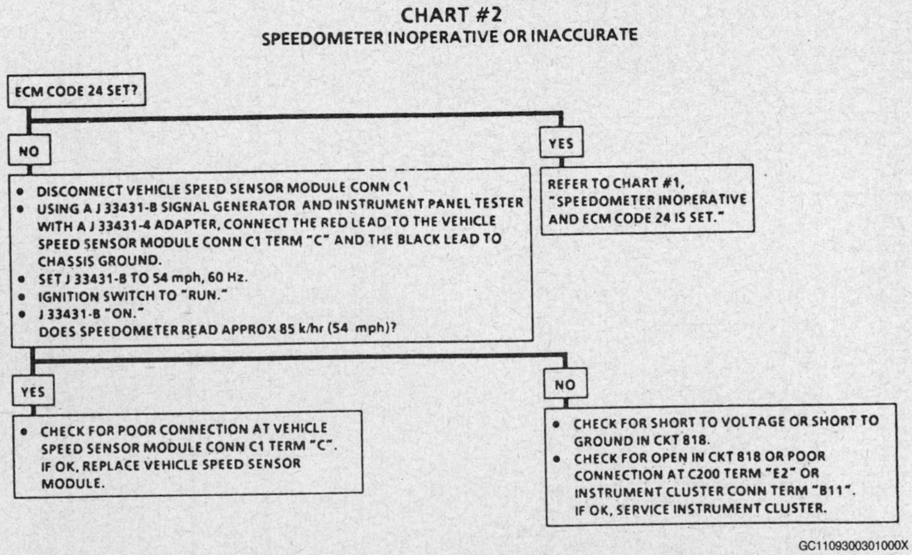
CHART #2
SPEEDOMETER INOPERATIVE OR INACCURATE
ECM CODE 24 SET?
NO
YES
REFER TO CHART #1, "SPEEDOMETER INOPERATIVE AND ECM CODE 24 IS SET."
• DISCONNECT VEHICLE SPEED SENSOR MODULE CONN C1
• USING A J 33431-B SIGNAL GENERATOR AND INSTRUMENT PANEL TESTER WITH A J 33431-4 ADAPTER, CONNECT THE RED LEAD TO THE VEHICLE SPEED SENSOR MODULE CONN C1 TERM "C" AND THE BLACK LEAD TO CHASSIS GROUND.
• SET J 33431-B TO 54 mph, 60 Hz.
• IGNITION SWITCH TO "RUN."
• J 33431-B "ON."
DOES SPEEDOMETER READ APPROX 85 k/hr (54 mph)?
YES
NO
• CHECK FOR POOR CONNECTION AT VEHICLE SPEED SENSOR MODULE CONN C1 TERM "C". IF OK, REPLACE VEHICLE SPEED SENSOR MODULE.
• CHECK FOR SHORT TO VOLTAGE OR SHORT TO GROUND IN CKT 818.
• CHECK FOR OPEN IN CKT 818 OR POOR CONNECTION AT C200 TERM "E2" OR INSTRUMENT CLUSTER CONN TERM "B11". IF OK, SERVICE INSTRUMENT CLUSTER.
GC1109300301000X

Fig. 43 Vehicle speed sensor troubleshooting chart No. 2. Fleetwood (RWD)

(1)
- ASSUMES SPEEDOMETER IS WORKING OK.
- RAISE DRIVE WHEELS.
- WITH ENGINE IDLING IN GEAR, SCAN TOOL SHOULD DISPLAY MPH ABOVE 0. DOES IT?

YES → DTC 24 IS INTERMITTENT.

NO →
- ENGINE STILL IDLING IN GEAR.
- BACKPROBE CKT 437 AT 37-WAY CONNECTOR WITH VOLTMETER TO GROUND.
- IS VOLTAGE VARYING BETWEEN 1 AND 12 VOLTS ?

YES → FAULTY ECM

NO → (2)
- IGNITION "OFF."
- DISCONNECT VSS BUFFER MODULE.
- IGNITION "ON."
- BACKPROBE CKT 437 AT 37-WAY CONNECTOR. WITH VOLTMETER TO GROUND.
- SHOULD DISPLAY 10 VOLTS OR MORE. DOES IT?

YES → CKT 437 OPEN BETWEEN 37-WAY CONNECTOR AND VSS BUFFER MODULE CONNECTOR OR FAULTY VSS BUFFER MODULE.

NO → CKT 437 SHORTED TO GROUND, OPEN BETWEEN ECM AND 37-WAY CONNECTOR, FAULTY CONNECTION OR FAULTY ECM.

GC1109300302000X

Fig. 44 Code 24: Vehicle Speed Sensor. Caprice, Impala SS & Roadmaster

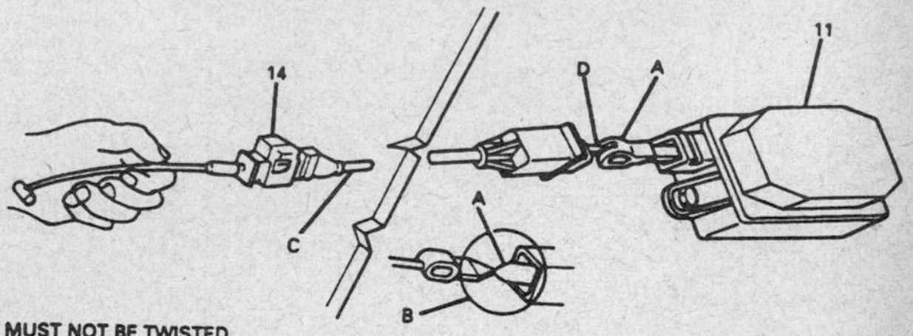

14
D
A
11
C
A
B

A RIBBON
B RIBBON MUST NOT BE TWISTED
C MARKINGS IN YELLOW FOR LT1 ENGINE, PINK FOR L32 ENGINE
D BEAD
11 MODULE ASSEMBLY, CRUISE CONTROL
14 CABLE ASSEMBLY, CRUISE CONTROL

GC1109300309000X

Fig. 46 Cruise control cable retainer removal

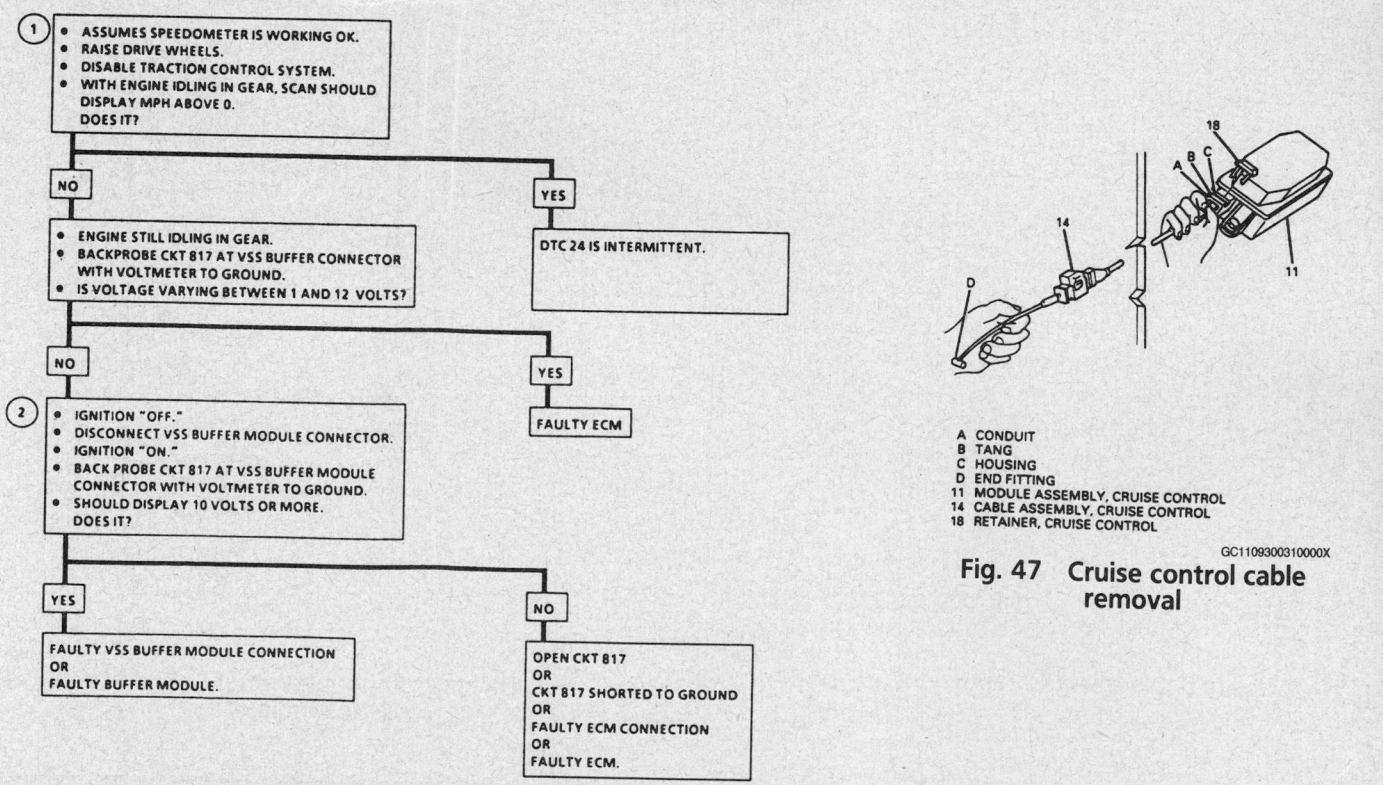

(1)
- ASSUMES SPEEDOMETER IS WORKING OK.
- RAISE DRIVE WHEELS.
- DISABLE TRACTION CONTROL SYSTEM.
- WITH ENGINE IDLING IN GEAR, SCAN SHOULD DISPLAY MPH ABOVE 0. DOES IT?

YES → DTC 24 IS INTERMITTENT.

NO →
- ENGINE STILL IDLING IN GEAR.
- BACKPROBE CKT 817 AT VSS BUFFER CONNECTOR WITH VOLTMETER TO GROUND.
- IS VOLTAGE VARYING BETWEEN 1 AND 12 VOLTS?

YES → FAULTY ECM

NO → (2)
- IGNITION "OFF."
- DISCONNECT VSS BUFFER MODULE CONNECTOR.
- IGNITION "ON."
- BACK PROBE CKT 817 AT VSS BUFFER MODULE CONNECTOR WITH VOLTMETER TO GROUND.
- SHOULD DISPLAY 10 VOLTS OR MORE. DOES IT?

YES → FAULTY VSS BUFFER MODULE CONNECTION OR FAULTY BUFFER MODULE.

NO → OPEN CKT 817 OR CKT 817 SHORTED TO GROUND OR FAULTY ECM CONNECTION OR FAULTY ECM.

GC1109300303000X

Fig. 45 Code 24: Vehicle Speed Sensor. Fleetwood (RWD)

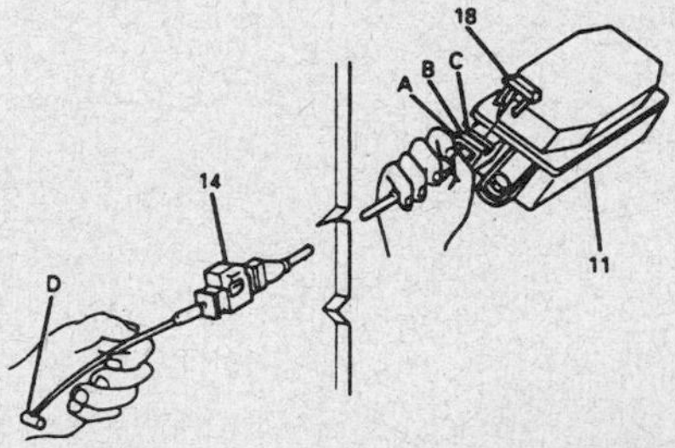

18
A
B
C
14
11
D

A CONDUIT
B TANG
C HOUSING
D END FITTING
11 MODULE ASSEMBLY, CRUISE CONTROL
14 CABLE ASSEMBLY, CRUISE CONTROL
18 RETAINER, CRUISE CONTROL

GC1109300310000X

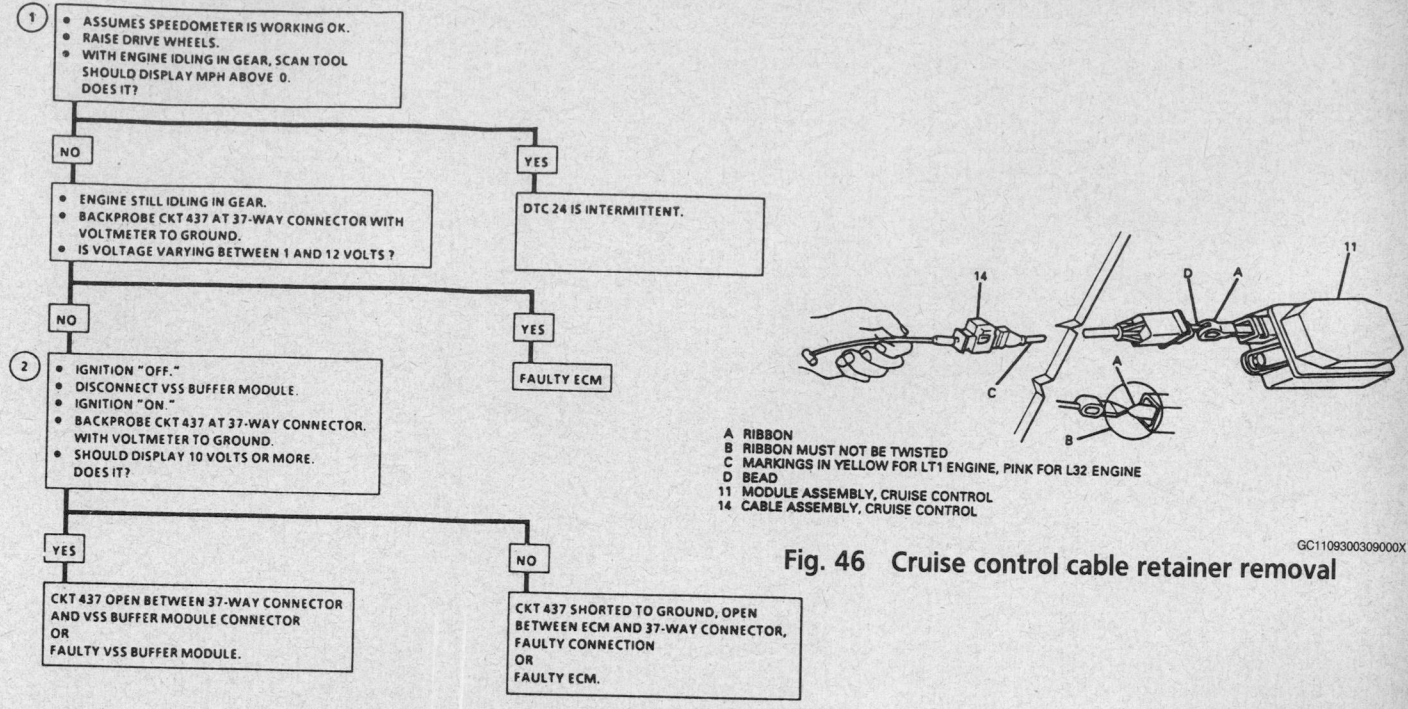

Fig. 47 Cruise control cable removal

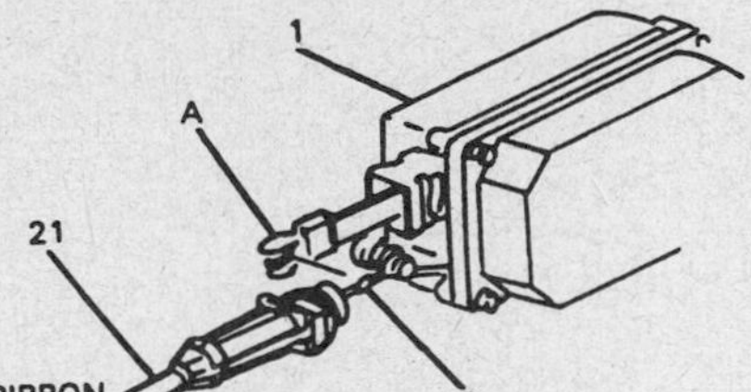

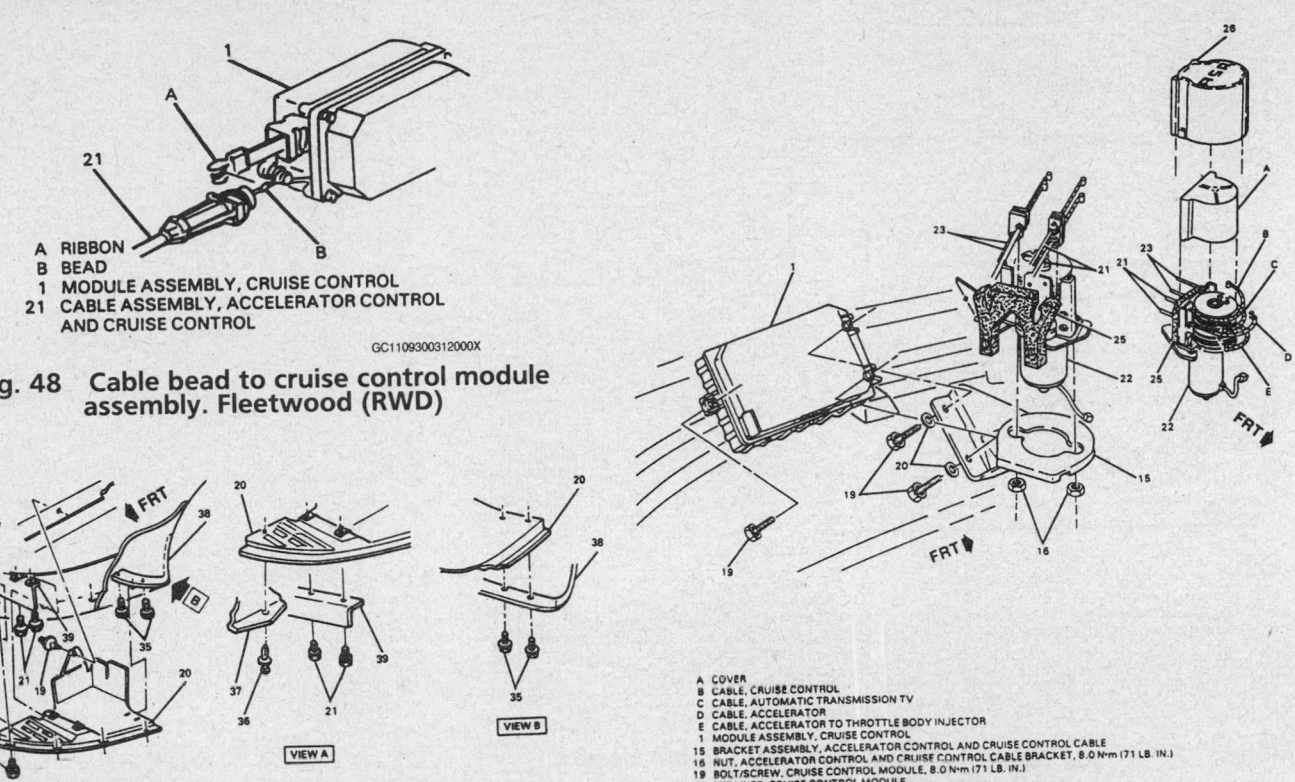

A RIBBON
B BEAD
1 MODULE ASSEMBLY, CRUISE CONTROL
21 CABLE ASSEMBLY, ACCELERATOR CONTROL AND CRUISE CONTROL

GC1109300312000X

Fig. 48 Cable bead to cruise control module assembly. Fleetwood (RWD)

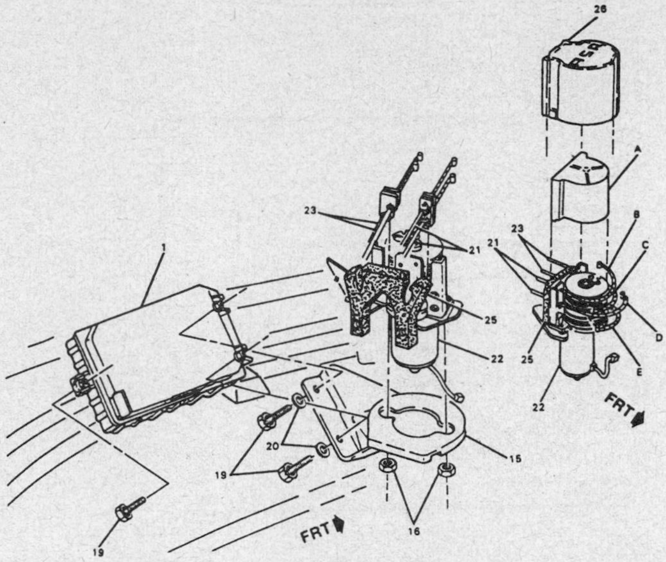

A COVER
B CABLE, CRUISE CONTROL
C CABLE, AUTOMATIC TRANSMISSION TV
D CABLE, ACCELERATOR
E CABLE, ACCELERATOR TO THROTTLE BODY INJECTOR
1 MODULE ASSEMBLY, CRUISE CONTROL
15 BRACKET ASSEMBLY, ACCELERATOR CONTROL AND CRUISE CONTROL CABLE
16 NUT, ACCELERATOR CONTROL AND CRUISE CONTROL CABLE BRACKET, 8.0 N·m (71 LB. IN.)
19 BOLT/SCREW, CRUISE CONTROL MODULE, 8.0 N·m (71 LB. IN.)
20 RETAINER, CRUISE CONTROL MODULE
21 CABLE ASSEMBLY, ACCELERATOR CONTROL AND CRUISE CONTROL
22 ADJUSTER ASSEMBLY, ACCELERATOR CONTROL AND CRUISE CONTROL CABLE
23 CABLE ASSEMBLY, ACCELERATOR CONTROL AND AUTOMATIC TRANSMISSION TV
25 SHIELD ASSEMBLY, ACCELERATOR CONTROL AND CRUISE CONTROL CABLE ADJUSTER
26 COVER, ACCELERATOR CONTROL AND CRUISE CONTROL CABLE ADJUSTER

GC1109300311000X

Fig. 49 Accelerator control & cruise control cable adjuster removal. Fleetwood (RWD) less V4U Coachbuilder Equipment Opetion

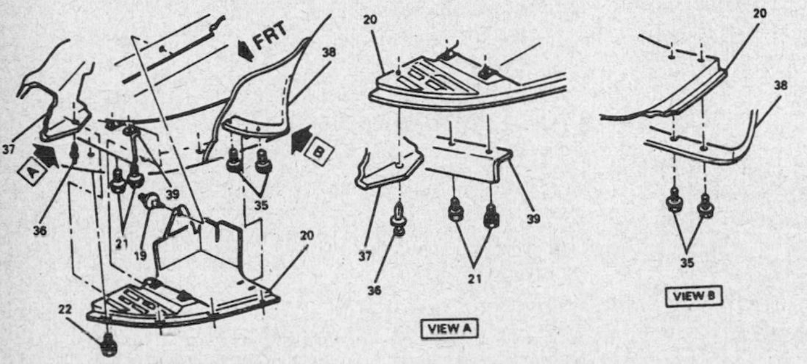

19 RETAINER, FRONT BUMPER FASCIA LOWER DEFLECTOR
20 DEFLECTOR, FRONT BUMPER FASCIA LOWER
21 BOLT/SCREW, RADIATOR AIR LOWER DEFLECTOR
22 BOLT/SCREW, FRONT BUMPER FASCIA LOWER DEFLECTOR
35 BOLT/SCREW, FRONT BUMPER FASCIA LOWER DEFLECTOR
36 RETAINER, FRONT BUMPER FASCIA LOWER DEFLECTOR
37 BAFFLE, RADIATOR AIR LOWER
38 LINER, FRONT WHEELHOUSE PANEL
39 DEFLECTOR, RADIATOR AIR LOWER

GC1109300313000X

Fig. 50 Front bumper fascia lower deflector removal. Camaro & Firebird

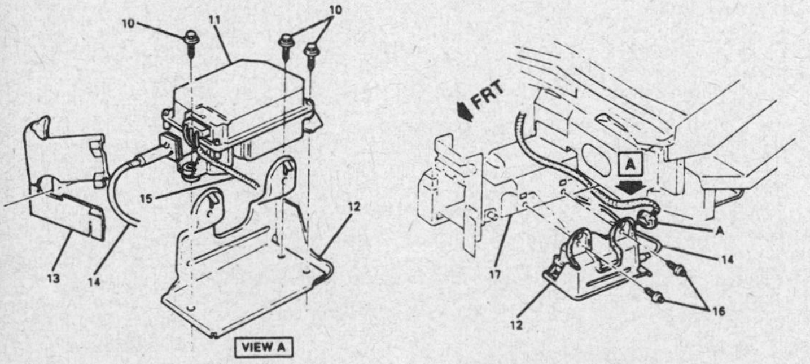

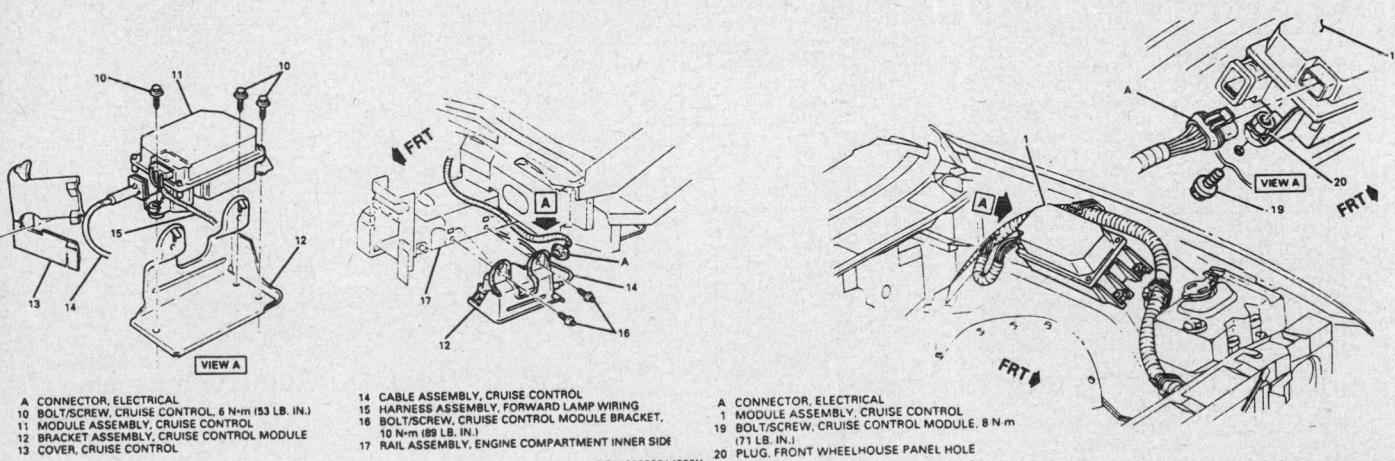

A CONNECTOR, ELECTRICAL
10 BOLT/SCREW, CRUISE CONTROL, 6 N·m (53 LB. IN.)
11 MODULE ASSEMBLY, CRUISE CONTROL
12 BRACKET ASSEMBLY, CRUISE CONTROL MODULE
13 COVER, CRUISE CONTROL
14 CABLE ASSEMBLY, CRUISE CONTROL
15 HARNESS ASSEMBLY, FORWARD LAMP WIRING
16 BOLT/SCREW, CRUISE CONTROL MODULE BRACKET, 10 N·m (89 LB. IN.)
17 RAIL ASSEMBLY, ENGINE COMPARTMENT INNER SIDE

GC1109300314000X

Fig. 51 Cruise control module removal. Camaro & Firebird

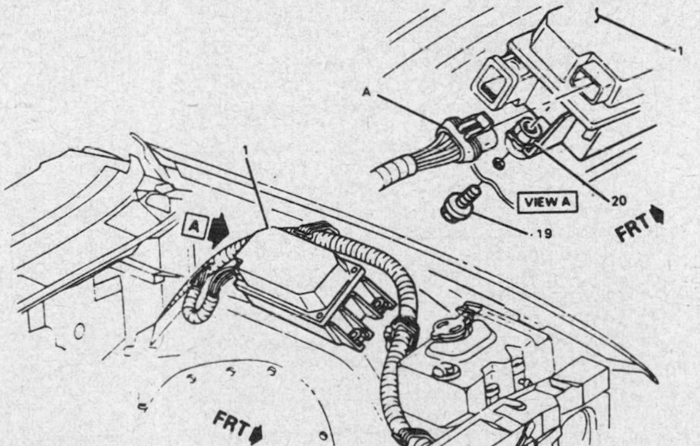

A CONNECTOR, ELECTRICAL
1 MODULE ASSEMBLY, CRUISE CONTROL
19 BOLT/SCREW, CRUISE CONTROL MODULE, 8 N·m (71 LB. IN.)
20 PLUG, FRONT WHEELHOUSE PANEL HOLE

GC1109300315000X

Fig. 52 Cruise control module removal. Caprice, Impala SS & Roadmaster

WIPER SYSTEMS

TABLE OF CONTENTS

Application Chart

Model	Year	System	Page No.
Achieva	1992–94	Permanent Magnet Depressed Park System	22-2
Beretta	1992–94	Permanent Magnet Depressed Park System	22-2
Bonneville	1992–94	Permanent Magnet Depressed Park System	22-2
Brougham	1992	Multiplex Pulse Wiper System	22-27
Camaro	1992–94	Permanent Magnet Depressed Park System	22-2
Caprice	1992–94	Permanent Magnet Depressed Park System	22-2
Cavalier	1992–94	Permanent Magnet Positive Park System	22-21
Century	1992–94	Permanent Magnet Depressed Park System	22-2
Concours	1993-94	Permanent Magnet Depressed Park System	22-2
Corsica	1992–94	Permanent Magnet Depressed Park System	22-2
Corvette	1992–94	Permanent Magnet Depressed Park System	22-2
Custom Cruiser	1992	Permanent Magnet Depressed Park System	22-2
Cutlass Ciera	1992–94	Permanent Magnet Depressed Park System	22-2
Cutlass Cruiser	1992–94	Permanent Magnet Depressed Park System	22-2
Cutlass Supreme	1992–94	Permanent Magnet Depressed Park System	22-2
DeVille	1992–94	Permanent Magnet Depressed Park System	22-2
Eighty Eight	1992–94	Permanent Magnet Depressed Park System	22-2
Eldorado	1992–94	Permanent Magnet Depressed Park System	22-2
Firebird	1992–94	Permanent Magnet Depressed Park System	22-2
Fleetwood (FWD)	1992	Permanent Magnet Depressed Park System	22-2
Fleetwood (RWD)	1993–94	Permanent Magnet Depressed Park System	22-2
Grand Am	1992–94	Permanent Magnet Depressed Park System	22-2
Gran Prix	1992–94	Permanent Magnet Depressed Park System	22-2
Impala SS	1994	Permanent Magnet Depressed Park System	22-2
LeSabre	1992–94	Permanent Magnet Depressed Park System	22-2
Metro	1992–94	One, Two & Three Speed Systems	22-28
Lumina	1992–94	Permanent Magnet Depressed Park System	22-2
Ninety Eight	1992–94	Permanent Magnet Depressed Park System	22-2
Park Avenue	1992–94	Permanent Magnet Depressed Park System	22-2
Prizm	1992–94	One, Two & Three Speed Systems	22-28
Regal	1992–94	Permanent Magnet Depressed Park System	22-2
Riviera	1992–93	Permanent Magnet Depressed Park System	22-2
Roadmaster	1992–94	Permanent Magnet Depressed Park System	22-2
Seville	1992–94	Permanent Magnet Depressed Park System	22-2
Skylark	1992-94	Permanent Magnet Depressed Park System	22-2
Storm	1992-93	One, Two & Three Speed Systems	22-28
Sunbird	1992–94	Permanent Magnet Positive Park System	22-21
Toronado	1992	Permanent Magnet Depressed Park System	22-2
Trofeo	1992	Permanent Magnet Depressed Park System	22-2

Permanent Magnet Depressed Park System

INDEX

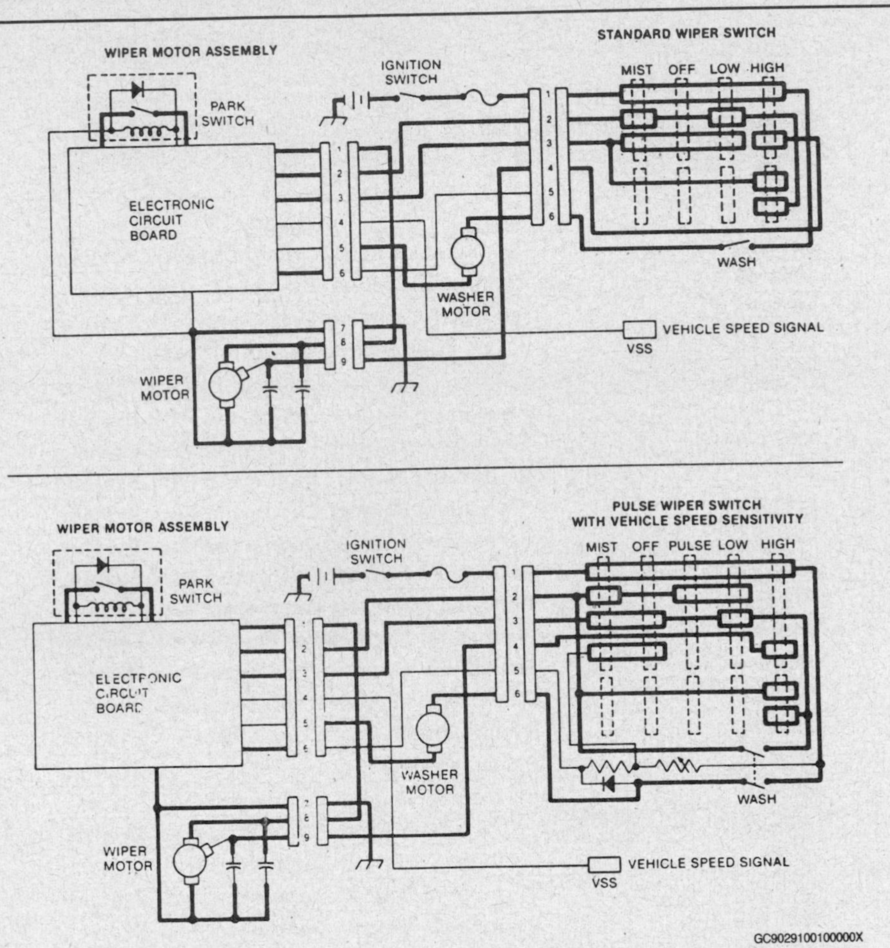
WIPER MOTOR ASSEMBLY
PARK SWITCH
IGNITION SWITCH
STANDARD WIPER SWITCH
MIST OFF LOW HIGH
ELECTRONIC CIRCUIT BOARD
WASHER MOTOR
WASH
VEHICLE SPEED SIGNAL
VSS
WIPER MOTOR
WIPER MOTOR ASSEMBLY
PARK SWITCH
IGNITION SWITCH
PULSE WIPER SWITCH WITH VEHICLE SPEED SENSITIVITY
MIST OFF PULSE LOW HIGH
ELECTRONIC CIRCUIT BOARD
WASHER MOTOR
WASH
VEHICLE SPEED SIGNAL
VSS
WIPER MOTOR
GC9029100100000X

Fig. 1 Wiper system circuit diagram. 1992 Except Camaro, Century, Corvette, Cutlass Ciera, Cutlass Cruiser & Firebird

DESCRIPTION

The Permanent Magnet Depressed Park (PMDP) windshield wiper and remote washer pump system consists of a depressed park wiper motor and a washer pump mounted on the washer fluid reservoir.

Based on the type of control switch used and whether an optional electronic printed circuit board is attached in the wiper cover, the system can serve as either a pulse type wiper system or a standard type system. Pulse timing and demand functions are controlled electronically on pulse systems. The pulse system also uses the vehicle speed signal to adjust the wiper delay time. The faster the vehicle is traveling, the shorter delay time between wipe cycles.

Electronic logic circuits on the pulse wiper system's printed circuit board establish all timing and washer commands. If the WASH switch is pressed, a wash is performed for as long as the switch is depressed. The wash action is followed by six seconds of dry wipes before shutoff. With the control switch in the LO or HI speed position, the respective brush circuit is completed to the 12 volt DC source and the wiper motor runs at that particular speed setting.

Moving the switch to the PULSE mode operates the wiper motor intermittently and the delay and be varied by moving the switch back and forth in the delay mode. An instantaneous wipe can be obtained by moving the switch to the MIST position.

SYSTEM DIAGNOSIS & TESTING

EXCEPT CORVETTE

1992

Refer to wiring circuit diagrams **Fig. 1 and 2**, wiper motor terminal checks **Figs. 3 and 4**, wiper switch tests **Figs. 5 through 8**, wiper/washer switch check charts **Fig. 9 and 10** and diagnosis charts **Figs. 11 through 22**, when performing system diagnosis and testing procedures.

1993–94

On all models except Eldorado and Se-

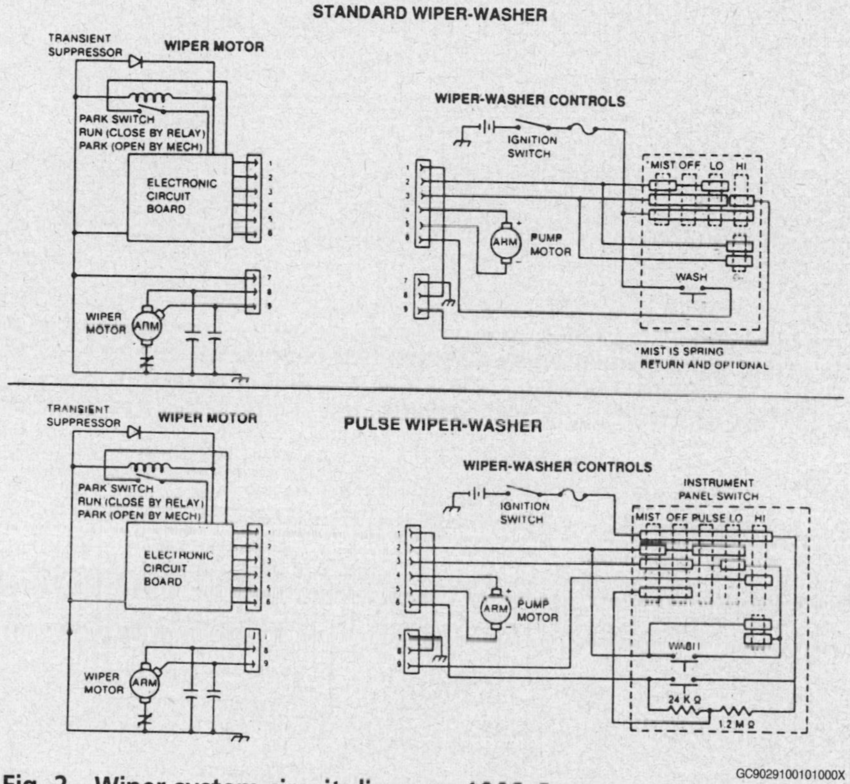
STANDARD WIPER-WASHER
TRANSIENT SUPPRESSOR
WIPER MOTOR
PARK SWITCH
RUN (CLOSE BY RELAY)
PARK (OPEN BY MECH)
ELECTRONIC CIRCUIT BOARD
WIPER MOTOR
ARM
WIPER-WASHER CONTROLS
IGNITION SWITCH
*MIST OFF LO HI
PUMP MOTOR
WASH
*MIST IS SPRING RETURN AND OPTIONAL
PULSE WIPER-WASHER
TRANSIENT SUPPRESSOR
WIPER MOTOR
PARK SWITCH
RUN (CLOSE BY RELAY)
PARK (OPEN BY MECH)
ELECTRONIC CIRCUIT BOARD
WIPER MOTOR
WIPER-WASHER CONTROLS
IGNITION SWITCH
INSTRUMENT PANEL SWITCH
MIST OFF PULSE LO HI
PUMP MOTOR
WASH
24 K Ω
1.2 M Ω
GC9029100101000X

Fig. 2 Wiper system circuit diagram. 1992 Camaro, Century, Cutlass Ciera, Cutlass Cruiser & Firebird

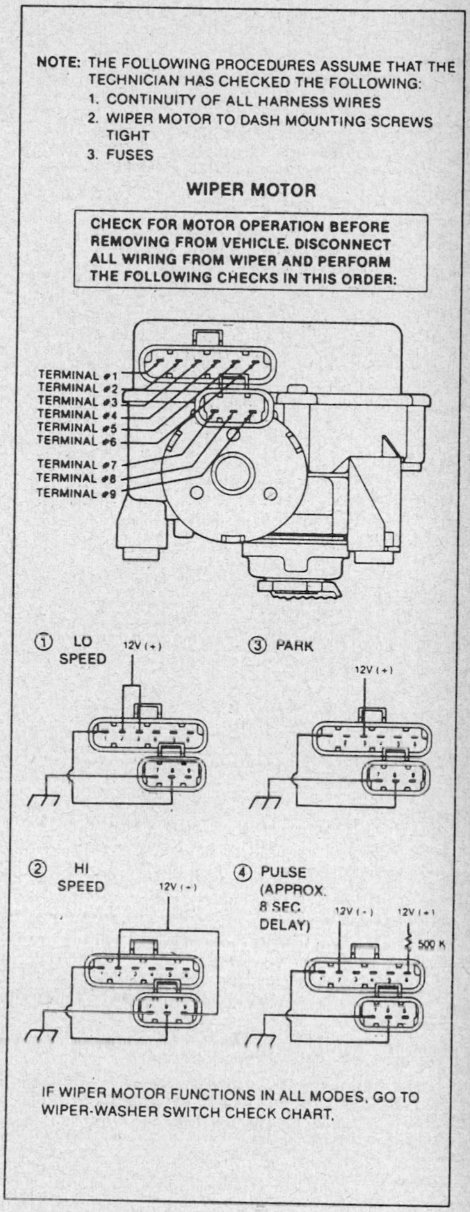
NOTE: THE FOLLOWING PROCEDURES ASSUME THAT THE TECHNICIAN HAS CHECKED THE FOLLOWING:
1. CONTINUITY OF ALL HARNESS WIRES
2. WIPER MOTOR TO DASH MOUNTING SCREWS TIGHT
3. FUSES
WIPER MOTOR
CHECK FOR MOTOR OPERATION BEFORE REMOVING FROM VEHICLE. DISCONNECT ALL WIRING FROM WIPER AND PERFORM THE FOLLOWING CHECKS IN THIS ORDER:
TERMINAL #1
TERMINAL #2
TERMINAL #3
TERMINAL #4
TERMINAL #5
TERMINAL #6
TERMINAL #7
TERMINAL #8
TERMINAL #9
① LO SPEED
12V (+)
③ PARK
12V (+)
② HI SPEED
12V (+)
④ PULSE (APPROX. 8 SEC. DELAY)
12V (-)
12V (+)
500 K
IF WIPER MOTOR FUNCTIONS IN ALL MODES, GO TO WIPER-WASHER SWITCH CHECK CHART.
GC9029100102000X

Fig. 3 Wiper motor terminal check. 1992 Except Camaro, Century, Corvette, Cutlass Ciera, Cutlass Cruiser & Firebird

ville, refer to wiring circuits **Figs. 23 through 28,** connector terminal identification **Figs. 29 and 30** and diagnostic charts **Figs. 31 through 47,** when performing system diagnosis and testing procedures.

On Eldorado and Seville models, refer to wiring circuit diagram **Fig. 48,** wiper motor terminal check **Fig. 49** wiper switch tests **Figs. 50 and 51** and diagnostic charts **Figs. 52 and 62** when performing system diagnosis and testing procedures.

CORVETTE

Refer to **Figs. 63 through 72** for system diagnostic charts.

PERMANENT MAGNET DEPRESSED PARK SYSTEM

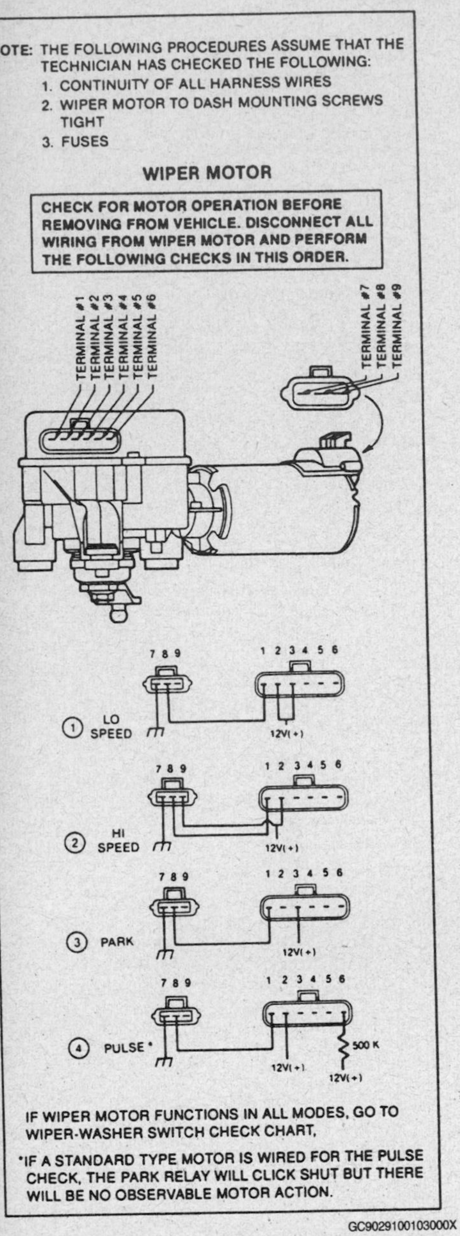
NOTE: THE FOLLOWING PROCEDURES ASSUME THAT THE TECHNICIAN HAS CHECKED THE FOLLOWING:
1. CONTINUITY OF ALL HARNESS WIRES
2. WIPER MOTOR TO DASH MOUNTING SCREWS TIGHT
3. FUSES
WIPER MOTOR
CHECK FOR MOTOR OPERATION BEFORE REMOVING FROM VEHICLE. DISCONNECT ALL WIRING FROM WIPER MOTOR AND PERFORM THE FOLLOWING CHECKS IN THIS ORDER.
TERMINAL #1
TERMINAL #2
TERMINAL #3
TERMINAL #4
TERMINAL #5
TERMINAL #6
TERMINAL #7
TERMINAL #8
TERMINAL #9
7 8 9
1 2 3 4 5 6
1 LO SPEED
12V(+)
2 HI SPEED
12V(+)
3 PARK
12V(+)
4 PULSE*
12V(+)
500 K
12V(+)
IF WIPER MOTOR FUNCTIONS IN ALL MODES, GO TO WIPER-WASHER SWITCH CHECK CHART.
*IF A STANDARD TYPE MOTOR IS WIRED FOR THE PULSE CHECK, THE PARK RELAY WILL CLICK SHUT BUT THERE WILL BE NO OBSERVABLE MOTOR ACTION.
GC9029100103000X

Fig. 4 Wiper motor terminal check. 1992 Camaro, Century, Cutlass Ciera, Cutlass Cruiser & Firebird

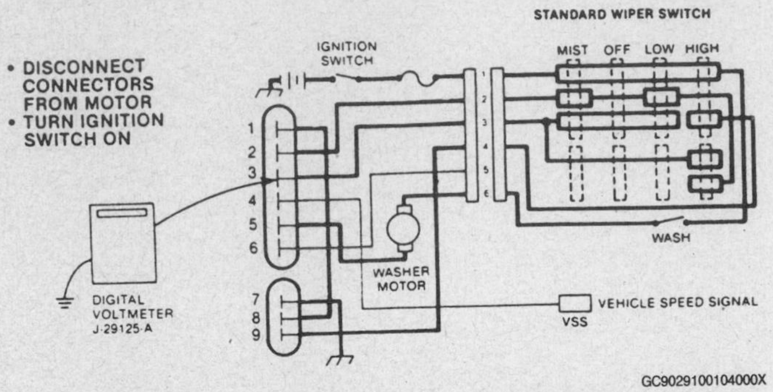
• DISCONNECT CONNECTORS FROM MOTOR
• TURN IGNITION SWITCH ON
IGNITION SWITCH
STANDARD WIPER SWITCH
MIST OFF LOW HIGH
WASH
WASHER MOTOR
DIGITAL VOLTMETER J-29125-A
VEHICLE SPEED SIGNAL
VSS
GC9029100104000X

Fig. 5 Wiper/washer switch test (standard). 1992 Except Camaro, Century, Corvette, Cutlass Ciera, Cutlass Cruiser & Firebird

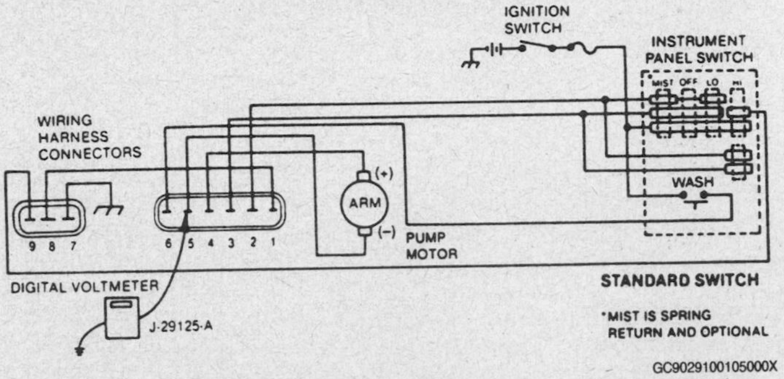
IGNITION SWITCH
INSTRUMENT PANEL SWITCH
WIRING HARNESS CONNECTORS
WASH
ARM
PUMP MOTOR
9 8 7
6 5 4 3 2 1
DIGITAL VOLTMETER
J-29125-A
STANDARD SWITCH
*MIST IS SPRING RETURN AND OPTIONAL
GC9029100105000X

Fig. 6 Wiper/washer switch test (standard). 1992 Camaro, Century, Cutlass Ciera, Cutlass Cruiser & Firebird

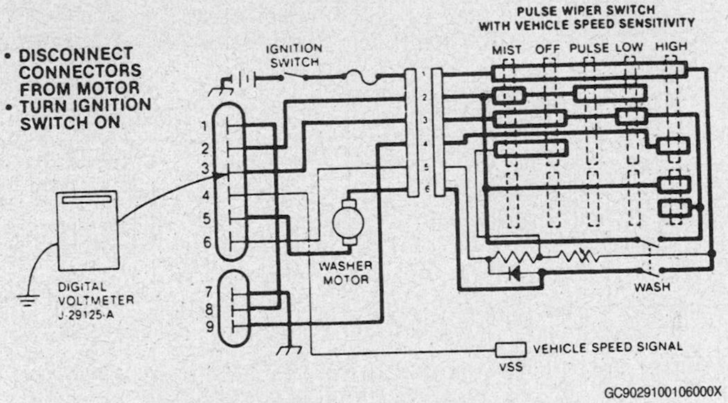
• DISCONNECT CONNECTORS FROM MOTOR
• TURN IGNITION SWITCH ON
IGNITION SWITCH
PULSE WIPER SWITCH WITH VEHICLE SPEED SENSITIVITY
MIST OFF PULSE LOW HIGH
WASHER MOTOR
WASH
DIGITAL VOLTMETER J-29125-A
VEHICLE SPEED SIGNAL
VSS
GC9029100106000X

Fig. 7 Wiper/washer switch test (pulse). 1992 Except Camaro, Century, Corvette, Cutlass Ciera, Cutlass Cruiser & Firebird

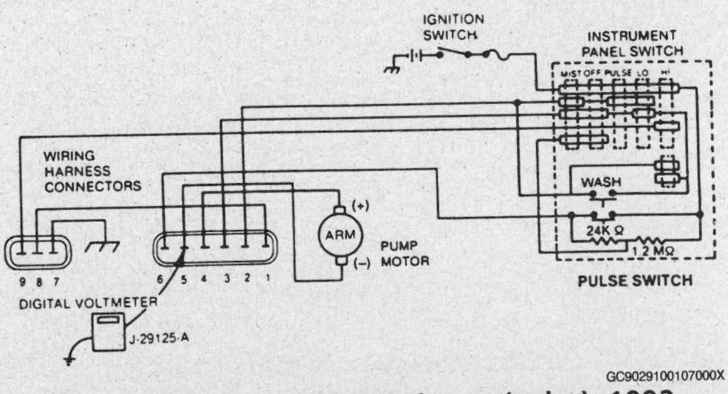
IGNITION SWITCH
INSTRUMENT PANEL SWITCH
WIRING HARNESS CONNECTORS
WASH
24K Ω
1.2 MΩ
ARM
PUMP MOTOR
9 8 7
6 5 4 3 2 1
DIGITAL VOLTMETER
J-29125-A
PULSE SWITCH
GC9029100107000X

Fig. 8 Wiper/washer switch test (pulse). 1992 Camaro, Century, Cutlass Ciera, Cutlass Cruiser & Firebird

	TERMINAL # \ SWITCH MODE	MIST	OFF	PULSE	LO	HI	WASH
PULSE	1	C TO 8	C TO 8	C TO 8	C TO 8	C TO 8	C TO 8
	2	B(+)	—	B(+)	B(+)	C TO 3	C TO 3
	3	B(+)	B(+)	—	B(+)	C TO 2	C TO 2
	4	—	—	—	—	—	—
	5	—	—	—	—	—	B(+)
	6	10-12V	10-12V	10-12V	10-12V	10-12V	B(+)
	7	GROUND	GROUND	GROUND	GROUND	GROUND	GROUND
	8	C TO 1	C TO 1	C TO 1	C TO 1	C TO 1	C TO 1
	9	—	—	—	—	B(+)	—
STANDARD	1	C TO 8	C TO 8		C TO 8	C TO 8	C TO 8
	2	B(+)	—		B(+)	C TO 3	C TO 3
	3	B(+)	B(+)		B(+)	C TO 2	C TO 2
	4	—	—		—	—	—
	5	—	—		—	—	B(+)
	6	—	—		—	—	—
	7	GROUND	GROUND		GROUND	GROUND	GROUND
	8	C TO 1	C TO 1		C TO 1	C TO 1	C TO 1
	9	—	—		—	B(+)	—

C = CONTINUITY

GC9029100108000X

Fig. 9 Wiper/washer switch check chart. 1992 Except Camaro, Century, Corvette, Cutlass Ciera, Cutlass Cruiser & Firebird

	TERMINAL # \ SWITCH MODE	MIST	OFF	PULSE	LO	HI †	WASH
PULSE	1	C	C	C	C	C	C
	2	B(+)	—	B(+)	B(+)	—	*B(+)
	3	B(+)	B(+)	—	B(+)	—	*B(+)
	4	—	—	—	—	—	—
	5	—	—	—	—	—	—
	6	10-12V	10-12V	10-12V	10-12V	10-12V	B(+)
	7	GROUND	GROUND	GROUND	GROUND	GROUND	GROUND
	8	C	C	C	C	C	C
	9	—	—	—	—	B(+)	—
STANDARD	1		C		C	C	C
	2		—		B(+)	—	*B(+)
	3		B(+)		B(+)	—	*B(+)
	4		—		—	—	—
	5		—		—	—	—
	6		—		—	—	B(+)
	7		GROUND		GROUND	GROUND	GROUND
	8		C		C	C	C
	9		—		—	B(+)	—

C = CONTINUITY † TERMINALS #2 & #3 CONNECTED TOGETHER. *EXCEPT ON HI.

GC9029100109000X

Fig. 10 Wiper/washer switch check chart. 1992 Camaro, Century, Cutlass Ciera, Cutlass Cruiser & Firebird

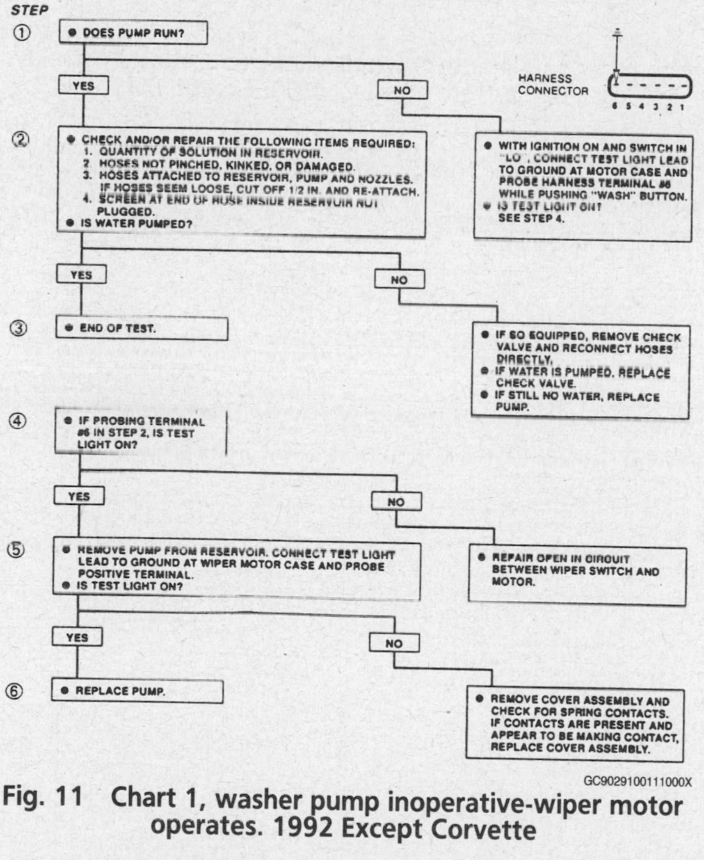
STEP
① • DOES PUMP RUN?
YES
NO
HARNESS CONNECTOR
6 5 4 3 2 1
② • CHECK AND/OR REPAIR THE FOLLOWING ITEMS REQUIRED:
1. QUANTITY OF SOLUTION IN RESERVOIR.
2. HOSES NOT PINCHED, KINKED, OR DAMAGED.
3. HOSES ATTACHED TO RESERVOIR, PUMP AND NOZZLES. IF HOSES SEEM LOOSE, CUT OFF 1/2 IN. AND RE-ATTACH.
4. SCREEN AT END OF HOSE INSIDE RESERVOIR NOT PLUGGED.
• IS WATER PUMPED?
• WITH IGNITION ON AND SWITCH IN "LO", CONNECT TEST LIGHT LEAD TO GROUND AT MOTOR CASE AND PROBE HARNESS TERMINAL #6 WHILE PUSHING "WASH" BUTTON.
• IS TEST LIGHT ON?
SEE STEP 4.
YES
NO
③ • END OF TEST.
• IF SO EQUIPPED, REMOVE CHECK VALVE AND RECONNECT HOSES DIRECTLY.
• IF WATER IS PUMPED, REPLACE CHECK VALVE.
• IF STILL NO WATER, REPLACE PUMP.
④ • IF PROBING TERMINAL #6 IN STEP 2, IS TEST LIGHT ON?
YES
NO
⑤ • REMOVE PUMP FROM RESERVOIR. CONNECT TEST LIGHT LEAD TO GROUND AT WIPER MOTOR CASE AND PROBE POSITIVE TERMINAL.
• IS TEST LIGHT ON?
• REPAIR OPEN IN CIRCUIT BETWEEN WIPER SWITCH AND MOTOR.
YES
NO
⑥ • REPLACE PUMP.
• REMOVE COVER ASSEMBLY AND CHECK FOR SPRING CONTACTS. IF CONTACTS ARE PRESENT AND APPEAR TO BE MAKING CONTACT, REPLACE COVER ASSEMBLY.

GC9029100111000X

Fig. 11 Chart 1, washer pump inoperative-wiper motor operates. 1992 Except Corvette

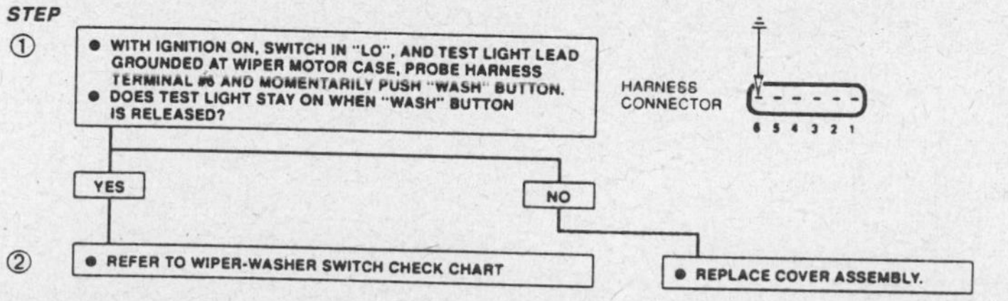
STEP
① • WITH IGNITION ON, SWITCH IN "LO", AND TEST LIGHT LEAD GROUNDED AT WIPER MOTOR CASE, PROBE HARNESS TERMINAL #6 AND MOMENTARILY PUSH "WASH" BUTTON.
• DOES TEST LIGHT STAY ON WHEN "WASH" BUTTON IS RELEASED?
HARNESS CONNECTOR
6 5 4 3 2 1
YES
NO
② • REFER TO WIPER-WASHER SWITCH CHECK CHART
• REPLACE COVER ASSEMBLY.

GC9029100112000X

Fig. 12 Chart 2, washer pumps continuously. 1992 Except Corvette

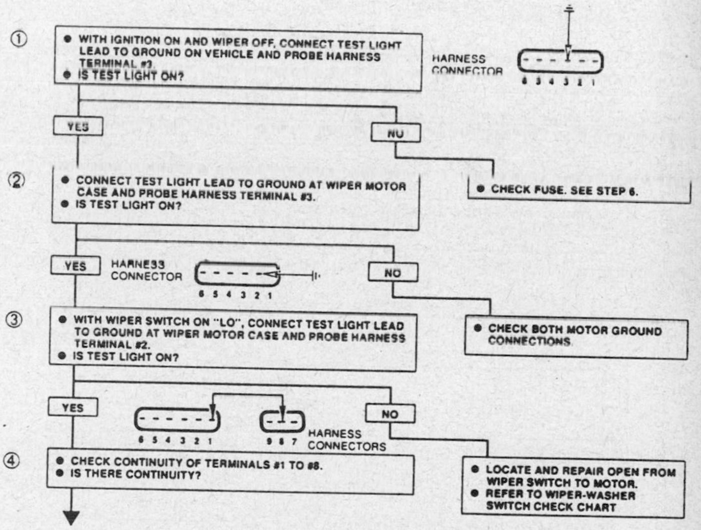
① • WITH IGNITION ON AND WIPER OFF, CONNECT TEST LIGHT LEAD TO GROUND ON VEHICLE AND PROBE HARNESS TERMINAL #3.
• IS TEST LIGHT ON?
HARNESS CONNECTOR
6 5 4 3 2 1
YES
NO
② • CONNECT TEST LIGHT LEAD TO GROUND AT WIPER MOTOR CASE AND PROBE HARNESS TERMINAL #3.
• IS TEST LIGHT ON?
• CHECK FUSE. SEE STEP 6.
YES
HARNESS CONNECTOR
6 5 4 3 2 1
NO
③ • WITH WIPER SWITCH ON "LO", CONNECT TEST LIGHT LEAD TO GROUND AT WIPER MOTOR CASE AND PROBE HARNESS TERMINAL #2.
• IS TEST LIGHT ON?
• CHECK BOTH MOTOR GROUND CONNECTIONS.
YES
NO
6 5 4 3 2 1
9 8 7
HARNESS CONNECTORS
④ • CHECK CONTINUITY OF TERMINALS #1 TO #8.
• IS THERE CONTINUITY?
• LOCATE AND REPAIR OPEN FROM WIPER SWITCH TO MOTOR.
• REFER TO WIPER-WASHER SWITCH CHECK CHART

GC9029100113010X

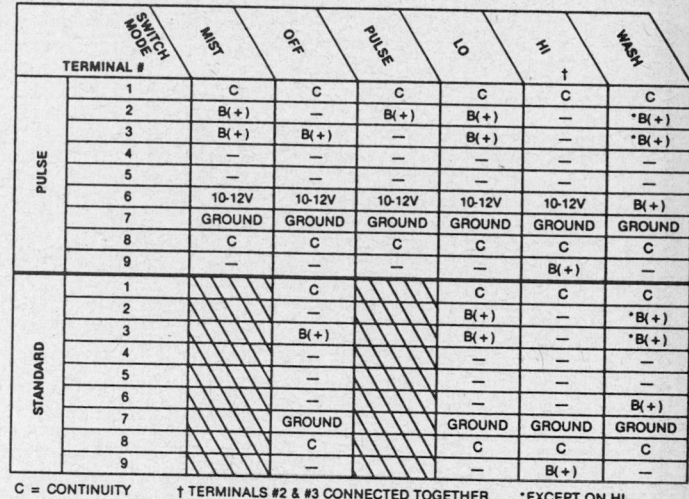

Fig. 13 Chart 3, wiper motor inoperative (Part 1 of 2). 1992 Except Corvette

(From previous step) YES → Step 5; NO → LOCATE AND REPAIR OPEN BETWEEN TERMINALS #1 & #8 IN WIRING HARNESS.

STEP

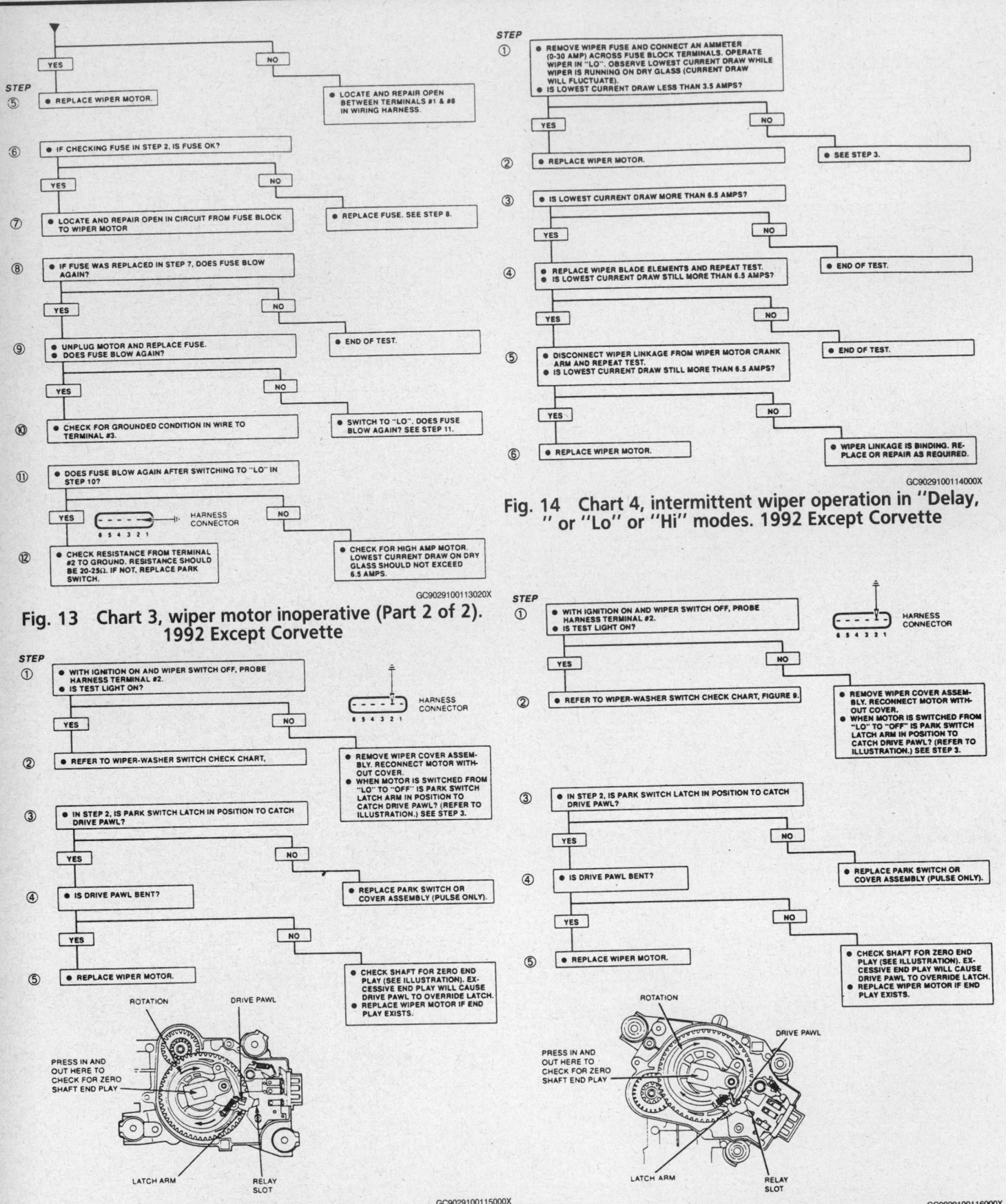

5. • REPLACE WIPER MOTOR.
6. • IF CHECKING FUSE IN STEP 2, IS FUSE OK?
   - YES → Step 7
   - NO → • REPLACE FUSE. SEE STEP 8.
7. • LOCATE AND REPAIR OPEN IN CIRCUIT FROM FUSE BLOCK TO WIPER MOTOR
8. • IF FUSE WAS REPLACED IN STEP 7, DOES FUSE BLOW AGAIN?
   - YES → Step 9
   - NO → • END OF TEST.
9. • UNPLUG MOTOR AND REPLACE FUSE.
   • DOES FUSE BLOW AGAIN?
   - YES → Step 10
   - NO → • SWITCH TO "LO". DOES FUSE BLOW AGAIN? SEE STEP 11.
10. • CHECK FOR GROUNDED CONDITION IN WIRE TO TERMINAL #3.
11. • DOES FUSE BLOW AGAIN AFTER SWITCHING TO "LO" IN STEP 10?
    - YES → Step 12 (HARNESS CONNECTOR 6 5 4 3 2 1)
    - NO → • CHECK FOR HIGH AMP MOTOR. LOWEST CURRENT DRAW ON DRY GLASS SHOULD NOT EXCEED 6.5 AMPS.
12. • CHECK RESISTANCE FROM TERMINAL #2 TO GROUND. RESISTANCE SHOULD BE 20-25Ω. IF NOT, REPLACE PARK SWITCH.

GC9029100113020X

Fig. 13 Chart 3, wiper motor inoperative (Part 2 of 2). 1992 Except Corvette

STEP

1. • WITH IGNITION ON AND WIPER SWITCH OFF, PROBE HARNESS TERMINAL #2.
   • IS TEST LIGHT ON?
   (HARNESS CONNECTOR 6 5 4 3 2 1)
   - YES → Step 2
   - NO → • REMOVE WIPER COVER ASSEMBLY. RECONNECT MOTOR WITHOUT COVER. • WHEN MOTOR IS SWITCHED FROM "LO" TO "OFF" IS PARK SWITCH LATCH ARM IN POSITION TO CATCH DRIVE PAWL? (REFER TO ILLUSTRATION.) SEE STEP 3.
2. • REFER TO WIPER-WASHER SWITCH CHECK CHART.
3. • IN STEP 2, IS PARK SWITCH LATCH IN POSITION TO CATCH DRIVE PAWL?
   - YES → Step 4
   - NO → • REPLACE PARK SWITCH OR COVER ASSEMBLY (PULSE ONLY).
4. • IS DRIVE PAWL BENT?
   - YES → Step 5
   - NO → • CHECK SHAFT FOR ZERO END PLAY (SEE ILLUSTRATION). EXCESSIVE END PLAY WILL CAUSE DRIVE PAWL TO OVERRIDE LATCH. • REPLACE WIPER MOTOR IF END PLAY EXISTS.
5. • REPLACE WIPER MOTOR.

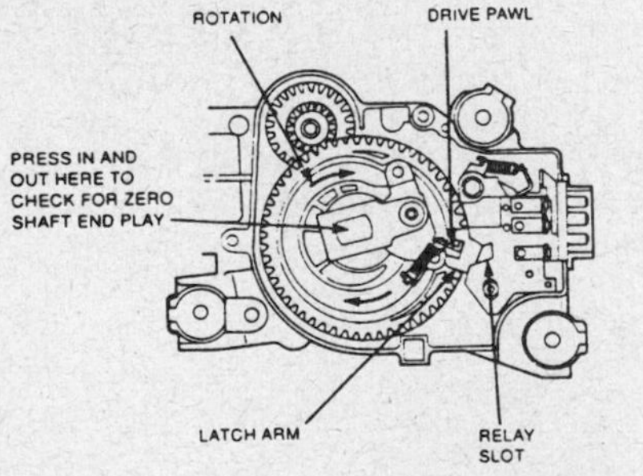
ROTATION
DRIVE PAWL
PRESS IN AND OUT HERE TO CHECK FOR ZERO SHAFT END PLAY
LATCH ARM
RELAY SLOT

GC9029100115000X

Fig. 15 Chart 5, wiper will not park. 1992 Except Camaro, Century, Corvette, Cutlass Ciera, Cutlass Cruiser & Firebird

STEP

1. • REMOVE WIPER FUSE AND CONNECT AN AMMETER (0-30 AMP) ACROSS FUSE BLOCK TERMINALS. OPERATE WIPER IN "LO". OBSERVE LOWEST CURRENT DRAW WHILE WIPER IS RUNNING ON DRY GLASS (CURRENT DRAW WILL FLUCTUATE).
   • IS LOWEST CURRENT DRAW LESS THAN 3.5 AMPS?
   - YES → Step 2
   - NO → • SEE STEP 3.
2. • REPLACE WIPER MOTOR.
3. • IS LOWEST CURRENT DRAW MORE THAN 6.5 AMPS?
   - YES → Step 4
   - NO → • END OF TEST.
4. • REPLACE WIPER BLADE ELEMENTS AND REPEAT TEST.
   • IS LOWEST CURRENT DRAW STILL MORE THAN 6.5 AMPS?
   - YES → Step 5
   - NO → • END OF TEST.
5. • DISCONNECT WIPER LINKAGE FROM WIPER MOTOR CRANK ARM AND REPEAT TEST.
   • IS LOWEST CURRENT DRAW STILL MORE THAN 6.5 AMPS?
   - YES → Step 6
   - NO → • WIPER LINKAGE IS BINDING. REPLACE OR REPAIR AS REQUIRED.
6. • REPLACE WIPER MOTOR.

GC9029100114000X

Fig. 14 Chart 4, intermittent wiper operation in "Delay," or "Lo" or "Hi" modes. 1992 Except Corvette

STEP

1. • WITH IGNITION ON AND WIPER SWITCH OFF, PROBE HARNESS TERMINAL #2.
   • IS TEST LIGHT ON?
   (HARNESS CONNECTOR 6 5 4 3 2 1)
   - YES → Step 2
   - NO → • REMOVE WIPER COVER ASSEMBLY. RECONNECT MOTOR WITHOUT COVER. • WHEN MOTOR IS SWITCHED FROM "LO" TO "OFF" IS PARK SWITCH LATCH ARM IN POSITION TO CATCH DRIVE PAWL? (REFER TO ILLUSTRATION.) SEE STEP 3.
2. • REFER TO WIPER-WASHER SWITCH CHECK CHART, FIGURE 9.
3. • IN STEP 2, IS PARK SWITCH LATCH IN POSITION TO CATCH DRIVE PAWL?
   - YES → Step 4
   - NO → • REPLACE PARK SWITCH OR COVER ASSEMBLY (PULSE ONLY).
4. • IS DRIVE PAWL BENT?
   - YES → Step 5
   - NO → • CHECK SHAFT FOR ZERO END PLAY (SEE ILLUSTRATION). EXCESSIVE END PLAY WILL CAUSE DRIVE PAWL TO OVERRIDE LATCH. • REPLACE WIPER MOTOR IF END PLAY EXISTS.
5. • REPLACE WIPER MOTOR.

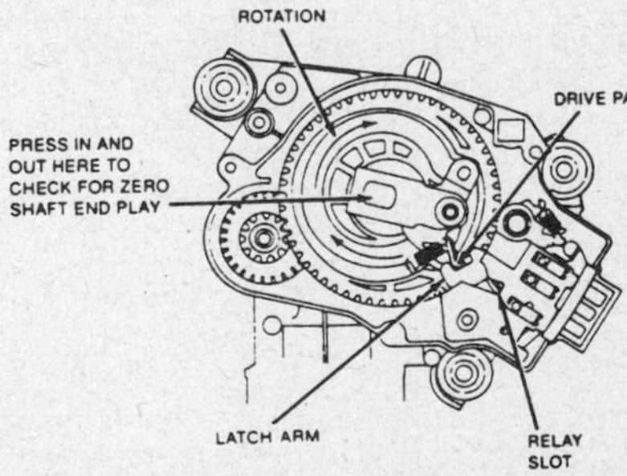
ROTATION
DRIVE PAWL
PRESS IN AND OUT HERE TO CHECK FOR ZERO SHAFT END PLAY
LATCH ARM
RELAY SLOT

GC9029100116000X

Fig. 16 Chart 5, wiper will not park. 1992 Camaro, Century, Cutlass Ciera, Cutlass Cruiser & Firebird

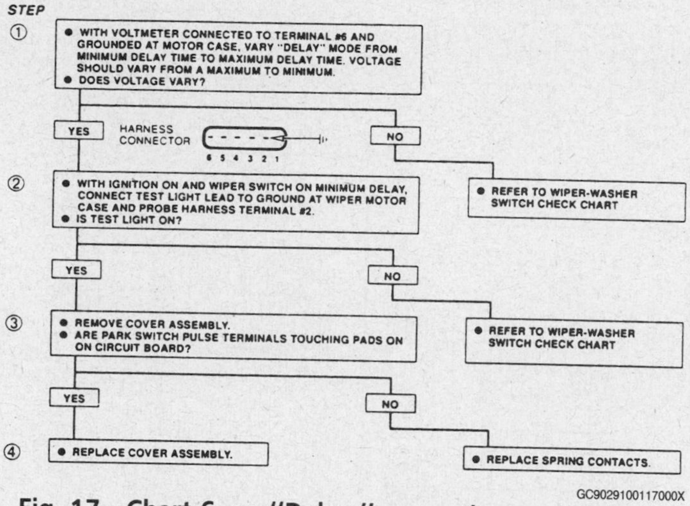
STEP
1
• WITH VOLTMETER CONNECTED TO TERMINAL #6 AND GROUNDED AT MOTOR CASE, VARY "DELAY" MODE FROM MINIMUM DELAY TIME TO MAXIMUM DELAY TIME. VOLTAGE SHOULD VARY FROM A MAXIMUM TO MINIMUM.
• DOES VOLTAGE VARY?
YES
HARNESS CONNECTOR
6 5 4 3 2 1
NO
2
• WITH IGNITION ON AND WIPER SWITCH ON MINIMUM DELAY, CONNECT TEST LIGHT LEAD TO GROUND AT WIPER MOTOR CASE AND PROBE HARNESS TERMINAL #2.
• IS TEST LIGHT ON?
• REFER TO WIPER-WASHER SWITCH CHECK CHART
YES
NO
3
• REMOVE COVER ASSEMBLY.
• ARE PARK SWITCH PULSE TERMINALS TOUCHING PADS ON ON CIRCUIT BOARD?
• REFER TO WIPER-WASHER SWITCH CHECK CHART
YES
NO
4
• REPLACE COVER ASSEMBLY.
• REPLACE SPRING CONTACTS.
GC9029100117000X

Fig. 17 Chart 6, no "Delay" or continuous "Delay"-motor operates in "Lo" and "Hi" modes. 1992 Except Corvette

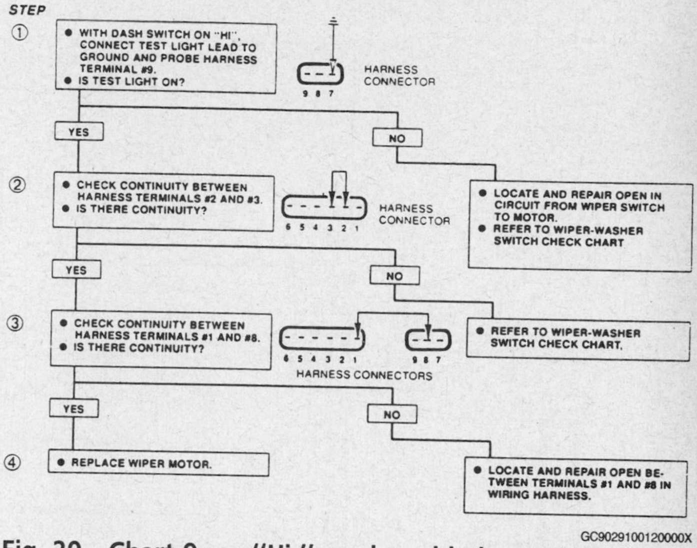
STEP
1
• WITH DASH SWITCH ON "HI", CONNECT TEST LIGHT LEAD TO GROUND AND PROBE HARNESS TERMINAL #9.
• IS TEST LIGHT ON?
HARNESS CONNECTOR
9 8 7
YES
NO
2
• CHECK CONTINUITY BETWEEN HARNESS TERMINALS #2 AND #3.
• IS THERE CONTINUITY?
HARNESS CONNECTOR
6 5 4 3 2 1
• LOCATE AND REPAIR OPEN IN CIRCUIT FROM WIPER SWITCH TO MOTOR.
• REFER TO WIPER-WASHER SWITCH CHECK CHART
YES
NO
3
• CHECK CONTINUITY BETWEEN HARNESS TERMINALS #1 AND #8.
• IS THERE CONTINUITY?
6 5 4 3 2 1
9 8 7
HARNESS CONNECTORS
• REFER TO WIPER-WASHER SWITCH CHECK CHART.
YES
NO
4
• REPLACE WIPER MOTOR.
• LOCATE AND REPAIR OPEN BETWEEN TERMINALS #1 AND #8 IN WIRING HARNESS.
GC9029100120000X

Fig. 20 Chart 9, no "Hi" mode or blades cycle in & out of park with switch in "Hi". 1992 Except Camaro, Century, Corvette, Cutlass Ciera, Cutlass Cruiser & Firebird

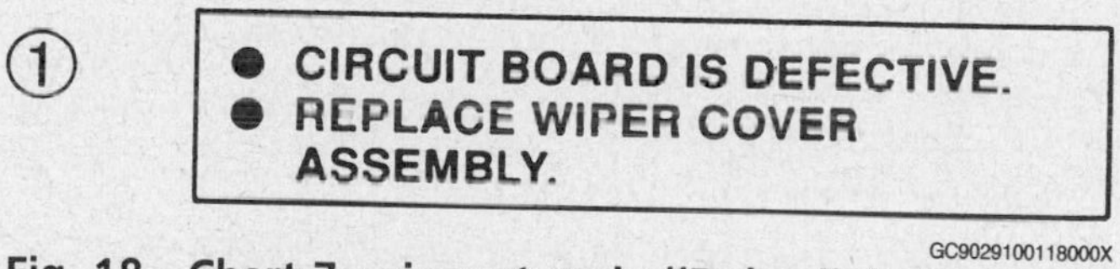
1
• CIRCUIT BOARD IS DEFECTIVE.
• REPLACE WIPER COVER ASSEMBLY.
GC9029100118000X

Fig. 18 Chart 7, wiper stays in "Delay" during wash cycle started in "Delay". 1992 Except Corvette

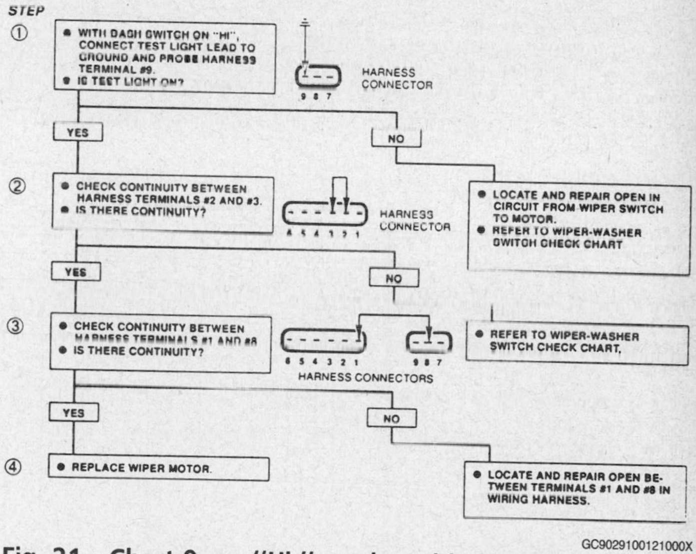
STEP
1
• WITH DASH SWITCH ON "HI", CONNECT TEST LIGHT LEAD TO GROUND AND PROBE HARNESS TERMINAL #9.
• IS TEST LIGHT ON?
HARNESS CONNECTOR
9 8 7
YES
NO
2
• CHECK CONTINUITY BETWEEN HARNESS TERMINALS #2 AND #3.
• IS THERE CONTINUITY?
HARNESS CONNECTOR
6 5 4 3 2 1
• LOCATE AND REPAIR OPEN IN CIRCUIT FROM WIPER SWITCH TO MOTOR.
• REFER TO WIPER-WASHER SWITCH CHECK CHART
YES
NO
3
• CHECK CONTINUITY BETWEEN HARNESS TERMINALS #1 AND #8
• IS THERE CONTINUITY?
6 5 4 3 2 1
9 8 7
HARNESS CONNECTORS
• REFER TO WIPER-WASHER SWITCH CHECK CHART.
YES
NO
4
• REPLACE WIPER MOTOR.
• LOCATE AND REPAIR OPEN BETWEEN TERMINALS #1 AND #8 IN WIRING HARNESS.
GC9029100121000X

Fig. 21 Chart 9, no "Hi" mode or blades cycle in & out of park with switch In "Hi". 1992 Camaro, Century, Cutlass Ciera, Cutlass Cruiser & Firebird

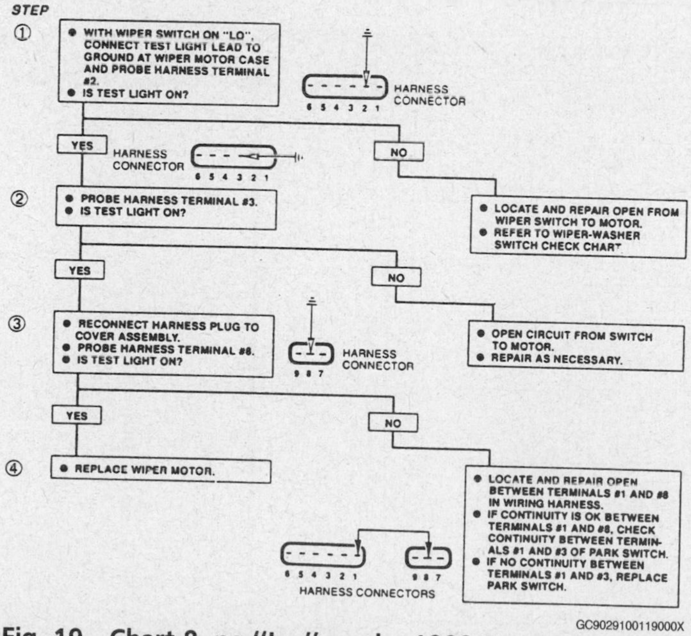
STEP
1
• WITH WIPER SWITCH ON "LO", CONNECT TEST LIGHT LEAD TO GROUND AT WIPER MOTOR CASE AND PROBE HARNESS TERMINAL #2.
• IS TEST LIGHT ON?
HARNESS CONNECTOR
6 5 4 3 2 1
YES
HARNESS CONNECTOR
6 5 4 3 2 1
NO
2
• PROBE HARNESS TERMINAL #3.
• IS TEST LIGHT ON?
• LOCATE AND REPAIR OPEN FROM WIPER SWITCH TO MOTOR.
• REFER TO WIPER-WASHER SWITCH CHECK CHART
YES
NO
3
• RECONNECT HARNESS PLUG TO COVER ASSEMBLY.
• PROBE HARNESS TERMINAL #8.
• IS TEST LIGHT ON?
HARNESS CONNECTOR
9 8 7
• OPEN CIRCUIT FROM SWITCH TO MOTOR.
• REPAIR AS NECESSARY.
YES
NO
4
• REPLACE WIPER MOTOR.
• LOCATE AND REPAIR OPEN BETWEEN TERMINALS #1 AND #8 IN WIRING HARNESS.
• IF CONTINUITY IS OK BETWEEN TERMINALS #1 AND #8, CHECK CONTINUITY BETWEEN TERMINALS #1 AND #3 OF PARK SWITCH.
• IF NO CONTINUITY BETWEEN TERMINALS #1 AND #3, REPLACE PARK SWITCH.
6 5 4 3 2 1
9 8 7
HARNESS CONNECTORS
GC9029100119000X

Fig. 19 Chart 8, no "Lo" mode. 1992 Except Corvette

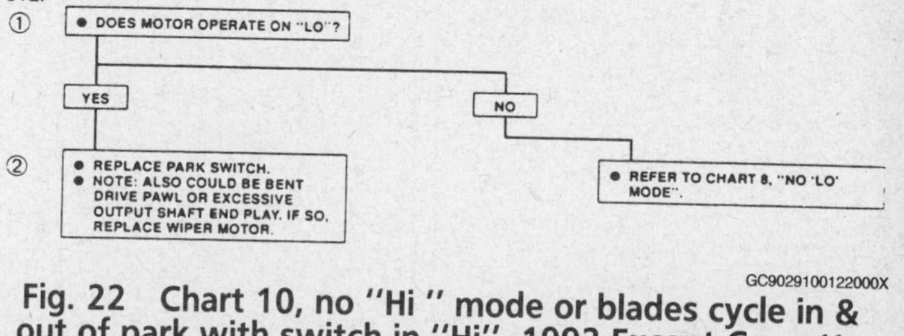
STEP
1
• DOES MOTOR OPERATE ON "LO"?
YES
NO
2
• REPLACE PARK SWITCH.
• NOTE: ALSO COULD BE BENT DRIVE PAWL OR EXCESSIVE OUTPUT SHAFT END PLAY. IF SO, REPLACE WIPER MOTOR.
• REFER TO CHART 8, "NO 'LO' MODE".
GC9029100122000X

Fig. 22 Chart 10, no "Hi" mode or blades cycle in & out of park with switch in "Hi". 1992 Except Corvette

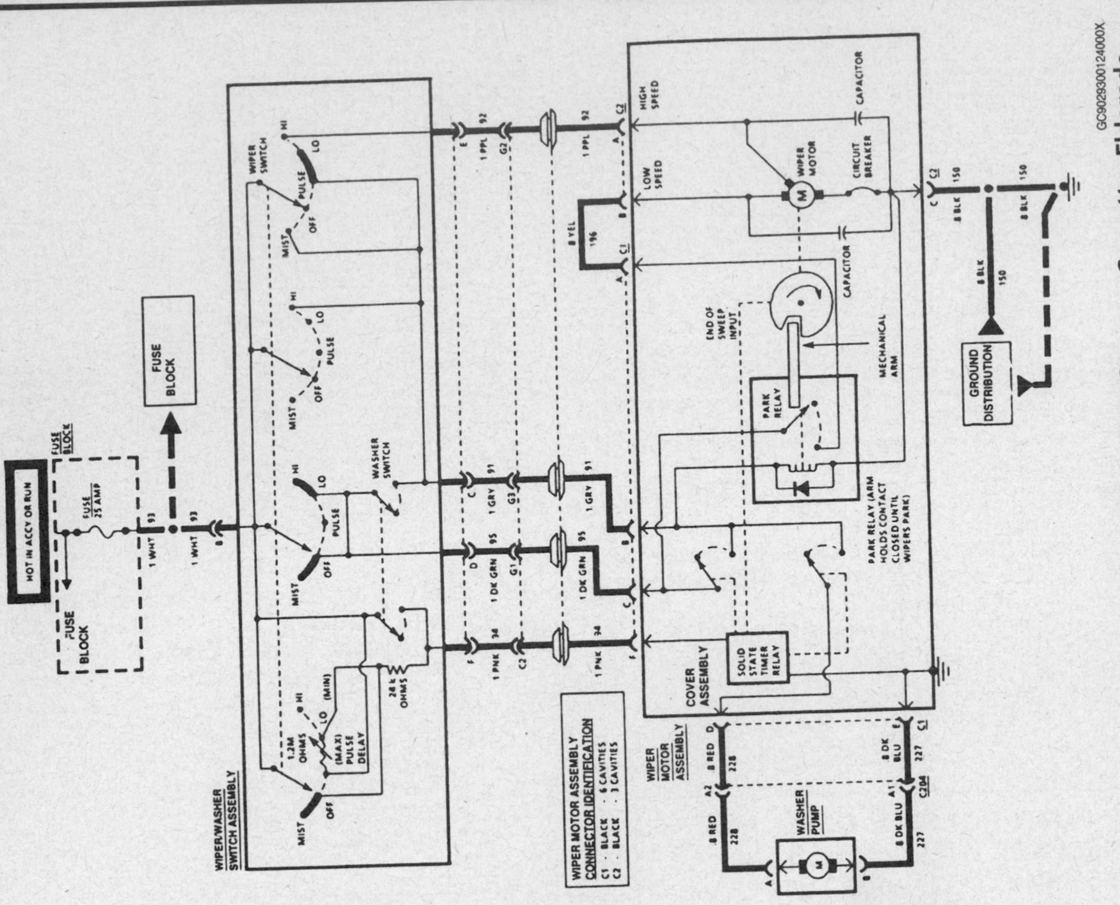
HOT IN ACCY OR RUN
FUSE BLOCK
FUSE 25 AMP
FUSE BLOCK
1 WHT 93
WIPER/WASHER SWITCH ASSEMBLY
MIST
OFF
PULSE
LO
HI
WIPER SWITCH
WASHER SWITCH
1.2M OHMS
(MAX) PULSE DELAY
(MIN)
24 K OHMS
1 PNK 94
1 DK GRN 95
1 GRY 91
1 PPL 92
8 YEL 196
WIPER MOTOR ASSEMBLY CONNECTOR IDENTIFICATION
C1 - BLACK - 6 CAVITIES
C2 - BLACK - 3 CAVITIES
COVER ASSEMBLY
SOLID STATE TIMER RELAY
PARK RELAY (ARM HOLDS CONTACT CLOSED UNTIL WIPERS PARK)
PARK RELAY
END OF SWEEP INPUT
MECHANICAL ARM
CAPACITOR
LOW SPEED
HIGH SPEED
WIPER MOTOR
CIRCUIT BREAKER
CAPACITOR
WIPER MOTOR ASSEMBLY
WASHER PUMP
8 RED 228
8 DK BLU 227
C204
8 BLK 150
GROUND DISTRIBUTION
GC9029300124000X

Fig. 24 Wiring circuit. 1993–94 Except Camaro, Corvette, Eldorado, Firebird & Seville

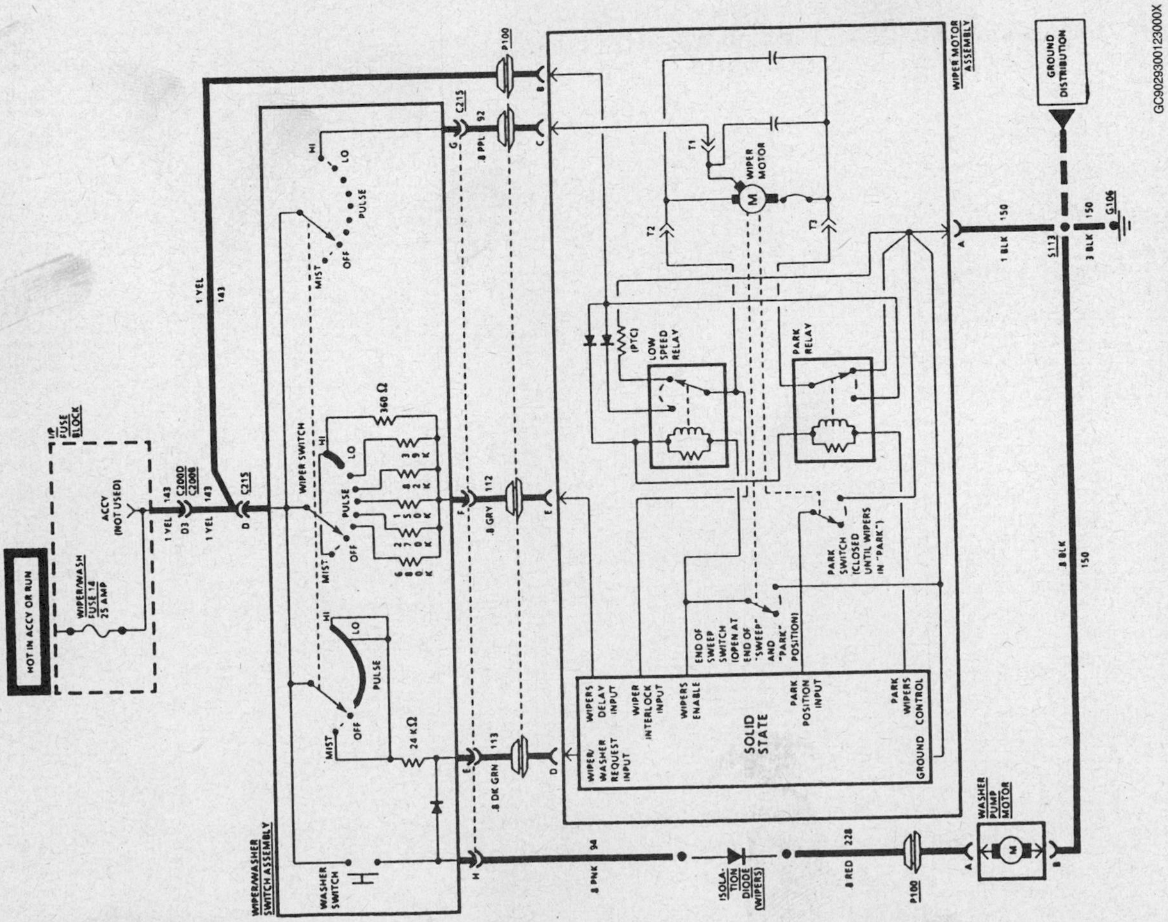
HOT IN ACCY OR RUN
WIPER/WASH FUSE 18 25 AMP
ACCY (NOT USED)
I/P FUSE BLOCK
1 YEL 143
C200D
C200B
C215
WIPER/WASHER SWITCH ASSEMBLY
WASHER SWITCH
MIST
OFF
PULSE
LO
HI
WIPER SWITCH
24 KΩ
360 Ω
.8 DK GRN 113
.8 GRY 112
.8 PPL 92
.8 PNK 94
ISOLATION DIODE (WIPERS)
.8 RED 228
P100
WIPER/WASHER REQUEST INPUT
WIPERS DELAY INPUT
WIPER INTERLOCK INPUT
WIPERS ENABLE
SOLID STATE
PARK POSITION INPUT
PARK WIPERS CONTROL
GROUND CONTROL
END OF SWEEP SWITCH (OPEN AT END OF "SWEEP" AND "PARK" POSITION)
PARK SWITCH (CLOSED UNTIL WIPERS IN "PARK")
LOW SPEED RELAY
PARK RELAY
(PTC)
WIPER MOTOR
WIPER MOTOR ASSEMBLY
WASHER PUMP MOTOR
.8 BLK 150
1 BLK 150
3 BLK 150
S113
G106
GROUND DISTRIBUTION
GC9029300123000X

Fig. 23 Wiring circuit. 1993–94 Camaro & Firebird

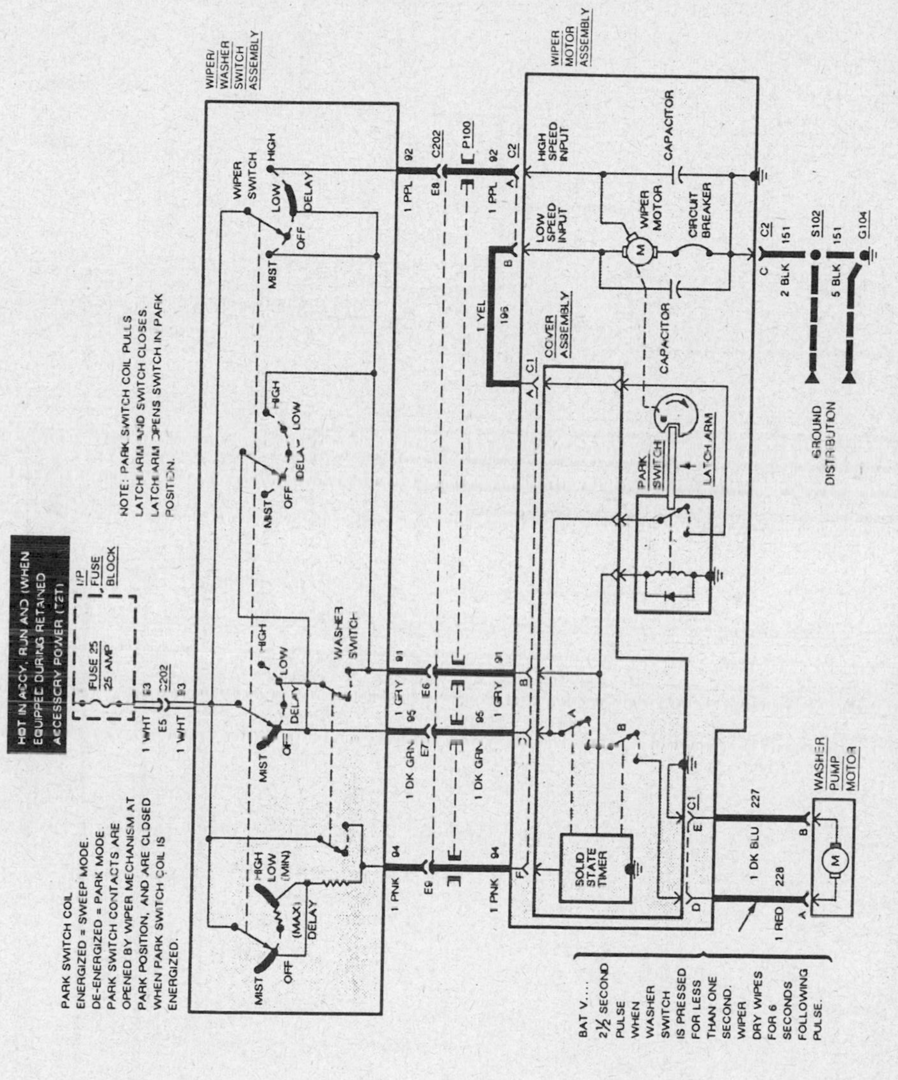
NOTE: PARK SWITCH COIL PULLS LATCH ARM AND SWITCH CLOSES. LATCH ARM OPENS SWITCH IN PARK POSITION.
WIPER/WASHER SWITCH ASSEMBLY
WIPER MOTOR ASSEMBLY
COVER ASSEMBLY
SOLID STATE TIMER
WASHER PUMP MOTOR
GROUND DISTRIBUTION
CAPACITOR
CIRCUIT BREAKER
PARK SWITCH
LATCH ARM
IP FUSE BLOCK
FUSE 25 25 AMP

Fig. 25 Wiring Circuit: 1994 88 & 98

GC902940024000X

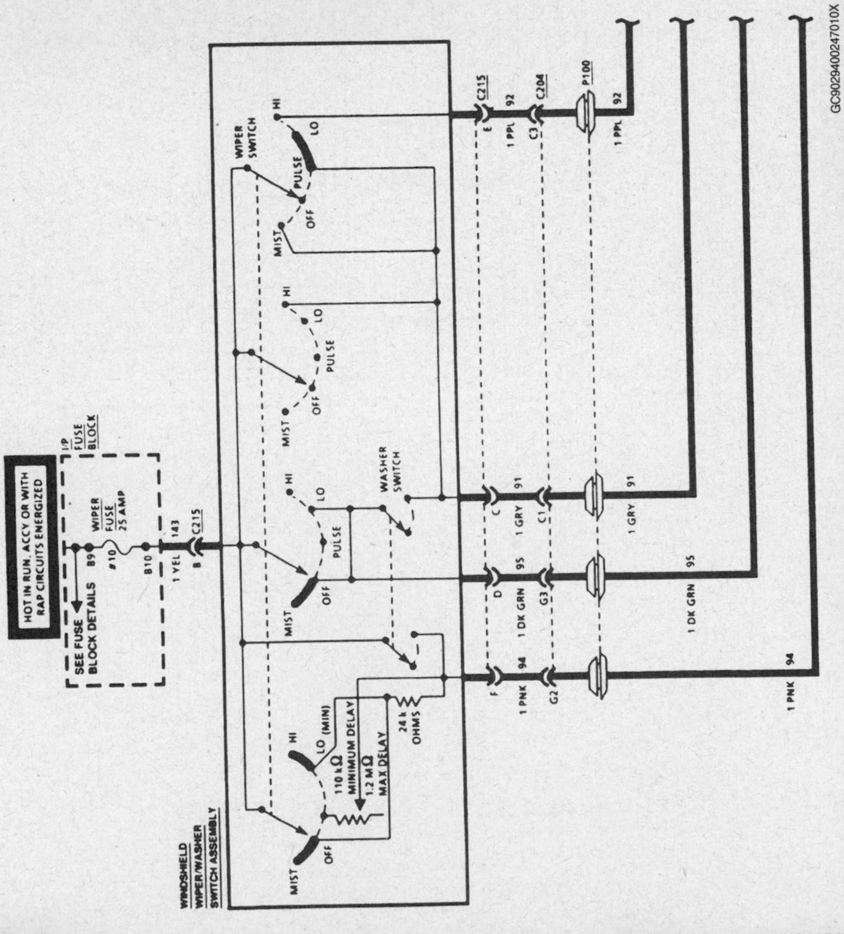

HOT IN RUN, ACCY OR WITH RAP CIRCUITS ENERGIZED
SEE FUSE BLOCK DETAILS
I/P FUSE BLOCK
WIPER FUSE #10 25 AMP
WINDSHIELD WIPER/WASHER SWITCH ASSEMBLY
WIPER SWITCH
WASHER SWITCH
MIST
OFF
PULSE
LO
HI
LO (MIN)
110 kΩ MINIMUM DELAY
1.2 MΩ MAX DELAY
24 k OHMS
C215
C204
P100
1 YEL
1 PPL
1 GRY
1 DK GRN
1 PNK
GC9029400247010X

Fig. 26 Wiring circuit (Part 1 of 2). 1994 Fleetwood

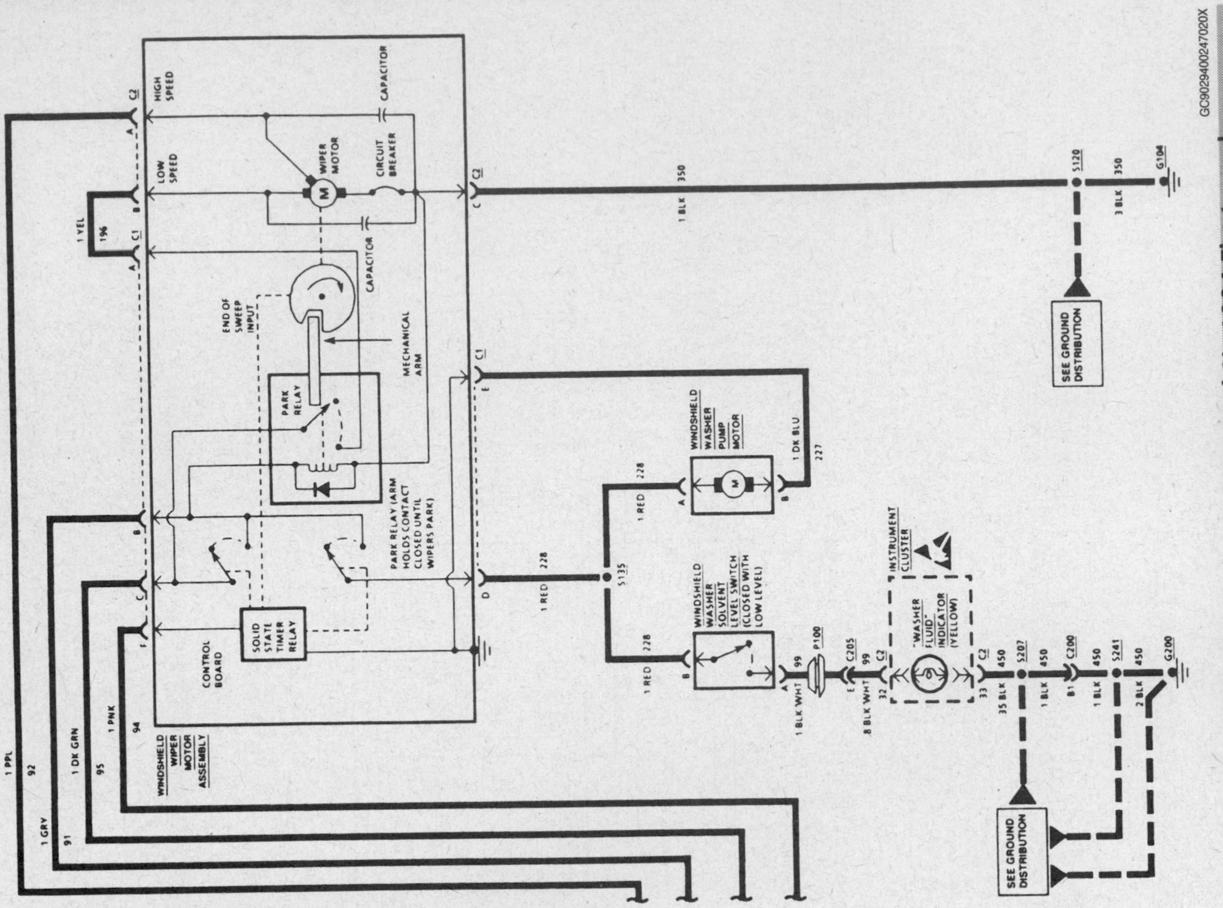

WINDSHIELD WIPER MOTOR ASSEMBLY
HIGH SPEED
LOW SPEED
WIPER MOTOR
CIRCUIT BREAKER
CAPACITOR
END OF SWEEP INPUT
MECHANICAL ARM
PARK RELAY
PARK RELAY (ARM HOLDS CONTACT CLOSED UNTIL WIPERS PARK)
SOLID STATE TIMER RELAY
CONTROL BOARD
WINDSHIELD WASHER PUMP MOTOR
WINDSHIELD WASHER SOLVENT LEVEL SWITCH (CLOSED WITH LOW LEVEL)
INSTRUMENT CLUSTER
"WASHER FLUID" INDICATOR (YELLOW)
SEE GROUND DISTRIBUTION
1 PPL
1 GRY
1 DK GRN
1 PNK
1 YEL
1 RED
1 DK BLU
1 BLK
1 BLK WHT
S135
S120
S207
S241
C200
C205
P100
G104
G200
GC9029400247020X

Fig. 26 Wiring circuit (Part 2 of 2). 1994 Fleetwood

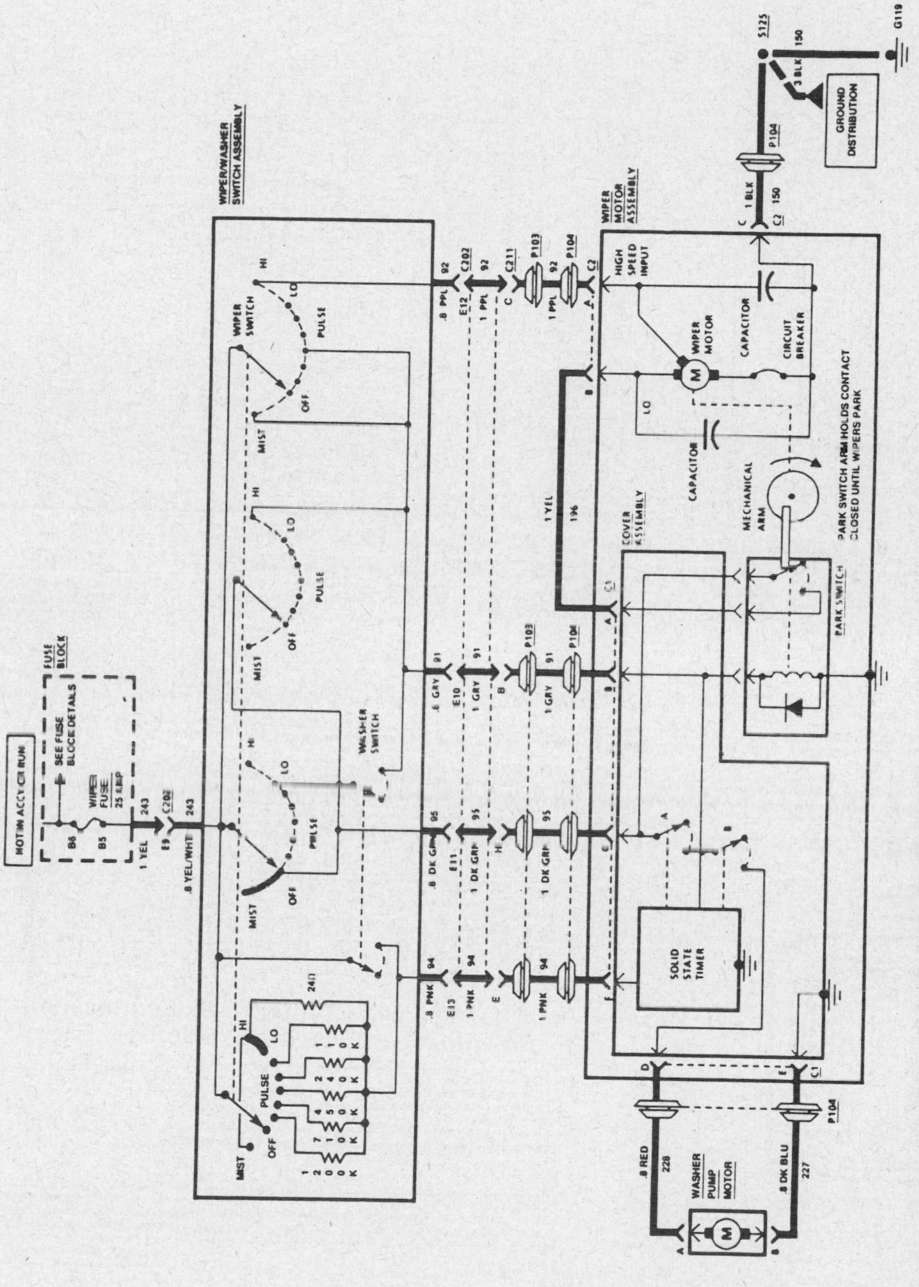
WIPER/WASHER SWITCH ASSEMBLY
FUSE BLOCK
SEE FUSE BLOCK DETAILS
WIPER FUSE 25 AMP
WIPER SWITCH
WASHER SWITCH
MIST
OFF
PULSE
LO
HI
WIPER MOTOR ASSEMBLY
HIGH SPEED INPUT
WIPER MOTOR
CAPACITOR
CIRCUIT BREAKER
MECHANICAL ARM
PARK SWITCH ARM HOLDS CONTACT CLOSED UNTIL WIPERS PARK
COVER ASSEMBLY
PARK SWITCH
SOLID STATE TIMER
WASHER PUMP MOTOR
GROUND DISTRIBUTION
S125
G119
P104
P103
C202
C211

Fig. 27 Wiring circuit: 1994 Century, Cutlass Ciera & Cutlass Cruiser

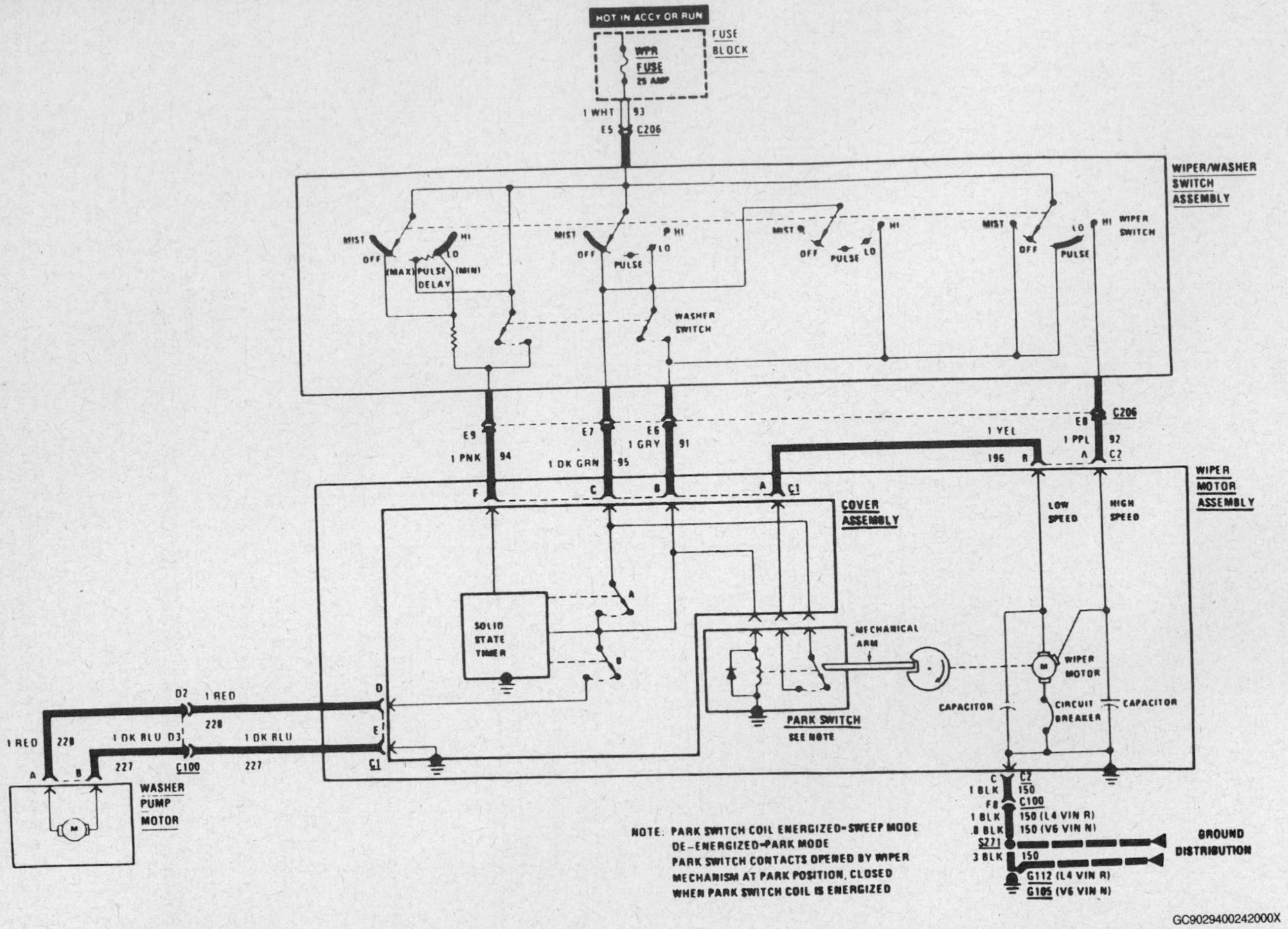
HOT IN ACCY OR RUN
FUSE BLOCK
WPR FUSE 25 AMP
WIPER/WASHER SWITCH ASSEMBLY
WASHER SWITCH
WIPER MOTOR ASSEMBLY
COVER ASSEMBLY
SOLID STATE TIMER
MECHANICAL ARM
PARK SWITCH
WIPER MOTOR
CIRCUIT BREAKER
CAPACITOR
LOW SPEED
HIGH SPEED
WASHER PUMP MOTOR
GROUND DISTRIBUTION
NOTE: PARK SWITCH COIL ENERGIZED=SWEEP MODE
DE-ENERGIZED=PARK MODE
PARK SWITCH CONTACTS OPENED BY WIPER MECHANISM AT PARK POSITION, CLOSED WHEN PARK SWITCH COIL IS ENERGIZED
GC9029400242000X

Fig. 28 Wiring circuit. 1994 Cutlass Supreme

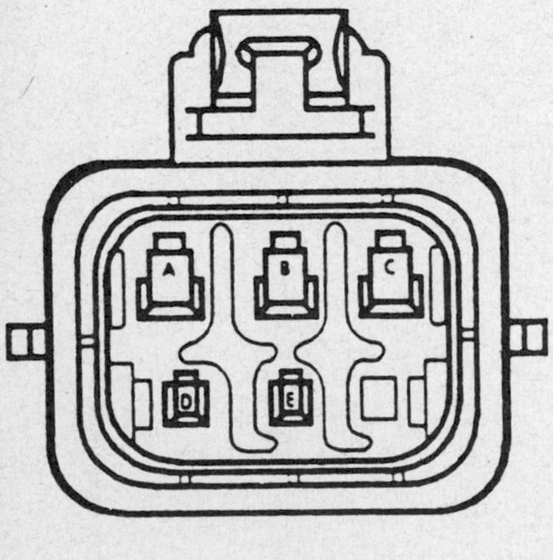

A BLK
B YEL
C PPL
D DK GRN
E GRY

GC9029300125000X

Fig. 29 Connector terminal identification. 1993–94 Camaro & Firebird

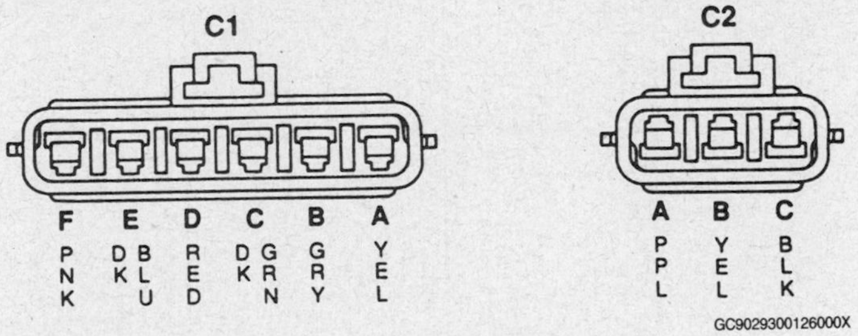
C1
F E D C B A
PNK DBLU RED DKGRN GRY YEL
C2
A B C
PPL YEL BLK
GC9029300126000X

Fig. 30 Connector terminal identification. 1993–94 Except Camaro, Corvette, Eldorado, Firebird & Seville

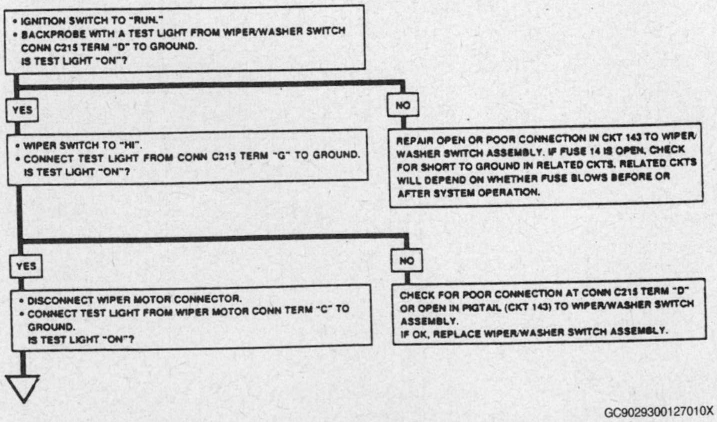
• IGNITION SWITCH TO "RUN."
• BACKPROBE WITH A TEST LIGHT FROM WIPER/WASHER SWITCH CONN C215 TERM "D" TO GROUND.
IS TEST LIGHT "ON"?
YES
NO
• WIPER SWITCH TO "HI".
• CONNECT TEST LIGHT FROM CONN C215 TERM "G" TO GROUND.
IS TEST LIGHT "ON"?
REPAIR OPEN OR POOR CONNECTION IN CKT 143 TO WIPER/WASHER SWITCH ASSEMBLY. IF FUSE 14 IS OPEN, CHECK FOR SHORT TO GROUND IN RELATED CKTS. RELATED CKTS WILL DEPEND ON WHETHER FUSE BLOWS BEFORE OR AFTER SYSTEM OPERATION.
YES
NO
• DISCONNECT WIPER MOTOR CONNECTOR.
• CONNECT TEST LIGHT FROM WIPER MOTOR CONN TERM "C" TO GROUND.
IS TEST LIGHT "ON"?
CHECK FOR POOR CONNECTION AT CONN C215 TERM "D" OR OPEN IN PIGTAIL (CKT 143) TO WIPER/WASHER SWITCH ASSEMBLY.
IF OK, REPLACE WIPER/WASHER SWITCH ASSEMBLY.
GC9029300127010X

Fig. 31 Chart 1, wipers do not operate in any mode, (Part 1 Of 2). 1993–94 Camaro & Firebird

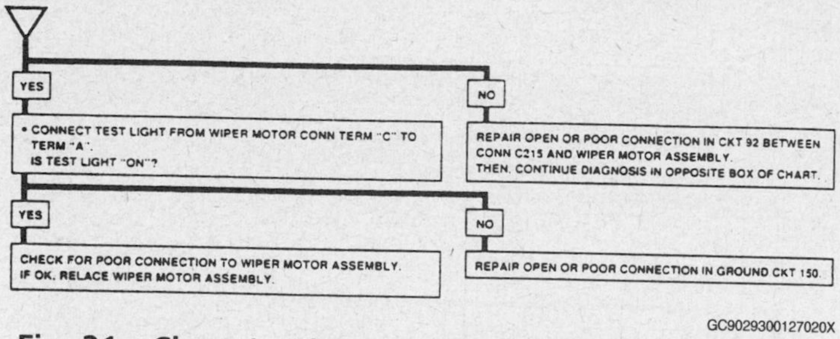
YES
NO
• CONNECT TEST LIGHT FROM WIPER MOTOR CONN TERM "C" TO TERM "A".
IS TEST LIGHT "ON"?
REPAIR OPEN OR POOR CONNECTION IN CKT 92 BETWEEN CONN C215 AND WIPER MOTOR ASSEMBLY.
THEN, CONTINUE DIAGNOSIS IN OPPOSITE BOX OF CHART.
YES
NO
CHECK FOR POOR CONNECTION TO WIPER MOTOR ASSEMBLY.
IF OK, RELACE WIPER MOTOR ASSEMBLY.
REPAIR OPEN OR POOR CONNECTION IN GROUND CKT 150.
GC9029300127020X

Fig. 31 Chart 1, wipers do not operate in any mode (Part 2 of 2). 1993–94 Camaro & Firebird

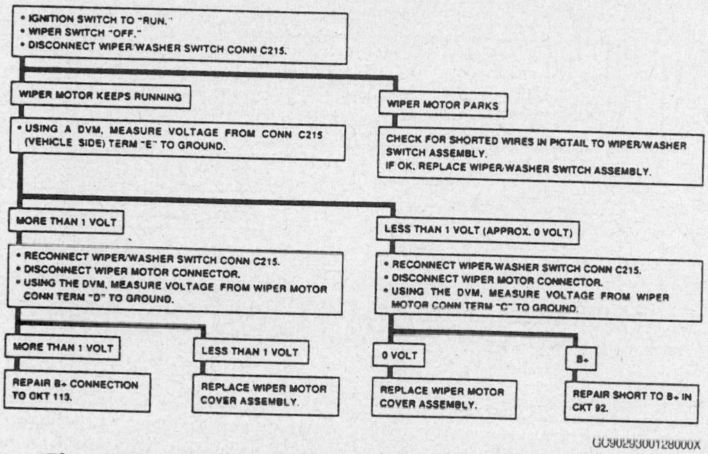
• IGNITION SWITCH TO "RUN."
• WIPER SWITCH "OFF."
• DISCONNECT WIPER/WASHER SWITCH CONN C215.
WIPER MOTOR KEEPS RUNNING
WIPER MOTOR PARKS
• USING A DVM, MEASURE VOLTAGE FROM CONN C215 (VEHICLE SIDE) TERM "E" TO GROUND.
CHECK FOR SHORTED WIRES IN PIGTAIL TO WIPER/WASHER SWITCH ASSEMBLY.
IF OK, REPLACE WIPER/WASHER SWITCH ASSEMBLY.
MORE THAN 1 VOLT
LESS THAN 1 VOLT (APPROX. 0 VOLT)
• RECONNECT WIPER/WASHER SWITCH CONN C215.
• DISCONNECT WIPER MOTOR CONNECTOR.
• USING THE DVM, MEASURE VOLTAGE FROM WIPER MOTOR CONN TERM "D" TO GROUND.
• RECONNECT WIPER/WASHER SWITCH CONN C215.
• DISCONNECT WIPER MOTOR CONNECTOR.
• USING THE DVM, MEASURE VOLTAGE FROM WIPER MOTOR CONN TERM "C" TO GROUND.
MORE THAN 1 VOLT
LESS THAN 1 VOLT
0 VOLT
B+
REPAIR B+ CONNECTION TO CKT 113.
REPLACE WIPER MOTOR COVER ASSEMBLY.
REPLACE WIPER MOTOR COVER ASSEMBLY.
REPAIR SHORT TO B+ IN CKT 92.
GC9029300128000X

Fig. 32 Chart 2, Wipers run when switch is off. 1993–94 Camaro & Firebird

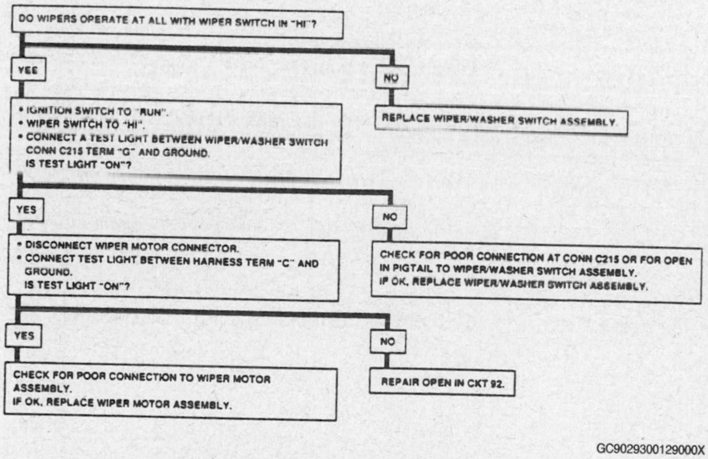
DO WIPERS OPERATE AT ALL WITH WIPER SWITCH IN "HI"?
YEE
NO
• IGNITION SWITCH TO "RUN".
• WIPER SWITCH TO "HI".
• CONNECT A TEST LIGHT BETWEEN WIPER/WASHER SWITCH CONN C215 TERM "G" AND GROUND.
IS TEST LIGHT "ON"?
REPLACE WIPER/WASHER SWITCH ASSEMBLY.
YES
NO
• DISCONNECT WIPER MOTOR CONNECTOR.
• CONNECT TEST LIGHT BETWEEN HARNESS TERM "C" AND GROUND.
IS TEST LIGHT "ON"?
CHECK FOR POOR CONNECTION AT CONN C215 OR FOR OPEN IN PIGTAIL TO WIPER/WASHER SWITCH ASSEMBLY.
IF OK, REPLACE WIPER/WASHER SWITCH ASSEMBLY.
YES
NO
CHECK FOR POOR CONNECTION TO WIPER MOTOR ASSEMBLY.
IF OK, REPLACE WIPER MOTOR ASSEMBLY.
REPAIR OPEN IN CKT 92.
GC9029300129000X

Fig. 33 Chart 3, No high speed mode. 1993–94 Camaro & Firebird

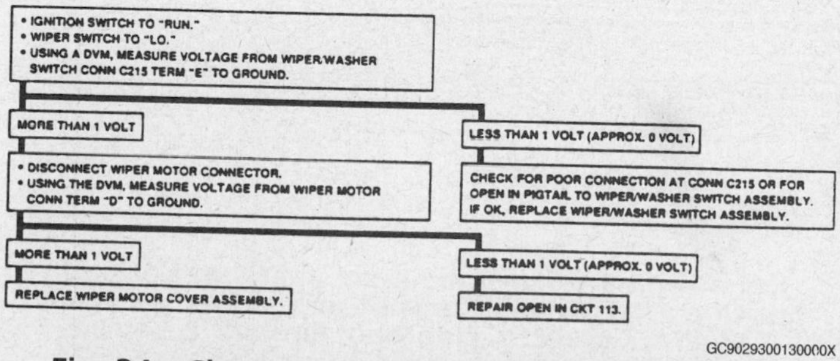
• IGNITION SWITCH TO "RUN."
• WIPER SWITCH TO "LO."
• USING A DVM, MEASURE VOLTAGE FROM WIPER/WASHER SWITCH CONN C215 TERM "E" TO GROUND.
MORE THAN 1 VOLT
LESS THAN 1 VOLT (APPROX. 0 VOLT)
• DISCONNECT WIPER MOTOR CONNECTOR.
• USING THE DVM, MEASURE VOLTAGE FROM WIPER MOTOR CONN TERM "D" TO GROUND.
CHECK FOR POOR CONNECTION AT CONN C215 OR FOR OPEN IN PIGTAIL TO WIPER/WASHER SWITCH ASSEMBLY.
IF OK, REPLACE WIPER/WASHER SWITCH ASSEMBLY.
MORE THAN 1 VOLT
LESS THAN 1 VOLT (APPROX. 0 VOLT)
REPLACE WIPER MOTOR COVER ASSEMBLY.
REPAIR OPEN IN CKT 113.
GC9029300130000X

Fig. 34 Chart 4, Low speed, pulse delay & mist modes inoperative. 1993–94 Camaro & Firebird

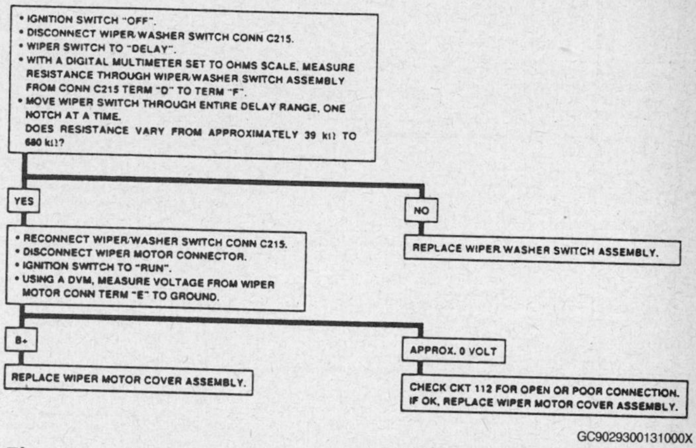
• IGNITION SWITCH "OFF".
• DISCONNECT WIPER/WASHER SWITCH CONN C215.
• WIPER SWITCH TO "DELAY".
• WITH A DIGITAL MULTIMETER SET TO OHMS SCALE, MEASURE RESISTANCE THROUGH WIPER/WASHER SWITCH ASSEMBLY FROM CONN C215 TERM "D" TO TERM "F".
• MOVE WIPER SWITCH THROUGH ENTIRE DELAY RANGE, ONE NOTCH AT A TIME.
DOES RESISTANCE VARY FROM APPROXIMATELY 39 kΩ TO 680 kΩ?
YES
NO
• RECONNECT WIPER/WASHER SWITCH CONN C215.
• DISCONNECT WIPER MOTOR CONNECTOR.
• IGNITION SWITCH TO "RUN".
• USING A DVM, MEASURE VOLTAGE FROM WIPER MOTOR CONN TERM "E" TO GROUND.
REPLACE WIPER WASHER SWITCH ASSEMBLY.
B+
APPROX. 0 VOLT
REPLACE WIPER MOTOR COVER ASSEMBLY.
CHECK CKT 112 FOR OPEN OR POOR CONNECTION.
IF OK, REPLACE WIPER MOTOR COVER ASSEMBLY.
GC9029300131000X

Fig. 35 Chart 5, Pulse delay operates incorrectly or not at all. 1993–94 Camaro & Firebird

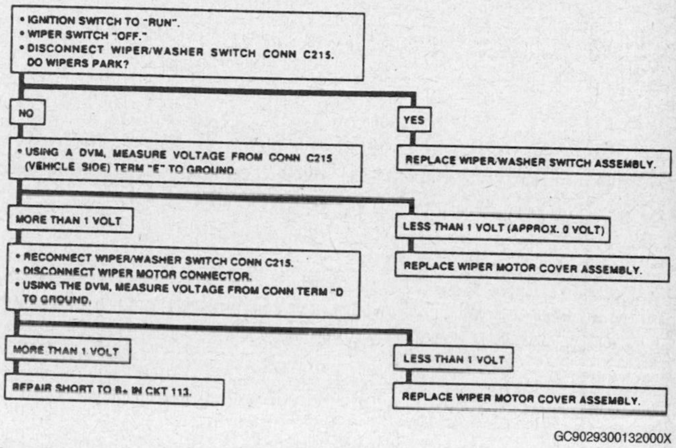
• IGNITION SWITCH TO "RUN".
• WIPER SWITCH "OFF."
• DISCONNECT WIPER/WASHER SWITCH CONN C215.
DO WIPERS PARK?
NO
YES
• USING A DVM, MEASURE VOLTAGE FROM CONN C215 (VEHICLE SIDE) TERM "E" TO GROUND.
REPLACE WIPER/WASHER SWITCH ASSEMBLY.
MORE THAN 1 VOLT
LESS THAN 1 VOLT (APPROX. 0 VOLT)
• RECONNECT WIPER/WASHER SWITCH CONN C215.
• DISCONNECT WIPER MOTOR CONNECTOR.
• USING THE DVM, MEASURE VOLTAGE FROM CONN TERM "D TO GROUND.
REPLACE WIPER MOTOR COVER ASSEMBLY.
MORE THAN 1 VOLT
LESS THAN 1 VOLT
REPAIR SHORT TO B+ IN CKT 113.
REPLACE WIPER MOTOR COVER ASSEMBLY.
GC9029300132000X

Fig. 36 Chart 6, Wipers stop randomly and do not park when switch is turned off. 1993–94 Camaro & Firebird

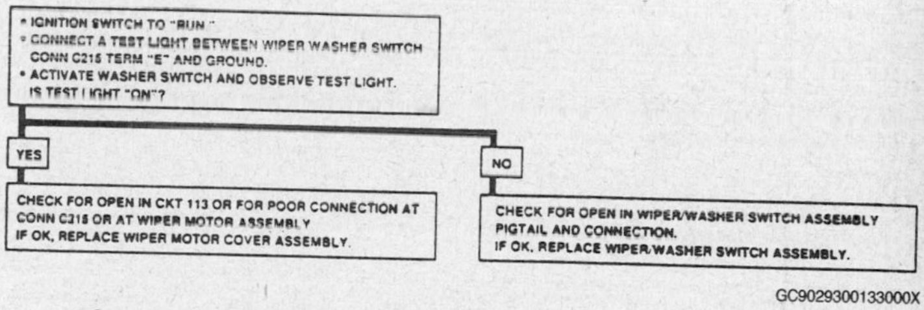
• IGNITION SWITCH TO "RUN."
• CONNECT A TEST LIGHT BETWEEN WIPER WASHER SWITCH CONN C215 TERM "E" AND GROUND.
• ACTIVATE WASHER SWITCH AND OBSERVE TEST LIGHT.
IS TEST LIGHT "ON"?
YES
NO
CHECK FOR OPEN IN CKT 113 OR FOR POOR CONNECTION AT CONN C215 OR AT WIPER MOTOR ASSEMBLY.
IF OK, REPLACE WIPER MOTOR COVER ASSEMBLY.
CHECK FOR OPEN IN WIPER/WASHER SWITCH ASSEMBLY PIGTAIL AND CONNECTION.
IF OK, REPLACE WIPER/WASHER SWITCH ASSEMBLY.
GC9029300133000X

Fig. 37 Chart 7, Wipers do not operate when washer switch is activated. 1993–94 Camaro & Firebird

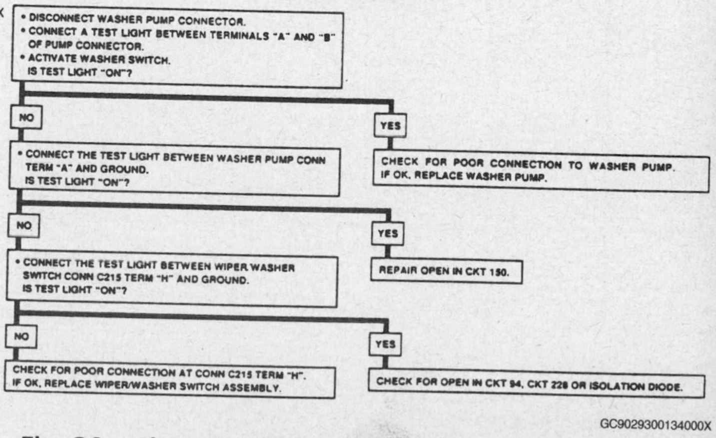
• DISCONNECT WASHER PUMP CONNECTOR.
• CONNECT A TEST LIGHT BETWEEN TERMINALS "A" AND "B" OF PUMP CONNECTOR.
• ACTIVATE WASHER SWITCH.
IS TEST LIGHT "ON"?
NO
YES
• CONNECT THE TEST LIGHT BETWEEN WASHER PUMP CONN TERM "A" AND GROUND.
IS TEST LIGHT "ON"?
CHECK FOR POOR CONNECTION TO WASHER PUMP.
IF OK, REPLACE WASHER PUMP.
NO
YES
• CONNECT THE TEST LIGHT BETWEEN WIPER/WASHER SWITCH CONN C215 TERM "H" AND GROUND.
IS TEST LIGHT "ON"?
REPAIR OPEN IN CKT 150.
NO
YES
CHECK FOR POOR CONNECTION AT CONN C215 TERM "H".
IF OK, REPLACE WIPER/WASHER SWITCH ASSEMBLY.
CHECK FOR OPEN IN CKT 94, CKT 228 OR ISOLATION DIODE.
GC9029300134000X

Fig. 38 Chart 8, Washer does not operate. 1993–94 Camaro & Firebird

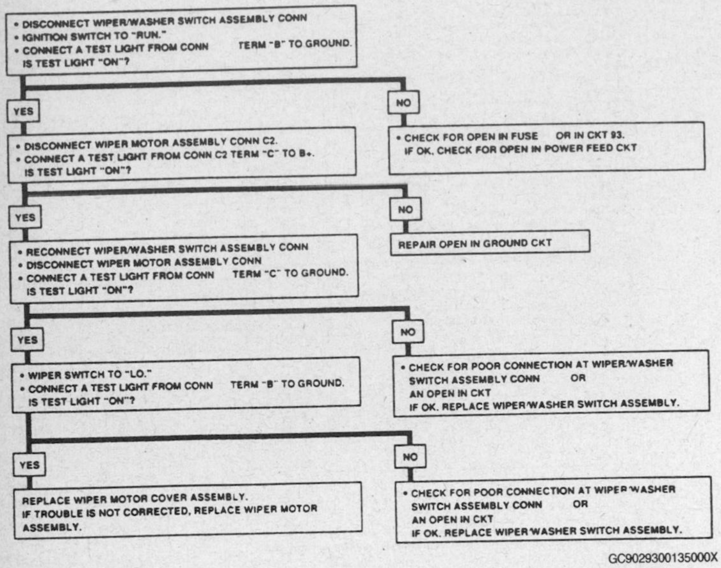
• DISCONNECT WIPER/WASHER SWITCH ASSEMBLY CONN
• IGNITION SWITCH TO "RUN."
• CONNECT A TEST LIGHT FROM CONN TERM "B" TO GROUND.
IS TEST LIGHT "ON"?
YES
NO
• DISCONNECT WIPER MOTOR ASSEMBLY CONN C2.
• CONNECT A TEST LIGHT FROM CONN C2 TERM "C" TO B+.
IS TEST LIGHT "ON"?
• CHECK FOR OPEN IN FUSE OR IN CKT 93.
IF OK, CHECK FOR OPEN IN POWER FEED CKT
YES
NO
REPAIR OPEN IN GROUND CKT
• RECONNECT WIPER/WASHER SWITCH ASSEMBLY CONN
• DISCONNECT WIPER MOTOR ASSEMBLY CONN
• CONNECT A TEST LIGHT FROM CONN TERM "C" TO GROUND.
IS TEST LIGHT "ON"?
YES
NO
• WIPER SWITCH TO "LO."
• CONNECT A TEST LIGHT FROM CONN TERM "B" TO GROUND.
IS TEST LIGHT "ON"?
• CHECK FOR POOR CONNECTION AT WIPER/WASHER SWITCH ASSEMBLY CONN OR
AN OPEN IN CKT
IF OK, REPLACE WIPER/WASHER SWITCH ASSEMBLY.
YES
NO
REPLACE WIPER MOTOR COVER ASSEMBLY.
IF TROUBLE IS NOT CORRECTED, REPLACE WIPER MOTOR ASSEMBLY.
• CHECK FOR POOR CONNECTION AT WIPER/WASHER SWITCH ASSEMBLY CONN OR
AN OPEN IN CKT
IF OK, REPLACE WIPER/WASHER SWITCH ASSEMBLY.
GC9029300135000X

Fig. 39 Chart 1, Wipers do not operate in any mode. 1993–94 Except Camaro, Corvette, Eldorado, Firebird & Seville

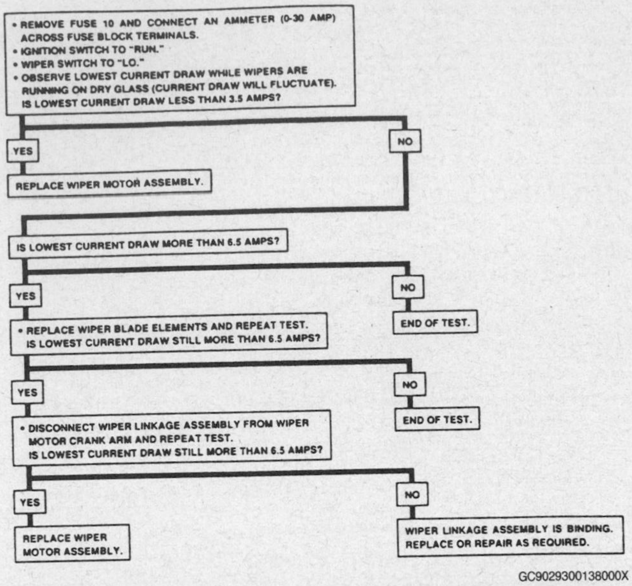
• REMOVE FUSE 10 AND CONNECT AN AMMETER (0-30 AMP) ACROSS FUSE BLOCK TERMINALS.
• IGNITION SWITCH TO "RUN."
• WIPER SWITCH TO "LO."
• OBSERVE LOWEST CURRENT DRAW WHILE WIPERS ARE RUNNING ON DRY GLASS (CURRENT DRAW WILL FLUCTUATE).
IS LOWEST CURRENT DRAW LESS THAN 3.5 AMPS?
YES
NO
REPLACE WIPER MOTOR ASSEMBLY.
IS LOWEST CURRENT DRAW MORE THAN 6.5 AMPS?
YES
NO
• REPLACE WIPER BLADE ELEMENTS AND REPEAT TEST.
IS LOWEST CURRENT DRAW STILL MORE THAN 6.5 AMPS?
END OF TEST.
YES
NO
• DISCONNECT WIPER LINKAGE ASSEMBLY FROM WIPER MOTOR CRANK ARM AND REPEAT TEST.
IS LOWEST CURRENT DRAW STILL MORE THAN 6.5 AMPS?
END OF TEST.
YES
NO
REPLACE WIPER MOTOR ASSEMBLY.
WIPER LINKAGE ASSEMBLY IS BINDING.
REPLACE OR REPAIR AS REQUIRED.
GC9029300138000X

Fig. 42 Chart 4, Wipers run intermittently in low or high speed settings. 1993–94 Except Camaro, Corvette, Eldorado, Firebird & Seville

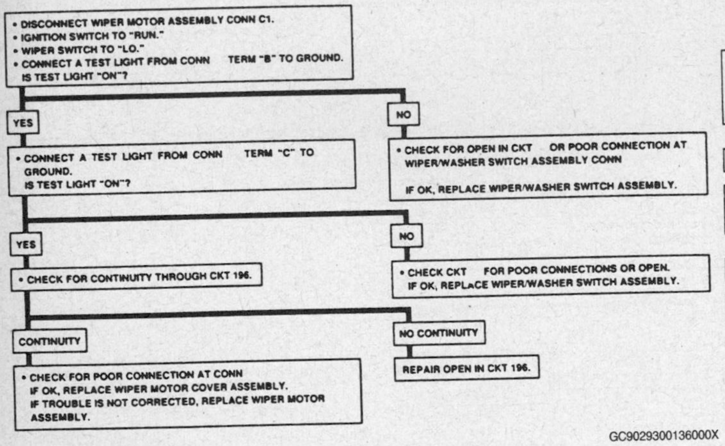
• DISCONNECT WIPER MOTOR ASSEMBLY CONN C1.
• IGNITION SWITCH TO "RUN."
• WIPER SWITCH TO "LO."
• CONNECT A TEST LIGHT FROM CONN TERM "B" TO GROUND.
IS TEST LIGHT "ON"?
YES
NO
• CONNECT A TEST LIGHT FROM CONN TERM "C" TO GROUND.
IS TEST LIGHT "ON"?
• CHECK FOR OPEN IN CKT OR POOR CONNECTION AT WIPER/WASHER SWITCH ASSEMBLY CONN
IF OK, REPLACE WIPER/WASHER SWITCH ASSEMBLY.
YES
NO
• CHECK FOR CONTINUITY THROUGH CKT 196.
• CHECK CKT FOR POOR CONNECTIONS OR OPEN.
IF OK, REPLACE WIPER/WASHER SWITCH ASSEMBLY.
CONTINUITY
NO CONTINUITY
• CHECK FOR POOR CONNECTION AT CONN
IF OK, REPLACE WIPER MOTOR COVER ASSEMBLY.
IF TROUBLE IS NOT CORRECTED, REPLACE WIPER MOTOR ASSEMBLY.
REPAIR OPEN IN CKT 196.
GC9029300136000X

Fig. 40 Chart 2, Wipers run at high speed only. 1993–94 Except Camaro, Corvette, Eldorado, Firebird & Seville

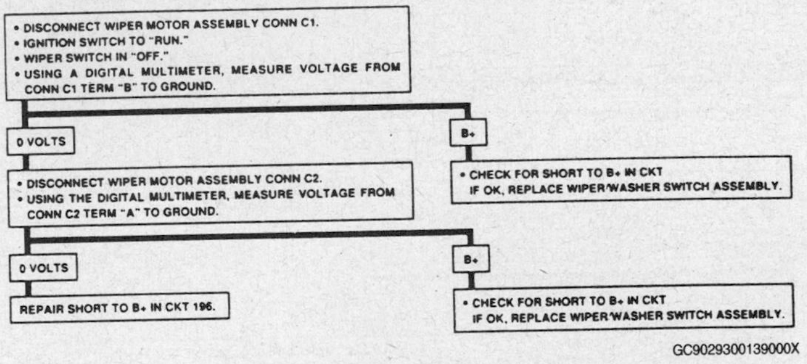
• DISCONNECT WIPER MOTOR ASSEMBLY CONN C1.
• IGNITION SWITCH TO "RUN."
• WIPER SWITCH IN "OFF."
• USING A DIGITAL MULTIMETER, MEASURE VOLTAGE FROM CONN C1 TERM "B" TO GROUND.
0 VOLTS
B+
• DISCONNECT WIPER MOTOR ASSEMBLY CONN C2.
• USING THE DIGITAL MULTIMETER, MEASURE VOLTAGE FROM CONN C2 TERM "A" TO GROUND.
• CHECK FOR SHORT TO B+ IN CKT
IF OK, REPLACE WIPER/WASHER SWITCH ASSEMBLY.
0 VOLTS
B+
REPAIR SHORT TO B+ IN CKT 196.
• CHECK FOR SHORT TO B+ IN CKT
IF OK, REPLACE WIPER/WASHER SWITCH ASSEMBLY.
GC9029300139000X

Fig. 43 Chart 5, Wipers will not turn off. 1993–94 Except Camaro, Corvette, Eldorado, Firebird & Seville

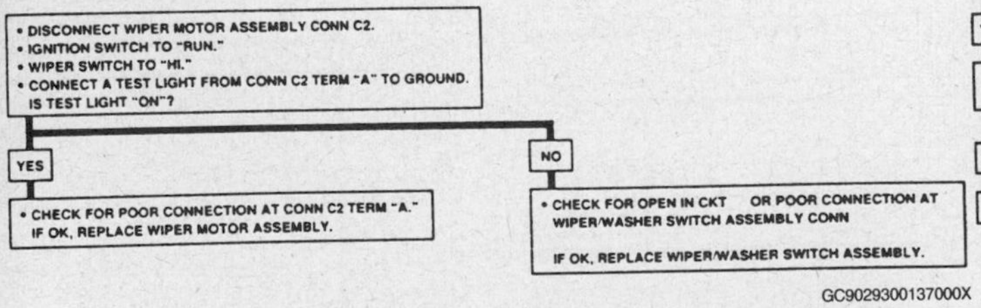
• DISCONNECT WIPER MOTOR ASSEMBLY CONN C2.
• IGNITION SWITCH TO "RUN."
• WIPER SWITCH TO "HI."
• CONNECT A TEST LIGHT FROM CONN C2 TERM "A" TO GROUND.
IS TEST LIGHT "ON"?
YES
NO
• CHECK FOR POOR CONNECTION AT CONN C2 TERM "A."
IF OK, REPLACE WIPER MOTOR ASSEMBLY.
• CHECK FOR OPEN IN CKT OR POOR CONNECTION AT WIPER/WASHER SWITCH ASSEMBLY CONN
IF OK, REPLACE WIPER/WASHER SWITCH ASSEMBLY.
GC9029300137000X

Fig. 41 Chart 3, Wipers run at low speed only. 1993–94 Except Camaro, Corvette, Eldorado, Firebird & Seville

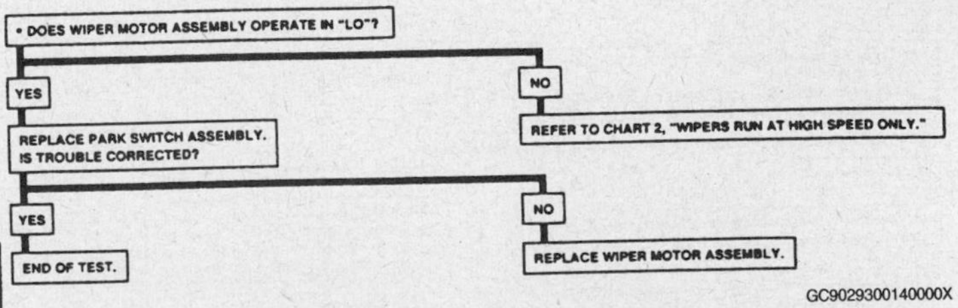
• DOES WIPER MOTOR ASSEMBLY OPERATE IN "LO"?
YES
NO
REPLACE PARK SWITCH ASSEMBLY.
IS TROUBLE CORRECTED?
REFER TO CHART 2, "WIPERS RUN AT HIGH SPEED ONLY."
YES
NO
END OF TEST.
REPLACE WIPER MOTOR ASSEMBLY.
GC9029300140000X

Fig. 44 Chart 6, Wipers cycle in and out of park position after wipers are shut off. 1993–94 Except Camaro, Corvette, Eldorado, Firebird & Seville

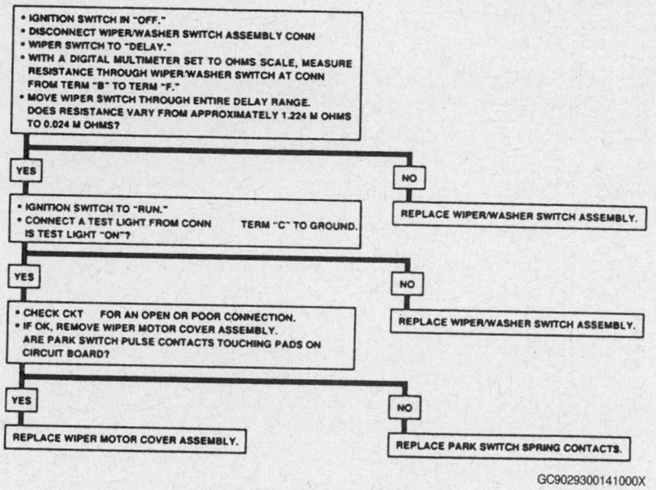
• IGNITION SWITCH IN "OFF."
• DISCONNECT WIPER/WASHER SWITCH ASSEMBLY CONN
• WIPER SWITCH TO "DELAY."
• WITH A DIGITAL MULTIMETER SET TO OHMS SCALE, MEASURE RESISTANCE THROUGH WIPER/WASHER SWITCH AT CONN FROM TERM "B" TO TERM "F."
• MOVE WIPER SWITCH THROUGH ENTIRE DELAY RANGE. DOES RESISTANCE VARY FROM APPROXIMATELY 1.224 M OHMS TO 0.024 M OHMS?
YES
NO
REPLACE WIPER/WASHER SWITCH ASSEMBLY.
• IGNITION SWITCH TO "RUN."
• CONNECT A TEST LIGHT FROM CONN TERM "C" TO GROUND. IS TEST LIGHT "ON"?
YES
NO
REPLACE WIPER/WASHER SWITCH ASSEMBLY.
• CHECK CKT FOR AN OPEN OR POOR CONNECTION.
• IF OK, REMOVE WIPER MOTOR COVER ASSEMBLY. ARE PARK SWITCH PULSE CONTACTS TOUCHING PADS ON CIRCUIT BOARD?
YES
NO
REPLACE WIPER MOTOR COVER ASSEMBLY.
REPLACE PARK SWITCH SPRING CONTACTS.
GC9029300141000X

Fig. 45 Chart 7, Pulse delay operates incorrectly or not at all. 1993- —94 Except Camaro, Corvette, Eldorado, Firebird & Seville

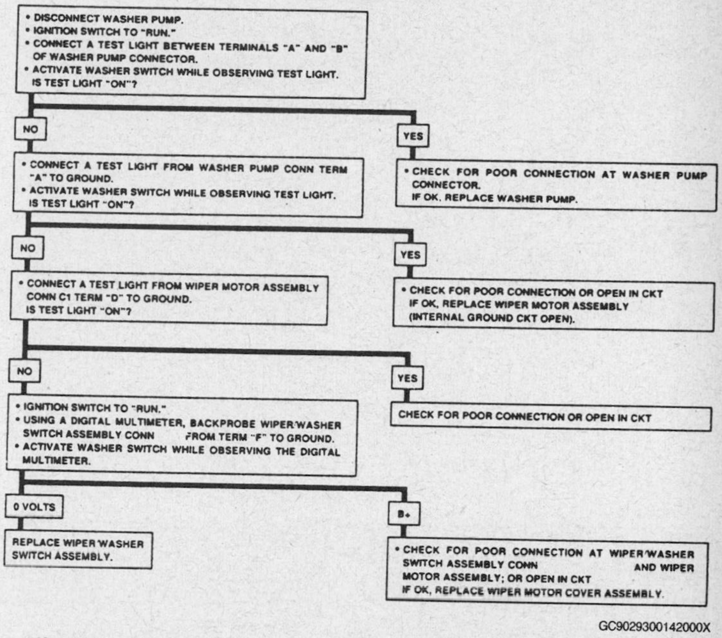
• DISCONNECT WASHER PUMP.
• IGNITION SWITCH TO "RUN."
• CONNECT A TEST LIGHT BETWEEN TERMINALS "A" AND "B" OF WASHER PUMP CONNECTOR.
• ACTIVATE WASHER SWITCH WHILE OBSERVING TEST LIGHT. IS TEST LIGHT "ON"?
NO
YES
• CHECK FOR POOR CONNECTION AT WASHER PUMP CONNECTOR. IF OK, REPLACE WASHER PUMP.
• CONNECT A TEST LIGHT FROM WASHER PUMP CONN TERM "A" TO GROUND.
• ACTIVATE WASHER SWITCH WHILE OBSERVING TEST LIGHT. IS TEST LIGHT "ON"?
NO
YES
• CHECK FOR POOR CONNECTION OR OPEN IN CKT IF OK, REPLACE WIPER MOTOR ASSEMBLY (INTERNAL GROUND CKT OPEN).
• CONNECT A TEST LIGHT FROM WIPER MOTOR ASSEMBLY CONN C1 TERM "D" TO GROUND. IS TEST LIGHT "ON"?
NO
YES
CHECK FOR POOR CONNECTION OR OPEN IN CKT
• IGNITION SWITCH TO "RUN."
• USING A DIGITAL MULTIMETER, BACKPROBE WIPER/WASHER SWITCH ASSEMBLY CONN FROM TERM "F" TO GROUND.
• ACTIVATE WASHER SWITCH WHILE OBSERVING THE DIGITAL MULTIMETER.
0 VOLTS
B+
REPLACE WIPER/WASHER SWITCH ASSEMBLY.
• CHECK FOR POOR CONNECTION AT WIPER/WASHER SWITCH ASSEMBLY CONN AND WIPER MOTOR ASSEMBLY; OR OPEN IN CKT IF OK, REPLACE WIPER MOTOR COVER ASSEMBLY.
GC9029300142000X

Fig. 46 Chart 8, Washer will not operate. 1993–94 Except Camaro, Corvette, Eldorado, Firebird & Seville

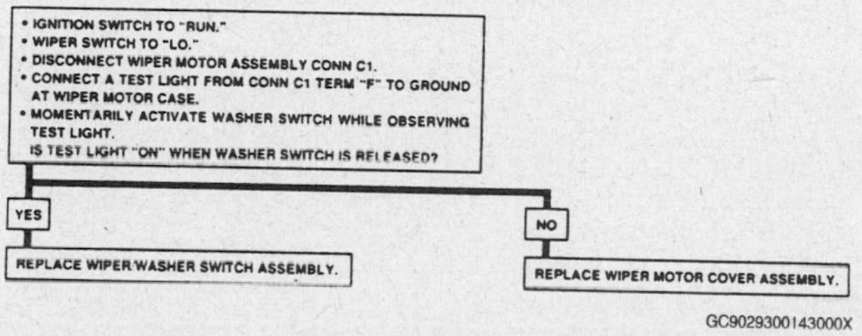
• IGNITION SWITCH TO "RUN."
• WIPER SWITCH TO "LO."
• DISCONNECT WIPER MOTOR ASSEMBLY CONN C1.
• CONNECT A TEST LIGHT FROM CONN C1 TERM "F" TO GROUND AT WIPER MOTOR CASE.
• MOMENTARILY ACTIVATE WASHER SWITCH WHILE OBSERVING TEST LIGHT. IS TEST LIGHT "ON" WHEN WASHER SWITCH IS RELEASED?
YES
NO
REPLACE WIPER/WASHER SWITCH ASSEMBLY.
REPLACE WIPER MOTOR COVER ASSEMBLY.
GC9029300143000X

Fig. 47 Chart 9, Washer will not shut off. 1993–94 Except Camaro, Corvette, Eldorado, Firebird & Seville

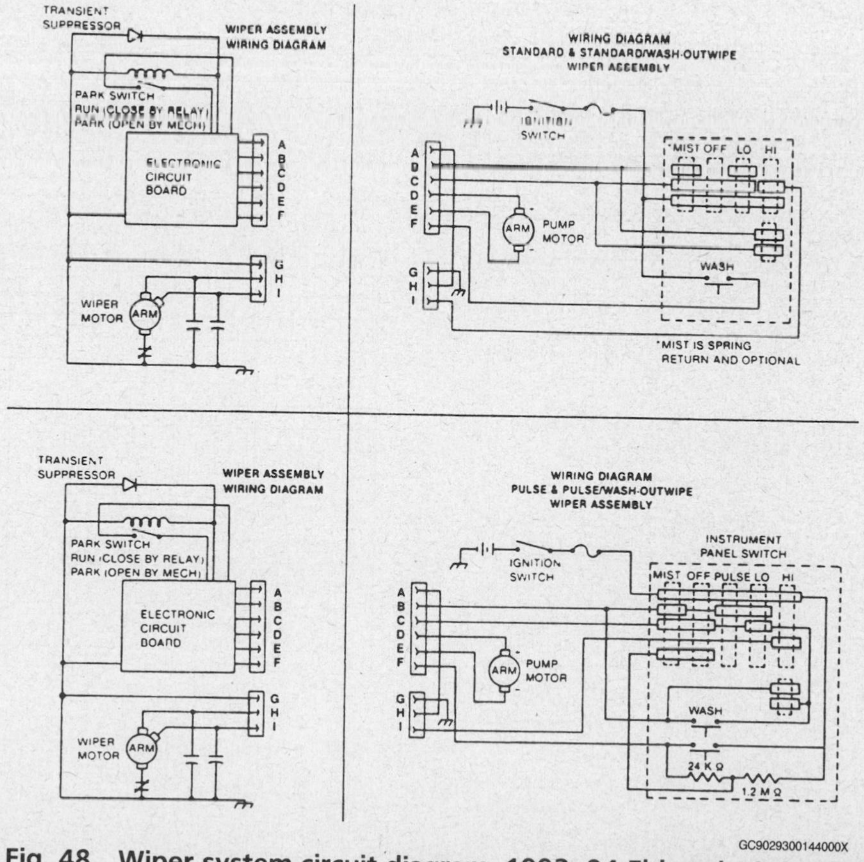
TRANSIENT SUPPRESSOR
WIPER ASSEMBLY WIRING DIAGRAM
PARK SWITCH
RUN (CLOSE BY RELAY)
PARK (OPEN BY MECH)
ELECTRONIC CIRCUIT BOARD
A B C D E F
G H I
WIPER MOTOR
ARM
WIRING DIAGRAM STANDARD & STANDARD/WASH-OUTWIPE WIPER ASSEMBLY
IGNITION SWITCH
*MIST OFF LO HI
PUMP MOTOR
WASH
*MIST IS SPRING RETURN AND OPTIONAL
WIRING DIAGRAM PULSE & PULSE/WASH-OUTWIPE WIPER ASSEMBLY
INSTRUMENT PANEL SWITCH
MIST OFF PULSE LO HI
24 K Ω
1.2 M Ω
GC9029300144000X

Fig. 48 Wiper system circuit diagram. 1993–94 Eldorado & Seville

NOTE: THE FOLLOWING PROCEDURES ASSUME THAT THE TECHNICIAN HAS CHECKED THE FOLLOWING:
1. CONTINUITY OF ALL HARNESS WIRES
2. WIPER MOTOR TO DASH MOUNTING SCREWS TIGHT
3. FUSES

WIPER MOTOR

CHECK FOR MOTOR OPERATION BEFORE REMOVING FROM VEHICLE. DISCONNECT ALL WIRING FROM WIPER AND PERFORM THE FOLLOWING CHECKS IN THIS ORDER:

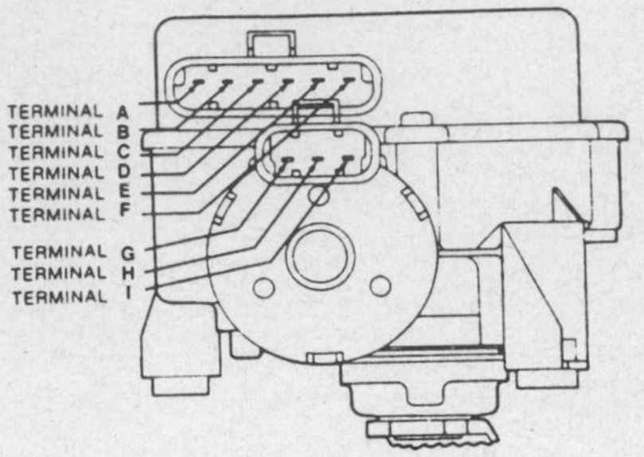
TERMINAL A
TERMINAL B
TERMINAL C
TERMINAL D
TERMINAL E
TERMINAL F
TERMINAL G
TERMINAL H
TERMINAL I

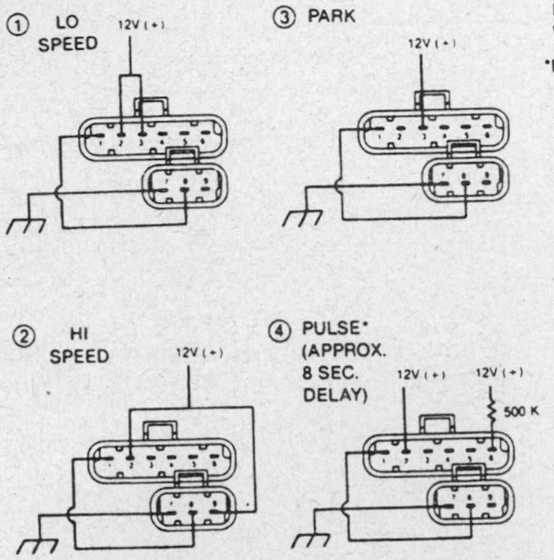
① LO SPEED
12V (+)
③ PARK
12V (+)
② HI SPEED
12V (+)
④ PULSE* (APPROX. 8 SEC. DELAY)
12V (+)
12V (+)
500 K

IF WIPER MOTOR FUNCTIONS IN ALL MODES, GO TO WIPER-WASHER SWITCH CHECK CHART.

*IF A STANDARD TYPE MOTOR IS WIRED FOR THE PULSE CHECK, THE PARK RELAY WILL CLICK SHUT BUT THERE WILL BE NO OBSERVABLE MOTOR ACTION.

GC9029300145000X

Fig. 49 Wiper motor terminal check. 1993–94 Eldorado & Seville

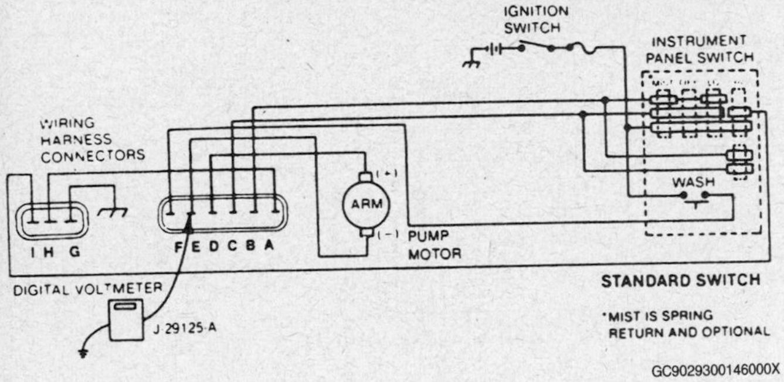
IGNITION SWITCH
INSTRUMENT PANEL SWITCH
WIRING HARNESS CONNECTORS
ARM
(+)
(-)
PUMP MOTOR
WASH
I H G
F E D C B A
DIGITAL VOLTMETER
J 29125-A
STANDARD SWITCH
*MIST IS SPRING RETURN AND OPTIONAL
GC9029300146000X

Fig. 50 Wiper/washer switch test standard. 1993–94 Eldorado & Seville

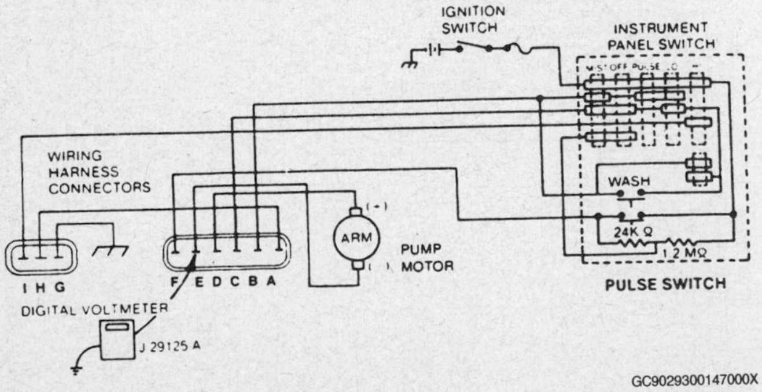
IGNITION SWITCH
INSTRUMENT PANEL SWITCH
WIRING HARNESS CONNECTORS
ARM
(+)
PUMP MOTOR
WASH
24K Ω
1.2 MΩ
I H G
F E D C B A
DIGITAL VOLTMETER
J 29125 A
PULSE SWITCH
GC9029300147000X

Fig. 51 Wiper/washer switch test pulse. 1993–94 Eldorado & Seville

	TERMINAL \ SWITCH MODE	MIST	OFF	PULSE	LO	HI †	WASH
PULSE	A	C	C	C	C	C	C
	B	B(+)	—	B(+)	B(+)	—	*B(+)
	C	B(+)	B(+)	—	B(+)	—	*B(+)
	D	—	—	—	—	—	—
	E	—	—	—	—	—	—
	F	10-12V	10-12V	10-12V	10-12V	10-12V	B(+)
	G	GROUND	GROUND	GROUND	GROUND	GROUND	GROUND
	H	C	C	C	C	C	C
	I	—	—	—	—	B(+)	—
STANDARD	A		C		C	C	C
	B		—		B(+)	—	*B(+)
	C		B(+)		B(+)	—	*B(+)
	D		—		—	—	—
	E		—		—	—	—
	F		—		—	—	B(+)
	G		GROUND		GROUND	GROUND	GROUND
	H		C		C	C	C
	I		—		—	B(+)	—

C = CONTINUITY † TERMINALS B & C CONNECTED TOGETHER *EXCEPT ON HI.

GC9029300148000X

Fig. 52 Wiper/washer switch check chart. 1993–94 Eldorado & Seville

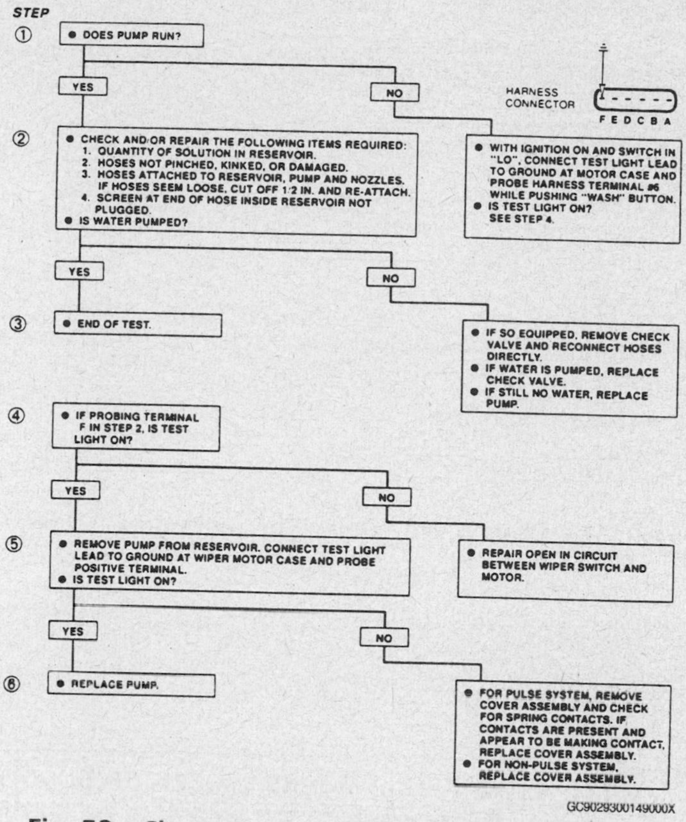
STEP
1 • DOES PUMP RUN?
YES
NO
HARNESS CONNECTOR
F E D C B A
2 • CHECK AND/OR REPAIR THE FOLLOWING ITEMS REQUIRED:
1. QUANTITY OF SOLUTION IN RESERVOIR.
2. HOSES NOT PINCHED, KINKED, OR DAMAGED.
3. HOSES ATTACHED TO RESERVOIR, PUMP AND NOZZLES. IF HOSES SEEM LOOSE, CUT OFF 1/2 IN. AND RE-ATTACH.
4. SCREEN AT END OF HOSE INSIDE RESERVOIR NOT PLUGGED.
• IS WATER PUMPED?
• WITH IGNITION ON AND SWITCH IN "LO", CONNECT TEST LIGHT LEAD TO GROUND AT MOTOR CASE AND PROBE HARNESS TERMINAL #6 WHILE PUSHING "WASH" BUTTON.
• IS TEST LIGHT ON? SEE STEP 4.
YES
NO
3 • END OF TEST.
• IF SO EQUIPPED, REMOVE CHECK VALVE AND RECONNECT HOSES DIRECTLY.
• IF WATER IS PUMPED, REPLACE CHECK VALVE.
• IF STILL NO WATER, REPLACE PUMP.
4 • IF PROBING TERMINAL F IN STEP 2, IS TEST LIGHT ON?
YES
NO
5 • REMOVE PUMP FROM RESERVOIR. CONNECT TEST LIGHT LEAD TO GROUND AT WIPER MOTOR CASE AND PROBE POSITIVE TERMINAL.
• IS TEST LIGHT ON?
• REPAIR OPEN IN CIRCUIT BETWEEN WIPER SWITCH AND MOTOR.
YES
NO
6 • REPLACE PUMP.
• FOR PULSE SYSTEM, REMOVE COVER ASSEMBLY AND CHECK FOR SPRING CONTACTS. IF CONTACTS ARE PRESENT AND APPEAR TO BE MAKING CONTACT, REPLACE COVER ASSEMBLY.
• FOR NON-PULSE SYSTEM, REPLACE COVER ASSEMBLY.
GC9029300149000X

Fig. 53 Chart 1, Washer pump inoperative-wiper motor operates. 1993–94 Eldorado & Seville

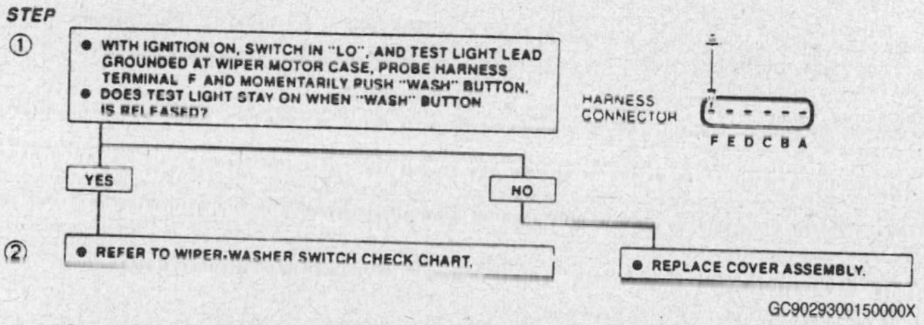
STEP
1 • WITH IGNITION ON, SWITCH IN "LO", AND TEST LIGHT LEAD GROUNDED AT WIPER MOTOR CASE, PROBE HARNESS TERMINAL F AND MOMENTARILY PUSH "WASH" BUTTON.
• DOES TEST LIGHT STAY ON WHEN "WASH" BUTTON IS RELEASED?
HARNESS CONNECTOR
F E D C B A
YES
NO
2 • REFER TO WIPER-WASHER SWITCH CHECK CHART.
• REPLACE COVER ASSEMBLY.
GC9029300150000X

Fig. 54 Chart 2, Washer pumps continuously. 1993–94 Eldorado & Seville

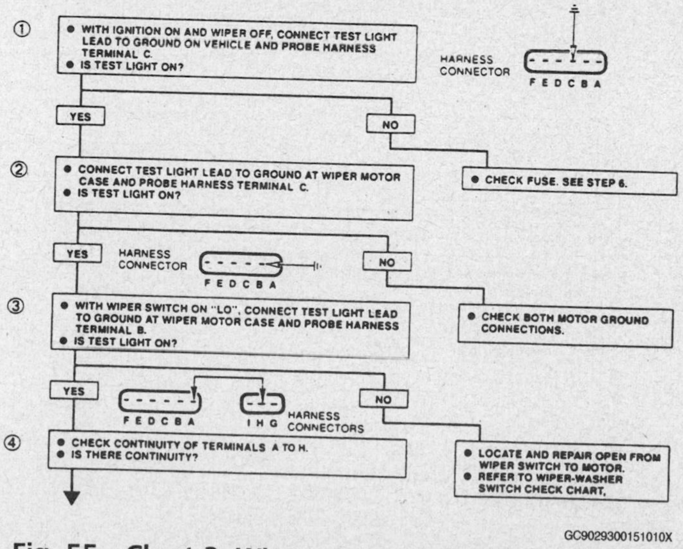
1 • WITH IGNITION ON AND WIPER OFF, CONNECT TEST LIGHT LEAD TO GROUND ON VEHICLE AND PROBE HARNESS TERMINAL C.
• IS TEST LIGHT ON?
HARNESS CONNECTOR
F E D C B A
YES
NO
2 • CONNECT TEST LIGHT LEAD TO GROUND AT WIPER MOTOR CASE AND PROBE HARNESS TERMINAL C.
• IS TEST LIGHT ON?
• CHECK FUSE. SEE STEP 6.
YES
HARNESS CONNECTOR
F E D C B A
NO
3 • WITH WIPER SWITCH ON "LO", CONNECT TEST LIGHT LEAD TO GROUND AT WIPER MOTOR CASE AND PROBE HARNESS TERMINAL B.
• IS TEST LIGHT ON?
• CHECK BOTH MOTOR GROUND CONNECTIONS.
YES
F E D C B A
I H G
HARNESS CONNECTORS
NO
4 • CHECK CONTINUITY OF TERMINALS A TO H.
• IS THERE CONTINUITY?
• LOCATE AND REPAIR OPEN FROM WIPER SWITCH TO MOTOR.
• REFER TO WIPER-WASHER SWITCH CHECK CHART.
GC9029300151010X

Fig. 55 Chart 3, Wiper motor inoperative (Part 1 of 2). 1993–94 Eldorado & Seville

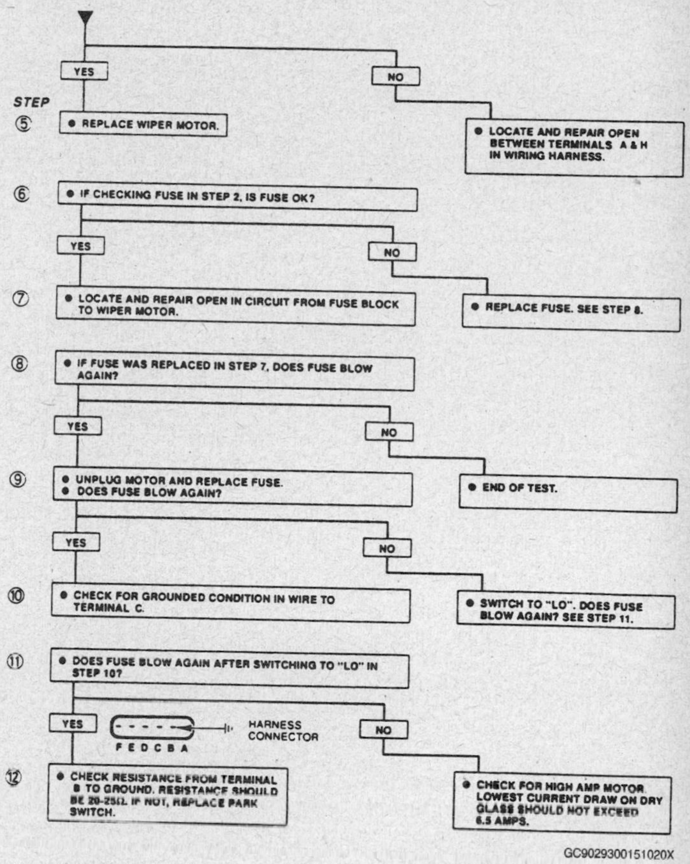
YES
NO
STEP
5 • REPLACE WIPER MOTOR.
• LOCATE AND REPAIR OPEN BETWEEN TERMINALS A & H IN WIRING HARNESS.
6 • IF CHECKING FUSE IN STEP 2, IS FUSE OK?
YES
NO
7 • LOCATE AND REPAIR OPEN IN CIRCUIT FROM FUSE BLOCK TO WIPER MOTOR.
• REPLACE FUSE. SEE STEP 8.
8 • IF FUSE WAS REPLACED IN STEP 7, DOES FUSE BLOW AGAIN?
YES
NO
9 • UNPLUG MOTOR AND REPLACE FUSE.
• DOES FUSE BLOW AGAIN?
• END OF TEST.
YES
NO
10 • CHECK FOR GROUNDED CONDITION IN WIRE TO TERMINAL C.
• SWITCH TO "LO". DOES FUSE BLOW AGAIN? SEE STEP 11.
11 • DOES FUSE BLOW AGAIN AFTER SWITCHING TO "LO" IN STEP 10?
YES
HARNESS CONNECTOR
F E D C B A
NO
12 • CHECK RESISTANCE FROM TERMINAL B TO GROUND. RESISTANCE SHOULD BE 20-25Ω. IF NOT, REPLACE PARK SWITCH.
• CHECK FOR HIGH AMP MOTOR LOWEST CURRENT DRAW ON DRY GLASS SHOULD NOT EXCEED 6.5 AMPS.
GC9029300151020X

Fig. 55 Chart 3, Wiper motor inoperative (Part 2 of 2). 1993–94 Eldorado & Seville

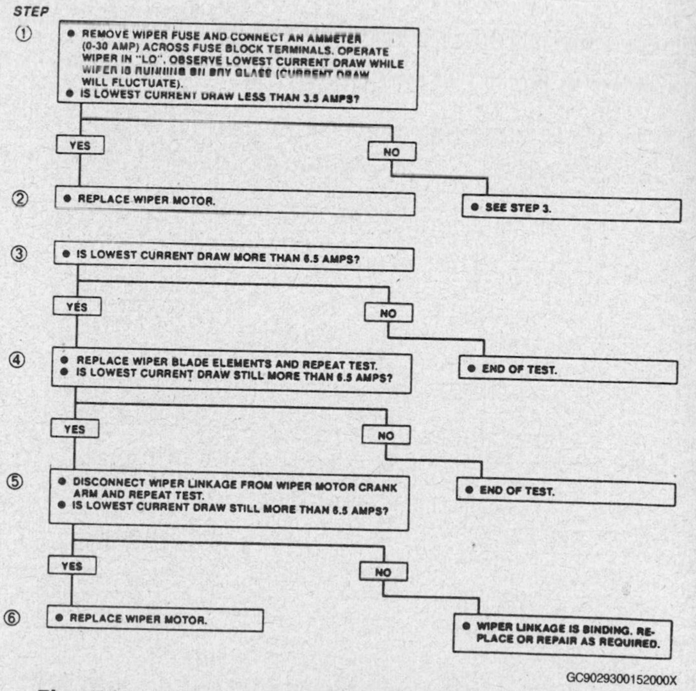
STEP
1 • REMOVE WIPER FUSE AND CONNECT AN AMMETER (0-30 AMP) ACROSS FUSE BLOCK TERMINALS. OPERATE WIPER IN "LO". OBSERVE LOWEST CURRENT DRAW WHILE WIPER IS RUNNING ON DRY GLASS (CURRENT DRAW WILL FLUCTUATE).
• IS LOWEST CURRENT DRAW LESS THAN 3.5 AMPS?
YES
NO
2 • REPLACE WIPER MOTOR.
• SEE STEP 3.
3 • IS LOWEST CURRENT DRAW MORE THAN 6.5 AMPS?
YES
NO
4 • REPLACE WIPER BLADE ELEMENTS AND REPEAT TEST.
• IS LOWEST CURRENT DRAW STILL MORE THAN 6.5 AMPS?
• END OF TEST.
YES
NO
5 • DISCONNECT WIPER LINKAGE FROM WIPER MOTOR CRANK ARM AND REPEAT TEST.
• IS LOWEST CURRENT DRAW STILL MORE THAN 6.5 AMPS?
• END OF TEST.
YES
NO
6 • REPLACE WIPER MOTOR.
• WIPER LINKAGE IS BINDING. REPLACE OR REPAIR AS REQUIRED.
GC9029300152000X

Fig. 56 Chart 4, Intermittent wiper operation in "Delay," or "Lo" or "Hi" modes. 1993–94 Eldorado & Seville

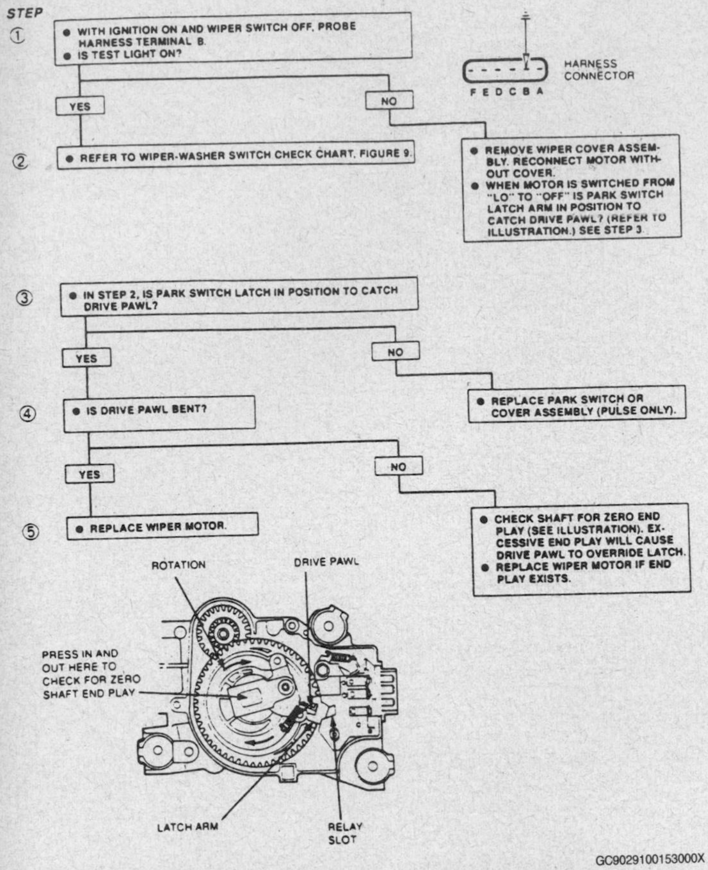

STEP
①
• WITH IGNITION ON AND WIPER SWITCH OFF, PROBE HARNESS TERMINAL B.
• IS TEST LIGHT ON?
HARNESS CONNECTOR
F E D C B A
YES
NO
②
• REFER TO WIPER-WASHER SWITCH CHECK CHART, FIGURE 9.
• REMOVE WIPER COVER ASSEMBLY. RECONNECT MOTOR WITHOUT COVER.
• WHEN MOTOR IS SWITCHED FROM "LO" TO "OFF" IS PARK SWITCH LATCH ARM IN POSITION TO CATCH DRIVE PAWL? (REFER TO ILLUSTRATION.) SEE STEP 3
③
• IN STEP 2, IS PARK SWITCH LATCH IN POSITION TO CATCH DRIVE PAWL?
YES
NO
④
• IS DRIVE PAWL BENT?
• REPLACE PARK SWITCH OR COVER ASSEMBLY (PULSE ONLY).
YES
NO
⑤
• REPLACE WIPER MOTOR.
• CHECK SHAFT FOR ZERO END PLAY (SEE ILLUSTRATION). EXCESSIVE END PLAY WILL CAUSE DRIVE PAWL TO OVERRIDE LATCH.
• REPLACE WIPER MOTOR IF END PLAY EXISTS.
ROTATION
DRIVE PAWL
PRESS IN AND OUT HERE TO CHECK FOR ZERO SHAFT END PLAY
LATCH ARM
RELAY SLOT
GC9029100153000X

Fig. 57 Chart 5, Wiper will not park. 1991–92 except Camaro, Century, Corvette, Cutlass Ciera/Cutlass Cruiser, & Firebird

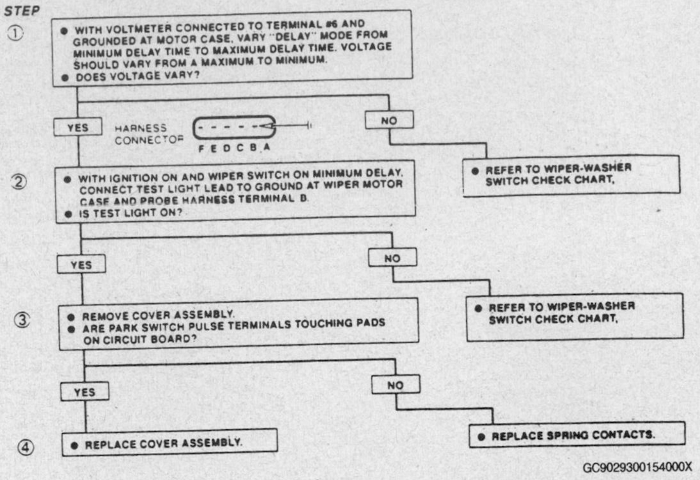

STEP
①
• WITH VOLTMETER CONNECTED TO TERMINAL #6 AND GROUNDED AT MOTOR CASE, VARY "DELAY" MODE FROM MINIMUM DELAY TIME TO MAXIMUM DELAY TIME. VOLTAGE SHOULD VARY FROM A MAXIMUM TO MINIMUM.
• DOES VOLTAGE VARY?
YES
HARNESS CONNECTOR
F E D C B A
NO
②
• WITH IGNITION ON AND WIPER SWITCH ON MINIMUM DELAY, CONNECT TEST LIGHT LEAD TO GROUND AT WIPER MOTOR CASE AND PROBE HARNESS TERMINAL B.
• IS TEST LIGHT ON?
• REFER TO WIPER-WASHER SWITCH CHECK CHART.
YES
NO
③
• REMOVE COVER ASSEMBLY.
• ARE PARK SWITCH PULSE TERMINALS TOUCHING PADS ON CIRCUIT BOARD?
• REFER TO WIPER-WASHER SWITCH CHECK CHART.
YES
NO
④
• REPLACE COVER ASSEMBLY.
• REPLACE SPRING CONTACTS.
GC9029300154000X

Fig. 58 Chart 6, No "Delay" or continuous "Delay"-motor operates in "Lo" & "Hi" modes. 1993–94 Eldorado & Seville

①
- CIRCUIT BOARD IS DEFECTIVE.
- REPLACE WIPER COVER ASSEMBLY.

GC9029300155000X

Fig. 59 Chart 7, Wiper stays in "Delay" during wash cycle started in "Delay". 1993–94 Eldorado & Seville

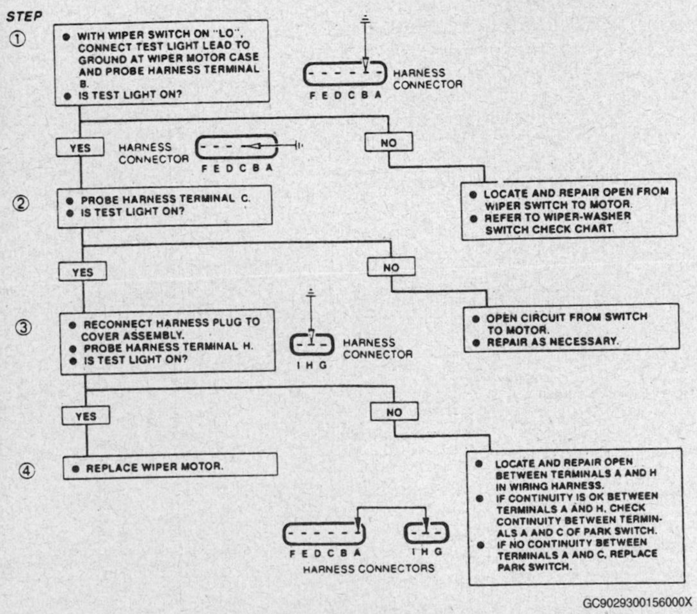

STEP
①
• WITH WIPER SWITCH ON "LO", CONNECT TEST LIGHT LEAD TO GROUND AT WIPER MOTOR CASE AND PROBE HARNESS TERMINAL B.
• IS TEST LIGHT ON?
HARNESS CONNECTOR
F E D C B A
YES
HARNESS CONNECTOR
F E D C B A
NO
②
• PROBE HARNESS TERMINAL C.
• IS TEST LIGHT ON?
• LOCATE AND REPAIR OPEN FROM WIPER SWITCH TO MOTOR.
• REFER TO WIPER-WASHER SWITCH CHECK CHART.
YES
NO
③
• RECONNECT HARNESS PLUG TO COVER ASSEMBLY.
• PROBE HARNESS TERMINAL H.
• IS TEST LIGHT ON?
I H G
HARNESS CONNECTOR
• OPEN CIRCUIT FROM SWITCH TO MOTOR.
• REPAIR AS NECESSARY.
YES
NO
④
• REPLACE WIPER MOTOR.
• LOCATE AND REPAIR OPEN BETWEEN TERMINALS A AND H IN WIRING HARNESS.
• IF CONTINUITY IS OK BETWEEN TERMINALS A AND H, CHECK CONTINUITY BETWEEN TERMINALS A AND C OF PARK SWITCH.
• IF NO CONTINUITY BETWEEN TERMINALS A AND C, REPLACE PARK SWITCH.
F E D C B A
I H G
HARNESS CONNECTORS
GC9029300156000X

Fig. 60 Chart 8, No "Lo" mode. 1993–94 Eldorado & Seville

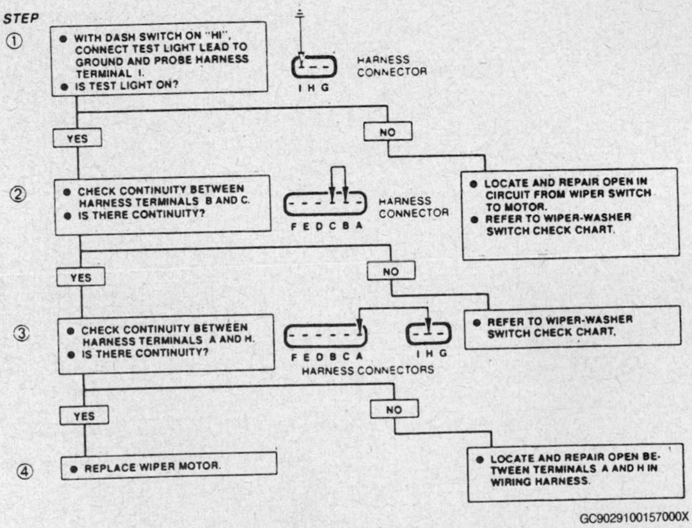

STEP
①
• WITH DASH SWITCH ON "HI", CONNECT TEST LIGHT LEAD TO GROUND AND PROBE HARNESS TERMINAL I.
• IS TEST LIGHT ON?
HARNESS CONNECTOR
I H G
YES
NO
②
• CHECK CONTINUITY BETWEEN HARNESS TERMINALS B AND C.
• IS THERE CONTINUITY?
HARNESS CONNECTOR
F E D C B A
• LOCATE AND REPAIR OPEN IN CIRCUIT FROM WIPER SWITCH TO MOTOR.
• REFER TO WIPER-WASHER SWITCH CHECK CHART.
YES
NO
③
• CHECK CONTINUITY BETWEEN HARNESS TERMINALS A AND H.
• IS THERE CONTINUITY?
F E D C B A
I H G
HARNESS CONNECTORS
• REFER TO WIPER-WASHER SWITCH CHECK CHART.
YES
NO
④
• REPLACE WIPER MOTOR.
• LOCATE AND REPAIR OPEN BETWEEN TERMINALS A AND H IN WIRING HARNESS.
GC9029100157000X

Fig. 61 Chart 9, No "Hi" mode or blades cycle in & out of park with switch in "Hi". 1992 except Camaro, Century, Corvette, Cutlass Ciera, Cutlass Cruiser, & Firebird

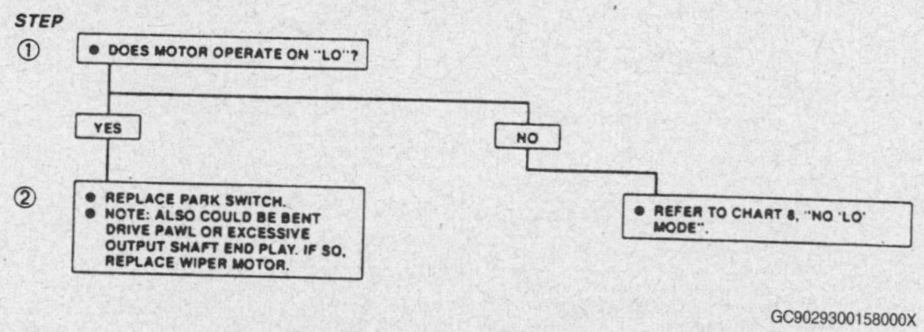
STEP
①
• DOES MOTOR OPERATE ON "LO"?
YES
NO
②
• REPLACE PARK SWITCH.
• NOTE: ALSO COULD BE BENT DRIVE PAWL OR EXCESSIVE OUTPUT SHAFT END PLAY. IF SO, REPLACE WIPER MOTOR.
• REFER TO CHART 8, "NO 'LO' MODE".
GC9029300158000X

Fig. 62 Chart 10, Blades cycle in & out of park with switch off. 1993–94 Eldorado & Seville

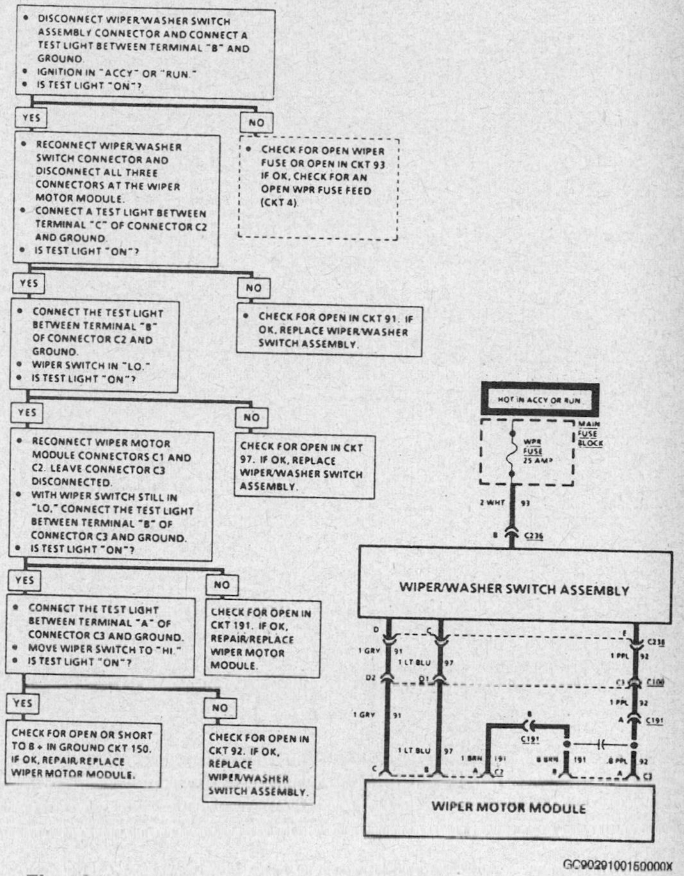
• DISCONNECT WIPER/WASHER SWITCH ASSEMBLY CONNECTOR AND CONNECT A TEST LIGHT BETWEEN TERMINAL "B" AND GROUND.
• IGNITION IN "ACCY" OR "RUN."
• IS TEST LIGHT "ON"?
YES
NO
• CHECK FOR OPEN WIPER FUSE OR OPEN IN CKT 93. IF OK, CHECK FOR AN OPEN WPR FUSE FEED (CKT 4).
• RECONNECT WIPER/WASHER SWITCH CONNECTOR AND DISCONNECT ALL THREE CONNECTORS AT THE WIPER MOTOR MODULE.
• CONNECT A TEST LIGHT BETWEEN TERMINAL "C" OF CONNECTOR C2 AND GROUND.
• IS TEST LIGHT "ON"?
YES
NO
• CHECK FOR OPEN IN CKT 91. IF OK, REPLACE WIPER/WASHER SWITCH ASSEMBLY.
• CONNECT THE TEST LIGHT BETWEEN TERMINAL "B" OF CONNECTOR C2 AND GROUND.
• WIPER SWITCH IN "LO."
• IS TEST LIGHT "ON"?
YES
NO
CHECK FOR OPEN IN CKT 97. IF OK, REPLACE WIPER/WASHER SWITCH ASSEMBLY.
• RECONNECT WIPER MOTOR MODULE CONNECTORS C1 AND C2. LEAVE CONNECTOR C3 DISCONNECTED.
• WITH WIPER SWITCH STILL IN "LO," CONNECT THE TEST LIGHT BETWEEN TERMINAL "B" OF CONNECTOR C3 AND GROUND.
• IS TEST LIGHT "ON"?
YES
NO
CHECK FOR OPEN IN CKT 191. IF OK, REPAIR/REPLACE WIPER MOTOR MODULE.
• CONNECT THE TEST LIGHT BETWEEN TERMINAL "A" OF CONNECTOR C3 AND GROUND.
• MOVE WIPER SWITCH TO "HI."
• IS TEST LIGHT "ON"?
YES
NO
CHECK FOR OPEN OR SHORT TO B+ IN GROUND CKT 150. IF OK, REPAIR/REPLACE WIPER MOTOR MODULE.
CHECK FOR OPEN IN CKT 92. IF OK, REPLACE WIPER/WASHER SWITCH ASSEMBLY.
HOT IN ACCY OR RUN
MAIN FUSE BLOCK
WPR FUSE 25 AMP
2 WHT
93
C236
WIPER/WASHER SWITCH ASSEMBLY
1 GRY
91
1 LT BLU
97
1 PPL
92
C100
C191
1 BRN
191
.8 BRN
.8 PPL
WIPER MOTOR MODULE
GC9029100150000X

Fig. 63 Chart 1, Wipers do not operate at any speed. 1992 Corvette

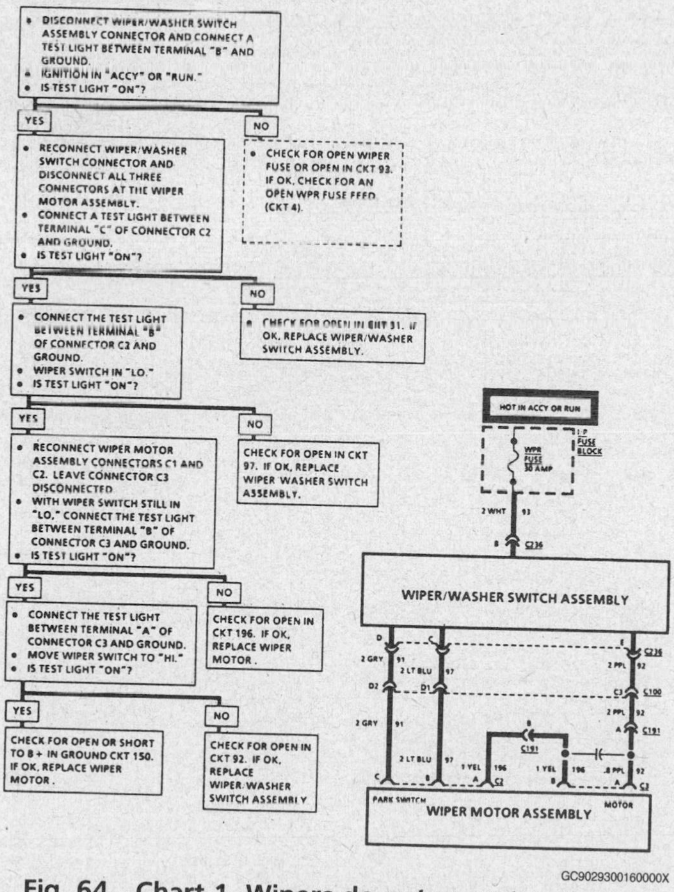
• DISCONNECT WIPER/WASHER SWITCH ASSEMBLY CONNECTOR AND CONNECT A TEST LIGHT BETWEEN TERMINAL "B" AND GROUND.
• IGNITION IN "ACCY" OR "RUN."
• IS TEST LIGHT "ON"?
YES
NO
• CHECK FOR OPEN WIPER FUSE OR OPEN IN CKT 93. IF OK, CHECK FOR AN OPEN WPR FUSE FEED (CKT 4).
• RECONNECT WIPER/WASHER SWITCH CONNECTOR AND DISCONNECT ALL THREE CONNECTORS AT THE WIPER MOTOR ASSEMBLY.
• CONNECT A TEST LIGHT BETWEEN TERMINAL "C" OF CONNECTOR C2 AND GROUND.
• IS TEST LIGHT "ON"?
YES
NO
• CHECK FOR OPEN IN CKT 91. IF OK, REPLACE WIPER/WASHER SWITCH ASSEMBLY.
• CONNECT THE TEST LIGHT BETWEEN TERMINAL "B" OF CONNECTOR C2 AND GROUND.
• WIPER SWITCH IN "LO."
• IS TEST LIGHT "ON"?
YES
NO
CHECK FOR OPEN IN CKT 97. IF OK, REPLACE WIPER WASHER SWITCH ASSEMBLY.
• RECONNECT WIPER MOTOR ASSEMBLY CONNECTORS C1 AND C2. LEAVE CONNECTOR C3 DISCONNECTED.
• WITH WIPER SWITCH STILL IN "LO," CONNECT THE TEST LIGHT BETWEEN TERMINAL "B" OF CONNECTOR C3 AND GROUND.
• IS TEST LIGHT "ON"?
YES
NO
CHECK FOR OPEN IN CKT 196. IF OK, REPLACE WIPER MOTOR.
• CONNECT THE TEST LIGHT BETWEEN TERMINAL "A" OF CONNECTOR C3 AND GROUND.
• MOVE WIPER SWITCH TO "HI."
• IS TEST LIGHT "ON"?
YES
NO
CHECK FOR OPEN OR SHORT TO B+ IN GROUND CKT 150. IF OK, REPLACE WIPER MOTOR.
CHECK FOR OPEN IN CKT 92. IF OK, REPLACE WIPER/WASHER SWITCH ASSEMBLY
HOT IN ACCY OR RUN
I/P FUSE BLOCK
WPR FUSE 30 AMP
2 WHT
93
C236
WIPER/WASHER SWITCH ASSEMBLY
2 GRY
91
2 LT BLU
97
2 PPL
92
C100
C191
1 YEL
196
.8 PPL
PARK SWITCH
WIPER MOTOR ASSEMBLY
MOTOR
GC9029300160000X

Fig. 64 Chart 1, Wipers do not operate at any speed. 1993–94 Corvette

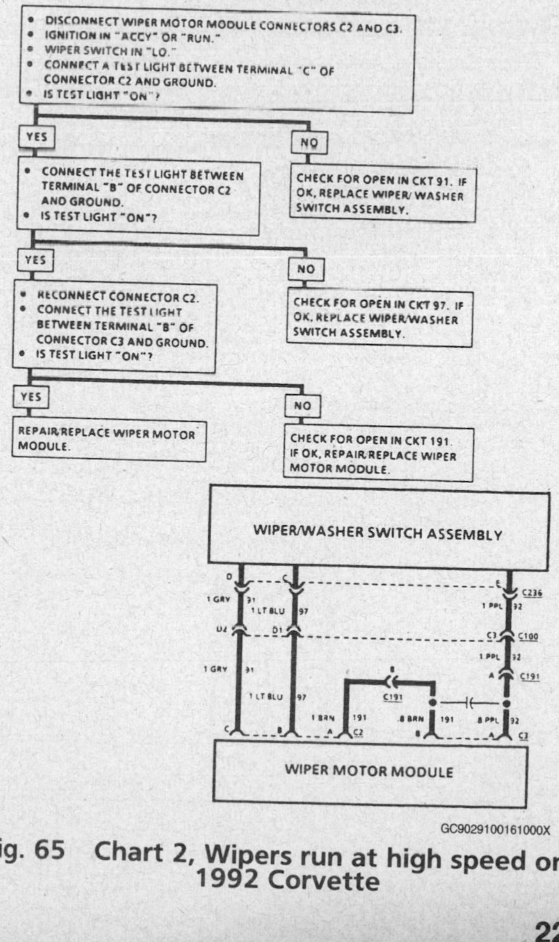
• DISCONNECT WIPER MOTOR MODULE CONNECTORS C2 AND C3.
• IGNITION IN "ACCY" OR "RUN."
• WIPER SWITCH IN "LO."
• CONNECT A TEST LIGHT BETWEEN TERMINAL "C" OF CONNECTOR C2 AND GROUND.
• IS TEST LIGHT "ON"?
YES
NO
• CONNECT THE TEST LIGHT BETWEEN TERMINAL "B" OF CONNECTOR C2 AND GROUND.
• IS TEST LIGHT "ON"?
CHECK FOR OPEN IN CKT 91. IF OK, REPLACE WIPER/ WASHER SWITCH ASSEMBLY.
YES
NO
• RECONNECT CONNECTOR C2.
• CONNECT THE TEST LIGHT BETWEEN TERMINAL "B" OF CONNECTOR C3 AND GROUND.
• IS TEST LIGHT "ON"?
CHECK FOR OPEN IN CKT 97. IF OK, REPLACE WIPER/WASHER SWITCH ASSEMBLY.
YES
NO
REPAIR/REPLACE WIPER MOTOR MODULE.
CHECK FOR OPEN IN CKT 191. IF OK, REPAIR/REPLACE WIPER MOTOR MODULE.
WIPER/WASHER SWITCH ASSEMBLY
1 GRY
91
1 LT BLU
97
1 PPL
92
C236
C100
C191
1 BRN
191
.8 BRN
.8 PPL
WIPER MOTOR MODULE
GC9029100161000X

Fig. 65 Chart 2, Wipers run at high speed only. 1992 Corvette

- DISCONNECT WIPER MOTOR ASSEMBLY CONNECTORS C2 AND C3.
- IGNITION IN "ACCY" OR "RUN."
- WIPER SWITCH IN "LO."
- CONNECT A TEST LIGHT BETWEEN TERMINAL "C" OF CONNECTOR C2 AND GROUND.
- IS TEST LIGHT "ON"?

NO: CHECK FOR OPEN IN CKT 91. IF OK, REPLACE WIPER/WASHER SWITCH ASSEMBLY.

YES:
- CONNECT THE TEST LIGHT BETWEEN TERMINAL "B" OF CONNECTOR C2 AND GROUND.
- IS TEST LIGHT "ON"?

NO: CHECK FOR OPEN IN CKT 97. IF OK, REPLACE WIPER/WASHER SWITCH ASSEMBLY.

YES:
- RECONNECT CONNECTOR C2.
- CONNECT THE TEST LIGHT BETWEEN TERMINAL "B" OF CONNECTOR C3 AND GROUND.
- IS TEST LIGHT "ON"?

YES: REPLACE WIPER MOTOR.

NO: CHECK FOR OPEN IN CKT 196. IF OK, REPLACE WIPER MOTOR.

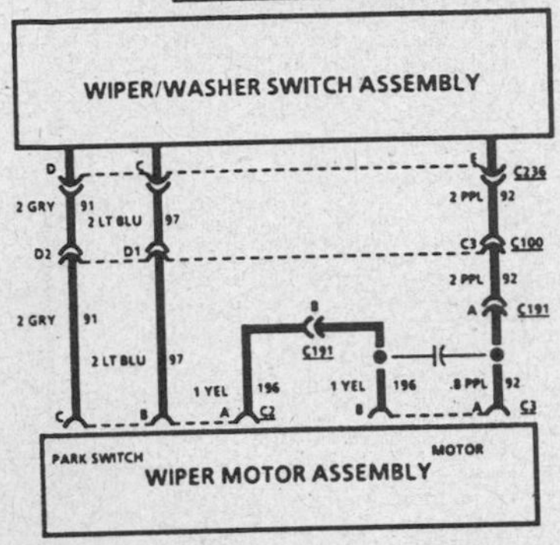
WIPER/WASHER SWITCH ASSEMBLY
PARK SWITCH
MOTOR
WIPER MOTOR ASSEMBLY

GC9029300162000X

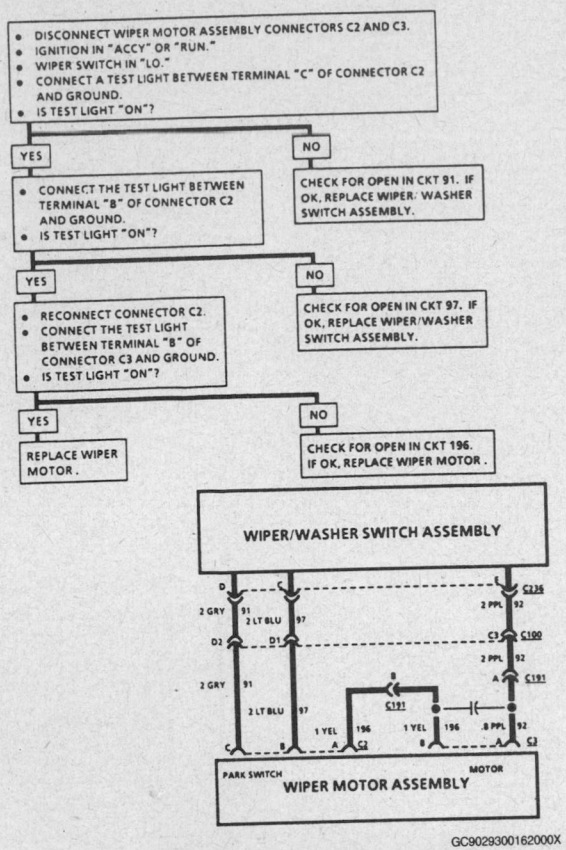

Fig. 66 Chart 2, Wipers run at high speed only. 1993–94 Corvette

- DISCONNECT THE THREE WIPER MOTOR ASSEMBLY CONNECTORS.
- IGNITION IN "ACCY" OR "RUN."
- WIPER SWITCH "OFF."
- CONNECT A TEST LIGHT BETWEEN TERMINAL "A" OF CONNECTOR C1 AND GROUND.
- IS TEST LIGHT "ON"?

YES: CHECK FOR SHORT TO B+ IN CKT 96. IF OK, REPLACE WIPER/WASHER SWITCH ASSEMBLY.

NO:
- CONNECT THE TEST LIGHT BETWEEN TERMINAL "B" OF CONNECTOR C2 AND GROUND.
- IS TEST LIGHT "ON"?

YES: CHECK FOR SHORT TO B+ IN CKT 97. IF OK, REPLACE WIPER/WASHER SWITCH ASSEMBLY.

NO:
- RECONNECT CONNECTORS C1 AND C2.
- CONNECT THE TEST LIGHT BETWEEN TERMINAL "B" OF CONNECTOR C3 AND GROUND.
- IS TEST LIGHT "ON"?

YES: CHECK FOR SHORT TO B+ IN CKT 196. IF OK, REPLACE WIPER MOTOR.

NO:
- CONNECT THE TEST LIGHT BETWEEN TERMINAL "A" OF CONNECTOR C3 AND GROUND.
- IS TEST LIGHT "ON"?

NO: REPLACE WIPER MOTOR.

YES: CHECK FOR SHORT TO B+ IN CKT 92. IF OK, REPLACE WIPER/WASHER SWITCH ASSEMBLY.

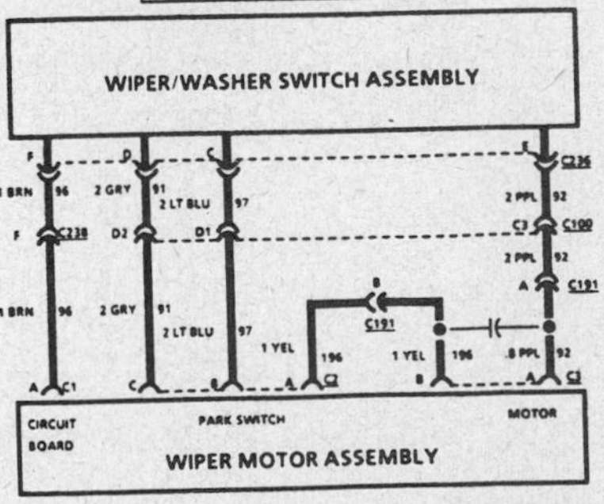
WIPER/WASHER SWITCH ASSEMBLY
CIRCUIT BOARD
PARK SWITCH
MOTOR
WIPER MOTOR ASSEMBLY

GC9029300164000X

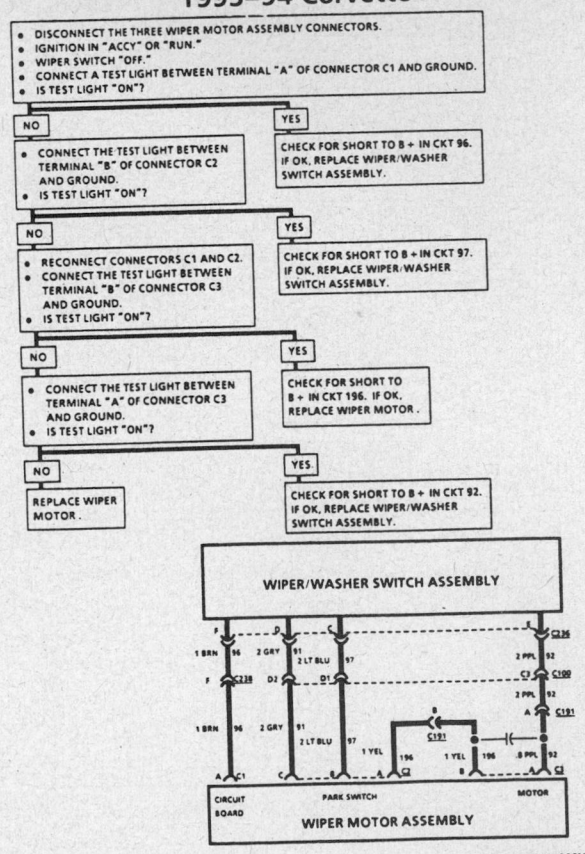

Fig. 68 Chart 3, Wipers will not shut off. 1993–94 Corvette

- DISCONNECT THE THREE WIPER MOTOR MODULE CONNECTORS.
- IGNITION IN "ACCY" OR "RUN."
- WIPER SWITCH "OFF."
- CONNECT A TEST LIGHT BETWEEN TERMINAL "A" OF CONNECTOR C1 AND GROUND.
- IS TEST LIGHT "ON"?

YES: CHECK FOR SHORT TO B+ IN CKT 96. IF OK, REPLACE WIPER/WASHER SWITCH ASSEMBLY.

NO:
- CONNECT THE TEST LIGHT BETWEEN TERMINAL "B" OF CONNECTOR C2 AND GROUND.
- IS TEST LIGHT "ON"?

YES: CHECK FOR SHORT TO B+ IN CKT 97. IF OK, REPLACE WIPER/WASHER SWITCH ASSEMBLY.

NO:
- RECONNECT CONNECTORS C1 AND C2.
- CONNECT THE TEST LIGHT BETWEEN TERMINAL "B" OF CONNECTOR C3 AND GROUND.
- IS TEST LIGHT "ON"?

YES: CHECK FOR SHORT TO B+ IN CKT 191. IF OK, REPAIR/REPLACE WIPER MOTOR MODULE.

NO:
- CONNECT THE TEST LIGHT BETWEEN TERMINAL "A" OF CONNECTOR C3 AND GROUND.
- IS TEST LIGHT "ON"?

NO: REPAIR/REPLACE WIPER MOTOR MODULE.

YES: CHECK FOR SHORT TO B+ IN CKT 92. IF OK, REPLACE WIPER/WASHER SWITCH ASSEMBLY.

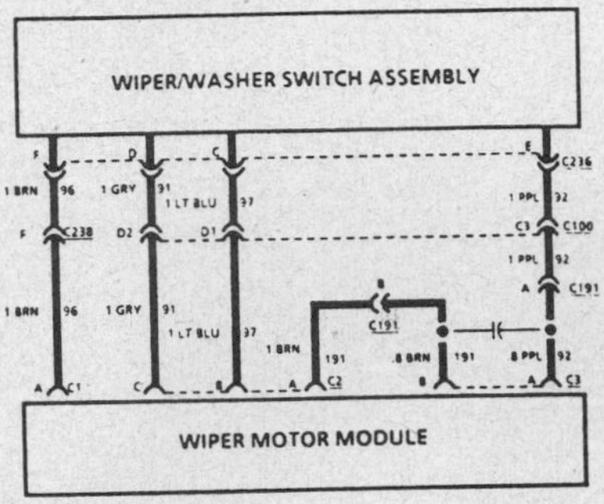
WIPER/WASHER SWITCH ASSEMBLY
WIPER MOTOR MODULE

GC9029100163000X

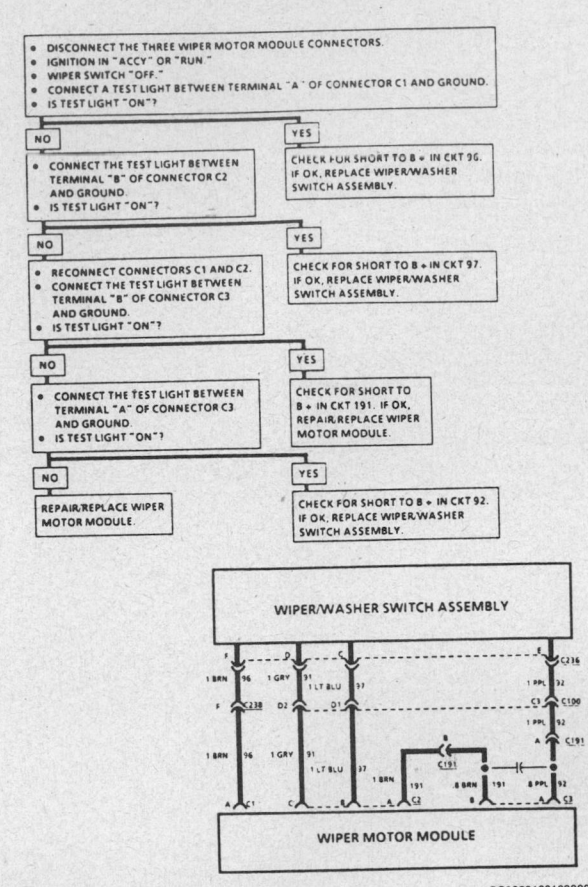

Fig. 67 Chart 3, Wipers will not shut off. 1992 Corvette

- DISCONNECT WIPER MOTOR MODULE CONNECTOR C3.
- IGNITION IN "ACCY" OR "RUN."
- WIPER SWITCH IN "HI."
- CONNECT A TEST LIGHT BETWEEN TERMINAL "A" OF CONNECTOR C3 AND GROUND.
- IS TEST LIGHT "ON"?

YES: REPAIR/REPLACE WIPER MOTOR MODULE.

NO: CHECK FOR OPEN IN CKT 92. IF OK, REPLACE WIPER/WASHER SWITCH ASSEMBLY.

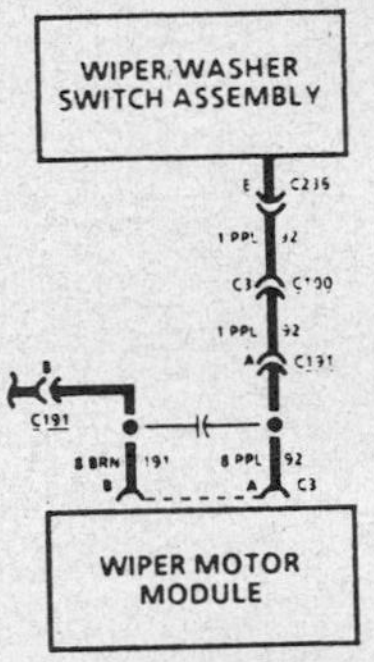
WIPER/WASHER SWITCH ASSEMBLY
WIPER MOTOR MODULE

GC9029100165000X

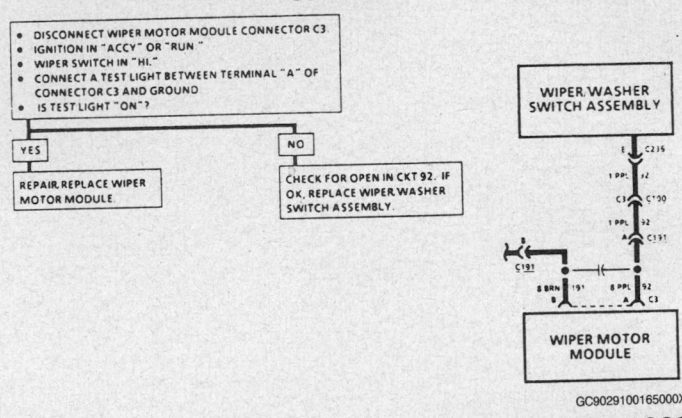

Fig. 69 Chart 4, Wipers run at low speed only. 1992 Corvette

- DISCONNECT WIPER MOTOR ASSEMBLY CONNECTOR C3.
- IGNITION IN "ACCY" OR "RUN."
- WIPER SWITCH IN "HI."
- CONNECT A TEST LIGHT BETWEEN TERMINAL "A" OF CONNECTOR C3 AND GROUND.
- IS TEST LIGHT "ON"?

YES: REPLACE WIPER MOTOR.

NO: CHECK FOR OPEN IN CKT 92. IF OK, REPLACE WIPER/WASHER SWITCH ASSEMBLY.

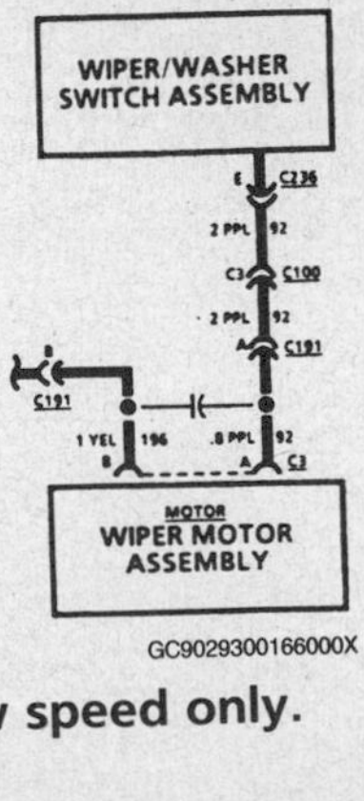
WIPER/WASHER SWITCH ASSEMBLY
MOTOR
WIPER MOTOR ASSEMBLY

GC9029300166000X

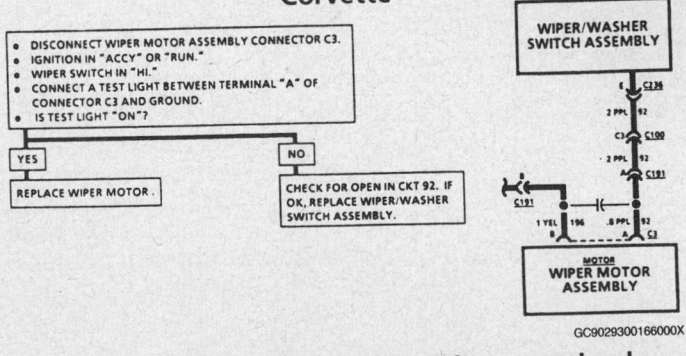

Fig. 70 Chart 4, Wipers run at low speed only. 1993–94 Corvette

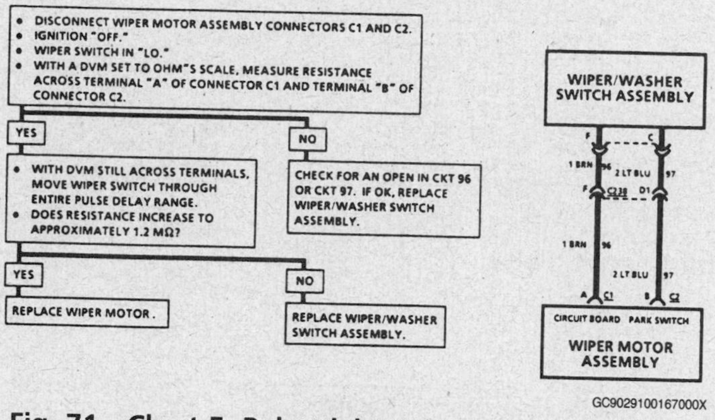

• DISCONNECT WIPER MOTOR ASSEMBLY CONNECTORS C1 AND C2.
• IGNITION "OFF."
• WIPER SWITCH IN "LO."
• WITH A DVM SET TO OHM"S SCALE, MEASURE RESISTANCE ACROSS TERMINAL "A" OF CONNECTOR C1 AND TERMINAL "B" OF CONNECTOR C2.
YES
NO
• WITH DVM STILL ACROSS TERMINALS, MOVE WIPER SWITCH THROUGH ENTIRE PULSE DELAY RANGE.
• DOES RESISTANCE INCREASE TO APPROXIMATELY 1.2 MΩ?
CHECK FOR AN OPEN IN CKT 96 OR CKT 97. IF OK, REPLACE WIPER/WASHER SWITCH ASSEMBLY.
YES
NO
REPLACE WIPER MOTOR.
REPLACE WIPER/WASHER SWITCH ASSEMBLY.
WIPER/WASHER SWITCH ASSEMBLY
1 BRN 96
2 LT BLU 97
CIRCUIT BOARD
PARK SWITCH
WIPER MOTOR ASSEMBLY
GC9029100167000X

Fig. 71 Chart 5, Pulse delay operates incorrectly or not at all. Corvette

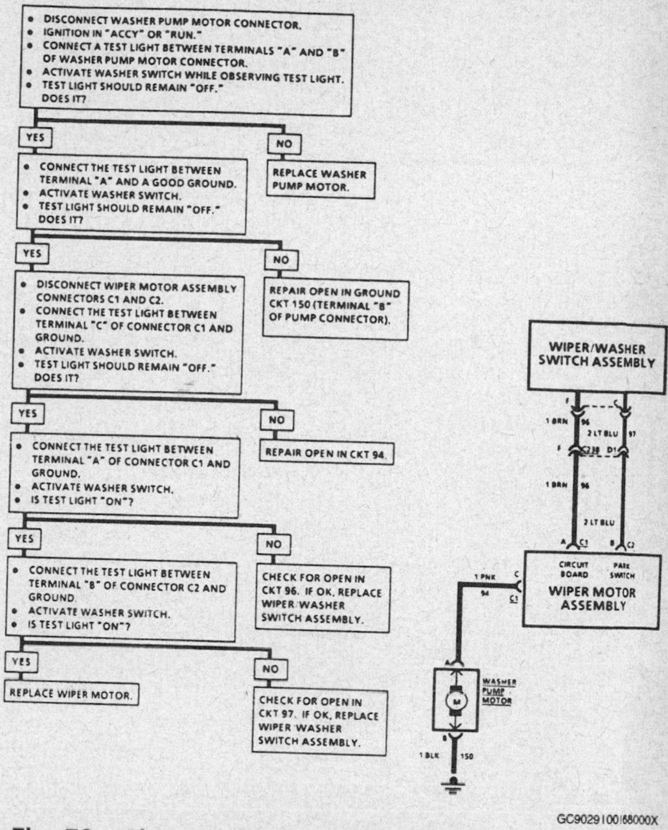

• DISCONNECT WASHER PUMP MOTOR CONNECTOR.
• IGNITION IN "ACCY" OR "RUN."
• CONNECT A TEST LIGHT BETWEEN TERMINALS "A" AND "B" OF WASHER PUMP MOTOR CONNECTOR.
• ACTIVATE WASHER SWITCH WHILE OBSERVING TEST LIGHT.
• TEST LIGHT SHOULD REMAIN "OFF." DOES IT?
YES
NO
REPLACE WASHER PUMP MOTOR.
• CONNECT THE TEST LIGHT BETWEEN TERMINAL "A" AND A GOOD GROUND.
• ACTIVATE WASHER SWITCH.
• TEST LIGHT SHOULD REMAIN "OFF." DOES IT?
YES
NO
REPAIR OPEN IN GROUND CKT 150 (TERMINAL "B" OF PUMP CONNECTOR).
• DISCONNECT WIPER MOTOR ASSEMBLY CONNECTORS C1 AND C2.
• CONNECT THE TEST LIGHT BETWEEN TERMINAL "C" OF CONNECTOR C1 AND GROUND.
• ACTIVATE WASHER SWITCH.
• TEST LIGHT SHOULD REMAIN "OFF." DOES IT?
YES
NO
REPAIR OPEN IN CKT 94.
• CONNECT THE TEST LIGHT BETWEEN TERMINAL "A" OF CONNECTOR C1 AND GROUND.
• ACTIVATE WASHER SWITCH.
• IS TEST LIGHT "ON"?
YES
NO
CHECK FOR OPEN IN CKT 96. IF OK, REPLACE WIPER WASHER SWITCH ASSEMBLY.
• CONNECT THE TEST LIGHT BETWEEN TERMINAL "B" OF CONNECTOR C2 AND GROUND.
• ACTIVATE WASHER SWITCH.
• IS TEST LIGHT "ON"?
YES
NO
REPLACE WIPER MOTOR.
CHECK FOR OPEN IN CKT 97. IF OK, REPLACE WIPER WASHER SWITCH ASSEMBLY.
WIPER/WASHER SWITCH ASSEMBLY
CIRCUIT BOARD
PARK SWITCH
WIPER MOTOR ASSEMBLY
WASHER PUMP MOTOR
GC9029100168000X

Fig. 72 Chart 6, Washer will not operate. Corvette

Permanent Magnet Positive Park System

INDEX

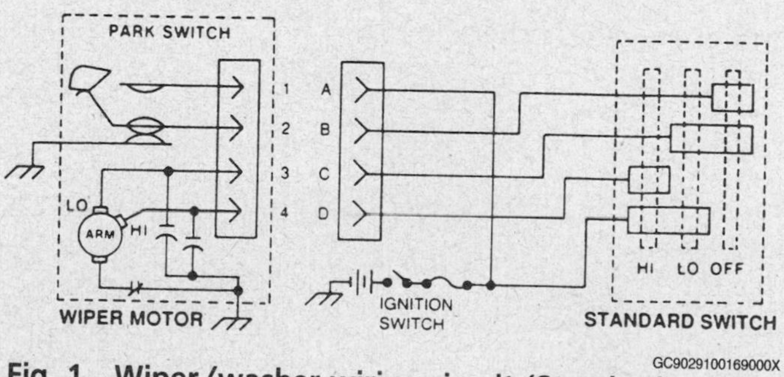

PARK SWITCH
1
2
3
4
A
B
C
D
LO
ARM
HI
HI
LO
OFF
WIPER MOTOR
IGNITION SWITCH
STANDARD SWITCH
GC9029100169000X

Fig. 1 Wiper/washer wiring circuit (Standard). 1992

DESCRIPTION

This wiper/washer system consists of a permanent magnet positive park wiper motor, a washer pump mounted on the fluid reservoir and wiper/washer control switch.

This system can be used for a standard wiper/washer system or a pulse wiper/washer system. The standard type wiper/washer system is controlled directly by the wiper/washer control switch. The pulse type wiper/washer system has a printed circuit board enclosed in the wiper housing cover that controls system functions. The printed circuit board is controlled by the wiper/washer control switch.

SYSTEM DIAGNOSIS & TESTING

1992

To properly diagnose this system refer to wiring circuits **Figs. 1 and 2** wiper motor on-vehicle check **Fig. 3**, wiper/washer switch tests **Figs. 4 and 5**, wiper/washer switch check chart **Fig. 6** and diagnosis tests **Figs. 7 through 17**.

1993–94

Refer to wiring circuits **Figs. 18 and 19** and diagnosis tests **Figs. 20 through 25** when performing system diagnosis and testing procedures.

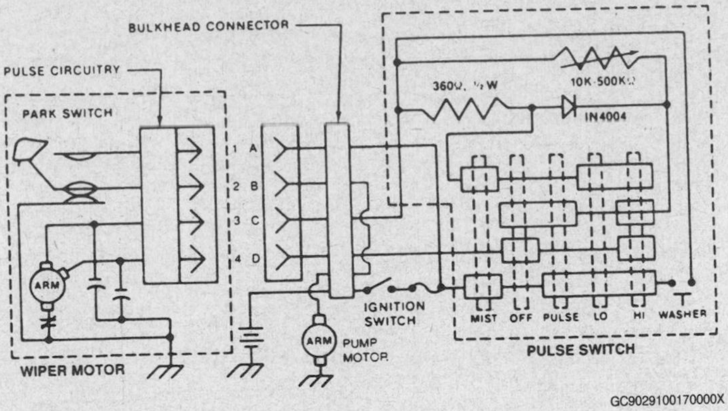
BULKHEAD CONNECTOR
PULSE CIRCUITRY
PARK SWITCH
1 A
2 B
3 C
4 D
ARM
WIPER MOTOR
ARM
PUMP MOTOR
IGNITION SWITCH
360Ω, ½ W
10K-500KΩ
IN4004
MIST OFF PULSE LO HI WASHER
PULSE SWITCH
GC9029100170000X

Fig. 2 Wiper/washer wiring circuit (Pulse). 1992

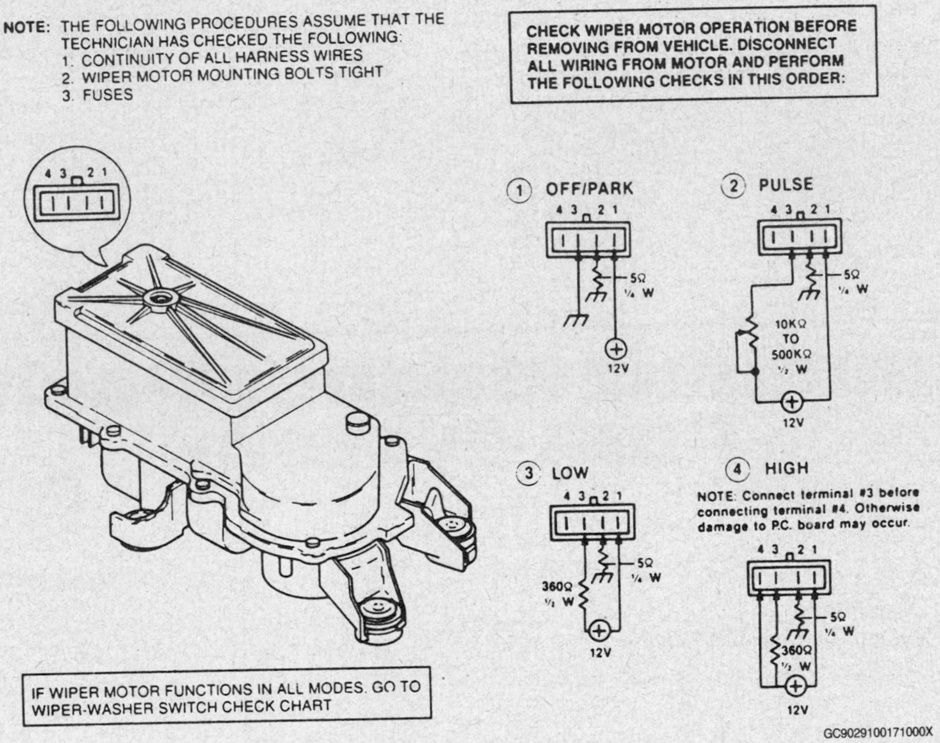
NOTE: THE FOLLOWING PROCEDURES ASSUME THAT THE TECHNICIAN HAS CHECKED THE FOLLOWING:
1. CONTINUITY OF ALL HARNESS WIRES
2. WIPER MOTOR MOUNTING BOLTS TIGHT
3. FUSES
CHECK WIPER MOTOR OPERATION BEFORE REMOVING FROM VEHICLE. DISCONNECT ALL WIRING FROM MOTOR AND PERFORM THE FOLLOWING CHECKS IN THIS ORDER:
4 3 2 1
1 OFF/PARK
5Ω ¼ W
12V
2 PULSE
10KΩ TO 500KΩ ½ W
3 LOW
360Ω ½ W
4 HIGH
NOTE: Connect terminal #3 before connecting terminal #4. Otherwise damage to P.C. board may occur.
IF WIPER MOTOR FUNCTIONS IN ALL MODES, GO TO WIPER-WASHER SWITCH CHECK CHART
GC9029100171000X

Fig. 3 Wiper motor on-vehicle check. 1992

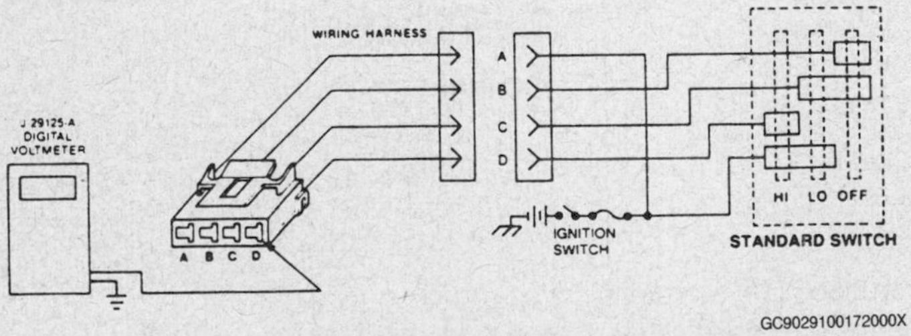
WIRING HARNESS
J 29125-A DIGITAL VOLTMETER
A B C D
IGNITION SWITCH
HI LO OFF
STANDARD SWITCH
GC9029100172000X

Fig. 4 Wiper/washer switch check (Standard). 1992

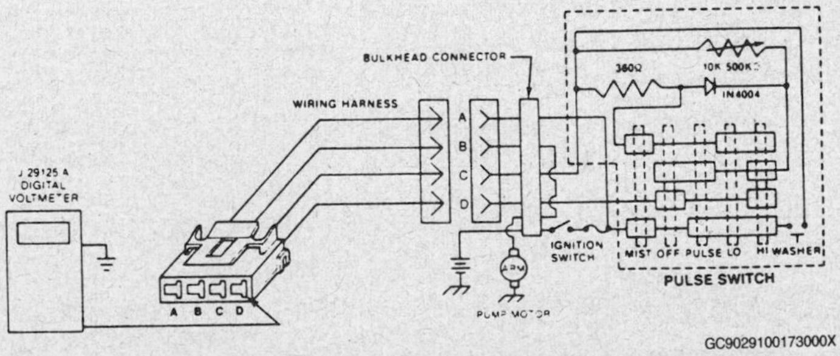
BULKHEAD CONNECTOR
WIRING HARNESS
J 29125 A DIGITAL VOLTMETER
360Ω
10K 500KΩ
IN4004
A B C D
IGNITION SWITCH
MIST OFF PULSE LO HI WASHER
PULSE SWITCH
PUMP MOTOR
GC9029100173000X

Fig. 5 Wiper/washer switch check (Pulse). 1992

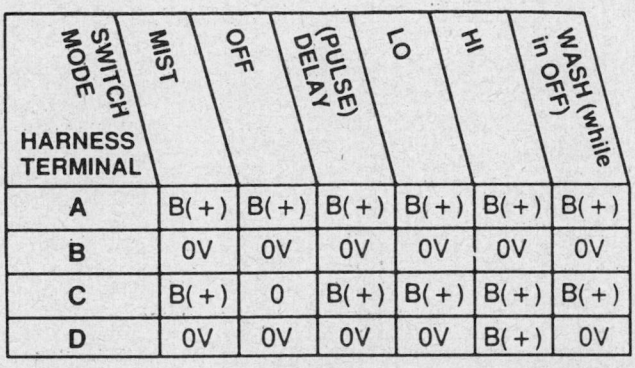

HARNESS TERMINAL \ SWITCH MODE	MIST	OFF	(PULSE) DELAY	LO	HI	WASH (while in OFF)
A	B(+)	B(+)	B(+)	B(+)	B(+)	B(+)
B	0V	0V	0V	0V	0V	0V
C	B(+)	0	B(+)	B(+)	B(+)	B(+)
D	0V	0V	0V	0V	B(+)	0V

GC9029100174000X

Fig. 6 Wiper/washer switch check chart. 1992

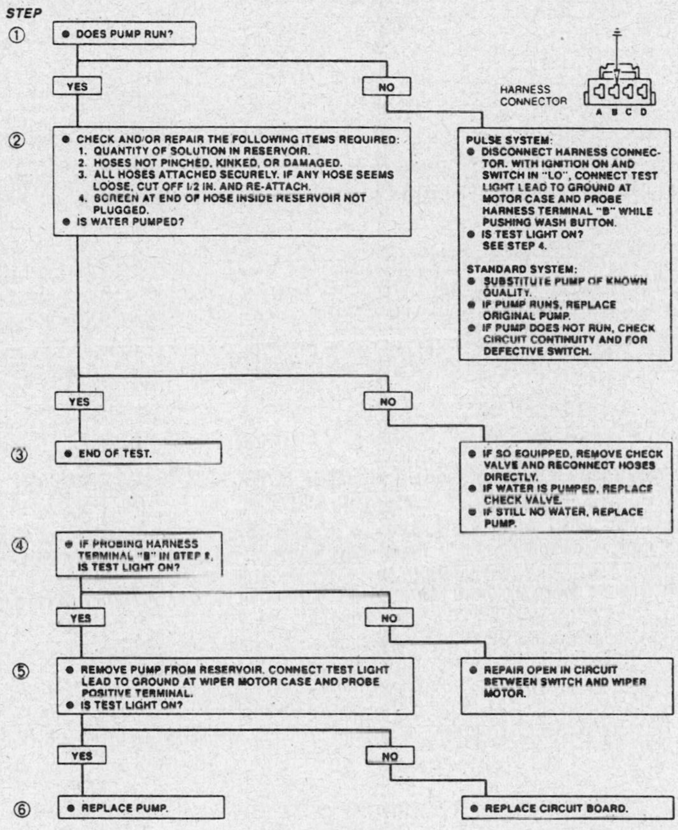
STEP
① ● DOES PUMP RUN?
YES
NO
HARNESS CONNECTOR
A B C D
② ● CHECK AND/OR REPAIR THE FOLLOWING ITEMS REQUIRED:
1. QUANTITY OF SOLUTION IN RESERVOIR.
2. HOSES NOT PINCHED, KINKED, OR DAMAGED.
3. ALL HOSES ATTACHED SECURELY. IF ANY HOSE SEEMS LOOSE, CUT OFF 1/2 IN. AND RE-ATTACH.
4. SCREEN AT END OF HOSE INSIDE RESERVOIR NOT PLUGGED.
● IS WATER PUMPED?
PULSE SYSTEM:
● DISCONNECT HARNESS CONNECTOR. WITH IGNITION ON AND SWITCH IN "LO", CONNECT TEST LIGHT LEAD TO GROUND AT MOTOR CASE AND PROBE HARNESS TERMINAL "B" WHILE PUSHING WASH BUTTON.
● IS TEST LIGHT ON? SEE STEP 4.
STANDARD SYSTEM:
● SUBSTITUTE PUMP OF KNOWN QUALITY.
● IF PUMP RUNS, REPLACE ORIGINAL PUMP.
● IF PUMP DOES NOT RUN, CHECK CIRCUIT CONTINUITY AND FOR DEFECTIVE SWITCH.
YES
NO
③ ● END OF TEST.
● IF SO EQUIPPED, REMOVE CHECK VALVE AND RECONNECT HOSES DIRECTLY.
● IF WATER IS PUMPED, REPLACE CHECK VALVE.
● IF STILL NO WATER, REPLACE PUMP.
④ ● IF PROBING HARNESS TERMINAL "B" IN STEP 2, IS TEST LIGHT ON?
YES
NO
⑤ ● REMOVE PUMP FROM RESERVOIR. CONNECT TEST LIGHT LEAD TO GROUND AT WIPER MOTOR CASE AND PROBE POSITIVE TERMINAL.
● IS TEST LIGHT ON?
● REPAIR OPEN IN CIRCUIT BETWEEN SWITCH AND WIPER MOTOR.
YES
NO
⑥ ● REPLACE PUMP.
● REPLACE CIRCUIT BOARD.
GC9029100175000X

Fig. 7 Chart 1, washer pump inoperative. 1992

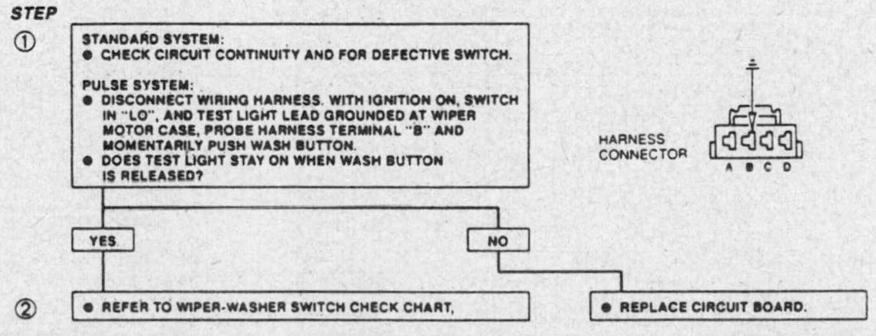
STEP
① STANDARD SYSTEM:
● CHECK CIRCUIT CONTINUITY AND FOR DEFECTIVE SWITCH.
PULSE SYSTEM:
● DISCONNECT WIRING HARNESS. WITH IGNITION ON, SWITCH IN "LO", AND TEST LIGHT LEAD GROUNDED AT WIPER MOTOR CASE, PROBE HARNESS TERMINAL "B" AND MOMENTARILY PUSH WASH BUTTON.
● DOES TEST LIGHT STAY ON WHEN WASH BUTTON IS RELEASED?
HARNESS CONNECTOR
A B C D
YES
NO
② ● REFER TO WIPER-WASHER SWITCH CHECK CHART,
● REPLACE CIRCUIT BOARD.
GC9029100176000X

Fig. 8 Chart 2, washer pumps continuously. 1992

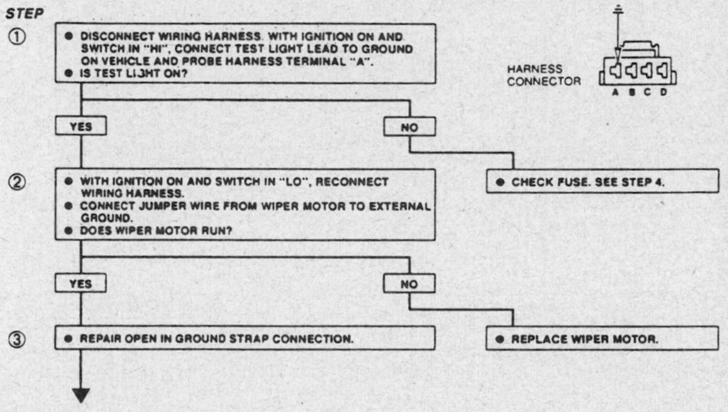
STEP
① ● DISCONNECT WIRING HARNESS. WITH IGNITION ON AND SWITCH IN "HI", CONNECT TEST LIGHT LEAD TO GROUND ON VEHICLE AND PROBE HARNESS TERMINAL "A".
● IS TEST LIGHT ON?
HARNESS CONNECTOR
A B C D
YES
NO
② ● WITH IGNITION ON AND SWITCH IN "LO", RECONNECT WIRING HARNESS.
● CONNECT JUMPER WIRE FROM WIPER MOTOR TO EXTERNAL GROUND.
● DOES WIPER MOTOR RUN?
● CHECK FUSE. SEE STEP 4.
YES
NO
③ ● REPAIR OPEN IN GROUND STRAP CONNECTION.
● REPLACE WIPER MOTOR.
GC9029100177010X

Fig. 9 Chart 3, wiper motor inoperative, (Part 1 of 2). 1992

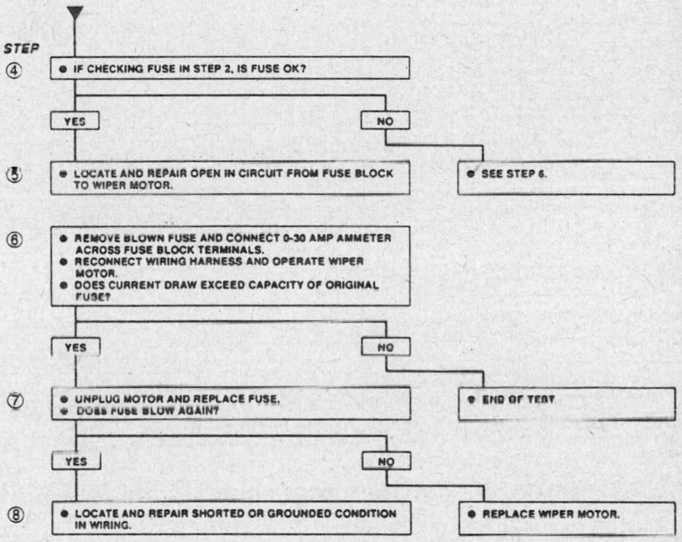
STEP
④ ● IF CHECKING FUSE IN STEP 2, IS FUSE OK?
YES
NO
⑤ ● LOCATE AND REPAIR OPEN IN CIRCUIT FROM FUSE BLOCK TO WIPER MOTOR.
● SEE STEP 6.
⑥ ● REMOVE BLOWN FUSE AND CONNECT 0-30 AMP AMMETER ACROSS FUSE BLOCK TERMINALS.
● RECONNECT WIRING HARNESS AND OPERATE WIPER MOTOR.
● DOES CURRENT DRAW EXCEED CAPACITY OF ORIGINAL FUSE?
YES
NO
⑦ ● UNPLUG MOTOR AND REPLACE FUSE.
● DOES FUSE BLOW AGAIN?
● END OF TEST
YES
NO
⑧ ● LOCATE AND REPAIR SHORTED OR GROUNDED CONDITION IN WIRING.
● REPLACE WIPER MOTOR.
GC9029100177020X

Fig. 9 Chart 3, wiper motor inoperative, (Part 2 of 2). 1992

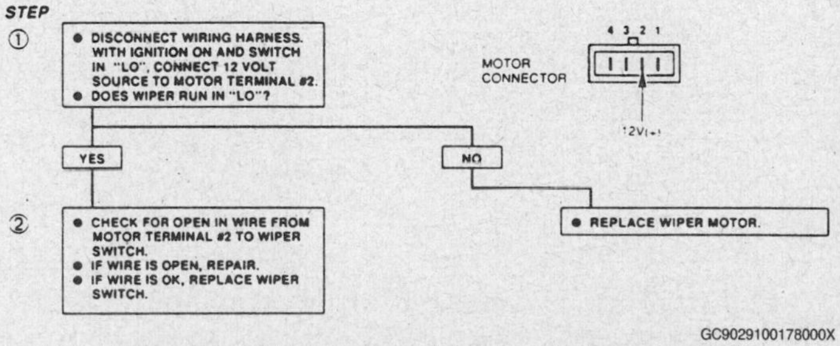
STEP
① ● DISCONNECT WIRING HARNESS. WITH IGNITION ON AND SWITCH IN "LO", CONNECT 12 VOLT SOURCE TO MOTOR TERMINAL #2.
● DOES WIPER RUN IN "LO"?
4 3 2 1
MOTOR CONNECTOR
12V(+)
YES
NO
② ● CHECK FOR OPEN IN WIRE FROM MOTOR TERMINAL #2 TO WIPER SWITCH.
● IF WIRE IS OPEN, REPAIR.
● IF WIRE IS OK, REPLACE WIPER SWITCH.
● REPLACE WIPER MOTOR.
GC9029100178000X

Fig. 10 Chart 4, no "LO" mode. 1992

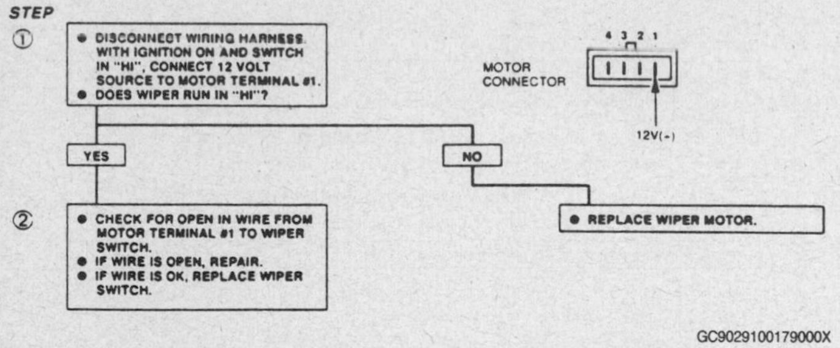
STEP
① • DISCONNECT WIRING HARNESS. WITH IGNITION ON AND SWITCH IN "HI", CONNECT 12 VOLT SOURCE TO MOTOR TERMINAL #1.
• DOES WIPER RUN IN "HI"?
MOTOR CONNECTOR
4 3 2 1
12V(+)
YES
NO
② • CHECK FOR OPEN IN WIRE FROM MOTOR TERMINAL #1 TO WIPER SWITCH.
• IF WIRE IS OPEN, REPAIR.
• IF WIRE IS OK, REPLACE WIPER SWITCH.
• REPLACE WIPER MOTOR.
GC9029100179000X

Fig. 11 Chart 5, no "HI " mode. 1992

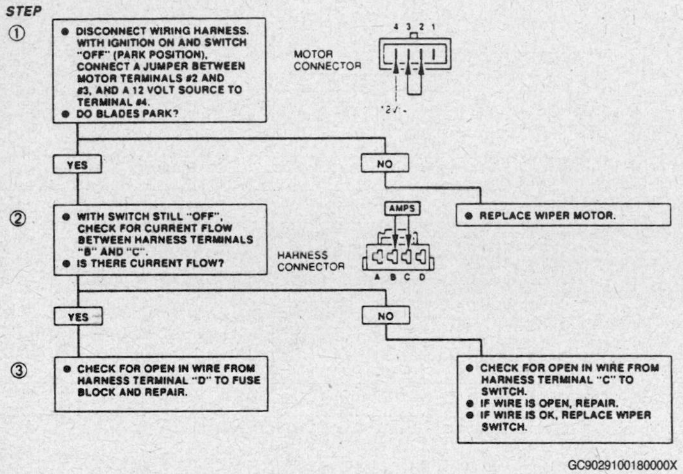
STEP
① • DISCONNECT WIRING HARNESS. WITH IGNITION ON AND SWITCH "OFF" (PARK POSITION), CONNECT A JUMPER BETWEEN MOTOR TERMINALS #2 AND #3, AND A 12 VOLT SOURCE TO TERMINAL #4.
• DO BLADES PARK?
MOTOR CONNECTOR
4 3 2 1
YES
NO
② • WITH SWITCH STILL "OFF", CHECK FOR CURRENT FLOW BETWEEN HARNESS TERMINALS "B" AND "C".
• IS THERE CURRENT FLOW?
AMPS
HARNESS CONNECTOR
A B C D
• REPLACE WIPER MOTOR.
YES
NO
③ • CHECK FOR OPEN IN WIRE FROM HARNESS TERMINAL "D" TO FUSE BLOCK AND REPAIR.
• CHECK FOR OPEN IN WIRE FROM HARNESS TERMINAL "C" TO SWITCH.
• IF WIRE IS OPEN, REPAIR.
• IF WIRE IS OK, REPLACE WIPER SWITCH.
GC9029100180000X

Fig. 12 Chart 6, wiper motor shuts off but blades do not park. 1992

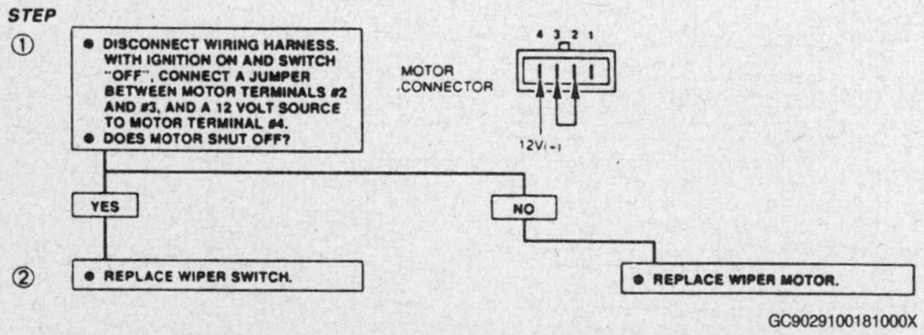
STEP
① • DISCONNECT WIRING HARNESS. WITH IGNITION ON AND SWITCH "OFF", CONNECT A JUMPER BETWEEN MOTOR TERMINALS #2 AND #3, AND A 12 VOLT SOURCE TO MOTOR TERMINAL #4.
• DOES MOTOR SHUT OFF?
MOTOR CONNECTOR
4 3 2 1
12V(+)
YES
NO
② • REPLACE WIPER SWITCH.
• REPLACE WIPER MOTOR.
GC9029100181000X

Fig. 13 Chart 7, wiper motor will not shut off. 1992

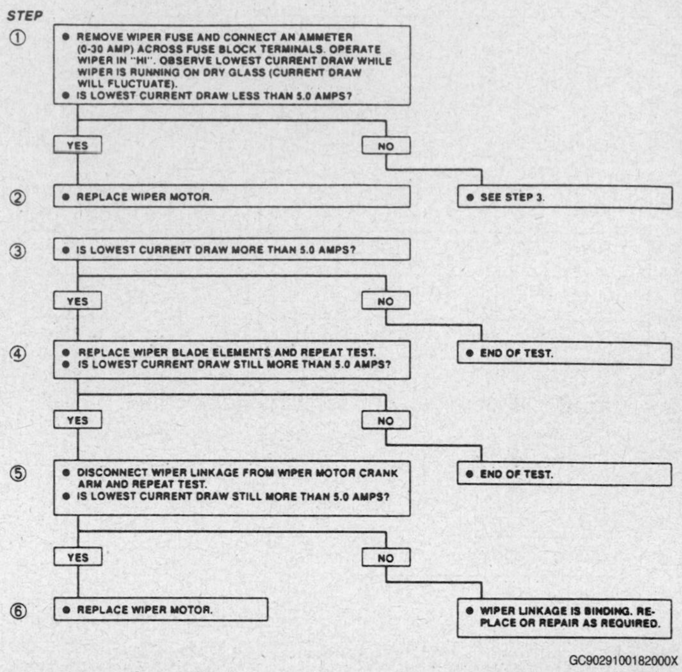
STEP
① • REMOVE WIPER FUSE AND CONNECT AN AMMETER (0-30 AMP) ACROSS FUSE BLOCK TERMINALS. OPERATE WIPER IN "HI". OBSERVE LOWEST CURRENT DRAW WHILE WIPER IS RUNNING ON DRY GLASS (CURRENT DRAW WILL FLUCTUATE).
• IS LOWEST CURRENT DRAW LESS THAN 5.0 AMPS?
YES
NO
② • REPLACE WIPER MOTOR.
• SEE STEP 3.
③ • IS LOWEST CURRENT DRAW MORE THAN 5.0 AMPS?
YES
NO
④ • REPLACE WIPER BLADE ELEMENTS AND REPEAT TEST.
• IS LOWEST CURRENT DRAW STILL MORE THAN 5.0 AMPS?
• END OF TEST.
YES
NO
⑤ • DISCONNECT WIPER LINKAGE FROM WIPER MOTOR CRANK ARM AND REPEAT TEST.
• IS LOWEST CURRENT DRAW STILL MORE THAN 5.0 AMPS?
• END OF TEST.
YES
NO
⑥ • REPLACE WIPER MOTOR.
• WIPER LINKAGE IS BINDING. REPLACE OR REPAIR AS REQUIRED.
GC9029100182000X

Fig. 14 Chart 8, intermittent wiper operation in "LO" of "HI" modes, blades stop at random positions. 1992

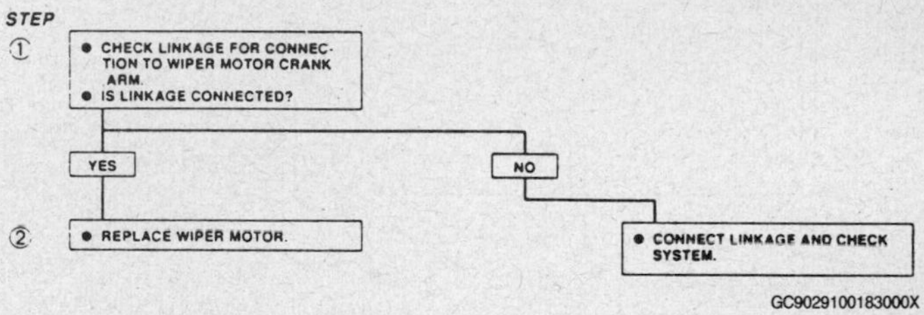
STEP
① • CHECK LINKAGE FOR CONNECTION TO WIPER MOTOR CRANK ARM.
• IS LINKAGE CONNECTED?
YES
NO
② • REPLACE WIPER MOTOR.
• CONNECT LINKAGE AND CHECK SYSTEM.
GC9029100183000X

Fig. 15 Chart 9, wiper motor runs, but blades do not move. 1992

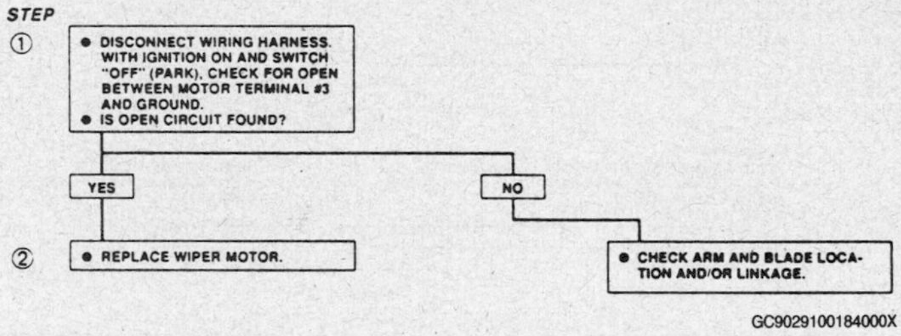
STEP
① • DISCONNECT WIRING HARNESS. WITH IGNITION ON AND SWITCH "OFF" (PARK), CHECK FOR OPEN BETWEEN MOTOR TERMINAL #3 AND GROUND.
• IS OPEN CIRCUIT FOUND?
YES
NO
② • REPLACE WIPER MOTOR.
• CHECK ARM AND BLADE LOCATION AND/OR LINKAGE.
GC9029100184000X

Fig. 16 Chart 10, blades park above park position. 1992

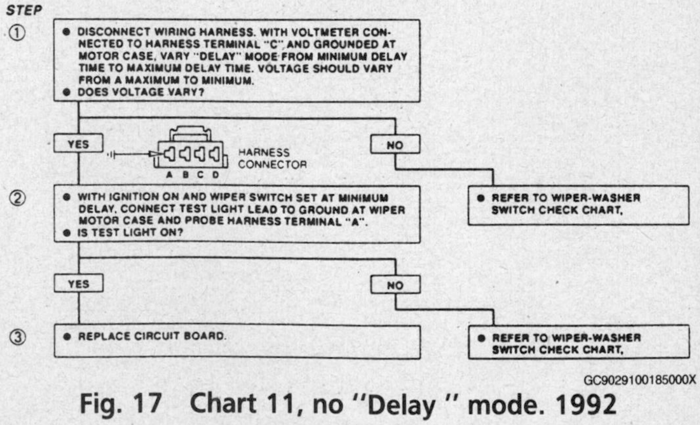
STEP
① • DISCONNECT WIRING HARNESS. WITH VOLTMETER CONNECTED TO HARNESS TERMINAL "C" AND GROUNDED AT MOTOR CASE, VARY "DELAY" MODE FROM MINIMUM DELAY TIME TO MAXIMUM DELAY TIME. VOLTAGE SHOULD VARY FROM A MAXIMUM TO MINIMUM.
• DOES VOLTAGE VARY?
YES
HARNESS CONNECTOR
A B C D
NO
② • WITH IGNITION ON AND WIPER SWITCH SET AT MINIMUM DELAY, CONNECT TEST LIGHT LEAD TO GROUND AT WIPER MOTOR CASE AND PROBE HARNESS TERMINAL "A".
• IS TEST LIGHT ON?
• REFER TO WIPER-WASHER SWITCH CHECK CHART.
YES
NO
③ • REPLACE CIRCUIT BOARD.
• REFER TO WIPER-WASHER SWITCH CHECK CHART.
GC9029100185000X

Fig. 17 Chart 11, no "Delay " mode. 1992

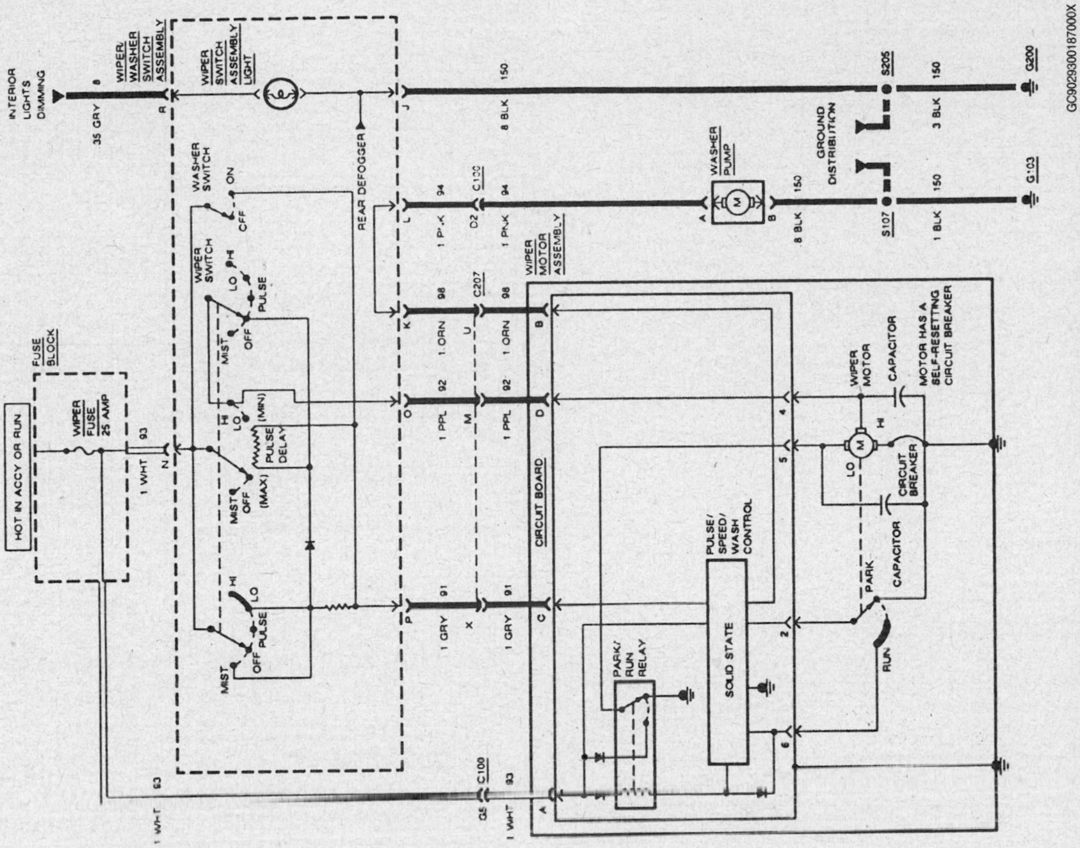
HOT IN ACCY OR RUN
FUSE BLOCK
WIPER FUSE 25 AMP
INTERIOR LIGHTS DIMMING
WIPER WASHER SWITCH ASSEMBLY
WIPER SWITCH ASSEMBLY LIGHT
WASHER SWITCH
WIPER SWITCH
REAR DEFOGGER
PULSE DELAY
CIRCUIT BOARD
PARK/ RUN RELAY
SOLID STATE
PULSE/ SPEED/ WASH CONTROL
WIPER MOTOR
CAPACITOR
CIRCUIT BREAKER
MOTOR HAS A SELF-RESETTING CIRCUIT BREAKER
WIPER MOTOR ASSEMBLY
WASHER PUMP
GROUND DISTRIBUTION
GC9029300187000X

Fig. 19 Wiper/washer system wiring circuit (Pulse). 1993–94

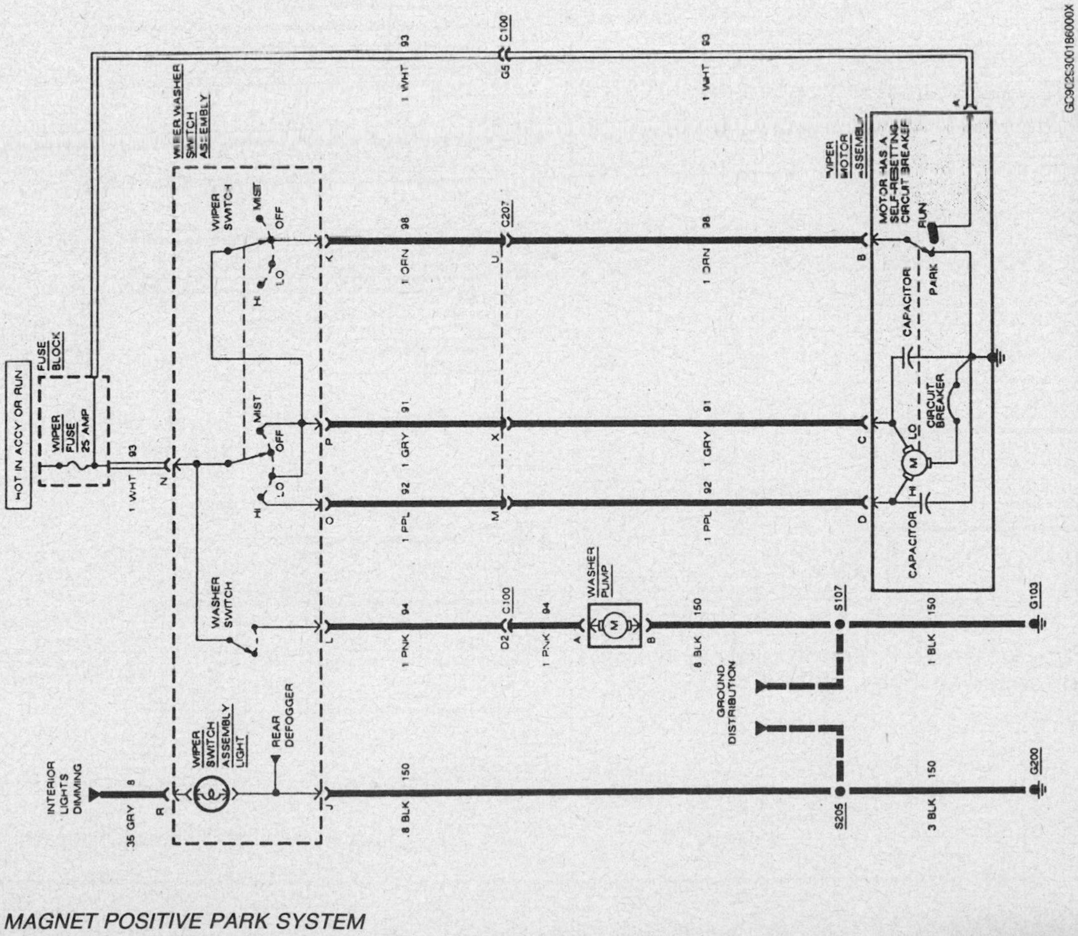
HOT IN ACCY OR RUN
FUSE BLOCK
WIPER FUSE 25 AMP
INTERIOR LIGHTS DIMMING
WIPER WASHER SWITCH ASSEMBLY
WIPER SWITCH ASSEMBLY LIGHT
WASHER SWITCH
WIPER SWITCH
REAR DEFOGGER
WASHER PUMP
GROUND DISTRIBUTION
WIPER MOTOR ASSEMBLY
MOTOR HAS A SELF-RESETTING CIRCUIT BREAKER
CAPACITOR
CIRCUIT BREAKER
GC9C2530018600X

Fig. 18 Wiper/washer system wiring circuit (Standard). 1993–94

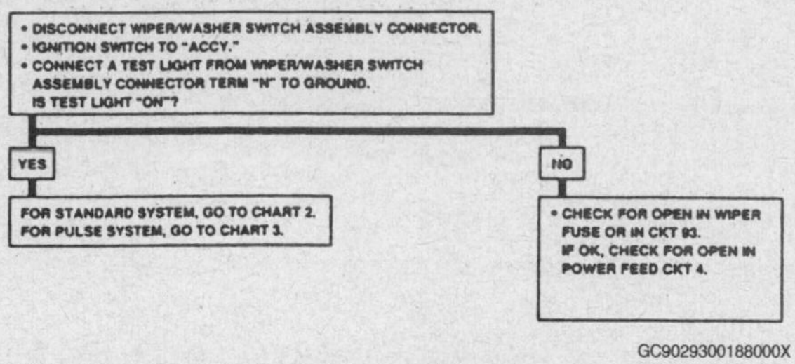
• DISCONNECT WIPER/WASHER SWITCH ASSEMBLY CONNECTOR.
• IGNITION SWITCH TO "ACCY."
• CONNECT A TEST LIGHT FROM WIPER/WASHER SWITCH ASSEMBLY CONNECTOR TERM "N" TO GROUND.
IS TEST LIGHT "ON"?
YES
NO
FOR STANDARD SYSTEM, GO TO CHART 2.
FOR PULSE SYSTEM, GO TO CHART 3.
• CHECK FOR OPEN IN WIPER FUSE OR IN CKT 93.
IF OK, CHECK FOR OPEN IN POWER FEED CKT 4.
GC9029300188000X

Fig. 20 Chart 1, wipers do not operate in any mode. 1993–94

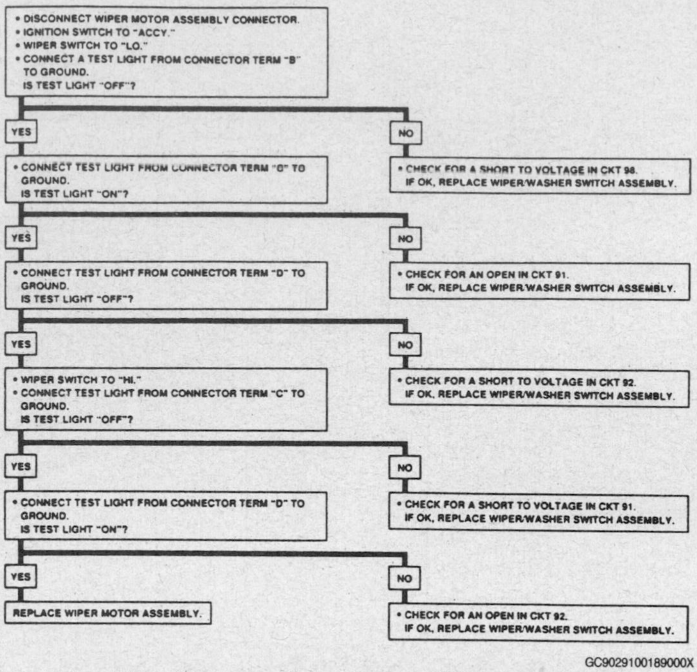
• DISCONNECT WIPER MOTOR ASSEMBLY CONNECTOR.
• IGNITION SWITCH TO "ACCY."
• WIPER SWITCH TO "LO."
• CONNECT A TEST LIGHT FROM CONNECTOR TERM "B" TO GROUND.
IS TEST LIGHT "OFF"?
YES
NO
• CONNECT TEST LIGHT FROM CONNECTOR TERM "C" TO GROUND.
IS TEST LIGHT "ON"?
• CHECK FOR A SHORT TO VOLTAGE IN CKT 98.
IF OK, REPLACE WIPER/WASHER SWITCH ASSEMBLY.
YES
NO
• CONNECT TEST LIGHT FROM CONNECTOR TERM "D" TO GROUND.
IS TEST LIGHT "OFF"?
• CHECK FOR AN OPEN IN CKT 91.
IF OK, REPLACE WIPER/WASHER SWITCH ASSEMBLY.
YES
NO
• WIPER SWITCH TO "HI."
• CONNECT TEST LIGHT FROM CONNECTOR TERM "C" TO GROUND.
IS TEST LIGHT "OFF"?
• CHECK FOR A SHORT TO VOLTAGE IN CKT 92.
IF OK, REPLACE WIPER/WASHER SWITCH ASSEMBLY.
YES
NO
• CONNECT TEST LIGHT FROM CONNECTOR TERM "D" TO GROUND.
IS TEST LIGHT "ON"?
• CHECK FOR A SHORT TO VOLTAGE IN CKT 91.
IF OK, REPLACE WIPER/WASHER SWITCH ASSEMBLY.
YES
NO
REPLACE WIPER MOTOR ASSEMBLY.
• CHECK FOR AN OPEN IN CKT 92.
IF OK, REPLACE WIPER/WASHER SWITCH ASSEMBLY.
GC9029100189000X

Fig. 21 Chart 2, wipers run at high speed only. 1993–94

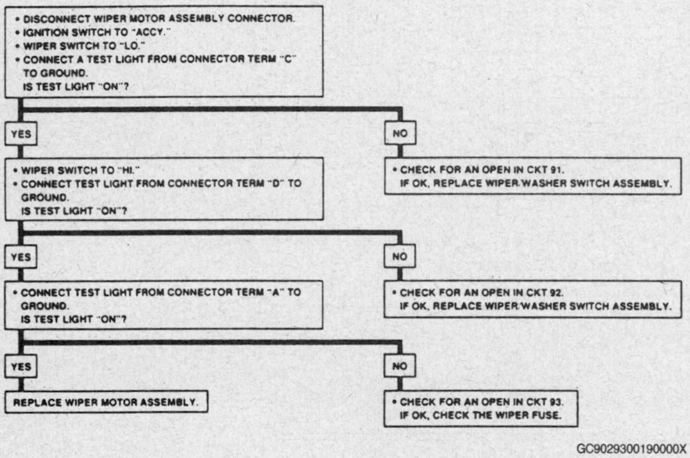
• DISCONNECT WIPER MOTOR ASSEMBLY CONNECTOR.
• IGNITION SWITCH TO "ACCY."
• WIPER SWITCH TO "LO."
• CONNECT A TEST LIGHT FROM CONNECTOR TERM "C" TO GROUND.
IS TEST LIGHT "ON"?
YES
NO
• WIPER SWITCH TO "HI."
• CONNECT TEST LIGHT FROM CONNECTOR TERM "D" TO GROUND.
IS TEST LIGHT "ON"?
• CHECK FOR AN OPEN IN CKT 91.
IF OK, REPLACE WIPER/WASHER SWITCH ASSEMBLY.
YES
NO
• CONNECT TEST LIGHT FROM CONNECTOR TERM "A" TO GROUND.
IS TEST LIGHT "ON"?
• CHECK FOR AN OPEN IN CKT 92.
IF OK, REPLACE WIPER/WASHER SWITCH ASSEMBLY.
YES
NO
REPLACE WIPER MOTOR ASSEMBLY.
• CHECK FOR AN OPEN IN CKT 93.
IF OK, CHECK THE WIPER FUSE.
GC9029300190000X

Fig. 22 Chart 3, wipers run at low speed only. 1993–94

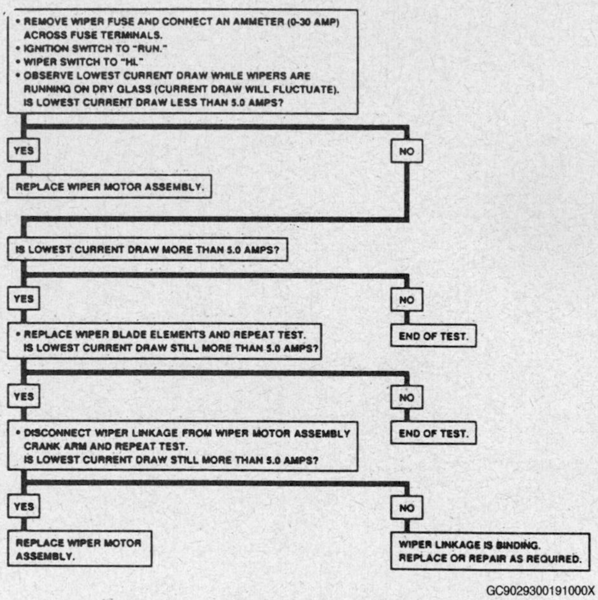
• REMOVE WIPER FUSE AND CONNECT AN AMMETER (0-30 AMP) ACROSS FUSE TERMINALS.
• IGNITION SWITCH TO "RUN."
• WIPER SWITCH TO "HI."
• OBSERVE LOWEST CURRENT DRAW WHILE WIPERS ARE RUNNING ON DRY GLASS (CURRENT DRAW WILL FLUCTUATE).
IS LOWEST CURRENT DRAW LESS THAN 5.0 AMPS?
YES
NO
REPLACE WIPER MOTOR ASSEMBLY.
IS LOWEST CURRENT DRAW MORE THAN 5.0 AMPS?
YES
NO
• REPLACE WIPER BLADE ELEMENTS AND REPEAT TEST.
IS LOWEST CURRENT DRAW STILL MORE THAN 5.0 AMPS?
END OF TEST.
YES
NO
• DISCONNECT WIPER LINKAGE FROM WIPER MOTOR ASSEMBLY CRANK ARM AND REPEAT TEST.
IS LOWEST CURRENT DRAW STILL MORE THAN 5.0 AMPS?
END OF TEST.
YES
NO
REPLACE WIPER MOTOR ASSEMBLY.
WIPER LINKAGE IS BINDING.
REPLACE OR REPAIR AS REQUIRED.
GC9029300191000X

Fig. 23 Chart 4, wipers will not turn off. 1993–94

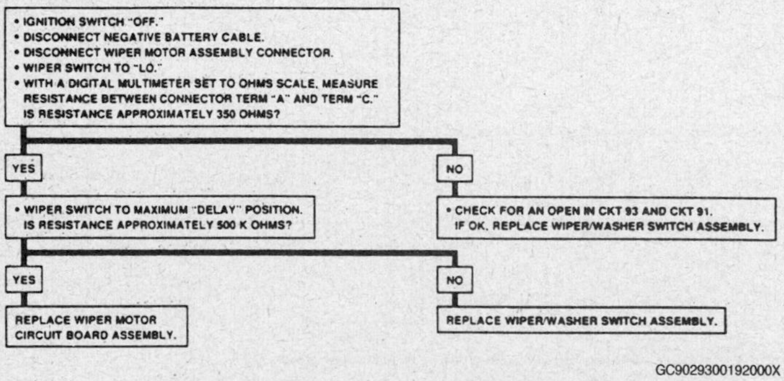
• IGNITION SWITCH "OFF."
• DISCONNECT NEGATIVE BATTERY CABLE.
• DISCONNECT WIPER MOTOR ASSEMBLY CONNECTOR.
• WIPER SWITCH TO "LO."
• WITH A DIGITAL MULTIMETER SET TO OHMS SCALE, MEASURE RESISTANCE BETWEEN CONNECTOR TERM "A" AND TERM "C."
IS RESISTANCE APPROXIMATELY 350 OHMS?
YES
NO
• WIPER SWITCH TO MAXIMUM "DELAY" POSITION.
IS RESISTANCE APPROXIMATELY 500 K OHMS?
• CHECK FOR AN OPEN IN CKT 93 AND CKT 91.
IF OK, REPLACE WIPER/WASHER SWITCH ASSEMBLY.
YES
NO
REPLACE WIPER MOTOR CIRCUIT BOARD ASSEMBLY.
REPLACE WIPER/WASHER SWITCH ASSEMBLY.
GC9029300192000X

Fig. 24 Chart 5, wipers run intermittently in low or high speed settings. 1993–94

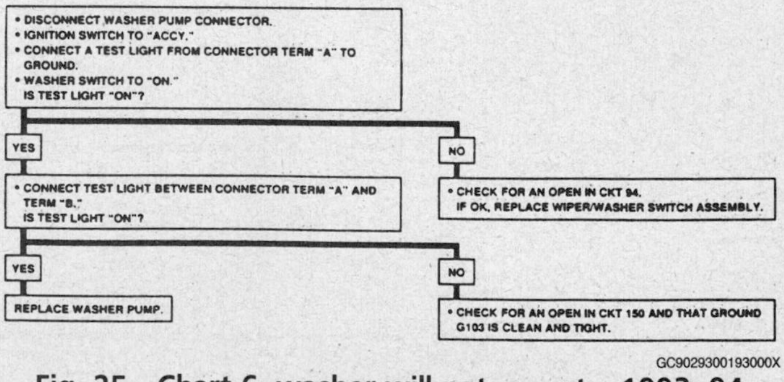
• DISCONNECT WASHER PUMP CONNECTOR.
• IGNITION SWITCH TO "ACCY."
• CONNECT A TEST LIGHT FROM CONNECTOR TERM "A" TO GROUND.
• WASHER SWITCH TO "ON."
IS TEST LIGHT "ON"?
YES
NO
• CONNECT TEST LIGHT BETWEEN CONNECTOR TERM "A" AND TERM "B."
IS TEST LIGHT "ON"?
• CHECK FOR AN OPEN IN CKT 94.
IF OK, REPLACE WIPER/WASHER SWITCH ASSEMBLY.
YES
NO
REPLACE WASHER PUMP.
• CHECK FOR AN OPEN IN CKT 150 AND THAT GROUND G103 IS CLEAN AND TIGHT.
GC9029300193000X

Fig. 25 Chart 6, washer will not operate. 1993–94

Multiplex Pulse Wiper System

INDEX

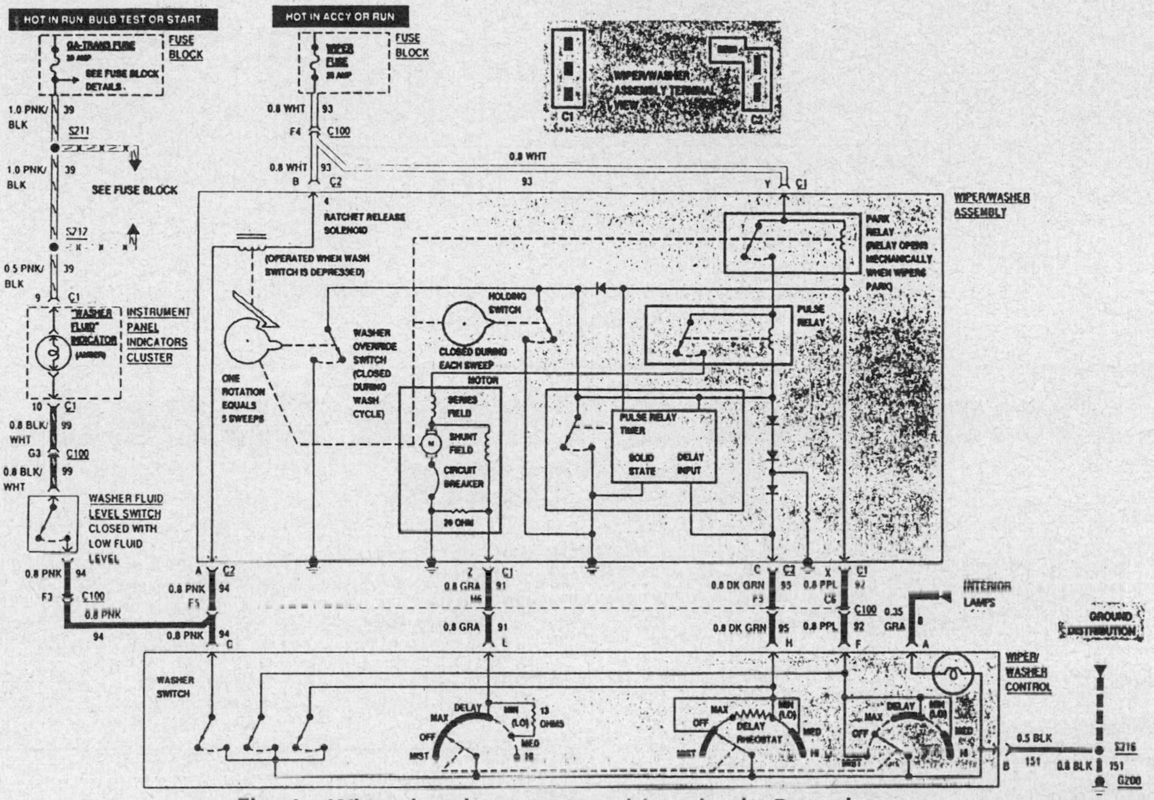

HOT IN RUN, BULB TEST OR START
HOT IN ACCY OR RUN
FUSE BLOCK
SEE FUSE BLOCK
INSTRUMENT PANEL INDICATORS CLUSTER
WASHER FLUID LEVEL SWITCH CLOSED WITH LOW FLUID LEVEL
RATCHET RELEASE SOLENOID
(OPERATED WHEN WASH SWITCH IS DEPRESSED)
ONE ROTATION EQUALS 5 SWEEPS
WASHER OVERRIDE SWITCH (CLOSED DURING WASH CYCLE)
HOLDING SWITCH
CLOSED DURING EACH SWEEP
MOTOR
SERIES FIELD
SHUNT FIELD
CIRCUIT BREAKER
20 OHM
PULSE RELAY TIMER
SOLID STATE
DELAY INPUT
PARK RELAY (RELAY OPENS MECHANICALLY WHEN WIPERS PARK)
PULSE RELAY
WIPER/WASHER ASSEMBLY
INTERIOR LAMPS
GROUND DISTRIBUTION
WASHER SWITCH
WIPER/WASHER CONTROL
DELAY
MAX
OFF
MIST
MIN (LO)
13 OHMS
MED
HI
DELAY RHEOSTAT

Fig 1 Wiper/washer system wiring circuit. Brougham

GC9029100194000X

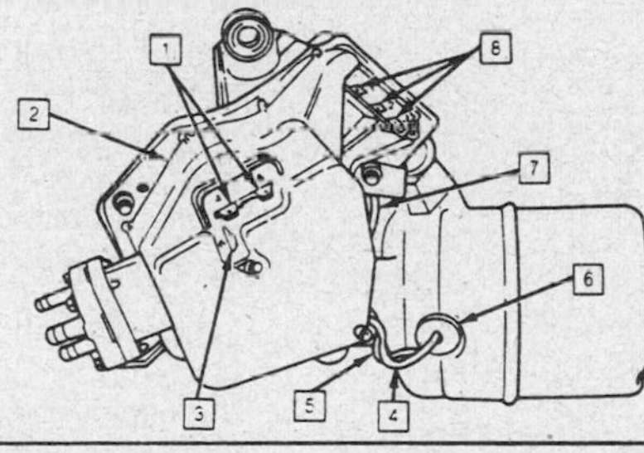

1. WASHER PUMP RELAY TERMINALS
2. DARK GRAY COVER
3. TIMING CIRCUIT TERMINAL
4. BLACK WITH PINK STRIPE WIRE (12V DC TO MOTOR WINDINGS FROM PULSE RELAY)
5. BLACK WIRE (MOTOR SHUNT FIELD GROUND WIRE)
6. MOTOR GROMMET
7. RED WIRE (12V DC TO PULSE RELAY)
8. WIPER MOTOR TERMINALS (PARK RELAY)

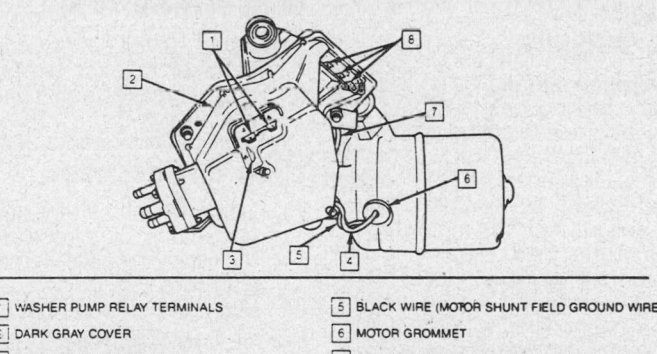

GC9029100195000X

Fig. 2 Multiplex pulse wiper motor & pump assembly (Cover in place). Brougham

DESCRIPTION

The multiplex pulse wiper system provides a controlled wiping action. The system can be identified by a single electrical lead to the timing circuit.

The wiper switch in "DELAY" mode can be varied from minimum to a maximum position by moving the control knob. The delay can vary from 0 to 12 seconds depending on the position of the knob.

The multiplex pulse wiper motor less the washer pump is the same as the stock standard depressed park wiper motor except for the concealed electrical leads.

When the motor is at low speed the motor shunt field is connected directly to ground at the control switch and there is no external resistance.

When the motor is at medium speed the shunt field is connected to ground through two external resistors (one 20 ohm resistor located in the parking relay and one 13 ohm resistor located in the control switch). The resistors are connected in parallel which provides an equivalent resistance of approximately 8 ohms.

When the motor is at high speed the circuit is open at the control switch and completed to ground through the 20 ohm resistor in the parking relay.

When the motor is in the pulse or delay mode, the parking relay coil ground circuit is maintained at the control switch which keeps it energized. This maintains the 12 volt DC current to the pulse relay coil. The relay coil ground circuit is opened at the control switch and the timing circuit controls the ground circuit.

SYSTEM DIAGNOSIS & TESTING

Refer to wiring circuit **Fig. 1** and terminal identification in **Figs. 2 & 3** for continuity and ground checks.

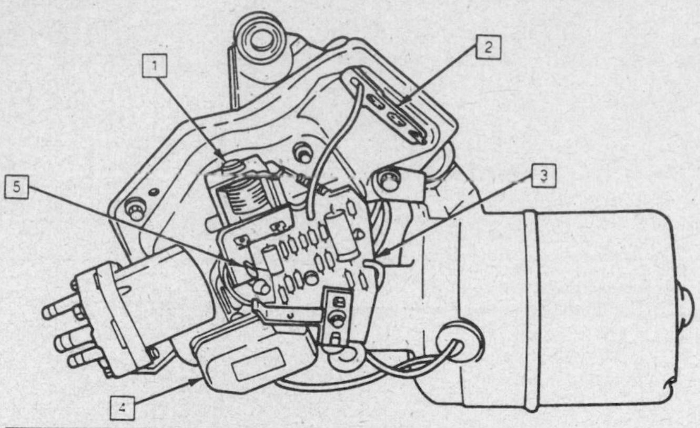
1
2
3
4
5

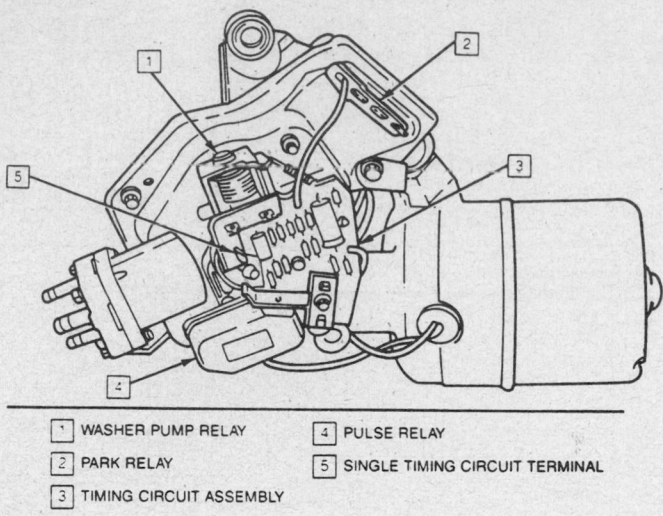

1 WASHER PUMP RELAY
2 PARK RELAY
3 TIMING CIRCUIT ASSEMBLY
4 PULSE RELAY
5 SINGLE TIMING CIRCUIT TERMINAL

GC9029100196000X

Fig. 3 Multiplex pulse wiper motor & pump assembly (Cover removed). Brougham

One, Two & Three Speed Systems

INDEX

DESCRIPTION

METRO

Standard (Non-Pulse) Wiper Operation

When the wiper switch is on low, battery voltage is applied to the wiper motor through the blue wire. When the wiper switch is in high, battery voltage is applied directly to motor through the blue/red wire to the high speed brushes.

When the wiper switch is turned off, the run/park switch in the wiper motor is still in the Run position. Voltage is still applied to the wiper motor at the low speed brushes through the run/park switch, blue/white and blue wires.

Pulse Wiper Operation

When the wiper switch is in delay position, a shunt is applied to two of the inputs at the pulse wiper relay by the wiper switch to start the pulse operation. The pulse wiper relay momentarily supplies battery voltage to wiper switch to run wiper motor. The wiper blades make one sweep and reach park, the park/run switch opens. The wiper blades remain in park until the pulse wiper relay supplies battery voltage to start another sweep. The delay time between sweeps is determined by circuits in the pulse wiper relay.

PRIZM & STORM

Windshield wiper operation is controlled by a dash or steering column mounted switch. The wiper feed circuit is protected by a fuse which is located in the fuse block on most models, or in an inline fuse holder on some models with pulse wipers. A circuit breaker, integral with the motor brush holder, protects the motor against overload. Pulse wipers, available on most models, use a variable resistor, a pulse control module, and/or a modified wiper motor to provide a delay wipe mode.

SYSTEM DIAGNOSIS & TESTING

METRO

Refer to **Fig. 1** for wiring circuit and **Figs. 5 and 6,** for complete system diagnosis and testing.

WIPER SWITCH TEST

Inspect wiper and washer switch for continuity, refer to **Fig. 7,** for switch connections.

WIPER MOTOR TEST

Low Speed Test

1. Using 12 volt battery, connect positive terminal to blue terminal on motor, and negative terminal to black lead wire **Fig. 8.**
2. Motor should rotate at 45 to 55 RPM.

High Speed Test

1. Using 12 volt battery, connect positive terminal to blue/red terminal on motor, and negative terminal to black lead wire **Fig. 8.**
2. Motor should rotate at 68 to 78 RPM.

Park Operation Test

1. Use 12 volt battery, connect positive terminal to yellow/blue terminal on motor, and negative terminal to black lead wire **Fig. 8.**
2. Using a jumper short the blue/white and blue terminals to each other.
3. Check whether motor shaft stops at a given position. **This position must conform to the start position.**
4. Repeat step 2 to confirm that shaft stops at the same position.

Checking Brush & Commutator

1. Check continuity between blue termi-

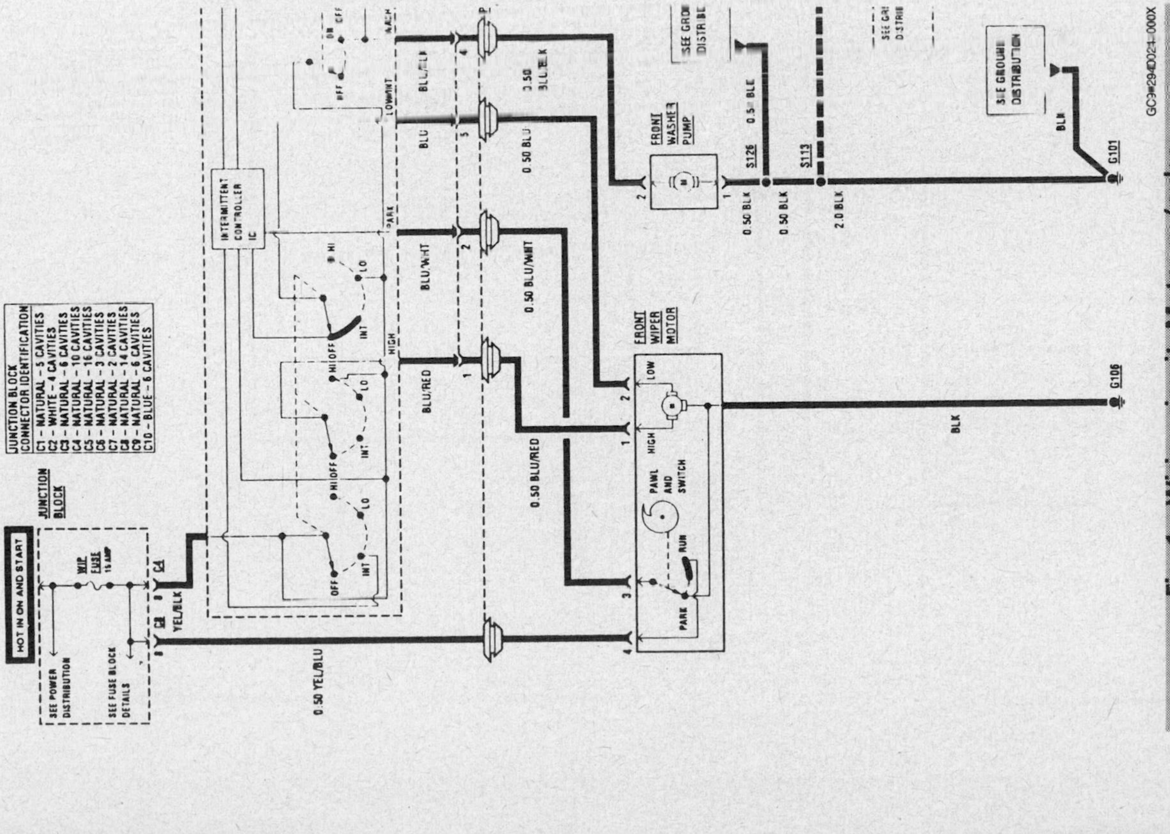
HOT IN ON AND START
JUNCTION BLOCK
WIP FUSE 15 AMP
SEE POWER DISTRIBUTION
SEE FUSE BLOCK DETAILS
JUNCTION BLOCK CONNECTOR IDENTIFICATION
C1 - NATURAL - 5 CAVITIES
C2 - WHITE - 4 CAVITIES
C3 - NATURAL - 6 CAVITIES
C4 - NATURAL - 10 CAVITIES
C5 - NATURAL - 16 CAVITIES
C6 - NATURAL - 3 CAVITIES
C7 - NATURAL - 2 CAVITIES
C8 - NATURAL - 14 CAVITIES
C9 - NATURAL - 6 CAVITIES
C10 - BLUE - 6 CAVITIES
INTERMITTENT CONTROLLER IC
0.50 YEL/BLU
YEL/BLK
BLU/RED
0.50 BLU/RED
BLU/WHT
0.50 BLU/WHT
BLU
0.50 BLU
BLU/BLK
0.50 BLU/BLK
FRONT WIPER MOTOR
PAWL AND SWITCH
PARK
RUN
HIGH
LOW
FRONT WASHER PUMP
S126
S113
0.50 BLK
2.0 BLK
BLK
G106
G101
SEE GROUND DISTRIBUTION
GC3#294D021-000X
Fig. 1 Wiring circuit. Metro w/pulse

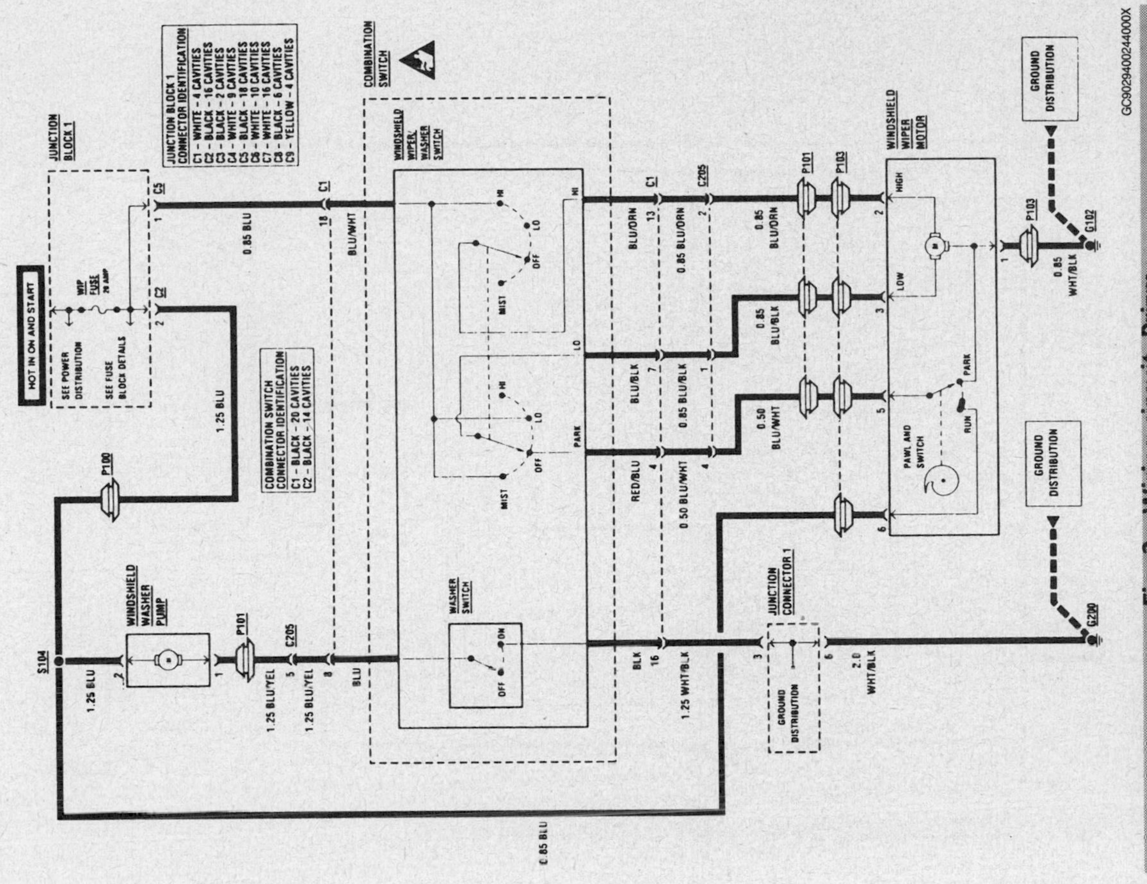
HOT IN ON AND START
JUNCTION BLOCK 1
WIP FUSE 20 AMP
SEE POWER DISTRIBUTION
SEE FUSE BLOCK DETAILS
JUNCTION BLOCK 1 CONNECTOR IDENTIFICATION
C1 - WHITE - 4 CAVITIES
C2 - BLACK - 16 CAVITIES
C3 - BLACK - 2 CAVITIES
C4 - WHITE - 9 CAVITIES
C5 - BLACK - 18 CAVITIES
C6 - WHITE - 10 CAVITIES
C7 - WHITE - 16 CAVITIES
C8 - BLACK - 6 CAVITIES
C9 - YELLOW - 4 CAVITIES
COMBINATION SWITCH
COMBINATION SWITCH CONNECTOR IDENTIFICATION
C1 - BLACK - 20 CAVITIES
C2 - BLACK - 14 CAVITIES
WINDSHIELD WIPER/WASHER SWITCH
WASHER SWITCH
WINDSHIELD WASHER PUMP
WINDSHIELD WIPER MOTOR
PAWL AND SWITCH
JUNCTION CONNECTOR 1
GROUND DISTRIBUTION
P100
P101
P103
S104
C205
G102
G200
0.85 BLU
1.25 BLU
BLU/WHT
BLU/ORN
0.85 BLU/ORN
BLU/BLK
0.85 BLU/BLK
RED/BLU
0.50 BLU/WHT
1.25 BLU/YEL
BLK
1.25 WHT/BLK
2.0 WHT/BLK
0.85 WHT/BLK
GC9029400244000X
Fig. 2 Wiring circuit. Prizm

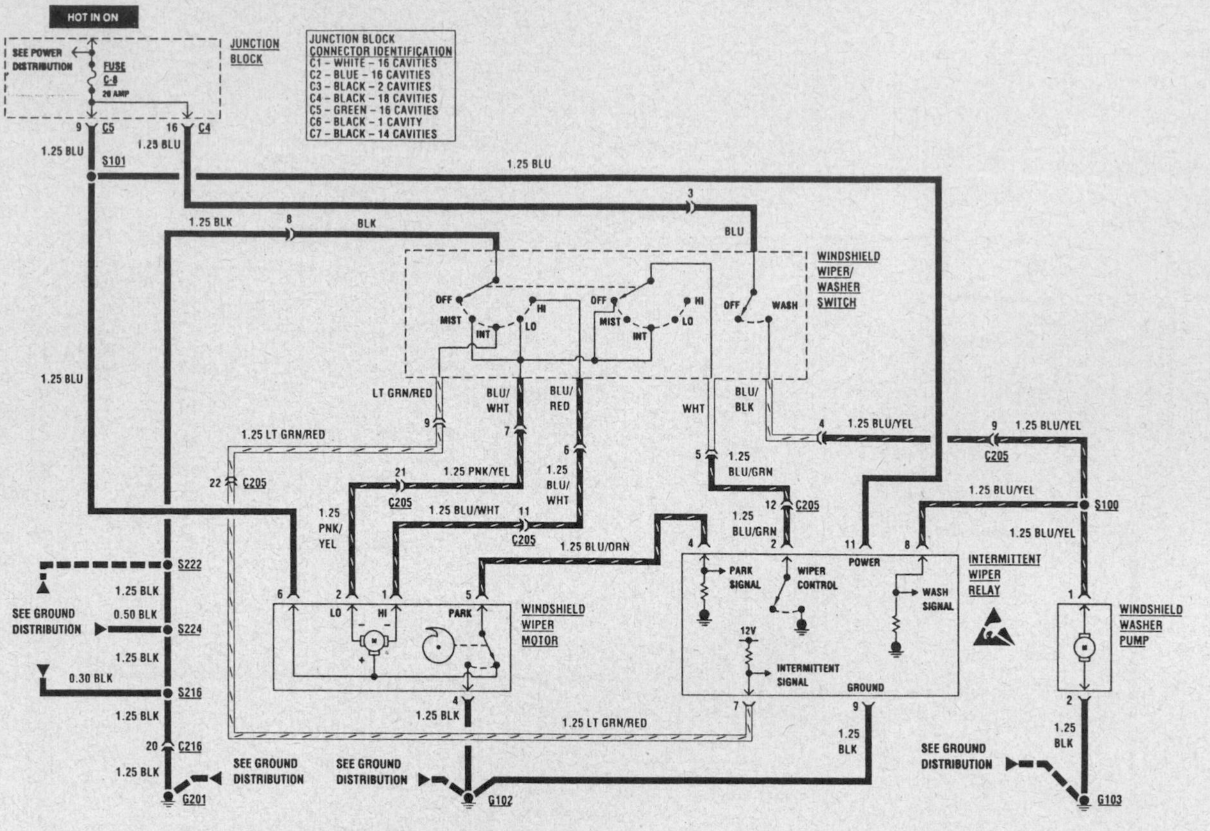
HOT IN ON
SEE POWER DISTRIBUTION
FUSE C-8 20 AMP
JUNCTION BLOCK
JUNCTION BLOCK CONNECTOR IDENTIFICATION
C1 – WHITE – 16 CAVITIES
C2 – BLUE – 16 CAVITIES
C3 – BLACK – 2 CAVITIES
C4 – BLACK – 18 CAVITIES
C5 – GREEN – 16 CAVITIES
C6 – BLACK – 1 CAVITY
C7 – BLACK – 14 CAVITIES
1.25 BLU
S101
1.25 BLK
BLK
BLU
WINDSHIELD WIPER/ WASHER SWITCH
OFF
MIST
INT
HI
LO
WASH
LT GRN/RED
BLU/ WHT
BLU/ RED
WHT
BLU/ BLK
1.25 BLU/YEL
C205
1.25 LT GRN/RED
1.25 PNK/YEL
1.25 BLU/ WHT
1.25 BLU/GRN
1.25 PNK/ YEL
1.25 BLU/WHT
1.25 BLU/ORN
S100
POWER
INTERMITTENT WIPER RELAY
PARK SIGNAL
WIPER CONTROL
WASH SIGNAL
12V
INTERMITTENT SIGNAL
GROUND
S222
SEE GROUND DISTRIBUTION
0.50 BLK
S224
0.30 BLK
S216
C216
WINDSHIELD WIPER MOTOR
PARK
WINDSHIELD WASHER PUMP
G201
G102
G103

GC9029300245000X

Fig. 3 Wiring circuit. Storm w/pulse

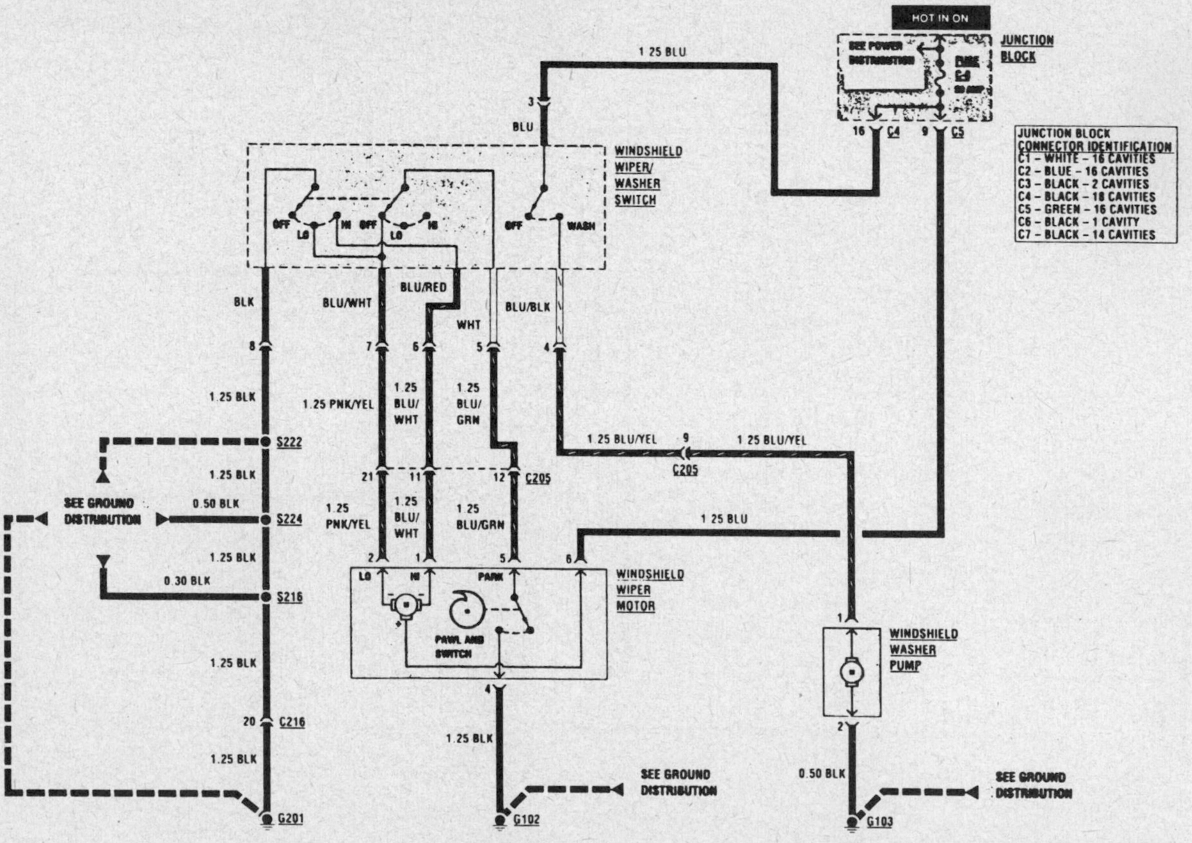
HOT IN ON
SEE POWER DISTRIBUTION
FUSE C-8 20 AMP
JUNCTION BLOCK
1.25 BLU
BLU
JUNCTION BLOCK CONNECTOR IDENTIFICATION
C1 – WHITE – 16 CAVITIES
C2 – BLUE – 16 CAVITIES
C3 – BLACK – 2 CAVITIES
C4 – BLACK – 18 CAVITIES
C5 – GREEN – 16 CAVITIES
C6 – BLACK – 1 CAVITY
C7 – BLACK – 14 CAVITIES
WINDSHIELD WIPER/ WASHER SWITCH
OFF
LO
HI
WASH
BLK
BLU/WHT
BLU/RED
WHT
BLU/BLK
1.25 BLK
1.25 PNK/YEL
1.25 BLU/ WHT
1.25 BLU/ GRN
1.25 BLU/YEL
C205
S222
SEE GROUND DISTRIBUTION
0.50 BLK
S224
0.30 BLK
S216
1.25 PNK/YEL
1.25 BLU/GRN
WINDSHIELD WIPER MOTOR
PARK
PAWL AND SWITCH
WINDSHIELD WASHER PUMP
C216
G201
G102
G103

GC9029300246000X

Fig. 4 Wiring circuit. Storm less pulse

SYSTEM DIAGNOSIS

WIPER/WASHER — DIAGNOSTIC CHART A

TEST		RESULT	ACTION
A1.	Turn ignition switch to "ON." Press Wash button.	FRONT WASHER PUMP operates, and wipers complete at least 1 sweep.	GO TO A2.
		FRONT WASHER PUMP does not operate.	GO TO A4.
		FRONT WASHER PUMP operates but wipers do not complete at least 1 full sweep.	GO TO A14.
		FRONT WASHER PUMP continues to operate after Wash Switch has been released.	GO TO A19.
		Wipers continue to operate continuously after Wash Switch has been released.	GO TO A20.
A2.	Press "LO" button.	Wipers operate at low speed.	GO TO A3.
		Wipers do not operate.	Replace FRONT WIPER/WASHER SWITCH.
		Wipers operate at high speed.	GO TO A8.
A3.	Press "HI" button.	Wipers operate at high speed.	All systems diagnosed are functioning normally.
		Wipers do not operate.	GO TO A10.
		Wipers operate at low speed.	GO TO A12.
A4.	Backprobe FRONT WIPER/WASHER SWITCH connector a test lamp from cavity 5 to chassis ground.	Test lamp does not light.	Repair open in YEL/BLU wire between JUNCTION BLOCK and FRONT WIPER/WASHER SWITCH.
		Test lamp lights.	GO TO A5.
A5.	Backprobe FRONT WIPER/WASHER SWITCH connector with a test lamp from cavity 7 to chassis ground. Press Wash button.	Test lamp does not light.	Replace FRONT WIPER/WASHER SWITCH.
		Test lamp lights.	GO TO A6.
A6.	Disconnect FRONT WASHER PUMP and FRONT WIPER/WASHER SWITCH connectors. Connect a digital multimeter from FRONT WASHER PUMP connector cavity 2 to FRONT WIPER/WASHER SWITCH connector cavity 7. Measure resistance.	More than 0.3 ohms.	Repair open in BLU/BLK wire between FRONT WIPER/WASHER SWITCH and FRONT WASHER PUMP.
		Less than 0.3 ohms.	GO TO A7.
A7.	Connect a digital multimeter from FRONT WASHER PUMP connector cavity 1 to chassis ground. Measure resistance.	More than 0.3 ohms.	Repair BLK ground wire between FRONT WASHER PUMP and G101 (XFi, Base, LSi – USA /Canada) or G200 (Convertible – USA).
		Less than 0.3 ohms.	Replace FRONT WASHER PUMP.
A8.	Backprobe FRONT WIPER MOTOR connector with a test lamp from cavity 1 to chassis ground.	Test lamp does not light.	Replace FRONT WIPER MOTOR.
		Test lamp lights.	GO TO A9.
A9.	Disconnect FRONT WIPER/WASHER SWITCH connector. Connect a test lamp from connector cavity 3 to chassis ground.	Test lamp lights.	Repair short to voltage in BLU/RED wire between FRONT WIPER/WASHER SWITCH and FRONT WIPER MOTOR.
		Test lamp does not light.	Replace FRONT WIPER/WASHER SWITCH.
A10.	Backprobe FRONT WIPER MOTOR connector with a test lamp from cavity 1 to chassis ground.	Test lamp lights.	Replace FRONT WIPER MOTOR.
		Test lamp does not light.	GO TO A11.
A11.	Backprobe FRONT WIPER/WASHER SWITCH with a test lamp from cavity 2 to chassis ground.	Test lamp lights.	Repair open in BLU/RED wire between FRONT WIPER/WASHER SWITCH and FRONT WIPER MOTOR.
		Test lamp does not light.	Replace FRONT WIPER/WASHER SWITCH.
A12.	Backprobe FRONT WIPER MOTOR connector with a test lamp from cavity 2 to chassis ground.	Test lamp does not light.	Replace FRONT WIPER MOTOR.
		Test lamp lights.	GO TO A13.
A13.	Disconnect FRONT WIPER/WASHER SWITCH connector. Connect a test lamp from connector cavity 6 to chassis ground.	Test lamp lights.	Repair short to voltage in BLU wire between FRONT WIPER/WASHER SWITCH and FRONT WIPER MOTOR.
		Test lamp does not light.	Replace FRONT WIPER/WASHER SWITCH.
A14.	Backprobe FRONT WIPER MOTOR connector with a test lamp from cavity 2 to chassis ground. Press Wash button.	Test lamp does not light.	Repair open in BLU wire between FRONT WIPER/WASHER SWITCH and FRONT WIPER MOTOR.
		Test lamp lights.	GO TO A15.
A15.	Backprobe FRONT WIPER MOTOR connector with a test lamp from cavity 4 to chassis ground. Press Wash button.	Test lamp does not light.	GO TO A16.
		Test lamp lights.	GO TO A17.
A16.	Backprobe JUNCTION BLOCK connector C8 with a test lamp from cavity 8 to chassis ground.	Test lamp lights.	Repair open in YEL/BLU wire between JUNCTION BLOCK and FRONT WIPER MOTOR.
		Test lamp does not light.	Replace JUNCTION BLOCK.
A17.	Manually move wipers up and out of PARK position. Backprobe FRONT WIPER MOTOR connector with a test lamp from cavity 3 to chassis ground.	Test lamp does not light.	Replace FRONT WIPER MOTOR.
		Test lamp lights.	GO TO A18.
A18.	Backprobe FRONT WIPER/WASHER SWITCH connector with a test lamp from cavity 4 to chassis ground.	Test lamp does not light.	Repair open in BLU/WHT wire between FRONT WIPER MOTOR and FRONT WIPER/WASHER SWITCH.
		Test lamp lights.	Replace FRONT WIPER/WASHER SWITCH.
A19.	Disconnect FRONT WIPER/WASHER SWITCH connector.	FRONT WASHER PUMP continues to operate.	Repair short to voltage in BLU/BLK wire between FRONT WIPER/WASHER SWITCH and FRONT WIPER MOTOR.
		FRONT WASHER PUMP stops operating.	Replace FRONT WIPER/WASHER SWITCH.
A20.	Disconnect FRONT WIPER/WASHER SWITCH connector.	Wipers continue to operate.	Repair short to voltage in BLU or BLU/WHT wire between FRONT WIPER/WASHER SWITCH and WIPER MOTOR.
		Wipers stop operating.	GO TO A21.
A21.	Make sure that wipers are in the fully down PARK position. Backprobe FRONT WIPER MOTOR connector with a test lamp from cavity 3 to chassis ground.	Test lamp lights.	Replace FRONT WIPER MOTOR.
		Test lamp does not light.	Replace FRONT WIPER/WASHER SWITCH.

GC9029100197000X

Fig. 5 System diagnostic chart. Metro less pulse wiper

nal and black lead wire.

2. If continuity is poor, check brush to commutator contact area.
3. If contact area is fouled, use suitable solvent to clean area. **When surface is coarse or burnt, use sandpaper to polish surface smooth.**
4. If necessary, replace brushes. **Replace brushes as a set.**

Intermittent Wiper Relay Test

1. Disconnect wiper/washer switch connector.
2. Using 12 volt battery, connect positive terminal to black terminal on connector, and negative terminal to yellow/blue terminal on connector **Fig. 9.**
3. Turn intermittent switch to OFF position, If an operating sound is heard from relay, it is operating properly. If no sound is heard, replace relay.

PRIZM

Refer to **Fig. 2,** for wiring circuit and **Figs. 10 and 11,** for complete system diagnosis.

WIPER SWITCH TEST

Inspect wiper/washer switch for continuity, refer to **Fig. 12,** for switch connections.

WIPER MOTOR TEST

Low Speed Test

1. Using 12 volt battery, connect positive terminal to terminal 2 on motor, and negative terminal to wiper motor body **Fig. 13.**
2. Motor should rotate at 45 to 55 RPM.

High Speed Test

1. Using 12 volt battery, connect positive terminal to terminal 1 on motor, and negative terminal to wiper motor body **Fig. 14-44.**
2. Motor should rotate at 69 to 83 RPM.

Park Operation Test

1. Use 12 volt battery, connect positive terminal to terminal 2 on motor, and negative terminal to wiper motor body **Fig. 15.**
2. Operate wiper motor at low speed.
3. Check whether motor shaft stops at a given position. **Time this disconnection so that wipers stop in any position other than their rest position.**
4. Install jumper wire between terminals 2 and 3, **Fig. 16.**
5. Connect battery positive lead to terminal 4.
6. Check that wiper motor stops running at rest position. If wiper motor operation is not as specified, replace motor.

STORM

Refer to **Figs. 3 and 4** for wiring circuits and **Figs. 17 and 18,** for complete system diagnosis.

WIPER SWITCH TEST

Inspect wiper and washer switch for continuity, refer to **Figs. 19 and 41,** for switch connections.

SYSTEM DIAGNOSIS

WIPER/WASHER: PULSE — DIAGNOSTIC CHART A

TEST		RESULT	ACTION
A1.	Turn ignition switch to "ON." Press Wash button.	FRONT WASHER PUMP operates, and wipers complete at least 1 sweep.	GO TO A2.
		FRONT WASHER PUMP does not operate.	GO TO A5.
		FRONT WASHER PUMP operates but wipers do not complete at least 1 full sweep.	GO TO A17.
		FRONT WASHER PUMP continues to operate after Wash Switch has been released.	GO TO A22.
		Wipers continue to operate continuously after Wash Switch has been released.	GO TO A23.
A2.	Press "LO" button.	Wipers operate at low speed.	GO TO A3.
		Wipers do not operate.	Replace FRONT WIPER/WASHER SWITCH.
		Wipers operate at high speed.	GO TO A9.
A3.	Press "HI" button.	Wipers operate at high speed.	GO TO A4.
		Wipers do not operate.	GO TO A11.
		Wipers operate at low speed.	GO TO A13.
A4.	Press "INT" button.	Wipers sweep once every 6 seconds.	All systems diagnosed are functioning normally.
		Wipers do not operate in the intermittent mode.	GO TO A15.
A5.	Backprobe FRONT WIPER/WASHER SWITCH connector with a test lamp from cavity 5 to chassis ground.	Test lamp does not light.	Repair open in YEL/BLU wire between JUNCTION BLOCK and FRONT WIPER/WASHER SWITCH.
		Test lamp lights.	GO TO A6.
A6.	Backprobe FRONT WIPER/WASHER SWITCH connector with a test lamp from cavity 7 to chassis ground. Press Wash button.	Test lamp does not light.	Replace FRONT WIPER/WASHER SWITCH.
		Test lamp lights.	GO TO A7.
A7.	Disconnect FRONT WASHER PUMP and FRONT WIPER/WASHER SWITCH connectors. Connect a digital multimeter from FRONT WASHER PUMP connector cavity 2 to FRONT WIPER/WASHER SWITCH connector cavity 7. Measure resistance.	More than 0.3 ohms.	Repair open in BLU/BLK wire between FRONT WIPER/WASHER SWITCH and FRONT WASHER PUMP.
		Less than 0.3 ohms.	GO TO A8.
A8.	Connect a digital multimeter from FRONT WASHER PUMP connector cavity 1 to chassis ground. Measure resistance.	More than 0.3 ohms.	Repair BLK ground wire between FRONT WASHER PUMP and G101 (XFi, Base, LSi – USA/Canada) or G200 (Convertible – USA).
		Less than 0.3 ohms.	Replace FRONT WASHER PUMP.
A9.	Backprobe FRONT WIPER MOTOR connector with a test lamp from cavity 1 to chassis ground.	Test lamp does not light.	Replace FRONT WIPER MOTOR.
		Test lamp lights.	GO TO A10.
A10.	Disconnect FRONT WIPER/WASHER SWITCH connector. Connect a test lamp from connector cavity 2 chassis ground.	Test lamp lights.	Repair short to voltage in BLU/RED wire between FRONT WIPER/WASHER SWITCH and FRONT WIPER MOTOR.
		Test lamp does not light.	Replace FRONT WIPER/WASHER SWITCH.
A11.	Backprobe FRONT WIPER MOTOR connector with a test lamp from cavity 1 to chassis ground.	Test lamp lights.	Replace FRONT WIPER MOTOR.
		Test lamp does not light.	GO TO A12.
A12.	Backprobe FRONT WIPER/WASHER SWITCH with a test lamp from cavity 2 to chassis ground.	Test lamp lights.	Repair open in BLU/RED wire between FRONT WIPER/WASHER SWITCH and FRONT WIPER MOTOR.
		Test lamp does not light.	Replace FRONT WIPER/WASHER SWITCH.
A13.	Backprobe FRONT WIPER MOTOR connector with a test lamp from cavity 2 to chassis ground.	Test lamp does not light.	Replace FRONT WIPER MOTOR.
		Test lamp lights.	GO TO A14.
A14.	Disconnect FRONT WIPER/WASHER SWITCH connector. Connect a test lamp from connector cavity 6 to chassis ground.	Test lamp lights.	Repair short to voltage in BLU wire between FRONT WIPER/WASHER SWITCH and FRONT WIPER MOTOR.
		Test lamp does not light.	Replace FRONT WIPER/WASHER SWITCH.
A15.	Disconnect FRONT WIPER/WASHER SWITCH connector. Connect a digital multimeter from connector cavity 1 to chassis ground. Measure resistance.	Less than 0.3 ohms.	Replace FRONT WIPER/WASHER SWITCH.
		More than 0.3 ohms.	GO TO A16.
A16.	Disconnect JUNCTION BLOCK connector C6. Connect a digital multimeter from JUNCTION BLOCK connector C6 to FRONT WIPER/WASHER SWITCH connector cavity 1. Measure resistance.	More than 0.3 ohms.	Repair BLK ground wire between JUNCTION BLOCK and FRONT WIPER/WASHER SWITCH.
		Less than 0.3 ohms.	Replace JUNCTION BLOCK.
A17.	Backprobe FRONT WIPER MOTOR connector with a test lamp from cavity 2 to chassis ground. Press Wash button.	Test lamp does not light.	Repair open in BLU wire between FRONT WIPER/WASHER SWITCH and FRONT WIPER MOTOR.
		Test lamp lights.	GO TO A18.
A18.	Backprobe FRONT WIPER MOTOR connector with a test lamp from cavity 4 to chassis ground. Press Wash button.	Test lamp does not light.	GO TO A19.
		Test lamp lights.	GO TO A20.
A19.	Backprobe JUNCTION BLOCK connector C8 with a test lamp from cavity 8 to chassis ground.	Test lamp lights.	Repair open in YEL/BLU wire between JUNCTION BLOCK and FRONT WIPER MOTOR.
		Test lamp does not light.	Replace JUNCTION BLOCK.
A20.	Manually move wipers up and out of PARK position. Backprobe FRONT WIPER MOTOR connector with a test lamp from cavity 3 to chassis ground.	Test lamp does not light.	Replace FRONT WIPER MOTOR.
		Test lamp lights.	GO TO A21.
A21.	Backprobe FRONT WIPER/WASHER SWITCH connector with a test lamp from cavity 4 to chassis ground.	Test lamp does not light.	Repair open in BLU/WHT wire between FRONT WIPER MOTOR and FRONT WIPER/WASHER SWITCH.
		Test lamp lights.	Replace FRONT WIPER/WASHER SWITCH.
A22.	Disconnect FRONT WIPER/WASHER SWITCH connector.	FRONT WASHER PUMP continues to operate	Repair short to voltage in BLU/BLK wire between FRONT WIPER/WASHER SWITCH and FRONT WIPER MOTOR.
		FRONT WASHER PUMP stops operating.	Replace FRONT WIPER/WASHER SWITCH.
A23.	Disconnect FRONT WIPER/WASHER SWITCH connector.	Wipers continue to operate.	Repair short to voltage in BLU or BLU/WHT wire between FRONT WIPER/WASHER SWITCH and WIPER MOTOR.
		Wipers stop operating.	GO TO A24.
A24.	Make sure that wipers are in the fully down PARK position. Backprobe FRONT WIPER MOTOR connector with a test lamp from cavity 3 to chassis ground.	Test lamp lights.	Replace FRONT WIPER MOTOR.
		Test lamp does not light.	Replace FRONT WIPER/WASHER SWITCH.

GC9029100198000X

Fig. 6 System diagnostic chart. Metro w/pulse wiper

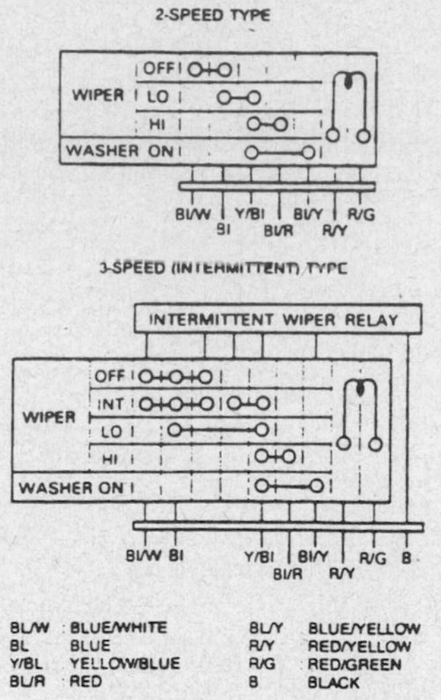
2-SPEED TYPE
WIPER
OFF
LO
HI
WASHER ON
Bl/W
Bl
Y/Bl
Bl/R
Bl/Y
R/Y
R/G
3-SPEED (INTERMITTENT) TYPE
INTERMITTENT WIPER RELAY
OFF
INT
LO
HI
WASHER ON
B
BL/W : BLUE/WHITE
BL : BLUE
Y/BL : YELLOW/BLUE
BL/R : RED
BL/Y : BLUE/YELLOW
R/Y : RED/YELLOW
R/G : RED/GREEN
B : BLACK

GC9029100199000X

Fig. 7 Wiper switch continuity chart. Metro

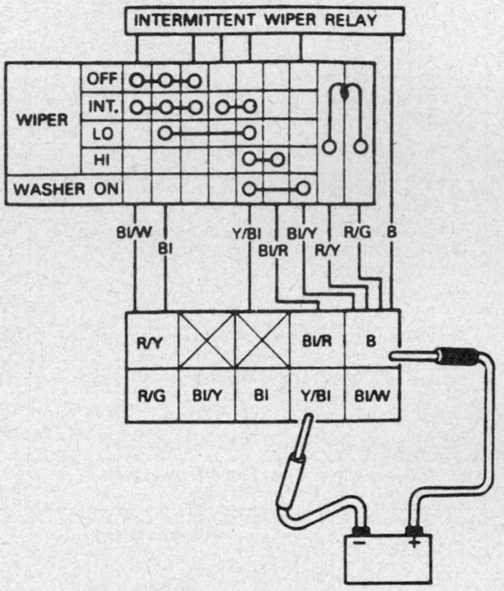
INTERMITTENT WIPER RELAY
WIPER
OFF
INT.
LO
HI
WASHER ON
Bl/W
Bl
Y/Bl
Bl/R
Bl/Y
R/Y
R/G
B

GC9029100200000X

Fig. 8 Connections to operate two & three speed wiper motor independent of vehicle wiring

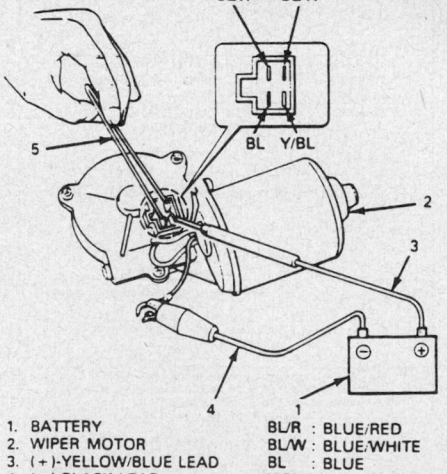

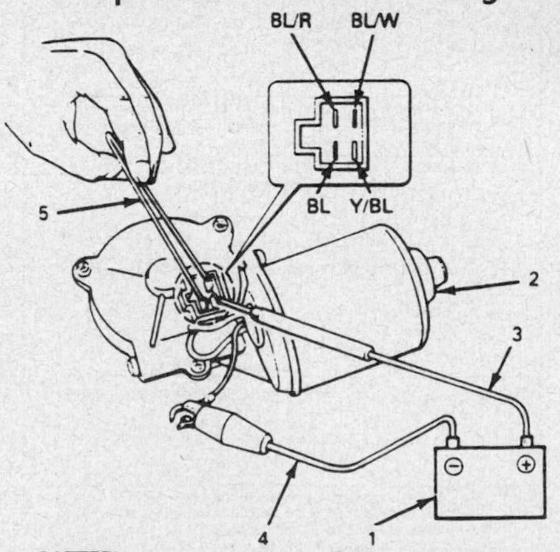
BL/R
BL/W
BL
Y/BL
1
2
3
4
5

1. BATTERY
2. WIPER MOTOR
3. (+)-YELLOW/BLUE LEAD
4. (−)-BLACK LEAD
5. JUMPER

BL/R : BLUE/RED
BL/W : BLUE/WHITE
BL : BLUE
Y/BL : YELLOW/BLUE

GC9029100201000X

Fig. 9 Intermittent wiper relay test connections. Metro

SYSTEM DIAGNOSIS

WIPER/WASHER — DIAGNOSTIC CHART A

TEST	RESULT	ACTION
A1. Turn ignition switch to "ON." Press Wash Switch and release.	WINDSHIELD WASHER PUMP operates.	GO TO A2.
	WINDSHIELD WASHER PUMP does not operate.	GO TO A5.
A2. Turn WINDSHIELD WIPER SWITCH to the "MIST" position and release.	Wipers sweep once and return to PARK.	GO TO A3.
	Wipers do not sweep.	GO TO A12.
	Wipers sweep but do not return to PARK.	GO TO A16.
	Wipers sweep more than once.	GO TO A20.
A3. Turn WINDSHIELD WIPER SWITCH to the "LO" position.	Wipers sweep at low speed.	GO TO A4.
	Wipers do not sweep.	Replace WINDSHIELD WIPER SWITCH.
	Wipers operate in high speed.	GO TO A22.
A4. Turn WINDSHIELD WIPER SWITCH the to "HI" position.	Wipers operate at high speed.	All systems diagnosed are functioning normally.
	Wipers do not sweep.	GO TO A24.
	Wipers operate in low speed.	GO TO A26.
A5. Backprobe WINDSHIELD WASHER PUMP connector with a test lamp from cavity 2 to chassis ground.	Test lamp does not light.	GO TO A6.
	Test lamp lights.	GO TO A7.
A6. Backprobe JUNCTION BLOCK 1 connector C2 with a test lamp from cavity 4 to chassis ground.	Test lamp lights.	Repair open in BLU wire between JUNCTION BLOCK 1 and WINDSHIELD WASHER PUMP.
	Test lamp does not light.	Replace JUNCTION BLOCK 1.
A7. Disconnect WINDSHIELD WIPER SWITCH connector. Connect a test lamp from connector cavity 8 to chassis ground.	Test lamp does not light.	GO TO A8.
	Test lamp lights.	GO TO A11.
A8. Backprobe WINDSHIELD WASHER DIODE connector with a test lamp from cavity 2 to chassis ground.	Test lamp lights.	Repair open in BLU/RED wire between WINDSHIELD WASHER DIODE and WINDSHIELD WIPER SWITCH.
	Test lamp does not light.	GO TO A9.
A9. Backprobe WINDSHIELD WASHER DIODE connector with a test lamp from cavity 1 to chassis ground.	Test lamp lights.	Replace WINDSHIELD WASHER DIODE.
	Test lamp does not light.	GO TO A10.
A10. Backprobe WINDSHIELD WASHER PUMP connector with a test lamp from cavity 1 to chassis ground.	Test lamp lights.	Repair open in BLU/YEL wire between WINDSHIELD WASHER PUMP and WINDSHIELD WASHER DIODE.
	Test lamp does not light.	Replace WINDSHIELD WASHER PUMP.
A11. Connect a digital multimeter from WINDSHIELD WIPER SWITCH connector cavity 16 to chassis ground. Measure resistance.	More than 0.3 ohms.	Repair WHT/BLK ground wire between WINDSHIELD WIPER SWITCH and G200.
	Less than 0.3 ohms.	Replace WINDSHIELD WIPER SWITCH.

00902910020201OX

Fig. 10 System diagnostic chart (Part 1 of 2) Prizm less pulse wiper

WIPER MOTOR TEST

Low Speed Test

1. Using 12 volt battery, connect positive terminal to "LO" terminal on motor, and negative terminal to wiper motor body **Fig. 20.**
2. Motor should rotate at 45 to 55 RPM.

High Speed Test

1. Using 12 volt battery, connect positive terminal to "HI" terminal on motor, and negative terminal to wiper motor body **Fig. 20.**
2. Motor should rotate at 69 to 83 RPM.

Park Operation Test

1. Use 12 volt battery, connect positive terminal to "Park" terminal on motor, and negative terminal to wiper motor body **Fig. 20.**
2. Operate wiper motor at high speed.
3. Check whether motor shaft stops at a given position. **This position must conform to the start position.**
4. Repeat step 2 to confirm that shaft stops at the same position.

SYSTEM DIAGNOSIS

WIPER/WASHER	DIAGNOSTIC CHART A (CONT'D)	
TEST	**RESULT**	**ACTION**
A12. Backprobe WINDSHIELD WIPER SWITCH connector with a test lamp from cavity 18 to chassis ground.	Test lamp does not light.	GO TO A13.
	Test lamp lights.	GO TO A14.
A13. Backprobe JUNCTION BLOCK 1 connector C5 with a test lamp from cavity 7 to chassis ground.	Test lamp lights.	Replace JUNCTION BLOCK 3.
	Test lamp does not light.	Replace JUNCTION BLOCK 1.
A14. Backprobe WINDSHIELD WIPER SWITCH connector with a test lamp from cavity 7 to chassis ground. Hold WINDSHIELD WIPER SWITCH in the "MIST" position.	Test lamp does not light.	Replace WINDSHIELD WIPER SWITCH.
	Test lamp lights.	GO TO A15.
A15. Backprobe WINDSHIELD WIPER MOTOR connector with a test lamp from cavity 2 to chassis ground.	Test lamp does not light.	Repair open in BLU/BLK wire between WINDSHIELD WIPER SWITCH and WINDSHIELD WIPER MOTOR.
	Test lamp lights.	Replace WINDSHIELD WIPER MOTOR.
A16. Backprobe WINDSHIELD WIPER MOTOR connector with a test lamp from cavity 4 to chassis ground.	Test lamp does not light.	GO TO A17.
	Test lamp lights.	GO TO A18.
A17. Backprobe JUNCTION BLOCK 3 connector C2 with a test lamp from cavity 5 to chassis ground.	Test lamp lights.	Repair open in BLU wire between JUNCTION BLOCK 3 and WINDSHIELD WIPER MOTOR.
	Test lamp does not light.	Replace JUNCTION BLOCK 3.
A18. Disconnect WINDSHIELD WIPER SWITCH connector. Connect a digital multimeter from terminal 4 to terminal 7 (WINDSHIELD WIPER SWITCH side). Measure resistance with WINDSHIELD WIPER SWITCH in "OFF."	More than 0.3 ohms.	Replace WINDSHIELD WIPER SWITCH.
	Less than 0.3 ohms.	GO TO A19.
A19. Disconnect WINDSHIELD WIPER MOTOR connector. Connect a digital multimeter from WINDSHIELD WIPER SWITCH connector cavity 4 to WINDSHIELD WIPER MOTOR connector cavity 3. Measure resistance.	More than 0.3 ohms.	Repair open in BLU/WHT wire between WINDSHIELD WIPER SWITCH And WINDSHIELD WIPER MOTOR.
	Less than 0.3 ohms.	Replace WINDSHIELD WIPER MOTOR.
A20. Disconnect WINDSHIELD WIPER MOTOR connector. Connect a test lamp from connector cavity 2 to chassis ground.	Test lamp does not light.	Replace WINDSHIELD WIPER MOTOR.
	Test lamp lights.	GO TO A21.
A21. Disconnect WINDSHIELD WIPER SWITCH connector. Connect a test lamp from connector cavity 7 to chassis ground.	Test lamp lights.	Repair short to voltage in BLU/BLK wire between WINDSHIELD WIPER SWITCH and WINDSHIELD WIPER MOTOR.
	Test lamp does not light.	Replace WINDSHIELD WIPER SWITCH.
A22. Disconnect WINDSHIELD WIPER MOTOR connector. Connect a test lamp from connector cavity 1 to chassis ground.	Test lamp does not light.	Replace WINDSHIELD WIPER MOTOR.
	Test lamp lights.	GO TO A23.
A23. Disconnect WINDSHIELD WIPER SWITCH connector. Connect a test lamp from connector cavity 13 to chassis ground.	Test lamp lights.	Repair short to voltage in BLU/ORN wire between WINDSHIELD WIPER SWITCH and WINDSHIELD WIPER MOTOR.
	Test lamp does not light.	Replace WINDSHIELD WIPER SWITCH.
A24. Backprobe WINDSHIELD WIPER SWITCH connector with a test lamp from cavity 13 to chassis ground.	Test lamp does not light.	Replace WINDSHIELD WIPER SWITCH.
	Test lamp lights.	GO TO A25.
A25. Backprobe WINDSHIELD WIPER MOTOR connector with a test lamp from cavity 1 to chassis ground.	Test lamp does not light.	Repair open in BLU/ORN wire between WINDSHIELD WIPER and WINDSHIELD WIPER MOTOR.
	Test lamp lights.	Replace WINDSHIELD WIPER MOTOR.
A26. Disconnect WINDSHIELD WIPER MOTOR connector. Connect a test lamp from connector cavity 2 to chassis ground.	Test lamp does not light.	Replace WINDSHIELD WIPER MOTOR.
	Test lamp lights.	GO TO A27.
A27. Disconnect WINDSHIELD WIPER SWITCH connector. Connect a test lamp from connector cavity 7 to chassis ground.	Test lamp lights.	Repair short to voltage in BLU/BLK wire between WINDSHIELD WIPER SWITCH and WINDSHIELD WIPER MOTOR.
	Test lamp does not light.	Replace WINDSHIELD WIPER SWITCH.

GC9029100202020X

Fig. 10 System diagnostic chart (Part 2 of 2). Prizm less pulse wiper

SYSTEM DIAGNOSIS

WIPER/WASHER: PULSE	DIAGNOSTIC CHART A	
TEST	**RESULT**	**ACTION**
A1. Turn ignition switch to "ON." Press Wash and release.	WINDSHIELD WASHER PUMP operates and wipers make 2-5 sweeps and return to PARK.	GO TO A2.
	WINDSHIELD WASHER PUMP does not operate.	GO TO A5.
	WINDSHIELD WASHER PUMP operates but wipers do not sweep.	GO TO A12.
	WINDSHIELD WASHER PUMP continues to operate.	GO TO A16.
	Wipers sweep but do not return to PARK.	GO TO A20.
	Wipers continue to operate.	GO TO A24.
A2. Turn WINDSHIELD WIPER SWITCH to the "LO" position.	Wipers sweep at low speed.	GO TO A3.
	Wipers do not sweep.	Replace WINDSHIELD WIPER SWITCH.
	Wipers operate in high speed.	GO TO A26.
A3. Turn WINDSHIELD WIPER SWITCH to the "HI" position.	Wipers operate at high speed.	GO TO A4.
	Wipers do not sweep.	GO TO A28.
	Wipers operate in low speed.	GO TO A30.
A4. Turn WINDSHIELD WIPER SWITCH to the "INT" position. Adjust delay time up and down.	Wipers operate in intermittent mode with delay times changing with adjustment.	All systems diagnosed are functioning normally.
	Wipers do not operate or do not operate in intermittent mode.	Replace WINDSHIELD WIPER SWITCH.
	Delay times do not change with adjustment.	Replace WINDSHIELD WIPER SWITCH.
A5. Backprobe WINDSHIELD WASHER PUMP connector with a test lamp from cavity 2 to chassis ground.	Test lamp does not light.	GO TO A6.
	Test lamp lights.	GO TO A7.
A6. Backprobe JUNCTION BLOCK 1 connector C2 with a test lamp from cavity 4 to chassis ground.	Test lamp lights.	Repair open in BLU wire between JUNCTION BLOCK 1 and WINDSHIELD WASHER PUMP.
	Test lamp does not light.	Replace JUNCTION BLOCK 1.
A7. Backprobe WINDSHIELD WASHER PUMP connector with a test lamp from cavity 1 to chassis ground.	Test lamp does not light.	Replace WINDSHIELD WASHER PUMP.
	Test lamp lights.	GO TO A8.
A8. Backprobe WINDSHIELD WASHER DIODE connector with a test lamp from cavity 1 to chassis ground.	Test lamp does not light.	Repair open in BLU/YEL wire between WINDSHIELD WASHER PUMP and WINDSHIELD WASHER DIODE.
	Test lamp lights.	GO TO A9.
A9. Backprobe WINDSHIELD WASHER DIODE connector with a test lamp from cavity 2 to chassis ground.	Test lamp does not light.	Replace WINDSHIELD WASHER DIODE.
	Test lamp lights.	GO TO A10.
A10. Backprobe WINDSHIELD WIPER SWITCH connector with a test lamp from cavity 8 to chassis ground.	Test lamp does not light.	Repair open in BLU/RED wire between WINDSHIELD WASHER DIODE and WINDSHIELD WIPER SWITCH.
	Test lamp lights.	GO TO A11.
A11. Backprobe WINDSHIELD WIPER SWITCH connector with a digital multimeter from cavity 16 to chassis ground.	More than 0.3 ohms.	Repair WHT/BLK ground wire between WINDSHIELD WIPER SWITCH and G200.
	Less than 0.3 ohms.	Replace WINDSHIELD WIPER SWITCH.
A12. Backprobe WINDSHIELD WIPER SWITCH connector with a test lamp from cavity 18 to chassis ground.	Test lamp does not light.	GO TO A13.
	Test lamp lights.	GO TO A14.
A13. Backprobe JUNCTION BLOCK 1 connector C5 with a test lamp from cavity 7 to chassis ground.	Test lamp lights.	Replace JUNCTION BLOCK 3.
	Test lamp does not light.	Replace JUNCTION BLOCK 1.
A14. Backprobe WINDSHIELD WIPER SWITCH connector with a test lamp from cavity 7 to chassis ground. Press Wash Switch.	Test lamp does not light.	Replace WINDSHIELD WIPER SWITCH.
	Test lamp lights.	GO TO A15.
A15. Backprobe WINDSHIELD WIPER MOTOR connector with a test lamp from cavity 2 to chassis ground. Press Wash Switch.	Test lamp does not light.	Repair open in BLU/BLK wire between WINDSHIELD WIPER SWITCH and WINDSHIELD WIPER MOTOR.
	Test lamp lights.	Replace WINDSHIELD WIPER MOTOR.
A16. Disconnect WINDSHIELD WIPER SWITCH connector.	WINDSHIELD WASHER PUMP stops.	Replace WINDSHIELD WIPER SWITCH.
	WINDSHIELD WASHER PUMP continues to operate.	GO TO A17.
A17. Remove WINDSHIELD WASHER DIODE.	WINDSHIELD WASHER PUMP stops.	GO TO A18.
	WINDSHIELD WASHER PUMP continues to operate.	GO TO A19.

GC9029100203010X

Fig. 11 System diagnostic chart (Part 1 of 2). Prizm w/pulse wiper

SYSTEM DIAGNOSIS

WIPER/WASHER: PULSE — DIAGNOSTIC CHART A (CONT'D)

TEST	RESULT	ACTION
A18. Connect a digital multimeter from WINDSHIELD WIPER SWITCH connector cavity 8 to chassis ground. Measure resistance.	Less than infinite.	Repair short to ground in BLU/RED wire between WINDSHIELD WASHER DIODE and WINDSHIELD WIPER SWITCH.
	Infinite.	Replace WINDSHIELD WASHER DIODE.
A19. Disconnect WINDSHIELD WASHER PUMP connector. Connect a digital multimeter from connector cavity 1 to chassis ground. Measure resistance.	Less than infinite.	Repair short to ground in BLU/YEL wire between WINDSHIELD WASHER PUMP and WINDSHIELD WASHER DIODE.
	Infinite.	Replace WINDSHIELD WASHER PUMP.
A20. Backprobe WINDSHIELD WIPER MOTOR connector with a test lamp from cavity 4 to chassis ground.	Test lamp does not light.	GO TO A21.
	Test lamp lights.	GO TO A22.
A21. Backprobe JUNCTION BLOCK 3 connector C2 with a test lamp from cavity 5 to chassis ground.	Test lamp lights.	Repair open in BLU wire between JUNCTION BLOCK 3 and WINDSHIELD WIPER MOTOR.
	Test lamp does not light.	Replace JUNCTION BLOCK 3.
A22. Disconnect WINDSHIELD WIPER SWITCH connector. Connect a digital multimeter from connector terminal 4 to terminal 7 (WINDSHIELD WIPER SWITCH side). Measure resistance with WINDSHIELD WIPER SWITCH in "OFF."	More than 0.3 ohms.	Replace WINDSHIELD WIPER SWITCH.
	Less than 0.3 ohms.	GO TO A23.
A23. Disconnect WINDSHIELD WIPER MOTOR connector. Connect a digital multimeter from WINDSHIELD WIPER SWITCH connector cavity 4 to WINDSHIELD WIPER MOTOR connector cavity 3. Measure resistance.	More than 0.3 ohms.	Repair open in BLU/WHT wire between WINDSHIELD WIPER SWITCH and WINDSHIELD WIPER MOTOR.
	Less than 0.3 ohms.	Replace WINDSHIELD WIPER MOTOR.
A24. Disconnect WINDSHIELD WIPER MOTOR connector. Connect a test lamp from connector cavity 2 to chassis ground.	Test lamp does not light.	Replace WINDSHIELD WIPER MOTOR.
	Test lamp lights.	GO TO A25.
A25. Disconnect WINDSHIELD WIPER SWITCH connector. Connect a test lamp from connector cavity 7 to chassis ground.	Test lamp lights.	Repair short to voltage in BLU/BLK wire between WINDSHIELD WIPER SWITCH and WINDSHIELD WIPER MOTOR.
	Test lamp does not light.	Replace WINDSHIELD WIPER SWITCH.
A26. Disconnect WINDSHIELD WIPER MOTOR connector. Connect a test lamp from connector cavity 1 to chassis ground.	Test lamp does not light.	Replace WINDSHIELD WIPER MOTOR.
	Test lamp lights.	GO TO A27.
A27. Disconnect WINDSHIELD WIPER SWITCH connector. Connect a test lamp from connector cavity 13 to chassis ground.	Test lamp lights.	Repair short to voltage in BLU/ORN wire between WINDSHIELD WIPER SWITCH and WINDSHIELD WIPER MOTOR.
	Test lamp does not light.	Replace WINDSHIELD WIPER SWITCH.
A28. Backprobe WINDSHIELD WIPER MOTOR connector with a test lamp from cavity 1 to chassis ground.	Test lamp lights.	Replace WINDSHIELD WIPER MOTOR.
	Test lamp does not light.	GO TO A29.
A29. Backprobe WINDSHIELD WIPER SWITCH connector with a test lamp from cavity 13 to chassis ground.	Test lamp lights.	Repair open in BLU/ORN wire between WINDSHIELD WIPER SWITCH and WINDSHIELD WIPER MOTOR.
	Test lamp does not light.	Replace WINDSHIELD WIPER SWITCH.
A30. Disconnect WINDSHIELD WIPER MOTOR connector. Connect a test lamp from connector cavity 2 to chassis ground.	Test lamp does not light.	Replace WINDSHIELD WIPER MOTOR.
	Test lamp lights.	GO TO A31.
A31. Disconnect WINDSHIELD WIPER SWITCH connector. Connect a test lamp from connector cavity 7 to chassis ground.	Test lamp lights.	Repair short to voltage in BLU/BLK wire between WINDSHIELD WIPER SWITCH and WINDSHIELD WIPER MOTOR.
	Test lamp does not light.	Replace WINDSHIELD WIPER SWITCH.

Fig. 7 System diagnosis chart (Part 2 of 2). Prizm w/pulse wiper

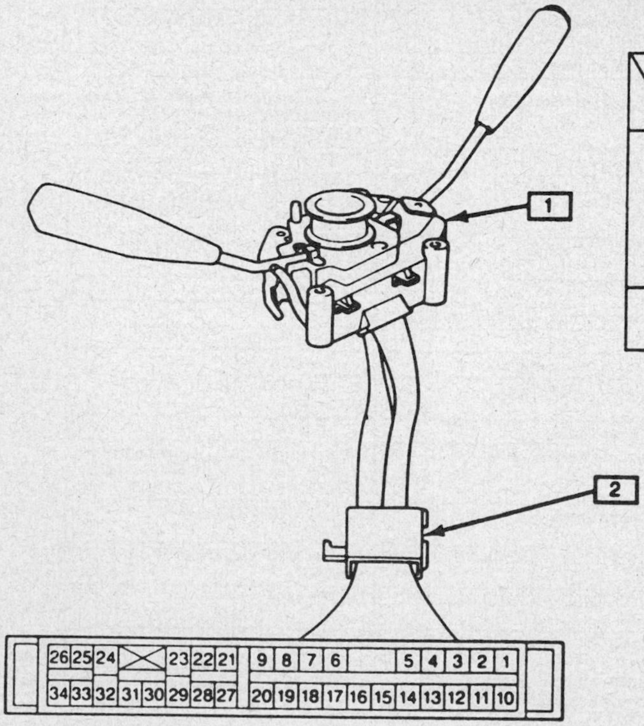
1
2
26 25 24 23 22 21 9 8 7 6 5 4 3 2 1
34 33 32 31 30 29 28 27 20 19 18 17 16 15 14 13 12 11 10

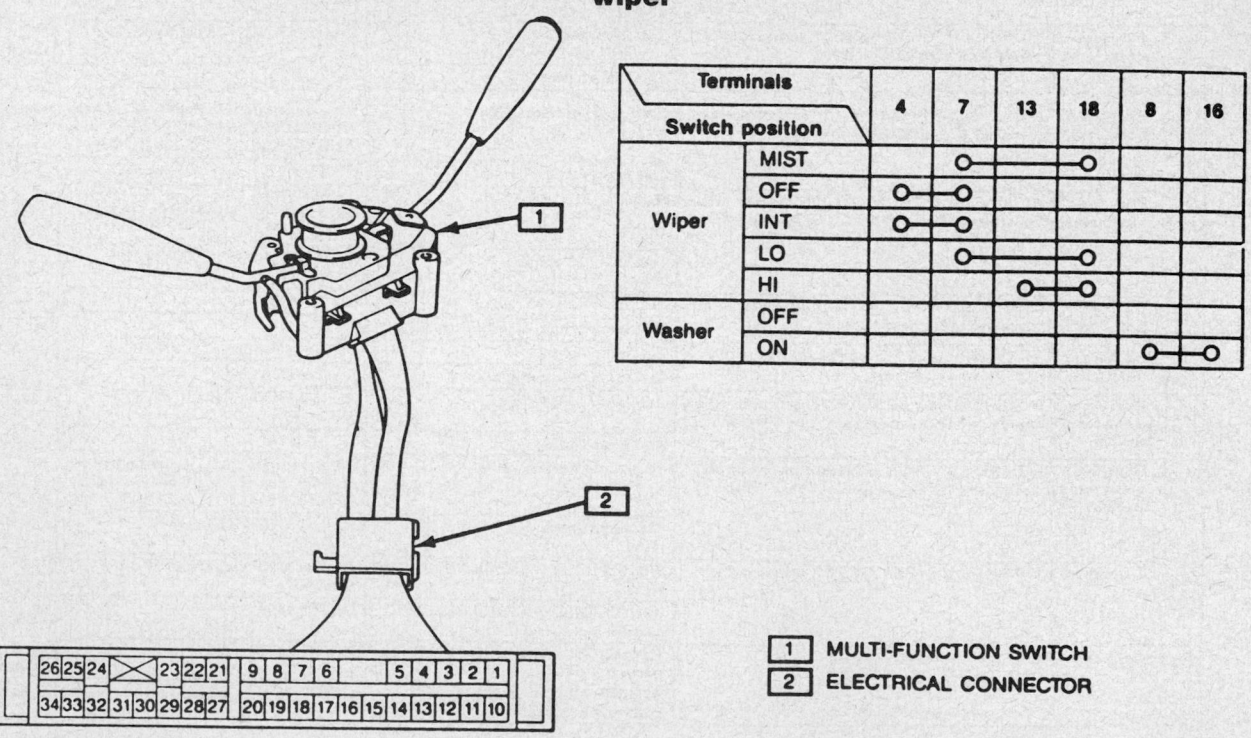

Switch position (Terminals)		4	7	13	18	8	16
Wiper	MIST		O		O		
	OFF	O	O				
	INT	O	O				
	LO		O		O		
	HI			O	O		
Washer	OFF						
	ON					O	O

1 MULTI-FUNCTION SWITCH
2 ELECTRICAL CONNECTOR

GC9029100204000X

Fig. 12 Windshield wiper switch. Prizm

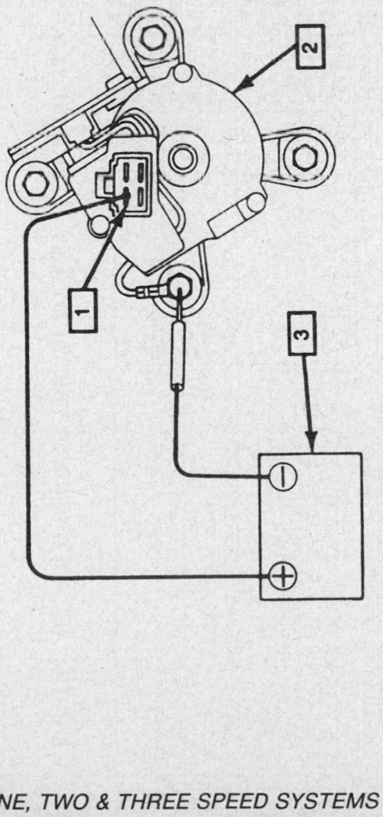
1
2
3

1 TERMINAL 2
2 WIPER MOTOR
3 BATTERY

GC90291002050000X

Fig. 13 Windshield wiper "Low" speed operation. Prizm

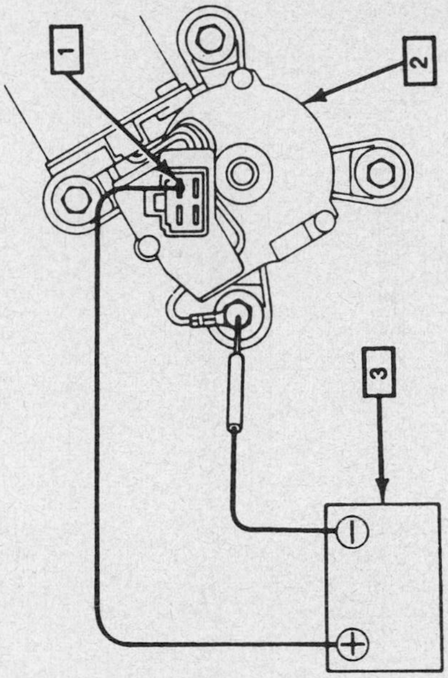
1
2
3

1 TERMINAL 1
2 WIPER MOTOR
3 BATTERY

GC90291002060000X

Fig. 14 Windshield wiper "High" speed operation. Prizm

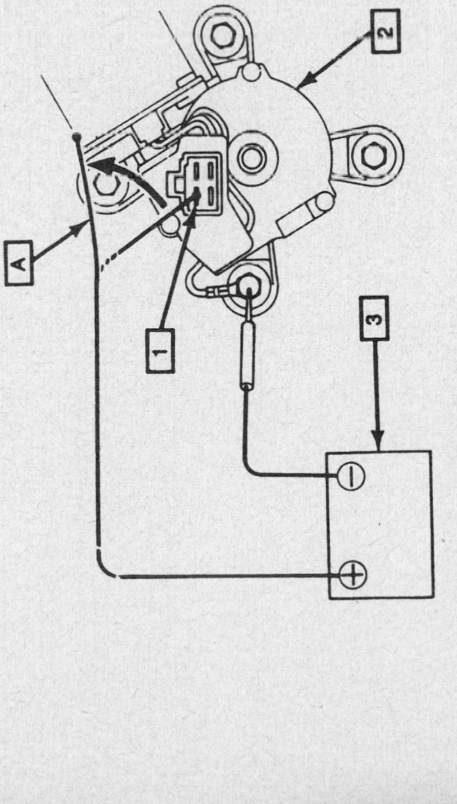
A
1
2
3

A DISCONNECT TERMINAL 2
1 TERMINAL 2
2 WIPER MOTOR
3 BATTERY

GC90291002070000X

Fig. 15 Windshield wiper terminal 2. Prizm

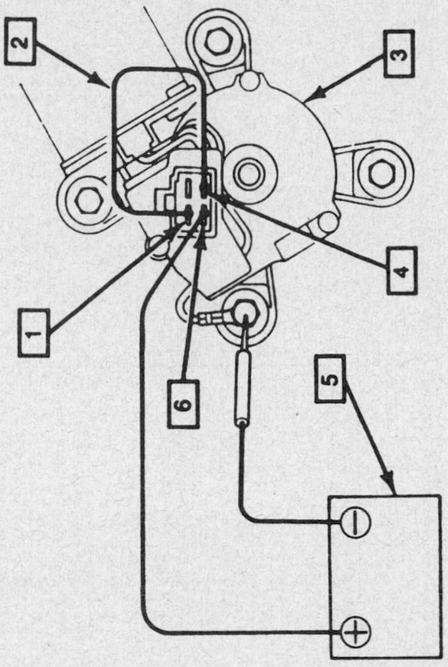
1
2
3
4
5
6

1 TERMINAL 2
2 JUMPER WIRE
3 WIPER MOTOR
4 TERMINAL 3
5 BATTERY
6 TERMINAL 4

GC90291002080000X

Fig. 16 Windshield wiper "Park" operation. Prizm

SYSTEM DIAGNOSIS

WIPER/WASHER — DIAGNOSTIC CHART A

	TEST	RESULT	ACTION
A1.	Turn ignition switch to "ON." Press WASH button.	WINDSHIELD WASHER PUMP operates.	GO TO A2.
		WINDSHIELD WASHER PUMP does not operate.	GO TO A5.
		WINDSHIELD WASHER PUMP continues to operate after WASH button has been released.	GO TO A10.
A2.	Press "LO" button.	Wipers sweep at low speed.	GO TO A3.
		Wipers do not sweep.	GO TO A11.
		Wipers sweep at high speed.	GO TO A16.
A3.	Press "HI" button.	Wipers sweep at high speed.	GO TO A4.
		Wipers do not sweep.	GO TO A18.
		Wipers sweep at low speed.	GO TO A20.
A4.	Press "OFF" button.	Wipers complete 1 full sweep and stop.	All systems diagnosed are functioning normally.
		Wipers do not complete 1 full sweep.	GO TO A22.
		Wipers continue for more than 2 sweeps.	GO TO A25.
A5.	Disconnect WINDSHIELD WASHER PUMP connector. Connect a digital multimeter from cavity 2 to chassis ground. Measure resistance.	More than 0.3 ohms.	Repair BLK ground wire between WINDSHIELD WASHER PUMP and G103.
		Less than 0.3 ohms.	GO TO A6.
A6.	Connect a test lamp from WINDSHIELD WASHER PUMP connector cavity 1 to chassis ground. Press WASH button.	Test lamp lights.	Replace WINDSHIELD WASHER PUMP.
		Test lamp does not light.	GO TO A7.
A7.	Backprobe WINDSHIELD WIPER/WASHER SWITCH connector with a test lamp from cavity 4 to chassis ground. Press WASH button.	Test lamp lights.	Repair open in BLU/YEL wire.
		Test lamp does not light.	GO TO A8.
A8.	Backprobe WINDSHIELD WIPER/WASHER SWITCH connector with a test lamp from cavity 3 to chassis ground.	Test lamp lights.	Replace WINDSHIELD WIPER/WASHER SWITCH.
		Test lamp does not light.	GO TO A9.
A9.	Backprobe JUNCTION BLOCK connector C4 with a test lamp from cavity 16 to chassis ground.	Test lamp does not light.	Replace JUNCTION BLOCK.
		Test lamp lights.	Repair open in BLU wire between JUNCTION BLOCK and WINDSHIELD WIPER/WASHER SWITCH.
A10.	Disconnect WINDSHIELD WIPER/WASHER SWITCH connector.	WINDSHIELD WASHER PUMP stops.	Replace WINDSHIELD WIPER/WASHER SWITCH.
		WINDSHIELD WASHER PUMP continues to operate.	Repair short to voltage in BLU/YEL wire between WINDSHIELD WIPER/WASHER SWITCH and WINDSHIELD WASHER PUMP.
A11.	Backprobe WINDSHIELD WIPER MOTOR connector with a fused jumper from cavity 2 to chassis ground.	WINDSHIELD WIPER MOTOR operates.	Remove jumper, GO TO A12.
		WINDSHIELD WIPER MOTOR does not operate.	Remove jumper, GO TO A14.
A12.	Disconnect WINDSHIELD WIPER/WASHER SWITCH connector. Connect a digital multimeter from connector terminal 8 to chassis ground. Measure resistance.	More than 0.3 ohms.	Repair BLK ground wire between WINDSHIELD WIPER/WASHER SWITCH and G201.
		Less than 0.3 ohms.	GO TO A13.
A13.	Disconnect WINDSHIELD WIPER MOTOR connector. Connect a digital multimeter from WINDSHIELD WIPER MOTOR connector cavity 2 to WINDSHIELD WIPER/WASHER SWITCH connector terminal 7. Measure resistance.	Less than 0.3 ohms.	Replace WINDSHIELD WIPER/WASHER SWITCH.
		More than 0.3 ohms.	Repair open in PNK/YEL wire between WINDSHIELD WIPER/WASHER SWITCH and WINDSHIELD WIPER MOTOR.
A14.	Backprobe WINDSHIELD WIPER MOTOR connector with a test lamp from cavity 6 to chassis ground.	Test lamp lights.	Replace WINDSHIELD WIPER MOTOR.
		Test lamp does not light.	GO TO A15.
A15.	Backprobe JUNCTION BLOCK connector C5 with a test lamp from cavity 9 to chassis ground.	Test lamp does not light.	Replace JUNCTION BLOCK.
		Test lamp lights.	Repair open in BLU wire between JUNCTION BLOCK and WINDSHIELD WIPER MOTOR.

GC9029100209010X

Fig. 17 System diagnostic chart (Part 1 of 2). Storm less pulse wiper

SYSTEM DIAGNOSIS

WIPER/WASHER — DIAGNOSTIC CHART A (CONT'D)

	TEST	RESULT	ACTION
A16.	Disconnect WINDSHIELD WIPER MOTOR connector. Connect a digital multimeter from cavity 1 to chassis ground. Measure resistance.	Infinite.	Replace WINDSHIELD WIPER MOTOR.
		Less than infinite.	GO TO A17.
A17.	Disconnect WINDSHIELD WIPER/WASHER SWITCH connector. Connect a digital multimeter from connector cavity 6 (switch side) to chassis ground. Measure resistance.	Less than infinite.	Replace WINDSHIELD WIPER/WASHER SWITCH.
		Infinite.	Repair short to ground in BLU/WHT wire between WINDSHIELD WIPER MOTOR and WINDSHIELD WIPER/WASHER SWITCH.
A18.	Disconnect WINDSHIELD WIPER MOTOR connector. Connect a digital multimeter from cavity 1 chassis ground. Measure resistance.	Less than 0.3 ohms.	Replace WINDSHIELD WIPER MOTOR.
		More than 0.3 ohms.	GO TO A19.
A19.	Backprobe WINDSHIELD WIPER/WASHER SWITCH connector with a digital multimeter from cavity 6 to chassis ground. Measure resistance.	More than 0.3 ohms.	Replace WINDSHIELD WIPER/WASHER SWITCH.
		Less than 0.3 ohms.	Repair open in BLU/WHT wire between WINDSHIELD WIPER/WASHER SWITCH and WINDSHIELD WIPER MOTOR.
A20.	Disconnect WINDSHIELD WIPER MOTOR connector. Connect a digital multimeter from cavity 2 to chassis ground. Measure resistance.	Infinite.	Replace WINDSHIELD WIPER MOTOR.
		Less than infinite.	GO TO A21.
A21.	Disconnect WINDSHIELD WIPER/WASHER SWITCH connector. Connect a digital multimeter from connector cavity 7 (switch side) to chassis ground. Measure resistance.	Less than infinite.	Replace WINDSHIELD WIPER/WASHER SWITCH.
		Infinite.	Repair short to ground in PNK/YEL wire between WINDSHIELD WIPER/WASHER SWITCH and WINDSHIELD WIPER MOTOR.
A22.	Disconnect WINDSHIELD WIPER MOTOR connector. Connect a digital multimeter from cavity 4 to chassis ground. Measure resistance.	More than 0.3 ohms.	Repair BLK ground wire between WINDSHIELD WIPER MOTOR and G102.
		Less than 0.3 ohms.	GO TO A23.
A23.	Connect a digital multimeter across WINDSHIELD WIPER MOTOR connector cavities 2 and 5. Measure resistance.	Less than 0.3 ohms.	Replace WINDSHIELD WIPER MOTOR.
		More than 0.3 ohms.	GO TO A24.
A24.	Disconnect WINDSHIELD WIPER/WASHER SWITCH connector. Connect a digital multimeter from WINDSHIELD WIPER/WASHER SWITCH connector terminal 5 (wiring harness side) to WINDSHIELD WIPER MOTOR connector cavity 5. Measure resistance.	Less than 0.3 ohms.	Replace WINDSHIELD WIPER/WASHER SWITCH.
		More than 0.3 ohms.	Repair open in BLU/GRN wire between WINDSHIELD WIPER/WASHER SWITCH and WINDSHIELDWIPER MOTOR.
A25.	Disconnect WINDSHIELD WIPER/WASHER SWITCH connector.	WINDSHIELD WIPER MOTOR continues to operate.	Repair short to ground in BLU/WHT or PNK/YEL wire between WINDSHIELD WIPER MOTOR and WINDSHIELD WIPER/WASHER SWITCH.
		WINDSHIELD WIPER MOTOR stops.	GO TO A26.
A26.	Disconnect WINDSHIELD WIPER MOTOR. Connect a digital multimeter from cavity 5 to chassis ground. Measure resistance.	Infinite.	Replace WINDSHIELD WIPER/WASHER SWITCH.
		Less than infinite.	Repair short to ground in BLU/GRN wire between WINDSHIELD WIPER/WASHER SWITCH and WINDSHIELD WIPER MOTOR.

GC9029100209020X

Fig. 17 System diagnostic chart (Part 2 of 2). Storm less pulse wiper

SYSTEM DIAGNOSIS

WIPER/WASHER: PULSE — DIAGNOSTIC CHART A

	TEST	RESULT	ACTION
A1.	Turn ignition switch to "ON." Press WASH button for one to two seconds and release.	WINDSHIELD WASHER PUMP operates and wipers complete at least one sweep.	GO TO A2.
		WINDSHIELD WASHER PUMP does not operate.	GO TO A6.
		WINDSHIELD WASHER PUMP operates but wipers do not sweep.	GO TO A11.
		WINDSHIELD WASHER PUMP continues to operate after WASH button is released.	GO TO A19.
		Wipers continue for more than two sweeps after WASH button is released.	GO TO A21.
		Wipers do not complete at least one full sweep.	GO TO A28.
A2.	Press and release OFF/MIST button.	Wipers complete one full sweep.	GO TO A3.
		Wipers do not operate.	GO TO A30.
A3.	Press "INT" button.	Wipers complete one full sweep every four seconds.	GO TO A4.
		Wipers do not operate.	GO TO A31.
A4.	Press "LO" button.	Wipers operate at low speed.	GO TO A5.
		Wipers do not operate.	Replace WINDSHIELD WIPER/WASHER SWITCH.
A5.	Press "HI" button.	Wipers operate at high speed.	All systems diagnosed in this cell are functioning normally.
		Wipers do not operate.	GO TO A33.
A6.	Disconnect WINDSHIELD WASHER PUMP connector. Connect a digital multimeter from cavity 2 to chassis ground. Measure resistance.	More than 0.3 ohms.	Repair BLK ground wire between WINDSHIELD WASHER PUMP and G103.
		Less than 0.3 ohms.	GO TO A7.
A7.	Connect a test lamp from WINDSHIELD WASHER PUMP cavity 1 to chassis ground. Press and hold WASH button.	Test lamp lights.	Replace WINDSHIELD WASHER PUMP.
		Test lamp does not light.	GO TO A8.
A8.	Backprobe WINDSHIELD WIPER/WASHER SWITCH with a test lamp from cavity 4 to chassis ground. Press and hold WASH button.	Test lamp lights.	Repair open in BLU/YEL wire between WINDSHIELD WIPER/WASHER SWITCH and WINDSHIELD WASHER PUMP.
		Test lamp does not light.	GO TO A9.
A9.	Backprobe WINDSHIELD WIPER/WASHER SWITCH connector with a test lamp from cavity 3 to chassis ground.	Test lamp lights.	Replace WINDSHIELD WIPER/WASHER SWITCH.
		Test lamp does not light.	GO TO A10.
A10.	Backprobe JUNCTION BLOCK connector C4 with a test lamp from cavity 16 to chassis ground.	Test lamp does not light.	Replace JUNCTION BLOCK.
		Test lamp lights.	Repair open in BLU wire between JUNCTION BLOCK and WINDSHIELD WIPER/WASHER SWITCH.
A11.	Backprobe WINDSHIELD WIPER MOTOR connector with a test lamp from cavity 6 to chassis ground.	Test lamp does not light.	Repair open in BLU wire between JUNCTION BLOCK and WINDSHIELD WIPER MOTOR.
		Test lamp lights.	GO TO A12.
A12.	Backprobe WINDSHIELD WIPER MOTOR connector with a fused jumper from cavity 2 to chassis ground.	WINDSHIELD WIPER MOTOR does not operate.	Replace WINDSHIELD WIPER MOTOR.
		WINDSHIELD WIPER MOTOR operates.	Remove jumper, GO TO A13.
A13.	Disconnect INTERMITTENT WIPER RELAY connector. Connect a test lamp from cavity 11 to chassis ground.	Test lamp does not light.	Repair open in BLU wire between INTERMITTENT WIPER RELAY and S101.
		Test lamp lights.	GO TO A14.
A14.	Connect a test lamp from cavity 8 to chassis ground. Press and hold WASH button.	Test lamp does not light.	Repair open in BLU/YEL wire between INTERMITTENT WIPER RELAY and S100.
		Test lamp lights.	GO TO A15.

GC9029100210010X

Fig. 18 System diagnostic chart (Part 1 of 2). Storm w/pulse wiper

SYSTEM DIAGNOSIS

WIPER/WASHER: PULSE	DIAGNOSTIC CHART A (CONT'D)	
TEST	**RESULT**	**ACTION**
A15. Connect a digital multimeter from INTERMITTENT WIPER RELAY connector cavity 9 to chassis ground. Measure resistance.	More than 0.3 ohms.	Repair BLK ground wire between INTERMITTENT WIPER RELAY and G102.
	Less than 0.3 ohms.	GO TO A16.
A16. Connect a fused jumper from INTERMITTENT WIPER RELAY connector cavity 2 to chassis ground.	WINDSHIELD WIPER MOTOR operates.	Replace INTERMITTENT WIPER RELAY.
	WINDSHIELD WIPER MOTOR does not operate.	Remove jumper, GO TO A17.
A17. Backprobe WINDSHIELD WIPER/WASHER SWITCH connector with a fused jumper from cavity 5 to chassis ground.	WINDSHIELD WIPER MOTOR operates.	Repair open in BLU/GRN wire between WINDSHIELD WIPER/WASHER SWITCH and WINDSHIELD WASHER PUMP.
	WINDSHIELD WIPER MOTOR does not operate.	Remove jumper, GO TO A18.
A18. Backprobe WINDSHIELD WIPER/WASHER SWITCH connector with a fused jumper from cavity 7 to chassis ground.	WINDSHIELD WIPER MOTOR operates.	Replace WINDSHIELD WIPER/ WASHER SWITCH.
	WINDSHIELD WIPER MOTOR does not operate.	Repair open in PNK/YEL wire between WINDSHIELD WIPER/WASHER SWITCH and WINDSHIELD WIPER MOTOR.
A19. Disconnect WINDSHIELD WIPER/WASHER SWITCH connector.	WINDSHIELD WASHER PUMP stops.	Replace WINDSHIELD WIPER/ WASHER SWITCH.
	WINDSHIELD WASHER PUMP continues to operate.	GO TO A20.
A20. Disconnect INTERMITTENT WIPER RELAY connector.	WINDSHIELD WASHER PUMP stops.	Replace INTERMITTENT WIPER RELAY.
	WINDSHIELD WASHER PUMP continues to operate.	Repair short to voltage in BLU/YEL wire between WINDSHIELD WIPER/ WASHER SWITCH, INTERMITTENT WIPER RELAY and WINDSHIELD WASHER PUMP.
A21. Disconnect INTERMITTENT WIPER RELAY connector.	WINDSHIELD WIPER MOTOR continues to operate.	GO TO A22.
	WINDSHIELD WIPER MOTOR stops.	GO TO A24.
A22. Disconnect WINDSHIELD WIPER/WASHER SWITCH connector.	WINDSHIELD WIPER MOTOR continues to operate.	Repair short to ground in BLU/WHT or PNK/YEL wire between WINDSHIELD WIPER/WASHER SWITCH and WINDSHIELD WIPER MOTOR.
	WINDSHIELD WIPER MOTOR stops.	GO TO A23.
A23. Connect a digital multimeter from INTERMITTENT WIPER RELAY connector cavity 2 to chassis ground. Measure resistance.	Infinite.	Replace WINDSHIELD WIPER/ WASHER SWITCH.
	Less than infinite.	Repair short to ground in BLU/GRN wire between WINDSHIELD WIPER/ WASHER SWITCH and INTERMIT-TENT WIPER RELAY.
A24. Connect a test lamp from INTERMITTENT WIPER RELAY connector cavity 4 to chassis ground. Press "LO" button.	Test lamp does not light.	GO TO A25.
	Test lamp lights only when wipers are in PARK position.	GO TO A26.
A25. Backprobe WINDSHIELD WIPER MOTOR connector with a test lamp from cavity 5 to chassis ground.	Test lamp does not light.	Replace WINDSHIELD WIPER MOTOR.
	Test lamp lights only when wipers are in PARK position.	Repair open in BLU/ORN wire between WINDSHIELD WIPER MOTOR and INTERMITTENT WIPER RELAY.
A26. Connect a digital multimeter from INTERMITTENT WIPER RELAY connector cavity 7 to chassis ground. Measure resistance.	Infinite.	Replace INTERMITTENT WIPER RELAY.
	Less than infinite.	GO TO A27.
A27. Disconnect WINDSHIELD WIPER/WASHER SWITCH connector. Connect a digital multimeter from cavity 9 (SWITCH side) to chassis ground. Measure resistance.	Less than infinite.	Replace WINDSHIELD WIPER/ WASHER SWITCH.
	Infinite.	Repair short to ground in LT GRN/ RED wire on WINDSHIELD WIPER/ WASHER SWITCH.
A28. Disconnect INTERMITTENT WIPER RELAY connector.	Test lamp lights only when wipers are in PARK position.	Replace INTERMITTENT WIPER RELAY.
	Test lamp lit continuously.	GO TO A29.
A29. Connect a test lamp from cavity 4 to chassis ground. Press "LO" button.	Test lamp does not light.	Replace WINDSHIELD WIPER MOTOR.
Disconnect WINDSHIELD WIPER MOTOR connector. Connect a test lamp from connector cavity 5 to chassis ground.	Test lamp lights.	Repair short to voltage in BLU/ORN wire between WINDSHIELD WIPER MOTOR and INTERMITTENT WIPER RELAY.
A30.	Less than 0.3 ohms.	Replace WINDSHIELD WIPER/ WASHER SWITCH.
Disconnect WINDSHIELD WIPER/WASHER SWITCH connector. Connect a digital multimeter from connector terminal 8 to chassis ground. Measure resistance.	More than 0.3 ohms.	Repair BLK ground wire between WINDSHIELD WIPER/WASHER SWITCH and G201.
A31.	Less than 0.3 ohms.	Replace INTERMITTENT WIPER RELAY.
Turn ignition switch to "OFF." Disconnect INTERMITTENT	More than 0.3 ohms.	GO TO A32.
A32. WIPER RELAY connector. Connect a digital multimeter from cavity 7 to chassis ground. Measure resistance.	More than 0.3 ohms.	Replace WINDSHIELD WIPER/ WASHER SWITCH.
Backprobe WINDSHIELD WIPER/WASHER SWITCH connector with a digital multimeter from cavity 9 to chassis ground. Measure resistance.	Less than 0.3 ohms.	Repair open in LT GRN/RED wire between WINDSHIELD WIPER/ WASHER SWITCH and INTERMITTENT WIPER RELAY.
A33.	WINDSHIELD WIPER MOTOR does not operate.	Replace WINDSHIELD WIPER MOTOR.
Backprobe WINDSHIELD WIPER MOTOR connector with a fused jumper from cavity 1 to chassis ground.	WINDSHIELD WIPER MOTOR operates.	Remove jumper, GO TO A34.
A34.	WINDSHIELD WIPER MOTOR operates.	Replace WINDSHIELD WIPER/ WASHER SWITCH.
Backprobe WINDSHIELD WIPER/WASHER SWITCH with a fused jumper from cavity 6 to chassis ground.	WINDSHIELD WIPER MOTOR does not operate.	Repair open in BLU/WHT wire between WINDSHIELD WIPER/ WASHER SWITCH and WINDSHIELD WIPER MOTOR.

GC9029100210020X

Fig. 18 System diagnostic chart (Part 2 of 2). Storm w/pulse wiper

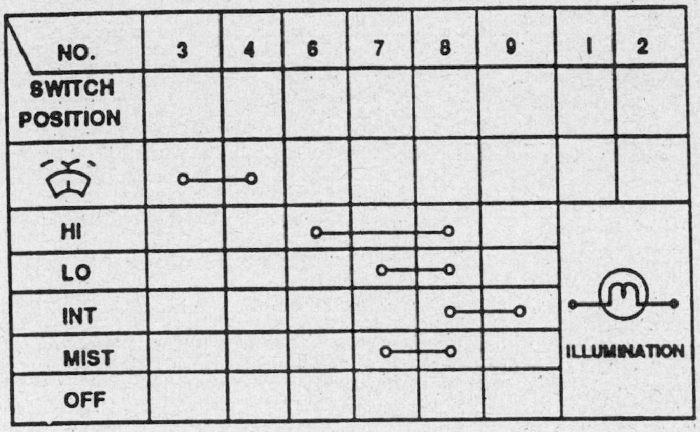
NO.
3
4
6
7
8
9
1
2
SWITCH POSITION
HI
LO
INT
MIST
OFF
ILLUMINATION
GC9029100211000X

Fig. 19 Wiper switch continuity chart. Storm

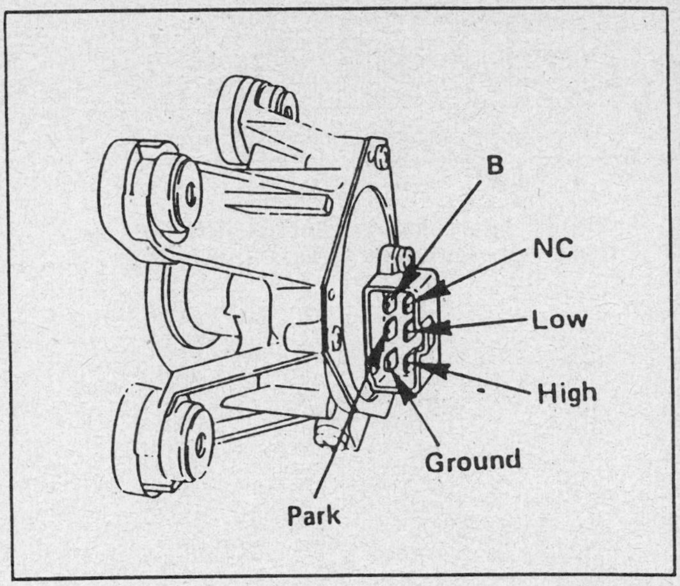
B
NC
Low
High
Ground
Park
GC9029100213000X

Fig. 20 Windshield wiper connections. Storm

Rear Window Wiper Systems

INDEX

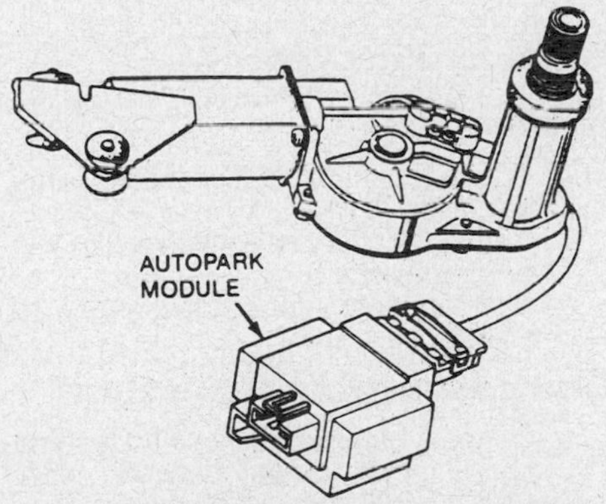
AUTOPARK MODULE
GC9029100214000X

Fig. 1 Rear wiper motor assembly. Century & Cutlass Cruiser wagons

DESCRIPTION

CENTURY & CUTLASS CRUISER WAGONS

These vehicles use a one speed, 12 volt, DC permanent magnet motor, **Fig. 1**. The motor drives a gearbox which in turn drives a wiper pivot that provides an oscillating output to the arm and blade.

The system operates only with the ignition in Run position, but will park if the ignition is turned off.

There are three electrical terminals on the motor, **Fig. 2.** Terminals A, B and C are used when the motor is in Run mode. A and C are positive and B is ground.

When wiper switch is set to OFF, only motor terminals A and B are used, with A being positive and the circuit being completed through the closed park switch terminals. A cam on the gear then opens at Park position and the wiper shuts off.

The autopark module supplies power to the rear wiper motor to allow the wiper arm to park if the ignition switch is turned off while the wiper is operating.

CAPRICE, CUSTOM CRUISER, IMPALA SS & ROADMASTER WAGONS

These vehicles use a one speed permanent magnet motor. The motor drives a gearbox which in turn drives a wiper pivot that provides an oscillating output to the arm and blade.

METRO & PRIZM

These vehicles use a one speed type motor.

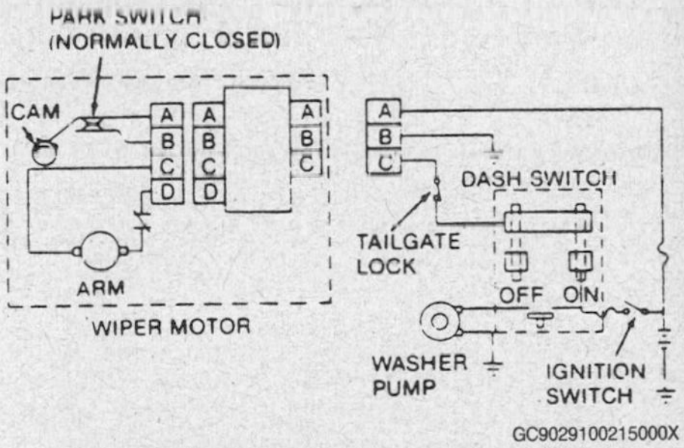
PARK SWITCH (NORMALLY CLOSED)
CAM
A
B
C
D
ARM
WIPER MOTOR
DASH SWITCH
TAILGATE LOCK
OFF
ON
WASHER PUMP
IGNITION SWITCH
GC9029100215000X

Fig. 2 Rear wiper motor wiring schematic. Century & Cutlass Cruiser wagons

STORM

These vehicles use a one speed type motor and are equipped with a separate type washer pump and reservoir located behind rear end trim panel.

SYSTEM DIAGNOSIS & TESTING

CENTURY & CUTLASS CRUISER WAGONS

Before removing wiper assembly from

REAR WINDOW WIPER SWITCH CHECK		
TERMINAL	SWITCH MODE	
	OFF	ON
A	B(+)	0V
B	0V	B(+)
C	GROUND	GROUND
D	0V	B(+)

GC9029100216000X

Fig. 3 Rear window wiper switch test chart. Century & Cutlass Cruiser wagons

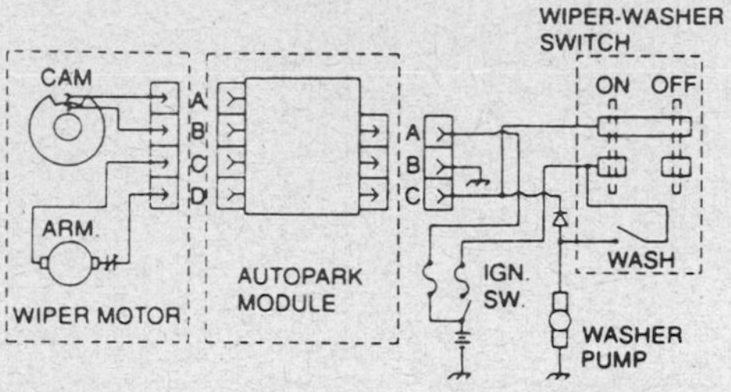
WIPER-WASHER SWITCH
CAM
A
B
C
D
ON
OFF
A
B
C
ARM
WASH
AUTOPARK MODULE
IGN. SW.
WIPER MOTOR
WASHER PUMP

GC9029100217000X

Fig. 4 Rear wiper motor wiring schematic. Caprice, Custom Cruiser, Impala SS & Roadmaster wagons

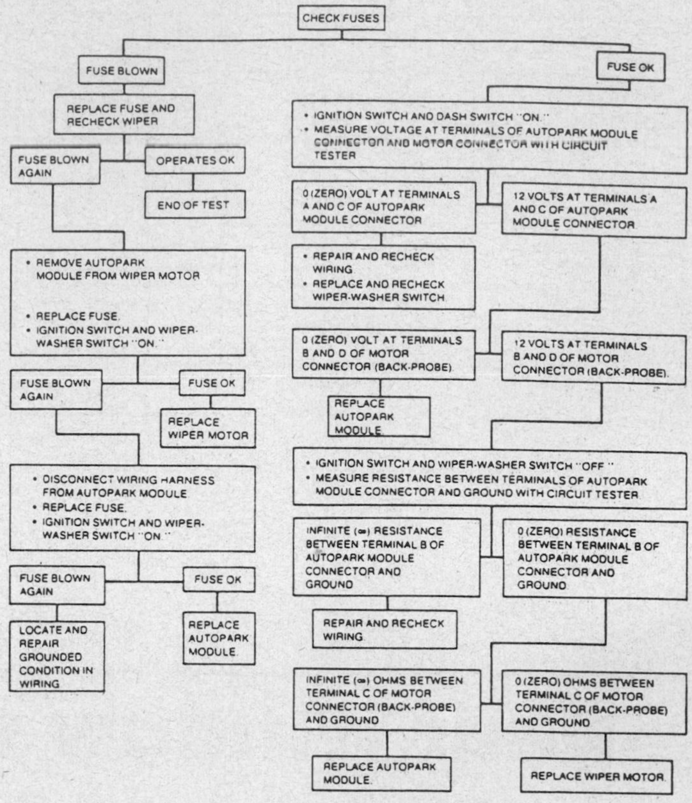
CHECK FUSES
FUSE BLOWN
FUSE OK
REPLACE FUSE AND RECHECK WIPER
• IGNITION SWITCH AND DASH SWITCH "ON."
• MEASURE VOLTAGE AT TERMINALS OF AUTOPARK MODULE CONNECTOR AND MOTOR CONNECTOR WITH CIRCUIT TESTER
FUSE BLOWN AGAIN
OPERATES OK
END OF TEST
0 (ZERO) VOLT AT TERMINALS A AND C OF AUTOPARK MODULE CONNECTOR
12 VOLTS AT TERMINALS A AND C OF AUTOPARK MODULE CONNECTOR
• REMOVE AUTOPARK MODULE FROM WIPER MOTOR
• REPLACE FUSE.
• IGNITION SWITCH AND WIPER-WASHER SWITCH "ON."
• REPAIR AND RECHECK WIRING.
• REPLACE AND RECHECK WIPER-WASHER SWITCH
0 (ZERO) VOLT AT TERMINALS B AND D OF MOTOR CONNECTOR (BACK-PROBE)
12 VOLTS AT TERMINALS B AND D OF MOTOR CONNECTOR (BACK-PROBE).
FUSE BLOWN AGAIN
FUSE OK
REPLACE WIPER MOTOR
REPLACE AUTOPARK MODULE
• DISCONNECT WIRING HARNESS FROM AUTOPARK MODULE
• REPLACE FUSE.
• IGNITION SWITCH AND WIPER-WASHER SWITCH "ON."
• IGNITION SWITCH AND WIPER-WASHER SWITCH "OFF."
• MEASURE RESISTANCE BETWEEN TERMINALS OF AUTOPARK MODULE CONNECTOR AND GROUND WITH CIRCUIT TESTER
INFINITE (∞) RESISTANCE BETWEEN TERMINAL B OF AUTOPARK MODULE CONNECTOR AND GROUND
0 (ZERO) RESISTANCE BETWEEN TERMINAL B OF AUTOPARK MODULE CONNECTOR AND GROUND
FUSE BLOWN AGAIN
FUSE OK
REPAIR AND RECHECK WIRING.
LOCATE AND REPAIR GROUNDED CONDITION IN WIRING
REPLACE AUTOPARK MODULE.
INFINITE (∞) OHMS BETWEEN TERMINAL C OF MOTOR CONNECTOR (BACK-PROBE) AND GROUND
0 (ZERO) OHMS BETWEEN TERMINAL C OF MOTOR CONNECTOR (BACK-PROBE) AND GROUND
REPLACE AUTOPARK MODULE.
REPLACE WIPER MOTOR

GC9029100218000X

Fig. 5 Rear wiper system diagnostic chart (wiper inoperative). Caprice, Custom Cruiser, Impala SS & Roadmaster wagons

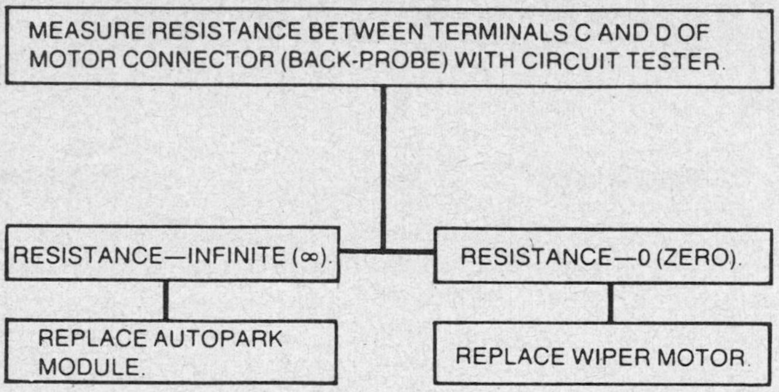
MEASURE RESISTANCE BETWEEN TERMINALS C AND D OF MOTOR CONNECTOR (BACK-PROBE) WITH CIRCUIT TESTER.
RESISTANCE—INFINITE (∞).
RESISTANCE—0 (ZERO).
REPLACE AUTOPARK MODULE.
REPLACE WIPER MOTOR.

GC9029100219000X

Fig. 6 Rear wiper system diagnostic chart (wiper will not park). Caprice, Custom Cruiser, Impala SS & Roadmaster wagons

TERMINAL	SWITCH MODE	
	OFF	ON
A	Battery Voltage	Battery Voltage
B	Ground	Ground
C	Zero Voltage	Battery Voltage

GC9029100220000X

Fig. 7 Rear window wiper switch test chart. Caprice, Custom Cruiser, Impala SS & Roadmaster wagons

vehicle, perform the following:

1. Disconnect wiring harness and apply 12 volts to motor terminals A and C and connect ground to terminal B. The motor should run.
2. To test for proper parking, apply 12 volts to terminal A and connect ground to terminal B. The wiper should park and shutoff.
3. If results are correct in steps 1 and 2, the problem is in the wiring harness or switch. After checking all wires for continuity and ensuring fuses are satisfactory, check switch by turning ignition switch on and probing connector to dash switch. Results should be as shown, **Fig. 3,** with respect to vehicle ground.

CAPRICE, CUSTOM CRUISER, IMPALA SS & ROADMASTER WAGONS

1. To test for proper motor operation, disconnect wiring harness and apply 12 volts to terminals A and C of autopark module and ground terminal B, **Fig. 4.** Motor should run.
2. To test for proper park operation, apply 12 volts to terminal A and ground terminal B. The wiper should go into park position and shutoff.
3. If wiper motor does not run in steps one and two, refer to diagnostic chart in **Fig. 5 and 6.**

Switch Test

Using a voltmeter, perform tests in **Fig. 7,** with ignition switch ON. If the voltage is not as specified, replace switch.

METRO

Refer to **Fig. 8,** for complete system diagnosis.

PRIZM

Refer to **Fig. 9,** for complete system diagnosis.

Switch Test

Using a digital multimeter, perform continuity tests in **Fig. 10.** If the continuity is not as specified, replace switch.

Motor Test

1. Connect battery positive lead to terminal 2, **Fig. 11.**
2. Connect battery negative lead to wiper motor body.
3. If wiper motor does not operate, replace motor.

Park Position Inspection

1. Connect battery positive lead to terminal 1, install jumper between terminals 2 and 3, **Fig. 12.**
2. Connect battery negative lead to wiper motor body.
3. If operation does not end in the "Park position, replace wiper motor.

STORM

Refer to **Fig. 13,** for complete system diagnosis.

Motor Test

Using a digital multimeter, take measurements and compare the results to the specifications in **Fig. 14.** If the motor does not operate as specified, replace motor.

SYSTEM DIAGNOSIS

REAR WIPER/WASHER	DIAGNOSTIC CHART A	
TEST	**RESULT**	**ACTION**
A1. Turn Rear Wiper Switch ON.	REAR WIPER MOTOR operates.	GO TO A2.
	REAR WIPER MOTOR does not operate.	GO TO A5.
A2. Turn Rear Wiper Switch OFF.	REAR WIPER MOTOR stops with wiper in PARK position.	GO TO A3.
	REAR WIPER MOTOR does not stop.	GO TO A9.
	Rear wiper does not return to PARK position.	GO TO A11.
A3. Press and hold Rear Washer Switch.	REAR WASHER PUMP and REAR WIPER MOTOR both operate.	GO TO A4.
	REAR WASHER PUMP does not operate.	Release switch and GO TO A14.
	REAR WIPER MOTOR does not operate.	Replace REAR WIPER/WASHER SWITCH.
A4. Release Rear Washer Switch.	REAR WASHER PUMP and REAR WIPER MOTOR both stop with wiper in PARK position.	All systems diagnosed are functioning normally.
	REAR WASHER PUMP does not stop.	GO TO A17.
	REAR WIPER MOTOR does not stop or rear wiper does not return to PARK position.	Replace REAR WIPER/WASHER SWITCH.
A5. Backprobe REAR WIPER/WASHER SWITCH connector with a test lamp from cavity 5 to chassis ground.	Test lamp does not light.	Repair open in YEL/BLU wire between JUNCTION BLOCK and REAR WIPER/WASHER SWITCH.
	Test lamp lights.	GO TO A6.
A6. Turn Rear Wiper Switch ON. Backprobe REAR WIPER/WASHER SWITCH connector with a test lamp from cavity 2 to chassis ground.	Test lamp does not light.	Replace REAR WIPER/WASHER SWITCH.
	Test lamp lights.	GO TO A7.
A7. Backprobe REAR WIPER MOTOR connector with a test lamp from cavity 4 to chassis ground.	Test lamp does not light.	Repair open in ORN wire between REAR WIPER/WASHER SWITCH and REAR WIPER MOTOR.
	Test lamp lights.	GO TO A8.
A8. Backprobe REAR WIPER MOTOR with a digital multimeter from ground terminal to G400. Measure resistance.	More than 0.3 ohms.	Repair BLK ground wire between REAR WIPER MOTOR and G400.
	Less than 0.3 ohms.	Replace REAR WIPER MOTOR.
A9. Disconnect REAR WIPER/WASHER SWITCH connector.	REAR WIPER MOTOR continues to operate.	Repair short to voltage in ORN wire between REAR WIPER/WASHER SWITCH and REAR WIPER MOTOR
	REAR WIPER MOTOR stops.	GO TO A10.
A10. Connect a digital multimeter across REAR WIPER/WASHER SWITCH terminals 2 and 5. Measure resistance.	Less than infinite.	Replace REAR WIPER/WASHER SWITCH.
	Infinite.	Replace REAR WIPER MOTOR.
A11. Backprobe REAR WIPER MOTOR connector with a test lamp from cavity 2 to chassis ground.	Test lamp does not light.	Repair open in YEL/BLU wire between JUNCTION BLOCK and REAR WIPER MOTOR.
	Test lamp lights.	GO TO A12.
A12. Backprobe REAR WIPER MOTOR connector with a test lamp from cavity 1 to chassis ground.	Test lamp does not light.	Replace REAR WIPER MOTOR.
	Test lamp lights.	GO TO A13.
A13. Backprobe REAR WIPER/WASHER SWITCH connector with a test lamp from cavity 3 to chassis ground.	Test lamp does not light.	Repair open in BLU/GRN wire between REAR WIPER MOTOR and REAR WIPER/WASHER SWITCH.
	Test lamp lights.	Replace REAR WIPER/WASHER SWITCH.
A14. Disconnect REAR WIPER/WASHER SWITCH connector. Connect a digital multimeter from cavity 5 to cavity 1. Measure resistance while pressing Rear Washer Switch.	More than 0.3 ohms.	Replace REAR WIPER/WASHER SWITCH.
	Less than 0.3 ohms.	Release switch and GO TO A15.
A15. Reconnect REAR WIPER/WASHER SWITCH connector. Backprobe REAR WASHER PUMP connector with a test lamp from cavity 2 to chassis ground while pressing Rear Washer Switch.	Test lamp does not light.	Repair open in BLK/GRN wire between REAR WIPER/WASHER SWITCH and REAR WASHER
	Test lamp lights.	GO TO A16.
A16. Disconnect REAR WASHER PUMP connector. Connect a digital multimeter from cavity 1 to chassis ground. Measure resistance.	More than 0.3 ohms.	Repair BLK ground wire between REAR WASHER PUMP and G101.
	Less than 0.3 ohms.	Replace REAR WASHER PUMP.
A17. Disconnect REAR WIPER/WASHER SWITCH connector.	REAR WASHER PUMP stops.	Replace REAR WIPER/WASHER SWITCH.
	REAR WASHER PUMP continues to operate.	Repair short to voltage in BLK/GRN wire between REAR WIPER/WASHER SWITCH and REAR WASHER PUMP.

GC9029100221000X

Fig. 8 System diagnostic chart. Metro rear wiper

1. Connect battery positive lead to terminal 2, **Fig. 15.**
2. Connect battery negative lead to wiper motor body.
3. If wiper motor does not operate as specified in **Fig. 14,** replace motor.

Park Position Inspection

1. Connect battery positive lead to terminal 2, **Fig. 15.**
2. Connect battery negative lead to wiper motor body.
3. Remove battery positive lead from terminal 2. Time this disconnection so that the wiper stops in any position other than "Park" position.
4. If operation does not end in the "Park position, replace wiper motor.

SYSTEM DIAGNOSIS

REAR WIPER/WASHER	DIAGNOSTIC CHART A		
	TEST	RESULT	ACTION
A1.	Press REAR WIPER SWITCH all the way to the WASH position.	Rear wiper sweeps and washer fluid is sprayed on rear window.	All systems diagnosed are functioning normally.
		Rear wiper sweeps but washer fluid is sprayed on front window.	GO TO A2.
		Rear wiper does not sweep.	GO TO A6.
		WASHER FLUID PUMP does not operate.	Check operation of front washer. If good, repair open in BLU/YEL wire between REAR WIPER SWITCH and S280.
A2.	Backprobe WASHER CHANGE VALVE connector with a test lamp from cavity 2 to chassis ground.	Test lamp does not light.	Repair open in JUNCTION BLOCK 3 or in BLU wire between JUNCTION BLOCK 3 and WASHER CHANGE VALVE.
		Test lamp lights.	GO TO A3.
A3.	Turn ignition switch to "OFF." Backprobe REAR WIPER SWITCH connector with a digital multimeter from cavity 1 to chassis ground. Measure resistance with switch pressed to WASH.	More than 0.3 ohms.	GO TO A4.
		Less than 0.3 ohms.	GO TO A5.
A4.	Backprobe REAR WIPER SWITCH with a digital multimeter from cavity 8 to chassis ground. Measure resistance.	More than 0.3 ohms.	Repair WHT/BLK ground wire between REAR WIPER SWITCH and G201 (Base, LSi) or G200 (GSi).
		Less than 0.3 ohms.	Replace REAR WIPER SWITCH.
A5.	Backprobe WASHER CHANGE VALVE connector with a digital multimeter from cavity 1 to chassis ground. Measure resistance with the REAR WIPER SWITCH pressed to WASH.	More than 0.3 ohms.	Repair open in PNK wire between WASHER CHANGE VALVE and REAR WIPER SWITCH.
		Less than 0.3 ohms.	Replace WASHER CHANGE VALVE.
A6.	Backprobe REAR WIPER SWITCH connector with a test lamp from cavity 2 to chassis ground.	Test lamp does not light.	Repair open in BLU wire or JUNCTION BLOCK 3 between JUNCTION BLOCK 1 and REAR WIPER SWITCH.
		Test lamp lights.	GO TO A7.
A7.	Backprobe REAR WIPER SWITCH connector with a test lamp from cavity 4 to chassis ground with switch pressed.	Test lamp does not light.	Replace REAR WIPER SWITCH.
		Test lamp lights.	GO TO A8.
A8.	Backprobe REAR WIPER MOTOR connector with a test lamp from cavity 3 to chassis ground with REAR WIPER SWITCH pressed.	Test lamp does not light.	Repair open in PNK wire between REAR WIPER SWITCH and REAR WIPER MOTOR.
		Test lamp lights.	GO TO A9.
A9.	Backprobe REAR WIPER MOTOR connector with a test lamp from cavity 1 to chassis ground.	Test lamp does not light.	Repair open in BLU wire between JUNCTION BLOCK 1 and REAR WIPER MOTOR.
		Test lamp lights.	GO TO A10.
A10.	Disconnect REAR WIPER MOTOR connector and REAR WIPER SWITCH connector. Connect a digital multimeter from REAR WIPER MOTOR connector cavity 2 to REAR WIPER SWITCH connector cavity 3. Measure resistance.	Less than 0.3 ohms.	Replace REAR WIPER MOTOR.
		More than 0.3 ohms.	Repair open in PNK/BLK wire between REAR WIPER MOTOR and REAR WIPER SWITCH.

GC9029100222000X

Fig. 9 System diagnostic chart. Prizm rear wiper

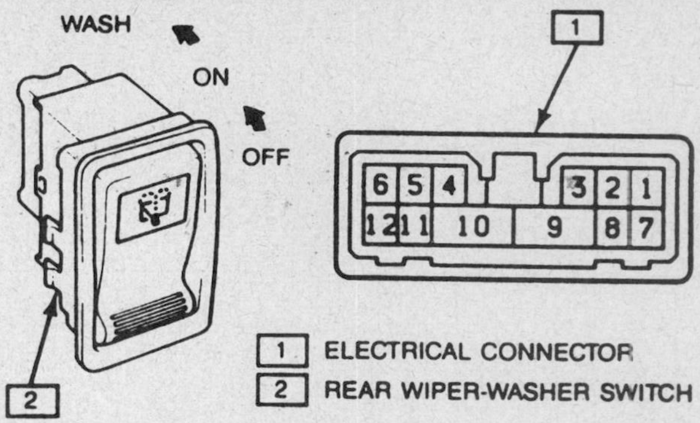

WASH
ON
OFF
1
2
6 5 4 3 2 1
12 11 10 9 8 7

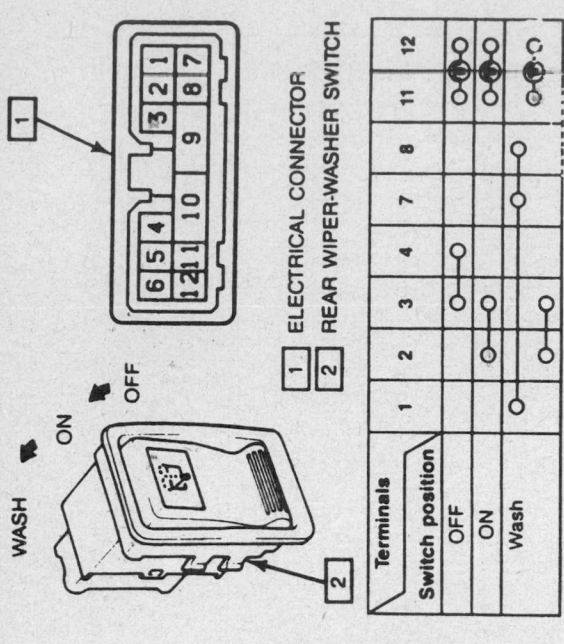

1 ELECTRICAL CONNECTOR
2 REAR WIPER-WASHER SWITCH

Switch position \ Terminals	1	2	3	4	7	8	11	12
OFF			O—	—O			O—⊗—	—O
ON		O—	—O				O—⊗—	—O
Wash	O—	O—	—O	——	—O—	—O	O—⊗—	—O

GC9029100223000X

Fig. 10 Rear wiper switch connections. Prizm

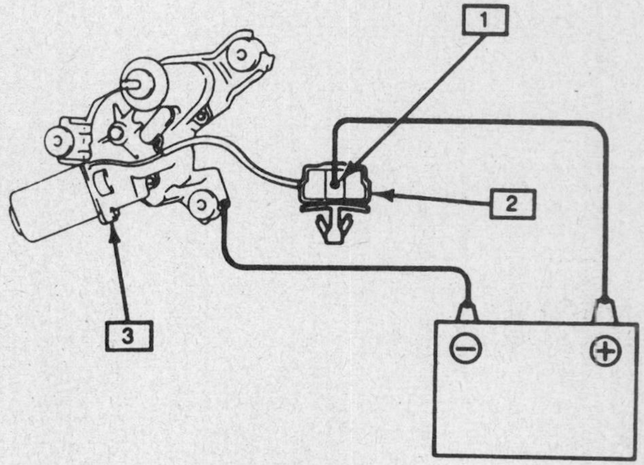

1
2
3

1 TERMINAL 2
2 ELECTRICAL CONNECTOR
3 REAR WIPER MOTOR

GC9029100224000X

Fig. 11 Rear wiper motor connections. Prizm

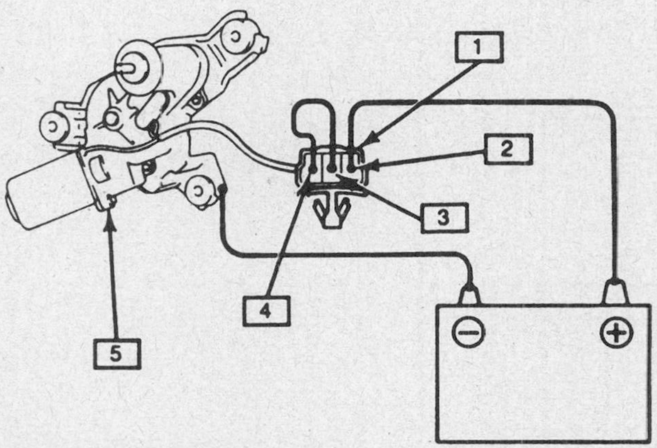
1
2
3
4
5

1 ELECTRICAL CONNECTOR
2 TERMINAL 1
3 TERMINAL 2
4 TERMINAL 3
5 REAR WIPER MOTOR

GC9029100225000X

Fig. 12 Rear wiper "Park" connections. Prizm

WIPER/WASHER — DIAGNOSTIC CHART A

	TEST	RESULT	ACTION
A1.	Turn ignition switch to "ON." Press REAR WIPER/ WASHER SWITCH to MIST/WASH (bottom of switch) and release.	REAR WASHER PUMP operates and REAR WIPER MOTOR sweeps once.	GO TO A2.
		REAR WASHER PUMP operates but REAR WIPER MOTOR does not sweep.	GO TO A5.
		REAR WIPER MOTOR sweeps once but REAR WASHER PUMP does not operate.	GO TO A8.
		REAR WIPER MOTOR and REAR WASHER PUMP do not operate.	GO TO A11.
		REAR WASHER PUMP and REAR WIPER MOTOR operate but REAR WIPER MOTOR does not complete one sweep.	GO TO A13.
A2.	Press REAR WIPER/WASHER SWITCH to WIPER (first detent on top of switch).	REAR WIPER MOTOR operates.	GO TO A3.
		REAR WIPER MOTOR does not operate.	Replace REAR WIPER/WASHER SWITCH.
A3.	Press REAR WIPER/WASHER SWITCH to WIPER/ WASHER (fully press top of switch).	REAR WIPER MOTOR and REAR WASHER PUMP operate.	GO TO A4.
		REAR WIPER MOTOR operates but REAR WASHER PUMP does not operate.	Replace REAR WIPER/WASHER SWITCH.
		REAR WASHER PUMP operates but REAR WIPER MOTOR does not operate.	Replace REAR WIPER/WASHER SWITCH.
A4.	Press REAR WIPER/WASHER SWITCH to OFF.	REAR WIPER MOTOR and REAR WASHER PUMP stop.	All systems diagnosed are functioning normally.
		REAR WIPER MOTOR or REAR WASHER PUMP continue to operate.	GO TO A15.
A5.	Disconnect REAR WIPER MOTOR connector. Connect a digital multimeter from cavity 3 to chassis ground. Measure resistance.	More than 0.3 ohms.	Repair BLK ground wire between REAR WIPER MOTOR and G401.
		Less than 0.3 ohms.	GO TO A6.
A6.	Connect a test lamp from REAR WIPER MOTOR connector cavity 2 to chassis ground. Observe test lamp while pressing REAR WIPER/WASHER SWITCH to MIST/WASH.	Test lamp lights.	Replace REAR WIPER MOTOR.
		Test lamp does not light.	GO TO A7.
A7.	Backprobe REAR WIPER/WASHER SWITCH connector with a test lamp from cavity 4 to chassis ground. Observe test lamp while pressing REAR WIPER/WASHER SWITCH to MIST/WASH.	Test lamp does not light.	Replace REAR WIPER/WASHER SWITCH.
		Test lamp lights.	Repair open in LT GRN/YEL wire between REAR WIPER/WASHER SWITCH and REAR WIPER MOTOR.
A8.	Disconnect REAR WASHER PUMP connector. Connect a digital multimeter from connector cavity 2 to chassis ground. Measure resistance.	More than 0.3 ohms.	Repair BLK ground wire between REAR WASHER PUMP and G404.
		Less than 0.3 ohms.	GO TO A9.
A9.	Connect a test lamp from REAR WASHER PUMP connector cavity 1 to chassis ground. Observe test lamp while pressing REAR WIPER/WASHER SWITCH to the MIST/WASH position.	Test lamp lights.	Replace REAR WASHER PUMP.
		Test lamp does not light.	GO TO A10.
A10.	Backprobe REAR WIPER/WASHER SWITCH connector with a test lamp from cavity 1 to chassis ground. Observe test lamp while pressing REAR WIPER/WASHER SWITCH to the MIST/WASH position.	Test lamp does not light.	Replace REAR WIPER/WASHER SWITCH.
		Test lamp lights.	Repair open in LT GRN/WHT wire between REAR WIPER/WASHER SWITCH and REAR WASHER PUMP.
A11.	Backprobe REAR WIPER/WASHER SWITCH connector with a test lamp from cavity 5 to chassis ground.	Test lamp lights.	Replace REAR WIPER/WASHER SWITCH.
		Test lamp does not light.	GO to A12.
A12.	Backprobe JUNCTION BLOCK connector C4 with a test lamp from cavity 4 to chassis ground.	Test lamp does not light.	Replace JUNCTION BLOCK.
		Test lamp lights.	Repair open in LT GRN/BLK wire between JUNCTION BLOCK and REAR WIPER/WASHER SWITCH.
A13.	Backprobe REAR WIPER MOTOR connector with a test lamp from cavity 1 to chassis ground.	Test lamp lights.	Replace REAR WIPER MOTOR.
		Test lamp does not light.	GO TO A14.
A14.	Backprobe JUNCTION BLOCK connector C7 with a test lamp from cavity 2 to chassis ground.	Test lamp does not light.	Replace JUNCTION BLOCK.
		Test lamp lights.	Repair open in LT GRN/BLK wire between JUNCTION BLOCK and REAR WIPER MOTOR.
A15.	Disconnect REAR WIPER/WASHER SWITCH connector.	REAR WIPER MOTOR or REAR WASHER PUMP stops operating.	Replace REAR WIPER/WASHER SWITCH.
		REAR WIPER MOTOR continues to operate.	Repair short to voltage in LT GRN/YEL wire between REAR WIPER/WASHER SWITCH and REAR WIPER MOTOR.
		REAR WASHER PUMP continues to operate.	Repair short to voltage in LT GRN/WHT wire between REAR WIPER/WASHER SWITCH and REAR WASHER PUMP.

GC9029100226000X

Fig. 13 System diagnostic chart. Storm rear wiper

REAR WIPER MOTOR	SPECIFICATIONS
RATED VOLTAGE	12V
OPERATING VOLTAGE	10-15V
STARTING VOLTAGE	8V
TESTING VOLTAGE	13.5V
CURRENT AT 10 KG-CM LOAD AT 15 KG-CM LOAD	2.0A OR LESS 2.5A OR LESS
STALL CURRENT	9A OR LESS
INSULATION RESISTANCE	1MΩ (MINIMUM)
SPEED (AT 10 KG-CM LOAD)	34-44 RPM

GC9029100227000X

Fig. 14 Rear wiper motor specifications. Storm

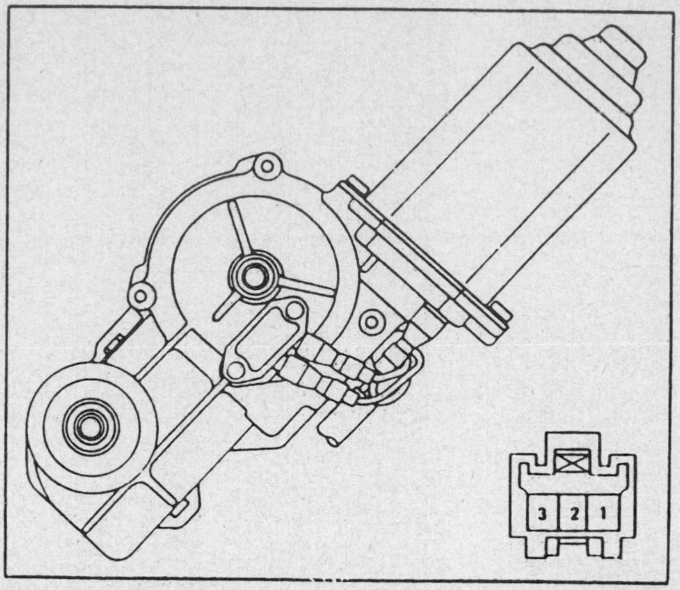
3 2 1

GC9029100228000X

Fig. 15 Rear wiper motor connections. Storm

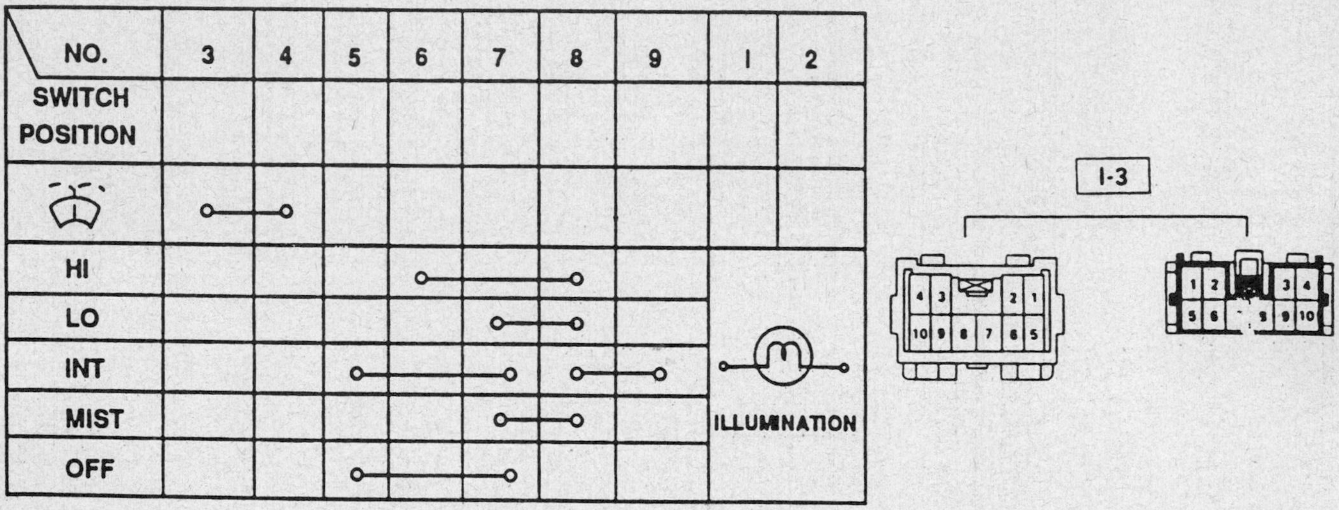
NO.
3
4
5
6
7
8
9
1
2
SWITCH POSITION
HI
LO
INT
MIST
OFF
ILLUMINATION
I-3
4 3 2 1
10 9 8 7 6 5
1 2 3 4
5 6 9 10

GC9029100212000X

Fig. 16 Windshield wiper cable continuity chart. Storm

PASSIVE RESTRAINT SYSTEMS

TABLE OF CONTENTS

Air Bag System

INDEX

AIR BAG SYSTEM DISARMING & ARMING

ACHIEVA, GRAND AM & SKYLARK

Disarming

The diagnostic energy reserve module or sensing and diagnostic module (DERM/SDM) can maintain enough voltage to cause air bag deployment for up to ten minutes after the ignition switch is turned off and the battery is disconnected. Servicing the SIR system during this period may result in accidental deployment and personal injury.

1. Ensure front wheels are pointed straight ahead.
2. Turn ignition switch to Lock position.
3. Remove AIR BAG fuse from fuse block.
4. Working through trap door located in the lefthand sound insulator, disconnect Connector Position Assurance (CPA) and yellow 2-way connector at base of steering column.

Arming

1. Turn ignition switch to the Lock position and remove key.
2. Working through trap door located in the lefthand sound insulator, connect Connector Position Assurance (CPA) and yellow 2-way connector at base of steering column.
3. Install AIR BAG fuse.
4. Turn ignition switch to the Run position and verify that the AIR BAG warning lamp flashes seven times and then turns off. If lamp does not operate as specified, refer to "Diagnosis & Testing."

BERETTA & CORSICA

Disarming

The diagnostic energy reserve module or sensing and diagnostic module (DERM/SDM) can maintain enough voltage to cause air bag deployment for up to ten minutes after the ignition switch is turned off and the battery is disconnected. Servicing the SIR system during this period may result in accidental deployment and personal injury.

1. Ensure front wheels are pointed straight ahead.
2. Turn ignition switch to Lock position and remove SIR or AIR BAG fuse.
3. Remove left sound insulator. **Remove courtesy lamp from sound insulator, if necessary.**
4. Disconnect Connector Position Assurance (CPA), then the yellow two-way SIR electrical connector at base of steering column.

Arming

1. **On models with passenger air bag,** connect CPA and yellow 2-way connector to passenger inflator pigtail, then install righthand sound insulator.
2. **On all models,** connect yellow two-way SIR electrical connector, then install Connector Position Assurance (CPA).
3. Install left sound insulator. **Install courtesy lamp to sound insulator, if applicable.**
4. Install SIR fuse to fuse block, turn ignition switch to Run position and ensure "Inflatable Restraint" lamp flashes 7 to 9 times, then turns off.

BONNEVILLE, LESABRE, PARK AVENUE, 88 & 98

Disarming

The diagnostic energy reserve module or sensing and diagnostic module (DERM/SDM) can maintain enough voltage to cause air bag deployment for up to ten minutes after the ignition switch is turned off and the battery is disconnected. Servicing the SIR system during this period may result in accidental deployment and personal injury.

1. Ensure front wheels are pointed straight ahead.
2. Turn ignition switch to Lock position and remove SIR or AIR BAG fuse.
3. Remove left sound insulator. **Remove courtesy lamp from sound insulator, if necessary.**
4. Disconnect Connector Position Assurance (CPA), then the yellow two-way SIR electrical connector at base of steering column.
5. **On models with passenger air bag,** remove righthand sound insulator and disconnect CPA and yellow 2-way connector from passenger inflator pigtail.

Arming

1. **On models with passenger air bag,** connect CPA and yellow 2-way con-

nector to passenger inflator pigtail, then install righthand sound insulator.

2. **On all models,** connect yellow two-way SIR electrical connector, then install Connector Position Assurance (CPA).
3. Install left sound insulator. **Install courtesy lamp to sound insulator, if applicable.**
4. Install SIR fuse to fuse block, turn ignition switch to Run position and ensure "Inflatable Restraint" lamp flashes 7 to 9 times, then turns off.

CAMARO & FIREBIRD

Disarming

The diagnostic energy reserve module or sensing and diagnostic module (DERM/SDM) can maintain enough voltage to cause air bag deployment for up to ten minutes after the ignition switch is turned off and the battery is disconnected. Servicing the SIR system during this period may result in accidental deployment and personal injury.

1. Ensure front wheels are pointed straight ahead.
2. Turn ignition switch to Lock position and remove SIR or AIR BAG fuse.
3. Remove left sound insulator. **Remove courtesy lamp from sound insulator, if necessary.**
4. Disconnect Connector Position Assurance (CPA), then the yellow two-way SIR electrical connector at base of steering column.
5. Remove glove compartment door assembly, then CPA and yellow 2-way connector from passenger inflator module.

Arming

1. Turn ignition switch to the Lock position and remove key.
2. Connect CPA and yellow 2-way connector to passenger inflator module, then install glove compartment door assembly.
3. Connect yellow two-way SIR electrical connector, then install Connector Position Assurance (CPA) near base of steering column.
4. Install left sound insulator. **Install courtesy lamp to sound insulator, if applicable.**
5. Install SIR fuse to fuse block, then verify that the "Inflatable Restraint" lamp flashes 7 to 9 times and then turns off. If lamp does not operate as specified, refer to "Diagnosis & Testing."

CAPRICE, CUSTOM CRUISER & ROADMASTER

Disarming

The diagnostic energy reserve module or sensing and diagnostic module (DERM/SDM) can maintain enough voltage to cause air bag deployment for up to ten minutes after the ignition switch is turned off and the battery is disconnected. Servicing the SIR system during this period may result in accidental deployment and personal injury.

1. Ensure front wheels are pointed straight ahead.
2. Turn ignition switch to Lock position and remove SIR or AIR BAG fuse from fuse block.
3. **On 1992-93 models**, remove Connector Position Assurance (CPA), then disconnect yellow two-way SIR electrical connector at base of steering column.
4. **On 1994 models,** remove Connector Position Assurance (CPA), then disconnect both yellow two-way SIR electrical connectors at base of steering column.

Arming

1. **On 1992-93 models,** connect yellow two-way SIR electrical connector at base of column, then install Connector Position Assurance (CPA).
2. **On 1994 models,** connect both yellow two-way SIR electrical connectors at base of column, then install Connector Position Assurance (CPA).
3. **On all models,** install SIR or AIR BAG fuse into fuse block, turn ignition switch to Run position and ensure "Inflatable Restraint" lamp flashes 7 to 9 times and then turns off.

CENTURY, CUTLASS CIERA & CUTLASS CRUISER

Disarming

The diagnostic energy reserve module or sensing and diagnostic module (DERM/SDM) can maintain enough voltage to cause air bag deployment for up to ten minutes after the ignition switch is turned off and the battery is disconnected. Servicing the SIR system during this period may result in accidental deployment and personal injury.

1. Ensure front wheels are pointed straight ahead.
2. Turn ignition switch to Lock position and remove SIR or AIR BAG fuse.
3. Remove left sound insulator. **Remove courtesy lamp from sound insulator, if necessary.**
4. Remove Connector Position Assurance (CPA), then disconnect yellow two-way SIR electrical connector at base of steering column.

Arming

1. Connect yellow two-way SIR electrical connector, then install Connector Position Assurance (CPA).
2. Install left sound insulator. **Install courtesy lamp to sound insulator, if applicable.**
3. Install SIR or AIR BAG fuse into fuse block, the turn ignition switch to Run position and ensure AIR BAG warning lamp flashes 7 times and then turns off. If warning lamp does not operate as specified, refer to "Diagnosis & Testing."

DEVILLE & FLEETWOOD

DISARMING

1992–93

The diagnostic energy reserve module or sensing and diagnostic module (DERM/SDM) can maintain enough voltage to cause air bag deployment for up to ten minutes after the ignition switch is turned off and the battery is disconnected. Servicing the SIR system during this period may result in accidental deployment and personal injury.

1. Ensure front wheels are pointed straight ahead.
2. Turn ignition switch to Lock position and remove SIR or AIR BAG fuse.
3. Remove left sound insulator. **Remove courtesy lamp from sound insulator, if necessary.**
4. Disconnect Connector Position Assurance (CPA), then the yellow two-way SIR electrical connector at base of steering column.

1994

The diagnostic energy reserve module or sensing and diagnostic module (DERM/SDM) can maintain enough voltage to cause air bag deployment for up to ten minutes after the ignition switch is turned off and the battery is disconnected. Servicing the SIR system during this period may result in accidental deployment and personal injury.

1. Ensure front wheels are pointed straight ahead.
2. Turn ignition key to the Lock position and remove key.
3. **On Fleetwood (RWD)**, remove AIR BAG fuse from instrument panel fuse block.
4. **On all models,** remove lefthand sound insulator from under steering column.
5. **On Fleetwood (RWD),** remove CPAs and disconnect both yellow 2-way connectors located near base of steering column.

ARMING

1992–93

1. Connect yellow two-way SIR electrical connector, then install Connector Position Assurance (CPA).
2. Install left sound insulator. **Install courtesy lamp to sound insulator, if applicable.**
3. Install SIR fuse to fuse block, turn ignition switch to Run position and ensure "Inflatable Restraint" lamp flashes 7 to 9 times, then turns off. If lamp does not operate as specified, refer to "Diagnosis & Testing."

1994

1. Turn ignition to the Lock position and remove key.
2. **On Deville,** connect 2-way yellow connector and install CPA at base of steering column.

3. **On Fleetwood (RWD),** connect both yellow 2-way connectors and install CPAs at base of steering column.
4. **On all models,** install lefthand sound insulator.
5. **On Fleetwood (RWD),** install AIR BAG fuse into instrument panel fuse block.
6. **On all models,** turn ignition switch to the Run position and verify that AIR BAG warning lamp flashes seven times and then turns off. If warning lamp does not operate as specified, refer to "Diagnosis & Testing."

CORVETTE

DISARMING

1992–93

The diagnostic energy reserve module (DERM) can maintain enough voltage to cause air bag deployment for up to ten minutes after the ignition switch is turned off and the battery is disconnected. Servicing the SIR system during this period may result in accidental deployment and personal injury.

1. Ensure front wheels are pointed straight ahead.
2. Turn ignition switch to Lock position and remove AIR BAG fuse.
3. Remove left sound insulator. **Remove courtesy lamp from sound insulator, if necessary.**
4. Disconnect Connector Position Assurance (CPA), then the yellow two-way SIR electrical connector at base of steering column.

1994

1. Ensure front wheels are pointed straight ahead.
2. Turn ignition switch to Lock position and remove key.
3. Remove AIR BAG fuse from instrument panel fuse block.
4. Remove trim panel from under steering column.
5. Remove Connector Position Assurance (CPA), then disconnect both yellow SIR connectors located near base of steering column.

ARMING

1992–93

1. **On models with passenger air bag,** connect CPA and yellow 2-way connector to passenger inflator pigtail, then install righthand sound insulator.
2. **On all models,** connect yellow two-way SIR electrical connector, then install Connector Position Assurance (CPA).
3. Install left sound insulator. **Install courtesy lamp to sound insulator, if applicable.**
4. Install SIR fuse to fuse block, turn ignition switch to Run position and ensure "Inflatable Restraint" lamp flashes 7 to 9 times, then turns off.

1994

1. Turn ignition key to the Lock position.
2. Connect both yellow SIR connectors and corresponding CPAs located near base of steering column.
3. Install trim panel under steering column.
4. Install AIR BAG fuse into instrument panel fuse block.
5. Turn ignition switch to the Run position and verify that the AIR BAG warning lamp flashes seven times and then turns off. If warning lamp does not operate as specified, refer to "Diagnosis & Testing."

CUTLASS SUPREME & REGAL

Disarming

The diagnostic energy reserve module or sensing and diagnostic module (DERM/SDM) can maintain enough voltage to cause air bag deployment for up to ten minutes after the ignition switch is turned off and the battery is disconnected. Servicing the SIR system during this period may result in accidental deployment and personal injury.

1. Ensure front wheels are pointed straight ahead.
2. Turn ignition switch to the Lock position.
3. Remove ARBG1 fuse from fuse block.
4. Remove trim panel from under steering column.
5. Disconnect Connector Position Assurance (CPA) and yellow 2-way connector at base of steering column.

Arming

The diagnostic energy reserve module or sensing and diagnostic module (DERM/SDM) can maintain enough voltage to cause air bag deployment for up to ten minutes after the ignition switch is turned off and the battery is disconnected. Servicing the SIR system during this period may result in accidental deployment and personal injury.

1. Turn ignition switch to the Lock position and remove key.
2. Connect Connector Position Assurance (CPA) and yellow 2-way connector at base of steering column.
3. Install trim panel under steering column.
4. Install ARBG1 fuse into fuse block.
5. Turn ignition switch to the Run position and verify that the AIR BAG warning lamp flashes seven times and then turns off. If lamp does not operate as specified, refer to "Diagnosis & Testing."

ELDORADO, RIVIERA, SEVILLE, TORONADO & TROFEO

Disarming

The diagnostic energy reserve module (DERM) can maintain enough voltage to cause air bag deployment for up to ten minutes after the ignition switch is turned off and the battery is disconnected. Servicing the SIR system during this period may result in accidental deployment and personal injury.

1. Ensure front wheels are pointed straight ahead.
2. Turn ignition switch to Lock position and remove SIR or AIR BAG fuse.
3. Remove left sound insulator. **Remove courtesy lamp from sound insulator, if necessary.**
4. Disconnect Connector Position Assurance (CPA), then the yellow two-way SIR electrical connector at base of steering column.
5. **On models with passenger air bag,** remove righthand sound insulator and disconnect CPA and yellow 2-way connector from passenger inflator pigtail.

Arming

1. **On models with passenger air bag,** connect CPA and yellow 2-way connector to passenger inflator pigtail, then install righthand sound insulator.
2. **On all models,** connect yellow two-way SIR electrical connector, then install Connector Position Assurance (CPA).
3. Install left sound insulator. **Install courtesy lamp to sound insulator, if applicable.**
4. Install SIR fuse to fuse block, turn ignition switch to Run position and ensure "Inflatable Restraint" lamp flashes 7 to 9 times, then turns off.

GRAND PRIX

Disarming

The diagnostic energy reserve module or sensing and diagnostic module (DERM/SDM) can maintain enough voltage to cause air bag deployment for up to ten minutes after the ignition switch is turned off and the battery is disconnected. Servicing the SIR system during this period may result in accidental deployment and personal injury.

1. Ensure front wheels are pointed straight ahead.
2. Turn ignition switch to the Lock position and remove key.
3. Remove AIR BAG fuse from instrument panel fuse block.
4. Remove trim panel from under steering column.
5. Disconnect Connector Position Assurance (CPA) and yellow 2-way connector at base of steering column.
6. Open glove compartment door and disconnect passenger's side Connector Position Assurance (CPA) and yellow 2-way connector.

Arming

1. Turn ignition switch to the Lock position and remove key.
2. Open glove compartment door and connect yellow 2-way connector and Connector Position Assurance (CPA).
3. Connect yellow 2-way connector and Connector Position Assurance (CPA) at base of steering column.

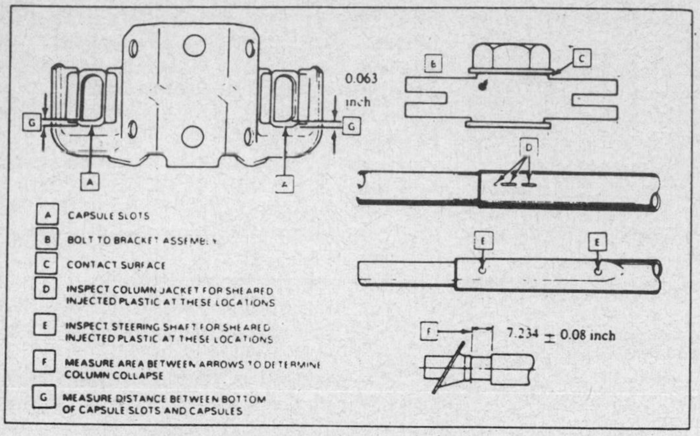
0.063 inch
G
G
A
A
B
C
D
E
E
F
7.234 ± 0.08 inch
A CAPSULE SLOTS
B BOLT TO BRACKET ASSEMBLY
C CONTACT SURFACE
D INSPECT COLUMN JACKET FOR SHEARED INJECTED PLASTIC AT THESE LOCATIONS
E INSPECT STEERING SHAFT FOR SHEARED INJECTED PLASTIC AT THESE LOCATIONS
F MEASURE AREA BETWEEN ARROWS TO DETERMINE COLUMN COLLAPSE
G MEASURE DISTANCE BETWEEN BOTTOM OF CAPSULE SLOTS AND CAPSULES

GC8019201303000X

Fig. 1 Steering column accident damage inspection. 1992 Camaro & Firebird

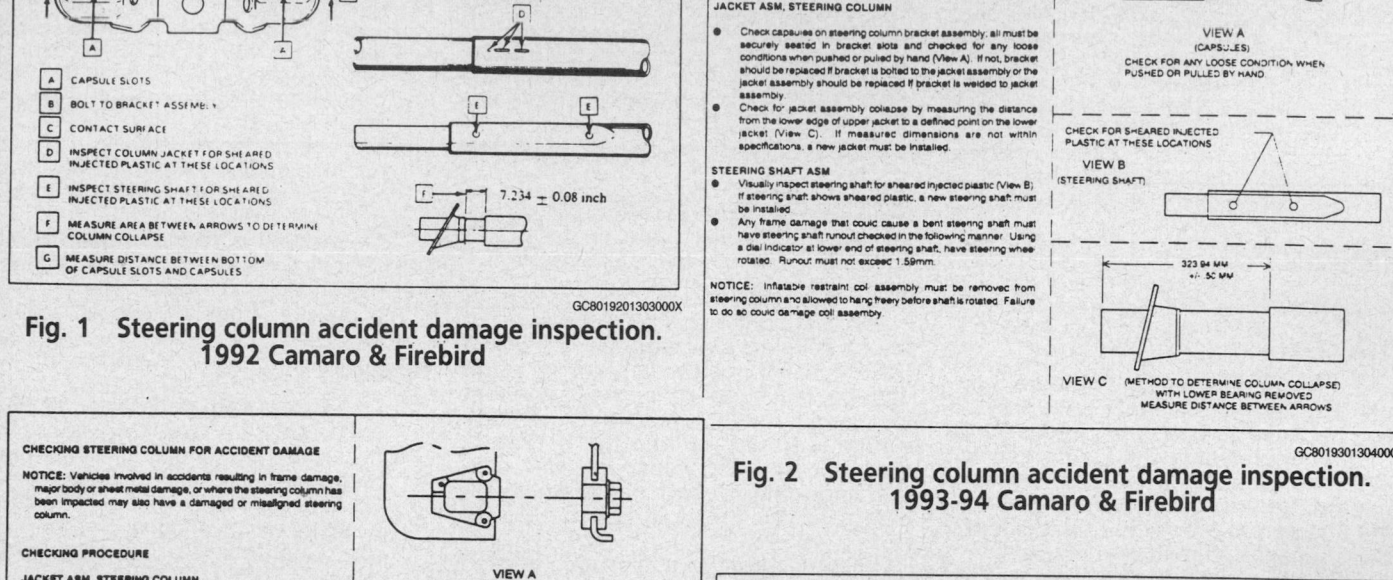

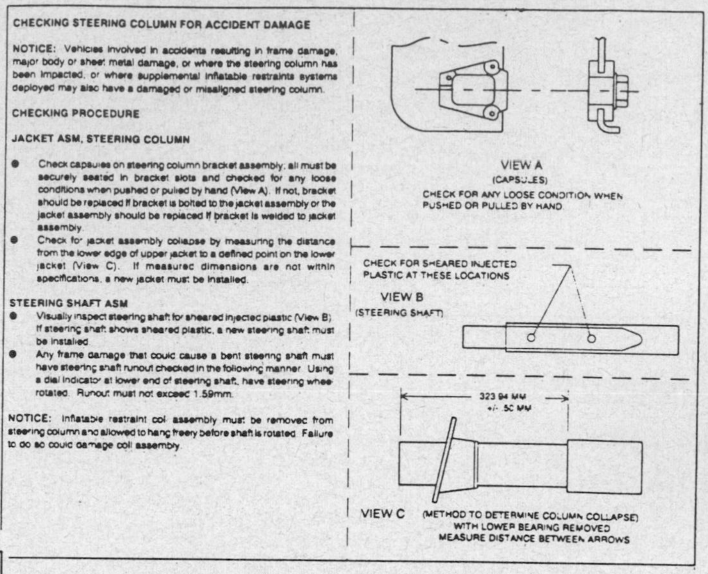
CHECKING STEERING COLUMN FOR ACCIDENT DAMAGE
NOTICE: Vehicles involved in accidents resulting in frame damage, major body or sheet metal damage, or where the steering column has been impacted, or where supplemental inflatable restraints systems deployed may also have a damaged or misaligned steering column.
CHECKING PROCEDURE
JACKET ASM, STEERING COLUMN
● Check capsules on steering column bracket assembly; all must be securely seated in bracket slots and checked for any loose conditions when pushed or pulled by hand (View A). If not, bracket should be replaced if bracket is bolted to the jacket assembly or the jacket assembly should be replaced if bracket is welded to jacket assembly.
● Check for jacket assembly collapse by measuring the distance from the lower edge of upper jacket to a defined point on the lower jacket (View C). If measured dimensions are not within specifications, a new jacket must be installed.
STEERING SHAFT ASM
● Visually inspect steering shaft for sheared injected plastic (View B). If steering shaft shows sheared plastic, a new steering shaft must be installed.
● Any frame damage that could cause a bent steering shaft must have steering shaft runout checked in the following manner. Using a dial indicator at lower end of steering shaft, have steering wheel rotated. Runout must not exceed 1.59mm.
NOTICE: Inflatable restraint coil assembly must be removed from steering column and allowed to hang freely before shaft is rotated. Failure to do so could damage coil assembly.
VIEW A
(CAPSULES)
CHECK FOR ANY LOOSE CONDITION WHEN PUSHED OR PULLED BY HAND.
CHECK FOR SHEARED INJECTED PLASTIC AT THESE LOCATIONS
VIEW B
(STEERING SHAFT)
323.94 MM
+/- .50 MM
VIEW C
(METHOD TO DETERMINE COLUMN COLLAPSE)
WITH LOWER BEARING REMOVED
MEASURE DISTANCE BETWEEN ARROWS

GC8019301304000X

Fig. 2 Steering column accident damage inspection. 1993-94 Camaro & Firebird

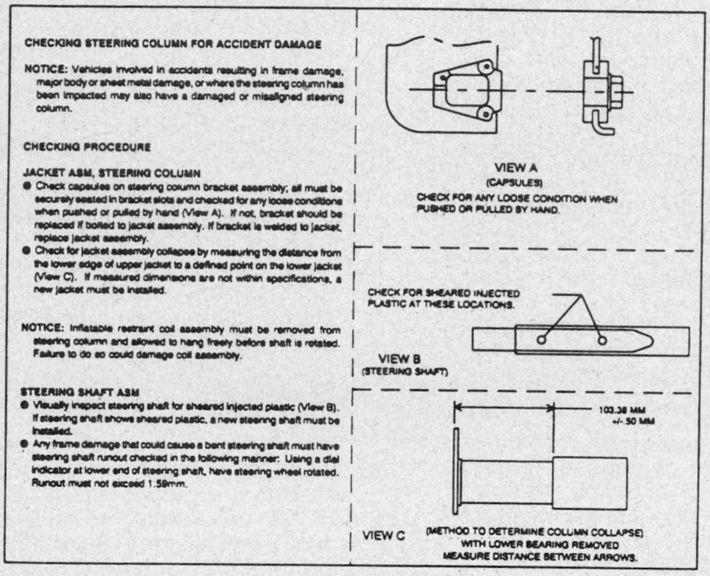
CHECKING STEERING COLUMN FOR ACCIDENT DAMAGE
NOTICE: Vehicles involved in accidents resulting in frame damage, major body or sheet metal damage, or where the steering column has been impacted may also have a damaged or misaligned steering column.
CHECKING PROCEDURE
JACKET ASM, STEERING COLUMN
● Check capsules on steering column bracket assembly; all must be securely seated in bracket slots and checked for any loose conditions when pushed or pulled by hand (View A). If not, bracket should be replaced if bolted to jacket assembly. If bracket is welded to jacket, replace jacket assembly.
● Check for jacket assembly collapse by measuring the distance from the lower edge of upper jacket to a defined point on the lower jacket (View C). If measured dimensions are not within specifications, a new jacket must be installed.
NOTICE: Inflatable restraint coil assembly must be removed from steering column and allowed to hang freely before shaft is rotated. Failure to do so could damage coil assembly.
STEERING SHAFT ASM
● Visually inspect steering shaft for sheared injected plastic (View B). If steering shaft shows sheared plastic, a new steering shaft must be installed.
● Any frame damage that could cause a bent steering shaft must have steering shaft runout checked in the following manner: Using a dial indicator at lower end of steering shaft, have steering wheel rotated. Runout must not exceed 1.59mm.
VIEW A
(CAPSULES)
CHECK FOR ANY LOOSE CONDITION WHEN PUSHED OR PULLED BY HAND.
CHECK FOR SHEARED INJECTED PLASTIC AT THESE LOCATIONS.
VIEW B
(STEERING SHAFT)
103.38 MM
+/- .50 MM
VIEW C
(METHOD TO DETERMINE COLUMN COLLAPSE)
WITH LOWER BEARING REMOVED
MEASURE DISTANCE BETWEEN ARROWS.

GC8019201305000X

Fig. 3 Steering column accident damage inspection. Beretta & Corsica

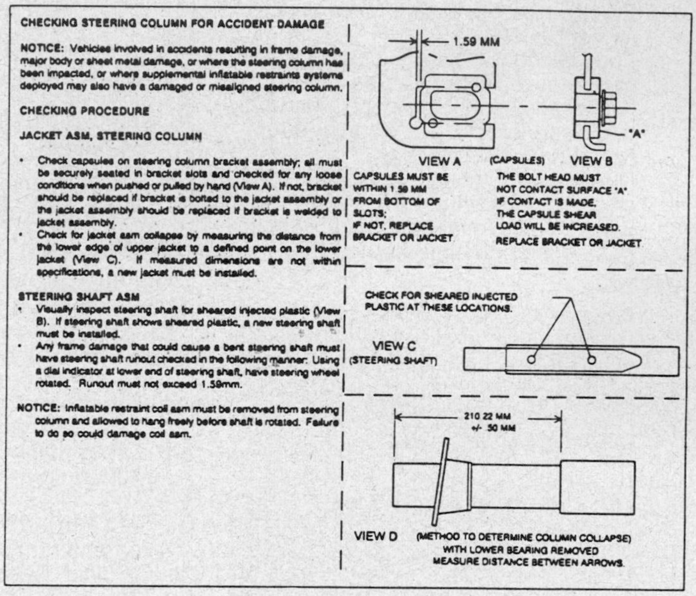
CHECKING STEERING COLUMN FOR ACCIDENT DAMAGE
NOTICE: Vehicles involved in accidents resulting in frame damage, major body or sheet metal damage, or where the steering column has been impacted, or where supplemental inflatable restraints systems deployed may also have a damaged or misaligned steering column.
CHECKING PROCEDURE
JACKET ASM, STEERING COLUMN
• Check capsules on steering column bracket assembly; all must be securely seated in bracket slots and checked for any loose conditions when pushed or pulled by hand (View A). If not, bracket should be replaced if bracket is bolted to the jacket assembly or the jacket assembly should be replaced if bracket is welded to jacket assembly.
• Check for jacket asm collapse by measuring the distance from the lower edge of upper jacket to a defined point on the lower jacket (View C). If measured dimensions are not within specifications, a new jacket must be installed.
STEERING SHAFT ASM
• Visually inspect steering shaft for sheared injected plastic (View B). If steering shaft shows sheared plastic, a new steering shaft must be installed.
• Any frame damage that could cause a bent steering shaft must have steering shaft runout checked in the following manner: Using a dial indicator at lower end of steering shaft, have steering wheel rotated. Runout must not exceed 1.59mm.
NOTICE: Inflatable restraint coil asm must be removed from steering column and allowed to hang freely before shaft is rotated. Failure to do so could damage coil asm.
1.59 MM
"A"
VIEW A
(CAPSULES)
VIEW B
CAPSULES MUST BE WITHIN 1.59 MM FROM BOTTOM OF SLOTS; IF NOT, REPLACE BRACKET OR JACKET.
THE BOLT HEAD MUST NOT CONTACT SURFACE "A". IF CONTACT IS MADE, THE CAPSULE SHEAR LOAD WILL BE INCREASED.
REPLACE BRACKET OR JACKET.
CHECK FOR SHEARED INJECTED PLASTIC AT THESE LOCATIONS.
VIEW C
(STEERING SHAFT)
210.22 MM
+/- .50 MM
VIEW D
(METHOD TO DETERMINE COLUMN COLLAPSE)
WITH LOWER BEARING REMOVED
MEASURE DISTANCE BETWEEN ARROWS.

GC8019201306000X

Fig. 4 Steering column accident damage inspection. Corvette

4. Install trim panel under steering column.
5. Install AIR BAG fuse into instrument panel fuse block.
6. Turn ignition switch to the Run position and verify that the INFLATABLE RESTRAINT warning lamp flashes seven times and then turns off. If lamp does not operate as specified, refer to "Diagnosis & Testing."

METRO

Disarming

The diagnostic energy reserve module (DERM) can maintain enough voltage to cause air bag deployment for up to ten minutes after the ignition switch is turned off and the battery is disconnected. Servicing the SIR system during this period may result in accidental deployment and personal injury.

1. **On 1992-93 models,** place steering wheel so that wheels are pointing straight ahead, then turn ignition switch to the Lock position.
2. **On all models,** remove SIR IG fuse from SIR fuse block.
3. Remove rear plastic access cover from inflator module housing.
4. Remove Connector Position Assurance (CPA), then disconnect yellow two-way SIR electrical connector inside inflator module housing.

Arming

1. Turn ignition switch to Lock position.
2. Connect yellow two-way SIR electrical connector inside inflator module housing, then install Connector Position Assurance (CPA).
3. Install SIR IG fuse into SIR fuse block, then the rear plastic access cover onto inflator module housing.
4. Turn ignition switch to Run position and ensure "Inflatable Restraint" lamp flashes 7 to 9 times and then turns off.

PRIZM

Disarming

1. Ensure front wheels are pointed straight ahead, then turn ignition switch to Lock position.
2. Remove IGN and CIG & RADIO fuse from junction block No. 1.
3. Remove Connector Position Assurance (CPA) and disconnect lower steering column (yellow two-cavity) connector at base of steering column.
4. **On models with passenger air bag,** open glove box door and gently pry

CHECKING STEERING COLUMN FOR ACCIDENT DAMAGE

NOTICE: Vehicles involved in accidents resulting in frame damage, major body or sheet metal damage, or where the steering column has been impacted, or where supplemental inflatable restraints systems deployed may also have a damaged or misaligned steering column.

CHECKING PROCEDURE

JACKET ASM, STEERING COLUMN

- Check capsules on steering column bracket assembly; all must be securely seated in bracket slots and checked for any loose conditions when pushed or pulled by hand (View A). If not, bracket should be replaced if bracket is bolted to the jacket assembly or the jacket assembly should be replaced if bracket is welded to jacket assembly.
- Check for jacket asm collapse by measuring the distance from the lower edge of upper jacket to a defined point on the lower jacket (View D). If measured dimensions are not within specifications, a new jacket must be installed.

SHIFT TUBE ASM

- Visually inspect shift tube for sheared injected plastic (View B). If shift tube shows sheared plastic, a new shift tube must be installed.
- Check operation of shift lever. If you can move lever to "Park" position without raising lever, it is an indication that upper shift tube plastic bearing is broken.

STEERING SHAFT ASM

- Visually inspect steering shaft for sheared injected plastic (View C). If steering shaft shows sheared plastic, a new steering shaft must be installed.
- Any frame damage that could cause a bent steering shaft must have steering shaft runout checked in the following manner: Using a dial indicator at lower end of steering shaft, have steering wheel rotated. Runout must not exceed 1.59mm.

NOTICE: Inflatable restraint coil asm must be removed from steering column and allowed to hang freely before shaft is rotated. Failure to do so could damage coil asm.

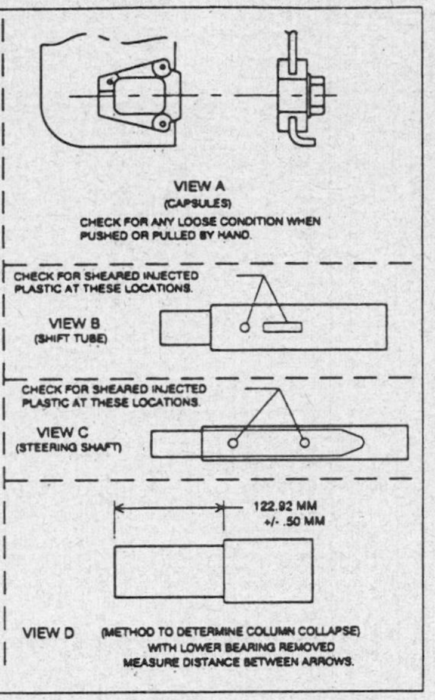

VIEW A
(CAPSULES)
CHECK FOR ANY LOOSE CONDITION WHEN PUSHED OR PULLED BY HAND.
CHECK FOR SHEARED INJECTED PLASTIC AT THESE LOCATIONS.
VIEW B
(SHIFT TUBE)
CHECK FOR SHEARED INJECTED PLASTIC AT THESE LOCATIONS.
VIEW C
(STEERING SHAFT)
122.92 MM
+/- .50 MM
VIEW D
(METHOD TO DETERMINE COLUMN COLLAPSE)
WITH LOWER BEARING REMOVED
MEASURE DISTANCE BETWEEN ARROWS.

GC8019201307000X

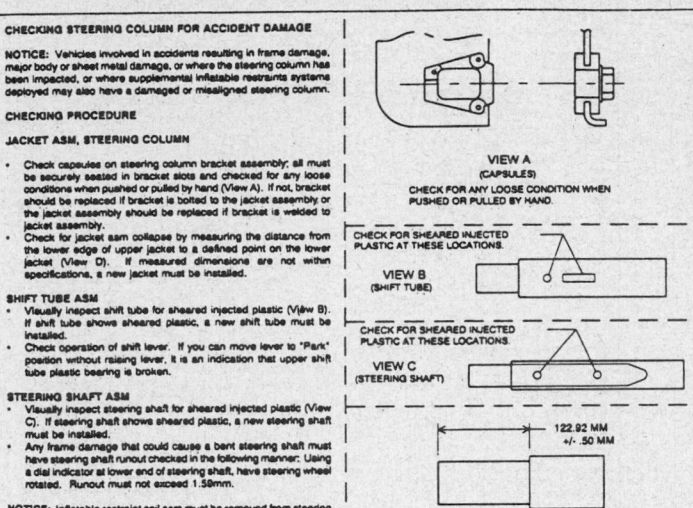

Fig. 5 Steering column accident damage inspection. 1992 Toronado & Trofeo

CHECKING STEERING COLUMN FOR ACCIDENT DAMAGE

NOTICE: Vehicles involved in accidents resulting in frame damage, major body or sheet metal damage, or where the steering column has been impacted, or where supplemental inflatable restraints systems deployed may also have a damaged or misaligned steering column.

CHECKING PROCEDURE

JACKET ASM, STEERING COLUMN

- Check capsules on steering column bracket assembly; all should be within 1.59mm from the bottom of the slots (View A). If not, bracket should be replaced if bracket is bolted to the jacket asm or the jacket asm should be replaced if bracket is welded to jacket asm.
- Check contact surface "A" on capsules (View B). The bolt head must not contact surface "A" or shear load would be increased. If contact is made, replace bracket asm or jacket asm.
- Check for jacket asm collapse by measuring the distance from the lower edge of upper jacket to a defined point on the lower jacket (View E). If measured dimensions are not within specifications, a new jacket must be installed.

SHIFT TUBE ASM

- Visually inspect shift tube for sheared injected plastic (View C). If shift tube shows sheared plastic, a new shift tube must be installed.
- Check operation of shift lever. If you can move lever to "Park" position without raising lever, it is an indication that upper shift tube plastic bearing is broken.

NOTICE: Inflatable restraint coil asm must be removed from steering column and allowed to hang freely before shaft is rotated. Failure to do so could damage coil assembly.

STEERING SHAFT ASM

- Visually inspect steering shaft for sheared injected plastic (View D). If steering shaft shows sheared plastic, a new steering shaft must be installed.
- Any frame damage that could cause a bent steering shaft must have steering shaft runout checked in the following manner: Using a dial indicator at lower end of steering shaft, have steering wheel rotated. Runout must not exceed 1.59mm.

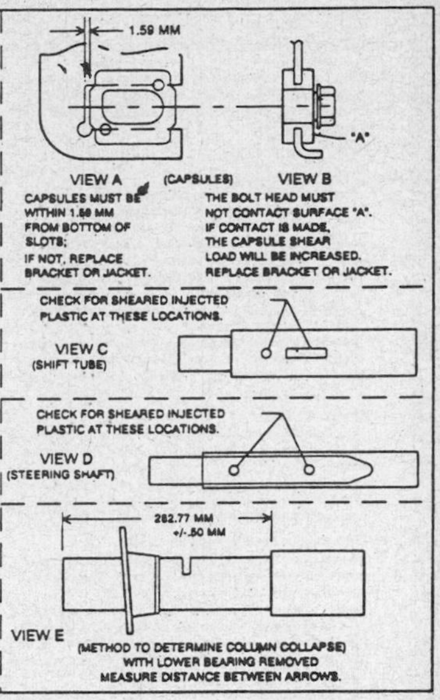

1.59 MM
"A"
VIEW A
(CAPSULES)
VIEW B
CAPSULES MUST BE WITHIN 1.59 MM FROM BOTTOM OF SLOTS;
IF NOT, REPLACE BRACKET OR JACKET.
THE BOLT HEAD MUST NOT CONTACT SURFACE "A".
IF CONTACT IS MADE, THE CAPSULE SHEAR LOAD WILL BE INCREASED.
REPLACE BRACKET OR JACKET.
CHECK FOR SHEARED INJECTED PLASTIC AT THESE LOCATIONS.
VIEW C
(SHIFT TUBE)
CHECK FOR SHEARED INJECTED PLASTIC AT THESE LOCATIONS.
VIEW D
(STEERING SHAFT)
282.77 MM
+/-.50 MM
VIEW E
(METHOD TO DETERMINE COLUMN COLLAPSE)
WITH LOWER BEARING REMOVED
MEASURE DISTANCE BETWEEN ARROWS.

GC8019201308000X

Fig. 6 Steering column accident damage inspection. Caprice, Custom Cruiser & Roadmaster

off passenger inflator module connector retainer.

5. Remove CPA and disconnect yellow 2-way connector from passenger inflator module.

Arming

1. Turn ignition switch to Lock position.
2. **On models with passenger air bag,** connect passenger inflator module 2-way connector and secure with CPA.
3. **On all models,** connect lower steering column yellow two-cavity connector and secure with CPA.
4. Install IGN and CIG & RADIO fuses.
5. Turn ignition switch to ACC or On positions and verify that the air bag indicator illuminates steady for approximately six seconds and then turns off.

STORM

Disarming

The diagnostic energy reserve module (DERM) can maintain enough voltage to cause air bag deployment for up to ten minutes after the ignition switch is turned off and the battery is disconnected. Servicing the SIR system during this period may result in accidental deployment and personal injury.

1. Place steering wheel so that wheels are pointing straight ahead, then turn ignition switch to Lock position.
2. Remove fuses C-22 and C-23 from fuse block.
3. Remove switch bezel from instrument panel, then disconnect electrical connector from switches.
4. Remove cigar lighter bezel from instrument panel, then disconnect cigar lighter electrical connectors.
5. Remove two screws and hood latch release handle from knee bolster, then the three screws, three bolts and two nuts retaining the knee bolster.
6. Disconnect lap cooler air duct from knee bolster, then remove knee bolster from vehicle.
7. Remove Connector Position Assurance (CPA), then disconnect orange three-way connector at the base of the steering column.

Arming

1. Turn ignition switch to Off position, then connect orange three-way connector at the base of the steering column.
2. Connect lap cooler air duct to knee bolster, then install knee bolster.
3. **Torque** knee bolster bolts and nuts to 89 inch lbs.
4. Install hood latch release handle to knee bolster.
5. Connect cigar lighter electrical connector, then snap cigar lighter bezel into place on instrument panel.
6. Connect switch bezel electrical connectors, then snap switch bezel into place on instrument panel.

PRECAUTIONS

1. **Inflator modules should not be subjected to temperatures above 150°F (65°C).**
2. **Discriminating sensors, inflator modules, arming sensors, or DRMs should not be used if they have been dropped from a height of more than three feet.**
3. **When a discriminating sensor or arming sensor is replaced, it must be positioned with the arrow of the sensor pointing toward the front of the vehicle. It is important that the discriminating sensors and arming sensor are mounted flat on their mounting surfaces. It is also important that the sensor mounting surface be free of dirt or any other foreign substance.**
4. **Do not apply power to the SIR system unless all components are connected or a diagnostic chart requests it, as this will set a trouble code.**
5. **When carrying a live inflator module, make sure the bag opening is pointed away from the body. In case of accidental deployment, the bag will then deploy with a small chance of injury. Never carry an inflator module by the wires or connector on the underside of the module. When placing a live inflator on a bench or other surface, always face the bag and trim cover up, away from the surface. Never rest a steering column assembly on the steering wheel with the inflator module face down and column vertical.**
6. **Failure to follow inflator module disposal procedures can result in air bag deployment. Undeployed inflator modules must not be disposed of through normal channels. The undeployed inflator module contains substances that can cause severe illness or personal injury if the sealed container is damaged during disposal.**
7. **When troubleshooting the SIR system, do not use electrical test equipment such as a battery powered or AC powered voltmeter or ohmmeter, or any type of electrical equipment other than those that are specified in this section. Do not use a non-powered probe type tester.**

COLLISION INSPECTION

1. The following items must be replaced or inspected anytime air bag deployment occurs:
   a. Inflator module.
   b. All system sensors.
   c. Coil assembly.
2. After any type of collision occurs, the following items must be checked:
   a. Steering column, **Figs. 1 through 12.**

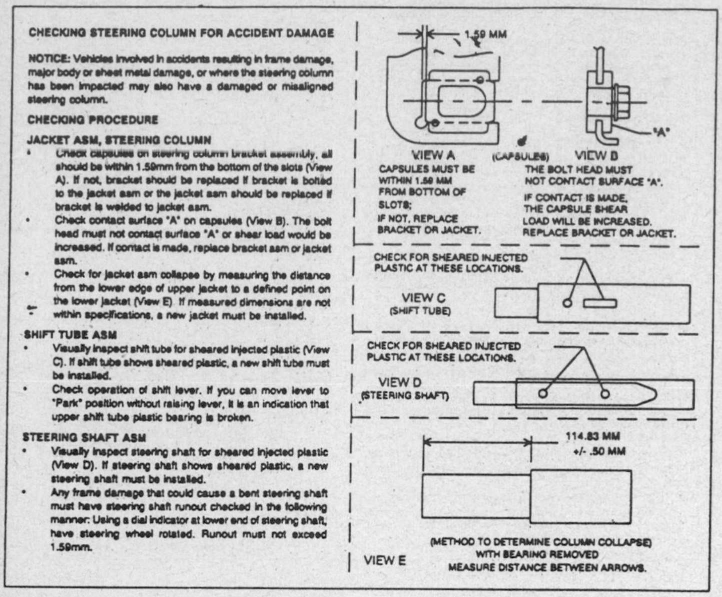
CHECKING STEERING COLUMN FOR ACCIDENT DAMAGE
NOTICE: Vehicles involved in accidents resulting in frame damage, major body or sheet metal damage, or where the steering column has been impacted may also have a damaged or misaligned steering column.
CHECKING PROCEDURE
JACKET ASM, STEERING COLUMN
• Check capsules on steering column bracket assembly, all should be within 1.59mm from the bottom of the slots (View A). If not, bracket should be replaced if bracket is bolted to the jacket asm or the jacket asm should be replaced if bracket is welded to jacket asm.
• Check contact surface "A" on capsules (View B). The bolt head must not contact surface "A" or shear load would be increased. If contact is made, replace bracket asm or jacket asm.
• Check for jacket asm collapse by measuring the distance from the lower edge of upper jacket to a defined point on the lower jacket (View E). If measured dimensions are not within specifications, a new jacket must be installed.
SHIFT TUBE ASM
• Visually inspect shift tube for sheared injected plastic (View C). If shift tube shows sheared plastic, a new shift tube must be installed.
• Check operation of shift lever. If you can move lever to "Park" position without raising lever, it is an indication that upper shift tube plastic bearing is broken.
STEERING SHAFT ASM
• Visually inspect steering shaft for sheared injected plastic (View D). If steering shaft shows sheared plastic, a new steering shaft must be installed.
• Any frame damage that could cause a bent steering shaft must have steering shaft runout checked in the following manner: Using a dial indicator at lower end of steering shaft, have steering wheel rotated. Runout must not exceed 1.59mm.
1.59 MM
"A"
VIEW A
(CAPSULES)
VIEW B
CAPSULES MUST BE WITHIN 1.59 MM FROM BOTTOM OF SLOTS; IF NOT, REPLACE BRACKET OR JACKET.
THE BOLT HEAD MUST NOT CONTACT SURFACE "A". IF CONTACT IS MADE, THE CAPSULE SHEAR LOAD WILL BE INCREASED. REPLACE BRACKET OR JACKET.
CHECK FOR SHEARED INJECTED PLASTIC AT THESE LOCATIONS.
VIEW C (SHIFT TUBE)
CHECK FOR SHEARED INJECTED PLASTIC AT THESE LOCATIONS.
VIEW D (STEERING SHAFT)
114.83 MM +/- .50 MM
VIEW E
(METHOD TO DETERMINE COLUMN COLLAPSE) WITH BEARING REMOVED MEASURE DISTANCE BETWEEN ARROWS.

GC8019201309000X

Fig. 7 Steering column accident damage inspection. Century, Cutlass Ciera & Cutlass Cruiser

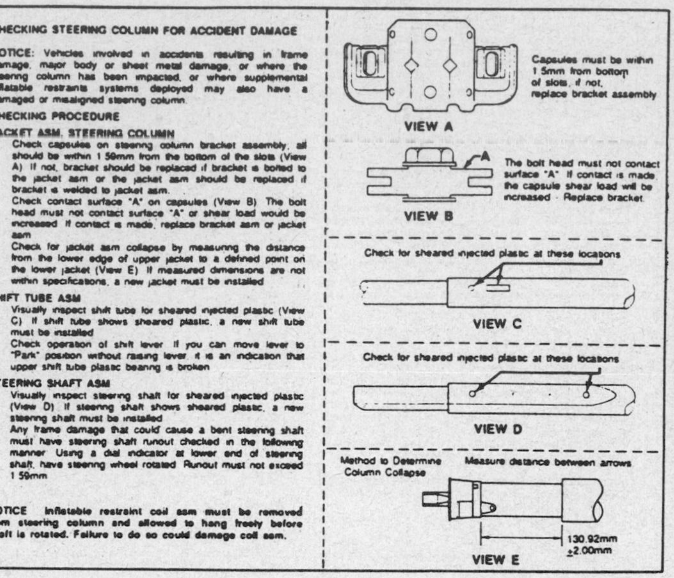
CHECKING STEERING COLUMN FOR ACCIDENT DAMAGE
NOTICE: Vehicles involved in accidents resulting in frame damage, major body or sheet metal damage, or where the steering column has been impacted, or where supplemental inflatable restraints systems deployed may also have a damaged or misaligned steering column.
CHECKING PROCEDURE
JACKET ASM, STEERING COLUMN
• Check capsules on steering column bracket assembly, all should be within 1.59mm from the bottom of the slots (View A). If not, bracket should be replaced if bracket is bolted to the jacket asm or the jacket asm should be replaced if bracket is welded to jacket asm.
• Check contact surface "A" on capsules (View B). The bolt head must not contact surface "A" or shear load would be increased. If contact is made, replace bracket asm or jacket asm.
• Check for jacket asm collapse by measuring the distance from the lower edge of upper jacket to a defined point on the lower jacket (View E). If measured dimensions are not within specifications, a new jacket must be installed.
SHIFT TUBE ASM
• Visually inspect shift tube for sheared injected plastic (View C). If shift tube shows sheared plastic, a new shift tube must be installed.
• Check operation of shift lever. If you can move lever to "Park" position without raising lever, it is an indication that upper shift tube plastic bearing is broken.
STEERING SHAFT ASM
• Visually inspect steering shaft for sheared injected plastic (View D). If steering shaft shows sheared plastic, a new steering shaft must be installed.
• Any frame damage that could cause a bent steering shaft must have steering shaft runout checked in the following manner. Using a dial indicator at lower end of steering shaft, have steering wheel rotated. Runout must not exceed 1.59mm.
NOTICE Inflatable restraint coil asm must be removed from steering column and allowed to hang freely before shaft is rotated. Failure to do so could damage coil asm.
Capsules must be within 1.5mm from bottom of slots, if not, replace bracket assembly
VIEW A
The bolt head must not contact surface "A". If contact is made, the capsule shear load will be increased. Replace bracket
VIEW B
Check for sheared injected plastic at these locations
VIEW C
Check for sheared injected plastic at these locations
VIEW D
Method to Determine Column Collapse
Measure distance between arrows
130.92mm ±2.00mm
VIEW E

GC8019201310000X

Fig. 8 Steering column accident damage inspection. Bonneville, LeSabre, Park Avenue, 88 & 98

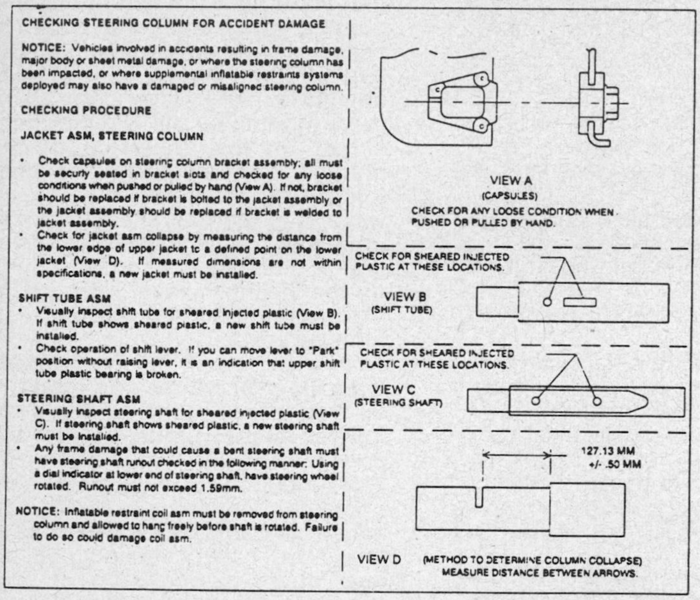
CHECKING STEERING COLUMN FOR ACCIDENT DAMAGE
NOTICE: Vehicles involved in accidents resulting in frame damage, major body or sheet metal damage, or where the steering column has been impacted, or where supplemental inflatable restraints systems deployed may also have a damaged or misaligned steering column.
CHECKING PROCEDURE
JACKET ASM, STEERING COLUMN
• Check capsules on steering column bracket assembly; all must be securly seated in bracket slots and checked for any loose conditions when pushed or pulled by hand (View A). If not, bracket should be replaced if bracket is bolted to the jacket assembly or the jacket assembly should be replaced if bracket is welded to jacket assembly.
• Check for jacket asm collapse by measuring the distance from the lower edge of upper jacket to a defined point on the lower jacket (View D). If measured dimensions are not within specifications, a new jacket must be installed.
SHIFT TUBE ASM
• Visually inspect shift tube for sheared injected plastic (View B). If shift tube shows sheared plastic, a new shift tube must be installed.
• Check operation of shift lever. If you can move lever to "Park" position without raising lever, it is an indication that upper shift tube plastic bearing is broken.
STEERING SHAFT ASM
• Visually inspect steering shaft for sheared injected plastic (View C). If steering shaft shows sheared plastic, a new steering shaft must be installed.
• Any frame damage that could cause a bent steering shaft must have steering shaft runout checked in the following manner: Using a dial indicator at lower end of steering shaft, have steering wheel rotated. Runout must not exceed 1.59mm.
NOTICE: Inflatable restraint coil asm must be removed from steering column and allowed to hang freely before shaft is rotated. Failure to do so could damage coil asm.
VIEW A (CAPSULES)
CHECK FOR ANY LOOSE CONDITION WHEN PUSHED OR PULLED BY HAND.
CHECK FOR SHEARED INJECTED PLASTIC AT THESE LOCATIONS.
VIEW B (SHIFT TUBE)
CHECK FOR SHEARED INJECTED PLASTIC AT THESE LOCATIONS.
VIEW C (STEERING SHAFT)
127.13 MM +/- .50 MM
VIEW D
(METHOD TO DETERMINE COLUMN COLLAPSE) MEASURE DISTANCE BETWEEN ARROWS.

GC8019201311000X

Fig. 9 Steering column accident damage inspection. Eldorado & Seville

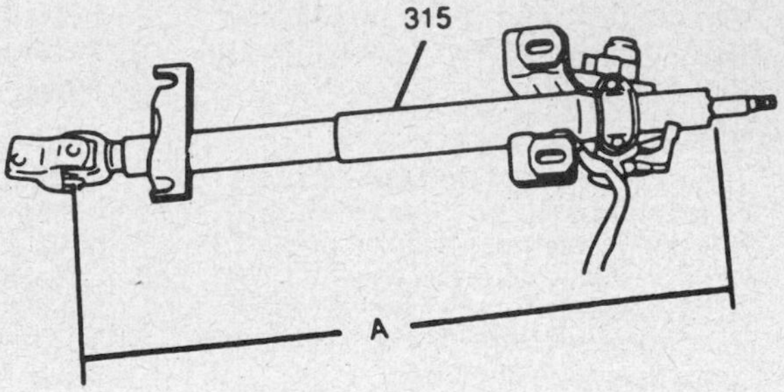
315
A

A 528 mm (20.79")

315 STEERING COLUMN

GC8019201312000X

Fig. 10 Steering column accident damage inspection. 1992-93 Metro

b. Any system sensors in the area of the collision.
c. Knee bolsters and mounting points.
d. Instrument panel steering column reinforcement plate.
e. Instrument panel braces.
f. Seat belts and mounting points.
g. Steering wheel.

3. Replace any item that shows signs of distortion, bending, cracking or other damage.

DIAGNOSIS & TESTING

Refer to MOTOR's Air Bag Manual for air bag system diagnosis and testing procedures.

COMPONENT SERVICE

Prior to performing service procedures, disarm air bag system as described under "Air Bag System Disarming & Arming." Refer to the "Tightening Specifications" chart when installing components.

ARMING SENSOR, REPLACE

ACHIEVA, GRAND AM & SKYLARK

1994

1. Disarm air bag system as described under "Air Bag System Disarming & Arming."
2. Remove glove compartment assembly.
3. Remove CPA and disconnect sensor electrical connector.
4. Remove sensor mounting bolts, then remove sensor.
5. Reverse procedure to install, noting the following:
   a. After completing installation, rearm air bag system as described under "Air Bag System Disarming & Arming."
   b. Turn ignition switch to On position and verify "Inflatable Restraint" indicator flashes 7 to 9 times, then turns off. If indicator does not respond, refer to "Diagnosis & Testing."

BERETTA & CORSICA

1992–93

1. Disarm air bag system as described

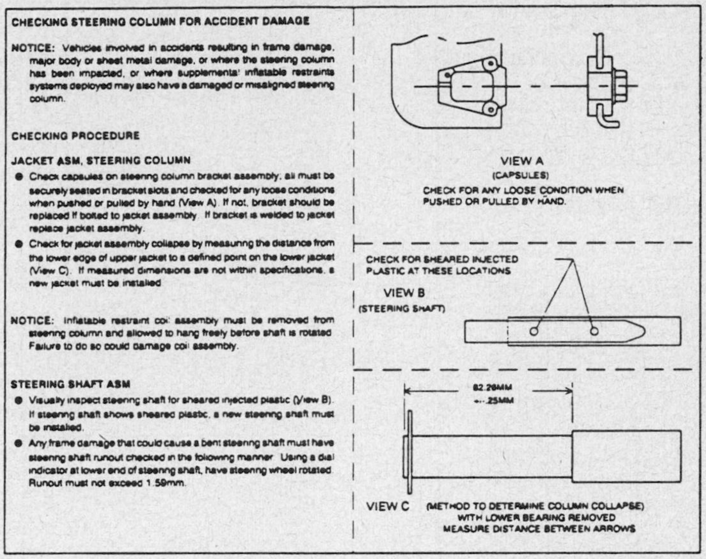
CHECKING STEERING COLUMN FOR ACCIDENT DAMAGE
NOTICE: Vehicles involved in accidents resulting in frame damage, major body or sheet metal damage, or where the steering column has been impacted, or where supplemental inflatable restraints systems deployed may also have a damaged or misaligned steering column.
CHECKING PROCEDURE
JACKET ASM, STEERING COLUMN
Check capsules on steering column bracket assembly; all must be securely seated in bracket slots and checked for any loose conditions when pushed or pulled by hand (View A). If not, bracket should be replaced if bolted to jacket assembly. If bracket is welded to jacket replace jacket assembly.
Check for jacket assembly collapse by measuring the distance from the lower edge of upper jacket to a defined point on the lower jacket (View C). If measured dimensions are not within specifications, a new jacket must be installed.
NOTICE: Inflatable restraint coil assembly must be removed from steering column and allowed to hang freely before shaft is rotated. Failure to do so could damage coil assembly.
STEERING SHAFT ASM
Visually inspect steering shaft for sheared injected plastic (View B). If steering shaft shows sheared plastic, a new steering shaft must be installed.
Any frame damage that could cause a bent steering shaft must have steering shaft runout checked in the following manner. Using a dial indicator at lower end of steering shaft, have steering wheel rotated. Runout must not exceed 1.59mm.
VIEW A
(CAPSULES)
CHECK FOR ANY LOOSE CONDITION WHEN PUSHED OR PULLED BY HAND.
CHECK FOR SHEARED INJECTED PLASTIC AT THESE LOCATIONS
VIEW B
(STEERING SHAFT)
82.26MM
+/-.25MM
VIEW C (METHOD TO DETERMINE COLUMN COLLAPSE)
WITH LOWER BEARING REMOVED
MEASURE DISTANCE BETWEEN ARROWS
GC8019201313000X

Fig. 11 Steering column accident damage inspection. Achieva, Grand Am & Skylark

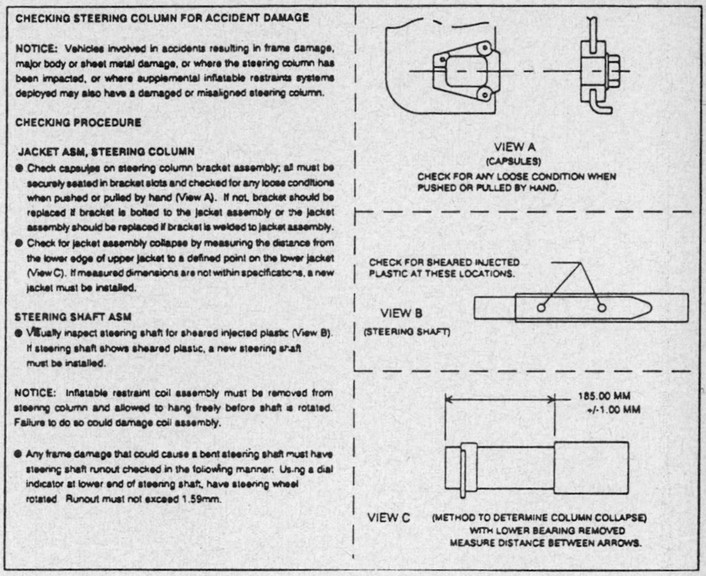
CHECKING STEERING COLUMN FOR ACCIDENT DAMAGE
NOTICE: Vehicles involved in accidents resulting in frame damage, major body or sheet metal damage, or where the steering column has been impacted, or where supplemental inflatable restraints systems deployed may also have a damaged or misaligned steering column.
CHECKING PROCEDURE
JACKET ASM, STEERING COLUMN
Check capsules on steering column bracket assembly; all must be securely seated in bracket slots and checked for any loose conditions when pushed or pulled by hand (View A). If not, bracket should be replaced if bracket is bolted to the jacket assembly or the jacket assembly should be replaced if bracket is welded to jacket assembly.
Check for jacket assembly collapse by measuring the distance from the lower edge of upper jacket to a defined point on the lower jacket (View C). If measured dimensions are not within specifications, a new jacket must be installed.
STEERING SHAFT ASM
Visually inspect steering shaft for sheared injected plastic (View B). If steering shaft shows sheared plastic, a new steering shaft must be installed.
NOTICE: Inflatable restraint coil assembly must be removed from steering column and allowed to hang freely before shaft is rotated. Failure to do so could damage coil assembly.
Any frame damage that could cause a bent steering shaft must have steering shaft runout checked in the following manner: Using a dial indicator at lower end of steering shaft, have steering wheel rotated. Runout must not exceed 1.59mm.
VIEW A
(CAPSULES)
CHECK FOR ANY LOOSE CONDITION WHEN PUSHED OR PULLED BY HAND.
CHECK FOR SHEARED INJECTED PLASTIC AT THESE LOCATIONS.
VIEW B
(STEERING SHAFT)
185.00 MM
+/-1.00 MM
VIEW C (METHOD TO DETERMINE COLUMN COLLAPSE)
WITH LOWER BEARING REMOVED
MEASURE DISTANCE BETWEEN ARROWS.
GC8019201314000X

Fig. 12 Steering column accident damage inspection. Cutlass Supreme, Grand Prix & Regal

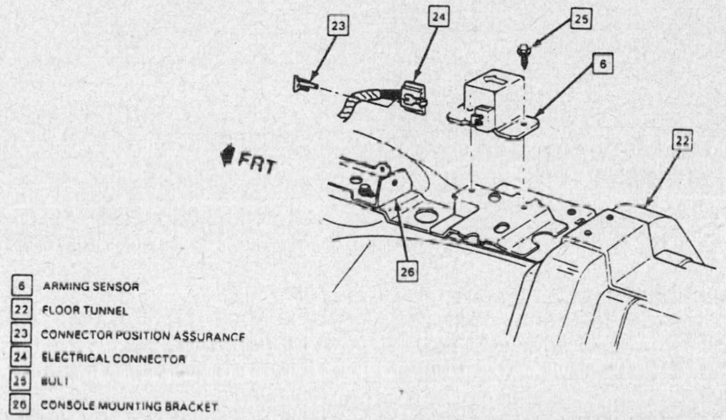
23
24
25
6
22
26
FRT
6 ARMING SENSOR
22 FLOOR TUNNEL
23 CONNECTOR POSITION ASSURANCE
24 ELECTRICAL CONNECTOR
25 BOLT
26 CONSOLE MOUNTING BRACKET
GC8019201315000X

Fig. 13 Arming sensor replacement. 1992 Camaro & Firebird

under "Air Bag System Disarming & Arming."
2. Remove glove compartment assembly.
3. Remove CPA and disconnect sensor electrical connector.
4. Remove sensor mounting bolts, then remove sensor.
5. Reverse procedure to install, noting the following:
   a. After completing installation, rearm air bag system as described under "Air Bag System Disarming & Arming."
   b. Turn ignition switch to On position and verify "Inflatable Restraint" indicator flashes 7 to 9 times, then turns off. If indicator does not respond, refer to "Diagnosis & Testing."

1994

1. Disarm air bag system as described under "Air Bag System Disarming & Arming."
2. Remove righthand sound insulator.
3. Open instrument panel compartment assembly.
4. Remove CPA and disconnect sensor electrical connector.
5. Remove sensor mounting bolts, then remove sensor.
6. Reverse procedure to install, noting the following:
   a. After completing installation, rearm air bag system as described under "Air Bag System Disarming & Arming."
   b. Turn ignition switch to On position and verify "Inflatable Restraint" indicator flashes 7 to 9 times, then turns off. If indicator does not respond, refer to "Diagnosis & Testing."

CAMARO & FIREBIRD

1992

1. Disarm air bag system as described under "Air Bag System Disarming & Arming."
2. Remove knee bolster as described under "Component Replacement."
3. Remove upper console.
4. Remove arming sensor retaining bolts, then disconnect arming sensor electrical connector and remove arming sensor, **Fig. 13.**
5. Reverse procedure to install, noting the following:
   a. Install arming sensor with arrow pointing toward front of vehicle.
   b. After completing installation, rearm air bag system as described under "Air Bag System Disarming & Arming."
   c. Turn ignition switch to On position and verify "Inflatable Restraint" indicator flashes 7 to 9 times, then turns off. If indicator does not respond, refer to "Diagnosis & Testing."

CAPRICE, CUSTOM CRUISER & ROADMASTER

1. Disarm air bag system as described under "Air Bag System Disarming & Arming."
2. Remove twilight sentinel module from bracket, if equipped.
3. Reposition dash mat for access, then disconnect CPA and arming sensor connector from body harness connector near top of instrument panel.
4. Remove mounting screws, then the arming sensor. **Fig. 14.**
5. Reverse procedure to install, noting the following:
   a. After completing installation, rearm air bag system as described under "Air Bag System Disarming & Arming."
   b. Turn ignition switch to On position and verify "Inflatable Restraint" indicator flashes 7 to 9 times, then turns off. If indicator does not respond, refer to "Diagnosis & Testing."

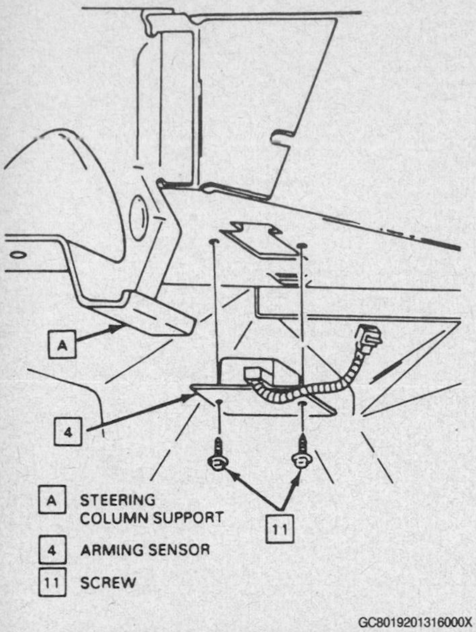
A
4
11
A STEERING COLUMN SUPPORT
4 ARMING SENSOR
11 SCREW
GC8019201316000X

Fig. 14 Arming sensor replacement. Caprice, Custom Cruiser & Roadmaster

CENTURY, CUTLASS CIERA & CUTLASS CRUISER

1. Disarm air bag system as described under "Air Bag System Disarming & Arming."
2. Remove instrument panel compartment and right outlets.
3. Remove electrical connector from retainer, then release connector position assurance (CPA) from connector and disconnect the connector.
4. Loosen sensor mounting bolts and remove sensor.
5. Reverse procedure to install, noting the following:
   a. Tighten to specifications.
   b. Ensure arming sensor is correctly mounted to mounting bracket.
   c. After completing installation, rearm air bag system as described under "Air Bag System Disarming & Arming."

CORVETTE

1992–93

1. Disarm air bag system as described under "Air Bag System Disarming & Arming."
2. Remove radio control.
3. Disconnect arming sensor connector from clip on righthand knee bolster inner bracket.
4. Remove SIR wiring harness to arming sensor CPA and disconnect arming sensor electrical connector.
5. Remove arming sensor retaining fasteners. **Fig. 15.**
6. Remove arming sensor.
7. Reverse procedure to install, noting the following:
   a. Install sensor with arrow pointing toward front of vehicle.
   b. After completing installation, rearm air bag system as described under "Air Bag System Disarming & Arming."
   c. Turn ignition switch to On position and verify "Inflatable Restraint" indicator flashes 7 to 9 times, then turns off. If indicator does not respond, refer to "Diagnosis & Testing."

CUTLASS SUPREME & REGAL

1994

1. Disarm air bag system as described under "Air Bag System Disarming & Arming."
2. **On models equipped with bench seats,** remove front seat.
3. **On models equipped with bucket seats,** remove center console.
4. **On all models,** disconnect connector position assurance (CPA) connector and electrical connector from arming sensor.
5. Remove arming sensor retaining fasteners.
6. Remove arming sensor.
7. Reverse procedure to install, noting the following:
   a. Install sensor with arrow pointing toward front of vehicle.
   b. After completing installation, rearm air bag system as described under "Air Bag System Disarming & Arming."

METRO & STORM

1. Disarm air bag system as described under "Air Bag System Disarming & Arming."
2. Disconnect battery ground cable.
3. Remove instrument panel, **Figs. 16 and 17.**
4. **On Storm,** disconnect defroster duct from cowl.
5. **On all models,** remove CPA and disconnect electrical connector.
6. Loosen sensor mounting bolts and remove sensor.
7. Reverse procedure to install, noting the following:
   a. Install sensor with arrow pointing toward front of vehicle.
   b. After completing installation, rearm air bag system as described under "Air Bag System Disarming & Arming."
   c. Place ignition switch in On position and verify "Inflatable Restraint" indicator flashes 7 to 9 times, then turns off. If indicator does not respond, refer to "Diagnosis & Testing."

DUAL SENSOR, REPLACE

DEVILLE & FLEETWOOD (FWD)

1992–93

1. Disarm air bag system as described under "Air Bag System Disarming & Arming."
2. Remove DERM as described under "Diagnostic Energy Reserve Module, Replace."
3. Remove nut retaining sensor connector.

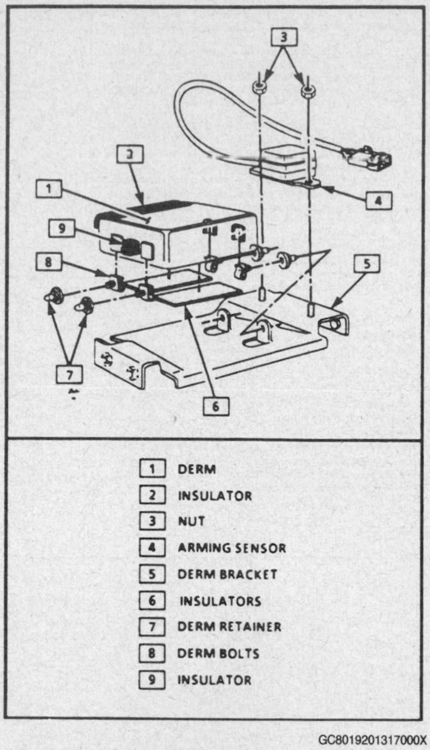
1 DERM
2 INSULATOR
3 NUT
4 ARMING SENSOR
5 DERM BRACKET
6 INSULATORS
7 DERM RETAINER
8 DERM BOLTS
9 INSULATOR
GC8019201317000X

Fig. 15 Arming sensor replacement. 1992-93 Corvette

4. Remove CPA and disconnect sensor electrical connector.
5. Remove nut retaining resistor module and two nuts retaining body computer module.
6. Remove DERM and body control module bracket.
7. Remove sensor mounting bolts and screws.
8. Remove sensor by rotating rear of sensor to disengage from mounting clip and pulling rearward.
9. Reverse procedure to install, noting the following:
   a. Install sensor with arrow pointing toward front of vehicle.
   b. Ensure front flange of sensor is engaged into spring clip on bracket.
   c. After completing installation, rearm air bag system as described under "Air Bag System Disarming & Arming."
   d. Turn ignition switch to On position and verify "Inflatable Restraint" indicator flashes 7 to 9 times, then turns off. If indicator does not respond, refer to "Diagnosis & Testing."

1994

Refer to "1992-93 Eldorado, Riviera, Seville, Toronado & Trofeo" in this section for dual sensor replacement procedure.

1992–93 ELDORADO, RIVIERA, SEVILLE, TORONADO & TROFEO

1. Disarm air bag system as described under "Air Bag System Disarming & Arming."
2. Remove body computer module and glove compartment assembly.

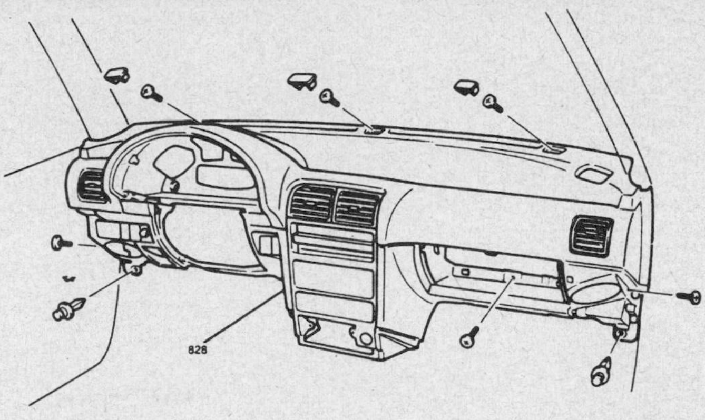
828
828 · INSTRUMENT PANEL
GC8019201318000X

Fig. 16 Exploded view of instrument panel. 1992-93 Metro

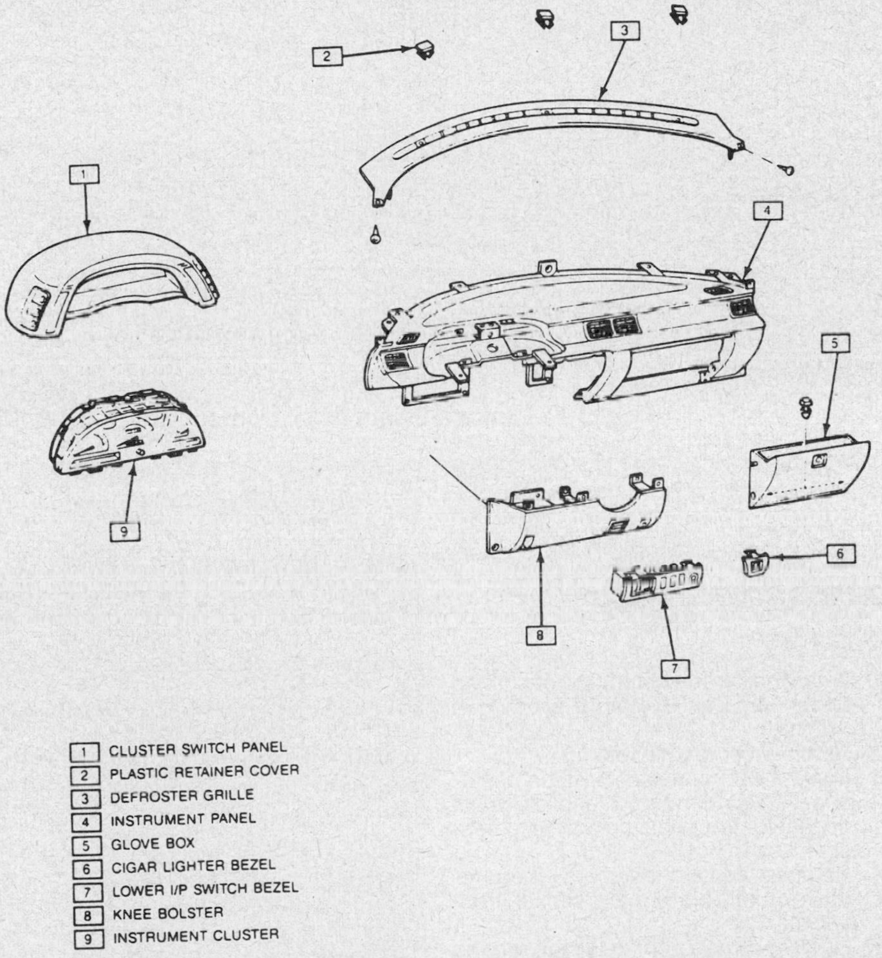
1
2
3
4
5
6
7
8
9
1 CLUSTER SWITCH PANEL
2 PLASTIC RETAINER COVER
3 DEFROSTER GRILLE
4 INSTRUMENT PANEL
5 GLOVE BOX
6 CIGAR LIGHTER BEZEL
7 LOWER I/P SWITCH BEZEL
8 KNEE BOLSTER
9 INSTRUMENT CLUSTER
GC8019201319000X

Fig. 17 Exploded view of instrument panel. Storm

3. Remove right side-glass defroster hose and position sound insulation away from cowl.
4. Disconnect sensor electrical connector and remove two retaining bolts.
5. Reverse procedure to install, noting the following:
   a. Install sensor with arrow pointing toward the front of vehicle.
   b. After completing installation, rearm air bag system as described under "Air Bag System Disarming & Arming."
   c. Turn ignition switch to On position and verify "Inflatable Restraint" indicator flashes 7 to 9 times, then turns off. If indicator does not respond, refer to "Diagnosis & Testing."

LESABRE, PARK AVENUE, 88 & 98

1992–93

1. Disarm air bag system as described under "Air Bag System Disarming & Arming."
2. Remove instrument panel assembly, **Figs. 18 and 19.**
3. Remove air distributor assembly, located behind instrument panel.
4. Remove push-type fastener retaining sensor electrical connector to theft deterrent/pass key control module bracket.
5. Remove CPA and dual sensor electrical connector.
6. Remove mounting bolts attaching sensor to front of dash.
7. Remove sensor by rotating rear of sensor to disengage from mounting clip and pulling rearward.
8. Reverse procedure to install, noting the following:
   a. Ensure front flange of sensor is engaged into spring clip on bracket.
   b. After completing installation, rearm air bag system as described under "Air Bag System Disarming & Arming."
   c. Turn ignition switch to On position and verify "Inflatable Restraint" indicator flashes 7 to 9 times, then turns off. If indicator does not respond, refer to "Diagnosis & Testing."

BONNEVILLE w/SINGLE AIR BAG

1992–93

1. Disarm air bag system as described under "Air Bag System Disarming & Arming."
2. Remove instrument panel assembly, **Fig. 20.**
3. Remove air distributor assembly.
4. Remove push type fastener retaining sensor pigtail to theft deterrent control module bracket.
5. Disconnect connector position assurance and sensor electrical connector.
6. Remove sensor mounting bolts.
7. Remove sensor by rotating rear of sensor to disengage from mounting clip and pulling rearward.
8. Reverse procedure to install. Tighten to specifications.
9. After completing installation, rearm air bag system as described under "Air Bag System Disarming & Arming."

BONNEVILLE w/DUAL AIR BAGS

1992–93

1. Disarm air bag system as described under "Air Bag System Disarming & Arming."
2. Remove instrument panel assembly, **Fig. 20.**
3. Disconnect connector position assurance and sensor electrical connector.
4. Remove steering column support bracket brace to pillar panel bolts.

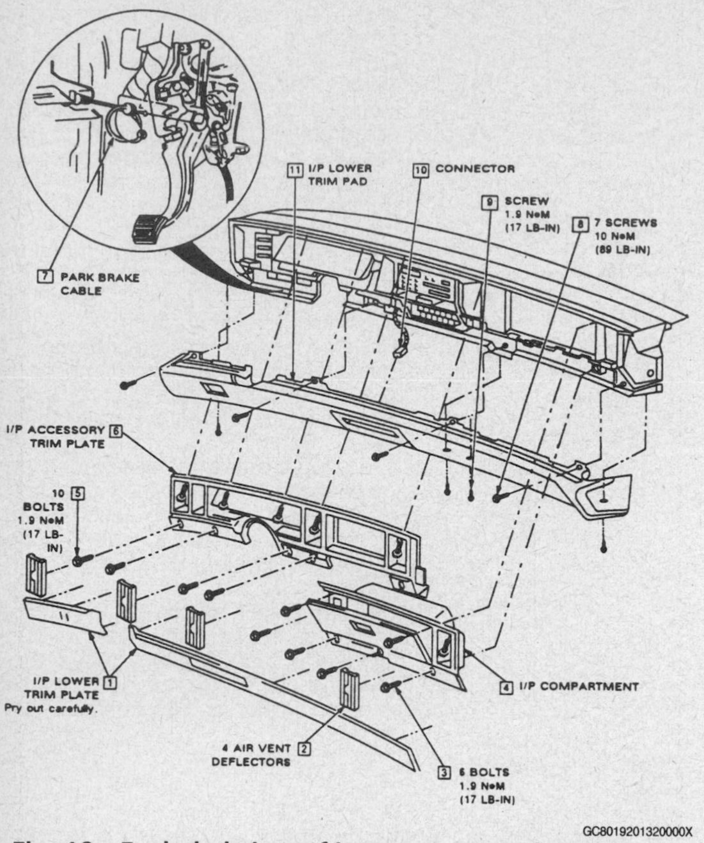
11 I/P LOWER TRIM PAD
10 CONNECTOR
9 SCREW 1.9 N•M (17 LB-IN)
8 7 SCREWS 10 N•M (89 LB-IN)
7 PARK BRAKE CABLE
I/P ACCESSORY TRIM PLATE 6
10 BOLTS 1.9 N•M (17 LB-IN) 5
I/P LOWER TRIM PLATE 1 Pry out carefully.
4 I/P COMPARTMENT
4 AIR VENT DEFLECTORS 2
3 6 BOLTS 1.9 N•M (17 LB-IN)
GC8019201320000X

Fig. 18 Exploded view of instrument panel. LeSabre & Park Avenue

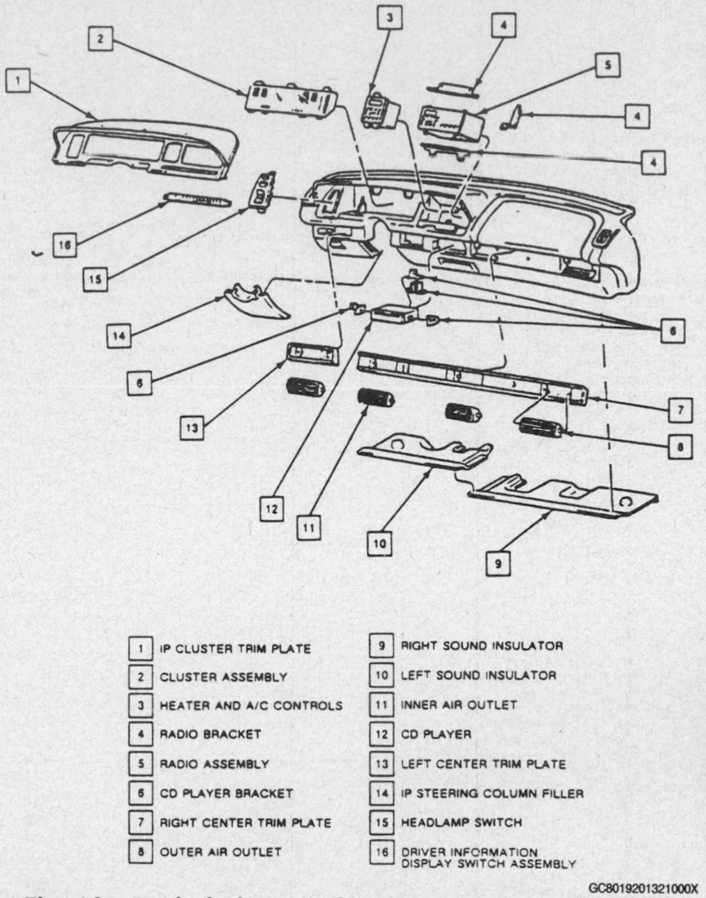
1 IP CLUSTER TRIM PLATE
2 CLUSTER ASSEMBLY
3 HEATER AND A/C CONTROLS
4 RADIO BRACKET
5 RADIO ASSEMBLY
6 CD PLAYER BRACKET
7 RIGHT CENTER TRIM PLATE
8 OUTER AIR OUTLET
9 RIGHT SOUND INSULATOR
10 LEFT SOUND INSULATOR
11 INNER AIR OUTLET
12 CD PLAYER
13 LEFT CENTER TRIM PLATE
14 IP STEERING COLUMN FILLER
15 HEADLAMP SWITCH
16 DRIVER INFORMATION DISPLAY SWITCH ASSEMBLY
GC8019201321000X

Fig. 19 Exploded view of instrument panel. 88 & 98

5. Remove steering column support bracket brace to steering column support bracket bolts.
6. Remove steering column support bracket brace.
7. Remove attaching bolts and sensor.
8. Reverse procedure to install. Tighten to specifications.
9. After completing installation, rearm air bag system as described under "Air Bag System Disarming & Arming."

DUAL POLE ARMING SENSOR, REPLACE

Use extreme caution when handling an air bag system sensor. Striking an air bag sensor could cause system deployment, resulting in personal injury and/or improper air bag system operation. All sensors and mounting bracket bolts must be properly tightened to ensure proper operation.

BONNEVILLE, LESABRE, PARK AVENUE, 88 & 98

1994

1. Disarm air bag system as described under "Air Bag System Disarming & Arming."
2. Remove instrument panel assembly, **Figs. 18 through 20.**
3. Disconnect connector position assurance and sensor electrical connector.
4. Remove attaching bolts and sensor.
5. Reverse procedure to install. Tighten to specifications.
6. After completing installation, rearm air bag system as described under "Air Bag System Disarming & Arming."

CAMARO & FIREBIRD

1993–94

1. Disarm air bag system as described under "Air Bag System Disarming & Arming."
2. Remove center console.
3. Disconnect connector position assurance (CPA) connector and electrical connector from dual pole arming sensor.
4. Remove sensor fasteners, then remove dual pole arming sensor from vehicle.
5. Reverse procedure to install, noting the following:
   a. Tighten to specifications.
   b. After completing installation, rearm air bag system as described under "Air Bag System Disarming & Arming."

CORVETTE

1994

1. Disarm air bag system as described under "Air Bag System Disarming & Arming."
2. Remove radio control.
3. Disconnect arming sensor connector from clip on righthand knee bolster inner bracket.
4. Remove SIR wiring harness to arming sensor CPA and disconnect arming sensor electrical connector.
5. Remove arming sensor retaining fasteners.
6. Remove arming sensor.
7. Reverse procedure to install, noting the following:
   a. Install sensor with arrow pointing toward front of vehicle.
   b. After completing installation, rearm air bag system as described under "Air Bag System Disarming & Arming."
   c. Turn ignition switch to On position and verify "Inflatable Restraint" indicator flashes 7 to 9 times, then turns off. If indicator does not respond, refer to "Diagnosis & Testing."

1993–94 ELDORADO & SEVILLE & 1994 DEVILLE & RIVIERA

1. Disarm air bag system as described under "Air Bag System Disarming & Arming."
2. Remove glove compartment.
3. Remove four screws and the glove compartment unit from instrument panel, then remove passenger's side air bag module as described under "Passenger Air Bag Module, Replace."
4. Remove two screws and one nut retaining radio chassis to bracket.

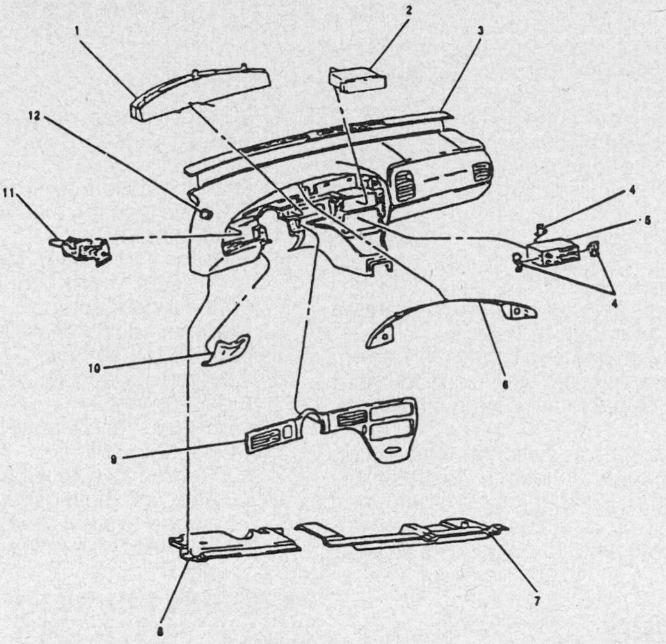
1
2
3
4
5
6
7
8
9
10
11
12

1	CLUSTER ASSEMBLY	7	RIGHT SOUND INSULATOR
2	HEATER AND A/C CONTROLS	8	LEFT SOUND INSULATOR
3	WINDSHIELD DEFROSTER GRILLE	9	IP TRIM PLATE ASSEMBLY
4	RADIO BRACKET	10	IP STEERING COLUMN FILLER
5	RADIO ASSEMBLY	11	HEADLAMP SWITCH ASSEMBLY
6	IP CLUSTER TRIM PLATE ASSEMBLY	12	SIDE WINDOW DEFOGGER OUTLET

GC8019201322000X

Fig. 20 Exploded view of instrument panel. Bonneville

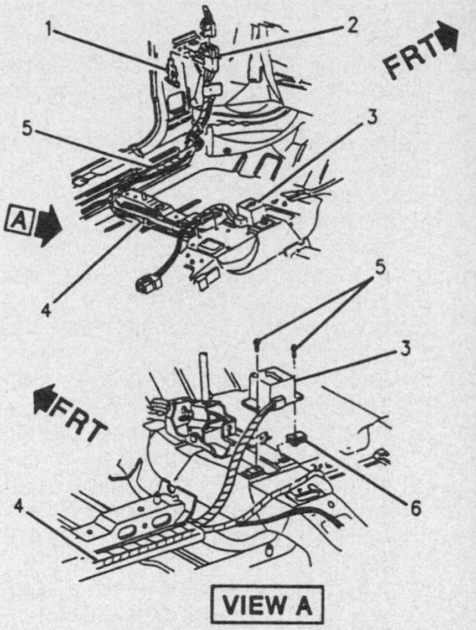
1
2
FRT
3
5
A
4
5
3
FRT
4
6
VIEW A

GC8019201323000X

Fig. 21 Passenger compartment sensor replacement. Beretta & Corsica

5. Disconnect electrical connectors and coax cable from radio chassis, then remove radio chassis from bracket.
6. Remove two screws retaining bracket assembly and set aside.
7. Disconnect connector position assurance (CPA) and electrical connector from sensor.
8. Loosen two bolts and remove dual pole arming sensor.
9. Reverse procedure to install, noting the following:
   a. Tighten mounting bolts to specifications.
   b. After completing installation, rearm air bag system as described under "Air Bag System Disarming & Arming."

FLEETWOOD (RWD)

1993

1. Disarm air bag system as described under "Air Bag System Disarming & Arming."
2. Remove accelerator pedal assembly.
3. Disconnect connector position assurance (CPA) and electrical connector.
4. Loosen fasteners from dual pole arming sensor.
5. Remove dual pole arming sensor.
6. Reverse procedure to install, noting the following:
   a. Tighten to specifications.
   b. After completing installation, rearm air bag system as described under "Air Bag System Disarming & Arming."

PASSENGER COMPARTMENT SENSOR, REPLACE

BERETTA, CORSICA & 1994 ACHIEVA, GRAND AM & SKYLARK

1. Disarm air bag system as described under "Air Bag System Disarming & Arming."
2. Remove console, left front seat and track guides.
3. Remove left side shroud panel and left front center pillar lower trim and carpet restrainer.
4. Remove CPA and disconnect sensor electrical connector.
5. Lift carpet to gain access to electrical harness routing conduits. **Fig. 21.**
6. Remove sensor mounting bolts, then snap open conduits and remove sensor wiring.
7. Remove passenger compartment sensor.
8. Reverse procedure to install, noting the following:
   a. Install sensor with arrow pointing toward front of vehicle.
   b. After completing installation, rearm air bag system as described under "Air Bag System Disarming & Arming."
   c. Turn ignition switch to On position and verify "Inflatable Restraint" indicator flashes 7 to 9 times, then turns off. If indicator does not respond, refer to "Diagnosis & Testing."

CENTURY, CUTLASS CIERA & CUTLASS CRUISER

1. Disarm air bag system as described under "Air Bag System Disarming & Arming."
2. Remove right sound insulator.
3. Remove sensor electrical connector from retainer, then release connector position assurance (CPA) from connector and disconnect connector.
4. Pull back carpet on tunnel for access to sensor.
5. Loosen sensor mounting bolts and remove sensor.
6. Reverse procedure to install, noting the following:
   a. Tighten to specifications.
   b. After completing installation, rearm air bag system as described under "Air Bag System Disarming & Arming."

DEVILLE, ELDORADO, FLEETWOOD, LESABRE, PARK AVENUE, RIVIERA, SEVILLE, TORONADO & TROFEO

The passenger compartment sensor and arming sensor are removed as an assembly. Refer to "Dual Sensor" or "Dual Pole Arming Sensor" for removal procedure.

CAMARO & FIREBIRD

1992

1. Disarm air bag system as described under "Air Bag System Disarming & Arming."
2. Remove knee bolster, refer to "Knee Bolster, Replace."
3. Remove console.
4. Remove heater air distribution duct.
5. Remove CPA and disconnect passenger compartment discriminating sensor electrical connector.
6. Remove sensor retaining bolts, then the sensor.
7. Reverse procedure to install, noting the following:
   a. Install sensor with arrow pointing toward front of vehicle.
   b. After completing installation, rearm air bag system as described under "Air Bag System Disarming & Arming."
   c. Turn ignition switch to On position and verify "Inflatable Restraint" indicator flashes 7 to 9 times, then turns off. If indicator does not respond, refer to "Diagnosis & Testing."

1993–94

1. Disarm air bag system as described under "Air Bag System Disarming & Arming."
2. Disconnect connector position assurance (CPA) and electrical connectors from sensor.
3. Loosen fasteners and remove passenger compartment sensor from vehicle.
4. Reverse procedure to install, noting the following:
   a. Tighten to specifications.
   b. After completing installation, rearm air bag system as described under "Air Bag System Disarming & Arming."

METRO

1. Disarm air bag system as described under "Air Bag System Disarming & Arming."
2. Disconnect battery ground cable.
3. Remove CPA and disconnect sensor electrical connector, below instrument panel, on right side of steering column.
4. Remove two mounting bolts, then remove sensor.
5. Reverse procedure to install, noting the following:
   a. Install sensor with arrow pointing toward front of vehicle.
   b. After completing installation, rearm air bag system as described under "Air Bag System Disarming & Arming."
   c. Turn ignition switch to On position and verify "Inflatable Restraint" indicator flashes 7 to 9 times, then turns off. If indicator does not respond, refer to "Diagnosis & Testing."

STORM

1. Disarm air bag system as described under "Air Bag System Disarming & Arming."
2. Remove front console bracket.
3. Disconnect electrical connector clip and sensor connector.
4. Remove two mounting bolts securing sensor.
5. Remove sensor.
6. Reverse procedure to install, noting the following:
   a. Install sensor with arrow pointing towards front of vehicle.
   b. After completing installation, rearm air bag system as described under "Air Bag System Disarming & Arming."
   c. Turn ignition switch to On position and verify "Inflatable Restraint" indicator flashes 7 to 9 times, then turns off. If indicator does not respond, refer to "Diagnosis & Testing."

FORWARD DISCRIMINATING SENSOR, REPLACE

ACHIEVA, BERETTA, CORSICA, GRAND AM & SKYLARK

1994

1. Disarm air bag system as described under "Air Bag System Disarming & Arming."
2. Remove CPA and disconnect sensor electrical connector located near righthand strut tower.
3. Remove nuts securing sensor.
4. Reverse procedure to install, noting the following:
   a. Install sensor with arrow pointing toward front of vehicle.
   b. After completing installation, rearm air bag system as described under "Air Bag System Disarming & Arming."
   c. Turn ignition switch to On position and verify "Inflatable Restraint" indicator flashes 7 to 9 times, then turns off. If indicator does not respond, refer to "Diagnosis & Testing."

LESABRE, PARK AVENUE, 88, 98 & BONNEVILLE

1. Disarm air bag system as described under "Air Bag System Disarming & Arming."
2. Disconnect connector position assurance and sensor pigtail electrical connection.
3. Remove sensor pigtail wiring from clips.
4. Remove bolts and upper radiator tie bar to grill reveal molding.
5. Remove sensor bolts and sensor.
6. Reverse procedure to install. Tighten to specifications.
7. After completing installation, rearm air bag system as described under "Air Bag System Disarming & Arming."

CENTURY, CUTLASS CIERA & CUTLASS CRUISER

1993–94

1. Disarm air bag system as described under "Air Bag System Disarming & Arming."
2. Remove grille from front of vehicle.
3. Remove sensor electrical connector from retainer.
4. Release connector position assurance (CPA) from connector and disconnect connector.
5. Remove sensor mounting bolts, then remove the sensor.
6. Reverse procedure to install, noting the following:
   a. Ensure sensor arrow points toward front of vehicle.
   b. Tighten to specifications.
   c. After completing installation, rearm air bag system as described under "Air Bag System Disarming & Arming."

CUTLASS SUPREME

1994

1. Disarm air bag system as described under "Air Bag System Disarming & Arming."
2. Remove headlamp and side marker lamp.
3. Release connector position assurance (CPA) from connector and disconnect connector.
4. Remove sensor mounting bolts, then remove the sensor.
5. Reverse procedure to install, noting the following:
   a. Ensure sensor arrow points toward front of vehicle.
   b. Tighten to specifications.
   c. After completing installation, rearm air bag system as described under "Air Bag System Disarming & Arming."

1993–94 FLEETWOOD (RWD) & 1994 CAPRICE & ROADMASTER

Left Sensor

1. Disarm air bag system as described under "Air Bag System Disarming & Arming."
2. Disconnect Connector Position Assurance (CPA) and sensor electrical connector.
3. Remove sensor mounting fasteners, then remove sensor from vehicle.
4. Reverse procedure to install, noting the following:
   a. Ensure arrow on top of sensor is pointing toward front of vehicle.
   b. Tighten to specifications.
   c. After completing installation, rearm air bag system as described under "Air Bag System Disarming & Arming."

Right Sensor

1. Disarm air bag system as described under "Air Bag System Disarming & Arming."
2. Remove battery, then disconnect

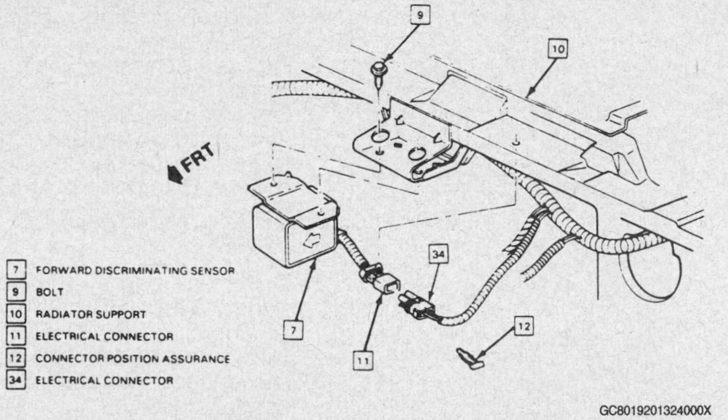
FRT
7 FORWARD DISCRIMINATING SENSOR
9 BOLT
10 RADIATOR SUPPORT
11 ELECTRICAL CONNECTOR
12 CONNECTOR POSITION ASSURANCE
34 ELECTRICAL CONNECTOR
GC8019201324000X

Fig. 22 Forward sensor replacement. 1992 Camaro & Firebird

Connector Position Assurance (CPA) and sensor electrical connector.
3. Remove sensor mounting fasteners, then remove sensor from vehicle.
4. Reverse procedure to install, noting the following:
   a. Ensure arrow on top of sensor is pointed toward front of vehicle.
   b. Tighten to specifications.
   c. After completing installation, rearm air bag system as described under "Air Bag System Disarming & Arming."

CAMARO & FIREBIRD

1993–94

1. Disarm air bag system as described under "Air Bag System Disarming & Arming."
2. Loosen sensor fasteners and lower sensor for access.
3. Disconnect connector position assurance (CPA) and electrical connectors.
4. Remove sensor from vehicle.
5. Reverse procedure to install, noting the following:
   a. Tighten to specifications.
   b. After completing installation, rearm air bag system as described under "Air Bag System Disarming & Arming."

FORWARD SENSORS, REPLACE

BERETTA & CORSICA

1. Disarm air bag system as described under "Air Bag System Disarming & Arming."
2. Remove right outer radiator upper air baffle.
3. Remove CPA and disconnect sensor electrical connector.
4. Remove wiring clips from upper radiator tie bar, then remove bolts securing bracket to upper radiator tie bar.
5. Remove nuts securing sensor to bracket.
6. Reverse procedure to install, noting the following:
   a. Install sensor with arrow pointing toward front of vehicle.
   b. After completing installation, rearm air bag system as described under "Air Bag System Disarming & Arming."
   c. Turn ignition switch to On position and verify "Inflatable Restraint" indicator flashes 7 to 9 times, then turns off. If indicator does not respond, refer to "Diagnosis & Testing."

CAMARO & FIREBIRD

1992

1. Disarm air bag system as described under "Air Bag System Disarming & Arming."
2. Remove air cleaner, then raise and support vehicle.
3. Remove radiator air upper baffle.
4. Remove CPA and disconnect Forward Discriminating Sensor electrical connector behind radiator support.
5. Remove forward discrimination sensor retaining bolts, then the sensor, **Fig. 22.**
6. Reverse procedure to install, noting the following:
   a. Install forward discriminating sensor with arrow pointing toward front of vehicle.
   b. After completing installation, rearm air bag system as described under "Air Bag System Disarming & Arming."
   c. Turn ignition switch to On position and verify "Inflatable Restraint" indicator flashes 7 to 9 times, then turns Off. If indicator does not respond, refer to "Diagnosis & Testing."

CAPRICE, CUSTOM CRUISER & ROADMASTER

1. Disarm air bag system as described under "Air Bag System Disarming & Arming."
2. Remove battery if necessary for access to right sensor.
3. Remove radiator support baffle.
4. Disconnect CPA and electrical connector from radiator support.
5. Remove mounting screws from sensor, then remove sensor.
6. Reverse procedure to install, noting the following:
   a. Install sensor with arrow pointing toward front of vehicle.
   b. After completing installation, rearm air bag system as described under "Air Bag System Disarming & Arming."
   c. Turn ignition switch to On position and verify "Inflatable Restraint" indicator flashes 7 to 9 times, then turns off. If indicator does not respond, refer to "Diagnosis & Testing."

CORVETTE

Left Sensor

1. Disarm air bag system as described under "Air Bag System Disarming & Arming."
2. Remove battery, ECM and ECM support.
3. Remove sensor mounting bolts then disconnect sensor electrical connector and remove sensor from vehicle.
4. Reverse procedure to install, noting the following:
   a. Install sensor with arrow pointing toward front of vehicle.
   b. After completing installation, rearm air bag system as described under "Air Bag System Disarming & Arming."
   c. Turn ignition switch to On position and verify "Inflatable Restraint" indicator flashes 7 to 9 times, then turns off. If indicator does not respond, refer to "Diagnosis & Testing."

Right Sensor

1. Disarm air bag system as described under "Air Bag System Disarming & Arming."
2. Remove six front righthand rocker panel retaining screws.
3. Remove right side front fender gill panel retaining bolts, then the fender.
4. Peel back rear portion of wheelwell to hood seal.
5. Remove right side lower wheelwell retaining bolts, then the wheelwell.
6. Remove two front windshield washer reservoir retaining bolts, then loosen remaining washer reservoir bolt.
7. Rotate reservoir to access sensor.
8. Remove sensor retaining bolts, then disconnect sensor electrical connector.
9. Reverse procedure to install, noting the following:
   a. Install sensor with arrow pointing toward front of vehicle.
   b. After completing installation, rearm air bag system as described under "Air Bag System Disarming & Arming."
   c. Turn ignition switch to the On position and verify proper operation of "INFL REST" lamp.

DEVILLE & FLEETWOOD (FWD)

1992–93

1. Disarm air bag system as described under "Air Bag System Disarming & Arming."
2. Disconnect forward sensor electrical connector, then remove harness retaining clips, **Fig. 23.**

3. Remove two sensor mounting bolts, then remove sensor.
4. Reverse procedure to install, noted the following:
   a. Install sensor with arrow pointing toward the front of vehicle.
   b. After completing installation, rearm air bag system as described under "Air Bag System Disarming & Arming."
   c. Turn ignition switch to On position and verify "Inflatable Restraint" indicator flashes 7 to 9 times, then turns off. If indicator does not respond, refer to "Diagnosis & Testing."

LESABRE, PARK AVENUE, 88 & 98

1992–93

1. Disarm air bag system as described under "Air Bag System Disarming & Arming."
2. Remove instrument panel assembly, **Figs. 18 and 19.**
3. Remove air distributor assembly, located behind instrument panel.
4. Remove push-type fastener retaining sensor electrical connector to theft deterrent/pass key control module bracket.
5. Remove CPA and dual sensor electrical connector.
6. Remove mounting bolts attaching sensor to front of dash.
7. Remove sensor, **Fig. 23,** by rotating rear of sensor to disengage from mounting clip and pulling rearward.
8. Reverse procedure to install, noting the following:
   a. Ensure front flange of sensor is engaged into spring clip on bracket.
   b. After completing installation, rearm air bag system as described under "Air Bag System Disarming & Arming."
   c. Turn ignition switch to On position and verify "Inflatable Restraint" indicator flashes 7 to 9 times, then turns off. If indicator does not respond, refer to "Diagnosis & Testing."

BONNEVILLE w/SINGLE AIR BAG

1992–93

1. Disarm air bag system as described under "Air Bag System Disarming & Arming."
2. Remove instrument panel assembly, **Fig. 20.**
3. Remove air distributor assembly.
4. Remove push type fastener retaining sensor pigtail to theft deterrent control module bracket.
5. Disconnect connector position assurance and sensor electrical connector.
6. Remove sensor mounting bolts.
7. Remove sensor by rotating rear of sensor to disengage from mounting clip and pulling rearward.
8. Reverse procedure to install. Tighten to specifications.
9. After completing installation, rearm air bag system as described under "Air Bag System Disarming & Arming."

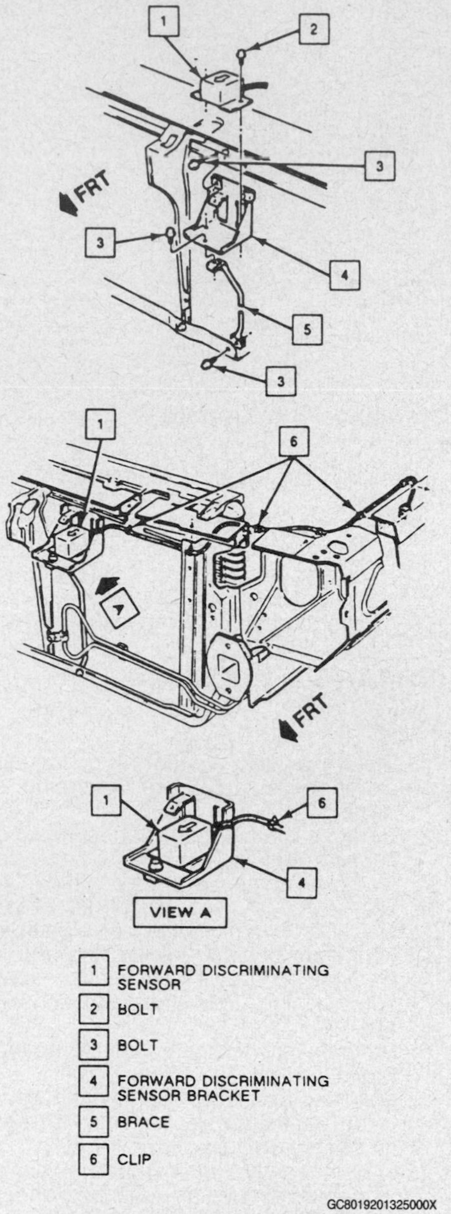

FRT
FRT
A
VIEW A
1 FORWARD DISCRIMINATING SENSOR
2 BOLT
3 BOLT
4 FORWARD DISCRIMINATING SENSOR BRACKET
5 BRACE
6 CLIP
GC8019201325000X

Fig. 23 Forward sensor replacement. 1992-93 DeVille, Fleetwood (FWD), LeSabre, Park Avenue, 88 & 98

BONNEVILLE w/DUAL AIR BAGS

1992–93

1. Disarm air bag system as described under "Air Bag System Disarming & Arming."
2. Remove instrument panel assembly, **Fig. 20.**
3. Disconnect connector position assurance and sensor electrical connector.
4. Remove steering column support bracket brace to pillar panel bolts.
5. Remove steering column support bracket brace to support bracket bolts.
6. Remove steering column support bracket brace.
7. Remove sensor attaching bolts, then the sensor.
8. Reverse procedure to install. After installation is complete, rearm air bag system as described under "Air Bag System Disarming & Arming."

RIVIERA, TORONADO & TROFEO

1. Disarm air bag system as described under "Air Bag System Disarming & Arming."
2. Disconnect battery ground cable.
3. Disconnect and remove wire harness conduit cover.
4. Disconnect CPA and sensor electrical connector.
5. Remove harness retaining clips and pull harness through radiator support brace.
6. Raise and support vehicle, then remove two tamper resistant bolts with insert bit tool No. J-38597 or equivalent.
7. Remove sensor from vehicle.
8. Reverse procedure to install, noting the following:
   a. Install sensor with arrow towards front of vehicle.
   b. After completing installation, rearm air bag system as described under "Air Bag System Disarming & Arming."
   c. Turn ignition switch to On position and verify "Inflatable Restraint" indicator flashes 7 to 9 times, then turns off. If indicator does not respond, refer to "Diagnosis & Testing."

1992–94 ELDORADO & SEVILLE & 1994 DEVILLE & RIVIERA

1. Disarm air bag system as described under "Air Bag System Disarming & Arming."
2. Remove radiator plastic support cover.
3. Remove windshield washer fluid reservoir.
4. Disconnect connector position assurance and sensor electrical connector.
5. Remove two sensor bolts and sensor.
6. Reverse procedure to install. Tighten to specifications.
7. After completing installation, rearm air bag system as described under "Air Bag System Disarming & Arming."

METRO

1. Disarm air bag system as described under "Air Bag System Disarming & Arming."
2. Disconnect battery ground cable.
3. Disconnect sensor connector from lamp support panel.
4. Remove CPA and sensor electrical connector.
5. Disconnect two sensor lead wire clamps and remove two sensor mounting bolts.
6. Remove sensor.
7. Reverse procedure to install, noting the following:

a. Install sensor with arrow pointing toward front of vehicle.
b. After completing installation, rearm air bag system as described under "Air Bag System Disarming & Arming."
c. Turn ignition switch to On position and verify "Inflatable Restraint" indicator flashes 7 to 9 times, then turns off. If indicator does not respond, refer to "Diagnosis & Testing."

PRIZM

1. Disarm air bag system as described under "Air Bag System Disarming & Arming."
2. Raise and support vehicle, then remove retaining clips and wheel housing from front wheelwell.
3. Disconnect forward sensor electrical connector.
4. Loosen two mounting bolts and remove forward sensor from vehicle. Discard mounting bolts following removal.
5. Reverse procedure to install, noting the following;
   a. Ensure forward sensor is installed with arrow on sensor pointing toward front of vehicle.
   b. Tighten to specifications.
   c. **Always secure with new mounting bolts.**
   d. After completing installation, rearm air bag system as described under "Air Bag System Disarming & Arming."

STORM

1. Disarm air bag system as described under "Air Bag System Disarming & Arming."
2. Disconnect battery ground cable.
3. Raise and support vehicle, then disconnect sensor electrical connector. **Fig. 24.**
4. Remove three mounting bolts and sensor from radiator support brace.
5. Reverse procedure to install, noting the following:
   a. Install sensor with arrow pointing toward front of vehicle.
   b. After completing installation, rearm air bag system as described under "Air Bag System Disarming & Arming."
   c. Turn ignition switch to On position and verify "Inflatable Restraint" indicator flashes 7 to 9 times, then turns off. If indicator does not respond, refer to "Diagnosis & Testing."

LEFTHAND & RIGHTHAND DISCRIMINATING SENSORS, REPLACE

1992–94 ELDORADO & SEVILLE & 1994 DEVILLE & RIVIERA

Left Sensor

1. Disarm air bag system as described under "Air Bag System Disarming & Arming."

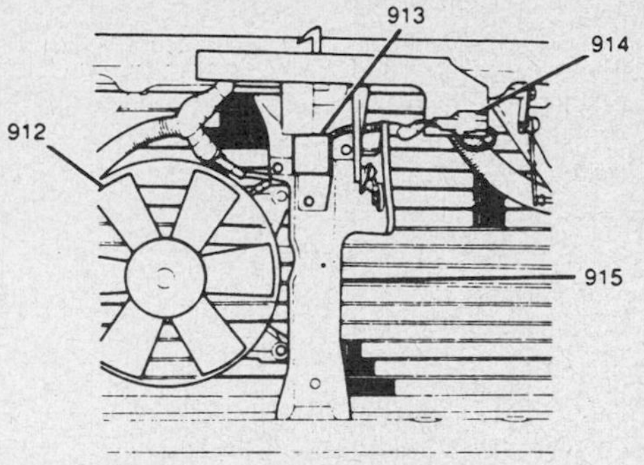
913
914
912
915

912 CONDENSER FAN
913 FORWARD DISCRIMINATING SENSOR
914 FORWARD DISCRIMINATING SENSOR CONNECTOR
915 RADIATOR CORE SUPPORT

GC8019201326000X

Fig. 24 Forward sensor replacement. Storm

2. Remove windshield washer fluid reservoir.
3. Disconnect connector position assurance and sensor electrical connector.
4. Remove two sensor bolts and sensor.
5. Reverse procedure to install. Tighten to specifications.
6. After completing installation, rearm air bag system as described under "Air Bag System Disarming & Arming."

Right Sensor

1. Disarm air bag system as described under "Air Bag System Disarming & Arming."
2. Reposition heater hose.
3. Disconnect connector position assurance and sensor electrical connector.
4. Remove two sensor bolts and sensor.
5. Reverse procedure to install. Tighten to specifications.
6. After completing installation, rearm air bag system as described under "Air Bag System Disarming & Arming."

MID-RAIL DISCRIMINATING SENSOR, REPLACE

BONNEVILLE, 88 & 98

1994

1. Disarm air bag system as described under "Air Bag System Disarming & Arming."
2. Raise and support vehicle.
3. Disconnect connector position assurance and sensor electrical connection.
4. Remove sensor attaching screws, then the sensor.
5. Reverse procedure to install. Tighten to specifications.
6. After completing installation, rearm air bag system as described under "Air Bag System Disarming & Arming."

PASSENGER COMPARTMENT DISCRIMINATING SENSOR, REPLACE

CUTLASS SUPREME & REGAL

1994

1. Disarm air bag system as described under "Air Bag System Disarming & Arming."
2. Disconnect connector position assurance and sensor electrical connection.
3. Remove sensor attaching screws, then the sensor.
4. Reverse procedure to install. Tighten to specifications.
5. After completing installation, rearm air bag system as described under "Air Bag System Disarming & Arming."

CENTER SENSOR ASSEMBLY, REPLACE

Prizm

Do not open the center sensor assembly case for any reason. Touching the connector pins or soldered components may cause electrostatic discharge (ESD) damage. Repair of a faulty center sensor assembly is by replacement only.

1. Disarm air bag system as described under "Air Bag System Disarming & Arming."
2. Disconnect battery ground cable, then remove console from vehicle.
3. Remove three bolts and console mounting bracket from floor, then remove rear seat cushion.
4. Loosen rear floor carpet to gain access to center sensor assembly bolts.
5. Disconnect center sensor assembly connectors.
6. Remove three bolts and the center sensor assembly from vehicle.
7. Reverse procedure to install, noting the following:
   a. Tighten to specifications.
   b. After completing installation, rearm air bag system as described under "Air Bag System Disarming & Arming."

KNEE BOLSTER, REPLACE

Beretta, Corsica & 1992 Camaro & Firebird

1. Disarm air bag system as described under "Air Bag System Disarming & Arming."
2. Remove knee bolster retaining screws, **Fig. 25.**
3. Reverse procedure to install, noting the following:
   a. After completing installation, rearm air bag system as described under "Air Bag System Disarming & Arming."
   b. Turn ignition switch to On position and verify "Inflatable Restraint" indicator flashes 7 to 9 times, then turns off. If indicator does not re-

spond, refer to "Diagnosis & Testing."

Caprice, Custom Cruiser & Roadmaster

1. Disarm air bag system as described under "Air Bag System Disarming & Arming."
2. Remove lower steering column trim panel.
3. Remove four bolster mounting screws.
4. Remove knee bolster.
5. Reverse procedure to install. After completing installation, rearm air bag system as described under "Air Bag System Disarming & Arming."

Corvette

1. Disarm air bag system as described under "Air Bag System Disarming & Arming."
2. Remove lower trim panel.
3. Remove console side trim panel left-hand upper two screws. Rotate access panel down to remove two knee bolster retaining bolts.
4. Remove knee bolster inner and outer bracket retaining screws.
5. Disconnect lap air outlet duct from lower duct assembly.
6. Remove knee bolster.
7. Reverse procedure to install, noting the following:
   a. After completing installation, rearm air bag system as described under "Air Bag System Disarming & Arming."
   b. Turn ignition switch to On position and verify proper operation of "INFL REST" lamp.

DeVille & Fleetwood (FWD)

1. Disarm air bag system as described under "Air Bag System Disarming & Arming."
2. Remove I/P lower trim panel.
3. Remove two twilight sentinel bracket retaining screws.
4. Remove two fuse block bracket retaining screws.
5. Remove two knee bolster tie bar retaining screws, **Fig. 26.**
6. Remove left side instrument panel retaining bolt.
7. Reverse procedure to install, noting the following:
   a. After completing installation, rearm air bag system as described under "Air Bag System Disarming & Arming."
   b. Turn ignition switch to On position and verify the "Inflatable Restraint" indicator flashes 7 to 9 times, then turns off. If indicator does not respond, refer to "Diagnosis & Testing."

Eldorado & Seville

1. Disarm air bag system as described under "Air Bag System Disarming & Arming."
2. Remove center trim plate.
3. Remove five screws securing knee bolster.
4. Remove knee bolster.

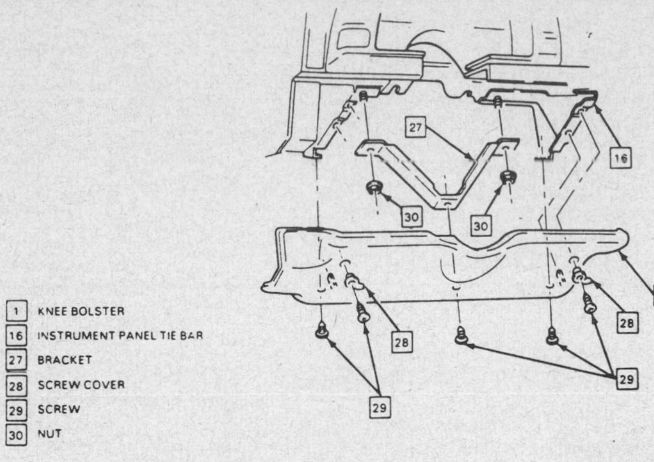

1 KNEE BOLSTER
16 INSTRUMENT PANEL TIE BAR
27 BRACKET
28 SCREW COVER
29 SCREW
30 NUT
GC8019201327000X

Fig. 25 Knee bolster replacement. 1992 Camaro & Firebird

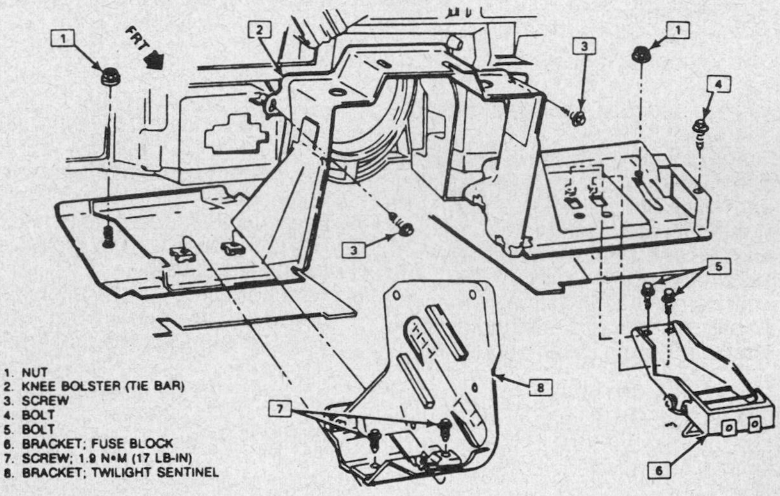

FRT
1. NUT
2. KNEE BOLSTER (TIE BAR)
3. SCREW
4. BOLT
5. BOLT
6. BRACKET; FUSE BLOCK
7. SCREW; 1.9 N•M (17 LB-IN)
8. BRACKET; TWILIGHT SENTINEL
GC8019201328000X

Fig. 26 Knee bolster replacement. DeVille & Fleetwood (FWD)

5. Reverse procedure to install. After completing installation, rearm air bag system as described under "Air Bag System Disarming & Arming."

Metro

1. Disarm air bag system as described under "Air Bag System Disarming & Arming."
2. Remove lower steering column trim panel and steering column reinforcement plate.
3. Remove two lower instrument panel retaining screws.
4. Remove five mounting screws and knee bolster from instrument panel support member.
5. Reverse procedure to install. After completing installation, rearm air bag system as described under "Air Bag System Disarming & Arming."

Prizm

1. Disarm air bag system as described under "Air Bag System Disarming & Arming."
2. Remove retaining clips and left front sill plate.
3. Loosen two screws and remove hood latch release handle from knee bolster.
4. Remove two bolt covers from front of knee bolster.
5. Remove four bolts and the knee bolster from instrument panel, disconnecting lap cooler air outlet from lap cooler air duct.
6. Reverse procedure to install, noting the following:
   a. Tighten to specifications.
   b. After completing installation, rearm air bag system as described under "Air Bag System Disarming & Arming."

Riviera

1. Disarm air bag system as described under "Air Bag System Disarming & Arming."
2. Remove instrument panel trim plate.
3. Remove front and rear console assemblies.
4. Remove six knee retaining bolster screws, then the knee bolster, **Fig. 27.**
5. Reverse procedure to install, noting the following:
   a. After completing installation, rearm air bag system as described under "Air Bag System Disarming & Arming."
   b. Turn ignition switch to On position

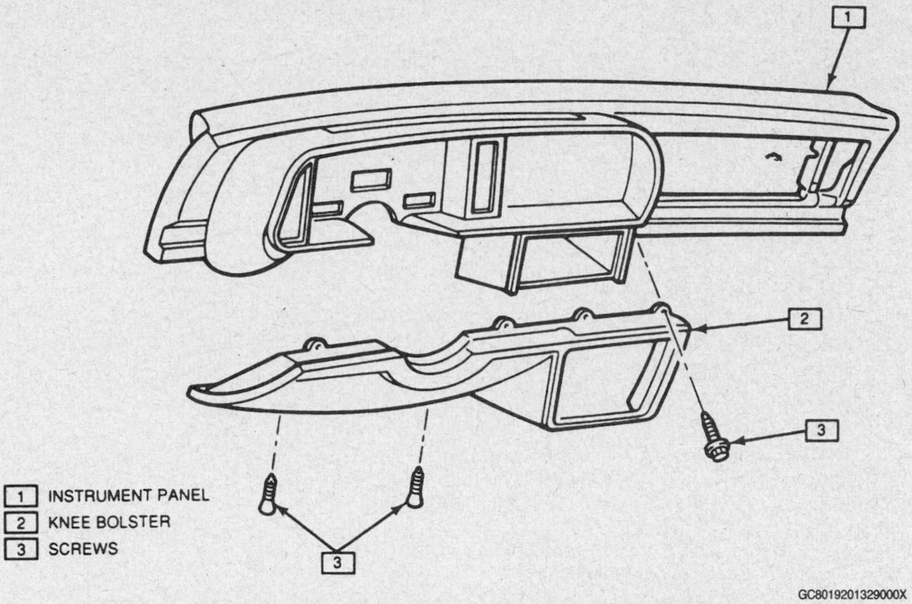
1
2
3
3
1 INSTRUMENT PANEL
2 KNEE BOLSTER
3 SCREWS
GC8019201329000X

Fig. 27 Knee bolster replacement. Riviera

and verify "Inflatable Restraint" indicator flashes 7 to 9 times, then turns off. If indicator does not respond, refer to "Diagnosis & Testing."

Storm

1. Disarm air bag system as described under "Air Bag System Disarming & Arming."
2. Remove left lower switch and dash lighter panel assemblies.
3. Remove hood release latch and cable.
4. Remove knee bolster.
5. Reverse procedure to install, noting the following:
   a. After completing installation, rearm air bag system as described under "Air Bag System Disarming & Arming."
   b. Turn ignition switch to On position and verify "Inflatable Restraint" indicator flashes 7 to 9 times, then turns off. If indicator does not respond, refer to "Diagnosis & Testing."

Toronado & Trofeo

1. Disarm air bag system as described under "Air Bag System Disarming & Arming."
2. Remove left side sound insulator.
3. Remove two bolster retaining screws, then remove the knee bolster.
4. Reverse procedure to install. After completing installation, rearm air bag system as described under "Air Bag System Disarming & Arming."

DRIVER AIR BAG MODULE, REPLACE

Always wear safety glasses and gloves. Wash hands with mild soap and water after handling a deployed module.

Except Metro, Prizm & Storm

1. Disarm air bag system as described under "Air Bag System Disarming & Arming."
2. Disconnect battery ground cable and wait ten minutes before removing air bag module.
3. Remove four bolts at rear of steering wheel, securing air bag module.
4. Rotate horn lead 1/4 turn and disconnect.
5. Disconnect electrical connectors and remove air bag module.
6. Reverse procedure to install, noting the following:
   a. After completing installation, rearm air bag system as described under "Air Bag System Disarming & Arming."
   b. Turn ignition switch to On position and verify "Inflatable Restraint" indicator flashes 7 to 9 times, then turns off. If indicator does not respond, refer to "Diagnosis & Testing."

Metro & Storm

1. Disarm air bag system as described under "Air Bag System Disarming & Arming."
2. Disconnect battery ground cable.
3. Remove four screws from rear of steering wheel.
4. Disconnect electrical connector and carefully remove air bag module from steering wheel.
5. Reverse procedure to install, noting the following:
   a. After completing installation, rearm air bag system as described under "Air Bag System Disarming & Arming."
   b. Turn ignition switch to On position and verify "Inflatable Restraint" indicator flashes 7 to 9 times, then turns off. If indicator does not respond, refer to "Diagnosis & Testing."

Prizm

1. Disarm air bag system as described under "Air Bag System Disarming & Arming."
2. Place front wheels in straight ahead position, then remove two side trim covers from steering column.
3. Remove two Torx screws and release connector position assurance (CPA) from air bag module.
4. Disconnect upper steering column connector and remove air bag module from steering wheel.
5. Reverse procedure to install, noting the following:
   a. Tighten to specifications.
   b. After completing installation, rearm air bag system as described under "Air Bag System Disarming & Arming."

PASSENGER AIR BAG MODULE, REPLACE

BONNEVILLE, LESABRE, PARK AVENUE & 1994 88 & 98

1. Disarm air bag system as described under "Air Bag System Disarming & Arming."
2. Remove instrument panel assembly, **Figs. 18 through 20.**
3. Remove air bag module to instrument panel nuts and bolts, **Fig. 28.**
4. Remove air bag module.
5. Reverse procedure to install, noting the following:
   a. Tighten to specifications.
   b. After completing installation, rearm air bag system as described under "Air Bag System Disarming & Arming."

1993–94 ELDORADO & SEVILLE & 1994 RIVIERA

1. Disarm air bag system as described under "Air Bag System Disarming & Arming."
2. Remove instrument panel upper trim panel.
3. Remove screw located behind trap door in rear of glove compartment retaining air bag module to bracket.
4. Remove four screws retaining air bag module to top of instrument panel.
5. Remove air bag module and wiring harness.
6. Reverse procedure to install, noting the following:
   a. Tighten to specifications.
   b. After completing installation, rearm air bag system as described under "Air Bag System Disarming & Arming."

1993–94 FLEETWOOD (RWD) & 1994 CAPRICE & ROADMASTER

1. Disarm air bag system as described under "Air Bag System Disarming & Arming."
2. Remove upper trim pad from instrument panel.

3. Disconnect connector position assurance (CPA) and electrical connector.
4. Loosen air bag module fasteners, then remove passenger air bag module from vehicle.
5. Reverse procedure to install, noting the following:
   a. Tighten to specifications.
   b. After completing installation, rearm air bag system as described under "Air Bag System Disarming & Arming."

CAMARO & FIREBIRD

1993–94

1. Disarm air bag system as described under "Air Bag System Disarming & Arming."
2. Remove I/P carrier assembly.
3. Disconnect connector position assurance (CPA) and electrical connectors from passenger air bag module.
4. Loosen fasteners and remove air bag module from vehicle.
5. Reverse procedure to install, noting the following:
   a. Tighten to specifications.
   b. After completing installation, rearm air bag system as described under "Air Bag System Disarming & Arming."

CORVETTE

1994

1. Disarm air bag system as described under "Air Bag System Disarming & Arming."
2. Remove instrument panel upper trim pad.
3. Disconnect connector position assurance (CPA) and electrical connectors from passenger air bag module.
4. Loosen fasteners and remove air bag module from vehicle, **Fig. 29.**
5. Reverse procedure to install, noting the following:
   a. Tighten to specifications.
   b. After completing installation, rearm air bag system as described under "Air Bag System Disarming & Arming."

PRIZM

1994

1. Disarm air bag system as described under "Air Bag System Disarming & Arming."
2. Remove plastic retainer nut and right-hand kick panel.
3. Remove four glove compartment attaching screws, then the glove compartment.
4. Remove four passenger's side air bag to instrument panel attaching bolts, then the air bag module.
5. Reverse procedure to install, noting the following:
   a. Tighten to specifications.
   b. After completing installation, rearm air bag system as described under "Air Bag System Disarming & Arming."

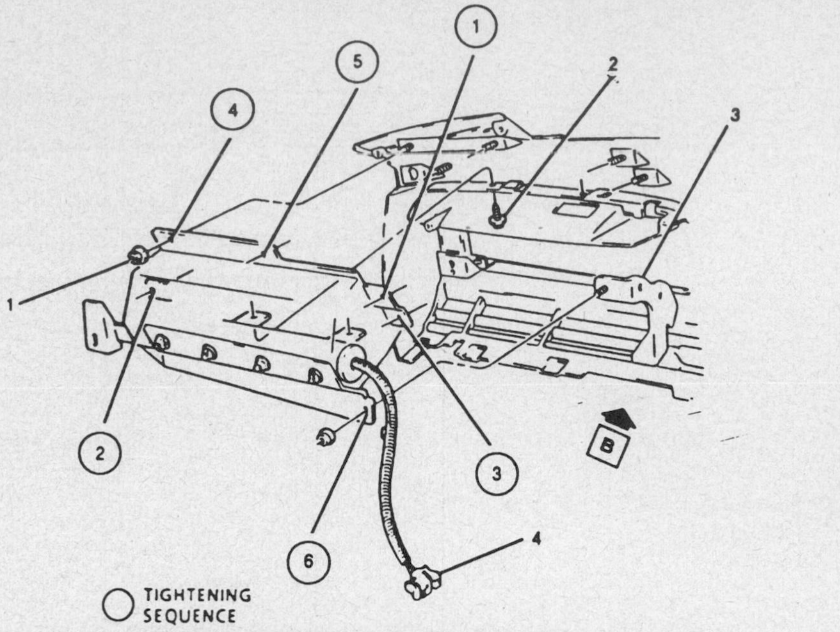
1
2
3
4
5
6
1
2
3
4
B
TIGHTENING SEQUENCE
1 INSTRUMENT PANEL
2 FASTENERS
3 KNEE BOLSTER (TIE BAR & STEERING COLUMN FILLER) BRACKET
4 INFLATOR MODULE PIGTAIL CONNECTOR
5 PASSENGER INFLATOR MODULE
GC8019201330000X

Fig. 28 Passenger's side air bag replacement. Bonneville, LeSabre, Park Avenue & 1994 88 & 98

GRAND PRIX

1994

1. Disarm air bag system as described under "Air Bag System Disarming & Arming."
2. Remove instrument panel compartment door.
3. Open passenger's side air bag module access panel.
4. Disconnect connector position assurance (CPA) and electrical connectors from passenger's side air bag module.
5. Remove four passenger's side air bag to instrument panel attaching bolts, then the air bag module.
6. Reverse procedure to install, noting the following:
   a. Tighten to specifications.
   b. After completing installation, rearm air bag system as described under "Air Bag System Disarming & Arming."

DIAGNOSTIC ENERGY RESERVE MODULE (DERM), REPLACE

Do not open the DERM case for any reason. Touching the connector pins or soldered components may cause electrostatic discharge damage. Repair of a faulty DERM is by replacement only.

BERETTA & CORSICA

1992–93

1. Disarm air bag system as described under "Air Bag System Disarming & Arming."
2. Remove right sound insulator.
3. Remove glove box assembly.
4. Loosen retaining nuts and slide DERM from bracket.
5. Unlatch orange connector lock then disconnect DERM electrical connector and remove DERM, **Fig. 30.**
6. Reverse procedure to install, noting the following:
   a. After completing installation, rearm air bag system as described under "Air Bag System Disarming & Arming."
   b. Turn ignition switch to On position and verify "Inflatable Restraint" indicator flashes 7 to 9 times, then turns off. If indicator does not respond, refer to "Diagnosis & Testing."

1994

Refer to "Achieva, Grand Am & Skylark" in this section for DERM replacement procedure.

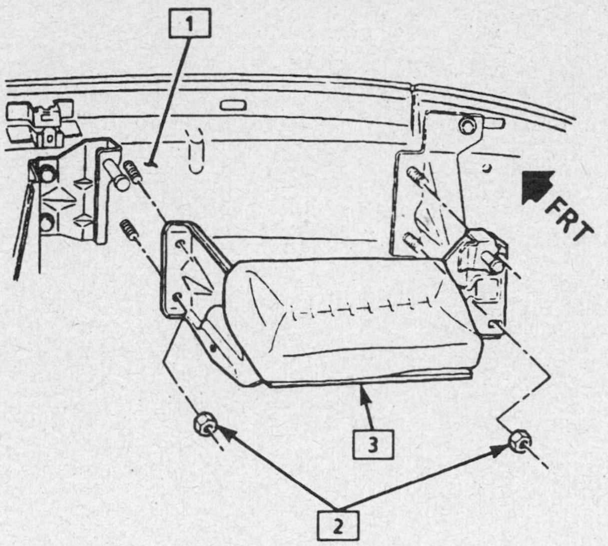
1
2
3

1 DASH PANEL ASSEMBLY

2 FASTENER

3 PASSENGER INFLATOR MODULE

GC8019201331000X

Fig. 29 Passenger's side air bag replacement. 1994 Corvette

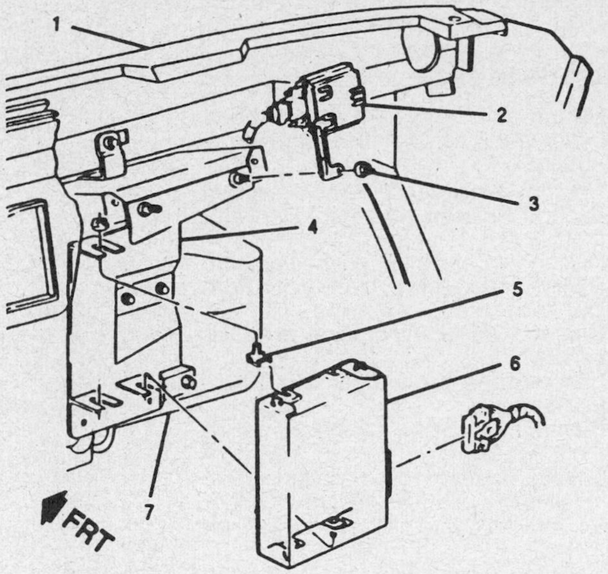
1
2
3
4
5
6
7
FRT

1 DASH

2 RESISTOR MODULE

3 NUT; 4 N·m (30 LB-FT)

4 BCM/DERM BRACKET

5 BOLT/SCREW

6 DIAGNOSTIC ENERGY RESERVE MODULE

7 HEATER AND A/C MODULE

GC8019201332000X

Fig. 30 DERM replacement. DeVille, Fleetwood (FWD) & 1992-93 Beretta & Corsica

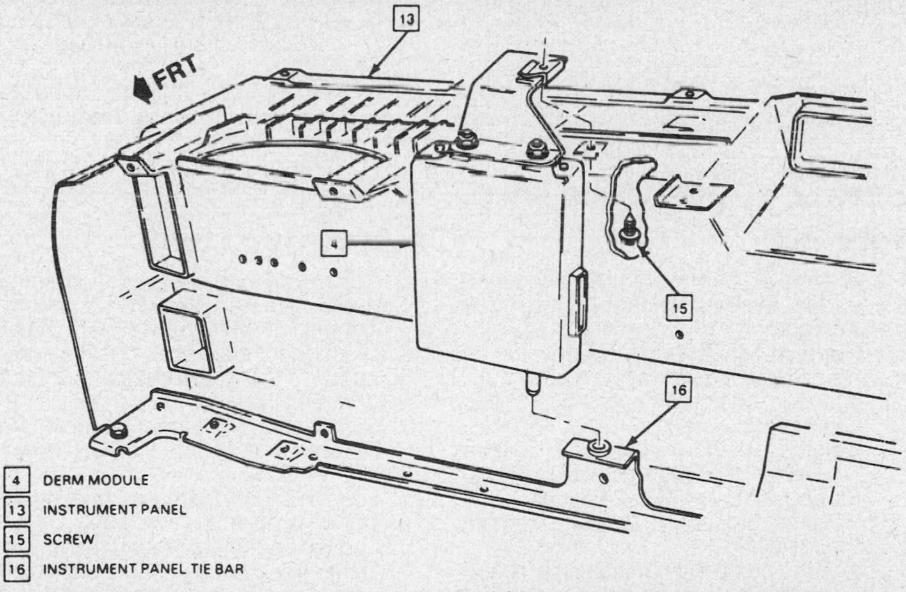
FRT
13
4
15
16
4 DERM MODULE
13 INSTRUMENT PANEL
15 SCREW
16 INSTRUMENT PANEL TIE BAR

GC8019201333000X

Fig. 31 DERM replacement. 1992 Camaro & Firebird

ACHIEVA, GRAND AM & SKYLARK

1994

1. Disarm air bag system as described under "Air Bag System Disarming & Arming."
2. Remove right sound insulator.
3. Open glove box assembly.
4. Remove DERM from bracket.
5. Disconnect connector position assurance (CPA) and electrical connector from DERM.
6. Reverse procedure to install, noting the following:
   a. After completing installation, rearm air bag system as described under "Air Bag System Disarming & Arming."
   b. Turn ignition switch to On position and verify "Inflatable Restraint" indicator flashes 7 to 9 times, then turns off. If indicator does not respond, refer to "Diagnosis & Testing."

CAMARO & FIREBIRD

1992

1. Disarm air bag system as described under "Air Bag System Disarming & Arming."
2. Remove instrument panel pad.
3. Remove side window defogger duct and retaining screws.
4. Remove DERM upper and lower retaining screws, **Fig. 31.**
5. Unlatch orange lock and disconnect DERM electrical connector.
6. Reverse procedure to install, noting the following:
   a. After completing installation, rearm air bag system as described under "Air Bag System Disarming & Arming."
   b. Turn ignition switch to On position and verify "Inflatable Restraint" indicator flashes 7 to 9 times, then turns off. If indicator does not respond, refer to "Diagnosis & Testing."

1993–94

1. Disarm air bag system as described under "Air Bag System Disarming & Arming."
2. Remove right side lower sound insulator pad, then remove the I/P compartment door assembly.
3. Disconnect Connector Position Assurance (CPA) connector and electrical connector from DERM.
4. Remove DERM from vehicle.
5. Reverse procedure to install. After completing installation, rearm air bag

system as described under "Air Bag System Disarming & Arming."

CAPRICE, CUSTOM CRUISER & ROADMASTER

1. Disarm air bag system as described under "Air Bag System Disarming & Arming."
2. Remove resistor module as described under "Resistor Module, Replacement."
3. Disconnect electrical connector from DERM and remove three nuts from DERM bracket.
4. Remove DERM and bracket as an assembly.
5. Loosen three nuts and remove DERM from bracket.
6. Reverse procedure to install, noting the following:
   a. After completing installation, rearm air bag system as described under "Air Bag System Disarming & Arming."
   b. Turn ignition switch to On position and verify "Inflatable Restraint" indicator flashes 7 to 9 times, then turns off. If indicator does not respond, refer to "Diagnosis & Testing."

CENTURY, CUTLASS CIERA & CUTLASS CRUISER

1. Disarm air bag system as described under "Air Bag System Disarming & Arming."
2. Remove right sound insulator.
3. Remove accelerator pedal and bracket assembly.
4. Release connector position assurance (CPA), then disconnect DERM electrical connector.
5. Loosen nuts and remove DERM from vehicle.
6. Reverse procedure to install, noting the following:
   a. Tighten to specifications.
   b. After completing installation, rearm air bag system as described under "Air Bag System Disarming & Arming."

CORVETTE

1. Disarm air bag system as described under "Air Bag System Disarming & Arming."
2. Remove knee bolster inner bracket and radio control.
3. Remove SIR wiring harness to DERM CPA and disconnect electrical connectors.
4. Remove DERM.
5. Reverse procedure to install, noting the following:
   a. After completing installation, rearm air bag system as described under "Air Bag System Disarming & Arming."
   b. Turn ignition switch to On position and verify "Inflatable Restraint" indicator flashes 7 to 9 times, then turns off. If indicator does not respond, refer to "Diagnosis & Testing."

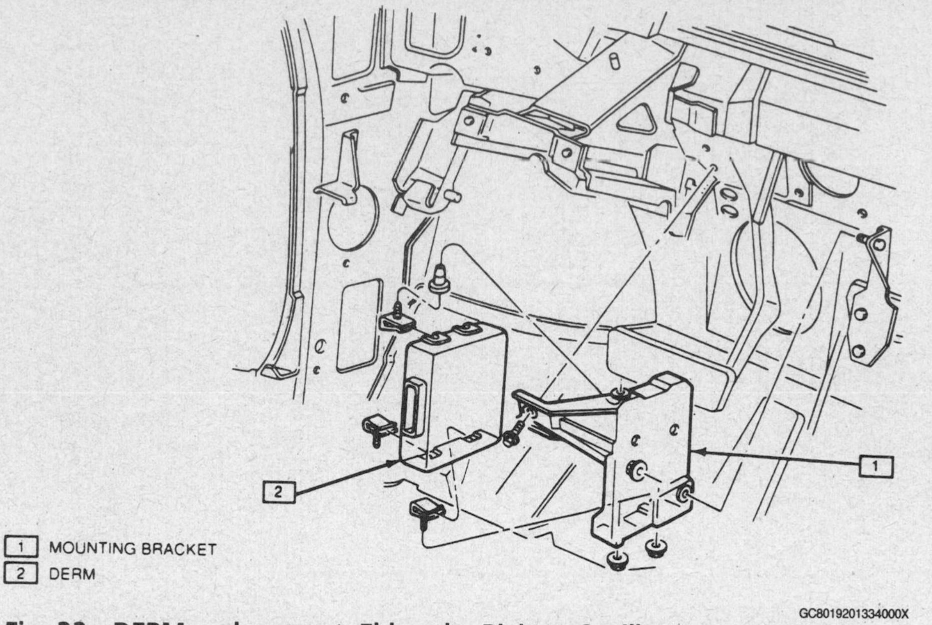
1
2
1 MOUNTING BRACKET
2 DERM
GC8019201334000X

Fig. 32 DERM replacement. Eldorado, Riviera, Seville, Toronado & Trofeo

CUTLASS SUPREME & REGAL

1994

1. Disarm air bag system as described under "Air Bag System Disarming & Arming."
2. Disconnect Connector Position Assurance (CPA) connector and electrical connector from DERM.
3. Remove DERM from mounting bracket.
4. Reverse procedure to install. After completing installation, rearm air bag system as described under "Air Bag System Disarming & Arming."

DEVILLE & FLEETWOOD (FWD)

1992–93

1. Disarm air bag system as described under "Air Bag System Disarming & Arming."
2. Remove right sound insulator.
3. Remove glove box assembly.
4. Loosen retaining nuts and slide DERM from bracket.
5. Unlatch orange connector lock then disconnect DERM electrical connector and remove DERM, **Fig. 30.**
6. Reverse procedure to install, noting the following:
   a. After completing installation, rearm air bag system as described under "Air Bag System Disarming & Arming."
   b. Turn ignition switch to On position and verify "Inflatable Restraint" indicator flashes 7 to 9 times, then turns off. If indicator does not respond, refer to "Diagnosis & Testing."

ELDORADO, RIVIERA, SEVILLE, TORONADO & TROFEO

1. Disarm air bag system as described under "Air Bag System Disarming & Arming."
2. Disconnect DERM electrical connector, **Fig. 32.**
3. Loosen DERM retaining nuts, located to the right of steering column.
4. Remove DERM from vehicle.
5. Reverse procedure to install, noting the following:
   a. After completing installation, rearm air bag system as described under "Air Bag System Disarming & Arming."
   b. Turn ignition switch to On position and verify "Inflatable Restraint" indicator flashes 7 to 9 times, then turns off. If indicator does not respond, refer to "Diagnosis & Testing."

FLEETWOOD (RWD)

1. Disarm air bag system as described under "Air Bag System Disarming & Arming."
2. Disconnect connector position assurance (CPA) and electrical connector from DERM.
3. Disconnect electrical connector from Retained Accessory Power (RAP) relay.
4. Loosen DERM fasteners, then remove DERM bracket.
5. Loosen fasteners from Transmission Converter Clutch (TCC) disable relay, then remove TCC disable relay for clearance.
6. Remove DERM from vehicle.
7. Reverse procedure to install, noting the following:
   a. Tighten to specifications.
   b. After completing installation, rearm air bag system as described under "Air Bag System Disarming & Arming."

METRO

1. Disarm air bag system as described under "Air Bag System Disarming & Arming."
2. Disconnect battery ground cable.

3. Remove orange connector lock and disconnect DERM electrical connector.
4. From below instrument panel, at right side steering column, remove DERM mounting bracket from steering column support member.
5. Disconnect and remove resistor module from DERM mounting bracket, then remove DERM from bracket.
6. Reverse procedure to install, noting the following:
   a. After completing installation, rearm air bag system as described under "Air Bag System Disarming & Arming."
   b. Turn ignition switch to On position and verify "Inflatable Restraint" indicator flashes 7 to 9 times, then turns off. If indicator does not respond, refer to "Diagnosis & Testing."

LESABRE & PARK AVENUE

1992–93

1. Disarm air bag system as described under "Air Bag System Disarming & Arming."
2. Remove righthand sound insulator.
3. Remove remote accessory control module (RAC) from bracket. **Do not disconnect.**
4. Remove mounting bolt from DERM bracket. Slide DERM from bracket.
5. Disconnect electrical connector from DERM, then remove nut attaching bracket to DERM.
6. Reverse procedure to install, noting the following:
   a. After completing installation, rearm air bag system as described under "Air Bag System Disarming & Arming."
   b. Turn ignition switch to On position and verify "Inflatable Restraint" indicator flashes 7 to 9 times, then turns off. If indicator does not respond, refer to "Diagnosis & Testing."

1994

Refer to "88, 98 & Bonneville" in this section for DERM replacement procedure.

STORM

1992–93

1. Disarm air bag system as described under "Air Bag System Disarming & Arming."
2. Disconnect battery ground cable.
3. Remove front console bracket and disconnect DERM electrical connector.
4. Remove four screws and nuts securing DERM yellow bracket.
5. Disconnect and remove resistor module from DERM mounting bracket.
6. Remove four retaining clips at DERM.
7. Remove DERM.
8. Reverse procedure to install, noting the following:
   a. After completing installation, rearm air bag system as described under "Air Bag System Disarming & Arming."
   b. Turn ignition switch to On position and verify "Inflatable Restraint" indicator flashes 7 to 9 times, then turns off. If indicator does not respond, refer to "Diagnosis & Testing."

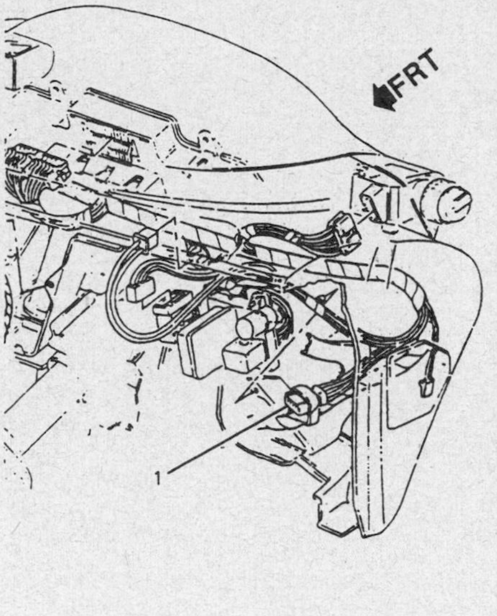
FRT
1

1 RESISTOR MODULE

GC8019201335000X

Fig. 33 Resistor module replacement. Beretta & Corsica

88, 98 & BONNEVILLE

1992–93

1. Disarm air bag system as described under "Air Bag System Disarming & Arming."
2. Remove instrument panel insert.
3. Remove remote accessory control module from multi-use bracket and position aside.
4. Remove spacer from underneath DERM.
5. Remove DERM from multi-use bracket by separating hook and loop tape, then disconnect electrical connector.
6. Reverse procedure to install.
7. After completing installation, rearm air bag system as described under "Air Bag System Disarming & Arming."

1994

1. Disarm air bag system as described under "Air Bag System Disarming & Arming."
2. Remove floor outlet.
3. Disconnect connector position assurance (CPA) and electrical from DERM.
4. Remove DERM from bracket.
5. Reverse procedure to install.
6. After completing installation, rearm air bag system as described under "Air Bag System Disarming & Arming."

SENSING & DIAGNOSTIC MODULE (SDM), REPLACE

CAPRICE, FLEETWOOD (RWD) & ROADMASTER

1994

1. Disarm air bag system as described under "Air Bag System Disarming & Arming."
2. Remove accelerator pedal assembly.
3. Disconnect connector position assurance (CPA) and electrical from SDM.
4. Loosen SDM fasteners, then remove SDM bracket.
5. Remove SDM from vehicle.
6. Reverse procedure to install, noting the following:
   a. Tighten to specifications.
   b. After completing installation, rearm air bag system as described under "Air Bag System Disarming & Arming."

GRAND PRIX

1994

1. Disarm air bag system as described under "Air Bag System Disarming & Arming."
2. Remove front righthand seat.
3. Disconnect connector position assurance (CPA) and electrical from SDM.
4. Loosen SDM fasteners, then remove SDM bracket.
5. Remove SDM from vehicle.
6. Reverse procedure to install, noting the following:
   a. Tighten to specifications.
   b. After completing installation, rearm air bag system as described under "Air Bag System Disarming & Arming."

RESISTOR MODULE, REPLACE

BERETTA & CORSICA

1. Disarm air bag system as described under "Air Bag System Disarming & Arming."
2. Remove tape securing resistor module to wiring harness.
3. Remove CPA and disconnect resistor module electrical connector.
4. Remove resistor module, **Fig. 33.**
5. Reverse procedure to install, noting the following:
   a. After completing installation, rearm air bag system as described under "Air Bag System Disarming & Arming."
   b. Turn ignition switch to On position and verify "Inflatable Restraint" indicator flashes 7 to 9 times, then turns off. If indicator does not respond, refer to "Diagnosis & Testing."

CAMARO & FIREBIRD

1992

1. Disarm air bag system as described under "Air Bag System Disarming & Arming."

2. Remove knee bolster, refer to "Knee Bolster, Replace."
3. Unsnap resistor module from left side tie bar, **Fig. 34,** then remove CPA and disconnect module electrical connector.
4. Reverse procedure to install, noting the following:
   a. After completing installation, rearm air bag system as described under "Air Bag System Disarming & Arming."
   b. Turn ignition switch to On position and verify "Inflatable Restraint" indicator flashes 7 to 9 times, then turns off. If indicator does not respond, refer to "Diagnosis & Testing."

CAPRICE, CUSTOM CRUISER & ROADMASTER

1. Disarm air bag system as described under "Air Bag System Disarming & Arming."
2. Disconnect CPA and electrical connector at resistor module.
3. Remove resistor module by sliding to the left on the DERM bracket.
4. Reverse procedure to install, noting the following:
   a. After completing installation, rearm air bag system as described under "Air Bag System Disarming & Arming."
   b. Turn ignition switch to On position and verify "Inflatable Restraint" indicator flashes 7 to 9 times, then turns off. If indicator does not respond, refer to "Diagnosis & Testing."

CENTURY, CUTLASS CIERA & CUTLASS CRUISER

The resistor module is part of the SIR wiring harness and is taped to the I/P wiring harness. The resistor module is located level with and to the right of the radio.

1. Disarm air bag system as described under "Air Bag System Disarming & Arming."
2. Remove radio.
3. Carefully cut tape attaching resistor module to the I/P wiring harness.
4. Release connector position assurance (CPA) and disconnect resistor module.
5. Remove resistor module from vehicle.
6. Reverse procedure to install. After completing installation, rearm air bag system as described under "Air Bag System Disarming & Arming."

CORVETTE

1. Disarm air bag system as described under "Air Bag System Disarming & Arming."
2. Remove radio control.
3. Disconnect resistor module from instrument carrier assembly.
4. Remove SIR wiring harness CPA and disconnect electrical connector from resistor module.
5. Remove resistor module.
6. Reverse procedure to install, noting the following:
   a. Following installation, rearm air bag system as described under "Air Bag System Arming."
   b. Turn ignition switch to On position and verify "Inflatable Restraint" indicator flashes 7 to 9 times, then turns off. If indicator does not respond, refer to "Diagnosis & Testing."

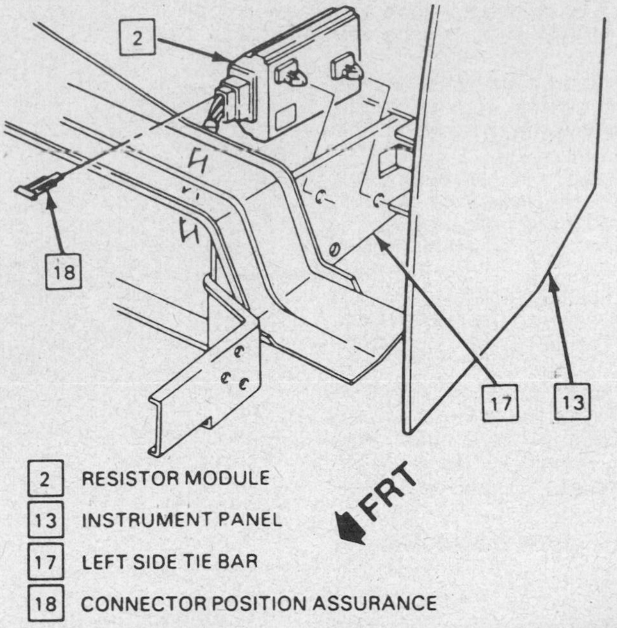
2
18
17
13
2 RESISTOR MODULE
13 INSTRUMENT PANEL
17 LEFT SIDE TIE BAR
18 CONNECTOR POSITION ASSURANCE
FRT
GC8019201336000X

Fig. 34 Resistor module replacement. 1992 Camaro & Firebird

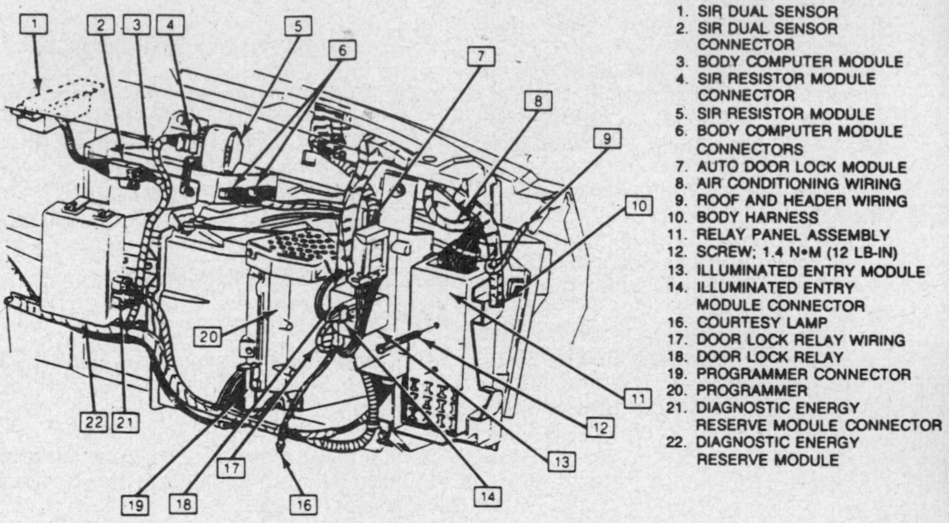
1. SIR DUAL SENSOR
2. SIR DUAL SENSOR CONNECTOR
3. BODY COMPUTER MODULE
4. SIR RESISTOR MODULE CONNECTOR
5. SIR RESISTOR MODULE
6. BODY COMPUTER MODULE CONNECTORS
7. AUTO DOOR LOCK MODULE
8. AIR CONDITIONING WIRING
9. ROOF AND HEADER WIRING
10. BODY HARNESS
11. RELAY PANEL ASSEMBLY
12. SCREW; 1.4 N•M (12 LB-IN)
13. ILLUMINATED ENTRY MODULE
14. ILLUMINATED ENTRY MODULE CONNECTOR
16. COURTESY LAMP
17. DOOR LOCK RELAY WIRING
18. DOOR LOCK RELAY
19. PROGRAMMER CONNECTOR
20. PROGRAMMER
21. DIAGNOSTIC ENERGY RESERVE MODULE CONNECTOR
22. DIAGNOSTIC ENERGY RESERVE MODULE
GC8019201337000X

Fig. 35 Resistor module replacement. 1992–93 DeVille & Fleetwood

DEVILLE & FLEETWOOD (FWD)

1992–93

1. Disarm air bag system as described under "Air Bag System Disarming & Arming."
2. Remove right sound insulator.
3. Remove glove box module.
4. Remove CPA, then disconnect resistor module electrical connector and remove module, **Fig. 35.**
5. Reverse procedure to install, noting the following:
   a. After completing installation, rearm air bag system as described under "Air Bag System Disarming & Arming."
   b. Turn ignition switch to On position and verify "Inflatable Restraint" indicator flashes 7 to 9 times, then turns off. If indicator does not respond, refer to "Diagnosis & Testing."

ELDORADO, SEVILLE & 1994 DEVILLE & RIVIERA

1. Disarm air bag system as described under "Air Bag System Disarming & Arming."
2. Remove steering column opening filler trim.

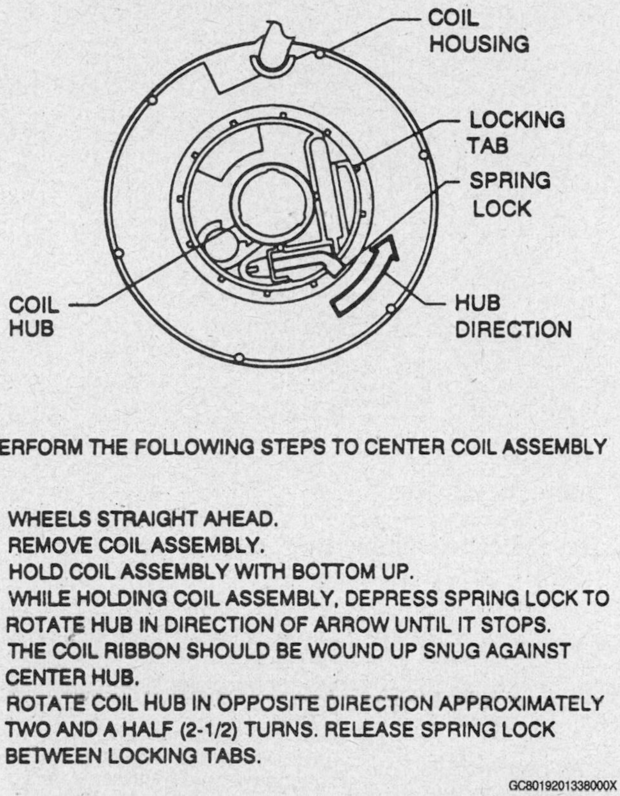
COIL HOUSING
LOCKING TAB
SPRING LOCK
COIL HUB
HUB DIRECTION
PERFORM THE FOLLOWING STEPS TO CENTER COIL ASSEMBLY
A. WHEELS STRAIGHT AHEAD.
B. REMOVE COIL ASSEMBLY.
C. HOLD COIL ASSEMBLY WITH BOTTOM UP.
D. WHILE HOLDING COIL ASSEMBLY, DEPRESS SPRING LOCK TO ROTATE HUB IN DIRECTION OF ARROW UNTIL IT STOPS.
E. THE COIL RIBBON SHOULD BE WOUND UP SNUG AGAINST CENTER HUB.
F. ROTATE COIL HUB IN OPPOSITE DIRECTION APPROXIMATELY TWO AND A HALF (2-1/2) TURNS. RELEASE SPRING LOCK BETWEEN LOCKING TABS.
GC8019201338000X

Fig. 36 SRI coil assembly centering procedure. Except Metro, Prizm & Storm

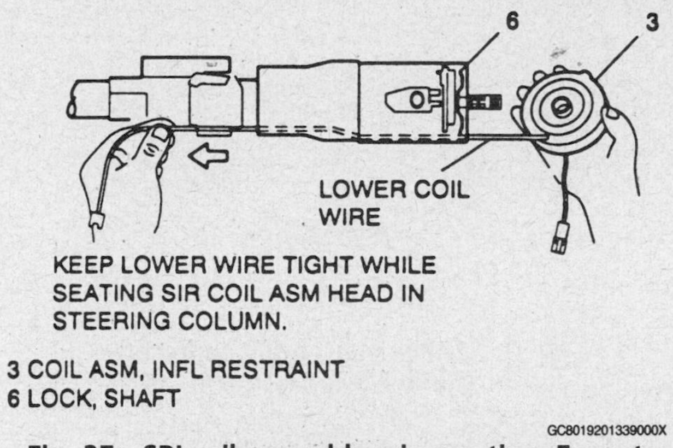
6
3
LOWER COIL WIRE
KEEP LOWER WIRE TIGHT WHILE SEATING SIR COIL ASM HEAD IN STEERING COLUMN.
3 COIL ASM, INFL RESTRAINT
6 LOCK, SHAFT
GC8019201339000X

Fig. 37 SRI coil assembly wire routing. Except Metro, Prizm & Storm

3. Remove steering column opening bracket.
4. Disconnect connector position assurance and electrical connector.
5. Remove resistor module.
6. Reverse procedure to install.
7. After completing installation, rearm air bag system as described under "Air Bag System Disarming & Arming."

METRO & STORM

The resistor module is removed with the DERM as an assembly. Refer to "Diagnostic Energy Reserve Module (DERM), Replace" for replacement procedure.

LESABRE & PARK AVENUE

1. Disarm air bag system as described under "Air Bag System Disarming & Arming."
2. Remove instrument panel lower trim plate, then the air vent deflector.
3. Remove three bolts and three screws securing glove compartment assembly to instrument panel.
4. Slide resistor module off of bracket.
5. Disconnect electrical connector and remove resistor module.
6. Reverse procedure to install, noting the following:
   a. After completing installation, rearm air bag system as described under "Air Bag System Disarming & Arming."
   b. Turn ignition switch to On position and verify "Inflatable Restraint" indicator flashes 7 to 9 times, then turns off. If indicator does not respond, refer to "Diagnosis & Testing."

RIVIERA, TORONADO & TROFEO

1. Disarm air bag system as described under "Air Bag System Disarming & Arming."
2. Disconnect battery ground cable.
3. Disconnect module from bracket behind left side of instrument panel.
4. Disconnect CPA and module electrical connector.
5. Remove resistor module.
6. Reverse procedure to install, noting the following:
   a. After completing installation, rearm air bag system as described under "Air Bag System Disarming & Arming."
   b. Turn ignition switch to On position and verify "Inflatable Restraint" indicator flashes 7 to 9 times, then turns off. If indicator does not respond, refer to "Diagnosis & Testing."

88, 98 & BONNEVILLE w/SINGLE AIR BAG

1992-93

1. Disarm air bag system as described under "Air Bag System Disarming & Arming."
2. Remove instrument panel compartment insert.
3. Remove resistor module from multi-use bracket.
4. Disconnect CPA and electrical connector from resistor module.
5. Reverse procedure to install.
6. After completing installation, rearm air bag system as described under "Air Bag System Disarming & Arming."

SIR/SRS COIL ASSEMBLY, REPLACE

Except Metro, Prizm & Storm

1. Position front wheel in the straight ahead position.
2. Disarm air bag system as described under "Air Bag System Disarming & Arming."
3. Remove driver's side air bag module as described "Driver Air Bag Module, Replace."
4. Disconnect electrical connectors and leads.
5. Remove retainer and nut, then remove steering wheel, using suitable steering wheel puller tool. Place alignment marks on steering wheel hub and steering column shaft for use during installation.
6. Place ignition switch in Lock position to retain coil assembly in the centered position.
7. Remove coil assembly retaining ring.
8. Lift coil assembly from steering shaft and allow to hang from wire.
9. Using a suitable tool, compress lock plate and remove retaining ring.
10. Remove lock plate, turn signal canceling cam and upper bearing spring, inner race seat and inner race.
11. Place turn signal lever in righthand turn position, then remove multifunction lever and hazard warning flasher knob.
12. Remove turn signal switch lever attaching screw, then remove lever.
13. Remove turn signal switch attaching screws and allow to hang from wire.
14. Disconnect SRI coil connector from turn signal switch electrical connector.
15. Using mechanics wire, gently pull SRI coil wire through steering column.
16. Remove SRI coil assembly.
17. Reverse procedure to install, noting the following:
    a. Ensure front wheels are in the straight ahead position.
    b. If coil assembly has become un-

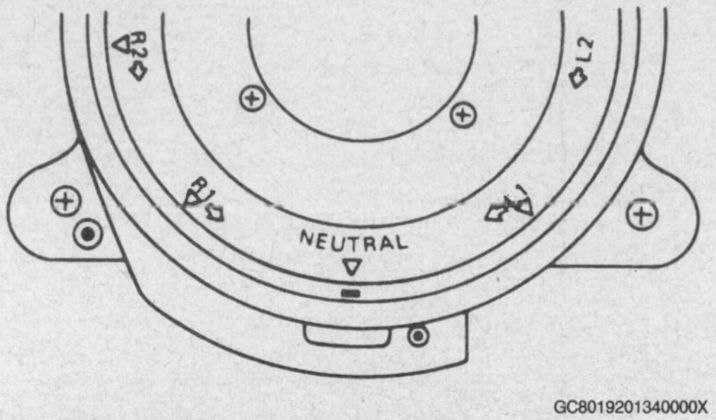
R2
L2
R1
NEUTRAL

GC8019201340000X

Fig. 38 SRI coil assembly centered position. Metro & Storm

centered, refer to **Fig. 36** for centering procedure.
   c. Ensure SRI wiring is tight while seating coil in column housing, **Fig. 37.**
   d. After completing installation, rearm air bag system as described under "Air Bag System Disarming & Arming."

Metro

1. Position front wheel in the straight ahead position.
2. Disarm air bag system as described under "Air Bag System Disarming & Arming."
3. Remove driver's side air bag module as described "Driver Air Bag Module, Replace."
4. Disconnect electrical connectors and leads.
5. Remove retainer and nut, then remove steering wheel, using suitable steering wheel puller tool. Place alignment marks on steering wheel hub and steering column shaft for use during installation.
6. Remove steering column covers.
7. Disconnect combination switch/SRI coil switch electrical connector.
8. Remove combination switch/SRI coil attaching screws, then remove switch and SRI coil.
9. Reverse procedure to install, noting the following:
   a. Ensure front wheels are in the straight ahead position.
   b. If SRI coil neutral mark is aligned with the alignment mark, **Fig. 38,** not further adjustment is required. If R1 mark is aligned with alignment mark, coil is off one turn to the right, adjust by turning one turn counterclockwise. If R2 mark is aligned with alignment mark, coil is off two turns to the right, adjust by turning two turns counterclockwise. If L1 mark is aligned with alignment mark, coil is off one turn to the left, adjust by turning one turn clockwise. If L2 mark is aligned with alignment mark, coil is off two turns to the left, adjust by turning two turns clockwise.
   c. After completing installation, rearm air bag system as described under "Air Bag System Disarming & Arming."

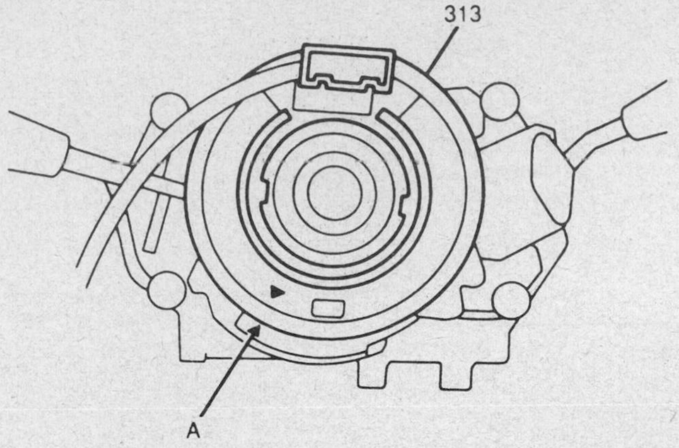
313
A

A ALIGNMENT MARKS

313 SRS COIL ASSEMBLY

GC8019201341000X

Fig. 39 SRI coil assembly centered position. Prizm

Prizm

1. Position front wheel in the straight ahead position.
2. Disarm air bag system as described under "Air Bag System Disarming & Arming."
3. Remove driver's side air bag module as described "Driver Air Bag Module, Replace."
4. Disconnect electrical connectors and leads.
5. Remove retainer and nut, then remove steering wheel, using suitable steering wheel puller tool. Place alignment marks on steering wheel and steering column shaft for use during installation.
6. Remove upper and lower steering column covers.
7. Remove two screws and disconnect hood release cable.
8. Remove knee bolster from instrument panel.
9. Remove tape holding SRS coil wiring harness to combination switch wiring harness.
10. Disconnect SRS coil electrical connector.
11. Remove SRS coil attaching screws and SRS coil.
12. Reverse procedure to install. noting the following:
    a. Ensure front wheels are in the straight ahead position.
    b. To center coil assembly, turn coil counterclockwise until stop is contacted. Turn coil assembly three turn clockwise, aligning the red marks, **Fig. 39.**
    c. After completing installation, rearm air bag system as described under "Air Bag System Disarming & Arming."

Storm

1. Position front wheels in straight ahead position.
2. Disarm air bag system as described under "Air Bag System Disarming & Arming."
3. Remove driver's side air bag module as described "Driver Air Bag Module, Replace."
4. Disconnect electrical connectors and leads.
5. Remove retainer and nut, then remove steering wheel, using suitable steering wheel puller tool. Place alignment marks on steering wheel and steering column shaft for use during installation.
6. Remove lower switch panel, dash lighter panel and hood release cable.
7. Remove lap air deflector attaching screws, then the lap air reflector.
8. Remove left lower dash trim panel attaching screws, then lower dash trim panel.
9. Remove upper steering column mounting bolts and lower column.
10. Remove two piece steering column cover attaching screws and cover.
11. Disconnect coil assembly wiring harness from turn signal switch, then remove four retaining screws and coil assembly.
12. Reverse procedure to install. noting the following:
    a. Ensure front wheels are in the straight ahead position.
    b. If SRI coil neutral mark is aligned with the alignment mark, **Fig. 38,** no further adjustment is required. If R1 mark is aligned with alignment mark, coil is off one turn to the right, adjust by turning one turn counterclockwise. If R2 mark is aligned with alignment mark, coil is off two turns to the right, adjust by turning two turns counterclockwise. If L1 mark is aligned with alignment mark, coil is off one turn to the left, adjust by turning one turn clockwise. If L2 mark is aligned with alignment mark, coil is off two turns to the left, adjust by turning two turns clockwise.
    c. After completing installation, rearm air bag system as described under "Air Bag System Disarming & Arming."

AIR BAG MODULE DISPOSAL

When a deployed module has been removed from a vehicle, it may be disposed of with any other scrap material. Handle with gloves and safety glasses and wash hands after handling. **The steering wheel module must be deactivated prior to disposal. The module contains explosive material. Failure to deactivate before disposing may result in personal injury.**

Some vehicle with SIR systems that have live (undeployed) air bag modules may have to be scrapped because they have completed their useful life or have been severely damaged in a non-deployment type accident. The following procedure should be followed when scrapping a vehicle with an undeployed module:

1. Place ignition switch in Off position.
2. Ensure steering wheel module is secured to steering wheel and that their is nobody in vehicle, and remove all loose objects from front seat.
3. Disconnect lower steering column connector and remove shorting clip from connector.
4. Cut lower steering column connector away from vehicle harness leaving at least 6 inches of wire at the connector.
5. Splice two 18 gauge wires, at least 20 feet long, into steering wheel module circuit wiring at base of steering column.
6. Stretch wires away from vehicle to their full length.
7. Apply 12 volts across wires to deploy module. **Do not touch steering wheel module area for 20 minutes, due to heat generated by deployment.**

TIGHTENING SPECIFICATIONS

Year	Component	Torque/Inch Lbs.
ACHIEVA, GRAND AM & SKYLARK		
1992-94	Arming Sensor Bolts	82
	Diagnostic Energy Reserve Module Nuts	35
	Forward Discriminating Sensor Bracket Bolts	80
	Forward Discriminating Sensor Nuts	80
	Inflator Module	89
	Nuts Securing Studs To Diagnostic Energy Reserve Module	22
	Passenger Compartment Discriminating Sensor Bolts	17①
BERETTA & CORSICA		
1992-94	Arming Sensor Bolts	80
	Diagnostic Energy Reserve Module Nuts	35
	Forward Discriminating Sensor Bracket Bolts	80
	Forward Discriminating Sensor Nuts	80
	Knee Bolster Panel Screws	13
	Nuts Securing Studs To Diagnostic Energy Reserve Module	22
	Passenger Compartment Discriminating Sensor Bolts	80
CAMARO & FIREBIRD		
1992	Arming Sensor Bolt	25
	Diagnostic Energy Reserve Module Screw	19
	Forward Discriminating Sensor Bolt	25
	Knee Bolster Screw	49
	Passenger Compartment Discriminating Sensor Bolt	25
1993-94	Arming Sensor Fastener	40
	Forward Discriminating Sensor	89
	Passenger Compartment Sensor	89
	Passenger Inflator Module	25
CAPRICE, CUSTOM CRUISER & ROADMASTER		
1992-94	Arming Sensor Mounting Screw	25
	Diagnostic Energy Reserve Module Bracket Mounting Bolt	53

Year	Component	Torque/Inch Lbs.
CAPRICE, CUSTOM CRUISER & ROADMASTER		
1992-94 —Cont'd	Diagnostic Energy Reserve Module To Bracket Nut	17
	Forward Discriminating Sensor Mounting Screw	25
	Knee Bolster Deflector Mounting Bolt	89
	Knee Bolster Mounting Bolt	53
	Steering Column Lower Trim Panel Screw	17
CENTURY, CUTLASS CIERA & CUTLASS CRUISER		
1992-94	DERM To Bracket Nuts	53
	Front Discriminating Sensor Mounting Bolts	44
	Passenger Compartment Discriminating Sensor Bolts	44
CORVETTE		
1992-94	Arming Sensor Bolts	11①
	Arming Sensor Nuts	107
	Driver Inflator Module	86
	Dual Pole Arming Sensor	108
	Forward Discriminating Sensor Bolts	19①
	Front Bumper Skid Bar To Drive Train & Front Suspension Frame Assembly Nuts	22①
	Front Bumper Skid Bar To Power Steering Cooler Bolts	89
	Front Bumper Skid Bar To Skid Plate Bracket Nuts	20①
	Knee Bolster Inner Console Area Bolts	89
	Knee Bolster Outer Console Area Bolts	17①
	I/P Inner Knee Bolster Bracket To Console Bracket Bolts	89
	I/P Inner Knee Bolster Bracket To Diagnostic Energy Reserve Module Bracket Area Bolts	89
	Passenger Inflator Module	108
CUTLASS SUPREME & REGAL		
1992-94	Arming Sensor	40
	Forward Discriminating Sensor	53

Continued

TIGHTENING SPECIFICATIONS-Continued

Year	Component	Torque/Inch Lbs.
CUTLASS SUPREME & REGAL -Continued		
1992-94 —Cont'd	Inflator Module	25
	Passenger Compartment Discriminating Sensor	53
DEVILLE & FLEETWOOD (FWD)		
1992-94	BCM Retaining Nuts	33
	DERM Nuts	35
	DERM/BCM Bracket Screw	13
	Dual Sensor	11 ①
	Dual Sensor Pigtail Wiring To BCM Stud Nut	35
	Forward Discriminating Sensor Bolts	82
	Forward Discriminating Sensor Bracket Brace To Lower Radiator Tie Bar Bolts	84
	Forward Discriminating Sensor Bracket To Brace Bolt	84
	Forward Discriminating Sensor Bracket To Upper Radiator Tie Bolts	84
	I/P Lower Brace Bolt	84
	I/P Lower Brace Nut	84
	I/P Column Reinforcement Plate Bolts	17
	I/P Steering Column Filler Screws	13
	Left Support Bracket Bolts	84
	Passenger Compartment Discriminating/Arming Sensor Bolts	84
	Resistor Module To BCM Stud Nut	35
	Steering Column Upper Support Bracket Brace Assembly Bolts/ Screws	84
	Steering Column Upper Support Bracket Brace Assembly To Steering Column Upper Support Bracket Bolts	62
ELDORADO & SEVILLE		
1992-94	Dual Pole Arming Sensor Mounting Bolts	98
	Dual Sensor Mounting Bolts	98
	Forward Discriminating Sensor Bracket Mounting Nuts & Bolts	98
	Forward Discriminating Sensor Mounting Bolts	98
	Left & Right Hand Discriminating Sensor Bolts	45
	Passenger Inflator Module	18
GRAND PRIX		
1992-94	Driver Inflator Module	25
	Passenger Inflator Module	53
	Passenger Inflator Module Tether Fasteners	35
	Sensing & Diagnostic Module Fasteners	40

Continued

TIGHTENING SPECIFICATIONS-Continued

Year	Component	Torque/Inch Lbs.
FLEETWOOD (RWD)		
1993-94	DERM Fasteners	17
	Dual Pole Arming Sensor	25
	Forward Discriminating Sensor	25
	Passenger Inflator Module	89
LESABRE		
1992-93	Dual Sensor Bolts	11①
	Forward Discriminating Sensor Mounting Bolts	12①
	Inflator Module Bolts	25
	Knee Deflector Nuts & Bolts	89
METRO		
1992-94	Arming Sensor Mounting Bolts	53
	DERM Mounting Bracket Bolts	44
	DERM To DERM Mounting Bracket Nuts	35
	Forward Discriminating Sensor Mounting Bolts	98
	Negative Battery Cable To Negative Battery Terminal Retainer	11①
	Passenger Compartment Discriminating Sensor Mounting Bolts	53
PARK AVENUE		
1992-93	Dual Sensor Bolts	84
	Forward Discriminating Sensor Bracket Mounting Nuts & Bolts	84
	Forward Discriminating Sensor Mounting Bolts	62
	Inflator Module Bolts	25
	Knee Deflector Nuts & Bolts	89
PRIZM		
1992-94	Center Sensor Assembly Bolts	115
	Console Mounting Bracket Bolts	89
	Forward Sensor Bolts	18①
	Inflator Module	78
	Knee Bolster Bolts	89
RIVIERA, TORONADO & TROFEO		
1992-93	Dual Sensor Mounting Bolts	98
	Forward Discriminating Sensor Bracket Mounting Nuts & Bolts	98
	Forward Discriminating Sensor Mounting Bolts	98
STORM		
1992-93	Arming Sensor Mounting Bolts	89
	Diagnostic Energy Reserve Module Yellow Bracket Retaining Nuts	35
	Diagnostic Energy Reserve Module Yellow Bracket Retaining Screws	44
	Forward Discriminating Sensor Mounting Bolts	97
	Knee Bolster Assembly Retaining Nut & Bolt	89
	Negative Battery Cable To Negative Battery Terminal Retainer	11①

Continued

TIGHTENING SPECIFICATIONS-Continued

Year	Component	Torque/Inch Lbs.
STORM		
1992-93 —Cont'd	Passenger Compartment Discriminating Sensor Mounting Bolts	89
88, 98 & BONNEVILLE w/SINGLE AIR BAG		
1992-93	Forward Discriminating Sensor Bolts	12①
	Forward Discriminating Sensor Bracket Bolts	84
	Passenger Compartment Discriminating Sensor/Arming Sensor Bolts	11①
	Upper Radiator Tie Bar To Grill Reveal Molding Bolts	84
BONNEVILLE, LESABRE, PARK AVENUE, 88 & 98 w/DUAL AIR BAGS		
1992-94	Dual Pole Arming Sensor Bolts	53
	Forward Discriminating Sensor Bolts	12①
	Forward Discriminating Sensor Bracket Bolts	84
	Passenger Compartment Discriminating Sensor Bolts	11①
	Passenger Inflator Module Bolts	17
	Passenger Inflator Module Nuts	89
	Steering Column Support Bracket Brace To Pillar Panel Bolts	89
	Steering Column Support Bracket Brace To Steering Column Support Bracket Bolts	62

①—Ft. lbs.

Automatic Seat Belts

INDEX

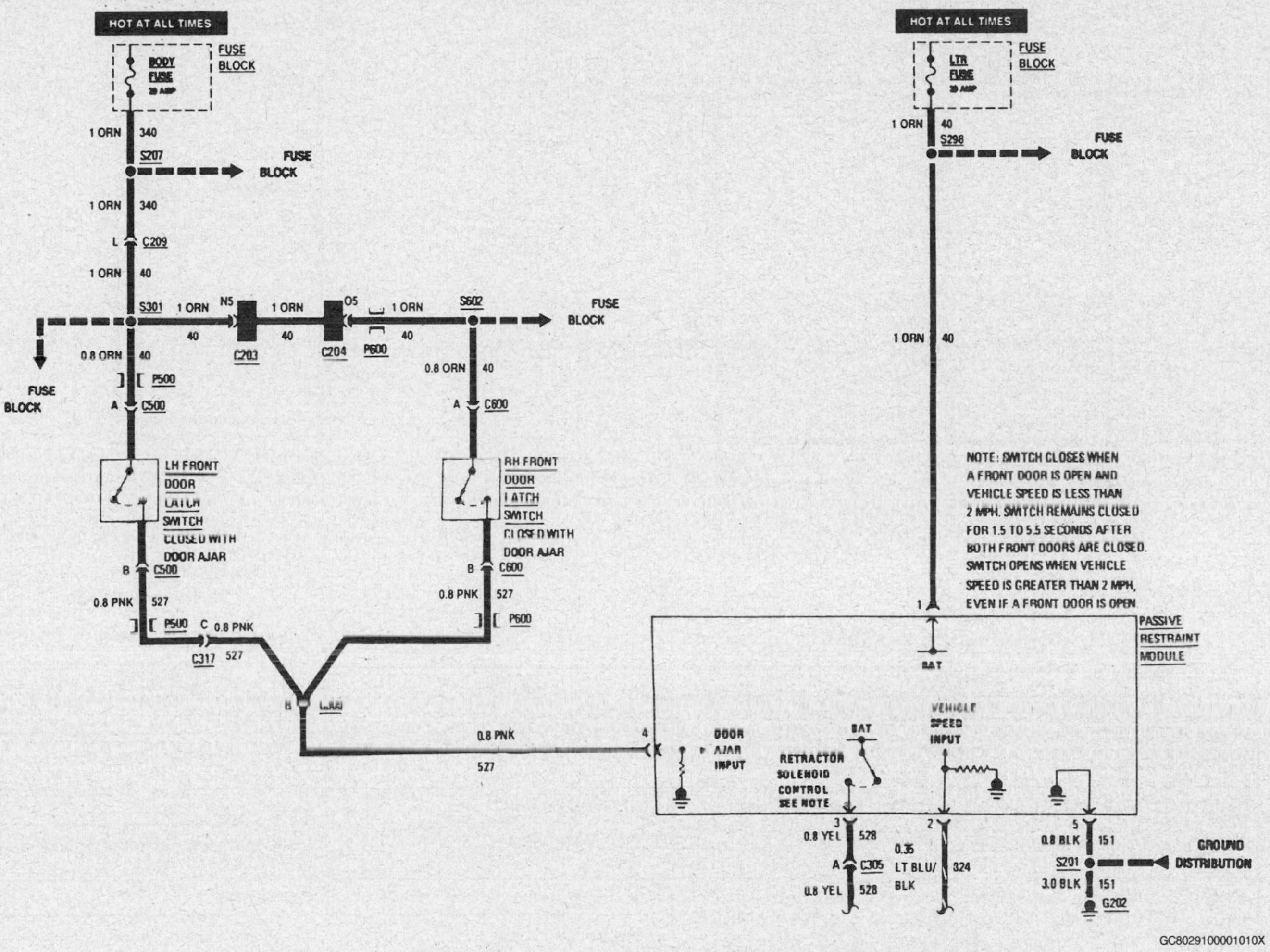

HOT AT ALL TIMES
BODY FUSE 20 AMP
FUSE BLOCK
1 ORN 340
S207
FUSE BLOCK
C209
1 ORN 40
S301
C203
C204
P600
S602
0.8 ORN 40
P500
C500
C600
LH FRONT DOOR LATCH SWITCH CLOSED WITH DOOR AJAR
RH FRONT DOOR LATCH SWITCH CLOSED WITH DOOR AJAR
0.8 PNK 527
C317
LTR FUSE 20 AMP
S298
NOTE: SWITCH CLOSES WHEN A FRONT DOOR IS OPEN AND VEHICLE SPEED IS LESS THAN 2 MPH. SWITCH REMAINS CLOSED FOR 1.5 TO 5.5 SECONDS AFTER BOTH FRONT DOORS ARE CLOSED. SWITCH OPENS WHEN VEHICLE SPEED IS GREATER THAN 2 MPH, EVEN IF A FRONT DOOR IS OPEN.
PASSIVE RESTRAINT MODULE
BAT
DOOR AJAR INPUT
RETRACTOR SOLENOID CONTROL SEE NOTE
VEHICLE SPEED INPUT
0.8 YEL 528
C305
0.35 LT BLU/BLK 324
0.8 BLK 151
S201
GROUND DISTRIBUTION
3.0 BLK 151
G202
GC8029100001010X

Fig. 1 Automatic safety belt wiring circuit (Part 1 of 2). Brougham

DESCRIPTION

BROUGHAM

The automatic safety belt system allows the safety belts to remained fastened while occupants enter and exit the vehicle. The main components of the system include a passive restraint module, left hand and right hand door latch switches and left hand and right hand shoulder and lap belt retractor solenoids. The purpose of the system is to keep the safety belt retractor mechanisms from locking up while the front doors are being opened and closed.

Battery voltage is applied, at all times, to both door latch switches. Whenever a front door is opened, the front door latch switch closes, voltage is applied through the switch to the passive restraint module, and the module detects a door ajar input. When the input is detected, the passive restraint module applies battery voltage to the shoulder and lap belt retractor solenoids. The retractor solenoids are permanently grounded so they become energized as soon as voltage is applied from the passive restraint module. When the retractor solenoids are energized, the safety belt lock mechanisms are disabled. Therefore, when a front door is opened, the safety belt for that door will not be allowed to lock up and interfere with normal opening and closing of the door. The passive restraint module continues to apply battery voltage to the belt retractor solenoids for 1.5 to 5.5 seconds after both front doors have been closed. This time-out period prevents the safety belts from locking up in a door slamming or immediate door reopening situations.

In addition to receiving an input from the door latch switches, the passive restraint module also receives a vehicle speed signal from the vehicle speed sensor buffer. Whenever the passive restraint module determines a vehicle speed of over two miles per hour, the battery voltage signal applied to the belt retractor solenoids is cancelled. This feature ensures safety belt lockup whenever the vehicle is in motion, regardless of input from the door latch switches or the 1.5 to 5.5 second timer.

In order to provide constant operation, the passive restraint module receives battery voltage at all times and is permanently grounded.

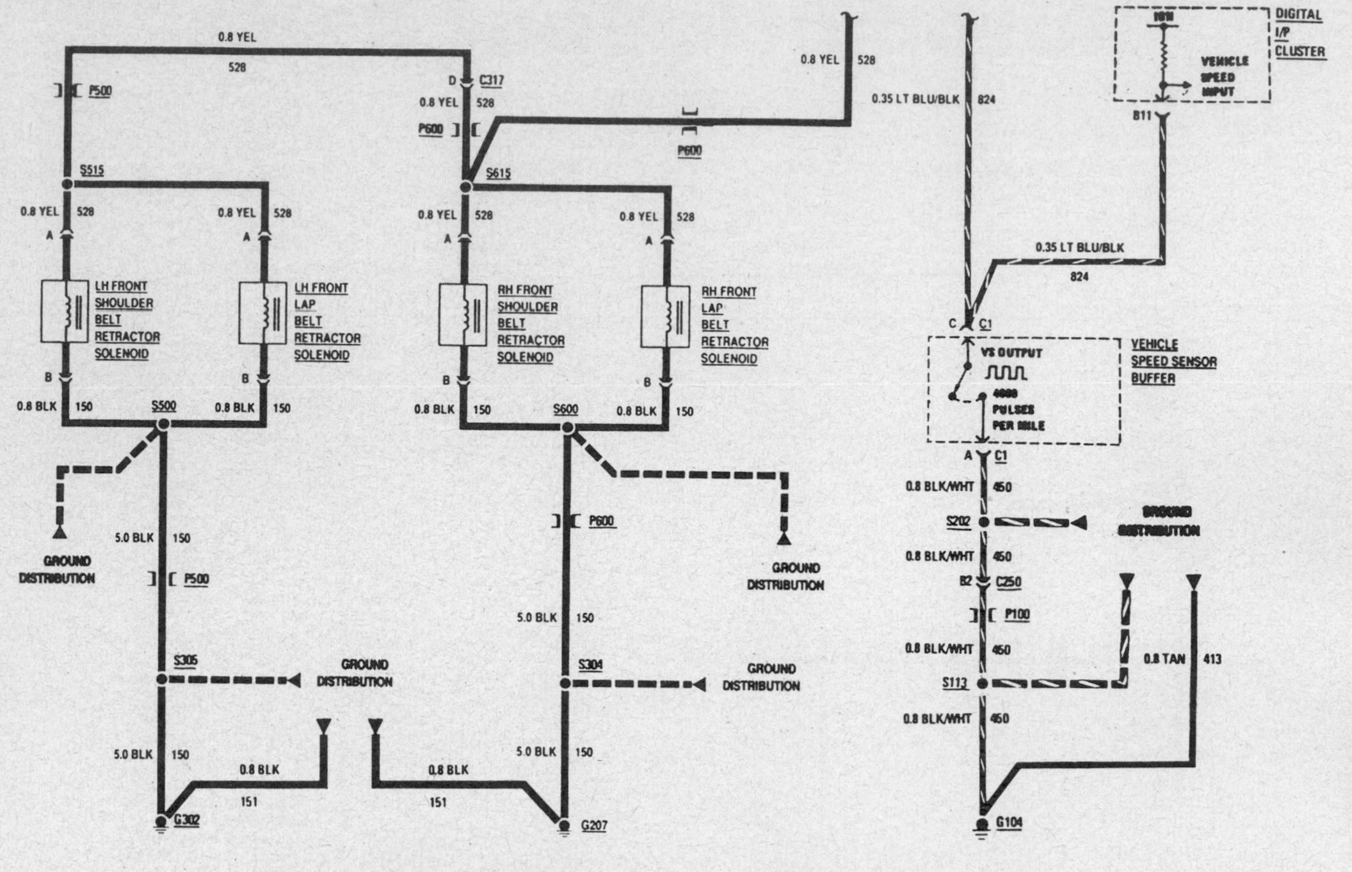

0.8 YEL
528
P500
C317
P600
S615
S515
LH FRONT SHOULDER BELT RETRACTOR SOLENOID
LH FRONT LAP BELT RETRACTOR SOLENOID
RH FRONT SHOULDER BELT RETRACTOR SOLENOID
RH FRONT LAP BELT RETRACTOR SOLENOID
0.8 BLK
150
S500
S600
GROUND DISTRIBUTION
5.0 BLK
S305
S304
151
G302
G207
DIGITAL I/P CLUSTER
VEHICLE SPEED INPUT
0.35 LT BLU/BLK
824
B11
C1
VS OUTPUT
4000 PULSES PER MILE
VEHICLE SPEED SENSOR BUFFER
0.8 BLK/WHT
450
S202
C250
P100
0.8 TAN
413
S113
G104
GC8029100001020X

Fig. 1 Automatic safety belt wiring circuit (Part 2 of 2). Brougham

TEST		RESULT	ACTION
A1.	Open LH front door. Backprobe PASSIVE RESTRAINT MODULE connector with a digital multimeter from cavity 3 to chassis ground. Measure voltage.	Less than 10.0 volts.	GO TO **A11.**
		More than 10.0 volts.	Leave multimeter connected and GO TO **A2.**
A2.	Close LH front door and wait 10 seconds. Measure voltage from PASSIVE RESTRAINT MODULE connector cavity 3 to chassis ground with all doors closed.	More than 10.0 volts.	GO TO **A16.**
		Less than 10.0 volts.	Leave multimeter connected and GO TO **A3.**
A3.	Open RH front door. Measure voltage from PASSIVE RESTRAINT MODULE connector cavity 3 to chassis ground.	Less than 10.0 volts.	GO TO **A20.**
		More than 10.0 volts.	Leave multimeter connected, close RH front door and GO TO **A4.**
A4.	Raise both rear wheels. Open LH front door. Start engine and place gear selector in "D." Increase rear wheel speed to 5 mph. Measure voltage from PASSIVE RESTRAINT MODULE connector cavity 3 to chassis ground.	More than 10.0 volts.	GO TO **A22.**
		Less than 10.0 volts.	Leave multimeter connected and GO TO **A5.**

GC8029100002010X

Fig. 2 Automatic safety belt diagnostic chart (Part 1 of 5). Brougham

LEMANS

The automatic safety belt system consists of a shoulder belt mounted to a carrier which moves along a guide rail between the A and B-pillars. When the front doors are opened, the shoulder belts move to the A-pillar. When the ignition switch is turned to "ON," the belts move to the B-pillar. This system also incorporates active lap belts which must be used with the motorized shoulder belts.

DIAGNOSIS & TESTING

BROUGHAM

Refer to wiring circuit, **Fig. 1**, and system diagnosis chart, **Fig. 2**, when diagnosing this system.

LEMANS

Refer to wiring circuit, **Fig. 3**, when performing the following diagnosis and testing procedures. Refer to the symptom table, **Fig. 4**, and related tests, **Figs. 5 through 10**, as directed.

TEST		RESULT	ACTION
A5.	Apply brake and reduce wheel speed to 0 mph. Place gear selector in "P." Measure voltage from PASSIVE RESTRAINT MODULE connector cavity 3 to chassis ground with LH front door still open.	More than 10.0 volts.	Replace PASSIVE RESTRAINT MODULE.
		Less than 10.0 volts.	Leave multimeter connected and GO TO **A6.**
A6.	Turn ignition switch to "OFF." Close LH front door, wait 10 seconds and reopen LH front door. Measure voltage from PASSIVE RESTRAINT MODULE connector cavity 3 to chassis ground.	Less than 10.0 volts.	Replace PASSIVE RESTRAINT MODULE.
		More than 10.0 volts.	GO TO **A7.**
A7.	Disconnect PASSIVE RESTRAINT MODULE connector. Disconnect LH FRONT SHOULDER BELT RETRACTOR SOLENOID. Connect a fused jumper from PASSIVE RESTRAINT MODULE connector cavity 1 to cavity 3. Listen for LH FRONT LAP BELT RETRACTOR SOLENOID operation while connecting jumper.	SOLENOID does not operate (Ltr Fuse or jumper fuse opens).	Repair short to ground in YEL (528) wire between PASSIVE RESTRAINT MODULE and SOLENOIDS.
		SOLENOID does not operate (fuses do not open).	Leave jumper connected and GO TO **A24.**
		SOLENOID operates.	Remove jumper and GO TO **A8.**
A8.	Connect LH FRONT SHOULDER BELT RETRACTOR SOLENOID connector. Disconnect LH FRONT LAP BELT RETRACTOR SOLENOID connector. Reconnect fused jumper from PASSIVE RESTRAINT MODULE connector cavity 1 to cavity 3 and listen for LH FRONT SHOULDER BELT RETRACTOR SOLENOID operation.	SOLENOID does not operate.	Leave jumper connected and GO TO **A26.**
		SOLENOID operates.	Remove jumper and GO TO **A9.**
A9.	Disconnect RH FRONT SHOULDER BELT RETRACTOR SOLENOID connector. Reconnect fused jumper from PASSIVE RESTRAINT MODULE connector cavity 1 to cavity 3. Listen for RH FRONT LAP BELT RETRACTOR SOLENOID operation while connecting jumper.	SOLENOID does not operate.	Leave jumper connected and GO TO **A28.**
		SOLENOID operates.	Remove jumper and GO TO **A10.**
A10.	Connect RH FRONT SHOULDER BELT RETRACTOR SOLENOID connector. Disconnect RH FRONT LAP BELT RETRACTOR SOLENOID connector. Reconnect fused jumper from PASSIVE RESTRAINT MODULE connector cavity 1 to cavity 3 and listen for RH FRONT SHOULDER BELT RETRACTOR SOLENOID operation.	SOLENOID does not operate.	Leave jumper connected and GO TO **A30.**
		SOLENOID operates.	All systems diagnosed in this cell are functioning normally.

GC8029100002020X

Fig. 2 Automatic safety belt diagnostic chart (Part 2 of 5). Brougham

TEST		RESULT	ACTION
A11.	Disconnect PASSIVE RESTRAINT MODULE connector. Connect a digital multimeter from connector cavity 1 to chassis ground. Measure voltage.	Less than 10.0 volts.	Repair open in ORN (40) wire between FUSE BLOCK and PASSIVE RESTRAINT MODULE.
		More than 10.0 volts.	GO TO **A12.**
A12.	Connect a digital multimeter from PASSIVE RESTRAINT MODULE connector cavity 3 to chassis ground. Measure resistance.	More than 0.3 ohms.	Repair BLK (151) ground wire.
		Less than 0.3 ohms.	GO TO **A13.**
A13.	Connect a digital multimeter from PASSIVE RESTRAINT MODULE connector cavity 4 to chassis ground. Measure voltage with LH front door open.	More than 10.0 volts.	Check circuit (528) for a short to ground. If OK, replace PASSIVE RESTRAINT MODULE.
		Less than 10.0 volts.	GO TO **A14.**
A14.	Backprobe LH FRONT DOOR LATCH SWITCH connector with a digital multimeter from cavity B to chassis ground. Measure voltage with LH front door open.	More than 10.0 volts.	Repair open in PNK (527) wire.
		Less than 10.0 volts.	GO TO **A15.**
A15.	Backprobe LH FRONT DOOR LATCH SWITCH connector with a digital multimeter from cavity A to chassis ground. Measure voltage.	More than 10.0 volts.	Replace LH FRONT DOOR LATCH SWITCH.
		Less than 10.0 volts.	Repair open in ORN (340) or (40) wire between FUSE BLOCK and LH FRONT DOOR LATCH SWITCH.
A16.	Disconnect PASSIVE RESTRAINT MODULE connector. Connect a digital multimeter from connector cavity 3 to chassis ground. Measure voltage.	More than 10.0 volts.	Repair short to voltage in YEL (528) wire.
		Less than 10.0 volts.	GO TO **A17.**
A17.	Connect a digital multimeter from PASSIVE RESTRAINT MODULE connector cavity 4 to chassis ground. Measure voltage with both front doors closed.	Less than 10.0 volts.	Replace PASSIVE RESTRAINT MODULE.
		More than 10.0 volts.	Leave multimeter connected and GO TO **A18.**
A18.	Disconnect LH FRONT DOOR LATCH SWITCH connector. Measure voltage from PASSIVE RESTRAINT MODULE connector cavity 4 to chassis ground.	Less than 10.0 volts.	Replace LH FRONT DOOR LATCH SWITCH.
		More than 10.0 volts.	GO TO **A19.**

GC8029100002030X

Fig. 2 Automatic safety belt diagnostic chart (Part 3 of 5). Brougham

TEST		RESULT	ACTION
A19.	Disconnect RH FRONT DOOR LATCH SWITCH connector. Measure voltage from PASSIVE RESTRAINT MODULE connector cavity 4 to chassis ground.	Less than 10.0 volts.	Replace RH FRONT DOOR LATCH SWITCH.
		More than 10.0 volts.	Repair short to voltage in PNK (527) wire.
A20.	Backprobe RH FRONT DOOR LATCH SWITCH connector with a digital multimeter from cavity B to chassis ground. Measure voltage with RH front door open.	More than 10.0 volts.	Repair open in PNK (527) wire between RH FRONT DOOR LATCH SWITCH and C305.
		Less than 10.0 volts.	GO TO **A21**.
A21.	Backprobe RH FRONT DOOR LATCH SWITCH connector with a digital multimeter from cavity A to chassis ground. Measure voltage.	More than 10.0 volts.	Replace RH FRONT DOOR LATCH SWITCH.
		Less than 10.0 volts.	Repair open in ORN (40) wire between S301 and RH FRONT DOOR LATCH SWITCH.
A22.	Turn ignition switch to "OFF." Lower the vehicle so that only the RH rear wheel is capable of spinning. (Keep the LH rear wheel in contact with the floor while leaving some clearance between the floor and the RH rear wheel.) Backprobe PASSIVE RESTRAINT MODULE connector with a digital multimeter from cavity 2 to chassis ground. Turn ignition switch to "RUN" (do not start engine) and observe voltage reading while manually rotating RH rear wheel with gear selector in "DRIVE."	Voltage fluctuates from greater than 8 volts to less than 3 volts while RH rear wheel is rotated.	Replace PASSIVE RESTRAINT MODULE.
		Voltage does not fluctuate.	GO TO **A23**.
A23.	Disconnect PASSIVE RESTRAINT MODULE connector and VEHICLE SPEED SENSOR BUFFER connector C1. Connect a digital multimeter from PASSIVE RESTRAINT MODULE connector cavity 2 to cavity C of VEHICLE SPEED SENSOR BUFFER connector C1. Measure resistance.	More than 0.3 ohms.	Repair LT BLU/BLK (824) wire between PASSIVE RESTRAINT MODULE and VEHICLE SPEED SENSOR BUFFER.
		Less than 0.3 ohms.	Repair terminal contact at cavity 2.
A24.	Disconnect LH FRONT LAP BELT RETRACTOR SOLENOID connector. Connect a digital multimeter from connector cavity A to chassis ground. Measure voltage.	Less than 10.0 volts.	Repair open in YEL (528) wire between PASSIVE RESTRAINT MODULE and LH FRONT LAP BELT RETRACTOR SOLENOID.
		More than 10.0 volts.	Go to **A25**.

GC8029100002040X

Fig. 2 Automatic safety belt diagnostic chart (Part 4 of 5). Brougham

TEST		RESULT	ACTION
A25.	Connect a digital multimeter from LH FRONT LAP BELT RETRACTOR SOLENOID connector cavity B to chassis ground. Measure resistance.	More than 0.3 ohms.	Repair BLK (150) ground wire.
		Less than 0.3 ohms	Replace LH SAFETY BELT RETRACTOR ASSEMBLY.
A26.	Disconnect LH FRONT SHOULDER BELT RETRACTOR SOLENOID connector. Connect a digital multimeter from connector cavity A to chassis ground. Measure voltage.	Less than 10.0 volts	Repair open in YEL (528) wire between S515 and LH FRONT SHOULDER BELT RETRACTOR SOLENOID
		More than 10.0 volts.	GO TO **A27**
A27.	Connect a digital multimeter from LH FRONT SHOULDER BELT RETRACTOR SOLENOID connector cavity B to chassis ground. Measure resistance.	More than 0.3 ohms.	Repair BLK (150) ground wire.
		Less than 0.3 ohms.	Replace LH SAFETY BELT RETRACTOR ASSEMBLY.
A28.	Disconnect RH FRONT LAP BELT RETRACTOR SOLENOID connector. Connect a digital multimeter from connector cavity A to chassis ground. Measure voltage.	Less than 10.0 volts	Repair open in YEL (528) wire between S615 and RH FRONT LAP BELT RETRACTOR SOLENOID.
		More than 10.0 volts	GO TO **A29**
A29.	Connect a digital multimeter from RH FRONT LAP BELT RETRACTOR SOLENOID connector cavity B to chassis ground. Measure resistance.	More than 0.3 ohms.	Repair BLK (150) ground wire.
		Less than 0.3 ohms.	Replace RH SAFETY BELT RETRACTOR ASSEMBLY.
A30.	Disconnect RH FRONT SHOULDER BELT RETRACTOR SOLENOID connector. Connect a digital multimeter from connector cavity A to chassis ground. Measure voltage.	Less than 10.0 volts.	Repair open in YEL (528) wire between S615 and RH FRONT SHOULDER BELT RETRACTOR SOLENOID.
		More than 10.0 volts.	GO TO **A31**.
A31.	Connect a digital multimeter from RH FRONT SHOULDER BELT RETRACTOR SOLENOID connector cavity B to chassis ground. Measure resistance.	More than 0.3 ohms.	Repair BLK (150) ground wire.
		Less than 0.3 ohms.	Replace RH SAFETY BELT RETRACTOR ASSEMBLY.

GC8029100002050X

Fig. 2 Automatic safety belt diagnostic chart (Part 5 of 5). Brougham

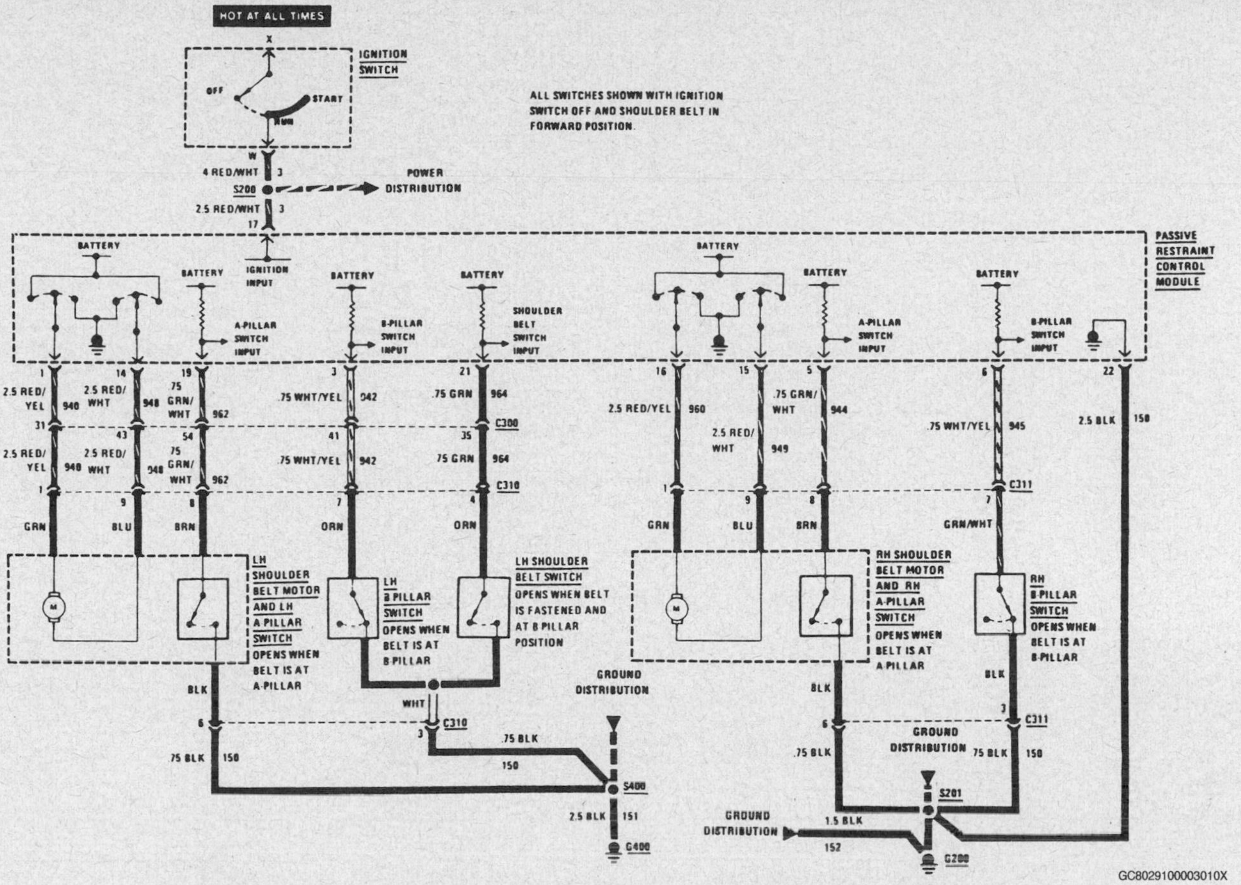
HOT AT ALL TIMES
IGNITION SWITCH
OFF
START
RUN
ALL SWITCHES SHOWN WITH IGNITION SWITCH OFF AND SHOULDER BELT IN FORWARD POSITION.
4 RED/WHT
S200
POWER DISTRIBUTION
2.5 RED/WHT
PASSIVE RESTRAINT CONTROL MODULE
BATTERY
IGNITION INPUT
A-PILLAR SWITCH INPUT
B-PILLAR SWITCH INPUT
SHOULDER BELT SWITCH INPUT
C300
C310
C311
LH SHOULDER BELT MOTOR AND LH A PILLAR SWITCH OPENS WHEN BELT IS AT A-PILLAR
LH B PILLAR SWITCH OPENS WHEN BELT IS AT B PILLAR
LH SHOULDER BELT SWITCH OPENS WHEN BELT IS FASTENED AND AT B PILLAR POSITION
RH SHOULDER BELT MOTOR AND RH A-PILLAR SWITCH OPENS WHEN BELT IS AT A PILLAR
RH B PILLAR SWITCH OPENS WHEN BELT IS AT B-PILLAR
GROUND DISTRIBUTION
S400
G400
S201
G200
GC8029100003010X

Fig. 3 Automatic safety belt wiring circuit (Part 1 of 2). LeMans

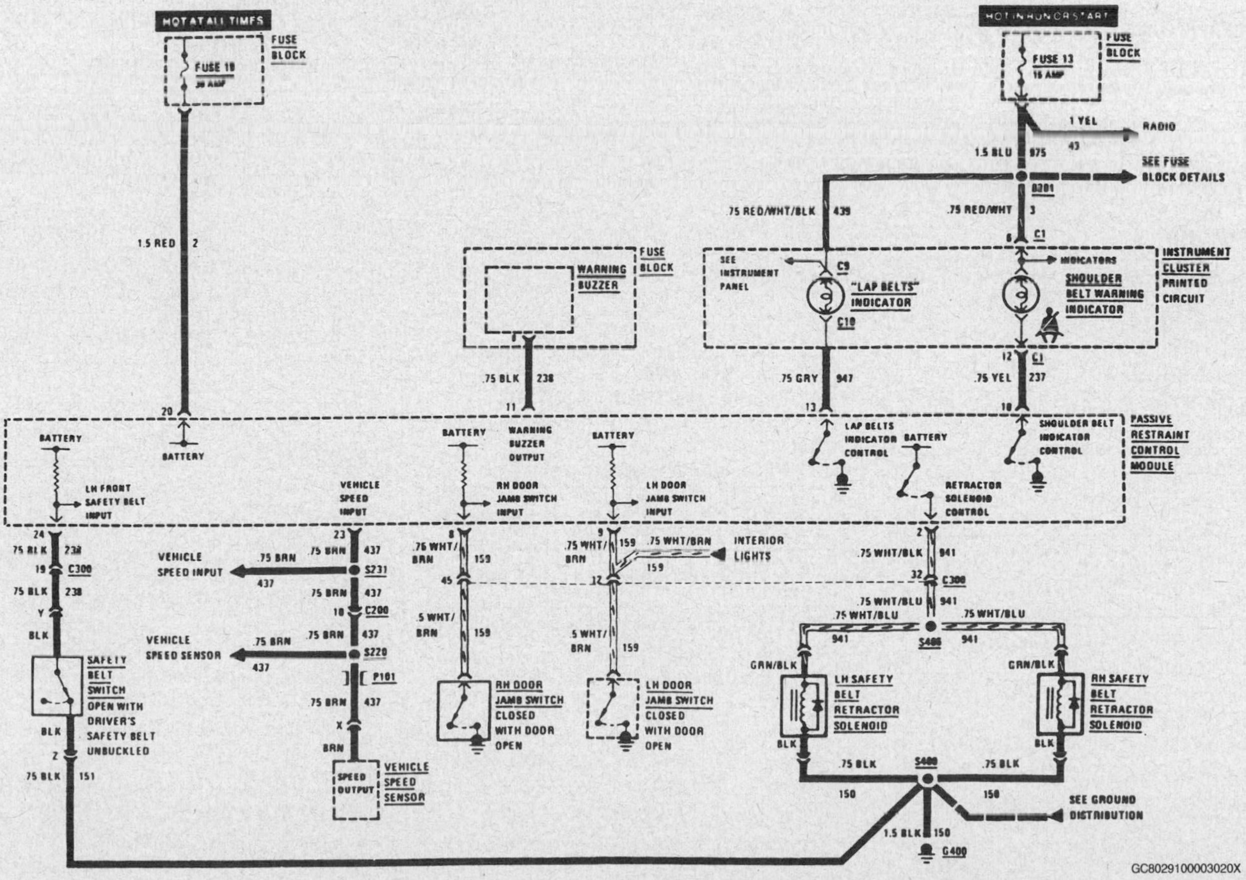
HOT AT ALL TIMES
FUSE BLOCK
FUSE 19
HOT IN RUN OR START
FUSE 13 15 AMP
RADIO
SEE FUSE BLOCK DETAILS
S201
WARNING BUZZER
INSTRUMENT CLUSTER PRINTED CIRCUIT
SEE INSTRUMENT PANEL
"LAP BELTS" INDICATOR
SHOULDER BELT WARNING INDICATOR
INDICATORS
PASSIVE RESTRAINT CONTROL MODULE
LH FRONT SAFETY BELT INPUT
VEHICLE SPEED INPUT
WARNING BUZZER OUTPUT
RH DOOR JAMB SWITCH INPUT
LH DOOR JAMB SWITCH INPUT
LAP BELTS INDICATOR CONTROL
SHOULDER BELT INDICATOR CONTROL
RETRACTOR SOLENOID CONTROL
INTERIOR LIGHTS
VEHICLE SPEED SENSOR
SAFETY BELT SWITCH OPEN WITH DRIVER'S SAFETY BELT UNBUCKLED
RH DOOR JAMB SWITCH CLOSED WITH DOOR OPEN
LH DOOR JAMB SWITCH CLOSED WITH DOOR OPEN
SPEED OUTPUT
LH SAFETY BELT RETRACTOR SOLENOID
RH SAFETY BELT RETRACTOR SOLENOID
S400
G400
SEE GROUND DISTRIBUTION
GC8029100003020X

Fig. 3 Automatic safety belt wiring circuit (Part 2 of 2). LeMans

SYMPTOM	DO TEST
Neither belt operates	A: Power and Ground Test
One belt remains in position at A-PILLAR	C: Shoulder Belt Motor and Switch Test
LAP BELTS Indicator remains on or does not come on	E: LAP BELTS Indicator Test F: Safety Belts Switch Test
Shoulder Belt Warning Indicator remains on after belt reaches B-PILLAR	B: Shoulder Belt Warning Indicator Test
Belt does not move freely while traveling on track	D: Belt Retractor Solenoid Test
Shoulder Belt Warning Indicator does not light	B: Shoulder Belt Warning Indicator Test

GC8029100004000X

Fig. 4 Symptom table. LeMans

DIAGNOSTIC CHART INDEX

Test	Description	Model	Page No.	Fig. No.
Test A	Power & Ground Test	LeMans	5-34	5
Test B	Shoulder Belt Warning Indicator Test	LeMans	5-34	6
Test C	Shoulder Belt Motor & Switch Test	LeMans	5-35	7
Test D	Belt Reatractor Solenoid Test	LeMans	5-35	8
Test E	Lap Belt Indicator Test	LeMans	5-35	9
Test F	Safety Belt Switch Test	LeMans	5-35	10

Measure: VOLTAGE
At: PASSIVE RESTRAINT CONTROL MODULE (Disconnected)
Condition:
- Ignition Switch: RUN

Measure Between	Correct Voltage	For Diagnosis
17 (RED/WHT) & Ground	Battery	See 1
17 (RED/WHT) & 22 (BLK)	Battery	See 2
20 (RED) & Ground	Battery	See 3

- If voltages are correct, replace Passive Restraint Control Module.

1. Check RED/WHT (3) wire for an open.
2. Check BLK (150) wire for an open.
3. Check RED (2) wire for an open.

GC8029100005000X

Fig. 5 Test A: Power & Ground Test. LeMans

Measure: VOLTAGE
At: PASSIVE RESTRAINT CONTROL MODULE CONNECTOR (Disconnected)
Condition:
- Ignition in RUN or START

Measure Between	Correct Voltage	For Diagnosis
10 (YEL) & Ground	Battery	See 1

- If voltage is correct, go to Test B; Table 2.

1. Check YEL (237) wire for an open. If wire is good, check bulb. Replace cluster if bulb is OK.

GC8029100006010X

Fig. 6 Test B: Shoulder Belt Warning Indicator Test (Part 1 of 3). LeMans

Measure: VOLTAGE
At: CONNECTOR C310 (Disconnected)
Condition:
- Ignition: RUN

Measure Between	Correct Votlage	For Diagnosis
4 (GRN) & Ground	Battery	See 1
4 (GRN) & 3 (BLK)	Battery	See 2

- If all voltages are correct, go to Test B; Table 3.

1. Check GRN (964) wire for an open or short to ground. If wire is OK, replace Passive Restraint Control Module.
2. Check/repair BLK (150) wire for an open.

GC8029100006020X

Fig. 6 Test B: Shoulder Belt Warning Indicator Test (Part 2 of 3). LeMans

Connect: FUSED JUMPER
At: CONNECTOR C310 (Disconnected)
Condition:
- Ignition: RUN

Connect Between	Correct Result	For Diagnosis
4 (GRN) & 3 (BLK)	Shoulder Belt Indicator lights	See 1

- If result is correct, replace LH Shoulder Belt Switch.

1. Replace Passive Restraint Control Module.

GC8029100006030X

Fig. 6 Test B: Shoulder Belt Warning Indicator Test (Part 3 of 3). LeMans

Measure: VOLTAGE
At: CONNECTOR C310 female half (LH)
CONNECTOR C311 female half (RH)
(Disconnected)
Condition:
- Ignition in RUN

Measure Between	Correct Voltage	For Diagnosis
8 (GRN/WHT) & Ground	Battery	See 1
8 (GRN/WHT) & 6 (BLK)	Battery	See 2
7 (WHT/YEL) & Ground	Battery	See 3
7 (WHT/YEL) & 3 (BLK)	Battery	See 2

- If all voltages are correct, go to Test B; Table 2.

1. Check GRN/WHT (964) or (944) for an open or short to ground. If wire is OK, replace Passive Restraint Control Module.
2. Repair open in BLK (150) wire.
3. Check WHT/YEL (942) or (945) wire for an open or short to ground. If wire is OK, replace Passive Restraint Control Module.

GC8029100009010X

Fig. 7 Test C: Shoulder Belt Motor & Switch Test (Part 1 of 3). LeMans

Measure: RESISTANCE
At: PASSIVE RESTRAINT CONTROL MODULE CONNECTOR (Disconnected)
Conditions:
- Ignition: OFF
- Shoulder Belts at A-PILLAR
- Shoulder Belts Buckled

Measure Between	Correct Measurement	For Diagnosis
19 (GRN/WHT) & Ground	More than 100 ohms	See 1
5 (GRN/WHT) & Ground	More than 100 ohms	See 1
3 (WHT/YEL) & Ground	Less than 10 ohms	See 2
6 (WHT/YEL) & Ground	Less than 10 ohms	See 2
• Shoulder Belts at B-PILLAR		
19 (GRN/WHT) & Ground	Less than 10 ohms	See 1
5 (GRN/WHT) & Ground	Less than 10 ohms	See 1
3 (WHT/YEL) & Ground	More than 100 ohms	See 2
6 (WHT/YEL) & Ground	More than 100 ohms	See 2
• LH and RH Doors Closed		
8 (WHT/BRN) & Ground	More than 100 ohms	See 3
9 (WHT/BRN) & Ground	More than 100 ohms	See 3
• LH and RH Doors open		
8 (WHT/BRN) & Ground	Less than 10 ohms	See 3
9 (WHT/BRN) & Ground	Less than 10 ohms	See 3

- If all measurements are correct, go to Table 3.

1. Replace respective Shoulder Belt Motor and A-PILLAR Switch.
2. Replace respective B-PILLAR Switch.
3. Check WHT/BRN (159) wire for an open or short to ground. If wire is OK, replace respective Door Jamb Switch.

GC8029100009020X

Fig. 7 Test C: Shoulder Belt Motor & Switch Test (Part 2 of 3). LeMans

Connect: FUSED JUMPER
At: C310 or C311 male half (Disconnected)
Condition:
Terminal 1 Connected to positive battery with Fused Jumper

Connect Between	Correct Results	For Diagnosis
9 (BLU) & Ground	Motor Runs	See 1

- If the result is correct, replace Passive Restraint Control Module.

1. Replace respective Shoulder Belt Motor and A-PILLAR Switch.

GC8029100009030X

Fig. 7 Test C: Shoulder Belt Motor & Switch Test (Part 3 of 3). LeMans

Measure: VOLTAGE
At: SUSPECT BELT RETRACTOR SOLENOID CONNECTOR (Disconnected)
Conditions:
- Ignition in RUN or START
- Doors: CLOSED
- Belt traveling between A-PILLAR and B-PILLAR

Measure Between	Correct Voltage	For Diagnosis
WHT/BLU & Ground	Battery	See 1
WHT/BLU & BLK	Battery	See 2

- If all voltage are correct, replace suspect solenoid.

1. Check WHT/BLU (941) wires for an open or a short to ground. If wires are good, replace module.
2. Check BLK (150) wires for an open.

GC8029100012000X

Fig. 8 Test D: Belt Retractor Solenoid Test. LeMans

Measure: VOLTAGE
At: PASSIVE RESTRAINT CONTROL MODULE CONNECTOR (Disconnected)
Condition:
- Ignition in RUN

Measure Between	Correct Voltage	For Diagnosis
13 (GRY) & Ground	Battery	See 1

- If voltage is correct, go to Test F.

1. Check bulb and GRY (947) wire for an open.

GC8029100013000X

Fig. 9 Test E: Lap Belts Indicator Test. LeMans

Measure: VOLTAGE
At: SAFETY BELT SWITCH CONNECTOR (Disconnected)
Condition:
- Ignition in RUN

Measure Between	Correct Voltage	For Diagnosis
A (BLK) & Ground	Battery	See 1
A (BLK) & B (BLK)	Battery	See 2
• Reconnect: SAFETY BELT SWITCH • Lap Belt: BUCKLED		
A (BLK) & B (BLK)	12 volts	See 3
• Lap Belt: UNBUCKLED		
A (BLK) & B (BLK)	0 Volts	See 3

- If all voltages are correct, replace Module.

1. Check BLK (238) wire for an open. If wires are good, replace Module.
2. Check BLK (151 and 150) wires for an open.
3. Replace SAFETY BELT Switch.

GC8029100014000X

Fig. 10 Test F: Safety Belt Switch Test. LeMans

COMPONENT REPLACEMENT

LEMANS

GUIDE RAIL

1. With belt locked at B-pillar, disconnect battery ground cable.
2. Remove shoulder belt from carrier.
3. **On hatchback models,** remove upper quarter trim panel.
4. **On all models,** remove guide rail trim panel.
5. Remove upper and lower bolts retaining lock mechanism.
6. Remove warning lamp switch from lock mechanism, then remove lock mechanism.
7. Loosen five retaining screws and remove guide rail.
8. Reverse procedure to install, noting the following:
   a. **Torque** mechanism to guide rail bolts to 26 ft. lbs.

DRIVE MOTOR ASSEMBLY

Hatchback

1. Disconnect battery ground cable.
2. Remove guide rail.
3. Remove bolts retaining drive motor and locking section.
4. Remove assembly by pulling down while turning the locking section 180°.
5. Reverse procedure to install, noting the following:
   a. **Torque** drive motor mounting bolts to 26 ft. lbs.
   b. **Torque** locking section mounting bolts to 15 ft. lbs.

Sedan

1. With belt locked at B-pillar, disconnect battery ground cable.
2. Remove front and rear sill plates.
3. Remove B-pillar upper and lower trim.
4. Remove two bolts, one screw and locking mechanism from guide rail.
5. Disconnect metal retaining clip and remove drive motor mounting nut.
6. Remove drive motor and disconnect electrical connector.
7. Reverse procedure to install, noting the following:
   a. **Torque** drive motor retaining nut to 26 ft. lbs.
   b. **Torque** locking mechanism screw and bolts to 15 ft. lbs.

DASH PANEL SERVICE

NOTE: On Air Bag Equipped Models, Refer To Air Bag System Precautions Located In The Front Of This Manual For System Disarming & Arming Procedures.

INDEX

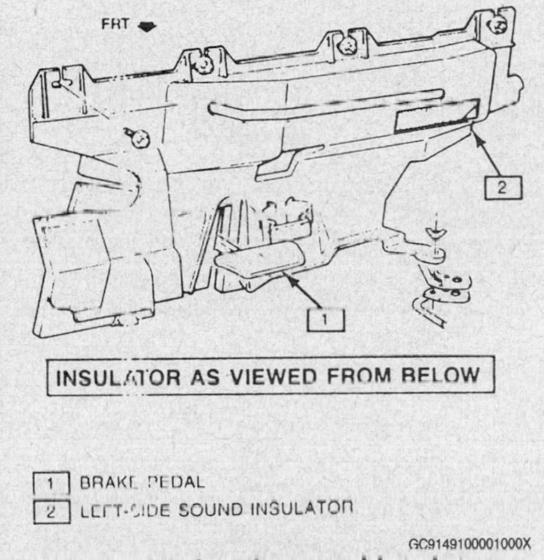

FRT
INSULATOR AS VIEWED FROM BELOW
1 BRAKE PEDAL
2 LEFT-SIDE SOUND INSULATOR
GC9149100001000X

Fig. 1 Left side sound insulator. Brougham

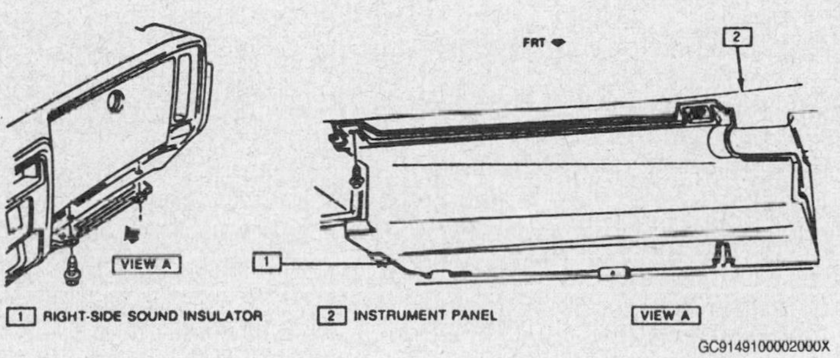

FRT
VIEW A
1 RIGHT-SIDE SOUND INSULATOR
2 INSTRUMENT PANEL
GC9149100002000X

Fig. 2 Right side sound insulator. Brougham

PRECAUTIONS

AIR BAG SYSTEMS

Refer to "Air Bag System Precautions" in the front of this manual for system disarming and arming procedures.

DASH PANEL

REPLACE

BROUGHAM

1. Disconnect battery ground cable.
2. Remove sound insulators, **Fig. 1 and 2.**
3. Remove screw securing left side A/C outlet duct extension and remove duct.
4. Remove two steering column cover retaining screws and lower cover.
5. Remove A/C left side outlet duct extension retaining screw, then the duct.
6. Remove instrument panel retaining screws at each end of instrument panel.
7. Remove top cover attaching screw through access hole located in top of glove box liner.
8. Remove four top cover to cowl retaining screws located in the defroster grilles.
9. Remove top cover by pulling panel up and out of retaining clips.
10. Using a 1/16 inch Allen wrench, loosen key on bottom of each center outlet grille directional knob, then remove knobs.
11. Remove four center trim panel retaining screws, then the trim panel.
12. Remove remaining grille directional knob.
13. Remove six trim panel retaining screws, then the trim panel.
14. Remove four instrument cluster retaining screws, **Fig. 3.**
15. Remove upper steering column mounting bolts and set column on front seat.
16. Remove two windshield wiper switch retaining screws.
17. Remove three headlamp switch to instrument panel retaining screws.
18. **On models equipped with cruise control,** remove two cruise control switch retaining screws, then slide switch forward.
19. Disconnect switch two piece electrical connector.
20. Remove twilight Sentinel wiring if equipped.
21. **On all models,** remove headlamp switch retaining nut, then the switch from housing.
22. Remove two 10mm mounting bolts and ground strap from chime mounting bracket.
23. Remove 10mm retaining nut from stud on bottom of radio chassis.
24. Pull chime module, bracket and chime wiring downward, then position aside.
25. Disconnect antenna lead.
26. Pull radio chassis down and pivot towards front of car until connector end of chassis is horizontal with floorpan.
27. Disconnect (2) electrical connectors from side opposite coax cable.
28. Pull chassis out from behind instrument panel and disconnect three electrical connectors.
29. Remove two ECC head retaining screws.
30. Disconnect electrical connector from ECC head, then the EEC.
31. Remove right side mirror remote control retaining screws, then the remote control.
32. Remove three glove box liner retaining screws, **Fig. 4.**
33. Remove four glove box door retaining screws, then remove accessory relay bracket and position aside.
34. Remove four upper instrument panel retaining screws and two lower instrument panel retaining bolts.
35. Disconnect instrument panel electrical connectors.

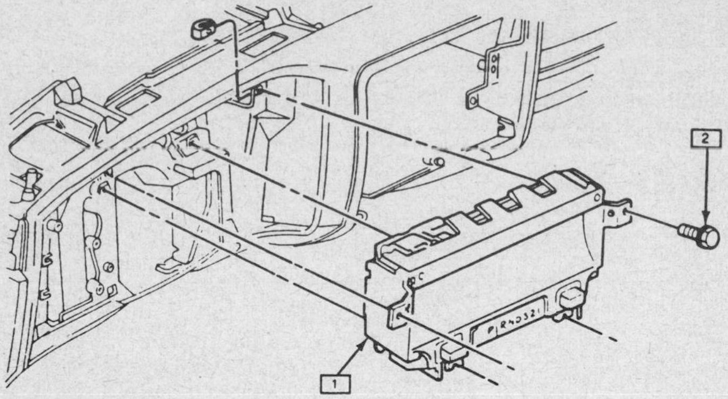
1
2
1 DIGITAL INSTRUMENT CLUSTER
2 MOUNTING BOLT (1 OF 4)
GC9149100003000X

Fig. 3 Instrument cluster removal. Brougham

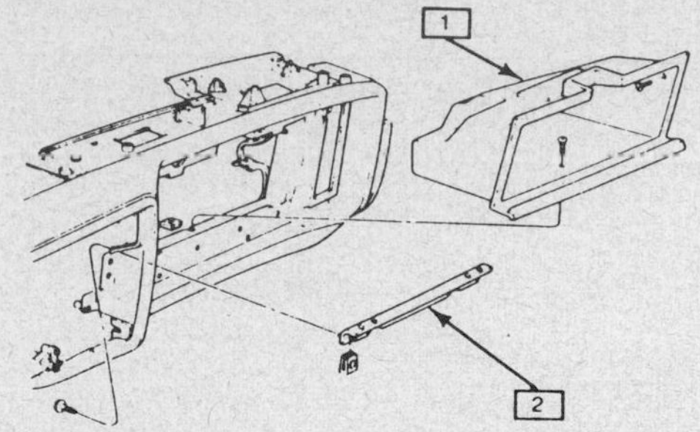
1
2
1 GLOVE BOX LINER
2 LINER BRACKET
GC9149100004000X

Fig. 4 Glove box liner removal. Brougham

36. Remove instrument panel.
37. Reverse procedure to install.

CORVETTE

Refer to **Fig. 5** when performing this procedure.

1. Remove driver knee bolster, then right hand lower trim panel and support.
2. Remove console and accessory trim plates.
3. Remove console to instrument panel bolt and screws, then console side trim plates.
4. Remove instrument panel to knee bolster brackets bolts and screws.
5. Remove stack bracket bolts.
6. Remove Driver Information Center (DIC) and Heater/Vent/Air Conditioning (HVAC) control and radio control.
7. Remove lateral accelerometer.
8. Remove upper trim pad, then cluster and headlamp switch.
9. Disconnect wire harness retainers from instrument panel.
10. Remove side window defogger outlet ducts.
11. Remove inside air temperature sensor.
12. Remove upper instrument panel brace, then upper and lower outer instrument panel to dash nuts from studs.
13. Remove fuse box by drilling out rivet heads.
14. Remove multi-use relay brackets.
15. Remove air distribution duct from instrument panel.
16. Disconnect harness connectors from instrument panel mounted modules.
17. Remove instrument panel from vehicle.
18. Reverse procedure to install.

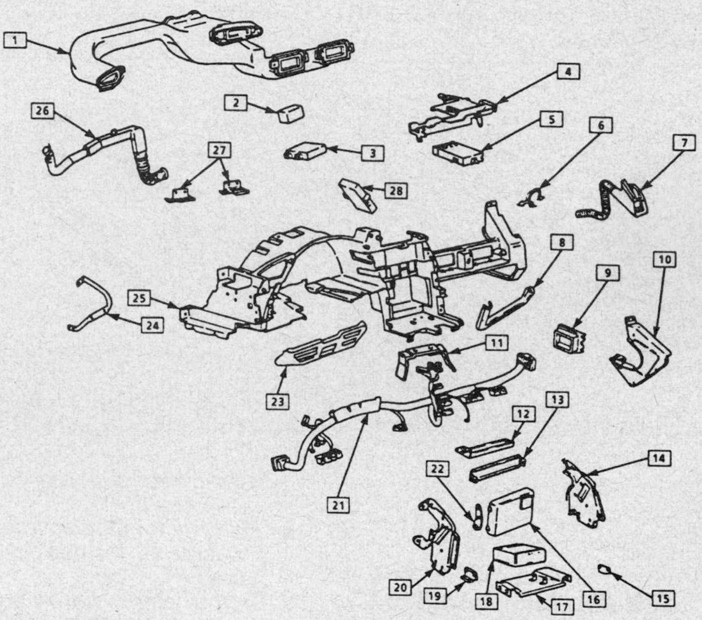
1 AIR DISTRIBUTOR DUCT
2 ALARM MODULE
3 PKE MODULE
4 MULTI USE RELAY BRACKET
5 CRUISE MODULE
6 PLASTIC 7" ADJUSTABLE STRAP RETAINER
7 SIDE WINDOW DEFOG OUTLET DUCT - RH
8 LOWER TRIM PANEL SUPPORT
9 WIRING HARNESS FUSE BLOCK BRACKET
10 KNEE BOLSTER OUTER BRACKET - RH
11 LOWER CENTER SUPPORT
12 CARRIER
13 KNEE BOLSTER INNER BRACKET BRACE
14 KNEE BOLSTER INNER BRACKET - RH
15 DERM BRACKET - RH
16 CENTRAL CONTROL MODULE
17 DERM/ARMING SENSOR BRACKET
18 DIAGNOSTIC ENERGY RESERVE MODULE (DERM)
19 DERM BRACKET - LH
20 KNEE BOLSTER INNER BRACKET - LH
21 I/P WIRING HARNESS
22 CENTRAL CONTROL MODULE BRACKET
23 KNEE BOLSTER, DRIVERS SIDE
24 KNEE BOLSTER OUTER BRACKET - LH
25 INSTRUMENT PANEL
26 SIDE WINDOW DEFOG OUTLET DUCT - LH
27 MULTI USE RELAY BRACKET - LH
28 LOW TIRE PRESSURE INDICATOR MODULE
GC9149200005000X

Fig. 5 I/P removal. Corvette

CENTURY

1. Disconnect battery ground cable.
2. Remove two screws from front of left side instrument panel sound insulator, **Fig. 6.**
3. Remove one bolt from rear left side and one nut from accelerator pedal bracket, then pull left sound insulator straight forward to remove.
4. Remove three screws from front of right side sound insulator, **Fig. 7.**
5. Remove nut from right back side, then pull right side sound insulator straight forward to remove.
6. Remove two screws from instrument panel filler panel, **Fig. 8.**
7. Gently pull forward on left side trim cover to release hooks on front of lower instrument panel filler panel.
8. Disconnect lap vent hose and ALDL connector, then remove instrument panel filler.
9. Remove two screws from steering column opening filler, **Fig. 9.**
10. Lower steering column by removing shift indicator clip, then the three retaining bolts and one nut.
11. Disconnect electrical connectors at steering column and disconnect parking brake cable.
12. Disconnect instrument panel harness connectors to body connectors at

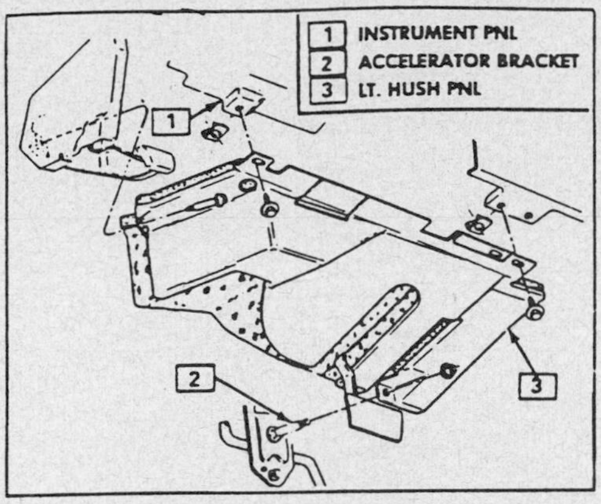
1 INSTRUMENT PNL
2 ACCELERATOR BRACKET
3 LT. HUSH PNL
1
2
3

GC9149100006000X

Fig. 6 LH side I/P sound insulator removal. Century

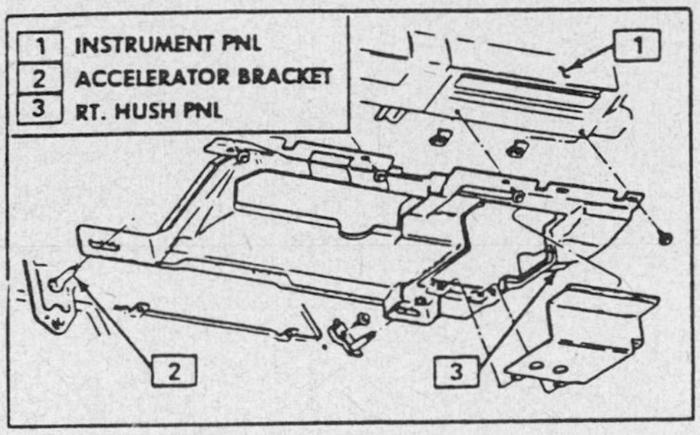
1 INSTRUMENT PNL
2 ACCELERATOR BRACKET
3 RT. HUSH PNL
1
2
3

GC9149100007000X

Fig. 7 RH side I/P sound insulator removal. Century

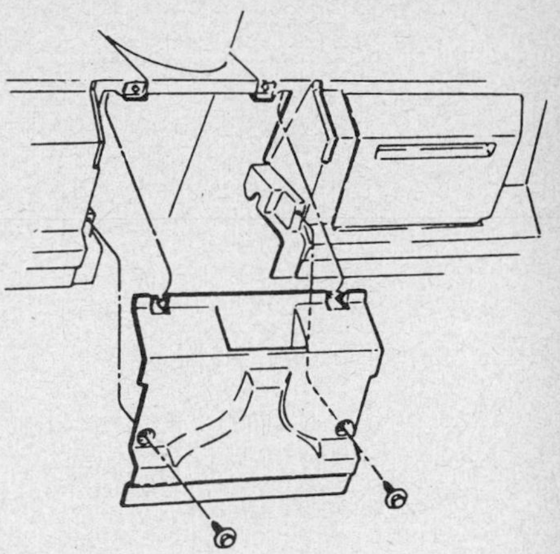

GC9149100008000X

Fig. 8 I/P filler panel removal. Century

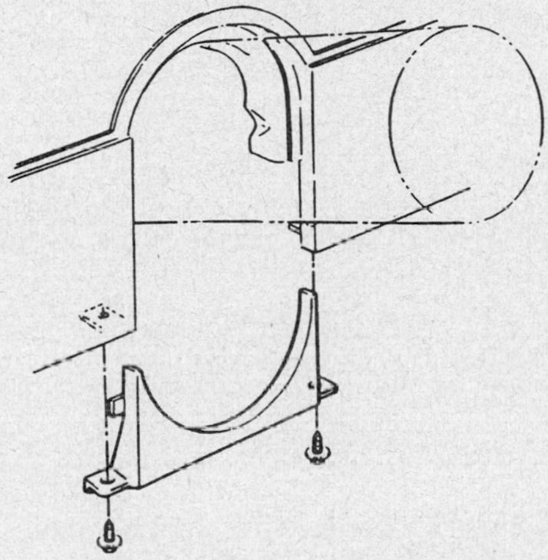

GC9149100009000X

Fig. 9 Steering column opening filler removal. Century

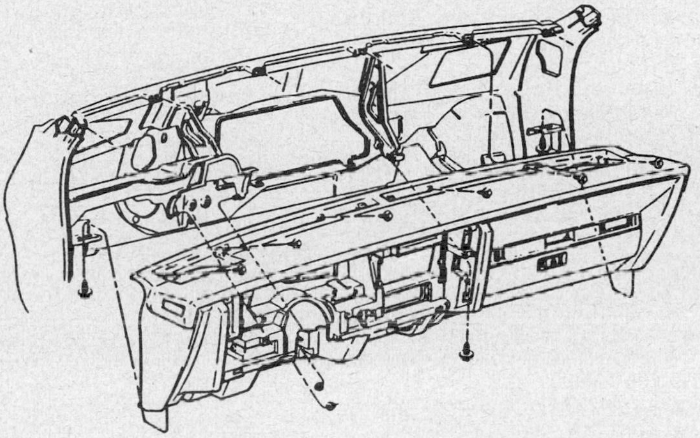

GC9149100010000X

Fig. 10 I/P removal. Century

junction block.

13. Disconnect speaker connectors, A/C vacuum harness and temperature door cable.
14. Disconnect emission harness connectors, antenna cable and side window defroster hoses.
15. **On 1992 models,** disconnect speedometer cable from engine compartment split if a two piece cable is used, or from the transmission for slack.
16. **On all models,** split bulk head connector by removing 1/4 inch bolt, then slide instrument panel side of connector out of clip.
17. Disconnect electrical connectors from windshield wiper motor, master brake cylinder and hood light.
18. Disconnect harness cowl connector, then feed harness through cowl.
19. Remove two screws, then pull speaker-defroster grille straight out.
20. Remove two nuts on both inner sides of steering column opening.
21. Remove three bolts on bottom side of instrument panel, then remove six screws in defroster area at top of instrument panel, **Fig. 10.**
22. **On 1992 models,** pull instrument panel forward and disconnect speedometer cable.
23. **On all models,** remove panel. **On vehicles equipped with digital instrument cluster,** the Vehicle Speed Sensor (VSS) buffer must be disconnected.
24. Reverse procedure to install.

CUTLASS CIERA & CUTLASS CRUISER

1. Disconnect battery ground cable.
2. Remove left and right sound insulators, **Figs. 11 and 12.**
3. **On models with center console,** proceed as follows:
   a. Open armrest and remove cassette holder.
   b. Remove six screws, then lift compartment straight up.
   c. Remove ashtray, then two screws in ashtray opening.
   d. **On models with column shifter,** open center compartment and remove two screws at rear of center compartment.
   e. **On models with console shifter,** use a small screwdriver to pry off snap ring that holds shift knob in place. Remove shift knob and remove two screws at rear of shifter plate.
   f. **On all models,** remove center compartment or shifter plate, **Fig. 13.**
   g. Pull console trim plate rearward, then disconnect the electrical connectors to DIS, ashtray light and lighter.
   h. Remove console trim plate, then remove two screws from console trim plate opening.
   i. Remove upper console, **Fig. 14.**
4. **On all models,** remove steering column collar by carefully prying rearward to release the five clips.
5. Remove outer air deflectors by pulling rearward.
6. Remove one bolt and one screw from deflector openings, then one bolt and one screw from steering column opening.
7. **On models with center console,** remove four bolts from ashtray trim cover. Remove ashtray trim cover and the two bolts holding accessory trim plate.
8. **On models less center console,** open ashtray and remove two bolts holding accessory trim plate.
9. **On models with column shift,** move shift lever to the 1 position.
10. **On all models,** remove accessory trim panel by carefully pulling rearward to release clips, **Fig. 15.**

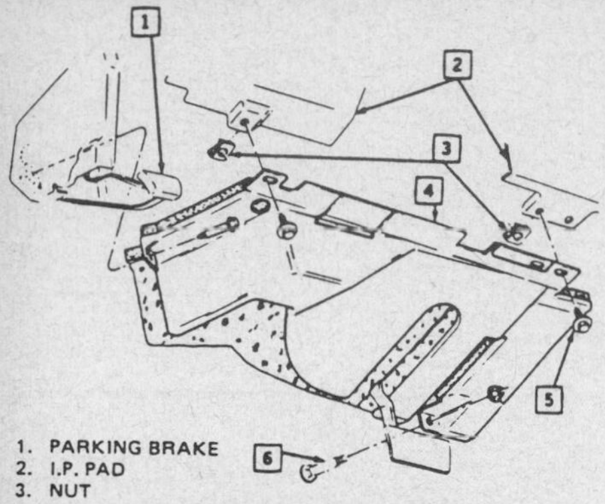

1. PARKING BRAKE
2. I.P. PAD
3. NUT
4. INSULATOR
5. FULLY DRIVEN, SEATED AND NOT STRIPPED
6. STUD ON ACCELERATOR SUPPORT

GC9149100011000X

Fig. 11 Left side I/P sound insulator removal. Cutlass Ciera & Cutlass Cruiser

11. Remove Torx screws from bottom and top of cluster trim plate, then remove trim plate, **Fig. 16.**
12. **On models with column shifter,** remove shift indicator clip from steering column shift bowl.
13. **On all models,** remove four bolts holding instrument cluster, pull cluster rearward and disconnect speedometer.
14. Remove speaker grilles by prying carefully.
15. Remove ventilation control assembly.
16. Remove parking brake release handle, then side window defogger hoses from heater outlet.
17. Disconnect steering column wiring harness from the steering column.
18. Remove wiper motor to cowl attaching bolts, then disconnect bulkhead connector at cowl.
19. Remove lower instrument panel attaching bolts, then using a small screwdriver remove defroster grille by carefully prying upward.
20. Remove upper instrument panel attaching bolts, **Fig. 17,** then open engine compartment hood.
21. Remove clip in engine compartment holding instrument panel wiring harness to cowl.
22. Disconnect electrical connectors from wiring harness in engine compartment.
23. Pull wiring harness through cowl opening into passenger compartment.
24. Tilt instrument panel forward and disconnect remaining electrical connectors and remove instrument panel.
25. Reverse procedure to install.

1992–93 DEVILLE & FLEETWOOD (FWD)

Refer to **Fig. 18** when performing this procedure.

1. Disconnect battery ground cable.
2. Remove right and left side sound insulators, **Fig. 19.**
3. Remove upper trim pad as shown in **Fig. 18.**
4. Remove lower steering column filler.
5. Remove steering column to support bracket attaching bolts, then lower steering column.
6. Remove lower instrument panel trim pad support.
7. Remove lower instrument panel brace retaining nut from accelerator pedal stud.
8. Disconnect electrical connectors between instrument panel and dash, then remove glove box switches.
9. Remove instrument panel to dash attaching screws, **Fig. 20.**
10. Remove trim pad assembly.
11. Reverse procedure to install.

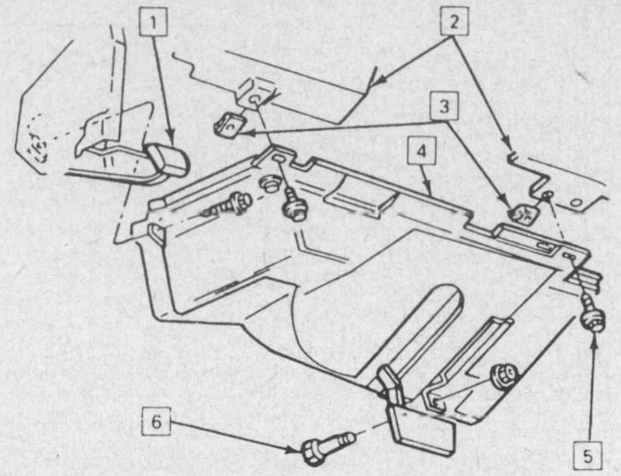

1. PARKING BRAKE
2. I.P. PAD
3. NUT
4. INSULATOR
5. FULLY DRIVEN, SEATED AND NOT STRIPPED
6. STUD ON ACCELERATOR SUPPORT

GC9149100012000X

Fig. 12 Right side I/P sound insulator removal. Cutlass Ciera & Cutlass Cruiser

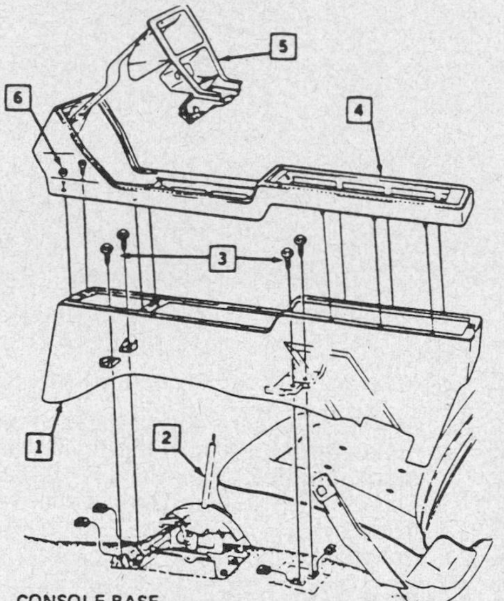

1. CONSOLE BASE
2. TRANSMISSION SHIFTER ASSEMBLY
3. 6 N·m (4 LBS. FT.)
4. PAD ASM.
5. COMPARTMENT ASM.
6. FULLY DRIVEN, SEATED AND NOT STRIPPED

GC9149100014000X

Fig. 14 Upper console removal. Cutlass Ciera & Cutlass Cruiser

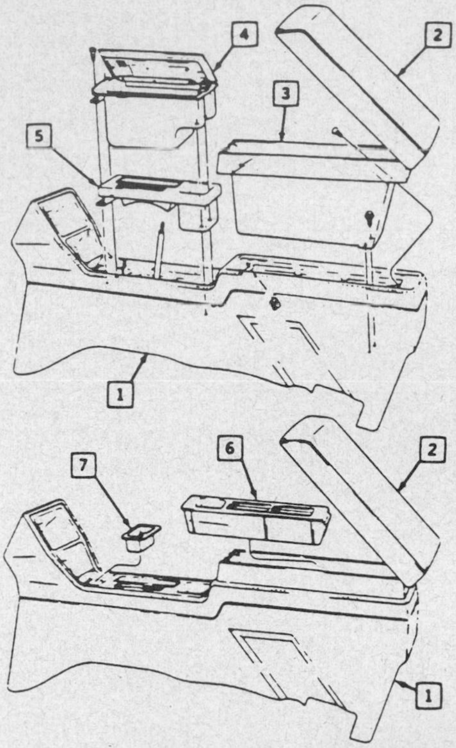

1. CONSOLE BASE
2. COMPARTMENT DOOR
3. COMPARTMENT
4. CENTER COMPARTMENT
5. SHIFTER PLATE
6. TAPE STORAGE
7. ASHTRAY

GC9149100013000X

Fig. 13 Center console assembly. Cutlass Ciera & Cutlass Cruiser

1994 CONCOURS & DEVILLE

1. Disconnect battery ground cable.
2. Using a small flat-bladed tool, remove defroster grille by prying upward.
3. Remove sunload and headlamp auto control sensors from defroster grille.
4. Remove three upper trim panel attaching screws through defroster grille opening.
5. Remove heater and A/C vents from front of instrument panel by releasing tab on each side from inside of vent and pulling out.
6. Remove four upper trim panel attaching screws through vent openings.
7. Remove upper trim panel from instrument panel.
8. Pull ignition and battery fuses from passenger compartment fuse panel, then the ignition fuse from engine compartment fuse panel.
9. Disconnect two electrical connectors from top of instrument cluster.
10. Remove four instrument cluster to instrument panel attaching screws.
11. Raise cluster to gain access to two PRNDL mechanism retaining screws and remove screws.
12. Remove instrument cluster from vehicle.
13. Remove right and left A/C vent trim panels.

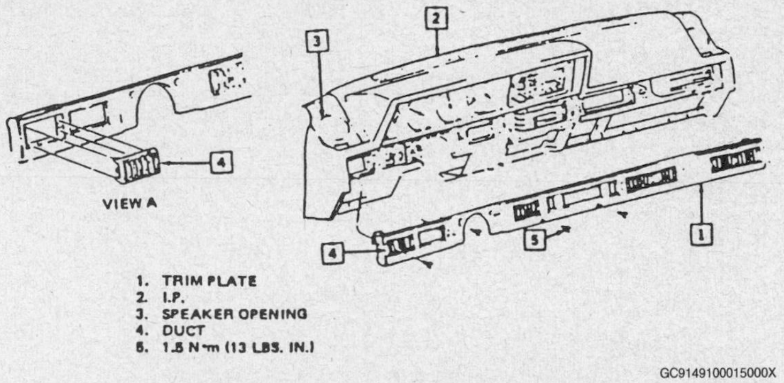
VIEW A
1. TRIM PLATE
2. I.P.
3. SPEAKER OPENING
4. DUCT
5. 1.5 N·m (13 LBS. IN.)
GC9149100015000X

Fig. 15 Accessory trim plate removal. Cutlass Ciera & Cutlass Cruiser

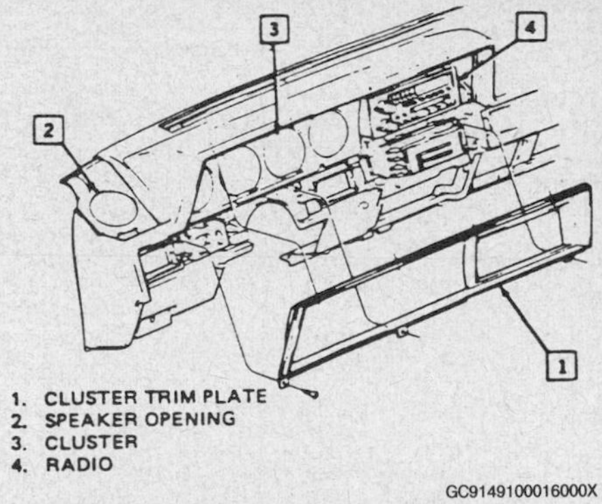
1. CLUSTER TRIM PLATE
2. SPEAKER OPENING
3. CLUSTER
4. RADIO
GC9149100016000X

Fig. 16 Cluster trim plate removal. Cutlass Ciera & Cutlass Cruiser

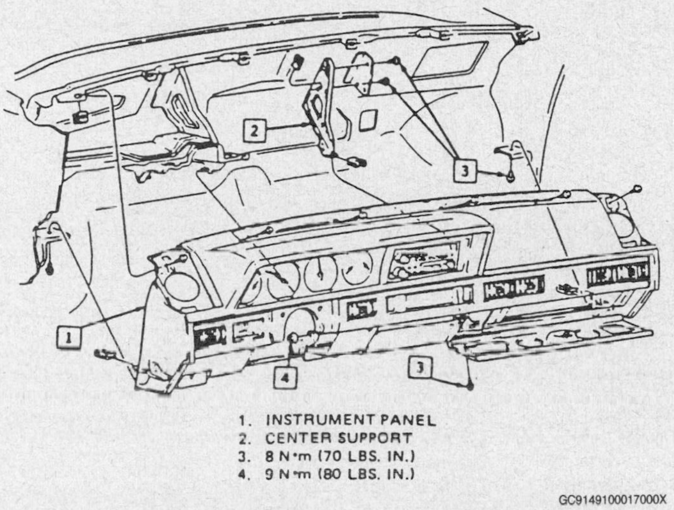
1. INSTRUMENT PANEL
2. CENTER SUPPORT
3. 8 N·m (70 LBS. IN.)
4. 9 N·m (80 LBS. IN.)
GC9149100017000X

Fig. 17 I/P removal. Cutlass Ciera & Cutlass Cruiser

14. Open trap door in rear of glove compartment and remove passenger inflatable restraint wiring connector from retaining clip on rear of glove compartment assembly.
15. Open glove compartment door and remove six glove compartment to instrument panel attaching screws.
16. Pull glove compartment assembly out a little and disconnect electrical connectors from glove compartment switches.
17. Remove glove compartment assembly from instrument panel.
18. Remove right and left sound insulators, **Fig. 21**.
19. Remove filler trim panel from under steering column by grasping the front and rear edges of the panel and pulling downward.
20. Remove four steering column opening bracket attaching screws.
21. Remove radio attaching screws and pull radio out a little, disconnect radio electrical connectors and antenna.
22. Remove headlamp switch module by pulling firmly on headlamp switch knob.
23. Remove two hood latch release assembly to instrument panel attaching bolts.
24. Place driver's seat in its' full rearward position.
25. Remove steering column upper and lower mounting bolts, then lower steering column.
26. Remove eight instrument panel mounting screws, then disconnect instrument panel electrical connectors, **Fig. 22**.
27. Remove shims at lower mounting screws.
28. With assistance from another technician, remove instrument panel from vehicle.
29. Reverse procedure to install.

PARK AVENUE & 1992–93 LESABRE

1. Disconnect battery ground cable.
2. Refer to **Fig. 23** for dash panel service.

98 & 88

1992–93

Refer to **Fig. 24** when performing this procedure.

1. Remove lower console if necessary.
2. Disconnect connectors from sensors (if equipped).
3. Remove instrument panel trim plates, **Fig. 25.**
4. Remove steering column filler screws from instrument panel, then steering column filler, **Fig. 26.**
5. Remove instrument panel compartment tray by pulling rearward.
6. Remove PRNDL cable and park brake release cable.
7. Remove bolts to instrument panel support brackets and center bracket, then lower steering column.
8. Remove bolts to dash nuts and instrument panel end support bracket, then pull assembly away from dash.
9. Disconnect electrical connectors.
10. Remove antenna coax cable.
11. Remove vacuum line.
12. Remove instrument panel assembly.
13. Reverse procedure to install.

1994

1. **On 88 LSS models**, remove console assembly as follows:
   a. Remove console front compartment assembly, **Fig. 27**
   b. Remove transmission shift knob.
   c. Remove console front compartment assembly.
   d. Remove console rear compartment lower insert.
   e. Remove console assembly attaching nuts.
   f. Disconnect all console electrical connectors.
   g. Remove console assembly from vehicle.
2. **On all models**, remove instrument panel molding by carefully pulling rearward, **Fig. 28**
3. Remove cluster trim plate to instrument panel attaching screws.
4. Tilt top of cluster trim plate rearward, then pull bottom of trim plate rearward.
5. Disconnect HVAC control head and head/park lamp switch connectors.
6. Disconnect HVAC control head vacuum harness connector.
7. Remove HVAC control head by carefully pushing one side outward.
8. Remove head/park lamp switch by carefully pushing one side outward.
9. Remove upper trim pad attaching screws, then the upper trim pad.
10. Remove passenger inflator module attaching bolts, then lift the inflator module and disconnect electrical connector. **Always place inflator module with trim cover up and away from any loose objects.**
11. Remove sound insulator to instrument panel attaching screws and

nuts, **Fig. 29**

12. Pull lefthand sound insulator down and rearward.
13. Disconnect Data Link Connector (DLC).
14. Remove fuse block cover, then separate fuse from sound insulator.
15. Disconnect turn signal flasher, then the courtesy lamp from sound insulator.
16. Pull righthand sound insulator down and rearward.
17. Disconnect courtesy lamp from sound insulator.
18. Remove plastic cap in knee bolster panel near door to access screw, **Fig. 30.**
19. Remove knee bolster to instrument panel attaching screws.
20. Pull knee bolster rearward and remove interior lamp control module.
21. Disconnect traction control/computer command ride switch connector.
22. Disconnect compartment/fuel door release switch connector.
23. Separate air temperature sensor from knee bolster.
24. Remove knee bolster from vehicle.
25. Remove deflector attaching bolts and nuts, then the deflector.
26. **On models with column shift,** disconnect PRNDL cable from steering column.
27. **On all models,** support column and remove two steering column support bracket to instrument panel attaching bolts.
28. Lower steering column. **Cover steering column with protective cloth to prevent any scratches when removing instrument panel.**
29. Remove instrument panel center bracket to dash center support bracket bolts.
30. Remove instrument panel to outer support bracket bolts and nuts, **Fig. 31.**
31. Pull instrument panel assembly away from dash and disconnect electrical connectors.
32. Separate antenna coax cable and vacuum line connector from instrument panel.
33. Remove instrument panel from vehicle.
34. Reverse procedure to install.

TORONADO & TROFEO

1. Disconnect battery ground cable.
2. Turn ignition to the Off position, then remove fuse No. 9 from fuse panel.
3. Remove four left side sound insulator retaining screws.
4. Disconnect courtesy lamp from panel and remove sound insulator from vehicle.
5. Remove four right side sound insulator retaining screws, **Fig. 32.**
6. Disconnect courtesy lamp from panel and remove sound insulator from vehicle.
7. Remove two knee bolster retaining screws, then remove bolster from vehicle, **Fig. 33.**
8. Remove four steering column reinforcement plate retaining screws, then remove plate from vehicle.

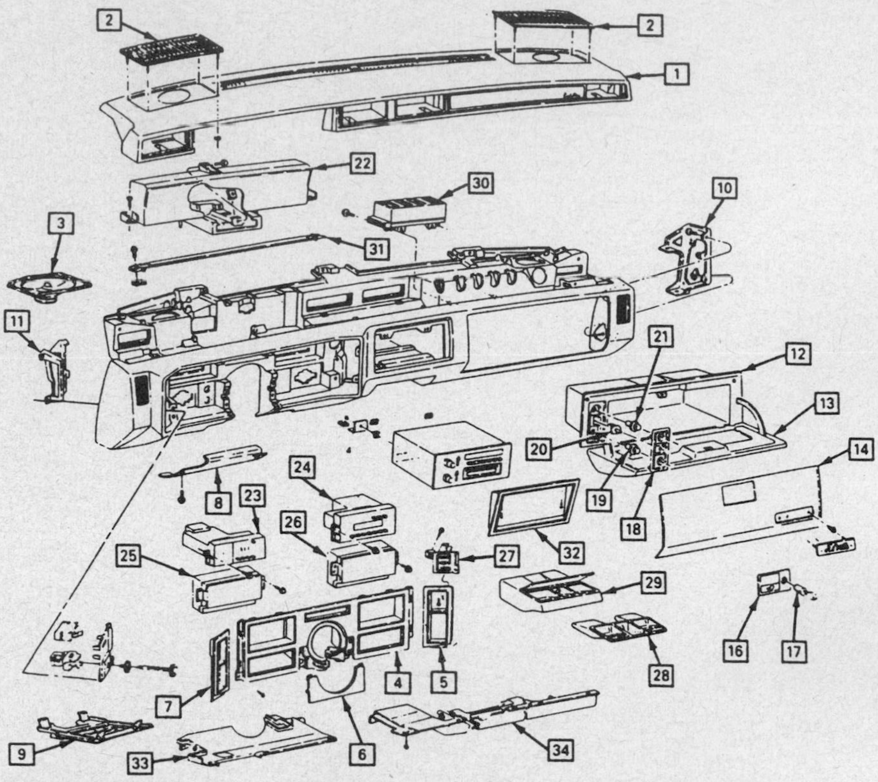

1. PAD ASSEMBLY, INSTRUMENT PANEL (I/P) UPPER TRIM PAD
2. GRILLE, FRONT SPEAKER
3. SPEAKER
4. PLATE, I/P CLUSTER CENTER TRIM
5. PLATE, I/P CLUSTER RIGHT-HAND TRIM
6. FILLER, STEERING COLUMN OPENING UPPER
7. PLATE, I/P CLUSTER LEFT-HAND TRIM
8. FILLER, I/P STEE NG COLUMN OPENING LOWE
9. COVER, FUSE PANEL ACCESS OPENING
10. BRACKET, I/P MOUNTING
11. BRACKET, HEADLIGHT SWITCH
12. BOX, GLOVE COMPARTMENT MODULE
13. PANEL, GLOVE BOX DOOR INNER
14. PANEL, GLOVE BOX DOOR OUTER
15. NAMEPLATE, GLOVE BOX
16. LATCH ASSEMBLY, GLOVE BOX
17. LOCK CYLINDER, GLOVE BOX LATCH ASSEMBLY
18. PLATE, GLOVE BOX SWITCHES
19. SWITCH, FUEL FILLER DOOR RELEASE
20. SWITCH, GLOVE BOX LIGHT
21. SWITCH, REAR DECK LID RELEASE
22. CLUSTER, SPEEDOMETER
23. DISPLAY, FUEL DATA CENTER
24. CONTROL, HEATER AND AIR CONDITIONER (A/C)
25. TELLTALE, LEFT-HAND INFORMATION CENTER
26. TELLTALE, RIGHT-HAND INFORMATION CENTER
27. SWITCH, CRUISE CONTROL ON-OFF
28. TRAY, ASH RECEPTACLE
29. HOUSING, ASHTRAY
30. ALARM, SEAT BELT WARNING, IGNITION KEY AND HEADLAMPS "ON" REMINDER
31. PLATE, I/P SPEEDOMETER CLUSTER
32. PLATE, RADIO TRIM
33. INSULATOR, LEFT-HAND SOUND
34. INSULATOR, RIGHT-HAND SOUND

GC9149100018000X

Fig. 18 Exploded view of I/P. 1992–93 DeVille & Fleetwood (FWD)

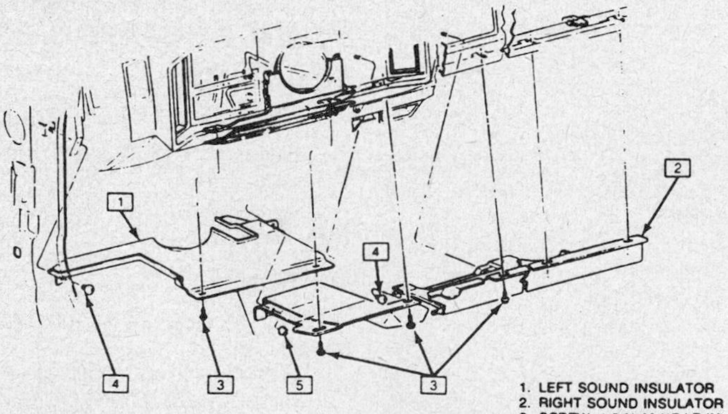

1. LEFT SOUND INSULATOR
2. RIGHT SOUND INSULATOR
3. SCREW; 1.9 N•M (17 LB-IN)
4. NUT
5. NUT; 9.5 N•M (84 LB-IN)

GC9149100019000X

Fig. 19 Insulator sound panel removal. 1992–93 DeVille & Fleetwood (FWD)

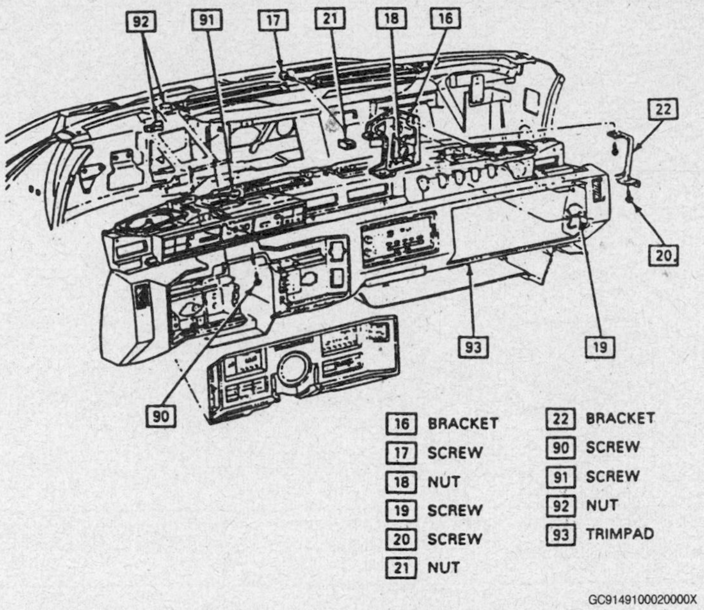
92
91
17
21
18
16
22
20
93
19
90
16 BRACKET
17 SCREW
18 NUT
19 SCREW
20 SCREW
21 NUT
22 BRACKET
90 SCREW
91 SCREW
92 NUT
93 TRIMPAD
GC9149100020000X

Fig. 20 I/P removal. 1992–93 DeVille & Fleetwood (FWD)

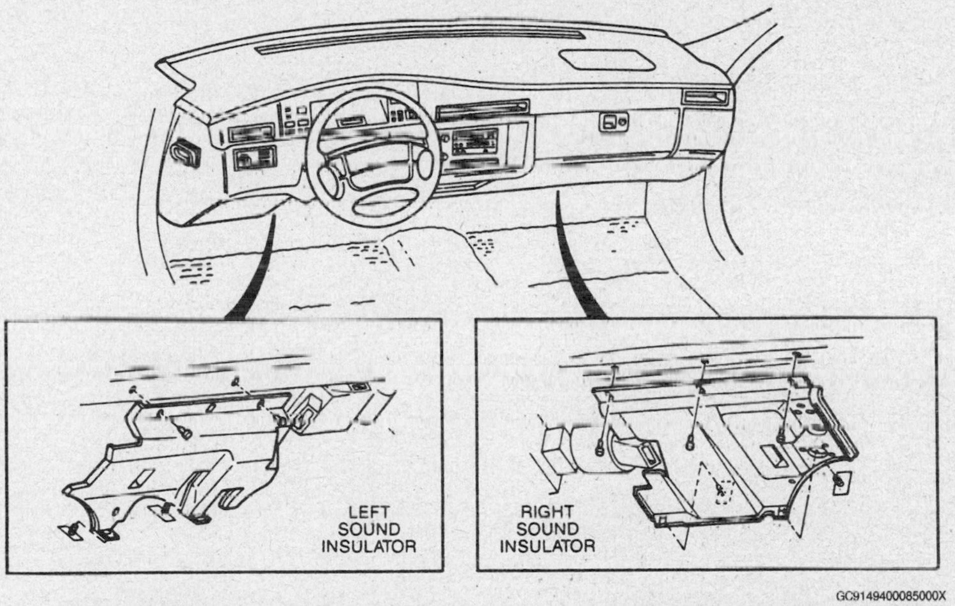
LEFT
SOUND
INSULATOR
RIGHT
SOUND
INSULATOR
GC9149400085000X

Fig. 21 Sound insulator removal. 1994 Concours & DeVille

9. Remove instrument panel cluster trim plate retaining screws, then remove plate from vehicle, **Fig. 34.**
10. Remove right and left side switch assembly retaining screws, then disconnect switch assemblies from electrical connectors and remove from vehicle.
11. Remove instrument panel cluster retaining screws, then pull cluster outward disengaging electrical connector.
12. Remove electronic climate control head retaining screws, if equipped.
13. **On models equipped with integral radio unit,** proceed as follows:
    a. Remove radio/ECC retaining screws.
    b. Remove radio bracket to radio retaining nuts.
    c. Disconnect radio electrical connectors and remove radio from vehicle.
14. **On models equipped with remote radio chassis,** proceed as follows:
    a. Open console storage tray and remove CD, cassette holder or phone handset if equipped.
    b. Remove four T-15 Torx screws.
    c. Remove storage tray liner, then disconnect two seat control electrical connectors and handset connector if equipped.
    d. Open ashtray and remove cigar lighter and ashtray bucket.
    e. Pull console trim plate upward, then disconnect trim plate bulb and cigar lighter electrical connectors.
    f. Remove console trim plate from vehicle.
    g. Remove three 10mm chassis to CRTC bracket retaining nuts.
    h. Disconnect six remote chassis and one coax lead electrical connectors.
15. **On all models,** remove four driver information display to mounting bracket retaining bolts.
16. Disconnect driver information display electrical connector and remove from vehicle.
17. Remove center A/C deflector, then unsnap and remove defroster grille.
18. Remove upper and lower left instrument panel retaining screws.
19. Remove hood release assembly, remaining instrument panel retaining screws and center instrument panel brace.
20. Remove four inflator module retaining screws located on back of steering wheel assembly.
21. Remove position assurance (CPA) and coil assembly connector from inflator module.
22. Remove inflator module from vehicle. **When carrying a live inflator, ensure the bag and trim cover are pointed away in case of accidental deployment. Do not carry inflator module by wires of connector on the underside of the module. Encase of accidental deployment, the bag will then deploy with minimal chance of injury. When placing a live inflator module on a bench or other surface, ensure the bag and trim cover faces in a upward direction. Never rest steering column assembly on the steering wheel with the inflator module face down and column vertical. This is necessary in case of accidental deployment. Otherwise, personal injury may result.**
23. Remove horn contact by pushing slightly and twisting counterclockwise.
24. Remove glove box door and glove box unit retaining screws.
25. Remove lower right instrument panel retaining bolt.
26. Remove fuse box retaining screws.
27. Remove console assembly to floor retaining screws and nuts.
28. Disconnect console electrical connectors and remove console from vehicle.
29. Disconnect instrument panel electrical connectors, then remove instrument panel.
30. Reverse procedure to install.

RIVIERA

1. Disconnect battery ground cable.
2. Turn ignition to the Off position, then remove fuse No. 14 from fuse panel.
3. Remove left side sound insulator retaining screws and nuts, **Fig. 35.**
4. Disconnect courtesy lamp from insulator panel and remove from vehicle.
5. Remove instrument panel cluster trim plate retaining screws, then remove plate from vehicle, **Fig. 36.**
6. Remove center air duct assembly.
7. Remove 13 instrument panel cluster retaining screws, then pull cluster out-

ward from instrument panel, **Fig. 37.**

8. Remove two headlamp switch to instrument panel retaining screws, then disconnect headlamp switch electrical connector and remove from vehicle.
9. Remove four electronic climate control head retaining screws, if equipped.
10. Remove climate control electrical connector then the climate control assembly.
11. **On models equipped with integral radio unit,** proceed as follows:
    a. Remove radio/ECC retaining screws.
    b. Remove radio bracket to radio retaining nuts.
    c. Disconnect radio electrical connectors and remove radio from vehicle.
12. **On models equipped with cassette tape/compact disc,** remove holder from rear console storage compartment.
13. Remove two outer and three inner console trim plate retaining screws, then the trim plate.
14. **On models equipped with CD player,** proceed as follows:
    a. Remove CD trim plate from instrument panel.
    b. Disconnect two CD player electrical connectors accessed through ashtray.
    c. Remove two T-15 Torx retaining screws to CD mounting bracket, then pull player and bracket forward.
    d. Remove two 10mm bracket to CD retaining nuts.
15. **On all models,** remove two front storage compartment retaining screws, then the storage compartment.
16. Remove right side sound insulator retaining screws and nuts.
17. Disconnect courtesy lamp from panel and remove sound insulator from vehicle.
18. Remove six knee bolster retaining screws, then remove bolster from vehicle.
19. Remove four steering column reinforcement plate retaining screws, then remove plate from vehicle.
20. Remove glove box door and glove box unit retaining screws.
21. Remove three upper trim pad retaining screws, then pull trim pad up and out of retaining clips to remove from vehicle, **Fig. 38.**
22. Remove lower left side instrument panel retaining bolt.
23. Remove hood release retaining screws.
24. Remove two instrument panel brace retaining screws, then the brace.
25. Remove four inflator module retaining screws located on back of steering wheel assembly.
26. Remove inflator module from vehicle. **When carrying a live inflator, ensure the bag and trim cover are pointed away in case of accidental deployment. Do not carry inflator module by wires of connector on underside of module. When placing a live inflator module on a bench or other surface, ensure the bag and trim cover faces in a upward direction. Never rest steering column assembly on the steering wheel with the inflator module face down and column vertical. This is necessary in case of accidental deployment. Otherwise, personal injury may result.**
27. Disconnect ignition wiring and multifunction switch electrical connectors.
28. Remove pinch bolt from intermediate shaft.
29. Remove upper and lower steering col-

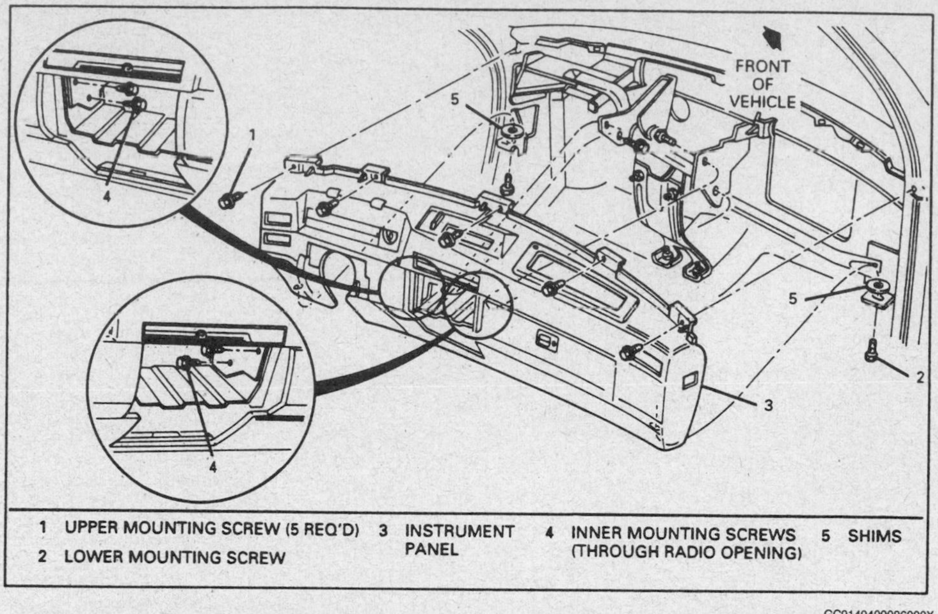
FRONT OF VEHICLE
1
2
3
4
5
1 UPPER MOUNTING SCREW (5 REQ'D)
2 LOWER MOUNTING SCREW
3 INSTRUMENT PANEL
4 INNER MOUNTING SCREWS (THROUGH RADIO OPENING)
5 SHIMS
GC9149400086000X

Fig. 22 Instrument panel removal. 1994 Concours & DeVille

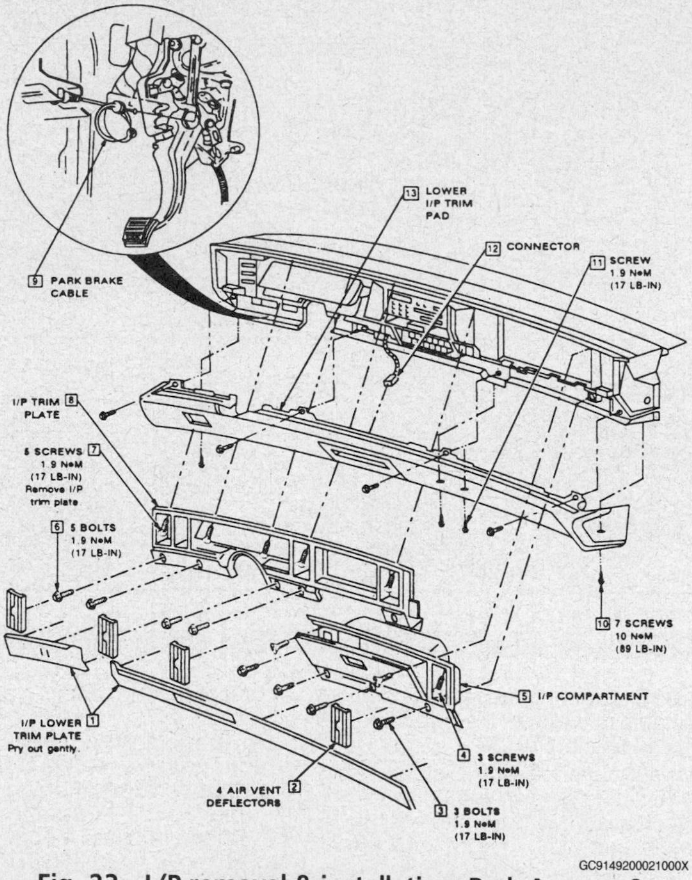
13 LOWER I/P TRIM PAD
12 CONNECTOR
11 SCREW 1.9 N•M (17 LB-IN)
9 PARK BRAKE CABLE
I/P TRIM 8 PLATE
6 SCREWS 7 1.9 N•M (17 LB-IN) Remove I/P trim plate
6 5 BOLTS 1.9 N•M (17 LB-IN)
10 7 SCREWS 10 N•M (89 LB-IN)
5 I/P COMPARTMENT
I/P LOWER 1 TRIM PLATE Pry out gently.
4 3 SCREWS 1.9 N•M (17 LB-IN)
4 AIR VENT 2 DEFLECTORS
3 3 BOLTS 1.9 N•M (17 LB-IN)
GC9149200021000X

Fig. 23 I/P removal & installation. Park Avenue & 1992–94 LeSabre

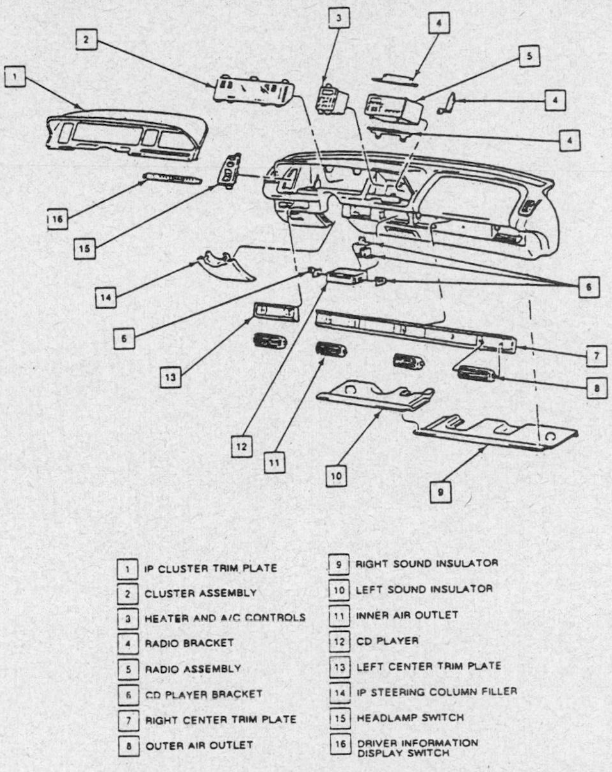
1 IP CLUSTER TRIM PLATE
2 CLUSTER ASSEMBLY
3 HEATER AND A/C CONTROLS
4 RADIO BRACKET
5 RADIO ASSEMBLY
6 CD PLAYER BRACKET
7 RIGHT CENTER TRIM PLATE
8 OUTER AIR OUTLET
9 RIGHT SOUND INSULATOR
10 LEFT SOUND INSULATOR
11 INNER AIR OUTLET
12 CD PLAYER
13 LEFT CENTER TRIM PLATE
14 IP STEERING COLUMN FILLER
15 HEADLAMP SWITCH
16 DRIVER INFORMATION DISPLAY SWITCH
GC9149200022000X

Fig. 24 Exploded view of I/P front. 98 & 1992–93 88

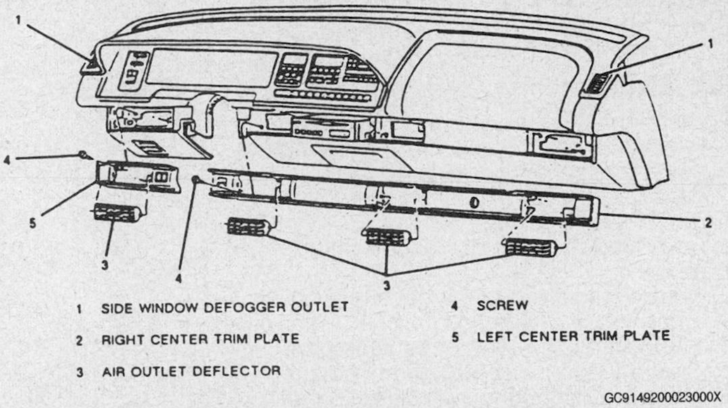
1 SIDE WINDOW DEFOGGER OUTLET
2 RIGHT CENTER TRIM PLATE
3 AIR OUTLET DEFLECTOR
4 SCREW
5 LEFT CENTER TRIM PLATE
GC9149200023000X

Fig. 25 Center trim plate assembly. 98 & 1992–93 88

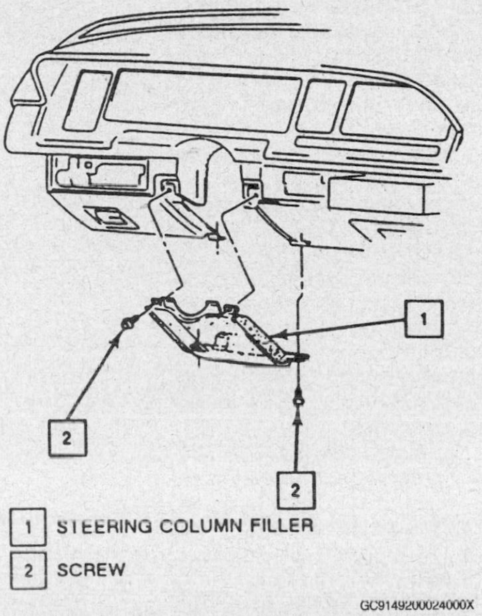
1 STEERING COLUMN FILLER
2 SCREW
GC9149200024000X

Fig. 26 I/P steering column filler. 98 & 1992–93 88

umn support brackets, then remove steering column from vehicle.
30. Remove lower right instrument panel retaining bolt and three upper instrument panel retaining screws.
31. Disconnect instrument panel electrical connectors, then remove instrument panel from vehicle, **Fig. 39.**
32. Reverse procedure to install.

ELDORADO & SEVILLE

1. Disconnect battery ground cable.
2. Remove instrument panel upper trim panel as follows:
   a. Pry defroster grill upward using a small flat bladed tool, then remove, **Fig. 40.**
   b. Disconnect sunload and auto control sensors from defroster grill.
   c. Remove screws retaining upper trim panel through defroster grill opening.
   d. Remove heat and A/C vents from front of instrument panel by gently prying on both sides and pulling out.
   e. Remove screws retaining upper trim panel through vent openings, then the upper trim panel.
3. Remove instrument panel cluster as follows:
   a. Remove ignition and battery fuses from rear compartment fuse panel and ignition fuse from engine compartment fuse panel.
   b. Disconnect two electrical connectors on top of instrument panel.
   c. Remove screws retaining cluster to instrument panel, **Fig. 41.**
   d. **On models with digital cluster,** raise cluster and remove two screws retaining PRNDL mechanism.
   e. **On all models,** remove cluster.
4. Remove right and left A/C vent trim panels.
5. Remove glove compartment as follows:
   a. Open glove compartment door and remove screws retaining glove compartment assembly to instrument panel.
   b. Pull glove compartment out slightly, then disconnect electrical connectors from glove compartment switches.
   c. Remove glove compartment.
6. Remove right and left sound insulators, **Fig. 42.**
7. Remove steering column opening filler trim and bracket, **Fig. 43.**
8. If equipped with full console, remove as follows:
   a. Remove storage compartment by pulling up and out.
   b. Remove shift handle retaining clip and handle, then the console upper trim plate.
   c. Disconnect cigar lighter electrical connector, then remove radio.
   d. Remove gear selector trim plate and PRNDL illumination lamp socket.
   e. Remove shifter plate upper mounting bolts, then the nuts retaining shifter assembly to floor.
   f. Remove nuts retaining console to floor through storage compartment opening.
   g. Disconnect console blower air supply duct, then slide console up and disconnect electrical connectors.
   h. Slide console back to clear shifter, then remove from vehicle.
9. Remove headlamp switch module from instrument panel by pulling outward on switch knob. Disconnect electrical connector.
10. Remove two bolts and hood latch release, then place drivers seat in full rearward position.
11. Remove steering column as described in "Steering Columns" section.
12. Remove screws retaining instrument panel, then disconnect electrical connectors.

13. Remove instrument panel from vehicle, **Fig. 44.**
14. Reverse procedure to install.

CAVALIER

1. Disconnect battery ground cable, then remove three screws from steering column opening filler, **Fig. 45,** and pull downward to disengage clips and remove.
2. Remove left and right sound insulators.
3. Remove instrument panel compartment housing as follows:
   a. Open instrument panel compartment door, **Fig. 46,** then remove screws attaching instrument panel housing to instrument panel.
   b. Pull out housing enough to disconnect rear compartment lid release switch and remove instrument panel compartment light and right courtesy lamp.
   c. Remove instrument panel compartment housing.
4. Remove console assembly, then the convenience center, **Fig. 47.**
5. Disconnect forward lamp and engine electrical harnesses from bulkhead connector.
6. Remove two corner instrument panel retaining screws, and one screw to instrument panel brace at left side of instrument panel opening, **Fig. 48.**
7. Remove defroster grilles, then the upper retaining screws located in defroster duct openings.
8. Remove steering column as described in "Steering Columns" section.
9. Pull instrument panel assembly out enough to disconnect all electrical connectors and vacuum lines.
10. Remove instrument panel assembly with electrical harness attached.
11. If necessary, remove electrical harness assembly.
12. Reverse procedure to install.

SUNBIRD

1. Disconnect battery ground cable, then remove left and right sound insulators.
2. Remove steering column opening filler by gently prying out.
3. Remove retaining screws and/or nut, then the right and left instrument panel trim plates. **It may be necessary to loosen righthand console housing bracket.**
4. Remove console housing as follows:
   a. Remove side panels by prying outward, then pull rearward to remove accessory trim plate.
   b. Remove console bracket to instrument panel nuts, housing to console bracket screws, then the housing assembly.
5. Remove instrument panel compartment/door as follows:
   a. Open instrument panel compartment door, then gently pull out compartment/door until retaining pins on door unsnap from their retainers.
   b. Unsnap instrument panel compartment strap from instrument panel center support, then remove instrument panel compartment/door.
6. Remove heater and A/C control, then the convenience center, **Fig. 49.**
7. Disconnect forward lamp and engine electrical harnesses from bulkhead connector.
8. Remove bulkhead from cowl, then the hood release handle.
9. Remove defroster grilles, then the upper instrument panel retaining screws located in defroster duct openings.
10. Remove two lower corner instrument panel retaining nuts, and one screw to instrument panel brace at left side of instrument panel opening.
11. Remove two nuts securing electrical harness to neutral start switch, if necessary, then the three steering column retaining bolts and lower column.
12. Pull instrument panel assembly out enough to disconnect all electrical connectors and vacuum lines.
13. Remove instrument panel assembly with electrical harness attached.
14. If necessary, remove electrical harness assembly.
15. Reverse procedure to install.

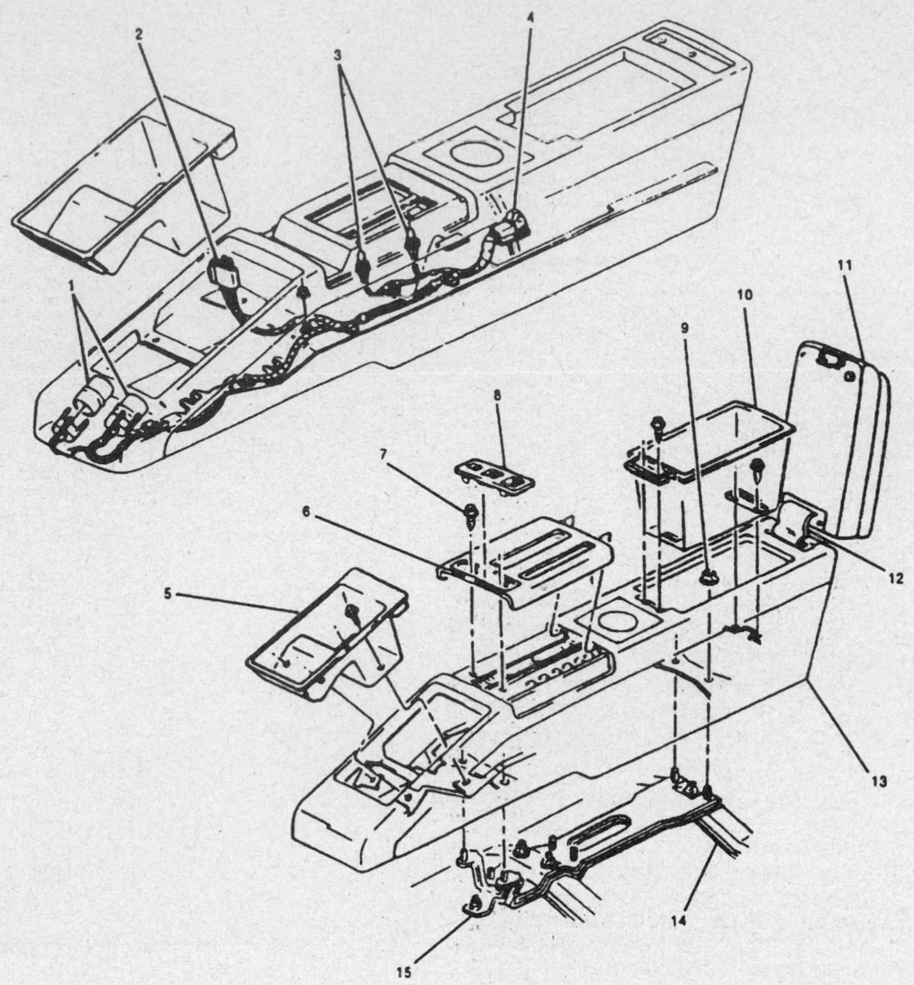
1
2
3
4
5
6
7
8
9
10
11
12
13
14
15

1 AUXILIARY POWER OUTLETS
2 CONNECTOR TO IP HARNESS
3 PRNDL LAMPS
4 CONNECTOR TO SHIFT INTERLOCK SOLENOID
5 CONSOLE FRONT COMPARTMENT ASSEMBLY
6 TRANS SHIFT OPENING TRIM PLATE
7 SCREW: 1.9 N·m (17 LB-IN)
8 COIN HOLDER ASSEMBLY
9 NUT: 10 N·m (88 LB-IN)
10 CONSOLE REAR COMPARTMENT INSERT
11 CONSOLE REAR COMPARTMENT DOOR
12 CONSOLE REAR COMPARTMENT DOOR HINGE
13 CONSOLE ASSEMBLY
14 UNDERBODY ASSEMBLY
15 CONSOLE BRACKET ASSEMBLY

GC9149400087000X

Fig. 27 Console assembly. 1994 88 LSS

BERETTA & CORSICA

Refer to **Fig. 50** when performing this procedure.

1. Disconnect battery ground cable.
2. Remove sound insulators and left speaker panel.
3. Disconnect electrical connectors.
4. Remove knee bolster and bulkhead.
5. Disconnect electrical connectors to brake switches and clutch pedal switches.
6. Remove heater and A/C control, then radio.
7. Remove defroster grille, then screws to cowl through defroster duct.

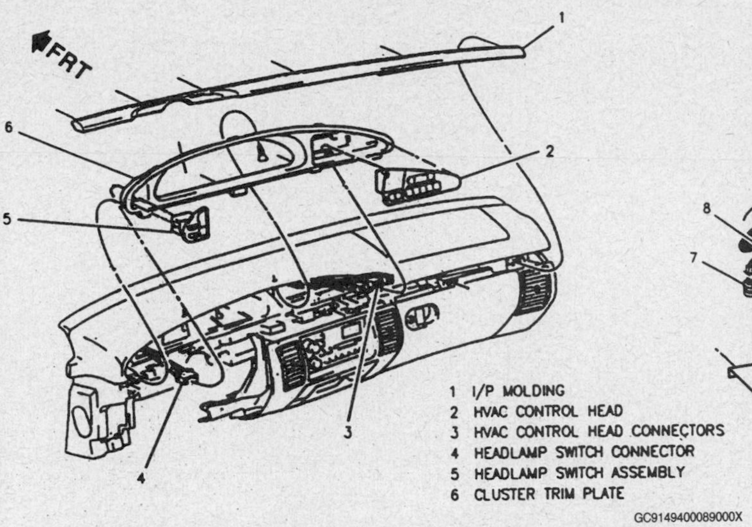
FRT
1 I/P MOLDING
2 HVAC CONTROL HEAD
3 HVAC CONTROL HEAD CONNECTORS
4 HEADLAMP SWITCH CONNECTOR
5 HEADLAMP SWITCH ASSEMBLY
6 CLUSTER TRIM PLATE
GC9149400089000X

Fig. 28 Cluster trim plate removal. 1994 88 & 98

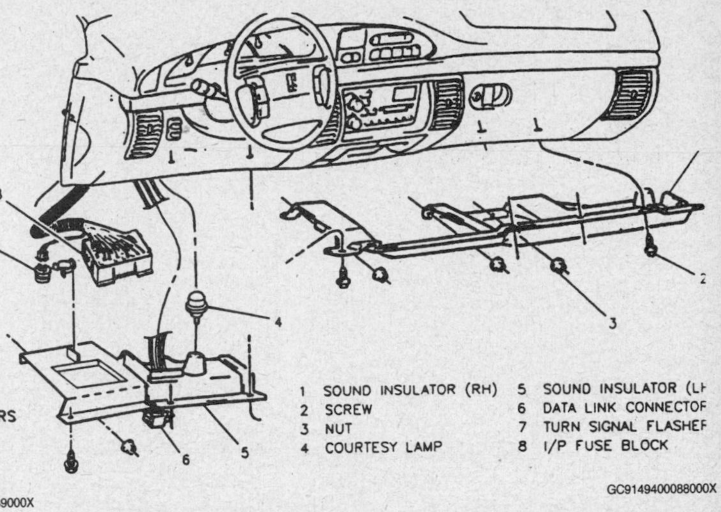
1 SOUND INSULATOR (RH)
2 SCREW
3 NUT
4 COURTESY LAMP
5 SOUND INSULATOR (LH
6 DATA LINK CONNECTOR
7 TURN SIGNAL FLASHER
8 I/P FUSE BLOCK
GC9149400088000X

Fig. 29 Sound insulator removal. 1994 88 & 98

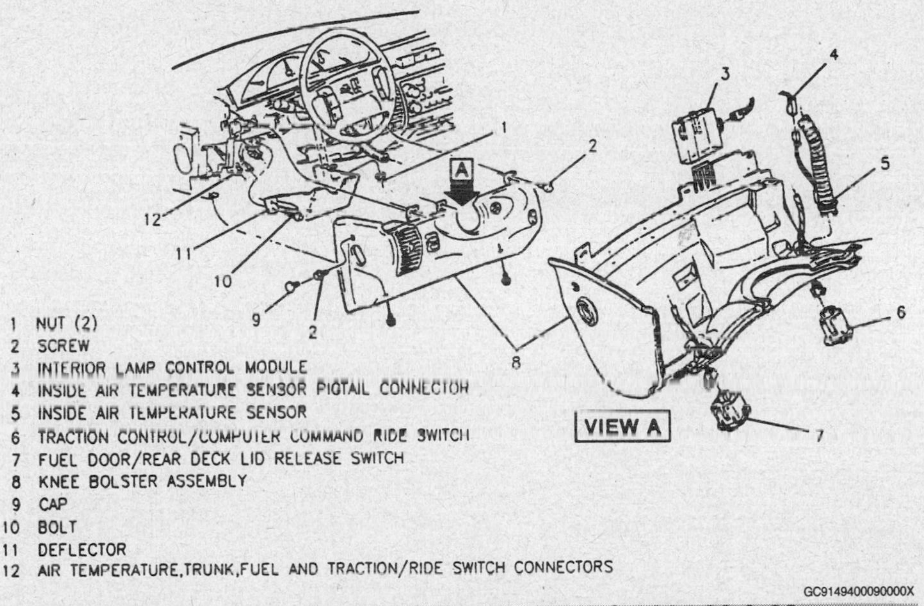
A
VIEW A
1 NUT (2)
2 SCREW
3 INTERIOR LAMP CONTROL MODULE
4 INSIDE AIR TEMPERATURE SENSOR PIGTAIL CONNECTOR
5 INSIDE AIR TEMPERATURE SENSOR
6 TRACTION CONTROL/COMPUTER COMMAND RIDE SWITCH
7 FUEL DOOR/REAR DECK LID RELEASE SWITCH
8 KNEE BOLSTER ASSEMBLY
9 CAP
10 BOLT
11 DEFLECTOR
12 AIR TEMPERATURE,TRUNK,FUEL AND TRACTION/RIDE SWITCH CONNECTORS
GC9149400090000X

Fig. 30 Knee bolster & deflector removal. 1994 88 & 98

8. Remove lower left nut, left support screw, the instrument panel compartment.
9. Disconnect electrical connectors: DERM, body harness and arming sensor.
10. Remove right support screw and lower right nut.
11. Lower steering column, then disconnect electrical connections.
12. Remove instrument panel from cowl.
13. Reverse procedure to install.

ACHIEVA & SKYLARK

1. Disconnect battery ground cable, then remove center instrument panel trim plate, radio and heater and A/C control.
2. Remove left instrument panel trim plate, then the instrument panel compartment.
3. Remove screw to brace in left side of instrument panel compartment, then disconnect 26 way body connector.
4. Remove left sound insulator, then the bulkhead.
5. Remove defroster grille, then the steering column filler.
6. Remove screw to left brace, lower instrument panel screws, then the console.
7. Remove steering column upper and lower covers, then disconnect electrical connectors on column.
8. Remove steering column bolts, then lower column and allow to rest on seat.
9. Disconnect electrical connectors to brake switches, then remove remaining screws through defroster duct.
10. Remove instrument panel from vehicle, **Fig. 51 and 52.**
11. Reverse procedure to install.

GRAND AM

1. Disconnect battery ground cable, then remove left sound insulator.
2. Remove steering column filler, drivers side air deflectors, then the instrument panel cover.
3. Remove left instrument panel trim plate, then the upper and lower instrument panel compartments.
4. Remove radio and heater and A/C control.
5. Remove defroster grille, then the upper instrument panel screw covers and screws.
6. Disconnect brake switches, then remove bulkhead.
7. Remove steering column upper and lower covers, steering column bolts, then lower column and allow to rest

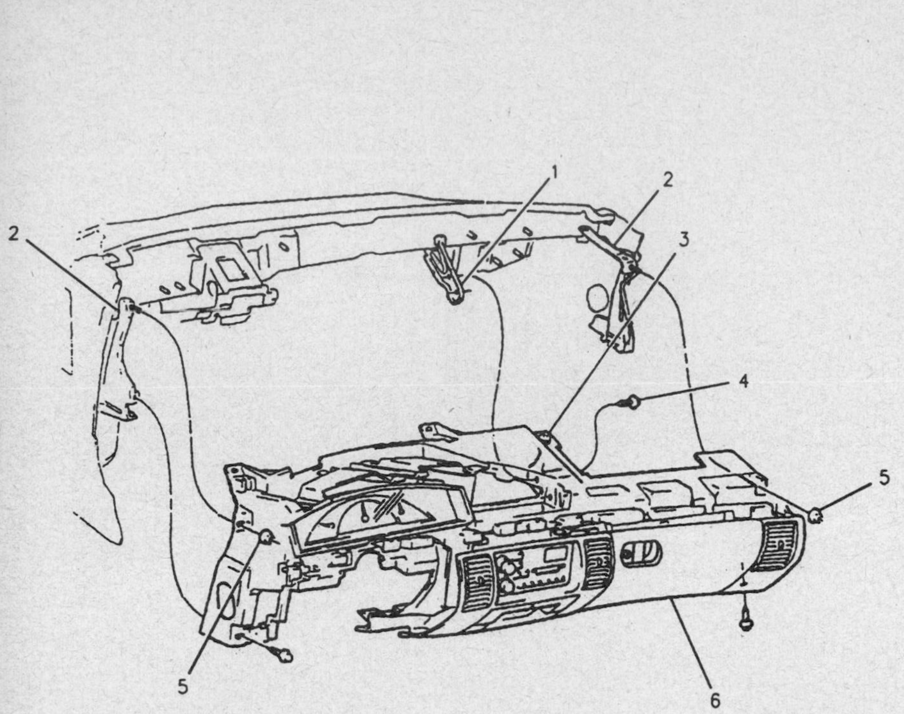
1
2
3
2
4
5
5
6

1 DASH CENTER SUPPORT BRACKET
2 I/P OUTER SUPPORT BRACKET
3 I/P CENTER SUPPORT BRACKET
4 BOLT (2)
5 NUT
6 I/P ASSEMBLY

GC9149400091000X

Fig. 31 Instrument panel removal. 1994 88 & 98

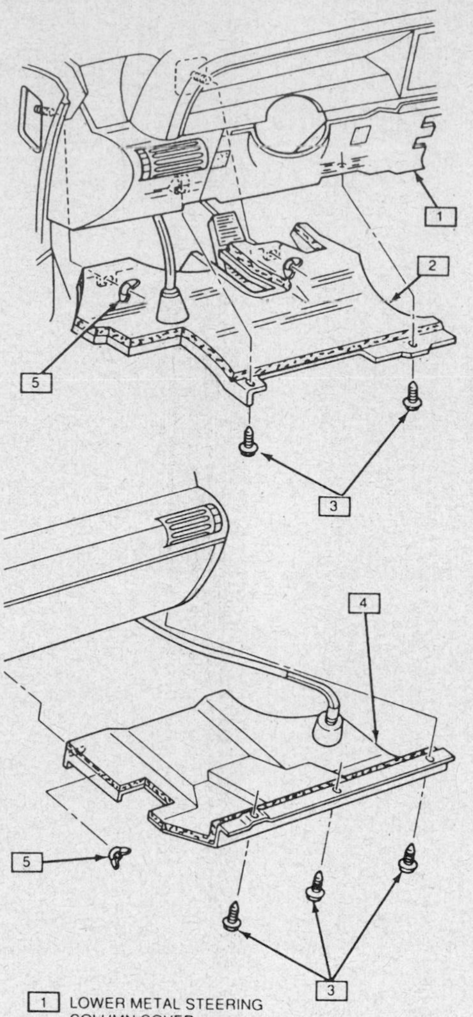
1
2
5
3
4
5
3

1 LOWER METAL STEERING COLUMN COVER
2 LEFT-SIDE SOUND INSULATOR
3 SCREWS
4 RIGHT-SIDE SOUND INSULATOR
5 WING NUTS

GC9149100025000X

Fig. 32 Sound insulators removal. Toronado/Trofeo

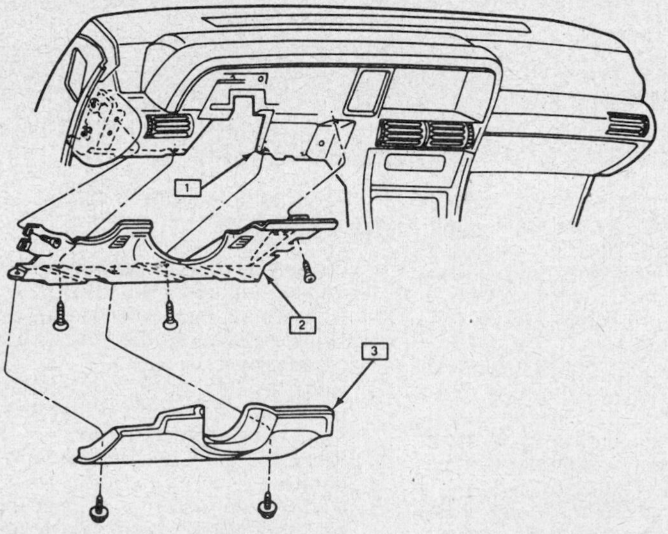
1
2
3

1 I/P PAD
2 I/P STEERING COLUMN REINFORCEMENT PLATE
3 KNEE BOLSTER

GC9149100026000X

Fig. 33 Knee bolster removal. Toronado/Trofeo

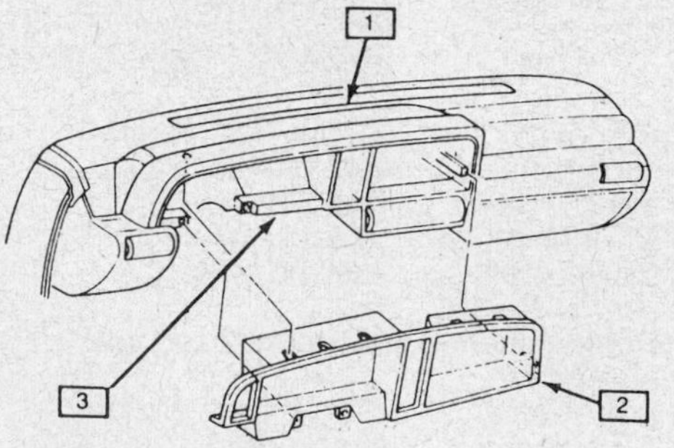
1
3
2

1 I/P PAD
2 I/P CLUSTER TRIM PLATE
3 I/P CLUSTER HOUSING (CLUSTER REMOVED)

GC9149100027000X

Fig. 34 I/P cluster trim plate removal. Toronado/Trofeo

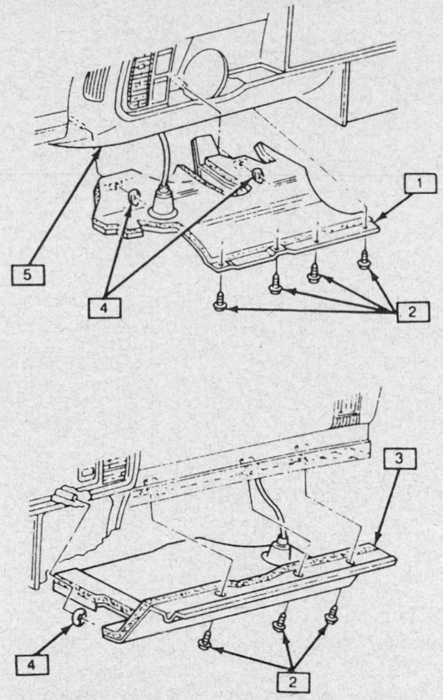
1
2
3
4
5
2
1 LEFT-SIDE SOUND INSULATOR
2 SCREWS
3 RIGHT-SIDE SOUND INSULATOR
4 WING NUTS
5 KNEE BOLSTER
GC9149100028000X

Fig. 35 I/P sound insulator removal. Riviera

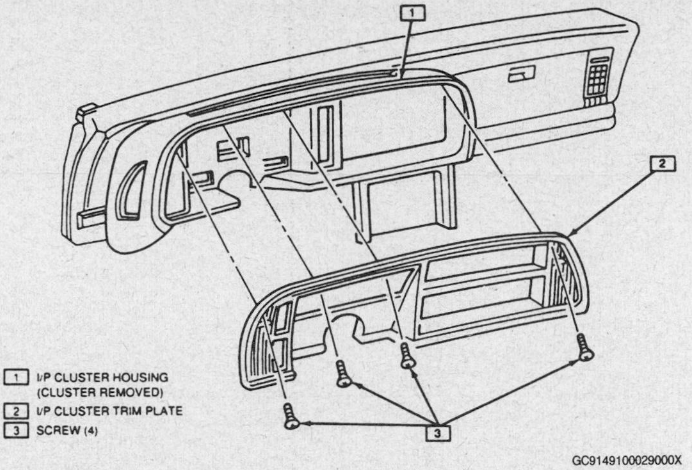
1
2
3
1 I/P CLUSTER HOUSING (CLUSTER REMOVED)
2 I/P CLUSTER TRIM PLATE
3 SCREW (4)
GC9149100029000X

Fig. 36 I/P cluster trim plate removal. Riviera

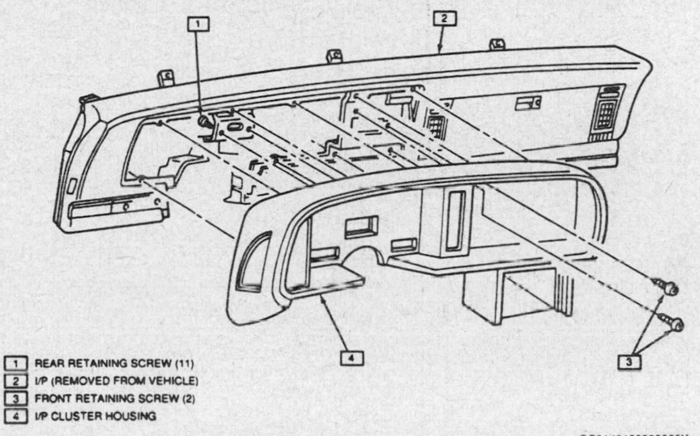
1
2
3
4
1 REAR RETAINING SCREW (11)
2 I/P (REMOVED FROM VEHICLE)
3 FRONT RETAINING SCREW (2)
4 I/P CLUSTER HOUSING
GC9149100030000X

Fig. 37 I/P cluster housing removal. Riviera

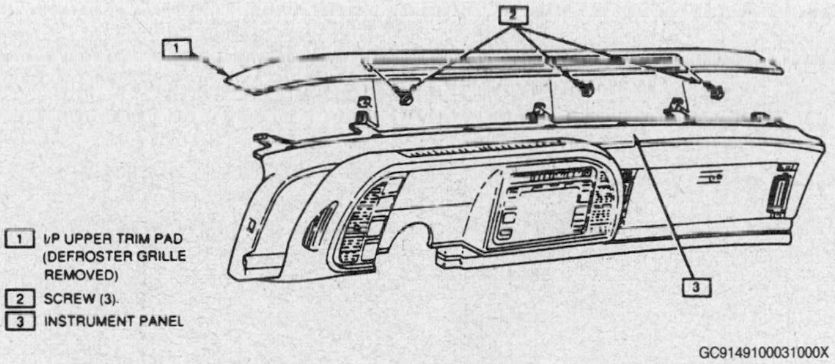
1
2
3
1 I/P UPPER TRIM PAD (DEFROSTER GRILLE REMOVED)
2 SCREW (3)
3 INSTRUMENT PANEL
GC9149100031000X

Fig. 38 I/P trim pad assembly removal. Riviera

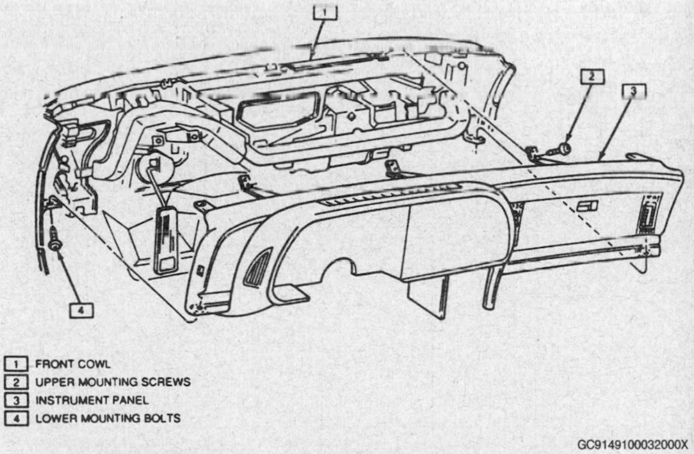
1
2
3
4
1 FRONT COWL
2 UPPER MOUNTING SCREWS
3 INSTRUMENT PANEL
4 LOWER MOUNTING BOLTS
GC9149100032000X

Fig. 39 I/P assembly removal. Riviera

on seat.

8. Remove right center support screw at left of instrument panel compartment opening, then the right sound insulator.
9. Disconnect 23 way electrical connector.
10. Remove lower instrument panel screws, then the instrument panel from vehicle, **Fig. 53.**
11. Reverse procedure to install.

CAMARO & FIREBIRD

1992

1. Disconnect battery ground cable.
2. Remove shifter handle and seven shift gate trim plate attaching screws.
3. Remove radio and A/C heater controller trim plate.
4. Remove A/C heater controller attaching screws, then pull controller rearward and disconnect electrical connections, vacuum connections and remove heater control cable.
5. Remove four radio retaining screws, then pull radio rearward and disconnect the power, speaker and antenna connectors.
6. Disconnect all console electrical connectors.
7. Remove six console hold-down and two console to instrument panel screws and remove console.
8. Remove instrument panel trim pad and hush panels, **Figs. 54 through 57.**
9. Remove right and left lower instrument panel covers and trim plates, **Fig. 58 and 59.**
10. Remove six instrument cluster attachment screws, then pull cluster back and disconnect speedometer cable and electrical connections.

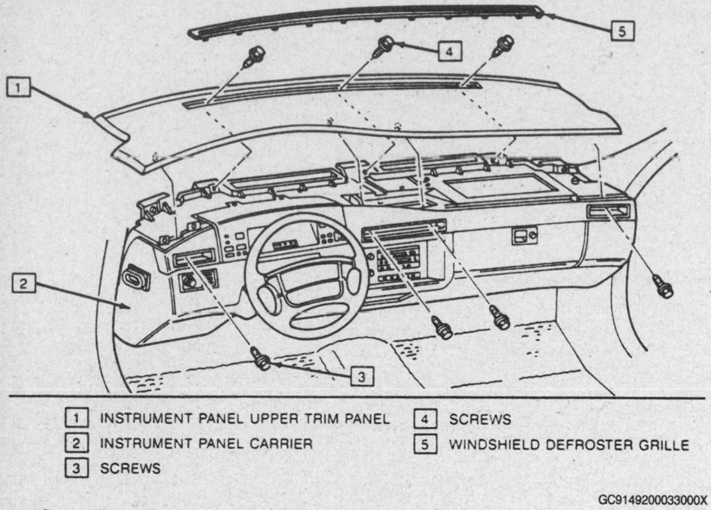
1 INSTRUMENT PANEL UPPER TRIM PANEL
2 INSTRUMENT PANEL CARRIER
3 SCREWS
4 SCREWS
5 WINDSHIELD DEFROSTER GRILLE
GC9149200033000X

Fig. 40 Upper trim panel removal. Eldorado & Seville

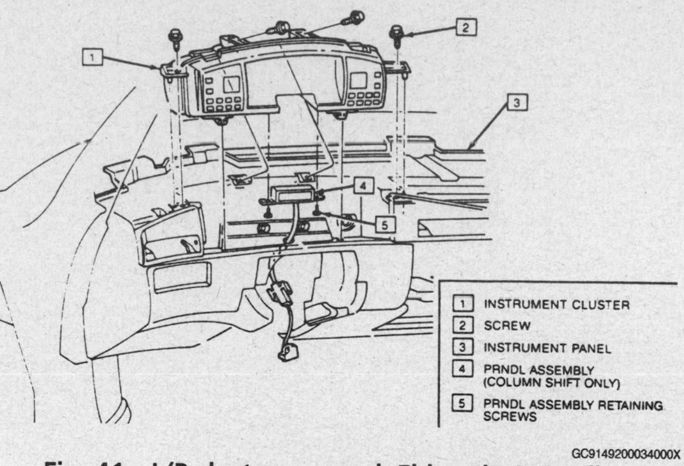
1 INSTRUMENT CLUSTER
2 SCREW
3 INSTRUMENT PANEL
4 PRNDL ASSEMBLY (COLUMN SHIFT ONLY)
5 PRNDL ASSEMBLY RETAINING SCREWS
GC9149200034000X

Fig. 41 I/P cluster removal. Eldorado & Seville

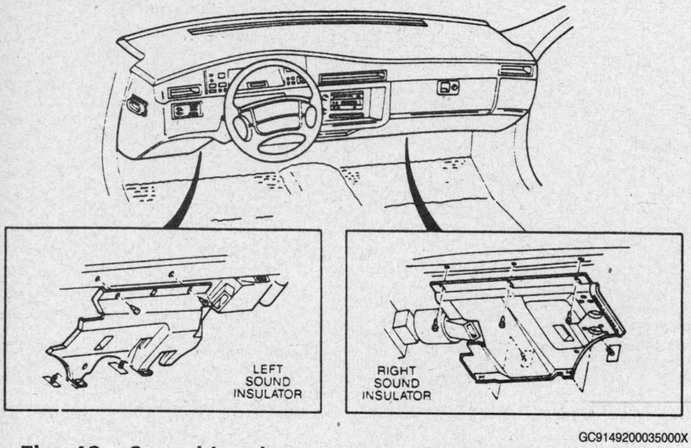
LEFT SOUND INSULATOR
RIGHT SOUND INSULATOR
GC9149200035000X

Fig. 42 Sound insulators removal. Eldorado & Seville

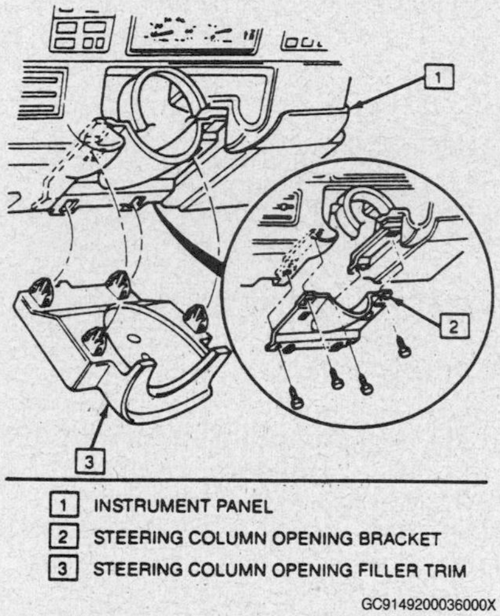
1 INSTRUMENT PANEL
2 STEERING COLUMN OPENING BRACKET
3 STEERING COLUMN OPENING FILLER TRIM
GC9149200036000X

Fig. 43 Steering column opening bracket & filler trim removal. Eldorado & Seville

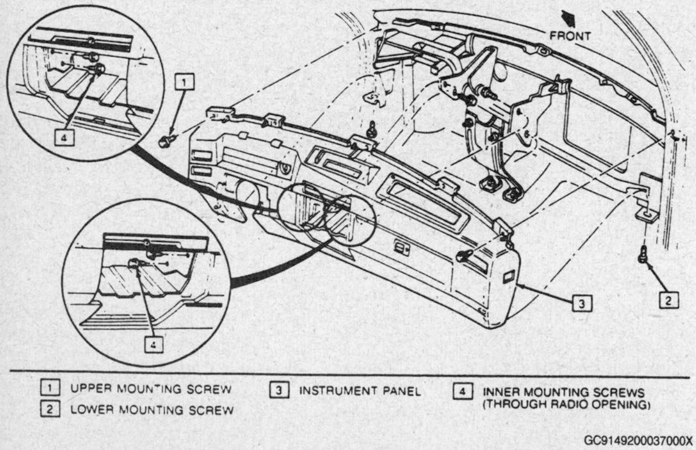
FRONT
1 UPPER MOUNTING SCREW
2 LOWER MOUNTING SCREW
3 INSTRUMENT PANEL
4 INNER MOUNTING SCREWS (THROUGH RADIO OPENING)
GC9149200037000X

Fig. 44 I/P removal. Eldorado & Seville

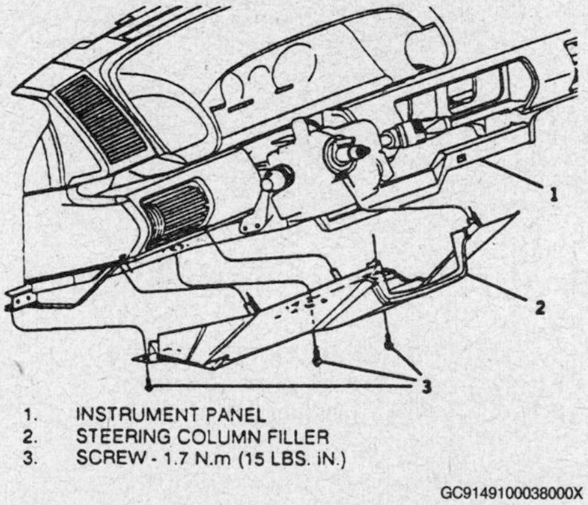
1. INSTRUMENT PANEL
2. STEERING COLUMN FILLER
3. SCREW - 1.7 N.m (15 LBS. IN.)
GC9149100038000X

Fig. 45 Steering column opening filler removal. Cavalier

11. Remove headlight switch assembly.
12. Lower the steering column, then remove five upper and six lower instrument panel carrier to cowl screws.
13. Disconnect instrument panel electrical harness at bulkhead connector and under dash.
14. Remove instrument panel carrier, **Fig. 60.**
15. Reverse procedure to install.

1993–94

1. Remove both sound insulator assemblies, **Fig. 61.**
2. Remove removable top assembly, then window rail trim panel assembly.
3. Remove knee bolster assembly and deflector**Fig. 62.**
4. Remove stop lamp switch before lowering steering column. **Failure to remove stop lamp switch before lowering steering column may cause the switch to be damaged or thrown out of adjustment resulting in a malfunctioning switch or premature brake failure.**
5. Lower steering column.
6. Remove trim panel and trim plate assemblies.
7. Remove bezel and instrument cluster

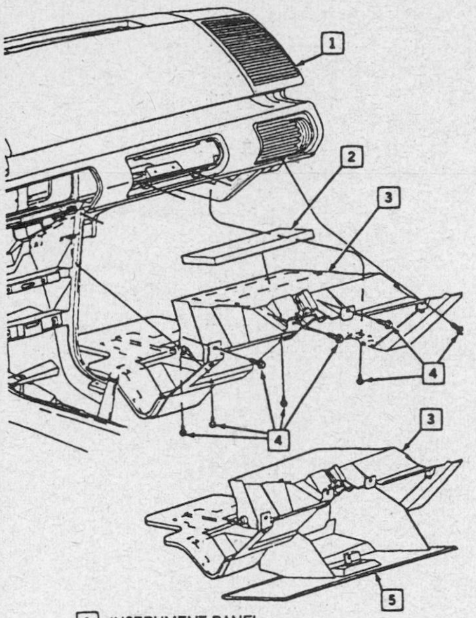

1 INSTRUMENT PANEL
2 INSULATOR
3 I.P. COMPARTMENT HOUSING
4 SCREW - 2 N.m (19 LBS. IN.)
5 I.P. COMPARTMENT DOOR

GC9149100039000X

Fig. 46 I/P compartment housing removal. Cavalier

assemblies.

8. Remove radio and temperature control assemblies.
9. Remove left side duct assemblies.
10. Remove transmission gear shift knob, cover and console assemblies.
11. Remove fuse block, then disconnect assembly line data link connector (ALDL).
12. Remove hazard and chime assembly.
13. Remove upper bolts and screws, lower nuts and reposition carrier.
14. Remove air duct and audio alarm assemblies.
15. Disconnect wiring harness from carrier, then remove carrier, **Fig. 63.**
16. Reverse procedure to install.

BONNEVILLE

1. **On models with center console,** remove console as follows:
   a. Remove transaxle control lever handle, **Fig. 64,**
   b. Remove ashtray, then the screws under ashtray.
   c. Carefully pry up console center trim plate, then rotate trim plate back.
   d. Remove trans lever and console bracket bolts.
   e. Open armrest bin lid and remove bin lower trim plate by lifting tab.
   f. Remove lower console to floor stud nuts.
   g. Remove front lower console vent clip, **Fig. 65.**
   h. Disconnect electrical connectors and remove lower console.
   i. Remove automatic transmission control assembly, release cables and automatic transmission cable bracket.
2. **On all models,** remove instrument panel trim plate, **Fig. 66.**
3. Remove steering column filler panel from under steering column.
4. Remove steering column support bracket to instrument panel attaching bolts and lower steering column.
5. Remove glove compartment insert retaining screws, then the insert.
6. Carefully pry defroster grill out of instrument panel.
7. Remove instrument panel attaching screws through defroster grill opening.
8. Remove steering column support bracket brace attaching bolts.
9. Remove instrument panel to dash panel attaching bolts.
10. Remove instrument panel to instrument panel support bracket attaching bolts.
11. Remove steering column support bracket bolts.
12. Disconnect instrument panel electrical connectors, including antenna coax cable.
13. Disconnect aspirator hose, then remove instrument panel.
14. Reverse procedure to install.

REGAL

Refer to **Fig. 67,** when performing this procedure.

1. Disconnect battery ground cable.
2. Remove speaker grilles by prying carefully at edge of grille.
3. Remove one instrument panel pad cover retaining screw from under each speaker grille.
4. Remove five screws under lower edge of instrument panel pad.
5. Remove pad by lifting front, pulling rearward to release, then lifting up and out.
6. Remove two speaker retaining bolts, then disconnect electrical connectors and remove speakers.
7. Remove one cluster trim plate retaining bolt on left side, then the trim plate.
8. Remove electrical connectors, then six cluster retaining bolts and the cluster.
9. With glove box open, remove gasket from around air outlet.
10. Remove two screws behind gasket, then open fuse block cover.
11. Remove two glove box retaining screws, located on the left side of glove box.
12. Disconnect electrical connector, then remove glove box.
13. Remove three bolts holding right side sound insulator.
14. Remove insulator by pushing towards front of car, then pulling down.
15. Remove four ventilation control assembly retaining bolts, then the control assembly and connectors.
16. Remove bolts securing radio, then the radio and connectors.
17. Remove bolts securing English/Metric switch, then the switch.
18. Remove bolts securing headlight switch, then the switch.
19. Remove four cassette player retaining bolts, then pulling unit rearward, disconnect electrical connectors.

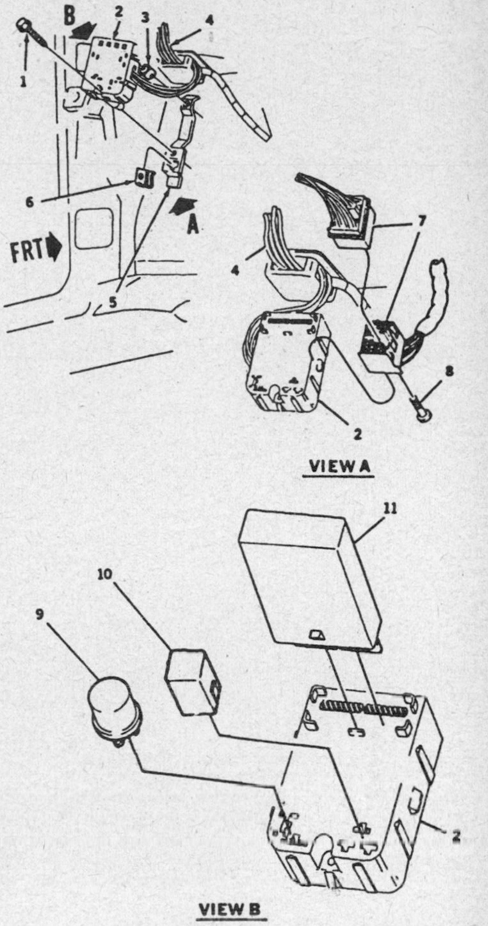
FRT
VIEW A
VIEW B

1. SCREW - 2 N.m (19 LBS. IN.)
2. CONVENIENCE CENTER
3. RETAINER
4. I/P HARNESS
5. BRACKET
6. NUT
7. I/P HARNESS CONNECTOR
8. BOLT - 7 N.m (62 LBS. IN.)
9. FLASHER ASM. HAZARD
10. HORN RELAY
11. MULTI-FUNCTION ALARM

GC9149100040000X

Fig. 47 Convenience center removal. Cavalier & Sunbird

20. Remove ashtray and bracket.
21. Remove two ALDL connector retaining bolts, then lower ALDL connector.
22. Remove two parking brake retaining bolts, then lower lever and pull to the right.
23. Remove bolt holding right side courtesy light, then disconnect electrical connector.
24. Remove two radio receiver retaining bolts, then the receiver, electrical and antenna connectors.
25. Remove one nut and two screws holding left side sound insulator.
26. Remove four steering column trim cover retaining screws, then the cover.
27. Remove four steering column retaining bolts, lower steering column.
28. Remove seven instrument panel carrier assembly retaining bolts, five at top and two at bottom.
29. Remove two carrier assembly retain-

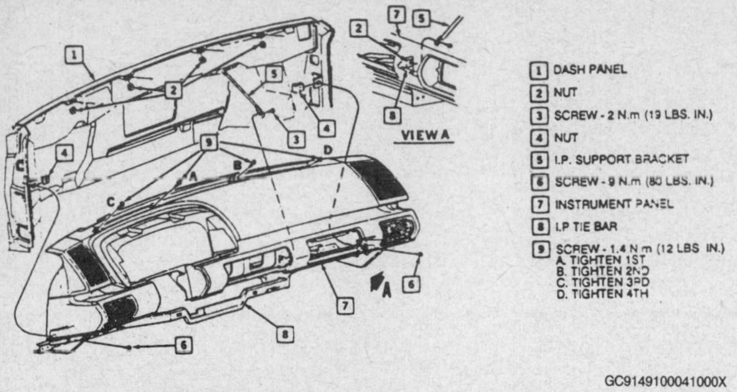
VIEW A
1 DASH PANEL
2 NUT
3 SCREW - 2 N.m (19 LBS. IN.)
4 NUT
5 I.P. SUPPORT BRACKET
6 SCREW - 9 N.m (80 LBS. IN.)
7 INSTRUMENT PANEL
8 I.P TIE BAR
9 SCREW - 1.4 N m (12 LBS IN.)
A. TIGHTEN 1ST
B. TIGHTEN 2ND
C. TIGHTEN 3RD
D. TIGHTEN 4TH
GC9149100041000X

Fig. 48 I/P removal. Cavalier

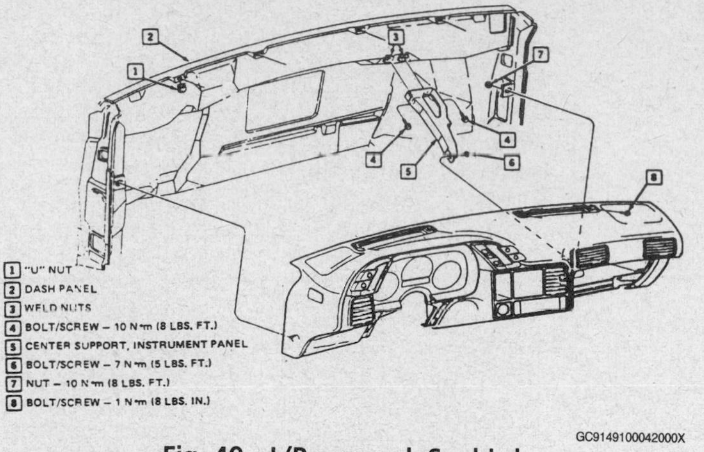
1 "U" NUT
2 DASH PANEL
3 WELD NUTS
4 BOLT/SCREW – 10 N·m (8 LBS. FT.)
5 CENTER SUPPORT, INSTRUMENT PANEL
6 BOLT/SCREW – 7 N·m (5 LBS. FT.)
7 NUT – 10 N·m (8 LBS. FT.)
8 BOLT/SCREW – 1 N·m (8 LBS. IN.)
GC9149100042000X

Fig. 49 I/P removal. Sunbird

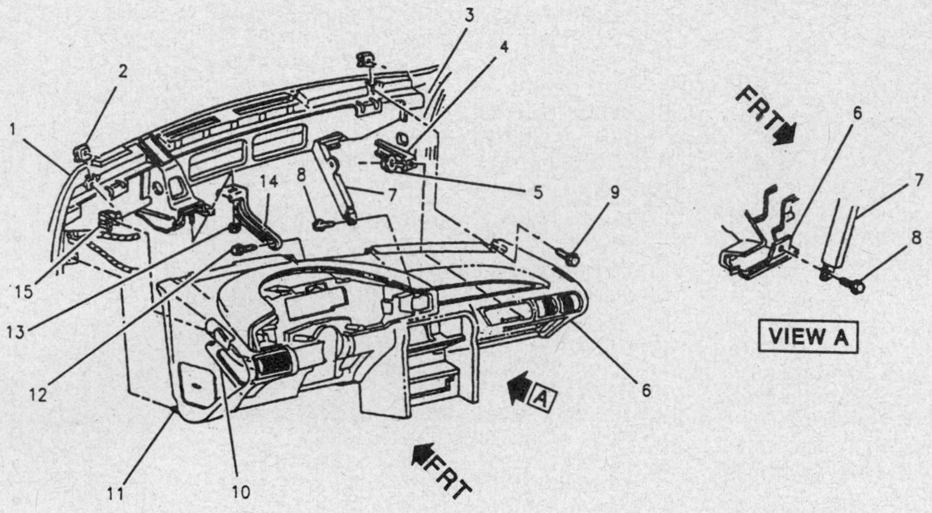
FRT
VIEW A
A
FRT

1 DASH PANEL
2 CLAMP-ON NUT
3 BODY LOCK PILLAR
4 SUPPORT
5 NUT
6 INSTRUMENT PANEL PAD
7 RIGHT REINFORCEMENT
8 BOLT
9 BOLT TO I/P
10 KNEE BOLSTER SUPPORT
11 MOUNTING BOLT
12 BOLT
13 NUT TO COLUMN
14 LEFT CENTER BRACE
15 KNEE BOLSTER BRACKET

GC9149200043000X

Fig. 50 Instrument panel assembly. Beretta & Corsica

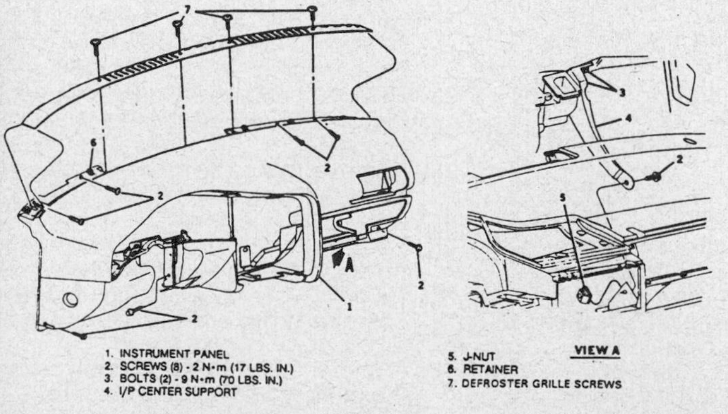
VIEW A
1. INSTRUMENT PANEL
2. SCREWS (8) - 2 N·m (17 LBS. IN.)
3. BOLTS (2) - 9 N·m (70 LBS. IN.)
4. I/P CENTER SUPPORT
5. J-NUT
6. RETAINER
7. DEFROSTER GRILLE SCREWS
GC9149100044000X

Fig. 51 I/P removal. Achieva

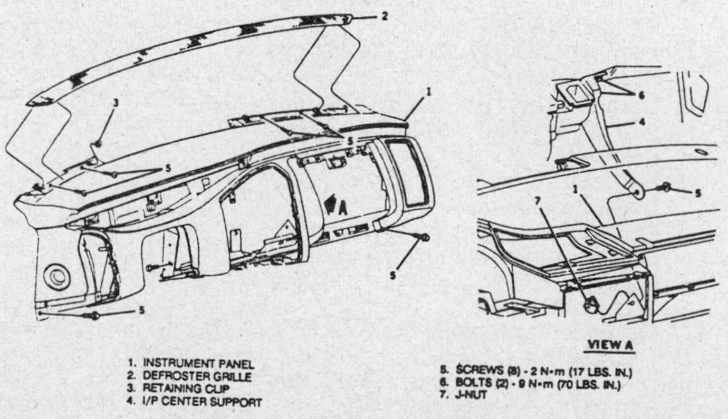
VIEW A
1. INSTRUMENT PANEL
2. DEFROSTER GRILLE
3. RETAINING CLIP
4. I/P CENTER SUPPORT
5. SCREWS (8) - 2 N·m (17 LBS. IN.)
6. BOLTS (2) - 9 N·m (70 LBS. IN.)
7. J-NUT
GC9149200045000X

Fig. 52 I/P removal. Skylark

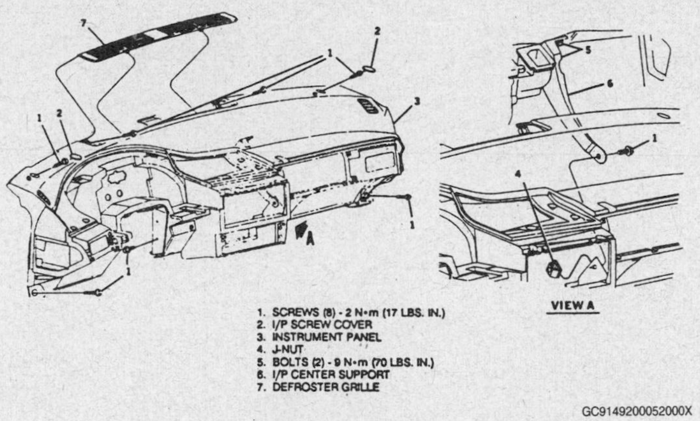
VIEW A
1. SCREWS (8) - 2 N·m (17 LBS. IN.)
2. I/P SCREW COVER
3. INSTRUMENT PANEL
4. J-NUT
5. BOLTS (2) - 9 N·m (70 LBS. IN.)
6. I/P CENTER SUPPORT
7. DEFROSTER GRILLE
GC9149200052000X

Fig. 53 I/P removal. Grand Am

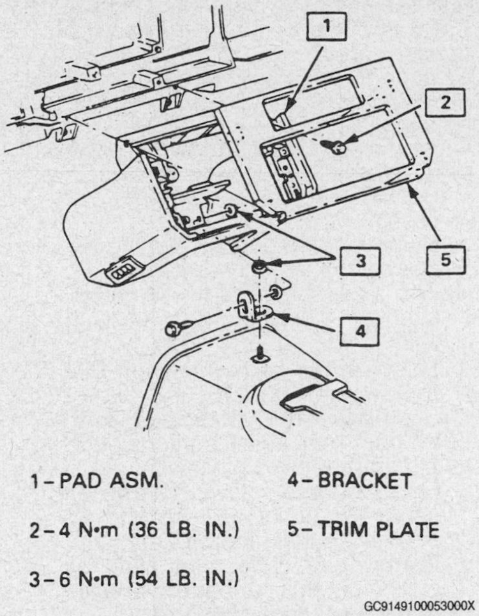
1-PAD ASM.
4-BRACKET
2-4 N·m (36 LB. IN.)
5-TRIM PLATE
3-6 N·m (54 LB. IN.)
GC9149100053000X

Fig. 54 I/P lower trim pad removal. 1992 Camaro & Firebird

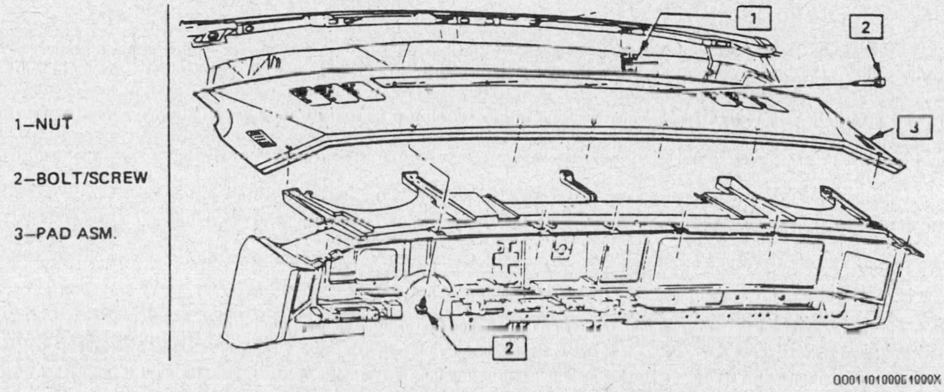
1-NUT
2-BOLT/SCREW
3-PAD ASM.

Fig. 55 I/P pad removal. 1992 Camaro & Firebird

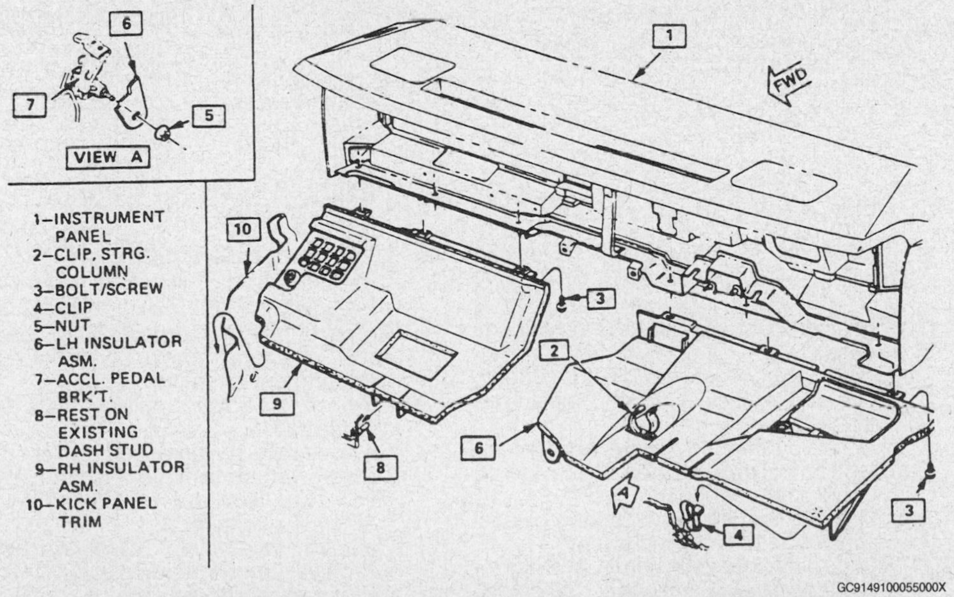
VIEW A
FWD
1-INSTRUMENT PANEL
2-CLIP, STRG. COLUMN
3-BOLT/SCREW
4-CLIP
5-NUT
6-LH INSULATOR ASM.
7-ACCL. PEDAL BRK'T.
8-REST ON EXISTING DASH STUD
9-RH INSULATOR ASM.
10-KICK PANEL TRIM
GC9149100055000X

Fig. 56 I/P hush panel removal (with A/C). 1992 Camaro & Firebird

ing bolts, located above steering column.

30. Remove five carrier assembly to air duct attaching bolts.
31. Remove three conduit retaining nuts, two above glove compartment and one through cassette compartment opening.
32. Remove nine clips holding wiring harness.
33. Remove instrument panel by pulling top out, then lifting panel up and out.
34. Reverse procedure to install.

CUTLASS SUPREME

Refer to Fig. 68, when performing this procedure.

1. Disconnect battery ground cable.
2. Open glove compartment door, then remove lower storage compartment by lifting it out.
3. Remove two screws inside glove compartment opening.
4. Remove defroster grille and deflector.
5. Remove two instrument panel upper pad retaining screws, located in defroster grille opening.
6. Remove five instrument panel cluster trim plate attaching screws.
7. Pull top of trim plate outward, then starting at one side of trim plate carefully pull bottom outward to release five spring clips.
8. Remove two screws at sides of instrument cluster opening.
9. Lift upper pad and disconnect electrical connector to glove compartment light, then remove upper pad.
10. Remove two screws attaching speakers to instrument panel.
11. Disconnect speaker electrical connectors, and remove speaker.
12. Remove radio assembly retaining screws, then pulling assembly rearward, disconnect antenna, speaker and electrical connectors.
13. Remove two screws holding left air

outlet trim plate to instrument panel.
14. Carefully pull at bottom of trim plate to release spring clips.
15. Disconnect electrical connector for headlight switch, and remove air outlet trim plate.
16. **On vehicles equipped with sport pod,** remove sport pod as follows:
    a. Remove two screws on bottom of assembly.
    b. Remove three screws holding assembly to instrument panel.
    c. Pull assembly outward and disconnect electrical connector to lighter.
    d. Remove four screws holding filler to instrument panel.
17. **On vehicles not equipped with sport pod,** remove left center air outlet plate assembly as follows:
    a. Remove three screws holding left center air outlet assembly to instrument panel trim plate.
    b. Remove air outlet trim plate by pulling carefully at bottom of plate to release spring clips.
18. **On all models,** remove left and right instrument panel sound insulators.
19. Remove two screws holding ALDL connector to instrument panel.
20. Remove four steering column trim plate attaching screws.
21. Pull trim cover rearward and disconnect trunk release electrical connector.
22. Remove two bolts at upper part of column and one bolt at lower part of column, then lower column.
23. Disconnect left and right courtesy light assemblies.
24. Remove two screws holding parking brake release handle to instrument panel.
25. Turn handle and remove it from instrument panel.
26. Remove three fuse block bracket to instrument panel attaching screws.
27. Remove seven screws holding main ventilation duct to the instrument panel.
28. Remove nut holding wiring harness clip to instrument panel.
29. Remove screw holding glove compartment light, then slide off bracket.
30. Remove two instrument panel attaching screws, located at lower left and right sides of panel.
31. Remove five instrument panel attaching screws at top of instrument panel.
32. Remove two instrument panel attaching screws at steering column support.
33. Remove instrument panel from vehicle.
34. Reverse procedure to install.

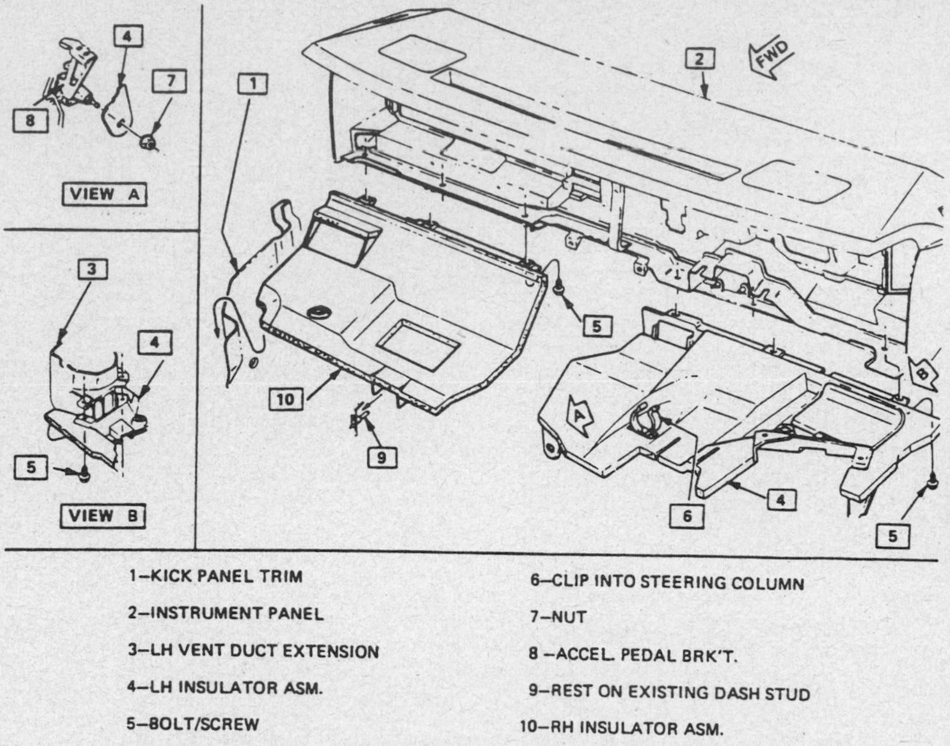
VIEW A
VIEW B
FWD
1—KICK PANEL TRIM
2—INSTRUMENT PANEL
3—LH VENT DUCT EXTENSION
4—LH INSULATOR ASM.
5—BOLT/SCREW
6—CLIP INTO STEERING COLUMN
7—NUT
8—ACCEL. PEDAL BRK'T.
9—REST ON EXISTING DASH STUD
10—RH INSULATOR ASM.
GC9149100056000X

Fig. 57 I/P hush panel removal (less A/C). 1992 Camaro & Firebird

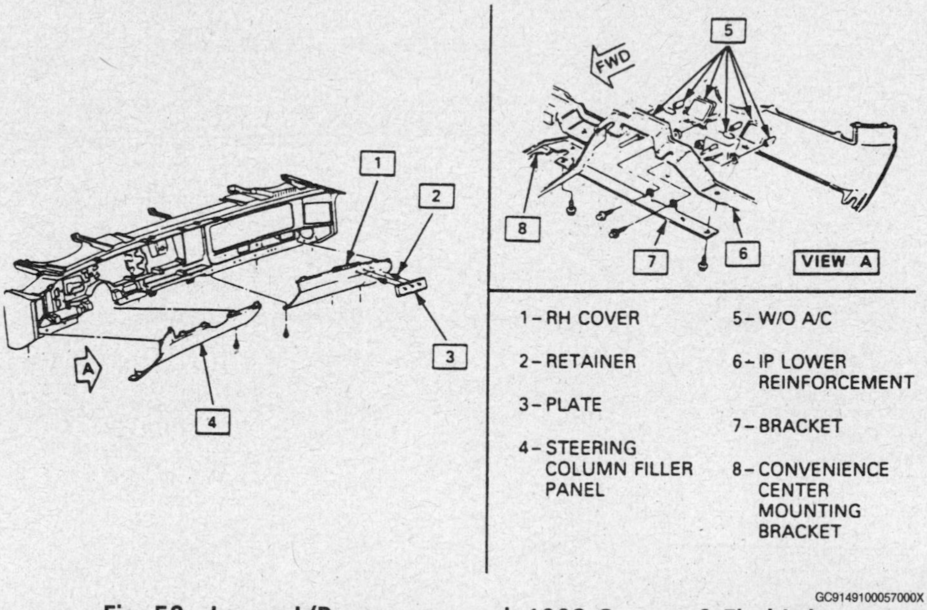
FWD
VIEW A
1-RH COVER
2-RETAINER
3-PLATE
4-STEERING COLUMN FILLER PANEL
5-W/O A/C
6-IP LOWER REINFORCEMENT
7-BRACKET
8-CONVENIENCE CENTER MOUNTING BRACKET
GC9149100057000X

Fig. 58 Lower I/P cover removal. 1992 Camaro & Firebird

GRAND PRIX

1992–93

Refer to **Fig. 69** when performing this procedure.

1. Disconnect battery ground cable.
2. Remove two instrument panel pad cover attaching screws at top of cluster trim plate.
3. Remove two screws securing glove compartment hinges to instrument panel.
4. Holding door at the bottom, open door, then lift door up and out to release.
5. Remove three glove compartment attaching screws, located at the top of glove compartment.
6. Remove two screws securing plastic clips under the compartment.
7. Slide glove compartment out of instrument panel and disconnect electrical connectors to light and trunk release switch.
8. Remove one instrument panel pad cover attaching screw above glove compartment opening.
9. Lift front of pad and pull rearward to release clips.
10. Remove light switch assembly retaining screw, then remove assembly by carefully pulling out to release two spring clips at the top.
11. Remove windshield wiper/washer switch assembly retaining screw, then remove assembly by carefully pulling out to release two spring clips at the top.

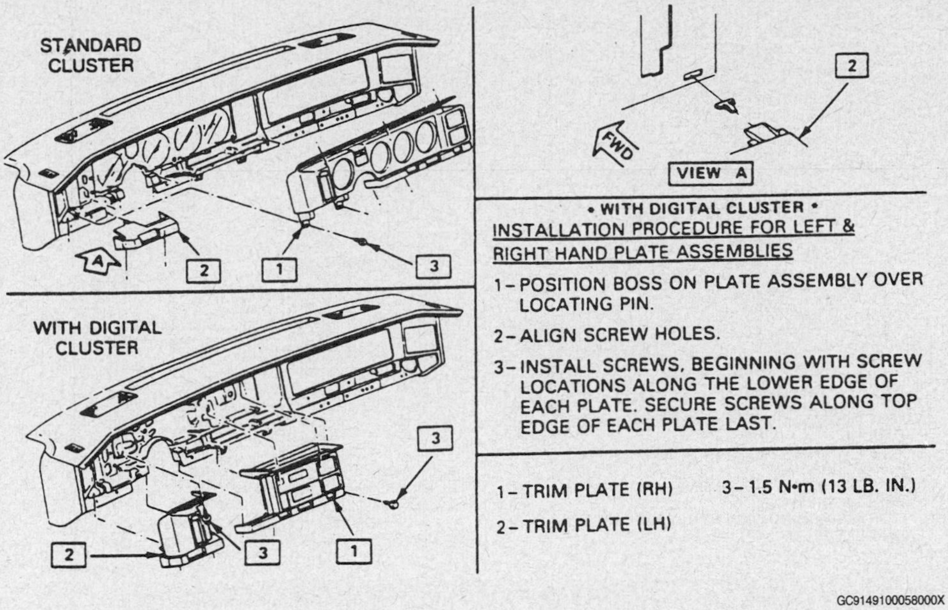
STANDARD CLUSTER
WITH DIGITAL CLUSTER
VIEW A
FWD
A
1
2
3
• WITH DIGITAL CLUSTER •
INSTALLATION PROCEDURE FOR LEFT & RIGHT HAND PLATE ASSEMBLIES
1 - POSITION BOSS ON PLATE ASSEMBLY OVER LOCATING PIN.
2 - ALIGN SCREW HOLES.
3 - INSTALL SCREWS, BEGINNING WITH SCREW LOCATIONS ALONG THE LOWER EDGE OF EACH PLATE. SECURE SCREWS ALONG TOP EDGE OF EACH PLATE LAST.
1 - TRIM PLATE (RH)
2 - TRIM PLATE (LH)
3 - 1.5 N•m (13 LB. IN.)
GC9149100058000X

Fig. 59 I/P trim plate removal. 1992 Camaro & Firebird

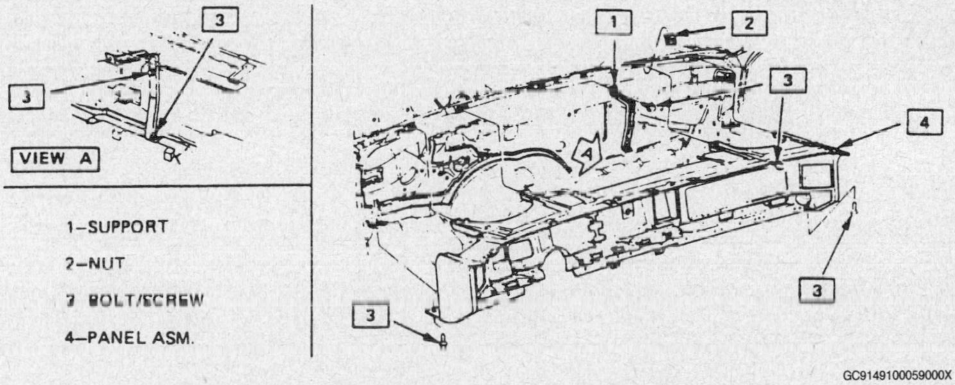
VIEW A
1—SUPPORT
2—NUT
3 BOLT/SCREW
4—PANEL ASM.
1
2
3
4
GC9149100059000X

Fig. 60 I/P removal. 1992 Camaro & Firebird

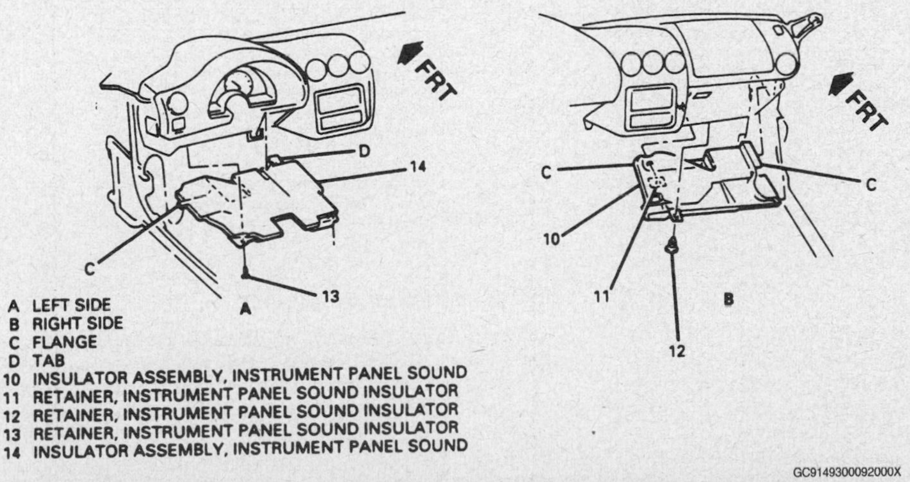
FRT
A LEFT SIDE
B RIGHT SIDE
C FLANGE
D TAB
10 INSULATOR ASSEMBLY, INSTRUMENT PANEL SOUND
11 RETAINER, INSTRUMENT PANEL SOUND INSULATOR
12 RETAINER, INSTRUMENT PANEL SOUND INSULATOR
13 RETAINER, INSTRUMENT PANEL SOUND INSULATOR
14 INSULATOR ASSEMBLY, INSTRUMENT PANEL SOUND
GC9149300092000X

Fig. 61 Sound insulator removal. 1993-94 Camaro & Firebird

12. Remove four cluster trim plate attaching screws, located inside switch openings.
13. Remove two cluster trim plate attaching screws from top of trim plate.
14. Remove two switch assembly connectors by sliding out of holders.
15. Remove two screws attaching clutch brake release lever, then disconnect linkage from brake assembly.
16. Remove two bolts securing ALDL connector, then lower connector.
17. Remove two left side sound insulator attaching screws, located on the rear edge of the insulator.
18. Remove one slide clip from front of insulator, then remove insulator.
19. Remove three attaching screws at the bottom of steering column cover.
20. Remove cover by carefully pulling rearward to release it from the three clips at the top.
21. Remove two bolts at upper part of steering column.
22. Remove two bolts at lower part of column, then lower column.
23. Disconnect electrical connectors at steering column.
24. Remove two screws securing right side sound insulator, then remove insulator.
25. Disconnect electrical connectors to fuse block.
26. Remove four bolts securing fuse block, and remove fuse block.
27. Disconnect electrical connector at HVAC assembly.
28. Remove two remote radio amplifier attaching screws, disconnect electrical connectors and remove amplifier.
29. Remove four radio trim plate attaching bolts, then trim plate.
30. Remove two ventilation control attaching screws.
31. Pull control rearward, disconnect electrical connectors.
32. Remove two radio control attaching bolts, disconnect electrical connectors and remove radio control assembly.
33. Remove two cassette player attaching bolts, disconnect electrical connectors and remove cassette player assembly.
34. Remove two radio receiver retaining nuts, disconnect electrical connectors and antenna connector, remove radio receiver.
35. Remove four cluster retaining screws, lift cluster and disconnect electrical connector, remove cluster.
36. Remove four radio speaker retaining screws, and remove both speaker assemblies.
37. Remove seven screws securing ventilation duct to instrument panel.
38. Remove three retaining nuts from wiring harness carrier.
39. Lift instrument panel carrier up and rearward then out through the passenger door.
40. Remove ventilation duct and wiring harness carrier as a unit.
41. Reverse procedure to install.

1994

Refer to **Fig. 70** when performing the

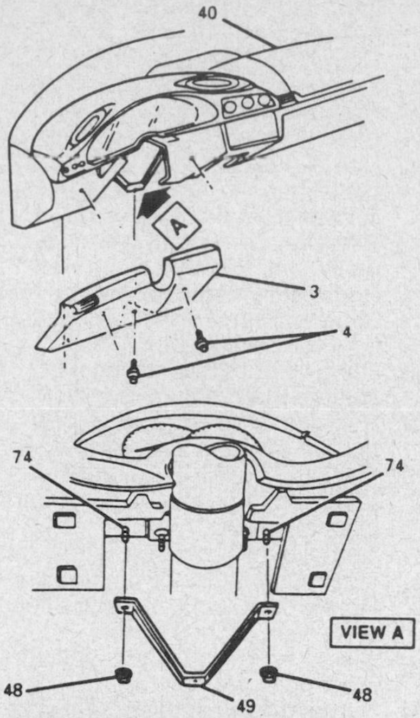

3 BOLSTER ASSEMBLY, INSTRUMENT PANEL DRIVER KNEE
4 BOLT/SCREW, INSTRUMENT PANEL DRIVER KNEE BOLSTER, 1.9 N•m (17 LB. IN.)
40 PANEL ASSEMBLY, INSTRUMENT
48 NUT, INSTRUMENT PANEL DRIVER KNEE BOLSTER DEFLECTOR
49 DEFLECTOR, INSTRUMENT PANEL DRIVER KNEE BOLSTER
74 STUD, INSTRUMENT PANEL DRIVER KNEE BOLSTER DEFLECTOR

GC9149300093000X

Fig. 62 Driver knee bolster & deflector removal. 1993-94 Camaro & Firebird

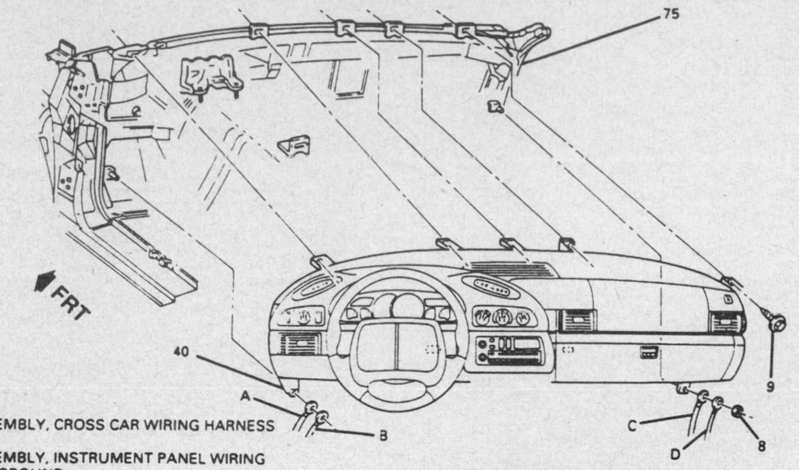

A WIRE ASSEMBLY, CROSS CAR WIRING HARNESS GROUND
B WIRE ASSEMBLY, INSTRUMENT PANEL WIRING HARNESS GROUND
C WIRE ASSEMBLY, INSTRUMENT PANEL WIRING HARNESS GROUND
D WIRE ASSEMBLY, INSTRUMENT PANEL WIRING HARNESS GROUND
8 NUT, INSTRUMENT PANEL, 25 N•m (18 LB. FT.)
9 BOLT/SCREW, INSTRUMENT PANEL, 1.9 N•m (17 LB. IN.)
40 PANEL ASSEMBLY, INSTRUMENT
75 CARRIER, INSTRUMENT PANEL

GC9149300094000X

Fig. 63 I/P removal. 1993-94 Camaro & Firebird

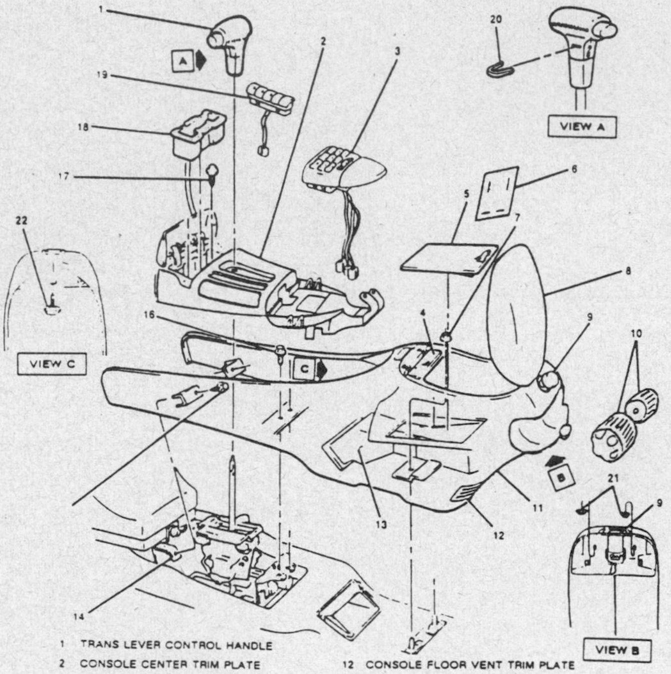

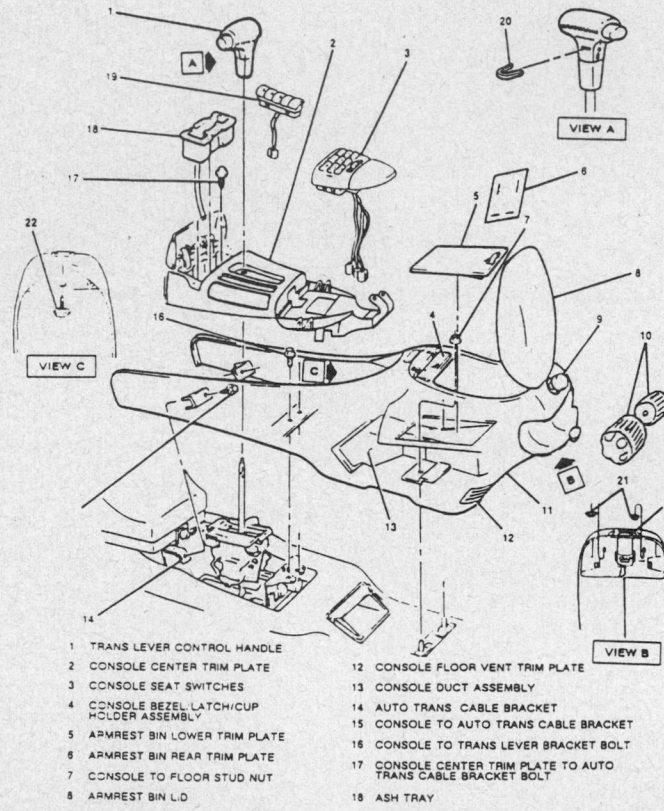

1 TRANS LEVER CONTROL HANDLE
2 CONSOLE CENTER TRIM PLATE
3 CONSOLE SEAT SWITCHES
4 CONSOLE BEZEL/LATCH/CUP HOLDER ASSEMBLY
5 ARMREST BIN LOWER TRIM PLATE
6 ARMREST BIN REAR TRIM PLATE
7 CONSOLE TO FLOOR STUD NUT
8 ARMREST BIN LID
9 CONSOLE CIGAR LIGHTER ASSEMBLY
10 CONSOLE VENT ASSEMBLY
11 LOWER CONSOLE
12 CONSOLE FLOOR VENT TRIM PLATE
13 CONSOLE DUCT ASSEMBLY
14 AUTO TRANS CABLE BRACKET
15 CONSOLE TO AUTO TRANS CABLE BRACKET
16 CONSOLE TO TRANS LEVER BRACKET BOLT
17 CONSOLE CENTER TRIM PLATE TO AUTO TRANS CABLE BRACKET BOLT
18 ASH TRAY
19 CONSOLE CENTER TRIM PLATE SWITCHES
20 TRANS LEVER CONTROL HANDLE RETAINER
21 NUTS
22 BOLT

GC9149200060000X

Fig. 64 Console removal. Bonneville

following replacement procedure.

1. Disconnect battery ground cable.
2. Remove front door inside carpet retainers.
3. Remove right and left sound insulators.
4. Remove windshield upper garnish moldings, **Figs. 71 and 72.**
5. Insert a flat blade screwdriver at the rearmost edge of the upper trim panel, pry panel up to release six upper trim panel retainers.
6. Left rear edge of upper trim panel approximately two inches, then pull panel rearward to remove.
7. Remove screws under lower instrument panel compartment.
8. Remove screws holding lower compartment hinge to instrument panel, then the screws at top of lower compartment.
9. Remove screws holding plastic clips under compartment.
10. Remove opening screw, then slide lower compartment out of instrument panel.
11. Disconnect electrical connectors to lamp and rear compartment lid release switch.
12. Remove theft deterrent module assembly attaching bolts, **Fig. 73.**
13. Remove module assembly bracket from tie bar assembly.
14. Disconnect module electrical connector.
15. Remove bolt from bottom tab on passenger inflator module.
16. Remove inflator module to bag bracket attaching bolts.
17. Remove passenger inflator module from instrument panel. **When carrying a live inflator, ensure the bag and trim cover are pointed away in case of accidental deployment. Do not carry inflator module by wires of connector on underside of module. When placing a live inflator module on a bench or other surface, ensure the bag and trim cover faces in a upward direction. Never rest steering column assembly on the steering wheel with the inflator**

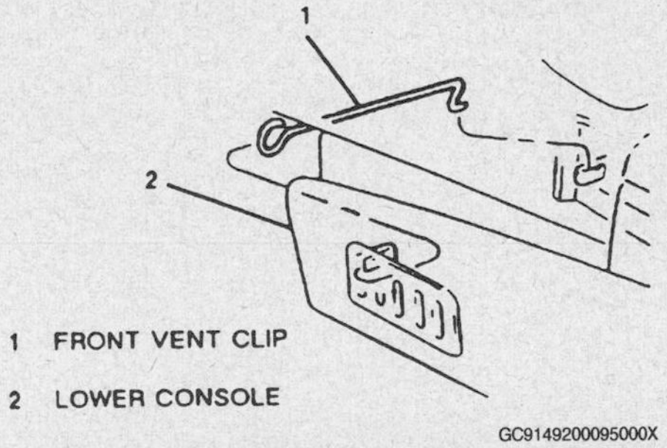
1
2
1 FRONT VENT CLIP
2 LOWER CONSOLE
GC9149200095000X

Fig. 65 Front lower console vent clip. Bonneville

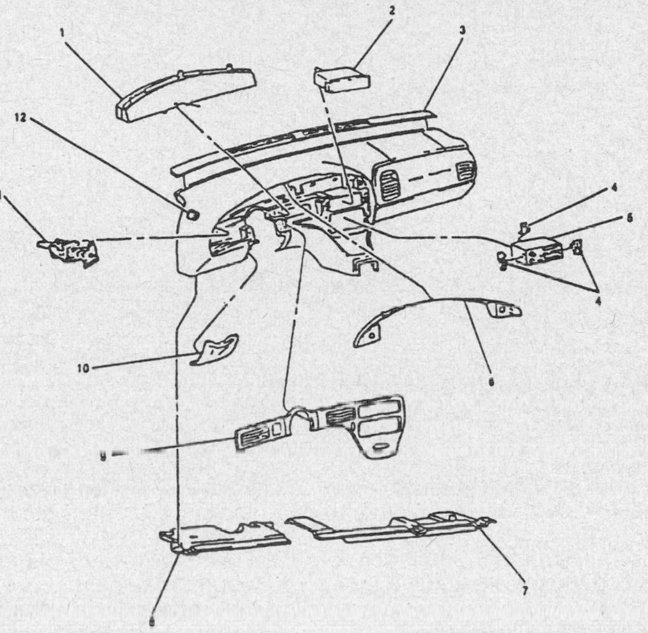
1
2
3
4
5
6
7
8
9
10
11
12

1 CLUSTER ASSEMBLY
2 HEATER AND A/C CONTROLS
3 WINDSHIELD DEFROSTER GRILLE
4 RADIO BRACKET
5 RADIO ASSEMBLY
6 IP CLUSTER TRIM PLATE ASSEMBLY
7 RIGHT SOUND INSULATOR
8 LEFT SOUND INSULATOR
9 IP TRIM PLATE ASSEMBLY
10 IP STEERING COLUMN FILLER
11 HEADLAMP SWITCH ASSEMBLY
12 SIDE WINDOW DEFOGGER OUTLET

GC9149200061000X

Fig. 66 I/P removal. Bonneville

module face down and column vertical. This is necessary in case of accidental deployment. Otherwise, personal injury may result.

18. Remove steering column opening filler.
19. **On models with center console,** remove console as follows:
    a. Using a screwdriver, remove shift handle snap ring.
    b. Remove shift handle.
    c. Remove console retaining screws from rear compartment.
    d. Remove front floor console shift opening trim, by prying two rear tabs gently with a small screwdriver.
    e. Raise armrest and remove ashtray and steel flame plate.
    f. Loosen screws inside ashtray area, then pry sides of base apart.
    g. Remove armrest at rear hinge area, from between base halves.
    h. Disconnect console wiring and electrical connectors.
    i. Remove console front and rear attaching bolts.
    j. Remove console assembly.
20. **On all models,** remove two instrument panel accessory trim plate attaching screws.
21. Pull instrument panel accessory trim plate rearward to release two steel retainers, then rotate trim plate rearward and up to release two tabs at top edge.
22. Rotate ventilation control assembly clockwise to unsnap.
23. Pull ventilation control assembly away from instrument panel and disconnect electrical connectors.
24. **On models with column shift,** set parking brake and position shift lever to L1.
25. Tilt steering column to its' lowest position.
26. Remove tilt lever assembly.
27. Insert screwdriver into slot in instrument panel cluster trim plate directly below headlamp switch.
28. Push screwdriver handle down, releasing tab, pull plate rearward.
29. Grasp trim plate at right end below right center A/C outlet and carefully pull to release clip.
30. Remove instrument cluster trim plate to instrument panel attaching screw.
31. Grasp bottom edge of cluster trim plate on both sides of steering column and pull to release two additional retaining clips.
32. Disconnect cigarette lighter electrical connector.
33. Insert screwdriver into slot at left upper corner of trim plate and raise handle.
34. Pull rearward at top center of trim plate to disengage plastic clip, then remove trim plate from vehicle.
35. Remove audio assembly mounting screws
36. Slide audio assembly out of instrument panel and disconnect electrical connectors.
37. Press two push-pin retainers at top of instrument cluster.
38. Rotate top of cluster rearward and disengage locating pins on bottom of cluster at instrument panel.
39. Disconnect cluster electrical connector and remove cluster.
40. Remove headlamp switch and trip calculator.
41. Disconnect fuse block electrical connector.
42. Rotate fuse block to release locking tabs, then remove fuse block.
43. Remove steering column to support bracket attaching bolts, then lower column.
44. Remove instrument panel attaching bolts and screws.
45. Remove lower compartment lamp and trunk release switch from instrument panel.
46. Remove instrument panel retaining clips and reposition wiring harness.
47. Remove instrument panel from vehicle.
48. Reverse procedure to install.

LEMANS

1. Disconnect battery ground cable.
2. Remove horn pad and disconnect horn lead.
3. Remove nut and retainer, mark shaft and wheel for assembly reference.
4. Using steering wheel puller tool No. J-3651 or equivalent, remove steering wheel.
5. If necessary remove contact ring from steering wheel.
6. Using a pointed plastic tool, pry package panel out of console.

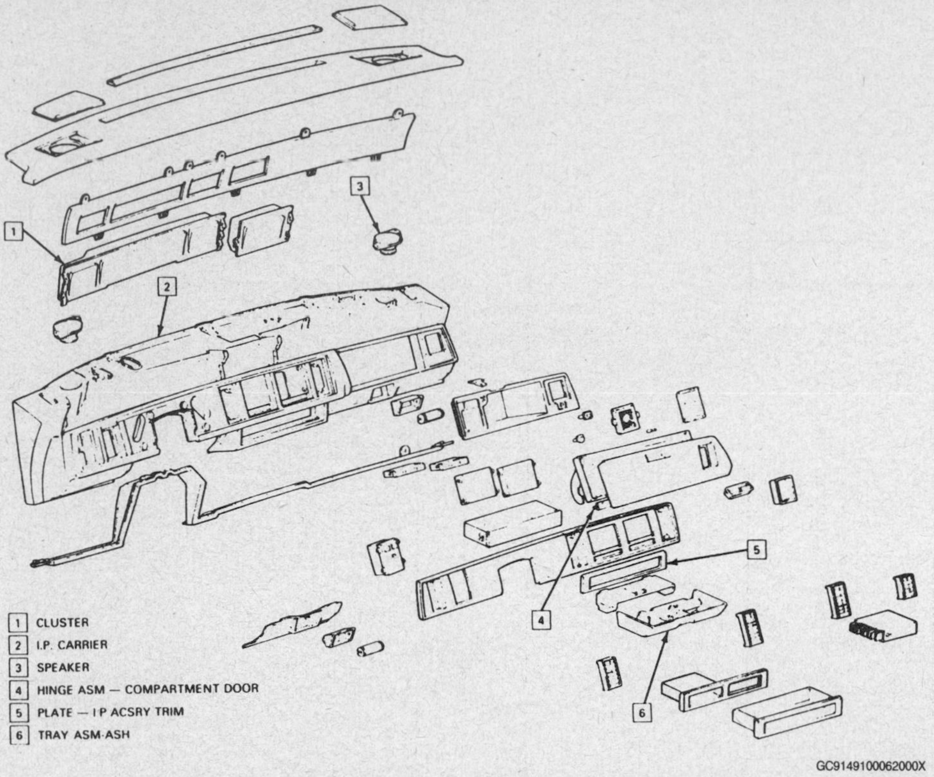
1
2
3
4
5
6
1 CLUSTER
2 I.P. CARRIER
3 SPEAKER
4 HINGE ASM — COMPARTMENT DOOR
5 PLATE — I P ACSRY TRIM
6 TRAY ASM-ASH
GC9149100062000X

Fig. 67 Exploded view of I/P assembly. Regal

7. Remove two screws from under ashtray.
8. **On models with automatic transmission,** pull gear selector lever off. Pull out indicator strap from cover, then remove retaining clips and cover.
9. **On models with manual transmission,** remove shift knob, trim plate and boot.
10. **On all models,** remove front center console, **Fig. 74.**
11. Remove two attaching screws, then pull center back and out,**Fig. 75.**
12. Remove right side hush panel, **Fig. 76.**
13. Open glove box door and pry off two retaining straps.
14. Remove two screws attaching glove box to instrument panel pad.
15. Remove A/C or heater control.
16. Turning steering wheel to gain access to turn signal switch housing attaching screws, remove turn signal switch housing.
17. Remove instrument panel trim plate, then remove dimmer switch from trim plate.
18. While pressing down on speedometer cable retainer spring, pull out speedometer cable.
19. Remove instrument cluster attaching screws, pull cluster rearward and disconnect electrical connectors.
20. Remove cluster from instrument panel.
21. Remove instrument panel center section.
22. Remove air nozzles and air vents from instrument panel.
23. Remove fuse box, disconnect wiring harness from all switches and lamps.
24. Disconnect wiring harness from instrument panel.
25. Remove six instrument panel screw on panel and remove instrument panel.
26. Reverse procedure to install.

METRO

1. Disconnect battery ground cable.
2. **On convertible models,** remove inflator module from steering wheel as described in "Passive Restraints" section.
3. **On all models,** remove lower steering column trim panel.
4. Remove steering wheel as described in "Electrical" section of "Metro" section.
5. **On convertible models,** remove SIR coil/combination switch assembly as described in "Passive Restraints" section.
6. **On hardtop models,** remove combination switch as described in "Electrical" section of "Metro" section.
7. **On all models,** remove right and left kick panels, then the right and left speaker grilles from instrument panel.
8. **On convertible models,** remove plastic retaining clips securing instrument panel to door jambs.
9. **On all models,** if equipped, remove front speakers from instrument panel.
10. Remove glove box inner panel, then disconnect A/C switch electrical connector, if equipped.
11. Remove heater control lever knobs, then the heater control unit cover plate.
12. Remove heater control unit from instrument panel.
13. **On models with manual transmission,** remove gearshift control lever upper boot from console.
14. **On all models,** remove console, ashtray and center console trim bezel.
15. Remove instrument panel center trim bezel, then the radio, if equipped.
16. Remove instrument panel cluster trim bezel, then disconnect electrical connectors from cluster trim bezel mounted switches, if equipped.
17. Disconnect retaining clip and speedometer cable at transaxle, then remove cluster assembly from instrument panel.
18. Disconnect ashtray illumination lamp, cigar lighter and cigar lighter illumination lamp bulb socket electrical connectors.
19. Remove retaining ring from rear of cigar lighter, then the cigar lighter from instrument panel.
20. **On convertible models,** remove two retaining screws from cluster cavity.
21. **On all models,** remove upper and lower instrument panel retaining screws, **Fig. 77,** and screw retaining instrument panel to bracket to floor pan.
22. Disconnect illumination controller electrical connector, then pull instrument panel from support member.
23. Remove screw retaining hood latch release lever, then disconnect cable from lever.

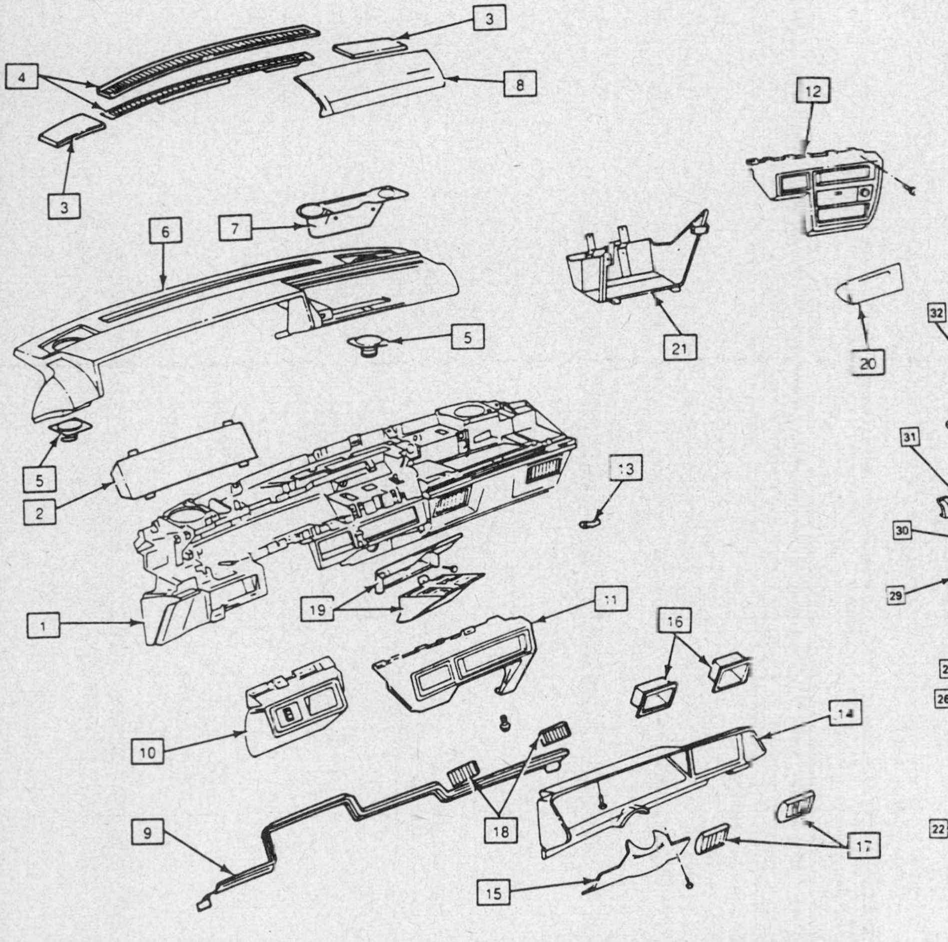

1. INSTRUMENT PANEL CARRIER
2. INSTRUMENT CLUSTER
3. SPEAKER COVERS
4. DEFROSTER DEFLECTOR GRILLE
5. SPEAKER
6. INSTRUMENT PANEL UPPER PAD
7. LOWER COMPARTMENT
8. COMPARTMENT DOOR (SPORT OPTION)
9. INSTRUMENT PANEL CARRIER TIE BAR
10. LEFT AIR OUTLET PLATE ASSEMBLY
11. LEFT CENTER AIR OUTLET PLATE ASSEMBLY
12. LEFT CENTER AIR OUTLET PLATE ASSEMBLY (SPORT OPTION)
13. SWITCH INSTRUMENT PANEL COMPARTMENT LIGHT
14. INSTRUMENT CLUSTER TRIM PLATE
15. STEERING COLUMN LOWER FILLER
16. RIGHT AND RIGHT CENTER AIR OUTLET HOUSINGS
17. RIGHT AND RIGHT CENTER AIR OUTLET GRILLES
18. LEFT AND LEFT CENTER AIR OUTLET GRILLES
19. ASH TRAY
20. ASH TRAY (SPORT OPTION)
21. LOWER FILLER ASSEMBLY

GC9149100096000X

Fig. 68 Exploded view of I/P. Cutlass Supreme

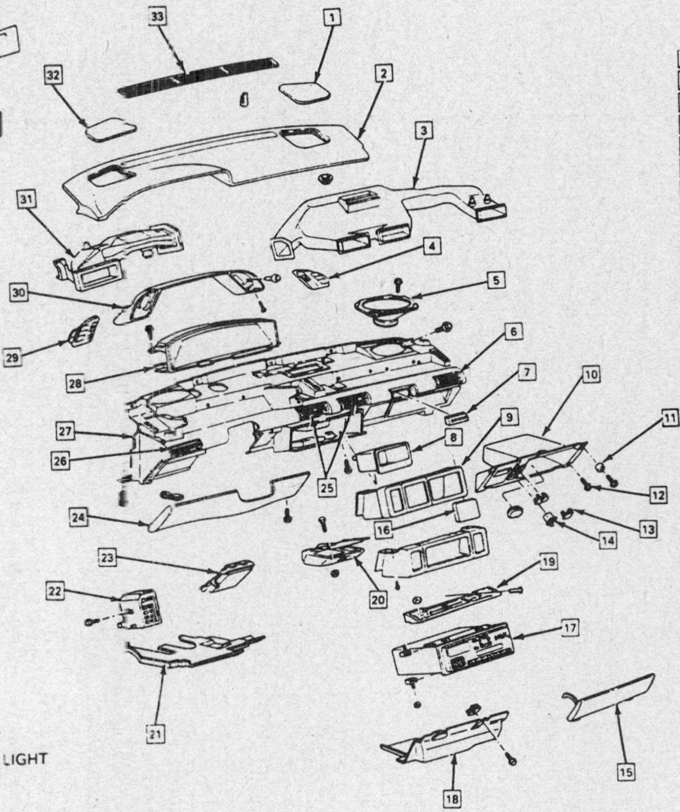

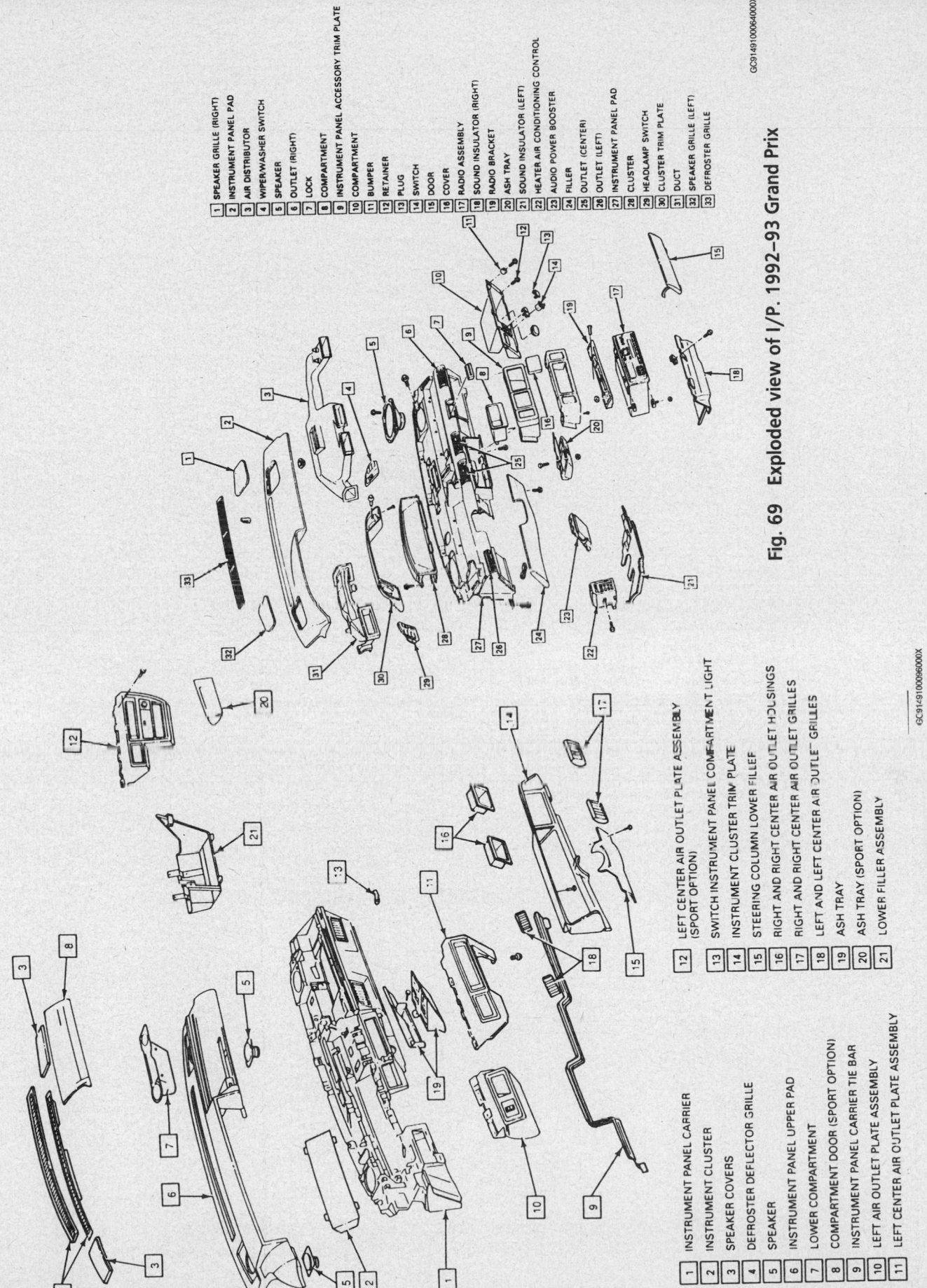

1. SPEAKER GRILLE (RIGHT)
2. INSTRUMENT PANEL PAD
3. AIR DISTRIBUTOR
4. WIPER/WASHER SWITCH
5. SPEAKER
6. OUTLET (RIGHT)
7. LOCK
8. COMPARTMENT
9. INSTRUMENT PANEL ACCESSORY TRIM PLATE
10. COMPARTMENT
11. BUMPER
12. RETAINER
13. PLUG
14. SWITCH
15. DOOR
16. COVER
17. RADIO ASSEMBLY
18. SOUND INSULATOR (RIGHT)
19. RADIO BRACKET
20. ASH TRAY
21. SOUND INSULATOR (LEFT)
22. HEATER AIR CONDITIONING CONTROL
23. AUDIO POWER BOOSTER
24. FILLER
25. OUTLET (CENTER)
26. OUTLET (LEFT)
27. INSTRUMENT PANEL PAD
28. CLUSTER
29. HEADLAMP SWITCH
30. CLUSTER TRIM PLATE
31. DUCT
32. SPEAKER GRILLE (LEFT)
33. DEFROSTER GRILLE

GC9149100064000X

Fig. 69 Exploded view of I/P. 1992–93 Grand Prix

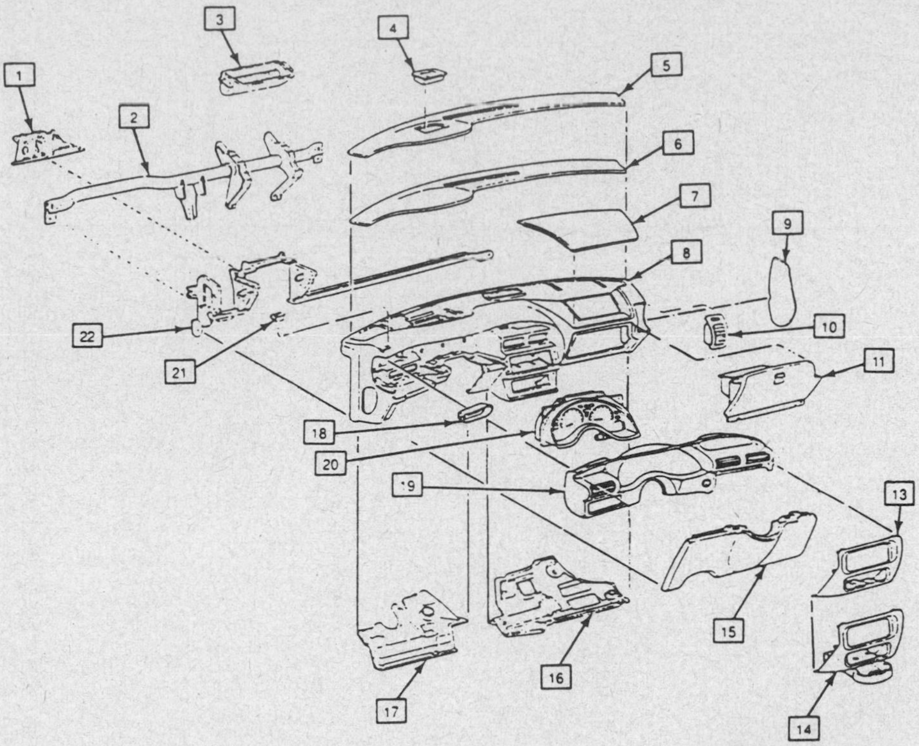

- 1 BRACKET ASSEMBLY, BRAKE PEDAL
- 2 BAR, BODY HINGE PILLAR TIE
- 3 MODULE, INFLATABLE RESTRAINT INSTRUMENT PANEL
- 4 HEAD UP DISPLAY, INSTRUMENT CLUSTER
- 5 PANEL, INSTRUMENT PANEL UPPER TRIM (W HUD)
- 6 PANEL, INSTRUMENT PANEL UPPER TRIM (W O HUD)
- 7 COVER, INFLATABLE RESTRAINT INSTRUMENT PANEL MODULE TRIM
- 8 PANEL, INSTRUMENT
- 9 DOOR, INSTRUMENT PANEL FUSE BLOCK ACCESSORY COVER
- 10 OUTLET, INSTRUMENT PANEL OUTER AIR
- 11 COMPARTMENT, INSTRUMENT PANEL
- 13 PLATE, INSTRUMENT PANEL ACCESSORY TRIM (W CONSOLE)
- 14 PLATE, INSTRUMENT PANEL ACCESSORY TRIM (W O CONSOLE)
- 15 FILLER, INSTRUMENT PANEL STEERING COLUMN OPENING
- 16 INSULATOR, INSTRUMENT PANEL SOUND (RH)
- 17 INSULATOR, INSTRUMENT PANEL SOUND (LH)
- 18 TRIP CALCULATOR
- 19 PLATE, INSTRUMENT PANEL CLUSTER TRIM
- 20 CLUSTER, INSTRUMENT
- 21 OUTLET, SIDE WINDOW DEFOGGER
- 22 BAR, INSTRUMENT PANEL LOWER TIE

GC9149400097000X

Fig. 70 Exploded view of I/P. 1994 Grand Prix

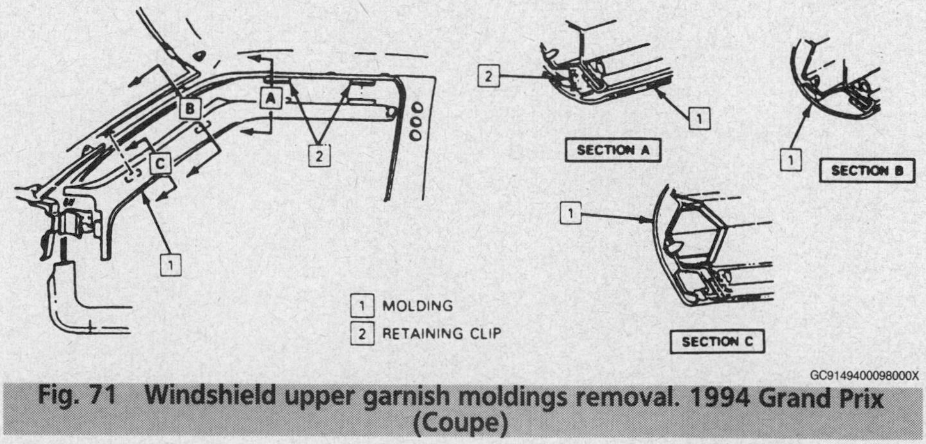
SECTION A
SECTION B
SECTION C
1 MOLDING
2 RETAINING CLIP

GC9149400098000X

Fig. 71 Windshield upper garnish moldings removal. 1994 Grand Prix (Coupe)

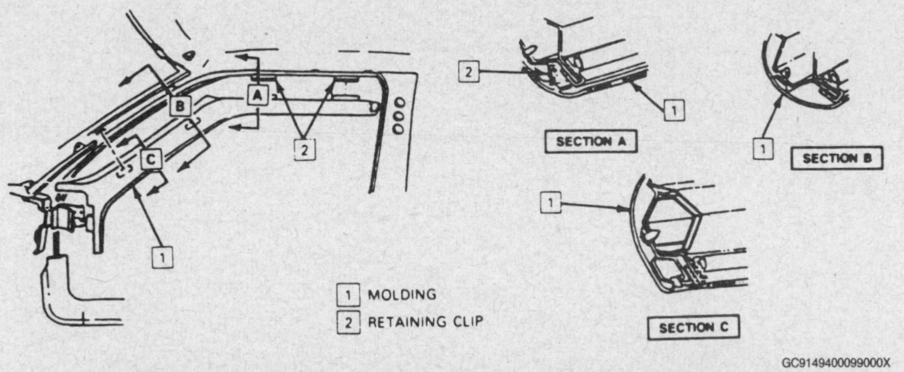

A
B
C
1
2
SECTION A
SECTION B
SECTION C
1 MOLDING
2 RETAINING CLIP
GC9149400099000X

Fig. 72 Windshield upper garnish moldings removal. 1994 Grand Prix (Sedan)

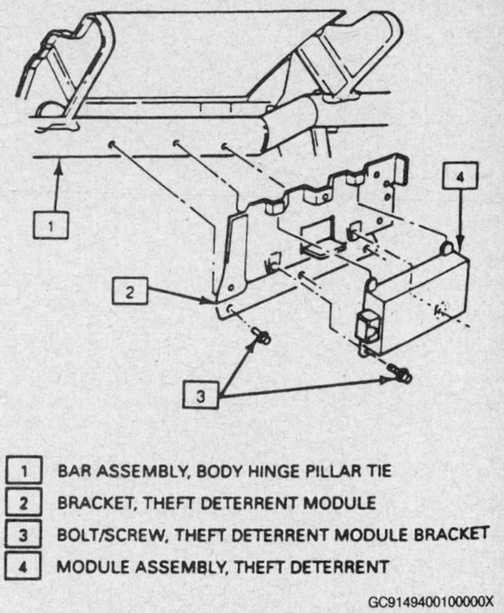

1
2
3
4
1 BAR ASSEMBLY, BODY HINGE PILLAR TIE
2 BRACKET, THEFT DETERRENT MODULE
3 BOLT/SCREW, THEFT DETERRENT MODULE BRACKET
4 MODULE ASSEMBLY, THEFT DETERRENT
GC9149400100000X

Fig. 73 Theft deterrent module assembly. 1994 Grand Prix

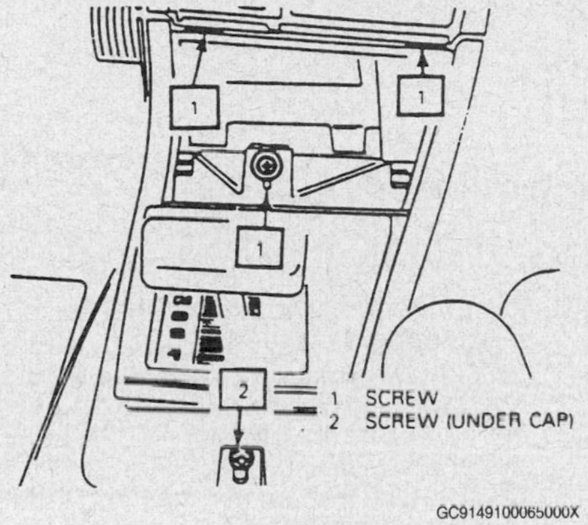

1
2
1 SCREW
2 SCREW (UNDER CAP)
GC9149100065000X

Fig. 74 front center console removal. LeMans

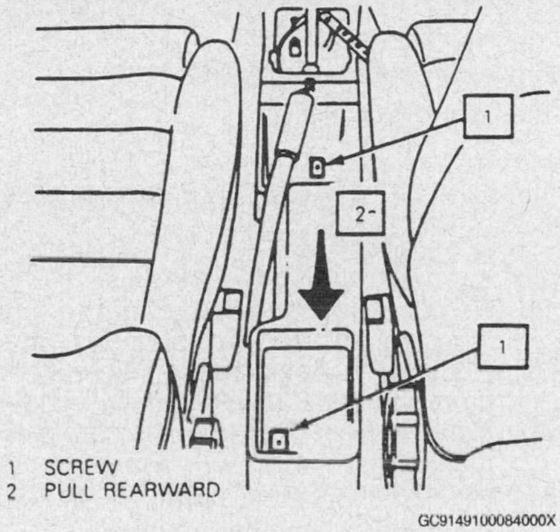

1
2
1 SCREW
2 PULL REARWARD
GC9149100084000X

Fig. 75 Center console removal. LeMans

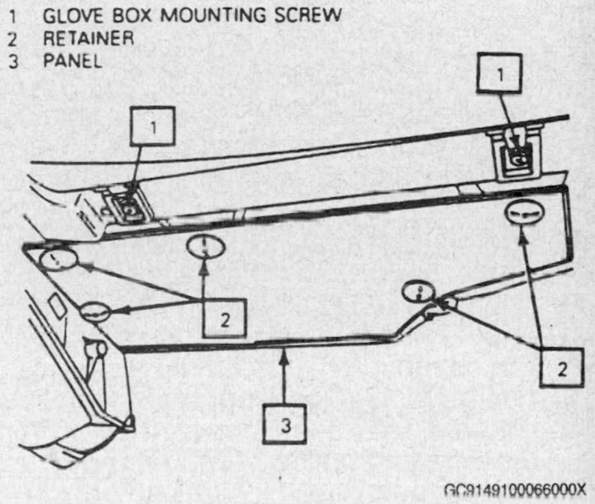

1 GLOVE BOX MOUNTING SCREW
2 RETAINER
3 PANEL
GC9149100066000X

Fig. 76 Right side hush panel removal. LeMans

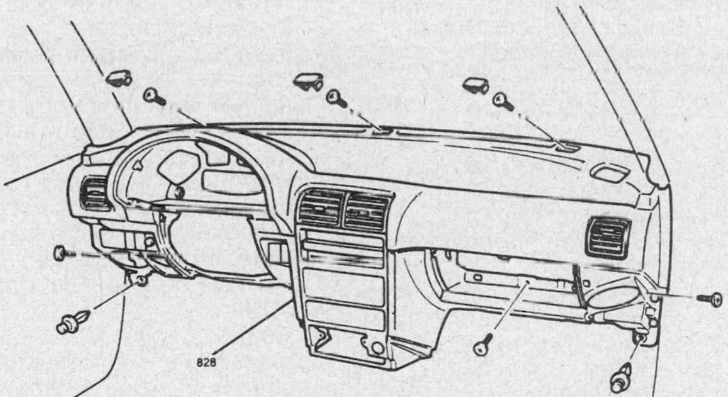

828
828 INSTRUMENT PANEL
GC9149200067000X

Fig. 77 I/P removal. Metro

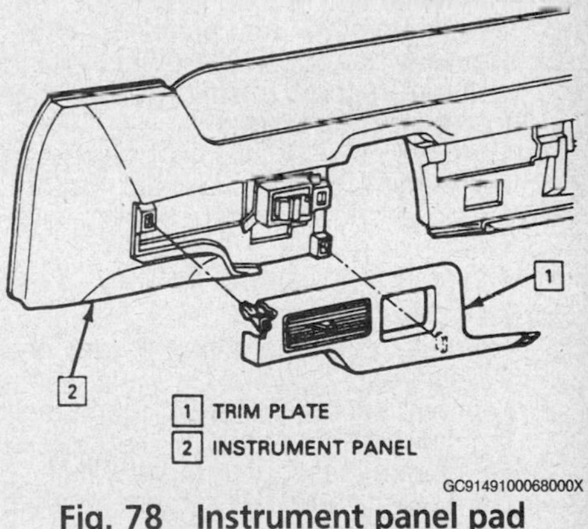

1 TRIM PLATE
2 INSTRUMENT PANEL
GC9149100068000X

Fig. 78 Instrument panel pad removal. 1992 Lumina

24. Disconnect wiring harnesses from instrument panel.
25. Remove instrument panel from vehicle.
26. Reverse procedure to install.

LUMINA

1992

1. Disconnect battery ground cable.
2. Remove instrument panel pad retaining screws under edge of instrument panel pad, **Fig. 78.**
3. Lift upward on front of pad assembly, then pull rearward to release.
4. Remove speaker retaining bolts, then lift speaker and disconnect speaker electrical connectors.
5. Disconnect instrument cluster assembly electrical connectors, then remove cluster retaining screws, **Fig. 79.**
6. Remove glove compartment door.
7. Remove glove compartment assembly retaining screws.
8. Disconnect glove compartment electrical connector.
9. Remove glove compartment assembly.
10. Remove right side sound insulator retaining screws.
11. Push insulator toward front of vehicle then pull downward to remove.
12. Remove ventilation system control retaining bolts.
13. Disconnect control assembly electrical connectors and remove from vehicle.
14. Remove radio retaining bolts, then disconnect electrical connectors and remove from vehicle.

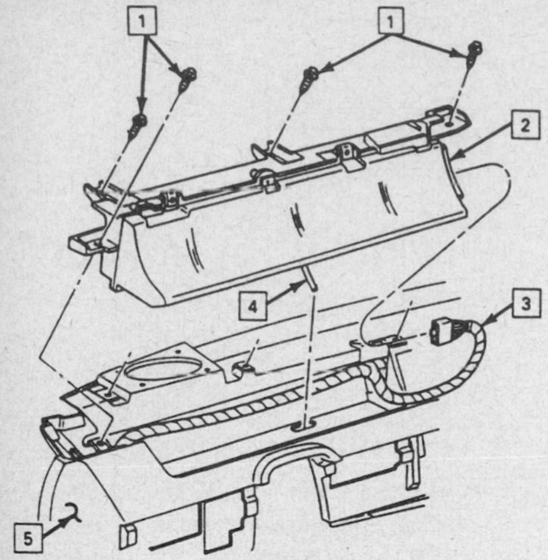
1
1
2
3
4
5
1 SCREWS
2 CLUSTER
3 CONNECTOR
4 PRNDL CABLE
5 INSTRUMENT PANEL CARRIER
GC9149100069000X

Fig. 79 I/P cluster removal. 1992 Lumina

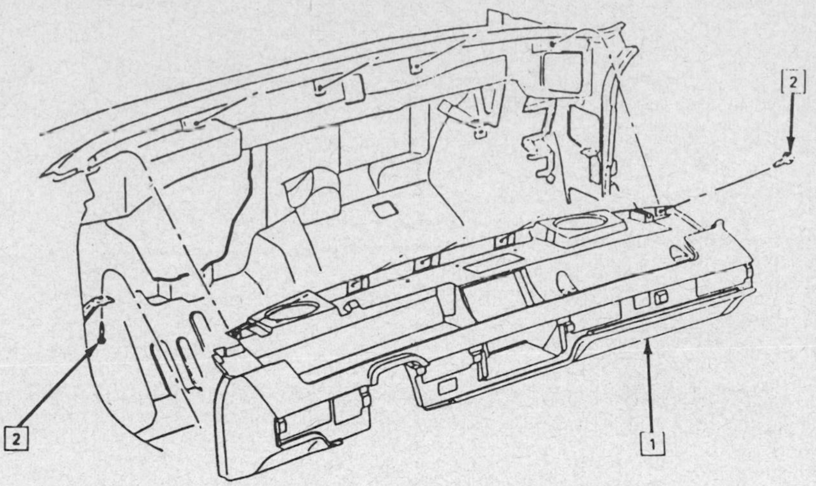
2
2
1
1 INSTRUMENT PANEL CARRIER
2 10 N·m (89 LB. IN.)
GC9149100070000X

Fig. 80 I/P carrier assembly removal. 1992 Lumina

15. Remove headlamp switch retaining screws, then disconnect switch electrical connector and remove from vehicle.
16. Remove ashtray, slide bracket retaining screws, then the bracket.
17. Remove ALDL cover.
18. Remove ALDL retaining screws then disconnect ALDL electrical connector.
19. Remove two parking brake release handle retaining screws then lower handle and pull to right to remove.
20. Disconnect fuse block electrical connectors.
21. Remove fuse block retaining screws, then the fuse block.
22. Remove left sound insulator and steering column trim panel.
23. Remove two upper and lower steering column support retaining bolts, then lower steering column.
24. Remove seven instrument panel carrier assembly retaining bolts, **Fig. 80.**
25. Remove carrier assembly from vehicle.
26. Reverse procedure to install.

1993–94

1. Remove instrument panel pad and trim plates.
2. Remove sound insulators, then steering column trim panel.
3. Remove accessory trim plate.
4. Remove audio system, then headlamp switch.
5. Remove instrument cluster assembly as follows:
   a. Remove air cleaner assembly.
   b. Remove screws holding cluster, then disconnect electrical connectors.
   c. Remove automatic transaxle control indicator cable, if equipped.
6. Remove ventilation controls, then data link connector (DLC).
7. Remove parking brake release handle, then ashtray and bracket.
8. Remove lower compartment, fuse block, then lower the steering column.
9. Remove two bolts above steering column and bolts from ventilation duct.
10. Remove front door opening carpet retainer.
11. Remove instrument panel center support bolts, then center support.
12. Disconnect instrument panel wiring harness, then remove instrument panel bolts.
13. Remove instrument panel by pulling top out, then lifting panel up and out.
14. Reverse procedure to install.

PRIZM

1992

Refer to **Fig. 81,** when performing the following procedure.

1. Disconnect battery ground cable.
2. Remove two steering wheel pad retaining bolts from back of steering wheel.
3. Remove steering wheel pad.
4. Disconnect horn switch electrical connector.
5. Remove steering wheel shaft nut.
6. Using steering wheel puller tool No. 1859-03 or equivalent, remove steering wheel.
7. Remove two hood release attaching screws lever.
8. Remove four lower left trim panel retaining screws, **Fig. 82.**
9. Disconnect speaker electrical connector, then remove A/C duct from lower A/C register, if equipped.
10. Remove seven steering column cover retaining screws.
11. Remove two trim bezel retaining screws.
12. Disconnect control/defogger switch electrical connector.
13. Disconnect rear wiper/washer switch, if equipped.
14. Disconnect two electrical connectors and cigar lighter from trim bezel.
15. Remove trim bezel, then four cluster bezel retaining screws.
16. Disconnect hazard flasher and dimmer switch electrical connectors.
17. Remove four instrument cluster retaining screws, **Fig. 83.**
18. Disconnect speedometer cable and remaining electrical connectors from instrument cluster.
19. Remove instrument cluster.
20. Remove two cup holder retaining screws, then the cup holder.
21. Remove four radio retaining screws, then pull radio from console.
22. Disconnect two radio electrical connectors and antenna from radio.
23. Remove three glove box door scuff plate retaining screws.
24. Remove one side trim panel retaining screw.
25. Remove cowl side trim, then five glove box and trim assembly retaining screws, **Fig. 84.**
26. Pull glove box out of trim assembly, then disconnect speaker electrical connector.
27. Remove glove box and trim assembly.
28. Remove glove box retaining pins and glove box door from trim panel.
29. Remove four heater and A/C control unit retaining screws.
30. Remove remaining console retaining screws, then the console.
31. Remove five instrument panel retaining screws, **Fig. 85.**
32. Disconnect three instrument panel electrical connectors and one relay unit from left side of instrument panel.
33. Remove one electrical connector from right side of instrument panel, then disconnect defroster duct retain-

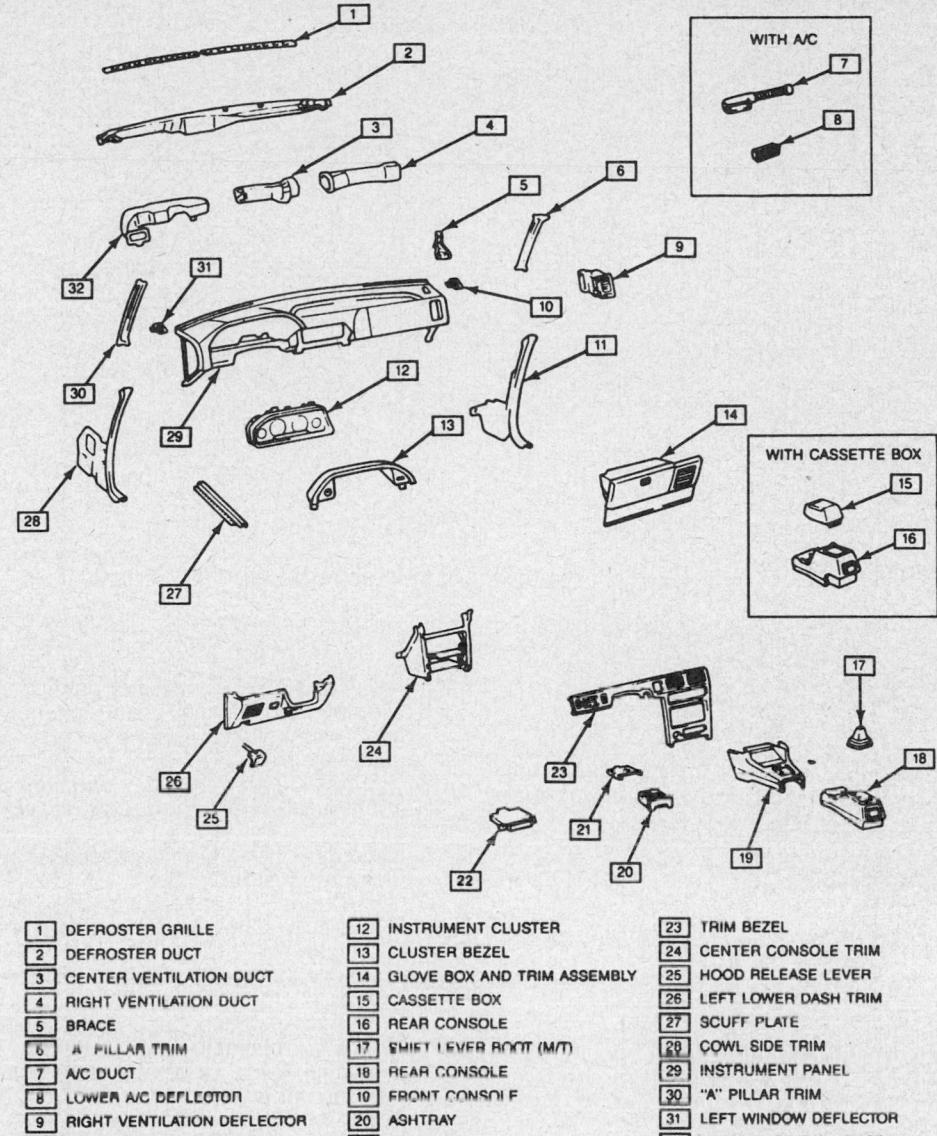

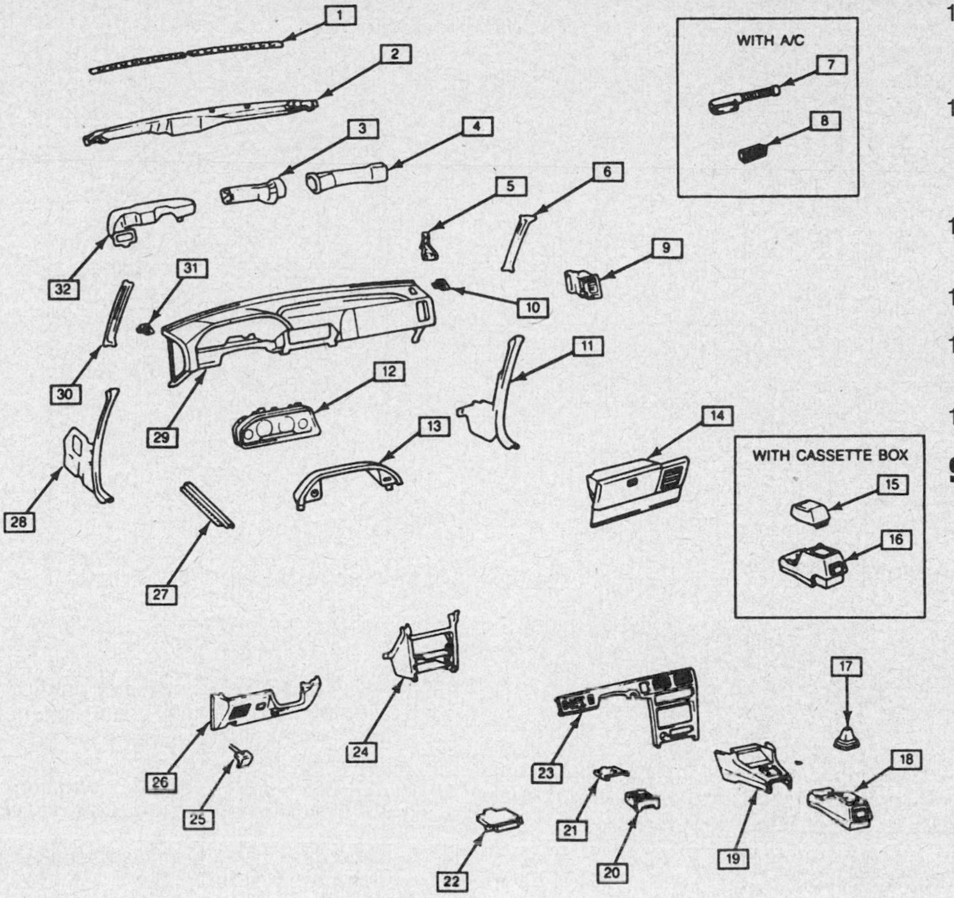
WITH A/C
WITH CASSETTE BOX
GC9149100071000X

1 DEFROSTER GRILLE
2 DEFROSTER DUCT
3 CENTER VENTILATION DUCT
4 RIGHT VENTILATION DUCT
5 BRACE
6 A PILLAR TRIM
7 A/C DUCT
8 LOWER A/C DEFLECTOR
9 RIGHT VENTILATION DEFLECTOR
10 RIGHT WINDOW DEFLECTOR
11 COWL SIDE TRIM
12 INSTRUMENT CLUSTER
13 CLUSTER BEZEL
14 GLOVE BOX AND TRIM ASSEMBLY
15 CASSETTE BOX
16 REAR CONSOLE
17 SHIFT LEVER BOOT (M/T)
18 REAR CONSOLE
19 FRONT CONSOLE
20 ASHTRAY
21 RETAINER
22 CUP HOLDER
23 TRIM BEZEL
24 CENTER CONSOLE TRIM
25 HOOD RELEASE LEVER
26 LEFT LOWER DASH TRIM
27 SCUFF PLATE
28 COWL SIDE TRIM
29 INSTRUMENT PANEL
30 "A" PILLAR TRIM
31 LEFT WINDOW DEFLECTOR
32 LEFT VENTILATION DUCT

Fig. 81 Exploded view of I/P. 1992 Prizm

ers and remove instrument panel.

34. Reverse procedure to install.

1993–94

Refer to **Fig. 86** when replacing the instrument panel.

1. Disconnect battery ground cable.
2. Remove A-pillar lower trim panel from both sides.
3. Remove steering wheel as follows:
   a. Place front wheel in straight ahead position.
   b. Remove inflator module.
   c. Remove horn electrical connector and cruise control electrical connector, if equipped.
   d. Remove steering wheel retaining nut, then place matchmarks on steering wheel and main shaft.
   e. Remove steering wheel using suitable puller.
4. Remove five screws and steering column upper and lower trim panels.
5. Remove center console.
6. Remove two screws and instrument cluster trim panel, disengaging two lower clips.
7. Remove four screws and instrument cluster assembly, disconnecting three electrical connectors.
8. Remove one screw and instrument panel left side ventilation duct. Unsnap and remove right side ventilation duct.
9. Disconnect left, center and right side electrical connectors and fuse blocks from under instrument panel.
10. Disconnect left and right ground wires.
11. Remove three heater control assembly screws and set heater control assembly aside.
12. **On models with cruise control,** remove cruise control module and disconnect electrical connector.
13. **On all models,** disconnect and remove ground wires from instrument panel support bracket.
14. Disconnect electrical connectors from heater evaporator case, then unclip and remove right and left lower B-pillar trim covers.
15. Disconnect rear door lock connectors, if equipped, then unclip and remove A-pillar trim covers and remote control mirror switch electrical connector, if equipped.
16. Remove two bolts and two nuts and disconnect steering column from instrument panel.
17. Remove four mounting bolts from instrument panel.
18. Remove instrument panel from vehicle by lifting up and pulling rearward, disengaging five clips, **Fig. 87**
19. Reverse procedure to install.

STORM

1. Disconnect battery ground cable. **After disconnecting battery, wait 10 minutes before proceeding with removal procedure. The Energy Reserve Module in the DERM may maintain SIR system voltage for a period after the battery is disconnected.**
2. Pull out on switch bezel, **Fig. 88,** then disconnect electrical connectors and remove bezel.
3. Pull out on cigar lighter bezel, then disconnect cigar lighter electrical connector and remove bezel, **Fig. 89.**
4. Remove two hood release retaining screws, then disconnect hood release cable, **Fig. 90.**
5. Remove knee bezel retaining screws and nuts.
6. Remove two glove box hinge pins, then the glove box.
7. Remove front console mounting bracket.
8. Remove two meter hood hole covers, **Fig. 90.**
9. Remove four meter hood retaining screws.
10. Disconnect lighting and windshield wiper switch electrical connectors.
11. Remove meter hood and meter assembly.
12. Remove three defroster grille plastic retaining covers, **Fig. 91.**
13. Remove three bolts and two screws from defroster grille assembly, then the defroster grille.
14. Remove four bolts, two screws and one nut attaching instrument panel assembly.
15. Remove electrical harness to instrument panel retaining clips.
16. Remove instrument panel assembly.
17. Reverse procedure to install.

FLEETWOOD (RWD)

1. Remove left and right molding assemblies.
2. Remove windshield washer nozzle grille from upper trim pad assembly as follows:
   a. Pry upward to unseat spring clips.
   b. Remove sunload sensor and light sensor assembly (photocell) from grille assembly by rotating counterclockwise.

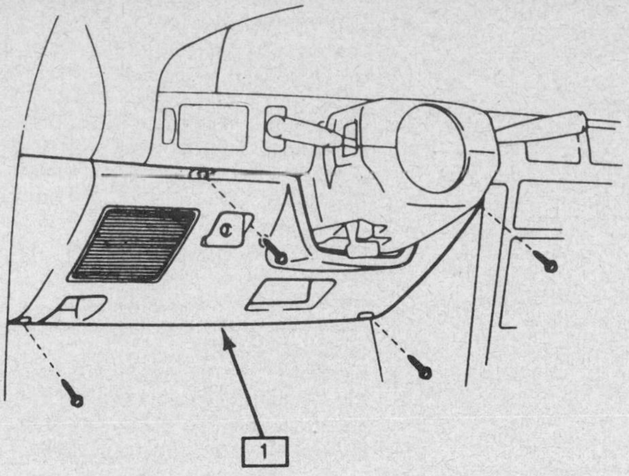
1
1 LEFT LOWER DASH TRIM
GC9149100072000X

Fig. 82 Lower left trim panel removal. 1992 Prizm

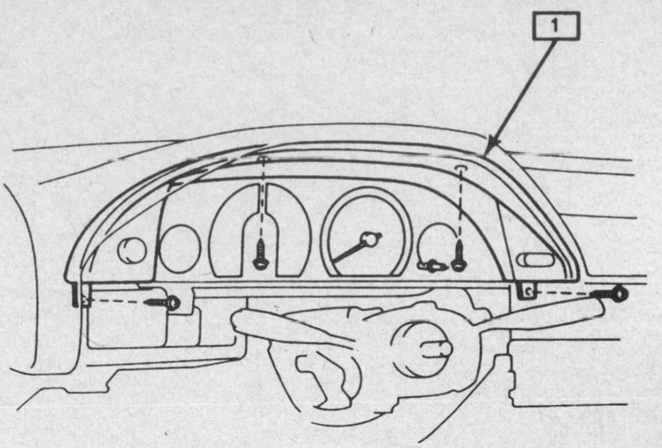
1
1 CLUSTER BEZEL
GC9149100073000X

Fig. 83 I/P cluster removal. 1992 Prizm

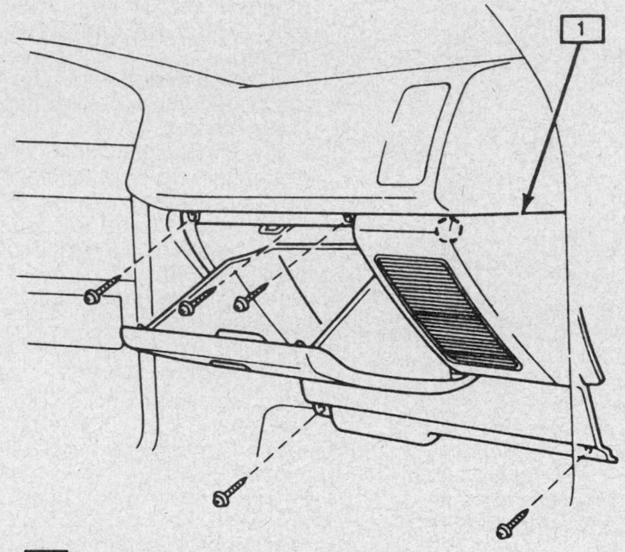
1
1 GLOVE BOX AND TRIM ASSEMBLY
GC9149100074000X

Fig. 84 Glove box assembly removal. 1992 Prizm

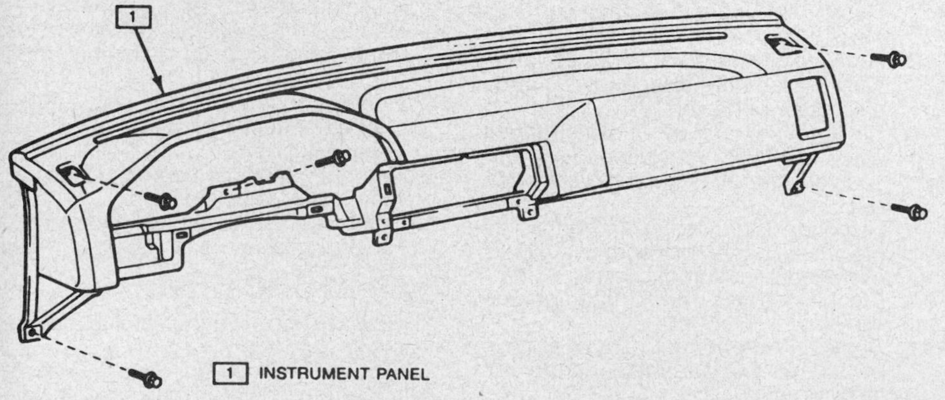
1
1 INSTRUMENT PANEL
GC9149100075000X

Fig. 85 I/P assembly removal. 1992 Prizm

3. Remove upper trim pad assembly, then left and right sound insulators.
4. Remove steering column opening filler assembly and knee bolster assembly.
5. Remove tilt wheel lever assembly and transmission shift indicator cable.
6. Remove cluster trim plate assembly, instrument cluster assembly and trim plate assembly, **Fig. 92.**
7. Remove heater and air conditioning control assembly, then radio assembly.
8. Disconnect and remove passenger inflator module as follows:
   a. Disconnect connector position assurance (CPA) and electrical connector.
   b. Disconnect fasteners from passenger inflator module.
   c. Remove passenger inflator module from vehicle.
9. Remove inside air temperature sensor assembly and duct.
10. Remove ashtray assembly.
11. Remove floor carpet retainer assemblies.
12. Remove instrument panel compartment, lamp and switch assemblies.
13. Remove rear compartment lid release switch assembly, then headlight switch assembly.
14. Remove steering column bracket nuts and lower steering column assembly.
15. Remove data link connector (DLC), **Fig. 93.**
16. Remove oil level module and coolant level sensor.
17. Remove instrument panel screws and nuts and lower tie bar bolt and screw.
18. Remove center lower brace bolt and screw attaching center lower brace to instrument panel assembly. Remove center lower brace and nut if necessary.
19. Remove instrument panel wiring harness assembly as follows:
   a. Disconnect harness assembly clips.
   b. Note harness assembly routing before removal.
20. Remove instrument panel, **Fig. 94.** Replace instrument panel nuts if necessary.

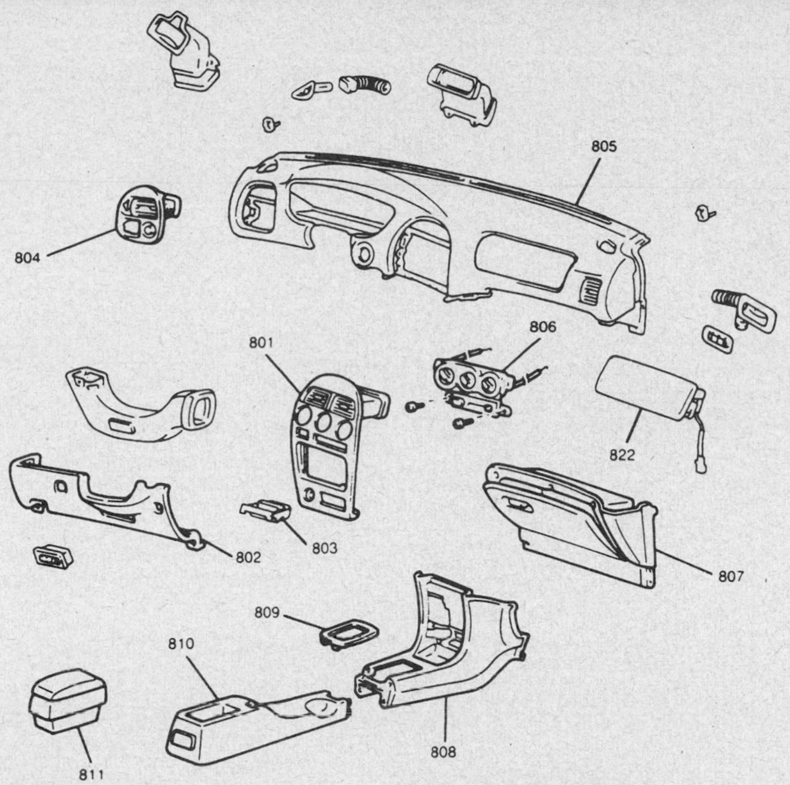
805
804
801
806
822
802
803
807
809
810
808
811

801 CENTER CONSOLE TRIM BEZEL
802 KNEE BOLSTER
803 ASHTRAY
804 INSTRUMENT PANEL LEFT-SIDE OUTLET TRIM BEZEL
805 INSTRUMENT PANEL
806 HEATER CONTROL ASSEMBLY
807 GLOVE BOX ASSEMBLY
808 CENTER CONSOLE
809 CENTER CONSOLE LOWER TRAY
810 REAR CENTER CONSOLE
811 ARM REST/STORAGE COMPARTMENT
822 PASSENGER INFLATOR MODULE

GC9149300101000X

Fig. 86 Exploded view of I/P. 1993-94 Prizm

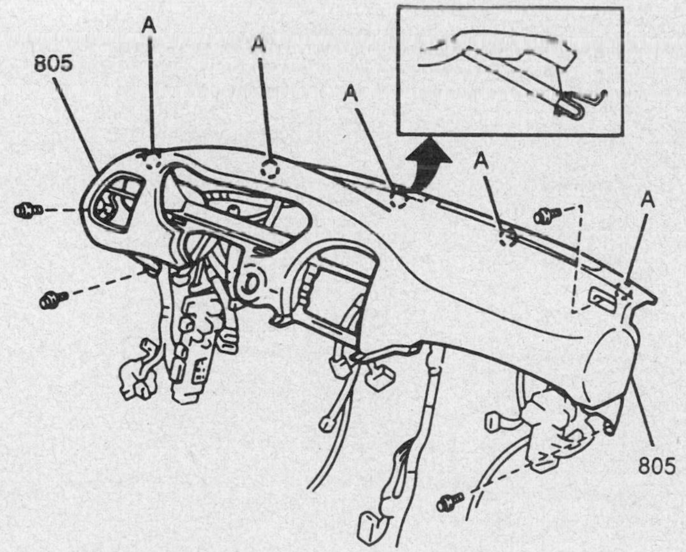
A
805
A
A
A
A
805

A CLIP LOCATIONS
805 INSTRUMENT PANEL

GC9149300076000X

Fig. 87 I/P assembly removal. 1993–94 Prizm

1 METER HOOD
2 METER ASSEMBLY
3 FRONT COVER HOLE COVER
4 FRONT COVER
5 INSTRUMENT PANEL ASSEMBLY

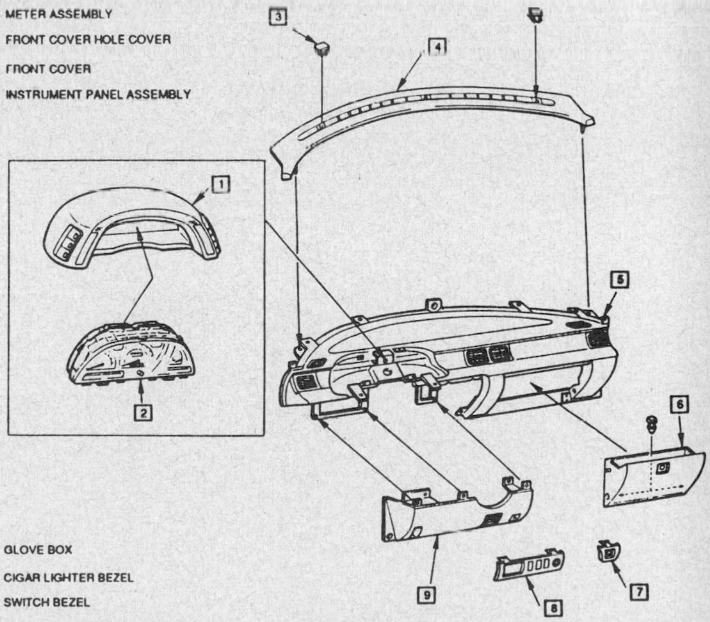
3
4
1
2
5
6
9
8
7

6 GLOVE BOX
7 CIGAR LIGHTER BEZEL
8 SWITCH BEZEL
9 KNEE PAD ASSEMBLY

GC9149100077000X

Fig. 88 I/P assembly. Storm

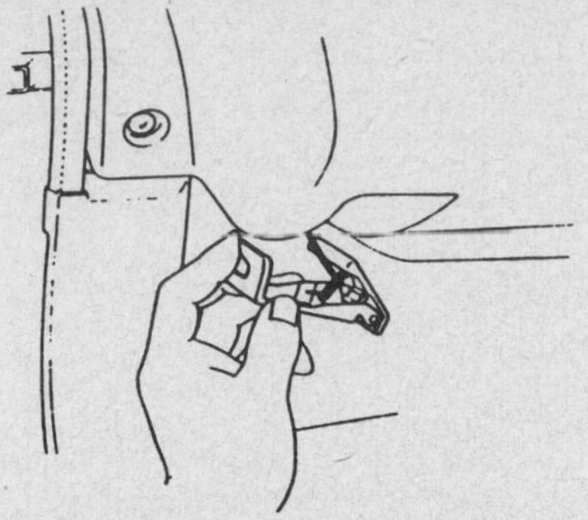

GC9149100078000X

Fig. 89 Disconnecting hood release cable. Storm

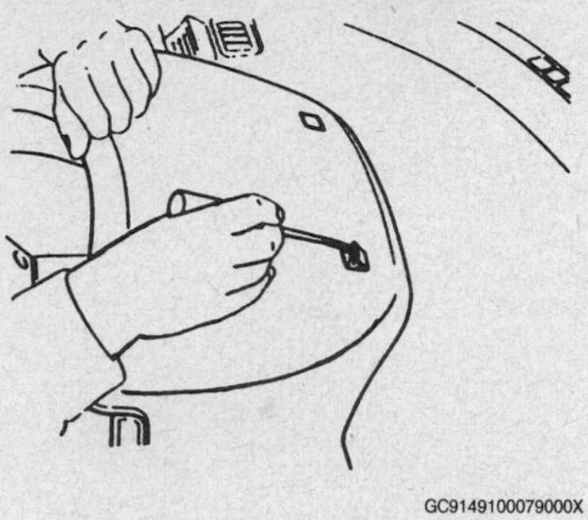

GC9149100079000X

Fig. 90 I/P hood retaining screws removal. Storm

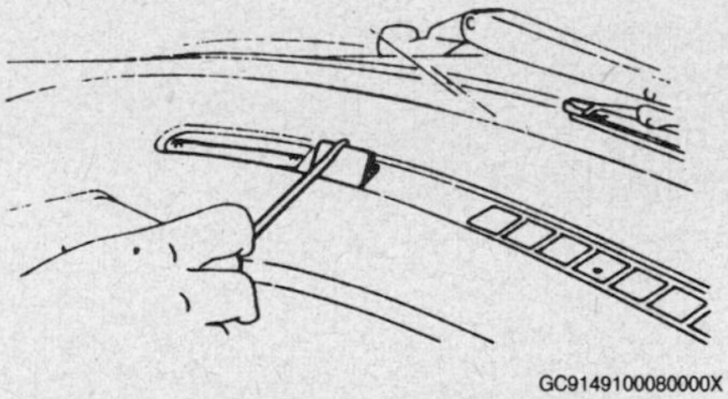

GC9149100080000X

Fig. 91 I/P front cover retaining screws removal. Storm

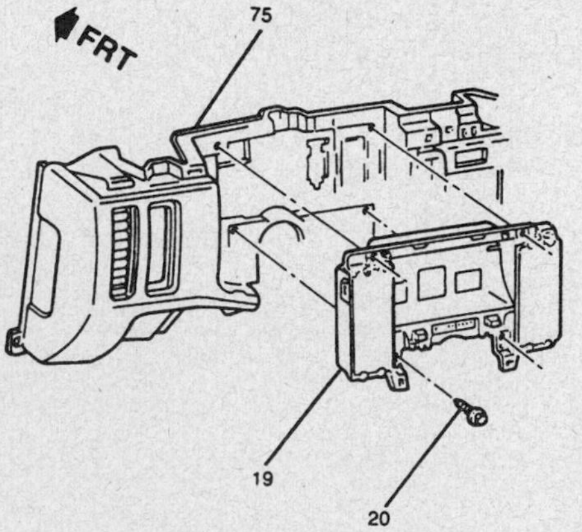
FRT
75
19
20

19 CLUSTER ASSEMBLY, INSTRUMENT
20 BOLT/SCREW, INSTRUMENT CLUSTER, 1.9 N•m (17 LB. IN.)
75 PANEL ASSEMBLY, INSTRUMENT

GC9149300081000X

Fig. 92 Instrument cluster assembly removal. 1993–94 Fleetwood (RWD)

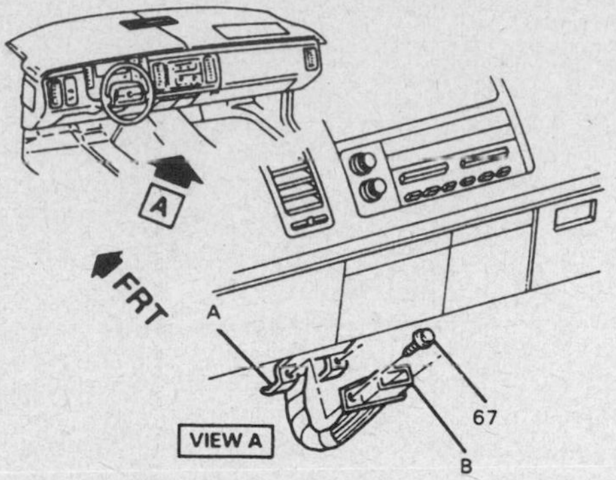
A
FRT
A
67
VIEW A
B

A BRACKET, DATA LINK CONNECTOR
B CONNECTOR, DATA LINK
67 BOLT/SCREW, INSTRUMENT PANEL WIRING HARNESS ENGINE CONTROL MODULE DATA LINK CONNECTOR, 1.9 N•m (17 LB. IN.)

GC9149300082000X

Fig. 93 Data link Connector (DLC) removal. 1993–94 Fleetwood (RWD)

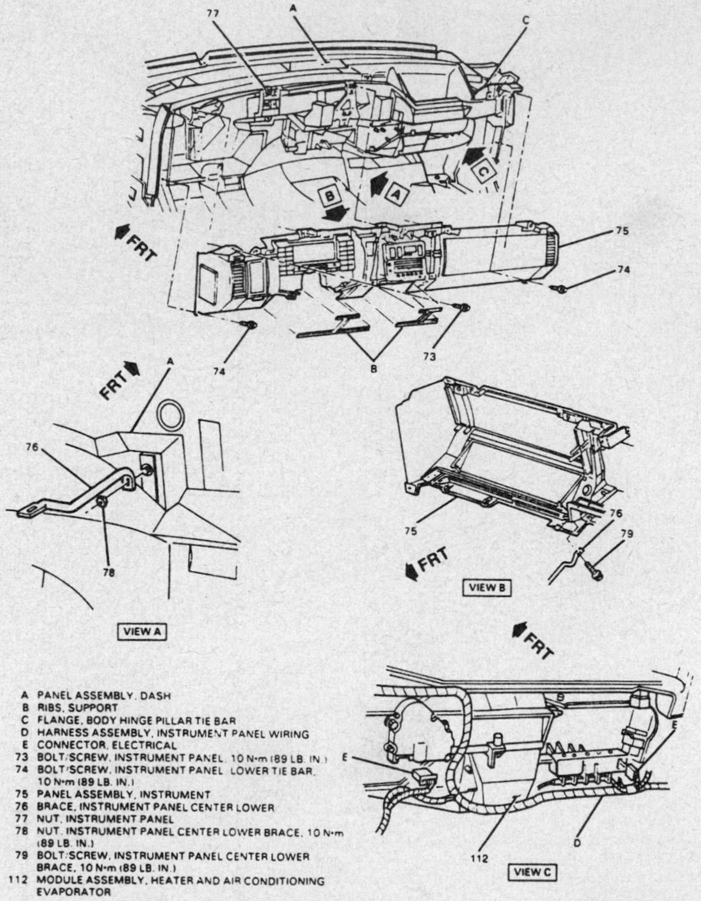
77
A
C
B
A
C
FRT
75
74
74
B
73
FRT
A
76
78
VIEW A
75
76
79
FRT
VIEW B
FRT
E
112
D
VIEW C

A PANEL ASSEMBLY, DASH
B RIBS, SUPPORT
C FLANGE, BODY HINGE PILLAR TIE BAR
D HARNESS ASSEMBLY, INSTRUMENT PANEL WIRING
E CONNECTOR, ELECTRICAL
73 BOLT/SCREW, INSTRUMENT PANEL, 10 N•m (89 LB. IN.)
74 BOLT/SCREW, INSTRUMENT PANEL LOWER TIE BAR, 10 N•m (89 LB. IN.)
75 PANEL ASSEMBLY, INSTRUMENT
76 BRACE, INSTRUMENT PANEL CENTER LOWER
77 NUT, INSTRUMENT PANEL
78 NUT, INSTRUMENT PANEL CENTER LOWER BRACE, 10 N•m (89 LB. IN.)
79 BOLT/SCREW, INSTRUMENT PANEL CENTER LOWER BRACE, 10 N•m (89 LB. IN.)
112 MODULE ASSEMBLY, HEATER AND AIR CONDITIONING EVAPORATOR

GC9149300083000X

Fig. 94 Instrument panel mounting. 1993–94 Fleetwood (RWD)

STEERING COLUMNS

NOTE: On Air Bag Equipped Models, Refer To "Air Bag System Precautions" Located In The Front Of This Manual For System Disarming & Arming Procedures.

INDEX

STEERING COLUMN EXPLODED VIEWS

Model	Year	Column Type		Fig. No.	Page No.
		Standard	Tilt		
Achieva	1992-94	X	—	25	25-16
	1992-94	—	X	28	25-19
Beretta & Corsica	1992-94	—	X	37	25-27
	1992-94	X	—	32	25-24
Bonneville	1992-94 ②	—	X	55	25-40
	1992-94 ①	—	X	57	25-42
Brougham	1992	—	X	64	25-45
Camaro & Firebird	1992-94	—	X	51	25-36
Caprice	1992-94	X	—	74	25-55
	1992-94	—	X	75	25-57
Cavalier	1992-94	X	—	24	25-15
	1992-94	—	X	27	25-18
Century	1992-94	X	—	65	25-46
	1992-94	—	X	66	25-47
Corvette	1992-94	—	X	52	25-37
Custom Cruiser	1992	X	—	74	25-55
	1992	—	X	75	25-57
Cutlass Ciera	1992-94	X	—	65	25-46
	1992-94	—	X	66	25-47
Cutlass Cruiser	1992-94	X	—	65	25-46
	1992-94	—	X	66	25-47
Cutlass Supreme	1992-94	X	—	43	25-30
	1992-93	—	X	47	25-32
	1994	—	X	48	25-33
DeVille	1992-94	—	X	55	25-40
Eldorado & Seville	1992	—	X	53	25-38
	1993-94 ②	—	X	67	25-49
	1993-94 ③	—	X	68	25-51
Fleetwood (FWD)	1992	—	X	55	25-40
Fleetwood (RWD)	1993-94	—	X	9	25-8
Grand Am	1992-94	X	—	25	25-16
	1992-94	—	X	28	25-19
Grand Prix	1992-94	X	—	43	25-30
	1992-93	—	X	47	25-32
	1994	—	X	48	25-33
Impala SS	1994 ⑤	X	—	74	25-55
	1994 ⑤	—	X	75	25-57
LeMans	1992-93	X	—	83	25-62
	1992-93	—	X	84	25-62
LeSabre	1992-94 ⑤	—	X	55	25-40
Lumina	1992-94	X	—	43	25-30
	1992-93	—	X	47	25-32
	1994	—	X	48	25-33
Metro	1992-94 ④	X	—	80	25-60
	1992-94 ⑤	X	—	22	25-14
Park Avenue	1992-94 ⑤	—	X	55	25-40
Prizm	1992	X	X	85	25-63
	1992	—	X	86	25-64
	1993-94	X	X	90	25-66
Riviera	1992-93	—	X	54	25-39

Continued

STEERING COLUMN EXPLODED VIEWS—Continued

Model	Year	Column Type		Fig. No.	Page No.
		Standard	Tilt		
Regal	1992–94	X	—	43	25-30
	1992–93	—	X	47	25-32
	1994	—	X	48	25-33
Roadmaster	1992–94	X	—	74	25-55
	1992–94	—	X	75	25-57
Skylark	1992–94	X	—	26	25-17
	1992–94	—	X	29	25-20
Sunbird	1992–94	X	—	30	25-21
	1992–94	—	X	31	25-22
Toronado & Trofeo	1992	—	X	56	25-41
88 & 98	1992–94①	—	X	57	25-42
	1992–94②	—	X	55	25-40

①—Floor shift.
②—Column shift.
③—Console shift.
④—Less SIR.
⑤—With SIR.

PRECAUTIONS

AIR BAG SYSTEMS

Refer to "Air Bag System Precautions" in the front of this manual for system disarming and arming procedures.

SERVICE

It is important that only the specified screws, bolts and nuts be used during the mandatory assembling sequence and torquod to specifications to insure proper breakaway action of column under impact. Avoid using excessively long bolts as they may prevent a portion of the steering column from collapsing under impact.

When removing or installing, steering wheel, ignition switch or lock, turn signal switch, adjusting transmission linkage, or installing and adjusting neutral-start or back-up light switch, refer to appropriate car chapter.

If a shift tube shows a sheared plastic injection, a new shift tube must be installed. If a steering shaft shows a sheared plastic, but it is not bent, it can be repaired by using a Service Steering Shaft Repair Kit part number 7810077. The kit contains instructions and dimensions for all steering columns. On some models, the attaching brackets will shear under impact and must also be replaced.

STEERING COLUMN DAMAGE

When the steering column is removed from the vehicle, it is extremely susceptible to damage. Dropping the steering column assembly on its end could collapse the steering shaft assembly or loosen plastic injections that keep the steering column assembly rigid. Leaning on the steering column assembly could cause the jacket to bend or deform. Any of these conditions could impair the steering column assembly's collapsible design. If the steering wheel must be removed, use only the specified steering wheel puller and steering wheel puller bolts. Never hammer on the end of the shaft.

TROUBLESHOOTING

Refer to **Figs. 1 and 2** for steering column troubleshooting.

STEERING COLUMN

REPLACE

CAPRICE, CUSTOM CRUISER, IMPALA SS & ROADMASTER

Removal

Wheels must be in a straight forward position and the key must be in the Lock position when removing or installing column to ensure proper alignment of components during installation.

Care must be taken when handling column with a live inflator module. Never point bag deploy surface toward you, and never stand column on steering wheel. Accidental deployment in these positions may cause injury. Always face bag deploy surface toward open space to allow for unrestricted expansion.

1. Remove the inflator module as follows:
   a. With the ignition switch in the Off position and the battery ground cable.
   b. Remove left side sound insulator.
   c. Remove the Torx screws from the back of the steering wheel, then remove the inflator module from steering wheel.
   d. Remove the horn contact by pushing lightly and twisting counterclockwise.
   e. Disconnect the coil assembly connector from inflator module.
2. Remove stop lamp switch.
3. Remove nut and bolt from pot joint coupling, attaching upper intermediate shaft to the steering column, **Fig. 3.**
4. Disconnect shift linkage from steering column.
5. If steering column is to be replaced or serviced, remove steering wheel as described in the "Electrical" section of the appropriate vehicle section in the front of this manual.
6. Remove steering column opening filler, then driver side knee bolster and deflector.
7. Remove bolts attaching toe plate to cowl, then the shift indicator cable from steering column.
8. Disconnect electrical connectors from column, then remove capsule nuts attaching column support bracket to instrument panel carrier. If shims are used, retain for use in installation.
9. Remove steering column from vehicle.

Installation

If a service replacement column is being installed, do not remove antirotation pin until after steering column has been connected to steering gear. Removing pin before column is installed or connected will damage SIR coil assembly.

1. Carefully place column into position in vehicle.
2. Raise column and loosely install capsule nuts, Install shims, if equipped.
3. **Torque** capsule nuts to 20 ft. lbs.
4. Install nut and bolt to pot joint, attaching upper intermediate shaft to steering column shaft. **Torque** to 40 ft. lbs.
5. Connect shift linkage to steering column.
6. Install toe plate attaching bolts and

ALL COLUMNS (NO MARK)
TILT COLUMN ONLY*

LOCK SYSTEM

Will Not Unlock
1. Shear flange on sector shaft collapsed.
2. Lock bolt damaged.
3. Damaged lock cylinder.
4. Damaged housing.
5. Damaged sector.
6. Damaged rack.

Will Not Lock
1. Lock bolt spring broken or defective.
2. Damaged sector.
3. Damaged lock cylinder
4. Burr on lock bolt.
5. Damaged housing.
6. Transmission linkage adjustment incorrect.
7. Damaged rack.
8. Interference between bowl and rack coupling*.
9. Ignition switch stuck.
10. Actuator rod restricted.

High Lock Effort
1. Lock cylinder damaged.
2. Ignition switch damaged.
3. Rack preload spring broken or deformed.
4. Burrs on sector, rack, housing, support or actuator rod coupling.
5. Bent sector shaft.
6. Damaged rack.
7. Extreme misalignment of housing to cover.*
8. Distorted coupling slot in rack.*
9. Bent actuator rod.
10. Ignition switch mounting bracket bent.
11. Improper shift linkage adjustment.

Will Stick In "Start"
1. Actuator rod deformed.
2. Check items under "High Lock Effort".

Key Cannot Be Removed In "Off-Lock"
1. Ignition switch is not set correctly.
2. Damaged lock cylinder.

Lock Cylinder Can Be Removed
1. Lock cylinder retaining screw missing.

COLUMN

Noise In Column
1. Intermediate shaft pinch bolt not tightened.
2. Column not correctly aligned.
3. Horn contact ring not lubricated.
4. Lack of grease on bearings.
5. Loose sight shields.*
6. Lower or upper steering shaft bearing worn or broken.
7. Shaft lock snap ring not seated.
8. Plastic spherical joint not lubricated.*

High Steering Shaft Effort
1. Column assembly misaligned.
2. Improperly installed or deformed dust seal.
3. Damaged upper or lower bearing.
4. Flash on I.D. of shift tube from plastic joint.
5. Tight intermediate steering shaft universal joint.

High Shift Effort (Automatic)
1. Column not aligned correctly in car.
2. Wave washer with burrs.*
3. Improperly installed dust seal.
4. Lack of grease on seal or bearing.
5. Improper screws used for ignition switch.
6. Burr on upper or lower end of shift tube.

Improper Transmission Shifting (Automatic Transmission)
1. Sheared shift tube joint or lower shift lever weld.
2. Improper transmission linkage adjustment.
3. Improper gate plate.

Lash In Mounted Column Assembly
1. IP to column upper and lower bracket mounting bolts loose.
2. Broken weld nuts on jacket.
3. IP upper bracket capsule sheared.
4. Loose shoes in housing.*
5. Loose tilt head pivot pins.*
6. Loose shoe lock pin in support.*
7. Loose support screws.
8. Column upper and lower bracket to jacket bolts loose.

GC6049100041000X

Fig. 1 Steering column troubleshooting

torque to 58 inch lbs.
7. Connect electrical connectors to column.
8. If a service replacement steering column is being installed, remove anti-rotation pin.
9. Install shift indicator cable clip to steering column and adjust shift indicator if necessary.
10. Install driver knee bolster and deflector, then the steering column opening filler.
11. If a service replacement steering column is being installed, remove hexagon locking nut, then the coil assembly shipping cover and disengage connector from cover.
12. Replace steering wheel if removed.
13. Connect battery ground cable.
14. Install stop lamp switch, adjust if necessary.

BONNEVILLE, DEVILLE, FLEETWOOD (FWD), LESABRE, PARK AVENUE, 88 & 98

Removal

Wheels must be in a straight forward position and the key must be in the Lock position when removing or installing column to ensure proper alignment of components during installation.

Care must be taken when handling column with a live inflator module. Never point bag deploy surface toward you, and never stand column on steering wheel. Accidental deployment in these positions may cause injury. Always face bag deploy surface toward open space to allow for unrestricted expansion.

1. Remove the inflator module as follows:
   a. With the ignition switch in the Off position and the battery ground cable.
   b. Remove left side sound insulator.
   c. Remove the Torx screws from the back of the steering wheel, then remove the inflator module from steering wheel.
   d. Remove the horn contact by pushing lightly and twisting counterclockwise.
   e. Disconnect the coil assembly connector from inflator module.
2. Remove instrument panel steering column trim plate.
3. Remove two screws retaining filler,

ALL COLUMNS (NO MARK)
TILT COLUMN ONLY*

Housing Scraping On Bowl
1. Bowl bent or not concentric with hub.*

Steering Wheel Loose
1. Excessive clearance between holes in support or housing and pivot pin diameters.*
2. Defective or missing anti-lash spring in spheres.*
3. Upper bearing not seated in housing.*
4. Upper bearing inner race seal missing.*
5. Loose support screws.
6. Bearing proload spring missing or broken.*

Steering Wheel Loose (Every Other Tilt Position)
1. Loose fit between shoe and shoe pivot pin.*
2. Shoe not free in slot.*

Steering Column Not Locking In Any Tilt Position
1. Shoe seized on its pivot pin.*
2. Shoe grooves may have burrs or dirt.*
3. Shoe lock spring weak or broken.*

Steering Wheel Fails To Return To Top Tilt Position
1. Pivot pins are bound up.*
2. Wheel tilt spring is defective.*
3. Turn signal switch wires too tight.*

Noise When Tilting Column
1. Upper tilt bumpers worn.*
2. Tilt spring rubbing in housing.*

Miscellaneous
1. Housing loose on jacket – will be noticed with ignition in "off-lock" and a torque applied to the steering wheel.

GC6049100042000X

Fig. 2 Steering column troubleshooting

thon four bolt/screws from column reinforcement plate and the reinforcement plate.
4. Disconnect any necessary electrical connectors.
5. Disconnect shift control cable at actuator, then remove four seal assembly mounting bolts, **Fig. 4.**
6. Remove bolt from upper knuckle of intermediate steering shaft, **Fig. 4.**
7. Remove nut and bolt holding lower brace assembly, then remove lower brace.
8. Remove remaining bracket bolts, then remove the lower support bracket.
9. Remove two column to upper support retaining bolts/screws, then the column.

Installation

1. Install lower support bracket to steering column, **Fig. 5.** Do not tighten fasteners at this time.
2. Install two bolts into upper support assembly, **Fig. 5.** Do not tighten completely.
3. Position steering column with lower support bracket slots over fasteners installed in step 2. Do not allow to hang freely and do not tighten fasteners.

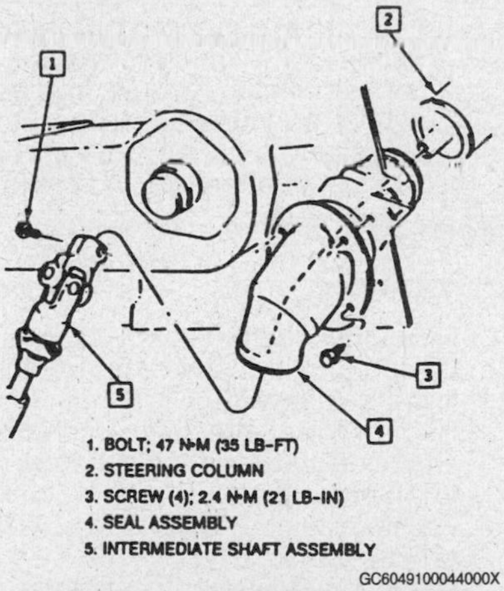
1. BOLT; 47 N·M (35 LB-FT)
2. STEERING COLUMN
3. SCREW (4); 2.4 N·M (21 LB-IN)
4. SEAL ASSEMBLY
5. INTERMEDIATE SHAFT ASSEMBLY
GC6049100044000X

Fig. 4 Intermediate shaft & boot installation. Bonneville, DeVille, Fleetwood (FWD), LeSabre, Park, Avenue, 88 & 98

4. Install two bolts through steering column into upper support assembly, but do not tighten.
5. Install upper knuckle of intermediate steering shaft on upper steering shaft. **Torque** bolt to 35 ft. lbs.

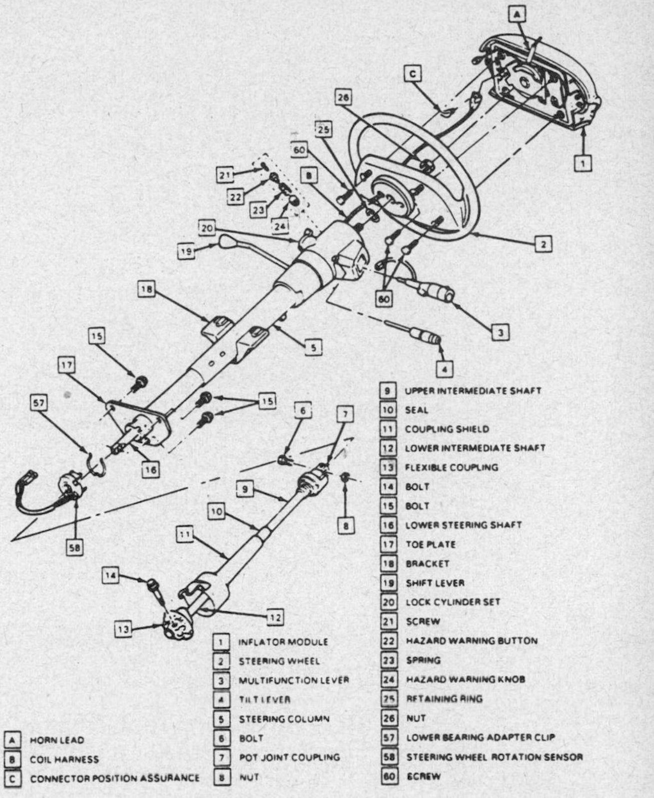
A HORN LEAD
B COIL HARNESS
C CONNECTOR POSITION ASSURANCE
1 INFLATOR MODULE
2 STEERING WHEEL
3 MULTIFUNCTION LEVER
4 TILT LEVER
5 STEERING COLUMN
6 BOLT
7 POT JOINT COUPLING
8 NUT
9 UPPER INTERMEDIATE SHAFT
10 SEAL
11 COUPLING SHIELD
12 LOWER INTERMEDIATE SHAFT
13 FLEXIBLE COUPLING
14 BOLT
15 BOLT
16 LOWER STEERING SHAFT
17 TOE PLATE
18 BRACKET
19 SHIFT LEVER
20 LOCK CYLINDER SET
21 SCREW
22 HAZARD WARNING BUTTON
23 SPRING
24 HAZARD WARNING KNOB
25 RETAINING RING
26 NUT
57 LOWER BEARING ADAPTER CLIP
58 STEERING WHEEL ROTATION SENSOR
60 SCREW
GC6049100043000X

Fig. 3 Steering column replacement. Caprice, Custom Cruiser, Impala SS & Roadmaster

6. Install seal assembly and **torque** four bolts to 21 inch lbs.
7. Remove left bolt from lower support bracket, then install lower brace assembly. **Torque** bolts to 84 inch lbs.
8. **Torque** remaining lower brace and bracket bolts to 84 inch lbs. and upper support assembly bolts to 20 ft. lbs.
9. **Torque** two lower support bracket through bolts to 20 ft. lbs., then connect shift control cable and electrical connections.
10. Install steering wheel inflator module as follows:
    a. With ignition off, install horn contact, then connect coil assembly connector to inflator module.
    b. Push coil assembly lead wires into channel in lower right portion of steering wheel, then install inflator module in steering wheel.
    c. **Torque** screws holding inflator module to steering wheel to 25 inch lbs.
    d. Install left side sound insulator.
    e. Connect battery ground cable.
11. Install reinforcement plate and **torque** bolts to 17 inch lbs.
12. Install instrument panel column filler and trim plate.

ELDORADO, RIVIERA, SEVILLE, TORONADO & TROFEO

Removal

Wheels must be in a straight forward position and the key must be in the

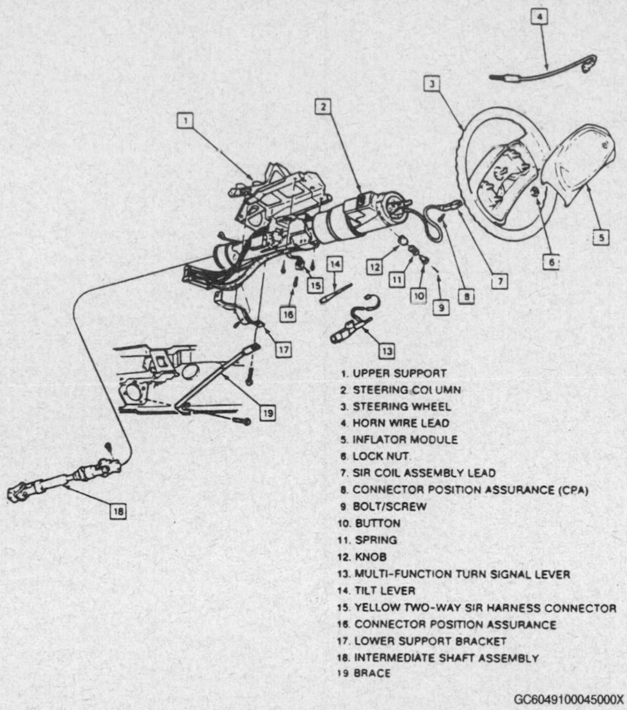
1. UPPER SUPPORT
2. STEERING COLUMN
3. STEERING WHEEL
4. HORN WIRE LEAD
5. INFLATOR MODULE
6. LOCK NUT
7. SIR COIL ASSEMBLY LEAD
8. CONNECTOR POSITION ASSURANCE (CPA)
9. BOLT/SCREW
10. BUTTON
11. SPRING
12. KNOB
13. MULTI-FUNCTION TURN SIGNAL LEVER
14. TILT LEVER
15. YELLOW TWO-WAY SIR HARNESS CONNECTOR
16. CONNECTOR POSITION ASSURANCE
17. LOWER SUPPORT BRACKET
18. INTERMEDIATE SHAFT ASSEMBLY
19. BRACE
GC6049100045000X

Fig. 5 Steering column replacement. Bonneville, DeVille, Fleetwood (FWD), LeSabre, Park Avenue, 88 & 98

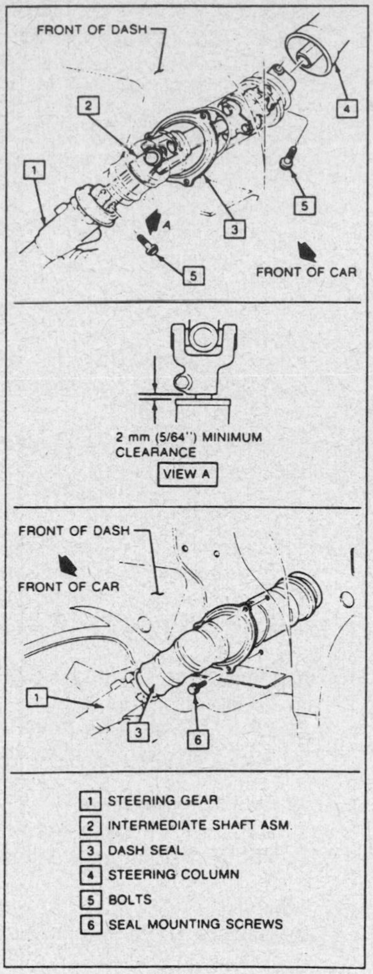
FRONT OF DASH
FRONT OF CAR
2 mm (5/64") MINIMUM CLEARANCE
VIEW A
FRONT OF DASH
FRONT OF CAR
1 STEERING GEAR
2 INTERMEDIATE SHAFT ASM.
3 DASH SEAL
4 STEERING COLUMN
5 BOLTS
6 SEAL MOUNTING SCREWS
GC6049100048000X

Fig. 6 Intermediate shaft & boot installation. Eldorado, Riviera, Seville, Toronado & Trofeo

Lock position when removing or installing column to ensure proper alignment of components during installation.

Care must be taken when handling column with a live inflator module. Never point bag deploy surface toward you, and never stand column on steering wheel. Accidental deployment in these positions may cause injury. Always face bag deploy surface toward open space to allow for unrestricted expansion.

1. Remove inflator module as follows:
   a. Remove screws from back of steering wheel, then the inflator module from steering wheel.
   b. Disconnect horn contact by pushing lightly and twisting counterclockwise.
   c. Disconnect coil assembly connector from inflator module.
2. Remove knee bolster and steering column reinforcement plate.
3. Disconnect electrical connectors from column.
4. Remove pinch bolt from intermediate shaft, **Fig. 6.**
5. Remove lower support bracket from vehicle.
6. Remove upper column support from instrument panel, then the column from vehicle.

Installation

1. Install column in vehicle and support at upper bracket with two bolts, **Fig. 7**, do not tighten at this time.
2. Install column lower support bracket in vehicle, do not tighten at this time.
3. Connect column intermediate shaft to steering rack, install pinch bolt and **torque** to 35 ft. lbs.
4. **Torque** upper and lower column support bolts to 20 ft. lbs. and lower bracket to column screws to 12 ft. lbs.
5. Connect electrical connectors to column.
6. Install knee bolster and column reinforcement plate.
7. Install steering wheel inflator module as follows:
   a. With ignition off, install horn contact, then connect coil assembly connector to inflator module.
   b. Install inflator module in steering wheel and **torque** screws to 27 inch lbs.
   c. Connect battery ground cable.

BROUGHAM

Removal

1. Disconnect battery ground cable.
2. Disconnect transmission linkage at lower shift lever.
3. Remove nut attaching intermediate shaft and column, then separate shaft from the column.
4. Remove column lower cover and lower fuse panel cover.
5. Remove lefthand A/C outlet duct.
6. Disconnect turn signal harness connector, park neutral switch, parking brake release hose and headlamp dimmer switch from column.
7. Remove clip retaining shift cable and loosen two upper support nuts.
8. Position carpet out of the way to gain access to the cowl insulator and seal fasteners.
9. Remove cowl insulator and cover seal.
10. Remove two upper column support nuts, then the column from vehicle.

Installation

1. Install column in vehicle and finger tighten upper mounting bracket nuts, **Fig. 8.**
2. Install nut securing column to the intermediate shaft and finger tighten.
3. Connect transmission linkage to lower shaft lever.
4. Connect shift cable and securing clip.
5. Install cowl seal and finger tighten nuts and bolts.
6. Connect turn signal harness, park neutral switch, parking brake release hose and headlamp dimmer switch connectors.
7. **Torque** upper column bracket nuts to 20 ft. lbs., cowl cover seal nuts and bolts to 35 inch lbs. and column to intermediate shaft bolt to 52 ft. lbs.
8. Install cowl seal insulator, lefthand A/C outlet duct, lower fuse panel cover and steering column lower cover.
9. Connect battery ground cable.

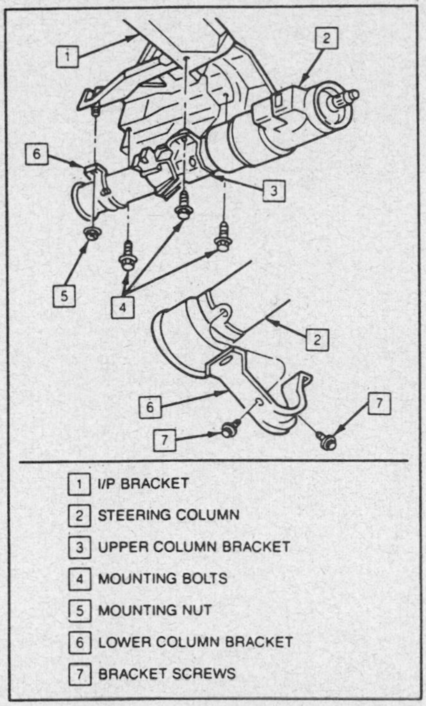
1
2
3
4
5
6
7
1 I/P BRACKET
2 STEERING COLUMN
3 UPPER COLUMN BRACKET
4 MOUNTING BOLTS
5 MOUNTING NUT
6 LOWER COLUMN BRACKET
7 BRACKET SCREWS
GC6049100049000X

Fig. 7 Steering column installation. Eldorado, Riviera, Seville, Toronado & Trofeo

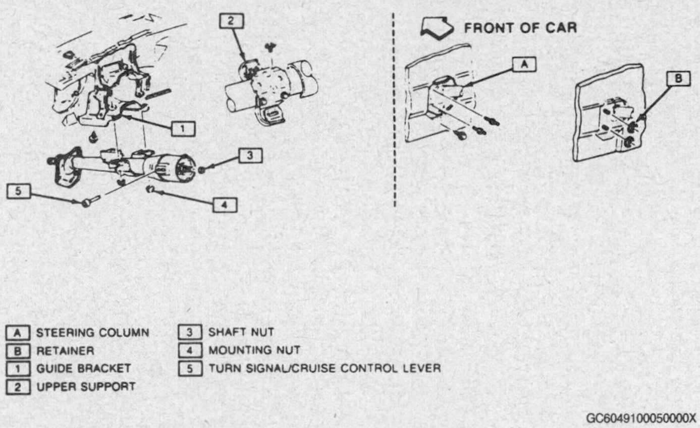
FRONT OF CAR
A STEERING COLUMN
B RETAINER
1 GUIDE BRACKET
2 UPPER SUPPORT
3 SHAFT NUT
4 MOUNTING NUT
5 TURN SIGNAL/CRUISE CONTROL LEVER
GC6049100050000X

Fig. 8 Steering column installation. Brougham

FLEETWOOD (RWD)

Removal

Front wheels must be straight ahead and the ignition switch in the Lock position before disconnecting the steering column assembly or the intermediate steering shaft assembly from the steering gear assembly. Failure to do so will cause the SIR coil assembly to become uncentered, which will case damage to the SIR coil assembly.

1. Remove stop lamp switch assembly.
2. Remove instrument panel steering column opening filler assembly.
3. Remove instrument panel driver knee bolster assembly and deflector.
4. Disconnect steering wheel rotation sensor electrical connector.
5. Remove bolt and nut from pot joint coupling, attaching upper intermediate steering shaft assembly to steering column assembly, **Fig. 9.**
6. Remove nuts attaching steering column bracket to instrument panel carrier, then lower the steering column assembly.
7. Disconnect shift indicator cable from steering column assembly.
8. Disconnect all electrical connectors, then remove automatic transmission range selector rod assembly from steering column.
9. Remove bolts attaching jacket to cowl, then remove the steering wheel assembly, if required.
10. Remove steering column assembly from vehicle.

Installation

If a service replacement steering column assembly is being installed, do not remove the anti-rotation pin until the steering column assembly has been connected to the steering gear. **Removing the anti-rotation pin before steering column is connected to the steering gear assembly may damage the SIR coil assembly.**

1. Place steering column in vehicle and install bolts securing jacket to cowl. **Torque** bolts to 58 inch lbs.
2. Connect electrical connectors, then remove anti-rotation pin if service replacement steering column assembly is being installed.
3. Connect indicator cable to steering column assembly, then install nuts attaching steering column bracket. **Torque** nuts to 20 ft. lbs.
4. Install bolt and nut to coupling, attaching upper intermediate steering shaft assembly to steering column assembly. **Torque** nut to 40 ft. lbs.
5. Connect steering wheel rotation sensor electrical connector.
6. Install automatic transmission range selector rod assembly to steering column assembly.
7. Adjust shift linkage, then install stop lamp switch assembly.
8. Install instrument panel driver knee bolster assembly and deflector.
9. Install instrument panel steering column opening filler assembly.
10. Remove hexagon locking nut, if a service replacement steering column is being installed.
11. Install steering wheel, if removed.

CAMARO & FIREBIRD

Removal

Wheels must be in a straight forward position and the key must be in the Lock position when removing or installing column to ensure proper alignment of components during installation.

Care must be taken when handling column with a live inflator module. Never point bag deploy surface toward you, and never stand column on steering wheel. Accidental deployment in these positions may cause injury. Always face bag deploy surface toward open space to allow for unrestricted expansion.

1. Remove the inflator module as follows:
   a. Remove the Torx screws from the back of the steering wheel, then remove the inflator module from steering wheel.
   b. Disconnect the coil assembly connector from inflator module.
2. Disconnect park lock cable from the ignition switch inhibitor, if applicable.
3. Remove bolt and nut from upper intermediate shaft clamp, **Fig. 10.**
4. Remove knee bolster and bracket and screws attaching toe pan cover to the cowl.
5. Disconnect electrical connectors and remove capsule nuts attaching column support bracket to the instrument panel.
6. Remove steering column from the vehicle.

Installation

1. Install steering column into the vehicle, then connect the park lock cable to the ignition switch inhibitor, if applicable.
2. Install the capsule nuts attaching the column support bracket to the instrument panel.
3. Install the bolt and nut to the clamp attaching the intermediate shaft to the steering column and **torque** to 44 ft. lbs.
4. Install screws attaching toe pan cover to the cowl and connect electrical connectors.
5. Install knee bolster and bracket and sound insulator panel.
6. Connect coil assembly to the inflator module, then install inflator module to the steering wheel and **torque** screws to 25 inch lbs.
7. Install left side sound insulator.

CORVETTE

Removal

Wheels must be in a straight forward position and the key must be in the Lock position when removing or installing column to ensure proper alignment of components during installation.

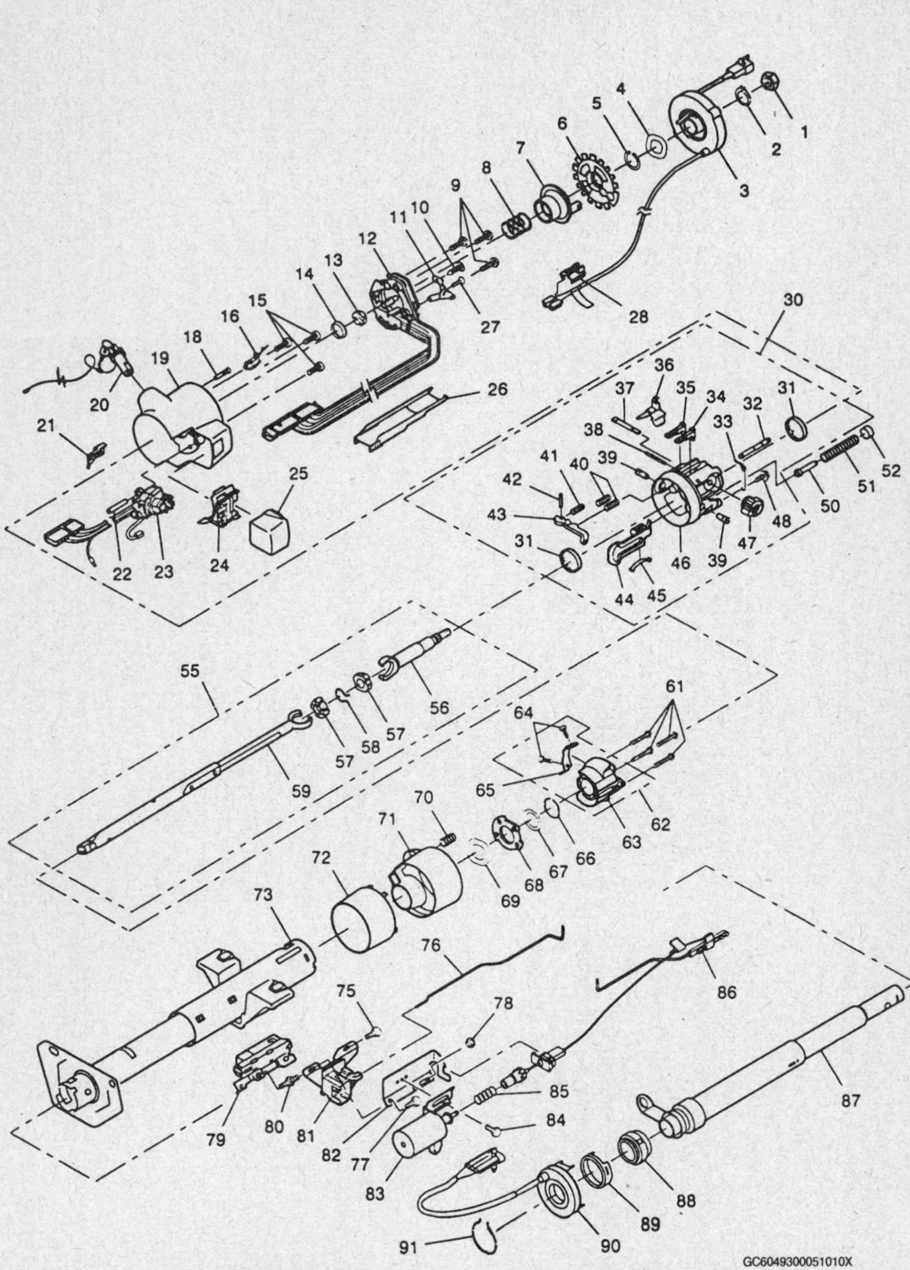

GC6049300051010X

Fig. 9 Exploded view of tilt steering column (Part 1 of 2). Fleetwood (RWD)

1-NUT, HEX LOCKING (M14x1.5)
2-RING, RETAINING
3-COIL ASM, INFL RESTRAINT
4-WASHER, WAVE
5-RING, RETAINING
6-LOCK, SHAFT
7-CAM ASM, TURN SIG CANCEL
8-SPRING, UPPER BEARING
9-SCREW, BNDG HD CR RECESS
10-SCREW, FLAT HD TAP
11-ARM, SIGNAL SWITCH
12-SWITCH ASM, TURN SIGNAL
13-SEAT, UPPER BRG INNER RACE
14-RACE, INNER
15-SCREW, PAN HD SOC TAP
16-SWITCH ASM, BUZZER
18-SCREW, LOCK RETAINING
19-COVER ASM, LOCK HOUSING
20-LOCK CYLINDER SET, STRG COL PASS KEY
21-ACTUATOR, DIMMER SW ROD
22-PIN, SWITCH ACTUATOR PIVOT
23-SWITCH ASM, PIVOT & (PULSE)
24-BASE PLATE, COL HSG CVR END
25-CAP, COL HSG COVER END
26-PROTECTOR, WIRING
27-SCREW, C/S TAP (#8-18)
28-SHROUD, CONNECTOR
30-HOUSING ASM, STRG COLUMN
31-BEARING ASM
32-BOLT, LOCK
33-SPRING, LOCK BOLT
34-SHOE, STEERING WHEEL LOCK
35-SHOE, STEERING WHEEL LOCK
36-SHIELD, WIRE PROTECTOR
37-SHAFT, DRIVE
38-PIN, DOWEL
39-PIN, PIVOT
40-SPRING, SHOE
41-SPRING, RELEASE LEVER
42-PIN, RELEASE LEVER
43-LEVER, SHOE RELEASE
44-RACK, SWITCH ACTUATOR
45-SPRING, RACK PRELOAD
46-HOUSING, STRG COLUMN
47-SECTOR, SWITCH ACTUATOR
48-SCREW, HEX WASHER HEAD
50-GUIDE, SPRING
51-SPRING, WHEEL TILT
52-RETAINER, SPRING
55-SHAFT ASM, STEERING
56-SHAFT ASM, RACE & UPPER
57-SPHERE, CENTERING
58-SPRING, JOINT PRELOAD
59-SHAFT ASM, LOWER STEERING
61-SCREW, SUPPORT
62-SUPPORT ASM, STRG COL HSG
63-SUPPORT, STRG COL HSG
64-SCREW, OVL HD CROSS RECESS
65-GATE, SHIFT LEVER
66-RING, SHIFT TUBE RETAINING
67-WASHER, THRUST
68-PLATE, LOCK
69-WASHER, WAVE
70-SPRING, SHIFT LEVER
71-BOWL ASM, GEARSHIFT LEVER
72-SHROUD, GEARSHIFT BOWL
73-JACKET ASM, STRG COL
75-SCREW, WASH HD (#10-24x.25)
76-ROD, DIMMER SWITCH
77-SCREW, HEX WASH HD TAP
78-NUT, HEXAGON
79-SWITCH ASM, IGNITION
80-STUD, DIMR & IGN SWITCH MTG
81-SWITCH ASM, DIMMER
82-BRACKET, SOLENOID
83-SOLENOID ASM, INTERLOCK
84-SCREW, HEX WASH HD (10-24X.25)
85-SPRING, BALL JOINT
86-ACTUATOR ASM, IGN SWITCH
87-TUBE ASM, SHIFT
88-BUSHING ASM, STRG SHAFT
89-RETAINER, BEARING ADAPTER
90-SENSOR ASM, ATTACHMENT PLATE &
91-CLIP, LOWER BEARING ADAPTER

Service Kits

201-RACK SERV KIT, COL SECTOR & -INCLUDES: 14,31,33,44,47,48
202-SPRING SERV KIT, TILT COLUMN -INCLUDES: 13,14,39,50,51,52
203-COIL SERV KIT, INFL RESTRAINT -INCLUDES: 3,28
204-SPHERE SERV KIT, TILT COLUMN -INCLUDES: 57,58
205-GREASE SERV KIT, (SYNTHETIC)
206-GREASE SERV KIT, BTSI

GC6049300051020X

Fig. 9 Exploded view of tilt steering column (Part 2 of 2). Fleetwood (RWD)

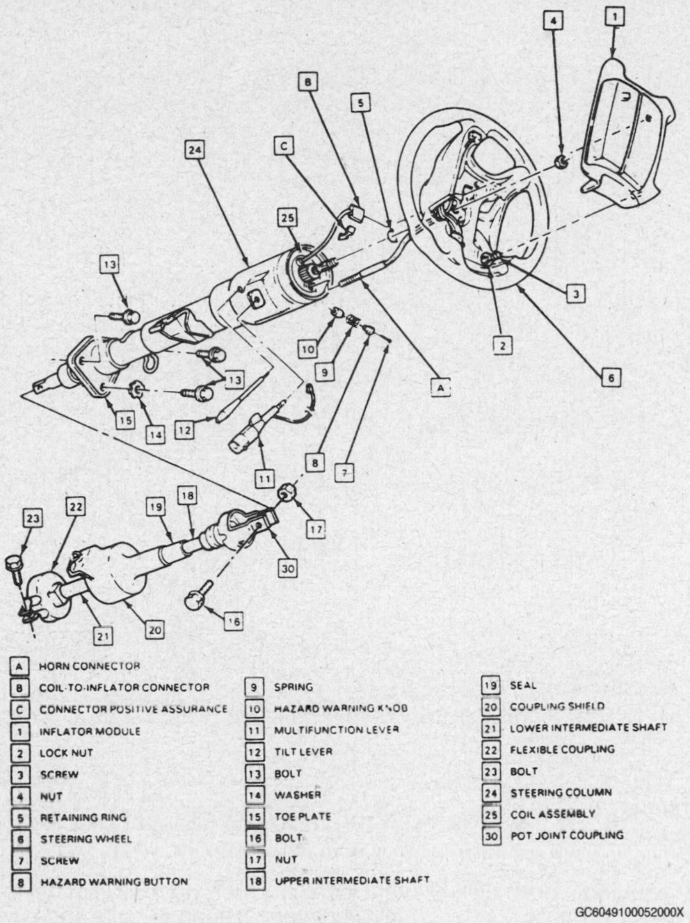
A HORN CONNECTOR
B COIL-TO-INFLATOR CONNECTOR
C CONNECTOR POSITIVE ASSURANCE
1 INFLATOR MODULE
2 LOCK NUT
3 SCREW
4 NUT
5 RETAINING RING
6 STEERING WHEEL
7 SCREW
8 HAZARD WARNING BUTTON
9 SPRING
10 HAZARD WARNING KNOB
11 MULTIFUNCTION LEVER
12 TILT LEVER
13 BOLT
14 WASHER
15 TOE PLATE
16 BOLT
17 NUT
18 UPPER INTERMEDIATE SHAFT
19 SEAL
20 COUPLING SHIELD
21 LOWER INTERMEDIATE SHAFT
22 FLEXIBLE COUPLING
23 BOLT
24 STEERING COLUMN
25 COIL ASSEMBLY
30 POT JOINT COUPLING
GC6049100052000X

Fig. 10 Steering column replacement. Camaro & Firebird

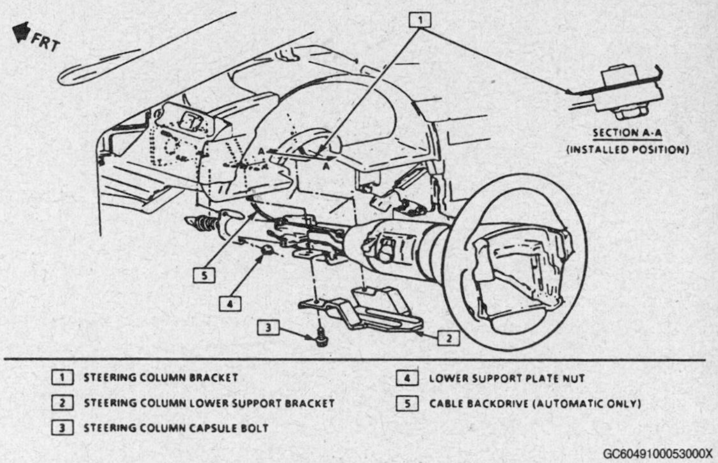
FRT
SECTION A-A
(INSTALLED POSITION)
1 STEERING COLUMN BRACKET
2 STEERING COLUMN LOWER SUPPORT BRACKET
3 STEERING COLUMN CAPSULE BOLT
4 LOWER SUPPORT PLATE NUT
5 CABLE BACKDRIVE (AUTOMATIC ONLY)
GC6049100053000X

Fig. 11 Steering column installation. Corvette

Care must be taken when handling column with a live inflator module. Never point bag deploy surface toward you, and never stand column on steering wheel. Accidental deployment in these positions may cause injury. Always face bag deploy surface toward open space to allow for unrestricted expansion.

1. Remove the inflator module as follows:
   a. Turn the ignition switch to the Off position and disconnect battery ground cable.
   b. Remove left side sound insulator.
   c. Install load tool No. J 37808 or equivalent, by connecting "base of column" lead of tool.
   d. Remove the Torx screws from the back of the steering wheel, then remove the inflator module from steering wheel.
   e. Disconnect the coil assembly connector from inflator module.
2. Remove steering wheel retaining nut, steering wheel and disconnect horn connector.
3. Remove intermediate shaft upper bolt.
4. Disconnect the (ALDL) Assembly Line Diagnostic Link connector and lamp from the sound insulator and remove sound insulator.
5. Remove column housing cover end cap by pulling toward front of vehicle.
6. Disconnect harness connector and grommet and remove multi-function lever by pulling toward driver side door.
7. Remove driver's side knee bolster and tilt lever.
8. Remove nuts from lower support plate and capsule bolts from reinforcement assembly.
9. Disconnect electrical connectors from column.
10. Remove sound insulator to column lower support bracket and nuts from the accelerator pedal bracket.
11. Remove steering column from vehicle.

Installation

1. Install steering column assembly in vehicle and insert lower steering shaft assembly into U-joint of intermediate shaft.
2. Install intermediate shaft upper bolt and loosely attach column and upper support plate to instrument panel reinforcement assembly with capsule bolts, **Fig. 11.**
3. Install cable back drive on models with automatic transmission, then loosely attach column nuts to support plate studs.
4. **Torque** intermediate shaft bolt to 26 ft. lbs., capsule bolts to 20 ft. lbs. and lower support plate nuts to 10 ft. lbs.
5. Connect electrical connectors to column and install driver's side knee bolster.
6. Install multi-function lever, harness and grommet, column housing cover end cap and tilt lever.
7. Align tilt lever tab into slot, with lever in Off position.
8. Install sound insulator bracket to column lower support and accelerator pedal bracket nuts. **Torque** accelerator pedal bracket nuts to 71 inch lbs.
9. Install steering wheel, retaining nut and connect horn connector.
10. Connect coil assembly to the inflator module, then install inflator module to the steering wheel, using new screws and **torque** screws to 87 inch lbs.
11. Remove load tool No. J 37808.
12. Install left side sound insulator, ALDL and lamp connectors.
13. Connect battery ground cable.

CENTURY, CUTLASS CIERA & CUTLASS CRUISER

Removal

1. Disconnect battery ground cable.
2. Remove left instrument panel sound absorber, trim pad and column trim collar.
3. Remove bolt and disconnect column to intermediate shaft connection.
4. Remove column support bracket bolts and nut.
5. Disconnect shift indicator cable and electrical connectors.
6. Disconnect shift cable at actuator and housing holder, then remove column assembly from vehicle.

Installation

1. Install column assembly in vehicle, **Fig. 12.**
2. Connect shift cable at actuator and housing holder, then the electrical connectors.
3. Connect shift indicator cable and install column bracket support bolts and nut.
4. Install intermediate shaft to column upper shaft pinch bolt and **torque** to 35 ft. lbs.
5. **Torque** column bracket support bolts

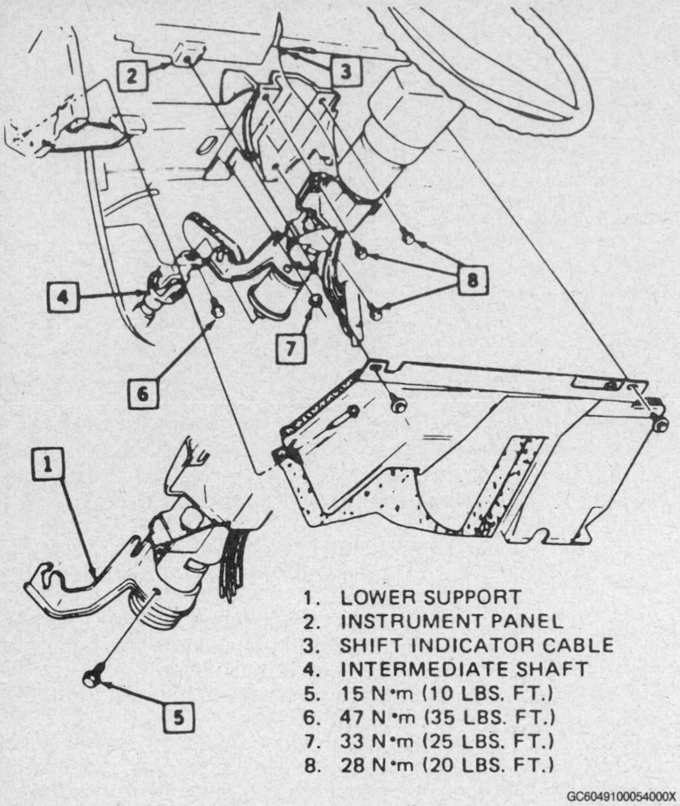
1. LOWER SUPPORT
2. INSTRUMENT PANEL
3. SHIFT INDICATOR CABLE
4. INTERMEDIATE SHAFT
5. 15 N•m (10 LBS. FT.)
6. 47 N•m (35 LBS. FT.)
7. 33 N•m (25 LBS. FT.)
8. 28 N•m (20 LBS. FT.)
GC6049100054000X

Fig. 12 Steering column installation. Century, Cutlass Ciera & Cutlass Cruiser

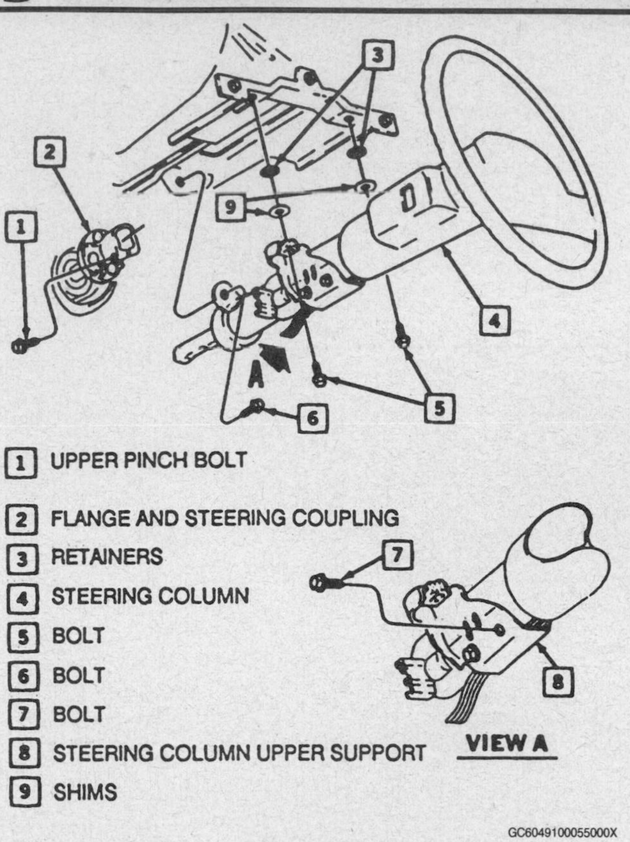
1 UPPER PINCH BOLT
2 FLANGE AND STEERING COUPLING
3 RETAINERS
4 STEERING COLUMN
5 BOLT
6 BOLT
7 BOLT
8 STEERING COLUMN UPPER SUPPORT
9 SHIMS
VIEW A
A
GC6049100055000X

Fig. 13 Steering column replacement. Beretta & Corsica

and nut to 20 ft. lbs.

6. Install column trim collar, left instrument panel trim pad and sound insulator, then connect battery ground cable.

BERETTA & CORSICA

Wheels must be in a straight forward position and the key must be in the Lock position when removing or installing column to ensure proper alignment of components during installation.

Care must be taken when handling column with a live inflator module. Never point bag deploy surface toward you, and never stand column on steering wheel. Accidental deployment in these positions may cause injury. Always face bag deploy surface toward open space to allow for unrestricted expansion.

1. Remove the inflator module as follows:
   a. With the ignition switch in the Off position and the battery ground cable.
   b. Remove left side sound insulator.
   c. Remove the Torx screws from the back of the steering wheel, then remove the inflator module from steering wheel.
   d. Remove the horn contact by pushing lightly and twisting counterclockwise.
   e. Disconnect the coil assembly connector from inflator module.
2. Disconnect hazard and turn signal electrical connector, then cruise switch terminal connector.
3. Remove column support bracket bolts, then flange and coupling pinch bolt, **Fig. 13.**
4. Remove upper and lower steering column support bolts.
5. Disconnect ignition and dimmer switch electrical connections.
6. Remove park lock cable from ignition switch.
7. Remove column assembly.
8. Reverse procedure to install noting the following:
   a. **Torque** lower steering column support bolts to 21 ft. lbs.
   b. **Torque** steering column support bracket to steering column to 22 ft. lbs.
   c. **Torque** upper steering column support bolts to 21 ft. lbs.
   d. **Torque** flange and coupling pinch bolt to 30 ft. lbs.

ACHIEVA, CAVALIER, GRAND AM, SKYLARK & SUNBIRD

Removal

1. Disconnect battery ground cable and remove left instrument panel sound insulator, lower trim panel or duct assembly, and steering column collar, as equipped.
2. If column is to be disassembled, remove horn contact pad and steering wheel.
3. Push back seal to expose flexible coupling, **Fig. 14,** then remove coupling pinch bolt.
4. Remove lower column support bracket bolt, then the upper bracket to instrument panel support bolts and lower column.
5. Disconnect column electrical connectors and shift indicator cable, if equipped.
6. Disconnect shift cable at actuator and housing holder, then remove steering column.

Installation

1. Insert steering shaft into flexible coupling.
2. Connect shift cable to actuator and housing holder.
3. Connect column electrical connectors and shift indicator cable.
4. Raise column into position, then install upper and lower bracket mounting bolts hand tight.
5. Install flexible coupling pinch bolt and **torque** bolt to 29 ft. lbs.
6. Ensure steering shaft is centered in mast jacket, repositioning column as needed, then **torque** mounting bolts to 20 ft. lbs.
7. Adjust shift cable and shift indicator as needed, then reverse remaining procedure to complete installation.

CUTLASS SUPREME, GRAND PRIX, LUMINA & REGAL

Removal

1. Remove air cleaner.
2. Disconnect battery ground cable, then remove steering wheel as necessary. **When removing steering wheel**

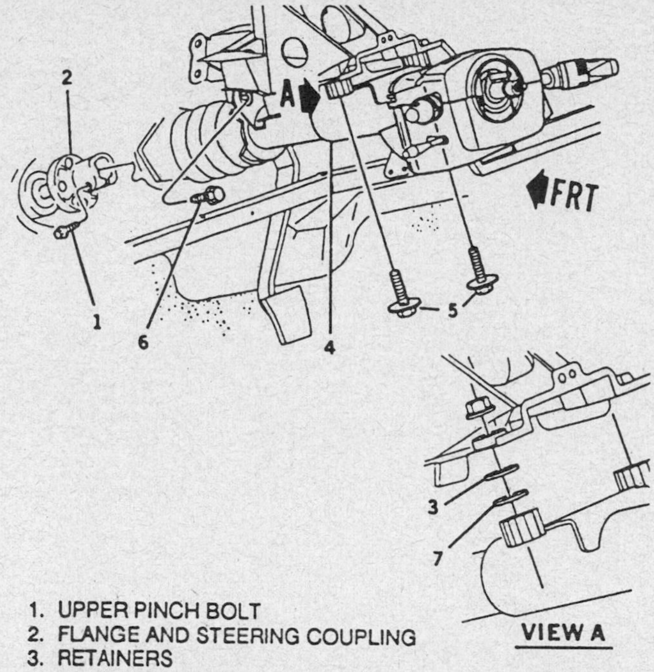
FRT
A
VIEW A

1. UPPER PINCH BOLT
2. FLANGE AND STEERING COUPLING
3. RETAINERS
4. STEERING COLUMN
5. BOLT
6. BOLT
7. SHIMS

GC6049100056000X

Fig. 14 Steering column installation. Achieva, Cavalier, Grand Am, Skylark & Sunbird

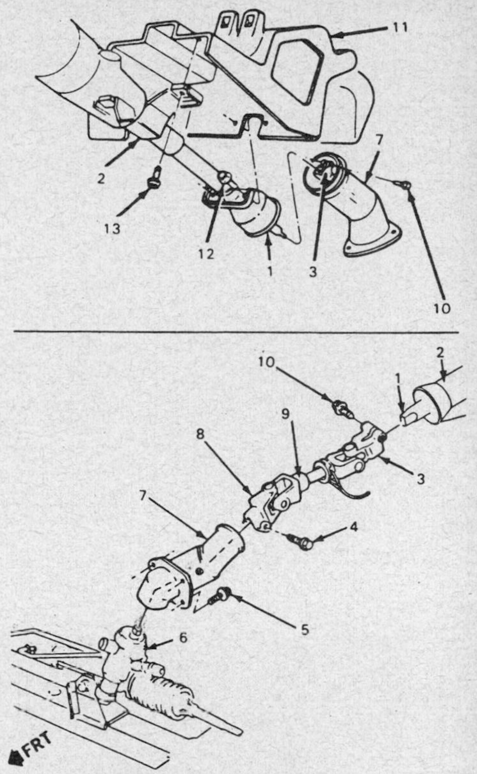
FRT

1 STEERING SHAFT-LOWER END
2 STEERING COLUMN ASSEMBLY
3 INTERMEDIATE SHAFT COUPLING-UPPER
4 PINCH BOLT-LOWER COUPLING
5 SCREW
6 STEERING GEAR
7 SEAL-INTERMEDIATE SHAFT
8 INTERMEDIATE SHAFT COUPLING-LOWER
9 INTERMEDIATE SHAFT
10 PINCH BOLT-UPPER COUPLING
11 BRACKET-BRAKE PEDAL
12 BOLT-LOWER STEERING COLUMN
13 BOLT-UPPER STEERING COLUMN

GC6049100057000X

Fig. 15 Steering column replacement. Cutlass Supreme, Grand Prix, Lumina & Regal

that is equipped with redundant steering wheel controls, insert wheel puller bolts only four to six threads deep to prevent bolts from going all the way through the hub.

3. Remove left hand sound insulator and the trim panel below steering column.
4. Unlock steering column, then push top of intermediate shaft seal down for access to upper intermediate shaft coupling and upper coupling pinch bolt.
5. Rotate intermediate shaft as necessary to remove upper coupling pinch bolt.
6. Disconnect shift indicator cable end and casing from steering column and transaxle shift lever, or park lock cable if equipped with floor shift.
7. Disconnect transaxle shift cable from ball stud on transaxle shift lever, then remove transaxle shift cable casing from steering column bracket by depressing two tabs.
8. Remove lower steering column attaching bolts, **Fig. 15,** then the upper steering column attaching bolts, and lower steering column to seat.
9. Disconnect electrical connector by loosening the screw and separating the two halves.
10. **On models equipped with floor shift and automatic transmission, an ignition switch inhibitor and park lock cable are used, proceed as follows:**
    a. Lower steering column to floor of vehicle.
    b. Remove shield or other upper column housing.

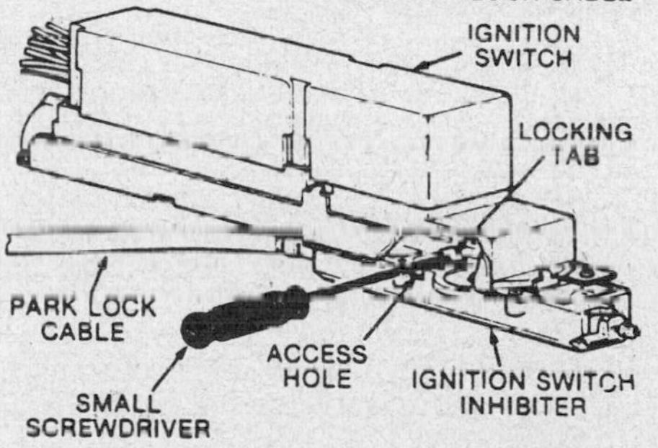
PUSH DOWN ON LOCKING TAB
TO RELEASE PARK LOCK CABLE
IGNITION
SWITCH
LOCKING
TAB
PARK LOCK
CABLE
ACCESS
HOLE
IGNITION SWITCH
INHIBITER
SMALL
SCREWDRIVER

GC6049100085000X

Fig. 16 Disconnecting park lock cable. Cutlass Supreme, Grand Prix, Lumina & Regal w/floor shift & automatic transmission

    c. Turn column lock cylinder to the On position.
    d. Disconnect park lock cable from ignition switch inhibitor with small screwdriver or punch, **Fig. 16.**
11. Withdraw lower end of steering shaft from upper intermediate shaft coupling and remove column. **It may be necessary to spread coupling clamp with a screwdriver to withdraw steering shaft.**

Installation

1. Install column back into vehicle and insert lower end of column shaft into upper intermediate shaft coupling.
2. Connect column electrical connector, tightening screw that draws the two halves together.
3. Connect transaxle shift cable and transaxle shift cable casing to column bracket and shift lever ball stud, or park lock cable if equipped with floor shift.
4. Install transaxle shift indicator cable end and casing and connect cable to transaxle shift lever.
5. Loosely install upper and lower steering column attaching bolts, then **torque** to 18 ft. lbs.
6. Install upper coupling pinch bolt into upper intermediate shaft coupling and **torque** to 35 ft. lbs.
7. Ensure clearance between lower shaft coupling and steering gear is at least .08 inch, then pull up intermediate shaft seal over lower column until it locks in place.
8. Install trim panel below steering column and the left hand sound insulator.
9. In stall steering wheel, if removed, then connect battery ground cable and confirm proper operation of all steering column components and functions.

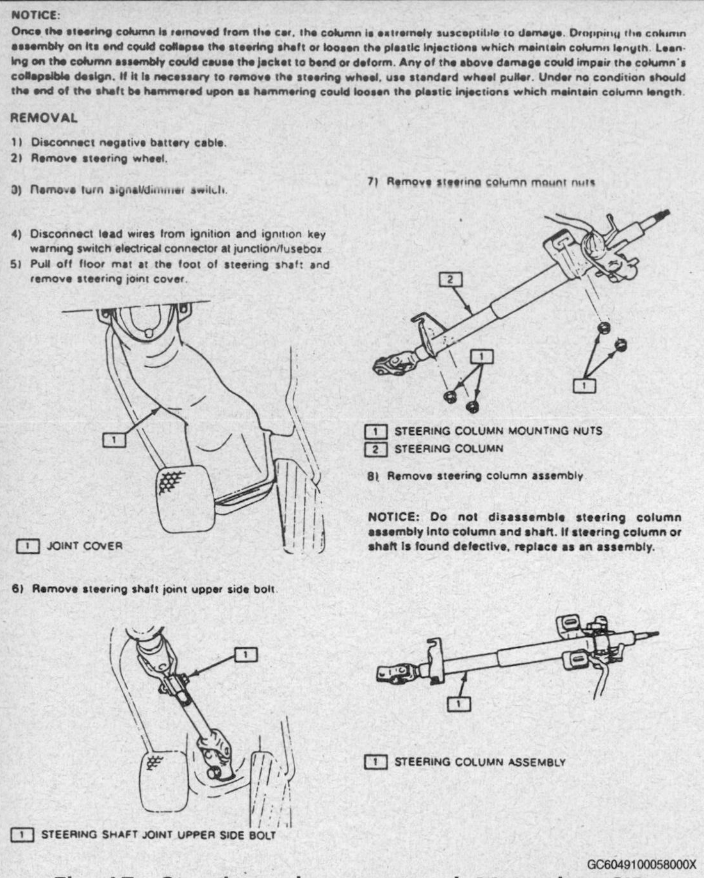
NOTICE:
Once the steering column is removed from the car, the column is extremely susceptible to damage. Dropping the column assembly on its end could collapse the steering shaft or loosen the plastic injections which maintain column length. Leaning on the column assembly could cause the jacket to bend or deform. Any of the above damage could impair the column's collapsible design. If it is necessary to remove the steering wheel, use standard wheel puller. Under no condition should the end of the shaft be hammered upon as hammering could loosen the plastic injections which maintain column length.
REMOVAL
1) Disconnect negative battery cable.
2) Remove steering wheel.
3) Remove turn signal/dimmer switch.
4) Disconnect lead wires from ignition and ignition key warning switch electrical connector at junction/fusebox
5) Pull off floor mat at the foot of steering shaft and remove steering joint cover.
1 JOINT COVER
6) Remove steering shaft joint upper side bolt.
1 STEERING SHAFT JOINT UPPER SIDE BOLT
7) Remove steering column mount nuts
1 STEERING COLUMN MOUNTING NUTS
2 STEERING COLUMN
8) Remove steering column assembly
NOTICE: Do not disassemble steering column assembly into column and shaft. If steering column or shaft is found defective, replace as an assembly.
1 STEERING COLUMN ASSEMBLY
GC6049100058000X

Fig. 17 Steering column removal. Metro less SIR

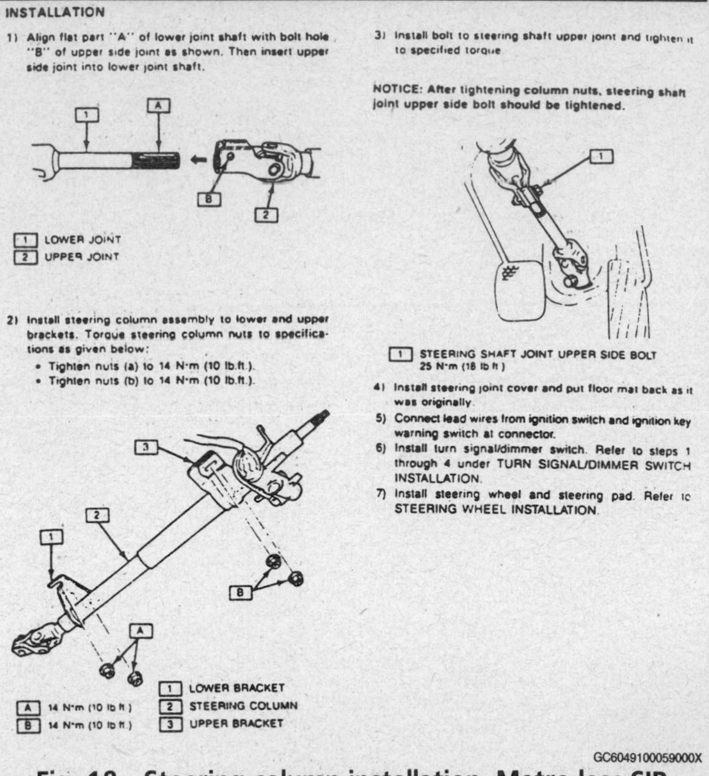
INSTALLATION
1) Align flat part "A" of lower joint shaft with bolt hole "B" of upper side joint as shown. Then insert upper side joint into lower joint shaft.
1 LOWER JOINT
2 UPPER JOINT
2) Install steering column assembly to lower and upper brackets. Torque steering column nuts to specifications as given below:
• Tighten nuts (a) to 14 N·m (10 lb.ft.).
• Tighten nuts (b) to 14 N·m (10 lb.ft.).
A 14 N·m (10 lb ft.)
B 14 N·m (10 lb ft.)
1 LOWER BRACKET
2 STEERING COLUMN
3 UPPER BRACKET
3) Install bolt to steering shaft upper joint and tighten it to specified torque.
NOTICE: After tightening column nuts, steering shaft joint upper side bolt should be tightened.
1 STEERING SHAFT JOINT UPPER SIDE BOLT 25 N·m (18 lb ft.)
4) Install steering joint cover and put floor mat back as it was originally.
5) Connect lead wires from ignition switch and ignition key warning switch at connector.
6) Install turn signal/dimmer switch. Refer to steps 1 through 4 under TURN SIGNAL/DIMMER SWITCH INSTALLATION.
7) Install steering wheel and steering pad. Refer to STEERING WHEEL INSTALLATION.
GC6049100059000X

Fig. 18 Steering column installation. Metro less SIR

10. Install air cleaner.

LEMANS

Removal

1. Disconnect battery ground cable.
2. Remove the turn signal/wiper switch lever as follows:
   a. Remove lower instrument cluster trim.
   b. Remove screws from upper cover panel by turning wheel 90° right or left for access.
   c. Remove the three screws from the lower panel. Pull handle from the lock release lever and unscrew tilt lever, if so equipped.
   d. Unclip switch from housing by pushing in on tab on either side of switch.
3. Disconnect wire harness and park lock actuation cable, if equipped.
4. Adjust steering to the straight ahead position, then remove pinch bolt from steering shaft flange.
5. Remove column jacket assembly lower mounting bolt from the instrument panel.
6. Remove shear plates below instrument panel as follows:
   a. Center punch the lefthand shear bolt, then drill a hole using a 1/8 inch drill bit.
   b. Install drive tool No. 1411 bolt extractor or equivalent, into hole and unscrew shear bolt.
   c. Remove shear plates.
7. Guide column assembly out of shaft flange and remove from vehicle.

Installation

1. Guide steering shaft into steering shaft flange and provide support for column until shear bolts are fastened.
2. Loosely mount shear plates on instrument panel, then install column jacket assembly lower mounting bolt to instrument panel and pinch bolt in steering shaft flange.
3. **Torque** column jacket assembly lower mounting bolt to 12 ft. lbs. and shear bolt and self locking nut to 16 ft. lbs.
4. Draw steering shaft upwards until the stop reaches the steering shaft ball bearing and **torque** pinch bolt to 18 ft. lbs.
5. Slide alignment bushing out of column allowing bushing to remain on steering shaft.
6. Connect wiring harness and park lock actuation cable, if equipped.
7. Connect electrical connectors to turn signal/wiper switch, then clip switch back into housing.
8. Install cover panels, lock release lever and tilt lever, if so equipped.
9. Install lower cluster trim, then connect battery ground cable.
10. Inspect steering for straight ahead position.

METRO

Models Less SIR

Refer to **Figs. 17 through 20** for removal and installation procedures.

Models w/SIR

Wheels must be in a straight forward position and the key must be in the Lock position when removing or installing column to ensure proper alignment of components during installation.

Care must be taken when handling column with a live inflator module. Never point bag deploy surface toward you, and never stand column on steering wheel. Accidental deployment in these positions may cause injury. Always face bag deploy surface toward open space to allow for unrestricted expansion.

1. Remove steering wheel as follows:
   a. Remove four screw from rear of steering wheel, then remove inflator module from steering wheel.
   b. Remove steering attaching nut.
   c. Attach wheel puller tool Nos. J 8433-1 and J 8433-3 or equivalents, **Fig. 21,** then remove steering wheel.
2. Remove steering shaft trim panel.
3. Remove lower column steering trim panel attaching screws, then trim panel.
4. Remove lower column reinforcement plate attaching screws, then plate.
5. Disconnect steering column electrical connectors.
6. **On models with automatic transmissions,** remove transaxle shift interlock cable from ignition switch.
7. **On all models,** remove column to steering shaft joint pinch bolt, **Fig. 22.**
8. Remove two upper and lower column attaching bolts, then column.
9. Measure column as shown in **Fig. 23.** If measurement is less than 20.96 inches, replace column.

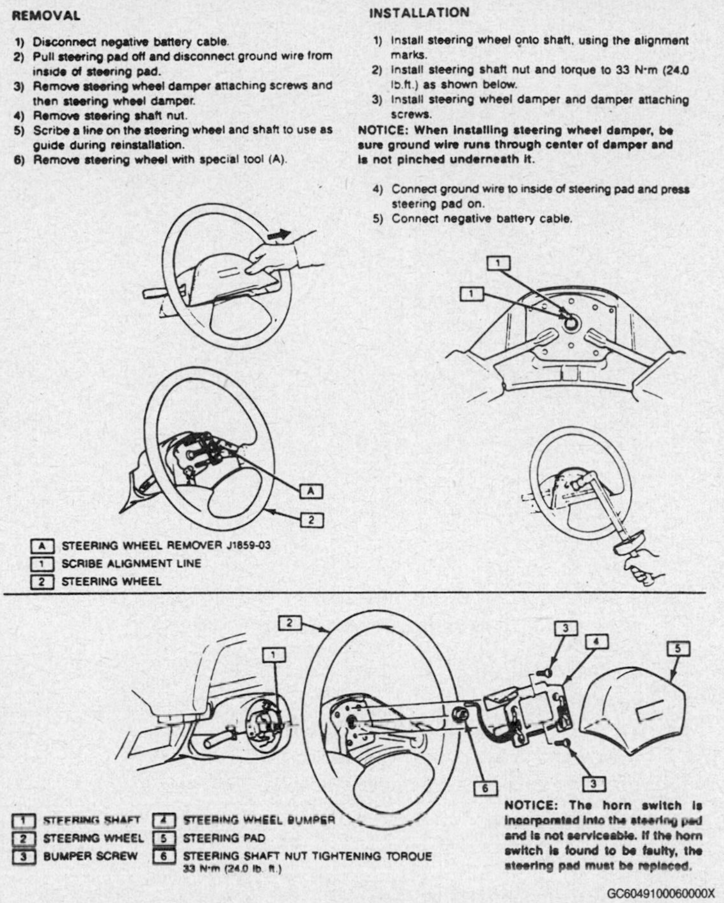
REMOVAL
1) Disconnect negative battery cable.
2) Pull steering pad off and disconnect ground wire from inside of steering pad.
3) Remove steering wheel damper attaching screws and then steering wheel damper.
4) Remove steering shaft nut.
5) Scribe a line on the steering wheel and shaft to use as guide during reinstallation.
6) Remove steering wheel with special tool (A).
INSTALLATION
1) Install steering wheel onto shaft, using the alignment marks.
2) Install steering shaft nut and torque to 33 N·m (24.0 lb.ft.) as shown below.
3) Install steering wheel damper and damper attaching screws.
NOTICE: When installing steering wheel damper, be sure ground wire runs through center of damper and is not pinched underneath it.
4) Connect ground wire to inside of steering pad and press steering pad on.
5) Connect negative battery cable.
A STEERING WHEEL REMOVER J1859-03
1 SCRIBE ALIGNMENT LINE
2 STEERING WHEEL
1 STEERING SHAFT
2 STEERING WHEEL
3 BUMPER SCREW
4 STEERING WHEEL BUMPER
5 STEERING PAD
6 STEERING SHAFT NUT TIGHTENING TORQUE 33 N·m (24.0 lb. ft.)
NOTICE: The horn switch is incorporated into the steering pad and is not serviceable. If the horn switch is found to be faulty, the steering pad must be replaced.
GC6049100060000X

Fig. 19 Steering wheel replacement. Metro less SIR

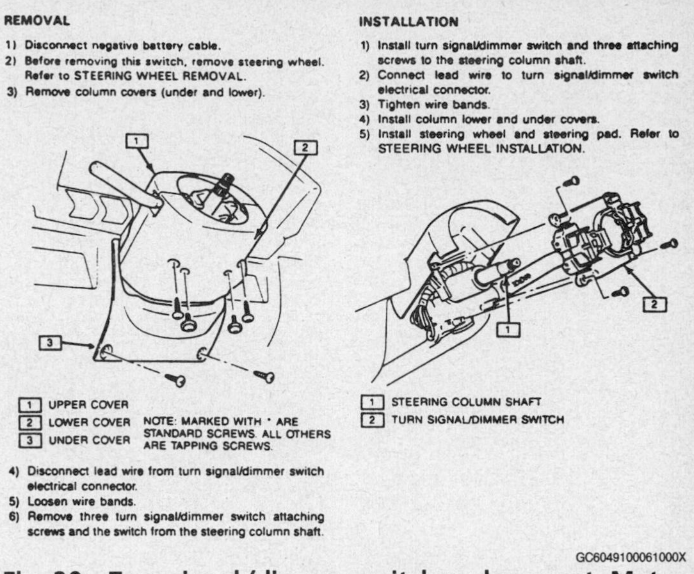
REMOVAL
1) Disconnect negative battery cable.
2) Before removing this switch, remove steering wheel. Refer to STEERING WHEEL REMOVAL.
3) Remove column covers (under and lower).
1 UPPER COVER
2 LOWER COVER
3 UNDER COVER
NOTE: MARKED WITH * ARE STANDARD SCREWS. ALL OTHERS ARE TAPPING SCREWS.
4) Disconnect lead wire from turn signal/dimmer switch electrical connector.
5) Loosen wire bands.
6) Remove three turn signal/dimmer switch attaching screws and the switch from the steering column shaft.
INSTALLATION
1) Install turn signal/dimmer switch and three attaching screws to the steering column shaft.
2) Connect lead wire to turn signal/dimmer switch electrical connector.
3) Tighten wire bands.
4) Install column lower and under covers.
5) Install steering wheel and steering pad. Refer to STEERING WHEEL INSTALLATION.
1 STEERING COLUMN SHAFT
2 TURN SIGNAL/DIMMER SWITCH
GC6049100061000X

Fig. 20 Turn signal/dimmer switch replacement. Metro less SIR

2. Unclip left front carpet retainer, then loosen two screws and disconnect hood release lever from knee bolster.
3. Remove two trim caps, then the four bolts securing knee bolster to the instrument panel.
4. Pull out instrument panel left-side ventilation duct.
5. Loosen five screws and remove upper and lower steering column trim covers.
6. Disconnect steering column electrical connectors.
7. Remove steering column pinch bolt.
8. Remove two bolts, two nuts and remove the steering column from the instrument panel.
9. Reverse procedure to install, noting the following:
   a. **Torque** steering column mounting bolts to 19 ft. lbs.
   b. **Torque** steering column pinch bolt to 26 ft. lbs.
   c. **Torque** knee bolster bolts to 89 inch lbs.

10. Reverse procedure to install noting the following:
    a. **Torque** upper and lower steering column attaching bolts to 124 inch lbs.
    b. **Torque** steering column to steering shaft pinch bolt to 18 ft. lbs.

PRIZM

1992

Removal

1. Disconnect battery ground cable.
2. Remove left side lower instrument finish panel, upper and lower column covers.
3. Disconnect multi-function and ignition switch harnesses.
4. Disconnect park lock cable from lock cylinder housing.
5. Remove air intake filter assembly to gain access to column yoke and disconnect yoke from steering gear.
6. Remove lower column bolts, then upper column bolts and remove steering column.

Installation

1. Install steering column securing with upper and lower column bolts. **Torque** bolts to 19 ft. lbs.
2. Connect shaft yoke to steering gear and **torque** bolt to 26 ft. lbs.
3. Install air intake filter assembly and connect multi-function and ignition switch harnesses.

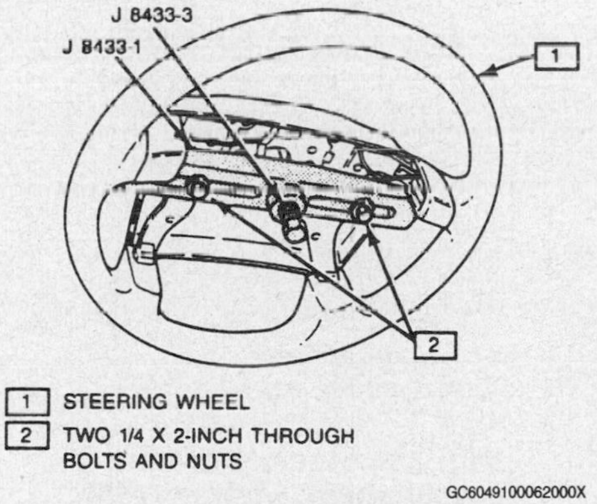
J 8433-3
J 8433-1
1 STEERING WHEEL
2 TWO 1/4 X 2-INCH THROUGH BOLTS AND NUTS
GC6049100062000X

Fig. 21 Steering wheel removal. Metro w/SIR

4. Connect park lock cable to lock cylinder housing, then install upper and lower column covers.
5. Install left side lower instrument finish panel, then connect battery ground cable.

1993–94

Wheels must be in straight ahead position and the key must be in the Lock position when removing or installing the steering column. Failure to do so may cause the air bag coil assembly to become uncentered and may result in unnecessary air bag system repairs.

1. Remove steering wheel.

STORM

Removal

Wheels must be in a straight forward position and the key must be in the Lock position when removing or installing column to ensure proper alignment of components during installation.

Care must be taken when handling column with a live inflator module. Never point bag deploy surface toward you, and never stand column on steering wheel. Accidental deployment in these positions may cause injury. Always face bag deploy surface toward open space to allow for unrestricted expansion.

1. Remove the inflator module as follows:
   a. With the ignition switch in the Off position, disconnect battery ground cable.
   b. Remove left side sound insulator.

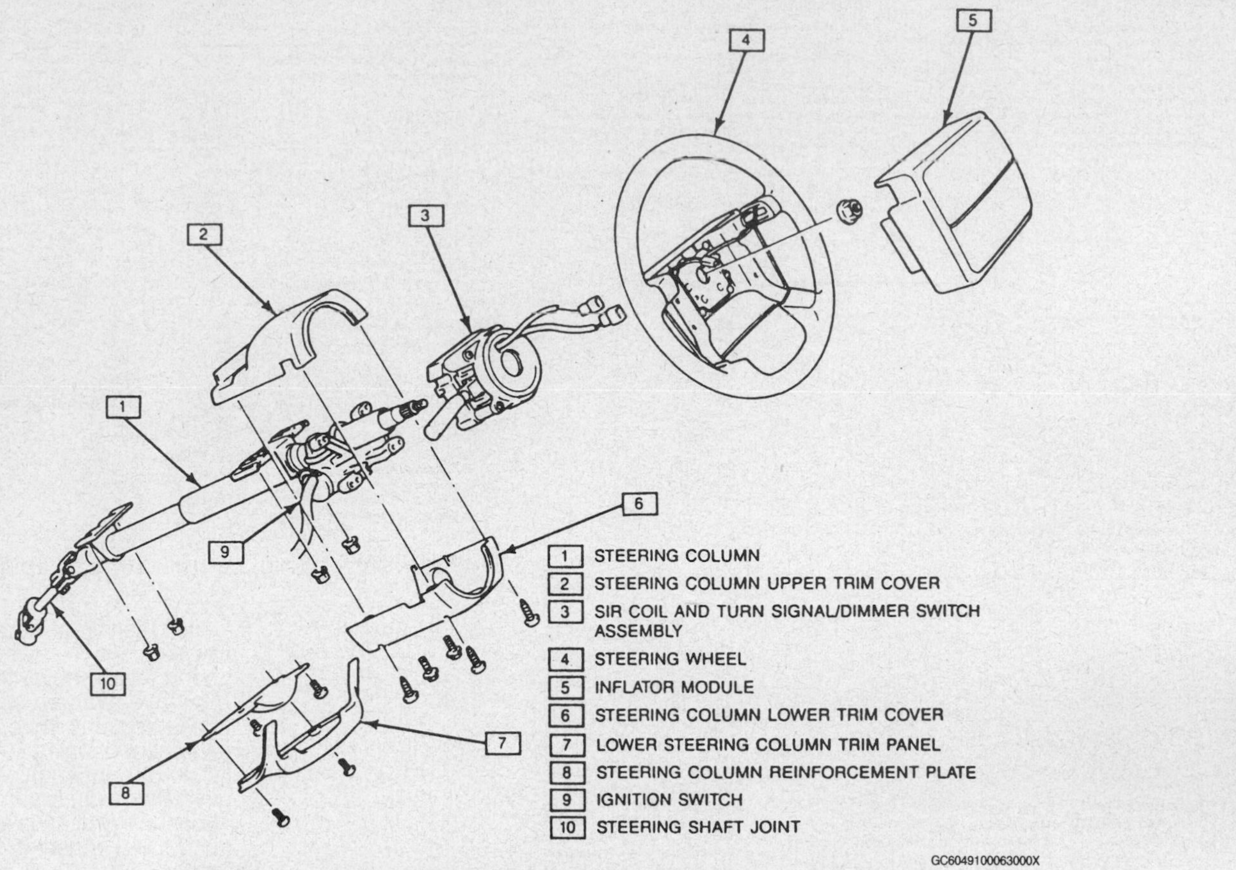
1 STEERING COLUMN
2 STEERING COLUMN UPPER TRIM COVER
3 SIR COIL AND TURN SIGNAL/DIMMER SWITCH ASSEMBLY
4 STEERING WHEEL
5 INFLATOR MODULE
6 STEERING COLUMN LOWER TRIM COVER
7 LOWER STEERING COLUMN TRIM PANEL
8 STEERING COLUMN REINFORCEMENT PLATE
9 IGNITION SWITCH
10 STEERING SHAFT JOINT
GC6049100063000X

Fig. 22 Exploded view of steering column. Metro w/SIR

c. Remove the Torx screws from the back of the steering wheel, then remove the inflator module from steering wheel.
d. Remove the horn contact by pushing lightly and twisting counterclockwise.
e. Disconnect the coil assembly connector from inflator module.
2. Remove steering wheel retaining nut and wheel from column using puller tool No. J 1859-03 or equivalent.
3. Remove lower switch panel and dash lighter panel.
4. Disconnect hood release cable and remove lap air deflector.
5. Remove left lower dash trim panel and upper column mounting bolts, then allow column to drop down.
6. Remove the two piece column cover and disconnect necessary electrical connectors.
7. Disconnect back drive cable from ignition switch, then remove pinch bolt from column knuckle.
8. Remove the two nuts from the lower column mount, then the column from vehicle.

Installation

1. Install column assembly into vehicle and secure with retaining nuts on lower column mount. **Torque** retaining nuts to 18 ft. lbs.
2. Connect intermediate shaft to column and install pinch bolt. **Torque** pinch bolt to 30 ft. lbs.

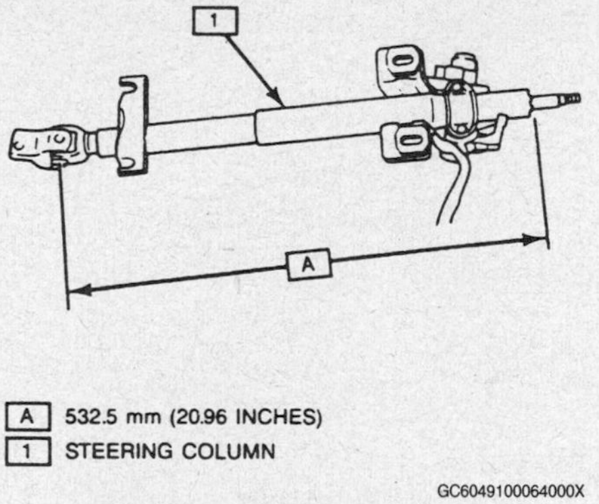
1
A
A 532.5 mm (20.96 INCHES)
1 STEERING COLUMN
GC6049100064000X

Fig. 23 Steering column measurement. Metro w/SIR

3. Connect back drive cable to ignition switch and necessary electrical connectors.
4. Install two piece column cover and upper column bolts. **Torque** bolts to 18 ft. lbs.
5. Install lower dash trim panel and lap air deflector.
6. Connect hood release cable, install lighter panel and lower switch panel.
7. Install steering wheel and retaining nut onto column and **torque** retaining nut to 25 ft. lbs.
8. Install steering wheel inflator module as follows:
   a. With ignition off, install horn contact, then connect coil assembly connector to inflator module.
   b. Push coil assembly lead wires into channel in lower right portion of steering wheel, then install inflator module in steering wheel.
   c. **Torque** screws holding inflator module to steering wheel to 25 inch lbs.
   d. Install left side sound insulator.
   e. Connect battery ground cable.

STEERING COLUMN SERVICE

Achieva, Cavalier, Grand Am & Skylark

STANDARD COLUMN

Refer to **Figs. 24 through 26** when servicing these steering columns.

STEERING COLUMN COVERS

1. Remove steering wheel as described in the "Electrical" section of the appropriate vehicle chapter in the front of this manual.
2. Remove cover screws, then the upper steering column cover.
3. Remove lower steering column cover screws, then the lower steering column cover.
4. Reverse procedure to install. **Torque** mounting screws to 49 inch lbs.

TURN SIGNAL SWITCH

Refer to the "Electrical" section of the

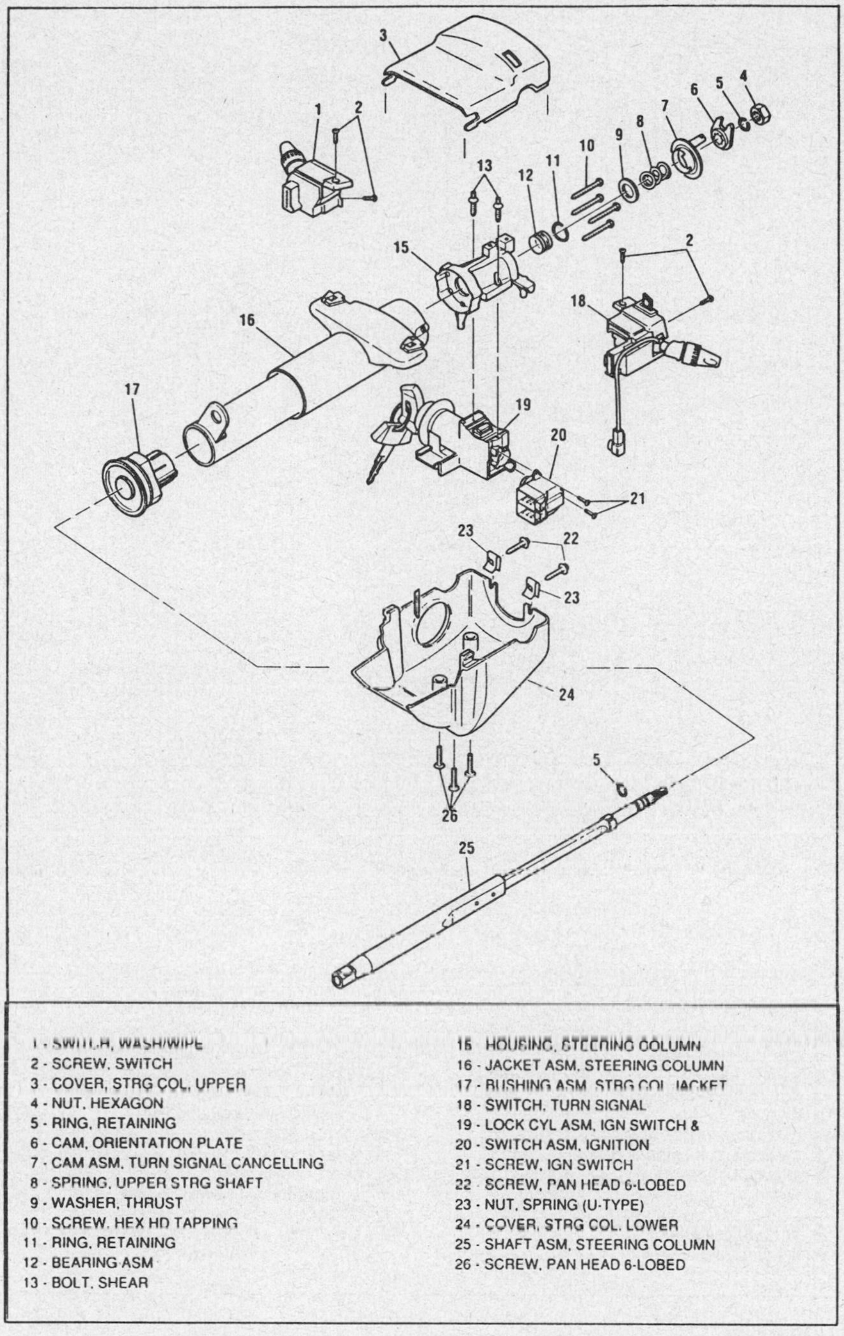
1 - SWITCH, WASH/WIPE
2 - SCREW, SWITCH
3 - COVER, STRG COL, UPPER
4 - NUT, HEXAGON
5 - RING, RETAINING
6 - CAM, ORIENTATION PLATE
7 - CAM ASM, TURN SIGNAL CANCELLING
8 - SPRING, UPPER STRG SHAFT
9 - WASHER, THRUST
10 - SCREW, HEX HD TAPPING
11 - RING, RETAINING
12 - BEARING ASM
13 - BOLT, SHEAR
15 - HOUSING, STEERING COLUMN
16 - JACKET ASM, STEERING COLUMN
17 - BUSHING ASM, STRG COL JACKET
18 - SWITCH, TURN SIGNAL
19 - LOCK CYL ASM, IGN SWITCH &
20 - SWITCH ASM, IGNITION
21 - SCREW, IGN SWITCH
22 - SCREW, PAN HEAD 6-LOBED
23 - NUT, SPRING (U-TYPE)
24 - COVER, STRG COL, LOWER
25 - SHAFT ASM, STEERING COLUMN
26 - SCREW, PAN HEAD 6-LOBED
GC6049100065000X

Fig. 24 Exploded view of standard steering column. Cavalier

appropriate vehicle chapter in the front of this manual for turn signal switch replacement.

WASH/WIPE SWITCH

Refer to the "Electrical" section of the appropriate vehicle chapter in the front of this manual for turn signal switch replacement.

IGNITION SWITCH

Refer to the "Electrical" section of the appropriate vehicle chapter in the front of this manual for turn signal switch replacement.

INTERLOCK SOLENOID

Column Shift

1. Remove steering wheel as described in the "Electrical" section of the appropriate vehicle section in the front of this manual.
2. Place shifter lever in Park position, then the ignition key in Off-Lock position and remove key.
3. Disconnect wire connector from interlock solenoid assembly.
4. Remove interlock solenoid mounting screws, then the interlock solenoid assembly.
5. Reverse procedure to install. **Torque** mounting screws to 21 inch lbs.

LOCK CYLINDER

Refer to the "Electrical" section of the appropriate vehicle chapter in the front of this manual for turn signal switch replacement.

PARK LOCK CABLE

Removal

1. Remove steering wheel as described in the "Electrical" section of the appropriate vehicle section in the front of this manual.
2. Place key in RUN position, then disconnect park lock cable from lock cylinder housing assembly.
3. **On models with column shift,** disconnect park lock cable from shift gate assembly.

Installation

1. Place key in RUN position and shift lever in PARK position.
2. Snap connector body of cable assembly to lock cylinder, ensuring locking tab is fully engaged into lock cylinder housing.
3. **On models with column shift,** place key in Off-Lock position and pull key half way out of lock cylinder housing.
4. **On all models,** route cable end fitting through park lock latch, then depress adjuster button and snap cable adjuster assembly to shift gate assembly.
5. Snap cable into cable retainer, then depress adjuster button and pull cable sheathing towards lock cylinder to remove lash from system.
6. Release sheathing, then release button.

SHIFT LEVER GATE & CLEVIS

Column Shift

1. Remove steering wheel as described in the "Electrical" section of the appropriate vehicle section in the front of this manual.
2. Remove shift lever, then the shift cable from shift cable ball stud.
3. Remove shoulder tapping screw, button head screw, shift pivot bushing and stud and clevis assembly.
4. Remove clevis spacer, shift lever spring, spring retainer, two flat head screws and shift lever gate assembly.
5. Reverse procedure to install, noting the following:
   a. **Torque** flat head screws to 14 ft. lbs., button head screw to 15 ft. lbs. and shoulder tapping screw to 119 inch lbs.
   b. Lubricate clevis spacer.

COLUMN JACKET BUSHING, ORIENTATION PLATE CAM, TURN SIGNAL CANCEL CAM, UPPER BEARING SPRING, BEARING, COLUMN SHAFT, COLUMN HOUSING & JACKET

Disassemble

1. Remove steering wheel as described

in the "Electrical" section of the appropriate vehicle section in the front of this manual.

2. Remove turn signal switch mounting screws and turn signal switch, letting switch hang freely.
3. Remove wash/wipe switch mounting screws and wash/wipe switch, letting switch hang freely.
4. Remove retaining ring using lock plate adapter tool Nos. J 23653-91 and lock plate compressor J 23653-C or equivalents, to compress orientation plate cam and upper bearing spring. Discard retaining ring.
5. Remove orientation plate cam, turn signal cancel cam assembly, upper bearing spring, thrust washer, bearing retainer and bearing assembly. Discard bearing retainer retaining ring.
6. Remove steering column from vehicle as described under "Steering Column, Replace."
7. Inspect steering column for damage.
8. Remove steering column jacket bushing assembly, then the steering column shaft assembly from lower end of steering column jacket assembly.
9. Remove retaining ring from shaft assembly and discard, then the four pan head tapping screws.
10. Disconnect park lock cable from lock cylinder housing assembly.
11. **On models with column shift,** disconnect park lock cable from shift gate assembly.
12. **On all models,** remove bearing and steering housing assembly from steering column jacket assembly.

Assemble

Ensure all fasteners are securely seated before applying torque. Failure to do so may result in component damage or malfunctioning of steering column.

1. Assemble bearing and steering housing assembly to steering column jacket assembly using four pan head tapping screws. **Torque** screws to 47 inch lbs.
2. Install new retaining ring to lower groove of steering shaft assembly, ensuring ring is firmly seated in groove.
3. Install steering column shaft assembly into lower end of steering column jacket assembly until bottomed.
4. Place key in Off-Lock position, remove key, rotate shaft until lock bolt engages and locks shaft in position, then insert key.
5. Install steering column jacket bushing assembly and snap into position.
6. Install bearing assembly, then lubricate.
7. Install bearing retainer, thrust washer, upper bearing spring and turn signal cancel cam assembly. Lubricate turn signal cancel cam assembly with synthetic grease.
8. Install orientation plate cam, then a new retaining ring using lock plate adapter and lock plate compressor to compress orientation plate cam and upper bearing spring. Ensure retaining ring is firmly seated in groove.

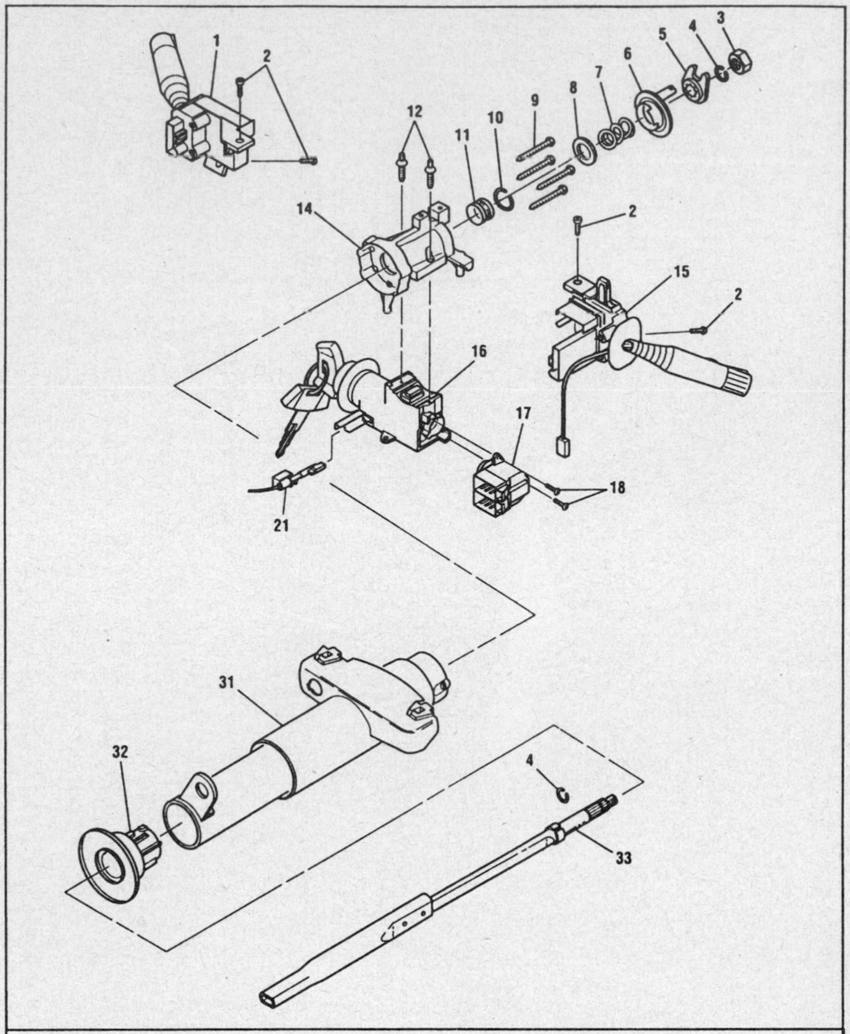

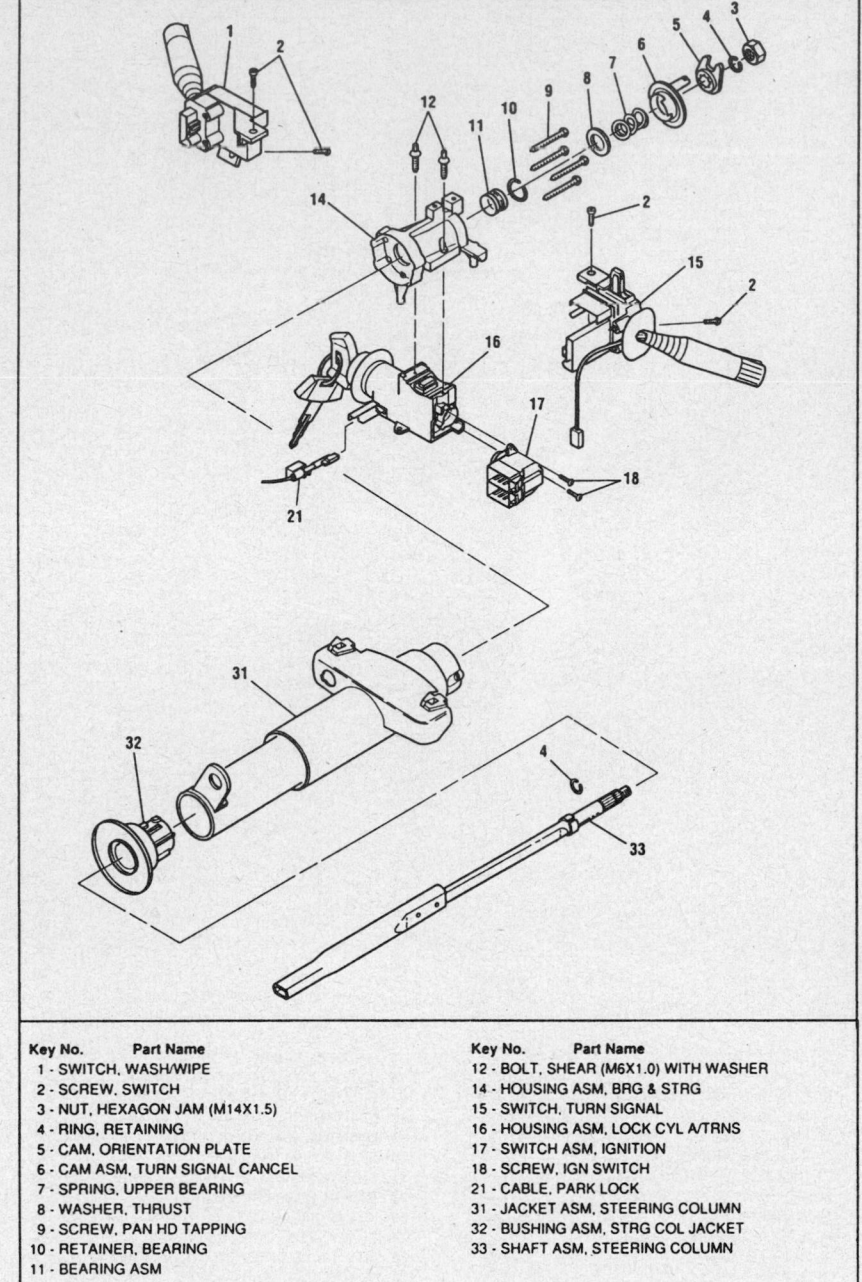

Key No.	Part Name	Key No.	Part Name
1	SWITCH, WASH/WIPE	12	BOLT, SHEAR (M6X1.0) WITH WASHER
2	SCREW, SWITCH	14	HOUSING ASM, BRG & STRG
3	NUT, HEXAGON JAM (M14X1.5)	15	SWITCH, TURN SIGNAL
4	RING, RETAINING	16	HOUSING ASM, LOCK CYL A/TRNS
5	CAM, ORIENTATION PLATE	17	SWITCH ASM, IGNITION
6	CAM ASM, TURN SIGNAL CANCEL	18	SCREW, IGN SWITCH
7	SPRING, UPPER BEARING	21	CABLE, PARK LOCK
8	WASHER, THRUST	31	JACKET ASM, STEERING COLUMN
9	SCREW, PAN HD TAPPING	32	BUSHING ASM, STRG COL JACKET
10	RETAINER, BEARING	33	SHAFT ASM, STEERING COLUMN
11	BEARING ASM		

GC6049200066000X

Fig. 25 Exploded view of standard steering column. Achieva & Grand Am

9. Install turn signal switch, wash/wipe switch and park lock cable as previously described.
10. Install steering wheel as described in the "Electrical" section of the appropriate vehicle section in the front of this manual.
11. Install steering column as described under "Steering Column, Replace."

TILT COLUMN

Refer to **Figs. 27 through 29** when servicing these steering columns.

STEERING COLUMN COVERS

Refer to "Standard Column" for procedure.

TURN SIGNAL SWITCH

Refer to "Standard Column" for procedure.

WASH/WIPE SWITCH

Refer to "Standard Column" for procedure.

IGNITION SWITCH

Refer to "Standard Column" for procedure.

INTERLOCK SOLENOID ASSEMBLY

Column Shift

Refer to "Standard Column" for procedure.

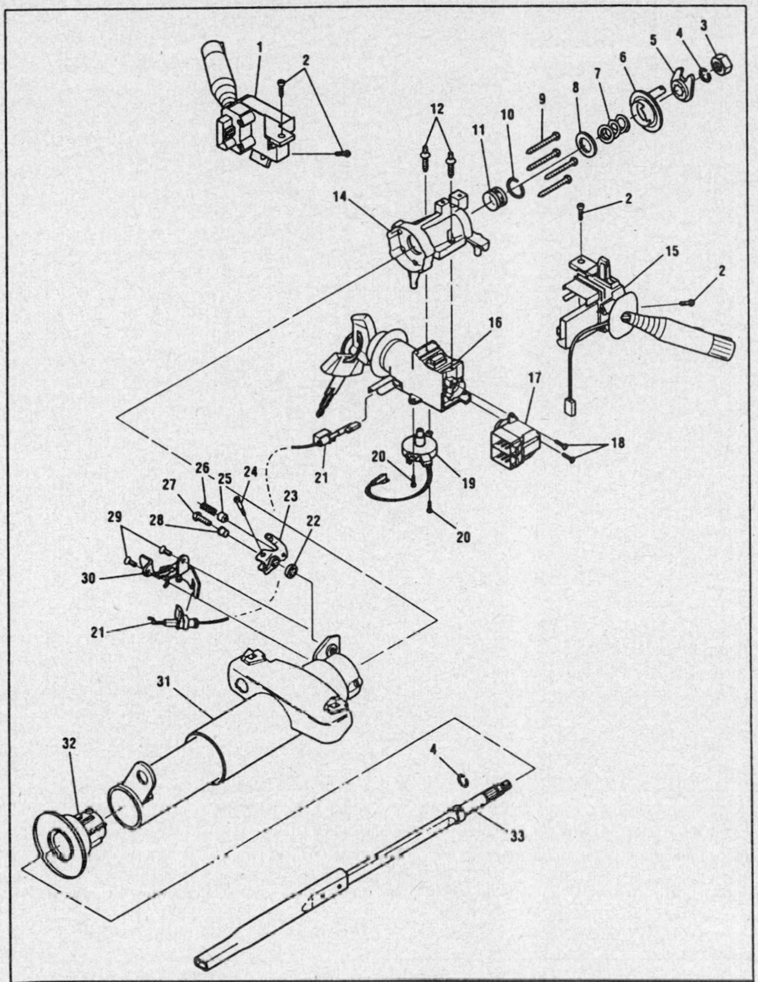

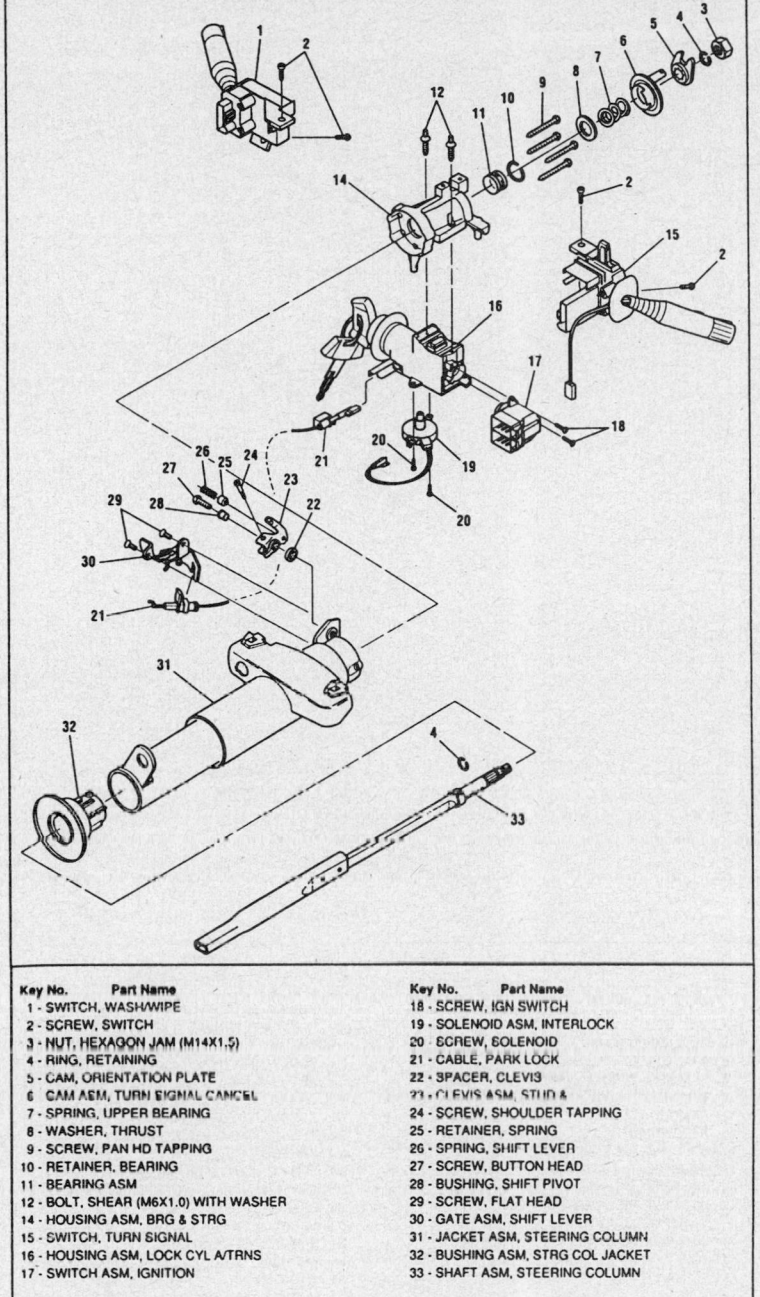

Key No.	Part Name	Key No.	Part Name
1	SWITCH, WASH/WIPE	18	SCREW, IGN SWITCH
2	SCREW, SWITCH	19	SOLENOID ASM, INTERLOCK
3	NUT, HEXAGON JAM (M14X1.5)	20	SCREW, SOLENOID
4	RING, RETAINING	21	CABLE, PARK LOCK
5	CAM, ORIENTATION PLATE	22	SPACER, CLEVIS
6	CAM ASM, TURN SIGNAL CANCEL	23	CLEVIS ASM, STUD &
7	SPRING, UPPER BEARING	24	SCREW, SHOULDER TAPPING
8	WASHER, THRUST	25	RETAINER, SPRING
9	SCREW, PAN HD TAPPING	26	SPRING, SHIFT LEVER
10	RETAINER, BEARING	27	SCREW, BUTTON HEAD
11	BEARING ASM	28	BUSHING, SHIFT PIVOT
12	BOLT, SHEAR (M6X1.0) WITH WASHER	29	SCREW, FLAT HEAD
14	HOUSING ASM, BRG & STRG	30	GATE ASM, SHIFT LEVER
15	SWITCH, TURN SIGNAL	31	JACKET ASM, STEERING COLUMN
16	HOUSING ASM, LOCK CYL A/TRNS	32	BUSHING ASM, STRG COL JACKET
17	SWITCH ASM, IGNITION	33	SHAFT ASM, STEERING COLUMN

GC6049200067000X

Fig. 26 Exploded view of standard steering column. Skylark

LOCK CYLINDER HOUSING

Refer to "Standard Column" for procedure.

PARK LOCK CABLE

Refer to "Standard Column" for procedure.

SHIFT LEVER GATE & CLEVIS

Column Shift

Refer to "Standard Column" for procedure.

COLUMN JACKET BUSHING, ORIENTATION PLATE CAM, TURN SIGNAL CANCEL CAM, UPPER BEARING SPRING, BEARING, COLUMN SHAFT, COLUMN HOUSING & COLUMN JACKET

Disassemble

1. Remove steering wheel as described in the "Electrical" section of the appropriate vehicle section in the front of this manual.
2. Remove turn signal switch mounting screws and turn signal switch, letting switch hang freely.
3. Remove wash/wipe switch mounting screws and wash/wipe switch, letting switch hang freely.
4. Remove retaining ring using lock plate adapter tool Nos. J 23653-91 and lock plate compressor tool No. J 23653-C or equivalents, to compress orientation plate cam and upper bearing spring. Discard retaining ring.
5. Remove orientation plate cam, turn signal cancel cam assembly, upper bearing spring, inner race seat, and inner race.
6. Pull tilt lever bracket on column housing assembly and tilt column all the way up.
7. Remove steering column from vehicle as described under "Steering Column, Replace."
8. Inspect steering column for damage.
9. Remove steering column jacket bushing from lower end of jacket assembly, then insert a Phillips head screwdriver into square opening in spring retainer, push down and turn counterclockwise to release retainer and wheel tilt spring.
10. Remove spring retainer and tilt spring, then the two pivot pins using pivot pin remover tool No. J 21854-01 or equivalent.
11. Place lock cylinder in RUN position, then pull tilt lever to release column housing and remove column housing from housing support.
12. Remove wire support screw and wire support, then the steering shaft assembly from housing support.
13. Remove tilt bumpers from housing support with pliers, then the pan head screws and housing support from jacket assembly.
14. If necessary, service steering shaft assembly as follows:
    a. **Before separating upper and lower shafts, note relationship of upper shaft with alignment mark in threaded end at 12 o'clock position and lower shaft pinch bolt groove at 9 o'clock position. Refer to this alignment for proper assembling.**
    b. Position upper shaft 90° to lower shaft and separate.
    c. Rotate centering sphere 90° and remove from upper shaft.
    d. Separate sphere halves and joint preload spring.

Assemble

Ensure all fasteners are securely seated before applying torque. Failure to do so may result in component damage or malfunctioning of steering column.

1. If necessary, assemble steering shaft as follows:
    a. Lubricate centering sphere halves and joint preload spring with lithium grease, then assemble spring between sphere halves with ends of spring in notches.
    b. Lubricate sphere end of upper shaft with lithium grease, then assemble sphere into upper shaft

and rotate sphere 90°.

c. Lubricate sphere end of lower shaft with lithium grease.

d. Place alignment notch on threaded end of upper shaft at 12 o'clock. Pinch bolt groove near end of lower shaft must be at 9 o'clock position.

e. Position upper shaft 90° to lower shaft, then engage and straighten.

2. Assemble housing support to jacket assembly with support screws. **Torque** screws to 12 ft. lbs.
3. Install tilt bumpers to housing support and snap into place.
4. Install steering shaft assembly into support housing.
5. Lubricate both bearings in column housing with lithium grease, then assemble column housing onto shaft assembly and column support.
6. Lubricate pivot pins with lithium grease, then install pivot pins until bottomed in housing. **Stake pivot pins to housing in three equally spaced locations. If there is no surface suitable for restaking, housing must be replaced.**
7. Pull tilt lever bracket on column housing assembly and tilt column all the way up.
8. Lubricate tilt spring with lithium grease, then install tilt spring with spring retainer. Ensure spring engages locating tab on support housing. Insert Phillips head screwdriver into square opening in spring retainer, push down and turn clockwise to lock in place.
9. Install wire support with wire support screw. **Torque** screw to 53 inch lbs.
10. Place key in Off-Lock position, remove key, rotate shaft until lock bolt engages and locks shaft in position.
11. Install inner race and inner race seat.
12. Install upper bearing spring and turn signal cancel cam assembly.
13. Install orientation plate cam, then a new retaining ring using lock plate adapter and lock plate compressor to compress orientation plate cam and upper bearing spring. Ensure retaining ring is firmly seated in groove.
14. Install turn signal switch, wash/wipe switch and park lock cable as previously described.
15. Install steering wheel as described in the "Electrical" section of the appropriate vehicle section in the front of this manual.

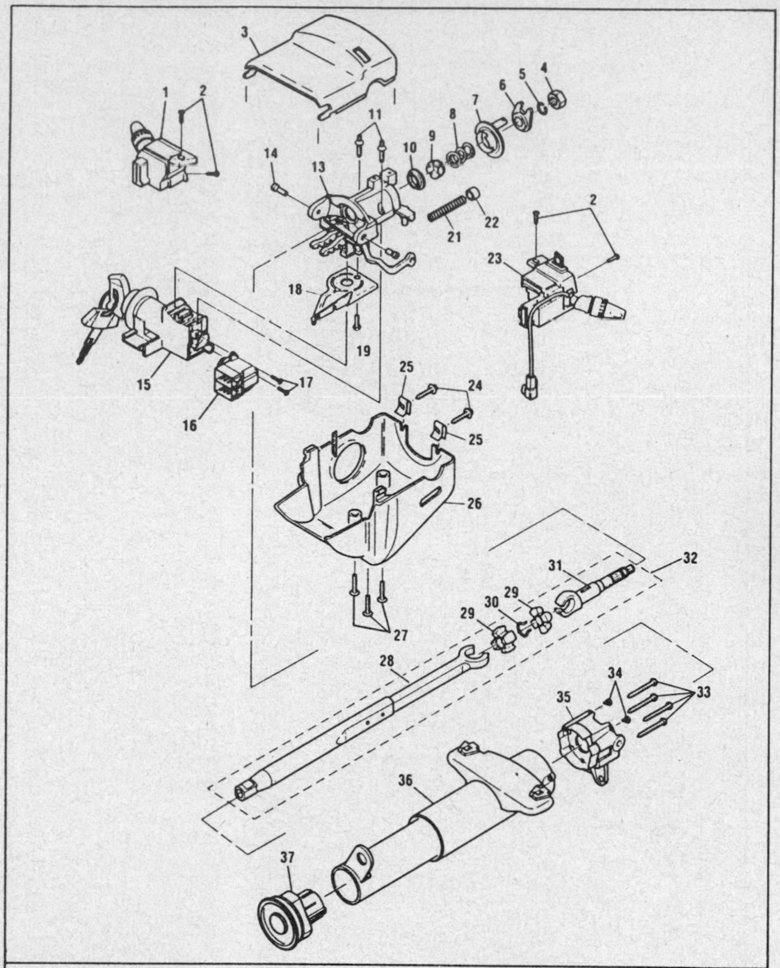

Key No.	Part Name	Key No.	Part Name
1	SWITCH, WASH/WIPE	19	SUPPORT, WIRE
2	SCREW, SWITCH	20	LEVER, TILT
3	COVER, STRG COL, UPPER	21	SPRING, WHEEL TILT
4	NUT, HEXAGON	22	RETAINER, SPRING
5	RING, RETAINING	23	SWITCH, TURN SIGNAL
6	CAM, ORIENTATION PLATE	24	SCREW, PAN HEAD 6-LOBED
7	CAM ASM, TURN SIGNAL CANCELLING	25	NUT, SPRING (U-TYPE)
8	SPRING, UPPER BEARING	26	COVER, STRG COL, LOWER
9	SEAT, INNER RACE	27	SCREW, PAN HEAD 6-LOBED
10	RACE, INNER	28	SHAFT ASM, LOWER STEERING
11	BOLT, SHEAR	29	SPHERE, CENTERING
13	HOUSING ASM, STEERING COLUMN	30	SPRING, JOINT PRELOAD
14	PIN, PIVOT	31	SHAFT ASM, RACE & UPPER
15	LOCK CYL ASM, IGN SWITCH &	32	SHAFT ASM, STEERING
16	SWITCH ASM, IGNITION	33	SCREW, HEX HD TAPPING
17	SCREW, IGN SWITCH	34	BUMPER, TILT
18	SCREW, WIRE SUPPORT	35	SUPPORT, STRG COLUMN HOUSING
19	SUPPORT, WIRE	36	JACKET ASM, STEERING COLUMN
		37	BUSHING ASM, STRG COL JACKET

GC6049100068000X

Fig. 27 Exploded view of tilt steering column. Cavalier

Sunbird

STANDARD COLUMN

Refer to **Fig. 30** when servicing these steering columns.

SHAFT LOCK, TURN SIGNAL CANCEL CAM, UPPER BEARING SPRING, THRUST WASHER, BUZZER SWITCH & COLUMN LOCK CYLINDER SET

Disassemble

1. Remove steering wheel as described in the "Electrical" section of the appropriate vehicle section in the front of this manual.
2. Disconnect battery ground cable.
3. Remove shaft lock cover, then the shaft lock retaining ring using plate compressor tool No. J 23653-C or equivalent, to depress shaft lock. Discard ring.
4. Remove shaft lock, turn signal cancelling cam assembly, upper bearing spring and thrust washer.
5. Move turn signal to the right turn position.
6. Remove multi-function lever and hazard knob assembly.
7. Remove screw and signal switch arm, then the turn signal switch screws.
8. Remove turn signal switch assembly and allow switch to hang freely.
9. Remove key from lock cylinder set, then the buzzer switch assembly.
10. Reinstall key in lock cylinder and turn to Lock position.
11. Remove retaining screw, then the lock cylinder set.

Assemble

Ensure all fasteners are securely seated before applying torque. Failure to do so may result in component damage or malfunctioning of steering column.

1. Install lock cylinder set and retaining screw. **Torque** screw to 40 inch lbs.

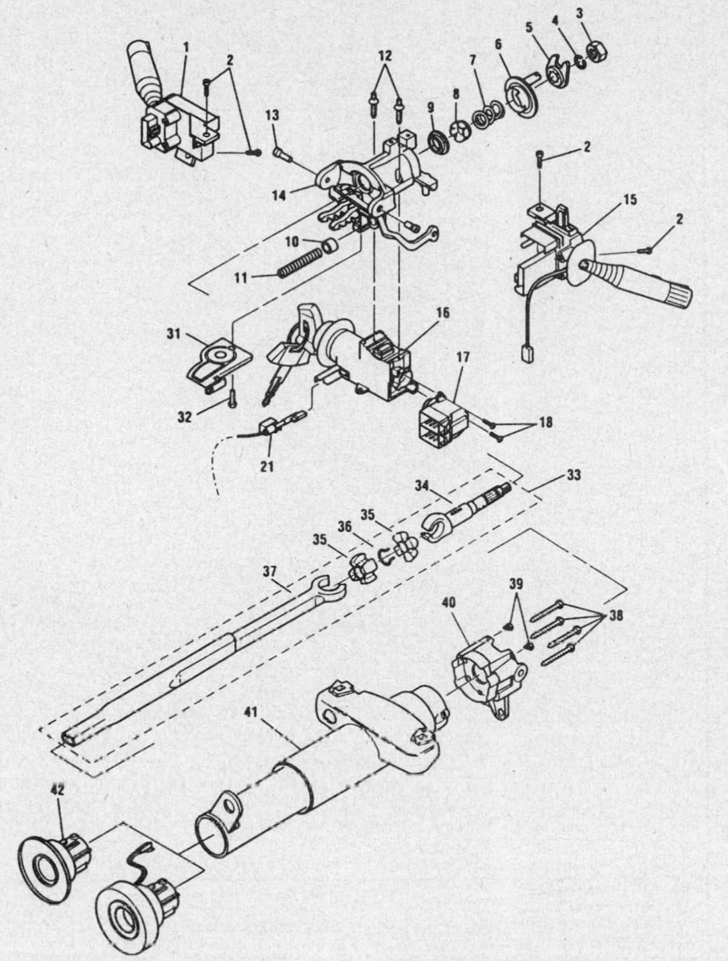

Key No.	Part Name	Key No.	Part Name
1	SWITCH, WASH/WIPE	16	HOUSING ASM, LOCK CYL A/TRNS
2	SCREW, SWITCH	17	SWITCH ASM, IGNITION
3	NUT, HEXAGON JAM (M14X1.5)	18	SCREW, IGN SWITCH
4	RING, RETAINING	21	CABLE, PARK LOCK
5	CAM, ORIENTATION PLATE	31	SUPPORT, WIRE
6	CAM ASM, TURN SIGNAL CANCEL	32	SCREW, WIRE SUPPORT
7	SPRING, UPPER BEARING	33	SHAFT ASM, STEERING
8	SEAT, INNER RACE	34	SHAFT ASM, RACE & UPPER
9	RACE, INNER	35	SPHERE, CENTERING
10	RETAINER, SPRING	36	SPRING, JOINT PRELOAD
11	SPRING, WHEEL TILT	37	SHAFT ASM, LOWER STEERING
12	BOLT, SHEAR (M6X1.0)	38	SCREW, PAN HD TAPPING
13	PIN, PIVOT	39	BUMPER, TILT
14	HOUSING ASM, BRG & STRG	40	SUPPORT, STRG COLUMN HOUSING
15	SWITCH, TURN SIGNAL	41	JACKET ASM, STEERING COLUMN
		42	BUSHING ASM, STRG COL JACKET

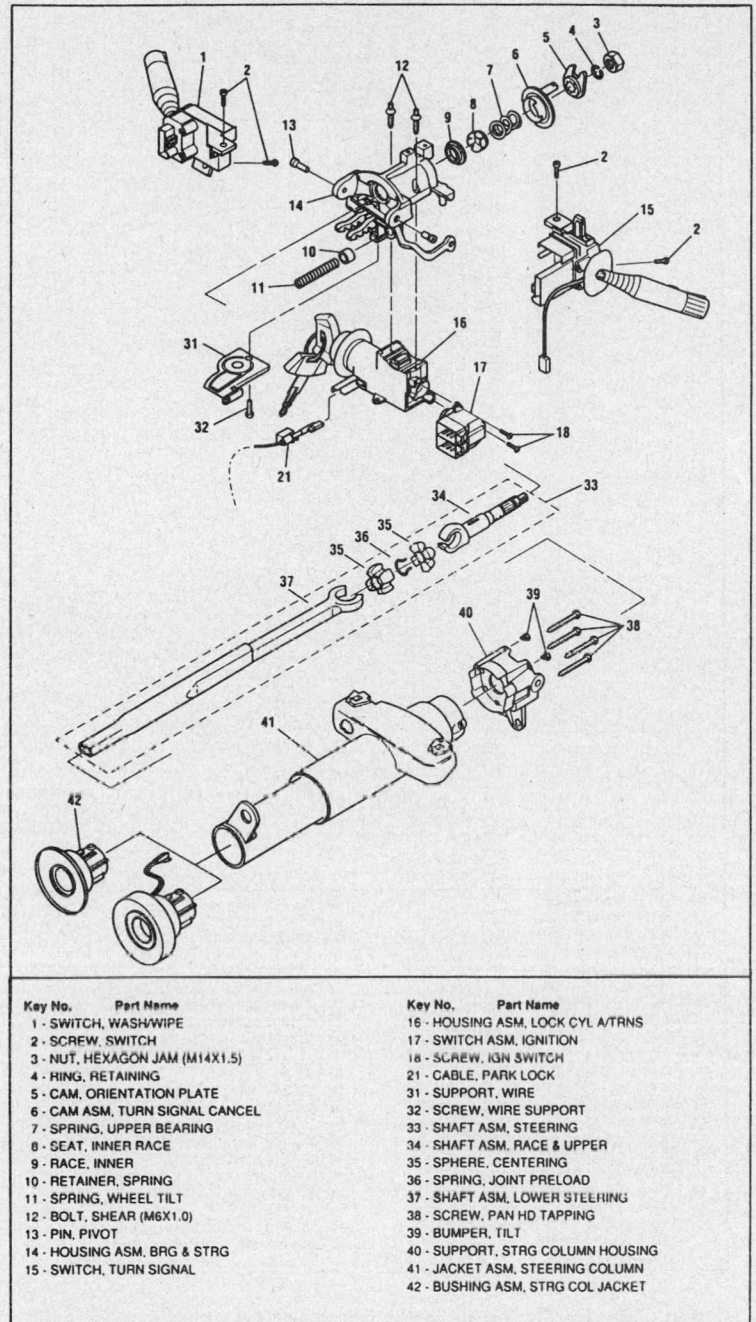

GC6049200069000X

Fig. 28 Exploded view of tilt steering column. Achieva & Grand Am

2. Remove key from lock cylinder set, then install buzzer switch assembly.
3. Reinstall key in lock cylinder set, then turn key to Lock position.
4. Install turn signal switch assembly and screws. **Torque** screws to 30 inch lbs.
5. Install signal switch arm and screw. **Torque** screw to 20 inch lbs.
6. Install hazard knob assembly and multi-function lever.
7. Install thrust washer, upper bearing spring and turn signal cancelling cam assembly. Lubricate cancelling cam with synthetic grease.
8. Install shaft lock and shaft lock retaining ring using plate compressor tool No. J 23653-C or equivalent, to depress shaft lock. Ring must be fully seated in groove.
9. Install shaft lock cover, then connect battery ground cable.
10. Install steering wheel as described in the "Electrical" section of the appropriate vehicle section in the front of this manual.

STEERING SHAFT, TURN SIGNAL SWITCH, COLUMN HOUSING, SWITCH ACTUATOR PIVOT, SPRING & BOLT, BEARING, SWITCH ACTUATOR SECTOR & IGNITION SWITCH ACTUATOR

Disassemble

1. Remove steering wheel as described in the "Electrical" section of the appropriate vehicle section in the front of this manual.
2. Disconnect battery ground cable.
3. Remove steering column from vehicle as described under "Steering Column, Replace."
4. Inspect steering column for damage.
5. Disassemble shaft lock, turn signal cancel cam, upper bearing spring, thrust washer, buzzer switch and lock cylinder set as previously described.
6. Remove steering shaft assembly, then the retaining ring from shaft.
7. Inspect column shaft assembly for damage.
8. Remove four support bolts, then the steering column support bracket assembly.
9. Remove wiring protector, turn signal switch assembly, washer head screw and hex nut.
10. Remove dimmer switch, dimmer switch rod and switch mounting stud.
11. Remove ignition switch, two cross recess screws and ignition switch inhibitor housing assembly.
12. Remove cover screws and lock housing cover assembly with floor shift lever bowl and shift bowl shroud. Pull housing cover from jacket and remove upper bearing retainer.
13. Remove three cross recess screws, floor shift lever bowl with shift bowl shroud, then the shroud from bowl.
14. If necessary, disassemble steering column housing as follows:
    a. Remove switch actuator rack with spring and bolt assembly, then the spring and bolt assembly from switch actuator rack.
    b. Remove switch actuator rod from rack, then the spring thrust washer from spring and bolt assembly.
    c. Remove switch actuator sector, rack preload spring, switch actuator pivot pin and switch actuator pivot assembly.
    d. Remove bearing retaining bushing using a punch, then the bearing assembly using a punch.

Assemble

Ensure all fasteners are securely seated before applying torque. Failure to do so may result in component damage or malfunctioning of steering column.

Use bearing retainer bushing to aid in seating bearing assembly into housing assembly. Tab on bushing must be fully seated into slot in housing assembly.

1. If necessary, assemble steering column housing as follows:
    a. Install bearing assembly, bearing retaining bushing, switch actuator

pivot assembly and switch actuator pivot pin. **Torque** pin to 27 inch lbs.

b. Install rack preload spring and switch actuator sector.

c. Assemble spring thrust washer to bolt assembly, switch actuator rod to switch actuator rack, then the spring and bolt assembly to switch actuator rack.

d. Assemble spring and bolt assembly with switch actuator rack to housing assembly. **First tooth of rack must interact with first and second tooth of sector. With rack fully inserted, block tooth of sector will rest in block tooth of rack.**

2. Assemble retaining ring to shaft assembly, then the shaft assembly to jacket assembly. Lubricate with lithium grease.
3. Assemble shift bowl shroud to floor shift lever bowl, then the bowl with shroud to steering column housing assembly.
4. Install three cross recess screws, then **torque** to 17 inch lbs.
5. Install turn signal switch connector through column housing assembly, then the upper bearing retainer.
6. Assemble lock housing cover assembly with bowl and shroud to jacket assembly.
7. Install cover screws and tighten in a clockwise order finger tight, then **torque** screws in same order to 47 inch lbs.
8. Adjust ignition switch assembly by moving switch slider to extreme left position, then one detent to right, Off-Lock position. **New ignition switch will be pinned in Off-Lock position, remove plastic pin after switch is installed on column.**
9. Install ignition switch and mounting stud to jacket, then **torque** stud to 35 inch lbs.
10. Install dimmer switch rod, assemble dimmer switch assembly to rod, then install washer head screw and hex nut finger tight.
11. Adjust dimmer switch by placing a 3/32 inch drill bit in hole on switch to limit travel, position switch on column and push against dimmer switch rod to remove all lash, then remove drill bit. **Torque** screw and nut to 35 inch lbs.
12. Install wiring protector, steering column support bracket assembly, then the four mounting bolts. **Torque** bolts to 22 ft. lbs.
13. Perform all assembly steps from "Shaft Lock, Turn Signal Cancelling Cam Assembly, Upper Bearing Spring, Thrust Washer, Buzzer Switch Assembly & Steering Column Lock Cylinder Set" as previously described.

TILT COLUMN

Refer to **Fig. 31** when servicing these steering columns.

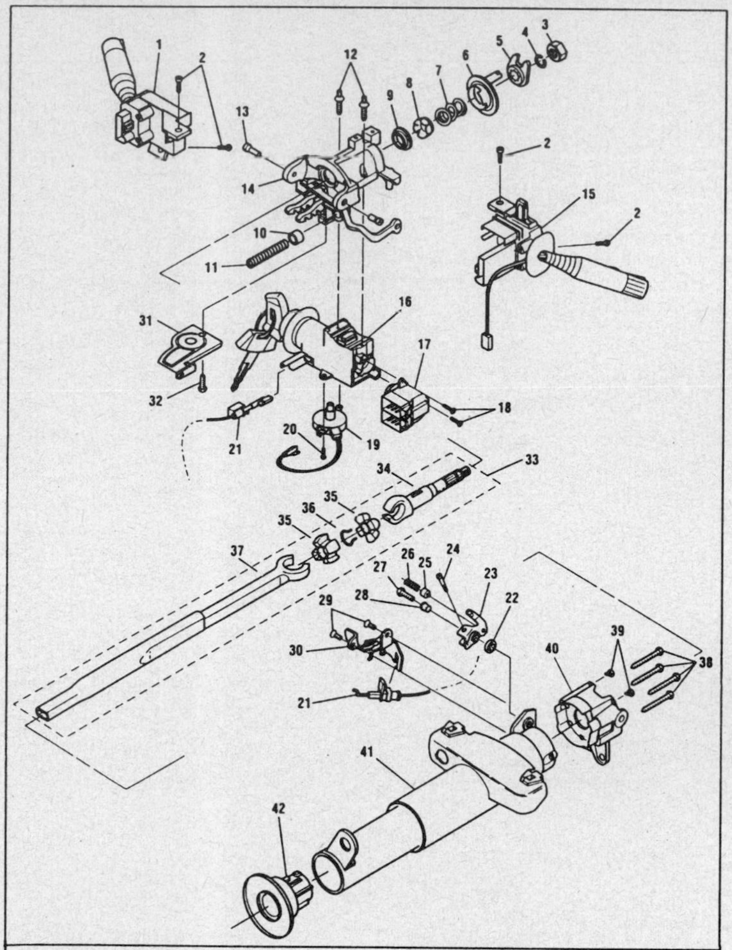

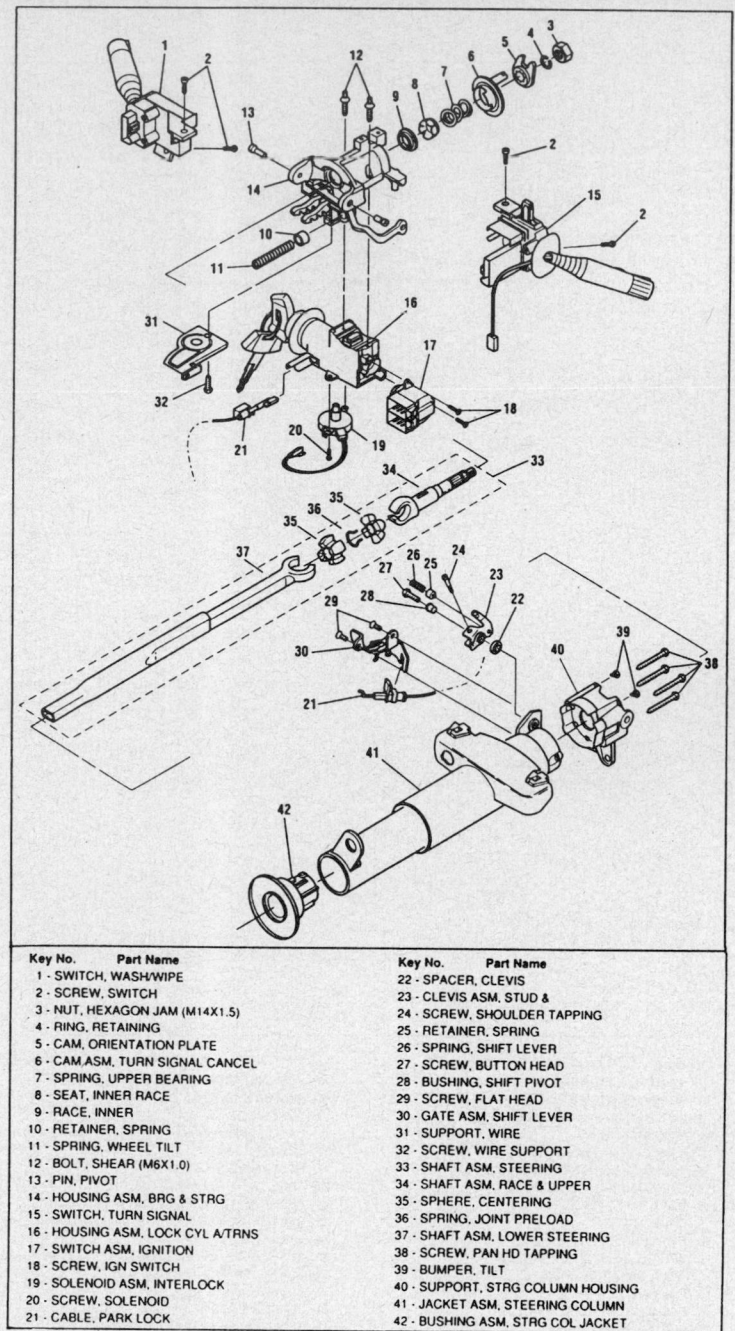

Key No.	Part Name	Key No.	Part Name
1	SWITCH, WASH/WIPE	22	SPACER, CLEVIS
2	SCREW, SWITCH	23	CLEVIS ASM, STUD &
3	NUT, HEXAGON JAM (M14X1.5)	24	SCREW, SHOULDER TAPPING
4	RING, RETAINING	25	RETAINER, SPRING
5	CAM, ORIENTATION PLATE	26	SPRING, SHIFT LEVER
6	CAM ASM, TURN SIGNAL CANCEL	27	SCREW, BUTTON HEAD
7	SPRING, UPPER BEARING	28	BUSHING, SHIFT PIVOT
8	SEAT, INNER RACE	29	SCREW, FLAT HEAD
9	RACE, INNER	30	GATE ASM, SHIFT LEVER
10	RETAINER, SPRING	31	SUPPORT, WIRE
11	SPRING, WHEEL TILT	32	SCREW, WIRE SUPPORT
12	BOLT, SHEAR (M6X1.0)	33	SHAFT ASM, STEERING
13	PIN, PIVOT	34	SHAFT ASM, RACE & UPPER
14	HOUSING ASM, BRG & STRG	35	SPHERE, CENTERING
15	SWITCH, TURN SIGNAL	36	SPRING, JOINT PRELOAD
16	HOUSING ASM, LOCK CYL A/TRNS	37	SHAFT ASM, LOWER STEERING
17	SWITCH ASM, IGNITION	38	SCREW, PAN HD TAPPING
18	SCREW, IGN SWITCH	39	BUMPER, TILT
19	SOLENOID ASM, INTERLOCK	40	SUPPORT, STRG COLUMN HOUSING
20	SCREW, SOLENOID	41	JACKET ASM, STEERING COLUMN
21	CABLE, PARK LOCK	42	BUSHING ASM, STRG COL JACKET

GC6049200070000X

Fig. 29 Exploded view of tilt steering column. Skylark

SHAFT LOCK, TURN SIGNAL CANCEL CAM, UPPER BEARING SPRING, UPPER BEARING INNER RACE SEAT, INNER RACE, BUZZER SWITCH & COLUMN LOCK CYLINDER SET

Disassemble

1. Remove steering wheel as described in the "Electrical" section of the appropriate vehicle section in the front of this manual.
2. Disconnect battery ground cable.
3. Remove shaft lock cover, then the shaft lock retaining ring using plate compressor J 23653-C or equivalent to depress shaft lock. Discard ring.
4. Remove shaft lock, turn signal cancelling cam assembly, upper bearing spring, upper bearing inner race seat and inner race.
5. Move turn signal to the right turn position.
6. Remove multi-function lever and hazard knob assembly.
7. Remove screw and signal switch arm, then the turn signal switch screws.
8. Remove turn signal switch assembly and allow switch to hang freely.
9. Remove key from lock cylinder set, then the buzzer switch assembly.
10. Reinstall key in lock cylinder and turn to Lock position.
11. Remove lock retaining screw, then the lock cylinder.

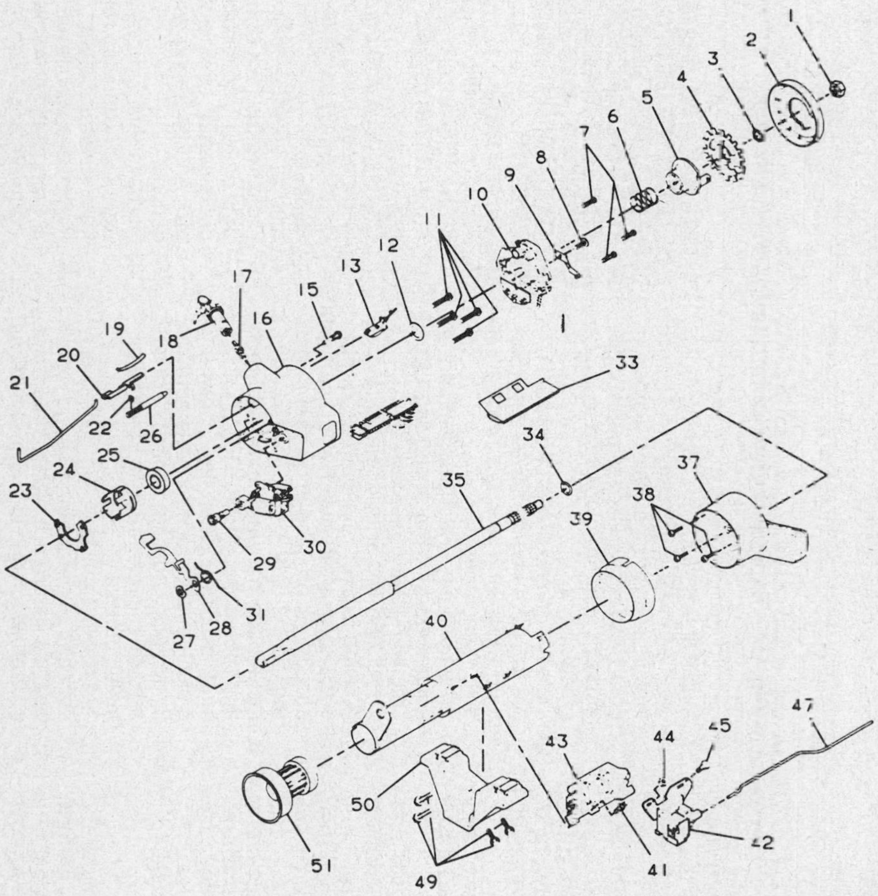
GC6049200071010X

Fig. 30 Exploded view of standard steering column (Part 1 of 2). Sunbird

1-NUT, HEXAGON LOCKING (M14x1.5)
2-COVER, SHAFT LOCK
3-RING, RETAINING
4-LOCK, STEERING SHAFT
5-CAM ASM, TURN SIG CANCELLING
6-SPRING, UPPER BEARING
7-SCREW, BIND HD CROSS RECESS
8-SCREW, RD WASH HD (M4.2x1.41)
9-ARM, ACTUATOR SWITCH
10-SWITCH ASM, TURN SIGNAL
11-SCREW, HEX WASHER HD TAP
12-WASHER, THRUST
13-SWITCH ASM, BUZZER
15-SCREW, LOCK RETAINING
16-HOUSING ASM, STRG COL
17-SECTOR, SWITCH ACTUATOR
18-LOCK CYLINDER SET, STRG COL
19-SPRING, RACK PRELOAD
20-RACK, SWITCH ACTUATOR
21-ROD, SWITCH ACTUATOR
22-WASHER, SPRING THRUST
23-RETAINER, UPPER BEARING
24-BUSHING, BEARING RETAINING
25-BEARING ASM
26-BOLT ASM, SPRING &
27-WASHER, WAVE
28-LEVER, KEY RELEASE
29-PIN, SWITCH ACTUATOR PIVOT
30-PIVOT ASM, SWITCH ACTUATOR
31-SPRING, KEY RELEASE
33-PROTECTOR, WIRING
34-RING, RETAINING
35-SHAFT ASM, STEERING
37-BOWL, FLOOR SHIFT LEVER
38-SCREW, BIND HD C/REC
39-SHROUD, SHIFT BOWL
40-JACKET ASM, STRG COL
41-STUD, DIMR & IGN SW MOUNTING
42-SWITCH ASM, DIMMER
43-SWITCH ASM, IGNITION
44-NUT, HEX (#10-24)
45-SCREW, WASH HD (#10-24 x .25)
47-ROD, DIMMER SWITCH ACTUATOR
49-BOLT, FLANGED HEX HD
50-BRACKET ASM, STRG COL SUPT
51-BUSHING, STRG COL JACKET

Service Kits

201-HSG ASM SERV SET, STRG COL
-INCLUDES: 16,17,23,24,25
202-GREASE SERV KIT, (SYNTHETIC)
203-RACK SERV ASM, SW AC ROD &
-INCLUDES: 20,21
204-ROD SERVICE KIT, DIMMER SWITCH
-INCLUDES 47
205-SECTOR SERV KIT, IGN SW ACTR
-INCLUDES 17

GC6049200071020X

Fig. 30 Exploded view of standard steering column (Part 2 of 2). Sunbird

Assemble

Ensure all fasteners are securely seated before applying torque. Failure to do so may result in component damage or malfunctioning of steering column.

1. Install lock cylinder and lock retaining screw. **Torque** screw to 22 inch lbs.
2. Remove key from lock cylinder set, then install buzzer switch assembly.
3. Reinstall key in lock cylinder set, then turn key to Lock position.
4. Install turn signal switch assembly and screws. **Torque** screws to 30 inch lbs.
5. Install signal switch arm and screw. **Torque** screw to 20 inch lbs.
6. Install hazard knob assembly and multi-function lever.
7. Install inner race, upper bearing inner race seat, upper bearing spring and turn signal cancelling cam assembly. Lubricate cancelling cam with synthetic grease.
8. Install shaft lock and shaft lock retaining ring using plate compressor tool No. J 23653-C or equivalent, to depress shaft lock. Ring must be fully seated in groove.
9. Install shaft lock cover, then connect battery ground cable.
10. Install steering wheel as described in the "Electrical" section of the appropriate vehicle section in the front of this manual.

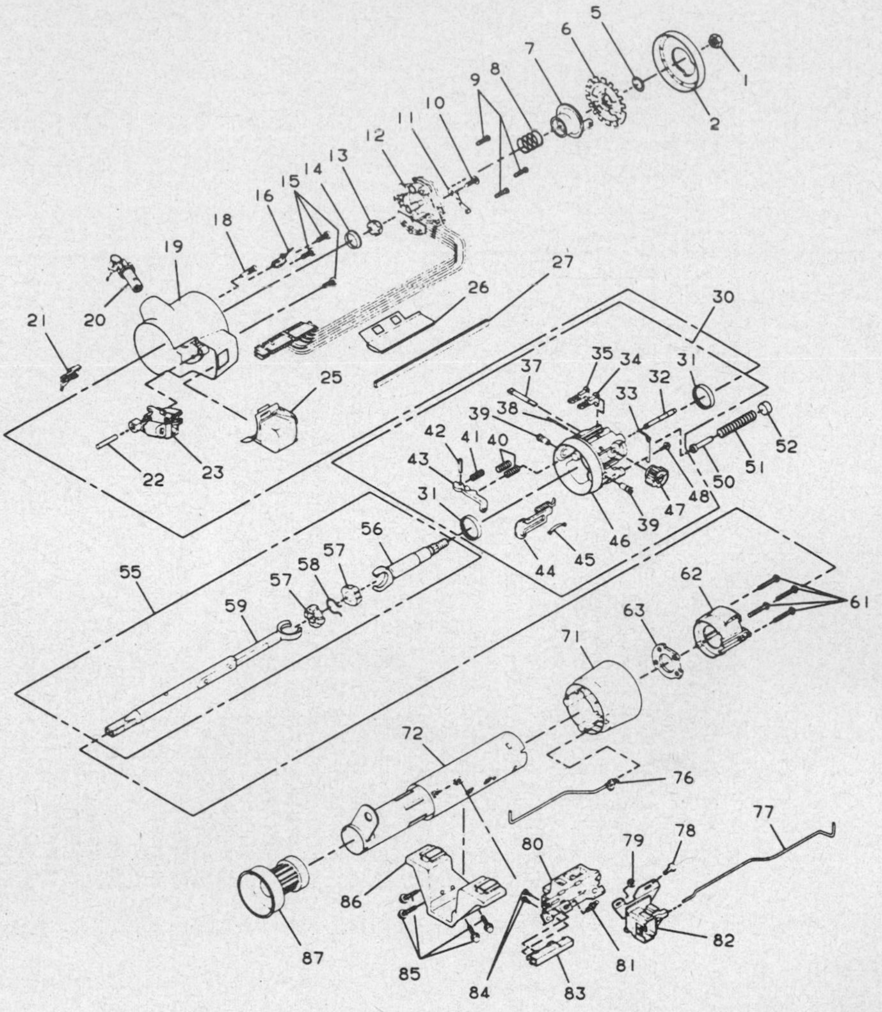
GC6049200072010X

Fig. 31 Exploded view of tilt steering column (Part 1 of 2). Sunbird

LOCK HOUSING COVER, COLUMN HOUSING COVER END CAP, PIVOT & PULSE SWITCH, DIMMER SWITCH ROD ACTUATOR & TILT SPRING

Disassemble

1. Remove steering wheel as described in the "Electrical" section of the appropriate vehicle section in the front of this manual.
2. Disconnect battery ground cable.
3. Disassemble shaft lock, turn signal cancel cam, upper bearing spring, upper bearing inner race seat, inner race, buzzer switch and lock cylinder set as previously described.
4. Remove tilt lever, cover screws and lock housing cover assembly. Let cover hang freely.
5. Remove column housing cover end cap with dimmer switch rod actuator, then the actuator from end cap.
6. Remove switch actuator pivot pin, then the pivot and pulse switch assembly.
7. Remove spring retainer using a cross recess head screwdriver to push retainer down and turn clockwise to release.
8. Remove spring and spring guide.

Assemble

Ensure all fasteners are securely seated before applying torque. Failure to do so may result in component damage or malfunctioning of steering column.

1. Install spring guide and spring. Lubricate with lithium grease.
2. Install spring retainer using a cross recess head screwdriver to push retainer down and turn clockwise to lock in place.
3. Install pivot and pulse switch assembly to lock housing cover assembly, then the switch actuator pivot pin to switch and cover.
4. Install dimmer switch rod actuator to column housing cover end cap. Lubricate with lithium grease.
5. Install end cap with actuator to lock housing cover assembly. Bottom edge of dimmer switch rod actuator should rest on bend in dimmer switch rod.
6. Install lock housing cover assembly and mounting screws. Tighten screw in 12 o'clock position first, screw in 8 o'clock position second, and screw in 3 o'clock position third. **Torque** screws in same order to 80 inch lbs.
7. Install tilt lever.
8. Assemble shaft lock, turn signal cancel cam, upper bearing spring, upper bearing inner race seat, inner race, buzzer switch and lock cylinder set as previously described.

TURN SIGNAL SWITCH, COLUMN HOUSING, STEERING WHEEL LOCK SHOE, SWITCH ACTUATOR SECTOR, SWITCH ACTUATOR RACK, BEARING, LOCK BOLT, STEERING SHAFT & COLUMN HOUSING SUPPORT

Disassemble

1. Remove steering wheel as described in the "Electrical" section of the appropriate vehicle section in the front of this manual.
2. Disconnect battery ground cable.
3. Remove steering column from vehicle as described under "Steering Column, Replace."
4. Inspect steering column for damage.
5. Disassemble lock housing cover, column housing cover end cap, pivot and pulse switch, dimmer switch rod actuator and tilt spring as previously described.
6. Remove turn signal switch assembly with lock housing cover assembly from steering column.
7. Remove four bolts and support bracket from steering column, then the wiring protectors and gently pull wire harness through column.

1-NUT, HEX LOCKING (M14x1.5)
2-COVER, SHAFT LOCK
5-RING, RETAINING
6-LOCK, SHAFT
7-CAM ASM, TURN SIG CANCEL
8-SPRING, UPPER BEARING
9-SCREW, BNDG HD CR RECESS
10-SCREW, RD WASH HD (M4.2x1.41)
11-ARM, SIGNAL SWITCH
12-SWITCH ASM, TURN SIGNAL
13-SEAT, UPPER BRG INNER RACE
14-RACE, INNER
15-SCREW, PAN HD SOC TAP
16-SWITCH ASM, BUZZER
18-SCREW, LOCK RETAINING
19-COVER ASM, LOCK HOUSING
20-LOCK CYLINDER SET, STRG COL
21-ACTUATOR, DIMMER SW ROD
22-PIN, SWITCH ACTUATOR PIVOT
23-SWITCH ASM, PIVOT & (PULSE)
25-CAP, COL HSG COVER END
26-PROTECTOR, WIRING
27-PROTECTOR, WIRING (CRUISE)
30-HOUSING ASM, STRG COLUMN
31-BEARING ASM
32-BOLT, LOCK
33-SPRING, LOCK BOLT
34-SHOE, STEERING WHEEL LOCK
35-SHOE, STEERING WHEEL LOCK
37-SHAFT, DRIVE
38-PIN, DOWEL
39-PIN, PIVOT
40-SPRING, SHOE
41-SPRING, RELEASE LEVER
42-PIN, RELEASE LEVER
43-LEVER, SHOE RELEASE
44-RACK, SWITCH ACTUATOR
45-SPRING, RACK PRELOAD
46-HOUSING, STRG COLUMN
47-SECTOR, SWITCH ACTUATOR
48-SCREW, HEX WASHER HEAD
50-GUIDE, SPRING
51-SPRING, WHEEL TILT
52-RETAINER, SPRING
55-SHAFT ASM, STEERING
56-SHAFT ASM, RACE & UPPER
57-SPHERE, CENTERING
58-SPRING, JOINT PRELOAD
59-SHAFT ASM, LOWER STEERING
61-SCREW, SUPPORT
62-SUPPORT ASM, STRG COL HSG
63-PLATE, LOCK
71-SHROUD, STRG COL HOUSING
72-JACKET ASM, STRG COL
76-ACTUATOR ASM, IGN SWITCH
77-ROD, DIMMER SWITCH
78-SCREW, WASH HD (#10-24x.25)
79-NUT, HEXAGON (#10-24)
80-SWITCH ASM, IGNITION
81-STUD, DIMR & IGN SW MTG
82-SWITCH ASM, DIMMER
83-HOUSING ASM, IGN SW INHIBITOR
84-SCREW, PAN HD C/REC (4-24 x .25)
85-BOLT, FLDG HEX HD (M8 x 1.25)
86-BRACKET ASM, STRG COL SUPT
87-BUSHING, STRG COL JACKET

Service Kits

201-RACK SERV KIT, COL SECTOR & -INCLUDES: 14,31,33,44,47,48
202-SPRING SERV KIT, TILT COLUMN -INCLUDES: 13,14,39,50,51,52
203-SPHERE SERV KIT, TILT COLUMN -INCLUDES: 57,58
204-GREASE SERV KIT, (SYNTHETIC)
205-COVER SERV ASM, LOCK HOUSING -INCLUDES: 19

GC6049200072020X

Fig. 31 Exploded view of tilt steering column (Part 2 of 2). Sunbird

8. Remove pivot pins using pivot pin remover tool No. J 21854-01 or equivalent, then reinstall tilt lever.
9. Remove steering column housing assembly, pull back on tilt lever and pull steering column housing assembly down and away from column.
10. If necessary, disassemble steering column housing as follows:
    a. Remove bearing assembly, hex head screw, lock bolt spring, lock bolt, switch actuator rack and rack preload spring.
    b. Remove driveshaft, switch actuator sector, then the release lever pin using lock shoe and release lever pin remover/installer tool No. J 22635 or equivalent.
    c. Remove shoe release lever, release lever spring, then the dowel pin using lock shoe and release lever pin remover/installer.
    d. Remove lock shoes and shoe springs.
11. If necessary, assemble steering column housing as follows:
    a. Install shoe springs and lock shoes, then the dowel pin using lock shoe and release lever pin remover/installer.
    b. Install release lever spring, shoe release lever, then the release lever pin using lock shoe and release lever pin remover/installer.
    c. Install switch actuator sector, driveshaft and rack preload spring, then assemble switch actuator rack to actuator sector.
    d. Assemble bearing assembly lubricated with lithium grease to column housing using steering column housing bearing installer tool No. J 38639 and driver handle tool No. J 8092 or equivalents.
    e. Install lock bolt, lock bolt spring and hex head screw. **Torque** screw to 35 inch lbs.
12. Remove steering column jacket bushing, then the steering column shaft assembly.
13. Inspect steering column shaft assembly for damage, then mark upper shaft assembly and lower steering shaft assembly to ensure proper assembly.
14. If necessary, disassemble steering column shaft assembly as follows:
    a. Disassemble upper shaft assembly from lower steering shaft assembly. Tilt 90° to each other and disengage.
    b. Disassemble centering sphere from upper shaft assembly. Rotate sphere 90° and slip out.
    c. Remove joint preload spring from centering sphere.
15. If necessary, assemble steering column shaft assembly as follows:
    a. Install joint preload spring to centering sphere, then lubricate centering sphere with lithium grease, slip into upper shaft assembly and rotate sphere 90°.
    b. Install upper shaft assembly to lower steering shaft assembly. Align marks and tilt assemblies 90° to each other.
16. Remove support screws, then the column housing support assembly with dimmer switch rod from steering column jacket assembly. Remove rod from support.
17. Remove lock plate from steering column jacket assembly, then the steering column housing shroud.
18. Remove hex nut and screw, then the dimmer switch assembly from rod.
19. Remove mounting stud and ignition switch assembly with switch actuator assembly.
20. Remove switch actuator assembly from switch assembly, then the two pan head screws from ignition switch and ignition switch inhibitor housing assembly.
21. Remove ignition switch inhibitor from ignition switch.

Assemble

Ensure all fasteners are securely seated before applying torque. Failure to do so may result in component damage or malfunctioning of steering column.

1. Install shroud to jacket, lock plate to steering column jacket assembly, then the dimmer switch rod to loop in column housing support assembly.
2. Install support assembly and mounting screws. **Torque** mounting screws to 77 inch lbs.
3. Install actuator assembly to groove in housing support assembly, then the steering shaft assembly to jacket assembly. Lubricate with lithium grease.
4. Install tilt lever, then the column housing assembly to column.
5. Position column housing and align switch actuator rack with pin on end of ignition switch actuator rack.
6. Pull back on tilt lever, pushing column housing onto column housing support assembly.
7. Release tilt lever to lock shoes onto dowel pins, then remove tilt lever.
8. Install pivot pins, lubricate with lithium grease, then press pin until firmly seated, two places.
9. Install steering column jacket bushing. Lubricate outer surface with lithium grease. Bushing locator lug must seat in jacket notch.
10. Adjust ignition switch assembly by

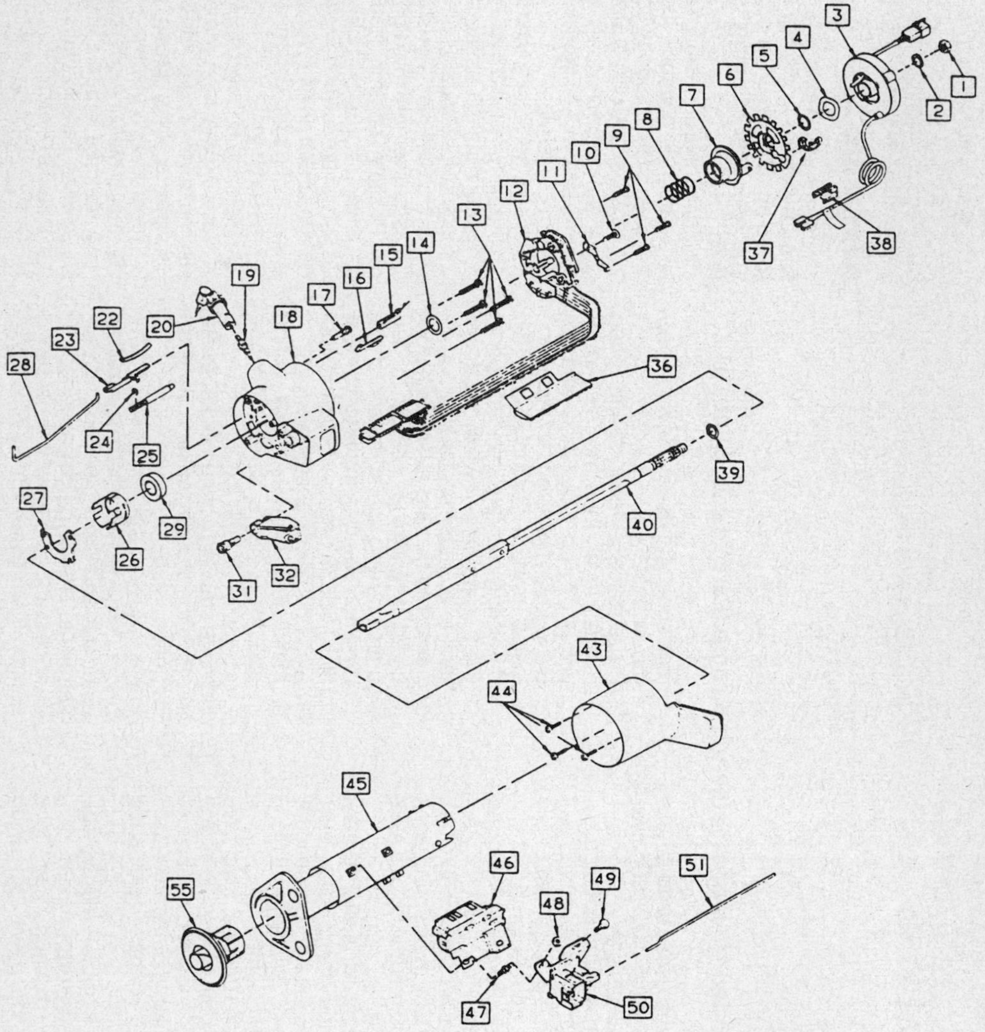
1
2
3
4
5
6
7
8
9
10
11
12
13
14
15
16
17
18
19
20
22
23
24
25
26
27
28
29
31
32
36
37
38
39
40
43
44
45
46
47
48
49
50
51
55

1	NUT, HEXAGON LOCKING (M14x1.5)
2	RING, RETAINING
3	COIL ASM, INFL RESTRAINT
4	WASHER, WAVE
5	RING, RETAINING
6	LOCK, SHAFT
7	CAM ASM, TURN SIG CANCELLING
8	SPRING, UPPER BEARING
9	SCREW, BINDING HD CROSS RECESS
10	SCREW, RD WASH HD (M4.2x1.41)
11	ARM, SIGNAL SWITCH
12	SWITCH ASM, TURN SIGNAL
13	SCREW, HEX WASHER HD TAPPING
14	WASHER, THRUST
15	SWITCH ASM, BUZZER
16	CLIP, BUZZER SWITCH RETAINING
17	SCREW, LOCK RETAINING
18	HOUSING ASM, STEERING COLUMN
19	SECTOR, SWITCH ACTUATOR
20	LOCK CYLINDER SET, STRG COLUMN
22	SPRING, RACK PRELOAD
23	RACK, SWITCH ACTUATOR
24	WASHER, SPRING THRUST
25	BOLT, LOCK
26	BUSHING, BEARING RETAINING
27	RETAINER, UPPER BEARING
28	ROD, SWITCH ACTUATOR
29	BEARING ASM
31	PIN, SWITCH ACTUATOR PIVOT
32	PIVOT ASM, SWITCH ACTUATOR
36	PROTECTOR, WIRING
37	SPACER, SHAFT LOCK
38	SHROUD, CONNECTOR
39	RING, RETAINING
40	SHAFT ASM, STEERING COLUMN
43	BOWL, FLOORSHIFT
44	SCREW, BINDING HD CROSS RECESS
45	JACKET ASM, STEERING COLUMN
46	SWITCH ASM, IGNITION
47	STUD, DIMR & IGN SW MOUNTING
48	NUT, HEX (#10-24 x .25)
49	SCREW, WASHER HD (#10-24 x .25)
50	SWITCH ASM, DIMMER
51	ROD, DIMMER SWITCH
55	BUSHING ASM, STRG COL JACKET

Service Kits

201	COIL SERV KIT, INFL RESTRAINT -INCLUDES: 3,4,38
202	GREASE SERV KIT, (SYNTHETIC)

GC6049100073000X -R-

Fig. 32 Exploded view of standard steering column. Beretta & Corsica

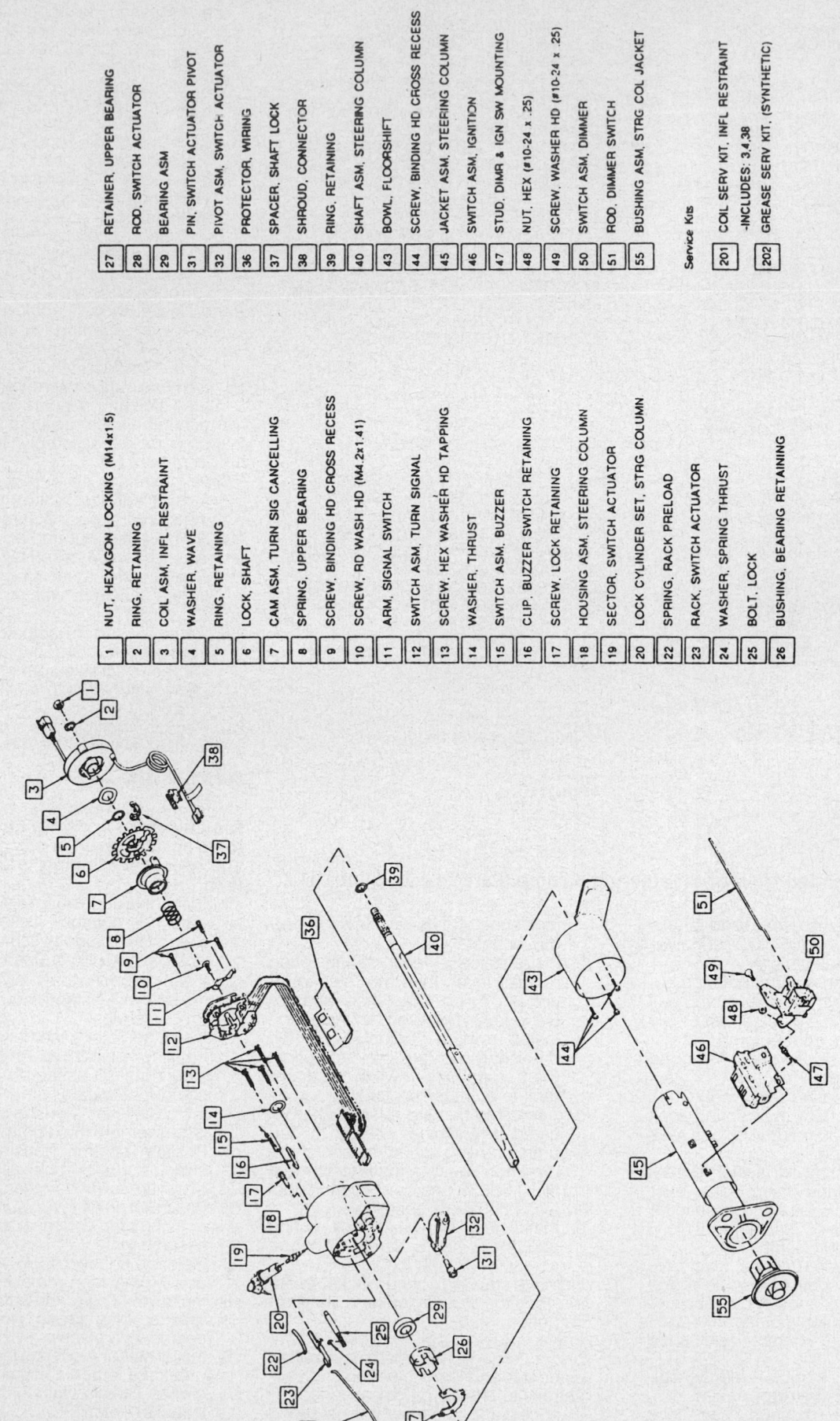

moving switch slider to extreme left position, then one detent to right, Off-Lock position. **When using a new ignition switch, the switch will be pinned in Off-Lock position. Remove plastic pin after switch is assembled to column.**

11. Install ignition switch and mounting stud, then **torque** stud to 35 inch lbs.
12. Install ignition switch inhibitor to ignition switch, then the two pan head screws. **Torque** screws to 30 inch lbs.
13. Install dimmer switch assembly to rod, then the screw and nut and tighten finger tight.
14. Adjust dimmer switch by placing a 3/32 inch drill bit in hole on switch to limit travel, position switch on column and push against dimmer switch rod to remove all lash, then remove drill bit. **Torque** screw and nut to 35 inch lbs.
15. Install turn signal switch assembly wire harness through lock housing cover assembly and steering column. Let switch hang freely.
16. Install wiring protectors, then the bracket with four bolts. **Torque** bolts to 22 ft. lbs.
17. Assemble lock housing cover, column housing cover end cap, pivot and pulse switch, dimmer switch rod actuator and tilt spring as previously described.
18. Install steering column into vehicle as described under "Steering Column, Replace."
19. Connect battery ground cable, then install steering wheel as described in the "Electrical" section of the appropriate vehicle section in the front of this manual.

Beretta & Corsica

STANDARD COLUMN

Care must be taken when handling column with a live inflator module. Never point bag deploy surface toward you, and never stand column on steering wheel. Accidental deployment in these positions may cause injury. Always face bag deploy surface toward open space to allow for unrestricted expansion.

INFLATOR MODULE, COIL, SHAFT LOCK, TURN SIGNAL CANCELLING CAM, UPPER BEARING SPRING, THRUST WASHER, TURN SIGNAL SWITCH, BUZZER SWITCH, LOCK CYLINDER SET & CENTERING COIL

Refer to **Fig. 32** for exploded view of steering column.

Disassemble

1. Remove inflator module from steering wheel as follows:
   a. Remove Torx screws from back of steering wheel.
   b. Remove connector position assurance (CPA) and connector from rear of inflator module.
   c. Remove inflator module.
2. Remove column as described under "Steering Column, Replace." The steering wheel must be straight and the column in the Lock position.
3. Remove horn connector to slip ring, then horn contact.
4. Remove steering wheel locknut.
5. Remove steering wheel using wheel puller tool No. J 1859-03 or equivalent. **When attaching puller to steering wheel, use care to prevent threading the side screws into the coil assembly.**
6. Remove coil assembly retaining ring.
7. Remove coil assembly off shaft end, allowing coil to hang freely. **The coil assembly will become uncentered if steering column is separated from gear and is allowed to rotate, or centering spring is pushed down letting hub rotate while coil is removed from column.**
8. Remove wave washer, then shaft lock spacer.
9. Using compressor tool No. J-23653-C or equivalent, depress shaft lock, then remove shaft lock retaining ring.
10. Remove shaft lock, then the turn signal cancelling cam assembly.
11. Remove upper bearing spring, then thrust washer.
12. Place turn signal in Right Turn position.
13. Remove multi-function lever and hazard knob assembly.
14. Remove signal switch assembly, then turn signal switch assembly. Position turn signal switch out of way. If removal of switch is necessary, disconnect electrical connector at base of column and remove wiring protector, then gently pull wire harness through gear shift lever bowl, column housing and lock housing cover.
15. Remove coil assembly.
16. Remove key from cylinder lock and remove buzzer switch and clip, then reinstall key in cylinder lock and place key in Lock position.
17. Remove lock retaining screw and lock cylinder set.

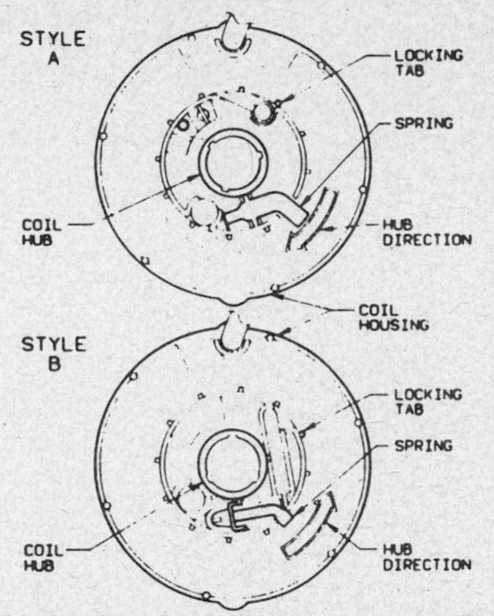
STYLE A
LOCKING TAB
SPRING
COIL HUB
HUB DIRECTION
COIL HOUSING
STYLE B
LOCKING TAB
SPRING
COIL HUB
HUB DIRECTION

Perform the following steps to center coil assembly:
A. **Remove coil assembly.**
B. **Hold coil assembly with clear bottom up to see coil ribbon.**
C. **NOTE: There are two different styles of coils. One rotates clockwise and the other rotates counterclockwise.**
D. **While holding coil assembly, depress spring lock to rotate hub in direction of arrow until it stops.**
E. **The coil ribbon should be wound up snug against center hub.**
F. **Rotate coil hub in opposite direction approximately two and a half (2-1/2) turns. Release spring lock between locking tabs in front of arrow.**

GC0049100074000X

Fig. 33 Coil assembly centering. Beretta & Corsica w/standard column

Assemble

Ensure all fasteners are securely seated before applying required torque.

1. Install lock cylinder set, **torque** lock retaining screw to 40 inch lbs.
2. Place key in Run position, then install buzzer switch and clip.
3. Route turn signal switch wiring harness through lock housing cover, column housing and gear shift lever bowl.
4. Route coil assembly wire through lock housing cover, column housing and gear shift lever bowl and allow coil to hang freely.
5. Install turn signal switch, **torque** attaching screws to 30 inch lbs.
6. Install switch arm, **torque** retaining screw to 20 inch lbs.
7. Install hazard knob, multi-function lever.
8. Install thrust washer, then the upper bearing spring.
9. Install turn signal cancelling cam assembly, then the shaft lock.
10. Using compressor tool No. J-23653-C or equivalent, to depress shaft lock, install shaft lock retaining ring. Ring must seat in groove on shaft.
11. Set steering shaft so that block teeth on upper steering shaft are at the 12 o'clock and 6 o'clock positions. The alignment mark at the end of shaft should be at 12 o'clock position. Set ignition switch to Lock position to ensure no damage occurs to the coil assembly.
12. Ensure coil assembly hub is centered, **Fig. 33.** The coil assembly will become uncentered if the column is separated from the steering gear and is allowed to rotate, or the coil is removed from the column without first locking in position with locking screw.
13. Install wave washer, then shaft lock spacer.
14. Install coil assembly, using horn tower on cancel cam on inner ring and projections on outer ring for alignment, then the coil assembly retaining ring.
15. Install steering wheel, then inflator module to steering wheel.

COLUMN HOUSING, SWITCH ACTUATOR PIVOT, LOCK BOLT, BEARING, SWITCH ACTUATOR, DIMMER & IGNITION SWITCH

Disassemble

1. Disassemble inflator module, coil, shaft lock, turn signal cancel cam, upper bearing spring, thrust washer, turn signal switch, buzzer switch, lock cyl-

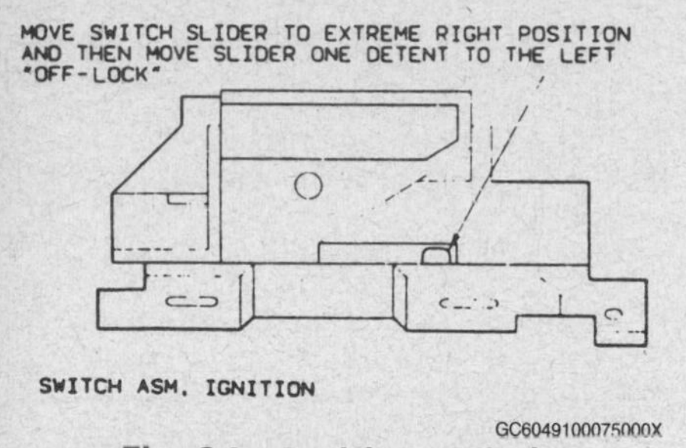
MOVE SWITCH SLIDER TO EXTREME RIGHT POSITION
AND THEN MOVE SLIDER ONE DETENT TO THE LEFT
"OFF-LOCK"
SWITCH ASM. IGNITION
GC6049100075000X

Fig. 34 Ignition switch adjustment. Beretta & Corsica w/standard column

inder set and centering coil as outlined previously.

2. Remove dimmer switch attaching screw and hex nut, dimmer switch, then dimmer switch rod.
3. Remove ignition switch attaching screw, then ignition switch.
4. Remove steering column housing assembly, then floorshift bowl.
5. Remove upper bearing retainer, then floorshift bowl from housing cover.
6. Remove ignition switch actuator assembly with lock bolt and spring washer.
7. Remove switch actuator pivot pin, then pivot pin assembly.
8. Remove bearing retainer bushing, then bearing assembly.
9. Remove switch actuator sector, then rack preload spring.

Assemble

1. Install rack preload spring, then switch actuator sector.
2. Install bearing assembly, then bearing retainer bushing.
3. Install switch actuator pivot assembly, then pivot pin. **Torque** pivot pin to 29 inch lbs.
4. Install actuator rod to actuator rack.
5. Install ignition switch actuator assembly, lock bolt, then spring thrust washer.
6. Install upper retainer, then floorshift bowl. **Torque** floorshift bowl attaching screws to 16 inch lbs.
7. Install ignition switch. Switch must be in the "Off-Lock" position.
8. Adjust ignition switch **Fig. 34**.
9. Install dimmer switch and adjust as follows:
   a. Place a 3/32 drill bit in hole on switch, **Fig. 35.**
   b. Place switch on column and push against switch rod to remove all lash, remove drill bit and **Torque** attaching nut and bolt to 35 inch lbs.
10. Assemble inflator module, coil, shaft lock, turn signal cancel cam, upper bearing spring, thrust washer, turn signal switch, buzzer switch, lock cylinder set and centering coil as outlined previously.

COLUMN JACKET BEARING & COLUMN SHAFT

Disassemble

1. Disassemble inflator module, coil, shaft lock, turn signal cancel Cam, upper bearing spring, thrust washer, turn signal switch, buzzer switch, lock cylinder set and centering coil as outlined previously.

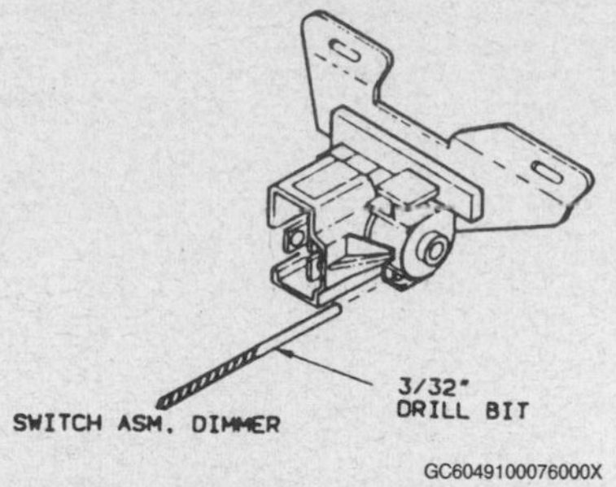
3/32"
DRILL BIT
SWITCH ASM. DIMMER
GC6049100076000X

Fig. 35 Dimmer switch adjustment. Beretta & Corsica w/standard column

2. Disassemble column housing, switch actuator pivot, lock bolt, bearing, switch actuator, dimmer and ignition switch as outlined previously.
3. Remove steering column jacket bushing assembly, then column shaft assembly, **Fig. 36.**
4. Remove retaining ring from shaft.

Assemble

1. Install retaining ring onto shaft.
2. Install shaft, then bushing assembly. Tab on bushing must fit into slot on end of steering column jacket.
3. Assemble inflator module, coil, shaft lock, turn signal cancel Cam, upper bearing spring, thrust washer, turn signal switch, buzzer switch, lock cylinder set and centering coil as outlined previously.
4. Assemble column housing, switch actuator pivot, lock bolt, bearing, switch actuator, dimmer and ignition switch as outlined previously.

TILT COLUMN

Care must be taken when handling column with a live inflator module. Never point bag deploy surface toward you, and never stand column on steering wheel. Accidental deployment in these positions may cause injury. Always face bag deploy surface toward open space to allow for unrestricted expansion.

INFLATOR MODULE, COIL, SHAFT LOCK, TURN SIGNAL CANCEL CAM, UPPER BEARING SPRING & SEAT, INNER RACE TURN SIGNAL SWITCH, BUZZER SWITCH & LOCK CYLINDER SET

Refer to **Fig. 37** for exploded view of steering column.

Disassemble

1. Remove inflator module from steering wheel as follows:
   a. Remove Torx screws from back of steering wheel.
   b. Remove connector position assurance (CPA) and connector from rear of inflator module.
   c. Remove inflator module.

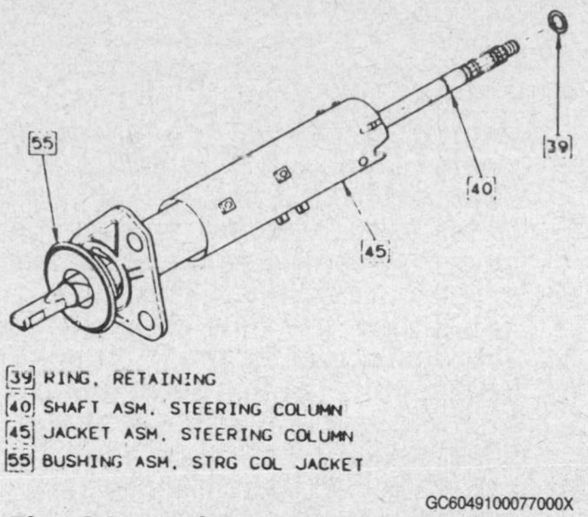
55
39
40
45
39 RING, RETAINING
40 SHAFT ASM. STEERING COLUMN
45 JACKET ASM. STEERING COLUMN
55 BUSHING ASM. STRG COL JACKET
GC6049100077000X

Fig. 36 Column jacket bushing & shaft assembly removal. Beretta & Corsica w/standard column

2. Remove column as described under "Steering Column, Replace." The steering wheel must be straight and the column in the Lock position.
3. Remove horn connector to slip ring, then horn contact.
4. Remove steering wheel locknut.
5. Remove steering wheel using wheel puller tool No. J 1859-03 or equivalent. **When attaching puller to steering wheel, use care to prevent threading the side screws into the coil assembly.**
6. Remove coil assembly retaining ring.
7. Remove coil assembly off shaft end, allowing coil to hang freely.
8. Using compressor tool No. J-23653-C or equivalent, depress shaft lock, then remove shaft lock retaining ring.
9. Remove shaft lock, then the turn signal cancelling cam.
10. Remove upper bearing spring, then the upper bearing seat.
11. Remove inner race, then place turn signal in Right Turn position.
12. Remove signal switch arm attaching screw and the arm, then the turn signal switch attaching screws.
13. Remove hazard knob, then position turn signal switch out of way. If removal of switch is necessary, remove retainer spring and wiring protector, then gently pull wire harness through gear shift lever bowl, column housing and lock housing cover.
14. Remove coil assembly.
15. Remove key from cylinder lock and remove buzzer switch and clip, then reinstall key in cylinder lock and place key in Lock position.
16. Remove lock retaining screw and lock cylinder set.

Assemble

Ensure all fasteners are securely seated before applying required torque.

1. Install lock cylinder set, **torque** lock retaining screw to 22 inch lbs.
2. Place key in Run position, then install buzzer switch and clip.
3. Route turn signal switch wiring harness through lock housing cover, column housing and gear shift lever bowl.
4. Route coil assembly wire through lock

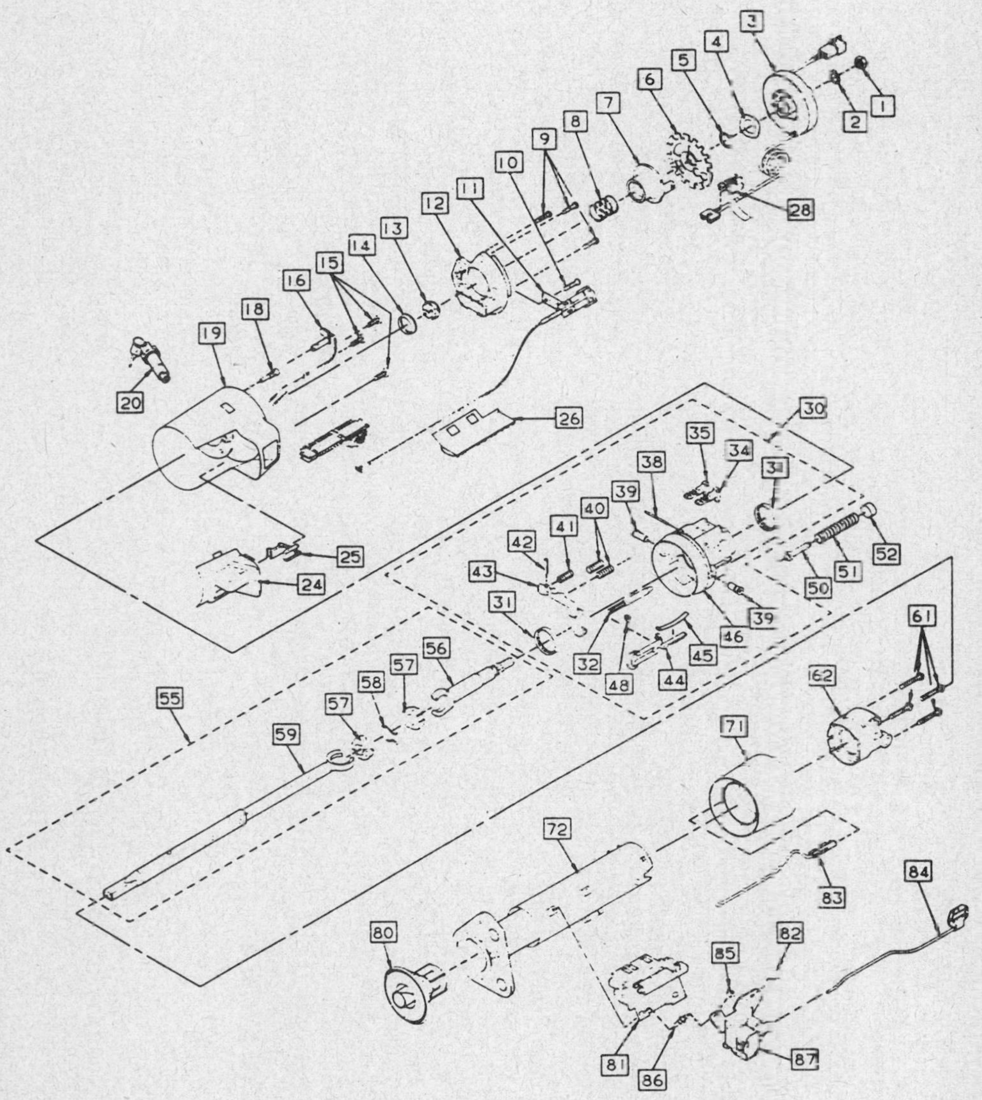

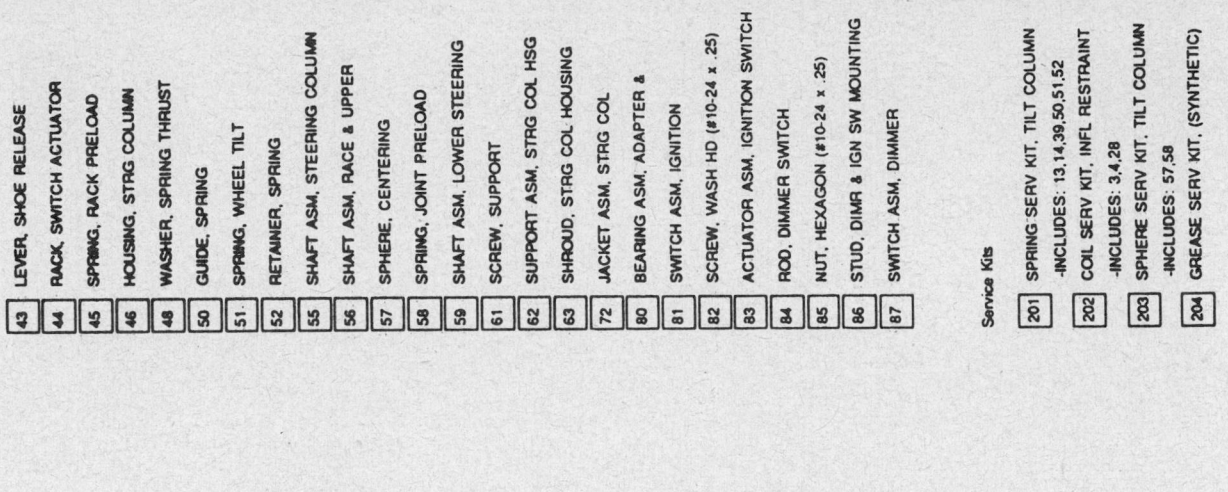

1	NUT, HEXAGON LOCKING (M14x1.5)
2	RING, RETAINING
3	COIL ASM, INFL RESTRAINT
4	WASHER, WAVE
5	RING, RETAINING
6	LOCK, SHAFT
7	CAM ASM, TURN SIG CANCELLING
8	SPRING, UPPER BEARING
9	SCREW, BINDING HD CROSS RECESS
10	SCREW, RD WASH HD (M4.2x1.41)
11	ARM, SIGNAL SWITCH
12	SWITCH ASM, TURN SIGNAL
13	SEAT, UPPER BRG INNER RACE
14	RACE, INNER
15	SCREW, PAN HD 6-LOBED SOC TAP
16	SWITCH ASM, BUZZER
18	SCREW, LOCK RETAINING
19	COVER ASM, LOCK HOUSING
20	LOCK CYLINDER SET, STRG COL
21	SCREW, FLT HD TAPPING
24	CAP, STRG COL HSG COVER END
25	ACTUATOR, DIMMER SWITCH ROD
26	PROTECTOR, WIRING
28	SHROUD, CONNECTOR
30	HOUSING ASM, STRG COLUMN
31	BEARING ASM
34	SHOE, STEERING WHEEL LOCK
35	SHOE, STEERING WHEEL LOCK
36	SHIELD, WIRE ABRASION
38	PIN, DOWEL
39	PIN, PIVOT
40	SPRING, SHOE
41	SPRING, RELEASE LEVER
42	PIN, RELEASE LEVER
43	LEVER, SHOE RELEASE
44	RACK, SWITCH ACTUATOR
45	SPRING, RACK PRELOAD
46	HOUSING, STRG COLUMN
48	WASHER, SPRING THRUST
50	GUIDE, SPRING
51	SPRING, WHEEL TILT
52	RETAINER, SPRING
55	SHAFT ASM, STEERING COLUMN
56	SHAFT ASM, RACE & UPPER
57	SPHERE, CENTERING
58	SPRING, JOINT PRELOAD
59	SHAFT ASM, LOWER STEERING
61	SCREW, SUPPORT
62	SUPPORT ASM, STRG COL HSG
63	SHROUD, STRG COL HOUSING
72	JACKET ASM, STRG COL
80	BEARING ASM, ADAPTER &
81	SWITCH ASM, IGNITION
82	SCREW, WASH HD (#10-24 x .25)
83	ACTUATOR ASM, IGNITION SWITCH
84	ROD, DIMMER SWITCH
85	NUT, HEXAGON (#10-24 x .25)
86	STUD, DIMR & IGN SW MOUNTING
87	SWITCH ASM, DIMMER

Service Kits

201	SPRING SERV KIT, TILT COLUMN -INCLUDES: 13,14,39,50,51,52
202	COIL SERV KIT, INFL RESTRAINT -INCLUDES: 3,4,28
203	SPHERE SERV KIT, TILT COLUMN -INCLUDES: 57,58
204	GREASE SERV KIT, (SYNTHETIC)

GC6049100078000X -R-

Fig. 37 Exploded view of tilt steering column. Beretta & Corsica

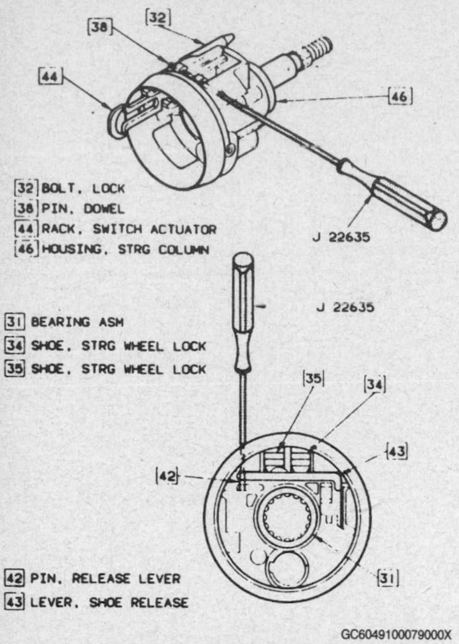
[38]
[32]
[44]
[46]
[32] BOLT, LOCK
[38] PIN, DOWEL
[44] RACK, SWITCH ACTUATOR
[46] HOUSING, STRG COLUMN
J 22635
J 22635
[31] BEARING ASM
[34] SHOE, STRG WHEEL LOCK
[35] SHOE, STRG WHEEL LOCK
[35]
[34]
[43]
[42]
[31]
[42] PIN, RELEASE LEVER
[43] LEVER, SHOE RELEASE
GC6049100079000X

Fig. 38 Disassembling steering column housing. Beretta & Corsica w/tilt column

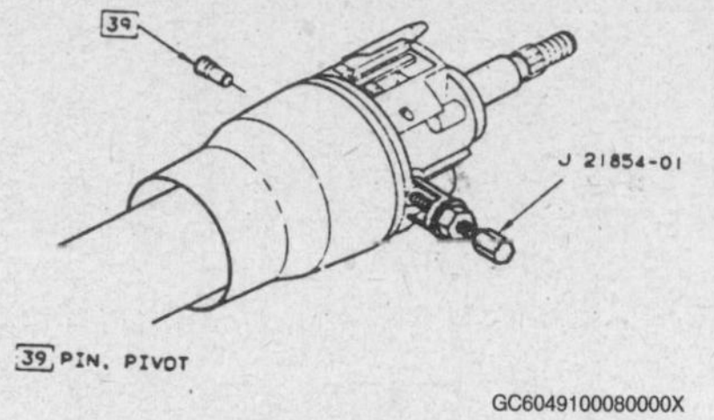
[39]
J 21854-01
[39] PIN, PIVOT
GC6049100080000X

Fig. 39 Pivot pin removal. Beretta & Corsica w/tilt column

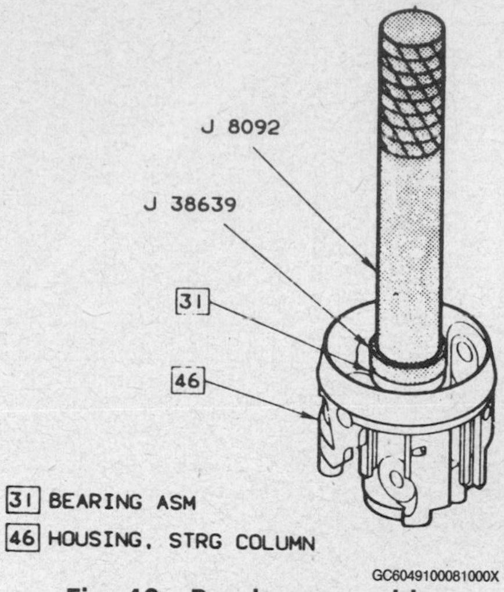
J 8092
J 38639
[31]
[46]
[31] BEARING ASM
[46] HOUSING, STRG COLUMN
GC6049100081000X

Fig. 40 Bearing assembly installation. Beretta & Corsica w/tilt column

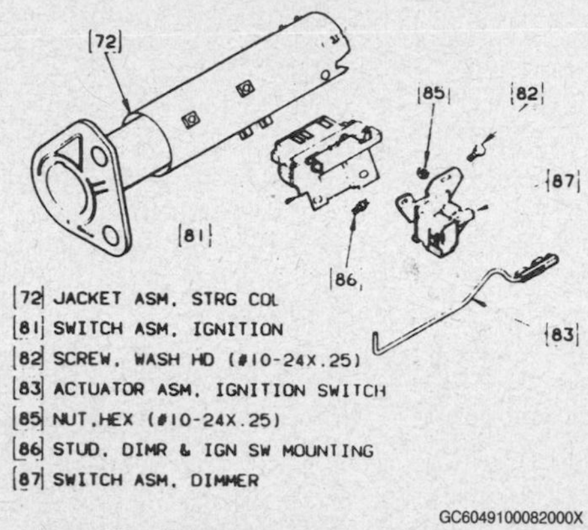
[72]
[85]
[82]
[87]
[81]
[86]
[83]
[72] JACKET ASM, STRG COL
[81] SWITCH ASM, IGNITION
[82] SCREW, WASH HD (#10-24X.25)
[83] ACTUATOR ASM, IGNITION SWITCH
[85] NUT,HEX (#10-24X.25)
[86] STUD, DIMR & IGN SW MOUNTING
[87] SWITCH ASM, DIMMER
GC6049100082000X

Fig. 41 Dimmer & ignition switch removal. Beretta & Corsica w/tilt column

housing cover, column housing and gear shift lever bowl and allow coil to hang freely.

5. Install turn signal switch, **torque** attaching screws to 30 inch lbs.
6. Install switch actuator pivot assembly, **torque** retaining screw to 20 inch lbs.
7. Install hazard knob, multi-function lever, then the inner race.
8. Install upper bearing inner race seat, then the upper bearing spring.
9. Install turn signal cancelling cam, then the shaft lock.
10. Using compressor tool No. J-23653-C or equivalent, to depress shaft lock, install shaft lock retaining ring, aligning to block tooth on shaft.
11. Ensure coil assembly hub is centered, **Fig. 33.** The coil assembly will become uncentered if the column is separated from the steering gear and is allowed to rotate, or the coil is removed from the column without first locking in position with locking screw.
12. Install wave washer.
13. Install coil assembly, using horn tower on cancel cam on inner ring and projections on outer ring for alignment, then the coil assembly retaining ring.
14. Install steering wheel, then inflator module to steering wheel.

LOCK HOUSING COVER, COVER END CAP, DIMMER SWITCH ROD ACTUATOR & TILT SPRING

Disassemble

1. Disassemble inflator module, coil, shaft lock, turn signal cancel cam, upper bearing spring and seat, inner race turn signal switch, buzzer switch and lock cylinder set as outlined previously.
2. Remove lock housing cover attaching screws and the cover, then the tilt lever.
3. Remove cover housing end cap, then dimmer switch rod actuator.
4. Using a cross recess head screwdriver, remove spring retainer. Push retainer down and turn counterclockwise to release.
5. Remove spring and spring guide.

Assemble

Ensure all fasteners are securely seated before applying required torque.

1. Coat spring guide and spring with lithium grease and install them, then install spring retainer. Push retainer down and turn clockwise to lock into place.
2. Install dimmer switch rod actuator to dimmer switch rod.
3. Install cover housing end cap.
4. Install lock housing cover. Tighten screw in 12 o'clock position first, screw in 8 o'clock position second and screw in 3 o'clock position third, then **torque** screws to 80 inch lbs. in same order.
5. Assemble inflator module, coil, shaft lock, turn signal cancel cam, upper bearing spring and seat, inner race turn signal switch, buzzer switch and lock cylinder set as outlined previously.

COLUMN HOUSING, LOCK SHOES, SWITCH ACTUATOR RACK BEARINGS & LOCK BOLT

Disassemble

1. Disassemble inflator module, coil, shaft lock, turn signal cancel cam, upper bearing spring and seat, inner race turn signal switch, buzzer switch and lock cylinder set as outlined previously.
2. Disassemble lock housing cover, cover end cap, dimmer switch rod actuator and tilt spring as previously outlined.
3. Remove pivot pin using tool No. J 21854-01 or equivalent, then reinstall tilt lever.
4. Remove steering column housing by pulling back on tilt lever and pull steering column housing down and away from steering column.
5. Disassemble steering column housing as follows:
   a. Remove bearing assembly, switch actuator rack, lock bolt and spring thrust washer, **Fig. 38.**
   b. Remove rack preload spring from housing.
   c. Remove release lever pin using tool No. J 22635 or equivalent, then shoe release lever.
   d. Remove dowel pin using tool No. J 22635 or equivalent, **Fig. 39.**
   e. Remove lock shoes and shoe springs.
   f. Reverse procedure to reassemble the steering column housing. When installing bearing assembly use tool Nos. J8092 and J 38629 or equivalents, **Fig. 40.**

Assemble

Ensure all fasteners are securely seated before applying required torque.

1. Install steering column housing to steering column as follows:
   a. Line up switch actuator rack with pin on end of ignition switch actuator assembly.
   b. Pull back on tilt lever, then push steering column housing onto steering column support assembly.
   c. Release tilt lever to lock shoes onto dowel pins.

d. Remove tilt lever.
2. Lubricate pivot pins using suitable lithium grease, press pins in until firmly seated.
3. Assemble inflator module, coil, shaft lock, turn signal cancel cam, upper bearing spring and seat, inner race turn signal switch, buzzer switch and lock cylinder set as outlined previously.
4. Assemble lock housing cover, cover end cap, dimmer switch rod actuator and tilt spring as previously outlined.

SHAFT, COLUMN HOUSING SUPPORT, IGNITION SWITCH, DIMMER SWITCH & JACKET BUSHING

Disassemble

1. Disassemble inflator module, coil, shaft lock, turn signal cancel cam, upper bearing spring and seat, inner race turn signal switch, buzzer switch and lock cylinder set as outlined previously.
2. Disassemble lock housing cover, cover end cap, dimmer switch rod actuator and tilt spring as previously outlined.
3. Disassemble "column housing, lock shoes, switch actuator rack bearings and lock bolt as outlined previously."
4. Remove steering column shaft assembly. **Mark upper and lower shaft assemblies to ensure proper assembling.**
5. Remove steering column support screw, steering column support assembly, then dimmer switch rod from jacket assembly.
6. Remove column housing shroud from jacket.
7. Remove ignition switch and dimmer switch as shown in **Fig. 41.**

Assemble

Ensure all fasteners are securely seated before applying required torque.

1. Install shroud to jacket, then dimmer switch rod to steering column support assembly.
2. Install support assembly, **torque** attaching screws to 47 inch lbs.
3. Install steering column shaft assembly. Refer to **Fig. 42** for proper shaft position.
4. Install steering column jacket bushing. Align tab on bushing with slot on end of jacket.
5. Install actuator assembly.
6. Assemble "column housing, lock shoes, switch actuator rack bearings and lock bolt as outlined previously."
7. Assemble lock housing cover, cover end cap, dimmer switch rod actuator and tilt spring as previously outlined.
8. Assemble inflator module, coil, shaft lock, turn signal cancel cam, upper bearing spring and seat, inner race turn signal switch, buzzer switch and lock cylinder set as outlined previously.
9. Install ignition switch to jacket. Install with switch in Off-Lock position, and shift bowl must not be in Park position **Fig. 34.**
10. Install dimmer switch and adjust as follows:
    a. Place a 3/32 drill bit in hole on switch, **Fig. 35.**
    b. Place switch on column and push against switch rod to remove all lash, remove drill bit and **Torque** attaching nut and bolt to 35 inch lbs.

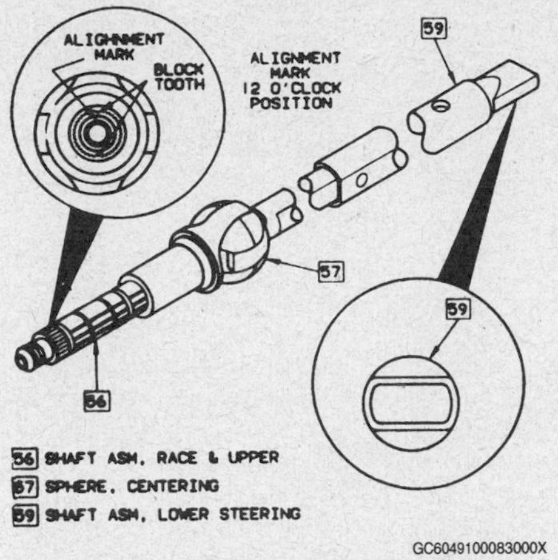
ALIGNMENT MARK
BLOCK TOOTH
ALIGNMENT MARK 12 O'CLOCK POSITION
59
57
59
56
56 SHAFT ASM, RACE & UPPER
57 SPHERE, CENTERING
59 SHAFT ASM, LOWER STEERING
GC6049100083000X

Fig. 42 Proper upper to lower shaft position. Beretta & Corsica w/tilt column

Cutlass Supreme, Grand Prix, Lumina & Regal

STANDARD COLUMN

Refer to **Fig. 43** when servicing this column.

TURN SIGNAL CANCEL CAM, PIVOT & PULSE SWITCH & TURN SIGNAL SWITCH

Disassemble

1. Remove nut retainer, jam nut and steering wheel.
2. Remove turn signal cancel cam assembly, hazard knob screw and hazard warning knob.
3. Position turn signal switch so that signal switch screws and housing cover screw can be removed through openings in switch.
4. Remove housing cover screw and column housing cover.
5. Disconnect wiring protector from opening in instrument panel bracket on jacket and bowl assembly and separate from wires.
6. Disconnect pivot and pulse switch connector from ignition and dimmer switch.
7. Remove pivot switch screw and pivot and pulse switch assembly.
8. Remove turn signal switch screws and disconnect turn signal switch connector from ignition and dimmer switch assembly connector.
9. Remove seventeen-way lock from turn signal connector and disconnect wires on alarm or buzzer assembly from turn signal connector with special tool No. J 35689-A or equivalent, **Fig. 44.** Wrap wire ends with tape to protect during removal and installation.
10. Remove turn signal switch assembly from column.

Assemble

1. Install turn signal switch assembly and **torque** screws to 35 inch lbs.
2. Connect wires from alarm or buzzer assembly to turn signal switch connector.
3. Install seventeen-way secondary lock to turn signal connector and snap in place.
4. Connect turn signal switch connector to ignition and dimmer switch connector and snap in place.
5. Install pivot and pulse switch assembly and **torque** screw to 18 inch lbs.
6. Connect pivot switch connector to ignition and dimmer switch connector and snap in place.
7. Install wiring protector as follows:
    a. Wrap protector around all wires passing through instrument panel bracket opening.
    b. Close protector so that interlocking grooves engage and slide protector into instrument panel bracket opening on jacket and bowl assembly and snap in place.
8. Install column housing cover and **torque** screw to 35 inch lbs.
9. Install hazard warning knob and **torque** screw to 9 inch lbs.
10. Lubricate bottom side of cancel cam with lithium grease and install turn signal cancel cam assembly.
11. Install steering wheel and jam nut, **torque** jam nut to 30 inch lbs. and secure with nut retainor.

STEERING SHAFT, STEERING COLUMN HOUSING, BEARING ASSEMBLIES, ALARM & STEERING COLUMN LOCK CYLINDER.

Disassemble

1. Remove turn signal cancel cam assembly, pivot & pulse switch assembly & turn signal switch assembly as previously described.
2. Remove two lower spring retainers and discard.
3. Remove lower bearing spring and lower bearing seat.
4. Remove adapter screws, adapter and lower bearing assembly.
5. Turn lock cylinder to the Run position.
6. Place opening in retaining ring over flat on steering shaft, then remove retaining ring with a screwdriver and discard.
7. Remove thrust washer, upper bearing spring and washer.
8. Remove steering shaft from lower end of jacket and bowl assembly.
9. Remove housing screws and column housing.
10. Remove housing spacer and bearing

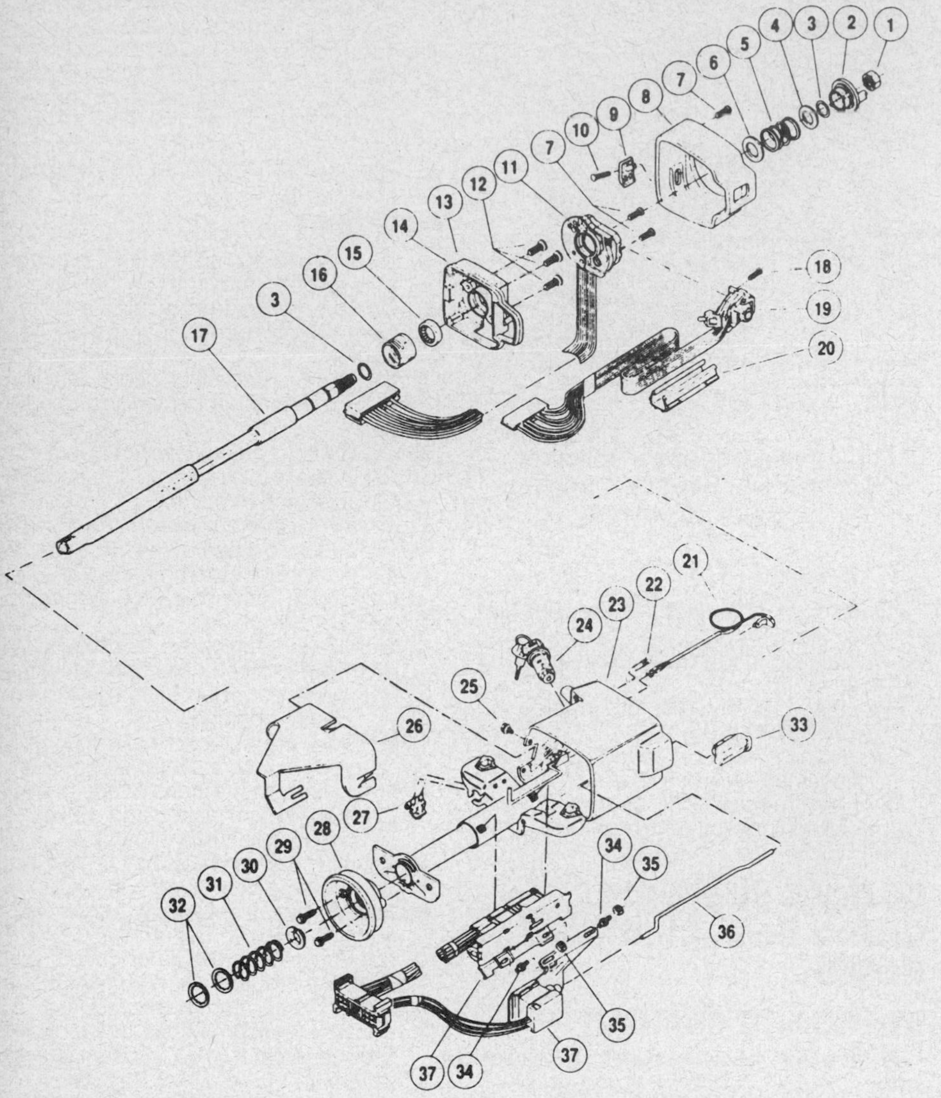
1
2
3
4
5
6
7
8
9
10
11
12
13
14
15
16
17
18
19
20
21
22
23
24
25
26
27
28
29
30
31
32
33
34
35
36
37

1-NUT, HEXAGON JAM (M14X1.5)
2-CAM ASM, SPACER & CANCELLING
3-RING, RETAINING
4-WASHER, THRUST
5-SPRING, UPPER BEARING
6-WASHER, THRUST
7-SCREW, PAN HD 6-LOBED SOC TAP
8-COVER, COLUMN HOUSING
9-KNOB, HAZARD WARNING
10-SCREW, OV HD C/REC (M3.5X1.27)
11-SWITCH ASM, TURN SIGNAL
12-SCREW, PAN HD 6-LOBED SOC TAP
13-HOUSING ASM, STRG COLUMN
14-HOUSING, STEERING COLUMN
15-BEARING ASM
16-SPACER, STRG COLUMN HOUSING
17-SHAFT ASM, STEERING
18-SCR, OVL HD 6-LOBED SOC TAP
19-SWITCH ASM, PIVOT & PULSE
20-PROTECTOR, WIRING
21-SWITCH ASM, BUZZER
22-SCREW, LOCK RETAINING
23-BOWL ASM, JACKET &
24-LOCK CYL SET, STRG COLUMN
25-SCREW, HEX WASHER HD TAPPING
26-SHIELD, BOWL
27-ADJUSTER ASM, PRNDL
28-BEARING ASM, ADAPTER &
29-SCREW, HEX WASHER HD TAPPING
30-SEAT, LOWER BEARING
31-SPRING, LOWER BEARING
32-RETAINER, LOWER SPRING
33-CAP, DIMMER SWITCH ROD
34-STUD DIMR & IGN SW MOUNTING
35-NUT, HEXAGON (#10-24)
36-ROD, DIMMER SW ACTUATOR
37-SWITCH ASM, COLUMN LOCK & IGN

GC6049100084000X

Fig. 43 Exploded view of standard steering column. Cutlass Supreme, Grand Prix, Lumina & Regal

with drift and discard.

11. Turn lock cylinder to the Off-Lock position and remove key.
12. Remove alarm assembly by lifting alarm tab with a screwdriver and gently pulling wires to remove.
13. Remove lock retaining screw and lock cylinder.
14. Remove rod cap from dimmer switch rod and jacket and bowl assembly.

Assemble

1. Install rod cap into jacket and bowl assembly.
2. Install lock cylinder and **torque** retaining screw to 27 inch lbs.
3. Install alarm assembly by pushing down into retaining bore until bottomed with plastic tab covering lock retaining screw.
4. Lubricate bearing with lithium grease and press into housing with a 1$^1/_2$ inch socket until bottomed.
5. Install housing spacer and column housing and **torque** screw to 88 inch lbs.
6. Turn lock cylinder to the Run position and insert steering shaft into the lower end of jacket and bowl assembly until shaft rests against bearing. The shaft will extend 2$^1/_2$ inches beyond the highest surface of column housing when installed properly.
7. Install thrust washer, upper bearing spring and thrust washer.
8. Wrap a two inch wide piece of shim stock .005 inch, around the shaft and slip a new retaining ring up to the thrust washer. Use two long handled screwdrivers and push on retaining ring until it seats in the retainer ring groove in shaft. Discard shim stock.
9. Install adapter and lower bearing assembly and **torque** adapter screws to 27 inch lbs.
10. Install lower bearing seat and lower bearing spring.
11. Install two new lower spring retainers and compress spring until retainers are positioned 1.14 inch from lower end of steering shaft.
12. Perform assemble steps for turn signal cancel cam assembly, pivot & pulse switch assembly & turn signal switch assembly as previously described.

IGNITION & DIMMER SWITCH

Disassemble

1. Place shift lever in the Park position and lock cylinder in the Off position.
2. Remove steering column from vehicle.
3. Disconnect turn signal switch and pivot and pulse switch connectors from ignition and dimmer switch assembly connector.

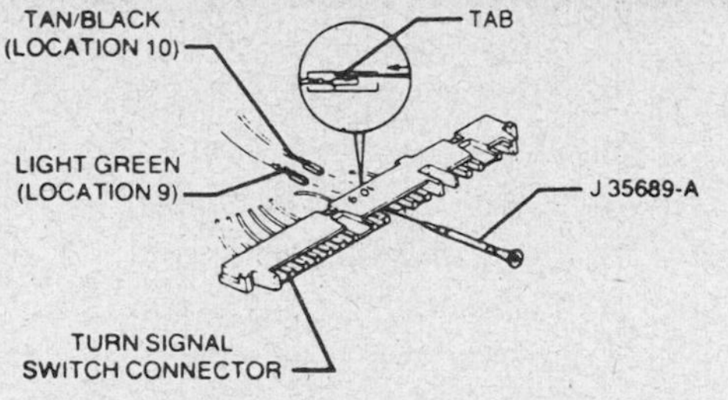
TAN/BLACK
(LOCATION 10)
TAB
LIGHT GREEN
(LOCATION 9)
J 35689-A
TURN SIGNAL
SWITCH CONNECTOR
GC6049100086000X

Fig. 44 Disconnecting switch wires. Cutlass Supreme, Grand Prix, Lumina & Regal w/standard column

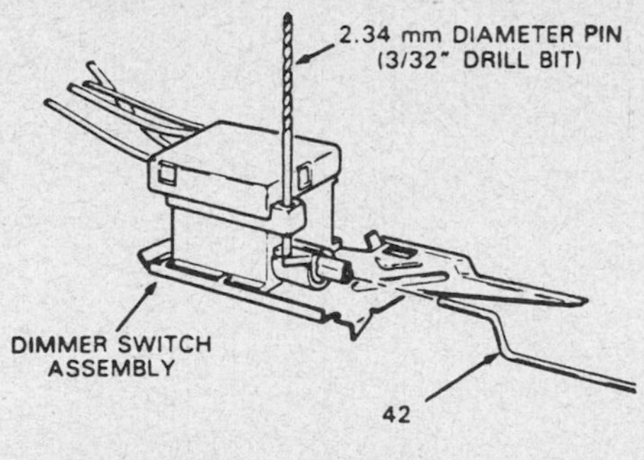
2.34 mm DIAMETER PIN
(3/32" DRILL BIT)
DIMMER SWITCH
ASSEMBLY
42
42-ROD, DIMMER SW ACTUATOR
GC6049100087000X

Fig. 45 Ignition switch & actuator installation. Cutlass Supreme, Grand Prix, Lumina & Regal w/standard column

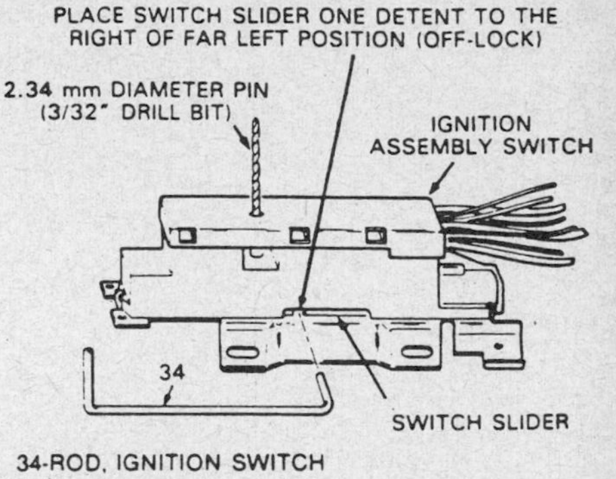
PLACE SWITCH SLIDER ONE DETENT TO THE
RIGHT OF FAR LEFT POSITION (OFF-LOCK)
2.34 mm DIAMETER PIN
(3/32" DRILL BIT)
IGNITION
ASSEMBLY SWITCH
34
SWITCH SLIDER
34-ROD, IGNITION SWITCH
GC6049100088000X

Fig. 46 Dimmer switch adjustment. Cutlass Supreme, Grand Prix, Lumina & Regal w/standard column

4. Remove bowl shield screw and nut and remove bowl shield.
5. Remove dimmer and ignition switch assembly as follows:
   a. Remove dimmer switch nut, upper mounting stud, then dimmer switch.
   b. Remove lower mounting stud and ignition switch from ignition switch actuator rod.
6. Remove dimmer switch actuator rod from rod cap.

Assemble

1. Place the ignition switch slider in the far left position and move back one detent to the right, Off-Lock position. **Fig. 45.**
2. Insert a 3/32 inch drill bit into the adjustment hole on ignition switch to hold switch slider in proper position during installation.
3. Install ignition switch to switch rod.
4. Install ignition switch to jacket and bowl assembly with lower mounting stud and **torque** stud to 35 inch lbs.
5. Remove drill bit from ignition switch and install dimmer switch actuator rod, tab first, through hole in instrument panel bracket and hole in dimmer switch rod cap.
6. Tab on rod must engage wide slot in rod cap and snap in place.
7. Install dimmer switch onto actuator rod and dimmer switch assembly on lower mounting stud with dimmer switch nut and upper mounting stud.
8. Adjust dimmer switch by inserting a 3/32 inch drill bit through hole in switch and push switch against actuator rod to remove all lash. **Fig. 46.**
9. **Torque** dimmer switch nut and upper mounting stud to 35 inch lbs.
10. Install shield screw and bowl shield nut and **torque** shield screw to 53 inch lbs. and bowl shield nut to 35 inch lbs.
11. Connect turn signal switch and pivot and pulse switch connectors to ignition and dimmer switch connector and snap in place.

TILT COLUMN

Refer to **Figs. 47 and 48**when servicing this column.

TURN SIGNAL CANCEL CAM, PIVOT & PULSE SWITCH & TURN SIGNAL SWITCH

Disassemble

1. Remove nut retainer, jam nut and steering wheel.
2. Remove turn signal cancel cam assembly, hazard knob screw and hazard warning knob.
3. Position turn signal switch so that signal switch screws and housing cover screw can be removed through openings in switch.
4. Remove housing cover screw and column housing cover.
5. Disconnect wiring protector from opening in instrument panel bracket on jacket and bowl assembly and separate from wires.
6. Disconnect pivot and pulse switch connector from ignition and dimmer switch.
7. Remove pivot switch screw and pivot and pulse switch assembly.
8. Remove turn signal switch screws and disconnect turn signal switch connector from ignition and dimmer switch assembly connector.
9. Remove seventeen-way lock from turn signal connector and disconnect wires on alarm or buzzer assembly from turn signal connector with special tool No. J 35689-A or equivalent, **Fig. 44.** Wrap wire ends with tape to protect during removal and installation.
10. Remove turn signal switch assembly from column.

Assemble

1. Install turn signal switch assembly and **torque** screws to 35 inch lbs.
2. Connect wires from alarm or buzzer assembly to turn signal switch connector.
3. Install seventeen-way secondary lock to turn signal connector and snap in place.
4. Connect turn signal switch connector to ignition and dimmer switch connector and snap in place.
5. Install pivot and pulse switch assembly and **torque** screw to 18 inch lbs.
6. Connect pivot switch connector to ignition and dimmer switch connector and snap in place.
7. Install wiring protector as follows:
   a. Wrap protector around all wires passing through instrument panel bracket opening.
   b. Close protector so that interlocking grooves engage and slide protector into instrument panel bracket opening on jacket and bowl assembly and snap in place.
8. Install column housing cover and **torque** screw to 35 inch lbs.
9. Install hazard warning knob and **torque** screw to 9 inch lbs.
10. Lubricate bottom side of cancel cam with lithium grease and install turn signal cancel cam assembly.
11. Install steering wheel and jam nut, **torque** jam nut to 30 inch lbs. and secure with nut retainer.

TILT LEVER & BRACKET, WHEEL TILT SPRING, LOWER BEARING, STEERING SHAFT & HOUSING, ALARM, STEERING COLUMN LOCK CYLINDER, COLUMN TILT BUMPERS & JACKET & BOWL

Disassemble

1. Remove turn signal cancel cam assembly, pivot and pulse switch assembly and turn signal switch assembly as previously described.
2. Pull tilt lever and tilt column all the way up.
3. Insert suitable Phillips tip screwdriver into square opening in spring retainer, push down and turn left to release retainer and wheel tilt spring.
4. Remove spring retainer, tilt spring and tilt spring guide.
5. Remove two lower spring retainers and discard.
6. Remove lower bearing spring and lower bearing seat.
7. Remove adapter screws, adapter and lower bearing assembly.
8. Remove two pivot pins from shaft and housing assembly with special tool No. J 21854-01 or equivalent.
9. Turn lock cylinder to the Run position and pull tilt lever to release shaft and housing assembly.
10. Remove shaft and housing assembly from jacket and bowl assembly.
11. Turn lock cylinder to the Off-Lock position and remove key.
12. Remove alarm assembly by lifting

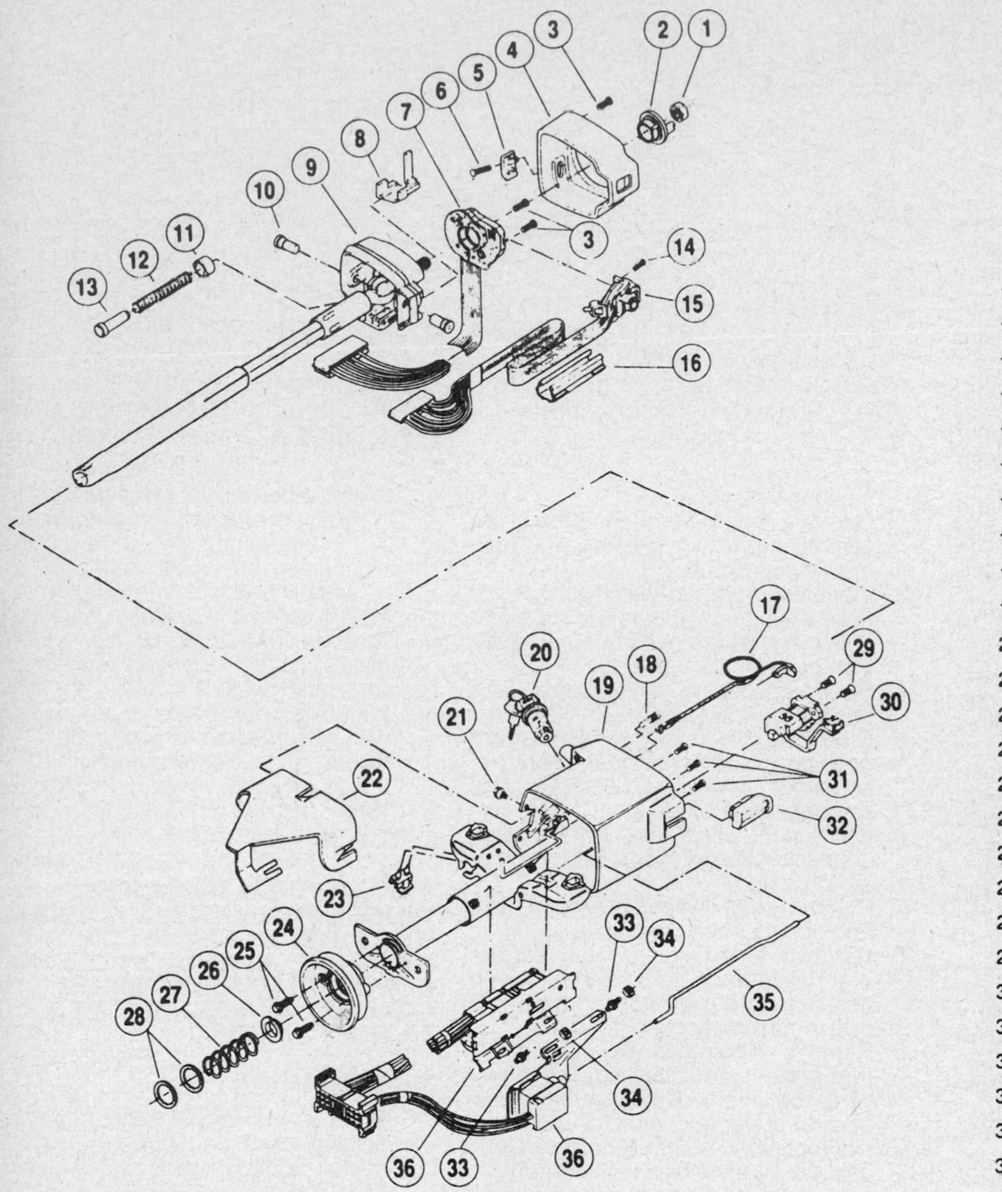

1 - NUT, HEXAGON JAM (M14X1.5)
2 - CAM ASM, SPACER & CANCELLING
3 - SCREW, PAN HD 6 - LOBED SOC TAP
4 - COVER, COLUMN HOUSING
5 - KNOB, HAZARD WARNING
6 - SCREW, OV HD C/REC (M3.5X1.27)
7 - SWITCH ASM, TURN SIGNAL
8 - CAP, HSG SHOE PIN RETAINER
9 - HOUSING ASM, SHAFT &
10 - PIN, PIVOT
11 - RETAINER, SPRING
12 - SPRING, WHEEL TILT
13 - GUIDE, TILT SPRING
14 - SCR, OVL HD 6 - LOBED SOC TAP
15 - SWITCH ASM, PIVOT & PULSE
16 - PROTECTOR, WIRING
17 - BUZZER SWITCH ASM
18 - SCREW, LOCK RETAINING
19 - BOWL ASM, JACKET &
20 - LOCK CYL SET, STRG COLUMN
21 - SCREW, HEX WASHER HD TAPPING
22 - SHIELD, BOWL
23 - ADJUSTER ASM, PRNDL
24 - BEARING ASM, ADAPTER &
25 - SCREW, HEX WASHER HD TAPPING
26 - SEAT, LOWER BEARING
27 - SPRING, LOWER BEARING
28 - RETAINER, LOWER SPRING
29 - SCR, OVL HD 6 - LOBED SOC TAP
30 - BRACKET ASM, TILT LEVER &
31 - BUMPER, COLUMN TILT
32 - CAP, DIMMER SWITCH ROD
33 - STUD, DIMR & IGN SW MOUNTING
34 - NUT, HEXAGON (#10 - 24)
35 - ROD, DIMMER SW ACTUATOR
36 - SWITCH ASM, IGNITION

GC6049100089000X

Fig. 47 Exploded view of tilt steering column. 1992–93 Cutlass Supreme, Grand Prix, Lumina & Regal

alarm tab with a screwdriver and gently pulling wires to remove.

13. Remove lock retaining screw and lock cylinder.
14. Remove column tilt bumpers with vise grips. If bumper is broken off use a 7/32 inch drill bit to remove remaining piece of bumper.
15. Remove tilt bracket screws and tilt lever and bracket assembly.
16. Remove rod cap from dimmer switch rod and jacket and bowl assembly.

Assemble

1. Install rod cap into jacket and bowl assembly.
2. Install tilt lever and bracket assembly into jacket and bowl assembly and **torque** tilt bracket screws to 35 inch lbs.
3. Install three tilt bumpers into jacket and bowl assembly until bottomed.
4. Install column lock cylinder and **torque** screw to 27 inch lbs.
5. Install alarm assembly by pushing down into retaining bore until bottomed with plastic tab covering lock retaining screw.
6. Insert key and turn lock cylinder to the Run position.
7. Install shaft and housing assembly.
8. Lubricate pivot pins with lithium grease and install into pivot holes in shaft and housing assembly until bottomed.
9. Pull tilt lever and tilt column all the way up.
10. Lubricate tilt spring guide with lithium grease and install tilt spring guide into tilt spring.
11. Install guide and tilt spring with spring retainer as follows:
    a. Ensure that recess in spring guide engages round locating tab in jacket and bowl assembly.
    b. Insert Phillips tip screwdriver into square opening in spring retainer, push down and turn right to lock in place.
12. Install adapter and lower bearing assembly and **torque** adapter screws to 27 inch lbs.
13. Install lower bearing seat and lower bearing spring.
14. Install two new lower spring retainers and compress spring until retainers are positioned 1.14 inch from lower end of steering shaft.
15. Perform assembling steps for turn signal cancel cam assembly, pivot and pulse switch assembly and turn signal switch assembly as previously described.

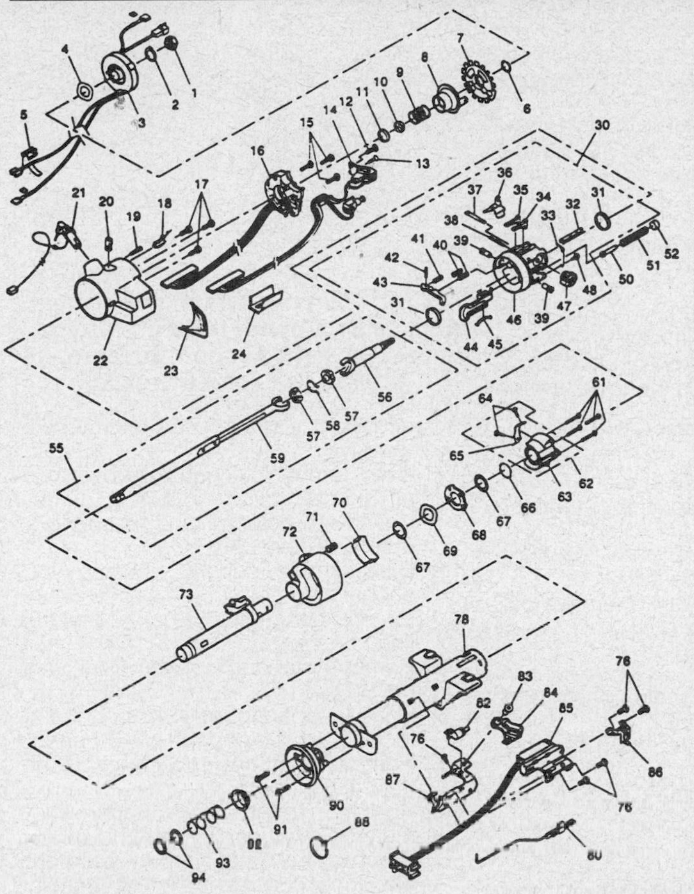

GC6049400150010X

Fig. 48 Exploded view of tilt steering column (Part 1 of 2). 1994 Cutlass Supreme, Grand Prix, Lumina & Regal

1-NUT, HEX LOCKING (M14x1.5)
2-RING, RETAINING
3-COIL ASM, INFL RESTRAINT
4-WASHER, WAVE
5-SHROUD, CONNECTOR
6-RING, RETAINING
7-LOCK, SHAFT
8-CAM ASM, TURN SIG CANCEL
9-SPRING, UPPER BEARING
10-SEAT, UPPER BRG INNER RACE
11-RACE, INNER
12-SCREW, RD WASH HD (M4.2X1.41)
13-SCREW, FLT HD TAPPING
14-SWITCH ASM, PIVOT PULSE DIMMER
15-SCREW, BNDG HD CR RECESS
16-SWITCH ASM, TURN SIGNAL
17-SCREW, PAN HD SOC TAP
18-SWITCH ASM, BUZZER
19-SCREW, LOCK RETAINING
20-KNOB, HAZARD WARNING SW
21-LOCK CYLINDER SET, STRG COL (PASS KEY)
22-SLEEVE ASM, LOCK COVER &
23-CAP, COVER HSG END
24-PROTECTOR, WIRING
30-HOUSING ASM, STRG COLUMN
31-BEARING ASM
32-BOLT, LOCK
33-SPRING, LOCK BOLT
34-SHOE, STEERING WHEEL LOCK
35-SHOE, STEERING WHEEL LOCK
36-SHIELD, WIRE PROTECTOR
37-SHAFT, DRIVE
38-PIN, DOWEL
39-PIN, PIVOT
40-SPRING, SHOE
41-SPRING, RELEASE LEVER
42-PIN, RELEASE LEVER
43-LEVER, SHOE RELEASE
44-RACK, SWITCH ACTUATOR
45-SPRING, RACK PRELOAD
46-HOUSING, STRG COLUMN
47-SECTOR, SWITCH ACTUATOR
48-SCREW, HEX WASHER HEAD
50-GUIDE, SPRING
51-SPRING, WHEEL TILT
52-RETAINER, SPRING
55-SHAFT ASM, STEERING
56-SHAFT ASM, RACE & UPPER
57-SPHERE, CENTERING
58-SPRING, JOINT PRELOAD
59-SHAFT ASM, LOWER STEERING
61-SCREW, SUPPORT
62-SUPPORT ASM, STRG COL HSG
63-SUPPORT, STRG COL HSG
64-SCREW, OVL HD CROSS RECESS
65-GATE, SHIFT LEVER
66-RING, SHIFT TUBE RETAINING
67-WASHER, THRUST
68-PLATE, LOCK
69-WASHER, WAVE
70-PROTECTOR, WIRING
71-SPRING, SHIFT LEVER
72-BOWL ASM, GEARSHIFT LEVER
73-TUBE ASM, SHIFT
78-JACKET ASM, STRG COL
80-ACTUATOR ASM, IGNITION SWITCH
82-SWITCH ASM, PARK POSITION
83-RETAINER, CAM
84-CAM ASM, CABLE SHIFT
85-SWITCH ASM, IGNITION
86-ADJUSTER ASM, PRNDL
87-BRACKET ASM, STUD &
88-STRAP, WIRE HARNESS
90-BEARING ASM, ADAPTER & LOWER
91-SCREW, HEX WASHER HD TAP
92-SEAT, LOWER BEARING
93-SPRING, LOWER BEARING
94-RETAINER, LOWER SPRING

Service Kits

201-RACK SERV KIT, COL SECTOR & -INCLUDES: 11,31,33,44,47,48
202-SPRING SERV KIT, TILT COLUMN -INCLUDES: 10,11,39,50,51,52
203-COIL SERV KIT, INFL RESTRAINT -INCLUDES: 3,4,5
204-SPHERE SERV KIT, TILT COLUMN -INCLUDES: 57,58
205-GREASE SERV KIT, (SYNTHETIC)

GC6049400150020X

Fig. 48 Exploded view of tilt steering column (Part 2 of 2). 1994 Cutlass Supreme, Grand Prix, Lumina & Regal

Ignition & Dimmer Switch

Refer to "Standard Column" for procedure.

Bonneville, Caprice, Custom Cruiser, Impala SS, LeSabre, Park Avenue, 88 & 98 Less SIR

SHAFT LOCK, TURN SIGNAL CANCEL CAM, UPPER BEARING SPRING & SEAT, INNER RACE, TURN SIGNAL SWITCH, BUZZER SWITCH & LOCK CYLINDER SET

Disassemble

Wheels of vehicle must be in straight ahead position. Failure to do so may cause improper alignment of some components during installation, resulting in column malfunction.

1. Place key in Lock position.
2. Disconnect battery ground cable.
3. Remove screws from back of steering wheel and horn pad, disconnecting horn lead from cam tower.
4. Remove retainer and jam nut, then, using puller tool No. J-1859-03 or equivalent, the steering wheel.
5. Using compressor tool No. J-23653-A or equivalent, depress shaft lock, then remove shaft lock retaining ring.
6. Remove shaft lock and shaft lock cover, then the turn signal cancelling cam.
7. Remove upper bearing spring, then the upper bearing seat.
8. Remove inner race.
9. Place turn signal in right turn position, then remove signal switch arm attaching screw and the arm.
10. Remove turn signal switch attaching screws and position switch out of way. If it is necessary to remove switch, remove wiring harness protector and hazard knob, then gently pull wire harness through gear shift lever bowl, column housing and lock housing cover.
11. Remove key from cylinder lock, and remove buzzer switch and clip, then reinsert key in cylinder lock and turn to Lock position.
12. Remove lock retaining screw and lock cylinder set.

Assemble

1. Install lock cylinder set, **torque** retaining screw to 26 inch lbs.
2. Place key in Run position, then install buzzer switch and clip.
3. Route turn signal switch wiring harness through lock housing cover, column housing and gear shift lever bowl, then secure switch, **torque** retaining screws to 26 inch lbs.
4. Install signal switch arm, **torque** retaining screw to 18 inch lbs.
5. Install hazard knob, then the inner race.
6. Install upper bearing seat, then the upper bearing spring.
7. Install turn signal cancelling cam, then the shaft lock.
8. Depress shaft lock, then install shaft lock retaining ring.
9. Install steering wheel, then the jam nut and retainer.
10. Install horn pad, then the wiring harness protector.
11. Connect battery ground cable.

LOCK HOUSING COVER, COVER END CAP, PIVOT & SWITCH, DIMMER SWITCH ROD ACTUATOR & TILT SPRING

Disassemble

1. Disassemble shaft lock, turn signal cancel cam, upper bearing spring and

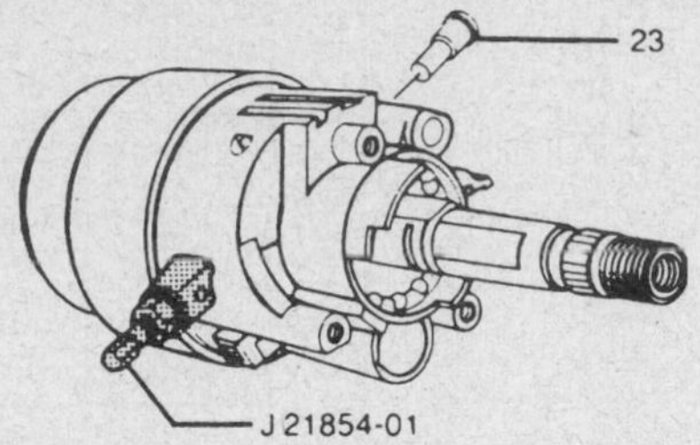
23
J 21854-01

23 PIN, PIVOT

GC6049100092000X

Fig. 49 Pivot pin removal. Bonneville, Caprice, Custom Cruiser, Impala SS, Park Avenue, LeSabre, 88 & 98 w/tilt column less SIR

seat, turn signal switch, buzzer switch and lock cylinder set as outlined previously.

2. Remove lock housing cover attaching screws and cover, then the tilt lever.
3. Remove cover housing end cap and the dimmer switch rod actuator.
4. **On models equipped with cruise control,** unplug cruise control connector and remove multi-function lever.
5. **On all models,** gently pull pivot switch wiring harness through column housing and gear shift lever bowl.
6. Remove pivot pin, then the pivot and switch assembly.
7. Remove spring retainer, then the spring and spring guide.

Assemble

1. Coat spring guide and spring with lithium grease and install, then install spring retainer.
2. Install pivot and switch assembly, then the pivot pin.
3. Route pivot and switch assembly wiring harness through gear shift lever bowl and column housing.
4. Install dimmer switch rod actuator, then the gear shift lever bowl, ensuring bottom edge of dimmer switch rod actuator rests on bend in dimmer switch rod.
5. Install cover housing end cap.
6. **On models equipped with cruise control,** plug in cruise control connector and install multi-function lever.
7. **On all models,** Install lock housing cover. Tighten screw in 12 o'clock position first, screw in 8 o'clock position second and screw in 4 o'clock position third, then **torque** in same order to 89 inch lbs.
8. Disassemble shaft lock, turn signal cancel cam, upper bearing spring and seat, turn signal switch, buzzer switch and lock cylinder set as outlined previously.

COLUMN HOUSING, LOCK SHOES, ACTUATOR SECTOR, SWITCH ACTUATOR RACK, BEARINGS & LOCK BOLT

Disassemble

1. Disassemble shaft lock, turn signal cancel cam, upper bearing spring and seat, turn signal switch, buzzer switch and lock cylinder set as outlined previously.
2. Disassemble lock housing cover, cover end cap, pivot and switch, dimmer switch rod actuator and tilt spring as outlined previously.
3. Using pivot pin remover tool No. J-21854-01 or equivalent, remove pivot pins, **Fig. 49.**
4. Reinstall tilt lever.
5. Remove column housing assembly by pulling back on tilt lever and pulling housing down and away from column.
6. Remove driveshaft, then the switch actuator sector.
7. Remove switch actuator rack and rack preload spring, then the release lever pin and release lever.
8. Remove release lever spring, then the dowel pin.
9. Remove lock shoes and lock shoe springs, then the bearings.
10. Remove hex head bolt, then the lock bolt spring and lock bolt.

Assemble

1. Install bearings to column housing, then install driveshaft.
2. Install actuator sector, then the lock shoes.
3. Install dowel pin, then the lock shoe springs.
4. Install release lever spring, then the release lever.
5. Install release lever pin, then the rack preload spring.
6. Install switch actuator rack to actuator sector.
7. Install lock bolt and lock bolt spring, then the hex head bolt.
8. Install column housing assembly to column as follows:
   a. Position column housing assembly and align switch actuator rack with pin on end of actuator rod.
   b. Pull back on tilt lever, pushing column housing assembly onto column housing support assembly.
   c. Release tilt lever to lock shoes.
9. Remove tilt lever.
10. Lubricate pivot pins with lithium grease and install them.
11. Assemble lock housing cover, cover end cap, pivot and switch, dimmer switch rod actuator and tilt spring as outlined previously.
12. Assemble shaft lock, turn signal cancel cam, upper bearing spring and seat, turn signal switch, buzzer switch and lock cylinder set as outlined previously.

SHAFT, COLUMN HOUSING SUPPORT, SHIFT TUBE, IGNITION SWITCH, DIMMER SWITCH & LOWER BEARING

Disassemble

1. Disassemble shaft lock, turn signal cancel cam, upper bearing spring and seat, turn signal switch, buzzer switch

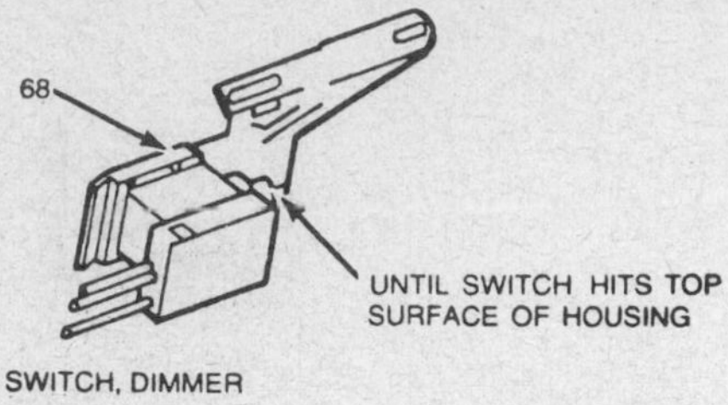
68
UNTIL SWITCH HITS TOP
SURFACE OF HOUSING

68. SWITCH, DIMMER

GC6049100093000X

Fig. 50 Dimmer switch adjustment. Bonneville, Caprice, Custom Cruiser, Impala SS, Park Avenue, LeSabre, 88 & 98 w/tilt column less SIR

and lock cylinder set as outlined previously.

2. Disassemble lock housing cover, cover end cap, pivot and switch, dimmer switch rod actuator and tilt spring as outlined previously.
3. Disassemble column housing, lock shoes, actuator sector, switch actuator rack, bearings and lock bolt as outlined previously.
4. Remove steering column from vehicle.
5. Remove bearing retainer, then the attaching screws and the lower bearing.
6. Remove shaft assembly then disconnect lower shaft.
7. Remove sphere from upper shaft, then the retainer clip from the sphere.
8. Remove housing support assembly attaching screws, then the housing support assembly and dimmer switch rod.
9. Remove hex nut and hex head bolt, then the dimmer switch and mounting stud.
10. Remove gear shift bowl.

Assemble

1. Install gear shift lever bowl to jacket, then the dimmer switch rod to housing support.
2. Install housing support assembly, **torque** attaching screws to 80 inch lbs.
3. Install actuator rod assembly to track in housing support.
4. Install ignition switch and mounting stud, then adjust switch, **Fig. 45.**
5. Install retaining clip and sphere to upper shaft.
6. Install lower shaft to upper shaft with block tooth on shaft lower end of upper shaft at 12 o'clock position and notch at end of lower shaft at 4 o'clock position.
7. Lubricate shaft assembly with lithium grease and install to column.
8. Install column housing assembly to column.
9. Position column assembly and align switch actuator rack with pin on end of actuator rod.
10. Pull back on tilt lever, pushing column housing assembly onto column housing support assembly.
11. Release tilt lever to lock shoes, then remove tilt lever.
12. Lubricate inner surface of lower bearing with lithium grease, then install bearing and retaining screws.

13. Install bearing retainer.
14. Install dimmer switch, hex nut and hex head bolt, then adjust dimmer switch, **Fig. 50.**
15. Install steering column to instrument panel.
16. Install tilt lever.
17. Assemble column housing, lock shoes, actuator sector, switch actuator rack, bearings and lock bolt as outlined previously.
18. Assemble lock housing cover, cover end cap, pivot and switch, dimmer switch rod actuator and tilt spring as outlined previously.
19. Assemble shaft lock, turn signal cancel cam, upper bearing spring and seat, turn signal switch, buzzer switch and lock cylinder set as outlined previously.

Bonneville, Camaro, Corvette, DeVille, Firebird, Fleetwood (FWD), LeSabre, Park Avenue, Riviera, Toronado, Trofeo, 88, 98, & 1992 Eldorado & Seville w/SIR

Care must be taken when handling column with a live inflator module. Never point bag deploy surface toward you, and never stand column on steering wheel. Accidental deployment in these positions may cause injury. Always face bag deploy surface toward open space to allow for unrestricted expansion.

COIL, SHAFT LOCK, TURN SIGNAL CANCELLING CAM, UPPER BEARING SPRING & SEAT, INNER RACE TURN SIGNAL SWITCH, BUZZER SWITCH & LOCK CYLINDER SET

Refer to **Figs. 51 through 57** when servicing this column.

Disassemble

The following procedure has been revised by a Technical Service Bulletin.

Wheel of vehicle must be in straight ahead position and key must be in Lock position.

1. Remove screws from back of steering wheel.
2. Remove restraint module from steering wheel.
3. Remove coil assembly plug from restraint module, then the horn contact from column.
4. Remove column as described under "Steering Column, Replace." The steering wheel must be straight and the column in the Lock position.
5. Remove hexagon locking nut, then, using puller tool No. J-1859-03 or equivalent, the steering wheel.
6. **On Riviera, Toronado and Trofeo models,** insert steering wheel puller bolts only four to six threads deep to prevent the bolts from going through the hub and damaging the coil assembly.
7. **On all models,** remove steering wheel shroud.
8. Remove lock screw from boss Home position on coil assembly to Center Lock position on coil assembly, **Fig. 58.**
9. Remove coil assembly retaining ring.
10. Remove coil assembly off shaft end, allowing coil to hang freely.
11. Using tool No. J-23653-A or equivalent, depress shaft lock, then remove shaft lock retaining ring.
12. Remove shaft lock, then the turn signal cancelling cam.
13. Remove upper bearing spring, then the upper bearing seat.
14. Remove inner race, then place turn signal in Right Turn position.
15. Remove signal switch arm attaching screw and the arm, then the turn signal switch attaching screws.
16. Remove hazard knob, then position turn signal switch out of way. If removal of switch is necessary, remove retainer spring and wiring protector, then gently pull wire harness through gear shift lever bowl, column housing and lock housing cover.
17. Remove coil assembly, if necessary, as follows:
    a. Disconnect POS assurance terminal, and, using tool No. J-35689-A or equivalent, disconnect wires from body connector assembly, **Fig. 59.**
    b. Tape wire ends, then gently pull wire through gear shift lever bowl, column housing, and lock housing cover.
18. Remove key from cylinder lock and remove buzzer switch and clip, then reinstall key in cylinder lock and place key in Lock position.
19. Remove lock retaining screw and lock cylinder set.

Assemble

Ensure all fasteners are securely seated before applying required torque.

1. Install lock cylinder set, **torque** lock retaining screw to 26 inch lbs.
2. Place key in Run position, then install buzzer switch and clip.
3. Route turn signal switch wiring harness through lock housing cover, column housing and gear shift lever bowl.
4. Route coil assembly wire through lock housing cover, column housing and gear shift lever bowl and allow coil to hang freely.
5. Install turn signal switch, **torque** attaching screws to 26 inch lbs.
6. Install wiring protector and retaining spring.
7. Install signal switch arm, **torque** retaining screw to 18 inch lbs.
8. Install hazard knob, then the inner race.
9. Install upper bearing seat, then the upper bearing spring.
10. Install turn signal cancelling cam, then the shaft lock.
11. Using tool No. J-23653-A or equivalent to depress shaft lock, install shaft lock retaining ring, aligning to block tooth on shaft.
12. Ensure coil assembly hub is centered, **Fig. 60. The coil assembly will become uncentered if the column is separated from the steering gear and is allowed to rotate, or the coil is removed from the column without first locking in position with locking screw.**
13. Install coil assembly, using horn tower on cancel cam on inner ring and projections on outer ring for alignment, then the coil assembly retaining ring. **Move lock screw from Center Lock position to Home position on coil assembly.**
14. Install steering wheel and steering wheel shroud, then the hexagon locking nut.
15. Install coil assembly plug to air bag module and the horn contact into column.
16. Install steering wheel module to steering wheel.
17. Using tool No. J-35689-A or equivalent, connect wires to connector body assembly and install POS assurance terminal, **Fig. 61.**
18. Install screws to back of steering column, then connect battery ground cable.

LOCK HOUSING COVER, COVER END CAP, PIVOT & SWITCH, DIMMER SWITCH ROD ACTUATOR & TILT SPRING

Disassemble

1. Disassemble coil, shaft lock, turn signal cancel cam, upper bearing spring and seat, inner race turn signal switch, buzzer switch and lock cylinder set as outlined previously.
2. Remove lock housing cover attaching screws and the cover, then the tilt lever.
3. Remove cover housing end cap, base plate, and dimmer switch rod actuator, then gently pull pivot switch wiring harness through column housing and gear shift lever bowl.
4. **On models equipped with cruise control,** unplug connector from base plate and remove multi-function lever.
5. **On all models,** remove pivot pin, then the pivot and switch assembly.
6. Remove spring retainer, then the spring and spring guide.

Assemble

Ensure all fasteners are securely seated before applying required torque.

1. Coat spring guide and spring with lithium grease and install them, then in-

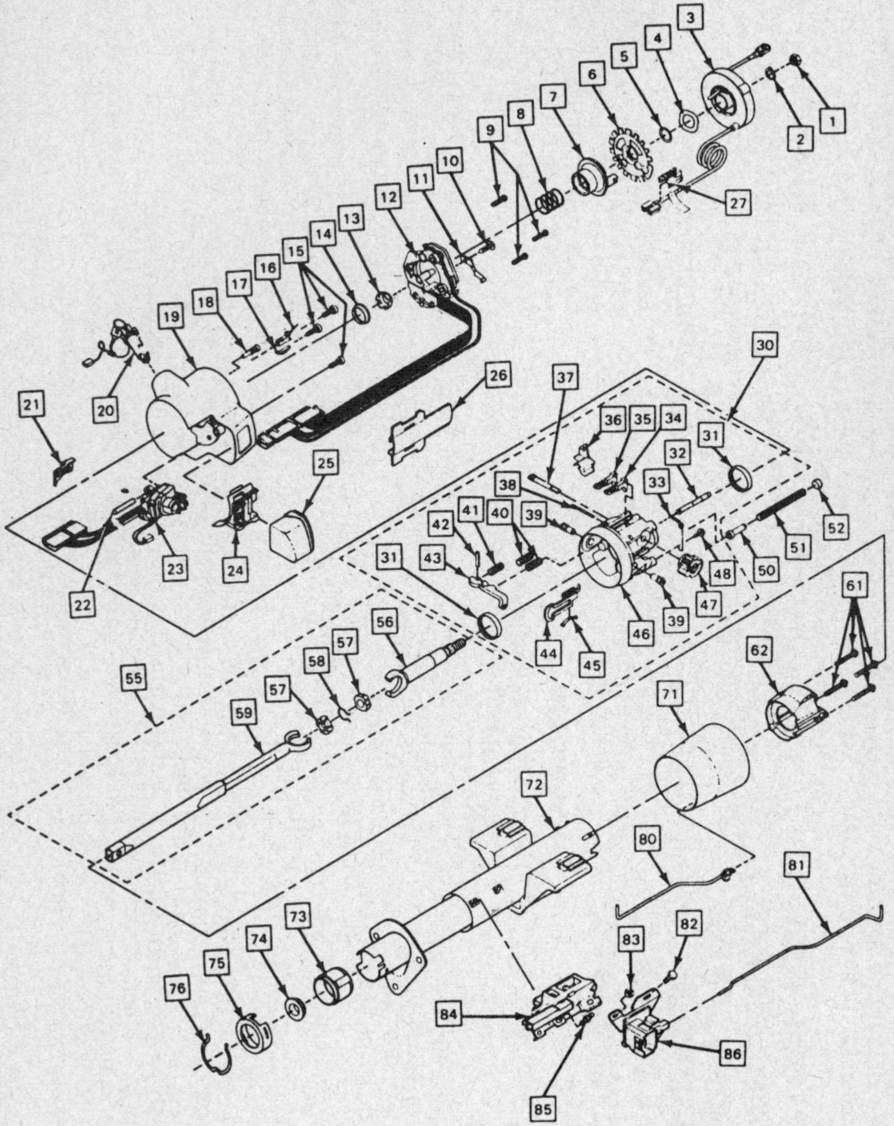

1 HEXAGON LOCKING NUT
2 RETAINING RING
3 COIL ASSEMBLY
4 WAVE WASHER
5 RETAINING RING
6 SHAFT LOCK
7 TURN SIGNAL CANCELLING CAM
8 UPPER BEARING SPRING
9 SCREW
10 SCREW
11 SIGNAL SWITCH ARM
12 TURN SIGNAL SWITCH
13 UPPER BEARING INNER RACE SEAT
14 INNER RACE
15 SCREW
16 BUZZER SWITCH
17 BUZZER SWITCH RETAINING CLIP
18 LOCK RETAINING SCREW
19 LOCK HOUSING COVER
20 VATS LOCK CYLINDER SET
21 DIMMER SWITCH ROD ACTUATOR
22 SWITCH ACTUATOR PIVOT PIN
23 PIVOT AND PULSE SWITCH
24 HOUSING COVER END BASE PLATE
25 HOUSING COVER END CAP
26 WIRING PROTECTOR
27 CONNECTOR SHROUD
30 STEERING COLUMN HOUSING
31 BEARING
32 LOCK BOLT
33 LOCK BOLT SPRING
34 STEERING WHEEL LOCK SHOE
35 STEERING WHEEL LOCK SHOE
36 WIRE ABRASION SHIELD
37 DRIVE SHAFT
38 DOWEL PIN
39 PIVOT PIN
40 SHOE SPRING
41 RELEASE LEVER SPRING
42 RELEASE LEVER PIN
43 SHOE RELEASE LEVER
44 SWITCH ACTUATOR RACK
45 RACK PRELOAD SPRING
46 STEERING COLUMN HOUSING
47 SWITCH ACTUATOR SECTOR
48 SCREW
50 SPRING GUIDE
51 WHEEL TILT SPRING
52 SPRING RETAINER
55 STEERING COLUMN SHAFT
56 RACE AND UPPER SHAFT
57 CENTERING SPHERE
58 JOINT PRELOAD SPRING
59 LOWER STEERING SHAFT
61 SCREW
62 STEERING COLUMN HOUSING SUPPORT
71 STEERING COLUMN HOUSING SHROUD
72 STEERING COLUMN JACKET
73 LOWER BEARING ADAPTER
74 BEARING
75 BEARING ADAPTER RETAINER
76 LOWER BEARING CLIP
80 IGNITION SWITCH ACTUATOR
81 DIMMER SWITCH ROD
82 SCREW
83 NUT
84 IGNITION SWITCH
85 DIMMER AND IGNITION SWITCH MOUNTING STUD
86 DIMMER SWITCH

GC6049100097000X -R-

Fig. 51 Exploded view of steering column. Camaro & Firebird w/SIR

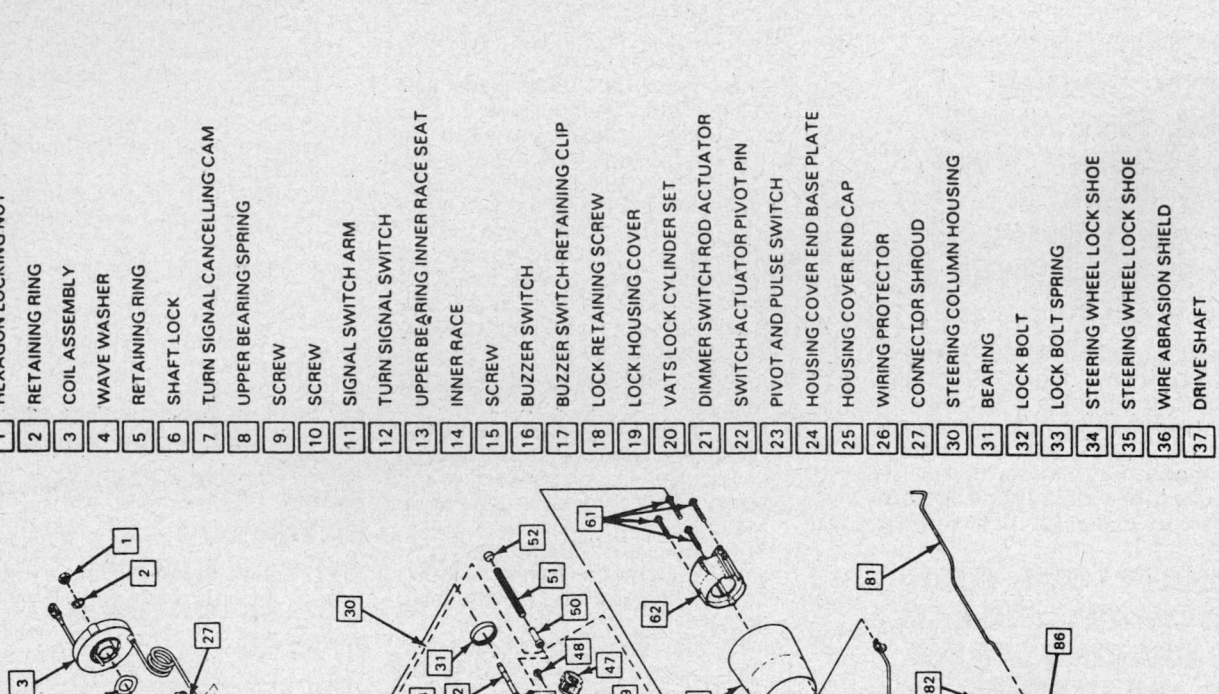

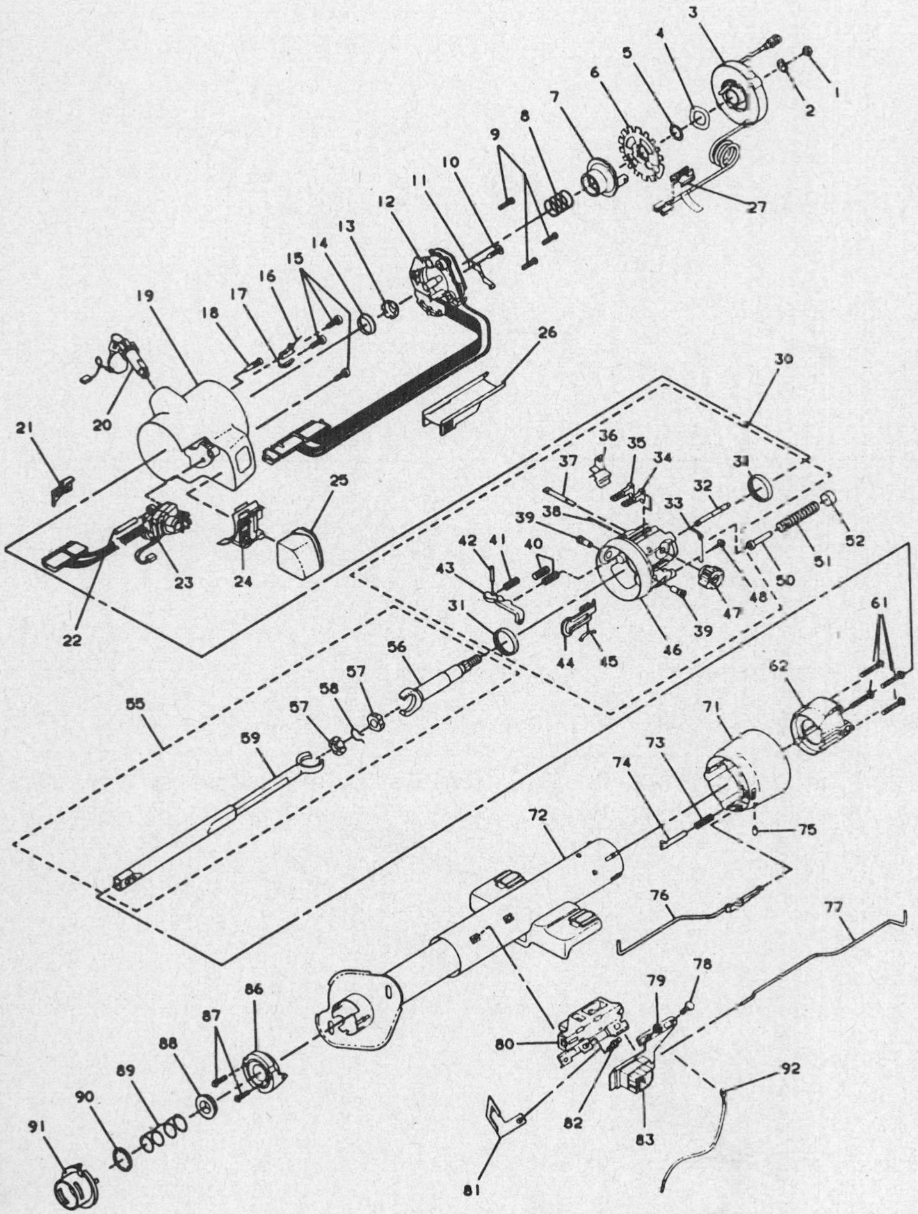
1
2
3
4
5
6
7
8
9
10
11
12
13
14
15
16
17
18
19
20
21
22
23
24
25
26
27
30
31
32
33
34
35
36
37
38
39
40
41
42
43
44
45
46
47
48
50
51
52
55
56
57
58
59
61
62
71
72
73
74
75
76
77
78
79
80
81
82
83
86
87
88
89
90
91
92

1-NUT, HEXAGON LOCKING (M14X1.5)
2-RING, RETAINING
3-COIL ASM, INFL RESTRAINT
4-WASHER, WAVE
5-RING, RETAINING
6-LOCK, SHAFT
7-CAM ASM, TURN SIG CANCELLING
8-SPRING, UPPER BEARING
9-SCREW, BINDING HD CROSS RECESS
10-SCREW, RD WASH HD (M4.2X1.41)
11-ARM, SIGNAL SWITCH
12-SWITCH ASM, TURN SIGNAL
13-SEAT, UPPER BEARING INNER RACE
14-RACE, INNER
15-SCREW, PAN HD 6-LOBED SOC TAP
16-SWITCH ASM, BUZZER
17-CLIP, BUZZER SWITCH RETAINING
18-SCREW, LOCK RETAINING
19-COVER ASM, LOCK HOUSING
20-LOCK CYLINDER SET, STRG COLUMN VATS
21-ACTUATOR, DIMMER SWITCH ROD
22-PIN, SWITCH ACTUATOR PIVOT
23-SWITCH ASM, PIVOT & (PULSE)
24-BASE PLATE, COL HSG COVER END
25-CAP, COL HSG COVER END
26-PROTECTOR, WIRING
27-SHROUD, CONNECTOR
30-HOUSING ASM, STRG COLUMN
31-BEARING ASM
32-BOLT, LOCK
33-SPRING, LOCK BOLT
34-SHOE, STEERING WHEEL LOCK
35-SHOE, STEERING WHEEL LOCK
36-SHIELD, WIRE ABRASION
37-SHAFT, DRIVE
38-PIN, DOWEL
39-PIN, PIVOT
40-SPRING, SHOE
41-SPRING, RELEASE LEVER
42-PIN, RELEASE LEVER
43-LEVER, SHOE RELEASE
44-RACK, SWITCH ACTUATOR
45-SPRING, RACK PRELOAD
46-HOUSING, STRG COLUMN
47-SECTOR, SWITCH ACTUATOR
48-SCREW, HEX WASHER HEAD
50-GUIDE, SPRING
51-SPRING, WHEEL TILT
52-RETAINER, SPRING
55-SHAFT ASM, STEERING COLUMN
56-SHAFT ASM, RACE & UPPER
57-SPHERE, CENTERING
58-SPRING, JOINT PRELOAD
59-SHAFT ASM, LOWER STEERING
61-SCREW, SUPPORT
62-SUPPORT ASM, STRG COL HSG
71-SHROUD, STRG COLUMN HOUSING
72-JACKET ASM, STRG COL
73-SPRING, CABLE BACKDRIVE PIN
74-PIN, CABLE BACKDRIVE
75-PIN, INHIBITOR
76-ACTUATOR ASM, IGNITION SWITCH
77-ROD, DIMMER SWITCH
78-SCREW, WASH HD (#10-24 X .25)
79-NUT, HEXAGON (#10-24 X .25)
80-SWITCH ASM, IGNITION
81-BRACKET, CABLE
82-STUD, DIMR & IGN SW MOUNTING
83-SWITCH ASM, DIMMER
86-BEARING ASM, ADAPTER &
87-SCREW, HEX WASHER HD TAPPING
88-SEAT, LOWER BEARING
89-SPRING, LOWER BEARING
90-RETAINER, LOWER SPRING
91-RETAINER (NON-SERVICEABLE)
92-WIRING ASM, HORN PAD GROUND

Service Kits

201-RACK SERV KIT, COLUMN SECTOR &
-INCLUDES: 14,31,33,44,47,48
202-SPRING SERV KIT, TILT COLUMN
-INCLUDES: 13,14,39,50,51,52
203-COIL SERV KIT, INFL RESTRAINT
-INCLUDES: 3,4,27
204-SPHERE SERV KIT, TILT COLUMN
-INCLUDES: 57,58

GC6049100098000X -R-

Fig. 52 Exploded view of steering column. Corvette w/SIR

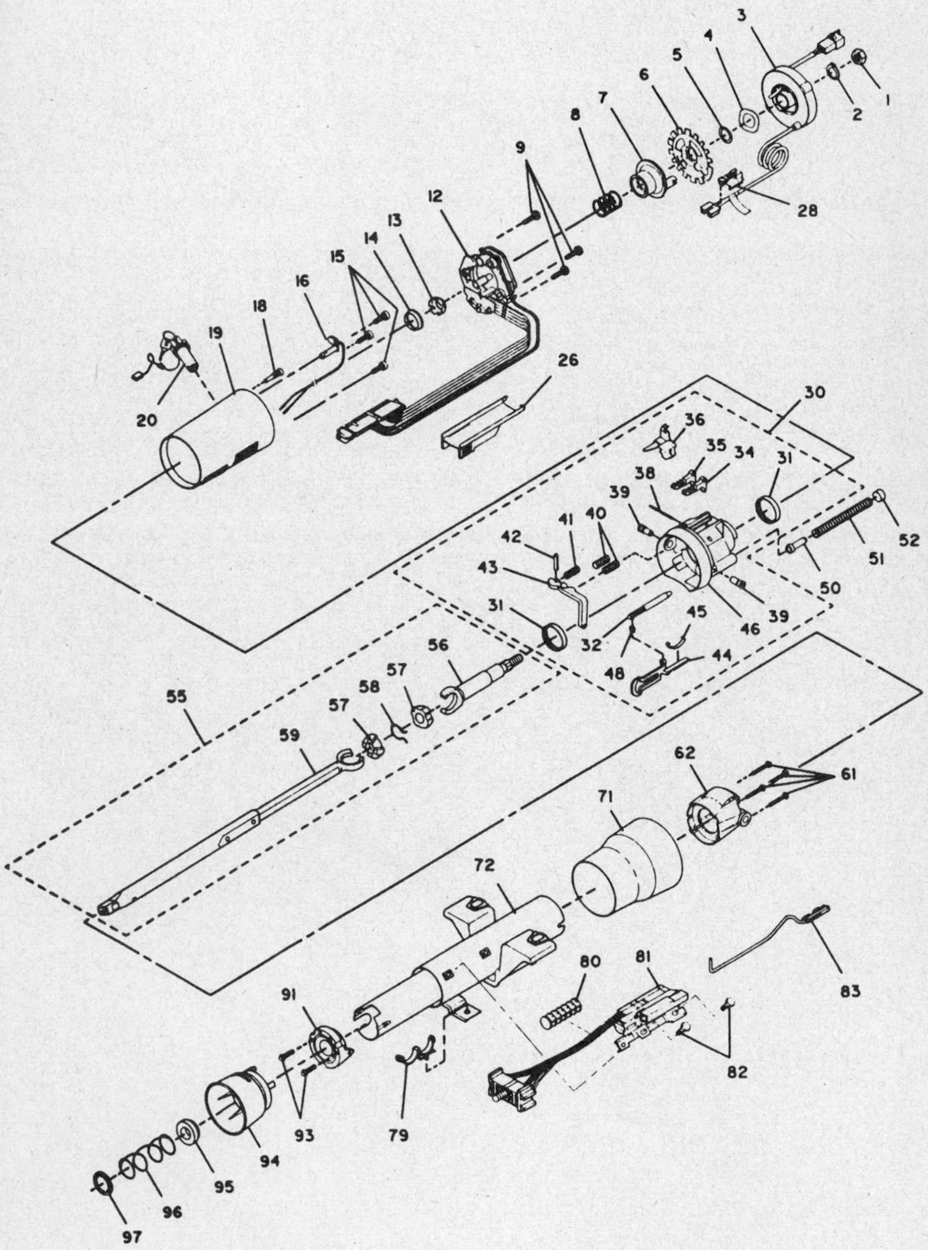
1
2
3
4
5
6
7
8
9
12
13
14
15
16
18
19
20
26
28
30
31
32
34
35
36
38
39
40
41
42
43
44
45
46
48
50
51
52
55
56
57
58
59
61
62
71
72
79
80
81
82
83
91
93
94
95
96
97

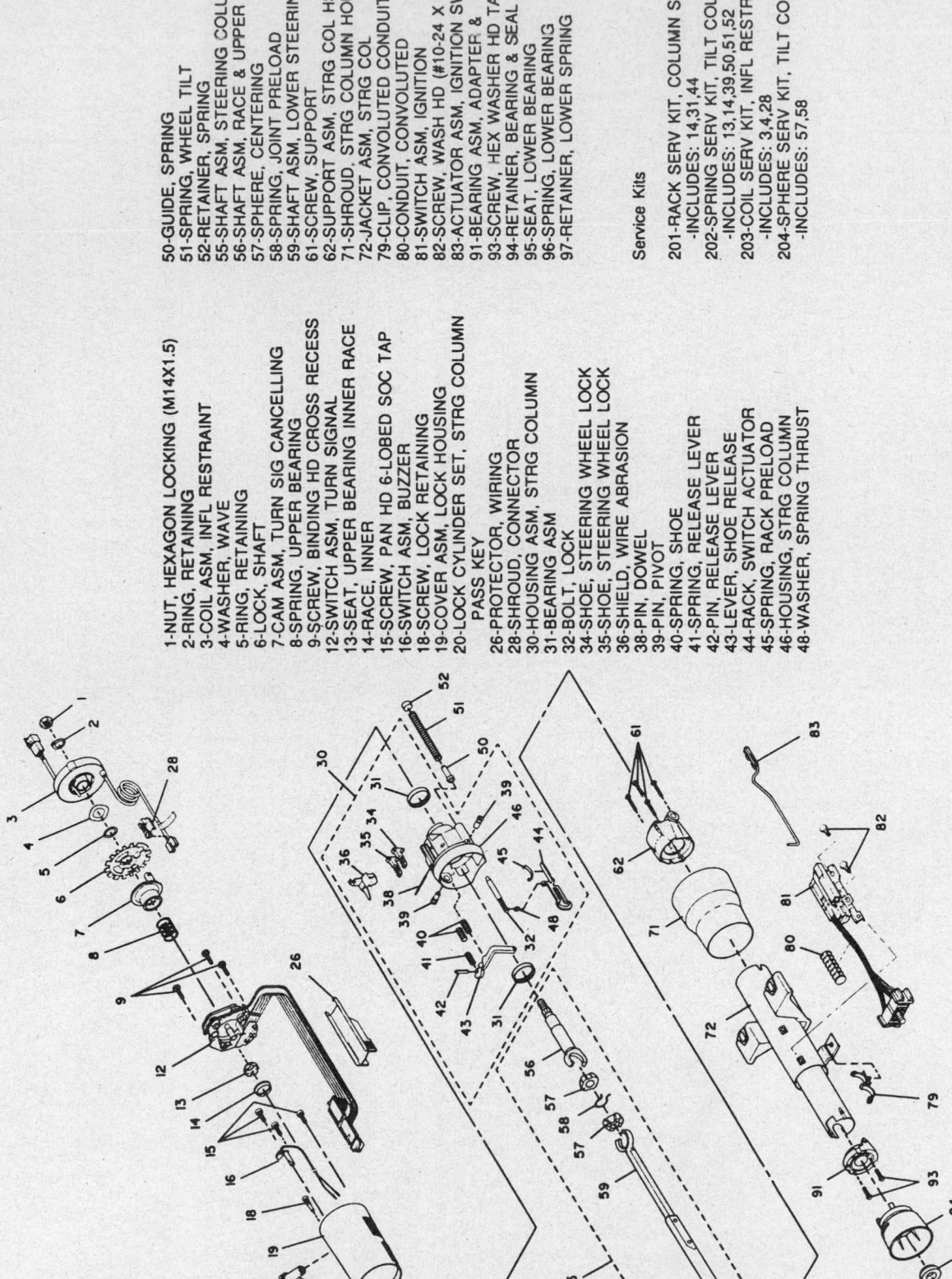

1-NUT, HEXAGON LOCKING (M14X1.5)
2-RING, RETAINING
3-COIL ASM, INFL RESTRAINT
4-WASHER, WAVE
5-RING, RETAINING
6-LOCK, SHAFT
7-CAM ASM, TURN SIG CANCELLING
8-SPRING, UPPER BEARING
9-SCREW, BINDING HD CROSS RECESS
12-SWITCH ASM, TURN SIGNAL
13-SEAT, UPPER BEARING INNER RACE
14-RACE, INNER
15-SCREW, PAN HD 6-LOBED SOC TAP
16-SWITCH ASM, BUZZER
18-SCREW, LOCK RETAINING
19-COVER ASM, LOCK HOUSING
20-LOCK CYLINDER SET, STRG COLUMN PASS KEY
26-PROTECTOR, WIRING
28-SHROUD, CONNECTOR
30-HOUSING ASM, STRG COLUMN
31-BEARING ASM
32-BOLT, LOCK
34-SHOE, STEERING WHEEL LOCK
35-SHOE, STEERING WHEEL LOCK
36-SHIELD, WIRE ABRASION
38-PIN, DOWEL
39-PIN, PIVOT
40-SPRING, SHOE
41-SPRING, RELEASE LEVER
42-PIN, RELEASE LEVER
43-LEVER, SHOE RELEASE
44-RACK, SWITCH ACTUATOR
45-SPRING, RACK PRELOAD
46-HOUSING, STRG COLUMN
48-WASHER, SPRING THRUST
50-GUIDE, SPRING
51-SPRING, WHEEL TILT
52-RETAINER, SPRING
55-SHAFT ASM, STEERING COLUMN
56-SHAFT ASM, RACE & UPPER
57-SPHERE, CENTERING
58-SPRING, JOINT PRELOAD
59-SHAFT ASM, LOWER STEERING
61-SCREW, SUPPORT
62-SUPPORT ASM, STRG COL HSG
71-SHROUD, STRG COLUMN HOUSING
72-JACKET ASM, STRG COL
79-CLIP, CONVOLUTED CONDUIT
80-CONDUIT, CONVOLUTED
81-SWITCH ASM, IGNITION
82-SCREW, WASH HD (#10-24 X .25)
83-ACTUATOR ASM, IGNITION SWITCH
91-BEARING ASM, ADAPTER &
93-SCREW, HEX WASHER HD TAPPING
94-RETAINER, BEARING & SEAL
95-SEAT, LOWER BEARING
96-SPRING, LOWER BEARING
97-RETAINER, LOWER SPRING

Service Kits

201-RACK SERV KIT, COLUMN SECTOR & -INCLUDES: 14,31,44
202-SPRING SERV KIT, TILT COLUMN -INCLUDES: 13,14,39,50,51,52
203-COIL SERV KIT, INFL RESTRAINT -INCLUDES: 3,4,28
204-SPHERE SERV KIT, TILT COLUMN -INCLUDES: 57,58

GC6049100099000X -R-

Fig. 53 Exploded view of steering column. 1992 Eldorado & Seville w/SIR

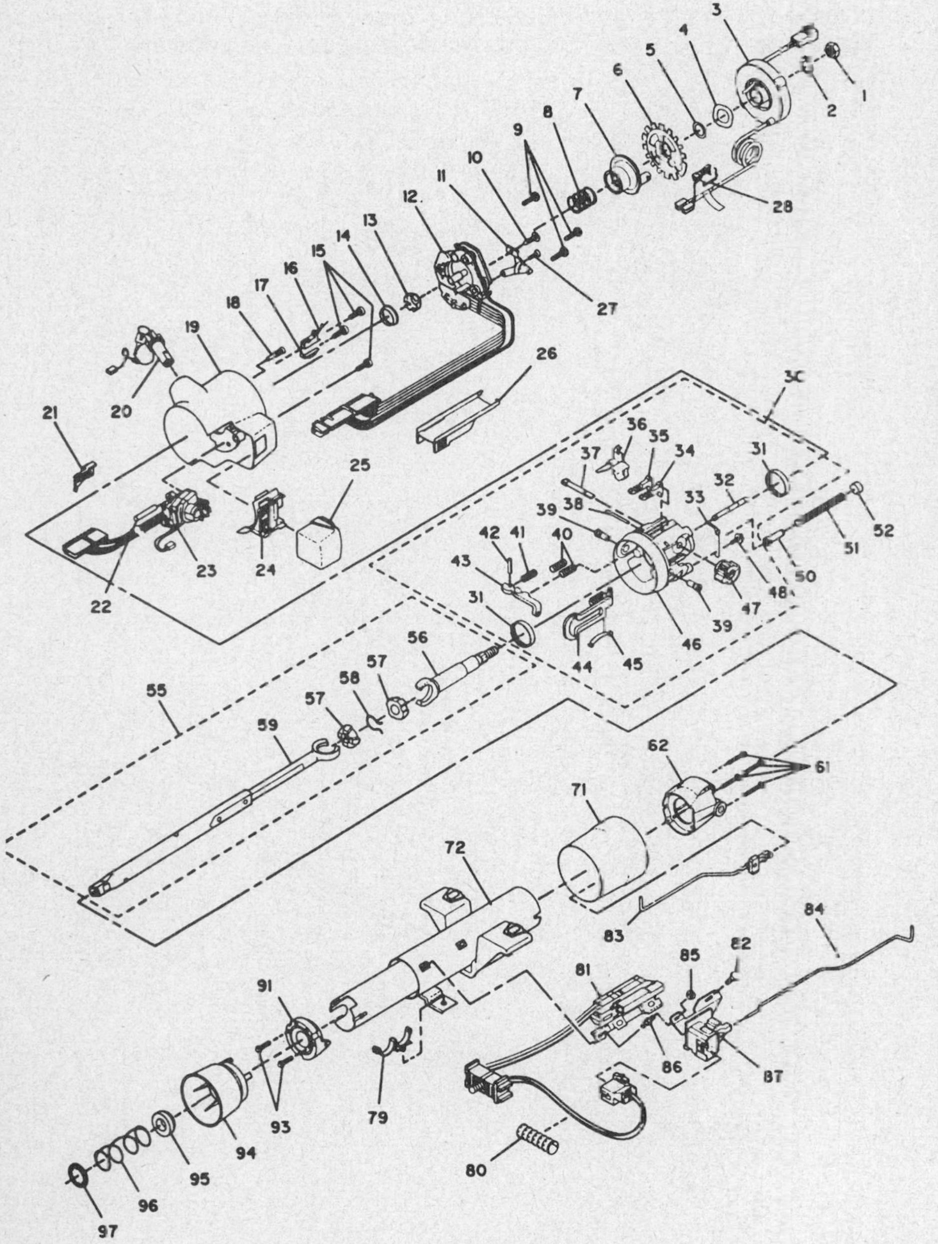

1-NUT, HEXAGON LOCKING (M14X1.5)
2-RING, RETAINING
3-COIL ASM, INFL RESTRAINT
4-WASHER, WAVE
5-RING, RETAINING
6-LOCK, SHAFT
7-CAM ASM, TURN SIG CANCELLING
8-SPRING, UPPER BEARING
9-SCREW, BINDING HD CROSS RECESS
10-SCREW, RD WASH HD (M4.2X1.41)
11-ARM, SIGNAL SWITCH
12-SWITCH ASM, TURN SIGNAL
13-SEAT, UPPER BEARING INNER RACE
14-RACE, INNER
15-SCREW, PAN HD 6-LOBED SOC TAP
16-SWITCH ASM, BUZZER
17-CLIP, BUZZER SWITCH RETAINING
18-SCREW, LOCK RETAINING
19-COVER ASM, LOCK HOUSING
20-LOCK CYLINDER SET, STRG COLUMN PASS KEY
21-ACTUATOR, DIMMER SWITCH ROD
22-PIN, SWITCH ACTUATOR PIVOT
23-SWITCH ASM, PIVOT & (PULSE)
24-BASE PLATE, COL HSG COVER END
25-CAP, COL HSG COVER END
26-PROTECTOR, WIRING
27-SCREW, FLT HD TAPPING
28-SHROUD, CONNECTOR
30-HOUSING ASM, STRG COLUMN
31-BEARING ASM
32-BOLT, LOCK
33-SPRING, LOCK BOLT
34-SHOE, STEERING WHEEL LOCK
35-SHOE, STEERING WHEEL LOCK
36-SHIELD, WIRE ABRASION
37-SHAFT, DRIVE
38-PIN, DOWEL
39-PIN, PIVOT
40-SPRING, SHOE
41-SPRING, RELEASE LEVER
42-PIN, RELEASE LEVER
43-LEVER, SHOE RELEASE
44-RACK, SWITCH ACTUATOR
45-SPRING, RACK PRELOAD
46-HOUSING, STRG COLUMN
47-SECTOR, SWITCH ACTUATOR
48-SCREW, HEX WASHER HEAD
50-GUIDE, SPRING
51-SPRING, WHEEL TILT
52-RETAINER, SPRING
55-SHAFT ASM, STEERING COLUMN
56-SHAFT ASM, RACE & UPPER
57-SPHERE, CENTERING
58-SPRING, JOINT PRELOAD
59-SHAFT ASM, LOWER STEERING
61-SCREW, SUPPORT
62-SUPPORT ASM, STRG COL HSG
71-SHROUD, STRG COLUMN HOUSING
72-JACKET ASM, STRG COL
79-CLIP, CONVOLUTED CONDUIT
80-CONDUIT, CONVOLUTED
81-SWITCH ASM, IGNITION
82-SCREW, WASH HD (#10-24 X .25)
83-ACTUATOR ASM, IGNITION SWITCH
84-ROD, DIMMER SWITCH
85-NUT, HEXAGON (#10-24 X .25)
86-STUD, DIMR & IGN SW MOUNTING
87-SWITCH ASM, DIMMER
91-BEARING ASM, ADAPTER &
93-SCREW, HEX WASHER HD TAPPING
94-RETAINER, BEARING & SEAL
95-SEAT, LOWER BEARING
96-SPRING, LOWER BEARING
97-RETAINER, LOWER SPRING

Service Kits

201-RACK SERV KIT, COLUMN SECTOR & -INCLUDES: 14,31,33,44,47,48
202-SPRING SERV KIT, TILT COLUMN -INCLUDES: 13,14,39,50,51,52
203-COIL SERV KIT, INFL RESTRAINT -INCLUDES: 3,4,28
204-SPHERE SERV KIT, TILT COLUMN -INCLUDES: 57,58

GC6049100100000X -R-

Fig. 54 Exploded view of steering column. Riviera w/SIR

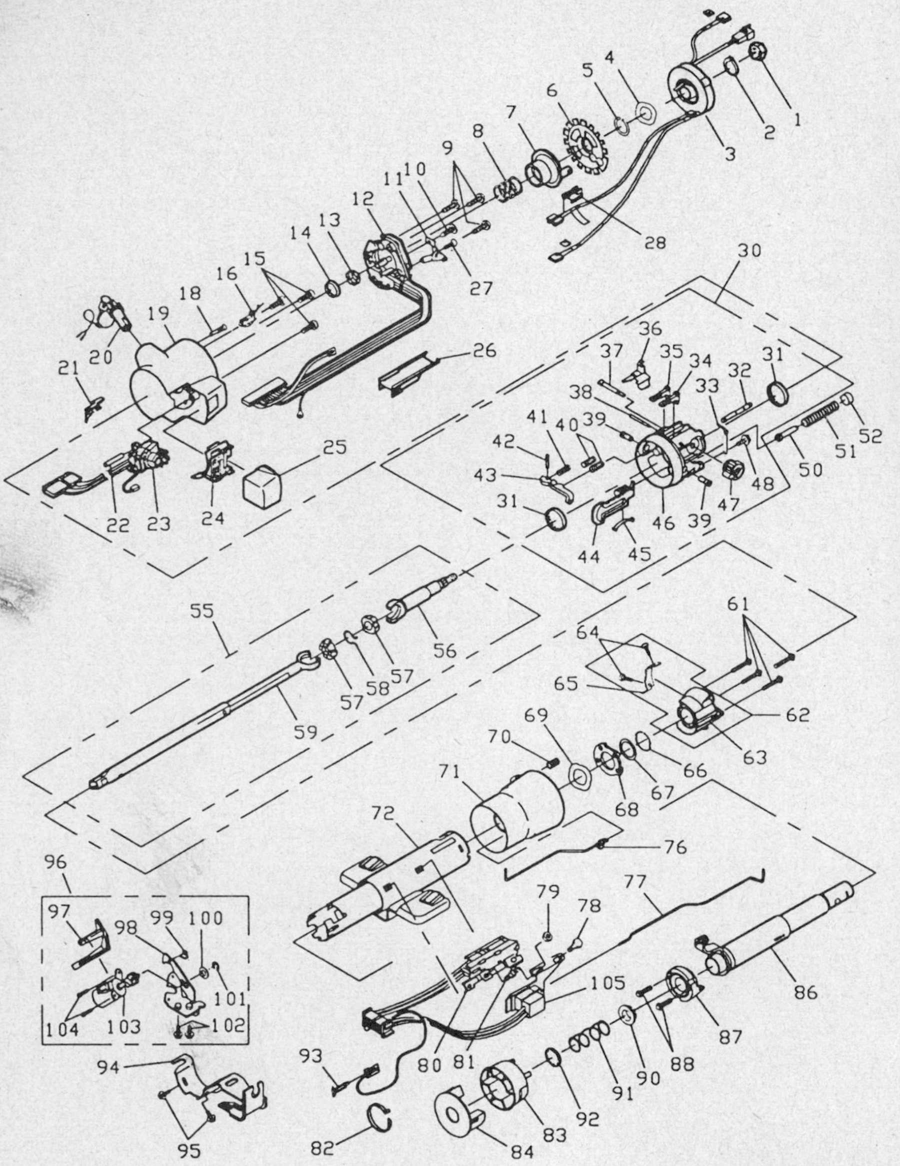

GC6049200101010X

Fig. 55 Exploded view of tilt steering column (Part 1 of 2). Bonneville, DeVille, Fleetwood (FWD), LeSabre, Park Avenue, 88 & 98 w/SIR & column shift

1–NUT, HEX LOCKING (M14x1.5)
2–RING, RETAINING
3–COIL ASM, INFL RESTRAINT
4–WASHER, WAVE
5–RING, RETAINING
6–LOCK, SHAFT
7–CAM ASM, TURN SIG CANCEL
8–SPRING, UPPER BEARING
9–SCREW, BNDG HD CR RECESS
10–SCREW, RD WASH HD (M4.2x1.41)
11–ARM ASM, SIGNAL SWITCH
12–SWITCH ASM, TURN SIGNAL
13–SEAT, UPPER BRG INNER RACE
14–RACE, INNER
15–SCREW, PAN HD SOC TAP
16–SWITCH ASM, BUZZER
18–SCREW, LOCK RETAINING
19–COVER ASM, LOCK HOUSING
20–LOCK CYLINDER SET, STRG COL (PASS KEY)
21–ACTUATOR, DIMMER SW ROD
22–PIN, SWITCH ACTUATOR PIVOT
23–SWITCH ASM, PIVOT & (PULSE)
24–BASE PLATE, COL HSG CVR END
25–CAP, COL HSG COVER END
26–PROTECTOR, WIRING
27–SCREW, FLT HD TAPPING
28–SHROUD, CONNECTOR
30–HOUSING ASM, STRG COLUMN
31–BEARING ASM
32–BOLT, LOCK
33–SPRING, LOCK BOLT
34–SHOE, STRG WHEEL LOCK
35–SHOE, STRG WHEEL LOCK
36–SHIELD, WIRE PROTECTOR
37–SHAFT, DRIVE
38–PIN, DOWEL
39–PIN, PIVOT
40–SPRING, SHOE
41–SPRING, RELEASE LEVER
42–PIN, RELEASE LEVER
43–LEVER, SHOE RELEASE
44–RACK, SWITCH ACTUATOR
45–SPRING, RACK PRELOAD
46–HOUSING, STRG COLUMN
47–SECTOR, SWITCH ACTUATOR
48–SCREW, HEX WASHER HEAD
50–GUIDE, SPRING
51–SPRING, WHEEL TILT
52–RETAINER, SPRING
55–SHAFT ASM, STEERING
56–SHAFT ASM, RACE & UPPER
57–SPHERE, CENTERING
58–SPRING, JOINT PRELOAD
59–SHAFT ASM, LOWER STEERING
61–SCREW, SUPPORT
62–SUPPORT ASM, STRG COL HSG
63–SUPPORT, STRG COL HSG
64–SCREW, OVL HD CROSS RECESS
65–GATE, SHIFT LEVER
66–RING, SHIFT TUBE RETAINING
67–WASHER, THRUST
68–PLATE, LOCK
69–WASHER, WAVE
70–SPRING, SHIFT LEVER
71–BOWL ASM, GEARSHIFT LEVER
72–JACKET ASM, STRG COL
76–ACTUATOR ASM, IGN SWITCH
77–ROD, DIMMER SWITCH
78–SCREW, WASH HD (#10–24x.25)
79–NUT, HEXAGON (#10–24)
80–SWITCH ASM, IGNITION & DIMR
81–STUD, DIMR & IGN SW MTG
82–STRAP, WIRE HARNESS
83–RETAINER, BEARING & SEAL
84–WASHER ASM, RETAINER
86–TUBE ASM, SHIFT
87–BEARING ASM, ADAPTER &
88–SCREW, HEX WASHER HD TAP
90–SEAT, LOWER BEARING
91–SPRING, LOWER BEARING
92–RETAINER, LOWER SPRING
93–CONNECTOR, AXIAL POS ASSUR
94–SUPPORT, STRG COL LOWER
95–BOLT, HEX FLNG HD (M6x1x14)
96–INTERLOCK ASM, SOLENOID &
97–SHIELD, INTERLOCK LEVER
98–LEVER ASM, INTLCK & BMPR
99–BUMPER, INTERLOCK LEVER
100–BUSHING, SOLENOID PIN
101–RING, RETAINING (METRIC 3CMI)
102–BOLT, HEX FLNG HD (M6x1x14)
103–SOLENOID ASM, INTERLOCK
104–SCREW, PAN HD 6-LOBED SOC TAP
105–SWITCH ASM, DIMMER

Service Kits

RACK SERV KIT, COL SECTOR & –INCLUDES: 14,31,33,44,47,48
SPRING SERV KIT, TILT COLUMN –INCLUDES: 13,14,39,50,51,52
COIL SERV KIT, INFL RESTRAINT –INCLUDES: 3,4,28
SPHERE SERV KIT, TILT COLUMN –INCLUDES: 57,58
GREASE SERV KIT, (SYNTHETIC)

GC6049200101020X

Fig. 55 Exploded view of tilt steering column (Part 2 of 2). Bonneville, DeVille, Fleetwood (FWD), LeSabre, Park Avenue, 88 & 98 w/SIR & column shift

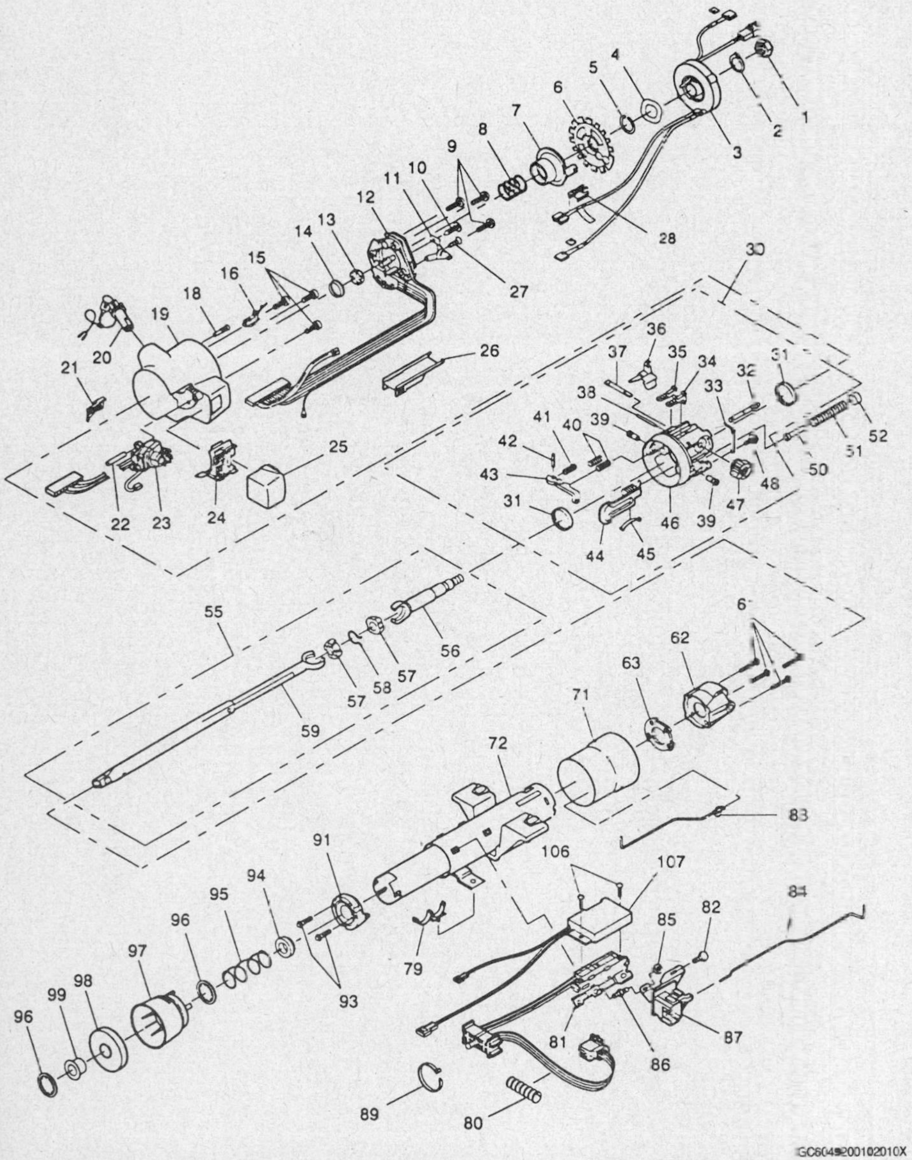

GC6049200102010X

Fig. 56 Exploded view of steering column (Part 1 of 2). Toronado & Trofeo w/SIR

1-NUT, HEX LOCKING (M14x1.5)
2-RING, RETAINING
3-COIL ASM, INFL RESTRAINT
4-WASHER, WAVE
5-RING, RETAINING
6-LOCK, SHAFT
7-CAM ASM, TURN SIG CANCEL
8-SPRING, UPPER BEARING
9-SCREW, BNDG HD CR RECESS
10-SCREW, RD WASH HD (M4.2x1.41)
11-ARM ASM, SIGNAL SWITCH
12-SWITCH ASM, TURN SIGNAL
13-SEAT, UPPER BRG INNER RACE
14-RACE, INNER
15-SCREW, PAN HD SOC TAP
16-SWITCH ASM, BUZZER
18-SCREW, LOCK RETAINING
19-COVER ASM, LOCK HOUSING
20-LOCK CYLINDER SET, STRG COL PASS KEY
21-ACTUATOR, DIMMER SW ROD
22-PIN, SWITCH ACTUATOR PIVOT
23-SWITCH ASM, PIVOT & (PULSE)
24-BASE PLATE, COL HSG CVR END
25-CAP, COL HSG COVER END
26-PROTECTOR, WIRING
27-SCREW, FLT HD TAPPING
28-SHROUD, CONNECTOR
30-HOUSING ASM, STRG COLUMN
31-BEARING ASM
32-BOLT, LOCK
33-SPRING, LOCK BOLT
34-SHOE, STEERING WHEEL LOCK
35-SHOE, STEERING WHEEL LOCK
36-SHIELD, WIRE PROTECTOR
37-SHAFT, DRIVE
38-PIN, DOWEL
39-PIN, PIVOT
40-SPRING, SHOE
41-SPRING, RELEASE LEVER
42-PIN, RELEASE LEVER
43-LEVER, SHOE RELEASE
44-RACK, SWITCH ACTUATOR
45-SPRING, RACK PRELOAD
46-HOUSING, STRG COLUMN
47-SECTOR, SWITCH ACTUATOR
48-SCREW, HEX WASHER HEAD
50-GUIDE, SPRING
51-SPRING, WHEEL TILT
52-RETAINER, SPRING
55-SHAFT ASM, STEERING
56-SHAFT ASM, RACE & UPPER
57-SPHERE, CENTERING
58-SPRING, JOINT PRELOAD
59-SHAFT ASM, LOWER STEERING
61-SCREW, SUPPORT
62-SUPPORT ASM, STRG COL HSG
63-PLATE, LOCK
71-SHROUD, STRG COLUMN HSG
72-JACKET ASM, STRG COL
79-CLIP, CONVOLUTED CONDUIT
80-CONDUIT, CONVOLUTED
81-SWITCH ASM, COL LOCK & IGN
82-SCREW, WASH HD (#10-24X.25)
83-ACTUATOR ASM, IGNITION SWITCH
84-ROD, DIMMER SWITCH
85-NUT, HEXAGON (#10-24)
86-STUD, DIMR & IGNITION SW MTG
87-SWITCH ASM, DIMMER
89-STRAP, WIRE HARNESS
91-BEARING ASM, ADAPTER &
93-SCREW, HEX WASHER HD TAP
94-SEAT, LOWER BEARING
95-SPRING, LOWER BEARING
96-RETAINER, LOWER SPRING
97-RETAINER, BEARING & SEAL
98-SEAL, STEERING SHAFT
99-BUSHING, SEAL RETAINING
106-SCREW, RD WASH HD (M4.2X1.41)
107-MODULE ASM, E & C INTERFACE

Service Kits

201-RACK SERV KIT, COL SECTOR &
-INCLUDES: 14,31,33,44,47,48
202-SPRING SERV KIT, TILT COLUMN
-INCLUDES: 13,14,39,50,51,52
203-COIL SERV KIT, INFL RESTRAINT
-INCLUDES: 3,4,28
204-SPHERE SERV KIT, TILT COLUMN
-INCLUDES: 57,58
205-GREASE SERV KIT, (SYNTHETIC)

GC6049200102020X

Fig. 56 Exploded view of steering column (Part 2 of 2). Toronado & Trofeo w/SIR

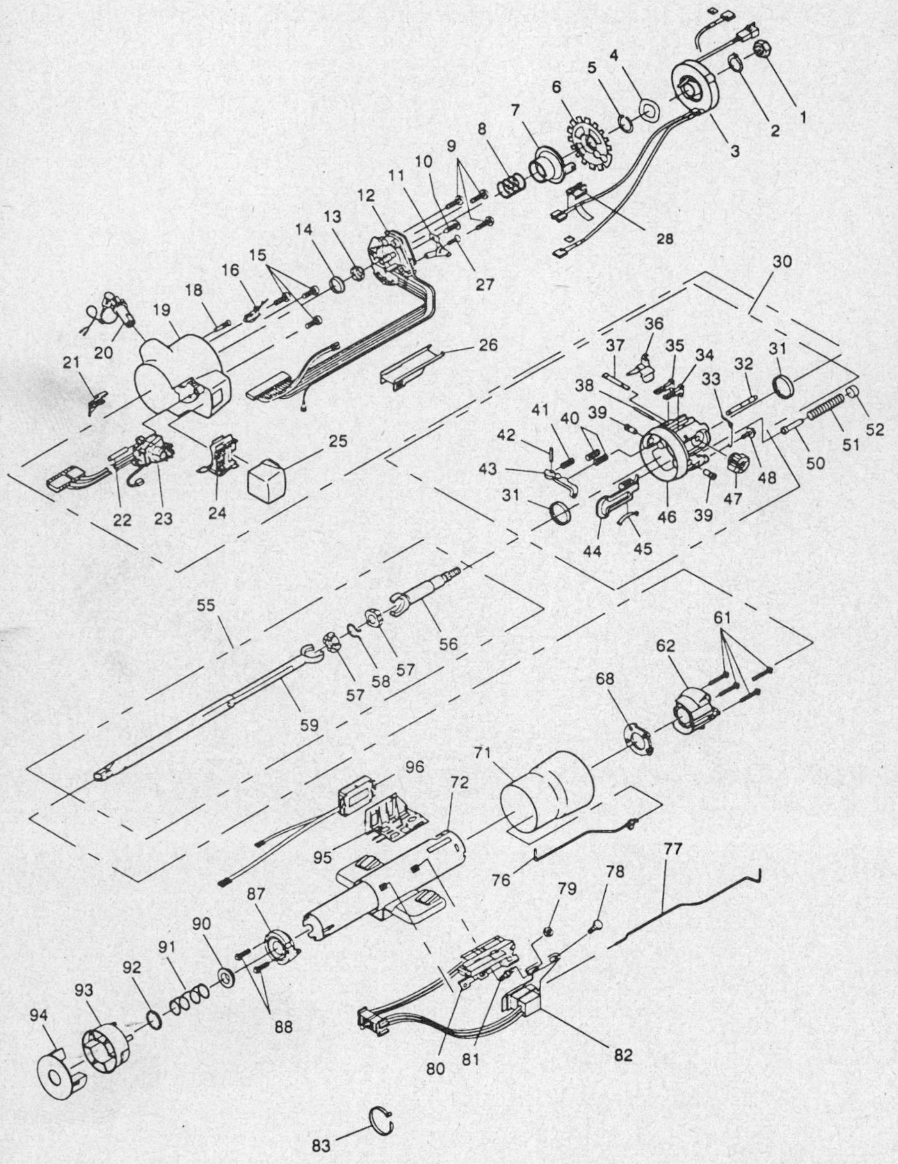

GC6049200103010X

Fig. 57 Exploded view of tilt steering column (Part 1 of 2). Bonneville, 88 & 98 w/SIR & floor shift

1-NUT, HEX LOCKING (M14x1.5)
2-RING, RETAINING
3-COIL ASM, INFL RESTRAINT
4-WASHER, WAVE
5-RING, RETAINING
6-LOCK, SHAFT
7-CAM ASM, TURN SIG CANCEL
8-SPRING, UPPER BEARING
9-SCREW, BNDG HD CR RECESS
10-SCREW, RD WASH HD (M4.2x1.41)
11-ARM ASM, SIGNAL SWITCH
12-SWITCH ASM, TURN SIGNAL
13-SEAT, UPPER BRG INNER RACE
14-RACE, INNER
15-SCREW, PAN HD SOC TAP
16-SWITCH ASM, BUZZER
18-SCREW, LOCK RETAINING
19-COVER ASM, LOCK HOUSING
20-LOCK CYLINDER SET, STRG COL (PASS KEY)
21-ACTUATOR, DIMMER SW ROD
22-PIN, SWITCH ACTUATOR PIVOT
23-SWITCH ASM, PIVOT & (PULSE)
24-BASE PLATE, COL HSG CVR END
25-CAP, COL HSG COVER END
26-PROTECTOR, WIRING
27-SCREW, FLT HD TAPPING
28-SHROUD, CONNECTOR
30-HOUSING ASM, STRG COLUMN
31-BEARING ASM
32-BOLT, LOCK
33-SPRING, LOCK BOLT
34-SHOE, STRG WHEEL LOCK
35-SHOE, STRG WHEEL LOCK
36-SHIELD, WIRE PROTECTOR
37-SHAFT, DRIVE
38-PIN, DOWEL
39-PIN, PIVOT
40-SPRING, SHOE
41-SPRING, RELEASE LEVER
42-PIN, RELEASE LEVER
43-LEVER, SHOE RELEASE
44-RACK, SWITCH ACTUATOR
45-SPRING, RACK PRELOAD
46-HOUSING, STRG COLUMN
47-SECTOR, SWITCH ACTUATOR
48-SCREW, HEX WASHER HEAD
50-GUIDE, SPRING
51-SPRING, WHEEL TILT
52-RETAINER, SPRING
55-SHAFT ASM, STEERING
56-SHAFT ASM, RACE & UPPER
57-SPHERE, CENTERING
58-SPRING, JOINT PRELOAD
59-SHAFT ASM, LOWER STEERING
61-SCREW, SUPPORT
62-SUPPORT ASM, STRG COL HSG
68-PLATE, LOCK
71-SHROUD, STRG COL HSG
72-JACKET ASM, STRG COL
76-ACTUATOR ASM, IGN SWITCH
77-ROD, DIMMER SWITCH
78-SCREW, WASH HD (#10-24x.25)
79-NUT, HEXAGON (#10-24)
80-SWITCH ASM, IGN & DIMMER
81-STUD, DIMR & IGN SW MTG
82-SWITCH ASM, DIMMER
83-STRAP, WIRE HARNESS
87-BEARING ASM, ADAPTER &
88-SCREW, HEX WASHER HD TAP
90-SEAT, LOWER BEARING
91-SPRING, LOWER BEARING
92-RETAINER, LOWER SPRING
93-RETAINER, BEARING & SEAL
94-WASHER ASM, RETAINER
95-BRACKET, E & C MODULE
96-MODULE ASM, E & C INTERFACE

Service Kits

201-RACK SERV KIT, COL SECTOR & -INCLUDES: 14,31,33,44,47,48
202-SPRING SERV KIT, TILT COLUMN -INCLUDES: 13,14,39,50,51,52
203-COIL SERV KIT, INFL RESTRAINT -INCLUDES: 3,4,28
204-SPHERE SERV KIT, TILT COLUMN -INCLUDES: 57,58
205-GREASE SERV KIT, (SYNTHETIC)

GC6049200103020X

Fig. 57 Exploded view of tilt steering column (Part 2 of 2). Bonneville, 88 & 98 w/SIR & floor shift

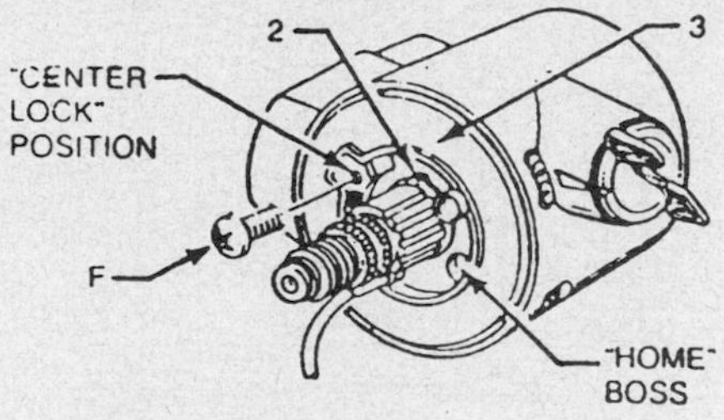
"CENTER LOCK" POSITION
2
3
F
"HOME" BOSS

2. RING, RETAINING
3. COIL ASM, INFL RESTRAINT
F. LOCK SCREW

GC6049100104000X

Fig. 58 Locking coil assembly. Bonneville, Camaro, Corvette, DeVille, Firebird, Fleetwood (FWD), LeSabre, Park Avenue, Riviera, Toronado, Trofeo, 88 & 98 & 1992 Eldorado & Seville

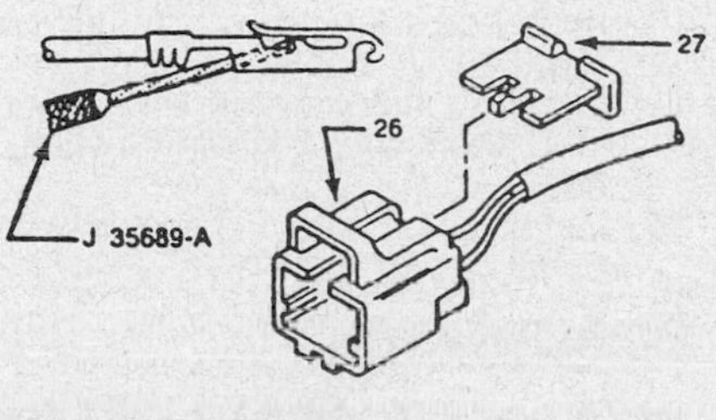
27
26
J 35689-A

26. CONNECTOR ASM, BODY
27. TERMINAL, POS ASSURANCE

GC6049100107000X

Fig. 61 Assembling connector body. Bonneville, Camaro, Corvette, DeVille, Firebird, Fleetwood (FWD), LeSabre, Park Avenue, Riviera, Toronado, Trofeo, 88 & 98 & 1992 Eldorado & Seville

stall spring retainer.
2. Install pivot and pulse switch assembly, then the pivot pin.
3. Route lock housing cover wire harness through gear shift lever bowl and column housing.
4. Install dimmer switch rod actuator to base plate, then the base plate to gear shift lever bowl, ensuring bottom edge of dimmer switch rod actuator rests on bend in dimmer switch rod.
5. Install cover housing end cap.
6. **On models equipped with cruise control,** plug multi-function lever connector and cruise control wires on wipe/wash switch together and mount on base plate and install multi-function lever.
7. **On all models,** install lock housing cover. Tighten screw in 12 o'clock position first, screw in 8 o'clock position second and screw in 4 o'clock position third, then **torque** screws to 89 inch lbs. in same order.
8. Assemble coil, shaft lock, turn signal cancel cam, upper bearing spring and seat, inner race turn signal switch, buzzer switch and lock cylinder set as outlined previously.

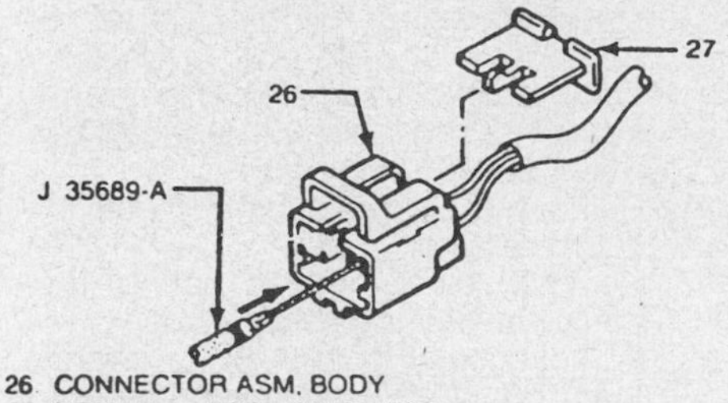
27
26
J 35689-A

26 CONNECTOR ASM, BODY
27 TERMINAL, POS ASSURANCE

GC6049100105000X

Fig. 59 Disassembling connector body. Bonneville, Camaro, Corvette, DeVille, Firebird, Fleetwood (FWD), LeSabre, Park Avenue, Riviera, Toronado, Trofeo, 88 & 98 & 1992 Eldorado & Seville

COLUMN HOUSING, LOCK SHOES, ACTUATOR SECTOR, SWITCH ACTUATOR RACK, BEARINGS & LOCK BOLT

Disassemble

1. Disassemble coil, shaft lock, turn signal cancel cam, upper bearing spring and seat, inner race turn signal switch, buzzer switch and lock cylinder set as outlined previously.
2. Disassemble lock housing cover, cover end cap, pivot and switch, dimmer switch rod actuator and tilt spring as outlined previously.
3. Remove lock housing cover attaching screws and the cover, then the tilt lever.
4. Remove cover housing end cap, base plate and dimmer switch rod actuator, then gently pull pivot switch wire harness through column housing and gear shift lever bowl.
5. **On models equipped with cruise control,** unplug connector from base plate and remove multi-function lever.
6. **On all models,** remove spring retainer, then the spring and spring guide.
7. Using tool No. J-21854-01 or equivalent, remove pivot pins, **Fig. 49,** then reinstall tilt lever.
8. Remove column housing assembly by pulling back on tilt lever and pulling housing down and away from column.
9. Remove driveshaft, then the switch actuator sector.
10. Remove switch actuator rack and rack preload spring, then the release lever pin.
11. Remove release lever, then the release lever spring.
12. Remove dowel pin, then the lock shoes.
13. Remove lock shoe springs, then the bearings.
14. Remove hex head bolt, then the lock bolt spring and lock bolt.

Assemble

Ensure all fasteners are securely seated before applying required torque.

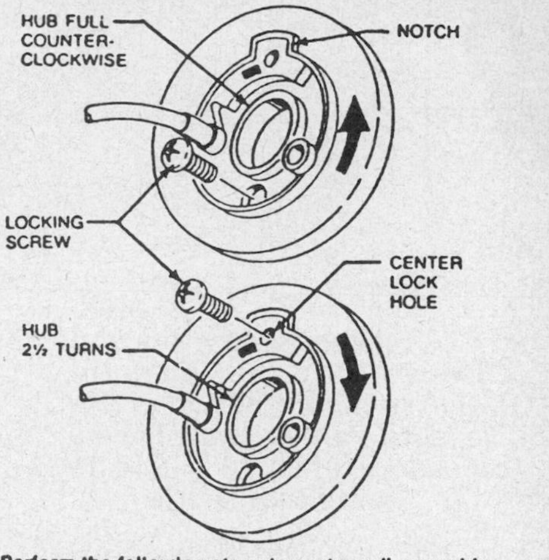
HUB FULL COUNTER-CLOCKWISE
NOTCH
LOCKING SCREW
CENTER LOCK HOLE
HUB 2½ TURNS

Perform the following steps to center coil assembly:
A. Remove coil assembly (3) from column
B. Lock screw to boss "Hcme" position, allowing hub to rotate
C. Hold coil assembly housing in one hand with steering wheel connector up
D. Rotate coil hub counterclockwise until it stops. Turn coil over to inspect coil position through the clear bottom. The coil ribbon should be wound up snug against center hub.
E. Rotate coil hub clockwise approximately two and a half (2½) turns until "Center Lock" hole is even with the notch in coil housing
F. Hold hub in position while installing lock screw to "Center Lock" hole

GC6049100106000X

Fig. 60 Centering coil assembly. Bonneville, Camaro, Corvette, DeVille, Firebird, Fleetwood (FWD), LeSabre, Park Avenue, Riviera, Toronado, Trofeo, 88 & 98 & 1992 Eldorado & Seville

1. Install bearings to column housing.
2. Install driveshaft, then the actuator sector.
3. Install lock shoes, then the dowel pin.
4. Install lock shoe springs, then the release lever spring.
5. Install release lever, then the release lever pin.
6. Install rack preload spring, then the switch actuator rack to actuator sector.
7. Install lock bolt, then the lock bolt spring.
8. Install hex head bolt.
9. Install column housing assembly to column as follows:
   a. Position column housing assembly and align switch actuator rack with pin on end of actuator rod.
   b. Pull back on tilt lever, pushing column housing assembly onto column housing support assembly, then release tilt lever to lock shoes.
10. Remove tilt lever.
11. Lubricate pivot pins with lithium grease and install them.
12. Assemble lock housing cover, cover end cap, pivot and switch, dimmer switch rod actuator and tilt spring as outlined previously.
13. Assemble coil, shaft lock, turn signal cancel cam, upper bearing spring and seat, inner race turn signal switch, buzzer switch and lock cylinder set as outlined previously.

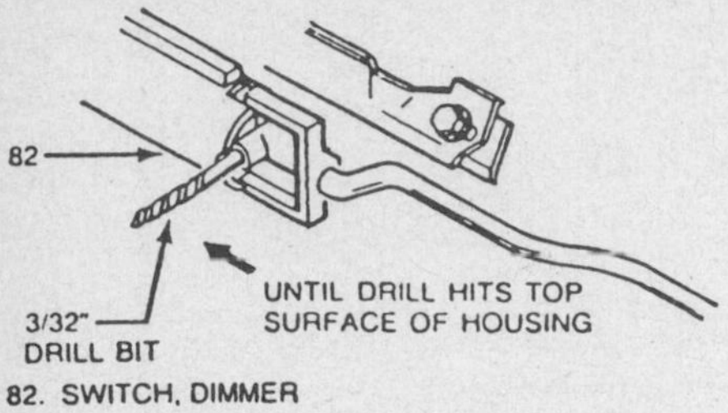
82
3/32"
DRILL BIT
UNTIL DRILL HITS TOP
SURFACE OF HOUSING
82. SWITCH, DIMMER
GC6049100108000X

Fig. 62 Dimmer switch adjustment. Bonneville, Camaro, Corvette, DeVille, Firebird, Fleetwood (FWD), LeSabre, Park Avenue, Riviera, Toronado, Trofeo, 88 & 98 & 1992 Eldorado & Seville

SHAFT, COLUMN HOUSING SUPPORT, SHIFT TUBE, IGNITION SWITCH, DIMMER SWITCH & LOWER BEARING

Disassemble

1. Disassemble coil, shaft lock, turn signal cancel cam, upper bearing spring and seat, inner race turn signal switch, buzzer switch and lock cylinder set as outlined previously.
2. Disassemble lock housing cover, cover end cap, pivot and switch, dimmer switch rod actuator and tilt spring as outlined previously.
3. Disassemble column housing, lock shoes, actuator sector, switch actuator rack, bearings and lock bolt as outlined previously.
4. Remove lock housing cover attaching screws and the cover, then the tilt lever.
5. Remove cover housing end cap, base plate and dimmer switch rod actuator, then gently pull pivot switch wire harness through column housing and gear shift lever bowl.
6. **On models equipped with cruise control,** unplug connector from base plate and remove multi-function lever.
7. **On all models,** remove spring retainer, then the spring and spring guide.
8. Using tool No. J-21854-01 or equivalent, remove pivot pins, **Fig. 49,** then reinstall tilt lever.
9. Remove column housing assembly by pulling back on tilt lever and pulling housing down and away from column.
10. Remove steering column from vehicle. **Once steering column is removed from vehicle, the column is extremely susceptible to damage. Dropping column assembly on its end could collapse steering shaft or loosen plastic injections that maintain column rigidity. Leaning on column assembly may cause jacket to bend or deform. Any of the above damage may impair column's collapsible design. If it is necessary to remove steering wheel, use only the specified steering wheel puller. Under no conditions should end of shaft be hammered on because hammering could loosen plastic injections that maintain column rigidity.**
11. Remove bearing retainer, then the spring retainer.
12. Remove lower bearing spring, then the lower bearing seat.
13. Remove screws and lower bearing, then the shaft assembly. Check for accident damage.
14. Remove lower shaft.
15. Remove sphere from shaft assembly, then the retainer clip from sphere.
16. Remove housing support assembly retaining screws, then the housing support assembly and dimmer switch rod.
17. Remove hex nut and hex head bolt, then the dimmer switch and mounting stud.
18. Remove ignition switch and actuator rod assembly, then the shift tube retaining ring.
19. Remove thrust washer, then the gear shift lever spring.
20. Using tool No. J-23072 or equivalent, remove shift tube.
21. Remove lock plate and wave washer, then the gear shift lever bowl.

Assemble

Ensure all fasteners are securely seated before applying required torque.

1. Install gear shift lever spring to gear shift lever bowl, then the gear shift lever bowl to the shift tube jacket.
2. Lubricate wave washer with lithium grease and install it.
3. Install lock plate, then, using tool No. J-23073-1-2-3 or equivalent, the shift tube.
4. Install thrust washer, then the shift tube retaining ring.
5. Install dimmer switch rod to housing support.
6. Install housing support assembly, **torque** attaching bolts to 79 inch lbs.
7. Install actuator rod assembly to track in housing support.
8. Install retaining clip and sphere to shaft assembly.
9. Install lower shaft to shaft assembly with block tooth on shaft end of shaft assembly at 12 o'clock position and notch at lower end of shaft at 4 o'clock position.
10. Lubricate shaft assembly with lithium grease and install to column.
11. Assemble lock housing cover, cover end cap, pivot and switch, dimmer switch rod actuator and tilt spring as outlined previously.
12. Assemble column housing, lock shoes, actuator sector, switch actuator rack, bearings and lock bolt as outlined previously.
13. Assemble coil, shaft lock, turn signal cancel cam, upper bearing spring and seat, inner race turn signal switch, buzzer switch and lock cylinder set as outlined previously.
14. Lubricate inner surface of lower bearing with lithium grease, then install lower bearing and screws.

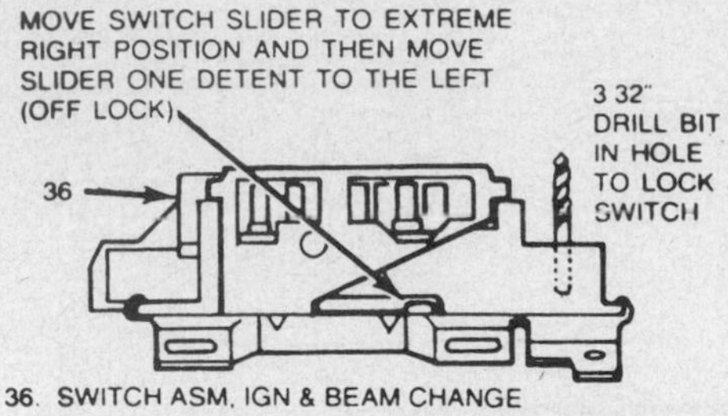
MOVE SWITCH SLIDER TO EXTREME RIGHT POSITION AND THEN MOVE SLIDER ONE DETENT TO THE LEFT (OFF LOCK)
3 32"
DRILL BIT
IN HOLE
TO LOCK
SWITCH
36
36. SWITCH ASM. IGN & BEAM CHANGE
GC6049100109000X

Fig. 63 Ignition switch adjustment. Bonneville, Camaro, Corvette, DeVille, Firebird, Fleetwood (FWD), LeSabre, Park Avenue, Riviera, Toronado, Trofeo, 88 & 98 & 1992 Eldorado & Seville

15. Install lower bearing seat, then the lower bearing spring.
16. Install spring retainer, then the bearing retainer.
17. Install dimmer switch, hex nut and hex head bolt, then adjust dimmer switch, **Fig. 62.**
18. Install ignition switch and mounting stud, then adjust ignition switch, **Fig. 63.**
19. Install column to vehicle instrument panel.

Brougham

TILT/TELESCOPIC COLUMN

Refer to **Fig. 64** when servicing this column.

Disassemble

1. Disconnect battery ground cable, then remove column from vehicle.
2. Turn ignition switch to the Run position.
3. Remove horn pad, switch and horn connector.
4. Remove three small bolts and unscrew telescoping adjuster from shaft.
5. Remove telescoping lever from column, nut from steering column shaft and steering wheel.
6. Remove key warning buzzer and retaining clip.
7. Remove lock cylinder retaining screw inside lock housing column cover and lock cylinder from column.
8. Remove hazard switch, tilt column lever and turn signal/cruise control lever.
9. Remove lock housing column cover, lower column cover and fuse panel cover.
10. Disconnect harness connector, then remove wiring protector and multi-function turn signal switch from column.
11. Install tilt lever and place column in the full up position.
12. Remove upper bearing seat, inner race and bearing.
13. Remove tilt spring retainer, spring and guide.
14. Use a punch to remove driveshaft and sector.
15. Remove pivot pins using special tool No. J 21854-01 or equivalent, **Fig. 49.**

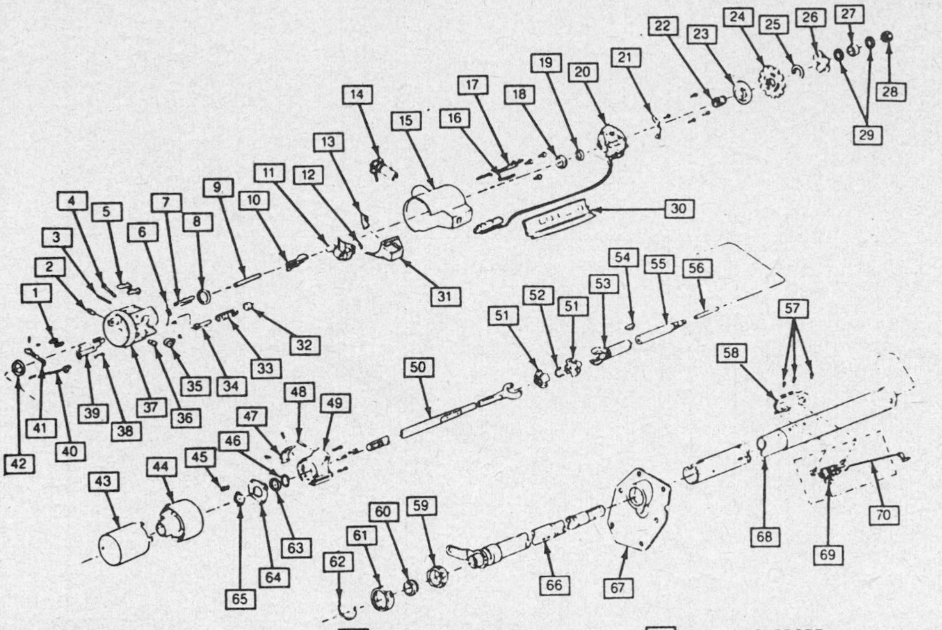

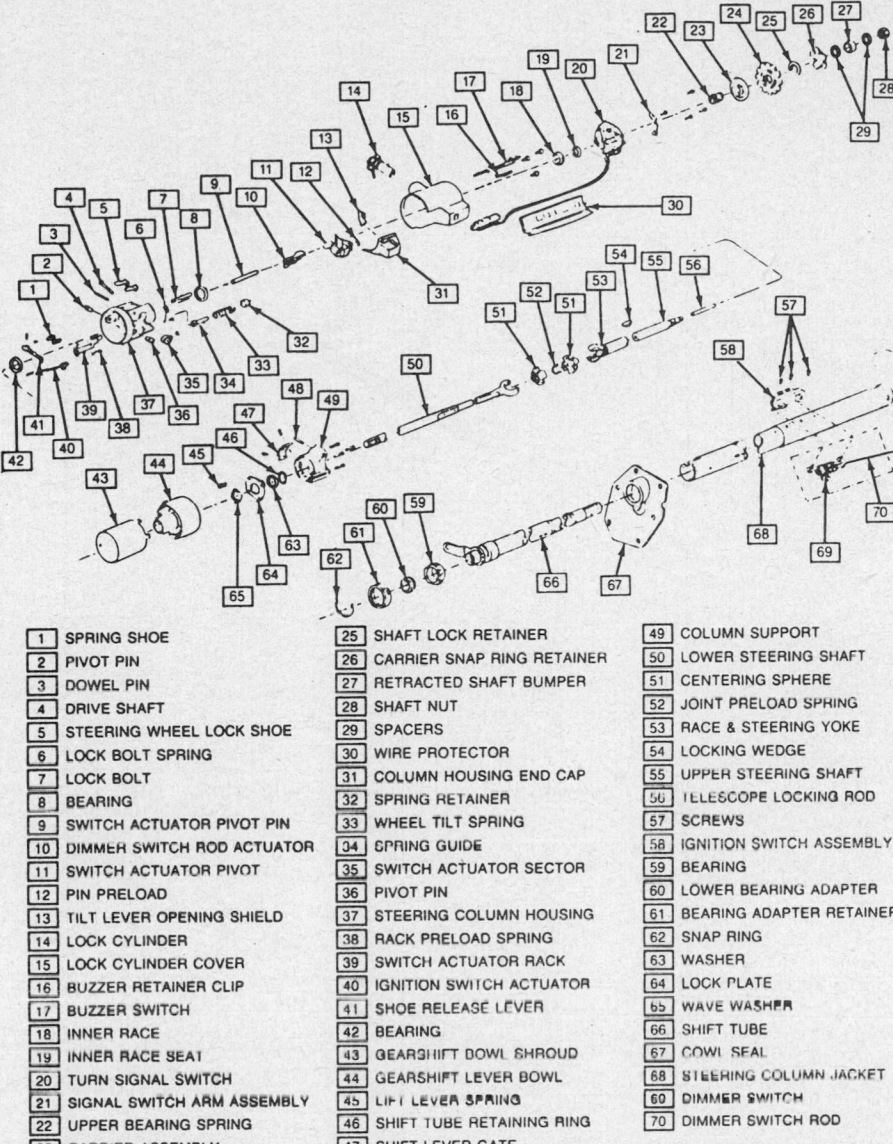

1 SPRING SHOE
2 PIVOT PIN
3 DOWEL PIN
4 DRIVE SHAFT
5 STEERING WHEEL LOCK SHOE
6 LOCK BOLT SPRING
7 LOCK BOLT
8 BEARING
9 SWITCH ACTUATOR PIVOT PIN
10 DIMMER SWITCH ROD ACTUATOR
11 SWITCH ACTUATOR PIVOT
12 PIN PRELOAD
13 TILT LEVER OPENING SHIELD
14 LOCK CYLINDER
15 LOCK CYLINDER COVER
16 BUZZER RETAINER CLIP
17 BUZZER SWITCH
18 INNER RACE
19 INNER RACE SEAT
20 TURN SIGNAL SWITCH
21 SIGNAL SWITCH ARM ASSEMBLY
22 UPPER BEARING SPRING
23 CARRIER ASSEMBLY
24 STEERING SHAFT LOCK
25 SHAFT LOCK RETAINER
26 CARRIER SNAP RING RETAINER
27 RETRACTED SHAFT BUMPER
28 SHAFT NUT
29 SPACERS
30 WIRE PROTECTOR
31 COLUMN HOUSING END CAP
32 SPRING RETAINER
33 WHEEL TILT SPRING
34 SPRING GUIDE
35 SWITCH ACTUATOR SECTOR
36 PIVOT PIN
37 STEERING COLUMN HOUSING
38 RACK PRELOAD SPRING
39 SWITCH ACTUATOR RACK
40 IGNITION SWITCH ACTUATOR
41 SHOE RELEASE LEVER
42 BEARING
43 GEARSHIFT BOWL SHROUD
44 GEARSHIFT LEVER BOWL
45 LIFT LEVER SPRING
46 SHIFT TUBE RETAINING RING
47 SHIFT LEVER GATE
48 DOWEL PIN
49 COLUMN SUPPORT
50 LOWER STEERING SHAFT
51 CENTERING SPHERE
52 JOINT PRELOAD SPRING
53 RACE & STEERING YOKE
54 LOCKING WEDGE
55 UPPER STEERING SHAFT
56 TELESCOPE LOCKING ROD
57 SCREWS
58 IGNITION SWITCH ASSEMBLY
59 BEARING
60 LOWER BEARING ADAPTER
61 BEARING ADAPTER RETAINER
62 SNAP RING
63 WASHER
64 LOCK PLATE
65 WAVE WASHER
66 SHIFT TUBE
67 COWL SEAL
68 STEERING COLUMN JACKET
69 DIMMER SWITCH
70 DIMMER SWITCH ROD

GC6049100094000X

Fig. 64 Exploded view of tilt/telescopic steering column. Brougham

16. Tilt housing by pulling upward on tilt lever and pulling housing upward until it stops. Move housing to the right to disengage rack from actuator.
17. Remove race and upper shaft assembly from lower shaft at centering sphere.
18. Remove gearshift lever, gate and column support.
19. Remove lock plate, retaining ring and washers.
20. Remove shift tube from shift bowl using special tool No. J 23072 or equivalent.
21. Remove lower bearing and retainer.

Assemble

1. Install lower bearing and retainer.
2. Install gear shift tube to bowl using special tool No. J 23073-01 or equivalent.
3. Install lock plate, retaining ring and washers.
4. Install column support, gearshift lever and gate.
5. Install race and upper shaft assembly to lower shaft at centering sphere.
6. Install tilt housing and new pivot pins.
7. Install driveshaft and sector.
8. Install tilt spring, retainer and guide.
9. Install upper bearing, seat and inner race.
10. Install multi-function switch to column, wiring protector and connect harness connector.
11. Install fuse panel, lower column and lock housing column covers.
12. Install hazard switch, turn signal/cruise control and tilt column levers to column.
13. Install lock cylinder and retaining screw to column.
14. Install key warning buzzer and retaining clip.
15. Install steering wheel to column shaft and **torque** nut to 35 ft. lbs.
16. Install telescope locking lever on shaft and telescope adjuster.
17. Position locking lever and bolts along the marks made by the bolts when tightened, **torque** bolts to 35 inch lbs.
18. Check operation of telescoping lever for proper release and tightening within the lever's range of motion. Ensure that the wheel is free to telescope when the lever is all the way to the left and securely locked when lever is all the way to the right. If necessary adjust using the slotted locking lever bolt holes.
19. Install horn contact wire and horn pad assembly, then connect battery ground cable.

Century, Cutlass Ciera & Cutlass Cruiser

STANDARD COLUMN

Refer to **Fig. 65** when servicing this column.

SHAFT LOCK, TURN SIGNAL CANCEL CAM, UPPER BEARING SPRING & SEAT, INNER RACE, TURN SIGNAL SWITCH, ALARM & LOCK CYLINDER SET

Disassemble

1. Disconnect battery ground cable.
2. Gently pull up on horn pad to remove.
3. Disconnect horn lead by gently pushing down on lead and turning to the left, spring will then come out of cancelling cam tower.
4. Remove retainer, nut and steering wheel.
5. Remove shaft lock retaining ring using special tool No. J 23653-C or equivalent, to depress shaft lock.
6. Remove shaft lock, turn signal cancelling cam, upper bearing spring and thrust washer.
7. Move turn signal to the right turn position.
8. Remove multi-function lever, screw and switch actuator arm.
9. Remove screws, hazard knob assembly and turn signal switch.
10. Remove wiring protector and gently pull harness through gearshift lever bowl, gearshift lever bowl shroud and lock cover assembly housing.
11. Remove key from lock cylinder and alarm assembly and clip.
12. Reinstall key and turn to the Lock position, remove lock retaining screw, then lock cylinder set.

Assemble

1. Install lock cylinder set and retaining screw and **torque** to 30 inch lbs.
2. Install key and turn to the Run position.
3. Install alarm assembly and clip.
4. Install turn signal switch harness through lock housing cover assembly, gearshift lever bowl and gearshift bowl shroud and connect.
5. Install turn signal switch and screws and **torque** to 35 inch lbs.

6. Install wiring protector, switch actuator arm and screw and **torque** to 20 inch lbs.
7. Install hazard knob assembly, multi-function lever, thrust washer, upper bearing spring and turn signal cancelling cam.
8. Install shaft lock and shaft lock retaining ring using compressor tool No. J 23653-C or equivalent, to depress shaft lock.
9. Install steering wheel and nut and **torque** to 30 ft. lbs.
10. Install horn lead and pad, then connect battery ground cable.

LOCK HOUSING COVER, COVER END CAP, PIVOT & PULSE SWITCH, IGNITION SWITCH ACTUATOR, UPPER BEARING, SWITCH ACTUATOR SECTOR, DIMMER & IGNITION SWITCH

Disassemble

1. Remove shaft lock, turn signal cancelling cam, upper bearing spring, upper bearing seat, inner race, turn signal switch, alarm assembly & lock cylinder set as previously described.
2. **On models equipped with cruise control,** remove housing cover end cap, disconnect multi-function lever connector and gently pull through shroud, bowl and cover and remove multi-function lever.
3. **On all models,** remove washer head screw, hex nut, dimmer switch and mounting stud.
4. Remove ignition switch, dimmer switch rod, cover screws and lock cover housing assembly.
5. Remove upper bearing retainer and gently pull pivot switch harness through gear shift bowl shroud and gear shift lever bowl.
6. Remove binding head cross recess screw, housing cover end cap and switch actuator pivot pin.
7. Remove pivot and pulse switch assembly, flat head cross recess screws and shift lever gate.
8. Remove ignition switch actuator assembly, spring and lock bolt assembly, spring thrust washer and rack preload spring.
9. Remove bearing retaining bushing and horn circuit contact.
10. Remove bearing assembly and switch actuator sector.

Assemble

1. Install switch actuator sector and bearing assembly.
2. Install bearing retaining bushing, horn circuit contact and rack preload spring.
3. Install ignition switch actuator assembly, spring and lock bolt assembly and spring thrust washer.
4. Install shift lever gate and **torque** screws to 44 inch lbs.
5. Install pivot and pulse switch assembly and switch actuator pivot pin.
6. **On models equipped with cruise**

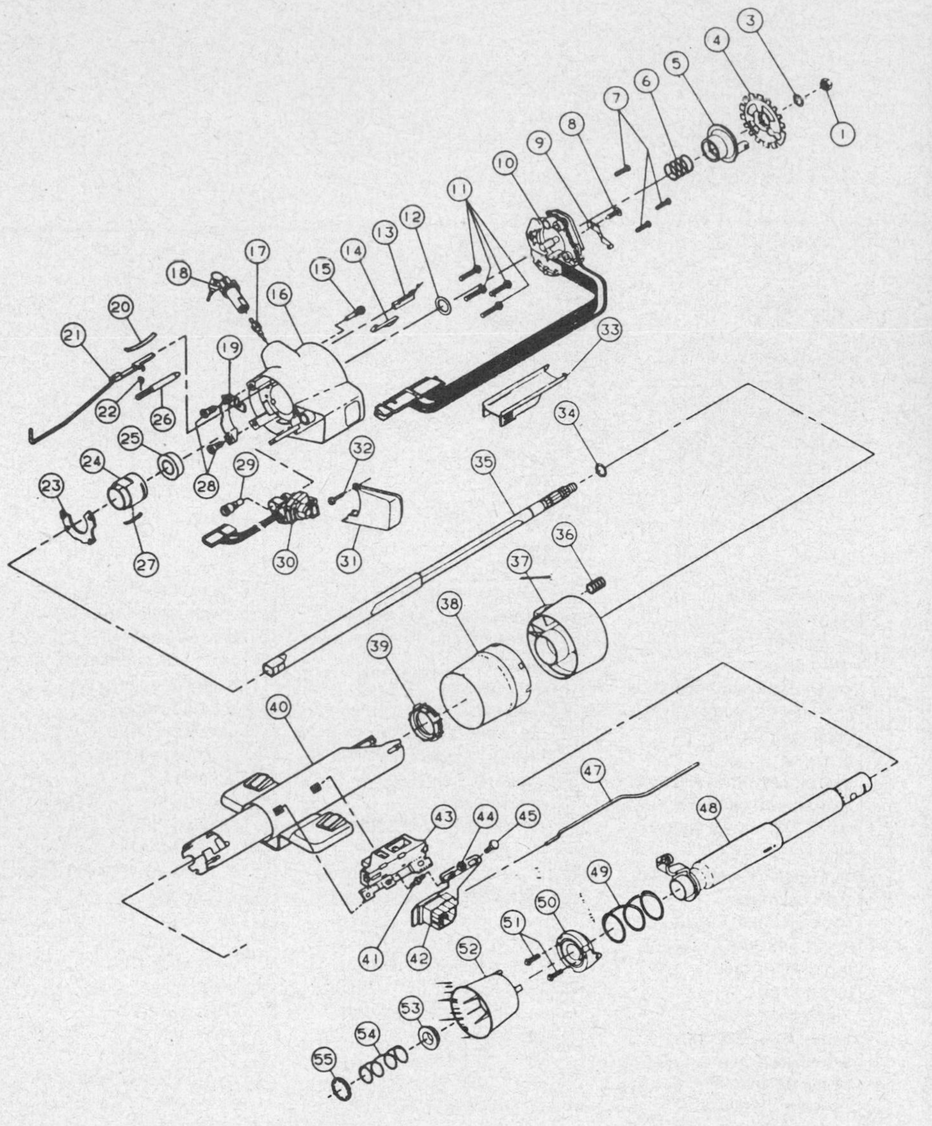

1	NUT, HEXAGON LOCKING (M14 × 1.5)	20	SPRING, RACK PRELOAD	38	SHROUD, GEARSHIFT BOWL
3	RING, RETAINING	21	ACTUATOR ASM, IGNITION SWITCH	39	BEARING, BOWL LOWER
4	LOCK, SHAFT	22	WASHER, SPRING THRUST	40	JACKET ASM, STRG COL
5	CAM ASM, TURN SIG CANCELLING	23	RETAINER, UPPER BEARING	41	STUD, DIMR & IGN SW MOUNTING
6	SPRING, UPPER BEARING	24	BUSHING, BEARING RETAINING	42	SWITCH ASM, DIMMER
7	SCREW, BINDING HD CROSS RECESS	25	BEARING ASM	43	SWITCH ASM, IGNITION
8	SCREW, RD WASH HD (M4.2 × 1.41)	26	BOLT ASM, SPRING &	44	NUT, HEXAGON (#10-24 × .25)
9	ARM, SIGNAL SWITCH	27	CONTACT, HORN CIRCUIT	45	SCREW, WASH HD (#10-24 × .25)
10	SWITCH ASM, TURN SIGNAL	28	SCREW, FLAT HEAD CROSS RECESS	47	ROD, DIMMER SWITCH
11	SCREW, HEX WASHER HD TAPPING	29	PIN, SWITCH ACTUATOR PIVOT	48	TUBE ASM, SHIFT
12	WASHER, THRUST	30	SWITCH ASM, PIVOT & (PULSE)	49	SPRING, LOWER BEARING
13	SWITCH ASM, BUZZER	31	CAP, COL HSG COVER END	50	BEARING ASM, ADAPTER &
14	CLIP, BUZZER SWITCH RETAINING	32	SCREW, BINDING HEAD CROSS RECESS	51	SCREW, HEX WASHER HD TAPPING
15	SCREW, LOCK RETAINING	33	PROTECTOR, WIRING	52	RETAINER, BEARING & SEAL
16	COVER ASM, LOCK HOUSING	34	RING, RETAINING	53	SEAT, LOWER BEARING
17	SECTOR, SWITCH ACTUATOR	35	SHAFT ASM, STEERING COLUMN	54	SPRING, SHIFT TUBE RETURN
18	LOCK CYLINDER SET, STRG COLUMN	36	SPRING, UPPER SHIFT LEVER	55	RETAINER, LOWER SPRING
19	GATE, SHIFT LEVER	37	BOWL, GEARSHIFT LEVER		

GC6049100095000X

Fig. 65 Exploded view of standard steering column. Century, Cutlass Ciera & Cutlass Cruiser

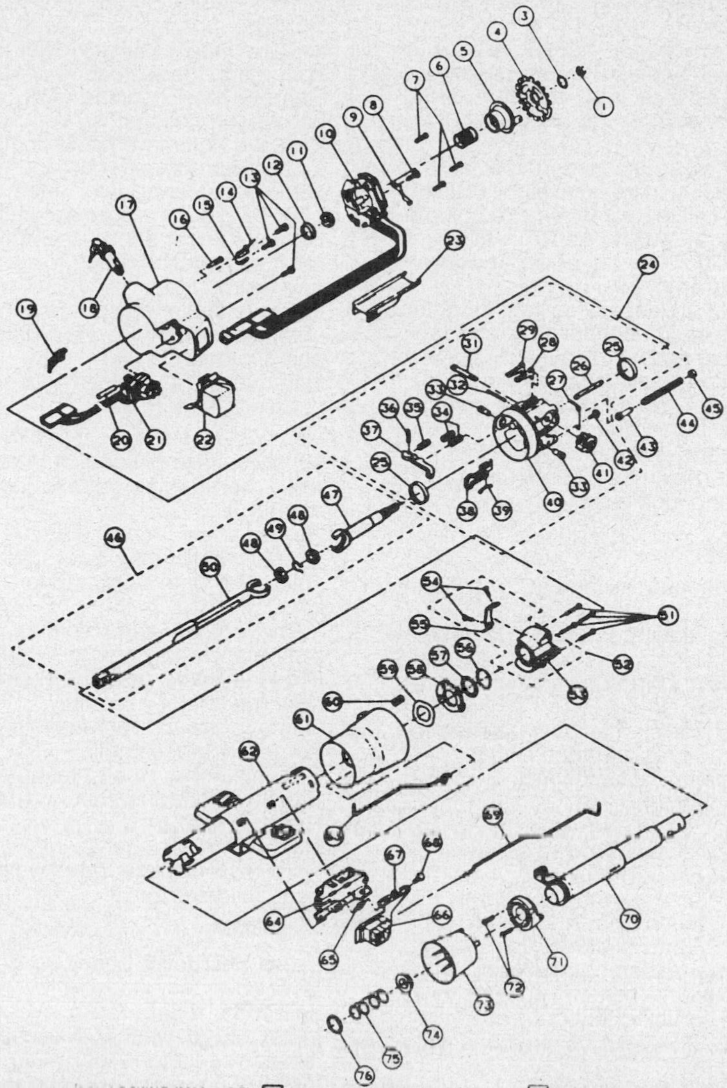

1	NUT, HEXAGON LOCKING (M14 × 1.5)	27	SPRING, LOCK BOLT	53	SUPPORT, STRG COL HSG
3	RING, RETAINING	28	SHOE, STEERING WHEEL LOCK	54	SCREW, OVAL HD CROSS RECESS
4	LOCK, SHAFT	29	SHOE, STEERING WHEEL LOCK	55	GATE, SHIFT LEVER
5	CAM ASM, TURN SIG CANCELLING	31	SHAFT, DRIVE	56	RING, SHIFT TUBE RETAINING
6	SPRING, UPPER BEARING	32	PIN, DOWEL	57	WASHER, THRUST
7	SCREW, BINDING HD CROSS RECESS	33	PIN, PIVOT	58	PLATE, LOCK
8	SCREW, RD WASH HD (M4.2 × 1.41)	34	SPRING, SHOE	59	WASHER, WAVE
9	ARM, SIGNAL SWITCH	35	SPRING, RELEASE LEVER	60	SPRING, SHIFT LEVER
10	SWITCH ASM, TURN SIGNAL	36	PIN, RELEASE LEVER	61	BOWL ASM, GEARSHIFT LEVER
11	SEAT, UPPER BEARING INNER RACE	37	LEVER, SHOE RELEASE	62	JACKET ASM, STRG COL
12	RACE, INNER	38	RACK, SWITCH ACTUATOR	63	ACTUATOR ASM, IGNITION SWITCH
13	SCREW, PAN HD 6-LOBED SOC TAP	39	SPRING, RACK PRELOAD	64	SWITCH ASM, IGNITION
14	SWITCH ASM, BUZZER	40	HOUSING, STRG COLUMN	65	STUD, DIMR & IGN SW MOUNTING
15	CLIP, BUZZER SWITCH RETAINING	41	SECTOR, SWITCH ACTUATOR	66	SWITCH ASM, DIMMER
16	SCREW, LOCK RETAINING	42	SCREW, HEX WASHER HEAD	67	NUT, HEXAGON (#10-24 × .25)
17	COVER ASM, LOCK HOUSING	43	GUIDE, SPRING	68	SCREW, WASH HD (#10-24 × .25)
18	LOCK CYLINDER SET, STRG COLUMN	44	SPRING, WHEEL TILT	69	ROD, DIMMER SWITCH
19	ACTUATOR, DIMMER SWITCH ROD	45	RETAINER, SPRING	70	TUBE ASM, SHIFT
20	PIN, SWITCH ACTUATOR PIVOT	46	SHAFT ASM, STEERING COLUMN	71	BEARING ASM, ADAPTER &
21	SWITCH ASM, PIVOT & (PULSE)	47	SHAFT ASM, RACE & UPPER	72	SCREW, HEX WASHER HD TAPPING
22	CAP, COL HSG COVER END	48	SPHERE, CENTERING	73	RETAINER, BEARING & SEAL
23	PROTECTOR, WIRING	49	SPRING, JOINT PRELOAD	74	SEAT, LOWER BEARING
24	HOUSING ASM, STRG COLUMN	50	SHAFT ASM, LOWER STEERING	75	SPRING, LOWER BEARING
25	BEARING ASM	51	SCREW, SUPPORT	76	RETAINER, LOWER SPRING
26	BOLT, LOCK	52	SUPPORT ASM, STRG COL HSG		

GC6049100096000X

Fig. 66 Exploded view of tilt steering column. Century, Cutlass Ciera & Cutlass Cruiser

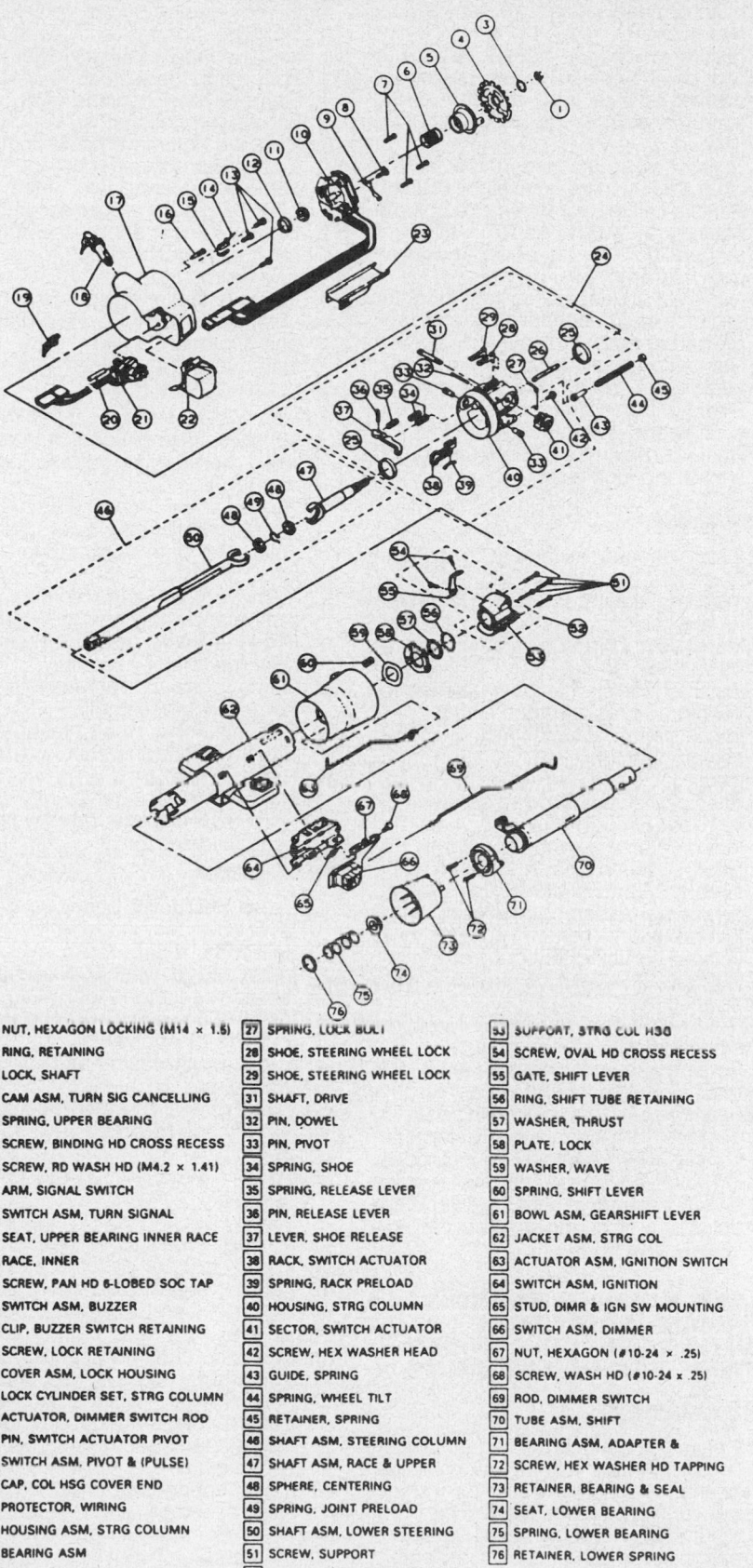

control, gently pull connector through cover assembly, bowl, and shroud and connect, then install multi-function lever.

7. **On all models,** install housing cover end cap and screw and **torque** screw to 18 inch lbs.
8. Gently pull pivot switch harness through bowl and shroud and connect.
9. Install upper bearing retainer, lock housing cover assembly and screws and **torque** screws to 97 inch lbs.
10. Install ignition switch and mounting stud and **torque** to 36 inch lbs.
11. Install dimmer switch rod, dimmer switch and hex nut and **torque** to 36 inch lbs.
12. Perform assembly steps for shaft lock, turn signal cancelling cam, upper bearing spring, upper bearing seat, inner race, turn signal switch, alarm assembly & lock cylinder set as previously described.

SHAFT, ADAPTER & BEARING, GEARSHIFT LEVER BOWL, SHIFT TUBE & BOWL LOWER BEARING

Disassemble

1. Disconnect battery ground cable.
2. Gently pull up on horn pad to remove and disconnect horn lead by pushing down and turning left to remove from cancelling cam tower.
3. Remove retainer, nut and steering wheel.
4. Remove column from vehicle.
5. Remove bearing and seal retainer, lower spring retainer, lower bearing spring and lower bearing seat.
6. Remove hex head screws, adapter and bearing assembly and shift tube return spring.
7. Remove column shaft assembly and check for accident damage.
8. Remove retaining ring, gearshift lever bowl and shroud.
9. Remove upper shift lever spring from bowl, shift tube assembly and bowl lower bearing.

Assemble

1. Install lower bowl bearing to jacket assembly and upper shift lever spring to bowl.
2. Install shift tube assembly, gearshift lever bowl and shroud.
3. Install shift tube return spring, adapter and bearing assembly, lubricating inner surface with lithium grease.
4. Install screws and **torque** to 27 inch lbs.
5. Install lower bearing seat, lower bearing spring, bearing and seal retainer.
6. Install steering wheel and **torque** nut to 30 ft. lbs.
7. Install retainer, horn lead and pad and connect battery ground cable.

TILT COLUMN

Refer to **Fig. 66.** when servicing this column.

SHAFT LOCK, TURN SIGNAL CANCEL CAM, UPPER, BEARING SPRING & SEAT, INNER RACE, TURN SIGNAL SWITCH, ALARM & LOCK CYLINDER SET

Refer to "Standard Column" for disassemble procedure.

LOCK HOUSING COVER, COVER END CAP, PIVOT & PULSE SWITCH, DIMMER SWITCH ROD ACTUATOR & TILT SPRING

Disassemble

1. Remove shaft lock, turn signal cancelling cam, upper bearing spring, upper bearing seat, inner race, turn signal switch, alarm assembly & lock cylinder set as previously described.
2. **On models equipped with cruise control,** remove housing cover end cap, unplug connector and gently pull through bowl assembly, then remove multi-function lever.
3. **On all models,** remove cover screws and lock housing cover assembly.
4. Remove tilt lever, cover end cap and dimmer switch rod actuator.
5. Gently pull pivot switch harness through bowl assembly and column housing.
6. Remove pivot pin, pivot and pulse switch assembly, spring retainer, spring and spring guide.

Assemble

1. Install spring guide and spring coated with lithium grease.
2. Install spring retainer, pivot and pulse switch assembly and pivot pin.
3. Feed pivot and pulse switch assembly harness through column housing and bowl assembly and connect.
4. Install dimmer switch rod actuator to cover end cap.
5. Install cover end cap to lock housing cover assembly. Bottom edge of dimmer switch rod actuator should rest on bend in dimmer switch rod.
6. Install lock housing cover assembly.
7. **On models equipped with cruise control,** gently pull connector through column housing and bowl assembly and connect, then install multi-function lever.
8. **On all models,** install lock housing cover assembly screws and **torque** to 80 inch lbs. Screw in the 12 o'clock position first, 8 o'clock position second and the 4 o'clock position last.
9. Perform assembly steps for shaft lock, turn signal cancelling cam, upper bearing spring, upper bearing seat, inner race, turn signal switch, alarm assembly & lock cylinder set as previously described.

COLUMN HOUSING, LOCK SHOES, ACTUATOR SECTOR, SWITCH ACTUATOR RACK, BEARINGS & LOCK BOLT

Disassemble

1. Remove shaft lock, turn signal cancelling cam, upper bearing spring, upper bearing seat, inner race, turn signal switch, alarm assembly & lock cylinder set, lock housing cover, cover end cap, pivot & pulse switch assembly, dimmer switch rod actuator & tilt spring assembly as previously described.
2. Remove pivot pins using special tool No. J 21854-01 or equivalent, **Fig. 49.**
3. Reinstall tilt lever and remove column housing by pulling back on tilt lever and pulling housing down and away from column.
4. Remove driveshaft, switch actuator sector, switch actuator rack and rack preload spring.
5. Remove release lever pin, shoe release lever and release lever spring.
6. Remove dowel pin, lock shoes, shoe springs and bearing assembly.
7. Remove hex head screw, lock bolt spring and lock bolt.

Assemble

1. Install bearing assembly to column housing.
2. Install driveshaft, switch actuator sector and lock shoes.
3. Install dowel pin, shoe springs and release lever spring.
4. Install shoe release lever, release lever pin and rack preload spring.
5. Install switch actuator rack to switch actuator sector.
6. Install lock bolt, lock bolt spring and hex head screw. **Torque** screw to 37 inch lbs.
7. Install column housing to column. Position column housing and align switch actuator rack with pin on end of actuator assembly. pull back on tilt lever, pushing column housing onto column housing support assembly. Release tilt lever to lock shoes onto dowel pins.
8. Remove tilt lever and install pivot pins lubricated with lithium grease.
9. Perform assembly steps for shaft lock, turn signal cancelling cam, upper bearing spring, upper bearing seat, inner race, turn signal switch, alarm assembly & lock cylinder set, lock housing cover, cover end cap, pivot & pulse switch assembly, dimmer switch rod actuator & tilt spring assembly as previously described.

SHAFT, COLUMN HOUSING SUPPORT, SHIFT TUBE, IGNITION SWITCH, DIMMER SWITCH & LOWER BEARING

Disassemble

1. Remove shaft lock, turn signal cancelling cam, upper bearing spring, upper bearing seat, inner race, turn signal switch, alarm assembly & lock cylinder set, lock housing cover, cover end cap, pivot & pulse switch assembly, dimmer switch rod actuator & tilt spring assembly, column housing, lock shoes, actuator sector assembly, switch actuator rack, bearings & lock bolt assembly as previously described.
2. Remove column from vehicle.
3. Remove bearing and seal retainer, lower spring retainer, lower bearing spring and lower bearing seat.
4. Remove hex head screws, adapter and bearing assembly.
5. Remove column shaft assembly and inspect for accident damage.
6. Mark upper and lower shaft assemblies to ensure proper assembly.
7. Remove upper shaft assembly, lower shaft assembly. Tilt 90° to each other and disengage.
8. Remove centering sphere from upper shaft assembly. Rotate sphere 90° and slip out.
9. Remove joint preload spring from centering sphere.
10. Remove screws, column housing support assembly and dimmer switch rod from steering column jacket assembly.
11. Remove rod from column housing support assembly and screws and shift lever gate from support assembly.
12. Remove hex nut, screw, dimmer switch assembly and mounting stud.
13. Remove ignition switch assembly and switch actuator assembly.
14. Remove switch actuator assembly from switch assembly.
15. Remove shift tube retaining ring, thrust washer and shift lever spring.
16. Remove shift tube using special tool No. J 23072 or equivalent.
17. Remove lock plate, wave washer and gearshift lever bowl.

Assemble

1. Install shift lever spring to gear shift lever bowl and gear shift lever bowl to shift tube jacket.
2. Install wave washer lubricated with lithium grease and lock plate.
3. Install shift tube using special tool No. J 23073 or equivalent.
4. Install thrust washer and shift tube retaining ring.
5. Install gate and screws to support assembly and **torque** screws to 27 inch lbs.
6. Install dimmer switch rod to support assembly.
7. Install column support assembly and **torque** screws to 80 inch lbs.
8. Install actuator assembly to track in housing support assembly.
9. Install joint preload spring to centering sphere.
10. Lubricate centering sphere with lithium grease and slip into upper shaft assembly and rotate 90°.
11. Ensure marks made on upper and lower shaft assemblies line up after assembling.
12. Install upper shaft assembly to lower shaft assembly, line up marks and tilt assemblies 90° to each other.
13. Install column shaft assembly lubricated with lithium grease to jacket assembly.
14. Perform assembling steps for shaft lock, turn signal cancelling cam, upper bearing spring, upper bearing seat, inner race, turn signal switch, alarm as-

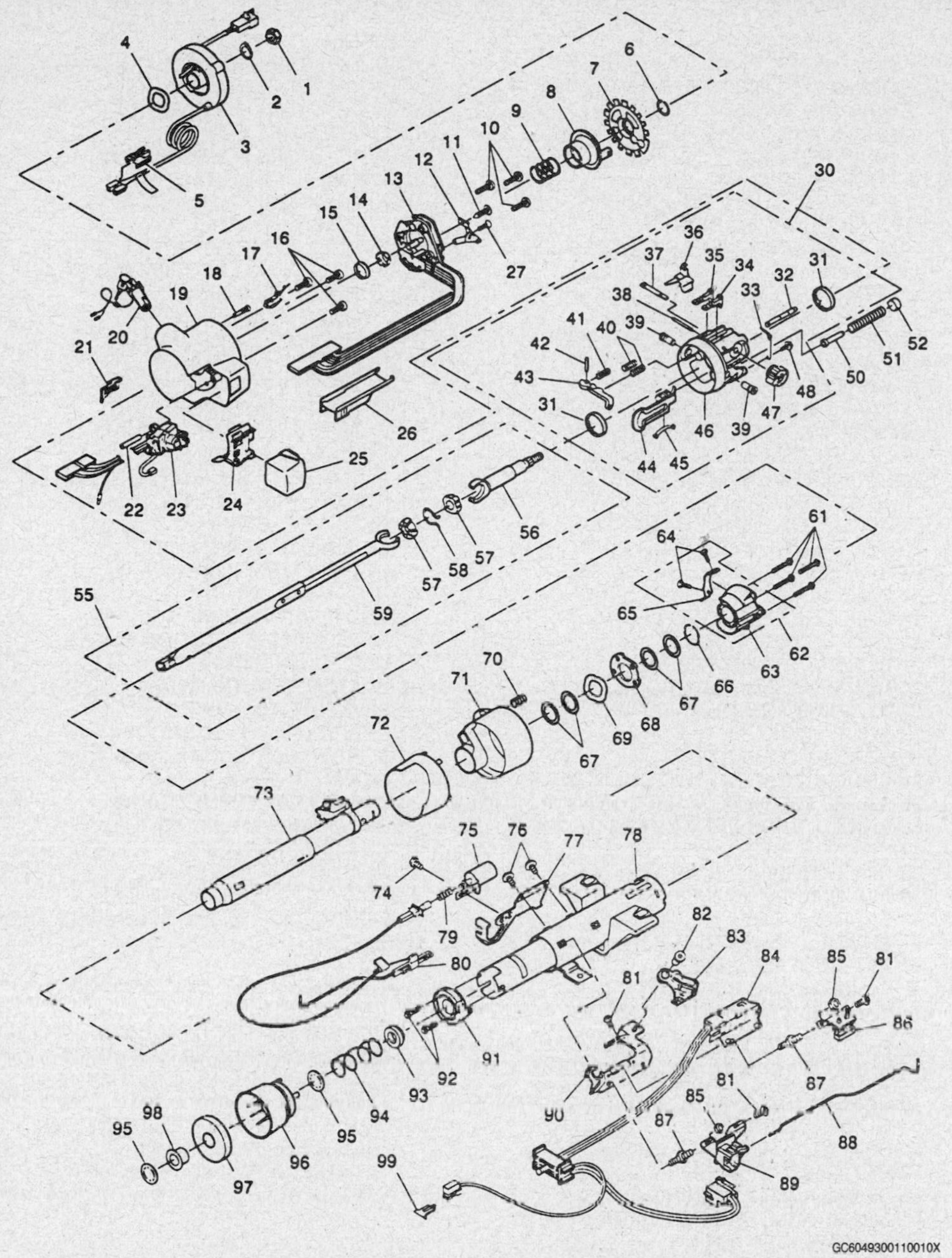
GC60493001100I0X

Fig. 67 Exploded view of column shift tilt steering column (Part 1 of 2). 1993–94 Eldorado & Seville

sembly & lock cylinder set, lock housing cover, cover end cap, pivot & pulse switch assembly, dimmer switch rod actuator & tilt spring assembly, column housing, lock shoes, actuator sector assembly, switch actuator rack, bearings & lock bolt assembly as previously described.

15. Install adapter and bearing assembly and lubricate inner surface with lithium grease.
16. Install screws and **torque** to 27 inch lbs.
17. Install lower bearing seat, lower bearing spring, lower spring retainer, bearing and seal retainer.
18. Install ignition switch assembly and mounting stud and **torque** to 36 inch lbs.
19. Install dimmer switch assembly, screw and nut and **torque** to 36 inch lbs.
20. Install column into vehicle.

1993–94 Eldorado & Seville

The steering wheel must be straight and the column in the Lock position. **Care must be taken when handling column with a live inflator module. Never point bag deploy surface toward you, and never stand column on steering wheel. Accidental deployment in these positions may cause injury. Always face bag deploy surface toward open space to allow for unrestricted expansion.**

Refer to **Figs. 67 and 68** for steering column service procedures.

UPPER COLUMN

The upper column consists of the following components: air bag coil assembly, shaft lock, turn signal cancelling cam assembly, upper bearing spring, upper bearing inner race seat, inner race, turn signal switch assembly, buzzer switch assembly and the steering column pass key lock cylinder set.

Disassemble

1. Remove inflator module and steering wheel as described in the appropriate "Electrical" section, then remove column from vehicle as described under "Steering Column, Replace.".
2. Remove coil assembly retaining ring, then the coil assembly.
3. Remove wave washer, then using removal tool No. J 23653-C or equivalent, to push down shaft lock, remove shaft lock retaining ring.
4. Remove shaft lock, then the turn signal cancelling cam assembly.
5. Remove upper bearing spring and upper bearing inner race seat.
6. Remove inner race, then move turn signal to Right Turn position (up).
7. Remove multi-function lever and hazard knob assembly.
8. Remove signal switch arm, then the turn signal switch screws.
9. Remove turn signal switch assembly as follows:
   a. Disconnect turn signal switch connector from the bulkhead connector.
   b. Remove wiring protector.
   c. Gently pull wire harness through column.
10. **Coil assembly will become uncentered if the steering column is separated from the steering gear and is allowed to rotate; or if the centering spring is pushed down, letting the hub rotate while the coil is removed from the steering column.**
11. Remove inflatable restraint coil assembly with wire harness from the coil assembly as follows:
    a. Remove the coil terminal from the vehicle harness.
    b. Remove yellow connector shroud from the black terminal connector.
    c. Remove wiring protector.
    d. Attach a length of mechanics wire to the coil terminal connector to aid in assembling.
    e. Gently pull wire through column.
12. Remove key from pass key lock cylinder set, **Fig. 69.**
13. Remove buzzer switch assembly, then reinsert key in pass key in lock cylinder. Ensure key is in Lock position.
14. Remove lock retaining screw, then remove pass key lock cylinder and harness as follows:
    a. Disconnect pivot switch connector from bulkhead connector and remove 13-way secondary lock.
    b. Disconnect two terminals of pass key wire harness from cavities 12 and 13 of switch connector.
    c. Remove wiring protector, then at-

tach a piece of mechanics wire to terminal to aid in assembling.
   d. Remove retaining clip from housing cover and gently pull wire harness through column.

Assemble

Route wire from pass key lock cylinder as shown in **Fig. 70,** and snap retaining clip into hole in housing. **Failure to do so may result in component damage or malfunction of pass key lock cylinder.**

1. Install pass key lock cylinder as follows:
   a. Install wire terminal through column and snap retaining clip into hole in housing.
   b. Connect two terminals of pass key wire harness to cavities 12 and 13 of pivot switch connector.
   c. Attach 13-way secondary lock to switch connector.
   d. Connect switch connector to bulkhead connector.
2. Install lock retaining screw. **Torque** to 22 inch lbs.
3. Install key from pass key lock cylinder set. Install buzzer switch assembly.
4. Reinstall key in pass key lock cylinder set. Ensure key is in Lock position.
5. Install turn signal switch assembly wire harness through steering column. Let switch hang freely and connect switch electrical connector to bulkhead connector.
6. Install coil assembly wire harness through column. Let coil hang freely, then connect yellow connector shroud to black terminal connector and connect to the vehicle harness.
7. Install turn signal switch assembly and screw. **Torque** screw to 30 inch lbs.
8. Install signal switch arm and screws. **Torque** screws to 20 inch lbs.
9. Install hazard knob assembly and multi-function lever.
10. Install inner race, upper bearing inner race seat and the upper bearing spring.
11. Install turn signal cancelling cam assembly. Lubricate with synthetic grease.
12. Install shaft lock.
13. Install new shaft lock retaining ring using installation tool No. J 23653-C or equivalent, to push down shaft lock. **Ring must be firmly seated in groove on shaft.**
14. Set steering shaft so block tooth on upper steering shaft is at the 12 o'clock position and the wheels are facing straight ahead. Set ignition switch to Lock position to ensure no damage occurs to the coil assembly.
15. Install wave washer.
16. **SIR coil assembly wires must be kept tight with no slack while installing SIR coil assembly. Failure to do so may cause wires to be kinked near the shaft lock area and cut when the steering wheel is turned.**
17. Ensure coil assembly is centered as follows:
   a. Remove coil assembly.

1-NUT, HEX LOCKING (M14x1.5)
2-RING, RETAINING
3-COIL ASM, INFL RESTRAINT
4-WASHER, WAVE
5-SHROUD, CONNECTOR
6-RING, RETAINING
7-LOCK, SHAFT
8-CAM ASM, TURN SIG CANCEL
9-SPRING, UPPER BEARING
10-SCREW, BNDG HD CR RECESS
11-SCREW, RD WASH HD (M4.2x1.41)
12-ARM ASM, SIGNAL SWITCH
13-SWITCH ASM, TURN SIGNAL
14-SEAT, UPPER BRG INNER RACE
15-RACE, INNER
16-SCREW, PAN HD SOC TAP
17-SWITCH ASM, BUZZER
18-SCREW, LOCK RETAINING
19-COVER ASM, LOCK HOUSING
20-LOCK CYLINDER SET, STRG COL PASS KEY
21-ACTUATOR, DIMMER SW ROD
22-PIN, SWITCH ACTUATOR PIVOT
23-SWITCH ASM, PIVOT & (PULSE)
24-BASE PLATE, COL HSG CVR END
25-CAP, COL HSG COVER END
26-PROTECTOR, WIRING
27-SCREW, FLT HD TAPPING
30-HOUSING ASM, STRG COLUMN
31-BEARING ASM
32-BOLT, LOCK
33-SPRING, LOCK BOLT
34-SHOE, STEERING WHEEL LOCK
35-SHOE, STEERING WHEEL LOCK
36-SHIELD, WIRE PROTECTOR
37-SHAFT, DRIVE
38-PIN, DOWEL
39-PIN, PIVOT
40-SPRING, SHOE
41-SPRING, RELEASE LEVER
42-PIN, RELEASE LEVER
43-LEVER, SHOE RELEASE
44-RACK, SWITCH ACTUATOR
45-SPRING, RACK PRELOAD
46-HOUSING, STRG COLUMN
47-SECTOR, SWITCH ACTUATOR
48-SCREW, HEX WASHER HEAD
50-GUIDE, SPRING
51-SPRING, WHEEL TILT
52-RETAINER, SPRING
55-SHAFT ASM, STEERING
56-SHAFT ASM, RACE & UPPER
57-SPHERE, CENTERING
58-SPRING, JOINT PRELOAD
59-SHAFT ASM, LOWER STEERING
61-SCREW, SUPPORT
62-SUPPORT ASM, STRG COL HSG
63-SUPPORT, STRG COL HSG
64-SCREW, OVL HD CROSS RECESS
65-GATE, SHIFT LEVER
66-RING, SHIFT TUBE RETAINING
67-WASHER, THRUST
68-PLATE, LOCK
69-WASHER, WAVE
70-SPRING, SHIFT LEVER
71-BOWL ASM, GEARSHIFT LEVER
72-SHROUD, GEARSHIFT BOWL
73-TUBE ASM, SHIFT
74-SCREW, WASH HD (#10-24X.25)
75-SOLENOID ASM, INTERLOCK
76-SCREW, HEX WASH HD (#10-24X.25)
77-BRACKET, SOLENOID
78-JACKET ASM, STRG COL
79-SPRING, BALL JOINT
80-ACTUATOR ASM, IGNITION SWITCH
81-SCREW, PAN HD SOC
82-RETAINER, CAM
83-CAM ASM, CABLE SHIFT
84-SWITCH ASM, IGNITION
85-NUT, HEXAGON
86-ADJUSTER ASM, PRNDL
87-STUD, DIMR & IGNITION SW MTG
88-ROD, DIMMER SWITCH
89-SWITCH ASM, DIMMER
90-BRACKET ASM, STUD &
91-BEARING ASM, ADAPTER &
92-SCREW, HEX WASHER HD TAP
93-SEAT, LOWER BEARING
94-SPRING, LOWER BEARING
95-RETAINER, LOWER SPRING
96-RETAINER, BEARING
97-SEAL, STEERING SHAFT
98-BUSHING, SEAL RETAINING
99-CONNECTOR, POS ASSURANCE TER

Service Kits

201-RACK SERV KIT, COL SECTOR & -INCLUDES: 15,31,33,44,47,48
202-SPRING SERV KIT, TILT COLUMN -INCLUDES: 14,15,39,50,51,52
203-COIL SERV KIT, INFL RESTRINT -INCLUDES: 3,4,5
204-SPHERE SERV KIT, TILT COLUMN -INCLUDES: 57,58
205-GREASE SERV KIT, (SYNTHETIC)

GC6049300110020X

Fig. 67 Exploded view of column shift tilt steering column (Part 2 of 2). 1993–94 Eldorado & Seville

   b. Hold coil assembly with clear bottom up to see coil ribbon.
   c. There are two different styles of coils. One rotates clockwise and the other rotates counterclockwise.
   d. While holding coil assembly, depress spring lock to rotate hub in direction of arrow shown in **Fig. 71,** until is stops.
   e. The coil ribbon should be wound up tight against the center hub.
   f. Rotate coil hub in opposite direction approximately 2 1/2 turns. Release spring lock between locking tabs in front of arrow, **Fig. 71.**
18. Install coil assembly as follows:
   a. Pull wire tight while positioning SIR coil to the steering shaft.
   b. Align opening in coil with horn tower and "locating bump" between two tabs on housing cover, **Fig. 72.**
   c. Seat coil assembly into steering column.
19. Install coil assembly retaining ring. **Ring must be firmly seated in groove on shaft.**
20. Gently pull lower coil assembly, turn signal, pass key, and pivot wires to remove any wire kinks that may be inside steering column assembly. Failure to do so may cause damage to wire harness.
21. Install wiring protector.
22. Install steering wheel.

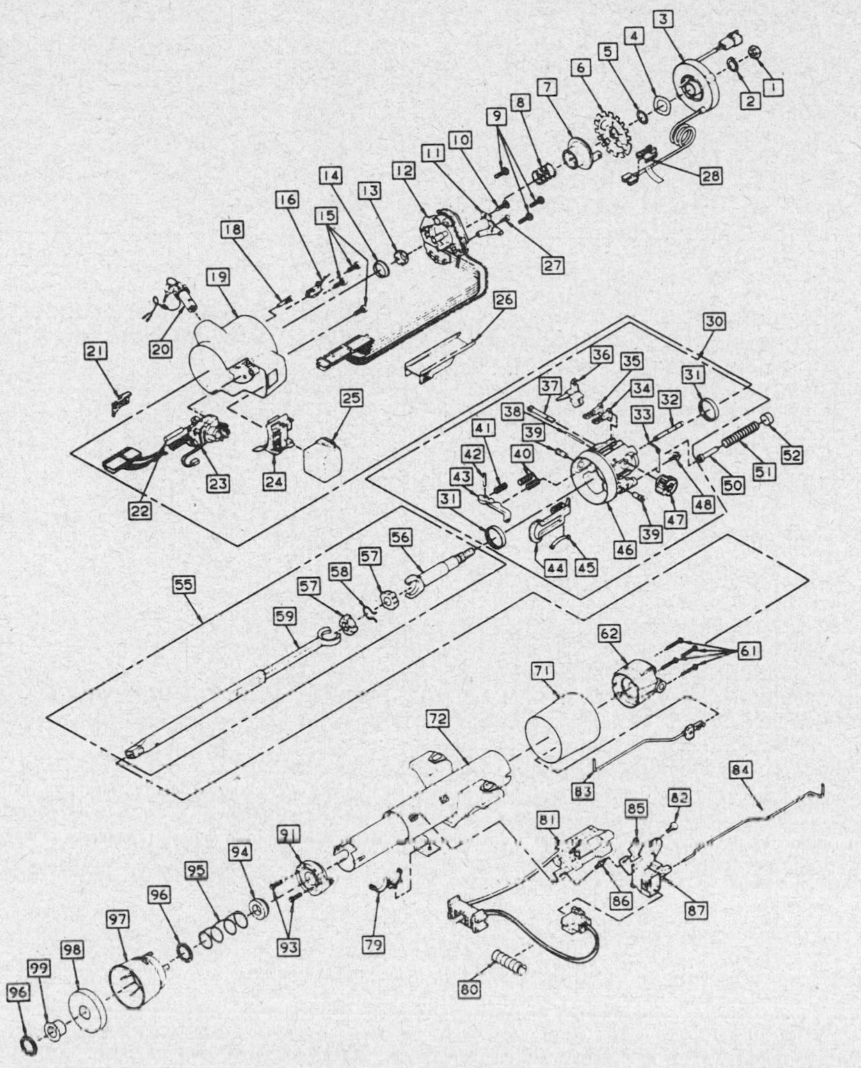

GC6049300111010X

Fig. 68 Exploded view of console shift tilt steering column (Part 1 of 2). 1993–94 Eldorado & Seville

HOUSING COVER

The housing cover consists of the following components: lock housing cover assembly, column housing cover end cap, pivot & pulse switch assembly, dimmer switch rod actuator and the tilt spring assembly.

Disassemble

1. Remove upper column as described under "Upper Column" disassembling procedures.
2. Remove housing end cap.
3. Remove cruise control and multi-function lever connectors from base plate and disconnect.
4. Remove multi-function lever.
5. Remove cover screws, then remove the tilt lever.
6. Remove lock housing cover assembly.
7. Remove base plate and dimmer switch rod actuator.
8. Remove switch actuator pivot pin, then the pivot and pulse switch assembly as follows:
   a. Allow switch to hang freely if removal is not required.
   b. Disconnect pivot and switch connector from bulkhead connector.
   c. Gently pull wire harness through column.
9. Remove spring retainer, spring and spring guide.

Assemble

1. Install spring guide and spring. Lubricate with lithium grease.
2. Using a cross recess screwdriver, push spring retainer down and turn clockwise to lock in place.
3. Install pivot and switch assembly to lock housing cover assembly.
4. Connect switch actuator pivot pin to switch and cover.
5. Pull pivot and switch assembly wire harness through steering column. Connect switch connector to bulkhead connector.
6. Install dimmer switch rod actuator to base plate. Lubricate with lithium grease.
7. Install base plate to lock housing cover assembly. Bottom edge of dimmer switch rod actuator must rest on bend in dimmer switch rod.
8. Install lock housing cover assembly.
9. Install screws. Tighten screw in 12 o'clock position first, 8 o'clock position second, and the screw in the 3 o'clock position last. **Torque** screws in same order to 80 inch lbs.
10. Connect multi-function lever and cruise control connectors together and mount on base plate.
11. Install housing cover end cap.
12. Assemble remainder of steering column as described under "Upper Column" assembling procedure.

MID COLUMN

The mid column consists of the following components: steering column housing assembly, steering wheel lock shoe, switch actuator sector, switch actuator rack, bearing assembly, lock bolt, steering column housing support assembly, steering shaft assembly and the shift tube assembly.

Disassemble

1. Disconnect battery ground cable, then remove steering column from vehicle as described under "Steering Column, Replace."
2. Perform all disassembling steps described under "Housing Cover."
3. Remove pivot pins using pivot pin removal tool No. J 21854-01 or equivalent. Reinstall tilt lever.
4. Remove steering column housing assembly. Pull back on tilt lever and pull steering column housing assembly down and away from column.
5. Remove the following components to disassemble the steering column housing assembly:
   a. Bearing assembly.
   b. Wire abrasion shield.
   c. Hex head screw.
   d. Lock bolt spring.
   e. Lock bolt.
   f. Switch actuator rack and rack preload spring.
   g. Driveshaft.
   h. Switch actuator sector.
   i. Release lever pin using lock shoe and release lever pin tool No. J 22635 or equivalent.
   j. Shoe release lever.
   k. Release lever spring.
   l. Dowel pin using lock show and release lever pin tool No. J 22635 or equivalent.
   m. Lock shoes and shoe springs.
6. Remove lower spring retainer.
7. Remove bearing and seal retainer.
8. Remove lower spring retainer.
9. Remove lower bearing spring and lower bearing seat.
10. Remove hex head bolts, then the adapter and bearing assembly.
11. Remove steering column shaft assembly.
12. Mark upper shaft assembly and lower steering shaft assembly to ensure proper assembly. Failure to assemble properly will cause steering wheel to

1-NUT, HEX LOCKING (M14x1.5)
2-RING, RETAINING
3-COIL ASM, INFL RESTRAINT
4-WASHER, WAVE
5-RING, RETAINING
6-LOCK, SHAFT
7-CAM ASM, TURN SIG CANCEL
8-SPRING, UPPER BEARING
9-SCREW, BNDG HD CR RECESS
10-SCREW, RD WASH HD (M4.2x1.41)
11-ARM ASM, SIGNAL SWITCH
12-SWITCH ASM, TURN SIGNAL
13-SEAT, UPPER BRG INNER RACE
14-RACE, INNER
15-SCREW, PAN HD SOC TAP
16-SWITCH ASM, BUZZER
18-SCREW, LOCK RETAINING
19-COVER ASM, LOCK HOUSING
20-LOCK CYLINDER SET, STRG COL PASS KEY
21-ACTUATOR, DIMMER SW ROD
22-PIN, SWITCH ACTUATOR PIVOT
23-SWITCH ASM, PIVOT & (PULSE)
24-BASE PLATE, COL HSG CVR END
25-CAP, COL HSG COVER END
26-PROTECTOR, WIRING
27-SCREW, FLT HD TAPPING
28-SHROUD, CONNECTOR
30-HOUSING ASM, STRG COLUMN
31-BEARING ASM
32-BOLT, LOCK
33-SPRING, LOCK BOLT
34-SHOE, STEERING WHEEL LOCK
35-SHOE, STEERING WHEEL LOCK
36-SHIELD, WIRE PROTECTOR
37-SHAFT, DRIVE
38-PIN, DOWEL
39-PIN, PIVOT
40-SPRING, SHOE
41-SPRING, RELEASE LEVER
42-PIN, RELEASE LEVER
43-LEVER, SHOE RELEASE
44-RACK, SWITCH ACTUATOR
45-SPRING, RACK PRELOAD
46-HOUSING, STRG COLUMN
47-SECTOR, SWITCH ACTUATOR
48-SCREW, HEX WASHER HEAD
50-GUIDE, SPRING
51-SPRING, WHEEL TILT
52-RETAINER, SPRING
55-SHAFT ASM, STEERING
56-SHAFT ASM, RACE & UPPER
57-SPHERE, CENTERING
58-SPRING, JOINT PRELOAD
59-SHAFT ASM, LOWER STEERING
61-SCREW, SUPPORT
62-SUPPORT ASM, STRG COL HSG
71-SHROUD, STRG COL HSG
72-JACKET ASM, STRG COL
79-CLIP, CONVOLUTED CONDUIT
80-CONDUIT, CONVOLUTED
81-SWITCH ASM, IGNITION
82-SCREW, WASH HD (#10-24X.25)
83-ACTUATOR ASM, IGNITION SWITCH
84-ROD, DIMMER SWITCH
85-NUT, HEXAGON (#10-24)
86-STUD, DIMR & IGNITION SW MTG
87-SWITCH ASM, DIMMER
91-BEARING ASM, ADAPTER &
93-SCREW, HEX WASHER HD TAP
94-SEAT, LOWER BEARING
95-SPRING, LOWER BEARING
96-RETAINER, LOWER SPRING
97-RETAINER, BEARING
98-SEAL, STEERING SHAFT
99-BUSHING, SEAL RETAINING

Service Kits

201-RACK SERV KIT, COL SECTOR & -INCLUDES: 14,31,33,44,47,48
202-SPRING SERV KIT, TILT COLUMN -INCLUDES: 13,14,39,50,51,52
203-COIL SERV KIT, INFL RESTRINT -INCLUDES: 3,4,28
204-SPHERE SERV KIT, TILT COLUMN -INCLUDES: 57,58
205-GREASE SERV KIT, (SYNTHETIC)

GC6049300111020X

Fig. 68 Exploded view of console shift tilt steering column (Part 2 of 2). 1993–94 Eldorado & Seville

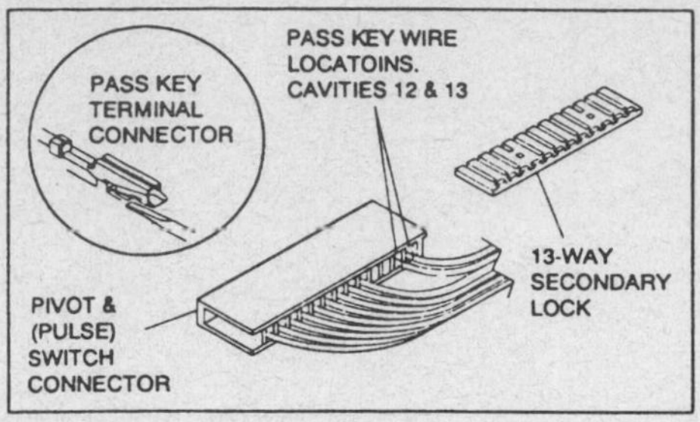
PASS KEY WIRE
LOCATOINS.
CAVITIES 12 & 13
PASS KEY
TERMINAL
CONNECTOR
13-WAY
SECONDARY
LOCK
PIVOT &
(PULSE)
SWITCH
CONNECTOR

GC6049300112000X

Fig. 69 Pass key wire connection locations. 1993–94 Eldorado & Seville

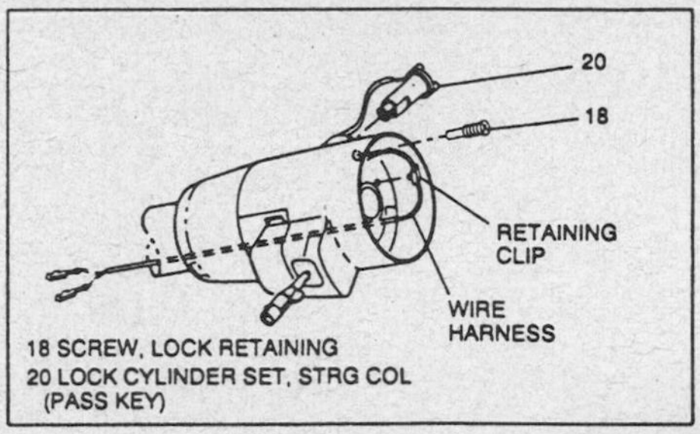
20
18
RETAINING
CLIP
WIRE
HARNESS
18 SCREW, LOCK RETAINING
20 LOCK CYLINDER SET, STRG COL
(PASS KEY)

GC6049300113000X

Fig. 70 Pass key wire installation. 1993–94 Eldorado, Fleetwood (RWD) & Seville

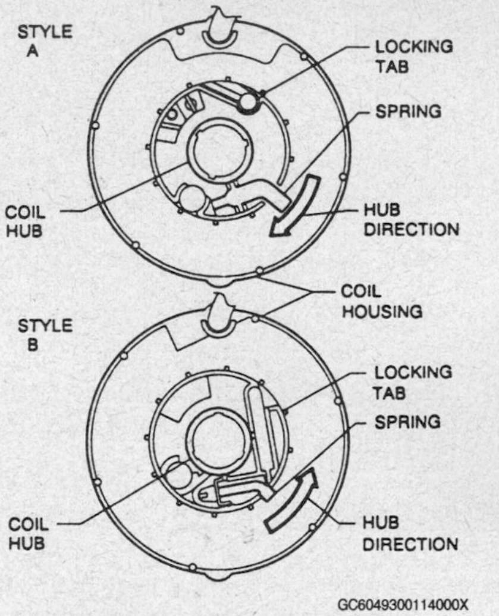
STYLE
A
LOCKING
TAB
SPRING
COIL
HUB
HUB
DIRECTION
COIL
HOUSING
STYLE
B
LOCKING
TAB
SPRING
COIL
HUB
HUB
DIRECTION

GC6049300114000X

Fig. 71 Coil assembly centering procedure. 1993–94 Eldorado, Fleetwood (RWD) & Seville

be turned 180°.

13. Disassemble steering column shaft assembly as follows:
    a. Separate upper shaft assembly from lower steering shaft assembly. Tilt 90° to each other and disengage.
    b. Separate centering sphere from upper shaft assembly by rotating sphere 90° and sliding out.
    c. Remove joint preload spring from centering sphere.
14. Remove support screws, then remove column housing support assembly with dimmer switch rod from the steering column jacket.
15. Remove oval head recess screws and shift lever gate from support.
16. Remove shift tube retaining ring, then the two thrust washers and the lock plate.
17. Remove wave washer and two thrust washers, then the gearshift lever bowl assembly with the gearshift bowl shroud and shift tube assembly.
18. Remove shroud from bowl.
19. Remove shift lever spring, then the shift tube from the bowl. Use a press is necessary.
20. Remove hex nut and pan head screw securing PRNDL adjuster assembly.
21. Remove PRNDL adjuster bracket and the dimmer switch assembly.
22. Remove dimmer and ignition switch mounting stud.
23. Remove ignition switch assembly from ignition switch actuator assembly.
24. Remove cam retainer.
25. Remove pan head screw and dimmer and ignition switch mounting stud.
26. Remove cable assembly with ignition switch actuator assembly as follows:
    a. Remove cable clip from upper location of steering column jacket assembly.
    b. Remove cable mounting clip from solenoid bracket.
    c. Remove ball joint socket from solenoid.
    d. Remove ball joint spring.

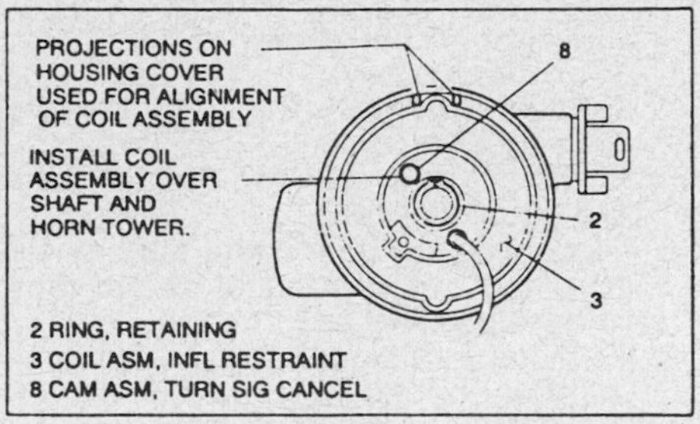
PROJECTIONS ON HOUSING COVER USED FOR ALIGNMENT OF COIL ASSEMBLY
INSTALL COIL ASSEMBLY OVER SHAFT AND HORN TOWER.
8
2
3
2 RING, RETAINING
3 COIL ASM, INFL RESTRAINT
8 CAM ASM, TURN SIG CANCEL
GC6049300115000X

Fig. 72 Coil assembly installation. 1993–94 Eldorado, Fleetwood (RWD) & Seville

27. Remove hex washer head screw securing interlock solenoid assembly and solenoid bracket to steering column jacket assembly.
28. Remove hex washer head screws securing solenoid bracket to steering column jacket assembly.

Assemble

1. Install solenoid bracket. **Torque** screws to 35 inch lbs.
2. Install interlock solenoid assembly, then finger tighten hex washer head screw.
3. Connect terminal connector to interlock solenoid assembly.
4. Install cable assembly with ignition switch actuator assembly, as follows:
   a. Install cable clip to upper location of jacket assembly.
   b. Allow lower cable to hang free.
5. Install stud and bracket assembly. **Torque** screw and stud to 35 inch lbs.
6. Install cable shift cam assembly and cam retainer. **Torque** retainer to 35 inch lbs.
7. Assemble gate and screws to support. **Torque** screws to 33 inch lbs.
8. Install dimmer switch rod to column housing support assembly.
9. Install support assembly and screws. **Torque** screws to 88 inch lbs.
10. Install shift tube lever spring to gearshift lever bowl assembly.
11. Attach bowl to shift tube assembly using shift tube installation tool No. J 23073-1 or equivalent.
12. Install gearshift bowl shroud to bowl.
13. Install shift tube with bowl to steering column jacket assembly.
14. Install two thrust washers and wave washer. Lubricate wave washer with lithium grease.
15. Install lock plate and two thrust washers.
16. Install shift tube retaining ring, then connect steering shaft assembly to jacket assembly.
17. Install tilt lever, then the column housing assembly to the column, as follows:
   a. Position column housing assembly and align switch actuator rack with pin on end of ignition switch actuator assembly.
   b. Pull back on tilt lever, pushing column housing assembly onto column housing support assembly.
   c. Release tilt lever to lock shoes and onto dowel pins.
   d. Remove tilt lever.
18. Install pivot pins. Lubricate with lithium grease, then press pin until firmly seated.
19. Install adapter and bearing assembly. Lubricate with lithium grease.
20. Install hex head screws. **Torque** to 30 inch lbs.
21. Install lower bearing seat and lower bearing spring. Press new lower spring retainer onto shaft to compress spring.
22. Measure distance from face of adapter and bearing assembly to lower spring retainer. Spring height must be 1.0 inch.
23. Install bearing and seal retainer, then the steering shaft seal.
24. Install seal retaining bushing and a new spring retainer.
25. Assemble remaining steering column components as described in the "Assemble" procedures.

Fleetwood (RWD)

Care must be taken when handling column with a live inflator module. Never point bag deploy surface toward you, and never stand column on steering wheel. Accidental deployment in these positions may cause injury. Always face bag deploy surface toward open space to allow for unrestricted expansion.

Refer to **Fig. 9** for steering column service procedures.

UPPER COLUMN

The upper column consists of the following components: Inflatable restraint coil assembly, shaft lock, turn signal cancelling cam assembly, upper bearing spring, upper bearing inner race seat, inner race, turn signal switch assembly, buzzer switch assembly and the steering column pass key lock cylinder set.

The steering wheel must be straight and the column in the Lock position.

Disassemble

1. Remove column from vehicle as described under "Steering Column, Replace."
2. Remove coil assembly retaining ring.
3. Remove inflatable restraint coil assembly, if required, as follows:
   a. Remove wave washer, then the shaft lock retaining ring using lock plate compressor tool No. J 23635-C or equivalent, to push down on shaft.
   b. Remove shaft lock, then the turn signal cancelling cam assembly.
   c. Remove upper bearing spring and the upper bearing race seat.
   d. Remove inner race, then place turn signal lever to "RIGHT TURN" position (up).
   e. Remove multi-function lever and hazard knob assembly.
   f. Remove screws and the signal switch arm.
   g. Remove turn signal switch mounting screws, then remove the turn signal switch assembly by removing the wiring protector and gently pulling wire harness through the column.
   h. Remove wiring protector, then attach a piece of mechanics wire to terminal connector harness to ease assembling.
   i. Gently pull wire through column and remove inflatable restraint coil assembly.
4. Remove key from pass key lock cylinder set.
5. Remove buzzer switch assembly, then reinsert key in pass key lock cylinder and move to Lock position.
6. Remove lock retaining screw, then remove pass key lock cylinder and harness as follows:
   a. Disconnect cylinder harness connector from vehicle wire harness.
   b. Remove wiring protector.
   c. Attach a piece of mechanics wire to terminals to ease in assembling.
   d. Gently pull wire harness through column.

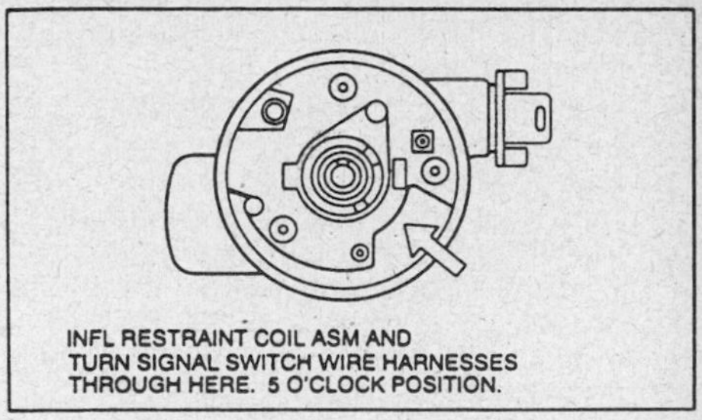
INFL RESTRAINT COIL ASM AND TURN SIGNAL SWITCH WIRE HARNESSES THROUGH HERE. 5 O'CLOCK POSITION.
GC6049300116000X

Fig. 73 Coil assembly wire installation. Fleetwood (RWD)

Assemble

1. Install pass key lock cylinder as follows:
   a. Route wire from pass key lock cylinder as shown in **Fig. 70,** and snap retaining clip into hole in housing. **Failure to do so may result in component damage or malfunction of pass key lock cylinder.**
   b. Pull wire terminals through column and snap retaining clip into hole in housing.
   c. Connect cylinder harness connector to vehicle wire harness.
2. Install lock retaining screw. **Torque** to 22 inch lbs.
3. Remove key from pass key lock cylinder set, install buzzer switch assembly, then reinsert key in pass key lock cylinder set. Ensure key is in Lock position.
4. Insert signal switch assembly wire harness through steering column. Allow switch to hang freely, then connect switch connector to vehicle wire harness.
5. Pull coil assembly wire harness through column, **Fig. 73.** Allow coil to hang freely.
6. Install turn signal switch assembly and mounting screws. **Torque** mounting screws to 30 inch lbs.

7. Install signal switch arm and screws. **Torque** screws to 20 inch lbs.
8. Install hazard knob assembly and multi-function lever.
9. Install inner race, upper bearing inner race seat and upper bearing spring.
10. Install turn signal cancelling cam assembly. Lubricate with synthetic grease.
11. Install shaft lock, then the new shaft lock retaining ring using lock plate compressor tool No. J 23653-C or equivalent, to push down shaft lock. **Retaining ring must be firmly seated in groove on shaft.**
12. Set steering shaft so block tooth on upper steering shaft is at the 12 o'clock position and the wheels are straight ahead, then set ignition switch to Lock position, to ensure no damage to coil assembly.
13. Install wave washer.
14. Coil assembly will become uncentered if the steering column is separated from the steering gear and is allowed to rotate, or if the centering spring is pushed down, allowing hub to rotate while coil is removed from column. If this occurs, center coil assembly by referring to **Fig. 71**, and performing the following:
    a. Ensure wheels are pointing straight ahead.
    b. Remove coil assembly.
    c. Hold coil assembly with clear bottom up to see coil ribbon.
    d. There are two different styles of coils, one rotates clockwise, the other rotates counterclockwise.
    e. While holding coil assembly, depress spring lock to rotate hub in direction of arrow, **Fig. 71**, until it stops.
    f. Coil ribbon should be wound up tightly against center hub.
    g. Rotate coil hub in opposite direction approximately 2 1/2 turns. Release spring lock between locking tabs in front of arrow.
15. If a new coil assembly is installed, assemble pre-centered coil assembly to steering column. Remove centering tab and dispose.
16. **SIR coil assembly wire must be kept tight with no slack while installing the coil assembly. failure to do so may cause wire to be kinked near shaft lock area and cut when the steering wheel is turned.**
17. Ensure coil assembly is centered. If not, perform procedure described in step 14
18. Install coil assembly as follows:
    a. Pull wire tight while positioning air bag coil to steering shaft.
    b. Align opening in coil with horn tower and "locating bump" between two tabs on housing cover, **Fig. 72.**
    c. Seat coil assembly into steering column.
19. Install coil assembly retaining ring. Ring must be firmly seated in groove on shaft.
20. Gently pull lower coil assembly, turn signal and pass key wires to remove any wire kinks that may be inside steering column assembly. Failure to do so may cause damage to wire harness.
21. Install wiring protector.

HOUSING COVER

Refer to the 1993-94 Eldorado & Seville "Housing Cover" assembling and disassembling procedures for housing cover service.

MID COLUMN

Refer to the 1993-94 Eldorado & Seville "Mid Column" assembling and disassembling procedures for mid column service.

ATTACHMENT PLATE, SENSOR & STEERING SHAFT BUSHING

Disassemble

1. Remove steering column from vehicle as described under "Steering Column, Replace."
2. Remove lower bearing adapter clip, then the sensor assembly.
3. Remove bearing adapter retainer, then the steering shaft bushing assembly.

Assemble

1. Assemble steering shaft bushing assembly to jacket assembly. Lubricate inner surface of bushing with lithium grease.
2. Install bearing adapter retainer, then the sensor assembly.
3. Install lower bearing adapter clip.

Caprice, Custom Cruiser, Impala SS & Roadmaster

STANDARD COLUMN

INFLATOR MODULE, STEERING WHEEL COIL, SHAFT LOCK, CANCELLING CAM, UPPER BEARING SPRING & SEAT, INNER RACE, TURN SIGNAL SWITCH, BUZZER SWITCH & LOCK CYLINDER SET

Disassemble

Refer to **Fig. 74** for exploded view of steering column.

With steering column, inflator module and steering wheel already removed as previously outlined in "Steering Column, Replace," proceed as follows:

1. Place key in "lock" position.
2. Remove coil assembly retaining ring, slide coil assembly off end of shaft, then remove wave washer.
3. Remove shaft lock retaining ring using compressor tool No. J 23653-C or equivalent, to depress shaft lock. **Use a 1/2 inch wrench to hold the shaft of tool J 23653 or equivalent when releasing the nut. Failure to do so may cause tool to fly off the steering column causing personal injury.**
4. Remove shaft lock, then the turn signal cancelling cam.
5. Remove upper bearing spring, then the thrust washer.
6. Place turn signal in "right turn" position, then remove signal switch arm attaching screw and the arm.
7. Remove turn signal switch attaching screws and position switch out of way. If it is necessary to remove switch, remove wiring harness protector and hazard knob, then gently pull wire harness through gear shift lever bowl, column housing and lock housing cover.
8. If necessary remove coil assembly as follows:
    a. Remove connector from terminal connector.
    b. Remove wire protector, then attach a wire to the coil assembly connector at the base of the steering column.
    c. Pull wire through lock housing cover and gearshift bowl shroud.
9. Remove key from cylinder lock, and remove buzzer switch and clip, then reinsert key in cylinder lock and turn to "lock" position.
10. Remove lock retaining screw and lock cylinder set.

Assemble

1. Install lock cylinder set, **torque** retaining screw to 22 inch lbs.
2. Place key in "run" position, then install buzzer switch and clip.
3. Route turn signal switch wiring harness through lock housing cover, column housing and gear shift lever bowl.
4. Place coil assembly wire through lock housing cover and gearshift bowl shroud.
5. Connect shroud connector to terminal connector.
6. Install turn signal and hazard warning switch.
7. Install signal switch arm, **torque** retaining screw to 10 inch lbs.
8. Install hazard knob.
9. Install thrust washer, then the upper bearing spring.
10. Install turn signal cancelling cam, then the shaft lock.
11. Depress shaft lock, then install shaft lock retaining ring.
12. Install steering wheel and inflator module as outlined in "Steering Column, Replace."

LOCK HOUSING COVER, COVER END CAP, PIVOT & PULSE SWITCH, IGNITION SWITCH ACTUATOR, LOCK BOLT, UPPER BEARING, SWITCH ACTUATOR SECTOR, DIMMER SWITCH & IGNITION SWITCH

Disassemble

1. Disassemble inflator module, coil, shaft lock, turn signal cancel cam, upper bearing spring and seat, inner

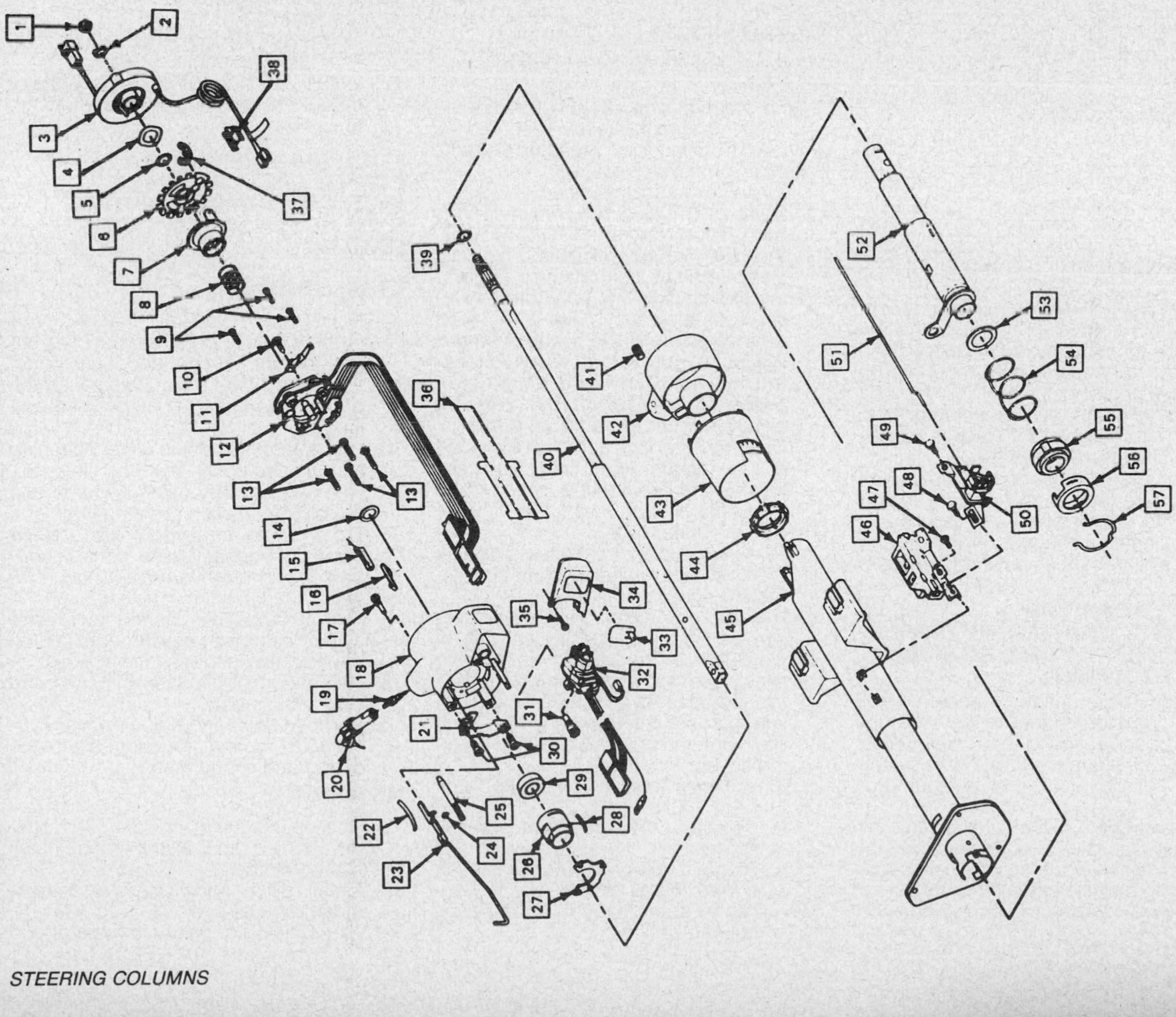
1
2
3
4
5
6
7
8
9
10
11
12
13
14
15
16
17
18
19
20
21
22
23
24
25
26
27
28
29
30
31
32
33
34
35
36
37
38
39
40
41
42
43
44
45
46
47
48
49
50
51
52
53
54
55
56
57

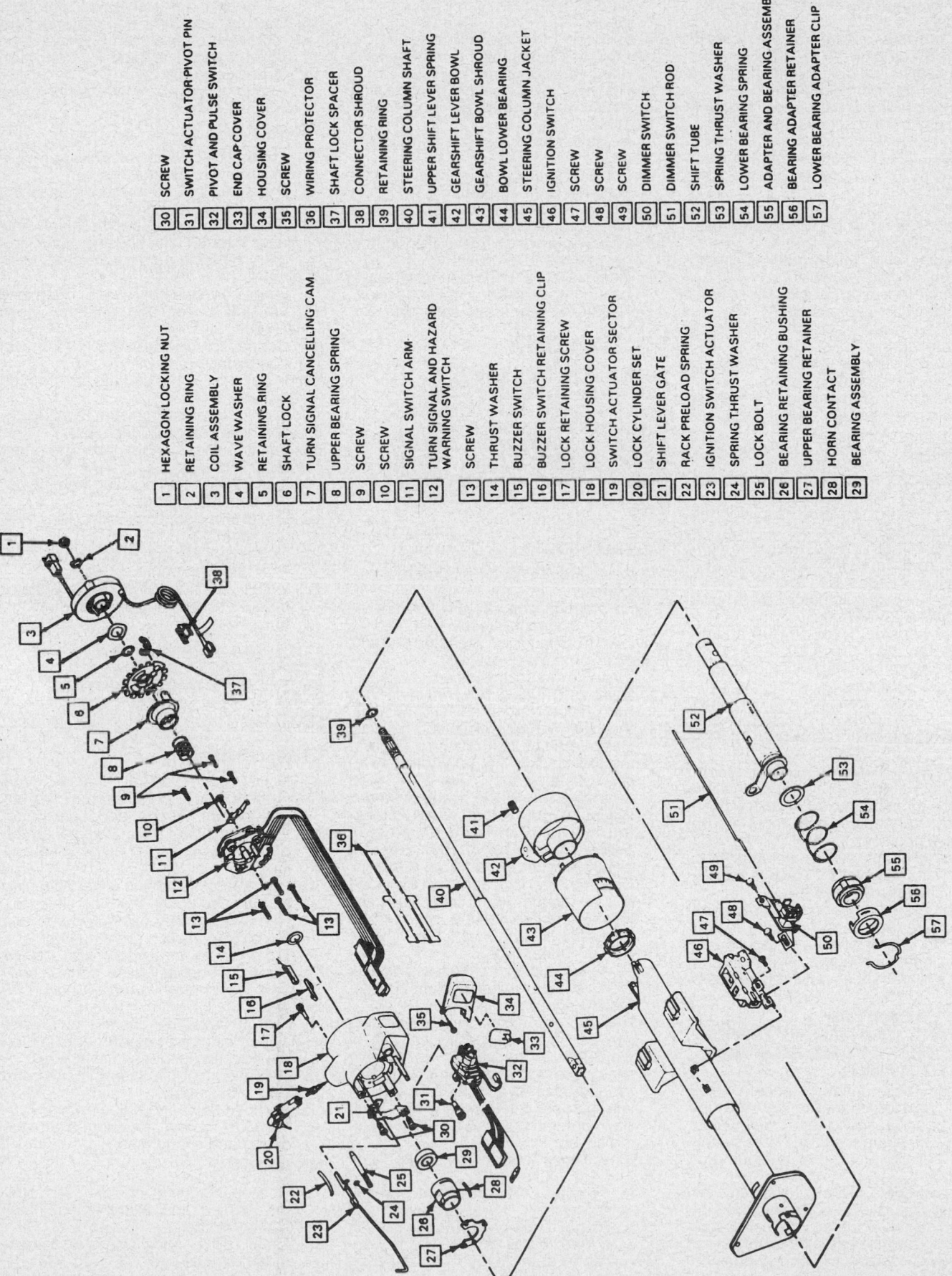

1	HEXAGON LOCKING NUT
2	RETAINING RING
3	COIL ASSEMBLY
4	WAVE WASHER
5	RETAINING RING
6	SHAFT LOCK
7	TURN SIGNAL CANCELLING CAM
8	UPPER BEARING SPRING
9	SCREW
10	SCREW
11	SIGNAL SWITCH ARM
12	TURN SIGNAL AND HAZARD WARNING SWITCH
13	SCREW
14	THRUST WASHER
15	BUZZER SWITCH
16	BUZZER SWITCH RETAINING CLIP
17	LOCK RETAINING SCREW
18	LOCK HOUSING COVER
19	SWITCH ACTUATOR SECTOR
20	LOCK CYLINDER SET
21	SHIFT LEVER GATE
22	RACK PRELOAD SPRING
23	IGNITION SWITCH ACTUATOR
24	SPRING THRUST WASHER
25	LOCK BOLT
26	BEARING RETAINING BUSHING
27	UPPER BEARING RETAINER
28	HORN CONTACT
29	BEARING ASSEMBLY
30	SCREW
31	SWITCH ACTUATOR PIVOT PIN
32	PIVOT AND PULSE SWITCH
33	END CAP COVER
34	HOUSING COVER
35	SCREW
36	WIRING PROTECTOR
37	SHAFT LOCK SPACER
38	CONNECTOR SHROUD
39	RETAINING RING
40	STEERING COLUMN SHAFT
41	UPPER SHIFT LEVER SPRING
42	GEARSHIFT LEVER BOWL
43	GEARSHIFT BOWL SHROUD
44	BOWL LOWER BEARING
45	STEERING COLUMN JACKET
46	IGNITION SWITCH
47	SCREW
48	SCREW
49	SCREW
50	DIMMER SWITCH
51	DIMMER SWITCH ROD
52	SHIFT TUBE
53	SPRING THRUST WASHER
54	LOWER BEARING SPRING
55	ADAPTER AND BEARING ASSEMBLY
56	BEARING ADAPTER RETAINER
57	LOWER BEARING ADAPTER CLIP

GC6049100117000X -R-

Fig. 74 Exploded view of standard steering column. Caprice, Custom Cruiser, Impala SS & Roadmaster

race, turn signal switch, buzzer switch and lock cylinder set as outlined previously.
2. **On models equipped with cruise control**, unplug multi-function lever and cruise control connectors, then remove multi-function lever.
3. **On all models,** remove lock housing cover attaching screws, then cover.
4. Remove lock bolt and spring thrust washer from ignition switch actuator.
5. Remove housing cover screws, then cover.
6. Remove switch actuator pivot pin, and pulse switch using pivot pin removal tool J 21854-01.
7. Remove shift lever gate attaching screws, then lever gate.
8. Remove retaining bushing, horn contact, then bearing assembly.
9. Remove switch actuator, then rack preload spring.
10. Remove dimmer switch attaching screws, then dimmer switch.
11. Remove ignition switch attaching screws, then ignition switch and actuator.

Assemble

1. Install rack preload spring, switch actuator, then bearing assembly.
2. Install bearing retaining bushing, then horn contact.
3. Install shift lever gate, **torque** attaching screws to 18 inch lbs.
4. Install pivot and pulse switch.
5. Install switch actuator pivot pin, **torque** to 27 inch lbs.
6. Install housing cover, **torque** attaching screws to 17 inch lbs.
7. Install switch actuator, lock bolt, then spring thrust washer.
8. Install upper bearing retainer, then lock cover housing. **Torque** cover housing attaching screws to 47 inch lbs.
9. Install ignition switch, **torque** attaching screw to 35 inch lbs. Ignition switch must be in Off-Unlock position and gearshift lever bowl must not be in park position.
10. Install dimmer switch actuator rod, then dimmer switch. **Torque** attaching screws to 28 inch lbs.
11. Assemble inflator module, coil, shaft lock, turn signal cancel cam, upper bearing spring and seat, inner race, turn signal switch, buzzer switch and lock cylinder set as outlined previously.

SHAFT, ADAPTER & BEARING, GEARSHIFT LEVER BOWL, SHIFT TUBE & LOWER BOWL BEARING

1. Disassemble inflator module, coil, shaft lock, turn signal cancel cam, upper bearing spring and seat, inner race, turn signal switch, buzzer switch and lock cylinder set as outlined previously.
2. Disassemble lock housing cover, cover end cap, pivot and pulse switch, ignition switch actuator, lock bolt, upper bearing, switch actuator sector, dimmer and ignition switch as outlined previously.
3. Remove steering column from vehicle as outlined in "Steering Column, Replace."
4. Remove lower bearing adapter clip, bearing adapter retainer, then adapter and bearing assembly.
5. Remove lower bearing spring, spring thrust washer, then steering column shaft.
6. Remove retaining spring from column shaft.
7. Remove gearshift lever bowl from the gearshift bowl shroud.
8. Remove gearshift bowl shroud from the gearshift lever bowl.
9. Remove upper shift lever spring from gearshift lever bowl.
10. Remove shift tube, then bowl lower bearing from steering column jacket.
11. Reverse procedure to assemble.

TILT COLUMN

INFLATOR MODULE, STEERING WHEEL COIL, SHAFT LOCK, CANCELLING CAM, UPPER BEARING SPRING, UPPER BEARING SEAT, INNER RACE, TURN SIGNAL SWITCH, BUZZER SWITCH & LOCK CYLINDER SET

Disassemble

Refer to **Fig. 75** exploded view of steering column.

With steering column, inflator module and steering wheel already removed as previously outlined in "Steering Column, Replace," proceed as follows:

1. Place key in Lock position.
2. Remove coil assembly retaining ring, slide coil assembly off end of shaft, then remove wave washer.
3. Remove shaft lock retaining ring using tool J 23653-C or equivalent to depress shaft lock. **Use a 1/2 inch wrench to hold the shaft of tool J 23653 or equivalent when releasing the nut. Failure to do so may cause tool to fly off the steering column causing personal injury.**
4. Remove shaft lock and shaft lock cover, then the turn signal cancelling cam.
5. Remove upper bearing spring, then the upper bearing seat.
6. Remove inner race.
7. Place turn signal in right turn position, then remove signal switch arm attaching screw and the arm.
8. Remove turn signal switch attaching screws and position switch out of way. If it is necessary to remove switch, remove wiring harness protector and hazard knob, then gently pull wire harness through gear shift lever bowl, column housing and lock housing cover.
9. If necessary remove coil assembly as follows:
   a. Remove connector from terminal connector.
   b. Remove wire protector, then attach a wire to the coil assembly connector at the base of the steering column.
   c. Pull wire through lock housing cover and gearshift bowl shroud.
10. Remove key from cylinder lock, and remove buzzer switch and clip, then reinsert key in cylinder lock and turn to Lock position.
11. Remove lock retaining screw and lock cylinder set.

Assemble

1. Install lock cylinder set, **torque** retaining screw to 22 inch lbs.
2. Place key in Run position, then install buzzer switch and clip.
3. Route turn signal switch wiring harness through lock housing cover, column housing and gear shift lever bowl.
4. Place coil assembly wire through lock housing cover and gearshift bowl shroud.
5. Connect shroud connector to terminal connector.
6. Install turn signal and hazard warning switch.
7. Install signal switch arm, **torque** retaining screw to 20 inch lbs.
8. Install hazard knob, then the inner race.
9. Install upper bearing seat, then the upper bearing spring.
10. Install turn signal cancelling cam, then the shaft lock.
11. Depress shaft lock, then install shaft lock retaining ring.
12. Install steering wheel and inflator module as outlined in "Steering Column, Replace."

LOCK HOUSING COVER, COVER END CAP, PIVOT & SWITCH, DIMMER SWITCH ROD ACTUATOR & TILT SPRING

Disassemble

1. Disassemble inflator module, coil, shaft lock, turn signal cancel cam, upper bearing spring and seat, inner race, turn signal switch, buzzer switch and lock cylinder set as outlined previously.
2. Remove lock housing cover attaching screws and cover, then the tilt lever.
3. Remove cover housing end cap and the dimmer switch rod actuator.
4. **On models equipped with cruise control,** unplug cruise control connector and remove multi-function lever.
5. **On all models,** gently pull pivot switch wiring harness through column housing and gear shift lever bowl.
6. Remove pivot pin, then the pivot and switch assembly.
7. Remove pivot and pulse switch.
8. Remove spring retainer, then the spring and spring guide.

Assemble

1. Coat spring guide and spring with lithium grease and install, then install spring retainer.
2. Install pivot and switch assembly, then the pivot pin.
3. Attach actuator pivot pin to pivot and

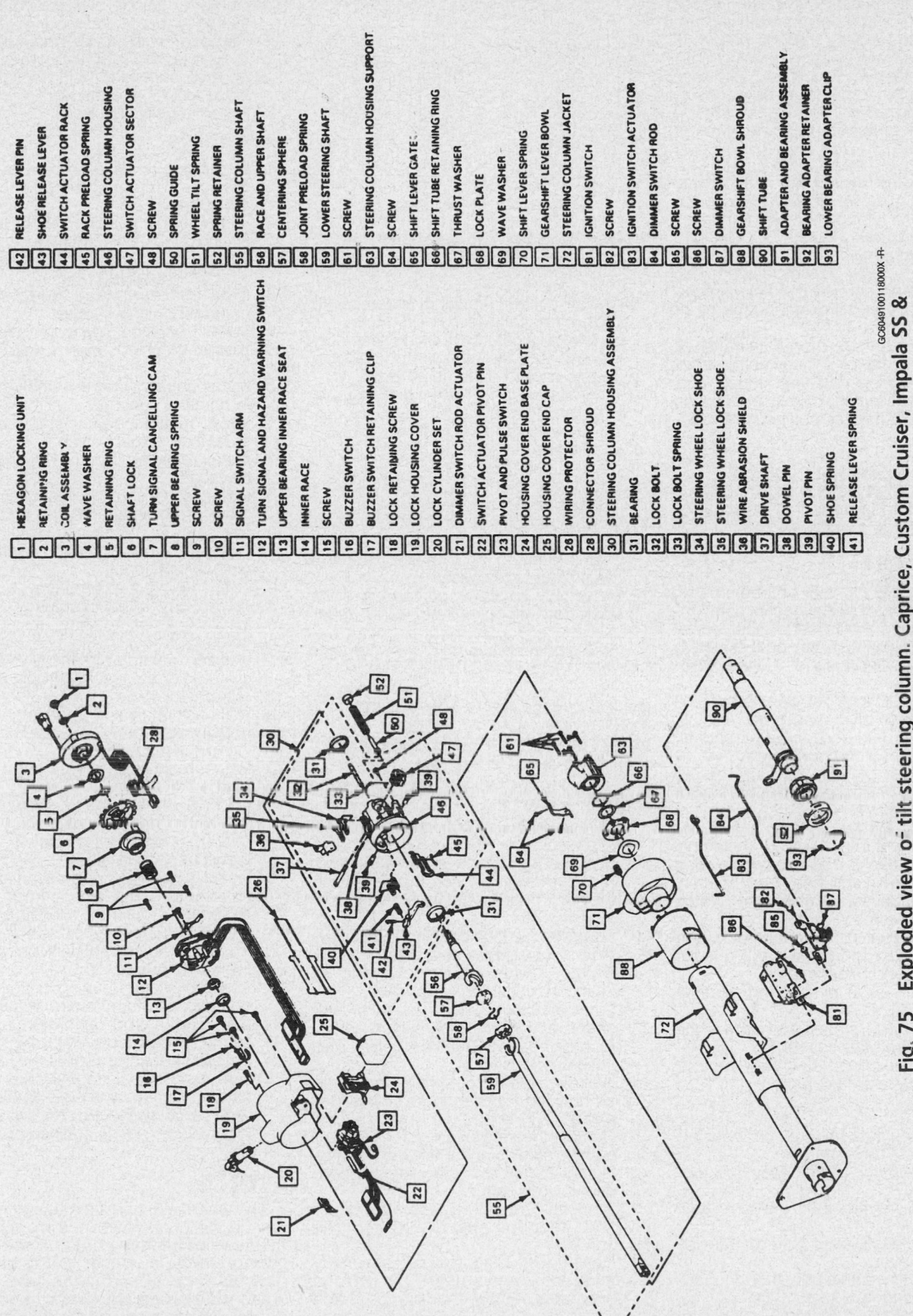

1	HEXAGON LOCKING UNIT
2	RETAINING RING
3	COIL ASSEMBLY
4	WAVE WASHER
5	RETAINING RING
6	SHAFT LOCK
7	TURN SIGNAL CANCELLING CAM
8	UPPER BEARING SPRING
9	SCREW
10	SCREW
11	SIGNAL SWITCH ARM
12	TURN SIGNAL AND HAZARD WARNING SWITCH
13	UPPER BEARING INNER RACE SEAT
14	INNER RACE
15	SCREW
16	BUZZER SWITCH
17	BUZZER SWITCH RETAINING CLIP
18	LOCK RETAINING SCREW
19	LOCK HOUSING COVER
20	LOCK CYLINDER SET
21	DIMMER SWITCH ROD ACTUATOR
22	SWITCH ACTUATOR PIVOT PIN
23	PIVOT AND PULSE SWITCH
24	HOUSING COVER END BASE PLATE
25	HOUSING COVER END CAP
26	WIRING PROTECTOR
28	CONNECTOR SHROUD
30	STEERING COLUMN HOUSING ASSEMBLY
31	BEARING
32	LOCK BOLT
33	LOCK BOLT SPRING
34	STEERING WHEEL LOCK SHOE
35	STEERING WHEEL LOCK SHOE
36	WIRE ABRASION SHIELD
37	DRIVE SHAFT
38	DOWEL PIN
39	PIVOT PIN
40	SHOE SPRING
41	RELEASE LEVER SPRING
42	RELEASE LEVER PIN
43	SHOE RELEASE LEVER
44	SWITCH ACTUATOR RACK
45	RACK PRELOAD SPRING
46	STEERING COLUMN HOUSING
47	SWITCH ACTUATOR SECTOR
48	SCREW
50	SPRING GUIDE
51	WHEEL TILT SPRING
52	SPRING RETAINER
55	STEERING COLUMN SHAFT
56	RACE AND UPPER SHAFT
57	CENTERING SPHERE
58	JOINT PRELOAD SPRING
59	LOWER STEERING SHAFT
61	SCREW
63	STEERING COLUMN HOUSING SUPPORT
64	SCREW
65	SHIFT LEVER GATE
66	SHIFT TUBE RETAINING RING
67	THRUST WASHER
68	LOCK PLATE
69	WAVE WASHER
70	SHIFT LEVER SPRING
71	GEARSHIFT LEVER BOWL
72	STEERING COLUMN JACKET
81	IGNITION SWITCH
82	SCREW
83	IGNITION SWITCH ACTUATOR
84	DIMMER SWITCH ROD
85	SCREW
86	SCREW
87	DIMMER SWITCH
88	GEARSHIFT BOWL SHROUD
90	SHIFT TUBE
91	ADAPTER AND BEARING ASSEMBLY
92	BEARING ADAPTER RETAINER
93	LOWER BEARING ADAPTER CLIP

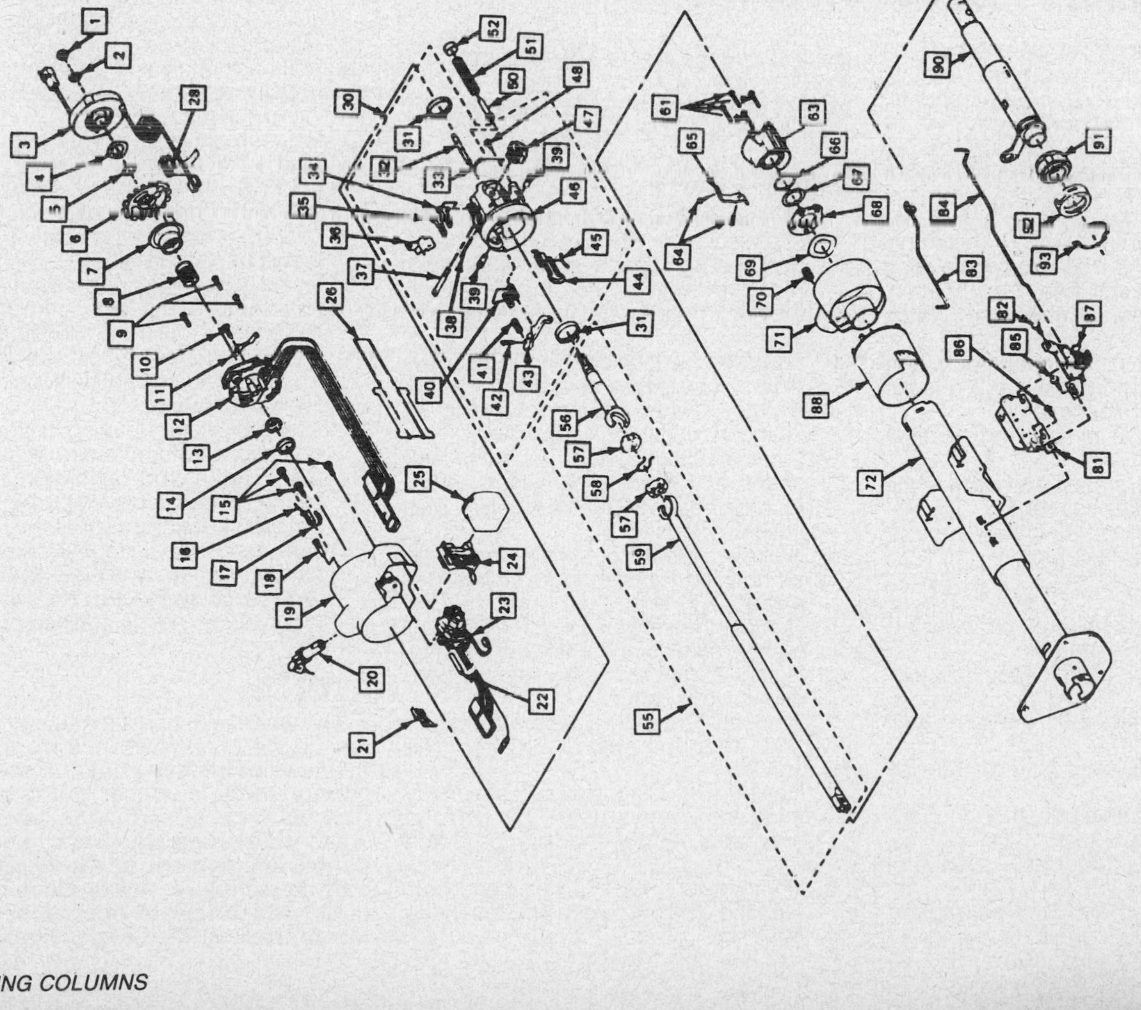

GC6049100118000X -R-

Fig. 75 Exploded view of tilt steering column. Caprice, Custom Cruiser, Impala SS & Roadmaster w/SIR

pulse switch, and lock housing cover.
4. Route pivot and pulse switch assembly wiring harness through gear shift lever bowl and column housing.
5. Install dimmer switch rod actuator, then the gear shift lever bowl, ensuring bottom edge of dimmer switch rod actuator rests on bend in dimmer switch rod.
6. Install cover housing end cap.
7. **On models equipped with cruise control,** plug in cruise control connector and install multi-function lever.
8. **On all models,** install lock housing cover. Tighten screw in 12 o'clock position first, screw in 8 o'clock position second and screw in 3 o'clock position third, then **torque** in same order to 80 inch lbs.
9. Assemble inflator module, coil, shaft lock, turn signal cancel cam, upper bearing spring and seat, inner race, turn signal switch, buzzer switch and lock cylinder set as outlined previously.

COLUMN HOUSING, LOCK SHOES, ACTUATOR SECTOR, SWITCH ACTUATOR RACK, BEARINGS & LOCK BOLT

Disassemble

1. Disassemble inflator module, coil, shaft lock, turn signal cancel cam, upper bearing spring and seat, inner race, turn signal switch, buzzer switch and lock cylinder set as outlined previously.
2. Disassemble lock housing cover, cover end cap, pivot and pulse switch, dimmer switch rod actuator and tilt spring as outlined previously.
3. Using pivot pin remover tool No. J-21854-01 or equivalent, remove pivot pins, **Fig. 49.**
4. Reinstall tilt lever.
5. Remove column housing assembly by pulling back on tilt lever and pulling housing down and away from column.
6. Remove driveshaft, then the switch actuator sector.
7. Remove switch actuator rack and rack preload spring, then the release lever pin and release lever.
8. Remove release lever spring, then the dowel pin.
9. Remove lock shoes and lock shoe springs, then the bearings.
10. Remove hex head bolt, then the lock bolt spring and lock bolt.

Assemble

1. Install bearings to column housing, then install driveshaft.
2. Install actuator sector, then the lock shoes.
3. Install dowel pin, then the lock shoe springs.
4. Install release lever spring, then the release lever.
5. Install release lever pin, then the rack preload spring.
6. Install switch actuator rack to actuator sector.
7. Install lock bolt and lock bolt spring, then the hex head bolt.

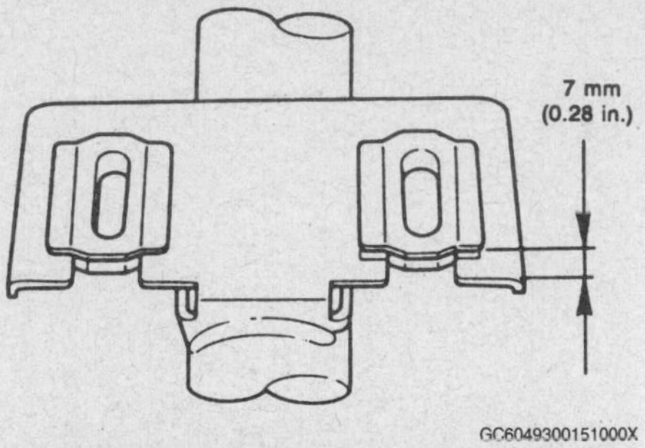
7 mm
(0.28 in.)
GC6049300151000X

Fig. 76 Slide block inspection. Storm

8. Install column housing assembly to column as follows:
   a. Position column housing assembly and align switch actuator rack with pin on end of actuator rod.
   b. Pull back on tilt lever, pushing column housing assembly onto column housing support assembly.
   c. Release tilt lever to lock shoes.
9. Remove tilt lever.
10. Lubricate pivot pins with lithium grease and install them.
11. Assemble lock housing cover, cover end cap, pivot and pulse switch, dimmer switch rod actuator and tilt spring as outlined previously.
12. Assemble inflator module, coil, shaft lock, turn signal cancel cam, upper bearing spring and seat, inner race, turn signal switch, buzzer switch and lock cylinder set as outlined previously.

SHAFT, COLUMN HOUSING SUPPORT, SHIFT TUBE, IGNITION SWITCH, DIMMER SWITCH & LOWER BEARING

Disassemble

1. Disassemble inflator module, coil, shaft lock, turn signal cancel cam, upper bearing spring and seat, inner race, turn signal switch, buzzer switch and lock cylinder set as outlined previously.
2. Disassemble lock housing cover, cover end cap, pivot and pulse switch, dimmer switch rod actuator and tilt spring as outlined previously.
3. Disassemble column housing, lock shoes, actuator sector, switch actuator rack, bearings and lock bolt as outlined previously.
4. Remove steering column from vehicle as outlined in "Steering Column, Replace."
5. Remove bearing retainer, then the attaching screws and the lower bearing.
6. Remove shaft assembly then disconnect lower shaft.
7. Remove centering sphere from upper shaft, then the retainer clip from the sphere.
8. Remove housing support assembly attaching screws, then the housing support assembly and dimmer switch rod.
9. Remove hex nut and hex head bolt, then the dimmer switch and mounting stud.
10. Remove ignition switch and ignition switch actuator.
11. Remove shift tube retaining ring, thrust washer, lock plate, wave washer, then shift tube using special tool No. J 23072 or equivalent.
12. Remove gear shift bowl.

Assemble

1. Install gear shift lever bowl to jacket, then the dimmer switch rod to housing support.
2. Install shift tube using special tool No. J 23073-01 or equivalent, wave washer, lock plate, thrust washer, then shift tube retaining ring.
3. Install dimmer switch rod to steering column housing support.
4. Install housing support assembly, **torque**attaching screws to 30 inch lbs.
5. Install actuator rod assembly to track in housing support.
6. Install ignition switch and mounting stud, then adjust switch.
7. Install retaining clip and sphere to upper shaft.
8. Install lower shaft to upper shaft with block tooth on shaft lower end of upper shaft at 12 o'clock position and notch at end of lower shaft at 4 o'clock position.
9. Lubricate shaft assembly with lithium grease and install to column.
10. Install column housing assembly to column.
11. Position column assembly and align switch actuator rack with pin on end of actuator rod.
12. Pull back on tilt lever, pushing column housing assembly onto column housing support assembly.
13. Release tilt lever to lock shoes, then remove tilt lever.
14. Lubricate inner surface of lower bearing with lithium grease, then install bearing and retaining screws.
15. Install bearing retainer.
16. Install dimmer switch, hex nut and hex head bolt, then adjust dimmer switch.
17. Assemble column housing, lock shoes, actuator sector, switch actuator rack, bearings and lock bolt as outlined previously.
18. Assemble lock housing cover, cover end cap, pivot and pulse switch, dimmer switch rod acturator and tilt spring as outlined previously.
19. Assemble inflator module, coil, shaft lock, turn signal cancel cam, upper bearing spring and seat, inner race, turn signal switch, buzzer switch and lock cylinder set as outlined previously.

Storm

The wheel must be straight and the column in the Lock position. **Care must be taken when handling column with a live inflator module. Never point bag deploy surface toward you, and never stand column on steering wheel. Accidental deployment in these positions may cause injury. Always face bag deploy surface toward open space to allow for unrestricted expansion.**

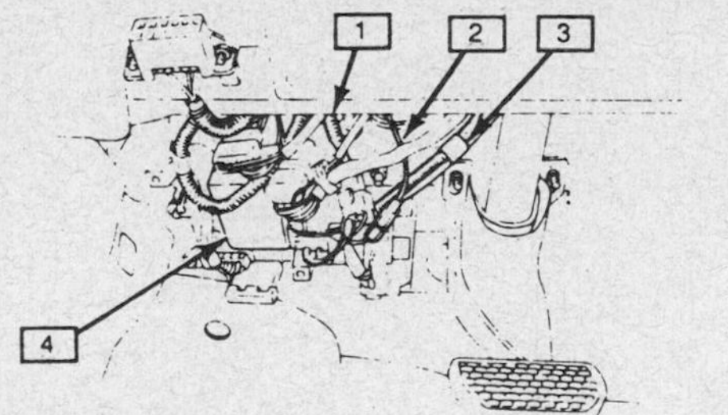
1
2
3
4

1 SIR HARNESS
2 MAIN WIRE HARNESS (HORN)
3 SIR COIL AND TURN SIGNAL/DIMMER SWITCH HARNESS
4 FUSE BLOCK

GC6049100122000X

Fig. 77 Electrical connector locations. Metro w/SIR

DISASSEMBLE

1. Remove the inflator module as follows:
   a. With the ignition switch in the Off position disconnect battery ground cable.
   b. Remove the SIR module screws and the SIR module.
2. Remove steering wheel retaining nut and steering wheel.
3. Remove horn switch screws and horn switch, rear steering wheel cover screws and rear cover.
4. Remove lower switch panel, dash lighter panel and hood release panel.
5. Remove lap air deflector and left lower dash trim panel.
6. Remove upper steering column mounting bolts and drop column down.
7. Remove two piece steering column cover, then disconnect coil assembly wiring harness from turn signal switch.
8. Remove four screws and coil assembly from turn signal switch.
9. Remove turn signal switch, then snap ring and spacer collar from steering shaft.
10. Remove ignition switch, then steering shaft from steering column.
11. Remove back drive cable and guide.
12. Inspect steering column for damage as follows:
    a. Check upper column tube bearing for abnormal noise or rotation difficulty, replace as necessary.
    b. Check slide block on steering column bracket assembly. Block be within .28 inch, **Fig. 76,** from the slots insert edge. If measurement is not within specifications, replace column.

ASSEMBLE

1. Install guide onto column, then ignition switch.
2. Install steering shaft into column, then install collar and snap ring onto column.
3. Install turn signal switch onto column, then four screws and coil assembly onto turn signal switch.
4. Connect coil assembly wiring harness into turn signal switch.

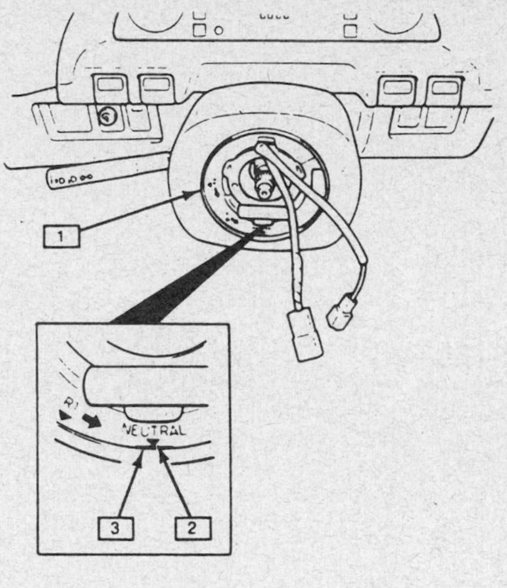
1
R1
NEUTRAL
3
2

1 SIR COIL
2 NEUTRAL MARK
3 ALIGNMENT MARK

GC6049100123000X

Fig. 78 Checking position of SIR coil. Metro w/SIR

5. Install two piece steering column cover, then install steering column and steering column mounting bolts and **torque** to 18 ft. lbs.
6. Install left lower dash trim panel and lap air deflector.
7. Install hood release panel, dash lighter panel and lower switch panel.
8. Install rear steering wheel cover, then connect horn contact switches into wheel.
9. Install steering wheel and retaining nut, **torque** nut to 25 ft. lbs.
10. Install SIR module and SIR module screws, **torque** screws to 44 inch lbs.
11. With the ignition switch in the Off position, connect the battery ground cable.

Metro

Refer to **Figs. 17 through 20** and **Figs. 80 through 82** when servicing this steering column.

SIR COIL & TURN SIGNAL & DIMMER SWITCH

Remove steering wheel as outlined in "Steering Column, Replace" in this section.

Refer to **Fig. 22** for exploded view of steering column.

1. Remove six screws retaining upper and lower steering column covers, then remove column covers.
2. Remove two electrical connectors from fuse box, one from the SIR harness, and one from the main wiring harness, **Fig. 77.**
3. Remove SIR coil and turn signal/dimmer switch attaching screws, then switch assembly.
4. Reverse procedure to install noting the following:

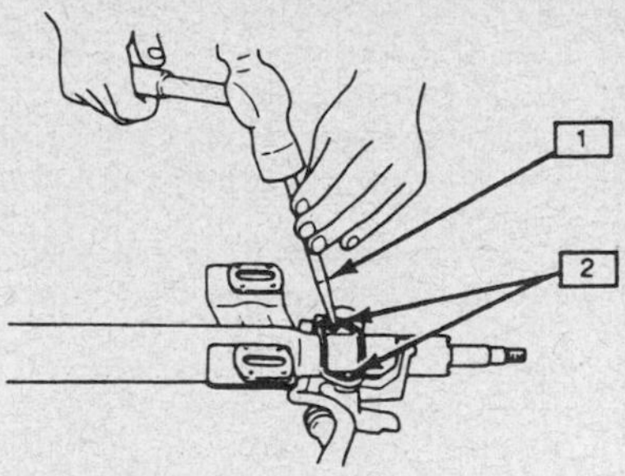
1
2

1 CENTER PUNCH
2 STEERING COLUMN LOCK BOLTS

GC6049100124000X

Fig. 79 Steering column lock bolts removal. Metro w/SIR

   a. Ensure that SIR coil is centered. If not position wheels of vehicle in the straightforward position.
   b. Check position of SIR coil, **Fig. 78.**
   c. If Neutral mark is at the alignment mark the coil is centered and no adjustment is necessary.
   d. If R1 mark is close to the alignment mark coil is one rotation off to the right from its center state and needs to be adjusted on turn counterclockwise. The R2 mark indicates that the coil is two rotations off.
   e. If L1 mark is close to the alignment mark coil is one rotation off to the left from its center state and needs to be adjusted on turn clockwise. The L2 mark indicates that the coil is two rotations off.
   f. To adjust remove SIR coil, hold coil lead at its base and turn in the direction specified in steps d and e. Then replace SIR coil.

STEERING COLUMN LOCK

Remove steering wheel as outlined in "Steering Column, Replace" in this section.

1. Remove ignition switch attaching screw, then switch.
2. Remove ignition key warning switch attaching screws, then switch.
3. Loosen and remove two steering column lock retaining bolts using a center punch, **Fig. 79. When using center punch do not damage aluminum parts of lock assembly.**
4. Turn ignition key to On or ACC position, then remove lock assembly from steering column.
5. Reverse procedure to install.

LeMans

STANDARD COLUMN

Refer to **Fig. 83** when servicing this column.

TURN SIGNAL SWITCH HOUSING, STEERING SHAFT, STEERING COLUMN HOUSING & IGNITION SWITCH HOUSING

Disassemble

1. Disconnect battery ground cable and remove steering wheel horn cap and horn leads.

2. Remove nut, retainer and steering wheel, then unclip contact ring from wheel if necessary.
3. Remove steering column as previously described in Steering Column, Replace section.
4. Remove alignment bushing from lower end of shaft assembly, then upper steering shaft spring.
5. Remove thrust washer, washer head tap screws and turn signal switch housing assembly.
6. Turn lock cylinder to the Run position and remove steering shaft from lower end of jacket assembly.
7. Remove shear bolts, shear bolt washers and ignition switch housing as follows:
   a. Drill off head of shear bolts down to shear bolt washers with a 1/4 inch drill bit.
   b. Separate washers and switch housing from column housing.
   c. Remove threaded end of shear bolts from ignition switch housing using vise grips.
8. Remove lock cylinder from ignition switch housing, ignition switch retaining screw and ignition switch assembly.
9. Remove shear bolts and column housing as follows:
   a. Drill off head of shear bolts with a 5/16 inch drill bit.
   b. Separate column housing from jacket assembly.
   c. Remove threaded end of shear bolts from jacket assembly using vise grips.

Assemble

1. Install column housing to jacket assembly using "new" shear bolts and **torque** until bolt head separates from body, approximately 11 ft. lbs.
2. Install ignition switch to ignition switch housing ensuring retaining pin engages ear on ignition switch. Ensure that the tab on the lock cylinder shaft and the slotted opening on the ignition switch are in alignment, the lock cylinder and ignition switch must be in the Run position prior to installation.
3. Install lock cylinder into ignition switch housing.
4. Install ignition switch housing to column housing using "new" shear bolts and washers and **torque** until bolt head separates from body, approximately 15 ft. lbs.
5. Turn lock cylinder to the Run position and install steering shaft assembly into lower end of jacket assembly until bottomed.
6. Turn lock cylinder to the Off-Lock position and remove key.
7. Rotate steering shaft until lock bolt engages and locks steering shaft in position.
8. Install signal switch housing to steering column housing with washer head tap screws and **torque** to 30 inch lbs.
9. Install alignment bushing over lower end of steering shaft and into lower end of jacket assembly.

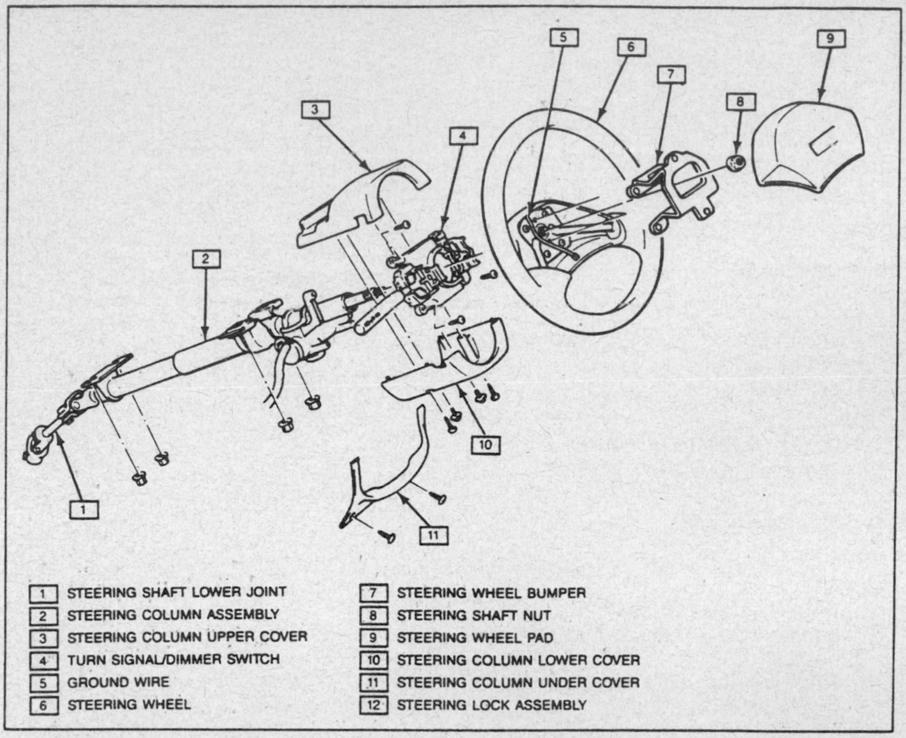
1 STEERING SHAFT LOWER JOINT
2 STEERING COLUMN ASSEMBLY
3 STEERING COLUMN UPPER COVER
4 TURN SIGNAL/DIMMER SWITCH
5 GROUND WIRE
6 STEERING WHEEL
7 STEERING WHEEL BUMPER
8 STEERING SHAFT NUT
9 STEERING WHEEL PAD
10 STEERING COLUMN LOWER COVER
11 STEERING COLUMN UNDER COVER
12 STEERING LOCK ASSEMBLY

GC6049100119000X

Fig. 80 Exploded view of steering column. Metro less SIR

10. Install steering column in car, refer to Steering Column, Replace section.
11. Install thrust washer and upper steering shaft spring on steering shaft.
12. Install contact ring if necessary, steering wheel, retainer and nut and **torque** nut to 13 ft. lbs.
13. Install horn leads and cap, then connect battery ground cable.

TILT COLUMN

Refer to **Fig. 84** when servicing this column.

TURN SIGNAL SWITCH HOUSING, STEERING SHAFT, STEERING COLUMN HOUSING & IGNITION SWITCH HOUSING

Disassemble

1. Disconnect battery ground cable and remove steering wheel horn cap and horn leads.
2. Remove nut, retainer and steering wheel, then unclip contact ring from wheel if necessary.
3. Remove steering column as previously described in Steering Column, Replace section.
4. Remove alignment bushing from lower end of shaft assembly, then canceling cam spring from upper end of shaft assembly.
5. Remove washer head tap screws and signal switch housing assembly.
6. Compress spring retainer and upper bearing spring with special tools No. J 36667 and J 23653-A or equivalent.
7. Remove retaining ring, spring retainer, upper bearing spring, inner race seat and inner race.
8. Pull tilt lever and tilt column all the way up.
9. Insert a Phillips tip screwdriver into square opening in spring retainer, push down and turn left to release retainer and tilt spring.
10. Remove spring retainer and tilt spring.
11. Remove two pivot pins using special tool No. J 21854-01 or equivalent.
12. Turn lock cylinder to the Run position and pull tilt lever to release column housing from housing support.
13. Remove shear bolts, shear bolt washers and ignition switch housing from column housing as follows:
    a. Drill off head of shear bolts down to shear bolt washers with a 1/4 inch drill bit.
    b. Separate washers and switch housing from column housing.
    c. Remove threaded end of shear bolts from ignition switch housing using vise grips.
14. Remove lock cylinder from ignition switch housing, ignition switch retaining screw and ignition switch assembly.
15. Remove steering shaft assembly from housing support.
16. Remove tilt bumpers using pliers.
17. Remove support screws and support housing from jacket assembly.
18. When necessary, the steering shaft assembly may be serviced as follows:
    a. Prior to separation of upper shaft and lower shaft, note relationship of upper shaft with lock bolt slot at 12 o'clock position and lower shaft pinch bolt groove at 7 o'clock position. Refer to this orientation for proper assembling.
    b. Position upper shaft 90° to lower shaft and separate.
    c. Rotate centering sphere 90° and remove from upper shaft.

REMOVAL

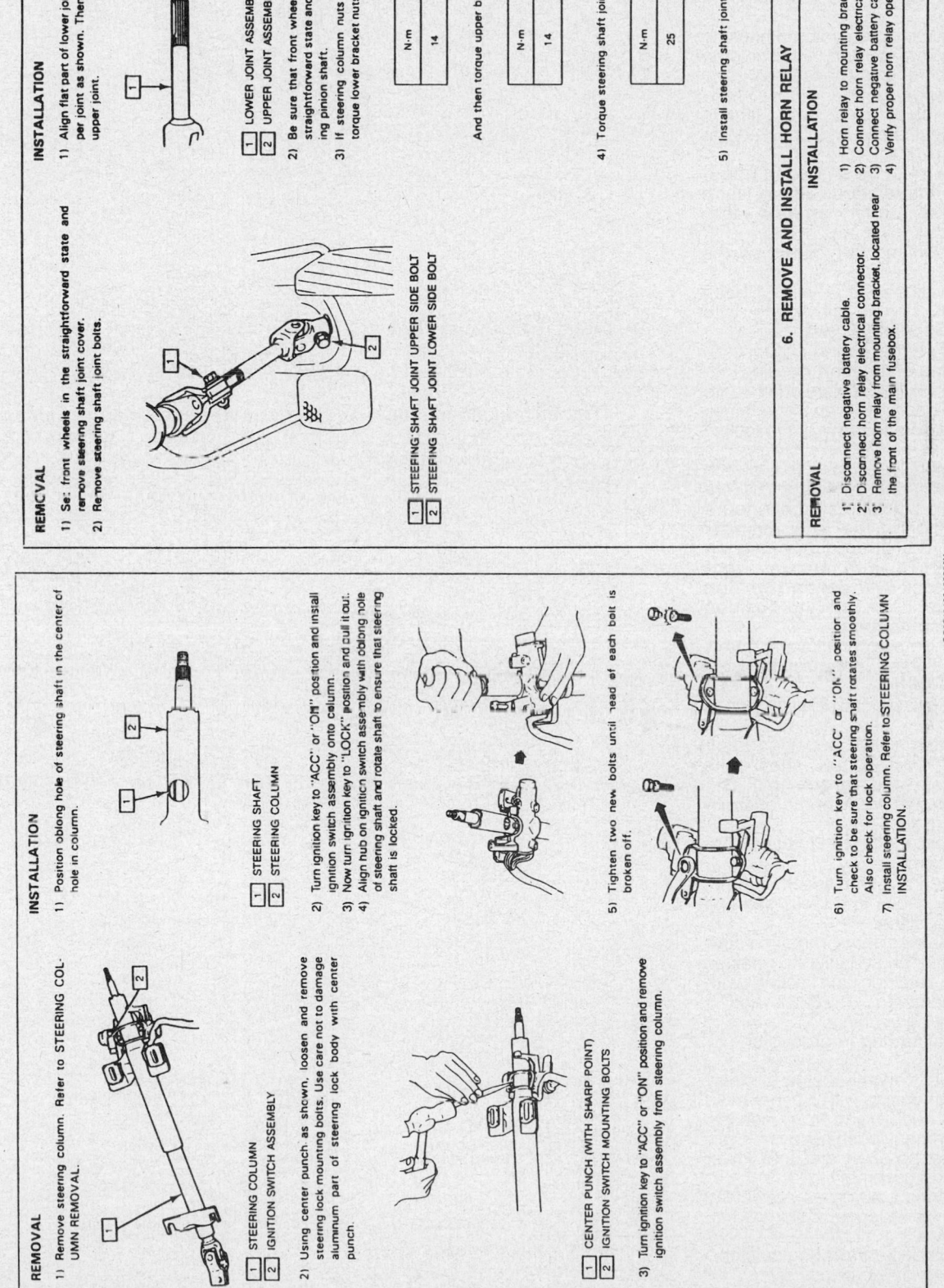

1) Remove steering column. Refer to STEERING COLUMN REMOVAL.

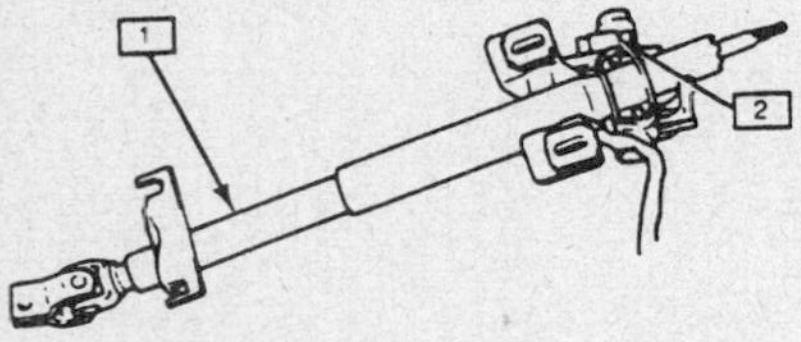
1
2

1 STEERING COLUMN
2 IGNITION SWITCH ASSEMBLY

2) Using center punch as shown, loosen and remove steering lock mounting bolts. Use care not to damage aluminum part of steering lock body with center punch.

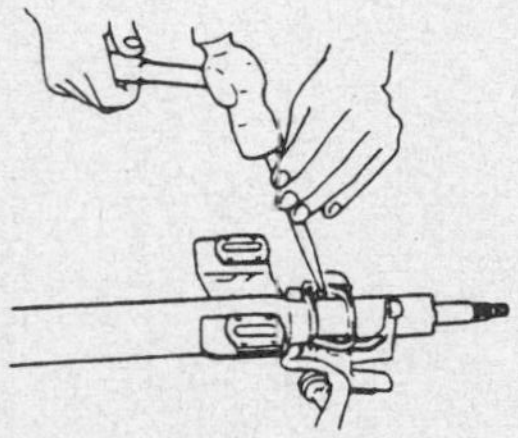

1 CENTER PUNCH (WITH SHARP POINT)
2 IGNITION SWITCH MOUNTING BOLTS

3) Turn ignition key to "ACC" or "ON" position and remove ignition switch assembly from steering column.

INSTALLATION

1) Position oblong hole of steering shaft in the center of hole in column.

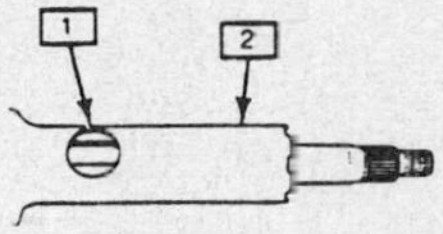
1
2

1 STEERING SHAFT
2 STEERING COLUMN

2) Turn ignition key to "ACC" or "ON" position and install ignition switch assembly onto column.
3) Now turn ignition key to "LOCK" position and pull it out.
4) Align hub on ignition switch assembly with oblong hole of steering shaft and rotate shaft to ensure that steering shaft is locked.

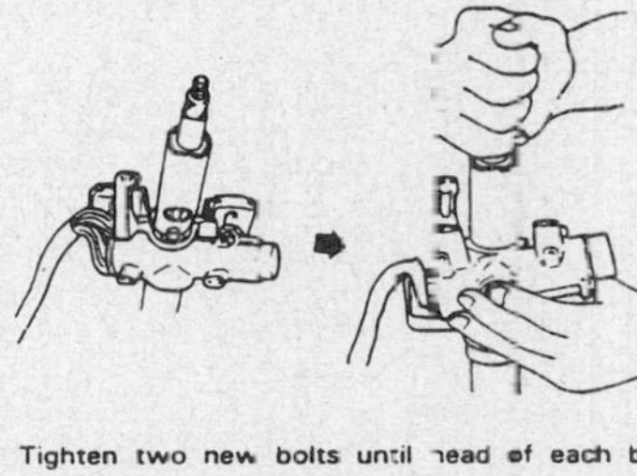

5) Tighten two new bolts until head of each bolt is broken off.

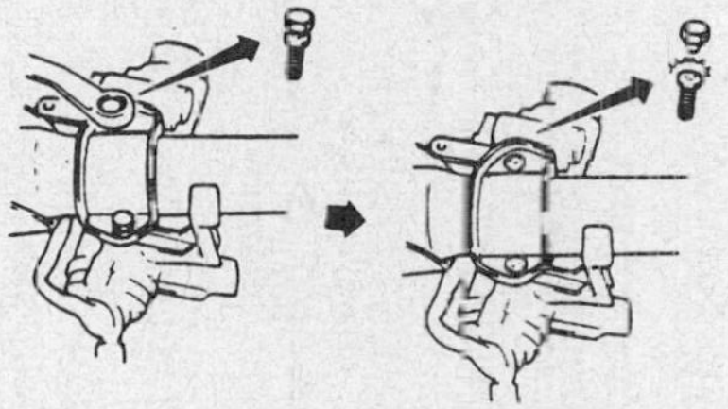

6) Turn ignition key to "ACC" or "ON" position and check to be sure that steering shaft rotates smoothly. Also check for lock operation.
7) Install steering column. Refer to STEERING COLUMN INSTALLATION.

GC6C43100120000X

Fig. 81 Steering lock replacement. Metro less SIR

REMOVAL

1) Set front wheels in the straightforward state and remove steering shaft joint cover.
2) Remove steering shaft joint bolts.

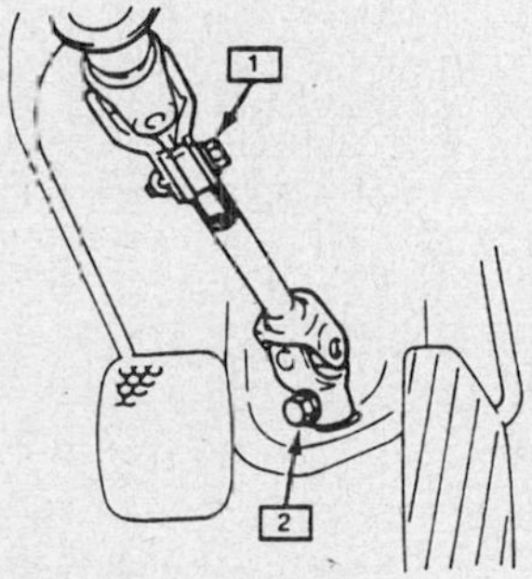
1
2

1 STEERING SHAFT JOINT UPPER SIDE BOLT
2 STEERING SHAFT JOINT LOWER SIDE BOLT

INSTALLATION

1) Align flat part of lower joint shaft with bolt hole of upper joint as shown. Then insert lower joint shaft into upper joint.

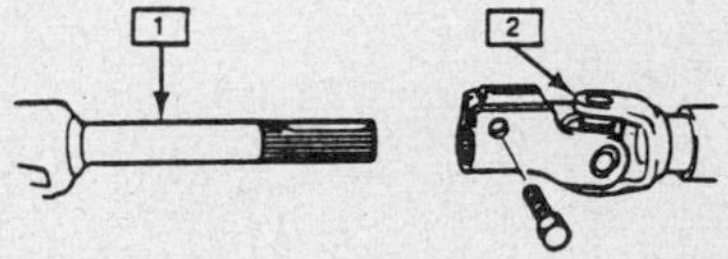
1
2

1 LOWER JOINT ASSEMBLY
2 UPPER JOINT ASSEMBLY

2) Be sure that front wheels and steering wheel are in straightforward state and insert lower joint into steering pinion shaft.
3) If steering column nuts were loosened in removal, torque lower bracket nuts to below specification first:

N·m	lb. ft.
14	10

And then torque upper bracket nuts to specification:

N·m	lb. ft.
14	10

4) Torque steering shaft joint bolts to specification:

N·m	lb. ft.
25	18

5) Install steering shaft joint cover.

6. REMOVE AND INSTALL HORN RELAY

REMOVAL

1) Disconnect negative battery cable.
2) Disconnect horn relay electrical connector.
3) Remove horn relay from mounting bracket, located near the front of the main fusebox.

INSTALLATION

1) Horn relay to mounting bracket.
2) Connect horn relay electrical connector.
3) Connect negative battery cable.
4) Verify proper horn relay operation.

GC6049100121000X

Fig. 82 Steering shaft lower joint & horn relay replacement. Metro less SIR

d. Separate sphere halves and joint preload spring.

Assemble

1. Install housing support to jacket assembly with support screws and **torque** to 12 ft. lbs.
2. Install tilt bumpers to housing support and snap into place, then install steering shaft assembly into support housing.
3. Lubricate bearings in column housing with lithium grease and install column housing onto shaft assembly and housing support.
4. Lubricate pivot pins with lithium grease and install until bottomed in housing.
5. **Pivot pins must be staked to housing after installation. Stake each pin at three equally spaced locations.**
6. Pull tilt lever and tilt column all the way up.
7. Lubricate tilt spring with lithium grease and install tilt spring with spring retainer as follows:
   a. Make sure that spring engages locating tab on support housing.
   b. Insert a Phillips tip screwdriver into square opening in spring retainer, push down and turn right to lock in place.
8. Install ignition switch to ignition switch housing ensuring retaining pin engages ear on ignition switch. **Ensure that the tab on the lock cylinder shaft and the slotted opening on the ignition switch are in alignment, the lock cylinder and ignition switch must be in the Run position prior to installation.**
9. Install ignition switch retaining screw and hand tighten, approximately 2.7 inch lbs. of **torque**.
10. Install lock cylinder into ignition switch housing.
11. Install ignition switch housing to column housing using "new" shear bolts and washers and **torque** until bolt head separates from body, approximately 15 ft. lbs.
12. Turn lock cylinder to the Off-Lock position and remove key.
13. Rotate steering shaft assembly until lock bolt engages and locks steering shaft into position.
14. Install inner race, inner race seat, upper bearing spring and spring retainer.
15. Compress retainer and spring with special tools No. J 26667 and J 23653-A or equivalents.
16. Install retaining ring in groove on upper shaft.
17. Install signal switch housing to steering column housing with washer head tap screws and **torque** to 30 inch lbs.
18. Install alignment bushing over lower end of steering shaft and into lower end of jacket assembly.
19. Install steering column as previously described in Steering Column, Replace section.
20. Install cancelling cam spring on steering shaft.
21. Install contact ring if necessary, steer-

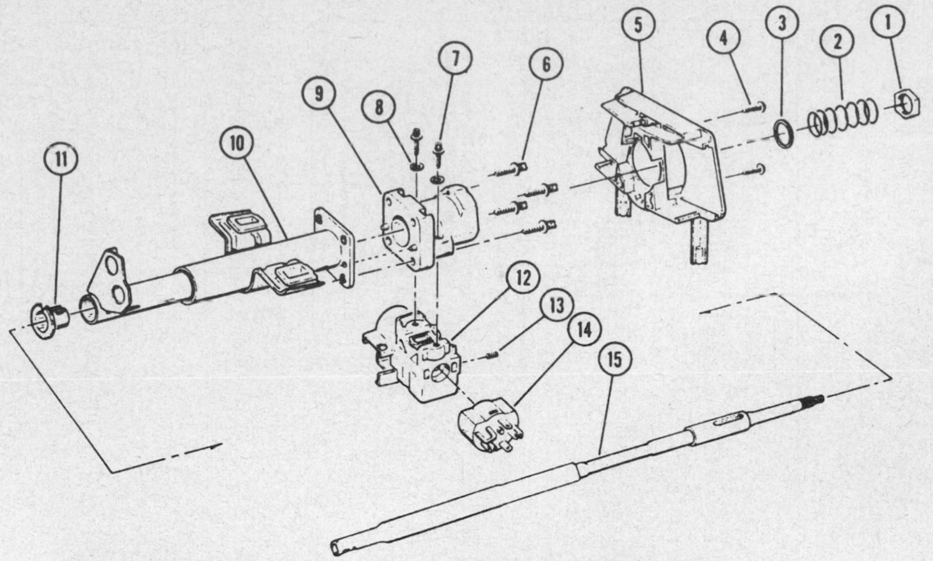

1- NUT, HEXAGON
2- SPRING, UPPER STRG SHAFT
3- WASHER, THRUST
4- SCREW, WASHER HD TAP
5- HOUSING ASM, SIGNAL SWITCH
6- BOLT, SHEAR
7- BOLT, SHEAR
8- WASHER, SHEAR BOLT
9- HOUSING, STEERING COLUMN
10- JACKET ASM, STEERING COLUMN
11- BUSHING, ALIGNMENT
12- HOUSING ASM, IGN SWITCH
13- SCREW, IGN SWITCH RETAINING
14- SWITCH ASM, IGNITION
15- SHAFT ASM, STEERING COLUMN

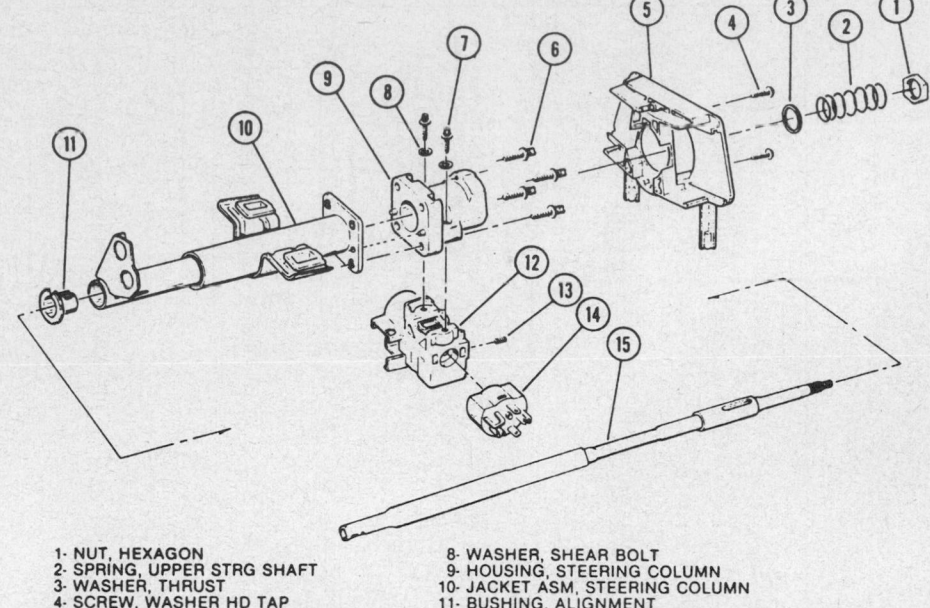

GC6049100125000X

Fig. 83 Exploded view of standard steering column. LeMans

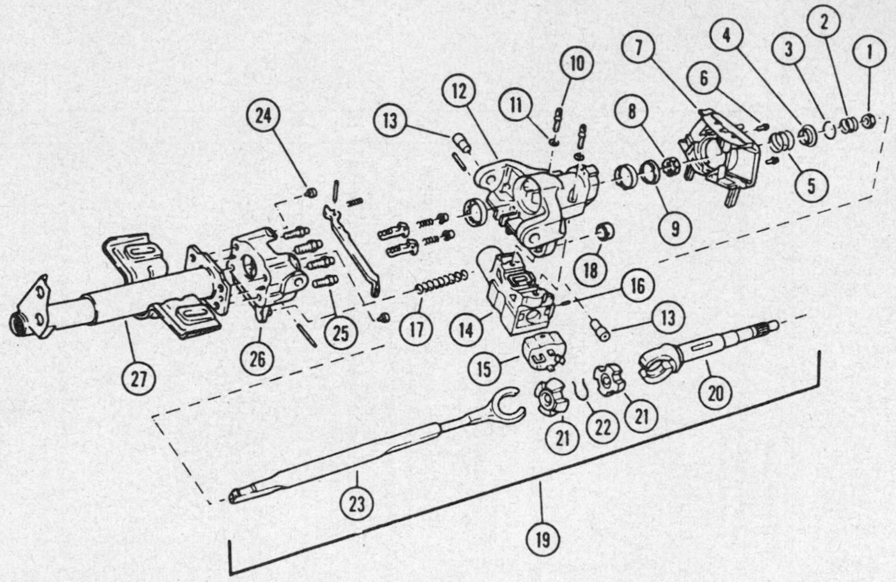

1- NUT, HEXAGON
2- SPRING, CANCELLING CAM
3- RING, RETAINING
4- RETAINER, SPRING
5- SPRING, UPPER BEARING
6- SCREW, HEX WASHER HD TAP
7- HOUSING ASM, SIGNAL SWITCH
8- SEAT, INNER RACE
9- RACE, INNER
10- BOLT, SHEAR
11- WASHER, SHEAR BOLT
12- HOUSING ASM, STEERING COLUMN
13- PIN, PIVOT
14- HOUSING ASM, IGN SWITCH
15- SWITCH ASM, IGNITION
16- SCREW, IGN SWITCH RETAINING
17- SPRING, WHEEL TILT
18- RETAINER, SPRING
19- SHAFT ASM, STEERING
20- SHAFT ASM, RACE & UPPER
21- SPHERE, CENTERING
22- SPRING, JOINT PRELOAD
23- SHAFT ASM, LOWER STEERING
24- BUMPER, TILT
25- SCREW, SUPPORT
26- SUPPORT, STRG COLUMN HOUSING
27- JACKET ASM, STEERING COLUMN

GC6049100126000X

Fig. 84 Exploded view of tilt steering column. LeMans

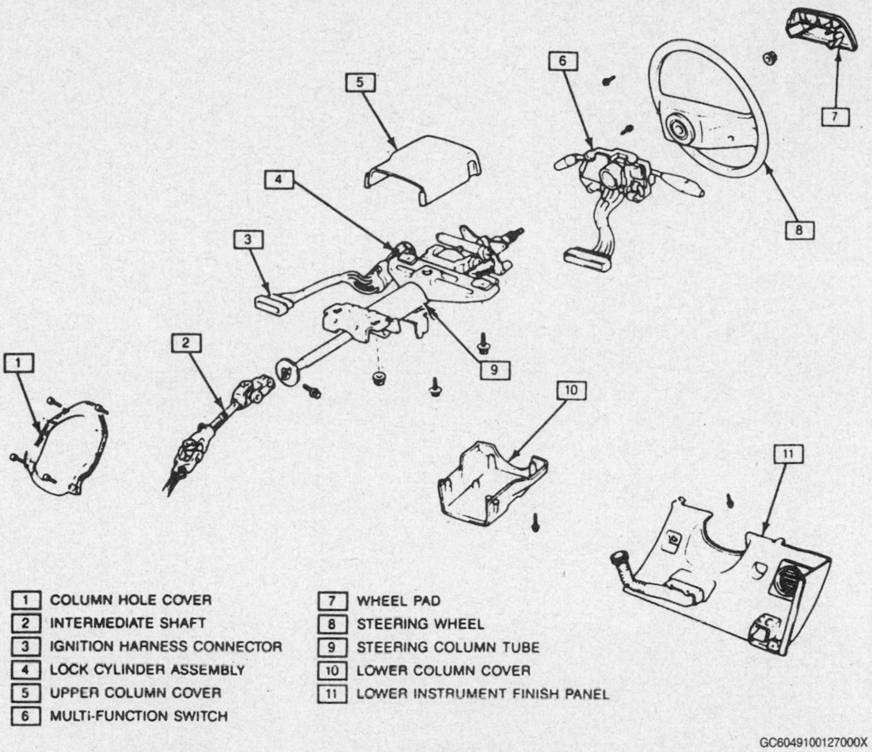
1
2
3
4
5
6
7
8
9
10
11
1 COLUMN HOLE COVER
2 INTERMEDIATE SHAFT
3 IGNITION HARNESS CONNECTOR
4 LOCK CYLINDER ASSEMBLY
5 UPPER COLUMN COVER
6 MULTI-FUNCTION SWITCH
7 WHEEL PAD
8 STEERING WHEEL
9 STEERING COLUMN TUBE
10 LOWER COLUMN COVER
11 LOWER INSTRUMENT FINISH PANEL
GC6049100127000X

Fig. 85 Exploded view of steering column. 1992 Prizm

ing wheel, retainer and nut and **torque** nut to 13 ft. lbs.

22. Install horn leads and cap, then connect battery ground cable.

STEERING SHAFT

Disassemble

1. When necessary, the steering shaft assembly may be serviced as follows:
   a. Prior to separation of upper shaft and lower shaft, note relationship of upper shaft with lock bolt slot at 12 o'clock position and lower shaft pinch bolt groove at 7 o'clock position. Refer to this orientation for proper assembling.
   b. Position upper shaft 90° to lower shaft and separate.
   c. Rotate centering sphere 90° and remove from upper shaft.
   d. Separate sphere halves and joint preload spring.

Assemble

1. Lubricate centering sphere halves and joint preload spring with lithium grease and install spring between sphere halves with ends of spring in notches.
2. Lubricate sphere end of upper and lower shaft with lithium grease and install sphere into upper shaft and rotate sphere 90°
3. To ensure proper operation, align upper shaft and lower shaft by placing lock bolt slot on upper shaft at 12 o'clock position and pinch bolt groove near end of lower shaft at 7 o'clock position.
4. Position upper shaft 90° to lower shaft and install upper shaft to lower shaft and straighten.

Prizm

1992

STANDARD COLUMN

Refer to **Fig. 85** when servicing this column.

Disassemble

1. Disconnect battery ground cable.
2. Remove steering wheel pad, horn switch connector, shaft nut and steering wheel.
3. Remove steering column as previously described in Steering Column, Replace section.
4. Secure column assembly into a vise, making sure not to damage column.
5. Remove lock cylinder housing as follows:
   a. Using a centering punch, mark the center of the tapered-head bolts securing the lock cylinder housing
   b. Using a .12-.16 inch drill bit, drill into the bolts then remove with a suitable bolt extractor.
6. Remove main shaft as follows:
   a. Using snap ring pliers, remove upper snap ring.
   b. Remove shaft from column tube, then snap ring from shaft.
7. Remove upper column tube bearing and check for abnormal noise or rotation difficulty. If bearing is faulty, replace.
8. Remove lock cylinder assembly and check for proper operation. If cylinder is faulty, replace.
9. Remove column tube bushing using a screwdriver, inspect for damage and replace if necessary.

Assemble

1. Install column tube bushing, then upper column tube bearing.
2. Install main shaft into column tube as follows:
   a. Using snap ring pliers, install snap ring in the inside groove of the main shaft.
   b. Insert main shaft into tube.
   c. Using snap ring pliers, connect shaft snap ring to column.
3. Install lock cylinder assembly.
4. Install lock cylinder housing onto column with "new" tapered-head bolts and **torque** bolts until the bolt heads break off.
5. Install column assembly as described in Steering Column, Replace section.
6. Install steering wheel and nut, **torque** bolt to 25 ft. lbs.
7. Install horn switch connector and horn pad, then connect battery ground cable.

TILT COLUMN

Refer to **Figs. 85 and 86** when servicing this column.

Disassemble

1. Disconnect battery ground cable.
2. Remove steering wheel pad, horn switch connector, shaft nut and steering wheel.
3. Remove steering column as previously described in Steering Column, Replace section.
4. Secure column assembly into a vise, making sure not to damage column.
5. Remove lock cylinder housing as follows:
   a. Using a centering punch, mark the center of the tapered-head bolts securing the lock cylinder housing
   b. Using a .12-.16 inch drill bit, drill into the bolts then remove with a suitable bolt extractor.
6. Remove two tension springs, then two bolts, two bushings and two compression springs.
7. Remove tilt levers retainers, then tilt pawls, two nuts and bolts and separate two pawls from collars.
8. Remove two pawl stoppers, then remove tilt lever, tilt sub-lever and lever lock bolt.
9. Remove lower column tube.
10. Remove column pivot bolts using special tools No. J 38256 or equivalent pivot bolt remover and a J 2619-01 or equivalent slide hammer, **Fig. 87.**
11. Separate upper and lower columns.
12. Remove mainshaft as follows;
    a. Using special tool No. J 38364 or equivalent, spring compressor, compress main shaft spring.
    b. Remove shaft snap ring with snap ring pliers.
    c. Separate main shaft from column.
    d. Remove thrust collar and bearing.
    e. Remove snap ring from shaft using snap ring pliers.
13. Remove wiring harness clamp, then steering support

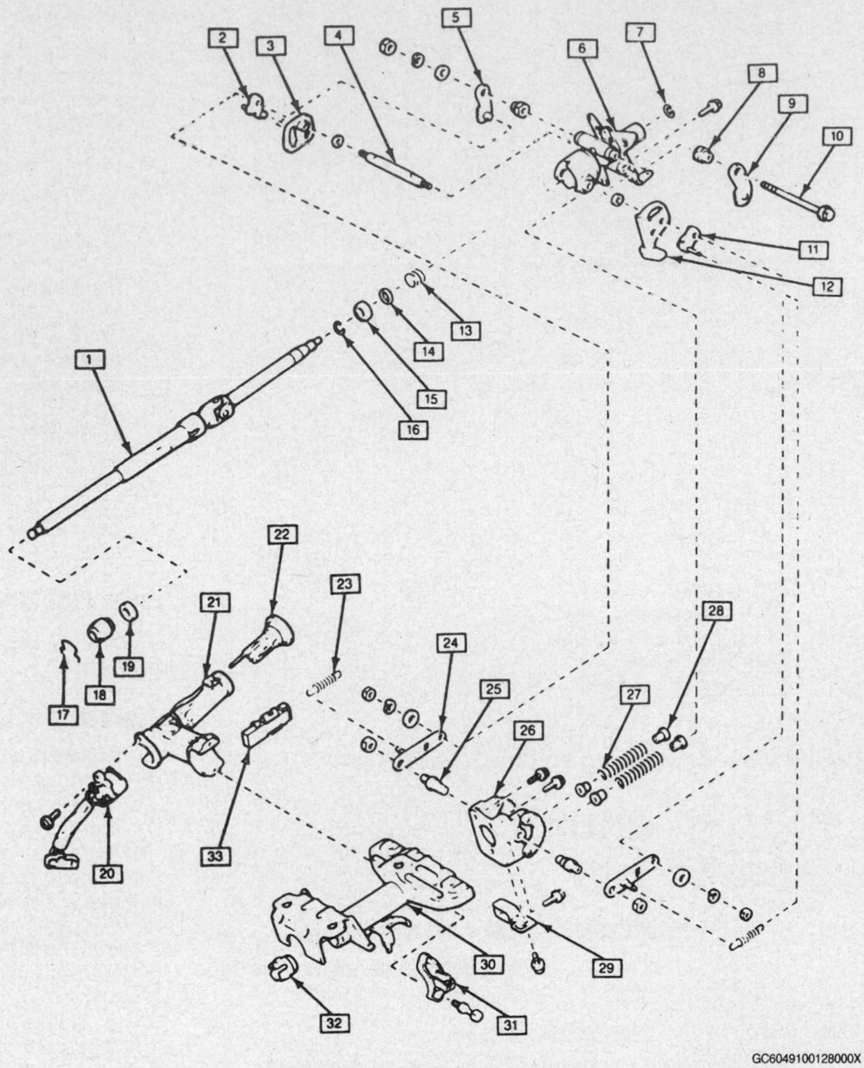
GC6049100128000X

Fig. 86 Exploded view of tilt steering shaft. 1992 Prizm

14. Remove snap ring from lower column tube using snap ring pliers, then remove main shaft collar.
15. Inspect lock cylinder assembly to ensure that lock mechanism operates properly. Replace if necessary.
16. Remove column tube bushing with a screwdriver and inspect for damage or unusual wear. Replace if necessary.

Assemble

Prior to assembling of steering column, apply GM 1050109 or equivalent grease to all parts indicated in **Fig. 88**

1. Install column tube bushing, then steering support to lower column.
2. **Torque** steering support to lower column bolts to 14 ft. lbs.
3. Install main shaft to column tube as follows:
   a. Using snap ring pliers, install snap ring.
   b. Install main shaft, bearing, collar and spring.
   c. Using compressor tool No. J 38364 or equivalent, compress main shaft spring and install a "new" snap ring with snap ring pliers.

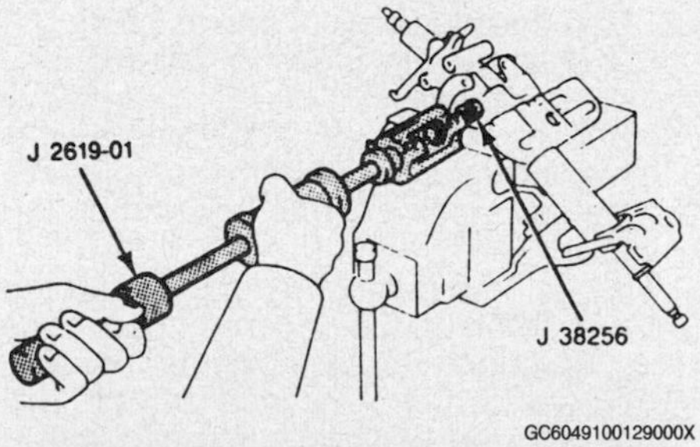
J 2619-01
J 38256
GC6049100129000X

Fig. 87 Pivot bolts removal. 1992 Prizm

4. Install wire harness clamp to column.
5. Install main shaft with upper and lower columns.
6. **Select the proper pivot bolts to match the upper column. If the column is marked with a number 1 on the side, select a grooveless bolt; if the upper column is marked with a number 2, select a grooved bolt. When one bolt has been selected, choose its opposite for the other side as both sides are different.**
7. Install pivot bolts, driving in with a hammer.
8. Install tilt lever lock bolt, tilt lever and sub lever.
9. Select collars for tilt pawl, **Fig. 89**
10. Insert collars into tilt pawls and install temporarily.
11. Engage tilt lever side pawls at the center of the ratchet and **torque** pawl nut to 70 inch lbs.
12. Install two tilt levers and **torque** tilt lever retainer forward nuts to 70 inch lbs. and retainer rearward nuts to 89 inch lbs.
13. Install two compression springs with bushings in each end and **torque** spring bolts to 70 inch lbs.
14. Install two tension springs.
15. Install lock cylinder housing onto column with "new" tapered-head bolts and **torque** bolts until the bolt heads break off.
16. Install column assembly as described in Steering Column, Replace section.
17. Install steering wheel and nut, **torque** bolt to 25 ft. lbs.

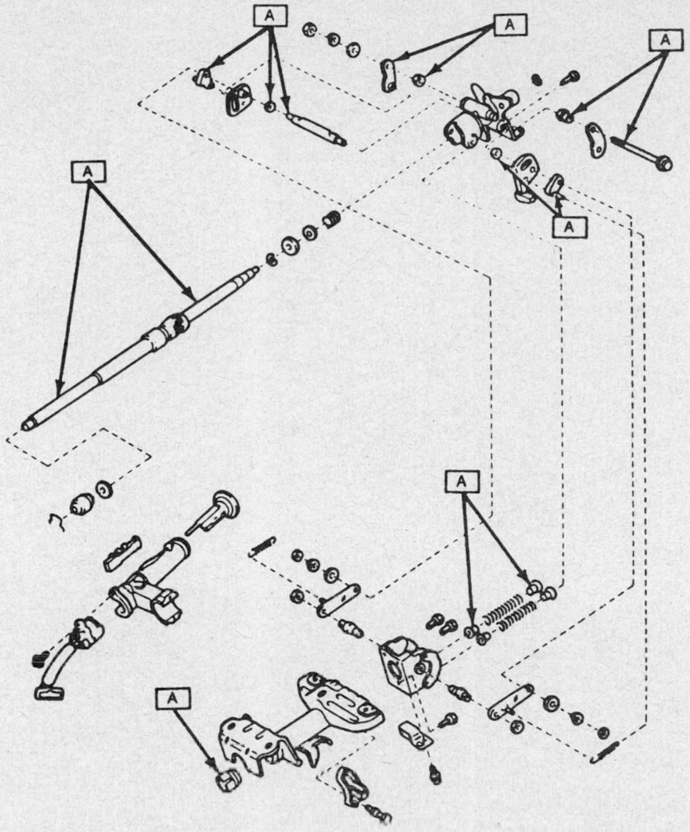
A
A
A
A
A
A
A

GC6049100130000X

Fig. 88 Tilt steering column grease points. 1992 Prizm

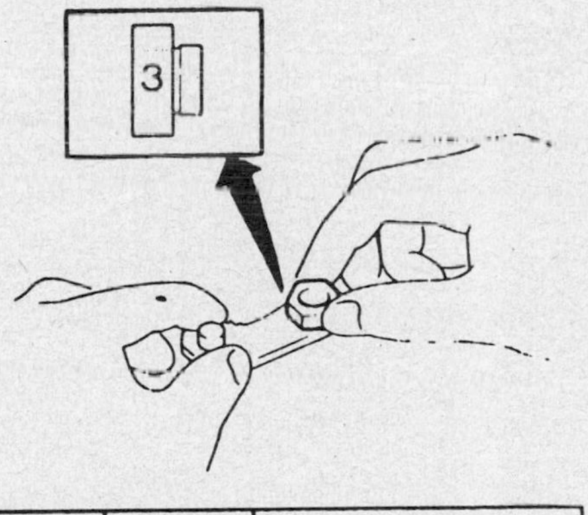
3

TILT LEVER SIDE	TILT SUB LEVER SIDE	OUTER DIAMETER
1	5	11.504–11.514 mm (0.4529–0.4533")
2	6	11.499–11.509 mm (0.4527–0.4531")
3	7	11.494–11.504 mm (0.4525–0.4529")
4	8	11.488–11.498 mm (0.4523–0.4527")

GC6049100131000X

Fig. 89 Collar selection. 1992 Prizm

18. Install horn switch connector and horn pad, then connect battery ground cable.

1993–94

The steering column cannot be serviced, a faulty column can be replaced only.

Disassemble

Refer to **Fig. 90**, for exploded view of steering column.

1. Disconnect combination switch electrical connector.
2. Loosen four screws and remove combination switch from steering column.
3. Remove ignition switch housing as follows:
   a. Using a suitable center punch, mark center of the tapered-head bolts securing the ignition switch housing.
   b. Using a .12-.16 inch (3-4 mm) drill bit, drill into tapered-head bolts.
   c. Remove two tapered-head bolts using a suitable bolt extractor, then remove the ignition switch housing.
4. Remove main shaft, noting the following:
   a. Using suitable snap ring pliers, remove upper snap ring.
   b. Remove shaft from steering column tube.
   c. Remove snap ring from shaft.

Assemble

1. Connect main shaft into column tube as follows:
   a. Using snap ring pliers, install snap ring to the inside groove of the main shaft.
   b. Insert main shaft into the tube.
   c. Using snap ring pliers, connect shaft snap ring to column.
2. Install ignition switch housing assembly to steering column, securing with two new tapered-head bolts. Tighten tapered-head bolts until heads snap off.
3. Install combination switch to steering column, securing with four screws.
4. Connect combination switch electrical connector.

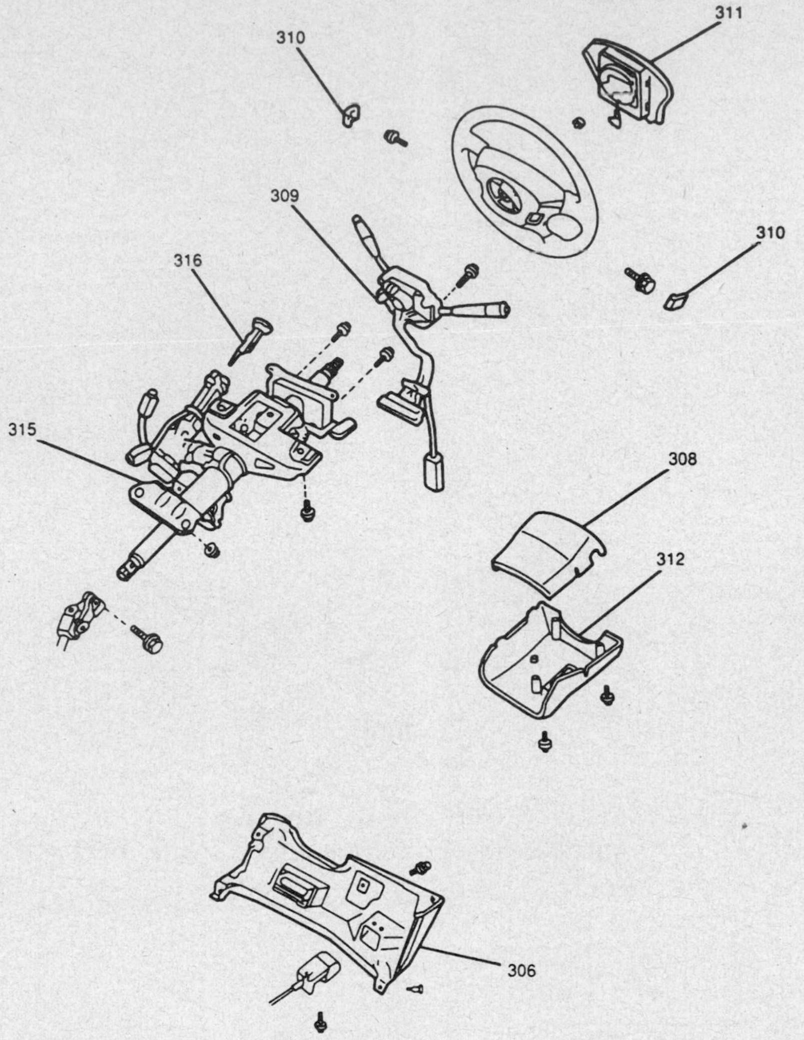
310
311
309
316
310
315
308
312
306
GC6049300132000X

306 KNEE BOLSTER
308 UPPER STEERING COLUMN COVER
309 COMBINATION SWITCH
310 SIDE TRIM COVERS
311 INFLATOR MODULE
312 LOWER STEERING COLUMN COVER
315 STEERING COLUMN ASSEMBLY
316 IGNITION SWITCH

Fig. 90 Exploded view of steering column. 1993–94 Prizm

MANUAL STEERING GEARS

TABLE OF CONTENTS

Application Chart

Year	Model	Steering Gear Type
1992-93	LeMans	Saginaw Rack & Pinion
1992-94	Metro	Suzuki Rack & Pinion
	Prizm	Toyota Rack & Pinion

Saginaw Rack & Pinion

INDEX

DESCRIPTION

The rack and pinion steering system consists of two main components, the rack and the pinion. The motion of turning the steering wheel is transferred to the pinion. The rotary motion of the pinion is then transferred through the pinion teeth which mesh with teeth on the rack, which gives the rack linear motion. The linear motion is then transmitted through the inner and outer tie rods to the steering knuckles which turn the wheels.

STEERING GEAR SERVICE

Refer to **Figs. 1 and 2** for service procedures on this Saginaw rack and pinion steering gear.

Refer to the rear of this section for tightening specifications.

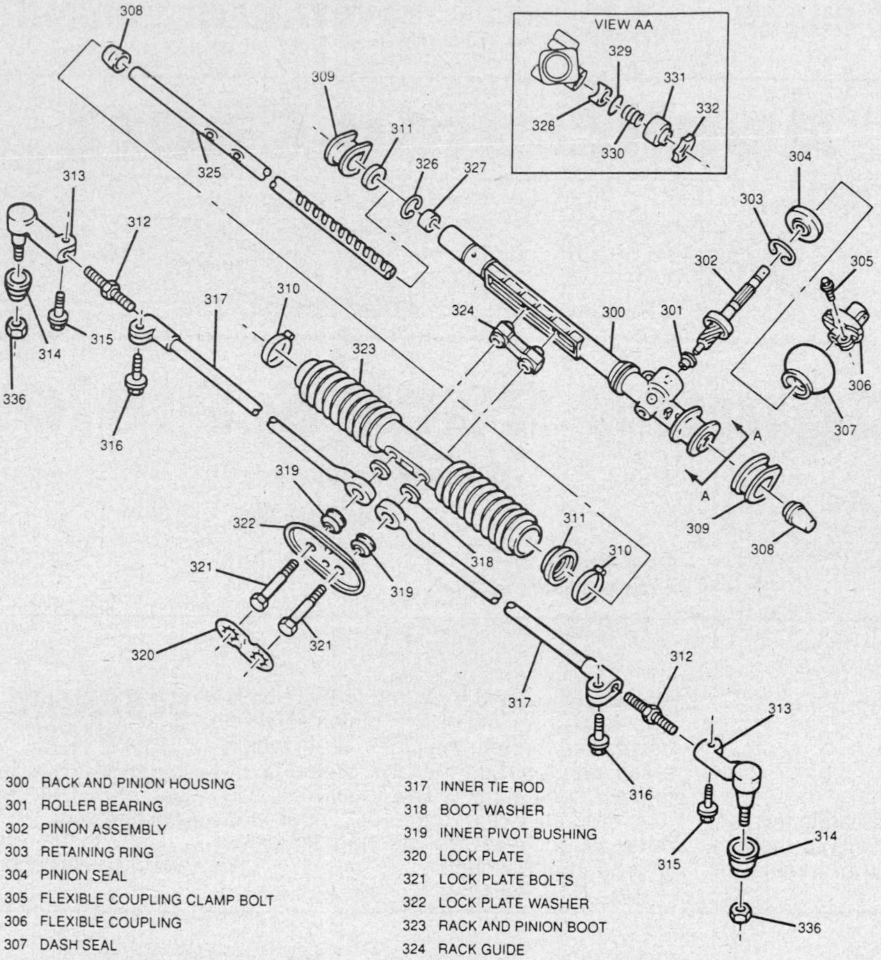
VIEW AA
308
309
311
326
327
325
313
312
317
310
324
300
301
302
303
304
305
306
307
323
314
315
336
316
319
322
321
320
318
A
329
328
330
331
332

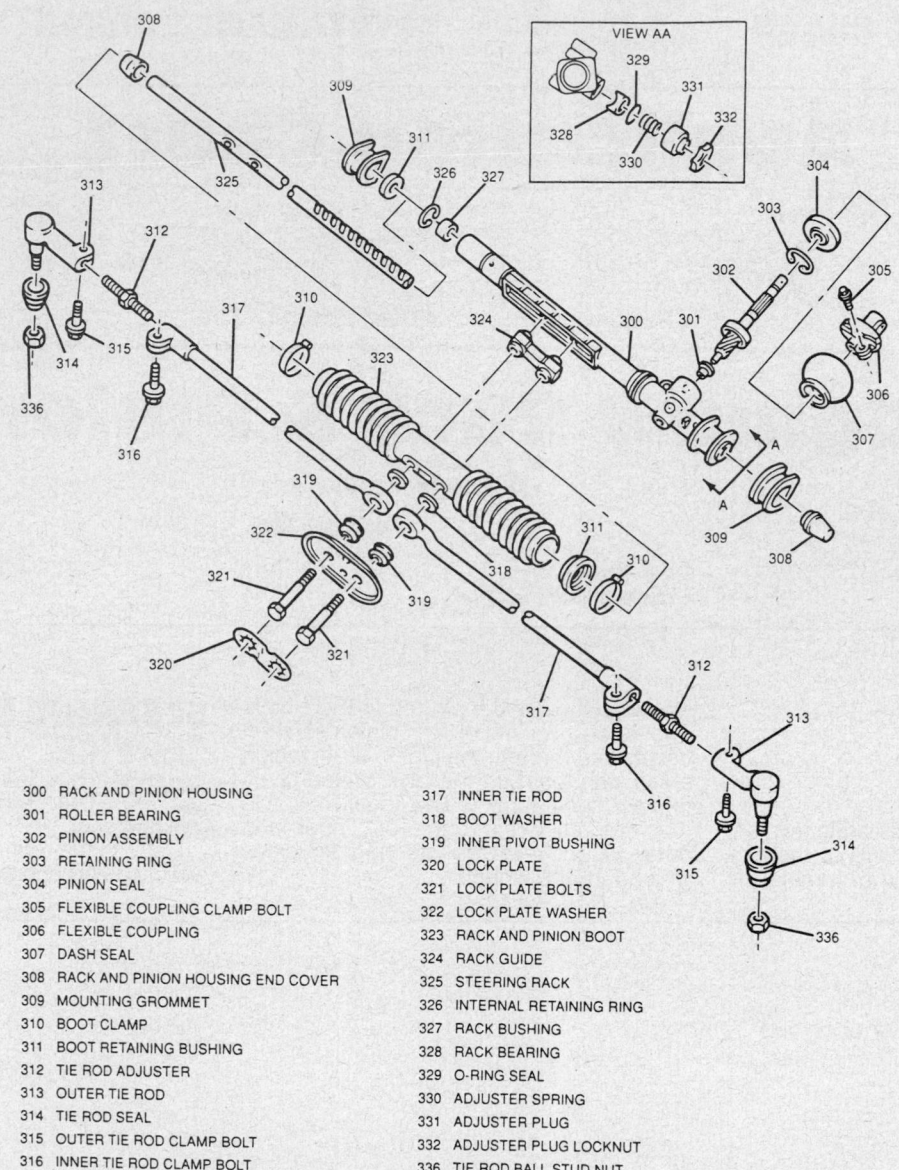

300 RACK AND PINION HOUSING
301 ROLLER BEARING
302 PINION ASSEMBLY
303 RETAINING RING
304 PINION SEAL
305 FLEXIBLE COUPLING CLAMP BOLT
306 FLEXIBLE COUPLING
307 DASH SEAL
308 RACK AND PINION HOUSING END COVER
309 MOUNTING GROMMET
310 BOOT CLAMP
311 BOOT RETAINING BUSHING
312 TIE ROD ADJUSTER
313 OUTER TIE ROD
314 TIE ROD SEAL
315 OUTER TIE ROD CLAMP BOLT
316 INNER TIE ROD CLAMP BOLT
317 INNER TIE ROD
318 BOOT WASHER
319 INNER PIVOT BUSHING
320 LOCK PLATE
321 LOCK PLATE BOLTS
322 LOCK PLATE WASHER
323 RACK AND PINION BOOT
324 RACK GUIDE
325 STEERING RACK
326 INTERNAL RETAINING RING
327 RACK BUSHING
328 RACK BEARING
329 O-RING SEAL
330 ADJUSTER SPRING
331 ADJUSTER PLUG
332 ADJUSTER PLUG LOCKNUT
336 TIE ROD BALL STUD NUT

GC6039100019000A

Fig. 1 Exploded view of Saginaw rack & pinion steering gear

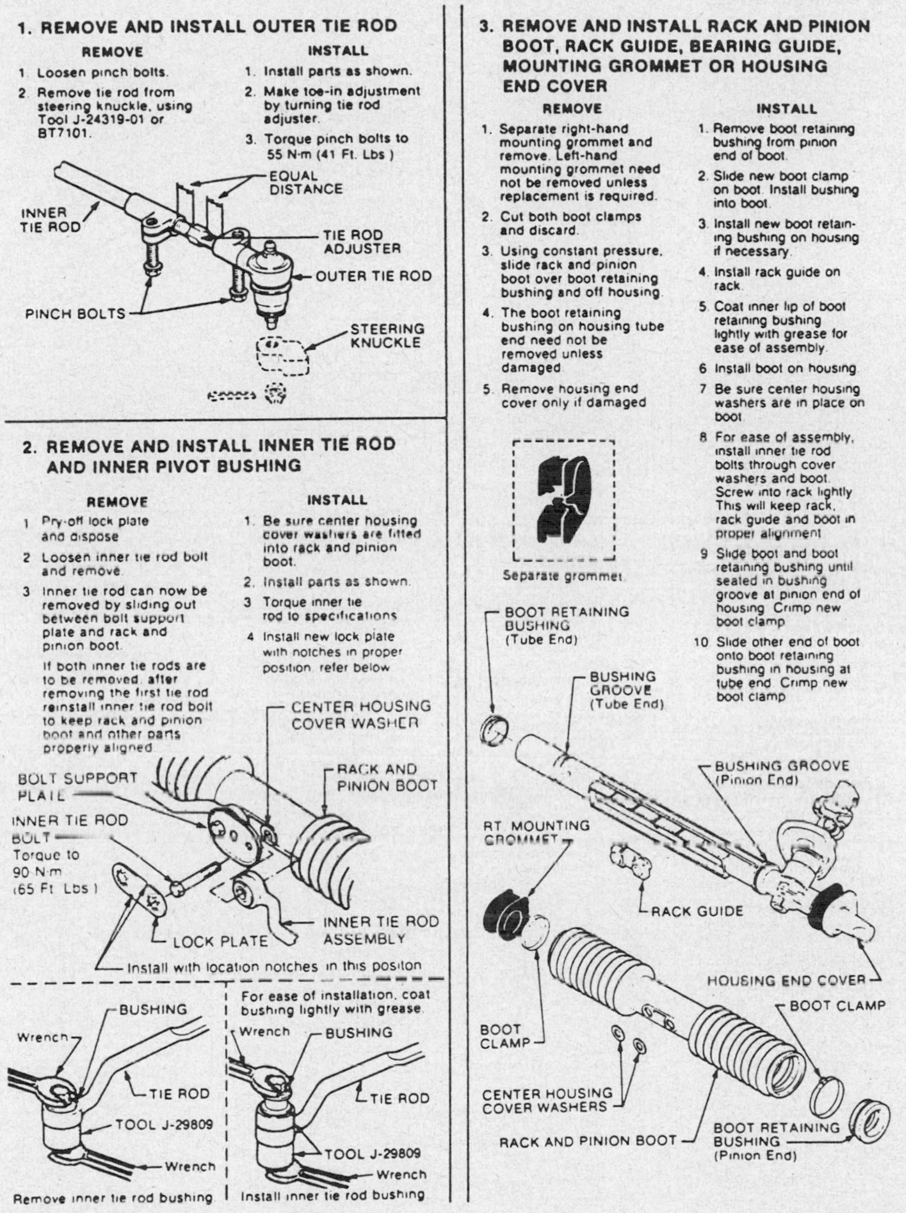
1. REMOVE AND INSTALL OUTER TIE ROD
REMOVE
1. Loosen pinch bolts.
2. Remove tie rod from steering knuckle, using Tool J-24319-01 or BT7101.
INSTALL
1. Install parts as shown.
2. Make toe-in adjustment by turning tie rod adjuster.
3. Torque pinch bolts to 55 N·m (41 Ft. Lbs.)
EQUAL DISTANCE
INNER TIE ROD
TIE ROD ADJUSTER
OUTER TIE ROD
PINCH BOLTS
STEERING KNUCKLE
2. REMOVE AND INSTALL INNER TIE ROD AND INNER PIVOT BUSHING
REMOVE
1 Pry-off lock plate and dispose
2 Loosen inner tie rod bolt and remove.
3 Inner tie rod can now be removed by sliding out between bolt support plate and rack and pinion boot.
If both inner tie rods are to be removed, after removing the first tie rod reinstall inner tie rod bolt to keep rack and pinion boot and other parts properly aligned.
INSTALL
1. Be sure center housing cover washers are fitted into rack and pinion boot.
2. Install parts as shown.
3 Torque inner tie rod to specifications
4 Install new lock plate with notches in proper position, refer below
CENTER HOUSING COVER WASHER
BOLT SUPPORT PLATE
RACK AND PINION BOOT
INNER TIE ROD BOLT
Torque to 90 N·m (65 Ft. Lbs.)
LOCK PLATE
INNER TIE ROD ASSEMBLY
Install with location notches in this positon
For ease of installation, coat bushing lightly with grease.
BUSHING
Wrench
TIE ROD
TOOL J-29809
Wrench
Remove inner tie rod bushing
Wrench
BUSHING
TIE ROD
TOOL J-29809
Wrench
Install inner tie rod bushing
3. REMOVE AND INSTALL RACK AND PINION BOOT, RACK GUIDE, BEARING GUIDE, MOUNTING GROMMET OR HOUSING END COVER
REMOVE
1. Separate right-hand mounting grommet and remove. Left-hand mounting grommet need not be removed unless replacement is required.
2. Cut both boot clamps and discard.
3. Using constant pressure, slide rack and pinion boot over boot retaining bushing and off housing.
4. The boot retaining bushing on housing tube end need not be removed unless damaged.
5. Remove housing end cover only if damaged
INSTALL
1. Remove boot retaining bushing from pinion end of boot.
2. Slide new boot clamp on boot. Install bushing into boot.
3. Install new boot retaining bushing on housing if necessary.
4. Install rack guide on rack.
5. Coat inner lip of boot retaining bushing lightly with grease for ease of assembly.
6 Install boot on housing.
7 Be sure center housing washers are in place on boot.
8 For ease of assembly, install inner tie rod bolts through cover washers and boot. Screw into rack lightly. This will keep rack, rack guide and boot in proper alignment.
9 Slide boot and boot retaining bushing until seated in bushing groove at pinion end of housing. Crimp new boot clamp.
10 Slide other end of boot onto boot retaining bushing in housing at tube end. Crimp new boot clamp.
Separate grommet
BOOT RETAINING BUSHING (Tube End)
BUSHING GROOVE (Tube End)
BUSHING GROOVE (Pinion End)
RT MOUNTING GROMMET
RACK GUIDE
HOUSING END COVER
BOOT CLAMP
BOOT CLAMP
CENTER HOUSING COVER WASHERS
RACK AND PINION BOOT
BOOT RETAINING BUSHING (Pinion End)
GC6039100020010X

Fig. 2 Saginaw rack & pinion steering gear service procedures. (Part 1 of 3)

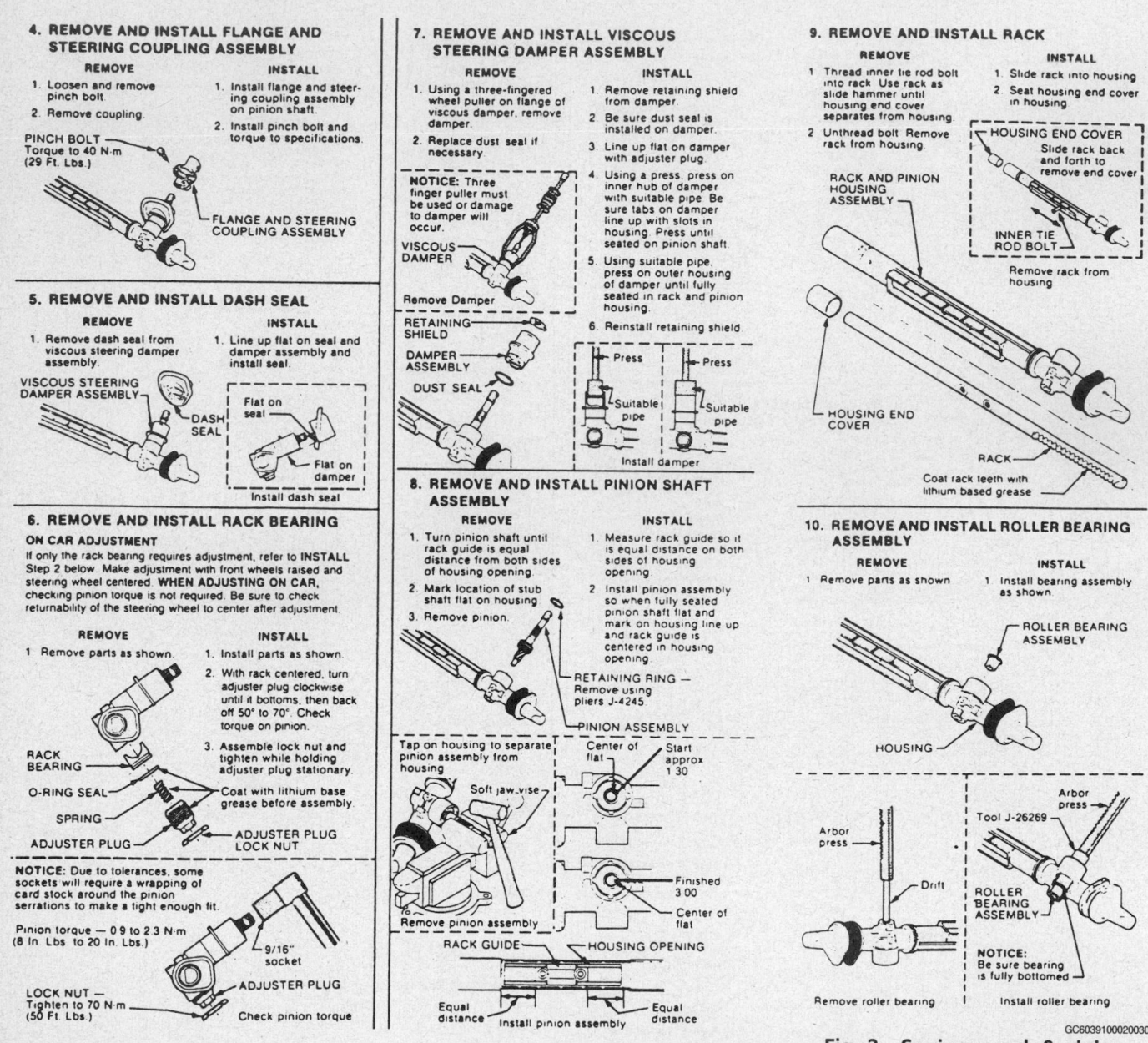

4. REMOVE AND INSTALL FLANGE AND STEERING COUPLING ASSEMBLY

REMOVE

1. Loosen and remove pinch bolt.
2. Remove coupling.

INSTALL

1. Install flange and steering coupling assembly on pinion shaft.
2. Install pinch bolt and torque to specifications.

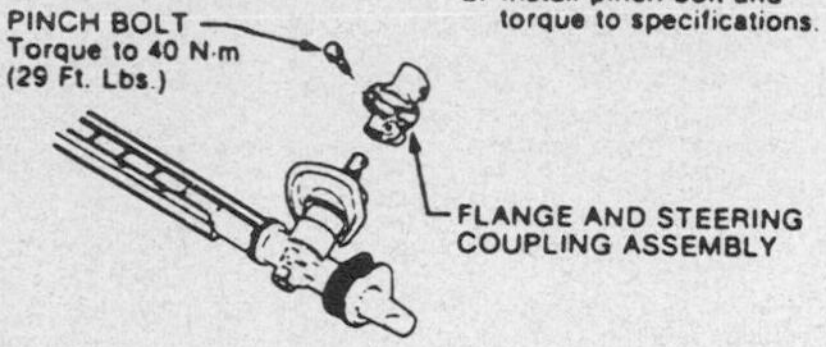
PINCH BOLT
Torque to 40 N·m
(29 Ft. Lbs.)
FLANGE AND STEERING
COUPLING ASSEMBLY

5. REMOVE AND INSTALL DASH SEAL

REMOVE

1. Remove dash seal from viscous steering damper assembly.

INSTALL

1. Line up flat on seal and damper assembly and install seal.

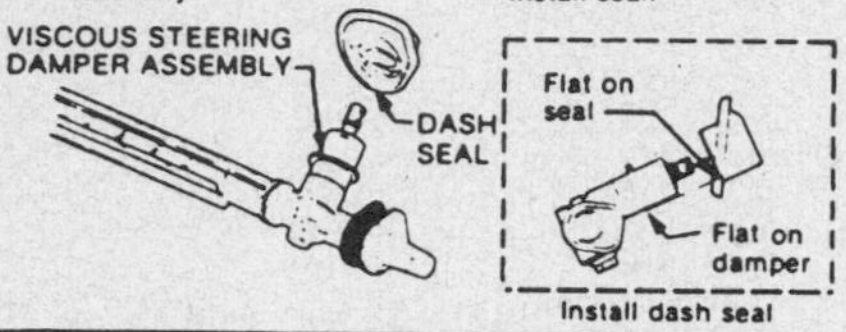
VISCOUS STEERING
DAMPER ASSEMBLY
DASH
SEAL
Flat on
seal
Flat on
damper
Install dash seal

6. REMOVE AND INSTALL RACK BEARING

ON CAR ADJUSTMENT

If only the rack bearing requires adjustment, refer to **INSTALL** Step 2 below. Make adjustment with front wheels raised and steering wheel centered. **WHEN ADJUSTING ON CAR,** checking pinion torque is not required. Be sure to check returnability of the steering wheel to center after adjustment.

REMOVE

1. Remove parts as shown.

INSTALL

1. Install parts as shown.
2. With rack centered, turn adjuster plug clockwise until it bottoms, then back off 50° to 70°. Check torque on pinion.
3. Assemble lock nut and tighten while holding adjuster plug stationary.

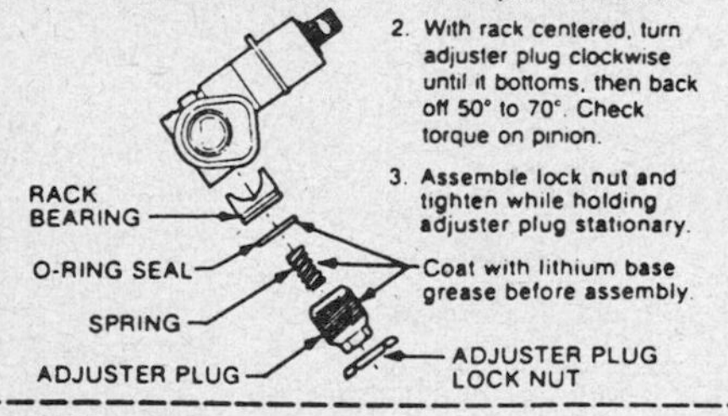
RACK
BEARING
O-RING SEAL
SPRING
ADJUSTER PLUG
Coat with lithium base
grease before assembly.
ADJUSTER PLUG
LOCK NUT

NOTICE: Due to tolerances, some sockets will require a wrapping of card stock around the pinion serrations to make a tight enough fit.

Pinion torque — 0.9 to 2.3 N·m (8 In. Lbs. to 20 In. Lbs.)

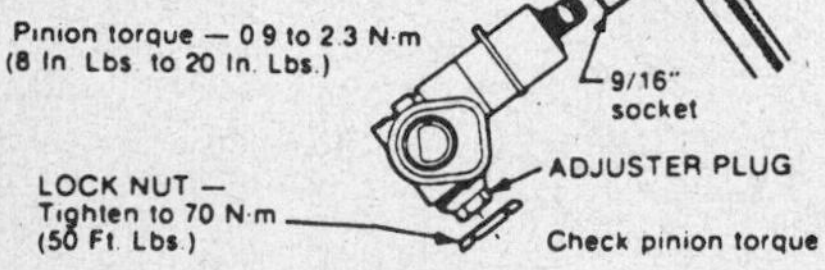
9/16"
socket
ADJUSTER PLUG
LOCK NUT —
Tighten to 70 N·m
(50 Ft. Lbs.)
Check pinion torque

7. REMOVE AND INSTALL VISCOUS STEERING DAMPER ASSEMBLY

REMOVE

1. Using a three-fingered wheel puller on flange of viscous damper, remove damper.
2. Replace dust seal if necessary.

NOTICE: Three finger puller must be used or damage to damper will occur.

INSTALL

1. Remove retaining shield from damper.
2. Be sure dust seal is installed on damper.
3. Line up flat on damper with adjuster plug.
4. Using a press, press on inner hub of damper with suitable pipe. Be sure tabs on damper line up with slots in housing. Press until seated on pinion shaft.
5. Using suitable pipe, press on outer housing of damper until fully seated in rack and pinion housing.
6. Reinstall retaining shield.

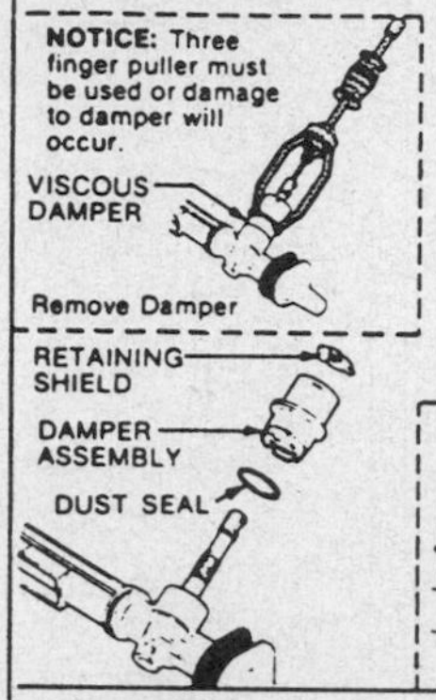
VISCOUS
DAMPER
Remove Damper
RETAINING
SHIELD
DAMPER
ASSEMBLY
DUST SEAL

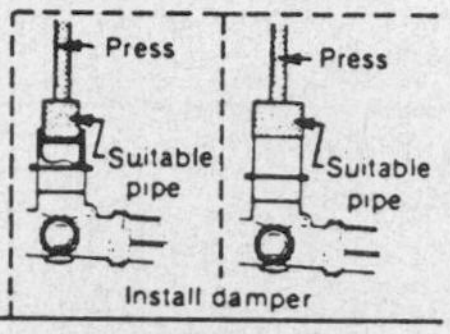
Press
Suitable
pipe
Press
Suitable
pipe
Install damper

8. REMOVE AND INSTALL PINION SHAFT ASSEMBLY

REMOVE

1. Turn pinion shaft until rack guide is equal distance from both sides of housing opening.
2. Mark location of stub shaft flat on housing.
3. Remove pinion.

INSTALL

1. Measure rack guide so it is equal distance on both sides of housing opening.
2. Install pinion assembly so when fully seated pinion shaft flat and mark on housing line up and rack guide is centered in housing opening.

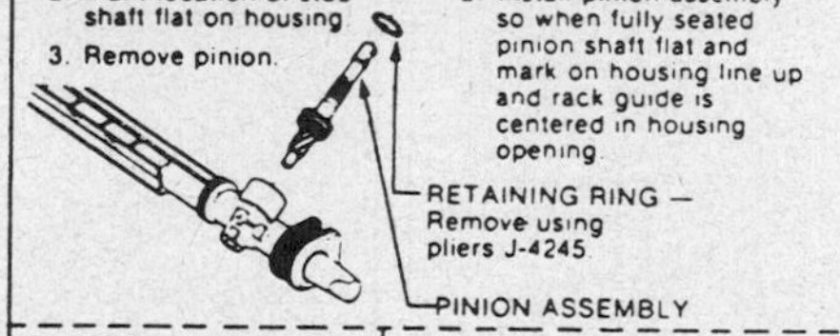
RETAINING RING —
Remove using
pliers J-4245
PINION ASSEMBLY

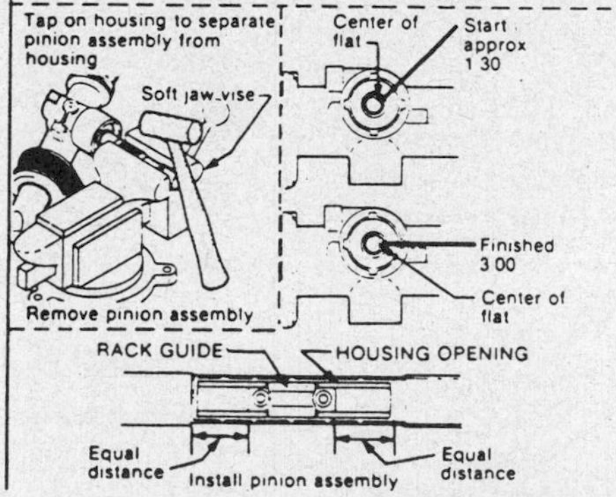
Tap on housing to separate
pinion assembly from
housing
Soft jaw vise
Remove pinion assembly
Center of
flat
Start
approx
1:30
Finished
3:00
Center of
flat
RACK GUIDE
HOUSING OPENING
Equal
distance
Install pinion assembly
Equal
distance

GC6039100020020X

Fig. 2 Saginaw rack & pinion steering gear service procedures. (Part 2 of 3)

9. REMOVE AND INSTALL RACK

REMOVE

1. Thread inner tie rod bolt into rack. Use rack as slide hammer until housing end cover separates from housing.
2. Unthread bolt. Remove rack from housing.

INSTALL

1. Slide rack into housing.
2. Seat housing end cover in housing.

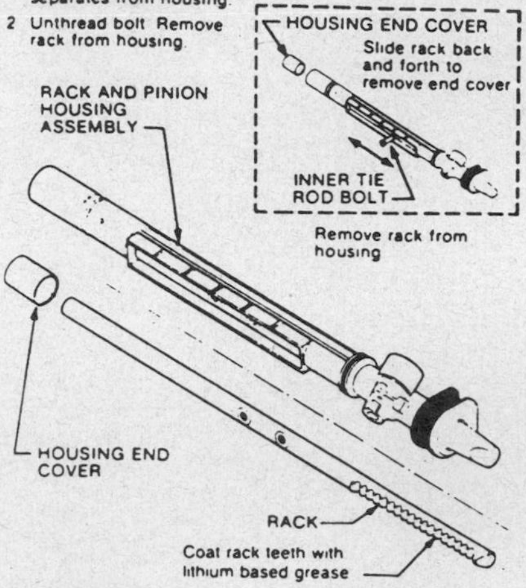
HOUSING END COVER
Slide rack back
and forth to
remove end cover
INNER TIE
ROD BOLT
Remove rack from
housing
RACK AND PINION
HOUSING
ASSEMBLY
HOUSING END
COVER
RACK
Coat rack teeth with
lithium based grease

10. REMOVE AND INSTALL ROLLER BEARING ASSEMBLY

REMOVE

1. Remove parts as shown.

INSTALL

1. Install bearing assembly as shown.

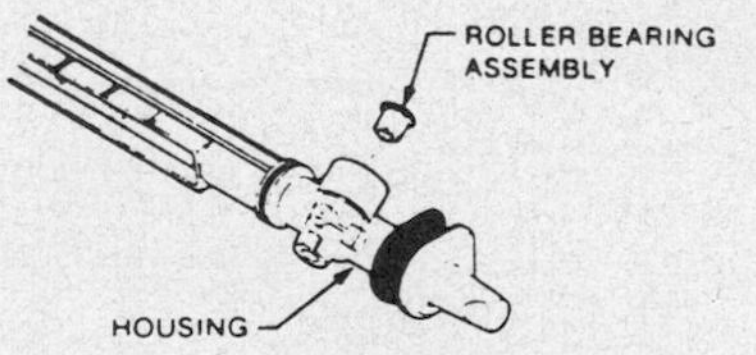
ROLLER BEARING
ASSEMBLY
HOUSING

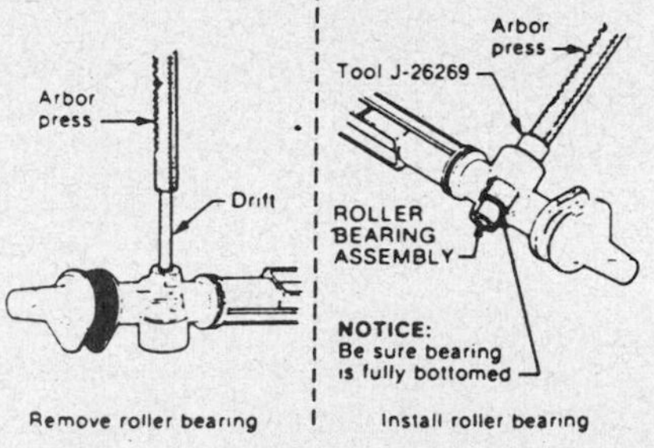
Arbor
press
Drift
Remove roller bearing
Arbor
press
Tool J-26269
ROLLER
BEARING
ASSEMBLY
NOTICE:
Be sure bearing
is fully bottomed
Install roller bearing

GC6039100020030X

Fig. 2 Saginaw rack & pinion steering gear service procedures. (Part 3 of 3)

Suzuki Rack & Pinion

INDEX

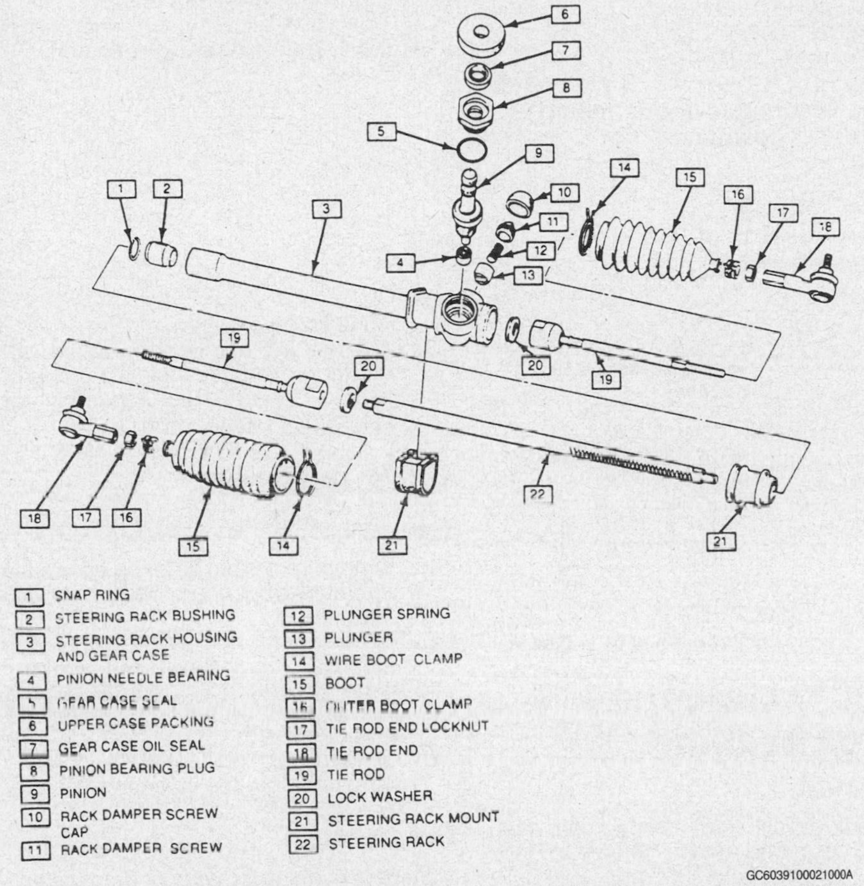

1 SNAP RING
2 STEERING RACK BUSHING
3 STEERING RACK HOUSING AND GEAR CASE
4 PINION NEEDLE BEARING
5 GEAR CASE SEAL
6 UPPER CASE PACKING
7 GEAR CASE OIL SEAL
8 PINION BEARING PLUG
9 PINION
10 RACK DAMPER SCREW CAP
11 RACK DAMPER SCREW
12 PLUNGER SPRING
13 PLUNGER
14 WIRE BOOT CLAMP
15 BOOT
16 OUTER BOOT CLAMP
17 TIE ROD END LOCKNUT
18 TIE ROD END
19 TIE ROD
20 LOCK WASHER
21 STEERING RACK MOUNT
22 STEERING RACK
GC6039100021000A

Fig. 1 Exploded view of manual rack & pinion steering assembly

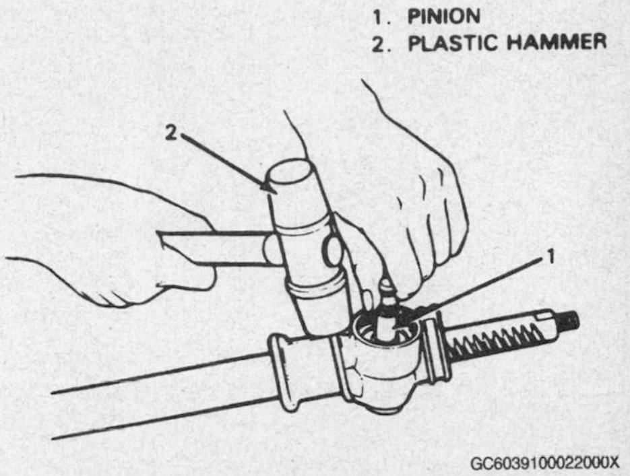

1. PINION
2. PLASTIC HAMMER
GC6039100022000X

Fig. 2 Separating pinion from housing

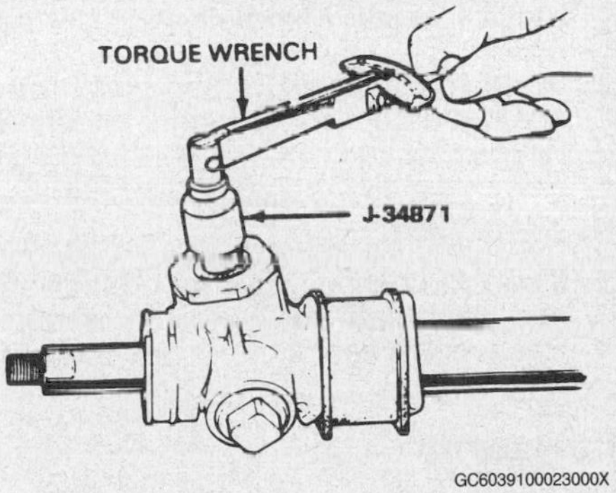

TORQUE WRENCH
J-34871
GC6039100023000X

Fig. 3 Checking pinion torque

DESCRIPTION

The rack and pinion steering system consists of two main components, the rack and the pinion. The motion of turning the steering wheel is transferred to the pinion. The rotary motion of the pinion is then transferred through the pinion teeth which mesh with teeth on the rack, which gives the rack linear motion. The linear motion is then transmitted through the inner and outer tie rods to the steering knuckles which turn the wheels.

STEERING GEAR SERVICE

Refer to Fig. 1 when servicing steering gear assembly.

STEERING PINION

Removal

1. Remove rack damper screw cap and damper screw.
2. Remove rack plunger spring and rack plunger.
3. Remove steering gear case packing.
4. Using a 43 mm socket, remove pinion bearing plug with oil seal.
5. Tap on position **Fig. 2** with a plastic hammer to separate pinion assembly from housing.

Inspection

1. Inspect pinion teeth for wear or damage.
2. Inspect oil seal for wear or damage.
3. Inspect plunger spring for deterioration and screw cap, screw and plunger for wear or damage.
4. Inspect gear case packing for damage. Replace all seals and any parts found defective.

Assembly

1. Apply grease to pinion teeth and gear case oil seal lip.
2. Install pinion assembly.
3. Install pinion case seal and bearing plug. **Torque** plug to 70. ft. lbs.
4. Install oil seal and gear case packing.
5. Install rack plunger, plunger spring and damper screw.
6. After tightening damper screw, back it off 90° and check rotational torque of pinion. Pinion **torque** should be 9.6 inch lbs., **Fig. 3.**

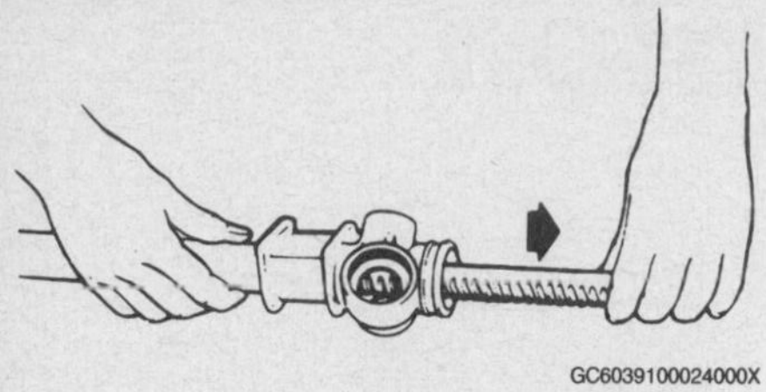
GC6039100024000X

Fig. 4 Rack removal from gear case

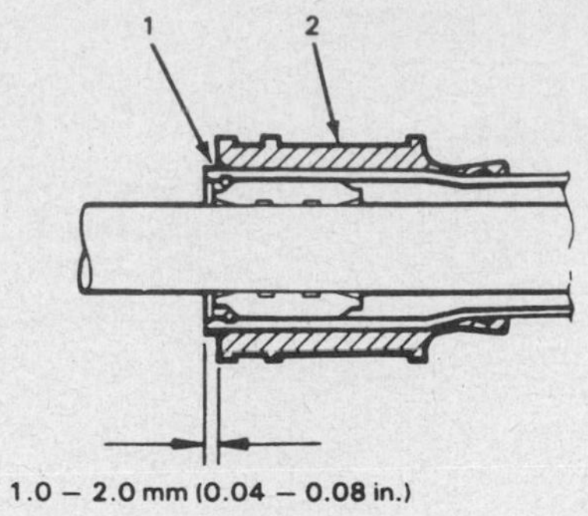
1. STEERING RACK HOUSING
2. RACK SIDE MOUNT
1
2
1.0 – 2.0 mm (0.04 – 0.08 in.)
GC6039100025000X

Fig. 5 Ensuring rack side mount is positioned

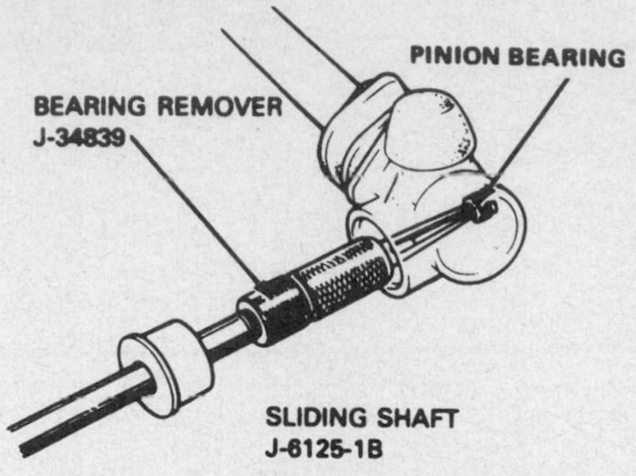
PINION BEARING
BEARING REMOVER
J-34839
SLIDING SHAFT
J-6125-1B
GC6039100026000X

Fig. 6 Pinion bearing removal

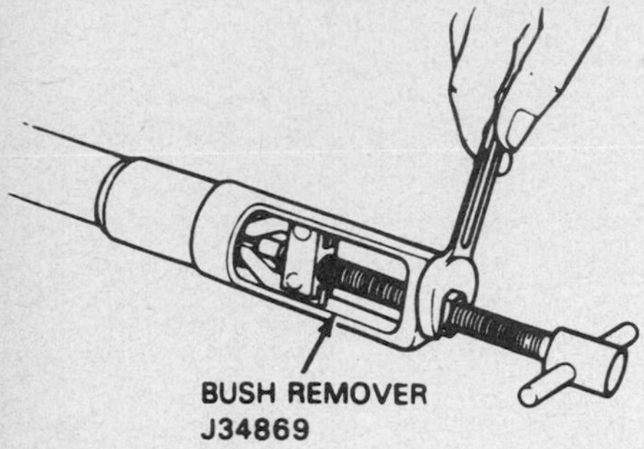
BUSH REMOVER
J34869
GC6039100027000X

Fig. 7 Rack bushing removal

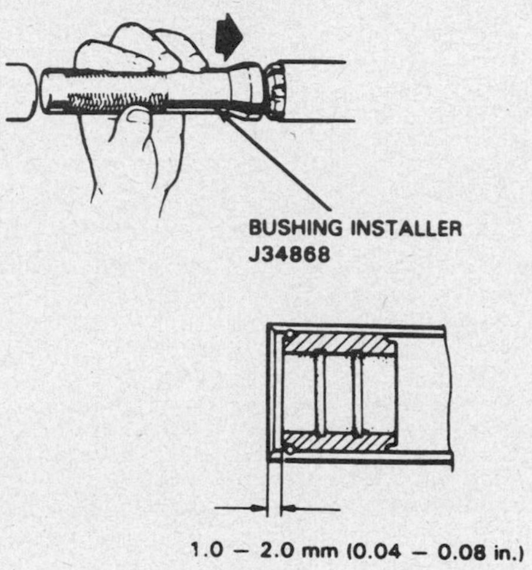
BUSHING INSTALLER
J34868
1.0 – 2.0 mm (0.04 – 0.08 in.)
GC6039100028000X

Fig. 8 Rack bushing installation

STEERING RACK

Removal

1. Remove boot wires and clips. Slide boots toward tie rod end.
2. Unbend tie rod lock washers and remove tie rods. Mark left and right tie rods.
3. Remove rack plunger and pinion assembly as described under Steering Pinion.
4. Remove rack from gear case **Fig. 4.**

Inspection

1. Inspect steering rack for deflection and rack teeth for wear or damage. Rack deflection should not exceed .016 inch.

Assembly

1. Apply a suitable lithium based grease to rack teeth surface.
2. Install rack into steering gear case, in opposite direction of removal.
3. Install pinion assembly and plunger assembly as described under "Steering Rack" Removal.
4. Install boot to steering rack housing, ensuring that rack side mount is positioned as shown in **Fig. 5.**
5. Install tie rods as described under "Steering Rack."

PINION BEARING

Removal

1. Remove rack from steering gear case as described under "Steering Rack Removal."
2. Remove pinion bearing using tools Nos. J-34839 and J-6125-1B, as shown in **Fig. 6.**

Inspection

Check pinion bearing for wear or damages. Replace if found defective.

Assembly

1. Apply a suitable lithium based grease to pinion bearing rollers.
2. Press fit pinion bearing into gear case using bearing installer tool No. J-34840 or equivalent.
3. After bearing has been installed, ensure that rollers are installed properly.
4. Refer to "Steering Rack Assembly" for steering rack installation.

RACK BUSHING

Removal

1. Remove rack from steering gear case as described under "Steering Rack Removal."
2. Remove snap ring. **When removing bushing, be careful not to pull bushing while holding gear case in vise as the housing may come off gear case.**
3. Remove bushing from rack housing using tool J-34869 or equivalent, **Fig. 7.**

Inspection

Inspect bushing for wear or damage and replace if necessary.

Assembly

1. Apply a suitable lithium based grease to inner surface of bushing.
2. Using bushing installer tool No.J-34868 or equivalent, install bushing into rack housing, ensuring bushing to housing clearance is as shown, **Fig. 8.**
3. Install snap ring.
4. Install steering rack assembly as described under Steering Rack Assembly.

Toyota Rack & Pinion

INDEX

DESCRIPTION

This steering system converts rotary motion to linear motion as follows; when the steering wheel is turned, rotary motion is transferred to the steering shaft, shaft joint and rack pinion. The pinion teeth mesh with teeth on the rack and the rotary motion is transferred to the rack and changed to linear motion. The linear force is then transmitted through the tie rods and to the steering knuckles which steer the front wheels.

STEERING GEAR SERVICE

DISASSEMBLE

1. Clamp steering gear housing in a suitable vise, **Figs. 1 and 2**.
2. Remove tie rod ends as follows:
   a. Place match marks on tie rod ends and tie rods.
   b. Loosen and remove locknuts and tie rod ends.
3. Remove rack boots.
4. Remove tie rods and locking washers as follows:
   a. Push back bent section of locking washer.
   b. Using tie rod housing wrench tool No. J-35414 and steering rack end wrench tool No. J-35418 or equivalents, remove tie rod.
5. Remove steering gear case upper oil seal as follows:
   a. Remove dust cover.
   b. Remove snap ring with suitable snap ring pliers.
   c. Remove oil seal.

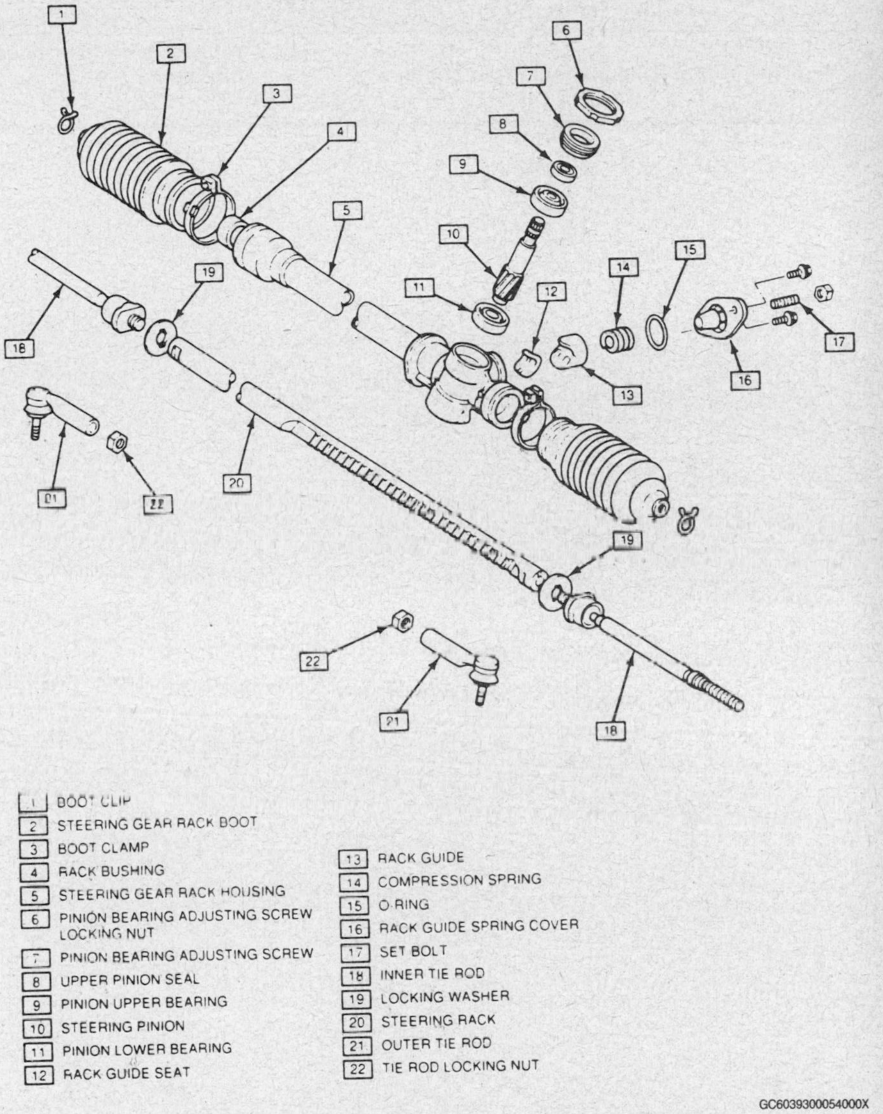
1 BOOT CLIP
2 STEERING GEAR RACK BOOT
3 BOOT CLAMP
4 RACK BUSHING
5 STEERING GEAR RACK HOUSING
6 PINION BEARING ADJUSTING SCREW LOCKING NUT
7 PINION BEARING ADJUSTING SCREW
8 UPPER PINION SEAL
9 PINION UPPER BEARING
10 STEERING PINION
11 PINION LOWER BEARING
12 RACK GUIDE SEAT
13 RACK GUIDE
14 COMPRESSION SPRING
15 O RING
16 RACK GUIDE SPRING COVER
17 SET BOLT
18 INNER TIE ROD
19 LOCKING WASHER
20 STEERING RACK
21 OUTER TIE ROD
22 TIE ROD LOCKING NUT
GC6039300054000X

Fig. 1 Exploded view of Toyota rack & pinion steering gear

ASSEMBLE

1. Coat new upper oil seal with manual steering gear lube No. 1052182 or equivalent, then install seal followed by snap ring and dust cover.
2. Install tie rods and locking washers as follows:
   a. Install new locking washer.
   b. Using tie rod housing wrench tool No. J-35414 and steering rack end wrench tool No. J-35418 or equivalents, install tie rods and **torque** to 53 ft. lbs.
   c. Stake locking claw washer with a brass bar and hammer.
3. Install rubber rack boots being careful not to twist or damage them.
4. Install tie rod ends as follows:
   a. Screw locknuts and tie rod ends onto tie rods until match marks are aligned.
   b. **Torque** tie rod end locknuts to 41 ft. lbs.

TIGHTENING SPECIFICATIONS

NOTE: All Specifications In Ft. Lbs. Unless Noted.

Year & Model	Adjuster Plug Locknut	Flange & Coupling Pinch Bolt	Coupling To Column Pinch Bolt	Inner Tie Rod Pinch Bolts	Outer Tie Rod Pinch Bolts	Inner Tie Rod Bolt	Pinion Preload ① ②	Inner Tie Rod Housing To Rack	Outer Tie Rod Jam Nut
LeMans	52	18	18	16	16	66	14 max.	—	44
Metro	70	18	18	—	33 ③	—	7 max.	63	32
Prizm	83	26	26	—	41 ③	53	3.5 max.	—	41

①—Inch lbs.
②—Effort required to sustain input shaft rotation with gear filled with lubricant.
③—Locknut

POWER STEERING

NOTE: Automatic Transmission Fluid Should Not Be Used In These Power Steering Systems. ATF Is Not Compatible With The Seals And Hoses Used In This System And Will Eventually Cause Damage. Also, Power Steering Fluid Must Withstand Very High Pressure (About 1400 psi), Whereas Transmission Fluid Does Not Have The Need To Operate At These Pressures. If ATF Has Been Added To A Power Steering System As In An Emergency Situation, The System Should Be Drained, Flushed And Refilled With Power Steering Fluid As Soon As Possible To Avoid Damage.

TABLE OF CONTENTS

Application Chart

Model	Front Wheel Drive Vehicles	Rear Wheel Drive Vehicles
Corvette, Camaro & Firbird①	—	Saginaw Rack & Pinion
Except Corvette, Camaro & Firebird①	—	Saginaw Rotary Valve
Except Prizm & Storm	Saginaw Rack & Pinion	—
Prizm	Toyota Rack & Pinion	—
Storm	Jidosha Kiki Rack & Pinion	—

①—1993-94 Camaro & Firebird.

Power Steering Pressure Specifications

Model	Year	Engine	Maximum Pressure Reading, Gauge Valve Open	Minimum Pressure Reading, Gauge Valve Closed
Achieva	1992–94	2.3L & 3.3L	150	1000②
Beretta	1992–94	2.2L, 2.3L & 3.1L	150	1000②
Bonneville	1992–94	3800	150	1000②
Brougham & Fleetwood (RWD)	1992-94	5.0L & 5.7L	200	1250
Camaro	1992	3.1L, 5.0L & 5.7L	200	1000
	1993-94	3.4L & 5.7L	150	1000②
Caprice & Impala SS	1992	4.3L, 5.0L & 5.7L	200	1000
	1993-94	4.3L, 5.0L & 5.7L	150	1000②
Cavalier	1992–94	2.2L & 3.1L	150	1000②
Century	1992	2.5L & 3.3L	150	1250
	1993-94	2.2L & 3.3L	150	②
Corsica	1992–94	2.2L, 2.3L & 3.1L	150	1000
Corvette	1992–94	5.7L	150	1250
Custom Cruiser	1992	5.0L & 5.7L	200	1000
Cutlass Ciera	1992	2.5L & 3.3L	150	1250
	1993-94	2.2L & 3.3L	150	②

Continued

Power Steering Pressure Specifications -Continued

Model	Year	Engine	Maximum Pressure Reading, Gauge Valve Open	Minimum Pressure Reading, Gauge Valve Closed
Cutlass Cruiser	1992	2.5L & 3.3L	150	1250
	1993-94	2.2L & 3.3L	150	②
Cutlass Supreme	1992-94	3.1L	150	②
	1992-94	3.4L	181	②
DeVille	1992	4.9L	200	1250
	1993-94	4.6L & 4.9L	150	1000②
Eldorado	1992	4.9L	200	1250
	1993-94	4.6L & 4.9L	200	1500②
Firebird	1992	3.1L	200	1000
	1992	5.0L & 5.7L	200	1000
	1993-94	3.4L & 5.7L	150	1000②
Fleetwood (FWD)	1992	4.9L	200	1250
Grand Am	1992-94	2.3L & 3.3L	150	1000②
Grand Prix	1992-94	3.1L	150	②
	1992-94	3.4L	181	②
LeMans	1992-93	1.6L	200	②
LeSabre	1992	3800	200	1250
	1993-94	3800	150	1000②
Lumina	1992	2.5L	200	②
	1992-94	3.1L	150	②
	1992-94	3.4L	181	②
	1993	2.2L	200	②
Park Avenue	1992	3800	200	1250
	1993-94	3800	150	1000②
Prizm	1992-94	1.6L	—	924
	1993-94	1.8L	—	924
Regal	1992	3.1L	150	1250
	1992	3800	200	1250
	1993-94	3.1L	150	②
	1993-94	3800	200	②
Riviera	1992-93	3800	200	1250
Roadmaster	1992-94	5.7L	150	1000②
Seville	1993-94	4.6L & 4.9L	200	1500②
Skylark	1992-94	2.3L, 3.1L & 3.3L	150	1000②
Storm	1992-93	1.6L & 1.8L	—	924
Sunbird	1992-94	2.0L & 3.1L	150	1000②
Toronado/Trofeo	1992	3800	200	1250
88	1992	3800	200	1000①
	1993-94	3800	150	1000②
98	1992	3800	200	1000①
	1993-94	3800	150	1000②

①—Except TC style pump, 1000 psi; TC style pump, 1250 psi.

②— Fully close and reopen valve three times. Record highest pressure readings each time valve is closed. Do not leave valve fully closed for more than five seconds. Each reading should be at least 1000 psi; readings should be within 50 psi of each other.

Power Steering Pumps

INDEX

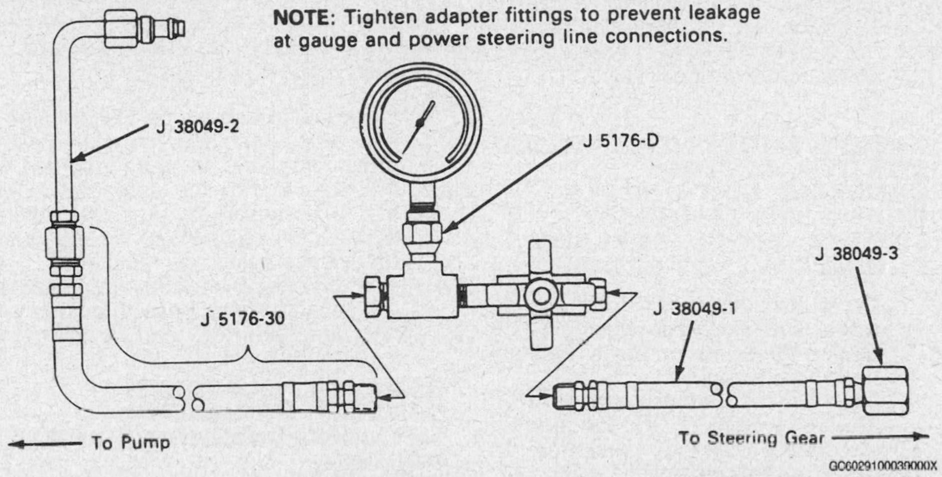

NOTE: Tighten adapter fittings to prevent leakage at gauge and power steering line connections.
J 38049-2
J 5176-D
J 38049-3
J 38049-1
J 5176-30
To Pump
To Steering Gear

Fig. 1 Power steering pressure gauge connections. Cutlass Supreme, Grand Prix, Lumina & Regal w/2.3L, 3.1L, 3.4L & 3800 Engines

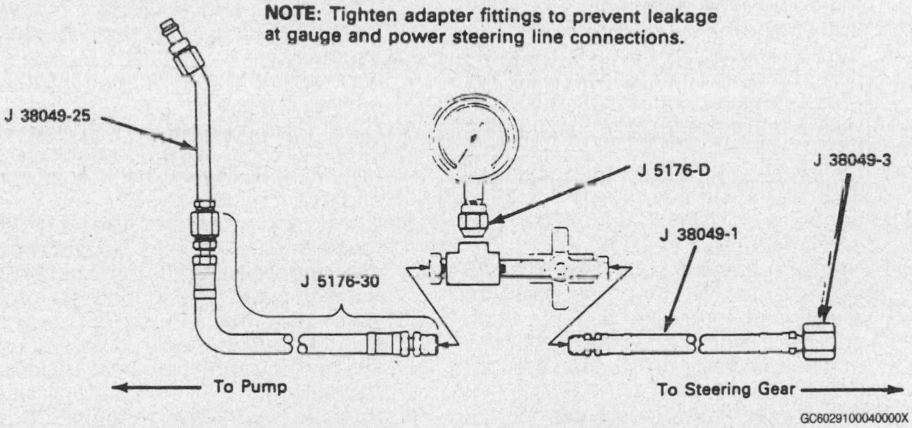

NOTE: Tighten adapter fittings to prevent leakage at gauge and power steering line connections.
J 38049-25
J 5176-D
J 38049-3
J 38049-1
J 5176-30
To Pump
To Steering Gear
GC6029100040000X

Fig. 2 Power steering pressure gauge connections. Lumina w/2.5L/4-151 Engine

DIAGNOSIS & TESTING

SYSTEM PRESSURE TEST

When performing system test procedures, power steering pressures can easily exceed 1000 psi. Extreme caution must be exercised when performing these tests to prevent personal injury.

CUTLASS SUPREME, GRAND PRIX, LUMINA & REGAL

Models w/2.3L/4-138, 3.1L/V6-191, 3.4L/V6-204 & 3800/V6-231 Engines

The following procedure has been revised by a Technical Service Bulletin.

1. **On models with 3.4L/V6-204 and 3800/V6-231 engines,** remove ECM cover/coolant reservoir and lay aside.
2. **On models with 3.1L/V6-204 engines,** remove fuse block shield and AIR belt, if equipped.
3. **On models with 3.1L/V6-204 and 3800/V6-231 engines,** partially remove serpentine belt.
4. **On all models,** open retaining clip from high pressure pipe.
5. Remove high pressure pipe from pump. **Catch any fluid that may drain to avoid fluid seepage into engine and keep high pressure pipe away from belt.**
6. **On models with 3.1L/V6-204 and 3800/V6-231 engines,** install serpentine belt.
7. **On all models,** install power steering pressure gauge tool No. J-5176-D or equivalent as shown in **Fig. 1.**
8. Open valve on pressure gauge.
9. Start engine and allow system to reach operating temperature. Stop engine and check fluid level, add if necessary.
10. Start engine and check pressure.
11. **On models with 3.4L/V6-204 engine,** pressure reading should be under 181 psi. If pressure is above 181 psi, check hoses for restrictions.
12. **On models with 2.3L/4-138 and 3.1L/V6-204 engines,** pressure reading should be under 150 psi. If pressure is above 150 psi, check hoses for restrictions.
13. **On models with 3800/V6-231 engine,** pressure reading should be under 200 psi. If pressure is above 200 psi, check hoses for restrictions.
14. **On all models,** with engine running, close valve fully three times for not more than five seconds each time. Each reading should show at least 1250 psi.
15. If pressures recorded are high enough and within 50 psi of each other, the pump is operating normally.
16. If pressures recorded are high enough but not within 50 psi of each other, the control valve in the pump is sticking. Remove but do not disassemble control valve and clean it with crocus cloth or a fine hone to remove any burrs.
17. If pressures recorded are less than 1250 psi, replace control valve and recheck. If pressures are still low, inspect pump rotor and vanes.
18. Shut off engine and remove pressure gauge.
19. **On models with 3.1L/V6-204 and 3800/V6-231 engines,** partially remove serpentine belt.
20. **On all models,** install high pressure pipe to pump and close retaining clip to pipe.
21. **On models with 3.1L/V6-204 and 3800/V6-231 engines,** install serpentine belt, fuse block shield and A.I.R. belt, if equipped.
22. **On models with 3.4L/V6-204 engine,** install ECM cover/coolant reservoir.
23. **On all models,** bleed system and check fluid level.

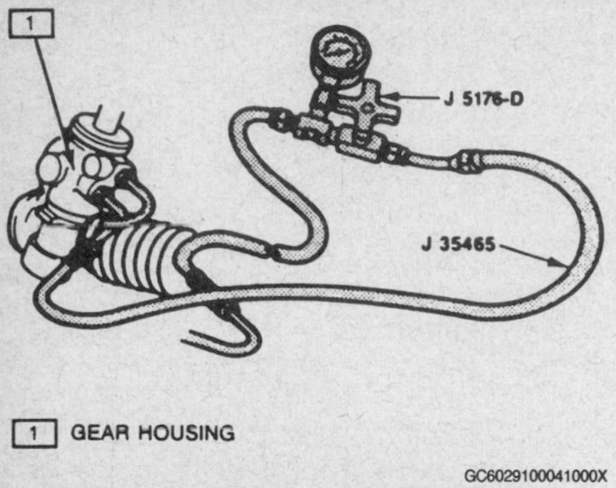
1
J 5176-D
J 35465
1 GEAR HOUSING
GC6029100041000X

Fig. 3 Power steering pressure gauge connections. Geo models

Lumina w/2.2L/4-134 & 2.5L/4-151 Engines

This procedure has been modified by Chevrolet technical service bulletin No. 90-45-3B.

1. Raise and support vehicle.
2. Remove high pressure pipe from pump. Catch any fluid that may drain out.
3. Install hoses tool No. J-38049-25 and tool No. J-5176-30 or equivalents on pump.
4. Lower vehicle and install pressure gauge J-5176-D or equivalent as shown in **Fig. 2.**
5. Open valve on pressure gauge.
6. Start engine and allow system to reach operating temperature. Stop engine and check fluid level, add if necessary.
7. Start engine and check pressure.
8. Pressure reading should be 80-125 psi. If pressure is above 200 psi, check hoses for restrictions and poppet valve for proper assembly.
9. With engine running, close valve fully three times for not more than five seconds each time. Each reading should show at least 1250 psi.
10. If pressures recorded are high enough and within 50 psi of each other, the pump is operating normally.
11. If pressures recorded are high enough but not within 50 psi of each other, the control valve in the pump is sticking. Remove but do not disassemble control valve and clean it with crocus cloth or a fine hone to remove any burrs.
12. If pressures recorded are less than 1250 psi, replace flow control valve and recheck. If pressures are still low, inspect rotor and vanes.
13. Shut off engine and remove pressure gauge.
14. Raise and support vehicle and install high pressure pipe to pump.
15. Lower vehicle and check fluid level.

GEO MODELS

1. Disconnect pressure line from gear housing.
2. Connect pressure gauge J-5176 and gauge adapter J-35465 to power steering system as shown in **Fig. 3.**
3. Bleed system, then start engine and turn steering wheel from right to left stops two or three times.
4. Shut off engine and ensure fluid temperature is at least 176°F and that fluid reservoir is full.
5. Start engine and run at idle speed. Check fluid pressure with valve on pressure gauge closed. If pressure is below 924 psi, power steering pump is defective and must be repaired or replaced as necessary. **Do not keep valve closed for more than 10 seconds. This could cause damage to power steering system.**
6. Open valve on power steering gear and record pressure reading at 1000 RPM and at 3000 RPM. If there is more than 71 psi difference between 1000 and 3000 RPM checks, repair or replace steering gear valve.

EXCEPT BERETTA, CAVALIER, CORSICA, CUTLASS SUPREME, GEO MODELS, GRAND AM, GRAND PRIX, LUMINA, REGAL, SKYLARK, SUNBIRD & 1992 ACHIEVA

1. **On all models except 1993-94 Camaro and Firebird with 5.7L/V8-350 engine,** disconnect pressure hose from pump.
2. **On 1993-94 Camaro and Firebird models with 5.7L/V8-350 engine,** disconnect pressure hose from remote reservoir assembly.
3. **On 1993-94 Camaro and Firebird models,** place drain pan under pump assembly (3.4L/V6-204 engine) or remote reservoir assembly (5.7L/V8-350 engine).
4. **On all models,**connect a spare pressure hose to pump, then connect pressure gauge tool No. J-5176-D or equivalent between both hoses, **Fig. 4.**
5. Open valve on gauge, then start engine and allow it to reach operating temperature. Check fluid level and add if necessary.
6. Pressure reading should be 80-125 psi. Refer to chart for proper pressure readings; if pressure is more than specified, check hoses for restrictions and poppet valve on steering gear for proper assembly.
7. Close valve fully three times for not more than five seconds each time. Refer to chart for pressure readings (models without T/C style pump).
8. If pressures recorded are high enough and within 50 psi of each other, the pump is operating normally.
9. If pressures recorded are high enough but are not within 50 psi of each other, the control valve in the pump is sticking. Remove but do not disassemble control valve and clean it with crocus cloth or a fine hone to remove any burrs. Flush system if fluid appears to be dirty.
10. If pressures recorded are less than specified replace control valve and recheck. If pressures are still low, inspect pump rotor and vanes.
11. If pump pressure meets specifications, leave valve open and turn steering wheel to both stops. Record highest pressures and compare with maximum pump pressure recorded. If pressure is not the same (at both stops) as maximum pressure, steering gear is leaking internally and must be disassembled and repaired.
12. Turn off engine and remove pressure gauge and spare hose, then reconnect pressure hose and restore fluid level to full level.

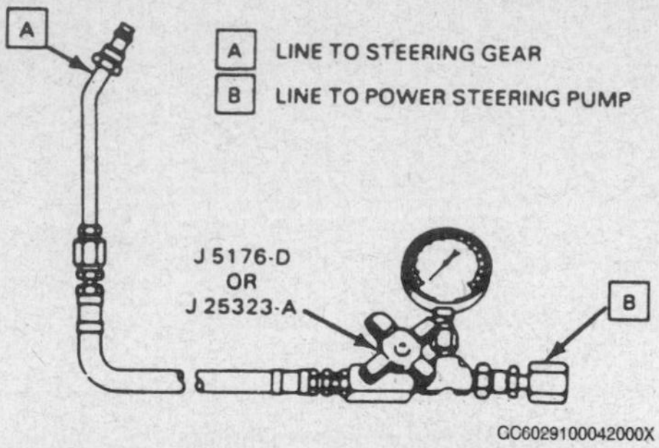
A
A LINE TO STEERING GEAR
B LINE TO POWER STEERING PUMP
J 5176-D
OR
J 25323-A
B
GC6029100042000X

Fig. 4 Power steering pressure gauge connections. Except Cavalier, Cutlass Supreme, Geo, Grand Am, Grand Prix, Lumina, Regal, Skylark, Sunbird & 1992 Beretta/Corsica

BERETTA, CAVALIER, CORSICA, GRAND AM, SKYLARK, SUNBIRD & 1992 ACHIEVA

1. Disconnect high pressure line at power steering pump.
2. Connect power steering analyzer tool No. J-25323-B or equivalent to power steering pressure line at power steering pump.
3. Shift vehicle to park or neutral and set parking brake.
4. Open valve on analyzer, then start engine and allow system to reach operating temperature. Check fluid level and add if necessary.
5. Check and note pressure and flow readings at idle speed. **Do not move steering wheel while engine is running, this will give inaccurate pressure readings.** Pressure readings should be less than 200 psi. If pressure is above 200 psi, check hoses for restrictions.
6. Partially close valve to build 700 psi and record flow. Subtract flow from flow reading taken previously. Flow should not drop more than 1 gallon per minute (GPM). If flow drops more than 1 GPM, replace ring, rotor and vanes in pump. Check if pressure plate and thrust plates are worn or damaged.
7. Close valve fully three times for not more than five seconds each time. All three readings should be within 50 psi of each other. If reading are not within 50 psi or the same, replace flow control valve ensuring it is free to move in its bore.
8. Increase engine speed to 1500 RPM and read flow. Subtract flow from flow reading taken previously. Flow should not vary more than 1 GPM. If flow varies more than 1 GPM, remove flow

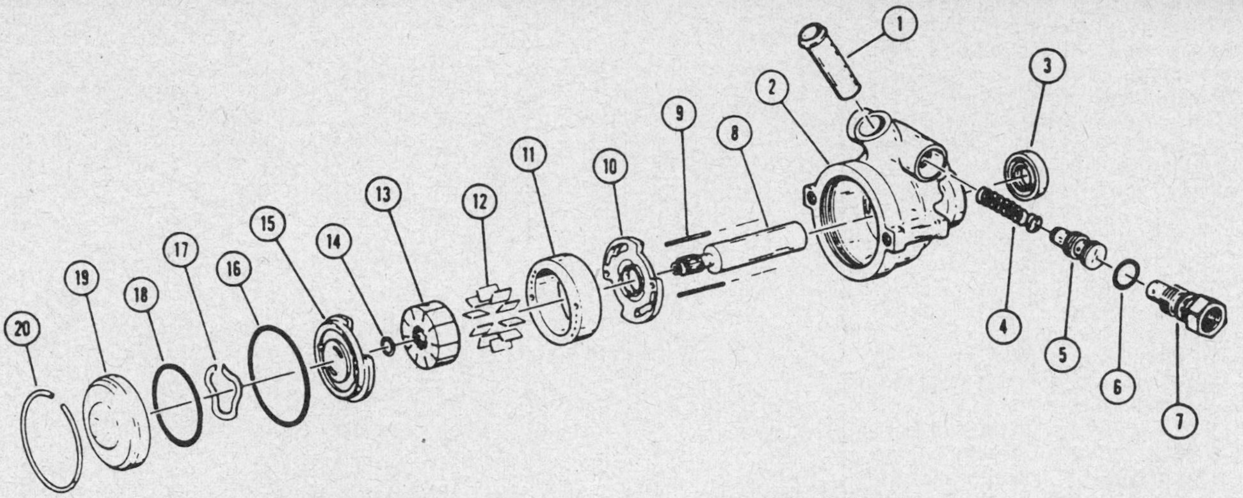
1
2
3
4
5
6
7
8
9
10
11
12
13
14
15
16
17
18
19
20

1-TUBE, RETURN
2-HOUSING ASM, HYD PUMP
3-SEAL, DRIVE SHAFT
4-SPRING, FLOW CONTROL
5-VALVE ASM, CONTROL
6-SEAL, O-RING
7-FITTING, O-RING UNION
8-SHAFT, DRIVE
9-PIN, PUMP RING DOWEL (2)
10-PLATE, THRUST
11-RING,PUMP
12-VANE (10)
13-ROTOR, PUMP
14-RING, SHAFT RETAINING
15-PLATE, PRESSURE
16-SEAL, O-RING
17-SPRING, PRESSURE PLATE
18-SEAL, O-RING
19-COVER, END
20-RING, RETAINING

GC6029100043000X

Fig. 5 Exploded view of CB series power steering pump

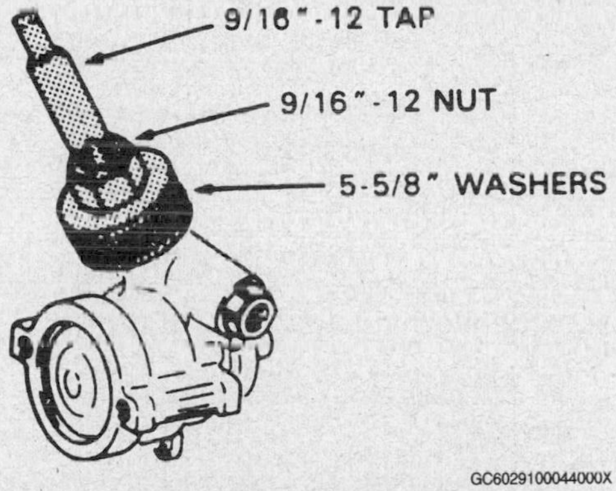
9/16"-12 TAP
9/16"-12 NUT
5-5/8" WASHERS

GC6029100044000X

Fig. 6 Return tube removal. CB series power steering pump

control valve and clean. **Do not disassemble flow control valve.**

9. Turn steering wheel all the way left and right. Record flow at each stop. Flow should drop below 1 GPM at 1500 RPM at each stop. If flow is OK, check steering gear for leakage.
10. After completing any repairs, remove analyzer and reconnect high pressure line to pump, then bleed system and fill fluid to full level.

POWER STEERING SYSTEM SERVICE

Component Service

CB SERIES PUMP

Disassemble

1. Disconnect battery ground cable, then remove power steering pump from vehicle. Refer to individual car chapters for procedures.
2. Remove union fitting with O-ring and the O-ring seal, **Fig. 5.**
3. Remove control valve assembly and flow control spring.
4. Protect driveshaft with shim stock and remove driveshaft seal by cutting with small chisel. Discard seal.
5. Remove return tube using tap, nut and washers, **Fig. 6**, as follows. **Plug return tube to prevent chips from entering pump.**
   a. Stack five 5/8 inch washers onto return tube.
   b. Run one 9/16 inch-12 nut midway up a 9/16 inch 12 tap.
   c. Install threaded end of tap into return tube until nut is positioned against washers.
   d. Using wrench, hold top stationary while turning nut clockwise.
6. Remove end cover retaining ring by inserting punch in access hole.
7. Gently push on driveshaft to assist in removing end cover, O-ring, pressure plate spring, pump ring, pump vanes and the driveshaft subassembly, consisting of pump rotor, thrust plate, driveshaft and shaft retaining ring.
8. Remove O-ring from housing.
9. Remove dowel pins, then the driveshaft seal if not previously removed.
10. Remove pressure plate, pressure plate spring and O-ring from end cover.
11. Remove shaft retaining ring from driveshaft, then the pump rotor and thrust plate.

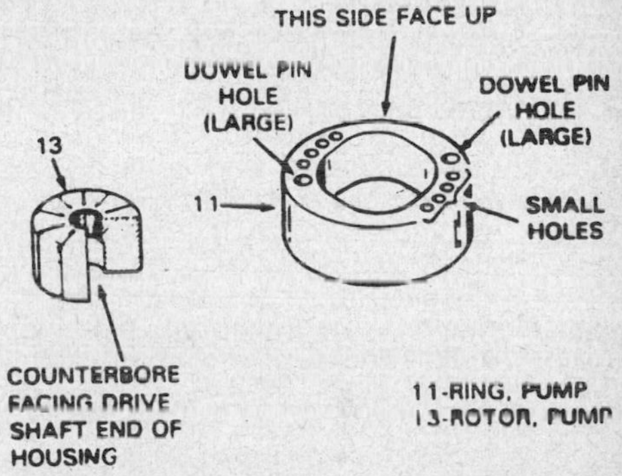
THIS SIDE FACE UP
DOWEL PIN HOLE (LARGE)
DOWEL PIN HOLE (LARGE)
13
11
SMALL HOLES
COUNTERBORE FACING DRIVE SHAFT END OF HOUSING
11-RING, PUMP
13-ROTOR, PUMP

GC6029100045000X

Fig. 7 Rotor and/or pump ring installation. CB series power steering pump

Inspection

1. Clean all parts in power steering fluid, then dry thoroughly.
2. Inspect pump ring, vanes, thrust plate, pressure plate and driveshaft for scoring, pitting or chatter marks, replacing parts as necessary.

Assemble

1. Lubricate new driveshaft seal with power steering fluid and, using seal installer tool No. J 7728 or equivalent, press driveshaft seal into pump housing.
2. Install pump ring dowel pins into housing.
3. Install thrust plate and pump rotor onto driveshaft, **Fig. 7.**
4. Install new shaft retaining ring onto driveshaft.
5. Install driveshaft subassembly into housing.

6. Install pump ring with holes positioned correctly onto dowel pins, **Fig. 7,** in housing.
7. Install vanes into pump rotor.
8. Lubricate new O-ring (large) with power steering fluid and install O-ring into end cover.
9. Install pressure plate and pressure plate spring.
10. Lubricate new O-ring (small) and install O-ring into end cover.
11. Lubricate outer edge of end cover with power steering fluid and press end cover into housing.
12. Insert retaining ring into groove in housing, with ring opening near access hole opening.
13. Remove plug and any chips, then coat end of new return tube with Loctite solvent part No. 75559 and Loctite adhesive part No. 290, or equivalents and press return tube into housing until bottomed.

REVERSE ROTATION

Disassemble

1. Disconnect battery ground cable, then remove power steering pump from vehicle. Refer to individual chassis chapter for procedure.
2. Remove retaining ring using punch in access hole, **Fig. 8.**
3. Remove internal components from pump assembly by gently pushing on driveshaft. Components should include pressure plate and subassembly, consisting of end cover, O-ring seal, pressure plate spring and pressure plate. Driveshaft subassembly, consisting of pump rotor, thrust plate, driveshaft and shaft retaining ring.
4. Remove O-ring from pump housing.
5. Remove dowel pins and driveshaft seal.
6. Remove end cover, pressure plate spring and O-ring from pressure plate.
7. Remove pump ring and vanes from driveshaft subassembly, then shaft retaining rings from driveshaft.
8. Remove thrust plate and pump rotor from driveshaft.

Inspection

1. Clean all parts in power steering fluid, then dry thoroughly.
2. Inspect pump ring, vanes, thrust plate, pressure plate, rotor and driveshaft for scoring, pitting or chatter marks, replacing parts as necessary.

Assemble

1. Lubricate new driveshaft seal with power steering fluid and, using seal installer tool No. J 7728 or equivalent, press driveshaft seal into pump housing.
2. Install pump ring dowel pins into housing.
3. Install thrust plate and pump rotor onto driveshaft.
4. Install new shaft retaining ring onto driveshaft.
5. Install driveshaft subassembly into housing.

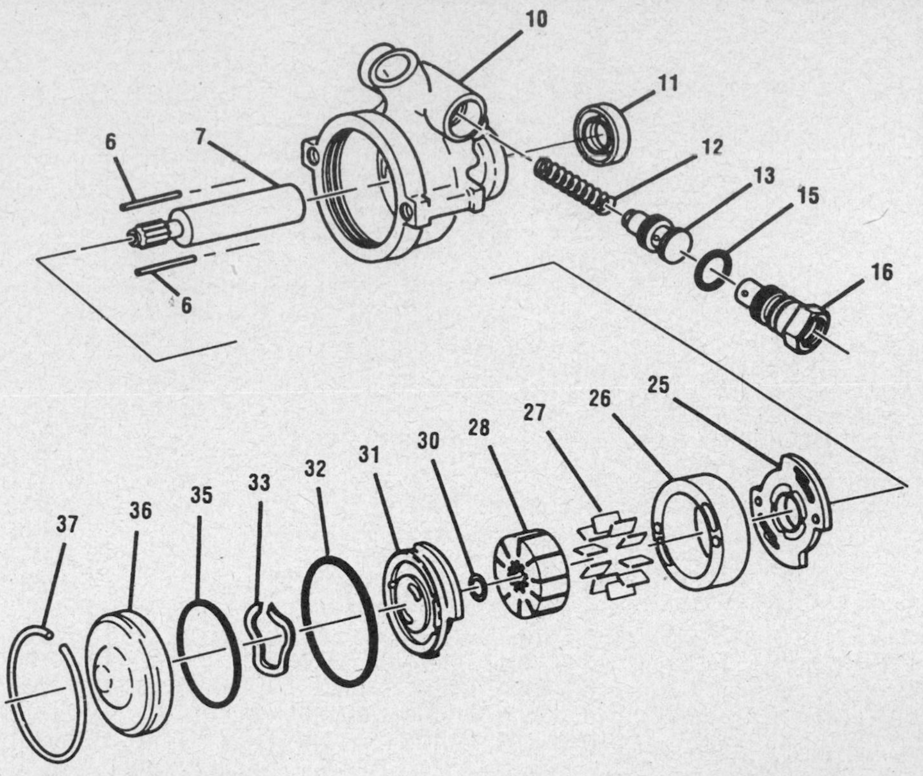
10
11
12
13
15
16
6
7
6
37
36
35
33
32
31
30
28
27
26
25

6 - PIN, PUMP RING DOWEL
7 - SHAFT, DRIVE
10 - HOUSING ASM, BUSHING &
11 - SEAL, DRIVE SHAFT
12 - SPRING, FLOW CONTROL
13 - VALVE ASM, CONTROL
15 - SEAL, O-RING
16 - FITTING, O-RING UNION
25 - PLATE, THRUST
26 - RING, PUMP
27 - VANE, PUMP
28 - ROTOR, PUMP
30 - RING, SHAFT RETAINING
31 - PLATE, PRESSURE
32 - SEAL, O-RING
33 - SPRING, PRESSURE PLATE
35 - SEAL, O-RING
36 - COVER, END
37 - RING, RETAINING

GC60291000460000X

Fig. 8 Power steering pump assembly overhaul. Reverse rotation

6. Install vanes into pump rotor.
7. Install pump ring, with holes positioned correctly onto dowel pins in housing.
8. Lubricate new O-ring with power steering fluid and install O-ring into groove in pump housing.
9. Install pressure plate and pressure plate spring.
10. Lubricate new O-ring and install O-ring into end cover.
11. Lubricate outer edge of end cover with power steering fluid and press end cover into housing.
12. Insert retaining ring into groove in housing, with ring opening near access hole opening.
13. Remove plug and any chips, then coat end of new return tube with Loctite solvent 75559 and Loctite 290 adhesive, or equivalents, and press return tube into housing until bottomed.

JIDOSHA KIKI

This pump is only serviced as an assembly, except for relief valve and pulley.

N & P SERIES PUMP

Refer to **Fig. 9** for service procedures on this power steering pump.

P SERIES L/RESERVOIR PUMP

Refer to **Figs. 10 and 11** for service procedures on this power steering pump.

TC SERIES PUMP

Refer to **Fig. 12** for service procedures on this power steering pump.

Power Steering System Bleed

Bleed power steering system after any component replacement, disconnecting fluid line or in case of steering system noise. Bleed system to prevent pump damage, stop steering noise and to ensure proper system operation. Before bleeding, inspect steering system. Check and correct if needed power steering lines touching frame body or engine. Also check all hose connections for looseness or leaks and tighten.

1. Switch ignition off.
2. Turn steering wheel full left.
3. Fill fluid reservoir to FULL COLD level. Leave cap off.
4. Raise front wheels off ground.

Continued on page 27-12

POWER STEERING PUMP ASSEMBLY
(N SERIES-REMOTE RESERVOIR)
(P SERIES-SUBMERGED)

1-SHAFT, DRIVE
2-SEAL, DRIVE SHAFT
3-SEAL, O-RING (HOUSING)
4-HOUSING ASM., PUMP
5-SPRING, FLOW CONTROL
6-VALVE ASM., CONTROL
7-SEAL, O-RING (HOUSING)
8-SEAL, O-RING (PRESSURE & END PLATE)
9-PIN, DOWEL
10-PLATE, THRUST
11-ROTOR, PUMP
12-RING, SHAFT RETAINING
13-VANE, PUMP
14-RING, PUMP
15-PLATE, PRESSURE
16-SPRING, PRESSURE PLATE
17-PLATE, END
18-RING, END PLATE RETAINING
19-SEAL, O-RING (HOUSING TO STUD)
20-RESERVOIR ASM.
21-CAP ASM., RESERVOIR
22-STUD OR BOLT, PUMP MOUNTING
23-SEAL, O-RING (FITTING ASM.)
24-FITTING ASM. (CONNECTOR &)
25-MAGNET
26-RESERVOIR ASM.
27-HOUSING ASM., PUMP
28-TUBE, RETURN

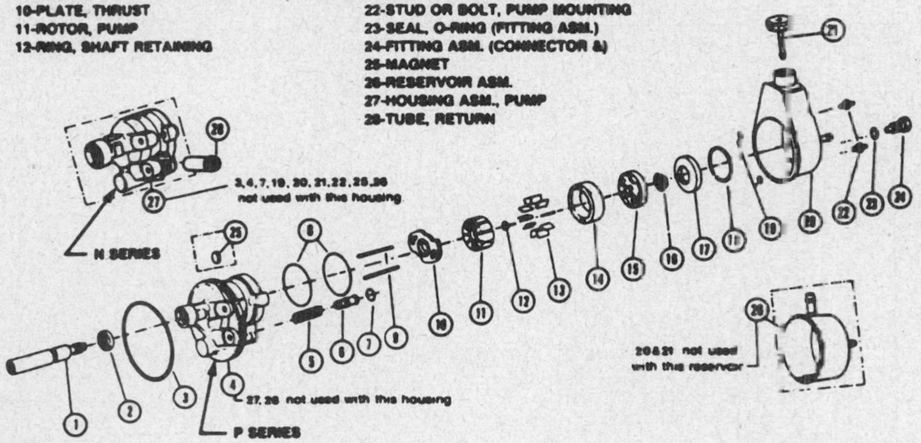
3, 4, 7, 19, 20, 21, 22, 25, 26
not used with this housing
N SERIES
20 & 21 not used
with this reservoir
27, 28 not used with this housing
P SERIES

BENCH REPAIR INDEX
(N&P SERIES PUMP)

TO REMOVE	EXPLODED VIEW NO.	PERFORM STEPS
Drive Shaft Seal	2	1
Pump Reservoir	20 or 26	2
Control Valve Asm.	6	2-3
End Plate	17	3
Rotating Group	1-10-11-12-13-14-15	2-3-4
O-Ring Seals (Rotating Group) & Drive Shaft	2-8	2-3-4-5
Return Tube	28	6

GC6029100047010X

Fig. 9 Power steering pump assembly overhaul (Part 1 of 2). N & P series

1. REMOVE AND INSTALL DRIVE SHAFT SEAL WITHOUT DISASSEMBLING THE PUMP

REMOVE

1. Protect drive shaft with shim stock
2. Use chisel to cut seal and remove

INSTALL

1. Coat drive shaft seal with hydraulic pump fluid. Refer to inset for drive shaft seal installation.

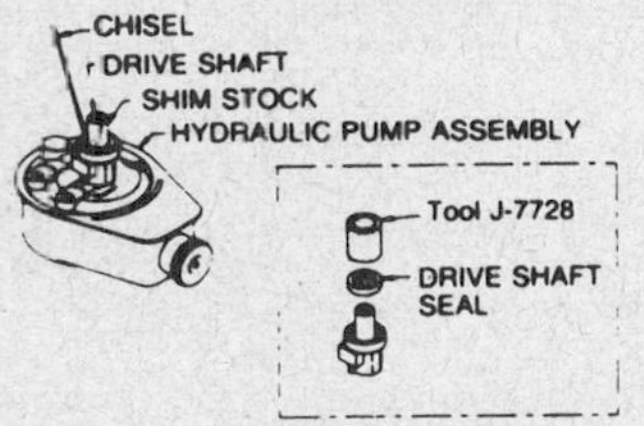
CHISEL
DRIVE SHAFT
SHIM STOCK
HYDRAULIC PUMP ASSEMBLY
Tool J-7728
DRIVE SHAFT SEAL

Install drive shaft seal

2. REMOVE AND INSTALL PUMP RESERVOIR ASSEMBLY

REMOVE

1. Drain oil from reservoir assembly before removal
2. Remove parts as shown

INSTALL

1. Use all new seals and lubricate with power steering fluid before installation
2. Install parts as shown.

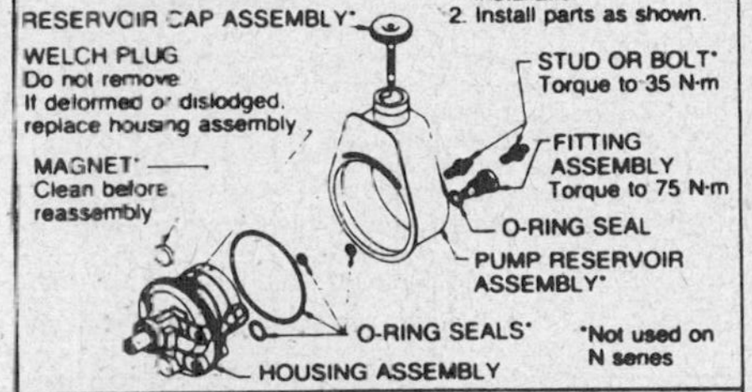
RESERVOIR CAP ASSEMBLY*
WELCH PLUG
Do not remove
If deformed or dislodged, replace housing assembly
MAGNET*
Clean before reassembly
STUD OR BOLT*
Torque to 35 N·m
FITTING ASSEMBLY
Torque to 75 N·m
O-RING SEAL
PUMP RESERVOIR ASSEMBLY*
O-RING SEALS*
HOUSING ASSEMBLY

*Not used on N series

3. REMOVE AND INSTALL END PLATE

REMOVE

1. Refer to inset for retaining ring removal.

INSTALL

1. Lubricate end plate and retaining ring. Install parts as shown. Refer to inset for positioning of retaining ring in housing.

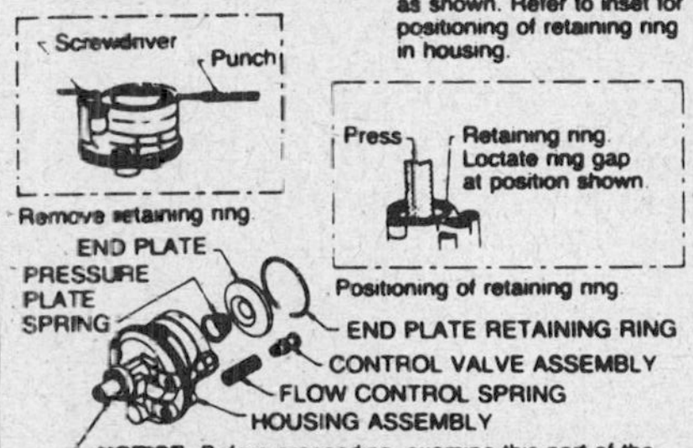
Screwdriver
Punch
Remove retaining ring
Press
Retaining ring.
Locate ring gap at position shown.
Positioning of retaining ring
END PLATE
PRESSURE PLATE SPRING
END PLATE RETAINING RING
CONTROL VALVE ASSEMBLY
FLOW CONTROL SPRING
HOUSING ASSEMBLY

NOTICE: Before proceeding, examine this part of the drive shaft. If it is corroded, clean with crocus cloth before removing. This will prevent damage to the shaft bushing which might require replacement of the entire housing

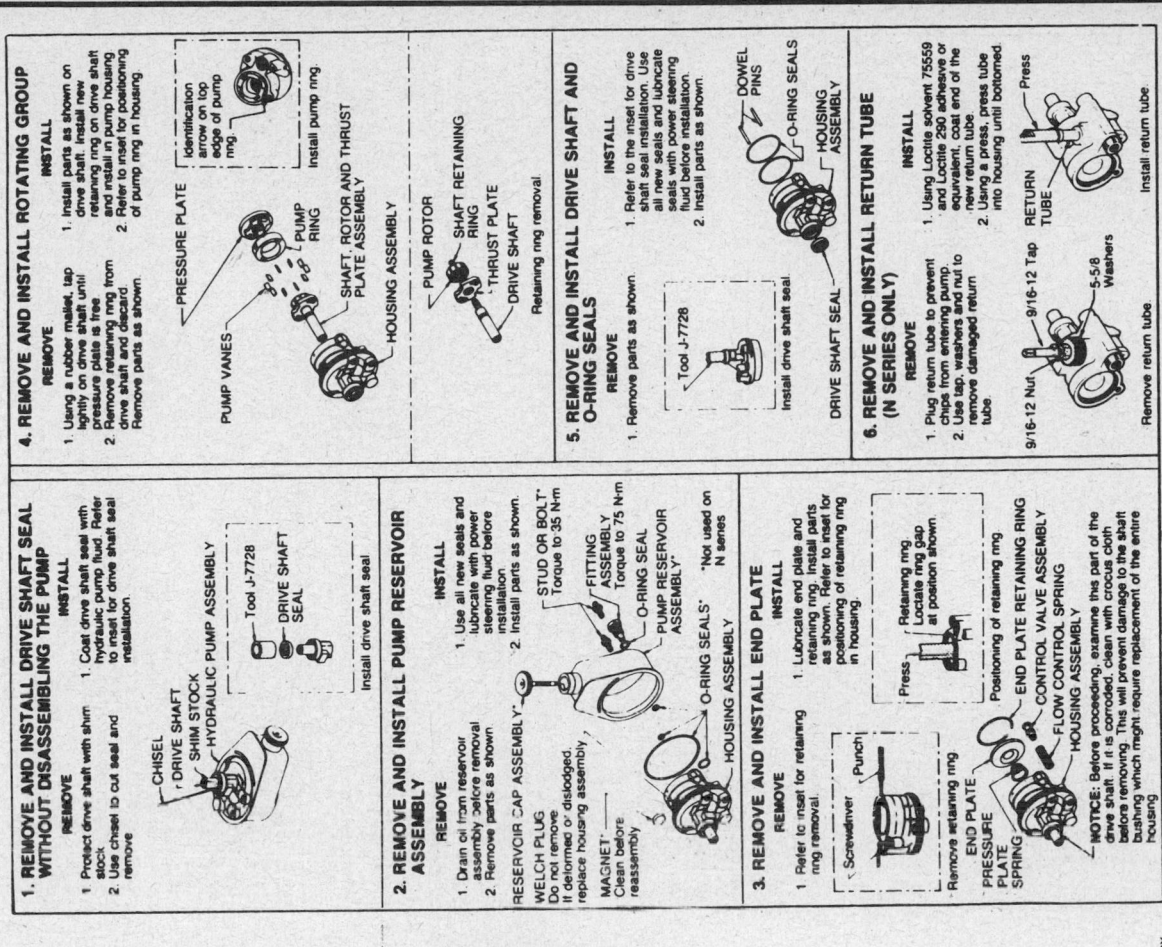

4. REMOVE AND INSTALL ROTATING GROUP

REMOVE

1. Using a rubber mallet, tap lightly on drive shaft until pressure plate is free.
2. Remove retaining ring from drive shaft and discard. Remove parts as shown.

INSTALL

1. Install parts as shown on drive shaft. Install new retaining ring on drive shaft and install in pump housing.
2. Refer to inset for positioning of pump ring in housing.

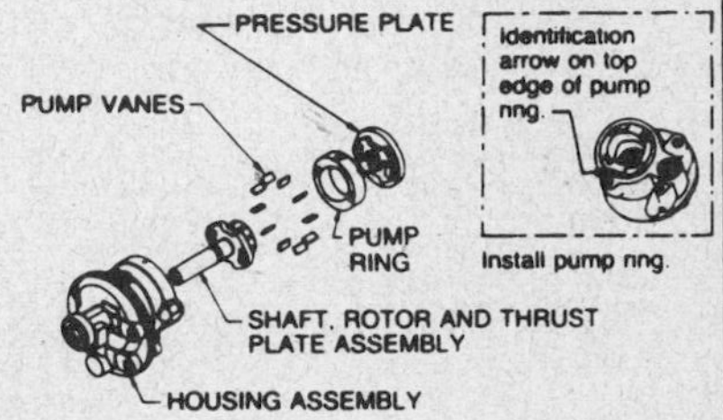
PRESSURE PLATE
PUMP VANES
PUMP RING
SHAFT, ROTOR AND THRUST PLATE ASSEMBLY
HOUSING ASSEMBLY
Identification arrow on top edge of pump ring.
Install pump ring.
PUMP ROTOR
SHAFT RETAINING RING
THRUST PLATE
DRIVE SHAFT

Retaining ring removal.

5. REMOVE AND INSTALL DRIVE SHAFT AND O-RING SEALS

REMOVE

1. Remove parts as shown.

INSTALL

1. Refer to the inset for drive shaft seal installation. Use all new seals and lubricate seals with power steering fluid before installation.
2. Install parts as shown.

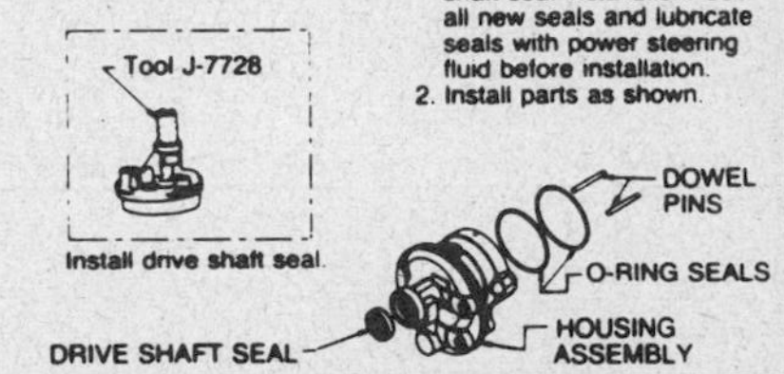
Tool J-7728
Install drive shaft seal.
DOWEL PINS
O-RING SEALS
HOUSING ASSEMBLY
DRIVE SHAFT SEAL

6. REMOVE AND INSTALL RETURN TUBE (N SERIES ONLY)

REMOVE

1. Plug return tube to prevent chips from entering pump.
2. Use tap, washers and nut to remove damaged return tube.

INSTALL

1. Using Loctite solvent 75559 and Loctite 290 adhesive or equivalent, coat end of the new return tube.
2. Using a press, press tube into housing until bottomed.

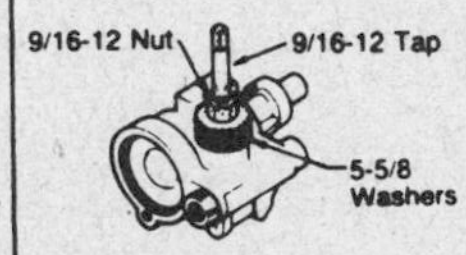
9/16-12 Nut
9/16-12 Tap
5-5/8 Washers

Remove return tube.

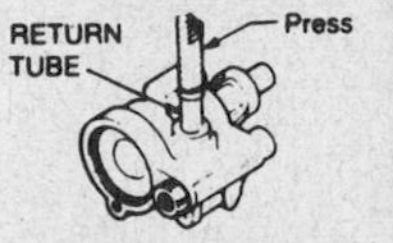
RETURN TUBE
Press

Install return tube.

GC6029100047020X

Fig. 9 Power steering pump assembly overhaul (Part 2 of 2). N & P series

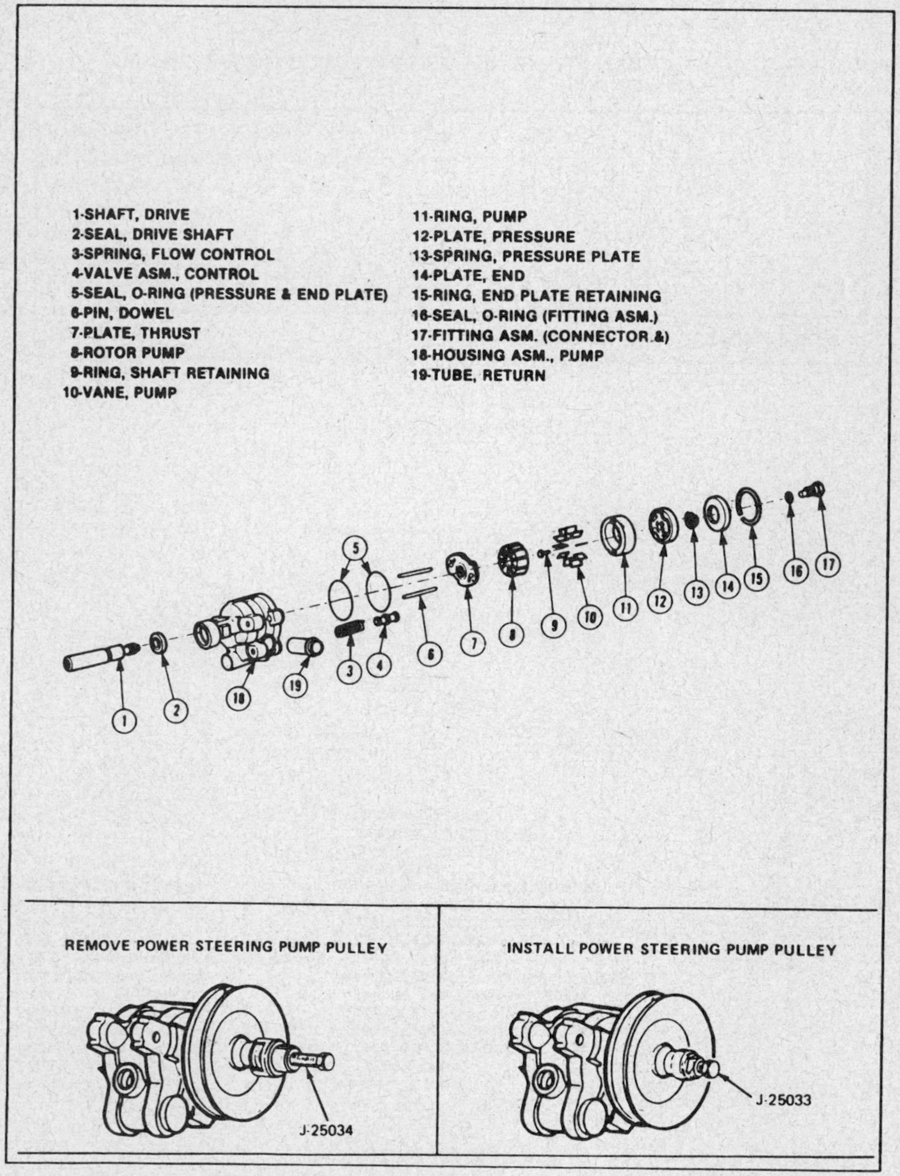
1-SHAFT, DRIVE
2-SEAL, DRIVE SHAFT
3-SPRING, FLOW CONTROL
4-VALVE ASM., CONTROL
5-SEAL, O-RING (PRESSURE & END PLATE)
6-PIN, DOWEL
7-PLATE, THRUST
8-ROTOR PUMP
9-RING, SHAFT RETAINING
10-VANE, PUMP
11-RING, PUMP
12-PLATE, PRESSURE
13-SPRING, PRESSURE PLATE
14-PLATE, END
15-RING, END PLATE RETAINING
16-SEAL, O-RING (FITTING ASM.)
17-FITTING ASM. (CONNECTOR &)
18-HOUSING ASM., PUMP
19-TUBE, RETURN
REMOVE POWER STEERING PUMP PULLEY
J-25034
INSTALL POWER STEERING PUMP PULLEY
J-25033
GC6029100048010X

Fig. 10 Power steering pump assembly overhaul (Part 1 of 2). P series, L/reservoir, except 1993–94 Camaro & Firebird

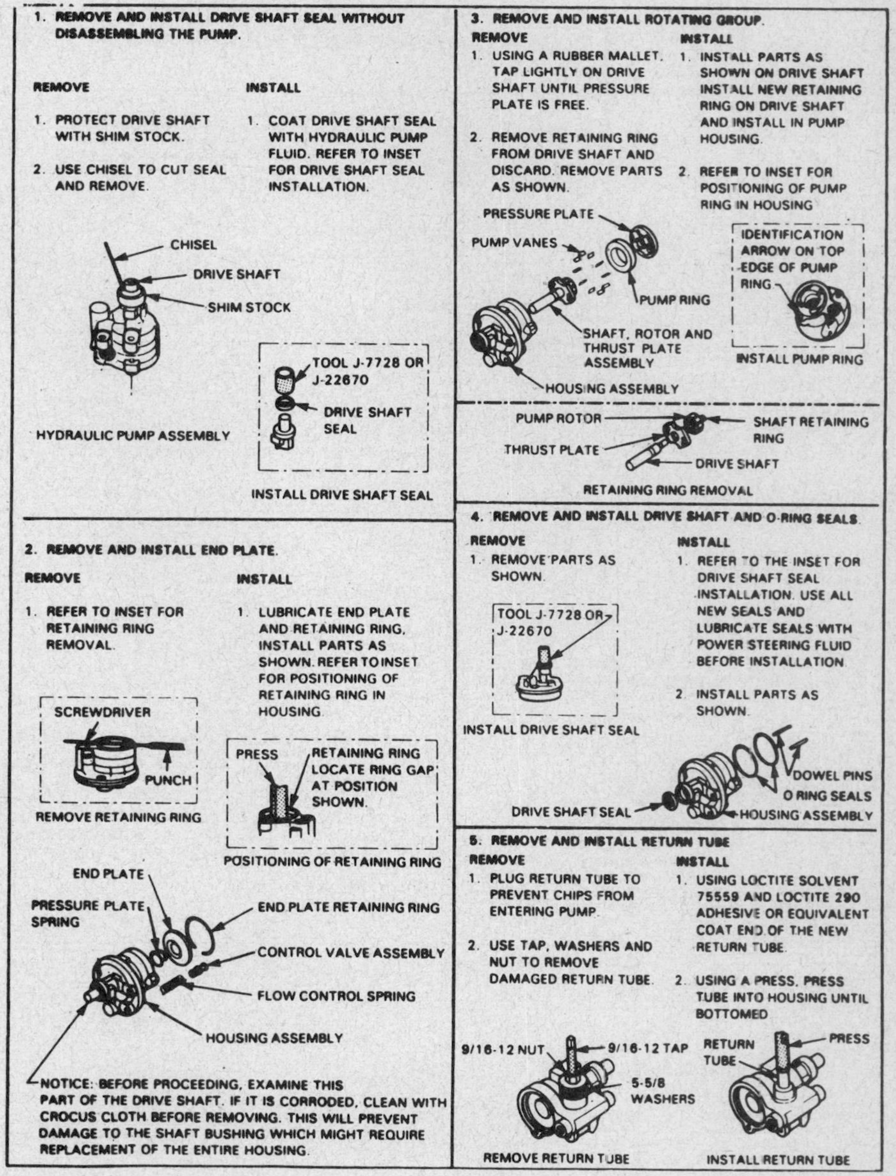
1. REMOVE AND INSTALL DRIVE SHAFT SEAL WITHOUT DISASSEMBLING THE PUMP.
REMOVE
1. PROTECT DRIVE SHAFT WITH SHIM STOCK.
2. USE CHISEL TO CUT SEAL AND REMOVE.
INSTALL
1. COAT DRIVE SHAFT SEAL WITH HYDRAULIC PUMP FLUID. REFER TO INSET FOR DRIVE SHAFT SEAL INSTALLATION.
CHISEL
DRIVE SHAFT
SHIM STOCK
HYDRAULIC PUMP ASSEMBLY
TOOL J-7728 OR J-22670
DRIVE SHAFT SEAL
INSTALL DRIVE SHAFT SEAL
2. REMOVE AND INSTALL END PLATE.
REMOVE
1. REFER TO INSET FOR RETAINING RING REMOVAL.
INSTALL
1. LUBRICATE END PLATE AND RETAINING RING, INSTALL PARTS AS SHOWN. REFER TO INSET FOR POSITIONING OF RETAINING RING IN HOUSING.
SCREWDRIVER
PUNCH
REMOVE RETAINING RING
PRESS
RETAINING RING LOCATE RING GAP AT POSITION SHOWN.
POSITIONING OF RETAINING RING
END PLATE
PRESSURE PLATE SPRING
END PLATE RETAINING RING
CONTROL VALVE ASSEMBLY
FLOW CONTROL SPRING
HOUSING ASSEMBLY
NOTICE: BEFORE PROCEEDING, EXAMINE THIS PART OF THE DRIVE SHAFT. IF IT IS CORRODED, CLEAN WITH CROCUS CLOTH BEFORE REMOVING. THIS WILL PREVENT DAMAGE TO THE SHAFT BUSHING WHICH MIGHT REQUIRE REPLACEMENT OF THE ENTIRE HOUSING.
3. REMOVE AND INSTALL ROTATING GROUP.
REMOVE
1. USING A RUBBER MALLET, TAP LIGHTLY ON DRIVE SHAFT UNTIL PRESSURE PLATE IS FREE.
2. REMOVE RETAINING RING FROM DRIVE SHAFT AND DISCARD. REMOVE PARTS AS SHOWN.
INSTALL
1. INSTALL PARTS AS SHOWN ON DRIVE SHAFT INSTALL NEW RETAINING RING ON DRIVE SHAFT AND INSTALL IN PUMP HOUSING.
2. REFER TO INSET FOR POSITIONING OF PUMP RING IN HOUSING
PRESSURE PLATE
PUMP VANES
PUMP RING
SHAFT, ROTOR AND THRUST PLATE ASSEMBLY
HOUSING ASSEMBLY
IDENTIFICATION ARROW ON TOP EDGE OF PUMP RING
INSTALL PUMP RING
PUMP ROTOR
THRUST PLATE
SHAFT RETAINING RING
DRIVE SHAFT
RETAINING RING REMOVAL
4. REMOVE AND INSTALL DRIVE SHAFT AND O-RING SEALS.
REMOVE
1. REMOVE PARTS AS SHOWN.
INSTALL
1. REFER TO THE INSET FOR DRIVE SHAFT SEAL INSTALLATION. USE ALL NEW SEALS AND LUBRICATE SEALS WITH POWER STEERING FLUID BEFORE INSTALLATION.
2. INSTALL PARTS AS SHOWN.
TOOL J-7728 OR J-22670
INSTALL DRIVE SHAFT SEAL
DOWEL PINS
O RING SEALS
DRIVE SHAFT SEAL
HOUSING ASSEMBLY
5. REMOVE AND INSTALL RETURN TUBE
REMOVE
1. PLUG RETURN TUBE TO PREVENT CHIPS FROM ENTERING PUMP.
2. USE TAP, WASHERS AND NUT TO REMOVE DAMAGED RETURN TUBE.
INSTALL
1. USING LOCTITE SOLVENT 75559 AND LOCTITE 290 ADHESIVE OR EQUIVALENT COAT END OF THE NEW RETURN TUBE.
2. USING A PRESS, PRESS TUBE INTO HOUSING UNTIL BOTTOMED
9/16-12 NUT
9/16-12 TAP
5-5/8 WASHERS
REMOVE RETURN TUBE
RETURN TUBE
PRESS
INSTALL RETURN TUBE
GC6029100048020X

Fig. 10 Power steering pump assembly overhaul (Part 2 of 2). P series, L/reservoir except 1993–94 Camaro & Firebird

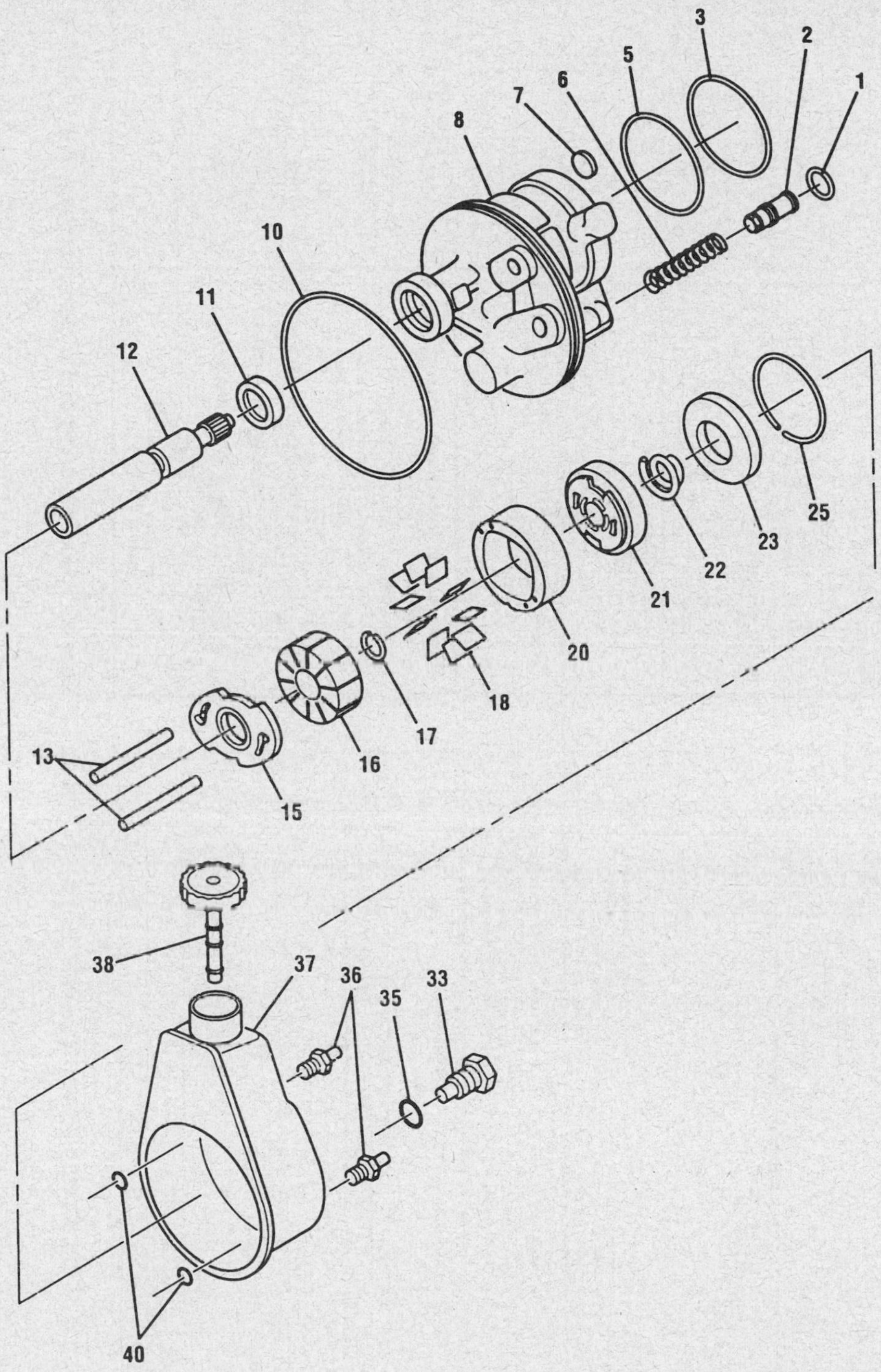
1
2
3
5
6
7
8
10
11
12
13
15
16
17
18
20
21
22
23
25
33
35
36
37
38
40

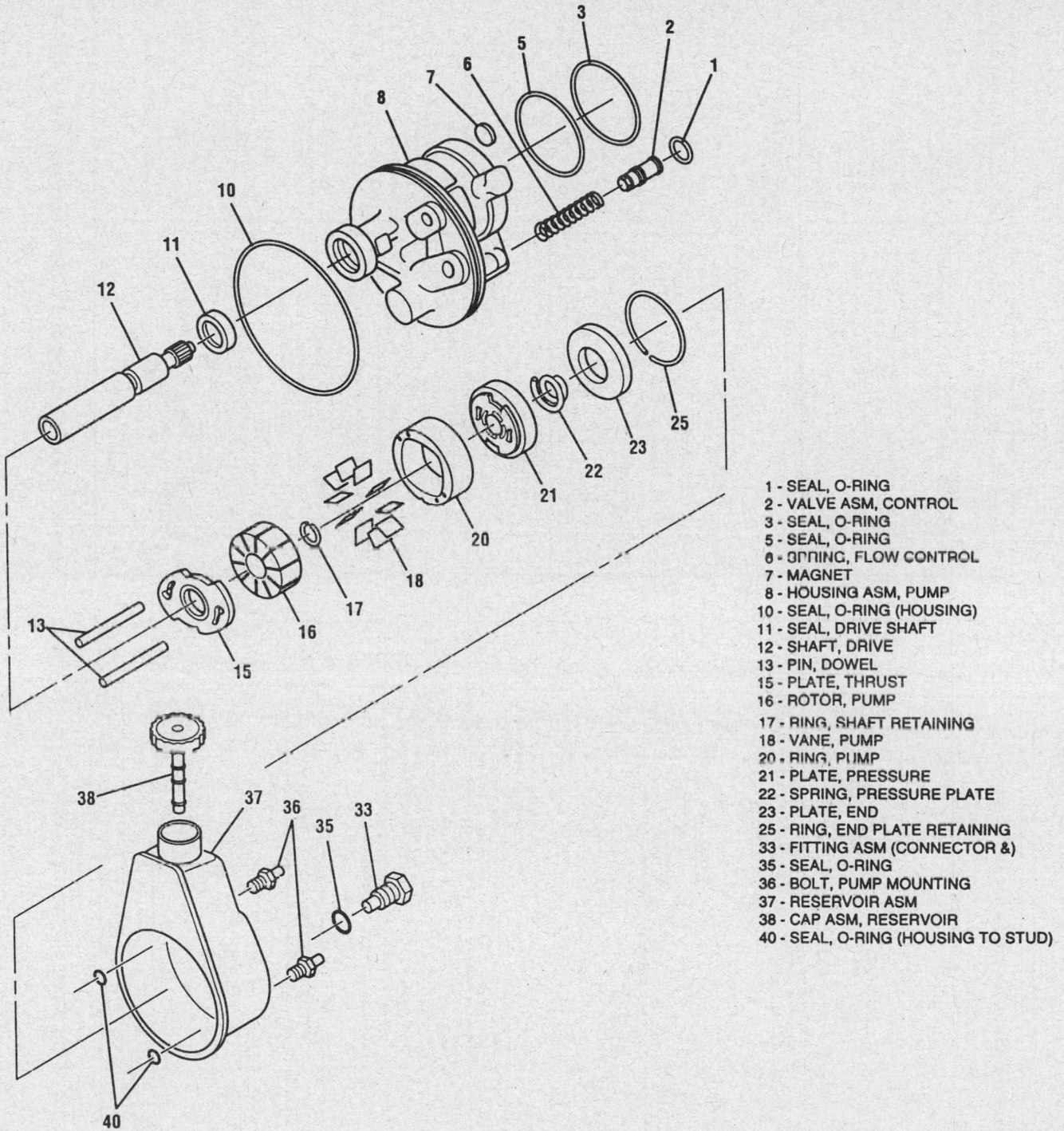

1 - SEAL, O-RING
2 - VALVE ASM, CONTROL
3 - SEAL, O-RING
5 - SEAL, O-RING
6 - SPRING, FLOW CONTROL
7 - MAGNET
8 - HOUSING ASM, PUMP
10 - SEAL, O-RING (HOUSING)
11 - SEAL, DRIVE SHAFT
12 - SHAFT, DRIVE
13 - PIN, DOWEL
15 - PLATE, THRUST
16 - ROTOR, PUMP
17 - RING, SHAFT RETAINING
18 - VANE, PUMP
20 - RING, PUMP
21 - PLATE, PRESSURE
22 - SPRING, PRESSURE PLATE
23 - PLATE, END
25 - RING, END PLATE RETAINING
33 - FITTING ASM (CONNECTOR &)
35 - SEAL, O-RING
36 - BOLT, PUMP MOUNTING
37 - RESERVOIR ASM
38 - CAP ASM, RESERVOIR
40 - SEAL, O-RING (HOUSING TO STUD)

GC6029300049000X

Fig. 11 Power steering pump assembly overhaul. P series, 1993–94 Camaro & Firebird

POWER STEERING PUMP ASSEMBLY (TC SERIES)

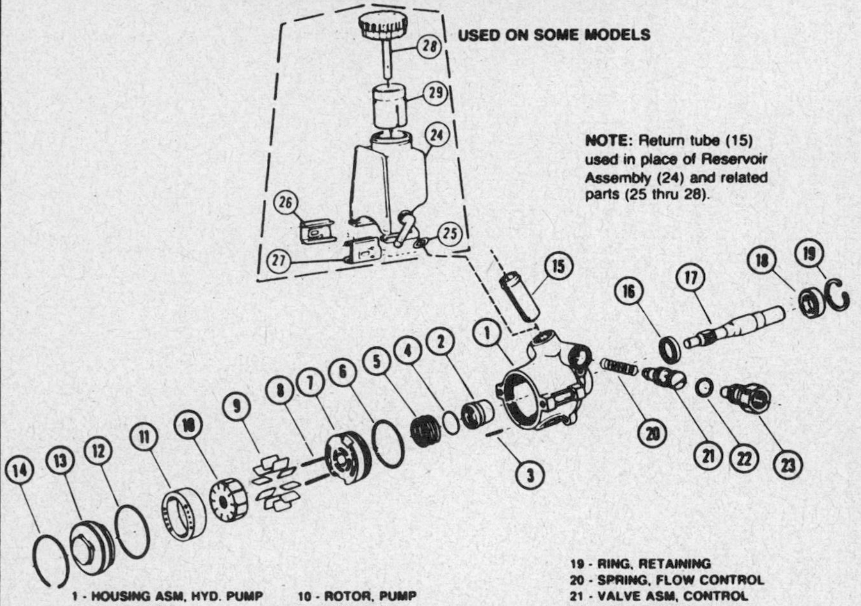
USED ON SOME MODELS
NOTE: Return tube (15) used in place of Reservoir Assembly (24) and related parts (25 thru 28).

1 - HOUSING ASM, HYD. PUMP
2 - SLEEVE ASM
3 - PIN, DOWEL
4 - SEAL, O-RING
5 - SPRING, PRESSURE PLATE
6 - SEAL, O-RING
7 - PLATE, PRESSURE
8 - PIN, PUMP RING DOWEL (2)
9 - VANE (10)
10 - ROTOR, PUMP
11 - RING, PUMP
12 - SEAL, O-RING
13 - PLATE ASM, THRUST
14 - RING, THRUST PLATE RETAINING
15 - TUBE, RETURN
16 - SEAL, DRIVE SHAFT
17 - SHAFT, DRIVE
18 - BEARING ASM, BALL
19 - RING, RETAINING
20 - SPRING, FLOW CONTROL
21 - VALVE ASM, CONTROL
22 - SEAL, O-RING
23 - FITTING, O-RING UNION
24 - RESERVOIR ASM, HYD. PUMP
25 - SEAL, O-RING
26 - CLIP, RESERVOIR RETAINING (LH)
27 - CLIP, RESERVOIR RETAINING (RH)
28 - CAPSTICK ASM, RESERVOIR
29 - BAFFLE, PUMP ASM.

BENCH REPAIR INDEX (TC SERIES)

TO REMOVE	EXPLODED VIEW NO.	PERFORM STEPS
Return Tube	15	7
Control Valve Asm.	21	2
Drive Shaft	17	3
Ball Bearing (Drive Shaft)	18	3
Drive Shaft Seal	16	3-4
Rotating Group	7-9-10-11-12-13	3&5
Sleeve Asm.	2	3-5-6
Hydraulic Pump Reservoir Asm.	24	1

GC6029100050010X

Fig. 12 Power steering pump assembly overhaul (Part 1 of 4). TC series

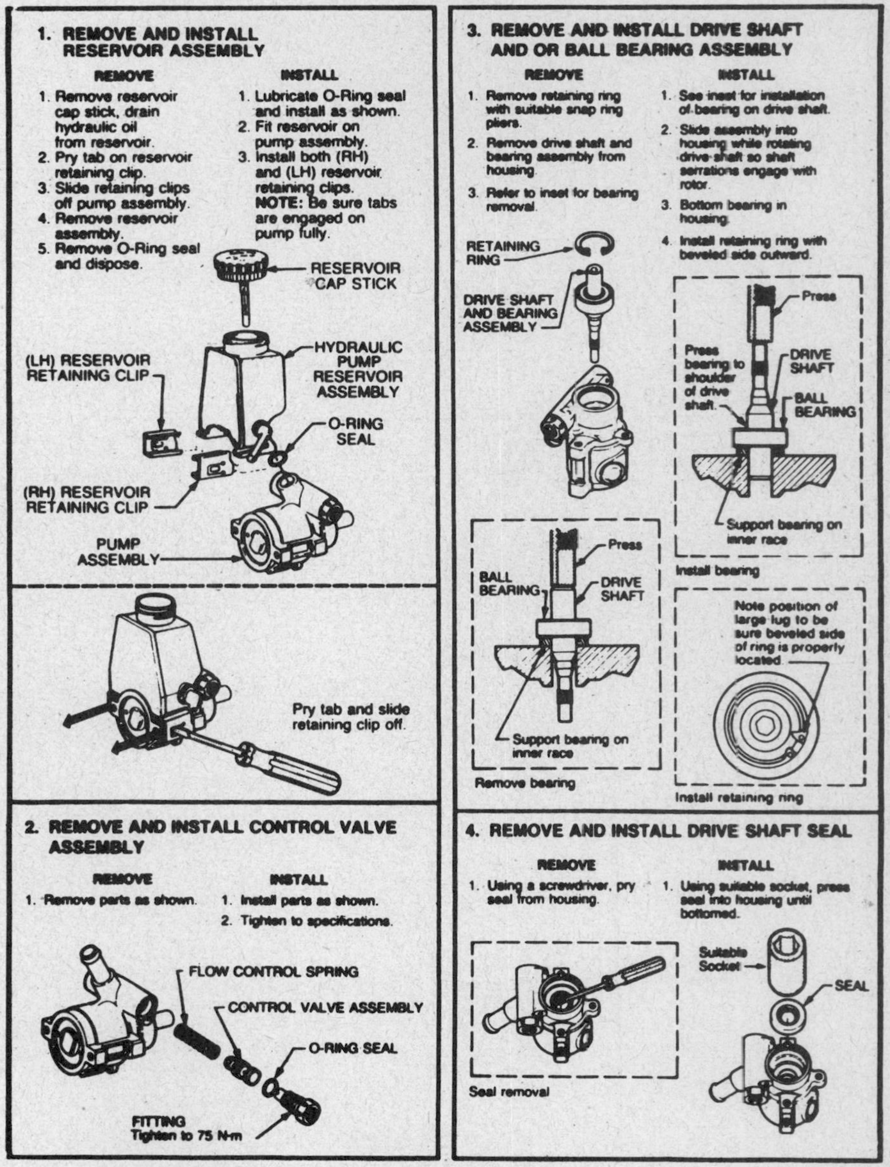
1. REMOVE AND INSTALL RESERVOIR ASSEMBLY
REMOVE
1. Remove reservoir cap stick, drain hydraulic oil from reservoir.
2. Pry tab on reservoir retaining clip.
3. Slide retaining clips off pump assembly.
4. Remove reservoir assembly.
5. Remove O-Ring seal and dispose.
INSTALL
1. Lubricate O-Ring seal and install as shown.
2. Fit reservoir on pump assembly.
3. Install both (RH) and (LH) reservoir retaining clips. NOTE: Be sure tabs are engaged on pump fully.
RESERVOIR CAP STICK
(LH) RESERVOIR RETAINING CLIP
HYDRAULIC PUMP RESERVOIR ASSEMBLY
O-RING SEAL
(RH) RESERVOIR RETAINING CLIP
PUMP ASSEMBLY
Pry tab and slide retaining clip off.
2. REMOVE AND INSTALL CONTROL VALVE ASSEMBLY
REMOVE
1. Remove parts as shown.
INSTALL
1. Install parts as shown.
2. Tighten to specifications.
FLOW CONTROL SPRING
CONTROL VALVE ASSEMBLY
O-RING SEAL
FITTING Tighten to 75 N·m
3. REMOVE AND INSTALL DRIVE SHAFT AND OR BALL BEARING ASSEMBLY
REMOVE
1. Remove retaining ring with suitable snap ring pliers.
2. Remove drive shaft and bearing assembly from housing.
3. Refer to inset for bearing removal.
INSTALL
1. See inset for installation of bearing on drive shaft.
2. Slide assembly into housing while rotating drive shaft so shaft serrations engage with rotor.
3. Bottom bearing in housing.
4. Install retaining ring with beveled side outward.
RETAINING RING
DRIVE SHAFT AND BEARING ASSEMBLY
Press
Press bearing to shoulder of drive shaft.
DRIVE SHAFT
BALL BEARING
Support bearing on inner race
Install bearing
Press
BALL BEARING
DRIVE SHAFT
Support bearing on inner race
Remove bearing
Note position of large lug to be sure beveled side of ring is properly located.
Install retaining ring
4. REMOVE AND INSTALL DRIVE SHAFT SEAL
REMOVE
1. Using a screwdriver, pry seal from housing.
INSTALL
1. Using suitable socket, press seal into housing until bottomed.
Suitable Socket
SEAL
Seal removal

GC6029100050020X

Fig. 12 Power steering pump assembly overhaul (Part 2 of 4). TC series

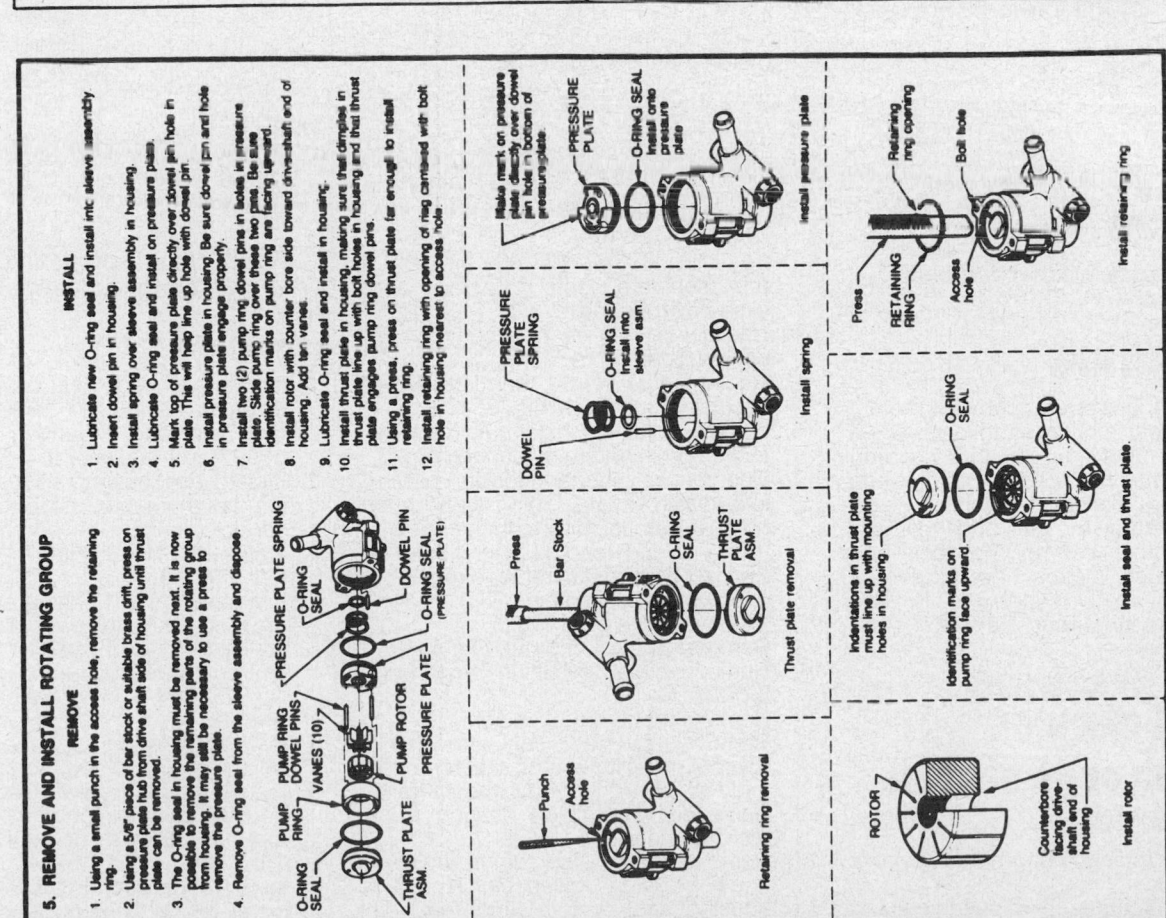

5. REMOVE AND INSTALL ROTATING GROUP

REMOVE

1. Using a small punch in the access hole, remove the retaining ring.
2. Using a 5/8" piece of bar stock or suitable brass drift, press on pressure plate hub from drive shaft side of housing until thrust plate can be removed.
3. The O-ring seal in housing must be removed next. It is now possible to remove the remaining parts of the rotating group from housing. It may still be necessary to use a press to remove the pressure plate.
4. Remove O-ring seal from the sleeve assembly and dispose.

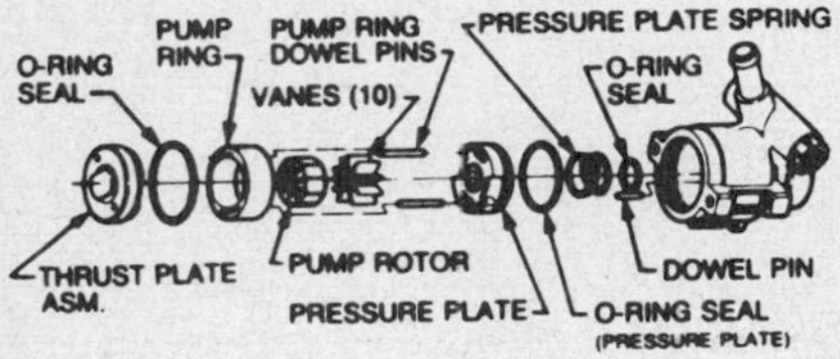
O-RING SEAL
PUMP RING
PUMP RING DOWEL PINS
VANES (10)
PRESSURE PLATE SPRING
O-RING SEAL
THRUST PLATE ASM.
PUMP ROTOR
PRESSURE PLATE
DOWEL PIN
O-RING SEAL (PRESSURE PLATE)

INSTALL

1. Lubricate new O-ring seal and install into sleeve assembly.
2. Insert dowel pin in housing.
3. Install spring over sleeve assembly in housing.
4. Lubricate O-ring seal and install on pressure plate.
5. Mark top of pressure plate directly over dowel pin hole in plate. This will help line up hole with dowel pin.
6. Install pressure plate in housing. Be sure dowel pin and hole in pressure plate engage properly.
7. Install two (2) pump ring dowel pins in holes in pressure plate. Slide pump ring over these two pins. Be sure identification marks on pump ring are facing upward.
8. Install rotor with counter bore side toward drive-shaft end of housing. Add ten vanes.
9. Lubricate O-ring seal and install in housing.
10. Install thrust plate in housing, making sure that dimples in thrust plate line up with bolt holes in housing and that thrust plate engages pump ring dowel pins.
11. Using a press, press on thrust plate far enough to install retaining ring.
12. Install retaining ring with opening of ring centered with bolt hole in housing nearest to access hole.

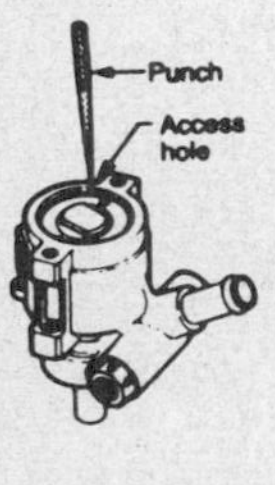
Punch
Access hole

Retaining ring removal

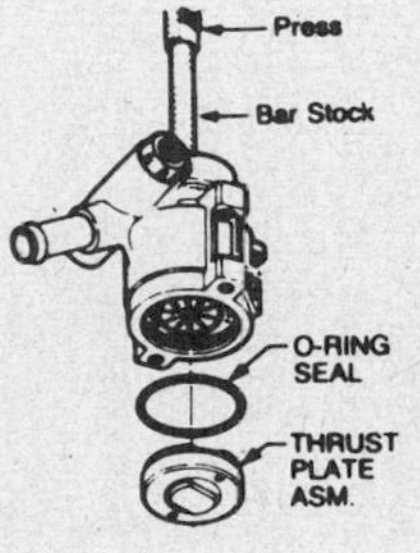
Press
Bar Stock
O-RING SEAL
THRUST PLATE ASM.

Thrust plate removal

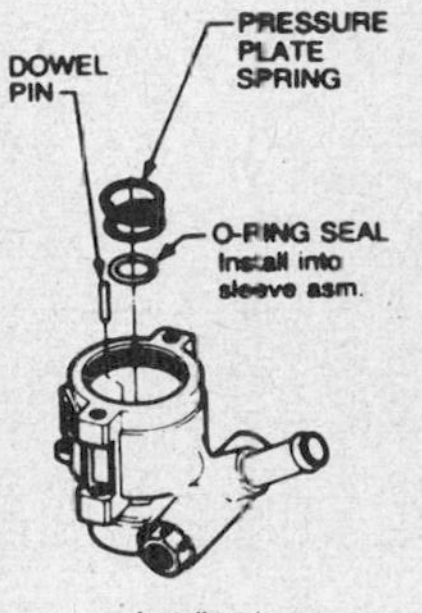
DOWEL PIN
PRESSURE PLATE SPRING
O-RING SEAL Install into sleeve asm.

Install spring

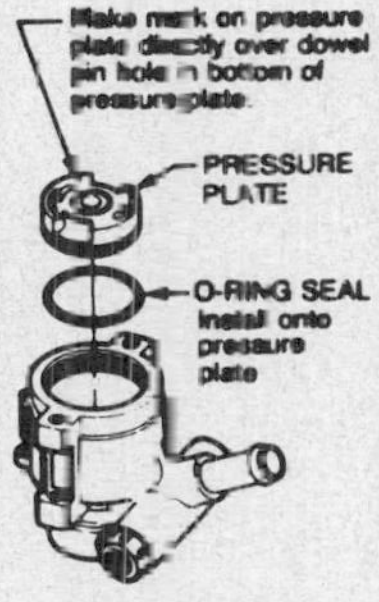
Make mark on pressure plate directly over dowel pin hole in bottom of pressure plate.
PRESSURE PLATE
O-RING SEAL Install onto pressure plate

Install pressure plate

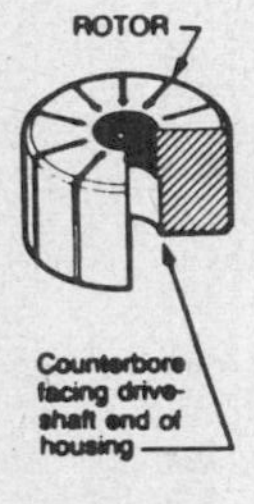
ROTOR
Counterbore facing drive-shaft end of housing

Install rotor

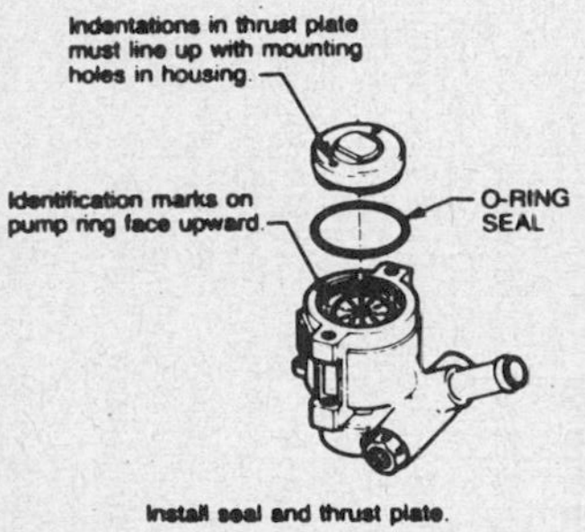
Indentations in thrust plate must line up with mounting holes in housing.
Identification marks on pump ring face upward.
O-RING SEAL

Install seal and thrust plate.

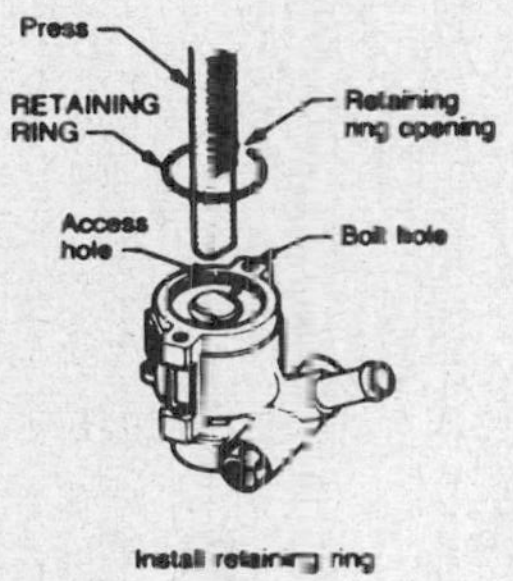
Press
RETAINING RING
Retaining ring opening
Access hole
Bolt hole

Install retaining ring

GC6029100050030X

Fig. 12 Power steering pump assembly overhaul (Part 3 of 4). TC series

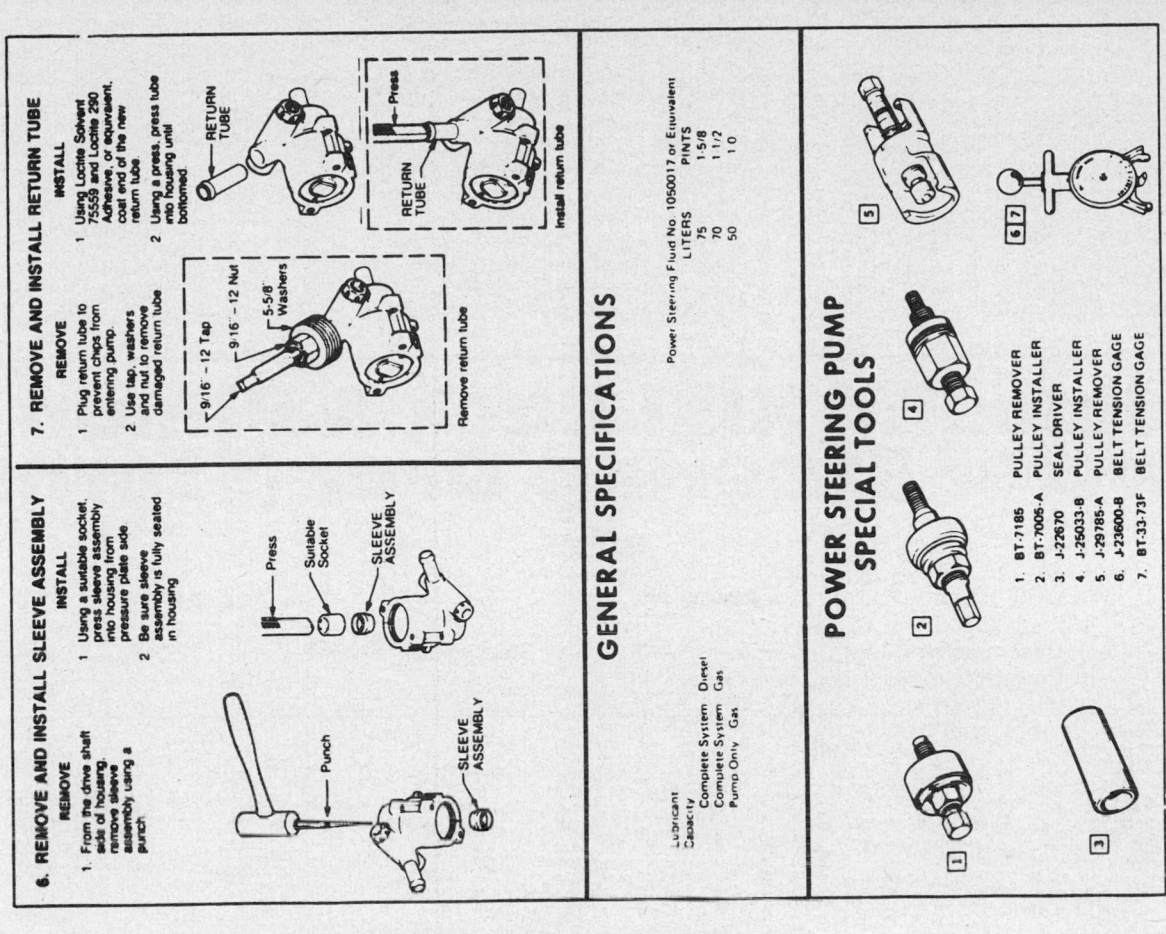

6. REMOVE AND INSTALL SLEEVE ASSEMBLY

REMOVE

1. From the drive shaft side of housing, remove sleeve assembly using a punch.

INSTALL

1. Using a suitable socket, press sleeve assembly into housing from pressure plate side.
2. Be sure sleeve assembly is fully seated in housing.

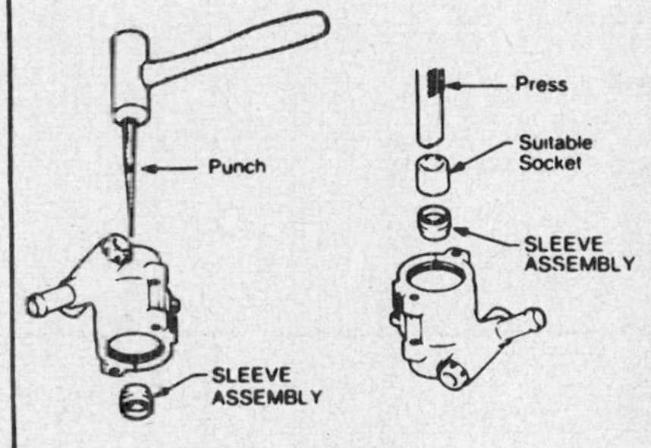
Punch
SLEEVE ASSEMBLY
Press
Suitable Socket
SLEEVE ASSEMBLY

7. REMOVE AND INSTALL RETURN TUBE

REMOVE

1. Plug return tube to prevent chips from entering pump.
2. Use tap, washers and nut to remove damaged return tube.

INSTALL

1. Using Loctite Solvent 75559 and Loctite 290 Adhesive, or equivalent, coat end of the new return tube.
2. Using a press, press tube into housing until bottomed.

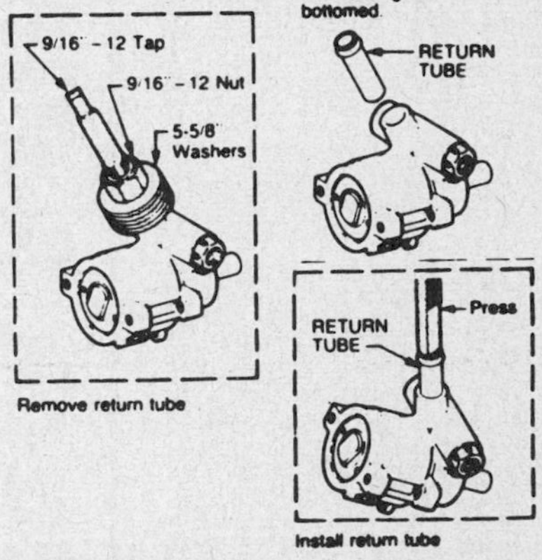
9/16" - 12 Tap
9/16" - 12 Nut
5-5/8" Washers
RETURN TUBE
RETURN TUBE
Press

Remove return tube

Install return tube

GENERAL SPECIFICATIONS

Lubricant	Power Steering Fluid No. 1050017 or Equivalent	
Capacity	LITERS	PINTS
Complete System Diesel	75	1-5/8
Complete System Gas	70	1 1/2
Pump Only Gas	50	1 0

POWER STEERING PUMP SPECIAL TOOLS

1
2
4

3

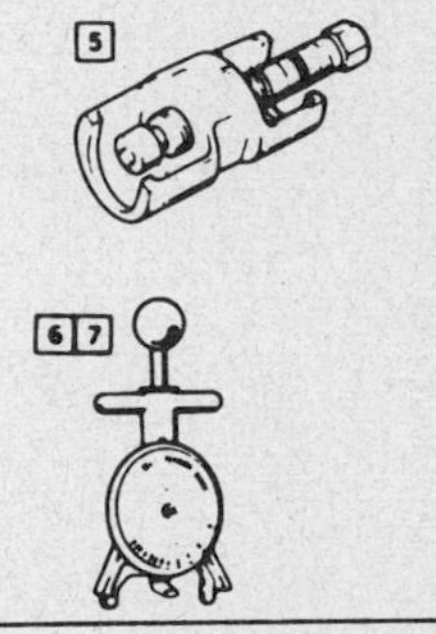
5
6 7

1. BT-7185 PULLEY REMOVER
2. BT-7005-A PULLEY INSTALLER
3. J-22670 SEAL DRIVER
4. J-25033-B PULLEY INSTALLER
5. J-29785-A PULLEY REMOVER
6. J-23600-B BELT TENSION GAGE
7. BT-33-73F BELT TENSION GAGE

GC6029100050040X

Fig. 12 Power steering pump assembly overhaul (Part 4 of 4). TC series

5. With assistant checking fluid level and condition, turn steering wheel lock-to lock at least 20 times. Engine remains off.
6. While turning wheel, check fluid constantly for any sign of bubbles. If bubbles present repeat previous step.
7. Start engine. With engine idling, maintain fluid level and install cap.
8. Return wheels to center. Lower front wheels to ground.
9. Keep engine running for two minutes at just above idle.
10. Turn steering wheel in both directions to verify proper operation.
11. If steering system operates properly, procedure is complete. If any problem remains, proceed as follows:
    a. **If foam, bubbles or discoloration exist in fluid,** switch ignition off. Wait two minutes. Recheck hose connections.
    b. Repeat bleed procedure.
    c. If condition still exists, replace O-ring seals and hose clamps. Then fill system and repeat bleed procedure.
    d. **If pump has whine or groan,** recheck hoses for possible contact with frame, body or engine while engine is running.
    e. If hoses are not rubbing, remove as much fluid from reservoir as possible using suction device, then refill with cool clean fluid.
    f. If noise persists, remove and replace power steering pump then repeat bleed procedure following replacement.

Jidosha Kiki Rack & Pinion Power Steering Gear (Storm)

INDEX

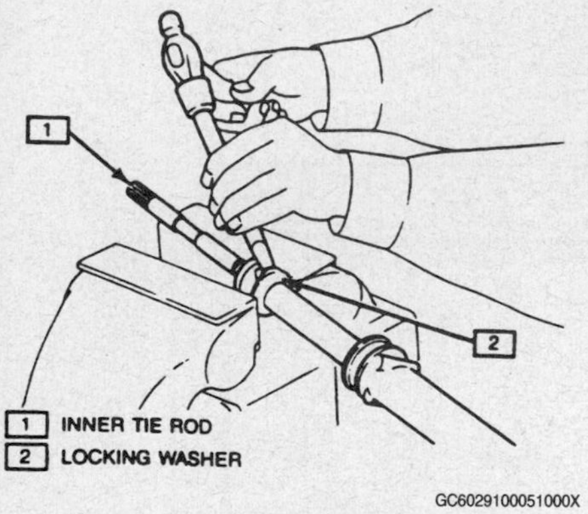

1
2
1 INNER TIE ROD
2 LOCKING WASHER
GC6029100051000X

Fig. 1 Lock washer removal

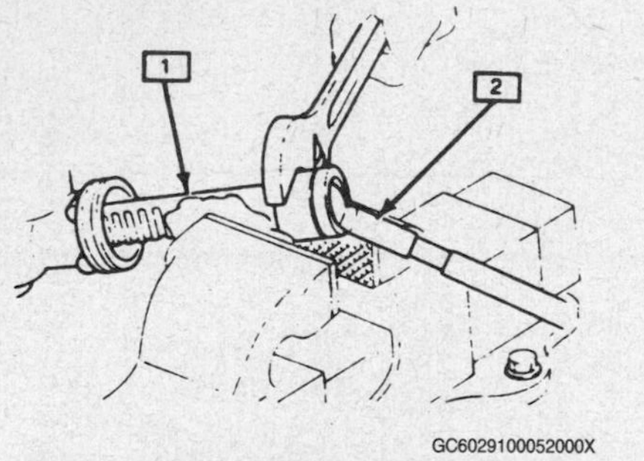

1
2
GC6029100052000X

Fig. 2 Inner tie rod assembly removal

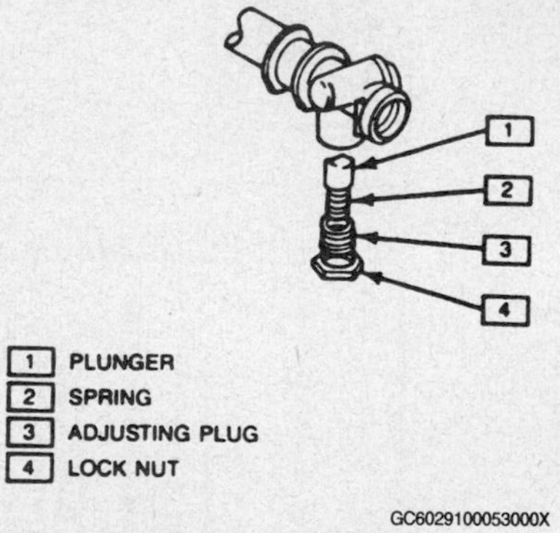

1
2
3
4
1 PLUNGER
2 SPRING
3 ADJUSTING PLUG
4 LOCK NUT
GC6029100053000X

Fig. 3 Plug, spring & plunger assembly adjustment

DESCRIPTION

This steering system converts rotary motion to linear motion as follows; when the steering wheel is turned, rotary motion is transferred to the steering shaft, shaft joint and rack pinion. The pinion teeth mesh with teeth on the rack and the rotary motion is transferred to the rack and changed to linear motion. The linear force is then transmitted through the tie rods and to the steering knuckles which steer the front wheels.

POWER STEERING SYSTEM SERVICE

STEERING GEAR SERVICE

Disassemble

1. Remove retaining ring and dust boot from rack.
2. Clamp steering gear in suitable vise.
3. Remove clamps from tie rod boots, then separate boots from rack and slide down tie rods.
4. Unstake locking washers between inner tie rods and rack, **Fig. 1.**
5. Remove right tie rod, then left tie rod assembly from rack, **Fig. 2.**
6. Loosen adjusting plug nut, then remove spring and rack plunger, **Fig. 3.**
7. Center rack and mark position of pinion valve. Rotate pinion gear until notch is parallel to rack, then carefully measure and record dimension "A," **Fig. 4.** This measurement must be used upon reassembly.
8. Remove valve plug, **Fig. 5.**
9. Remove pinion fixing nut, **Fig. 6.**
10. Remove pinion retaining snap ring, **Fig. 7.**
11. Remove rack from housing.
12. Remove inner rack seal and shock damper using inner rack seal remover tool No. 38304-5 or equivalent,**Fig. 8.**
13. Remove lower pinion bearing from rack housing.
14. Remove bearing and seal from valve housing using lower pinion valve housing seal and bearing remover tool No. 38304-1 or equivalent, **Fig. 9.**

Assemble

1. Install inner rack seal onto rack seal ring installer, tool No. J 33997-3 using rack seal ring expander, tool No. J 33997-2 or equivalent.
2. Install upper bearing and seal into pinion valve housing using lower pinion valve housing seal and bearing installer tool No. J 38304-4 or equivalent, **Fig. 10.**
3. Install rack into housing and seat inner rack seal using pack piston ring installer tool No. J 38304-7 or equivalent and inner rack seal installer tool No. J 38304-6 or equivalent, **Figs. 11 and 12.**
4. Install seal holder on to housing, then retaining ring on seal holder.
5. Install pinion valve assembly into housing using pinion ring compressor tool No. 38304-8 or equivalent, **Fig. 13.**
6. Install lower bearing on pinion valve.
7. Install pinion fixing nut and **torque** to 29 ft. lbs.

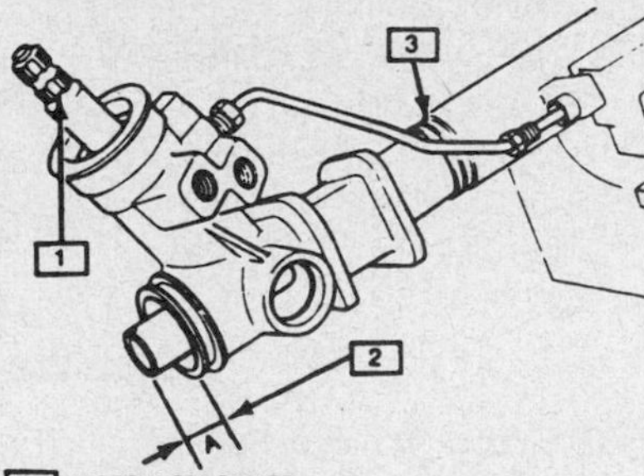

1
2
3
A

1 NOTCH ON SHAFT
2 DIMENSION "A"
3 RACK HOUSING

GC6029100054000X

Fig. 4 Pinion shaft measurement location

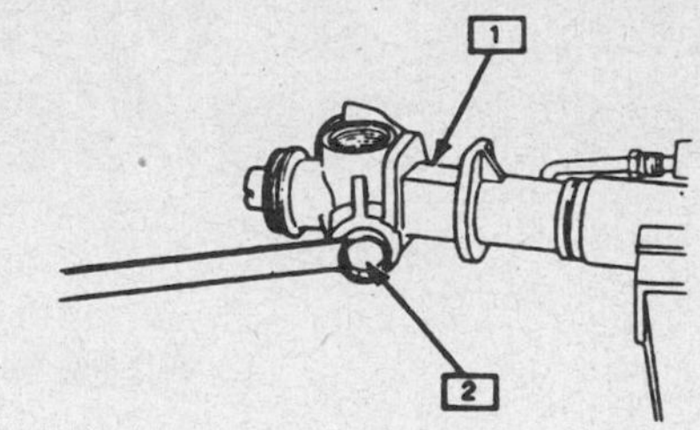

1
2

1 RACK HOUSING
2 VALVE PLUG

GC6029100055000X

Fig. 5 Valve plug removal

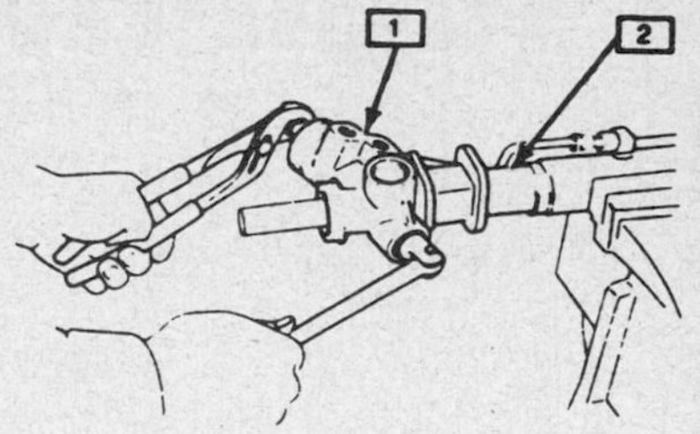

1
2

1 PINION HOUSING
2 RACK HOUSING

GC6029100056000X

Fig. 6 Pinion fixing nut removal

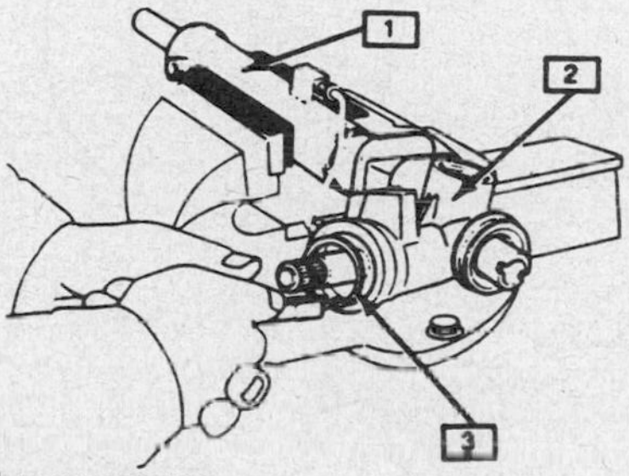

1
2
3

1 RACK HOUSING
2 PINION HOUSING
3 PINION RETAINING RING

GC6029100057000X

Fig. 7 Retaining snap ring removal

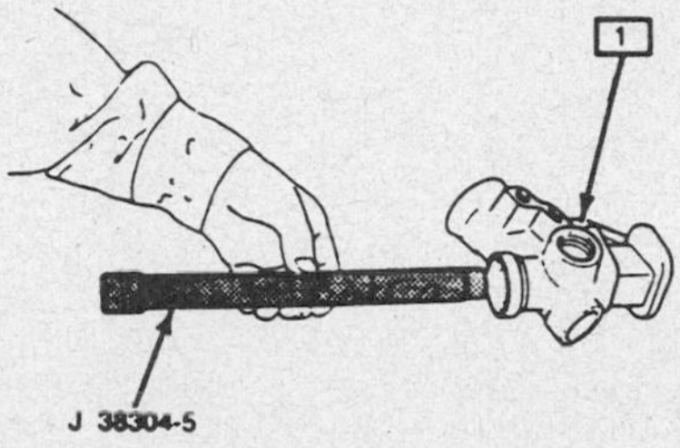

1
J 38304-5

1 PINION VALVE HOUSING

GC6029100058000X

Fig. 8 Inner rack seal & shock damper removal

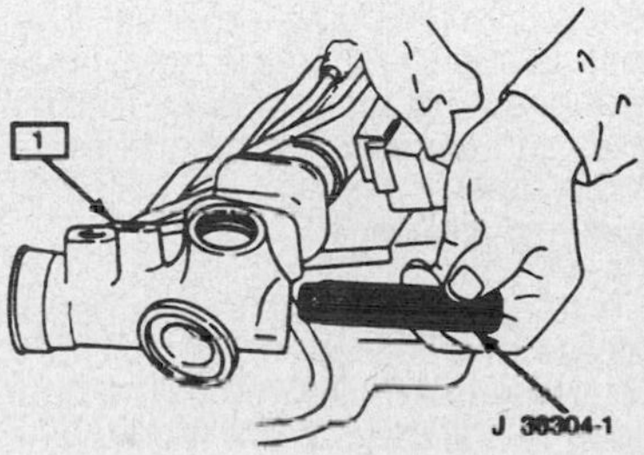

1
J 38304-1

1 PINION VALVE HOUSING

GC6029100059000X

Fig. 9 Pinion bearing removal

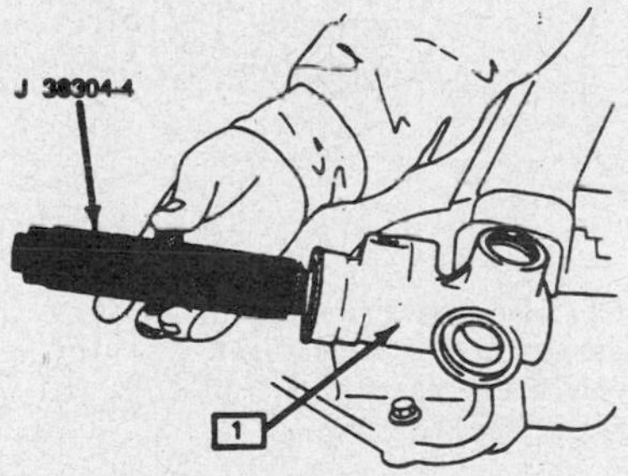

J 38304-4
1

1 PINION VALVE HOUSING

GC6029100060000X

Fig. 10 Pinion valve bearing & seal installation

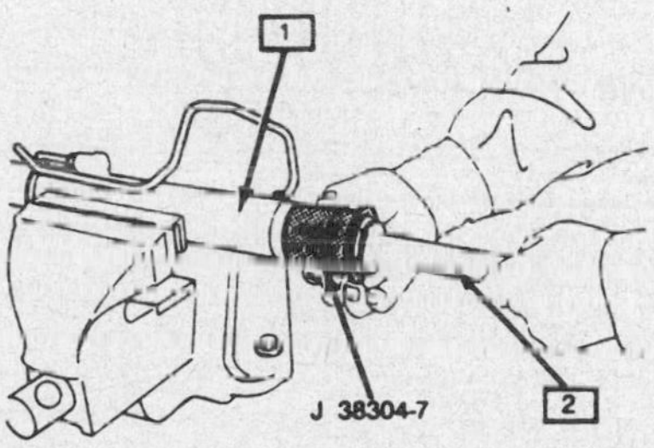

1
J 38304-7
2

1 RACK HOUSING
2 RACK GEAR

GC6029100061000X

Fig. 11 Inner rack seal installation

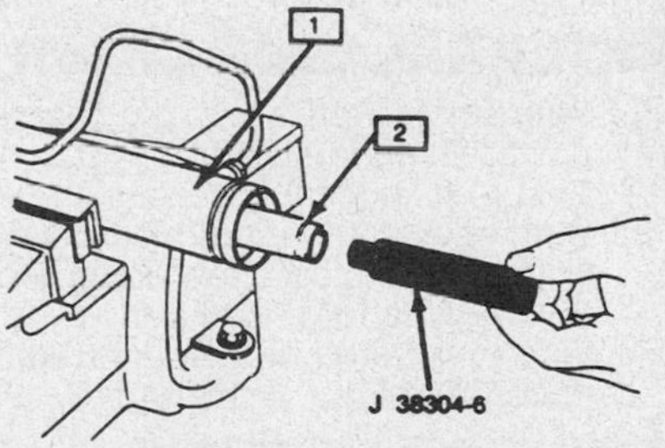

1
2
J 38304-6

1 RACK HOUSING
2 RACK GEAR

GC6029100062000X

Fig. 12 Inner rack seal seating

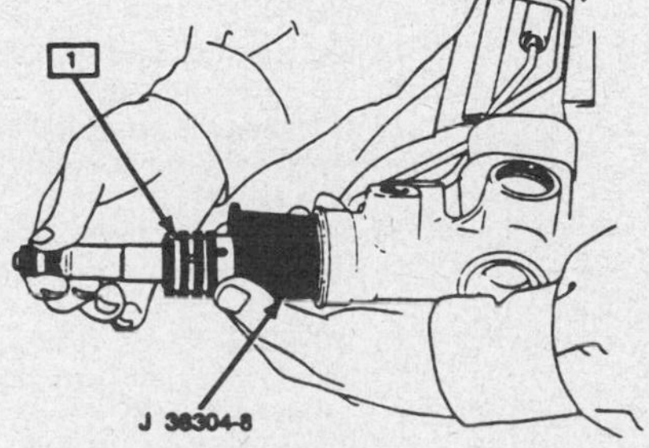

1
J 38304-8

1 PINION VALVE ASSEMBLY

GC6029100063000X

Fig. 13 Pinion valve assembly installation

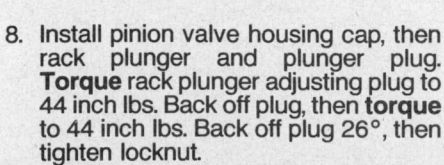

8. Install pinion valve housing cap, then rack plunger and plunger plug. **Torque** rack plunger adjusting plug to 44 inch lbs. Back off plug, then **torque** to 44 inch lbs. Back off plug 26°, then tighten locknut.
9. Install upper pinion valve seal, then retaining ring on upper pinion valve seal.
10. Install left tie rod assembly, then **torque** inner tie rod to 65 ft. lbs. and peen over stake washer. Install left tie rod boot.
11. Install right tie rod assembly, then **torque** inner tie rod to 65 ft. lbs. and peen over stake washer. Install right tie rod boot.

Saginaw Rack & Pinion Power Steering Gear

INDEX

DESCRIPTION

This power steering gear assembly incorporates an integral tube and housing, containing a pinion shaft and steering rack. The tube and housing are joined by a plastic injection-bonding process. The pinion shaft is supported in the housing by thrust bearings and bushings. A bushing and bulkhead assembly supports the steering in the tube.

OPERATION

A rotary-type valve body is used to control the hydraulic steering assist. Fluid under pressure is directed to the gear housing and into the valve body. The valve body then directs fluid to the power cylinder.

A spool valve, connected to the stub shaft by a locating pin, rotates within the valve body. Fluid directional passages, machined into the spool valve, are aligned with fluid passages in the valve body as the spool valve rotates. Fluid is directed through these passages, into either side of the power cylinder through the externally mounted oil lines.

DIAGNOSIS & TESTING

EXTERNAL LEAK CHECK

1. With engine off, wipe dry the entire power steering system.
2. Ensure fluid level is correct.
3. Start engine, then turn steering wheel from stop to stop a few times. Do not hold at stop for a long period.
4. Find exact area of leak and repair as necessary, **Figs. 1 through 3.**

POWER STEERING SYSTEM SERVICE

FWD EXCEPT ACHIEVA, BERETTA, CAVALIER, CORSICA, GRAND AM, LEMANS, SKYLARK & SUNBIRD

To prevent damage to the rack and pinion boot seal when removing it, the following should be noted. Slide the small end of the boot towards the rack until the groove is exposed. Place a

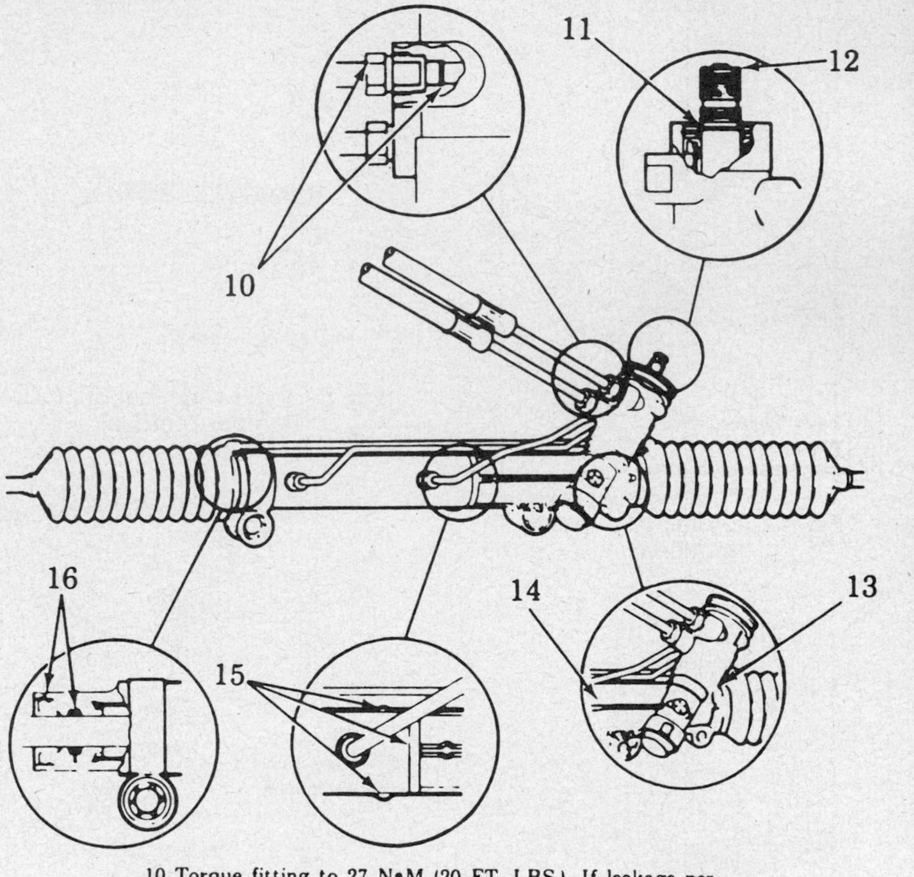
11
12
10
16
15
14
13

10 Torque fitting to 27 N•M (20 FT. LBS.). If leakage persists, replace "O" ring seal. If leakage is due to damaged threads, repair fitting nut or replace line as required. If housing threads are badly damaged, replace housing.

11 Replace dust and stub shaft seals.

12 If leakage is observed between torsion bar and stub shaft, replace the valve assembly.

13 If leakage is observed at driver side and is not affected by the direction of turn, replace pinion shaft seal.

14 If leakage is observed at the housing end and spurts when bottomed in left turn, replace inner rack seal.

15 Replace inner rack seal.

16 If leakage is observed at passenger side, it is necessary to remove bulkhead and replace both "O" ring seals and lip seal.

GC6029100090000X

Fig. 1 Power rack & pinion steering gear leak diagnosis. FWD except Achieva, Beretta, Cavalier, Corsica, Grand Am, LeMans, Skylark & Sunbird

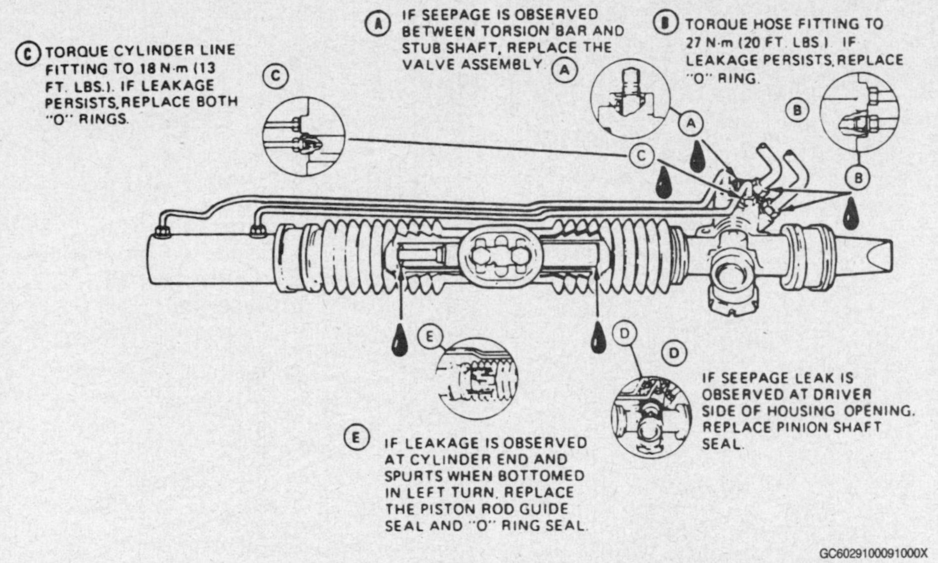
(C) TORQUE CYLINDER LINE FITTING TO 18 N·m (13 FT. LBS.). IF LEAKAGE PERSISTS, REPLACE BOTH "O" RINGS.
(A) IF SEEPAGE IS OBSERVED BETWEEN TORSION BAR AND STUB SHAFT, REPLACE THE VALVE ASSEMBLY.
(B) TORQUE HOSE FITTING TO 27 N·m (20 FT. LBS.). IF LEAKAGE PERSISTS, REPLACE "O" RING.
(D) IF SEEPAGE LEAK IS OBSERVED AT DRIVER SIDE OF HOUSING OPENING, REPLACE PINION SHAFT SEAL.
(E) IF LEAKAGE IS OBSERVED AT CYLINDER END AND SPURTS WHEN BOTTOMED IN LEFT TURN, REPLACE THE PISTON ROD GUIDE SEAL AND "O" RING SEAL.
GC6029100091000X

Fig. 2 Power rack & pinion steering gear leak diagnosis. FWD Achieva, Beretta, Cavalier, Corsica, Grand Am, LeMans, Skylark & Sunbird

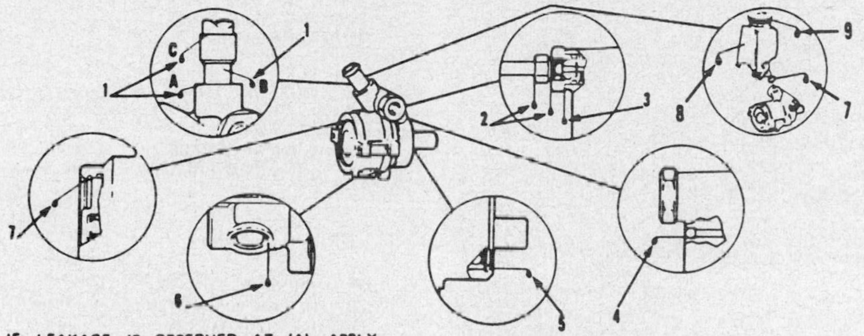
1. IF LEAKAGE IS OBSERVED AT (A), APPLY LOCTITE SAFETY SOLVENT AND LOCTITE 290 OR EQUIVALENT TO TUBE/ HOUSING CONNECTION. IF LEAKAGE IS FROM (B), REPLACE RETURN TUBE. IF LEAKAGE IS FROM (C), REPLACE HOSE OR CLAMP
2. TORQUE FITTING TO 27 N·m (20 FT. LBS.). IF LEAKAGE PERSISTS, REPLACE "O" RING SEAL.
3. TORQUE FITTING TO 75 N·m (55 FT. LBS.). IF LEAKAGE PERSISTS, REPLACE "O" RING SEAL
4. SEAT BALL IN HOUSING WITH BLUNT PUNCH APPLY LOCTITE SAFETY SOLVENT AND LOCTITE 290 OR EQUIVALENT TO AREA
5. REPLACE DRIVE SHAFT SEAL. MAKE CERTAIN THAT DRIVE SHAFT IS CLEAN AND FREE OF PITTING IN SEAL AREA.
6. SEAT PLUG IN HOUSING. APPLY LOCTITE SAFETY SOLVENT AND LOCTITE 290 OR EQUIVALENT TO AREA.
7. REPLACE "O" RING SEAL.
8. REPLACE RESERVIOR IF CRACKED OR DENTED
9. IF CAP LEAKS WITH CORRECT FLUID LEVEL, REPLACE CAP
GC6029100092000X

Fig. 3 Power steering pump leak diagnosis. FWD models w/rack & pinion steering

small rubber band in the groove, then slide the small end of the boot over the rubber band and off the threaded end of the tie rod. This will prevent boot damage.

OUTER TIE ROD

1. Remove cotter pin and hex slotted nut from outer tie rod assembly, **Figs. 4 and 5.**
2. Loosen jam nut, then remove outer tie rod from steering knuckle using steering linkage remover tool No. J 24319-01 or equivalent.
3. Remove outer tie rod from inner tie rod.
4. Reverse procedure to install, noting the following:
   a. **Torque** hex slotted nut to 35 ft. lbs. with a maximum of 45 ft. lbs. to install cotter pin.
   b. Adjust toe by turning inner tie rod.
   c. **Torque** jam nut against outer tie rod to 50 ft. lbs.

RACK & PINION BOOT & BREATHER TUBE

Removal

1. Remove outer tie rod.
2. Remove hex jam nut from inner tie rod assembly.
3. Remove tie rod end clamp, **Fig. 6**, then remove and discard boot clamp with side cutters.
4. Mark location of breather tube on housing before removing tube, then remove boot and breather tube.

Installation

1. Install new boot clamp onto boot.
2. Apply grease to inner tie rod or housing as shown in **Fig. 7.**
3. Align and install breather tube.
4. Install boot onto housing until seated in housing groove tang.
5. Position boot clamp on boot and crimp.
6. Position tie rod end clamp on boot and secure with pliers.

INNER TIE ROD

Removal

1. Remove rack and pinion steering assembly from vehicle.
2. Remove outer tie rod from inner tie rod assembly, then rack and pinion boot.
3. Place wrench on flat of rack assembly and place wrench on flats of inner tie rod housing, **Fig. 8.**
4. Rotate housing counterclockwise until inner tie rod separates from rack.

Installation

Rack must be held during inner tie rod installation to prevent internal gear damage.

1. Install inner tie rod on rack and **torque** to 70 ft. lbs., **Fig. 9.**
2. Support rack and housing of inner tie rod assembly, then stake both sides of inner tie rod housing to flats on rack, **Fig. 10.**
3. Check both stakes by inserting a .010 inch feeler gauge between rack and housing stake.
4. Slide shock damper over housing until it engages.
5. Install boot and rack outer tie rod, then rack and pinion assembly to vehicle.

RACK BEARING PRELOAD

Make adjustment with front wheels raised and steering wheel centered. Check returnability of steering wheel to center after adjustment.

1. Loosen locknut, then turn adjuster plug clockwise until it bottoms in housing, then back off 50° to 70°.
2. **Torque** locknut to 50 ft. lbs. while holding adjuster plug.

PINION & VALVE ASSEMBLY

Removal

1. Remove rack and pinion steering assembly from vehicle.
2. Remove adjuster plug locknut from adjuster plug, **Fig. 11.**
3. Remove adjuster plug from housing, then adjuster spring and rack bearing.
4. Remove retaining ring from valve bore of housing then, the dust cover, **Fig. 12.**
5. Holding stub shaft, remove hex locknut from pinion and valve assembly. **Stub shaft must be held to prevent damage to pinion teeth.**
6. With rack centered, mark location of stub shaft notch on housing, then measure distance "A," as shown in **Fig. 13.**
7. Using a suitable press, press threaded end of pinion until the pinion and valve assembly is almost removed. Mark a second location of stub shaft notch on housing. The second mark is used to position notch prior to reassembly.

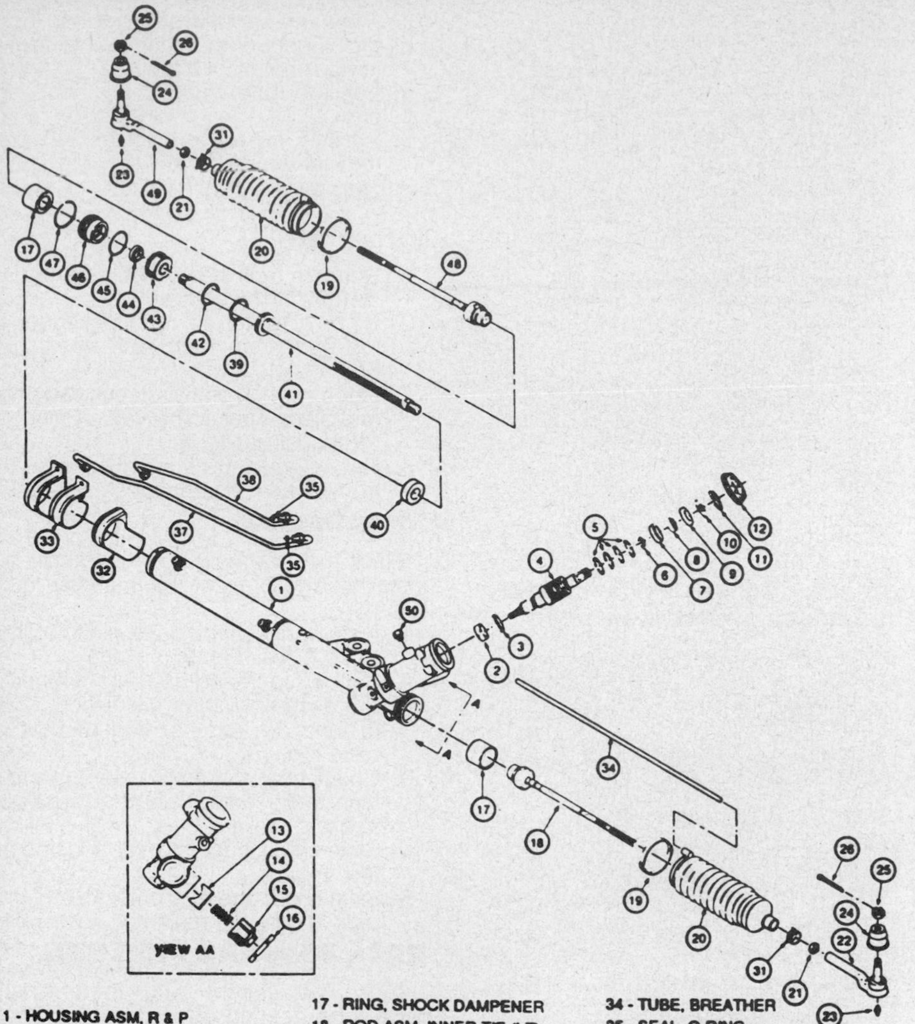

1 - HOUSING ASM, R & P
2 - BUSHING, UPPER PINION
3 - SEAL, RACK & PINION
4 - VALVE ASM, PINION &
5 - RING, VALVE BODY
6 - RING, RETAINING
7 - ANNULUS, STUB SHAFT BEARING
8 - BEARING ASM, NEEDLE
9 - SEAL, STUB SHAFT
10 - SEAL, STUB SHAFT DUST
11 - RING, RETAINING
12 - ADAPTER, SEAL
13 - BEARING, RACK
14 - SPRING, ADJUSTER
15 - PLUG, ADJUSTER
16 - NUT, ADJUSTER PLUG LOCK
17 - RING, SHOCK DAMPENER
18 - ROD ASM, INNER TIE (LT)
19 - CLAMP, BOOT
20 - BOOT, RACK & PINION
21 - NUT, HEX JAM
22 - ROD ASM, OUTER TIE (LT)
23 - FITTING, LUBRICATION
24 - SEAL, TIE ROD
25 - NUT, HEXAGON SLOTTED
26 - PIN, COTTER
27 - BEARING ASM, BALL
28 - RING, RETAINING
29 - NUT, HEX LOCK
30 - COVER, DUST
31 - CLAMP, TIE ROD END
32 - GROMMET, MOUNTING
33 - BRACKET ASM, MOUNTING
34 - TUBE, BREATHER
35 - SEAL, O-RING
36 - THIS NUMBER NOT USED
37 - LINE ASM, CYLINDER (LT)
38 - LINE ASM, CYLINDER (RT)
39 - THIS NUMBER NOT USED
40 - SEAL, INNER RACK
41 - RACK ASM, PISTON & STEERING
42 - RING PISTON
43 - BULKHEAD, CYLINDER INNER
44 - SEAL, RACK & PINION (BULKHEAD)
45 - SEAL, O-RING
46 - BULKHEAD, CYLINDER OUTER
47 - RING, BULKHEAD RETAINING
48 - ROD ASM, INNER TIE (RT)
49 - ROD ASM, OUTER TIE (RT)
50 - PLUG ASM, O-RING

GC6029100064000X

Fig. 4 Exploded view of power rack & pinion assembly. FWD except Achieva, Beretta, Cavalier, Corsica, Grand Am, LeMans, Skylark & Sunbird

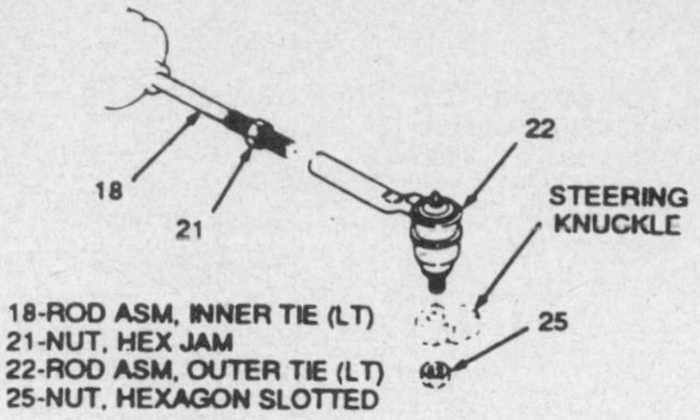
18
21
22
STEERING KNUCKLE
25
18-ROD ASM, INNER TIE (LT)
21-NUT, HEX JAM
22-ROD ASM, OUTER TIE (LT)
25-NUT, HEXAGON SLOTTED

GC6029100065000X

Fig. 5 Outer tie rod replacement

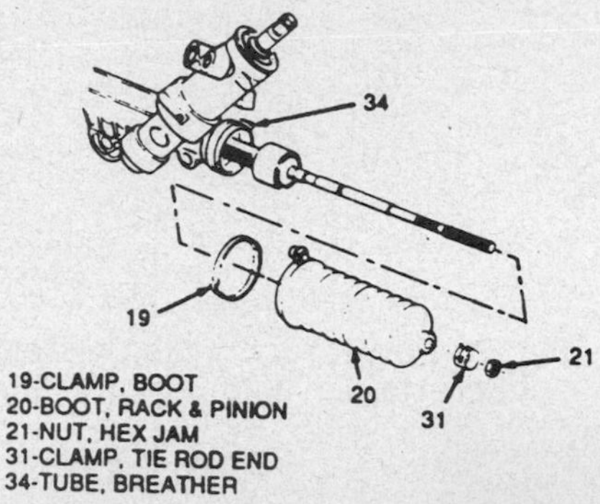
34
19
20
21
31
19-CLAMP, BOOT
20-BOOT, RACK & PINION
21-NUT, HEX JAM
31-CLAMP, TIE ROD END
34-TUBE, BREATHER

GC6029100066000X

Fig. 6 Boot replacement

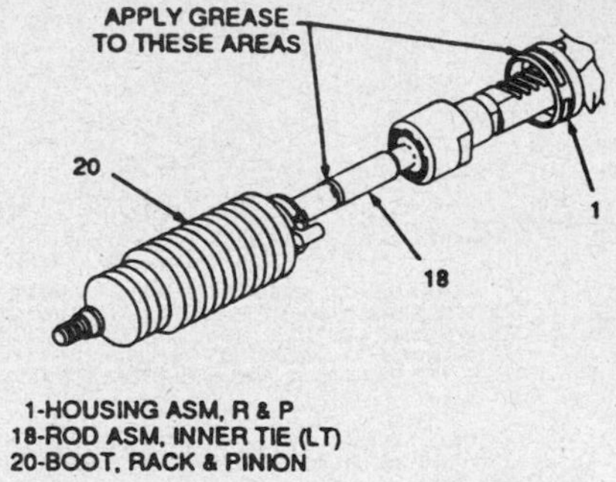
APPLY GREASE TO THESE AREAS
20
1
18
1-HOUSING ASM, R & P
18-ROD ASM, INNER TIE (LT)
20-BOOT, RACK & PINION

GC6029100067000X

Fig. 7 Boot seal application

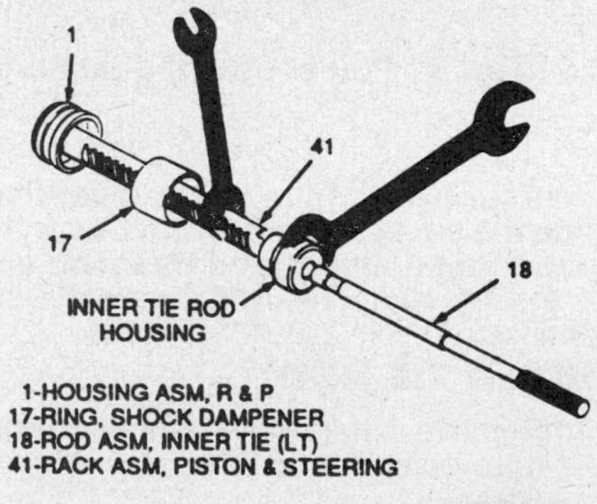
1
41
17
18
INNER TIE ROD HOUSING
1-HOUSING ASM, R & P
17-RING, SHOCK DAMPENER
18-ROD ASM, INNER TIE (LT)
41-RACK ASM, PISTON & STEERING

GC6029100068000X

Fig. 8 Inner tie rod removal

8. Remove stub shaft dust seal, stub shaft seal, stub shaft bearing annulus assembly and pinion and valve assembly with retaining ring and valve body rings attached.
9. If necessary, remove valve body rings from pinion and valve assembly, then clean ring grooves. Inspect pinion and valve assembly for broken drive pin. If found, replace gear assembly.

Installation

1. If valve body rings are to be replaced, apply grease to ring grooves and rings and Install new rings, ensure split tabs are engaged and staggered, **Fig. 4.**
2. Place pinion and valve assembly into clear pinion and valve assembly ring protector tool No. 37090 or equivalent. Allow to set for at least three minutes.
3. Center rack in housing, refer to measurement "A" taken during disassembly.
4. Wipe housing bore clean and apply grease to valve housing bore. Inspect stub shaft bearing annulus for damage and ensure bearing is flush with annulus.
5. Align notch on valve stub shaft with second mark on housing made during disassembly.
6. Install pinion and valve assembly with spool shaft retaining ring and valve body rings installed into housing using clear pinion and valve assembly ring protector tool No. 37090 or equivalent to prevent ring damage.

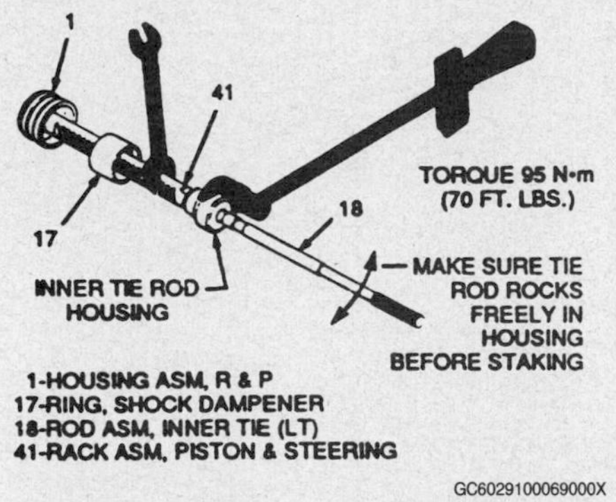
TORQUE 95 N•m
(70 FT. LBS.)
INNER TIE ROD
HOUSING
MAKE SURE TIE
ROD ROCKS
FREELY IN
HOUSING
BEFORE STAKING
1-HOUSING ASM, R & P
17-RING, SHOCK DAMPENER
18-ROD ASM, INNER TIE (LT)
41-RACK ASM, PISTON & STEERING
GC6029100069000X

Fig. 9 Inner tie rod installation

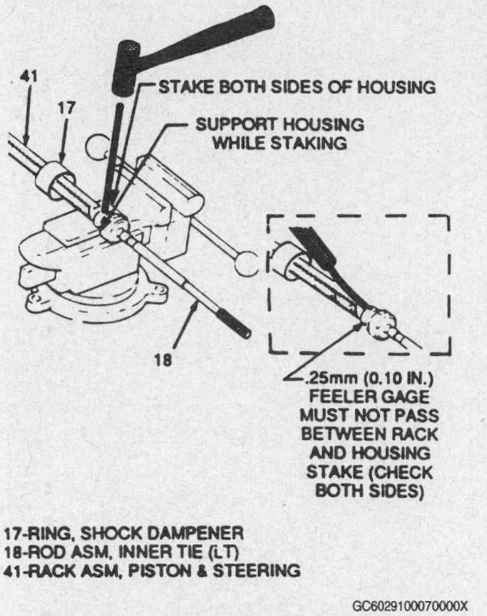
STAKE BOTH SIDES OF HOUSING
SUPPORT HOUSING
WHILE STAKING
.25mm (0.10 IN.)
FEELER GAGE
MUST NOT PASS
BETWEEN RACK
AND HOUSING
STAKE (CHECK
BOTH SIDES)
17-RING, SHOCK DAMPENER
18-ROD ASM, INNER TIE (LT)
41-RACK ASM, PISTON & STEERING
GC6029100070000X

Fig. 10 Inner tie rod staking procedure

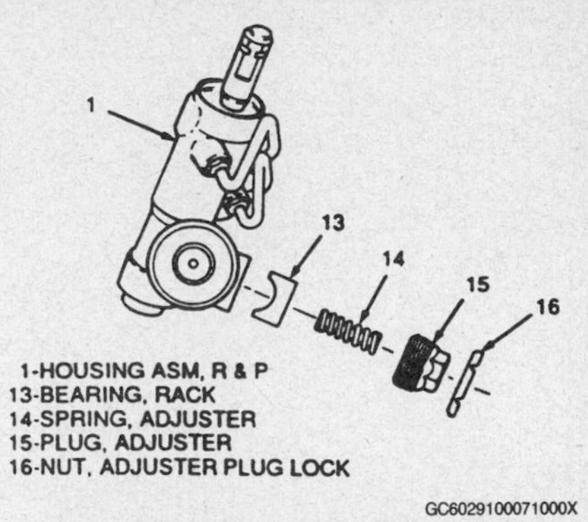
1-HOUSING ASM, R & P
13-BEARING, RACK
14-SPRING, ADJUSTER
15-PLUG, ADJUSTER
16-NUT, ADJUSTER PLUG LOCK
GC6029100071000X

Fig. 11 Rack bearing removal

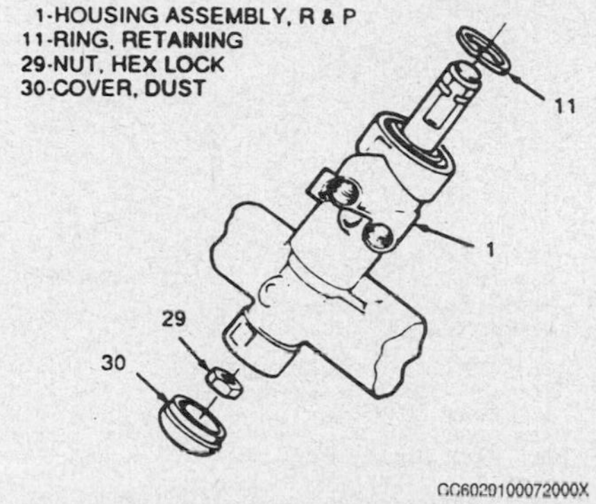
1-HOUSING ASSEMBLY, R & P
11-RING, RETAINING
29-NUT, HEX LOCK
30-COVER, DUST
GC6029100072000X

Fig. 12 Retaining ring & locknut removal

7. Install pinion and valve assembly onto rack using clear pinion and valve assembly ring protector tool No. J 37090 or equivalent and pinion seal installer tool No. J 29822 or equivalent. **Do not hammer or use excessive force.**
8. Ensure notch in stub shaft and first mark on housing are lined up while rack is centered in housing. Refer to measurement "A" taken during disassembly.
9. Hold valve stub shaft and thread hex locknut into pinion, then **torque** to 26 ft lbs. **If stub shaft is not held, damage to pinion teeth will result.**
10. Install dust cover onto housing.
11. Install stub shaft bearing annulus assembly onto valve stub shaft.
12. Place seal protector tool No. J 29810 or equivalent onto valve stub shaft, then apply a small quantity of grease between stub shaft seals.
13. Install stub shaft seal and stub shaft dust seal over protector and into housing.
14. Install retaining ring into groove in housing.
15. Lubricate stub shaft and dust seal area, then coat rack bearing, adjuster spring and adjuster plug with lithium grease and install in housing.
16. With rack centered in housing, turn adjuster plug clockwise until it bottoms in housing, then back off 50° to 70°. Check torque on pinion. Maximum pinion preload torque is 16 inch lbs.
17. Install adjuster plug locknut to adjuster plug, then tighten firmly against housing while holding adjuster plug stationary.
18. Install rack and pinion assembly, then flush power steering system.

ACHIEVA, BERETTA, CAVALIER, CORSICA, GRAND AM, LEMANS, SKYLARK & SUNBIRD

OUTER TIE ROD

1. Remove cotter pin, then hex slotted nut from outer tie rod ball stud, **Figs. 14 and 15.**
2. Loosen outer tie rod pinch bolts, then separate outer tie rod from steering knuckle using steering linkage puller, tool No. J 24319-01 or equivalent.
3. Remove outer tie rod from tie rod adjuster.
4. Reverse procedure to install, noting the following:
   a. **On all models except LeMans, torque** hex slotted nut to 35 ft. lbs., with a maximum of 50 ft. lbs. to install cotter pin.
   b. **On LeMans models, torque** nut to 44 ft. lbs., with a maximum of 55 ft. lbs. to install cotter pin.
   c. **On all models,** adjust toe by turning tie rod adjuster.
   d. **Torque** pinch bolts to 15 ft. lbs. on LeMans models and 41 ft. lbs. on all models except LeMans.

INNER TIE ROD

1. Remove and dispose of lock plate from inner tie rod bolts, **Fig. 16.**
2. Remove inner tie rod bolt.
3. Slide out and remove inner tie rod between bolt support plate and rack and pinion boot. **If both inner tie rods are to be removed, after removing the first tie rod, reinstall bolt to keep rack and pinion and other parts aligned.**
4. Reverse procedure to install. Ensure center housing cover washers are fitted into rack and pinion boot. **Torque** inner tie rod bolts to 65 ft. lbs. and install new lock plate with notches in proper position over flats of inner tie rod bolts.

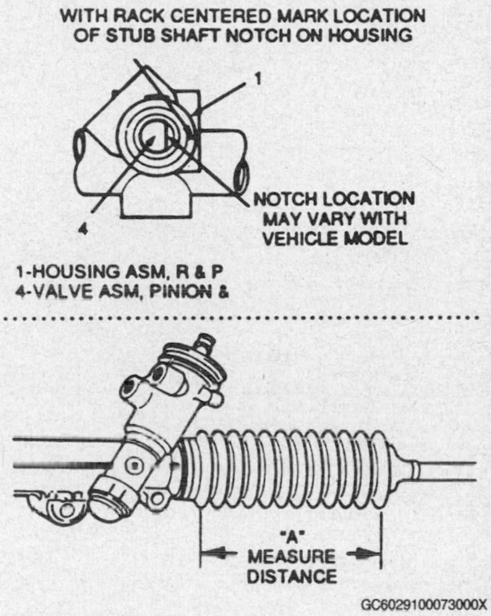
WITH RACK CENTERED MARK LOCATION
OF STUB SHAFT NOTCH ON HOUSING
NOTCH LOCATION
MAY VARY WITH
VEHICLE MODEL
1-HOUSING ASM, R & P
4-VALVE ASM, PINION &
"A"
MEASURE
DISTANCE
GC6029100073000X

Fig. 13 Housing reference mark

INNER PIVOT BUSHINGS

Refer to **Figs. 17 and 18** for replacement procedure.

FLANGE & STEERING COUPLING ASSEMBLY

1. Remove rack and pinion assembly from vehicle.
2. Remove pinch bolt from flange and steering coupling assembly, then the coupling, **Fig. 19.**
3. Reverse procedure to install. **Torque** pinch bolt to 29 ft. lbs.

HYDRAULIC CYLINDER LINES

Refer to **Fig. 14** for replacement procedure. Ensure new O-rings are installed. **Torque** line fittings at valve end to 14 ft. lbs. and at cylinder end to 20 ft. lbs.

RACK GUIDE

Removal

1. Remove rack and pinion steering assembly from vehicle.
2. Remove lock plate from inner tie rod bolts and discard, **Figs. 14 and 20.**
3. Remove inner tie rod bolts, bolt support plate, cylinder lines and inner tie rod assemblies.

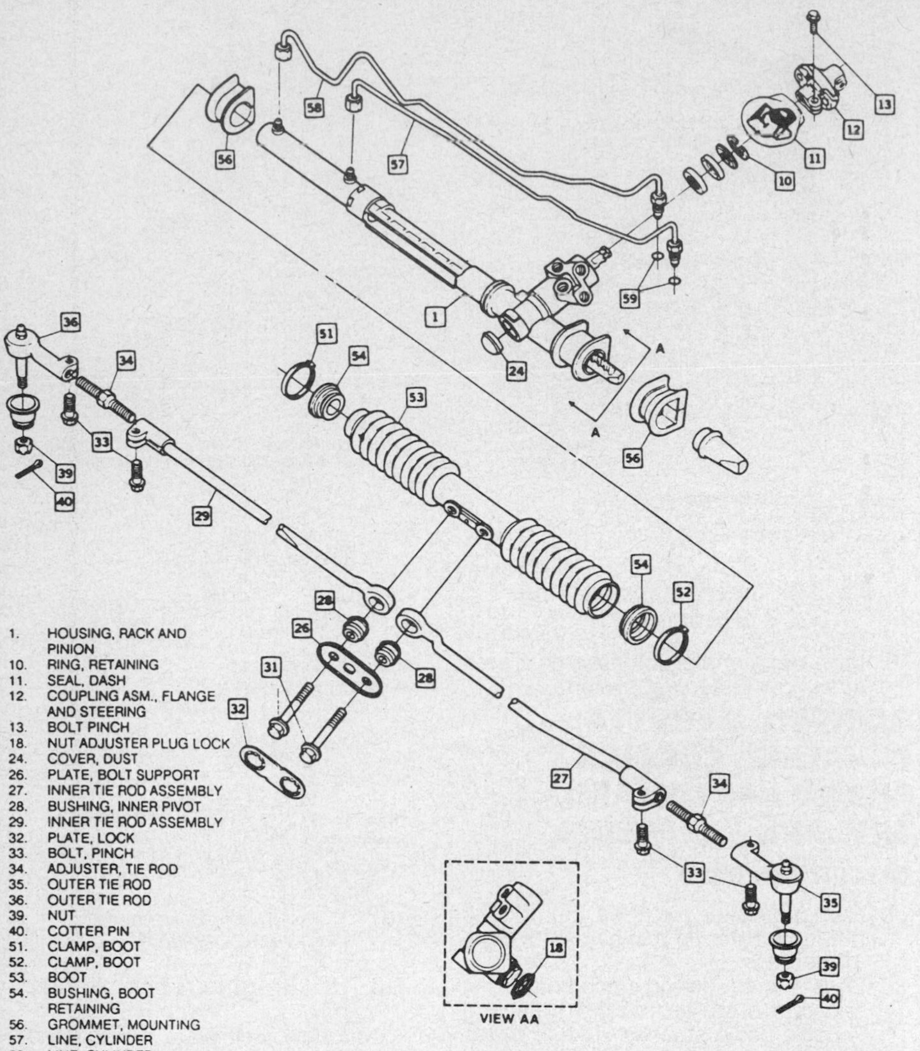
VIEW AA

1. HOUSING, RACK AND PINION
10. RING, RETAINING
11. SEAL, DASH
12. COUPLING ASM., FLANGE AND STEERING
13. BOLT PINCH
18. NUT ADJUSTER PLUG LOCK
24. COVER, DUST
26. PLATE, BOLT SUPPORT
27. INNER TIE ROD ASSEMBLY
28. BUSHING, INNER PIVOT
29. INNER TIE ROD ASSEMBLY
32. PLATE, LOCK
33. BOLT, PINCH
34. ADJUSTER, TIE ROD
35. OUTER TIE ROD
36. OUTER TIE ROD
39. NUT
40. COTTER PIN
51. CLAMP, BOOT
52. CLAMP, BOOT
53. BOOT
54. BUSHING, BOOT RETAINING
56. GROMMET, MOUNTING
57. LINE, CYLINDER
58. LINE, CYLINDER
59. O-RING

GC6029100074000X

Fig. 14 Exploded view of power rack & pinion assembly. Achieva, Beretta, Cavalier, Corsica, Grand Am, LeMans, Skylark & Sunbird

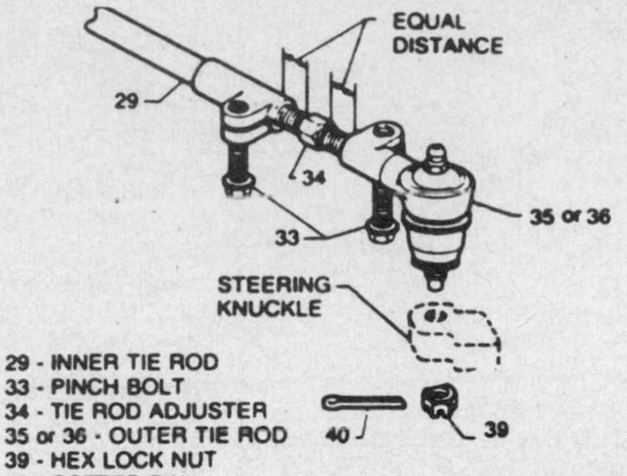
EQUAL DISTANCE
STEERING KNUCKLE

29 - INNER TIE ROD
33 - PINCH BOLT
34 - TIE ROD ADJUSTER
35 or 36 - OUTER TIE ROD
39 - HEX LOCK NUT
40 - COTTER PIN

GC6029100075000X

Fig. 15 Outer tie rod assembly

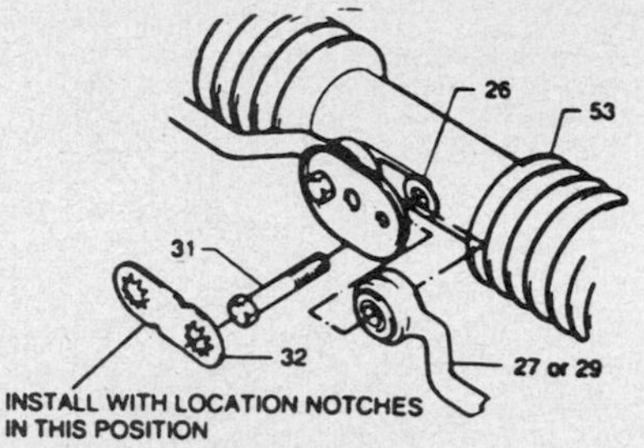

INSTALL WITH LOCATION NOTCHES IN THIS POSITION

26 - CENTER COVER HSG WASHER
27 OR 29 - INNER TIE ROD ASSEMBLY
31 - INNER TIE ROD BOLTS
32 - LOCK PLATE
53 - RACK & PINION BOOT

GC6029100076000X

Fig. 16 Inner tie rod assembly

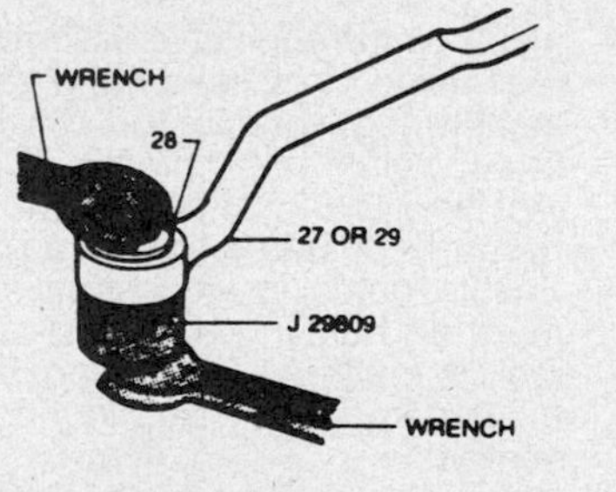
WRENCH
27 OR 29
J 29809
WRENCH

27 OR 29 - INNER TIE ROD
28 - PIVOT BUSHING

GC6029100077000X

Fig. 17 Inner pivot bushing removal

4. Cut and remove mounting grommet and boot clamp.
5. Slide boot retaining bushing from rack and pinion boot, then boot assembly from rack and pinion housing.
6. Insert rack guide assembly from rod and rack assembly if necessary.

Installation

1. Slide boot retaining bushing from rack and pinion housing.
2. Slide new boot clamp on rack and pinion boot and install boot retaining bushing into rack and pinion boot.
3. Install rack guide on rack.
4. Coat inner lip of boot retaining bushing lightly with grease, then install boot on housing. Ensure that center housing cover washers are in place on boot.
5. Install inner tie rod bolts through cover washers and rack and pinion boot. Screw into rack lightly.
6. Slide boot and boot retaining bushing until seated in bushing groove in housing. Crimp new boot clamp.
7. Slide other end of boot into boot groove on cylinder end of housing.
8. Slide other end of boot into boot groove on cylinder end of housing and crimp new boot clamp. **Bridge of boot clamp must be crimped over split in boot retaining bushing to ensure proper sealing, Fig. 21.**
9. Install new lock plate with notches in proper position over flats of inner tie rod bolts.

RACK BEARINGS

Removal

1. Remove rack and pinion assembly from vehicle.
2. Remove adjuster plug nut from adjuster plug, then adjuster plug from housing, **Fig. 22.**
3. Remove adjuster spring and rack bearing with O-ring seal attached.

Installation

1. Coat parts with lithium grease, then install rack bearing with O-ring seal adjuster spring and adjuster plug into housing.
2. With rack centered in housing, turn adjuster plug clockwise until it bottoms in housing, then back off 35° to 45° and check torque on pinion. Maximum pinion preload torque is 16 inch lbs.
3. Install locknut to adjuster plug and **torque** to 50 ft. lbs. while holding adjuster plug stationary, **Fig. 23.**

STUB SHAFT SEALS & UPPER BEARING

Removal

1. Remove rack and pinion assembly from vehicle.
2. Remove retaining ring and dust cover, **Fig. 24.**
3. While holding stub shaft, remove locknut from pinion. **If stub shaft is not held, damage to pinion teeth will occur.**

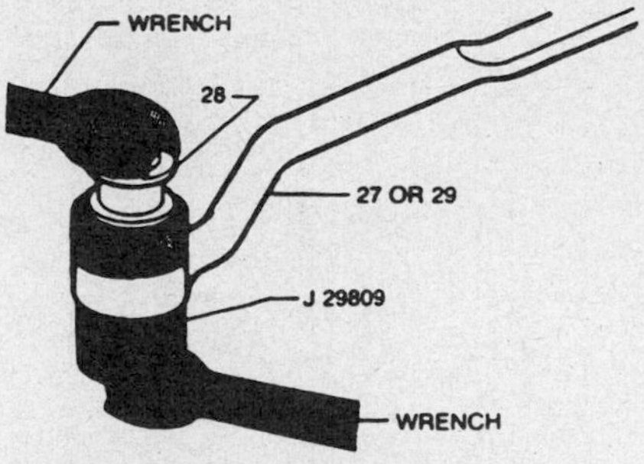
WRENCH
28
27 OR 29
J 29809
WRENCH

27 OR 29 – INNER TIE ROD ASSEMBLY
28 – PIVOT BUSHING

GC6029100078000X

Fig. 18 Inner pivot bushing installation

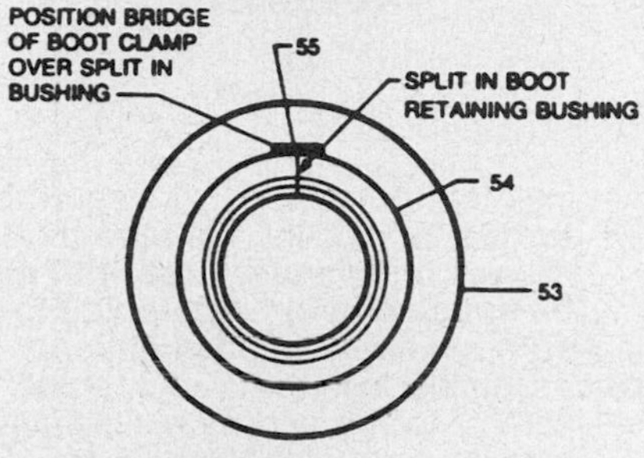
POSITION BRIDGE OF BOOT CLAMP OVER SPLIT IN BUSHING
55
SPLIT IN BOOT RETAINING BUSHING
54
53

53 - RACK AND PINION BOOT
54 - BOOT RETAINING BUSHING
55 - BOOT CLAMP

GC6029100081000X

Fig. 21 Boot clamp position

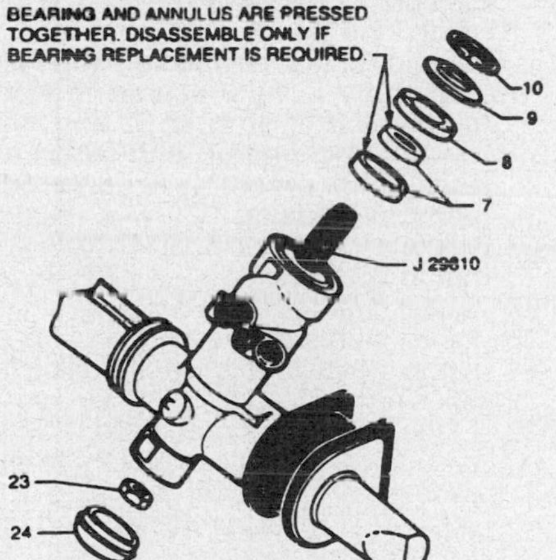
BEARING AND ANNULUS ARE PRESSED TOGETHER. DISASSEMBLE ONLY IF BEARING REPLACEMENT IS REQUIRED.
10
9
8
7
J 29810
23
24

7 – STUB SHAFT ANNULUS & BEARING
8 – STUB SHAFT SEAL
9 – STUB SHAFT DUST SEAL
10 – RETAINING RING
23 – HEX LOCK NUT
24 – DUST COVER

GC6029100084000X

Fig. 24 Stub shaft seals & upper bearing assembly

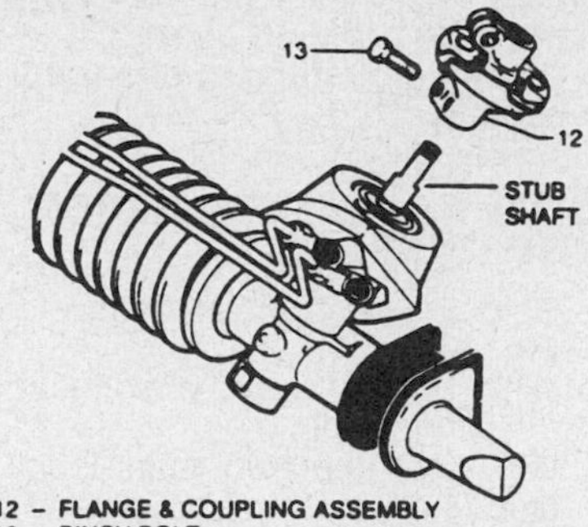
13
12
STUB SHAFT

12 – FLANGE & COUPLING ASSEMBLY
13 – PINCH BOLT

GC6029100079000X

Fig. 19 Flange & steering coupling assembly

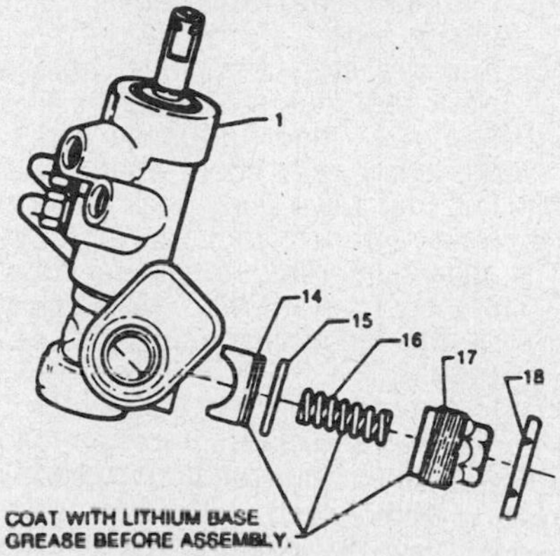
1
14
15
16
17
18
COAT WITH LITHIUM BASE GREASE BEFORE ASSEMBLY.

1 – HOUSING ASSEMBLY
14 – RACK BEARING
15 – O-RING SEAL
16 – ADJUSTER SPRING
17 – ADJUSTER PLUG
18 – ADJUSTER PLUG LOCK NUT

GC6029100082000X

Fig. 22 Rack bearing assembly

4 – PINION & VALVE ASSEMBLY
5 – SPOOL SHAFT RETAINING RING
6 – VALVE BODY RINGS

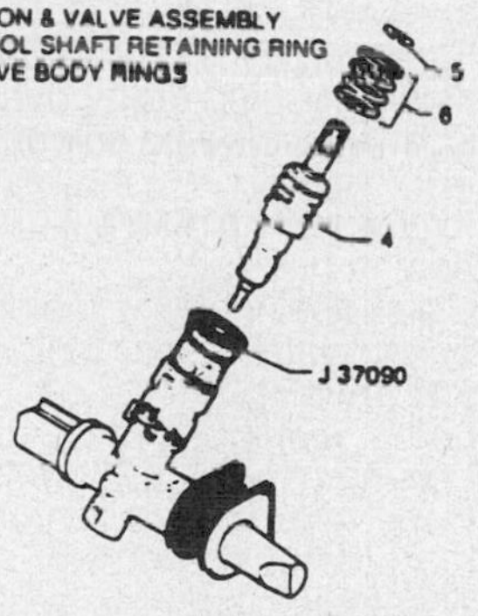
5
6
4
J 37090

GC6029100085000X

Fig. 25 Pinion & valve assembly

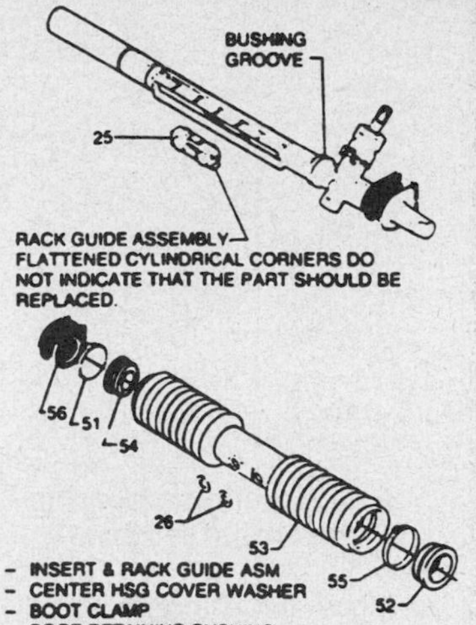
BUSHING GROOVE
25
RACK GUIDE ASSEMBLY– FLATTENED CYLINDRICAL CORNERS DO NOT INDICATE THAT THE PART SHOULD BE REPLACED.
56
51
54
26
53
55
52

25 – INSERT & RACK GUIDE ASM
26 – CENTER HSG COVER WASHER
51 – BOOT CLAMP
52 – BOOT RETAINING BUSHING
53 – RACK & PINION BOOT
55 – BOOT CLAMP
56 – MOUNTING GROMMET

GC6029100080000X

Fig. 20 Boot & rack guide assembly

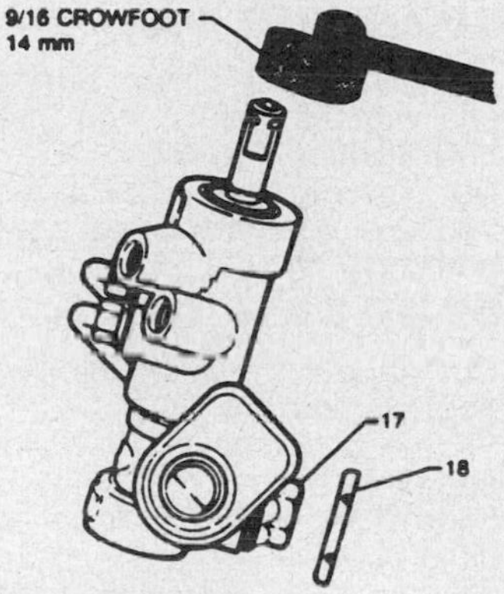
9/16 CROWFOOT 14 mm
17
18

17 – ADJUSTER PLUG
18 – ADJUSTER PLUG LOCK NUT

GC6029100083000X

Fig. 23 Rack bearing adjustment

4. Using a suitable press, press on threaded end of pinion until flush with ball bearing assembly. Complete removal of valve and pinion assembly is not required.
5. Remove stub shaft dust seal, stub shaft seal and stub shaft bearing annulus assembly from valve end of housing.

Installation

1. Install annulus assembly into gear.
2. Place seal protector, tool No. J 29810 or equivalent, onto stub shaft and install stub shaft seal and stub shaft dust seal over protector and into housing.
3. While holding the stub shaft firmly, seat locknut and **torque** to 26 ft. lbs.

PINION & VALVE ASSEMBLY

Removal

1. Turn stub shaft until rack guide is equal distance from both sides of housing opening, then mark location of stub shaft notch on housing, **Fig. 25.**
2. Using a suitable press, press on threaded end of pinion until it is possible to remove valve and pinion assembly from housing.
3. Replace valve body rings if necessary.

Installation

1. Install rack so it is centered in housing.
2. Using valve body ring protector tool No. J 33057 or equivalent to prevent damaging valve body rings, install valve and pinion assembly.
3. When pinion and valve assembly is fully seated, ensure notch in stub shaft and mark on housing line up, and rack is centered in housing.

RACK BEARING PRELOAD

On Vehicle Adjustment

Make adjustment with front wheels raised and steering wheel centered. Be sure to check returnability of steering wheel to center after adjustment.

1. Loosen locknut, then turn adjuster plug clockwise until it bottoms in housing, then back off 35° to 45°.
2. **Torque** locknut to adjuster plug to 50 ft. lbs. while holding adjuster plug.

PINION BEARING ASSEMBLY

1. Remove bearing retainer ring, **Fig. 26.**

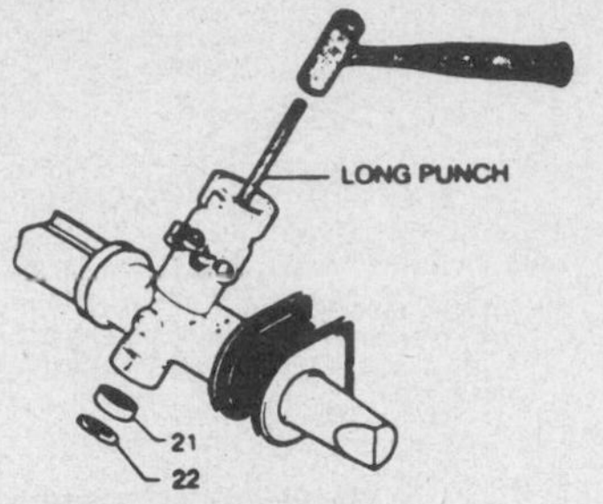
LONG PUNCH
21
22

21 – PINION BEARING ASSEMBLY
22 – RETAINING RING

GC6029100086000X

Fig. 26 Pinion bearing assembly removal

2. Using a drift or punch, gently tap on bearing until removed.
3. To install, use a suitable socket and press on outer race of bearing until firmly seated.
4. Install retaining ring.

UPPER PINION BUSHING & PINION SHAFT SEAL

1. Remove upper pinion bushing and seal with a forceful punch, then install new bushing, **Fig. 27.**
2. Using pinion seal installer, tool No. J 29822 or equivalent, seat new seal in housing with seal tip facing up.

BOOT OR RACK GUIDE

1. Cut off RH mounting grommet and boot clamps, **Fig. 14.**
2. Slide boot retaining bushing from rack and pinion boot.
3. Slide boot assembly from rack and pinion housing.
4. Remove insert and rack guide assembly as necessary.
5. Slide boot retaining bushing from rack and pinion boot.
6. Slide new boot clamp onto rack and pinion boot.
7. Insert boot retaining bushing into rack and pinion boot.
8. Coat inner lip of boot retaining bushing lightly with suitable grease to facilitate assembly, then slide assembly onto housing assembly.
9. Ensure center housing cover washers are in place on rack and pinion boot.
10. For ease of assembly, insert inner tie rod bolt through center housing cover washers, insert and rack guide and lightly thread bolt into rod and rack assembly to keep components in proper alignment.
11. Place boot retaining bushing onto cylinder tube of rack and pinion assembly, then slide into end of rack and pinion boot.
12. Slide boot clamp over cylinder end of housing and position on rack and pinion boot.
13. Slide rack and pinion boot and boot retaining bushing until seated in bushing groove in housing.
14. Position boot clamp on rack and pinion boot and crimp clamp.
15. Position bridge of boot clamp over split in boot retaining bushing and crimp clamp. **Bridge of boot clamp must be crimped over split in boot retaining bushing to ensure proper sealing.**

ROD & RACK & CYLINDER TUBE ASSEMBLY

1. Remove dust cover from housing, **Fig. 14.**
2. While holding stub shaft, remove locknut from pinion.
3. With gear centered, mark location of stub shaft notch on housing to aid in proper installation of the pinion and valve assembly.
4. Using a press, press on threaded end of pinion until it is possible to remove the pinion and valve assembly from the housing.
5. Remove stub shaft dust seal, stub shaft seal, stub shaft bearing annulus assembly, then the pinion and valve assembly with spool shaft retaining ring and valve body rings attached.
6. Using wrench, tool No. J 36343 or equivalent, remove cylinder tube assembly from housing. **Mark location of fittings on housing before removal.**
7. Remove piston rod guide rack from housing and disassemble as follows:
   a. Remove hex nut from rod and rack assembly.
   b. Remove rack piston with O-ring seal, piston ring and piston rod guide assembly.
   c. Remove O-ring seal and piston rod seal from piston rod guide.
8. Remove retaining ring from housing.
9. Remove pinion bearing assembly from housing.
10. Remove pinion shaft seal and upper pinion bushing from housing.
11. Coat all seals with power steering fluid.
12. Install upper pinion bushing into valve bore in housing.
13. Using seal installer tool No. J 29822 or equivalent, seat pinion shaft seal into housing.
14. Using suitable press, install pinion bearing assembly into housing.
15. Install retaining ring in groove in housing, positioning properly.
16. Assemble piston rod seal and O-ring seal to piston rod guide.
17. Assemble O-ring seal and piston ring to rack piston.
18. Slide seal back-up washer, piston rod guide assembly and rack piston onto rod and rack assembly.
19. Install hex nut on rod and rack assembly. On models except LeMans, torque to 30 ft. lbs.; on LeMans, torque to 22 ft. lbs.
20. Slide piston rod guide assembly into housing.
21. Apply one small drop of Loctite 242 or equivalent in three equally spaced locations around threaded portion of housing. **Be sure to use sealant sparingly to ensure ease of removal of cylinder tube assembly if future repairs are necessary.**
22. Slide cylinder tube assembly over rack piston ring to housing, then, using torque wrench or equivalent, **torque** to 82 ft. lbs. **Be sure to align fittings on cylinder tube with mark on housing before tightening to ensure cylinder line installation.**

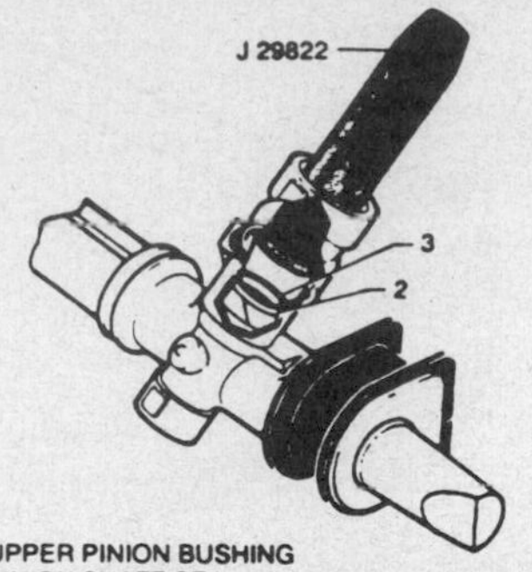
J 29822
3
2

2 – UPPER PINION BUSHING
3 – PINION SHAFT SEAL

GC6029100087000X

Fig. 27 Pinion shaft seal & bushing removal

23. Assemble insert and rack guide assembly to rod and rack assembly in housing.
24. Center rack guide assembly in housing window opening.
25. Using protector tool No. J 33057 or equivalent, install pinion and valve assembly, together with new valve body rings, and spool shaft retaining ring into housing. **When pinion and valve assembly is fully seated in housing, notch in stub shaft and mark on housing line up and insert and rack guide assembly is centered in window housing.**
26. While holding stub shaft, **torque** locknut to 26 ft. lbs.
27. Install dust cover on housing.
28. Install stub shaft bearing annulus assembly onto stub shaft and slide into housing.
29. Place seal protector tool No. J 29810 or equivalent onto stub shaft, then slide stub shaft seal and stub shaft dust seal over protector and into housing.
30. Install retaining ring into groove in housing.
31. Coat rack bearing, with O-ring seal attached, adjuster spring and the adjuster plug with lithium base grease and install in housing.
32. With rack centered in window in housing, turn adjuster plug clockwise until it bottoms in housing, then back off 50-70°. Check pinion preload **torque,** which should not exceed 16 inch lbs.
33. Install locknut on adjuster plug and **torque** to 50 ft. lbs. while holding adjuster plug stationary.

CORVETTE & 1993–94 CAMARO & FIREBIRD

For service procedures on this power rack and pinion steering gear assembly, refer to **Figs. 28 and 29.**

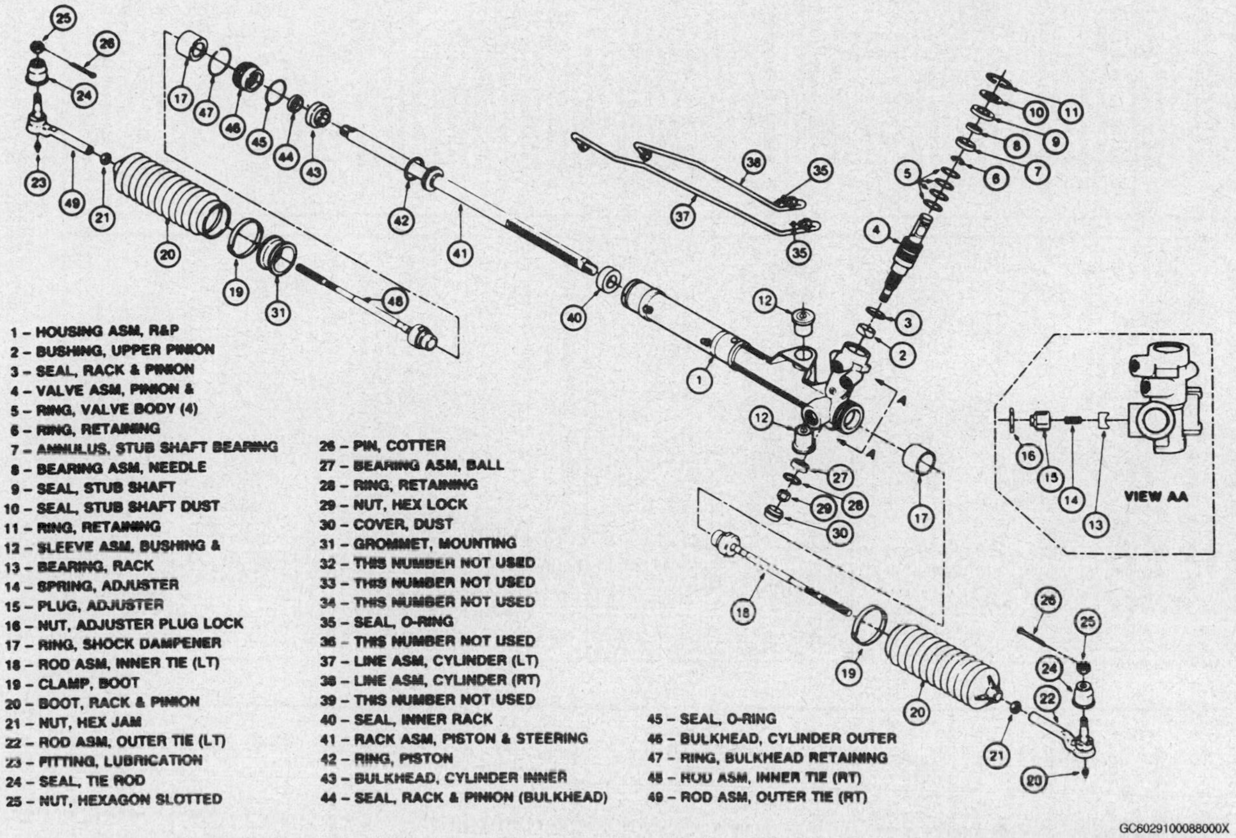

VIEW AA
1 – HOUSING ASM, R&P
2 – BUSHING, UPPER PINION
3 – SEAL, RACK & PINION
4 – VALVE ASM, PINION &
5 – RING, VALVE BODY (4)
6 – RING, RETAINING
7 – ANNULUS, STUB SHAFT BEARING
8 – BEARING ASM, NEEDLE
9 – SEAL, STUB SHAFT
10 – SEAL, STUB SHAFT DUST
11 – RING, RETAINING
12 – SLEEVE ASM, BUSHING &
13 – BEARING, RACK
14 – SPRING, ADJUSTER
15 – PLUG, ADJUSTER
16 – NUT, ADJUSTER PLUG LOCK
17 – RING, SHOCK DAMPENER
18 – ROD ASM, INNER TIE (LT)
19 – CLAMP, BOOT
20 – BOOT, RACK & PINION
21 – NUT, HEX JAM
22 – ROD ASM, OUTER TIE (LT)
23 – FITTING, LUBRICATION
24 – SEAL, TIE ROD
25 – NUT, HEXAGON SLOTTED
26 – PIN, COTTER
27 – BEARING ASM, BALL
28 – RING, RETAINING
29 – NUT, HEX LOCK
30 – COVER, DUST
31 – GROMMET, MOUNTING
32 – THIS NUMBER NOT USED
33 – THIS NUMBER NOT USED
34 – THIS NUMBER NOT USED
35 – SEAL, O-RING
36 – THIS NUMBER NOT USED
37 – LINE ASM, CYLINDER (LT)
38 – LINE ASM, CYLINDER (RT)
39 – THIS NUMBER NOT USED
40 – SEAL, INNER RACK
41 – RACK ASM, PISTON & STEERING
42 – RING, PISTON
43 – BULKHEAD, CYLINDER INNER
44 – SEAL, RACK & PINION (BULKHEAD)
45 – SEAL, O-RING
46 – BULKHEAD, CYLINDER OUTER
47 – RING, BULKHEAD RETAINING
48 – ROD ASM, INNER TIE (RT)
49 – ROD ASM, OUTER TIE (RT)
GC6029100088000X

Fig. 28 Exploded view of power rack & pinion assembly. Corvette (1993–94 Camaro & Firebird Similar)

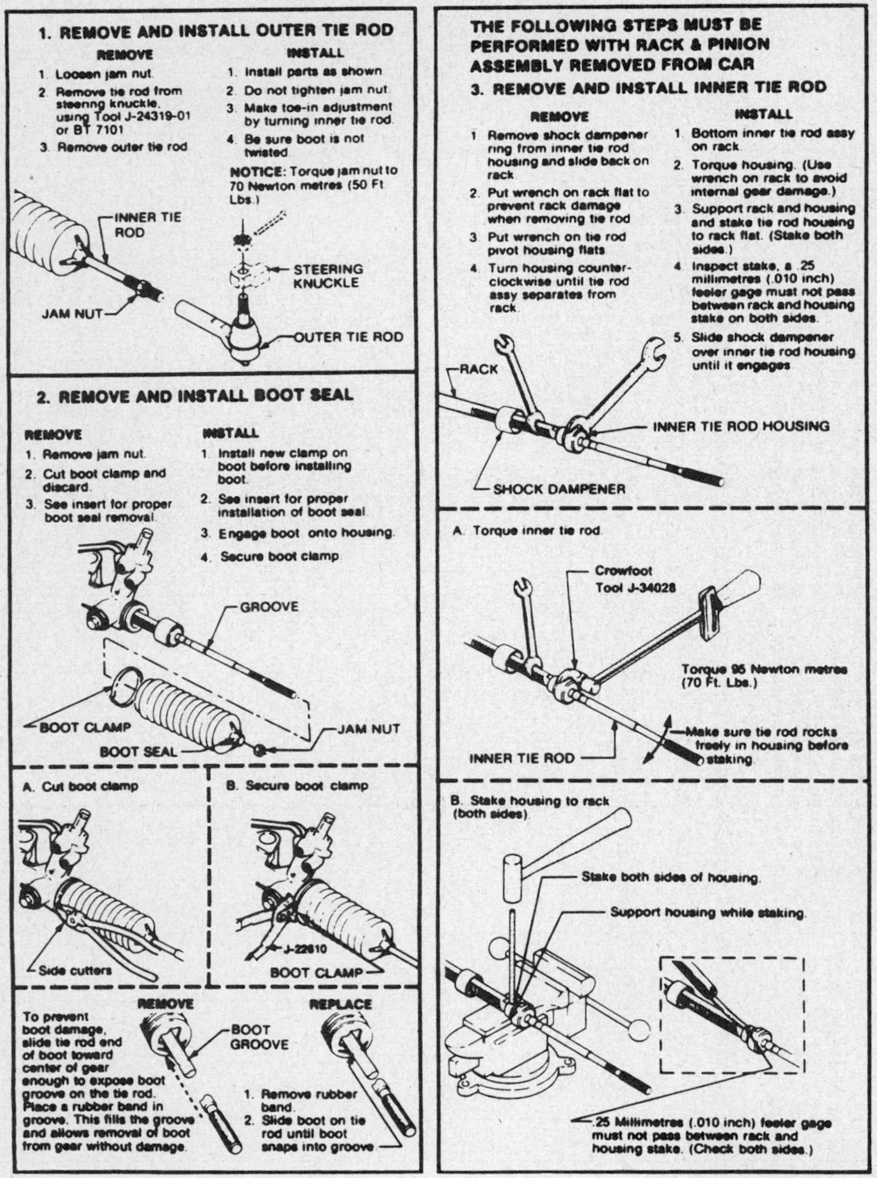
1. REMOVE AND INSTALL OUTER TIE ROD
REMOVE
1. Loosen jam nut.
2. Remove tie rod from steering knuckle, using Tool J-24319-01 or BT 7101
3. Remove outer tie rod
INSTALL
1. Install parts as shown
2. Do not tighten jam nut
3. Make toe-in adjustment by turning inner tie rod.
4. Be sure boot is not twisted.
NOTICE: Torque jam nut to 70 Newton metres (50 Ft Lbs.)
INNER TIE ROD
STEERING KNUCKLE
JAM NUT
OUTER TIE ROD
2. REMOVE AND INSTALL BOOT SEAL
REMOVE
1. Remove jam nut.
2. Cut boot clamp and discard.
3. See insert for proper boot seal removal.
INSTALL
1. Install new clamp on boot before installing boot.
2. See insert for proper installation of boot seal.
3. Engage boot onto housing.
4. Secure boot clamp
GROOVE
BOOT CLAMP
JAM NUT
BOOT SEAL
A. Cut boot clamp
Side cutters
B. Secure boot clamp
J-22610
BOOT CLAMP
REMOVE
To prevent boot damage, slide tie rod end of boot toward center of gear enough to expose boot groove on the tie rod. Place a rubber band in groove. This fills the groove and allows removal of boot from gear without damage.
BOOT GROOVE
REPLACE
1. Remove rubber band.
2. Slide boot on tie rod until boot snaps into groove.
THE FOLLOWING STEPS MUST BE PERFORMED WITH RACK & PINION ASSEMBLY REMOVED FROM CAR
3. REMOVE AND INSTALL INNER TIE ROD
REMOVE
1. Remove shock dampener ring from inner tie rod housing and slide back on rack.
2. Put wrench on rack flat to prevent rack damage when removing tie rod
3. Put wrench on tie rod pivot housing flats
4. Turn housing counter-clockwise until tie rod assy separates from rack.
INSTALL
1. Bottom inner tie rod assy on rack.
2. Torque housing. (Use wrench on rack to avoid internal gear damage.)
3. Support rack and housing and stake tie rod housing to rack flat. (Stake both sides.)
4. Inspect stake, a .25 millimetres (.010 inch) feeler gage must not pass between rack and housing stake on both sides.
5. Slide shock dampener over inner tie rod housing until it engages
RACK
INNER TIE ROD HOUSING
SHOCK DAMPENER
A. Torque inner tie rod.
Crowfoot Tool J-34028
Torque 95 Newton metres (70 Ft. Lbs.)
Make sure tie rod rocks freely in housing before staking.
INNER TIE ROD
B. Stake housing to rack (both sides).
Stake both sides of housing.
Support housing while staking.
.25 Millimetres (.010 inch) feeler gage must not pass between rack and housing stake. (Check both sides.)
GC6029100089010X

Fig. 29 Service procedures, power rack & pinion assembly (Part 1 of 3). Corvette (1993–94 Camaro & Firebird Similar)

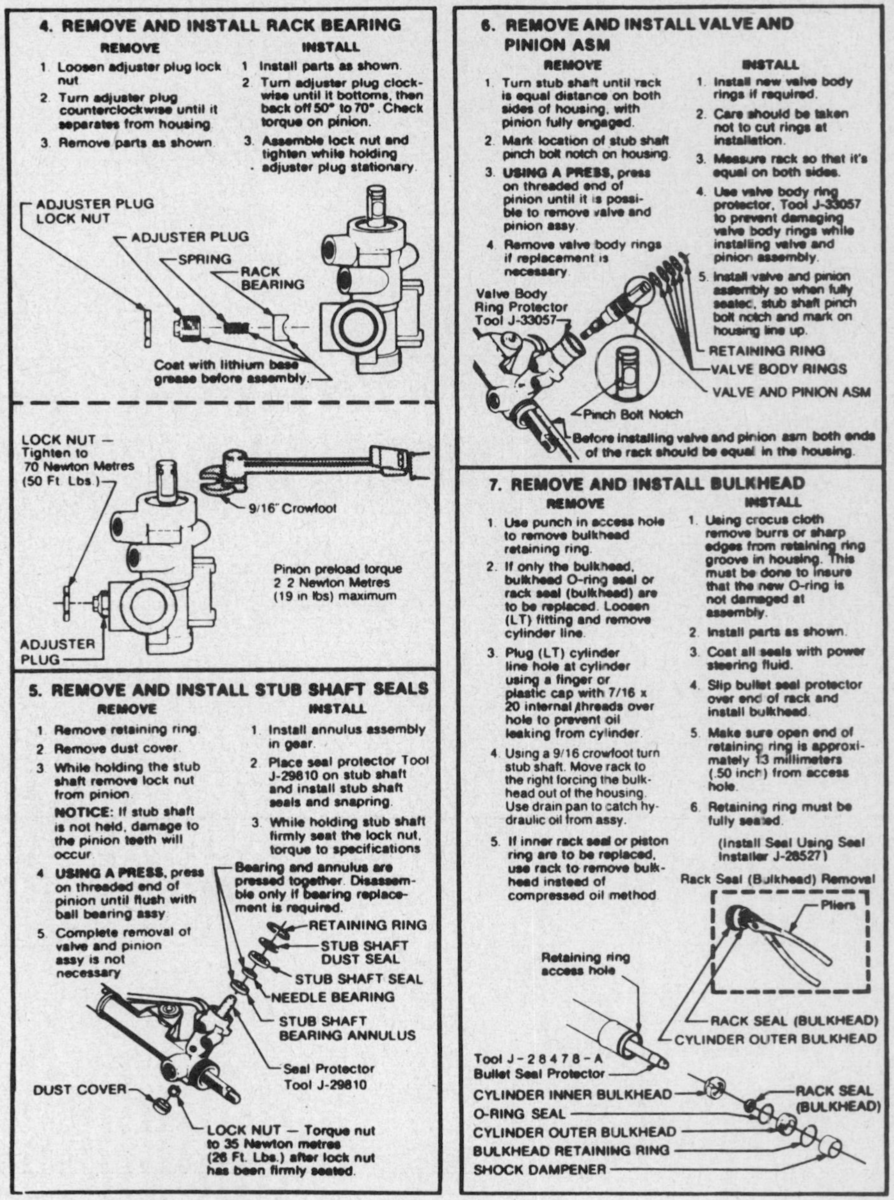
4. REMOVE AND INSTALL RACK BEARING
REMOVE
1. Loosen adjuster plug lock nut
2. Turn adjuster plug counterclockwise until it separates from housing
3. Remove parts as shown.
INSTALL
1. Install parts as shown.
2. Turn adjuster plug clockwise until it bottoms, then back off 50° to 70°. Check torque on pinion.
3. Assemble lock nut and tighten while holding adjuster plug stationary.
ADJUSTER PLUG LOCK NUT
ADJUSTER PLUG
SPRING
RACK BEARING
Coat with lithium base grease before assembly.
LOCK NUT — Tighten to 70 Newton Metres (50 Ft. Lbs.)
9/16" Crowfoot
Pinion preload torque 2.2 Newton Metres (19 in lbs) maximum
ADJUSTER PLUG
5. REMOVE AND INSTALL STUB SHAFT SEALS
REMOVE
1. Remove retaining ring.
2. Remove dust cover.
3. While holding the stub shaft remove lock nut from pinion.
NOTICE: If stub shaft is not held, damage to the pinion teeth will occur.
4. USING A PRESS, press on threaded end of pinion until flush with ball bearing assy.
5. Complete removal of valve and pinion assy is not necessary
INSTALL
1. Install annulus assembly in gear.
2. Place seal protector Tool J-29810 on stub shaft and install stub shaft seals and snapring.
3. While holding stub shaft firmly seat the lock nut, torque to specifications
Bearing and annulus are pressed together. Disassemble only if bearing replacement is required.
RETAINING RING
STUB SHAFT DUST SEAL
STUB SHAFT SEAL
NEEDLE BEARING
STUB SHAFT BEARING ANNULUS
Seal Protector Tool J-29810
DUST COVER
LOCK NUT — Torque nut to 35 Newton metres (26 Ft. Lbs.) after lock nut has been firmly seated.
6. REMOVE AND INSTALL VALVE AND PINION ASM
REMOVE
1. Turn stub shaft until rack is equal distance on both sides of housing, with pinion fully engaged.
2. Mark location of stub shaft pinch bolt notch on housing.
3. USING A PRESS, press on threaded end of pinion until it is possible to remove valve and pinion assy.
4. Remove valve body rings if replacement is necessary.
INSTALL
1. Install new valve body rings if required.
2. Care should be taken not to cut rings at installation.
3. Measure rack so that it's equal on both sides.
4. Use valve body ring protector, Tool J-33057 to prevent damaging valve body rings while installing valve and pinion assembly.
5. Install valve and pinion assembly so when fully seated, stub shaft pinch bolt notch and mark on housing line up.
Valve Body Ring Protector Tool J-33057
RETAINING RING
VALVE BODY RINGS
VALVE AND PINION ASM
Pinch Bolt Notch
Before installing valve and pinion asm both ends of the rack should be equal in the housing.
7. REMOVE AND INSTALL BULKHEAD
REMOVE
1. Use punch in access hole to remove bulkhead retaining ring.
2. If only the bulkhead, bulkhead O-ring seal or rack seal (bulkhead) are to be replaced. Loosen (LT) fitting and remove cylinder line.
3. Plug (LT) cylinder line hole at cylinder using a finger or plastic cap with 7/16 x 20 internal threads over hole to prevent oil leaking from cylinder.
4. Using a 9/16 crowfoot turn stub shaft. Move rack to the right forcing the bulkhead out of the housing. Use drain pan to catch hydraulic oil from assy.
5. If inner rack seal or piston ring are to be replaced, use rack to remove bulkhead instead of compressed oil method
INSTALL
1. Using crocus cloth remove burrs or sharp edges from retaining ring groove in housing. This must be done to insure that the new O-ring is not damaged at assembly.
2. Install parts as shown.
3. Coat all seals with power steering fluid.
4. Slip bullet seal protector over end of rack and install bulkhead.
5. Make sure open end of retaining ring is approximately 13 millimeters (.50 inch) from access hole.
6. Retaining ring must be fully seated.
(Install Seal Using Seal Installer J-28527)
Rack Seal (Bulkhead) Removal
Pliers
Retaining ring access hole
RACK SEAL (BULKHEAD)
CYLINDER OUTER BULKHEAD
Tool J-28478-A Bullet Seal Protector
CYLINDER INNER BULKHEAD
RACK SEAL (BULKHEAD)
O-RING SEAL
CYLINDER OUTER BULKHEAD
BULKHEAD RETAINING RING
SHOCK DAMPENER
GC6029100089020X

Fig. 29 Service procedures, power rack & pinion assembly (Part 2 of 3). Corvette (1993–94 Camaro & Firebird Similar)

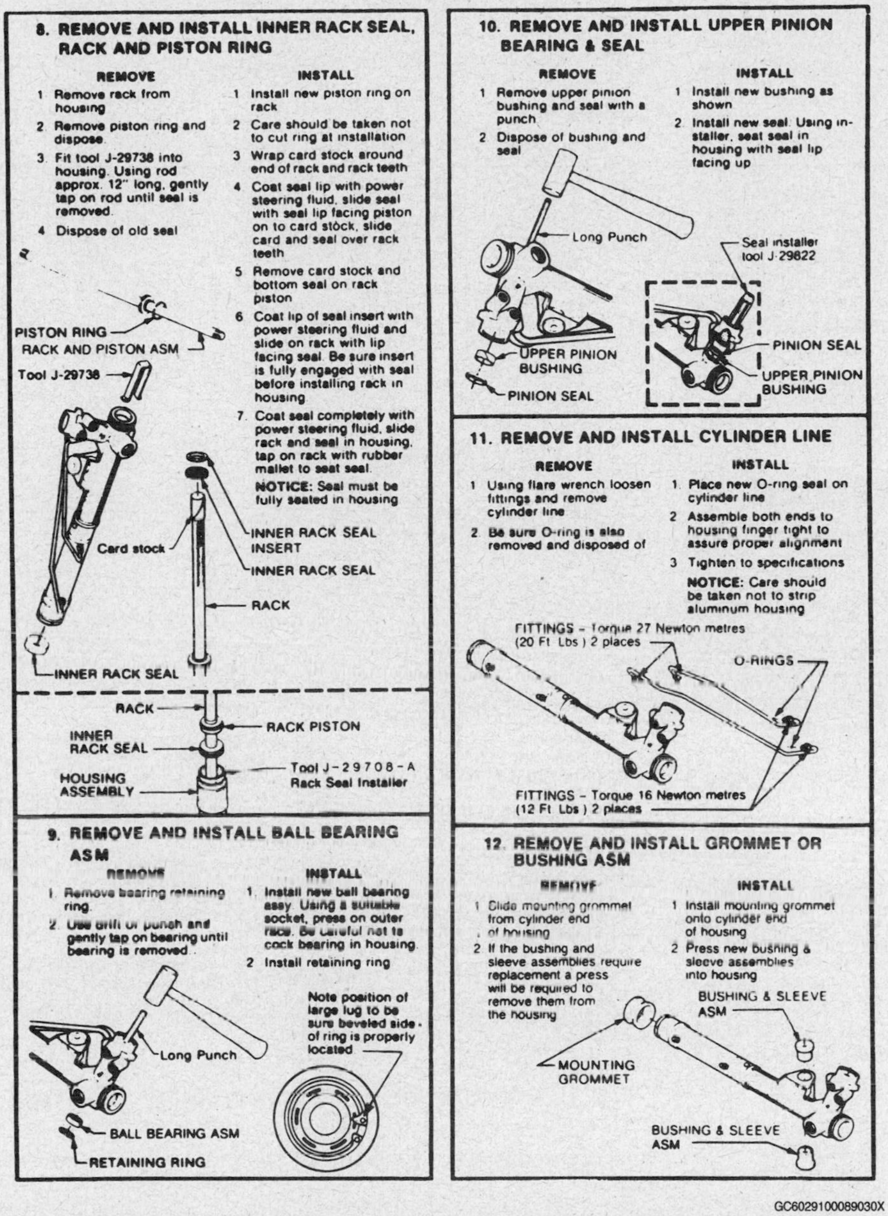
8. REMOVE AND INSTALL INNER RACK SEAL, RACK AND PISTON RING
REMOVE
1 Remove rack from housing
2 Remove piston ring and dispose.
3 Fit tool J-29738 into housing. Using rod approx. 12" long, gently tap on rod until seal is removed.
4 Dispose of old seal
INSTALL
1 Install new piston ring on rack
2 Care should be taken not to cut ring at installation
3 Wrap card stock around end of rack and rack teeth
4 Coat seal lip with power steering fluid, slide seal with seal lip facing piston on to card stock, slide card and seal over rack teeth
5 Remove card stock and bottom seal on rack piston
6 Coat lip of seal insert with power steering fluid and slide on rack with lip facing seal. Be sure insert is fully engaged with seal before installing rack in housing.
7. Coat seal completely with power steering fluid, slide rack and seal in housing, tap on rack with rubber mallet to seat seal.
NOTICE: Seal must be fully seated in housing
PISTON RING
RACK AND PISTON ASM
Tool J-29738
Card stock
INNER RACK SEAL INSERT
INNER RACK SEAL
RACK
INNER RACK SEAL
RACK
RACK PISTON
INNER RACK SEAL
HOUSING ASSEMBLY
Tool J-29708-A Rack Seal Installer
9. REMOVE AND INSTALL BALL BEARING ASM
REMOVE
1. Remove bearing retaining ring.
2. Use drift or punch and gently tap on bearing until bearing is removed.
INSTALL
1. Install new ball bearing assy. Using a suitable socket, press on outer race. Be careful not to cock bearing in housing.
2 Install retaining ring
Note position of large lug to be sure beveled side of ring is properly located
Long Punch
BALL BEARING ASM
RETAINING RING
10. REMOVE AND INSTALL UPPER PINION BEARING & SEAL
REMOVE
1 Remove upper pinion bushing and seal with a punch.
2 Dispose of bushing and seal
INSTALL
1 Install new bushing as shown
2. Install new seal. Using installer, seat seal in housing with seal lip facing up
Long Punch
Seal installer tool J-29822
PINION SEAL
UPPER PINION BUSHING
UPPER PINION BUSHING
PINION SEAL
11. REMOVE AND INSTALL CYLINDER LINE
REMOVE
1 Using flare wrench loosen fittings and remove cylinder line
2. Be sure O-ring is also removed and disposed of
INSTALL
1. Place new O-ring seal on cylinder line
2 Assemble both ends to housing finger tight to assure proper alignment
3 Tighten to specifications
NOTICE: Care should be taken not to strip aluminum housing
FITTINGS – Torque 27 Newton metres (20 Ft. Lbs.) 2 places
O-RINGS
FITTINGS – Torque 16 Newton metres (12 Ft. Lbs.) 2 places
12. REMOVE AND INSTALL GROMMET OR BUSHING ASM
REMOVE
1 Slide mounting grommet from cylinder end of housing
2 If the bushing and sleeve assemblies require replacement a press will be required to remove them from the housing
INSTALL
1 Install mounting grommet onto cylinder end of housing
2 Press new bushing & sleeve assemblies into housing
BUSHING & SLEEVE ASM
MOUNTING GROMMET
BUSHING & SLEEVE ASM
GC6029100089030X

Fig. 29 Service procedures, power rack & pinion assembly (Part 3 of 3). Corvette (1993–94 Camaro & Firebird Similar)

Saginaw Rotary Valve Type Power Steering Gear

INDEX

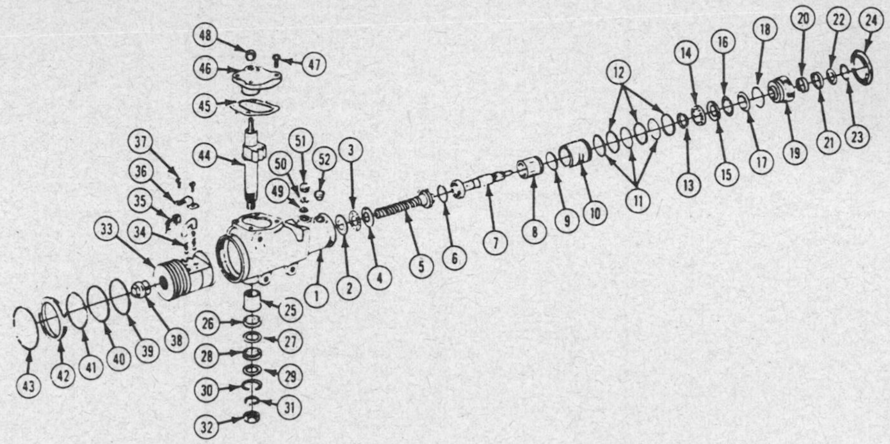

1	HOUSING, STEERING GEAR	18	SEAL, "O" RING (ADJUSTER)	35	GUIDE, BALL RETURN (2)
2	RACE, THRUST BEARING (WORM)	19	PLUG, ADJUSTER	36	CLAMP, BALL RETURN GUIDE
3	BEARING ASSY, ROLLER THRUST (WORM)	20	BEARING, NEEDLE	37	SCREW ASSY, LOCKWASHER & (2)
4	RACE, THRUST BEARING (WORM)	21	SEAL, STUB SHAFT	38	PLUG, RACK PISTON
5	WORM, STEERING	22	SEAL, STUB SHAFT DUST	39	SEAL, "O" RING (RACK PISTON)
6	SEAL, "O" RING (STUB SHAFT)	23	RING, RETAINING	40	RING, RACK PISTON
7	SHAFT, STUB	24	NUT, ADJUSTER PLUG LOCK	41	SEAL, "O" RING (HOUSING END PLUG)
8	SPOOL, VALVE	25	BEARING ASSY, NEEDLE (PITMAN SHAFT)	42	PLUG, HOUSING END
9	SEAL, "O" RING (SPOOL)	26	SEAL, PITMAN SHAFT (SINGLE LIP)	43	RING, RETAINING (HOUSING END PLUG)
10	BODY, VALVE	27	WASHER, SEAL BACK-UP (PITMAN SHAFT)	44	GEAR ASSY, PITMAN SHAFT
11	RING, VALVE BODY (3)	28	SEAL, PITMAN SHAFT (DOUBLE LIP)	45	SEAL ASSY, GASKET
12	SEAL, "O" RING (VALVE BODY) (3)	29	WASHER, SEAL BACK-UP (PITMAN SHAFT)	46	COVER ASSY, HOUSING SIDE
13	RETAINER, BEARING (ADJUSTER)	30	RING, RETAINING (PITMAN SHAFT SEAI	47	BOLT, HEX HEAD (SIDE COVER) (4)
14	SPACER, THRUST BEARING	31	WASHER, PITMAN SHAFT LOCK	48	NUT, LASH ADJUSTER
15	RACE, UPPER THRUST BEARING (SMALL)	32	NUT, PITMAN SHAFT	49	SPRING, CHECK VALVE
16	BEARING, UPPER THRUST	33	NUT, RACK PISTON	50	POPPET, CHECK VALVE
17	RACE, UPPER THRUST BEARING (LARGE)	34	BALL	51	CONNECTOR, INVERTED FLARE
				52	CONNECTOR, INVERTED FLARE

GC6029100093000X

Fig. 1 Exploded view of Saginaw rotary valve type power steering gear

DESCRIPTION

The Saginaw rotary valve steering gear incorporates a recirculating ball system in which steel balls act as a rolling thread between a steering worm shaft and the rack piston.

POWER STEERING SYSTEM SERVICE

Component Service

Whenever a part which forms a sealing surface for an O-ring is removed, the O-ring seal should also be removed and replaced with a new seal. Whenever one of the Pitman shaft or stub shaft seals are removed, all adjacent seals should be removed and replaced with new seals. Lubricate all new seals with power steering fluid to facilitate assembly.

For service procedures on this power steering gear assembly, refer to **Figs. 1 and 2.**

Adjustments

Adjustment of steering gear in the vehicle is not recommended because of the difficulty encountered in adjusting the worm thrust bearing preload and confirming the effects of the hydraulic fluid in the gear. Since a gear adjustment is made only as a correction and not a periodic adjustment, it is better to take the extra time and make the adjustment correctly the first time.

Since a handling stability complaint can be caused by improperly adjusted worm thrust bearings as well as an improper gear over-center adjustment, it is necessary that the steering gear assembly be removed from vehicle and both thrust bearing and over-center preload be checked and corrected as necessary. An in-vehicle check of steering gear will not show a thrust bearing adjustment error.

Valve assembly and seal drag should be 1-4 inch lbs. Thrust bearing preload should be 3-4 inch lbs. in excess of valve assembly and seal drag.

OVER CENTER ADJUSTMENT

Brougham & Fleetwood (RWD)

Refer to **Fig. 2,** for proper procedure. Over-center adjustment should be 5-11 inch lbs. (new gear) or 4-5 inch lbs. (used gear) in excess of combined thrust bearing preload.

Except Brougham & Fleetwood (RWD)

1. Rotate stub shaft back and forth to drain fluid.
2. Turn pitman shaft adjuster screw counterclockwise until fully extended, then turn back one full turn, **Fig. 3.**
3. Rotate stub shaft from stop to stop and count the turns.
4. Starting at either stop, turn the stub shaft back one-half the total number of turns.
5. When the gear is centered, the flat on stub shaft should face upward and be parallel with side cover and master spline on pitman shaft should be in-line with adjuster screw, **Fig. 4.**
6. Rotate stub shaft 45° each side of center using a torque wrench with handle in vertical position, **Fig. 5,** record the highest drag torque measured on or near center.
7. Adjust over-center drag torque by loosening adjuster locknut and turning the pitman shaft adjuster screw clockwise until correct drag torque is obtained. On new steering gears (under 400 miles) add 5-11 inch lbs. to previously measured worm bearing preload. Do not exceed total preload of 18 inch lbs. On used steering gears (400 miles or more) add 4-5 inch lbs. to previously measured worm bearing preload. Do not exceed total gear preload of 13 inch lbs.
8. Hold adjuster screw and **torque** adjuster locknut to 20 ft. lbs. on 1992 models and 22 ft. lbs. on 1993-94 models.

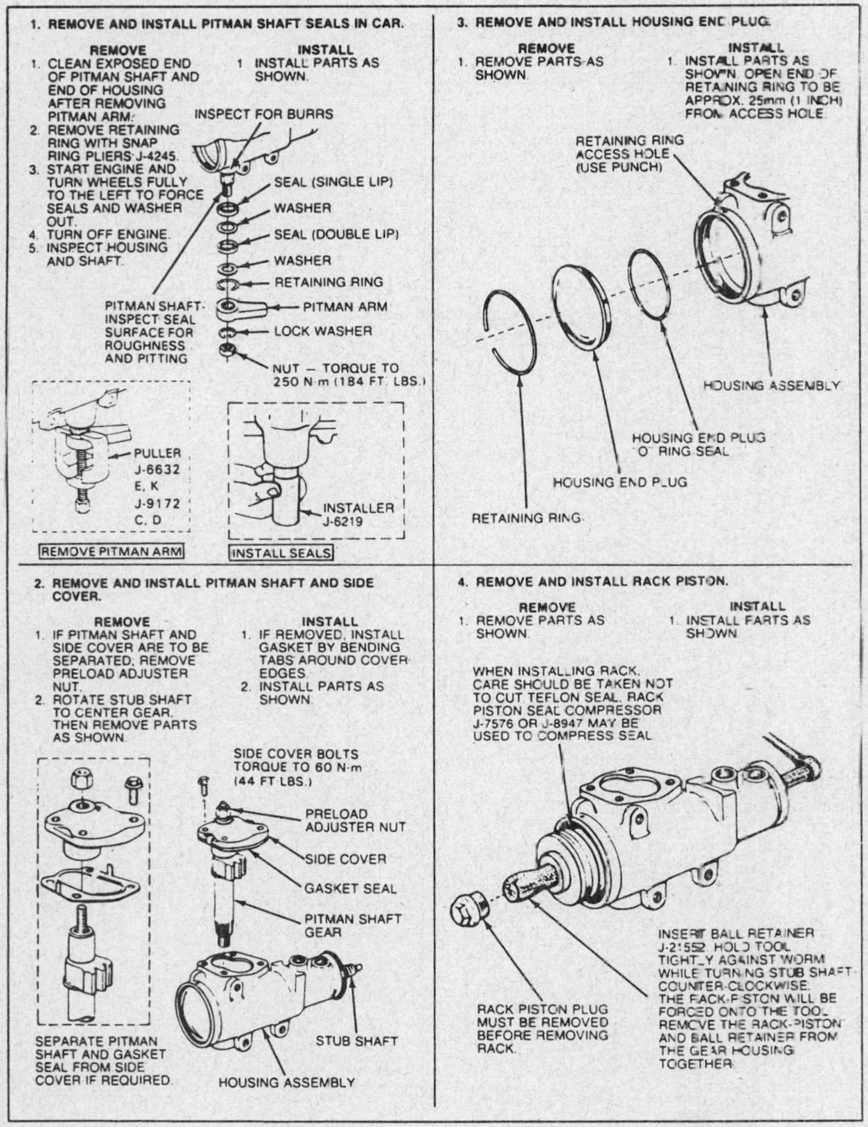

1. REMOVE AND INSTALL PITMAN SHAFT SEALS IN CAR.
REMOVE
1. CLEAN EXPOSED END OF PITMAN SHAFT AND END OF HOUSING AFTER REMOVING PITMAN ARM.
2. REMOVE RETAINING RING WITH SNAP RING PLIERS J-4245.
3. START ENGINE AND TURN WHEELS FULLY TO THE LEFT TO FORCE SEALS AND WASHER OUT.
4. TURN OFF ENGINE.
5. INSPECT HOUSING AND SHAFT.
INSTALL
1. INSTALL PARTS AS SHOWN.
INSPECT FOR BURRS
SEAL (SINGLE LIP)
WASHER
SEAL (DOUBLE LIP)
WASHER
RETAINING RING
PITMAN SHAFT-INSPECT SEAL SURFACE FOR ROUGHNESS AND PITTING
PITMAN ARM
LOCK WASHER
NUT — TORQUE TO 250 N·m (184 FT. LBS.)
PULLER J-6632 E, K J-9172 C, D
INSTALLER J-6219
REMOVE PITMAN ARM
INSTALL SEALS
3. REMOVE AND INSTALL HOUSING END PLUG.
REMOVE
1. REMOVE PARTS AS SHOWN.
INSTALL
1. INSTALL PARTS AS SHOWN. OPEN END OF RETAINING RING TO BE APPROX. 25mm (1 INCH) FROM ACCESS HOLE.
RETAINING RING ACCESS HOLE (USE PUNCH)
HOUSING ASSEMBLY
HOUSING END PLUG "O" RING SEAL
HOUSING END PLUG
RETAINING RING
2. REMOVE AND INSTALL PITMAN SHAFT AND SIDE COVER.
REMOVE
1. IF PITMAN SHAFT AND SIDE COVER ARE TO BE SEPARATED, REMOVE PRELOAD ADJUSTER NUT.
2. ROTATE STUB SHAFT TO CENTER GEAR, THEN REMOVE PARTS AS SHOWN.
INSTALL
1. IF REMOVED, INSTALL GASKET BY BENDING TABS AROUND COVER EDGES.
2. INSTALL PARTS AS SHOWN.
SIDE COVER BOLTS TORQUE TO 60 N·m (44 FT LBS.)
PRELOAD ADJUSTER NUT
SIDE COVER
GASKET SEAL
PITMAN SHAFT GEAR
STUB SHAFT
HOUSING ASSEMBLY
SEPARATE PITMAN SHAFT AND GASKET SEAL FROM SIDE COVER IF REQUIRED.
4. REMOVE AND INSTALL RACK PISTON.
REMOVE
1. REMOVE PARTS AS SHOWN.
INSTALL
1. INSTALL PARTS AS SHOWN.
WHEN INSTALLING RACK, CARE SHOULD BE TAKEN NOT TO CUT TEFLON SEAL. RACK PISTON SEAL COMPRESSOR J-7576 OR J-8947 MAY BE USED TO COMPRESS SEAL.
RACK PISTON PLUG MUST BE REMOVED BEFORE REMOVING RACK.
INSERT BALL RETAINER J-21552. HOLD TOOL TIGHTLY AGAINST WORM WHILE TURNING STUB SHAFT COUNTER-CLOCKWISE. THE RACK-PISTON WILL BE FORCED ONTO THE TOOL. REMOVE THE RACK-PISTON AND BALL RETAINER FROM THE GEAR HOUSING TOGETHER.
GC6029100094010X

Fig. 2 Service procedures, Saginaw power steering gear (Part 1 of 4)

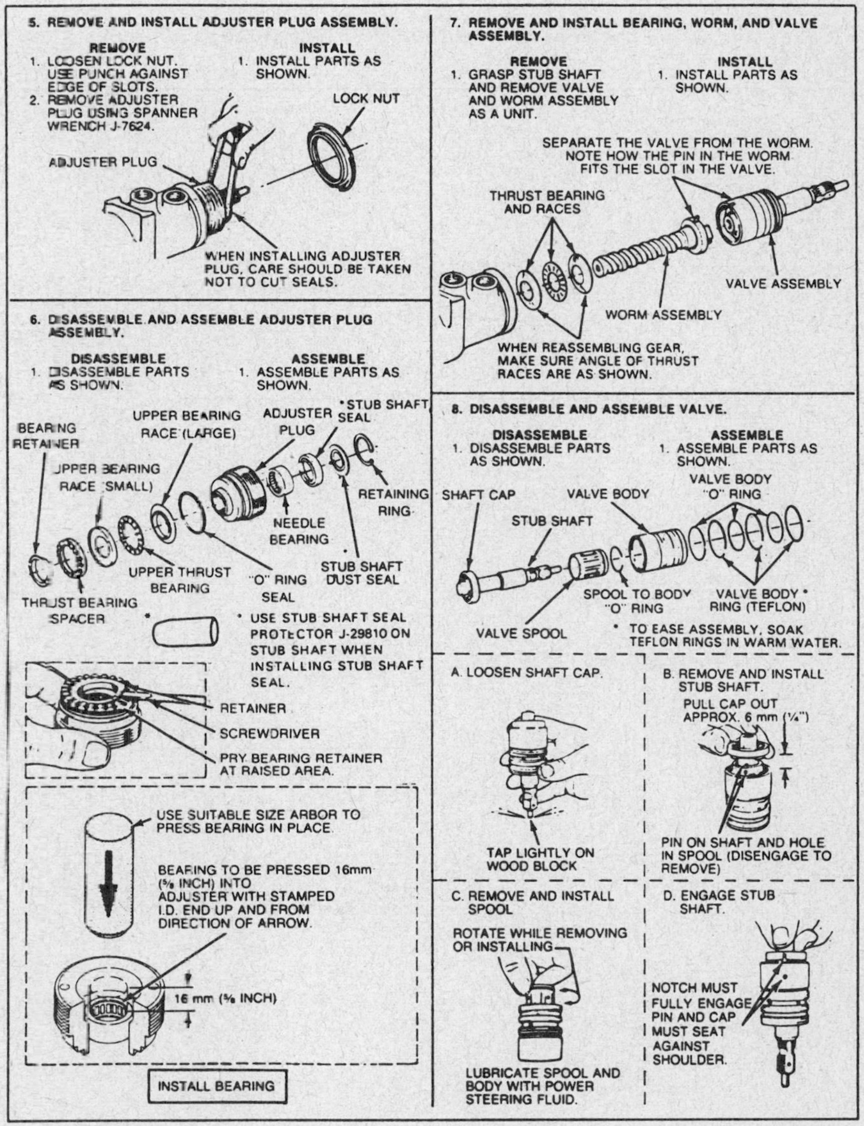

5. REMOVE AND INSTALL ADJUSTER PLUG ASSEMBLY.
REMOVE
1. LOOSEN LOCK NUT. USE PUNCH AGAINST EDGE OF SLOTS.
2. REMOVE ADJUSTER PLUG USING SPANNER WRENCH J-7624.
INSTALL
1. INSTALL PARTS AS SHOWN.
LOCK NUT
ADJUSTER PLUG
WHEN INSTALLING ADJUSTER PLUG, CARE SHOULD BE TAKEN NOT TO CUT SEALS.
6. DISASSEMBLE AND ASSEMBLE ADJUSTER PLUG ASSEMBLY.
DISASSEMBLE
1. DISASSEMBLE PARTS AS SHOWN.
ASSEMBLE
1. ASSEMBLE PARTS AS SHOWN.
BEARING RETAINER
UPPER BEARING RACE (LARGE)
ADJUSTER PLUG
*STUB SHAFT SEAL
UPPER BEARING RACE (SMALL)
RETAINING RING
NEEDLE BEARING
UPPER THRUST BEARING
"O" RING SEAL
STUB SHAFT DUST SEAL
THRUST BEARING SPACER
* USE STUB SHAFT SEAL PROTECTOR J-29810 ON STUB SHAFT WHEN INSTALLING STUB SHAFT SEAL.
RETAINER
SCREWDRIVER
PRY BEARING RETAINER AT RAISED AREA.
USE SUITABLE SIZE ARBOR TO PRESS BEARING IN PLACE.
BEARING TO BE PRESSED 16mm (5/8 INCH) INTO ADJUSTER WITH STAMPED I.D. END UP AND FROM DIRECTION OF ARROW.
16 mm (5/8 INCH)
INSTALL BEARING
7. REMOVE AND INSTALL BEARING, WORM, AND VALVE ASSEMBLY.
REMOVE
1. GRASP STUB SHAFT AND REMOVE VALVE AND WORM ASSEMBLY AS A UNIT.
INSTALL
1. INSTALL PARTS AS SHOWN.
SEPARATE THE VALVE FROM THE WORM. NOTE HOW THE PIN IN THE WORM FITS THE SLOT IN THE VALVE.
THRUST BEARING AND RACES
VALVE ASSEMBLY
WORM ASSEMBLY
WHEN REASSEMBLING GEAR, MAKE SURE ANGLE OF THRUST RACES ARE AS SHOWN.
8. DISASSEMBLE AND ASSEMBLE VALVE.
DISASSEMBLE
1. DISASSEMBLE PARTS AS SHOWN.
ASSEMBLE
1. ASSEMBLE PARTS AS SHOWN.
SHAFT CAP
VALVE BODY
VALVE BODY "O" RING
STUB SHAFT
SPOOL TO BODY "O" RING
VALVE BODY * RING (TEFLON)
VALVE SPOOL
* TO EASE ASSEMBLY, SOAK TEFLON RINGS IN WARM WATER.
A. LOOSEN SHAFT CAP.
TAP LIGHTLY ON WOOD BLOCK
B. REMOVE AND INSTALL STUB SHAFT.
PULL CAP OUT APPROX. 6 mm (1/4")
PIN ON SHAFT AND HOLE IN SPOOL (DISENGAGE TO REMOVE)
C. REMOVE AND INSTALL SPOOL
ROTATE WHILE REMOVING OR INSTALLING
LUBRICATE SPOOL AND BODY WITH POWER STEERING FLUID.
D. ENGAGE STUB SHAFT.
NOTCH MUST FULLY ENGAGE PIN AND CAP MUST SEAT AGAINST SHOULDER.
GC6029100094020X

Fig. 2 Service procedures, Saginaw power steering gear (Part 2 of 4)

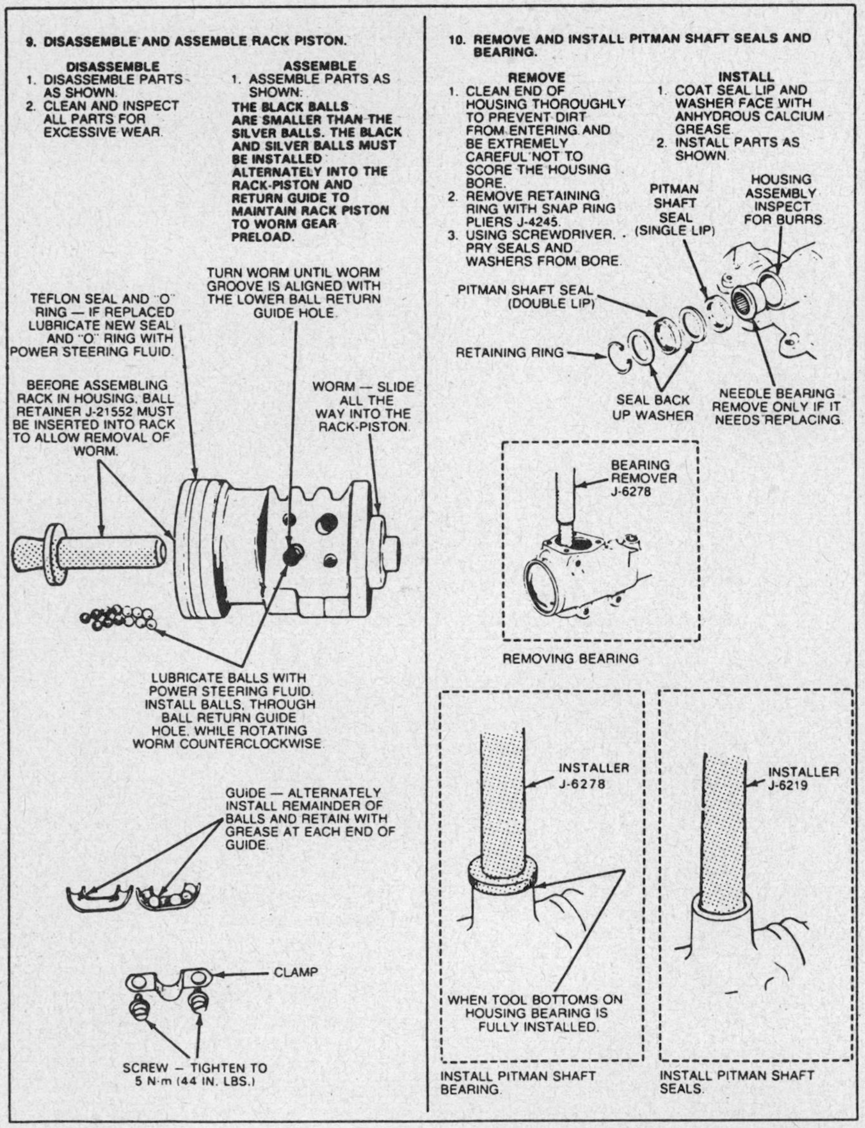
9. DISASSEMBLE AND ASSEMBLE RACK PISTON.
DISASSEMBLE
1. DISASSEMBLE PARTS AS SHOWN.
2. CLEAN AND INSPECT ALL PARTS FOR EXCESSIVE WEAR.
ASSEMBLE
1. ASSEMBLE PARTS AS SHOWN.
THE BLACK BALLS ARE SMALLER THAN THE SILVER BALLS. THE BLACK AND SILVER BALLS MUST BE INSTALLED ALTERNATELY INTO THE RACK-PISTON AND RETURN GUIDE TO MAINTAIN RACK PISTON TO WORM GEAR PRELOAD.
TEFLON SEAL AND "O" RING — IF REPLACED LUBRICATE NEW SEAL AND "O" RING WITH POWER STEERING FLUID.
TURN WORM UNTIL WORM GROOVE IS ALIGNED WITH THE LOWER BALL RETURN GUIDE HOLE.
BEFORE ASSEMBLING RACK IN HOUSING, BALL RETAINER J-21552 MUST BE INSERTED INTO RACK TO ALLOW REMOVAL OF WORM.
WORM — SLIDE ALL THE WAY INTO THE RACK-PISTON.
LUBRICATE BALLS WITH POWER STEERING FLUID. INSTALL BALLS, THROUGH BALL RETURN GUIDE HOLE, WHILE ROTATING WORM COUNTERCLOCKWISE.
GUIDE — ALTERNATELY INSTALL REMAINDER OF BALLS AND RETAIN WITH GREASE AT EACH END OF GUIDE.
CLAMP
SCREW — TIGHTEN TO 5 N·m (44 IN. LBS.)
10. REMOVE AND INSTALL PITMAN SHAFT SEALS AND BEARING.
REMOVE
1. CLEAN END OF HOUSING THOROUGHLY TO PREVENT DIRT FROM ENTERING AND BE EXTREMELY CAREFUL NOT TO SCORE THE HOUSING BORE.
2. REMOVE RETAINING RING WITH SNAP RING PLIERS J-4245.
3. USING SCREWDRIVER, PRY SEALS AND WASHERS FROM BORE.
INSTALL
1. COAT SEAL LIP AND WASHER FACE WITH ANHYDROUS CALCIUM GREASE.
2. INSTALL PARTS AS SHOWN.
PITMAN SHAFT SEAL (SINGLE LIP)
HOUSING ASSEMBLY INSPECT FOR BURRS
PITMAN SHAFT SEAL (DOUBLE LIP)
RETAINING RING
SEAL BACK UP WASHER
NEEDLE BEARING REMOVE ONLY IF IT NEEDS REPLACING.
BEARING REMOVER J-6278
REMOVING BEARING
INSTALLER J-6278
WHEN TOOL BOTTOMS ON HOUSING BEARING IS FULLY INSTALLED.
INSTALL PITMAN SHAFT BEARING.
INSTALLER J-6219
INSTALL PITMAN SHAFT SEALS.
GC6029100094030X

Fig. 2 Service procedures, Saginaw power steering gear (Part 3 of 4)

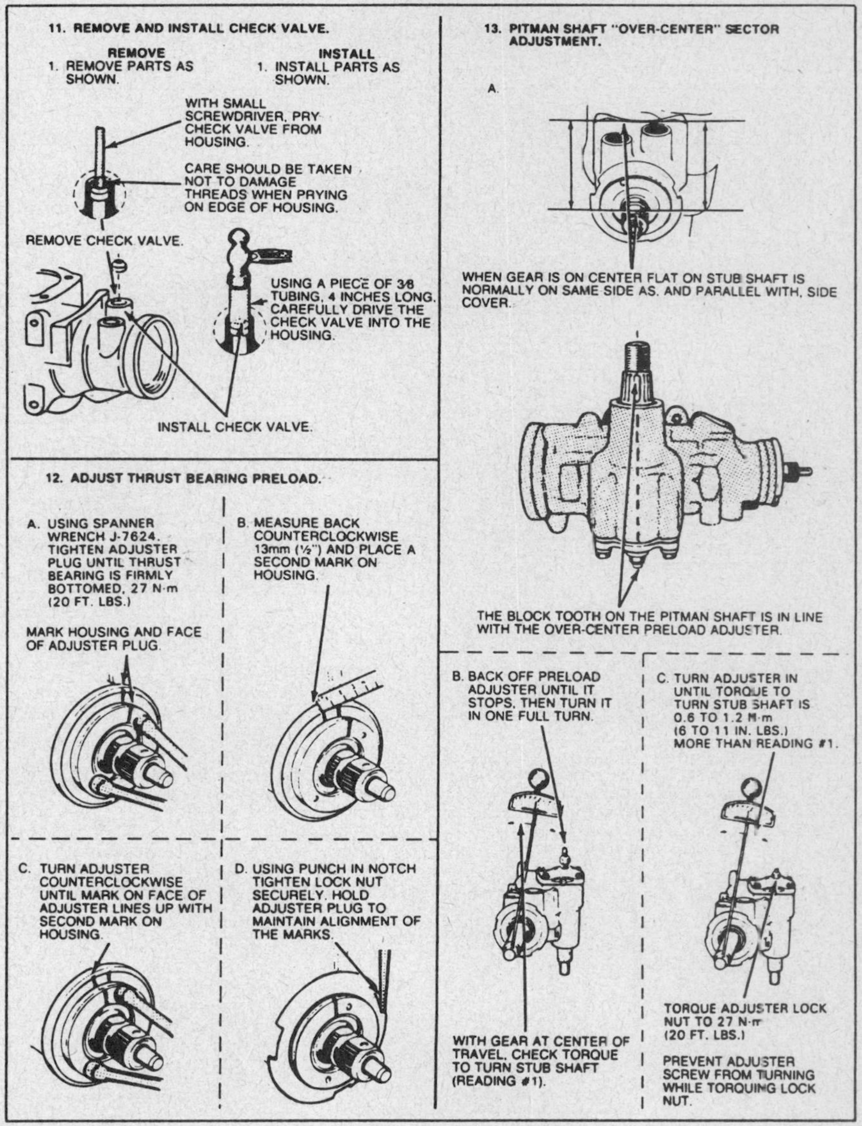
11. REMOVE AND INSTALL CHECK VALVE.
REMOVE
1. REMOVE PARTS AS SHOWN.
INSTALL
1. INSTALL PARTS AS SHOWN.
WITH SMALL SCREWDRIVER, PRY CHECK VALVE FROM HOUSING.
CARE SHOULD BE TAKEN NOT TO DAMAGE THREADS WHEN PRYING ON EDGE OF HOUSING.
REMOVE CHECK VALVE.
USING A PIECE OF 3/8 TUBING, 4 INCHES LONG, CAREFULLY DRIVE THE CHECK VALVE INTO THE HOUSING.
INSTALL CHECK VALVE.
12. ADJUST THRUST BEARING PRELOAD.
A. USING SPANNER WRENCH J-7624, TIGHTEN ADJUSTER PLUG UNTIL THRUST BEARING IS FIRMLY BOTTOMED, 27 N·m (20 FT. LBS.)
MARK HOUSING AND FACE OF ADJUSTER PLUG.
B. MEASURE BACK COUNTERCLOCKWISE 13mm (½") AND PLACE A SECOND MARK ON HOUSING.
C. TURN ADJUSTER COUNTERCLOCKWISE UNTIL MARK ON FACE OF ADJUSTER LINES UP WITH SECOND MARK ON HOUSING.
D. USING PUNCH IN NOTCH TIGHTEN LOCK NUT SECURELY. HOLD ADJUSTER PLUG TO MAINTAIN ALIGNMENT OF THE MARKS.
13. PITMAN SHAFT "OVER-CENTER" SECTOR ADJUSTMENT.
A.
WHEN GEAR IS ON CENTER FLAT ON STUB SHAFT IS NORMALLY ON SAME SIDE AS, AND PARALLEL WITH, SIDE COVER.
THE BLOCK TOOTH ON THE PITMAN SHAFT IS IN LINE WITH THE OVER-CENTER PRELOAD ADJUSTER.
B. BACK OFF PRELOAD ADJUSTER UNTIL IT STOPS, THEN TURN IT IN ONE FULL TURN.
WITH GEAR AT CENTER OF TRAVEL, CHECK TORQUE TO TURN STUB SHAFT (READING #1).
C. TURN ADJUSTER IN UNTIL TORQUE TO TURN STUB SHAFT IS 0.6 TO 1.2 N·m (6 TO 11 IN. LBS.) MORE THAN READING #1.
TORQUE ADJUSTER LOCK NUT TO 27 N·m (20 FT. LBS.)
PREVENT ADJUSTER SCREW FROM TURNING WHILE TORQUING LOCK NUT.
GC6029100094040X

Fig. 2 Service procedures, Saginaw power steering gear (Part 4 of 4)

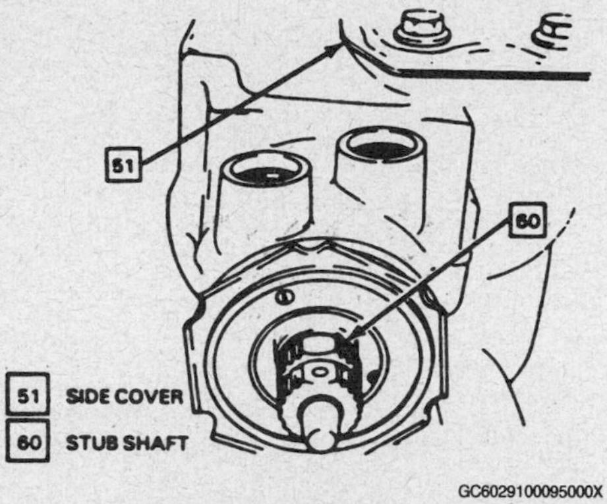
51
60
51 SIDE COVER
60 STUB SHAFT
GC6029100095000X

Fig. 3 Stub shaft alignment. Except Brougham & Fleetwood (RWD)

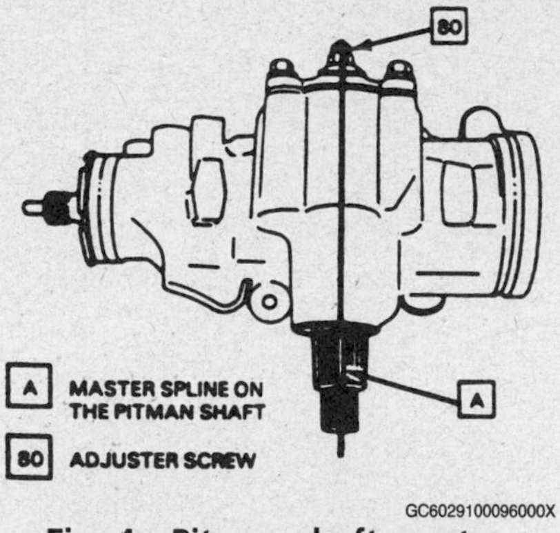
80
A
A MASTER SPLINE ON THE PITMAN SHAFT
80 ADJUSTER SCREW
GC6029100096000X

Fig. 4 Pitman shaft master spline alignment. Except Brougham & Fleetwood (RWD)

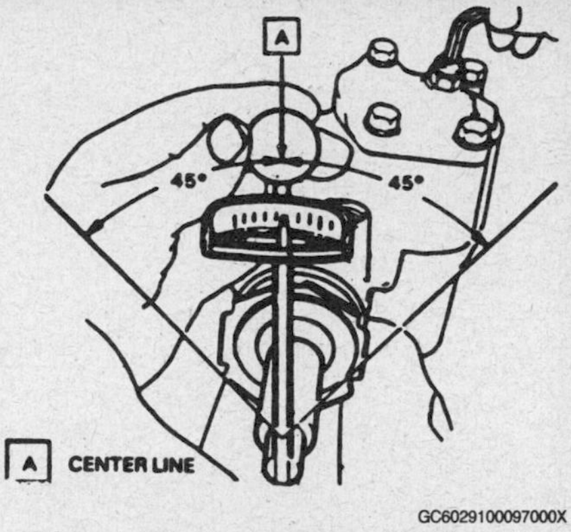
A
45°
45°
A CENTER LINE
GC6029100097000X

Fig. 5 Over center rotational torque inspection. Except Brougham & Fleetwood (RWD)

Toyota (Prizm) Rack & Pinion Power Steering Gear

INDEX

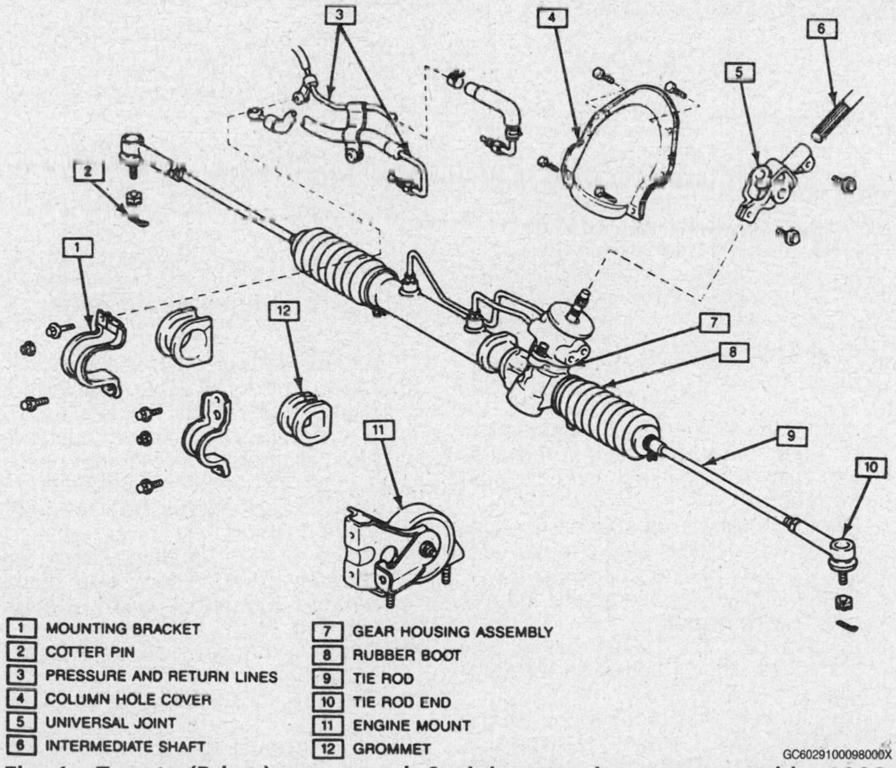
1
2
3
4
5
6
7
8
9
10
11
12
1 MOUNTING BRACKET
2 COTTER PIN
3 PRESSURE AND RETURN LINES
4 COLUMN HOLE COVER
5 UNIVERSAL JOINT
6 INTERMEDIATE SHAFT
7 GEAR HOUSING ASSEMBLY
8 RUBBER BOOT
9 TIE ROD
10 TIE ROD END
11 ENGINE MOUNT
12 GROMMET
GC6029100098000X

Fig. 1 Toyota (Prizm) power rack & pinion steering gear assembly. 1992

DESCRIPTION

This steering system converts rotary motion to linear motion as follows; when the steering wheel is turned, rotary motion is transferred to the steering shaft, shaft joint and rack pinion. The pinion teeth mesh with teeth on the rack and the rotary motion is transferred to the rack and changed to linear motion. The linear force is then transmitted through the tie rods and to the steering knuckles which steer the front wheels.

POWER STEERING SYSTEM SERVICE

REMOVAL

The power steering gear is non-serviceable and therefore must be replaced as a unit. To remove the power steering gear proceed as follows:

1. Remove steering unit from vehicle and place in suitable vise, **Fig. 1.**
2. Remove power steering lines.
3. Scribe alignment mark on tie rod end and tie rod, then remove tie rod ends.
4. Remove rack boots, then bend back locking washer using appropriate punch or chisel and remove.
5. Using tie rod housing wrench tool No. J 35414 and steering rack end wrench tool No. J 35418 or equivalent, remove tie rod.
6. Remove dust cover, snap ring and oil seal.

DISASSEMBLE

1992

1. Remove steering unit from vehicle and place in suitable vise, **Fig. 2.**
2. Remove right and left turn pressure pipes between valve housing and cylinder using injection line wrench tool No. J-29698-A or equivalent.
3. Place match marks on tie rod ends and tie rods, then remove tie rod ends, **Fig. 3.**
4. Remove both rack boots.

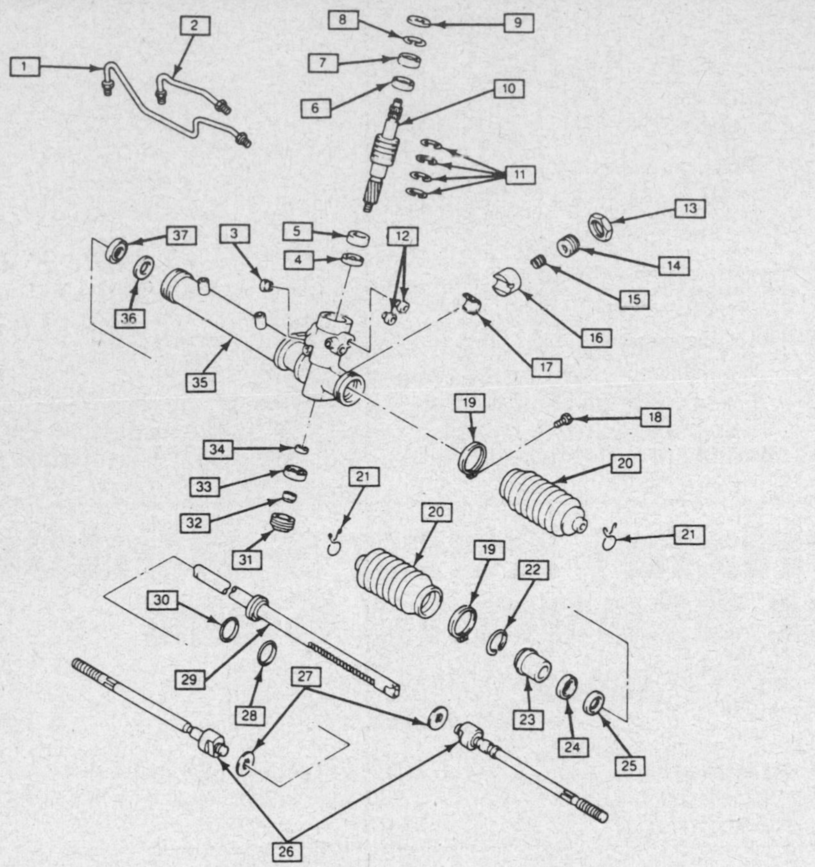

1 RIGHT TURN OIL PRESSURE PIPE
2 LEFT TURN OIL PRESSURE PIPE
3 UNION SEAT (AIR)
4 OIL SEAL (6.5 mm THICK)
5 RACK HOUSING BUSHING
6 UPPER BEARING
7 RACK HOUSING SEAL (7.8 mm THICK)
8 SNAP RING
9 DUST COVER
10 CONTROL VALVE
11 CONTROL VALVE SNAP RING (TEFLON)
12 UNION SEAT (PRESSURE FEED TUBE)
13 RACK GUIDE CAP LOCKING NUT
14 RACK GUIDE SPRING CAP
15 RACK GUIDE SPRING
16 RACK GUIDE
17 RACK GUIDE SEAT
18 SCREW
19 BOOT CLAMP
20 RACK BOOT
21 HOSE CLAMP
22 END STOPPER SNAP RING
23 RACK HOUSING STOPPER
24 SPACER (6 mm THICK)
25 OUTER OIL SEAL
26 RACK END
27 CLAW WASHER
28 TEFLON O-RING
29 STEERING RACK
30 OUTER O-RING
31 RACK HOUSING CAP
32 CONTROL VALVE LOCKING NUT
33 LOWER BEARING
34 CONTROL VALVE SPACER
35 STEERING RACK HOUSING
36 SPACER (2 mm THICK)
37 INNER OIL SEAL

GC6029100099000X

Fig. 2 Exploded view of Toyota (Prizm) power rack & pinion steering gear assembly. 1992

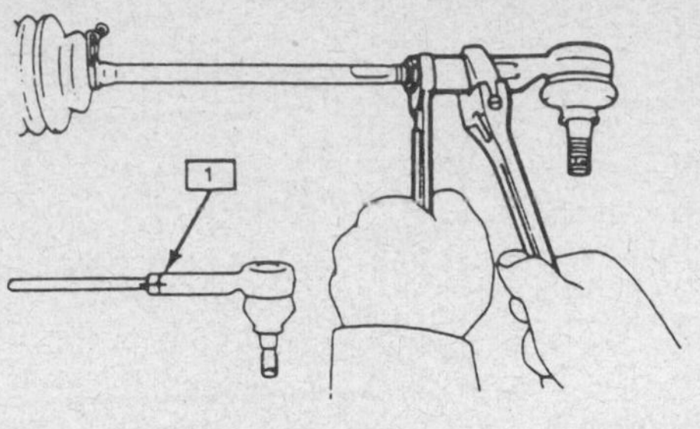
1

1 MATCH MARKS

GC6029100100000X

Fig. 3 Tie rod ends removal. 1992

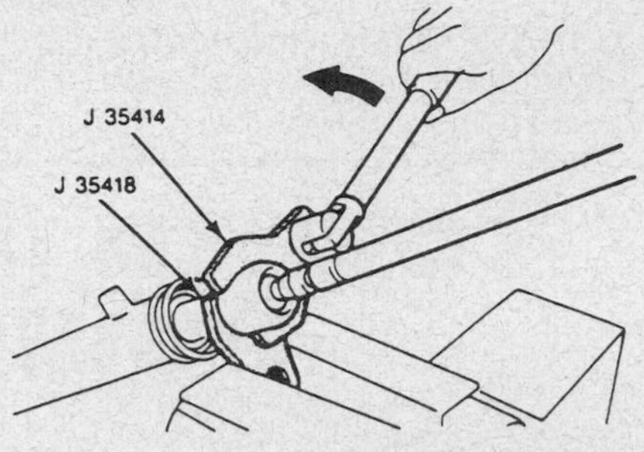
J 35414
J 35418

GC6029100101000X

Fig. 4 Tie rod removal. 1992

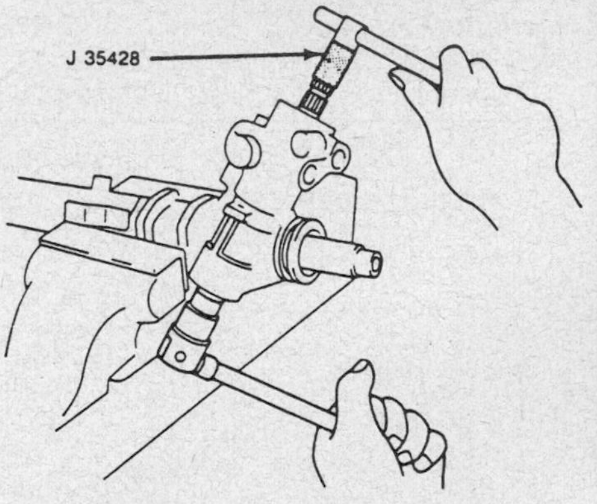
J 35428

GC6029100102000X

Fig. 5 Lower valve nut removal. 1992

5. Unstake claw washers retaining both tie rods to steering rack, then remove using tie rod housing wrench tool No. J-35414 and steering rack end wrench tool No. J-35418 or equivalents, **Fig. 4.**
6. Remove steering rack guide cap nut, cap, spring, rack guide and seat using rack guide spring cap wrench tool No. J-35423 and spring cap locknut wrench tool No. J-35692 or equivalents.
7. Remove rack housing dust cover, housing snap ring and housing cap.
8. Remove lower valve nut, lower bearing and spacer using pinion preload socket tool No. J-35428 or equivalent, **Fig. 5.**
9. Remove pinion valve using steering gear bushing remover tool No. J-35420 or equivalent, **Fig. 6.**
10. Remove cylinder end stopper snap ring, cylinder end stopper and spacer.
11. Lightly tap rack end with a brass bar and hammer to free rack from housing, then remove rack and oil seal from housing.
12. Remove cylinder oil seal and spacer using rack cylinder seal remover tool No. J-35434 or equivalent, **Fig. 7.**
13. Clean all disassembled parts. **Do not use a wire brush.**
14. Inspect rack bar for corrosion, pits, scratches, dents, teeth wear or damage.
15. Measure steering rack runout using a suitable dial indicator. If runout is greater than .012 inch, replace rack bar, **Fig. 8.**
16. Remove inner (teflon) and outer O-ring seal.
17. Measure control valve shaft outer diameter using a suitable micrometer. Maximum shaft outside diameter should not exceed 1.0925 inches. If measurement exceeds specified limit, replace control valve shaft.
18. Measure control valve bushing inner diameter using V.C. tool No. J-26900-5 or equivalent. Maximum bushing inside diameter should not exceed 1.1102 inches. If measurement exceeds specified limit, replace control valve bushing.
19. Remove inner bushing from valve housing using steering gear bushing remover tool No. J-35420 or equivalent, **Fig. 9.**
20. Remove housing oil seal using a brass bar.
21. Remove four control valve (Teflon) rings.
22. Inspect housing union seat for damage, corrosion or excessive wear. If necessary, remove using a screw extractor and replace seat.

ASSEMBLE

1992

1. Install new inner (Teflon) and outer O-ring seals as follows:

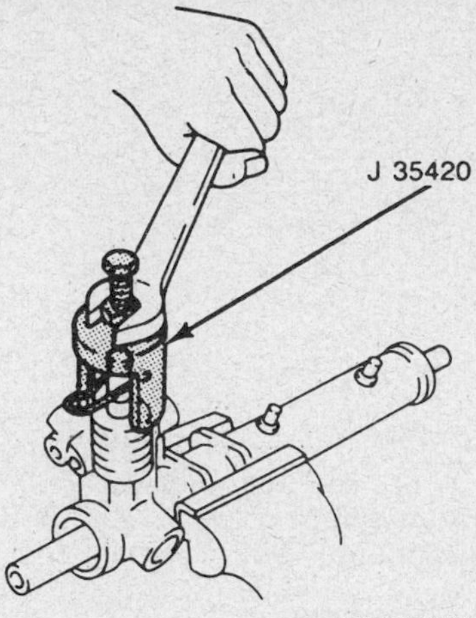
J 35420
GC6029100103000X

Fig. 6 Pinion valve removal. 1992

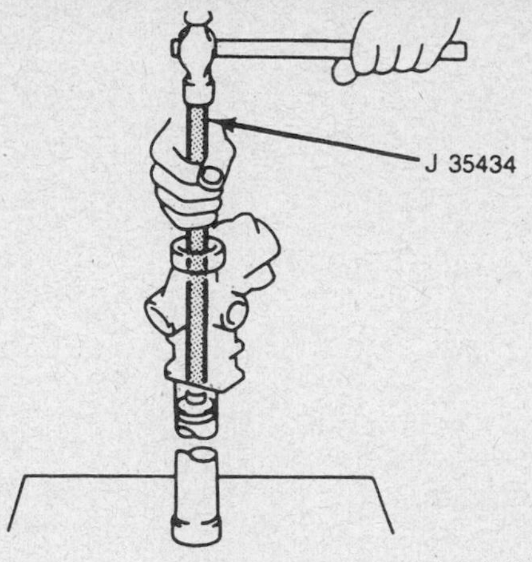
J 35434
GC6029100104000X

Fig. 7 Cylinder inner oil seal removal. 1992

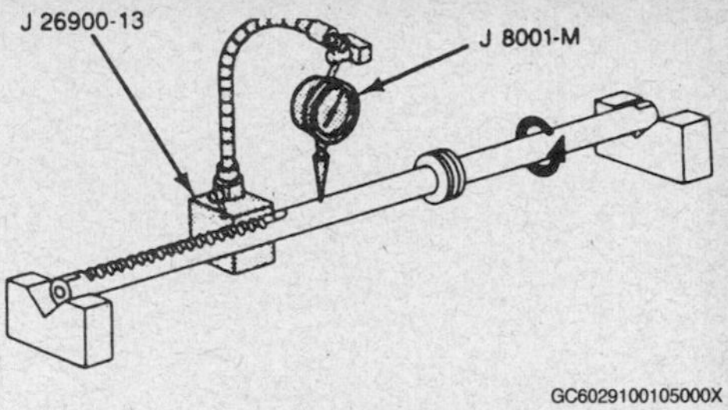
J 26900-13
J 8001-M
GC6029100105000X

Fig. 8 Steering rack bar runout measurement. 1992

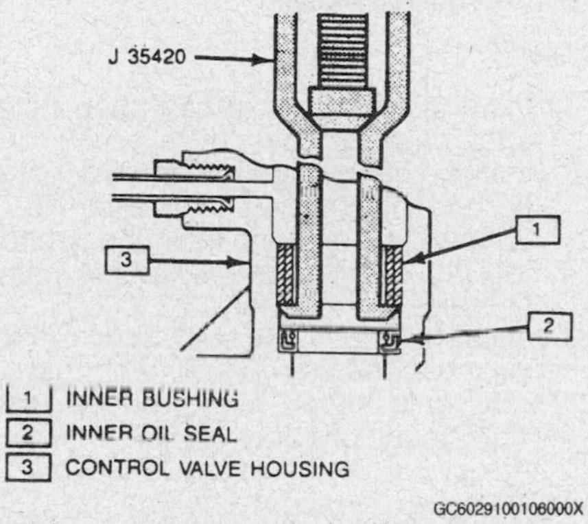
J 35420
1
2
3
1 INNER BUSHING
2 INNER OIL SEAL
3 CONTROL VALVE HOUSING
GC6029100106000X

Fig. 9 Inner pinion valve bushing removal. 1992

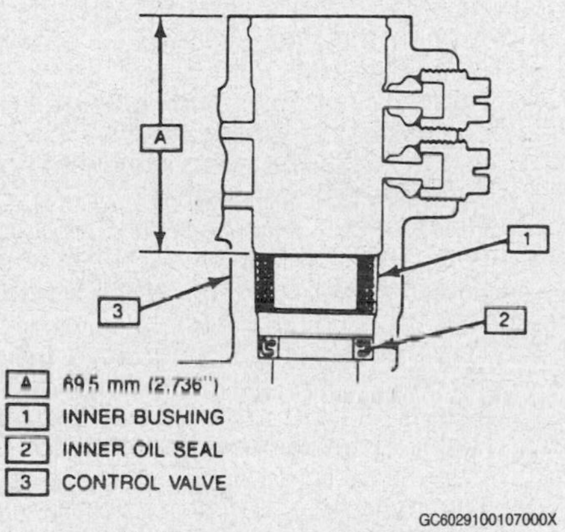
A
1
2
3
A 69.5 mm (2.736")
1 INNER BUSHING
2 INNER OIL SEAL
3 CONTROL VALVE
GC6029100107000X

Fig. 10 Proper inner bushing installation. 1992

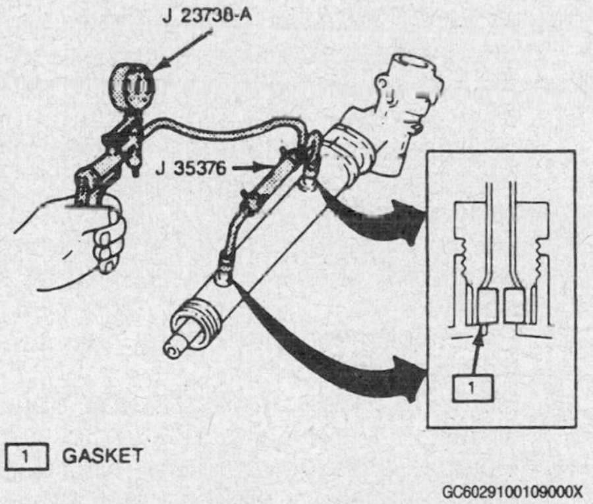
J 23738-A
J 35376
1
1 GASKET
GC6029100109000X

Fig. 12 Pressure testing cylinder seals. 1992

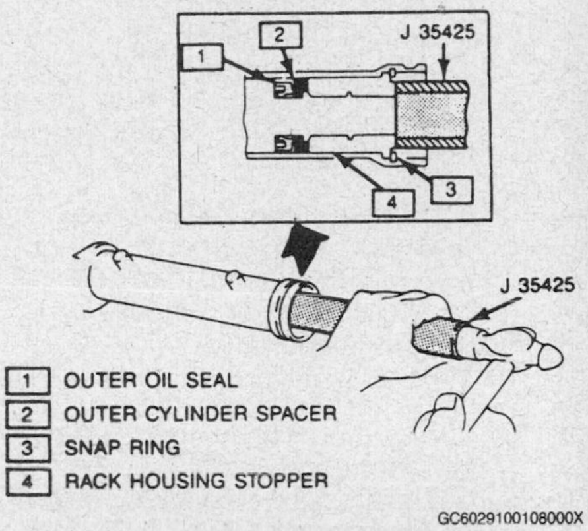
J 35425
1
2
3
4
J 35425
1 OUTER OIL SEAL
2 OUTER CYLINDER SPACER
3 SNAP RING
4 RACK HOUSING STOPPER
GC6029100108000X

Fig. 11 Rack housing stopper position. 1992

a. Expand Teflon ring slightly with fingers.
b. Install Teflon ring to steering rack piston.
c. Coat Teflon ring with suitable power steering fluid and snug it down with fingers.

2. Install new pinion valve (Teflon) rings.
3. Coat new housing oil seal with suitable power steering fluid and install.
4. Install inner bushing to valve housing with inner pinion bushing installer tool No. J-35695 and driver handle tool No. J-8092 or equivalents, **Fig. 10. Bushing must be installed to a depth of 2.736 inches.**
5. Coat pinion valve with suitable power steering fluid, then install and inspect for proper operation. Remove valve after inspection.
6. Clean rack teeth, then cover teeth with electrical tape. Tape both ends of rack bar and ensure air bleed holes are covered to prevent damage to oil seal lips.
7. Coat cylinder bore and new inner oil seal with suitable power steering fluid, then install inner oil seal onto rack, lip end first.
8. Install a .079 inch cylinder spacer.
9. Cover rack teeth with electrical tape, then coat cylinder outer seal with suitable power steering fluidand install on rack, lip end first.
10. Coat cylinder bore with suitable power steering fluid, then carefully install steering rack into cylinder. Push inner oil seal, piston seal ring and outer oil seal into bore being careful not to damage components on cylinder bore end or snap ring groove.
11. Install a .236 inch cylinder spacer with shallow side facing out.
12. Coat rack housing stopper with suitable power steering fluid, then install rack housing stopper onto rack and push into cylinder bore.
13. Install rack into cylinder. Tap end of rack with a fiber hammer to seat inner seal and spacer.
14. Seal rack housing stopper using power rack pinion bearing and seal installer tool No. J-35425 or equivalent. Stopper should be in far enough to expose snap ring groove, **Fig. 11.**
15. Install snap ring to cylinder end stopper.
16. Test inner and outer seals as follows:
    a. Install valve stem seal tester tool No. J-23728 and cylinder pressure tester tool No. J-35376 or equivalents, **Fig. 12.**
    b. Apply 15 inches Hg.
    c. If vacuum does not hold for a minimum of 30 seconds, replace faulty seals.
17. Install pinion valve into housing.
18. Install rack housing upper bearing using power rack pinion bearing and seal installer tool No. J-35425 or equivalent.
19. Coat rack housing oil seal and snap ring with suitable power steering fluid, then install rack housing oil seal, snap ring and dust cover.
20. Install spacer and lower bearing on pinion valve shaft.
21. Install new self-locking nut on pinion shaft using pinion preload socket tool No. J-35428 or equivalent, **Fig. 13. Torque** pinion shaft locknut to 43 ft. lbs.
22. Coat threads of new rack housing cap with suitable power steering fluid, then install new rack housing cap and **torque** to 51 ft. lbs. Stake housing using a hammer and chisel.
23. Install rack guide seat, rack guide and rack guide spring.
24. Coat threads of rack guide spring cap with thread sealer part No. 1052080

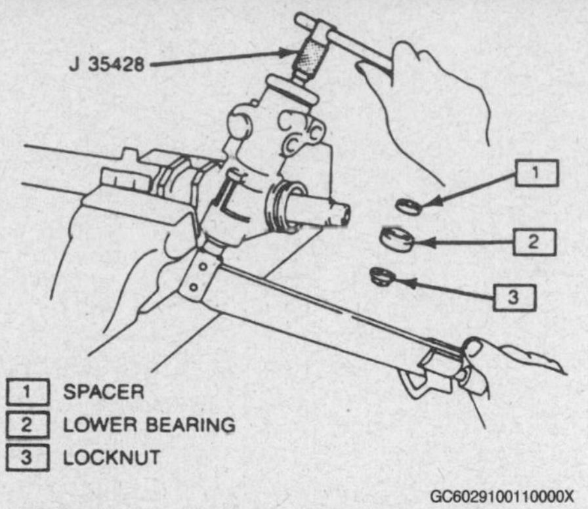
J 35428
1
2
3
1 SPACER
2 LOWER BEARING
3 LOCKNUT
GC6029100110000X

Fig. 13 Pinion shaft locknut installation. 1992

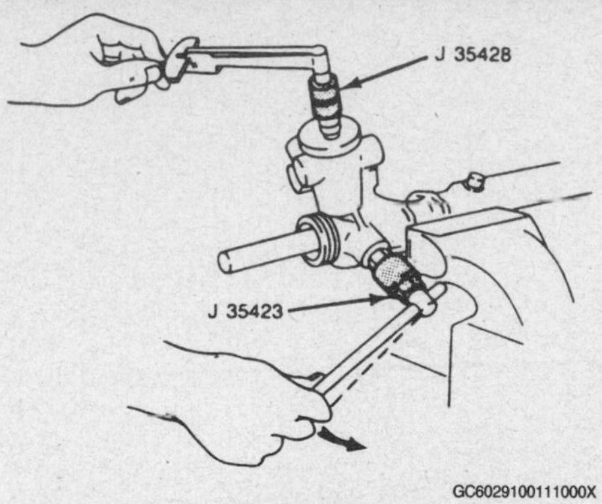
J 35428
J 35423
GC6029100111000X

Fig. 14 Rack guide spring cap preload adjustment. 1992

or equivalent, then install using rack guide spring cap wrench tool No. J-35423 or equivalent. **Torque** rack guide spring cap to 18 ft. lbs.

25. Adjust total preload as follows:
    a. Turn rack guide spring cap 12 degrees counterclockwise.
    b. Turn pinion valve shaft right and left 3 to 4 times.
    c. Using a torque wrench and pinion preload socket tool No. J-35428 or equivalent, adjust pinion valve to 7-11 inch lbs., then install rack guide spring cap locking nut and **torque** to 33 ft. lbs., **Fig. 14.**
    d. Recheck preload of pinion valve. If preload is not 7-11 inch lbs., readjust preload.
26. Install tie rods and new claw washers. **Torque** tie rods to 61 ft. lbs., then using a brass bar and hammer, stake claw washers.
27. Ensure air bleed hole is clear of grease and contaminants, then coat inside of steering rack boots small end with suitable power steering fluid.
28. install steering rack boots to steering rack being careful not to damage or twist boots during installation.
29. Install clips securing boots to steering rack with open ends of clips facing outward.
30. Install locknuts and tie rod ends on to tie rods until matchmarks are aligned. **Torque** tie rod locknuts to 41 ft. lbs.
31. Install left and right turn pressure pipes using injection line wrench tool No. J-29698-A or equivalent. **Torque** pipe fittings to 32 ft. lbs.

1993–94

1. Remove steering unit, **Fig. 15.** from vehicle and place in suitable vise.
2. Remove right and left turn pressure pipes between valve housing and cylinder using injection line wrench tool No. J-29698-A or equivalent.
3. Place match marks on tie rod ends and tie rods, then remove tie rod ends.
4. Remove both rack boots.
5. Unstake claw washers retaining both tie rods to steering rack, then remove using tie rod housing wrench tool No. J-35414 and steering rack end wrench tool No. J-35418 or equivalents.
6. Remove steering rack guide cap nut, cap, spring, rack guide and seat using rack guide spring cap wrench tool No. J-35309-2 and spring cap locknut wrench tool No. J-35692 or equivalents, **Fig. 16.**
7. Remove control valve locknut from control using pinion preload socket tool No. J-35428 or equivalent to hold control valve stationary.
8. Remove dust cover from top of pinion gear, then two bolts, control valve housing and gasket from steering rack housing, **Fig. 17.**
9. Turn cylinder end stopper using cylinder end stopper end wrench or equivalent until both ends of cylinder end stopper wire appear in slot on top of steering rack housing.
10. Turn cylinder end stopper using cylinder end stopper end wrench or equivalent so that loose end of cylinder end stopper wire is fed out of slot on top of steering rack housing.
11. Remove cylinder end stopper wire and cylinder end stopper from steering rack housing, **Fig. 18.** Install a rack seal protector tool No. J-36595 or equivalent onto toothed portion on steering rack to protect inner steering rack fluid seal.
12. Remove steering rack and steering rack outer spacer from steering rack housing.
13. Remove steering rack outer fluid seal from outer spacer.
14. Remove O-ring from steering outer spacer.
15. Remove steering rack inner fluid seal and spacer from steering rack housing using rack cylinder seal remover tool No. J-35434-1 with drive handle tool No. J-35343-2 or equivalents.
16. Remove steering rack housing lower bearing from steering rack housing using a brass drift punch and hammer.
17. Remove steering rack upper bearing using a control valve bearing remover tool No. J-39902 with drive handle tool No. J-35343-2 or equivalents.
18. Clean all disassembled parts. **Do not use a wire brush.**
19. Inspect rack bar for corrosion, pits, scratches, dents, teeth wear or damage.
20. Measure steering rack runout using a suitable dial indicator. If runout is greater than .006 inch, replace steering rack.

INSTALLATION

1992

1. Install a new upper oil seal, then install snap ring and dust cover.
2. Install a new claw washer; then, using tie rod housing wrench tool No. J 351414 and steering rack end wrench tool No. J 35418 or equivalents install tie rods and **torque** to 53 ft. lbs.
3. Install rubber rack boot, then screw locknuts and tie rod ends onto the tie rods until match marks are aligned. **Torque** locknut to 41 ft. lbs.
4. Adjust toe-in, then **torque** locknut to 41 ft. lbs.
5. Install power steering lines, **torque** nuts to 8 ft. lbs.
6. Install steering assembly into vehicle.

1993–94

1. Install steering rack housing upper bearing into steering rack housing using control valve bearing stopper tool No. J-39903 and driver handle tool No. J-7079-2 or equivalents, **Fig. 19.**
2. Install steering rack inner fluid seal and spacer into steering rack housing using rack seal protector tool No. J-36595 or equivalent and steering rack. Place rack seal protector tool No. tool No. J-36595 or equivalent over toothed portion of steering rack and slide fluid seal and spacer over rack seal protector tool No. J-36595 or equivalent and onto steering rack. Install steering rack into steering rack housing and tap gently with plastic mallet until inner fluid seal and spacer have been seated.
3. Remove rack seal protector tool No. J-36595 or equivalent from steering rack.
4. Install new O-ring onto steering rack outer spacer.
5. Install new steering rack outer fluid seal into steering rack outer spacer.
6. Install cylinder end stopper into steering rack housing as follows:
    a. Turn cylinder end stopper using cylinder end stopper wrench tool No. J-39901 or equivalent until wire end hole appears in slot on top of steering rack housing.

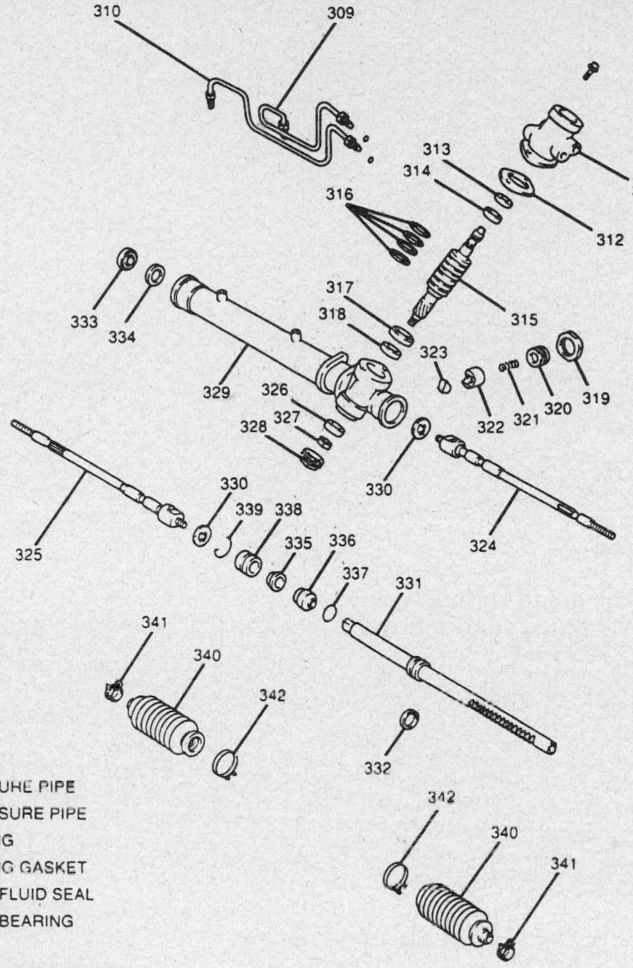
310
309
313
314
311
316
312
317
318
315
333
334
323
329
326
319
327
320
328
321
322
330
330
339
338
335
336
324
325
337
331
341
340
342
332
342
340
341

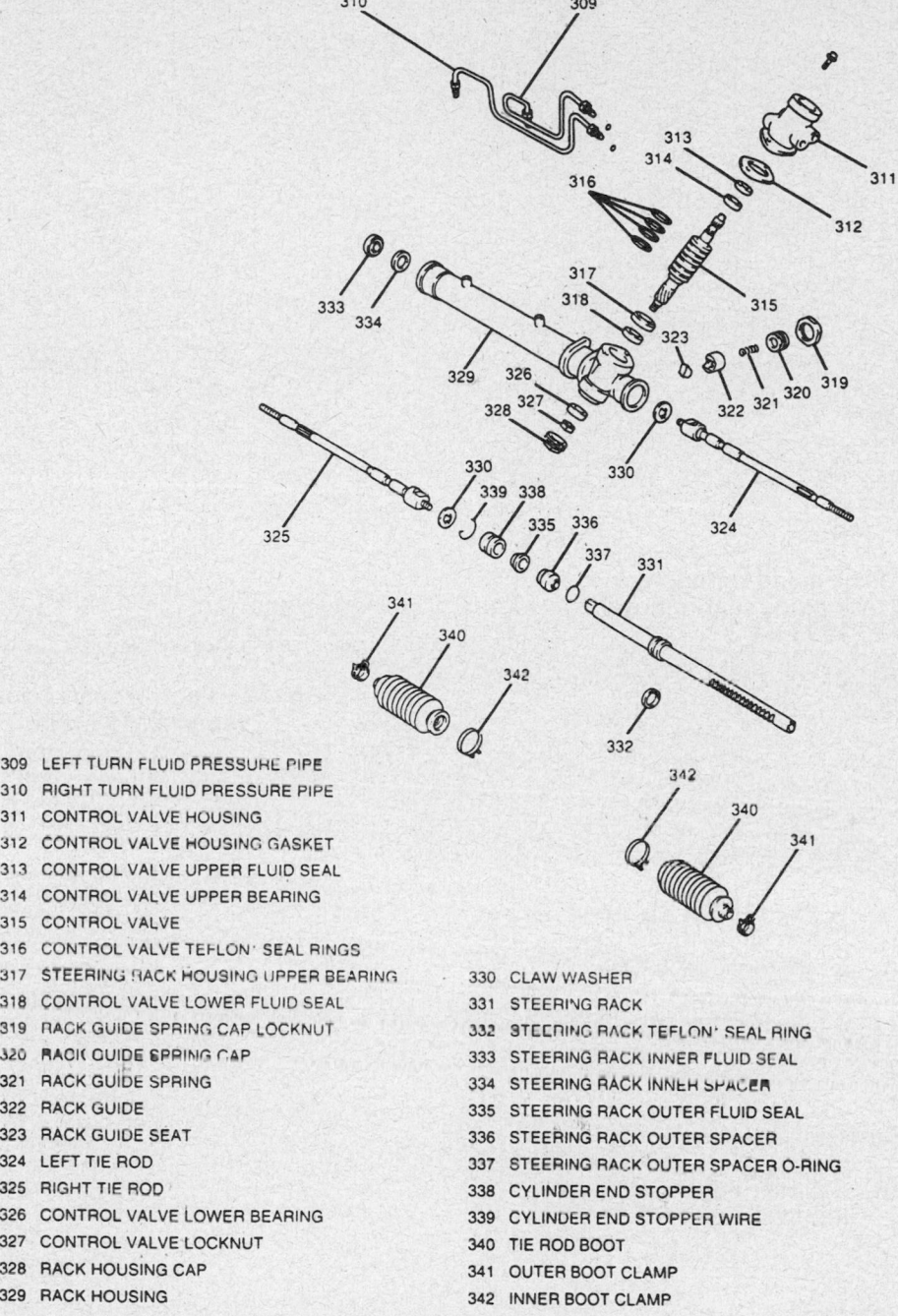

309 LEFT TURN FLUID PRESSURE PIPE
310 RIGHT TURN FLUID PRESSURE PIPE
311 CONTROL VALVE HOUSING
312 CONTROL VALVE HOUSING GASKET
313 CONTROL VALVE UPPER FLUID SEAL
314 CONTROL VALVE UPPER BEARING
315 CONTROL VALVE
316 CONTROL VALVE TEFLON' SEAL RINGS
317 STEERING RACK HOUSING UPPER BEARING
318 CONTROL VALVE LOWER FLUID SEAL
319 RACK GUIDE SPRING CAP LOCKNUT
320 RACK GUIDE SPRING CAP
321 RACK GUIDE SPRING
322 RACK GUIDE
323 RACK GUIDE SEAT
324 LEFT TIE ROD
325 RIGHT TIE ROD
326 CONTROL VALVE LOWER BEARING
327 CONTROL VALVE LOCKNUT
328 RACK HOUSING CAP
329 RACK HOUSING
330 CLAW WASHER
331 STEERING RACK
332 STEERING RACK TEFLON' SEAL RING
333 STEERING RACK INNER FLUID SEAL
334 STEERING RACK INNER SPACER
335 STEERING RACK OUTER FLUID SEAL
336 STEERING RACK OUTER SPACER
337 STEERING RACK OUTER SPACER O-RING
338 CYLINDER END STOPPER
339 CYLINDER END STOPPER WIRE
340 TIE ROD BOOT
341 OUTER BOOT CLAMP
342 INNER BOOT CLAMP

GC6029300112000X

Fig. 15 Exploded view of Toyota (Prizm) power rack & pinion steering gear assembly. 1993-94

b. Place hooked end of cylinder end stopper wire into wire end of hole of cylinder end stopper and turn cylinder end stopper using cylinder end stopper wrench tool No. J-39901 while feeding cylinder end stopper wire into slot on top of steering rack housing.
c. Continue to turn cylinder end stopper until both ends of cylinder end stopper wire are no longer visible.

7. Inspect steering rack fluid seal integrity using cylinder pressure tester tool No. J-35376 or equivalent and suitable vacuum pipe, **Fig. 20**. Apply 15 inch Hg. of vacuum to steering rack housing and observe vacuum pump. If pressure tester indicates a loss of vacuum, inspect steering rack inner and outer fluid seals.
8. Install new control valve housing gasket and control valve housing onto steering rack housing, then **torque** two bolts to 13 ft. lbs.
9. Install dust cover onto top of pinion gear.
10. Install steering rack housing lower bearing and new control valve locknut onto control valve using pinion preload socket tool No. J-35428 or equivalent to hold control valve stationary.
11. Apply Loctite pipe sealant or equivalent to threaded portion of rack housing cap.
12. Install housing cap into steering rack housing and **torque**cap to 51 ft. lbs., **Fig. 21.** Apply Loctite pipe sealant or equivalent to threaded portion of rack guide spring cap.
13. Install rack guide spring cap into steering rack housing using locknut wrench tool No. J-35309-2 or equivalent and **torque** to 18 ft. lbs.
14. Adjust total pinion preload as follows:
    a. Loosen rack guide spring cap 15° (1/24 of a turn) using locknut wrench tool No. J-35309-2 or equivalent.

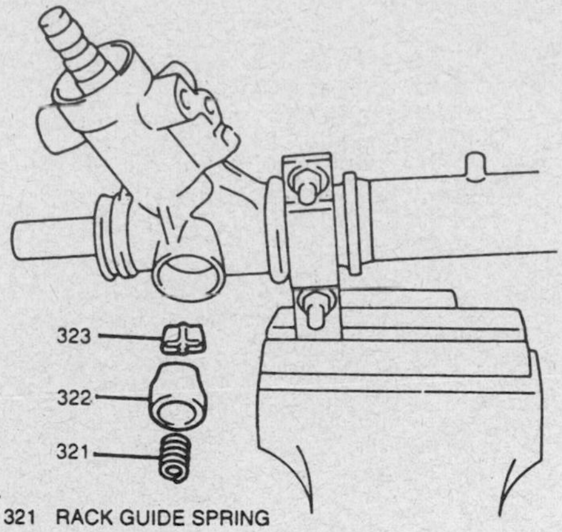
323
322
321

321 RACK GUIDE SPRING
322 RACK GUIDE
323 RACK GUIDE SEAT

GC6029300113000X

Fig. 16 Rack guide spring, rack guide and rack guide seat removal. 1993-94

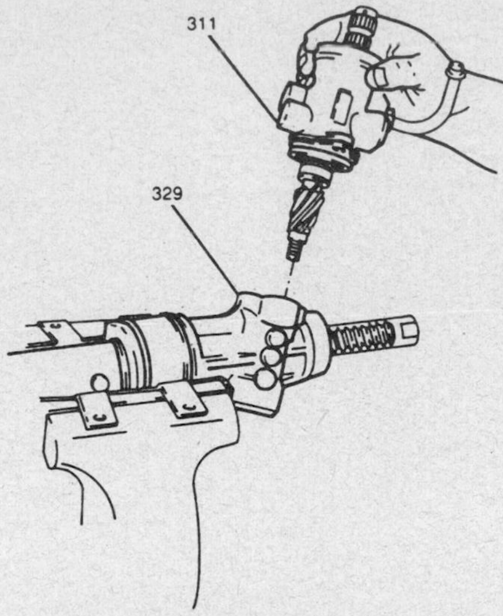
311
329

311 CONTROL VALVE HOUSING
329 STEERING RACK HOUSING

GC6029300114000X

Fig. 17 Control valve housing removal. 1993-94

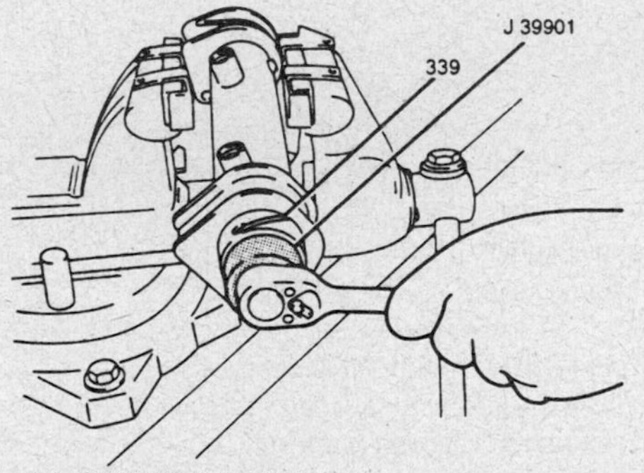
J 39901
339

339 CYLINDER END STOPPER WIRE

GC6029300115000X

Fig. 18 Cylinder end stopper wire removal. 1993-94

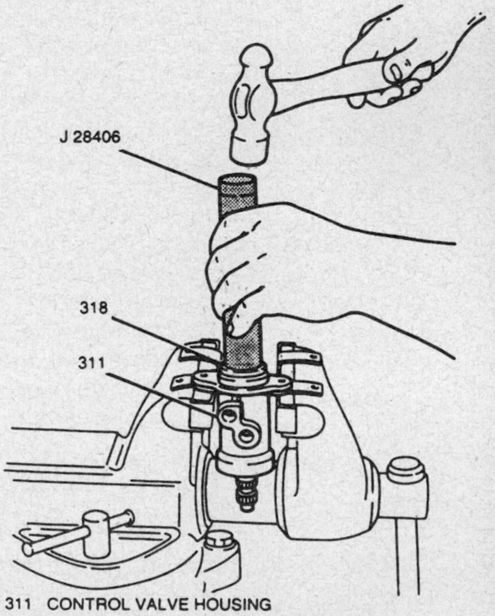
J 28406
318
311

311 CONTROL VALVE HOUSING
318 CONTROL VALVE LOWER FLUID SEAL

GC6029300116000X

Fig. 19 Steering rack housing upper bearing installation. 1993-94

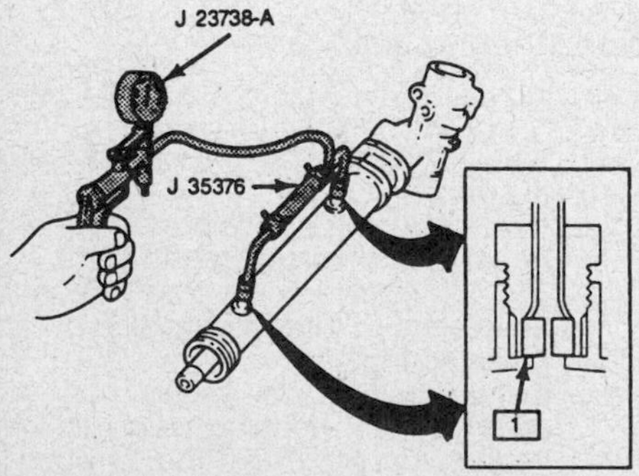
J 23738-A
J 35376
1

1 GASKET

GC6029300117000X

Fig. 20 Steering rack fluid seal integrity testing. 1993-94

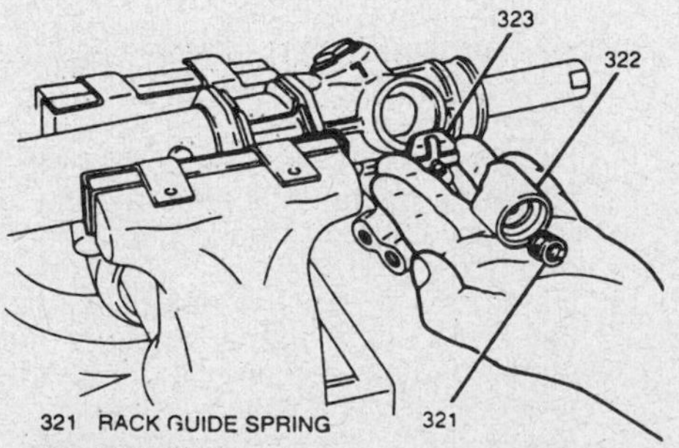
323
322
321

321 RACK GUIDE SPRING
322 RACK GUIDE
323 RACK GUIDE SEAT

GC6029300118000X

Fig. 21 Rack guide spring, rack guide and rack guide seat installation. 1993-94

b. Turn pinion shaft to right and left one rotation each.
c. Loosen rack guide spring cap using locknut wrench tool No. J-35309-2 or equivalent until all tension on rack guide spring is released.
d. Tighten rack guide spring cap using locknut wrench tool No. J-35309-2 or equivalent gradually until pinion preload is within specifications. Measure total pinion preload (starting torque) using pinion preload socket tool No. J-35428 or equivalent and a torque wrench. Standard pinion preload should be 6.9-11.3 ft. lbs.

15. Install rack guide spring cap locknut onto rack guide spring cap using locknut wrench tool No. J-35309-2 or equivalent while holding rack guide spring cap stationary **torque** rack guide spring cap locknut to 33 ft. lbs.
16. Install tie rods onto steering rack using tie rod housing wrench tool No. J-35414 and steering rack end wrench tool No. J-35418, then **torque** tie rods to 61 ft. lbs.
17. Stake both claw washers, then slide both tie rod boots toward steering rack housing.
18. Install inner and outer boot clamps to both boots.
19. Inspect right and left turn fluid pressure pipe O-rings for cuts or other damage, replacing as necessary.
20. Install right and left turn fluid pressure pipes to power steering gear, then **torque** four fluid pressure pipe flare nuts to 18 ft. lbs.
21. Remove power steering gear from vise.

TECHNICAL SERVICE BULLETINS

VEHICLE LEAD OR PULL

Some vehicles may experience lead or pull. Do not replace the steering gear to fix a lead or pull on 1993-94 vehicles as this will not solve the problem. It will temporarily mask the real problem due to higher internal friction in the new gear. However, the condition will resurface when the new gear is worn in with mileage. Refer to the Prizm "Wheel Alignment" section for further TSB information on vehicle lead or pull.

TIGHTENING SPECIFICATIONS

NOTE: All Specifications In Ft. Lbs. Unless Otherwise Noted.

ACHIEVA, BERETTA, CAVALIER, CORSICA, GRAND AM, LEMANS, SKYLARK & SUNBIRD

Year	Adjuster Plug Locknut	Coupling To Stub Shaft	Coupling To Steering Column	Inner Tie Rod Bolts	Pinion Locknut	Pinion Preload	Power Steering Line Fittings	Rack & Pinion Mounting Clamp Nuts	Rod & Piston Assembly To Rack	Tie Rod End To Steering Knuckle Nut	Tie Rod Pinch Bolts
1992–94	50	③	⑥	65	26	16①	②	22	65	④	⑤

①—Inch lbs.
②—Valve end, 14 ft. lbs.; cylinder end, 20 ft. lbs.
③—Except LeMans, 37 ft. lbs.; LeMans, 18 ft. lbs.
④—Except LeMans, 35 ft. lbs.; LeMans, 44 ft. lbs.
⑤—Except LeMans, 41 ft. lbs.; LeMans, 15 ft. lbs.
⑥—Except LeMans, 34 ft. lbs.; LeMans, 18 ft. lbs.

MODELS w/SAGINAW RACK & PINION POWER STEERING EXCEPT ACHIEVA, BERETTA, CAVALIER, CORSICA, GRAND AM, LEMANS, SKYLARK & SUNBIRD

Year	Adjuster Plug Locknut	Inner Tie Rod Housing To Rack	Intermediate Shaft Pinch Bolts	Outer Tie Rod Jam Nut	Pinion Locknut	Pinion Preload①	Power Steering Line Fittings	Tie Rod Pinch Bolts
1992–94	50	70	35	30	26	16①	②	41

①—Inch lbs.
②—Valve end, 12 ft. lbs.; cylinder end, 20 ft. lbs.

PRIZM & STORM

Model	Inner Tie Rod Pinch Bolts	Pinion Preload ①	Power Steering Line Fittings	Inner Tie Rod Housing To Rack	Outer Tie Rod Jam Nut
1992–94					
Prizm	26	—	7-11	32	41
Storm	—	65	44①	20	41

①—Inch lbs.

DISC BRAKES

NOTE: Refer To "Application Chart" To Determine Which Type Brakes Are Used On Vehicle Being Serviced.

TABLE OF CONTENTS

Application Chart

Model	Year	Front/Rear Brakes	Application
BUICK			
Century	1992-94	Front	AC Delco Single Piston Type 2
LeSabre	1992-94	Front	AC Delco Single Piston Type 2
Park Avenue	1992-94	Front	AC Delco Single Piston Type 2
Regal	1992-94	Front	AC Delco Dual Piston
		Rear	AC Delco Single Piston Type 1
Riviera	1992-93	Front	AC Delco Single Piston Type 3
		Rear	AC Delco Single Piston Type 2
Roadmaster	1992-94	Front	AC Delco Single Piston Type 1
Skylark	1992-94	Front	AC Delco Single Piston Type 2
CADILLAC			
Brougham	1992	Front	AC Delco Single Piston Type 1
DeVille	1992-94	Front	AC Delco Single Piston Type 2
Eldorado	1992-94	Front	AC Delco Single Piston Type 2
		Rear	AC Delco Single Piston Type 2

Model	Year	Front/Rear Brakes	Application
CADILLAC-Continued			
Fleetwood FWD	1992	Front	AC Delco Single Piston Type 2
Fleetwood RWD	1993-94	Front	AC Delco Single Piston Type 1
Seville	1992-94	Front	AC Delco Single Piston Type 2
		Rear	AC Delco Single Piston Type 2
CHEVROLET			
Beretta	1992-94	Front	AC Delco Single Piston Type 2
Camaro	1992	Front (Standard)	AC Delco Single Piston Type 1
		Front (Optional)	PBR Dual Piston
	1993-94	Front	AC Delco Single Piston Type 2
	1992-94	Rear	PBR Single Piston
Caprice & Impala SS	1992-94	Front	AC Delco Single Piston Type 1
Cavalier	1992-94	Front	AC Delco Single Piston Type 2
Corsica	1992-94	Front	AC Delco Single Piston Type 2
Corvette	1992-94	Front	PBR Dual Piston
		Rear	PBR Single Piston

Model	Year	Front/Rear Brakes	Application
CHEVROLET -Continued			
Lumina	1992-94	Front	AC Delco Dual Piston
	1992-94	Rear	AC Delco Single Piston Type 3
GEO			
Metro	1992-94	Front	Aisin Seiki Type 2
Prizm	1992-94	Front	Toyota/GM
	1992	Rear	Toyota/GM
Storm	1992-93	Front	Aisin Seiki Type 1
OLDSMOBILE			
Achieva	1992-94	Front	AC Delco Single Piston Type 2
Custom Cruiser	1992	Front	AC Delco Single Piston Type 1
Cutlass Ciera	1992-94	Front	AC Delco Single Piston Type 2
Cutlass Cruiser	1992	Front	AC Delco Single Piston Type 2
Cutlass Supreme	1992-94	Front	AC Delco Dual Piston
		Rear	AC Delco Single Piston Type 3
Eighty-Eight	1992-94	Front	Delco-Moraine Single Piston Type 2
Ninety-Eight	1992-94	Front	AC Delco Single Piston Type 2

Model	Year	Front/Rear Brakes	Application
OLDSMOBILE -Continued			
Toronado	1992	Front	AC Delco Single Piston Type 3
		Rear	AC Delco Single Piston Type 4
Trofeo	1992	Front	AC Delco Single Piston Type 3
		Rear	AC Delco Single Piston Type 4
PONTIAC			
Bonneville	1992-94	Front	AC Delco Single Piston Type 2
Firebird	1992	Front (Standard)	AC Delco Single Piston Type 1
		Front (Optional)	PBR Dual Piston
	1993-94	Front	AC Delco Single Piston Type 2
	1992-94	Rear	PBR Single Piston
Grand Am	1992-94	Front	AC Delco Single Piston Type 2
Grand Prix	1992-94	Front	AC Delco Dual Piston
	1992-94	Rear	AC Delco Single Piston Type 3
LeMans	1992-93	Front	DAEWOO Single Piston
Sunbird	1992-94	Front	AC Delco Single Piston Type 2

Aisin-Seiki Single Piston Front Disc Brake (Type 1)

INDEX

PRECAUTIONS

1. Grease or any other foreign material must be kept off the brake linings, caliper, surfaces of the disc and external surfaces of the hub, during service procedures. Handling the brake disc and caliper should be done in a way to avoid deformation of the disc and nicking or scratching brake linings.
2. If inspection reveals rubber piston seals are worn or damaged, they should be replaced immediately.
3. During removal and installation of a wheel assembly, exercise care so as not to interfere with or damage the caliper splash shield, or bleeder screw.
4. Front wheel bearings preload should be adjusted to specifications .
5. Be sure vehicle is centered on hoist before servicing any of the front end components to avoid bending or damaging the disc splash shield on full right or left wheel turns.
6. Before the vehicle is moved after any brake service work, be sure to obtain a firm brake pedal.
7. The assembly bolts of two piece caliper housings should not be disturbed unless the caliper requires service.

DESCRIPTION

This single piston sliding caliper assembly, **Fig. 1 and 2**, is mounted to a support bracket by two slide pins. The caliper assembly slides on the two mounting pins. Upon brake application, fluid pressure against the piston forces the inboard shoe and lining assembly against the inboard side of the disc. This action causes the caliper assembly to slide until the outboard lining comes into contact with the disc.

TROUBLESHOOTING

BRAKE ROUGHNESS

The most common cause of brake chatter on disc brakes is a variation in thickness of the disc. If roughness or vibration is encountered during highway operation or if pedal pulsation is experienced at low speeds, the disc may have excessive thickness variation. To check for this con-

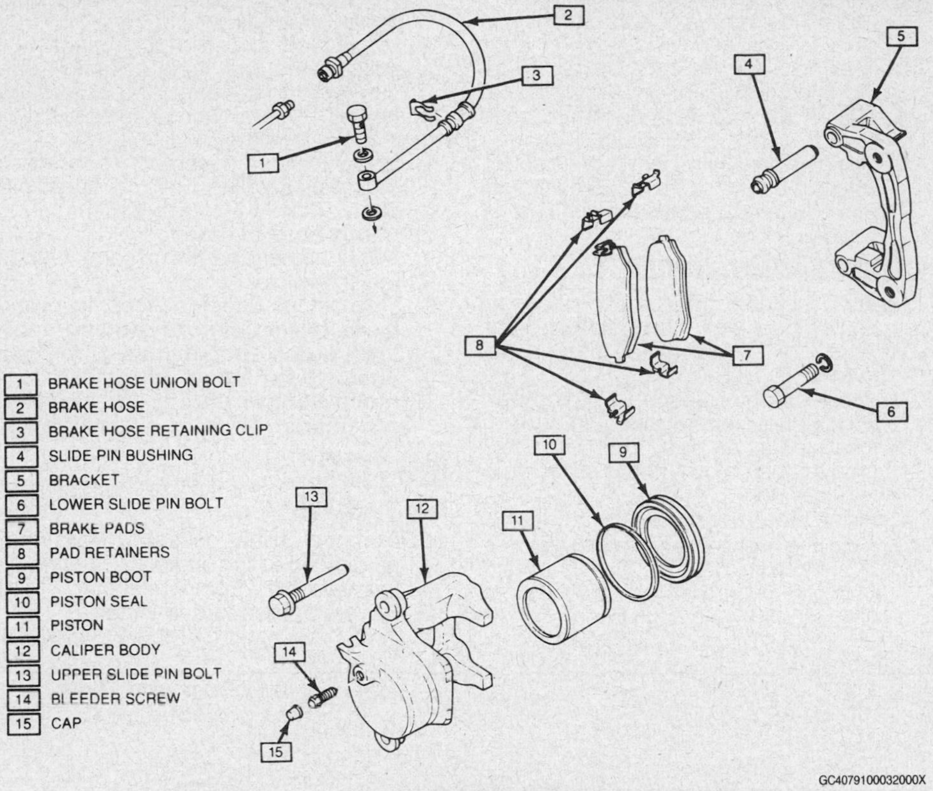
1 BRAKE HOSE UNION BOLT
2 BRAKE HOSE
3 BRAKE HOSE RETAINING CLIP
4 SLIDE PIN BUSHING
5 BRACKET
6 LOWER SLIDE PIN BOLT
7 BRAKE PADS
8 PAD RETAINERS
9 PISTON BOOT
10 PISTON SEAL
11 PISTON
12 CALIPER BODY
13 UPPER SLIDE PIN BOLT
14 BLEEDER SCREW
15 CAP
GC4079100032000X

Fig. 1 Exploded view of disc brake caliper assembly. Metro except convertible

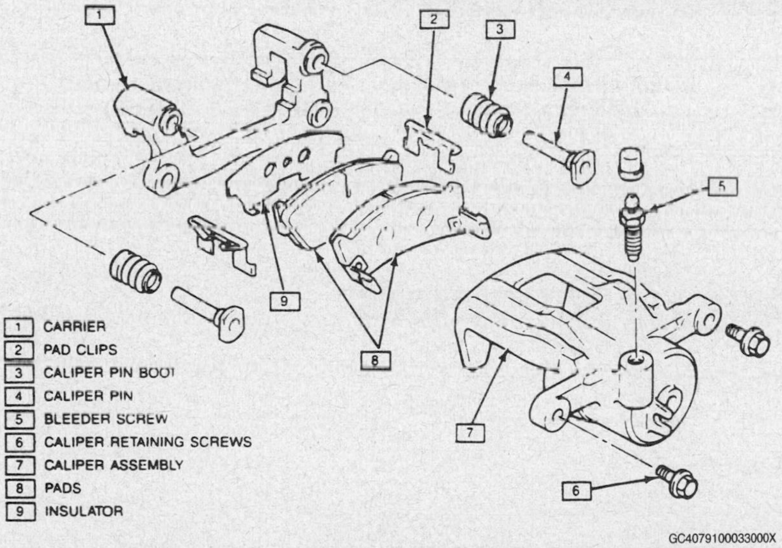
1 CARRIER
2 PAD CLIPS
3 CALIPER PIN BOOT
4 CALIPER PIN
5 BLEEDER SCREW
6 CALIPER RETAINING SCREWS
7 CALIPER ASSEMBLY
8 PADS
9 INSULATOR
GC4079100033000X

Fig. 2 Exploded view of disc brake caliper assembly. Metro convertible

dition, measure the disc at 12 points with a micrometer at a radius approximately one inch from edge of disc. If thickness measurements vary by more than .0005 inch, the disc should be replaced with a new one.

Excessive lateral runout of braking disc may cause a "knocking back" of the pistons, possibly creating increased pedal travel and vibration when brakes are applied.

Before checking the runout, wheel bearings should be adjusted. The readjustment is very important and will be required at the completion of the test to prevent bearing failure. Be sure to make the adjustment according to the recommendations given under "Front Wheel Bearings, Adjust" in the car chapters.

BRAKE SYSTEM BLEED

Pressure bleeding is recommended for all hydraulic disc brake systems.

The disc brake hydraulic system can be bled manually or with pressure bleeding equipment. The brake pedal will require pumping and frequent checking of fluid level in master cylinder during bleeding operation.

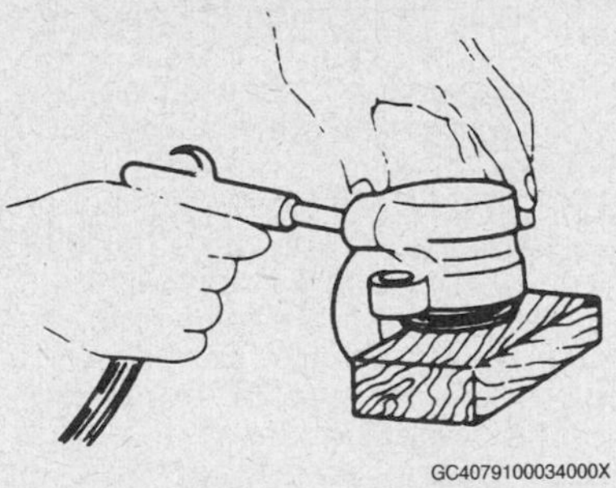
GC4079100034000X

Fig. 3 Caliper piston removal

Never use brake fluid that has been drained from hydraulic system when bleeding the brakes. Be sure the disc brake pistons are returned to their normal positions and that the shoe and lining assemblies are properly seated. Before driving the vehicle, check brake operation to be sure that a firm pedal has been obtained.

BRAKE PAD SERVICE

1. Remove approximately 2/3 of brake fluid from master cylinder.
2. Raise and support vehicle.
3. Mark relationship between front wheel and axle, then remove wheel and tire assembly.
4. Remove 2 caliper slide pins from bracket.
5. Unfasten caliper, and support with a length of wire, leaving hydraulic lines connected.
6. Remove brake pads, shims, wear indicators and retainers, **Figs. 1 and 2.**
7. Reverse procedure to install.

CALIPER SERVICE

CALIPER REMOVAL

1. Disconnect negative battery cable.
2. Remove approximately 2/3 of brake fluid from master cylinder.
3. Raise and support vehicle.
4. Mark relationship between front wheel and axle, then remove wheel and tire assembly.
5. If caliper assembly is to be serviced, remove inlet fitting attaching bolt, copper washer, and inlet fitting from caliper housing. Plug opening in inlet fitting to prevent fluid loss and contamination. **Do not crimp brake hose, as this may damage internal structure of hose. If only shoe and lining assemblies are to be replaced, do not disconnect brake line fitting from caliper.**
6. Remove caliper slide pins and the caliper. If only shoe and lining assemblies are to be replaced, suspend caliper from chassis using suitable hanger. **Do not allow caliper to hang by brake hose.**
7. Remove shoe and lining assembly.
8. Remove bracket attaching bolts and the bracket.
9. Remove slide pin boot from bracket.

CALIPER DISASSEMBLY

1. Remove caliper assembly as outlined previously, then drain brake fluid from caliper.
2. Use clean shop towels to pad interior of caliper assembly, then remove piston by directing compressed air into caliper brake hose inlet hole, **Fig. 3. Use just enough air pressure to ease piston out of bore. Do not place fingers in front of piston for any reason when applying compressed air. This could result in serious personal injury.**
3. Remove dust boot from piston.
4. Using a small piece of wood or plastic, remove piston seal from bore. **Do not use a metal tool of any kind to remove seal as it may damage bore.**
5. Remove bleeder valve.
6. Inspect piston for scoring, nicks, corrosion, and wear and replace as needed.
7. Inspect caliper housing and seal groove for corrosion, nicks, scoring and excessive wear, and use crocus cloth to polish away corrosion from housing bore. Replace caliper housing if corrosion in and around seal groove will not clean up with crocus cloth.
8. Clean all parts with denatured alcohol. Dry with unlubricated compressed air. Blow out all passages in housing and bleeder valve.

CALIPER ASSEMBLY

1. Apply suitable grease to piston seal and cylinder wall, then install the seal. Check to ensure piston seal is not twisted.
2. Apply suitable grease to sliding portion of piston and install dust boot.
3. Insert edge of dust boot into boot groove, then slowly force piston fully into cylinder.
4. Install bleeder valve.

CALIPER INSTALLATION

1. Apply suitable grease to inner face of slide pin boot.
2. Install slide pin boot to bracket.
3. Install bracket and attaching bolts.
4. Install shoe and lining assembly, ensure wear indicators are located on trailing edge of shoe assemblies during forward wheel rotation.
5. Install caliper assembly to bracket. Tighten attaching bolts to specifications.
6. Attach hose to caliper.
7. Install wheel and tire assembly, then lower vehicle.
8. Fill master cylinder to proper level and bleed brakes. **Before moving vehicle, pump brake pedal several times to be sure it is firm. Do not move vehicle until a firm pedal is obtained.**

ROTOR

REPLACE

1. Remove caliper assembly from rotor as described in "Brake Pad Service."
2. Remove rotor from wheel hub.
3. Reverse procedure to install.

DISC BRAKE SPECIFICATIONS

ROTOR SPECIFICATIONS

Model	Year	Nominal Thickness	Minimum Refinish Thickness	Thickness Variation (Parallelism)	Lateral Runout (T.I.R.)
Storm	1992-93	.866	.811	.0005	.005

TIGHTENING SPECIFICATIONS

Component	Torque/Ft. Lbs.
Bleeder Valve	89①
Brake Hose Union Bolt	14
Brake Pipe Fittings	113①
Caliper Mounting Bracket	76
Caliper Mounting Slide Pins	36

①—Inch Lbs.

Aisin-Seiki Single Piston Front Disc Brake (Type 2)

INDEX

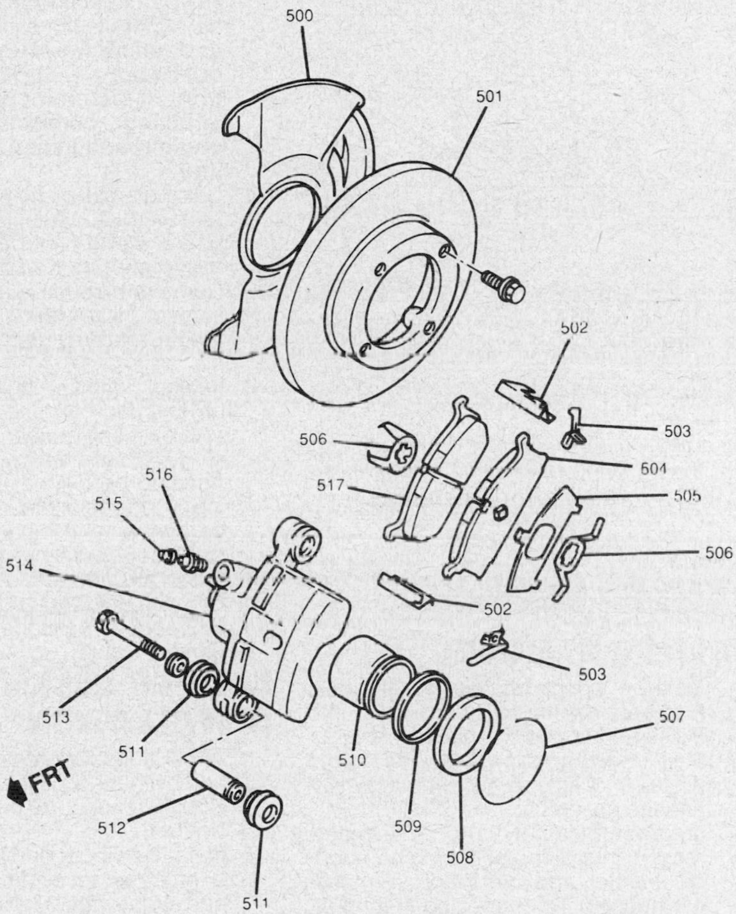

500
501
502
503
506
516
515
517
504
505
506
514
502
503
513
511
510
507
509
508
512
511
FRT

500	DISC BRAKE BACKING PLATE	509	PISTON SEAL
501	DISC BRAKE ROTOR	510	PISTON
502	BRAKE-TO-KNUCKLE CLIP	511	BUSHING BOOT
503	ANTI-RATTLE SPRING	512	SLIDE BUSHING
504	OUTBOARD BRAKE PAD	513	CALIPER MOUNTING BOLT (ONE OF TWO)
505	OUTER SHIM	514	CALIPER
506	CENTER RETAINING CLIP	515	VALVE CAP
507	PISTON BOOT RETAINING RING	516	BLEEDER VALVE
508	PISTON BOOT	517	INBOARD BRAKE PAD

GC4079100035000X

Fig. 1 Exploded view of brake caliper

PRECAUTIONS

1. Grease or any other foreign material must be kept off the brake linings, caliper, surfaces of the disc and external surfaces of the hub, during service procedures. Handling the brake disc and caliper should be done in a way to avoid deformation of the disc and nicking or scratching brake linings.
2. If inspection reveals rubber piston seals are worn or damaged, they should be replaced immediately.
3. During removal and installation of a wheel assembly, exercise care so as not to interfere with or damage the caliper splash shield, or bleeder screw.
4. Front wheel bearings preload should be adjusted to specifications .
5. Be sure vehicle is centered on hoist before servicing any of the front end components to avoid bending or damaging the disc splash shield on full right or left wheel turns.
6. Before the vehicle is moved after any brake service work, be sure to obtain a firm brake pedal.
7. The assembly bolts of two piece caliper housings should not be disturbed unless the caliper requires service.

DESCRIPTION

This single piston sliding caliper assembly, **Fig. 1**, is mounted to a support bracket by two slide pins. The caliper assembly slides on the two mounting pins. Upon brake application, fluid pressure against the piston forces the inboard shoe and lining assembly against the inboard side of the disc. This action causes the caliper assembly to slide until the outboard lining comes into contact with the disc.

TROUBLESHOOTING

BRAKE ROUGHNESS

The most common cause of brake chatter on disc brakes is a variation in thickness of the disc. If roughness or vibration is encountered during highway operation or if pedal pulsation is experienced at low speeds, the disc may have excessive thickness variation. To check for this condition, measure the disc at 12 points with

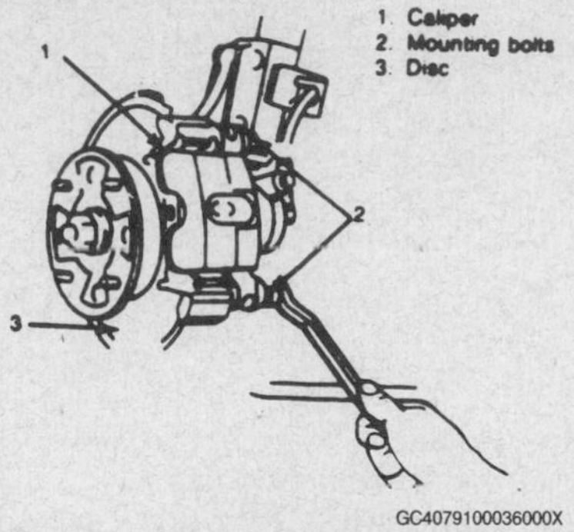
1. Caliper
2. Mounting bolts
3. Disc
GC4079100036000X

Fig. 2 Caliper mounting bolts removal

a micrometer at a radius approximately one inch from edge of disc. If thickness measurements vary by more than .0005 inch, the disc should be replaced with a new one.

Excessive lateral runout of braking disc may cause a "knocking back" of the pistons, possibly creating increased pedal travel and vibration when brakes are applied.

Before checking the runout, wheel bearings should be adjusted. The readjustment is very important and will be required at the completion of the test to prevent bearing failure. Be sure to make the adjustment according to the recommendations given under "Front Wheel Bearings, Adjust" in the car chapters.

BRAKE SYSTEM BLEED

Pressure bleeding is recommended for all hydraulic disc brake systems.

The disc brake hydraulic system can be bled manually or with pressure bleeding equipment. The brake pedal will require pumping and frequent checking of fluid level in master cylinder during bleeding operation.

Never use brake fluid that has been drained from hydraulic system when bleeding the brakes. Be sure the disc brake pistons are returned to their normal positions and that the shoe and lining assemblies are properly seated. Before driving the vehicle, check brake operation to be sure that a firm pedal has been obtained.

BRAKE PAD SERVICE

1. Raise and support vehicle and remove wheel.
2. Remove caliper mounting bolts, **Fig. 2.**
3. Remove caliper from knuckle, taking care not to drop inside pad. If only shoe and lining assemblies are to be replaced, suspend caliper from chassis using suitable hanger. **Do not allow caliper to hang by brake hose.**
4. Remove outside pad.
5. Install pad clips, No. 1 & 2, then outside pad to knuckle, **Fig. 3.**
6. Install caliper and inside pad to knuckle, **Fig. 4.** Position outer springs over caliper as shown.
7. Tighten caliper bolts to specifications.
8. Install front wheel.
9. Lower vehicle and perform brake test.

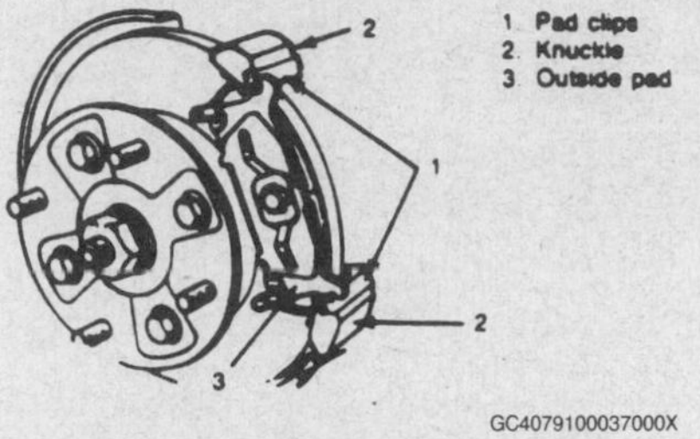
1. Pad clips
2. Knuckle
3. Outside pad
GC4079100037000X

Fig. 3 Outside pad installation

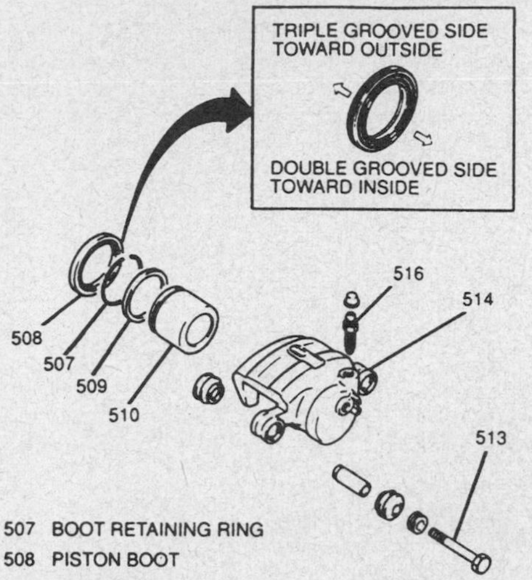
TRIPLE GROOVED SIDE TOWARD OUTSIDE
DOUBLE GROOVED SIDE TOWARD INSIDE
516
514
508
507
509
510
513

507 BOOT RETAINING RING
508 PISTON BOOT
509 PISTON SEAL
510 PISTON
513 CALIPER MOUNTING BOLT
514 CALIPER
516 BLEEDER VALVE

GC4079100039000X

Fig. 5 Caliper boot installation

CALIPER SERVICE

CALIPER REMOVAL

1. Remove approximately 2/3 of brake fluid from master cylinder.
2. Raise and support vehicle.
3. Mark relationship between front wheel and axle, then remove wheel and tire assembly.
4. If caliper assembly is to be serviced, remove inlet fitting attaching bolt, copper washer, and inlet fitting from caliper housing. Plug opening in inlet fitting to prevent fluid loss and contamination. **Do not crimp brake hose, as this may damage internal structure of hose. If only shoe and lining assemblies are to be replaced, do not disconnect brake line fitting from caliper.**
5. Remove caliper mounting bolts.
6. Remove caliper from knuckle. **Be careful not to drop inside pad which will come off with caliper.**

CALIPER DISASSEMBLY

1. Remove caliper assembly as outlined previously, then drain brake fluid from caliper.

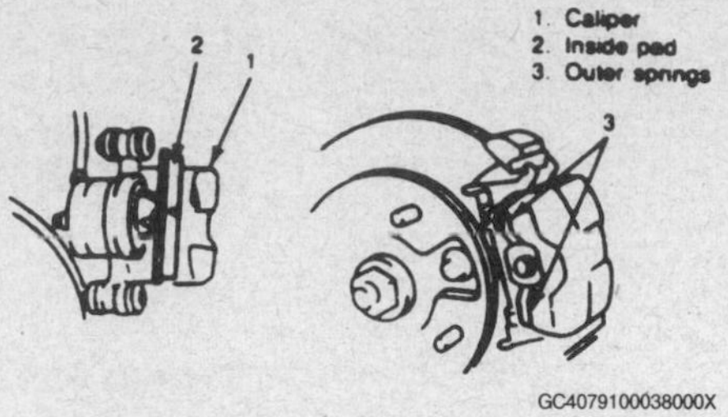
1. Caliper
2. Inside pad
3. Outer springs
GC4079100038000X

Fig. 4 Inside pad & caliper installation

2. Remove cylinder boot set ring and boot from cylinder groove, **Fig. 1.**
3. Use clean shop towels to pad interior of caliper assembly, then remove piston by directing compressed air into caliper brake hose inlet hole. **Use just enough air pressure to ease piston out of bore. Do not place fingers in front of piston for any reason when applying compressed air. This could result in serious personal injury.**
4. Using a small piece of wood or plastic, remove piston seal from bore. **Do not use a metal tool of any kind to remove seal as it may damage bore.**
5. Remove bleeder valve.
6. Inspect piston for scoring, nicks, corrosion, and wear and replace as needed.
7. Inspect caliper housing and seal groove for corrosion, nicks, scoring and excessive wear, and use crocus cloth to polish away corrosion from housing bore. Replace caliper housing if corrosion in and around seal groove will not clean up with crocus cloth.
8. Clean all parts with denatured alcohol. Dry with unlubricated compressed air. Blow out all passages in housing and bleeder valve.

CALIPER ASSEMBLY & INSTALLATION

1. Apply suitable grease to piston seal and cylinder wall, then install the seal. Check to ensure piston seal is not twisted.
2. Install new boot on piston so side with 2 grooves faces in toward cylinder and side with 3 grooves faces out, **Fig. 5.**
3. Install piston in caliper so it projects about .4 inch to ease installation of boot on caliper housing. Install boot on caliper housing, then install set ring.
4. Install bleeder valve.
5. Check that caliper slide bushings are lubricated with rubber grease. Check that slide bushing in each carrier hole can be moved smoothly in each direction.
6. Install caliper and inside pad on knuckle.
7. Tighten caliper bolts.
8. Connect brake hose, then bleed hydraulic system.
9. Install wheel.

10. Lower vehicle and test brakes. **Before moving vehicle, pump brake pedal several times to be sure it is firm. Do not move vehicle until a firm pedal is obtained.**

ROTOR

REPLACE

1. Remove caliper assembly from rotor as described in "Brake Pad Service."
2. Remove rotor from wheel hub.
3. Reverse procedure to install.

DISC BRAKE SPECIFICATIONS

ROTOR SPECIFICATIONS

Model	Year	Nominal Thickness	Minimum Refinish Thickness	Maximum Lateral Runout	Maximum Scoring Depth	Maximum Thickness Variation
Metro	1992-94	.394	.315	.004	.015	.0005

TIGHTENING SPECIFICATIONS

Component	Torque/Ft. Lbs.
Bleeder Valves	89①
Backing Plate Bolts	17
Caliper Mounting Bolts	22
Spindle Nut	129
Union Bolt	17

①—Inch Lbs.

Daewoo Single Piston Front Disc Brake

INDEX

PRECAUTIONS

1. Grease or any other foreign material must be kept off the brake linings, caliper, surfaces of the disc and external surfaces of the hub, during service procedures. Handling the brake disc and caliper should be done in a way to avoid deformation of the disc and nicking or scratching brake linings.
2. If inspection reveals rubber piston seals are worn or damaged, they should be replaced immediately.
3. During removal and installation of a wheel assembly, exercise care so as not to interfere with or damage the caliper splash shield, or bleeder screw.
4. Front wheel bearings preload should be adjusted to specifications .
5. Be sure vehicle is centered on hoist before servicing any of the front end components to avoid bending or damaging the disc splash shield on full right or left wheel turns.
6. Before the vehicle is moved after any brake service work, be sure to obtain a firm brake pedal.
7. The assembly bolts of two piece caliper housings should not be disturbed unless the caliper requires service.

DESCRIPTION

This caliper has a single bore, **Fig. 1**, and is mounted to the steering knuckle with two mounting bolts. Upon brake application, hydraulic pressure is converted by the caliper to stopping force. This force acts equally against the piston and the bottom of the caliper bore to move the piston outward and to slide the caliper inward resulting in a clamping action on the rotor. This clamping action forces the lining against the rotor, creating friction to stop the vehicle.

TROUBLESHOOTING

BRAKE ROUGHNESS

The most common cause of brake chatter on disc brakes is a variation in thickness of the disc. If roughness or vibration is encountered during highway operation

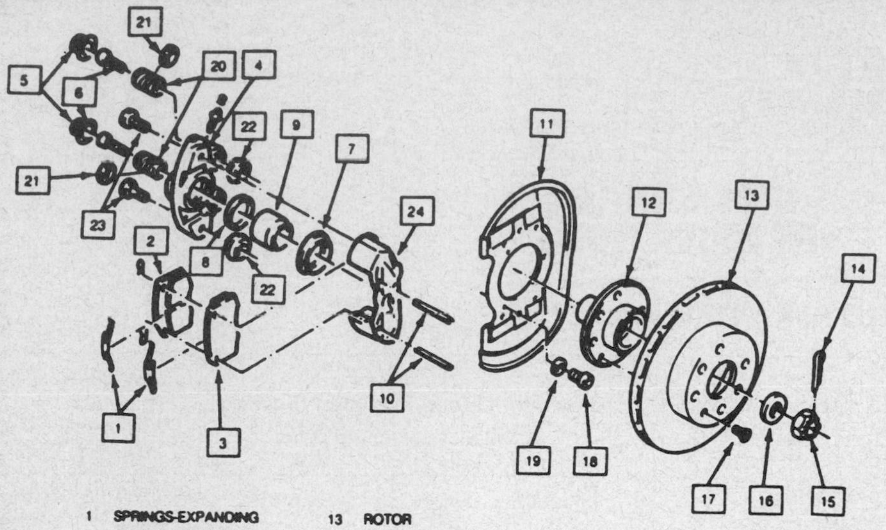

1 SPRINGS-EXPANDING
2 SHOE-INBOARD
3 SHOE-OUTBOARD
4 HOUSING-CALIPER
5 CAP-BLEEDER VALVE
6 VALVE-BLEEDER
7 BOOT-PISTON
8 SEAL-PISTON
9 PISTON-CALIPER
10 PINS-RETAINING
11 SHIELD
12 HUB-WHEEL
13 ROTOR
14 PIN-COTTER
15 NUT-WHEEL HUB
16 WASHER-WHEEL HUB
17 SCREW-DETENT
18 SCREW-SHIELD
19 WASHER-SHIELD
20 PLUG-BLEEDER VALVE
21 WASHER-BLEEDER VALVE
22 SPACER-CALIPER HOUSING
23 BOLT-CALIPER HOUSING
24 RETAINING FRAME

GC4079100040000X

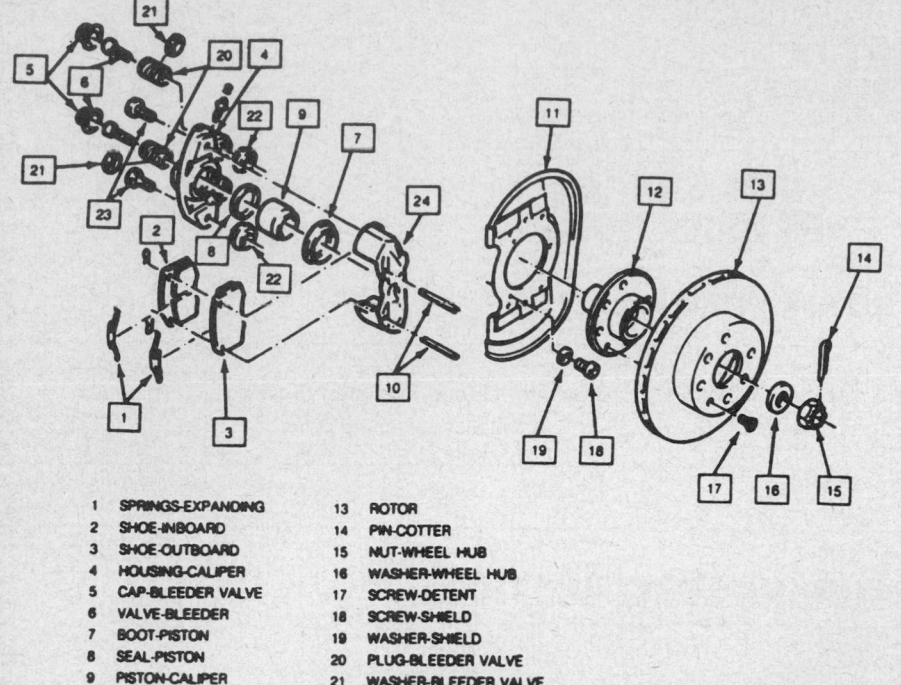

Fig. 1 Exploded view of brake caliper assembly

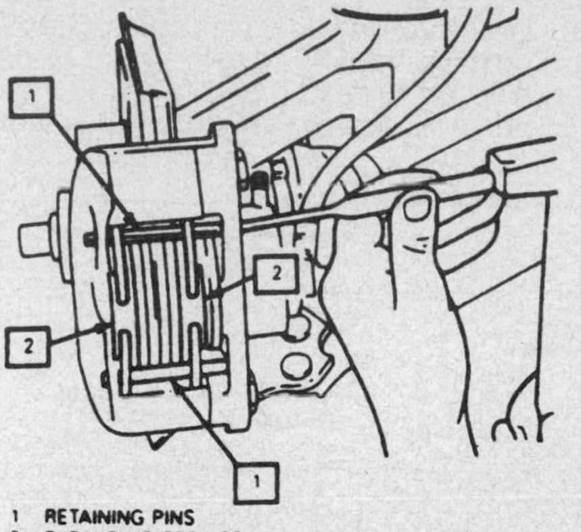

1 RETAINING PINS
2 EXPANDING SPRINGS

GC4079100041000X

Fig. 2 Brake pad retaining pin removal

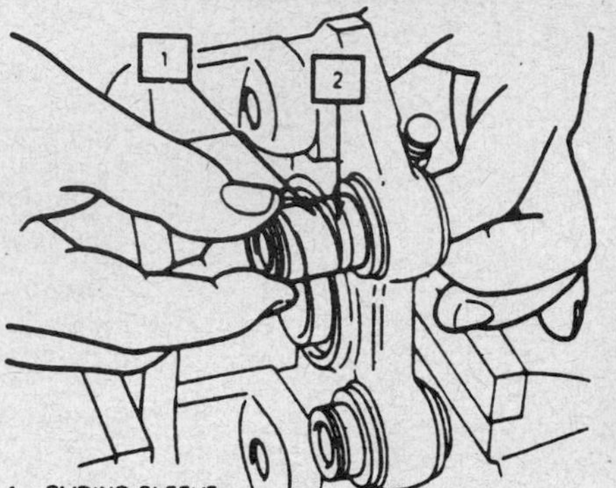

1 SLIDING SLEEVE
2 SEAL

GC4079100042000X

Fig. 3 Caliper sliding sleeve removal

or if pedal pulsation is experienced at low speeds, the disc may have excessive thickness variation. To check for this condition, measure the disc at 12 points with a micrometer at a radius approximately one inch from edge of disc. If thickness measurements vary by more than .0005 inch, the disc should be replaced with a new one.

Excessive lateral runout of braking disc may cause a "knocking back" of the pistons, possibly creating increased pedal travel and vibration when brakes are applied.

Before checking the runout, wheel bearings should be adjusted. The readjustment is very important and will be required at the completion of the test to prevent bearing failure. Be sure to make the adjustment according to the recommendations given under "Front Wheel Bearings, Adjust" in the car chapters.

BRAKE SYSTEM BLEED

Pressure bleeding is recommended for all hydraulic disc brake systems.

The disc brake hydraulic system can be bled manually or with pressure bleeding equipment. **On vehicles with disc brakes** the brake pedal will require more pumping and frequent checking of fluid level in master cylinder during bleeding operation.

Never use brake fluid that has been drained from hydraulic system when bleeding the brakes. Be sure the disc brake pistons are returned to their normal positions and that the shoe and lining assemblies are properly seated. Before driving the vehicle, check brake operation to be sure that a firm pedal has been obtained.

BRAKE PAD SERVICE

Caliper removal is not required to replace shoe and linings.

1. Remove approximately 2/3 of brake fluid from master cylinder.
2. Raise and support vehicle.
3. Mark relationship between front wheel and hub, then remove wheel and tire assembly.
4. Carefully drive pad retaining pins from inside out, **Fig. 2.**
5. Bottom piston into caliper bore using suitable pliers, then remove brake pads.
6. Reverse procedure to install, noting the following:
   a. Install brake pads with wear sensor to the piston side.
   b. Ensure pads can be moved back and forth slightly when installed.
   c. Install retaining pins from outside in, ensuring openings align.
   d. Upon completion of installation, lower vehicle and pump brake pedal several times to properly position brake pads.

CALIPER SERVICE

CALIPER, REPLACE

1. Remove approximately 2/3 of brake fluid from master cylinder.
2. Raise and support vehicle.
3. Mark relationship between front wheel and hub, then remove wheel and tire assembly.
4. Bottom piston into caliper bore using suitable pliers to provide clearance between brake pads and rotor.
5. Disconnect brake hose from caliper. Plug openings in brake hose and caliper to prevent leakage and contamination. **Do not crimp brake hose, as this may damage internal structure of hose.**
6. Remove outer protective caps from caliper housing seats.
7. Remove caliper attaching bolts, and the caliper.
8. Reverse procedure to install, noting the following:
   a. Original equipment caliper attaching bolts are micro-encapsulated. After removal of these bolts, threads in steering knuckle must be re-cut using a M12 X 1.5 thread tap.
   b. Install new caliper attaching bolts not micro-encapsulated and tighten to specification.
   c. Install brake hose inlet fitting attaching bolt.
   d. Install new outer protective caps. Ensure caps seat evenly on caliper.
   e. Upon completion of installation, bleed hydraulic system, then lower vehicle. **Before moving vehicle, pump brake pedal several times to be sure it is firm. Do not move vehicle until a firm pedal is obtained.**

CALIPER DISASSEMBLE

1. Remove caliper and brake pads as previously described.
2. Remove inner protective caps for sliding sleeves.
3. Remove piston boot from housing.
4. Move sliding sleeve slightly toward protective cap and remove cap from groove in sleeve.
5. Remove boot from piston and housing.
6. Press sliding sleeves out of housing, **Fig. 3,** then remove seals using a suitable wood or plastic tool.
7. Clean outside of caliper, then drain brake fluid from caliper.
8. Use clean shop towels to pad interior of caliper assembly, then remove piston by directing compressed air into caliper brake hose inlet hole, **Use just enough air pressure to ease piston out of bore. Do not place fingers in front of piston for any reason when applying compressed air. This could result in serious personal injury.**
9. Secure caliper assembly in a suitable vise, then remove caliper retaining frame attaching bolts and the frame.
10. Remove piston seal from groove in caliper bore using a suitable wood or plastic tool. **Do not use a metal tool of any kind to remove seal as it may damage bore.**
11. Remove bleeder valve from caliper.
12. Inspect piston for scoring, nicks, corrosion, and wear and replace as needed.
13. Inspect caliper housing and seal groove for corrosion, nicks, scoring and excessive wear, and use crocus cloth to polish away corrosion from housing bore. Replace caliper housing if corrosion in and around seal groove will not clean up with crocus cloth.
14. Clean all parts with denatured alcohol. Dry with unlubricated compressed air. Blow out all passages in housing and bleeder valve.

CALIPER ASSEMBLE

1. Lubricate, then install new piston seal into caliper bore. Ensure seal is not twisted.
2. Install lubricated piston into caliper bore, ensuring piston does not jam and piston seal is properly seated. **Leave piston exposed enough to permit installation of boot in groove.**
3. Position boot in piston groove and press onto caliper housing. Seat boot using dust boot seal installer tool No. J36538 or equivalent.
4. Install caliper retaining frame, tighten attaching bolts to specifications.
5. Apply suitable grease to sliding sleeves, then install seals in center groove of sliding sleeves.
6. Position sliding sleeves in caliper with inner protective cap groove facing piston. **Leave sleeves exposed enough to permit installation of protective caps.**
7. Install new protective caps into sliding sleeve grooves and press onto caliper housing collar. Seat caps using sliding sleeve dust boot installer tool No. J36647 or equivalent.
8. Push sliding sleeves into housing, then install bleeder valve.
9. Install brake pads and caliper as previously described. Bleed hydraulic system, **Before moving vehicle, pump brake pedal several times to be sure it is firm. Do not move vehicle until a firm pedal is obtained.**

ROTOR

REPLACE

1. Remove caliper assembly from rotor as described in "Brake Pad Service."
2. Remove detent screw from rotor.
3. Remove rotor from wheel hub.
4. Reverse procedure to install.

DISC BRAKE SPECIFICATIONS

ROTOR SPECIFICATIONS

Model	Year	Nominal Thickness	Minimum Refinish Thickness	Thickness Variation (Parallelism)	Lateral Runout (T.I.R.)
LeMans	1992-93	.94	.83	.0004	.004

TIGHTENING SPECIFICATIONS

Component	Torque/Ft. Lbs.
Brake Hose To Caliper	29
Caliper Bleeder Screw	80 ①
Caliper To Steering Knuckle	70
Rotor To Front Wheel Hub	35 ①
Wheel Lug Nuts	66

①—Inch Lbs.

AC-Delco Single Piston Front Disc Brake (Type 1)

INDEX

PRECAUTIONS

1. Grease or any other foreign material must be kept off the brake linings, caliper, surfaces of the disc and external surfaces of the hub, during service procedures. Handling the brake disc and caliper should be done in a way to avoid deformation of the disc and nicking or scratching brake linings.
2. If inspection reveals rubber piston seals are worn or damaged, they should be replaced immediately.
3. During removal and installation of a wheel assembly, exercise care so as not to interfere with or damage the caliper splash shield, or bleeder screw.
4. Front wheel bearings preload should be adjusted to specifications .
5. Be sure vehicle is centered on hoist before servicing any of the front end components to avoid bending or damaging the disc splash shield on full right or left wheel turns.
6. Before the vehicle is moved after any brake service work, be sure to obtain a firm brake pedal.
7. The assembly bolts of two piece caliper housings should not be disturbed unless the caliper requires service.

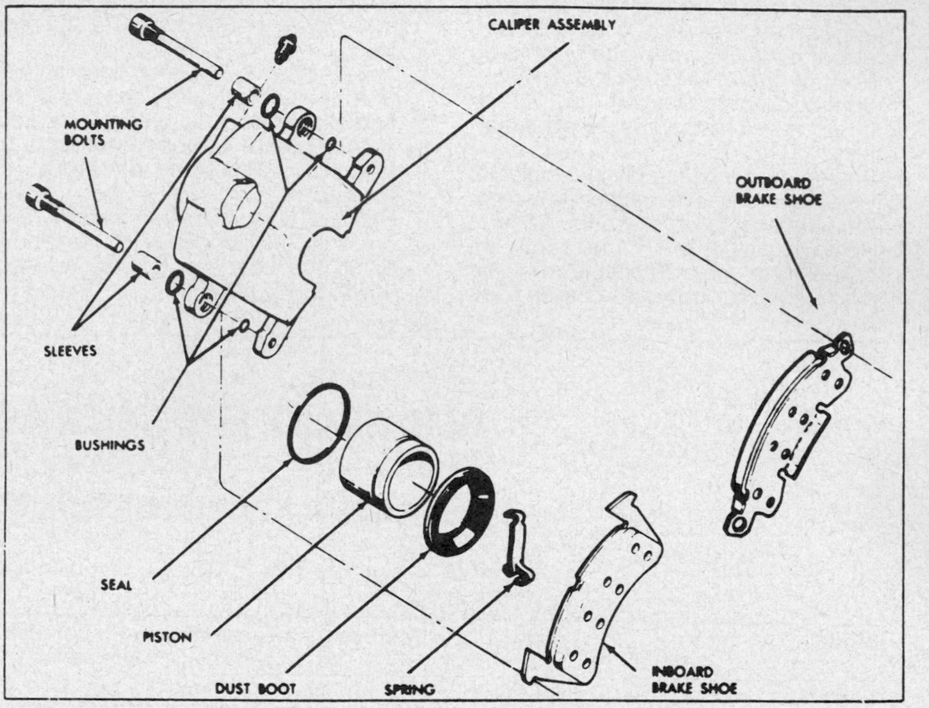
CALIPER ASSEMBLY
MOUNTING BOLTS
OUTBOARD BRAKE SHOE
SLEEVES
BUSHINGS
SEAL
PISTON
DUST BOOT
SPRING
INBOARD BRAKE SHOE

GC4079100043000X

Fig. 1 Typical AC-Delco 3000/3075/3100 series caliper exploded view

DESCRIPTION

This single piston sliding caliper assembly, **Fig. 1,** incorporates a one piece housing with the inboard side of the housing bored for the piston. A seal within the housing bore provides a hydraulic seal between the piston and housing wall.

A spring steel scraper (wear sensor) is incorporated on each inboard shoe. When the shoe lining has worn to within .030 inch of the shoe, the sensor scrapes the rotor and emits an audible high frequency sound indicating that the linings should be replaced.

The caliper assembly slides on the mounting bolts. Upon brake application, fluid pressure against the piston forces the inboard shoe and lining assembly against the inboard side of the disc. This action causes the caliper assembly to slide until the outboard lining comes into contact with the disc. As pressure builds up, the linings are pressed against the disc with increased force.

TROUBLESHOOTING

BRAKE ROUGHNESS

The most common cause of brake chatter on disc brakes is a variation in thickness of the disc. If roughness or vibration is encountered during highway operation or if pedal pulsation is experienced at low speeds, the disc may have excessive thickness variation. To check for this condition, measure the disc at 12 points with a micrometer at a radius approximately one inch from edge of disc. If thickness measurements vary by more than .0005 inch, the disc should be replaced with a new one.

Excessive lateral runout of braking disc may cause a "knocking back" of the pistons, possibly creating increased pedal travel and vibration when brakes are applied.

Before checking the runout, wheel bearings should be adjusted. The readjustment is very important and will be required at the completion of the test to prevent bearing failure. Be sure to make the adjustment according to the recommendations given under "Front Wheel Bearings, Adjust" in the car chapters.

BRAKE SYSTEM BLEED

Pressure bleeding is recommended for all hydraulic disc brake systems.

The disc brake hydraulic system can be bled manually or with pressure bleeding equipment. **On vehicles with disc brakes** the brake pedal will require more pumping and frequent checking of fluid level in master cylinder during bleeding operation.

Never use brake fluid that has been drained from hydraulic system when bleeding the brakes. Be sure the disc brake pistons are returned to their normal positions and that the shoe and lining as-

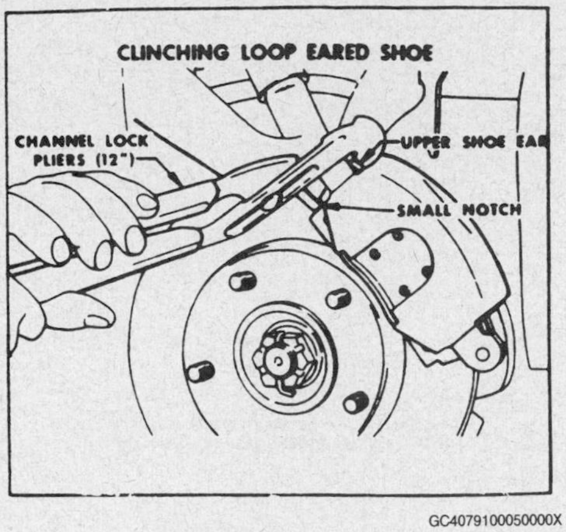
CLINCHING LOOP EARED SHOE
CHANNEL LOCK PLIERS (12")
UPPER SHOE EAR
SMALL NOTCH
GC4079100050000X

Fig. 2 Clinching loop eared brake shoe

semblies are properly seated. Before driving the vehicle, check brake operation to be sure that a firm pedal has been obtained.

BRAKE PAD SERVICE

REMOVAL

1. Remove caliper assembly from steering knuckle as described in "Caliper Removal" under "Caliper Service."
2. Remove inboard shoe. Dislodge outboard shoe and position caliper on the front suspension so the brake hose will not support the weight of the caliper.
3. Remove shoe support spring from piston.
4. Remove two sleeves from inboard ears of the caliper.
5. Remove four rubber bushings from the grooves in each of the caliper ears.

INSTALLATION

1. Lubricate new sleeves, rubber bushings, bushing grooves and mounting bolt ends with Delco Silicone Lube or its equivalent.
2. Install new bushings and sleeves in caliper ears. **Position the sleeve so that the end toward the shoe is flush with the machined surface of the ear.**
3. Install shoe support spring by positioning single tang end of spring into notch cut at top of inboard shoe. Press remaining end of spring over bottom edge of shoe until shoe is engaged securely.
4. Position inboard shoe with spring attached into caliper with ear end facing downward and bottom end facing upward with spring resting on inside diameter of piston. Press downward on both ends of shoe until shoe contacts piston and support spring contacts piston inside diameter. **Some inboard replacement brake pads incorporate wear sensors and have a specific left and righthand assembly. Properly installed, the wear sensor will face toward the rear of caliper.**

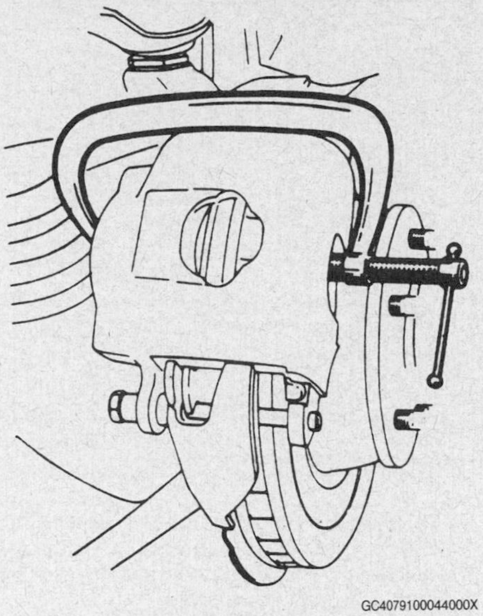
GC4079100044000X

Fig. 3 Compressing piston and shoes w/C-clamp

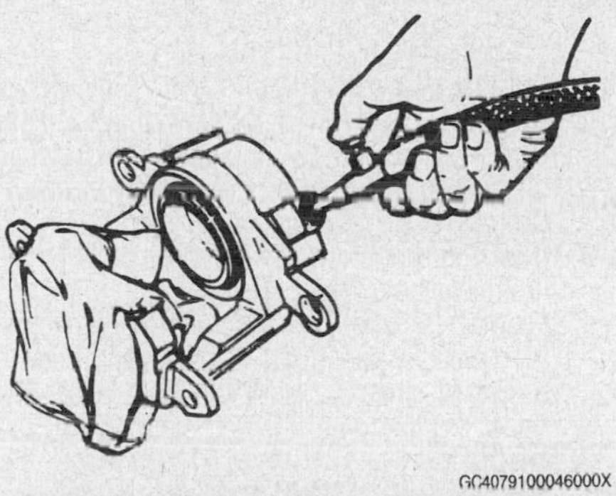
GC4079100046000X

Fig. 5 Caliper piston removal

5. Position outboard shoe in caliper with shoe ears over caliper ears and tab at bottom of shoe engaged in caliper cutout.
6. With shoes installed, lift caliper and rest bottom edge of outboard lining on outer edge of brake disc to be sure there is no clearance between outboard shoe tab and caliper abutment.
7. Install caliper and tighten mounting bolts to specifications.
8. Clinch upper ears of outboard shoe by positioning pliers with one jaw on top of upper ear and one jaw in notch on bottom shoe opposite ear, **Fig. 2.** Ears are to be flat against caliper housing with no radial clearance. If clearance exists, repeat clinching procedure. **Before moving vehicle, pump brake pedal several times to be sure it is firm. Do not move vehicle until a firm pedal is obtained. On some models with low drag calipers, apply approximately 175 pounds of pressure to the brake pedal three times to properly seat the caliper and related components.**

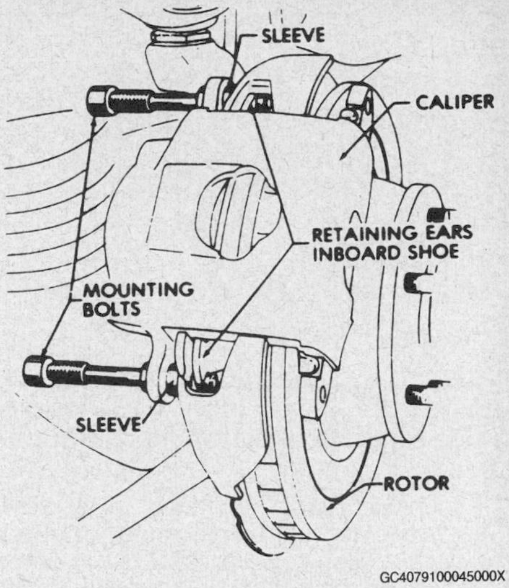
SLEEVE
CALIPER
RETAINING EARS INBOARD SHOE
MOUNTING BOLTS
SLEEVE
ROTOR
GC4079100045000X

Fig. 4 Caliper & mounting bolts

CALIPER SERVICE

CALIPER REMOVAL

1. Siphon enough brake fluid out of the master cylinder to bring fluid level to 1/3 full to avoid fluid overflow when the caliper piston is pushed back into its bore.
2. Raise vehicle and remove front wheels.
3. Using a C-clamp, as illustrated in **Fig. 3**, push piston back into its bore.
4. If caliper assembly is to be serviced, remove inlet fitting attaching bolt, copper washer, and inlet fitting from caliper housing. Plug opening in inlet fitting to prevent fluid loss and contamination. **Do not crimp brake hose, as this may damage internal structure of hose. If only shoe and lining assemblies are to be replaced, do not disconnect brake line fitting from caliper.**
5. Remove two mounting bolts, **Fig. 4**, and lift caliper away from disc. If only shoe and lining assemblies are to be replaced, suspend caliper from chassis using suitable hanger. **Do not allow caliper to hang by brake hose.**

CALIPER DISASSEMBLY

1. Remove caliper as outlined above.
2. Clean outside of caliper, then drain brake fluid from caliper.
3. Use clean shop towels to pad interior of caliper assembly, then remove piston by directing compressed air into caliper brake hose inlet hole, **Fig. 5. Use just enough air pressure to ease piston out of bore. Do not place fingers in front of piston for any reason when applying compressed air. This could result in serious personal injury.**
4. Carefully pry dust boot out of bore.
5. Using a small piece of wood or plastic, remove piston seal from bore. **Do not use a metal tool of any kind to remove seal as it may damage bore.**
6. Remove bleeder valve.
7. Inspect piston for scoring, nicks, corrosion, and wear and replace as needed.

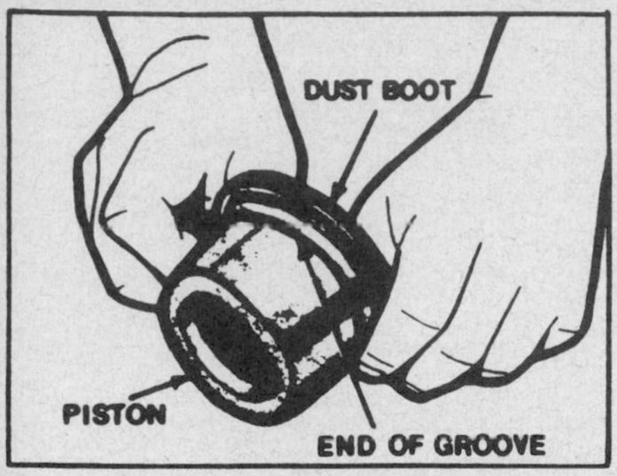
DUST BOOT
PISTON
END OF GROOVE

GC4079100047000X

Fig. 6 Boot to piston installation

8. Inspect caliper housing and seal groove for corrosion, nicks, scoring and excessive wear, and use crocus cloth to polish away corrosion from housing bore. Replace caliper housing if corrosion in and around seal groove will not clean up with crocus cloth.
9. Clean all parts with denatured alcohol. Dry with unlubricated compressed air. Blow out all passages in housing and bleeder valve.

CALIPER ASSEMBLY

1. Lubricate caliper piston bore and new piston seal with clean brake fluid. Position seal in bore groove. **Ensure seal is not twisted.**
2. Lubricate piston with clean brake fluid and assemble a new boot into the groove in the piston so the fold faces the open end of the piston, **Fig. 6.**
3. Using care not to unseat the seal, insert piston into bore and force the piston to the bottom of the bore.
4. Position dust boot in caliper counterbore and install, using suitable seal installer, **Fig. 7. Check the boot installation to be sure the retaining ring molded into the boot is not bent and that the boot is installed below the caliper face and evenly all around. If the boot is not fully installed, dirt and moisture may enter the bore and cause corrosion.**
5. Install the brake hose in the caliper using a new copper gasket.
6. Install shoes and reinstall caliper assembly.

CALIPER INSTALLATION

1. Position caliper over disc, lining up holes in caliper with holes in mounting bracket. If brake hose was not disconnected during removal, be sure not to kink it during installation.

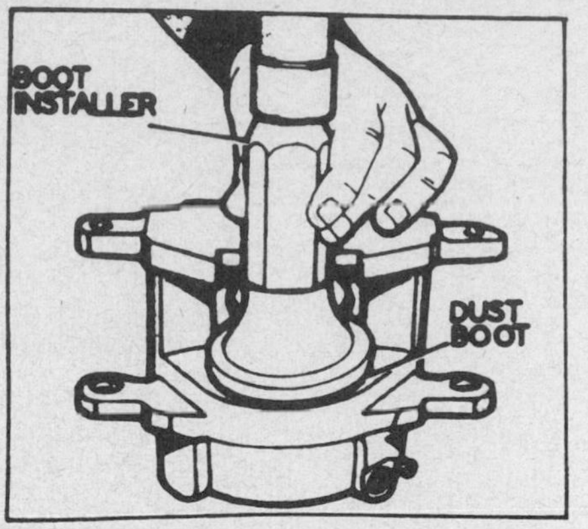
BOOT INSTALLER
DUST BOOT

GC4079100048000X

Fig. 7 Boot to caliper installation

2. Start mounting bolts through sleeves in inboard caliper ears and the mounting bracket, making sure ends of bolts pass under ears on inboard shoe. **Right and left calipers must not be interchanged.**
3. Push mounting bolts through to engage holes in the outboard ears. Then thread mounting bolts into bracket.
4. Tighten mounting bolts to specifications.
5. Check the dimensions between each caliper stop and caliper, **Fig. 8.**
6. If brake hose was removed, reconnect it and bleed the calipers.
7. Replace front wheels, lower vehicle and add brake fluid to master cylinder to bring level to 1/4 inch from top. **Before moving vehicle, pump brake pedal several times to be sure it is firm. Do not move vehicle until a firm pedal is obtained. On some models with low drag calipers, apply approximately 175 pounds of pressure to the brake pedal three times to properly seat the caliper and related components.**

ROTOR

REPLACE

1. Remove caliper assembly from steering knuckle as described in "Caliper Removal" under "Caliper Service."
2. **On models with anti-lock brakes,** proceed as follows:

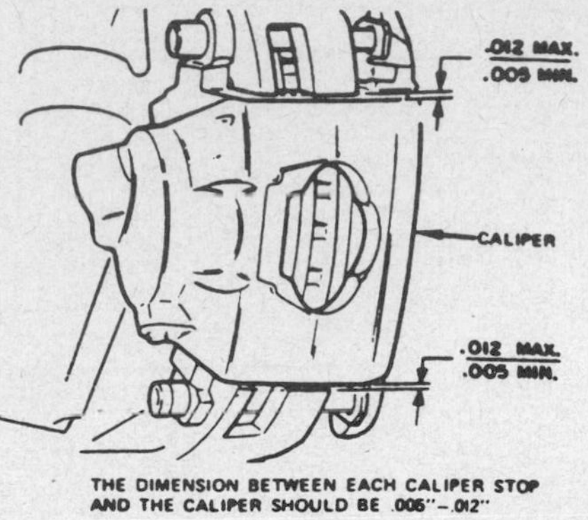
.012 MAX.
.005 MIN.
CALIPER
.012 MAX.
.005 MIN.
THE DIMENSION BETWEEN EACH CALIPER STOP AND THE CALIPER SHOULD BE .005"-.012"

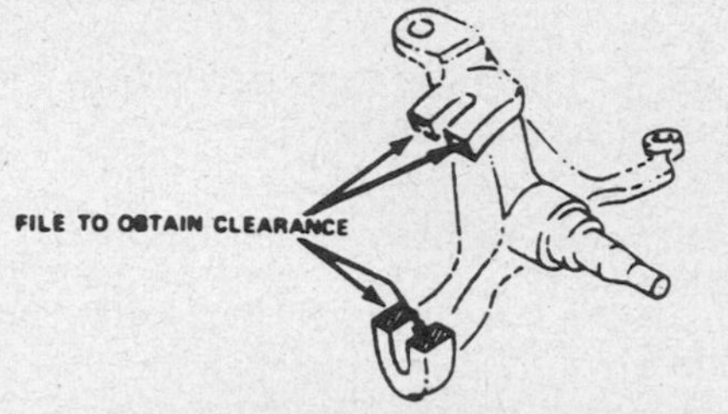
FILE TO OBTAIN CLEARANCE

GC4079100049000X

Fig. 8 Checking clearance between caliper & stops

   a. Remove wheel speed sensor retaining bolt from rear side of steering knuckle.
   b. Remove wheel speed sensor from steering knuckle and position aside.
3. **On all models,** remove wheel bearing lubricant cap from center of rotor.
4. Remove cotter pin, nut and washer from steering knuckle assembly.
5. Carefully pull brake rotor from steering knuckle.
6. Reverse procedure to install, prior to installing cotter pin onto the steering knuckle, adjust wheel bearing as follows:
   a. **Torque** nut to 21 ft. lbs. while turning brake rotor clockwise. This will remove any grease or burrs which may cause excessive wheel bearing play.
   b. Back off nut to a "just loose" position.
   c. Hand tighten nut until the next slot.
   d. Install cotter pin and wheel bearing lubricant cap.

DISC BRAKE SPECIFICATIONS

CALIPER SPECIFICATIONS

Year	Model	Caliper Bore Dia. Inch.
BUICK		
1992-94	Roadmaster	2.94
CADILLAC		
1992	Brougham	2.94
1993-94	Fleetwood RWD	2.94
CHERVOLET		
1992	Camaro	2.52

Year	Model	Caliper Bore Dia. Inch.
CHEVROLET-Continued		
1992-94	Caprice & Impala SS	2.94
OLDSMOBILE		
1992	Custom Cruiser	2.94
PONTIAC		
1992	Firebird	2.52

ROTOR SPECIFICATIONS

Model	Year	Nominal Thickness	Minimum Refinish Thickness	Thickness Variation (Parallelism)	Lateral Runout (T.I.R.)
BUICK					
Roadmaster	1992-94	1.043	.980	.0005	.005
CADILLAC					
Brougham	1992	1.031	.980	.0005	.004
Fleetwood RWD	1993-94	1.043	.965	.0005	.004
CHERVOLET					
Camaro	1992	1.043	.965	.0005	.005
Caprice & Impala SS	1992-94	1.043	.980	.0005	.005
OLDSMOBILE					
Custom Cruiser	1992	1.043	.980	.0005	.005
PONTIAC					
Firebird	1992	1.043	.965	.0005	.005

TIGHTENING SPECIFICATIONS

Component	Torque Ft. Lbs.
Brake Hose To Caliper	33
Caliper Bleeder Screw	115
Caliper Mounting Bolts	38
Wheel Lug Nuts	100

AC-Delco Single Piston Front Disc Brake (Type 2)

INDEX

PRECAUTIONS

1. Grease or any other foreign material must be kept off the brake linings, caliper, surfaces of the disc and external surfaces of the hub, during service procedures. Handling the brake disc and caliper should be done in a way to avoid deformation of the disc and nicking or scratching brake linings.
2. If inspection reveals rubber piston seals are worn or damaged, they should be replaced immediately.
3. During removal and installation of a wheel assembly, exercise care so as not to interfere with or damage the caliper splash shield, or bleeder screw.
4. Front wheel bearings preload should be adjusted to specifications .
5. Be sure vehicle is centered on hoist before servicing any of the front end components to avoid bending or damaging the disc splash shield on full right or left wheel turns.
6. Before the vehicle is moved after any brake service work, be sure to obtain a firm brake pedal.
7. The assembly bolts of two piece caliper housings should not be disturbed unless the caliper requires service.

DESCRIPTION

The caliper has a single piston and is mounted to the support bracket by two mounting bolts, **Figs. 1 through 4.** The caliper assembly slides on the two mounting bolts. Upon brake application, fluid pressure against the piston forces the inboard shoe and lining assembly against the inboard side of the disc. This action causes the caliper assembly to slide until the outboard lining comes into contact with the disc. As pressure builds up the linings are pressed against the disc with increased force.

TROUBLESHOOTING

BRAKE ROUGHNESS

The most common cause of brake chatter on disc brakes is a variation in thickness of the disc. If roughness or vibration is encountered during highway operation or if pedal pulsation is experienced at low speeds, the disc may have excessive thickness variation. To check for this condition, measure the disc at 12 points with a micrometer at a radius approximately one inch from edge of disc. If thickness measurements vary by more than .0005 inch, the disc should be replaced with a new one.

Excessive lateral runout of braking disc may cause a "knocking back" of the pistons, possibly creating increased pedal travel and vibration when brakes are applied.

Before checking the runout, wheel bearings should be adjusted. The readjustment is very important and will be required at the completion of the test to prevent bearing failure. Be sure to make the adjustment according to the recommendations given under "Front Wheel Bearings, Adjust" in the car chapters.

BRAKE SYSTEM BLEED

Pressure bleeding is recommended for all hydraulic disc brake systems.

The disc brake hydraulic system can be bled manually or with pressure bleeding equipment. The brake pedal will require pumping and frequent checking of fluid level in master cylinder during bleeding operation.

Never use brake fluid that has been drained from hydraulic system when bleeding the brakes. Be sure the disc brake pistons are returned to their normal positions and that the shoe and lining assemblies are properly seated. Before driving the vehicle, check brake operation to be sure that a firm pedal has been obtained.

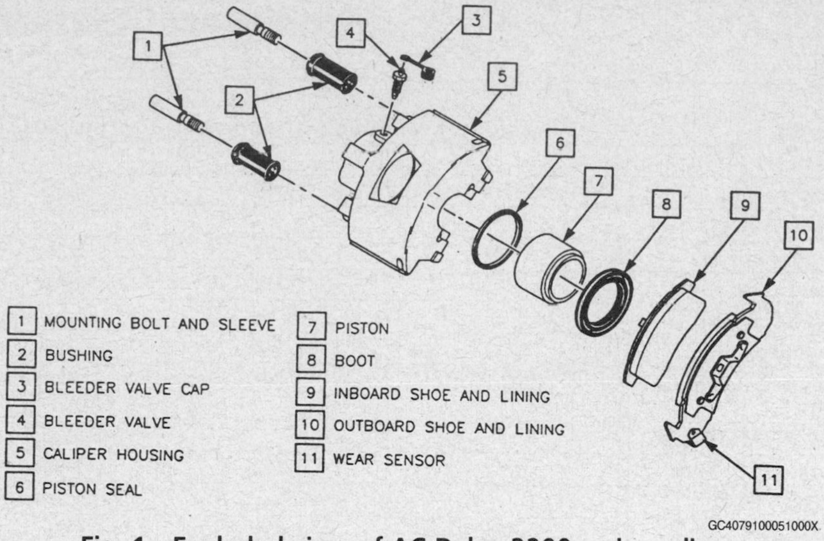
1 MOUNTING BOLT AND SLEEVE
2 BUSHING
3 BLEEDER VALVE CAP
4 BLEEDER VALVE
5 CALIPER HOUSING
6 PISTON SEAL
7 PISTON
8 BOOT
9 INBOARD SHOE AND LINING
10 OUTBOARD SHOE AND LINING
11 WEAR SENSOR
GC4079100051000X

Fig. 1 Exploded view of AC-Delco 3200 series caliper

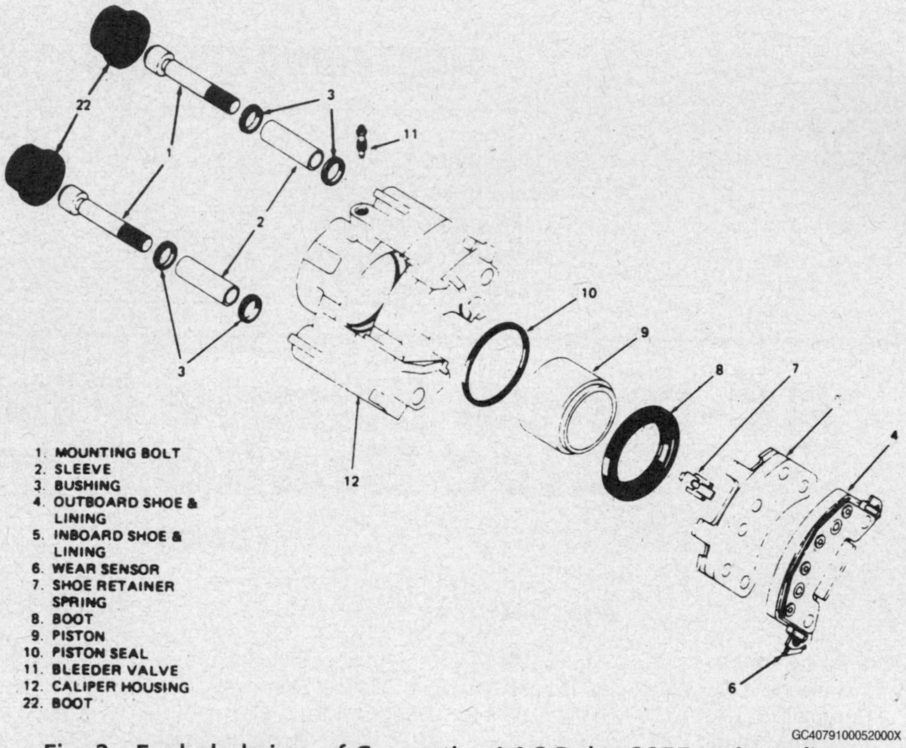
1. MOUNTING BOLT
2. SLEEVE
3. BUSHING
4. OUTBOARD SHOE & LINING
5. INBOARD SHOE & LINING
6. WEAR SENSOR
7. SHOE RETAINER SPRING
8. BOOT
9. PISTON
10. PISTON SEAL
11. BLEEDER VALVE
12. CALIPER HOUSING
22. BOOT
GC4079100052000X

Fig. 2 Exploded view of Generation I AC-Delco 3257 series caliper

BRAKE PAD SERVICE

REMOVAL

1. Remove caliper assembly as described in "Caliper Service."
2. Remove shoe and lining assemblies from caliper, **Figs. 1 through 4,** noting the following:
   a. **On models with tab mount outer shoe (all except series 3264),** straighten bent over shoe tabs with suitable pliers.
   b. **On models with spring mount outer shoe (series 3264),** insert screwdriver between shoe and caliper and disengage buttons on shoe from holes in caliper.
3. Remove sleeves and bushings from grooves in caliper mounting bolt holes, **Figs. 1 through 4.**

INSTALLATION

1. Lubricate new bushings with suitable grease, install bushings in caliper grooves, then insert sleeves through bushings.
2. Install retaining spring onto inboard shoe and lining assembly, **Fig. 5,** if equipped, then install inboard shoe into caliper housing.
3. Install outboard shoe and lining assembly into caliper housing ensuring wear sensor is properly positioned. **On models with spring mount shoe (series 3264),** ensure buttons on shoe are properly engaged in holes in caliper.
4. Install caliper assembly as outlined.
5. **On models with tab mount outer shoe (except series 3264),** clinch outboard shoe to brake caliper as follows:
   a. Apply brakes several times to ensure caliper piston is extended and shoes are fully seated.
   b. Wedge a large flat blade screwdriver between outboard shoe flange and hat section of rotor, **Fig. 6.**
   c. Hold outer pad against caliper with suitable clamp or by applying moderate pressure on brake pedal.
   d. Position a ball peen hammer on outboard shoe tab, **Fig. 7,** then using a larger brass hammer, lightly tap the ball peen hammer to bend

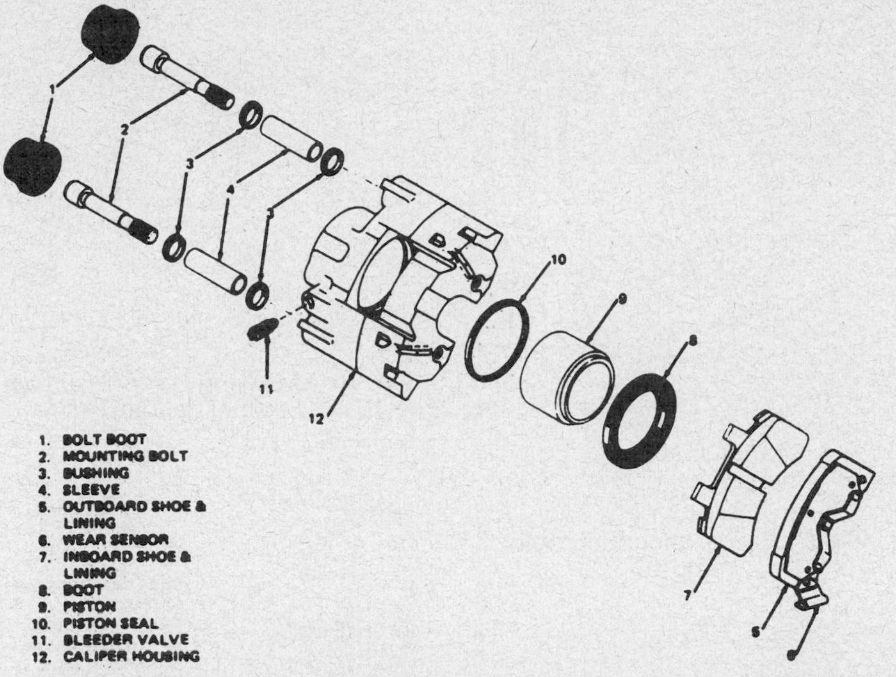
1. BOLT BOOT
2. MOUNTING BOLT
3. BUSHING
4. SLEEVE
5. OUTBOARD SHOE & LINING
6. WEAR SENSOR
7. INBOARD SHOE & LINING
8. BOOT
9. PISTON
10. PISTON SEAL
11. BLEEDER VALVE
12. CALIPER HOUSING
GC4079100053000X

Fig. 3 Exploded view of Generation I AC-Delco 3264 series caliper

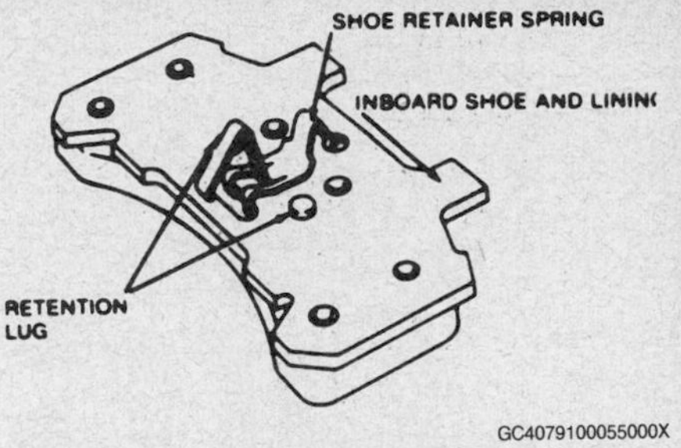
SHOE RETAINER SPRING
INBOARD SHOE AND LINING
RETENTION LUG
GC4079100055000X

Fig. 5 Retainer spring installation on inboard shoe

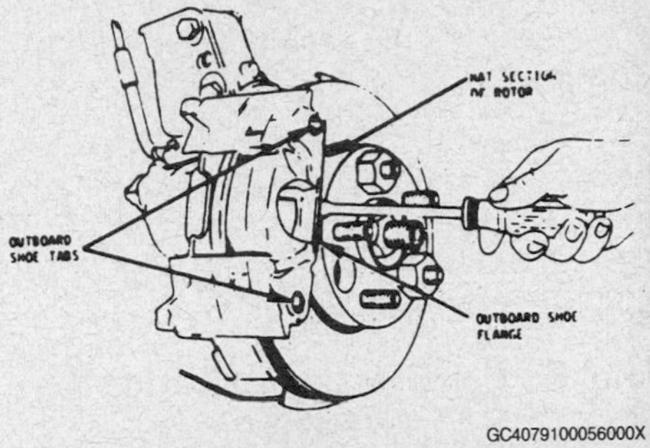
GC4079100056000X

Fig. 6 Positioning screwdriver between outboard shoe flange & hat section of rotor

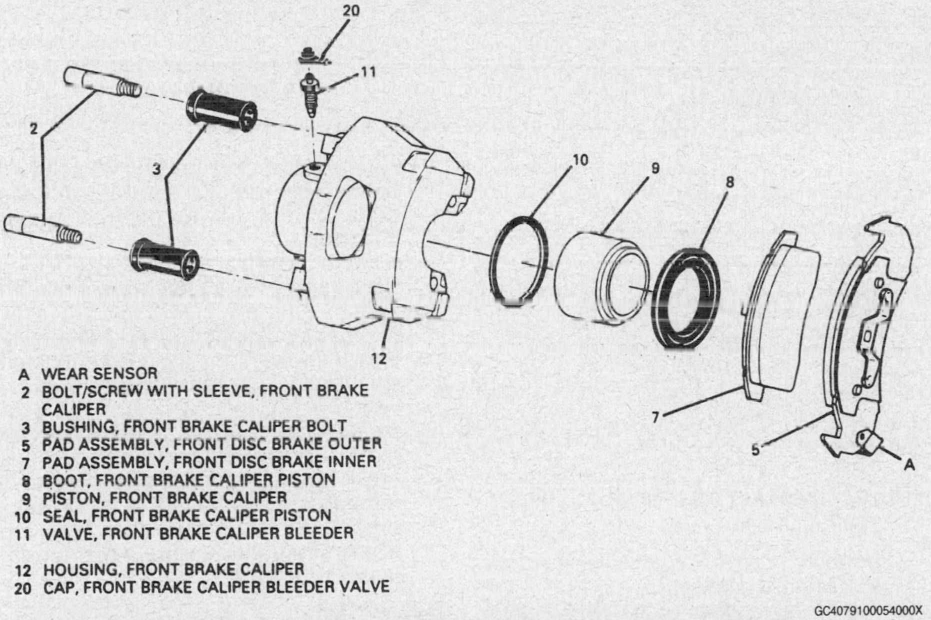
A WEAR SENSOR
2 BOLT/SCREW WITH SLEEVE, FRONT BRAKE CALIPER
3 BUSHING, FRONT BRAKE CALIPER BOLT
5 PAD ASSEMBLY, FRONT DISC BRAKE OUTER
7 PAD ASSEMBLY, FRONT DISC BRAKE INNER
8 BOOT, FRONT BRAKE CALIPER PISTON
9 PISTON, FRONT BRAKE CALIPER
10 SEAL, FRONT BRAKE CALIPER PISTON
11 VALVE, FRONT BRAKE CALIPER BLEEDER
12 HOUSING, FRONT BRAKE CALIPER
20 CAP, FRONT BRAKE CALIPER BLEEDER VALVE
GC4079100054000X

Fig. 4 Exploded view of Generation II AC-Delco 3257 & 3264 series caliper

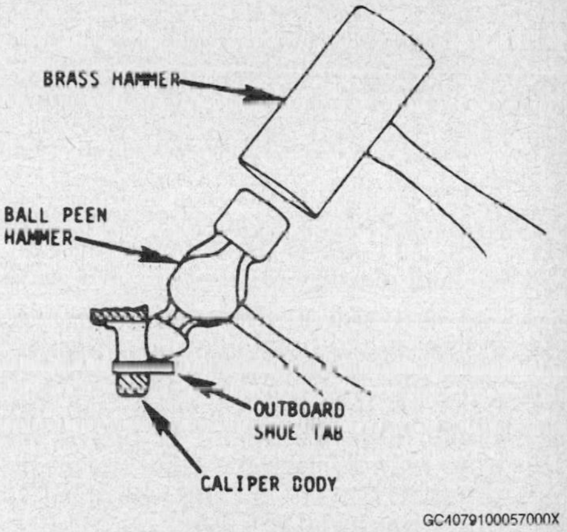
BRASS HAMMER
BALL PEEN HAMMER
OUTBOARD SHOE TAB
CALIPER BODY
GC4079100057000X

Fig. 7 Positioning hammer to clinch brake pad tabs

the outboard shoe tab. Tabs must be bent around casting to approximately 45°.

e. After both tabs have been bent pressure should be released and outboard shoe should be locked into position. If shoe is loose, repeat steps a. through d. **If an outboard shoe is removed from the caliper, or the tabs unclinched for any reason, then it will be necessary to replace the shoe and lining assemblies. Do not re-clinch outboard shoe locking tabs after having removed shoe from caliper.**

CALIPER SERVICE

CALIPER REMOVAL

1. Remove approximately 2/3 of brake fluid from master cylinder.
2. Raise and support front of vehicle, then remove wheel and tire assembly.
3. Position suitable pliers over inboard pad and housing as shown in **Fig. 8**, and squeeze pliers to compress caliper piston.
4. If caliper assembly is being removed for service, remove inlet fitting attaching bolt, copper washer, and inlet fitting from caliper housing. Plug opening in inlet fitting to prevent fluid loss and contamination. **Do not crimp brake hose, as this may damage internal structure of hose. If only shoe and lining assemblies are to be replaced, do not disconnect brake line fitting from caliper.**
5. Remove Allen head caliper mounting bolts, **Fig. 9.** If bolts show signs of corrosion, use new bolts when installing caliper assembly.
6. Remove caliper assembly from disc. If only shoe and lining assemblies are to be replaced, using a length of wire suspend caliper from spring coil. Never allow caliper to hang from brake hose.

CALIPER DISASSEMBLY

1. Clean outside of caliper, then drain brake fluid from caliper.
2. Use clean shop towels to pad interior of caliper assembly, then remove pis-

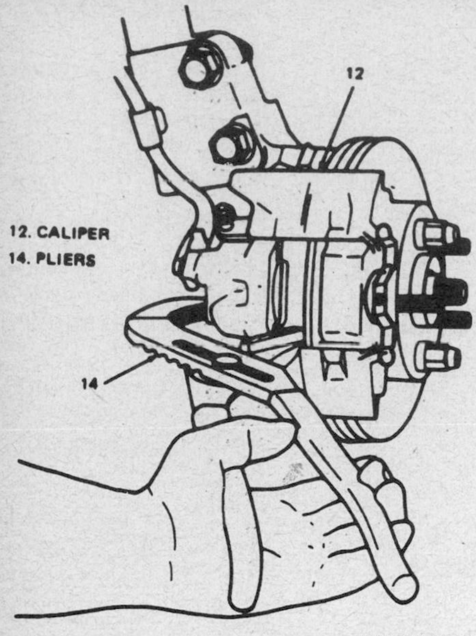
12
12. CALIPER
14. PLIERS
14
GC4079100058000X

Fig. 8 Compressing caliper piston w/pliers

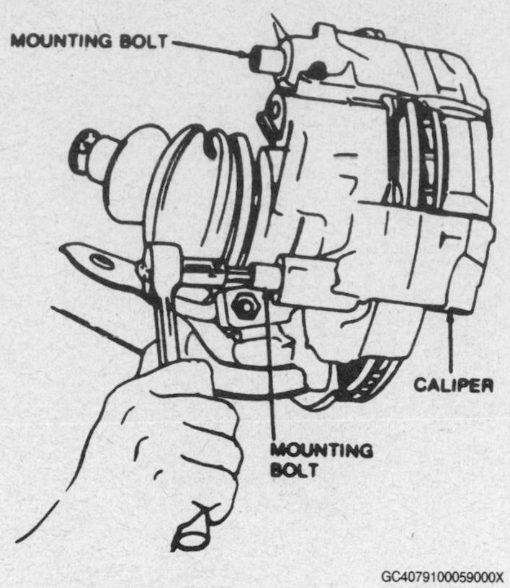
MOUNTING BOLT
CALIPER
MOUNTING BOLT
GC4079100059000X

Fig. 9 Caliper mounting bolts removal

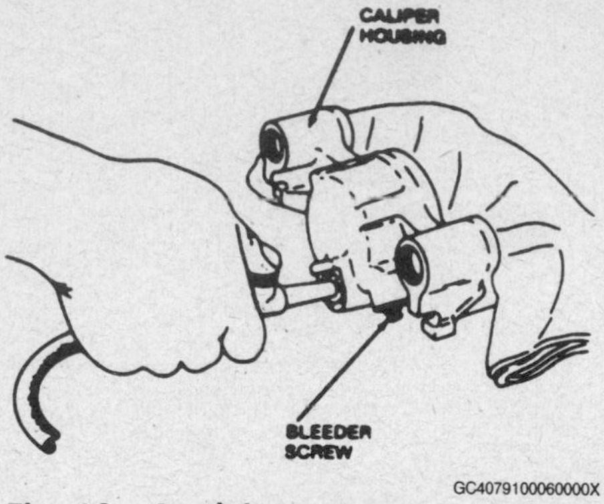
CALIPER HOUSING
BLEEDER SCREW
GC4079100060000X

Fig. 10 Applying compressed air to caliper line port

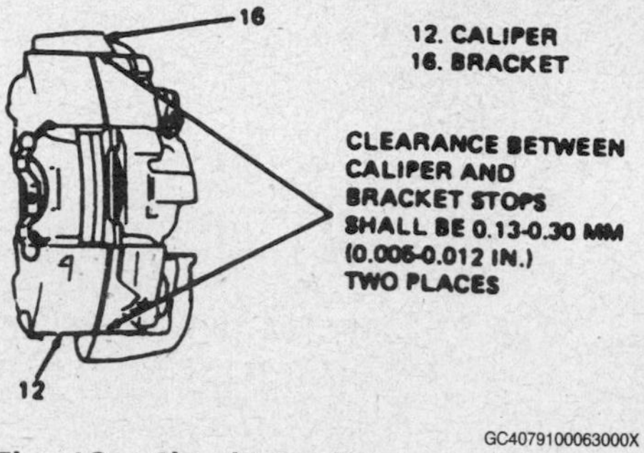
16
12. CALIPER
16. BRACKET
CLEARANCE BETWEEN CALIPER AND BRACKET STOPS SHALL BE 0.13-0.30 MM (0.005-0.012 IN.) TWO PLACES
12
GC4079100063000X

Fig. 13 Checking clearance between caliper & stops

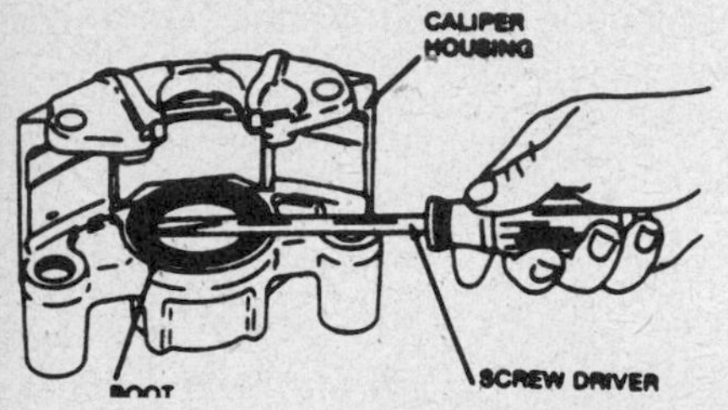
CALIPER HOUSING
SCREW DRIVER
GC4079100061000X

Fig. 11 Dust boot removal

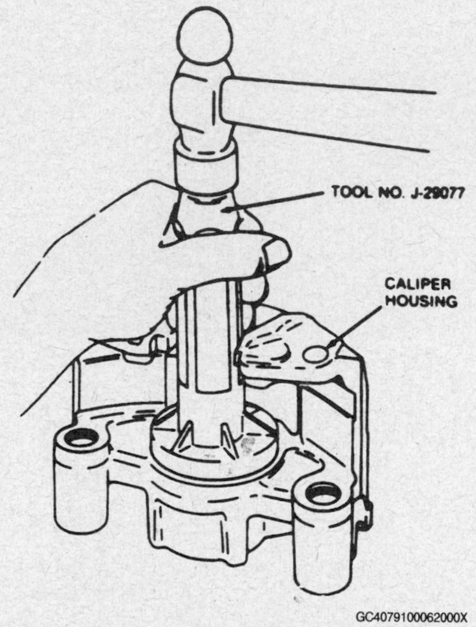
TOOL NO. J-29077
CALIPER HOUSING
GC4079100062000X

Fig. 12 Seating dust boot in caliper

ton by directing compressed air into caliper brake hose inlet hole, **Fig. 10. Use just enough air pressure to ease piston out of bore. Do not place fingers in front of piston for any reason when applying compressed air. This could result in serious personal injury.**

3. Using a screwdriver, remove dust boot from caliper bore, **Fig. 11.**
4. Using a small piece of wood or plastic, remove piston seal from bore. **Do not use a metal tool of any kind to remove seal as it may damage bore.**
5. Remove bleeder valve.
6. Inspect piston for scoring, nicks, corrosion, and wear and replace as needed.
7. Inspect caliper housing and seal groove for corrosion, nicks, scoring and excessive wear, and use crocus cloth to polish away corrosion from housing bore. Replace caliper housing if corrosion in and around seal groove will not clean up with crocus cloth.
8. Clean all parts with denatured alcohol. Dry with unlubricated compressed air. Blow out all passages in housing and bleeder valve.

CALIPER ASSEMBLY

1. Lubricate piston seal with clean brake fluid, then install piston seal into caliper bore groove. Check to ensure piston seal is not twisted.
2. Lubricate caliper bore with clean brake fluid.
3. Insert piston into caliper bore, then force piston down until piston bottoms in bore.
4. Position outer diameter of dust boot in caliper housing counterbore, then seat boot as shown in **Fig. 12.**
5. Install bleeder screw on caliper housing.

CALIPER INSTALLATION

1. Position caliper assembly over disc and align mounting bolt holes. If brake hoses were not disconnected during removal, use care not to kink hoses during installation.
2. Install mounting bolts and tighten to specifications, **Fig. 9.**
3. Check the dimensions between each caliper stop and caliper, **Fig. 13.** If necessary remove caliper and file ends of bracket to provide proper clearance.
4. If brake hose fitting was disconnected during removal, install brake hose fitting.
5. Fill master cylinder. Bleed brake system if brake line was disconnected and recheck master cylinder fluid level.
6. Install wheel and tire assembly on vehicle, then lower vehicle and check brake system operation. **Before moving vehicle, pump brake pedal several times to be sure it is firm. Do not move vehicle until a firm pedal is obtained.**

ROTOR

REPLACE

EXCEPT CAMARO & FIREBIRD

1. Raise and support vehicle, then remove tire and wheel assembly.
2. Remove caliper assembly from rotor as described in "Caliper Service."
3. Remove caliper assembly mounting bracket attaching bolts, then the mounting bracket.
4. Remove rotor from hub and bearing assembly.
5. Reverse procedure to install.

CAMARO & FIREBIRD

1. Remove caliper as described in "Cali-

per Removal" under "Caliper Service.
2. Remove caliper mounting bracket attaching bolts, then the caliper mounting bracket.
3. Remove wheel bearing lubricant cap from center of rotor.
4. Remove cotter pin, nut and washer from steering knuckle assembly.
5. Carefully pull brake rotor from steering knuckle.
6. Reverse procedure to install, prior to installing cotter pin onto the steering knuckle, adjust wheel bearing as follows:
   a. **Torque** nut to 21 ft. lbs. while turning brake rotor clockwise. This will remove any grease or burrs which may cause excessive wheel bearing play.
   b. Back off nut to a "just loose" position.
   c. Hand tighten nut until the next slot.
   d. Install cotter pin and wheel bearing lubricant cap.

DISC BRAKE SPECIFICATIONS

CALIPER SPECIFICATIONS

Year	Model	Caliper Bore Dia. Inch.
BUICK		
1992-94	Century	①
1992-94	LeSabre	2.52
1992-94	Park Avenue	2.52
1992-94	Skylark	2.24
CADILLAC		
1992-94	DeVille	2.52
1992-94	Eldorado	2.52
1992	Fleetwood FWD	2.52
1992-94	Seville	2.52
CHEVROLET		
1992-94	Beretta	2.25
1993-94	Camaro	2.50
1992-94	Cavalier	2.24
1992-94	Corsica	2.25
OLDSMOBILE		
1992-94	Achieva	2.24
1992-94	Cutlass Ciera	①
1992-94	Eighty-Eight	2.52
1992-94	Ninety-Eight	2.52
PONTIAC		
1992-94	Bonneville	2.52
1993-94	Firebird	2.50
1993-94	Grand Am	2.24
1992-94	Sunbird	2.24

①—Front standard, 2.50 inches; front heavy duty, 1.50 inches.
②—Front, 2.5 inches, rear 1.5 inches.

ROTOR SPECIFICATIONS

Model	Year	Nominal Thickness	Minimum Refinish Thickness	Thickness Variation (Parallelism)	Lateral Runout (T.I.R.)
BUICK					
Century	1992-93②	.885	.830	.0005	.004
	1992-93 ①	1.043	.972	.0005	.004
	1994	1.028	.972	.0005	.004
LeSabre	1992-94	1.043	.972	.0005	.004
Park Avenue	1992-94	1.043	.972	.0005	.004
Skylark	1992-94	.806	.786	.0005	.004
CADILLAC					
DeVille	1992-94	1.276	1.226	.0005	.004
Eldorado	1992-94	1.260	1.250	.0005	.004
Fleetwood FWD	1992	1.276	1.226	.0005	.004
Seville	1992-94	1.260	1.250	.0005	.002
CHEVROLET					
Beretta	1992-94	.885	.830	.0005	.004
Cavalier	1992-94	.885	.830	.0005	.004
Camaro	1993-94	.795	.744	.0005	.006
Corsica	1992-94	.885	.830	.0005	.004
OLDSMOBILE					
Achieva	1992-94	.806	.786	.0005	.004
Cutlass Ciera & Cutlass Cruiser	1992-93②	.885	.830	.0005	.004
	1992-93 ①	1.043	.957	.0005	.004
	1994	1.028	.957	.0005	.004

Continued

ROTOR SPECIFICATIONS-Continued

Model	Year	Nominal Thickness	Minimum Refinish Thickness	Thickness Variation (Parallelism)	Lateral Runout (T.I.R.)
OLDSMOBILE					
Eighty-Eight	1992-94	1.043	.972	.0005	.004
Ninety-Eight	1992-94	1.276	1.226	.0005	.004
PONTIAC					
Bonneville	1992-94	1,043	.972	.0005	.004
Firebird	1993-94	.795	.744	.0005	.006
Grand Am	1992-94	.806	.786	.0005	.004
Sunbird	1992-94	.885	.830	.0005	.004

①—Medium & heavy duty.
②—Light duty.

TIGHTENING SPECIFICATIONS

Component	Torque/Ft. Lbs.
Brake Hose To Caliper	32
Caliper Bleeder Screw	9
Caliper Bracket Mounting Bolts	83
Caliper Mounting Bolts	63
Wheel Speed Sensor Mounting Bolt	9
Wheel Lug Nuts	100

AC-Delco Single Piston Front Disc Brake (Type 3)

INDEX

PRECAUTIONS

1. Grease or any other foreign material must be kept off the brake linings, caliper, surfaces of the disc and external surfaces of the hub, during service procedures. Handling the brake disc and caliper should be done in a way to avoid deformation of the disc and nicking or scratching brake linings.
2. If inspection reveals rubber piston seals are worn or damaged, they should be replaced immediately.
3. During removal and installation of a wheel assembly, exercise care so as not to interfere with or damage the caliper splash shield, or bleeder screw.
4. Front wheel bearings preload should be adjusted to specifications .
5. Be sure vehicle is centered on hoist before servicing any of the front end components to avoid bending or damaging the disc splash shield on full right or left wheel turns.
6. Before the vehicle is moved after any brake service work, be sure to obtain a firm brake pedal.
7. The assembly bolts of two piece caliper housings should not be disturbed unless the caliper requires service.

DESCRIPTION

This caliper, **Fig. 1,** has a single bore and is mounted to the support bracket with two mounting bolts. Hydraulic pressure, created by applying force to the brake pedal, is converted by the caliper into friction. The hydraulic pressure is applied equally against the piston and the bottom of the caliper bore moving the piston outward and the housing inward, resulting in a clamping action on the brake rotor.

TROUBLESHOOTING

BRAKE ROUGHNESS

The most common cause of brake chatter on disc brakes is a variation in thickness of the disc. If roughness or vibration is encountered during highway operation or if pedal pulsation is experienced at low speeds, the disc may have excessive thickness variation. To check for this condition, measure the disc at 12 points with a micrometer at a radius approximately

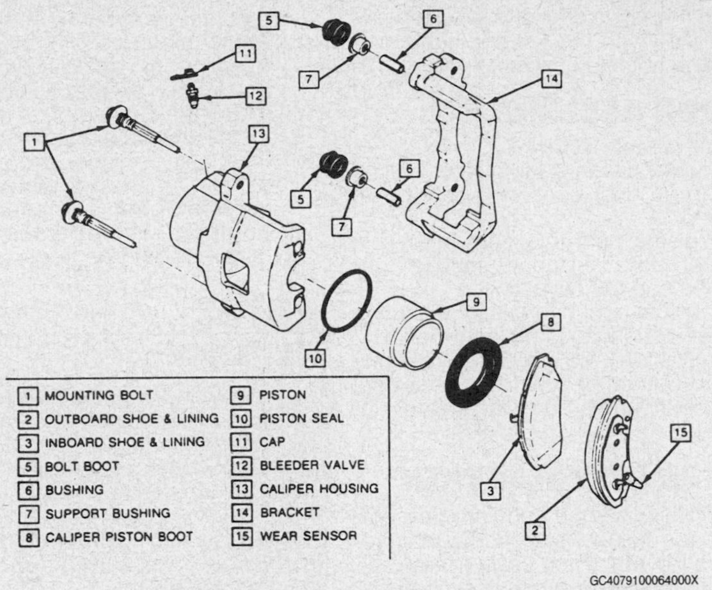
1 MOUNTING BOLT
2 OUTBOARD SHOE & LINING
3 INBOARD SHOE & LINING
5 BOLT BOOT
6 BUSHING
7 SUPPORT BUSHING
8 CALIPER PISTON BOOT
9 PISTON
10 PISTON SEAL
11 CAP
12 BLEEDER VALVE
13 CALIPER HOUSING
14 BRACKET
15 WEAR SENSOR
GC4079100064000X

Fig. 1 Exploded view of AC-Delco series 3264M front disc brake caliper

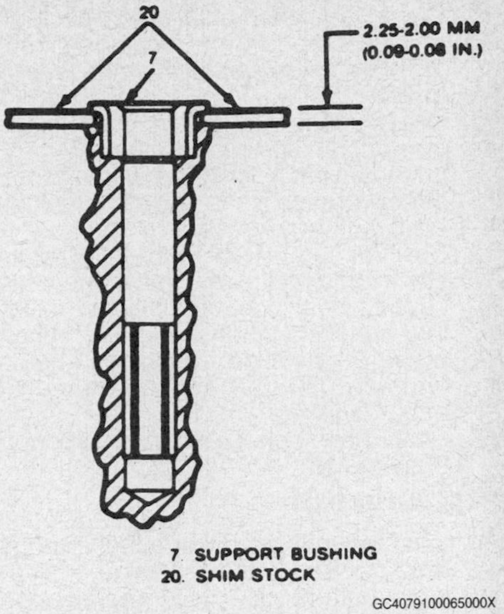
20
7
2.25-2.00 MM
(0.09-0.08 IN.)
7. SUPPORT BUSHING
20. SHIM STOCK
GC4079100065000X

Fig. 2 Support bushing installation

one inch from edge of disc. If thickness measurements vary by more than .0005 inch, the disc should be replaced with a new one.

Excessive lateral runout of braking disc may cause a "knocking back" of the pistons, possibly creating increased pedal travel and vibration when brakes are applied.

Before checking the runout, wheel bearings should be adjusted. The readjustment is very important and will be required at the completion of the test to prevent bearing failure. Be sure to make the adjustment according to the recommendations given under "Front Wheel Bearings, Adjust" in the car chapters.

BRAKE SYSTEM BLEED

Pressure bleeding is recommended for all hydraulic disc brake systems.

The disc brake hydraulic system can be bled manually or with pressure bleeding equipment. **On vehicles with disc brakes** the brake pedal will require more pumping and frequent checking of fluid level in master cylinder during bleeding operation.

Never use brake fluid that has been drained from hydraulic system when bleeding the brakes. Be sure the disc brake pistons are returned to their normal positions and that the shoe and lining assemblies are properly seated. Before driving the vehicle, check brake operation to be sure that a firm pedal has been obtained.

BRAKE PAD SERVICE

REMOVAL

1. Remove caliper assembly as outlined.
2. Remove outboard shoe and lining assembly, using screwdriver to disengage shoe springs from holes in caliper housing.
3. Remove inboard shoe and lining assembly, unsnapping shoe retainer spring from caliper piston bore.
4. If new shoe and lining assemblies are to be installed, compress piston into housing with suitable clamp or pliers, taking care not to damage piston.

INSTALLATION

1. If new shoe and lining assemblies are being installed, compress piston into caliper bore, taking care not to damage piston.
2. Install inboard shoe, snapping shoe retainer spring into piston bore, and ensure shoe is flat against piston.
3. Install outboard shoe assembly, snapping shoe springs into holes in caliper, and ensure shoe is flat against caliper housing.

CALIPER SERVICE

CALIPER REMOVAL

1. Drain approximately 2/3 of brake fluid from master cylinder assembly.
2. Raise and support vehicle, then mark position of wheel and remove tire and wheel assembly.
3. If caliper is to be serviced or replaced, remove bolt securing inlet fitting, then disconnect brake hose, and plug end to prevent loss of fluid and contamination. **Do not crimp brake hose, as this may damage internal structure of hose. If only shoe and lining assemblies are being replaced, do not disconnect brake hose from caliper.**
4. Remove caliper to support mounting bolts, then lift caliper off support. If only shoe and lining assemblies are to be replaced, suspend caliper from chassis using suitable hanger. **Do not allow caliper to hang by brake hose.**
5. Remove insulators (4) from caliper support if equipped, **Fig. 1.**

CALIPER DISASSEMBLY

1. Drain brake fluid from caliper and clean thoroughly.
2. Use clean shop towels to pad inside of caliper, then remove piston by applying compressed air to fluid inlet port. Use only enough air pressure to ease piston from bore. **Keep fingers away from piston to avoid injury as piston is forced out.**
3. Pry dust boot from caliper, taking care not to damage housing bore.
4. With a small wood or plastic tool remove piston seal from caliper bore. **Do not use metal tool since this may damage caliper bore or seal groove.**
5. Inspect piston for scoring nicks, corro sion, wear and damage and replace as needed.
6. Inspect caliper housing and seal groove for corrosion, nicks, scoring and excessive wear. Use crocus cloth to polish away corrosion from housing bore. Replace caliper housing if corrosion in and around seal groove will not clean up with crocus cloth.
7. Remove bleeder screw from caliper housing, **Fig. 1.**
8. Clean components with denatured alcohol and dry with unlubricated compressed air. Blow out all passages in housing and bleeder valve.

MOUNTING BRACKET SERVICE

Removal

1. Remove caliper as outlined previously.
2. Remove mounting bracket attaching bolts, then mounting bracket.

Bushing & Boot Replacement

1. Remove mounting bracket from vehicle.
2. Remove bolt boots from support bushings, **Fig. 1.**

3. Clamp bracket in a suitable vise, then pry support bushings from inner bushings in bracket ears with small screwdriver.
4. Using a paper clip, pull inner bushings from mounting bracket ears.
5. Lubricate inner bushings with silicone based grease, then install bushings flush with bracket ears.
6. Position .080-.090 inch thick shim stock on bracket ear face, then tap support bushings, with plastic mallet, into inner bushings, **Fig. 2.** When properly installed, bushing should protrude .080-.090 inch above bracket ear face.
7. Snap new bolt boots over support bushing lip.

Installation

1. Coat mounting bracket attaching bolt threads with Loctite sealant or equivalent. **Failure to use sealant on mounting bolts may result in loosening of caliper to knuckle attachment.**
2. Align mounting bracket holes, then install mounting bracket and tighten attaching bolts to specifications.

CALIPER ASSEMBLY

1. Install bleeder screw.
2. Lubricate piston seal, piston, caliper bore and dust boot with new brake fluid.
3. Roll piston seal into seal groove in caliper bore, ensuring seal is fully seated and not twisted.
4. Install dust boot over piston, ensuring lip of boot engages piston groove.
5. Install piston in caliper bore, press piston to bottom of bore, then seat boot in caliper counterbore with suitable installer.

CALIPER INSTALLATION

1. If first design shoe and lining assemblies are being installed, mount insulators (4), **Fig. 1,** on caliper bracket.
2. Position caliper on mounting bracket, ensuring insulators, first design, and mounting bolt boots remain in place.
3. Apply thin coating of silicone grease to caliper mounting bolts, install bolts and tighten to specifications.
4. Install brake hose, if removed.
5. Install wheels and lower vehicle.
6. Fill master cylinder and bleed brakes as needed. **Do not attempt to move vehicle until brake pedal has been pumped several times and a firm brake pedal has been obtained.**

ROTOR

REPLACE

1. Raise and support vehicle.
2. Remove tire and wheel assembly.
3. Insert a suitable drift punch through caliper and into rotor, then remove hub nut and washer.
4. Remove caliper as described in "Caliper Service" and position aside.
5. Remove rotor from hub and bearing assembly.
6. Reverse procedure to install.

DISC BRAKE SPECIFICATIONS

CALIPER SPECIFICATIONS

Year	Model	Caliper Bore Dia. Inch.
1992-93	All	2.50

ROTOR SPECIFICATIONS

Model	Year	Nominal Thickness	Minimum Refinish Thickness	Thickness Variation (Parallelism)	Lateral Runout (T.I.R.)
All	1992-93	1.260	1.220	.0005	.002

TIGHTENING SPECIFICATIONS

Component	Torque/Ft. Lbs.
Accumulator	24①
Brake Hose To Caliper	30
Caliper Bleeder Screw	62
Caliper Mounting Bolts	79
Caliper Mounting Bracket To Knuckle	148
Hub Nut	180
Pressure Switch	18①
Wheel Lug Nuts	100
Wheel Speed Sensor Retaining Bolt	59①

①—w/Anti-lock brakes.

AC-Delco Dual Piston Front Disc Brake

INDEX

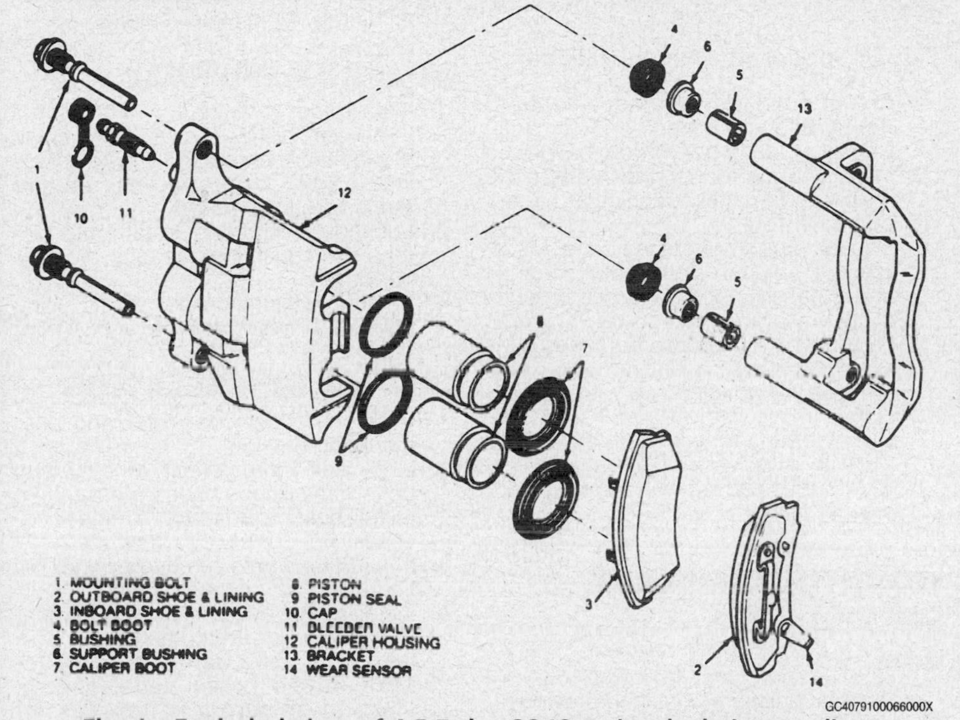

1. MOUNTING BOLT
2. OUTBOARD SHOE & LINING
3. INBOARD SHOE & LINING
4. BOLT BOOT
5. BUSHING
6. SUPPORT BUSHING
7. CALIPER BOOT
8. PISTON
9 PISTON SEAL
10. CAP
11 BLEEDER VALVE
12 CALIPER HOUSING
13. BRACKET
14 WEAR SENSOR
GC4079100066000X

Fig. 1 Exploded view of AC-Delco 3242 series dual piston caliper

PRECAUTIONS

1. Grease or any other foreign material must be kept off the brake linings, caliper, surfaces of the disc and external surfaces of the hub, during service procedures. Handling the brake disc and caliper should be done in a way to avoid deformation of the disc and nicking or scratching brake linings.
2. If inspection reveals rubber piston seals are worn or damaged, they should be replaced immediately.
3. During removal and installation of a wheel assembly, exercise care so as not to interfere with or damage the caliper splash shield, or bleeder screw.
4. Front wheel bearings preload should be adjusted to specifications .
5. Be sure vehicle is centered on hoist before servicing any of the front end components to avoid bending or damaging the disc splash shield on full right or left wheel turns.
6. Before the vehicle is moved after any brake service work, be sure to obtain a firm brake pedal.
7. The assembly bolts of two piece caliper housings should not be disturbed unless the caliper requires service.

DESCRIPTION

This dual piston sliding caliper, **Fig. 1,** is comprised of two interconnected bores and is attached to a mounting bracket with two mounting bolts. Hydraulic pressure acting on the bottom of the caliper bores forces the pistons outward, enabling the caliper to slide inward, thereby clamping the brake shoes against the rotor.

TROUBLESHOOTING

BRAKE ROUGHNESS

The most common cause of brake chatter on disc brakes is a variation in thickness of the disc. If roughness or vibration is encountered during highway operation or if pedal pulsation is experienced at low speeds, the disc may have excessive thickness variation. To check for this condition, measure the disc at 12 points with a micrometer at a radius approximately one inch from edge of disc. If thickness measurements vary by more than .0005 inch, the disc should be replaced with a new one.

Excessive lateral runout of braking disc may cause a "knocking back" of the pistons, possibly creating increased pedal travel and vibration when brakes are applied.

Before checking the runout, wheel bearings should be adjusted. The readjustment is very important and will be required at the completion of the test to prevent bearing failure. Be sure to make the adjustment according to the recommendations given under "Front Wheel Bearings, Adjust" in the car chapters.

BRAKE SYSTEM BLEED

Pressure bleeding is recommended for all hydraulic disc brake systems.

The disc brake hydraulic system can be bled manually or with pressure bleeding equipment. **On vehicles with disc brakes** the brake pedal will require more pumping and frequent checking of fluid level in master cylinder during bleeding operation.

Never use brake fluid that has been drained from hydraulic system when bleeding the brakes. Be sure the disc brake pistons are returned to their normal positions and that the shoe and lining assemblies are properly seated. Before driving the vehicle, check brake operation to be sure that a firm pedal has been obtained.

BRAKE PAD SERVICE

REMOVAL

1. Remove caliper as outlined previously.
2. Lift upward on outward shoe retaining spring of outboard shoe until it clears center lug, then remove shoe from caliper.
3. Pull inboard shoe outward to disengage retainer springs from pistons,

then remove inboard shoe from caliper.

INSTALLATION

1. Install inboard shoe into caliper, ensuring retainer spring tangs are fully positioned into pistons.
2. Snap outboard shoe retaining spring over housing center lug, then install outboard shoe into caliper.
3. Install brake caliper as outlined further on.

CALIPER SERVICE

CALIPER REMOVAL

1. Siphon enough brake fluid out of the master cylinder to bring fluid level to 1/3 full to avoid fluid overflow when the caliper pistons are pushed back into bores.
2. Raise vehicle and remove front wheels.
3. Mark relationship between wheel to hub and bearing assembly. Remove tire and wheel assembly.
4. Using a suitable C-clamp and block of wood, push pistons back together into caliper bores.
5. If caliper assembly is to be serviced, remove inlet fitting attaching bolt, copper washer, and inlet fitting from caliper housing. Plug opening in inlet fitting to prevent fluid loss and contamination. **Do not crimp brake hose, as this may damage internal structure of hose. If only shoe and lining assemblies are to be replaced, do not disconnect brake line fitting from caliper.**
6. Remove two mounting bolts, then remove caliper. If only shoe and lining assemblies are to be replaced, suspend caliper from chassis using suitable hanger. **Do not allow caliper to hang by brake hose.**

CALIPER DISASSEMBLY

1. Remove caliper assembly as outlined previously, then drain brake fluid from caliper.
2. Position shop towel in interior part of caliper, then slowly apply compressed air to inlet port and remove pistons. **It is imperative that one piston be partially installed to facilitate removal of second piston from bore. A pad or wooden spacer may be used to prevent complete removal of first piston.**
3. Remove piston boots from caliper bores, then using suitable wooden or plastic tool, pry piston seals from caliper bore grooves. **Do not use a metal tool of any kind to remove seal as it may damage bore.**
4. Remove bleeder valve from caliper.
5. Inspect piston for scoring, nicks, corrosion, and wear and replace as needed.
6. Inspect caliper housing and seal grooves for corrosion, nicks, scoring and excessive wear, and use crocus cloth to polish away corrosion from housing bore. Replace caliper housing if corrosion in and around seal grooves will not clean up with crocus cloth.
7. Clean all parts with denatured alcohol. Dry with unlubricated compressed air. Blow out all passages in housing and bleeder valve.

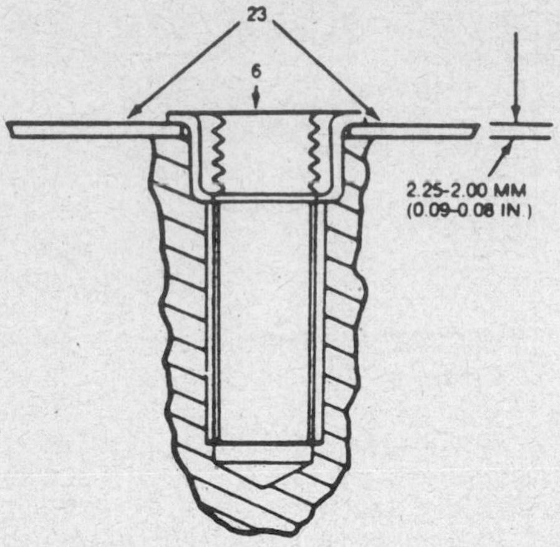
23
6
2.25-2.00 MM
(0.09-0.08 IN.)
6. SUPPORT BUSHING
23. SHIM STOCK
GC4079100067000X
Fig. 2 Support bushing installation

MOUNTING BRACKET SERVICE

Removal

1. Remove caliper as outlined previously.
2. Using suitable Torx bit, remove mounting bracket attaching bolts and the mounting bracket.

Bushing & Boot Replacement

1. Remove mounting bracket from vehicle.
2. Remove bolt boots from support bushings, **Fig. 1.**
3. Clamp bracket in a suitable vise, then pry support bushings from inner bushings in bracket ears with small screwdriver.
4. Using a paper clip, pull inner bushings from mounting bracket ears.
5. Lubricate inner bushings with silicone based grease, then install bushings flush with bracket ears.
6. Position .080-.090 inch thick shim stock on bracket ear face, then drive support bushings into inner bushings, **Fig. 2.** When properly installed, bushing should protrude .080-.090 inch above bracket ear face.
7. Snap new bolt boots over support bushing lip.

Installation

1. Coat mounting bracket attaching bolt threads with Loctite sealant or equivalent.
2. Align mounting bracket holes, then install mounting bracket and tighten attaching bolts to specifications.

CALIPER ASSEMBLY

1. Install bleeder valve.
2. Lubricate piston seals with clean brake fluid, then carefully install seals into caliper bore grooves. **Ensure seals are not twisted.**
3. Lubricate boots and install onto pistons, then push pistons fully into caliper bores.
4. Seat boots into caliper bores using boot seal installer tool No. J-36349 or equivalent.

CALIPER INSTALLATION

1. Position caliper over rotor and onto mounting bracket.
2. Lubricate entire length of mounting bolts with silicone based grease, then install bolts and tighten to specifications.
3. If inlet fitting was removed, install fitting using new copper washer.
4. Install front wheels, fill master cylinder to proper level, then bleed brake system as required. **Before moving vehicle, pump brake pedal several times to be sure it is firm. Do not move vehicle until a firm pedal is obtained.**

ROTOR

REPLACE

1. Raise and support vehicle, then remove tire and wheel assembly.
2. Remove caliper and caliper mounting bracket as described in "Caliper Service."
3. Remove rotor from hub and bearing assembly.
4. Reverse procedure to install.

DISC BRAKE SPECIFICATIONS

CALIPER SPECIFICATIONS

Year	Model	Caliper Bore Dia. Inch.
1992-94	All	1.654

ROTOR SPECIFICATIONS

Model	Year	Nominal Thickness	Discard Thickness	Thickness Variation (Parallelism)	Lateral Runout (T.I.R.)
All	1992-94	1.039	.972	.0005	.003

TIGHTENING SPECIFICATIONS

Component	Torque/Ft. Lbs.
Brake Hose Bracket Bolt	18
Brake Hose To Caliper Inlet Fitting Bolt	32
Brake Pipe Connection	11
Caliper Bleeder Valve	62①
Caliper Mounting Bracket Bolt	148
Caliper Slide Bolt	80

①—Inch lbs.

PBR Dual Piston Front Disc Brake

INDEX

PRECAUTIONS

1. Grease or any other foreign material must be kept off the brake linings, caliper, surfaces of the disc and external surfaces of the hub, during service procedures. Handling the brake disc and caliper should be done in a way to avoid deformation of the disc and nicking or scratching brake linings.
2. If inspection reveals rubber piston seals are worn or damaged, they should be replaced immediately.
3. During removal and installation of a wheel assembly, exercise care so as not to interfere with or damage the caliper splash shield, or bleeder screw.
4. Front wheel bearings preload should be adjusted to specifications .
5. Be sure vehicle is centered on hoist before servicing any of the front end components to avoid bending or damaging the disc splash shield on full right or left wheel turns.
6. Before the vehicle is moved after any brake service work, be sure to obtain a firm brake pedal.
7. The assembly bolts of two piece caliper housings should not be disturbed unless the caliper requires service.

DESCRIPTION

This front caliper, **Fig. 1**, consists of dual pistons and an aluminum housing which is suspended on the shoe and lining assemblies. Hydraulic pressure, created by applying force to the brake pedal, acts equally against the pistons and the bottom of the caliper bores to move the pistons outward. This action slides the caliper inward, resulting in a clamping action on the brake rotor. This clamping action forces the linings against the rotor, creating the friction necessary to stop the vehicle.

TROUBLESHOOTING

BRAKE ROUGHNESS

The most common cause of brake chatter on disc brakes is a variation in thickness of the disc. If roughness or vibration is encountered during highway operation or if pedal pulsation is experienced at low speeds, the disc may have excessive thickness variation. To check for this condition, measure the disc at 12 points with a micrometer at a radius approximately one inch from edge of disc. If thickness measurements vary by more than .0005 inch, the disc should be replaced with a new one.

Excessive lateral runout of braking disc may cause a "knocking back" of the pistons, possibly creating increased pedal travel and vibration when brakes are applied.

Before checking the runout, wheel bearings should be adjusted. The readjustment is very important and will be required at the completion of the test to prevent bearing failure. Be sure to make the adjustment according to the recommendations given under "Front Wheel Bearings, Adjust" in the car chapters.

BRAKE SYSTEM BLEED

Pressure bleeding is recommended for all hydraulic disc brake systems.

The disc brake hydraulic system can be bled manually or with pressure bleeding equipment. **On vehicles with disc brakes** the brake pedal will require more pumping and frequent checking of fluid level in master cylinder during bleeding operation.

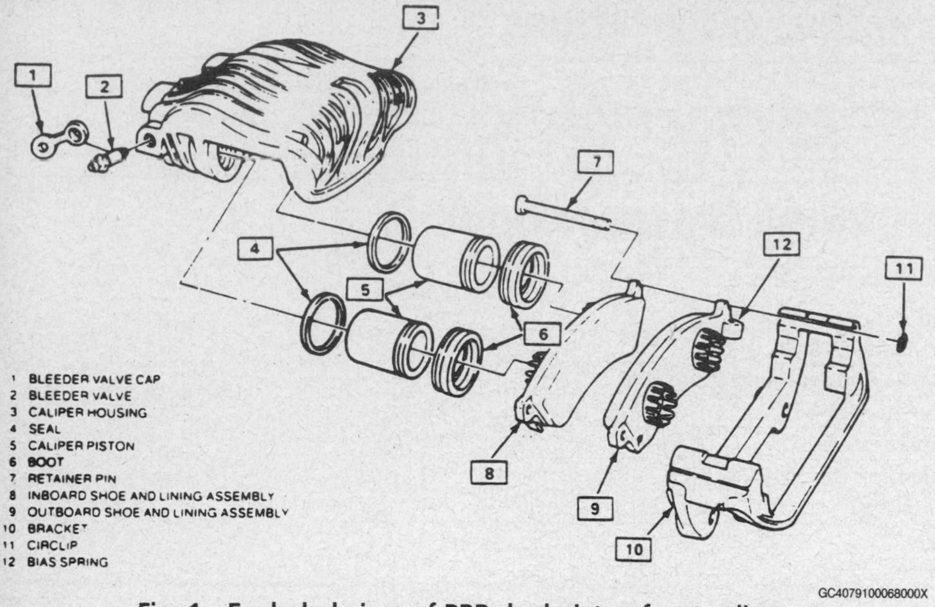
1 BLEEDER VALVE CAP
2 BLEEDER VALVE
3 CALIPER HOUSING
4 SEAL
5 CALIPER PISTON
6 BOOT
7 RETAINER PIN
8 INBOARD SHOE AND LINING ASSEMBLY
9 OUTBOARD SHOE AND LINING ASSEMBLY
10 BRACKET
11 CIRCLIP
12 BIAS SPRING
GC4079100068000X

Fig. 1 Exploded view of PBR dual piston front caliper

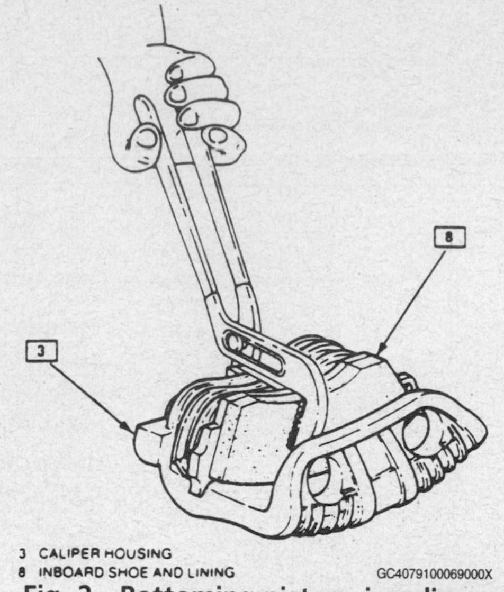
3 CALIPER HOUSING
8 INBOARD SHOE AND LINING
GC4079100069000X

Fig. 2 Bottoming pistons in caliper bore

Never use brake fluid that has been drained from hydraulic system when bleeding the brakes. Be sure the disc brake pistons are returned to their normal positions and that the shoe and lining assemblies are properly seated. Before driving the vehicle, check brake operation to be sure that a firm pedal has been obtained.

BRAKE PAD SERVICE

REMOVAL

1. Remove brake caliper as outlined previously.
2. Position suitable pliers over caliper and center of inboard shoe and lining as shown, **Fig. 2**, then squeeze pliers to bottom pistons in caliper bores.
3. Remove shoe and lining assemblies.

INSTALLATION

1. Install inboard shoe and lining, ensuring tangs on shoe fully engage pistons. When properly installed, shoe should be flush with piston.
2. Install outboard shoe and lining into caliper housing, ensuring insulators are fully seated into holes in outboard side of housing.
3. Install caliper as outlined further on.

CALIPER SERVICE

CALIPER REMOVAL

1. Remove 2/3 of the total brake fluid capacity from master cylinder reservoir.
2. Raise and support vehicle, then remove tire and wheel assembly.
3. Install two wheel retaining nuts to retain rotor in position.
4. If caliper requires overhaul, remove inlet fitting attaching bolt, then disconnect inlet fitting from caliper housing. Discard the two gaskets, then plug openings in inlet fitting and caliper to prevent loss or contamination of fluid. **Do not crimp brake hose, as this may damage internal structure of hose.**
5. Remove circlip (11) and retaining pin (7), **Fig. 1**, then pull caliper off rotor and mounting bracket. If only shoe and linings require replacement, suspend caliper from upper control arm to prevent damage to brake hose.

CALIPER DISASSEMBLY

1. Remove shoe and lining assemblies as previously described.
2. Pad interior of caliper housing with shop towels to prevent damage to pistons during removal.
3. Position shop towel in interior part of caliper, then slowly apply compressed air to inlet port and remove pistons. **It is imperative that one piston be partially installed to facilitate removal of second piston from bore. A pad or wooden spacer may be used to prevent complete removal of first piston.**
4. Remove dust boots from pistons.
5. Using a small piece of wood or plastic, remove piston seal from bore. **Do not use a metal tool of any kind to remove seal as it may damage bore.**
6. Remove bleeder valve cap and bleeder valve.
7. Inspect piston for scoring, nicks, corrosion, and wear and replace as needed.
8. Inspect caliper housing and seal groove for corrosion, nicks, scoring and excessive wear, and use crocus cloth to polish away corrosion from housing bore. Replace caliper housing if corrosion in and around seal groove will not clean up with crocus cloth.
9. Clean all parts with denatured alcohol. Dry with unlubricated compressed air. Blow out all passages in housing and bleeder valve.

CALIPER ASSEMBLY

1. Install cap onto bleeder valve, then install bleeder valve into caliper.
2. Using clean brake fluid, lubricate piston seals, then install seals into caliper bore grooves. Ensure seals are not twisted during installation.
3. Using clean brake fluid, lubricate caliper bores and piston assemblies.
4. Install boot over end of piston. Place piston into caliper bore, then push downward until fully bottomed in bore. Ensure boot is properly seated into groove around piston and into groove in caliper bore.
5. Repeat step 4 for remaining piston.
6. Install shoes and linings as outlined further on, then bleed brake system.

CALIPER INSTALLATION

1. Ensure guiding surfaces on shoe and lining assemblies and mounting bracket are seated correctly, then position caliper over rotor and onto mounting bracket.
2. Press caliper housing downward to compress bias springs (12), **Fig. 1**, then install new retainer pin and circlip. **Two sets of retainer pins are available for service, one for base calipers and one for heavy duty. Since the circlip grooves are cut in different positions, ensure the correct retainer pin is used.**
3. If caliper was overhauled, reconnect inlet fitting using new gaskets, then bleed brake system as required.
4. Reinstall wheel and tire assembly, then lower vehicle.
5. Fill master cylinder to proper level, then pump brake pedal firmly and slowly three times to bring pads into contact with brake rotor.

ROTOR

REPLACE

1. Remove caliper as described in "Caliper, Service."
2. Remove caliper mounting bracket attaching bolts, then the mounting bracket.
3. Remove rotor from hub assembly.
4. Reverse procedure to install.

DISC BRAKE SPECIFICATIONS

CALIPER SPECIFICATIONS

Year	Model	Caliper Bore Dia. Inch.
1992-94	All	1.50

ROTOR SPECIFICATIONS

Model	Year	Nominal Thickness	Minimum Refinish Thickness	Thickness Variation (Parallelism)	Lateral Runout (T.I.R.)
CHEVROLET					
Camaro	1992	1.043	.987	.0005	.006
Corvette	1992-94①	.795	.744	.0005	.006
	1992-94②	1.110	1.059	.0005	.006
PONTIAC					
Firebird	1992	1.043	.987	.0005	.006

①—Standard Brake System.
②—Heavy Duty Brake System.

TIGHTENING SPECIFICATIONS

Component	Torque/Ft. Lbs.
Brake Hose To Caliper	30
Caliper Bleeder Screw	80
Front Caliper Mounting Bracket	166
Wheel Lug Nuts	100

AC-Delco Single Piston Rear Disc Brake (Type 1)

INDEX

PRECAUTIONS

1. Grease or any other foreign material must be kept off the brake linings, caliper, surfaces of the disc and external surfaces of the hub, during service procedures. Handling the brake disc and caliper should be done in a way to avoid deformation of the disc and nicking or scratching brake linings.
2. If inspection reveals rubber piston seals are worn or damaged, they should be replaced immediately.
3. During removal and installation of a wheel assembly, exercise care so as not to interfere with or damage the caliper splash shield, or bleeder screw.
4. Front wheel bearings preload should be adjusted to specifications .
5. Be sure vehicle is centered on hoist before servicing any of the front end components to avoid bending or damaging the disc splash shield on full right or left wheel turns.
6. Before the vehicle is moved after any brake service work, be sure to obtain a firm brake pedal.
7. The assembly bolts of two piece caliper housings should not be disturbed unless the caliper requires service.

DESCRIPTION

Upon application of the brakes, **Fig. 1 and 2,** the cone and piston move out as one part. The nut remains stationary on the high lead screw and a gap develops between the cone and nut. When lining wear occurs, the cone and piston do not return to their original position, thereby leaving a small gap equal to the lining wear between the nut and cone. The adjusting spring causes the nut to rotate on the high lead screw to close the gap and adjust the caliper.

Upon application of parking brake, the lever rotation causes the high lead screw to turn and the nut to move down the screw, thereby loading through the cone and the cone-clutch interface of the piston, resulting in a clamp load on the linings. When the parking brake is released, the cone rotates on the clutch interface to adjust the caliper. The clutch interface prevents the cone from turning when the parking brake is applied.

TROUBLESHOOTING

BRAKE ROUGHNESS

The most common cause of brake chatter on disc brakes is a variation in thickness of the disc. If roughness or vibration is encountered during highway operation or if pedal pulsation is experienced at low speeds, the disc may have excessive thickness variation. To check for this condition, measure the disc at 12 points with a micrometer at a radius approximately one inch from edge of disc. If thickness measurements vary by more than .0005 inch, the disc should be replaced with a new one.

Excessive lateral runout of braking disc may cause a "knocking back" of the pistons, possibly creating increased pedal travel and vibration when brakes are applied.

Before checking the runout, wheel bearings should be adjusted. The readjustment is very important and will be required at the completion of the test to prevent bearing failure. Be sure to make the adjustment according to the recommendations given under "Front Wheel Bearings, Adjust" in the car chapters.

BRAKE SYSTEM BLEED

Pressure bleeding is recommended for all hydraulic disc brake systems.

The disc brake hydraulic system can be bled manually or with pressure bleeding equipment. The brake pedal will require pumping and frequent checking of fluid level in master cylinder during bleeding operation.

Never use brake fluid that has been drained from hydraulic system when bleeding the brakes. Be sure the disc brake pistons are returned to their normal positions and that the shoe and lining assemblies are properly seated. Before driving the vehicle, check brake operation to be sure that a firm pedal has been obtained.

BRAKE PAD SERVICE

1. Remove caliper as described previously and remove shoe and lining.
2. Remove and discard the two caliper mounting sleeves and the four bushings. Using silicone lubricant, install new bushings and seals. **Sleeves are installed in inner bushings.**
3. Remove and discard piston two-way check valve and install a new one,

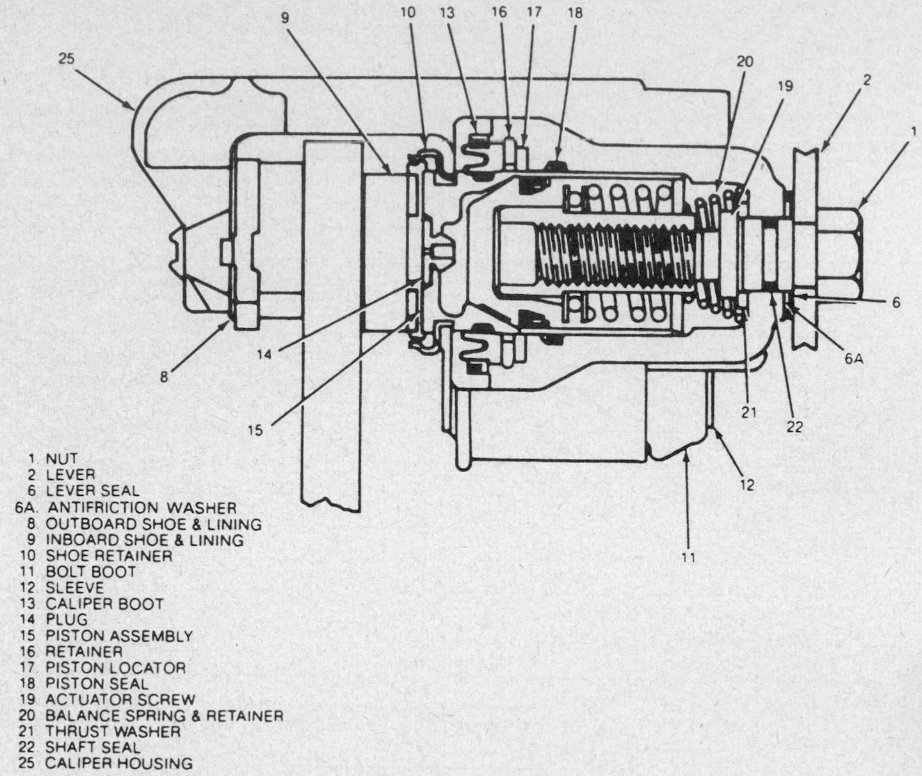
1 NUT
2 LEVER
6 LEVER SEAL
6A. ANTIFRICTION WASHER
8 OUTBOARD SHOE & LINING
9 INBOARD SHOE & LINING
10 SHOE RETAINER
11 BOLT BOOT
12 SLEEVE
13 CALIPER BOOT
14 PLUG
15 PISTON ASSEMBLY
16 RETAINER
17 PISTON LOCATOR
18 PISTON SEAL
19 ACTUATOR SCREW
20 BALANCE SPRING & RETAINER
21 THRUST WASHER
22 SHAFT SEAL
25 CALIPER HOUSING

GC4079100070000X

Fig. 1 Cross-sectional view of typical AC-Delco rear disc brake

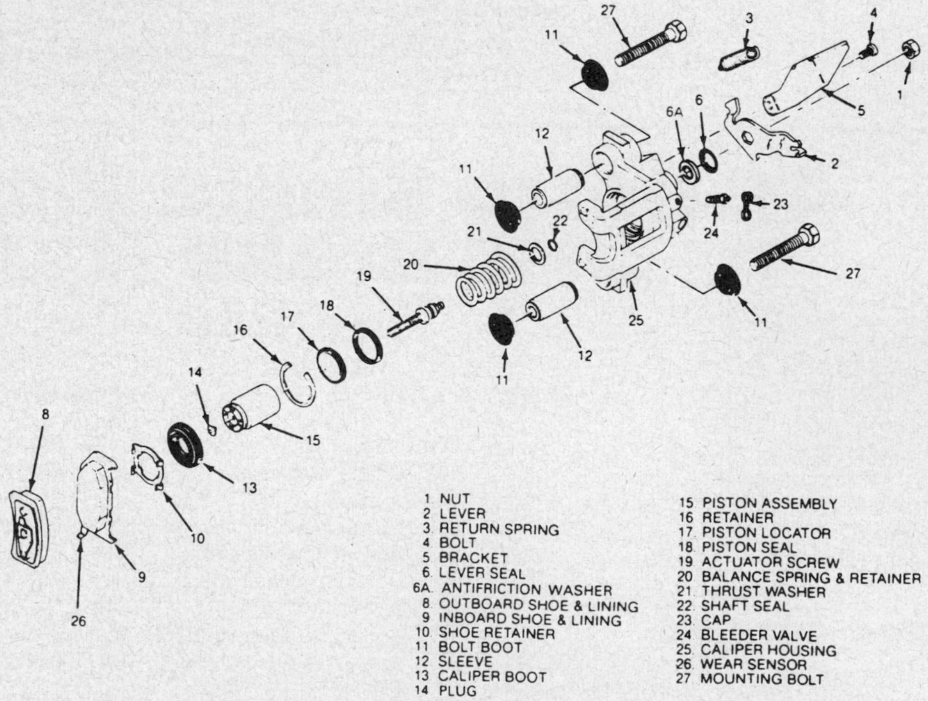
1 NUT
2 LEVER
3 RETURN SPRING
4 BOLT
5 BRACKET
6 LEVER SEAL
6A. ANTIFRICTION WASHER
8 OUTBOARD SHOE & LINING
9 INBOARD SHOE & LINING
10 SHOE RETAINER
11 BOLT BOOT
12 SLEEVE
13 CALIPER BOOT
14 PLUG
15 PISTON ASSEMBLY
16 RETAINER
17 PISTON LOCATOR
18 PISTON SEAL
19 ACTUATOR SCREW
20 BALANCE SPRING & RETAINER
21 THRUST WASHER
22 SHAFT SEAL
23 CAP
24 BLEEDER VALVE
25 CALIPER HOUSING
26 WEAR SENSOR
27 MOUNTING BOLT

GC4079100071000X

Fig. 2 Exploded view of rear disc brake caliper

Fig. 3. If leakage is noted from end of piston after check valve is removed caliper must be overhauled.

4. Position new inboard shoe assembly on piston. The D-shaped tab must fit into indentation in piston. If piston requires rotation, use spanner wrench to rotate piston, **Fig. 4. Install new spring retainers as applicable.**
5. Install new outboard shoe assembly onto caliper. Install caliper and **torque** mounting bolts to 30 ft. lbs.
6. Position channel lock pliers over

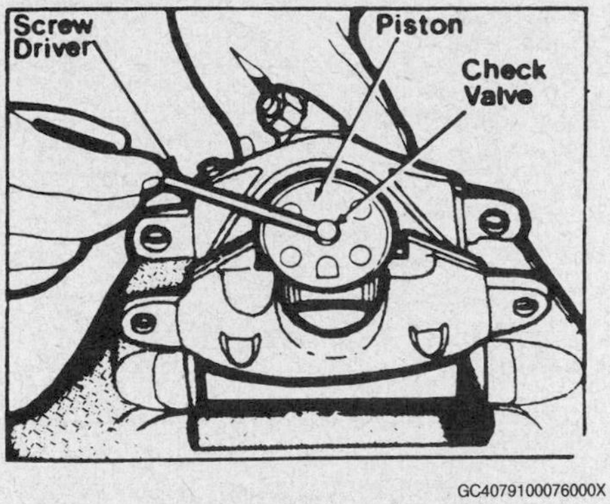
Screw Driver
Piston
Check Valve
GC4079100076000X

Fig. 3 Piston check valve removal

brake shoe ears, if equipped, and bottom edge of caliper. While holding moderate force on brake pedal, clinch outboard shoe.

CALIPER SERVICE

CALIPER REMOVAL

Do not mix power steering fluid with brake fluid. If brake seals contact steering fluid or steering seals contact brake fluid, damage will result.

1. Remove two thirds of the total brake fluid capacity from the master cylinder front reservoir, to prevent overflow of brake fluid.
2. Support vehicle on a hoist and remove tire and wheel assembly.
3. Install one nut with flat side facing rotor to prevent rotor from falling out when caliper is removed.
4. Loosen parking brake cable tension at equalizer, then remove cable from parking brake lever and remove return spring, locknut, lever, lever seal and anti-friction washer. **Lever must be held in place while removing nut.**
5. Clean surface in area of lever seal, then using a 7 inch (or larger) C-clamp, with the solid end on lever stop and screw end on back of outboard lining, turn clamp until piston is bottomed in caliper. **Do not position C-clamp on actuator screw.**
6. Before removing clamp, lubricate housing surface under lever seal with silicone lubricant.
7. Install anti-friction washer, a new lever seal and lever. **Install lever on hex with arm pointing downward.**
8. Rotate lever toward front of vehicle and while holding in this position, install nut and **torque** to 25 ft. lbs. and rotate lever back to stop.
9. Disconnect brake line from caliper and plug openings to prevent loss of fluid and contamination. **Do not crimp brake hose, as this may damage internal structure of hose.**
10. Remove the brass bolt from block, if applicable. **If brake line nut is seized, brass bolt and block can be removed with brake line attached by removing bolt. Plug openings to prevent loss of fluid and entry of dirt.**
11. Remove caliper mounting bolts and remove caliper.

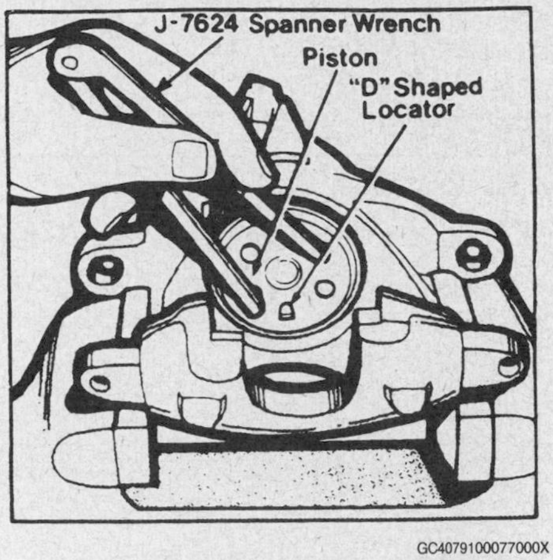
J-7624 Spanner Wrench
Piston
"D" Shaped Locator
GC4079100077000X

Fig. 4 Piston rotation in boot

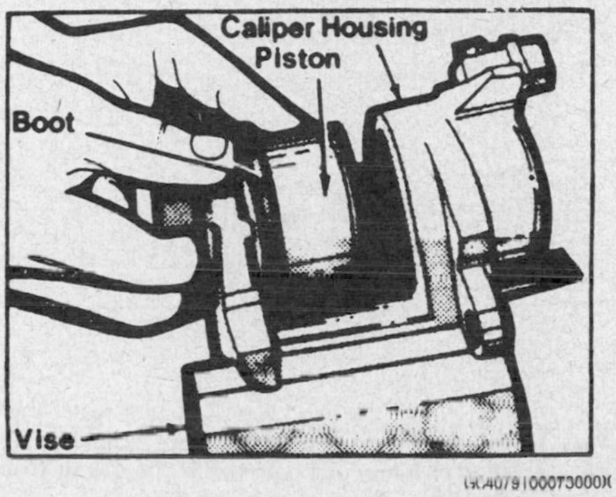
Caliper Housing
Piston
Boot
Vise
GC4079100073000X

Fig. 6 Piston positioning in caliper

12. Reverse procedure to install and **torque** caliper mounting bolts to 30 ft. lbs. **When installing brass bolt and block, use two new copper gaskets. Torque bolt or connector to 30 ft. lbs.**

CALIPER DISASSEMBLY

1. Clamp caliper in a vise and remove the two mounting sleeves and four bushings, **Fig. 2.**
2. Remove shoe dampening spring from end of piston.
3. If installed, remove locknut, lever seal, and anti-friction washer.
4. Rotate parking brake lever in parking brake apply direction to remove piston from housing, **Fig. 5.** If piston will not move, Use a 9/16 inch wrench, rotate actuator screw clockwise on right-hand caliper or counterclockwise on lefthand caliper until the piston moves from housing. **Pad caliper with shop cloths when removing piston.**
5. Remove balance spring, then remove actuator screw by pressing on thread end.
6. Remove shaft seal, and thrust washer from actuator screw.
7. Remove dust boot. **Take care not to scratch caliper housing or bore.**
8. Using a small piece of wood or plastic, remove piston seal from bore. **Do not use a metal tool of any kind to remove seal as it may damage bore.**
9. Remove bleeder screw, fitting, copper washers, and bolt. Remove bracket only if damaged.

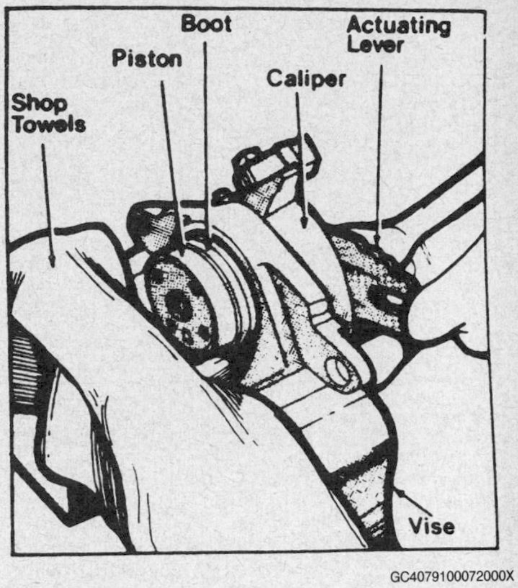
Boot
Actuating Lever
Piston
Caliper
Shop Towels
Vise
GC4079100072000X

Fig. 5 Piston removal from bore

10. Inspect piston for scoring, nicks, corrosion, and wear and replace as needed.
11. Inspect caliper housing and seal groove for corrosion, nicks, scoring and excessive wear, and use crocus cloth to polish away corrosion from housing bore. Replace caliper housing if corrosion in and around seal groove will not clean up with crocus cloth.
12. Clean all parts with denatured alcohol. Dry with unlubricated compressed air. Blow out all passages in housing and bleeder valve.

CALIPER ASSEMBLY

1. Install bleeder screw and **torque** to 116 inch lbs., then install bracket, if removed, and **torque** to 31 ft. lbs.
2. Install fitting and bolt, if equipped, using new copper washer and **torque** to 24 ft. lbs.
3. Lubricate and install new piston seal. **Make sure is not twisted.**
4. Install new boot onto piston assembly with lip of boot located in piston groove and boot fold toward end of piston that contact inboard brake shoe.
5. Install new thrust washer on actuator screw, with copper side of washer towards the piston assembly.
6. Install lubricated shaft seal on actuator screw, then install actuator screw in piston.
7. Coat piston seal with clean brake fluid. Install balance spring into piston and install assembly into caliper housing, **Fig. 6.**
8. With piston installer tool No. J-23072 or equivalent push piston fully into caliper housing, **Fig. 7. The piston must be pushed straight into caliper to prevent damage to the actuator screw seal as it passes through hole in rear of piston bore.**
9. Before removing piston installer tool No. J-23072, install lubricated anti-friction washer, new lever seal, lever and locknut. Position lever away from

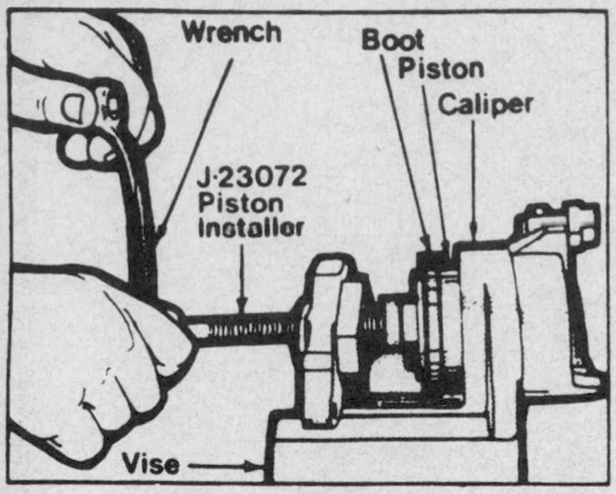
Wrench
Boot
Piston
Caliper
J-23072
Piston
Installer
Vise

GC4079100074000X

Fig. 7 Piston installation into caliper

stop, rotate forward and hold lever in position, then **torque** nut to 35 ft. lbs.

10. Remove piston installer tool No. J-23072, rotate lever back to stop and install return spring.
11. With dust boot installer tool No. J-26296 or equivalent, drive boot until seal bottoms in caliper housing, **Fig. 8.**
12. Install dampening spring in groove in end of piston.

ROTOR

REPLACE

1. Remove caliper as described in "Caliper Service."
2. Using caliper mounting bracket attaching bolts, then the mounting bracket.
3. Remove rotor from hub and bearing assembly.
4. Reverse procedure to install, adjust parking brake as described under "Adjustments."

ADJUSTMENTS

PARKING BRAKE

1. Lubricate parking brake cables at underbody rub points and at equalizer hooks and ensure free movement of all cables.
2. With parking brake fully released, jack up both rear wheels.

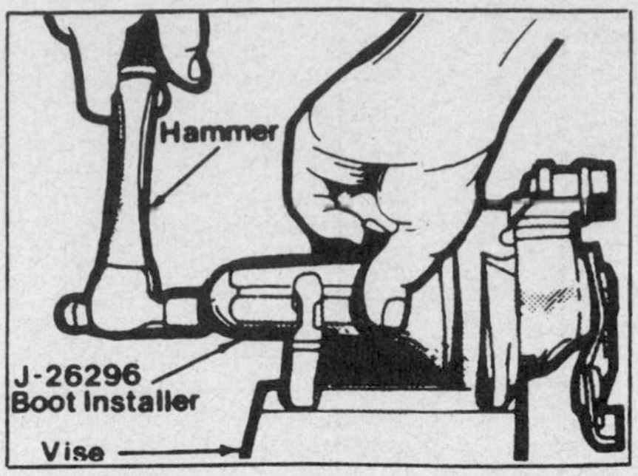
Hammer
J-26296
Boot Installer
Vise

GC4079100075000X

Fig. 8 Boot installation into caliper

3. Remove slack from cable by holding brake cable stud and tightening equalizer nut. **After tightening nut, check that caliper levers are against stops on caliper housing. If not, loosen cable until levers return to stops.**
4. Actuate parking brake several times to check adjustment.

DISC BRAKE SPECIFICATIONS

CALIPER SPECIFICATIONS

Year	Model	Caliper Bore Dia. Inch.
BUICK		
1992-94	Regal	1.38

ROTOR SPECIFICATIONS

Model	Year	Nominal Thickness	Minimum Refinish Thickness	Thickness Variation (Parallelism)	Lateral Runout (T.I.R.)
BUICK					
Regal	1992-94	.492	.441	.0005	.004

TIGHTENING SPECIFICATIONS

Component	Torque/Ft. Lbs.
Bleeder Valve	115②
Bracket Retaining Bolt	32
Caliper Mounting Bolt	92
Inlet Fitting	32
Lever Attaching Nut	35
Rotor Nut①	25
Shield Attaching Bolt	89②

—①Tool No. J 37160-A
—②Inch Lbs.

AC-Delco Single Piston Rear Disc Brake (Type 2)

INDEX

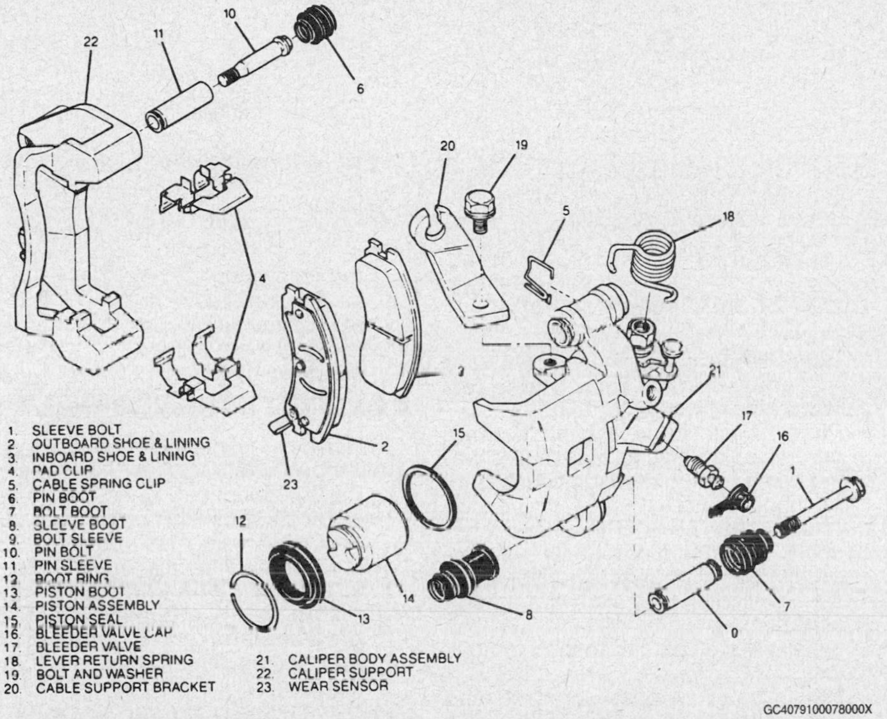

22
11
10
6
20
19
5
18
4
3
2
23
15
21
17
16
1
12
14
13
8
9
7
1. SLEEVE BOLT
2. OUTBOARD SHOE & LINING
3. INBOARD SHOE & LINING
4. PAD CLIP
5. CABLE SPRING CLIP
6. PIN BOOT
7. BOLT BOOT
8. SLEEVE BOOT
9. BOLT SLEEVE
10. PIN BOLT
11. PIN SLEEVE
12. BOOT RING
13. PISTON BOOT
14. PISTON ASSEMBLY
15. PISTON SEAL
16. BLEEDER VALVE CAP
17. BLEEDER VALVE
18. LEVER RETURN SPRING
19. BOLT AND WASHER
20. CABLE SUPPORT BRACKET
21. CALIPER BODY ASSEMBLY
22. CALIPER SUPPORT
23. WEAR SENSOR
GC4079100078000X

Fig. 1 Disassembled view of AC-Delco single piston rear disc brake caliper. Type 2

PRECAUTIONS

1. Grease or any other foreign material must be kept off the brake linings, caliper, surfaces of the disc and external surfaces of the hub, during service procedures. Handling the brake disc and caliper should be done in a way to avoid deformation of the disc and nicking or scratching brake linings.
2. If inspection reveals rubber piston seals are worn or damaged, they should be replaced immediately.
3. During removal and installation of a wheel assembly, exercise care so as not to interfere with or damage the caliper splash shield, or bleeder screw.
4. Front wheel bearings preload should be adjusted to specifications .
5. Be sure vehicle is centered on hoist before servicing any of the front end components to avoid bending or damaging the disc splash shield on full right or left wheel turns.
6. Before the vehicle is moved after any brake service work, be sure to obtain a firm brake pedal.
7. The assembly bolts of two piece caliper housings should not be disturbed unless the caliper requires service.

DESCRIPTION

The caliper assembly, **Fig. 1,** has a single bore and is mounted to the support bracket with two mounting bolt and sleeve assemblies. Hydraulic pressure created by applying the brake pedal, is converted by the caliper to a stopping force. This force acts equally against the piston and the bottom of the piston bore to move the piston outward and to slide the caliper inward resulting in a clamping action. This clamping action presses the linings against the rotor, creating friction to stop the vehicle.

When the parking brake is applied, the external caliper parking brake lever moves and rotates a spindle within the caliper housing. As the spindle rotates, a connecting rod is pushed against an internal adjusting screw which is threaded into a sleeve nut in the piston assembly. This causes the piston assembly to move outward bringing the inboard shoe and lining assembly against the rotor. As the inboard shoe and lining contacts the rotor, a reaction force causes the caliper housing to slide inward pressing the outboard shoe and lining against the rotor.

The piston assembly contains a self adjusting mechanism to keep the parking brake in proper adjustment. As the linings are worn, the piston moves through the seal to maintain proper lining to rotor clearance. The park brake adjusts to proper clearances through an internal sleeve nut that rotates and moves as one unit with the piston.

TROUBLESHOOTING

BRAKE ROUGHNESS

The most common cause of brake chatter on disc brakes is a variation in thickness of the disc. If roughness or vibration is encountered during highway operation or if pedal pulsation is experienced at low speeds, the disc may have excessive thickness variation. To check for this condition, measure the disc at 12 points with a micrometer at a radius approximately one inch from edge of disc. If thickness measurements vary by more than .0005 inch, the disc should be replaced with a new one.

Excessive lateral runout of braking disc may cause a "knocking back" of the pistons, possibly creating increased pedal travel and vibration when brakes are applied.

Before checking the runout, wheel bearings should be adjusted. The readjustment is very important and will be required at the completion of the test to prevent bearing failure. Be sure to make the adjustment according to the recommendations given under "Front Wheel Bearings, Adjust" in the car chapters.

BRAKE SYSTEM BLEED

Pressure bleeding is recommended for all hydraulic disc brake systems.

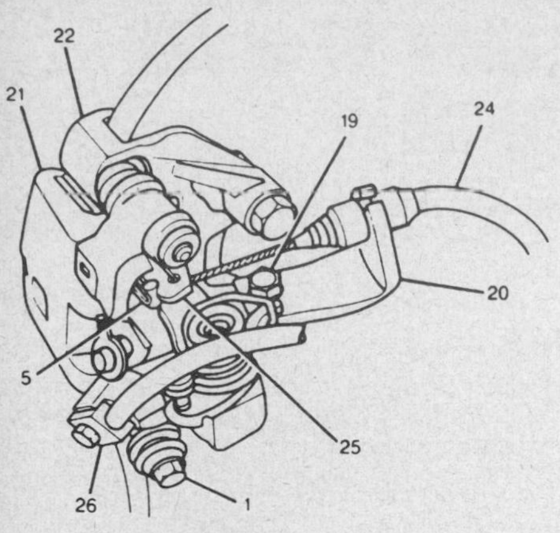
22
21
19
24
20
5
25
26
1

1 SLEEVE BOLT
5 CABLE SPRING CLIP
19 BOLT AND WASHER
20 CABLE SUPPORT BRACKET
21 CALIPER BODY ASSEMBLY
22 CALIPER SUPPORT
24 PARKING BRAKE CABLE
25 PARKING BRAKE LEVER
26 BRAKE HOSE

GC4079100079000X

Fig. 2 Caliper installation

The disc brake hydraulic system can be bled manually or with pressure bleeding equipment. The brake pedal will require pumping and frequent checking of fluid level in master cylinder during bleeding operation.

Never use brake fluid that has been drained from hydraulic system when bleeding the brakes. Be sure the disc brake pistons are returned to their normal positions and that the shoe and lining assemblies are properly seated. Before driving the vehicle, check brake operation to be sure that a firm pedal has been obtained.

BRAKE PAD SERVICE

1. Remove 2/3 of brake fluid from master cylinder reservoir.
2. Raise and support vehicle.
3. Mark relationship of wheel to axle flange, then remove wheel and tire assembly.
4. Remove bolt and washer attaching cable support bracket to caliper body, **Fig. 2.**
5. Remove sleeve bolt and pivot caliper assembly up, **Fig. 3. Do not completely remove caliper assembly body.**
6. Remove outboard and inboard shoe and linings and two pad clips from caliper support.
7. Using a suitable spanner type tool in piston slots to turn piston assembly and thread it into caliper body assembly.
8. After bottoming piston, lift inner edge of boot next to piston assembly and press out any trapped air.
9. Ensure slots in end of piston are positioned as shown in **Fig. 4** before pivoting caliper body assembly down over shoe and linings in caliper support. Use suitable spanner type tool to turn piston as necessary.
10. Install pad clips and outboard and inboard shoe and linings in caliper support. **Ensure wear sensor is on outboard shoe positioned downward at leading edge of rotor during forward wheel rotation.**

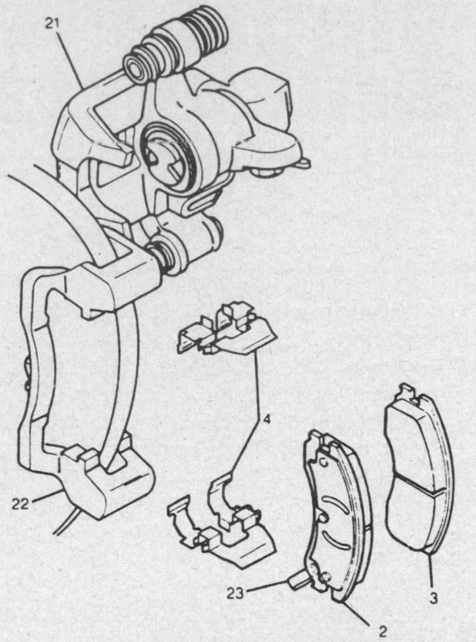
21
4
22
23
3
2

2 OUTBOARD SHOE & LINING
3 INBOARD SHOE & LINING
4 PAD CLIP
21 CALIPER BODY ASSEMBLY
22 CALIPER SUPPORT
23 WEAR SENSOR

GC4079100083000X

Fig. 3 Shoe & lining installation

11. Pivot caliper body assembly down over shoe and lining assemblies being careful not to damage piston boot on inboard shoe.
12. After caliper body is in position, recheck installation of pad clips. If necessary, use a small screwdriver to reseat or center pad clips on support abutments.
13. Install sleeve bolt and **torque** to 20 ft. lbs.
14. Install cable support bracket and **torque** bolt to 32 ft. lbs.
15. Install wheels and tires aligning previous marks, then lower vehicle.
16. Apply approximately 175 lbs. of force to brake pedal three times to seat shoe and linings against rotor.

CALIPER SERVICE

CALIPER, REPLACE

1. Raise and support vehicle.
2. Mark relationship of wheel to axle flange, then remove wheel and tire assembly.
3. Remove brake hose from caliper, **Fig. 2.** Plug openings in caliper and brake hose to prevent fluid loss and contamination.
4. Lift up on end of cable spring to free end of cable from lever, then disconnect parking brake cable from lever.
5. Remove bolt and washer attaching cable support bracket to caliper body assembly.
6. Remove sleeve bolt and caliper body assembly.
7. Reverse procedure to install noting the following:
   a. **Torque** sleeve bolt to 20 ft. lbs.
   b. **Torque** cable support bracket to 32 ft. lbs.
   c. Bleed brakes.

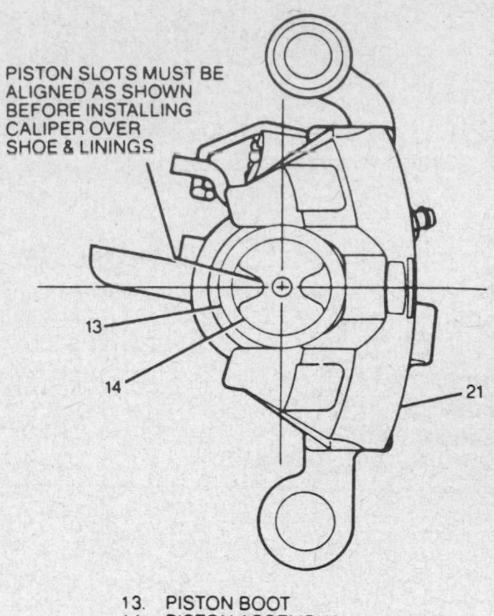
PISTON SLOTS MUST BE
ALIGNED AS SHOWN
BEFORE INSTALLING
CALIPER OVER
SHOE & LININGS
13
14
21

13. PISTON BOOT
14. PISTON ASSEMBLY
21. CALIPER BODY ASSEMBLY

GC4079100084000X

Fig. 4 Positioning piston slots

CALIPER DISASSEMBLY

1. Remove caliper from vehicle as described under "Caliper Replace."
2. Pad interior of caliper assembly with a clean shop towel, then remove piston assembly using low pressure compressed air into caliper inlet hole, **Fig. 5. Do not place fingers in front of piston in an attempt to catch or protect piston when applying compressed air. This could result in serious injury.**
3. Using a small screwdriver, pry up one end of boot ring, **Fig. 6.** Work boot ring out of caliper groove.
4. Using a small wooden or plastic tool, remove piston seal from caliper bore groove.
5. Remove bleeder valve and bleeder valve cap.
6. If lever return spring replacement is required, remove by using a screwdriver to disengage return spring from parking brake lever, then unhook spring from stopper pin, **Fig. 7.**
7. Remove pin boot, pin bolt, then the bolt sleeve and sleeve bolt from caliper body.
8. Remove pin bolt and pin sleeve from caliper support.
9. Clean all parts in clean denatured alcohol, then dry with unlubricated low pressure compressed air. Blow out all passages in caliper body and bleeder valve.
10. Inspect piston assembly for nicks, cracks, wear or corrosion. Replace piston if any damage is found.
11. Inspect piston bore for scoring, nicks, wear or corrosion. Use crocus cloth to

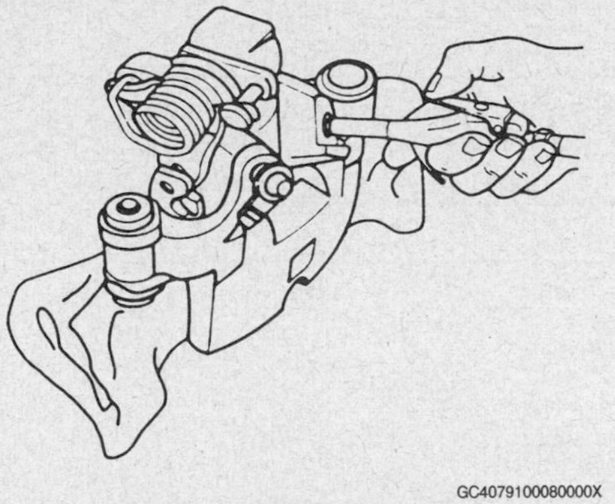
GC4079100080000X

Fig. 5 Removing piston

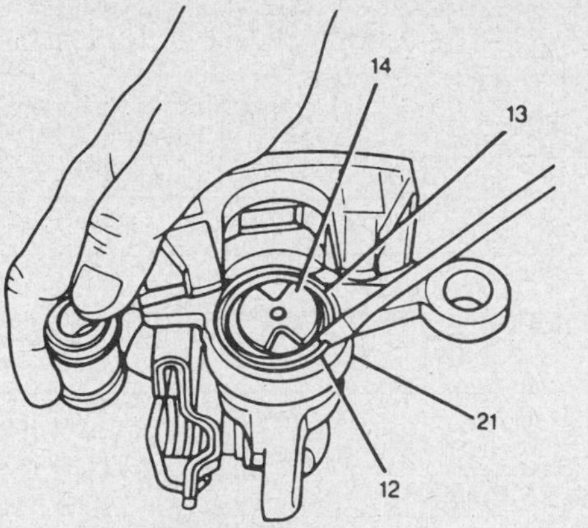
14
13
21
12
GC4079100081000X

12. BOOT RING
13. PISTON BOOT
14. PISTON ASSEMBLY
21. CALIPER BODY ASSEMBLY

Fig. 6 Removing boot ring

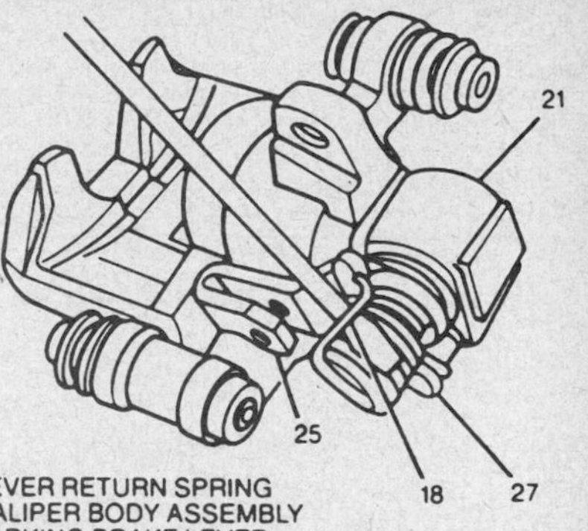
21
25
18
27
GC4079100082000X

18. LEVER RETURN SPRING
21. CALIPER BODY ASSEMBLY
25. PARKING BRAKE LEVER
27. STOPPER PIN

Fig. 7 Removing lever return spring

polish out light corrosion. Replace caliper if any heavy corrosion is found. **Do not hone caliper bore.**

12. Inspect seal groove for nicks or burrs. If found, replace caliper.
13. Inspect boots for cuts, tears or deterioration. If damaged, replace boots.
14. Inspect bolt sleeve and pin sleeve for corrosion or damage. Replace corroded or damaged sleeves. **Do not attempt to polish away corrosion.**

CALIPER ASSEMBLY

1. Lubricate pin sleeve with silicone grease, then install pin bolts and pin sleeve to caliper support. **Torque** bolts to 20 ft. lbs.
2. Lubricate sleeve boot with silicone grease, then compress lip on sleeve boot and push it all the way through caliper body assembly until lip emerges and seals on inboard face of caliper ear.
3. Lubricate push bolt sleeve with silicone grease, then push it in through lip end of boot until boot seats in sleeve groove at other end.
4. Install bolt boot onto caliper body.
5. Install small end of pin boot over pin sleeve until boot seats in pin groove.
6. If removed, position new lever return spring with hook end around stopper pin, then pry other end of spring over lever.
7. Install bleeder valve and bleeder valve cap. **Torque** bleeder valve to 8 ft. lbs.
8. Lubricate new piston seal with clean brake fluid and install in groove in caliper bore ensuring it is not twisted.
9. Install piston boot onto piston assembly.
10. Lubricate piston assembly with clean brake fluid.
11. Start piston assembly in by hand, then thread into bottom of caliper bore using spanner type tool in slots in end of piston assembly.
12. Ensure outside edge of piston boot is smoothly seated in counterbore of caliper body assembly.
13. Work boot ring into groove near open end of caliper bore using care not to pinch piston boot between boot ring and caliper body.
14. After installing ring, lift inner edge of boot next to piston assembly and press out any trapped air. Boot must lay flat.
15. Install caliper on vehicle as described under "Caliper Service."

ROTOR

REPLACE

1. Remove caliper assembly as described under "Caliper Service."
2. Remove caliper mounting bracket attaching bolts, then the mounting bracket.
3. Remove rotor from hub and bearing assembly.
4. Reverse procedure to install, adjust parking brake as described under "Adjustments."

ADJUSTMENTS

PARKING BRAKE

1. Cycle brake system as follows:
   a. Apply service brake with a pedal force of 150 lbs. and release.
   b. Fully apply parking brake using approximately 125 lbs. of force on final stroke, and release.
   c. Apply and release parking brake two additional times as described above.
2. Check parking brake pedal assembly for full release by turning ignition on and inspecting brake warning light. Light should be off. If brake warning light is on and parking brake appears to be fully released, operate the manual pedal release lever and pull downward on front park brake cable to remove slack from pedal assembly.
3. Raise and support vehicle.
4. Check parking brake levers on rear calipers. Levers should be against the stops on caliper housing. If levers are not against stops, check for binding in rear brake cables and position levers against stops.
5. Tighten parking brake cable at adjuster until either left or right lever begins to move off of stop.
6. Loosen adjuster until lever which moved off of stop in step four is again resting on stop. **Both levers should be resting on caliper stops after completing this step.**
7. Operate parking brake several times to check adjustment. A firm pedal feel should be obtained by pumping pedal less than one stroke.
8. Inspect left and right caliper levers. Both levers must be resting on stops after adjustment of parking brake.
9. Check operation of parking brake. If possible, place vehicle on a grade and check parking brake holding ability.

DISC BRAKE SPECIFICATIONS

CALIPER SPECIFICATIONS

Year	Model	Caliper Bore Dia. Inch.
1992-94	All	1.38

ROTOR SPECIFICATIONS

Model	Year	Nominal Thickness	Minimum Refinish Thickness	Thickness Variation (Parallelism)	Lateral Runout (T.I.R.)
All	1992-94	.433	.389	.0005	.002

TIGHTENING SPECIFICATIONS

Component	Torque/Ft. Lbs.
Brake Hose To Caliper	32
Caliper Bleeder Screw	9
Caliper Bracket Mounting Bolts	83
Caliper Mounting Bolts	63
Master Cylinder To Booster	22
Wheel Speed Sensor Mounting Bolt	9
Wheel Lug Nuts	100

AC-Delco Single Piston Rear Disc Brake (Type 3)

INDEX

PRECAUTIONS

1. Grease or any other foreign material must be kept off the brake linings, caliper, surfaces of the disc and external surfaces of the hub, during service procedures. Handling the brake disc and caliper should be done in a way to avoid deformation of the disc and nicking or scratching brake linings.
2. If inspection reveals rubber piston seals are worn or damaged, they should be replaced immediately.
3. During removal and installation of a wheel assembly, exercise care so as not to interfere with or damage the caliper splash shield, or bleeder screw.
4. Front wheel bearings preload should be adjusted to specifications .
5. Be sure vehicle is centered on hoist before servicing any of the front end components to avoid bending or damaging the disc splash shield on full right or left wheel turns.
6. Before the vehicle is moved after any brake service work, be sure to obtain a firm brake pedal.
7. The assembly bolts of two piece caliper housings should not be disturbed unless the caliper requires service.

DESCRIPTION

This rear caliper, **Fig. 1,** has a single bore and is mounted to the support bracket with two mounting bolts. Hydraulic pressure, created by applying force to the brake pedal, is converted by the caliper into friction. The hydraulic pressure is applied equally against the piston and the bottom of the caliper bore moving the piston outward and the caliper housing inward, resulting in a clamping action on the brake rotor.

The caliper includes an integral parking brake mechanism. When the parking brake is applied, the lever turns an actuator screw which is threaded into a nut in the caliper piston. As the actuator screw turns, the piston is forced out, applying force on the rotor. The piston contains a self-adjusting mechanism to keep the parking brake in proper adjustment and to ensure proper clearance when the parking brake is released.

TROUBLESHOOTING

BRAKE ROUGHNESS

The most common cause of brake chatter on disc brakes is a variation in thickness of the disc. If roughness or vibration is encountered during highway operation or if pedal pulsation is experienced at low speeds, the disc may have excessive thickness variation. To check for this condition, measure the disc at 12 points with a micrometer at a radius approximately one inch from edge of disc. If thickness measurements vary by more than .0005 inch, the disc should be replaced with a new one.

Excessive lateral runout of braking disc may cause a "knocking back" of the pistons, possibly creating increased pedal travel and vibration when brakes are applied.

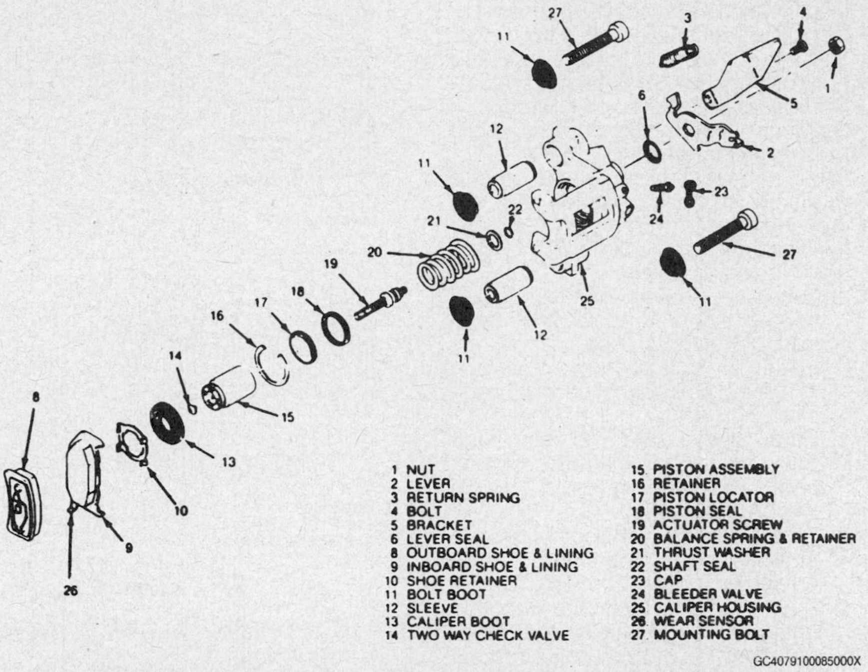
1 NUT
2 LEVER
3 RETURN SPRING
4 BOLT
5 BRACKET
6 LEVER SEAL
8 OUTBOARD SHOE & LINING
9 INBOARD SHOE & LINING
10 SHOE RETAINER
11 BOLT BOOT
12 SLEEVE
13 CALIPER BOOT
14 TWO WAY CHECK VALVE
15 PISTON ASSEMBLY
16 RETAINER
17 PISTON LOCATOR
18 PISTON SEAL
19 ACTUATOR SCREW
20 BALANCE SPRING & RETAINER
21 THRUST WASHER
22 SHAFT SEAL
23 CAP
24 BLEEDER VALVE
25 CALIPER HOUSING
26 WEAR SENSOR
27 MOUNTING BOLT
GC4079100085000X

Fig. 1 Exploded view of AC-Delco 7735 series rear caliper

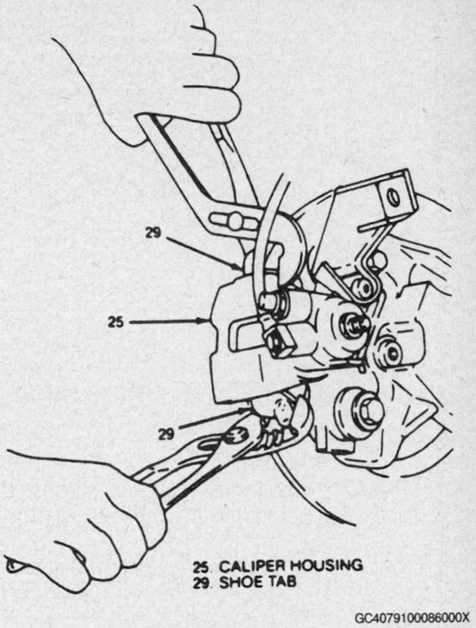
25. CALIPER HOUSING
29. SHOE TAB
GC4079100086000X

Fig. 2 Bottoming piston in caliper bore

Before checking the runout, wheel bearings should be adjusted. The readjustment is very important and will be required at the completion of the test to prevent bearing failure. Be sure to make the adjustment according to the recommendations given under "Front Wheel Bearings, Adjust" in the car chapters.

BRAKE SYSTEM BLEED

Pressure bleeding is recommended for all hydraulic disc brake systems.

The disc brake hydraulic system can be bled manually or with pressure bleeding equipment. The brake pedal will require pumping and frequent checking of fluid level in master cylinder during bleeding operation.

Never use brake fluid that has been drained from hydraulic system when bleeding the brakes. Be sure the disc brake pistons are returned to their normal positions and that the shoe and lining assemblies are properly seated. Before driving the vehicle, check brake operation to be sure that a firm pedal has been obtained.

BRAKE PAD SERVICE

REMOVAL

1. Remove caliper as outlined previously.
2. Remove outboard shoe assembly, disengaging buttons on shoe from holes in caliper.
3. Remove inboard shoe assembly, pressing in on edge of shoe from open side of caliper and tilting shoe outward to release it from retainer.
4. Remove two-way check valve from end of piston with screwdriver. **If leakage is noted from piston hole after removing check valve, caliper must be overhauled.**

INSTALLATION

1. Lubricate, then install two-way check valve into piston.
2. Install inboard shoe assembly as follows:
   a. Engage inboard shoe edge in retainer tabs closest to caliper bridge, then press down and snap shoe tabs at open side of caliper. Ensure shoe lays flat against piston.
   b. Ensure buttons on back of shoe engage D-shaped notches in piston. Rotate piston as needed with spanner wrench tool No. J-7624 or equivalent. Piston is properly aligned when one of the D-shaped notches is nearest caliper bridge.
   c. Wear sensor should be at the leading edge of shoe during forward wheel rotation.
3. Install outboard shoe assembly, snapping shoe springs into holes in caliper. Ensure pad lays flat against caliper.

CALIPER SERVICE

CALIPER REMOVAL

1. Drain approximately 2/3 of brake fluid from master cylinder assembly.
2. Raise and support vehicle, then remove tire and wheel assembly.
3. Loosen tension on parking brake cable at equalizer, then disconnect cable and remove return spring from parking brake lever, **Fig. 1.**
4. Hold parking brake lever in position, loosen retaining nut, then remove nut, lever and seal.
5. Position two adjustable pliers over inboard shoe tabs and flanges on caliper housing as shown, **Fig. 2**, then bottom piston in caliper bore.
6. Reinstall lever seal, lever and retaining nut.
7. If caliper assembly is to be serviced, remove inlet fitting attaching bolt, copper washer, and inlet fitting from caliper housing. Plug opening in inlet fitting to prevent fluid loss and contamination. **Do not crimp brake hose, as this may damage internal structure of hose. If only shoe and lining assemblies are to be replaced, do not disconnect brake line fitting from caliper.**
8. Remove caliper mounting bolts, then lift caliper from mounting bracket. If only shoe and lining assemblies are being replaced, suspend caliper from chassis with suitable hanger. **Do not allow caliper to hang from brake hose.**

CALIPER DISASSEMBLY

1. Remove caliper assembly as outlined previously.
2. Secure caliper assembly in vise and drive out sleeves and bolt boots. Insulate interior of caliper with shop towels.
3. Rotate shoe retainer until tabs are aligned with notches in piston, then remove shoe retainer, **Fig. 1.**
4. Remove locknut, lever, and lever seal, if installed.
5. Remove piston by rotating actuator screw in parking brake apply direction to work piston from caliper bore **Fig. 3.**
6. Remove balance spring (20), then remove actuator screw by pressing on threaded end, **Fig. 1.**
7. Remove seal and thrust washer from actuator screw.
8. Pry dust boot from caliper taking care not to damage caliper bore.
9. Remove piston locator retainer, then the locator.
10. Using a small piece of wood or plastic, remove piston seal from bore. **Do not use a metal tool of any kind to remove seal as it may damage bore.**

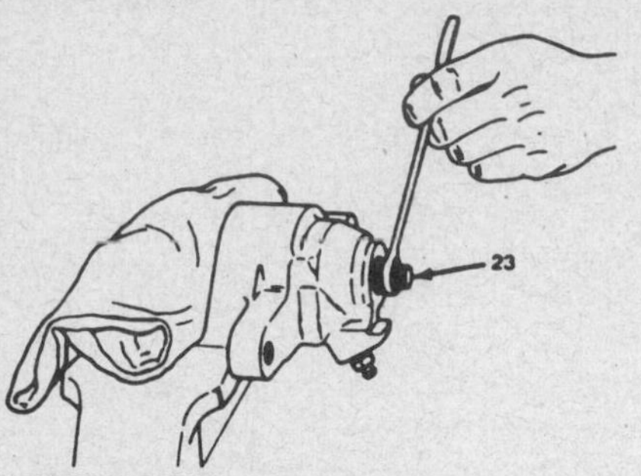
23
23. ACTUATOR SCREW
GC4079100087000X

Fig. 3 Piston removal from caliper

11. Remove bleeder screw. Remove bracket (5) and bolt (4), **Fig. 1**, if damaged.
12. Inspect piston for scoring, nicks, corrosion, and wear and replace as needed.
13. Inspect caliper housing and seal groove for corrosion, nicks, scoring and excessive wear, and use crocus cloth to polish away corrosion from housing bore. Replace caliper housing if corrosion in and around seal groove will not clean up with crocus cloth.
14. Clean all parts with denatured alcohol. Dry with unlubricated compressed air. Blow out all passages in housing and bleeder valve.

CALIPER ASSEMBLY

1. Install bleeder screw.
2. If removed, install bracket (5) and bolt (4), **Fig. 1**, then tighten bolt to specifications.
3. Lubricate piston seals and bore grooves with new brake fluid, then roll piston seal into seal groove in bore, ensuring seal is fully seated and not twisted.
4. Lubricate piston locator with new brake fluid, then position locator on piston using piston locator installer tool No. J-36627 or equivalent.
5. Install thrust washer on actuator screw, with grayish side towards caliper housing, then install lubricated shaft seal onto actuator screw.
6. Install actuator screw into piston assembly.
7. Install balance spring in piston recess in housing.
8. Install piston assembly, pressing piston in until locator is past retainer groove, turn actuator screw as necessary to allow piston assembly to move toward bottom of caliper bore, then install retainer ring.
9. Install lubricated dust boot over piston with inside lip in groove in piston and boot fold toward end of piston that contacts brake shoe, then bottom piston in caliper bore.
10. Install lubricated lever seal over end of actuator screw, ensuring seal bead is against caliper housing.
11. Install parking brake lever over actuator screw, rotate lever away from stop, then hold lever and **torque** retaining nut to 32 ft. lbs. After tightening retaining nut, rotate lever back to stop.
12. Seat dust boot in caliper counterbore using suitable driver.
13. Install shoe retainer in groove on end of piston, ensuring retainer tabs are properly aligned with piston notches.
14. Install sleeves and bolt boots into caliper housing as follows:
    a. Lubricate sleeves, bolt boots and caliper mounting bolt holes with silicone based grease.
    b. Install one bolt boot into groove in mounting bolt hole of caliper housing.
    c. Push sleeve into mounting bolt hole, past inner diameter of bolt boot, and position as shown in view A of **Fig. 4.**
    d. Install second bolt boot in groove at other end of mounting bolt hole as shown in view B of **Fig. 4.**
    e. Push sleeve in opposite direction until grooves of sleeve seat in inner diameter of both bolt boots as shown in view C of **Fig. 4.**
    f. Repeat steps b through e to install remaining bolt boots and sleeve.
15. Install caliper as outlined further on.

CALIPER INSTALLATION

1. Push sleeves inward, away from inboard brake shoe.
2. Reconnect brake hose bracket to suspension, then position caliper over rotor and onto mounting bracket.
3. Install mounting bolts and tighten to specifications.
4. Reinstall bracket (5) and bolt (4), **Fig. 1,** tighten bolt to specifications, then reconnect brake line to caliper using new copper washers.
5. Remove retaining nut, parking brake lever and lever seal, then clean area around seal and actuator screw.
6. Lubricate, then install lever seal. Ensure seal is fully seated against caliper.
7. Install parking brake lever onto actuator screw hex, ensuring lever faces downward, then install retaining nut.
8. While holding lever against stop on caliper, **torque** retaining nut to 35 ft. lbs.
9. Install lever return spring, then reconnect parking brake cable.
10. Install wheels and lower vehicle, then fill master cylinder and bleed brakes as needed. **Before moving vehicle, pump brake pedal several times to be sure it is firm. Do not move vehicle until a firm pedal is obtained.**
11. After installation is completed, adjust parking brake as follows:
    a. Depress brake pedal several times to seat linings.
    b. Fully apply and release parking brake approximately three times. Each full application may require two full pedal strokes.
    c. Raise and support vehicle, then remove rear wheels. Reinstall two wheel nuts to retain rotor.
    d. Turn ignition switch on, and observe brake warning light. Light should be Off. If light remains on, operate manual brake release and pull downward on front parking brake cable to remove slack from pedal assembly.
    e. Check that parking brake levers on both calipers are against caliper stops. If not, check for binding at rear cables. If cables are not binding proceed to next step.
    f. Loosen adjustment at equalizer until both parking brake levers are against caliper stops.
    g. Tighten cable at equalizer until either parking brake lever moves off caliper stop, then loosen cable until lever just contacts stop. With cable properly adjusted, a firm pedal should be obtained by pumping parking brake two full strokes. Rear wheels should be fully locked.
    h. After adjustment is completed, install wheels and lower vehicle.

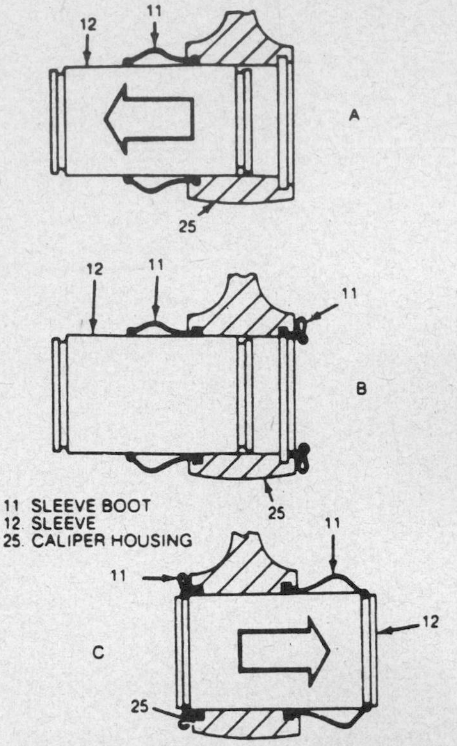
12
11
A
25
12
11
11
B
11 SLEEVE BOOT
12 SLEEVE
25 CALIPER HOUSING
25
11
11
12
C
25
GC4079100088000X

Fig. 4 Bolt boot & sleeve installation

ROTOR
REPLACE

1. Remove caliper assembly as described under "Caliper Service."
2. Remove caliper mounting bracket attaching bolts, then the mounting bracket.
3. Remove rotor from hub and bearing assembly.
4. Reverse procedure to install, adjust parking brake as described under "Adjustments."

ADJUSTMENTS

PARKING BRAKE

1. Apply service brake pedal three times with a force of approximately 175 lbs.
2. Fully apply and release parking brake three times. Full application may require two pedal strokes.
3. Raise and support vehicle, then mark relationship between wheel and axle flange.
4. Check parking brake pedal assembly for full release as follows:
   a. Turn ignition switch to On position.
   b. If "Brake" lamp is illuminated, operate manual brake release and pull downward on front parking brake cable to remove slack from pedal assembly.
5. Remove rear wheel and tire assemblies, then install two lug nuts to retain each rotor assembly.
6. If two parking brake levers on both calipers are not against lever stops on caliper housings, check for binding in rear cables and/or loosen cables at adjuster until both left and right levers are against their stops.
7. Tighten parking brake cable at adjuster until either the left or right lever begins to move off the stop, then loosen adjustment until lever moves back barely touching stop.
8. Operate parking brake several times to check adjustments. A firm pedal feel should be obtained by pumping pedal two full strokes and rear wheels should not rotate forward when parking brake is fully applied.
9. Install wheel and tire assemblies, aligning marks made in step 3.

DISC BRAKE SPECIFICATIONS

CALIPER SPECIFICATIONS

Year	Model	Caliper Bore Dia. Inch.
1992-94	All	1.654

ROTOR SPECIFICATIONS

Model	Year	Nominal Thickness	Minimum Refinish Thickness	Thickness Variation (Parallelism)	Lateral Runout (T.I.R.)
All	1992-94	.492	.444	.0005	.003

TIGHTENING SPECIFICATIONS

Component	Torque/ Ft. Lbs.
Brake Hose To Caliper	32
Caliper Bleeder Screw	9
Caliper Bracket Mounting Bolts	83
Caliper Mounting Bolts	63
Master Cylinder To Booster	22
Wheel Speed Sensor Mounting Bolt	9
Wheel Lug Nuts	100

PBR SINGLE PISTON REAR DISC BRAKE

INDEX

PRECAUTIONS

1. Grease or any other foreign material must be kept off the brake linings, caliper, surfaces of the disc and external surfaces of the hub, during service procedures. Handling the brake disc and caliper should be done in a way to avoid deformation of the disc and nicking or scratching brake linings.
2. If inspection reveals rubber piston seals are worn or damaged, they should be replaced immediately.
3. During removal and installation of a wheel assembly, exercise care so as not to interfere with or damage the caliper splash shield, or bleeder screw.
4. Front wheel bearings preload should be adjusted to specifications .
5. Be sure vehicle is centered on hoist before servicing any of the front end components to avoid bending or damaging the disc splash shield on full right or left wheel turns.
6. Before the vehicle is moved after any brake service work, be sure to obtain a firm brake pedal.
7. The assembly bolts of two piece caliper housings should not be disturbed unless the caliper requires service.

DESCRIPTION

This rear caliper, **Fig. 1,** consists of a single piston and an aluminum housing which is suspended in a mounting bracket through two slide pins. Hydraulic pressure, created by applying force to the brake pedal, acts equally against the piston and the bottom of the caliper bore to move the piston outward. This action slides the caliper inward, resulting in a clamping action on the brake rotor. This clamping action forces the linings against the rotor, creating the friction necessary to stop the vehicle.

The parking brake mechanism on this caliper is completely independent of the hydraulic brake system. When the parking brake is applied, the lever on the caliper causes the pushrod, actuating collar and clamp rod assembly to move outward. This causes the caliper to move inward, mechanically forcing the linings against the rotor.

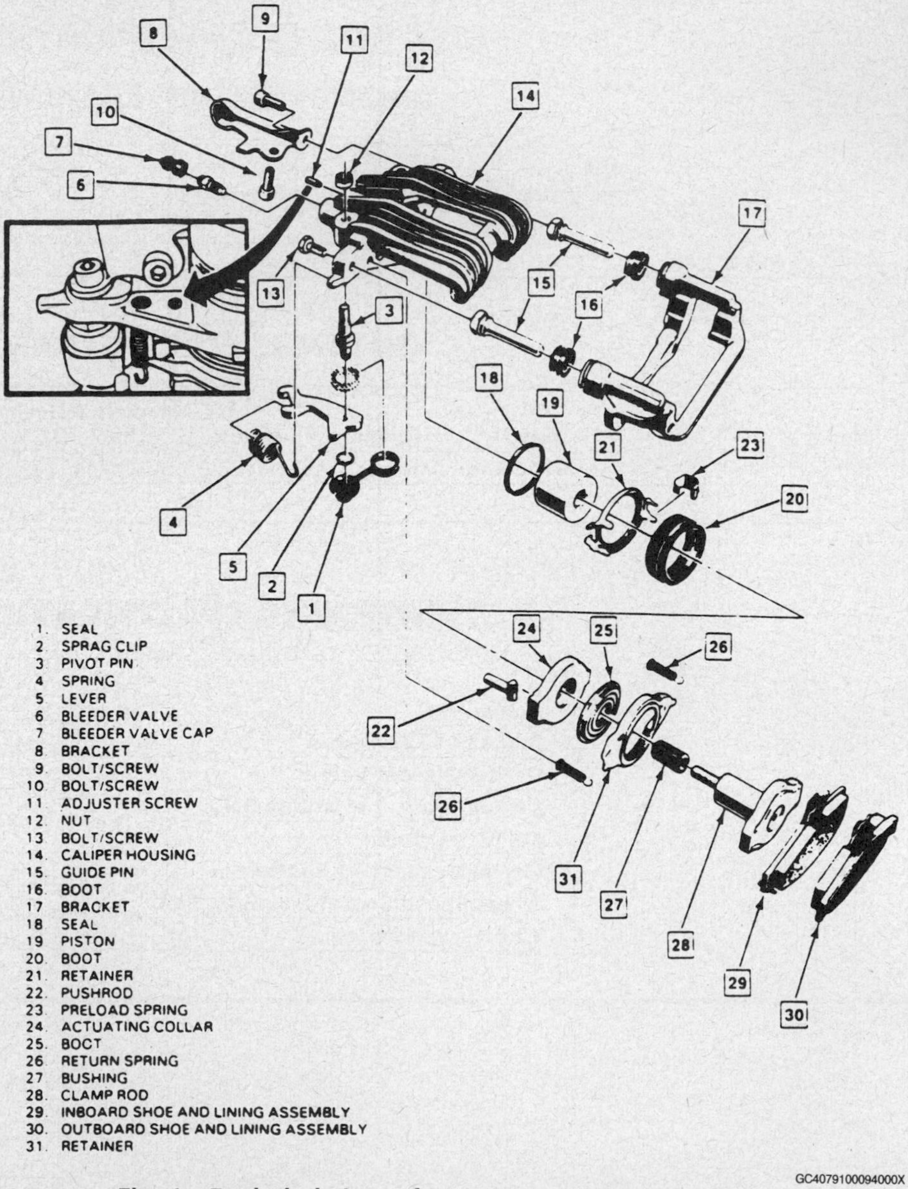
1. SEAL
2. SPRAG CLIP
3. PIVOT PIN
4. SPRING
5. LEVER
6. BLEEDER VALVE
7. BLEEDER VALVE CAP
8. BRACKET
9. BOLT/SCREW
10. BOLT/SCREW
11. ADJUSTER SCREW
12. NUT
13. BOLT/SCREW
14. CALIPER HOUSING
15. GUIDE PIN
16. BOOT
17. BRACKET
18. SEAL
19. PISTON
20. BOOT
21. RETAINER
22. PUSHROD
23. PRELOAD SPRING
24. ACTUATING COLLAR
25. BOOT
26. RETURN SPRING
27. BUSHING
28. CLAMP ROD
29. INBOARD SHOE AND LINING ASSEMBLY
30. OUTBOARD SHOE AND LINING ASSEMBLY
31. RETAINER
GC4079100094000X

Fig. 1 Exploded view of PBR single piston rear caliper

TROUBLESHOOTING
BRAKE ROUGHNESS

The most common cause of brake chatter on disc brakes is a variation in thickness of the disc. If roughness or vibration is encountered during highway operation or if pedal pulsation is experienced at low speeds, the disc may have excessive thickness variation. To check for this con-

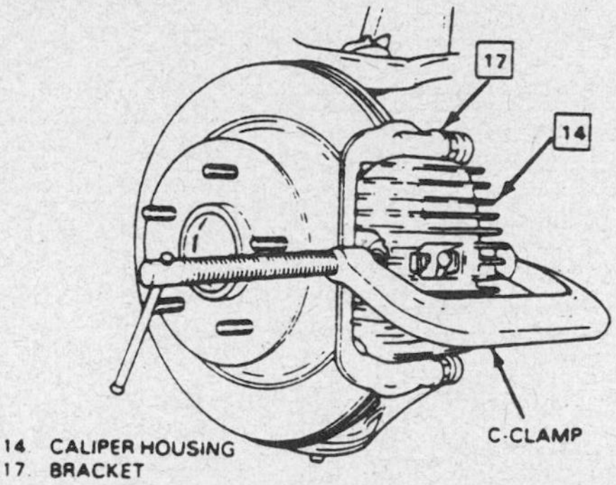
17
14
C-CLAMP
14 CALIPER HOUSING
17 BRACKET
GC4079100095000X

Fig. 2 Bottoming piston in caliper bore

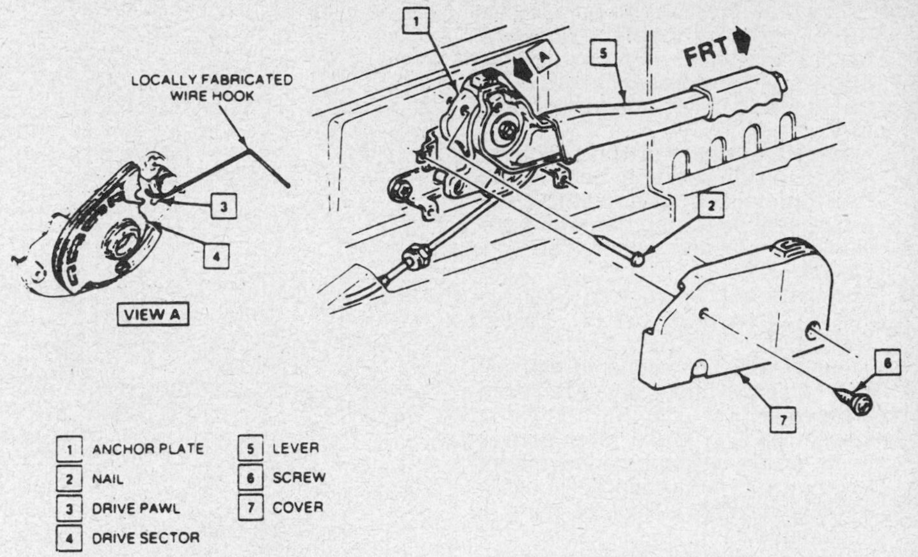
LOCALLY FABRICATED
WIRE HOOK
VIEW A
FRT
1 ANCHOR PLATE
2 NAIL
3 DRIVE PAWL
4 DRIVE SECTOR
5 LEVER
6 SCREW
7 COVER
GC4079100096000X

Fig. 3 Disabling parking brake automatic adjuster mechanism

dition, measure the disc at 12 points with a micrometer at a radius approximately one inch from edge of disc. If thickness measurements vary by more than .0005 inch, the disc should be replaced with a new one.

Excessive lateral runout of braking disc may cause a "knocking back" of the pistons, possibly creating increased pedal travel and vibration when brakes are applied.

Before checking the runout, wheel bearings should be adjusted. The readjustment is very important and will be required at the completion of the test to prevent bearing failure. Be sure to make the adjustment according to the recommendations given under "Front Wheel Bearings, Adjust" in the car chapters.

BRAKE SYSTEM BLEED

Pressure bleeding is recommended for all hydraulic disc brake systems.

The disc brake hydraulic system can be bled manually or with pressure bleeding equipment. The brake pedal will require pumping and frequent checking of fluid level in master cylinder during bleeding operation.

Never use brake fluid that has been drained from hydraulic system when bleeding the brakes. Be sure the disc brake pistons are returned to their normal positions and that the shoe and lining assemblies are properly seated. Before driving the vehicle, check brake operation to be sure that a firm pedal has been obtained.

BRAKE PAD SERVICE

REMOVAL

1. Remove 2/3 of the total brake fluid capacity from master cylinder reservoir.
2. Raise and support vehicle, then remove tire and wheel assembly.
3. Install two wheel retaining nuts to retain rotor in position.
4. Position one end of a suitable C-clamp against inlet fitting bolt, and the other end against outboard shoe and lining, then tighten clamp as shown, **Fig. 2,** until piston fully bottoms in caliper bore.
5. Remove upper guide pin bolt and discard.
6. Loosen lower guide pin bolt, then pivot caliper downward on the lower guide pin bolt to expose the shoe & lining assemblies. Use care to avoid damaging brake hose.
7. Remove shoes and linings from mounting bracket.

INSTALLATION

1. Install outboard shoe and lining onto mounting bracket, ensuring insulator on shoe is positioned toward caliper housing.
2. Install inboard shoe and lining. Ensure wear sensor is positioned nearest caliper piston. When properly installed, sensor should be in trailing position when wheel is rotated in forward direction.
3. Pivot caliper into position over shoes and linings. Ensure springs on outboard shoe do not protrude through inspection hole in housing. If protrusion is evident, lift caliper housing and readjust position of outboard shoe and lining.
4. Install new upper guide pin bolt and **torque** to 26 ft. lbs., then **torque** lower bolt to 16 ft. lbs.
5. Fill master cylinder to proper level, then pump brake pedal firmly and slowly three times to bring pads into contact with brake rotor.

CALIPER SERVICE

CALIPER REMOVAL

1. Disable parking brake automatic adjuster as follows:
   a. Working from inside vehicle, remove driver seat cushion, then the parking brake lever cover screws and cover.
   b. Using .080 inch gauge wire, fabricate a tool to disengage drive pawl from sector, **Fig. 3.**
   c. Using tool mentioned above, disengage drive pawl from sector, then insert a nail through anchor plate to keep drive pawl in disengaged position.
   d. Pull up on lever until it aligns with pawl, then depress button until lever is fully downward.
   e. Visually inspect that anchor plate is fully against stud. If not, repeat procedure as needed.
   f. Pull front parking brake cable rearward to slacken cable at caliper assembly.
2. Raise and support vehicle, then remove tire and wheel assembly.
3. Install two wheel retaining nuts to retain rotor in position.
4. If caliper requires overhaul, remove inlet fitting attaching bolt, then disconnect inlet fitting from caliper housing. Discard the two gaskets, then plug openings in inlet fitting and caliper to prevent loss or contamination of fluid.
5. Remove caliper lever return spring. Discard spring if coils are open.
6. Disconnect parking brake cable from lever (5) and caliper bracket (8), **Fig. 1.**
7. Remove upper and lower guide pin bolts, then remove caliper from rotor and mounting bracket. If caliper does not require overhaul, suspend it from suspension to prevent damage to brake line.

CALIPER DISASSEMBLY

1. Remove caliper as previously outlined.
2. Remove the two return springs from actuating collar, then pull collar out of caliper housing and remove clamp rod (28) and bushing (27), **Fig. 1.** Discard bushing.
3. Bend back boot retainer tabs, then remove retainers (21, 31), boots (20, 25) and pushrod (22) from actuating collar. Remove preload spring (23) from retainer (31), then discard retainers and boots.
4. Use clean shop towels to pad interior of caliper assembly, then remove piston by directing compressed air into caliper brake hose inlet hole, **Use just**

enough air pressure to ease piston out of bore. Do not place fingers in front of piston for any reason when applying compressed air. This could result in serious personal injury.

5. Using a small piece of wood or plastic, remove piston seal from bore. **Do not use a metal tool of any kind to remove seal as it may damage bore.**
6. Remove bleeder valve cap and bleeder valve.
7. Remove seal (1), sprag clip (2) and lever (5) from pivot pin (3). Discard sprag clip.
8. Clean all metal components with suitable solvent, then dry with compressed air.
9. Inspect parking brake lever components, piston, caliper bore and mounting bracket for scoring, excessive wear or corrosion. Replace parts as necessary.

CALIPER ASSEMBLY

1. Using clean brake fluid, lubricate piston seal, then install seal into caliper bore groove. Ensure seal is not twisted during installation.
2. Using clean brake fluid, lubricate caliper bore and piston.
3. Place piston into caliper bore, then push downward until fully bottomed in bore.
4. Apply lubricant provided in repair kit to actuating collar (24), then install pushrod (22), new boots (20, 25) and new retainers (21, 31) onto collar, **Fig. 1.** Clamp retainers firmly against collar, then bend tabs on retainer (21) to hold assembly together.
5. Reconnect preload spring (23) onto retainer (31).
6. Apply lubricant provided in repair kit to clamp rod (28), then slide rod through holes in boot (25) and actuating collar (24). Ensure boot is firmly positioned against reaction plate on clamp rod.
7. Lubricate new compliance bushing (27), then install bushing onto clamp rod (28).
8. Lubricate grooved bead of inner boot (20), boot groove in caliper housing and actuating collar with lubricant provided in repair kit.
9. Push clamp rod to bottom of piston mating hole, then pull actuating collar (24) and seat inner boot (20) into boot groove in caliper housing.
10. Ensure pushrod (22) is positioned in hole in caliper housing, then install bleeder cap and valve.
11. If removed, install pivot pin (3) and new nut (12) onto caliper, **torque** nut to 16 ft. lbs., then lubricate parking brake lever (5) and pivot pin.
12. Install pivot pin seal (1), parking brake lever and new sprag clip (2), ensuring teeth of sprag clip face away from lever, then snap seal cap over pivot pin.
13. Install the two collar return springs (26) onto retainer (31). Ensure retainer enters springs at end of second coil.
14. Install adjustment screw (11) into caliper housing until actuating collar is parallel to piston bore face of housing.

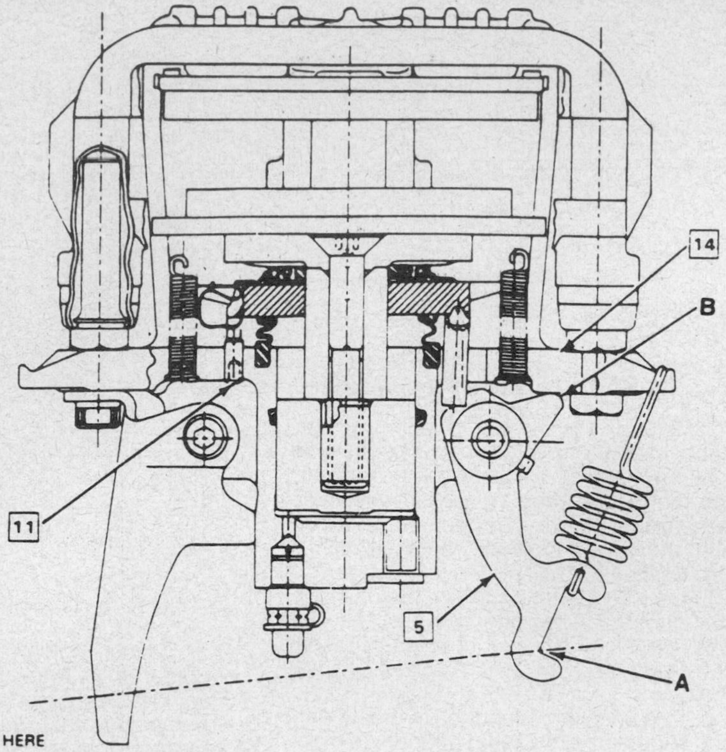
14
B
11
5
A
A. APPLY PRESSURE HERE
B. MEASURE HERE
5. LEVER
11 ADJUSTER SCREW
14. CALIPER HOUSING
GC4079100097000X

Fig. 4 Parking brake free travel adjustment

15. Lubricate guide pins with suitable grease, then slide boots onto pins.
16. Fill boots with grease, then install into mounting bracket. Ensure boots are properly positioned in grooves in pins and mounting bracket.
17. Install caliper and bleed brake system, then adjust parking brake free travel as outlined under "Caliper Installation.

CALIPER INSTALLATION

1. Install shoe and lining assemblies, if removed, as outlined previously.
2. Position caliper over rotor and onto mounting bracket, then install upper and lower guide pin bolts. **Torque** upper bolt to 26 ft. lbs. and lower bolt to 16 ft. lbs.
3. Attach parking brake cable to caliper bracket and lever, then install lever return spring.
4. If removed, install inlet fitting using new gaskets, then bleed brake system.
5. If caliper was overhauled, adjust parking brake free travel as follows:
   a. Have an assistant apply a light load to brake pedal until rotor can no longer be turned by hand.
   b. Apply pressure to caliper lever in direction shown in **Fig. 4.**
   c. Measure free travel between caliper lever and housing. Free travel should be .024-.028 inch. If free travel is not as specified, proceed to next step.
   d. Remove adjustment screw, then clean thread adhesive from threads.
   e. Coat threads with new adhesive, reinstall adjustment screw, then turn as required until specified free travel is obtained. **Turning screw clockwise increases free travel, while counterclockwise rotation decreases travel.**
   f. Release brake pedal, then firmly apply brake pedal three times and recheck free travel. Repeat adjustment procedure as necessary.
6. Remove nail from anchor plate installed during caliper removal procedure.
7. Apply and release parking brake three times, then lift lever upward and ensure parking brake fully engages at 7-9 clicks.
8. Release parking brake. No brake drag should exist and no gap between caliper housings and parking levers should be evident.
9. Install parking brake lever cover, screws and driver's cushion.
10. Reinstall tire and wheel assembly, then check and refill master cylinder as required.
11. Start engine and pump brake pedal several times to seat brake linings.

ROTOR

REPLACE

1. Remove caliper as described in "Caliper Service."
2. Remove caliper mounting bracket attaching bolts, then the mounting bracket.

3. Remove rotor from hub and bearing assembly.
4. Reverse procedure to install, adjust parking brake as described under "Adjustments."

ADJUSTMENTS

PARKING BRAKE

1. Release parking brake lever, then raise and support vehicle.
2. Remove rear wheels then install lug nuts on two opposite wheel studs to hold brake rotor in position.
3. Back caliper pistons into bores.
4. Loosen parking brake cable adjusting nut until there is no tension on parking brake shoes.
5. Turn each brake rotor until parking brake shoe star adjuster is visible through hole in rotor.
6. Adjusting one side at a time, tighten adjuster until rotor cannot be turned by hand, then back star wheel off 5 to 7 notches. **Adjust parking brake shoes by inserting a suitable tool through hole in rotor. On drivers side, tighten adjuster by moving handle of tool upwards. On passenger side, tighten adjuster by moving handle of tool downward.**
7. Install rear wheels and pull parking lever up two notches.
8. Tighten cable adjusting nut at equalizer until there is drag on wheels.
9. Release parking brake lever and check adjustment. No drag should be felt when rotating wheels.

DISC BRAKE SPECIFICATIONS

CALIPER SPECIFICATIONS

Model	Year	Caliper Bore Dia. Inch.
CHEVROLET		
Camaro	1992	1.6
	1993-94	1.595
Corvette	1992-94	1.6
PONTIAC		
Firebird	1992	1.6
	1993-94	1.595

ROTOR SPECIFICATIONS

Model	Year	Nominal Thickness	Minimum Refinish Thickness	Thickness Variation (Parallelism)	Lateral Runout (T.I.R.)
Camaro	1992	.795	.744	.0005	.006
	1993-94	.787	.733	.0005	.006
Corvette	1992-94	1.110①	1.059	.0005	.006
		.795②	.744	.0005	.006
PONTIAC					
Firebird	1992	.795	.744	.0005	.005
	1993-94	.787	.733	.0005	.006

①—Heavy duty.
②—Standard.

TIGHTENING SPECIFICATIONS

Component	Torque Ft./ Lbs
Brake hose to caliper	30
Caliper Bleeder Screw	80①
Front Caliper Mounting Bracket	166
Rear Bracket Mounting Bolt	70
Rear Lower Guide Pin Bolt	16
Rear Pivot Pin Nut	16
Rear Upper Guide Pin Bolt	26
Wheel Lug Nuts	100

①—Inch lbs.

Toyota/GM Single Piston Caliper

INDEX

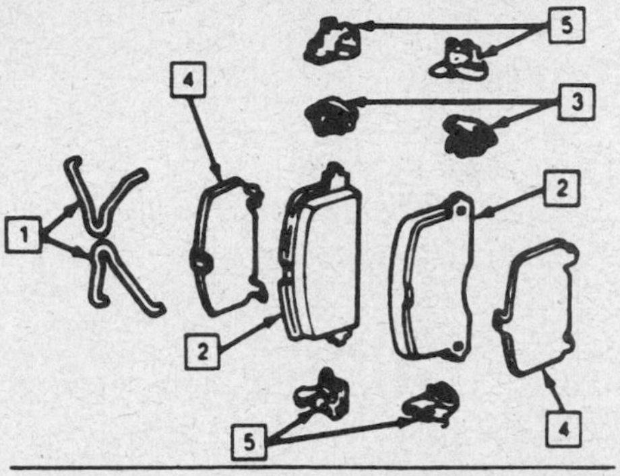

1
2
3
4
5
1. ANTI-RATTLE SPRINGS
2. BRAKE PADS
3. WEAR INDICATOR
4. ANTI-SQUEAL SHIMS
5. SUPPORT PLATES
GC4079100101000X

Fig. 1 Front brake pad assembly

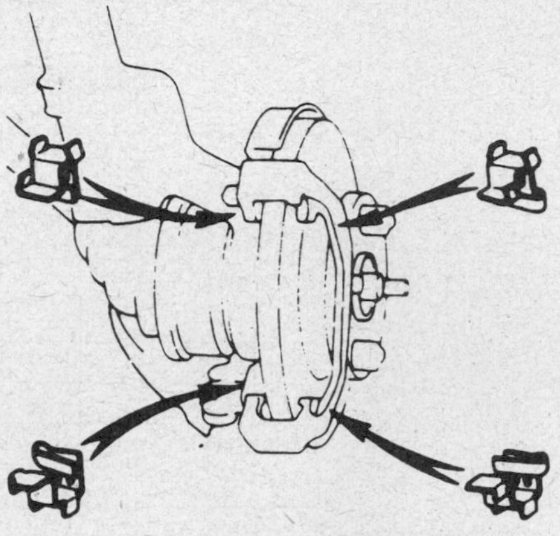

GC4079100099000X

Fig. 2 Front caliper support installation

PRECAUTIONS

1. Grease or any other foreign material must be kept off the brake linings, caliper, surfaces of the disc and external surfaces of the hub, during service procedures. Handling the brake disc and caliper should be done in a way to avoid deformation of the disc and nicking or scratching brake linings.
2. If inspection reveals rubber piston seals are worn or damaged, they should be replaced immediately.
3. During removal and installation of a wheel assembly, exercise care so as not to interfere with or damage the caliper splash shield, or bleeder screw.
4. Front wheel bearings preload should be adjusted to specifications .
5. Be sure vehicle is centered on hoist before servicing any of the front end components to avoid bending or damaging the disc splash shield on full right or left wheel turns.
6. Before the vehicle is moved after any brake service work, be sure to obtain a firm brake pedal.
7. The assembly bolts of two piece caliper housings should not be disturbed unless the caliper requires service.

DESCRIPTION

The caliper is a single bore design and is mounted to a carrier assembly. Hydraulic pressure, created by applying brake pedal, is converted by caliper to a stopping force. This force acts equally against the piston and bottom of caliper bore to move the piston outward and to slide caliper inward resulting in a clamping action on the rotor. The clamping action forces linings against the rotor, creating friction necessary to stop the vehicle.

TROUBLESHOOTING

BRAKE ROUGHNESS

The most common cause of brake chatter on disc brakes is a variation in thickness of the disc. If roughness or vibration is encountered during highway operation or if pedal pulsation is experienced at low speeds, the disc may have excessive thickness variation. To check for this condition, measure the disc at 12 points with a micrometer at a radius approximately one inch from edge of disc. If thickness measurements vary by more than .0005 inch, the disc should be replaced with a new one.

Excessive lateral runout of braking disc may cause a "knocking back" of the pistons, possibly creating increased pedal travel and vibration when brakes are applied.

Before checking the runout, wheel bearings should be adjusted. The readjustment is very important and will be required at the completion of the test to prevent bearing failure. Be sure to make the adjustment according to the recommendations given under "Front Wheel Bearings, Adjust" in the car chapters.

BRAKE SYSTEM BLEED

Pressure bleeding is recommended for all hydraulic disc brake systems.

The disc brake hydraulic system can be bled manually or with pressure bleeding equipment. The brake pedal will require more pumping and frequent checking of fluid level in master cylinder during bleeding operation.

Never use brake fluid that has been drained from hydraulic system when bleeding the brakes. Be sure the disc brake pistons are returned to their normal positions and that the shoe and lining assemblies are properly seated. Before driving the vehicle, check brake operation to be sure that a firm pedal has been obtained.

BRAKE PAD SERVICE

FRONT

Replace brake pads on one wheel at a time to prevent opposite side caliper piston from being forced out of bore.

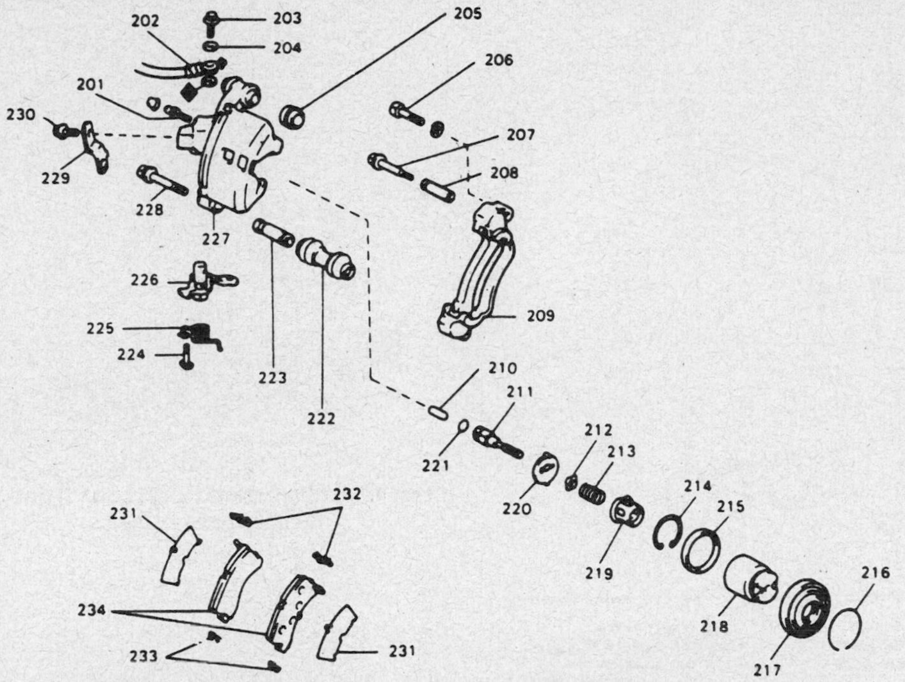
202
203
204
205
206
201
230
207
208
229
228
227
226
209
225
224
223
210
211
222
212
213
221
232
231
220
214
215
219
216
234
218
233
231
217

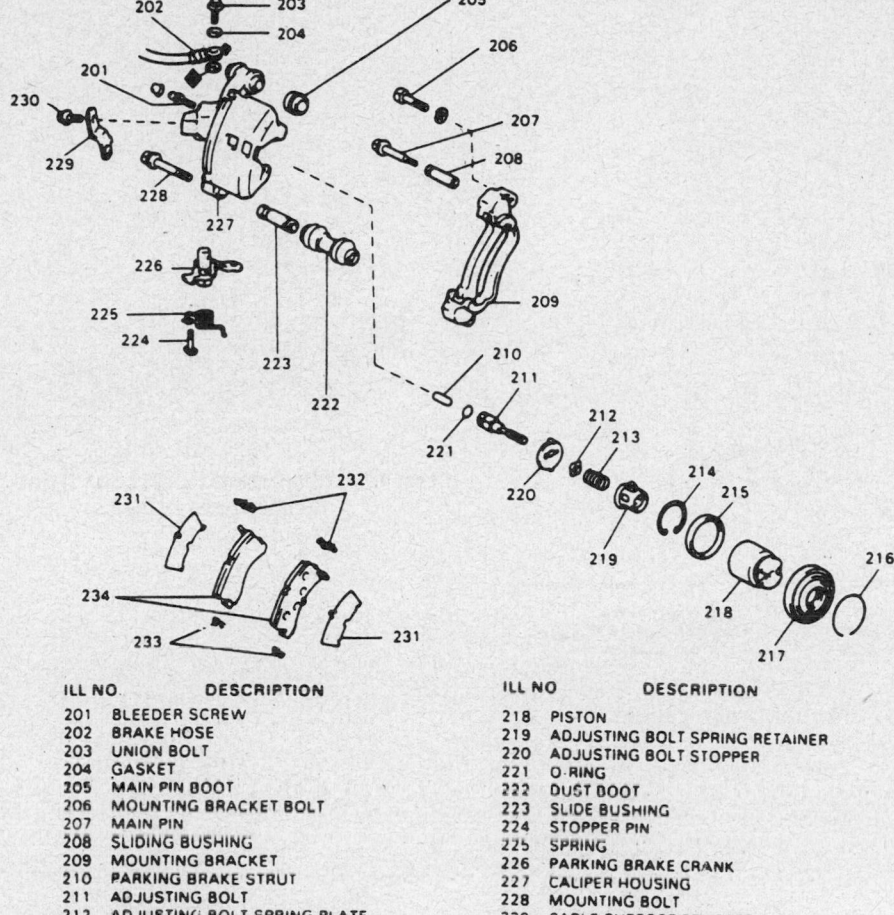

ILL NO	DESCRIPTION	ILL NO	DESCRIPTION
201	BLEEDER SCREW	218	PISTON
202	BRAKE HOSE	219	ADJUSTING BOLT SPRING RETAINER
203	UNION BOLT	220	ADJUSTING BOLT STOPPER
204	GASKET	221	O-RING
205	MAIN PIN BOOT	222	DUST BOOT
206	MOUNTING BRACKET BOLT	223	SLIDE BUSHING
207	MAIN PIN	224	STOPPER PIN
208	SLIDING BUSHING	225	SPRING
209	MOUNTING BRACKET	226	PARKING BRAKE CRANK
210	PARKING BRAKE STRUT	227	CALIPER HOUSING
211	ADJUSTING BOLT	228	MOUNTING BOLT
212	ADJUSTING BOLT SPRING PLATE	229	CABLE SUPPORT BRACKET
213	SPRING	230	CABLE SUPPORT BRACKET BOLT
214	SNAP RING	231	ANTI-SQUEAL SHIM
215	PISTON SEAL	232	ANTI-RATTLE SPRING
216	SET RING	233	PAD SUPPORT PLATE
217	BOOT	234	PAD

GC4079100100000X

Fig. 3 Exploded view of front caliper assembly

Removal

1. Remove caliper as outlined, leaving brake hose connected, and secure caliper aside.
2. Remove 2 anti-rattle clips, then the brake pads, **Fig. 1.**
3. Remove pad wear indicator plates and anti-squeal shims.
4. Remove support plates.

Installation

1. Install new support plates on caliper mounting bracket, **Fig. 2.**
2. Install new wear indicators and anti-squeal shims on each pad, **Fig. 1,** then position pads in caliper mounting bracket. **Ensure arrow on wear indicator is pointing in rotating direction of rotor.**
3. Install anti-rattle springs.
4. Seat piston in caliper bore, then install caliper and mounting bolts, and **torque** bolts to 18. ft lbs.
5. Refill master cylinder and bleed brakes as needed.

REAR

Replace brake pads on one wheel at a time to prevent opposite side caliper piston from being forced out of bore.

Removal

1. Siphon 2/3 of the brake fluid from master cylinder, raise and support vehicle, and remove wheels.
2. Reinstall 2 wheel nuts to retain rotor.
3. Remove caliper mounting bolt, then swing caliper upward to expose brake components. **Do not remove main pin from caliper.**
4. Remove brake pads, anti-squeal shims, anti-rattle springs and the two support plates, **Fig. 3.**

Installation

1. Install new pad support plates to lower part of mounting bracket.
2. Install new anti-rattle springs to upper side of mounting bracket.
3. Position new anti-squeal shims to backside of each brake pad, then install pads onto mounting bracket. Ensure pads are positioned so wear indicators are on top side.
4. Using brake piston driver tool No. J-37149 or equivalent, **Fig. 4,** slowly turn piston clockwise and press into caliper bore until it locks in position at bottom of bore.

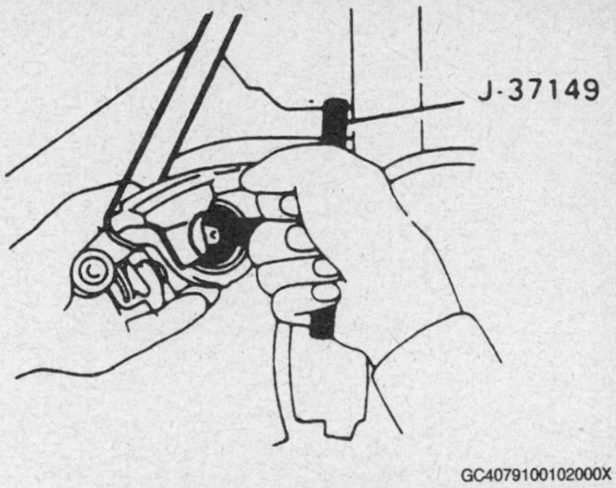
J-37149

GC4079100102000X

Fig. 4 Pressing piston into caliper bore

5. With pad protrusion fitted into piston stopper groove, swing caliper downward and install mounting bolt. **Torque** bolt to 14 ft. lbs.
6. Fill master cylinder to proper level, then depress brake pedal several times to seat linings and to actuate parking brake automatic adjuster.

CALIPER SERVICE

FRONT CALIPER

Removal

1. Siphon 2/3 of the brake fluid from master cylinder, raise and support vehicle, and remove wheels.
2. Reinstall 2 wheel nuts to retain rotor, then remove caliper mounting bolts, **Fig. 5.**
3. Remove union nut securing brake hose to caliper and drain fluid into suitable container. **If caliper is only being removed for brake pad replacement, do not disconnect brake hose.**
4. Compress piston as needed, then remove caliper. If brake hose remains connected, secure caliper aside to prevent hose from being stretched.

Disassemble

1. Remove 2 caliper slide bushings, 4 dust boots and spacer collars, **Fig. 3.**
2. Pry out caliper dust boot retaining ring and remove dust boot.
3. Place clean shop towels in caliper web to protect piston, then apply compressed air to caliper fluid inlet to force piston from bore. **Keep fingers clear of caliper web when removing piston. Use only enough air pressure to ease piston out of bore, or piston may be damaged.**
4. Remove piston seal from caliper bore, taking care not to mar machined surface of caliper.
5. Remove bleeder valve.
6. Clean components with alcohol and wipe dry with clean, lint free shop towels. Blow out caliper body and fluid passages with clean, filtered compressed air.
7. Inspect caliper and piston for damage, distortion, excessive wear and pitting, and replace as needed.
8. Replace mounting bolts, collars and caliper slides if they are damaged or worn.

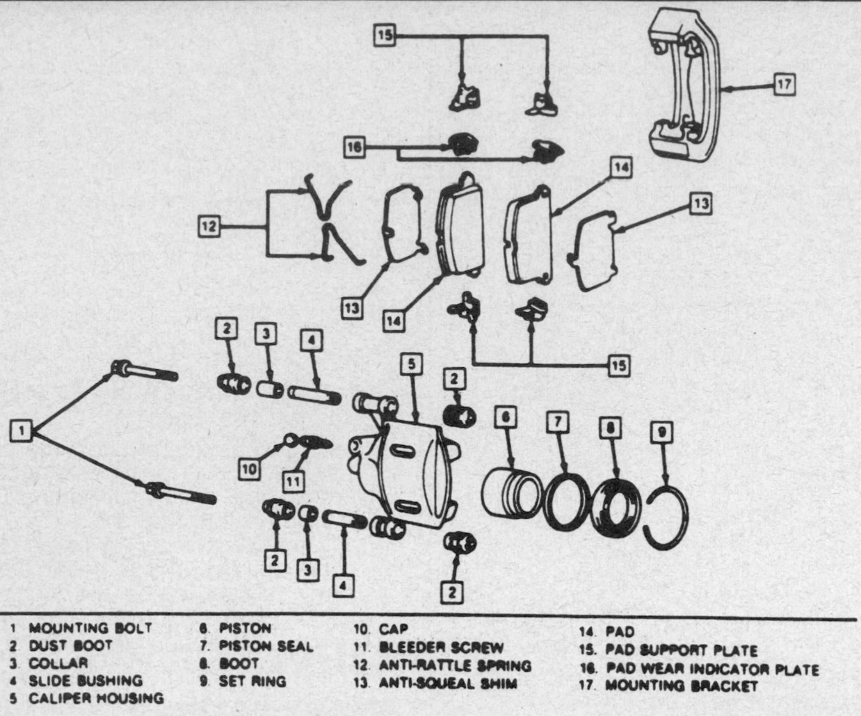
1 MOUNTING BOLT
2 DUST BOOT
3 COLLAR
4 SLIDE BUSHING
5 CALIPER HOUSING
6 PISTON
7 PISTON SEAL
8 BOOT
9 SET RING
10 CAP
11 BLEEDER SCREW
12 ANTI-RATTLE SPRING
13 ANTI-SQUEAL SHIM
14 PAD
15 PAD SUPPORT PLATE
16 PAD WEAR INDICATOR PLATE
17 MOUNTING BRACKET
GC4079100098000X

Fig. 5 Exploded view of Toyota/GM rear brake caliper

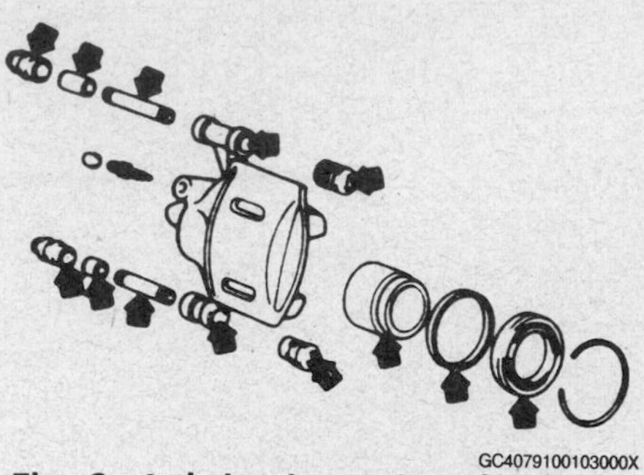
GC4079100103000X

Fig. 6 Lubrication points for front caliper assembly

Assemble

1. Apply lithium soap base glycol grease to components shown in **Fig. 4**.
2. Install piston seal in caliper, ensuring seal is squarely seated in groove.
3. Press piston into bore, ensuring piston enters bore straight.
4. Seat piston dust boot in caliper groove, then install retaining ring.
5. Install 2 collars and 4 slide bushing dust boots, **Fig. 5,** rotating boots as they are pressed in to ensure they are fully seated.
6. Install slide bushings through dust boots, ensuring boots remain seated in caliper grooves.

Installation

1. Seat piston in caliper bore, taking care not to damage piston.
2. Ensure support plates, **Fig. 2**, and anti-rattle springs are properly positioned, then mount caliper over rotor onto mounting bracket.
3. Install caliper mounting bolts and **torque** bolts to 18 ft. lbs.
4. Install brake hose and mounting bolts, using new copper gaskets, then **torque** bolt to 17 ft. lbs.
5. Refill master cylinder and bleed brake system.

REAR CALIPER

Removal

1. Siphon $^2/_3$ of the brake fluid from master cylinder, raise and support vehicle, and remove wheels.
2. Reinstall 2 wheel nuts to retain rotor.
3. Remove union nut securing brake hose to caliper and drain fluid into suitable container.
4. Remove clip from parking brake and disconnect parking brake cable.
5. Remove caliper mounting bolt, lift caliper, then remove parking brake pin clip.
6. While pushing parking brake crank, **Fig. 3**, remove pin.
7. Lift caliper and remove from vehicle.

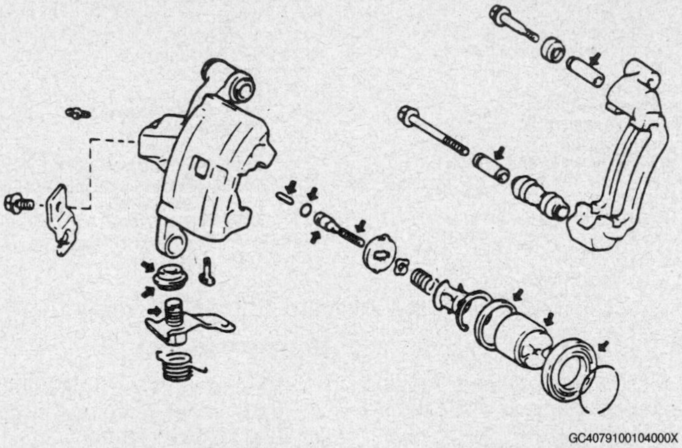
GC4079100104000X

Fig. 7 Lubrication points for rear caliper assembly

Disassemble

1. Remove sliding bushing and the four dust boots, **Fig. 3.**
2. Using a suitable screwdriver, remove caliper set ring and boot.
3. Using brake piston driver tool No. J-37149 or equivalent, rotate piston out of caliper bore.
4. Pry piston seal from caliper bore.
5. Position adjusting bolt guide nut tool No. J-37150 or equivalent over adjusting bolt, tighten tool, then remove snap ring from caliper bore and pull out adjusting bolt and components.
6. Remove parking brake strut and cable support bracket, then the parking brake crank torsion spring.
7. Remove parking brake crank, then the crank boot by tapping on metal portion of boot with screwdriver or similar tool. **Do not remove crank boot unless boot is damaged or excessively worn.**
8. Using a suitable punch, drive stopper pin from caliper.
9. Inspect all components for damage, wear or corrosion, and replace as necessary.

Assemble

1. Clean all parts not included in repair kit and dry with compressed air.
2. Lubricate all components indicated in **Fig. 7** with lithium based grease.
3. Install stopper pin into caliper until pin protrudes .98 inch outward as shown in **Fig. 8.**
4. If removed during disassembly, tap parking brake crank boot into position in caliper using a 24mm socket.
5. Install parking brake crank. Ensure crank boot aligns with groove of crank

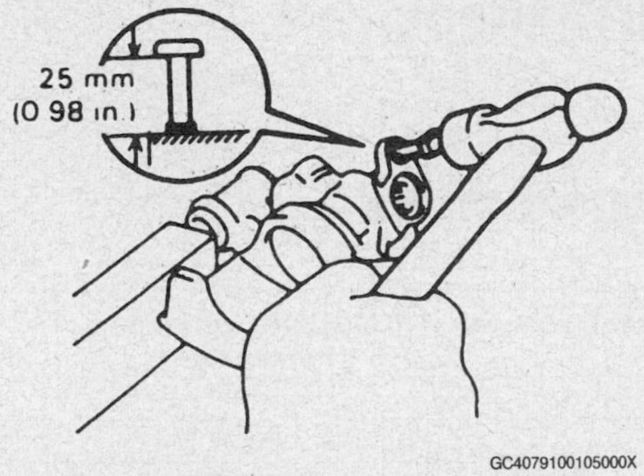
25 mm
(0 98 in)
GC4079100105000X

Fig. 8 Stopper pin installation

seal.

6. Install cable support bracket, then press surface of bracket flush against caliper and **torque** bolt to 34 ft. lbs. When properly installed, clearance between parking brake crank and support bracket should be .236 inch.
7. Install torsion spring, then check that parking brake crank subassembly touches stopper pin.
8. Install parking brake strut. **Before adjusting strut, ensure needle bearing rollers do not catch on caliper bore.**
9. Position new O-ring onto adjusting bolt, then assemble stopper, plate, spring and spring retainer onto bolt. Hand tighten assembly using adjusting bolt guide nut tool No. J-37150 or equivalent. When properly assembled, inscribed surface of stopper should face upward and notches of spring retainer should align with notches of stopper.
10. Position adjusting bolt subassembly into caliper, then install snap ring, ensuring opening faces toward bleeder side of caliper. Pull upward on adjusting bolt and ensure bolt does not move.
11. Check operation of parking brake by moving crank by hand. Adjusting bolt should move smoothly, with no evidence of binding.
12. Install piston seal into caliper bore, then using brake piston driver tool No. J-37149 or equivalent, install piston and bottom in bore by turning tool clockwise.
13. Align center of piston stopper groove with protrusion of caliper bore.
14. Install boot and set ring into caliper.
15. Using a 21mm socket and suitable vise, press new main pin boot into caliper housing.
16. Install sliding bushing and bolt, then install caliper as outlined previously.

Installation

1. Position caliper over mounting bracket, then install mounting bolt and **torque** to 14 ft. lbs.
2. Install parking brake clip.
3. Install brake hose and union bolt, using new copper gaskets, then **torque** bolt to 22 ft. lbs.
4. Refill master cylinder and bleed brake system.
5. Adjust parking brake as follows:
   a. Pull upward on parking brake lever several times, then fully release lever.
   b. Depress brake pedal several times to automatically adjust brake.
   c. When properly adjusted, parking brake crank should just contact stopper pin.

ROTOR

REPLACE

FRONT

1. Remove front caliper as described under "Front Caliper" in "Caliper Service.
2. Remove four anti-rattle springs from caliper carrier.
3. Remove caliper carrier mounting bolts, then the caliper carrier.
4. Remove brake rotor from wheel hub. If rotor cannot be removed by hand, install two 8mm bolts into rotor. Tightening the bolts will force the rotor off the wheel hub.
5. Reverse procedure to install.

REAR

1. Remove rear caliper as described under "Rear Caliper" in "Caliper Service.
2. Remove brake pads as described in "Brake Pad Service."
3. Remove rotor from wheel hub.
4. Reverse procedure to install, adjust parking brake as described in "Adjustments."

ADJUSTMENTS

PARKING BRAKE

1. Check that parking brake lever travel is correct by pulling parking brake lever all the way up and counting the number of clicks.
2. Parking brake lever travel should be 4 to 7 clicks. If not, remove console, loosen locknut and turn adjusting nut until travel is correct.

DISC BRAKE SPECIFICATIONS

ROTOR SPECIFICATIONS

Model	Year	Nominal Thickness	Minimum Refinish Thickness ①	Thickness Variation (Parallelism)	Lateral Runout (T.I.R.)
FRONT					
Geo Prizm	1992	.709	.669	.0005	.0035
	1993-94	.866	.787	.0005	.0035
REAR					
Geo Prizm	1992	.354	.315	.0005	.0039

①—All brake rotors have a discard dimension cast into them. This is a wear dimension, not a refinish dimension. Any rotor that does not meet specifications should be discarded.

TIGHTENING SPECIFICATIONS

Component	Torque/Ft. Lbs.
Brake Hose Union Bolt	22
Caliper Carrier Mounting Bolts	65
Caliper Mounting Bolts	25
Parking Brake Jam Nut	53①
Parking Brake Lock Nut	53①
Union Bolt	22

①—Inch lbs.

DRUM BRAKES

NOTE: Refer To "Application Chart" To Determine Which Type Brakes Are Used On Vehicle Being Serviced.

TABLE OF CONTENTS

Application Chart

Model	Year	Application	Page 29-
BUICK			
Century	1992	Type 4	8
	1993-94	Type 8	19
LeSabre	1992-94	Type 8	19
Park Avenue	1992-94	Type 8	19
Roadmaster	1992-94	Type 1	2
Skylark	1992-94	Type 4	8
CADILLAC			
Brougham	1992	Type 1	2
DeVille	1992-94	Type 8	19
Fleetwood FWD	1992	Type 8	19
Fleetwood RWD	1993–94	Type 1	2
CHEVROLET			
Beretta	1992–94	Type 4	8
Camaro	1992-94	Type 2	2
Caprice	1992-94	Type 1	2
Cavalier	1992-94	Type 4	8
Corsica	1992–94	Type 4	8
Impala SS	1994	Type 1	2
GEO			
Metro	1992-94	Type 7	15
Prizm	1992-94	Type 5	10
Storm	1992-93	Type 6	13
OLDSMOBILE			
Achieva	1992-94	Type 4	8
Custom Cruiser	1992	Type 1	2
Cutlass Ciera	1992	Type 4	8
	1993–94	Type 8	19
Cutlass Cruiser	1992	Type 4	8
	1993-94	Type 8	19
Eighty-Eight	1992-94	Type 8	19
Ninety-Eight	1992–94	Type 8	19
PONTIAC			
Bonneville	1992-94	Type 8	19
Firebird	1992-94	Type 2	2
Grand Am	1992-94	Type 4	8
LeMans	1992-93	Type 3	5
Sunbird	1992-94	Type 4	8

Types 1 & 2

INDEX

PRECAUTIONS

When working on or around brake assemblies, care must be taken to prevent breathing asbestos dust, as many manufacturers incorporate asbestos fibers in the production of brake linings. During routine service operations the amount of asbestos dust from brake lining wear is at a low level due to a chemical breakdown during use, and a few precautions will minimize exposure.

1. Do not sand or grind brake linings unless suitable local exhaust ventilation equipment is used to prevent excessive asbestos exposure.
2. Wear a suitable respirator approved for asbestos dust use during all repair procedures.
3. When cleaning brake dust from brake parts, use a vacuum cleaner with a highly efficient filter system. If a suitable vacuum cleaner is not available, use a water soaked rag. **Do not use compressed air or dry brush to clean brake parts.**
4. Keep work area clean using same equipment as for cleaning brake parts.
5. Properly dispose of rags and vacuum cleaner bags by placing them in plastic bags.
6. Do not smoke or eat while working on brake systems. **Never use gasoline, kerosene, alcohol, motor oil, transmission fluid, or any fluid containing mineral oil to clean brake system components. These fluids will damage the rubber caps and seals. If system contamination is suspected, check brake fluid in the reservoir for dirt, discoloration, or separation (breakdown) of the brake fluid into distinct layers. Drain and flush the hydraulic system with clean brake fluid if contamination is suspected.**

INSPECTION

1. Inspect components for damage and unusual wear. Replace as necessary.
2. Inspect wheel cylinders. Boots which are torn, cut or heat damaged indicate need for wheel cylinder replacement. **On type 1 brakes,** remove wheel cylinder links. Fluid spill from boot center hole indicates cup leakage and need for wheel cylinder replacement. **On type 2 brakes,** use a small screwdriver to pry center hole of boot away from piston. If fluid spills from center hole, cup leakage is indicated and wheel cylinder should be replaced. **On all types,** light fluid coatings on piston within cylinder is considered normal.
3. Inspect backing plate for evidence of axle seal leakage. If leakage exists, refer to individual car chapters for axle seal replacement procedures.
4. Inspect backing plate attaching bolts, and ensure they are tight.
5. Using fine emery cloth or other suitable abrasive, clean rust and dirt from shoe contact surface on backing plate.

BRAKE DRUMS

Any time the brake drums are removed for brake service, the braking surface diameter should be checked with a suitable brake drum micrometer at several points to determine if they are within the safe oversize limit stamped on the brake drum outer surface. If the braking surface diameter exceeds specifications, the drum must be replaced. If the braking surface diameter is within specifications, drums should be cleaned and inspected for cracks, scores, deep grooves, taper, out of round and heat spotting. If drums are cracked or heat spotted, they must be replaced. Minor scores should be removed with sandpaper. Grooves and large scores can only be removed by machining with special equipment, as long as the braking surface is within specifications stamped on brake drum outer surface. Any brake drum sufficiently out of round to cause vehicle vibration or noise while braking or showing taper should also be machined, removing only enough stock to true up the brake drum.

After a brake drum is machined, wipe the braking surface diameter with a denatured alcohol soaked cloth. If one brake drum is machined, the other should also be machined to the same diameter to maintain equal braking forces.

BRAKE LININGS & SPRINGS

Inspect brake linings for excessive wear, damage, oil, grease or brake fluid contamination. If any of the above conditions exists, brake linings should be replaced. Do not attempt to replace only one set of brake shoes; they should be replaced as an axle set only to maintain equal braking forces. Examine brake shoe webbing, hold-down and return springs for signs of overheating indicated by a slight blue color. If any component exhibits overheating signs, replace hold-down and return springs with new ones. Overheated springs lose their pull and could cause brake linings to wear out prematurely. Inspect all springs for sags, bends and external damage and replace as necessary.

Inspect hold-down retainers and pins for bends, rust and corrosion. If any of the above is found, replace as required.

BACKING PLATE

Inspect backing plate shoe contact surface for grooves that may restrict shoe movement and cannot be removed by lightly sanding with emery cloth or other suitable abrasive. If backing plate exhibits above condition, it should be replaced. Also inspect for signs of cracks, warpage and excessive rust, indicating need for replacement.

ADJUSTER MECHANISM

Inspect all components for rust, corrosion, bends and fatigue. Replace as necessary. **On adjuster mechanism equipped with adjuster cable,** inspect cable for kinks, fraying or elongation of eyelet and replace as necessary.

PARKING BRAKE CABLE

Inspect parking brake cable end for kinks, fraying and elongation and replace as necessary. Use a small hose clamp to compress clamp where it enters backing plate to remove.

BRAKE SERVICE

REMOVAL

1. Raise and support rear of vehicle, then remove tire and wheel assembly.
2. Remove brake drum. If brake lining is dragging on brake drum, back off brake adjustment by rotating adjustment screw. Refer to individual car chapter for procedure. **If brake drum is rusted or corroded to axle flange and cannot be removed, lightly tap axle flange to drum mounting surface with a suitable hammer.**
3. Using brake spring pliers or equivalent, unhook primary and secondary return springs, **Fig. 1 and 2. Observe location of brake parts being removed to aid during installation.**

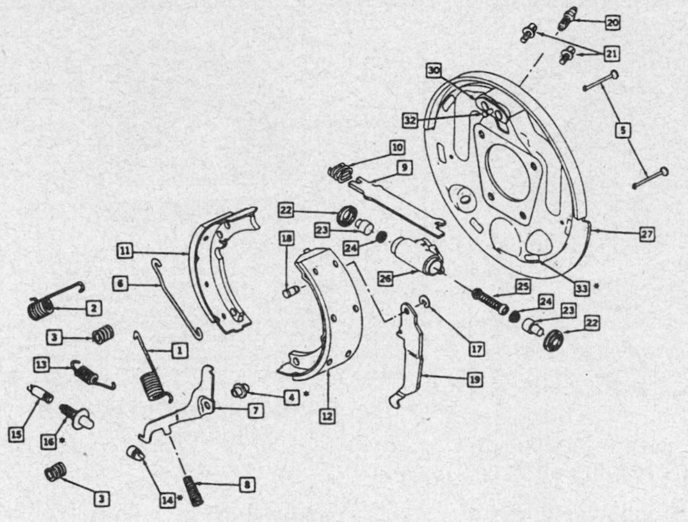

1 RETURN SPRING
2 RETURN SPRING
3 HOLD-DOWN SPRING
4 BEARING SLEEVE
5 HOLD-DOWN PIN
6 ACTUATOR LINK
7 ACTUATOR LEVER
8 LEVER RETURN SPRING
9 PARKING BRAKE STRUT
10 STRUT SPRING
11 PRIMARY SHOE AND LINING
12 SECONDARY SHOE AND LINING
13 ADJUSTING SCREW SPRING
14 SOCKET
15 PIVOT NUT
16 ADJUSTING SCREW
17 RETAINING RING
18 PIN
19 PARKING BRAKE LEVER
20 BLEEDER VALVE
21 BOLT
22 BOOT
23 PISTON
24 SEAL
25 SPRING ASSEMBLY
26 WHEEL CYLINDER
27 BACKING PLATE
30 SHOE RETAINER
32 ANCHOR PIN
33 SHOE PADS (8 PLACES)

GC4089100009000X

Fig. 1 Drum brake assembly. Type 1, typical

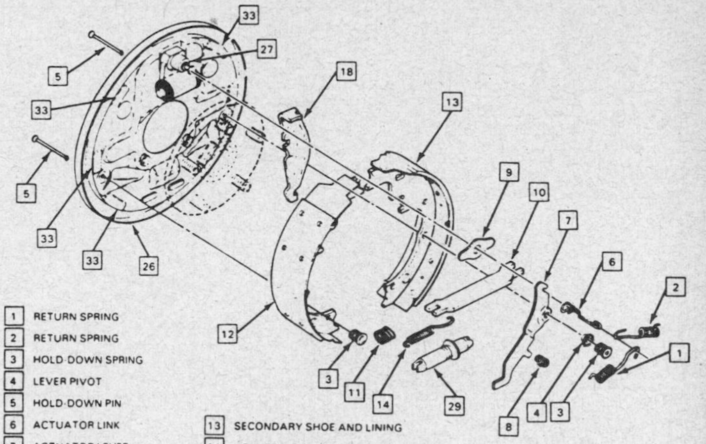

1 RETURN SPRING
2 RETURN SPRING
3 HOLD-DOWN SPRING
4 LEVER PIVOT
5 HOLD-DOWN PIN
6 ACTUATOR LINK
7 ACTUATOR LEVER
8 LEVER RETURN SPRING
9 SHOE GUIDE
10 PARKING BRAKE STRUT
11 STRUT SPRING
12 PRIMARY SHOE AND LINING
13 SECONDARY SHOE AND LINING
14 ADJUSTING SCREW SPRING
18 PARKING BRAKE LEVER
26 BACKING PLATE
27 ANCHOR PIN
29 ADJUSTING SCREW ASSEMBLY
33 SHOE PAD

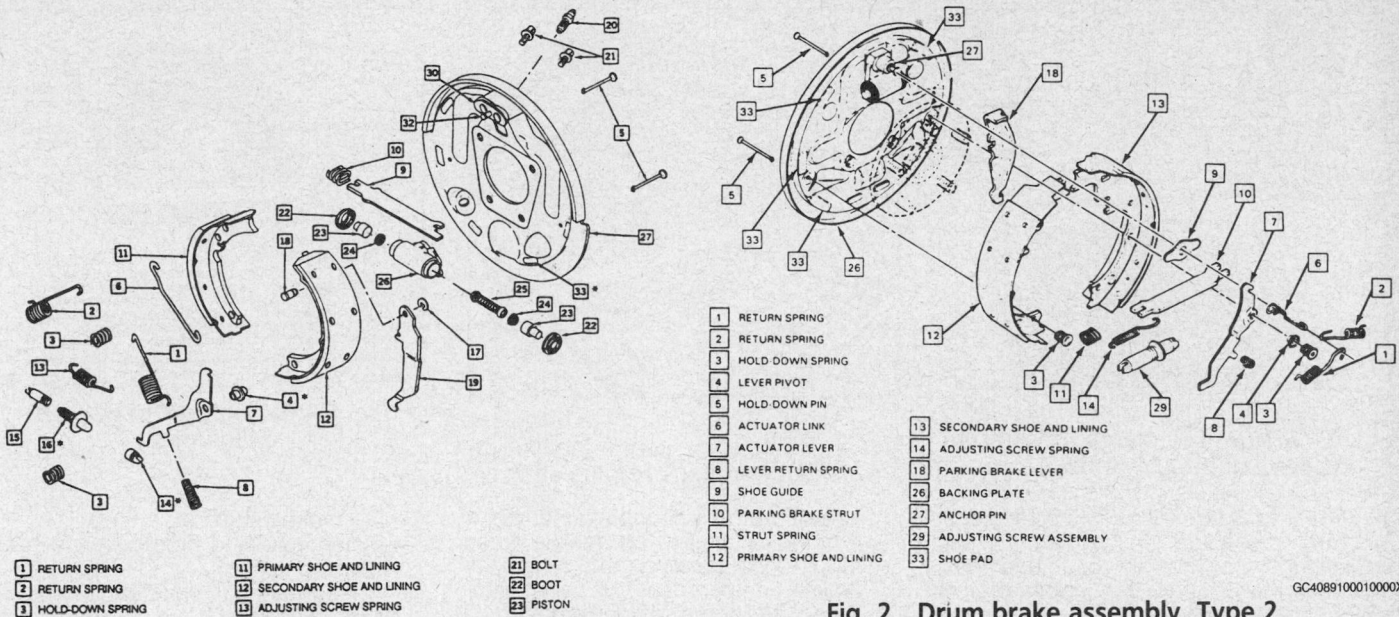

GC4089100010000X

Fig. 2 Drum brake assembly. Type 2

4. Remove brake hold-down springs with suitable tool.
5. Lift actuating lever, then unhook actuating link from anchor pin and remove.
6. Remove actuating lever(s) and return spring.
7. Spread shoes apart and remove parking brake strut and spring.
8. Disconnect parking brake cable from lever, then remove brake shoes from backing plate.
9. Separate brake shoes by removing adjusting screw and spring, then unhook parking brake lever from shoe assembly.
10. Clean dirt from brake drum, backing plate and all other components. **Do not use compressed air or dry brush to clean brake parts. Many brake parts contain asbestos fibers which, if inhaled, can cause serious injury. Clean brake parts with a water soaked rag or a suitable vacuum cleaner to minimize airborne dust.**

INSTALLATION

1. Lubricate parking brake lever fulcrum with suitable brake lube, then attach lever to brake shoe. Ensure lever operates smoothly.
2. Connect brake shoes with adjusting screw spring, then position adjusting screw. **Ensure adjusting screw star wheel does not contact adjusting screw spring after installation and also ensure righthand thread adjusting screw is installed on left side of vehicle and lefthand thread adjusting screw is installed on right side of vehicle. When brake shoe installation is completed, ensure starwheel lines up with adjusting hole in backing plate.**
3. Lightly lubricate backing plate shoe contact surfaces with suitable brake lube, then the area where parking brake cable contacts backing plate.
4. Install brake shoes on backing plate while engaging wheel cylinder links (if equipped) with shoe webbing. Connect parking brake cable to parking brake lever. **The primary shoe (short lining) faces towards front of vehicle.**
5. Install actuating levers, actuating link and return spring, **Figs. 1 and 2.**
6. Install hold-down springs with suitable tool.
7. Install primary and secondary shoe return springs using brake spring pliers or equivalent.
8. Using suitable brake drum to shoe gauge, measure brake drum inside diameter. Adjust brake shoes to dimension obtained on outside portion of gauge.
9. Install brake drum, wheel and tire assembly.
10. If any hydraulic connections have been opened, bleed brake system.
11. Adjust parking brake. Refer to individual car chapters for procedures.
12. Inspect all hydraulic lines and connections for leakage and repair as necessary.
13. Check master cylinder fluid level and replenish as necessary.
14. Check brake pedal for proper feel and return.
15. Lower vehicle and road test. **Do not severely apply brakes immediately after installation of new brake linings or permanent damage may occur to linings, and/or brake drums may become scored. Brakes must be used moderately during first several hundred miles of operation to ensure proper burnishing of linings.**

ADJUSTMENTS

These brakes have self-adjusting shoe mechanisms that assure correct lining-to-drum clearances at all times. The automatic adjusters operate only when the brakes are applied as the car is moving rearward.

Although the brakes are self-adjusting, an initial adjustment is necessary after the brake shoes have been relined or replaced, or when the length of the adjusting screw has been changed during some other service operation.

Frequent usage of an automatic transmission forward range to halt reverse vehicle motion may prevent the automatic adjusters from functioning, thereby inducing low pedal heights. Should low pedal heights be encountered, it is recommended that numerous forward and reverse stops be made until satisfactory pedal height is obtained. **If a low pedal condition cannot be corrected by making numerous reverse stops (provided the hydraulic system is free of air) it indicates that the self-adjusting mechanism is not functioning. Therefore, it will be necessary to remove the brake drum, clean, free up and lubricate the adjusting mechanism. Then adjust the brakes as follows, being sure the parking brake is fully released.**

SERVICE BRAKE ADJUSTMENT

Type 1

In as much as there is no way to adjust

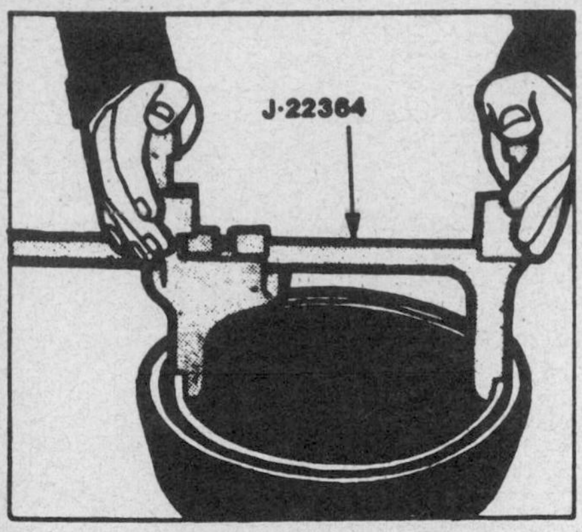
J-22364

GC4089100011000X

Fig. 3 Brake shoe gauge measuring inside diameter of brake drum

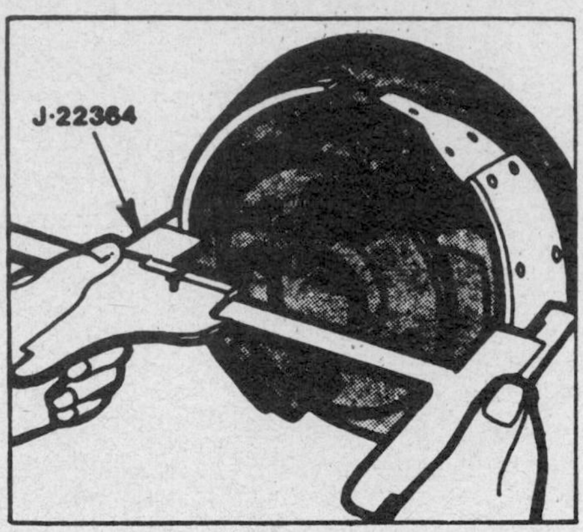
J-22364

GC4089100012000X

Fig. 4 Brake shoe gauge measuring outside diameter of brake shoes

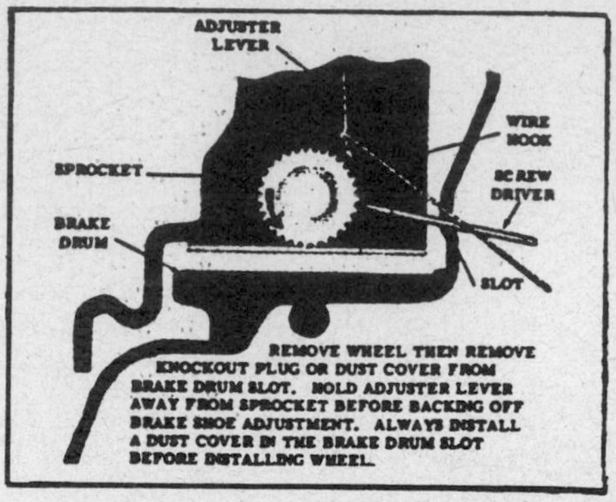
ADJUSTER LEVER
WIRE HOOK
SPROCKET
SCREW DRIVER
BRAKE DRUM
SLOT
REMOVE WHEEL THEN REMOVE KNOCKOUT PLUG OR DUST COVER FROM BRAKE DRUM SLOT. HOLD ADJUSTER LEVER AWAY FROM SPROCKET BEFORE BACKING OFF BRAKE SHOE ADJUSTMENT. ALWAYS INSTALL A DUST COVER IN THE BRAKE DRUM SLOT BEFORE INSTALLING WHEEL.

GC4089100013000X

Fig. 5 Backing off brake shoe adjustment

these brakes with the drums installed, the following procedure is mandatory after new linings are installed, or it becomes necessary to change the length of the brake shoe adjusting screw.

1. With brake drums removed, position the caliper shown in **Fig. 3,** to the inside diameter of the drum, then tighten the clamp screw.
2. Next position brake shoe end of the caliper tool over the brake shoes as shown in **Fig. 4.**
3. Rotate the gauge slightly around the shoes to ensure that the gauge contacts the linings at the largest diameter.
4. Adjust brake shoes until the gauge is a snug fit on the linings at the point of largest lining diameter. **If it is necessary to back off the brake shoe adjustment, it will be necessary to hold the adjuster lever away from the adjuster screw, Fig. 5.**

Type 2

1. Using a suitable punch, knock out lanced area in backing plate or drum. If drum is installed on vehicle when this is done, remove drum and clean brake compartment of all metal. **When adjustment is completed, a new hole cover must be installed in the backing plate.**
2. Using brake adjusting tool No. J-6166 or equivalent, turn brake adjusting screw to expand brake shoes at each wheel until wheel can just be turned by hand. Drag should be equal on all wheels.
3. **On all except Camaro,** back off adjusting screw at each wheel 30 notches.
4. **On Camaro,** back off screw 12 notches.
5. **On all models,** if shoe still drags slightly on drum, back off adjusting screw an additional one or two notches.
6. When adjusting screw has been backed off approximately 12 notches, brakes should be free of drag. Heavy drag at this point indicates tight parking brake cables.
7. Install adjusting hole cover in brake backing plate.
8. Check parking brake for proper adjustment.

PARKING BRAKE ADJUSTMENT

1. Jack up both rear wheels.
2. Apply parking brake three notches.
3. **Type 1,** tighten adjusting nut until right rear wheel can just be rotated rearward but is locked when forward rotation is attempted.
4. **Type 2,** tighten adjusting nut until left rear wheel can just be rotated rearward but is locked when forward rotation is attempted.
5. Release parking brake and check to ensure rear wheels rotate freely in either direction with no brake drag.

DRUM BRAKE SPECIFICATIONS

Year	Model	Brake Drum Inside Dia. Inch
BUICK		
1992-94	Roadmaster	①
CADILLAC		
1992	Brougham	11
1993–94	Fleetwood RWD	11
CHEVROLET		
1992-94	Camaro	①
1992-94	Caprice	①
1994	Impala SS	①
OLDSMOBILE		
1992	Custom Cruiser	①
PONTIAC		
1992-94	Firebird	①

①—With 4¾ inch bolt circle, 9.5 inches; w/5 inch bolt circle, 11 inches.

TIGHTENING SPECIFICATIONS

Component	Torque/Ft. Lbs.
CHEVROLET CAMARO & PONTIAC FIREBIRD	
Base Front Caliper Mounting Bolts	37
Brake Hose To Caliper	30
Caliper Bleeder Screw	115①②
Heavy Duty Front Caliper Bracket	137
Heavy Duty Caliper Adapter Bracket	85
Master Cylinder To Booster	24
Pivot Pin Nut	16
Rear Caliper Bracket	70
Rear Caliper Guide Pin (Hex Head)	26
Rear Caliper Guide Pin (Allen Head)	16
Wheel Cylinder Bleeder Screw	53①
Wheel Cylinder Line Fitting	11
Backing Plate To Axle Housing Nut	43
Wheel Lug Nuts	81

Component	Torque/Ft. Lbs.
BUICK ROADMASTER/CADILLAC BROUGHAM/ FLEETWOOD RWD, CHEVROLET CAPRICE & IMPALA SS & OLDSMOBILE CUSTOM CRUISER	
Brake Hose To Caliper	33
Caliper Bleeder Screw	115①
Caliper Mounting Bolts	38
Master Cylinder To Booster	20
Wheel Cylinder Bleeder Screw	62①
Wheel Cylinder Line Fitting	18
Wheel Cylinder To Backing Plate	13
Wheel Lug Nuts	100

①—Inch Lbs.
②—Heavy duty front & rear caliper bleeder screw, 80 inch lbs.

Type 3

INDEX

PRECAUTIONS

When working on or around brake assemblies, care must be taken to prevent breathing asbestos dust, as many manufacturers incorporate asbestos fibers in the production of brake linings. During routine service operations the amount of asbestos dust from brake lining wear is at a low level due to a chemical breakdown during use, and a few precautions will minimize exposure.

1. Do not sand or grind brake linings unless suitable local exhaust ventilation equipment is used to prevent excessive asbestos exposure.
2. Wear a suitable respirator approved for asbestos dust use during all repair procedures.
3. When cleaning brake dust from brake parts, use a vacuum cleaner with a highly efficient filter system. If a suitable vacuum cleaner is not available, use a water soaked rag. **Do not use compressed air or dry brush to clean brake parts.**
4. Keep work area clean using same equipment as for cleaning brake parts.
5. Properly dispose of rags and vacuum cleaner bags by placing them in plastic bags.
6. Do not smoke or eat while working on brake systems. **Never use gasoline, kerosene, alcohol, motor oil, transmission fluid, or any fluid containing mineral oil to clean brake system components. These fluids will damage the rubber caps and seals. If system contamination is suspected, check brake fluid in the reservoir for dirt, discoloration, or separation (breakdown) of the brake fluid into distinct layers. Drain and flush the hydraulic system with clean brake fluid if contamination is suspected.**

INSPECTION

1. If any parts are of doubtful strength or quality due to heat discoloration, or are worn, replace them.
2. Inspect wheel cylinder dust boots for signs of excessive wear or damage.
3. Inspect adjusting screw for smooth operation over full length.
4. Clean adjusting screw components in denatured alcohol.
5. Apply suitable lubricant to adjuster screw threads, inside diameter of socket and socket face. Adequate lubrication is achieved when a continuous bead of lubricant is at open end of adjuster nut and socket when threads are fully engaged.
6. Clean dirt and/or rust from brake drum, backing plate and all other components. **Do not use compressed air or dry brush to clean brake parts. Many brake parts contain asbestos fibers which, if inhaled, can cause serious injury. Clean brake parts with a water soaked rag or a suitable vacuum cleaner to minimize airborne dust.**
7. Ensure adjuster nut turns freely on adjuster screw.

BRAKE DRUMS

Any time the brake drums are removed for brake service, the braking surface diameter should be checked with a suitable brake drum micrometer at several points to determine if they are within the safe oversize limit stamped on the brake drum outer surface. If the braking surface diameter exceeds specifications, the drum must be replaced. If the braking surface diameter is within specifications, drums should be cleaned and inspected for cracks, scores, deep grooves, taper, out of round and heat spotting. If drums are cracked or heat spotted, they must be replaced. Minor scores should be removed with sandpaper. Grooves and large scores can only be removed by machining with special equipment, as long as the braking surface is

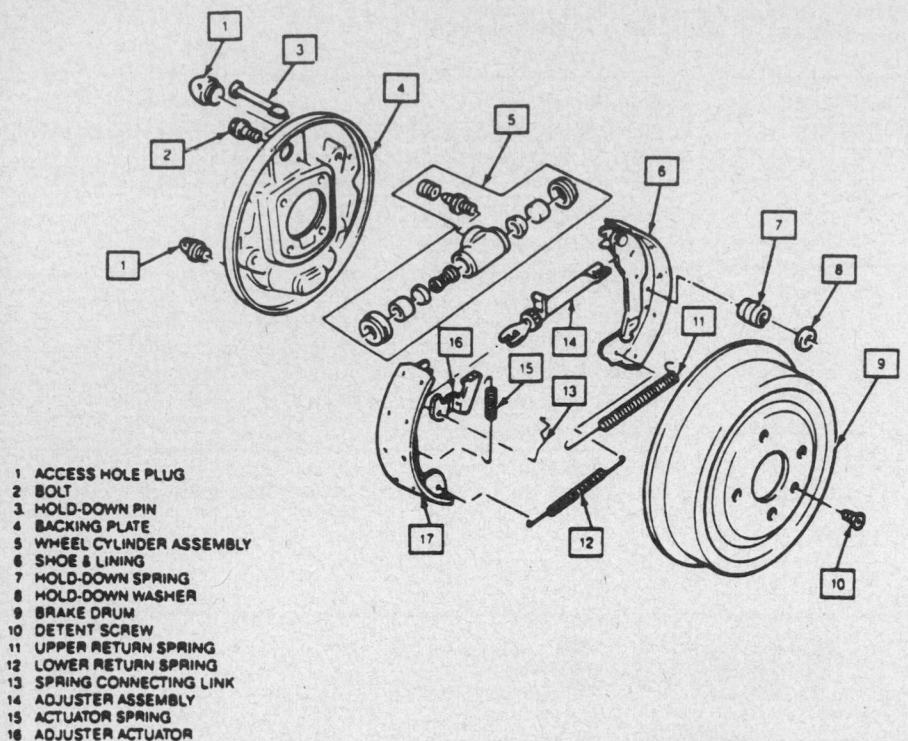

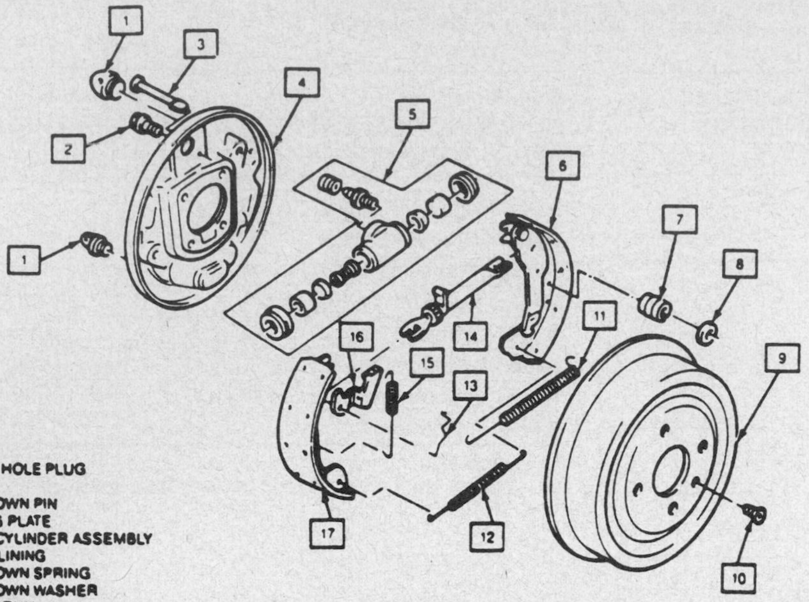
1 ACCESS HOLE PLUG
2 BOLT
3 HOLD-DOWN PIN
4 BACKING PLATE
5 WHEEL CYLINDER ASSEMBLY
6 SHOE & LINING
7 HOLD-DOWN SPRING
8 HOLD-DOWN WASHER
9 BRAKE DRUM
10 DETENT SCREW
11 UPPER RETURN SPRING
12 LOWER RETURN SPRING
13 SPRING CONNECTING LINK
14 ADJUSTER ASSEMBLY
15 ACTUATOR SPRING
16 ADJUSTER ACTUATOR
17 ADJUSTER SHOE & LINING
GC4089100014000X

Fig. 1 Drum brake assembly

within specifications stamped on brake drum outer surface. Any brake drum sufficiently out of round to cause vehicle vibration or noise while braking or showing taper should also be machined, removing only enough stock to true up the brake drum.

After a brake drum is machined, wipe the braking surface diameter with a denatured alcohol soaked cloth. If one brake drum is machined, the other should also be machined to the same diameter to maintain equal braking forces.

BRAKE LININGS & SPRINGS

Inspect brake linings for excessive wear, damage, oil, grease or brake fluid contamination. If any of the above conditions exists, brake linings should be replaced. Do not attempt to replace only one set of brake shoes; they should be replaced as an axle set only to maintain equal braking forces. Examine brake shoe webbing, hold-down and return springs for signs of overheating indicated by a slight blue color. If any component exhibits overheating signs, replace hold-down and return springs with new ones. Overheated springs lose their pull and could cause brake linings to wear out prematurely. Inspect all springs for sags, bends and external damage and replace as necessary.

Inspect hold-down retainers and pins for bends, rust and corrosion. If any of the above is found, replace as required.

BACKING PLATE

Inspect backing plate shoe contact surface for grooves that may restrict shoe movement and cannot be removed by lightly sanding with emery cloth or other suitable abrasive. If backing plate exhibits above condition, it should be replaced. Also inspect for signs of cracks, warpage and excessive rust, indicating need for replacement.

ADJUSTER MECHANISM

Inspect all components for rust, corrosion, bends and fatigue. Replace as necessary. **On adjuster mechanism equipped with adjuster cable,** inspect cable for kinks, fraying or elongation of eyelet and replace as necessary.

PARKING BRAKE CABLE

Inspect parking brake cable end for kinks, fraying and elongation and replace as necessary. Use a small hose clamp to compress clamp where it enters backing plate to remove.

BRAKE SERVICE

REMOVAL

1. Raise and support vehicle.
2. Mark relationship between rear wheel and hub, then remove wheel and tire assembly.
3. Remove brake drum detent screw, then the brake drum. If drum is difficult to remove, proceed as follows:
   a. Ensure parking brake cable is released.
   b. Loosen parking brake cable.
   c. Remove access hole plug from backing plate, then move parking brake lever until lever stop rests on brake shoe.

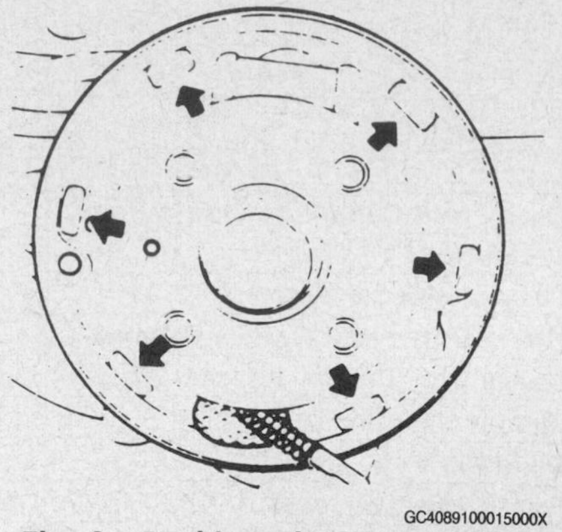
GC4089100015000X

Fig. 2 Backing plate lubrication points

4. Remove upper and lower return springs, then the adjuster actuator and actuator spring, **Fig. 1.**
5. Press brake shoes outward slightly and remove adjuster assembly.
6. Remove hold-down springs, washers and pins using a suitable tool.
7. Remove brake shoes from backing plate and parking brake cable.

INSTALLATION

1. Lubricate backing plate at points shown, **Fig. 2.**
2. Connect parking brake lever to parking brake cable.
3. Ensure parking brake cable is properly routed, then install shoes and lining to backing plate with hold-down spring, washer and pin.
4. Position adjuster shoe and lining and lower return spring against backing plate. Ensure spring is properly positioned under anchor plate.
5. Install hold-down spring, washer and pin.
6. Turn adjuster in to stop, then install adjuster assembly, **Fig. 3.** Ensure spring clip is positioned toward backing plate.
7. Install adjuster actuator onto pin and actuator spring.
8. Install spring connecting link to pin and press into brake hole.
9. Connect upper spring from connecting link to brake shoe.
10. Install brake drum and detent screw, then the wheel and tire assembly.
11. Adjust service and parking brakes as necessary.

ADJUSTMENTS

SERVICE BRAKE ADJUSTMENT

1. Raise and support vehicle.
2. Mark relationship between rear wheels and hubs, then remove wheel and tire assemblies.
3. Remove brake drum setscrew, then the brake drum. If drum is difficult to remove, proceed as follows:
   a. Ensure parking brake cable releases.
   b. Loosen parking brake cable.
   c. Remove access hole plug from

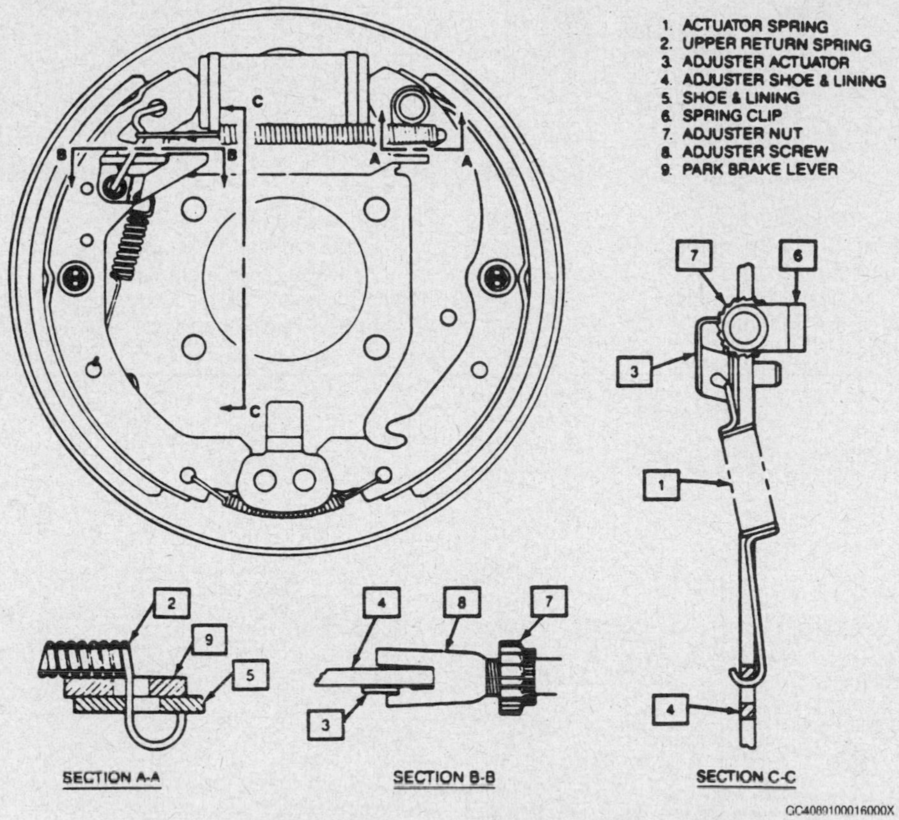
1. ACTUATOR SPRING
2. UPPER RETURN SPRING
3. ADJUSTER ACTUATOR
4. ADJUSTER SHOE & LINING
5. SHOE & LINING
6. SPRING CLIP
7. ADJUSTER NUT
8. ADJUSTER SCREW
9. PARK BRAKE LEVER
SECTION A-A
SECTION B-B
SECTION C-C
GC4089100016000X

Fig. 3 Cross-sectional view of drum brake assembly

backing plate, then move parking brake lever until lever stop rests on brake shoe.

4. Turn adjuster assembly in as far as possible, **Fig. 3.**
5. Ensure parking brake lever stops make contact with edge of shoe web. If contact is not evident, loosen parking brake cable at equalizer as necessary.
6. Install brake drums and wheels. then lower vehicle.
7. Depress brake pedal at least ten times until clicking of adjustment actuator is no longer heard.
8. Adjust parking brake as necessary.

PARKING BRAKE ADJUSTMENT

1. Adjust service brakes as previously described.
2. Ensure parking brakes are fully released.
3. Raise and support vehicle.
4. Ensure parking brake cable moves freely, then turn self-locking nut until rear wheels are difficult to turn.
5. Back off self-locking nut until rear wheels are just free to turn.

DRUM BRAKE SPECIFICATIONS

Year	Model	Brake Drum Inside Dia. Inch
1992–93	LeMans	7.87

TIGHTENING SPECIFICATIONS

Component	Torque/Ft. Lbs.
Anchor Plate To Rear Axle	21
Booster To Support Bracket	13
Brake Hose To Caliper	29
Brake Drum To Wheel Hub	35①
Caliper Bleeder Screw	80①
Caliper To Steering Knuckle	70
Master Cylinder To Booster	13
Rotor To Front Wheel Hub	35①
Wheel Cylinder Bleeder Screw	80①
Wheel Cylinder To Backing Plate	80①
Wheel Lug Nuts	66

①—Inch Lbs.

Type 4

INDEX

PRECAUTIONS

When working on or around brake assemblies, care must be taken to prevent breathing asbestos dust, as many manufacturers incorporate asbestos fibers in the production of brake linings. During routine service operations the amount of asbestos dust from brake lining wear is at a low level due to a chemical breakdown during use, and a few precautions will minimize exposure.

1. Do not sand or grind brake linings unless suitable local exhaust ventilation equipment is used to prevent excessive asbestos exposure.
2. Wear a suitable respirator approved for asbestos dust use during all repair procedures.
3. When cleaning brake dust from brake parts, use a vacuum cleaner with a highly efficient filter system. If a suitable vacuum cleaner is not available, use a water soaked rag. **Do not use compressed air or dry brush to clean brake parts.**
4. Keep work area clean using same equipment as for cleaning brake parts.
5. Properly dispose of rags and vacuum cleaner bags by placing them in plastic bags.
6. Do not smoke or eat while working on brake systems. **Never use gasoline, kerosene, alcohol, motor oil, transmission fluid, or any fluid containing mineral oil to clean brake system components. These fluids will damage the rubber caps and seals. If system contamination is suspected, check brake fluid in the reservoir for dirt, discoloration, or separation (breakdown) of the brake fluid into distinct layers. Drain and flush the hydraulic system with clean brake fluid if contamination is suspected.**

INSPECTION

1. Inspect brake components for damage and/or wear. Replace as necessary.
2. Inspect wheel cylinders. Excessive fluid indicates cup leakage and need for wheel cylinder replacement.
3. Inspect backing plate for evidence of axle seal leakage.
4. Inspect backing plate attaching bolts. Ensure bolts are tight.
5. Check adjuster operation. If adjusters are worn, frozen or loose, replace adjuster and backing plate assembly as required.
6. Using fine emery cloth or other suitable abrasive, clean rust and/or dirt from shoe contact surface on backing plate.

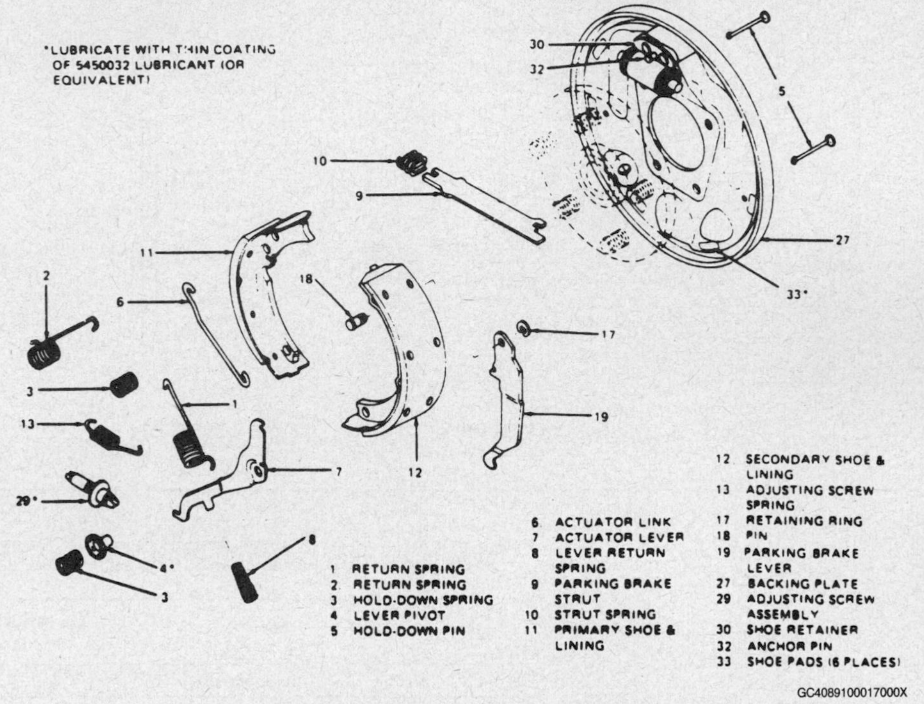

*LUBRICATE WITH THIN COATING OF 5450032 LUBRICANT (OR EQUIVALENT)
1 RETURN SPRING
2 RETURN SPRING
3 HOLD-DOWN SPRING
4 LEVER PIVOT
5 HOLD-DOWN PIN
6 ACTUATOR LINK
7 ACTUATOR LEVER
8 LEVER RETURN SPRING
9 PARKING BRAKE STRUT
10 STRUT SPRING
11 PRIMARY SHOE & LINING
12 SECONDARY SHOE & LINING
13 ADJUSTING SCREW SPRING
17 RETAINING RING
18 PIN
19 PARKING BRAKE LEVER
27 BACKING PLATE
29 ADJUSTING SCREW ASSEMBLY
30 SHOE RETAINER
32 ANCHOR PIN
33 SHOE PADS (6 PLACES)
GC4089100017000X

Fig. 1 Drum brake assembly

BRAKE DRUMS

Any time the brake drums are removed for brake service, the braking surface diameter should be checked with a suitable brake drum micrometer at several points to determine if they are within the safe oversize limit stamped on the brake drum outer surface. If the braking surface diameter exceeds specifications, the drum must be replaced. If the braking surface diameter is within specifications, drums should be cleaned and inspected for cracks, scores, deep grooves, taper, out of round and heat spotting. If drums are cracked or heat spotted, they must be replaced. Minor scores should be removed with sandpaper. Grooves and large scores can only be removed by machining with special equipment, as long as the braking surface is within specifications stamped on brake drum outer surface. Any brake drum sufficiently out of round to cause vehicle vibration or noise while braking or showing taper should also be machined, removing only enough stock to true up the brake drum.

After a brake drum is machined, wipe the braking surface diameter with a denatured alcohol soaked cloth. If one brake drum is machined, the other should also be machined to the same diameter to maintain equal braking forces.

BRAKE LININGS & SPRINGS

Inspect brake linings for excessive wear, damage, oil, grease or brake fluid contamination. If any of the above conditions exists, brake linings should be replaced. Do not attempt to replace only one set of brake shoes; they should be replaced as an axle set only to maintain equal braking forces. Examine brake shoe webbing, hold-down and return springs for signs of overheating indicated by a slight blue color. If any component exhibits overheating signs, replace hold-down and return

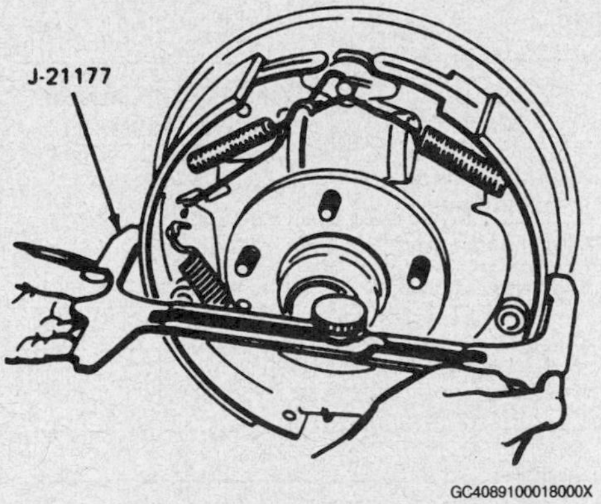
J-21177
GC4089100018000X

Fig. 2 Brake drum inside diameter measurement

springs with new ones. Overheated springs lose their pull and could cause brake linings to wear out prematurely. Inspect all springs for sags, bends and external damage and replace as necessary.

Inspect hold-down retainers and pins for bends, rust and corrosion. If any of the above is found, replace as required.

BACKING PLATE

Inspect backing plate shoe contact surface for grooves that may restrict shoe movement and cannot be removed by lightly sanding with emery cloth or other suitable abrasive. If backing plate exhibits above condition, it should be replaced. Also inspect for signs of cracks, warpage and excessive rust, indicating need for replacement.

ADJUSTER MECHANISM

Inspect all components for rust, corrosion, bends and fatigue. Replace as necessary. **On adjuster mechanism equipped with adjuster cable**, inspect cable for kinks, fraying or elongation of eyelet and replace as necessary.

PARKING BRAKE CABLE

Inspect parking brake cable end for kinks, fraying and elongation and replace as necessary. Use a small hose clamp to compress clamp where it enters backing plate to remove.

BRAKE SERVICE

REMOVAL

1. Raise and support rear of vehicle, then remove tire and wheel assembly.
2. Remove brake drum. If brake lining is dragging on brake drum, back off brake adjustment by rotating adjusting screw. Refer to individual car chapter for procedure. **If brake drum is rusted or corroded to axle flange and cannot be removed, lightly tap axle flange to drum mounting surface with a suitable hammer.**
3. Using brake spring pliers or equivalent, remove brake return springs, **Fig. 1.**
4. Using suitable pliers, remove hold-down springs and lever pivot.
5. While lifting up on actuator lever, disconnect actuating link.
6. Remove actuator lever and return spring.
7. Remove parking brake strut and spring.
8. Disconnect parking brake cable, then remove brake shoe and lining assembly.
9. Remove adjusting screw assembly and spring as follows:
   a. Note position of adjusting spring.
   b. Remove retaining ring, pin, and parking brake lever from secondary shoe.
   c. Remove adjusting screw and spring. **Do not interchange adjusting screws from right and left brake assemblies.**

INSTALLATION

1. Install parking brake lever, pin and retaining ring onto secondary shoe.
2. Apply silicone brake lubricant onto adjuster screw threads, inside diameter of socket and socket face. Adequate lubrication is achieved when a continuous bead of lubricant is at open end of pivot nut and socket when adjuster threads are completely engaged.
3. Install adjusting screw assembly and spring. **Spring coils must not overlap star wheel. Do not interchange right and lefthand springs.**
4. Connect parking brake cable, then install shoe and lining assembly.
5. Using a suitable tool, spread brake shoes apart, then install parking brake strut and spring. **Ensure parking brake strut is properly positioned. Ensure strut end without spring engages parking brake lever. Ensure strut end with spring engages primary brake shoe.**
6. Install actuator lever and return spring.
7. Install actuator link onto anchor pin.
8. While holding up on actuator lever, install link onto lever.
9. Install hold-down pins, lever pivot and hold-down springs.
10. Install shoe return springs.
11. Install brake drum, tire and wheel assembly.
12. If any hydraulic connections have been opened, bleed brake system.
13. Adjust brakes. Refer to individual car chapters for procedure.

ADJUSTMENTS

The rear drum brakes have self-adjusting shoe mechanisms that assure correct lining-to-drum clearances at all times. The automatic adjusters operate only when the service brakes are applied.

Although the brakes are self-adjusting, an initial adjustment is necessary after the brake shoes have been replaced, or when

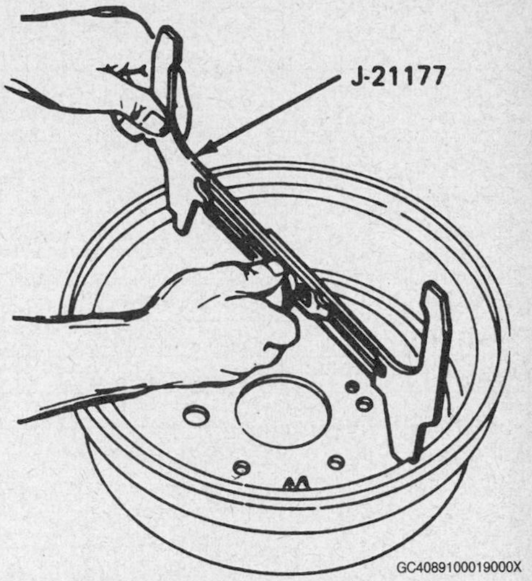
J-21177
GC4089100019000X

Fig. 3 Brake shoe clearance adjustment

the length of the star wheel adjuster has been changed during some other service operation.

SERVICE BRAKE ADJUSTMENT

1. Raise and support vehicle, then remove rear wheels and brake drums.
2. Check to make sure parking brake cable linkage and levers on secondary brake shoe are in "free" position.
3. Using brake shoe measuring tool No. J-21177 or equivalent, measure drum inside diameter, **Fig. 2.**
4. Turn brake adjusting screw to expand shoes to .050 inch less than diameter obtained on outside caliper portion of brake shoe measuring tool No. J-21177, **Fig. 3.**
5. Adjust parking brake. **Whenever rear drum brakes are serviced, the parking brake linkage cable at the equalizer must always be readjusted to prevent possible damage to brake shoes.**
6. Install brake drums, wheels and tires and lower vehicle to ground.
7. Drive vehicle and apply and release service brake 30-35 times with normal pedal force. Allow about one second between brake applications until satisfactory pedal height is obtained.

PARKING BRAKE ADJUSTMENT

1. Jack up both rear wheels.
2. **On hand operated parking brakes,** apply parking brake three to five notches. **On foot operated brakes,** apply parking brake two notches.
3. Tighten adjusting nut until right rear wheel can just be rotated rearward but is locked when forward rotation is attempted.
4. Release parking brake and check to ensure rear wheels rotate freely in either direction with no brake drag.

DRUM BRAKE SPECIFICATIONS

Year	Model	Brake Drum Inside Dia. Inch
BUICK		
1992–94	Century	8.86
1992–94	Skylark	7.87
CHEVROLET		
1993–94	Beretta	7.87
1992–94	Cavalier	7.87
1993–94	Corsica	7.87

Year	Model	Brake Drum Inside Dia. Inch
OLDSMOBILE		
1992–94	Achieva	7.87
1992	Cutlass Ciera	8.86
1992	Cutlass Cruiser	8.86
PONTIAC		
1992–94	Grand Am	7.87
1992–94	Sunbird	7.87

TIGHTENING SPECIFICATIONS

Component	Torque/Ft. Lbs.
Brake Hose To Caliper	32
Caliper Bleeder Screw	115①
Caliper Mounting Bolts	38
Master Cylinder To Booster	20
Wheel Cylinder To Backing Plate	15
Wheel Lug Nuts	100
Wheel Speed Sensor Mounting Bolts	62①

①—Inch Lbs.

Type 5

INDEX

PRECAUTIONS

When working on or around brake assemblies, care must be taken to prevent breathing asbestos dust, as many manufacturers incorporate asbestos fibers in the production of brake linings. During routine service operations the amount of asbestos dust from brake lining wear is at a low level due to a chemical breakdown during use, and a few precautions will minimize exposure.

1. Do not sand or grind brake linings unless suitable local exhaust ventilation equipment is used to prevent excessive asbestos exposure.
2. Wear a suitable respirator approved for asbestos dust use during all repair procedures.
3. When cleaning brake dust from brake parts, use a vacuum cleaner with a highly efficient filter system. If a suitable vacuum cleaner is not available, use a water soaked rag. **Do not use compressed air or dry brush to clean brake parts.**
4. Keep work area clean using same equipment as for cleaning brake parts.
5. Properly dispose of rags and vacuum cleaner bags by placing them in plastic bags.
6. Do not smoke or eat while working on brake systems. **Never use gasoline, kerosene, alcohol, motor oil, transmission fluid, or any fluid containing mineral oil to clean brake system components. These fluids will damage the rubber caps and seals. If system contamination is suspected, check brake fluid in the reservoir for dirt, discoloration, or separation (breakdown) of the brake fluid into distinct layers. Drain and flush the hydraulic system with clean brake fluid if contamination is suspected.**

INSPECTION

1. Check brake drum, shoes, strut, auto adjuster lever, springs and backing plate for wear, distortion, cracks or other abnormal conditions.
2. If any parts are of doubtful strength or quality due to damage, heat discoloration, stress or wear, replace them.
3. Measure brake drum inside diameter and the brake shoe lining thickness.
4. Inspect lining and drum for proper contact.

BRAKE DRUMS

Any time the brake drums are removed for brake service, the braking surface diameter should be checked with a suitable brake drum micrometer at several points to determine if they are within the safe oversize limit stamped on the brake drum outer surface. If the braking surface diameter exceeds specifications, the drum must

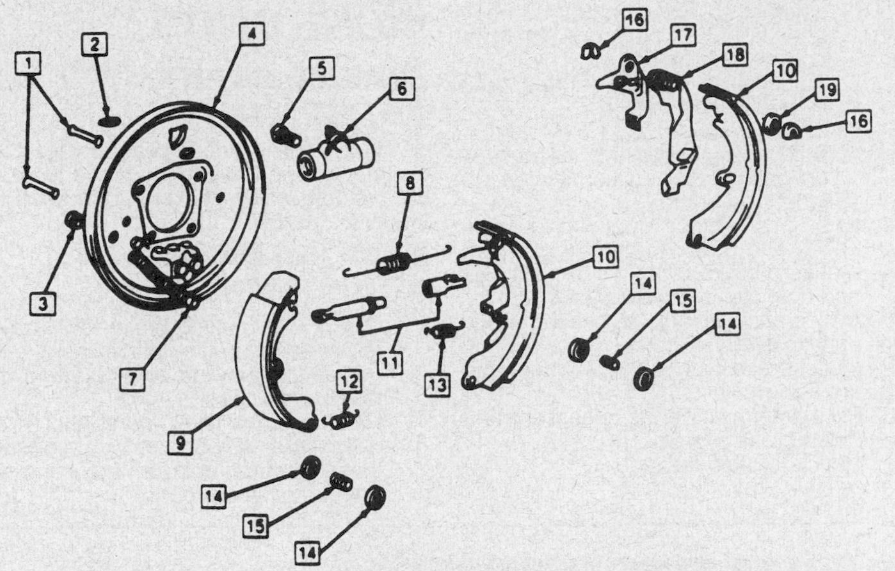
1
2
3
4
5
6
7
8
9
10
11
12
13
14
15
16
17
18
19

1. HOLD-DOWN PIN
2. PLUG
3. INSPECTION HOLE PLUG
4. BACKING PLATE
5. BOLT
6. WHEEL CYLINDER
7. PARKING BRAKE CABLE
8. RETURN SPRING
9. FRONT SHOE
10. REAR SHOE
11. STRUT
12. ANCHOR SPRING
13. ADJUSTING LEVER SPRING
14. RETAINER
15. HOLD-DOWN SPRING
16. C-WASHER
17. AUTOMATIC ADJUSTING LEVER
18. PARKING BRAKE LEVER
19. SHIM

GC4089100024000X

Fig. 1 Drum brake assembly

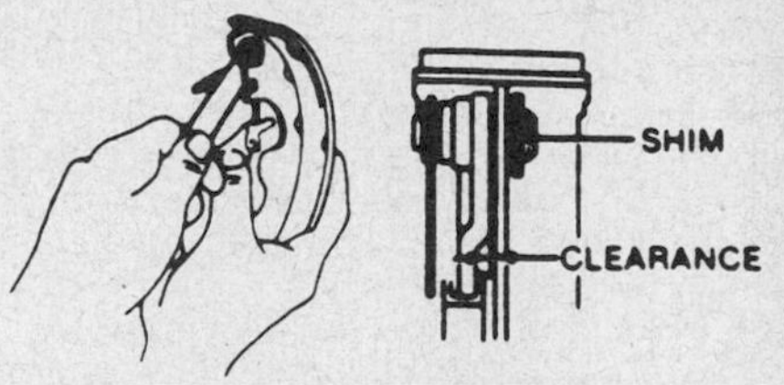
SHIM
CLEARANCE

SHIM THICKNESS	
THICKNESS	THICKNESS
0.2 MM (0.008 IN.)	0.5 MM (0.020 IN.)
0.3 MM (0.012 IN.)	0.6 MM (0.024 IN.)
0.4 MM (0.016 IN.)	0.9 MM (0.035 IN.)

GC4089100025000X

Fig. 2 Lever to shoe clearance check

be replaced. If the braking surface diameter is within specifications, drums should be cleaned and inspected for cracks, scores, deep grooves, taper, out of round and heat spotting. If drums are cracked or heat spotted, they must be replaced. Minor scores should be removed with sandpaper. Grooves and large scores can only be removed by machining with special equipment, as long as the braking surface is within specifications stamped on brake drum outer surface. Any brake drum sufficiently out of round to cause vehicle vibration or noise while braking or showing taper should also be machined, removing only enough stock to true up the brake drum.

After a brake drum is machined, wipe the braking surface diameter with a denatured alcohol soaked cloth. If one brake drum is machined, the other should also be machined to the same diameter to maintain equal braking forces.

BRAKE LININGS & SPRINGS

Inspect brake linings for excessive wear, damage, oil, grease or brake fluid contamination. If any of the above conditions exists, brake linings should be replaced. Do not attempt to replace only one set of brake shoes; they should be replaced as an axle set only to maintain equal braking forces. Examine brake shoe webbing, hold-down and return springs for signs of overheating indicated by a slight blue color. If any component exhibits overheating signs, replace hold-down and return springs with new ones. Overheated springs lose their pull and could cause brake linings to wear out prematurely. Inspect all springs for sags, bends and external damage and replace as necessary.

Inspect hold-down retainers and pins for bends, rust and corrosion. If any of the above is found, replace as required.

BACKING PLATE

Inspect backing plate shoe contact surface for grooves that may restrict shoe movement and cannot be removed by lightly sanding with emery cloth or other suitable abrasive. If backing plate exhibits above condition, it should be replaced. Also inspect for signs of cracks, warpage and excessive rust, indicating need for replacement.

ADJUSTER MECHANISM

Inspect all components for rust, corrosion, bends and fatigue. Replace as necessary. **On adjuster mechanism equipped with adjuster cable,** inspect cable for kinks, fraying or elongation of eyelet and replace as necessary.

PARKING BRAKE CABLE

Inspect parking brake cable end for kinks, fraying and elongation and replace as necessary. Use a small hose clamp to compress clamp where it enters backing plate to remove.

BRAKE SERVICE

REMOVAL

1. Raise and support vehicle.
2. Mark relationship of wheel to axle, then remove wheel and tire assembly.
3. Remove brake drum. If drum is difficult to remove, insert screwdriver through hole in backing plate and hold automatic adjusting lever away from adjusting bolt, then, using a second screwdriver, reduce brake shoe adjustment.
4. Remove return spring, **Fig. 1**
5. Remove hold-down spring, retainers and pin retaining front shoe.
6. Disconnect anchor spring from front shoe, then remove front shoe.
7. Remove anchor spring.
8. Remove hold-down spring, retainers and pin retaining rear shoe.
9. Using screwdriver, disconnect parking brake cable from anchor plate.
10. Using pliers, disconnect parking brake cable from lever and remove rear shoe together with strut.
11. Remove adjusting lever spring, then the strut together with return spring.
12. Remove parking brake lever and automatic adjusting lever from rear shoe by prying out "C" washer and removing shims and levers.
13. Clean dirt from brake drum, backing plate and all other components. **Do not use compressed air or dry brush to clean brake parts. Many brake parts contain asbestos fibers which, if inhaled, can cause serious injury. Clean brake parts with a water soaked rag or a suitable vacuum cleaner to minimize airborne dust.**

INSTALLATION

1. Apply suitable lubricant to backing plate brake shoe contact points, anchor plate brake shoe contact points, strut and adjusting bolt contact points and the strut and brake shoe contact points.
2. Install parking brake lever and automatic adjusting lever to rear shoe as follows:
   a. Temporarily install levers and shim with a new "C" washer.
   b. Using feeler gauge, measure clearance between shoe and lever, **Fig. 2.**
   c. If clearance is not 0-.0138 inch, adjust by installing replacement shim.
   d. Using pliers, stake "C" washer.
3. Set strut and return spring in place on rear shoe and install adjusting lever spring.
4. Install rear shoe as follows:
   a. Using pliers, connect parking brake cable to lever.

b. Pass parking brake cable through notch in anchor plate.
c. Set rear shoe in place with end of shoe inserted in wheel cylinder and other end in anchor plate.
d. Install hold-down spring, retainers and pin.

5. Install front shoe as follows:
   a. Install anchor spring between front and rear shoes.
   b. Set front shoe in place with end of shoe inserted in wheel cylinder and the strut in place.
   c. Install hold-down spring, retainers and pin.
   d. Connect return spring.
6. Check operation of automatic adjuster mechanism as follows:
   a. Move parking brake lever of rear shoe back and forth and check whether adjusting bolt turns. If bolt does not turn, check brakes for incorrect installation.
   b. Adjust strut length to shortest possible distance.
   c. Install brake drum.
   d. Pull parking brake lever all the way up until a clicking sound can no longer be heard.
7. Check clearance between brake shoes and drum. Remove drum and measure brake drum inside diameter and diameter of brake shoes.
8. If clearance is not .024 inch, check parking brake system.
9. Install brake drum and the wheel and tire assembly.
10. Fill master cylinder as necessary and bleed brake system.
11. Check for fluid leakage.

ADJUSTMENTS

SERVICE BRAKE ADJUSTMENT

Adjustment is accomplished automatically by pulling the parking brake lever all the way up until a clicking sound can no longer be heard.

PARKING BRAKE ADJUSTMENT

1. Check that parking brake lever travel is correct by pulling parking brake lever all the way up and counting the number of clicks.
2. Parking brake lever travel should be 4-7 clicks. If not, remove console, loosen locknut and turn adjusting nut until travel is correct.

DRUM BRAKE SPECIFICATIONS

Year	Model	Brake Drum Inside Dia. Inch
GEO		
1992–94	Prizm	7.87

TIGHTENING SPECIFICATIONS

Component	Torque/Ft. Lbs.
Brake Hose To Caliper	11
Caliper Carrier Mounting Bolts	65
Caliper Mounting Bolts	19
Master Cylinder Retaining Nut	115①
Wheel Lug Nuts	76

①—Inch Lbs.

Type 6

INDEX

PRECAUTIONS

When working on or around brake assemblies, care must be taken to prevent breathing asbestos dust, as many manufacturers incorporate asbestos fibers in the production of brake linings. During routine service operations the amount of asbestos dust from brake lining wear is at a low level due to a chemical breakdown during use, and a few precautions will minimize exposure.

1. Do not sand or grind brake linings unless suitable local exhaust ventilation equipment is used to prevent excessive asbestos exposure.
2. Wear a suitable respirator approved for asbestos dust use during all repair procedures.
3. When cleaning brake dust from brake parts, use a vacuum cleaner with a highly efficient filter system. If a suitable vacuum cleaner is not available, use a water soaked rag. **Do not use compressed air or dry brush to clean brake parts.**
4. Keep work area clean using same equipment as for cleaning brake parts.
5. Properly dispose of rags and vacuum cleaner bags by placing them in plastic bags.
6. Do not smoke or eat while working on brake systems. **Never use gasoline, kerosene, alcohol, motor oil, transmission fluid, or any fluid containing mineral oil to clean brake system components. These fluids will damage the rubber caps and seals. If system contamination is suspected, check brake fluid in the reservoir for dirt, discoloration, or separation (breakdown) of the brake fluid into distinct layers. Drain and flush the hydraulic system with clean brake fluid if contamination is suspected.**

INSPECTION

1. If any parts are of doubtful strength or quality due to heat discoloration, or are worn, replace them.
2. Inspect wheel cylinder dust boots for signs of excessive wear or damage.
3. Inspect auto adjuster gear for smooth operation over full length.
4. Clean adjusting gear components in denatured alcohol.
5. Apply suitable lubricant to adjuster screw threads, inside diameter of socket and socket face. Adequate lubrication is achieved when a continuous bead of lubricant is at open end of adjuster nut and socket when threads are fully engaged.
6. Clean dirt and/or rust from brake drum, backing plate and all other components. **Do not use compressed air or dry brush to clean brake parts. Many brake parts contain asbestos fibers which, if inhaled, can cause serious injury. Clean brake parts with a water soaked rag or a suitable vacuum cleaner to minimize airborne dust.**
7. Ensure adjuster gear turns freely on adjuster screw.

BRAKE DRUMS

Any time the brake drums are removed for brake service, the braking surface diameter should be checked with a suitable brake drum micrometer at several points to determine if they are within the safe oversize limit stamped on the brake drum outer surface. If the braking surface diameter exceeds specifications, the drum must be replaced. If the braking surface diameter is within specifications, drums should be cleaned and inspected for cracks, scores, deep grooves, taper, out of round and heat spotting. If drums are cracked or heat spotted, they must be replaced. Minor scores should be removed with sandpaper. Grooves and large scores can only be removed by machining with special equipment, as long as the braking surface is within specifications stamped on brake drum outer surface. Any brake drum sufficiently out of round to cause vehicle vibration or noise while braking or showing taper should also be machined, removing only enough stock to true up the brake drum.

After a brake drum is machined, wipe the braking surface diameter with a denatured alcohol soaked cloth. If one brake drum is machined, the other should also be machined to the same diameter to maintain equal braking forces.

BRAKE LININGS & SPRINGS

Inspect brake linings for excessive wear, damage, oil, grease or brake fluid contamination. If any of the above conditions exists, brake linings should be replaced. Do not attempt to replace only one set of brake shoes; they should be replaced as an axle set only to maintain equal braking forces. Examine brake shoe webbing, hold-down and return springs for signs of overheating indicated by a slight blue color. If any component exhibits overheating signs, replace hold-down and return springs with new ones. Overheated springs lose their pull and could cause brake linings to wear out prematurely. Inspect all springs for sags, bends and external damage and replace as necessary.

Inspect hold-down retainers and pins for bends, rust and corrosion. If any of the above is found, replace as required.

BACKING PLATE

Inspect backing plate shoe contact surface for grooves that may restrict shoe movement and cannot be removed by lightly sanding with emery cloth or other suitable abrasive. If backing plate exhibits above condition, it should be replaced. Also inspect for signs of cracks, warpage and excessive rust, indicating need for replacement.

ADJUSTER MECHANISM

Inspect all components for rust, corrosion, bends and fatigue. Replace as necessary. **On adjuster mechanism equipped with adjuster cable,** inspect cable for kinks, fraying or elongation of eyelet and replace as necessary.

PARKING BRAKE CABLE

Inspect parking brake cable end for kinks, fraying and elongation and replace as necessary. Use a small hose clamp to compress clamp where it enters backing plate to remove.

BRAKE SERVICE

REMOVAL

1. Raise and support rear of vehicle.
2. Remove wheels, then brake hubs and drums.
3. Remove return spring and auto adjuster spring.
4. Remove leading shoe hold-down spring and pin, **Fig. 1.**
5. Remove leading shoe and auto adjuster.
6. Remove trailing shoe hold-down spring and pin, then shoe.
7. Disconnect parking brake cable from

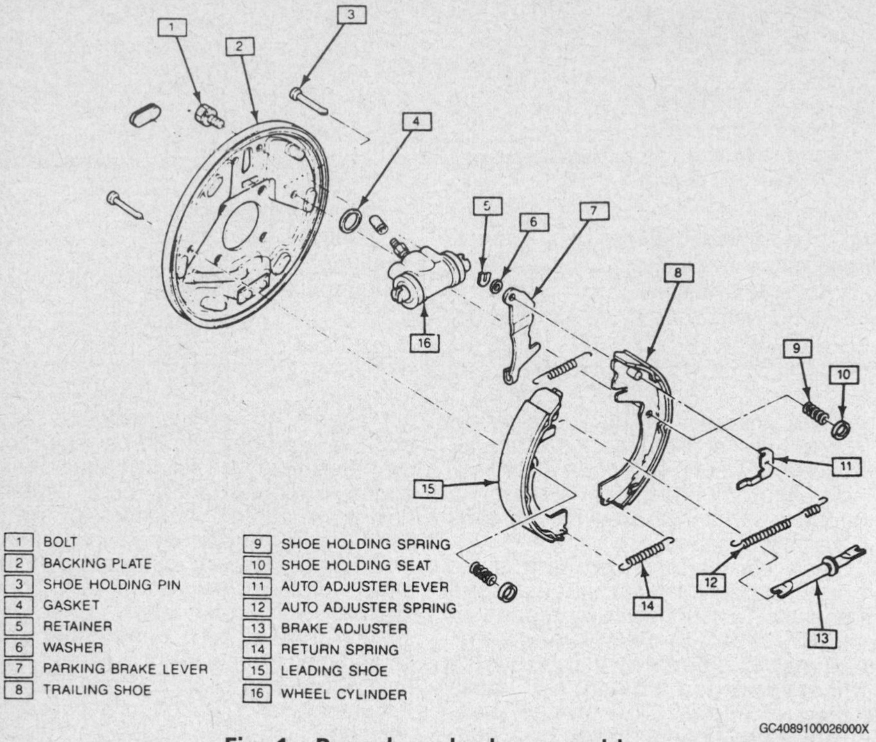
1 BOLT
2 BACKING PLATE
3 SHOE HOLDING PIN
4 GASKET
5 RETAINER
6 WASHER
7 PARKING BRAKE LEVER
8 TRAILING SHOE
9 SHOE HOLDING SPRING
10 SHOE HOLDING SEAT
11 AUTO ADJUSTER LEVER
12 AUTO ADJUSTER SPRING
13 BRAKE ADJUSTER
14 RETURN SPRING
15 LEADING SHOE
16 WHEEL CYLINDER
GC4089100026000X

Fig. 1 Rear drum brake assembly

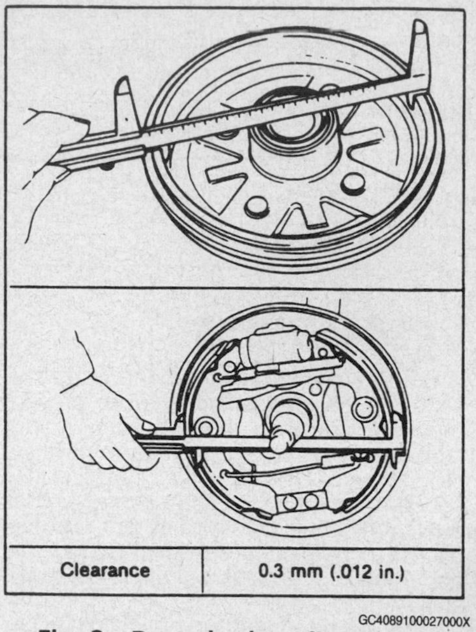
Clearance
0.3 mm (.012 in.)
GC4089100027000X

Fig. 2 Drum brake adjustment

lever, then remove trailing shoe.
8. Remove parking brake lever from trailing shoe.

INSTALLATION

1. Apply suitable lubricant to backing plate and cylinder piston brake shoe contact points, adjuster and parking lever pin contact points.
2. Install parking brake lever to trailing shoe, then connect parking brake cable to lever.
3. Install trailing shoe to backing plate with hold-down pin and spring, then install brake adjuster.
4. Install leading shoe to backing plate with hold-down pin and spring.
5. Install auto adjuster lever and auto adjuster spring, then install return spring.
6. Install brake drum, then adjust brakes. Refer to individual car chapters for procedure.
7. Adjust bearing preload. Refer to individual car chapters for procedure.
8. If hydraulic connections have been opened, bleed system.

ADJUSTMENTS

SERVICE BRAKE ADJUSTMENT

1. Measure brake drum inside diameter and brake shoe diameter, **Fig. 2.**
2. Ensure clearance between diameters is as specified, **Fig. 2.**

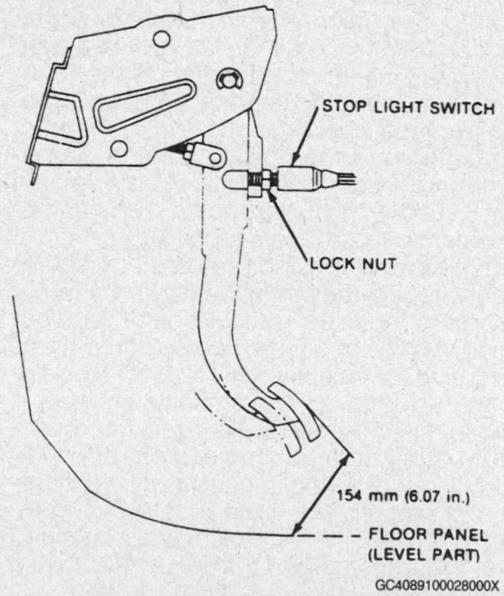
STOP LIGHT SWITCH
LOCK NUT
154 mm (6.07 in.)
FLOOR PANEL
(LEVEL PART)
GC4089100028000X

Fig. 3 Brake pedal height adjustment

PARKING BRAKE ADJUSTMENT

Parking brake stroke should measure 7 to 9 notches with approximately 14 lbs. pressure applied. Lever stroke is automatically adjusted when rear brakes are adjusted. If stroke is not within specifications after adjusting rear brakes, it may be adjusted by rotating the cable turnbuckle.

BRAKE PEDAL HEIGHT ADJUSTMENT

1. Ensure pedal is fully returned by pedal return spring, then measure brake pedal height, **Fig. 3.**
2. If measurement does not meet specifications, perform adjustment as follows:
   a. Loosen stop light switch and the locknut on pushrod.
   b. Adjust pushrod until brake pedal extends approximately 6.07 inches from floorboard.
   c. Position tip of stop lamp switch to rest lightly on pedal arm rubber stop.
   d. Carefully rotate stop lamp switch until freeplay between pedal arm and pushrod is eliminated from brake pedal.
   e. Tighten locknut.

DRUM BRAKE SPECIFICATIONS

Year	Model	Brake Drum Inside Dia. Inch
GEO		
1992–93	Storm	7.87

TIGHTENING SPECIFICATIONS

Component	Torque/Ft. Lbs.
Brake Hose To Caliper	113①
Caliper Bracket Mounts	76
Caliper Side Pins	36
Master Cylinder Retaining Nut	115①
Wheel Lug Nuts	87

①—Inch Lbs.

Type 7

INDEX

PRECAUTIONS

When working on or around brake assemblies, care must be taken to prevent breathing asbestos dust, as many manufacturers incorporate asbestos fibers in the production of brake linings. During routine service operations the amount of asbestos dust from brake lining wear is at a low level due to a chemical breakdown during use, and a few precautions will minimize exposure.

1. Do not sand or grind brake linings unless suitable local exhaust ventilation equipment is used to prevent excessive asbestos exposure.
2. Wear a suitable respirator approved for asbestos dust use during all repair procedures.
3. When cleaning brake dust from brake parts, use a vacuum cleaner with a highly efficient filter system. If a suitable vacuum cleaner is not available, use a water soaked rag. **Do not use compressed air or dry brush to clean brake parts.**
4. Keep work area clean using same equipment as for cleaning brake parts.
5. Properly dispose of rags and vacuum cleaner bags by placing them in plastic bags.
6. Do not smoke or eat while working on brake systems. **Never use gasoline, kerosene, alcohol, motor oil, transmission fluid, or any fluid containing mineral oil to clean brake system components. These fluids will damage the rubber caps and seals. If system contamination is suspected, check brake fluid in the reservoir for dirt, discoloration, or separation (breakdown) of the brake fluid into distinct layers. Drain and flush the hydraulic system with clean brake fluid if contamination is suspected.**

INSPECTION

1. If any parts are of doubtful strength or quality due to heat discoloration, or are worn, replace them.
2. Inspect wheel cylinder dust boots for signs of excessive wear or damage. If any leakage is apparent replace or rebuild wheel cylinder.
3. Clean dirt and/or rust from brake drum, backing plate and all other components. **Do not use compressed air or dry brush to clean brake parts. Many brake parts contain asbestos fibers which, if inhaled, can cause serious injury. Clean brake parts with a water soaked rag or a suitable vacuum cleaner to minimize airborne dust.**

BRAKE DRUMS

Any time the brake drums are removed for brake service, the braking surface diameter should be checked with a suitable brake drum micrometer at several points to determine if they are within the safe oversize limit stamped on the brake drum outer surface. If the braking surface diameter exceeds specifications, the drum must be replaced. If the braking surface diameter is within specifications, drums should be cleaned and inspected for cracks, scores, deep grooves, taper, out of round and heat spotting. If drums are cracked or heat spotted, they must be replaced. Minor scores should be removed with sandpaper. Grooves and large scores can only be removed by machining with special equipment, as long as the braking surface is within specifications stamped on brake drum outer surface. Any brake drum sufficiently out of round to cause vehicle vibration or noise while braking or showing taper should also be machined, removing only enough stock to true up the brake drum.

After a brake drum is machined, wipe the braking surface diameter with a denatured alcohol soaked cloth. If one brake drum is machined, the other should also be machined to the same diameter to maintain equal braking forces.

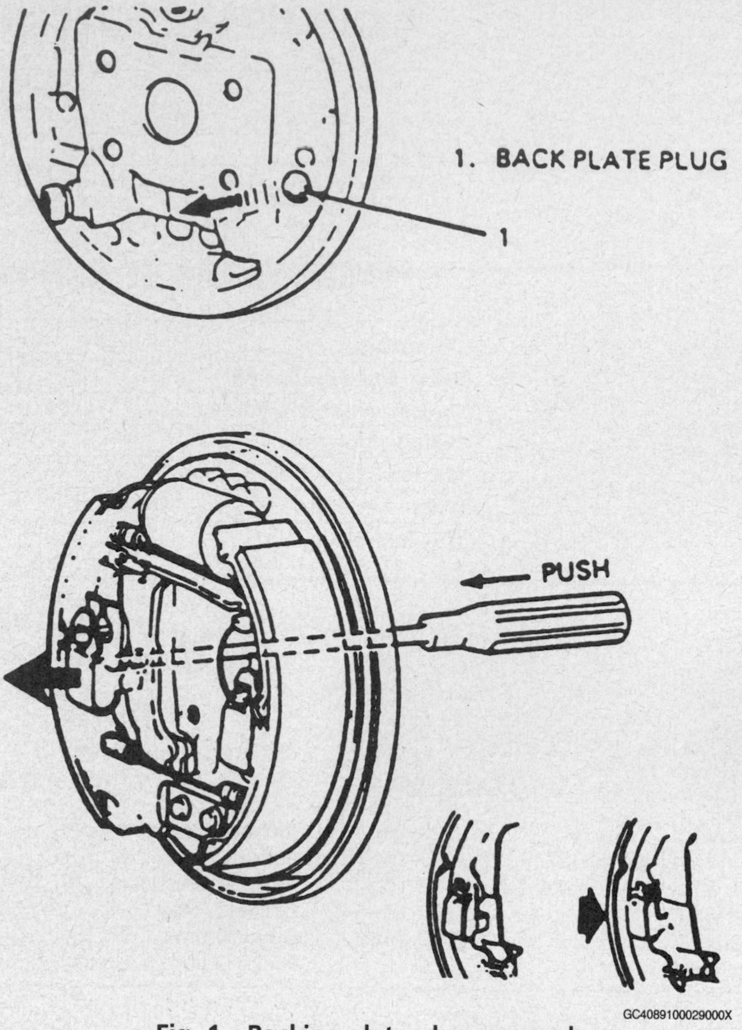
1. BACK PLATE PLUG
1
PUSH
GC4089100029000X
Fig. 1 Backing plate plug removal

BRAKE LININGS & SPRINGS

Inspect brake linings for excessive wear, damage, oil, grease or brake fluid contamination. If any of the above conditions exists, brake linings should be replaced. Do not attempt to replace only one set of brake shoes; they should be replaced as an axle set only to maintain equal braking forces. Examine brake shoe webbing, hold-down and return springs for signs of overheating indicated by a slight blue color. If any component exhibits overheating signs, replace hold-down and return springs with new ones. Overheated springs lose their pull and could cause brake linings to wear out prematurely. Inspect all springs for sags, bends and external damage and replace as necessary.

Inspect hold-down retainers and pins for bends, rust and corrosion. If any of the above is found, replace as required.

BACKING PLATE

Inspect backing plate shoe contact surface for grooves that may restrict shoe movement and cannot be removed by lightly sanding with emery cloth or other suitable abrasive. If backing plate exhibits above condition, it should be replaced. Also inspect for signs of cracks, warpage and excessive rust, indicating need for replacement.

ADJUSTER MECHANISM

Inspect all components for rust, corrosion, bends and fatigue. Replace as necessary. **On adjuster mechanism equipped with adjuster cable,** inspect cable for kinks, fraying or elongation of eyelet and replace as necessary.

PARKING BRAKE CABLE

Inspect parking brake cable end for kinks, fraying and elongation and replace as necessary. Use a small hose clamp to compress clamp where it enters backing plate to remove.

BRAKE SERVICE

REMOVAL

1. Raise and support vehicle.
2. Remove spindle cap by hammering lightly at 3 points around cap.
3. Remove cotter pin or unfasten staked portion of nut, then remove castle nut and washer.
4. Loosen parking brake cable adjusting nuts.
5. Remove backing plate plug, **Fig. 1.**
6. Insert screwdriver into plug hole until it contacts shoe hold-down spring and push in direction shown, **Fig. 1.** This pushes hold-down spring up and releases parking brake shoe lever from hold-down spring, resulting in added clearance between shoe and drum.
7. Using slide hammer tool No. J-2619-01 and brake drum remover tool No. J-34866 or equivalents, pull off brake drum.
8. Remove brake shoe hold-down springs by turning hold-down pins.
9. Disconnect parking brake cable from parking brake shoe lever and remove brake shoes.
10. Remove spring 1 in **Fig. 2,** pull primary shoe in direction of arrow and disengage strut 4 and return spring 2.
11. Disconnect return spring 3 from shoe.
12. Disconnect parking brake shoe lever from shoe.

INSTALLATION

1. Assemble brake shoes, levers and springs as shown in **Fig. 3.**
2. Push shoe hold-down springs down into place. Turn hold-down pins to engage springs.
3. To minimize dimension 'A-A,' **Fig. 4,** push strut towards backplate while pushing out on shoe as shown.
4. Position tab of spring clip behind parking lever.
5. Install brake drum and **torque** castle nut to 58-86.5 ft. lbs. Install cotter pin.
6. Install spindle cap.
7. Install wheel.
8. Depress brake pedal several times to obtain proper drum to shoe clearance and adjust parking brake.
9. Check that brake drum does not drag.
10. Lower vehicle and test brake operation.

ADJUSTMENTS

SERVICE BRAKE ADJUSTMENT

Adjustment is accomplished automatically by applying brake pedal 3 to 5 times with 66 lbs. of pressure. Brake pedal should be cycled 3 to 5 times when replacement components are installed to assure proper adjustment.

PARKING BRAKE ADJUSTMENT

Parking brake lever should be adjusted so lever comes up 4 to 9 notches with 44 to 55 lbs. of pull applied.

Adjust travel by loosening adjustment nuts, **Fig. 5.**

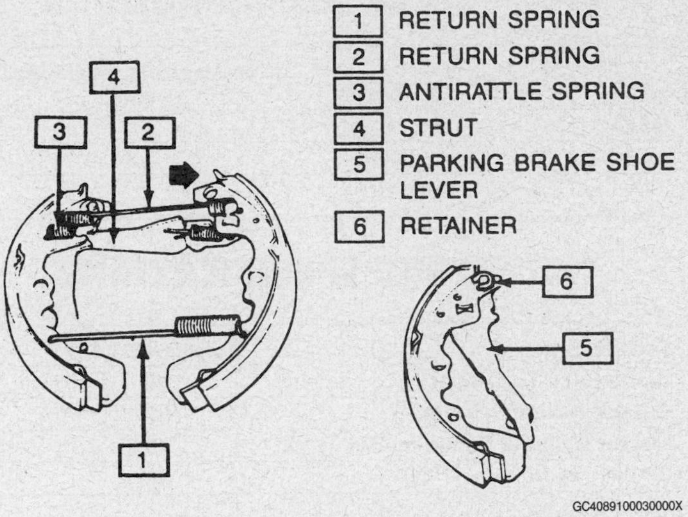
1 RETURN SPRING
2 RETURN SPRING
3 ANTIRATTLE SPRING
4 STRUT
5 PARKING BRAKE SHOE LEVER
6 RETAINER
GC4089100030000X

Fig. 2 Brake shoe return spring identification

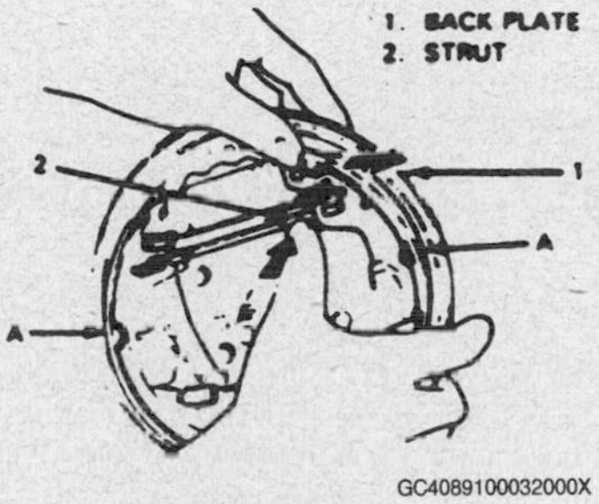
1. BACK PLATE
2. STRUT
A
GC4089100032000X

Fig. 4 Brake lining installation

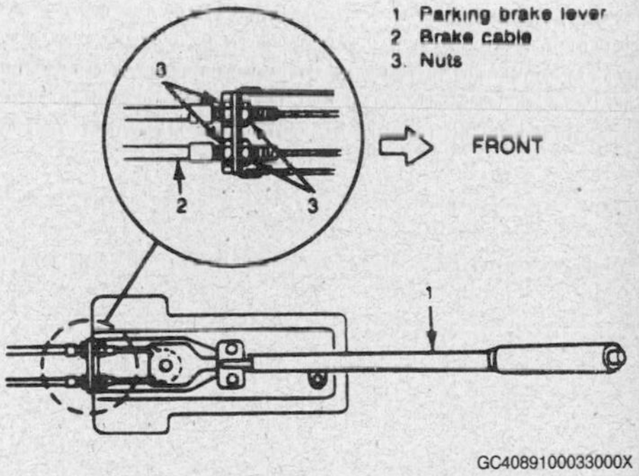
1. Parking brake lever
2. Brake cable
3. Nuts
FRONT
GC4089100033000X

Fig. 5 Parking brake adjustment

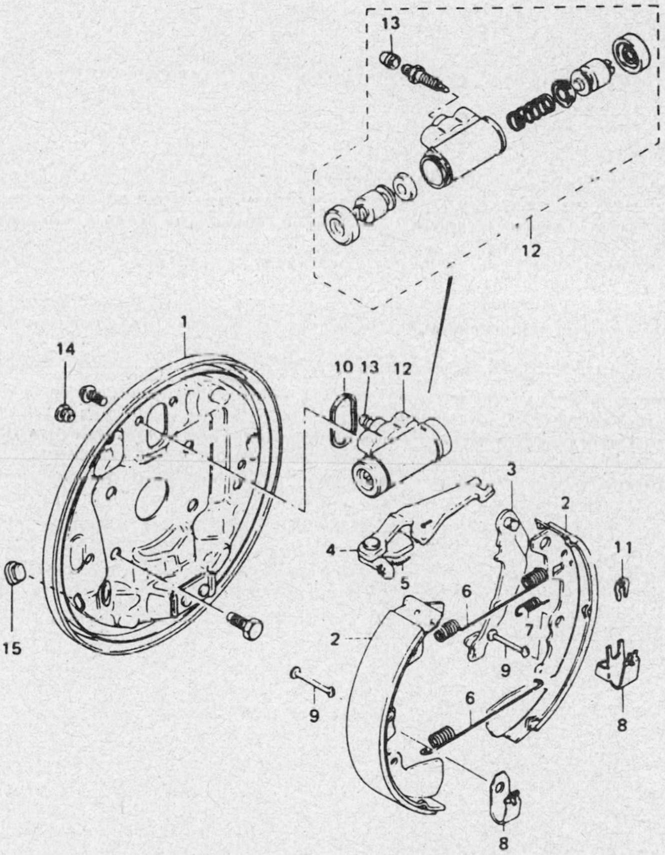

1. Brake back plate
2. Brake shoe
3. Parking brake shoe lever
4. Brake strut
5. Quadrant spring
6. Shoe return spring
7. Antirattle spring
8. Shoe hold down spring
9. Shoe hold down pin
10. Packing
11. Parking level retainer
12. Wheel cylinder
13. Bleeder plug cap
14. Rubber plug
15. Rubber plug

GC4089100031000X

Fig. 3 Rear brake unit assemble

DRUM BRAKE SPECIFICATIONS

Year	Model	Brake Drum Inside Dia. Inch
GEO		
1992–94	Metro	7.09

TIGHTENING SPECIFICATIONS

Component	Torque/Ft. Lbs.
Brake Hose To Caliper	17
Caliper Mounting Bolts	22
Master Cylinder Retaining Nut	10
Wheel Lug Nuts	44

①—Inch Lbs.

Type 8

INDEX

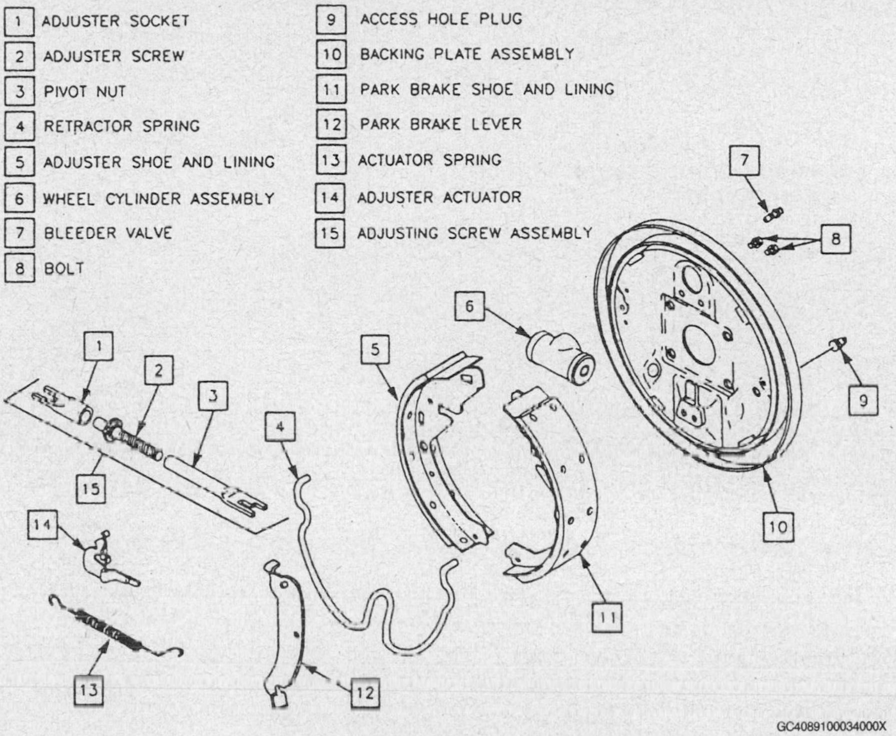

1 ADJUSTER SOCKET
2 ADJUSTER SCREW
3 PIVOT NUT
4 RETRACTOR SPRING
5 ADJUSTER SHOE AND LINING
6 WHEEL CYLINDER ASSEMBLY
7 BLEEDER VALVE
8 BOLT
9 ACCESS HOLE PLUG
10 BACKING PLATE ASSEMBLY
11 PARK BRAKE SHOE AND LINING
12 PARK BRAKE LEVER
13 ACTUATOR SPRING
14 ADJUSTER ACTUATOR
15 ADJUSTING SCREW ASSEMBLY
GC4089100034000X

Fig. 1 Brake drum assembly

DESCRIPTION

This brake assembly is of an advanced design. It operates with fewer parts, but is equal to other drum brake systems in performance. In this assembly, a single spring holds both shoe and lining to the backing plate, and acts as a retractor spring for the shoe and lining assemblies, **Fig. 1**.

PRECAUTIONS

When working on or around brake assemblies, care must be taken to prevent breathing asbestos dust, as many manufacturers incorporate asbestos fibers in the production of brake linings. During routine service operations the amount of asbestos dust from brake lining wear is at a low level due to a chemical breakdown during use, and a few precautions will minimize exposure.

1. Do not sand or grind brake linings unless suitable local exhaust ventilation equipment is used to prevent excessive asbestos exposure.
2. Wear a suitable respirator approved for asbestos dust use during all repair procedures.
3. When cleaning brake dust from brake parts, use a vacuum cleaner with a highly efficient filter system. If a suitable vacuum cleaner is not available, use a water soaked rag. **Do not use compressed air or dry brush to clean brake parts.**
4. Keep work area clean using same equipment as for cleaning brake parts.
5. Properly dispose of rags and vacuum cleaner bags by placing them in plastic bags.
6. Do not smoke or eat while working on brake systems. **Never use gasoline, kerosene, alcohol, motor oil, transmission fluid, or any fluid containing mineral oil to clean brake system components. These fluids will damage the rubber caps and seals. If system contamination is suspected, check brake fluid in the reservoir for dirt, discoloration, or separation (breakdown) of the brake fluid into distinct layers. Drain and flush the hydraulic system with clean brake fluid if contamination is suspected.**

INSPECTION

1. If any parts are of doubtful strength or quality due to heat discoloration, or are worn, replace them.
2. Inspect wheel cylinder dust boots for signs of excessive wear or damage. If any leakage is apparent replace wheel cylinder.
3. Clean dirt and/or rust from brake drum, backing plate and all other components. **Do not use compressed air or dry brush to clean brake parts. Many brake parts contain asbestos fibers which, if inhaled, can cause serious injury. Clean brake parts with a water soaked rag or a suitable vacuum cleaner to minimize airborne dust.**

BRAKE DRUMS

Any time the brake drums are removed for brake service, the braking surface diameter should be checked with a suitable

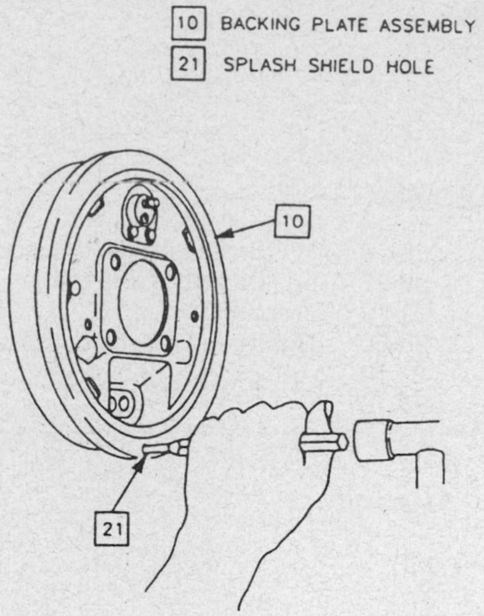
10 BACKING PLATE ASSEMBLY
21 SPLASH SHIELD HOLE
10
21
GC4089100035000X

Fig. 2 Loosening drum through splash shield

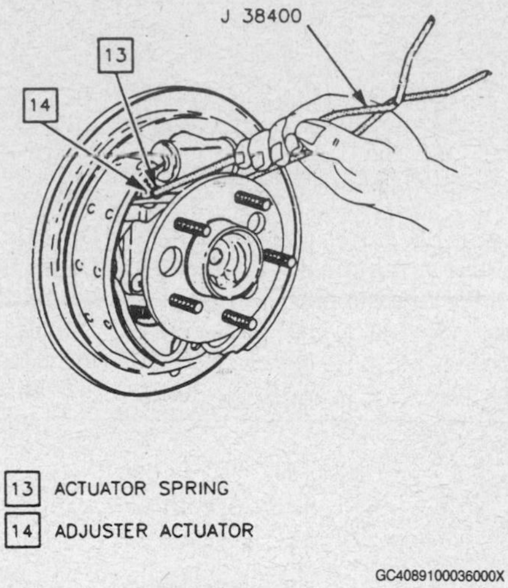
J 38400
13
14
13 ACTUATOR SPRING
14 ADJUSTER ACTUATOR
GC4089100036000X

Fig. 3 Actuator spring removal

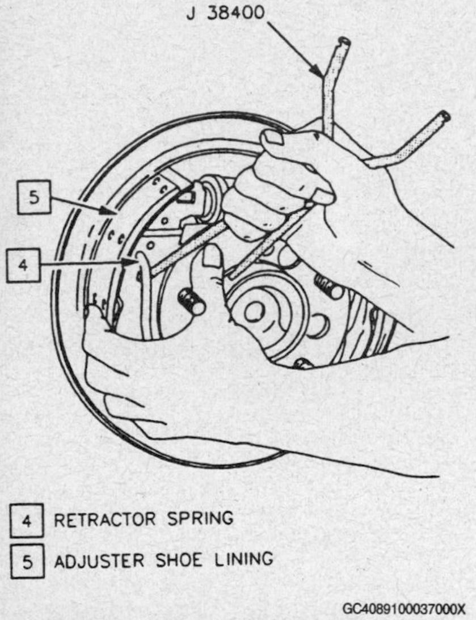
J 38400
5
4
4 RETRACTOR SPRING
5 ADJUSTER SHOE LINING
GC4089100037000X

Fig. 4 Retractor spring disengagement

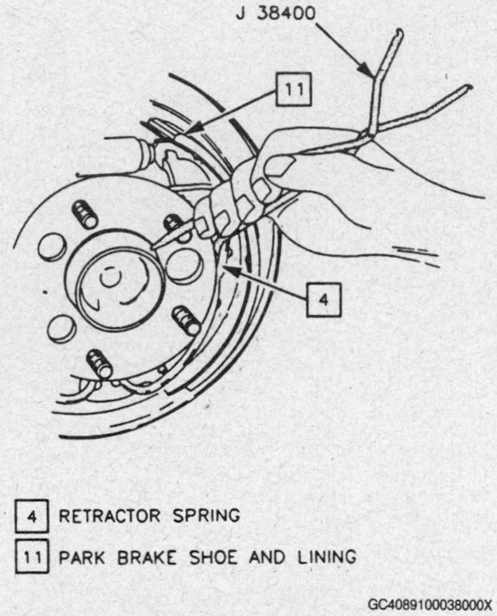
J 38400
11
4
4 RETRACTOR SPRING
11 PARK BRAKE SHOE AND LINING
GC4089100038000X

Fig. 5 Spring end installation onto shoe web

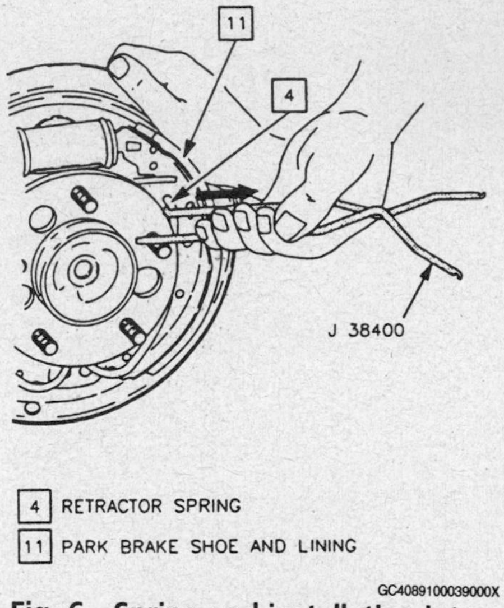
11
4
J 38400
4 RETRACTOR SPRING
11 PARK BRAKE SHOE AND LINING
GC4089100039000X

Fig. 6 Spring end installation into shoe slot

brake drum micrometer at several points to determine if they are within the safe oversize limit stamped on the brake drum outer surface. If the braking surface diameter exceeds specifications, the drum must be replaced. If the braking surface diameter is within specifications, drums should be cleaned and inspected for cracks, scores, deep grooves, taper, out of round and heat spotting. If drums are cracked or heat spotted, they must be replaced. Minor scores should be removed with sandpaper. Grooves and large scores can only be removed by machining with special equipment, as long as the braking surface is within specifications stamped on brake drum outer surface. Any brake drum sufficiently out of round to cause vehicle vibration or noise while braking or showing taper should also be machined, removing only enough stock to true up the brake drum.

After a brake drum is machined, wipe the braking surface diameter with a denatured alcohol soaked cloth. If one brake drum is machined, the other should also be machined to the same diameter to maintain equal braking forces.

BRAKE LININGS & SPRINGS

Inspect brake linings for excessive wear, damage, oil, grease or brake fluid contamination. If any of the above conditions exists, brake linings should be replaced. Do not attempt to replace only one set of brake shoes; they should be replaced as an axle set only to maintain equal braking forces. Examine brake shoe webbing, hold-down and return springs for signs of overheating indicated by a slight blue color. If any component exhibits overheating signs, replace hold-down and return springs with new ones. Overheated springs lose their pull and could cause brake linings to wear out prematurely. Inspect all springs for sags, bends and external damage and replace as necessary.

Inspect hold-down retainers and pins for bends, rust and corrosion. If any of the above is found, replace as required.

BACKING PLATE

Inspect backing plate shoe contact surface for grooves that may restrict shoe movement and cannot be removed by lightly sanding with emery cloth or other suitable abrasive. If backing plate exhibits above condition, it should be replaced. Also inspect for signs of cracks, warpage and excessive rust, indicating need for replacement.

ADJUSTER MECHANISM

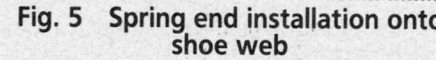

Inspect all components for rust, corro-

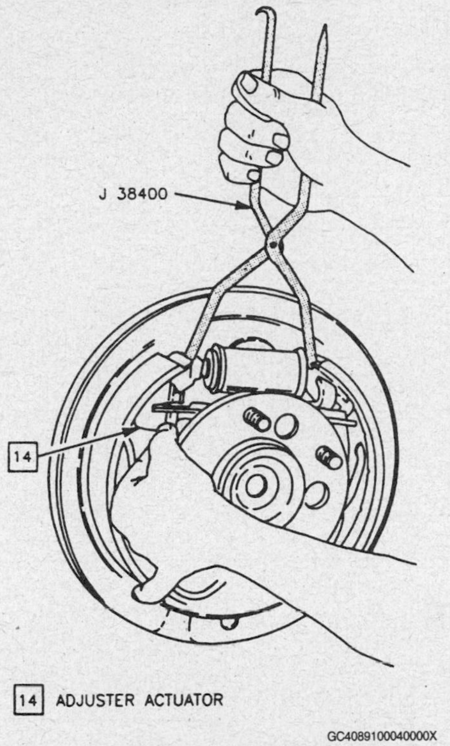
J 38400
14
14 ADJUSTER ACTUATOR
GC4089100040000X

Fig. 7 Shoe spreading to install adjuster actuator

sion, bends and fatigue. Replace as necessary. **On adjuster mechanism equipped with adjuster cable**, inspect cable for kinks, fraying or elongation of eyelet and replace as necessary.

PARKING BRAKE CABLE

Inspect parking brake cable end for kinks, fraying and elongation and replace as necessary. Use a small hose clamp to compress clamp where it enters backing plate to remove.

BRAKE SERVICE

REMOVAL

1. Raise and support vehicle.
2. Mark relationship of wheel to axle, then remove wheel and tire assembly.
3. Remove brake drum. If drum is difficult to remove, proceed as follows:
   a. Ensure parking brake is released.
   b. Back off parking brake cable adjustment.
   c. Remove access hole plug from backing plate, insert screwdriver through hole and push parking brake lever off its stop.
   d. Insert punch through hole in splash shield **Fig. 2**, tap on punch to loosen drum. Then remove drum.
4. Remove actuator spring using special brake tool J 38400 or equivalent to pry loop end of spring from adjuster actuator, **Fig. 3. When removing the retractor spring do not over stretch the spring, this will reduce its effectiveness.**
5. Remove end of retractor spring from adjuster shoe and lining assembly using special brake tool J 38400 or equivalent, **Fig. 4. Keep finger away from retractor spring to prevent fingers from being pinched.**
6. Remove adjuster shoe and lining assembly, adjuster actuator, then adjusting screw assembly.
7. Remove park brake lever from shoe assembly, do not remove parking brake cable from lever unless parking brake lever is being replaced.
8. Remove retractor spring from park brake shoe and lining.
9. Pry end of retractor spring toward axle using special brake tool J 38400 or equivalent, until it snap off shoe web onto backing plate. Remove park brake shoe.

INSTALLATION

1. Lubricate raised shoe pads on backing plate, anchor surfaces on backing plate, and adjuster screw threads using brake lubricant No. 1052196 or equivalent.
2. Install retractor spring if removed by hooking center spring section under tab on anchor.
3. Install park shoe and lining assembly as follows:
   a. Place shoe on backing plate.
   b. Using special brake tool J 38400 or equivalent, pull end of retractor spring up to rest on web of brake shoe, **Fig. 5.**
   c. Using special brake tool J 38400 or equivalent, pull end of retractor spring over until if locks into slot of brake shoe, **Fig. 6.**
4. Install park brake lever.
5. Install adjuster screw and adjuster shoe as follows:
   a. Place shoe on backing plate.
   b. Using special brake tool J 38400 or equivalent, pull end of retractor spring up to rest on web of brake shoe.
   c. Using special brake tool J 38400 or equivalent, pull end of retractor spring over until if locks into slot of brake shoe.
6. Install adjuster actuator by spreading shoes using special brake tool J 38400 or equivalent, **Fig. 7.** Then install adjuster actuator.
7. Install actuator spring.
8. Adjust brakes using suitable adjustment tool. Lining diameter should be 0.050 inches less than inside diameter of each drum.
9. Install drums, wheels and tires, aligning marks made during removal.

ADJUSTMENTS

SERVICE BRAKE ADJUSTMENT

1. Raise and support vehicle.
2. Mark relationship of wheel to axle, then remove wheel and tire assembly.
3. Remove brake drum. If drum is difficult to remove, proceed as follows:
   a. Ensure parking brake is released.
   b. Back off parking brake cable adjustment.

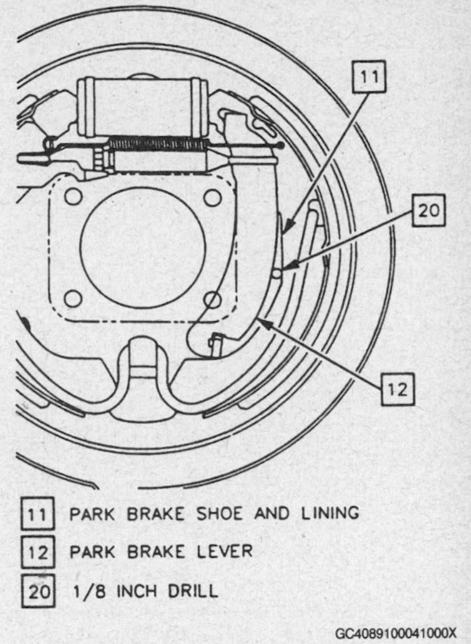
11
20
12
11 PARK BRAKE SHOE AND LINING
12 PARK BRAKE LEVER
20 1/8 INCH DRILL
GC4089100041000X

Fig. 8 Parking brake adjustment

   c. Remove access hole plug from backing plate, insert screwdriver through hole and push parking brake lever off its stop.
   d. Insert punch through hole in splash shield **Fig. 2,** tap on punch to loosen drum. Then remove drum.
4. Measure inside diameter of drum using special tool J 21177-A or J22364-01 or equivalent.
5. Adjust by turning star wheel adjuster. Lining diameter should be 0.050 inches less than inside diameter of each drum.
6. Install drums, wheels and tires.
7. Lower vehicle, then torque wheel lug nuts to specifications.

PARKING BRAKE ADJUSTMENT

1. Adjust brakes as outlined in "Service Brake Adjustment."
2. Apply and release parking brake 5 times to 10 clicks.
3. Ensure that pedal is fully released by turning ignition switch "On" the brake warning light should be "Off."
4. If brake warning lamp is "On," operate pedal release lever and pull downward on parking brake cable.
5. Apply parking brake to four clicks.
6. Raise and support vehicle, then remove access hole plug.
7. Adjust cable until and 1/8 inch drill bit can be inserted through access hole into space between shoe web and park lever, **Fig. 8.** Proper adjustment is when a 1/8 inch drill bit will fit in the space and a 1/4 inch drill bit will not fit.
8. Release brake, then check that wheels rotate freely.
9. Replace access hole plug, then lower vehicle.

DRUM BRAKE SPECIFICATIONS

Year	Model	Drum Brake Inside Dia. Inch
BUICK		
1993–94	Century	8.86
1992–94	LeSabre	8.86
CADILLAC		
1992	Fleetwood FWD	8.86
OLDSMOBILE		
1993–94	Cutlass Ciera	8.86
1993–94	Cutlass Cruiser	8.86
1992–94	Eighty-Eight	8.86
1993–94	Ninety-Eight	8.86
PONTIAC		
1992-94	Bonneville	8.86

TIGHTENING SPECIFICATIONS

Component	Torque/Ft. Lbs.
Brake Hose To Caliper	33
Caliper Bleeder Screw	115①
Caliper Mounting Bolts	38
Master Cylinder To Booster	22
Wheel Cylinder Bleeder Screw	48①
Wheel Cylinder Line Fitting	11
Wheel Cylinder To Backing Plate	106①
Wheel Lug Nuts	100

①—Inch lbs.

HYDRAULIC BRAKE SYSTEMS

INDEX

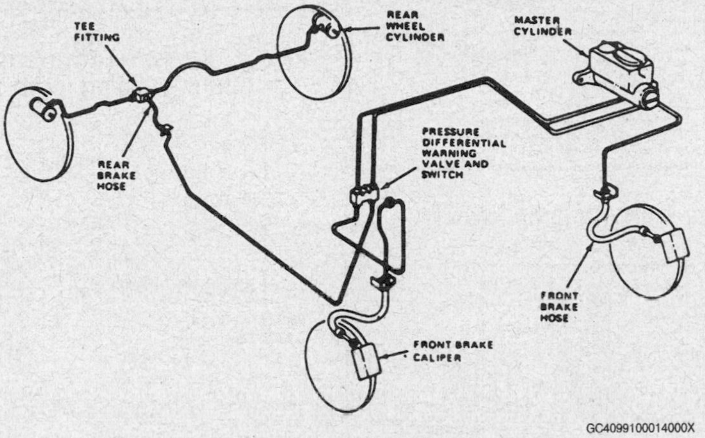

TEE FITTING
REAR WHEEL CYLINDER
MASTER CYLINDER
PRESSURE DIFFERENTIAL WARNING VALVE AND SWITCH
REAR BRAKE HOSE
FRONT BRAKE HOSE
FRONT BRAKE CALIPER
GC4099100014000X

Fig. 1 Front & rear split brake system

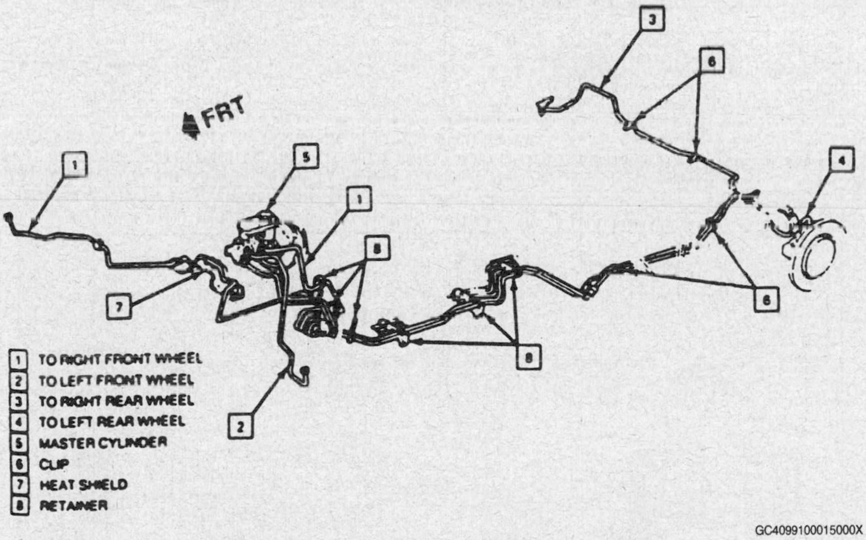

FRT
1 TO RIGHT FRONT WHEEL
2 TO LEFT FRONT WHEEL
3 TO RIGHT REAR WHEEL
4 TO LEFT REAR WHEEL
5 MASTER CYLINDER
6 CLIP
7 HEAT SHIELD
8 RETAINER
GC4099100015000X

Fig. 2 Diagonally split brake system

DESCRIPTION

SYSTEM OPERATION

Front & Rear Split System

When the brake pedal is depressed, both the primary (front brake) and the secondary (rear brake) master cylinder pistons are moved simultaneously to exert hydraulic fluid pressure on their respective systems, **Fig. 1.**

If the rear (secondary) brake system fails, initial brake pedal movement will cause the unrestricted secondary piston to bottom in the master cylinder bore. Primary piston movement will displace hydraulic fluid in the primary section of the master cylinder to actuate the front brake system.

If the front (primary) brake system fails, initial brake pedal movement will cause the unrestricted primary piston to bottom out against the secondary piston. Continued downward movement of the brake pedal moves the secondary piston to displace hydraulic fluid in the rear brake system to actuate the rear brakes.

Diagonally Split System

This system operates on the same principle as conventional front and rear split systems, using primary and secondary master cylinders which move simultaneously to exert hydraulic pressure on their respective systems. The hydraulic brake lines on this system, however, have been diagonally split front to rear (left front to right rear and right front to left rear) in place of separate lines to the front and rear wheels, **Fig. 2.**

In the event of a system failure, the remaining non-failed system will do all the braking on one front wheel and one rear wheel, thus maintaining 50% of the total braking force.

COMPONENT DESCRIPTION

BRAKE WARNING LAMP SWITCHES

There are four basic types of brake warning lamp switches as shown, **Figs. 3 through 6.** When a pressure differential occurs between the front and rear brake systems, the valves will shuttle toward the side with the low pressure.

In the switch shown in **Fig. 3,** movement of the differential valve forces the switch plunger upward over the tapered shoulder of the valve to close the switch contacts and light the dual brake warning lamp, signaling a brake system failure.

In **Fig. 4,** the valve assembly consists of two valves in a common bore that are spring loaded toward the centered position. The spring-loaded switch contact plunger rests on top of the valves in the centered position (right view). When a pressure differential occurs between the front and rear brake systems, the valves will shuttle toward the side with the low pressure. The spring-loaded switch plunger is "triggered" and the ground circuit for the warning lamp is completed, lighting the lamp (left view).

In **Fig. 5,** as pressure falls in one system, the other system's normal pressure forces the piston to the inoperative side, contacting the switch terminal, causing the warning lamp on the instrument panel to glow.

Fig. 6 shows the switch mounted directly in the master cylinder assembly. Whenever there is a specified differential pressure, the switch piston will activate the brake failure warning switch and cause the brake warning lamp to glow.

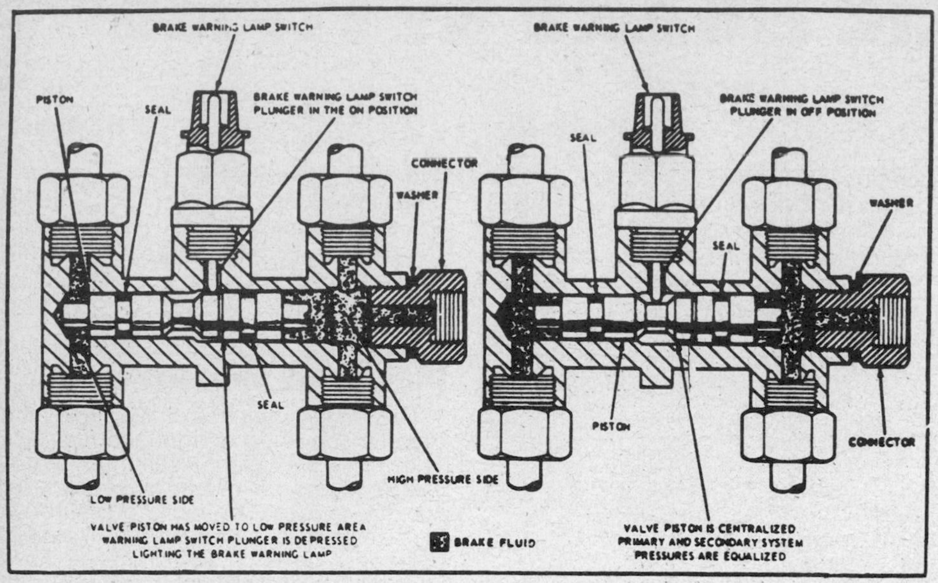
BRAKE WARNING LAMP SWITCH
BRAKE WARNING LAMP SWITCH PLUNGER IN THE ON POSITION
PISTON
SEAL
CONNECTOR
WASHER
SEAL
LOW PRESSURE SIDE
HIGH PRESSURE SIDE
VALVE PISTON HAS MOVED TO LOW PRESSURE AREA WARNING LAMP SWITCH PLUNGER IS DEPRESSED LIGHTING THE BRAKE WARNING LAMP
BRAKE FLUID
BRAKE WARNING LAMP SWITCH
BRAKE WARNING LAMP SWITCH PLUNGER IN OFF POSITION
SEAL
WASHER
SEAL
PISTON
CONNECTOR
VALVE PISTON IS CENTRALIZED PRIMARY AND SECONDARY SYSTEM PRESSURES ARE EQUALIZED
GC4099100016000X

Fig. 3 Pressure differential valve & brake warning lamp switch

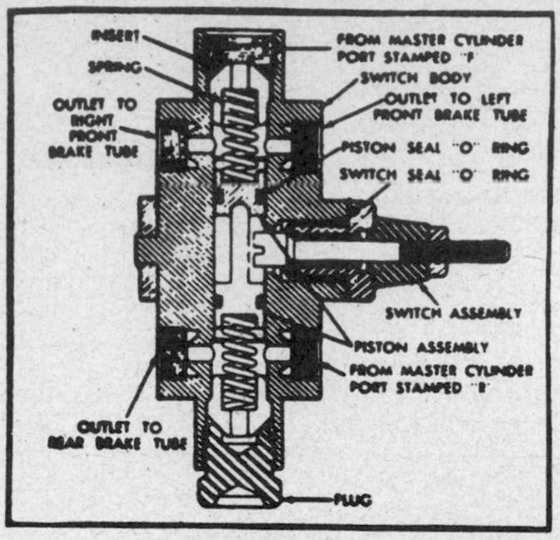
INSERT
SPRING
OUTLET TO RIGHT FRONT BRAKE TUBE
FROM MASTER CYLINDER PORT STAMPED "F"
SWITCH BODY
OUTLET TO LEFT FRONT BRAKE TUBE
PISTON SEAL "O" RING
SWITCH SEAL "O" RING
SWITCH ASSEMBLY
PISTON ASSEMBLY
FROM MASTER CYLINDER PORT STAMPED "R"
OUTLET TO REAR BRAKE TUBE
PLUG
GC4099100018000X

Fig. 5 Pressure differential valve & brake warning lamp switch

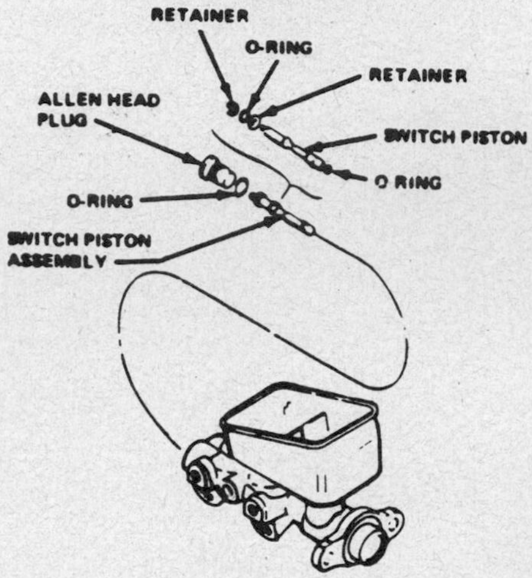
RETAINER
O-RING
RETAINER
ALLEN HEAD PLUG
SWITCH PISTON
O RING
O-RING
SWITCH PISTON ASSEMBLY
GC4099100019000X

Fig. 6 Dual master cylinder with built in warning lamp switch

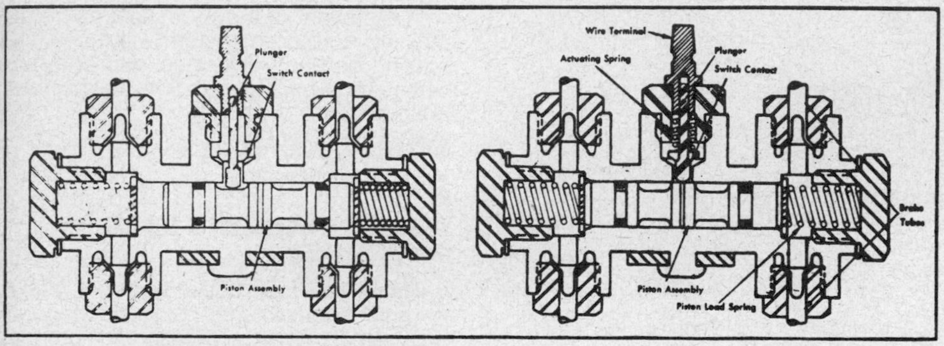
Plunger
Switch Contact
Piston Assembly
Wire Terminal
Actuating Spring
Plunger
Switch Contact
Brake Tubes
Piston Assembly
Piston Load Spring
GC4099100017000X

Fig. 4 Pressure differential valve & brake warning lamp switch

Testing Warning Lamp Operation

The warning lamp should illuminate when the ignition switch is in the start position, and turn off when the switch returns to run. If the brake lamp remains on after the ignition returns to run, check fluid level in master cylinder reservoir and inspect parking brake. If the warning lamp does not turn on during cranking, check for defective bulb or blown fuse.

COMBINATION VALVE

The combination valve, **Fig. 7** is a metering valve, failure warning switch, and a proportioner in one assembly and is used on disc brake applications. The metering valve delays front disc braking until the rear drum brake shoes contact the drum. The failure warning switch is actuated in event of front or rear brake system failure, in turn activating a dash warning lamp. The proportioner balances front to rear braking action during rapid deceleration.

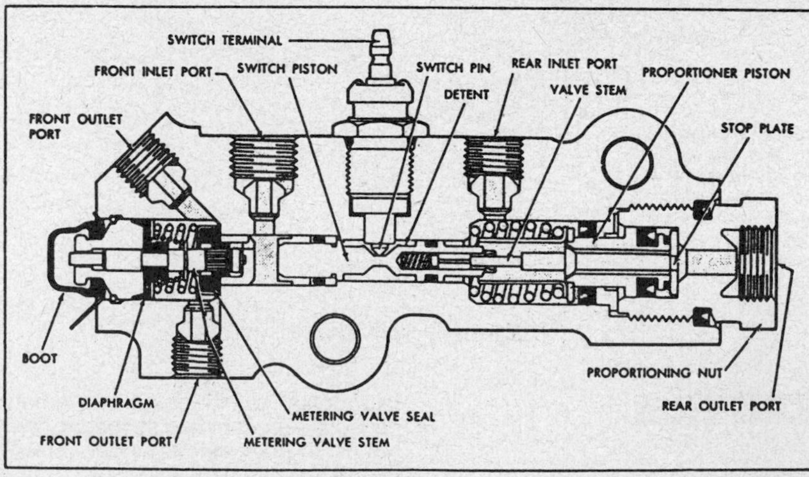
SWITCH TERMINAL
FRONT INLET PORT
SWITCH PISTON
SWITCH PIN
REAR INLET PORT
PROPORTIONER PISTON
DETENT
VALVE STEM
FRONT OUTLET PORT
STOP PLATE
BOOT
PROPORTIONING NUT
DIAPHRAGM
REAR OUTLET PORT
METERING VALVE SEAL
FRONT OUTLET PORT
METERING VALVE STEM
GC4099100020000X

Fig. 7 Combination valve

Metering Valve

When the brakes are not applied, the metering valve permits the brake fluid to flow through the valve, thus allowing the fluid to expand and contract with temperature changes.

When the brakes are initially applied, the metering valve stem moves to the left, preventing fluid to flow through the valve to the front disc brakes. This is accomplished by the smooth end of the metering valve stem contacting the metering valve seal lip at 4 to 30 psi, **Fig. 8.** The metering valve spring holds the retainer against the seal until a predetermined pressure is produced at the valve inlet port which overcomes the spring pressure and permits hydraulic pressure to actuate the front disc brakes, **Fig. 9.** The increased pressure into the valve is metered through the valve

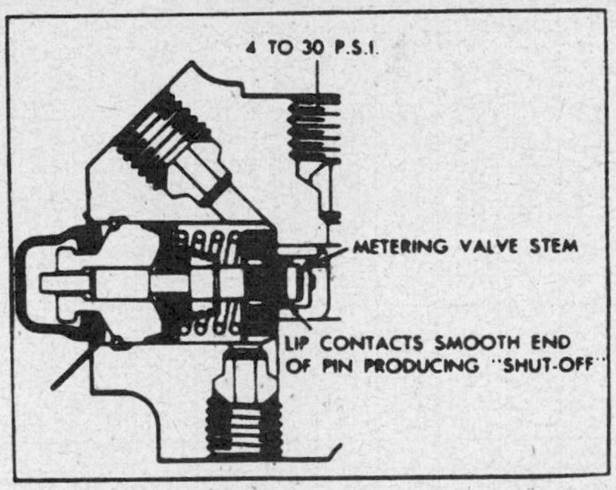
4 TO 30 P.S.I.
METERING VALVE STEM
LIP CONTACTS SMOOTH END
OF PIN PRODUCING "SHUT-OFF"
GC4099100021000X

Fig. 8 Metering valve. Initial braking

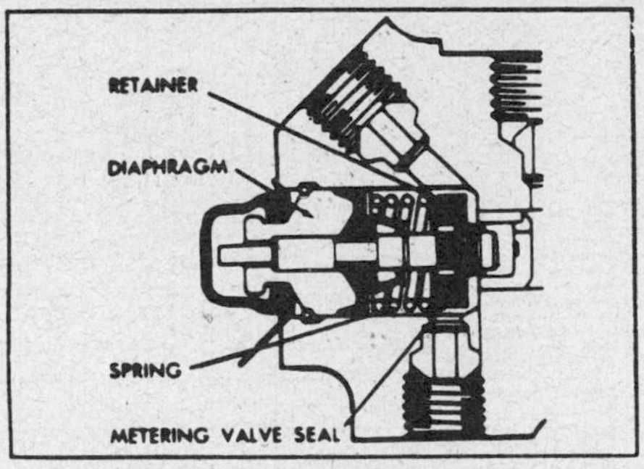
RETAINER
DIAPHRAGM
SPRING
METERING VALVE SEAL
GC4099100022000X

Fig. 9 Metering valve. continued braking

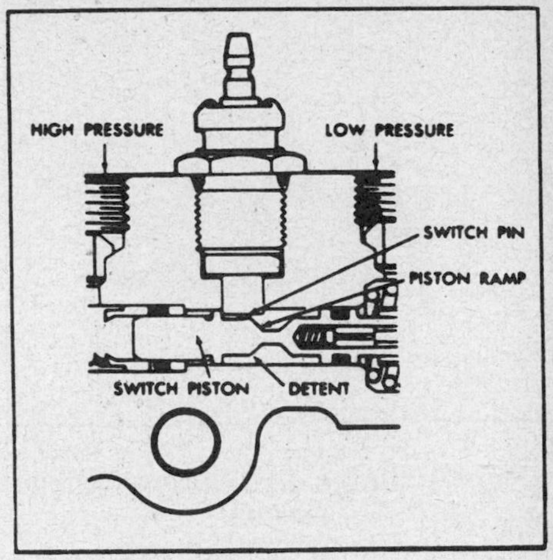
HIGH PRESSURE
LOW PRESSURE
SWITCH PIN
PISTON RAMP
SWITCH PISTON
DETENT
GC4099100023000X

Fig. 10 Failure warning switch. Rear system failure

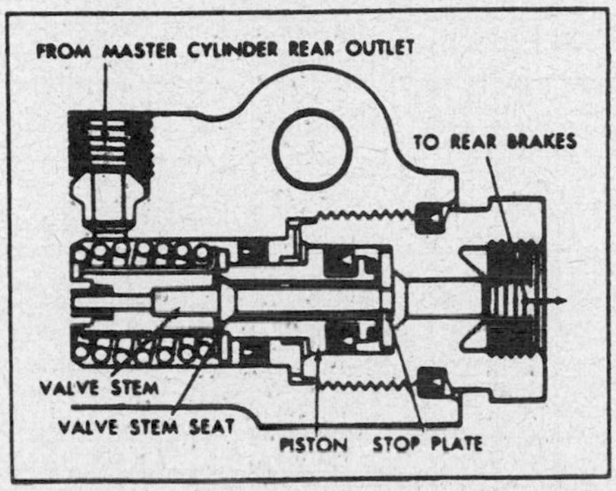
FROM MASTER CYLINDER REAR OUTLET
TO REAR BRAKES
VALVE STEM
VALVE STEM SEAT
PISTON
STOP PLATE
GC4099100024000X

Fig. 11 Proportioner. Rapid deceleration

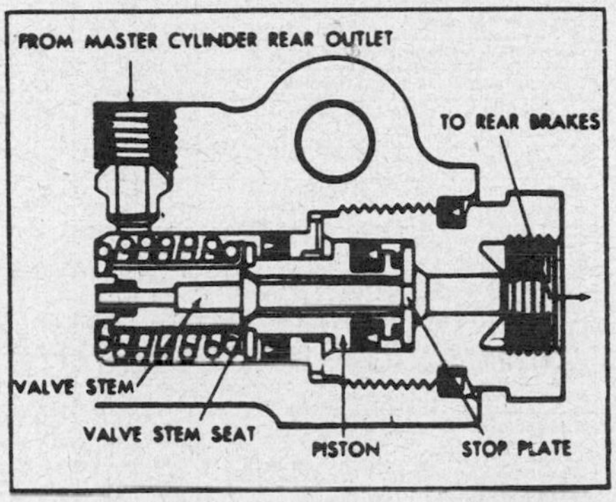
FROM MASTER CYLINDER REAR OUTLET
TO REAR BRAKES
VALVE STEM
VALVE STEM SEAT
PISTON
STOP PLATE
GC4099100025000X

Fig. 12 Proportioner. Normal braking

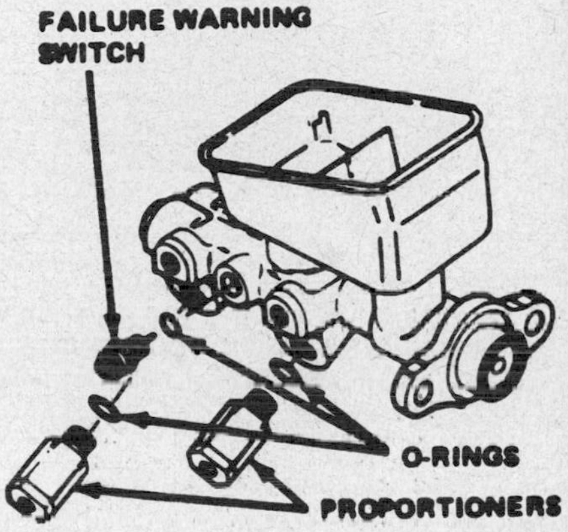
FAILURE WARNING SWITCH
O-RINGS
PROPORTIONERS
GC4099100026000X

Fig. 13 Proportioners installed in master cylinder

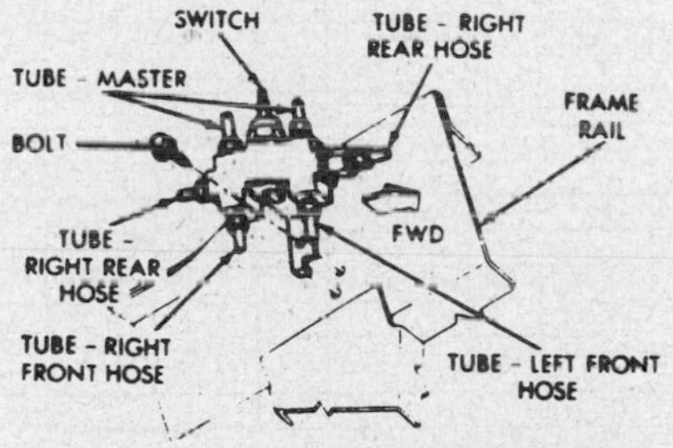
SWITCH
TUBE - RIGHT REAR HOSE
TUBE - MASTER
FRAME RAIL
BOLT
FWD
TUBE - RIGHT REAR HOSE
TUBE - RIGHT FRONT HOSE
TUBE - LEFT FRONT HOSE
GC4099100027000X

Fig. 14 Distribution switch. Diagonally split brake systems

seal, to the front disc brakes, producing an increased force on the diaphragm. The diaphragm then pulls the pin, in turn pulling the retainer and reduces the spring pressure on the metering valve seal. Eventually, the pressure reaches a point at which the spring is pulled away by the diaphragm pin and retainer, leaving the metering valve unrestricted, permitting full pressure to pass through the metering valve.

Failure Warning Switch

If the rear brake system fails, the front system pressure forces the switch piston to the right, **Fig. 10.** The switch pin is then forced up into the switch, completing the electrical circuit and activates the dash warning lamp.

When repairs are made and pressure returns to the system, the piston moves to the left, resetting the switch. The detent on the piston requires approximately 100 to 450 psi to permit full reset of the piston. In event of front brake system failure, the piston moves to the left and the same sequence of events is followed as for rear system failure except the piston resets to the right.

Fluid Level Sensor

This sensor mounted on the master cylinder will activate the Brake Warning lamp if a low brake fluid level is detected. The lamp will turn off once the fluid level is corrected.

Proportioning Or Pressure Control Valve

During rapid deceleration, a portion of vehicle weight is transferred to the front wheels. This resultant loss of weight at rear wheels must be compensated for to avoid early rear wheel skid. The proportioner or pressure control valve reduces rear brake system pressure, delaying rear wheel skid. When the proportioner or pressure control valve is incorporated in the combination valve assembly, pressure developed within the valve acts against the large end of the piston, overcoming the spring pressure, moving the piston left, **Fig. 11.** The piston then contacts the stem seat and restricts line pressure through the valve.

During normal braking operation, the proportioner or pressure control valve is not functional. Brake fluid flows into the proportioner or pressure control valve between the piston center hole and the valve stem, through the stop plate and to the rear brakes. Spring pressure loads the piston during normal braking, causing it to rest against the stop plate, **Fig. 12.**

On diagonally split brake systems, two proportioners or pressure control valves are used. One controls the left rear brake, the other the right rear brake. The proportioners or pressure control valves are installed in the master cylinder rear brake outlet ports, **Fig. 13.**

BRAKE DISTRIBUTION VALVE & SWITCH

This switch assembly, **Fig. 14,** is used on some diagonally split brake systems and Corvette four wheel disc brake systems. It is connected to the outlet ports of the master cylinder and to the brake warning lamp and warns the driver if either the primary or secondary brake system has failed.

When hydraulic pressure is equal in both primary and secondary brake systems, the switch remains centered, **Fig. 15.** If pressure fails in one of the systems, the piston moves toward the inoperative side, **Fig. 16.** The shoulder of the piston contacts the switch terminal, providing a ground and lighting the warning lamp.

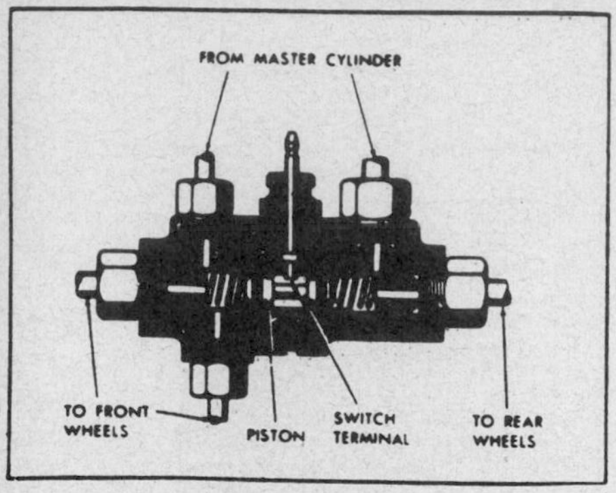
FROM MASTER CYLINDER
TO FRONT WHEELS
PISTON
SWITCH TERMINAL
TO REAR WHEELS

GC4099100028000X

Fig. 15 Brake distribution switch. Normal

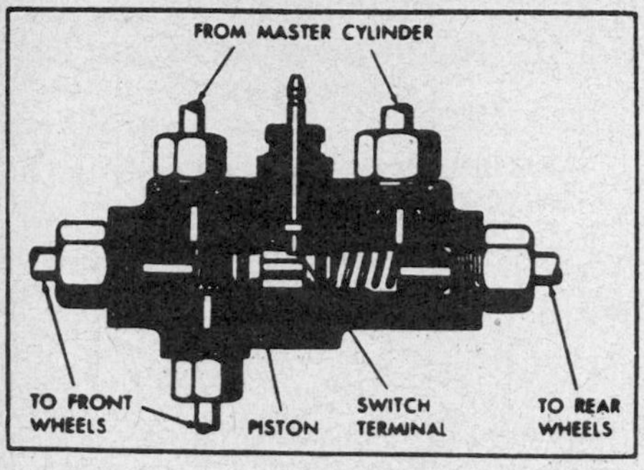
FROM MASTER CYLINDER
TO FRONT WHEELS
PISTON
SWITCH TERMINAL
TO REAR WHEELS

GC4099100029000X

Fig. 16 Brake distribution switch. Failed

TROUBLESHOOTING

When troubleshooting the hydraulic brake system, perform the following checks and inspections as outlined below. If problem still exists within system, refer to **Fig. 17** first, then to **Figs. 18 and 19** as necessary.

CHECKING FOR FLUID LEAKAGE

Start engine and depress the brake pedal. If the pedal gradually falls under constant pressure, the hydraulic system may be leaking. Raise the vehicle on a lift and check all tubing lines and backing plates for signs of leakage. It may be necessary to lift or remove the carpeting or floor mats to check for booster or master cylinder leakage.

ROAD TESTING

When testing brakes, ensure the road is level and dry. Test brakes at both light and heavy pedal pressure. Do not lock up brakes or slide tires during a brake test.

Check the tires on the vehicle before performing a brake test. Tires should be equally inflated, identical in size and with equal tread pattern. Excessive camber and caster will cause the brakes to pull. An overloaded vehicle will also brake erratically.

DIAGNOSIS & TESTING

Refer to **Fig. 20** for diagnosis chart.

CAUSE \ SYMPTOM	Excessive Brake Pedal Travel	Brake Pedal Travel Gradually Increases	Excessive Brake Pedal Effort	Excessive Braking Action	Brakes Slow To Respond	Brakes Slow To Release	Brakes Drag	Uneven Braking Action (Side To Side)	Uneven Braking Action (Front To Rear)	Scraping Noise From Brakes	Brakes Squeak During Application*	Brakes Squeak During Stop*	Brakes Chatter (Roughness)	Brakes Groan At End Of Stop*	Brake Warning Lamp Glows During Stop
Leaking Brake Line or Connection	X	XX							X						XX
Leaking Wheel Cylinder or Piston Seal	X	XX		X				X							X
Leaking Master Cylinder	X	XX													X
Air in Brake System	XX								X						XX
Contaminated or Improper Brake Fluid					X	X	X								X
Leaking Vacuum System			XX		X										
Restricted Air Passage in Power Head			X		XX	X									
Damaged Power Head			X	X	X	X	X								
Improperly Assembled Power Head Valving			X	X	X	X	XX								
Worn Out Brake Lining-Replace			X	X				X	X	X	X	X		X	
Uneven Brake Lining Wear-Replace and Correct	X			X				X	X	X	X	XX		X	X
Glazed Brake Lining			XX		X			X	X		X	X			
Incorrect Lining Material-Replace			X	X				X	X			X		X	
Contaminated Brake Lining-Replace				XX				XX	XX	X	X	X		X	
Linings Damaged by Abusive Use-Replace			X	XX				X	X	X	X	X		X	
Excessive Brake Lining Dust			X	XX				XX	XX		X	XX		X	
Heat Spotted or Scored Brake Drums or Rotors				X				X	X		X	X	XX	X	
Out-of-Round or Vibrating Brake Drums												X	XX		
Improper Thickness Variation on Brake Rotors													XX		
Excessive Lateral Run-Out													X		
Faulty Automatic Adjusters	X						X	X	X						X
Incorrect Wheel Cylinder Sizes			X	X				X	X						
Weak or Incorrect Brake Shoe Retention Springs				X		X	XX	X	X	XX	X	XX			
Brake Assembly Attachments-Missing or Loose	X						X	X	X	X		X	X	X	
Insufficient Brake Shoe Guide Lubricant						X	X	X	X	XX	XX				
Restricted Brake Fluid Passage or Sticking Wheel Cylinder Piston		X	X		X	X	X	X	X						
Faulty Metering Valve	X		X	X	X	X	X		X						X
Brake Pedal Linkage Interference or Binding			X		X	XX	XX								
Improperly Adjusted Parking Brake							X								
Drums Tapered or Threaded										XX					
Incorrect Front End Alignment								XX							
Incorrect Tire Pressure								X	X						
Incorrect Wheel Bearing Adjustment	X									X			X		
Loose Front Suspension Attachments								X		XX			X	X	
Out-of-Balance Wheel Assemblies													XX		
Operator Riding Brake Pedal	X	X	X				X		X					X	
Improperly Adjusted Booster Pushrod	X					X	XX								X
Sticking Wheel Cylinder or Caliper Pistons			X			X	X	X	X						
Faulty Proportioning Valve			X		X	X	X								

XX — Indicates more probable cause(s)   X — Indicates other causes   *May be a normal condition.

GC4099100030010X

Fig. 17 Brake diagnosis chart (Part 1 of 2). Front disc/rear drum system

COMPONENT REPLACEMENT

MASTER CYLINDER

1. Disconnect wire connector from brake warning pressure switch.
2. Disconnect brake lines from master cylinder.
3. Remove two master cylinder mounting nuts, then the master cylinder.
4. Reverse procedure to install.

COMPONENT SERVICE

MASTER CYLINDER OVERHAUL

EXCEPT CORVETTE

Disassemble

Refer to **Figs. 21 and 22** when performing the following procedures.

1. Remove master cylinder from vehicle as follows:
   a. Disconnect and plug hydraulic lines.
   b. Remove two master cylinder attaching nuts, then the master cylinder.
2. Remove reservoir cover and diaphragm. Discard old brake fluid in reservoir.
3. Inspect cover and diaphragm. Replace if cut, cracked or deformed.
4. Remove fluid level switch, if equipped.
5. **On models with compact master cylinder,** remove proportioner valve assembly, **Fig. 22.**
6. Depress primary piston and remove lock ring.
7. Plug primary fluid outlet (outlet nearest to cowl when master cylinder is installed), then apply compressed air

CAUSE / SYMPTOM	Excessive Brake Pedal Travel	Brake Pedal Travel Gradually Increases	Excessive Brake Pedal Effort	Excessive Braking Action	Brakes Slow To Respond	Brakes Slow To Release	Brakes Drag	Uneven Braking Action (Side To Side)	Uneven Braking Action (Front To Rear)	Scraping Noise From Brakes	Brakes Squeak During Application*	Brakes Squeak During Stop*	Brakes Chatter (Roughness)	Brakes Groan At End Of Stop*	Brake Warning Lamp Glows
Leaking Brake Line or Connection	X	XX	X						X						XX
Leaking Piston Seal	X	XX	X	X				X	X						X
Leaking Master Cylinder	X	XX	X						X						X
Air in Brake System	XX		X						X						XX
Contaminated or Improper Brake Fluid	X				X	X	X	X	X						X
Leaking Vacuum System			XX		X										
Restricted Air Passage in Power Head		X	X		XX	X									
Damaged Power Head		X	X	X	X	XX									
Worn Out Brake Lining			X	X				X	X	X	X	X		X	
Uneven Brake Lining Wear-Replace	X			X				X	X	X	X	XX		X	X
Glazed Brake Lining			XX		X			X	X		X	X			
Incorrect Lining Material-Replace			X	X		X		X	X			X		X	
Contaminated Brake Lining-Replace				XX		X		XX	XX	X	X	X		X	
Linings Damaged by Abusive Use-Replace			X	XX				X	X	X	X	X		X	
Heat Spotted or Scored Discs				X				X	X		X	X	XX	X	
Improper Thickness Variation	X												XX		
Excessive Lateral Run-Out	X												X		
Automatic Adjuster Problem	X	X					X	X	X						X
Brake Assembly Attachments-Missing or Loose	X						X	X	X	X		X	X	X	
Restricted Brake Fluid Passage		X	X		X	X	X	X	X						X
Improperly Adjusted Stoplamp Switch Or Cruise Control Vacuum Dump							X								
Metering Valve Problem		X	X	X	X	X	X		X						X
Proportioning Valve Problem		X	X	X	X	X	X		X						X
Brake Pedal Linkage Interference or Binding			X		X	XX	XX								
Improperly Adjusted Parking Brake							X		X						
Improper Length Booster Pushrod	X			X		X	XX		X						
Incorrect Front End Alignment								XX							
Incorrect Tire Pressure								X	X						
Incorrect Wheel Bearing Adjustment	X									X			X		
Loose Front Suspension Attachments							X	X		XX			X	X	
Out-of-Balance Wheel Assemblies													XX		
Operator Riding Brake Pedal			X				X		X					X	
Sticking Caliper or Wheel Cylinder Pistons					X	X	XX	X	X						
Park Brake Switch Circuit Grounded															XX
Park Brake Not Releasing						X		X							XX

XX — Indicates more probable cause(s) *May be a normal condition.
X — Indicates other causes

GC4099100030020X

Fig. 17 Brake diagnosis chart (Part 2 of 2). Four wheel disc system

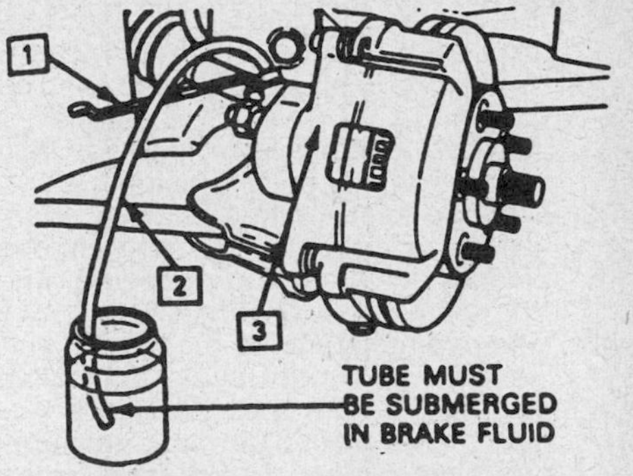
1
2
3
TUBE MUST
BE SUBMERGED
IN BRAKE FLUID

1 BLEEDER WRENCH 3 CALIPER
2 TUBE

GC4099100032000X

Fig. 18 Bleeding brakes

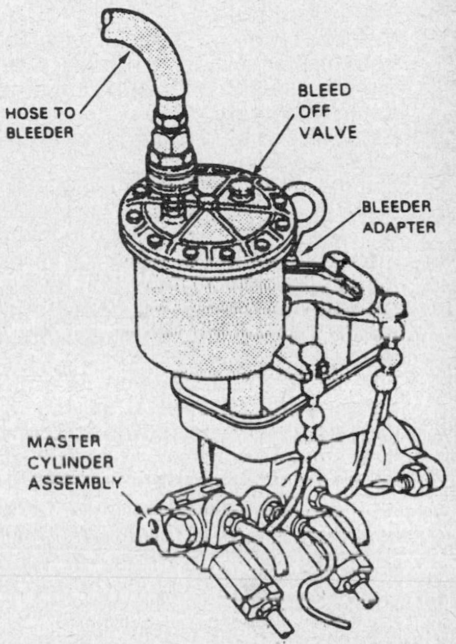
HOSE TO
BLEEDER
BLEED
OFF
VALVE
BLEEDER
ADAPTER
MASTER
CYLINDER
ASSEMBLY

GC4099100033000X

Fig. 19 Installing pressure bleeder adapter

into secondary fluid outlet to remove primary and secondary pistons.
8. Remove spring retainer and seals from secondary piston.
9. Clamp master cylinder in a vise as shown in **Fig. 23,** then remove reservoir using a pry bar. Remove reservoir grommets.
10. Inspect master cylinder bore for corrosion. **Do not use abrasive material on master cylinder bore.** Replace if bore is corroded.

Assemble

Clean all parts not included in repair kit with brake fluid. **Do not dry with compressed air.** Lubricate all rubber parts with clean brake fluid prior to installation.

1. Lubricate new reservoir grommets with silicone brake lube, then press grommets into master cylinder body. Ensure grommets are properly seated.
2. Lay reservoir upside down on flat, hard surface. Press master cylinder body onto reservoir using rocking motion.
3. Install new seals on secondary piston, then the spring retainer.
4. Install spring and secondary piston assembly into cylinder.
5. Install primary piston. Depress primary piston into cylinder, then install lock ring.
6. Install fluid level switch, if equipped.
7. **On models with compact master cylinder,** install proportioner valve assembly, **Fig. 22.**
8. Fit diaphragm into reservoir cover, then install cover onto reservoir.
9. Install master cylinder and bleed brake system.

CORVETTE

1. Remove reservoir cap and diaphragm from reservoir.
2. Drain fluid, then remove master cylinder prime pipe clamp and prime pipe.
3. Remove reservoir retaining screw and reservoir, **Fig. 24.**
4. Remove reservoir O-rings from reservoir wells.
5. Slightly depress piston and remove retaining ring with retaining ring pliers.
6. Invert cylinder so the reservoir wells face downward. Depress the primary and secondary pistons with a brass rod or wooden dowel until fully bottomed in bore. The secondary stop pin should fall freely from the cylinder.
7. Gently bump open end of cylinder body against a piece of wood to dislodge the primary piston, then remove primary piston.
8. Gently bump open end of cylinder body against a piece of wood to dislodge the secondary piston and center the valve assembly, then remove secondary piston. **Do not remove or disturb screw which retains primary spring to secondary piston. This has been set to a predetermined height and will severely affect cylinder performance if setting is changed.**
9. Remove secondary return spring from secondary piston assembly.

10. Remove spring retainer from secondary piston using a small screwdriver to lift crimp to allow retainer to slide off piston, **Fig. 25.**
11. Remove center valve plunger and spring from secondary piston.
12. Remove seal retainer using a sharp knife or razor blade to cut and remove plastic retaining cup retaining ring from primary piston, **Fig. 26.**
13. Remove recuperating guide.
14. Remove all rubber seals from both pistons, **Fig. 27 and 28. Take extreme care not to damage any surfaces on piston, particularly areas where seals seat.**
15. Remove pressure differential switch assembly. **Do not disassemble spring or probe from switch body.**
16. Remove end plug and O-ring. **Care must be taken not to lose small electrical bias spring located just inside end plug.**
17. Remove warning switch assembly from master cylinder assembly. **Keep warning switch and probe together as an assembly.**
18. Remove end plug, O-ring and electrical bias spring.
19. Gently tap cylinder body against a piece of wood to dislodge proportioning valve spool assembly then, remove proportioning valve spool assembly including O-ring and spacer. **Do not disassemble proportioning valve, it is serviced as an assembly only.**
20. **The proportioning valve is prelubricated with a special grease, do not use a cleaning solution to clean it or parts included in repair kit. Clean all other parts in denatured alcohol. Use filtered unlubricated compressed air to dry all parts and passages within the cylinder.**
21. Reverse procedure to assemble, ensuring that all seals and parts are lubricated with clean brake fluid.

The same types of brake trouble are encountered with power brakes as with standard brakes. Before checking power brake system for source of trouble, refer to the brake system diagnosis charts. After these possible causes have been eliminated, check for cause as outlined below:

HARD PEDAL

CAUSE	CORRECTION
Broken or damaged hydraulic brake pipes.	Inspect and replace as necessary.
Vacuum failure.	Check for: Faulty vacuum check valve or grommet. Replace. Collapsed or damaged vacuum hose. Replace. Plugged or loose vacuum fitting. Repair. Faulty air valve seal or support plate seal. Replace. Damaged floating control valve. Replace. Bad stud welds on front or rear housing or power head. Replace unless easily repaired.
Faulty diaphragm.	Replace.
Restricted air filter element.	Replace.
Worn or distorted reaction plate or levers.	Replace plate or levers.
Cracked or broken power pistons or retainer.	Replace power pistons and piston rod retainer.

GRABBY BRAKES
(Apparent Off-On Condition)

CAUSE	CORRECTION
Broken or damaged hydraulic brake pipes	Inspect and replace as necessary
Insufficient fluid in master cylinder.	Fill reservoirs with approved brake fluid. Check for leaks.
Faulty master cylinder seals.	Repair or replace as necessary
Cracked master cylinder casting.	Replace.
Leaks in pipes or connections at disc brake calipers or wheel cylinders.	Inspect and repair as necessary
Air in hydraulic system.	Bleed system.

BRAKES FAIL TO RELEASE

CAUSE	CORRECTION
Blocked passage in power piston	Inspect and repair or replace as necessary.
Air valve sticking shut.	Check for proper lubrication of air valve "O" ring.
Broken piston return spring.	Replace.
Broken air valve spring.	Replace.
Tight pedal linkage.	Repair or replace as necessary.

GC4099100031000X

Fig. 20 Power brake diagnosis chart

WHEEL CYLINDER OVERHAUL

1. Raise and support vehicle.
2. Remove wheel, drum and brake shoes.
3. Disconnect hydraulic line at wheel cylinder. **Do not pull metal line away from cylinder, as this may kink or bend line.** Line will separate from cylinder when cylinder is moved away from brake backing plate.
4. Remove wheel cylinder-to-brake plate attaching screws, then the wheel cylinder.
5. Remove boots, pistons, springs and cups from cylinder, **Fig. 29.**
6. Clean all parts with brake fluid.
7. Inspect cylinder bore. A scored bore may be honed as long as the diameter is not increased by more than .005 inch. Replace worn or damaged parts as necessary.
8. Ensure hands are clean before proceeding with assembly. Lubricate cylinder wall and rubber cups with brake fluid, then install springs, cups, pistons and boots in housing.
9. Wipe end of hydraulic line to remove any foreign matter, then place wheel cylinder in position. Enter tubing into cylinder and start threads on fitting.
10. Secure cylinder to backing plate, then complete tightening of tubing fitting.
11. Install brake shoes, drum and wheel.
12. Bleed system as outlined previously, then adjust brakes.

BRAKE SYSTEM BLEED

MANUAL BLEEDING

Pressure bleeding is recommended for all hydraulic systems. However, if a pressure bleeder is unavailable, use the following procedure. **Brake fluid damages painted surfaces. Immediately clean any spilled fluid.**

1. Remove vacuum reserve by pumping brakes several times with engine off.
2. Fill master cylinder reservoir with clean brake fluid. Check fluid level often during bleeding procedure; do not let reservoir fall below half full.
3. If necessary, bleed master cylinder as follows:
   a. Disconnect master cylinder forward brake line connection until fluid flows from reservoir. Reconnect and tighten brake line.
   b. Instruct an assistant to slowly depress brake pedal one time and hold.
   c. Crack open front brake line connection again, purging air from cylinder.
   d. Retighten connection and slowly release brake pedal.
   e. Wait 15 seconds, then repeat until all air is purged.

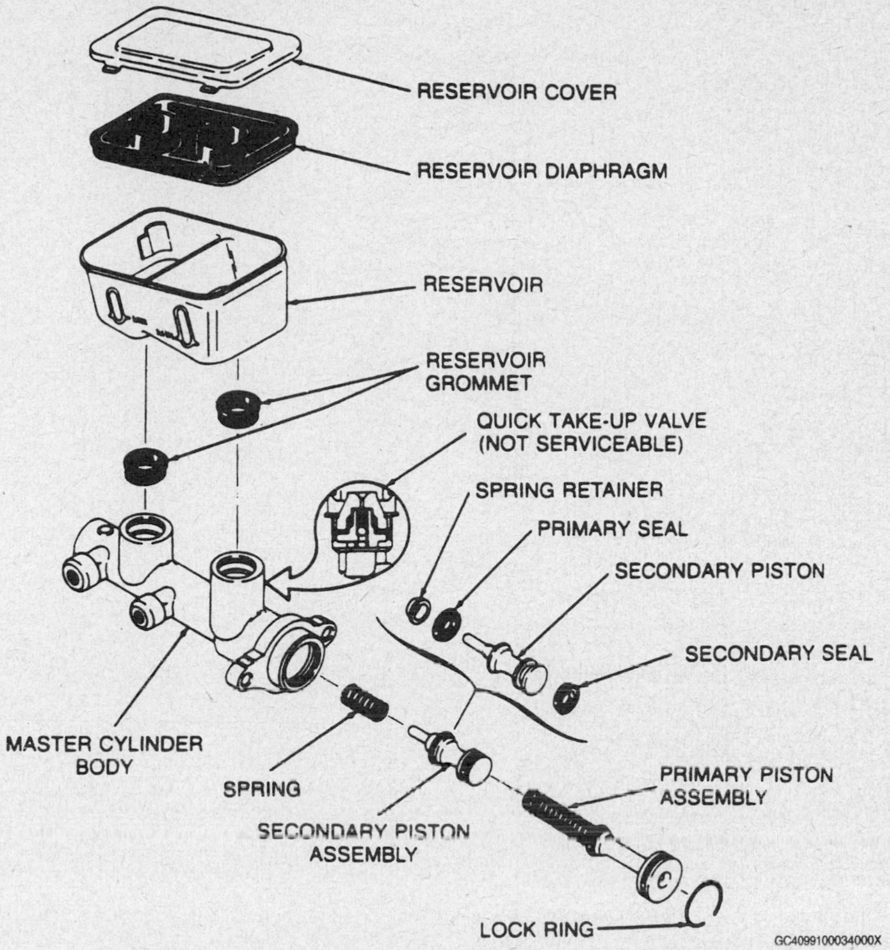
RESERVOIR COVER
RESERVOIR DIAPHRAGM
RESERVOIR
RESERVOIR GROMMET
QUICK TAKE-UP VALVE (NOT SERVICEABLE)
SPRING RETAINER
PRIMARY SEAL
SECONDARY PISTON
SECONDARY SEAL
MASTER CYLINDER BODY
SPRING
PRIMARY PISTON ASSEMBLY
SECONDARY PISTON ASSEMBLY
LOCK RING
GC4099100034000X

Fig. 21 Dual master cylinder assembly. Composite type

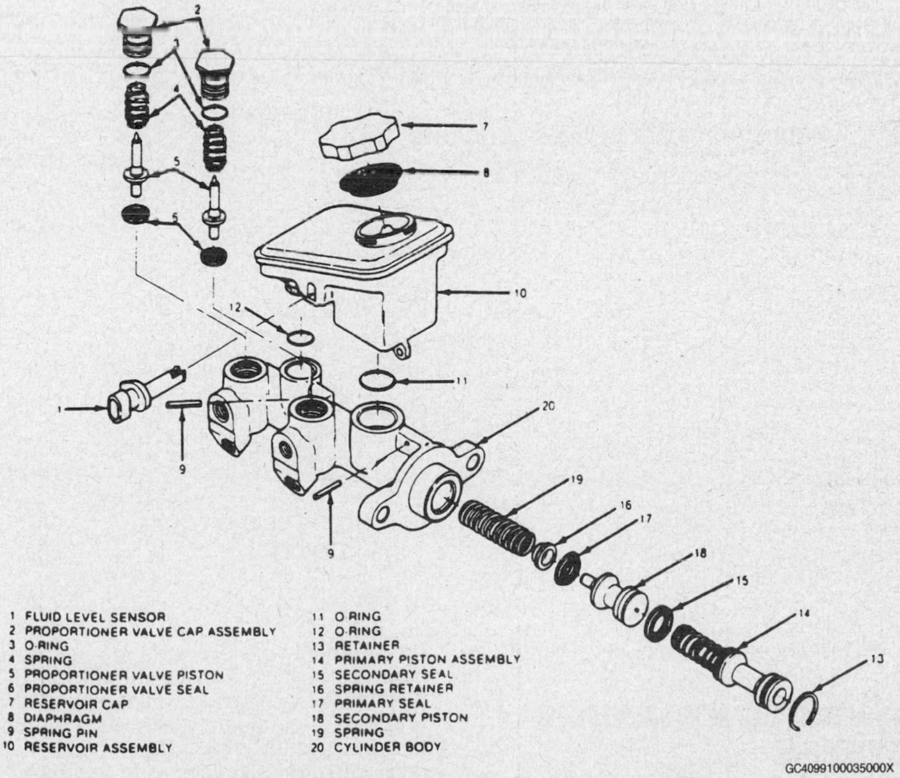
1 FLUID LEVEL SENSOR
2 PROPORTIONER VALVE CAP ASSEMBLY
3 O-RING
4 SPRING
5 PROPORTIONER VALVE PISTON
6 PROPORTIONER VALVE SEAL
7 RESERVOIR CAP
8 DIAPHRAGM
9 SPRING PIN
10 RESERVOIR ASSEMBLY
11 O-RING
12 O-RING
13 RETAINER
14 PRIMARY PISTON ASSEMBLY
15 SECONDARY SEAL
16 SPRING RETAINER
17 PRIMARY SEAL
18 SECONDARY PISTON
19 SPRING
20 CYLINDER BODY
GC4099100035000X

Fig. 22 Compact master cylinder assembly

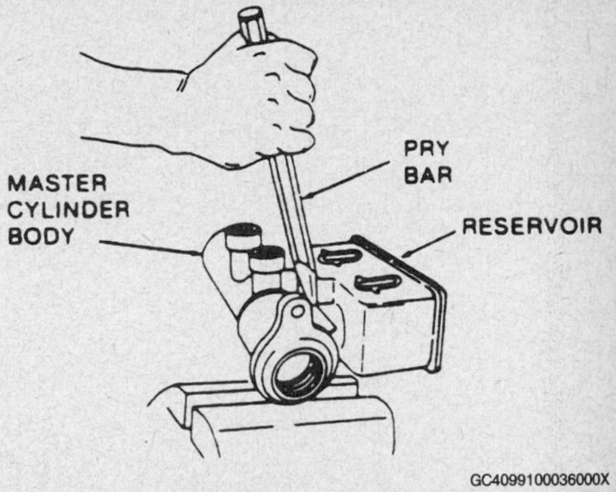
MASTER CYLINDER BODY
PRY BAR
RESERVOIR
GC4099100036000X

Fig. 23 Removing master cylinder reservoir. Composite type

f. Bleed the rearward (nearest the cowl) brake line connection by repeating steps a through e.

4. Loosen, then slightly retighten bleeder valves at all four wheels. Repair any broken, stripped or frozen valves at this time.
5. Proceed to appropriate wheel first and follow set sequence according to "Wheel Bleeding Sequence."
6. Place transparent tube over bleeder valve, then allow tube to hang down into transparent container, **Fig. 18.** Ensure end of tube is submerged in clean brake fluid.
7. Instruct an assistant to slowly depress brake pedal one time and hold.
8. Crack open bleeder valve, purging air from cylinder. Retighten bleeder screw and slowly release pedal.
9. Wait 15 seconds, then repeat steps 7 and 8. Repeat these steps until all air is bled from system.

PRESSURE BLEEDING

1. Loosen, then slightly retighten bleeder valves at all four wheels. Repair any broken, stripped or frozen valves at this time.
2. Using a diaphragm type pressure bleeder, install suitable bleeder adapter to master cylinder, **Fig. 19.**
3. Charge bleeder ball to 20-25 psi.
4. Connect pressure bleeder line to adapter.
5. Open line valve on pressure bleeder, then depress bleed-off valve on adapter until a small amount of brake fluid is released.
6. Raise and support vehicle.
7. Proceed to appropriate wheel first and follow set sequence according to "Wheel Bleeding Sequence."
8. Place transparent tube over bleeder valve, then allow tube to hang down into transparent container, **Fig. 18.** Ensure end of tube is submerged in clean brake fluid.
9. Open bleeder valve 1/2 to 3/4 turn and allow fluid to flow into container until all air is purged from line.

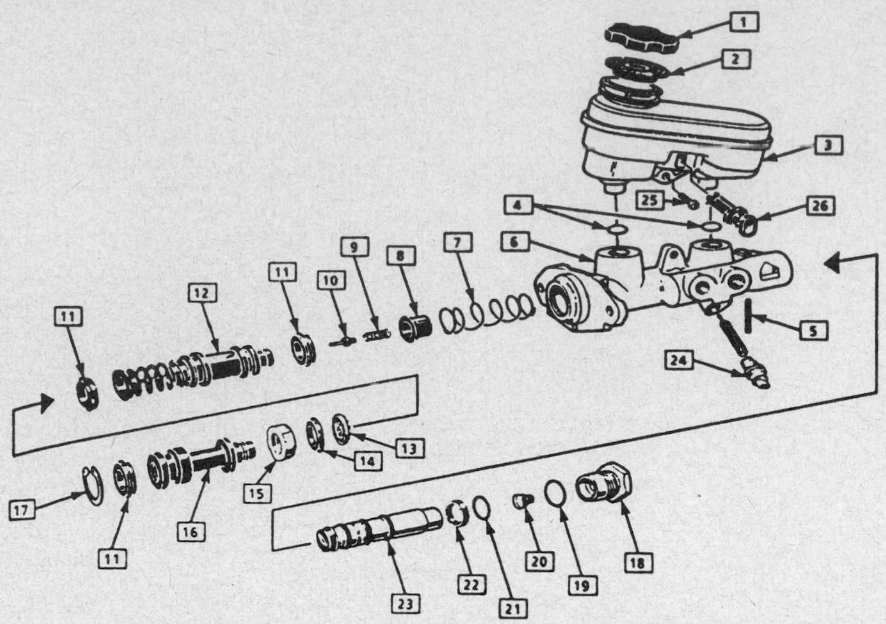

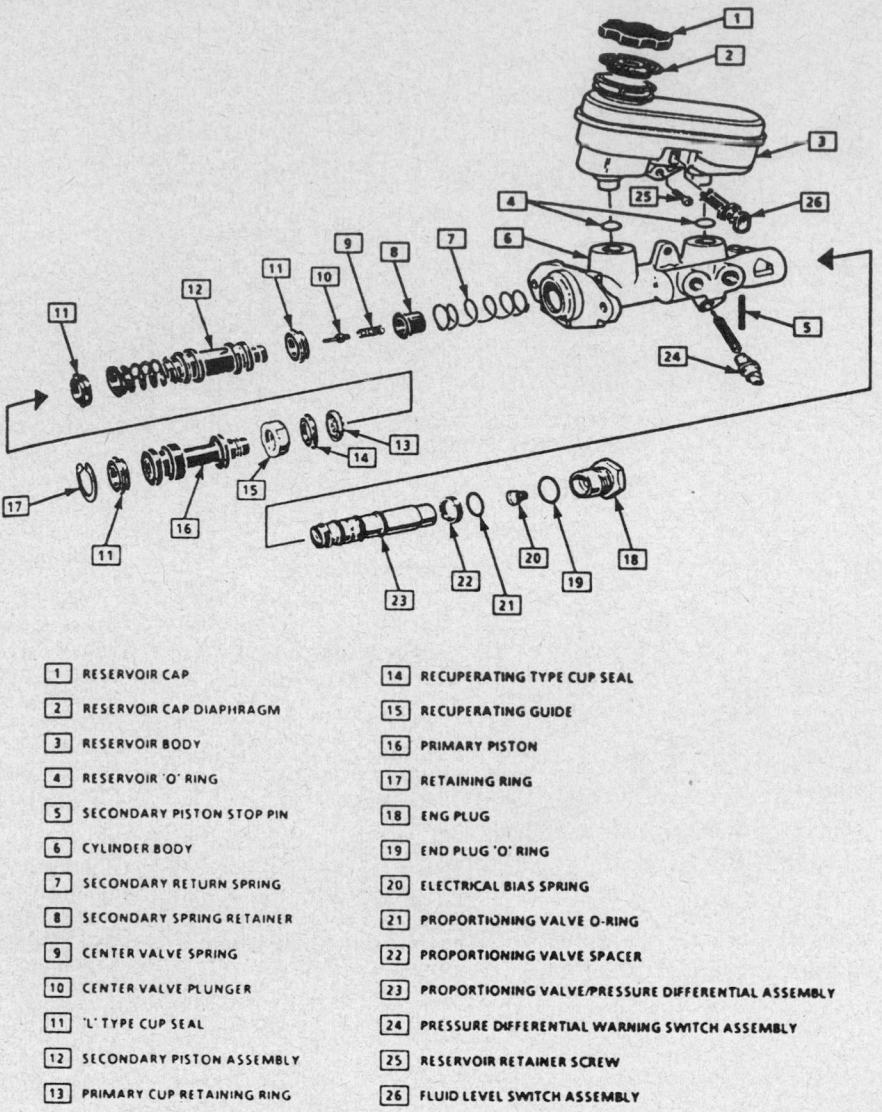

1. RESERVOIR CAP
2. RESERVOIR CAP DIAPHRAGM
3. RESERVOIR BODY
4. RESERVOIR 'O' RING
5. SECONDARY PISTON STOP PIN
6. CYLINDER BODY
7. SECONDARY RETURN SPRING
8. SECONDARY SPRING RETAINER
9. CENTER VALVE SPRING
10. CENTER VALVE PLUNGER
11. 'L' TYPE CUP SEAL
12. SECONDARY PISTON ASSEMBLY
13. PRIMARY CUP RETAINING RING
14. RECUPERATING TYPE CUP SEAL
15. RECUPERATING GUIDE
16. PRIMARY PISTON
17. RETAINING RING
18. ENG PLUG
19. END PLUG 'O' RING
20. ELECTRICAL BIAS SPRING
21. PROPORTIONING VALVE O-RING
22. PROPORTIONING VALVE SPACER
23. PROPORTIONING VALVE/PRESSURE DIFFERENTIAL ASSEMBLY
24. PRESSURE DIFFERENTIAL WARNING SWITCH ASSEMBLY
25. RESERVOIR RETAINER SCREW
26. FLUID LEVEL SWITCH ASSEMBLY

GC4099200037000X

Fig. 24 Composite master cylinder. Corvette

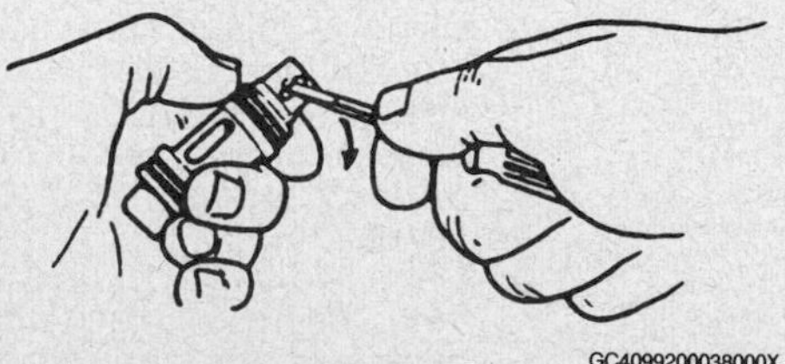

GC4099200038000X

Fig. 25 Lifting crimp on secondary spring retainer. Corvette

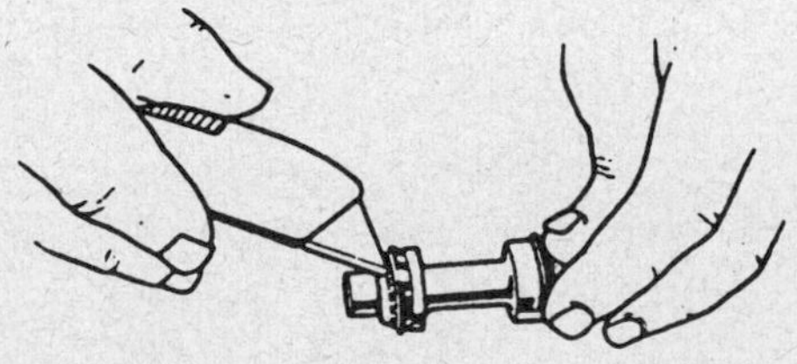

GC4099200039000X

Fig. 26 Cutting seal retainer. Corvette

WHEEL BLEEDING SEQUENCE

Rear wheel drive models: if manual bleeding, RR-LR-RF-LF; if pressure bleeding, bleed front brakes together and rear brakes together.

Front wheel drive models: RR-LF-LR-RF

FLUSHING HYDRAULIC SYSTEM

If brake fluid is old, rusty or contaminated, or whenever new parts are installed in hydraulic system, the system must be flushed. Bleed brakes, allowing at least one quart of clean brake fluid to pass through system. Any rubber parts in hydraulic system which were exposed to contaminated fluid must be replaced.

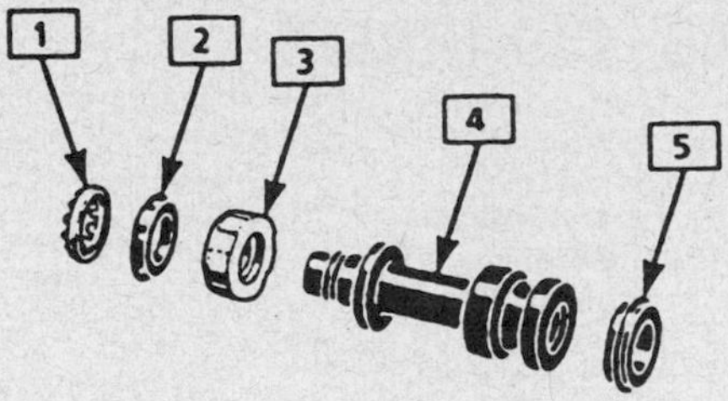
1
2
3
4
5

1 PRIMARY CUP RETAINING RING
2 RECUPERATING TYPE CUP SEAL
3 RECUPERATING GUIDE
4 PRIMARY PISTON
5 'L' TYPE CUP SEAL

GC4099200040000X

Fig. 27 Primary piston components. Corvette

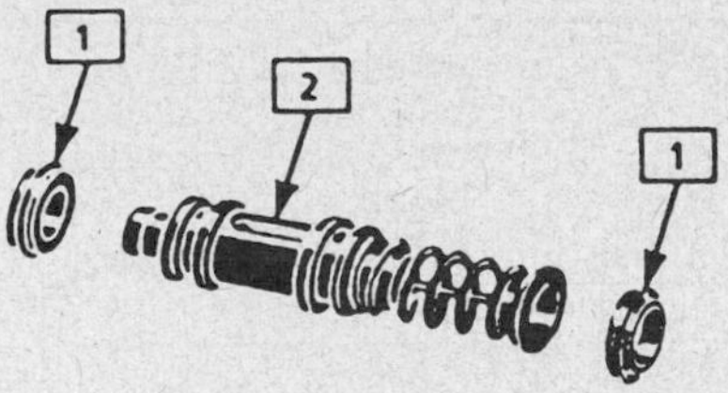
1
2
1

1 'L' TYPE CUP SEAL
2 SECONDARY PISTON ASSEMBLY

GC4099200041000X

Fig. 28 Secondary piston components. Corvette

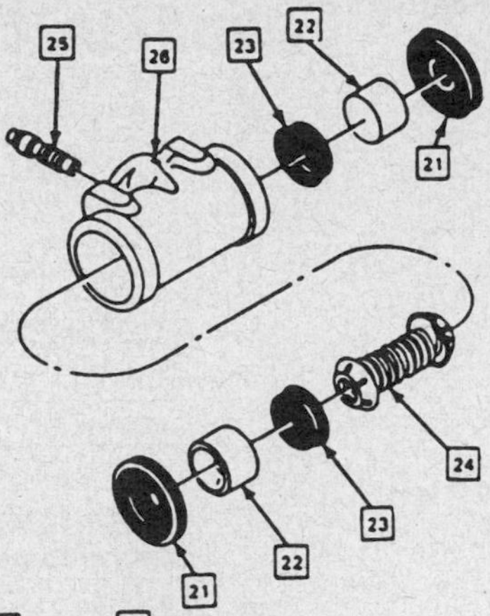
25
26
23
22
21
24
23
22
21

21 BOOT
22 PISTON
23 SEAL
24 SPRING ASSEMBLY
25 BLEEDER VALVE
26 CYLINDER BODY

GC4099100042000X

Fig. 29 Exploded view of wheel cylinder

HYDRAULIC BRAKE SYSTEM SPECIFICATIONS

Model	Year	Master Cylinder Bore Dia., Inch	Front Caliper Bore Dia., Inch	Rear Caliper Bore Dia., Inch	Wheel Cylinder Bore Dia., Inch
BUICK					
Century	1992–94	①	—	—	②
LeSabre	1992–94	1.000	2.52	—	.937
Park Avenue	1992–94	1.000	2.52	—	.937
Regal	1992–94	.945	1.65	1.378	—
Riviera	1992–93	1.000	2.52	1.50	—
Roadmaster	1992–94	1.125	2.952	—	③
Skylark	1992–94	.874	2.244	—	.689
CADILLAC					
Brougham	1992	⑦	2.952	—	1.00
DeVille	1992–94	1.000	2.52	—	.937
Eldorado	1992–94	1.000	2.52	1.50	—
Fleetwood (FWD)	1992–93	1.000	2.52	—	.937
Fleetwood (RWD)	1993–94	1.125	2.952	—	1.00
Seville	1992–94	1.000	2.52	—	.937
CHEVROLET					
Beretta	1992–94	.875	2.25	—	⑤
Camaro	1992	⑧	⑨	1.60	.748
	1993–94	1.000	2.500	1.595	.810
Caprice	1992	1.125	2.952	—	.748⑩
	1993–94	1.125	2.952	—	④
Cavalier	1992–94	.874	2.244	—	.625
Corsica	1992–94	.875	2.25	—	⑤
Corvette	1992–94	.870	1.50	1.60	—
Impala SS	1994	1.125	2.952	—	1.000
Lumina	1992–94	.945	1.65	1.378	—
GEO					
Metro	1992–94	.810	1.889	—	.620
Prizm	1992–94	.812	2.01	—	.690
Prizm GSI	1992–94	.874	2.13	1.19	—

Continued

HYDRAULIC BRAKE SYSTEM SPECIFICATIONS—Continued

Model	Year	Master Cylinder Bore Dia., Inch	Front Caliper Bore Dia., Inch	Rear Caliper Bore Dia., Inch	Wheel Cylinder Bore Dia., Inch
Storm	1992–93	⑪	2.00	—	.600
OLDSMOBILE					
Achieva	1992–94	.874	2.244	—	.689
Custom Cruiser	1992	1.125	2.952	—	.748
Cutlass Ciera	1992–94	.945	1.65	1.378	—
Cutlass Cruiser	1992–94	.944	—	—	⑫
Cutlass Supreme	1992–94	.945	1.65	1.378	—
Toronado	1992	1.000	2.52	1.50	—
Trofeo	1992	1.000	2.52	1.50	—
88/98	1992–94	1.000	2.52	—	.937
PONTIAC					
Bonneville	1992–94	1.000	2.52	—	.937
Firebird	1992	⑧	2.5⑥	1.60	.748
	1993–94	1.000	2.500	1.595	.810
Grand Am	1992–94	.874	2.244	—	.689
Grand Prix	1992–94	.945	1.65	1.378	—
LeMans	1992–94	.874	—	—	.678
Sunbird	1992–94	.874	2.244	—	.625
Trans Am	1992-94	⑧	2.5⑥	1.60	.748

①—Light duty, .874. Medium & heavy duty, .944.
②—Sedan/coupe, .689. Wagon: medium duty, .811, heavy duty, .748.
③—1992, .748 inch; 1993, 1.00 inch.
④—Standard duty, .874 inch; heavy duty, 1.00 inch.
⑤—Anchor plate drum brakes, .625, Leading/Trailing drum brakes, .748.
⑥—Heavy duty, 1.50.
⑦—Main bore, 1.126. Quick Take Up bore, 1.574.
⑧—Disc & drum system, .945. Four wheel disc system, 1.00.
⑨—Standard, 2.52. Heavy duty, 1.50.
⑩—Heavy duty, .937.
⑪—Single overhead cam, .810. Dual overhead cam, .875.
⑫—Coupe/sedan standard, .689. Coupe/sedan medium duty & wagon standard, .811. All heavy duty, .748.

POWER BRAKE UNITS

INDEX

APPLICATION CHART

Model	Power Brake Type
BUICK	
Century	AC-Delco Tandem Diaphragm
LeSabre	AC-Delco Tandem Diaphragm
Park Avenue	AC-Delco Tandem Diaphragm
Regal	AC-Delco Tandem Diaphragm
Riviera	AC-Delco Tandem Diaphragm
Roadmaster	AC-Delco Tandem Diaphragm
Skylark	AC-Delco Tandem Diaphragm
CADILLAC	
Brougham	AC-Delco Tandem Diaphragm
DeVille	AC-Delco Tandem Diaphragm
Eldorado	AC-Delco Tandem Diaphragm
Fleetwood (FWD)	AC-Delco Tandem Diaphragm
Fleetwood (RWD)	AC-Delco Tandem Diaphragm
Seville	AC-Delco Tandem Diaphragm
CHEVROLET	
Beretta	AC-Delco Tandem Diaphragm
Camaro	AC-Delco Tandem Diaphragm
Caprice	AC-Delco Tandem Diaphragm
Cavalier	AC-Delco Tandem Diaphragm
Corsica	AC-Delco Tandem Diaphragm
Corvette (VIN P)	BCIA Single Diaphragm
Corvette (VIN J)	BCIA Tandem Diaphragm
Lumina	AC-Delco Tandem Diaphragm
GEO	
Metro	Geo Metro Single Diaphragm
Prizm	Toyota/GM Single Diaphragm
Storm	Geo Storm Single Diaphragm
OLDSMOBILE	
Achieva	AC-Delco Tandem Diaphragm
Custom Cruiser	AC-Delco Tandem Diaphragm
Cutlass Ciera	AC-Delco Tandem Diaphragm
Cutlass Cruiser	AC-Delco Tandem Diaphragm
Cutlass Supreme	AC-Delco Tandem Diaphragm
Toronado	AC-Delco Tandem Diaphragm
Trofeo	AC-Delco Tandem Diaphragm
88	AC-Delco Tandem Diaphragm
98	AC-Delco Tandem Diaphragm
PONTIAC	
Bonneville	AC-Delco Tandem Diaphragm
Firebird	AC-Delco Tandem Diaphragm
Grand AM	AC-Delco Tandem Diaphragm
Grand Prix	AC-Delco Tandem Diaphragm
LeMans	Pontiac LeMans Single Diaphragm
Sunbird	AC-Delco Tandem Diaphragm
Trans Am	AC-Delco Tandem Diaphragm

PRECAUTIONS

1. After disassembling a power brake unit, soak all metal parts in solvent.
2. Use only alcohol on parts containing rubber. After the parts have been thoroughly cleaned and rinsed in solvent, they should be rewashed in clean alcohol before assembling.
3. Use compressed air to blow dirt and cleaning fluid from the recesses and internal passages.
4. Always use all the parts furnished in the repair kit.
5. **Use extreme caution when disassembling power assist mechanisms, as suddenly releasing internal spring tension could cause damage or personal injury.**
6. **On models with hydro-boost assist systems,** do not disassemble the accumulator. If the accumulator is damaged or diagnosed as faulty, it must be replaced as an assembly.

DESCRIPTION

AC-DELCO TANDEM DIAPHRAGM TYPE

This unit utilizes a vacuum power chamber, consisting of a front and rear shell, housing divider, front and rear diaphragm, plate assemblies, hydraulic pushrod and a diaphragm return spring, **Figs. 1 and 2.**

The unit operates in much the same manner as the single diaphragm unit described previously. The diaphragm and plate assemblies utilize the pressure differential between the engine intake manifold vacuum and atmospheric pressure to assist in braking.

AC-DELCO SINGLE DIAPHRAGM TYPE

The AC-Delco power booster assembly, **Fig. 3**is located along the bulkhead in the left side engine compartment, between the brake pedal and master cylinder. It is designed to take advantage of the vacuum produced by the engine. The applied force created when brake pedal is applied is mechanically increased with assistance of engine vacuum.

BCIA SINGLE & TANDEM DIAPHRAGM TYPE

These boosters have a lightweight cast alloy housing, **Figs. 4 and 5**. Vacuum is applied to the front and rear housings. When the brake pedal is released, negative pressure is equalized on both sides of the diaphragm(s) and power piston assembly. Spring tension holds the piston at the rest position. When brakes are applied, the atmospheric port in the power piston is opened. Negative pressure in the front chamber pulls the diaphragm(s) and vacuum piston assembly, reaction disc and output rod forward. Pressure on the master cylinder piston is increased. When brakes are released, the atmospheric port in the valve assembly is closed. Negative pressure is equalized on both sides of the diaphragm(s) and piston assembly. Spring tension forces the piston back to the rest position. When the atmospheric port is opened, air is drawn into the rear chamber through a filter in the valve assembly.

TROUBLESHOOTING

AC-DELCO TANDEM DIAPHRAGM TYPE

Hard Pedal

1. Internal vacuum leak.
2. Faulty control valve.

Brakes Grab

1. Faulty control valve.

Slow Or No Release

1. Faulty pushrod adjustment.
2. Bind in linkage.

BCIA SINGLE & TANDEM DIAPHRAGM TYPE

Brakes Grab

1. Internal vacuum leak.
2. Faulty control valve

Excessive Pedal Effort

1. Leak in booster vacuum supply.
2. Glazed linings.
3. Contaminated brake fluid.
4. Restricted filter or booster valve air passage.
5. Leak in booster vacuum supply.
6. Damaged booster or improperly assembled booster valve.

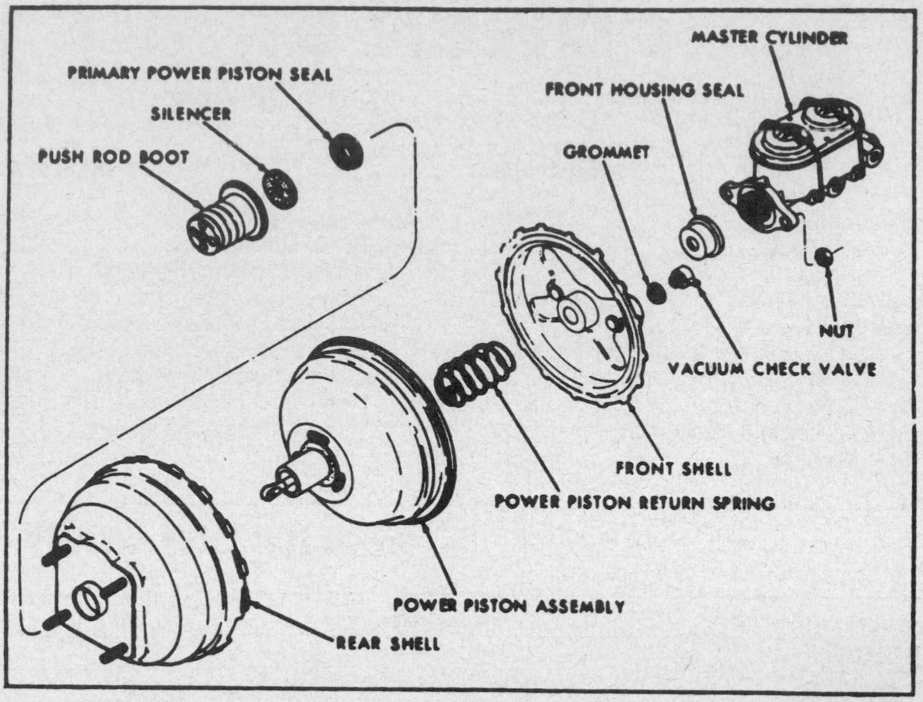
MASTER CYLINDER
PRIMARY POWER PISTON SEAL
FRONT HOUSING SEAL
SILENCER
GROMMET
PUSH ROD BOOT
NUT
VACUUM CHECK VALVE
FRONT SHELL
POWER PISTON RETURN SPRING
POWER PISTON ASSEMBLY
REAR SHELL

GC4099100046000X

Fig. 1 Exploded view of AC-Delco tandem diaphragm booster

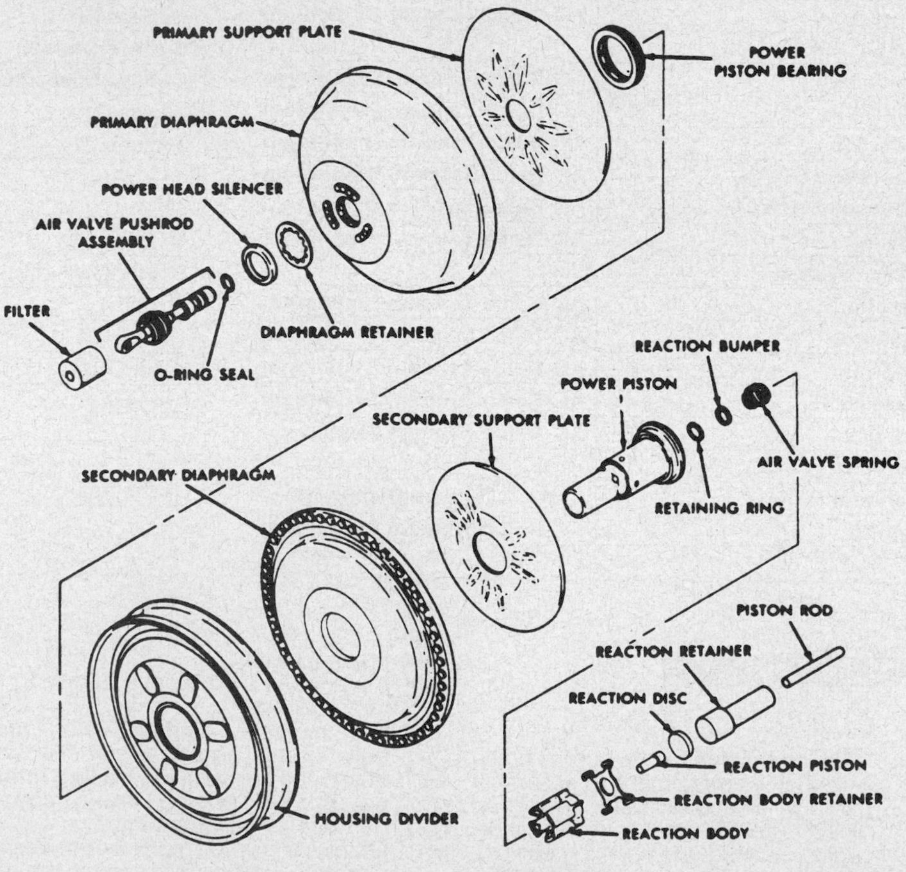
PRIMARY SUPPORT PLATE
POWER PISTON BEARING
PRIMARY DIAPHRAGM
POWER HEAD SILENCER
AIR VALVE PUSHROD ASSEMBLY
FILTER
DIAPHRAGM RETAINER
O-RING SEAL
REACTION BUMPER
POWER PISTON
SECONDARY SUPPORT PLATE
AIR VALVE SPRING
SECONDARY DIAPHRAGM
RETAINING RING
PISTON ROD
REACTION RETAINER
REACTION DISC
REACTION PISTON
REACTION BODY RETAINER
HOUSING DIVIDER
REACTION BODY

GC4099100047000X

Fig. 2 Exploded view of power head assembly. AC-Delco tandem diaphragm booster

Brakes Slow To Respond

1. Restricted filter or booster valve air passage.
2. Contaminated brake fluid.
3. Leak in booster vacuum supply.
4. Damaged booster or improperly assembled booster valve.

Brakes Slow To Release Or Drag

1. Damaged booster assembly.
2. Improperly assembled booster valve.
3. Pedal linkage damaged or improperly adjusted.
4. Restricted booster sir passage.
5. Insufficient caliper guide lubrication; damaged or defective calipers.
6. Contaminated brake fluid.

Low Or Spongy Brake Pedal

1. Worn linings.
2. Air or leaks in hydraulic system.
3. Defective master cylinder.
4. Defective wheel cylinders or calipers.
5. Improperly adjusted pedal linkage or booster pushrod.
6. Defective rear brake adjuster.

Brakes Drag

1. Improperly adjusted parking brake or binding cables.
2. Improperly adjusted pedal linkage or booster pushrod.
3. Improperly adjusted or binding pedal linkage.
4. Defective booster return spring.
5. Sticking caliper or wheel cylinder piston.
6. Defective master cylinder.

TOYOTA/GM SINGLE DIAPHRAGM TYPE

Brakes Grab

1. Contaminated, worn or faulty brake linings.
2. Drum or brake rotor out of round.
3. Faulty brake booster.

Hard Pedal/Brakes Inefficient

1. Contaminated, glazed or faulty brake linings.
2. Frozen caliper piston.
3. Faulty vacuum pump, or leak in booster vacuum supply system.
4. Faulty brake booster.

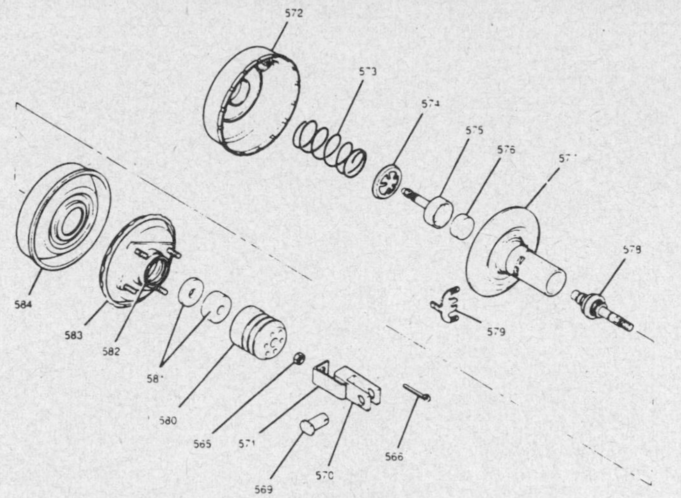

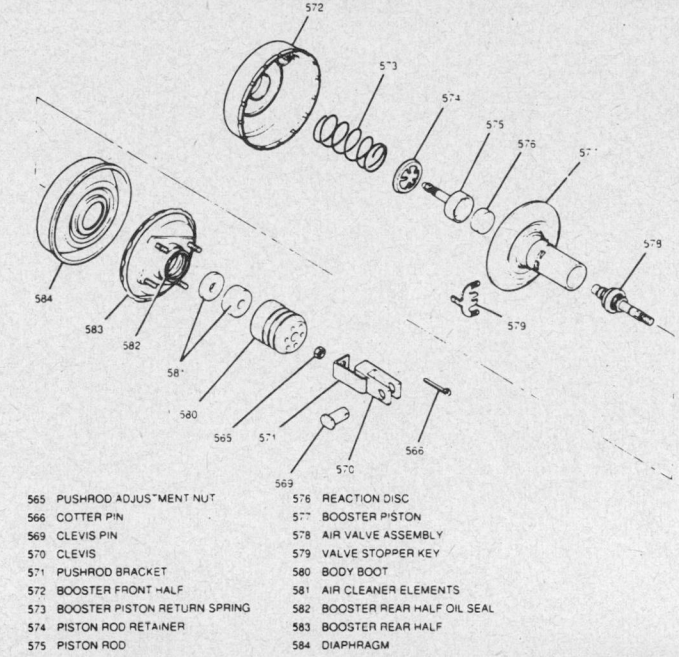

565 PUSHROD ADJUSTMENT NUT
566 COTTER PIN
569 CLEVIS PIN
570 CLEVIS
571 PUSHROD BRACKET
572 BOOSTER FRONT HALF
573 BOOSTER PISTON RETURN SPRING
574 PISTON ROD RETAINER
575 PISTON ROD
576 REACTION DISC
577 BOOSTER PISTON
578 AIR VALVE ASSEMBLY
579 VALVE STOPPER KEY
580 BODY BOOT
581 AIR CLEANER ELEMENTS
582 BOOSTER REAR HALF OIL SEAL
583 BOOSTER REAR HALF
584 DIAPHRAGM

GC4099400052000X

Fig. 3 Exploded view of Geo Metro single diaphragm booster

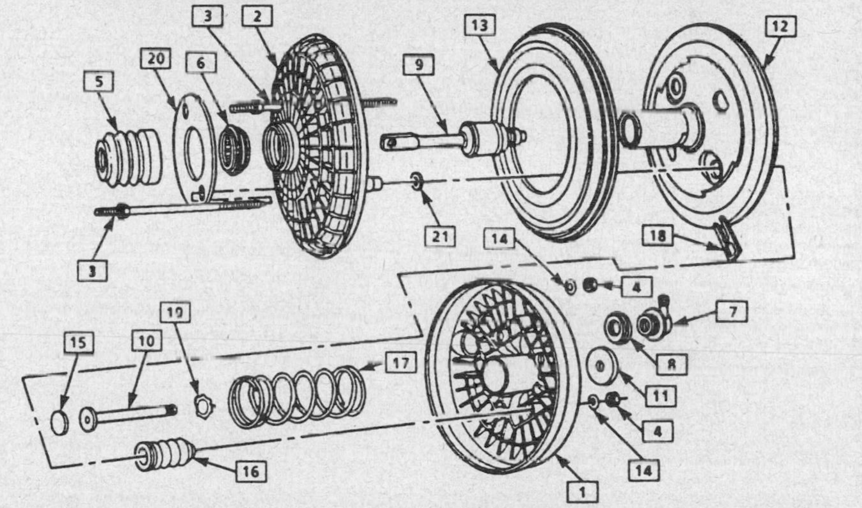

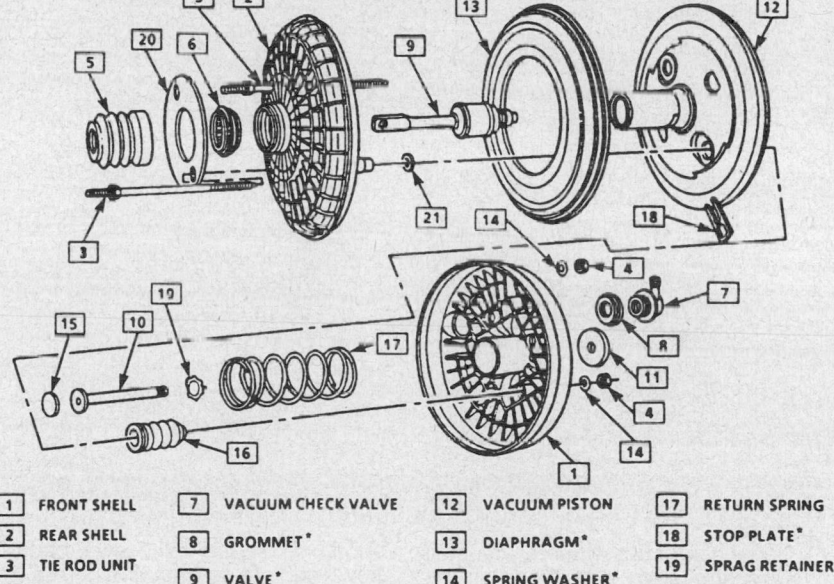

1 FRONT SHELL
2 REAR SHELL
3 TIE ROD UNIT
4 NUT
5 BOOT*
6 REAR SEAL*
7 VACUUM CHECK VALVE
8 GROMMET*
9 VALVE*
10 OUTPUT PUSH ROD
11 FRONT SEAL
12 VACUUM PISTON
13 DIAPHRAGM*
14 SPRING WASHER*
15 REACTION DISC*
16 TIE ROD BOOT*
17 RETURN SPRING
18 STOP PLATE*
19 SPRAG RETAINER*
20 GASKET
21 STEEL WASHER*
* REPAIR KIT

GC4099100048000X

Fig. 4 Exploded view of BCIA single diaphragm brake booster (VIN P). Corvette

ADJUSTMENTS

BRAKE PEDAL

Toyota/GM Single Diaphragm Type

1. With engine running and brake pedal in rest position, measure distance between face of pedal and floor mat.
2. If distance is not 5.79-6.18 inches, adjust pedal height as follows:
   a. Remove left lower instrument panel trim section and air duct.
   b. Loosen stop lamp switch sufficiently to gain clearance for pedal adjustment.
   c. Loosen locknut and rotate pedal pushrod as needed to obtain specified pedal height, then tighten locknut.
   d. Adjust position of brake light switch so that plunger lightly contacts pedal stopper and brake lamps are off when pedal is released.
   e. Check pedal free travel.
3. With engine stopped, depress brake pedal several times to ensure there is no vacuum pressure in booster.
4. Release pedal, then press pedal down until the beginning of resistance is felt, measuring the pedal travel. **Pedal free travel is the amount that the brake booster air valve is moved by the pedal pushrod.**
5. If pedal travel is not .12-.24 inch, adjust pedal freeplay as follows:
   a. Adjust pedal free travel by loosening locknut and rotating pedal pushrod.
   b. Ensure brake lamp switch and

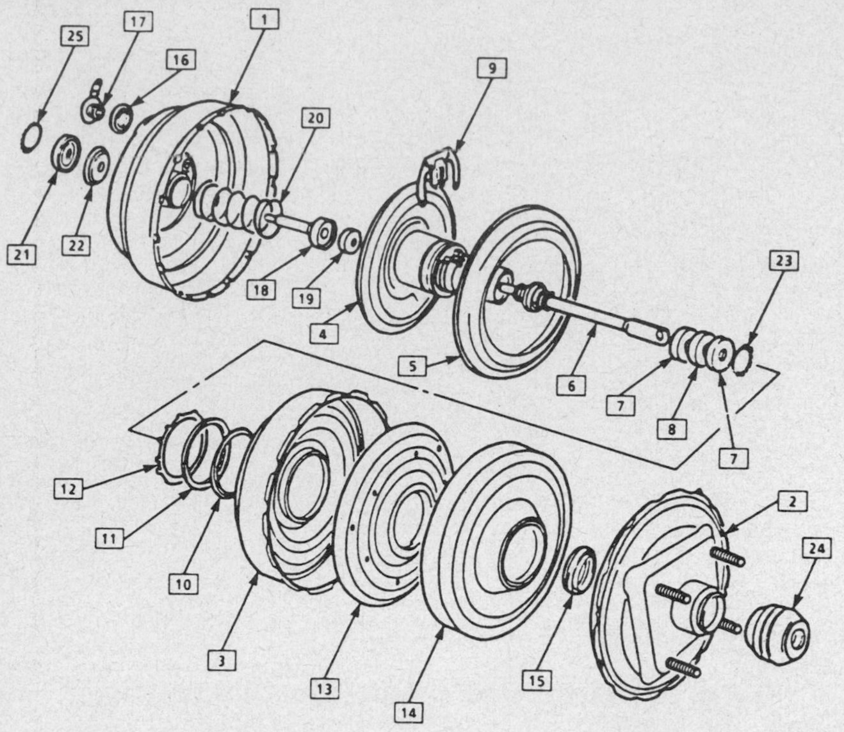

1 FRONT SHELL ASSEMBLY	14 REAR DIAPHRAGM*
2 REAR SHELL ASSEMBLY	15 REAR SEAL*
3 CENTER PLATE	16 GROMMET
4 VALVE BODY	17 CHECK VALVE
5 FRONT DIAPHRAGM*	18 OUTPUT PUSHROD
6 INPUT PUSHROD*	19 REACTION DISC*
7 FILTER*	20 RETURN SPRING
8 SILENCER*	21 FRONT SEAL*
9 KEY RETAINER	22 STOP PLATE*
10 RING BEARING*	23 RETAINER*
11 CENTER PLATE SEAL*	24 BOOT*
12 RETAINER CLIP	25 FRONT SEAL RETAINER
13 PRESSURE PLATE	* REPAIR KIT

GC4099300053000X

Fig. 5 Exploded view of BCIA tandem diaphragm brake booster (VIN J). Corvette

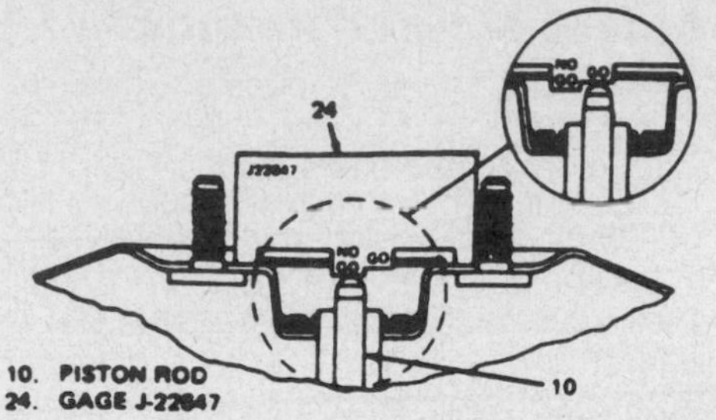
10. PISTON ROD
24. GAGE J-22847

GC4099100043000X

Fig. 6 Master cylinder pushrod adjustment. AC-Delco type vacuum booster

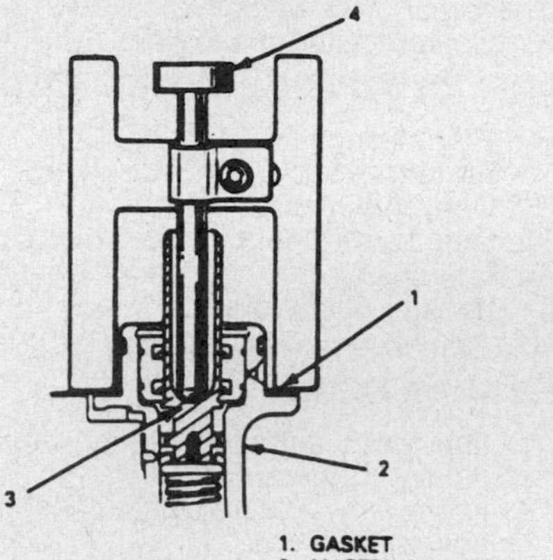
1. GASKET
2. MASTER CYLINDER
3. PISTON
4. PIN HEAD

GC4099100044000X

Fig. 7 Master cylinder adjustment tool

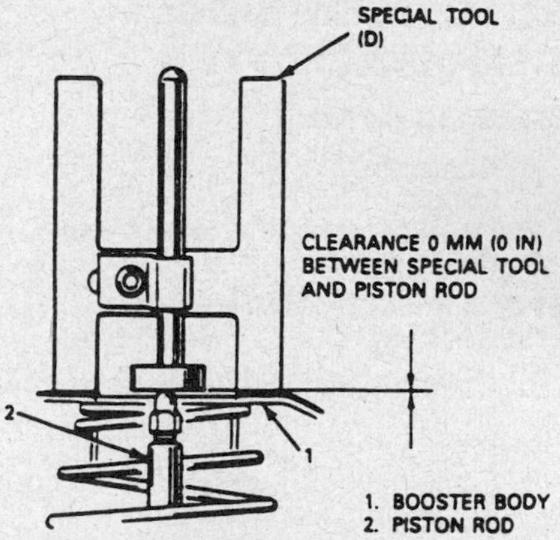
SPECIAL TOOL (D)
CLEARANCE 0 MM (0 IN) BETWEEN SPECIAL TOOL AND PISTON ROD
1. BOOSTER BODY
2. PISTON ROD

GC4099100045000X

Fig. 8 Booster piston rod adjustment

pedal height are properly adjusted, then start engine and confirm that free travel still exists.

c. Check pedal reserve distance.

6. Release parking brake, then start engine.
7. Depress brake pedal, then measure distance from face of pedal to floor mat. If pedal reserve distance is not more than 2.56 inch with an applied force of 110.2 lbs., check and repair brake system as needed.

PUSHROD

Proper adjustment of the master cylinder pushrod is necessary to ensure proper operation of the power brake system. A pushrod that is too long will cause the master cylinder piston to close off the compensating port, preventing hydraulic pressure from being released and resulting in brake drag. A pushrod that is too short will cause excessive brake pedal travel and cause groaning noises to come from the booster when the brakes are applied. A properly adjusted pushrod that remains assembled to the booster with which it was matched during production should not require service adjustment. However, if the booster, master cylinder or pushrod are serviced, the pushrod may require adjustment.

There are two methods that can be used to check for proper pushrod length and installation: the gauge method and air method. Usually, if the power unit pushrod requires adjustment, use the power unit repair kit gauge. The gauge measures from the end of the pushrod to the power unit shell.

GAUGE METHOD
AC-Delco Type

On these models, the master cylinder pushrod length is fixed and is usually only checked after the unit has been overhauled.

1. Assemble booster unit and install pushrod, ensuring pushrod is fully seated.
2. Position go/no go gauge furnished in repair kit over pushrod as shown in **Fig. 6**
3. If pushrod height is not within limits of gauge, install service adjustable pushrod and adjust rod to obtain correct height.
4. Install power unit and check adjust-

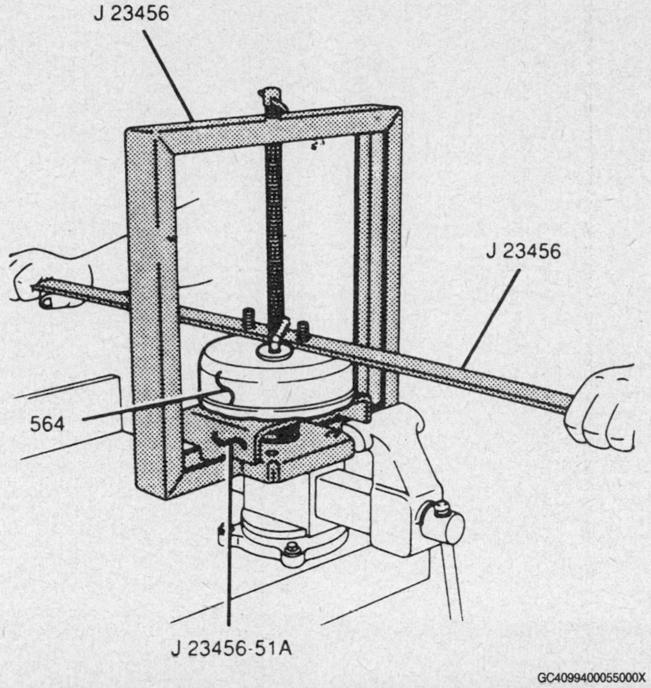
J 23456
J 23456
564
J 23456-51A
GC4099400055000X

Fig. 9 AC-Delco brake booster holding tools

ment, ensuring master cylinder compensating port is open with engine running and brake pedal released.

Single Diaphragm Type

This unit is used on late model GEO Metro. The length of the booster piston rod is adjusted to provide specified clearance between the piston rod end and master cylinder piston. Before making an adjustment, push piston rod several times to ensure reaction disc is in place. Ensure gasket is installed to master cylinder and keep inside of booster at atmospheric pressure.

1. Place booster pin rod gauge tool No. J 34873 or equivalent, on master cylinder and push pin until it contacts piston, **Fig. 7.**
2. Turn tool upside down and place it on booster. Adjust booster piston rod length until rod end contacts pin head.
3. Adjust clearance by turning adjusting bolt of piston rod, **Fig. 8.** If negative pressure is applied to booster with engine at idle, piston to piston rod clearance should measure 0.004-0.020 inch.

AIR METHOD

1. Be sure master cylinder attaching nuts are tight.
2. Remove master cylinder filler cap.
3. With brake released, force compressed air into the hydraulic outlet of the master cylinder. **Regulate air pressure to a value of approximately 5 psi, to prevent spraying brake fluid from master cylinder. Care must be taken not to allow brake fluid to contact painted surfaces of vehicle, skin or eyes, as damage or personal injury will result.**
4. If air passes through the compensating port, which is the smaller of the two holes in the bottom of the master cylinder reservoir, the adjustment is satisfactory.
5. If air does not flow through the compensating port, adjust the pushrod as required, either by means of the adjustment screw (if provided) or by adding shims between the master cylinder and power unit shell until the air flows freely.
6. Reconnect brake lines and bleed system.

GENERAL SERVICE

Two basic types of power assist mechanisms are used: vacuum assist diaphragm assemblies, which use engine vacuum or, in some cases vacuum pressure developed by an external vacuum pump. The second type is a hydraulic pressure assist mechanism, which use pressure developed by an external pump (usually the power steering pump). Both systems act to increase the force exerted on the master cylinder piston by the operator. This in turn increases the hydraulic pressure delivered to the wheel cylinders, while decreasing driver effort necessary to obtain acceptable stopping performance.

Vacuum assist units are similar in operation and get their energy by opposing engine vacuum to atmospheric pressure. A piston and cylinder, flexible diaphragm (bellows) utilize this energy to provide brake assistance. The fundamental difference between these types of vacuum assist systems lies simply in how the diaphragm within the power unit is suspended when the brakes are not applied.

In order to properly diagnose vacuum assist system malfunctions it is important to know whether the diaphragm within a power unit is air suspended or vacuum suspended. Air-suspended units are under atmospheric pressure until the brakes are applied. Engine vacuum is then admitted, causing the piston or diaphragm to move (or the bellows to collapse). Vacuum-suspended types are balanced with engine vacuum until the brake pedal is depressed, allowing atmospheric pressure to unbalance the unit and apply force to the brake system.

Regardless of whether the brakes are vacuum or hydraulically assisted, certain general service procedures apply. Only specified, clean brake fluid should be used in brake system. On hydro-boost systems, use of the specified hydraulic fluid in the boost circuit is essential to proper system operation. Care must be taken not to mix the fluids of the two separate operating circuits. Use of improper fluids, or contaminated fluid will cause damage to the seals and valves.

POWER BRAKE UNIT SERVICE

AC-DELCO TANDEM DIAPHRAGM TYPE

OVERHAUL

Disassemble

1. Remove pedal pushrod boot, silencer, check valve, vacuum switch and grommets, as equipped, then the front housing seal.
2. Scribe matching marks between front and rear housing sections, then mount booster assembly in suitable holding fixture with rear housing facing up.
3. Apply pressure to housing with holding fixture forcing screw and rotate rear housing counterclockwise to unlock housing halves.
4. Slowly release spring tension, then remove booster assembly from holding fixture. **Do not allow spring tension to release suddenly, as damage or personal injury may result.**
5. Lift off rear housing, then remove primary power piston bearing from housing.
6. Remove power piston group and return spring from front housing, **Fig. 1.**
7. Remove master cylinder piston rod and reaction retainer from front of piston, then the silencer from the rear of the assembly, **Fig. 2.**
8. Hold piston assembly at edges of divider and strike pedal pushrod against work surface to dislodge diaphragm retainer.
9. Remove primary diaphragm and support plate, secondary power piston bearing and housing divider, then the secondary diaphragm and support plate from piston, noting installation position of components.
10. Clean and inspect components as outlined in "General Service," then replace as needed. **Do not disassemble power piston. If service is required, power piston must be replaced as an assembly.**

Assemble

1. Position power piston assembly on work surface with pedal pushrod facing up.
2. Lubricate inner lip of secondary diaphragm, fit diaphragm over support plate, then install assembly onto power piston.
3. Install secondary power piston bearing into divider with flat surface of bearing on side of divider with 6 lugs, **Fig. 2.**
4. Install guide sleeve tool No. J 28458 or equivalent, over power piston, lubricate inner diameter of secondary bearing, then install divider assembly with lugged side facing up.
5. Lubricate inner lip of primary diaphragm. Fit diaphragm over support plate, then install diaphragm assembly on power piston.
6. Ensure diaphragms and support plates are properly positioned.
7. Install new diaphragm retainer, then seat retainer on power piston using guide sleeve tool No. J 28458 or equivalent, and tap with a hammer.
8. Install primary power piston bearing in rear housing, then lubricate inner diameter of bearing.
9. Mount front housing in holding fixture tool No. J 23456 or equivalent, then install diaphragm return spring, power piston group and the rear housing assembly, **Fig. 1.**
10. Ensure housing scribe marks are properly aligned, then press housing sections together with holding fixture forcing screw. **Assembling of housing can be facilitated by applying vacuum to front housing port. Block opening for vacuum switch, if equipped.**
11. Rotate rear housing clockwise to lock housing, then stake two tabs 180° apart to secure assembly. Do not stake tabs which have previously been used.
12. Lubricate grommets and front seal, install grommets, check valve and vacuum switch, as equipped, then the front housing seal.
13. Install silencer and pedal pushrod boot.

GEO METRO SINGLE DIAPHRAGM TYPE

Refer to **Fig. 3** during service procedure.

OVERHAUL

Disassemble

1. Remove booster pushrod clevis and adjustment nut from air valve assembly.
2. Using pliers, flatten two index tabs which fall between the two raised points on opposite sides of perimeter of both booster halves.
3. Mount booster in a vise with holding tool No. J 23456 and J 23456-51A or equivalents, **Fig. 9.** Tighten fixture enough to secure booster and allowing rotation of booster front half.
4. Scribe a mark across both booster halves to facilitate final assembling.
5. Using tool No. J 23456 or equivalent, rotate front half of booster until all indexing tabs are aligned with indention on rear half of booster.
6. Slowly loosen the tool center screw and separate booster halves.
7. Remove both booster halves, booster piston return spring and piston rod, and retainer from holding fixture.
8. Remove body boot, two air cleaner elements and booster piston from piston groove.
9. Remove valve stopper key from booster piston while working air valve in and in-and-out motion.
10. Using seal tools No. J 34874, J 7079-2 and J 35379 or equivalents, drive rear booster half seal out with a hammer.
11. Replace any parts that are corroded, nicked, scored, distorted or excessively worn.

Assemble

1. Before installation, apply a liberal coat of silicone grease to the following:
   a. Inside of rear booster half oil seal.
   b. Entire surface of reaction disc.
   c. Outside of air valve assembly seal.
   d. Entire surface of diaphragm.
   e. Sliding surface of air valve
2. Using seal tools No. J 34874, J 7079-2 and J 35379 or equivalents, drive new rear booster half seal in with a hammer.
3. Install reaction disc to piston rod, then air valve assembly to booster piston, diaphragm booster piston by hand.
4. Install valve stopper key to booster piston while compressing air valve assembly.
5. Install booster rear half, then both air cleaner elements to air valve assembly.
6. Secure body boot on rear booster body and air valve assembly, then rear booster half to holding tool No. J 23456 and J 23456-51A or equivalents.
7. Assemble piston rod, piston rod retainer and piston return spring to rear booster, then front booster to rear half aligning piston return spring.
8. Tighten center screw of tool No. J 23456 or equivalent, bringing both booster halves together. **Ensure that both halves mate squarely and align with indexing tabs in rear halve indentation.**
9. Rotate front half of booster using the tool until the twelve indexing tabs catch under lip of rear half of booster.
10. Align scribe mark made prior to disassembling, then remove booster assembly from tools.
11. Using pliers, reposition any flattened indexing tabs to secure assembly.

BCIA SINGLE DIAPHRAGM TYPE

OVERHAUL

Disassembly

1. Remove vacuum check valve from front housing.
2. Loosen tie rod nuts several turns (approximately 1/2 inch), but do not remove nuts.
3. Pry housing shells apart using a thin blade screw driver, taking care not to chip or mar housing shells, or cut diaphragm.
4. Clamp housing shells together with suitable holding fixtures, then remove tie rod nuts and spring washers. **Failure to secure housing shells prior to removing tie rod nuts may allow housing shells to separate due to spring tension, causing damage and/or personal injury.**
5. Slowly loosen clamp securing housing shells, then separate front shell and remove return spring, grommet and front seal from housing.
6. Remove pedal pushrod boot, gasket and tie rods from rear shell, **Fig. 4.**
7. Separate diaphragm bead from rear shell, tie rod boots from posts on shell, then remove vacuum piston assembly.
8. Remove diaphragm and tie rod boots from piston.
9. Remove rear seal from shell and washers from tie rod posts.
10. Remove output rod, retainer and reaction disc.
11. Remove stop plate from vacuum piston, pressing on open end while pulling on closed end of plate.
12. Remove valve assembly from vacuum piston. **Do not disassemble valve assembly. If service is required, entire valve assembly must be replaced.**

Assembly

Lubricate components where indicated with silicone grease.

1. Lubricate outer surface of valve assembly, then insert valve into vacuum piston and secure valve with stop plate, **Fig. 4.** Ensure plate is in fully locked position.
2. Lubricate reaction disc, then install disc in vacuum piston.
3. Install new tie rod boots in openings in vacuum piston, then liberally coat insides of boots with silicone grease.
4. Lubricate outer lip of diaphragm, then fit diaphragm into vacuum piston.
5. Press rear seal into shell, lubricate inner diameter of seal, then install washers over tie rod posts on rear shell.
6. Mount vacuum piston assembly in rear shell, pushing tie rod boots over posts. Ensure diaphragm bead is properly located around perimeter of shell.
7. Install tie rods through bores in rear shell.
8. Mount rear shell assembly in fixture J-23456-51A or equivalent, lubricate output rod, then install rod and new retainer in vacuum piston. **Do not alter adjustment of convex screw on output rod. Rod length is determined during manufacturing and should not be disturbed.**
9. Seat new front seal in front shell with

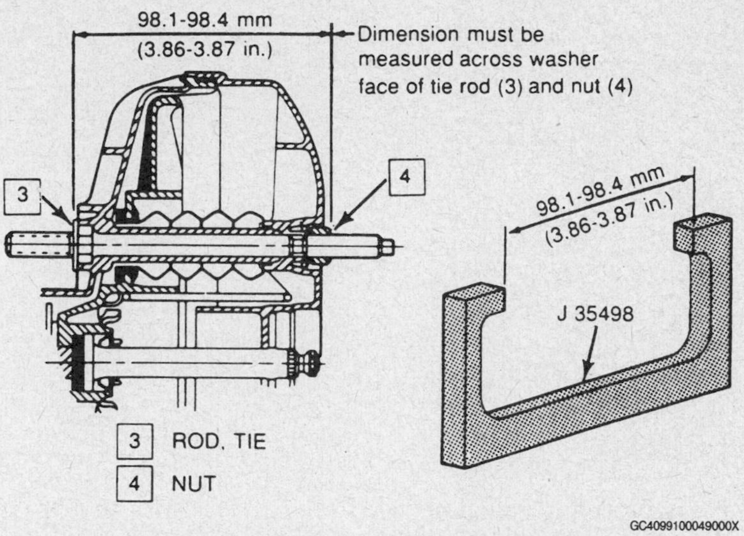
98.1-98.4 mm
(3.86-3.87 in.)
Dimension must be measured across washer face of tie rod (3) and nut (4)
3
4
98.1-98.4 mm
(3.86-3.87 in.)
J 35498
3 ROD, TIE
4 NUT
GC4099100049000X

Fig. 10 Measuring booster shell assembly. BCIA booster

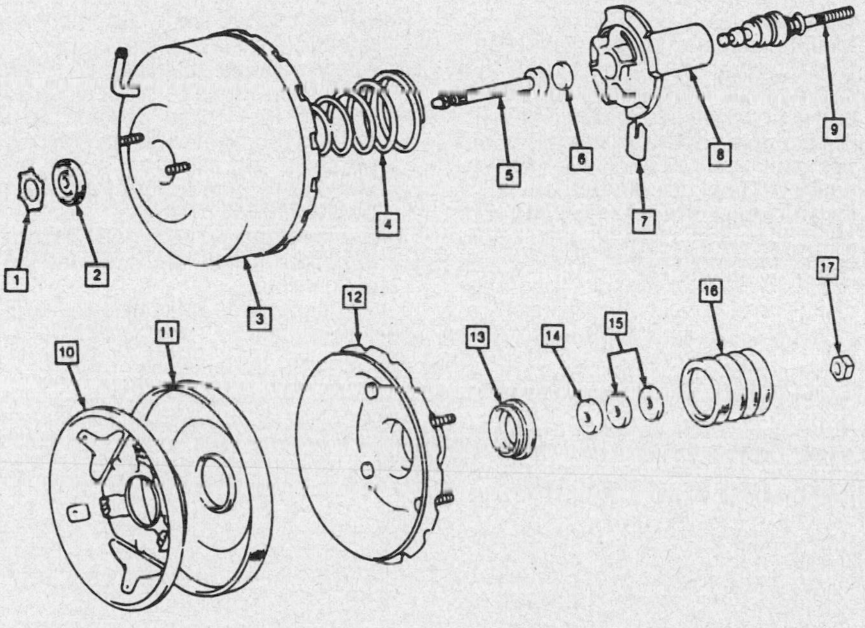
1
2
3
4
5
6
7
8
9
10
11
12
13
14
15
16
17
1. CIRCULAR RING
2. BODY SEAL
3. FRONT BODY
4. DIAPHRAGM SPRING
5. PUSH ROD
6. REACTION DISC
7. STOPPER KEY
8. VALVE BODY
9. OPERATING ROD
10. BOOSTER PISTON
11. DIAPHRAGM
12. REAR BODY
13. BODY SEAL
14. SPONGE ELEMENT
15. FELT ELEMENT
16. BOOT
17. NUT
GC4099100050000X

Fig. 11 Toyota/GM brake booster exploded view

metal face of seal toward outside.

10. Position return spring in vacuum piston, then install front housing. Ensure diaphragm bead remains properly positioned.
11. Press shell halves together by hand, then install spring washers and new retaining nuts on tie rods. Ensure concave side of washers face shell. **Use only new replacement nuts furnished with repair kit when assembling booster shells.**
12. Tighten nuts evenly until shells are .20 inch apart, then ensure diaphragm bead is still properly positioned.
13. Continue tightening nuts evenly, approximately 1/2 turn at a time. Gauge housing assembly with tool J-35498 or equivalent as shown in **Fig. 10.**
14. Housing shells are properly assembled when distance between face of washer (3) and face of nut (4) is 3.87-4.86 inches, **Fig. 10.**
15. Reverse steps 1 and 2 of disassembly procedure to complete assembly.

BCIA TANDEM DIAPHRAGM TYPE

1. Remove vacuum check valve.
2. Place power booster in suitable holder tools No. J 23456 and J 23456-61A or equivalents, then loosen nuts and spring washers.
3. Hold booster shells together, then remove nuts and washers.
4. Loosen tool No. J 23456 until spring pressure is released, then remove power booster from holding tools.
5. Remove front shell, return spring, grommet, front shell seal, boot, tie rods and gasket from rear shell.
6. Remove vacuum piston, then loosen bead of diaphragm from rear shell.
7. Remove rear seal from rear shell.
8. Disassemble diaphragm from tie rod boots and vacuum piston.
9. Remove output pushrod, sprag retainer and stop plate from vacuum piston.
10. Remove valve assembly from vacuum piston, the reaction disc.
11. Reverse procedure to install thoroughly lubricating the following with silicone grease:
    a. Reaction disc.
    b. OD valve assembly
    c. Inside of tie rod boots.
    d. Diaphragm OD lip.
    e. Rear seal ID.
    f. Output pushrod.

TOYOTA/GM SINGLE DIAPHRAGM TYPE

OVERHAUL

Disassemble

1. Attach holding fixture tool No. J-22805-01 or equivalent, to front of booster, then mount fixture in vise. Mounting holes of holding fixture may have to be elongated toward inside in order to accommodate booster master cylinder studs.
2. Scribe matching marks between front and rear booster shells to aid assembling.
3. Remove nut from pedal pushrod and boot from rear shell, **Fig. 11.**
4. Attach lever tool No. J-9504-01 or equivalent, to booster mounting studs. Rotate rear shell counterclockwise to unlock housing, separate booster shells, then remove holding fixtures. **Do not suddenly release spring tension when separating booster shells.**
5. Remove diaphragm spring and pushrod from front shell.
6. Remove diaphragm and piston assembly from rear shell.
7. Support rear shell inboard of mounting studs, then drive out rear seal using a spacer.
8. Rotate valve body clockwise, then separate valve body and diaphragm from booster piston.
9. Push pedal pushrod into valve body, supporting valve body on cushioned work surface, then remove stopper key from side of valve body.
10. Pull pushrod from valve body, then remove two felt and one sponge element, noting position for assembling.
11. Remove reaction disc from front of valve body.
12. Pry out retaining ring, then remove seal from front shell.

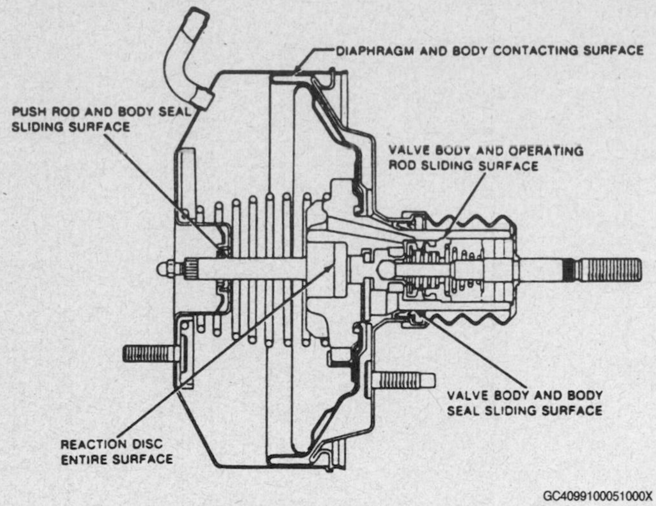
DIAPHRAGM AND BODY CONTACTING SURFACE
PUSH ROD AND BODY SEAL SLIDING SURFACE
VALVE BODY AND OPERATING ROD SLIDING SURFACE
VALVE BODY AND BODY SEAL SLIDING SURFACE
REACTION DISC ENTIRE SURFACE
GC4099100051000X

Fig. 12 Brake booster lubrication points

Assemble

Apply silicone grease to components indicated in **Fig. 12** prior to assembling.

1. Install new seal in front shell, then secure with new retaining ring.
2. Install holding fixture tool No. J-22805-01 or equivalent, on front shell, then mount holding fixture in vise.
3. Support front of valve body on cushioned work surface, press pedal pushrod into valve body, then secure pushrod by inserting stopper key into side of valve body.
4. Pull up on pushrod to ensure key is properly seated. Install elements (2 felt and 1 sponge), in rear of valve body, then the reaction disc in front of valve body, **Fig. 11.**
5. Mount diaphragm on booster piston.
6. Insert valve body assembly into booster piston, then rotate valve body counterclockwise to lock in position.
7. Support rear shell from inside, inboard of mounting studs, and drive new rear seal into place using a spacer.
8. Install diaphragm assembly into rear shell, then the pushrod and return spring into front shell.
9. Position rear shell and diaphragm assembly over front shell, then install rotating lever tool No. J-9504-01 or equivalent, ensuring matching marks will be aligned when assembly is rotated to locked position.
10. Apply vacuum to inlet port in front shell, then rotate rear housing clockwise to the locked position. **If rear shell is too tight to be rotated when pressed into position, apply more silicone grease to lip of diaphragm contacting front shell.**
11. Remove rotating lever and holding fixture, then install rear boot and pedal pushrod nut.
12. Adjust pushrod as outlined.

ANTI-LOCK BRAKES

TABLE OF CONTENTS

Corvette (Bosch ABS/ASR 2U Type)

NOTE: On Air Bag Equipped Models, Refer To "Air Bag System Precautions" Located In The Front Of This Manual For System Disarming & Arming Procedures.

NOTE: Electrical Symbol & Wire Color Code Identification Located In The Front Of This Manual May Be Used As An Aid When Using Wiring Circuits Found In This Section.

INDEX

PRECAUTIONS

AIR BAG SYSTEMS

Refer to "Air Bag System Precautions" in the front of this manual for system disarming and arming procedures.

DESCRIPTION

SYSTEM

The anti-lock brake system (ABS) with an integrated acceleration slip regulation (ASR) system, **Fig. 1**, maintains vehicle maneuverability under severe braking conditions on most road surfaces. The ABS/ASR systems monitors each wheel speed during braking. The Electronic Brake & Traction Control Module (EBTCM) uses this information to produce signals to prevent the braking wheels from locking.

The modulator valve regulates brake fluid pressure based on road conditions as interpreted by the , regardless of master cylinder output pressure. The modulator valve can maintain, reduce and increase brake fluid pressure to the calipers under ABS conditions, but it can not increase pressure above that applied from the master cylinder. However, during ASR operation, the modulator can apply pressure to the rear calipers if the requires that a wheel be slowed or regulated.

The ASR traction system uses engine spark retard, throttle close down and rear brake intervention to provide better acceleration and vehicle stability. The ASR system can function up to maximum vehicle speed. The system enhances the directional control, traction and maneuverability. The ASR system uses input information from wheel speed, vehicle speed, to allow traction priority to low speeds and direc-

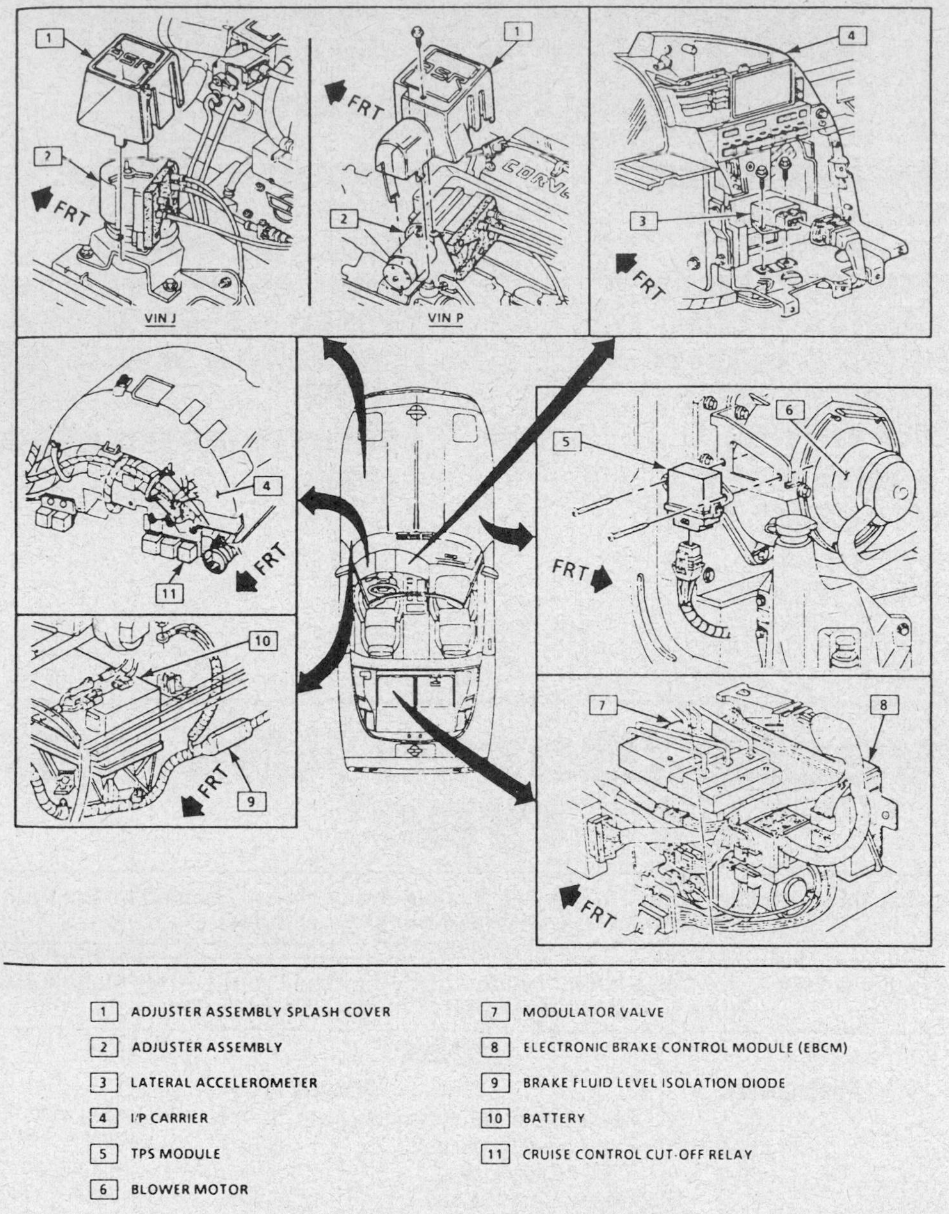
VIN J
VIN P
FRT
1 ADJUSTER ASSEMBLY SPLASH COVER
2 ADJUSTER ASSEMBLY
3 LATERAL ACCELEROMETER
4 I/P CARRIER
5 TPS MODULE
6 BLOWER MOTOR
7 MODULATOR VALVE
8 ELECTRONIC BRAKE CONTROL MODULE (EBCM)
9 BRAKE FLUID LEVEL ISOLATION DIODE
10 BATTERY
11 CRUISE CONTROL CUT-OFF RELAY
GC4029200395000X

Fig. 1 Bosch ABS/ASR brake system

tional control at high speeds, vehicle acceleration and throttle position, during low vehicle acceleration the controls are more sensitive and brake application input.

The ABS/ASR common components are four wheel speed sensors and sensor rings, master cylinder reservoir which supplies the ABS/ASR modulator valve, the EBTCM and wire harness. The ABS/ASR components that are specific to the ASR system are the adjuster assembly - throttle and cruise control cables, prime pipe from master cylinder to modulator valve, ASR Off switch, spark retard table added to the ECM, throttle position sensor (TPS) module, cruise control cutoff relay, ASR lamps and lateral accelerometer.

SYSTEM COMPONENTS

Modulator Valve

The modulator valve assembly, located in the rear compartment behind the left-hand seat, contains a recirculation pump with separate circuits for the front and rear brakes. During the ABS pressure reduction function the modulator valve transfers fluid from the brake calipers back to the master cylinder. During the ASR brake intervention function, the valve transfers fluid from the master cylinder reservoir to the rear brake calipers.

The ASR portions of the hydraulics circuit to the ABS hydraulic include and additional three way valve added to the rear brakes. These valves control each rear brake individually and use an additional rear brake pipe. The load valve is used to isolate the master cylinder prime pipe from the pump during brake application and ABS control, the valve is spring loaded to the open position. The two way pilot valve is electronically operated to isolate the master cylinder from the pump during ASR operation. When the pilot valve is closed, the pump can direct fluid to the rear brake circuit, with excess fluid passing through the pressure limiting valve. The master cylinder positive center valve is designed to open when the secondary piston returns to the rest position. This happens when the center valve pintle contacts a cross shaft at the rest position, ensuring pressure relief if excess fluid is pumped into the master cylinder.

Electronic Brake & Traction Control Module (EBTCM)

The EBTCM is located in the rear compartment behind the lefthand seat. The EBTCM receives information from the ECM, wheel speed sensor and the TPS module. The information is output to the ECM, modulator valve assembly and the adjuster assembly. The EBTCM determines when the ASR system should be actuated through timing retard, throttle close down and brake intervention. The ignition retard signal is based on engine RPM. Engine RPM information is received from the tach filter circuit on models equipped with VIN P engine or from the direct ignition module on models equipped with VIN J engine. The EBTCM controls the amount of adjuster assembly output and throttle rate. As required, the EBTCM controls the modulator valve assembly pressure. The EBTCM will disable the ASR system when the ignition switch is On but the engine is not running.

The EBTCM must reset its idle position detection capabilities whenever a new throttle position sensor or throttle body is installed.

Lateral Acceleration Switch (Accelerometer)

The lateral acceleration switch is made up of two mercury switches connected in series. They are used to detect if the vehicle is cornering faster than a predetermined curve speed. When this speed is exceeded, one of two switches opens up and sends a signal to control module.

The lateral acceleration switch is located under the A/C control head on the floor pan. This switch is not serviceable and should be replaced as an assembly.

Wheel Speed Sensors

Rotational speed of each wheel is detected separately by an inductive wheel speed sensor, **Fig. 2.** Electrical signal sensed from the speed sensors are transmitted to control module.

In this system, front wheels are controlled individually and rear wheels together. Control of rear wheels works on the "Select Low" principle. "Select Low" means wheel with the greatest tendency to lock-up (lower tire to road friction coefficient), determines level of control.

Wheel speed sensors are installed in knuckles. Toothed rings are pressed onto front hub and bearing assemblies and rear driveshaft spindles. **The wheel speed sensors do not require adjustment.**

Throttle Position Sensor (TPS) Module

The TPS module is located in the engine compartment near the RH side of the blower case. The module is used to allow the EBTCM to read the TPS signal. The TPS module scales the TPS signal, indicates the ground difference between the ECM and the EBTCM and buffers the signal so the TPS signal to the ECM is not affected by the EBTCM. The EBTCM uses the information for determining potential adjuster assembly requirements for engine torque management.

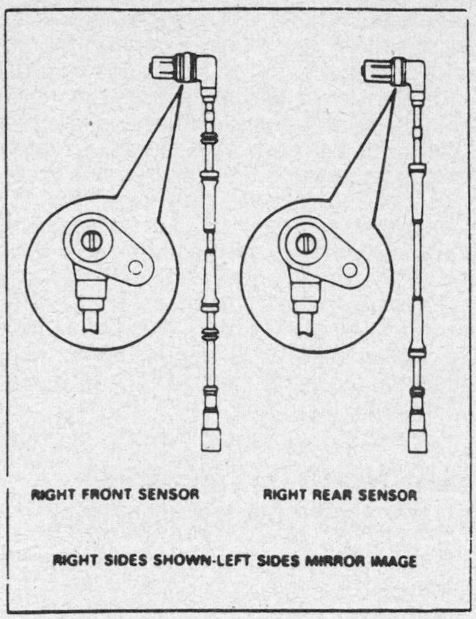
RIGHT FRONT SENSOR
RIGHT REAR SENSOR
RIGHT SIDES SHOWN-LEFT SIDES MIRROR IMAGE
GC4029100397000X

Fig. 2 Wheel speed sensor

OPERATION

When ignition switch is turned to On position, amber ANTI-LOCK warning lamp in the instrument panel illuminates. When engine is started, it goes out. If ABS warning light does not go out or comes on permanently while driving, it indicates a fault in ABS system.

When starting vehicle, the control module performs a functional check of electrical circuitry. The test cycle checks components of the monitoring circuit as well as the logic section. Test sample signals are sent to the control module, which checks whether or not the correct output signals are available.

Since the ABS system may not be used every day, there is an additional test which actually runs the modulator valve. Whenever ignition switch is turned to On position and vehicle reaches 4 mph, the test starts. Operation of the modular valve can be heard and felt, if the driver's foot is on the brake pedal. This test is performed once, each time the vehicle is started.

This system continuously monitors the following components: modulator valve, control module, lateral acceleration switch, wheel speed sensors, wiring harness and relays.

The control module constantly monitors its own supply voltage. If supply voltage drops below a predetermined value, ABS will be switched Off and the amber ANTI-LOCK lamp will come on. When supplied voltage returns to or exceeds the predetermined value, ANTI-LOCK lamp will go off. If a fault occurs in ABS, the ANTI-LOCK warning lamp comes on and ABS will be switched off. The system will remain off until vehicle is restarted at which time the functional check is repeated.

TROUBLESHOOTING

Refer to "Intermittents & Poor Connections" under "Diagnosis & Testing" for troubleshooting procedures.

DIAGNOSIS & TESTING

DESCRIPTION

When the vehicle is started, the EBTCM performs a functional test of the electrical circuits. The test cycle inspects the monitoring system components and system logic; the cycle is completed in about six seconds. An additional AUTO test operates the modulator valve assembly when the vehicle is started and vehicle speed reaches 4 mph in forward or reverse. The modulator valve assembly, EBTCM, lateral accelerometer, wheel speed sensors and wiring harness and relays are continuously monitored.

The EBTCM monitors its own voltage supply, if the supply drops below a specified minimum value, the ABS/ASR lamp will not be illuminated and the Service ABS lamp will be illuminated. When voltage exceeds the specified minimum value the Service ABS lamp will go out. If a fault occurs in the ABS system the warning lamp will be illuminated, the ABS system will be turned Off until the ignition switch is cycled Off then On, then the functional inspection will be repeated. The standard brake system will remain fully operational. Under normal driving conditions the ABS functions the same as a standard power assisted brake system.

Brake pedal pulsation and occasional tire noise are normal during ABS operation on dry pavement. During light braking in a turn, the rear brake pressure may be modulated to enhance vehicle stability under certain conditions. A slight brake pedal vibration may be experienced during light braking during lateral acceleration speeds above 30 mph.

INTERMITTENTS & POOR CONNECTIONS

Most intermittents are caused by faulty electrical connections or wiring, although a sticking or faulty relay or solenoid can be a problem. Check for the following items:

1. Poor mating of connector halves, or terminal not fully seated in the connector body (backed out).
2. Dirt or corrosion on the terminals. The terminals must be clean and free of foreign material which may impede proper terminal contact.
3. Damaged connector body, exposing the terminals to moisture or dirt, as well as not maintaining proper terminal orientation with the component or mating surface.
4. Improperly formed or damaged terminals. All connector terminals in problem circuits should be checked carefully to ensure full contact tension. Use corresponding mating terminal to check for proper tension.
5. The J 35616-A Connector Test Adapter Kit must be used whenever a diagnostic procedure requests checking or probing a terminal. Using the adapter will ensure no damage to the terminal will occur, as well as giving an idea of whether contact tension is sufficient.

6. Poor terminal-to-wire connection. Some conditions which fall under this description are poor crimps, poor solder joints, crimping over wire insulation rather than the wire itself, corrosion in the wire-to-terminal contact area, etc.
7. Wire insulation which has rubbed through, causing an intermittent short as the bare area touches other wiring or parts of the vehicle.
8. Wiring broken inside the insulation. This condition could cause a continuity check to show a good circuit, but if only one or two strands of a multistrand type wire are intact, resistance would be far too high.

PRELIMINARY INSPECTION

Refer to ABS wiring circuit **Figs. 3 through 5** when performing diagnostic procedures and **Figs. 6 and 7** for ABS functional tests.

If a malfunction in the ABS system occurs, check the following before using the code diagnostic charts:

1. Inspect fusible link.
2. Ensure ABS connectors are properly connected.
3. Ensure control module connectors is properly connected.
4. Inspect ABS system grounds.

ACCESSING DIAGNOSTIC TROUBLE CODES

TECH 1

Refer to "Tech 1 Diagnostics" for accessing trouble code procedure.

CENTRAL CONTROL MODULE (CCM)

Automatic Mode

1. Ground ALDL pin G, then turn ignition switch to On position. If A/C fuse is blown CCM will not receive IGN 3 power and will not enter diagnostic mode and code 16 will be indicated.
2. CCM will display codes and module for which they apply in an automatic code display sequence. ABS/ASR EBTCM is module 9.
3. Each code is displayed for three seconds followed by a one second pause before the next code is displayed. There will be a three second pause between code display sequence for each module.
4. Each module code list end will be indicated by an "- - -."
5. If a communication problem between ECM or EBTCM and CCM is indicated the speedometer will display Err.

Manual Mode

The manual mode may be entered after the automatic mode sequence has been completed. When manual mode is entered the speedometer will be blank and the trip monitor will display 1.0 indicating module 1 (CCM). Driver Information Center (DIC) buttons control manual diagnostic functions. Fuel info indicates previous value, gauges is previous test, fuel reset is previous module, eng met is next value, trip odo is next test and trip reset is next module. The speedometer will indicate "- - -" if the end or the beginning of a list of codes is reached using the DIC buttons or no codes are indicated for the module being tested. To display ABS/ASR codes trip monitor must indicate 9.1 to clear ABS/ASR codes 9.7 must be indicated.

DIAGNOSTIC TROUBLE CODE INTERPRETATION

Refer to **Fig. 8**, for trouble code identification.

CODE DIAGNOSIS

Refer to **Figs. 9 through 93**, for code diagnostic procedures and brake warning system wiring diagrams.

CLEARING DIAGNOSTIC TROUBLE CODES

Tech 1 Method

1. Ensure ignition switch is Off, then connect Tech 1 scan tool with suitable brake cartridge.
2. Select ABS/ASR system features.
3. Select F2 Trouble Codes.
4. Select Clear Codes.
5. Remove Tech 1 tool, then test drive vehicle.

CCM Method

1. Turn ignition switch to Off position.
2. Connect suitable jumper wire between ALDL terminals A and G.
3. Turn ignition switch On.
4. Depress DIC trip reset button repeatedly to display 9.0 in trip monitor.
5. Depress DIC trip odo twice to change display to 9.7.
6. Hold eng/met button until "- - -" appears in speedometer area.
7. Remove jumper from ALDL.

Ignition Cycle Default

If the ignition is cycled 50 times without a particular fault reappearing, that particular fault code will be erased and the ignition cycle counter will be reset to zero.

TECH 1 DIAGNOSTICS

When using the Tech 1 scan tool for ABS/ASR system diagnostics, the ABS and ASR systems are disabled and the Service ABS and Service ASR indicator lamps will be illuminated. Normal power assisted braking is still applicable. After completion of all diagnostic procedures, turn the ignition switch Off for at least 10 seconds and disconnect Tech 1 tool, then the system will return to normal operation. The valve solenoid relay is turned Off by the EBTCM when a code is set. When monitoring the data list with the Tech 1, the valve solenoid relay will be noted as Off, this is normal and should not be considered a system problem. Also when monitoring the data list, the throttle angle readings may stop updating. This is normal and should not be considered as system problem.

The Tech 1 has five test modes for diagnosis and testing of the ABS/ASR system as follows:

1. Mode F0 - Data List: Tech 1 monitors wheel speed data and brake switch status.
2. Mode F1 - Code History: In this mode, fault code history is displayed and includes the number of ignition cycles since the codes was set and other system information. Up to three codes are included in the ABS history data.
3. Mode F2 - Trouble Codes: In this test, trouble codes stored by the EBTCM may be displayed or cleared.
4. Mode F3 - Snapshot: In this test, displays data before and after a snapshot triggering condition which may not set a code.
5. Mode F4 - Miscellaneous Tests: In this mode, the Tech 1 performs modulator valve assembly functional tests, lamp output tests, pilot valve tests and ASR tests to assist in problem isolation during diagnostics.
6. Mode F5 - TPS Learn: If the TPS or throttle body has been replaced, the EBTCM must learn the TPS idle position voltage. This is required to ensure effective engine torque reduction during ASR operation.

MODE F3: SNAPSHOT

Conditions that will trigger the Tech 1 snapshot feature are as follows:

1. Loss of serial data.
2. Valve solenoid relay less then 11 volts (low voltage.)
3. Valve solenoid relay Off, less then two volts (relay will be Off if codes are set).
4. One wheel speed sensor ±8 mph of others (intermittent wheel speed).
5. Three wheel speed sensor ±3 mph of each other and one ±5 mph of the others (wheel speed out of range).
6. Low brake fluid.
7. Lateral accelerometer greater then 4.35 or less then 1.05 volts (out of range).
8. System voltage more then 17 volts (high voltage).
9. Sudden engine RPM change greater then 1100 RPM (intermittent engine RPM).
10. Brake switch state change of On-Off-On in less then 200 milliseconds (intermittent brake switch).

MODE F4: ABS TESTS

AUTO Test

The auto test cycles each valve solenoid, pump motor and relays to inspect component operation. This test is the same as the auto test the system performs

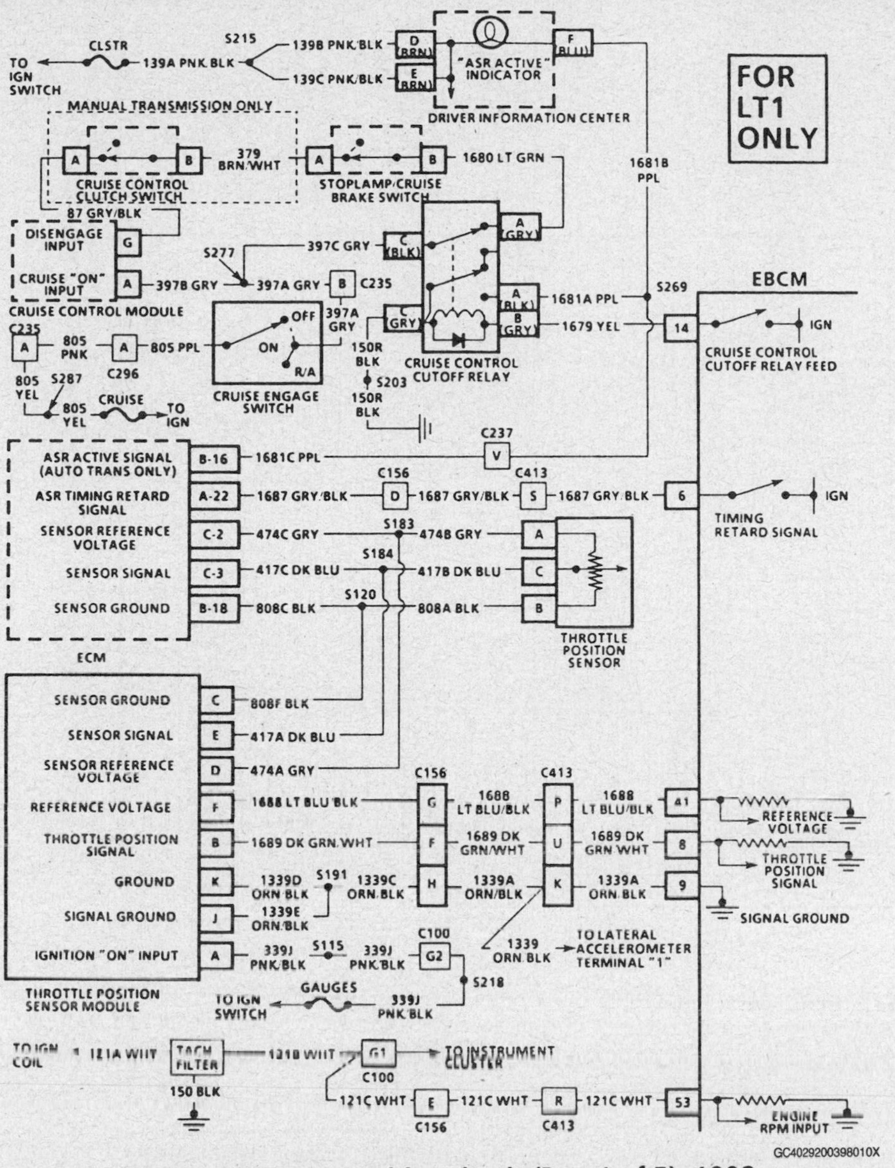
FOR LT1 ONLY
TO IGN SWITCH
CLSTR
139A PNK BLK
S215
139B PNK/BLK
139C PNK/BLK
"ASR ACTIVE" INDICATOR
DRIVER INFORMATION CENTER
MANUAL TRANSMISSION ONLY
CRUISE CONTROL CLUTCH SWITCH
379 BRN/WHT
STOPLAMP/CRUISE BRAKE SWITCH
1680 LT GRN
1681B PPL
87 GRY/BLK
DISENGAGE INPUT
CRUISE "ON" INPUT
CRUISE CONTROL MODULE
S277
397C GRY
397B GRY
397A GRY
C235
1681A PPL
S269
1679 YEL
EBCM
CRUISE CONTROL CUTOFF RELAY FEED
IGN
805 PNK
805 PPL
C296
805 YEL
S287
CRUISE
TO IGN
CRUISE ENGAGE SWITCH
OFF
ON
R/A
150R BLK
S203
CRUISE CONTROL CUTOFF RELAY
C237
ASR ACTIVE SIGNAL (AUTO TRANS ONLY)
1681C PPL
ASR TIMING RETARD SIGNAL
1687 GRY/BLK
C156
C413
TIMING RETARD SIGNAL
SENSOR REFERENCE VOLTAGE
474C GRY
S183
474B GRY
SENSOR SIGNAL
417C DK BLU
S184
417B DK BLU
SENSOR GROUND
808C BLK
S120
808A BLK
THROTTLE POSITION SENSOR
ECM
SENSOR GROUND
808F BLK
SENSOR SIGNAL
417A DK BLU
SENSOR REFERENCE VOLTAGE
474A GRY
REFERENCE VOLTAGE
1688 LT BLU/BLK
THROTTLE POSITION SIGNAL
1689 DK GRN/WHT
GROUND
1339D ORN/BLK
S191
1339C ORN/BLK
1339A ORN/BLK
SIGNAL GROUND
1339E ORN/BLK
C100
1339 ORN/BLK
TO LATERAL ACCELEROMETER TERMINAL "1"
IGNITION "ON" INPUT
339J PNK/BLK
S115
S218
THROTTLE POSITION SENSOR MODULE
TO IGN SWITCH
GAUGES
TO IGN COIL
121A WHT
TACH FILTER
121B WHT
TO INSTRUMENT CLUSTER
150 BLK
121C WHT
ENGINE RPM INPUT
GC4029200398010X

Fig. 3 ABS system wiring circuit (Part 1 of 5). 1992

when vehicle speed reaches 4 mph in forward or reverse. Stored codes will be indicated upon completion of the test.

1. With ignition switch in Off position.
2. Connect Tech 1 scan tool with appropriate brake cartridge.
3. Turn ignition switch to On position.
4. Select F4, Misc Tests.
5. Select F1, Auto Test.
6. Depress enter key to run auto test.
7. Record any stored codes.

Valve Solenoid—Pressure Hold

The pressure hold test activates the hydraulic wheel circuit valve in the pressure hold position. In that position the valve will not allow master cylinder pressure to be delivered to the wheel circuit. In this test, the tech 1 tool operates the valve to the pressure position which will allow wheel movement with brake pedal application.

1. With ignition switch in Off position.
2. Connect Tech 1 scan tool with appropriate brake cartridge.
3. Turn ignition switch to On position.
4. Raise and support vehicle with wheels about six inches from floor.
5. Select valve solenoid test, then depress Tech 1 tool HOLD PRESSURE.
6. Depress brake pedal.
7. Attempt to turn rear wheel, movement should be indicated.

Valve Solenoid—Pressure Reduction

The pressure reduction test activates the hydraulic wheel circuit valve, placing it in the pressure reduce position. In that position, the valve allows caliper pressure to return to the master cylinder. During this test the wheel should be moveable with brake pressure applied.

1. With ignition switch in Off position.
2. Connect Tech 1 scan tool with appropriate brake cartridge.
3. Turn ignition switch to On position.
4. Raise and support vehicle with wheels about six inches from floor.
5. Have an assistant depress brake pedal.
6. Select valve solenoid test, then depress Tech 1 tool RELEASE PRESSURE.
7. Depress brake pedal, turn rear wheel, movement should be indicated.

Lamp Test

The lamp test is used to inspect the Service ABS, Service ASR, ABS Active, ASR Active and ASR Off lamp operation.

1. With ignition switch in Off position.
2. Connect Tech 1 scan tool with appropriate brake cartridge.
3. Turn ignition switch to On position.
4. Select F4, Misc. Tests.
5. Select F2, Lamp Test.
6. Select lamp to be tested.
7. Depress up arrow to turn lamp On and down arrow to turn lamp Off.

Pilot Valve Test

The test indicates whether the pilot valve in the modulator valve assembly moves to the position which blocks pressure to the master cylinder. The pilot valve blocks pressure to the master cylinder before pump motor activation and fluid pressure application to the rear wheel circuits during ASR activation.

1. With ignition switch in Off position.
2. Connect Tech 1 scan tool with appropriate brake cartridge.
3. Turn ignition switch to On position.
4. Raise and support vehicle with wheels about six inches from floor.
5. Select F4, Misc. Tests.
6. Select F3, Pilot Valve Test.
7. Have assistant depress Tech 1 up arrow, then depress and hold brake pedal.
8. Attempt to move rear wheel by hand, no movement should be indicated.

ASR Test

The ASR test runs the pump motor to apply fluid pressure to the rear wheel circuits. The "Pilot Valve Test" as outlined previously must be run prior to the ASR test.

1. With ignition switch in Off position.
2. Connect Tech 1 scan tool with appropriate brake cartridge.
3. Turn ignition switch to On position.
4. Raise and support vehicle with wheels about six inches from floor.
5. Select F4, Misc. Tests.
6. Select F4, ASR Test.
7. Perform pilot valve test to confirm valve operation.
8. Depress up arrow to begin ASR test.
9. Attempt to move rear wheel by hand, no movement should be indicated.

MODE 5: TPS LEARN

When a throttle position sensor or throttle body assembly are replaced the TPS must relearn the TPS idle position voltage.

1. Place ignition switch in Off position.
2. Connect Tech 1 scan tool with appropriate brake system cartridge.
3. Turn ignition switch On.
4. Follow menus to reach ABS/ASR feature.
5. Select F5, TPS LEARN.
6. Depress up arrow to begin learn procedure.
7. Wait for Tech 1 tool to indicate COMPLETE.
8. Disconnect Tech 1 scan tool.

Continued on page 32-75

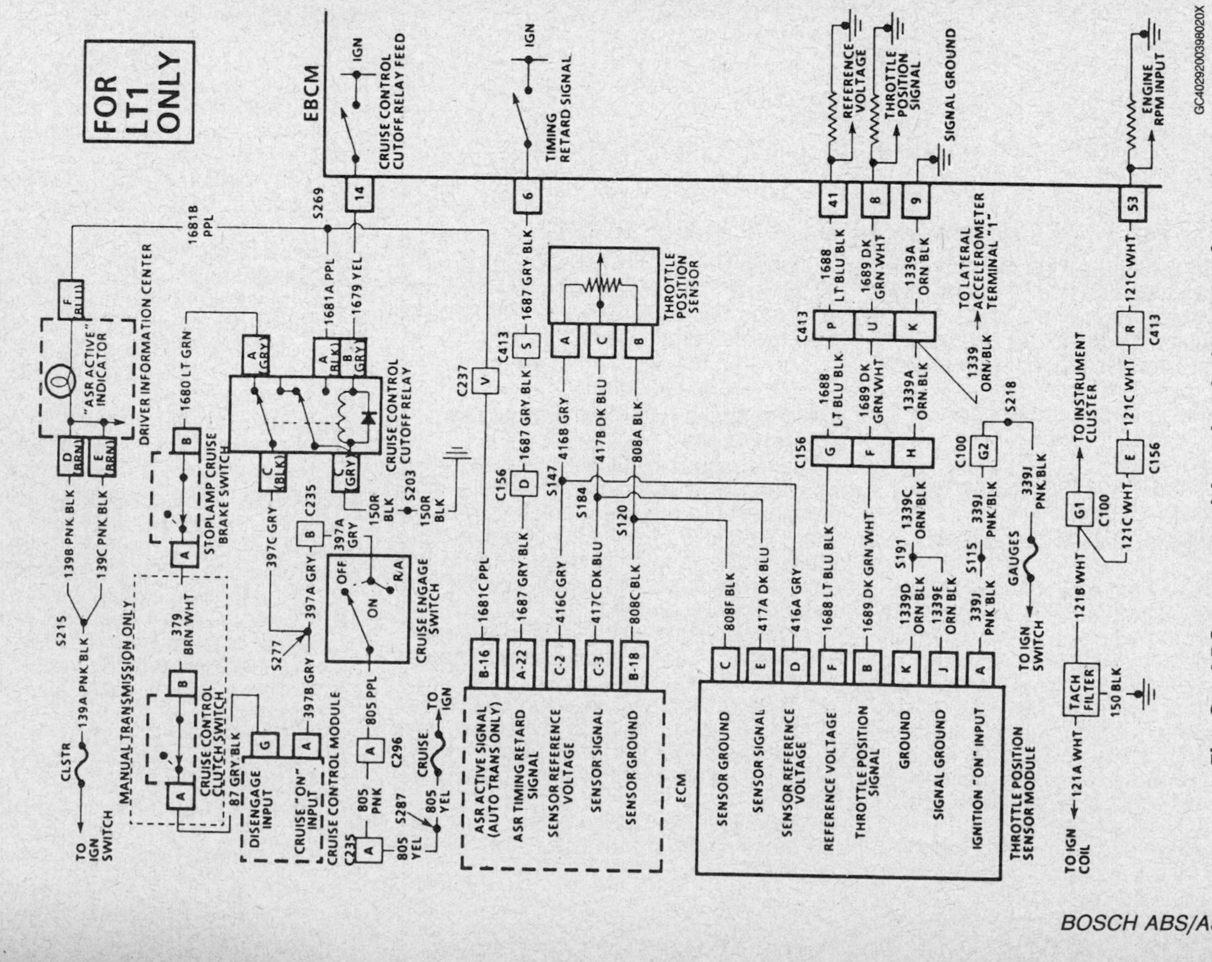
FOR LT1 ONLY
EBCM
TO IGN SWITCH
CLSTR
139A PNK BLK
S215
139B PNK BLK
139C PNK BLK
DRIVER INFORMATION CENTER
"ASR ACTIVE" INDICATOR
1680 LT GRN
1681B PPL
S269
1681A PPL
1679 YEL
CRUISE CONTROL CUTOFF RELAY FEED
IGN
CRUISE CONTROL CUTOFF RELAY
TIMING RETARD SIGNAL
MANUAL TRANSMISSION ONLY
CRUISE CONTROL CLUTCH SWITCH
379 BRN WHT
STOPLAMP CRUISE BRAKE SWITCH
87 GRY BLK
397C GRY
397A GRY
397B GRY
S277
C235
150R BLK
S203
CRUISE ENGAGE SWITCH
OFF
ON
R/A
DISENGAGE INPUT
CRUISE "ON" INPUT
CRUISE CONTROL MODULE
805 PPL
C296
805 PNK
S287
805 YEL
CRUISE
TO IGN
C237
1681C PPL
C413
1687 GRY BLK
C156
S147
416B GRY
416C GRY
S184
417B DK BLU
417C DK BLU
S120
808A BLK
808C BLK
THROTTLE POSITION SENSOR
ASR ACTIVE SIGNAL (AUTO TRANS ONLY)
ASR TIMING RETARD SIGNAL
SENSOR REFERENCE VOLTAGE
SENSOR SIGNAL
SENSOR GROUND
ECM
808F BLK
417A DK BLU
416A GRY
1688 LT BLU BLK
1689 DK GRN WHT
1339D ORN BLK
1339E ORN BLK
S191
1339C ORN BLK
339J PNK BLK
S115
REFERENCE VOLTAGE
THROTTLE POSITION SIGNAL
SIGNAL GROUND
1339A ORN BLK
1339 ORN/BLK
TO LATERAL ACCELEROMETER TERMINAL "1"
GROUND
IGNITION "ON" INPUT
THROTTLE POSITION SENSOR MODULE
GAUGES
TO IGN SWITCH
C100
S218
TO INSTRUMENT CLUSTER
121A WHT
121B WHT
121C WHT
TO IGN COIL
TACH FILTER
150 BLK
ENGINE RPM INPUT
GC402920039802OX

Fig. 3 ABS system wiring circuit (Part 2 of 5). 1992

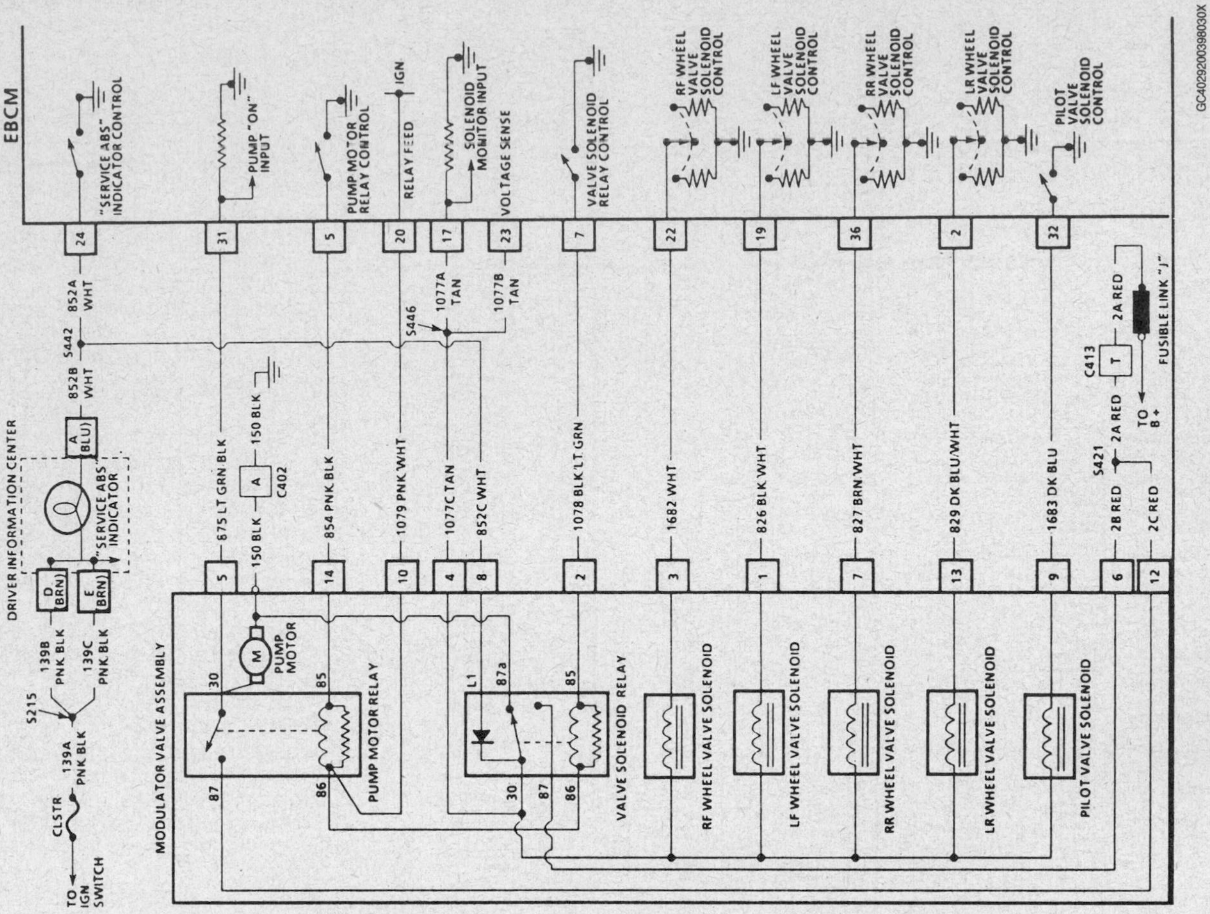
EBCM
TO IGN SWITCH
CLSTR
139A PNK BLK
S215
139B PNK BLK
139C PNK BLK
DRIVER INFORMATION CENTER
"SERVICE ABS" INDICATOR
852B WHT
S442
852A WHT
"SERVICE ABS" INDICATOR CONTROL
MODULATOR VALVE ASSEMBLY
PUMP MOTOR
PUMP MOTOR RELAY
VALVE SOLENOID RELAY
RF WHEEL VALVE SOLENOID
LF WHEEL VALVE SOLENOID
RR WHEEL VALVE SOLENOID
LR WHEEL VALVE SOLENOID
PILOT VALVE SOLENOID
675 LT GRN BLK
150 BLK
C402
854 PNK BLK
1079 PNK WHT
1077C TAN
852C WHT
S446
1077A TAN
1077B TAN
1078 BLK LT GRN
1682 WHT
826 BLK WHT
827 BRN WHT
829 DK BLU/WHT
1683 DK BLU
2B RED
S421
2A RED
C413
TO B+
2C RED
FUSIBLE LINK "J"
PUMP "ON" INPUT
PUMP MOTOR RELAY CONTROL
RELAY FEED
IGN
SOLENOID MONITOR INPUT
VOLTAGE SENSE
VALVE SOLENOID RELAY CONTROL
RF WHEEL VALVE SOLENOID CONTROL
LF WHEEL VALVE SOLENOID CONTROL
RR WHEEL VALVE SOLENOID CONTROL
LR WHEEL VALVE SOLENOID CONTROL
PILOT VALVE SOLENOID CONTROL
GC402920039803OX

Fig. 3 ABS system wiring circuit (Part 3 of 5). 1992

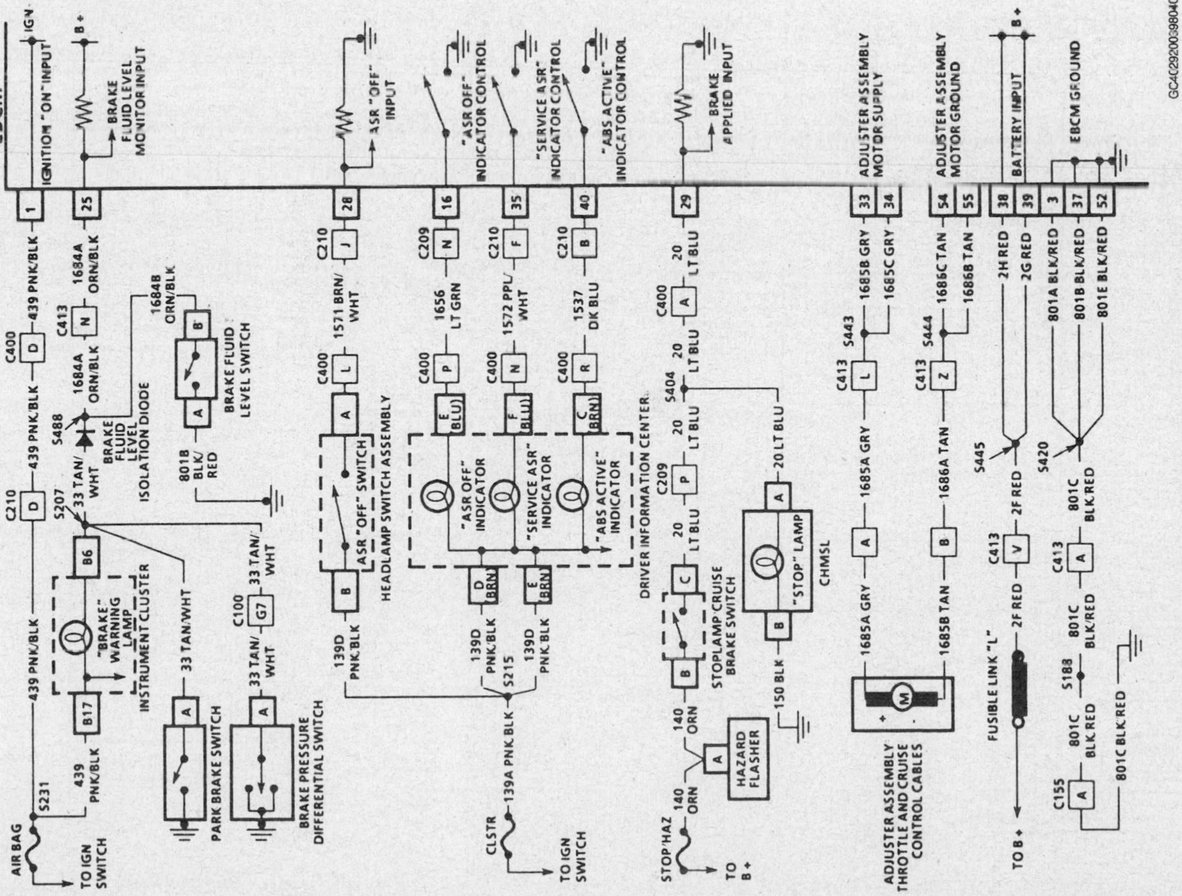
EBCM
IGNITION "ON" INPUT
BRAKE FLUID LEVEL MONITOR INPUT
ASR "OFF" INPUT
"ASR OFF" INDICATOR CONTROL
"SERVICE ASR" INDICATOR CONTROL
"ABS ACTIVE" INDICATOR CONTROL
BRAKE APPLIED INPUT
ADJUSTER ASSEMBLY MOTOR SUPPLY
ADJUSTER ASSEMBLY MOTOR GROUND
BATTERY INPUT
EBCM GROUND
INSTRUMENT CLUSTER
"BRAKE" WARNING LAMP
BRAKE FLUID LEVEL ISOLATION DIODE
BRAKE FLUID LEVEL SWITCH
PARK BRAKE SWITCH
BRAKE PRESSURE DIFFERENTIAL SWITCH
HEADLAMP SWITCH ASSEMBLY
ASR "OFF" SWITCH
DRIVER INFORMATION CENTER
"ASR OFF" INDICATOR
"SERVICE ASR" INDICATOR
"ABS ACTIVE" INDICATOR
STOPLAMP CRUISE BRAKE SWITCH
"STOP" LAMP
CHMSL
HAZARD FLASHER
ADJUSTER ASSEMBLY THROTTLE AND CRUISE CONTROL CABLES
FUSIBLE LINK "L"
AIR BAG
TO IGN SWITCH
CLSTR
STOP/HAZ
TO B+
GC4C29200398040X

Fig. 3 ABS system wiring circuit (Part 4 of 5). 1992

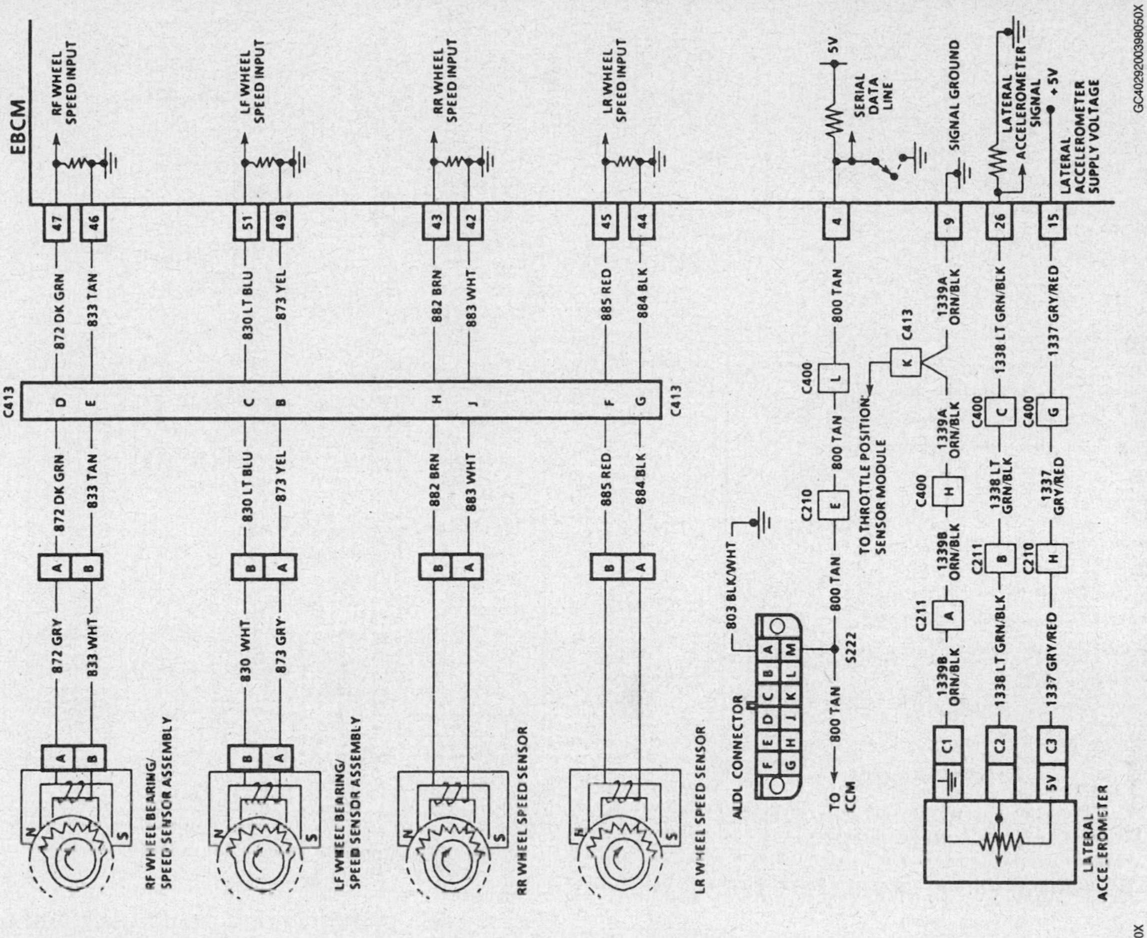
EBCM
RF WHEEL SPEED INPUT
LF WHEEL SPEED INPUT
RR WHEEL SPEED INPUT
LR WHEEL SPEED INPUT
SERIAL DATA LINE
SIGNAL GROUND
LATERAL ACCELEROMETER SIGNAL
LATERAL ACCELEROMETER SUPPLY VOLTAGE
RF WHEEL BEARING/SPEED SENSOR ASSEMBLY
LF WHEEL BEARING/SPEED SENSOR ASSEMBLY
RR WHEEL SPEED SENSOR
LR WHEEL SPEED SENSOR
ALDL CONNECTOR
TO CCM
TO THROTTLE POSITION SENSOR MODULE
LATERAL ACCELEROMETER
GC4C29200398050X

Fig. 3 ABS system wiring circuit (Part 5 of 5). 1992

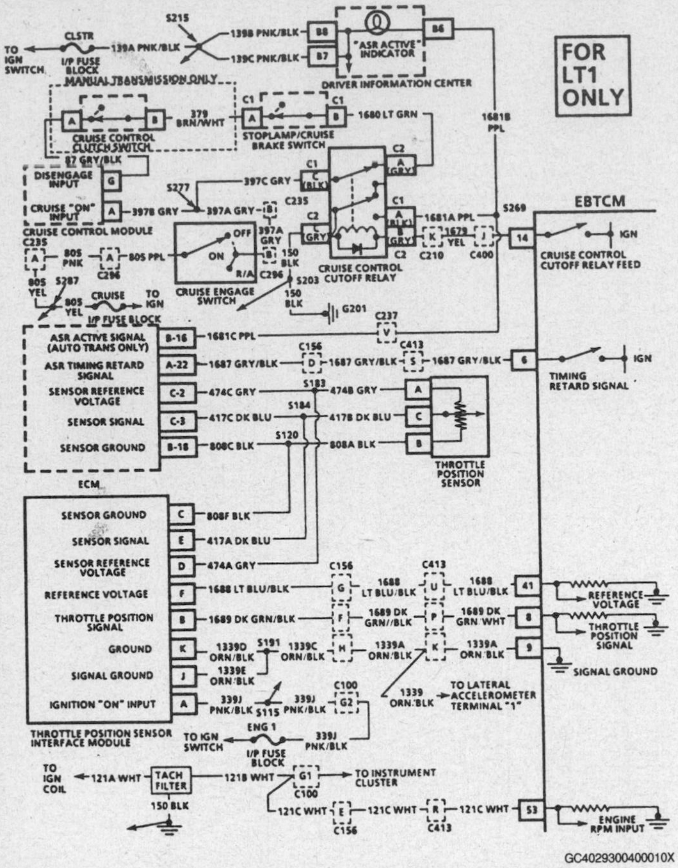
FOR LT1 ONLY
EBTCM
DRIVER INFORMATION CENTER
"ASR ACTIVE" INDICATOR
CRUISE CONTROL CLUTCH SWITCH
STOPLAMP/CRUISE BRAKE SWITCH
CRUISE CONTROL MODULE
CRUISE ENGAGE SWITCH
CRUISE CONTROL CUTOFF RELAY
CRUISE CONTROL CUTOFF RELAY FEED
TIMING RETARD SIGNAL
THROTTLE POSITION SENSOR
ECM
THROTTLE POSITION SENSOR INTERFACE MODULE
REFERENCE VOLTAGE
THROTTLE POSITION SIGNAL
SIGNAL GROUND
TO LATERAL ACCELEROMETER TERMINAL "1"
TO INSTRUMENT CLUSTER
ENGINE RPM INPUT
GC4029300400010X

Fig. 4 ABS system wiring circuit (Part 1 of 6). 1993

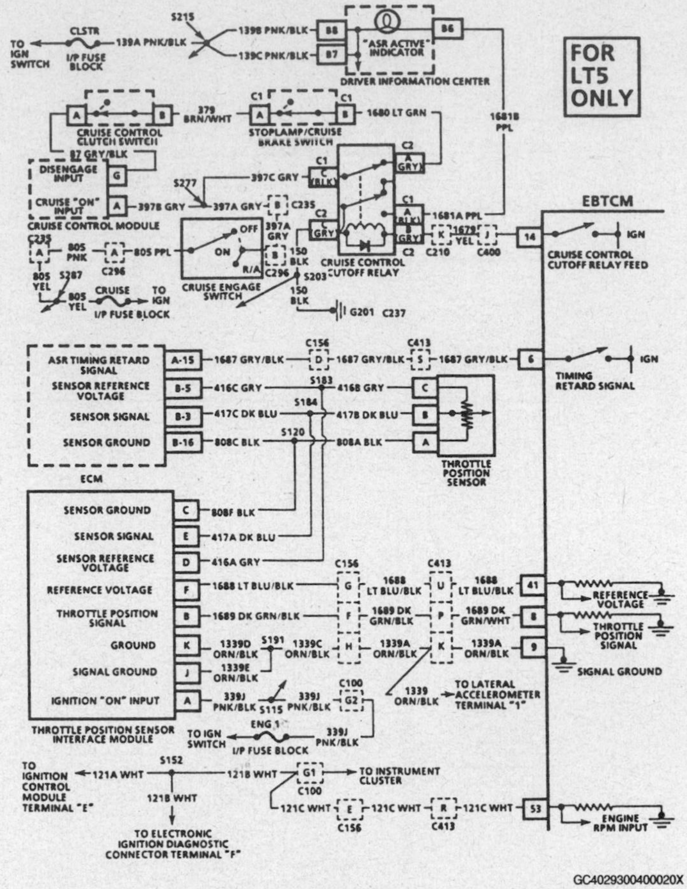
FOR LT5 ONLY
EBTCM
DRIVER INFORMATION CENTER
"ASR ACTIVE" INDICATOR
CRUISE CONTROL CLUTCH SWITCH
STOPLAMP/CRUISE BRAKE SWITCH
CRUISE CONTROL MODULE
CRUISE ENGAGE SWITCH
CRUISE CONTROL CUTOFF RELAY
CRUISE CONTROL CUTOFF RELAY FEED
TIMING RETARD SIGNAL
THROTTLE POSITION SENSOR
ECM
THROTTLE POSITION SENSOR INTERFACE MODULE
REFERENCE VOLTAGE
THROTTLE POSITION SIGNAL
SIGNAL GROUND
TO LATERAL ACCELEROMETER TERMINAL "1"
TO INSTRUMENT CLUSTER
TO ELECTRONIC IGNITION DIAGNOSTIC CONNECTOR TERMINAL "F"
ENGINE RPM INPUT
GC4029300400020X

Fig. 4 ABS system wiring circuit (Part 2 of 6). 1993

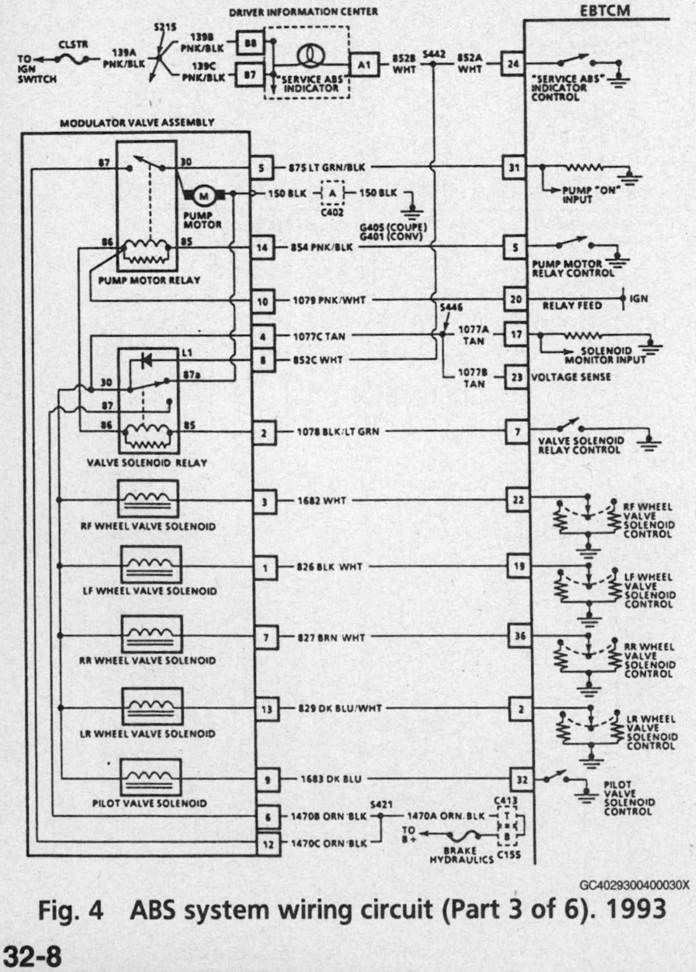
DRIVER INFORMATION CENTER
EBTCM
"SERVICE ABS" INDICATOR
"SERVICE ABS" INDICATOR CONTROL
MODULATOR VALVE ASSEMBLY
PUMP MOTOR
PUMP MOTOR RELAY
PUMP "ON" INPUT
PUMP MOTOR RELAY CONTROL
RELAY FEED
SOLENOID MONITOR INPUT
VOLTAGE SENSE
VALVE SOLENOID RELAY
VALVE SOLENOID RELAY CONTROL
RF WHEEL VALVE SOLENOID
LF WHEEL VALVE SOLENOID
RR WHEEL VALVE SOLENOID
LR WHEEL VALVE SOLENOID
PILOT VALVE SOLENOID
PILOT VALVE SOLENOID CONTROL
BRAKE HYDRAULICS
GC4029300400030X

Fig. 4 ABS system wiring circuit (Part 3 of 6). 1993

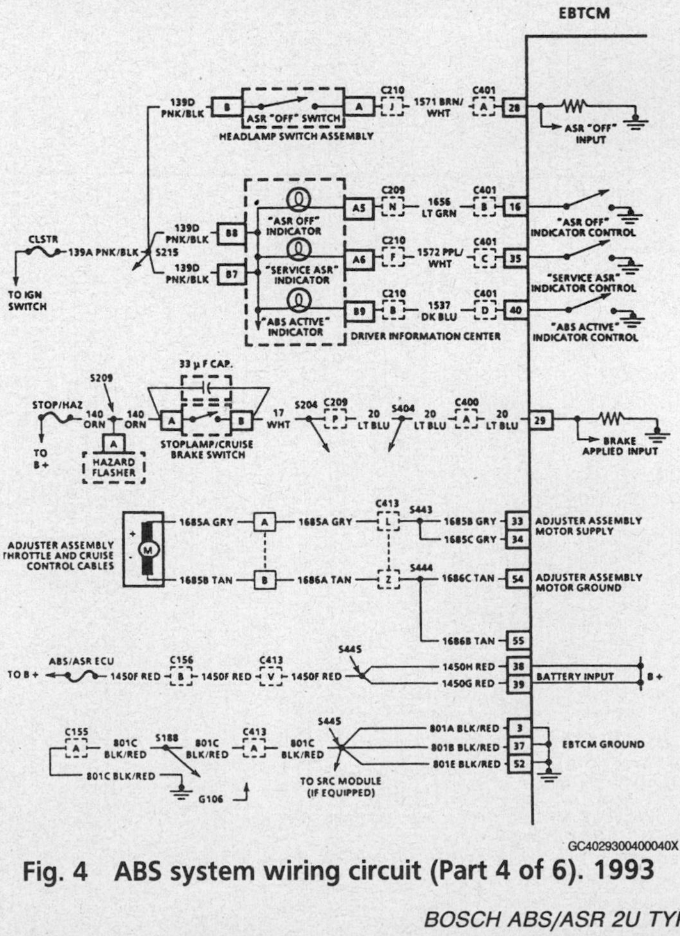
EBTCM
ASR "OFF" SWITCH
HEADLAMP SWITCH ASSEMBLY
ASR "OFF" INPUT
"ASR OFF" INDICATOR
"SERVICE ASR" INDICATOR
"ABS ACTIVE" INDICATOR
DRIVER INFORMATION CENTER
"ASR OFF" INDICATOR CONTROL
"SERVICE ASR" INDICATOR CONTROL
"ABS ACTIVE" INDICATOR CONTROL
33 μF CAP.
HAZARD FLASHER
STOPLAMP/CRUISE BRAKE SWITCH
BRAKE APPLIED INPUT
ADJUSTER ASSEMBLY THROTTLE AND CRUISE CONTROL CABLES
ADJUSTER ASSEMBLY MOTOR SUPPLY
ADJUSTER ASSEMBLY MOTOR GROUND
BATTERY INPUT
EBTCM GROUND
TO SRC MODULE (IF EQUIPPED)
GC4029300400040X

Fig. 4 ABS system wiring circuit (Part 4 of 6). 1993

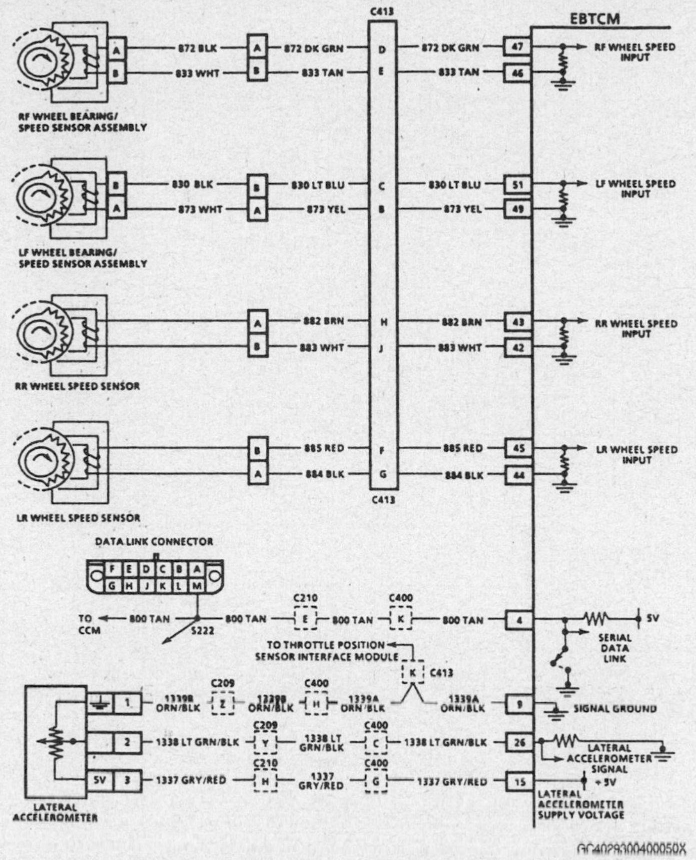

EBTCM
C413
RF WHEEL BEARING/ SPEED SENSOR ASSEMBLY
RF WHEEL SPEED INPUT
LF WHEEL BEARING/ SPEED SENSOR ASSEMBLY
LF WHEEL SPEED INPUT
RR WHEEL SPEED SENSOR
RR WHEEL SPEED INPUT
LR WHEEL SPEED SENSOR
LR WHEEL SPEED INPUT
DATA LINK CONNECTOR
TO CCM
SERIAL DATA LINK
TO THROTTLE POSITION SENSOR INTERFACE MODULE
SIGNAL GROUND
LATERAL ACCELEROMETER SIGNAL
LATERAL ACCELEROMETER SUPPLY VOLTAGE
LATERAL ACCELEROMETER
GC4029300400050X

Fig. 4 ABS system wiring circuit (Part 5 of 6). 1993

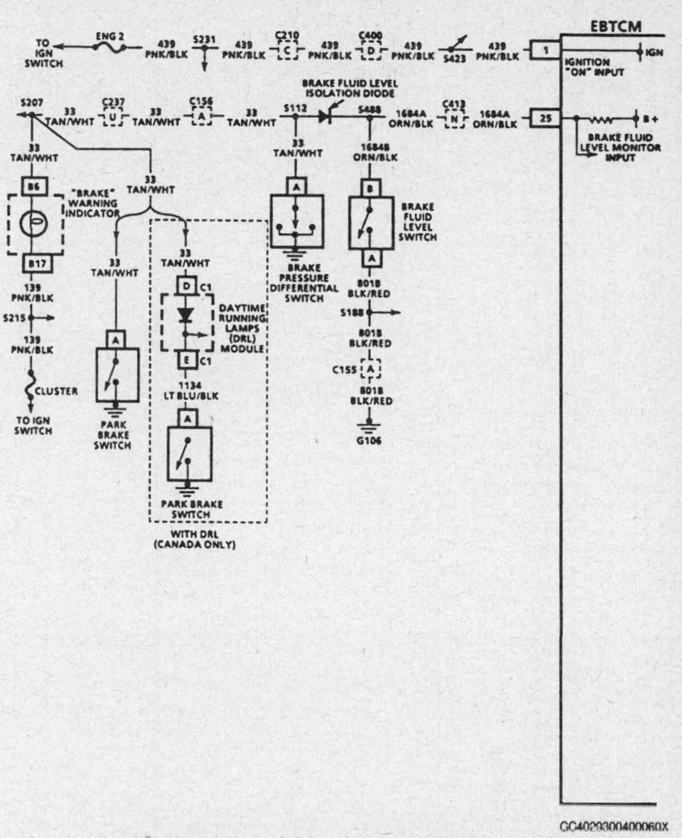

EBTCM
TO IGN SWITCH
IGNITION "ON" INPUT
BRAKE FLUID LEVEL ISOLATION DIODE
BRAKE FLUID LEVEL MONITOR INPUT
"BRAKE" WARNING INDICATOR
CLUSTER
TO IGN SWITCH
PARK BRAKE SWITCH
DAYTIME RUNNING LAMPS (DRL) MODULE
BRAKE PRESSURE DIFFERENTIAL SWITCH
BRAKE FLUID LEVEL SWITCH
WITH DRL (CANADA ONLY)
G106
GC4029300400060X

Fig. 4 ABS system wiring circuit (Part 6 of 6). 1993

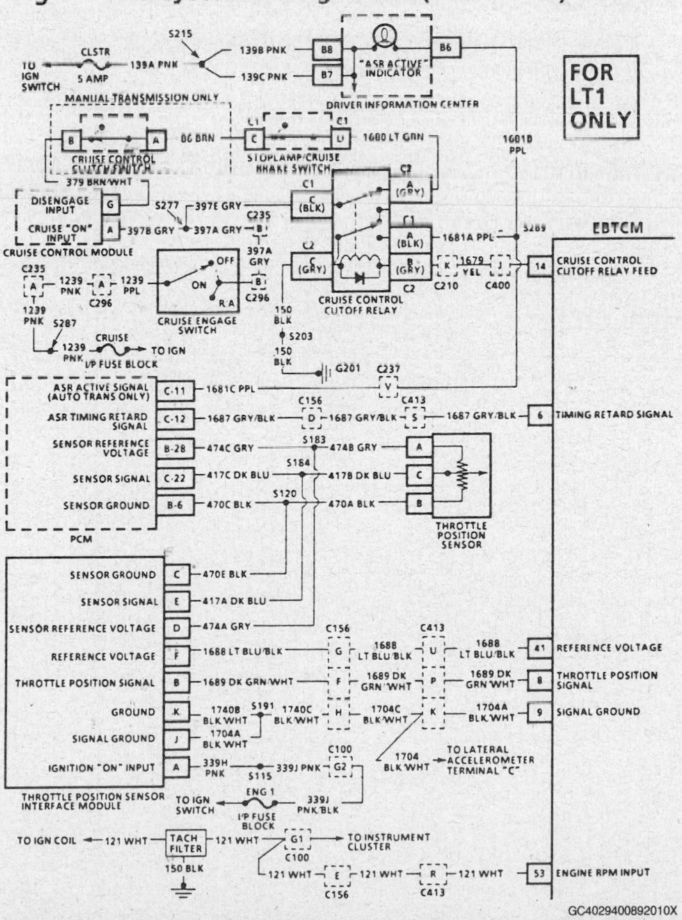

FOR LT1 ONLY
"ASR ACTIVE" INDICATOR
DRIVER INFORMATION CENTER
MANUAL TRANSMISSION ONLY
CRUISE CONTROL CLUTCH SWITCH
STOPLAMP/CRUISE BRAKE SWITCH
CRUISE CONTROL MODULE
CRUISE ENGAGE SWITCH
CRUISE CONTROL CUTOFF RELAY
EBTCM
CRUISE CONTROL CUTOFF RELAY FEED
TIMING RETARD SIGNAL
PCM
THROTTLE POSITION SENSOR
REFERENCE VOLTAGE
THROTTLE POSITION SIGNAL
SIGNAL GROUND
THROTTLE POSITION SENSOR INTERFACE MODULE
TO LATERAL ACCELEROMETER TERMINAL "C"
TO IGN COIL
TO INSTRUMENT CLUSTER
ENGINE RPM INPUT
GC4029400892010X

Fig. 5 ABS system wiring circuit (Part 1 of 6). 1994

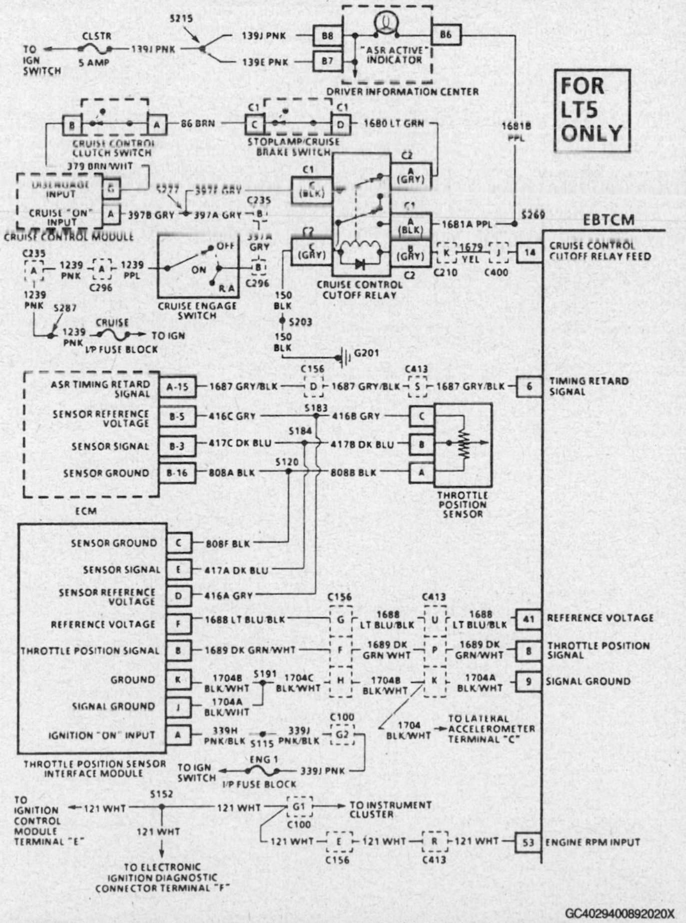

FOR LT5 ONLY
"ASR ACTIVE" INDICATOR
DRIVER INFORMATION CENTER
CRUISE CONTROL CLUTCH SWITCH
STOPLAMP/CRUISE BRAKE SWITCH
CRUISE CONTROL MODULE
CRUISE ENGAGE SWITCH
CRUISE CONTROL CUTOFF RELAY
EBTCM
CRUISE CONTROL CUTOFF RELAY FEED
TIMING RETARD SIGNAL
ECM
THROTTLE POSITION SENSOR
REFERENCE VOLTAGE
THROTTLE POSITION SIGNAL
SIGNAL GROUND
THROTTLE POSITION SENSOR INTERFACE MODULE
TO LATERAL ACCELEROMETER TERMINAL "C"
TO INSTRUMENT CLUSTER
TO ELECTRONIC IGNITION DIAGNOSTIC CONNECTOR TERMINAL "F"
ENGINE RPM INPUT
GC4029400892020X

Fig. 5 ABS system wiring circuit (Part 2 of 6). 1994

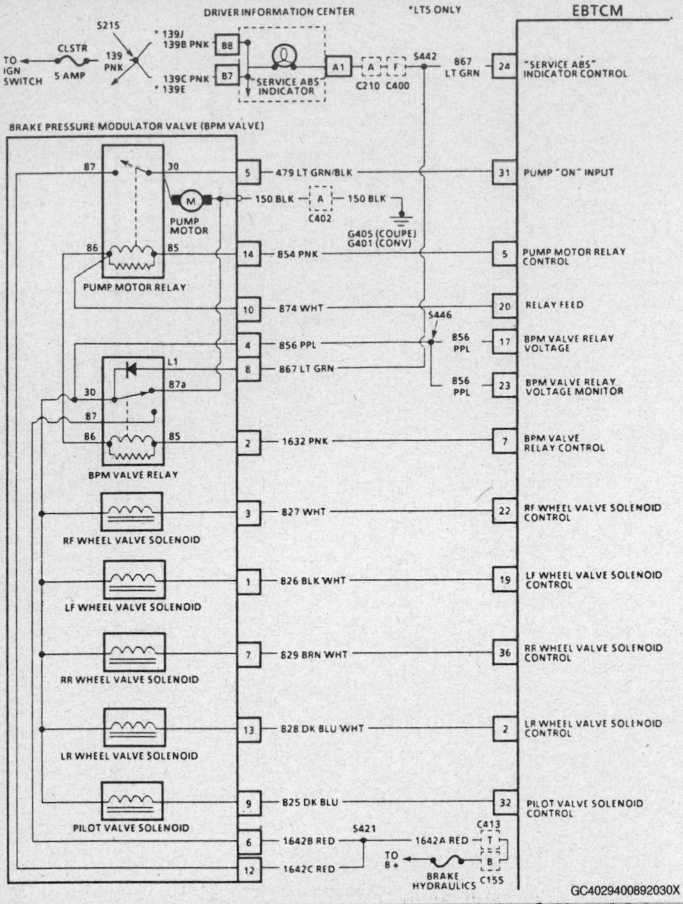
EBTCM
DRIVER INFORMATION CENTER
*LT5 ONLY
"SERVICE ABS" INDICATOR
"SERVICE ABS" INDICATOR CONTROL
BRAKE PRESSURE MODULATOR VALVE (BPM VALVE)
PUMP MOTOR
PUMP MOTOR RELAY
BPM VALVE RELAY
PUMP "ON" INPUT
PUMP MOTOR RELAY CONTROL
RELAY FEED
BPM VALVE RELAY VOLTAGE
BPM VALVE RELAY VOLTAGE MONITOR
BPM VALVE RELAY CONTROL
RF WHEEL VALVE SOLENOID
LF WHEEL VALVE SOLENOID
RR WHEEL VALVE SOLENOID
LR WHEEL VALVE SOLENOID
PILOT VALVE SOLENOID
RF WHEEL VALVE SOLENOID CONTROL
LF WHEEL VALVE SOLENOID CONTROL
RR WHEEL VALVE SOLENOID CONTROL
LR WHEEL VALVE SOLENOID CONTROL
PILOT VALVE SOLENOID CONTROL
G405 (COUPE)
G401 (CONV)
BRAKE HYDRAULICS
GC4029400892030X

Fig. 5 ABS system wiring circuit (Part 3 of 6). 1994

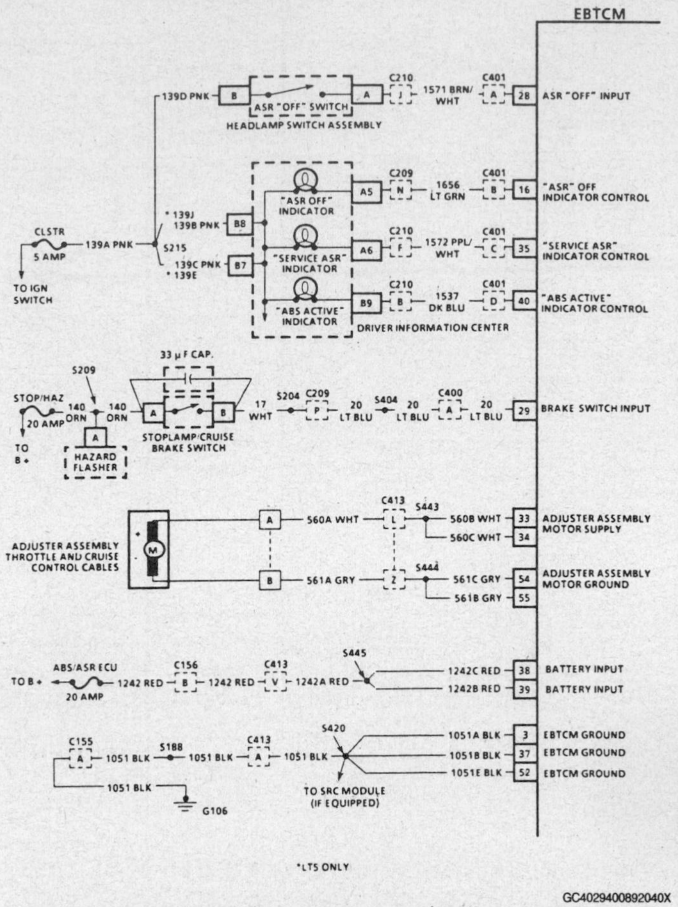
EBTCM
ASR "OFF" SWITCH
HEADLAMP SWITCH ASSEMBLY
ASR "OFF" INPUT
"ASR OFF" INDICATOR
"SERVICE ASR" INDICATOR
"ABS ACTIVE" INDICATOR
DRIVER INFORMATION CENTER
"ASR" OFF INDICATOR CONTROL
"SERVICE ASR" INDICATOR CONTROL
"ABS ACTIVE" INDICATOR CONTROL
33 μF CAP.
HAZARD FLASHER
STOPLAMP/CRUISE BRAKE SWITCH
BRAKE SWITCH INPUT
ADJUSTER ASSEMBLY THROTTLE AND CRUISE CONTROL CABLES
ADJUSTER ASSEMBLY MOTOR SUPPLY
ADJUSTER ASSEMBLY MOTOR GROUND
ABS/ASR ECU
BATTERY INPUT
EBTCM GROUND
TO SRC MODULE (IF EQUIPPED)
G106
*LT5 ONLY
GC4029400892040X

Fig. 5 ABS system wiring circuit (Part 4 of 6). 1994

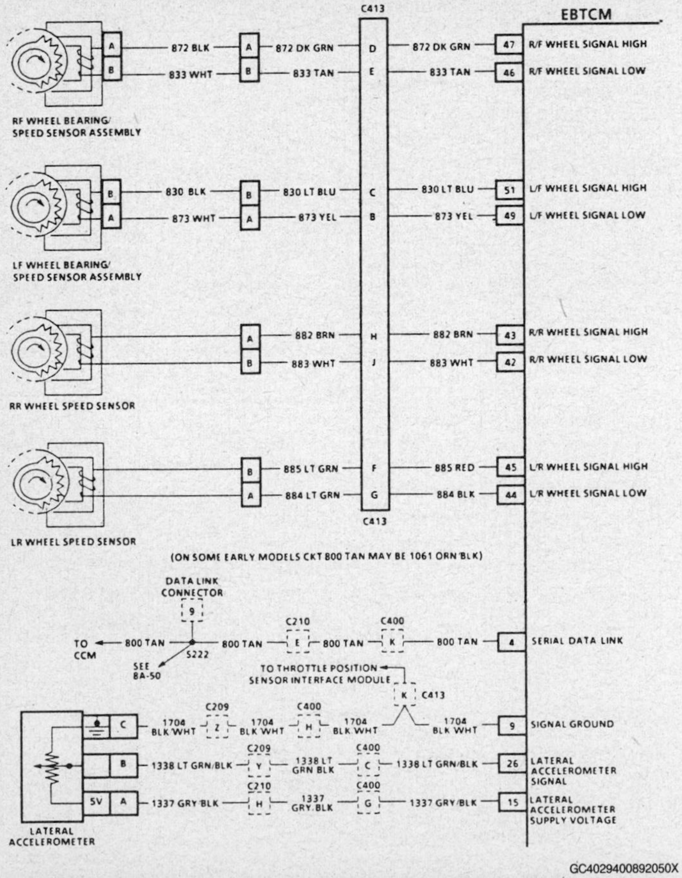
EBTCM
C413
RF WHEEL BEARING/ SPEED SENSOR ASSEMBLY
R/F WHEEL SIGNAL HIGH
R/F WHEEL SIGNAL LOW
LF WHEEL BEARING/ SPEED SENSOR ASSEMBLY
L/F WHEEL SIGNAL HIGH
L/F WHEEL SIGNAL LOW
RR WHEEL SPEED SENSOR
R/R WHEEL SIGNAL HIGH
R/R WHEEL SIGNAL LOW
LR WHEEL SPEED SENSOR
L/R WHEEL SIGNAL HIGH
L/R WHEEL SIGNAL LOW
(ON SOME EARLY MODELS CKT 800 TAN MAY BE 1061 ORN/BLK)
DATA LINK CONNECTOR
SERIAL DATA LINK
TO THROTTLE POSITION SENSOR INTERFACE MODULE
SIGNAL GROUND
LATERAL ACCELEROMETER SIGNAL
LATERAL ACCELEROMETER SUPPLY VOLTAGE
LATERAL ACCELEROMETER
GC4029400892050X

Fig. 5 ABS system wiring circuit (Part 5 of 6). 1994

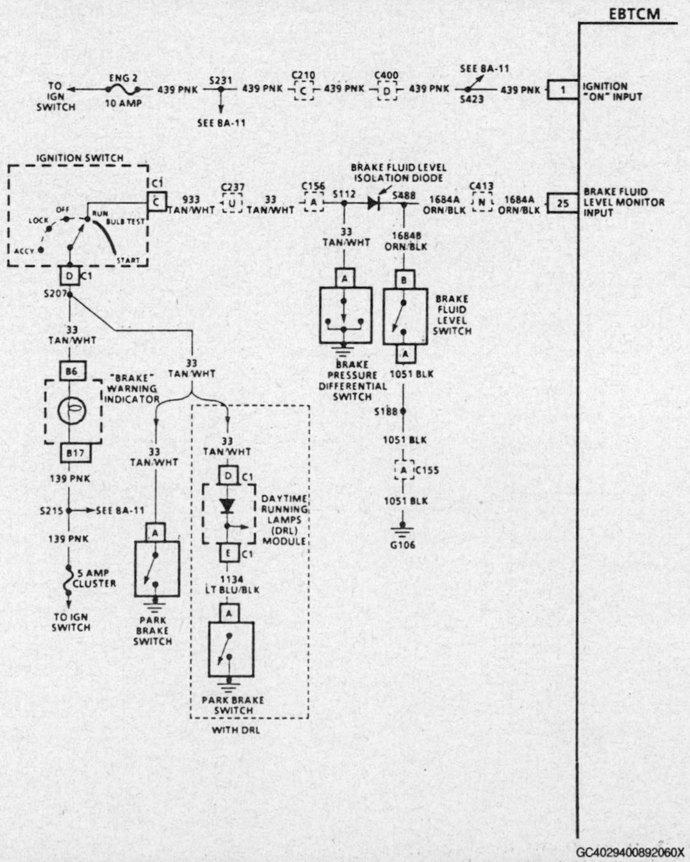
EBTCM
TO IGN SWITCH
ENG 2 10 AMP
SEE 8A-11
IGNITION "ON" INPUT
IGNITION SWITCH
BRAKE FLUID LEVEL ISOLATION DIODE
BRAKE FLUID LEVEL MONITOR INPUT
"BRAKE" WARNING INDICATOR
BRAKE PRESSURE DIFFERENTIAL SWITCH
BRAKE FLUID LEVEL SWITCH
DAYTIME RUNNING LAMPS (DRL) MODULE
PARK BRAKE SWITCH
WITH DRL
5 AMP CLUSTER
G106
GC4029400892060X

Fig. 5 ABS system wiring circuit (Part 6 of 6). 1994

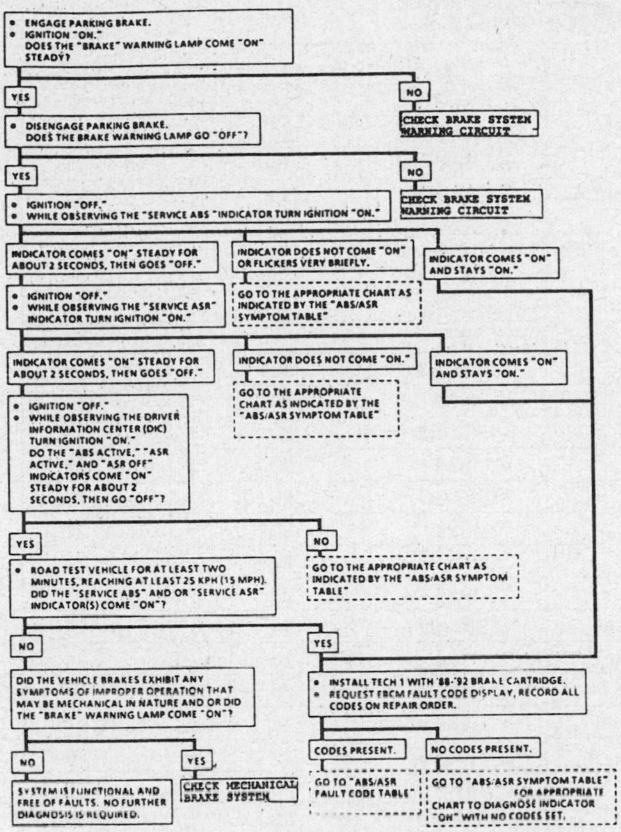

• ENGAGE PARKING BRAKE.
• IGNITION "ON."
DOES THE "BRAKE" WARNING LAMP COME "ON" STEADY?
YES
NO
CHECK BRAKE SYSTEM WARNING CIRCUIT
• DISENGAGE PARKING BRAKE.
DOES THE BRAKE WARNING LAMP GO "OFF"?
YES
NO
CHECK BRAKE SYSTEM WARNING CIRCUIT
• IGNITION "OFF."
• WHILE OBSERVING THE "SERVICE ABS "INDICATOR TURN IGNITION "ON."
INDICATOR COMES "ON" STEADY FOR ABOUT 2 SECONDS, THEN GOES "OFF."
INDICATOR DOES NOT COME "ON" OR FLICKERS VERY BRIEFLY.
INDICATOR COMES "ON" AND STAYS "ON."
• IGNITION "OFF."
• WHILE OBSERVING THE "SERVICE ASR" INDICATOR TURN IGNITION "ON."
GO TO THE APPROPRIATE CHART AS INDICATED BY THE "ABS/ASR SYMPTOM TABLE"
INDICATOR COMES "ON" STEADY FOR ABOUT 2 SECONDS, THEN GOES "OFF."
INDICATOR DOES NOT COME "ON."
INDICATOR COMES "ON" AND STAYS "ON."
GO TO THE APPROPRIATE CHART AS INDICATED BY THE "ABS/ASR SYMPTOM TABLE"
• IGNITION "OFF."
• WHILE OBSERVING THE DRIVER INFORMATION CENTER (DIC) TURN IGNITION "ON."
DO THE "ABS ACTIVE," "ASR ACTIVE," AND "ASR OFF" INDICATORS COME "ON" STEADY FOR ABOUT 2 SECONDS, THEN GO "OFF"?
YES
NO
• ROAD TEST VEHICLE FOR AT LEAST TWO MINUTES, REACHING AT LEAST 25 KPH (15 MPH). DID THE "SERVICE ABS" AND OR "SERVICE ASR" INDICATOR(S) COME "ON"?
GO TO THE APPROPRIATE CHART AS INDICATED BY THE "ABS/ASR SYMPTOM TABLE"
NO
YES
DID THE VEHICLE BRAKES EXHIBIT ANY SYMPTOMS OF IMPROPER OPERATION THAT MAY BE MECHANICAL IN NATURE AND OR DID THE "BRAKE" WARNING LAMP COME "ON"?
• INSTALL TECH 1 WITH '88-'92 BRAKE CARTRIDGE.
• REQUEST EBCM FAULT CODE DISPLAY, RECORD ALL CODES ON REPAIR ORDER.
NO
YES
CODES PRESENT.
NO CODES PRESENT.
SYSTEM IS FUNCTIONAL AND FREE OF FAULTS. NO FURTHER DIAGNOSIS IS REQUIRED.
CHECK MECHANICAL BRAKE SYSTEM
GO TO "ABS/ASR FAULT CODE TABLE"
GO TO "ABS/ASR SYMPTOM TABLE" FOR APPROPRIATE CHART TO DIAGNOSE INDICATOR "ON" WITH NO CODES SET.

GC4029200399000X

Fig. 6 ABS/ASR functional test. 1992

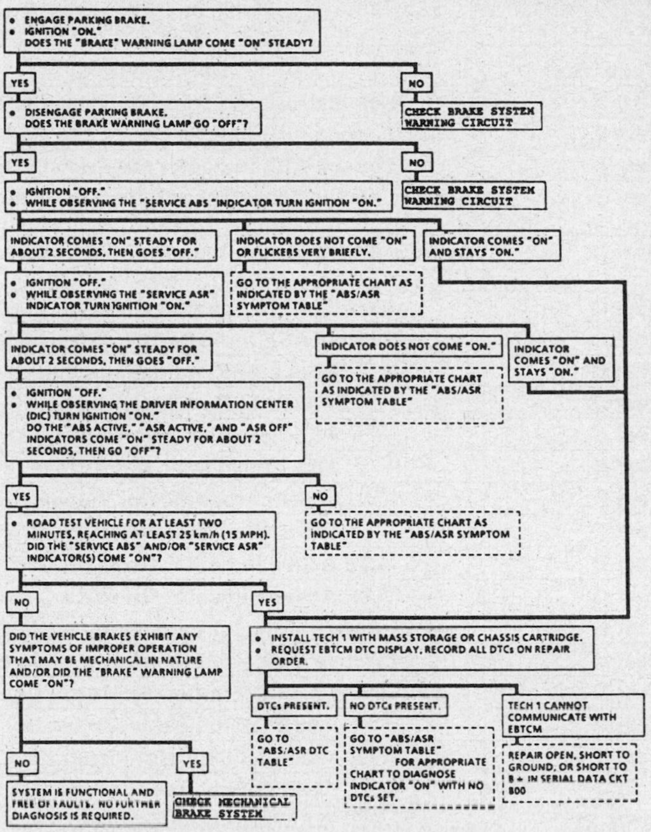

• ENGAGE PARKING BRAKE.
• IGNITION "ON."
DOES THE "BRAKE" WARNING LAMP COME "ON" STEADY?
YES
NO
CHECK BRAKE SYSTEM WARNING CIRCUIT
• DISENGAGE PARKING BRAKE.
DOES THE BRAKE WARNING LAMP GO "OFF"?
YES
NO
CHECK BRAKE SYSTEM WARNING CIRCUIT
• IGNITION "OFF."
• WHILE OBSERVING THE "SERVICE ABS "INDICATOR TURN IGNITION "ON."
INDICATOR COMES "ON" STEADY FOR ABOUT 2 SECONDS, THEN GOES "OFF."
INDICATOR DOES NOT COME "ON" OR FLICKERS VERY BRIEFLY.
INDICATOR COMES "ON" AND STAYS "ON."
• IGNITION "OFF."
• WHILE OBSERVING THE "SERVICE ASR" INDICATOR TURN IGNITION "ON."
GO TO THE APPROPRIATE CHART AS INDICATED BY THE "ABS/ASR SYMPTOM TABLE"
INDICATOR COMES "ON" STEADY FOR ABOUT 2 SECONDS, THEN GOES "OFF."
INDICATOR DOES NOT COME "ON."
INDICATOR COMES "ON" AND STAYS "ON."
GO TO THE APPROPRIATE CHART AS INDICATED BY THE "ABS/ASR SYMPTOM TABLE"
• IGNITION "OFF."
• WHILE OBSERVING THE DRIVER INFORMATION CENTER (DIC) TURN IGNITION "ON."
DO THE "ABS ACTIVE," "ASR ACTIVE," AND "ASR OFF" INDICATORS COME "ON" STEADY FOR ABOUT 2 SECONDS, THEN GO "OFF"?
YES
NO
• ROAD TEST VEHICLE FOR AT LEAST TWO MINUTES, REACHING AT LEAST 25 km/h (15 MPH). DID THE "SERVICE ABS" AND/OR "SERVICE ASR" INDICATOR(S) COME "ON"?
GO TO THE APPROPRIATE CHART AS INDICATED BY THE "ABS/ASR SYMPTOM TABLE"
NO
YES
DID THE VEHICLE BRAKES EXHIBIT ANY SYMPTOMS OF IMPROPER OPERATION THAT MAY BE MECHANICAL IN NATURE AND/OR DID THE "BRAKE" WARNING LAMP COME "ON"?
• INSTALL TECH 1 WITH MASS STORAGE OR CHASSIS CARTRIDGE.
• REQUEST EBTCM DTC DISPLAY, RECORD ALL DTCs ON REPAIR ORDER.
DTCs PRESENT.
NO DTCs PRESENT.
TECH 1 CANNOT COMMUNICATE WITH EBTCM
GO TO "ABS/ASR DTC TABLE"
GO TO "ABS/ASR SYMPTOM TABLE" FOR APPROPRIATE CHART TO DIAGNOSE INDICATOR "ON" WITH NO DTCs SET.
REPAIR OPEN, SHORT TO GROUND, OR SHORT TO B+ IN SERIAL DATA CKT 800
NO
YES
SYSTEM IS FUNCTIONAL AND FREE OF FAULTS. NO FURTHER DIAGNOSIS IS REQUIRED.
CHECK MECHANICAL BRAKE SYSTEM

GC4029300401000X

Fig. 7 ABS/ASR functional test. 1993–94

Code	Definition
21	RF Wheel Speed Sensor Fault
23	RF Wheel Speed Sensor Continuity Fault
25	LF Wheel Speed Sensor Fault
27	LF Wheel Speed Sensor Continuity Fault
28	Wheel Speed Sensor Frequency Error
31	RR Wheel Speed Sensor Fault
33	RR Wheel Speed Sensor Continuity Fault
35	LR Wheel Speed Sensor Fault
37	LR Wheel Speed Sensor Continuity Fault
41	RF Solenoid Valve Fault
44	Pilot Valve Solenoid Fault
45	LF Solenoid Valve Fault
51	RR Solenoid Valve Fault
55	LR Solenoid Valve Fault

Code	Definition
57	Cruise Control Output Monitoring Fault
58	EBTCM Internal Adjuster Assembly Fault
61	Pump Motor Or Motor Relay Fault
62	Tach Pulses Fault
63	Valve Solenoid Relay Fault
64	Throttle Position Signal Fault
65	Adjuster Assembly Fault
66	Adjuster Assembly Control Fault
71	EBTCM Fault
72	Serial Data Link Fault
73	Spark Retard Monitoring Fault
74	Low Voltage
75	Lateral Accelerometer Wiring Fault
76	Lateral Accelerometer Signal Out Of Range
83	Brake Fluid Level Low

Fig. 8 Trouble code identification.

DIAGNOSTIC CHART INDEX

Code/Test	Description	Year	Page No. 32-	Fig. No.
Test A	Service ABS Indicator On w/No Codes Set	1992	14	9
Test A	Service ABS Indicator On w/No Codes Set	1993	14	10
Test A	Service ABS Indicator On w/No Codes Set	1994	15	11
Test B	Service ABS Indicator Inoperative Or Flickers w/Ignition On	1992–93	16	12
Test B	Service ABS Indicator Inoperative Or Flickers w/Ignition On	1994	17	13
Test C	Service ASR Indicator On w/No Codes Set	1992–93	17	14
Test C	Service ASR Indicator On w/No Codes Set	1994	18	15
Test D	Service ASR Indicator Inoperative	1992–93	18	16
Test D	Service ASR Indicator Inoperative	1994	19	17
Test E	ABS Active Indicator Always On	1992–93	20	18
Test E	ABS Active Indicator Always On	1994	20	19
Test F	ABS Active Indicator Inoperative	1992–93	21	20
Test F	ABS Active Indicator Inoperative	1994	22	21
Test G	ASR Active Indicator On w/No Codes Set	1992–93	22	22
Test G	ASR Active Indicator On w/No Codes Set	1994	23	23
Test H	ASR Active Indicator Inoperative w/No Codes Set	1992–93	24	24
Test H	ASR Active Indicator Inoperative w/No Codes Set	1994	25	25
Test I	ASR Off Indicator Always On	1992–93	25	26
Test I	ASR Off Indicator Always On	1994	26	27
Test J	ASR Off Indicator Inoperative	1992–93	27	28
Test J	ASR Off Indicator Inoperative	1994	28	29
Code 21	RF Wheel Speed Sensor Fault	1992–93	28	30
Code 21	RF Wheel Speed Sensor Fault	1994	29	31
Code 23	RF Wheel Speed Sensor Continuity Fault	1992–93	29	32
Code 23	RF Wheel Speed Sensor Continuity Fault	1994	30	33
Code 25	LF Wheel Speed Sensor Fault	1992–93	30	34
Code 25	LF Wheel Speed Sensor Fault	1994	31	35
Code 27	LF Wheel Speed Sensor Continuity Fault	1992–93	31	36
Code 27	LF Wheel Speed Sensor Continuity Fault	1994	32	37
Code 28	Wheel Speed Sensor Frequency Error	1992–93	32	38
Code 28	Wheel Speed Sensor Frequency Error	1994	33	39
Code 31	RR Wheel Speed Sensor Fault	1992–93	33	40
Code 31	RR Wheel Speed Sensor Fault	1994	34	41
Code 33	RR Wheel Speed Sensor Continuity Fault	1992–93	34	42
Code 33	RR Wheel Speed Sensor Continuity Fault	1994	35	43
Code 35	LR Wheel Speed Sensor Fault	1992–93	35	44
Code 35	LR Wheel Speed Sensor Fault	1994	36	45
Code 37	LR Wheel Speed Sensor Continuity Fault	1992–93	36	46
Code 37	LR Wheel Speed Sensor Continuity Fault	1994	37	47
Code 41	RF Solenoid Valve Fault	1992–93	37	48
Code 41	RF Solenoid Valve Fault	1994	38	49
Code 44	Pilot Valve Solenoid Fault	1992–93	39	50
Code 44	Pilot Valve Solenoid Fault	1994	40	51
Code 45	LF Solenoid Valve Fault	1992–93	40	52
Code 45	LF Solenoid Valve Fault	1994	41	53
Code 51	RR Solenoid Valve Fault	1992–93	41	54
Code 51	RR Solenoid Valve Fault	1994	42	55
Code 55	LR Solenoid Valve Fault	1992–93	42	56
Code 55	LR Solenoid Valve Fault	1994	43	57
Code 57	Cruise Control Output Monitoring Fault	1992–93	43	58
Code 57	Cruise Control Output Monitoring Fault	1994	44	59
Code 58	EBTCM Internal Adjuster Assembly Fault	1992–93	45	60
Code 58	EBTCM Internal Adjuster Assembly Fault	1994	45	61

Continued

DIAGNOSTIC CHART INDEX—Continued

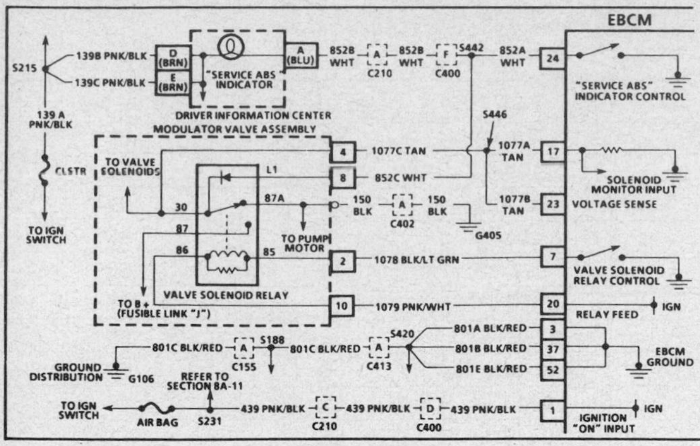
EBCM
S215
139B PNK/BLK
139C PNK/BLK
"SERVICE ABS" INDICATOR
DRIVER INFORMATION CENTER
139 A PNK/BLK
852B WHT
C210
C400
S442
852A WHT
"SERVICE ABS" INDICATOR CONTROL
MODULATOR VALVE ASSEMBLY
S446
TO VALVE SOLENOIDS
CLSTR
1077C TAN
1077A TAN
852C WHT
SOLENOID MONITOR INPUT
1077B TAN
VOLTAGE SENSE
150 BLK
C402
G405
TO IGN SWITCH
TO PUMP MOTOR
1078 BLK/LT GRN
VALVE SOLENOID RELAY CONTROL
VALVE SOLENOID RELAY
TO B+ (FUSIBLE LINK "J")
1079 PNK/WHT
RELAY FEED
IGN
801C BLK/RED
S188
C155
S420
801A BLK/RED
801B BLK/RED
801E BLK/RED
C413
GROUND DISTRIBUTION
G106
REFER TO SECTION 8A-11
EBCM GROUND
TO IGN SWITCH
AIR BAG
S231
439 PNK/BLK
IGNITION "ON" INPUT

CHART A

"SERVICE ABS" INDICATOR "ON" WITH NO CODES SET

Test Description: Number(s) below refer to circled number(s) on the diagnostic chart.

1. This test confirms that a fault condition exists.
2. This test determines whether the fault is due to a fault code setting condition, an indicator low side circuit fault, or an EBCM supply power fault.
3. This test determines whether the supply power fault is in the power feed to the EBCM or the ground feed to the EBCM.
4. This test checks whether the power feed fault is due to an open fuse.
5. This test checks for an open power feed circuit.
6. This test checks for an open in the ground feed to the EBCM.
7. This test checks whether the fuse failure is due to a short to ground.

GC402920040200AX

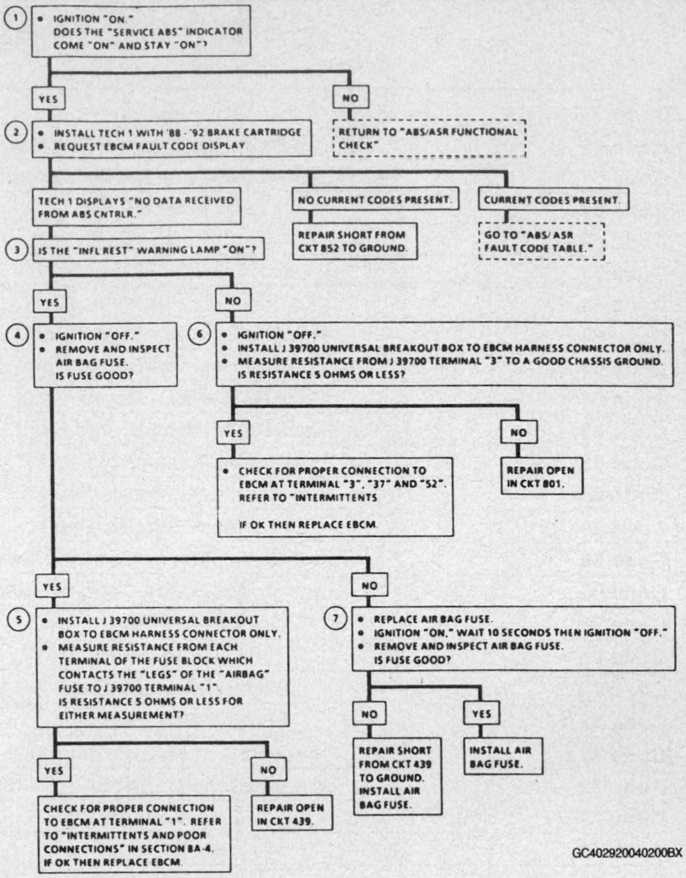
1 • IGNITION "ON." DOES THE "SERVICE ABS" INDICATOR COME "ON" AND STAY "ON"?
YES
NO
RETURN TO "ABS/ASR FUNCTIONAL CHECK"
2 • INSTALL TECH 1 WITH '88 - '92 BRAKE CARTRIDGE. • REQUEST EBCM FAULT CODE DISPLAY.
TECH 1 DISPLAYS "NO DATA RECEIVED FROM ABS CNTRLR."
NO CURRENT CODES PRESENT.
CURRENT CODES PRESENT.
REPAIR SHORT FROM CKT 852 TO GROUND.
GO TO "ABS/ASR FAULT CODE TABLE."
3 IS THE "INFL REST" WARNING LAMP "ON"?
YES
NO
4 • IGNITION "OFF." • REMOVE AND INSPECT AIR BAG FUSE. IS FUSE GOOD?
6 • IGNITION "OFF." • INSTALL J 39700 UNIVERSAL BREAKOUT BOX TO EBCM HARNESS CONNECTOR ONLY. • MEASURE RESISTANCE FROM J 39700 TERMINAL "3" TO A GOOD CHASSIS GROUND. IS RESISTANCE 5 OHMS OR LESS?
YES
NO
• CHECK FOR PROPER CONNECTION TO EBCM AT TERMINAL "3", "37" AND "52". REFER TO "INTERMITTENTS. IF OK THEN REPLACE EBCM.
REPAIR OPEN IN CKT 801.
YES
NO
5 • INSTALL J 39700 UNIVERSAL BREAKOUT BOX TO EBCM HARNESS CONNECTOR ONLY. • MEASURE RESISTANCE FROM EACH TERMINAL OF THE FUSE BLOCK WHICH CONTACTS THE "LEGS" OF THE "AIRBAG" FUSE TO J 39700 TERMINAL "1". IS RESISTANCE 5 OHMS OR LESS FOR EITHER MEASUREMENT?
7 • REPLACE AIR BAG FUSE. • IGNITION "ON," WAIT 10 SECONDS THEN IGNITION "OFF." • REMOVE AND INSPECT AIR BAG FUSE. IS FUSE GOOD?
NO
YES
REPAIR SHORT FROM CKT 439 TO GROUND. INSTALL AIR BAG FUSE.
INSTALL AIR BAG FUSE.
YES
NO
CHECK FOR PROPER CONNECTION TO EBCM AT TERMINAL "1". REFER TO "INTERMITTENTS AND POOR CONNECTIONS" IN SECTION 8A-4. IF OK THEN REPLACE EBCM.
REPAIR OPEN IN CKT 439.

GC402920040200BX

Fig. 9 Test A: Service ABS Indicator On w/No Codes Set. 1992

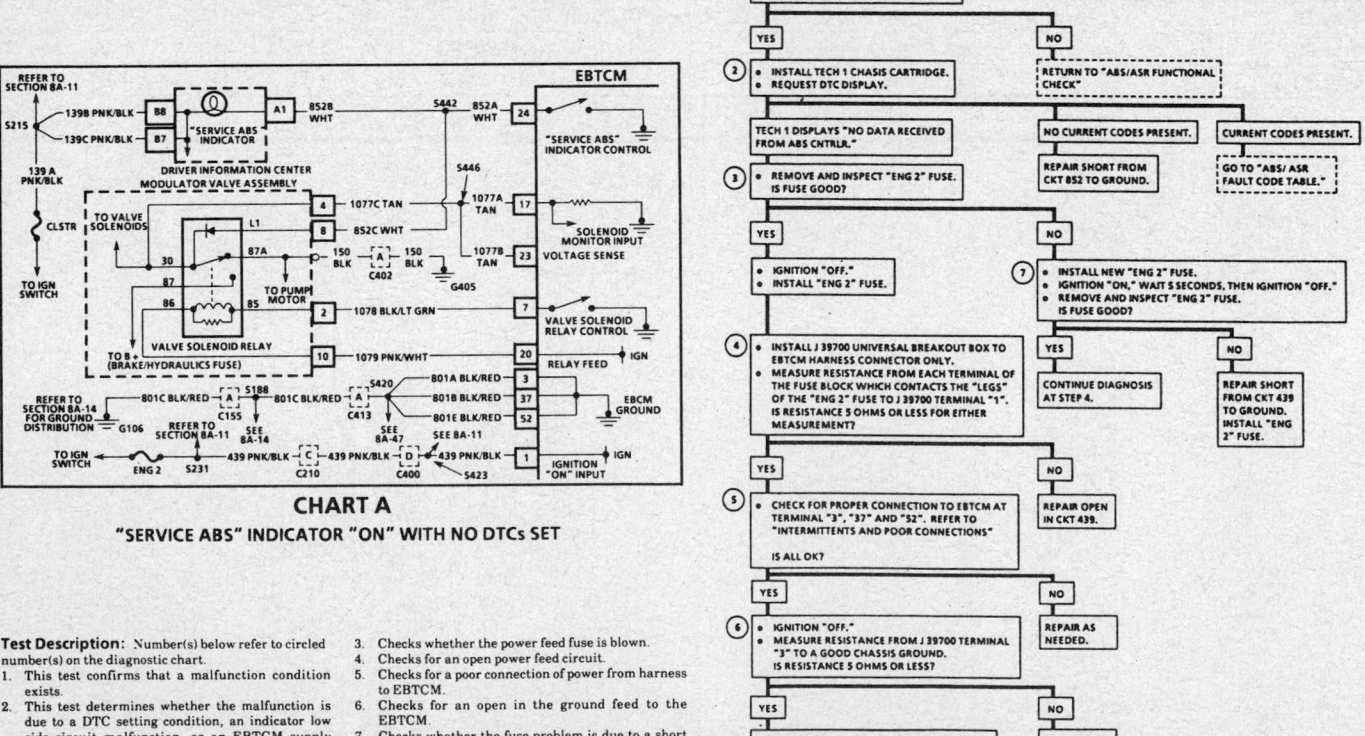

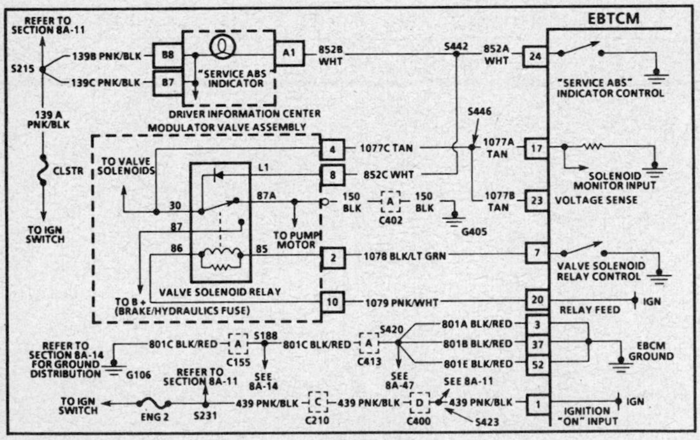
REFER TO SECTION 8A-11
EBTCM
S215
139B PNK/BLK
139C PNK/BLK
B8
B7
"SERVICE ABS" INDICATOR
A1
852B WHT
S442
852A WHT
"SERVICE ABS" INDICATOR CONTROL
139 A PNK/BLK
DRIVER INFORMATION CENTER
MODULATOR VALVE ASSEMBLY
S446
TO VALVE SOLENOIDS
CLSTR
1077C TAN
1077A TAN
852C WHT
SOLENOID MONITOR INPUT
150 BLK
C402
1077B TAN
VOLTAGE SENSE
G405
TO IGN SWITCH
TO PUMP MOTOR
1078 BLK/LT GRN
VALVE SOLENOID RELAY CONTROL
VALVE SOLENOID RELAY
TO B+ (BRAKE/HYDRAULICS FUSE)
1079 PNK/WHT
RELAY FEED
IGN
REFER TO SECTION 8A-14 FOR GROUND DISTRIBUTION
G106
801C BLK/RED
S188
C155
REFER TO SECTION 8A-11
SEE 8A-14
S420
801A BLK/RED
801B BLK/RED
801E BLK/RED
C413
SEE 8A-47
SEE 8A-11
EBCM GROUND
TO IGN SWITCH
ENG 2
S231
439 PNK/BLK
C210
C400
S423
IGNITION "ON" INPUT

CHART A

"SERVICE ABS" INDICATOR "ON" WITH NO DTCs SET

Test Description: Number(s) below refer to circled number(s) on the diagnostic chart.

1. This test confirms that a malfunction condition exists.
2. This test determines whether the malfunction is due to a DTC setting condition, an indicator low side circuit malfunction, or an EBTCM supply power malfunction.
3. Checks whether the power feed fuse is blown.
4. Checks for an open power feed circuit.
5. Checks for a poor connection of power from harness to EBTCM.
6. Checks for an open in the ground feed to the EBTCM.
7. Checks whether the fuse problem is due to a short to ground.

GC402930040300AX

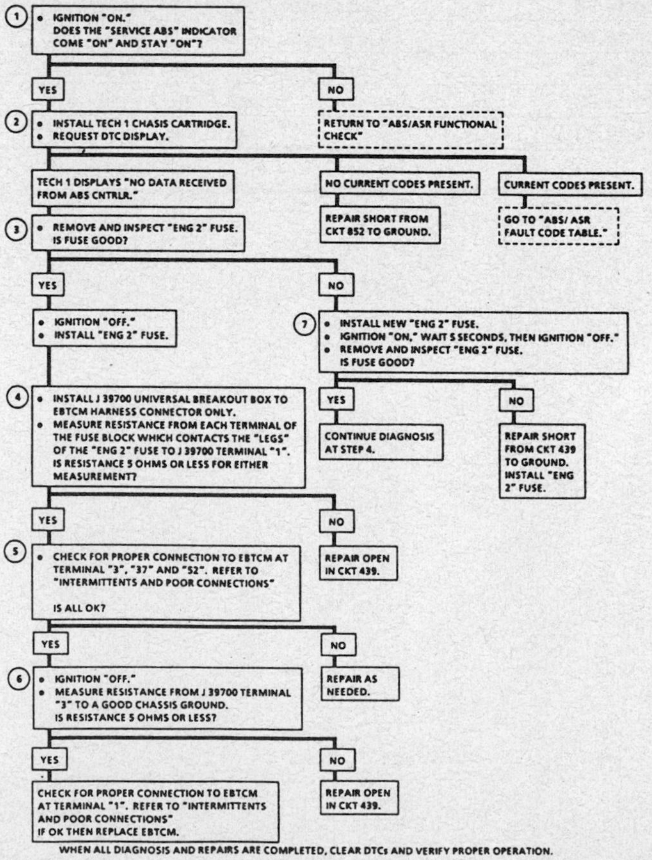
1 • IGNITION "ON." DOES THE "SERVICE ABS" INDICATOR COME "ON" AND STAY "ON"?
YES
NO
2 • INSTALL TECH 1 CHASSIS CARTRIDGE. • REQUEST DTC DISPLAY.
RETURN TO "ABS/ASR FUNCTIONAL CHECK"
TECH 1 DISPLAYS "NO DATA RECEIVED FROM ABS CNTRLR."
NO CURRENT CODES PRESENT.
CURRENT CODES PRESENT.
REPAIR SHORT FROM CKT 852 TO GROUND.
GO TO "ABS/ ASR FAULT CODE TABLE."
3 • REMOVE AND INSPECT "ENG 2" FUSE. IS FUSE GOOD?
YES
NO
• IGNITION "OFF." • INSTALL "ENG 2" FUSE.
7 • INSTALL NEW "ENG 2" FUSE. • IGNITION "ON," WAIT 5 SECONDS, THEN IGNITION "OFF." • REMOVE AND INSPECT "ENG 2" FUSE. IS FUSE GOOD?
4 • INSTALL J 39700 UNIVERSAL BREAKOUT BOX TO EBTCM HARNESS CONNECTOR ONLY. • MEASURE RESISTANCE FROM EACH TERMINAL OF THE FUSE BLOCK WHICH CONTACTS THE "LEGS" OF THE "ENG 2" FUSE TO J 39700 TERMINAL "1". IS RESISTANCE 5 OHMS OR LESS FOR EITHER MEASUREMENT?
YES
NO
CONTINUE DIAGNOSIS AT STEP 4.
REPAIR SHORT FROM CKT 439 TO GROUND. INSTALL "ENG 2" FUSE.
YES
NO
5 • CHECK FOR PROPER CONNECTION TO EBTCM AT TERMINAL "3", "37" AND "52". REFER TO "INTERMITTENTS AND POOR CONNECTIONS" IS ALL OK?
REPAIR OPEN IN CKT 439.
YES
NO
6 • IGNITION "OFF." • MEASURE RESISTANCE FROM J 39700 TERMINAL "3" TO A GOOD CHASSIS GROUND. IS RESISTANCE 5 OHMS OR LESS?
REPAIR AS NEEDED.
YES
NO
CHECK FOR PROPER CONNECTION TO EBTCM AT TERMINAL "1". REFER TO "INTERMITTENTS AND POOR CONNECTIONS" IF OK THEN REPLACE EBTCM.
REPAIR OPEN IN CKT 439.
WHEN ALL DIAGNOSIS AND REPAIRS ARE COMPLETED, CLEAR DTCs AND VERIFY PROPER OPERATION.

GC402930040300BX

Fig. 10 Test A: Service ABS Indicator On w/No Codes Set. 1993

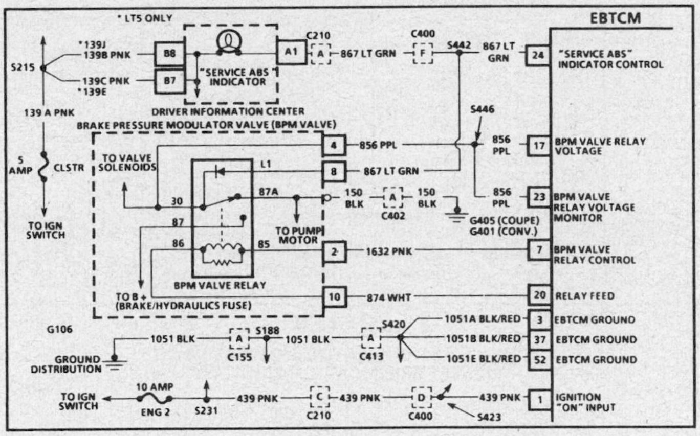
* LTS ONLY
EBTCM
S215
*139J
139B PNK
139C PNK
*139E
B8
B7
"SERVICE ABS" INDICATOR
A1
C210
A
867 LT GRN
C400
F
S442
867 LT GRN
24
"SERVICE ABS" INDICATOR CONTROL
139 A PNK
DRIVER INFORMATION CENTER
BRAKE PRESSURE MODULATOR VALVE (BPM VALVE)
S446
5 AMP
CLSTR
TO VALVE SOLENOIDS
4
856 PPL
856 PPL
17
BPM VALVE RELAY VOLTAGE
L1
8
867 LT GRN
87A
150 BLK
A
C402
150 BLK
856 PPL
23
BPM VALVE RELAY VOLTAGE MONITOR
30
87
G405 (COUPE)
G401 (CONV.)
TO IGN SWITCH
86
85
TO PUMP MOTOR
2
1632 PNK
7
BPM VALVE RELAY CONTROL
BPM VALVE RELAY
TO B+ (BRAKE/HYDRAULICS FUSE)
10
874 WHT
20
RELAY FEED
G106
S420
1051A BLK/RED
3
EBTCM GROUND
1051 BLK
S188
C155
1051 BLK
C413
1051B BLK/RED
37
EBTCM GROUND
GROUND DISTRIBUTION
1051E BLK/RED
52
EBTCM GROUND
10 AMP
TO IGN SWITCH
ENG 2
S231
439 PNK
C
C210
439 PNK
D
C400
439 PNK
S423
1
IGNITION "ON" INPUT

CHART A

(Page 1 of 2)

"SERVICE ABS" INDICATOR "ON" WITH NO DTCs SET

Chart Test Description: Number(s) below refer to circled number(s) on the diagnostic chart.

1. Confirms that a malfunction condition exists.
2. Determines whether the malfunction is due to a DTC setting condition, an indicator low side circuit malfunction, or an EBTCM supply power malfunction.
3. Checks whether the power feed fuse is blown.
4. Checks for an open power feed circuit.
5. Checks for an open in the ground feed to the EBTCM.
6. Checks for proper connection of EBTCM ground CKT(s) 1051A, 1051B, and 1051E.
7. Checks whether the fuse malfunction is due to a short to ground.
8. Identifies if the short to ground found in Step 7 is in CKT 439 or the EBTCM.

GC402940085201AX

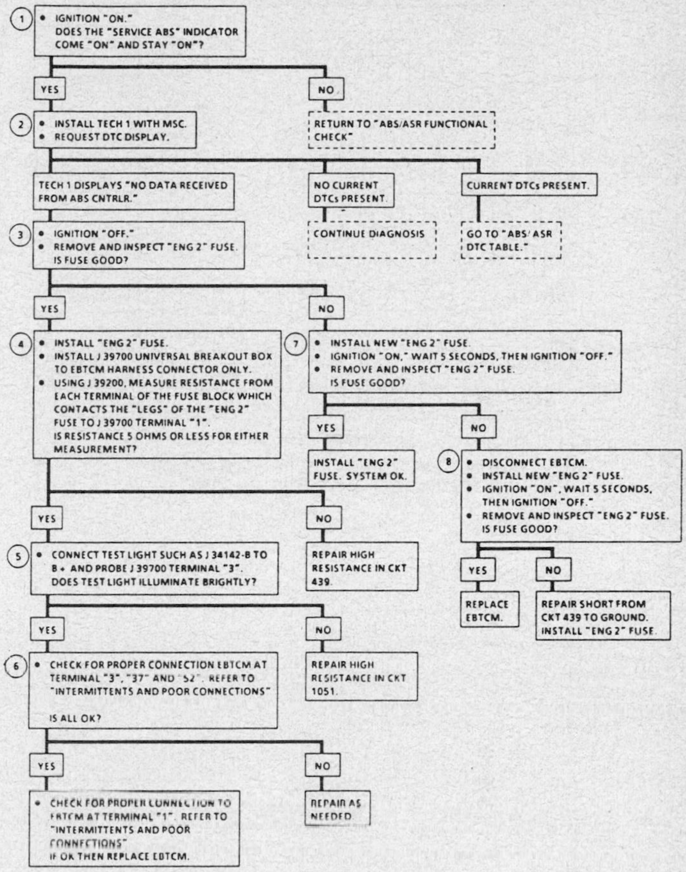
1 • IGNITION "ON."
DOES THE "SERVICE ABS" INDICATOR COME "ON" AND STAY "ON"?
YES
NO
2 • INSTALL TECH 1 WITH MSC.
• REQUEST DTC DISPLAY.
RETURN TO "ABS/ASR FUNCTIONAL CHECK"
TECH 1 DISPLAYS "NO DATA RECEIVED FROM ABS CNTRLR."
NO CURRENT DTCs PRESENT.
CURRENT DTCs PRESENT.
CONTINUE DIAGNOSIS
GO TO "ABS/ASR DTC TABLE."
3 • IGNITION "OFF."
• REMOVE AND INSPECT "ENG 2" FUSE.
IS FUSE GOOD?
YES
NO
4 • INSTALL "ENG 2" FUSE.
• INSTALL J 39700 UNIVERSAL BREAKOUT BOX TO EBTCM HARNESS CONNECTOR ONLY.
• USING J 39200, MEASURE RESISTANCE FROM EACH TERMINAL OF THE FUSE BLOCK WHICH CONTACTS THE "LEGS" OF THE "ENG 2" FUSE TO J 39700 TERMINAL "1".
IS RESISTANCE 5 OHMS OR LESS FOR EITHER MEASUREMENT?
7 • INSTALL NEW "ENG 2" FUSE.
• IGNITION "ON," WAIT 5 SECONDS, THEN IGNITION "OFF."
• REMOVE AND INSPECT "ENG 2" FUSE.
IS FUSE GOOD?
YES
NO
INSTALL "ENG 2" FUSE. SYSTEM OK.
8 • DISCONNECT EBTCM.
• INSTALL NEW "ENG 2" FUSE.
• IGNITION "ON", WAIT 5 SECONDS, THEN IGNITION "OFF."
• REMOVE AND INSPECT "ENG 2" FUSE.
IS FUSE GOOD?
YES
NO
5 • CONNECT TEST LIGHT SUCH AS J 34142-B TO B+ AND PROBE J 39700 TERMINAL "3".
DOES TEST LIGHT ILLUMINATE BRIGHTLY?
REPAIR HIGH RESISTANCE IN CKT 439.
YES
NO
REPLACE EBTCM.
REPAIR SHORT FROM CKT 439 TO GROUND. INSTALL "ENG 2" FUSE.
YES
NO
6 • CHECK FOR PROPER CONNECTION EBTCM AT TERMINAL "3", "37" AND "52". REFER TO "INTERMITTENTS AND POOR CONNECTIONS"
IS ALL OK?
REPAIR HIGH RESISTANCE IN CKT 1051.
YES
NO
• CHECK FOR PROPER CONNECTION TO EBTCM AT TERMINAL "1". REFER TO "INTERMITTENTS AND POOR CONNECTIONS"
IF OK THEN REPLACE EBTCM.
REPAIR AS NEEDED.

GC402940085201BX

Fig. 11 Test A: Service ABS Indicator On w/No Codes Set (Part 1 of 2). 1994

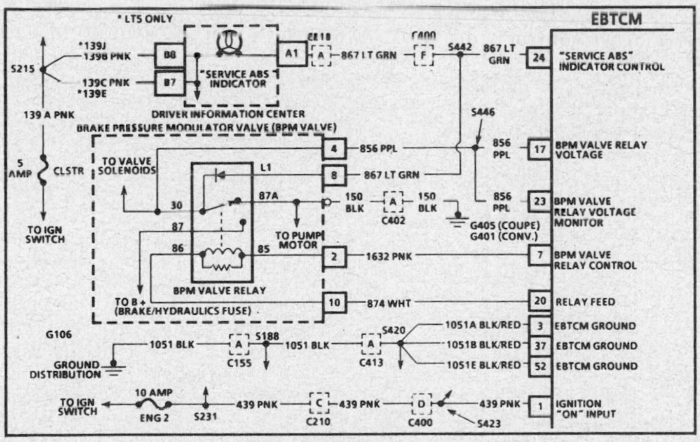

CHART A

(Page 2 of 2)

"SERVICE ABS" INDICATOR "ON" WITH NO DTCs SET

Chart Test Description: Number(s) below refer to circled number(s) on the diagnostic chart.

9. Determines whether the malfunction is due to a short to ground in CKT 867.
10. Ensures the malfunction is not due to an internal short to ground in the BPM valve.
11. Checks for an internal short to ground in the BPM valve relay.
12. Determines whether the malfunction is due to physical damage of the EBTCM, BPM valve connectors or the EBTCM.

GC402940085202AX

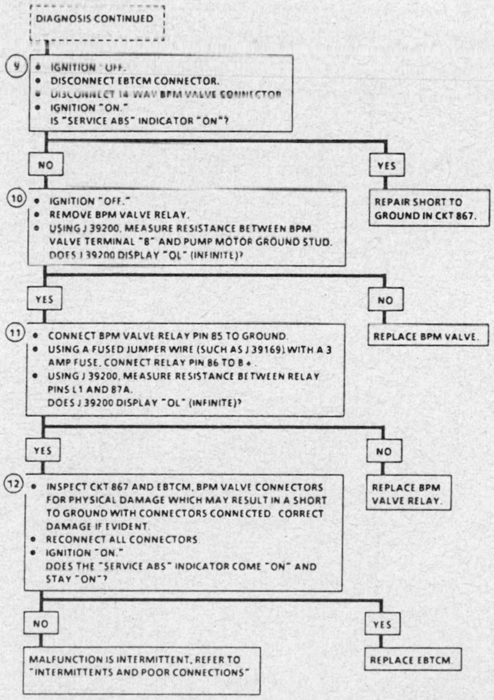
DIAGNOSIS CONTINUED
9 • IGNITION "OFF."
• DISCONNECT EBTCM CONNECTOR.
• DISCONNECT 14 WAY BPM VALVE CONNECTOR
• IGNITION "ON."
IS "SERVICE ABS" INDICATOR "ON"?
NO
YES
10 • IGNITION "OFF."
• REMOVE BPM VALVE RELAY.
• USING J 39200, MEASURE RESISTANCE BETWEEN BPM VALVE TERMINAL "8" AND PUMP MOTOR GROUND STUD.
DOES J 39200 DISPLAY "OL" (INFINITE)?
REPAIR SHORT TO GROUND IN CKT 867.
YES
NO
11 • CONNECT BPM VALVE RELAY PIN 85 TO GROUND.
• USING A FUSED JUMPER WIRE (SUCH AS J 39169) WITH A 3 AMP FUSE, CONNECT RELAY PIN 86 TO B+.
• USING J 39200, MEASURE RESISTANCE BETWEEN RELAY PINS L1 AND 87A.
DOES J 39200 DISPLAY "OL" (INFINITE)?
REPLACE BPM VALVE.
YES
NO
12 • INSPECT CKT 867 AND EBTCM, BPM VALVE CONNECTORS FOR PHYSICAL DAMAGE WHICH MAY RESULT IN A SHORT TO GROUND WITH CONNECTORS CONNECTED. CORRECT DAMAGE IF EVIDENT.
• RECONNECT ALL CONNECTORS.
• IGNITION "ON."
DOES THE "SERVICE ABS" INDICATOR COME "ON" AND STAY "ON"?
REPLACE BPM VALVE RELAY.
NO
YES
MALFUNCTION IS INTERMITTENT. REFER TO "INTERMITTENTS AND POOR CONNECTIONS"
REPLACE EBTCM.

GC402940085202BX

Fig. 11 Test A: Service ABS Indicator On w/No Codes Set (Part 2 of 2). 1994

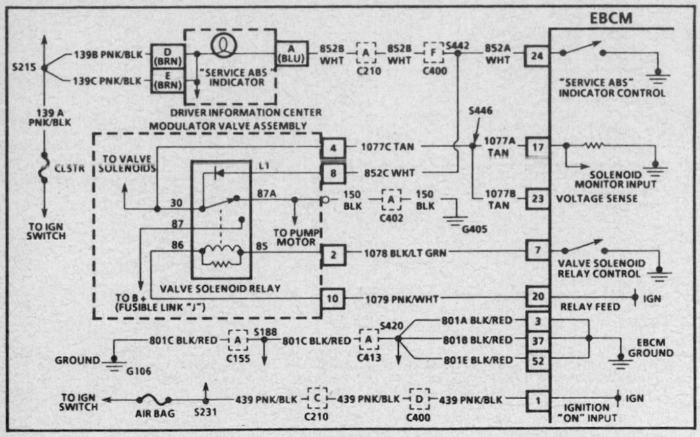
EBCM
S215
139B PNK/BLK
139C PNK/BLK
D (BRN)
E (BRN)
A (BLU)
"SERVICE ABS" INDICATOR
852B WHT
C210
852B WHT
C400
S442
852A WHT
24
"SERVICE ABS" INDICATOR CONTROL
139 A PNK/BLK
DRIVER INFORMATION CENTER
MODULATOR VALVE ASSEMBLY
S446
CLSTR
TO VALVE SOLENOIDS
L1
4
1077C TAN
1077A TAN
17
8
852C WHT
SOLENOID MONITOR INPUT
30
87A
150 BLK
C402
150 BLK
1077B TAN
23
VOLTAGE SENSE
TO IGN SWITCH
87
86
85
TO PUMP MOTOR
G405
2
1078 BLK/LT GRN
7
VALVE SOLENOID RELAY CONTROL
VALVE SOLENOID RELAY
TO B+ (FUSIBLE LINK "J")
10
1079 PNK/WHT
20
RELAY FEED
IGN
S420
801A BLK/RED
3
801B BLK/RED
37
801E BLK/RED
52
EBCM GROUND
801C BLK/RED
S188
801C BLK/RED
C155
C413
GROUND
G106
TO IGN SWITCH
AIR BAG
S231
439 PNK/BLK
C210
439 PNK/BLK
C400
439 PNK/BLK
1
IGNITION "ON" INPUT
IGN

CHART B

"SERVICE ABS" INDICATOR INOPERATIVE OR FLICKERS BRIEFLY AT IGNITION "ON"

Test Description: Number(s) below refer to circled number(s) on the diagnostic chart.

1. This test confirms that a fault condition exists.
2. This test checks the integrity of the indicator bulb.
3. This test checks for an indicator low side circuit open.
4. This test checks for an indicator low side circuit short to B+.
5. This test determines whether the fault is due to an EBCM circuit fault or an open in the DIC printed circuit.

GC402920040400AX

1992

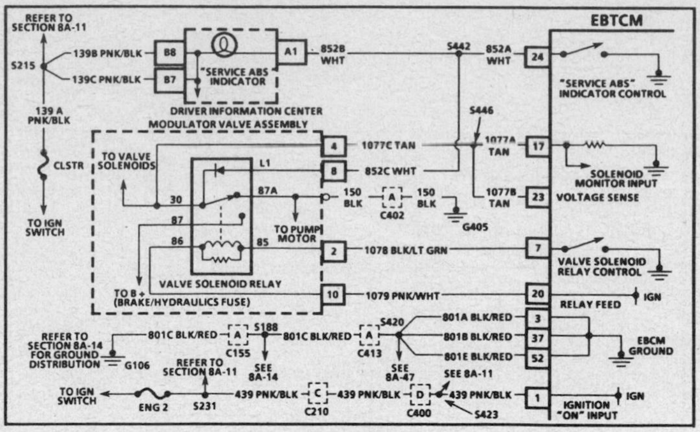
REFER TO SECTION 8A-11
EBTCM
S215
139B PNK/BLK
139C PNK/BLK
B8
B7
A1
"SERVICE ABS" INDICATOR
852B WHT
S442
852A WHT
24
"SERVICE ABS" INDICATOR CONTROL
139 A PNK/BLK
DRIVER INFORMATION CENTER
MODULATOR VALVE ASSEMBLY
S446
CLSTR
TO VALVE SOLENOIDS
L1
4
1077C TAN
1077A TAN
17
8
852C WHT
SOLENOID MONITOR INPUT
30
87A
150 BLK
C402
150 BLK
1077B TAN
23
VOLTAGE SENSE
TO IGN SWITCH
87
86
85
TO PUMP MOTOR
G405
2
1078 BLK/LT GRN
7
VALVE SOLENOID RELAY CONTROL
VALVE SOLENOID RELAY
TO B+ (BRAKE/HYDRAULICS FUSE)
10
1079 PNK/WHT
20
RELAY FEED
IGN
S420
801A BLK/RED
3
801B BLK/RED
37
801E BLK/RED
52
EBCM GROUND
REFER TO SECTION 8A-14 FOR GROUND DISTRIBUTION
801C BLK/RED
S188
801C BLK/RED
C155
C413
G106
REFER TO SECTION 8A-11
SEE 8A-14
SEE 8A-47
SEE 8A-11
TO IGN SWITCH
ENG 2
S231
439 PNK/BLK
C210
439 PNK/BLK
C400
S423
439 PNK/BLK
1
IGNITION "ON" INPUT
IGN

CHART B

"SERVICE ABS" INDICATOR INOPERATIVE OR FLICKERS BRIEFLY AT IGNITION "ON"

Test Description: Number(s) below refer to circled number(s) on the diagnostic chart.

1. This test confirms that a malfunction condition exists.
2. This test checks the integrity of the indicator bulb.
3. This test checks for an indicator low side circuit open.
4. This test checks for an indicator low side circuit short to B+.
5. This test determines whether the malfunction is due to an EBTCM circuit malfunction or an open in the DIC printed circuit.

GC402920040400BX

1993

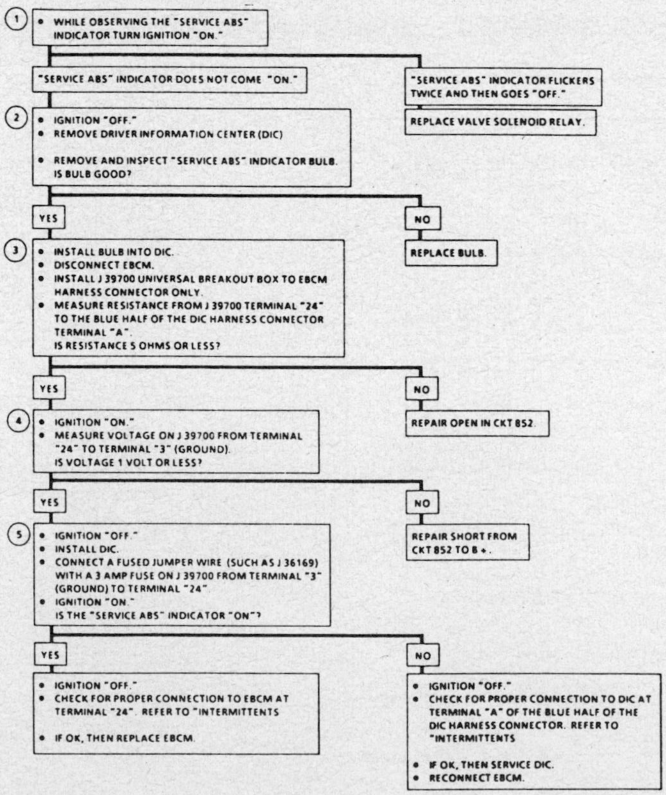
1
• WHILE OBSERVING THE "SERVICE ABS" INDICATOR TURN IGNITION "ON."
"SERVICE ABS" INDICATOR DOES NOT COME "ON."
"SERVICE ABS" INDICATOR FLICKERS TWICE AND THEN GOES "OFF."
REPLACE VALVE SOLENOID RELAY.
2
• IGNITION "OFF."
• REMOVE DRIVER INFORMATION CENTER (DIC)
• REMOVE AND INSPECT "SERVICE ABS" INDICATOR BULB. IS BULB GOOD?
YES
NO
REPLACE BULB.
3
• INSTALL BULB INTO DIC.
• DISCONNECT EBCM.
• INSTALL J 39700 UNIVERSAL BREAKOUT BOX TO EBCM HARNESS CONNECTOR ONLY.
• MEASURE RESISTANCE FROM J 39700 TERMINAL "24" TO THE BLUE HALF OF THE DIC HARNESS CONNECTOR TERMINAL "A". IS RESISTANCE 5 OHMS OR LESS?
YES
NO
REPAIR OPEN IN CKT 852.
4
• IGNITION "ON."
• MEASURE VOLTAGE ON J 39700 FROM TERMINAL "24" TO TERMINAL "3" (GROUND). IS VOLTAGE 1 VOLT OR LESS?
YES
NO
REPAIR SHORT FROM CKT 852 TO B+.
5
• IGNITION "OFF."
• INSTALL DIC.
• CONNECT A FUSED JUMPER WIRE (SUCH AS J 36169) WITH A 3 AMP FUSE ON J 39700 FROM TERMINAL "3" (GROUND) TO TERMINAL "24".
• IGNITION "ON." IS THE "SERVICE ABS" INDICATOR "ON"?
YES
NO
• IGNITION "OFF."
• CHECK FOR PROPER CONNECTION TO EBCM AT TERMINAL "24". REFER TO "INTERMITTENTS
• IF OK, THEN REPLACE EBCM.
• IGNITION "OFF."
• CHECK FOR PROPER CONNECTION TO DIC AT TERMINAL "A" OF THE BLUE HALF OF THE DIC HARNESS CONNECTOR. REFER TO "INTERMITTENTS
• IF OK, THEN SERVICE DIC.
• RECONNECT EBCM.

GC402920040400CX

Fig. 12 Test B: Service ABS Indicator Inoperative Or Flickers w/Ignition On. 1992–93

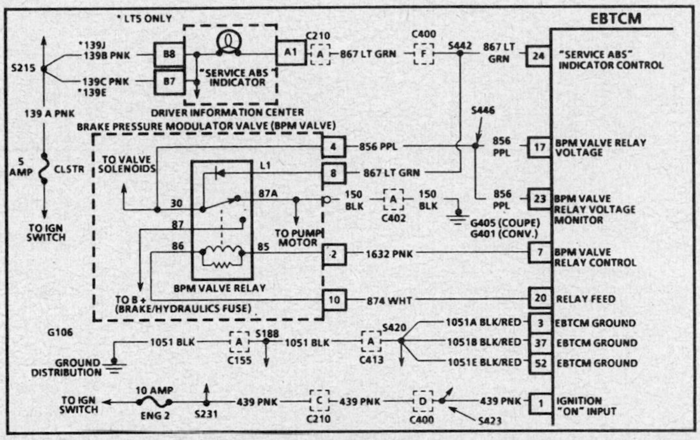

EBTCM
* LTS ONLY
*139J
-139B PNK
S215
-139C PNK
*139E
B8
B7
"SERVICE ABS" INDICATOR
A1
C210
A
867 LT GRN
C400
F
S442
867 LT GRN
24
"SERVICE ABS" INDICATOR CONTROL
139 A PNK
DRIVER INFORMATION CENTER
BRAKE PRESSURE MODULATOR VALVE (BPM VALVE)
S446
5 AMP
CLSTR
TO VALVE SOLENOIDS
4
856 PPL
856 PPL
17
BPM VALVE RELAY VOLTAGE
L1
8
867 LT GRN
30
87A
150 BLK
A
C402
150 BLK
856 PPL
23
BPM VALVE RELAY VOLTAGE MONITOR
G405 (COUPE)
G401 (CONV.)
87
TO IGN SWITCH
TO PUMP MOTOR
86
85
2
1632 PNK
7
BPM VALVE RELAY CONTROL
TO B+ (BRAKE/HYDRAULICS FUSE)
BPM VALVE RELAY
10
874 WHT
20
RELAY FEED
G106
1051 BLK
A
C155
S188
1051 BLK
A
C413
S420
1051A BLK/RED
3
EBTCM GROUND
1051B BLK/RED
37
EBTCM GROUND
1051E BLK/RED
52
EBTCM GROUND
GROUND DISTRIBUTION
10 AMP
TO IGN SWITCH
ENG 2
S231
439 PNK
C
C210
439 PNK
D
C400
439 PNK
S423
1
IGNITION "ON" INPUT

CHART B

"SERVICE ABS" INDICATOR INOPERATIVE OR FLICKERS BRIEFLY AT IGNITION "ON"

Chart Test Description: Number(s) below refer to circled number(s) on the diagnostic chart.

1. Confirms that a malfunction condition exists.
2. Check to see if the indicator can be turned "ON" manually.
3. Checks the integrity of the indicator bulb.
4. Checks for an indicator low side circuit open.
5. Checks for an indicator low side circuit short to B+.

GC402940085300AX

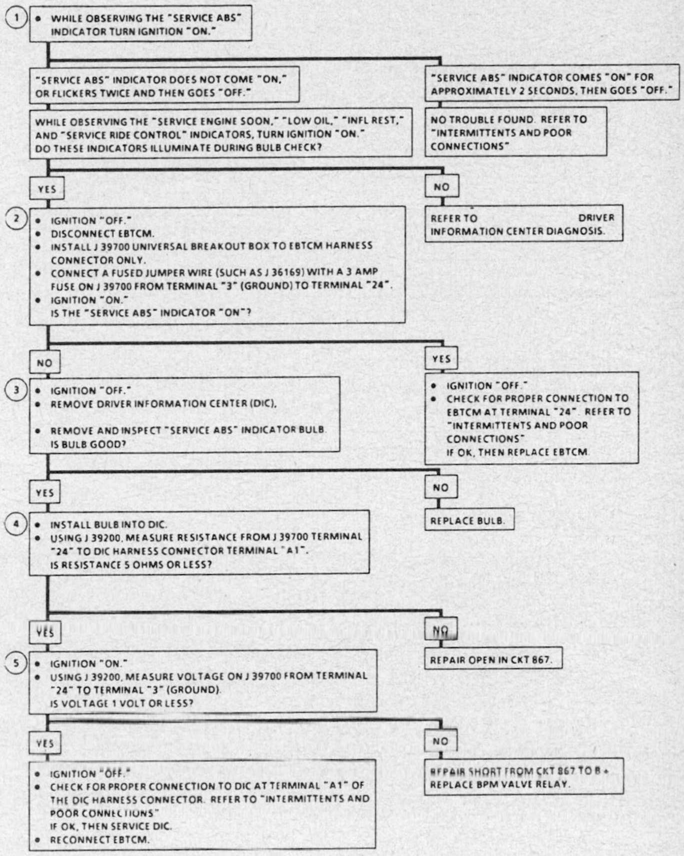

1 • WHILE OBSERVING THE "SERVICE ABS" INDICATOR TURN IGNITION "ON."
"SERVICE ABS" INDICATOR DOES NOT COME "ON," OR FLICKERS TWICE AND THEN GOES "OFF."
"SERVICE ABS" INDICATOR COMES "ON" FOR APPROXIMATELY 2 SECONDS, THEN GOES "OFF."
WHILE OBSERVING THE "SERVICE ENGINE SOON," "LOW OIL," "INFL REST," AND "SERVICE RIDE CONTROL" INDICATORS, TURN IGNITION "ON." DO THESE INDICATORS ILLUMINATE DURING BULB CHECK?
NO TROUBLE FOUND. REFER TO "INTERMITTENTS AND POOR CONNECTIONS"
YES
NO
2 • IGNITION "OFF." • DISCONNECT EBTCM. • INSTALL J 39700 UNIVERSAL BREAKOUT BOX TO EBTCM HARNESS CONNECTOR ONLY. • CONNECT A FUSED JUMPER WIRE (SUCH AS J 36169) WITH A 3 AMP FUSE ON J 39700 FROM TERMINAL "3" (GROUND) TO TERMINAL "24". • IGNITION "ON." IS THE "SERVICE ABS" INDICATOR "ON"?
REFER TO DRIVER INFORMATION CENTER DIAGNOSIS.
NO
YES
3 • IGNITION "OFF." • REMOVE DRIVER INFORMATION CENTER (DIC). • REMOVE AND INSPECT "SERVICE ABS" INDICATOR BULB. IS BULB GOOD?
• IGNITION "OFF." • CHECK FOR PROPER CONNECTION TO EBTCM AT TERMINAL "24". REFER TO "INTERMITTENTS AND POOR CONNECTIONS" IF OK, THEN REPLACE EBTCM.
YES
NO
REPLACE BULB.
4 • INSTALL BULB INTO DIC. • USING J 39200, MEASURE RESISTANCE FROM J 39700 TERMINAL "24" TO DIC HARNESS CONNECTOR TERMINAL "A1". IS RESISTANCE 5 OHMS OR LESS?
YES
NO
REPAIR OPEN IN CKT 867.
5 • IGNITION "ON." • USING J 39200, MEASURE VOLTAGE ON J 39700 FROM TERMINAL "24" TO TERMINAL "3" (GROUND). IS VOLTAGE 1 VOLT OR LESS?
YES
NO
• IGNITION "OFF." • CHECK FOR PROPER CONNECTION TO DIC AT TERMINAL "A1" OF THE DIC HARNESS CONNECTOR. REFER TO "INTERMITTENTS AND POOR CONNECTIONS" IF OK, THEN SERVICE DIC. • RECONNECT EBTCM.
REPAIR SHORT FROM CKT 867 TO B+. REPLACE BPM VALVE RELAY.

GC402940085300BX

Fig. 13 Test B: Service ABS Indicator Inoperative Or Flickers w/Ignition On. 1994

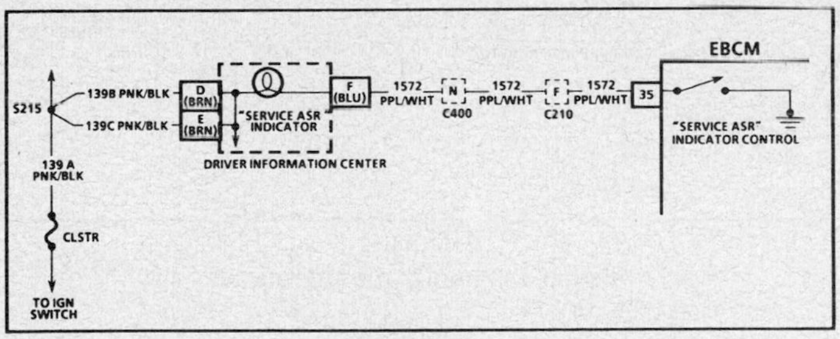

EBCM
S215
139B PNK/BLK
139C PNK/BLK
D (BRN)
E (BRN)
"SERVICE ASR" INDICATOR
F (BLU)
1572 PPL/WHT
N
C400
1572 PPL/WHT
F
C210
1572 PPL/WHT
35
"SERVICE ASR" INDICATOR CONTROL
139 A PNK/BLK
DRIVER INFORMATION CENTER
CLSTR
TO IGN SWITCH

CHART C

"SERVICE ASR" INDICATOR "ON" WITH NO CODES SET

Test Description: Number(s) below refer to circled number(s) on the diagnostic chart.

1. This test confirms that a fault condition exists.
2. This test checks if the fault is due to a fault code setting condition.
3. This test checks whether the fault is due to an indicator low side circuit short to ground or an EBCM circuit fault.

GC402920040500AX

1992

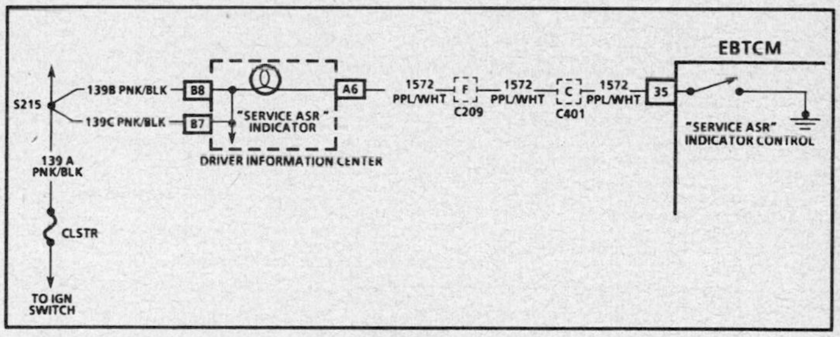

EBTCM
S215
139B PNK/BLK
139C PNK/BLK
B8
B7
"SERVICE ASR" INDICATOR
A6
1572 PPL/WHT
F
C209
1572 PPL/WHT
C
C401
1572 PPL/WHT
35
"SERVICE ASR" INDICATOR CONTROL
139 A PNK/BLK
DRIVER INFORMATION CENTER
CLSTR
TO IGN SWITCH

CHART C

"SERVICE ASR" INDICATOR "ON" WITH NO DTCs SET

Test Description: Number(s) below refer to circled number(s) on the diagnostic chart.

1. This test confirms that a malfunction condition exists.
2. This test checks if the malfunction is due to a DTC setting condition.
3. This test checks whether the malfunction is due to an indicator low side circuit short to ground or an EBTCM circuit malfunction.

GC402930040500BX

1993

Fig. 14 Test C: Service ASR Indicator On w/No Codes Set (Part 1 of 2). 1992-93

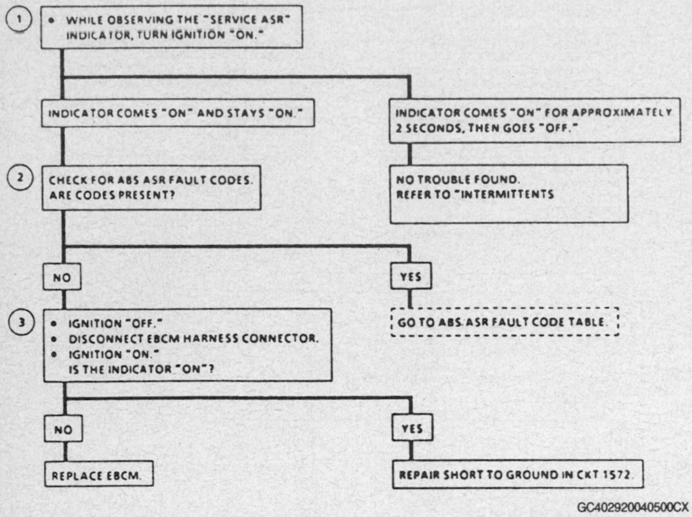
1
• WHILE OBSERVING THE "SERVICE ASR" INDICATOR, TURN IGNITION "ON."
INDICATOR COMES "ON" AND STAYS "ON."
INDICATOR COMES "ON" FOR APPROXIMATELY 2 SECONDS, THEN GOES "OFF."
2
CHECK FOR ABS ASR FAULT CODES. ARE CODES PRESENT?
NO TROUBLE FOUND. REFER TO "INTERMITTENTS
NO
YES
GO TO ABS ASR FAULT CODE TABLE.
3
• IGNITION "OFF."
• DISCONNECT EBCM HARNESS CONNECTOR.
• IGNITION "ON." IS THE INDICATOR "ON"?
NO
YES
REPLACE EBCM.
REPAIR SHORT TO GROUND IN CKT 1572.
GC402920040500CX

Fig. 14 Test C: Service ASR Indicator On w/No Codes Set (Part 2 of 2). 1992-93

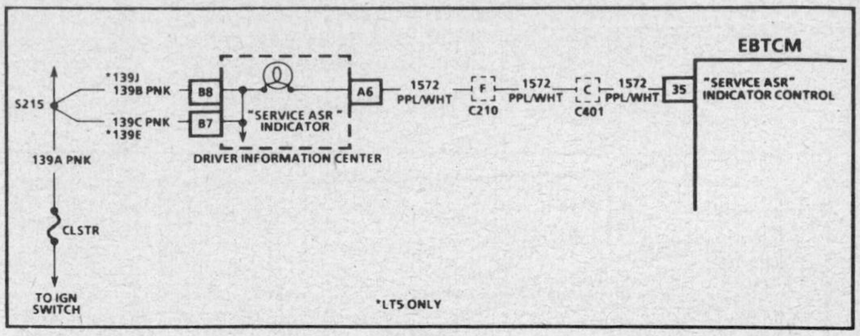
EBTCM
*139J
139B PNK
139C PNK
*139E
S215
B8
B7
"SERVICE ASR" INDICATOR
DRIVER INFORMATION CENTER
A6
1572 PPL/WHT
F
C210
1572 PPL/WHT
C
C401
1572 PPL/WHT
35
"SERVICE ASR" INDICATOR CONTROL
139A PNK
CLSTR
TO IGN SWITCH
*LTS ONLY

CHART C

"SERVICE ASR" INDICATOR "ON" WITH NO DTCs SET

Chart Test Description: Number(s) below refer to circled number(s) on the diagnostic chart.

1. Confirms that a malfunction condition exists.
2. Checks if the malfunction is due to a DTC setting condition.
3. Determines whether the malfunction is due to an indicator low side circuit short to ground or an EBTCM circuit malfunction.

GC402940085400AX

Fig. 15 Test C: Service ASR Indicator On w/No Codes Set (Part 1 of 2). 1994

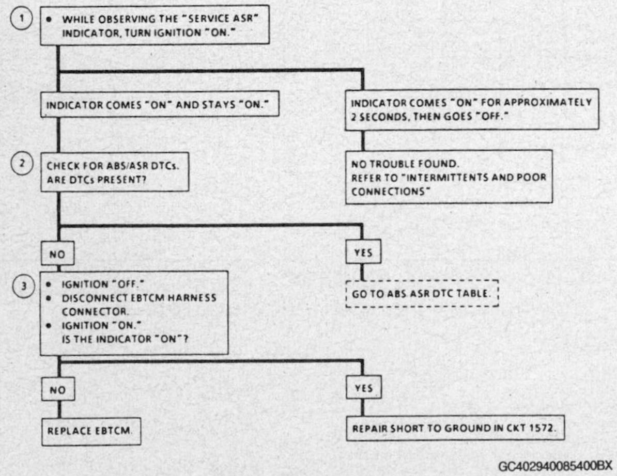
1
• WHILE OBSERVING THE "SERVICE ASR" INDICATOR, TURN IGNITION "ON."
INDICATOR COMES "ON" AND STAYS "ON."
INDICATOR COMES "ON" FOR APPROXIMATELY 2 SECONDS, THEN GOES "OFF."
2
CHECK FOR ABS/ASR DTCs. ARE DTCs PRESENT?
NO TROUBLE FOUND. REFER TO "INTERMITTENTS AND POOR CONNECTIONS"
NO
YES
GO TO ABS ASR DTC TABLE.
3
• IGNITION "OFF."
• DISCONNECT EBTCM HARNESS CONNECTOR.
• IGNITION "ON." IS THE INDICATOR "ON"?
NO
YES
REPLACE EBTCM.
REPAIR SHORT TO GROUND IN CKT 1572.
GC402940085400BX

Fig. 15 Test C: Service ASR Indicator On w/No Codes Set (Part 2 of 2). 1994

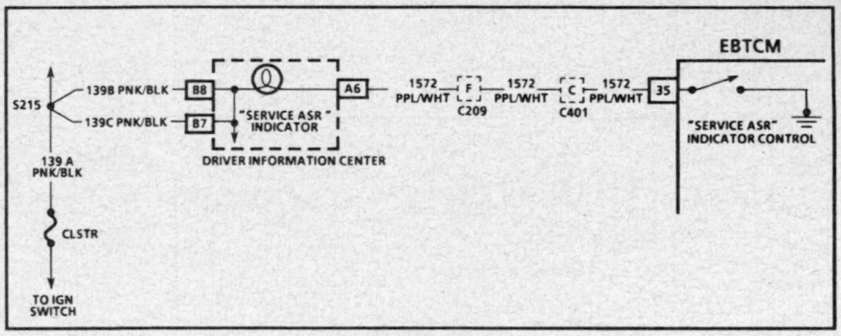
EBTCM
139B PNK/BLK
139C PNK/BLK
S215
B8
B7
"SERVICE ASR" INDICATOR
DRIVER INFORMATION CENTER
A6
1572 PPL/WHT
F
C209
1572 PPL/WHT
C
C401
1572 PPL/WHT
35
"SERVICE ASR" INDICATOR CONTROL
139 A PNK/BLK
CLSTR
TO IGN SWITCH

CHART D

"SERVICE ASR" INDICATOR INOPERATIVE

Test Description: Number(s) below refer to circled number(s) on the diagnostic chart.

1. This test confirms that a malfunction condition exists.
2. This test checks the integrity of the indicator bulb.
3. This test checks for an indicator low side circuit open.
4. This test checks for an indicator low side circuit short to B+.
5. This test determines whether the malfunction is due to an EBTCM circuit malfunction or an open in the DIC printed circuit.

GC402920040600AX

1992

Fig. 16 Test D: Service ASR Indicator Inoperative (Part 1 of 2). 1992–93

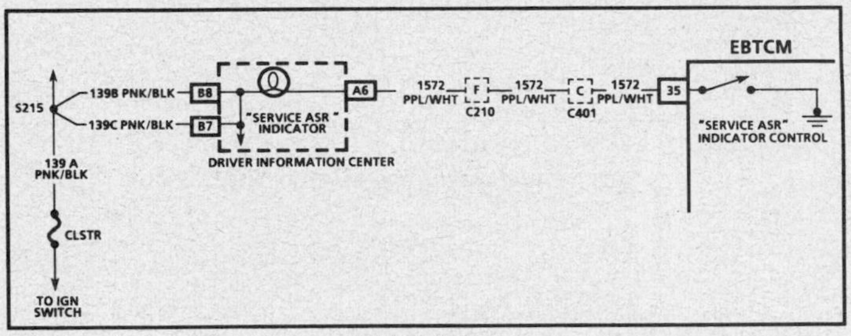
EBTCM
S215
139B PNK/BLK
139C PNK/BLK
B8
B7
A6
"SERVICE ASR" INDICATOR
DRIVER INFORMATION CENTER
1572 PPL/WHT
F
C210
1572 PPL/WHT
C
C401
1572 PPL/WHT
35
"SERVICE ASR" INDICATOR CONTROL
139 A PNK/BLK
CLSTR
TO IGN SWITCH

CHART D

"SERVICE ASR" INDICATOR INOPERATIVE

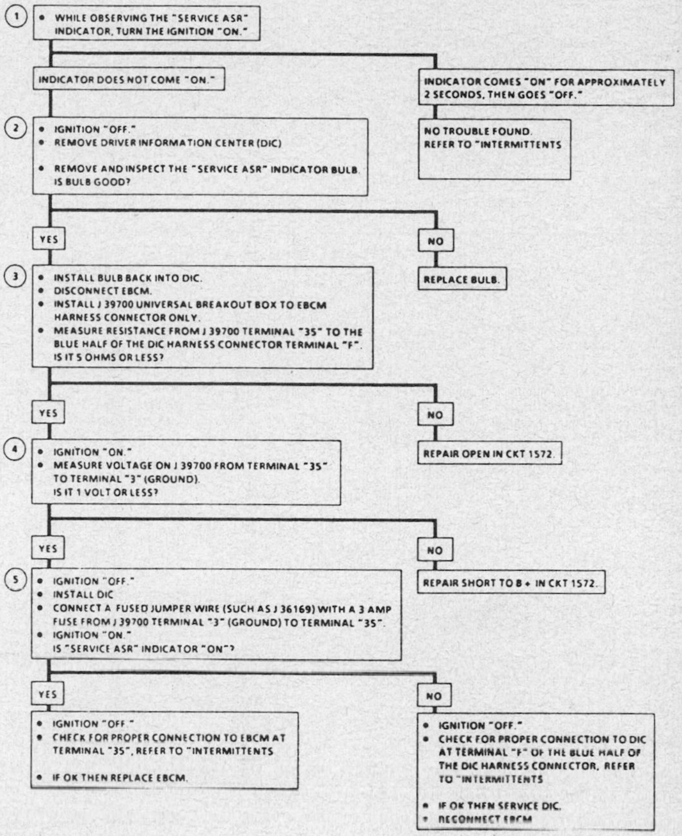
1
WHILE OBSERVING THE "SERVICE ASR" INDICATOR, TURN THE IGNITION "ON."
INDICATOR DOES NOT COME "ON."
INDICATOR COMES "ON" FOR APPROXIMATELY 2 SECONDS, THEN GOES "OFF."
NO TROUBLE FOUND. REFER TO "INTERMITTENTS
2
IGNITION "OFF."
REMOVE DRIVER INFORMATION CENTER (DIC)
REMOVE AND INSPECT THE "SERVICE ASR" INDICATOR BULB. IS BULB GOOD?
YES
NO
REPLACE BULB.
3
INSTALL BULB BACK INTO DIC.
DISCONNECT EBCM.
INSTALL J 39700 UNIVERSAL BREAKOUT BOX TO EBCM HARNESS CONNECTOR ONLY.
MEASURE RESISTANCE FROM J 39700 TERMINAL "35" TO THE BLUE HALF OF THE DIC HARNESS CONNECTOR TERMINAL "F". IS IT 5 OHMS OR LESS?
YES
NO
REPAIR OPEN IN CKT 1572.
4
IGNITION "ON."
MEASURE VOLTAGE ON J 39700 FROM TERMINAL "35" TO TERMINAL "3" (GROUND). IS IT 1 VOLT OR LESS?
YES
NO
REPAIR SHORT TO B+ IN CKT 1572.
5
IGNITION "OFF."
INSTALL DIC
CONNECT A FUSED JUMPER WIRE (SUCH AS J 36169) WITH A 3 AMP FUSE FROM J 39700 TERMINAL "3" (GROUND) TO TERMINAL "35".
IGNITION "ON."
IS "SERVICE ASR" INDICATOR "ON"?
YES
NO
IGNITION "OFF."
CHECK FOR PROPER CONNECTION TO EBCM AT TERMINAL "35", REFER TO "INTERMITTENTS
IF OK THEN REPLACE EBCM.
IGNITION "OFF."
CHECK FOR PROPER CONNECTION TO DIC AT TERMINAL "F" OF THE BLUE HALF OF THE DIC HARNESS CONNECTOR. REFER TO "INTERMITTENTS
IF OK THEN SERVICE DIC.
RECONNECT EBCM

Test Description: Number(s) below refer to circled number(s) on the diagnostic chart.

1. This test confirms that a malfunction condition exists.
2. This test checks the integrity of the indicator bulb.
3. This test checks for an indicator low side circuit open.
4. This test checks for an indicator low side circuit short to B+.
5. This test determines whether the malfunction is due to an EBTCM circuit malfunction or an open in the DIC printed circuit.

GC402030040600BX

1993

GC402920040600CX

Fig. 16 Test D: Service ASR indicator inoperative (Part 2 of 2). 1992–93

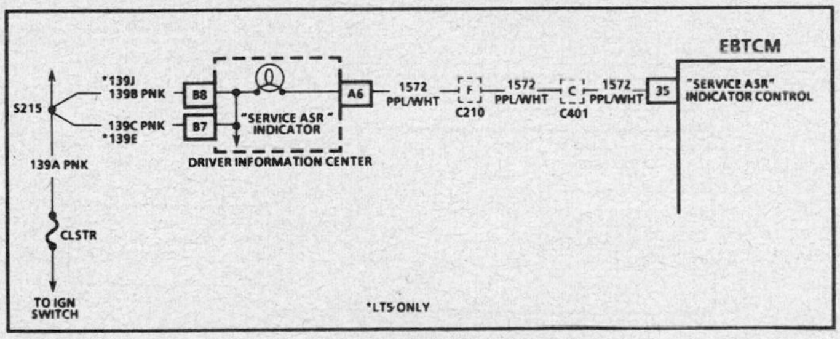
EBTCM
S215
*139J
139B PNK
139C PNK
*139E
B8
B7
A6
"SERVICE ASR" INDICATOR
DRIVER INFORMATION CENTER
1572 PPL/WHT
F
C210
1572 PPL/WHT
C
C401
1572 PPL/WHT
35
"SERVICE ASR" INDICATOR CONTROL
139A PNK
CLSTR
TO IGN SWITCH
*LTS ONLY

CHART D

"SERVICE ASR" INDICATOR INOPERATIVE

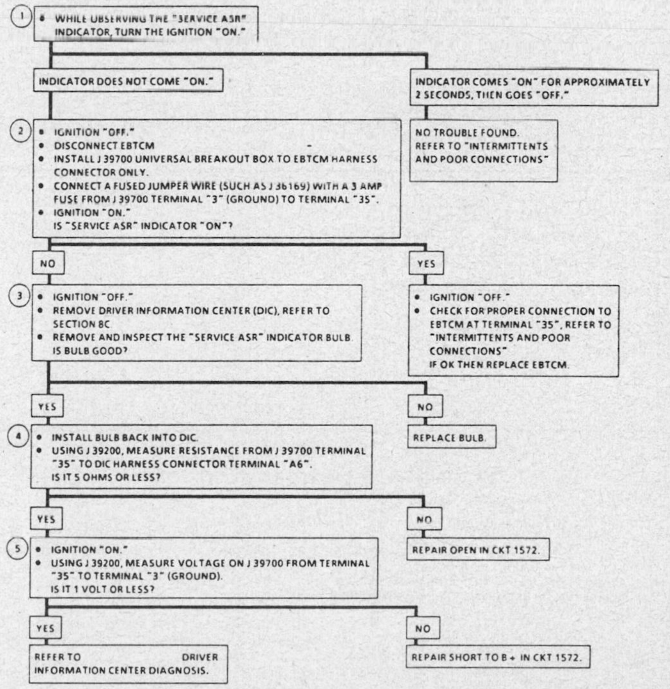
1
WHILE OBSERVING THE "SERVICE ASR" INDICATOR, TURN THE IGNITION "ON."
INDICATOR DOES NOT COME "ON."
INDICATOR COMES "ON" FOR APPROXIMATELY 2 SECONDS, THEN GOES "OFF."
NO TROUBLE FOUND. REFER TO "INTERMITTENTS AND POOR CONNECTIONS"
2
IGNITION "OFF."
DISCONNECT EBTCM
INSTALL J 39700 UNIVERSAL BREAKOUT BOX TO EBTCM HARNESS CONNECTOR ONLY.
CONNECT A FUSED JUMPER WIRE (SUCH AS J 36169) WITH A 3 AMP FUSE FROM J 39700 TERMINAL "3" (GROUND) TO TERMINAL "35".
IGNITION "ON."
IS "SERVICE ASR" INDICATOR "ON"?
NO
YES
3
IGNITION "OFF."
REMOVE DRIVER INFORMATION CENTER (DIC), REFER TO SECTION 8C.
REMOVE AND INSPECT THE "SERVICE ASR" INDICATOR BULB. IS BULB GOOD?
IGNITION "OFF."
CHECK FOR PROPER CONNECTION TO EBTCM AT TERMINAL "35", REFER TO "INTERMITTENTS AND POOR CONNECTIONS"
IF OK THEN REPLACE EBTCM.
YES
NO
REPLACE BULB.
4
INSTALL BULB BACK INTO DIC.
USING J 39200, MEASURE RESISTANCE FROM J 39700 TERMINAL "35" TO DIC HARNESS CONNECTOR TERMINAL "A6". IS IT 5 OHMS OR LESS?
YES
NO
REPAIR OPEN IN CKT 1572.
5
IGNITION "ON."
USING J 39200, MEASURE VOLTAGE ON J 39700 FROM TERMINAL "35" TO TERMINAL "3" (GROUND). IS IT 1 VOLT OR LESS?
YES
NO
REFER TO DRIVER INFORMATION CENTER DIAGNOSIS.
REPAIR SHORT TO B+ IN CKT 1572.

Chart Test Description: Number(s) below refer to circled number(s) on the diagnostic chart.

1. Confirms that a malfunction condition exists.
2. Checks to see if the indicator can be turned "ON" manually.
3. Checks the integrity of the indicator bulb.
4. Checks for an indicator low side circuit open.
5. Checks for an indicator low side circuit short to B+.

GC402940085500AX

GC402940085500BX

Fig. 17 Test D: Service ASR Indicator Inoperative. 1994

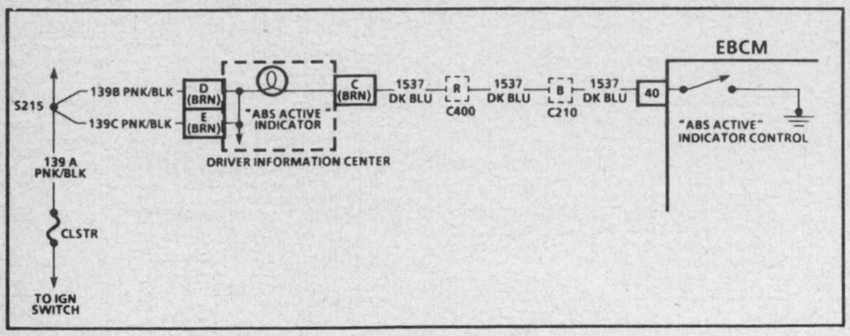
EBCM
S215
139B PNK/BLK
139C PNK/BLK
D (BRN)
E (BRN)
C (BRN)
"ABS ACTIVE" INDICATOR
DRIVER INFORMATION CENTER
1537 DK BLU
R
C400
B
C210
40
"ABS ACTIVE" INDICATOR CONTROL
139 A PNK/BLK
CLSTR
TO IGN SWITCH

CHART E

"ABS ACTIVE" INDICATOR ALWAYS "ON"

Test Description: Number(s) below refer to circled number(s) on the diagnostic chart.

1. This test confirms that a fault condition exists.
2. This test checks if the fault is due to a fault code setting condition.
3. This test checks whether the fault is due to an indicator low side circuit short to ground or an EBCM circuit fault.

GC402930040700AX

1992

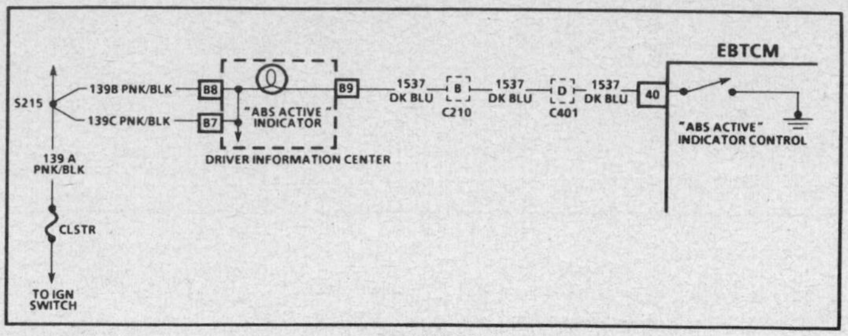
EBTCM
S215
139B PNK/BLK
139C PNK/BLK
B8
B7
B9
"ABS ACTIVE" INDICATOR
DRIVER INFORMATION CENTER
1537 DK BLU
B
C210
D
C401
40
"ABS ACTIVE" INDICATOR CONTROL
139 A PNK/BLK
CLSTR
TO IGN SWITCH

CHART E

"ABS ACTIVE" INDICATOR ALWAYS "ON"

Test Description: Number(s) below refer to circled number(s) on the diagnostic chart.

1. This test confirms that a malfunction condition exists.
2. This test checks if the malfunction is due to a DTC setting condition.
3. This test checks whether the malfunction is due to an indicator low side circuit short to ground or an EBTCM circuit malfunction.

GC402930040700BX

1993

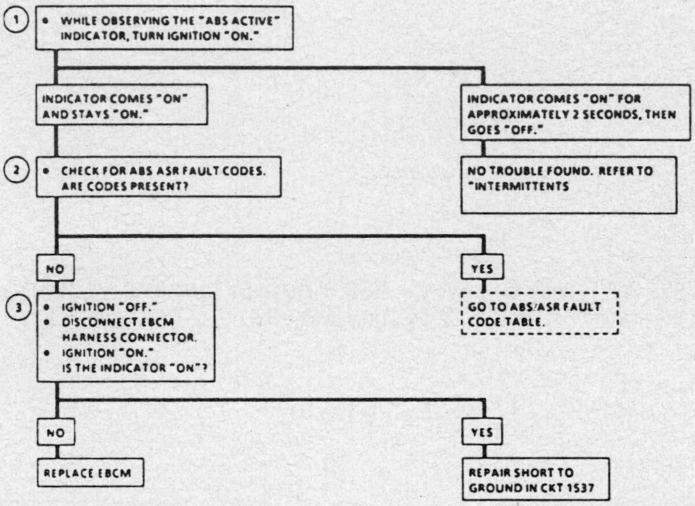
1
• WHILE OBSERVING THE "ABS ACTIVE" INDICATOR, TURN IGNITION "ON."
INDICATOR COMES "ON" AND STAYS "ON."
INDICATOR COMES "ON" FOR APPROXIMATELY 2 SECONDS, THEN GOES "OFF."
2
• CHECK FOR ABS ASR FAULT CODES. ARE CODES PRESENT?
NO TROUBLE FOUND. REFER TO "INTERMITTENTS
NO
YES
3
• IGNITION "OFF."
• DISCONNECT EBCM HARNESS CONNECTOR.
• IGNITION "ON." IS THE INDICATOR "ON"?
GO TO ABS/ASR FAULT CODE TABLE.
NO
YES
REPLACE EBCM
REPAIR SHORT TO GROUND IN CKT 1537

GC402920040700CX

Fig. 18 Test E: ABS Active Indicator Always On 1992–93

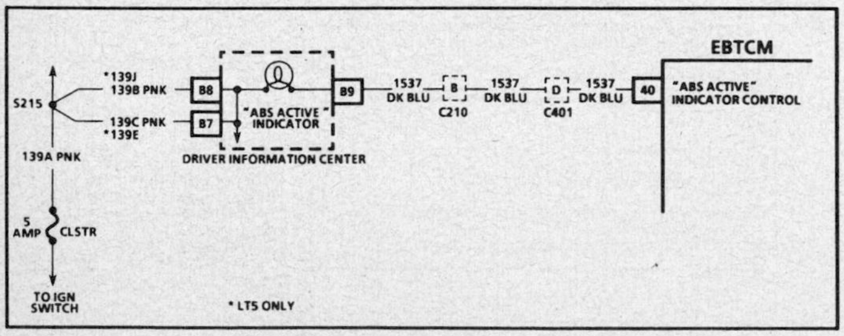
EBTCM
S215
*139J
139B PNK
139C PNK
*139E
B8
B7
B9
"ABS ACTIVE" INDICATOR
DRIVER INFORMATION CENTER
1537 DK BLU
B
C210
D
C401
40
"ABS ACTIVE" INDICATOR CONTROL
139A PNK
5 AMP
CLSTR
TO IGN SWITCH
* LTS ONLY

CHART E

"ABS ACTIVE" INDICATOR ALWAYS "ON"

Chart Test Description: Number(s) below refer to circled number(s) on the diagnostic chart.

1. Confirms that a malfunction condition exists.
2. Checks if the malfunction is due to a DTC setting condition.
3. Determines whether the malfunction is due to an indicator low side circuit short to ground or an EBTCM circuit malfunction.

GC402940085600AX

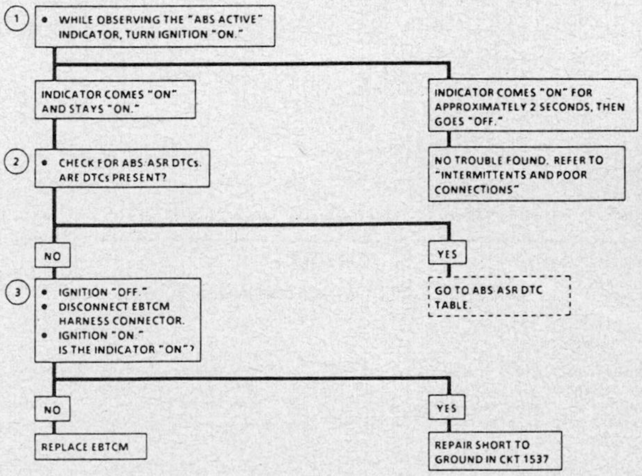
1
• WHILE OBSERVING THE "ABS ACTIVE" INDICATOR, TURN IGNITION "ON."
INDICATOR COMES "ON" AND STAYS "ON."
INDICATOR COMES "ON" FOR APPROXIMATELY 2 SECONDS, THEN GOES "OFF."
2
• CHECK FOR ABS ASR DTCs. ARE DTCs PRESENT?
NO TROUBLE FOUND. REFER TO "INTERMITTENTS AND POOR CONNECTIONS"
NO
YES
3
• IGNITION "OFF."
• DISCONNECT EBTCM HARNESS CONNECTOR.
• IGNITION "ON." IS THE INDICATOR "ON"?
GO TO ABS ASR DTC TABLE.
NO
YES
REPLACE EBTCM
REPAIR SHORT TO GROUND IN CKT 1537

GC402940085600BX

Fig. 19 Test E: ABS Active Indicator Always On. 1994

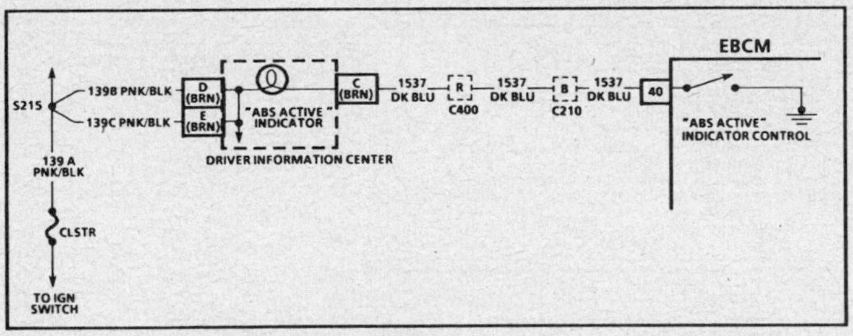
EBCM
S215
139B PNK/BLK
139C PNK/BLK
D (BRN)
E (BRN)
"ABS ACTIVE" INDICATOR
C (BRN)
1537 DK BLU
R
C400
1537 DK BLU
B
C210
1537 DK BLU
40
"ABS ACTIVE" INDICATOR CONTROL
DRIVER INFORMATION CENTER
139 A PNK/BLK
CLSTR
TO IGN SWITCH

CHART F

"ABS ACTIVE" INDICATOR INOPERATIVE

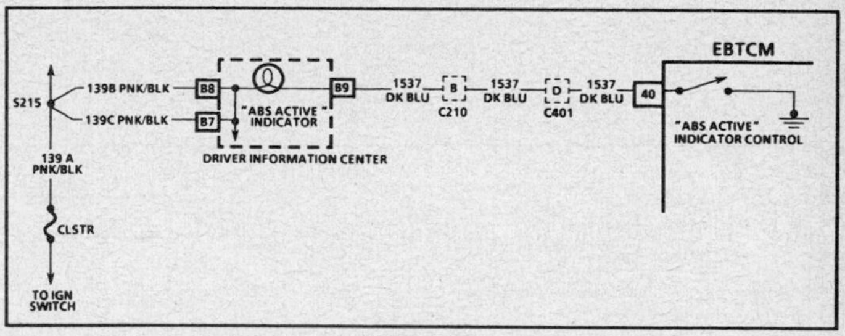
EBTCM
S215
139B PNK/BLK
139C PNK/BLK
B8
B7
"ABS ACTIVE" INDICATOR
B9
1537 DK BLU
B
C210
1537 DK BLU
D
C401
1537 DK BLU
40
"ABS ACTIVE" INDICATOR CONTROL
DRIVER INFORMATION CENTER
139 A PNK/BLK
CLSTR
TO IGN SWITCH

CHART F

"ABS ACTIVE" INDICATOR INOPERATIVE

Test Description: Number(s) below refer to circled number(s) on the diagnostic chart.

1. This test confirms that a fault condition exists.
2. This test checks the integrity of the indicator bulb.
3. This test checks for an indicator low side circuit open.
4. This test checks for an indicator low side circuit short to B+.
5. This test determines whether the fault is due to an EBCM circuit fault or an open in the DIC printed circuit.

GC402920040800AX

1992

Test Description: Number(s) below refer to circled number(s) on the diagnostic chart.

1. This test confirms that a malfunction condition exists.
2. This test checks the integrity of the indicator bulb.
3. This test checks for an indicator low side circuit open.
4. This test checks for an indicator low side circuit short to B+.
5. This test determines whether the malfunction is due to an EBTCM circuit malfunction or an open in the DIC printed circuit.

GC402930040800BX

1993

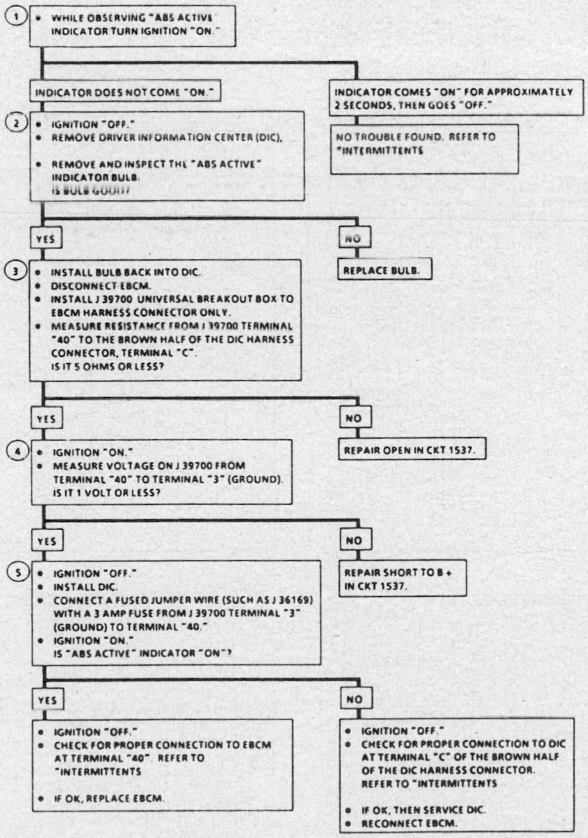
1
• WHILE OBSERVING "ABS ACTIVE INDICATOR TURN IGNITION "ON."
INDICATOR DOES NOT COME "ON."
INDICATOR COMES "ON" FOR APPROXIMATELY 2 SECONDS, THEN GOES "OFF."
NO TROUBLE FOUND. REFER TO "INTERMITTENTS
2
• IGNITION "OFF."
• REMOVE DRIVER INFORMATION CENTER (DIC),
• REMOVE AND INSPECT THE "ABS ACTIVE" INDICATOR BULB.
YES
NO
REPLACE BULB.
3
• INSTALL BULB BACK INTO DIC.
• DISCONNECT EBCM.
• INSTALL J 39700 UNIVERSAL BREAKOUT BOX TO EBCM HARNESS CONNECTOR ONLY.
• MEASURE RESISTANCE FROM J 39700 TERMINAL "40" TO THE BROWN HALF OF THE DIC HARNESS CONNECTOR, TERMINAL "C".
IS IT 5 OHMS OR LESS?
YES
NO
REPAIR OPEN IN CKT 1537.
4
• IGNITION "ON."
• MEASURE VOLTAGE ON J 39700 FROM TERMINAL "40" TO TERMINAL "3" (GROUND).
IS IT 1 VOLT OR LESS?
YES
NO
REPAIR SHORT TO B + IN CKT 1537.
5
• IGNITION "OFF."
• INSTALL DIC.
• CONNECT A FUSED JUMPER WIRE (SUCH AS J 36169) WITH A 3 AMP FUSE FROM J 39700 TERMINAL "3" (GROUND) TO TERMINAL "40."
• IGNITION "ON."
IS "ABS ACTIVE" INDICATOR "ON"?
YES
NO
• IGNITION "OFF."
• CHECK FOR PROPER CONNECTION TO EBCM AT TERMINAL "40". REFER TO "INTERMITTENTS
• IF OK, REPLACE EBCM.
• IGNITION "OFF."
• CHECK FOR PROPER CONNECTION TO DIC AT TERMINAL "C" OF THE BROWN HALF OF THE DIC HARNESS CONNECTOR. REFER TO "INTERMITTENTS
• IF OK, THEN SERVICE DIC.
• RECONNECT EBCM.

GC402920040800CX

Fig. 20 Test F: ABS Active Indicator Inoperative. 1992-93

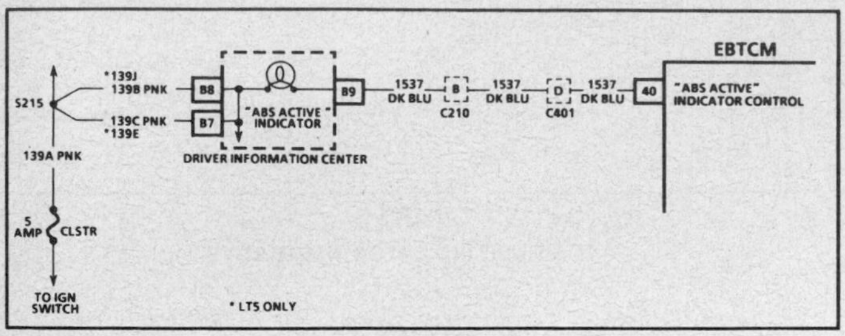
EBTCM
S215
*139J
139B PNK
139C PNK
*139E
139A PNK
B8
B7
B9
"ABS ACTIVE" INDICATOR
DRIVER INFORMATION CENTER
1537 DK BLU
C210
C401
40
"ABS ACTIVE" INDICATOR CONTROL
5 AMP
CLSTR
TO IGN SWITCH
* LT5 ONLY

CHART F
"ABS ACTIVE" INDICATOR INOPERATIVE

Chart Test Description: Number(s) below refer to circled number(s) on the diagnostic chart.

1. Confirms that a malfunction condition exists.
2. Checks to see if the indicator can be turned "ON" manually.
3. Checks the integrity of the indicator bulb.
4. Checks for an indicator low side circuit open.
5. Checks for an indicator low side circuit short to B+.

GC402940085700AX

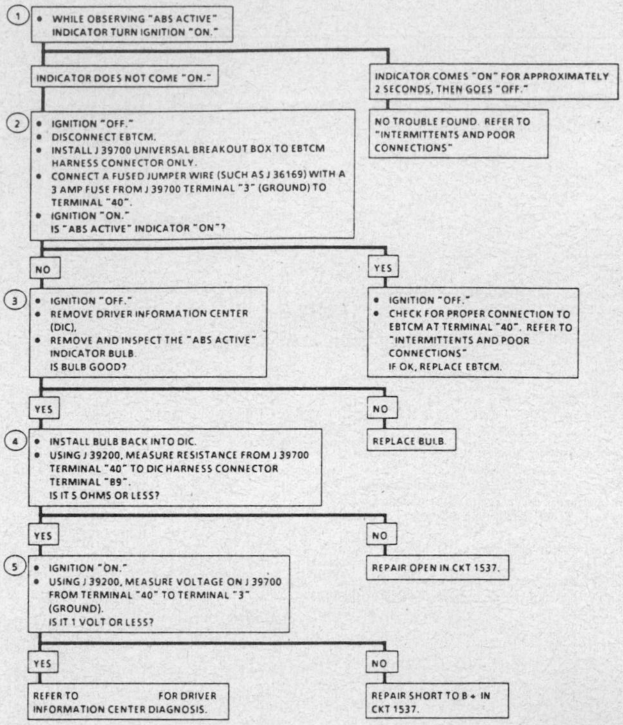
1 • WHILE OBSERVING "ABS ACTIVE" INDICATOR TURN IGNITION "ON."
INDICATOR DOES NOT COME "ON."
INDICATOR COMES "ON" FOR APPROXIMATELY 2 SECONDS, THEN GOES "OFF."
NO TROUBLE FOUND. REFER TO "INTERMITTENTS AND POOR CONNECTIONS"
2 • IGNITION "OFF." • DISCONNECT EBTCM. • INSTALL J 39700 UNIVERSAL BREAKOUT BOX TO EBTCM HARNESS CONNECTOR ONLY. • CONNECT A FUSED JUMPER WIRE (SUCH AS J 36169) WITH A 3 AMP FUSE FROM J 39700 TERMINAL "3" (GROUND) TO TERMINAL "40". • IGNITION "ON." IS "ABS ACTIVE" INDICATOR "ON"?
NO
YES
3 • IGNITION "OFF." • REMOVE DRIVER INFORMATION CENTER (DIC). • REMOVE AND INSPECT THE "ABS ACTIVE" INDICATOR BULB. IS BULB GOOD?
• IGNITION "OFF." • CHECK FOR PROPER CONNECTION TO EBTCM AT TERMINAL "40". REFER TO "INTERMITTENTS AND POOR CONNECTIONS" IF OK, REPLACE EBTCM.
YES
NO
4 • INSTALL BULB BACK INTO DIC. • USING J 39200, MEASURE RESISTANCE FROM J 39700 TERMINAL "40" TO DIC HARNESS CONNECTOR TERMINAL "B9". IS IT 5 OHMS OR LESS?
REPLACE BULB.
YES
NO
5 • IGNITION "ON." • USING J 39200, MEASURE VOLTAGE ON J 39700 FROM TERMINAL "40" TO TERMINAL "3" (GROUND). IS IT 1 VOLT OR LESS?
REPAIR OPEN IN CKT 1537.
YES
NO
REFER TO FOR DRIVER INFORMATION CENTER DIAGNOSIS.
REPAIR SHORT TO B+ IN CKT 1537.

GC402940085700BX

Fig. 21 Test F: ABS Active Indicator Inoperative. 1994

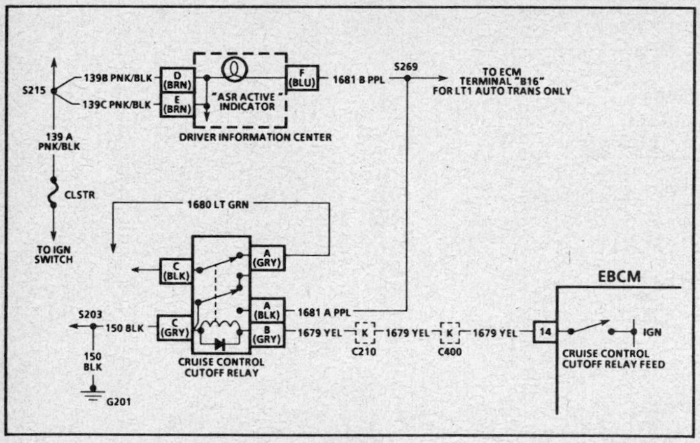
S215
139B PNK/BLK
139C PNK/BLK
D (BRN)
E (BRN)
F (BLU)
"ASR ACTIVE" INDICATOR
DRIVER INFORMATION CENTER
1681 B PPL
S269
TO ECM TERMINAL "B16" FOR LT1 AUTO TRANS ONLY
139 A PNK/BLK
CLSTR
TO IGN SWITCH
1680 LT GRN
C (BLK)
A (GRY)
A (BLK)
B (GRY)
C (GRY)
S203
150 BLK
150 BLK
G201
1681 A PPL
1679 YEL
C210
C400
14
EBCM
IGN
CRUISE CONTROL CUTOFF RELAY
CRUISE CONTROL CUTOFF RELAY FEED

CHART G
"ASR ACTIVE" INDICATOR "ON" WITH NO CODES SET

Test Description: Number(s) below refer to circled number(s) on the diagnostic chart.

1. This test confirms that a fault condition exists.
2. This test checks whether the fault is due to a fault code setting condition, specifically Code 57.
3. This test determines whether the fault is due to an indicator low side circuit short to ground or stuck contacts in the Cruise Control Cutoff Relay.

GC402920040900AX

1992

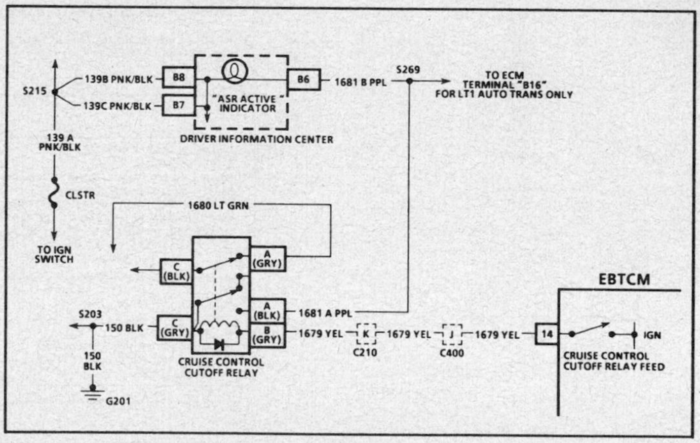
S215
139B PNK/BLK
139C PNK/BLK
B8
B7
B6
"ASR ACTIVE" INDICATOR
DRIVER INFORMATION CENTER
1681 B PPL
S269
TO ECM TERMINAL "B16" FOR LT1 AUTO TRANS ONLY
139 A PNK/BLK
CLSTR
TO IGN SWITCH
1680 LT GRN
C (BLK)
A (GRY)
A (BLK)
B (GRY)
C (GRY)
S203
150 BLK
150 BLK
G201
1681 A PPL
1679 YEL
C210
C400
14
EBTCM
IGN
CRUISE CONTROL CUTOFF RELAY
CRUISE CONTROL CUTOFF RELAY FEED

CHART G
"ASR ACTIVE" INDICATOR "ON" WITH NO DTCs SET

Test Description: Number(s) below refer to circled number(s) on the diagnostic chart.

1. This test confirms that a malfunction condition exists.
2. This test checks whether the malfunction is due to a DTC setting condition, specifically DTC 57.
3. This test determines whether the malfunction is due to an indicator low side circuit short to ground or stuck contacts in the cruise control cutoff relay.

GC402930040900BX

1993

Fig. 22 Test G: ASR Active Indicator On w/No Codes Set (Part 1 of 2). 1992–93

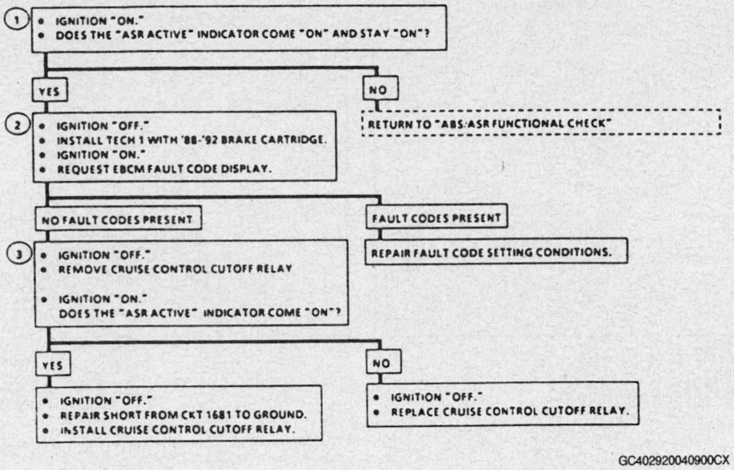
1
• IGNITION "ON."
• DOES THE "ASR ACTIVE" INDICATOR COME "ON" AND STAY "ON"?
YES
NO
RETURN TO "ABS/ASR FUNCTIONAL CHECK"
2
• IGNITION "OFF."
• INSTALL TECH 1 WITH '88-'92 BRAKE CARTRIDGE.
• IGNITION "ON."
• REQUEST EBCM FAULT CODE DISPLAY.
NO FAULT CODES PRESENT
FAULT CODES PRESENT
REPAIR FAULT CODE SETTING CONDITIONS.
3
• IGNITION "OFF."
• REMOVE CRUISE CONTROL CUTOFF RELAY
• IGNITION "ON."
DOES THE "ASR ACTIVE" INDICATOR COME "ON"?
YES
NO
• IGNITION "OFF."
• REPAIR SHORT FROM CKT 1681 TO GROUND.
• INSTALL CRUISE CONTROL CUTOFF RELAY.
• IGNITION "OFF."
• REPLACE CRUISE CONTROL CUTOFF RELAY.
GC402920040900CX

Fig. 22 Test G: ASR Active Indicator On w/No Codes Set (Part 2 of 2). 1992–93

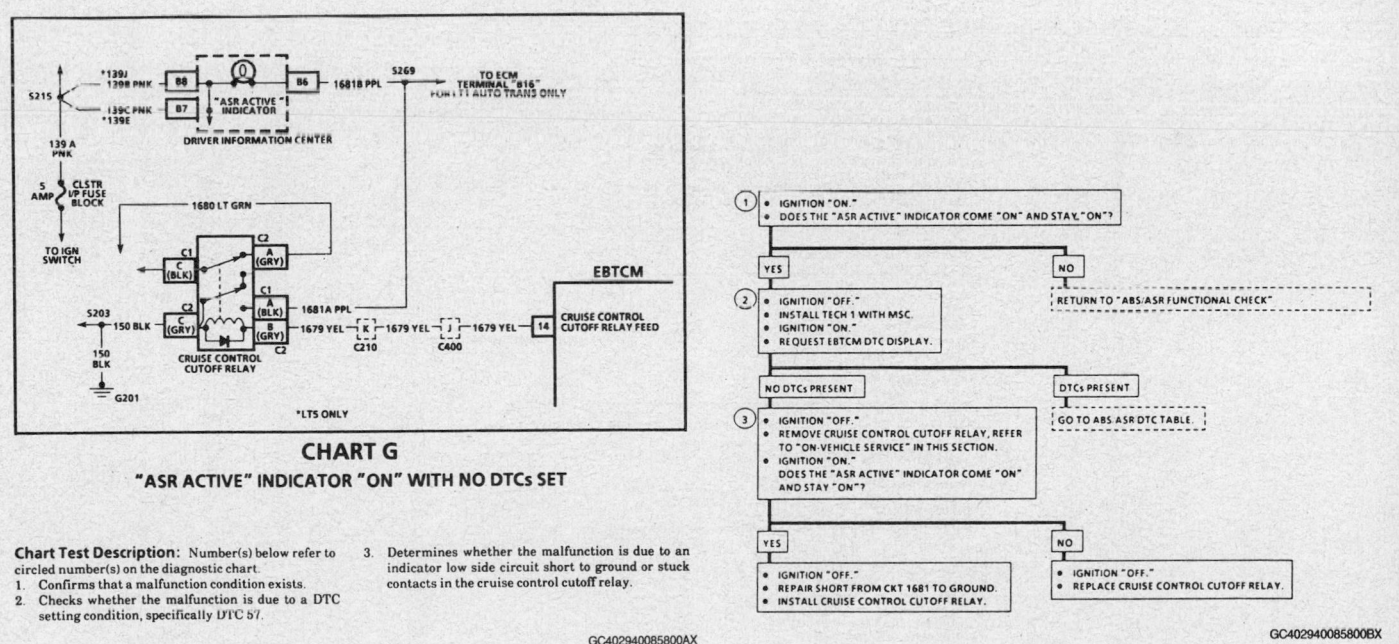

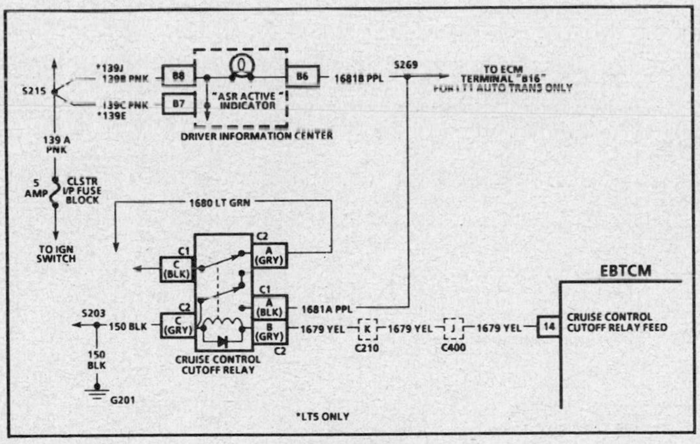
*139J
139B PNK
B8
B6
1681B PPL
S269
TO ECM TERMINAL "B16" FOR LT1 AUTO TRANS ONLY
S215
139C PNK
*139E
B7
"ASR ACTIVE" INDICATOR
DRIVER INFORMATION CENTER
139 A PNK
5 AMP
CLSTR I/P FUSE BLOCK
TO IGN SWITCH
1680 LT GRN
C1
C (BLK)
C2
A (GRY)
C1
A (BLK)
1681A PPL
S203
150 BLK
C2
C (GRY)
B (GRY)
C2
1679 YEL
K
C210
1679 YEL
J
C400
1679 YEL
14
EBTCM
CRUISE CONTROL CUTOFF RELAY FEED
150 BLK
G201
CRUISE CONTROL CUTOFF RELAY
*LT5 ONLY

CHART G

"ASR ACTIVE" INDICATOR "ON" WITH NO DTCs SET

Chart Test Description: Number(s) below refer to circled number(s) on the diagnostic chart.

1. Confirms that a malfunction condition exists.
2. Checks whether the malfunction is due to a DTC setting condition, specifically DTC 57.
3. Determines whether the malfunction is due to an indicator low side circuit short to ground or stuck contacts in the cruise control cutoff relay.

GC402940085800AX

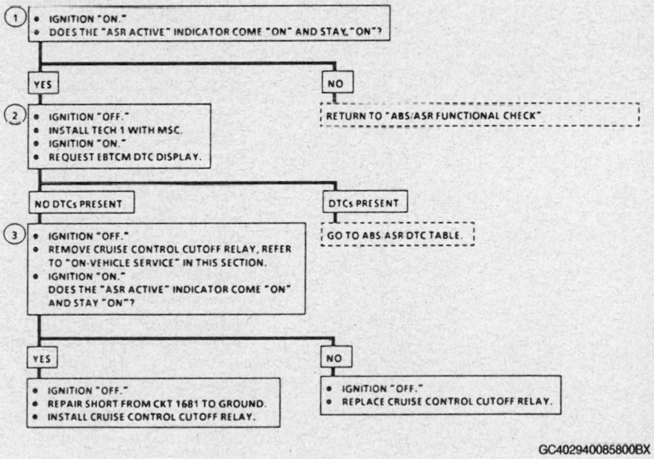
1
• IGNITION "ON."
• DOES THE "ASR ACTIVE" INDICATOR COME "ON" AND STAY "ON"?
YES
NO
RETURN TO "ABS/ASR FUNCTIONAL CHECK"
2
• IGNITION "OFF."
• INSTALL TECH 1 WITH MSC.
• IGNITION "ON."
• REQUEST EBTCM DTC DISPLAY.
NO DTCs PRESENT
DTCs PRESENT
GO TO ABS/ASR DTC TABLE.
3
• IGNITION "OFF."
• REMOVE CRUISE CONTROL CUTOFF RELAY, REFER TO "ON-VEHICLE SERVICE" IN THIS SECTION.
• IGNITION "ON."
DOES THE "ASR ACTIVE" INDICATOR COME "ON" AND STAY "ON"?
YES
NO
• IGNITION "OFF."
• REPAIR SHORT FROM CKT 1681 TO GROUND.
• INSTALL CRUISE CONTROL CUTOFF RELAY.
• IGNITION "OFF."
• REPLACE CRUISE CONTROL CUTOFF RELAY.
GC402940085800BX

Fig. 23 Test G: ASR Active Indicator On w/No Codes Set. 1994

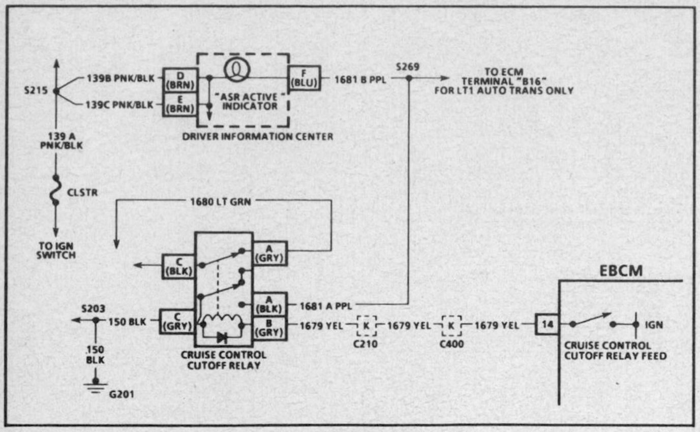
S215
139B PNK/BLK
139C PNK/BLK
D (BRN)
E (BRN)
F (BLU)
"ASR ACTIVE" INDICATOR
1681 B PPL
S269
TO ECM TERMINAL "B16" FOR LT1 AUTO TRANS ONLY
DRIVER INFORMATION CENTER
139 A PNK/BLK
CLSTR
TO IGN SWITCH
1680 LT GRN
C (BLK)
A (GRY)
A (BLK)
B (GRY)
C (GRY)
1681 A PPL
S203
150 BLK
1679 YEL
K
C210
C400
14
IGN
EBCM
150 BLK
G201
CRUISE CONTROL CUTOFF RELAY
CRUISE CONTROL CUTOFF RELAY FEED

CHART H

"ASR ACTIVE" INDICATOR INOPERATIVE WITH NO CODES SET

Test Description: Number(s) below refer to circled number(s) on the diagnostic chart.

1. This test confirms that a fault condition exists.
2. This test checks whether the fault is due to a fault code setting condition, specifically Code 57.
3. This determines whether the fault is due to stuck contacts in the Cruise Control Cutoff Relay or a fault in the indicator low side circuit.
4. This test checks whether the indicator low side circuit fault is a short to B+.
5. This test checks the integrity of the indicator bulb.
6. This test determines whether the fault is an open in the indicator low side circuit or an open in the DIC printed circuit.

GC402920041000AX

1992

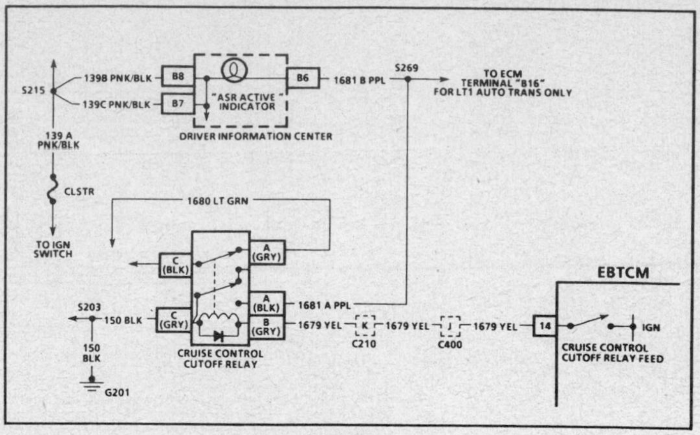
S215
139B PNK/BLK
139C PNK/BLK
B8
B7
B6
"ASR ACTIVE" INDICATOR
1681 B PPL
S269
TO ECM TERMINAL "B16" FOR LT1 AUTO TRANS ONLY
DRIVER INFORMATION CENTER
139 A PNK/BLK
CLSTR
TO IGN SWITCH
1680 LT GRN
C (BLK)
A (GRY)
A (BLK)
B (GRY)
C (GRY)
1681 A PPL
S203
150 BLK
1679 YEL
K
J
C210
C400
14
IGN
EBTCM
150 BLK
G201
CRUISE CONTROL CUTOFF RELAY
CRUISE CONTROL CUTOFF RELAY FEED

CHART H

"ASR ACTIVE" INDICATOR INOPERATIVE WITH NO DTCs SET

Test Description: Number(s) below refer to circled number(s) on the diagnostic chart.

1. This test confirms that a malfunction condition exists.
2. This test checks whether the malfunction is due to a DTC setting condition, specifically DTC 57.
3. This determines whether the malfunction is due to stuck contacts in the cruise control cutoff relay or a malfunction in the indicator low side circuit.
4. This test checks whether the indicator low side circuit malfunction is a short to B+.
5. This test checks the integrity of the indicator bulb.
6. This test determines whether the malfunction is an open in the indicator low side circuit or an open in the DIC printed circuit.

GC402930041000BX

1993

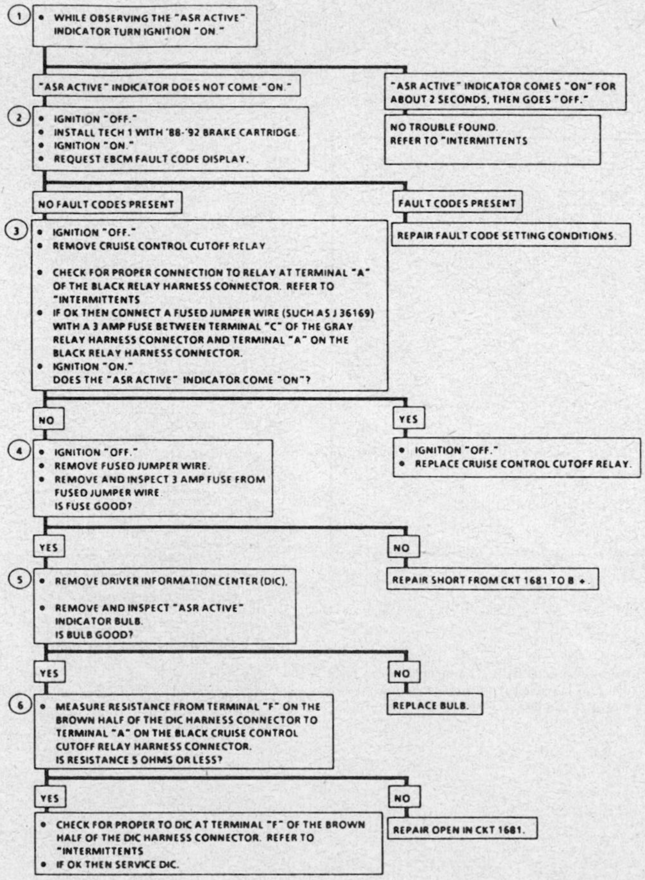
1 • WHILE OBSERVING THE "ASR ACTIVE" INDICATOR TURN IGNITION "ON."
"ASR ACTIVE" INDICATOR DOES NOT COME "ON."
"ASR ACTIVE" INDICATOR COMES "ON" FOR ABOUT 2 SECONDS, THEN GOES "OFF."
NO TROUBLE FOUND. REFER TO "INTERMITTENTS
2 • IGNITION "OFF." • INSTALL TECH 1 WITH '88-'92 BRAKE CARTRIDGE. • IGNITION "ON." • REQUEST EBCM FAULT CODE DISPLAY.
NO FAULT CODES PRESENT
FAULT CODES PRESENT
REPAIR FAULT CODE SETTING CONDITIONS.
3 • IGNITION "OFF." • REMOVE CRUISE CONTROL CUTOFF RELAY
• CHECK FOR PROPER CONNECTION TO RELAY AT TERMINAL "A" OF THE BLACK RELAY HARNESS CONNECTOR. REFER TO "INTERMITTENTS
• IF OK THEN CONNECT A FUSED JUMPER WIRE (SUCH AS J 36169) WITH A 3 AMP FUSE BETWEEN TERMINAL "C" OF THE GRAY RELAY HARNESS CONNECTOR AND TERMINAL "A" ON THE BLACK RELAY HARNESS CONNECTOR.
• IGNITION "ON." DOES THE "ASR ACTIVE" INDICATOR COME "ON"?
NO
YES
• IGNITION "OFF." • REPLACE CRUISE CONTROL CUTOFF RELAY.
4 • IGNITION "OFF." • REMOVE FUSED JUMPER WIRE. • REMOVE AND INSPECT 3 AMP FUSE FROM FUSED JUMPER WIRE. IS FUSE GOOD?
YES
NO
REPAIR SHORT FROM CKT 1681 TO B +.
5 • REMOVE DRIVER INFORMATION CENTER (DIC).
• REMOVE AND INSPECT "ASR ACTIVE" INDICATOR BULB. IS BULB GOOD?
YES
NO
REPLACE BULB.
6 • MEASURE RESISTANCE FROM TERMINAL "F" ON THE BROWN HALF OF THE DIC HARNESS CONNECTOR TO TERMINAL "A" ON THE BLACK CRUISE CONTROL CUTOFF RELAY HARNESS CONNECTOR. IS RESISTANCE 5 OHMS OR LESS?
YES
NO
REPAIR OPEN IN CKT 1681.
• CHECK FOR PROPER TO DIC AT TERMINAL "F" OF THE BROWN HALF OF THE DIC HARNESS CONNECTOR. REFER TO "INTERMITTENTS
• IF OK THEN SERVICE DIC.

GC402920041000CX

Fig. 24 Test H: ASR Active Indicator Inoperative w/No Codes Set. 1992-93

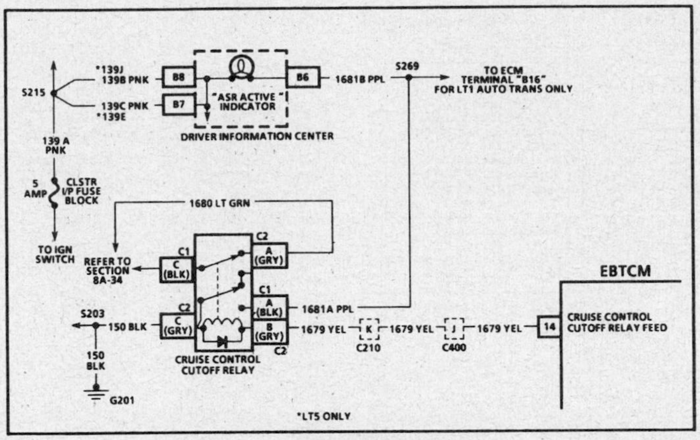
S215
139A PNK
5 AMP
CLSTR I/P FUSE BLOCK
TO IGN SWITCH
"ASR ACTIVE" INDICATOR
DRIVER INFORMATION CENTER
S269
TO ECM TERMINAL "B16" FOR LT1 AUTO TRANS ONLY
1680 LT GRN
REFER TO SECTION 8A-34
S203
150 BLK
G201
CRUISE CONTROL CUTOFF RELAY
1681A PPL
1679 YEL
C210
C400
EBTCM
CRUISE CONTROL CUTOFF RELAY FEED
*LT5 ONLY

CHART H

"ASR ACTIVE" INDICATOR INOPERATIVE WITH NO DTCs SET

Chart Test Description: Number(s) below refer to circled number(s) on the diagnostic chart.

1. Confirms that a malfunction condition exists.
2. Checks whether the malfunction is due to a DTC setting condition, specifically DTC 57.
3. Determines whether the malfunction is due to stuck contacts in the cruise control cutoff relay or a malfunction in the indicator low side circuit.
4. Checks whether the indicator low side circuit malfunction is a short to B +.
5. Checks the integrity of the indicator bulb.
6. Determines whether the malfunction is an open in the indicator low side circuit or an open in the DIC printed circuit.

GC402940085900AX

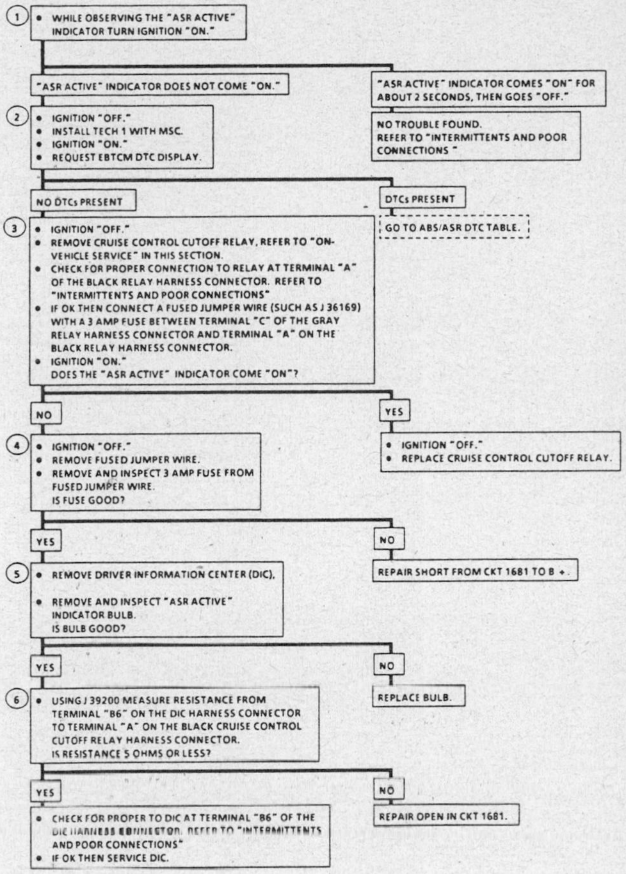
1 • WHILE OBSERVING THE "ASR ACTIVE" INDICATOR TURN IGNITION "ON."
"ASR ACTIVE" INDICATOR DOES NOT COME "ON."
"ASR ACTIVE" INDICATOR COMES "ON" FOR ABOUT 2 SECONDS, THEN GOES "OFF."
NO TROUBLE FOUND. REFER TO "INTERMITTENTS AND POOR CONNECTIONS"
2 • IGNITION "OFF." • INSTALL TECH 1 WITH MSC. • IGNITION "ON." • REQUEST EBTCM DTC DISPLAY.
NO DTCs PRESENT
DTCs PRESENT
GO TO ABS/ASR DTC TABLE.
3 • IGNITION "OFF." • REMOVE CRUISE CONTROL CUTOFF RELAY, REFER TO "ON-VEHICLE SERVICE" IN THIS SECTION. • CHECK FOR PROPER CONNECTION TO RELAY AT TERMINAL "A" OF THE BLACK RELAY HARNESS CONNECTOR. REFER TO "INTERMITTENTS AND POOR CONNECTIONS" • IF OK THEN CONNECT A FUSED JUMPER WIRE (SUCH AS J 36169) WITH A 3 AMP FUSE BETWEEN TERMINAL "C" OF THE GRAY RELAY HARNESS CONNECTOR AND TERMINAL "A" ON THE BLACK RELAY HARNESS CONNECTOR. • IGNITION "ON." DOES THE "ASR ACTIVE" INDICATOR COME "ON"?
NO
YES
• IGNITION "OFF." • REPLACE CRUISE CONTROL CUTOFF RELAY.
4 • IGNITION "OFF." • REMOVE FUSED JUMPER WIRE. • REMOVE AND INSPECT 3 AMP FUSE FROM FUSED JUMPER WIRE. IS FUSE GOOD?
YES
NO
REPAIR SHORT FROM CKT 1681 TO B +.
5 • REMOVE DRIVER INFORMATION CENTER (DIC). • REMOVE AND INSPECT "ASR ACTIVE" INDICATOR BULB. IS BULB GOOD?
YES
NO
REPLACE BULB.
6 • USING J 39200 MEASURE RESISTANCE FROM TERMINAL "B6" ON THE DIC HARNESS CONNECTOR TO TERMINAL "A" ON THE BLACK CRUISE CONTROL CUTOFF RELAY HARNESS CONNECTOR. IS RESISTANCE 5 OHMS OR LESS?
YES
NO
REPAIR OPEN IN CKT 1681.
• CHECK FOR PROPER TO DIC AT TERMINAL "B6" OF THE DIC HARNESS CONNECTOR. REFER TO "INTERMITTENTS AND POOR CONNECTIONS" • IF OK THEN SERVICE DIC.

GC402940085900BX

Fig. 25 Test H: ASR Active Indicator Inoperative w/No Codes Set. 1994

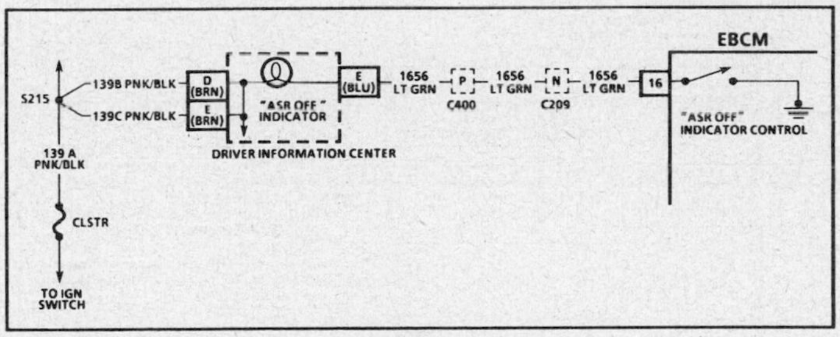
EBCM
S215
139B PNK/BLK
139C PNK/BLK
"ASR OFF" INDICATOR
1656 LT GRN
C400
C209
"ASR OFF" INDICATOR CONTROL
DRIVER INFORMATION CENTER
139 A PNK/BLK
CLSTR
TO IGN SWITCH

CHART I

"ASR OFF" INDICATOR ALWAYS "ON"

Test Description: Number(s) below refer to circled number(s) on the diagnostic chart.

1. This test confirms that a fault condition exists.
2. This test checks whether the fault is due to a fault code setting condition.
3. This test determines whether the fault is due to an indicator low side circuit short to ground or an EBCM circuit fault.
4. This test determines whether the extended "ON" time of the indicator is due to an "ASR OFF" input to the EBCM or an EBCM circuit fault.

GC402920041100AX

1992

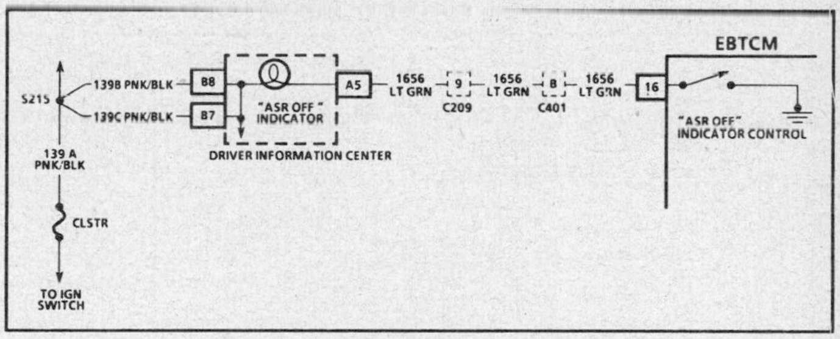
EBTCM
S215
139B PNK/BLK
139C PNK/BLK
"ASR OFF" INDICATOR
1656 LT GRN
C209
C401
"ASR OFF" INDICATOR CONTROL
DRIVER INFORMATION CENTER
139 A PNK/BLK
CLSTR
TO IGN SWITCH

CHART I

"ASR OFF" INDICATOR ALWAYS "ON"

Test Description: Number(s) below refer to circled number(s) on the diagnostic chart.

1. This test confirms that a malfunction condition exists.
2. This test checks whether the malfunction is due to a DTC setting condition.
3. This test determines whether the malfunction is due to an indicator low side circuit short to ground or an EBTCM circuit malfunction.
4. This test determines whether the extended "ON" time of the indicator is due to an "ASR OFF" input to the EBTCM or an EBTCM circuit malfunction.

GC402930041100BX

1993

Fig. 26 Test I: ASR Off Indicator Always On (Part 1 of 2). 1992–93

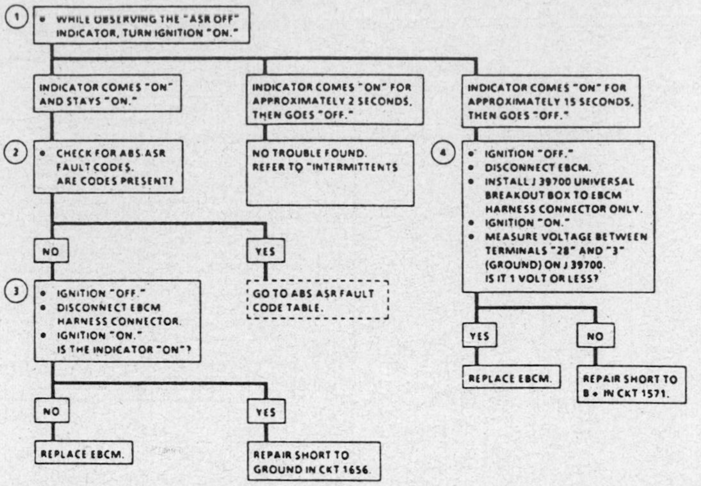

1 • WHILE OBSERVING THE "ASR OFF" INDICATOR, TURN IGNITION "ON."
INDICATOR COMES "ON" AND STAYS "ON."
INDICATOR COMES "ON" FOR APPROXIMATELY 2 SECONDS, THEN GOES "OFF."
INDICATOR COMES "ON" FOR APPROXIMATELY 15 SECONDS, THEN GOES "OFF."
2 • CHECK FOR ABS ASR FAULT CODES. ARE CODES PRESENT?
NO TROUBLE FOUND. REFER TO "INTERMITTENTS"
4 • IGNITION "OFF." • DISCONNECT EBCM. • INSTALL J 39700 UNIVERSAL BREAKOUT BOX TO EBCM HARNESS CONNECTOR ONLY. • IGNITION "ON." • MEASURE VOLTAGE BETWEEN TERMINALS "28" AND "3" (GROUND) ON J 39700. IS IT 1 VOLT OR LESS?
NO
YES
GO TO ABS ASR FAULT CODE TABLE.
3 • IGNITION "OFF." • DISCONNECT EBCM HARNESS CONNECTOR. • IGNITION "ON." IS THE INDICATOR "ON"?
YES
NO
REPLACE EBCM.
REPAIR SHORT TO B+ IN CKT 1571.
NO
YES
REPLACE EBCM.
REPAIR SHORT TO GROUND IN CKT 1656.

GC402920041100CX

Fig. 26 Test I: ASR Off Indicator Always On (Part 2 of 2). 1992–93

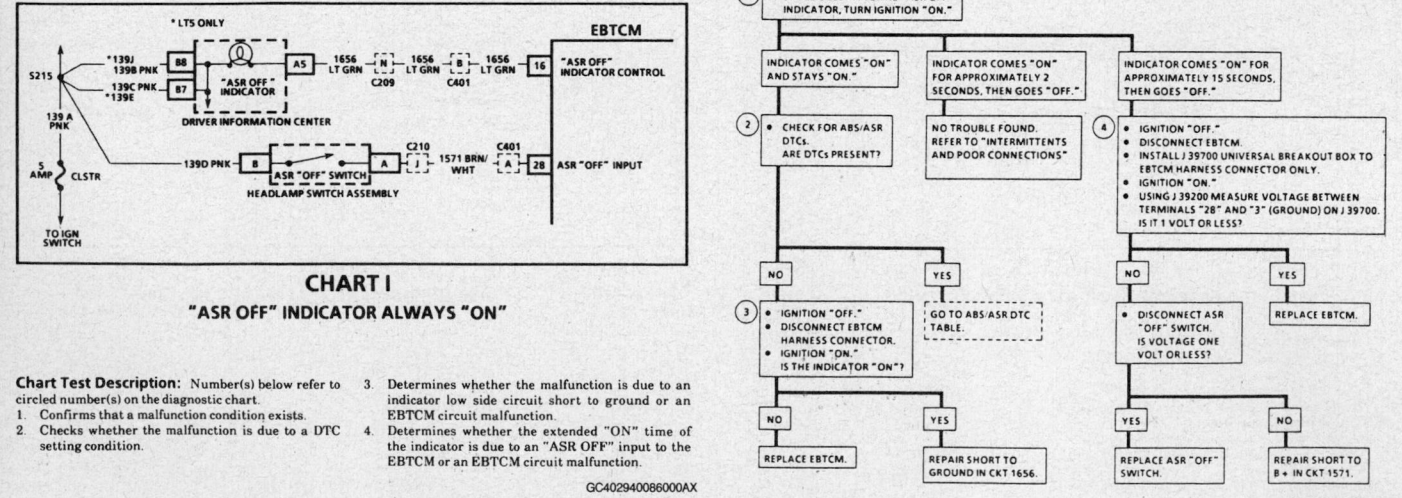

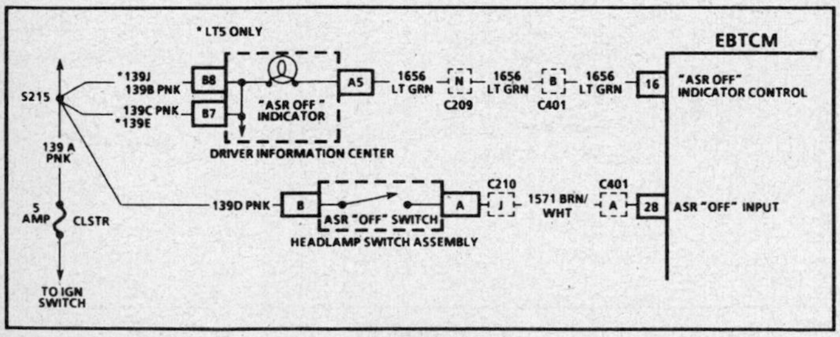

* LTS ONLY
EBTCM
S215
*139J
139B PNK
B8
139C PNK
*139E
B7
"ASR OFF" INDICATOR
A5
1656 LT GRN
N
C209
1656 LT GRN
B
C401
1656 LT GRN
16
"ASR OFF" INDICATOR CONTROL
DRIVER INFORMATION CENTER
139 A PNK
5 AMP
CLSTR
139D PNK
B
ASR "OFF" SWITCH
A
C210
J
1571 BRN/WHT
C401
A
28
ASR "OFF" INPUT
HEADLAMP SWITCH ASSEMBLY
TO IGN SWITCH

CHART I

"ASR OFF" INDICATOR ALWAYS "ON"

Chart Test Description: Number(s) below refer to circled number(s) on the diagnostic chart.

1. Confirms that a malfunction condition exists.
2. Checks whether the malfunction is due to a DTC setting condition.
3. Determines whether the malfunction is due to an indicator low side circuit short to ground or an EBTCM circuit malfunction.
4. Determines whether the extended "ON" time of the indicator is due to an "ASR OFF" input to the EBTCM or an EBTCM circuit malfunction.

GC402940086000AX

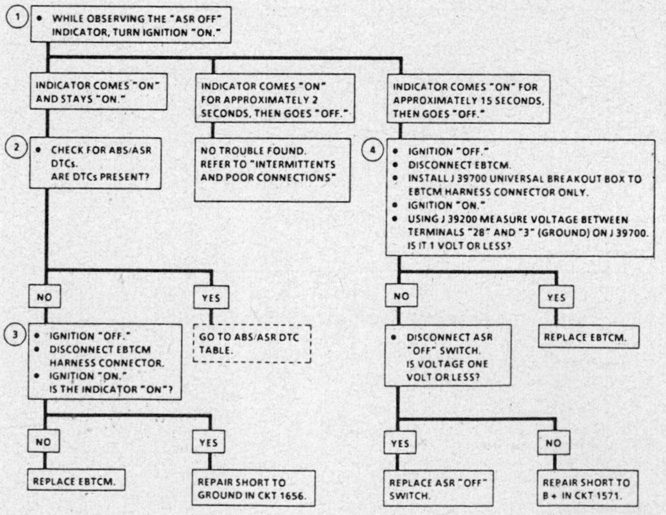

1 • WHILE OBSERVING THE "ASR OFF" INDICATOR, TURN IGNITION "ON."
INDICATOR COMES "ON" AND STAYS "ON."
INDICATOR COMES "ON" FOR APPROXIMATELY 2 SECONDS, THEN GOES "OFF."
INDICATOR COMES "ON" FOR APPROXIMATELY 15 SECONDS, THEN GOES "OFF."
2 • CHECK FOR ABS/ASR DTCs. ARE DTCs PRESENT?
NO TROUBLE FOUND. REFER TO "INTERMITTENTS AND POOR CONNECTIONS"
4 • IGNITION "OFF." • DISCONNECT EBTCM. • INSTALL J 39700 UNIVERSAL BREAKOUT BOX TO EBTCM HARNESS CONNECTOR ONLY. • IGNITION "ON." • USING J 39200 MEASURE VOLTAGE BETWEEN TERMINALS "28" AND "3" (GROUND) ON J 39700. IS IT 1 VOLT OR LESS?
NO
YES
GO TO ABS/ASR DTC TABLE.
NO
YES
REPLACE EBTCM.
3 • IGNITION "OFF." • DISCONNECT EBTCM HARNESS CONNECTOR. • IGNITION "ON." IS THE INDICATOR "ON"?
• DISCONNECT ASR "OFF" SWITCH. IS VOLTAGE ONE VOLT OR LESS?
NO
YES
REPLACE EBTCM.
REPAIR SHORT TO GROUND IN CKT 1656.
YES
NO
REPLACE ASR "OFF" SWITCH.
REPAIR SHORT TO B+ IN CKT 1571.

GC402940086000BX

Fig. 27 Test I: ASR Off Indicator Always On. 1994

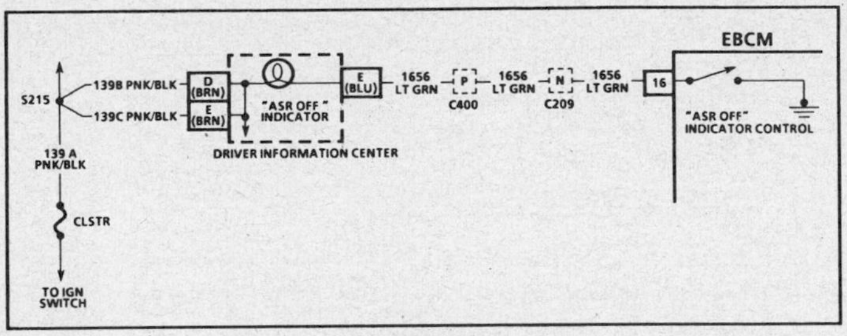
EBCM
S215
139B PNK/BLK
139C PNK/BLK
D (BRN)
E (BRN)
"ASR OFF" INDICATOR
E (BLU)
DRIVER INFORMATION CENTER
1656 LT GRN
P
C400
1656 LT GRN
N
C209
1656 LT GRN
16
"ASR OFF" INDICATOR CONTROL
139 A PNK/BLK
CLSTR
TO IGN SWITCH

CHART J

"ASR OFF" INDICATOR INOPERATIVE

Test Description: Number(s) below refer to circled number(s) on the diagnostic chart.

1. This test confirms that a fault condition exists.
2. This test checks the integrity of the indicator bulb.
3. This test checks for an indicator low side circuit open.
4. This test checks for an indicator low side circuit short to B+.
5. This test determines whether the fault is due to an EBCM circuit fault or an open in the DIC printed circuit.

GC402920041200AX

1992

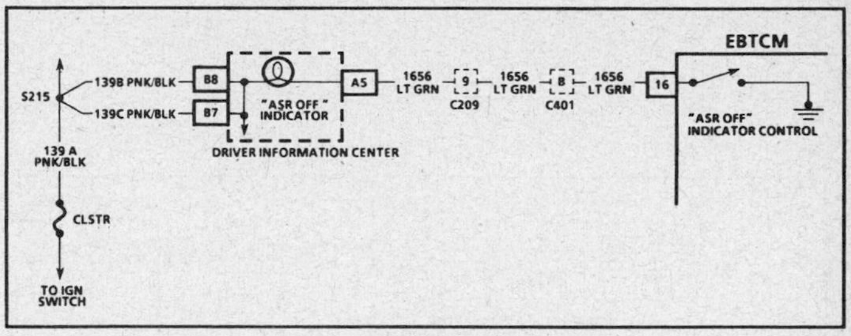
EBTCM
S215
139B PNK/BLK
139C PNK/BLK
B8
B7
"ASR OFF" INDICATOR
A5
DRIVER INFORMATION CENTER
1656 LT GRN
9
C209
1656 LT GRN
B
C401
1656 LT GRN
16
"ASR OFF" INDICATOR CONTROL
139 A PNK/BLK
CLSTR
TO IGN SWITCH

CHART J

"ASR OFF" INDICATOR INOPERATIVE

Test Description: Number(s) below refer to circled number(s) on the diagnostic chart.

1. This test confirms that a malfunction condition exists.
2. This test checks the integrity of the indicator bulb.
3. This test checks for an indicator low side circuit open.
4. This test checks for an indicator low side circuit short to B+.
5. This test determines whether the malfunction is due to an EBTCM circuit malfunction or an open in the DIC printed circuit.

GC402930041200BX

1993

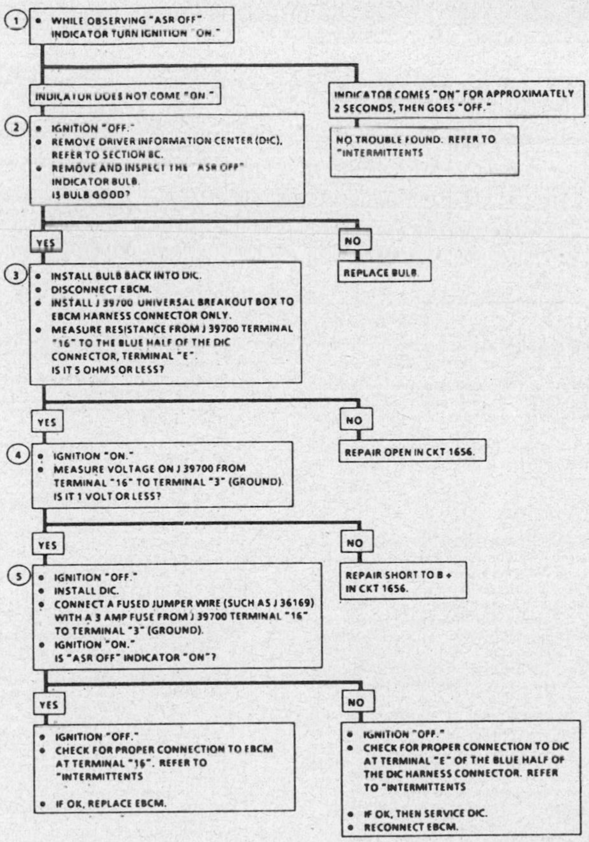
1
• WHILE OBSERVING "ASR OFF" INDICATOR TURN IGNITION "ON."
INDICATOR DOES NOT COME "ON."
INDICATOR COMES "ON" FOR APPROXIMATELY 2 SECONDS, THEN GOES "OFF."
NO TROUBLE FOUND. REFER TO "INTERMITTENTS
2
• IGNITION "OFF."
• REMOVE DRIVER INFORMATION CENTER (DIC), REFER TO SECTION 8C.
• REMOVE AND INSPECT THE "ASR OFF" INDICATOR BULB.
IS BULB GOOD?
YES
NO
REPLACE BULB.
3
• INSTALL BULB BACK INTO DIC.
• DISCONNECT EBCM.
• INSTALL J 39700 UNIVERSAL BREAKOUT BOX TO EBCM HARNESS CONNECTOR ONLY.
• MEASURE RESISTANCE FROM J 39700 TERMINAL "16" TO THE BLUE HALF OF THE DIC CONNECTOR, TERMINAL "E".
IS IT 5 OHMS OR LESS?
YES
NO
REPAIR OPEN IN CKT 1656.
4
• IGNITION "ON."
• MEASURE VOLTAGE ON J 39700 FROM TERMINAL "16" TO TERMINAL "3" (GROUND).
IS IT 1 VOLT OR LESS?
YES
NO
REPAIR SHORT TO B + IN CKT 1656.
5
• IGNITION "OFF."
• INSTALL DIC.
• CONNECT A FUSED JUMPER WIRE (SUCH AS J 36169) WITH A 3 AMP FUSE FROM J 39700 TERMINAL "16" TO TERMINAL "3" (GROUND).
• IGNITION "ON."
IS "ASR OFF" INDICATOR "ON"?
YES
NO
• IGNITION "OFF."
• CHECK FOR PROPER CONNECTION TO EBCM AT TERMINAL "16". REFER TO "INTERMITTENTS
• IF OK, REPLACE EBCM.
• IGNITION "OFF."
• CHECK FOR PROPER CONNECTION TO DIC AT TERMINAL "E" OF THE BLUE HALF OF THE DIC HARNESS CONNECTOR. REFER TO "INTERMITTENTS
• IF OK, THEN SERVICE DIC.
• RECONNECT EBCM.

GC402920041200CX

Fig. 28 Test J: ASR Off Indicator Inoperative. 1992-93

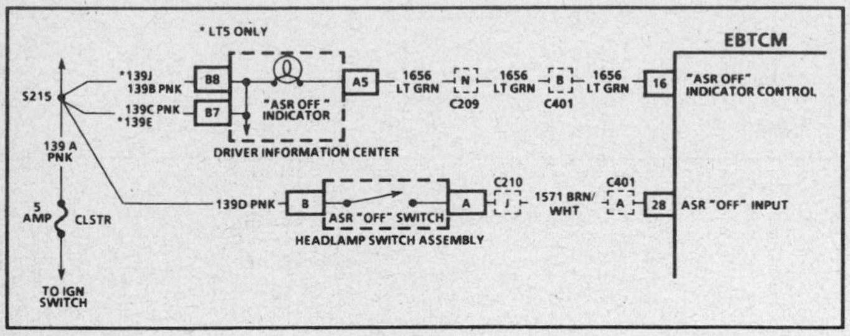

* LTS ONLY
EBTCM
S215
*139J
139B PNK
139C PNK
*139E
B8
B7
A5
1656 LT GRN
N
C209
1656 LT GRN
B
C401
1656 LT GRN
16
"ASR OFF" INDICATOR CONTROL
"ASR OFF" INDICATOR
DRIVER INFORMATION CENTER
139 A PNK
5 AMP
CLSTR
139D PNK
B
A
"ASR "OFF" SWITCH
C210
1571 BRN/WHT
C401
28
ASR "OFF" INPUT
HEADLAMP SWITCH ASSEMBLY
TO IGN SWITCH

CHART J

"ASR OFF" INDICATOR INOPERATIVE

Chart Test Description: Number(s) below refer to circled number(s) on the diagnostic chart.

1. Confirms that a malfunction condition exists.
2. Determines whether the malfunction is due to an EBTCM circuit malfunction or an open in the DIC printed circuit.
3. Checks the integrity of the indicator bulb.
4. Checks for an indicator low side circuit open.
5. Checks for an indicator low side circuit short to B+.

GC402940086100AX

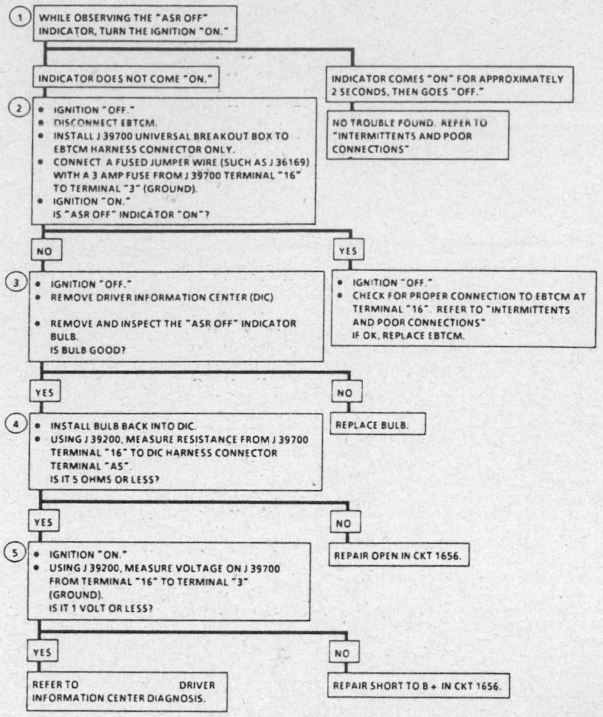

1 WHILE OBSERVING THE "ASR OFF" INDICATOR, TURN THE IGNITION "ON."
INDICATOR DOES NOT COME "ON."
INDICATOR COMES "ON" FOR APPROXIMATELY 2 SECONDS, THEN GOES "OFF."
NO TROUBLE FOUND. REFER TO "INTERMITTENTS AND POOR CONNECTIONS"
2 • IGNITION "OFF."
• DISCONNECT EBTCM.
• INSTALL J 39700 UNIVERSAL BREAKOUT BOX TO EBTCM HARNESS CONNECTOR ONLY.
• CONNECT A FUSED JUMPER WIRE (SUCH AS J 36169) WITH A 3 AMP FUSE FROM J 39700 TERMINAL "16" TO TERMINAL "3" (GROUND).
• IGNITION "ON."
IS "ASR OFF" INDICATOR "ON"?
NO
YES
3 • IGNITION "OFF."
• REMOVE DRIVER INFORMATION CENTER (DIC)
• REMOVE AND INSPECT THE "ASR OFF" INDICATOR BULB.
IS BULB GOOD?
• IGNITION "OFF."
• CHECK FOR PROPER CONNECTION TO EBTCM AT TERMINAL "16". REFER TO "INTERMITTENTS AND POOR CONNECTIONS"
IF OK, REPLACE EBTCM.
YES
NO
4 • INSTALL BULB BACK INTO DIC.
• USING J 39200, MEASURE RESISTANCE FROM J 39700 TERMINAL "16" TO DIC HARNESS CONNECTOR TERMINAL "A5".
IS IT 5 OHMS OR LESS?
REPLACE BULB.
YES
NO
5 • IGNITION "ON."
• USING J 39200, MEASURE VOLTAGE ON J 39700 FROM TERMINAL "16" TO TERMINAL "3" (GROUND).
IS IT 1 VOLT OR LESS?
REPAIR OPEN IN CKT 1656.
YES
NO
REFER TO DRIVER INFORMATION CENTER DIAGNOSIS.
REPAIR SHORT TO B + IN CKT 1656.

GC402940086100BX

Fig. 29 Test J: ASR Off Indicator Inoperative. 1994

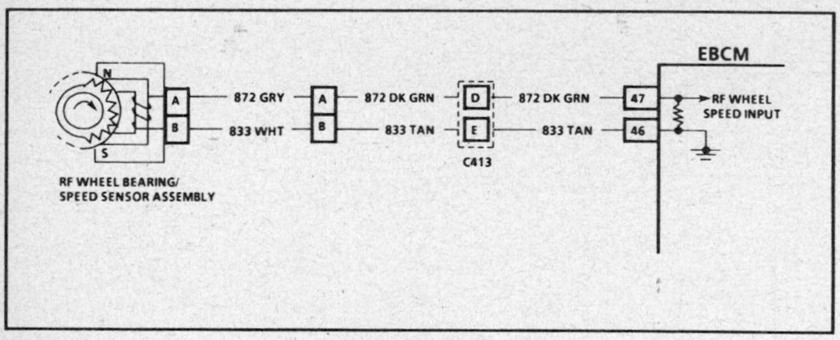

EBCM
N
A
B
S
872 GRY
833 WHT
A
B
872 DK GRN
833 TAN
D
E
C413
872 DK GRN
833 TAN
47
46
RF WHEEL SPEED INPUT
RF WHEEL BEARING/ SPEED SENSOR ASSEMBLY

CODE 21

RF WHEEL SPEED SENSOR FAULT

Circuit Description:

The toothed wheel generates a voltage pulse as it moves past the sensor; each tooth-gap-tooth series on the wheel generates these pulses. The frequency of these pulses is used by the EBCM to determine wheel speed. The amount of voltage generated in each pulse depends on the air gap between the sensor and the toothed wheel, and on wheel speed.

The "SERVICE ABS" and "SERVICE ASR" indicators will be "ON" and Code 21 is set if there is a short to voltage or ground in CKT 872 or 833, or a faulty speed sensor. The testing for this fault occurs when the vehicle is in motion; it will not set with the ignition "ON" and the vehicle at rest.

Test Description: Number(s) below refer to circled number(s) on the diagnostic chart.

1. Checks for proper resistance in the sensor itself.
2. Checks for a short to battery in either of the Speed Sensor circuit wires.
3. Checks for a short between the Speed Sensor circuit wires.
4. Checks for a short to ground in the Speed Sensor input circuit wire. The ground may be either a "hard" short to ground, or a resistive (partial) short. A short with a resistance less than 2 megohms, though not a hard short, can still cause Code 21 to set.
5. Checks if the code resets during a road test. If so, since Tests 1-4 have validated that the circuitry and components are good, intermittent problems are suspected.
6. Checks wiring and connectors for intermittents.
7. Replace the Wheel Bearing/Speed Sensor Assembly, as it is likely the cause of a code reset experienced during the road test, since other portions of the circuit have checked out OK. If the code resets after sensor replacement, the EBCM must be concluding there is a problem present in the Speed Sensor circuit when there is not.

Diagnostic Aids:

Be sure the speed sensor wiring is properly routed and retained. This will help prevent false signals due to electrical noise being picked up by the wiring.

It is very important that a thorough inspection of the wiring and connectors be performed. Failure to carefully and fully inspect wiring and connectors may result in misdiagnosis, causing part replacement with reappearance of the fault.

The Tech 1 can also be used to monitor the wheel speeds during a road test. Watch the wheel speeds being displayed on the Tech 1 to see if any of the readings are unusual, such as one sensor varying in speed from the other three, a signal going intermittently high or low, etc. If this does not identify the intermittent, wet the speed sensor harness on the underside of the vehicle and road test monitoring wheel speeds with the Tech 1.

GC402920041300AX

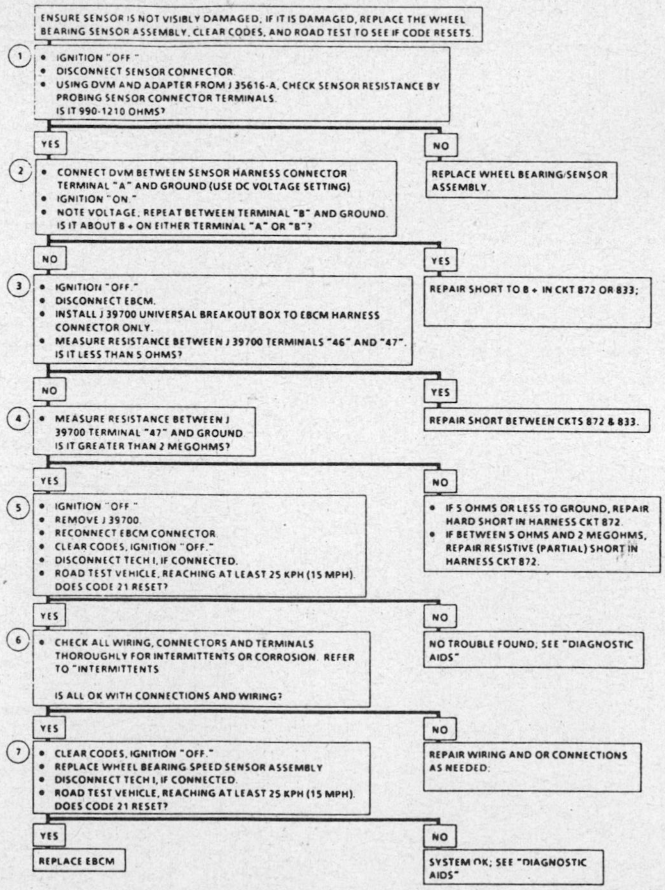

ENSURE SENSOR IS NOT VISIBLY DAMAGED. IF IT IS DAMAGED, REPLACE THE WHEEL BEARING SENSOR ASSEMBLY, CLEAR CODES, AND ROAD TEST TO SEE IF CODE RESETS.
1 • IGNITION "OFF."
• DISCONNECT SENSOR CONNECTOR.
• USING DVM AND ADAPTER FROM J 35616-A, CHECK SENSOR RESISTANCE BY PROBING SENSOR CONNECTOR TERMINALS.
IS IT 990-1210 OHMS?
YES
NO
2 • CONNECT DVM BETWEEN SENSOR HARNESS CONNECTOR TERMINAL "A" AND GROUND (USE DC VOLTAGE SETTING)
• IGNITION "ON."
• NOTE VOLTAGE; REPEAT BETWEEN TERMINAL "B" AND GROUND.
IS IT ABOUT B + ON EITHER TERMINAL "A" OR "B"?
REPLACE WHEEL BEARING/SENSOR ASSEMBLY.
NO
YES
3 • IGNITION "OFF."
• DISCONNECT EBCM.
• INSTALL J 39700 UNIVERSAL BREAKOUT BOX TO EBCM HARNESS CONNECTOR ONLY.
• MEASURE RESISTANCE BETWEEN J 39700 TERMINALS "46" AND "47".
IS IT LESS THAN 5 OHMS?
REPAIR SHORT TO B + IN CKT 872 OR 833;
NO
YES
4 • MEASURE RESISTANCE BETWEEN J 39700 TERMINAL "47" AND GROUND
IS IT GREATER THAN 2 MEGOHMS?
REPAIR SHORT BETWEEN CKTS 872 & 833.
YES
NO
5 • IGNITION "OFF."
• REMOVE J 39700.
• RECONNECT EBCM CONNECTOR.
• CLEAR CODES, IGNITION "OFF."
• DISCONNECT TECH I, IF CONNECTED.
• ROAD TEST VEHICLE, REACHING AT LEAST 25 KPH (15 MPH).
DOES CODE 21 RESET?
• IF 5 OHMS OR LESS TO GROUND, REPAIR HARD SHORT IN HARNESS CKT 872.
• IF BETWEEN 5 OHMS AND 2 MEGOHMS, REPAIR RESISTIVE (PARTIAL) SHORT IN HARNESS CKT 872.
YES
NO
6 • CHECK ALL WIRING, CONNECTORS AND TERMINALS THOROUGHLY FOR INTERMITTENTS OR CORROSION. REFER TO "INTERMITTENTS"
IS ALL OK WITH CONNECTIONS AND WIRING?
NO TROUBLE FOUND; SEE "DIAGNOSTIC AIDS"
YES
NO
7 • CLEAR CODES, IGNITION "OFF."
• REPLACE WHEEL BEARING SPEED SENSOR ASSEMBLY
• DISCONNECT TECH I, IF CONNECTED.
• ROAD TEST VEHICLE, REACHING AT LEAST 25 KPH (15 MPH).
DOES CODE 21 RESET?
REPAIR WIRING AND OR CONNECTIONS AS NEEDED.
YES
NO
REPLACE EBCM
SYSTEM OK; SEE "DIAGNOSTIC AIDS"

GC402920041300BX

Fig. 30 Code 21: RF Wheel Speed Sensor Fault. 1992–93

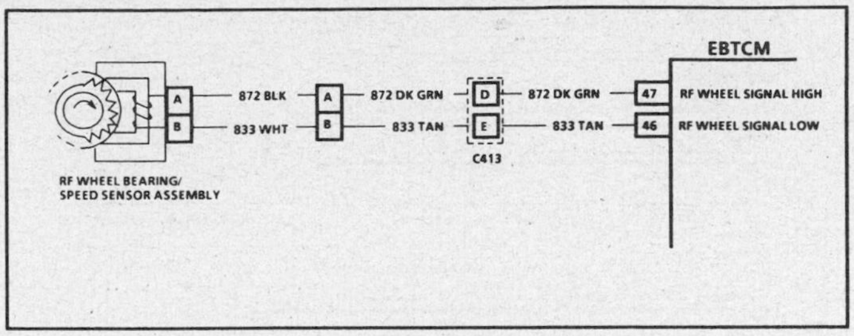

EBTCM
872 BLK
833 WHT
A
B
872 DK GRN
833 TAN
D
E
C413
47
46
RF WHEEL SIGNAL HIGH
RF WHEEL SIGNAL LOW
RF WHEEL BEARING/
SPEED SENSOR ASSEMBLY

DTC 21

RF WHEEL SPEED SENSOR CIRCUIT MALFUNCTION

Circuit Description:
The toothed wheel generates a voltage pulse as it moves past the sensor; each tooth-gap-tooth series on the wheel generates these pulses. The frequency of these pulses is used by the EBTCM to determine wheel speed. The amount of voltage generated in each pulse depends on the air gap between the sensor and the toothed wheel, and on wheel speed.

DTC Will Set When: There is a short to voltage or ground in CKT 872 or 833, or a malfunctioning speed sensor. The testing for this malfunction occurs when the vehicle is in motion; it will not set with the ignition "ON" and the vehicle at rest.

Action Taken: The "SERVICE ABS" and "SERVICE ASR" indicators will be "ON."

DTC Chart Test Description: Number(s) below refer to circled number(s) on the diagnostic chart.

1. Checks for proper resistance in the sensor itself.
2. Checks for a short to battery in either of the speed sensor circuit wires.
3. Checks for a short between the speed sensor circuit wires.
4. Checks for a short to ground in the speed sensor input circuit wire. The ground may be either a "hard" short to ground, or a resistive (partial) short. A short with a resistance less than 2 megohms, though not a hard short, can still cause DTC 21 to set.
5. Checks if the DTC resets during a road test. If so, since tests 1-4 have validated that the circuitry and components are good, intermittent malfunctions are suspected.
6. Checks wiring and connectors for intermittents.
7. Replace the wheel bearing/speed sensor assembly, as it is likely the cause of a DTC reset experienced during the road test, since other portions of the circuit have checked out OK. If the DTC resets after sensor replacement, the EBTCM must be concluding there is a malfunction present in the speed sensor circuit when there is not.

Diagnostic Aids: Be sure the speed sensor wiring is properly routed and retained. This will help prevent false signals due to electrical noise being picked up by the wiring.

It is very important that a thorough inspection of the wiring and connectors be performed. Failure to carefully and fully inspect wiring and connectors may result in misdiagnosis, causing part replacement with reappearance of the malfunction.

The Tech 1 can also be used to monitor the wheel speeds during a road test. Watch the wheel speeds being displayed on the Tech 1 to see if any of the readings are unusual, such as one sensor varying in speed from the other three, a signal going intermittently high or low, etc. If this does not identify the intermittent, wet the speed sensor harness on the underside of the vehicle and road test monitoring wheel speeds with the Tech 1

GC402940086200AX

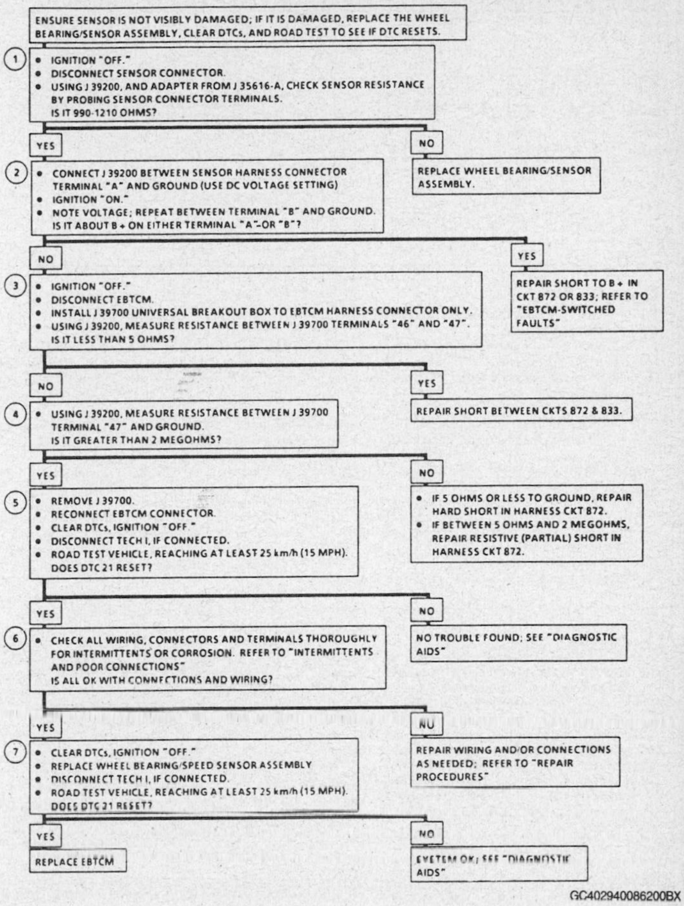

ENSURE SENSOR IS NOT VISIBLY DAMAGED; IF IT IS DAMAGED, REPLACE THE WHEEL BEARING/SENSOR ASSEMBLY, CLEAR DTCs, AND ROAD TEST TO SEE IF DTC RESETS.
1
• IGNITION "OFF."
• DISCONNECT SENSOR CONNECTOR.
• USING J 39200, AND ADAPTER FROM J 35616-A, CHECK SENSOR RESISTANCE BY PROBING SENSOR CONNECTOR TERMINALS.
IS IT 990-1210 OHMS?
YES
NO
REPLACE WHEEL BEARING/SENSOR ASSEMBLY.
2
• CONNECT J 39200 BETWEEN SENSOR HARNESS CONNECTOR TERMINAL "A" AND GROUND (USE DC VOLTAGE SETTING)
• IGNITION "ON."
• NOTE VOLTAGE; REPEAT BETWEEN TERMINAL "B" AND GROUND.
IS IT ABOUT B + ON EITHER TERMINAL "A"-OR "B"?
NO
YES
REPAIR SHORT TO B + IN CKT 872 OR 833; REFER TO "EBTCM-SWITCHED FAULTS"
3
• IGNITION "OFF."
• DISCONNECT EBTCM.
• INSTALL J 39700 UNIVERSAL BREAKOUT BOX TO EBTCM HARNESS CONNECTOR ONLY.
• USING J 39200, MEASURE RESISTANCE BETWEEN J 39700 TERMINALS "46" AND "47".
IS IT LESS THAN 5 OHMS?
NO
YES
REPAIR SHORT BETWEEN CKTS 872 & 833.
4
• USING J 39200, MEASURE RESISTANCE BETWEEN J 39700 TERMINAL "47" AND GROUND.
IS IT GREATER THAN 2 MEGOHMS?
YES
NO
• IF 5 OHMS OR LESS TO GROUND, REPAIR HARD SHORT IN HARNESS CKT 872.
• IF BETWEEN 5 OHMS AND 2 MEGOHMS, REPAIR RESISTIVE (PARTIAL) SHORT IN HARNESS CKT 872.
5
• REMOVE J 39700.
• RECONNECT EBTCM CONNECTOR.
• CLEAR DTCs, IGNITION "OFF."
• DISCONNECT TECH I, IF CONNECTED.
• ROAD TEST VEHICLE, REACHING AT LEAST 25 km/h (15 MPH).
DOES DTC 21 RESET?
YES
NO
NO TROUBLE FOUND; SEE "DIAGNOSTIC AIDS"
6
• CHECK ALL WIRING, CONNECTORS AND TERMINALS THOROUGHLY FOR INTERMITTENTS OR CORROSION. REFER TO "INTERMITTENTS AND POOR CONNECTIONS"
IS ALL OK WITH CONNECTIONS AND WIRING?
YES
NO
REPAIR WIRING AND/OR CONNECTIONS AS NEEDED; REFER TO "REPAIR PROCEDURES"
7
• CLEAR DTCs, IGNITION "OFF."
• REPLACE WHEEL BEARING/SPEED SENSOR ASSEMBLY
• DISCONNECT TECH I, IF CONNECTED.
• ROAD TEST VEHICLE, REACHING AT LEAST 25 km/h (15 MPH).
DOES DTC 21 RESET?
YES
REPLACE EBTCM
NO
SYSTEM OK; SEE "DIAGNOSTIC AIDS"

GC402940086200BX

Fig. 31 Code 21: RF Wheel Speed Sensor Fault. 1994

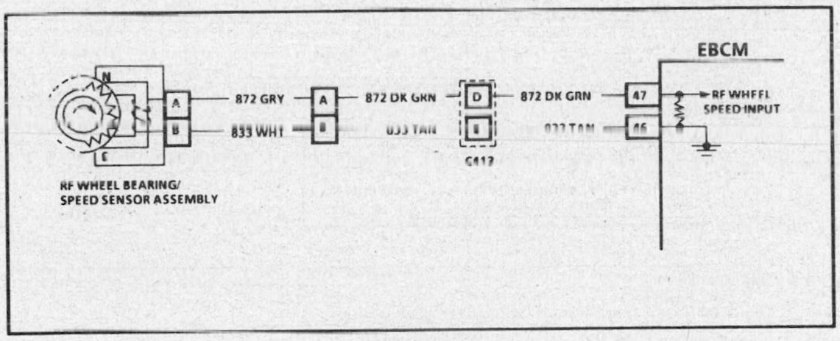

EBCM
N
E
A
B
872 GRY
833 WHT
872 DK GRN
833 TAN
D
E
C413
872 DK GRN
833 TAN
47
46
RF WHEEL SPEED INPUT
RF WHEEL BEARING/
SPEED SENSOR ASSEMBLY

CODE 23

RF WHEEL SPEED SENSOR CONTINUITY FAULT

Circuit Description:
The toothed wheel generates a voltage pulse as it moves past the sensor; each tooth-gap-tooth series on the wheel generates these pulses. The frequency of these pulses is used by the EBCM to determine wheel speed. The amount of voltage generated in each pulse depends on the air gap between the sensor and the toothed wheel, and on wheel speed.

The "SERVICE ABS" and "SERVICE ASR" indicators will be "ON" and Code 23 is set if there is a short to voltage or an open in CKT 872 or 833, or a faulty speed sensor. The testing for this fault occurs with the ignition "ON" and the vehicle at rest.

Test Description: Number(s) below refer to circled number(s) on the diagnostic chart.

1. Checks for proper resistance in the sensor itself.
2. Checks for a short to battery in either of the Speed Sensor circuit wires.
3. Checks for an open in both the Speed Sensor circuit wires.
4. Manipulates wiring and connectors, trying to induce a intermittent fault not currently present.
5. This test checks if the code resets on key-up. If so, since Tests 1-4 have validated that the circuitry and components are good, the Wheel Bearing/Speed Sensor assembly may be causing the fault.
6. Checks if Code 21 sets during a road test.
7. Code 23 sets when the vehicle is at rest; Code 21 sets with a problem in the Speed Sensor circuitry with the vehicle in motion. If problems are still present, Code 21 would set during the road test, not a 23. If the Code 21 sets at this point, the Code 21 diagnostics should be used.
8. The wheel speed sensor may be causing an intermittent fault. If Code 23 resets after sensor replacement, the EBCM must be concluding there is a problem present in the Speed Sensor circuit when there is not.

Diagnostic Aids:

Be sure the speed sensor wiring is properly routed and retained. This will help prevent false signals due to electrical noise being picked up by the wiring.

It is very important that a thorough inspection of the wiring and connectors be performed. Failure to carefully and fully inspect wiring and connectors may result in misdiagnosis, causing part replacement with reappearance of the fault.

GC402920041400AX

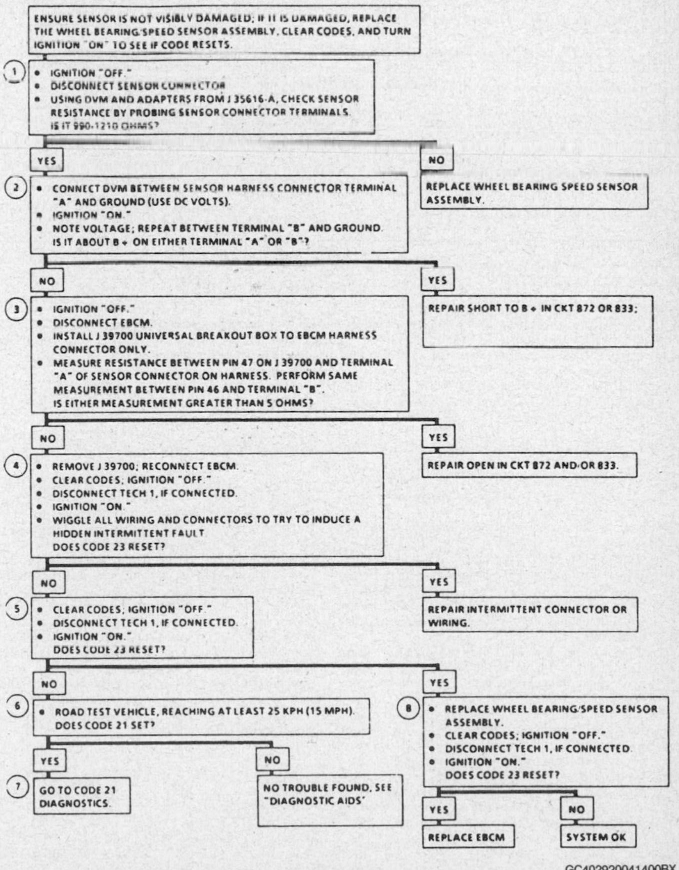

ENSURE SENSOR IS NOT VISIBLY DAMAGED; IF IT IS DAMAGED, REPLACE THE WHEEL BEARING/SPEED SENSOR ASSEMBLY, CLEAR CODES, AND TURN IGNITION "ON" TO SEE IF CODE RESETS.
1
• IGNITION "OFF."
• DISCONNECT SENSOR CONNECTOR
• USING DVM AND ADAPTERS FROM J 35616-A, CHECK SENSOR RESISTANCE BY PROBING SENSOR CONNECTOR TERMINALS.
IS IT 990-1210 OHMS?
YES
NO
REPLACE WHEEL BEARING SPEED SENSOR ASSEMBLY.
2
• CONNECT DVM BETWEEN SENSOR HARNESS CONNECTOR TERMINAL "A" AND GROUND (USE DC VOLTS).
• IGNITION "ON."
• NOTE VOLTAGE; REPEAT BETWEEN TERMINAL "B" AND GROUND.
IS IT ABOUT B + ON EITHER TERMINAL "A" OR "B"?
NO
YES
REPAIR SHORT TO B + IN CKT 872 OR 833;
3
• IGNITION "OFF."
• DISCONNECT EBCM.
• INSTALL J 39700 UNIVERSAL BREAKOUT BOX TO EBCM HARNESS CONNECTOR ONLY.
• MEASURE RESISTANCE BETWEEN PIN 47 ON J 39700 AND TERMINAL "A" OF SENSOR CONNECTOR ON HARNESS. PERFORM SAME MEASUREMENT BETWEEN PIN 46 AND TERMINAL "B".
IS EITHER MEASUREMENT GREATER THAN 5 OHMS?
NO
YES
REPAIR OPEN IN CKT 872 AND/OR 833.
4
• REMOVE J 39700; RECONNECT EBCM.
• CLEAR CODES; IGNITION "OFF."
• DISCONNECT TECH 1, IF CONNECTED.
• IGNITION "ON."
• WIGGLE ALL WIRING AND CONNECTORS TO TRY TO INDUCE A HIDDEN INTERMITTENT FAULT
DOES CODE 23 RESET?
NO
YES
REPAIR INTERMITTENT CONNECTOR OR WIRING.
5
• CLEAR CODES; IGNITION "OFF."
• DISCONNECT TECH 1, IF CONNECTED.
• IGNITION "ON."
DOES CODE 23 RESET?
NO
YES
6
• ROAD TEST VEHICLE, REACHING AT LEAST 25 KPH (15 MPH).
DOES CODE 21 SET?
YES
NO
7
GO TO CODE 21 DIAGNOSTICS.
NO TROUBLE FOUND, SEE "DIAGNOSTIC AIDS"
8
• REPLACE WHEEL BEARING/SPEED SENSOR ASSEMBLY.
• CLEAR CODES; IGNITION "OFF."
• DISCONNECT TECH 1, IF CONNECTED.
• IGNITION "ON."
DOES CODE 23 RESET?
YES
NO
REPLACE EBCM
SYSTEM OK

GC402920041400BX

Fig. 32 Code 23: RF Wheel Speed Sensor Continuity Fault. 1992–93

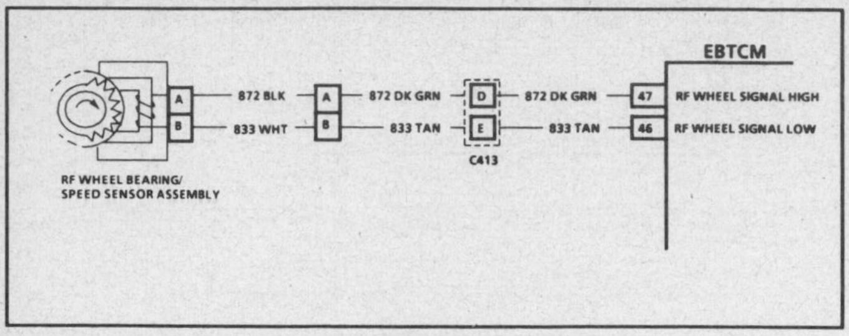
EBTCM
872 BLK
833 WHT
A
B
872 DK GRN
833 TAN
D
E
C413
47
46
RF WHEEL SIGNAL HIGH
RF WHEEL SIGNAL LOW
RF WHEEL BEARING/
SPEED SENSOR ASSEMBLY

DTC 23

RF WHEEL SPEED SENSOR CIRCUIT CONTINUITY MALFUNCTION

Circuit Description:

The toothed wheel generates a voltage pulse as it moves past the sensor; each tooth-gap-tooth series on the wheel generates these pulses. The frequency of these pulses is used by the EBTCM to determine wheel speed. The amount of voltage generated in each pulse depends on the air gap between the sensor and the toothed wheel, and on wheel speed.

DTC Will Set When: There is a short to voltage or an open in CKT 872 or 833, or a malfunctioning speed sensor. The testing for this malfunction occurs with the ignition "ON" and the vehicle at rest.

Action Taken: The "SERVICE ABS" and "SERVICE ASR" indicators will be "ON."

DTC Chart Test Description: Number(s) below refer to circled number(s) on the diagnostic chart.

1. Checks for proper resistance in the sensor itself.
2. Checks for a short to battery in either of the speed sensor circuit wires.
3. Checks for an open in both the speed sensor circuit wires.
4. Manipulates wiring and connectors, trying to induce an intermittent malfunction not currently present.
5. Checks if the DTC resets on key-up. If so, since tests 1-4 have validated that the circuitry and components are good, the wheel bearing/speed sensor assembly may be causing the malfunction.
6. Checks if DTC 21 sets during a road test.
7. DTC 23 sets when the vehicle is at rest; DTC 21 sets with a malfunction in the speed sensor circuitry with the vehicle in motion. If malfunctions are still present, DTC 21 would set during the road test, not a 23. If the DTC 21 sets at this point, the DTC 21 diagnostics should be used.
8. The wheel speed sensor may be causing an intermittent malfunction. If DTC 23 resets after sensor replacement, the EBTCM must be concluding there is a malfunction present in the speed sensor circuit when there is not.

Diagnostic Aids: Be sure the speed sensor wiring is properly routed and retained. This will help prevent false signals due to electrical noise being picked up by the wiring.

It is very important that a thorough inspection of the wiring and connectors be performed. Failure to carefully and fully inspect wiring and connectors may result in misdiagnosis, causing part replacement with reappearance of the malfunction.

GC402940086300AX

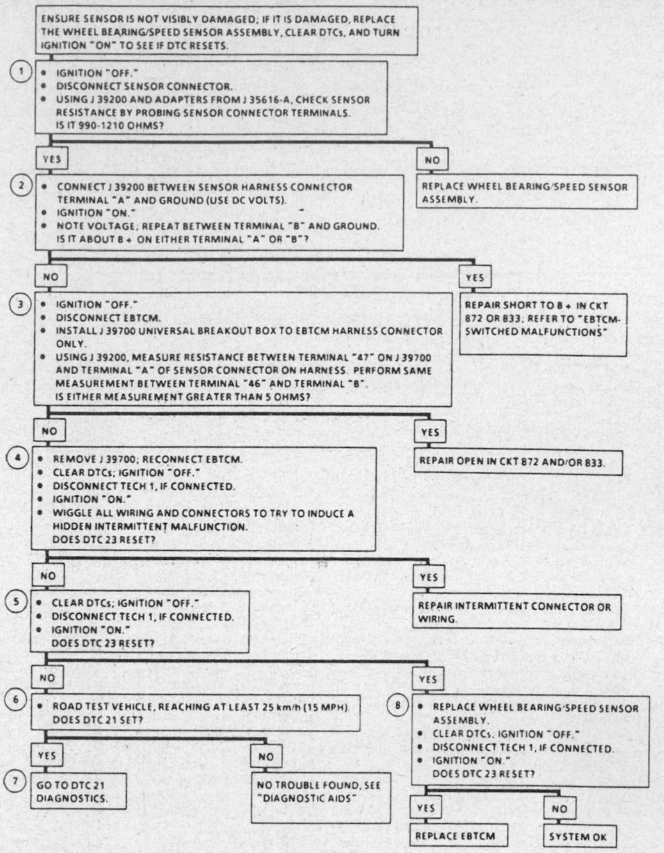
ENSURE SENSOR IS NOT VISIBLY DAMAGED; IF IT IS DAMAGED, REPLACE THE WHEEL BEARING/SPEED SENSOR ASSEMBLY, CLEAR DTCs, AND TURN IGNITION "ON" TO SEE IF DTC RESETS.
1
• IGNITION "OFF."
• DISCONNECT SENSOR CONNECTOR.
• USING J 39200 AND ADAPTERS FROM J 35616-A, CHECK SENSOR RESISTANCE BY PROBING SENSOR CONNECTOR TERMINALS.
IS IT 990-1210 OHMS?
YES
NO
REPLACE WHEEL BEARING/SPEED SENSOR ASSEMBLY.
2
• CONNECT J 39200 BETWEEN SENSOR HARNESS CONNECTOR TERMINAL "A" AND GROUND (USE DC VOLTS).
• IGNITION "ON."
• NOTE VOLTAGE; REPEAT BETWEEN TERMINAL "B" AND GROUND.
IS IT ABOUT B+ ON EITHER TERMINAL "A" OR "B"?
NO
YES
REPAIR SHORT TO B+ IN CKT 872 OR 833; REFER TO "EBTCM-SWITCHED MALFUNCTIONS"
3
• IGNITION "OFF."
• DISCONNECT EBTCM.
• INSTALL J 39700 UNIVERSAL BREAKOUT BOX TO EBTCM HARNESS CONNECTOR ONLY.
• USING J 39200, MEASURE RESISTANCE BETWEEN TERMINAL "47" ON J 39700 AND TERMINAL "A" OF SENSOR CONNECTOR ON HARNESS. PERFORM SAME MEASUREMENT BETWEEN TERMINAL "46" AND TERMINAL "B".
IS EITHER MEASUREMENT GREATER THAN 5 OHMS?
NO
YES
REPAIR OPEN IN CKT 872 AND/OR 833.
4
• REMOVE J 39700; RECONNECT EBTCM.
• CLEAR DTCs; IGNITION "OFF."
• DISCONNECT TECH 1, IF CONNECTED.
• IGNITION "ON."
• WIGGLE ALL WIRING AND CONNECTORS TO TRY TO INDUCE A HIDDEN INTERMITTENT MALFUNCTION.
DOES DTC 23 RESET?
NO
YES
REPAIR INTERMITTENT CONNECTOR OR WIRING.
5
• CLEAR DTCs; IGNITION "OFF."
• DISCONNECT TECH 1, IF CONNECTED.
• IGNITION "ON."
DOES DTC 23 RESET?
NO
YES
6
• ROAD TEST VEHICLE, REACHING AT LEAST 25 km/h (15 MPH).
DOES DTC 21 SET?
8
• REPLACE WHEEL BEARING/SPEED SENSOR ASSEMBLY.
• CLEAR DTCs, IGNITION "OFF."
• DISCONNECT TECH 1, IF CONNECTED.
• IGNITION "ON."
DOES DTC 23 RESET?
YES
NO
7
GO TO DTC 21 DIAGNOSTICS.
NO TROUBLE FOUND, SEE "DIAGNOSTIC AIDS"
YES
NO
REPLACE EBTCM
SYSTEM OK

GC402940086300BX

Fig. 33 Code 23: RF Wheel Speed Sensor Continuity Fault. 1994

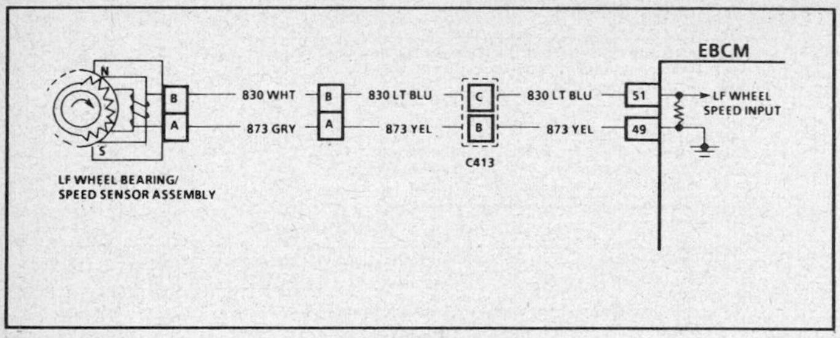
EBCM
N
S
B
A
830 WHT
873 GRY
830 LT BLU
873 YEL
C
B
C413
51
49
LF WHEEL SPEED INPUT
LF WHEEL BEARING/
SPEED SENSOR ASSEMBLY

CODE 25

LF WHEEL SPEED SENSOR FAULT

Circuit Description:

The toothed wheel generates a voltage pulse as it moves past the sensor; each tooth-gap-tooth series on the wheel generates these pulses. The frequency of these pulses is used by the EBCM to determine wheel speed. The amount of voltage generated in each pulse depends on the air gap between the sensor and the toothed wheel, and on wheel speed.

The "SERVICE ABS" and "SERVICE ASR" indicators will be "ON" and Code 25 is set if there is a short to voltage or ground in CKT 830 or 873, or a faulty speed sensor. The testing for this fault occurs when the vehicle is in motion; it will not set with the ignition "ON" and the vehicle at rest.

Test Description: Number(s) below refer to circled number(s) on the diagnostic chart.

1. Checks for proper resistance in the sensor itself.
2. Checks for a short to battery in either of the Speed Sensor circuit wires.
3. Checks for a short between the Speed Sensor circuit wires.
4. Checks for a short to ground in the Speed Sensor input circuit wire. The ground may be either a "hard" short to ground, or a resistive (partial) short. A short with a resistance less than 2 megohms, though not a hard short, can still cause Code 25 to set.
5. Checks if the code resets during a road test. If so, since Tests 1-4 have validated that the circuitry and components are good, intermittent problems are suspected.
6. Checks wiring and connectors for intermittents.
7. Replace the Wheel Bearing/Speed Sensor Assembly, as it is likely the cause of a code reset experienced during the road test, since other portions of the circuit have checked out OK. If the code resets after sensor replacement, the EBCM must be concluding there is a problem present in the Speed Sensor circuit when there is not.

Diagnostic Aids:

Be sure the speed sensor wiring is properly routed and retained. This will help prevent false signals due to electrical noise being picked up by the wiring.

It is very important that a thorough inspection of the wiring and connectors be performed. Failure to carefully and fully inspect wiring and connectors may result in misdiagnosis, causing part replacement with reappearance of the fault.

The Tech 1 can also be used to monitor the wheel speeds during a road test. Watch the wheel speeds being displayed on the Tech 1 to see if any of the readings are unusual, such as one sensor varying in speed from the other three, a signal going intermittently high or low, etc. If this does not identify the intermittent, wet the speed sensor harness on the underside of the vehicle and road test monitoring wheel speeds with the Tech 1.

GC402920041500AX

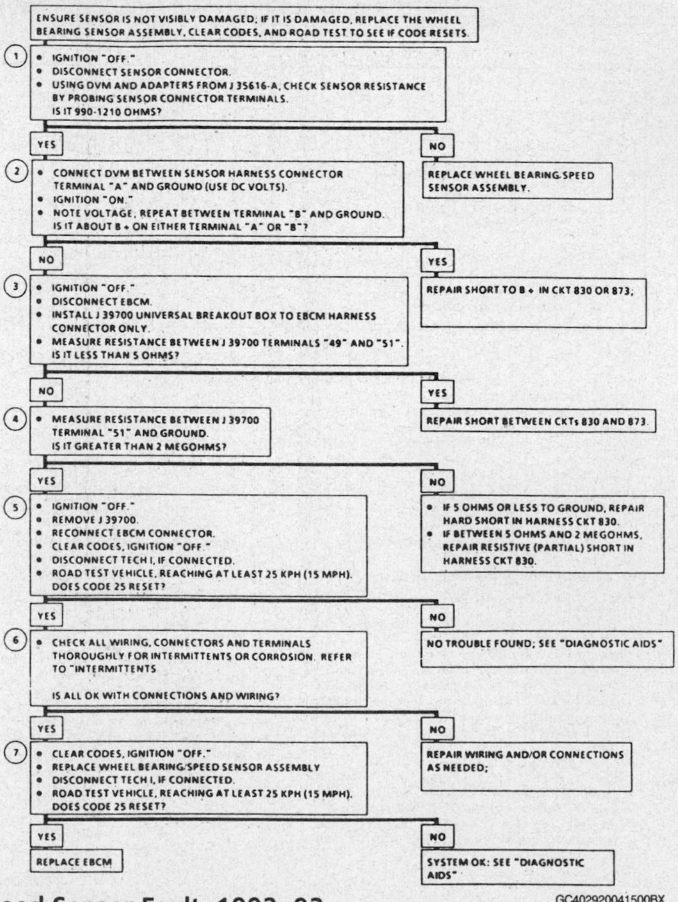
ENSURE SENSOR IS NOT VISIBLY DAMAGED; IF IT IS DAMAGED, REPLACE THE WHEEL BEARING SENSOR ASSEMBLY, CLEAR CODES, AND ROAD TEST TO SEE IF CODE RESETS.
1
• IGNITION "OFF."
• DISCONNECT SENSOR CONNECTOR.
• USING DVM AND ADAPTERS FROM J 35616-A, CHECK SENSOR RESISTANCE BY PROBING SENSOR CONNECTOR TERMINALS.
IS IT 990-1210 OHMS?
YES
NO
REPLACE WHEEL BEARING SPEED SENSOR ASSEMBLY.
2
• CONNECT DVM BETWEEN SENSOR HARNESS CONNECTOR TERMINAL "A" AND GROUND (USE DC VOLTS).
• IGNITION "ON."
• NOTE VOLTAGE; REPEAT BETWEEN TERMINAL "B" AND GROUND.
IS IT ABOUT B+ ON EITHER TERMINAL "A" OR "B"?
NO
YES
REPAIR SHORT TO B+ IN CKT 830 OR 873;
3
• IGNITION "OFF."
• DISCONNECT EBCM.
• INSTALL J 39700 UNIVERSAL BREAKOUT BOX TO EBCM HARNESS CONNECTOR ONLY.
• MEASURE RESISTANCE BETWEEN J 39700 TERMINALS "49" AND "51".
IS IT LESS THAN 5 OHMS?
NO
YES
REPAIR SHORT BETWEEN CKTs 830 AND 873.
4
• MEASURE RESISTANCE BETWEEN J 39700 TERMINAL "51" AND GROUND.
IS IT GREATER THAN 2 MEGOHMS?
YES
NO
• IF 5 OHMS OR LESS TO GROUND, REPAIR HARD SHORT IN HARNESS CKT 830.
• IF BETWEEN 5 OHMS AND 2 MEGOHMS, REPAIR RESISTIVE (PARTIAL) SHORT IN HARNESS CKT 830.
5
• IGNITION "OFF."
• REMOVE J 39700.
• RECONNECT EBCM CONNECTOR.
• CLEAR CODES, IGNITION "OFF."
• DISCONNECT TECH I, IF CONNECTED.
• ROAD TEST VEHICLE, REACHING AT LEAST 25 KPH (15 MPH).
DOES CODE 25 RESET?
YES
NO
NO TROUBLE FOUND; SEE "DIAGNOSTIC AIDS"
6
• CHECK ALL WIRING, CONNECTORS AND TERMINALS THOROUGHLY FOR INTERMITTENTS OR CORROSION. REFER TO "INTERMITTENTS
IS ALL OK WITH CONNECTIONS AND WIRING?
YES
NO
REPAIR WIRING AND/OR CONNECTIONS AS NEEDED;
7
• CLEAR CODES, IGNITION "OFF."
• REPLACE WHEEL BEARING SPEED SENSOR ASSEMBLY
• DISCONNECT TECH I, IF CONNECTED.
• ROAD TEST VEHICLE, REACHING AT LEAST 25 KPH (15 MPH).
DOES CODE 25 RESET?
YES
NO
REPLACE EBCM
SYSTEM OK: SEE "DIAGNOSTIC AIDS"

GC402920041500BX

Fig. 34 Code 25: LF Wheel Speed Sensor Fault. 1992–93

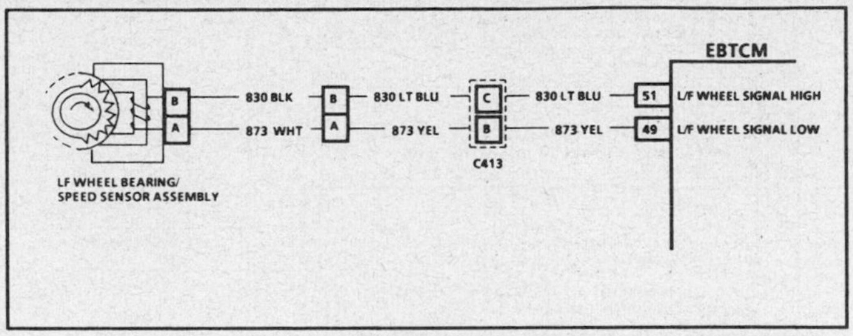

EBTCM
B
A
830 BLK
873 WHT
B
A
830 LT BLU
873 YEL
C
B
C413
830 LT BLU
873 YEL
51
49
L/F WHEEL SIGNAL HIGH
L/F WHEEL SIGNAL LOW
LF WHEEL BEARING/
SPEED SENSOR ASSEMBLY

DTC 25

LF WHEEL SPEED SENSOR CIRCUIT MALFUNCTION

Circuit Description:

The toothed wheel generates a voltage pulse as it moves past the sensor; each tooth-gap-tooth series on the wheel generates these pulses. The frequency of these pulses is used by the EBTCM to determine wheel speed. The amount of voltage generated in each pulse depends on the air gap between the sensor and the toothed wheel, and on wheel speed.

DTC Will Set When: There is a short to voltage or ground in CKT 830 or 873, or a malfunctioning speed sensor. The testing for this malfunction occurs when the vehicle is in motion; it will not set with the ignition "ON" and the vehicle at rest.

Action Taken: The "SERVICE ABS" and "SERVICE ASR" indicators will be "ON."

DTC Chart Test Description: Number(s) below refer to circled number(s) on the diagnostic chart.

1. Checks for proper resistance in the sensor itself.
2. Checks for a short to battery in either of the speed sensor circuit wires.
3. Checks for a short between the speed sensor circuit wires.
4. Checks for a short to ground in the speed sensor input circuit wire. The ground may be either a "hard" short to ground, or a resistive (partial) short. A short with a resistance less than 2 megohms, though not a hard short, can still cause DTC 25 to set.
5. Checks if the DTC resets during a road test. If so, since tests 1-4 have validated that the circuitry and components are good, intermittent malfunctions are suspected.
6. Checks wiring and connectors for intermittents.
7. Replace the wheel bearing/speed sensor assembly, as it is likely the cause of a DTC reset experienced during the road test, since other portions of the circuit have checked out OK. If the DTC resets after sensor replacement, the EBTCM must be concluding there is a malfunction present in the speed sensor circuit when there is not.

Diagnostic Aids: Be sure the speed sensor wiring is properly routed and retained. This will help prevent false signals due to electrical noise being picked up by the wiring.

It is very important that a thorough inspection of the wiring and connectors be performed. Failure to carefully and fully inspect wiring and connectors may result in misdiagnosis, causing part replacement with reappearance of the malfunction.

The Tech 1 can also be used to monitor the wheel speeds during a road test. Watch the wheel speeds being displayed on the Tech 1 to see if any of the readings are unusual, such as one sensor varying in speed from the other three, a signal going intermittently high or low, etc. If this does not identify the intermittent, wet the speed sensor harness on the underside of the vehicle and road test monitoring wheel speeds with the Tech 1.

GC402940086400AX

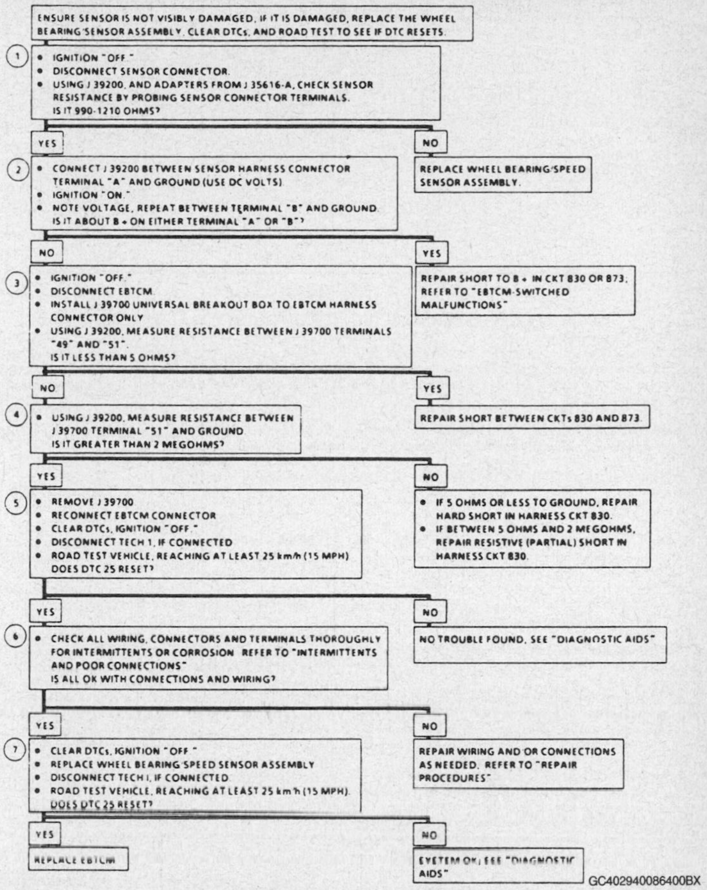

ENSURE SENSOR IS NOT VISIBLY DAMAGED, IF IT IS DAMAGED, REPLACE THE WHEEL BEARING/SENSOR ASSEMBLY. CLEAR DTCs, AND ROAD TEST TO SEE IF DTC RESETS.
1
• IGNITION "OFF."
• DISCONNECT SENSOR CONNECTOR.
• USING J 39200, AND ADAPTERS FROM J 35616-A, CHECK SENSOR RESISTANCE BY PROBING SENSOR CONNECTOR TERMINALS.
IS IT 990-1210 OHMS?
YES
NO
REPLACE WHEEL BEARING/SPEED SENSOR ASSEMBLY.
2
• CONNECT J 39200 BETWEEN SENSOR HARNESS CONNECTOR TERMINAL "A" AND GROUND (USE DC VOLTS).
• IGNITION "ON."
• NOTE VOLTAGE, REPEAT BETWEEN TERMINAL "B" AND GROUND.
IS IT ABOUT B + ON EITHER TERMINAL "A" OR "B"?
NO
YES
REPAIR SHORT TO B + IN CKT 830 OR 873; REFER TO "EBTCM-SWITCHED MALFUNCTIONS"
3
• IGNITION "OFF."
• DISCONNECT EBTCM.
• INSTALL J 39700 UNIVERSAL BREAKOUT BOX TO EBTCM HARNESS CONNECTOR ONLY
• USING J 39200, MEASURE RESISTANCE BETWEEN J 39700 TERMINALS "49" AND "51".
IS IT LESS THAN 5 OHMS?
NO
YES
REPAIR SHORT BETWEEN CKTs 830 AND 873.
4
• USING J 39200, MEASURE RESISTANCE BETWEEN J 39700 TERMINAL "51" AND GROUND
IS IT GREATER THAN 2 MEGOHMS?
YES
NO
• IF 5 OHMS OR LESS TO GROUND, REPAIR HARD SHORT IN HARNESS CKT 830.
• IF BETWEEN 5 OHMS AND 2 MEGOHMS, REPAIR RESISTIVE (PARTIAL) SHORT IN HARNESS CKT 830.
5
• REMOVE J 39700
• RECONNECT EBTCM CONNECTOR
• CLEAR DTCs, IGNITION "OFF."
• DISCONNECT TECH 1, IF CONNECTED
• ROAD TEST VEHICLE, REACHING AT LEAST 25 km/h (15 MPH)
DOES DTC 25 RESET?
YES
NO
NO TROUBLE FOUND, SEE "DIAGNOSTIC AIDS"
6
• CHECK ALL WIRING, CONNECTORS AND TERMINALS THOROUGHLY FOR INTERMITTENTS OR CORROSION. REFER TO "INTERMITTENTS AND POOR CONNECTIONS"
IS ALL OK WITH CONNECTIONS AND WIRING?
YES
NO
REPAIR WIRING AND/OR CONNECTIONS AS NEEDED. REFER TO "REPAIR PROCEDURES"
7
• CLEAR DTCs, IGNITION "OFF."
• REPLACE WHEEL BEARING/SPEED SENSOR ASSEMBLY
• DISCONNECT TECH 1, IF CONNECTED
• ROAD TEST VEHICLE, REACHING AT LEAST 25 km/h (15 MPH).
DOES DTC 25 RESET?
YES
NO
REPLACE EBTCM
SYSTEM OK; SEE "DIAGNOSTIC AIDS"

GC402940086400BX

Fig. 35 Code 25: LF Wheel Speed Sensor Fault. 1994

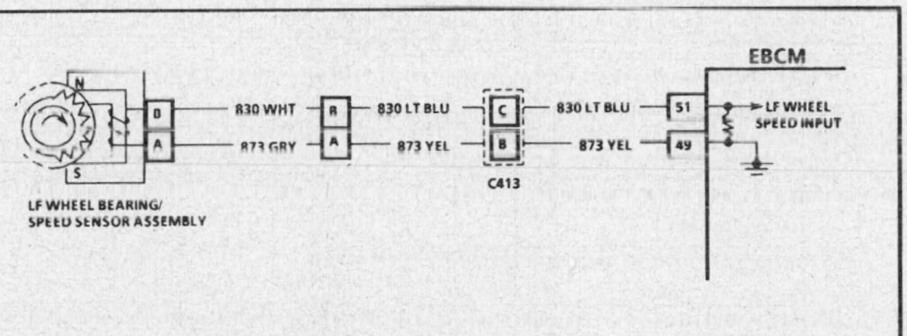

EBCM
N
S
B
A
830 WHT
873 GRY
B
A
830 LT BLU
873 YEL
C
B
C413
830 LT BLU
873 YEL
51
49
LF WHEEL SPEED INPUT
LF WHEEL BEARING/
SPEED SENSOR ASSEMBLY

CODE 27

LF WHEEL SPEED SENSOR CONTINUITY FAULT

Circuit Description:

The toothed wheel generates a voltage pulse as it moves past the sensor; each tooth-gap-tooth series on the wheel generates these pulses. The frequency of these pulses is used by the EBCM to determine wheel speed. The amount of voltage generated in each pulse depends on the air gap between the sensor and the toothed wheel, and on wheel speed.

The "SERVICE ABS" and "SERVICE ASR" indicators will be "ON" and Code 27 is set if there is a short to voltage or an open in CKT 830 or 873, or a faulty speed sensor. The testing for this fault occurs with the ignition "ON" and the vehicle at rest.

Test Description: Number(s) below refer to circled number(s) on the diagnostic chart.

1. Checks for proper resistance in the sensor itself.
2. Checks for a short to battery in either of the Speed Sensor circuit wires.
3. Checks for an open in both the Speed Sensor circuit wires.
4. Manipulates wiring and connectors, trying to induce a intermittent fault not currently present.
5. This test checks if the code resets on key up. If so, since Tests 1-4 have validated that the circuitry and components are good, the Wheel Bearing/Speed Sensor assembly may be causing the fault.
6. Checks if Code 25 sets during a road test.
7. Code 27 sets when the vehicle is at rest; Code 25 sets with a problem in the Speed Sensor circuitry with the vehicle in motion. If problems are still present, Code 25 would set during the road test, not a 27. If the Code 25 sets at this point, the Code 25 diagnostics should be used.
8. The wheel speed sensor may be causing an intermittent fault. If Code 27 resets after sensor replacement, the EBCM must be concluding there is a problem present in the Speed Sensor circuit when there is not.

Diagnostic Aids:

Be sure the speed sensor wiring is properly routed and retained. This will help prevent false signals due to electrical noise being picked up by the wiring.

It is very important that a thorough inspection of the wiring and connectors be performed. Failure to carefully and fully inspect wiring and connectors may result in misdiagnosis, causing part replacement with reappearance of the fault.

GC402920041600AX

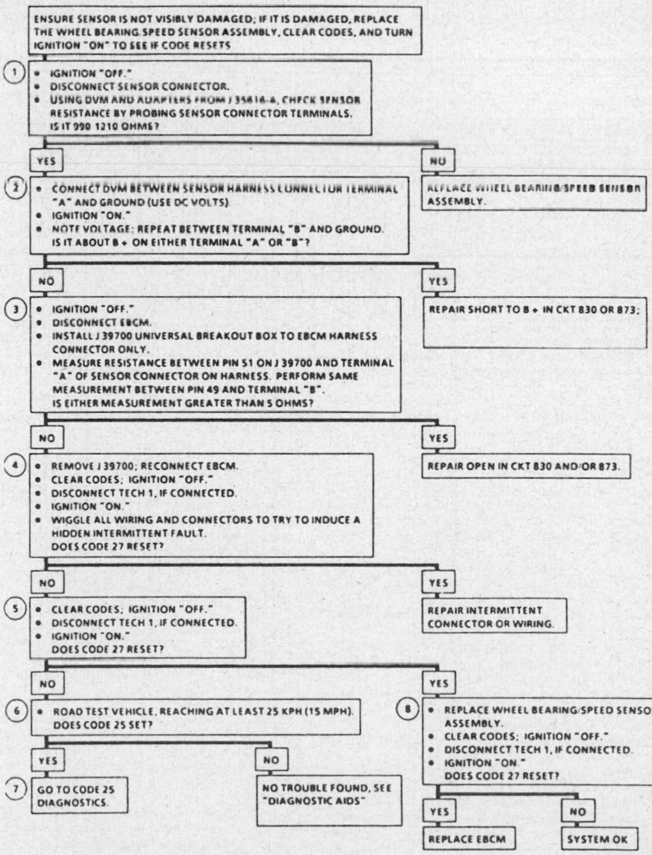

ENSURE SENSOR IS NOT VISIBLY DAMAGED; IF IT IS DAMAGED, REPLACE THE WHEEL BEARING/SPEED SENSOR ASSEMBLY, CLEAR CODES, AND TURN IGNITION "ON" TO SEE IF CODE RESETS
1
• IGNITION "OFF."
• DISCONNECT SENSOR CONNECTOR.
• USING DVM AND ADAPTERS FROM J 35616-A, CHECK SENSOR RESISTANCE BY PROBING SENSOR CONNECTOR TERMINALS.
IS IT 990-1210 OHMS?
YES
NO
REPLACE WHEEL BEARING/SPEED SENSOR ASSEMBLY.
2
• CONNECT DVM BETWEEN SENSOR HARNESS CONNECTOR TERMINAL "A" AND GROUND (USE DC VOLTS).
• IGNITION "ON."
• NOTE VOLTAGE; REPEAT BETWEEN TERMINAL "B" AND GROUND.
IS IT ABOUT B + ON EITHER TERMINAL "A" OR "B"?
NO
YES
REPAIR SHORT TO B + IN CKT 830 OR 873;
3
• IGNITION "OFF."
• DISCONNECT EBCM.
• INSTALL J 39700 UNIVERSAL BREAKOUT BOX TO EBCM HARNESS CONNECTOR ONLY.
• MEASURE RESISTANCE BETWEEN PIN 51 ON J 39700 AND TERMINAL "A" OF SENSOR CONNECTOR ON HARNESS. PERFORM SAME MEASUREMENT BETWEEN PIN 49 AND TERMINAL "B".
IS EITHER MEASUREMENT GREATER THAN 5 OHMS?
NO
YES
REPAIR OPEN IN CKT 830 AND/OR 873.
4
• REMOVE J 39700; RECONNECT EBCM.
• CLEAR CODES; IGNITION "OFF."
• DISCONNECT TECH 1, IF CONNECTED.
• IGNITION "ON."
• WIGGLE ALL WIRING AND CONNECTORS TO TRY TO INDUCE A HIDDEN INTERMITTENT FAULT.
DOES CODE 27 RESET?
NO
YES
REPAIR INTERMITTENT CONNECTOR OR WIRING.
5
• CLEAR CODES; IGNITION "OFF."
• DISCONNECT TECH 1, IF CONNECTED.
• IGNITION "ON."
DOES CODE 27 RESET?
NO
YES
6
• ROAD TEST VEHICLE, REACHING AT LEAST 25 KPH (15 MPH).
DOES CODE 25 SET?
YES
NO
7
GO TO CODE 25 DIAGNOSTICS.
NO TROUBLE FOUND, SEE "DIAGNOSTIC AIDS"
8
• REPLACE WHEEL BEARING/SPEED SENSOR ASSEMBLY.
• CLEAR CODES; IGNITION "OFF."
• DISCONNECT TECH 1, IF CONNECTED.
• IGNITION "ON."
DOES CODE 27 RESET?
YES
NO
REPLACE EBCM
SYSTEM OK

GC402920041600BX

Fig. 36 Code 27: LF Wheel Speed Sensor Continuity Fault. 1992–93

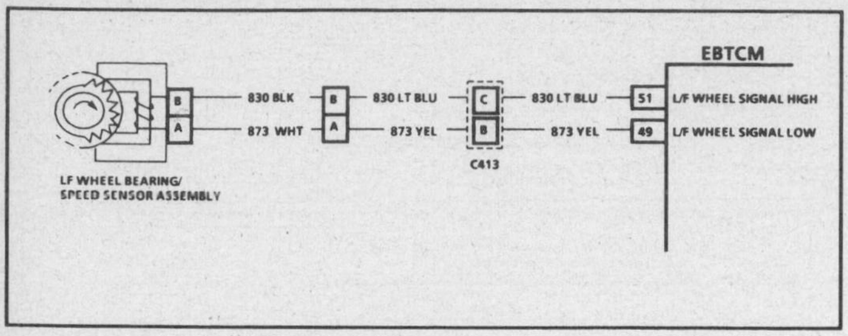
EBTCM
830 BLK
873 WHT
830 LT BLU
873 YEL
830 LT BLU
873 YEL
C413
51
49
L/F WHEEL SIGNAL HIGH
L/F WHEEL SIGNAL LOW
LF WHEEL BEARING/
SPEED SENSOR ASSEMBLY

DTC 27

LF WHEEL SPEED SENSOR CIRCUIT CONTINUITY MALFUNCTION

Circuit Description:

The toothed wheel generates a voltage pulse as it moves past the sensor; each tooth-gap-tooth series on the wheel generates these pulses. The frequency of these pulses is used by the EBTCM to determine wheel speed. The amount of voltage generated in each pulse depends on the air gap between the sensor and the toothed wheel, and on wheel speed.

DTC Will Set When: There is a short to voltage or an open in CKT 830 or 873, or a malfunctioning speed sensor. The testing for this malfunction occurs with the ignition "ON" and the vehicle at rest.

Action Taken: The "SERVICE ABS" and "SERVICE ASR" indicators will be "ON."

DTC Chart Test Description: Number(s) below refer to circled number(s) on the diagnostic chart.

1. Checks for proper resistance in the sensor itself.
2. Checks for a short to battery in either of the speed sensor circuit wires.
3. Checks for an open in both the speed sensor circuit wires.
4. Manipulates wiring and connectors, trying to induce an intermittent malfunction not currently present.
5. Checks if the DTC resets on key-up. If so, since tests 1-4 have validated that the circuitry and components are good, the wheel bearing/speed sensor assembly may be causing the malfunction.
6. Checks if DTC 25 sets during a road test.
7. DTC 27 sets when the vehicle is at rest; DTC 25 sets with a malfunction in the speed sensor circuitry with the vehicle in motion. If malfunctions are still present, DTC 25 would set during the road test, not a 27. If the DTC 25 sets at this point, the DTC 25 diagnostics should be used.
8. The wheel speed sensor may be causing an intermittent malfunction. If DTC 27 resets after sensor replacement, the EBTCM must be concluding there is a malfunction present in the speed sensor circuit when there is not.

Diagnostic Aids: Be sure the speed sensor wiring is properly routed and retained. This will help prevent false signals due to electrical noise being picked up by the wiring.

It is very important that a thorough inspection of the wiring and connectors be performed. Failure to carefully and fully inspect wiring and connectors may result in misdiagnosis, causing part replacement with reappearance of the malfunction.

GC402940086500AX

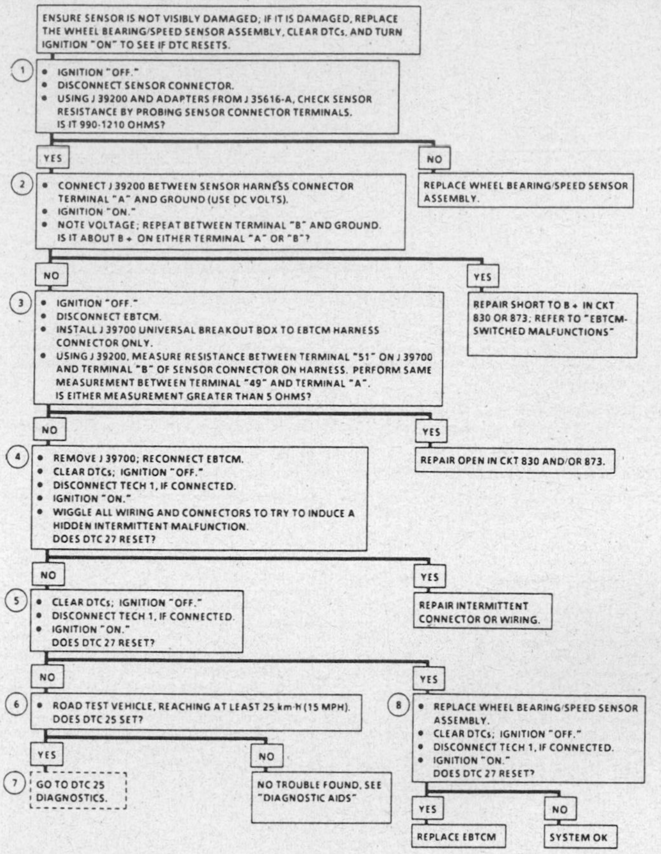
ENSURE SENSOR IS NOT VISIBLY DAMAGED; IF IT IS DAMAGED, REPLACE THE WHEEL BEARING/SPEED SENSOR ASSEMBLY, CLEAR DTCs, AND TURN IGNITION "ON" TO SEE IF DTC RESETS.
1
• IGNITION "OFF."
• DISCONNECT SENSOR CONNECTOR.
• USING J 39200 AND ADAPTERS FROM J 35616-A, CHECK SENSOR RESISTANCE BY PROBING SENSOR CONNECTOR TERMINALS. IS IT 990-1210 OHMS?
YES
NO
REPLACE WHEEL BEARING/SPEED SENSOR ASSEMBLY.
2
• CONNECT J 39200 BETWEEN SENSOR HARNESS CONNECTOR TERMINAL "A" AND GROUND (USE DC VOLTS).
• IGNITION "ON."
• NOTE VOLTAGE; REPEAT BETWEEN TERMINAL "B" AND GROUND. IS IT ABOUT B+ ON EITHER TERMINAL "A" OR "B"?
NO
YES
REPAIR SHORT TO B+ IN CKT 830 OR 873; REFER TO "EBTCM-SWITCHED MALFUNCTIONS"
3
• IGNITION "OFF."
• DISCONNECT EBTCM.
• INSTALL J 39700 UNIVERSAL BREAKOUT BOX TO EBTCM HARNESS CONNECTOR ONLY.
• USING J 39200, MEASURE RESISTANCE BETWEEN TERMINAL "51" ON J 39700 AND TERMINAL "B" OF SENSOR CONNECTOR ON HARNESS. PERFORM SAME MEASUREMENT BETWEEN TERMINAL "49" AND TERMINAL "A". IS EITHER MEASUREMENT GREATER THAN 5 OHMS?
NO
YES
REPAIR OPEN IN CKT 830 AND/OR 873.
4
• REMOVE J 39700; RECONNECT EBTCM.
• CLEAR DTCs; IGNITION "OFF."
• DISCONNECT TECH 1, IF CONNECTED.
• IGNITION "ON."
• WIGGLE ALL WIRING AND CONNECTORS TO TRY TO INDUCE A HIDDEN INTERMITTENT MALFUNCTION. DOES DTC 27 RESET?
NO
YES
REPAIR INTERMITTENT CONNECTOR OR WIRING.
5
• CLEAR DTCs; IGNITION "OFF."
• DISCONNECT TECH 1, IF CONNECTED.
• IGNITION "ON." DOES DTC 27 RESET?
NO
YES
6
• ROAD TEST VEHICLE, REACHING AT LEAST 25 km/h (15 MPH). DOES DTC 25 SET?
8
• REPLACE WHEEL BEARING/SPEED SENSOR ASSEMBLY.
• CLEAR DTCs; IGNITION "OFF."
• DISCONNECT TECH 1, IF CONNECTED.
• IGNITION "ON." DOES DTC 27 RESET?
YES
NO
7
GO TO DTC 25 DIAGNOSTICS.
NO TROUBLE FOUND, SEE "DIAGNOSTIC AIDS"
YES
NO
REPLACE EBTCM
SYSTEM OK

GC402940086500BX

Fig. 37 Code 27: LF Wheel Speed Sensor Continuity Fault. 1994

EBCM
N
S
WHEEL SPEED INPUT
WHEEL SPEED SENSOR

CODE 28

WHEEL SPEED SENSOR FREQUENCY ERROR

Circuit Description:

The toothed wheel generates a voltage pulse as it moves past the sensor; each tooth-gap-tooth series on the wheel generates these pulses. The frequency of these pulses is used by the EBCM to determine wheel speed. The amount of voltage generated in each pulse depends on the air gap between the sensor and the toothed wheel, and on wheel speed.

The "SERVICE ABS" and "SERVICE ASR" indicators will be "ON" and Code 28 is set if the EBCM cannot specifically identify which wheel speed sensor is causing the frequency error problem. If it can define the specific speed sensor causing the problem, the Sensor Fault code associated with the sensor (21, 25, 31, 35) will be set instead of Code 28.

Test Description: Number(s) below refer to circled number(s) on the diagnostic chart.

1. Checks wiring and connections for problems. It is critical that this step is performed thoroughly, as wiring/connector problems are the most likely cause for this code.
2. Uses the Tech 1 to monitor for vehicle electrical/electronic system "noise" being picked up by the speed sensor circuits.
3. Uses the Tech 1 to monitor the wheel speed sensors while the vehicle is operating. If the Tech 1 Auto-Trigger Snapshot mode triggers, the speed sensor or the wiring and/or connectors are going intermittent during the road test.
4. Checks for proper resistance in the sensor itself.

5a. Replace rear wheel speed sensor as the likely cause of the triggering intermittent.

5b. Replaces front wheel speed sensor as the likely cause of the triggering intermittent.

6. Uses the Tech 1 to monitor the wheel speed sensors while the vehicle is operating. If the Tech 1 Auto-Trigger Snapshot mode triggers, the EBCM must be concluding there is a problem with wheel speed sensor frequencies when there is not.
7. Checks for a short to ground in the seed sensor input circuit wires. The circuit to be tested depends on which speed sensor triggered the Tech 1. The ground may be either a "hard" short to ground, or a resistive (partial) short. A short with a resistance less than 2 megohms, though not a hard short, can still cause Code 28 to set.

Diagnostic Aids:

Code 28 may be set by running the Tech 1 Auto Test if the throttle angle readings are not updating while in the Data List mode. If this is the case, clear codes, disconnect Tech 1, and road test to at least 25 kph (15 mph) to see if code resets.

Rear Speed Sensors Only:

Check the toothed wheel for any large grooves, gouges, marks, etc. that might influence the tooth's signal at the wheel speed sensor. Also check for a buildup of foreign material in the gaps between teeth in the toothed wheel; this material may cause this fault.

A worn hub/bearing assembly may cause this fault in extreme cases; the bearing play allows the sensor-to-toothed-ring gap to change excessively.

GC402920041700AX

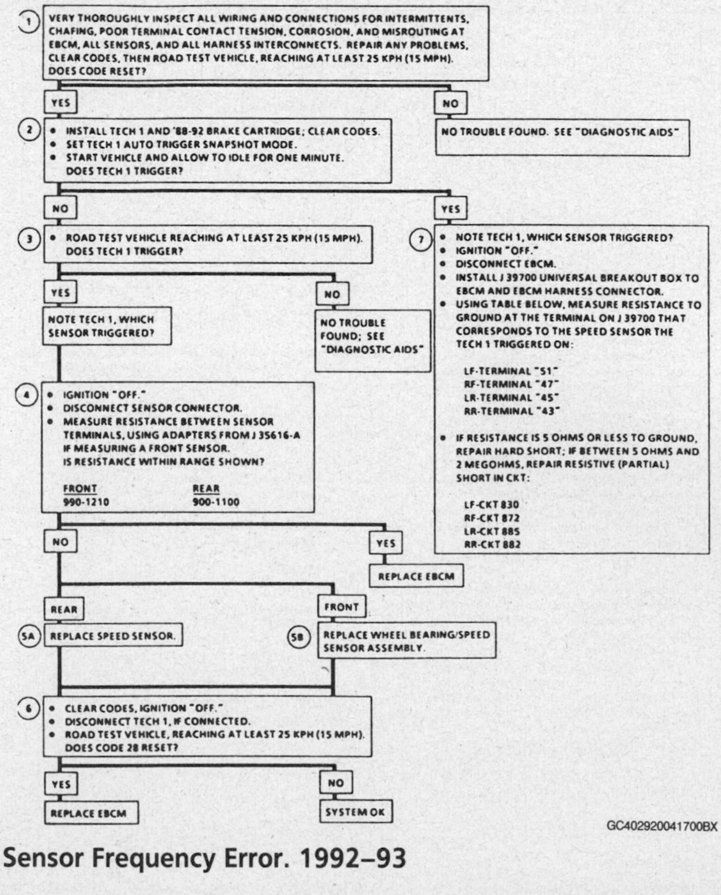
1
VERY THOROUGHLY INSPECT ALL WIRING AND CONNECTIONS FOR INTERMITTENTS, CHAFING, POOR TERMINAL CONTACT TENSION, CORROSION, AND MISROUTING AT EBCM, ALL SENSORS, AND ALL HARNESS INTERCONNECTS. REPAIR ANY PROBLEMS, CLEAR CODES, THEN ROAD TEST VEHICLE, REACHING AT LEAST 25 KPH (15 MPH). DOES CODE RESET?
YES
NO
NO TROUBLE FOUND. SEE "DIAGNOSTIC AIDS"
2
• INSTALL TECH 1 AND '88-92 BRAKE CARTRIDGE; CLEAR CODES.
• SET TECH 1 AUTO TRIGGER SNAPSHOT MODE.
• START VEHICLE AND ALLOW TO IDLE FOR ONE MINUTE. DOES TECH 1 TRIGGER?
NO
YES
3
• ROAD TEST VEHICLE REACHING AT LEAST 25 KPH (15 MPH). DOES TECH 1 TRIGGER?
7
• NOTE TECH 1, WHICH SENSOR TRIGGERED?
• IGNITION "OFF."
• DISCONNECT EBCM.
• INSTALL J 39700 UNIVERSAL BREAKOUT BOX TO EBCM AND EBCM HARNESS CONNECTOR.
• USING TABLE BELOW, MEASURE RESISTANCE TO GROUND AT THE TERMINAL ON J 39700 THAT CORRESPONDS TO THE SPEED SENSOR THE TECH 1 TRIGGERED ON:
LF-TERMINAL "51"
RF-TERMINAL "47"
LR-TERMINAL "45"
RR-TERMINAL "43"
• IF RESISTANCE IS 5 OHMS OR LESS TO GROUND, REPAIR HARD SHORT; IF BETWEEN 5 OHMS AND 2 MEGOHMS, REPAIR RESISTIVE (PARTIAL) SHORT IN CKT:
LF-CKT 830
RF-CKT 872
LR-CKT 885
RR-CKT 882
YES
NO
NOTE TECH 1, WHICH SENSOR TRIGGERED?
NO TROUBLE FOUND; SEE "DIAGNOSTIC AIDS"
4
• IGNITION "OFF."
• DISCONNECT SENSOR CONNECTOR.
• MEASURE RESISTANCE BETWEEN SENSOR TERMINALS, USING ADAPTERS FROM J 35616-A IF MEASURING A FRONT SENSOR. IS RESISTANCE WITHIN RANGE SHOWN?
FRONT 990-1210
REAR 900-1100
NO
YES
REPLACE EBCM
REAR
FRONT
5A
REPLACE SPEED SENSOR.
5B
REPLACE WHEEL BEARING/SPEED SENSOR ASSEMBLY.
6
• CLEAR CODES, IGNITION "OFF."
• DISCONNECT TECH 1, IF CONNECTED.
• ROAD TEST VEHICLE, REACHING AT LEAST 25 KPH (15 MPH). DOES CODE 28 RESET?
YES
NO
REPLACE EBCM
SYSTEM OK

GC402920041700BX

Fig. 38 Code 28: Wheel Speed Sensor Frequency Error. 1992–93

EBTCM
WHEEL SIGNAL HIGH
WHEEL SIGNAL LOW
WHEEL SPEED SENSOR

DTC 28

WHEEL SPEED SENSOR CIRCUIT FREQUENCY ERROR

Circuit Description:

The toothed wheel generates a voltage pulse as it moves past the sensor; each tooth-gap-tooth series on the wheel generates these pulses. The frequency of these pulses is used by the EBTCM to determine wheel speed. The amount of voltage generated in each pulse depends on the air gap between the sensor and the toothed wheel, and on wheel speed.

DTC Will Set When: The EBTCM cannot specifically identify which wheel speed sensor is causing the frequency error malfunction. If it can define the specific speed sensor causing the malfunction, the sensor DTC associated with the sensor (21, 25, 31, 35) will be set instead of DTC 28.

Action Taken: The "SERVICE ABS" and "SERVICE ASR" indicators will be "ON."

DTC Chart Test Description: Number(s) below refer to circled number(s) on the diagnostic chart.

1. Checks wiring and connections for malfunctions. It is critical that this step is performed thoroughly, as wiring/connector malfunctions are the most likely cause for this DTC.
2. Uses the Tech 1 to monitor for vehicle electrical/electronic system "noise" being picked up by the speed sensor circuits.
3. Uses the Tech 1 to monitor the wheel speed sensors while the vehicle is operating. If the Tech 1 auto-trigger snapshot mode triggers, the speed sensor or the wiring and/or connectors are going intermittent during the road test.
4. Checks for proper resistance in the sensor itself.

5a. Replace rear wheel speed sensor as the likely cause of the triggering intermittent.

5b. Replaces front wheel speed sensor as the likely cause of the triggering intermittent.

6. Uses the Tech 1 to monitor the wheel speed sensors while the vehicle is operating. If the Tech 1 auto-trigger snapshot mode triggers, the EBTCM must be concluding there is a malfunction with wheel speed sensor frequencies when there is not.
7. Checks for a short to ground in the speed sensor input circuit wires. The circuit to be tested depends on which speed sensor triggered the Tech 1. The ground may be either a "hard" short to ground, or a resistive (partial) short. A short with a resistance less than 2 megohms, though not a hard short, can still cause DTC 28 to set.

Diagnostic Aids: DTC 28 may be set by running the Tech 1 auto test if the throttle angle readings are not updating while in the data list mode. If this is the case, clear DTCs, disconnect Tech 1, and road test to at least 25 km/h (15 mph) to see if DTC resets.

Rear Speed Sensors Only:

Check the toothed wheel for any large grooves, gouges, marks, etc. that might influence the tooth's signal at the wheel speed sensor. Also check for a buildup of foreign material in the gaps between teeth in the toothed wheel; this material may cause this malfunction.

A worn hub/bearing assembly may cause this malfunction in extreme cases; the bearing play allows the sensor-to-toothed-ring gap to change excessively.

GC402940086600AX

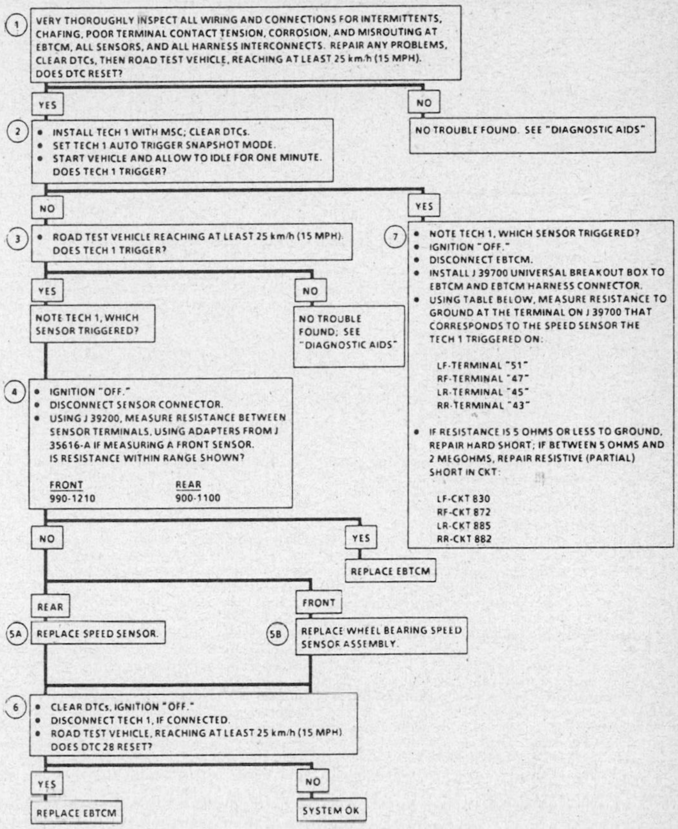
1
VERY THOROUGHLY INSPECT ALL WIRING AND CONNECTIONS FOR INTERMITTENTS, CHAFING, POOR TERMINAL CONTACT TENSION, CORROSION, AND MISROUTING AT EBTCM, ALL SENSORS, AND ALL HARNESS INTERCONNECTS. REPAIR ANY PROBLEMS, CLEAR DTCs, THEN ROAD TEST VEHICLE, REACHING AT LEAST 25 km/h (15 MPH). DOES DTC RESET?
YES
NO
NO TROUBLE FOUND. SEE "DIAGNOSTIC AIDS"
2
• INSTALL TECH 1 WITH MSC; CLEAR DTCs.
• SET TECH 1 AUTO TRIGGER SNAPSHOT MODE.
• START VEHICLE AND ALLOW TO IDLE FOR ONE MINUTE. DOES TECH 1 TRIGGER?
NO
YES
3
• ROAD TEST VEHICLE REACHING AT LEAST 25 km/h (15 MPH). DOES TECH 1 TRIGGER?
YES
NO
NOTE TECH 1, WHICH SENSOR TRIGGERED?
NO TROUBLE FOUND; SEE "DIAGNOSTIC AIDS"
7
• NOTE TECH 1, WHICH SENSOR TRIGGERED?
• IGNITION "OFF."
• DISCONNECT EBTCM.
• INSTALL J 39700 UNIVERSAL BREAKOUT BOX TO EBTCM AND EBTCM HARNESS CONNECTOR.
• USING TABLE BELOW, MEASURE RESISTANCE TO GROUND AT THE TERMINAL ON J 39700 THAT CORRESPONDS TO THE SPEED SENSOR THE TECH 1 TRIGGERED ON:
LF-TERMINAL "51"
RF-TERMINAL "47"
LR-TERMINAL "45"
RR-TERMINAL "43"
• IF RESISTANCE IS 5 OHMS OR LESS TO GROUND, REPAIR HARD SHORT; IF BETWEEN 5 OHMS AND 2 MEGOHMS, REPAIR RESISTIVE (PARTIAL) SHORT IN CKT:
LF-CKT 830
RF-CKT 872
LR-CKT 885
RR-CKT 882
4
• IGNITION "OFF."
• DISCONNECT SENSOR CONNECTOR.
• USING J 39200, MEASURE RESISTANCE BETWEEN SENSOR TERMINALS, USING ADAPTERS FROM J 35616-A IF MEASURING A FRONT SENSOR. IS RESISTANCE WITHIN RANGE SHOWN?
FRONT
990-1210
REAR
900-1100
NO
YES
REPLACE EBTCM
REAR
FRONT
5A
REPLACE SPEED SENSOR.
5B
REPLACE WHEEL BEARING SPEED SENSOR ASSEMBLY.
6
• CLEAR DTCs, IGNITION "OFF."
• DISCONNECT TECH 1, IF CONNECTED.
• ROAD TEST VEHICLE, REACHING AT LEAST 25 km/h (15 MPH). DOES DTC 28 RESET?
YES
NO
REPLACE EBTCM
SYSTEM OK

GC402940086600BX

Fig. 39 Code 28: Wheel Speed Sensor Frequency Error. 1994

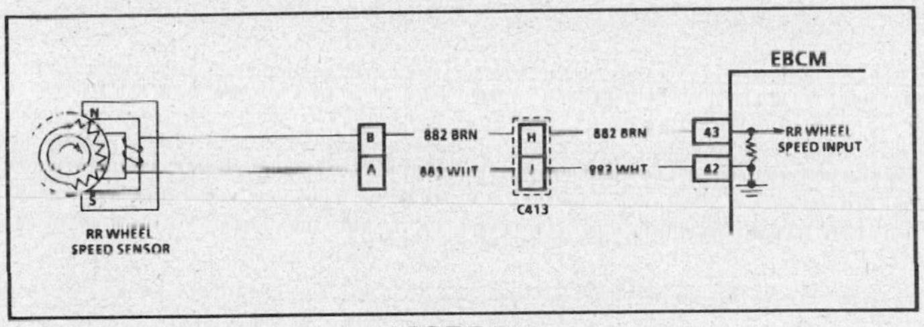
EBCM
N
S
B
A
882 BRN
883 WHT
H
J
882 BRN
883 WHT
C413
43
42
RR WHEEL SPEED INPUT
RR WHEEL SPEED SENSOR

CODE 31

RR WHEEL SPEED SENSOR FAULT

Circuit Description:

The toothed wheel generates a voltage pulse as it moves past the sensor, each tooth gap tooth series on the wheel generates these pulses. The frequency of these pulses is used by the EBCM to determine wheel speed. The amount of voltage generated in each pulse depends on the air gap between the sensor and the toothed wheel, and on wheel speed.

The "SERVICE ABS" and "SERVICE ASR" indicators will be "ON" and Code 31 is set if there is a short to voltage or ground in CKT 882 or 883, or a faulty speed sensor. The testing for this fault occurs when the vehicle is in motion; it will not set with the ignition "ON" and the vehicle at rest.

Test Description: Number(s) below refer to circled number(s) on the diagnostic chart.

1. Checks for proper resistance in the sensor itself.
2. Checks for a short to battery in either of the Speed Sensor circuit wires.
3. Checks for a short between the Speed Sensor circuit wires.
4. Checks for a short to ground in the Speed Sensor input circuit wire. The ground may be either a "hard" short to ground, or a resistive (partial) short. A short with a resistance less than 2 megohms, though not a hard short, can still cause Code 31 to set.
5. Checks if the code resets during a road test. If so, since Tests 1-4 have validated that all of the circuitry and components are good, intermittent problems are suspected.
6. Checks wiring and connectors for intermittents.
7. Checks for sensor mounting, toothed wheel, and rear wheel bearing problems which may be causing the problem. Check the toothed wheel for any large grooves, gouges, marks, etc. that might influence the tooth's signal at the wheel speed sensor. Also check for a buildup of foreign material in the gaps between teeth in the toothed wheel; this material may cause this fault.
8. Replace the Speed Sensor Assembly, as it is likely the cause of a code reset experienced during the road test, since other portions of the circuit have checked out OK.

Diagnostic Aids:

A worn hub-bearing assembly may cause this fault in extreme cases; the bearing play allows the sensor-to-toothed-ring gap to change excessively.

Be sure the speed sensor wiring is properly routed and retained. This will help prevent false signals due to electrical noise being picked up by the wiring.

It is very important that a thorough inspection of the wiring and connectors be performed. Failure to carefully and fully inspect wiring and connectors may result in misdiagnosis, causing part replacement with reappearance of the fault.

The Tech 1 can also be used to monitor the wheel speeds during a road test. Watch the wheel speeds being displayed on the Tech 1 to see if any of the readings are unusual, such as one sensor varying in speed from the other three, a signal going intermittently high or low, etc. If this does not identify the intermittent, wet the speed sensor harness on the underside of the vehicle and road test monitoring wheel speeds with the Tech 1.

GC402920041800AX

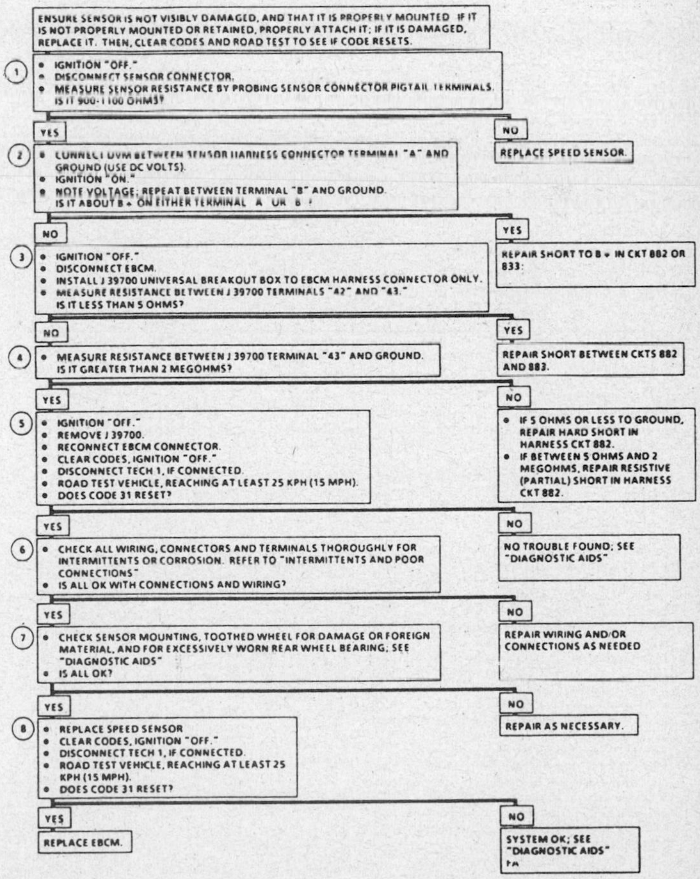
ENSURE SENSOR IS NOT VISIBLY DAMAGED, AND THAT IT IS PROPERLY MOUNTED. IF IT IS NOT PROPERLY MOUNTED OR RETAINED, PROPERLY ATTACH IT; IF IT IS DAMAGED, REPLACE IT. THEN, CLEAR CODES AND ROAD TEST TO SEE IF CODE RESETS.
1
• IGNITION "OFF."
• DISCONNECT SENSOR CONNECTOR.
• MEASURE SENSOR RESISTANCE BY PROBING SENSOR CONNECTOR PIGTAIL TERMINALS. IS IT 900-1100 OHMS?
YES
NO
REPLACE SPEED SENSOR.
2
• CONNECT DVM BETWEEN SENSOR HARNESS CONNECTOR TERMINAL "A" AND GROUND (USE DC VOLTS).
• IGNITION "ON."
• NOTE VOLTAGE; REPEAT BETWEEN TERMINAL "B" AND GROUND. IS IT ABOUT B+ ON EITHER TERMINAL "A" OR "B"?
NO
YES
REPAIR SHORT TO B+ IN CKT 882 OR 833.
3
• IGNITION "OFF."
• DISCONNECT EBCM.
• INSTALL J 39700 UNIVERSAL BREAKOUT BOX TO EBCM HARNESS CONNECTOR ONLY.
• MEASURE RESISTANCE BETWEEN J 39700 TERMINALS "42" AND "43." IS IT LESS THAN 5 OHMS?
NO
YES
REPAIR SHORT BETWEEN CKTS 882 AND 883.
4
• MEASURE RESISTANCE BETWEEN J 39700 TERMINAL "43" AND GROUND. IS IT GREATER THAN 2 MEGOHMS?
YES
NO
• IF 5 OHMS OR LESS TO GROUND, REPAIR HARD SHORT IN HARNESS CKT 882.
• IF BETWEEN 5 OHMS AND 2 MEGOHMS, REPAIR RESISTIVE (PARTIAL) SHORT IN HARNESS CKT 882.
5
• IGNITION "OFF."
• REMOVE J 39700.
• RECONNECT EBCM CONNECTOR.
• CLEAR CODES, IGNITION "OFF."
• DISCONNECT TECH 1, IF CONNECTED.
• ROAD TEST VEHICLE, REACHING AT LEAST 25 KPH (15 MPH).
• DOES CODE 31 RESET?
YES
NO
NO TROUBLE FOUND; SEE "DIAGNOSTIC AIDS"
6
• CHECK ALL WIRING, CONNECTORS AND TERMINALS THOROUGHLY FOR INTERMITTENTS OR CORROSION. REFER TO "INTERMITTENTS AND POOR CONNECTIONS"
• IS ALL OK WITH CONNECTIONS AND WIRING?
YES
NO
REPAIR WIRING AND/OR CONNECTIONS AS NEEDED
7
• CHECK SENSOR MOUNTING, TOOTHED WHEEL FOR DAMAGE OR FOREIGN MATERIAL, AND FOR EXCESSIVELY WORN REAR WHEEL BEARING; SEE "DIAGNOSTIC AIDS"
• IS ALL OK?
YES
NO
REPAIR AS NECESSARY.
8
• REPLACE SPEED SENSOR
• CLEAR CODES, IGNITION "OFF."
• DISCONNECT TECH 1, IF CONNECTED.
• ROAD TEST VEHICLE, REACHING AT LEAST 25 KPH (15 MPH).
• DOES CODE 31 RESET?
YES
NO
REPLACE EBCM.
SYSTEM OK; SEE "DIAGNOSTIC AIDS"

GC402920041800BX

Fig. 40 Code 31: RR Wheel Speed Sensor Fault. 1992–93

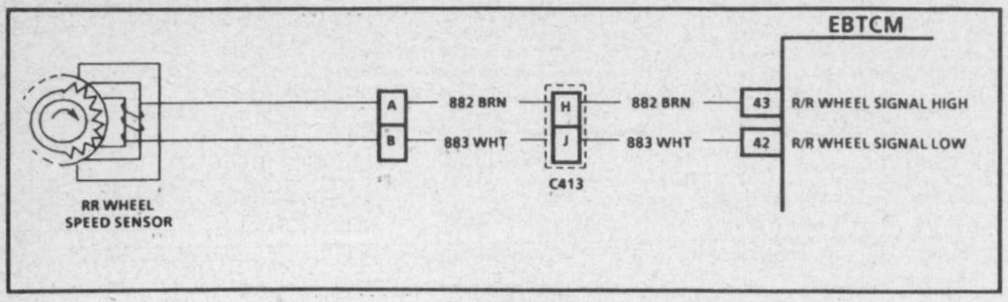
EBTCM
882 BRN
883 WHT
A
B
H
J
C413
43
42
R/R WHEEL SIGNAL HIGH
R/R WHEEL SIGNAL LOW
RR WHEEL
SPEED SENSOR

DTC 31

RR WHEEL SPEED SENSOR CIRCUIT MALFUNCTION

Circuit Description:

The toothed wheel generates a voltage pulse as it moves past the sensor; each tooth-gap-tooth series on the wheel generates these pulses. The frequency of these pulses is used by the EBTCM to determine wheel speed. The amount of voltage generated in each pulse depends on the air gap between the sensor and the toothed wheel, and on wheel speed.

DTC Will Set When: There is a short to voltage or an open in CKT 882 or 883, or a malfunctioning speed sensor. The testing for this malfunction occurs with the ignition "ON" and the vehicle at rest.

Action Taken: The "SERVICE ABS" and "SERVICE ASR" indicators will be "ON."

DTC Chart Test Description: Number(s) below refer to circled number(s) on the diagnostic chart.

1. Checks for proper resistance in the sensor itself.
2. Checks for a short to battery in either of the speed sensor circuit wires.
3. Checks for a short between the speed sensor circuit wires.
4. Checks for a short to ground in the speed sensor input circuit wire. The ground may be either a "hard" short to ground, or a resistive (partial) short. A short with a resistance less than 2 megohms, though not a hard short, can still cause DTC 31 to set.
5. Checks if the DTC resets during a road test. If so, since tests 1-4 have validated that all of the circuitry and components are good, intermittent malfunctions are suspected.
6. Checks wiring and connectors for intermittents.
7. Checks for sensor mounting, toothed wheel, and rear wheel bearing malfunctions which may be causing the malfunction. Check the toothed wheel for any large grooves, gouges, marks, etc. that might influence the tooth's signal at the wheel speed sensor. Also check for a buildup of foreign material in the gaps between teeth in the toothed wheel; this material may cause this malfunction.
8. Replace the speed sensor assembly, as it is likely the cause of a DTC reset experienced during the road test, since other portions of the circuit have checked out OK.

Diagnostic Aids: A worn hub-bearing assembly may cause this malfunction in extreme cases; the bearing play allows the sensor-to-toothed-ring gap to change excessively.

Be sure the speed sensor wiring is properly routed and retained. This will help prevent false signals due to electrical noise being picked up by the wiring.

It is very important that a thorough inspection of the wiring and connectors be performed. Failure to carefully and fully inspect wiring and connectors may result in misdiagnosis, causing part replacement with reappearance of the malfunction.

The Tech 1 can also be used to monitor the wheel speeds during a road test. Watch the wheel speeds being displayed on the Tech 1 to see if any of the readings are unusual, such as one sensor varying in speed from the other three, a signal going intermittently high or low, etc. If this does not identify the intermittent, wet the speed sensor harness on the underside of the vehicle and road test monitoring wheel speeds with the Tech 1.

GC402940086700AX

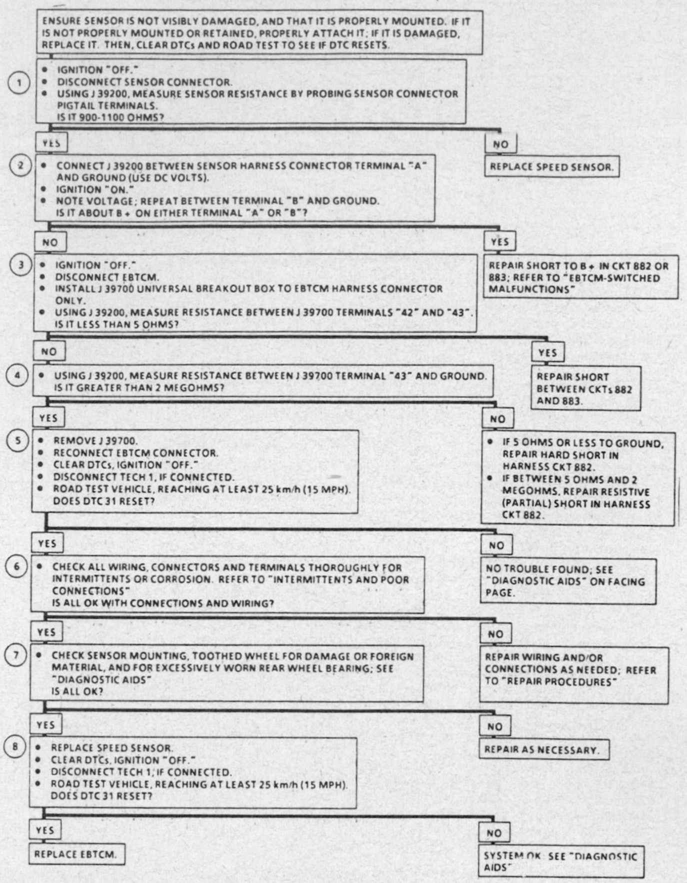
ENSURE SENSOR IS NOT VISIBLY DAMAGED, AND THAT IT IS PROPERLY MOUNTED. IF IT IS NOT PROPERLY MOUNTED OR RETAINED, PROPERLY ATTACH IT; IF IT IS DAMAGED, REPLACE IT. THEN, CLEAR DTCs AND ROAD TEST TO SEE IF DTC RESETS.
1
• IGNITION "OFF."
• DISCONNECT SENSOR CONNECTOR.
• USING J 39200, MEASURE SENSOR RESISTANCE BY PROBING SENSOR CONNECTOR PIGTAIL TERMINALS.
IS IT 900-1100 OHMS?
YES
NO
REPLACE SPEED SENSOR.
2
• CONNECT J 39200 BETWEEN SENSOR HARNESS CONNECTOR TERMINAL "A" AND GROUND (USE DC VOLTS).
• IGNITION "ON."
• NOTE VOLTAGE; REPEAT BETWEEN TERMINAL "B" AND GROUND.
IS IT ABOUT B+ ON EITHER TERMINAL "A" OR "B"?
NO
YES
REPAIR SHORT TO B+ IN CKT 882 OR 883; REFER TO "EBTCM-SWITCHED MALFUNCTIONS"
3
• IGNITION "OFF."
• DISCONNECT EBTCM.
• INSTALL J 39700 UNIVERSAL BREAKOUT BOX TO EBTCM HARNESS CONNECTOR ONLY.
• USING J 39200, MEASURE RESISTANCE BETWEEN J 39700 TERMINALS "42" AND "43".
IS IT LESS THAN 5 OHMS?
NO
YES
REPAIR SHORT BETWEEN CKTs 882 AND 883.
4
• USING J 39200, MEASURE RESISTANCE BETWEEN J 39700 TERMINAL "43" AND GROUND.
IS IT GREATER THAN 2 MEGOHMS?
YES
NO
• IF 5 OHMS OR LESS TO GROUND, REPAIR HARD SHORT IN HARNESS CKT 882.
• IF BETWEEN 5 OHMS AND 2 MEGOHMS, REPAIR RESISTIVE (PARTIAL) SHORT IN HARNESS CKT 882.
5
• REMOVE J 39700.
• RECONNECT EBTCM CONNECTOR.
• CLEAR DTCs, IGNITION "OFF."
• DISCONNECT TECH 1, IF CONNECTED.
• ROAD TEST VEHICLE, REACHING AT LEAST 25 km/h (15 MPH).
DOES DTC 31 RESET?
YES
NO
NO TROUBLE FOUND; SEE "DIAGNOSTIC AIDS" ON FACING PAGE.
6
• CHECK ALL WIRING, CONNECTORS AND TERMINALS THOROUGHLY FOR INTERMITTENTS OR CORROSION. REFER TO "INTERMITTENTS AND POOR CONNECTIONS"
IS ALL OK WITH CONNECTIONS AND WIRING?
YES
NO
REPAIR WIRING AND/OR CONNECTIONS AS NEEDED; REFER TO "REPAIR PROCEDURES"
7
• CHECK SENSOR MOUNTING, TOOTHED WHEEL FOR DAMAGE OR FOREIGN MATERIAL, AND FOR EXCESSIVELY WORN REAR WHEEL BEARING; SEE "DIAGNOSTIC AIDS"
IS ALL OK?
YES
NO
REPAIR AS NECESSARY.
8
• REPLACE SPEED SENSOR.
• CLEAR DTCs, IGNITION "OFF."
• DISCONNECT TECH 1, IF CONNECTED.
• ROAD TEST VEHICLE, REACHING AT LEAST 25 km/h (15 MPH).
DOES DTC 31 RESET?
YES
REPLACE EBTCM.
NO
SYSTEM OK. SEE "DIAGNOSTIC AIDS"

GC402940086700BX

Fig. 41 Code 31: RR Wheel Speed Sensor Fault. 1994

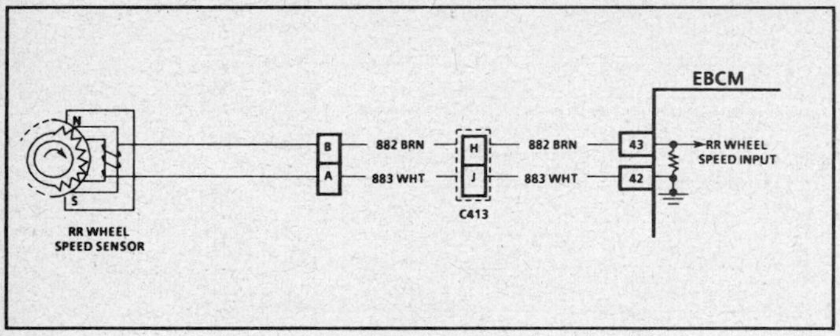
EBCM
N
S
882 BRN
883 WHT
B
A
H
J
C413
43
42
RR WHEEL SPEED INPUT
RR WHEEL
SPEED SENSOR

CODE 33

RR WHEEL SPEED SENSOR CONTINUITY FAULT

Circuit Description:

The toothed wheel generates a voltage pulse as it moves past the sensor; each tooth-gap-tooth series on the wheel generates these pulses. The frequency of these pulses is used by the EBCM to determine wheel speed. The amount of voltage generated in each pulse depends on the air gap between the sensor and the toothed wheel, and on wheel speed.

The "SERVICE ABS" and "SERVICE ASR" indicators will be "ON" and Code 33 is set if there is a short to voltage or an open in CKT 882 or 883, or a faulty speed sensor. The testing for this fault occurs with the ignition "ON" and the vehicle at rest.

Test Description: Number(s) below refer to circled number(s) on the diagnostic chart.

1. Checks for proper resistance in the sensor itself.
2. Checks for a short to battery in either of the Speed Sensor circuit wires.
3. Checks for an open in both the Speed Sensor circuit wires.
4. Manipulates wiring and connectors, trying to induce a intermittent fault not currently present.
5. This test checks if the code resets on key-up. If so, since Tests 1-4 have validated that the circuitry and components are good, the Speed Sensor may be causing the fault.
6. Checks if Code 31 sets during a road test.
7. Code 33 sets when the vehicle is at rest; Code 31 sets with a problem in the Speed Sensor circuitry with the vehicle in motion. If problems are still present, Code 31 would set during the road test, not a 33. If the Code 33 sets at this point, the Code 31 diagnostics should be used.
8. The wheel speed sensor may be causing an intermittent fault. If Code 33 resets after sensor replacement, the EBCM must be concluding there is a problem present in the Speed Sensor circuit when there is not.

Diagnostic Aids:

Be sure the speed sensor wiring is properly routed and retained. This will help prevent false signals due to electrical noise being picked up by the wiring.

It is very important that a thorough inspection of the wiring and connectors be performed. Failure to carefully and fully inspect wiring and connectors may result in misdiagnosis, causing part replacement with reappearance of the fault.

GC402920041900AX

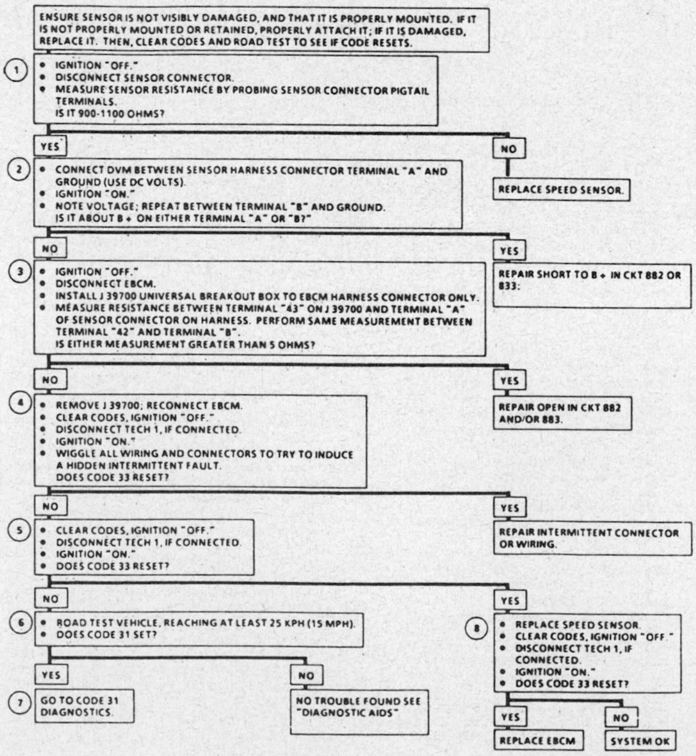
ENSURE SENSOR IS NOT VISIBLY DAMAGED, AND THAT IT IS PROPERLY MOUNTED. IF IT IS NOT PROPERLY MOUNTED OR RETAINED, PROPERLY ATTACH IT; IF IT IS DAMAGED, REPLACE IT. THEN, CLEAR CODES AND ROAD TEST TO SEE IF CODE RESETS.
1
• IGNITION "OFF."
• DISCONNECT SENSOR CONNECTOR.
• MEASURE SENSOR RESISTANCE BY PROBING SENSOR CONNECTOR PIGTAIL TERMINALS.
IS IT 900-1100 OHMS?
YES
NO
REPLACE SPEED SENSOR.
2
• CONNECT DVM BETWEEN SENSOR HARNESS CONNECTOR TERMINAL "A" AND GROUND (USE DC VOLTS).
• IGNITION "ON."
• NOTE VOLTAGE; REPEAT BETWEEN TERMINAL "B" AND GROUND.
IS IT ABOUT B+ ON EITHER TERMINAL "A" OR "B"?
NO
YES
REPAIR SHORT TO B+ IN CKT 882 OR 833:
3
• IGNITION "OFF."
• DISCONNECT EBCM.
• INSTALL J 39700 UNIVERSAL BREAKOUT BOX TO EBCM HARNESS CONNECTOR ONLY.
• MEASURE RESISTANCE BETWEEN TERMINAL "43" ON J 39700 AND TERMINAL "A" OF SENSOR CONNECTOR ON HARNESS. PERFORM SAME MEASUREMENT BETWEEN TERMINAL "42" AND TERMINAL "B".
IS EITHER MEASUREMENT GREATER THAN 5 OHMS?
NO
YES
REPAIR OPEN IN CKT 882 AND/OR 883.
4
• REMOVE J 39700; RECONNECT EBCM.
• CLEAR CODES, IGNITION "OFF."
• DISCONNECT TECH 1, IF CONNECTED.
• IGNITION "ON."
• WIGGLE ALL WIRING AND CONNECTORS TO TRY TO INDUCE A HIDDEN INTERMITTENT FAULT.
DOES CODE 33 RESET?
NO
YES
REPAIR INTERMITTENT CONNECTOR OR WIRING.
5
• CLEAR CODES, IGNITION "OFF."
• DISCONNECT TECH 1, IF CONNECTED.
• IGNITION "ON."
• DOES CODE 33 RESET?
NO
YES
6
• ROAD TEST VEHICLE, REACHING AT LEAST 25 KPH (15 MPH).
• DOES CODE 31 SET?
8
• REPLACE SPEED SENSOR.
• CLEAR CODES, IGNITION "OFF."
• DISCONNECT TECH 1, IF CONNECTED.
• IGNITION "ON."
• DOES CODE 33 RESET?
YES
NO
7
GO TO CODE 31 DIAGNOSTICS.
NO TROUBLE FOUND SEE "DIAGNOSTIC AIDS"
YES
NO
REPLACE EBCM
SYSTEM OK

GC402920041900BX

Fig. 42 Code 33: RR Wheel Speed Sensor Continuity Fault. 1992–93

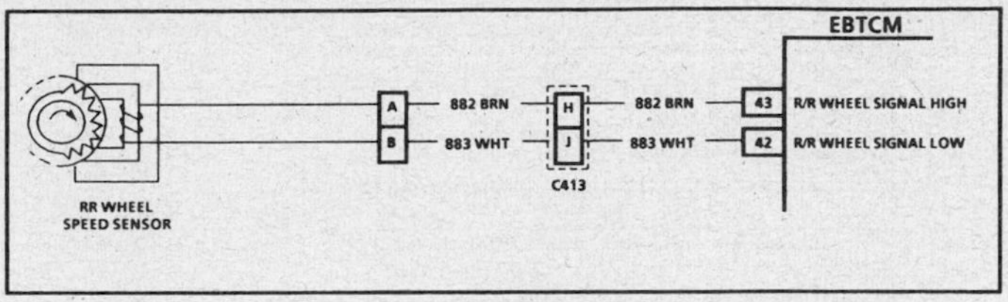
EBTCM
882 BRN
883 WHT
A
B
H
J
C413
43
42
R/R WHEEL SIGNAL HIGH
R/R WHEEL SIGNAL LOW
RR WHEEL
SPEED SENSOR

DTC 33

RR WHEEL SPEED SENSOR CIRCUIT CONTINUITY MALFUNCTION

Circuit Description:

The toothed wheel generates a voltage pulse as it moves past the sensor; each tooth-gap-tooth series on the wheel generates these pulses. The frequency of these pulses is used by the EBTCM to determine wheel speed. The amount of voltage generated in each pulse depends on the air gap between the sensor and the toothed wheel, and on wheel speed.

DTC Will Set When: There is a short to voltage or ground in CKT 882 or 883, or a malfunctioning speed sensor. The testing for this malfunction occurs when the vehicle is in motion; it will not set with the ignition "ON" and the vehicle at rest.

Action Taken: The "SERVICE ABS" and "SERVICE ASR" indicators will be "ON."

DTC Chart Test Description: Number(s) below refer to circled number(s) on the diagnostic chart.

1. Checks for proper resistance in the sensor itself.
2. Checks for a short to battery in either of the speed sensor circuit wires.
3. Checks for an open in both of the speed sensor circuit wires.
4. Manipulates wiring and connectors, trying to induce an intermittent malfunction not currently present.
5. Checks if the DTC resets on key-up. If so, since tests 1-4 have validated that the circuitry and components are good, the speed sensor may be causing the malfunction.
6. Checks if DTC 31 sets during a road test.
7. DTC 33 sets when the vehicle is at rest, DTC 31 sets with a malfunction in the speed sensor circuitry with the vehicle in motion. If malfunctions are still present, DTC 31 would set during the road test, not a 33. If the DTC 31 sets at this point, the DTC 31 diagnostics should be used.
8. The wheel speed sensor may be causing an intermittent malfunction. If DTC 33 resets after sensor replacement, the EBTCM must be concluding there is a malfunction present in the speed sensor circuit when there is not.

Diagnostic Aids: Be sure the speed sensor wiring is properly routed and retained. This will help prevent false signals due to electrical noise being picked up by the wiring.

It is very important that a thorough inspection of the wiring and connectors be performed. Failure to carefully and fully inspect wiring and connectors may result in misdiagnosis, causing part replacement with reappearance of the malfunction.

GC402940086800AX

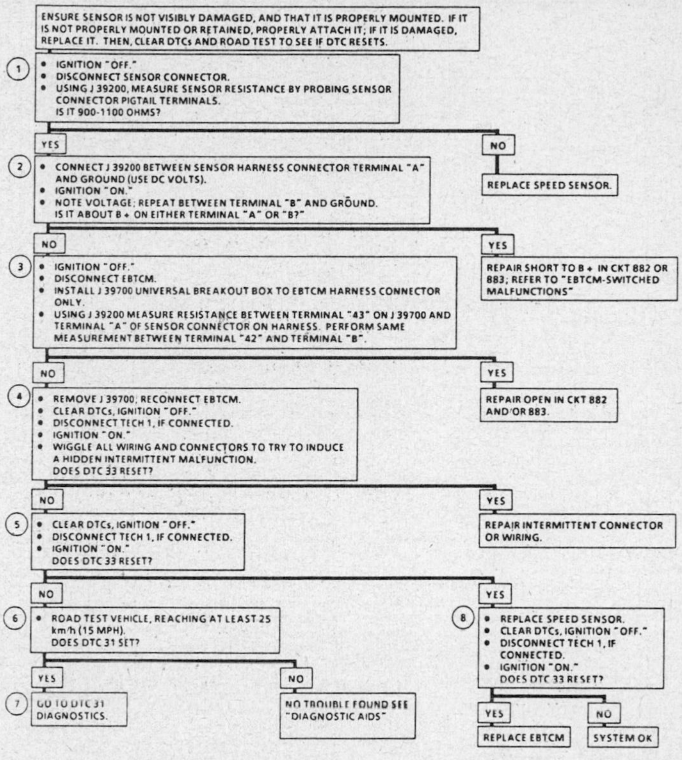
ENSURE SENSOR IS NOT VISIBLY DAMAGED, AND THAT IT IS PROPERLY MOUNTED. IF IT IS NOT PROPERLY MOUNTED OR RETAINED, PROPERLY ATTACH IT; IF IT IS DAMAGED, REPLACE IT. THEN, CLEAR DTCs AND ROAD TEST TO SEE IF DTC RESETS.
1
• IGNITION "OFF."
• DISCONNECT SENSOR CONNECTOR.
• USING J 39200, MEASURE SENSOR RESISTANCE BY PROBING SENSOR CONNECTOR PIGTAIL TERMINALS.
IS IT 900-1100 OHMS?
YES
NO
REPLACE SPEED SENSOR.
2
• CONNECT J 39200 BETWEEN SENSOR HARNESS CONNECTOR TERMINAL "A" AND GROUND (USE DC VOLTS).
• IGNITION "ON."
• NOTE VOLTAGE; REPEAT BETWEEN TERMINAL "B" AND GROUND.
IS IT ABOUT B+ ON EITHER TERMINAL "A" OR "B?"
NO
YES
REPAIR SHORT TO B+ IN CKT 882 OR 883; REFER TO "EBTCM-SWITCHED MALFUNCTIONS"
3
• IGNITION "OFF."
• DISCONNECT EBTCM.
• INSTALL J 39700 UNIVERSAL BREAKOUT BOX TO EBTCM HARNESS CONNECTOR ONLY.
• USING J 39200 MEASURE RESISTANCE BETWEEN TERMINAL "43" ON J 39700 AND TERMINAL "A" OF SENSOR CONNECTOR ON HARNESS. PERFORM SAME MEASUREMENT BETWEEN TERMINAL "42" AND TERMINAL "B".
NO
YES
REPAIR OPEN IN CKT 882 AND/OR 883.
4
• REMOVE J 39700; RECONNECT EBTCM.
• CLEAR DTCs, IGNITION "OFF."
• DISCONNECT TECH 1, IF CONNECTED.
• IGNITION "ON."
• WIGGLE ALL WIRING AND CONNECTORS TO TRY TO INDUCE A HIDDEN INTERMITTENT MALFUNCTION.
DOES DTC 33 RESET?
NO
YES
REPAIR INTERMITTENT CONNECTOR OR WIRING.
5
• CLEAR DTCs, IGNITION "OFF."
• DISCONNECT TECH 1, IF CONNECTED.
• IGNITION "ON."
DOES DTC 33 RESET?
NO
YES
6
• ROAD TEST VEHICLE, REACHING AT LEAST 25 km/h (15 MPH).
DOES DTC 31 SET?
8
• REPLACE SPEED SENSOR.
• CLEAR DTCs, IGNITION "OFF."
• DISCONNECT TECH 1, IF CONNECTED.
• IGNITION "ON."
DOES DTC 33 RESET?
YES
NO
7
GO TO DTC 31 DIAGNOSTICS.
NO TROUBLE FOUND SEE "DIAGNOSTIC AIDS"
YES
NO
REPLACE EBTCM
SYSTEM OK

GC402940086800BX

Fig. 43 Code 33: RR Wheel Speed Sensor Continuity Fault. 1994

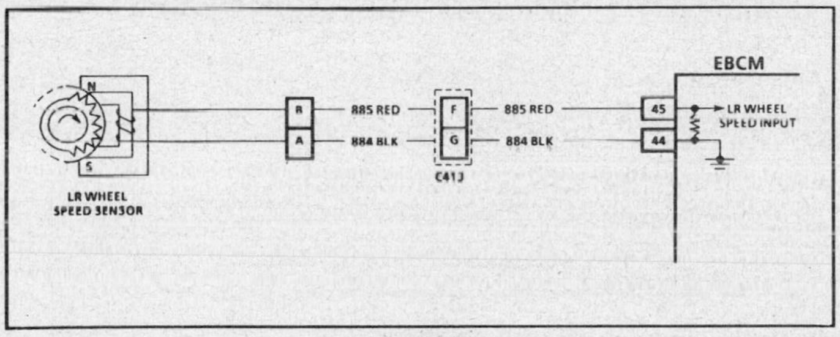
EBCM
N
S
R
A
885 RED
884 BLK
F
G
C413
45
44
LR WHEEL SPEED INPUT
LR WHEEL SPEED SENSOR

CODE 35

LR WHEEL SPEED SENSOR FAULT

Circuit Description:

The toothed wheel generates a voltage pulse as it moves past the sensor; each tooth-gap-tooth series on the wheel generates these pulses. The frequency of these pulses is used by the EBCM to determine wheel speed. The amount of voltage generated in each pulse depends on the air gap between the sensor and the toothed wheel, and on wheel speed.

The "SERVICE ABS" and "SERVICE ASR" indicators will be "ON" and Code 35 is set if there is a short to voltage or ground in CKT 885 or 884, or a faulty speed sensor. The testing for this fault occurs when the vehicle is in motion; it will not set with the ignition "ON" and the vehicle at rest.

Test Description: Number(s) below refer to circled number(s) on the diagnostic chart.

1. Checks for proper resistance in the sensor itself.
2. Checks for a short to battery in either of the Speed Sensor circuit wires.
3. Checks for a short between the Speed Sensor circuit wires.
4. Checks for a short to ground in the Speed Sensor input circuit wire. The ground may be either a "hard" short to ground, or a resistive (partial) short. A short with a resistance less than 2 megohms, though not a hard short, can still cause Code 35 to set.
5. Checks if the code resets during a road test. If so, since Tests 1-4 have validated that all of the circuitry and components are good, intermittent problems are suspected.
6. Checks wiring and connectors for intermittents.
7. Checks for sensor mounting, toothed wheel, and rear wheel bearing problems which may be causing the problem. Check the toothed wheel for any large grooves, gouges, marks, etc. that might influence the tooth's signal at the wheel speed sensor. Also check for a buildup of foreign material in the gaps between teeth in the toothed wheel; this material may cause this fault.
8. Replace the Speed Sensor Assembly, as it is likely the cause of a code reset experienced during the road test, since other portions of the circuit have checked out OK.

Diagnostic Aids:

A worn hub-bearing assembly may cause this fault in extreme cases; the bearing play allows the sensor-to-toothed-ring gap to change excessively.

Be sure the speed sensor wiring is properly routed and retained. This will help prevent false signals due to electrical noise being picked up by the wiring.

It is very important that a thorough inspection of the wiring and connectors be performed. Failure to carefully and fully inspect wiring and connectors may result in misdiagnosis, causing part replacement with reappearance of the fault.

The Tech 1 can also be used to monitor the wheel speeds during a road test. Watch the wheel speeds being displayed on the Tech 1 to see if any of the readings are unusual, such as one sensor varying in speed from the other three, a signal going intermittently high or low, etc. If this does not identify the intermittent, wet the speed sensor harness on the underside of the vehicle and road test monitoring wheel speeds with the Tech 1.

GC402920042000AX

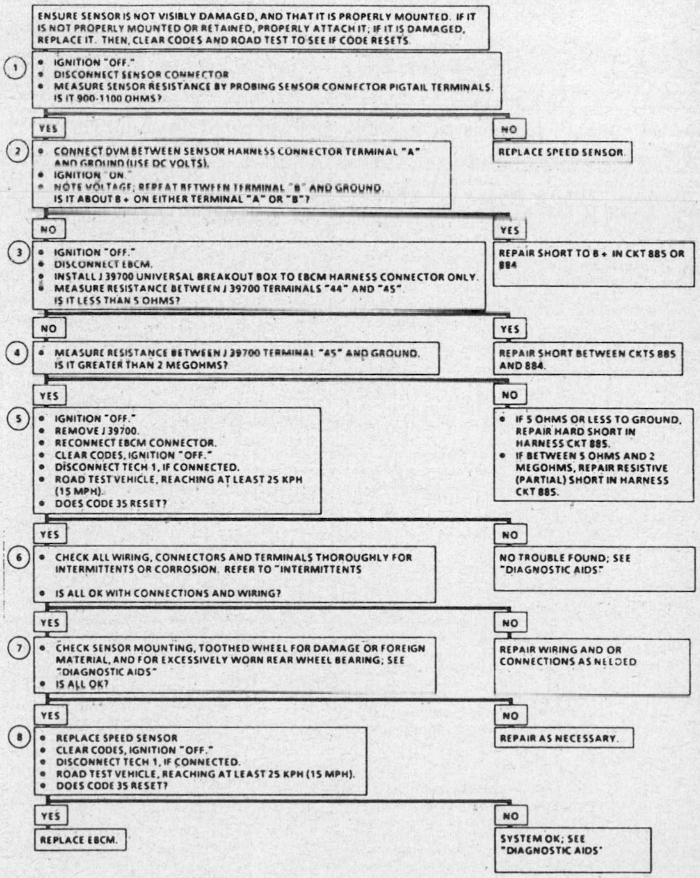
ENSURE SENSOR IS NOT VISIBLY DAMAGED, AND THAT IT IS PROPERLY MOUNTED. IF IT IS NOT PROPERLY MOUNTED OR RETAINED, PROPERLY ATTACH IT; IF IT IS DAMAGED, REPLACE IT. THEN, CLEAR CODES AND ROAD TEST TO SEE IF CODE RESETS.
1
• IGNITION "OFF."
• DISCONNECT SENSOR CONNECTOR
• MEASURE SENSOR RESISTANCE BY PROBING SENSOR CONNECTOR PIGTAIL TERMINALS.
IS IT 900-1100 OHMS?
YES
NO
REPLACE SPEED SENSOR.
2
• CONNECT DVM BETWEEN SENSOR HARNESS CONNECTOR TERMINAL "A" AND GROUND (USE DC VOLTS).
• IGNITION "ON."
• NOTE VOLTAGE; REPEAT BETWEEN TERMINAL "B" AND GROUND.
IS IT ABOUT B+ ON EITHER TERMINAL "A" OR "B"?
NO
YES
REPAIR SHORT TO B+ IN CKT 885 OR 884
3
• IGNITION "OFF."
• DISCONNECT EBCM.
• INSTALL J 39700 UNIVERSAL BREAKOUT BOX TO EBCM HARNESS CONNECTOR ONLY.
• MEASURE RESISTANCE BETWEEN J 39700 TERMINALS "44" AND "45".
IS IT LESS THAN 5 OHMS?
NO
YES
REPAIR SHORT BETWEEN CKTS 885 AND 884.
4
• MEASURE RESISTANCE BETWEEN J 39700 TERMINAL "45" AND GROUND.
IS IT GREATER THAN 2 MEGOHMS?
YES
NO
• IF 5 OHMS OR LESS TO GROUND, REPAIR HARD SHORT IN HARNESS CKT 885.
• IF BETWEEN 5 OHMS AND 2 MEGOHMS, REPAIR RESISTIVE (PARTIAL) SHORT IN HARNESS CKT 885.
5
• IGNITION "OFF."
• REMOVE J 39700.
• RECONNECT EBCM CONNECTOR.
• CLEAR CODES, IGNITION "OFF."
• DISCONNECT TECH 1, IF CONNECTED.
• ROAD TEST VEHICLE, REACHING AT LEAST 25 KPH (15 MPH).
• DOES CODE 35 RESET?
YES
NO
NO TROUBLE FOUND; SEE "DIAGNOSTIC AIDS"
6
• CHECK ALL WIRING, CONNECTORS AND TERMINALS THOROUGHLY FOR INTERMITTENTS OR CORROSION. REFER TO "INTERMITTENTS"
• IS ALL OK WITH CONNECTIONS AND WIRING?
YES
NO
REPAIR WIRING AND OR CONNECTIONS AS NEEDED
7
• CHECK SENSOR MOUNTING, TOOTHED WHEEL FOR DAMAGE OR FOREIGN MATERIAL, AND FOR EXCESSIVELY WORN REAR WHEEL BEARING; SEE "DIAGNOSTIC AIDS"
• IS ALL OK?
YES
NO
REPAIR AS NECESSARY.
8
• REPLACE SPEED SENSOR
• CLEAR CODES, IGNITION "OFF."
• DISCONNECT TECH 1, IF CONNECTED.
• ROAD TEST VEHICLE, REACHING AT LEAST 25 KPH (15 MPH).
• DOES CODE 35 RESET?
YES
NO
REPLACE EBCM.
SYSTEM OK; SEE "DIAGNOSTIC AIDS"

GC402920042000BX

Fig. 44 Code 35: LR Wheel Speed Sensor Fault. 1992–93

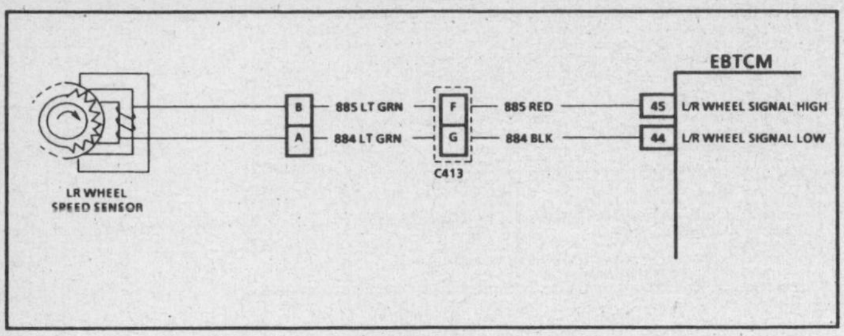
EBTCM
B 885 LT GRN
A 884 LT GRN
F 885 RED
G 884 BLK
C413
45 L/R WHEEL SIGNAL HIGH
44 L/R WHEEL SIGNAL LOW
LR WHEEL SPEED SENSOR

DTC 35

LR WHEEL SPEED SENSOR CIRCUIT MALFUNCTION

Circuit Description:

The toothed wheel generates a voltage pulse as it moves past the sensor; each tooth-gap-tooth series on the wheel generates these pulses. The frequency of these pulses is used by the EBTCM to determine wheel speed. The amount of voltage generated in each pulse depends on the air gap between the sensor and the toothed wheel, and on wheel speed.

DTC Will Set When: There is a short to voltage or ground in CKT 885 or 884, or a malfunctioning speed sensor. The testing for this malfunction occurs when the vehicle is in motion; it will not set with the ignition "ON" and the vehicle at rest.

Action Taken: The "SERVICE ABS" and "SERVICE ASR" indicators will be "ON."

DTC Chart Test Description: Number(s) below refer to circled number(s) on the diagnostic chart.

1. Checks for proper resistance in the sensor itself.
2. Checks for a short to battery in either of the speed sensor circuit wires.
3. Checks for a short between the speed sensor circuit wires.
4. Checks for a short to ground in the speed sensor input circuit wire. The ground may be either a "hard" short to ground, or a resistive (partial) short. A short with a resistance less than 2 megohms, though not a hard short, can still cause DTC 35 to set.
5. Checks if the DTC resets during a road test. If so, since tests 1-4 have validated that all of the circuitry and components are good, intermittent malfunctions are suspected.
6. Checks wiring and connectors for intermittents.
7. Checks for sensor mounting, toothed wheel, and rear wheel bearing malfunctions which may be causing the malfunction. Check the toothed wheel for any large grooves, gouges, marks, etc. that might influence the tooth's signal at the wheel speed sensor. Also check for a buildup of foreign material in the gaps between teeth in the toothed wheel; this material may cause this malfunction.
8. Replace the speed sensor assembly, as it is likely the cause of a DTC reset experienced during the road test, since other portions of the circuit have checked out OK.

Diagnostic Aids: A worn hub-bearing assembly may cause this malfunction in extreme cases; the bearing play allows the sensor-to-toothed-ring gap to change excessively.

Be sure the speed sensor wiring is properly routed and retained. This will help prevent false signals due to electrical noise being picked up by the wiring.

It is very important that a thorough inspection of the wiring and connectors be performed. Failure to carefully and fully inspect wiring and connectors may result in misdiagnosis, causing part replacement with reappearance of the malfunction.

The Tech 1 can also be used to monitor the wheel speeds during a road test. Watch the wheel speeds being displayed on the Tech 1 to see if any of the readings are unusual, such as one sensor varying in speed from the other three, a signal going intermittently high or low, etc. If this does not identify the intermittent, wet the speed sensor harness on the underside of the vehicle and road test monitoring wheel speeds with the Tech 1.

GC402940086900AX

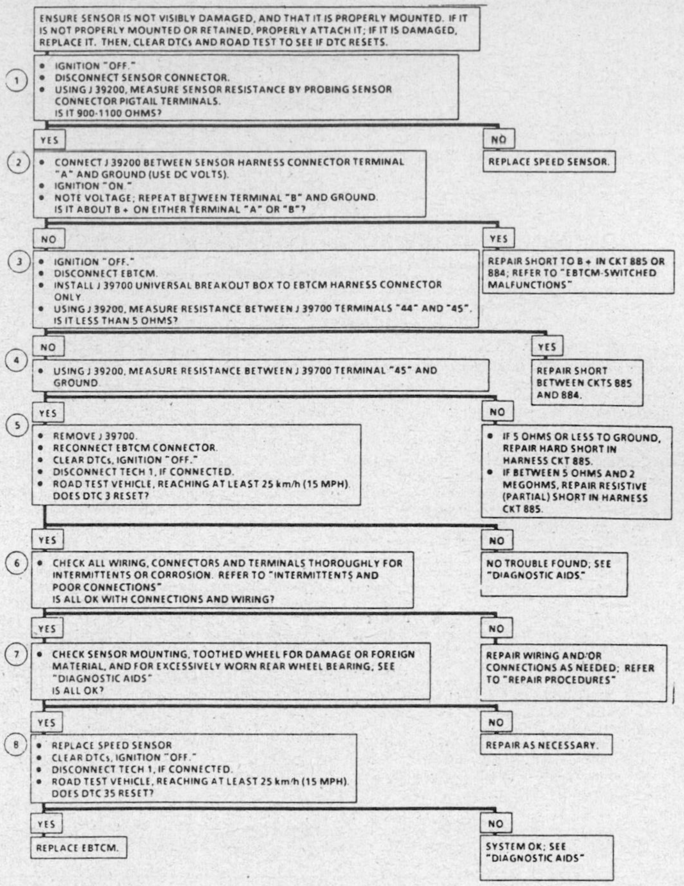
ENSURE SENSOR IS NOT VISIBLY DAMAGED, AND THAT IT IS PROPERLY MOUNTED. IF IT IS NOT PROPERLY MOUNTED OR RETAINED, PROPERLY ATTACH IT; IF IT IS DAMAGED, REPLACE IT. THEN, CLEAR DTCs AND ROAD TEST TO SEE IF DTC RESETS.
1
• IGNITION "OFF."
• DISCONNECT SENSOR CONNECTOR.
• USING J 39200, MEASURE SENSOR RESISTANCE BY PROBING SENSOR CONNECTOR PIGTAIL TERMINALS.
IS IT 900-1100 OHMS?
YES
NO
REPLACE SPEED SENSOR.
2
• CONNECT J 39200 BETWEEN SENSOR HARNESS CONNECTOR TERMINAL "A" AND GROUND (USE DC VOLTS).
• IGNITION "ON."
• NOTE VOLTAGE; REPEAT BETWEEN TERMINAL "B" AND GROUND.
IS IT ABOUT B+ ON EITHER TERMINAL "A" OR "B"?
NO
YES
REPAIR SHORT TO B+ IN CKT 885 OR 884; REFER TO "EBTCM-SWITCHED MALFUNCTIONS"
3
• IGNITION "OFF."
• DISCONNECT EBTCM.
• INSTALL J 39700 UNIVERSAL BREAKOUT BOX TO EBTCM HARNESS CONNECTOR ONLY.
• USING J 39200, MEASURE RESISTANCE BETWEEN J 39700 TERMINALS "44" AND "45".
IS IT LESS THAN 5 OHMS?
NO
YES
REPAIR SHORT BETWEEN CKTS 885 AND 884.
4
• USING J 39200, MEASURE RESISTANCE BETWEEN J 39700 TERMINAL "45" AND GROUND.
YES
NO
• IF 5 OHMS OR LESS TO GROUND, REPAIR HARD SHORT IN HARNESS CKT 885.
• IF BETWEEN 5 OHMS AND 2 MEGOHMS, REPAIR RESISTIVE (PARTIAL) SHORT IN HARNESS CKT 885.
5
• REMOVE J 39700.
• RECONNECT EBTCM CONNECTOR.
• CLEAR DTCs, IGNITION "OFF."
• DISCONNECT TECH 1, IF CONNECTED.
• ROAD TEST VEHICLE, REACHING AT LEAST 25 km/h (15 MPH).
DOES DTC 3 RESET?
YES
NO
NO TROUBLE FOUND; SEE "DIAGNOSTIC AIDS"
6
• CHECK ALL WIRING, CONNECTORS AND TERMINALS THOROUGHLY FOR INTERMITTENTS OR CORROSION. REFER TO "INTERMITTENTS AND POOR CONNECTIONS"
IS ALL OK WITH CONNECTIONS AND WIRING?
YES
NO
REPAIR WIRING AND/OR CONNECTIONS AS NEEDED; REFER TO "REPAIR PROCEDURES"
7
• CHECK SENSOR MOUNTING, TOOTHED WHEEL FOR DAMAGE OR FOREIGN MATERIAL, AND FOR EXCESSIVELY WORN REAR WHEEL BEARING. SEE "DIAGNOSTIC AIDS"
IS ALL OK?
YES
NO
REPAIR AS NECESSARY.
8
• REPLACE SPEED SENSOR
• CLEAR DTCs, IGNITION "OFF."
• DISCONNECT TECH 1, IF CONNECTED.
• ROAD TEST VEHICLE, REACHING AT LEAST 25 km/h (15 MPH).
DOES DTC 35 RESET?
YES
NO
REPLACE EBTCM.
SYSTEM OK; SEE "DIAGNOSTIC AIDS"

GC402940086900BX

Fig. 45 Code 35: LR Wheel Speed Sensor Fault. 1994

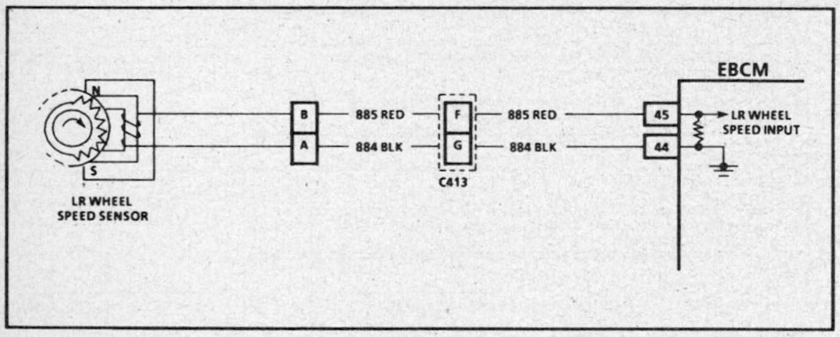
EBCM
N
S
B 885 RED
A 884 BLK
F 885 RED
G 884 BLK
C413
45
44
LR WHEEL SPEED INPUT
LR WHEEL SPEED SENSOR

CODE 37

LR WHEEL SPEED SENSOR CONTINUITY FAULT

Circuit Description:

The toothed wheel generates a voltage pulse as it moves past the sensor; each tooth-gap-tooth series on the wheel generates these pulses. The frequency of these pulses is used by the EBCM to determine wheel speed. The amount of voltage generated in each pulse depends on the air gap between the sensor and the toothed wheel, and on wheel speed.

The "SERVICE ABS" and "SERVICE ASR" indicators will be "ON" and Code 37 is set if there is a short to voltage or an open in CKT 885 or 884, or a faulty speed sensor. The testing for this fault occurs with the ignition "ON" and the vehicle at rest.

Test Description: Number(s) below refer to circled number(s) on the diagnostic chart.

1. Checks for proper resistance in the sensor itself.
2. Checks for a short to battery in either of the Speed Sensor circuit wires.
3. Checks for an open in both the Speed Sensor circuit wires.
4. Manipulates wiring and connectors, trying to induce a intermittent fault not currently present.
5. This test checks if the code resets on key-up. If so, since Tests 1-4 have validated that the circuitry and components are good, the Speed Sensor may be causing the fault.
6. Checks if Code 35 sets during a road test.
7. Code 37 sets when the vehicle is at rest; Code 35 sets with a problem in the Speed Sensor circuitry with the vehicle in motion. If problems are still present, Code 35 would set during the road test, not a 37. If the Code 35 sets at this point, the Code 35 diagnostics should be used.
8. The wheel speed sensor may be causing an intermittent fault. If Code 37 resets after sensor replacement, the EBCM must be concluding there is a problem present in the Speed Sensor circuit when there is not.

Diagnostic Aids:

Be sure the speed sensor wiring is properly routed and retained. This will help prevent false signals due to electrical noise being picked up by the wiring.

It is very important that a thorough inspection of the wiring and connectors be performed. Failure to carefully and fully inspect wiring and connectors may result in misdiagnosis, causing part replacement with reappearance of the fault.

GC402920042100AX

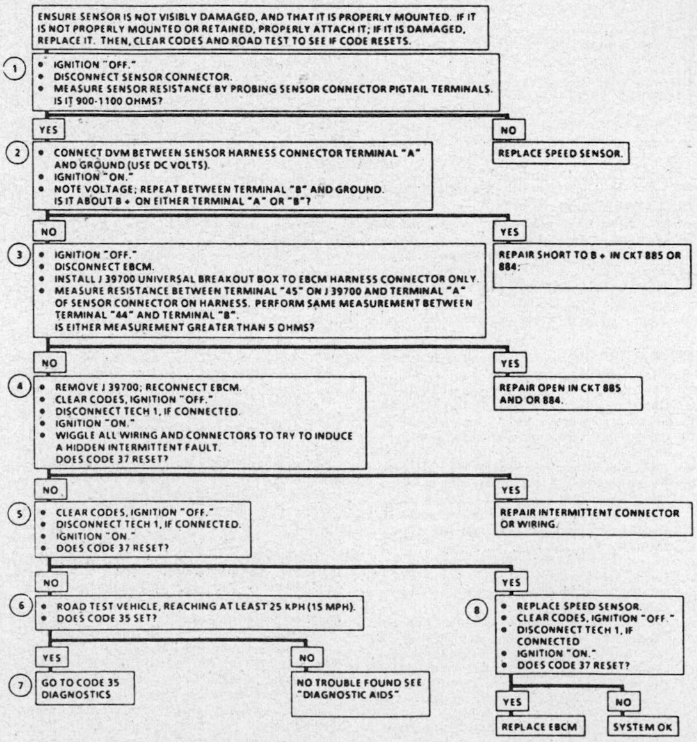
ENSURE SENSOR IS NOT VISIBLY DAMAGED, AND THAT IT IS PROPERLY MOUNTED. IF IT IS NOT PROPERLY MOUNTED OR RETAINED, PROPERLY ATTACH IT; IF IT IS DAMAGED, REPLACE IT. THEN, CLEAR CODES AND ROAD TEST TO SEE IF CODE RESETS.
1
• IGNITION "OFF."
• DISCONNECT SENSOR CONNECTOR.
• MEASURE SENSOR RESISTANCE BY PROBING SENSOR CONNECTOR PIGTAIL TERMINALS.
IS IT 900-1100 OHMS?
YES
NO
REPLACE SPEED SENSOR.
2
• CONNECT DVM BETWEEN SENSOR HARNESS CONNECTOR TERMINAL "A" AND GROUND (USE DC VOLTS).
• IGNITION "ON."
• NOTE VOLTAGE; REPEAT BETWEEN TERMINAL "B" AND GROUND.
IS IT ABOUT B+ ON EITHER TERMINAL "A" OR "B"?
NO
YES
REPAIR SHORT TO B+ IN CKT 885 OR 884.
3
• IGNITION "OFF."
• DISCONNECT EBCM.
• INSTALL J 39700 UNIVERSAL BREAKOUT BOX TO EBCM HARNESS CONNECTOR ONLY.
• MEASURE RESISTANCE BETWEEN TERMINAL "45" ON J 39700 AND TERMINAL "A" OF SENSOR CONNECTOR ON HARNESS. PERFORM SAME MEASUREMENT BETWEEN TERMINAL "44" AND TERMINAL "B".
IS EITHER MEASUREMENT GREATER THAN 5 OHMS?
NO
YES
REPAIR OPEN IN CKT 885 AND OR 884.
4
• REMOVE J 39700; RECONNECT EBCM.
• CLEAR CODES, IGNITION "OFF."
• DISCONNECT TECH 1, IF CONNECTED.
• IGNITION "ON."
• WIGGLE ALL WIRING AND CONNECTORS TO TRY TO INDUCE A HIDDEN INTERMITTENT FAULT.
DOES CODE 37 RESET?
NO
YES
REPAIR INTERMITTENT CONNECTOR OR WIRING.
5
• CLEAR CODES, IGNITION "OFF."
• DISCONNECT TECH 1, IF CONNECTED.
• IGNITION "ON."
• DOES CODE 37 RESET?
NO
YES
6
• ROAD TEST VEHICLE, REACHING AT LEAST 25 KPH (15 MPH).
• DOES CODE 35 SET?
YES
NO
7
GO TO CODE 35 DIAGNOSTICS
NO TROUBLE FOUND SEE "DIAGNOSTIC AIDS"
8
• REPLACE SPEED SENSOR.
• CLEAR CODES, IGNITION "OFF."
• DISCONNECT TECH 1, IF CONNECTED
• IGNITION "ON."
• DOES CODE 37 RESET?
YES
NO
REPLACE EBCM
SYSTEM OK

GC402920042100BX

Fig. 46 Code 37: LR Wheel Speed Sensor Continuity Fault. 1992-93

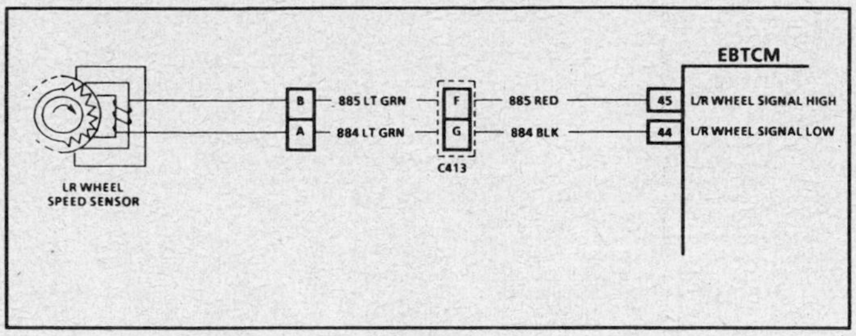
EBTCM
885 LT GRN
884 LT GRN
885 RED
884 BLK
C413
L/R WHEEL SIGNAL HIGH
L/R WHEEL SIGNAL LOW
LR WHEEL SPEED SENSOR

DTC 37

LR WHEEL SPEED SENSOR CIRCUIT CONTINUITY MALFUNCTION

Circuit Description:

The toothed wheel generates a voltage pulse as it moves past the sensor; each tooth-gap-tooth series on the wheel generates these pulses. The frequency of these pulses is used by the EBTCM to determine wheel speed. The amount of voltage generated in each pulse depends on the air gap between the sensor and the toothed wheel, and on wheel speed.

DTC Will Set When: There is a short to voltage or an open in CKT 885 or 884, or a malfunctioning speed sensor. The testing for this malfunction occurs with the ignition "ON" and the vehicle at rest.

Action Taken: The "SERVICE ABS" and "SERVICE ASR" indicators will be "ON."

DTC Chart Test Description: Number(s) below refer to circled number(s) on the diagnostic chart.

1. Checks for proper resistance in the sensor itself.
2. Checks for a short to battery in either of the speed sensor circuit wires.
3. Checks for an open in both the speed sensor circuit wires.
4. Manipulates wiring and connectors, trying to induce an intermittent malfunction not currently present.
5. Checks if the DTC resets on key-up. If so, since tests 1-4 have validated that the circuitry and components are good, the speed sensor may be causing the malfunction.
6. Checks if DTC 35 sets during a road test.
7. DTC 37 sets when the vehicle is at rest; DTC 35 sets with a malfunction in the speed sensor circuitry with the vehicle in motion. If malfunctions are still present, DTC 35 would set during the road test, not a 37. If the DTC 35 sets at this point, the DTC 35 diagnostics should be used.
8. The wheel speed sensor may be causing an intermittent malfunction. If DTC 37 resets after sensor replacement, the EBTCM must be concluding there is a malfunction present in the speed sensor circuit when there is not.

Diagnostic Aids: Be sure the speed sensor wiring is properly routed and retained. This will help prevent false signals due to electrical noise being picked up by the wiring.

It is very important that a thorough inspection of the wiring and connectors be performed. Failure to carefully and fully inspect wiring and connectors may result in misdiagnosis, causing part replacement with reappearance of the malfunction.

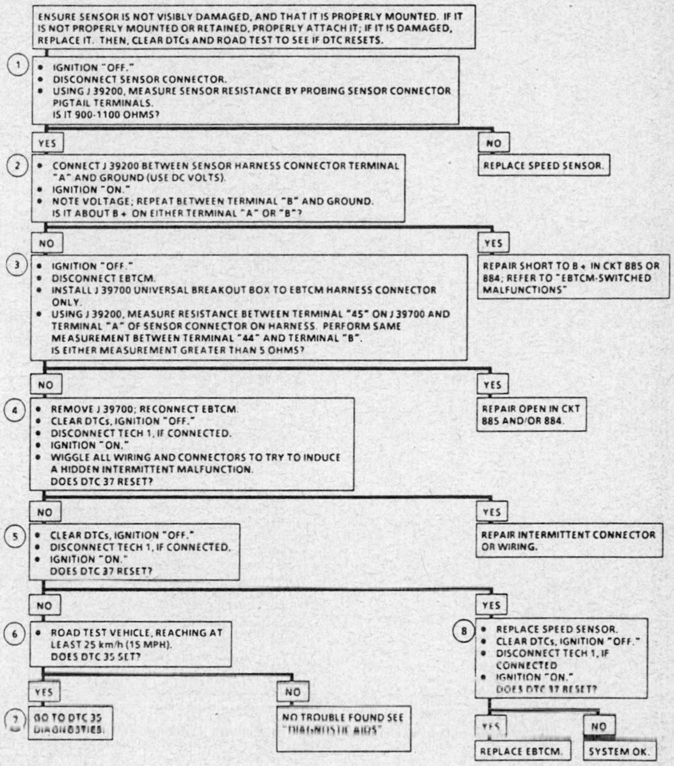
ENSURE SENSOR IS NOT VISIBLY DAMAGED, AND THAT IT IS PROPERLY MOUNTED. IF IT IS NOT PROPERLY MOUNTED OR RETAINED, PROPERLY ATTACH IT; IF IT IS DAMAGED, REPLACE IT. THEN, CLEAR DTCs AND ROAD TEST TO SEE IF DTC RESETS.
1
• IGNITION "OFF."
• DISCONNECT SENSOR CONNECTOR.
• USING J 39200, MEASURE SENSOR RESISTANCE BY PROBING SENSOR CONNECTOR PIGTAIL TERMINALS.
IS IT 900-1100 OHMS?
YES
NO
REPLACE SPEED SENSOR.
2
• CONNECT J 39200 BETWEEN SENSOR HARNESS CONNECTOR TERMINAL "A" AND GROUND (USE DC VOLTS).
• IGNITION "ON."
• NOTE VOLTAGE; REPEAT BETWEEN TERMINAL "B" AND GROUND.
IS IT ABOUT B+ ON EITHER TERMINAL "A" OR "B"?
NO
YES
REPAIR SHORT TO B+ IN CKT 885 OR 884; REFER TO "EBTCM-SWITCHED MALFUNCTIONS"
3
• IGNITION "OFF."
• DISCONNECT EBTCM.
• INSTALL J 39700 UNIVERSAL BREAKOUT BOX TO EBTCM HARNESS CONNECTOR ONLY.
• USING J 39200, MEASURE RESISTANCE BETWEEN TERMINAL "45" ON J 39700 AND TERMINAL "A" OF SENSOR CONNECTOR ON HARNESS. PERFORM SAME MEASUREMENT BETWEEN TERMINAL "44" AND TERMINAL "B".
IS EITHER MEASUREMENT GREATER THAN 5 OHMS?
NO
YES
REPAIR OPEN IN CKT 885 AND/OR 884.
4
• REMOVE J 39700; RECONNECT EBTCM.
• CLEAR DTCs, IGNITION "OFF."
• DISCONNECT TECH 1, IF CONNECTED.
• IGNITION "ON."
• WIGGLE ALL WIRING AND CONNECTORS TO TRY TO INDUCE A HIDDEN INTERMITTENT MALFUNCTION.
DOES DTC 37 RESET?
NO
YES
REPAIR INTERMITTENT CONNECTOR OR WIRING.
5
• CLEAR DTCs, IGNITION "OFF."
• DISCONNECT TECH 1, IF CONNECTED.
• IGNITION "ON."
DOES DTC 37 RESET?
NO
YES
6
• ROAD TEST VEHICLE, REACHING AT LEAST 25 km/h (15 MPH).
DOES DTC 35 SET?
8
• REPLACE SPEED SENSOR.
• CLEAR DTCs, IGNITION "OFF."
• DISCONNECT TECH 1, IF CONNECTED
• IGNITION "ON."
DOES DTC 37 RESET?
YES
NO
7
GO TO DTC 35 DIAGNOSTICS.
NO TROUBLE FOUND SEE "DIAGNOSTIC AIDS"
YES
NO
REPLACE EBTCM.
SYSTEM OK.

GC402940087000AX

Fig. 47 Code 37: LR Wheel Speed Sensor Continuity Fault. 1994

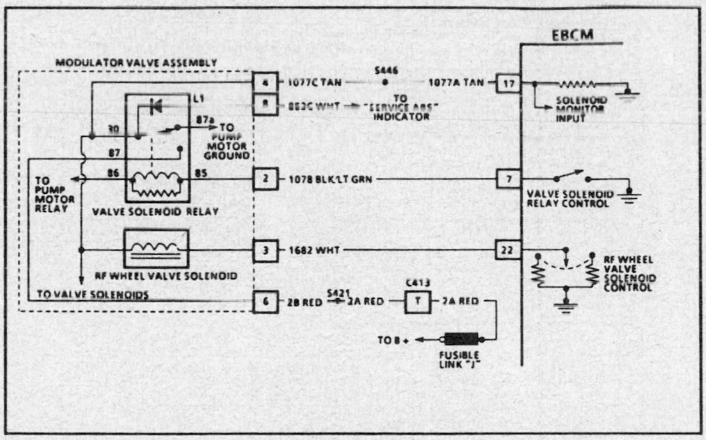
EBCM
MODULATOR VALVE ASSEMBLY
1077C TAN
S446
1077A TAN
SOLENOID MONITOR INPUT
TO "SERVICE ABS" INDICATOR
TO PUMP MOTOR GROUND
TO PUMP MOTOR RELAY
VALVE SOLENOID RELAY
1078 BLK/LT GRN
VALVE SOLENOID RELAY CONTROL
1682 WHT
RF WHEEL VALVE SOLENOID
RF WHEEL VALVE SOLENOID CONTROL
TO VALVE SOLENOIDS
2B RED
S421
2A RED
C413
TO B+
FUSIBLE LINK "J"

CODE 41

RF VALVE SOLENOID FAULT

Circuit Description:

The wheel valve solenoid circuits are supplied with battery power when the ignition is "ON." The EBCM controls the valve functions by permitting one of three levels of current flow (0, 2.5, 5 amps) to the solenoid.

If the EBCM senses a discrepancy such as an open or ground in the circuit, the Valve Solenoid Relay will turn "OFF," the "SERVICE ABS" and "SERVICE ASR" lights will come "ON," and Code 41 will set.

Test Description: Number(s) below refer to circled number(s) on the diagnostic chart.

1. Checks the integrity of CKTs 1682 and 1077, the RF Valve Solenoid circuitry internal to the Modulator Valve Assembly, and the RF Valve Solenoid coil.
2. Checks for a short to battery in CKT 1682, using EBCM terminal 3 as ground.
3. Checks for a short to ground in CKT 1682, using EBCM terminal 3 as ground.
4. Checks wiring and connectors for intermittents.
5. Uses the Tech 1 to exercise the RF Valve Solenoid and check it for proper operation.
6. Determines whether the code was set by an intermittent condition or an EBCM fault.
7. Determines whether a problem found in Step 1 is due to an open in CKT 1682 or a faulty Modulator Valve Assembly.

Diagnostic Aids:

All tests using J 39700 Universal Breakout Box terminal 3 are using the terminal as ground. These tests, of course, assume that the ground CKT 801 at terminal 3 is good.

If Codes 41 and 45 are both set the fault is likely to be a short to B+ on CKT 1682.

If Codes 41 and 55 are both set the fault is likely to be a short to B+ on CKT 829.

GC402920042200AX

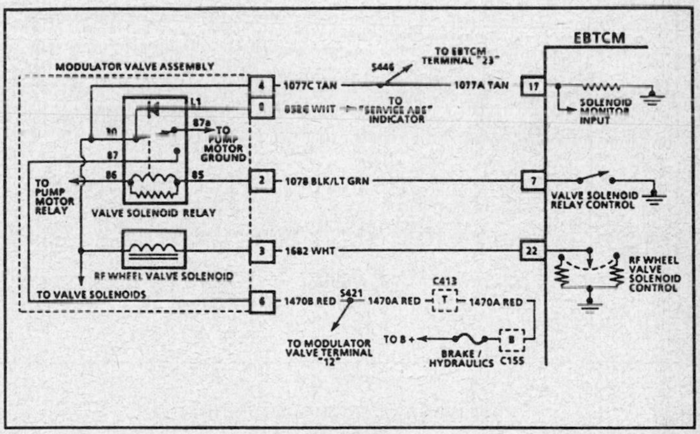
EBTCM
MODULATOR VALVE ASSEMBLY
TO EBTCM TERMINAL "23"
S446
1077C TAN
1077A TAN
SOLENOID MONITOR INPUT
TO "SERVICE ABS" INDICATOR
TO PUMP MOTOR GROUND
TO PUMP MOTOR RELAY
VALVE SOLENOID RELAY
1078 BLK/LT GRN
VALVE SOLENOID RELAY CONTROL
1682 WHT
RF WHEEL VALVE SOLENOID
RF WHEEL VALVE SOLENOID CONTROL
TO VALVE SOLENOIDS
1470B RED
S421
1470A RED
C413
TO MODULATOR VALVE TERMINAL "12"
TO B+
BRAKE / HYDRAULICS
C155

DTC 41

RF VALVE SOLENOID MALFUNCTION

Circuit Description:

The wheel valve solenoid circuits are supplied with battery power when the ignition is "ON." The EBTCM controls the valve functions by permitting one of three levels of current flow (0, 2.5, 5 amps) to the solenoid.

If the EBTCM senses a discrepancy such as an open or ground in the circuit, the valve solenoid relay will turn "OFF," the "SERVICE ABS" and "SERVICE ASR" lights will come "ON," and DTC 41 will set.

Test Description: Number(s) below refer to circled number(s) on the diagnostic chart.

1. Checks the integrity of CKTs 1682 and 1077, the RF valve solenoid circuitry internal to the modulator valve assembly, and the RF valve solenoid coil.
2. Checks for a short to battery in CKT 1682, using EBTCM terminal "3" as ground.
3. Checks for a short to ground in CKT 1682, using EBTCM terminal "3" as ground.
4. Checks wiring and connectors for intermittents.
5. Uses the Tech 1 to exercise the RF valve solenoid and check it for proper operation.
6. Determines whether the DTC was set by an intermittent condition or an EBTCM malfunction.
7. Determines whether a problem found in Step 1 is due to an open in CKT 1682 or a malfunctioning modulator valve assembly.

Diagnostic Aids:

All tests using J 39700 Universal Breakout Box terminal "3" are using the terminal as ground. These tests, of course, assume that the ground CKT 801 at terminal "3" is good.

If DTCs 41 and 45 are both set the malfunction is likely to be a short to B+ on CKT 1682.

If DTCs 41 and 55 are both set the malfunction is likely to be a short to B+ on CKT 829.

GC402920042200BX

Fig. 48 Code 41: RF Solenoid Valve Fault (Part 1 of 2). 1992–93

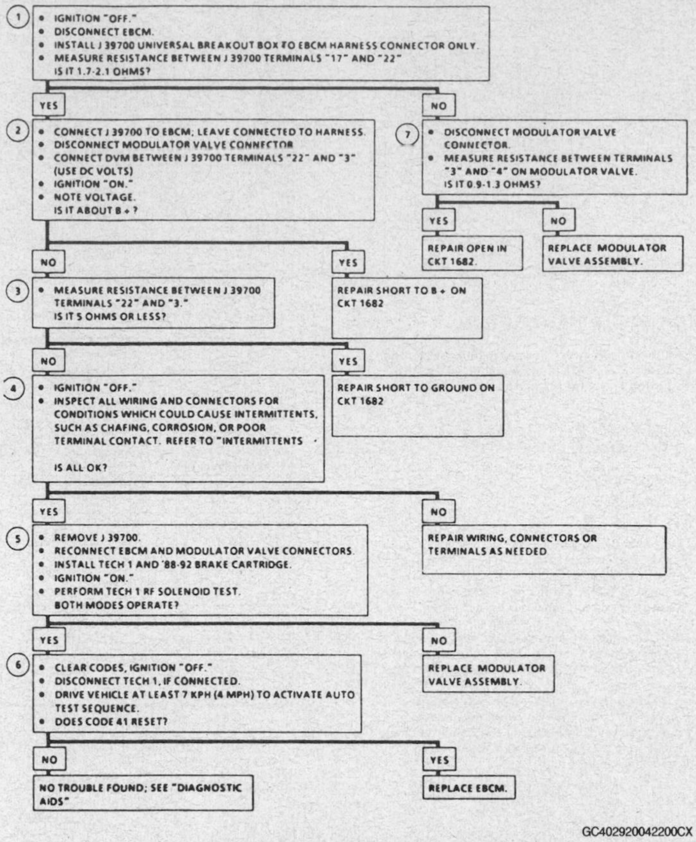
1
IGNITION "OFF."
DISCONNECT EBCM.
INSTALL J 39700 UNIVERSAL BREAKOUT BOX TO EBCM HARNESS CONNECTOR ONLY.
MEASURE RESISTANCE BETWEEN J 39700 TERMINALS "17" AND "22"
IS IT 1.7-2.1 OHMS?
YES
NO
2
CONNECT J 39700 TO EBCM; LEAVE CONNECTED TO HARNESS.
DISCONNECT MODULATOR VALVE CONNECTOR
CONNECT DVM BETWEEN J 39700 TERMINALS "22" AND "3" (USE DC VOLTS)
IGNITION "ON."
NOTE VOLTAGE.
IS IT ABOUT B + ?
7
DISCONNECT MODULATOR VALVE CONNECTOR.
MEASURE RESISTANCE BETWEEN TERMINALS "3" AND "4" ON MODULATOR VALVE.
IS IT 0.9-1.3 OHMS?
YES
NO
REPAIR OPEN IN CKT 1682.
REPLACE MODULATOR VALVE ASSEMBLY.
NO
YES
3
MEASURE RESISTANCE BETWEEN J 39700 TERMINALS "22" AND "3."
IS IT 5 OHMS OR LESS?
REPAIR SHORT TO B + ON CKT 1682
NO
YES
4
IGNITION "OFF."
INSPECT ALL WIRING AND CONNECTORS FOR CONDITIONS WHICH COULD CAUSE INTERMITTENTS, SUCH AS CHAFING, CORROSION, OR POOR TERMINAL CONTACT. REFER TO "INTERMITTENTS
IS ALL OK?
REPAIR SHORT TO GROUND ON CKT 1682
YES
NO
5
REMOVE J 39700.
RECONNECT EBCM AND MODULATOR VALVE CONNECTORS.
INSTALL TECH 1 AND '88-92 BRAKE CARTRIDGE.
IGNITION "ON."
PERFORM TECH 1 RF SOLENOID TEST.
BOTH MODES OPERATE?
REPAIR WIRING, CONNECTORS OR TERMINALS AS NEEDED
YES
NO
6
CLEAR CODES, IGNITION "OFF."
DISCONNECT TECH 1, IF CONNECTED.
DRIVE VEHICLE AT LEAST 7 KPH (4 MPH) TO ACTIVATE AUTO TEST SEQUENCE.
DOES CODE 41 RESET?
REPLACE MODULATOR VALVE ASSEMBLY.
NO
YES
NO TROUBLE FOUND; SEE "DIAGNOSTIC AIDS"
REPLACE EBCM.
GC402920042200CX

Fig. 48 Code 41: RF Solenoid Valve Fault (Part 2 of 2). 1992–93

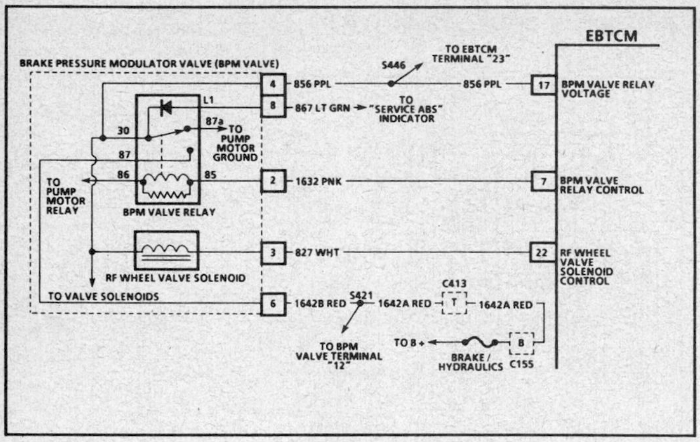
EBTCM
BRAKE PRESSURE MODULATOR VALVE (BPM VALVE)
TO EBTCM TERMINAL "23"
S446
4
856 PPL
856 PPL
17
BPM VALVE RELAY VOLTAGE
L1
8
867 LT GRN
TO "SERVICE ABS" INDICATOR
30
87a
TO PUMP MOTOR GROUND
87
86
85
TO PUMP MOTOR RELAY
2
1632 PNK
7
BPM VALVE RELAY CONTROL
BPM VALVE RELAY
3
827 WHT
22
RF WHEEL VALVE SOLENOID CONTROL
RF WHEEL VALVE SOLENOID
TO VALVE SOLENOIDS
C413
6
1642B RED
S421
1642A RED
T
1642A RED
TO BPM VALVE TERMINAL "12"
TO B +
B
BRAKE / HYDRAULICS
C155

DTC 41

RF VALVE SOLENOID MALFUNCTION

Circuit Description:

The wheel valve solenoid circuits are supplied with battery power when the ignition is "ON." The EBTCM controls the valve functions by permitting one of three levels of current flow (0, 2.5, 5 amps) to the solenoid.

DTC Will Set When: The EBTCM senses a discrepancy such as an open or ground in the circuit.

Action Taken: The BPM valve relay will turn "OFF" and the "SERVICE ABS" and "SERVICE ASR" indicators will come "ON."

DTC Chart Test Description: Number(s) below refer to circled number(s) on the diagnostic chart.

1. Checks the integrity of CKTs 827 and 856, the RF valve solenoid circuitry internal to the BPM valve assembly, and the RF valve solenoid coil.
2. Checks for a short to battery in CKT 827, using EBTCM terminal "3" as ground.
3. Checks for a short to ground in CKT 827, using EBTCM terminal "3" as ground.
4. Checks wiring and connectors for intermittents.
5. Uses the Tech 1 to exercise the RF valve solenoid and check it for proper operation.
6. Determines whether the DTC was set by an intermittent condition or an EBTCM malfunction.
7. Determines whether a malfunction found in Step 1 is due to an open in CKT 827 or a malfunctioning BPM valve assembly.

Diagnostic Aids: All tests using J 39700 Universal Breakout Box terminal "3" are using the terminal as ground. These tests, of course, assume that the ground CKT 1051 at terminal "3" is good.

If DTCs 41 and 45 are both set the malfunction is likely to be a short to B + on CKT 827.

If DTCs 41 and 55 are both set the malfunction is likely to be a short to B + on CKT 828.

GC402940087100AX

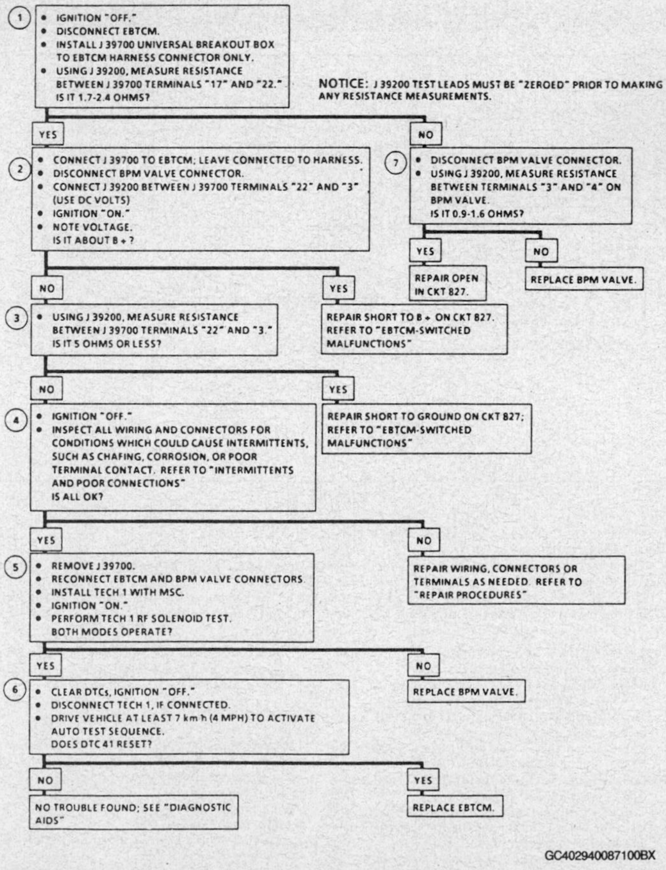
1
IGNITION "OFF."
DISCONNECT EBTCM.
INSTALL J 39700 UNIVERSAL BREAKOUT BOX TO EBTCM HARNESS CONNECTOR ONLY.
USING J 39200, MEASURE RESISTANCE BETWEEN J 39700 TERMINALS "17" AND "22."
IS IT 1.7-2.4 OHMS?
NOTICE: J 39200 TEST LEADS MUST BE "ZEROED" PRIOR TO MAKING ANY RESISTANCE MEASUREMENTS.
YES
NO
2
CONNECT J 39700 TO EBTCM; LEAVE CONNECTED TO HARNESS.
DISCONNECT BPM VALVE CONNECTOR.
CONNECT J 39200 BETWEEN J 39700 TERMINALS "22" AND "3" (USE DC VOLTS)
IGNITION "ON."
NOTE VOLTAGE.
IS IT ABOUT B + ?
7
DISCONNECT BPM VALVE CONNECTOR.
USING J 39200, MEASURE RESISTANCE BETWEEN TERMINALS "3" AND "4" ON BPM VALVE.
IS IT 0.9-1.6 OHMS?
YES
NO
REPAIR OPEN IN CKT 827.
REPLACE BPM VALVE.
NO
YES
3
USING J 39200, MEASURE RESISTANCE BETWEEN J 39700 TERMINALS "22" AND "3."
IS IT 5 OHMS OR LESS?
REPAIR SHORT TO B + ON CKT 827. REFER TO "EBTCM-SWITCHED MALFUNCTIONS"
NO
YES
4
IGNITION "OFF."
INSPECT ALL WIRING AND CONNECTORS FOR CONDITIONS WHICH COULD CAUSE INTERMITTENTS, SUCH AS CHAFING, CORROSION, OR POOR TERMINAL CONTACT. REFER TO "INTERMITTENTS AND POOR CONNECTIONS"
IS ALL OK?
REPAIR SHORT TO GROUND ON CKT 827; REFER TO "EBTCM-SWITCHED MALFUNCTIONS"
YES
NO
5
REMOVE J 39700.
RECONNECT EBTCM AND BPM VALVE CONNECTORS.
INSTALL TECH 1 WITH MSC.
IGNITION "ON."
PERFORM TECH 1 RF SOLENOID TEST.
BOTH MODES OPERATE?
REPAIR WIRING, CONNECTORS OR TERMINALS AS NEEDED. REFER TO "REPAIR PROCEDURES"
YES
NO
6
CLEAR DTCs, IGNITION "OFF."
DISCONNECT TECH 1, IF CONNECTED.
DRIVE VEHICLE AT LEAST 7 km/h (4 MPH) TO ACTIVATE AUTO TEST SEQUENCE.
DOES DTC 41 RESET?
REPLACE BPM VALVE.
NO
YES
NO TROUBLE FOUND; SEE "DIAGNOSTIC AIDS"
REPLACE EBTCM.
GC402940087100BX

Fig. 49 Code 41: RF Solenoid Valve Fault. 1994

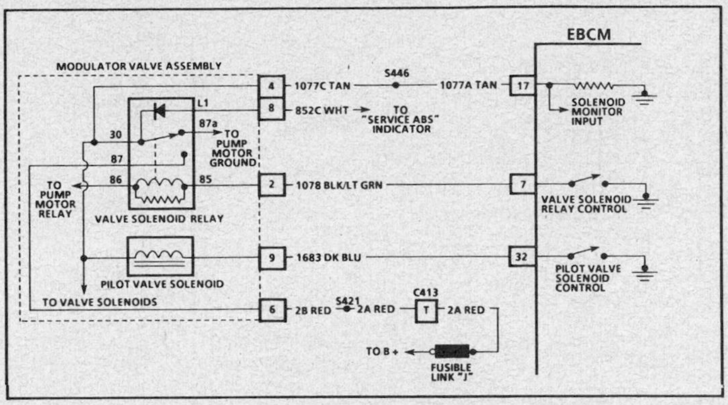
EBCM
MODULATOR VALVE ASSEMBLY
1077C TAN
S446
1077A TAN
852C WHT
TO "SERVICE ABS" INDICATOR
SOLENOID MONITOR INPUT
L1
87a
30
87
86
85
TO PUMP MOTOR GROUND
TO PUMP MOTOR RELAY
1078 BLK/LT GRN
VALVE SOLENOID RELAY
VALVE SOLENOID RELAY CONTROL
1683 DK BLU
PILOT VALVE SOLENOID
PILOT VALVE SOLENOID CONTROL
TO VALVE SOLENOIDS
2B RED
S421
2A RED
C413
TO B+
FUSIBLE LINK "J"

CODE 44

PILOT VALVE SOLENOID FAULT

Circuit Description:

The Pilot Valve Solenoid circuit is supplied with battery power when the ignition is "ON." The EBCM controls the valve by grounding the circuit when necessary.

If the EBCM senses a discrepancy such as an open or ground in the circuit, the Valve Solenoid Relay will turn "OFF," the "SERVICE ABS" and "SERVICE ASR" lights will come "ON," and Code 44 will set.

Test Description: Number(s) below refer to circled number(s) on the diagnostic chart.

1. Checks the integrity of CKTs 1683 and 1077, the Pilot Valve Solenoid circuitry internal to the Modulator Valve Assembly, and the Pilot Valve Solenoid coil.
2. Checks for a short to battery in CKT 1683, using EBCM terminal 3 as ground.
3. Checks for a short to ground in CKT 1683, using EBCM terminal 3 as ground.
4. Checks for connector or wiring problems which could cause intermittents.
5. Uses the Tech 1 to exercise the Pilot Valve Solenoid and check it for proper operation.
6. Determines whether the code was set by an intermittent condition or an EBCM fault.
7. Determines whether a problem found in Step 1 is due to an open in CKT 1683 or a faulty Modulator Valve Assembly.

Diagnostic Aids:

All tests using J 39700 Universal Breakout Box terminal 3 are using the terminal as ground. These tests, of course, assume that the ground CKT 801 at terminal 3 is good.

GC402920042300AX

1992

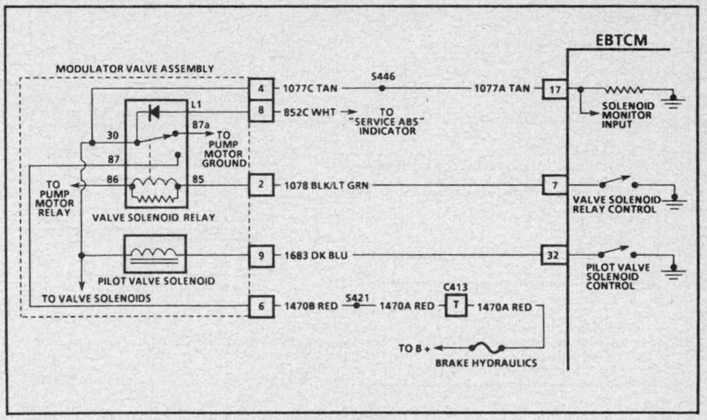
EBTCM
MODULATOR VALVE ASSEMBLY
1077C TAN
S446
1077A TAN
852C WHT
TO "SERVICE ABS" INDICATOR
SOLENOID MONITOR INPUT
L1
87a
30
87
86
85
TO PUMP MOTOR GROUND
TO PUMP MOTOR RELAY
1078 BLK/LT GRN
VALVE SOLENOID RELAY
VALVE SOLENOID RELAY CONTROL
1683 DK BLU
PILOT VALVE SOLENOID
PILOT VALVE SOLENOID CONTROL
TO VALVE SOLENOIDS
1470B RED
S421
1470A RED
C413
TO B+
BRAKE HYDRAULICS

DTC 44

PILOT VALVE SOLENOID MALFUNCTION

Circuit Description:

The pilot valve solenoid circuit is supplied with battery power when the ignition is "ON." The EBTCM controls the valve by grounding the circuit when necessary.

If the EBTCM senses a discrepancy such as an open or ground in the circuit, the valve solenoid relay will turn "OFF," the "SERVICE ABS" and "SERVICE ASR" lights will come "ON," and DTC 44 will set.

Test Description: Number(s) below refer to circled number(s) on the diagnostic chart.

1. Checks the integrity of CKTs 1683 and 1077, the pilot valve solenoid circuitry internal to the modulator valve assembly, and the pilot valve solenoid coil.
2. Checks for a short to battery in CKT 1683, using EBTCM terminal "3" as ground.
3. Checks for a short to ground in CKT 1683, using EBTCM terminal "3" as ground.
4. Checks for connector or wiring problems which could cause intermittents.
5. Uses the Tech 1 to exercise the pilot valve solenoid and check it for proper operation.
6. Determines whether the DTC was set by an intermittent condition or an EBTCM malfunction.
7. Determines whether a problem found in Step 1 is due to an open in CKT 1683 or a malfunctioning modulator valve assembly.

Diagnostic Aids:

All tests using J 39700 Universal Breakout Box terminal "3" are using the terminal as ground. These tests, of course, assume that the ground CKT 801 at terminal "3" is good.

GC402930042300BX

1993

Fig. 50 Code 44: Pilot Valve Solenoid Fault (Part 1 of 2). 1992–93

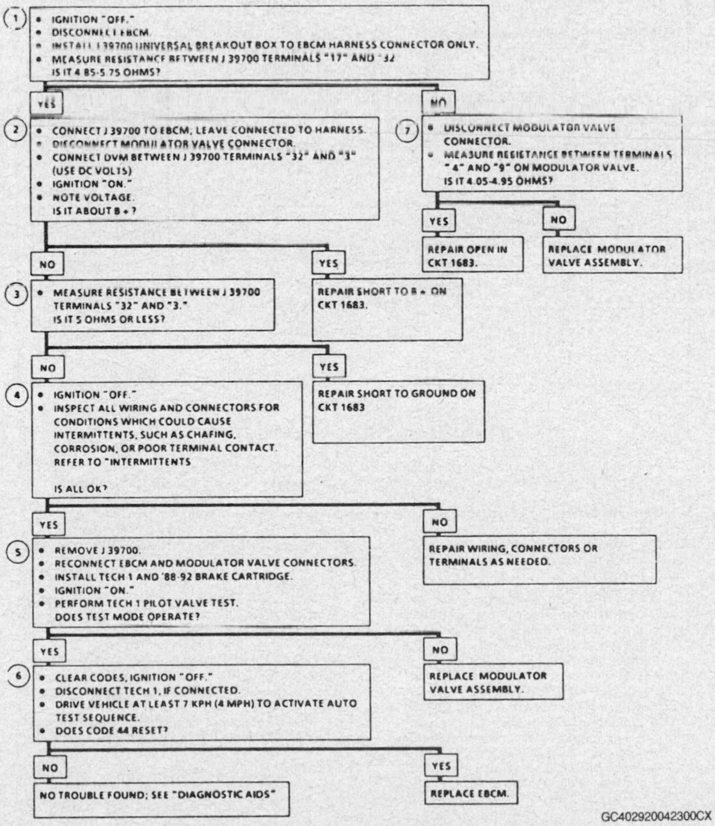
1
IGNITION "OFF."
DISCONNECT EBCM.
INSTALL J 39700 UNIVERSAL BREAKOUT BOX TO EBCM HARNESS CONNECTOR ONLY.
MEASURE RESISTANCE BETWEEN J 39700 TERMINALS "17" AND "32"
IS IT 4.85-5.75 OHMS?
YES
NO
2
CONNECT J 39700 TO EBCM, LEAVE CONNECTED TO HARNESS.
DISCONNECT MODULATOR VALVE CONNECTOR.
CONNECT DVM BETWEEN J 39700 TERMINALS "32" AND "3" (USE DC VOLTS)
IGNITION "ON."
NOTE VOLTAGE.
IS IT ABOUT B+?
7
DISCONNECT MODULATOR VALVE CONNECTOR.
MEASURE RESISTANCE BETWEEN TERMINALS "4" AND "9" ON MODULATOR VALVE.
IS IT 4.05-4.95 OHMS?
YES
NO
REPAIR OPEN IN CKT 1683.
REPLACE MODULATOR VALVE ASSEMBLY.
NO
YES
3
MEASURE RESISTANCE BETWEEN J 39700 TERMINALS "32" AND "3."
IS IT 5 OHMS OR LESS?
REPAIR SHORT TO B+ ON CKT 1683.
NO
YES
4
IGNITION "OFF."
INSPECT ALL WIRING AND CONNECTORS FOR CONDITIONS WHICH COULD CAUSE INTERMITTENTS, SUCH AS CHAFING, CORROSION, OR POOR TERMINAL CONTACT. REFER TO "INTERMITTENTS
IS ALL OK?
REPAIR SHORT TO GROUND ON CKT 1683
YES
NO
5
REMOVE J 39700.
RECONNECT EBCM AND MODULATOR VALVE CONNECTORS.
INSTALL TECH 1 AND '88-92 BRAKE CARTRIDGE.
IGNITION "ON."
PERFORM TECH 1 PILOT VALVE TEST.
DOES TEST MODE OPERATE?
REPAIR WIRING, CONNECTORS OR TERMINALS AS NEEDED.
YES
NO
6
CLEAR CODES, IGNITION "OFF."
DISCONNECT TECH 1, IF CONNECTED.
DRIVE VEHICLE AT LEAST 7 KPH (4 MPH) TO ACTIVATE AUTO TEST SEQUENCE.
DOES CODE 44 RESET?
REPLACE MODULATOR VALVE ASSEMBLY.
NO
YES
NO TROUBLE FOUND; SEE "DIAGNOSTIC AIDS"
REPLACE EBCM.

GC402920042300CX

Fig. 50 Code 44: Pilot Valve Soenoid Fault (Part 2 of 2). 1992-93

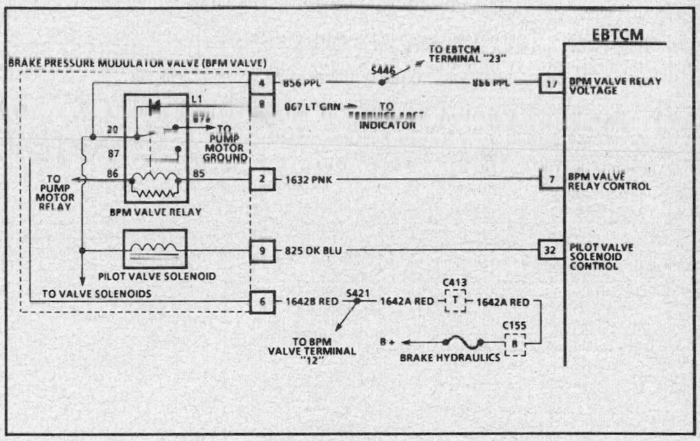
EBTCM
BRAKE PRESSURE MODULATOR VALVE (BPM VALVE)
TO EBTCM TERMINAL "23"
S446
856 PPL
BPM VALVE RELAY VOLTAGE
067 LT GRN
TO "SERVICE ABS" INDICATOR
L1
87a
30
87
86
85
TO PUMP MOTOR GROUND
TO PUMP MOTOR RELAY
1632 PNK
BPM VALVE RELAY
BPM VALVE RELAY CONTROL
825 DK BLU
PILOT VALVE SOLENOID
PILOT VALVE SOLENOID CONTROL
TO VALVE SOLENOIDS
1642B RED
S421
1642A RED
C413
TO BPM VALVE TERMINAL "12"
B+
BRAKE HYDRAULICS
C155

DTC 44

PILOT VALVE SOLENOID MALFUNCTION

Circuit Description:

The pilot valve solenoid circuit is supplied with battery power when the ignition is "ON." The EBTCM controls the valve by grounding the circuit when necessary.

DTC Will Set When: The EBTCM senses a discrepancy such as an open or ground in the circuit.

Action Taken: The BPM valve relay will turn "OFF" and the "SERVICE ABS" and "SERVICE ASR" indicators will come "ON."

DTC Chart Test Description: Number(s) below refer to circled number(s) on the diagnostic chart.

1. Checks the integrity of CKTs 825 and 856, the pilot valve solenoid circuitry internal to the BPM valve assembly, and the pilot valve solenoid coil.
2. Checks for a short to battery in CKT 825, using EBTCM terminal "3" as ground.
3. Checks for a short to ground in CKT 825, using EBTCM terminal "3" as ground.
4. Checks for connector or wiring malfunctions which could cause intermittents.
5. Uses the Tech 1 to exercise the pilot valve solenoid and check it for proper operation.
6. Determines whether the DTC was set by an intermittent condition or an EBTCM malfunction.
7. Determines whether a malfunction found in Step 1 is due to an open in CKT 825 or a malfunctioning BPM valve assembly.

Diagnostic Aids: All tests using J 39700 Universal Breakout Box terminal "3" are using the terminal as ground. These tests, of course, assume that the ground CKT 1051 at terminal "3" is good.

GC402940087200AX

Fig. 51 Code 44: Pilot Valve Solenoid Fault (Part 1 of 2). 1994

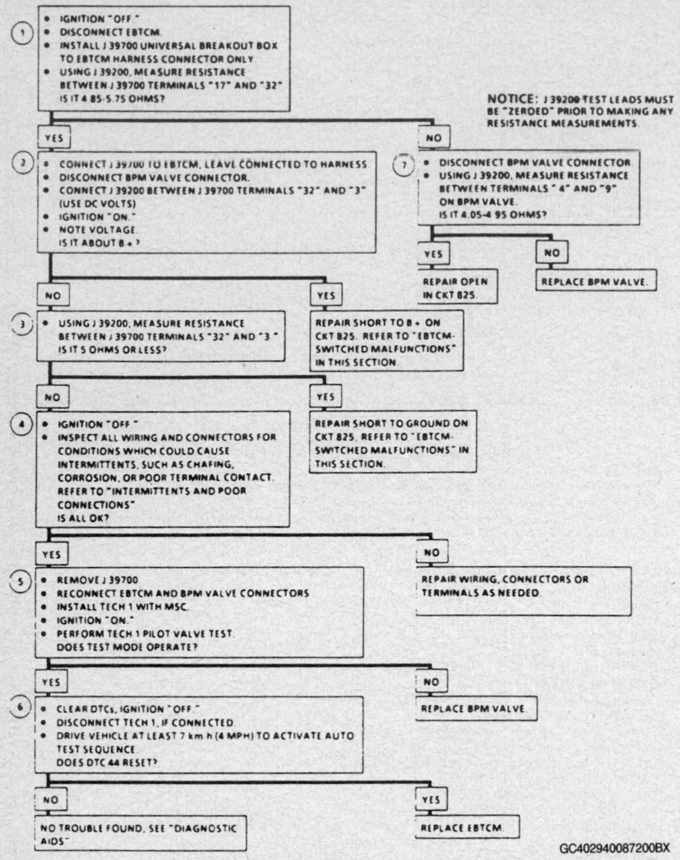

1 • IGNITION "OFF." • DISCONNECT EBTCM. • INSTALL J 39700 UNIVERSAL BREAKOUT BOX TO EBTCM HARNESS CONNECTOR ONLY. • USING J 39200, MEASURE RESISTANCE BETWEEN J 39700 TERMINALS "17" AND "32". IS IT 4.85-5.75 OHMS?
NOTICE: J 39200 TEST LEADS MUST BE "ZEROED" PRIOR TO MAKING ANY RESISTANCE MEASUREMENTS.
YES
NO
2 • CONNECT J 39700 TO EBTCM, LEAVE CONNECTED TO HARNESS. • DISCONNECT BPM VALVE CONNECTOR. • CONNECT J 39200 BETWEEN J 39700 TERMINALS "32" AND "3" (USE DC VOLTS) • IGNITION "ON." • NOTE VOLTAGE. IS IT ABOUT B + ?
7 • DISCONNECT BPM VALVE CONNECTOR. • USING J 39200, MEASURE RESISTANCE BETWEEN TERMINALS "4" AND "9" ON BPM VALVE. IS IT 4.05-4.95 OHMS?
YES
NO
REPAIR OPEN IN CKT 825.
REPLACE BPM VALVE.
NO
YES
3 • USING J 39200, MEASURE RESISTANCE BETWEEN J 39700 TERMINALS "32" AND "3". IS IT 5 OHMS OR LESS?
REPAIR SHORT TO B + ON CKT 825. REFER TO "EBTCM-SWITCHED MALFUNCTIONS" IN THIS SECTION.
NO
YES
4 • IGNITION "OFF." • INSPECT ALL WIRING AND CONNECTORS FOR CONDITIONS WHICH COULD CAUSE INTERMITTENTS, SUCH AS CHAFING, CORROSION, OR POOR TERMINAL CONTACT. REFER TO "INTERMITTENTS AND POOR CONNECTIONS" IS ALL OK?
REPAIR SHORT TO GROUND ON CKT 825. REFER TO "EBTCM-SWITCHED MALFUNCTIONS" IN THIS SECTION.
YES
NO
5 • REMOVE J 39700. • RECONNECT EBTCM AND BPM VALVE CONNECTORS. • INSTALL TECH 1 WITH MSC. • IGNITION "ON." • PERFORM TECH 1 PILOT VALVE TEST. DOES TEST MODE OPERATE?
REPAIR WIRING, CONNECTORS OR TERMINALS AS NEEDED.
YES
NO
6 • CLEAR DTCs, IGNITION "OFF." • DISCONNECT TECH 1, IF CONNECTED. • DRIVE VEHICLE AT LEAST 7 km/h (4 MPH) TO ACTIVATE AUTO TEST SEQUENCE. DOES DTC 44 RESET?
REPLACE BPM VALVE.
NO
YES
NO TROUBLE FOUND, SEE "DIAGNOSTIC AIDS"
REPLACE EBTCM.
GC402940087200BX

Fig. 51 Code 44: Pilot Valve Solenoid Fault (Part 2 of 2). 1994

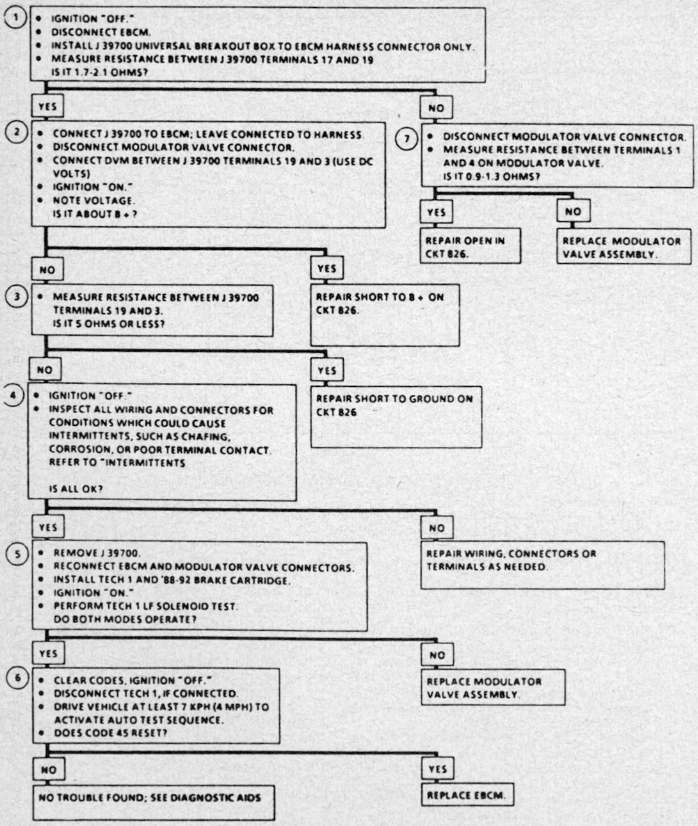

1 • IGNITION "OFF." • DISCONNECT EBCM. • INSTALL J 39700 UNIVERSAL BREAKOUT BOX TO EBCM HARNESS CONNECTOR ONLY. • MEASURE RESISTANCE BETWEEN J 39700 TERMINALS 17 AND 19. IS IT 1.7-2.1 OHMS?
YES
NO
2 • CONNECT J 39700 TO EBCM; LEAVE CONNECTED TO HARNESS. • DISCONNECT MODULATOR VALVE CONNECTOR. • CONNECT DVM BETWEEN J 39700 TERMINALS 19 AND 3 (USE DC VOLTS) • IGNITION "ON." • NOTE VOLTAGE. IS IT ABOUT B + ?
7 • DISCONNECT MODULATOR VALVE CONNECTOR. • MEASURE RESISTANCE BETWEEN TERMINALS 1 AND 4 ON MODULATOR VALVE. IS IT 0.9-1.3 OHMS?
YES
NO
REPAIR OPEN IN CKT 826.
REPLACE MODULATOR VALVE ASSEMBLY.
NO
YES
3 • MEASURE RESISTANCE BETWEEN J 39700 TERMINALS 19 AND 3. IS IT 5 OHMS OR LESS?
REPAIR SHORT TO B + ON CKT 826.
NO
YES
4 • IGNITION "OFF." • INSPECT ALL WIRING AND CONNECTORS FOR CONDITIONS WHICH COULD CAUSE INTERMITTENTS, SUCH AS CHAFING, CORROSION, OR POOR TERMINAL CONTACT. REFER TO "INTERMITTENTS" IS ALL OK?
REPAIR SHORT TO GROUND ON CKT 826
YES
NO
5 • REMOVE J 39700. • RECONNECT EBCM AND MODULATOR VALVE CONNECTORS. • INSTALL TECH 1 AND '88-92 BRAKE CARTRIDGE. • IGNITION "ON." • PERFORM TECH 1 LF SOLENOID TEST. DO BOTH MODES OPERATE?
REPAIR WIRING, CONNECTORS OR TERMINALS AS NEEDED.
YES
NO
6 • CLEAR CODES, IGNITION "OFF." • DISCONNECT TECH 1, IF CONNECTED. • DRIVE VEHICLE AT LEAST 7 KPH (4 MPH) TO ACTIVATE AUTO TEST SEQUENCE. • DOES CODE 45 RESET?
REPLACE MODULATOR VALVE ASSEMBLY.
NO
YES
NO TROUBLE FOUND; SEE DIAGNOSTIC AIDS
REPLACE EBCM.

Fig. 52 Code 45: LF Solenoid Valve Fault (Part 2 of 2). 1992-93

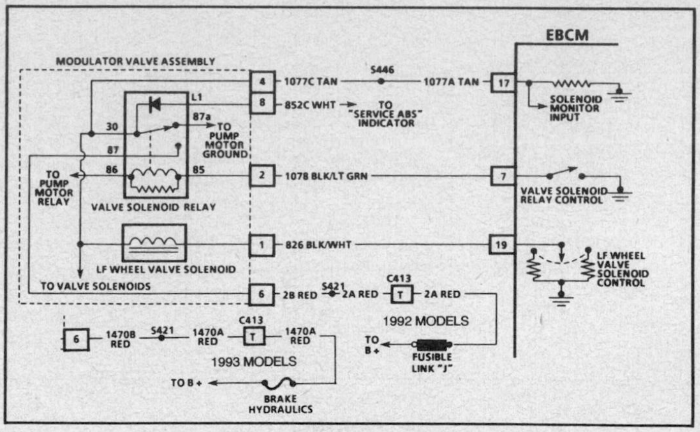

EBCM
MODULATOR VALVE ASSEMBLY
1077C TAN
S446
1077A TAN
852C WHT
TO "SERVICE ABS" INDICATOR
SOLENOID MONITOR INPUT
TO PUMP MOTOR GROUND
TO PUMP MOTOR RELAY
1078 BLK/LT GRN
VALVE SOLENOID RELAY
VALVE SOLENOID RELAY CONTROL
826 BLK/WHT
LF WHEEL VALVE SOLENOID
LF WHEEL VALVE SOLENOID CONTROL
TO VALVE SOLENOIDS
2B RED
S421
2A RED
C413
1992 MODELS
1470B RED
1470A RED
1993 MODELS
TO B+
FUSIBLE LINK "J"
BRAKE HYDRAULICS

CODE 45

LF VALVE SOLENOID FAULT

Circuit Description:

The wheel valve solenoid circuits are supplied with battery power when the ignition is "ON." The EBCM controls the valve functions by permitting one of three levels of current flow (0, 2.5, 5 amps) to the solenoid.

If the EBCM senses a discrepancy such as an open or ground in the circuit, the Valve Solenoid Relay will turn "OFF," the "SERVICE ABS" and "SERVICE ASR" lights will come "ON," and Code 45 will set.

Test Description: Number(s) below refer to circled number(s) on the diagnostic chart.

1. Checks the integrity of CKTs 826 and 1077, the LF Valve Solenoid circuitry internal to the Modulator Valve Assembly, and the LF Valve Solenoid coil.
2. Checks for a short to battery in CKT 826, using EBCM terminal 3 as ground.
3. Checks for a short to ground in CKT 826, using EBCM terminal 3 as ground.
4. Checks wiring and connectors for intermittents.
5. Uses the Tech 1 to exercise the LF Valve Solenoid and check it for proper operation.
6. Determines whether the code was set by an intermittent condition or an EBCM fault.
7. Determines whether a problem found in Step 1 is due to an open in CKT 826 or a faulty Modulator Valve Assembly.

Diagnostic Aids:

All tests using J 39700 Universal Breakout Box terminal 3 are using the terminal as ground. These tests, of course, assume that the ground CKT 801 at terminal 3 is good.

If Codes 41 and 45 are both set the fault is likely to be a short to B + on CKT 826.

GC402920042400AX

Fig. 52 Code 45: LF Solenoid Valve Fault (Part 1 of 2). 1992-93

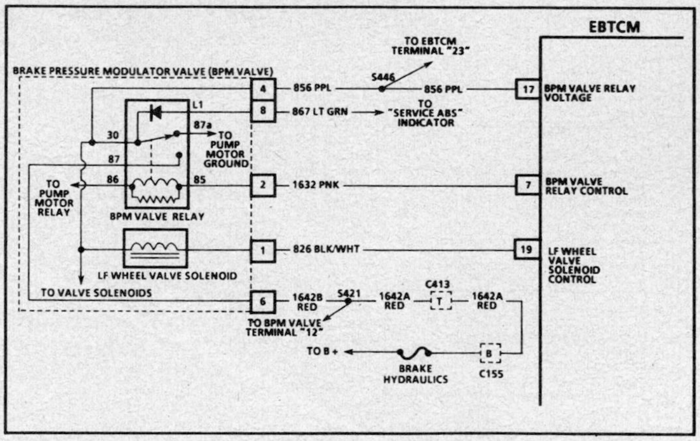

EBTCM
TO EBTCM TERMINAL "23"
BRAKE PRESSURE MODULATOR VALVE (BPM VALVE)
856 PPL
S446
856 PPL
BPM VALVE RELAY VOLTAGE
867 LT GRN
TO "SERVICE ABS" INDICATOR
TO PUMP MOTOR GROUND
TO PUMP MOTOR RELAY
1632 PNK
BPM VALVE RELAY
BPM VALVE RELAY CONTROL
826 BLK/WHT
LF WHEEL VALVE SOLENOID
LF WHEEL VALVE SOLENOID CONTROL
TO VALVE SOLENOIDS
1642B RED
S421
1642A RED
C413
TO BPM VALVE TERMINAL "12"
TO B+
BRAKE HYDRAULICS
C155

DTC 45

LF VALVE SOLENOID MALFUNCTION

Circuit Description:

The wheel valve solenoid circuits are supplied with battery power when the ignition is "ON." The EBTCM controls the valve functions by permitting one of three levels of current flow (0, 2.5, 5 amps) to the solenoid.

DTC Will Set When: The EBTCM senses a discrepancy such as an open or ground in the circuit.

Action Taken: The BPM valve relay will turn "OFF" and the "SERVICE ABS" and "SERVICE ASR" indicators will come "ON."

DTC Chart Test Description: Number(s) below refer to circled number(s) on the diagnostic chart.

1. Checks the integrity of CKTs 826 and 856, the LF valve solenoid circuitry internal to the BPM valve assembly, and the LF valve solenoid coil.
2. Checks for a short to battery in CKT 826, using EBTCM terminal "3" as ground.
3. Checks for a short to ground in CKT 826, using EBTCM terminal "3" as ground.
4. Checks wiring and connectors for intermittents.
5. Uses the Tech 1 to exercise the LF valve solenoid and check it for proper operation.
6. Determines whether the DTC was set by an intermittent condition or an EBTCM malfunction.
7. Determines whether a malfunction found in Step 1 is due to an open in CKT 826 or a malfunctioning BPM valve assembly.

Diagnostic Aids: All tests using J 39700 Universal Breakout Box terminal "3" are using the terminal as ground. These tests, of course, assume that the ground CKT 1051 at terminal "3" is good.

If DTCs 41 and 45 are both set the malfunction is likely to be a short to B + on CKT 826.

GC402940087300AX

Fig. 53 Code 45: LF Solenoid Valve Fault (Part 1 of 2). 1994

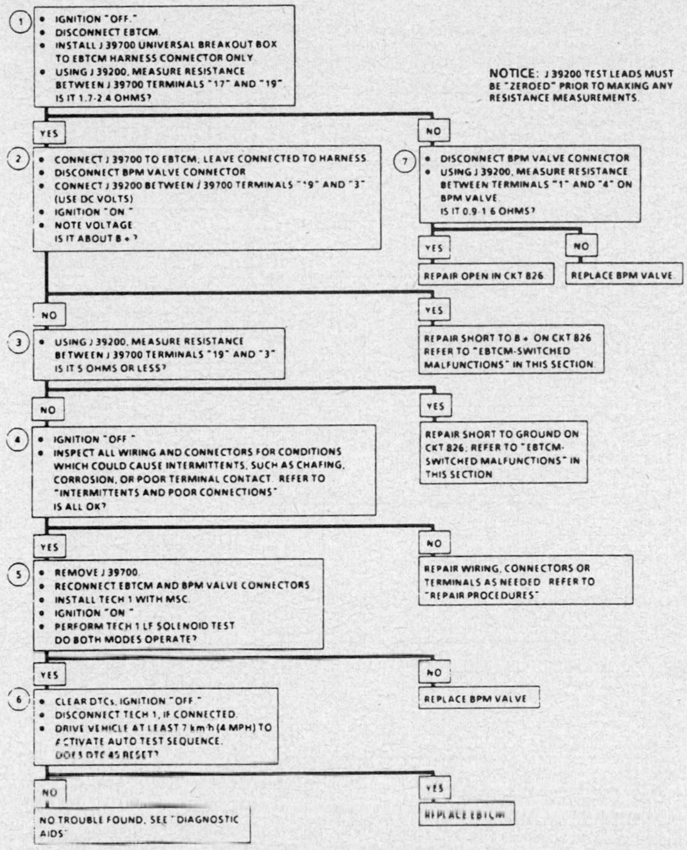
1
• IGNITION "OFF."
• DISCONNECT EBTCM.
• INSTALL J 39700 UNIVERSAL BREAKOUT BOX TO EBTCM HARNESS CONNECTOR ONLY
• USING J 39200, MEASURE RESISTANCE BETWEEN J 39700 TERMINALS "17" AND "19". IS IT 1.7-2.4 OHMS?
NOTICE: J 39200 TEST LEADS MUST BE "ZEROED" PRIOR TO MAKING ANY RESISTANCE MEASUREMENTS.
YES
NO
2
• CONNECT J 39700 TO EBTCM; LEAVE CONNECTED TO HARNESS.
• DISCONNECT BPM VALVE CONNECTOR
• CONNECT J 39200 BETWEEN J 39700 TERMINALS "19" AND "3" (USE DC VOLTS)
• IGNITION "ON."
• NOTE VOLTAGE. IS IT ABOUT B+?
7
• DISCONNECT BPM VALVE CONNECTOR
• USING J 39200, MEASURE RESISTANCE BETWEEN TERMINALS "1" AND "4" ON BPM VALVE. IS IT 0.9-1.6 OHMS?
YES
NO
REPAIR OPEN IN CKT 826.
REPLACE BPM VALVE.
NO
YES
3
• USING J 39200, MEASURE RESISTANCE BETWEEN J 39700 TERMINALS "19" AND "3" IS IT 5 OHMS OR LESS?
REPAIR SHORT TO B+ ON CKT 826 REFER TO "EBTCM-SWITCHED MALFUNCTIONS" IN THIS SECTION.
NO
YES
4
• IGNITION "OFF."
• INSPECT ALL WIRING AND CONNECTORS FOR CONDITIONS WHICH COULD CAUSE INTERMITTENTS, SUCH AS CHAFING, CORROSION, OR POOR TERMINAL CONTACT. REFER TO "INTERMITTENTS AND POOR CONNECTIONS" IS ALL OK?
REPAIR SHORT TO GROUND ON CKT 826; REFER TO "EBTCM-SWITCHED MALFUNCTIONS" IN THIS SECTION
YES
NO
5
• REMOVE J 39700.
• RECONNECT EBTCM AND BPM VALVE CONNECTORS
• INSTALL TECH 1 WITH MSC.
• IGNITION "ON."
• PERFORM TECH 1 LF SOLENOID TEST DO BOTH MODES OPERATE?
REPAIR WIRING, CONNECTORS OR TERMINALS AS NEEDED. REFER TO "REPAIR PROCEDURES"
YES
NO
6
• CLEAR DTCs, IGNITION "OFF."
• DISCONNECT TECH 1, IF CONNECTED.
• DRIVE VEHICLE AT LEAST 7 km/h (4 MPH) TO ACTIVATE AUTO TEST SEQUENCE. DOES DTC 45 RESET?
REPLACE BPM VALVE
NO
YES
NO TROUBLE FOUND. SEE "DIAGNOSTIC AIDS"
REPLACE EBTCM

Fig. 53 Code 45: LF Solenoid Valve Fault (Part 2 of 2). 1994

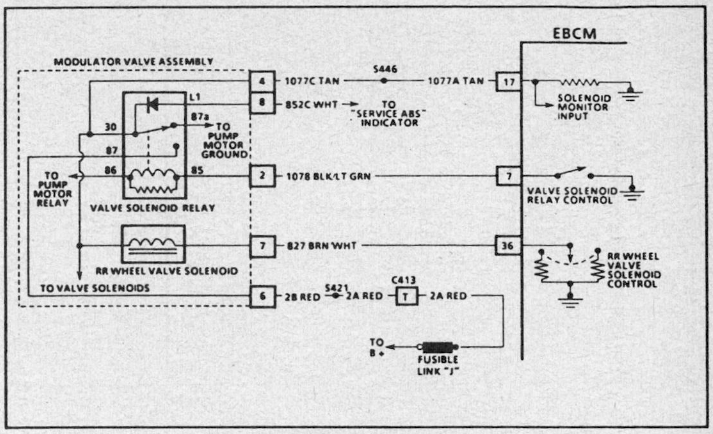
EBCM
MODULATOR VALVE ASSEMBLY
4
1077C TAN
S446
1077A TAN
17
SOLENOID MONITOR INPUT
L1
8
852C WHT
TO "SERVICE ABS" INDICATOR
87a
TO PUMP MOTOR GROUND
30
87
86
85
TO PUMP MOTOR RELAY
VALVE SOLENOID RELAY
2
1078 BLK/LT GRN
7
VALVE SOLENOID RELAY CONTROL
RR WHEEL VALVE SOLENOID
827 BRN WHT
36
RR WHEEL VALVE SOLENOID CONTROL
TO VALVE SOLENOIDS
6
2B RED
S421
2A RED
C413
T
2A RED
TO B+
FUSIBLE LINK "J"

CODE 51

RR VALVE SOLENOID FAULT

Circuit Description:

The wheel valve solenoid circuits are supplied with battery power when the ignition is "ON." The EBCM controls the valve functions by permitting one of three levels of current flow (0, 2.5, 5 amps) to the solenoid.

If the EBCM senses a discrepancy such as an open or ground in the circuit, the Valve Solenoid Relay will turn "OFF," the "SERVICE ABS" and "SERVICE ASR" lights will come "ON," and Code 51 will set.

Test Description: Number(s) below refer to circled number(s) on the diagnostic chart.

1. Checks the integrity of CKTs 827 and 1077, the RR Valve Solenoid circuitry internal to the Modulator Valve Assembly, and the RR Valve Solenoid coil.
2. Checks for a short to battery in CKT 827, using EBCM terminal 3 as ground.
3. Checks for a short to ground in CKT 827, using EBCM terminal 3 as ground.
4. Checks wiring and connectors for intermittents.
5. Uses the Tech 1 to exercise the RR Valve Solenoid and check it for proper operation.
6. Determines whether the code was set by an intermittent condition or an EBCM fault.
7. Determines whether a problem found in Step 1 is due to an open in CKT 827 or a faulty Modulator Valve Assembly.

Diagnostic Aids:

All tests using J 39700 Universal Breakout Box terminal 3 are using the terminal as ground. These tests, of course, assume that the ground CKT 801 at terminal 3 is good.

GC402920042500AX

Fig. 54 Code 51: RR Solenoid Valve Fault (Part 1 of 2). 1992-93

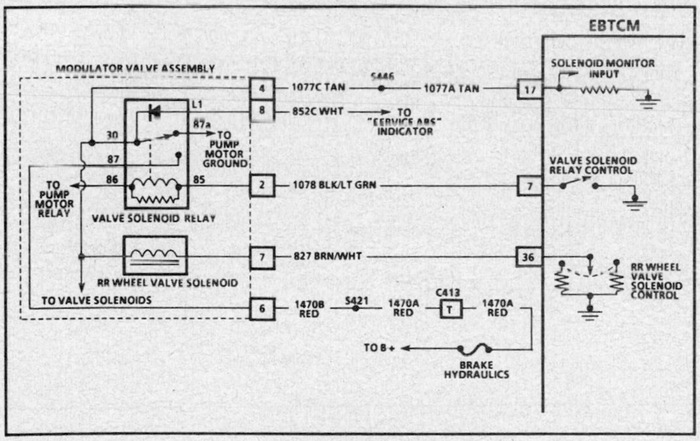
EBTCM
MODULATOR VALVE ASSEMBLY
4
1077C TAN
S446
1077A TAN
17
SOLENOID MONITOR INPUT
L1
8
852C WHT
TO "SERVICE ABS" INDICATOR
87a
TO PUMP MOTOR GROUND
30
87
86
85
TO PUMP MOTOR RELAY
VALVE SOLENOID RELAY
2
1078 BLK/LT GRN
7
VALVE SOLENOID RELAY CONTROL
RR WHEEL VALVE SOLENOID
827 BRN/WHT
36
RR WHEEL VALVE SOLENOID CONTROL
TO VALVE SOLENOIDS
6
1470B RED
S421
1470A RED
C413
T
1470A RED
TO B+
BRAKE HYDRAULICS

DTC 51

RR VALVE SOLENOID MALFUNCTION

Circuit Description:

The wheel valve solenoid circuits are supplied with battery power when the ignition is "ON." The EBTCM controls the valve functions by permitting one of three levels of current flow (0, 2.5, 5 amps) to the solenoid.

If the EBTCM senses a discrepancy such as an open or ground in the circuit, the valve solenoid relay will turn "OFF," the "SERVICE ABS" and "SERVICE ASR" lights will come "ON," and DTC 51 will set.

Test Description: Number(s) below refer to circled number(s) on the diagnostic chart.

1. Checks the integrity of CKTs 827 and 1077, the RR valve solenoid circuitry internal to the modulator valve assembly, and the RR valve solenoid coil.
2. Checks for a short to battery in CKT 827, using EBTCM terminal "3" as ground.
3. Checks for a short to ground in CKT 827, using EBTCM terminal "3" as ground.
4. Checks wiring and connectors for intermittents.
5. Uses the Tech 1 to exercise the RR valve solenoid and check it for proper operation.
6. Determines whether the DTC was set by an intermittent condition or an EBTCM malfunction.
7. Determines whether a problem found in Step 1 is due to an open in CKT 827 or a malfunctioning modulator valve assembly.

Diagnostic Aids:

All tests using J 39700 Universal Breakout Box terminal "3" are using the terminal as ground. These tests, of course, assume that the ground CKT 801 at terminal "3" is good.

GC402930042500BX

1993

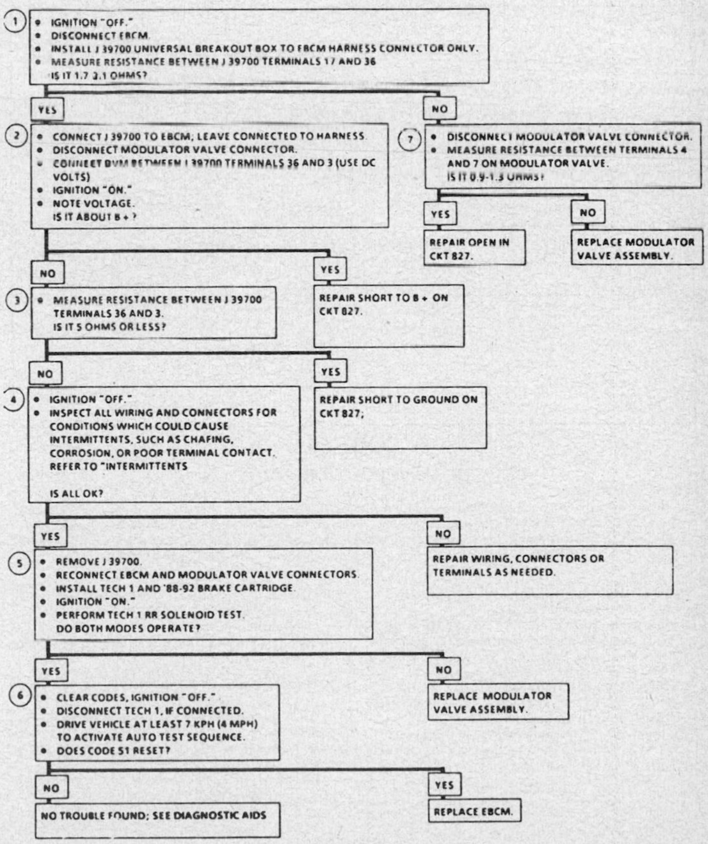
1
• IGNITION "OFF."
• DISCONNECT EBCM.
• INSTALL J 39700 UNIVERSAL BREAKOUT BOX TO EBCM HARNESS CONNECTOR ONLY.
• MEASURE RESISTANCE BETWEEN J 39700 TERMINALS 17 AND 36 IS IT 1.7-2.1 OHMS?
YES
NO
2
• CONNECT J 39700 TO EBCM; LEAVE CONNECTED TO HARNESS.
• DISCONNECT MODULATOR VALVE CONNECTOR.
• CONNECT DVM BETWEEN J 39700 TERMINALS 36 AND 3 (USE DC VOLTS)
• IGNITION "ON."
• NOTE VOLTAGE. IS IT ABOUT B+?
7
• DISCONNECT MODULATOR VALVE CONNECTOR.
• MEASURE RESISTANCE BETWEEN TERMINALS 4 AND 7 ON MODULATOR VALVE. IS IT 0.9-1.3 OHMS?
YES
NO
REPAIR OPEN IN CKT 827.
REPLACE MODULATOR VALVE ASSEMBLY.
NO
YES
3
• MEASURE RESISTANCE BETWEEN J 39700 TERMINALS 36 AND 3. IS IT 5 OHMS OR LESS?
REPAIR SHORT TO B+ ON CKT 827.
NO
YES
4
• IGNITION "OFF."
• INSPECT ALL WIRING AND CONNECTORS FOR CONDITIONS WHICH COULD CAUSE INTERMITTENTS, SUCH AS CHAFING, CORROSION, OR POOR TERMINAL CONTACT. REFER TO "INTERMITTENTS IS ALL OK?
REPAIR SHORT TO GROUND ON CKT 827;
YES
NO
5
• REMOVE J 39700.
• RECONNECT EBCM AND MODULATOR VALVE CONNECTORS.
• INSTALL TECH 1 AND '88-92 BRAKE CARTRIDGE.
• IGNITION "ON."
• PERFORM TECH 1 RR SOLENOID TEST. DO BOTH MODES OPERATE?
REPAIR WIRING, CONNECTORS OR TERMINALS AS NEEDED.
YES
NO
6
• CLEAR CODES, IGNITION "OFF."
• DISCONNECT TECH 1, IF CONNECTED.
• DRIVE VEHICLE AT LEAST 7 KPH (4 MPH) TO ACTIVATE AUTO TEST SEQUENCE.
• DOES CODE 51 RESET?
REPLACE MODULATOR VALVE ASSEMBLY.
NO
YES
NO TROUBLE FOUND; SEE DIAGNOSTIC AIDS
REPLACE EBCM.

GC402920042500CX

Fig. 54 Code 51: RR Solenoid Valve Fault (Part 2 of 2). 1992-93

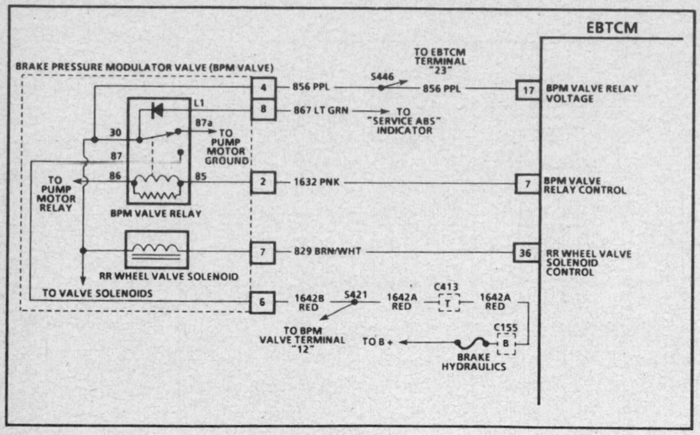
EBTCM
BRAKE PRESSURE MODULATOR VALVE (BPM VALVE)
TO EBTCM TERMINAL "23"
856 PPL
S446
856 PPL
BPM VALVE RELAY VOLTAGE
867 LT GRN
TO "SERVICE ABS" INDICATOR
TO PUMP MOTOR GROUND
TO PUMP MOTOR RELAY
BPM VALVE RELAY
1632 PNK
BPM VALVE RELAY CONTROL
829 BRN/WHT
RR WHEEL VALVE SOLENOID CONTROL
RR WHEEL VALVE SOLENOID
TO VALVE SOLENOIDS
1642B RED
S421
1642A RED
C413
1642A RED
TO BPM VALVE TERMINAL "12"
TO B+
C155
BRAKE HYDRAULICS

DTC 51

RR VALVE SOLENOID MALFUNCTION

Circuit Description:

The wheel valve solenoid circuits are supplied with battery power when the ignition is "ON." The EBTCM controls the valve functions by permitting one of three levels of current flow (0, 2.5, 5 amps) to the solenoid.

DTC Will Set When: The EBTCM senses a discrepancy such as an open or ground in the circuit.

Action Taken: The BPM valve relay will turn "OFF" and the "SERVICE ABS" and "SERVICE ASR" indicators will come "ON."

DTC Chart Test Description: Number(s) below refer to circled number(s) on the diagnostic chart.

1. Checks the integrity of CKTs 829 and 856, the RR valve solenoid circuitry internal to the BPM valve assembly, and the RR valve solenoid coil.
2. Checks for a short to battery in CKT 829, using EBTCM terminal "3" as ground.
3. Checks for a short to ground in CKT 829, using EBTCM terminal "3" as ground.
4. Checks wiring and connectors for intermittents.
5. Uses the Tech 1 to exercise the RR valve solenoid and check it for proper operation.
6. Determines whether the DTC was set by an intermittent condition or an EBTCM malfunction.
7. Determines whether a malfunction found in Step 1 is due to an open in CKT 829 or a malfunctioning BPM valve assembly.

Diagnostic Aids: All tests using J 39700 Universal Breakout Box terminal "3" are using the terminal as ground. These tests, of course, assume that the ground CKT 1051 at terminal "3" is good.

GC402940087400AX

(1)
- IGNITION "OFF."
- DISCONNECT EBTCM.
- INSTALL J 39700 UNIVERSAL BREAKOUT BOX TO EBTCM HARNESS CONNECTOR ONLY.
- USING J 39200, MEASURE RESISTANCE BETWEEN J 39700 TERMINALS "17" AND "36". IS IT 1.7-2.4 OHMS?

NOTICE: J 39200 TEST LEADS MUST BE "ZEROED" PRIOR TO MAKING ANY RESISTANCE MEASUREMENTS

YES → (2)
- CONNECT J 39700 TO EBTCM; LEAVE CONNECTED TO HARNESS.
- DISCONNECT BPM VALVE CONNECTOR.
- CONNECT J 39200 BETWEEN J 39700 TERMINALS "36" AND "3" (USE DC VOLTS).
- IGNITION "ON."
- NOTE VOLTAGE. IS IT ABOUT B+?

NO → (7)
- DISCONNECT BPM VALVE CONNECTOR.
- USING J 39200, MEASURE RESISTANCE BETWEEN TERMINALS "4" AND "7" ON BPM VALVE. IS IT 0.9-1.6 OHMS?

YES → REPAIR OPEN IN CKT 829.

NO → REPLACE BPM VALVE.

(2) YES → REPAIR SHORT TO B+ ON CKT 829. REFER TO "EBTCM-SWITCHED MALFUNCTIONS" IN THIS SECTION.

(2) NO → (3)
- USING J 39200, MEASURE RESISTANCE BETWEEN J 39700 TERMINALS "36" AND "3". IS IT 5 OHMS OR LESS?

YES → REPAIR SHORT TO GROUND ON CKT 829; REFER TO "EBTCM-SWITCHED MALFUNCTIONS"

NO → (4)
- IGNITION "OFF."
- INSPECT ALL WIRING AND CONNECTORS FOR CONDITIONS WHICH COULD CAUSE INTERMITTENTS, SUCH AS CHAFING, CORROSION, OR POOR TERMINAL CONTACT. REFER TO "INTERMITTENTS AND POOR CONNECTIONS" IS ALL OK?

NO → REPAIR WIRING, CONNECTORS OR TERMINALS AS NEEDED. REFER TO "REPAIR PROCEDURES"

YES → (5)
- REMOVE J 39700.
- RECONNECT EBTCM AND BPM VALVE CONNECTORS.
- INSTALL TECH 1 WITH MSC.
- IGNITION "ON."
- PERFORM TECH 1 RR SOLENOID TEST. DO BOTH MODES OPERATE?

NO → REPLACE BPM VALVE.

YES → (6)
- CLEAR DTCs, IGNITION "OFF."
- DISCONNECT TECH 1, IF CONNECTED.
- DRIVE VEHICLE AT LEAST 7 km/h (4 MPH) TO ACTIVATE AUTO TEST SEQUENCE. DOES DTC 51 RESET?

NO → NO TROUBLE FOUND; REFER TO "DIAGNOSTIC AIDS"

YES → REPLACE EBTCM.

GC402940087400BX

Fig. 55 Code 51: RR Solenoid Valve Fault. 1994

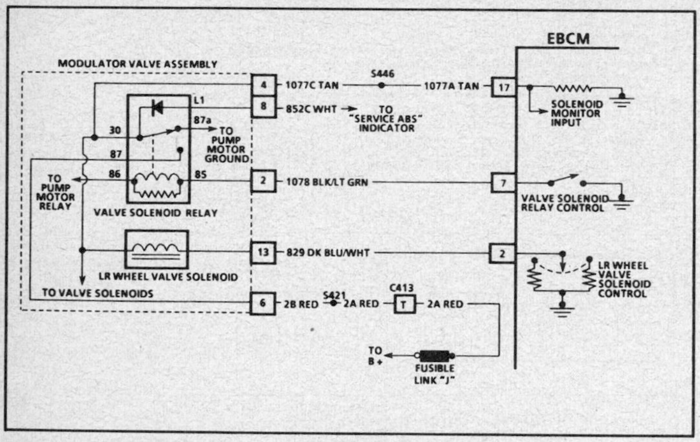
EBCM
MODULATOR VALVE ASSEMBLY
1077C TAN
S446
1077A TAN
SOLENOID MONITOR INPUT
852C WHT
TO "SERVICE ABS" INDICATOR
TO PUMP MOTOR GROUND
TO PUMP MOTOR RELAY
VALVE SOLENOID RELAY
1078 BLK/LT GRN
VALVE SOLENOID RELAY CONTROL
829 DK BLU/WHT
LR WHEEL VALVE SOLENOID CONTROL
LR WHEEL VALVE SOLENOID
TO VALVE SOLENOIDS
2B RED
S421
2A RED
C413
2A RED
TO B+
FUSIBLE LINK "J"

CODE 55

LR VALVE SOLENOID FAULT

Circuit Description:

The wheel valve solenoid circuits are supplied with battery power when the ignition is "ON." The EBCM controls the valve functions by permitting one of three levels of current flow (0, 2.5, 5 amps) to the solenoid.

If the EBCM senses a discrepancy such as an open or ground in the circuit, the Valve Solenoid Relay will turn "OFF," the "SERVICE ABS" and "SERVICE ASR" lights will come "ON," and Code 55 will set.

Test Description: Number(s) below refer to circled number(s) on the diagnostic chart.

1. Checks the integrity of CKTs 829 and 1077, the LR Valve Solenoid circuitry internal to the Modulator Valve Assembly, and the LR Valve Solenoid coil.
2. Checks for a short to battery in CKT 829, using EBCM terminal 3 as ground.
3. Checks for a short to ground in CKT 829, using EBCM terminal 3 as ground.
4. Checks wiring and connectors for intermittents.
5. Uses the Tech 1 to exercise the LR Valve Solenoid and check it for proper operation.
6. Determines whether the code was set by an intermittent condition or an EBCM fault.
7. Determines whether a problem found in Step 1 is due to an open in CKT 829 or a faulty Modulator Valve Assembly.

Diagnostic Aids:

All tests using J 39700 Universal Breakout Box terminal 3 are using the terminal as ground. These tests, of course, assume that the ground CKT 801 at terminal 3 is good.

If Codes 41 and 55 are both set the fault is likely to be a short to B+ on CKT 829.

GC402920042600AX

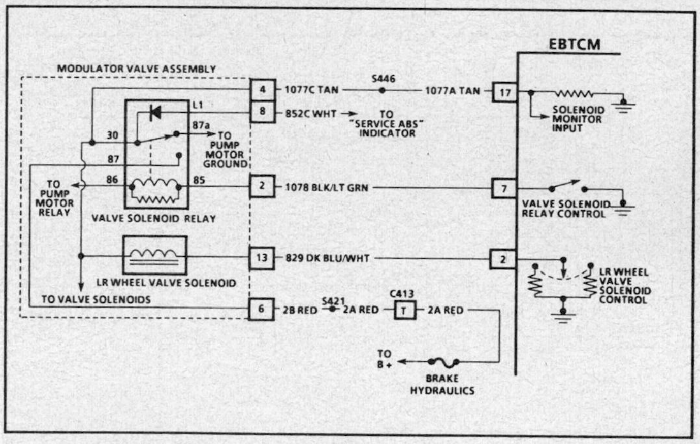
EBTCM
MODULATOR VALVE ASSEMBLY
1077C TAN
S446
1077A TAN
SOLENOID MONITOR INPUT
852C WHT
TO "SERVICE ABS" INDICATOR
TO PUMP MOTOR GROUND
TO PUMP MOTOR RELAY
VALVE SOLENOID RELAY
1078 BLK/LT GRN
VALVE SOLENOID RELAY CONTROL
829 DK BLU/WHT
LR WHEEL VALVE SOLENOID CONTROL
LR WHEEL VALVE SOLENOID
TO VALVE SOLENOIDS
2B RED
S421
2A RED
C413
2A RED
TO B+
BRAKE HYDRAULICS

DTC 55

LR VALVE SOLENOID MALFUNCTION

Circuit Description:

The wheel valve solenoid circuits are supplied with battery power when the ignition is "ON." The EBTCM controls the valve functions by permitting one of three levels of current flow (0, 2.5, 5 amps) to the solenoid.

If the EBTCM senses a discrepancy such as an open or ground in the circuit, the valve solenoid relay will turn "OFF," the "SERVICE ABS" and "SERVICE ASR" lights will come "ON," and DTC 55 will set.

Test Description: Number(s) below refer to circled number(s) on the diagnostic chart.

1. Checks the integrity of CKTs 829 and 1077, the LR valve solenoid circuitry internal to the modulator valve assembly, and the LR valve solenoid coil.
2. Checks for a short to battery in CKT 829, using EBTCM terminal "3" as ground.
3. Checks for a short to ground in CKT 829, using EBTCM terminal "3" as ground.
4. Checks wiring and connectors for intermittents.
5. Uses the Tech 1 to exercise the LR valve solenoid and check it for proper operation.
6. Determines whether the DTC was set by an intermittent condition or an EBTCM malfunction.
7. Determines whether a problem found in Step 1 is due to an open in CKT 829 or a malfunctioning modulator valve assembly.

Diagnostic Aids:

All tests using J 39700 Universal Breakout Box terminal "3" are using the terminal as ground. These tests, of course, assume that the ground CKT 801 at terminal "3" is good.

If DTCs 41 and 55 are both set the malfunction is likely to be a short to B+ on CKT 829.

GC402930042600BX

1992 1993

Fig. 56 Code 55: LR Solenoid Valve Fault (Part 1 of 2). 1992–93

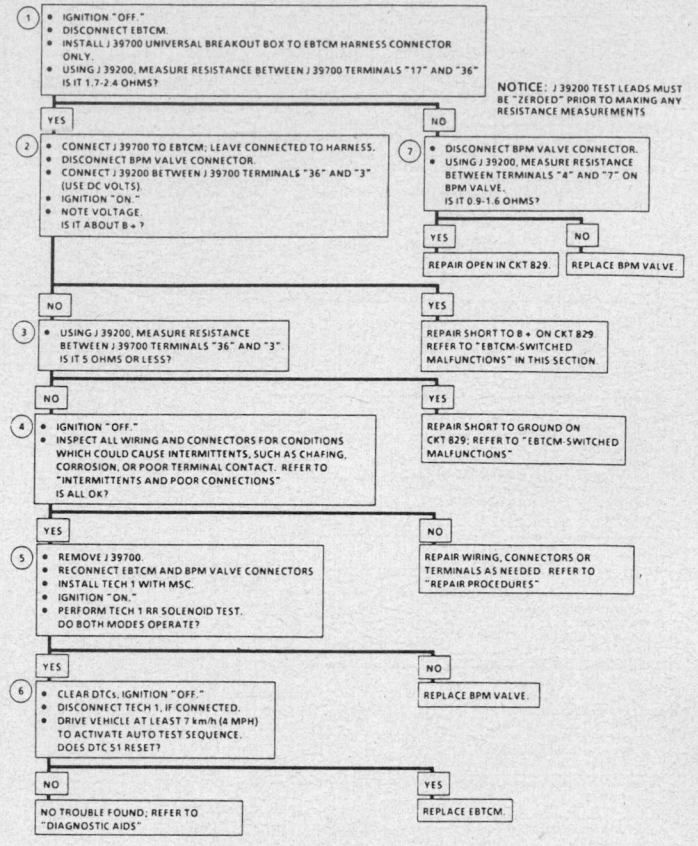

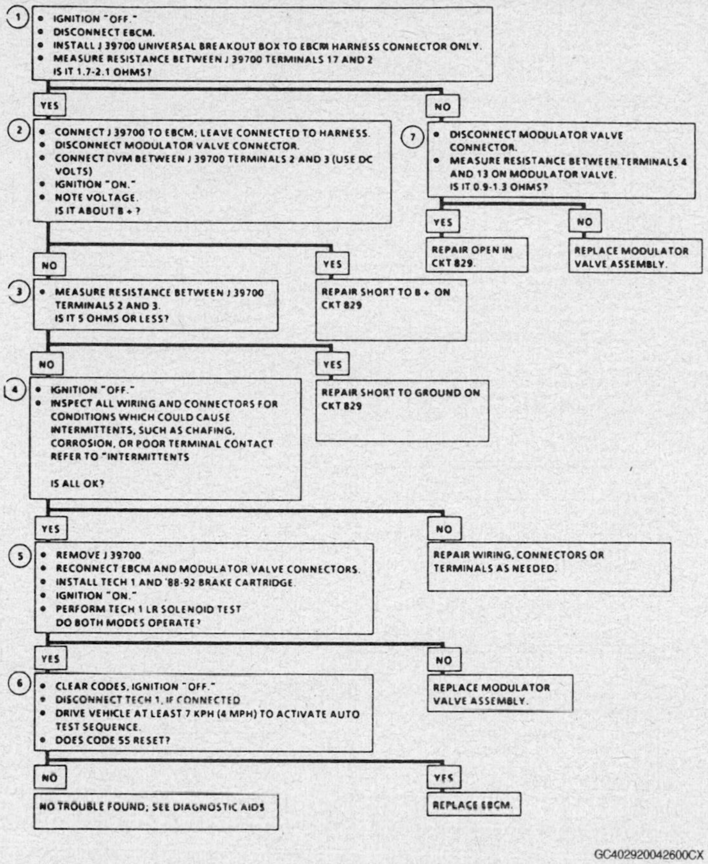

1 • IGNITION "OFF." • DISCONNECT EBCM. • INSTALL J 39700 UNIVERSAL BREAKOUT BOX TO EBCM HARNESS CONNECTOR ONLY. • MEASURE RESISTANCE BETWEEN J 39700 TERMINALS 17 AND 2 IS IT 1.7-2.1 OHMS?
YES
NO
2 • CONNECT J 39700 TO EBCM, LEAVE CONNECTED TO HARNESS. • DISCONNECT MODULATOR VALVE CONNECTOR. • CONNECT DVM BETWEEN J 39700 TERMINALS 2 AND 3 (USE DC VOLTS) • IGNITION "ON." • NOTE VOLTAGE. IS IT ABOUT B+?
7 • DISCONNECT MODULATOR VALVE CONNECTOR. • MEASURE RESISTANCE BETWEEN TERMINALS 4 AND 13 ON MODULATOR VALVE. IS IT 0.9-1.3 OHMS?
YES
NO
REPAIR OPEN IN CKT 829.
REPLACE MODULATOR VALVE ASSEMBLY.
NO
YES
3 • MEASURE RESISTANCE BETWEEN J 39700 TERMINALS 2 AND 3. IS IT 5 OHMS OR LESS?
REPAIR SHORT TO B+ ON CKT 829
NO
YES
4 • IGNITION "OFF." • INSPECT ALL WIRING AND CONNECTORS FOR CONDITIONS WHICH COULD CAUSE INTERMITTENTS, SUCH AS CHAFING, CORROSION, OR POOR TERMINAL CONTACT REFER TO "INTERMITTENTS IS ALL OK?
REPAIR SHORT TO GROUND ON CKT 829
YES
NO
5 • REMOVE J 39700. • RECONNECT EBCM AND MODULATOR VALVE CONNECTORS. • INSTALL TECH 1 AND '88-92 BRAKE CARTRIDGE. • IGNITION "ON." • PERFORM TECH 1 LR SOLENOID TEST DO BOTH MODES OPERATE?
REPAIR WIRING, CONNECTORS OR TERMINALS AS NEEDED.
YES
NO
6 • CLEAR CODES, IGNITION "OFF." • DISCONNECT TECH 1, IF CONNECTED • DRIVE VEHICLE AT LEAST 7 KPH (4 MPH) TO ACTIVATE AUTO TEST SEQUENCE. • DOES CODE 55 RESET?
REPLACE MODULATOR VALVE ASSEMBLY.
NO
YES
NO TROUBLE FOUND; SEE DIAGNOSTIC AIDS
REPLACE EBCM.
GC402920042600CX

Fig. 56 Code 55: Solenoid Valve Fault (Part 2 of 2). 1992-93

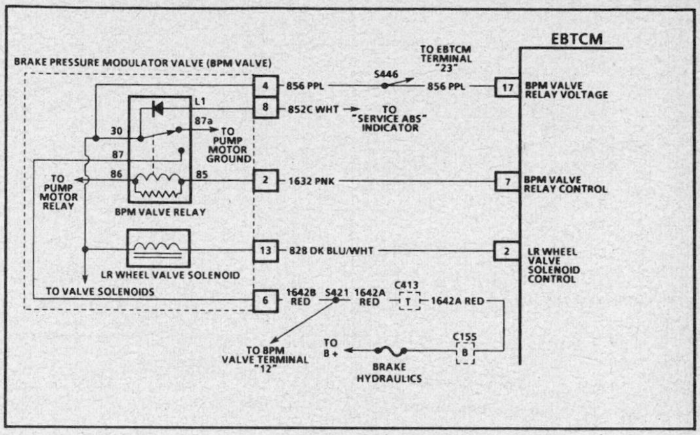

EBTCM
BRAKE PRESSURE MODULATOR VALVE (BPM VALVE)
TO EBTCM TERMINAL "23"
S446
856 PPL
852C WHT
TO "SERVICE ABS" INDICATOR
BPM VALVE RELAY VOLTAGE
TO PUMP MOTOR GROUND
TO PUMP MOTOR RELAY
1632 PNK
BPM VALVE RELAY CONTROL
BPM VALVE RELAY
828 DK BLU/WHT
LR WHEEL VALVE SOLENOID CONTROL
LR WHEEL VALVE SOLENOID
TO VALVE SOLENOIDS
1642B RED
S421
1642A RED
C413
TO BPM VALVE TERMINAL "12"
TO B+
BRAKE HYDRAULICS
C155

DTC 55

LR VALVE SOLENOID MALFUNCTION

Circuit Description:

The wheel valve solenoid circuits are supplied with battery power when the ignition is "ON." The EBTCM controls the valve functions by permitting one of three levels of current flow (0, 2.5, 5 amps) to the solenoid.

DTC Will Set When: The EBTCM senses a discrepancy such as an open or ground in the circuit.

Action Taken: The BPM valve relay will turn "OFF" and the "SERVICE ABS" and "SERVICE ASR" indicators will come "ON."

DTC Chart Test Description: Number(s) below refer to circled number(s) on the diagnostic chart.

1. Checks the integrity of CKTs 828 and 856, the LR valve solenoid circuitry internal to the BPM valve assembly, and the LR valve solenoid coil.
2. Checks for a short to battery in CKT 828, using EBTCM terminal "3" as ground.
3. Checks for a short to ground in CKT 828, using EBTCM terminal "3" as ground.
4. Checks wiring and connectors for intermittents.
5. Uses the Tech 1 to exercise the LR valve solenoid and check it for proper operation.
6. Determines whether the DTC was set by an intermittent condition or an EBTCM malfunction.
7. Determines whether a malfunction found in Step 1 is due to an open in CKT 828 or a malfunctioning BPM valve assembly.

Diagnostic Aids: All tests using J 39700 Universal Breakout Box terminal "3" are using the terminal as ground. These tests, of course, assume that the ground CKT 1051 at terminal "3" is good.

If DTCs 41 and 55 are both set the malfunction is likely to be a short to B+ on CKT 828.

GC402940087500AX

Fig. 57 Code 55: LR Solenoid Valve Fault (Part 1 of 2). 1994

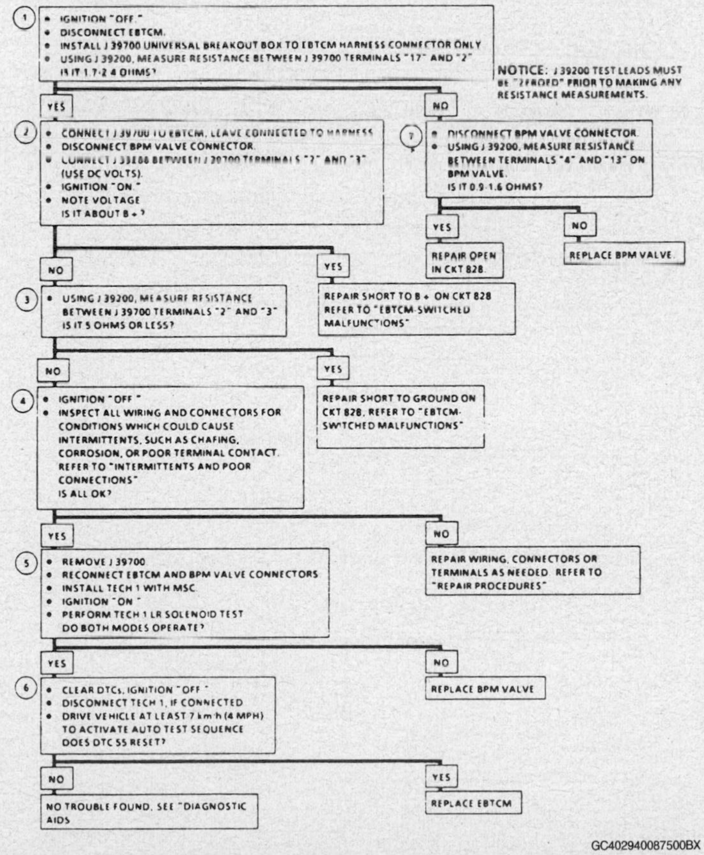

1 • IGNITION "OFF." • DISCONNECT EBTCM. • INSTALL J 39700 UNIVERSAL BREAKOUT BOX TO EBTCM HARNESS CONNECTOR ONLY • USING J 39200, MEASURE RESISTANCE BETWEEN J 39700 TERMINALS "17" AND "2" IS IT 1.7-2.4 OHMS?
NOTICE: J 39200 TEST LEADS MUST BE "ZEROED" PRIOR TO MAKING ANY RESISTANCE MEASUREMENTS.
YES
NO
2 • CONNECT J 39700 TO EBTCM, LEAVE CONNECTED TO HARNESS • DISCONNECT BPM VALVE CONNECTOR. • CONNECT J 33188 BETWEEN J 39700 TERMINALS "2" AND "3" (USE DC VOLTS). • IGNITION "ON." • NOTE VOLTAGE IS IT ABOUT B+?
7 • DISCONNECT BPM VALVE CONNECTOR. • USING J 39200, MEASURE RESISTANCE BETWEEN TERMINALS "4" AND "13" ON BPM VALVE. IS IT 0.9-1.6 OHMS?
YES
NO
REPAIR OPEN IN CKT 828.
REPLACE BPM VALVE.
NO
YES
3 • USING J 39200, MEASURE RESISTANCE BETWEEN J 39700 TERMINALS "2" AND "3" IS IT 5 OHMS OR LESS?
REPAIR SHORT TO B+ ON CKT 828 REFER TO "EBTCM-SWITCHED MALFUNCTIONS"
NO
YES
4 • IGNITION "OFF" • INSPECT ALL WIRING AND CONNECTORS FOR CONDITIONS WHICH COULD CAUSE INTERMITTENTS, SUCH AS CHAFING, CORROSION, OR POOR TERMINAL CONTACT. REFER TO "INTERMITTENTS AND POOR CONNECTIONS" IS ALL OK?
REPAIR SHORT TO GROUND ON CKT 828, REFER TO "EBTCM-SWITCHED MALFUNCTIONS"
YES
NO
5 • REMOVE J 39700 • RECONNECT EBTCM AND BPM VALVE CONNECTORS • INSTALL TECH 1 WITH MSC. • IGNITION "ON" • PERFORM TECH 1 LR SOLENOID TEST DO BOTH MODES OPERATE?
REPAIR WIRING, CONNECTORS OR TERMINALS AS NEEDED. REFER TO "REPAIR PROCEDURES"
YES
NO
6 • CLEAR DTCs, IGNITION "OFF" • DISCONNECT TECH 1, IF CONNECTED • DRIVE VEHICLE AT LEAST 7 km/h (4 MPH) TO ACTIVATE AUTO TEST SEQUENCE DOES DTC 55 RESET?
REPLACE BPM VALVE
NO
YES
NO TROUBLE FOUND. SEE "DIAGNOSTIC AIDS
REPLACE EBTCM
GC402940087500BX

Fig. 57 Code 55: LR Solenoid Valve Fault (Part 2 of 2). 1994

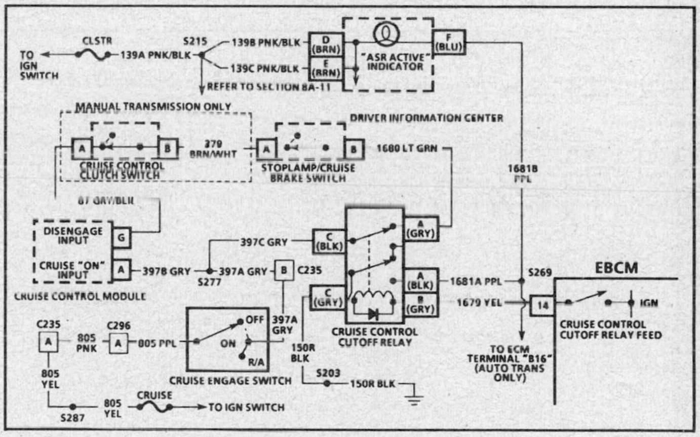

TO IGN SWITCH
CLSTR
139A PNK/BLK
S215
139B PNK/BLK
139C PNK/BLK
"ASR ACTIVE" INDICATOR
REFER TO SECTION 8A-11
MANUAL TRANSMISSION ONLY
DRIVER INFORMATION CENTER
CRUISE CONTROL CLUTCH SWITCH
379 BRN/WHT
STOPLAMP/CRUISE BRAKE SWITCH
1680 LT GRN
1681B PPL
87 GRY/BLK
DISENGAGE INPUT
CRUISE "ON" INPUT
CRUISE CONTROL MODULE
397C GRY
397B GRY
397A GRY
S277
C235
EBCM
1681A PPL
S269
1679 YEL
IGN
CRUISE CONTROL CUTOFF RELAY FEED
CRUISE CONTROL CUTOFF RELAY
TO ECM TERMINAL "B16" (AUTO TRANS ONLY)
C296
805 PNK
805 PPL
805 YEL
OFF
ON
R/A
CRUISE ENGAGE SWITCH
150R BLK
S203
S287
CRUISE
TO IGN SWITCH

CODE 57

CRUISE CONTROL OUTPUT MONITORING FAULT

Circuit Description:

The Cruise Control Output Monitoring circuit is used to determine the state of CKT 1679. The Cruise Control Cutoff Relay completes the cruise control engage circuit through terminals C2 and A1 when the cruise is requested to be "ON", the brake pedal is not depressed, and there is not an ASR event taking place. Whenever the Cruise Control Cutoff Relay is activated by the EBCM supplying B+ to CKT 1679, the cruise control circuit is opened by the relay switch moving off relay terminal A1.

The "SERVICE ASR" light will come "ON" and Code 57 will set if CKT 1679 is always high when the EBCM requests energization of the relay coil, which should take the circuit low.

Test Description: Number(s) below refer to circled number(s) on the diagnostic chart.

1. Checks the relay coil for proper resistance.
2. Checks the integrity of CKT 150 to ground.
3. Checks for an open in CKT 1679.
4. Checks for a short to B+ in CKT 1679, which would keep CKT 1679 high at all times.
5. Checks for an EBCM-switched short to B+.
6. Checks for recurrence of Code 57 after checks on other system components and wiring have been made. If the code comes back, the EBCM must be concluding there is a problem present in CKT 1679 when there is not.
7. Checks for proper system operation after faulty relay diagnosed in Step 1 has been replaced.
8. Checks for additional code-setting problems other than faulty relay diagnosed in Step 1 and replace in Step 7.

Diagnostic Aids:

All tests using J 39700 Universal Breakout Box terminal 3 are using the terminal as ground. These tests, of course, assume that the ground CKT 801 at terminal 3 is good.

If the "ASR ACTIVE" lamp is always "ON" and cruise control will not engage, the fault is likely a short to B+ on CKT 1679.

GC402920042700AX

1992

Fig. 58 Code 57: Cruise Control Output Monitoring Fault (Part 1 of 2). 1992-93

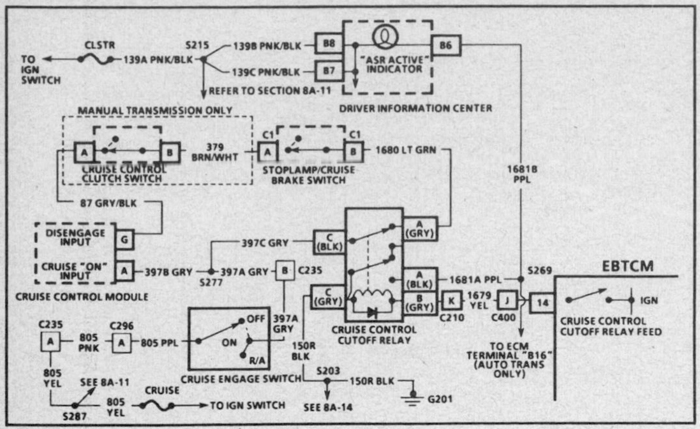
TO IGN SWITCH
CLSTR
139A PNK/BLK
S215
139B PNK/BLK
139C PNK/BLK
B8
B7
B6
"ASR ACTIVE" INDICATOR
REFER TO SECTION 8A-11
DRIVER INFORMATION CENTER
MANUAL TRANSMISSION ONLY
CRUISE CONTROL CLUTCH SWITCH
379 BRN/WHT
C1
STOPLAMP/CRUISE BRAKE SWITCH
1680 LT GRN
1681B PPL
87 GRY/BLK
DISENGAGE INPUT
CRUISE "ON" INPUT
CRUISE CONTROL MODULE
397C GRY
397B GRY
397A GRY
S277
C235
(GRY)
(BLK)
1681A PPL
S269
EBTCM
1679 YEL
C210
C400
14
IGN
CRUISE CONTROL CUTOFF RELAY
CRUISE CONTROL CUTOFF RELAY FEED
C296
805 PNK
805 PPL
OFF
ON
R/A
397A GRY
150R BLK
S203
CRUISE ENGAGE SWITCH
TO ECM TERMINAL "B16" (AUTO TRANS ONLY)
805 YEL
SEE 8A-11
CRUISE
S287
TO IGN SWITCH
SEE 8A-14
G201

Circuit Description:

The cruise control output monitoring circuit is used to determine the state of CKT 1679. The cruise control cutoff relay completes the cruise control engage circuit through terminals C2 and A1 when the cruise is requested to be "ON," the brake pedal is not depressed, and there is not an ASR event taking place. Whenever the cruise control cutoff relay is activated by the EBTCM supplying B+ to CKT 1679, the cruise control circuit is opened by the relay switch moving off relay terminal A1.

The "SERVICE ASR" light will come "ON" and DTC 57 will set if CKT 1679 is always high when the EBTCM requests energization of the relay coil, which should take the circuit low.

Test Description: Number(s) below refer to circled number(s) on the diagnostic chart.

1. Checks the relay coil for proper resistance.
2. Checks the integrity of CKT 150 to ground.
3. Checks for an open in CKT 1679.
4. Checks for a short to B+ in CKT 1679, which would keep CKT 1679 high at all times.
5. Checks for an EBTCM-switched short to B+.
6. Checks for recurrence of DTC 57 after checks on other system components and wiring have been made. If the DTC comes back, the EBTCM must be concluding there is a problem present in CKT 1679 when there is not.
7. Checks for proper system operation after malfunctioning relay diagnosed in Step 1 has been replaced.
8. Checks for additional DTC-setting problems other than malfunctioning relay diagnosed in Step 1 and replace in Step 7.

Diagnostic Aids:

All tests using J 39700 Universal Breakout Box terminal "3" are using the terminal as ground. These tests, of course, assume that the ground CKT 801 at terminal "3" is good.

If the "ASR ACTIVE" lamp is always "ON" and cruise control will not engage, the malfunction is likely a short to B+ on CKT 1679.

GC402930042700BX

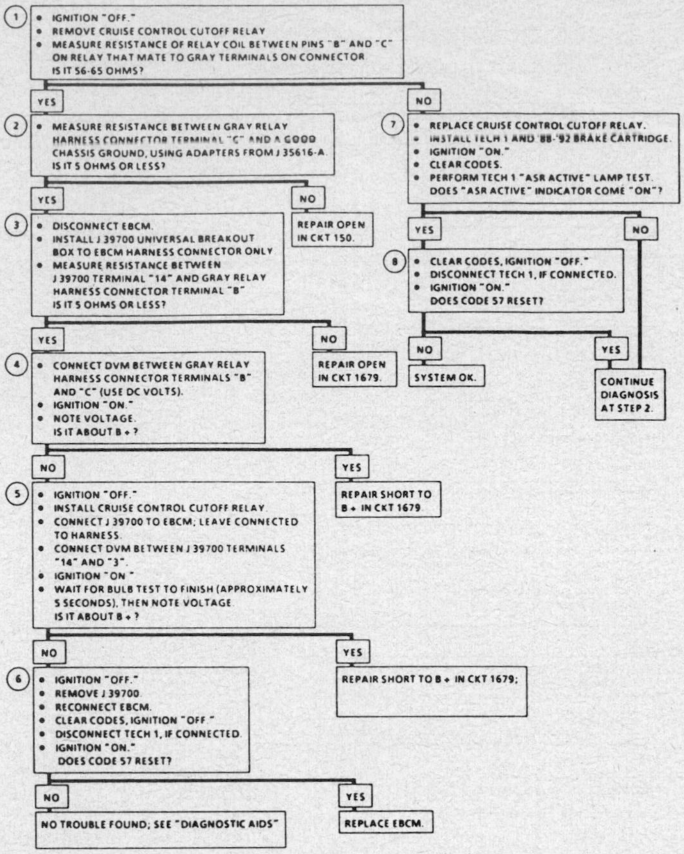
1 IGNITION "OFF."
REMOVE CRUISE CONTROL CUTOFF RELAY
MEASURE RESISTANCE OF RELAY COIL BETWEEN PINS "B" AND "C" ON RELAY THAT MATE TO GRAY TERMINALS ON CONNECTOR
IS IT 56-65 OHMS?
YES
NO
2 MEASURE RESISTANCE BETWEEN GRAY RELAY HARNESS CONNECTOR TERMINAL "C" AND A GOOD CHASSIS GROUND, USING ADAPTERS FROM J 35616-A.
IS IT 5 OHMS OR LESS?
YES
NO
REPAIR OPEN IN CKT 150.
3 DISCONNECT EBCM.
INSTALL J 39700 UNIVERSAL BREAKOUT BOX TO EBCM HARNESS CONNECTOR ONLY
MEASURE RESISTANCE BETWEEN J 39700 TERMINAL "14" AND GRAY RELAY HARNESS CONNECTOR TERMINAL "B"
IS IT 5 OHMS OR LESS?
YES
NO
REPAIR OPEN IN CKT 1679.
4 CONNECT DVM BETWEEN GRAY RELAY HARNESS CONNECTOR TERMINALS "B" AND "C" (USE DC VOLTS).
IGNITION "ON."
NOTE VOLTAGE.
IS IT ABOUT B+?
NO
YES
REPAIR SHORT TO B+ IN CKT 1679.
5 IGNITION "OFF."
INSTALL CRUISE CONTROL CUTOFF RELAY.
CONNECT J 39700 TO EBCM; LEAVE CONNECTED TO HARNESS.
CONNECT DVM BETWEEN J 39700 TERMINALS "14" AND "3".
IGNITION "ON."
WAIT FOR BULB TEST TO FINISH (APPROXIMATELY 5 SECONDS), THEN NOTE VOLTAGE.
IS IT ABOUT B+?
NO
YES
REPAIR SHORT TO B+ IN CKT 1679;
6 IGNITION "OFF."
REMOVE J 39700.
RECONNECT EBCM.
CLEAR CODES, IGNITION "OFF."
DISCONNECT TECH 1, IF CONNECTED.
IGNITION "ON."
DOES CODE 57 RESET?
NO
YES
NO TROUBLE FOUND; SEE "DIAGNOSTIC AIDS"
REPLACE EBCM.
7 REPLACE CRUISE CONTROL CUTOFF RELAY.
INSTALL TECH 1 AND '88-'92 BRAKE CARTRIDGE.
IGNITION "ON."
CLEAR CODES.
PERFORM TECH 1 "ASR ACTIVE" LAMP TEST.
DOES "ASR ACTIVE" INDICATOR COME "ON"?
YES
NO
8 CLEAR CODES, IGNITION "OFF."
DISCONNECT TECH 1, IF CONNECTED.
IGNITION "ON."
DOES CODE 57 RESET?
NO
YES
SYSTEM OK.
CONTINUE DIAGNOSIS AT STEP 2.

GC402920042700CX

1993

Fig. 58 Code 57: Cruise Control Output Monitoring Fault (Part 2 of 2). 1992–93

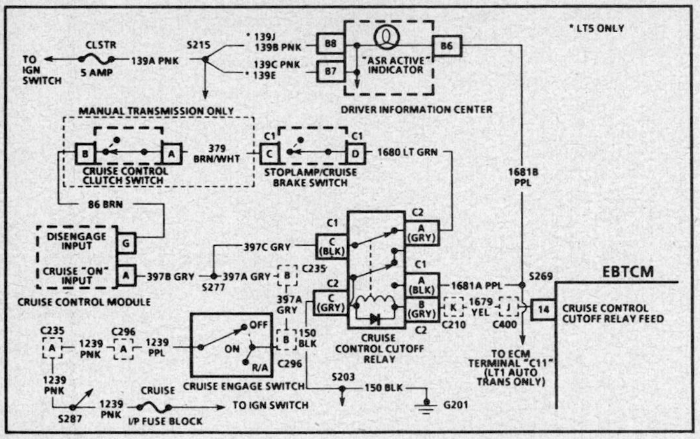
* LTS ONLY
TO IGN SWITCH
CLSTR
5 AMP
139A PNK
S215
139J
139B PNK
139C PNK
139E
B8
B7
B6
"ASR ACTIVE" INDICATOR
DRIVER INFORMATION CENTER
MANUAL TRANSMISSION ONLY
CRUISE CONTROL CLUTCH SWITCH
379 BRN/WHT
STOPLAMP/CRUISE BRAKE SWITCH
1680 LT GRN
1681B PPL
86 BRN
DISENGAGE INPUT
CRUISE "ON" INPUT
CRUISE CONTROL MODULE
397C GRY
397B GRY
397A GRY
S277
C235
(GRY)
(BLK)
1681A PPL
S269
EBTCM
1679 YEL
C210
C400
14
CRUISE CONTROL CUTOFF RELAY
CRUISE CONTROL CUTOFF RELAY FEED
C296
1239 PNK
1239 PPL
OFF
ON
R/A
150 BLK
S203
CRUISE ENGAGE SWITCH
TO ECM TERMINAL "C11" (LT1 AUTO TRANS ONLY)
CRUISE
S287
I/P FUSE BLOCK
TO IGN SWITCH
G201

Circuit Description:

The cruise control output monitoring circuit is used to determine the state of CKT 1679. The cruise control cutoff relay completes the cruise control engage circuit through terminals "C" of connector "C1" and "A" of connector "C2" when the cruise is requested to be "ON," the brake pedal is not depressed, and there is not an ASR event taking place. Whenever the cruise control cutoff relay is activated by the EBTCM supplying B+ to CKT 1679, the cruise control circuit is opened by the relay switch moving off relay terminal "A" of connector "C2".

DTC Will Set When: If CKT 1679 is always high when the EBTCM is not requesting energization of the relay coil, which should take the circuit low.

Action Taken: The "SERVICE ASR" indicator will come "ON."

DTC Chart Test Description: Number(s) below refer to circled number(s) on the diagnostic chart.

1. Checks the relay coil for proper resistance.
2. Checks the integrity of CKT 150 to ground.
3. Checks for an open in CKT 1679.
4. Checks for a short to B+ in CKT 1679, which would keep CKT 1679 high at all times.
5. Checks for an EBTCM-switched short to B+.
6. Checks for recurrence of DTC 57 after checks on other system components and wiring have been made. If the DTC comes back, the EBTCM must be concluding there is a malfunction present in CKT 1679 when there is not.
7. Checks for proper system operation after malfunctioning relay diagnosed in Step 1 has been replaced.
8. Checks for additional DTC-setting malfunctions other than malfunctioning relay diagnosed in Step 1 and replace in Step 7.

Diagnostic Aids: All tests using J 39700 Universal Breakout Box terminal "3" are using the terminal as ground. These tests, of course, assume that the ground CKT 1051 at terminal "3" is good.

Insure relay pin "B" of connector "C2" and pin "C" of connector "C1" are not internally shorted together.

If the "ASR ACTIVE" lamp is always "ON" and cruise control will not engage, the malfunction is likely a short to B+ on CKT 1679.

GC402940087600AX

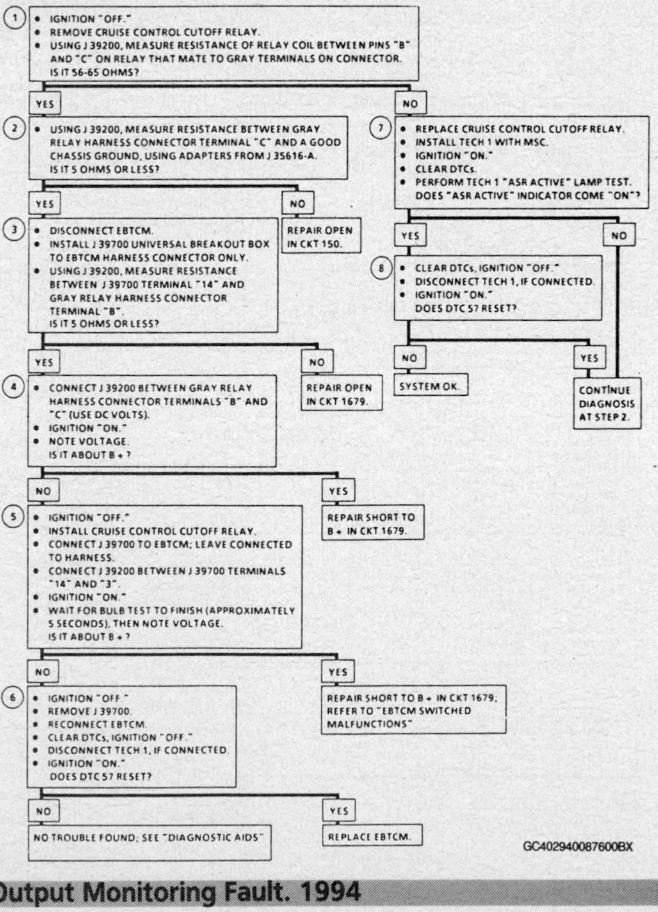
1 IGNITION "OFF."
REMOVE CRUISE CONTROL CUTOFF RELAY.
USING J 39200, MEASURE RESISTANCE OF RELAY COIL BETWEEN PINS "B" AND "C" ON RELAY THAT MATE TO GRAY TERMINALS ON CONNECTOR.
IS IT 56-65 OHMS?
YES
NO
2 USING J 39200, MEASURE RESISTANCE BETWEEN GRAY RELAY HARNESS CONNECTOR TERMINAL "C" AND A GOOD CHASSIS GROUND, USING ADAPTERS FROM J 35616-A.
IS IT 5 OHMS OR LESS?
YES
NO
REPAIR OPEN IN CKT 150.
3 DISCONNECT EBTCM.
INSTALL J 39700 UNIVERSAL BREAKOUT BOX TO EBTCM HARNESS CONNECTOR ONLY.
USING J 39200, MEASURE RESISTANCE BETWEEN J 39700 TERMINAL "14" AND GRAY RELAY HARNESS CONNECTOR TERMINAL "B".
IS IT 5 OHMS OR LESS?
YES
NO
REPAIR OPEN IN CKT 1679.
4 CONNECT J 39200 BETWEEN GRAY RELAY HARNESS CONNECTOR TERMINALS "B" AND "C" (USE DC VOLTS).
IGNITION "ON."
NOTE VOLTAGE.
IS IT ABOUT B+?
NO
YES
REPAIR SHORT TO B+ IN CKT 1679.
5 IGNITION "OFF."
INSTALL CRUISE CONTROL CUTOFF RELAY.
CONNECT J 39700 TO EBTCM; LEAVE CONNECTED TO HARNESS.
CONNECT J 39200 BETWEEN J 39700 TERMINALS "14" AND "3".
IGNITION "ON."
WAIT FOR BULB TEST TO FINISH (APPROXIMATELY 5 SECONDS), THEN NOTE VOLTAGE.
IS IT ABOUT B+?
NO
YES
REPAIR SHORT TO B+ IN CKT 1679; REFER TO "EBTCM SWITCHED MALFUNCTIONS"
6 IGNITION "OFF."
REMOVE J 39700.
RECONNECT EBTCM.
CLEAR DTCs, IGNITION "OFF."
DISCONNECT TECH 1, IF CONNECTED.
IGNITION "ON."
DOES DTC 57 RESET?
NO
YES
NO TROUBLE FOUND; SEE "DIAGNOSTIC AIDS"
REPLACE EBTCM.
7 REPLACE CRUISE CONTROL CUTOFF RELAY.
INSTALL TECH 1 WITH MSC.
IGNITION "ON."
CLEAR DTCs.
PERFORM TECH 1 "ASR ACTIVE" LAMP TEST.
DOES "ASR ACTIVE" INDICATOR COME "ON"?
YES
NO
8 CLEAR DTCs, IGNITION "OFF."
DISCONNECT TECH 1, IF CONNECTED.
IGNITION "ON."
DOES DTC 57 RESET?
NO
YES
SYSTEM OK.
CONTINUE DIAGNOSIS AT STEP 2.

GC402940087600BX

Fig. 59 Code 57: Cruise Control Output Monitoring Fault. 1994

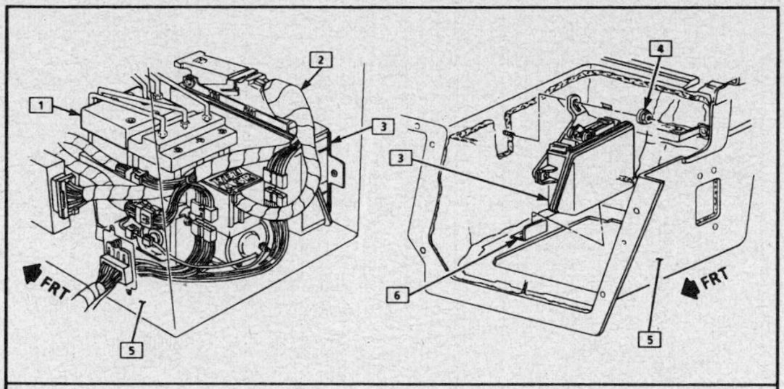

1
2
3
4
5
6
FRT

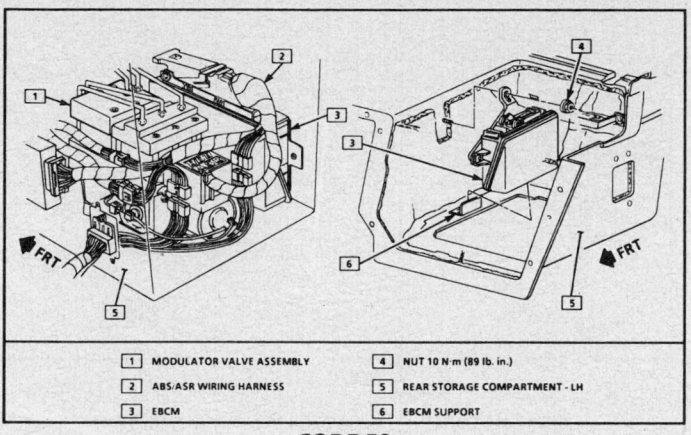

1 MODULATOR VALVE ASSEMBLY	4 NUT 10 N·m (89 lb. in.)
2 ABS/ASR WIRING HARNESS	5 REAR STORAGE COMPARTMENT - LH
3 EBCM	6 EBCM SUPPORT

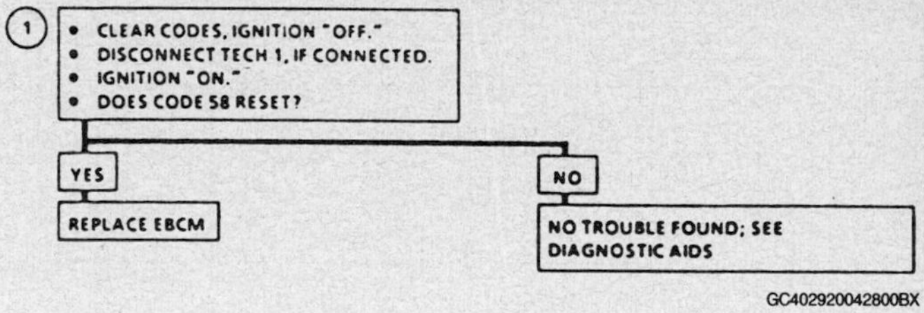

1
CLEAR CODES, IGNITION "OFF."
DISCONNECT TECH 1, IF CONNECTED.
IGNITION "ON."
DOES CODE 58 RESET?
YES
NO
REPLACE EBCM
NO TROUBLE FOUND; SEE DIAGNOSTIC AIDS
GC402920042800BX

CODE 58

EBCM INTERNAL ADJUSTER ASSEMBLY FAULT

Circuit Description:

The EBCM contains a microprocessor for ABS/ASR calculations and functions, as well as a microprocessor for Adjuster Assembly calculations and functions. If the two microprocessors cannot communicate with each other properly, Code 58 will set.

Test Description: Number(s) below refer to circled number(s) on the diagnostic chart.

1. Clears codes and checks for Code 58 reset. If the code resets, the microprocessor communication problem does exist within the EBCM.

GC402920042800AX

Fig. 60 Code 58: EBTCM Internal Adjuster Assembly Fault. 1992–93

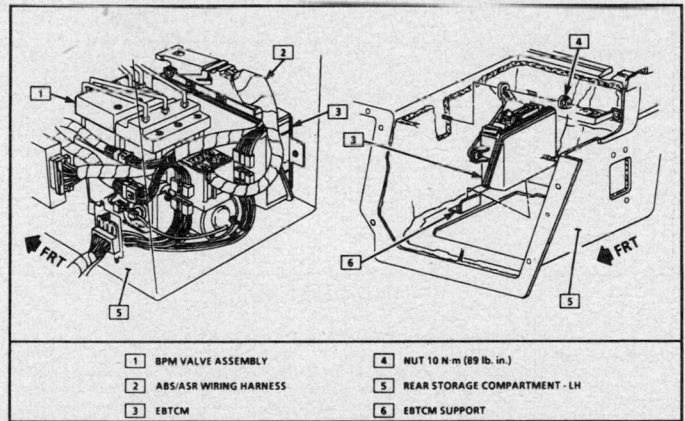

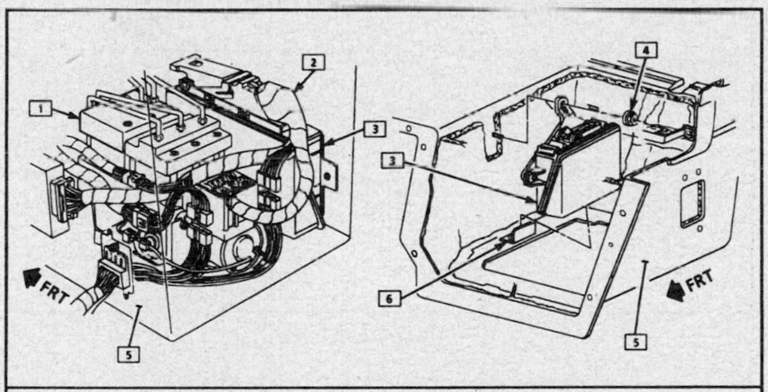

1
2
3
4
5
6
FRT

1 BPM VALVE ASSEMBLY	4 NUT 10 N·m (89 lb. in.)
2 ABS/ASR WIRING HARNESS	5 REAR STORAGE COMPARTMENT - LH
3 EBTCM	6 EBTCM SUPPORT

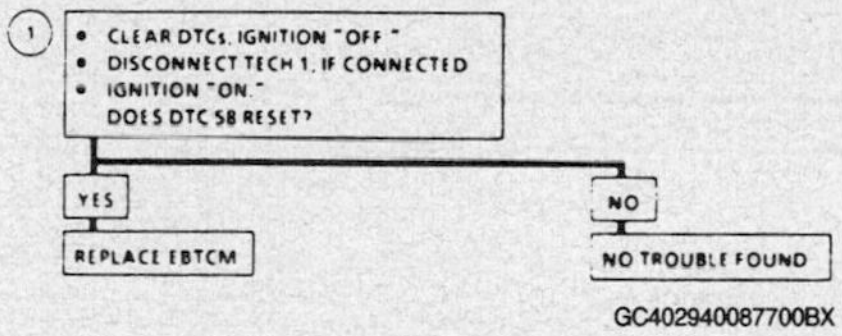

1
CLEAR DTCs, IGNITION "OFF."
DISCONNECT TECH 1, IF CONNECTED
IGNITION "ON."
DOES DTC 58 RESET?
YES
NO
REPLACE EBTCM
NO TROUBLE FOUND
GC402940087700BX

DTC 58

EBTCM INTERNAL ADJUSTER ASSEMBLY MALFUNCTION

Circuit Description:

The EBTCM contains a microprocessor for ABS/ASR calculations and functions, as well as a microprocessor for adjuster assembly calculations and functions.

DTC Will Set When: If the two microprocessors cannot communicate with each other properly.

DTC Chart Test Description: Number(s) below refer to circled number(s) on the diagnostic chart.

1. Clears DTCs and checks for DTC 58 reset. If the DTC resets, the microprocessor communication malfunction does exist within the EBTCM.

GC402940087700AX

Fig. 61 Code 58: EBTCM Internal Adjuster Assembly Fault. 1994

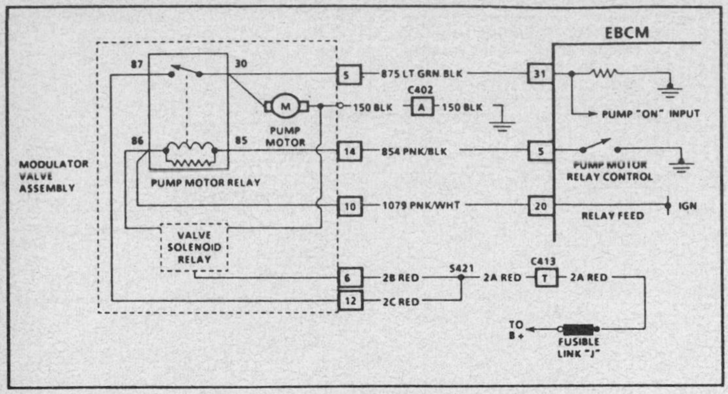

CODE 61

PUMP MOTOR OR PUMP MOTOR RELAY FAULT

Circuit Description:

When the pump motor relay is grounded by the EBCM, it closes and provides B+ to operate the pump. Once the motor circuit is energized, a "Pump ON" signal is sensed by the EBCM through CKT 875 to verify pump operation.

The "SERVICE ABS" and "SERVICE ASR" indicators will be "ON" and Code 61 will set if B+ is present at the pump motor without pump motor relay activation from the EBCM, or if B+ is NOT present at the pump motor within 60 milliseconds after the EBCM requests pump motor relay activation.

Test Description: Number(s) below refer to circled number(s) on the diagnostic chart.

1. Checks the Pump Motor Relay coil for proper resistance.
2. Checks for an open in power feed CKT 2C.
3. Determines if the Pump Motor Relay contacts are stuck closed.
4. Determines if the Pump Motor Relay contacts are stuck open.
5. Checks the integrity of the Pump Motor and Pump Motor Relay circuitry internal to the Modulator Valve Assembly.
6. Checks for an open in CKT 875.
7. Checks for a short to ground in CKT 875.
8. Checks for a short to B+ in CKT 875.

Diagnostic Aids:

All tests using J 39700 Universal Breakout Box terminal 3 are using that terminal as ground. These tests, of course, assume that the ground CKT 801 at terminal 3 is good.

It is very important that a thorough inspection of the wiring and connectors be performed. Failure to carefully and fully inspect wiring and connectors may result in misdiagnosis, causing part replacement with reappearance of the fault.

GC402920042900AX

1992

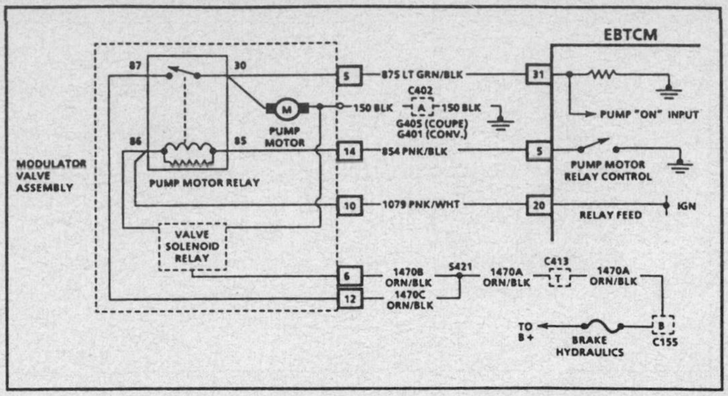

DTC 61

PUMP MOTOR OR PUMP MOTOR RELAY MALFUNCTION

Circuit Description:

When the pump motor relay is grounded by the EBTCM, it closes and provides B+ to operate the pump. Once the motor circuit is energized, a "Pump ON" signal is sensed by the EBTCM through CKT 875 to verify pump operation.

The "SERVICE ABS" and "SERVICE ASR" indicators will be "ON" and DTC 61 will set if B+ is present at the pump motor without pump motor relay activation from the EBTCM, or if B+ is NOT present at the pump motor within 60 milliseconds after the EBTCM requests pump motor relay activation.

Test Description: Number(s) below refer to circled number(s) on the diagnostic chart.

1. Checks the pump motor relay coil for proper resistance.
2. Checks for an open in power feed CKT 2C.
3. Determines if the pump motor relay contacts are stuck closed.
4. Determines if the pump motor relay contacts are stuck open.
5. Checks the integrity of the pump motor and pump motor relay circuitry internal to the modulator valve assembly.
6. Checks for an open in CKT 875.
7. Checks for a short to ground in CKT 875.
8. Checks for a short to B+ in CKT 875.

Diagnostic Aids:

All tests using J 39700 Universal Breakout Box terminal "3" are using that terminal as ground. These tests, of course, assume that the ground CKT 801 at terminal "3" is good.

It is very important that a thorough inspection of the wiring and connectors be performed. Failure to carefully and fully inspect wiring and connectors may result in misdiagnosis, causing part replacement with reappearance of the malfunction.

GC402930042900BX

1993

Fig. 62 Code 61: Pump Motor Or Motor Relay Fault (Part 1 of 3). 1992–93

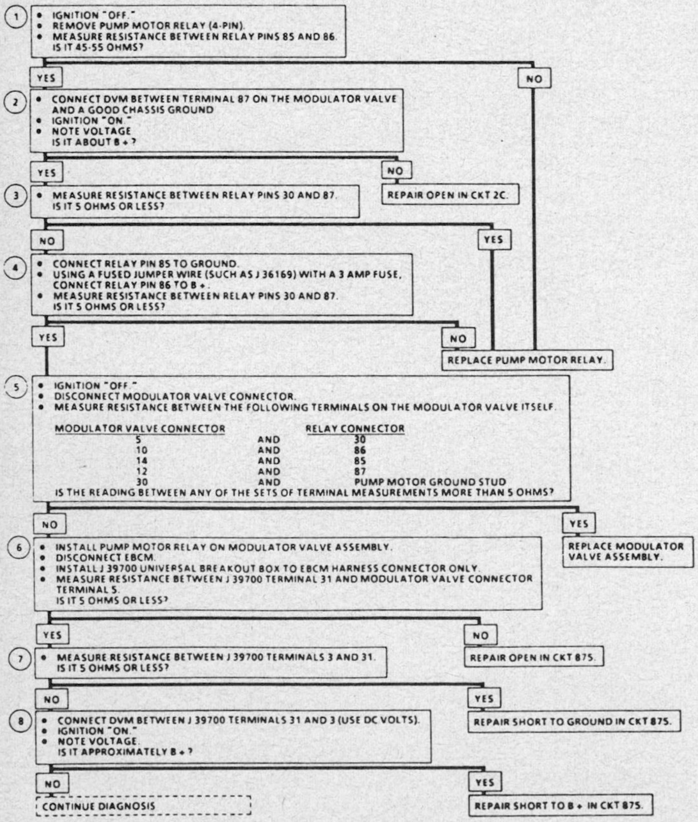

1 • IGNITION "OFF."
• REMOVE PUMP MOTOR RELAY (4-PIN).
• MEASURE RESISTANCE BETWEEN RELAY PINS 85 AND 86.
IS IT 45-55 OHMS?
YES
NO
2 • CONNECT DVM BETWEEN TERMINAL 87 ON THE MODULATOR VALVE AND A GOOD CHASSIS GROUND
• IGNITION "ON."
• NOTE VOLTAGE.
IS IT ABOUT B+?
YES
NO
REPAIR OPEN IN CKT 2C.
3 • MEASURE RESISTANCE BETWEEN RELAY PINS 30 AND 87.
IS IT 5 OHMS OR LESS?
NO
YES
4 • CONNECT RELAY PIN 85 TO GROUND.
• USING A FUSED JUMPER WIRE (SUCH AS J 36169) WITH A 3 AMP FUSE, CONNECT RELAY PIN 86 TO B+.
• MEASURE RESISTANCE BETWEEN RELAY PINS 30 AND 87.
IS IT 5 OHMS OR LESS?
YES
NO
REPLACE PUMP MOTOR RELAY.
5 • IGNITION "OFF."
• DISCONNECT MODULATOR VALVE CONNECTOR.
• MEASURE RESISTANCE BETWEEN THE FOLLOWING TERMINALS ON THE MODULATOR VALVE ITSELF.
MODULATOR VALVE CONNECTOR AND RELAY CONNECTOR
5 AND 30
10 AND 86
14 AND 85
12 AND 87
30 AND PUMP MOTOR GROUND STUD
IS THE READING BETWEEN ANY OF THE SETS OF TERMINAL MEASUREMENTS MORE THAN 5 OHMS?
NO
YES
REPLACE MODULATOR VALVE ASSEMBLY.
6 • INSTALL PUMP MOTOR RELAY ON MODULATOR VALVE ASSEMBLY.
• DISCONNECT EBCM.
• INSTALL J 39700 UNIVERSAL BREAKOUT BOX TO EBCM HARNESS CONNECTOR ONLY.
• MEASURE RESISTANCE BETWEEN J 39700 TERMINAL 31 AND MODULATOR VALVE CONNECTOR TERMINAL 5.
IS IT 5 OHMS OR LESS?
YES
NO
REPAIR OPEN IN CKT 875.
7 • MEASURE RESISTANCE BETWEEN J 39700 TERMINALS 3 AND 31.
IS IT 5 OHMS OR LESS?
NO
YES
REPAIR SHORT TO GROUND IN CKT 875.
8 • CONNECT DVM BETWEEN J 39700 TERMINALS 31 AND 3 (USE DC VOLTS).
• IGNITION "ON."
• NOTE VOLTAGE.
IS IT APPROXIMATELY B+?
NO
YES
CONTINUE DIAGNOSIS
REPAIR SHORT TO B+ IN CKT 875.

GC402920042900CX

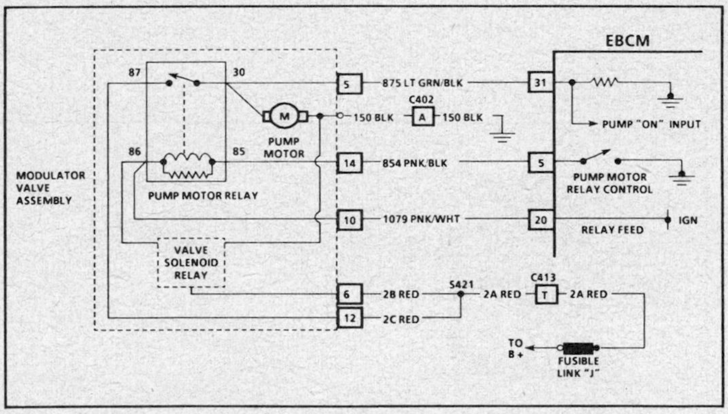

CODE 61

PUMP MOTOR OR PUMP MOTOR RELAY FAULT

Circuit Description:

When the pump motor relay is grounded by the EBCM, it closes and provides B+ to operate the pump. Once the motor circuit is energized, a "Pump ON" signal is sensed by the EBCM through CKT 875 to verify pump operation.

The "SERVICE ABS" and "SERVICE ASR" indicators will be "ON" and Code 61 will set if B+ is present at the pump motor without pump motor relay activation from the EBCM, or if B+ is NOT present at the pump motor within 60 milliseconds after the EBCM requests pump motor relay activation.

Test Description: Number(s) below refer to circled number(s) on the diagnostic chart.

9. Checks for an open in CKT 854.
10. Checks for a short to ground in CKT 854.
11. Checks for a short to B+ in CKT 854.
12. Checks wiring and connectors for intermittents.
13. Uses the Tech 1 to check for proper operation of the Pump Motor and associated circuitry.
14. Determines whether the problem found in Step 13 was due to a faulty EBCM or an open in Pump Motor ground CKT 150.

Diagnostic Aids:

All tests using J 39700 Universal Breakout Box terminal 3 are using that terminal as ground. These tests, of course, assume that the ground CKT 801 at terminal 3 is good.

It is very important that a thorough inspection of the wiring and connectors be performed. Failure to carefully and fully inspect wiring and connectors may result in misdiagnosis, causing part replacement with reappearance of the fault.

GC402920042900DX

1992

Fig. 62 Code 61: Pump Motor Or Motor Relay Fault (Part 2 of 3). 1992–93

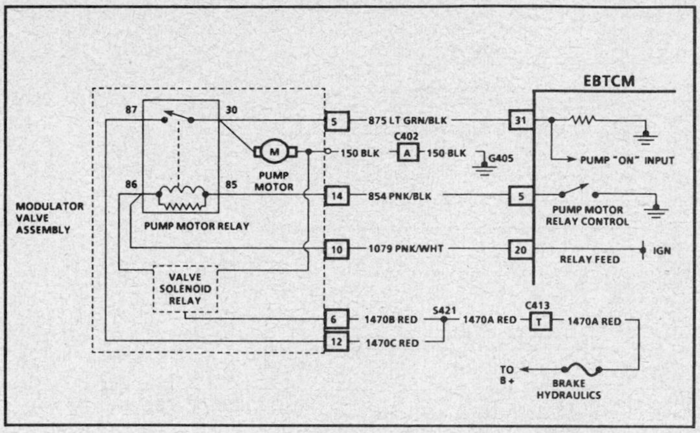
EBTCM
87
30
5
875 LT GRN/BLK
31
C402
150 BLK
A
150 BLK
G405
PUMP "ON" INPUT
PUMP MOTOR
86
85
14
854 PNK/BLK
5
PUMP MOTOR RELAY CONTROL
MODULATOR VALVE ASSEMBLY
PUMP MOTOR RELAY
10
1079 PNK/WHT
20
RELAY FEED
IGN
VALVE SOLENOID RELAY
S421
C413
6
1470B RED
1470A RED
T
1470A RED
12
1470C RED
TO B+
BRAKE HYDRAULICS

DTC 61

PUMP MOTOR OR PUMP MOTOR RELAY MALFUNCTION

Circuit Description:

When the pump motor relay is grounded by the EBTCM, it closes and provides B+ to operate the pump. Once the motor circuit is energized, a "Pump ON" signal is sensed by the EBTCM through CKT 875 to verify pump operation.

The "SERVICE ABS" and "SERVICE ASR" indicators will be "ON" and DTC 61 will set if B+ is present at the pump motor without pump motor relay activation from the EBTCM, or if B+ is NOT present at the pump motor within 60 milliseconds after the EBTCM requests pump motor relay activation.

Test Description: Number(s) below refer to circled number(s) on the diagnostic chart.

9. Checks for an open in CKT 854.
10. Checks for a short to ground in CKT 854.
11. Checks for a short to B+ in CKT 854.
12. Checks wiring and connectors for intermittents.
13. Uses the Tech 1 to check for proper operation of the pump motor and associated circuitry.
14. Determines whether the problem found in Step 13 was due to a malfunctioning EBTCM or an open in pump motor ground CKT 150.

Diagnostic Aids:

All tests using J 39700 Universal Breakout Box terminal "3" are using that terminal as ground. These tests, of course, assume that the ground CKT 801 at terminal "3" is good.

It is very important that a thorough inspection of the wiring and connectors be performed. Failure to carefully and fully inspect wiring and connectors may result in misdiagnosis, causing part replacement with reappearance of the malfunction.

GC402930042900EX

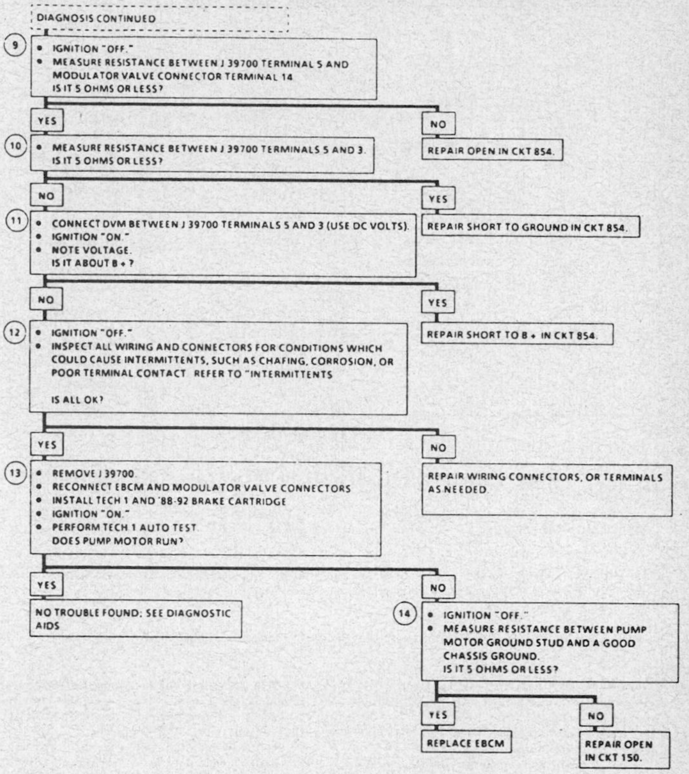
DIAGNOSIS CONTINUED
9
• IGNITION "OFF."
• MEASURE RESISTANCE BETWEEN J 39700 TERMINAL 5 AND MODULATOR VALVE CONNECTOR TERMINAL 14.
IS IT 5 OHMS OR LESS?
YES
NO
REPAIR OPEN IN CKT 854.
10
• MEASURE RESISTANCE BETWEEN J 39700 TERMINALS 5 AND 3.
IS IT 5 OHMS OR LESS?
NO
YES
REPAIR SHORT TO GROUND IN CKT 854.
11
• CONNECT DVM BETWEEN J 39700 TERMINALS 5 AND 3 (USE DC VOLTS).
• IGNITION "ON."
• NOTE VOLTAGE.
IS IT ABOUT B+?
NO
YES
REPAIR SHORT TO B+ IN CKT 854.
12
• IGNITION "OFF."
• INSPECT ALL WIRING AND CONNECTORS FOR CONDITIONS WHICH COULD CAUSE INTERMITTENTS, SUCH AS CHAFING, CORROSION, OR POOR TERMINAL CONTACT. REFER TO "INTERMITTENTS
IS ALL OK?
YES
NO
REPAIR WIRING CONNECTORS, OR TERMINALS AS NEEDED.
13
• REMOVE J 39700.
• RECONNECT EBCM AND MODULATOR VALVE CONNECTORS
• INSTALL TECH 1 AND '88-92 BRAKE CARTRIDGE
• IGNITION "ON."
• PERFORM TECH 1 AUTO TEST.
DOES PUMP MOTOR RUN?
YES
NO
NO TROUBLE FOUND; SEE DIAGNOSTIC AIDS.
14
• IGNITION "OFF."
• MEASURE RESISTANCE BETWEEN PUMP MOTOR GROUND STUD AND A GOOD CHASSIS GROUND.
IS IT 5 OHMS OR LESS?
YES
NO
REPLACE EBCM
REPAIR OPEN IN CKT 150.

GC402920042900FX

1993

Fig. 62 Code 61: Pump Motor Or Motor Relay Fault (Part 3 of 3). 1992–93

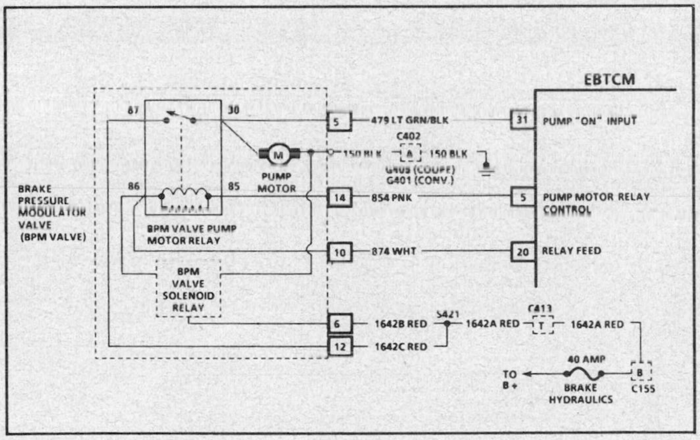
EBTCM
87
30
5
479 LT GRN/BLK
31
PUMP "ON" INPUT
C402
150 BLK
A
150 BLK
G409 (COUPE)
G401 (CONV.)
PUMP MOTOR
BRAKE PRESSURE MODULATOR VALVE (BPM VALVE)
86
85
14
854 PNK
5
PUMP MOTOR RELAY CONTROL
BPM VALVE PUMP MOTOR RELAY
10
874 WHT
20
RELAY FEED
BPM VALVE SOLENOID RELAY
S421
C413
6
1642B RED
1642A RED
T
1642A RED
12
1642C RED
40 AMP
TO B+
BRAKE HYDRAULICS
B
C155

DTC 61

(Page 1 of 2)

PUMP MOTOR OR PUMP MOTOR RELAY MALFUNCTION

Circuit Description:

When the pump motor relay is grounded by the EBTCM, it closes and provides B+ to operate the pump. Once the motor circuit is energized, a "Pump ON" signal is sensed by the EBTCM through CKT 479 to verify pump operation.

DTC Will Set When: If B+ is present at the pump motor without pump motor relay activation from the EBTCM, or if B+ is NOT present at the pump motor within 60 milliseconds after the EBTCM requests pump motor relay activation.

Action Taken: The "SERVICE ABS" and "SERVICE ASR" indicators will be "ON."

DTC Chart Test Description: Number(s) below refer to circled number(s) on the diagnostic chart.

1. Checks the pump motor relay coil for proper resistance.
2. Checks for an open in power feed CKT 1642.
3. Determines if the pump motor relay contacts are stuck closed.
4. Determines if the pump motor relay contacts are stuck open.
5. Checks the integrity of the pump motor and pump motor relay circuitry internal to the BPM valve assembly.
6. Checks for an open in CKT 479.
7. Checks for a short to ground in CKT 479.
8. Checks for a short to B+ in CKT 479.

Diagnostic Aids: All tests using J 39700 Universal Breakout Box terminal "3" are using that terminal as ground. These tests, of course, assume that the ground CKT 1051 at terminal "3" is good.

It is very important that a thorough inspection of the wiring and connectors be performed. Failure to carefully and fully inspect wiring and connectors may result in misdiagnosis, causing part replacement with reappearance of the malfunction.

GC402940087801AX

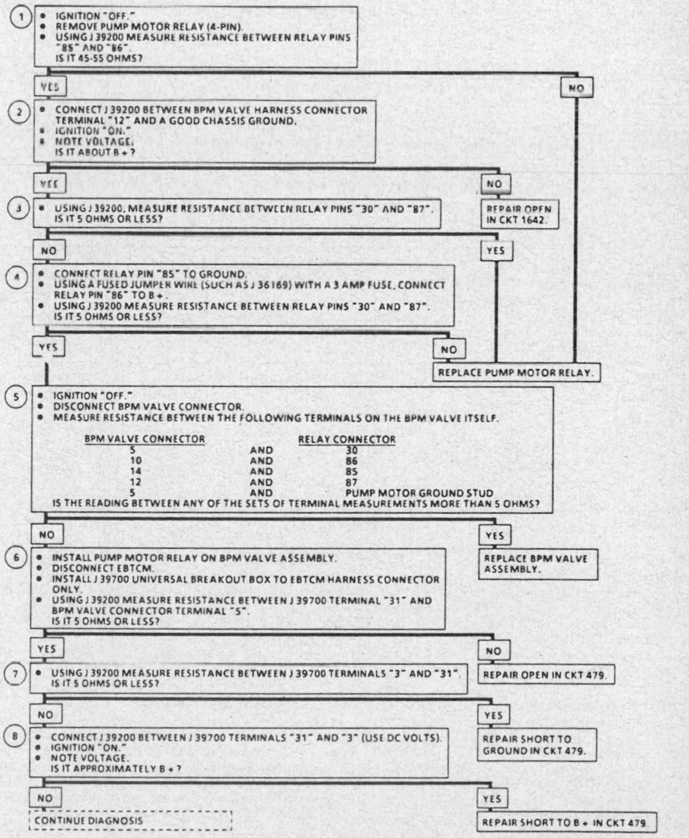
1
• IGNITION "OFF."
• REMOVE PUMP MOTOR RELAY (4-PIN).
• USING J 39200 MEASURE RESISTANCE BETWEEN RELAY PINS "85" AND "86".
IS IT 45-55 OHMS?
YES
NO
2
• CONNECT J 39200 BETWEEN BPM VALVE HARNESS CONNECTOR TERMINAL "12" AND A GOOD CHASSIS GROUND.
• IGNITION "ON."
• NOTE VOLTAGE.
IS IT ABOUT B+?
YES
NO
REPAIR OPEN IN CKT 1642.
3
• USING J 39200, MEASURE RESISTANCE BETWEEN RELAY PINS "30" AND "87".
IS IT 5 OHMS OR LESS?
NO
YES
4
• CONNECT RELAY PIN "85" TO GROUND.
• USING A FUSED JUMPER WIRE (SUCH AS J 36169) WITH A 3 AMP FUSE, CONNECT RELAY PIN "86" TO B+.
• USING J 39200 MEASURE RESISTANCE BETWEEN RELAY PINS "30" AND "87".
IS IT 5 OHMS OR LESS?
YES
NO
REPLACE PUMP MOTOR RELAY.
5
• IGNITION "OFF."
• DISCONNECT BPM VALVE CONNECTOR.
• MEASURE RESISTANCE BETWEEN THE FOLLOWING TERMINALS ON THE BPM VALVE ITSELF.
BPM VALVE CONNECTOR / RELAY CONNECTOR
5 AND 30
10 AND 86
14 AND 85
12 AND 87
5 AND PUMP MOTOR GROUND STUD
IS THE READING BETWEEN ANY OF THE SETS OF TERMINAL MEASUREMENTS MORE THAN 5 OHMS?
NO
YES
REPLACE BPM VALVE ASSEMBLY.
6
• INSTALL PUMP MOTOR RELAY ON BPM VALVE ASSEMBLY.
• DISCONNECT EBTCM.
• INSTALL J 39700 UNIVERSAL BREAKOUT BOX TO EBTCM HARNESS CONNECTOR ONLY.
• USING J 39200 MEASURE RESISTANCE BETWEEN J 39700 TERMINAL "31" AND BPM VALVE CONNECTOR TERMINAL "5".
IS IT 5 OHMS OR LESS?
YES
NO
REPAIR OPEN IN CKT 479.
7
• USING J 39200 MEASURE RESISTANCE BETWEEN J 39700 TERMINALS "3" AND "31".
IS IT 5 OHMS OR LESS?
NO
YES
REPAIR SHORT TO GROUND IN CKT 479.
8
• CONNECT J 39200 BETWEEN J 39700 TERMINALS "31" AND "3" (USE DC VOLTS).
• IGNITION "ON."
• NOTE VOLTAGE.
IS IT APPROXIMATELY B+?
NO
YES
CONTINUE DIAGNOSIS
REPAIR SHORT TO B+ IN CKT 479.

GC402940087801BX

Fig. 63 Code 61: Pump Motor Or Motor Relay Fault (Part 1 of 2). 1994

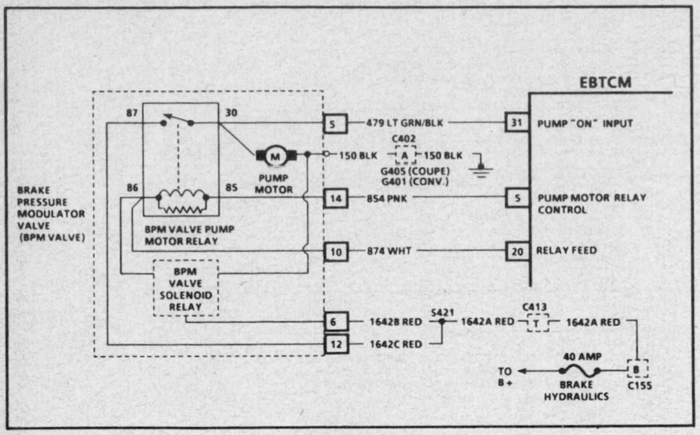
EBTCM
87
30
479 LT GRN/BLK
PUMP "ON" INPUT
C402
150 BLK
150 BLK
G405 (COUPE)
G401 (CONV.)
PUMP MOTOR
BRAKE PRESSURE MODULATOR VALVE (BPM VALVE)
86
85
854 PNK
PUMP MOTOR RELAY CONTROL
BPM VALVE PUMP MOTOR RELAY
874 WHT
RELAY FEED
BPM VALVE SOLENOID RELAY
S421
C413
1642B RED
1642A RED
1642A RED
1642C RED
40 AMP
TO B+
BRAKE HYDRAULICS
C155

DTC 61

(Page 2 of 2)

PUMP MOTOR OR PUMP MOTOR RELAY MALFUNCTION

Circuit Description:

When the pump motor relay is grounded by the EBTCM, it closes and provides B+ to operate the pump. Once the motor circuit is energized, a "Pump ON" signal is sensed by the EBTCM through CKT 479 to verify pump operation.

DTC Will Set When: If B+ is present at the pump motor without pump motor relay activation from the EBTCM, or if B+ is NOT present at the pump motor within 60 milliseconds after the EBTCM requests pump motor relay activation.

Action Taken: The "SERVICE ABS" and "SERVICE ASR" indicators will be "ON."

DTC Chart Test Description: Number(s) below refer to circled number(s) on the diagnostic chart.

9. Checks for an open in CKT 854.
10. Checks for a short to ground in CKT 854.
11. Checks for a short to B+ in CKT 854.
12. Checks wiring and connectors for intermittents.
13. Uses the Tech 1 to check for proper operation of the pump motor and associated circuitry.
14. Determines whether the malfunction found in Step 13 was due to a malfunctioning EBTCM or an open in pump motor ground CKT 150.

Diagnostic Aids: All tests using J 39700 Universal Breakout Box terminal "3" are using that terminal as ground. These tests, of course, assume that the ground CKT 1051 at terminal "3" is good.

It is very important that a thorough inspection of the wiring and connectors be performed. Failure to carefully and fully inspect wiring and connectors may result in misdiagnosis, causing part replacement with reappearance of the malfunction.

GC402940087802AX

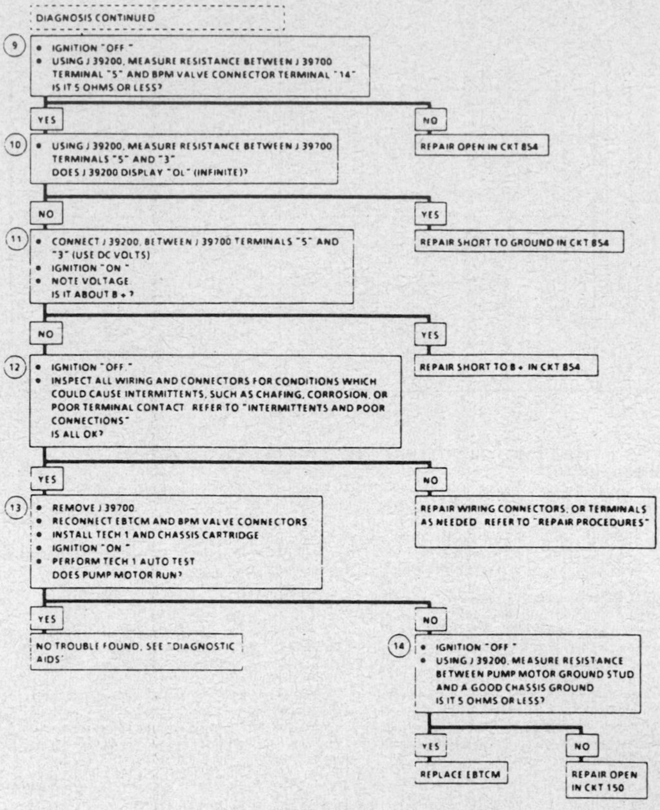
DIAGNOSIS CONTINUED
9
• IGNITION "OFF."
• USING J 39200, MEASURE RESISTANCE BETWEEN J 39700 TERMINAL "5" AND BPM VALVE CONNECTOR TERMINAL "14."
IS IT 5 OHMS OR LESS?
YES
NO
REPAIR OPEN IN CKT 854
10
• USING J 39200, MEASURE RESISTANCE BETWEEN J 39700 TERMINALS "5" AND "3."
DOES J 39200 DISPLAY "OL" (INFINITE)?
NO
YES
REPAIR SHORT TO GROUND IN CKT 854
11
• CONNECT J 39200, BETWEEN J 39700 TERMINALS "5" AND "3" (USE DC VOLTS)
• IGNITION "ON."
• NOTE VOLTAGE.
IS IT ABOUT B+?
NO
YES
REPAIR SHORT TO B+ IN CKT 854
12
• IGNITION "OFF."
• INSPECT ALL WIRING AND CONNECTORS FOR CONDITIONS WHICH COULD CAUSE INTERMITTENTS, SUCH AS CHAFING, CORROSION, OR POOR TERMINAL CONTACT. REFER TO "INTERMITTENTS AND POOR CONNECTIONS."
IS ALL OK?
YES
NO
REPAIR WIRING CONNECTORS, OR TERMINALS AS NEEDED. REFER TO "REPAIR PROCEDURES."
13
• REMOVE J 39700.
• RECONNECT EBTCM AND BPM VALVE CONNECTORS.
• INSTALL TECH 1 AND CHASSIS CARTRIDGE.
• IGNITION "ON."
• PERFORM TECH 1 AUTO TEST.
DOES PUMP MOTOR RUN?
YES
NO
NO TROUBLE FOUND. SEE "DIAGNOSTIC AIDS."
14
• IGNITION "OFF."
• USING J 39200, MEASURE RESISTANCE BETWEEN PUMP MOTOR GROUND STUD AND A GOOD CHASSIS GROUND.
IS IT 5 OHMS OR LESS?
YES
NO
REPLACE EBTCM
REPAIR OPEN IN CKT 150

GC402940087802BX

Fig. 63 Code 61: Pump Motor Or Motor Relay Fault (Part 2 of 2). 1994

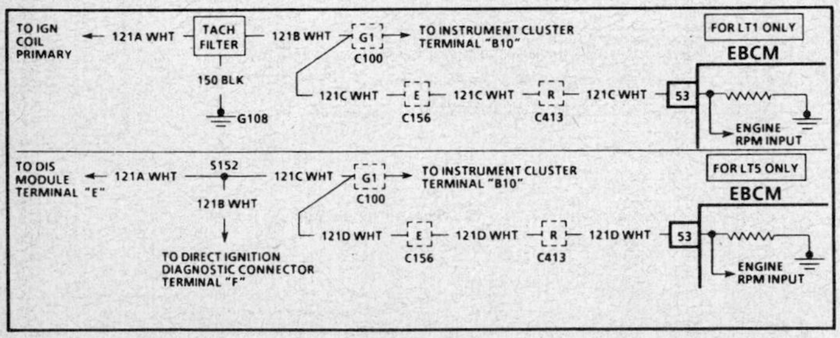
TO IGN COIL PRIMARY
121A WHT
TACH FILTER
121B WHT
G1
C100
TO INSTRUMENT CLUSTER TERMINAL "B10"
FOR LT1 ONLY
EBCM
150 BLK
G108
121C WHT
E
C156
121C WHT
R
C413
121C WHT
53
ENGINE RPM INPUT
TO DIS MODULE TERMINAL "E"
121A WHT
S152
121C WHT
121B WHT
TO INSTRUMENT CLUSTER TERMINAL "B10"
FOR LT5 ONLY
EBCM
121D WHT
121D WHT
121D WHT
TO DIRECT IGNITION DIAGNOSTIC CONNECTOR TERMINAL "F"
ENGINE RPM INPUT

CODE 62

TACH PULSES FAULT

Circuit Description:

The Tach Pulses Circuit provides the EBCM with an indication of engine rpm to help determine ASR control methods and rates when as ASR event takes place.

The "SERVICE ASR" indicator will be "ON" and Code 62 will set if there is a short to ground, short to B+, or an open in CKT 121.

Test Description: Number(s) below refer to circled number(s) on the diagnostic chart.

1. Checks if the instrument panel tachometer works properly. If so, there is likely an open between the common connection point of the I/P tach wiring and the CKT 121 wiring at bulkhead connector C100 terminal "G1".
2. Checks for a short to B+ in CKT 121.
3. Checks for a short to ground in CKT 121.

Diagnostic Aids:

A short to ground in CKT 121 with the LT1 (VIN P) engine may cause driveability problems. If the ground is on the ignition system side of the tach filter, there may be a no-start or extremely poor driveability condition. However, these symptoms do not apply to the LT5 (VIN J) engine.

GC402920043000AX

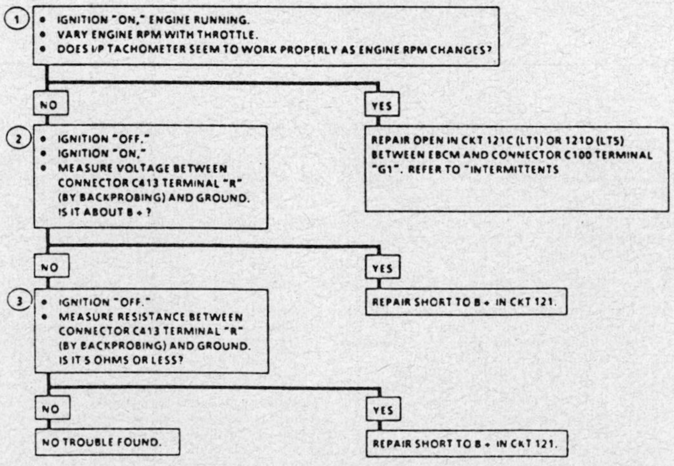
1
• IGNITION "ON," ENGINE RUNNING.
• VARY ENGINE RPM WITH THROTTLE.
• DOES I/P TACHOMETER SEEM TO WORK PROPERLY AS ENGINE RPM CHANGES?
NO
YES
REPAIR OPEN IN CKT 121C (LT1) OR 121D (LT5) BETWEEN EBCM AND CONNECTOR C100 TERMINAL "G1". REFER TO "INTERMITTENTS."
2
• IGNITION "OFF."
• IGNITION "ON."
• MEASURE VOLTAGE BETWEEN CONNECTOR C413 TERMINAL "R" (BY BACKPROBING) AND GROUND.
IS IT ABOUT B+?
NO
YES
REPAIR SHORT TO B+ IN CKT 121.
3
• IGNITION "OFF."
• MEASURE RESISTANCE BETWEEN CONNECTOR C413 TERMINAL "R" (BY BACKPROBING) AND GROUND.
IS IT 5 OHMS OR LESS?
NO
YES
NO TROUBLE FOUND.
REPAIR SHORT TO B+ IN CKT 121.

GC402920043000BX

Fig. 64 Code 62: Tach Pulses Fault. 1992–93

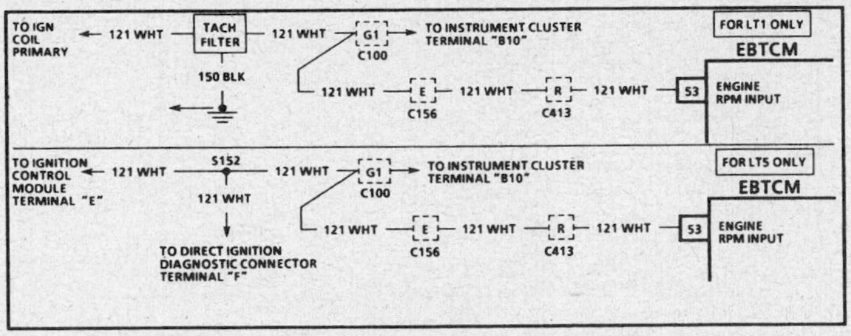

TO IGN COIL PRIMARY
121 WHT
TACH FILTER
121 WHT
G1
C100
TO INSTRUMENT CLUSTER TERMINAL "B10"
FOR LT1 ONLY
EBTCM
150 BLK
121 WHT
E
C156
121 WHT
R
C413
121 WHT
53
ENGINE RPM INPUT
TO IGNITION CONTROL MODULE TERMINAL "E"
121 WHT
S152
121 WHT
G1
C100
TO INSTRUMENT CLUSTER TERMINAL "B10"
FOR LT5 ONLY
EBTCM
121 WHT
TO DIRECT IGNITION DIAGNOSTIC CONNECTOR TERMINAL "F"
121 WHT
E
C156
121 WHT
R
C413
121 WHT
53
ENGINE RPM INPUT

DTC 62

TACH PULSES MALFUNCTION

Circuit Description:

The tach pulses circuit provides the EBTCM with an indication of engine RPM to help determine ASR control methods and rates when as ASR event takes place.

DTC Will Set When: There is a short to ground, short to B + or an open in CKT 121.

Action Taken: The "SERVICE ASR" indicator will be "ON."

DTC Chart Test Description: Number(s) below refer to circled number(s) on the diagnostic chart.

1. Checks if the instrument panel tachometer works properly. If so, there is likely an open between the common connection point of the I/P tach wiring and the CKT 121 wiring at bulkhead connector C100 terminal "G1".
2. Checks for a short to B + in CKT 121.
3. Checks for a short to ground in CKT 121.

Diagnostic Aids: A short to ground in CKT 121 with the LT1 (VIN P) engine may cause driveability malfunctions. If the ground is on the ignition system side of the tach filter, there may be a no-start or extremely poor driveability condition. However, these symptoms do not apply to the LT5 (VIN J) engine.

GC402940087900AX

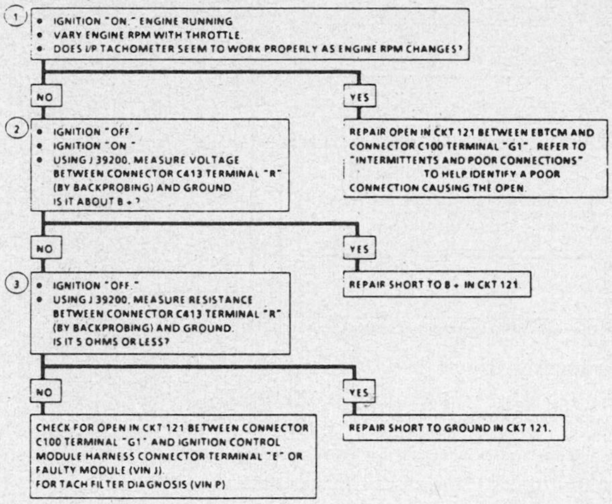

1
• IGNITION "ON," ENGINE RUNNING
• VARY ENGINE RPM WITH THROTTLE.
• DOES I/P TACHOMETER SEEM TO WORK PROPERLY AS ENGINE RPM CHANGES?
NO
YES
2
• IGNITION "OFF."
• IGNITION "ON."
• USING J 39200, MEASURE VOLTAGE BETWEEN CONNECTOR C413 TERMINAL "R" (BY BACKPROBING) AND GROUND
IS IT ABOUT B + ?
REPAIR OPEN IN CKT 121 BETWEEN EBTCM AND CONNECTOR C100 TERMINAL "G1". REFER TO "INTERMITTENTS AND POOR CONNECTIONS" TO HELP IDENTIFY A POOR CONNECTION CAUSING THE OPEN.
NO
YES
3
• IGNITION "OFF."
• USING J 39200, MEASURE RESISTANCE BETWEEN CONNECTOR C413 TERMINAL "R" (BY BACKPROBING) AND GROUND.
IS IT 5 OHMS OR LESS?
REPAIR SHORT TO B + IN CKT 121.
NO
YES
CHECK FOR OPEN IN CKT 121 BETWEEN CONNECTOR C100 TERMINAL "G1" AND IGNITION CONTROL MODULE HARNESS CONNECTOR TERMINAL "E" OR FAULTY MODULE (VIN J).
FOR TACH FILTER DIAGNOSIS (VIN P)
REPAIR SHORT TO GROUND IN CKT 121.

GC402940087900BX

Fig. 65 Code 62: Tach Pulses Fault. 1994

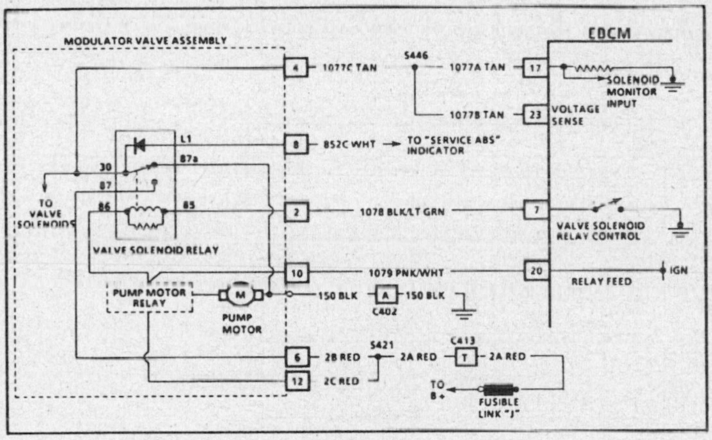

EBCM
MODULATOR VALVE ASSEMBLY
4
1077C TAN
S446
1077A TAN
17
SOLENOID MONITOR INPUT
1077B TAN
23
VOLTAGE SENSE
L1
87a
8
852C WHT
TO "SERVICE ABS" INDICATOR
30
87
86
85
TO VALVE SOLENOIDS
2
1078 BLK/LT GRN
7
VALVE SOLENOID RELAY CONTROL
VALVE SOLENOID RELAY
10
1079 PNK/WHT
20
RELAY FEED
IGN
PUMP MOTOR RELAY
M
150 BLK
A
150 BLK
C402
PUMP MOTOR
S421
C413
6
2B RED
2A RED
T
2A RED
12
2C RED
TO B+
FUSIBLE LINK "J"

CODE 63

VALVE SOLENOID RELAY FAULT

Circuit Description:

The Valve Solenoid Relay has two functions. When the ignition is "ON" and the EBCM is operating, the relay provides voltage to actuate the Valve Solenoids. However, the Valve Solenoids do not use this voltage unless the EBCM provides the ground. The second function of the Valve Solenoid Relay is to provide a ground path for illumination of the "SERVICE ABS" lamp if the relay loses power or ground.

The "SERVICE ABS" and "SERVICE ASR" indicators will be "ON" and Code 63 will set if the Valve Solenoid Relay voltage falls to less than 5 volts.

Test Description: Number(s) below refer to circled number(s) on the diagnostic chart.

1. Checks for the availability of battery voltage to the Valve Solenoid Relay through Fusible Link J and CKT 2.
2. Checks the Valve Solenoid Relay coil for proper resistance.
3. Checks for the Valve Solenoid Relay contacts being internally open when in the relay-unenergized position.
4. Checks for the Valve Solenoid Relay contacts being stuck open when in the relay-energized position.
5. Checks the integrity of the Valve Solenoid Relay circuitry internal to the Modulator Valve Assembly.
6. Checks for an open in ground CKT 150.
7. Checks for an open in CKT 1077.

Diagnostic Aids:

All tests using J 39700 Universal Breakout Box terminal 3 are using that terminal as ground. These tests, of course, assume that the ground CKT 801 at terminal 3 is good.

It is very important that a thorough inspection of the wiring and connectors be performed. Failure to carefully and fully inspect wiring and connectors may result in misdiagnosis, causing part replacement with reappearance of the fault.

GC402920043100AX

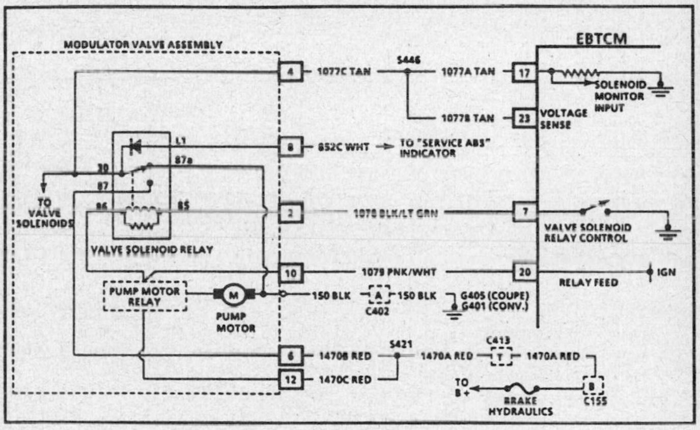

EBTCM
MODULATOR VALVE ASSEMBLY
4
1077C TAN
S446
1077A TAN
17
SOLENOID MONITOR INPUT
1077B TAN
23
VOLTAGE SENSE
L1
87a
8
852C WHT
TO "SERVICE ABS" INDICATOR
30
87
86
85
TO VALVE SOLENOIDS
2
1078 BLK/LT GRN
7
VALVE SOLENOID RELAY CONTROL
VALVE SOLENOID RELAY
10
1079 PNK/WHT
20
RELAY FEED
IGN
PUMP MOTOR RELAY
M
150 BLK
A
150 BLK
G405 (COUPE)
G401 (CONV.)
C402
PUMP MOTOR
S421
C413
6
1470B RED
1470A RED
T
1470A RED
12
1470C RED
TO B+
BRAKE HYDRAULICS
B
C155

DTC 63

VALVE SOLENOID RELAY MALFUNCTION

Circuit Description:

The valve solenoid relay has two functions. When the ignition is "ON" and the EBTCM is operating, the relay provides voltage to actuate the valve solenoids. However, the valve solenoids do not use this voltage unless the EBTCM provides the ground. The second function of the valve solenoid relay is to provide a ground path for illumination of the "SERVICE ABS" lamp if the relay loses power or ground.

The "SERVICE ABS" and "SERVICE ASR" indicators will be "ON" and DTC 63 will set if the valve solenoid relay voltage falls to less than 5 volts.

Test Description: Number(s) below refer to circled number(s) on the diagnostic chart.

1. Checks for the availability of battery voltage to the valve solenoid relay through the BRAKE HYDRAULICS fuse and CKT 1470.
2. Checks the valve solenoid relay coil for proper resistance.
3. Checks for the valve solenoid relay contacts being internally open when in the relay-unenergized position.
4. Checks for the valve solenoid relay contacts being stuck open when in the relay-energized position.
5. Checks the integrity of the valve solenoid relay circuitry internal to the modulator valve assembly.
6. Checks for an open in ground CKT 150.
7. Checks for an open in CKT 1077.

Diagnostic Aids:

All tests using J 39700 Universal Breakout Box terminal "3" are using that terminal as ground. These tests, of course, assume that the ground CKT 801 at terminal "3" is good.

It is very important that a thorough inspection of the wiring and connectors be performed. Failure to carefully and fully inspect wiring and connectors may result in misdiagnosis, causing part replacement with reappearance of the malfunction.

GC402920043100BX

1992 | 1993

Fig. 66 Code 63: Valve Solenoid Relay Fault (Part 1 of 3). 1992–93

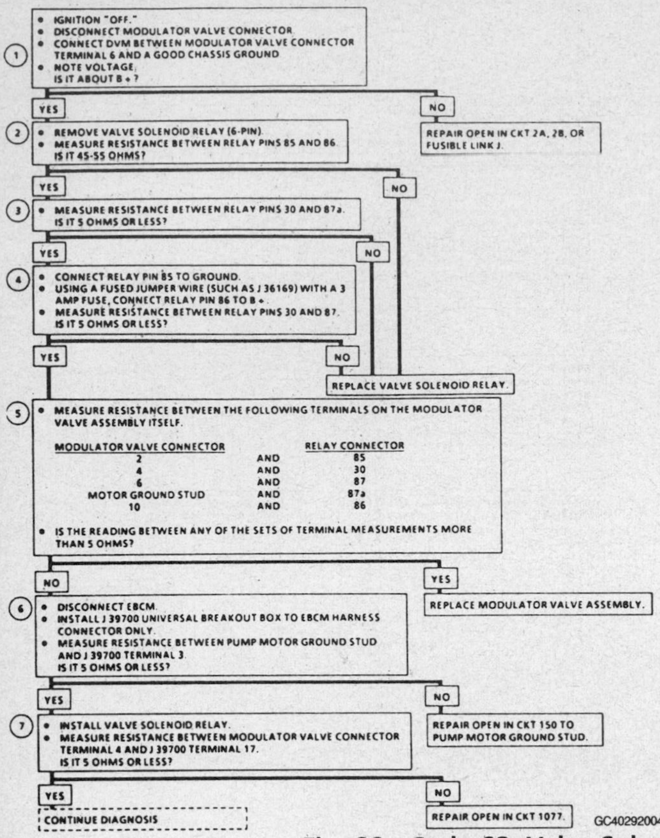
1
• IGNITION "OFF."
• DISCONNECT MODULATOR VALVE CONNECTOR.
• CONNECT DVM BETWEEN MODULATOR VALVE CONNECTOR TERMINAL 6 AND A GOOD CHASSIS GROUND.
• NOTE VOLTAGE. IS IT ABOUT B + ?
YES
NO
REPAIR OPEN IN CKT 2A, 2B, OR FUSIBLE LINK J.
2
• REMOVE VALVE SOLENOID RELAY (6-PIN).
• MEASURE RESISTANCE BETWEEN RELAY PINS 85 AND 86. IS IT 45-55 OHMS?
YES
NO
3
• MEASURE RESISTANCE BETWEEN RELAY PINS 30 AND 87a. IS IT 5 OHMS OR LESS?
YES
NO
4
• CONNECT RELAY PIN 85 TO GROUND.
• USING A FUSED JUMPER WIRE (SUCH AS J 36169) WITH A 3 AMP FUSE, CONNECT RELAY PIN 86 TO B +.
• MEASURE RESISTANCE BETWEEN RELAY PINS 30 AND 87. IS IT 5 OHMS OR LESS?
YES
NO
REPLACE VALVE SOLENOID RELAY.
5
• MEASURE RESISTANCE BETWEEN THE FOLLOWING TERMINALS ON THE MODULATOR VALVE ASSEMBLY ITSELF.
MODULATOR VALVE CONNECTOR | RELAY CONNECTOR
2 AND 85
4 AND 30
6 AND 87
MOTOR GROUND STUD AND 87a
10 AND 86
• IS THE READING BETWEEN ANY OF THE SETS OF TERMINAL MEASUREMENTS MORE THAN 5 OHMS?
NO
YES
REPLACE MODULATOR VALVE ASSEMBLY.
6
• DISCONNECT EBCM.
• INSTALL J 39700 UNIVERSAL BREAKOUT BOX TO EBCM HARNESS CONNECTOR ONLY.
• MEASURE RESISTANCE BETWEEN PUMP MOTOR GROUND STUD AND J 39700 TERMINAL 3. IS IT 5 OHMS OR LESS?
YES
NO
REPAIR OPEN IN CKT 150 TO PUMP MOTOR GROUND STUD.
7
• INSTALL VALVE SOLENOID RELAY.
• MEASURE RESISTANCE BETWEEN MODULATOR VALVE CONNECTOR TERMINAL 4 AND J 39700 TERMINAL 17. IS IT 5 OHMS OR LESS?
YES
NO
CONTINUE DIAGNOSIS
REPAIR OPEN IN CKT 1077.

GC402920043100CX

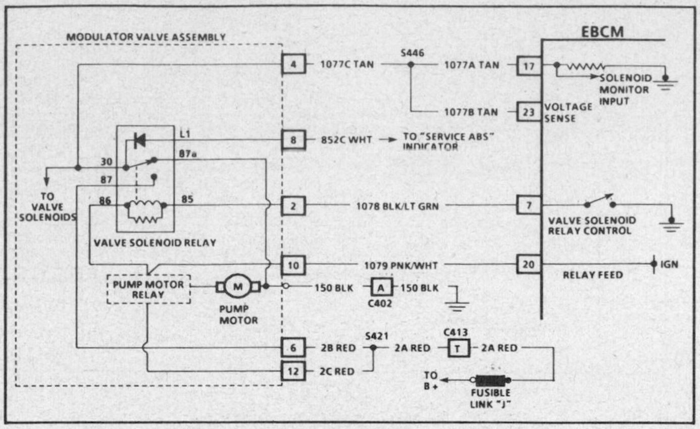
MODULATOR VALVE ASSEMBLY
EBCM
4
1077C TAN
S446
1077A TAN
17
SOLENOID MONITOR INPUT
1077B TAN
23
VOLTAGE SENSE
L1
87a
30
87
TO VALVE SOLENOIDS
86
85
VALVE SOLENOID RELAY
8
852C WHT
TO "SERVICE ABS" INDICATOR
2
1078 BLK/LT GRN
7
VALVE SOLENOID RELAY CONTROL
10
1079 PNK/WHT
20
RELAY FEED
IGN
PUMP MOTOR RELAY
M
PUMP MOTOR
150 BLK
A
150 BLK
C402
6
2B RED
S421
2A RED
C413
T
2A RED
12
2C RED
TO B +
FUSIBLE LINK "J"

CODE 63

VALVE SOLENOID RELAY FAULT

Circuit Description:

The Valve Solenoid Relay has two functions. When the ignition is "ON" and the EBCM is operating, the relay provides voltage to actuate the Valve Solenoids. However, the Valve Solenoids do not use this voltage unless the EBCM provides the ground. The second function of the Valve Solenoid Relay is to provide a ground path for illumination of the "SERVICE ABS" lamp if the relay loses power or ground.

The "SERVICE ABS" and "SERVICE ASR" indicators will be "ON" and Code 63 will set if the Valve Solenoid Relay voltage falls to less than 5 volts.

Test Description: Number(s) below refer to circled number(s) on the diagnostic chart.

8. Checks for a short to ground in CKT 1077.
9. Checks for a short to B + in CKT 1077.
10. Checks for an open in CKT 1079.
11. Checks for a short to ground in CKT 1079.
12. Checks for an open in CKT 1078.
13. Checks for a short to ground in CKT 1078.
14. Checks wiring and connectors for intermittents.
15. Determines whether the code was set due to an intermittent condition or an EBCM fault.

Diagnostic Aids:

All tests using J 39700 Universal Breakout Box terminal 3 are using that terminal as ground. These tests, of course, assume that the ground CKT 801 at terminal 3 is good.

It is very important that a thorough inspection of the wiring and connectors be performed. Failure to carefully and fully inspect wiring and connectors may result in misdiagnosis, causing part replacement with reappearance of the fault.

GC402920043100DX

Fig. 66 Code 63: Valve Solenoid Relay Fault (Part 2 of 3).1992–93

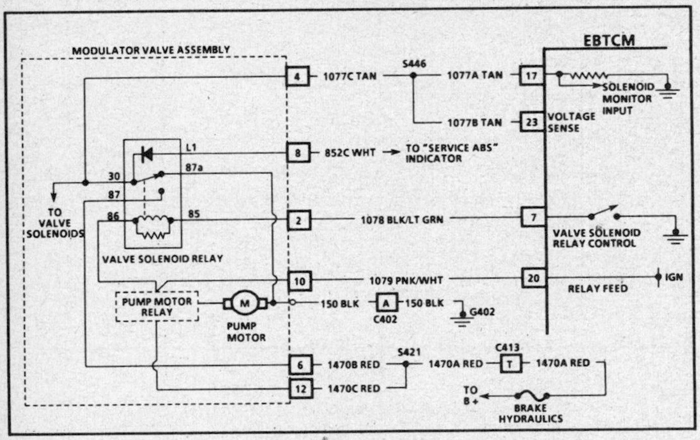
MODULATOR VALVE ASSEMBLY
EBTCM
4
1077C TAN
S446
1077A TAN
17
SOLENOID MONITOR INPUT
1077B TAN
23
VOLTAGE SENSE
L1
87a
30
87
TO VALVE SOLENOIDS
86
85
VALVE SOLENOID RELAY
8
852C WHT
TO "SERVICE ABS" INDICATOR
2
1078 BLK/LT GRN
7
VALVE SOLENOID RELAY CONTROL
10
1079 PNK/WHT
20
RELAY FEED
IGN
PUMP MOTOR RELAY
M
PUMP MOTOR
150 BLK
A
150 BLK
C402
G402
6
1470B RED
S421
1470A RED
C413
T
1470A RED
12
1470C RED
TO B +
BRAKE HYDRAULICS

DTC 63

VALVE SOLENOID RELAY MALFUNCTION

Circuit Description:

The valve solenoid relay has two functions. When the ignition is "ON" and the EBTCM is operating, the relay provides voltage to actuate the valve solenoids. However, the valve solenoids do not use this voltage unless the EBTCM provides the ground. The second function of the valve solenoid relay is to provide a ground path for illumination of the "SERVICE ABS" lamp if the relay loses power or ground.

The "SERVICE ABS" and "SERVICE ASR" indicators will be "ON" and DTC 63 will set if the valve solenoid relay voltage falls to less than 5 volts.

Test Description: Number(s) below refer to circled number(s) on the diagnostic chart.

8. Checks for a short to ground in CKT 1077.
9. Checks for a short to B + in CKT 1077.
10. Checks for an open in CKT 1079.
11. Checks for a short to ground in CKT 1079.
12. Checks for an open in CKT 1078.
13. Checks for a short to ground in CKT 1078.
14. Checks wiring and connectors for intermittents.
15. Determines whether the DTC was set due to an intermittent condition or an EBTCM malfunction.

Diagnostic Aids:

All tests using J 39700 Universal Breakout Box terminal "3" are using that terminal as ground. These tests, of course, assume that the ground CKT 801 at terminal "3" is good.

It is very important that a thorough inspection of the wiring and connectors be performed. Failure to carefully and fully inspect wiring and connectors may result in misdiagnosis, causing part replacement with reappearance of the malfunction.

GC402930043100EX

1993

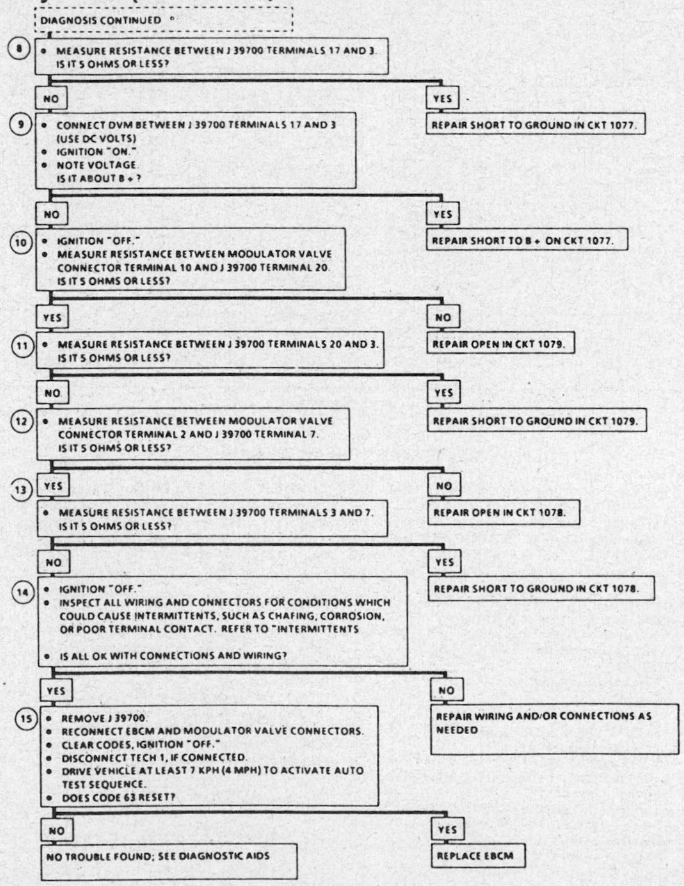
DIAGNOSIS CONTINUED
8
• MEASURE RESISTANCE BETWEEN J 39700 TERMINALS 17 AND 3. IS IT 5 OHMS OR LESS?
NO
YES
REPAIR SHORT TO GROUND IN CKT 1077.
9
• CONNECT DVM BETWEEN J 39700 TERMINALS 17 AND 3 (USE DC VOLTS).
• IGNITION "ON."
• NOTE VOLTAGE. IS IT ABOUT B + ?
NO
YES
REPAIR SHORT TO B + ON CKT 1077.
10
• IGNITION "OFF."
• MEASURE RESISTANCE BETWEEN MODULATOR VALVE CONNECTOR TERMINAL 10 AND J 39700 TERMINAL 20. IS IT 5 OHMS OR LESS?
YES
NO
REPAIR OPEN IN CKT 1079.
11
• MEASURE RESISTANCE BETWEEN J 39700 TERMINALS 20 AND 3. IS IT 5 OHMS OR LESS?
NO
YES
REPAIR SHORT TO GROUND IN CKT 1079.
12
• MEASURE RESISTANCE BETWEEN MODULATOR VALVE CONNECTOR TERMINAL 2 AND J 39700 TERMINAL 7. IS IT 5 OHMS OR LESS?
13
YES
NO
REPAIR OPEN IN CKT 1078.
• MEASURE RESISTANCE BETWEEN J 39700 TERMINALS 3 AND 7. IS IT 5 OHMS OR LESS?
NO
YES
REPAIR SHORT TO GROUND IN CKT 1078.
14
• IGNITION "OFF."
• INSPECT ALL WIRING AND CONNECTORS FOR CONDITIONS WHICH COULD CAUSE INTERMITTENTS, SUCH AS CHAFING, CORROSION, OR POOR TERMINAL CONTACT. REFER TO "INTERMITTENTS."
• IS ALL OK WITH CONNECTIONS AND WIRING?
YES
NO
REPAIR WIRING AND/OR CONNECTIONS AS NEEDED.
15
• REMOVE J 39700.
• RECONNECT EBCM AND MODULATOR VALVE CONNECTORS.
• CLEAR CODES, IGNITION "OFF."
• DISCONNECT TECH 1, IF CONNECTED.
• DRIVE VEHICLE AT LEAST 7 KPH (4 MPH) TO ACTIVATE AUTO TEST SEQUENCE.
• DOES CODE 63 RESET?
NO
YES
NO TROUBLE FOUND; SEE DIAGNOSTIC AIDS
REPLACE EBCM

GC402920043100FX

Fig. 66 Code 63: Valve Solenoid Relay Fault (Part 3 of 3). 1992–93

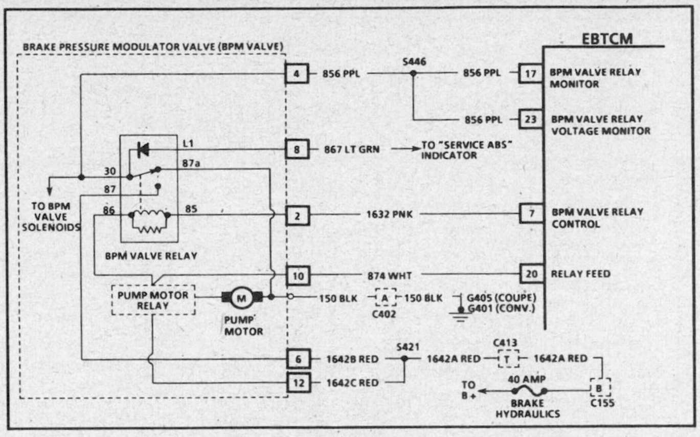
BRAKE PRESSURE MODULATOR VALVE (BPM VALVE)
EBTCM
856 PPL
S446
BPM VALVE RELAY MONITOR
BPM VALVE RELAY VOLTAGE MONITOR
L1
867 LT GRN
TO "SERVICE ABS" INDICATOR
87a
30
87
TO BPM VALVE SOLENOIDS
86
85
1632 PNK
BPM VALVE RELAY CONTROL
BPM VALVE RELAY
874 WHT
RELAY FEED
PUMP MOTOR RELAY
150 BLK
C402
G405 (COUPE)
G401 (CONV.)
PUMP MOTOR
S421
C413
1642B RED
1642A RED
1642C RED
TO B+
40 AMP
BRAKE HYDRAULICS
C155

DTC 63
(Page 1 of 2)
BPM VALVE RELAY MALFUNCTION

Circuit Description:
The BPM valve relay has two functions. When the ignition is "ON" and the EBTCM is operating, the relay provides voltage to actuate the valve solenoids. However, the valve solenoids do not use this voltage unless the EBTCM provides the ground. The second function of the BPM valve relay is to provide a ground path for illumination of the "SERVICE ABS" lamp if the relay loses power or ground.

DTC Will Set When: The BPM valve relay voltage falls to less than 5 volts.

Action Taken: The "SERVICE ABS" and "SERVICE ASR" indicators will be "ON."

DTC Chart Test Description: Number(s) below refer to circled number(s) on the diagnostic chart.
1. Checks for the availability of battery voltage to the BPM valve relay through the "BRAKE HYDRAULICS" fuse and CKT 1642.
2. Checks the BPM valve relay coil for proper resistance.
3. Checks for the BPM valve relay contacts being internally open when in the relay-unenergized position.
4. Checks for the BPM valve relay contacts being stuck open when in the relay-energized position.
5. Checks the integrity of the BPM valve relay circuitry internal to the BPM valve assembly.
6. Checks for an open in ground CKT 150.
7. Checks for an open in CKT 856.

Diagnostic Aids: All tests using J 39700 Universal Breakout Box terminal "3" are using that terminal as ground. These tests, of course, assume that the ground CKT 1051 at terminal "3" is good.

It is very important that a thorough inspection of the wiring and connectors be performed. Failure to carefully and fully inspect wiring and connectors may result in misdiagnosis, causing part replacement with reappearance of the malfunction.

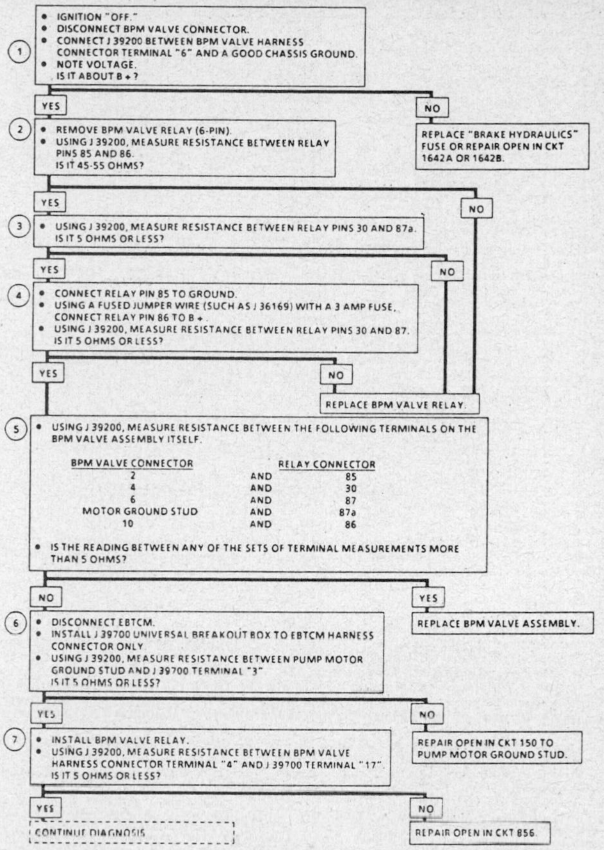
1
• IGNITION "OFF."
• DISCONNECT BPM VALVE CONNECTOR.
• CONNECT J 39200 BETWEEN BPM VALVE HARNESS CONNECTOR TERMINAL "6" AND A GOOD CHASSIS GROUND.
• NOTE VOLTAGE.
IS IT ABOUT B+?
YES
NO
REPLACE "BRAKE HYDRAULICS" FUSE OR REPAIR OPEN IN CKT 1642A OR 1642B.
2
• REMOVE BPM VALVE RELAY (6-PIN).
• USING J 39200, MEASURE RESISTANCE BETWEEN RELAY PINS 85 AND 86.
IS IT 45-55 OHMS?
YES
NO
3
• USING J 39200, MEASURE RESISTANCE BETWEEN RELAY PINS 30 AND 87a.
IS IT 5 OHMS OR LESS?
YES
NO
4
• CONNECT RELAY PIN 85 TO GROUND.
• USING A FUSED JUMPER WIRE (SUCH AS J 36169) WITH A 3 AMP FUSE, CONNECT RELAY PIN 86 TO B+.
• USING J 39200, MEASURE RESISTANCE BETWEEN RELAY PINS 30 AND 87.
IS IT 5 OHMS OR LESS?
YES
NO
REPLACE BPM VALVE RELAY.
5
• USING J 39200, MEASURE RESISTANCE BETWEEN THE FOLLOWING TERMINALS ON THE BPM VALVE ASSEMBLY ITSELF.
BPM VALVE CONNECTOR / RELAY CONNECTOR
2 AND 85
4 AND 30
6 AND 87
MOTOR GROUND STUD AND 87a
10 AND 86
• IS THE READING BETWEEN ANY OF THE SETS OF TERMINAL MEASUREMENTS MORE THAN 5 OHMS?
NO
YES
REPLACE BPM VALVE ASSEMBLY.
6
• DISCONNECT EBTCM.
• INSTALL J 39700 UNIVERSAL BREAKOUT BOX TO EBTCM HARNESS CONNECTOR ONLY.
• USING J 39200, MEASURE RESISTANCE BETWEEN PUMP MOTOR GROUND STUD AND J 39700 TERMINAL "3".
IS IT 5 OHMS OR LESS?
YES
NO
REPAIR OPEN IN CKT 150 TO PUMP MOTOR GROUND STUD.
7
• INSTALL BPM VALVE RELAY.
• USING J 39200, MEASURE RESISTANCE BETWEEN BPM VALVE HARNESS CONNECTOR TERMINAL "4" AND J 39700 TERMINAL "17".
IS IT 5 OHMS OR LESS?
YES
NO
CONTINUE DIAGNOSIS
REPAIR OPEN IN CKT 856.

GC40294000001AX

Fig. 67 Code 63: BPM Valve Relay Fault (Part 1 of 2). 1994

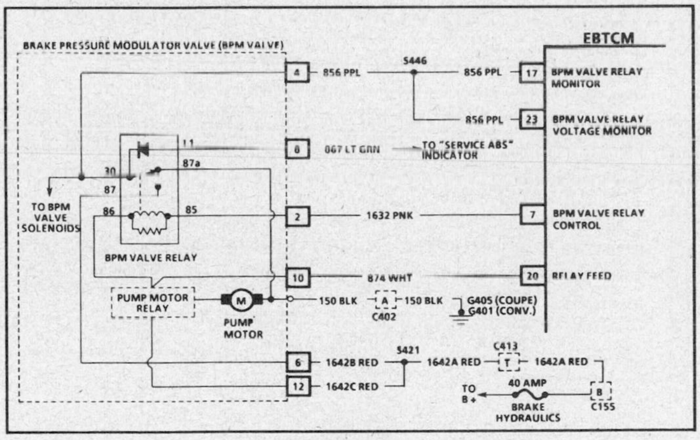
BRAKE PRESSURE MODULATOR VALVE (BPM VALVE)
EBTCM
856 PPL
S446
BPM VALVE RELAY MONITOR
BPM VALVE RELAY VOLTAGE MONITOR
L1
867 LT GRN
TO "SERVICE ABS" INDICATOR
87a
30
87
TO BPM VALVE SOLENOIDS
86
85
1632 PNK
BPM VALVE RELAY CONTROL
BPM VALVE RELAY
874 WHT
RELAY FEED
PUMP MOTOR RELAY
150 BLK
C402
G405 (COUPE)
G401 (CONV.)
PUMP MOTOR
S421
C413
1642B RED
1642A RED
1642C RED
TO B+
40 AMP
BRAKE HYDRAULICS
C155

DTC 63
(Page 2 of 2)
BPM VALVE RELAY MALFUNCTION

Circuit Description:
The BPM valve relay has two functions. When the ignition is "ON" and the EBTCM is operating, the relay provides voltage to actuate the valve solenoids. However, the valve solenoids do not use this voltage unless the EBTCM provides the ground. The second function of the BPM valve relay is to provide a ground path for illumination of the "SERVICE ABS" lamp if the relay loses power or ground.

DTC Will Set When: The BPM valve relay voltage falls to less than 5 volts.

Action Taken: The "SERVICE ABS" and "SERVICE ASR" indicators will be "ON."

DTC Chart Test Description: Number(s) below refer to circled number(s) on the diagnostic chart.
8. Checks for a short to ground in CKT 856.
9. Checks for a short to B+ in CKT 856.
10. Checks for an open in CKT 874.
11. Checks for a short to ground in CKT 874.
12. Checks for an open in CKT 1632.
13. Checks for a short to ground in CKT 1632.
14. Checks wiring and connectors for intermittents.
15. Determines whether the DTC was set due to an intermittent condition or an EBTCM malfunction.

Diagnostic Aids: All tests using J 39700 Universal Breakout Box terminal "3" are using that terminal as ground. These tests, of course, assume that the ground CKT 1051 at terminal "3" is good.

It is very important that a thorough inspection of the wiring and connectors be performed. Failure to carefully and fully inspect wiring and connectors may result in misdiagnosis, causing part replacement with reappearance of the malfunction.

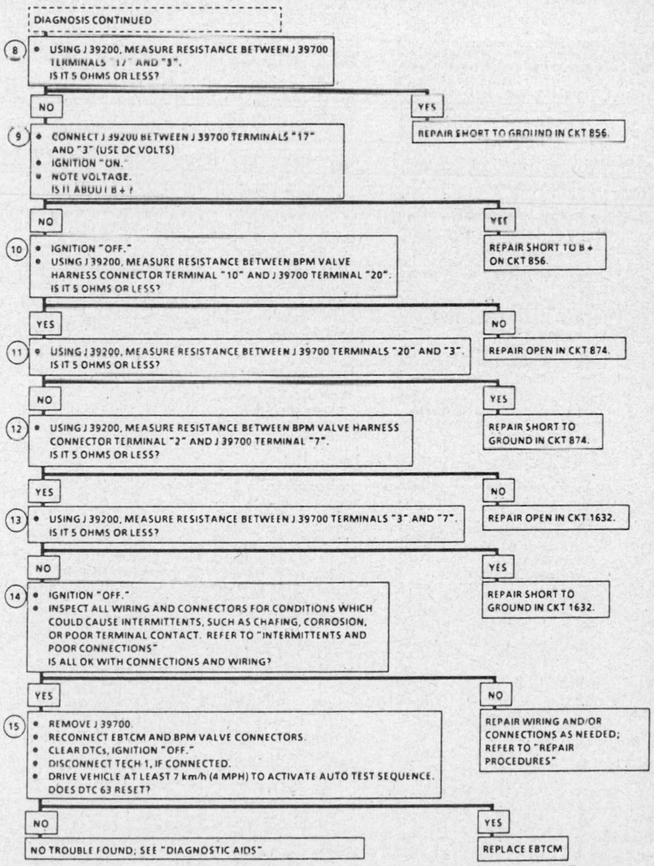
DIAGNOSIS CONTINUED
8
• USING J 39200, MEASURE RESISTANCE BETWEEN J 39700 TERMINALS "17" AND "3".
IS IT 5 OHMS OR LESS?
NO
YES
REPAIR SHORT TO GROUND IN CKT 856.
9
• CONNECT J 39200 BETWEEN J 39700 TERMINALS "17" AND "3" (USE DC VOLTS)
• IGNITION "ON."
• NOTE VOLTAGE.
IS IT ABOUT B+?
NO
YES
REPAIR SHORT TO B+ ON CKT 856.
10
• IGNITION "OFF."
• USING J 39200, MEASURE RESISTANCE BETWEEN BPM VALVE HARNESS CONNECTOR TERMINAL "10" AND J 39700 TERMINAL "20".
IS IT 5 OHMS OR LESS?
YES
NO
REPAIR OPEN IN CKT 874.
11
• USING J 39200, MEASURE RESISTANCE BETWEEN J 39700 TERMINALS "20" AND "3".
IS IT 5 OHMS OR LESS?
NO
YES
REPAIR SHORT TO GROUND IN CKT 874.
12
• USING J 39200, MEASURE RESISTANCE BETWEEN BPM VALVE HARNESS CONNECTOR TERMINAL "2" AND J 39700 TERMINAL "7".
IS IT 5 OHMS OR LESS?
YES
NO
REPAIR OPEN IN CKT 1632.
13
• USING J 39200, MEASURE RESISTANCE BETWEEN J 39700 TERMINALS "3" AND "7".
IS IT 5 OHMS OR LESS?
NO
YES
REPAIR SHORT TO GROUND IN CKT 1632.
14
• IGNITION "OFF."
• INSPECT ALL WIRING AND CONNECTORS FOR CONDITIONS WHICH COULD CAUSE INTERMITTENTS, SUCH AS CHAFING, CORROSION, OR POOR TERMINAL CONTACT. REFER TO "INTERMITTENTS AND POOR CONNECTIONS"
IS ALL OK WITH CONNECTIONS AND WIRING?
YES
NO
REPAIR WIRING AND/OR CONNECTIONS AS NEEDED; REFER TO "REPAIR PROCEDURES"
15
• REMOVE J 39700.
• RECONNECT EBTCM AND BPM VALVE CONNECTORS.
• CLEAR DTCs, IGNITION "OFF."
• DISCONNECT TECH 1, IF CONNECTED.
• DRIVE VEHICLE AT LEAST 7 km/h (4 MPH) TO ACTIVATE AUTO TEST SEQUENCE.
DOES DTC 63 RESET?
NO
YES
NO TROUBLE FOUND; SEE "DIAGNOSTIC AIDS"
REPLACE EBTCM

GC402940088002AX GC402940088002BX

Fig. 67 Code 63: BPM Valve Relay Fault (Part 2 of 2). 1994

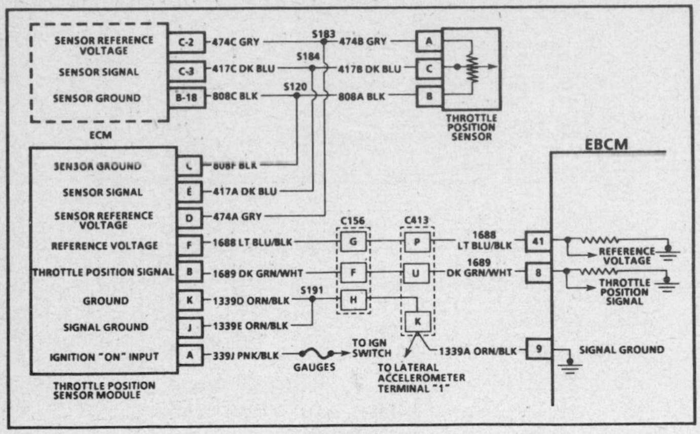
SENSOR REFERENCE VOLTAGE
SENSOR SIGNAL
SENSOR GROUND
ECM
C-2
C-3
B-18
474C GRY
417C DK BLU
808C BLK
S183
S184
S120
474B GRY
417B DK BLU
808A BLK
A
C
B
THROTTLE POSITION SENSOR
EBCM
SENSOR GROUND
SENSOR SIGNAL
SENSOR REFERENCE VOLTAGE
REFERENCE VOLTAGE
THROTTLE POSITION SIGNAL
GROUND
SIGNAL GROUND
IGNITION "ON" INPUT
THROTTLE POSITION SENSOR MODULE
808F BLK
417A DK BLU
474A GRY
1688 LT BLU/BLK
1689 DK GRN/WHT
1339D ORN/BLK
1339E ORN/BLK
339J PNK/BLK
C156
C413
S191
GAUGES
TO IGN SWITCH
TO LATERAL ACCELEROMETER TERMINAL "1"
1339A ORN/BLK
REFERENCE VOLTAGE
THROTTLE POSITION SIGNAL
SIGNAL GROUND

CODE 64

THROTTLE POSITION SIGNAL FAULT LT1 ONLY

Circuit Description:

The Throttle Position Signal circuit is used by the EBCM to monitor the actual throttle position versus desired throttle position to monitor and control engine torque during an ASR event. The Throttle Position Sensor Module is used to allow EBCM monitoring of the TPS signal without affecting the TPS signal to the ECM.

Code 64 will set if the EBCM is not receiving reference voltage or a TPS signal from the Throttle Position Sensor Module.

Test Description: Number(s) below refer to circled number(s) on the diagnostic chart.

1. Checks for TPS-related ECM trouble codes. Many of the same conditions which could cause an ASR Code 64 will also cause ECM codes. The ECM codes should be repaired first to eliminate those problems from affecting the ASR Code 64 condition.
2. Checks for a Lateral Accelerometer Code 75. Since the Lateral Accelerometer and the TPS Module share the same ground, a Code 75 likely indicates an open in CKT 1339.
3. Checks for a short to ground in CKT 1689.
4. Checks for a short to ground in CKT 1688.
5. Checks for proper voltage in CKT 1688 at the EBCM connection. (This voltage measurement is only appropriate when the EBCM is disconnected from the circuit).
6. Checks for proper voltage in CKT 1689 at the EBCM connection. (This voltage measurement is only appropriate when the EBCM is disconnected from the circuit).
7. Checks for an additional Code 64 problem after ground CKT 1339 is repaired.
8. Determines if a problem found in Step 5 is due to a fuse, CKT 339J, or CKT 1688.
9. Determines if a problem found in Steps 5 and 13 is due to an open in CKT 1688 or a faulty TPS Module.

GC402920043200AX

1992

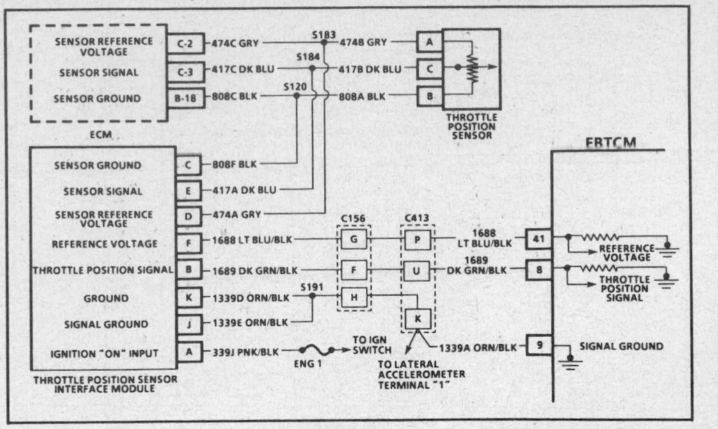
SENSOR REFERENCE VOLTAGE
SENSOR SIGNAL
SENSOR GROUND
ECM
C-2
C-3
B-18
474C GRY
417C DK BLU
808C BLK
S183
S184
S120
474B GRY
417B DK BLU
808A BLK
THROTTLE POSITION SENSOR
EBTCM
SENSOR GROUND
SENSOR SIGNAL
SENSOR REFERENCE VOLTAGE
REFERENCE VOLTAGE
THROTTLE POSITION SIGNAL
GROUND
SIGNAL GROUND
IGNITION "ON" INPUT
THROTTLE POSITION SENSOR INTERFACE MODULE
808F BLK
417A DK BLU
474A GRY
1688 LT BLU/BLK
1689 DK GRN/BLK
1339D ORN/BLK
1339E ORN/BLK
339J PNK/BLK
C156
C413
S191
ENG 1
TO IGN SWITCH
TO LATERAL ACCELEROMETER TERMINAL "1"
1339A ORN/BLK
REFERENCE VOLTAGE
THROTTLE POSITION SIGNAL
SIGNAL GROUND

DTC 64

THROTTLE POSITION SIGNAL MALFUNCTION LT1 ONLY

Circuit Description:

The throttle position signal circuit is used by the EBTCM to monitor the actual throttle position versus desired throttle position to monitor and control engine torque during an ASR event. The Throttle Position Sensor Interface Module is used to allow EBTCM monitoring of the TP sensor signal without affecting the TP sensor signal to the ECM.

DTC 64 will set if the EBTCM is not receiving reference voltage or a TP sensor signal from the Throttle Position Sensor Interface Module.

Test Description: Number(s) below refer to circled number(s) on the diagnostic chart.

1. Checks for TP sensor-related ECM DTCs. Many of the same conditions which could cause an ASR DTC 64 will also cause ECM DTCs. The ECM DTCs should be repaired first to eliminate those problems from affecting the ASR DTC 64 condition.
2. Checks for a lateral accelerometer DTC 75. Since the lateral Accelerometer and the TP Sensor Interface Module share the same ground, a DTC 75 likely indicates an open in CKT 1339.
3. Checks for a short to ground in CKT 1689.
4. Checks for a short to ground in CKT 1688.
5. Checks for proper voltage in CKT 1688 at the EBTCM connection. (This voltage measurement is only appropriate when the EBTCM is disconnected from the circuit).
6. Checks for proper voltage in CKT 1689 at the EBTCM connection. (This voltage measurement is only appropriate when the EBTCM is disconnected from the circuit).
7. Checks for an additional DTC 64 problem after ground CKT 1339 is repaired.
8. Determines if a problem found in Step 5 is due to a fuse, CKT 339J, or CKT 1688.
9. Determines if a problem found in Steps 5 and 13 is due to an open in CKT 1688 or a malfunctioning TP Sensor Interface Module.

1993

GC402930043200BX

Fig. 68 Code 64: Throttle Position Signal Fault (Part 1 of 3). 1992–93 LT1

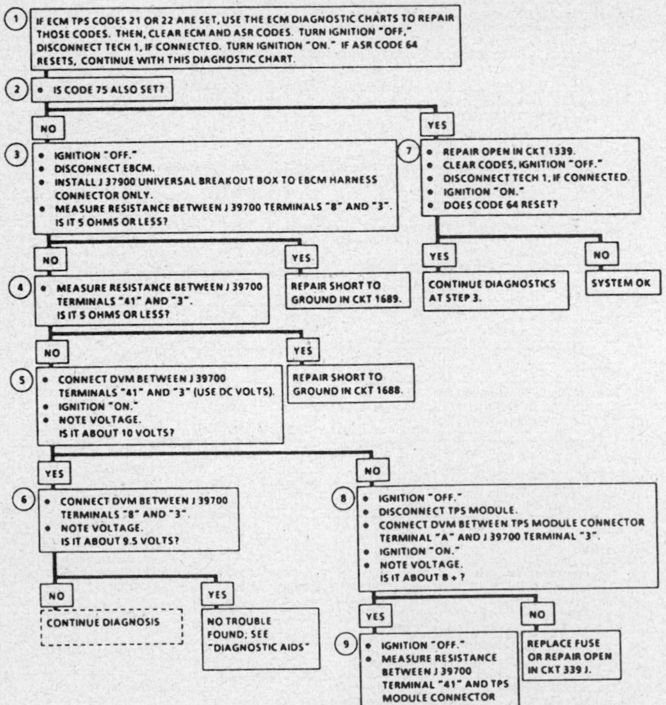
1 IF ECM TPS CODES 21 OR 22 ARE SET, USE THE ECM DIAGNOSTIC CHARTS TO REPAIR THOSE CODES. THEN, CLEAR ECM AND ASR CODES. TURN IGNITION "OFF," DISCONNECT TECH 1, IF CONNECTED. TURN IGNITION "ON." IF ASR CODE 64 RESETS, CONTINUE WITH THIS DIAGNOSTIC CHART.
2 • IS CODE 75 ALSO SET?
NO
YES
3 • IGNITION "OFF." • DISCONNECT EBCM. • INSTALL J 37900 UNIVERSAL BREAKOUT BOX TO EBCM HARNESS CONNECTOR ONLY. • MEASURE RESISTANCE BETWEEN J 39700 TERMINALS "8" AND "3". IS IT 5 OHMS OR LESS?
7 • REPAIR OPEN IN CKT 1339. • CLEAR CODES, IGNITION "OFF." • DISCONNECT TECH 1, IF CONNECTED. • IGNITION "ON." • DOES CODE 64 RESET?
NO
YES
REPAIR SHORT TO GROUND IN CKT 1689.
YES
NO
CONTINUE DIAGNOSTICS AT STEP 3.
SYSTEM OK
4 • MEASURE RESISTANCE BETWEEN J 39700 TERMINALS "41" AND "3". IS IT 5 OHMS OR LESS?
NO
YES
REPAIR SHORT TO GROUND IN CKT 1688.
5 • CONNECT DVM BETWEEN J 39700 TERMINALS "41" AND "3" (USE DC VOLTS). • IGNITION "ON." • NOTE VOLTAGE. IS IT ABOUT 10 VOLTS?
YES
NO
6 • CONNECT DVM BETWEEN J 39700 TERMINALS "8" AND "3". • NOTE VOLTAGE. IS IT ABOUT 9.5 VOLTS?
8 • IGNITION "OFF." • DISCONNECT TPS MODULE. • CONNECT DVM BETWEEN TPS MODULE CONNECTOR TERMINAL "A" AND J 39700 TERMINAL "3". • IGNITION "ON." • NOTE VOLTAGE. IS IT ABOUT B + ?
NO
YES
CONTINUE DIAGNOSIS
NO TROUBLE FOUND; SEE "DIAGNOSTIC AIDS"
YES
NO
9 • IGNITION "OFF." • MEASURE RESISTANCE BETWEEN J 39700 TERMINAL "41" AND TPS MODULE CONNECTOR TERMINAL "F". • IS IT 5 OHMS OR LESS?
REPLACE FUSE OR REPAIR OPEN IN CKT 339 J.
YES
NO
REPLACE TPS MODULE
REPAIR OPEN IN CKT 1688.

GC402920043200CX

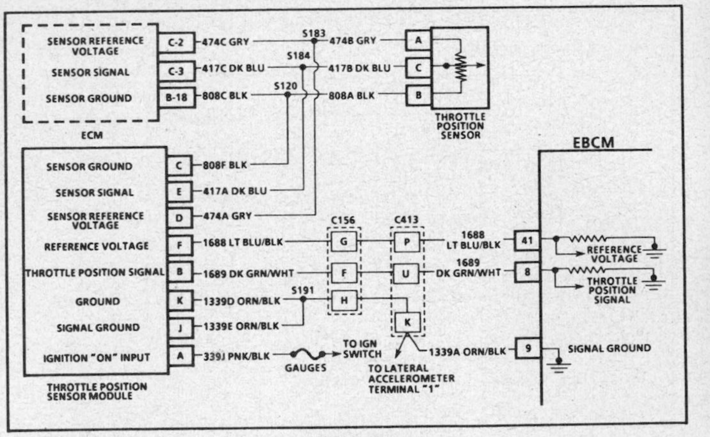
SENSOR REFERENCE VOLTAGE
SENSOR SIGNAL
SENSOR GROUND
ECM
C-2
C-3
B-18
474C GRY
417C DK BLU
808C BLK
S183
S184
S120
474B GRY
417B DK BLU
808A BLK
THROTTLE POSITION SENSOR
EBCM
SENSOR GROUND
SENSOR SIGNAL
SENSOR REFERENCE VOLTAGE
REFERENCE VOLTAGE
THROTTLE POSITION SIGNAL
GROUND
SIGNAL GROUND
IGNITION "ON" INPUT
THROTTLE POSITION SENSOR MODULE
808F BLK
417A DK BLU
474A GRY
1688 LT BLU/BLK
1689 DK GRN/WHT
1339D ORN/BLK
1339E ORN/BLK
339J PNK/BLK
C156
C413
S191
GAUGES
TO IGN SWITCH
TO LATERAL ACCELEROMETER TERMINAL "1"
1339A ORN/BLK
REFERENCE VOLTAGE
THROTTLE POSITION SIGNAL
SIGNAL GROUND

CODE 64

THROTTLE POSITION SIGNAL FAULT LT1 ONLY

Circuit Description:

The Throttle Position Signal circuit is used by the EBCM to monitor the actual throttle position versus desired throttle position to monitor and control engine torque during an ASR event. The Throttle Position Sensor Module is used to allow EBCM monitoring of the TPS signal without affecting the TPS signal to the ECM.

Code 64 will set if the EBCM is not receiving reference voltage or a TPS signal from the Throttle Position Sensor Module.

Test Description: Number(s) below refer to circled number(s) on the diagnostic chart.

10. Checks for an open in CKT 1689.
11. Checks for TPS reference voltage from the ECM at the TPS Module connector.
12. Checks for TPS signal voltage on CKT 808F at the TPS Module connector.
13. Checks for an open in TPS signal ground CKT 474A to the TPS Module connector.
14. Checks for an open in signal ground CKT 1339 to the TPS Module connector.
15. Checks for Code 64 reset after most system components have checked OK.
16. Replaces TPS Module as likely cause of Code reset in Step 15. If the code resets again, the EBCM must be concluding there is a problem present when there is not.

Diagnostic Aids:

It is very important that a thorough inspection of the wiring and connectors be performed. Failure to carefully and fully inspect wiring and connectors may result in misdiagnosis, causing part replacement with reappearance of the fault.

1992

GC402920043200DX

Fig. 68 Code 64: Throttle Position Signal Fault (Part 2 of 3). 1992–93 LT1

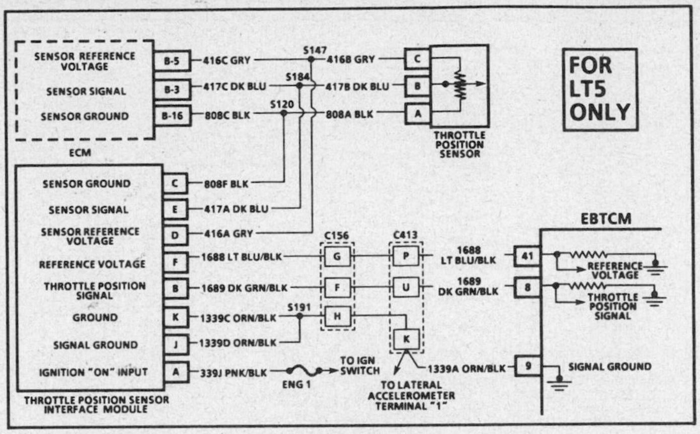
SENSOR REFERENCE VOLTAGE
SENSOR SIGNAL
SENSOR GROUND
ECM
B-5
B-3
B-16
416C GRY
417C DK BLU
808C BLK
S147
S184
S120
416B GRY
417B DK BLU
808A BLK
THROTTLE POSITION SENSOR
FOR LT5 ONLY
SENSOR GROUND
SENSOR SIGNAL
SENSOR REFERENCE VOLTAGE
REFERENCE VOLTAGE
THROTTLE POSITION SIGNAL
GROUND
SIGNAL GROUND
IGNITION "ON" INPUT
808F BLK
417A DK BLU
416A GRY
1688 LT BLU/BLK
1689 DK GRN/BLK
1339C ORN/BLK
1339D ORN/BLK
339J PNK/BLK
C156
C413
S191
ENG 1
TO IGN SWITCH
TO LATERAL ACCELEROMETER TERMINAL "1"
1339A ORN/BLK
EBTCM
REFERENCE VOLTAGE
THROTTLE POSITION SIGNAL
SIGNAL GROUND
THROTTLE POSITION SENSOR INTERFACE MODULE

DTC 64

THROTTLE POSITION SIGNAL MALFUNCTION LT5 ONLY

Circuit Description:

The throttle position signal circuit is used by the EBTCM to monitor the actual throttle position versus desired throttle position to monitor and control engine torque during an ASR event. The Throttle Position Sensor Interface Module is used to allow EBTCM monitoring of the TP sensor signal without affecting the TP sensor signal to the ECM.

DTC 64 will set if the EBTCM is not receiving reference voltage or a TP sensor signal from the Throttle Position Sensor Interface Module.

Test Description: Number(s) below refer to circled number(s) on the diagnostic chart.

10. Checks for an open in CKT 1689.
11. Checks for TP sensor reference voltage from the ECM at the TP Sensor Interface Module connector.
12. Checks for TP sensor signal voltage on CKT 808F at the TP Sensor Interface Module connector.
13. Checks for an open in TP sensor signal ground CKT 416A to the TP Sensor Interface Module connector.
14. Checks for an open in signal ground CKT 1339 to the TP Sensor Interface Module connector.
15. Checks for DTC 64 reset after most system components have checked OK.
16. Replaces TP Sensor Interface Module as likely cause of DTC reset in Step 15. If the DTC resets again, the EBTCM must be concluding there is a problem present when there is not.

Diagnostic Aids:

It is very important that a thorough inspection of the wiring and connectors be performed. Failure to carefully and fully inspect wiring and connectors may result in misdiagnosis, causing part replacement with reappearance of the malfunction.

GC402930043200EX

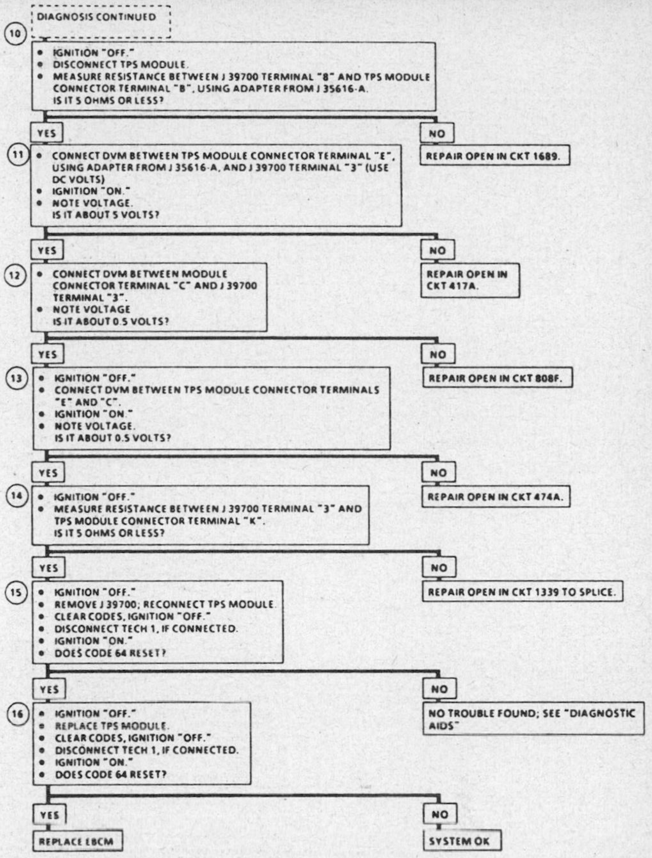
DIAGNOSIS CONTINUED
10
• IGNITION "OFF."
• DISCONNECT TPS MODULE.
• MEASURE RESISTANCE BETWEEN J 39700 TERMINAL "B" AND TPS MODULE CONNECTOR TERMINAL "B", USING ADAPTER FROM J 35616-A.
IS IT 5 OHMS OR LESS?
YES
NO
REPAIR OPEN IN CKT 1689.
11
• CONNECT DVM BETWEEN TPS MODULE CONNECTOR TERMINAL "E", USING ADAPTER FROM J 35616-A, AND J 39700 TERMINAL "3" (USE DC VOLTS)
• IGNITION "ON."
• NOTE VOLTAGE.
IS IT ABOUT 5 VOLTS?
YES
NO
REPAIR OPEN IN CKT 417A.
12
• CONNECT DVM BETWEEN MODULE CONNECTOR TERMINAL "C" AND J 39700 TERMINAL "3".
• NOTE VOLTAGE
IS IT ABOUT 0.5 VOLTS?
YES
NO
REPAIR OPEN IN CKT 808F.
13
• IGNITION "OFF."
• CONNECT DVM BETWEEN TPS MODULE CONNECTOR TERMINALS "E" AND "C".
• IGNITION "ON."
• NOTE VOLTAGE.
IS IT ABOUT 0.5 VOLTS?
YES
NO
REPAIR OPEN IN CKT 474A.
14
• IGNITION "OFF."
• MEASURE RESISTANCE BETWEEN J 39700 TERMINAL "3" AND TPS MODULE CONNECTOR TERMINAL "K".
IS IT 5 OHMS OR LESS?
YES
NO
REPAIR OPEN IN CKT 1339 TO SPLICE.
15
• IGNITION "OFF."
• REMOVE J 39700; RECONNECT TPS MODULE.
• CLEAR CODES, IGNITION "OFF."
• DISCONNECT TECH 1, IF CONNECTED.
• IGNITION "ON."
• DOES CODE 64 RESET?
YES
NO
NO TROUBLE FOUND; SEE "DIAGNOSTIC AIDS"
16
• IGNITION "OFF."
• REPLACE TPS MODULE.
• CLEAR CODES, IGNITION "OFF."
• DISCONNECT TECH 1, IF CONNECTED.
• IGNITION "ON."
• DOES CODE 64 RESET?
YES
NO
REPLACE EBCM
SYSTEM OK

GC402920043200FX

1993

Fig. 68 Code 64: Throttle Position Signal Fault (Part 2 of 3). 1992–93 LT1

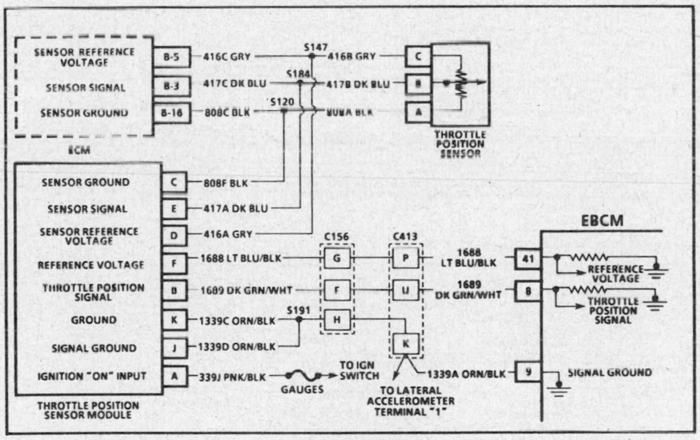
SENSOR REFERENCE VOLTAGE
SENSOR SIGNAL
SENSOR GROUND
ECM
B-5
B-3
B-16
416C GRY
417C DK BLU
808C BLK
S147
S184
S120
416B GRY
417B DK BLU
THROTTLE POSITION SENSOR
SENSOR GROUND
SENSOR SIGNAL
SENSOR REFERENCE VOLTAGE
REFERENCE VOLTAGE
THROTTLE POSITION SIGNAL
GROUND
SIGNAL GROUND
IGNITION "ON" INPUT
808F BLK
417A DK BLU
416A GRY
1688 LT BLU/BLK
1689 DK GRN/WHT
1339C ORN/BLK
1339D ORN/BLK
339J PNK/BLK
C156
C413
S191
GAUGES
TO IGN SWITCH
TO LATERAL ACCELEROMETER TERMINAL "1"
1339A ORN/BLK
EBCM
REFERENCE VOLTAGE
THROTTLE POSITION SIGNAL
SIGNAL GROUND
THROTTLE POSITION SENSOR MODULE

CODE 64

THROTTLE POSITION SIGNAL FAULT LT5 ONLY

Circuit Description:

The Throttle Position Signal circuit is used by the EBCM to monitor the actual throttle position versus desired throttle position to monitor and control engine torque during an ASR event. The Throttle Position Sensor Module is used to allow EBCM monitoring of the TPS signal without affecting the TPS signal to the ECM.

Code 64 will set if the EBCM is not receiving reference voltage or a TPS signal from the Throttle Position Sensor Module.

Test Description: Number(s) below refer to circled number(s) on the diagnostic chart.

1. Checks for TPS-related ECM trouble codes. Many of the same conditions which could cause an ASR Code 64 will also cause ECM codes. The ECM codes should be repaired first to eliminate those problems from affecting the ASR Code 64 condition.
2. Checks for an Lateral Accelerometer Code 75. Since the Lateral Accelerometer and the TPS Module share the same ground, a Code 75 likely indicates an open in CKT 1339.
3. Checks for a short to ground in CKT 1689.
4. Checks for a short to ground in CKT 1688.
5. Checks for proper voltage in CKT 1688 at the EBCM connection. (This voltage measurement is only appropriate when the EBCM is disconnected from the circuit).
6. Checks for proper voltage in CKT 1689 at the EBCM connection. (This voltage measurement is only appropriate when the EBCM is disconnected from the circuit).
7. Checks for an additional Code 64 problem after ground CKT 1339 is repaired.
8. Determines if a problem found in Step 5 is due to a fuse, CKT 339J, or CKT 1688.
9. Determines if a problem found in Steps 5 and 13 is due to an open in CKT 1688 or a faulty TPS Module.

GC402930043300AX

1992

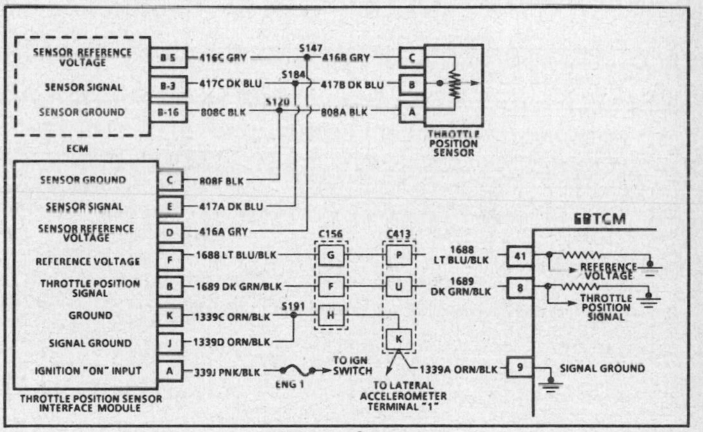
SENSOR REFERENCE VOLTAGE
SENSOR SIGNAL
SENSOR GROUND
ECM
416C GRY
417C DK BLU
808C BLK
S147
S184
S120
416B GRY
417B DK BLU
808A BLK
THROTTLE POSITION SENSOR
SENSOR GROUND
SENSOR SIGNAL
SENSOR REFERENCE VOLTAGE
REFERENCE VOLTAGE
THROTTLE POSITION SIGNAL
GROUND
SIGNAL GROUND
IGNITION "ON" INPUT
808F BLK
417A DK BLU
416A GRY
1688 LT BLU/BLK
1689 DK GRN/BLK
1339C ORN/BLK
1339D ORN/BLK
339J PNK/BLK
C156
C413
S191
ENG 1
TO IGN SWITCH
TO LATERAL ACCELEROMETER TERMINAL "1"
1339A ORN/BLK
EBTCM
REFERENCE VOLTAGE
THROTTLE POSITION SIGNAL
SIGNAL GROUND
THROTTLE POSITION SENSOR INTERFACE MODULE

DTC 64

THROTTLE POSITION SIGNAL MALFUNCTION LT5 ONLY

Circuit Description:

The throttle position signal circuit is used by the EBTCM to monitor the actual throttle position versus desired throttle position to monitor and control engine torque during an ASR event. The throttle position sensor interface module is used to allow EBTCM monitoring of the TP sensor signal without affecting the TP sensor signal to the ECM.

DTC 64 will set if the EBTCM is not receiving reference voltage or a TP sensor signal from the Throttle Position Sensor Interface Module.

Test Description: Number(s) below refer to circled number(s) on the diagnostic chart.

1. Checks for TP sensor-related ECM DTCs. Many of the same conditions which could cause an ASR DTC 64 will also cause ECM DTCs. The ECM DTCs should be repaired first to eliminate those problems from affecting the ASR DTC 64 condition.
2. Checks for an lateral accelerometer DTC 75. Since the lateral accelerometer and the TP Sensor Interface Module share the same ground, a DTC 75 likely indicates an open in CKT 1339.
3. Checks for a short to ground in CKT 1689.
4. Checks for a short to ground in CKT 1688.
5. Checks for proper voltage in CKT 1688 at the EBTCM connection. (This voltage measurement is only appropriate when the EBTCM is disconnected from the circuit).
6. Checks for proper voltage in CKT 1689 at the EBTCM connection. (This voltage measurement is only appropriate when the EBTCM is disconnected from the circuit).
7. Checks for an additional DTC 64 problem after ground CKT 1339 is repaired.
8. Determines if a problem found in Step 5 is due to a fuse, CKT 339J, or CKT 1688.
9. Determines if a problem found in Steps 5 and 13 is due to an open in CKT 1688 or a malfunctioning TP Sensor Interface Module.

GC402930043300BX

1993

Fig. 69 Code 64: Throttle Position Signal Fault (Part 1 of 3). 1992–93 LT5

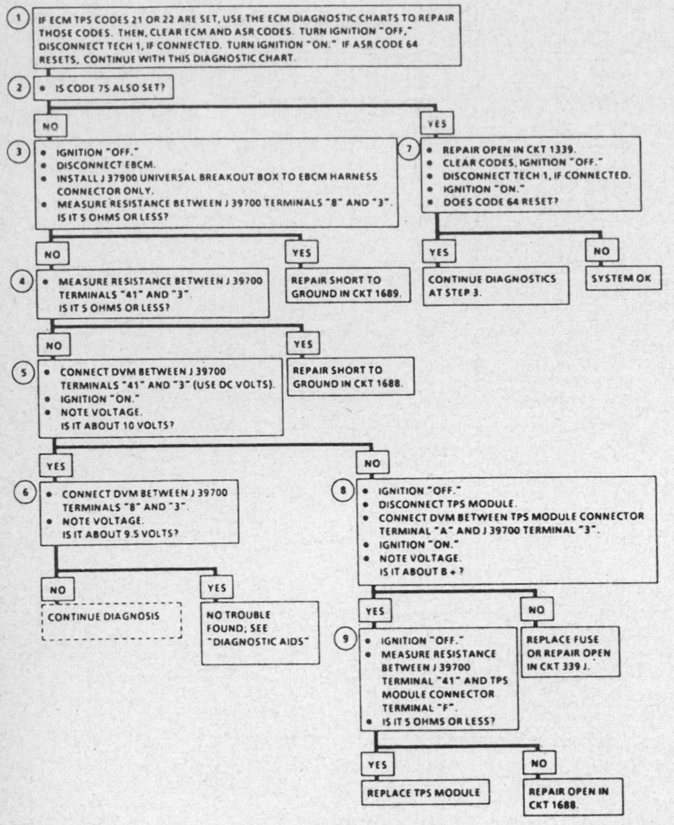
1 IF ECM TPS CODES 21 OR 22 ARE SET, USE THE ECM DIAGNOSTIC CHARTS TO REPAIR THOSE CODES. THEN, CLEAR ECM AND ASR CODES. TURN IGNITION "OFF," DISCONNECT TECH 1, IF CONNECTED. TURN IGNITION "ON." IF ASR CODE 64 RESETS, CONTINUE WITH THIS DIAGNOSTIC CHART.
2 • IS CODE 75 ALSO SET?
NO
YES
3 • IGNITION "OFF." • DISCONNECT EBCM. • INSTALL J 37900 UNIVERSAL BREAKOUT BOX TO EBCM HARNESS CONNECTOR ONLY. • MEASURE RESISTANCE BETWEEN J 39700 TERMINALS "8" AND "3". IS IT 5 OHMS OR LESS?
7 • REPAIR OPEN IN CKT 1339. • CLEAR CODES, IGNITION "OFF." • DISCONNECT TECH 1, IF CONNECTED. • IGNITION "ON." • DOES CODE 64 RESET?
NO
YES
YES
NO
4 • MEASURE RESISTANCE BETWEEN J 39700 TERMINALS "41" AND "3". IS IT 5 OHMS OR LESS?
REPAIR SHORT TO GROUND IN CKT 1689.
CONTINUE DIAGNOSTICS AT STEP 3.
SYSTEM OK
NO
YES
5 • CONNECT DVM BETWEEN J 39700 TERMINALS "41" AND "3" (USE DC VOLTS). • IGNITION "ON." • NOTE VOLTAGE. IS IT ABOUT 10 VOLTS?
REPAIR SHORT TO GROUND IN CKT 1688.
YES
NO
6 • CONNECT DVM BETWEEN J 39700 TERMINALS "8" AND "3". • NOTE VOLTAGE. IS IT ABOUT 9.5 VOLTS?
8 • IGNITION "OFF." • DISCONNECT TPS MODULE. • CONNECT DVM BETWEEN TPS MODULE CONNECTOR TERMINAL "A" AND J 39700 TERMINAL "3". • IGNITION "ON." • NOTE VOLTAGE. IS IT ABOUT B+?
NO
YES
CONTINUE DIAGNOSIS
NO TROUBLE FOUND; SEE "DIAGNOSTIC AIDS"
YES
NO
9 • IGNITION "OFF." • MEASURE RESISTANCE BETWEEN J 39700 TERMINAL "41" AND TPS MODULE CONNECTOR TERMINAL "F". • IS IT 5 OHMS OR LESS?
REPLACE FUSE OR REPAIR OPEN IN CKT 339J.
YES
NO
REPLACE TPS MODULE
REPAIR OPEN IN CKT 1688.
GC402920043300CX

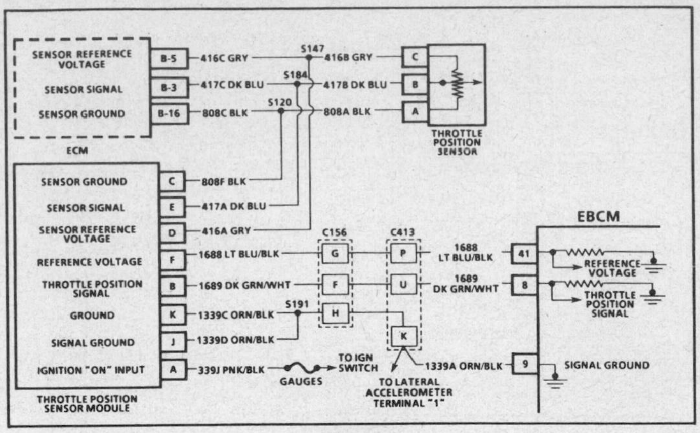
SENSOR REFERENCE VOLTAGE
SENSOR SIGNAL
SENSOR GROUND
B-5
B-3
B-16
416C GRY
417C DK BLU
808C BLK
S147
S184
S120
416B GRY
417B DK BLU
808A BLK
C
B
A
THROTTLE POSITION SENSOR
ECM
SENSOR GROUND
SENSOR SIGNAL
SENSOR REFERENCE VOLTAGE
REFERENCE VOLTAGE
THROTTLE POSITION SIGNAL
GROUND
SIGNAL GROUND
IGNITION "ON" INPUT
C
E
D
F
B
K
J
A
808F BLK
417A DK BLU
416A GRY
1688 LT BLU/BLK
1689 DK GRN/WHT
1339C ORN/BLK
1339D ORN/BLK
339J PNK/BLK
C156
C413
G
P
F
U
H
K
S191
GAUGES
TO IGN SWITCH
TO LATERAL ACCELEROMETER TERMINAL "1"
1339A ORN/BLK
1688 LT BLU/BLK
1689 DK GRN/WHT
41
8
9
EBCM
REFERENCE VOLTAGE
THROTTLE POSITION SIGNAL
SIGNAL GROUND
THROTTLE POSITION SENSOR MODULE

CODE 64
THROTTLE POSITION SIGNAL FAULT LT5 ONLY

Circuit Description:

The Throttle Position Signal circuit is used by the EBCM to monitor the actual throttle position versus desired throttle position to monitor and control engine torque during an ASR event. The Throttle Position Sensor Module is used to allow EBCM monitoring of the TPS signal without affecting the TPS signal to the ECM.

Code 64 will set if the EBCM is not receiving reference voltage or a TPS signal from the Throttle Position Sensor Module.

Test Description: Number(s) below refer to circled number(s) on the diagnostic chart.

10. Checks for an open in CKT 1689.
11. Checks for TPS reference voltage from the ECM at the TPS Module connector.
12. Checks for TPS signal voltage on CKT 808F at the TPS Module connector.
13. Checks for an open in TPS signal ground CKT 416A to the TPS Module connector.
14. Checks for an open in signal ground CKT 1339 to the TPS Module connector.
15. Checks for Code 64 reset after most system components have checked OK.
16. Replaces TPS Module as likely cause of Code reset in Step 15. If the code resets again, the EBCM must be concluding there is a problem present when there is not.

Diagnostic Aids:

It is very important that a thorough inspection of the wiring and connectors be performed. Failure to carefully and fully inspect wiring and connectors may result in misdiagnosis, causing part replacement with reappearance of the fault.

GC402920043300DX

1992

Fig. 69 Code 64: Throttle Position Signal Fault (Part 2 of 3). 1992–93 LT5

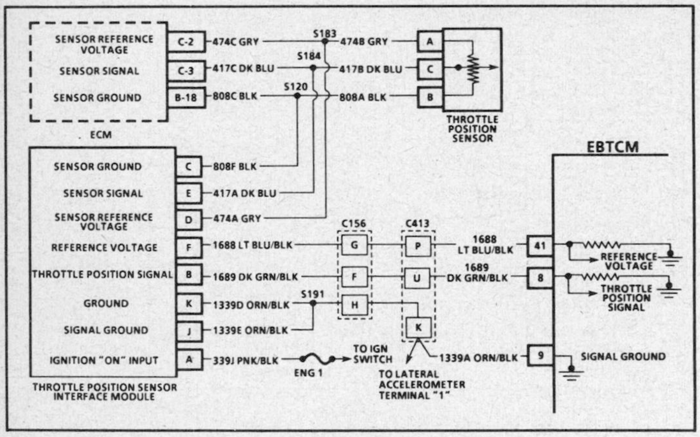
SENSOR REFERENCE VOLTAGE
SENSOR SIGNAL
SENSOR GROUND
C-2
C-3
B-18
474C GRY
417C DK BLU
808C BLK
S183
S184
S120
474B GRY
417B DK BLU
808A BLK
A
C
B
THROTTLE POSITION SENSOR
ECM
EBTCM
SENSOR GROUND
SENSOR SIGNAL
SENSOR REFERENCE VOLTAGE
REFERENCE VOLTAGE
THROTTLE POSITION SIGNAL
GROUND
SIGNAL GROUND
IGNITION "ON" INPUT
808F BLK
417A DK BLU
474A GRY
1688 LT BLU/BLK
1689 DK GRN/BLK
1339D ORN/BLK
1339E ORN/BLK
339J PNK/BLK
C156
C413
S191
ENG 1
TO IGN SWITCH
TO LATERAL ACCELEROMETER TERMINAL "1"
1339A ORN/BLK
1688 LT BLU/BLK
1689 DK GRN/BLK
41
8
9
REFERENCE VOLTAGE
THROTTLE POSITION SIGNAL
SIGNAL GROUND
THROTTLE POSITION SENSOR INTERFACE MODULE

DTC 64
THROTTLE POSITION SIGNAL MALFUNCTION LT1 ONLY

Circuit Description:

The throttle position signal circuit is used by the EBTCM to monitor the actual throttle position versus desired throttle position to monitor and control engine torque during an ASR event. The throttle position sensor module is used to allow EBTCM monitoring of the TP sensor signal without affecting the TP sensor signal to the ECM.

DTC 64 will set if the EBTCM is not receiving reference voltage or a TP sensor signal from the Throttle Position Sensor Interface Module.

Test Description: Number(s) below refer to circled number(s) on the diagnostic chart.

10. Checks for an open in CKT 1689.
11. Checks for TP sensor reference voltage from the ECM at the TP Sensor Interface Module connector.
12. Checks for TP sensor signal voltage on CKT 808F at the TP sensor interface module connector.
13. Checks for an open in TP sensor signal ground CKT 474A to the TP Sensor Interface Module connector.
14. Checks for an open in signal ground CKT 1339 to the TP Sensor Interface Module connector.
15. Checks for DTC 64 reset after most system components have checked OK.
16. Replaces TP Sensor Interface Module as likely cause of DTC reset in Step 15. If the DTC resets again, the EBTCM must be concluding there is a problem present when there is not.

Diagnostic Aids:

It is very important that a thorough inspection of the wiring and connectors be performed. Failure to carefully and fully inspect wiring and connectors may result in misdiagnosis, causing part replacement with reappearance of the malfunction.

GC402930043300EX

1993

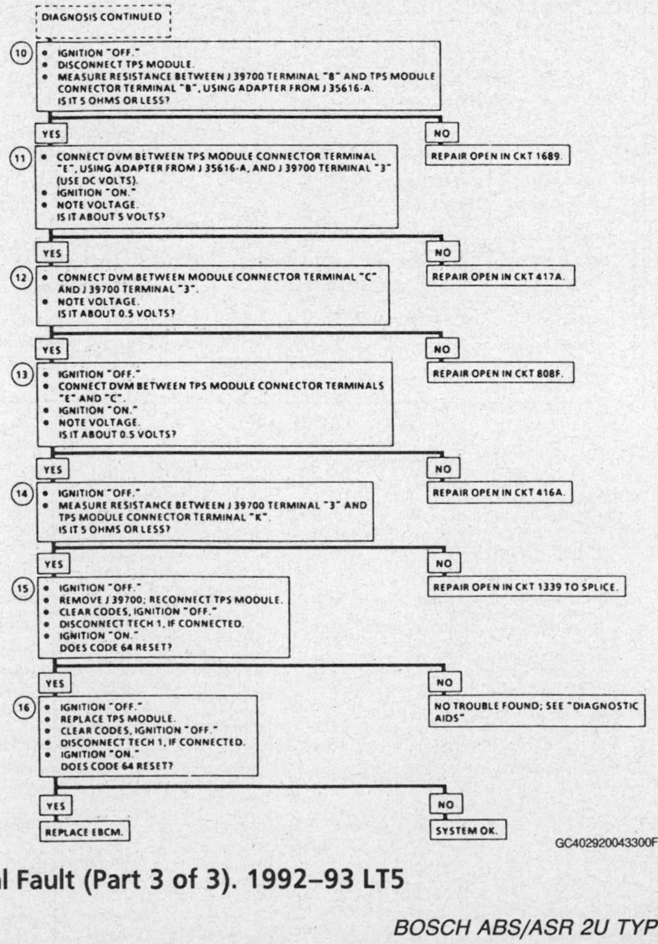
DIAGNOSIS CONTINUED
10 • IGNITION "OFF." • DISCONNECT TPS MODULE. • MEASURE RESISTANCE BETWEEN J 39700 TERMINAL "8" AND TPS MODULE CONNECTOR TERMINAL "B", USING ADAPTER FROM J 35616-A. IS IT 5 OHMS OR LESS?
YES
NO
REPAIR OPEN IN CKT 1689.
11 • CONNECT DVM BETWEEN TPS MODULE CONNECTOR TERMINAL "E", USING ADAPTER FROM J 35616-A, AND J 39700 TERMINAL "3" (USE DC VOLTS). • IGNITION "ON." • NOTE VOLTAGE. IS IT ABOUT 5 VOLTS?
YES
NO
REPAIR OPEN IN CKT 417A.
12 • CONNECT DVM BETWEEN MODULE CONNECTOR TERMINAL "C" AND J 39700 TERMINAL "3". • NOTE VOLTAGE. IS IT ABOUT 0.5 VOLTS?
YES
NO
REPAIR OPEN IN CKT 808F.
13 • IGNITION "OFF." • CONNECT DVM BETWEEN TPS MODULE CONNECTOR TERMINALS "E" AND "C". • IGNITION "ON." • NOTE VOLTAGE. IS IT ABOUT 0.5 VOLTS?
YES
NO
REPAIR OPEN IN CKT 416A.
14 • IGNITION "OFF." • MEASURE RESISTANCE BETWEEN J 39700 TERMINAL "3" AND TPS MODULE CONNECTOR TERMINAL "K". IS IT 5 OHMS OR LESS?
YES
NO
REPAIR OPEN IN CKT 1339 TO SPLICE.
15 • IGNITION "OFF." • REMOVE J 39700; RECONNECT TPS MODULE. • CLEAR CODES, IGNITION "OFF." • DISCONNECT TECH 1, IF CONNECTED. • IGNITION "ON." DOES CODE 64 RESET?
YES
NO
NO TROUBLE FOUND; SEE "DIAGNOSTIC AIDS"
16 • IGNITION "OFF." • REPLACE TPS MODULE. • CLEAR CODES, IGNITION "OFF." • DISCONNECT TECH 1, IF CONNECTED. • IGNITION "ON." DOES CODE 64 RESET?
YES
NO
REPLACE EBCM.
SYSTEM OK.
GC402920043300FX

Fig. 69 Code 64: Throttle Position Signal Fault (Part 3 of 3). 1992–93 LT5

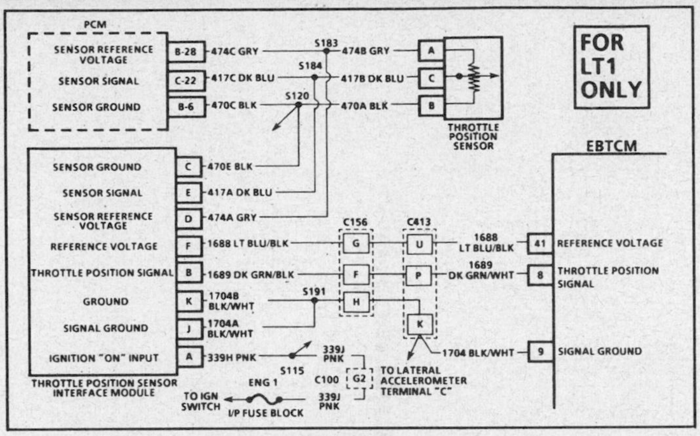
PCM
SENSOR REFERENCE VOLTAGE
SENSOR SIGNAL
SENSOR GROUND
B-28
C-22
B-6
474C GRY
417C DK BLU
470C BLK
S183
S184
S120
474B GRY
417B DK BLU
470A BLK
A
C
B
THROTTLE POSITION SENSOR
FOR LT1 ONLY
EBTCM
SENSOR GROUND
SENSOR SIGNAL
SENSOR REFERENCE VOLTAGE
REFERENCE VOLTAGE
THROTTLE POSITION SIGNAL
GROUND
SIGNAL GROUND
IGNITION "ON" INPUT
470E BLK
417A DK BLU
474A GRY
1688 LT BLU/BLK
1689 DK GRN/BLK
1704B BLK/WHT
1704A BLK/WHT
339H PNK
S191
C156
C413
G
F
H
U
P
K
1688 LT BLU/BLK
1689 DK GRN/WHT
1704 BLK/WHT
41
8
9
REFERENCE VOLTAGE
THROTTLE POSITION SIGNAL
SIGNAL GROUND
339J PNK
S115
C100
G2
TO LATERAL ACCELEROMETER TERMINAL "C"
ENG 1
TO IGN SWITCH
I/P FUSE BLOCK
THROTTLE POSITION SENSOR INTERFACE MODULE

DTC 64

Circuit Description:

The throttle position signal circuit is used by the EBTCM to monitor the actual throttle position versus desired throttle position to monitor and control engine torque during an ASR event. The throttle position sensor interface module is used to allow EBTCM monitoring of the TP sensor signal without affecting the TP sensor signal to the PCM.

DTC Will Set When: The EBTCM is not receiving reference voltage or a TP sensor signal from the throttle position sensor interface module.

DTC Chart Test Description: Number(s) below refer to circled number(s) on the diagnostic chart.

1. Checks for TP sensor-related PCM DTCs. Many of the same conditions which could cause an ASR DTC 64 will also cause PCM DTCs. The PCM DTCs should be repaired first to eliminate those malfunctions from affecting the ASR DTC 64 condition.
2. Checks for a lateral accelerometer DTC 75. Since the lateral accelerometer and the TP sensor interface module share the same ground, a DTC 75 likely indicates an open in CKT 1704.
3. Checks for a short to ground in CKT 1689.
4. Checks for a short to ground in CKT 1688.
5. Checks for proper voltage in CKT 1688 at the EBTCM connection. (This voltage measurement is only appropriate when the EBTCM is disconnected from the circuit.)
6. Checks for proper voltage in CKT 1689 at the EBTCM connection. (This voltage measurement is only appropriate when the EBTCM is disconnected from the circuit.)
7. Checks for an additional DTC 64 malfunction after ground CKT 1704 is repaired.
8. Determines if a malfunction found in Step 5 is due to a fuse, CKT 339, or CKT 1688.
9. Determines if a malfunction found in Steps 5 and 13 is due to an open in CKT 1688 or a malfunctioning TP sensor interface module.

GC402940088101AX

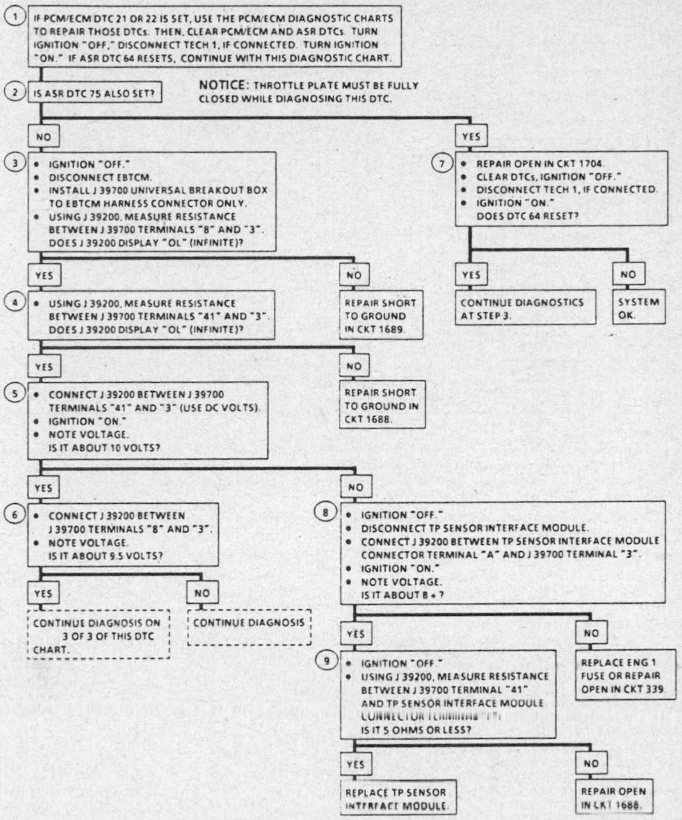
1
IF PCM/ECM DTC 21 OR 22 IS SET, USE THE PCM/ECM DIAGNOSTIC CHARTS TO REPAIR THOSE DTCs. THEN, CLEAR PCM/ECM AND ASR DTCs. TURN IGNITION "OFF," DISCONNECT TECH 1, IF CONNECTED. TURN IGNITION "ON." IF ASR DTC 64 RESETS, CONTINUE WITH THIS DIAGNOSTIC CHART.
2
IS ASR DTC 75 ALSO SET?
NOTICE: THROTTLE PLATE MUST BE FULLY CLOSED WHILE DIAGNOSING THIS DTC.
NO
YES
3
• IGNITION "OFF."
• DISCONNECT EBTCM.
• INSTALL J 39700 UNIVERSAL BREAKOUT BOX TO EBTCM HARNESS CONNECTOR ONLY.
• USING J 39200, MEASURE RESISTANCE BETWEEN J 39700 TERMINALS "8" AND "3". DOES J 39200 DISPLAY "OL" (INFINITE)?
7
• REPAIR OPEN IN CKT 1704.
• CLEAR DTCs, IGNITION "OFF."
• DISCONNECT TECH 1, IF CONNECTED.
• IGNITION "ON." DOES DTC 64 RESET?
YES
NO
YES
NO
REPAIR SHORT TO GROUND IN CKT 1689.
CONTINUE DIAGNOSTICS AT STEP 3.
SYSTEM OK.
4
• USING J 39200, MEASURE RESISTANCE BETWEEN J 39700 TERMINALS "41" AND "3". DOES J 39200 DISPLAY "OL" (INFINITE)?
YES
NO
REPAIR SHORT TO GROUND IN CKT 1688.
5
• CONNECT J 39200 BETWEEN J 39700 TERMINALS "41" AND "3" (USE DC VOLTS).
• IGNITION "ON."
• NOTE VOLTAGE. IS IT ABOUT 10 VOLTS?
YES
NO
6
• CONNECT J 39200 BETWEEN J 39700 TERMINALS "8" AND "3".
• NOTE VOLTAGE. IS IT ABOUT 9.5 VOLTS?
8
• IGNITION "OFF."
• DISCONNECT TP SENSOR INTERFACE MODULE.
• CONNECT J 39200 BETWEEN TP SENSOR INTERFACE MODULE CONNECTOR TERMINAL "A" AND J 39700 TERMINAL "3".
• IGNITION "ON."
• NOTE VOLTAGE. IS IT ABOUT B + ?
YES
NO
CONTINUE DIAGNOSIS ON 3 OF 3 OF THIS DTC CHART.
CONTINUE DIAGNOSIS
YES
NO
9
• IGNITION "OFF."
• USING J 39200, MEASURE RESISTANCE BETWEEN J 39700 TERMINAL "41" AND TP SENSOR INTERFACE MODULE
IS IT 5 OHMS OR LESS?
REPLACE ENG 1 FUSE OR REPAIR OPEN IN CKT 339.
YES
NO
REPLACE TP SENSOR INTERFACE MODULE.
REPAIR OPEN IN CKT 1688.

GC402940088101BX

Fig. 70 Code 64: Throttle Position Signal Fault (Part 1 of 3). 1994 LT1

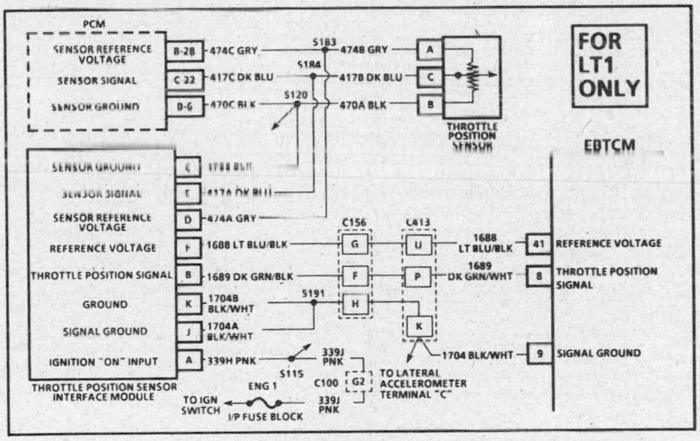
PCM
SENSOR REFERENCE VOLTAGE
SENSOR SIGNAL
B-28
C 22
B-6
474C GRY
417C DK BLU
S183
S184
S120
474B GRY
417B DK BLU
470A BLK
A
C
B
THROTTLE POSITION
FOR LT1 ONLY
EBTCM
SENSOR REFERENCE VOLTAGE
REFERENCE VOLTAGE
THROTTLE POSITION SIGNAL
GROUND
SIGNAL GROUND
IGNITION "ON" INPUT
474A GRY
1688 LT BLU/BLK
1689 DK GRN/BLK
1704B BLK/WHT
1704A BLK/WHT
339H PNK
S191
C156
C413
G
F
H
U
P
K
1688 LT BLU/BLK
1689 DK GRN/WHT
1704 BLK/WHT
41
8
9
REFERENCE VOLTAGE
THROTTLE POSITION SIGNAL
SIGNAL GROUND
339J PNK
S115
C100
G2
TO LATERAL ACCELEROMETER TERMINAL "C"
ENG 1
TO IGN SWITCH
I/P FUSE BLOCK
THROTTLE POSITION SENSOR INTERFACE MODULE

DTC 64

(Page 2 of 3)

THROTTLE POSITION SIGNAL MALFUNCTION

LT1 ONLY

Circuit Description:

The throttle position signal circuit is used by the EBTCM to monitor the actual throttle position versus desired throttle position to monitor and control engine torque during an ASR event. The throttle position sensor module is used to allow EBTCM monitoring of the TP sensor signal without affecting the TP sensor signal to the PCM.

DTC Will Set When: The EBTCM is not receiving reference voltage or a TP sensor signal from the throttle position sensor interface module.

DTC Chart Test Description: Number(s) below refer to circled number(s) on the diagnostic chart.

10. Checks for an open in CKT 1689.
11. Checks for TP sensor reference voltage from the PCM at the TP sensor interface module connector.
12. Checks for TP sensor signal voltage on CKT 417A at the TP sensor interface module connector.
13. Checks for an open in TP sensor signal ground CKT 470E to the TP sensor interface module connector.
14. Checks for an open in signal ground CKT 1704 to the TP sensor interface module connector.
15. Checks for DTC 64 reset after most system components have checked OK.
16. Replaces TP sensor interface module as likely cause of DTC reset in Step 15. If the DTC resets again, the EBTCM must be concluding there is a malfunction present when there is not.

Diagnostic Aids: It is very important that a thorough inspection of the wiring and connectors be performed. Failure to carefully and fully inspect wiring and connectors may result in misdiagnosis, causing part replacement with reappearance of the malfunction.

GC402940088102AX

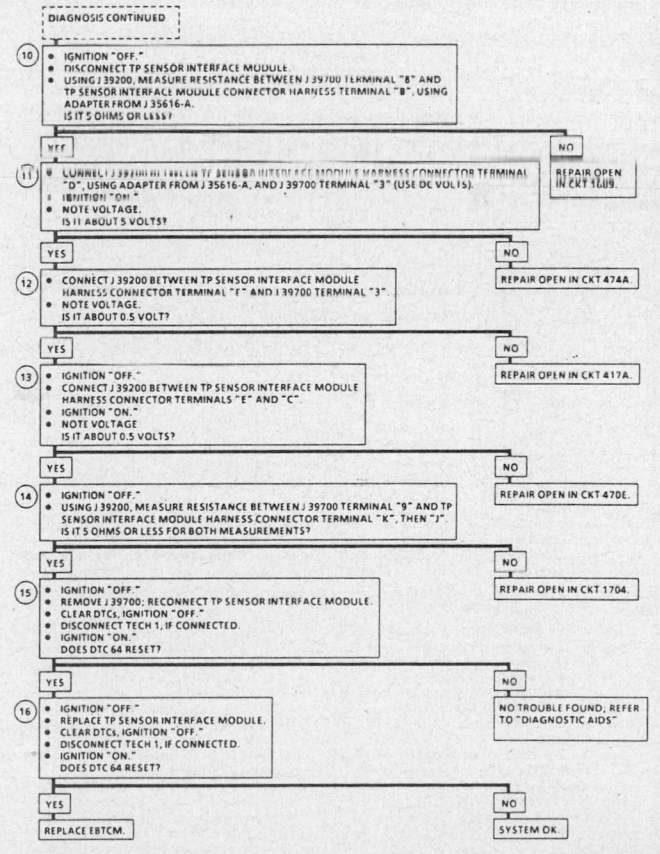

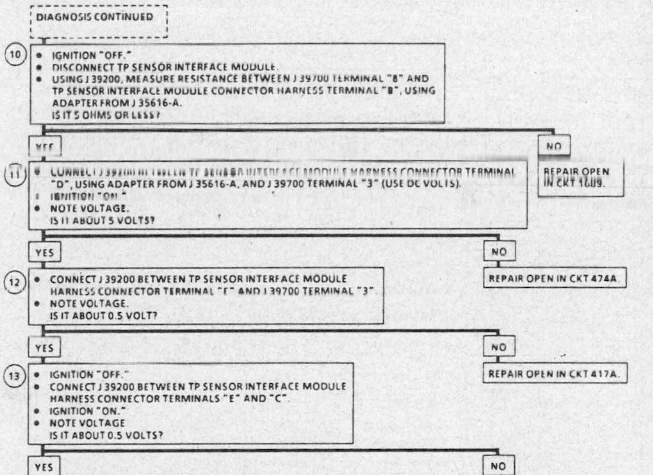
DIAGNOSIS CONTINUED
10
• IGNITION "OFF."
• DISCONNECT TP SENSOR INTERFACE MODULE.
• USING J 39200, MEASURE RESISTANCE BETWEEN J 39700 TERMINAL "8" AND TP SENSOR INTERFACE MODULE CONNECTOR HARNESS TERMINAL "B", USING ADAPTER FROM J 35616-A. IS IT 5 OHMS OR LESS?
NO
REPAIR OPEN
11
"D", USING ADAPTER FROM J 35616-A, AND J 39700 TERMINAL "3" (USE DC VOLTS).
• NOTE VOLTAGE.
YES
NO
REPAIR OPEN IN CKT 474A.
12
• CONNECT J 39200 BETWEEN TP SENSOR INTERFACE MODULE
• NOTE VOLTAGE. IS IT ABOUT 0.5 VOLT?
YES
NO
REPAIR OPEN IN CKT 417A.
13
• IGNITION "OFF."
• CONNECT J 39200 BETWEEN TP SENSOR INTERFACE MODULE HARNESS CONNECTOR TERMINALS "E" AND "C".
• IGNITION "ON."
• NOTE VOLTAGE IS IT ABOUT 0.5 VOLTS?
YES
NO
REPAIR OPEN IN CKT 470E.
14
• IGNITION "OFF."
• USING J 39200, MEASURE RESISTANCE BETWEEN J 39700 TERMINAL "9" AND TP SENSOR INTERFACE MODULE HARNESS CONNECTOR TERMINAL "K", THEN "J". IS IT 5 OHMS OR LESS FOR BOTH MEASUREMENTS?
YES
NO
REPAIR OPEN IN CKT 1704.
15
• IGNITION "OFF."
• REMOVE J 39700; RECONNECT TP SENSOR INTERFACE MODULE.
• CLEAR DTCs, IGNITION "OFF."
• DISCONNECT TECH 1, IF CONNECTED.
• IGNITION "ON." DOES DTC 64 RESET?
YES
NO
NO TROUBLE FOUND; REFER TO "DIAGNOSTIC AIDS"
16
• IGNITION "OFF."
• REPLACE TP SENSOR INTERFACE MODULE.
• CLEAR DTCs, IGNITION "OFF."
• DISCONNECT TECH 1, IF CONNECTED.
• IGNITION "ON." DOES DTC 64 RESET?
YES
NO
REPLACE EBTCM.
SYSTEM OK.

GC402940088102BX

Fig. 70 Code 64: Throttle position signal fault (Part 2 of 3). 1994 LT1

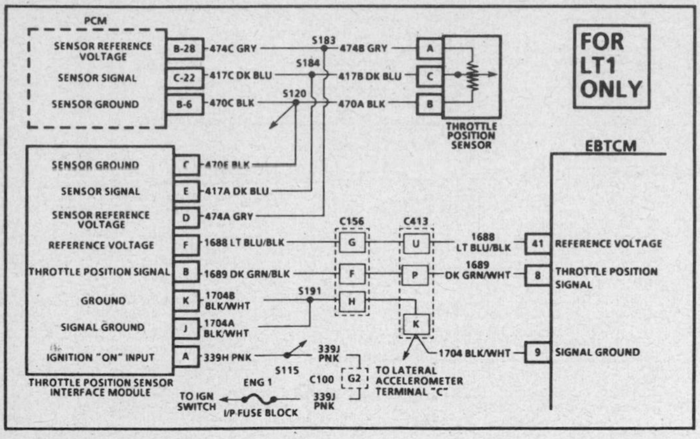
PCM
SENSOR REFERENCE VOLTAGE
SENSOR SIGNAL
SENSOR GROUND
B-28
C-22
B-6
474C GRY
417C DK BLU
470C BLK
S183
S184
S120
474B GRY
417B DK BLU
470A BLK
A
C
B
THROTTLE POSITION SENSOR
FOR LT1 ONLY
EBTCM
SENSOR GROUND
SENSOR SIGNAL
SENSOR REFERENCE VOLTAGE
REFERENCE VOLTAGE
THROTTLE POSITION SIGNAL
GROUND
SIGNAL GROUND
IGNITION "ON" INPUT
470E BLK
417A DK BLU
474A GRY
1688 LT BLU/BLK
1689 DK GRN/BLK
1704B BLK/WHT
1704A BLK/WHT
339H PNK
S191
C156
C413
1688 LT BLU/BLK
1689 DK GRN/WHT
41
8
9
REFERENCE VOLTAGE
THROTTLE POSITION SIGNAL
1704 BLK/WHT
SIGNAL GROUND
339J PNK
S115
ENG 1
C100
G2
TO LATERAL ACCELEROMETER TERMINAL "C"
339J PNK
THROTTLE POSITION SENSOR INTERFACE MODULE
TO IGN SWITCH
I/P FUSE BLOCK

Circuit Description:

The throttle position signal circuit is used by the EBTCM to monitor the actual throttle position versus desired throttle position to monitor and control engine torque during an ASR event. The throttle position sensor interface module is used to allow EBTCM monitoring of the TP sensor signal without affecting the TP sensor signal to the PCM.

DTC Will Set When: The EBTCM is not receiving reference voltage or a TP sensor signal from the throttle position sensor interface module.

DTC Chart Test Description: Number(s) below refer to circled number(s) on the diagnostic chart.

17. Determines whether the malfunction is due to a short to B+ in the pump motor relay control or pump motor relay feed circuitry.
18. Checks for an internal short to B+ in the BPM valve relay.
19. Checks for an internal short to B+ in the pump motor relay.
20. With the BPM valve relay and the pump motor relay removed, disconnect the BPM valve connector. If voltage at either J 39700 terminal "5" or "20" is greater than one volt, a short to B+ exists in CKT 854 and/or CKT 874. If voltage is less than one volt, an internal short to B+ exists in the BPM valve.
21. Checks for a short to B+ in CKT 1704.
22. Verifies whether the short to B+ is due to a malfunctioning TP sensor interface module.
23. Checks TP sensor interface module connector and wiring for intermittents.
24. Ensures DTC 64 does not reset due to a malfunctioning EBTCM.

GC402940088103AX

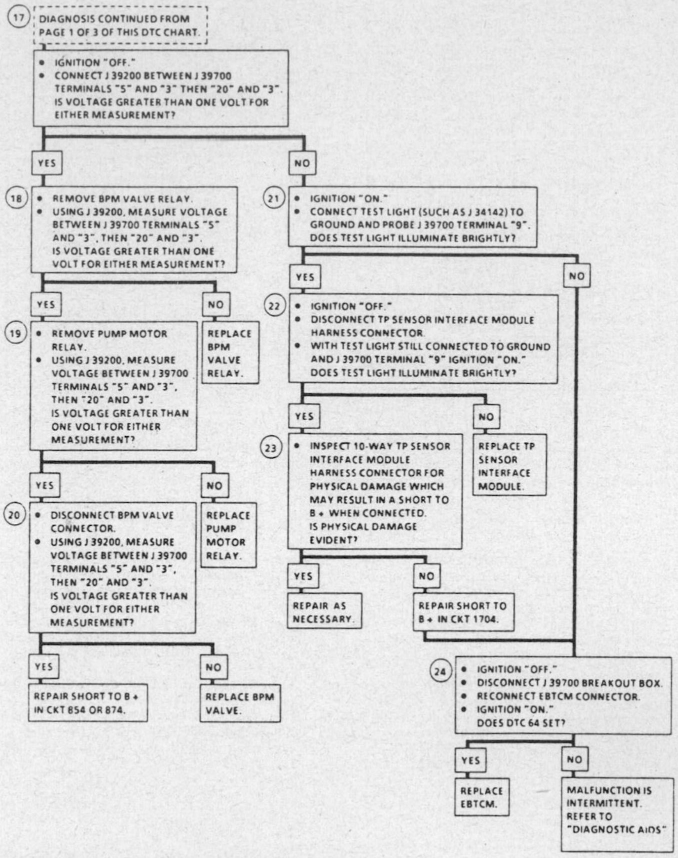
17 DIAGNOSIS CONTINUED FROM PAGE 1 OF 3 OF THIS DTC CHART.
• IGNITION "OFF."
• CONNECT J 39200 BETWEEN J 39700 TERMINALS "5" AND "3" THEN "20" AND "3". IS VOLTAGE GREATER THAN ONE VOLT FOR EITHER MEASUREMENT?
YES
NO
18 • REMOVE BPM VALVE RELAY.
• USING J 39200, MEASURE VOLTAGE BETWEEN J 39700 TERMINALS "5" AND "3", THEN "20" AND "3". IS VOLTAGE GREATER THAN ONE VOLT FOR EITHER MEASUREMENT?
21 • IGNITION "ON."
• CONNECT TEST LIGHT (SUCH AS J 34142) TO GROUND AND PROBE J 39700 TERMINAL "9". DOES TEST LIGHT ILLUMINATE BRIGHTLY?
YES
NO
REPLACE BPM VALVE RELAY.
19 • REMOVE PUMP MOTOR RELAY.
• USING J 39200, MEASURE VOLTAGE BETWEEN J 39700 TERMINALS "5" AND "3", THEN "20" AND "3". IS VOLTAGE GREATER THAN ONE VOLT FOR EITHER MEASUREMENT?
YES
NO
22 • IGNITION "OFF."
• DISCONNECT TP SENSOR INTERFACE MODULE HARNESS CONNECTOR.
• WITH TEST LIGHT STILL CONNECTED TO GROUND AND J 39700 TERMINAL "9" IGNITION "ON." DOES TEST LIGHT ILLUMINATE BRIGHTLY?
YES
NO
23 • INSPECT 10-WAY TP SENSOR INTERFACE MODULE HARNESS CONNECTOR FOR PHYSICAL DAMAGE WHICH MAY RESULT IN A SHORT TO B+ WHEN CONNECTED. IS PHYSICAL DAMAGE EVIDENT?
REPLACE TP SENSOR INTERFACE MODULE.
YES
NO
REPLACE PUMP MOTOR RELAY.
20 • DISCONNECT BPM VALVE CONNECTOR.
• USING J 39200, MEASURE VOLTAGE BETWEEN J 39700 TERMINALS "5" AND "3", THEN "20" AND "3". IS VOLTAGE GREATER THAN ONE VOLT FOR EITHER MEASUREMENT?
YES
NO
REPAIR AS NECESSARY.
REPAIR SHORT TO B+ IN CKT 1704.
YES
NO
REPAIR SHORT TO B+ IN CKT 854 OR 874.
REPLACE BPM VALVE.
24 • IGNITION "OFF."
• DISCONNECT J 39700 BREAKOUT BOX.
• RECONNECT EBTCM CONNECTOR.
• IGNITION "ON." DOES DTC 64 SET?
YES
NO
REPLACE EBTCM.
MALFUNCTION IS INTERMITTENT. REFER TO "DIAGNOSTIC AIDS"

GC402940088103BX

Fig. 70 Code 64: Throttle Position Signal Fault (Part 3 of 3). 1994 LT1

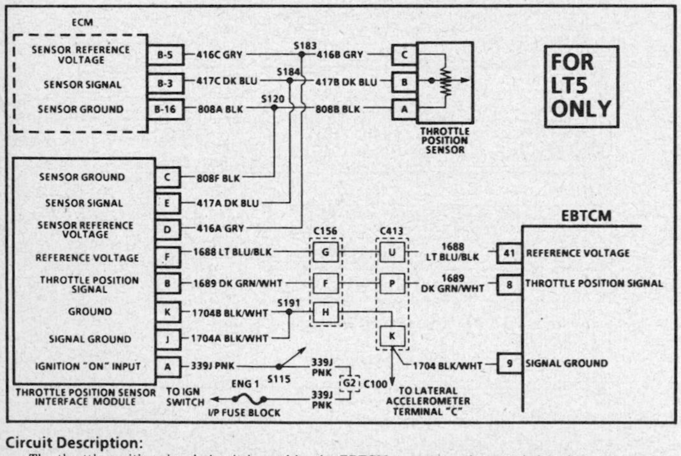
ECM
SENSOR REFERENCE VOLTAGE
SENSOR SIGNAL
SENSOR GROUND
B-5
B-3
B-16
416C GRY
417C DK BLU
808A BLK
S183
S184
S120
416B GRY
417B DK BLU
808B BLK
C
B
A
THROTTLE POSITION SENSOR
FOR LT5 ONLY
EBTCM
SENSOR GROUND
SENSOR SIGNAL
SENSOR REFERENCE VOLTAGE
REFERENCE VOLTAGE
THROTTLE POSITION SIGNAL
GROUND
SIGNAL GROUND
IGNITION "ON" INPUT
808F BLK
417A DK BLU
416A GRY
1688 LT BLU/BLK
1689 DK GRN/WHT
1704B BLK/WHT
1704A BLK/WHT
339J PNK
S191
C156
C413
1688 LT BLU/BLK
1689 DK GRN/WHT
41
8
9
REFERENCE VOLTAGE
THROTTLE POSITION SIGNAL
1704 BLK/WHT
SIGNAL GROUND
339J PNK
S115
ENG 1
G2
C100
TO LATERAL ACCELEROMETER TERMINAL "C"
339J PNK
THROTTLE POSITION SENSOR INTERFACE MODULE
TO IGN SWITCH
I/P FUSE BLOCK

Circuit Description:

The throttle position signal circuit is used by the EBTCM to monitor the actual throttle position versus desired throttle position to monitor and control engine torque during an ASR event. The throttle position sensor module is used to allow EBTCM monitoring of the TP sensor signal without affecting the TP sensor signal to the ECM.

DTC Will Set When: The EBTCM is not receiving reference voltage or a TP sensor signal from the throttle position sensor interface module.

DTC Chart Test Description: Number(s) below refer to circled number(s) on the diagnostic chart.

1. Checks for TP sensor-related ECM DTCs. Many of the same conditions which could cause an ASR DTC 64 will also cause ECM DTCs. The ECM DTCs should be repaired first to eliminate those malfunctions from affecting the ASR DTC 64 condition.
2. Checks for an lateral accelerometer DTC 75. Since the lateral accelerometer and the TP sensor interface module share the same ground, a DTC 75 likely indicates an open in CKT 1704.
3. Checks for a short to ground in CKT 1689.
4. Checks for a short to ground in CKT 1688.
5. Checks for proper voltage in CKT 1688 at the EBTCM connection. (This voltage measurement is only appropriate when the EBTCM is disconnected from the circuit.)
6. Checks for proper voltage in CKT 1689 at the EBTCM connection. (This voltage measurement is only appropriate when the EBTCM is disconnected from the circuit.)
7. Checks for an additional DTC 64 malfunction after ground CKT 1704 is repaired.
8. Determines if a malfunction found in Step 5 is due to a fuse, CKT 339, or CKT 1688.
9. Determines if a malfunction found in Steps 5 and 13 is due to an open in CKT 1688 or a malfunctioning TP sensor interface module.

GC402940088201AX

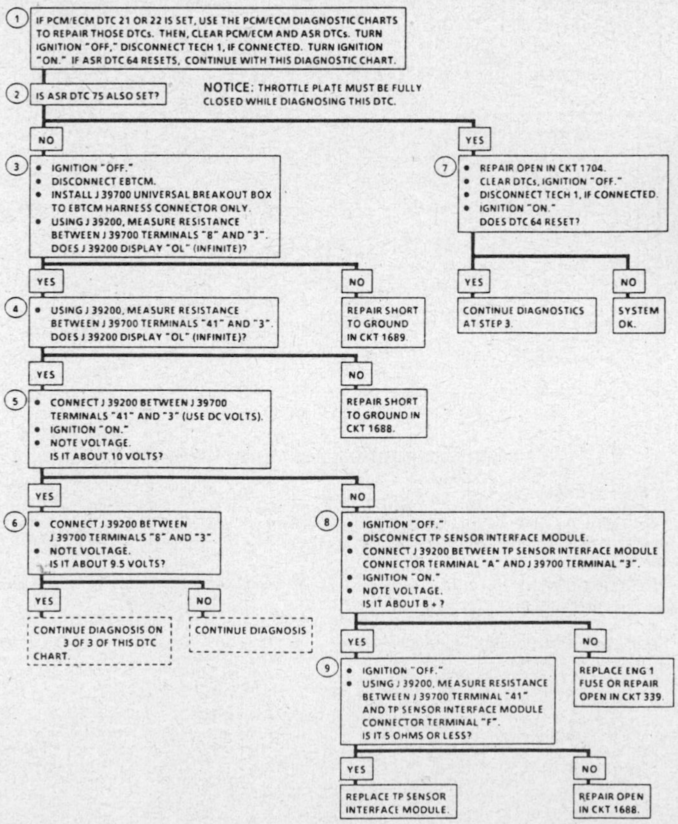
1 IF PCM/ECM DTC 21 OR 22 IS SET, USE THE PCM/ECM DIAGNOSTIC CHARTS TO REPAIR THOSE DTCs. THEN, CLEAR PCM/ECM AND ASR DTCs. TURN IGNITION "OFF," DISCONNECT TECH 1, IF CONNECTED. TURN IGNITION "ON." IF ASR DTC 64 RESETS, CONTINUE WITH THIS DIAGNOSTIC CHART.
2 IS ASR DTC 75 ALSO SET?
NOTICE: THROTTLE PLATE MUST BE FULLY CLOSED WHILE DIAGNOSING THIS DTC.
NO
YES
3 • IGNITION "OFF."
• DISCONNECT EBTCM.
• INSTALL J 39700 UNIVERSAL BREAKOUT BOX TO EBTCM HARNESS CONNECTOR ONLY.
• USING J 39200, MEASURE RESISTANCE BETWEEN J 39700 TERMINALS "8" AND "3". DOES J 39200 DISPLAY "OL" (INFINITE)?
7 • REPAIR OPEN IN CKT 1704.
• CLEAR DTCs, IGNITION "OFF."
• DISCONNECT TECH 1, IF CONNECTED.
• IGNITION "ON." DOES DTC 64 RESET?
YES
NO
YES
NO
4 • USING J 39200, MEASURE RESISTANCE BETWEEN J 39700 TERMINALS "41" AND "3". DOES J 39200 DISPLAY "OL" (INFINITE)?
REPAIR SHORT TO GROUND IN CKT 1689.
CONTINUE DIAGNOSTICS AT STEP 3.
SYSTEM OK.
YES
NO
5 • CONNECT J 39200 BETWEEN J 39700 TERMINALS "41" AND "3" (USE DC VOLTS).
• IGNITION "ON."
• NOTE VOLTAGE. IS IT ABOUT 10 VOLTS?
REPAIR SHORT TO GROUND IN CKT 1688.
YES
NO
6 • CONNECT J 39200 BETWEEN J 39700 TERMINALS "8" AND "3".
• NOTE VOLTAGE. IS IT ABOUT 9.5 VOLTS?
8 • IGNITION "OFF."
• DISCONNECT TP SENSOR INTERFACE MODULE.
• CONNECT J 39200 BETWEEN TP SENSOR INTERFACE MODULE CONNECTOR TERMINAL "A" AND J 39700 TERMINAL "3".
• IGNITION "ON."
• NOTE VOLTAGE. IS IT ABOUT B+?
YES
NO
CONTINUE DIAGNOSIS ON 3 OF 3 OF THIS DTC CHART.
CONTINUE DIAGNOSIS
YES
NO
9 • IGNITION "OFF."
• USING J 39200, MEASURE RESISTANCE BETWEEN J 39700 TERMINAL "41" AND TP SENSOR INTERFACE MODULE CONNECTOR TERMINAL "F". IS IT 5 OHMS OR LESS?
REPLACE ENG 1 FUSE OR REPAIR OPEN IN CKT 339.
YES
NO
REPLACE TP SENSOR INTERFACE MODULE.
REPAIR OPEN IN CKT 1688.

GC4029400882u1BX

Fig. 71 Code 64: Throttle Position Signal Fault (Part 1 of 3). 1994 LT5

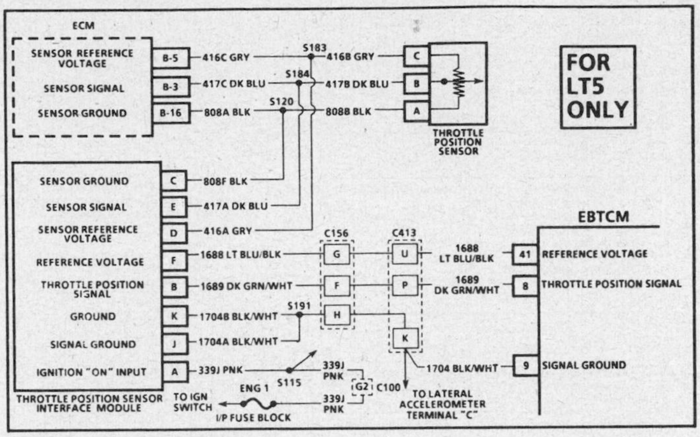
ECM
SENSOR REFERENCE VOLTAGE
SENSOR SIGNAL
SENSOR GROUND
B-5
B-3
B-16
416C GRY
417C DK BLU
808A BLK
S183
S184
S120
416B GRY
417B DK BLU
808B BLK
C
B
A
THROTTLE POSITION SENSOR
FOR LT5 ONLY
SENSOR GROUND
SENSOR SIGNAL
SENSOR REFERENCE VOLTAGE
REFERENCE VOLTAGE
THROTTLE POSITION SIGNAL
GROUND
SIGNAL GROUND
IGNITION "ON" INPUT
C
E
D
F
B
K
J
A
808F BLK
417A DK BLU
416A GRY
1688 LT BLU/BLK
1689 DK GRN/WHT
1704B BLK/WHT
1704A BLK/WHT
339J PNK
C156
C413
G
F
H
U
P
K
S191
1688 LT BLU/BLK
1689 DK GRN/WHT
1704 BLK/WHT
EBTCM
41
8
9
REFERENCE VOLTAGE
THROTTLE POSITION SIGNAL
SIGNAL GROUND
339J PNK
G2
C100
ENG 1
S115
339J PNK
THROTTLE POSITION SENSOR INTERFACE MODULE
TO IGN SWITCH
I/P FUSE BLOCK
TO LATERAL ACCELEROMETER TERMINAL "C"

Circuit Description:

The throttle position signal circuit is used by the EBTCM to monitor the actual throttle position versus desired throttle position to monitor and control engine torque during an ASR event. The throttle position sensor interface module is used to allow EBTCM monitoring of the TP sensor signal without affecting the TP sensor signal to the ECM.

DTC Will Set When: The EBTCM is not receiving reference voltage or a TP sensor signal from the throttle position sensor interface module.

DTC Chart Test Description: Number(s) below refer to circled number(s) on the diagnostic chart.

10. Checks for an open in CKT 1689.
11. Checks for TP sensor reference voltage from the ECM at the TP sensor interface module connector.
12. Checks for TP sensor signal voltage on CKT 417A at the TP sensor interface module connector.
13. Checks for an open in TP sensor signal ground CKT 808F to the TP sensor interface module connector.
14. Checks for an open in signal ground CKT 1704 to the TP sensor interface module connector.
15. Checks for DTC 64 reset after most system components have checked OK.
16. Replaces TP sensor interface module as likely cause of DTC reset in Step 15. If the DTC resets again, the EBTCM must be concluding there is a malfunction present when there is not.

GC402940088202AX

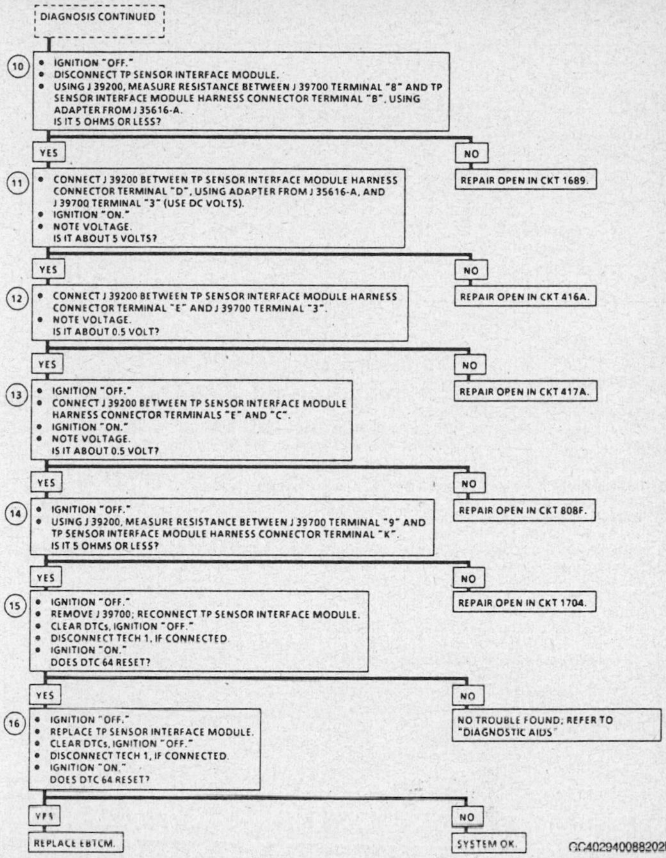
DIAGNOSIS CONTINUED
10
• IGNITION "OFF."
• DISCONNECT TP SENSOR INTERFACE MODULE.
• USING J 39200, MEASURE RESISTANCE BETWEEN J 39700 TERMINAL "8" AND TP SENSOR INTERFACE MODULE HARNESS CONNECTOR TERMINAL "B", USING ADAPTER FROM J 35616-A.
IS IT 5 OHMS OR LESS?
YES
NO
REPAIR OPEN IN CKT 1689.
11
• CONNECT J 39200 BETWEEN TP SENSOR INTERFACE MODULE HARNESS CONNECTOR TERMINAL "D", USING ADAPTER FROM J 35616-A, AND J 39700 TERMINAL "3" (USE DC VOLTS).
• IGNITION "ON."
• NOTE VOLTAGE.
IS IT ABOUT 5 VOLTS?
YES
NO
REPAIR OPEN IN CKT 416A.
12
• CONNECT J 39200 BETWEEN TP SENSOR INTERFACE MODULE HARNESS CONNECTOR TERMINAL "E" AND J 39700 TERMINAL "3".
• NOTE VOLTAGE.
IS IT ABOUT 0.5 VOLT?
YES
NO
REPAIR OPEN IN CKT 417A.
13
• IGNITION "OFF."
• CONNECT J 39200 BETWEEN TP SENSOR INTERFACE MODULE HARNESS CONNECTOR TERMINALS "E" AND "C".
• IGNITION "ON."
• NOTE VOLTAGE.
IS IT ABOUT 0.5 VOLT?
YES
NO
REPAIR OPEN IN CKT 808F.
14
• IGNITION "OFF."
• USING J 39200, MEASURE RESISTANCE BETWEEN J 39700 TERMINAL "9" AND TP SENSOR INTERFACE MODULE HARNESS CONNECTOR TERMINAL "K".
IS IT 5 OHMS OR LESS?
YES
NO
REPAIR OPEN IN CKT 1704.
15
• IGNITION "OFF."
• REMOVE J 39700; RECONNECT TP SENSOR INTERFACE MODULE.
• CLEAR DTCs, IGNITION "OFF."
• DISCONNECT TECH 1, IF CONNECTED.
• IGNITION "ON."
DOES DTC 64 RESET?
YES
NO
NO TROUBLE FOUND; REFER TO "DIAGNOSTIC AIDS"
16
• IGNITION "OFF."
• REPLACE TP SENSOR INTERFACE MODULE.
• CLEAR DTCs, IGNITION "OFF."
• DISCONNECT TECH 1, IF CONNECTED.
• IGNITION "ON."
DOES DTC 64 RESET?
YES
NO
REPLACE EBTCM.
SYSTEM OK.

GC402940088202BX

Fig. 71 Code 64: Throttle Position Signal Fault (Part 2 of 3). 1994 LT5

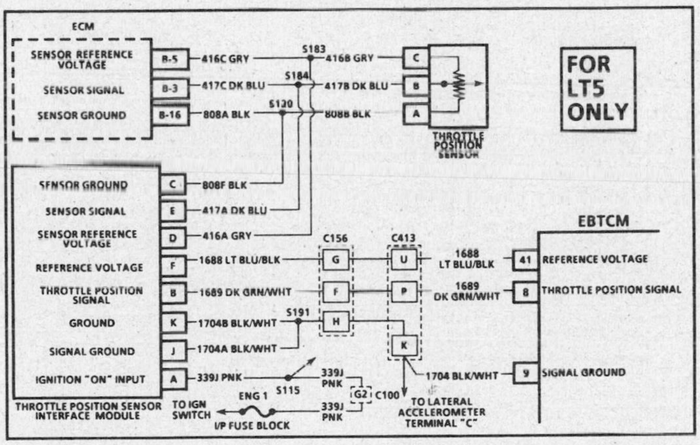
ECM
SENSOR REFERENCE VOLTAGE
SENSOR SIGNAL
SENSOR GROUND
B-5
B-3
B-16
416C GRY
417C DK BLU
808A BLK
S183
S184
S120
416B GRY
417B DK BLU
808B BLK
C
B
A
THROTTLE POSITION SENSOR
FOR LT5 ONLY
SENSOR GROUND
SENSOR SIGNAL
SENSOR REFERENCE VOLTAGE
REFERENCE VOLTAGE
THROTTLE POSITION SIGNAL
GROUND
SIGNAL GROUND
IGNITION "ON" INPUT
808F BLK
417A DK BLU
416A GRY
1688 LT BLU/BLK
1689 DK GRN/WHT
1704B BLK/WHT
1704A BLK/WHT
339J PNK
C156
C413
S191
1704 BLK/WHT
EBTCM
REFERENCE VOLTAGE
THROTTLE POSITION SIGNAL
SIGNAL GROUND
ENG 1
S115
THROTTLE POSITION SENSOR INTERFACE MODULE
TO IGN SWITCH
I/P FUSE BLOCK
TO LATERAL ACCELEROMETER TERMINAL "C"

Circuit Description:

The throttle position signal circuit is used by the EBTCM to monitor the actual throttle position versus desired throttle position to monitor and control engine torque during an ASR event. The throttle position sensor interface module is used to allow EBTCM monitoring of the TP sensor signal without affecting the TP sensor signal to the ECM.

DTC Will Set When: The EBTCM is not receiving reference voltage or a TP sensor signal from the throttle position sensor interface module.

DTC Chart Test Description: Number(s) below refer to circled number(s) on the diagnostic chart.

17. Determines whether the malfunction is due to a short to B+ in the pump motor relay control or pump motor relay feed circuitry.
18. Checks for an internal short to B+ in the BPM valve relay.
19. Checks for an internal short to B+ in the pump motor relay.
20. With the BPM valve relay and the pump motor relay removed, disconnect the BPM valve connector. If voltage at either J 39700 terminal "5" or "20" is greater than one volt, a short to B+ exists in CKT 854 and/or CKT 874. If voltage is less than one volt, an internal short to B+ exists in the BPM valve.
21. Checks for a short to B+ in CKT 1704.
22. Verifies whether the short to B+ is due to a malfunctioning TP sensor interface module.
23. Checks TP sensor interface module connector and wiring for intermittents.
24. Ensures DTC 64 does not reset due to a malfunctioning EBTCM.

Diagnostic Aids: It is very important that a thorough inspection of the wiring and connectors be performed. Failure to carefully and fully inspect wiring and connectors may result in misdiagnosis, causing part replacement with reappearance of the malfunction.

GC402940088203AX

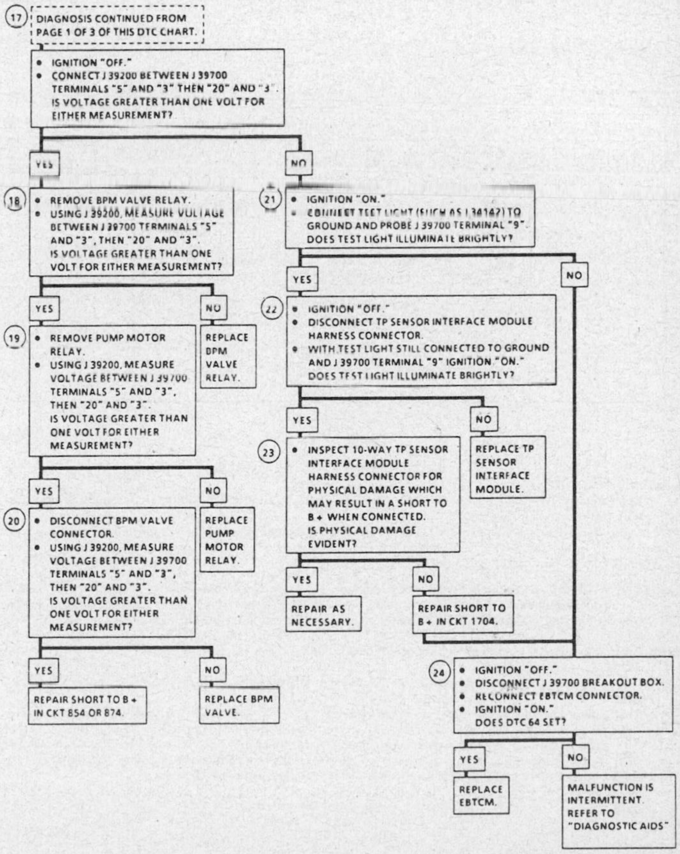
17
DIAGNOSIS CONTINUED FROM PAGE 1 OF 3 OF THIS DTC CHART.
• IGNITION "OFF."
• CONNECT J 39200 BETWEEN J 39700 TERMINALS "5" AND "3" THEN "20" AND "3".
IS VOLTAGE GREATER THAN ONE VOLT FOR EITHER MEASUREMENT?
YES
NO
18
• REMOVE BPM VALVE RELAY.
• USING J 39200, MEASURE VOLTAGE BETWEEN J 39700 TERMINALS "5" AND "3", THEN "20" AND "3".
IS VOLTAGE GREATER THAN ONE VOLT FOR EITHER MEASUREMENT?
YES
NO
REPLACE BPM VALVE RELAY.
19
• REMOVE PUMP MOTOR RELAY.
• USING J 39200, MEASURE VOLTAGE BETWEEN J 39700 TERMINALS "5" AND "3", THEN "20" AND "3".
IS VOLTAGE GREATER THAN ONE VOLT FOR EITHER MEASUREMENT?
YES
NO
REPLACE PUMP MOTOR RELAY.
20
• DISCONNECT BPM VALVE CONNECTOR.
• USING J 39200, MEASURE VOLTAGE BETWEEN J 39700 TERMINALS "5" AND "3", THEN "20" AND "3".
IS VOLTAGE GREATER THAN ONE VOLT FOR EITHER MEASUREMENT?
YES
NO
REPAIR SHORT TO B+ IN CKT 854 OR 874.
REPLACE BPM VALVE.
21
• IGNITION "ON."
• CONNECT TEST LIGHT (SUCH AS J 34142) TO GROUND AND PROBE J 39700 TERMINAL "9".
DOES TEST LIGHT ILLUMINATE BRIGHTLY?
YES
NO
22
• IGNITION "OFF."
• DISCONNECT TP SENSOR INTERFACE MODULE HARNESS CONNECTOR.
• WITH TEST LIGHT STILL CONNECTED TO GROUND AND J 39700 TERMINAL "9" IGNITION "ON."
DOES TEST LIGHT ILLUMINATE BRIGHTLY?
YES
NO
REPLACE TP SENSOR INTERFACE MODULE.
23
• INSPECT 10-WAY TP SENSOR INTERFACE MODULE HARNESS CONNECTOR FOR PHYSICAL DAMAGE WHICH MAY RESULT IN A SHORT TO B+ WHEN CONNECTED.
IS PHYSICAL DAMAGE EVIDENT?
YES
NO
REPAIR AS NECESSARY.
REPAIR SHORT TO B+ IN CKT 1704.
24
• IGNITION "OFF."
• DISCONNECT J 39700 BREAKOUT BOX.
• RECONNECT EBTCM CONNECTOR.
• IGNITION "ON."
DOES DTC 64 SET?
YES
NO
REPLACE EBTCM.
MALFUNCTION IS INTERMITTENT. REFER TO "DIAGNOSTIC AIDS"

GC402940088203BX

Fig. 71 Code 64: Throttle Position Signal Fault (Part 3 of 3). 1994 LT5

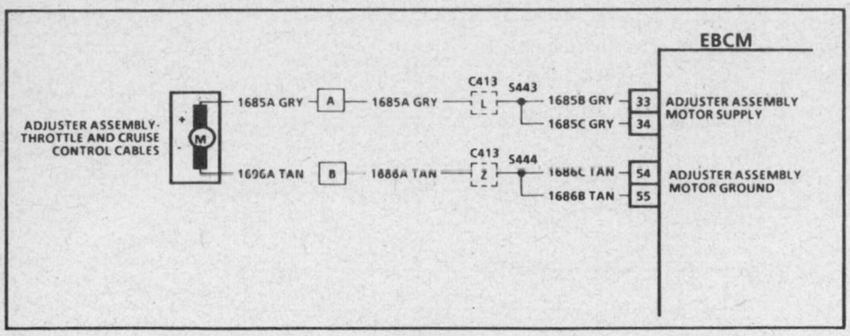
EBCM
ADJUSTER ASSEMBLY-THROTTLE AND CRUISE CONTROL CABLES
M
1685A GRY
A
1685A GRY
C413
L
S443
1685B GRY
1685C GRY
33
34
ADJUSTER ASSEMBLY MOTOR SUPPLY
1696A TAN
B
1686A TAN
C413
Z
S444
1686C TAN
1686B TAN
54
55
ADJUSTER ASSEMBLY MOTOR GROUND

CODE 65

ADJUSTER ASSEMBLY FAULT

Circuit Description:

The Adjuster Assembly circuit provides both power and ground to the Adjuster Assembly to help control engine torque during an ASR event.

Code 65 will set if CKT 1685 or CKT 1686 are shorted to ground, shorted to B+, shorted to each other, or both open at the same time. The ASR system will be disabled for the remainder of the ignition cycle and the "SERVICE ASR" lamp will illuminate.

Test Description: Number(s) below refer to circled number(s) on the diagnostic chart.

1. Checks for proper Adjuster Assembly motor winding resistance.
2. Checks for open(s) in CKT 1685B and/or 1685C.
3. Checks for open(s) in CKT 1686B and/or 1686C.
4. Checks for a short between CKTs 1685 and 1686.
5. Checks for short(s) to B+ in CKT 1685B and/or 1685C.
6. Checks wiring and connectors for intermittents and/or shorts. Information given under "Intermittents and Poor Connections" details conditions which can cause intermittents and how to identify them. The Adjuster Assembly requires special wiring repair procedures. Use only the instructions as shown under "Adjuster Assembly Wiring Repair" in this section if wiring repairs on the Adjuster Assembly are needed.

Diagnostic Aids:

It is very important that a thorough inspection of the wiring and connectors be performed. Failure to carefully and fully inspect wiring and connectors may result in misdiagnosis, causing part replacement with reappearance of the fault.

GC402920043400AX

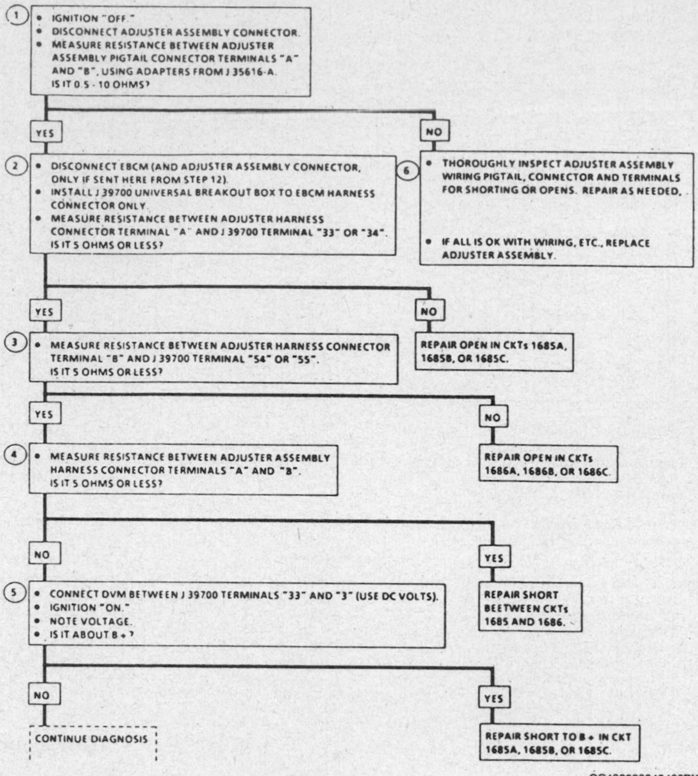
1
IGNITION "OFF."
DISCONNECT ADJUSTER ASSEMBLY CONNECTOR.
MEASURE RESISTANCE BETWEEN ADJUSTER ASSEMBLY PIGTAIL CONNECTOR TERMINALS "A" AND "B", USING ADAPTERS FROM J 35616-A.
IS IT 0.5 - 10 OHMS?
YES
NO
2
DISCONNECT EBCM (AND ADJUSTER ASSEMBLY CONNECTOR, ONLY IF SENT HERE FROM STEP 12).
INSTALL J 39700 UNIVERSAL BREAKOUT BOX TO EBCM HARNESS CONNECTOR ONLY.
MEASURE RESISTANCE BETWEEN ADJUSTER HARNESS CONNECTOR TERMINAL "A" AND J 39700 TERMINAL "33" OR "34".
IS IT 5 OHMS OR LESS?
6
THOROUGHLY INSPECT ADJUSTER ASSEMBLY WIRING PIGTAIL, CONNECTOR AND TERMINALS FOR SHORTING OR OPENS. REPAIR AS NEEDED.
IF ALL IS OK WITH WIRING, ETC., REPLACE ADJUSTER ASSEMBLY.
YES
NO
3
MEASURE RESISTANCE BETWEEN ADJUSTER HARNESS CONNECTOR TERMINAL "B" AND J 39700 TERMINAL "54" OR "55".
IS IT 5 OHMS OR LESS?
REPAIR OPEN IN CKTs 1685A, 1685B, OR 1685C.
YES
NO
4
MEASURE RESISTANCE BETWEEN ADJUSTER ASSEMBLY HARNESS CONNECTOR TERMINALS "A" AND "B".
IS IT 5 OHMS OR LESS?
REPAIR OPEN IN CKTs 1686A, 1686B, OR 1686C.
NO
YES
5
CONNECT DVM BETWEEN J 39700 TERMINALS "33" AND "3" (USE DC VOLTS).
IGNITION "ON."
NOTE VOLTAGE.
IS IT ABOUT B+?
REPAIR SHORT BEETWEEN CKTs 1685 AND 1686.
NO
YES
CONTINUE DIAGNOSIS
REPAIR SHORT TO B+ IN CKT 1685A, 1685B, OR 1685C.

GC402920043400BX

Fig. 72 Code 65: Adjuster Assembly Fault (Part 1 of 2). 1992

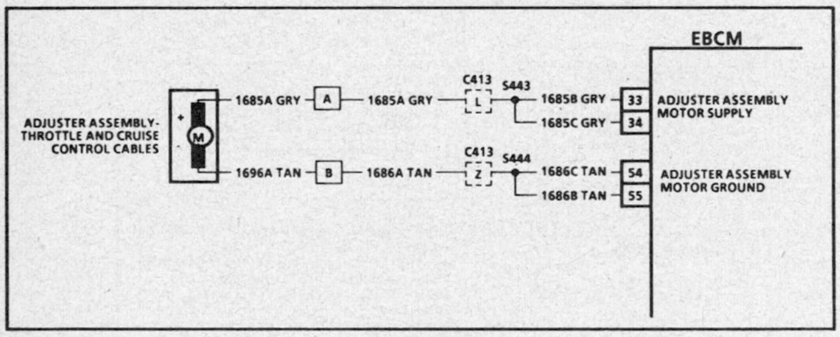
EBCM
ADJUSTER ASSEMBLY-THROTTLE AND CRUISE CONTROL CABLES
M
1685A GRY
A
1685A GRY
C413
L
S443
1685B GRY
1685C GRY
33
34
ADJUSTER ASSEMBLY MOTOR SUPPLY
1696A TAN
B
1686A TAN
C413
Z
S444
1686C TAN
1686B TAN
54
55
ADJUSTER ASSEMBLY MOTOR GROUND

CODE 65

ADJUSTER ASSEMBLY FAULT

Circuit Description:

The Adjuster Assembly circuit provides both power and ground to the Adjuster Assembly to help control engine torque during an ASR event.

Code 65 will set if CKT 1685 or CKT 1686 are shorted to ground, shorted to B+, shorted to each other, or both open at the same time. The ASR system will be disabled for the remainder of the ignition cycle and the "SERVICE ASR" lamp will illuminate.

Test Description: Number(s) below refer to circled number(s) on the diagnostic chart.

7. Checks for short(s) to B+ in CKT 1686B and/or 1686C.
8. Checks for short(s) to ground in CKT 1685B and/or 1685C.
9. Checks for short(s) to ground in CKT 1686B and/or 1686C.
10. Checks for continued code setting after wiring and Adjuster Assembly inspections.
11. Sets throttle to a position which enables one of the EBCM's special monitoring systems of the Adjuster Assembly circuits, checking for a code reset. If the code resets, the EBCM is likely at fault.
12. Checks for shorts to B+ or ground that are EBCM-switched. If you have reached Step 12 for a second time after performing checks for EBCM-switched faults, the EBCM is likely at fault for the code reset.

Diagnostic Aids:

It is very important that a thorough inspection of the wiring and connectors be performed. Failure to carefully and fully inspect wiring and connectors may result in misdiagnosis, causing part replacement with reappearance of the fault.

GC402920043400CX

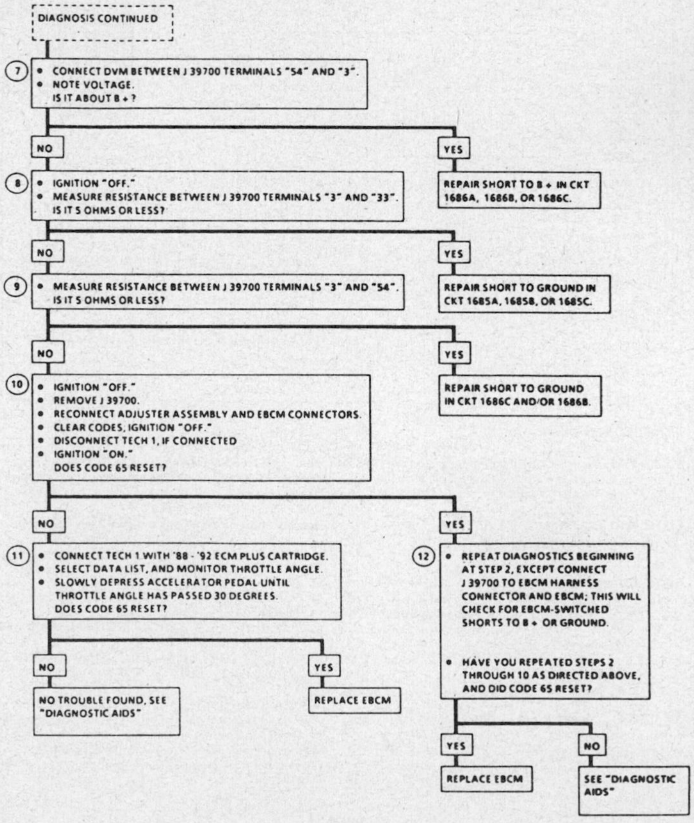
DIAGNOSIS CONTINUED
7
CONNECT DVM BETWEEN J 39700 TERMINALS "54" AND "3".
NOTE VOLTAGE.
IS IT ABOUT B+?
NO
YES
8
IGNITION "OFF."
MEASURE RESISTANCE BETWEEN J 39700 TERMINALS "3" AND "33".
IS IT 5 OHMS OR LESS?
REPAIR SHORT TO B+ IN CKT 1686A, 1686B, OR 1686C.
NO
YES
9
MEASURE RESISTANCE BETWEEN J 39700 TERMINALS "3" AND "54".
IS IT 5 OHMS OR LESS?
REPAIR SHORT TO GROUND IN CKT 1685A, 1685B, OR 1685C.
NO
YES
10
IGNITION "OFF."
REMOVE J 39700.
RECONNECT ADJUSTER ASSEMBLY AND EBCM CONNECTORS.
CLEAR CODES, IGNITION "OFF."
DISCONNECT TECH 1, IF CONNECTED
IGNITION "ON."
DOES CODE 65 RESET?
REPAIR SHORT TO GROUND IN CKT 1686C AND/OR 1686B.
NO
YES
11
CONNECT TECH 1 WITH '88 - '92 ECM PLUS CARTRIDGE.
SELECT DATA LIST, AND MONITOR THROTTLE ANGLE.
SLOWLY DEPRESS ACCELERATOR PEDAL UNTIL THROTTLE ANGLE HAS PASSED 30 DEGREES.
DOES CODE 65 RESET?
12
REPEAT DIAGNOSTICS BEGINNING AT STEP 2, EXCEPT CONNECT J 39700 TO EBCM HARNESS CONNECTOR AND EBCM; THIS WILL CHECK FOR EBCM-SWITCHED SHORTS TO B+ OR GROUND.
HAVE YOU REPEATED STEPS 2 THROUGH 10 AS DIRECTED ABOVE, AND DID CODE 65 RESET?
NO
YES
NO TROUBLE FOUND, SEE "DIAGNOSTIC AIDS"
REPLACE EBCM
YES
NO
REPLACE EBCM
SEE "DIAGNOSTIC AIDS"

GC402920043400DX

Fig. 72 Code 65: Adjuster Assembly Fault (Part 2 of 2). 1992

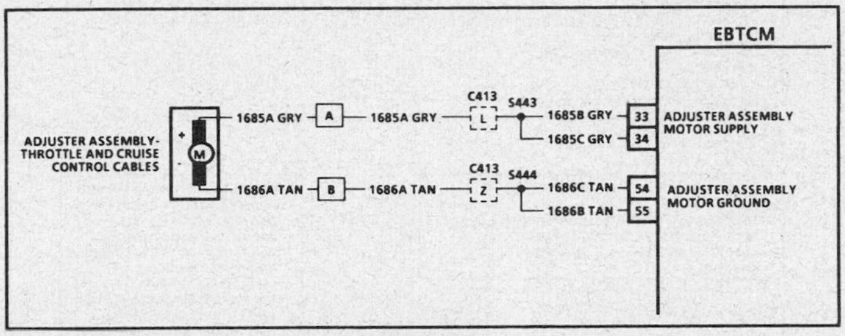
EBTCM
ADJUSTER ASSEMBLY-
THROTTLE AND CRUISE
CONTROL CABLES
M
1685A GRY
A
1685A GRY
C413
L
S443
1685B GRY
33
1685C GRY
34
ADJUSTER ASSEMBLY
MOTOR SUPPLY
1686A TAN
B
1686A TAN
C413
Z
S444
1686C TAN
54
1686B TAN
55
ADJUSTER ASSEMBLY
MOTOR GROUND

DTC 65

(Page 1 of 2)

ADJUSTER ASSEMBLY MALFUNCTION

Circuit Description:

The adjuster assembly circuit provides both power and ground to the adjuster assembly to help control engine torque during an ASR event.

DTC 65 will set if CKT 1685 or CKT 1686 are shorted to ground, shorted to B+, shorted to each other, or both open at the same time. The ASR system will be disabled for the remainder of the ignition cycle and the "SERVICE ASR" lamp will illuminate.

Test Description: Number(s) below refer to circled number(s) on the diagnostic chart.

1. Checks for proper Adjuster Assembly motor winding resistance. It is very important to do the "rotate & release" procedure before measuring to allow the motor to reach the "home" position.
2. Checks for open(s) in CKT 1685B and/or 1685C.
3. Checks for open(s) in CKT 1686B and/or 1686C.
4. Checks for a short between CKTs 1685 and 1686
5. Checks for short(s) to B+ in CKT 1685B and/or 1685C.
6. Repeats "rotate & release" procedure from Step 1. The Adjuster Assembly resistance should be 0.5-10 ohms at least once after the "rotate and release" procedure.
7. Sets throttle to a position which enables one of the EBCM's special monitoring systems of the Adjuster Assembly circuits, checking for a code reset.
8. Checks wiring and connectors for intermittents and/or shorts. Information given under "Intermittents and Poor Connections" details conditions which can cause intermittents and how to identify them. The Adjuster Assembly requires special wiring repair procedures. Use only the instructions as shown under "Adjuster Assembly Wiring Repair" in this section if wiring repairs on the Adjuster Assembly are needed.

Diagnostic Aids:

It is very important that a thorough inspection of the wiring and connectors be performed. Failure to carefully and fully inspect wiring and connectors may result in misdiagnosis, causing part replacement with rappearance of the fault.

If the "SERVICE ABS," "SERVICE ASR," "ABS ACTIVE," "ASR ACTIVE," and "ASR OFF" indicators all come "ON" when the ignition is turned "ON" but do not turn "OFF" after a few seconds (bulb check). Check for a poor connection or an open in ground CKT 801, especially at the connection point to the engine.

GC402930043500AX

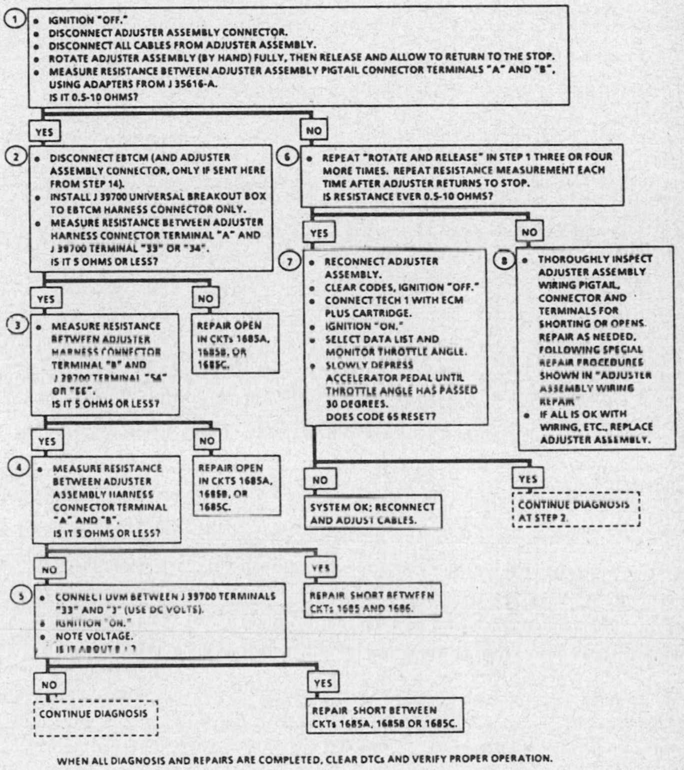
1
• IGNITION "OFF."
• DISCONNECT ADJUSTER ASSEMBLY CONNECTOR.
• DISCONNECT ALL CABLES FROM ADJUSTER ASSEMBLY.
• ROTATE ADJUSTER ASSEMBLY (BY HAND) FULLY, THEN RELEASE AND ALLOW TO RETURN TO THE STOP.
• MEASURE RESISTANCE BETWEEN ADJUSTER ASSEMBLY PIGTAIL CONNECTOR TERMINALS "A" AND "B", USING ADAPTERS FROM J 35616-A.
IS IT 0.5-10 OHMS?
YES
NO
2
• DISCONNECT EBTCM (AND ADJUSTER ASSEMBLY CONNECTOR, ONLY IF SENT HERE FROM STEP 14).
• INSTALL J 39700 UNIVERSAL BREAKOUT BOX TO EBTCM HARNESS CONNECTOR ONLY.
• MEASURE RESISTANCE BETWEEN ADJUSTER HARNESS CONNECTOR TERMINAL "A" AND J 39700 TERMINAL "33" OR "34".
IS IT 5 OHMS OR LESS?
YES
NO
3
• MEASURE RESISTANCE BETWEEN ADJUSTER HARNESS CONNECTOR TERMINAL "B" AND J 39700 TERMINAL "54" OR "55".
IS IT 5 OHMS OR LESS?
REPAIR OPEN IN CKTs 1685A, 1685B, OR 1685C.
YES
NO
4
• MEASURE RESISTANCE BETWEEN ADJUSTER ASSEMBLY HARNESS CONNECTOR TERMINAL "A" AND "B".
IS IT 5 OHMS OR LESS?
REPAIR OPEN IN CKTS 1685A, 1685B, OR 1685C.
NO
YES
5
• CONNECT DVM BETWEEN J 39700 TERMINALS "33" AND "3" (USE DC VOLTS).
• IGNITION "ON."
• NOTE VOLTAGE.
IS IT ABOUT B+?
REPAIR SHORT BETWEEN CKTs 1685 AND 1686.
NO
YES
CONTINUE DIAGNOSIS
REPAIR SHORT BETWEEN CKTs 1685A, 1685B OR 1685C.
6
• REPEAT "ROTATE AND RELEASE" IN STEP 1 THREE OR FOUR MORE TIMES. REPEAT RESISTANCE MEASUREMENT EACH TIME AFTER ADJUSTER RETURNS TO STOP.
IS RESISTANCE EVER 0.5-10 OHMS?
YES
NO
7
• RECONNECT ADJUSTER ASSEMBLY.
• CLEAR CODES, IGNITION "OFF."
• CONNECT TECH 1 WITH ECM PLUS CARTRIDGE.
• IGNITION "ON."
• SELECT DATA LIST AND MONITOR THROTTLE ANGLE.
• SLOWLY DEPRESS ACCELERATOR PEDAL UNTIL THROTTLE ANGLE HAS PASSED 30 DEGREES.
DOES CODE 65 RESET?
8
• THOROUGHLY INSPECT ADJUSTER ASSEMBLY WIRING PIGTAIL, CONNECTOR AND TERMINALS FOR SHORTING OR OPENS. REPAIR AS NEEDED, FOLLOWING SPECIAL REPAIR PROCEDURES SHOWN IN "ADJUSTER ASSEMBLY WIRING REPAIR"
• IF ALL IS OK WITH WIRING, ETC., REPLACE ADJUSTER ASSEMBLY.
NO
YES
SYSTEM OK; RECONNECT AND ADJUST CABLES.
CONTINUE DIAGNOSIS AT STEP 2.
WHEN ALL DIAGNOSIS AND REPAIRS ARE COMPLETED, CLEAR DTCs AND VERIFY PROPER OPERATION.

GC402930043500BX

Fig. 73 Code 65: Adjuster Assembly Fault (Part 1 of 2). 1993

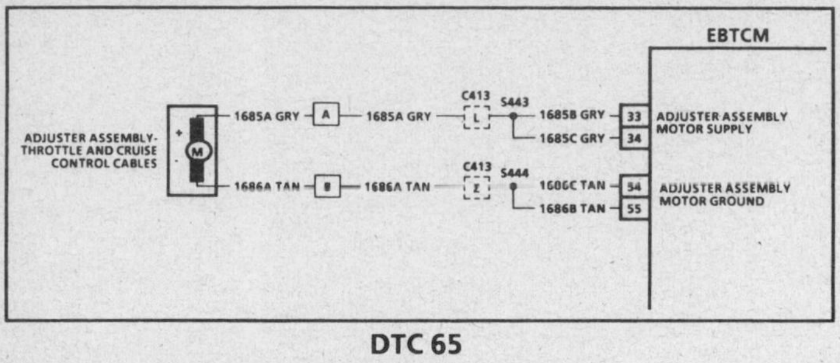
EBTCM
ADJUSTER ASSEMBLY-THROTTLE AND CRUISE CONTROL CABLES
M
1685A GRY
A
1685A GRY
C413
L
S443
1685B GRY
1685C GRY
33
34
ADJUSTER ASSEMBLY MOTOR SUPPLY
1686A TAN
B
1686A TAN
C413
Z
S444
1686C TAN
1686B TAN
54
55
ADJUSTER ASSEMBLY MOTOR GROUND

DTC 65

(Page 2 of 2)

ADJUSTER ASSEMBLY MALFUNCTION

Circuit Description:

The adjuster assembly circuit provides both power and ground to the adjuster assembly to help control engine torque during an ASR event.

DTC 65 will set if CKT 1685 or CKT 1686 are shorted to ground, shorted to B +, shorted to each other, or both open at the same time. The ASR system will be disabled for the remainder of the ignition cycle and the "SERVICE ASR" lamp will illuminate.

Test Description: Number(s) below refer to circled number(s) on the diagnostic chart.

9. Checks for short(s) to B + in CKT 1686B and/or 1686C.
10. Checks for short(s) to ground in CKT 1685B and/or 1685C.
11. Checks for short(s) to ground in CKT 1686B and/or 1686C.
12. Checks for continued code setting after wiring and Adjuster Assembly inspections.
13. Sets throttle to a position which enables one of the EBCM's special monitoring systems of the Adjuster Assembly circuits, checking for a code reset. If the code resets, the EBCM is likely at fault.
14. Checks for shorts to B + or ground that are EBCM-switched. If you have reached Step 14 for a second time after performing checks for EBCM-switched faults, the EBCM is likely at fault for the code reset.

Diagnostic Aids:

It is very important that a thorough inspection of the wiring and connectors be performed. Failure to carefully and fully inspect wiring and connectors may result in misdiagnosis, causing part replacement with reappearance of the fault.

If the "SERVICE ABS," "SERVICE ASR," "ABS ACTIVE," "ASR ACTIVE," and "ASR OFF" indicators all come "ON" when the ignition is turned "ON" but do not turn "OFF" after a few seconds (bulb check). Check for a poor connection or an open in ground CKT 801, especially at the connection point to the engine.

GC402930043500CX

DIAGNOSIS CONTINUED

(9)
- CONNECT DVM BETWEEN J 39700 TERMINALS "54" AND "3".
- NOTE VOLTAGE.
  IS IT ABOUT B + ?

NO → step 10. YES → REPAIR SHORT TO B + IN CKT 1686A, 1686B, OR 1686C.

(10)
- IGNITION "OFF."
- MEASURE RESISTANCE BETWEEN J 39700 TERMINALS "3" AND "33".
  IS IT 5 OHMS OR LESS?

NO → step 11. YES → REPAIR SHORT TO GROUND IN CKT 1685A, 1685B, OR 1685C.

(11)
- MEASURE RESISTANCE BETWEEN J 39700 TERMINALS "3" AND "54".
  IS IT 5 OHMS OR LESS?

NO → step 12. YES → REPAIR SHORT TO GROUND IN CKT 1686C AND/OR 1686B.

(12)
- IGNITION "OFF."
- REMOVE J 39700.
- RECONNECT ADJUSTER ASSEMBLY AND EBTCM CONNECTORS.
- CLEAR DTCs, IGNITION "OFF."
- DISCONNECT TECH 1, IF CONNECTED.
- IGNITION "ON."
  DOES DTC 65 RESET?

NO → step 13. YES → step 14.

(13)
- CONNECT TECH 1 WITH ECM PLUS CARTRIDGE.
- IGNITION "ON."
- SELECT DATA LIST, AND MONITOR THROTTLE ANGLE.
- SLOWLY DEPRESS ACCELERATOR PEDAL UNTIL THROTTLE ANGLE HAS PASSED 30 DEGREES.
  DOES DTC 65 RESET?

NO → NO TROUBLE FOUND, SEE "DIAGNOSTIC AIDS". YES → REPLACE EBTCM.

(14)
- REPEAT DIAGNOSTICS BEGINNING AT STEP 2, EXCEPT CONNECT J 39700 TO EBTCM HARNESS CONNECTOR AND EBTCM; THIS WILL CHECK FOR EBTCM-SWITCHED SHORTS TO B + OR GROUND. REFER TO "EBTCM-SWITCHED MALFUNCTIONS" IN THIS SECTION.
- HAVE YOU REPEATED STEPS 2 THROUGH 12 AS DIRECTED ABOVE, AND DID DTC 65 RESET?

YES → REPLACE EBTCM. NO → SEE "DIAGNOSTIC AIDS".

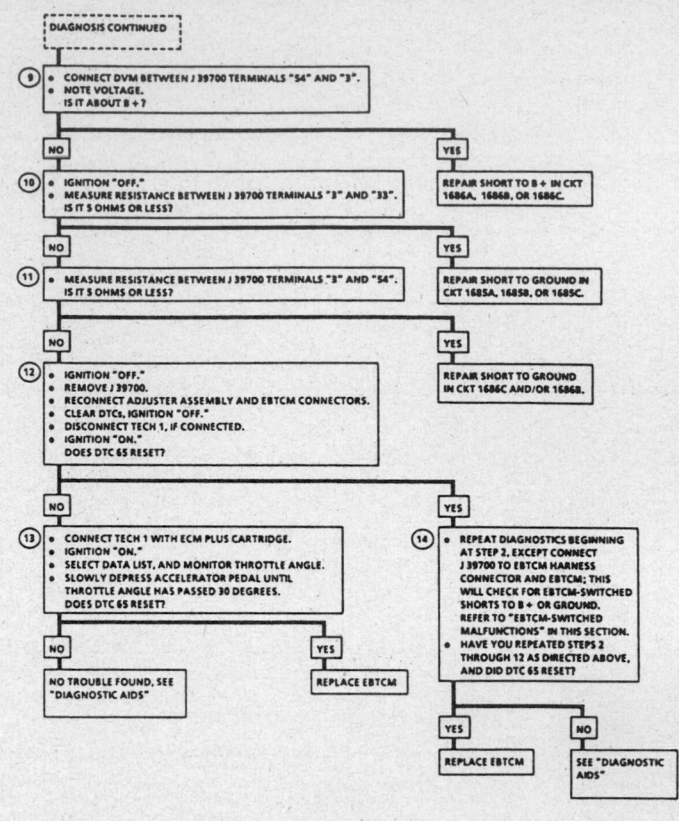

WHEN ALL DIAGNOSIS AND REPAIRS ARE COMPLETED, CLEAR DTCs AND VERIFY PROPER OPERATION.

GC402930043500DX

Fig. 73 Code 65: Adjuster Assembly Fault (Part 2 of 2). 1993

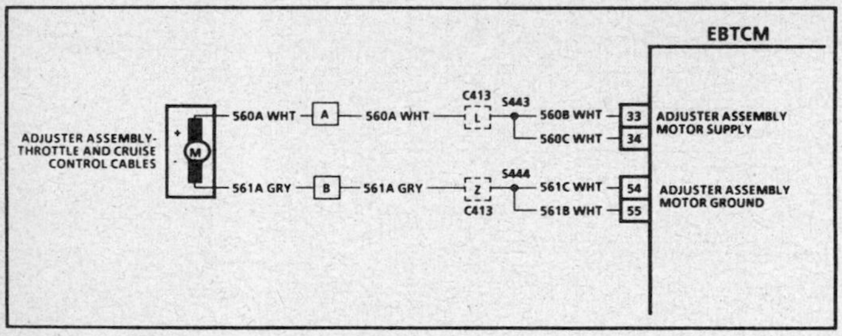
EBTCM
ADJUSTER ASSEMBLY-THROTTLE AND CRUISE CONTROL CABLES
M
560A WHT
A
560A WHT
C413
L
S443
560B WHT
560C WHT
33
34
ADJUSTER ASSEMBLY MOTOR SUPPLY
561A GRY
B
561A GRY
Z
C413
S444
561C WHT
561B WHT
54
55
ADJUSTER ASSEMBLY MOTOR GROUND

DTC 65

(Page 1 of 2)

ADJUSTER ASSEMBLY CIRCUIT MALFUNCTION

Circuit Description:

The adjuster assembly circuit provides both power and ground to the adjuster assembly to help control engine torque during an ASR event.

DTC Will Set When: If CKT 560 or CKT 561 are shorted to ground, shorted to B +, shorted to each other, or both open at the same time.

Action Taken: The ASR system will be disabled for the remainder of the ignition cycle and the "SERVICE ASR" indicator will be "ON."

DTC Chart Test Description: Number(s) below refer to circled number(s) on the diagnostic chart.

1. Checks for proper adjuster assembly motor winding resistance. It is very important to do the "rotate & release" procedure before measuring to allow the motor to reach the "home" position.
2. Checks for a poor power feed to the EBTCM through CKT 1242, which may be sensed by the EBTCM to be an open.
3. Checks for open(s) in CKT 560B and/or 560C.
4. Checks for open(s) in CKT 561B and/or 561C.
5. Checks for a short between CKTs 560 and 561.
6. Checks for short(s) to B + in CKT 560.
7. Repeats "rotate & release" procedure from Step 1. The adjuster assembly resistance should be 0.5-10 ohms at least once after the "rotate and release" procedure.
8. Sets throttle to a position which enables one of the EBTCMs special monitoring systems of the adjuster assembly circuits, checking for a DTC reset.
9. Checks wiring and connectors for intermittents and/or shorts. Information given under "Intermittents and Poor Connections" details conditions which can cause intermittents and how to identify them. The adjuster assembly requires special wiring repair procedures. Use only the instructions as shown under "Adjuster Assembly Wiring Repair" in this section if wiring repairs on the adjuster assembly are needed.

Diagnostic Aids: It is very important that a thorough inspection of the wiring and connectors be performed. Failure to carefully and fully inspect wiring and connectors may result in misdiagnosis, causing part replacement with reappearance of the malfunction.

If the "SERVICE ABS," "SERVICE ASR," "ABS ACTIVE," "ASR ACTIVE," and "ASR OFF" indicators all come "ON" when the ignition is turned "ON" but do not turn "OFF" after a few seconds (bulb check), check for a poor connection or an open in ground CKT 1051, especially at the connection point to the engine.

GC402940088301AX

(1)
- IGNITION "OFF."
- DISCONNECT ADJUSTER ASSEMBLY CONNECTOR.
- DISCONNECT ALL CABLES FROM ADJUSTER ASSEMBLY.
- ROTATE ADJUSTER ASSEMBLY (BY HAND) FULLY, THEN RELEASE AND ALLOW TO RETURN TO THE STOP.
- USING J 39200, MEASURE RESISTANCE BETWEEN ADJUSTER ASSEMBLY PIGTAIL CONNECTOR TERMINALS "A" AND "B", USING ADAPTERS FROM J 35616-A.
  IS IT 0.5-10 OHMS?

YES → step 2. NO → step 7.

(2)
- DISCONNECT EBTCM (AND ADJUSTER ASSEMBLY CONNECTOR ONLY IF SENT HERE FROM STEP 15).
- INSTALL J 39700 UNIVERSAL BREAKOUT BOX TO EBTCM HARNESS CONNECTOR ONLY.
- CONNECT UNPOWERED TEST LIGHT BETWEEN J 39700 TERMINALS "3" AND "38", AND "3" AND "39".
  DOES BULB GLOW BRIGHTLY BOTH TIMES?

YES → step 3. NO → REPAIR POOR POWER FEED CONDITION IN CKT 1242.

(3)
- USING J 39200, MEASURE RESISTANCE BETWEEN ADJUSTER HARNESS CONNECTOR TERMINAL "A" AND J 39700 TERMINAL "33" OR "34".
  IS IT 5 OHMS OR LESS?

YES → step 4. NO → REPAIR OPEN IN CKTs 560A, 560B, OR 560C.

(4)
- USING J 39200, MEASURE RESISTANCE BETWEEN ADJUSTER HARNESS CONNECTOR TERMINAL "B" AND J 39700 TERMINAL "54" OR "55".
  IS IT 5 OHMS OR LESS?

YES → step 5. NO → REPAIR OPEN IN CKTS 561A, 561B, OR 561C.

(5)
- USING J 39200, MEASURE RESISTANCE BETWEEN ADJUSTER ASSEMBLY HARNESS CONNECTOR TERMINALS "A" AND "B".
  IS IT 5 OHMS OR LESS?

NO → step 6. YES → REPAIR SHORT BETWEEN CKTs 560 AND 561.

(6)
- CONNECT J 39200 BETWEEN J 39700 TERMINALS "33" AND "3" (USE DC VOLTS).
- IGNITION "ON."
- NOTE VOLTAGE.
  IS IT ABOUT B + ?

NO → CONTINUE DIAGNOSIS. YES → REPAIR SHORT BETWEEN CKTs 560A, 560B OR 560C AND B +.

(7)
- REPEAT "ROTATE AND RELEASE" IN STEP 1 THREE OR FOUR MORE TIMES. REPEAT RESISTANCE MEASUREMENT EACH TIME AFTER ADJUSTER RETURNS TO STOP.
  IS RESISTANCE EVER 0.5-10 OHMS?

YES → step 8. NO → step 9.

(8)
- RECONNECT ADJUSTER ASSEMBLY.
- CLEAR DTCs, IGNITION "OFF."
- CONNECT TECH 1 WITH MSC.
- IGNITION "ON."
- SELECT DATA LIST AND MONITOR THROTTLE ANGLE.
- SLOWLY DEPRESS ACCELERATOR PEDAL UNTIL THROTTLE ANGLE HAS PASSED 30 DEGREES.
  DOES DTC 65 RESET?

NO → SYSTEM OK; RECONNECT AND ADJUST CABLES. YES → CONTINUE DIAGNOSIS AT STEP 2.

(9)
- THOROUGHLY INSPECT ADJUSTER ASSEMBLY WIRING PIGTAIL, CONNECTOR AND TERMINALS FOR SHORTING OR OPENS. REPAIR AS NEEDED, FOLLOWING SPECIAL REPAIR PROCEDURES SHOWN IN "ADJUSTER ASSEMBLY WIRING REPAIR"
- IF ALL IS OK WITH WIRING, ETC., REPLACE ADJUSTER ASSEMBLY.

GC402940088301BX

Fig. 74 Code 65: Adjuster Assembly Fault (Part 1 of 2). 1994

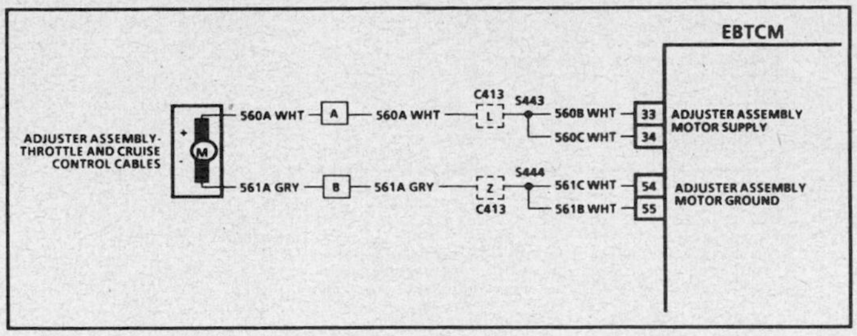
EBTCM
ADJUSTER ASSEMBLY-THROTTLE AND CRUISE CONTROL CABLES
560A WHT
A
560A WHT
C413
S443
L
560B WHT
560C WHT
33
34
ADJUSTER ASSEMBLY MOTOR SUPPLY
561A GRY
B
561A GRY
S444
Z
C413
561C WHT
561B WHT
54
55
ADJUSTER ASSEMBLY MOTOR GROUND

DTC 65

(Page 2 of 2)

ADJUSTER ASSEMBLY CIRCUIT MALFUNCTION

Circuit Description:

The adjuster assembly circuit provides both power and ground to the adjuster assembly to help control engine torque during an ASR event.

DTC Will Set When: If CKT 560 or CKT 561 are shorted to ground, shorted to B+, shorted to each other, or both open at the same time.

Action Taken: The ASR system will be disabled for the remainder of the ignition cycle and the "SERVICE ASR" indicator will be "ON."

DTC Chart Test Description: Number(s) below refer to circled number(s) on the diagnostic chart.

10. Checks for short(s) to B+ in CKT 561B and/or 561C.
11. Checks for short(s) to ground in CKT 560B and/or 560C.
12. Checks for short(s) to ground in CKT 561B and/or 561C.
13. Checks for continued DTC setting after wiring and adjuster assembly inspections.
14. Sets throttle to a position which enables one of the EBTCM's special monitoring systems of the adjuster assembly circuits, checking for a DTC reset. If the DTC resets, the EBTCM is likely at fault.
15. Checks for shorts to B+ or ground that are EBTCM-switched. If you have reached Step 15 for a second time after performing checks for EBTCM-switched faults, the EBTCM is likely at fault for the DTC reset.

Diagnostic Aids: It is very important that a thorough inspection of the wiring and connectors be performed. Failure to carefully and fully inspect wiring and connectors may result in misdiagnosis, causing part replacement with reappearance of the malfunction.

If the "SERVICE ABS," "SERVICE ASR," "ABS ACTIVE," "ASR ACTIVE," and "ASR OFF" indicators all come "ON" when the ignition is turned "ON" but do not turn "OFF" after a few seconds (bulb check), check for a poor connection or an open in ground CKT 1051, especially at the connection point to the engine.

GC402940088302AX

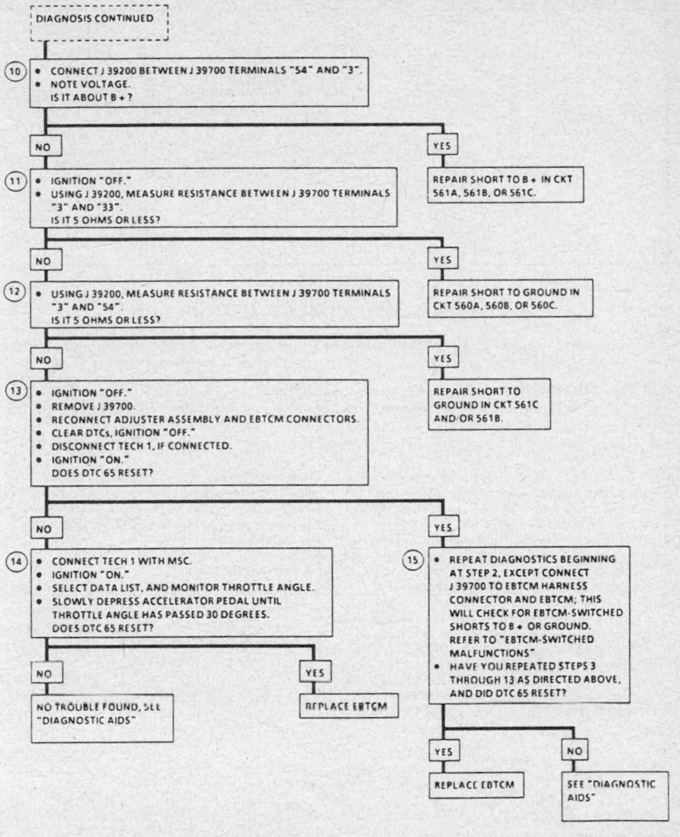
DIAGNOSIS CONTINUED
10
• CONNECT J 39200 BETWEEN J 39700 TERMINALS "54" AND "3".
• NOTE VOLTAGE.
IS IT ABOUT B+?
NO
YES
REPAIR SHORT TO B+ IN CKT 561A, 561B, OR 561C.
11
• IGNITION "OFF."
• USING J 39200, MEASURE RESISTANCE BETWEEN J 39700 TERMINALS "3" AND "33".
IS IT 5 OHMS OR LESS?
NO
YES
REPAIR SHORT TO GROUND IN CKT 560A, 560B, OR 560C.
12
• USING J 39200, MEASURE RESISTANCE BETWEEN J 39700 TERMINALS "3" AND "54".
IS IT 5 OHMS OR LESS?
NO
YES
REPAIR SHORT TO GROUND IN CKT 561C AND/OR 561B.
13
• IGNITION "OFF."
• REMOVE J 39700.
• RECONNECT ADJUSTER ASSEMBLY AND EBTCM CONNECTORS.
• CLEAR DTCs, IGNITION "OFF."
• DISCONNECT TECH 1, IF CONNECTED.
• IGNITION "ON."
DOES DTC 65 RESET?
NO
YES
14
• CONNECT TECH 1 WITH MSC.
• IGNITION "ON."
• SELECT DATA LIST, AND MONITOR THROTTLE ANGLE.
• SLOWLY DEPRESS ACCELERATOR PEDAL UNTIL THROTTLE ANGLE HAS PASSED 30 DEGREES.
DOES DTC 65 RESET?
NO
YES
NO TROUBLE FOUND, SEE "DIAGNOSTIC AIDS"
REPLACE EBTCM
15
• REPEAT DIAGNOSTICS BEGINNING AT STEP 2, EXCEPT CONNECT J 39700 TO EBTCM HARNESS CONNECTOR AND EBTCM; THIS WILL CHECK FOR EBTCM-SWITCHED SHORTS TO B+ OR GROUND. REFER TO "EBTCM-SWITCHED MALFUNCTIONS"
• HAVE YOU REPEATED STEPS 3 THROUGH 13 AS DIRECTED ABOVE, AND DID DTC 65 RESET?
YES
NO
REPLACE EBTCM
SEE "DIAGNOSTIC AIDS"

GC402940088302BX

Fig. 74 Code 65: Adjuster Assembly Fault (Part 2 of 2). 1994

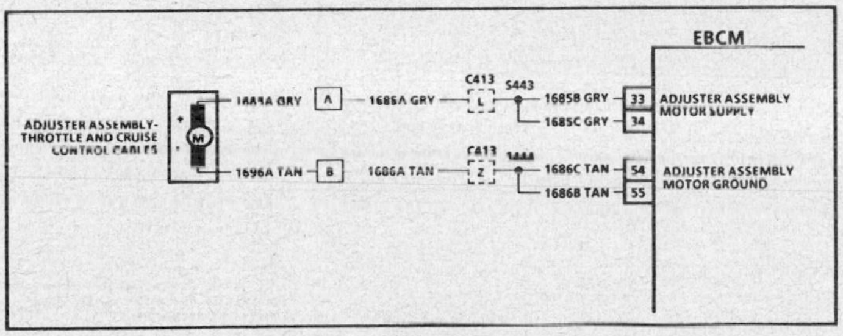
EBCM
ADJUSTER ASSEMBLY-THROTTLE AND CRUISE CONTROL CABLES
1685A GRY
A
1685A GRY
C413
S443
L
1685B GRY
1685C GRY
33
34
ADJUSTER ASSEMBLY MOTOR SUPPLY
1686A TAN
B
1686A TAN
C413
S444
Z
1686C TAN
1686B TAN
54
55
ADJUSTER ASSEMBLY MOTOR GROUND

CODE 66

ADJUSTER ASSEMBLY CONTROL FAULT

Circuit Description:

The Adjuster Assembly circuit provides both power and ground to the Adjuster Assembly to help control engine torque during an ASR event.

Code 66 will set if, during an ASR event, the EBCM delivers current greater than 16 amps to the Adjuster Assembly for more than three seconds without the Adjuster Assembly reaching its desired position.

Test Description: Number(s) below refer to circled number(s) on the diagnostic chart.

1. Checks to see if ASR Code 65 is set, since Code 65 conditions might affect Code 66.
2. Checks for any mechanical binding of the Adjuster Assembly, attached cables, and components to which the cables are attached, which could cause excessive load on the Adjuster Assembly.
3. Since Code 66 only sets during an ASR event, this check raises the vehicle on a hoist such that the rear wheels will spin while the fronts do not, inducing the system into attempting ASR control. The throttle angle must be greater than 15%, and less than 50%, and the system must attempt ASR control for greater than 3 seconds to ensure that the code-setting throttle and timing parameters are met when checking for a Code 66 reset.

Diagnostic Aids:

It may be helpful to disconnect all cables from the adjuster assembly and move them manually throughout their entire operating range. Also check the components to which the cables are attached for binding.

Important

- After cables are reconnected to the Adjuster Assembly, perform "Adjustment Procedure-Adjuster Assembly - Accelerator and Cruise Control Cables"

GC402920043600AX

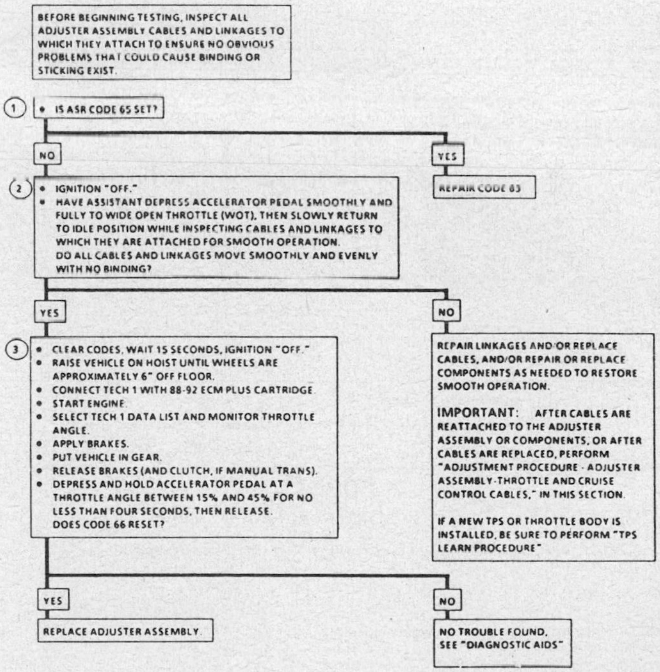
BEFORE BEGINNING TESTING, INSPECT ALL ADJUSTER ASSEMBLY CABLES AND LINKAGES TO WHICH THEY ATTACH TO ENSURE NO OBVIOUS PROBLEMS THAT COULD CAUSE BINDING OR STICKING EXIST.
1
• IS ASR CODE 65 SET?
NO
YES
REPAIR CODE 65
2
• IGNITION "OFF."
• HAVE ASSISTANT DEPRESS ACCELERATOR PEDAL SMOOTHLY AND FULLY TO WIDE OPEN THROTTLE (WOT), THEN SLOWLY RETURN TO IDLE POSITION WHILE INSPECTING CABLES AND LINKAGES TO WHICH THEY ARE ATTACHED FOR SMOOTH OPERATION.
DO ALL CABLES AND LINKAGES MOVE SMOOTHLY AND EVENLY WITH NO BINDING?
YES
NO
3
• CLEAR CODES, WAIT 15 SECONDS, IGNITION "OFF."
• RAISE VEHICLE ON HOIST UNTIL WHEELS ARE APPROXIMATELY 6" OFF FLOOR.
• CONNECT TECH 1 WITH 88-92 ECM PLUS CARTRIDGE
• START ENGINE.
• SELECT TECH 1 DATA LIST AND MONITOR THROTTLE ANGLE.
• APPLY BRAKES.
• PUT VEHICLE IN GEAR.
• RELEASE BRAKES (AND CLUTCH, IF MANUAL TRANS).
• DEPRESS AND HOLD ACCELERATOR PEDAL AT A THROTTLE ANGLE BETWEEN 15% AND 45% FOR NO LESS THAN FOUR SECONDS, THEN RELEASE.
DOES CODE 66 RESET?
REPAIR LINKAGES AND/OR REPLACE CABLES, AND/OR REPAIR OR REPLACE COMPONENTS AS NEEDED TO RESTORE SMOOTH OPERATION.
IMPORTANT: AFTER CABLES ARE REATTACHED TO THE ADJUSTER ASSEMBLY OR COMPONENTS, OR AFTER CABLES ARE REPLACED, PERFORM "ADJUSTMENT PROCEDURE - ADJUSTER ASSEMBLY-THROTTLE AND CRUISE CONTROL CABLES," IN THIS SECTION.
IF A NEW TPS OR THROTTLE BODY IS INSTALLED, BE SURE TO PERFORM "TPS LEARN PROCEDURE"
YES
NO
REPLACE ADJUSTER ASSEMBLY.
NO TROUBLE FOUND, SEE "DIAGNOSTIC AIDS"

GC402920043600BX

Fig. 75 Code 66: Adjuster Assembly Control Fault. 1992–93

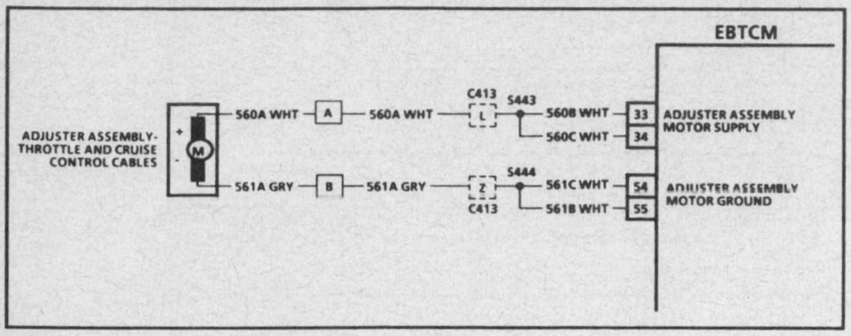
EBTCM
ADJUSTER ASSEMBLY-THROTTLE AND CRUISE CONTROL CABLES
M
560A WHT
A
560A WHT
C413
S443
L
560B WHT
560C WHT
33
34
ADJUSTER ASSEMBLY MOTOR SUPPLY
561A GRY
B
561A GRY
S444
Z
C413
561C WHT
561B WHT
54
55
ADJUSTER ASSEMBLY MOTOR GROUND

DTC 66

ADJUSTER ASSEMBLY CONTROL MALFUNCTION

Circuit Description:

The adjuster assembly circuit provides both power and ground to the adjuster assembly to help control engine torque during an ASR event.

DTC Will Set When: If (during an ASR event) the EBTCM delivers current greater than 16 amps to the adjuster assembly for more than three seconds without the adjuster assembly reaching its desired position.

DTC Chart Test Description: Number(s) below refer to circled number(s) on the diagnostic chart.

1. Checks to see if ASR DTC 65 is set, since DTC 65 conditions might affect DTC 66.
2. Checks for any mechanical binding of the adjuster assembly, attached cables, and components to which the cables are attached, which could cause excessive load on the adjuster assembly.
3. Since DTC 66 only sets during an ASR event, this check raises the vehicle on a hoist such that the rear wheels will spin while the fronts do not, inducing the system into attempting ASR control. The throttle angle must be greater than 15%, and less than 50%, and the system must attempt ASR control for greater than 3 seconds to ensure that the DTC setting throttle and timing parameters are met when checking for a DTC 66 reset.

Diagnostic Aids: It may be helpful to disconnect all cables from the adjuster assembly and move them manually throughout their entire operating range. Also check the components to which the cables are attached for binding.

Important

- After cables are reconnected to the adjuster assembly, perform "Adjustment Procedure-Adjuster Assembly - Accelerator and Cruise Control Cables" in this section.

GC402940088400AX

BEFORE BEGINNING TESTING, INSPECT ALL ADJUSTER ASSEMBLY CABLES AND LINKAGES TO WHICH THEY ATTACH TO ENSURE NO OBVIOUS PROBLEMS THAT COULD CAUSE BINDING OR STICKING EXIST.

(1)
- IS ASR DTC 65 SET?

YES: REPAIR DTC 65

NO:

(2)
- IGNITION "OFF."
- HAVE ASSISTANT DEPRESS ACCELERATOR PEDAL SMOOTHLY AND FULLY TO WIDE OPEN THROTTLE (WOT), THEN SLOWLY RETURN TO IDLE POSITION WHILE INSPECTING CABLES AND LINKAGES TO WHICH THEY ARE ATTACHED FOR SMOOTH OPERATION. DO ALL CABLES AND LINKAGES MOVE SMOOTHLY AND EVENLY WITH NO BINDING?

NO: REPAIR LINKAGES AND/OR REPLACE CABLES, AND OR REPAIR OR REPLACE COMPONENTS AS NEEDED TO RESTORE SMOOTH OPERATION.

IMPORTANT: AFTER CABLES ARE REATTACHED TO THE ADJUSTER ASSEMBLY OR COMPONENTS, OR AFTER CABLES ARE REPLACED, PERFORM "ADJUSTMENT PROCEDURE - ADJUSTER ASSEMBLY-THROTTLE AND CRUISE CONTROL CABLES," IN THIS SECTION.

IF A NEW TP SENSOR OR THROTTLE BODY IS INSTALLED, BE SURE TO PERFORM "TP SENSOR LEARN PROCEDURE"

YES:

(3)
- CLEAR DTC(s), WAIT 15 SECONDS, IGNITION "OFF."
- RAISE VEHICLE ON HOIST UNTIL WHEELS ARE APPROXIMATELY 6" OFF FLOOR.
- CONNECT TECH 1 WITH ECM PLUS CARTRIDGE.
- START ENGINE.
- SELECT TECH 1 DATA LIST AND MONITOR THROTTLE ANGLE.
- APPLY BRAKES.
- PUT VEHICLE IN GEAR.
- RELEASE BRAKES (AND CLUTCH, IF MANUAL TRANS).
- DEPRESS AND HOLD ACCELERATOR PEDAL AT A THROTTLE ANGLE BETWEEN 15% AND 45% FOR NO LESS THAN FOUR SECONDS, THEN RELEASE. DOES DTC 66 RESET?

YES: REPLACE ADJUSTER ASSEMBLY.

NO: NO TROUBLE FOUND, SEE "DIAGNOSTIC AIDS"

GC402940088400BX

Fig. 76 Code 66: Adjuster Assembly Control Fault. 1994

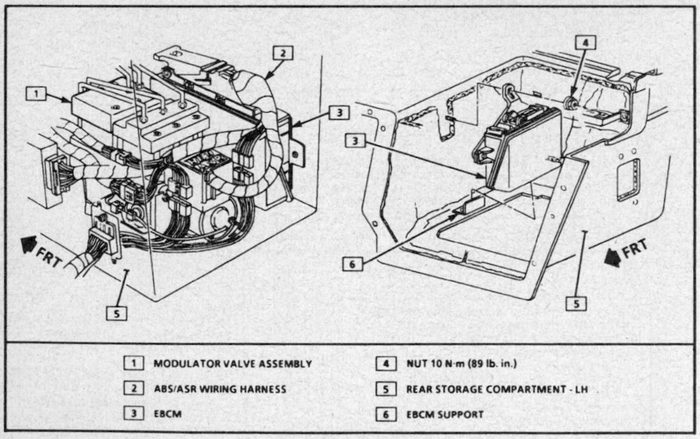
FRT
FRT
1
2
3
4
5
6
1 MODULATOR VALVE ASSEMBLY
2 ABS/ASR WIRING HARNESS
3 EBCM
4 NUT 10 N·m (89 lb. in.)
5 REAR STORAGE COMPARTMENT - LH
6 EBCM SUPPORT

CODE 71

EBCM INTERNAL FAULT

Circuit Description:

The EBCM performs various diagnostic checks on itself. If it finds a problem, Code 71 will set.

Test Description: Number(s) below refer to circled number(s) on the diagnostic chart.

1. Checks for good connections from the harness to the EBCM itself.
2. Checks to see if the fault was false. If Code 71 resets, replace the EBCM.

GC402920043700AX

(1)
- IGNITION "OFF."
- CHECK EBCM CONNECTOR CAREFULLY TO ENSURE GOOD ELECTRICAL CONTACT AT ALL TERMINALS, AND THAT CONNECTOR IS PROPERLY RETAINED WHEN CONNECTED. IS ALL OK?

NO: REPAIR TERMINAL(S), CONNECTOR OR CONNECTOR RETENTION AS NECESSARY REFER TO "INTERMITTENTS

YES:

(2)
- CLEAR CODES, IGNITION "OFF."
- DISCONNECT TECH 1, IF CONNECTED.
- IGNITION "ON."
- DOES CODE 71 RESET?

YES: REPLACE EBCM.

NO: NO TROUBLE FOUND; SEE "DIAGNOSTIC AIDS"

GC402920043700BX

Fig. 77 Code 71: EBTCM Fault. 1992–93

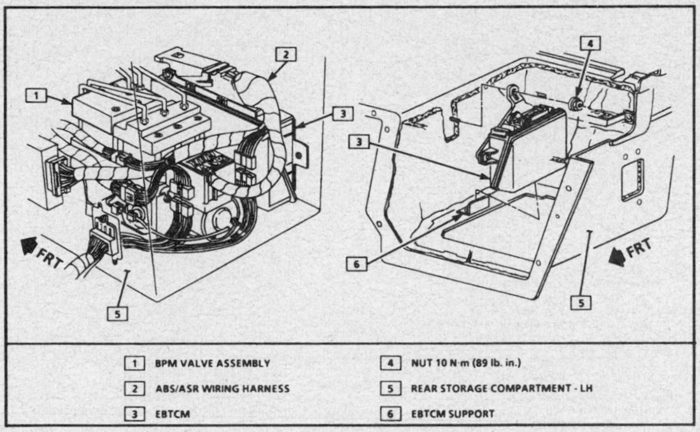
1
2
3
4
5
6
FRT
1 BPM VALVE ASSEMBLY
2 ABS/ASR WIRING HARNESS
3 EBTCM
4 NUT 10 N·m (89 lb. in.)
5 REAR STORAGE COMPARTMENT - LH
6 EBTCM SUPPORT

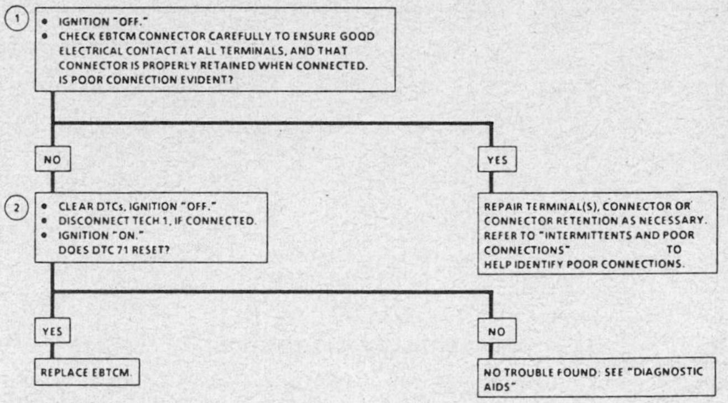
1 • IGNITION "OFF."
• CHECK EBTCM CONNECTOR CAREFULLY TO ENSURE GOOD ELECTRICAL CONTACT AT ALL TERMINALS, AND THAT CONNECTOR IS PROPERLY RETAINED WHEN CONNECTED. IS POOR CONNECTION EVIDENT?
NO
YES
2 • CLEAR DTCs, IGNITION "OFF."
• DISCONNECT TECH 1, IF CONNECTED.
• IGNITION "ON."
DOES DTC 71 RESET?
REPAIR TERMINAL(S), CONNECTOR OR CONNECTOR RETENTION AS NECESSARY. REFER TO "INTERMITTENTS AND POOR CONNECTIONS" TO HELP IDENTIFY POOR CONNECTIONS.
YES
NO
REPLACE EBTCM.
NO TROUBLE FOUND: SEE "DIAGNOSTIC AIDS"
GC402940088500BX

DTC 71

EBTCM INTERNAL MALFUNCTION

Circuit Description:

The EBTCM performs various diagnostic checks on itself. If it finds a malfunction, DTC 71 will set.

DTC Chart Test Description: Number(s) below refer to circled number(s) on the diagnostic chart.

1. Checks for good connections from the harness to the EBTCM itself.
2. Checks to see if the malfunction was false. If DTC 71 resets, replace the EBTCM.

GC402940088500AX

Fig. 78 Code 71: EBTCM Fault. 1994

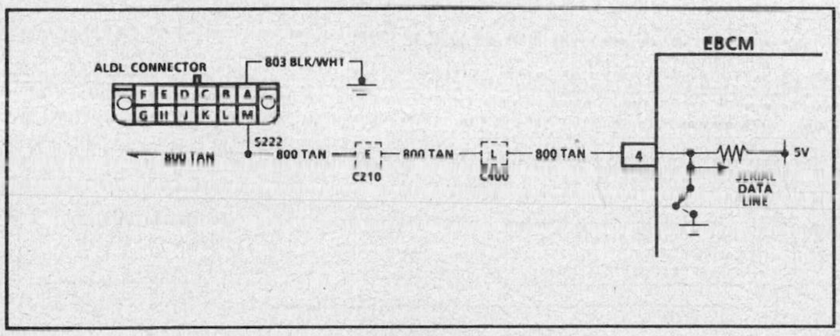
ALDL CONNECTOR
803 BLK/WHT
F E D C B A
G H J K L M
S222
800 TAN
800 TAN
E
C210
800 TAN
L
C400
800 TAN
4
EBCM
5V
SERIAL DATA LINE

CODE 72

SERIAL DATA LINK FAULT

Circuit Description:

The Serial Data Link is an asynchronous link operating at 8192 bits per second.

Code 72 will set and the "SERVICE ASR" indicator will illuminate if the EBCM detects three consecutive serial data link messages that are ignored due to errors in transmission.

Test Description: Number(s) below refer to circled number(s) on the diagnostic chart.

1. This test checks to see if the off-board device can communicate with the EBCM. CCM code display mode can also be used to communicate the the EBCM. Refer to "Display ABS/ASR Fault Codes" for details. If the CCM cannot communicate with the EBCM, it will display "Err" when the EBCM is selected for code display.
2. This test checks for a short to battery in the ABS/ASR serial data circuit.
3. This test checks for a short to ground in the ABS/ASR serial data circuit.
4. This test checks for an open in the ABS/ASR serial data circuit.
5. This test checks to see if the off-board device can communicate with the EBCM.
6. If the connections at the EBCM and ALDL connector are OK, replace the EBCM.

Diagnostic Aids:

The problem may be intermittent. Try performing the tests shown while "wiggling" wiring and connectors; this can often cause the fault to appear.

CCM Code 41 will likely be set along with this code if the problem is a short to ground or B+ on the Serial Data circuit.

If ABS/ASR Code 72 is set and CCM Code 41 is not, the fault is likely to be an open between the EBCM and the CCM.

GC402920043800AX

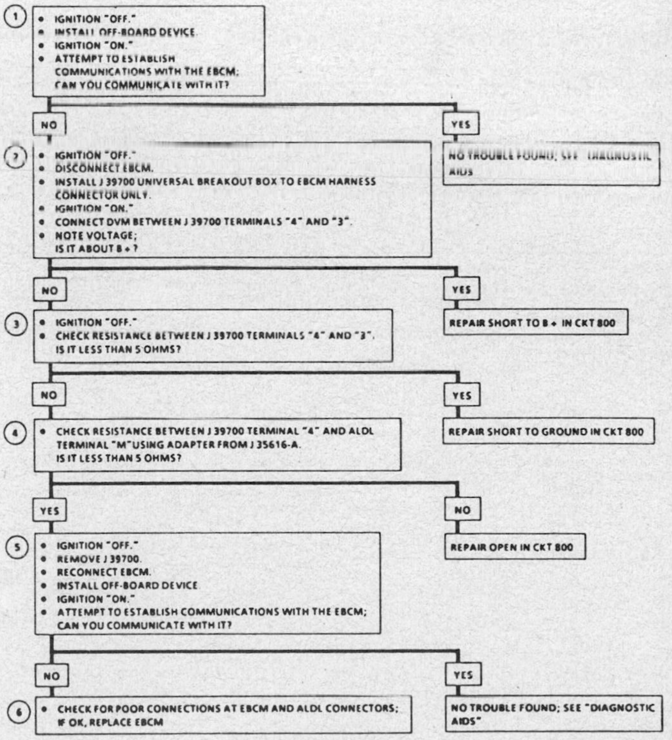
1 • IGNITION "OFF."
• INSTALL OFF-BOARD DEVICE.
• IGNITION "ON."
• ATTEMPT TO ESTABLISH COMMUNICATIONS WITH THE EBCM; CAN YOU COMMUNICATE WITH IT?
NO
YES
2 • IGNITION "OFF."
• DISCONNECT EBCM.
• INSTALL J 39700 UNIVERSAL BREAKOUT BOX TO EBCM HARNESS CONNECTOR ONLY.
• IGNITION "ON."
• CONNECT DVM BETWEEN J 39700 TERMINALS "4" AND "3".
• NOTE VOLTAGE; IS IT ABOUT B+?
NO
YES
3 • IGNITION "OFF."
• CHECK RESISTANCE BETWEEN J 39700 TERMINALS "4" AND "3". IS IT LESS THAN 5 OHMS?
REPAIR SHORT TO B+ IN CKT 800
NO
YES
4 • CHECK RESISTANCE BETWEEN J 39700 TERMINAL "4" AND ALDL TERMINAL "M" USING ADAPTER FROM J 35616-A. IS IT LESS THAN 5 OHMS?
REPAIR SHORT TO GROUND IN CKT 800
YES
NO
5 • IGNITION "OFF."
• REMOVE J 39700.
• RECONNECT EBCM.
• INSTALL OFF-BOARD DEVICE.
• IGNITION "ON."
• ATTEMPT TO ESTABLISH COMMUNICATIONS WITH THE EBCM; CAN YOU COMMUNICATE WITH IT?
REPAIR OPEN IN CKT 800
NO
YES
6 • CHECK FOR POOR CONNECTIONS AT EBCM AND ALDL CONNECTORS; IF OK, REPLACE EBCM
NO TROUBLE FOUND; SEE "DIAGNOSTIC AIDS"
GC402920043800BX

Fig. 79 Code 72: Serial Data Link Fault. 1992–93

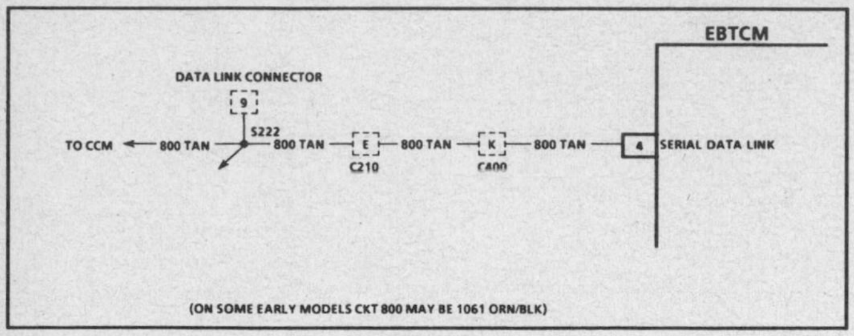
EBTCM
DATA LINK CONNECTOR
9
S222
TO CCM
800 TAN
800 TAN
E
C210
800 TAN
K
C400
800 TAN
4
SERIAL DATA LINK
(ON SOME EARLY MODELS CKT 800 MAY BE 1061 ORN/BLK)

DTC 72

SERIAL DATA LINE MALFUNCTION

Circuit Description:
The serial data link is an asynchronous link operating at 8192 bits per second.

DTC Will Set When: The EBTCM detects three consecutive serial data line messages that are ignored due to errors in the transmission.

Action Taken: The "SERVICE ASR" indicator will be "ON."

DTC Chart Test Description: Number(s) below refer to circled number(s) on the diagnostic chart.
1. Checks to see if the off-board device can communicate with the EBTCM. CCM DTC display mode can also be used to communicate to the EBTCM. Refer to "Display ABS/ASR DTCs" for details. If the CCM cannot communicate with the EBTCM, it will display "Err" when the EBTCM is selected for DTC display.

Diagnostic Aids: The malfunction may be intermittent. Try performing the tests shown while "wiggling" wiring and connectors; this can often cause the malfunction to appear.

CCM DTC 41 will likely be set along with this DTC if the malfunction is a short to ground or B+ on the serial data circuit.

If ABS/ASR DTC 72 is set and CCM DTC 41 is not, the malfunction is likely to be an open between the EBTCM and the CCM.

GC402940088600AX

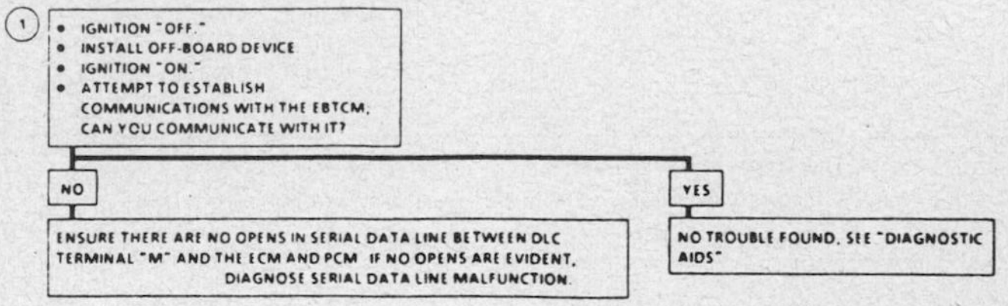
1
• IGNITION "OFF."
• INSTALL OFF-BOARD DEVICE
• IGNITION "ON."
• ATTEMPT TO ESTABLISH COMMUNICATIONS WITH THE EBTCM. CAN YOU COMMUNICATE WITH IT?
NO
YES
ENSURE THERE ARE NO OPENS IN SERIAL DATA LINE BETWEEN DLC TERMINAL "M" AND THE ECM AND PCM. IF NO OPENS ARE EVIDENT, DIAGNOSE SERIAL DATA LINE MALFUNCTION.
NO TROUBLE FOUND. SEE "DIAGNOSTIC AIDS"

GC402940088600BX

Fig. 80 Code 72: Serial Data Link Fault. 1994

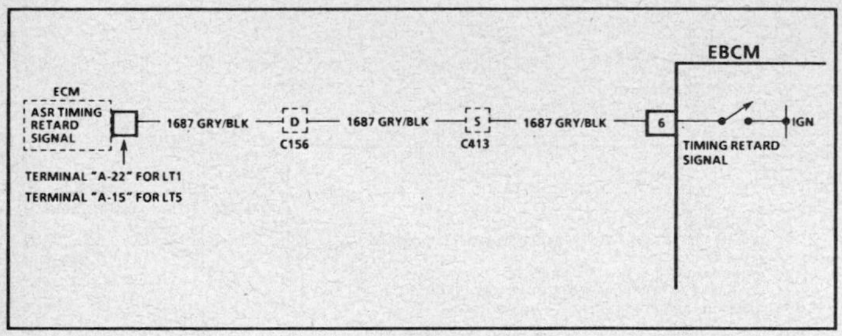
EBCM
ECM
ASR TIMING RETARD SIGNAL
1687 GRY/BLK
D
C156
1687 GRY/BLK
5
C413
1687 GRY/BLK
6
IGN
TIMING RETARD SIGNAL
TERMINAL "A-22" FOR LT1
TERMINAL "A-15" FOR LT5

CODE 73

SPARK RETARD MONITORING FAULT

Circuit Description:
The EBCM, upon sensing the need for ASR intervention, requests spark retard from the ECM by supplying B+ to CKT 1687.

Code 73 will set if the EBCM senses an open, short to B+, or short to ground on CKT 1687.

Test Description: Number(s) below refer to circled number(s) on the diagnostic chart.
1. Checks for a short to B+ on CKT 1687.
2. Checks for a short to ground on CKT 1687.
3. Checks CKT 1687 and internal ECM circuitry for proper resistance.
4. Checks for code reset after the rest of the system has checked OK.
5. Checks if a problem found in Step 3 is due to an open in CKT 1687 or an internally-faulty ECM.

Diagnostic Aids:

It is very important that a thorough inspection of the wiring and connectors be performed. Failure to carefully and fully inspect wiring and connectors may result in misdiagnosis, causing part replacement with reappearance of the fault.

GC402920043900AX

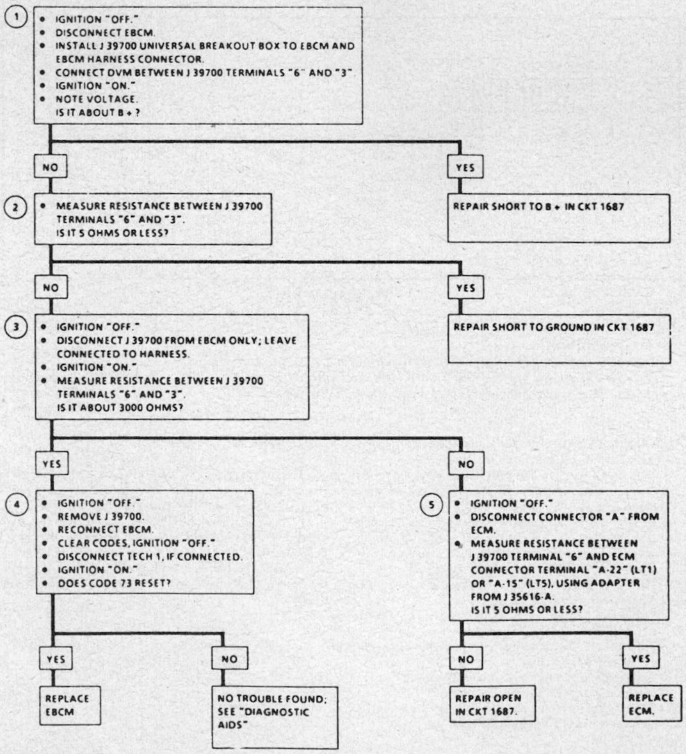
1
• IGNITION "OFF."
• DISCONNECT EBCM.
• INSTALL J 39700 UNIVERSAL BREAKOUT BOX TO EBCM AND EBCM HARNESS CONNECTOR.
• CONNECT DVM BETWEEN J 39700 TERMINALS "6" AND "3".
• IGNITION "ON."
• NOTE VOLTAGE. IS IT ABOUT B+?
NO
YES
REPAIR SHORT TO B+ IN CKT 1687
2
• MEASURE RESISTANCE BETWEEN J 39700 TERMINALS "6" AND "3". IS IT 5 OHMS OR LESS?
NO
YES
REPAIR SHORT TO GROUND IN CKT 1687
3
• IGNITION "OFF."
• DISCONNECT J 39700 FROM EBCM ONLY; LEAVE CONNECTED TO HARNESS.
• IGNITION "ON."
• MEASURE RESISTANCE BETWEEN J 39700 TERMINALS "6" AND "3". IS IT ABOUT 3000 OHMS?
YES
NO
4
• IGNITION "OFF."
• REMOVE J 39700.
• RECONNECT EBCM.
• CLEAR CODES, IGNITION "OFF."
• DISCONNECT TECH 1, IF CONNECTED.
• IGNITION "ON."
• DOES CODE 73 RESET?
5
• IGNITION "OFF."
• DISCONNECT CONNECTOR "A" FROM ECM.
• MEASURE RESISTANCE BETWEEN J 39700 TERMINAL "6" AND ECM CONNECTOR TERMINAL "A-22" (LT1) OR "A-15" (LT5), USING ADAPTER FROM J 35616-A. IS IT 5 OHMS OR LESS?
YES
NO
NO
YES
REPLACE EBCM
NO TROUBLE FOUND; SEE "DIAGNOSTIC AIDS"
REPAIR OPEN IN CKT 1687.
REPLACE ECM.

GC402920043900BX

Fig. 81 Code 73: Spark Retard Monitoring Fault. 1992–93

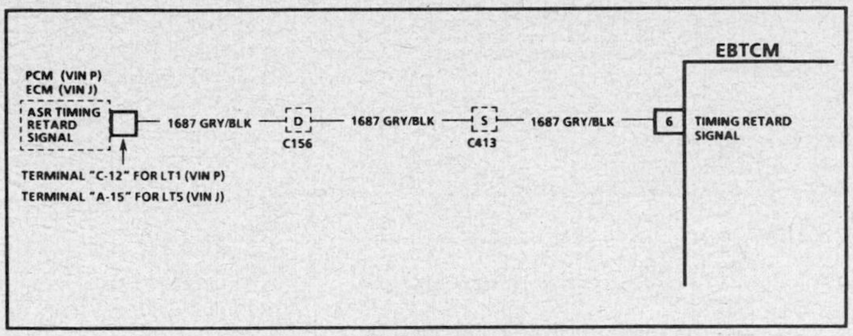
PCM (VIN P)
ECM (VIN J)
ASR TIMING RETARD SIGNAL
1687 GRY/BLK
D
C156
1687 GRY/BLK
S
C413
1687 GRY/BLK
EBTCM
6
TIMING RETARD SIGNAL
TERMINAL "C-12" FOR LT1 (VIN P)
TERMINAL "A-15" FOR LT5 (VIN J)

DTC 73

SPARK RETARD MONITORING MALFUNCTION

Circuit Description:
The EBTCM, upon sensing the need for ASR intervention, requests spark retard from the ECM (VIN J) or PCM (VIN P) by supplying B+ to CKT 1687.

DTC Will Set When: The EBTCM senses an open, short to B+, or short to ground on CKT 1687.

DTC Chart Test Description: Number(s) below refer to circled number(s) on the diagnostic chart.
1. Checks for a short to B+ on CKT 1687.
2. Checks for a short to ground on CKT 1687.
3. Checks CKT 1687 and internal ECM (VIN J) or PCM (VIN P) circuitry for proper resistance.
4. Checks for DTC reset after the rest of the system has checked OK.
5. Checks if a malfunction found in Step 3 is due to an open in CKT 1687 or an internally-malfunctioning ECM (VIN J) or PCM (VIN P).

Diagnostic Aids: It is very important that a thorough inspection of the wiring and connectors be performed. Failure to carefully and fully inspect wiring and connectors may result in misdiagnosis, causing part replacement with reappearance of the malfunction.

GC402940088700AX

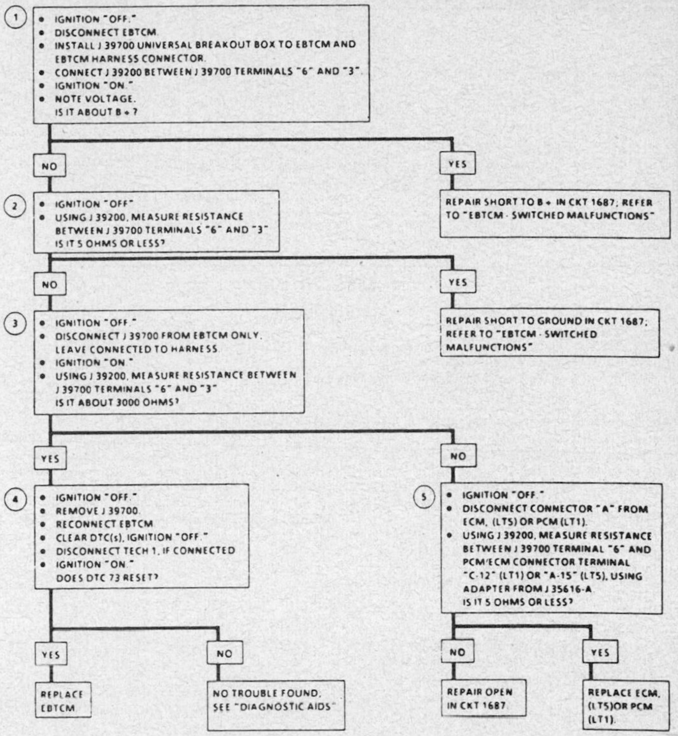
1
• IGNITION "OFF."
• DISCONNECT EBTCM.
• INSTALL J 39700 UNIVERSAL BREAKOUT BOX TO EBTCM AND EBTCM HARNESS CONNECTOR.
• CONNECT J 39200 BETWEEN J 39700 TERMINALS "6" AND "3".
• IGNITION "ON."
• NOTE VOLTAGE.
IS IT ABOUT B+?
NO
YES
REPAIR SHORT TO B+ IN CKT 1687; REFER TO "EBTCM - SWITCHED MALFUNCTIONS"
2
• IGNITION "OFF"
• USING J 39200, MEASURE RESISTANCE BETWEEN J 39700 TERMINALS "6" AND "3"
IS IT 5 OHMS OR LESS?
NO
YES
REPAIR SHORT TO GROUND IN CKT 1687; REFER TO "EBTCM - SWITCHED MALFUNCTIONS"
3
• IGNITION "OFF."
• DISCONNECT J 39700 FROM EBTCM ONLY. LEAVE CONNECTED TO HARNESS.
• IGNITION "ON."
• USING J 39200, MEASURE RESISTANCE BETWEEN J 39700 TERMINALS "6" AND "3"
IS IT ABOUT 3000 OHMS?
YES
NO
4
• IGNITION "OFF."
• REMOVE J 39700.
• RECONNECT EBTCM
• CLEAR DTC(s), IGNITION "OFF."
• DISCONNECT TECH 1, IF CONNECTED
• IGNITION "ON."
DOES DTC 73 RESET?
5
• IGNITION "OFF."
• DISCONNECT CONNECTOR "A" FROM ECM, (LT5) OR PCM (LT1).
• USING J 39200, MEASURE RESISTANCE BETWEEN J 39700 TERMINAL "6" AND PCM/ECM CONNECTOR TERMINAL "C-12" (LT1) OR "A-15" (LT5), USING ADAPTER FROM J 35616-A.
IS IT 5 OHMS OR LESS?
YES
NO
NO
YES
REPLACE EBTCM
NO TROUBLE FOUND; SEE "DIAGNOSTIC AIDS"
REPAIR OPEN IN CKT 1687
REPLACE ECM, (LT5)OR PCM (LT1).

GC402940088700BX

Fig. 82 Code 73: Spark Retard Monitoring Fault. 1994

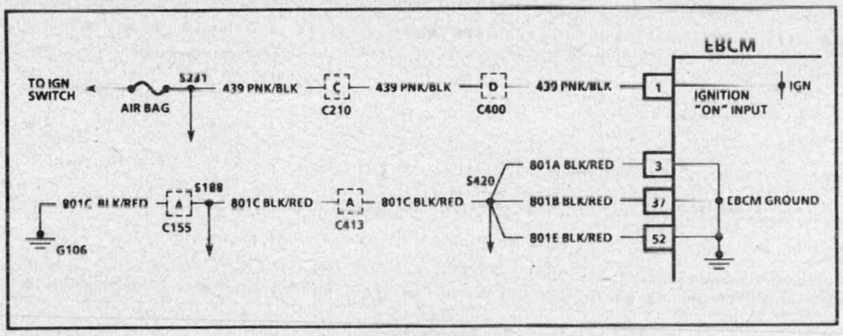
TO IGN SWITCH
AIR BAG
S201
439 PNK/BLK
C
C210
439 PNK/BLK
D
C400
439 PNK/BLK
EBCM
1
IGNITION "ON" INPUT
IGN
801C BLK/RED
G106
A
C155
S188
801C BLK/RED
A
C413
801C BLK/RED
S420
801A BLK/RED
801B BLK/RED
801E BLK/RED
3
37
52
EBCM GROUND

CODE 74

LOW VOLTAGE

Circuit Description:
The EBCM, requires a certain minimum voltage to operate properly. It monitors the ignition feed circuit to determine if voltage fails below a minimum level.
Code 74 will set if the EBCM operating voltage falls below 9.0 volts.

Test Description: Number(s) below refer to circled number(s) on the diagnostic chart.
1. Checks that AIRBAG fuse feeding the EBCM ignition circuit is good.
2. Measures for appropriate voltage from the EBCM ignition circuit, using each of the three EBCM ground lines to complete the circuit.
3. Checks EBCM connector terminals for good contact, i.e. not spread open, backed out of connector, corroded, etc.
4. Checks EBCM connector for good retention to EBCM when installed.
5. Checks for code reset after other portions of the system have tested as OK.
6. Determines if a problem found in Step 2 is due to an open or poor connection in the EBCM Ignition Feed CKT 439, or poor ground(s) in CKT 801.

Diagnostic Aids:

It is very important that a thorough inspection of the wiring and connectors be performed. Failure to carefully and fully inspect wiring and connectors may result in misdiagnosis, causing part replacement with reappearance of the fault.

GC402920044000AX

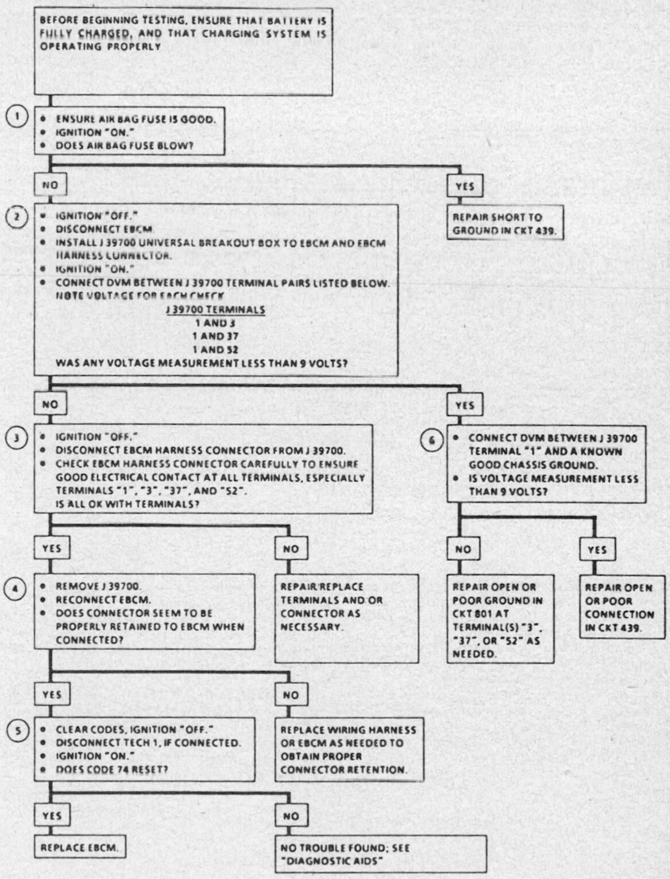
BEFORE BEGINNING TESTING, ENSURE THAT BATTERY IS FULLY CHARGED, AND THAT CHARGING SYSTEM IS OPERATING PROPERLY
1
• ENSURE AIR BAG FUSE IS GOOD.
• IGNITION "ON."
• DOES AIR BAG FUSE BLOW?
NO
YES
REPAIR SHORT TO GROUND IN CKT 439.
2
• IGNITION "OFF."
• DISCONNECT EBCM.
• INSTALL J 39700 UNIVERSAL BREAKOUT BOX TO EBCM AND EBCM HARNESS CONNECTOR.
• IGNITION "ON."
• CONNECT DVM BETWEEN J 39700 TERMINAL PAIRS LISTED BELOW. NOTE VOLTAGE FOR EACH CHECK
J 39700 TERMINALS
1 AND 3
1 AND 37
1 AND 52
WAS ANY VOLTAGE MEASUREMENT LESS THAN 9 VOLTS?
NO
YES
3
• IGNITION "OFF."
• DISCONNECT EBCM HARNESS CONNECTOR FROM J 39700.
• CHECK EBCM HARNESS CONNECTOR CAREFULLY TO ENSURE GOOD ELECTRICAL CONTACT AT ALL TERMINALS, ESPECIALLY TERMINALS "1", "3", "37", AND "52".
IS ALL OK WITH TERMINALS?
6
• CONNECT DVM BETWEEN J 39700 TERMINAL "1" AND A KNOWN GOOD CHASSIS GROUND.
• IS VOLTAGE MEASUREMENT LESS THAN 9 VOLTS?
YES
NO
NO
YES
4
• REMOVE J 39700.
• RECONNECT EBCM.
• DOES CONNECTOR SEEM TO BE PROPERLY RETAINED TO EBCM WHEN CONNECTED?
REPAIR/REPLACE TERMINALS AND/OR CONNECTOR AS NECESSARY.
REPAIR OPEN OR POOR GROUND IN CKT 801 AT TERMINAL(S) "3", "37", OR "52" AS NEEDED.
REPAIR OPEN OR POOR CONNECTION IN CKT 439.
YES
NO
5
• CLEAR CODES, IGNITION "OFF."
• DISCONNECT TECH 1, IF CONNECTED.
• IGNITION "ON."
• DOES CODE 74 RESET?
REPLACE WIRING HARNESS OR EBCM AS NEEDED TO OBTAIN PROPER CONNECTOR RETENTION.
YES
NO
REPLACE EBCM.
NO TROUBLE FOUND; SEE "DIAGNOSTIC AIDS"

GC402920044000BX

Fig. 83 Code 74: Low Voltage. 1992

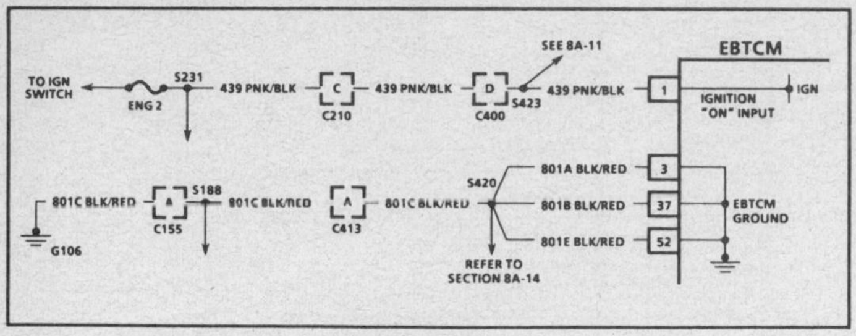
SEE 8A-11
EBTCM
TO IGN SWITCH
S231
ENG 2
439 PNK/BLK
C
C210
439 PNK/BLK
D
C400
S423
439 PNK/BLK
1
IGNITION "ON" INPUT
IGN
801A BLK/RED
3
S420
801B BLK/RED
37
EBTCM GROUND
801E BLK/RED
52
801C BLK/RED
A
S188
C155
801C BLK/RED
A
C413
801C BLK/RED
G106
REFER TO SECTION 8A-14

DTC 74

LOW VOLTAGE

Circuit Description:

The EBTCM, requires a certain minimum voltage to operate properly. It monitors the ignition feed circuit to determine if voltage fails below a minimum level.

DTC 74 will set if the EBTCM operating voltage falls below 9.0 volts.

Test Description: Number(s) below refer to circled number(s) on the diagnostic chart.

1. Checks that ENG2 fuse feeding the EBTCM ignition circuit is good.
2. Measures for appropriate voltage from the EBTCM ignition circuit, using each of the three EBTCM ground lines to complete the circuit.
3. Checks EBTCM connector terminals for good contact, i.e. not spread open, backed out of connector, corroded, etc.
4. Checks EBTCM connector for good retention to EBTCM when installed.
5. Checks for DTC reset after other portions of the system have tested as OK.
6. Determines if a problem found in Step 2 is due to an open or poor connection in the EBTCM ignition feed CKT 439, or poor ground(s) in CKT 801.

Diagnostic Aids:

It is very important that a thorough inspection of the wiring and connectors be performed. Failure to carefully and fully inspect wiring and connectors may result in misdiagnosis, causing part replacement with reappearance of the malfunction.

GC402930044100AX

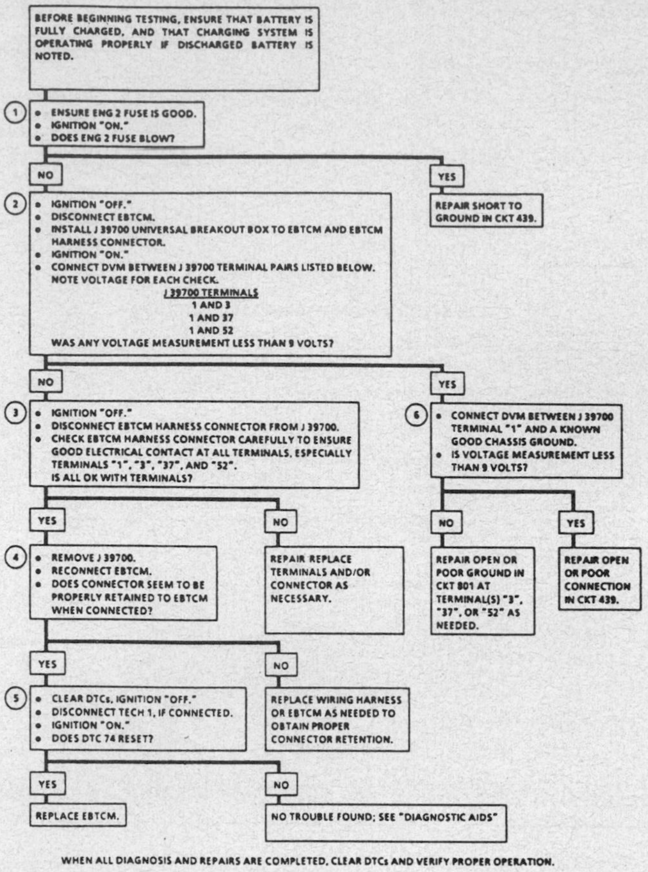
BEFORE BEGINNING TESTING, ENSURE THAT BATTERY IS FULLY CHARGED, AND THAT CHARGING SYSTEM IS OPERATING PROPERLY IF DISCHARGED BATTERY IS NOTED.
1
• ENSURE ENG 2 FUSE IS GOOD.
• IGNITION "ON."
• DOES ENG 2 FUSE BLOW?
NO
YES
REPAIR SHORT TO GROUND IN CKT 439.
2
• IGNITION "OFF."
• DISCONNECT EBTCM.
• INSTALL J 39700 UNIVERSAL BREAKOUT BOX TO EBTCM AND EBTCM HARNESS CONNECTOR.
• IGNITION "ON."
• CONNECT DVM BETWEEN J 39700 TERMINAL PAIRS LISTED BELOW. NOTE VOLTAGE FOR EACH CHECK.
J 39700 TERMINALS
1 AND 3
1 AND 37
1 AND 52
WAS ANY VOLTAGE MEASUREMENT LESS THAN 9 VOLTS?
NO
YES
3
• IGNITION "OFF."
• DISCONNECT EBTCM HARNESS CONNECTOR FROM J 39700.
• CHECK EBTCM HARNESS CONNECTOR CAREFULLY TO ENSURE GOOD ELECTRICAL CONTACT AT ALL TERMINALS, ESPECIALLY TERMINALS "1", "3", "37", AND "52".
IS ALL OK WITH TERMINALS?
6
• CONNECT DVM BETWEEN J 39700 TERMINAL "1" AND A KNOWN GOOD CHASSIS GROUND.
• IS VOLTAGE MEASUREMENT LESS THAN 9 VOLTS?
YES
NO
NO
YES
4
• REMOVE J 39700.
• RECONNECT EBTCM.
• DOES CONNECTOR SEEM TO BE PROPERLY RETAINED TO EBTCM WHEN CONNECTED?
REPAIR REPLACE TERMINALS AND/OR CONNECTOR AS NECESSARY.
REPAIR OPEN OR POOR GROUND IN CKT 801 AT TERMINAL(S) "3", "37", OR "52" AS NEEDED.
REPAIR OPEN OR POOR CONNECTION IN CKT 439.
YES
NO
5
• CLEAR DTCs, IGNITION "OFF."
• DISCONNECT TECH 1, IF CONNECTED.
• IGNITION "ON."
• DOES DTC 74 RESET?
REPLACE WIRING HARNESS OR EBTCM AS NEEDED TO OBTAIN PROPER CONNECTOR RETENTION.
YES
NO
REPLACE EBTCM.
NO TROUBLE FOUND; SEE "DIAGNOSTIC AIDS"
WHEN ALL DIAGNOSIS AND REPAIRS ARE COMPLETED, CLEAR DTCs AND VERIFY PROPER OPERATION.

GC402930044100BX

Fig. 84 Code 74: Low Voltage. 1993

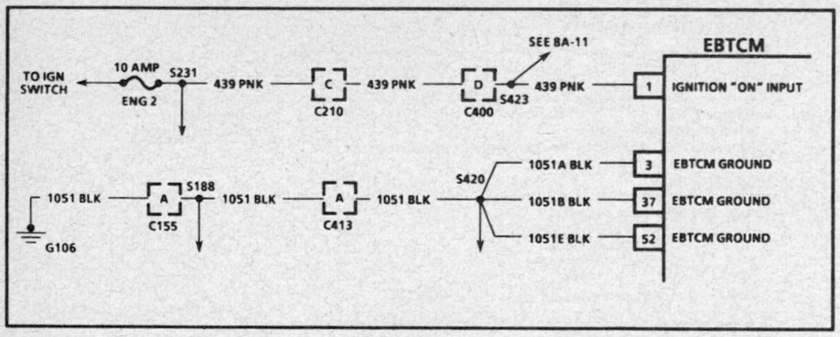
SEE 8A-11
EBTCM
TO IGN SWITCH
10 AMP
S231
ENG 2
439 PNK
C
C210
439 PNK
D
C400
S423
439 PNK
1
IGNITION "ON" INPUT
1051A BLK
3
EBTCM GROUND
S420
1051B BLK
37
EBTCM GROUND
1051E BLK
52
EBTCM GROUND
1051 BLK
A
S188
C155
1051 BLK
A
C413
1051 BLK
G106

DTC 74

LOW VOLTAGE

Circuit Description:

The EBTCM, requires a certain minimum voltage to operate properly. It monitors the ignition feed circuit to determine if voltage falls below a minimum level.

DTC Will Set When: The EBTCM operating voltage falls below 9.0 volts.

DTC Chart Test Description: Number(s) below refer to circled number(s) on the diagnostic chart.

1. Checks that ENG2 fuse feeding the EBTCM ignition circuit is good.
2. Measures for appropriate voltage from the EBTCM ignition circuit, using each of the three EBTCM ground lines to complete the circuit.
3. Checks EBTCM connector terminals for good contact, i.e. not spread open, backed out of connector, corroded, etc.
4. Checks EBTCM connector for good retention to EBTCM when installed.
5. Checks for DTC reset after other portions of the system have tested as OK.
6. Determines if a malfunction found in Step 2 is due to an open or poor connection in the EBTCM ignition feed CKT 439, or poor ground(s) in CKT 1051.

Diagnostic Aids: It is very important that a thorough inspection of the wiring and connectors be performed. Failure to carefully and fully inspect wiring and connectors may result in misdiagnosis, causing part replacement with reappearance of the malfunction.

GC402940088800AX

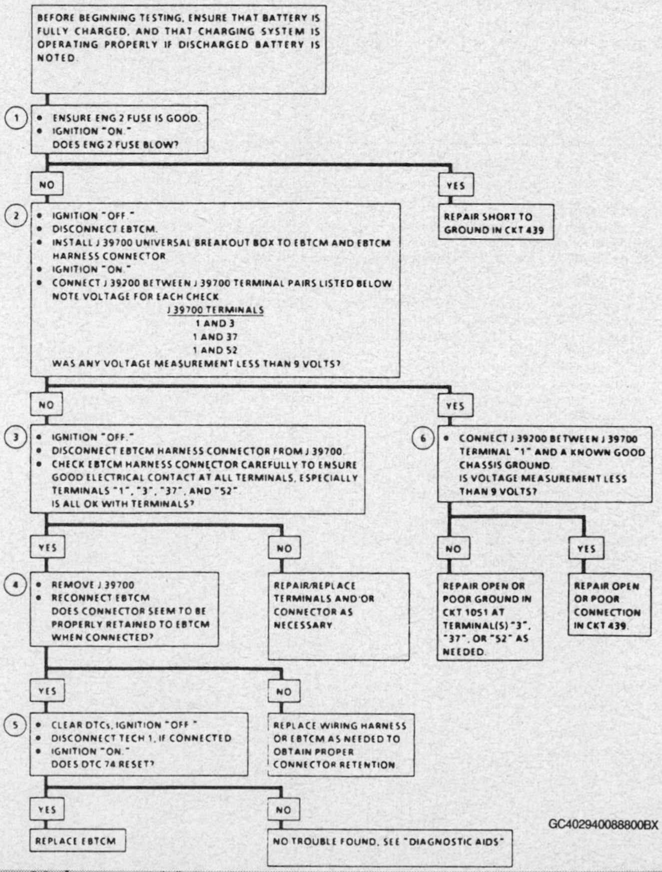
BEFORE BEGINNING TESTING, ENSURE THAT BATTERY IS FULLY CHARGED, AND THAT CHARGING SYSTEM IS OPERATING PROPERLY IF DISCHARGED BATTERY IS NOTED.
1
• ENSURE ENG 2 FUSE IS GOOD.
• IGNITION "ON."
DOES ENG 2 FUSE BLOW?
NO
YES
REPAIR SHORT TO GROUND IN CKT 439
2
• IGNITION "OFF."
• DISCONNECT EBTCM.
• INSTALL J 39700 UNIVERSAL BREAKOUT BOX TO EBTCM AND EBTCM HARNESS CONNECTOR
• IGNITION "ON."
• CONNECT J 39200 BETWEEN J 39700 TERMINAL PAIRS LISTED BELOW NOTE VOLTAGE FOR EACH CHECK
J 39700 TERMINALS
1 AND 3
1 AND 37
1 AND 52
WAS ANY VOLTAGE MEASUREMENT LESS THAN 9 VOLTS?
NO
YES
3
• IGNITION "OFF."
• DISCONNECT EBTCM HARNESS CONNECTOR FROM J 39700.
• CHECK EBTCM HARNESS CONNECTOR CAREFULLY TO ENSURE GOOD ELECTRICAL CONTACT AT ALL TERMINALS, ESPECIALLY TERMINALS "1", "3", "37", AND "52".
IS ALL OK WITH TERMINALS?
6
• CONNECT J 39200 BETWEEN J 39700 TERMINAL "1" AND A KNOWN GOOD CHASSIS GROUND.
IS VOLTAGE MEASUREMENT LESS THAN 9 VOLTS?
YES
NO
NO
YES
4
• REMOVE J 39700
• RECONNECT EBTCM
DOES CONNECTOR SEEM TO BE PROPERLY RETAINED TO EBTCM WHEN CONNECTED?
REPAIR/REPLACE TERMINALS AND/OR CONNECTOR AS NECESSARY.
REPAIR OPEN OR POOR GROUND IN CKT 1051 AT TERMINAL(S) "3", "37", OR "52" AS NEEDED.
REPAIR OPEN OR POOR CONNECTION IN CKT 439.
YES
NO
5
• CLEAR DTCs, IGNITION "OFF."
• DISCONNECT TECH 1, IF CONNECTED
• IGNITION "ON."
DOES DTC 74 RESET?
REPLACE WIRING HARNESS OR EBTCM AS NEEDED TO OBTAIN PROPER CONNECTOR RETENTION.
YES
NO
REPLACE EBTCM
NO TROUBLE FOUND. SEE "DIAGNOSTIC AIDS"

GC402940088800BX

Fig. 85 Code 74: Low Voltage. 1994

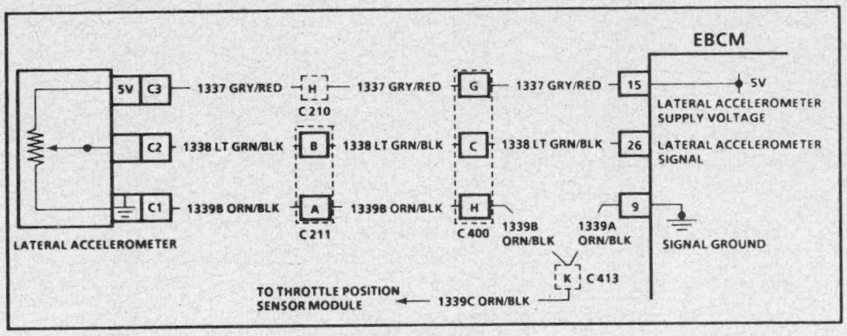
EBCM
5V
C3
1337 GRY/RED
H
C 210
G
15
5V
LATERAL ACCELEROMETER SUPPLY VOLTAGE
C2
1338 LT GRN/BLK
B
C
26
LATERAL ACCELEROMETER SIGNAL
C1
1339B ORN/BLK
A
C 211
H
C 400
1339B ORN/BLK
1339A ORN/BLK
9
SIGNAL GROUND
LATERAL ACCELEROMETER
K
C 413
TO THROTTLE POSITION SENSOR MODULE
1339C ORN/BLK

CODE 75

LATERAL ACCELEROMETER WIRING FAULT

Circuit Description:
The Lateral Accelerometer circuitry provides a signal to the EBCM which reflects the severity of a vehicle turn, i.e. the "yaw" forces on the vehicle. The EBCM uses this information to modify the control of the rear wheel brakes, to help prevent loss of control in a turn due to light brake pedal application at speeds above 50 km/h (30 mph).

Code 75 will set if the EBCM senses the Lateral Accelerometer voltage to be out of its permissible range due to an electrical wiring fault.

Test Description: Number(s) below refer to circled number(s) on the diagnostic chart.

1. Checks for an ASR Code 64, which, along with a Code 75, likely indicates an open in CKT 1339.
2. Checks for short to B+ on CKT 1338. The Lateral Accelerometer should also be replaced if this condition is found, since it will be damaged by the fault.
3. Checks for short to B+ on CKT 1337. The Lateral Accelerometer should also be replaced if this condition is found, since it will be damaged by the fault.
4. Checks for a short to ground in CKT 1338.
5. Checks for a short to ground in CKT 1337.
6. Checks for an appropriate supply voltage to the accelerometer from the EBCM, using the EBCM supply and ground terminals. If either is faulty, the supply voltage will not be present; the EBCM should be replaced.
7. Checks for a Code 75 reset after Code 64 conditions are repaired.

Diagnostic Aids:

It is very important that a thorough inspection of the wiring and connectors be performed. Failure to carefully and fully inspect wiring and connectors may result in misdiagnosis, causing part replacement with reappearance of the fault.

All tests using J 39700 Universal Breakout Box terminal 3 are using that terminal as ground. These tests, of course, assume that the ground CKT 801 at terminal 3 is good.

GC402920044200AX

1992

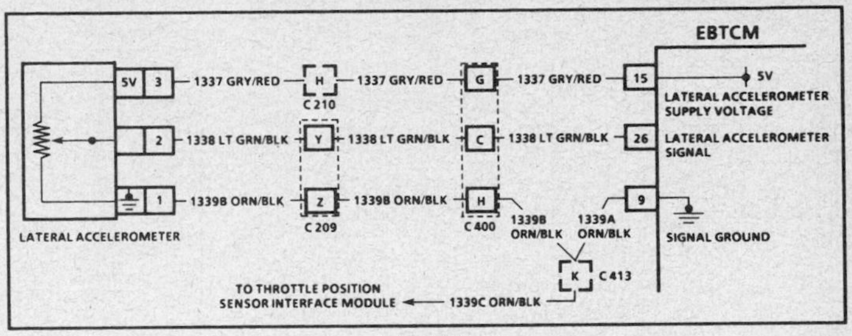
EBTCM
5V
3
1337 GRY/RED
H
C 210
G
15
5V
LATERAL ACCELEROMETER SUPPLY VOLTAGE
2
1338 LT GRN/BLK
Y
C
26
LATERAL ACCELEROMETER SIGNAL
1
1339B ORN/BLK
Z
C 209
H
C 400
1339B ORN/BLK
1339A ORN/BLK
9
SIGNAL GROUND
LATERAL ACCELEROMETER
K
C 413
TO THROTTLE POSITION SENSOR INTERFACE MODULE
1339C ORN/BLK

DTC 75

LATERAL ACCELEROMETER WIRING MALFUNCTION

Circuit Description:
The lateral accelerometer circuitry provides a signal to the EBTCM which reflects the severity of a vehicle turn, i.e. the "yaw" forces on the vehicle. The EBTCM uses this information to modify the control of the rear wheel brakes, to help prevent loss of control in a turn due to light brake pedal application at speeds above 50 km/h (30 mph).

DTC 75 will set if the EBTCM senses the lateral accelerometer voltage to be out of its permissible range due to an electrical wiring malfunction.

Test Description: Number(s) below refer to circled number(s) on the diagnostic chart.

1. Checks for an ASR DTC 64, which, along with a DTC 75, likely indicates an open in CKT 1339.
2. Checks for short to B+ on CKT 1338. The lateral accelerometer should also be replaced if this condition is found, since it will be damaged by the malfunction.
3. Checks for short to B+ on CKT 1337. The lateral accelerometer should also be replaced if this condition is found, since it will be damaged by the malfunction
4. Checks for a short to ground in CKT 1338.
5. Checks for a short to ground in CKT 1337.
6. Checks for an appropriate supply voltage to the accelerometer from the EBTCM, using the EBTCM supply and ground terminals. If either is malfunctioning, the supply voltage will not be present; the EBTCM should be replaced.
7. Checks for a DTC 75 reset after DTC 64 conditions are repaired.

Diagnostic Aids:

It is very important that a thorough inspection of the wiring and connectors be performed. Failure to carefully and fully inspect wiring and connectors may result in misdiagnosis, causing part replacement with reappearance of the malfunction.

All tests using J 39700 Universal Breakout Box terminal "3" are using that terminal as ground. These tests, of course, assume that the ground CKT 801 at terminal "3" is good.

GC402930044200BX

1993

Fig. 86 Code 75: Lateral Accelerometer Wiring Fault (Part 1 of 3). 1992–93

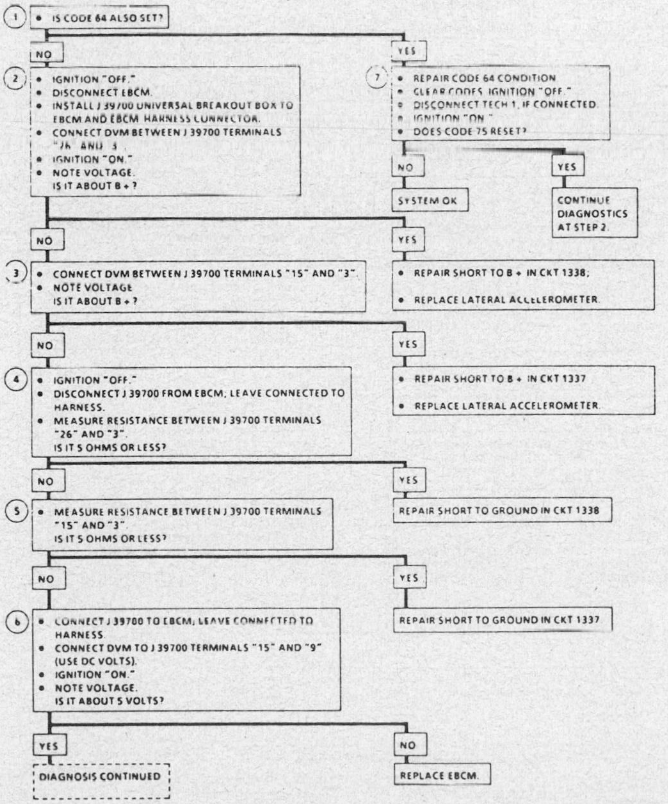
1 • IS CODE 64 ALSO SET?
NO
YES
2 • IGNITION "OFF."
• DISCONNECT EBCM.
• INSTALL J 39700 UNIVERSAL BREAKOUT BOX TO EBCM AND EBCM HARNESS CONNECTOR.
• CONNECT DVM BETWEEN J 39700 TERMINALS "26" AND "3".
• IGNITION "ON."
• NOTE VOLTAGE.
IS IT ABOUT B+?
7 • REPAIR CODE 64 CONDITION
• CLEAR CODES, IGNITION "OFF."
• DISCONNECT TECH 1, IF CONNECTED.
• IGNITION "ON."
• DOES CODE 75 RESET?
NO
YES
SYSTEM OK
CONTINUE DIAGNOSTICS AT STEP 2.
NO
YES
3 • CONNECT DVM BETWEEN J 39700 TERMINALS "15" AND "3".
• NOTE VOLTAGE
IS IT ABOUT B+?
• REPAIR SHORT TO B+ IN CKT 1338;
• REPLACE LATERAL ACCELEROMETER.
NO
YES
4 • IGNITION "OFF."
• DISCONNECT J 39700 FROM EBCM; LEAVE CONNECTED TO HARNESS.
• MEASURE RESISTANCE BETWEEN J 39700 TERMINALS "26" AND "3".
IS IT 5 OHMS OR LESS?
• REPAIR SHORT TO B+ IN CKT 1337
• REPLACE LATERAL ACCELEROMETER.
NO
YES
5 • MEASURE RESISTANCE BETWEEN J 39700 TERMINALS "15" AND "3".
IS IT 5 OHMS OR LESS?
REPAIR SHORT TO GROUND IN CKT 1338
NO
YES
6 • CONNECT J 39700 TO EBCM; LEAVE CONNECTED TO HARNESS.
• CONNECT DVM TO J 39700 TERMINALS "15" AND "9" (USE DC VOLTS).
• IGNITION "ON."
• NOTE VOLTAGE.
IS IT ABOUT 5 VOLTS?
REPAIR SHORT TO GROUND IN CKT 1337
YES
NO
DIAGNOSIS CONTINUED
REPLACE EBCM.

GC402920044200CX

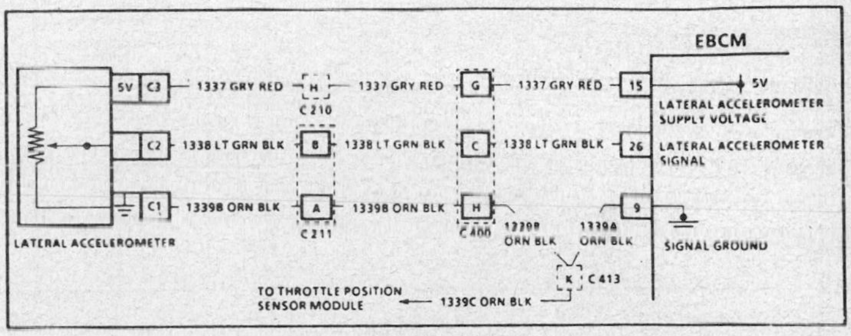
EBCM
5V
C3
1337 GRY RED
H
C 210
G
15
5V
LATERAL ACCELEROMETER SUPPLY VOLTAGE
C2
1338 LT GRN BLK
B
C
26
LATERAL ACCELEROMETER SIGNAL
C1
1339B ORN BLK
A
C 211
H
C 400
1339B ORN BLK
1339A ORN BLK
9
SIGNAL GROUND
LATERAL ACCELEROMETER
K
C 413
TO THROTTLE POSITION SENSOR MODULE
1339C ORN BLK

CODE 75

LATERAL ACCELEROMETER WIRING FAULT

Circuit Description:
The Lateral Accelerometer circuitry provides a signal to the EBCM which reflects the severity of a vehicle turn, i.e. the "yaw" forces on the vehicle. The EBCM uses this information to modify the control of the rear wheel brakes, to help prevent loss of control in a turn due to light brake pedal application at speeds above 50 km/h (30 mph).

Code 75 will set if the EBCM senses the Lateral Accelerometer voltage to be out of its permissible range due to an electrical wiring fault.

Test Description: Number(s) below refer to circled number(s) on the diagnostic chart.

8. Checks for short to B+ on CKT 1339
9. Checks for correct vehicle-stationary (no yaw) signal from the lateral accelerometer.
10. Checks for code reset after most other portions of the system have checked as OK
11. Replaces Lateral Accelerometer first as likely cause of code reset in Step 8. If Code 75 resets after Lateral Accelerometer replacement, the EBCM must be interpreting a fault condition when none exists
12. Checks for an appropriate supply voltage to the accelerometer from the EBCM through CKTs 1337 and 1339.
13. Determines if a problem found in Step 11 is due to an open in CKT 1337 or an open in CKT 1339 from the Lateral Accelerometer harness connector up to the CKT 1339 splice to the Throttle Position Sensor Module.
14. Determines if a problem found in Step 11 is due to an open in CKT 1338 or a faulty Lateral Accelerometer.

Diagnostic Aids:

It is very important that a thorough inspection of the wiring and connectors be performed. Failure to carefully and fully inspect wiring and connectors may result in misdiagnosis, causing part replacement with reappearance of the fault.

All tests using J 39700 Universal Breakout Box terminal 3 are using that terminal as ground. These tests, of course, assume that the ground CKT 801 at terminal 3 is good

GC402920044200DX

1992

Fig. 86 Code 75: Lateral Accelerometer Wiring Fault (Part 2 of 3). 1992-93

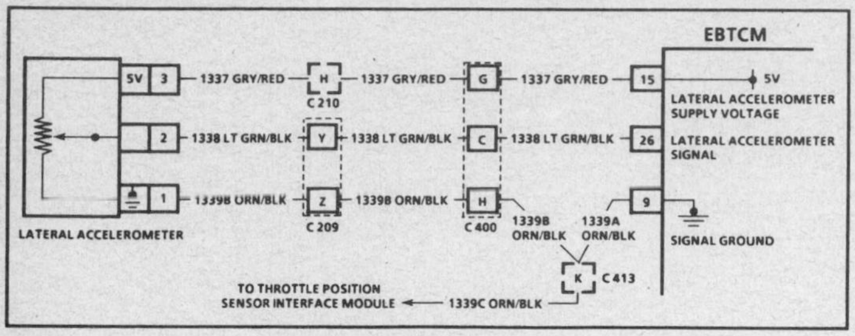
EBTCM
5V
3
1337 GRY/RED
H
C 210
1337 GRY/RED
G
1337 GRY/RED
15
5V
LATERAL ACCELEROMETER SUPPLY VOLTAGE
2
1338 LT GRN/BLK
Y
1338 LT GRN/BLK
C
1338 LT GRN/BLK
26
LATERAL ACCELEROMETER SIGNAL
1
1339B ORN/BLK
Z
C 209
1339B ORN/BLK
H
C 400
1339B ORN/BLK
1339A ORN/BLK
9
SIGNAL GROUND
LATERAL ACCELEROMETER
K
C 413
TO THROTTLE POSITION SENSOR INTERFACE MODULE
1339C ORN/BLK

DTC 75

LATERAL ACCELEROMETER WIRING MALFUNCTION

Circuit Description:

The lateral accelerometer circuitry provides a signal to the EBTCM which reflects the severity of a vehicle turn, i.e. the "yaw" forces on the vehicle. The EBTCM uses this information to modify the control of the rear wheel brakes, to help prevent loss of control in a turn due to light brake pedal application at speeds above 50 km/h (30 mph).

DTC 75 will set if the EBTCM senses the lateral accelerometer voltage to be out of its permissible range due to an electrical wiring malfunction.

Test Description: Number(s) below refer to circled number(s) on the diagnostic chart.

8. Checks for short to B+ on CKT 1339.
9. Checks for correct vehicle-stationary (no yaw) signal from the lateral accelerometer.
10. Checks for DTC reset after most other portions of the system have checked as OK.
11. Replaces lateral accelerometer first as likely cause of DTC reset in Step 8. If DTC 75 resets after lateral accelerometer replacement, the EBTCM must be interpreting a malfaction condition when none exists.
12. Checks for an appropriate supply voltage to the accelerometer from the EBTCM through CKTs 1337 and 1339.
13. Determines if a problem found in Step 11 is due to an open in CKT 1337 or an open in CKT 1339 from the Lateral Accelerometer harness connector up to the CKT 1339 splice to the Throttle Position Sensor Interface Module.
14. Determines if a problem found in Step 11 is due to an open in CKT 1338 or a malfunctioning lateral accelerometer.

Diagnostic Aids:

It is very important that a thorough inspection of the wiring and connectors be performed. Failure to carefully and fully inspect wiring and connectors may result in misdiagnosis, causing part replacement with reappearance of the malfunction.

All tests using J 39700 Universal Breakout Box terminal "3" are using that terminal as ground. These tests, of course, assume that the ground CKT 801 at terminal "3" is good.

GC402930044200EX

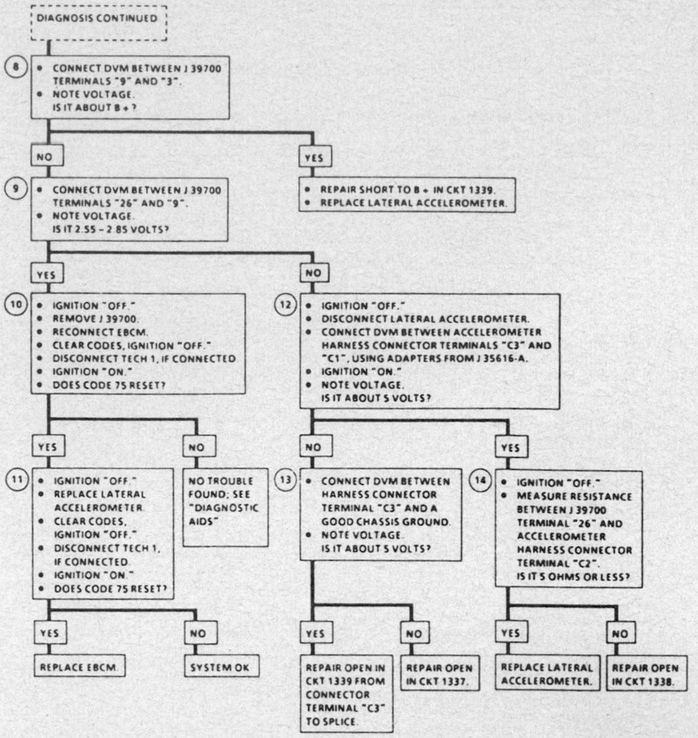
DIAGNOSIS CONTINUED
8
• CONNECT DVM BETWEEN J 39700 TERMINALS "9" AND "3".
• NOTE VOLTAGE.
IS IT ABOUT B+?
NO
YES
9
• CONNECT DVM BETWEEN J 39700 TERMINALS "26" AND "9".
• NOTE VOLTAGE.
IS IT 2.55 - 2.85 VOLTS?
• REPAIR SHORT TO B+ IN CKT 1339.
• REPLACE LATERAL ACCELEROMETER.
YES
NO
10
• IGNITION "OFF."
• REMOVE J 39700.
• RECONNECT EBCM.
• CLEAR CODES, IGNITION "OFF."
• DISCONNECT TECH 1, IF CONNECTED
• IGNITION "ON."
• DOES CODE 75 RESET?
12
• IGNITION "OFF."
• DISCONNECT LATERAL ACCELEROMETER.
• CONNECT DVM BETWEEN ACCELEROMETER HARNESS CONNECTOR TERMINALS "C3" AND "C1", USING ADAPTERS FROM J 35616-A.
• IGNITION "ON."
• NOTE VOLTAGE.
IS IT ABOUT 5 VOLTS?
YES
NO
NO
YES
11
• IGNITION "OFF."
• REPLACE LATERAL ACCELEROMETER.
• CLEAR CODES, IGNITION "OFF."
• DISCONNECT TECH 1, IF CONNECTED.
• IGNITION "ON."
• DOES CODE 75 RESET?
NO TROUBLE FOUND; SEE "DIAGNOSTIC AIDS"
13
• CONNECT DVM BETWEEN HARNESS CONNECTOR TERMINAL "C3" AND A GOOD CHASSIS GROUND.
• NOTE VOLTAGE.
IS IT ABOUT 5 VOLTS?
14
• IGNITION "OFF."
• MEASURE RESISTANCE BETWEEN J 39700 TERMINAL "26" AND ACCELEROMETER HARNESS CONNECTOR TERMINAL "C2".
IS IT 5 OHMS OR LESS?
YES
NO
YES
NO
YES
NO
REPLACE EBCM.
SYSTEM OK
REPAIR OPEN IN CKT 1339 FROM CONNECTOR TERMINAL "C3" TO SPLICE.
REPAIR OPEN IN CKT 1337.
REPLACE LATERAL ACCELEROMETER.
REPAIR OPEN IN CKT 1338.

GC402920044200FX

1993

Fig. 86 Code 75: Lateral Accelerometer Wiring Fault (Part 3 of 3). 1992–93

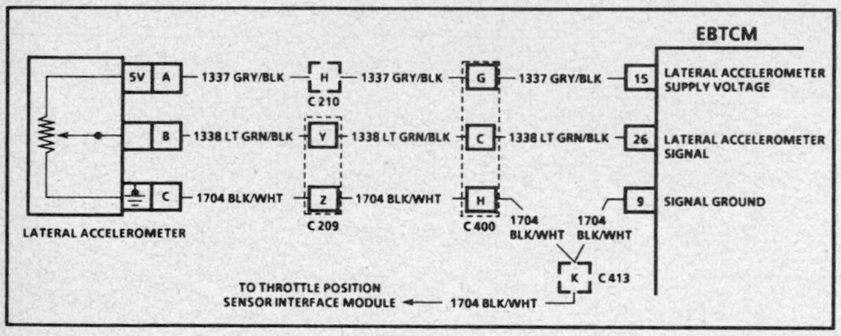
EBTCM
5V
A
1337 GRY/BLK
H
C 210
1337 GRY/BLK
G
1337 GRY/BLK
15
LATERAL ACCELEROMETER SUPPLY VOLTAGE
B
1338 LT GRN/BLK
Y
1338 LT GRN/BLK
C
1338 LT GRN/BLK
26
LATERAL ACCELEROMETER SIGNAL
C
1704 BLK/WHT
Z
C 209
1704 BLK/WHT
H
C 400
1704 BLK/WHT
1704 BLK/WHT
9
SIGNAL GROUND
LATERAL ACCELEROMETER
K
C 413
TO THROTTLE POSITION SENSOR INTERFACE MODULE
1704 BLK/WHT

DTC 75

(Page 1 of 2)

LATERAL ACCELEROMETER CIRCUIT MALFUNCTION

Circuit Description:

The lateral accelerometer circuitry provides a signal to the EBTCM which reflects the severity of a vehicle turn, i.e. the "yaw" forces on the vehicle. The EBTCM uses this information to modify the control of the rear wheel brakes, to help prevent loss of control in a turn due to light brake pedal application at speeds above 50 km/h (30 mph).

DTC Will Set When: The EBTCM senses the lateral accelerometer voltage to be out of its permissible range due to an electrical wiring malfunction.

DTC Chart Test Description: Number(s) below refer to circled number(s) on the diagnostic chart.

1. Checks for an ASR DTC 64, which, along with a DTC 75, likely indicates an open in CKT 1704.
2. Checks for short to B+ on CKT 1338. The lateral accelerometer should also be replaced if this condition is found, since it will be damaged by the malfunction.
3. Checks for short to B+ on CKT 1337. The lateral accelerometer should also be replaced if this condition is found, since it will be damaged by the malfunction.
4. Checks for a short to ground in CKT 1338.
5. Checks for a short to ground in CKT 1337.
6. Checks for an appropriate supply voltage to the accelerometer from the EBTCM, using the EBTCM supply and ground terminals. If either is malfunctioning, the supply voltage will not be present; the EBTCM should be replaced.
7. Ensures the lateral accelerometer is not internally shorted to ground.
8. Checks for a DTC 75 reset after DTC 64 conditions are repaired.

Diagnostic Aids: It is very important that a thorough inspection of the wiring and connectors be performed. Failure to carefully and fully inspect wiring and connectors may result in misdiagnosis, causing part replacement with reappearance of the malfunction.

All tests using J 39700 Universal Breakout Box terminal "3" are using that terminal as ground. These tests, of course, assume that the ground CKT 1051 at terminal "3" is good.

GC402940088901AX

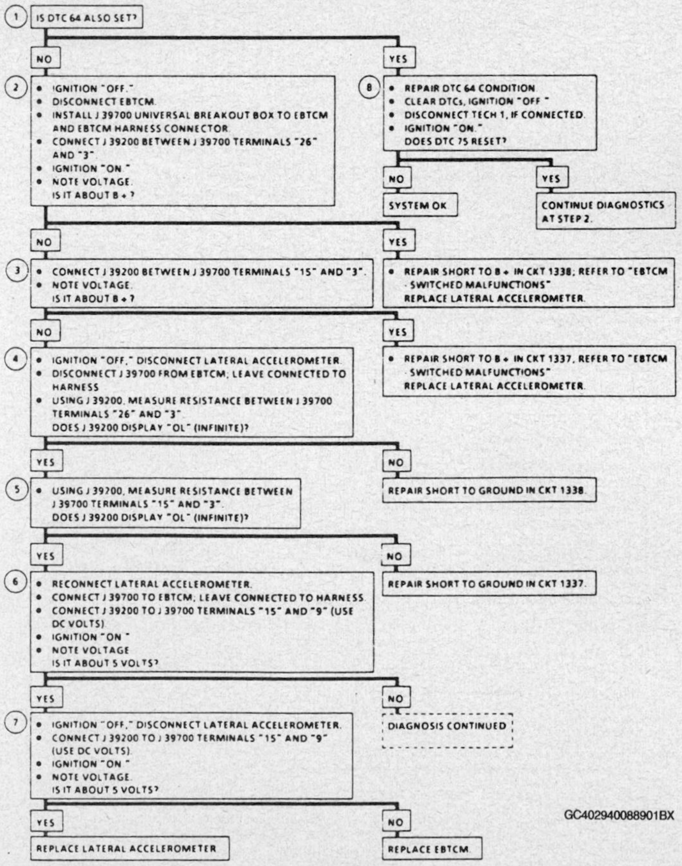
1
IS DTC 64 ALSO SET?
NO
YES
2
• IGNITION "OFF."
• DISCONNECT EBTCM.
• INSTALL J 39700 UNIVERSAL BREAKOUT BOX TO EBTCM AND EBTCM HARNESS CONNECTOR.
• CONNECT J 39200 BETWEEN J 39700 TERMINALS "26" AND "3".
• IGNITION "ON."
• NOTE VOLTAGE.
IS IT ABOUT B+?
8
• REPAIR DTC 64 CONDITION
• CLEAR DTCs, IGNITION "OFF."
• DISCONNECT TECH 1, IF CONNECTED.
• IGNITION "ON."
DOES DTC 75 RESET?
NO
YES
SYSTEM OK
CONTINUE DIAGNOSTICS AT STEP 2.
NO
YES
3
• CONNECT J 39200 BETWEEN J 39700 TERMINALS "15" AND "3".
• NOTE VOLTAGE.
IS IT ABOUT B+?
• REPAIR SHORT TO B+ IN CKT 1338; REFER TO "EBTCM SWITCHED MALFUNCTIONS"
REPLACE LATERAL ACCELEROMETER.
NO
YES
4
• IGNITION "OFF," DISCONNECT LATERAL ACCELEROMETER.
• DISCONNECT J 39700 FROM EBTCM; LEAVE CONNECTED TO HARNESS
• USING J 39200, MEASURE RESISTANCE BETWEEN J 39700 TERMINALS "26" AND "3".
DOES J 39200 DISPLAY "OL" (INFINITE)?
• REPAIR SHORT TO B+ IN CKT 1337, REFER TO "EBTCM SWITCHED MALFUNCTIONS"
REPLACE LATERAL ACCELEROMETER.
YES
NO
5
• USING J 39200, MEASURE RESISTANCE BETWEEN J 39700 TERMINALS "15" AND "3".
DOES J 39200 DISPLAY "OL" (INFINITE)?
REPAIR SHORT TO GROUND IN CKT 1338.
YES
NO
6
• RECONNECT LATERAL ACCELEROMETER.
• CONNECT J 39700 TO EBTCM; LEAVE CONNECTED TO HARNESS.
• CONNECT J 39200 TO J 39700 TERMINALS "15" AND "9" (USE DC VOLTS).
• IGNITION "ON."
• NOTE VOLTAGE
IS IT ABOUT 5 VOLTS?
REPAIR SHORT TO GROUND IN CKT 1337.
YES
NO
7
• IGNITION "OFF," DISCONNECT LATERAL ACCELEROMETER.
• CONNECT J 39200 TO J 39700 TERMINALS "15" AND "9" (USE DC VOLTS).
• IGNITION "ON."
• NOTE VOLTAGE.
IS IT ABOUT 5 VOLTS?
DIAGNOSIS CONTINUED
YES
NO
REPLACE LATERAL ACCELEROMETER.
REPLACE EBTCM.

GC402940088901BX

Fig. 87 Code 75: Lateral Accelerometer Wiring Fault (Part 1 of 2). 1994

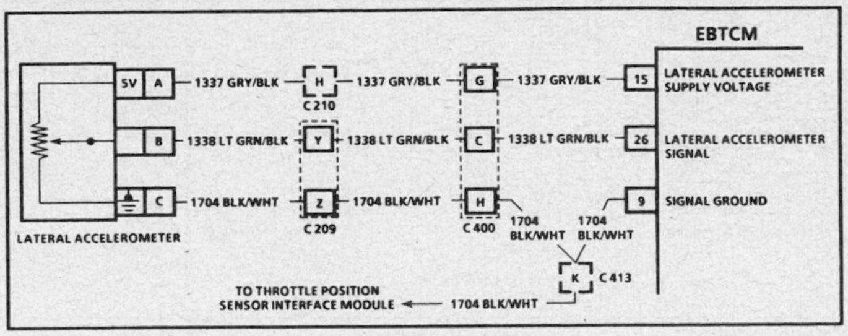
EBTCM
5V
A
1337 GRY/BLK
H
C 210
G
15
LATERAL ACCELEROMETER SUPPLY VOLTAGE
B
1338 LT GRN/BLK
Y
C
26
LATERAL ACCELEROMETER SIGNAL
C
1704 BLK/WHT
Z
C 209
H
C 400
9
SIGNAL GROUND
1704 BLK/WHT
LATERAL ACCELEROMETER
K
C413
TO THROTTLE POSITION SENSOR INTERFACE MODULE
1704 BLK/WHT

DTC 75

(Page 2 of 2)

LATERAL ACCELEROMETER CIRCUIT MALFUNCTION

Circuit Description:

The lateral accelerometer circuitry provides a signal to the EBTCM which reflects the severity of a vehicle turn, i.e. the "yaw" forces on the vehicle. The EBTCM uses this information to modify the control of the rear wheel brakes, to help prevent loss of control in a turn due to light brake pedal application at speeds above 50 km/h (30 mph).

DTC Will Set When: The EBTCM senses the lateral accelerometer voltage to be out of its permissible range due to an electrical wiring malfunction.

DTC Chart Test Description: Number(s) below refer to circled number(s) on the diagnostic chart.

9. Checks for correct vehicle-stationary (no yaw) signal from the lateral accelerometer.
10. Checks for DTC reset after most other portions of the system have checked as OK.
11. Replaces lateral accelerometer first as likely cause of DTC reset in Step 8. If DTC 75 resets after lateral accelerometer replacement, the EBTCM must be interpreting a malfunction condition when none exists.
12. Checks for an appropriate supply voltage to the accelerometer from the EBTCM through CKTs 1337 and 1704.
13. Determines if a malfunction found in Step 11 is due to an open in CKT 1337 or an open in CKT 1704 from the lateral accelerometer harness connector up to the CKT 1704 splice to the throttle position sensor interface module.
14. Determines if a malfunction found in Step 11 is due to an open in CKT 1338 or a malfunctioning lateral accelerometer.
15. Isolates CKT(s) 1337 and 1338 to determine if the lateral accelerometer is malfunctioning, or a short exists between CKT(s) 1337 and 1338.

Diagnostic Aids: It is very important that a thorough inspection of the wiring and connectors be performed. Failure to carefully and fully inspect wiring and connectors may result in misdiagnosis, causing part replacement with reappearance of the malfunction.

All tests using J 39700 Universal Breakout Box terminal "3" are using that terminal as ground. These tests, of course, assume that the ground CKT 1051 at terminal "3" is good.

GC402940088902AX

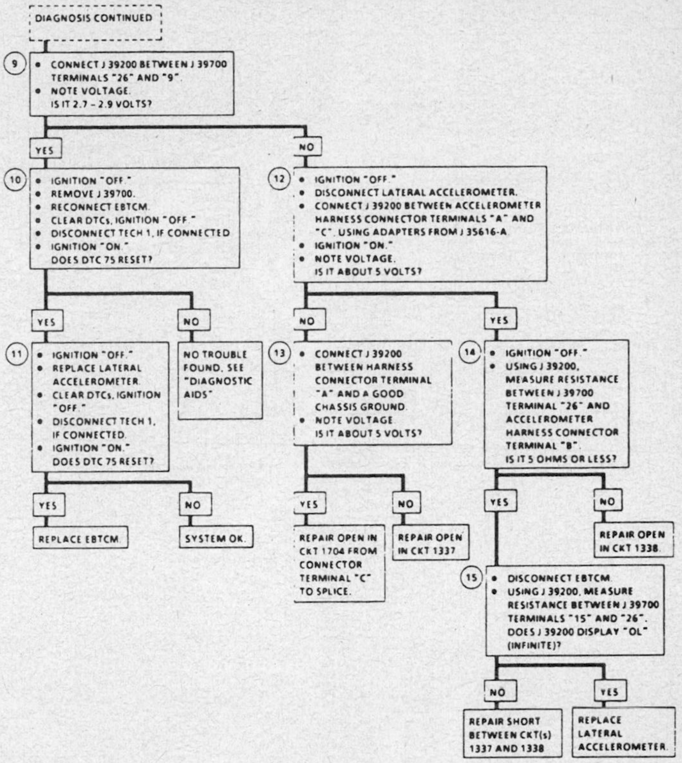
DIAGNOSIS CONTINUED
9
CONNECT J 39200 BETWEEN J 39700 TERMINALS "26" AND "9".
NOTE VOLTAGE.
IS IT 2.7 – 2.9 VOLTS?
YES
NO
10
IGNITION "OFF."
REMOVE J 39700.
RECONNECT EBTCM.
CLEAR DTCs, IGNITION "OFF."
DISCONNECT TECH 1, IF CONNECTED.
IGNITION "ON."
DOES DTC 75 RESET?
12
IGNITION "OFF."
DISCONNECT LATERAL ACCELEROMETER.
CONNECT J 39200 BETWEEN ACCELEROMETER HARNESS CONNECTOR TERMINALS "A" AND "C", USING ADAPTERS FROM J 35616-A.
IGNITION "ON."
NOTE VOLTAGE.
IS IT ABOUT 5 VOLTS?
YES
NO
NO
YES
11
IGNITION "OFF."
REPLACE LATERAL ACCELEROMETER.
CLEAR DTCs, IGNITION "OFF."
DISCONNECT TECH 1, IF CONNECTED.
IGNITION "ON."
DOES DTC 75 RESET?
NO TROUBLE FOUND. SEE "DIAGNOSTIC AIDS"
13
CONNECT J 39200 BETWEEN HARNESS CONNECTOR TERMINAL "A" AND A GOOD CHASSIS GROUND.
NOTE VOLTAGE.
IS IT ABOUT 5 VOLTS?
14
IGNITION "OFF."
USING J 39200, MEASURE RESISTANCE BETWEEN J 39700 TERMINAL "26" AND ACCELEROMETER HARNESS CONNECTOR TERMINAL "B".
IS IT 5 OHMS OR LESS?
YES
NO
YES
NO
YES
NO
REPLACE EBTCM
SYSTEM OK
REPAIR OPEN IN CKT 1704 FROM CONNECTOR TERMINAL "C" TO SPLICE.
REPAIR OPEN IN CKT 1337
REPAIR OPEN IN CKT 1338.
15
DISCONNECT EBTCM.
USING J 39200, MEASURE RESISTANCE BETWEEN J 39700 TERMINALS "15" AND "26".
DOES J 39200 DISPLAY "OL" (INFINITE)?
NO
YES
REPAIR SHORT BETWEEN CKT(s) 1337 AND 1338
REPLACE LATERAL ACCELEROMETER.

GC402940088902BX

Fig. 87 Code 75: Lateral Accelerometer Wiring Fault (Part 2 of 2). 1994

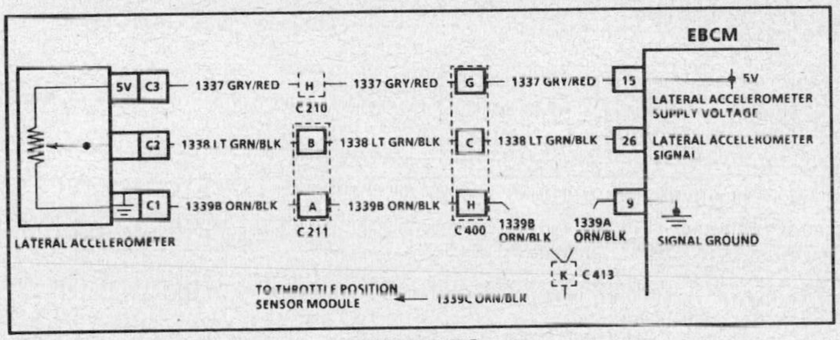
EBCM
5V
C3
1337 GRY/RED
H
C 210
G
15
5V
LATERAL ACCELEROMETER SUPPLY VOLTAGE
C2
1338 LT GRN/BLK
B
C
26
LATERAL ACCELEROMETER SIGNAL
C1
1339B ORN/BLK
A
C 211
H
C 400
9
1339B ORN/BLK
1339A ORN/BLK
SIGNAL GROUND
LATERAL ACCELEROMETER
K
C413
TO THROTTLE POSITION SENSOR MODULE
1339C ORN/BLK

CODE 76

LATERAL ACCELEROMETER SIGNAL OUT OF RANGE

Circuit Description:

The Lateral Accelerometer circuitry provides a signal to the EBCM which reflects the severity of a vehicle turn, i.e. the "yaw" forces on the vehicle. The EBCM uses this information to modify the control of the rear wheel brakes, to help prevent loss of control in a turn due to light brake pedal application at speeds above 50 km/h (30 mph).

Code 76 will set when the Lateral Accelerometer signal is out of range for 7.5 minutes or more.

Test Description: Number(s) below refer to circled number(s) on the diagnostic chart.

1. Checks if another ABS/ASR system code may be causing the Code 76 to set.
2. Checks for appropriate signal voltage at a 0g (no-turn, stationary) condition.
3. Checks for appropriate signal voltage for a full-scale left-hand turn. The full-scale left turn is simulated by the right side of the Lateral Accelerometer being exposed to the 1g force of gravity.
4. Repairs other ABS/ASR code problems that may affect Code 76, then checks for Code 76 reset.
5. Checks wiring and connectors for intermittents and/or shorts.
6. Checks for Code 76 reset after Lateral Accelerometer is replaced; Lateral Accelerometer is causing problem noted in Step 2, since Code 75 would identify other problems that could cause Step 2 to measure incorrectly, and the existence of Code 75 was eliminated in Step 1. If Code 76 resets after Lateral Accelerometer replacement, the EBCM is interpreting a problem when it should not be.

Diagnostic Aids:

It is very important that a thorough inspection of the wiring and connectors be performed. Failure to carefully and fully inspect wiring and connectors may result in misdiagnosis, causing part replacement with reappearance of the fault.

It is possible that the customer may complain of pedal pulsation during normal straight-line braking if the Lateral Accelerometer has failed.

GC402920044300AX

1992

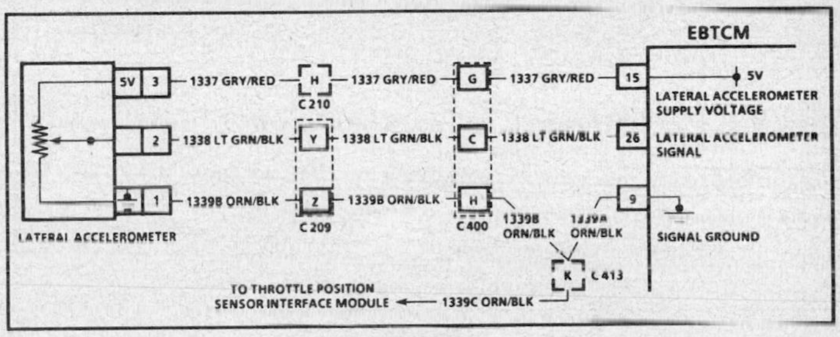
EBTCM
5V
3
1337 GRY/RED
H
C 210
G
15
5V
LATERAL ACCELEROMETER SUPPLY VOLTAGE
2
1338 LT GRN/BLK
Y
C
26
LATERAL ACCELEROMETER SIGNAL
1
1339B ORN/BLK
Z
C 209
H
C 400
9
1339B ORN/BLK
1339A ORN/BLK
SIGNAL GROUND
LATERAL ACCELEROMETER
K
C413
TO THROTTLE POSITION SENSOR INTERFACE MODULE
1339C ORN/BLK

DTC 76

LATERAL ACCELEROMETER SIGNAL OUT OF RANGE

Circuit Description:

The lateral accelerometer circuitry provides a signal to the EBTCM which reflects the severity of a vehicle turn, i.e. the "yaw" forces on the vehicle. The EBTCM uses this information to modify the control of the rear wheel brakes, to help prevent loss of control in a turn due to light brake pedal application at speeds above 50 km/h (30 mph).

DTC 76 will set when the lateral accelerometer signal is out of range for 7.5 minutes or more.

Test Description: Number(s) below refer to circled number(s) on the diagnostic chart.

1. Checks if another ABS/ASR system DTC may be causing the DTC 76 to set.
2. Checks for appropriate signal voltage at a 0g (no-turn, stationary) condition.
3. Checks for appropriate signal voltage for a full-scale left-hand turn. The full-scale left turn is simulated by the right side of the lateral accelerometer being exposed to the 1g force of gravity.
4. Repairs other ABS/ASR code problems that may affect DTC 76, then checks for DTC 76 reset.
5. Checks wiring and connectors for intermittents and/or shorts.
6. Checks for DTC 76 reset after lateral accelerometer is replaced; lateral accelerometer is causing problem noted in Step 2, since DTC 75 would identify other problems that could cause Step 2 to measure incorrectly, and the existence of DTC 75 was eliminated in Step 1. If DTC 76 resets after lateral accelerometer replacement, the EBTCM is interpreting a problem when it should not be.

Diagnostic Aids:

It is very important that a thorough inspection of the wiring and connectors be performed. Failure to carefully and fully inspect wiring and connectors may result in misdiagnosis, causing part replacement with reappearance of the malfunction.

It is possible that the customer may complain of pedal pulsation during normal straight-line braking if the lateral accelerometer has failed.

GC402930044300BX

1993

Fig. 88 Code 76: Lateral Accelerometer Signal Out Of Range (Part 1 of 3). 1992–93

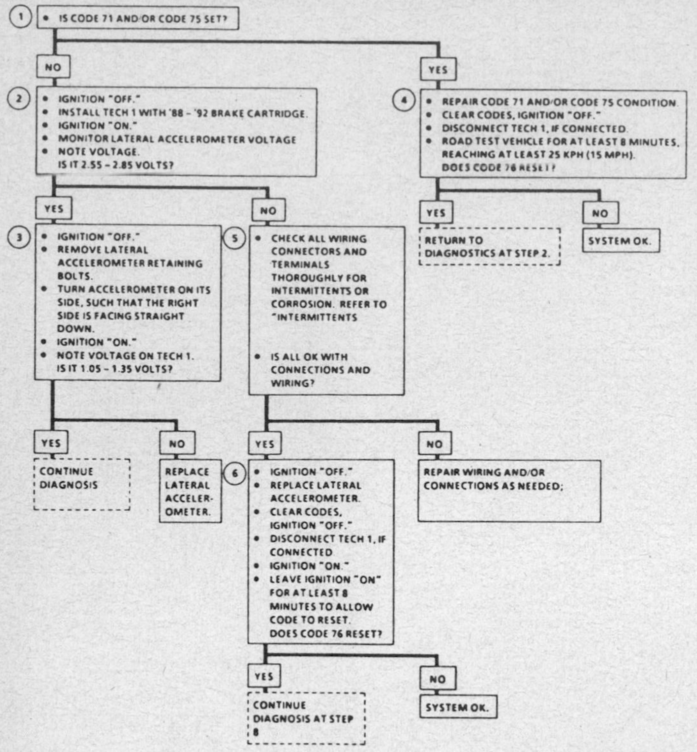

1 • IS CODE 71 AND/OR CODE 75 SET?
NO
YES
2 • IGNITION "OFF." • INSTALL TECH 1 WITH '88 - '92 BRAKE CARTRIDGE. • IGNITION "ON." • MONITOR LATERAL ACCELEROMETER VOLTAGE • NOTE VOLTAGE. IS IT 2.55 - 2.85 VOLTS?
4 • REPAIR CODE 71 AND/OR CODE 75 CONDITION. • CLEAR CODES, IGNITION "OFF." • DISCONNECT TECH 1, IF CONNECTED. • ROAD TEST VEHICLE FOR AT LEAST 8 MINUTES, REACHING AT LEAST 25 KPH (15 MPH). DOES CODE 76 RESET?
YES
NO
YES
NO
RETURN TO DIAGNOSTICS AT STEP 2.
SYSTEM OK.
3 • IGNITION "OFF." • REMOVE LATERAL ACCELEROMETER RETAINING BOLTS. • TURN ACCELEROMETER ON ITS SIDE, SUCH THAT THE RIGHT SIDE IS FACING STRAIGHT DOWN. • IGNITION "ON." • NOTE VOLTAGE ON TECH 1. IS IT 1.05 - 1.35 VOLTS?
5 • CHECK ALL WIRING CONNECTORS AND TERMINALS THOROUGHLY FOR INTERMITTENTS OR CORROSION. REFER TO "INTERMITTENTS" • IS ALL OK WITH CONNECTIONS AND WIRING?
YES
NO
YES
NO
CONTINUE DIAGNOSIS
REPLACE LATERAL ACCELEROMETER.
6 • IGNITION "OFF." • REPLACE LATERAL ACCELEROMETER. • CLEAR CODES, IGNITION "OFF." • DISCONNECT TECH 1, IF CONNECTED • IGNITION "ON." • LEAVE IGNITION "ON" FOR AT LEAST 8 MINUTES TO ALLOW CODE TO RESET. DOES CODE 76 RESET?
REPAIR WIRING AND/OR CONNECTIONS AS NEEDED;
YES
NO
CONTINUE DIAGNOSIS AT STEP 8
SYSTEM OK.

GC402920044300CX

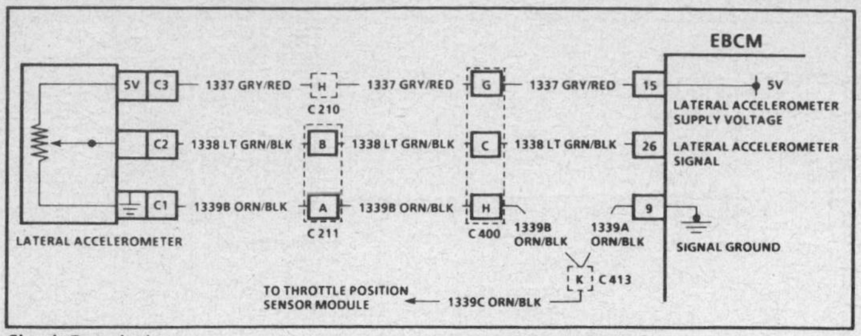

EBCM
5V C3
1337 GRY/RED
H
C210
1337 GRY/RED
G
1337 GRY/RED
15
5V
LATERAL ACCELEROMETER SUPPLY VOLTAGE
C2
1338 LT GRN/BLK
B
1338 LT GRN/BLK
C
1338 LT GRN/BLK
26
LATERAL ACCELEROMETER SIGNAL
C1
1339B ORN/BLK
A
C211
1339B ORN/BLK
H
C400
1339B ORN/BLK
1339A ORN/BLK
9
SIGNAL GROUND
LATERAL ACCELEROMETER
K C413
TO THROTTLE POSITION SENSOR MODULE
1339C ORN/BLK

Circuit Description:

The Lateral Accelerometer circuitry provides a signal to the EBCM which reflects the severity of a vehicle turn, i.e. the "yaw" forces on the vehicle. The EBCM uses this information to modify the control of the rear wheel brakes, to help prevent loss of control in a turn due to light brake pedal application at speeds above 50 km/h (30 mph).

Code 76 will set when the Lateral Accelerometer signal is out of range for 7.5 minutes or more.

Test Description: Number(s) below refer to circled number(s) on the diagnostic chart.

7. Checks for appropriate signal voltage for a full-scale right-hand turn. The full-scale right turn is simulated by the left side of the Lateral Accelerometer being exposed to the 1g force of gravity.
8. Checks for code reset after most other portions of the system have checked as OK.
9. Checks for the Lateral Accelerometer causing the Step 5 code reset, using the Tech 1 snapshot feature. In Snapshot Mode, the Tech 1 will trigger if the Lateral Accelerometer suddenly changes signal greater than high and low calibrated parameters. It is important when road-testing not to make any SEVERE directional changes that might incorrectly cause the Tech 1 to trigger by "spiking" the Lateral Accelerometer signal.
10. Checks if Lateral Accelerometer was replaced in Step 6. If so, the EBCM is at fault. If not, the Lateral Accelerometer may be faulty and should be replaced before continuing with diagnosis.
11. Road tests to check for continuing Code 76 reset. If Code 76 resets, the EBCM is interpreting a problem when it should not be.

Diagnostic Aids:

It is very important that a thorough inspection of the wiring and connectors be performed. Failure to carefully and fully inspect wiring and connectors may result in misdiagnosis, causing part replacement with reappearance of the fault.

It is possible that the customer may complain of pedal pulsation during normal light straight-line braking if the Lateral Accelerometer has failed.

GC402920044300DX

1992

Fig. 88 Code 76: Lateral Accelerometer Signal Out Of Range (Part 2 of 3). 1992–93

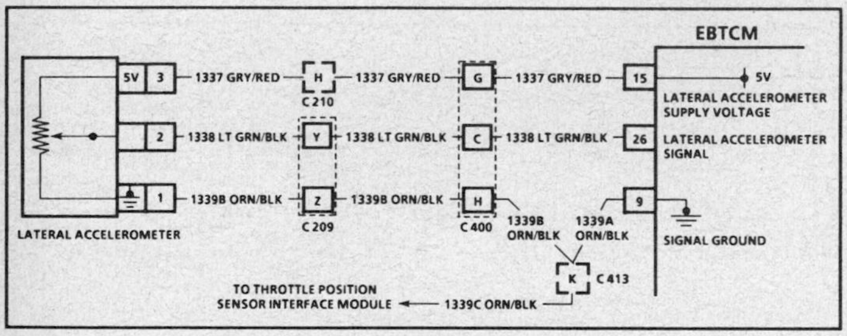

EBTCM
5V 3
1337 GRY/RED
H
C210
1337 GRY/RED
G
1337 GRY/RED
15
5V
LATERAL ACCELEROMETER SUPPLY VOLTAGE
2
1338 LT GRN/BLK
Y
1338 LT GRN/BLK
C
1338 LT GRN/BLK
26
LATERAL ACCELEROMETER SIGNAL
1
1339B ORN/BLK
Z
C209
1339B ORN/BLK
H
C400
1339B ORN/BLK
1339A ORN/BLK
9
SIGNAL GROUND
LATERAL ACCELEROMETER
K C413
TO THROTTLE POSITION SENSOR INTERFACE MODULE
1339C ORN/BLK

DTC 76

LATERAL ACCELEROMETER SIGNAL OUT OF RANGE

Circuit Description:

The lateral accelerometer circuitry provides a signal to the EBTCM which reflects the severity of a vehicle turn, i.e. the "yaw" forces on the vehicle. The EBTCM uses this information to modify the control of the rear wheel brakes, to help prevent loss of control in a turn due to light brake pedal application at speeds above 50 km/h (30 mph).

DTC 76 will set when the lateral accelerometer signal is out of range for 7.5 minutes or more.

Test Description: Number(s) below refer to circled number(s) on the diagnostic chart.

7. Checks for appropriate signal voltage for a full-scale right-hand turn. The full-scale right turn is simulated by the left side of the lateral accelerometer being exposed to the 1g force of gravity.
8. Checks for DTC reset after most other portions of the system have checked as OK.
9. Checks for the lateral accelerometer causing the Step 5 DTC reset, using the Tech 1 snapshot feature. In snapshot mode, the Tech 1 will trigger if the lateral accelerometer suddenly changes signal greater than high and low calibrated parameters. It is important when road-testing not to make any SEVERE directional changes that might incorrectly cause the Tech 1 to trigger by "spiking" the lateral accelerometer signal.
10. Checks if Lateral Accelerometer was replaced in Step 6. If so, the EBTCM is at fault. If not, the lateral accelerometer may be faulty and should be replaced before continuing with diagnosis.
11. Road tests to check for continuing DTC 76 reset. If DTC 76 resets, the EBTCM is interpreting a problem when it should not be.

Diagnostic Aids:

It is very important that a thorough inspection of the wiring and connectors be performed. Failure to carefully and fully inspect wiring and connectors may result in misdiagnosis, causing part replacement with reappearance of the malfunction.

It is possible that the customer may complain of pedal pulsation during normal light straight-line braking if the lateral accelerometer has failed.

GC402930044300EX

1993

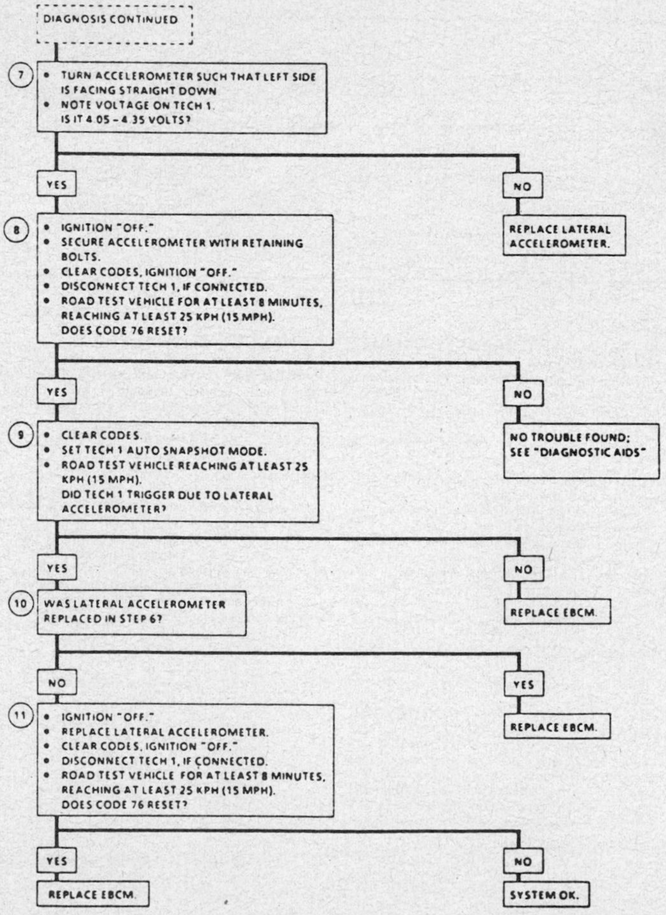

DIAGNOSIS CONTINUED
7 • TURN ACCELEROMETER SUCH THAT LEFT SIDE IS FACING STRAIGHT DOWN • NOTE VOLTAGE ON TECH 1. IS IT 4.05 - 4.35 VOLTS?
YES
NO
8 • IGNITION "OFF." • SECURE ACCELEROMETER WITH RETAINING BOLTS. • CLEAR CODES, IGNITION "OFF." • DISCONNECT TECH 1, IF CONNECTED. • ROAD TEST VEHICLE FOR AT LEAST 8 MINUTES, REACHING AT LEAST 25 KPH (15 MPH). DOES CODE 76 RESET?
REPLACE LATERAL ACCELEROMETER.
YES
NO
9 • CLEAR CODES. • SET TECH 1 AUTO SNAPSHOT MODE. • ROAD TEST VEHICLE REACHING AT LEAST 25 KPH (15 MPH). DID TECH 1 TRIGGER DUE TO LATERAL ACCELEROMETER?
NO TROUBLE FOUND; SEE "DIAGNOSTIC AIDS"
YES
NO
10 WAS LATERAL ACCELEROMETER REPLACED IN STEP 6?
REPLACE EBCM.
NO
YES
11 • IGNITION "OFF." • REPLACE LATERAL ACCELEROMETER. • CLEAR CODES, IGNITION "OFF." • DISCONNECT TECH 1, IF CONNECTED. • ROAD TEST VEHICLE FOR AT LEAST 8 MINUTES, REACHING AT LEAST 25 KPH (15 MPH). DOES CODE 76 RESET?
REPLACE EBCM.
YES
NO
REPLACE EBCM.
SYSTEM OK.

GC402920044300FX

Fig. 88 Code 76: Lateral Accelerometer Signal Out Of Range (Part 3 of 3). 1992–93

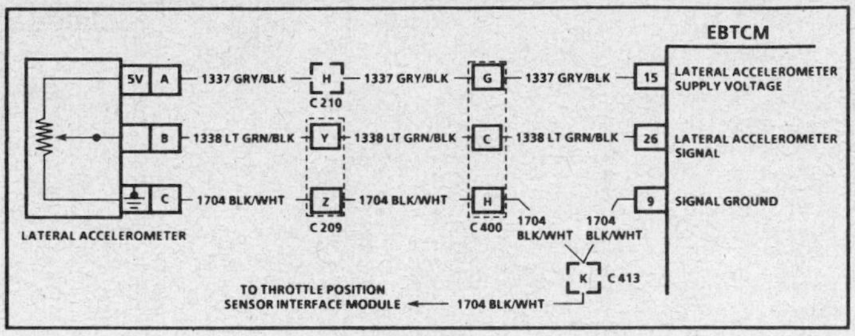
EBTCM
5V
A
B
C
1337 GRY/BLK
1338 LT GRN/BLK
1704 BLK/WHT
H
Y
Z
C210
C209
G
C
H
C400
15
26
9
LATERAL ACCELEROMETER SUPPLY VOLTAGE
LATERAL ACCELEROMETER SIGNAL
SIGNAL GROUND
1704 BLK/WHT
K
C413
LATERAL ACCELEROMETER
TO THROTTLE POSITION SENSOR INTERFACE MODULE

DTC 76

(Page 1 of 2)

LATERAL ACCELEROMETER SIGNAL OUT OF RANGE

Circuit Description:

The lateral accelerometer circuitry provides a signal to the EBTCM which reflects the severity of a vehicle turn, i.e. the "yaw" forces on the vehicle. The EBTCM uses this information to modify the control of the rear wheel brakes, to help prevent loss of control in a turn due to light brake pedal application at speeds above 50 km/h (30 mph).

DTC Will Set When: The lateral accelerometer signal is out of range for 7.5 minutes or more.

DTC Chart Test Description: Number(s) below refer to circled number(s) on the diagnostic chart.

1. Checks if another ABS/ASR system DTC may be causing the DTC 76 to set.
2. Checks for appropriate signal voltage at a 0g (no-turn, stationary) condition.
3. Checks for appropriate signal voltage for a full-scale right-hand turn. The full-scale left turn is simulated by the left side of the lateral accelerometer being exposed to the 1g force of gravity.
4. Repairs other ABS/ASR DTC malfunctions that may affect DTC 76, then checks for DTC 76 reset.
5. Checks wiring and connectors for intermittents and/or shorts.
6. Checks for DTC 76 reset after lateral accelerometer is replaced; lateral accelerometer is causing the malfunction noted in Step 2, since DTC 75 would identify other malfunctions that could cause Step 2 to measure incorrectly, and the existence of DTC 76 was eliminated in Step 1. If DTC 76 resets after lateral accelerometer replacement, the EBTCM is interpreting a malfunction when it should not be.

Diagnostic Aids: It is very important that a thorough inspection of the wiring and connectors be performed. Failure to carefully and fully inspect wiring and connectors may result in misdiagnosis, causing part replacement with reappearance of the malfunction.

It is possible that the customer may complain of pedal pulsation during normal straight-line braking if the lateral accelerometer has failed.

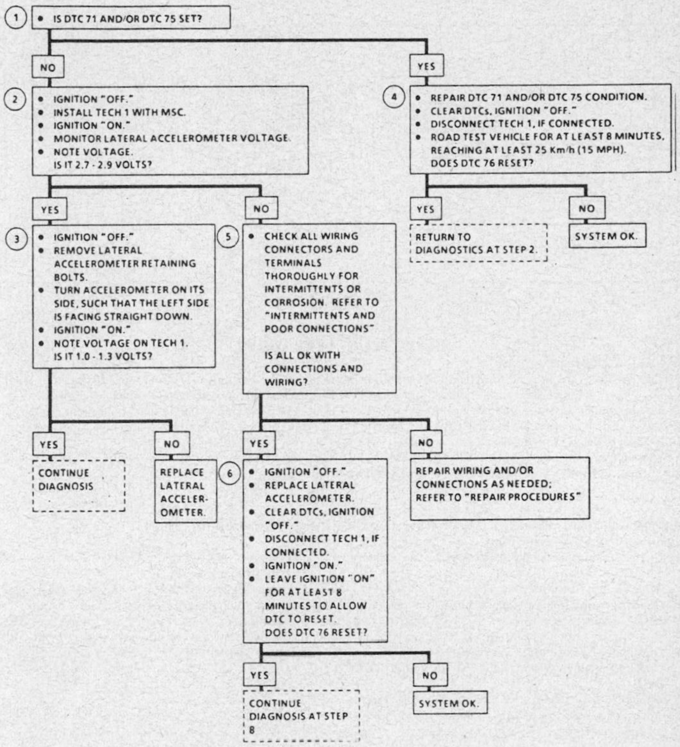
1 • IS DTC 71 AND/OR DTC 75 SET?
NO
YES
2 • IGNITION "OFF." • INSTALL TECH 1 WITH MSC. • IGNITION "ON." • MONITOR LATERAL ACCELEROMETER VOLTAGE. • NOTE VOLTAGE. IS IT 2.7 - 2.9 VOLTS?
4 • REPAIR DTC 71 AND/OR DTC 75 CONDITION. • CLEAR DTCs, IGNITION "OFF." • DISCONNECT TECH 1, IF CONNECTED. • ROAD TEST VEHICLE FOR AT LEAST 8 MINUTES, REACHING AT LEAST 25 Km/h (15 MPH). DOES DTC 76 RESET?
YES
NO
YES
NO
RETURN TO DIAGNOSTICS AT STEP 2.
SYSTEM OK.
3 • IGNITION "OFF." • REMOVE LATERAL ACCELEROMETER RETAINING BOLTS. • TURN ACCELEROMETER ON ITS SIDE, SUCH THAT THE LEFT SIDE IS FACING STRAIGHT DOWN. • IGNITION "ON." • NOTE VOLTAGE ON TECH 1. IS IT 1.0 - 1.3 VOLTS?
5 • CHECK ALL WIRING CONNECTORS AND TERMINALS THOROUGHLY FOR INTERMITTENTS OR CORROSION. REFER TO "INTERMITTENTS AND POOR CONNECTIONS" IS ALL OK WITH CONNECTIONS AND WIRING?
YES
NO
YES
NO
CONTINUE DIAGNOSIS
REPLACE LATERAL ACCELER-OMETER.
6 • IGNITION "OFF." • REPLACE LATERAL ACCELEROMETER. • CLEAR DTCs, IGNITION "OFF." • DISCONNECT TECH 1, IF CONNECTED. • IGNITION "ON." • LEAVE IGNITION "ON" FOR AT LEAST 8 MINUTES TO ALLOW DTC TO RESET. DOES DTC 76 RESET?
REPAIR WIRING AND/OR CONNECTIONS AS NEEDED; REFER TO "REPAIR PROCEDURES"
YES
NO
CONTINUE DIAGNOSIS AT STEP 8
SYSTEM OK.

GC402940009001AX

Fig. 89 Code 76: Lateral Accelerometer Signal Out Of Range (Part 1 of 2). 1994

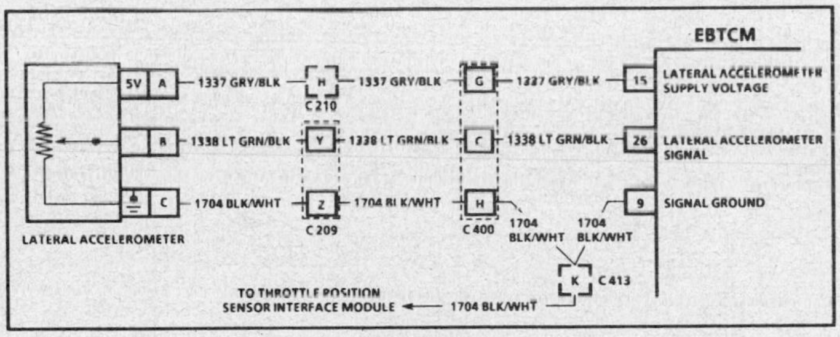
EBTCM
5V
A
B
C
1337 GRY/BLK
1338 LT GRN/BLK
1704 BLK/WHT
H
Y
Z
C210
C209
G
C
H
C400
15
26
9
LATERAL ACCELEROMETER SUPPLY VOLTAGE
LATERAL ACCELEROMETER SIGNAL
SIGNAL GROUND
1704 BLK/WHT
K
C413
LATERAL ACCELEROMETER
TO THROTTLE POSITION SENSOR INTERFACE MODULE

DTC 76

(Page 2 of 2)

LATERAL ACCELEROMETER SIGNAL OUT OF RANGE

Circuit Description:

The lateral accelerometer circuitry provides a signal to the EBTCM which reflects the severity of a vehicle turn, i.e. the "yaw" forces on the vehicle. The EBTCM uses this information to modify the control of the rear wheel brakes, to help prevent loss of control in a turn due to light brake pedal application at speeds above 50 km/h (30 mph).

DTC Will Set When: The lateral accelerometer signal is out of range for 7.5 minutes or more.

DTC Chart Test Description: Number(s) below refer to circled number(s) on the diagnostic chart.

7. Checks for appropriate signal voltage for a full-scale left-hand turn. The full-scale right turn is simulated by the right side of the lateral accelerometer being exposed to the 1g force of gravity.
8. Checks for DTC reset after most other portions of the system have checked as OK.
9. Checks for the lateral accelerometer causing the Step 5 DTC reset, using the Tech 1 snapshot feature. In snapshot mode, the Tech 1 will trigger if the lateral accelerometer suddenly changes signal greater than high and low calibrated parameters. It is important when road-testing not to make any SEVERE directional changes that might incorrectly cause the Tech 1 to trigger by "spiking" the lateral accelerometer signal.
10. Checks if lateral accelerometer was replaced in Step 6. If so, the EBTCM is at fault. If not, the lateral accelerometer may be faulty and should be replaced before continuing with diagnosis.
11. Road tests to check for continuing DTC 76 reset. If DTC 76 resets, the EBTCM is interpreting a malfunction when it should not be.

Diagnostic Aids: It is very important that a thorough inspection of the wiring and connectors be performed. Failure to carefully and fully inspect wiring and connectors may result in misdiagnosis, causing part replacement with reappearance of the malfunction.

It is possible that the customer may complain of pedal pulsation during normal light straight-line braking if the lateral accelerometer has failed.

GC402940089002AX

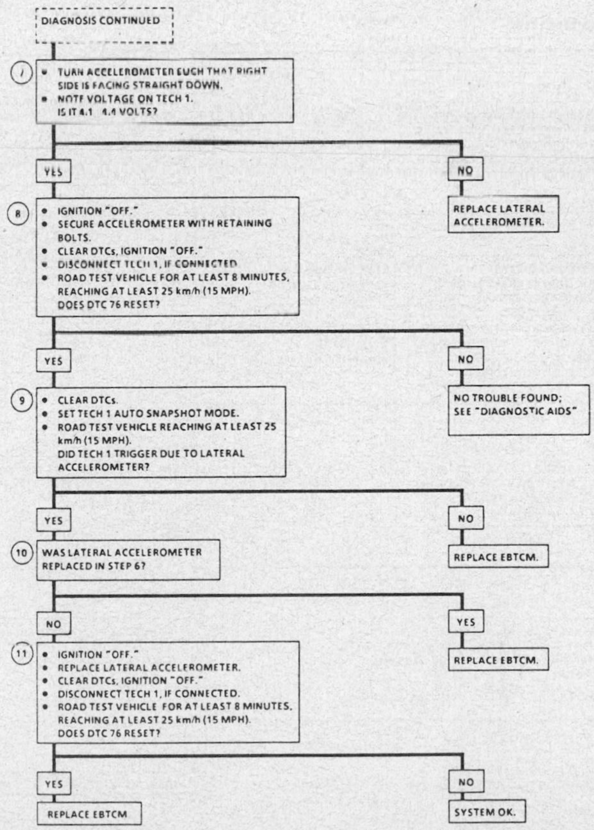
DIAGNOSIS CONTINUED
7 • TURN ACCELEROMETER SUCH THAT RIGHT SIDE IS FACING STRAIGHT DOWN. • NOTE VOLTAGE ON TECH 1. IS IT 4.1 - 4.4 VOLTS?
YES
NO
REPLACE LATERAL ACCELEROMETER.
8 • IGNITION "OFF." • SECURE ACCELEROMETER WITH RETAINING BOLTS. • CLEAR DTCs, IGNITION "OFF." • DISCONNECT TECH 1, IF CONNECTED. • ROAD TEST VEHICLE FOR AT LEAST 8 MINUTES, REACHING AT LEAST 25 km/h (15 MPH). DOES DTC 76 RESET?
YES
NO
NO TROUBLE FOUND; SEE "DIAGNOSTIC AIDS"
9 • CLEAR DTCs. • SET TECH 1 AUTO SNAPSHOT MODE. • ROAD TEST VEHICLE REACHING AT LEAST 25 km/h (15 MPH). DID TECH 1 TRIGGER DUE TO LATERAL ACCELEROMETER?
YES
NO
REPLACE EBTCM.
10 WAS LATERAL ACCELEROMETER REPLACED IN STEP 6?
NO
YES
REPLACE EBTCM.
11 • IGNITION "OFF." • REPLACE LATERAL ACCELEROMETER. • CLEAR DTCs, IGNITION "OFF." • DISCONNECT TECH 1, IF CONNECTED. • ROAD TEST VEHICLE FOR AT LEAST 8 MINUTES, REACHING AT LEAST 25 km/h (15 MPH). DOES DTC 76 RESET?
YES
NO
REPLACE EBTCM
SYSTEM OK.

GC402940089002BX

Fig. 89 Code 76: Lateral Accelerometer Signal Out Of Range (Part 2 of 2). 1994

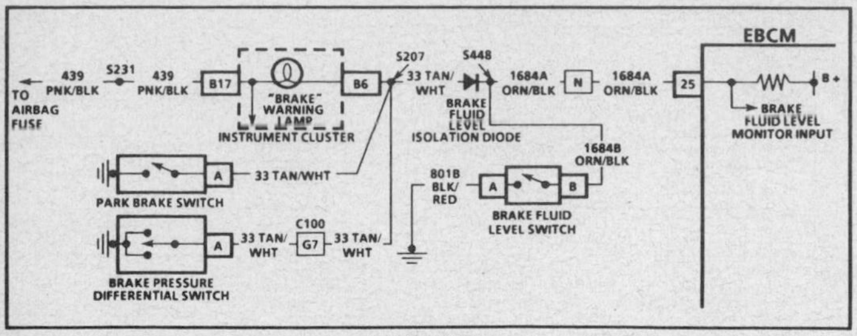
EBCM
TO AIRBAG FUSE
439 PNK/BLK
S231
439 PNK/BLK
B17
"BRAKE" WARNING LAMP
INSTRUMENT CLUSTER
B6
S207
33 TAN/WHT
S448
BRAKE FLUID LEVEL ISOLATION DIODE
1684A ORN/BLK
N
1684A ORN/BLK
25
B+
BRAKE FLUID LEVEL MONITOR INPUT
PARK BRAKE SWITCH
33 TAN/WHT
A
1684B ORN/BLK
801B BLK/RED
BRAKE FLUID LEVEL SWITCH
C100
33 TAN/WHT
G7
33 TAN/WHT
BRAKE PRESSURE DIFFERENTIAL SWITCH

CODE 83

BRAKE FLUID LEVEL LOW

Circuit Description:

The Brake Fluid Level circuit monitors the fluid level in the master cylinder reservoir. If the fluid level becomes low, as indicated by the Brake Fluid Level Switch, the ABS/ASR system is disabled. This is done to prevent introduction of air into the brake system. The Fluid Level Isolation Diode is used to prevent disabling ABS/ASR if illumination of the red "BRAKE" warning lamp occurs for reasons of brake pressure differential or application of the parking brake.

Code 83 will set and the "SERVICE ABS" and "SERVICE ASR" lamps will illuminate if CKT 1684 is low (grounded). **For some 1992 vehicles, the engine must be running for this code to set.**

Test Description: Number(s) below refer to circled number(s) on the diagnostic chart.

1. Checks for proper brake fluid level in the master cylinder reservoir.
2. Checks for illumination of the red "BRAKE" warning lamp for reasons other than parking brake engagement.
3. Checks for Brake Fluid Level Switch stuck closed.
4. Checks for short from CKT 1684 to ground CKT 801B.
5. Checks for short from CKT 1684 to chassis ground.
6. Adds fluid, noted to be low in Step 1, then checks for code reset.

Diagnostic Aids:

For some 1992 vehicles, the engine must be running for this code to set.

It is very important that a thorough inspection of the wiring and connectors be performed. Failure to carefully and fully inspect wiring and connectors may result in misdiagnosis, causing part replacement with reappearance of the fault.

GC402920044400AX

1992

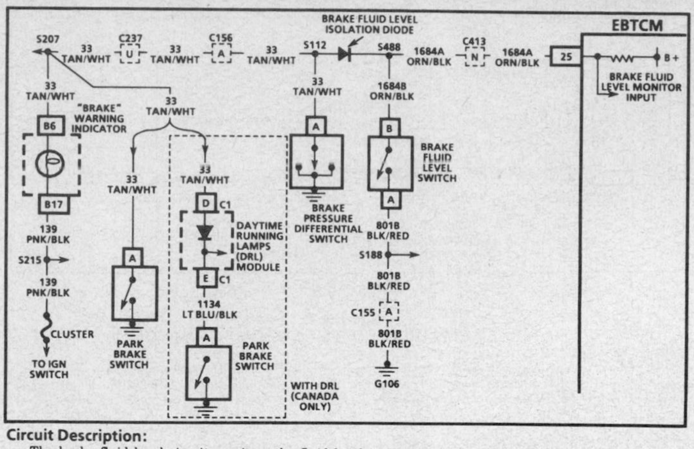
EBTCM
BRAKE FLUID LEVEL ISOLATION DIODE
S207
33 TAN/WHT
C237
U
33 TAN/WHT
C156
A
33 TAN/WHT
S112
S488
1684A ORN/BLK
C413
N
1684A ORN/BLK
25
B+
BRAKE FLUID LEVEL MONITOR INPUT
33 TAN/WHT
"BRAKE" WARNING INDICATOR
B6
B17
139 PNK/BLK
S215
139 PNK/BLK
CLUSTER
TO IGN SWITCH
33 TAN/WHT
PARK BRAKE SWITCH
DAYTIME RUNNING LAMPS (DRL) MODULE
1134 LT BLU/BLK
WITH DRL (CANADA ONLY)
BRAKE PRESSURE DIFFERENTIAL SWITCH
1684B ORN/BLK
BRAKE FLUID LEVEL SWITCH
801B BLK/RED
S188
C155
G106

Circuit Description:

The brake fluid level circuit monitors the fluid level in the master cylinder reservoir. If the fluid level becomes low, as indicated by the brake fluid level switch, the ABS/ASR system is disabled. This is done to prevent introduction of air into the brake system. The fluid level isolation diode is used to prevent disabling ABS/ASR if illumination of the red "BRAKE" warning lamp occurs for reasons of brake pressure differential or application of the parking brake.

DTC 83 will set and the "SERVICE ABS" and "SERVICE ASR" lamps will illuminate if the engine is running and CKT 1684 is low (grounded).

Test Description: Number(s) below refer to circled number(s) on the diagnostic chart.

1. Checks for proper brake fluid level in the master cylinder reservoir.
2. Checks for illumination of the red "BRAKE" warning lamp for reasons other than parking brake engagement. Refer to "Warning Lamp Operation" in SECTION 5 for details.
3. Checks for brake fluid level switch stuck closed.
4. Checks for short from CKT 1684 to ground CKT 801B.
5. Checks for short from CKT 1684 to chassis ground.
6. Adds fluid, noted to be low in Step 1, then checks for DTC reset.

Diagnostic Aids:

The engine must be running for this DTC to set.

It is very important that a thorough inspection of the wiring and connectors be performed. Failure to carefully and fully inspect wiring and connectors may result in misdiagnosis, causing part replacement with reappearance of the malfunction.

GC402930044400BX

1993

Fig. 90 Code 83: Brake Fluid Level Low (Part 1 of 3). 1992–93

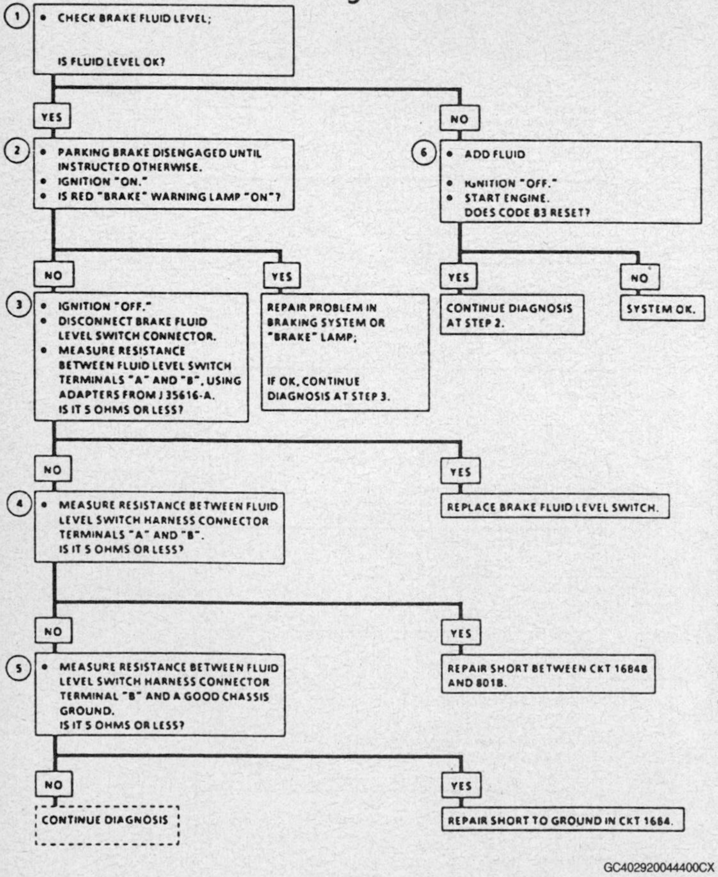
1 • CHECK BRAKE FLUID LEVEL; IS FLUID LEVEL OK?
YES
NO
2 • PARKING BRAKE DISENGAGED UNTIL INSTRUCTED OTHERWISE. • IGNITION "ON." • IS RED "BRAKE" WARNING LAMP "ON"?
6 • ADD FLUID • IGNITION "OFF." • START ENGINE. DOES CODE 83 RESET?
NO
YES
YES
NO
3 • IGNITION "OFF." • DISCONNECT BRAKE FLUID LEVEL SWITCH CONNECTOR. • MEASURE RESISTANCE BETWEEN FLUID LEVEL SWITCH TERMINALS "A" AND "B", USING ADAPTERS FROM J 35616-A. IS IT 5 OHMS OR LESS?
REPAIR PROBLEM IN BRAKING SYSTEM OR "BRAKE" LAMP; IF OK, CONTINUE DIAGNOSIS AT STEP 3.
CONTINUE DIAGNOSIS AT STEP 2.
SYSTEM OK.
NO
YES
4 • MEASURE RESISTANCE BETWEEN FLUID LEVEL SWITCH HARNESS CONNECTOR TERMINALS "A" AND "B". IS IT 5 OHMS OR LESS?
REPLACE BRAKE FLUID LEVEL SWITCH.
NO
YES
5 • MEASURE RESISTANCE BETWEEN FLUID LEVEL SWITCH HARNESS CONNECTOR TERMINAL "B" AND A GOOD CHASSIS GROUND. IS IT 5 OHMS OR LESS?
REPAIR SHORT BETWEEN CKT 1684B AND 801B.
NO
YES
CONTINUE DIAGNOSIS
REPAIR SHORT TO GROUND IN CKT 1684.

GC402920044400CX

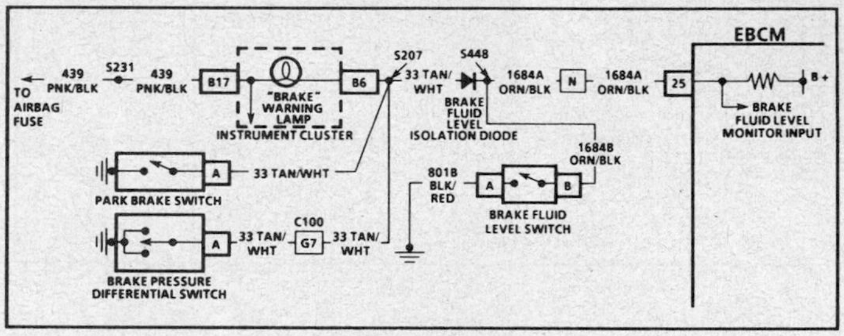
EBCM
TO AIRBAG FUSE
439 PNK/BLK
S231
439 PNK/BLK
B17
"BRAKE" WARNING LAMP
INSTRUMENT CLUSTER
B6
S207
33 TAN/WHT
S448
BRAKE FLUID LEVEL ISOLATION DIODE
1684A ORN/BLK
N
1684A ORN/BLK
25
B+
BRAKE FLUID LEVEL MONITOR INPUT
PARK BRAKE SWITCH
33 TAN/WHT
1684B ORN/BLK
801B BLK/RED
BRAKE FLUID LEVEL SWITCH
C100
33 TAN/WHT
G7
33 TAN/WHT
BRAKE PRESSURE DIFFERENTIAL SWITCH

CODE 83

BRAKE FLUID LEVEL LOW

Circuit Description:

The Brake Fluid Level circuit monitors the fluid level in the master cylinder reservoir. If the fluid level becomes low, as indicated by the Brake Fluid Level Switch, the ABS/ASR system is disabled. This is done to prevent introduction of air into the brake system. The Fluid Level Isolation Diode is used to prevent disabling ABS/ASR if illumination of the red "BRAKE" warning lamp occurs for reasons of brake pressure differential or application of the parking brake.

Code 83 will set and the "SERVICE ABS" and "SERVICE ASR" lamps will illuminate if CKT 1684 is low (grounded). **For some 1992 vehicles, the engine must be running for this code to set.**

Test Description: Number(s) below refer to circled number(s) on the diagnostic chart.

7. Checks for continuing code reset after checks in Steps 1-5.
8. Checks for code reset when parking brake is engaged, likely due to a faulty diode.
9. Checks for parking brake switch stuck closed.
10. Checks for short to ground in parking brake switch CKT 33.
11. Replaces faulty diode found in Step 7 or Step 10, then checks for code reset. If code resets, the EBCM is determining there is a problem in CKT 1684 and related circuitry when there is not.

Diagnostic Aids:

For some 1992 vehicles, the engine must be running for this code to set.

It is very important that a thorough inspection of the wiring and connectors be performed. Failure to carefully and fully inspect wiring and connectors may result in misdiagnosis, causing part replacement with reappearance of the fault.

GC402920044400DX

1992

Fig. 90 Code 83: Brake Fluid Level Low (Part 2 of 3). 1992–93

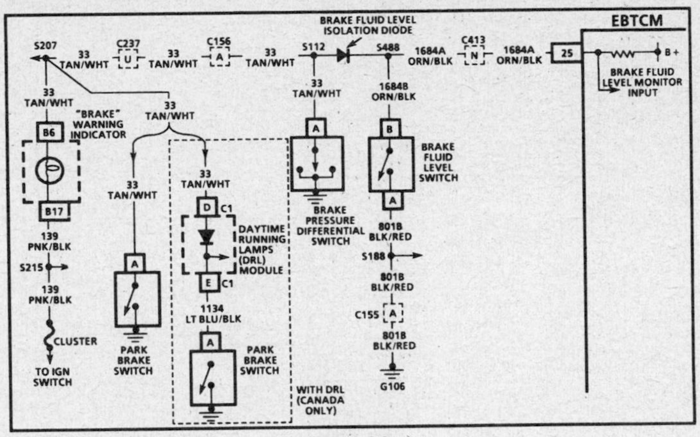

EBTCM
BRAKE FLUID LEVEL ISOLATION DIODE
S207
C237
C156
S112
S488
C413
33 TAN/WHT
1684A ORN/BLK
25
B+
BRAKE FLUID LEVEL MONITOR INPUT
1684B ORN/BLK
"BRAKE" WARNING INDICATOR
B6
B17
139 PNK/BLK
S215
CLUSTER
TO IGN SWITCH
PARK BRAKE SWITCH
DAYTIME RUNNING LAMPS (DRL) MODULE
1134 LT BLU/BLK
BRAKE PRESSURE DIFFERENTIAL SWITCH
BRAKE FLUID LEVEL SWITCH
801B BLK/RED
S188
C155
G106
WITH DRL (CANADA ONLY)

DTC 83

BRAKE FLUID LEVEL LOW

Circuit Description:

The brake fluid level circuit monitors the fluid level in the master cylinder reservoir. If the fluid level becomes low, as indicated by the brake fluid level switch, the ABS/ASR system is disabled. This is done to prevent introduction of air into the brake system. The fluid level isolation diode is used to prevent disabling ABS/ASR if illumination of the red "BRAKE" warning lamp occurs for reasons of brake pressure differential or application of the parking brake.

DTC 83 will set and the "SERVICE ABS" and "SERVICE ASR" lamps will illuminate if the engine is running and CKT 1684 is low (grounded).

Test Description: Number(s) below refer to circled number(s) on the diagnostic chart.

7. Checks for continuing DTC reset after checks in Steps 1-5.
8. Checks for DTC reset when parking brake is engaged, likely due to a malfunctioning diode.
9. Checks for parking brake switch stuck closed.
10. Checks for short to ground in parking brake switch CKT 33.
11. Replaces malfunctioning diode found in Step 7 or Step 10, then checks for DTC reset. If DTC resets, the EBTCM is determining there is a problem in CKT 1684 and related circuitry when there is not.

Diagnostic Aids:

The engine must be running for this DTC to set.

It is very important that a thorough inspection of the wiring and connectors be performed. Failure to carefully and fully inspect wiring and connectors may result in misdiagnosis, causing part replacement with reappearance of the malfunction.

GC402030011100EX

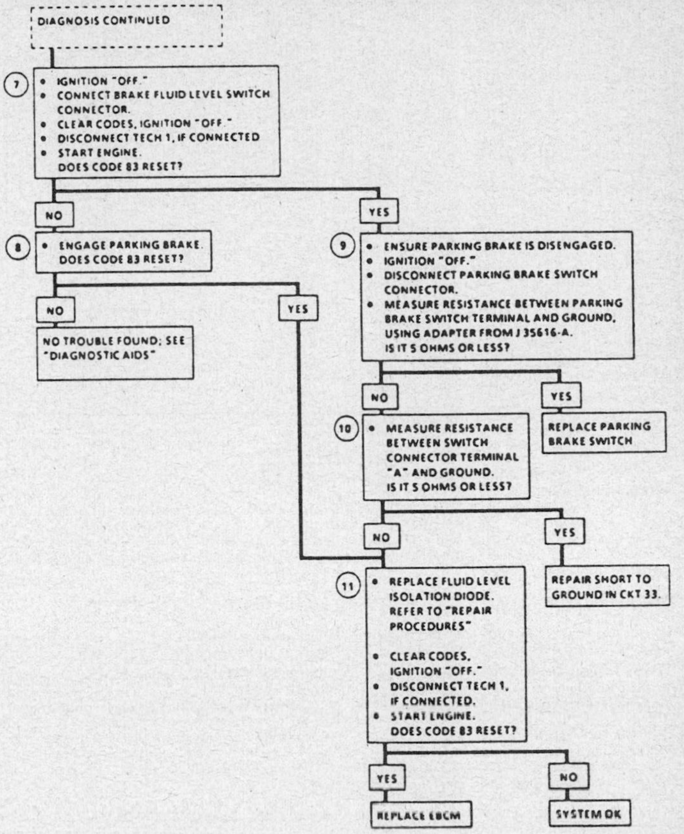

DIAGNOSIS CONTINUED
7
• IGNITION "OFF."
• CONNECT BRAKE FLUID LEVEL SWITCH CONNECTOR.
• CLEAR CODES, IGNITION "OFF."
• DISCONNECT TECH 1, IF CONNECTED
• START ENGINE.
DOES CODE 83 RESET?
NO
YES
8
• ENGAGE PARKING BRAKE.
DOES CODE 83 RESET?
9
• ENSURE PARKING BRAKE IS DISENGAGED.
• IGNITION "OFF."
• DISCONNECT PARKING BRAKE SWITCH CONNECTOR.
• MEASURE RESISTANCE BETWEEN PARKING BRAKE SWITCH TERMINAL AND GROUND, USING ADAPTER FROM J 35616-A.
IS IT 5 OHMS OR LESS?
NO
YES
NO TROUBLE FOUND; SEE "DIAGNOSTIC AIDS"
NO
YES
10
• MEASURE RESISTANCE BETWEEN SWITCH CONNECTOR TERMINAL "A" AND GROUND.
IS IT 5 OHMS OR LESS?
REPLACE PARKING BRAKE SWITCH
NO
YES
11
• REPLACE FLUID LEVEL ISOLATION DIODE. REFER TO "REPAIR PROCEDURES"
• CLEAR CODES, IGNITION "OFF."
• DISCONNECT TECH 1, IF CONNECTED.
• START ENGINE.
DOES CODE 83 RESET?
REPAIR SHORT TO GROUND IN CKT 33.
YES
NO
REPLACE EBCM
SYSTEM OK

GC402920044400FX

1993

Fig. 90 Code 83: Brake Fluid Level Low (Part 3 of 3). 1992–93

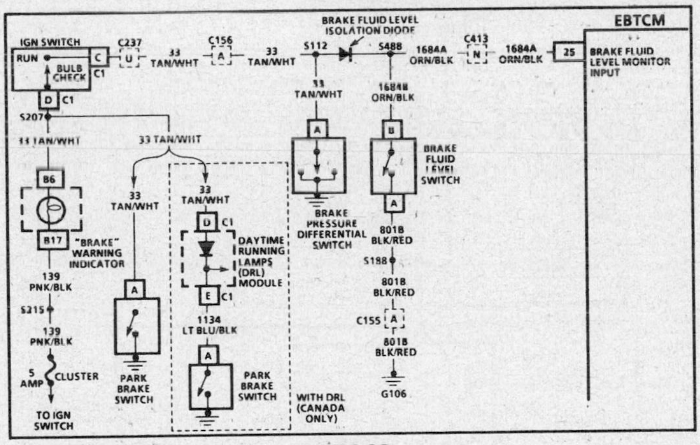

IGN SWITCH
RUN
BULB CHECK
C237
C156
S112
S488
C413
EBTCM
BRAKE FLUID LEVEL ISOLATION DIODE
33 TAN/WHT
1684A ORN/BLK
25
BRAKE FLUID LEVEL MONITOR INPUT
1684B ORN/BLK
S207
B6
B17
"BRAKE" WARNING INDICATOR
139 PNK/BLK
S215
5 AMP
CLUSTER
TO IGN SWITCH
PARK BRAKE SWITCH
DAYTIME RUNNING LAMPS (DRL) MODULE
1134 LT BLU/BLK
BRAKE PRESSURE DIFFERENTIAL SWITCH
BRAKE FLUID LEVEL SWITCH
801B BLK/RED
S188
C155
G106
WITH DRL (CANADA ONLY)

DTC 83

(Page 1 of 2)

BRAKE FLUID LEVEL LOW

Circuit Description:

The brake fluid level circuit monitors the fluid level in the master cylinder reservoir. If the fluid level becomes low, as indicated by the brake fluid level switch, the ABS/ASR system is disabled. This is done to prevent introduction of air into the brake system. The fluid level isolation diode is used to prevent disabling ABS/ASR if illumination of the red "BRAKE" warning lamp occurs for reasons of brake pressure differential or application of the parking brake.

DTC Will Set When: The engine is running and CKT 1684 is low (grounded).

Action Taken: The "SERVICE ABS" and "SERVICE ASR" indicators will be "ON."

DTC Chart Test Description: Number(s) below refer to circled number(s) on the diagnostic chart.

1. Checks for proper brake fluid level in the master cylinder reservoir.
2. Checks for illumination of the red "BRAKE" warning lamp for reasons other than parking brake engagement. Refer to "Warning Lamp Operation"
3. Checks for brake fluid level switch stuck closed.
4. Checks for short from CKT 1684 to ground CKT 1051.
5. Checks for short from CKT 1684 to chassis ground.
6. Adds fluid, noted to be low in Step 1, then checks for DTC reset.

Diagnostic Aids: The engine must be running for this DTC to set.

It is very important that a thorough inspection of the wiring and connectors be performed. Failure to carefully and fully inspect wiring and connectors may result in misdiagnosis, causing part replacement with reappearance of the malfunction.

GC402940089101AX

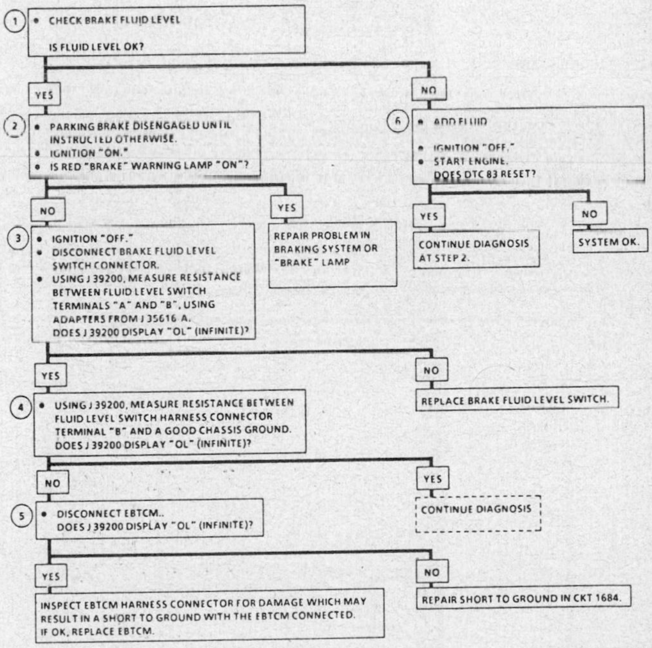

1
• CHECK BRAKE FLUID LEVEL
IS FLUID LEVEL OK?
YES
NO
2
• PARKING BRAKE DISENGAGED UNTIL INSTRUCTED OTHERWISE.
• IGNITION "ON."
• IS RED "BRAKE" WARNING LAMP "ON"?
6
• ADD FLUID
• IGNITION "OFF."
• START ENGINE.
DOES DTC 83 RESET?
NO
YES
YES
NO
3
• IGNITION "OFF."
• DISCONNECT BRAKE FLUID LEVEL SWITCH CONNECTOR.
• USING J 39200, MEASURE RESISTANCE BETWEEN FLUID LEVEL SWITCH TERMINALS "A" AND "B", USING ADAPTERS FROM J 35616 A.
DOES J 39200 DISPLAY "OL" (INFINITE)?
REPAIR PROBLEM IN BRAKING SYSTEM OR "BRAKE" LAMP
CONTINUE DIAGNOSIS AT STEP 2.
SYSTEM OK.
YES
NO
4
• USING J 39200, MEASURE RESISTANCE BETWEEN FLUID LEVEL SWITCH HARNESS CONNECTOR TERMINAL "B" AND A GOOD CHASSIS GROUND.
DOES J 39200 DISPLAY "OL" (INFINITE)?
REPLACE BRAKE FLUID LEVEL SWITCH.
NO
YES
5
• DISCONNECT EBTCM..
DOES J 39200 DISPLAY "OL" (INFINITE)?
CONTINUE DIAGNOSIS
YES
NO
INSPECT EBTCM HARNESS CONNECTOR FOR DAMAGE WHICH MAY RESULT IN A SHORT TO GROUND WITH THE EBTCM CONNECTED. IF OK, REPLACE EBTCM.
REPAIR SHORT TO GROUND IN CKT 1684.

GC402940089101BX

Fig. 91 Code 83: Brake Fluid Level Low (Part 1 of 2). 1994

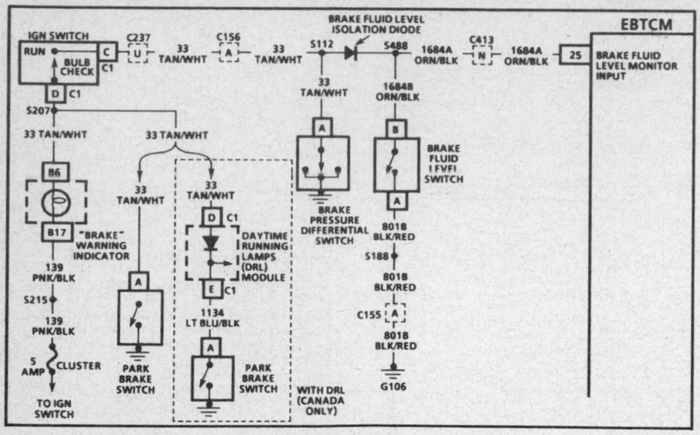
IGN SWITCH
RUN
BULB CHECK
C237
C156
BRAKE FLUID LEVEL ISOLATION DIODE
S112
S488
1684A ORN/BLK
C413
EBTCM
BRAKE FLUID LEVEL MONITOR INPUT
33 TAN/WHT
1684B ORN/BLK
S207
"BRAKE" WARNING INDICATOR
139 PNK/BLK
S215
5 AMP
CLUSTER
TO IGN SWITCH
PARK BRAKE SWITCH
DAYTIME RUNNING LAMPS (DRL) MODULE
1134 LT BLU/BLK
WITH DRL (CANADA ONLY)
BRAKE PRESSURE DIFFERENTIAL SWITCH
BRAKE FLUID LEVEL SWITCH
801B BLK/RED
S188
C155
G106

DTC 83

(Page 2 of 2)

BRAKE FLUID LEVEL LOW

Circuit Description:

The brake fluid level circuit monitors the fluid level in the master cylinder reservoir. If the fluid level becomes low, as indicated by the brake fluid level switch, the ABS/ASR system is disabled. This is done to prevent introduction of air into the brake system. The fluid level isolation diode is used to prevent disabling ABS/ASR if illumination of the red "BRAKE" warning lamp occurs for reasons of brake pressure differential or application of the parking brake.

DTC Will Set When: The engine is running and CKT 1684 is low (grounded).

Action Taken: The "SERVICE ABS" and "SERVICE ASR" indicators will be "ON."

DTC Chart Test Description: Number(s) below refer to circled number(s) on the diagnostic chart.

7. Checks for continuing DTC reset after checks in Steps 1-5.
8. Checks for DTC reset when parking brake is engaged, likely due to a malfunctioning diode.
9. Checks for parking brake switch stuck closed.
10. Replaces malfunctioning diode found in Step 7 or Step 10, then checks for DTC reset. If DTC resets, the EBTCM is determining there is a malfunction in CKT 1684 and related circuitry when there is not.

Diagnostic Aids: The engine must be running for this DTC to set.

It is very important that a thorough inspection of the wiring and connectors be performed. Failure to carefully and fully inspect wiring and connectors may result in misdiagnosis, causing part replacement with reappearance of the malfunction.

GC402940089102AX

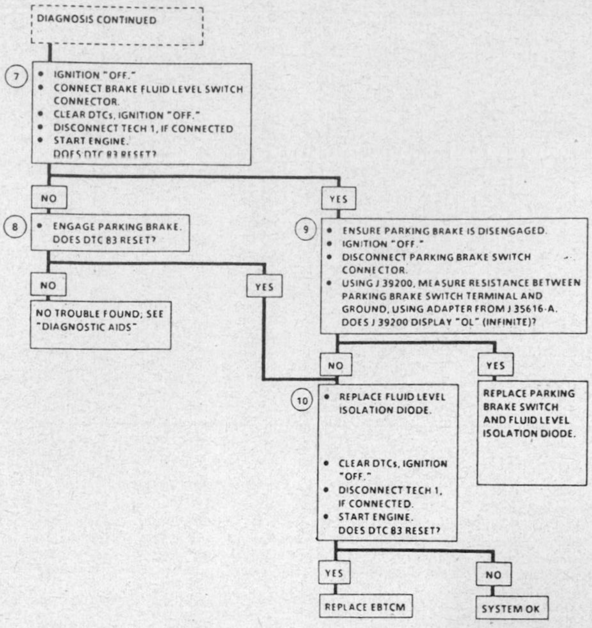
DIAGNOSIS CONTINUED
7
• IGNITION "OFF."
• CONNECT BRAKE FLUID LEVEL SWITCH CONNECTOR.
• CLEAR DTCs, IGNITION "OFF."
• DISCONNECT TECH 1, IF CONNECTED
• START ENGINE.
DOES DTC 83 RESET?
NO
YES
8
• ENGAGE PARKING BRAKE.
DOES DTC 83 RESET?
NO
YES
NO TROUBLE FOUND; SEE "DIAGNOSTIC AIDS"
9
• ENSURE PARKING BRAKE IS DISENGAGED.
• IGNITION "OFF."
• DISCONNECT PARKING BRAKE SWITCH CONNECTOR.
• USING J 39200, MEASURE RESISTANCE BETWEEN PARKING BRAKE SWITCH TERMINAL AND GROUND, USING ADAPTER FROM J 35616-A.
DOES J 39200 DISPLAY "OL" (INFINITE)?
NO
YES
10
• REPLACE FLUID LEVEL ISOLATION DIODE.
• CLEAR DTCs, IGNITION "OFF."
• DISCONNECT TECH 1, IF CONNECTED.
• START ENGINE.
DOES DTC 83 RESET?
REPLACE PARKING BRAKE SWITCH AND FLUID LEVEL ISOLATION DIODE.
YES
NO
REPLACE EBTCM
SYSTEM OK

GC402940089102BX

Fig. 91 Code 83: Brake Fluid Level Low (Part 2 of 2). 1994

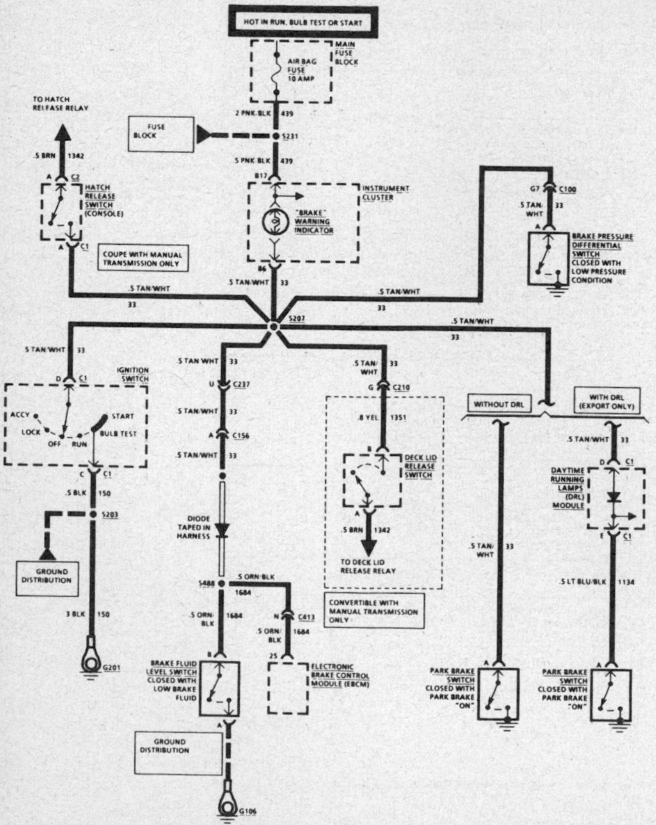
HOT IN RUN, BULB TEST OR START
MAIN FUSE BLOCK
AIR BAG FUSE 10 AMP
TO HATCH RELEASE RELAY
FUSE BLOCK
S231
HATCH RELEASE SWITCH (CONSOLE)
COUPE WITH MANUAL TRANSMISSION ONLY
INSTRUMENT CLUSTER
"BRAKE" WARNING INDICATOR
BRAKE PRESSURE DIFFERENTIAL SWITCH CLOSED WITH LOW PRESSURE CONDITION
S207
IGNITION SWITCH
ACCY
LOCK
OFF
RUN
START
BULB TEST
S203
GROUND DISTRIBUTION
DIODE TAPED IN HARNESS
DECK LID RELEASE SWITCH
TO DECK LID RELEASE RELAY
CONVERTIBLE WITH MANUAL TRANSMISSION ONLY
WITHOUT DRL
WITH DRL (EXPORT ONLY)
DAYTIME RUNNING LAMPS (DRL) MODULE
S488
BRAKE FLUID LEVEL SWITCH CLOSED WITH LOW BRAKE FLUID
ELECTRONIC BRAKE CONTROL MODULE (EBCM)
PARK BRAKE SWITCH CLOSED WITH PARK BRAKE "ON"
G201
G106

GC4029200445000X

Fig. 92 Brake warning system wiring diagram. 1992

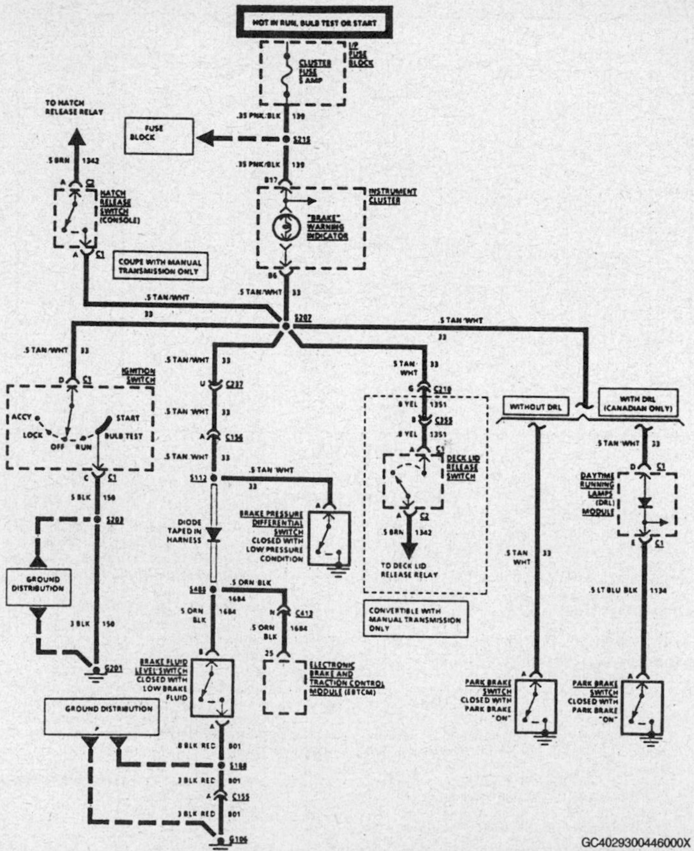
HOT IN RUN, BULB TEST OR START
CLUSTER FUSE 5 AMP
I/P FUSE BLOCK
TO HATCH RELEASE RELAY
FUSE BLOCK
S215
HATCH RELEASE SWITCH (CONSOLE)
COUPE WITH MANUAL TRANSMISSION ONLY
INSTRUMENT CLUSTER
"BRAKE" WARNING INDICATOR
S207
IGNITION SWITCH
ACCY
LOCK
OFF
RUN
START
BULB TEST
S203
GROUND DISTRIBUTION
DIODE TAPED IN HARNESS
BRAKE PRESSURE DIFFERENTIAL SWITCH CLOSED WITH LOW PRESSURE CONDITION
DECK LID RELEASE SWITCH
TO DECK LID RELEASE RELAY
CONVERTIBLE WITH MANUAL TRANSMISSION ONLY
WITHOUT DRL
WITH DRL (CANADIAN ONLY)
DAYTIME RUNNING LAMPS (DRL) MODULE
S488
BRAKE FLUID LEVEL SWITCH CLOSED WITH LOW BRAKE FLUID
ELECTRONIC BRAKE AND TRACTION CONTROL MODULE (EBTCM)
PARK BRAKE SWITCH CLOSED WITH PARK BRAKE "ON"
G201
S188
C155
G106

GC4029300446000X

Fig. 93 Brake warning system wiring diagram. 1993–94

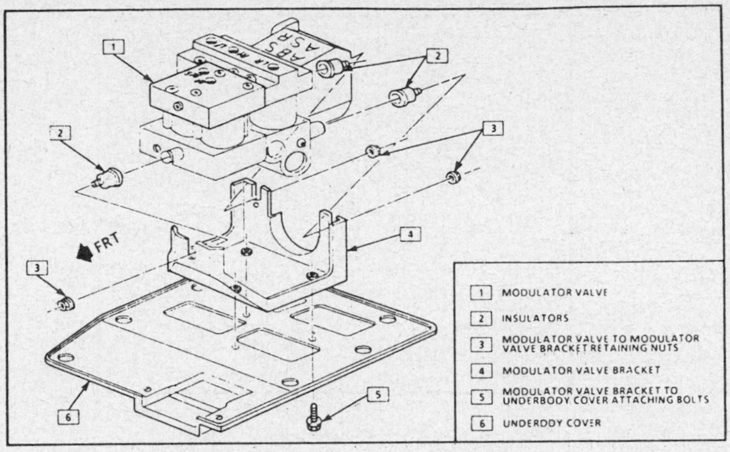
1
2
3
4
5
6
FRT
1 MODULATOR VALVE
2 INSULATORS
3 MODULATOR VALVE TO MODULATOR VALVE BRACKET RETAINING NUTS
4 MODULATOR VALVE BRACKET
5 MODULATOR VALVE BRACKET TO UNDERBODY COVER ATTACHING BOLTS
6 UNDERBODY COVER
GC4029200447000X

Fig. 94 Modulator valve location

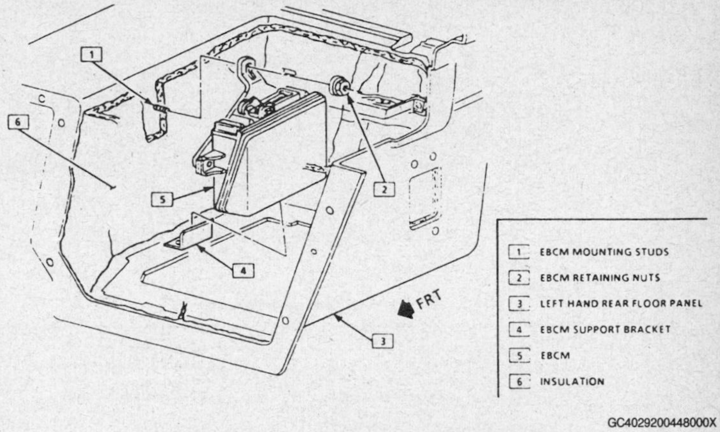
1
2
3
4
5
6
FRT
1 EBCM MOUNTING STUDS
2 EBCM RETAINING NUTS
3 LEFT HAND REAR FLOOR PANEL
4 EBCM SUPPORT BRACKET
5 EBCM
6 INSULATION
GC4029200448000X

Fig. 95 Control module location

SYSTEM SERVICE

Precaution

Before performing any service procedure on the ABS system, the following precautions should be followed:

1. The control module must be disconnected before performing any electric welding on these vehicles.
2. Use caution not to subject control module to a maximum heat of 185°F for longer than 2 hours.
3. After replacement of any ABS component, the entire ABS system should be tested.
4. Ensure inlet and outlet brake lines are properly routed.
5. Do not use a fast charger for starting engine.
6. Never disconnect battery from vehicle when engine is running.
7. Do not connect or disconnect control module electrical connector with ignition switch in On position. Ensure all harness connectors are securely connected.
8. No screws on the modulator valve should be loosened. If screws are loosened, it is no longer possible to get brake circuit leak-tight.
9. When replacing modulator valve, it should be removed through access panel in rear storage compartment. Ensure vehicle interior and exterior are protected to avoid damage from brake fluid spillage. Do not remove bottom of storage compartment to replace modulator valve.
10. Ensure rear storage compartment is wiped clean after replacing modulator valve.
11. Do not support suspension components by wheel speed sensor wires.
12. Wheel speed sensors are a tight fit into knuckle, but should be pushed in by hand. Do not hammer sensors into position.
13. Each replacement wheel speed sensor is identified with a white tag, located approximately 3/4 inch from neck of sensor, labeled L (left), or R (right).
14. Tire and wheel assemblies should be removed when replacing wheel speed sensors.
15. **On 1992 models,** wheel speed sensors should be given an anti-corrosion coating, use sealant No. 12345489 or equivalent, prior to installation. Do not use grease.
16. **On all models,** ensure proper routing, position, mounting and location of all components, wiring, connectors, clips, bracket and brake pipes, when performing ABS/ASR service.
17. Use caution not to use silicone type brake fluid.

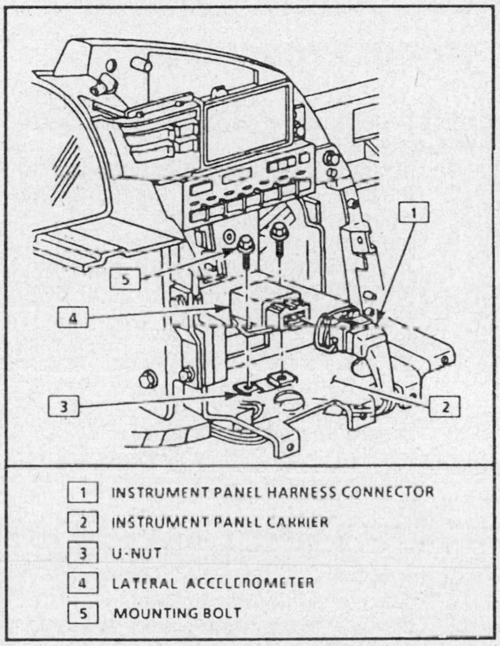
1
2
3
4
5
1 INSTRUMENT PANEL HARNESS CONNECTOR
2 INSTRUMENT PANEL CARRIER
3 U-NUT
4 LATERAL ACCELEROMETER
5 MOUNTING BOLT
GC4029200449000X

Fig. 96 Lateral acceleration switch (accelerometer)

On-Vehicle Service

When a diagnostic Test refers to removing, replacing or checking a component for proper mounting, refer to "Component Replacement."

After all diagnosis and repairs are completed, road test the vehicle to ensure proper ABS operation and that the SERVICE ABS light does not illuminate. If the Tech 1 was used for diagnosis, disconnect it from the ALDL connector and turn the ignition Off before road testing the vehicle. This is required to reset the EBTCM, it is disabled during Tech 1 diagnostics and does not reset until serial data communication is stopped and ignition power is lost.

Brake System Bleed

MANUAL BLEED

Pressure bleeding is recommended for all hydraulic systems. However, if a pressure bleeder is unavailable, use the following procedure. **Brake fluid damages painted surfaces. Immediately clean any spilled fluid.**

1. Remove vacuum reserve by pumping brakes several times with engine off.
2. Fill master cylinder reservoir with clean brake fluid. Check fluid level often during bleeding procedure; do not lot reservoir fall below half full.
3. If necessary, bleed master cylinder as follows:
   a. Disconnect master cylinder forward brake line connection until fluid flows from reservoir. Reconnect and tighten brake line.
   b. Instruct an assistant to slowly depress brake pedal one time and hold.
   c. Crack open front brake line connection again, purging air from cylinder.
   d. Retighten connection and slowly release brake pedal.
   e. Wait 15 seconds, then repeat until all air is purged.
   f. Bleed the rearward (nearest the cowl) brake line connection by repeating steps a through e.
4. Loosen, then slightly retighten bleeder valves at all four wheels. Repair any broken, stripped or frozen valves at this time.
5. Proceed to appropriate wheel first and follow set sequence according to "Wheel Bleeding Sequence."
6. Place transparent tube over bleeder valve, then allow tube to hang down into transparent container.
   Ensure end of tube is submerged in clean brake fluid.

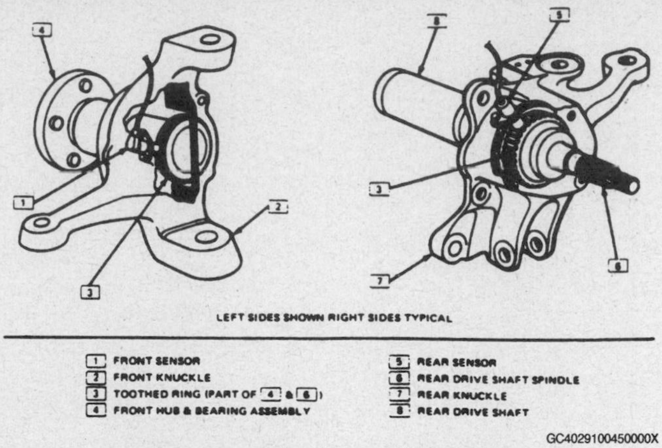
LEFT SIDES SHOWN RIGHT SIDES TYPICAL
1 FRONT SENSOR
2 FRONT KNUCKLE
3 TOOTHED RING (PART OF 4 & 6)
4 FRONT HUB & BEARING ASSEMBLY
5 REAR SENSOR
6 REAR DRIVE SHAFT SPINDLE
7 REAR KNUCKLE
8 REAR DRIVE SHAFT
GC4029100450000X

Fig. 97 Wheel speed sensors

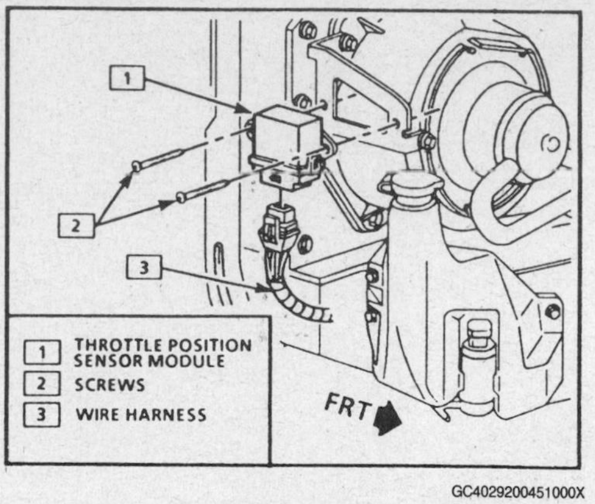
1 THROTTLE POSITION SENSOR MODULE
2 SCREWS
3 WIRE HARNESS
FRT
GC4029200451000X

Fig. 98 TPS module. 1992

7. Instruct an assistant to slowly depress brake pedal one time and hold.
8. Crack open bleeder valve, purging air from cylinder. Retighten bleeder screw and slowly release pedal.
9. Wait 15 seconds, then repeat steps 7 and 8. Repeat these steps until all air is bled from system.

PRESSURE BLEED

1. Loosen, then slightly retighten bleeder valves at all four wheels. Repair any broken, stripped or frozen valves at this time.
2. Using a diaphragm type pressure bleeder, install suitable bleeder adapter to master cylinder.
3. Charge bleeder ball to 20-25 psi.
4. Connect pressure bleeder line to adapter.
5. Open line valve on pressure bleeder, then depress bleed-off valve on adapter until a small amount of brake fluid is released.
6. Raise and support vehicle.
7. Proceed to appropriate wheel first and follow set sequence according to "Wheel Bleeding Sequence."
8. Place transparent tube over bleeder valve, then allow tube to hang down into transparent container.
   Ensure end of tube is submerged in clean brake fluid.
9. Open bleeder valve 1/2 to 3/4 turn and allow fluid to flow into container until all air is purged from line.

WHEEL BLEED SEQUENCE

Rear wheel drive models: if manual bleeding, RR-LR-RF-LF; if pressure bleeding, bleed front brakes together and rear brakes together.

Front wheel drive models: RR-LF-LR-RF

HYDRAULIC SYSTEM FLUSH

If brake fluid is old, rusty or contaminated, or whenever new parts are installed in hydraulic system, the system must be flushed. Bleed brakes, allowing at least one quart of clean brake fluid to pass through system. Any rubber parts in hydraulic system which were exposed to contaminated fluid must be replaced.

Component Replace

MODULATOR VALVE

Do not remove rear storage compartment panel opening cover to replace modulator valve.

1. Disconnect battery ground cable.
2. Remove rear storage compartment door and frame assembly.
3. Remove sound insulator pad.
4. **On models equipped with selective ride control,** disconnect wiring harness with selective ride control module.
5. **On all models,** disconnect brake pipes from modulator valve, noting pipe position.
6. Raise and support vehicle.
7. Remove modulator valve bracket to underbody cover attaching bolts, **Fig. 94.**
8. Lower vehicle.
9. Disconnect ground wire from modulator valve.
10. Remove valve from bracket.
11. Remove pump motor and solenoid valve relays.
12. Reverse procedure to install, noting the following:
    a. **Torque** modulator valve attaching nuts and valve bracket to underbody cover attaching bolts to 86 inch lbs.
    b. Ensure brake pipes are correctly connected to valve. If brake pipes are switched, wheel lockup will occur and personal injury may result.
    c. **Torque** valve brake pipes to 13 ft. lbs.
    d. Use only DOT 3 brake fluid, do not use silicone brake fluid or system damage will result.
    e. Ensure sound insulator pad covers valve or excessive system noise may result.

CONTROL MODULE

1. Disconnect battery ground cable.
2. **On Coupe models,** open left rear storage compartment cover.
3. **On convertible models,** remove storage compartment frame and covers.
4. **On all models,** remove sound insulator pad.
5. Pull EBTCM electrical connector retaining clip to release front of connector, then slide connector toward front of vehicle to release rear of connector.
6. Remove EBTCM attaching nut, then remove EBTCM, **Fig. 95.**
7. Reverse procedure to install, noting the following:
   a. **Torque** EBTCM attaching nut to 8 ft. lbs.
   b. Ensure wiring harness connector is tight and fully seated.
   c. Ensure sound insulator pad covers valve or excessive system noise may result.

LATERAL ACCELERATION SWITCH (ACCELEROMETER)

1. Disconnect battery ground cable.
2. Remove console trim plate.
3. Remove accessory trim plate.
4. Remove radio control assembly.
5. Depress ABS/ASR harness to lateral accelerometer electrical connector to release, **Fig. 96.**
6. Remove accelerometer to I/P carrier attaching bolts.
7. Remove lateral accelerometer from I/P carrier.
8. Reverse procedure to install, noting the following:
   a. Ensure accelerometer electrical connector is tight and fully seated.
   b. **Torque** accelerometer attaching bolts to 29 inch lbs.

WHEEL SPEED SENSOR

Front

The front wheel speed sensor is part of the wheel hub assembly and must be serviced as an assembly.

Rear

1. Disconnect battery ground cable.
2. Raise and support vehicle, then remove tire and wheel assembly.
3. Remove sensor electrical connector from bracket, then disconnect sensor connector.

4. Remove sensor wire grommets from brackets, noting sensor wire routing for reassembly.
5. Remove sensor to knuckle attaching bolts, then the sensor, **Fig. 97.**
6. Reverse procedure to install, noting the following:
   a. **On 1992 models,** coat new wheel speed sensor with anti-corrosion compound No. 12345489, or equivalent prior to installation.
   b. **On all models,** do not use hammer to install sensor.
   c. **On 1992 models, torque** sensor attaching bolt to 86 inch. lbs.

WIRING HARNESS

1. Disconnect battery ground cable.
2. Remove left rear storage compartment cover.
3. **On Coupe models,** disconnect EBTCM wiring harness electrical connector.
4. **On Convertible models,** proceed as follows:
   a. Remove EBTCM attaching nut.
   b. Pull connector retaining clip to release front of connector.
   c. Push retaining clip back down without locking front of connector.
   d. Push EBTCM toward front of vehicle as possible.
   e. Lift front of connector to release connector rear.
5. **On models equipped with Selective Ride Control,** disconnect selective ride control module electrical connector.
6. **On all models,** disconnect wheel speed sensor electrical connectors.
7. **On models equipped with Selective Ride Control,** disconnect selective ride control actuator electrical connector.
8. **On all models,** disconnect body harness connector.
9. Remove modulator valve cover.
10. Disconnect modulator valve electrical connector.
11. Remove wiring harness, noting harness routing.
12. Reverse procedure to install, noting the following:
    a. Ensure all connectors are tight and fully seated.
    b. Ensure EBTCM connector retaining clip is locked.

THROTTLE POSITION SENSOR MODULE

1992

1. Disconnect battery ground cable.
2. Disconnect TPS module electric connector, **Fig. 98.**
3. Remove module attaching screws, then remove module.
4. Reverse procedure to install. **Torque** TPS module attaching screws to 13 inch lbs.

Brougham, Caprice, Custom Cruiser, Fleetwood (RWD), Impala SS, Riviera, Roadmaster, Toronado, Trofeo & 1993–94 DeVille, Eldorado & Seville (Bosch 2 U Type)

NOTE: On Air Bag Equipped Models, Refer To "Air Bag System Precautions" Located In The Front Of This Manual For System Disarming & Arming Procedures.

NOTE: Wire Code Identification And Symbol Identification Located In The Front Of This Manual Can Be Used As An Aid When Using Wiring Circuits Found In This Section.

INDEX

PRECAUTIONS

AIR BAG SYSTEMS

Refer to "Air Bag System Precautions" in the front of this manual for system disarming and arming procedures.

DESCRIPTION

SYSTEM

The function of the Anti-Lock Brake System (ABS) is to minimize wheel lockup during heavy braking on most road surfaces. The system performs this function by monitoring wheel speed and controlling the brake fluid pressure to each front wheel and both rear wheels during braking. This allows the driver to retain directional stability and better steering capability.

1993-94 Eldorado, Seville & DeVille models with the 4.6L Northstar engine are also equipped with a real-time traction control system (TCS). The purpose of the traction control system is to prevent excessive wheel spin during acceleration or when turning a corner at high speed. The TCS also prevents wheel slip on slippery surfaces such as ice-covered roads; this allows for improved acceleration and improved stability while driving. The ABS and TCS are both part of the same hydraulic and electrical system.

TORQUE MANAGEMENT

1993-94 DeVille, Eldorado & Seville w/4.6L Northstar Engine

Traction control is simultaneously controlled by the PCM in the event that applying the brakes does not provide necessary traction. The PCM receives a torque request via a Pulse Width Modulated (PWM) signal from the EBTCM/EBCM requesting the desired torque level for proper traction control system operation. Torque reduction will be indicated if the duty cycle of the PWM signal is between 10% (100% torque reduction) and 90% (no torque reduction) and at least one (up to five) cylinder is requested to be disabled (the outside limits are used for diagnostic purposes and open or shorted PWM circuit). The percent duty cycle will indicate the percent torque required. The PCM will selectively disable fuel to certain cylinders to achieve this reduction. The timing of this action will be controlled by the EBTCM/EBCM with the following constraints:

1. The PCM will not allow traction control fuel shutoff if: engine coolant temperature is less than -40°C, greater than or equal to 131°C or low coolant level is detected.
2. Cylinders will be disabled under the following circumstance: engine speed is greater than or equal to 600 RPM.

PCM OVERRIDE

1993-94 DeVille, Eldorado & Seville w/4.6L Northstar Engine

Traction control enable, PS24 may be used to temporarily disable traction control. When PS24 is selected, the display will alternate between -- -- for one second and the current state of traction control disable (99 for override active and 00 for override not active). Pressing the WARMER button will disable traction control for the next eleven cycles and display 99. The TRACTION DISABLED message will be displayed for the duration of this override. No TCS diagnostic trouble codes will be set. Pressing the COOLER button will allow normal program control of traction control and display 00.

SYSTEM COMPONENTS

ELECTRONIC BRAKE CONTROL MODULE (EBCM)

Except 1993-94 DeVille, Eldorado & Seville

The EBCM is a small control computer located under the trim panel on the lefthand side of passenger compartment on wagon models, and on the lefthand side of the luggage compartment on sedan models. This computer monitors the speed of each wheel and the electrical status of the hydraulic modulator. The primary functions of EBCM are to detect wheel locking, control the brake function while in anti-lock mode and monitor system for correct electrical operation. The EBCM also controls the display of the ABS diagnostic codes. If the EBCM detects a fault, it can disable the ABS system and activate the ABS warning lamp.

1993-94 DeVille, Eldorado & Seville

The EBTCM or EBCM (if not equipped with traction control), is a small control computer located in the trunk in the center of the electronics bay, which monitors the speed of each wheel as well as several other functions internal to the BPM (brake pressure modulator) valve. The EBTCM/EBCM's main functions are to detect wheel locking or wheel slip tendencies, control the brake system while in anti-lock mode or traction control mode and monitor the system for proper operation.

On vehicles equipped with the 4.6L Northstar engine, the EBTCM/EBCM communicates torque requests (PWM signals) and receives delivered torque (PWM signals) from the PCM. The EBTCM/EBCM also communicates with the ABS/TCS diagnostic trouble codes (DTC) while in diagnostic mode to the IPC via serial data.

ACCELERATOR & CRUISE CONTROL CABLE ADJUSTER ASSEMBLY

Fleetwood (RWD)

The adjuster is mounted in the engine compartment and is used as a cable extender. It moves the throttle lever cam on the throttle body toward the closed throttle position when the traction control system requests it to reduce engine power to control wheel spin. The EBCM provides control logic.

ACCELERATOR PEDAL ASSEMBLY

Fleetwood (RWD)

To prevent overstressing of the adjuster assembly and transmission TV cable assembly due to over travel of the accelerator pedal, a spring loaded cable adjuster has been added. Refer to Speed Control section for replacement or adjustment.

OVER VOLTAGE PROTECTION RELAY (OVP)

This relay located on the EBCM mounting bracket, protects the EBCM from possible spike voltage, due to a faulty alternator regulator.

WHEEL SPEED SENSORS

The wheel speed sensors are located at each front wheel and on the rear axle differential on Caprice, Impala SS, Custom Cruiser and Roadmaster models. On Eldorado, Riviera, DeVille, Seville, Toronado and Trofeo models, wheel speed sensors are located at each wheel. These sensors transmit wheel speed information to the EBCM using a small amount of AC voltage.

HYDRAULIC MODULATOR VALVE

The hydraulic modulator (also known as brake pressure modulator (BPM)) is located on the front lefthand side of the engine compartment, provides brake fluid modulation for each individual wheel circuit as required during anti-lock braking. During anti-lock braking, the modulator can maintain or reduce brake fluid pressure independent of the pressure generated in the master cylinder.

SOLENOID VALVES

The solenoid valves are located inside the hydraulic modulator are not serviceable. The solenoid valves increase, decrease or maintain the brake fluid pressure to the wheel circuits. During anti-lock braking the valves are controlled by signals received by the EBCM. During normal braking, the valves are positioned in a pressure increase or open position.

PUMP MOTOR

The pump motor located in the modulator circulates brake fluid back to the master cylinder circuit during anti-lock braking.

ABS VALVE RELAY & PUMP RELAY

Eldorado, Riviera, DeVille, Seville, Toronado & Trofeo

These two relays are the only parts of the hydraulic modulator that can be serviced. The valve relay provides power to the three solenoid valves in the modulator. The pump relay provides power to the pump motor during anti-lock braking.

ABS/TCS SYSTEM OPERATION

The BPM valve regulates brake fluid pressure based on road conditions as interpreted by the EBTCM/EBCM, regardless of master cylinder output pressure. The BPM valve can maintain, reduce or increase brake fluid pressure to the brake calipers under ABS conditions, but it cannot increase pressure above that applied from the master cylinder. However, during TCS operation, the BPM valve can apply to the front brake calipers if the EBTCM/EBCM requires that a wheel be slowed or regulated.

TCS PILOT VALVES (VEHICLE EQUIPPED W/TCS)

There are two pilot valves within the BPM valve. These valves isolate the master cylinder so the pump motor can build brake fluid pressure to the front brakes during traction control. Unlike the ABS solenoid, the pilot valves do not modulate. They are normally open and then closed during traction control operation.

TCS PRIME PIPE & NOZZLE (VEHICLE EQUIPPED W/TCS)

On the side of the BPM valve there is the TCS prime pipe nozzle. The pump draws fluid during traction control through the 6mm prime pipe. This prime pipe is a rubber hose which runs up to the master cylinder reservoir to provide the BPM valve with brake fluid when necessary for traction control operation. It is a low pressure line.

TCS PRIME PIPE BLEED SCREW (VEHICLE EQUIPPED W/TCS)

On the side of the BPM valve, near the TCS prime pipe nozzle, is the TCS prime pipe bleed screw. This allows bleeding of the TCS prime pipe. The prime pipe must be bled anytime the master cylinder, the reservoir or BPM valve is replaced or if the reservoir fluid level becomes too low due to a leak in the system or brake system service.

TROUBLESHOOTING

Refer to "Diagnosis & Testing" for trouble shooting procedures.

DIAGNOSIS & TESTING

When a malfunction occurs in the ABS system, the EBCM will activate the amber Anti-Lock Warning Lamp. Before performing diagnosis on the ABS system when the warning lamp comes on, check that the EBCM connector and all other system electrical connectors are secure and that fuses are satisfactory. Refer to **Figs. 1 through 9** for ABS system functional check(s). Sometimes use of the compact spare will activate a wheel sensor fault code and deactivate the ABS system, if this occurs, recycle the ignition switch to reset the system.

There are trouble codes that may be set by the EBCM, **Figs. 10 through 16.** All codes except 72 will cause the EBCM to disable the ABS system, allowing power assisted braking only.

The EBCM performs an automatic (AUTO) test once each ignition cycle when vehicle reaches approximately 4 mph. The AUTO test cycles each solenoid valve and pump motor to check component operation. If any error is detected during this test the EBCM will set a trouble code. This test may be heard and felt while it is taking place and should be considered normal mode of operation.

The EBCM can display codes only when the "Diagnostic Service Mode" has been entered. There are two ways to enter the diagnostic service mode, either using a TECH 1 diagnostic computer, or by grounding pin "H" of the ALDL connector and using "Flash Code Diagnosis." The use of a TECH 1 computer is recommended for diagnosing the ABS system.

INTERMITTENTS & POOR CONNECTIONS

Intermittent failures in the anti-lock brake system may be difficult to accurately diagnose. The ABS trouble codes which may be stored by the EBCM are not designated as current or history codes. These codes can be helpful in diagnosing intermittent conditions.

If an intermittent condition is being diagnosed, the ABS system can be used in the following manner to help isolate the suspected circuit.

1. Display, then clear any ABS trouble codes present in the EBCM.
2. Test drive vehicle, attempting to repeat failure condition. A description of driving conditions under which the last failure occurred can be helpful.
3. After duplicating condition, stop the vehicle, then display any trouble codes stored.
4. If no codes were stored, proceed to "Symptom Diagnosis."
5. If a code was stored, check electrical connections and wiring for the following:
   a. Poor mating of connector halves.
   b. Terminals not fully seated in connector halves.
   c. Improperly formed, or damaged terminals. All connector terminals in a problem circuit should be carefully reformed to increase contact tension.
   d. Poor terminal to wire connection. In most cases, this will require removing wire from connector body.
6. If a complaint of intermittent warning lamp operation is encountered, the following circuits to the EBCM should be checked:
   a. Low system voltage. If low voltage is detected at the EBCM, the Anti-lock lamp will illuminate until normal operating voltage is detected.
   b. Low brake fluid. This condition in the Pressure Modulator Valve (PMV) reservoir will cause the Brake and Anti-lock lamps to illuminate. When an acceptable fluid level is registered, the lamps will no longer be illuminated.
7. Any condition which results in interruption of power to the EBCM or hydraulic unit may cause the warning lamps to turn on intermittently. These circuits include the main relay, pump motor relay, fuses and related wiring.

EBTCM/EBCM SWITCHED FAULTS

The J 39700 Universal Breakout Box is connected both to the ABS/TCS wiring harness and the EBTCM/EBCM. The EBTCM/EBCM provides power or ground on many circuits only when it is powered up and operational. If a diagnostic test indicates a short to the system voltage or ground, turn ignition Off and disconnect J 39700 from the EBTCM/EBCM. Leave it connected to the harness, then repeat the test which indicated the short (turn ignition On if the test directs to do so). If the short is now not present, it is likely that the short is to circuit from the EBTCM/EBCM when the EBTCM/EBCM is operating. Inspect the wiring harness and connectors to determine the location of the problem, then repair the short condition as needed. Examples of switched power and ground circuits are as follows: Power: 854, Ground: 833; Power: 1715, Ground: 595; Power: 851, Grounds: 886, 883, 884, 856, 874, 594 and 1676.

If the above process does not show fault as EBTCM/EBCM—switched, the short is likely located in other circuits than those mentioned. If continued diagnostics are necessary after this process, always turn ignition Off and reconnect J 39700 to the EBTCM/EBCM before continuing the chart, unless specified to do otherwise.

THROTTLE POSITION SENSOR LEARN

FLEETWOOD (RWD)

If a new throttle position sensor or throttle body is installed, the EBTCM must -learn- the throttle position sensor idle position voltage with the new component(s) installed. This is necessary to ensure effective engine torque reduction during TCS events. The procedure required TECH 1 or T-100 (CAMS) unit; the following procedure is descried as using a TECH 1 unit.

1. Turn ignition Off, then connect Chassis or Mass Storage Cartridge.
2. Turn ignition On, then follow menus to reach ABS/TCS features.
3. Select F5: TP SENSOR LEARN, then press UP arrow to begin learn procedure.
4. Wait for TECH 1 to indicate COMPLETE, then turn ignition Off and disconnect TECH 1.

FLASH CODE DIAGNOSIS

Flash code diagnosis can only be used to identify codes in the EBCM history. The flash code diagnostic mode cannot be initiated if the Anti-Lock warning lamp is on steady.

To initiate flash code diagnostics, ground pin "H" of the diagnostic connector, then turn ignition on. Flash Code Diagnostics will remain on as long as pin "H" is grounded, serial data line communication has not been initiated, and vehicle speed is less than 4 mph.

Approximately three seconds after ALDL has been grounded, the EBCM will begin flashing the Anti-Lock Indicator Lamp in flash code sequence. The flash code sequence **Fig. 17** will begin with Code 12 flashing three times to signal the beginning of the trouble code display. Each stored code will than be flashed three times. After all codes have been displayed, the sequence will repeat, starting with Code 12.

Current Codes 41, 45, 55, 61 and 63 can only be read using the TECH 1 diagnostic computer. If these codes are present as history codes only, they can be read through flash code diagnosis.

When performing diagnosis on Caprice, Impala SS, Custom Cruiser and Roadmaster models refer to wiring circuits **Figs.18 and 19**, code charts **Figs. 20 through 46**, A charts **Figs. 47 and 48** and B charts **Figs. 49 and 50.**

When performing diagnosis on Brougham models refer to wiring circuits **Fig. 51**, code charts **Figs. 52 through 64**, A Test **Fig. 65**, B Test **Fig. 66**, C Test **Fig. 67**, and D Test **Fig. 68.**

When performing diagnosis on 1992 Eldorado, Riviera, Seville, Toronado and Trofeo models refer to wiring circuits **Figs. 69 and 70**, code charts **Figs. 71 through 86**, A Test **Fig. 87**, B Test **Fig. 88**, C Test **Fig. 89**, and D Test **Fig. 90.**

When performing diagnosis on 1993-94 Eldorado, DeVille and Seville models, refer to wiring circuits **Figs. 91 and 92**, code charts **Figs. 93 through 118**, A Test **Fig. 119**, B Test **Fig. 120**, C Test **Fig. 121**, and D Test **Fig. 122.**

When performing diagnosis on 1993-94 Fleetwood RWD models refer: to wiring circuit **Fig. 123**, for 1993 and **Fig. 124**, for 1994 models. Code charts **Figs. 125 through 149**, A Test **Fig. 150**, B Test **Fig. 151**, C Test **Fig. 152**, D Test **Fig. 153**, E Test **Fig. 154**, and F Test **Fig. 155.**

TECH 1 DIAGNOSTICS

When using the TECH 1 for ABS system diagnosis, the ABS system is disabled when communication with the TECH 1. The Anti-Lock indicator lamp will be lit, indicating only power assisted braking is possible. A Bosch ABS adapter is required when connecting the TECH 1 to the ALDL connector.

When performing diagnosis on Caprice, Impala SS, Custom Cruiser and Roadmaster models refer to wiring circuits **Figs. and 18**, code charts **Figs. 20 through 46**, A charts **Figs. and 47** and B charts **Figs. and 49.**

When performing diagnosis on Brougham models refer to wiring circuits **Fig. 51**, code charts **Figs. 52 through 64**, A Test **Fig. 65**, B Test **Fig. 66**, C Test **Fig. 67**, and D Test **Fig. 68.**

When performing diagnosis on 1992 Eldorado, Riviera, Seville, Toronado and Trofeo models refer to wiring circuits **Figs. 69 and 70**, code charts **Figs. 71 through 86**, A Test **Fig. 87**, B Test **Fig. 88**, C Test **Fig. 89**, and D Test **Fig. 90.**

When performing diagnosis on 1993-94 Eldorado and Seville models, refer to wiring circuits **Fig. 91 and 92**, code charts **Figs. 93 through 118**, A Test **Fig. 119**, B Test **Fig. 120**, C Test **Fig. 121**, and D Test **Fig. 122.**

When performing diagnosis on 1993-94 Fleetwood RWD models refer, to wiring circuit **Fig. 123**, for 1993 models and **Fig. 124**, for 1994 models. Code charts **Figs. 125 through 149**, A Test **Fig. 150**, B Test **Fig. 151**, C Test **Fig. 152**, D Test **Fig. 153**, E Test **Fig. 154**, and F Test **Fig. 155.**

TECH 1 TEST MODES

Mode F0: Data List

In this mode, TECH 1 continuously monitors wheel speed data and brake switch status. When monitoring speed data, the TECH 1 screen displays signals being sent from wheel speed sensors to the EBCM. In this mode, vehicle can be driven while TECH 1 displays speed data. These reading can be compared with actual vehicle speed to check proper operation. Speed signals can also can be compared with each other to determine whether they are within specification.

If one speed signal differs greatly from another signal, improper operation of that sensor may be indicated. Intermittent speed signals can be located in the DATA LIST mode by checking for signals that vary for no reason.

In DATA LIST mode, the TECH 1 screen displays brake switch operation. When brake pedal is depressed, screen reads ON; when pedal is released, screen reads OFF.

Mode F1: Code History

In this mode, trouble code history is displayed. This data include how many ignition cycles since the trouble code first occurred, brake switch status, vehicle speed and ABS state when fault occurred. Up to three codes are included in the ABS history data.

Mode F2: Trouble Codes

In this mode, the TECH 1 displays trouble codes stored in the EBCM. The EBCM can store up to three different trouble codes. The TECH 1 can also clear codes when in this mode.

When this mode is accessed, trouble codes are displayed, with a three second interval between each code displayed. When each code is displayed, it will be accompanied by a brief description of what that code represents.

After displaying trouble codes, the TECH 1 can be ordered to clear any trouble codes stored in the EBCM. The TECH 1 will respond to a clear codes command by displaying either an "ABS CODES CLEARED" or "CODES CLEAR FAIL" on the screen.

The EBCM stores other information about trouble codes which may prove useful in diagnosis procedure. This function is called "ENHANCED DIAGNOSTIC DATA." The TECH 1 can be ordered to display any of the following ENHANCED DIAGNOSTIC DATA:

1. **Brake Switch Status,** indicates whether brake light switch was ON or OFF when code was set.
2. **ABS State,** indicates whether or not anti-lock mode was engaged when code was set.
3. **Vehicle Speed,** indicates vehicle speed when code was set.
4. **Ignition Cycles,** indicates how many ignition cycles have occurred since code was set.

Mode F3: ABS Snapshot

The ABS snapshot will help to isolate problems caused by the speed sensor signals which may cause intermittent operation of the ABS system. The ABS SNAPSHOT mode captures data before and after a trigger condition.

If "MANUAL TRIGGER" is selected, the TECH 1 will wait for "ENTER" to be pressed before storing speed sensor information. When TECH 1 is waiting for "ENTER" or "F9" to be pressed, a "W" will be displayed in the lower righthand corner of the display. While the TECH 1 is waiting for the trigger, it continuously stores ABS speed sensor data. The TECH 1 can store up to 81 samples of ABS data before the trigger, and 81 samples after the trigger. If more than 81 samples occur before the trigger, the oldest data will be discarded. It takes approximately eight seconds for the TECH 1 to store 81 samples.

As soon as "ENTER" or "F9" is pressed, the TECH 1 will begin to store speed sensor data, this is indicated by an "I" displayed on the screen. When data storage is full, the data point when the "ENTER" button was pressed will be displayed indicated by ")" on the display.

To view the speed information that was stored, use the UP ARROW and DOWN ARROW keys. The numbers on the display indicate the sample number relative to the trigger. An " + 1" on the display indicates the first sample after the "ENTER" button was pressed. An "-1" on the display indicates the sample proceeding the time when "ENTER" was pressed. By selecting the up and down arrow keys, all of the stored data can be displayed and examined for conditions which might indicate a problem. While displaying data, select F7 to convert English to Metric or select "ENTER" to convert number in the righthand lower corner of the screen to time in seconds.

If "AUTOMATIC TRIGGER" is selected, the TECH 1 will store data which may deviate from normal operating conditions but may not set a code. For example, when driving over bumpy roads or railroad tracks, the wheel speed signal may change rapidly or drop out. This condition may be caused by loose connections or intermittent wiring problems. Using the "AUTOMATIC TRIGGER," data will be stored when the TECH 1 recognizes that a wheel speed signal has deviated from it normal operating range. While the TECH 1 is waiting for a trigger, the "ENTER" or "F9 button may be used to force a trigger. While displaying the information, the cause of the trigger can be displayed by selecting F3.

Mode F4: ABS Tests

This mode performs functional tests on the ABS system which help verify proper system operation. Error conditions can be further identified by testing and observing test results. In the "ABS TESTS" mode the following test can be performed:

1. **Solenoid Valve-Pressure Reduction:** This test indicates whether specific solenoid valves in the hydraulic modulator release pressure to assigned hydraulic wheel circuits.
2. **Solenoid Valve-Hold Pressure:** This test indicates whether specific solenoid valves in the hydraulic modulator hold pressure in assigned hydraulic wheel circuits.
3. **AUTO Test:** This test cycles each solenoid valve and operates the pump

motor briefly. The EBCM will store an error code if test conditions fail.

The "PRESSURE REDUCE" test activates a selected hydraulic wheel circuit valve, placing it in the pressure reduce position. Valve action can then be verified by checking the appropriate wheel for proper brake action. The TECH 1 will indicate whether the valve action was commanded properly. This test used in conjunction with the "PRESSURE HOLD" test, completely checks each solenoid valve. With the aid of an assistant, perform the following procedure.

1. Have assistant press brake pedal.
2. Set TECH 1 to command "PRESSURE REDUCE" mode.
3. Try to spin wheel being tested, wheel should spin due to reduce command.

The "PRESSURE HOLD" test activates a selected hydraulic wheel circuit valve, placing it in the pressure hold position. Valve action can then be verified by checking the appropriate wheel for proper brake action. The TECH 1 will indicate whether the valve action was commanded properly. This test used in conjunction with the "PRESSURE REDUCE" test, completely checks each solenoid valve. With the aid of an assistant, perform the following procedure.

1. Spin wheel freely, then set TECH 1 to command "PRESSURE HOLD."
2. Have assistant press brake pedal.
3. Try to spin wheel being tested, wheel should spin due to hold command, even though brake is applied.

CLEARING CODES

The trouble codes in the EBCM memory are erased in one of three ways, diagnostic request line procedure, TECH 1 "CLEAR CODES" selection and ignition cycle default.

Whichever method is used, ensure to verify proper system operation and absence of codes when clearing procedure is completed.

The EBCM will not allow codes to be cleared until all codes have been displayed. Codes cannot be cleared by unplugging the EBCM, disconnecting the battery cables, or turning off the ignition.

Diagnostic Line Procedure

1. Turn ignition switch off, then attach a jumper to ALDL connector terminal "H."
2. Attach a jumper wire to ALDL connector terminal "A," then connect both jumper wires to each other.
3. Turn ignition switch to the "RUN" position.
4. Disconnect jumpers for approximately one second then reconnect jumpers for no less than one second intervals taking them apart briefly between intervals. Repeat this action four times within 10 seconds, leaving jumpers connected upon completion of the fourth interval. Check ANTI-LOCK indicator. Only Code 12 should be present. If not, trouble codes have not been properly cleared. Begin clearing procedures again at step 1. If codes are cleared, wait at least 15 seconds before turning ignition off.

TECH 1 Procedure

Before clearing codes, check and note history code data, as this information will also be cleared.

Select appropriate menu, and select the clear codes function. Verify that codes are cleared by using the TECH 1 to read codes. If any code other than Code 12 is present, either codes were not cleared, or an ABS fault still exists.

Ignition Cycle Default

If vehicle power is cycled 100 times without a particular fault reappearing, that particular fault code will be erased from the EBCM memory, and ignition cycle counter will be reset to zero.

SYSTEM SERVICE

SERVICE PRECAUTIONS

Before performing any repairs on the ABS system, note the following precautions:

Continued on page 32-180

DIAGNOSTIC CHART INDEX

Test	Description	Year	Page No. 32-	Fig. No.
BROUGHAM				
—	ABS Functional Check	1992	85	3
Code 21	RF Wheel Speed Sensor Fault	1992	111	52
Code 22	RF Toothed Wheel Frequency Error	1992	112	53
Code 25	LF Wheel Speed Sensor Fault	1992	113	54
Code 26	LF Toothed Wheel Frequency Error	1992	114	55
Code 35	LR Wheel Speed Sensor Fault	1992	114	56
Code 36	Rear Axle Toothed Wheel Frequency Error	1992	115	57
Code 41	RF Solenoid Valve Fault	1992	116	58
Code 45	LF Solenoid Valve Fault	1992	116	59
Code 55	Rear Axle Solenoid Valve Fault	1992	117	60
Code 61	Pump Motor Circuit Failure	1992	118	61
Code 63	Solenoid Valve Relay Fault	1992	119	62
Code 71	EBCM Fault	1992	120	63
Code 72	Serial Data Link Error	1992	120	64
Test A	No System Power	1992	120	65
Test B	ABS Indicator On w/No Codes Set	1992	121	66
Test C	ABS Indicator Inoperative w/Key On	1992	121	67
Test D	Valve Cycling During Normal Stops	1992	122	68
CAPRICE, CUSTOM CRUISER, IMPALA SS & ROADMASTER				
—	ABS Functional Check	1992–93	84	1
—	ABS Functional Check	1994	84	2
Code 21	RF Wheel Speed Sensor Fault	1992–93	89	20
Code 21	RF Wheel Speed Sensor Fault	1994	90	21
Code 22	RF Toothed Wheel Frequency Error	1992–93	91	22
Code 23	RF Wheel Speed Sensor Circuit Continuity Fault	1994	92	23
Code 25	LF Wheel Speed Sensor Fault	1992–93	92	24
Code 25	LF Wheel Speed Sensor Fault	1994	93	25

Continued

DIAGNOSTIC CHART INDEX —Continued

Test	Description	Year	Page No. 32-	Fig. No.
CAPRICE, CUSTOM CRUISER, IMPALA SS & ROADMASTER -Continued				
Code 26	LF Toothed Wheel Frequency Error	1992–93	94	26
Code 27	LF Wheel Speed Sensor Circuit Continuity Fault	1994	95	27
Code 28	Wheel Speed Sensor Circuit Frequency Fault	1994	95	28
Code 35	Rear Axle Speed Sensor Fault	1992–93	96	29
Code 35	Rear Wheel Speed Sensor Circuit Fault	1994	97	30
Code 36	Rear Axle Toothed Wheel Frequency Error	1992	98	31
Code 36	Rear Axle Toothed Wheel Frequency Error	1993	99	32
Code 37	Rear Wheel Speed Sensor Circuit Continuity Fault	1994	99	33
Code 41	RF Solenoid Valve Fault	1992–93	100	34
Code 41	RF Solenoid Valve Fault	1994	100	35
Code 45	LF Solenoid Valve Fault	1992–93	101	36
Code 45	LF Solenoid Valve Fault	1994	101	37
Code 55	Rear Wheels Solenoid Valve Fault	1992–93	102	38
Code 55	Rear Solenoid Valve Fault	1994	102	39
Code 61	Pump Motor Or Relay Fault	1992–93	103	40
Code 61	Pump Motor Or Relay Fault	1994	104	41
Code 63	Solenoid Valve Relay Fault	1992–93	105	42
Code 63	BPM Valve Relay Fault	1994	106	43
Code 71	EBCM Fault	1992–93	107	44
Code 71	EBCM Fault	1994	107	45
Code 72	EBCM Serial Line Data Fault	1992	108	46
Test A	ABS Indicator On w/No Codes Set Or TECH 1 Unable To Receive Data	1992–93	109	47
Test A	ABS Indicator On w/No Codes Set Or TECH 1 Unable To Receive Data	1994	109	48
Test B	ABS Indicator Inoperative Or Indicator Flashes Very Briefly At Ignition On	1992–93	110	49
Test B	ABS Indicator Inoperative Or Indicator Flashes Very Briefly At Ignition On	1994	110	50
ELDORADO, RIVIERA, SEVILLE, TORONADO & TROFEO & 1993-94 DEVILLE				
—	ABS Functional Check	1992	85	3
Test 1	ABS Functional Check	1993-94	85	4
Test 2	ABS Functional Check	1993–94	85	5
Test 3	ABS Functional Check	1993-94	85	6
Test 4	ABS Functional Check	1993-94	86	7
Test 5	ABS Functional Check	1993-94	86	8
Code 21	RF Wheel Speed Sensor Fault	1992	123	71
Code 21	Right Front Wheel Speed Sensor Fault	1993-94	138	93
Code 22	RF Toothed Wheel Frequency Error	1992	124	72
Code 22	Right Front Wheel Speed Sensor Frequency Error	1993-94	139	94
Code 23	Right Front Wheel Speed Sensor Continuity Fault	1993-94	140	95
Code 25	LF Wheel Speed Sensor Fault	1992	125	73
Code 25	Left Front Wheel Speed Sensor Fault	1993-94	140	96
Code 26	LF Toothed Wheel Frequency Error	1992	126	74
Code 26	Left Front Wheel Speed Sensor Frequency Error	1993-94	141	97
Code 27	Left Front Wheel Speed Sensor Continuity Fault	1993-94	142	98
Code 28	Wheel Speed Sensor Frequency Error	1993-94	142	99
Code 31	RR Wheel Speed Sensor Fault	1992	127	75
Code 31	Right Rear Wheel Speed Sensor Fault	1993-94	143	100
Code 32	RR Toothed Wheel Frequency Error	1992	128	76
Code 32	Right Rear Wheel Speed Sensor Frequency Error	1993-94	144	101
Code 33	Right Rear Wheel Speed Sensor Continuity Fault	1993-94	144	102
Code 35	LR Wheel Speed Sensor Fault	1992	128	77

Continued

DIAGNOSTIC CHART INDEX —Continued

Test	Description	Year	Page No. 32-	Fig. No.
ELDORADO, RIVIERA, SEVILLE, TORONADO & TROFEO & 1993-94 DEVILLE				
Code 35	Left Rear Wheel Speed Sensor Fault	1993-94	145	103
Code 36	LR Toothed Wheel Frequency Error	1992	129	78
Code 36	Left Rear Wheel Speed Sensor Frequency Error	1993-94	146	104
Code 37	Left Rear Wheel Speed Sensor Continuity Fault	1993-94	146	105
Code 41	RF Solenoid Valve Fault	1992	130	79
Code 41	Right Front ABS Valve Solenoid Fault	1993-94	147	106
Code 44	Right Front TCS Pilot Valve Fault	1993-94	148	107
Code 45	LF Solenoid Valve Fault	1992	130	80
Code 45	Left Front ABS Valve Solenoid Fault	1993-94	149	108
Code 48	Left Front TCS Pilot Valve Fault	1993-94	150	109
Code 51	Right Rear ABS Valve Solenoid Fault	1993-94	151	110
Code 55	Rear Solenoid Valve Fault	1992	131	81
Code 55	Left Rear Valve Solenoid Valve (With TCS); Rear Valve Solenoid Valve Fault (Less TCS),	1993-94	152	111
Code 61	Pump Motor Circuit Fault (Eldorado & Seville)	1992	131	82
Code 61	Pump Motor Circuit Fault (Riviera, Toronado & Trofeo)	1992	132	83
Code 61	Pump Motor Or Pump Motor Relay Fault	1993-94	153	112
Code 63	Solenoid Valve Relay Fault	1992	133	84
Code 63	Valve Relay Fault	1993-94	154	113
Code 67	Brake Light Switch Fault	1993-94	156	114
Code 71	EBCM Fault	1992	134	85
Code 71	EBTCM/EBCM Internal Fault	1993-94	156	115
Code 72	Serial Line Data Fault	1992	134	86
Code 72	Serial Data Link Fault	1993-94	156	116
Code 73	PCM-EBTCM/EBCM PWM Signal Fault	1993-94	157	117
Code 83	Low Brake Fluid Level	1993-94	157	118
Test A	No System Power	1992	135	87
Test A	Anti-Lock Indicator & Traction Disabled Message On w/No Codes Set Or No TCS Data	1993-94	158	119
Test B	ABS Indicator On w/No Codes Set	1992	136	88
Test B	Anti-Look Indicator On w/No Codes Set	1993-94 Eldorado,	158	120
Test C	ABS Indicator Inoperative At Key On	1992	137	89
Test C	Valve Cycling (Chatter) During Normal Stops (Unwanted ABS Modulation)	1993-94	159	121
Test D	Valve Cycling During Normal Stops	1992	137	90
Test D	Traction Control Operation Check, No DTCs Set	1993-94	159	122
FLEETWOOD (RWD)				
—	ABS Functional Check	1993–94	86	9
Code 21	Right Front Wheel Speed Sensor Malfunction	1993-94	162	125
Code 23	Right Front Wheel Speed Sensor Continuity Malfunction	1993-94	162	126
Code 25	Left Front Wheel Speed Sensor Malfunction	1993-94	163	127
Code 26	Left Front Wheel Speed Sensor Continuity Malfunction	1993-94	163	128
Code 28	Wheel Speed Sensor Frequency Error	1993-94	164	129
Code 31	Right Rear Wheel Speed Sensor Malfunction	1993-94	164	130
Code 33	Right Rear Wheel Speed Sensor Continuity Malfunction	1993-94	165	131
Code 35	Left Rear Wheel Speed Sensor Malfunction	1993-94	165	132
Code 36	Left Rear Wheel Speed Sensor Continuity Malfunction	1993-94	166	133
Code 41	Right Front Valve Solenoid Malfunction	1993-94	166	134
Code 44	Pilot Valve Solenoid Malfunction	1993-94	167	135
Code 45	Left Front Valve Solenoid Malfunction	1993-94	167	136
Code 51	Right Front Valve Solenoid Malfunction	1993-94	168	137
Code 55	Left Rear Valve Solenoid Malfunction	1993-94	168	138

Continued

DIAGNOSTIC CHART INDEX —Continued

Test	Description	Year	Page No. 32-	Fig. No.
FLEETWOOD (RWD)-Continued				
Code 57	TCC Disable Relay Output Malfunction	1993-94	169	139
Code 58	EBTCM Internal Adjuster Assembly Malfunction	1993-94	169	140
Code 61	Pump Motor Or Pump Motor Relay Malfunction	1993-94	170	141
Code 62	RPM Signal Malfunction	1993-94	171	142
Code 63	Valve Solenoid Relay Malfunction	1993-94	171	143
Code 64	Throttle Position Signal Malfunction	1993-94	172	144
Code 65	Adjuster Assembly Malfunction	1993-94	173	145
Code 66	Adjuster Assembly Control Malfunction	1993-94	174	146
Code 71	EBTCM Internal Malfunction	1993-94	175	147
Code 72	Serial Data Link Malfunction	1993-94	175	148
Code 83	Brake Fluid Differential Pressure Malfunction	1993-94	176	149
Test A	Anti-Lock Indicator On w/No Codes Set	1993-94	177	150
Test B	Anti-Lock Indicator Inoperative Or Flickers Briefly At Ignition On	1993-94	177	151
Test C	Traction Control Indicator On w/No Codes Set	1993-94	178	152
Test D	Traction Control Indicator Inoperative	1993-94	178	153
Test E	Traction Engaged Indicator On w/No Codes Set	1993-94	179	154
Test F	Traction Engaged Indicator Inoperative w/No Codes Set	1993-94	179	155

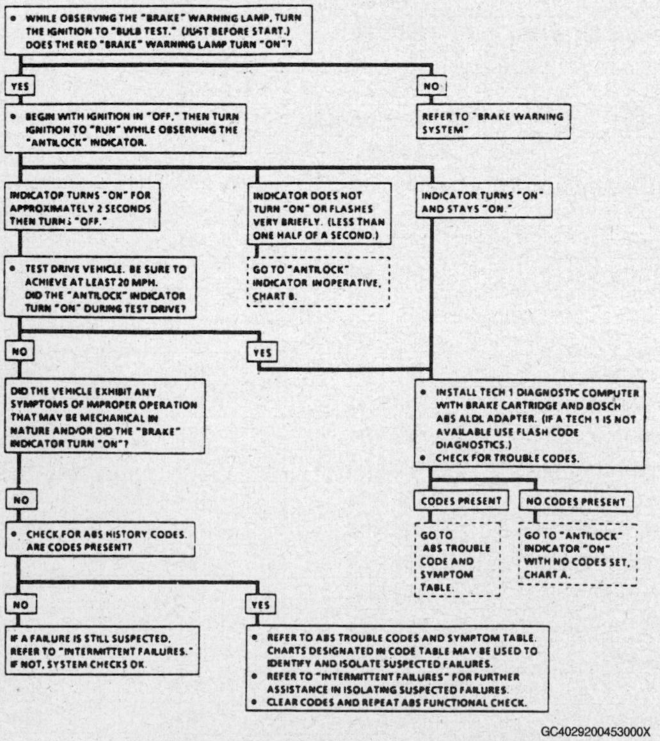
• WHILE OBSERVING THE "BRAKE" WARNING LAMP, TURN THE IGNITION TO "BULB TEST." (JUST BEFORE START.) DOES THE RED "BRAKE" WARNING LAMP TURN "ON"?
YES
NO
• BEGIN WITH IGNITION IN "OFF," THEN TURN IGNITION TO "RUN" WHILE OBSERVING THE "ANTILOCK" INDICATOR.
REFER TO "BRAKE WARNING SYSTEM"
INDICATOR TURNS "ON" FOR APPROXIMATELY 2 SECONDS THEN TURNS "OFF."
INDICATOR DOES NOT TURN "ON" OR FLASHES VERY BRIEFLY. (LESS THAN ONE HALF OF A SECOND.)
INDICATOR TURNS "ON" AND STAYS "ON."
GO TO "ANTILOCK" INDICATOR INOPERATIVE, CHART B.
• TEST DRIVE VEHICLE. BE SURE TO ACHIEVE AT LEAST 20 MPH. DID THE "ANTILOCK" INDICATOR TURN "ON" DURING TEST DRIVE?
NO
YES
DID THE VEHICLE EXHIBIT ANY SYMPTOMS OF IMPROPER OPERATION THAT MAY BE MECHANICAL IN NATURE AND/OR DID THE "BRAKE" INDICATOR TURN "ON"?
• INSTALL TECH 1 DIAGNOSTIC COMPUTER WITH BRAKE CARTRIDGE AND BOSCH ABS ALDL ADAPTER. (IF A TECH 1 IS NOT AVAILABLE USE FLASH CODE DIAGNOSTICS.)
• CHECK FOR TROUBLE CODES.
CODES PRESENT
NO CODES PRESENT
NO
• CHECK FOR ABS HISTORY CODES. ARE CODES PRESENT?
GO TO ABS TROUBLE CODE AND SYMPTOM TABLE.
GO TO "ANTILOCK" INDICATOR "ON" WITH NO CODES SET, CHART A.
NO
YES
IF A FAILURE IS STILL SUSPECTED, REFER TO "INTERMITTENT FAILURES." IF NOT, SYSTEM CHECKS OK.
• REFER TO ABS TROUBLE CODES AND SYMPTOM TABLE. CHARTS DESIGNATED IN CODE TABLE MAY BE USED TO IDENTIFY AND ISOLATE SUSPECTED FAILURES.
• REFER TO "INTERMITTENT FAILURES" FOR FURTHER ASSISTANCE IN ISOLATING SUSPECTED FAILURES.
• CLEAR CODES AND REPEAT ABS FUNCTIONAL CHECK.
GC4029200453000X

Fig. 1 ABS Functional Check. 1992–93 Caprice, Custom Cruiser & Roadmaster.

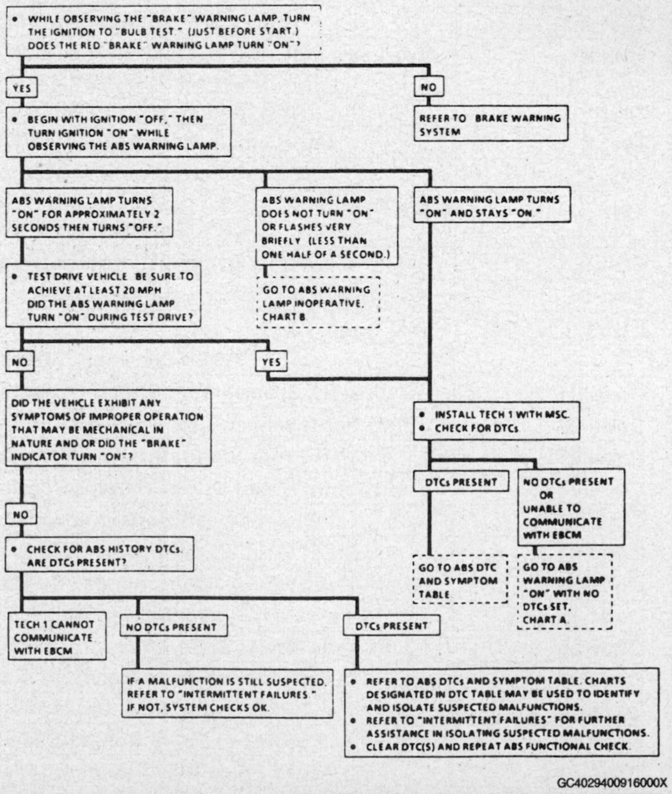
• WHILE OBSERVING THE "BRAKE" WARNING LAMP, TURN THE IGNITION TO "BULB TEST." (JUST BEFORE START.) DOES THE RED "BRAKE" WARNING LAMP TURN "ON"?
YES
NO
• BEGIN WITH IGNITION "OFF," THEN TURN IGNITION "ON" WHILE OBSERVING THE ABS WARNING LAMP.
REFER TO BRAKE WARNING SYSTEM
ABS WARNING LAMP TURNS "ON" FOR APPROXIMATELY 2 SECONDS THEN TURNS "OFF."
ABS WARNING LAMP DOES NOT TURN "ON" OR FLASHES VERY BRIEFLY (LESS THAN ONE HALF OF A SECOND.)
ABS WARNING LAMP TURNS "ON" AND STAYS "ON."
• TEST DRIVE VEHICLE. BE SURE TO ACHIEVE AT LEAST 20 MPH. DID THE ABS WARNING LAMP TURN "ON" DURING TEST DRIVE?
GO TO ABS WARNING LAMP INOPERATIVE, CHART B
NO
YES
DID THE VEHICLE EXHIBIT ANY SYMPTOMS OF IMPROPER OPERATION THAT MAY BE MECHANICAL IN NATURE AND OR DID THE "BRAKE" INDICATOR TURN "ON"?
• INSTALL TECH 1 WITH MSC.
• CHECK FOR DTCs.
DTCs PRESENT
NO DTCs PRESENT OR UNABLE TO COMMUNICATE WITH EBCM
NO
• CHECK FOR ABS HISTORY DTCs. ARE DTCs PRESENT?
GO TO ABS DTC AND SYMPTOM TABLE
GO TO ABS WARNING LAMP "ON" WITH NO DTCs SET, CHART A.
TECH 1 CANNOT COMMUNICATE WITH EBCM
NO DTCs PRESENT
DTCs PRESENT
IF A MALFUNCTION IS STILL SUSPECTED, REFER TO "INTERMITTENT FAILURES." IF NOT, SYSTEM CHECKS OK.
• REFER TO ABS DTCs AND SYMPTOM TABLE. CHARTS DESIGNATED IN DTC TABLE MAY BE USED TO IDENTIFY AND ISOLATE SUSPECTED MALFUNCTIONS.
• REFER TO "INTERMITTENT FAILURES" FOR FURTHER ASSISTANCE IN ISOLATING SUSPECTED MALFUNCTIONS.
• CLEAR DTC(S) AND REPEAT ABS FUNCTIONAL CHECK.
GC4029400916000X

Fig. 2 ABS Functional Check. 1994 Caprice, Impala SS & Roadmaster.

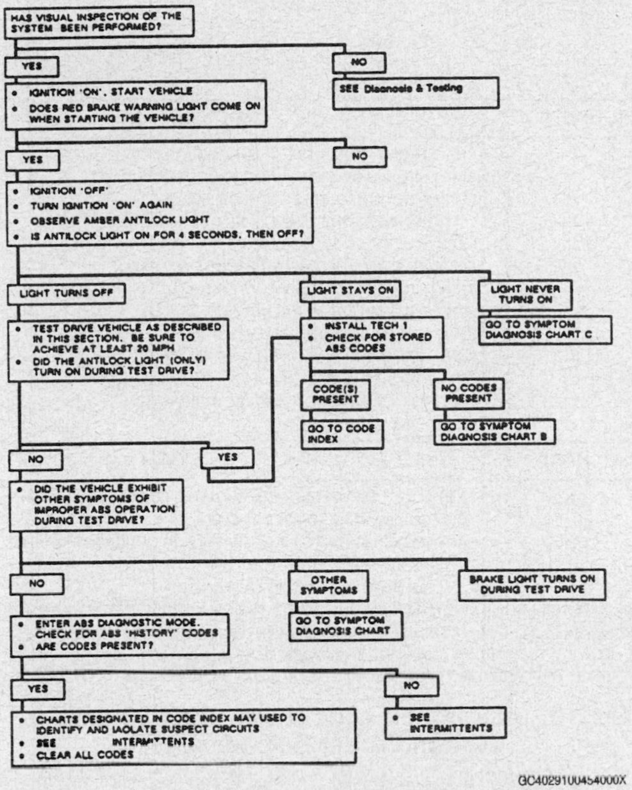
HAS VISUAL INSPECTION OF THE SYSTEM BEEN PERFORMED?
YES
NO
SEE Diagnosis & Testing
• IGNITION 'ON'. START VEHICLE
• DOES RED BRAKE WARNING LIGHT COME ON WHEN STARTING THE VEHICLE?
YES
NO
• IGNITION 'OFF'
• TURN IGNITION 'ON' AGAIN
• OBSERVE AMBER ANTILOCK LIGHT
• IS ANTILOCK LIGHT ON FOR 4 SECONDS, THEN OFF?
LIGHT TURNS OFF
LIGHT STAYS ON
LIGHT NEVER TURNS ON
• TEST DRIVE VEHICLE AS DESCRIBED IN THIS SECTION. BE SURE TO ACHIEVE AT LEAST 20 MPH
• DID THE ANTILOCK LIGHT (ONLY) TURN ON DURING TEST DRIVE?
• INSTALL TECH 1
• CHECK FOR STORED ABS CODES
GO TO SYMPTOM DIAGNOSIS CHART C
CODE(S) PRESENT
NO CODES PRESENT
GO TO CODE INDEX
GO TO SYMPTOM DIAGNOSIS CHART B
NO
YES
• DID THE VEHICLE EXHIBIT OTHER SYMPTOMS OF IMPROPER ABS OPERATION DURING TEST DRIVE?
NO
OTHER SYMPTOMS
BRAKE LIGHT TURNS ON DURING TEST DRIVE
• ENTER ABS DIAGNOSTIC MODE. CHECK FOR ABS 'HISTORY' CODES
• ARE CODES PRESENT?
GO TO SYMPTOM DIAGNOSIS CHART
YES
NO
• CHARTS DESIGNATED IN CODE INDEX MAY USED TO IDENTIFY AND ISOLATE SUSPECT CIRCUITS
• SEE INTERMITTENTS
• CLEAR ALL CODES
• SEE INTERMITTENTS
GC4029100454000X

Fig. 3 ABS Functional Check. Riviera, 1992 Brougham, Eldorado & Seville, Toronado & Trofeo

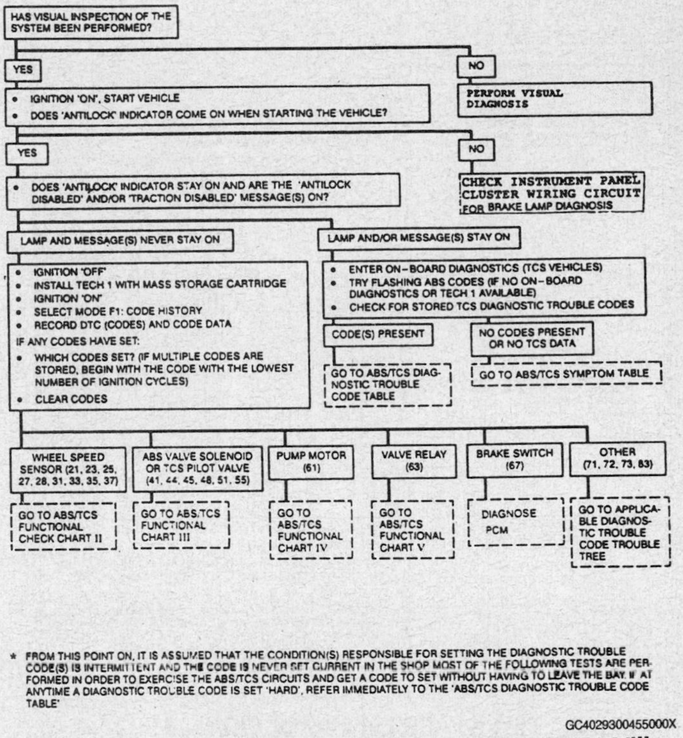
HAS VISUAL INSPECTION OF THE SYSTEM BEEN PERFORMED?
YES
NO
• IGNITION 'ON', START VEHICLE
• DOES 'ANTILOCK' INDICATOR COME ON WHEN STARTING THE VEHICLE?
PERFORM VISUAL DIAGNOSIS
YES
NO
• DOES 'ANTILOCK' INDICATOR STAY ON AND ARE THE 'ANTILOCK DISABLED' AND/OR 'TRACTION DISABLED' MESSAGE(S) ON?
CHECK INSTRUMENT PANEL CLUSTER WIRING CIRCUIT FOR BRAKE LAMP DIAGNOSIS
LAMP AND MESSAGE(S) NEVER STAY ON
LAMP AND/OR MESSAGE(S) STAY ON
• IGNITION 'OFF'
• INSTALL TECH 1 WITH MASS STORAGE CARTRIDGE
• IGNITION 'ON'
• SELECT MODE F1: CODE HISTORY
• RECORD DTC (CODES) AND CODE DATA
IF ANY CODES HAVE SET:
• WHICH CODES SET? (IF MULTIPLE CODES ARE STORED, BEGIN WITH THE CODE WITH THE LOWEST NUMBER OF IGNITION CYCLES)
• CLEAR CODES
• ENTER ON-BOARD DIAGNOSTICS (TCS VEHICLES)
• TRY FLASHING ABS CODES (IF NO ON-BOARD DIAGNOSTICS OR TECH 1 AVAILABLE)
• CHECK FOR STORED TCS DIAGNOSTIC TROUBLE CODES
CODE(S) PRESENT
NO CODES PRESENT OR NO TCS DATA
GO TO ABS/TCS DIAGNOSTIC TROUBLE CODE TABLE
GO TO ABS/TCS SYMPTOM TABLE
WHEEL SPEED SENSOR (21, 23, 25, 27, 28, 31, 33, 35, 37)
ABS VALVE SOLENOID OR TCS PILOT VALVE (41, 44, 45, 48, 51, 55)
PUMP MOTOR (61)
VALVE RELAY (63)
BRAKE SWITCH (67)
OTHER (71, 72, 73, 83)
GO TO ABS/TCS FUNCTIONAL CHECK CHART II
GO TO ABS/TCS FUNCTIONAL CHART III
GO TO ABS/TCS FUNCTIONAL CHART IV
GO TO ABS/TCS FUNCTIONAL CHART V
DIAGNOSE PCM
GO TO APPLICABLE DIAGNOSTIC TROUBLE CODE TROUBLE TREE
* FROM THIS POINT ON, IT IS ASSUMED THAT THE CONDITION(S) RESPONSIBLE FOR SETTING THE DIAGNOSTIC TROUBLE CODE(S) IS INTERMITTENT AND THE CODE IS NEVER SET CURRENT IN THE SHOP MOST OF THE FOLLOWING TESTS ARE PERFORMED IN ORDER TO EXERCISE THE ABS/TCS CIRCUITS AND GET A CODE TO SET WITHOUT HAVING TO LEAVE THE BAY. IF AT ANYTIME A DIAGNOSTIC TROUBLE CODE IS SET 'HARD', REFER IMMEDIATELY TO THE 'ABS/TCS DIAGNOSTIC TROUBLE CODE TABLE'
GC4029300455000X

Fig. 4 Test 1: ABS Functional Check. 1993-94 DeVille, Eldorado & Seville

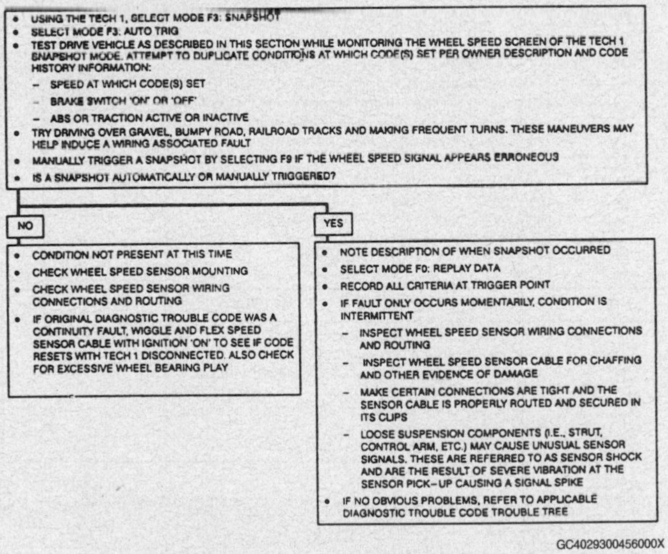
• USING THE TECH 1, SELECT MODE F3: SNAPSHOT
• SELECT MODE F3: AUTO TRIG
• TEST DRIVE VEHICLE AS DESCRIBED IN THIS SECTION WHILE MONITORING THE WHEEL SPEED SCREEN OF THE TECH 1 SNAPSHOT MODE. ATTEMPT TO DUPLICATE CONDITIONS AT WHICH CODE(S) SET PER OWNER DESCRIPTION AND CODE HISTORY INFORMATION:
– SPEED AT WHICH CODE(S) SET
– BRAKE SWITCH 'ON' OR 'OFF'
– ABS OR TRACTION ACTIVE OR INACTIVE
• TRY DRIVING OVER GRAVEL, BUMPY ROAD, RAILROAD TRACKS AND MAKING FREQUENT TURNS. THESE MANEUVERS MAY HELP INDUCE A WIRING ASSOCIATED FAULT
• MANUALLY TRIGGER A SNAPSHOT BY SELECTING F9 IF THE WHEEL SPEED SIGNAL APPEARS ERRONEOUS
• IS A SNAPSHOT AUTOMATICALLY OR MANUALLY TRIGGERED?
NO
YES
• CONDITION NOT PRESENT AT THIS TIME
• CHECK WHEEL SPEED SENSOR MOUNTING
• CHECK WHEEL SPEED SENSOR WIRING CONNECTIONS AND ROUTING
• IF ORIGINAL DIAGNOSTIC TROUBLE CODE WAS A CONTINUITY FAULT, WIGGLE AND FLEX SPEED SENSOR CABLE WITH IGNITION 'ON' TO SEE IF CODE RESETS WITH TECH 1 DISCONNECTED. ALSO CHECK FOR EXCESSIVE WHEEL BEARING PLAY
• NOTE DESCRIPTION OF WHEN SNAPSHOT OCCURRED
• SELECT MODE F0: REPLAY DATA
• RECORD ALL CRITERIA AT TRIGGER POINT
• IF FAULT ONLY OCCURS MOMENTARILY, CONDITION IS INTERMITTENT
– INSPECT WHEEL SPEED SENSOR WIRING CONNECTIONS AND ROUTING
– INSPECT WHEEL SPEED SENSOR CABLE FOR CHAFFING AND OTHER EVIDENCE OF DAMAGE
– MAKE CERTAIN CONNECTIONS ARE TIGHT AND THE SENSOR CABLE IS PROPERLY ROUTED AND SECURED IN ITS CLIPS
– LOOSE SUSPENSION COMPONENTS (I.E., STRUT, CONTROL ARM, ETC.) MAY CAUSE UNUSUAL SENSOR SIGNALS. THESE ARE REFERRED TO AS SENSOR SHOCK AND ARE THE RESULT OF SEVERE VIBRATION AT THE SENSOR PICK-UP CAUSING A SIGNAL SPIKE
• IF NO OBVIOUS PROBLEMS, REFER TO APPLICABLE DIAGNOSTIC TROUBLE CODE TROUBLE TREE
GC4029300456000X

Fig. 5 Test 2: ABS Functional Check. 1993–94 DeVille, Eldorado & Seville

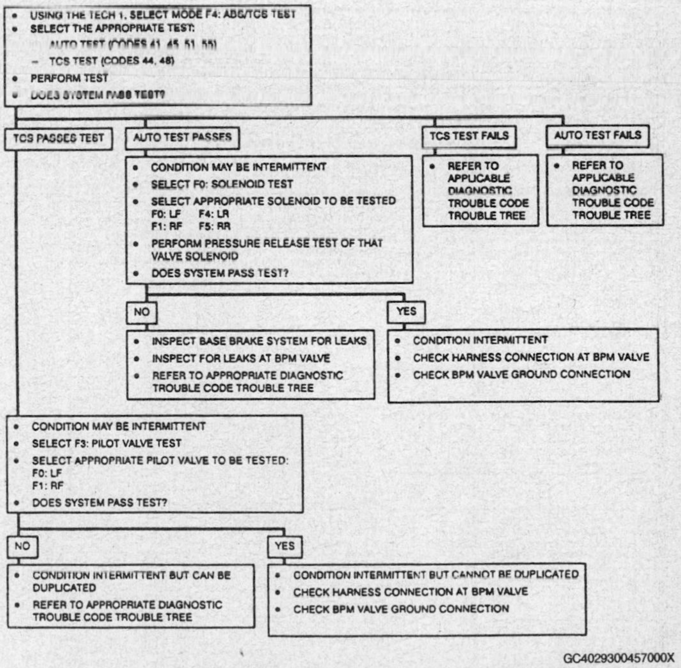
• USING THE TECH 1, SELECT MODE F4: ABS/TCS TEST
• SELECT THE APPROPRIATE TEST:
– AUTO TEST (CODES 41, 45, 51, 55)
– TCS TEST (CODES 44, 48)
• PERFORM TEST
• DOES SYSTEM PASS TEST?
TCS PASSES TEST
AUTO TEST PASSES
TCS TEST FAILS
AUTO TEST FAILS
• CONDITION MAY BE INTERMITTENT
• SELECT F0: SOLENOID TEST
• SELECT APPROPRIATE SOLENOID TO BE TESTED
F0: LF F4: LR
F1: RF F5: RR
• PERFORM PRESSURE RELEASE TEST OF THAT VALVE SOLENOID
• DOES SYSTEM PASS TEST?
• REFER TO APPLICABLE DIAGNOSTIC TROUBLE CODE TROUBLE TREE
• REFER TO APPLICABLE DIAGNOSTIC TROUBLE CODE TROUBLE TREE
NO
YES
• INSPECT BASE BRAKE SYSTEM FOR LEAKS
• INSPECT FOR LEAKS AT BPM VALVE
• REFER TO APPROPRIATE DIAGNOSTIC TROUBLE CODE TROUBLE TREE
• CONDITION INTERMITTENT
• CHECK HARNESS CONNECTION AT BPM VALVE
• CHECK BPM VALVE GROUND CONNECTION
• CONDITION MAY BE INTERMITTENT
• SELECT F3: PILOT VALVE TEST
• SELECT APPROPRIATE PILOT VALVE TO BE TESTED:
F0: LF
F1: RF
• DOES SYSTEM PASS TEST?
NO
YES
• CONDITION INTERMITTENT BUT CAN BE DUPLICATED
• REFER TO APPROPRIATE DIAGNOSTIC TROUBLE CODE TROUBLE TREE
• CONDITION INTERMITTENT BUT CANNOT BE DUPLICATED
• CHECK HARNESS CONNECTION AT BPM VALVE
• CHECK BPM VALVE GROUND CONNECTION
GC4029300457000X

Fig. 6 Test 3: ABS Functional Check. 1993-94 DeVille, Eldorado & Seville

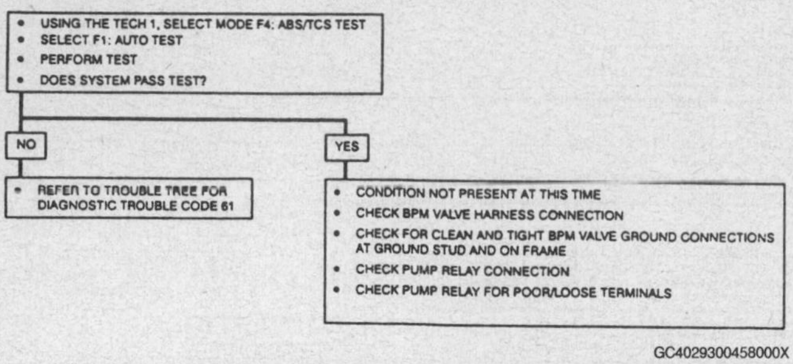
USING THE TECH 1, SELECT MODE F4: ABS/TCS TEST
SELECT F1: AUTO TEST
PERFORM TEST
DOES SYSTEM PASS TEST?
NO
YES
REFER TO TROUBLE TREE FOR DIAGNOSTIC TROUBLE CODE 61
CONDITION NOT PRESENT AT THIS TIME
CHECK BPM VALVE HARNESS CONNECTION
CHECK FOR CLEAN AND TIGHT BPM VALVE GROUND CONNECTIONS AT GROUND STUD AND ON FRAME
CHECK PUMP RELAY CONNECTION
CHECK PUMP RELAY FOR POOR/LOOSE TERMINALS
GC4029300458000X

Fig. 7 Test 4: ABS Functional Check. 1993-94 DeVille, Eldorado & Seville

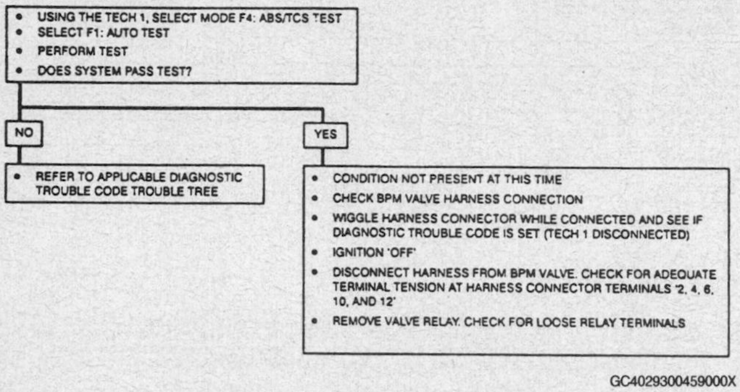
USING THE TECH 1, SELECT MODE F4: ABS/TCS TEST
SELECT F1: AUTO TEST
PERFORM TEST
DOES SYSTEM PASS TEST?
NO
YES
REFER TO APPLICABLE DIAGNOSTIC TROUBLE CODE TROUBLE TREE
CONDITION NOT PRESENT AT THIS TIME
CHECK BPM VALVE HARNESS CONNECTION
WIGGLE HARNESS CONNECTOR WHILE CONNECTED AND SEE IF DIAGNOSTIC TROUBLE CODE IS SET (TECH 1 DISCONNECTED)
IGNITION 'OFF'
DISCONNECT HARNESS FROM BPM VALVE. CHECK FOR ADEQUATE TERMINAL TENSION AT HARNESS CONNECTOR TERMINALS "2, 4, 6, 10, AND 12"
REMOVE VALVE RELAY. CHECK FOR LOOSE RELAY TERMINALS
GC4029300459000X

Fig. 8 Test 5: ABS Functional Check. 1993-94 DeVille, Eldorado & Seville

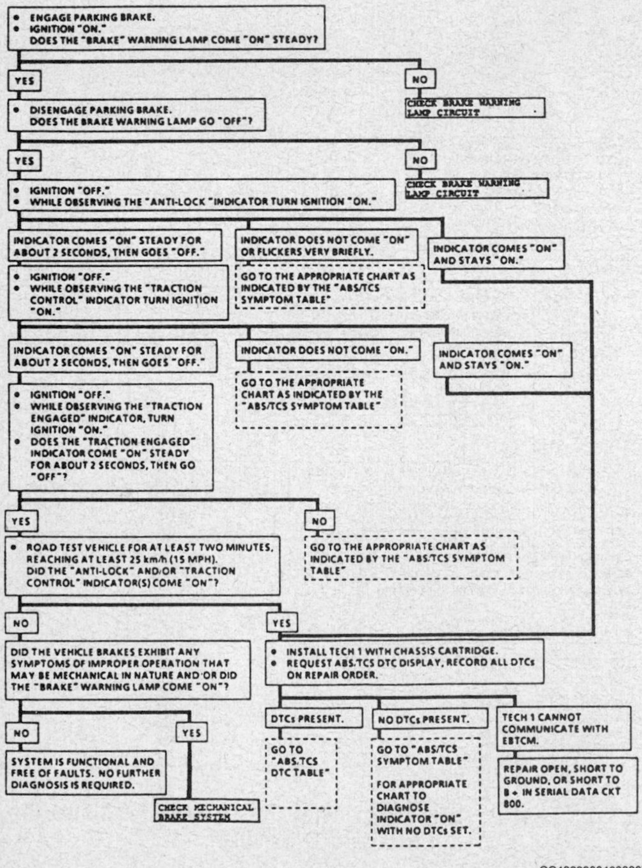
ENGAGE PARKING BRAKE.
IGNITION "ON."
DOES THE "BRAKE" WARNING LAMP COME "ON" STEADY?
YES
NO
CHECK BRAKE WARNING LAMP CIRCUIT
DISENGAGE PARKING BRAKE.
DOES THE BRAKE WARNING LAMP GO "OFF"?
YES
NO
CHECK BRAKE WARNING LAMP CIRCUIT
IGNITION "OFF."
WHILE OBSERVING THE "ANTI-LOCK "INDICATOR TURN IGNITION "ON."
INDICATOR COMES "ON" STEADY FOR ABOUT 2 SECONDS, THEN GOES "OFF."
INDICATOR DOES NOT COME "ON" OR FLICKERS VERY BRIEFLY.
INDICATOR COMES "ON" AND STAYS "ON."
IGNITION "OFF."
WHILE OBSERVING THE "TRACTION CONTROL" INDICATOR TURN IGNITION "ON."
GO TO THE APPROPRIATE CHART AS INDICATED BY THE "ABS/TCS SYMPTOM TABLE"
INDICATOR COMES "ON" STEADY FOR ABOUT 2 SECONDS, THEN GOES "OFF."
INDICATOR DOES NOT COME "ON."
INDICATOR COMES "ON" AND STAYS "ON."
GO TO THE APPROPRIATE CHART AS INDICATED BY THE "ABS/TCS SYMPTOM TABLE"
IGNITION "OFF."
WHILE OBSERVING THE "TRACTION ENGAGED" INDICATOR, TURN IGNITION "ON."
DOES THE "TRACTION ENGAGED" INDICATOR COME "ON" STEADY FOR ABOUT 2 SECONDS, THEN GO "OFF"?
YES
NO
ROAD TEST VEHICLE FOR AT LEAST TWO MINUTES, REACHING AT LEAST 25 km/h (15 MPH).
DID THE "ANTI-LOCK" AND/OR "TRACTION CONTROL" INDICATOR(S) COME "ON"?
GO TO THE APPROPRIATE CHART AS INDICATED BY THE "ABS/TCS SYMPTOM TABLE"
NO
YES
DID THE VEHICLE BRAKES EXHIBIT ANY SYMPTOMS OF IMPROPER OPERATION THAT MAY BE MECHANICAL IN NATURE AND/OR DID THE "BRAKE" WARNING LAMP COME "ON"?
INSTALL TECH 1 WITH CHASSIS CARTRIDGE.
REQUEST ABS/TCS DTC DISPLAY, RECORD ALL DTCs ON REPAIR ORDER.
NO
YES
SYSTEM IS FUNCTIONAL AND FREE OF FAULTS. NO FURTHER DIAGNOSIS IS REQUIRED.
CHECK MECHANICAL BRAKE SYSTEM
DTCs PRESENT.
NO DTCs PRESENT.
TECH 1 CANNOT COMMUNICATE WITH EBTCM.
GO TO "ABS/TCS DTC TABLE"
GO TO "ABS/TCS SYMPTOM TABLE" FOR APPROPRIATE CHART TO DIAGNOSE INDICATOR "ON" WITH NO DTCs SET.
REPAIR OPEN, SHORT TO GROUND, OR SHORT TO B+ IN SERIAL DATA CKT 800.
GC4029300460000X

Fig. 9 ABS Functional Check. 1993–94 Fleetwood (RWD)

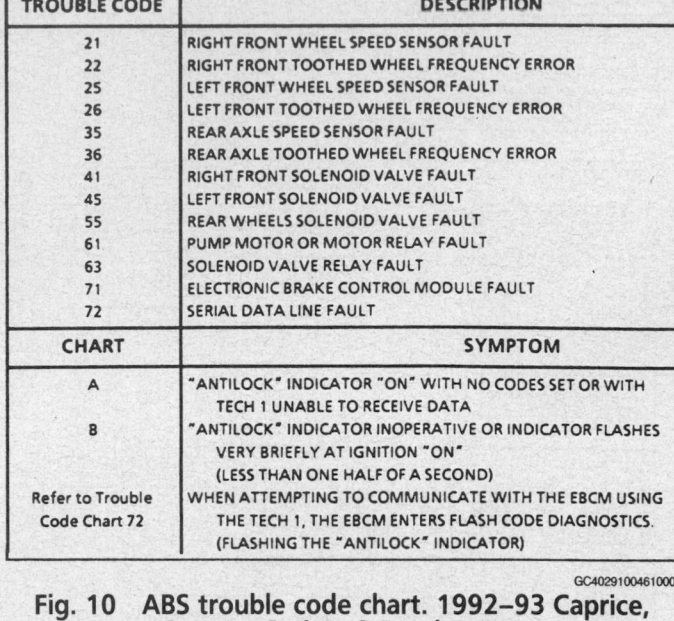

TROUBLE CODE	DESCRIPTION
21	RIGHT FRONT WHEEL SPEED SENSOR FAULT
22	RIGHT FRONT TOOTHED WHEEL FREQUENCY ERROR
25	LEFT FRONT WHEEL SPEED SENSOR FAULT
26	LEFT FRONT TOOTHED WHEEL FREQUENCY ERROR
35	REAR AXLE SPEED SENSOR FAULT
36	REAR AXLE TOOTHED WHEEL FREQUENCY ERROR
41	RIGHT FRONT SOLENOID VALVE FAULT
45	LEFT FRONT SOLENOID VALVE FAULT
55	REAR WHEELS SOLENOID VALVE FAULT
61	PUMP MOTOR OR MOTOR RELAY FAULT
63	SOLENOID VALVE RELAY FAULT
71	ELECTRONIC BRAKE CONTROL MODULE FAULT
72	SERIAL DATA LINE FAULT
CHART	**SYMPTOM**
A	"ANTILOCK" INDICATOR "ON" WITH NO CODES SET OR WITH TECH 1 UNABLE TO RECEIVE DATA
B	"ANTILOCK" INDICATOR INOPERATIVE OR INDICATOR FLASHES VERY BRIEFLY AT IGNITION "ON" (LESS THAN ONE HALF OF A SECOND)
Refer to Trouble Code Chart 72	WHEN ATTEMPTING TO COMMUNICATE WITH THE EBCM USING THE TECH 1, THE EBCM ENTERS FLASH CODE DIAGNOSTICS. (FLASHING THE "ANTILOCK" INDICATOR)

GC4029100461000X

Fig. 10 ABS trouble code chart. 1992–93 Caprice, Custom Cruiser & Roadmaster

DTC	DESCRIPTION
21	RF WHEEL SPEED SENSOR CIRCUIT MALFUNCTION
23	RF WHEEL SPEED SENSOR CIRCUIT CONTINUITY MALFUNCTION
25	LF WHEEL SPEED SENSOR CIRCUIT MALFUNCTION
27	LF WHEEL SPEED SENSOR CIRCUIT CONTINUITY MALFUNCTION
28	WHEEL SPEED SENSOR CIRCUIT FREQUENCY MALFUNCTION
35	REAR WHEEL SPEED SENSOR CIRCUIT MALFUNCTION
37	REAR WHEEL SPEED SENSOR CIRCUIT CONTINUITY MALFUNCTION
41	RF VALVE SOLENOID MALFUNCTION
45	LF VALVE SOLENOID MALFUNCTION
55	REAR VALVE SOLENOID MALFUNCTION
61	BPM VALVE PUMP MOTOR OR PUMP MOTOR RELAY MALFUNCTION (1 of 2)
63	BPM VALVE RELAY MALFUNCTION (1 of 2)
71	EBCM INTERNAL MALFUNCTION (EBCM FAULT)
CHART	**SYMPTOM**
A	ABS WARNING LAMP "ON" WITH NO DTCs SET OR WITH TECH 1 UNABLE TO RECEIVE DATA
B	ABS WARNING LAMP INOPERATIVE OR LAMP FLASHES VERY BRIEFLY AT IGNITION "ON" (LESS THAN ONE HALF OF A SECOND) "BRAKE" INDICATOR "ON" "BRAKE" INDICATOR INOPERATIVE

GC4029400917000X

Fig. 11 ABS trouble code chart. 1994 Caprice, Impala SS & Roadmaster.

ABS CODE	SYSTEM
21	RIGHT FRONT WHEEL SPEED SENSOR FAULT
22	RIGHT FRONT TOOTHED WHEEL FREQUENCY ERROR
25	LEFT FRONT WHEEL SPEED SENSOR FAULT
26	LEFT FRONT TOOTHED WHEEL FREQUENCY ERROR
31	RIGHT REAR WHEEL SPEED SENSOR FAULT
32	RIGHT REAR TOOTHED WHEEL FREQUENCY ERROR
35	LEFT REAR SPEED SENSOR FAULT
36	LEFT REAR TOOTHED WHEEL FREQUENCY ERROR
41	RIGHT FRONT SOLENOID VALVE FAULT
45	LEFT FRONT SOLENOID VALVE FAULT
55	REAR SOLENOID VALVE FAULT
61	MOTOR PUMP CIRCUIT FAULT
63	SOLENOID VALVE RELAY FAULT
71	ELECTRONIC BRAKE CONTROL MODULE FAULT
72	SERIAL DATA LINK FAULT (TECH 1 ERROR)
GO TO CHART	**SYMPTOM**
A	NO SYSTEM POWER
B	ANTILOCK LIGHT ON, NO CODES SET
C	ANTILOCK LIGHT INOPERATIVE AT KEY-ON
D	VALVE CYCLING (CHATTER) DURING NORMAL STOPS.

GC4029100462000X

Fig. 12 ABS trouble code chart. Riviera, 1992 Brougham, Eldorado, Seville, Toronado & Trofeo

ABS/TCS FAULT CODE TABLE

FAULT CODE	DESCRIPTION
21	RF WHEEL SPEED SENSOR FAULT
22	RF WHEEL SPEED SENSOR FREQUENCY ERROR
23	RF WHEEL SPEED SENSOR CONTINUITY FAULT
25	LF WHEEL SPEED SENSOR FAULT
26	LF WHEEL SPEED SENSOR FREQUENCY ERROR
27	LF WHEEL SPEED SENSOR CONTINUITY FAULT
28	WHEEL SPEED SENSOR FREQUENCY ERROR
31	RR WHEEL SPEED SENSOR FAULT
32	RR WHEEL SPEED SENSOR FREQUENCY ERROR
33	RR WHEEL SPEED SENSOR CONTINUITY FAULT
35	LR WHEEL SPEED SENSOR FAULT
36	LR WHEEL SPEED SENSOR FREQUENCY ERROR
37	LR WHEEL SPEED SENSOR CONTINUITY FAULT
41	RF ABS VALVE SOLENOID FAULT
44	RF TCS PILOT VALVE FAULT
45	LF ABS VALVE SOLENOID FAULT
48	LF TCS PILOT VALVE FAULT
51	RR ABS VALVE SOLENOID FAULT
55	LR VALVE SOLENOID FAULT (TCS)
55	REAR VALVE SOLENOID FAULT (NON-TCS)
61	PUMP MOTOR OR PUMP MOTOR RELAY FAULT
63	VALVE RELAY CIRCUIT FAULT
67	BRAKE LIGHT SWITCH FAULT
71	EBTCM/EBCM INTERNAL FAULT
72	SERIAL DATA LINK FAULT
73	PCM-EBTCM/EBCM PWM SIGNAL FAULT (4.6L)
83	BRAKE FLUID LEVEL LOW

GC4029300463000X

Fig. 13 ABS trouble code chart. 1993-94 DeVille, Eldorado & Seville

ABS/TCS DTC TABLE

DIAGNOSTIC TROUBLE CODE	DESCRIPTION
21	RF WHEEL SPEED SENSOR MALFUNCTION
23	RF WHEEL SPEED SENSOR CONTINUITY MALFUNCTION
25	LF WHEEL SPEED SENSOR MALFUNCTION
27	LF WHEEL SPEED SENSOR CONTINUITY MALFUNCTION
28	WHEEL SPEED SENSOR FREQUENCY ERROR
31	RR WHEEL SPEED SENSOR MALFUNCTION
33	RR WHEEL SPEED SENSOR CONTINUITY MALFUNCTION
35	LR WHEEL SPEED SENSOR MALFUNCTION
37	LR WHEEL SPEED SENSOR CONTINUITY MALFUNCTION
41	RF VALVE SOLENOID MALFUNCTION
44	PILOT VALVE SOLENOID MALFUNCTION
45	LF VALVE SOLENOID MALFUNCTION
51	RR VALVE SOLENOID MALFUNCTION
55	LR VALVE SOLENOID MALFUNCTION
57	TCC DISABLE RELAY OUTPUT MALFUNCTION
58	EBTCM INTERNAL ADJUSTER ASSEMBLY MALFUNCTION
61	PUMP MOTOR OR PUMP MOTOR RELAY MALFUNCTION
62	RPM SIGNAL MALFUNCTION
63	VALVE SOLENOID RELAY CIRCUIT MALFUNCTION
64	THROTTLE POSITION SIGNAL MALFUNCTION
65	ADJUSTER ASSEMBLY MALFUNCTION
66	ADJUSTER ASSEMBLY CONTROL MALFUNCTION
71	EBTCM INTERNAL MALFUNCTION
72	SERIAL DATA LINK MALFUNCTION
83	BRAKE DIFFERENTIAL PRESSURE MALFUNCTION

GC4029300464000X

Fig. 14 ABS trouble code chart. 1993–94 Fleetwood (RWD)

ABS/TCS SYMPTOM TABLE

CHART	DESCRIPTION
A	'ANTILOCK' INDICATOR AND 'TRACTION DISABLED' MESSAGE 'ON' – NO TCS CODES SET / NO TCS DATA
B	'ANTILOCK' INDICATOR 'ON'
C	VALVE CYCLING DURING NORMAL STOPS (UNWANTED ABS MODULATION)
D	TRACTION CONTROL OPERATION CHECK
•	'ANTILOCK' INDICATOR INOPERATIVE

GC4029300465000X

Fig. 15 ABS symptom table. 1993-94 DeVille, Eldorado & Seville

ABS/TCS SYMPTOM TABLE

CHART	SYMPTOM
A	"ANTI-LOCK" INDICATOR "ON" WITH NO DTCs SET
B	"ANTI-LOCK" INDICATOR INOPERATIVE OR FLICKERS BRIEFLY AT IGNITION "ON"
C	"TRACTION CONTROL" INDICATOR "ON" WITH NO DTCs SET
D	"TRACTION CONTROL" INDICATOR INOPERATIVE
E	"TRACTION ENGAGED" INDICATOR "ON" WITH NO DTCs SET
F	"TRACTION ENGAGED" INDICATOR INOPERATIVE WITH NO DTCs SET

GC4029300466000X

Fig. 16 ABS symptom table. 1993–94 Fleetwood (RWD)

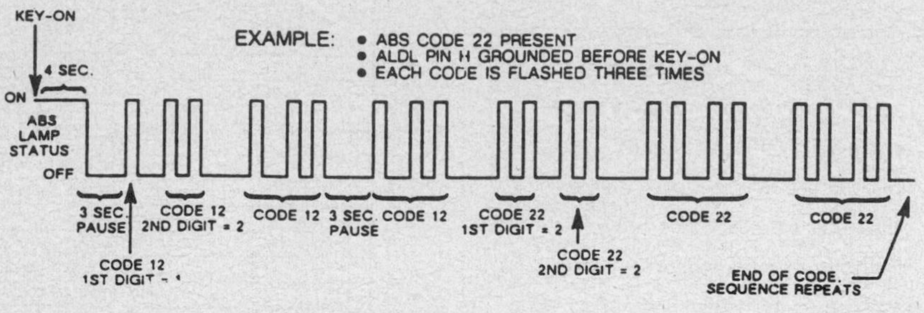
KEY-ON
4 SEC.
ON
ABS LAMP STATUS
OFF
EXAMPLE: • ABS CODE 22 PRESENT
• ALDL PIN H GROUNDED BEFORE KEY-ON
• EACH CODE IS FLASHED THREE TIMES
3 SEC. PAUSE
CODE 12 2ND DIGIT = 2
CODE 12
3 SEC. PAUSE
CODE 12
CODE 22 1ST DIGIT = 2
CODE 22
CODE 22
CODE 12 1ST DIGIT = 1
CODE 22 2ND DIGIT = 2
END OF CODE, SEQUENCE REPEATS
GC4029100467000X

Fig. 17 ABS flash code diagnosis

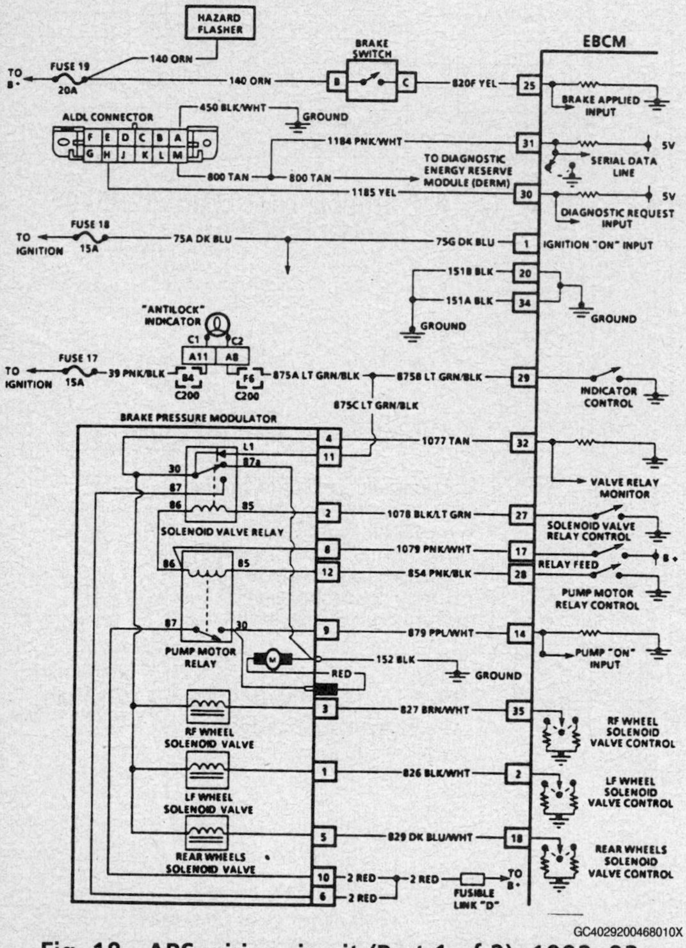
HAZARD FLASHER
EBCM
BRAKE SWITCH
TO B+
FUSE 19 20A
140 ORN
820F YEL
BRAKE APPLIED INPUT
ALDL CONNECTOR
450 BLK/WHT
GROUND
1184 PNK/WHT
SERIAL DATA LINE
5V
TO DIAGNOSTIC ENERGY RESERVE MODULE (DERM)
800 TAN
1185 YEL
DIAGNOSTIC REQUEST INPUT
TO IGNITION
FUSE 18 15A
75A DK BLU
75G DK BLU
IGNITION "ON" INPUT
151B BLK
151A BLK
GROUND
"ANTILOCK" INDICATOR
FUSE 17 15A
39 PNK/BLK
875A LT GRN/BLK
875B LT GRN/BLK
875C LT GRN/BLK
C200
INDICATOR CONTROL
BRAKE PRESSURE MODULATOR
1077 TAN
VALVE RELAY MONITOR
SOLENOID VALVE RELAY
1078 BLK/LT GRN
SOLENOID VALVE RELAY CONTROL
1079 PNK/WHT
RELAY FEED
854 PNK/BLK
PUMP MOTOR RELAY CONTROL
PUMP MOTOR RELAY
879 PPL/WHT
PUMP "ON" INPUT
152 BLK
RED
GROUND
RF WHEEL SOLENOID VALVE
827 BRN/WHT
RF WHEEL SOLENOID VALVE CONTROL
LF WHEEL SOLENOID VALVE
826 BLK/WHT
LF WHEEL SOLENOID VALVE CONTROL
REAR WHEELS SOLENOID VALVE
829 DK BLU/WHT
REAR WHEELS SOLENOID VALVE CONTROL
2 RED
FUSIBLE LINK "D"
TO B+
GC4029200468010X

Fig. 18 ABS wiring circuit (Part 1 of 2). 1992–93 Caprice, Custom Cruiser & Roadmaster

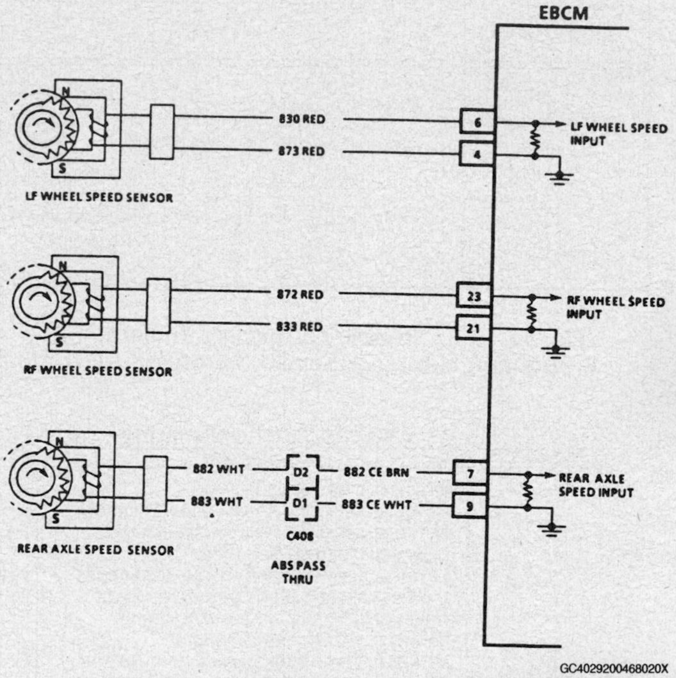
EBCM
830 RED
873 RED
LF WHEEL SPEED INPUT
LF WHEEL SPEED SENSOR
872 RED
833 RED
RF WHEEL SPEED INPUT
RF WHEEL SPEED SENSOR
882 WHT
883 WHT
882 CE BRN
883 CE WHT
C408
ABS PASS THRU
REAR AXLE SPEED INPUT
REAR AXLE SPEED SENSOR
GC4029200468020X

Fig. 18 ABS wiring circuit (Part 2 of 2). 1992–93 Caprice, Custom Cruiser & Roadmaster

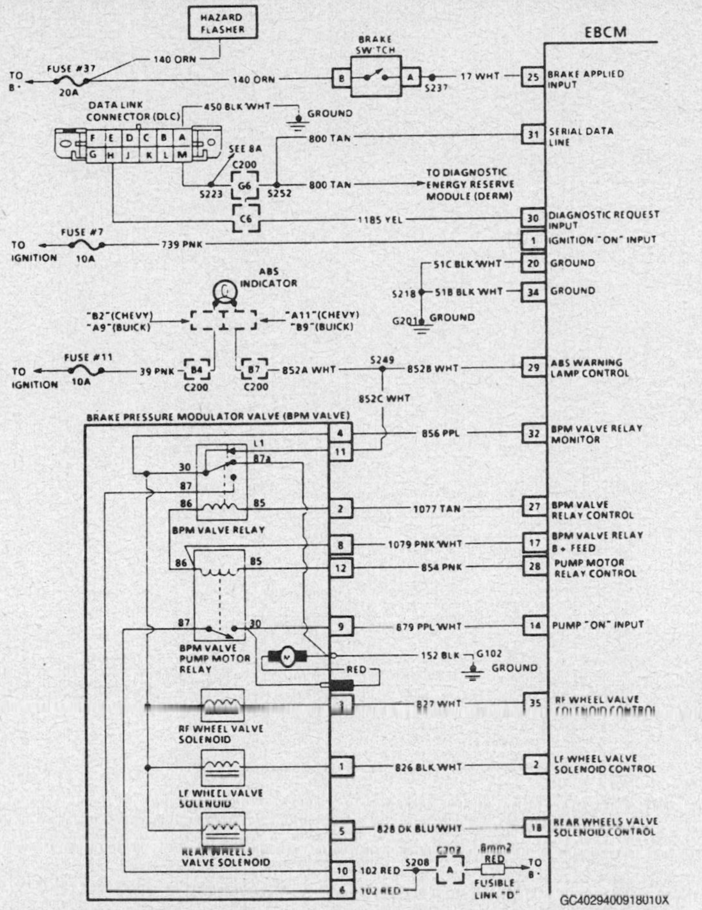

HAZARD FLASHER
BRAKE SWITCH
EBCM
TO B+
FUSE #37 20A
140 ORN
17 WHT
S237
BRAKE APPLIED INPUT
DATA LINK CONNECTOR (DLC)
450 BLK WHT
GROUND
800 TAN
SERIAL DATA LINE
SEE 8A
C200
S223
S252
TO DIAGNOSTIC ENERGY RESERVE MODULE (DERM)
1185 YEL
DIAGNOSTIC REQUEST INPUT
TO IGNITION
FUSE #7 10A
739 PNK
IGNITION "ON" INPUT
ABS INDICATOR
51C BLK WHT
GROUND
S218
51B BLK WHT
G201
"B2" (CHEVY) "A9" (BUICK)
"A11" (CHEVY) "B9" (BUICK)
FUSE #11 10A
39 PNK
852A WHT
S249
852B WHT
852C WHT
ABS WARNING LAMP CONTROL
BRAKE PRESSURE MODULATOR VALVE (BPM VALVE)
856 PPL
BPM VALVE RELAY MONITOR
BPM VALVE RELAY
1077 TAN
BPM VALVE RELAY CONTROL
1079 PNK WHT
BPM VALVE RELAY B+ FEED
854 PNK
PUMP MOTOR RELAY CONTROL
879 PPL WHT
PUMP "ON" INPUT
BPM VALVE PUMP MOTOR RELAY
152 BLK
G102
GROUND
RED
827 WHT
RF WHEEL VALVE SOLENOID CONTROL
RF WHEEL VALVE SOLENOID
826 BLK WHT
LF WHEEL VALVE SOLENOID CONTROL
LF WHEEL VALVE SOLENOID
828 DK BLU WHT
REAR WHEELS VALVE SOLENOID CONTROL
REAR WHEELS VALVE SOLENOID
102 RED
S208
FUSIBLE LINK "D"
GC4029400918010X

Fig. 19 ABS wiring circuit (Part 1 of 2). 1994 Caprice, Impala SS & Roadmaster

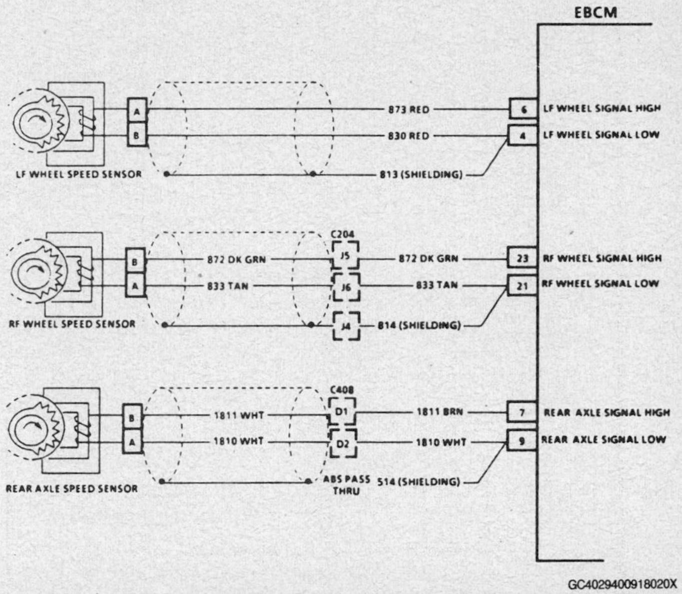

EBCM
LF WHEEL SPEED SENSOR
873 RED
830 RED
813 (SHIELDING)
LF WHEEL SIGNAL HIGH
LF WHEEL SIGNAL LOW
RF WHEEL SPEED SENSOR
C204
872 DK GRN
833 TAN
814 (SHIELDING)
RF WHEEL SIGNAL HIGH
RF WHEEL SIGNAL LOW
REAR AXLE SPEED SENSOR
C408
1811 WHT
1810 WHT
1811 BRN
1810 WHT
ABS PASS THRU
514 (SHIELDING)
REAR AXLE SIGNAL HIGH
REAR AXLE SIGNAL LOW
GC4029400918020X

Fig. 19 ABS wiring circuit (Part 2 of 2). 1994 Caprice, Impala SS & Roadmaster

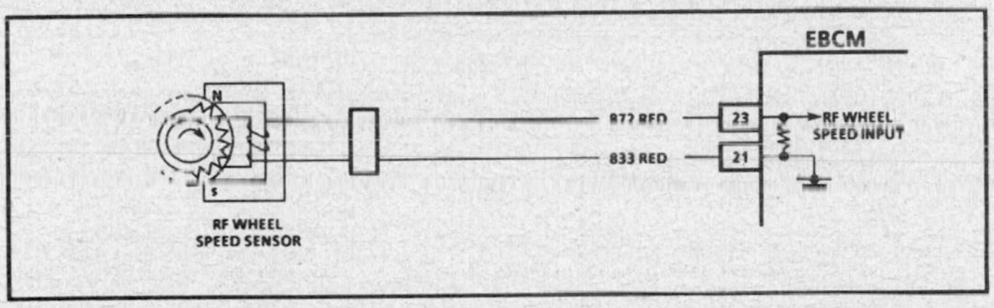

EBCM
872 RED
833 RED
RF WHEEL SPEED INPUT
RF WHEEL SPEED SENSOR
GC402920046900AX

Circuit Description:

As each wheel turns, the speed sensor for that wheel creates an AC voltage as the toothed ring rotates by the stationary sensor. The sensor consists of a permanent magnet and coil generating voltage by magnetic induction. The frequency and voltage of the induced signal is proportional to wheel speed.

The EBCM uses the speed sensor signal to calculate vehicle reference speed, individual speed, acceleration and slip values for each wheel which determine when antilock control is required.

Failure Conditions:

The EBCM performs two types of tests on the speed sensors to check continuity and output. Any condition which would result in lack of continuity or output on the right front wheel speed sensor circuit could result in setting Code 21. These conditions include an open, short to ground or short to B+ in CKT 872, an open in CKT 833 or an open across the sensor coil. Conditions which cause a low output from the speed sensor, such as a shorted sensor coil or an improperly installed sensor, will also set a Code 21.

Action Taken:

If a failure is detected which causes a speed sensor Code 21 to set, antilock braking is disabled and the EBCM turns "ON" the "Antilock" indicator for the remainder of the ignition cycle. If the failure is intermittent, the EBCM will enable the system at the next ignition cycle and a history Code 21 will be present.

Important

- The RF wheel speed sensor is located in the RF steering knuckle. In order to prevent electromagnetic interference from disturbing the speed sensor signal, the sensor wires are twisted together 9 times for every foot of wire. If wiring repairs are necessary, refer to "Wiring Repair Procedures"

Test Description: Number(s) below refer to circled number(s) on the diagnostic chart.

1. Checks for a correct resistance reading of the sensor itself.
2. Checks for a short between the wires for the RF wheel speed sensor.
3. Checks for an open, high resistance or short to voltage in the wires between the speed sensor and the EBCM.
4. Checks for a short to ground in CKT 872.
5. Checks for an "Intermittent" in the RF wheel speed sensor circuitry. If no "Intermittent" is found in the wiring, it may be in the sensor itself. Replace the sensor and road test the vehicle. If the code returns, replace the EBCM.

Diagnostic Aids:

Setting of speed sensor fault codes may be caused by improperly mounted sensors or improper wire routing. Verify that the sensor is properly mounted and free of foreign material such as metallic particles, dirt or grease. Verify that sensor wires are properly routed and secure. Improper RF Wheel Speed Sensor wire routing may cause Code 25 and/or Code 35 to set. To aid in troubleshooting intermittent conditions the Tech 1 can be used while test driving the vehicle however, antilock braking will be disabled. Refer to the Tech 1 Brake Cartridge Operators Manual for additional information. If this does not identify the intermittent, wet the speed sensor harness on the underside of the vehicle and road test monitoring wheel speeds with the Tech 1.

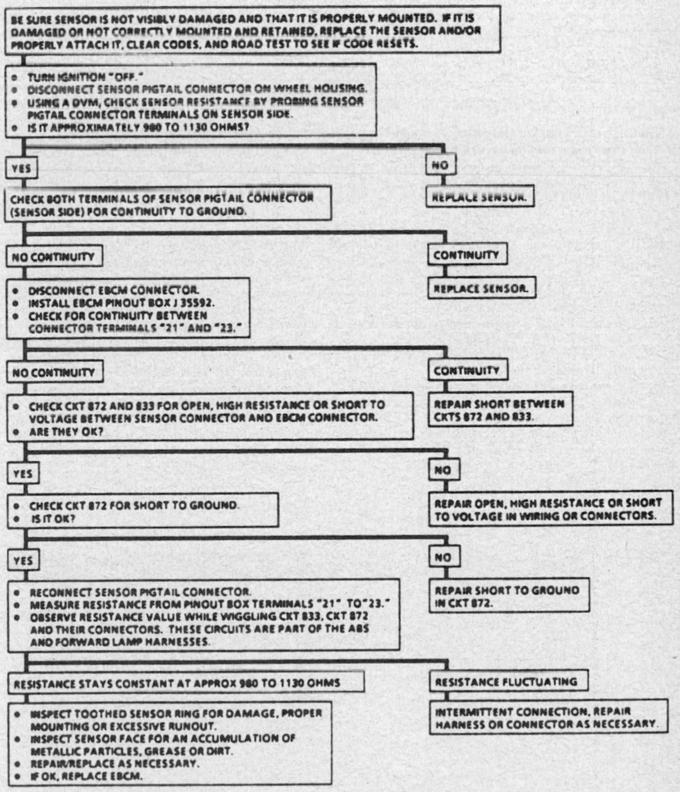

BE SURE SENSOR IS NOT VISIBLY DAMAGED AND THAT IT IS PROPERLY MOUNTED. IF IT IS DAMAGED OR NOT CORRECTLY MOUNTED AND RETAINED, REPLACE THE SENSOR AND/OR PROPERLY ATTACH IT, CLEAR CODES, AND ROAD TEST TO SEE IF CODE RESETS.
• TURN IGNITION "OFF."
• DISCONNECT SENSOR PIGTAIL CONNECTOR ON WHEEL HOUSING.
• USING A DVM, CHECK SENSOR RESISTANCE BY PROBING SENSOR PIGTAIL CONNECTOR TERMINALS ON SENSOR SIDE.
• IS IT APPROXIMATELY 980 TO 1130 OHMS?
YES
NO
REPLACE SENSOR.
CHECK BOTH TERMINALS OF SENSOR PIGTAIL CONNECTOR (SENSOR SIDE) FOR CONTINUITY TO GROUND.
NO CONTINUITY
CONTINUITY
REPLACE SENSOR.
• DISCONNECT EBCM CONNECTOR.
• INSTALL EBCM PINOUT BOX J 35592.
• CHECK FOR CONTINUITY BETWEEN CONNECTOR TERMINALS "21" AND "23."
NO CONTINUITY
CONTINUITY
REPAIR SHORT BETWEEN CKTS 872 AND 833.
• CHECK CKT 872 AND 833 FOR OPEN, HIGH RESISTANCE OR SHORT TO VOLTAGE BETWEEN SENSOR CONNECTOR AND EBCM CONNECTOR.
• ARE THEY OK?
YES
NO
REPAIR OPEN, HIGH RESISTANCE OR SHORT TO VOLTAGE IN WIRING OR CONNECTORS.
• CHECK CKT 872 FOR SHORT TO GROUND.
• IS IT OK?
YES
NO
REPAIR SHORT TO GROUND IN CKT 872.
• RECONNECT SENSOR PIGTAIL CONNECTOR.
• MEASURE RESISTANCE FROM PINOUT BOX TERMINALS "21" TO "23."
• OBSERVE RESISTANCE VALUE WHILE WIGGLING CKT 833, CKT 872 AND THEIR CONNECTORS. THESE CIRCUITS ARE PART OF THE ABS AND FORWARD LAMP HARNESSES.
RESISTANCE STAYS CONSTANT AT APPROX 980 TO 1130 OHMS
RESISTANCE FLUCTUATING
INTERMITTENT CONNECTION. REPAIR HARNESS OR CONNECTOR AS NECESSARY.
• INSPECT TOOTHED SENSOR RING FOR DAMAGE, PROPER MOUNTING OR EXCESSIVE RUNOUT.
• INSPECT SENSOR FACE FOR AN ACCUMULATION OF METALLIC PARTICLES, GREASE OR DIRT.
• REPAIR/REPLACE AS NECESSARY.
• IF OK, REPLACE EBCM.

GC402920046900BX

Fig. 20 Code 21: RF Wheel Speed Sensor Fault. 1992–93 Caprice, Custom Cruiser & Roadmaster

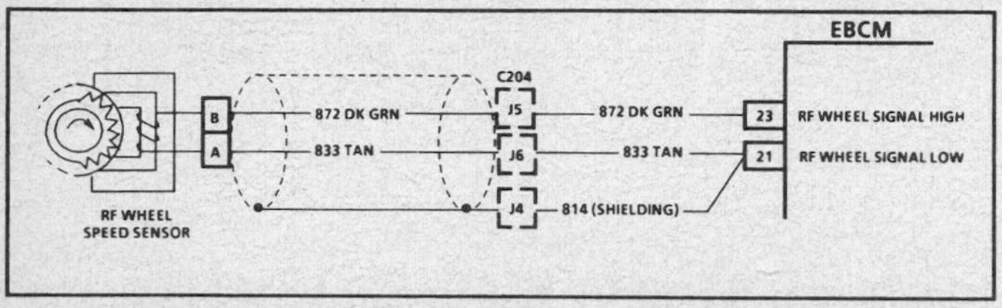
EBCM
C204
872 DK GRN
833 TAN
B
A
J5
J6
J4
872 DK GRN
833 TAN
814 (SHIELDING)
23
21
RF WHEEL SIGNAL HIGH
RF WHEEL SIGNAL LOW
RF WHEEL
SPEED SENSOR

DTC 21

RF WHEEL SPEED SENSOR CIRCUIT MALFUNCTION

Circuit Description:

As each wheel turns, the speed sensor for that wheel creates an AC voltage as the toothed ring rotates by the stationary sensor. The sensor consists of a permanent magnet and coil generating voltage by magnetic induction. The frequency and voltage of the induced signal is proportional to wheel speed.

The EBCM uses the speed sensor signal to calculate vehicle reference speed, individual speed, acceleration and slip values for each wheel which determine when antilock control is required.

DTC 21 Will Set When: There is a short to voltage or ground in CKT 872 or 833, or a malfunctioning speed sensor. The testing for this malfunction occurs when the vehicle is in motion; it will not set with the ignition "ON" and the vehicle at rest.

Action Taken: If a malfunction is detected which causes a speed sensor DTC 21 to set, antilock braking is disabled and the EBCM turns "ON" the ABS warning lamp for the remainder of the ignition cycle. If the malfunction is intermittent, the EBCM will enable the system at the next ignition cycle and a history DTC 21 will be present.

[?] Important

- The RF wheel speed sensor is located in the RF steering knuckle. In order to prevent electromagnetic interference from disturbing the speed sensor signal, the sensor wires are twisted together 9 times for every foot of wire.

DTC Chart Test Description: Number(s) below refer to circled number(s) on the diagnostic chart.

1. Checks for a short to battery in either of the speed sensor circuit wires.
2. Checks for a short between the speed sensor circuit wires.
3. Checks for a short to ground in the speed sensor input circuit wire. The ground may be either a "hard" short to ground, or a resistive (partial) short. A short with a resistance less than 2 megohms, though not a hard short, can still cause DTC 21 to set.
4. Checks if the DTC resets during a road test. If so, since tests 1-4 have validated that the circuitry and components are good, intermittent malfunctions are suspected.
5. Checks wiring and connectors for intermittents.
6. Replace the wheel bearing/speed sensor assembly, as it is likely the cause of a DTC reset experienced during the road test, since other portions of the circuit have checked out OK. If the DTC resets after sensor replacement, the EBCM must be concluding there is a malfunction present in the speed sensor circuit when there is not.
7. Ensures DTC was not set due to electromagnetic interference.

Diagnostic Aids: Setting of speed sensor DTCs may be caused by improperly mounted sensors or improper wire routing. Verify that the sensor is properly mounted and free of foreign material such as metallic particles, dirt or grease. Verify that sensor wires are properly routed and secure. Improper RF wheel speed sensor wire routing may cause DTC 25 and/or DTC 35 to set. To aid in troubleshooting intermittent conditions the Tech 1 can be used while test driving the vehicle however, antilock braking will be disabled. Refer to the Tech 1 Brake Cartridge Operators Manual for additional information. If this does not identify the intermittent, wet the speed sensor harness on the underside of the vehicle and road test monitoring wheel speeds with the Tech 1.

GC402940092000AX

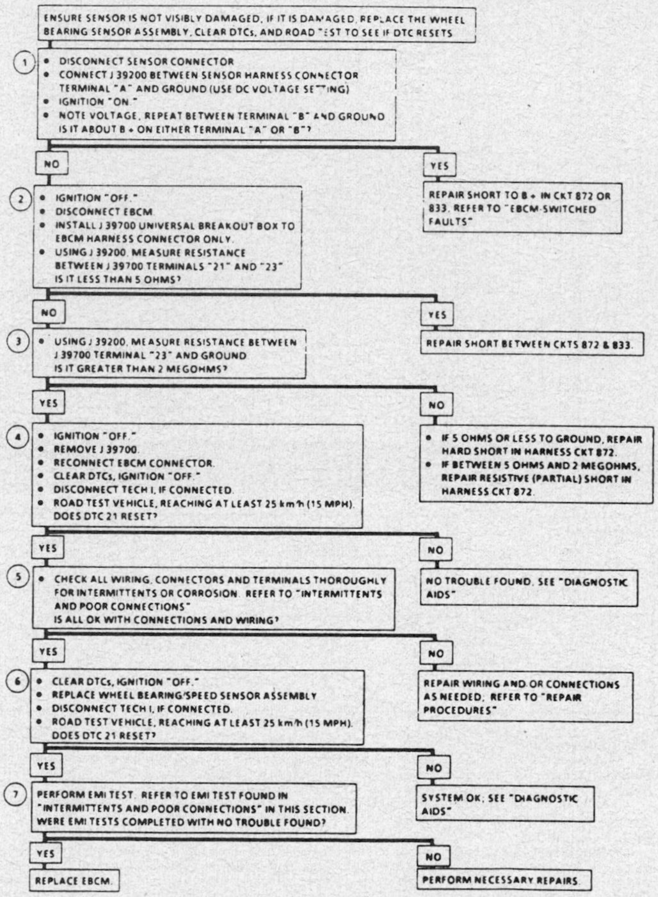
ENSURE SENSOR IS NOT VISIBLY DAMAGED. IF IT IS DAMAGED, REPLACE THE WHEEL BEARING SENSOR ASSEMBLY, CLEAR DTCs, AND ROAD TEST TO SEE IF DTC RESETS
1
• DISCONNECT SENSOR CONNECTOR
• CONNECT J 39200 BETWEEN SENSOR HARNESS CONNECTOR TERMINAL "A" AND GROUND (USE DC VOLTAGE SETTING)
• IGNITION "ON."
• NOTE VOLTAGE, REPEAT BETWEEN TERMINAL "B" AND GROUND IS IT ABOUT B + ON EITHER TERMINAL "A" OR "B"?
NO
YES
REPAIR SHORT TO B + IN CKT 872 OR 833. REFER TO "EBCM-SWITCHED FAULTS"
2
• IGNITION "OFF."
• DISCONNECT EBCM.
• INSTALL J 39700 UNIVERSAL BREAKOUT BOX TO EBCM HARNESS CONNECTOR ONLY.
• USING J 39200, MEASURE RESISTANCE BETWEEN J 39700 TERMINALS "21" AND "23" IS IT LESS THAN 5 OHMS?
NO
YES
REPAIR SHORT BETWEEN CKTS 872 & 833.
3
• USING J 39200, MEASURE RESISTANCE BETWEEN J 39700 TERMINAL "23" AND GROUND IS IT GREATER THAN 2 MEGOHMS?
YES
NO
• IF 5 OHMS OR LESS TO GROUND, REPAIR HARD SHORT IN HARNESS CKT 872.
• IF BETWEEN 5 OHMS AND 2 MEGOHMS, REPAIR RESISTIVE (PARTIAL) SHORT IN HARNESS CKT 872.
4
• IGNITION "OFF."
• REMOVE J 39700.
• RECONNECT EBCM CONNECTOR.
• CLEAR DTCs, IGNITION "OFF."
• DISCONNECT TECH I, IF CONNECTED.
• ROAD TEST VEHICLE, REACHING AT LEAST 25 km/h (15 MPH). DOES DTC 21 RESET?
YES
NO
NO TROUBLE FOUND. SEE "DIAGNOSTIC AIDS"
5
• CHECK ALL WIRING, CONNECTORS AND TERMINALS THOROUGHLY FOR INTERMITTENTS OR CORROSION. REFER TO "INTERMITTENTS AND POOR CONNECTIONS" IS ALL OK WITH CONNECTIONS AND WIRING?
YES
NO
REPAIR WIRING AND OR CONNECTIONS AS NEEDED; REFER TO "REPAIR PROCEDURES"
6
• CLEAR DTCs, IGNITION "OFF."
• REPLACE WHEEL BEARING/SPEED SENSOR ASSEMBLY
• DISCONNECT TECH I, IF CONNECTED.
• ROAD TEST VEHICLE, REACHING AT LEAST 25 km/h (15 MPH). DOES DTC 21 RESET?
YES
NO
SYSTEM OK; SEE "DIAGNOSTIC AIDS"
7
PERFORM EMI TEST. REFER TO EMI TEST FOUND IN "INTERMITTENTS AND POOR CONNECTIONS" IN THIS SECTION. WERE EMI TESTS COMPLETED WITH NO TROUBLE FOUND?
YES
REPLACE EBCM.
NO
PERFORM NECESSARY REPAIRS.

GC402940092000BX

Fig. 21 Code 21: RF Wheel Speed Sensor Fault. 1994 Caprice, Impala SS & Roadmaster

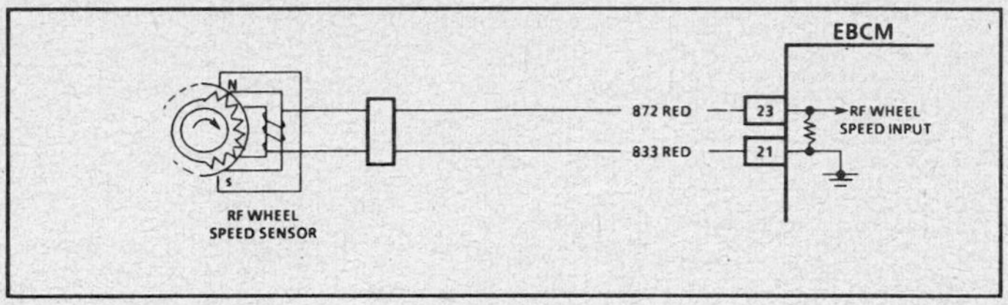
EBCM
872 RED
833 RED
23
21
RF WHEEL SPEED INPUT
N
S
RF WHEEL SPEED SENSOR

GC402920047000AX

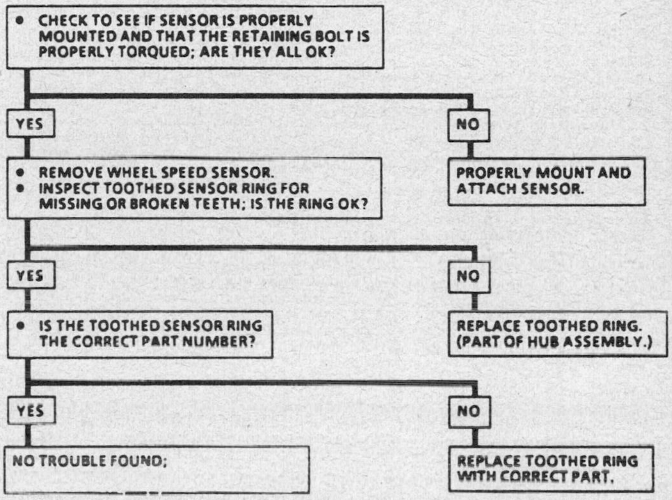
• CHECK TO SEE IF SENSOR IS PROPERLY MOUNTED AND THAT THE RETAINING BOLT IS PROPERLY TORQUED; ARE THEY ALL OK?
YES
NO
• REMOVE WHEEL SPEED SENSOR.
• INSPECT TOOTHED SENSOR RING FOR MISSING OR BROKEN TEETH; IS THE RING OK?
PROPERLY MOUNT AND ATTACH SENSOR.
YES
NO
• IS THE TOOTHED SENSOR RING THE CORRECT PART NUMBER?
REPLACE TOOTHED RING. (PART OF HUB ASSEMBLY.)
YES
NO
NO TROUBLE FOUND;
REPLACE TOOTHED RING WITH CORRECT PART.

GC402920047000CX

DTC 22

RF TOOTHED RING (FREQUENCY ERROR)

Circuit Description:

As each wheel turns, the speed sensor for that wheel creates an AC voltage as the toothed ring rotates by the stationary sensor. The sensor consists of a permanent magnet and coil generating voltage by magnetic induction. The frequency and voltage of the induced signal is proportional to wheel speed.

The EBCM uses the speed sensor signal to calculate vehicle reference speed, individual speed, acceleration and slip values for each wheel which determine when antilock control is required.

Failure Conditions:

DTC 22 will set if improper speed signals are being generated by the toothed ring. Causes of improper speed signals include; an incorrect number of teeth or damaged teeth present on the toothed ring, toothed ring or sensor face covered with dirt, grease or metallic particles that may impair magnetic induction.

DTC 22 may also set if the mini-spare tire has previously been used or the size of the tires on the vehicle differ. In addition to DTC 22, DTCs 26 and 36 may also set if the mini-spare tire has been used. If it is known that the spare tire was used, clear DTCs and test drive the vehicle again. Verify that DTCs do not set.

Action Taken:

If a failure is detected which causes a speed sensor DTC 22 to set, antilock braking is disabled and the EBCM turns "ON" the "ANTILOCK" indicator for the remainder of the ignition cycle. If the failure is intermittent, the EBCM will enable the system at the next ignition cycle and a history DTC 22 will be present.

Test Description: Number(s) below refer to circled number(s) on the diagnostic chart.

1. Checks for properly mounted sensor and mounting torque.
2. Checks for a physical problem with the toothed ring.
3. Checks for contamination on sensor face or toothed ring.

Diagnostic Aids:

A worn hub/bearing assembly may cause this fault in extreme cases; the bearing play allows the sensor-to-toothed ring gap to change excessively.

Check for a buildup of foreign material in the gaps between teeth on the toothed ring; this material may cause this error.

Also, check the toothed ring for any large grooves, gouges, marks, etc., that might influence the tooth's signal at the wheel speed sensor.

Remove and inspect wheel speed sensor for damage or contamination. If OK, and DTC 22 is still present, refer to DTC 21 chart.

GC402920047000BX

Fig. 22 Code 22: RF Toothed Wheel Frequency Error. 1992–93 Caprice, Custom Cruiser & Roadmaster

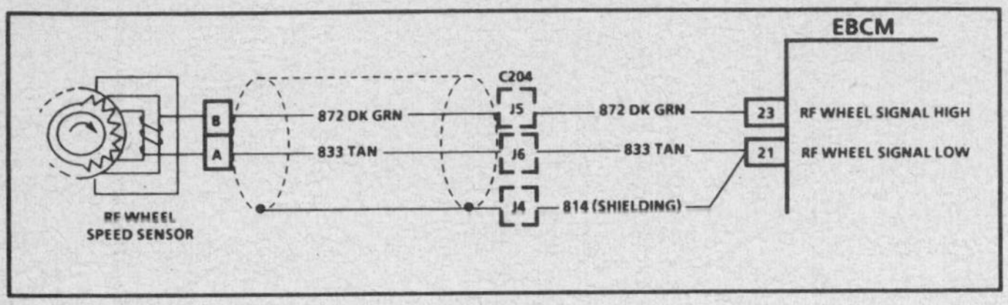
EBCM
C204
872 DK GRN
833 TAN
B
A
J5
J6
J4
814 (SHIELDING)
23
21
RF WHEEL SIGNAL HIGH
RF WHEEL SIGNAL LOW
RF WHEEL
SPEED SENSOR

DTC 23

RF WHEEL SPEED SENSOR CIRCUIT CONTINUITY MALFUNCTION

Circuit Description:

The toothed wheel generates a voltage pulse as it moves past the sensor; each tooth-gap-tooth series on the wheel generates these pulses. The frequency of these pulses is used by the EBCM to determine wheel speed. The amount of voltage generated in each pulse depends on the air gap between the sensor and the toothed wheel, and on wheel speed.

DTC 23 Will Set When: There is a short to voltage or an open in CKT 872 or 833, or a malfunctioning speed sensor. The testing for this malfunction occurs with the ignition "ON" and the vehicle at rest.

Action Taken: Antilock braking is disabled. The ABS warning lamp will be "ON" for the remainder of the ignition cycle. If the malfunction is intermittent, the EBCM will enable the system at the next ignition cycle and a history DTC 23 will be present.

DTC Chart Test Description: Number(s) below refer to circled number(s) on the diagnostic chart.

1. Checks for a short to battery in either of the speed sensor circuit wires.
2. Checks for an open in both the speed sensor circuit wires.
3. Manipulates wiring and connectors, trying to induce a intermittent malfunction not currently present.
4. This test checks if the DTC resets on key-up. If so, since tests 1-4 have validated that the circuitry and components are good, the wheel bearing/speed sensor assembly may be causing the malfunction.
5. Checks if DTC 21 sets during a road test.
6. DTC 23 sets when the vehicle is at rest; DTC 21 sets with a malfunction in the speed sensor circuitry with the vehicle in motion. If malfunctions are still present, DTC 21 would set during the road test, not a 23. If the DTC 21 sets at this point, the DTC 21 diagnostics should be used.
7. The wheel speed sensor may be causing an intermittent malfunction. If DTC 23 resets after sensor replacement, the EBCM must be concluding there is a malfunction present in the speed sensor circuit when there is not.
8. Ensures DTC was not set due to electromagnetic interference.

Diagnostic Aids: Be sure the speed sensor wiring is properly routed and retained. This will help prevent false signals due to electrical noise being picked up by the wiring.

It is very important that a thorough inspection of the wiring and connectors be performed. Failure to carefully and fully inspect wiring and connectors may result in misdiagnosis, causing part replacement with reappearance of the malfunction.

GC402940092100AX

ENSURE SENSOR IS NOT VISIBLY DAMAGED; IF IT IS DAMAGED, REPLACE THE WHEEL BEARING/SPEED SENSOR ASSEMBLY, CLEAR DTCs, AND TURN IGNITION "ON" TO SEE IF DTC RESETS.

(1)
- CONNECT J 39200 BETWEEN SENSOR HARNESS CONNECTOR TERMINAL "A" AND GROUND (USE DC VOLTS).
- IGNITION "ON."
- NOTE VOLTAGE; REPEAT BETWEEN TERMINAL "B" AND GROUND. IS IT ABOUT B+ ON EITHER TERMINAL "A" OR "B"?

YES: REPAIR SHORT TO B+ IN CKT 872 OR 833; REFER TO "EBCM-SWITCHED MALFUNCTIONS"

NO:

(2)
- IGNITION "OFF."
- DISCONNECT EBCM.
- INSTALL J 35592 PINOUT BOX TO EBCM HARNESS CONNECTOR ONLY
- USING J 39200, MEASURE RESISTANCE BETWEEN TERMINAL "21" ON J 35592 AND TERMINAL "A" OF SENSOR CONNECTOR ON HARNESS. PERFORM SAME MEASUREMENT BETWEEN TERMINAL "23" AND TERMINAL "B". IS EITHER MEASUREMENT GREATER THAN 5 OHMS?

YES: REPAIR OPEN IN CKT 872 AND/OR 833.

NO:

(3)
- REMOVE J 35592; RECONNECT EBCM.
- CLEAR DTCs; IGNITION "OFF."
- DISCONNECT TECH 1, IF CONNECTED.
- IGNITION "ON."
- WIGGLE ALL WIRING AND CONNECTORS TO TRY TO INDUCE A HIDDEN INTERMITTENT MALFUNCTION. DOES DTC 23 RESET?

YES: REPAIR INTERMITTENT CONNECTOR OR WIRING.

NO:

(4)
- CLEAR DTCs; IGNITION "OFF."
- DISCONNECT TECH 1, IF CONNECTED.
- IGNITION "ON." DOES DTC 23 RESET?

NO:

(5)
- ROAD TEST VEHICLE, REACHING AT LEAST 25 km/h (15 MPH). DOES DTC 21 SET?

YES: (6) GO TO DTC 21 DIAGNOSTICS.

NO: NO TROUBLE FOUND, SEE "DIAGNOSTIC AIDS"

YES:

(7)
- REPLACE WHEEL BEARING/SPEED SENSOR ASSEMBLY.
- CLEAR DTCs; IGNITION "OFF."
- DISCONNECT TECH 1, IF CONNECTED.
- IGNITION "ON." DOES DTC 23 RESET?

NO: SYSTEM OK

YES:

(8)
- PERFORM EMI TEST. REFER TO EMI TEST FOUND IN "INTERMITTENTS AND POOR CONNECTIONS" IN THIS SECTION. WERE EMI TESTS COMPLETED WITH NO TROUBLE FOUND?

YES: REPLACE EBCM.

NO: PERFORM NECESSARY REPAIRS.

GC402940092100BX

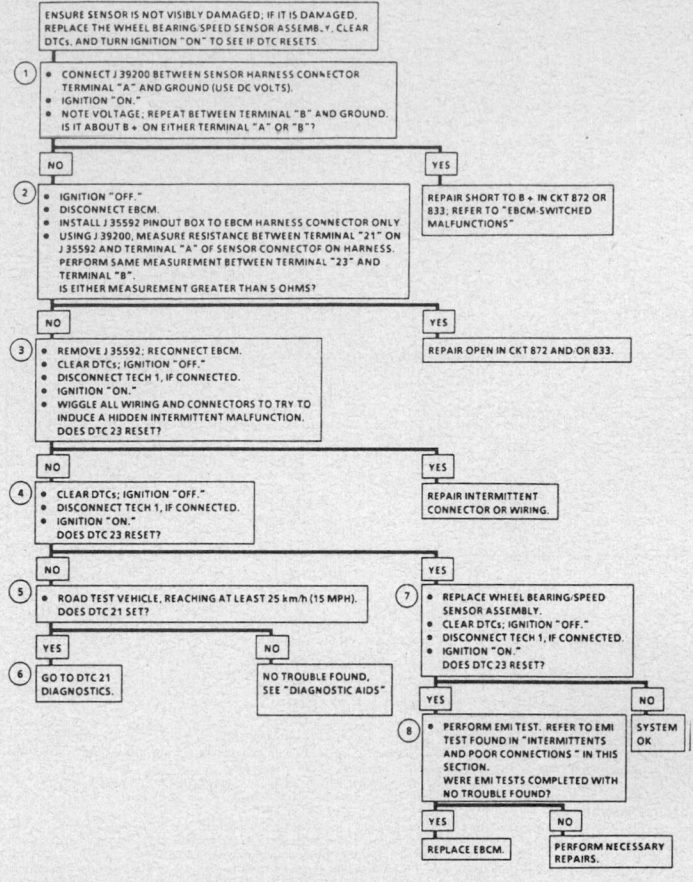

Fig. 23 Code 23: RF Wheel Speed Sensor Circuit Continuity Fault. 1994 Caprice, Impala SS & Roadmaster

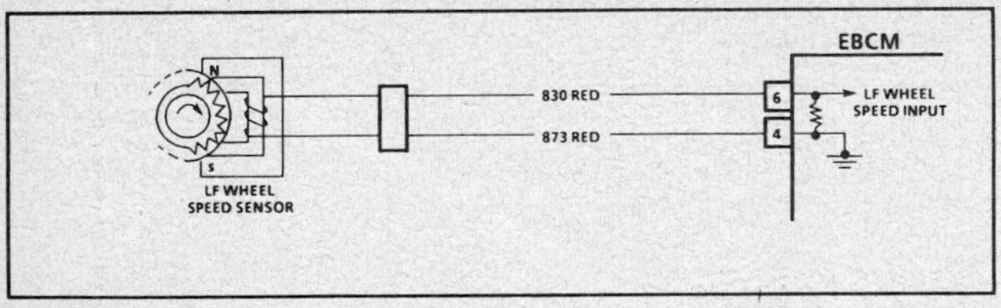
EBCM
N
S
830 RED
873 RED
6
4
LF WHEEL
SPEED INPUT
LF WHEEL
SPEED SENSOR

Circuit Description:

As each wheel turns, the speed sensor for that wheel creates an AC voltage as the toothed ring rotates by the stationary sensor. The sensor consists of a permanent magnet and coil generating voltage by magnetic induction. The frequency and voltage of the induced signal is proportional to wheel speed.

The EBCM uses the speed sensor signal to calculate vehicle reference speed, individual speed, acceleration and slip values for each wheel which determine when antilock control is required.

Failure Conditions:

The EBCM performs two types of tests on the speed sensors to check continuity and output. Any condition which would result in lack of continuity or output on the right front wheel speed sensor circuit could result in setting DTC 25. These conditions include an open, short to ground or short to B+ in CKT 830, an open in CKT 873 or an open across the sensor coil. Conditions which cause a low output from the speed sensor, such as a shorted sensor coil or an improperly installed sensor, will also set a DTC 25.

Action Taken:

If a failure is detected which causes a speed sensor DTC 25 to set, antilock braking is disabled and the EBCM turns "ON" the "ANTILOCK" indicator for the remainder of the ignition cycle. If the failure is intermittent, the EBCM will enable the system at the next ignition cycle and a history DTC 25 will be present.

Important

- The LF wheel speed sensor is located in the LF steering knuckle. In order to prevent electromagnetic interference from disturbing the wheel speed sensor signal, the sensor wires are twisted together 9 times for every foot of wire. If wiring repairs are necessary, refer to "Wiring Repair Procedures" in SECTION 8A-5.

Test Description: Number(s) below refer to circled number(s) on the diagnostic chart.

1. Checks for a correct resistance reading of the sensor itself.
2. Checks for a short to ground internal to the sensor.
3. Checks for a short between the wires for the LF wheel speed sensor.
4. Checks for a short to B+ on either CKT 830 or CKT 873.
5. Checks for a short to ground on either CKT 830 or CKT 873.
6. Checks for an open circuit or high resistance in CKT 830 or CKT 873.
7. Checks for an "Intermittent" in the LF wheel speed sensor circuitry. If no "Intermittent" is found in the wiring, it may be in the sensor itself. Replace the sensor and road test the vehicle. If the code returns, replace the EBCM.

Diagnostic Aids:

Setting of speed sensor DTCs may be caused by improperly mounted sensors or improper wire routing. Verify that the sensor is properly mounted and free of foreign material such as metallic particles, dirt or grease. Verify that sensor wires are properly routed and secure. Improper LF wheel speed sensor wire routing may cause DTC 21 and/or DTC 35 to set. To aid in troubleshooting intermittent conditions the Tech 1 can be used while test driving the vehicle however, antilock braking will be disabled. Refer to the Tech 1 Brake Cartridge Operators Manual for additional information. If this does not identify the intermittent, wet the speed sensor harness on the underside of the vehicle and road test monitoring wheel speeds with the Tech 1.

GC402920047100AX

BE SURE SENSOR IS NOT VISIBLY DAMAGED AND THAT IT IS PROPERLY MOUNTED. IF IT IS DAMAGED OR NOT CORRECTLY MOUNTED AND RETAINED, REPLACE THE SENSOR AND/OR PROPERLY ATTACH IT, CLEAR CODES, AND ROAD TEST TO SEE IF CODE RESETS.

- TURN IGNITION "OFF."
- DISCONNECT SENSOR PIGTAIL CONNECTOR ON WHEEL HOUSING.
- USING A DVM, CHECK SENSOR RESISTANCE BY PROBING SENSOR PIGTAIL CONNECTOR TERMINALS ON SENSOR SIDE.
- IS IT APPROXIMATELY 980 TO 1130 OHMS?

NO: REPLACE SENSOR.

YES: CHECK BOTH TERMINALS OF SENSOR PIGTAIL CONNECTOR (SENSOR SIDE) FOR CONTINUITY TO GROUND.

CONTINUITY: REPLACE SENSOR.

NO CONTINUITY:

- DISCONNECT EBCM CONNECTOR.
- INSTALL EBCM PINOUT BOX J 35592.
- CHECK FOR CONTINUITY BETWEEN CONNECTOR TERMINALS "4" AND "6".

CONTINUITY: REPAIR SHORT BETWEEN CKTS 873 AND 830.

NO CONTINUITY:

- CHECK CKT 873 AND 830 FOR OPEN, HIGH RESISTANCE OR SHORT TO VOLTAGE BETWEEN SENSOR CONNECTOR AND EBCM CONNECTOR.
- ARE THEY OK?

NO: REPAIR OPEN, HIGH RESISTANCE OR SHORT TO VOLTAGE IN WIRING OR CONNECTORS.

YES:

- CHECK CKT 830 FOR SHORT TO GROUND.
- IS IT OK?

NO: REPAIR SHORT TO GROUND IN CKT 830.

YES:

- RECONNECT SENSOR PIGTAIL CONNECTOR.
- MEASURE RESISTANCE FROM PINOUT BOX TERMINALS "4" TO "6"
- OBSERVE RESISTANCE VALUE WHILE WIGGLING CKT 830, CKT 873 AND THEIR CONNECTORS. THESE CIRCUITS ARE PART OF THE ABS AND FORWARD LAMP HARNESSES.

RESISTANCE FLUCTUATING: INTERMITTENT CONNECTION, REPAIR HARNESS OR CONNECTOR AS NECESSARY.

RESISTANCE STAYS CONSTANT AT APPROX 980 TO 1130 OHMS:

- INSPECT TOOTHED SENSOR RING FOR DAMAGE, PROPER MOUNTING OR EXCESSIVE RUNOUT.
- INSPECT SENSOR FACE FOR AN ACCUMULATION OF METALLIC PARTICLES, GREASE OR DIRT.
- REPAIR/REPLACE AS NECESSARY.
- IF OK, REPLACE EBCM.

GC402920047100BX

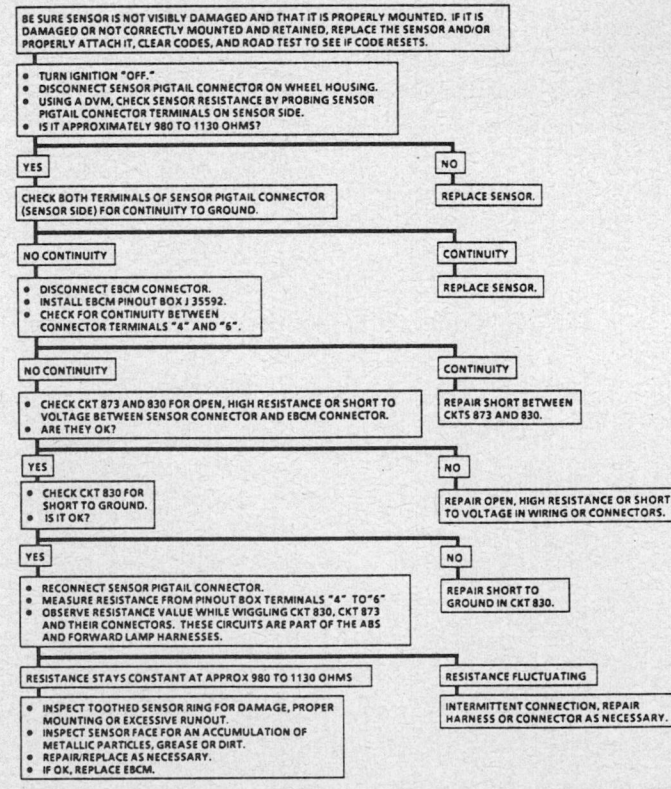

Fig. 24 Code 25: LF Wheel Speed Sensor Fault. 1992–93 Caprice, Custom Cruiser & Roadmaster

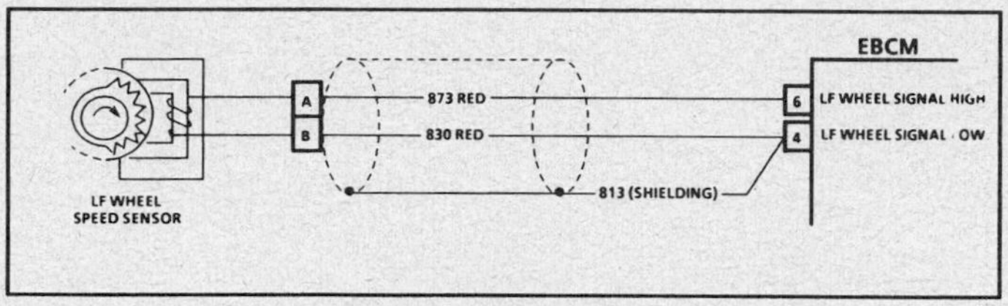
EBCM
873 RED
830 RED
LF WHEEL SIGNAL HIGH
LF WHEEL SIGNAL LOW
813 (SHIELDING)
LF WHEEL SPEED SENSOR
A
B
6
4

DTC 25

LF WHEEL SPEED SENSOR CIRCUIT MALFUNCTION

Circuit Description:

As each wheel turns, the speed sensor for that wheel creates an AC voltage as the toothed ring rotates by the stationary sensor. The sensor consists of a permanent magnet and coil generating voltage by magnetic induction. The frequency and voltage of the induced signal is proportional to wheel speed.

The EBCM uses the speed sensor signal to calculate vehicle reference speed, individual speed, acceleration and slip values for each wheel which determine when antilock control is required.

DTC 25 Will Set When: There is a short to voltage or ground in CKT 830 or 873, or a malfunctioning speed sensor. The testing for this malfunction occurs when the vehicle is in motion; it will not set with the ignition "ON" and the vehicle at rest.

Action Taken: If a malfunction is detected which causes a speed sensor DTC 25 to set, antilock braking is disabled and the EBCM turns "ON" the ABS warning lamp for the remainder of the ignition cycle. If the malfunction is intermittent, the EBCM will enable the system at the next ignition cycle and a history DTC 25 will be present.

[!] Important

- The LF wheel speed sensor is located in the LF steering knuckle. In order to prevent electromagnetic interference from disturbing the wheel speed sensor signal, the sensor wires are twisted together 9 times for every foot of wire.

DTC Chart Test Description: Number(s) below refer to circled number(s) on the diagnostic chart.

1. Checks for a short to battery in either of the speed sensor circuit wires.
2. Checks for a short between the speed sensor circuit wires.
3. Checks for a short to ground in the speed sensor input circuit wire. The ground may be either a "hard" short to ground, or a resistive (partial) short. A short with a resistance less than 2 megohms, though not a hard short, can still cause DTC 25 to set.
4. Checks if the DTC resets during a road test. If so, since tests 1-4 have validated that the circuitry and components are good, intermittent malfunctions are suspected.
5. Checks wiring and connectors for intermittents.
6. Replace the wheel bearing/speed sensor assembly, as it is likely the cause of a DTC reset experienced during the road test, since other portions of the circuit have checked out OK. If the DTC resets after sensor replacement, the EBCM must be concluding there is a malfunction present in the speed sensor circuit when there is not.
7. Ensures DTC was not set due to electromagnetic interference.

Diagnostic Aids: Setting of speed sensor DTCs may be caused by improperly mounted sensors or improper wire routing. Verify that the sensor is properly mounted and free of foreign material such as metallic particles, dirt or grease. Verify that sensor wires are properly routed and secure. Improper LF wheel speed sensor wire routing may cause DTC 21 and/or DTC 35 to set. To aid in troubleshooting intermittent conditions the Tech 1 can be used while test driving the vehicle however, antilock braking will be disabled. Refer to the Tech 1 Brake Cartridge Operators Manual for additional information. If this does not identify the intermittent, wet the speed sensor harness on the underside of the vehicle and road test monitoring wheel speeds with the Tech 1.

GC402940092200AX

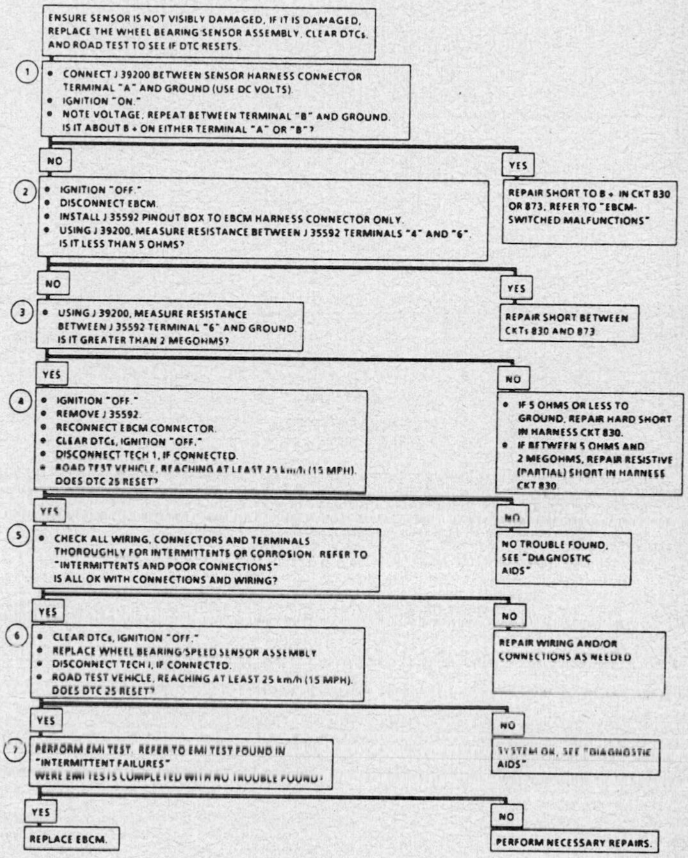
ENSURE SENSOR IS NOT VISIBLY DAMAGED, IF IT IS DAMAGED, REPLACE THE WHEEL BEARING SENSOR ASSEMBLY. CLEAR DTCs. AND ROAD TEST TO SEE IF DTC RESETS.
1 • CONNECT J 39200 BETWEEN SENSOR HARNESS CONNECTOR TERMINAL "A" AND GROUND (USE DC VOLTS). • IGNITION "ON." • NOTE VOLTAGE. REPEAT BETWEEN TERMINAL "B" AND GROUND. IS IT ABOUT B + ON EITHER TERMINAL "A" OR "B"?
NO
YES
REPAIR SHORT TO B + IN CKT 830 OR 873. REFER TO "EBCM-SWITCHED MALFUNCTIONS"
2 • IGNITION "OFF." • DISCONNECT EBCM. • INSTALL J 35592 PINOUT BOX TO EBCM HARNESS CONNECTOR ONLY. • USING J 39200, MEASURE RESISTANCE BETWEEN J 35592 TERMINALS "4" AND "6". IS IT LESS THAN 5 OHMS?
NO
YES
REPAIR SHORT BETWEEN CKTs 830 AND 873
3 • USING J 39200, MEASURE RESISTANCE BETWEEN J 35592 TERMINAL "6" AND GROUND. IS IT GREATER THAN 2 MEGOHMS?
YES
NO
• IF 5 OHMS OR LESS TO GROUND, REPAIR HARD SHORT IN HARNESS CKT 830. • IF BETWEEN 5 OHMS AND 2 MEGOHMS, REPAIR RESISTIVE (PARTIAL) SHORT IN HARNESS CKT 830.
4 • IGNITION "OFF." • REMOVE J 35592. • RECONNECT EBCM CONNECTOR. • CLEAR DTCs, IGNITION "OFF." • DISCONNECT TECH 1, IF CONNECTED. • ROAD TEST VEHICLE, REACHING AT LEAST 25 km/h (15 MPH). DOES DTC 25 RESET?
YES
NO
NO TROUBLE FOUND, SEE "DIAGNOSTIC AIDS"
5 • CHECK ALL WIRING, CONNECTORS AND TERMINALS THOROUGHLY FOR INTERMITTENTS OR CORROSION. REFER TO "INTERMITTENTS AND POOR CONNECTIONS" IS ALL OK WITH CONNECTIONS AND WIRING?
YES
NO
REPAIR WIRING AND/OR CONNECTIONS AS NEEDED
6 • CLEAR DTCs, IGNITION "OFF." • REPLACE WHEEL BEARING/SPEED SENSOR ASSEMBLY • DISCONNECT TECH I, IF CONNECTED. • ROAD TEST VEHICLE, REACHING AT LEAST 25 km/h (15 MPH). DOES DTC 25 RESET?
YES
NO
SYSTEM OK, SEE "DIAGNOSTIC AIDS"
7 PERFORM EMI TEST. REFER TO EMI TEST FOUND IN "INTERMITTENT FAILURES" WERE EMI TESTS COMPLETED WITH NO TROUBLE FOUND?
YES
REPLACE EBCM.
NO
PERFORM NECESSARY REPAIRS.

GC402940092200BX

Fig. 25 Code 25: LF Wheel Speed Sensor Fault. 1994 Caprice, Impala SS & Roadmaster

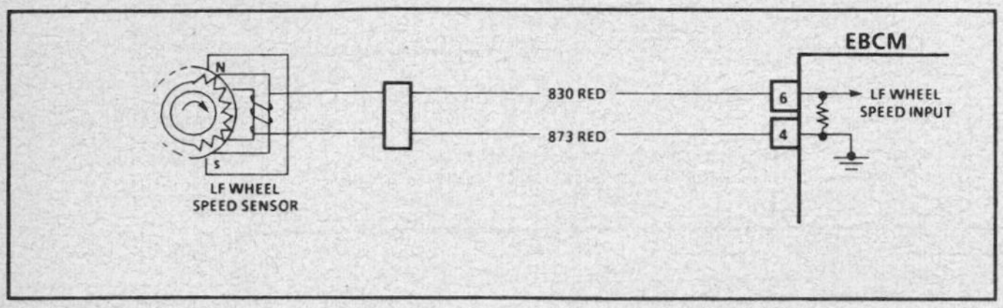
EBCM
N
S
830 RED
873 RED
6
4
LF WHEEL SPEED INPUT
LF WHEEL SPEED SENSOR

GC402920047200AX

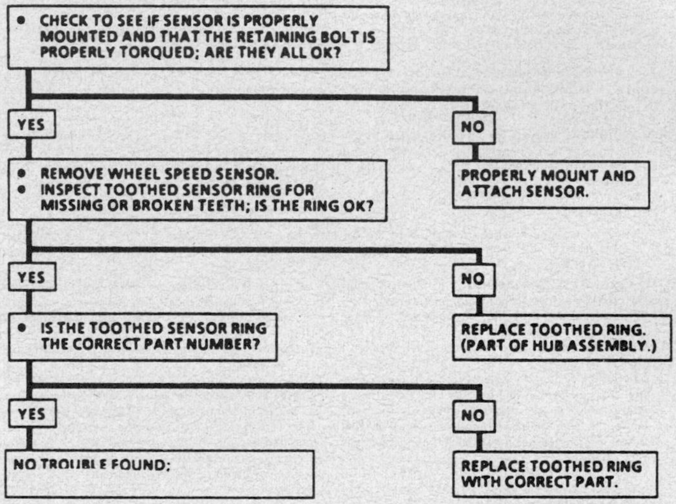
• CHECK TO SEE IF SENSOR IS PROPERLY MOUNTED AND THAT THE RETAINING BOLT IS PROPERLY TORQUED; ARE THEY ALL OK?
YES
NO
• REMOVE WHEEL SPEED SENSOR.
• INSPECT TOOTHED SENSOR RING FOR MISSING OR BROKEN TEETH; IS THE RING OK?
PROPERLY MOUNT AND ATTACH SENSOR.
YES
NO
• IS THE TOOTHED SENSOR RING THE CORRECT PART NUMBER?
REPLACE TOOTHED RING. (PART OF HUB ASSEMBLY.)
YES
NO
NO TROUBLE FOUND;
REPLACE TOOTHED RING WITH CORRECT PART.

GC402920047200CX

DTC 26

LF TOOTHED RING
(FREQUENCY ERROR)

Circuit Description:

As each wheel turns, the speed sensor for that wheel creates an AC voltage as the toothed ring rotates by the stationary sensor. The sensor consists of a permanent magnet and coil generating voltage by magnetic induction. The frequency and voltage of the induced signal is proportional to wheel speed.

The EBCM uses the speed sensor signal to calculate vehicle reference speed, individual speed, acceleration and slip values for each wheel which determine when antilock control is required.

Failure Conditions:

DTC 26 will set if improper speed signals are being generated by the toothed ring. Causes of improper speed signals include; an incorrect number of teeth or damaged teeth present on the toothed ring, toothed ring or sensor face covered with dirt, grease or metallic particles that may impair magnetic induction.

DTC 26 may also set if the mini-spare tire has previously been used or the size of the tires on the vehicle differ. In addition to DTC 26, DTCs 22 and 36 may also set if the mini-spare tire has been used. If it is known that the spare tire was used, clear DTCs and test drive the vehicle again. Verify that DTCs do not set.

Action Taken:

If a failure is detected which causes a speed sensor DTC 26 to set, antilock braking is disabled and the EBCM turns "ON" the "ANTILOCK" indicator for the remainder of the ignition cycle. If the failure is intermittent, the EBCM will enable the system at the next ignition cycle and a history DTC 26 will be present.

Test Description: Number(s) below refer to circled number(s) on the diagnostic chart.

1. Checks for properly mounted sensor and mounting torque.
2. Checks for a physical problem with the toothed ring.
3. Checks for contamination on sensor face or toothed ring.

Diagnostic Aids:

A worn hub/bearing assembly may cause this fault in extreme cases: the bearing play allows the sensor-to-toothed ring gap to change excessively.

Check for a buildup of foreign material in the gaps between teeth on the toothed ring; this material may cause this error.

Also, check the toothed ring for any large grooves, gouges, marks, etc., that might influence the tooth's signal at the wheel speed sensor.

Remove and inspect wheel speed sensor for damage or contamination. If OK, and DTC 26 is still present refer to DTC 25 chart.

GC402920047200BX

Fig. 26 Code 26: LF Toothed Wheel Frequency Error. 1992–93 Caprice, Custom Cruiser & Roadmaster

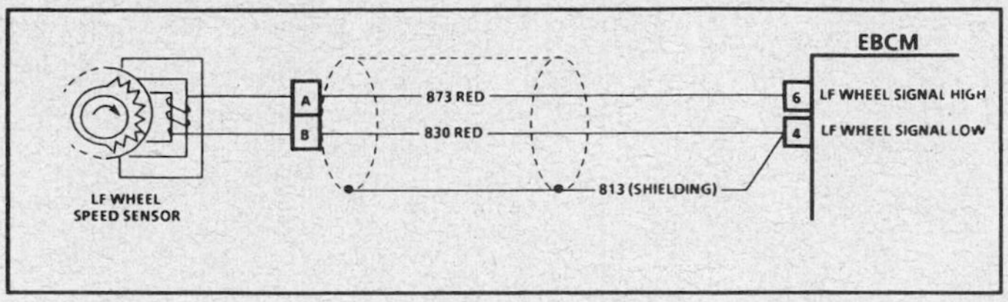
EBCM
873 RED
830 RED
813 (SHIELDING)
A
B
6 LF WHEEL SIGNAL HIGH
4 LF WHEEL SIGNAL LOW
LF WHEEL SPEED SENSOR

DTC 27

LF WHEEL SPEED SENSOR CIRCUIT CONTINUITY MALFUNCTION

Circuit Description:

The toothed wheel generates a voltage pulse as it moves past the sensor; each tooth-gap-tooth series on the wheel generates these pulses. The frequency of these pulses is used by the EBCM to determine wheel speed. The amount of voltage generated in each pulse depends on the air gap between the sensor and the toothed wheel, and on wheel speed.

DTC 27 Will Set When: There is a short to voltage or an open in CKT 830 or 873, or a malfunctioning speed sensor. The testing for this malfunction occurs with the ignition "ON" and the vehicle at rest.

Action Taken: Antilock braking is disabled. The ABS warning lamp will be "ON" for the remainder of the ignition cycle. If the malfunction is intermittent, the EBCM will enable the system at the next ignition cycle and a history DTC 27 will be present.

DTC Chart Test Description: Number(s) below refer to circled number(s) on the diagnostic chart.

1. Checks for a short to battery in either of the speed sensor circuit wires.
2. Checks for an open in both the speed sensor circuit wires.
3. Manipulates wiring and connectors, trying to induce a intermittent malfunction not currently present.
4. This test checks if the DTC resets on key-up. If so, since tests 1-4 have validated that the circuitry and components are good, the wheel bearing/speed sensor assembly may be causing the malfunction.
5. Checks if DTC 25 sets during a road test.
6. DTC 27 sets when the vehicle is at rest; DTC 25 sets with a malfunction in the speed sensor circuitry with the vehicle in motion. If malfunctions are still present, DTC 25 would set during the road test, not a 27. If the DTC 25 sets at this point, the DTC 25 diagnostics should be used.
7. The wheel speed sensor may be causing an intermittent malfunction. If DTC 27 resets after sensor replacement, the EBCM must be concluding there is a malfunction present in the speed sensor circuit when there is not.
8. Ensures DTC was not set due to electromagnetic interference.

Diagnostic Aids: Be sure the speed sensor wiring is properly routed and retained. This will help prevent false signals due to electrical noise being picked up by the wiring.

It is very important that a thorough inspection of the wiring and connectors be performed. Failure to carefully and fully inspect wiring and connectors may result in misdiagnosis, causing part replacement with reappearance of the malfunction.

GC402940092300AX

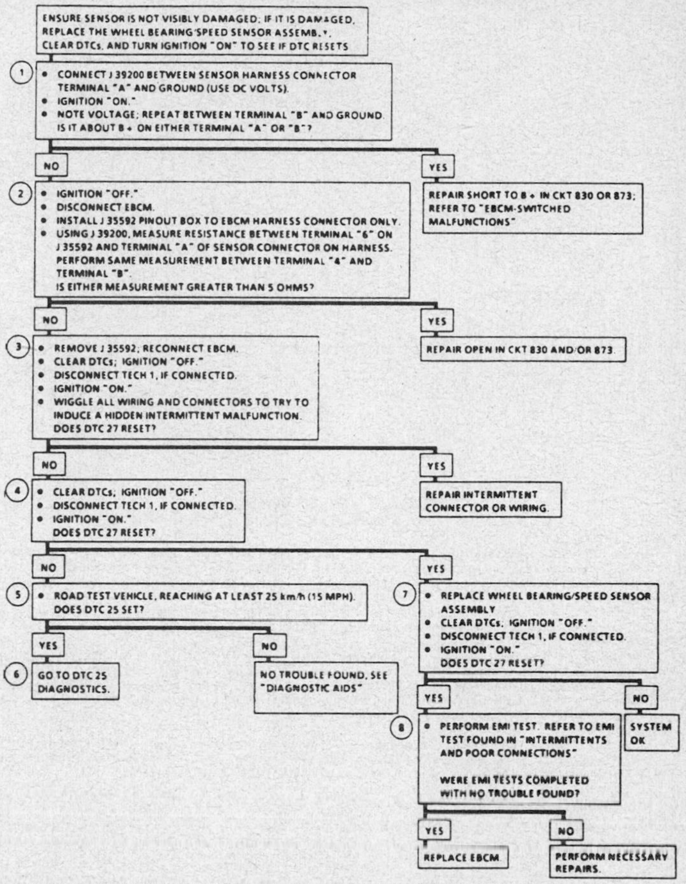
ENSURE SENSOR IS NOT VISIBLY DAMAGED; IF IT IS DAMAGED, REPLACE THE WHEEL BEARING/SPEED SENSOR ASSEMBLY, CLEAR DTCs, AND TURN IGNITION "ON" TO SEE IF DTC RESETS
1
• CONNECT J 39200 BETWEEN SENSOR HARNESS CONNECTOR TERMINAL "A" AND GROUND (USE DC VOLTS).
• IGNITION "ON."
• NOTE VOLTAGE; REPEAT BETWEEN TERMINAL "B" AND GROUND. IS IT ABOUT B+ ON EITHER TERMINAL "A" OR "B"?
NO
YES
REPAIR SHORT TO B+ IN CKT 830 OR 873; REFER TO "EBCM-SWITCHED MALFUNCTIONS"
2
• IGNITION "OFF."
• DISCONNECT EBCM.
• INSTALL J 35592 PINOUT BOX TO EBCM HARNESS CONNECTOR ONLY.
• USING J 39200, MEASURE RESISTANCE BETWEEN TERMINAL "6" ON J 35592 AND TERMINAL "A" OF SENSOR CONNECTOR ON HARNESS. PERFORM SAME MEASUREMENT BETWEEN TERMINAL "4" AND TERMINAL "B". IS EITHER MEASUREMENT GREATER THAN 5 OHMS?
NO
YES
REPAIR OPEN IN CKT 830 AND/OR 873.
3
• REMOVE J 35592; RECONNECT EBCM.
• CLEAR DTCs; IGNITION "OFF."
• DISCONNECT TECH 1, IF CONNECTED.
• IGNITION "ON."
• WIGGLE ALL WIRING AND CONNECTORS TO TRY TO INDUCE A HIDDEN INTERMITTENT MALFUNCTION. DOES DTC 27 RESET?
NO
YES
REPAIR INTERMITTENT CONNECTOR OR WIRING.
4
• CLEAR DTCs; IGNITION "OFF."
• DISCONNECT TECH 1, IF CONNECTED.
• IGNITION "ON." DOES DTC 27 RESET?
NO
YES
5
• ROAD TEST VEHICLE, REACHING AT LEAST 25 km/h (15 MPH). DOES DTC 25 SET?
YES
NO
6
GO TO DTC 25 DIAGNOSTICS.
NO TROUBLE FOUND, SEE "DIAGNOSTIC AIDS"
7
• REPLACE WHEEL BEARING/SPEED SENSOR ASSEMBLY
• CLEAR DTCs; IGNITION "OFF."
• DISCONNECT TECH 1, IF CONNECTED.
• IGNITION "ON." DOES DTC 27 RESET?
YES
NO
SYSTEM OK
8
• PERFORM EMI TEST. REFER TO EMI TEST FOUND IN "INTERMITTENTS AND POOR CONNECTIONS"
WERE EMI TESTS COMPLETED WITH NO TROUBLE FOUND?
YES
NO
REPLACE EBCM.
PERFORM NECESSARY REPAIRS.

Fig. 27 Code 27: LF Wheel Speed Sensor Circuit Continuity Fault. 1994 Caprice, Impala SS & Roadmaster

EBCM
WHEEL SIGNAL HIGH
WHEEL SIGNAL LOW

DTC 28

WHEEL SPEED SENSOR CIRCUIT FREQUENCY MALFUNCTION

Circuit Description:

The toothed wheel generates a voltage pulse as it moves past the sensor; each tooth-gap-tooth series on the wheel generates these pulses. The frequency of these pulses is used by the EBCM to determine wheel speed. The amount of voltage generated in each pulse depends on the air gap between the sensor and the toothed wheel, and on wheel speed.

DTC 28 Will Set When: The EBCM cannot specifically identify which wheel speed sensor is causing the frequency error malfunction. If it can define the specific speed sensor causing the malfunction, the sensor DTC associated with the sensor (21, 25, 31, 35) will be set instead of DTC 28.

Action Taken: Antilock braking is disabled. The ABS warning lamp will be "ON" for the remainder of the ignition cycle. If the malfunction is intermittent, the EBCM will enable the system at the next ignition cycle and a history DTC 28 will be present.

DTC Chart Test Description: Number(s) below refer to circled number(s) on the diagnostic chart.

The ABS warning lamp will be turned "ON" and ABS will be disabled.

1. Checks wiring and connections for malfunctions. It is critical that this step is performed thoroughly, as wiring/connector malfunctions are the most likely cause for this DTC.
2. Uses the Tech 1 to monitor for vehicle electrical/electronic system "noise" being picked up by the speed sensor circuits.
3. Uses the Tech 1 to monitor the wheel speed sensors while the vehicle is operating. If the Tech 1 auto-trigger snapshot mode triggers, the speed sensor or the wiring and/or connectors are going intermittent during the road test.
4. Checks for proper resistance in the sensor itself.

5a. Replace rear wheel speed sensor as the likely cause of the triggering intermittent.

5b. Replaces front wheel speed sensor as the likely cause of the triggering intermittent.

6. Ensures malfunction is not due to suspected wheel speed sensor.
7. Checks for a short to ground in the speed sensor input circuit wires. The circuit to be tested depends on which speed sensor triggered the Tech 1. The ground may be either a "hard" short to ground, or a resistive (partial) short. A short with a resistance less than 2 megohms, though not a hard short, can still cause DTC 28 to set.
8. Ensures DTC was not set due to electromagnetic interference.

Diagnostic Aids: Check the toothed wheel for any large grooves, gouges, marks, etc. that might influence the tooth's signal at the wheel speed sensor. Also check for a buildup of foreign material in the gaps between teeth in the toothed wheel; this material may cause this malfunction.

A worn hub/bearing assembly may cause this malfunction in extreme cases; the bearing play allows the sensor-to-toothed ring gap to change excessively.

GC402940092400AX

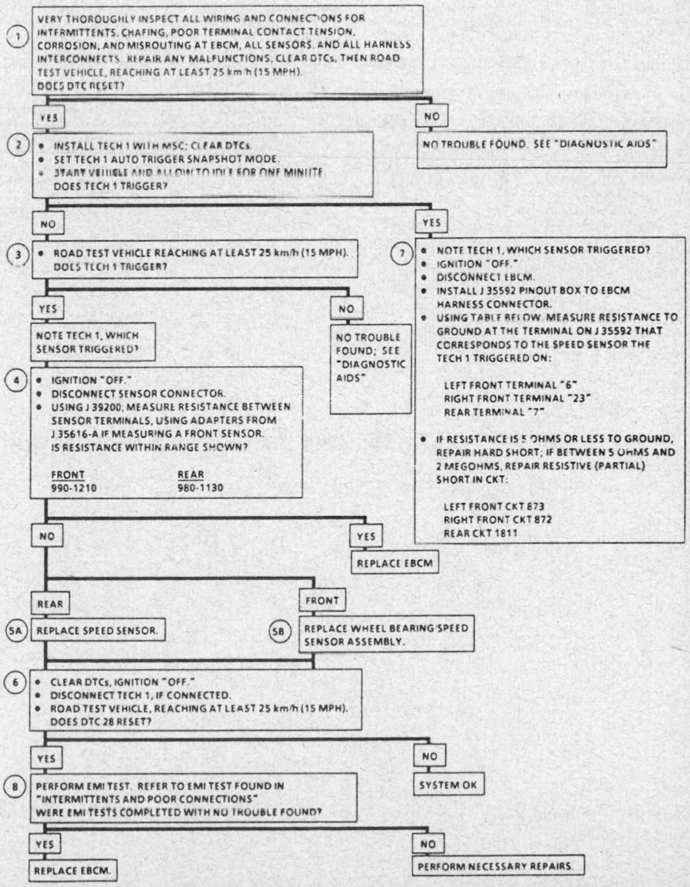
1
VERY THOROUGHLY INSPECT ALL WIRING AND CONNECTIONS FOR INTERMITTENTS, CHAFING, POOR TERMINAL CONTACT TENSION, CORROSION, AND MISROUTING AT EBCM, ALL SENSORS, AND ALL HARNESS INTERCONNECTS. REPAIR ANY MALFUNCTIONS, CLEAR DTCs, THEN ROAD TEST VEHICLE, REACHING AT LEAST 25 km/h (15 MPH). DOES DTC RESET?
YES
NO
NO TROUBLE FOUND. SEE "DIAGNOSTIC AIDS"
2
• INSTALL TECH 1 WITH MSC; CLEAR DTCs.
• SET TECH 1 AUTO TRIGGER SNAPSHOT MODE.
• START VEHICLE AND ALLOW TO IDLE FOR ONE MINUTE. DOES TECH 1 TRIGGER?
NO
YES
3
• ROAD TEST VEHICLE REACHING AT LEAST 25 km/h (15 MPH). DOES TECH 1 TRIGGER?
YES
NO
NOTE TECH 1, WHICH SENSOR TRIGGERED?
NO TROUBLE FOUND; SEE "DIAGNOSTIC AIDS"
4
• IGNITION "OFF."
• DISCONNECT SENSOR CONNECTOR.
• USING J 39200, MEASURE RESISTANCE BETWEEN SENSOR TERMINALS, USING ADAPTERS FROM J 35616-A IF MEASURING A FRONT SENSOR. IS RESISTANCE WITHIN RANGE SHOWN?
FRONT 990-1210
REAR 980-1130
7
• NOTE TECH 1, WHICH SENSOR TRIGGERED?
• IGNITION "OFF."
• DISCONNECT EBCM.
• INSTALL J 35592 PINOUT BOX TO EBCM HARNESS CONNECTOR.
• USING TABLE BELOW, MEASURE RESISTANCE TO GROUND AT THE TERMINAL ON J 35592 THAT CORRESPONDS TO THE SPEED SENSOR THE TECH 1 TRIGGERED ON:
LEFT FRONT TERMINAL "6"
RIGHT FRONT TERMINAL "23"
REAR TERMINAL "7"
• IF RESISTANCE IS 5 OHMS OR LESS TO GROUND, REPAIR HARD SHORT; IF BETWEEN 5 OHMS AND 2 MEGOHMS, REPAIR RESISTIVE (PARTIAL) SHORT IN CKT:
LEFT FRONT CKT 873
RIGHT FRONT CKT 872
REAR CKT 1811
NO
YES
REPLACE EBCM
REAR
FRONT
5A
REPLACE SPEED SENSOR.
5B
REPLACE WHEEL BEARING/SPEED SENSOR ASSEMBLY.
6
• CLEAR DTCs, IGNITION "OFF."
• DISCONNECT TECH 1, IF CONNECTED.
• ROAD TEST VEHICLE, REACHING AT LEAST 25 km/h (15 MPH). DOES DTC 28 RESET?
YES
NO
SYSTEM OK
8
PERFORM EMI TEST. REFER TO EMI TEST FOUND IN "INTERMITTENTS AND POOR CONNECTIONS" WERE EMI TESTS COMPLETED WITH NO TROUBLE FOUND?
YES
NO
REPLACE EBCM.
PERFORM NECESSARY REPAIRS.

Fig. 28 Code 28: Wheel Speed Sensor Circuit Frequency Fault. 1994 Caprice, Impala SS & Roadmaster

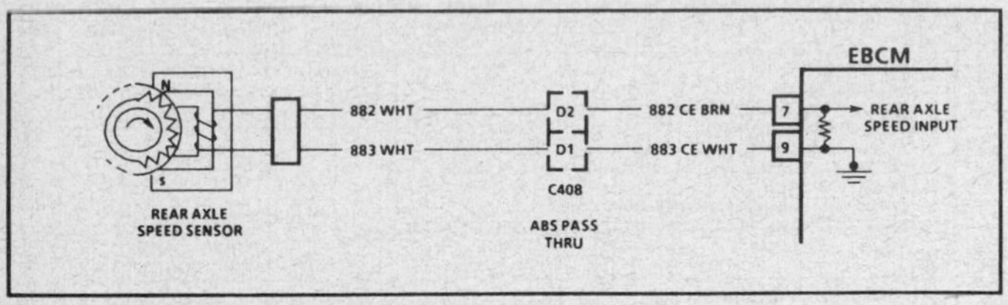
EBCM
882 WHT
883 WHT
D2
D1
882 CE BRN
883 CE WHT
7
9
REAR AXLE SPEED INPUT
N
S
REAR AXLE SPEED SENSOR
C408
ABS PASS THRU

GC402920047300AX

DTC 35

REAR AXLE SPEED SENSOR
(SENSOR FAULT)

Circuit Description:

As the differential pinion gear turns, the speed sensor creates an AC voltage as the toothed ring (mounted to the differential pinion gear) rotates by the stationary sensor. The sensor consists of a permanent magnet and coil generating voltage by magnetic induction. The frequency and voltage of the induced signal is proportional to rear axle speed.

The EBCM uses the speed sensor signal to calculate vehicle reference speed, individual speed, acceleration and slip values for the rear wheels which determine when antilock control is required.

Failure Conditions:

The EBCM performs two types of tests on the speed sensor to check continuity and output. Any condition which would result in lack of continuity or output on the rear axle speed sensor circuit could result in setting DTC 35. These conditions include an open, short to ground or short to B+ in CKT 882, an open in CKT 883 or an open across the sensor coil. Conditions which cause a low output from the speed sensor, such as a shorted sensor coil or an improperly installed sensor, will also set a DTC 35.

Action Taken:

If a failure is detected which causes a speed sensor DTC 35 to set, antilock braking is disabled and the EBCM turns "ON" the "ANTILOCK" indicator for the remainder of the ignition cycle. If the failure is intermittent, the EBCM will enable the system at the next ignition cycle and a history DTC 35 will be present.

Important

- The rear axle speed sensor is located in the rear axle housing. In order to prevent electromagnetic interference from disturbing the speed sensor signal, the sensor wires are twisted together 9 times for every foot of wire. If wiring repairs are necessary, refer to "Wiring Repair Procedures" in SECTION 8A-5.

Test Description: Number(s) below refer to circled number(s) on the diagnostic chart.

1. Checks for a correct resistance reading of the sensor itself.
2. Checks for a short to ground internal to the sensor.
3. Checks for a short between the wires for the rear axle speed sensor.
4. Checks for a short to B+ on either CKT 882 or CKT 883.
5. Checks for a short to ground on either CKT 882 or CKT 883.
6. Checks for an open circuit or high resistance in CKT 882 or CKT 883.
7. Checks for an "Intermittent" in the rear axle speed sensor circuitry. If no intermittent is found in the wiring, it may be in the sensor itself. Replace the sensor and road test the vehicle. If the code returns, replace the EBCM.

Diagnostic Aids:

Setting of speed sensor DTCs may be caused by improperly mounted sensors or improper wire routing. Verify that the sensor is properly mounted and free of foreign material such as metallic particles, dirt or grease. If rear axle service was performed and the rear axle toothed wheel was removed it must be replaced. Verify that sensor wires are properly routed and secure. Improper rear axle wheel speed sensor wire routing may cause DTC 21 and/or DTC 25 to set. To aid in troubleshooting intermittent conditions the Tech 1 can be used while test driving the vehicle however, antilock braking will be disabled. Refer to the Tech 1 Brake Cartridge Operators Manual for additional information. If this does not identify the intermittent, wet the speed sensor harness on the underside of the vehicle and road test monitoring wheel speeds with the Tech 1.

GC402920047300BX

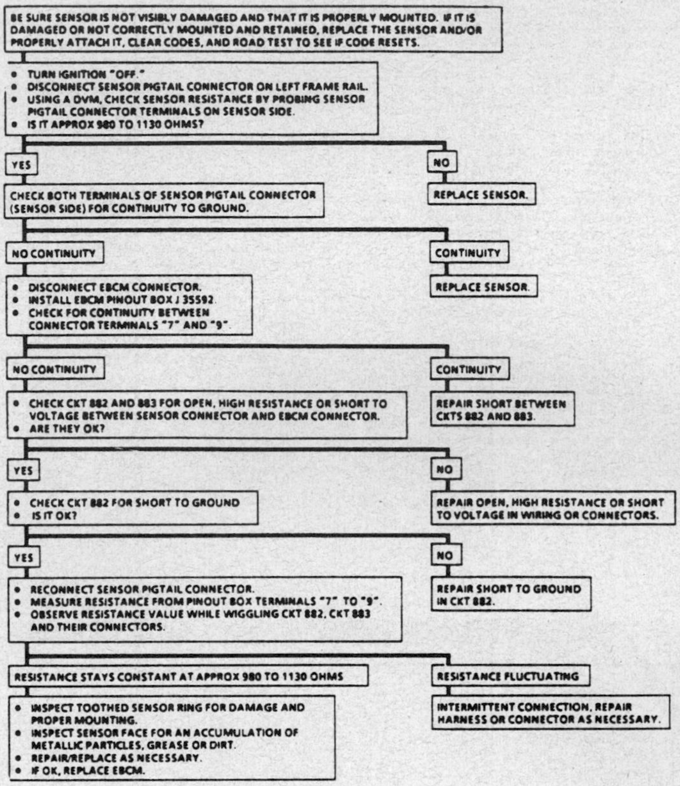
BE SURE SENSOR IS NOT VISIBLY DAMAGED AND THAT IT IS PROPERLY MOUNTED. IF IT IS DAMAGED OR NOT CORRECTLY MOUNTED AND RETAINED, REPLACE THE SENSOR AND/OR PROPERLY ATTACH IT, CLEAR CODES, AND ROAD TEST TO SEE IF CODE RESETS.
• TURN IGNITION "OFF."
• DISCONNECT SENSOR PIGTAIL CONNECTOR ON LEFT FRAME RAIL.
• USING A DVM, CHECK SENSOR RESISTANCE BY PROBING SENSOR PIGTAIL CONNECTOR TERMINALS ON SENSOR SIDE.
• IS IT APPROX 980 TO 1130 OHMS?
YES
NO
CHECK BOTH TERMINALS OF SENSOR PIGTAIL CONNECTOR (SENSOR SIDE) FOR CONTINUITY TO GROUND.
REPLACE SENSOR.
NO CONTINUITY
CONTINUITY
• DISCONNECT EBCM CONNECTOR.
• INSTALL EBCM PINOUT BOX J 35592.
• CHECK FOR CONTINUITY BETWEEN CONNECTOR TERMINALS "7" AND "9".
REPLACE SENSOR.
NO CONTINUITY
CONTINUITY
• CHECK CKT 882 AND 883 FOR OPEN, HIGH RESISTANCE OR SHORT TO VOLTAGE BETWEEN SENSOR CONNECTOR AND EBCM CONNECTOR.
• ARE THEY OK?
REPAIR SHORT BETWEEN CKTS 882 AND 883.
YES
NO
• CHECK CKT 882 FOR SHORT TO GROUND
• IS IT OK?
REPAIR OPEN, HIGH RESISTANCE OR SHORT TO VOLTAGE IN WIRING OR CONNECTORS.
YES
NO
• RECONNECT SENSOR PIGTAIL CONNECTOR.
• MEASURE RESISTANCE FROM PINOUT BOX TERMINALS "7" TO "9".
• OBSERVE RESISTANCE VALUE WHILE WIGGLING CKT 882, CKT 883 AND THEIR CONNECTORS.
REPAIR SHORT TO GROUND IN CKT 882.
RESISTANCE STAYS CONSTANT AT APPROX 980 TO 1130 OHMS
RESISTANCE FLUCTUATING
• INSPECT TOOTHED SENSOR RING FOR DAMAGE AND PROPER MOUNTING.
• INSPECT SENSOR FACE FOR AN ACCUMULATION OF METALLIC PARTICLES, GREASE OR DIRT.
• REPAIR/REPLACE AS NECESSARY.
• IF OK, REPLACE EBCM.
INTERMITTENT CONNECTION. REPAIR HARNESS OR CONNECTOR AS NECESSARY.

GC402920047300CX

Fig. 29 Code 35: Rear Axle Speed Sensor Fault. 1992–93 Caprice, Custom Cruiser & Roadmaster

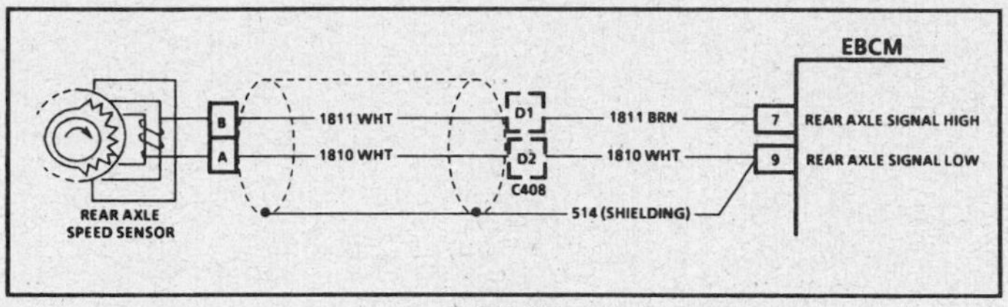
EBCM
1811 WHT
1810 WHT
B
A
D1
D2
C408
1811 BRN
1810 WHT
7
9
REAR AXLE SIGNAL HIGH
REAR AXLE SIGNAL LOW
514 (SHIELDING)
REAR AXLE
SPEED SENSOR

DTC 35

REAR WHEEL SPEED SENSOR CIRCUIT MALFUNCTION

Circuit Description:

As the differential pinion gear turns, the speed sensor creates an AC voltage as the toothed ring (mounted to the differential pinion gear) rotates by the stationary sensor. The sensor consists of a permanent magnet and coil generating voltage by magnetic induction. The frequency and voltage of the induced signal is proportional to rear axle speed.

The EBCM uses the speed sensor signal to calculate vehicle reference speed, individual speed, acceleration and slip values for the rear wheels which determine when antilock control is required.

DTC 35 Will Set When: There is a short to voltage or ground in CKT 1811 or 1810 or a malfunctioning speed sensor. The testing for this malfunction occurs when the vehicle is in motion; it will not set with the ignition "ON" and the vehicle at rest.

Action Taken: If a malfunction is detected which causes a speed sensor DTC 35 to set, antilock braking is disabled and the EBCM turns "ON" the ABS warning lamp for the remainder of the ignition cycle. If the malfunction is intermittent, the EBCM will enable the system at the next ignition cycle and a history DTC 35 will be present.

Important

- The rear axle speed sensor is located in the rear axle housing. In order to prevent electromagnetic interference from disturbing the speed sensor signal, the sensor wires are twisted together 9 times for every foot of wire.

DTC Chart Test Description: Number(s) below refer to circled number(s) on the diagnostic chart.

1. Checks for a short to battery in either of the speed sensor circuit wires.
2. Checks for a short between the speed sensor circuit wires.
3. Checks for a short to ground in the speed sensor input circuit wire. The ground may be either a "hard" short to ground, or a resistive (partial) short. A short with a resistance less than 2 megohms, though not a hard short, can still cause DTC 35 to set.
4. Checks if the DTC resets during a road test. If so, since tests 1-4 have validated that all of the circuitry and components are good, intermittent malfunctions are suspected.
5. Checks wiring and connectors for intermittents.
6. Checks for sensor mounting, toothed wheel, and rear wheel bearing malfunctions which may be causing the malfunction. Check the toothed wheel for any large grooves, gouges, marks, etc. that might influence the tooth's signal at the wheel speed sensor. Also check for a buildup of foreign material in the gaps between teeth in the toothed wheel; this material may cause this malfunction.
7. Replace the speed sensor assembly, as it is likely the cause of a DTC reset experienced during the road test, since other portions of the circuit have checked out OK.
8. Ensures DTC was not set due to electromagnetic interference.

Diagnostic Aids: Setting of speed sensor DTCs may be caused by improperly mounted sensors or improper wire routing. Verify that the sensor is properly mounted and free of foreign material such as metallic particles, dirt or grease. If rear axle [illegible] performed and the rear axle toothed wheel was removed it must be replaced. Verify that sensor wires are properly routed and secure. Improper rear axle wheel speed sensor wire routing may cause DTC 21 and/or DTC 25 to set. To aid in troubleshooting intermittent conditions the Tech 1 can be used while test driving the vehicle however, antilock braking will be disabled. Refer to the Tech 1 Brake Cartridge Operators Manual for additional information. If this does not identify the intermittent, wet the speed sensor harness on the underside of the vehicle and road test monitoring wheel speeds with the Tech 1.

GC402940092500AX

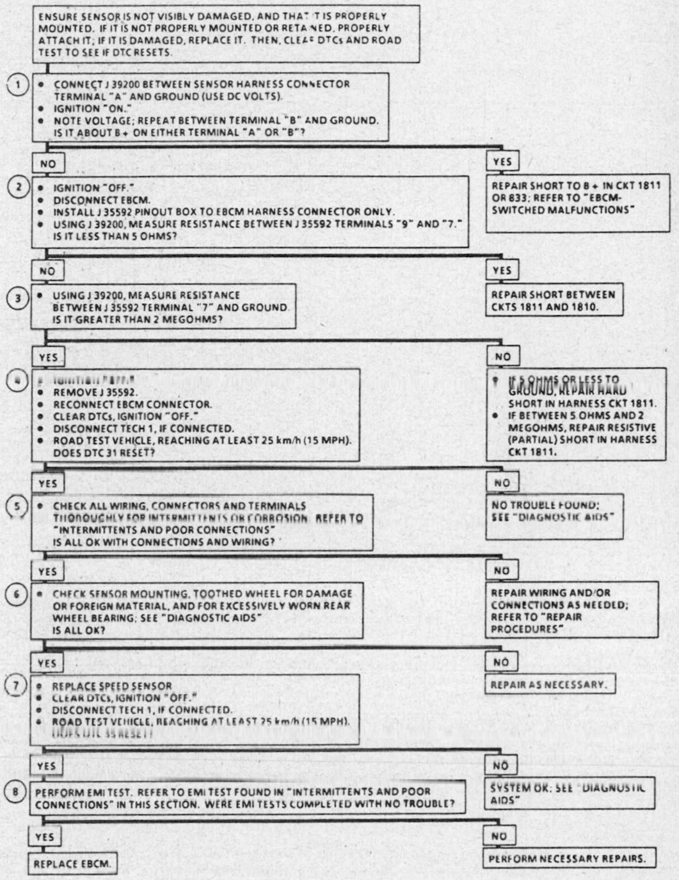
ENSURE SENSOR IS NOT VISIBLY DAMAGED, AND THAT IT IS PROPERLY MOUNTED. IF IT IS NOT PROPERLY MOUNTED OR RETAINED, PROPERLY ATTACH IT; IF IT IS DAMAGED, REPLACE IT. THEN, CLEAR DTCs AND ROAD TEST TO SEE IF DTC RESETS.
1
• CONNECT J 39200 BETWEEN SENSOR HARNESS CONNECTOR TERMINAL "A" AND GROUND (USE DC VOLTS).
• IGNITION "ON."
• NOTE VOLTAGE; REPEAT BETWEEN TERMINAL "B" AND GROUND. IS IT ABOUT B+ ON EITHER TERMINAL "A" OR "B"?
NO
YES
REPAIR SHORT TO B+ IN CKT 1811 OR 833; REFER TO "EBCM-SWITCHED MALFUNCTIONS"
2
• IGNITION "OFF."
• DISCONNECT EBCM.
• INSTALL J 35592 PINOUT BOX TO EBCM HARNESS CONNECTOR ONLY.
• USING J 39200, MEASURE RESISTANCE BETWEEN J 35592 TERMINALS "9" AND "7." IS IT LESS THAN 5 OHMS?
NO
YES
REPAIR SHORT BETWEEN CKTS 1811 AND 1810.
3
• USING J 39200, MEASURE RESISTANCE BETWEEN J 35592 TERMINAL "7" AND GROUND. IS IT GREATER THAN 2 MEGOHMS?
YES
NO
• IF 5 OHMS OR LESS TO GROUND, REPAIR HARD SHORT IN HARNESS CKT 1811.
• IF BETWEEN 5 OHMS AND 2 MEGOHMS, REPAIR RESISTIVE (PARTIAL) SHORT IN HARNESS CKT 1811.
4
• REMOVE J 35592.
• RECONNECT EBCM CONNECTOR.
• CLEAR DTCs, IGNITION "OFF."
• DISCONNECT TECH 1, IF CONNECTED.
• ROAD TEST VEHICLE, REACHING AT LEAST 25 km/h (15 MPH). DOES DTC 31 RESET?
YES
NO
NO TROUBLE FOUND; SEE "DIAGNOSTIC AIDS"
5
• CHECK ALL WIRING, CONNECTORS AND TERMINALS THOROUGHLY FOR INTERMITTENTS OR CORROSION. REFER TO "INTERMITTENTS AND POOR CONNECTIONS" IS ALL OK WITH CONNECTIONS AND WIRING?
YES
NO
REPAIR WIRING AND/OR CONNECTIONS AS NEEDED; REFER TO "REPAIR PROCEDURES"
6
• CHECK SENSOR MOUNTING, TOOTHED WHEEL FOR DAMAGE OR FOREIGN MATERIAL, AND FOR EXCESSIVELY WORN REAR WHEEL BEARING; SEE "DIAGNOSTIC AIDS" IS ALL OK?
YES
NO
REPAIR AS NECESSARY.
7
• REPLACE SPEED SENSOR
• CLEAR DTCs, IGNITION "OFF."
• DISCONNECT TECH 1, IF CONNECTED.
• ROAD TEST VEHICLE, REACHING AT LEAST 25 km/h (15 MPH).
YES
NO
SYSTEM OK; SEE "DIAGNOSTIC AIDS"
8
PERFORM EMI TEST. REFER TO EMI TEST FOUND IN "INTERMITTENTS AND POOR CONNECTIONS" IN THIS SECTION. WERE EMI TESTS COMPLETED WITH NO TROUBLE?
YES
REPLACE EBCM.
NO
PERFORM NECESSARY REPAIRS.

GC402940092500BX

Fig. 30 Code 35: Rear Wheel Speed Sensor Circuit Fault. 1994 Caprice, Impala SS & Roadmaster

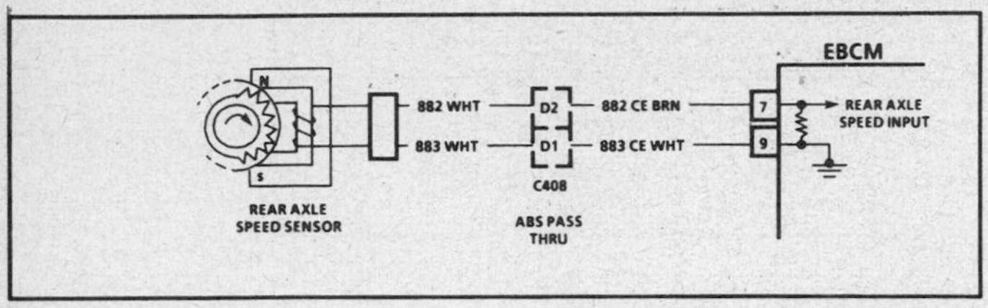
EBCM
882 WHT
D2
882 CE BRN
7
REAR AXLE
SPEED INPUT
883 WHT
D1
883 CE WHT
9
C408
REAR AXLE
SPEED SENSOR
ABS PASS
THRU

GC402920047400AX

CODE 36

REAR AXLE TOOTHED WHEEL (FREQUENCY ERROR)

Circuit Description:

As the differential pinion gear turns, the speed sensor creates an AC voltage as the toothed ring (mounted to the differential pinion gear) rotates by the stationary sensor. The sensor consists of a permanent magnet and coil generating voltage by magnetic induction. The frequency and voltage of the induced signal is proportional to rear axle speed.

The EBCM uses the speed sensor signal to calculate vehicle reference speed, individual speed, acceleration and slip values for the rear wheels which determine when antilock control is required.

Failure Conditions:

Code 36 will set if improper speed signals are being generated by the toothed wheel. Causes of improper speed signals include; an incorrect number of teeth or damaged teeth present on the toothed wheel, toothed wheel or sensor face covered with dirt, grease or metallic particles that may impair magnetic induction.

Code 36 may also set if the mini-spare tire has previously been used or the size of the tires on the vehicle differ. In addition to Code 36, Codes 22 and 26 may also set if the mini-spare tire has been used. If it is known that the spare tire was used, clear codes and test drive the vehicle again. Verify that codes do not set.

Action Taken:

If a failure is detected which causes a speed sensor Code 36 to set, antilock braking is disabled and the EBCM turns "ON" the "Antilock" indicator for the remainder of the ignition cycle. If the failure is intermittent, the EBCM will enable the system at the next ignition cycle and a history Code 36 will be present.

Test Description: Number(s) below refer to circled number(s) on the diagnostic chart.

1. Checks for properly mounted sensor and mounting torque.
2. Checks for a physical problem with the toothed wheel.
3. Checks for an improper sensor ring.

Diagnostic Aids:

Check for a buildup of foreign material in the gaps between teeth on the toothed wheel; this material may cause this error.

Also, check the toothed wheel for any large grooves, gouges, marks, etc., that might influence the tooth's signal at the speed sensor.

Inspect speed sensor for damage or contamination. If OK, and Code 36 is still present, refer to Code 35 chart.

GC402920047400BX

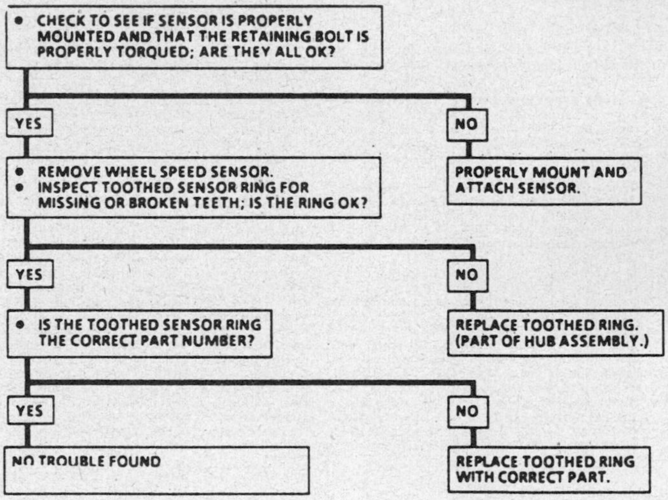
• CHECK TO SEE IF SENSOR IS PROPERLY MOUNTED AND THAT THE RETAINING BOLT IS PROPERLY TORQUED; ARE THEY ALL OK?
YES
NO
• REMOVE WHEEL SPEED SENSOR.
• INSPECT TOOTHED SENSOR RING FOR MISSING OR BROKEN TEETH; IS THE RING OK?
PROPERLY MOUNT AND ATTACH SENSOR.
YES
NO
• IS THE TOOTHED SENSOR RING THE CORRECT PART NUMBER?
REPLACE TOOTHED RING. (PART OF HUB ASSEMBLY.)
YES
NO
NO TROUBLE FOUND
REPLACE TOOTHED RING WITH CORRECT PART.

GC402920047400CX

Fig. 31 Code 36: Rear Axle Toothed Wheel Frequency Error. 1992 Caprice, Custom Cruiser & Roadmaster

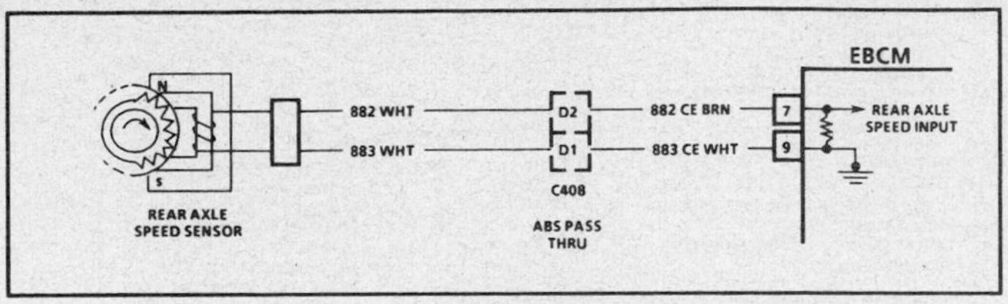
EBCM
882 WHT
883 WHT
D2
D1
C408
882 CE BRN
883 CE WHT
7
9
REAR AXLE SPEED INPUT
N
S
REAR AXLE SPEED SENSOR
ABS PASS THRU

DTC 36

REAR AXLE TOOTHED RING (FREQUENCY ERROR)

Circuit Description:

As the differential pinion gear turns, the speed sensor creates an AC voltage as the toothed ring (mounted to the differential pinion gear) rotates by the stationary sensor. The sensor consists of a permanent magnet and coil generating voltage by magnetic induction. The frequency and voltage of the induced signal is proportional to rear axle speed.

The EBCM uses the speed sensor signal to calculate vehicle reference speed, individual speed, acceleration and slip values for the rear wheels which determine when antilock control is required.

Failure Conditions:

DTC 36 will set if improper speed signals are being generated by the toothed ring. Causes of improper speed signals include; an incorrect number of teeth or damaged teeth present on the toothed ring, toothed ring or sensor face covered with dirt, grease or metallic particles that may impair magnetic induction.

DTC 36 may also set if the mini-spare tire has previously been used or the size of the tires on the vehicle differ. In addition to DTC 36, DTCs 22 and 26 may also set if the mini-spare tire has been used. If it is known that the spare tire was used, clear DTCs and test drive the vehicle again. Verify that DTCs do not set.

Action Taken:

If a failure is detected which causes a speed sensor DTC 36 to set, antilock braking is disabled and the EBCM turns "ON" the "ANTILOCK" indicator for the remainder of the ignition cycle. If the failure is intermittent, the EBCM will enable the system at the next ignition cycle and a history DTC 36 will be present.

Test Description: Number(s) below refer to circled number(s) on the diagnostic chart.

1. Checks for properly mounted sensor and mounting torque.
2. Checks for a physical problem with the toothed ring.
3. Checks for contamination on sensor face or toothed ring.

Diagnostic Aids:

Check for a buildup of foreign material in the gaps between teeth on the toothed ring; this material may cause this error.

Also, check the toothed ring for any large grooves, gouges, marks, etc., that might influence the tooth's signal at the speed sensor.

Inspect speed sensor for damage or contamination. If OK, and DTC 36 is still present, refer to DTC 35 chart.

GC402930047500AX

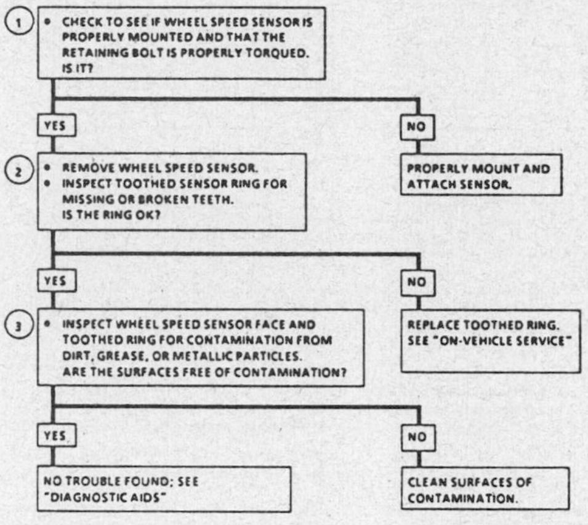
1
• CHECK TO SEE IF WHEEL SPEED SENSOR IS PROPERLY MOUNTED AND THAT THE RETAINING BOLT IS PROPERLY TORQUED. IS IT?
YES
NO
PROPERLY MOUNT AND ATTACH SENSOR.
2
• REMOVE WHEEL SPEED SENSOR.
• INSPECT TOOTHED SENSOR RING FOR MISSING OR BROKEN TEETH. IS THE RING OK?
YES
NO
REPLACE TOOTHED RING. SEE "ON-VEHICLE SERVICE"
3
• INSPECT WHEEL SPEED SENSOR FACE AND TOOTHED RING FOR CONTAMINATION FROM DIRT, GREASE, OR METALLIC PARTICLES. ARE THE SURFACES FREE OF CONTAMINATION?
YES
NO
NO TROUBLE FOUND; SEE "DIAGNOSTIC AIDS"
CLEAN SURFACES OF CONTAMINATION.

GC402930047500BX

Fig. 32 Code 36: Rear Axle Toothed Wheel Frequency Error. 1993 Caprice & Roadmaster

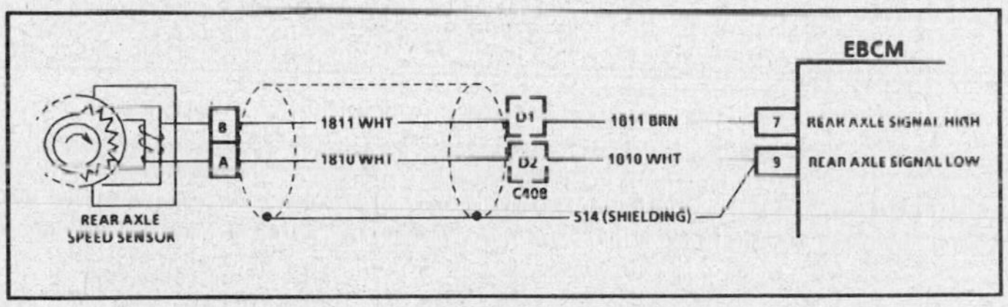
EBCM
1811 WHT
1810 WHT
B
A
D1
D2
C408
1811 BRN
1810 WHT
7
9
REAR AXLE SIGNAL HIGH
REAR AXLE SIGNAL LOW
514 (SHIELDING)
REAR AXLE SPEED SENSOR

DTC 37

REAR WHEEL SPEED SENSOR CIRCUIT CONTINUITY MALFUNCTION

Circuit Description:

The toothed wheel generates a voltage pulse as it moves past the sensor; each tooth-gap-tooth series on the wheel generates these pulses. The frequency of these pulses is used by the EBCM to determine wheel speed. The amount of voltage generated in each pulse depends on the air gap between the sensor and the toothed wheel, and on wheel speed.

DTC 37 Will Set When: There is a short to voltage or an open in CKT 1811 or 1810, or a malfunctioning speed sensor. The testing for this malfunction occurs with the ignition "ON" and the vehicle at rest.

Action Taken: Antilock braking is disabled. The ABS warning lamp will be "ON" for the remainder of the ignition cycle. If the malfunction is intermittent, the EBCM will enable the system at the next ignition cycle and a history DTC 37 will be present.

DTC Chart Test Description: Number(s) below refer to circled number(s) on the diagnostic chart.

1. Checks for a short to battery in either of the speed sensor circuit wires.
2. Checks for an open in both the speed sensor circuit wires.
3. Manipulates wiring and connectors, trying to induce a intermittent malfunction not currently present.
4. This test checks if the DTC resets on key up. If so, since tests 1-4 have validated that the circuitry and components are good, the speed sensor may be causing the malfunction.
5. Checks if DTC 35 sets during a road test.
6. DTC 37 sets when the vehicle is at rest; DTC 35 sets with a malfunction in the speed sensor circuitry with the vehicle in motion. If malfunctions are still present, DTC 35 would set during the road test, not a 37. If the DTC 37 sets at this point, the DTC 35 diagnostics should be used.
7. The wheel speed sensor may be causing an intermittent malfunction. If DTC 37 resets after sensor replacement, the EBCM must be concluding there is a malfunction present in the speed sensor circuit when there is not.
8. Ensures DTC was not set due to electromagnetic interference.

Diagnostic Aids: Be sure the speed sensor wiring is properly routed and retained. This will help prevent false signals due to electrical noise being picked up by the wiring.

It is very important that a thorough inspection of the wiring and connectors be performed. Failure to carefully and fully inspect wiring and connectors may result in misdiagnosis, causing part replacement with reappearance of the malfunction.

GC402940092600AX

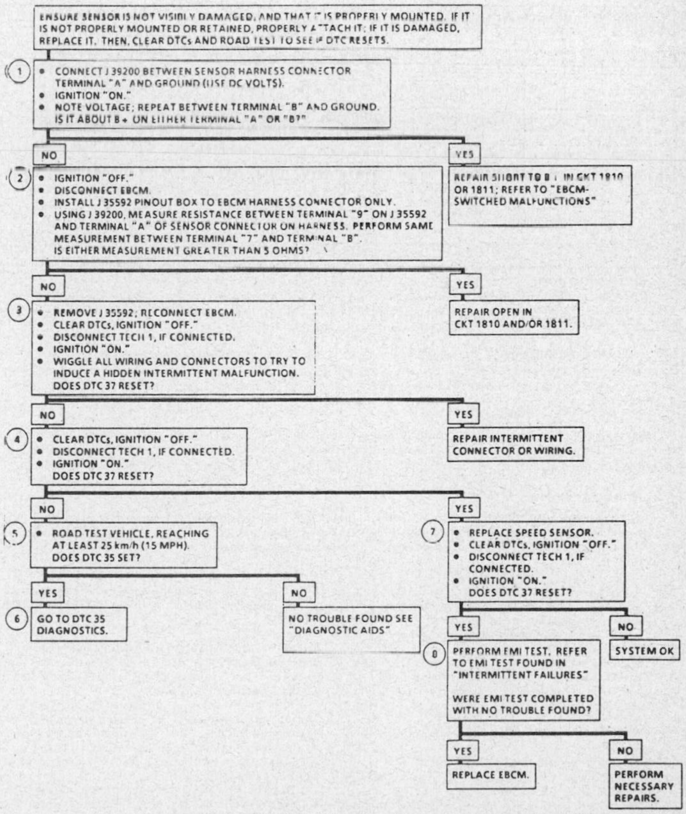
ENSURE SENSOR IS NOT VISIBLY DAMAGED, AND THAT IT IS PROPERLY MOUNTED. IF IT IS NOT PROPERLY MOUNTED OR RETAINED, PROPERLY ATTACH IT; IF IT IS DAMAGED, REPLACE IT. THEN, CLEAR DTCs AND ROAD TEST TO SEE IF DTC RESETS.
1
• CONNECT J 39200 BETWEEN SENSOR HARNESS CONNECTOR TERMINAL "A" AND GROUND (USE DC VOLTS).
• IGNITION "ON."
• NOTE VOLTAGE; REPEAT BETWEEN TERMINAL "B" AND GROUND. IS IT ABOUT B+ ON EITHER TERMINAL "A" OR "B?"
NO
YES
REPAIR SHORT TO B+ IN CKT 1810 OR 1811; REFER TO "EBCM-SWITCHED MALFUNCTIONS"
2
• IGNITION "OFF."
• DISCONNECT EBCM.
• INSTALL J 35592 PINOUT BOX TO EBCM HARNESS CONNECTOR ONLY.
• USING J 39200, MEASURE RESISTANCE BETWEEN TERMINAL "9" ON J 35592 AND TERMINAL "A" OF SENSOR CONNECTOR ON HARNESS. PERFORM SAME MEASUREMENT BETWEEN TERMINAL "7" AND TERMINAL "B". IS EITHER MEASUREMENT GREATER THAN 5 OHMS?
NO
YES
REPAIR OPEN IN CKT 1810 AND/OR 1811.
3
• REMOVE J 35592; RECONNECT EBCM.
• CLEAR DTCs, IGNITION "OFF."
• DISCONNECT TECH 1, IF CONNECTED.
• IGNITION "ON."
• WIGGLE ALL WIRING AND CONNECTORS TO TRY TO INDUCE A HIDDEN INTERMITTENT MALFUNCTION. DOES DTC 37 RESET?
NO
YES
REPAIR INTERMITTENT CONNECTOR OR WIRING.
4
• CLEAR DTCs, IGNITION "OFF."
• DISCONNECT TECH 1, IF CONNECTED.
• IGNITION "ON." DOES DTC 37 RESET?
NO
YES
5
• ROAD TEST VEHICLE, REACHING AT LEAST 25 km/h (15 MPH). DOES DTC 35 SET?
YES
NO
6
GO TO DTC 35 DIAGNOSTICS.
NO TROUBLE FOUND SEE "DIAGNOSTIC AIDS"
7
• REPLACE SPEED SENSOR.
• CLEAR DTCs, IGNITION "OFF."
• DISCONNECT TECH 1, IF CONNECTED.
• IGNITION "ON." DOES DTC 37 RESET?
YES
NO
SYSTEM OK
PERFORM EMI TEST. REFER TO EMI TEST FOUND IN "INTERMITTENT FAILURES"
WERE EMI TEST COMPLETED WITH NO TROUBLE FOUND?
YES
NO
REPLACE EBCM.
PERFORM NECESSARY REPAIRS.

GC402940092600BX

Fig. 33 Code 37, Rear Wheel Speed Sensor Circuit Continuity Fault. 1994 Caprice, Impala SS & Roadmaster

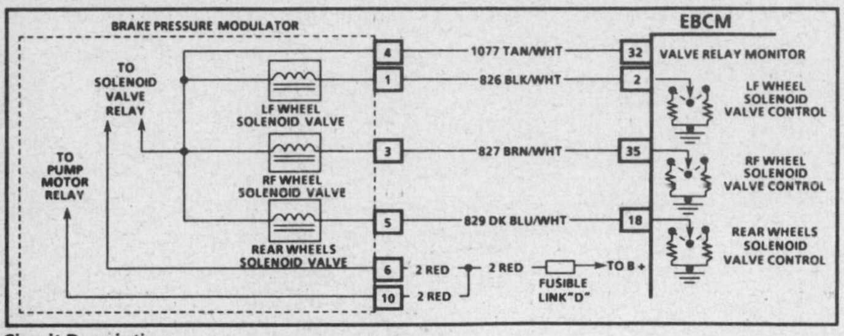
BRAKE PRESSURE MODULATOR
EBCM
TO SOLENOID VALVE RELAY
TO PUMP MOTOR RELAY
LF WHEEL SOLENOID VALVE
RF WHEEL SOLENOID VALVE
REAR WHEELS SOLENOID VALVE
1077 TAN/WHT
826 BLK/WHT
827 BRN/WHT
829 DK BLU/WHT
2 RED
2 RED
2 RED
FUSIBLE LINK "D"
TO B+
VALVE RELAY MONITOR
LF WHEEL SOLENOID VALVE CONTROL
RF WHEEL SOLENOID VALVE CONTROL
REAR WHEELS SOLENOID VALVE CONTROL

Circuit Description:
With the ignition in "Run," "Bulb Test" or "Start," the EBCM applies voltage to the coil of the solenoid valve relay. The EBCM will complete an internal self-check before providing ground to the coil. Once energized, the relay will provide B + to the solenoid valves.

Failure Conditions: Code 41 will set when the expected position of the right front solenoid valve does not match the commanded position from the EBCM (if valve line voltage does not match expected value). Conditions which could cause Code 41 to set are damage to the right front solenoid, an open or short to ground or battery voltage on CKT 827.

Action Taken: If a failure is detected which causes a valve Code 41 to set, antilock braking is disabled and the EBCM turns "ON" the "Antilock" indicator for the remainder of the ignition cycle. If the failure is intermittent, the EBCM will enable the system at the next ignition cycle and a history Code 41 will be present.

Important
- The Auto test (as described under "ABS Self Diagnostics") is performed once during each ignition cycle when the vehicle reaches approximately 4 mph. This test may be heard and felt while it is taking place and should be considered a normal mode of operation. This test can also be performed by using the Tech 1 in "ABS Tests" mode F4.

Test Description: Number(s) below refer to circled number(s) on the diagnostic chart.
1. This test checks the integrity of CKTs 827 and 1077, the RF Solenoid Valve Circuitry internal to the Brake Pressure Modulator and the RF Solenoid Valve Coil.
2. This test checks for a short to ground in CKT 827.
3. This test checks for a short to B + in CKT 827.
4. This test checks for connector or wiring problems which may cause an intermittent condition.
5. This test uses the Tech 1 to check for proper Solenoid Valve operation.
6. This test determines whether the code was set by an intermittent condition or an EBCM fault.
7. This test determines whether the problem revealed in Step 1 is due to a faulty Brake Pressure Modulator or a wiring problem.
8. This test determines whether the problem is an open CKT 827 or a short from CKT 827 to CKT 1077.

Diagnostic Aids:

All tests which require a connection to Pinout Box terminal "20" are using this terminal as ground. This assumes that the integrity of ground CKT 151 has been maintained.

It is important that a thorough inspection of the wiring and connectors be performed prior to road testing the vehicle. This code can only be set when the vehicle is in motion. Failure to properly inspect wiring and connectors may result in a misdiagnosis of a faulty Brake Pressure Modulator or EBCM.

If Codes 41 and 45 are both set the fault is likely to be a short to B + on CKT 827.

If Codes 41 and 55 are both set the fault is likely to be a short to B + on CKT 829.

GC402920047600AX

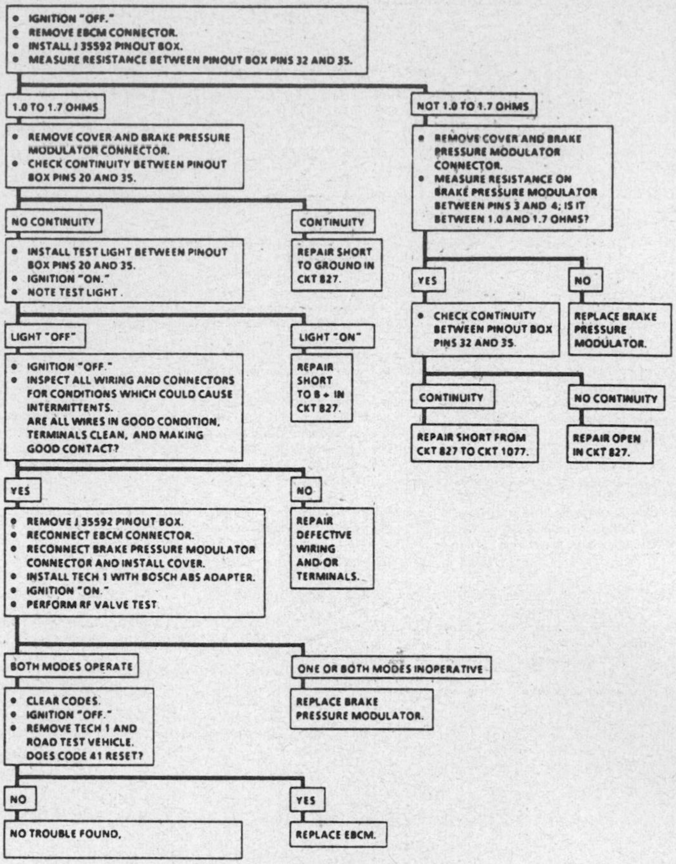
• IGNITION "OFF."
• REMOVE EBCM CONNECTOR.
• INSTALL J 35592 PINOUT BOX.
• MEASURE RESISTANCE BETWEEN PINOUT BOX PINS 32 AND 35.
1.0 TO 1.7 OHMS
NOT 1.0 TO 1.7 OHMS
• REMOVE COVER AND BRAKE PRESSURE MODULATOR CONNECTOR.
• CHECK CONTINUITY BETWEEN PINOUT BOX PINS 20 AND 35.
• REMOVE COVER AND BRAKE PRESSURE MODULATOR CONNECTOR.
• MEASURE RESISTANCE ON BRAKE PRESSURE MODULATOR BETWEEN PINS 3 AND 4; IS IT BETWEEN 1.0 AND 1.7 OHMS?
NO CONTINUITY
CONTINUITY
• INSTALL TEST LIGHT BETWEEN PINOUT BOX PINS 20 AND 35.
• IGNITION "ON."
• NOTE TEST LIGHT.
REPAIR SHORT TO GROUND IN CKT 827.
YES
NO
• CHECK CONTINUITY BETWEEN PINOUT BOX PINS 32 AND 35.
REPLACE BRAKE PRESSURE MODULATOR.
LIGHT "OFF"
LIGHT "ON"
• IGNITION "OFF."
• INSPECT ALL WIRING AND CONNECTORS FOR CONDITIONS WHICH COULD CAUSE INTERMITTENTS.
ARE ALL WIRES IN GOOD CONDITION, TERMINALS CLEAN, AND MAKING GOOD CONTACT?
REPAIR SHORT TO B + IN CKT 827.
CONTINUITY
NO CONTINUITY
REPAIR SHORT FROM CKT 827 TO CKT 1077.
REPAIR OPEN IN CKT 827.
YES
NO
• REMOVE J 35592 PINOUT BOX.
• RECONNECT EBCM CONNECTOR.
• RECONNECT BRAKE PRESSURE MODULATOR CONNECTOR AND INSTALL COVER.
• INSTALL TECH 1 WITH BOSCH ABS ADAPTER.
• IGNITION "ON."
• PERFORM RF VALVE TEST.
REPAIR DEFECTIVE WIRING AND/OR TERMINALS.
BOTH MODES OPERATE
ONE OR BOTH MODES INOPERATIVE
• CLEAR CODES.
• IGNITION "OFF."
• REMOVE TECH 1 AND ROAD TEST VEHICLE.
DOES CODE 41 RESET?
REPLACE BRAKE PRESSURE MODULATOR.
NO
YES
NO TROUBLE FOUND.
REPLACE EBCM.

GC402920047600BX

Fig. 34 Code 41: RF Solenoid Valve Fault. 1992–93 Caprice, Custom Cruiser & Roadmaster

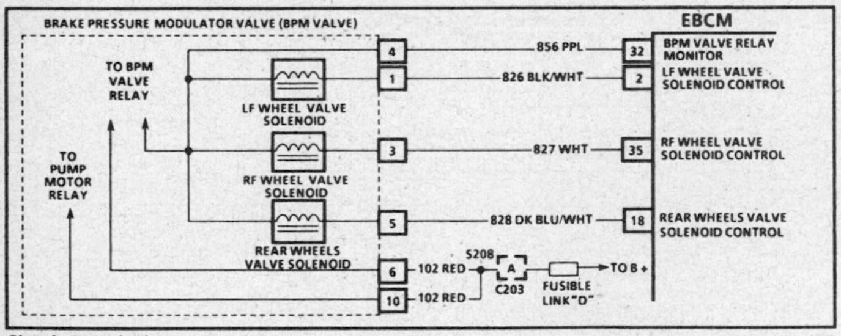
BRAKE PRESSURE MODULATOR VALVE (BPM VALVE)
EBCM
TO BPM VALVE RELAY
TO PUMP MOTOR RELAY
LF WHEEL VALVE SOLENOID
RF WHEEL VALVE SOLENOID
REAR WHEELS VALVE SOLENOID
856 PPL
826 BLK/WHT
827 WHT
828 DK BLU/WHT
102 RED
102 RED
S208
C203
FUSIBLE LINK "D"
TO B+
BPM VALVE RELAY MONITOR
LF WHEEL VALVE SOLENOID CONTROL
RF WHEEL VALVE SOLENOID CONTROL
REAR WHEELS VALVE SOLENOID CONTROL

Circuit Description:
With the ignition in "Run," "Bulb Test" or "Start," the EBCM applies voltage to the coil of the BPM valve relay. The EBCM will complete an internal self check before providing ground to the coil. Once energized, the relay will provide B + to the valve solenoids.

DTC 41 Will Set When: The expected position of the right front valve solenoid does not match the commanded position from the EBCM (if valve line voltage does not match expected value). Conditions which could cause DTC 41 to set are damage to the right front solenoid, an open or short to ground or battery voltage on CKT 827.

Action Taken: If a malfunction is detected which causes a valve DTC 41 to set, antilock braking is disabled and the EBCM turns "ON" the ABS warning lamp for the remainder of the ignition cycle. If the malfunction is intermittent, the EBCM will enable the system at the next ignition cycle and a history DTC 41 will be present.

Important
- The auto test (as described under "ABS Self Diagnostics") is performed once during each ignition cycle when the vehicle reaches approximately 4 mph. This test may be heard and felt while it is taking place and should be considered a normal mode of operation. This test can also be performed by using the Tech 1 in "Misc Tests" mode F4.

DTC Chart Test Description: Number(s) below refer to circled number(s) on the diagnostic chart.
1. This test checks the integrity of CKTs 827 and 856, the RF valve solenoid circuitry internal to the BPM valve and the RF valve solenoid coil.
2. This test checks for a short to ground in CKT 827.
3. This test checks for a short to B + in CKT 827.
4. This test checks for connector or wiring malfunctions which may cause an intermittent condition.
5. This test uses the Tech 1 to check for proper valve solenoid operation.
6. This test determines whether the DTC was set by an intermittent condition or an EBCM malfunction.
7. This test determines whether the malfunction revealed in Step 1 is due to a malfunctioning BPM valve or a wiring malfunction.
8. This test determines whether the malfunction is an open CKT 827 or a short from CKT 827 to CKT 856.

Diagnostic Aids: All tests which require a connection to Pinout Box Pin 20 are using this pin as ground. This assumes that the integrity of ground CKT 51 has been maintained.

It is important that a thorough inspection of the wiring and connectors be performed prior to road testing the vehicle. This DTC can only be set when the vehicle is in motion. Failure to properly inspect wiring and connectors may result in a misdiagnosis of a malfunctioning BPM valve or EBCM.

If DTCs 41 and 45 are both set the malfunction is likely to be a short to B + on CKT 827.

If DTCs 41 and 55 are both set the malfunction is likely to be a short to B + on CKT 828.

GC402940092700AX

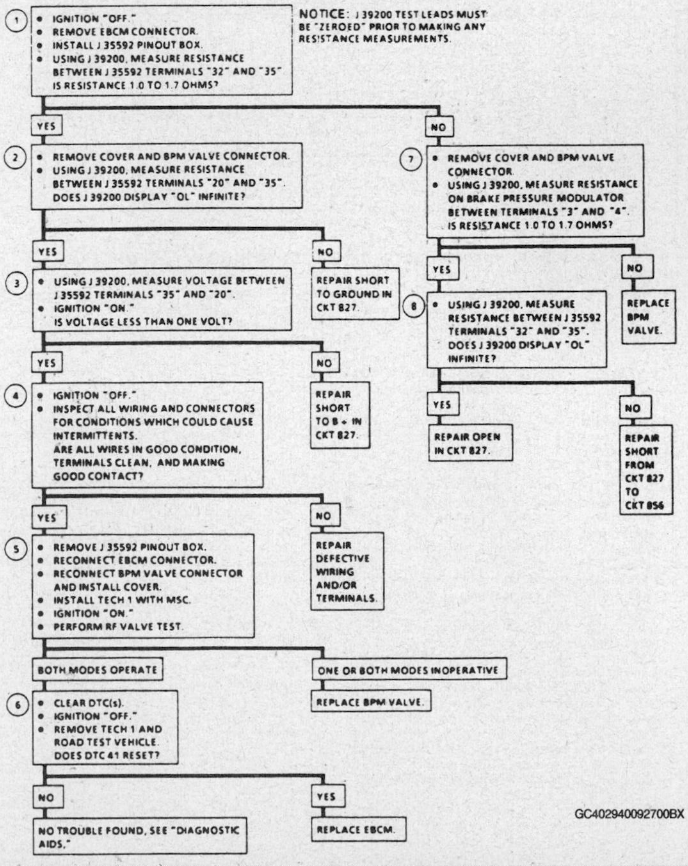
1
• IGNITION "OFF."
• REMOVE EBCM CONNECTOR.
• INSTALL J 35592 PINOUT BOX.
• USING J 39200, MEASURE RESISTANCE BETWEEN J 35592 TERMINALS "32" AND "35". IS RESISTANCE 1.0 TO 1.7 OHMS?
NOTICE: J 39200 TEST LEADS MUST BE "ZEROED" PRIOR TO MAKING ANY RESISTANCE MEASUREMENTS.
YES
NO
2
• REMOVE COVER AND BPM VALVE CONNECTOR.
• USING J 39200, MEASURE RESISTANCE BETWEEN J 35592 TERMINALS "20" AND "35". DOES J 39200 DISPLAY "OL" INFINITE?
7
• REMOVE COVER AND BPM VALVE CONNECTOR.
• USING J 39200, MEASURE RESISTANCE ON BRAKE PRESSURE MODULATOR BETWEEN TERMINALS "3" AND "4". IS RESISTANCE 1.0 TO 1.7 OHMS?
YES
NO
REPAIR SHORT TO GROUND IN CKT 827.
YES
NO
3
• USING J 39200, MEASURE VOLTAGE BETWEEN J 35592 TERMINALS "35" AND "20".
• IGNITION "ON."
IS VOLTAGE LESS THAN ONE VOLT?
8
• USING J 39200, MEASURE RESISTANCE BETWEEN J 35592 TERMINALS "32" AND "35". DOES J 39200 DISPLAY "OL" INFINITE?
REPLACE BPM VALVE.
YES
NO
YES
NO
4
• IGNITION "OFF."
• INSPECT ALL WIRING AND CONNECTORS FOR CONDITIONS WHICH COULD CAUSE INTERMITTENTS.
ARE ALL WIRES IN GOOD CONDITION, TERMINALS CLEAN, AND MAKING GOOD CONTACT?
REPAIR SHORT TO B + IN CKT 827.
REPAIR OPEN IN CKT 827.
REPAIR SHORT FROM CKT 827 TO CKT 856
YES
NO
5
• REMOVE J 35592 PINOUT BOX.
• RECONNECT EBCM CONNECTOR.
• RECONNECT BPM VALVE CONNECTOR AND INSTALL COVER.
• INSTALL TECH 1 WITH MSC.
• IGNITION "ON."
• PERFORM RF VALVE TEST.
REPAIR DEFECTIVE WIRING AND/OR TERMINALS.
BOTH MODES OPERATE
ONE OR BOTH MODES INOPERATIVE
6
• CLEAR DTC(s).
• IGNITION "OFF."
• REMOVE TECH 1 AND ROAD TEST VEHICLE.
DOES DTC 41 RESET?
REPLACE BPM VALVE.
NO
YES
NO TROUBLE FOUND, SEE "DIAGNOSTIC AIDS."
REPLACE EBCM.

GC402940092700BX

Fig. 35 Code 41: RF Solenoid Valve Fault. 1994 Caprice, Impala SS & Roadmaster

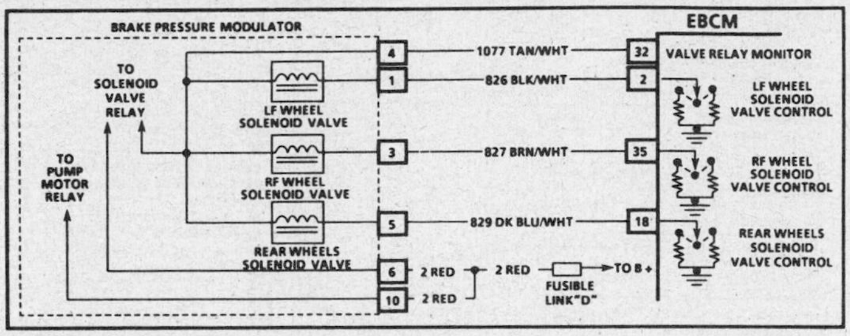
BRAKE PRESSURE MODULATOR
EBCM
TO SOLENOID VALVE RELAY
LF WHEEL SOLENOID VALVE
TO PUMP MOTOR RELAY
RF WHEEL SOLENOID VALVE
REAR WHEELS SOLENOID VALVE
4
1
3
5
6
10
1077 TAN/WHT
826 BLK/WHT
827 BRN/WHT
829 DK BLU/WHT
2 RED
2 RED
2 RED
TO B+
FUSIBLE LINK "D"
32
2
35
18
VALVE RELAY MONITOR
LF WHEEL SOLENOID VALVE CONTROL
RF WHEEL SOLENOID VALVE CONTROL
REAR WHEELS SOLENOID VALVE CONTROL

Circuit Description:
With the ignition in "Run," "Bulb Test" or "Start," the EBCM applies voltage to the coil of the solenoid valve relay. The EBCM will complete an internal self-check before providing ground to the coil. Once energized, the relay will provide B+ to the solenoid valves.

Failure Conditions: Code 45 will set when the expected position of the right front solenoid valve does not match the commanded position from the EBCM (if valve line voltage does not match expected value). Conditions which could cause Code 45 to set are damage to the left front solenoid, an open or short to ground or battery voltage on CKT 826.

Action Taken: If a failure is detected which causes a valve Code 45 to set, antilock braking is disabled and the EBCM turns "ON" the "Antilock" indicator for the remainder of the ignition cycle. If the failure is intermittent, the EBCM will enable the system at the next ignition cycle and a history Code 45 will be present.

Important

- The Auto test (as described under "ABS Self Diagnostics") is performed once during each ignition cycle when the vehicle reaches approximately 4 mph. This test may be heard and felt while it is taking place and should be considered a normal mode of operation. This test can also be performed by using the Tech 1 in "ABS Tests" mode F4.

Test Description: Number(s) below refer to circled number(s) on the diagnostic chart.

1. This test checks the integrity of CKTs 826 and 1077, the LF Solenoid Valve Circuitry internal to the Brake Pressure Modulator and the LF Solenoid Valve Coil.
2. This test checks for a short to ground in CKT 826.
3. This test checks for a short to B+ in CKT 826.
4. This test checks for connector or wiring problems which may cause an intermittent condition.
5. This test uses the Tech 1 to check for proper Solenoid Valve operation.
6. This test determines whether the code was set by an intermittent condition or an EBCM fault.
7. This test determines whether the problem revealed in Step 1 is due to a faulty Brake Pressure Modulator or a wiring problem.
8. This test determines whether the problem is an open CKT 826 or a short from CKT 826 to CKT 1077.

Diagnostic Aids:

All tests which require a connection to Pinout Box terminal "20" are using this terminal as ground. This assumes that the integrity of ground CKT 151 has been maintained.

It is important that a thorough inspection of the wiring and connectors be performed prior to road testing the vehicle. This code can only be set when the vehicle is in motion. Failure to properly inspect wiring and connectors may result in a misdiagnosis of a faulty Brake Pressure Modulator or EBCM.

If Codes 45 and 45 are both set the fault is likely to be a short to B+ on CKT 827.

If Codes 41 and 55 are both set the fault is likely to be a short to B+ on CKT 826 or a short to ground on CKT 1079.

GC402920047700AX

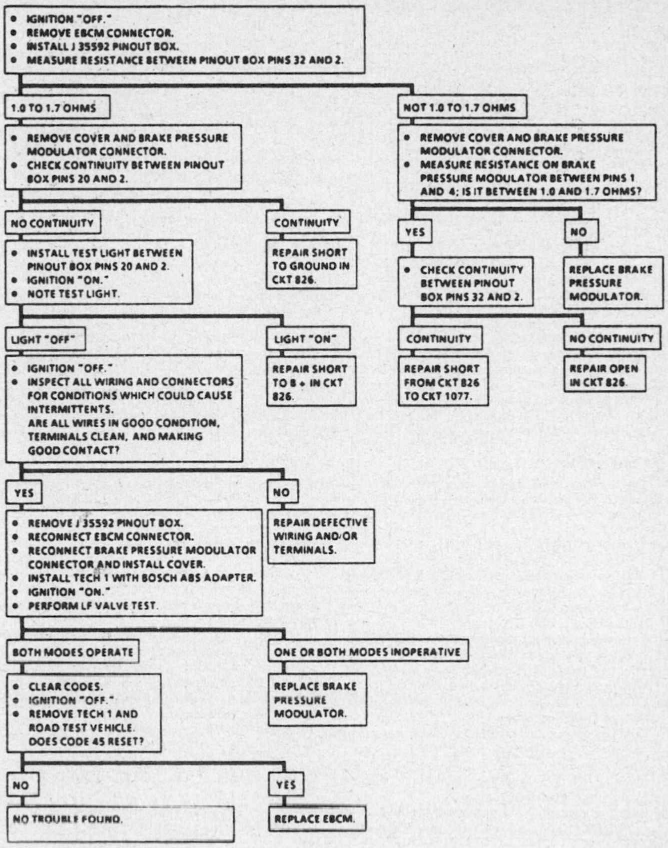
• IGNITION "OFF."
• REMOVE EBCM CONNECTOR.
• INSTALL J 35592 PINOUT BOX.
• MEASURE RESISTANCE BETWEEN PINOUT BOX PINS 32 AND 2.
1.0 TO 1.7 OHMS
NOT 1.0 TO 1.7 OHMS
• REMOVE COVER AND BRAKE PRESSURE MODULATOR CONNECTOR.
• CHECK CONTINUITY BETWEEN PINOUT BOX PINS 20 AND 2.
• REMOVE COVER AND BRAKE PRESSURE MODULATOR CONNECTOR.
• MEASURE RESISTANCE ON BRAKE PRESSURE MODULATOR BETWEEN PINS 1 AND 4; IS IT BETWEEN 1.0 AND 1.7 OHMS?
NO CONTINUITY
CONTINUITY
YES
NO
• INSTALL TEST LIGHT BETWEEN PINOUT BOX PINS 20 AND 2.
• IGNITION "ON."
• NOTE TEST LIGHT.
REPAIR SHORT TO GROUND IN CKT 826.
• CHECK CONTINUITY BETWEEN PINOUT BOX PINS 32 AND 2.
REPLACE BRAKE PRESSURE MODULATOR.
LIGHT "OFF"
LIGHT "ON"
CONTINUITY
NO CONTINUITY
• IGNITION "OFF."
• INSPECT ALL WIRING AND CONNECTORS FOR CONDITIONS WHICH COULD CAUSE INTERMITTENTS.
ARE ALL WIRES IN GOOD CONDITION, TERMINALS CLEAN, AND MAKING GOOD CONTACT?
REPAIR SHORT TO B+ IN CKT 826.
REPAIR SHORT FROM CKT 826 TO CKT 1077.
REPAIR OPEN IN CKT 826.
YES
NO
• REMOVE J 35592 PINOUT BOX.
• RECONNECT EBCM CONNECTOR.
• RECONNECT BRAKE PRESSURE MODULATOR CONNECTOR AND INSTALL COVER.
• INSTALL TECH 1 WITH BOSCH ABS ADAPTER.
• IGNITION "ON."
• PERFORM LF VALVE TEST.
REPAIR DEFECTIVE WIRING AND/OR TERMINALS.
BOTH MODES OPERATE
ONE OR BOTH MODES INOPERATIVE
• CLEAR CODES.
• IGNITION "OFF."
• REMOVE TECH 1 AND ROAD TEST VEHICLE.
DOES CODE 45 RESET?
REPLACE BRAKE PRESSURE MODULATOR.
NO
YES
NO TROUBLE FOUND.
REPLACE EBCM.

GC402920047700BX

Fig. 36 Code 45: LF Solenoid Valve Fault. 1992–93 Caprice, Custom Cruiser & Roadmaster

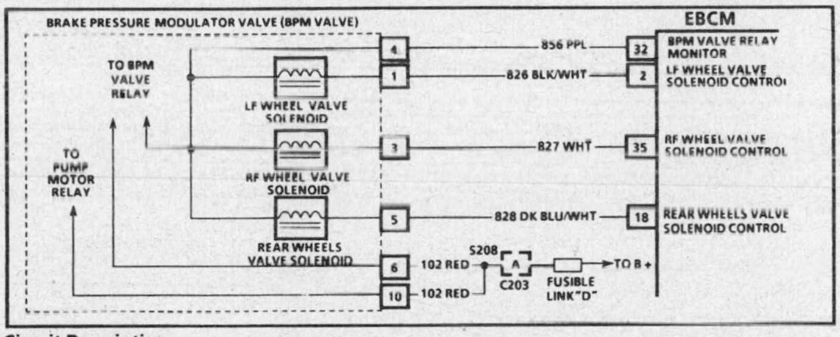
BRAKE PRESSURE MODULATOR VALVE (BPM VALVE)
EBCM
TO BPM VALVE RELAY
LF WHEEL VALVE SOLENOID
TO PUMP MOTOR RELAY
RF WHEEL VALVE SOLENOID
REAR WHEELS VALVE SOLENOID
4
1
3
5
6
10
856 PPL
826 BLK/WHT
827 WHT
828 DK BLU/WHT
102 RED
102 RED
S208
C203
FUSIBLE LINK "D"
TO B+
32
2
35
18
BPM VALVE RELAY MONITOR
LF WHEEL VALVE SOLENOID CONTROL
RF WHEEL VALVE SOLENOID CONTROL
REAR WHEELS VALVE SOLENOID CONTROL

Circuit Description:
With the ignition in "Run," "Bulb Test" or "Start," the EBCM applies voltage to the coil of the BPM valve relay. The EBCM will complete an internal self-check before providing ground to the coil. Once energized, the relay will provide B+ to the valve solenoids.

DTC 45 Will Set When: The expected position of the left front valve solenoid does not match the commanded position from the EBCM (if valve line voltage does not match expected value). Conditions which could cause DTC 45 to set are damage to the left front solenoid, an open or short to ground or battery voltage on CKT 826.

Action Taken: If a malfunction is detected which causes a valve DTC 45 to set, antilock braking is disabled and the EBCM turns "ON" the ABS warning lamp for the remainder of the ignition cycle. If the malfunction is intermittent, the EBCM will enable the system at the next ignition cycle and a history DTC 45 will be present.

Important

- The auto test (as described under "ABS Self Diagnostics") is performed once during each ignition cycle when the vehicle reaches approximately 4 mph. This test may be heard and felt while it is taking place and should be considered a normal mode of operation. This test can also be performed by using the Tech 1 in "Misc. Tests" mode F4.

DTC Chart Test Description: Number(s) below refer to circled number(s) on the diagnostic chart.

1. This test checks the integrity of CKTs 826 and 856, the LF valve solenoid circuitry internal to the BPM valve and the LF valve solenoid coil.
2. This test checks for a short to ground in CKT 826.
3. This test checks for a short to B+ in CKT 826.
4. This test checks for connector or wiring malfunctions which may cause an intermittent condition.
5. This test uses the Tech 1 to check for proper valve solenoid operation.
6. This test determines whether the DTC was set by an intermittent condition or an EBCM malfunction.
7. This test determines whether the malfunction revealed in Step 1 is due to a malfunctioning BPM valve or a wiring malfunction.
8. This test determines whether the malfunction is an open CKT 826 or a short from CKT 826 to CKT 856.

Diagnostic Aids: All tests which require a connection to Pinout Box Pin 20 are using this pin as ground. This assumes that the integrity of ground CKT 51 has been maintained.

It is important that a thorough inspection of the wiring and connectors be performed prior to road testing the vehicle. This DTC can only be set when the vehicle is in motion. Failure to properly inspect wiring and connectors may result in a misdiagnosis of a faulty BPM valve or EBCM.

If DTCs 41 and 45 are both set the malfunction is likely to be a short to B+ on CKT 827.

If DTCs 45 and 55 are both set the malfunction is likely to be a short to B+ on CKT 826.

GC402940092800AX

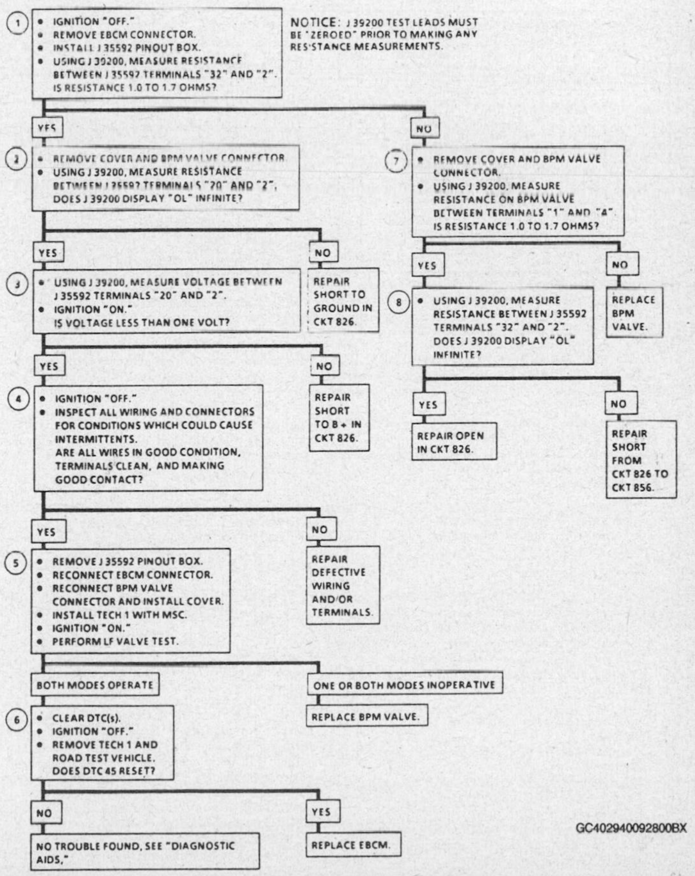
1
• IGNITION "OFF."
• REMOVE EBCM CONNECTOR.
• INSTALL J 35592 PINOUT BOX.
• USING J 39200, MEASURE RESISTANCE BETWEEN J 35592 TERMINALS "32" AND "2".
IS RESISTANCE 1.0 TO 1.7 OHMS?
NOTICE: J 39200 TEST LEADS MUST BE "ZEROED" PRIOR TO MAKING ANY RESISTANCE MEASUREMENTS.
YES
NO
2
• REMOVE COVER AND BPM VALVE CONNECTOR.
• USING J 39200, MEASURE RESISTANCE BETWEEN J 35592 TERMINALS "20" AND "2".
DOES J 39200 DISPLAY "OL" INFINITE?
7
• REMOVE COVER AND BPM VALVE CONNECTOR.
• USING J 39200, MEASURE RESISTANCE ON BPM VALVE BETWEEN TERMINALS "1" AND "4".
IS RESISTANCE 1.0 TO 1.7 OHMS?
YES
NO
YES
NO
3
• USING J 39200, MEASURE VOLTAGE BETWEEN J 35592 TERMINALS "20" AND "2".
• IGNITION "ON."
IS VOLTAGE LESS THAN ONE VOLT?
REPAIR SHORT TO GROUND IN CKT 826.
8
• USING J 39200, MEASURE RESISTANCE BETWEEN J 35592 TERMINALS "32" AND "2".
DOES J 39200 DISPLAY "OL" INFINITE?
REPLACE BPM VALVE.
YES
NO
4
• IGNITION "OFF."
• INSPECT ALL WIRING AND CONNECTORS FOR CONDITIONS WHICH COULD CAUSE INTERMITTENTS.
ARE ALL WIRES IN GOOD CONDITION, TERMINALS CLEAN, AND MAKING GOOD CONTACT?
REPAIR SHORT TO B+ IN CKT 826.
YES
NO
REPAIR OPEN IN CKT 826.
REPAIR SHORT FROM CKT 826 TO CKT 856.
YES
NO
5
• REMOVE J 35592 PINOUT BOX.
• RECONNECT EBCM CONNECTOR.
• RECONNECT BPM VALVE CONNECTOR AND INSTALL COVER.
• INSTALL TECH 1 WITH MSC.
• IGNITION "ON."
• PERFORM LF VALVE TEST.
REPAIR DEFECTIVE WIRING AND/OR TERMINALS.
BOTH MODES OPERATE
ONE OR BOTH MODES INOPERATIVE
6
• CLEAR DTC(s).
• IGNITION "OFF."
• REMOVE TECH 1 AND ROAD TEST VEHICLE.
DOES DTC 45 RESET?
REPLACE BPM VALVE.
NO
YES
NO TROUBLE FOUND, SEE "DIAGNOSTIC AIDS."
REPLACE EBCM.

GC402940092800BX

Fig. 37 Code 45: LF Solenoid Valve Fault. 1994 Caprice, Impala SS & Roadmaster

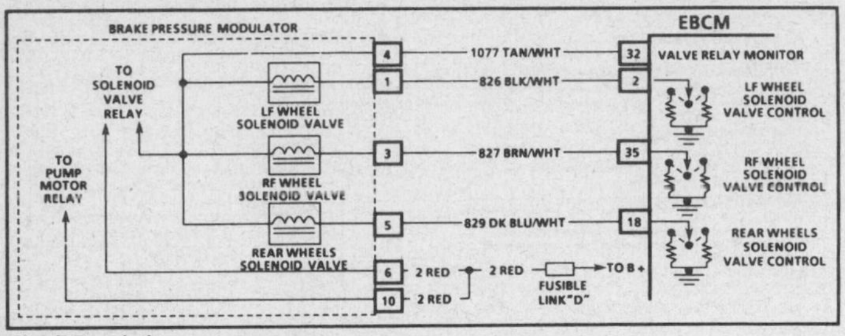
BRAKE PRESSURE MODULATOR
EBCM
TO SOLENOID VALVE RELAY
TO PUMP MOTOR RELAY
LF WHEEL SOLENOID VALVE
RF WHEEL SOLENOID VALVE
REAR WHEELS SOLENOID VALVE
1077 TAN/WHT
826 BLK/WHT
827 BRN/WHT
829 DK BLU/WHT
2 RED
2 RED
2 RED
FUSIBLE LINK "D"
TO B+
VALVE RELAY MONITOR
LF WHEEL SOLENOID VALVE CONTROL
RF WHEEL SOLENOID VALVE CONTROL
REAR WHEELS SOLENOID VALVE CONTROL
4
1
3
5
6
10
32
2
35
18

Circuit Description:
With the ignition in "Run," "Bulb Test" or "Start," the EBCM applies voltage to the coil of the solenoid valve relay. The EBCM will complete an internal self-check before providing ground to the coil. Once energized, the relay will provide B+ to the solenoid valves.

Failure Conditions: Code 55 will set when the expected position of the right front solenoid valve does not match the commanded position from the EBCM (if valve line voltage does not match expected value). Conditions which could cause Code 55 to set are damage to the left front solenoid, an open or short to ground or battery voltage on CKT 829.

Action Taken: If a failure is detected which causes a valve Code 55 to set, antilock braking is disabled and the EBCM turns "ON" the "Antilock" indicator for the remainder of the ignition cycle. If the failure is intermittent, the EBCM will enable the system at the next ignition cycle and a history Code 55 will be present.

Important

- The Auto test (as described under "ABS Self Diagnostics") is performed once during each ignition cycle when the vehicle reaches approximately 4 mph. This test may be heard and felt while it is taking place and should be considered a normal mode of operation. This test can also be performed by using the Tech 1 in "ABS Tests" mode F4.

Test Description: Number(s) below refer to circled number(s) on the diagnostic chart.

1. This test checks the integrity of CKTs 829 and 1077, the Rear Solenoid Valve Circuitry internal to the Brake Pressure Modulator and the Rear Solenoid Valve Coil.
2. This test checks for a short to ground in CKT 829.
3. This test checks for a short to B+ in CKT 829.
4. This test checks for connector or wiring problems which may cause an intermittent condition.
5. This test uses the Tech 1 to check for proper Solenoid Valve operation.
6. This test determines whether the code was set by an intermittent condition or an EBCM fault.
7. This test determines whether the problem revealed in Step 1 is due to a faulty Brake Pressure Modulator or a wiring problem.
8. This test determines whether the problem is an open CKT 829 or a short from CKT 829 to CKT 1077.

Diagnostic Aids:

All tests which require a connection to Pinout Box terminal "20" are using this terminal as ground. This assumes that the integrity of ground CKT 151 has been maintained.

It is important that a thorough inspection of the wiring and connectors be performed prior to road testing the vehicle. This code can only be set when the vehicle is in motion. Failure to properly inspect wiring and connectors may result in a misdiagnosis of a faulty Brake Pressure Modulator or EBCM.

If Codes 41 and 45 are both set the fault is likely to be a short to B+ on CKT 829.

If Codes 45 and 55 are both set the fault is likely to be a short to B+ on CKT 826 or a short to ground on CKT 1079.

GC402920047800AX

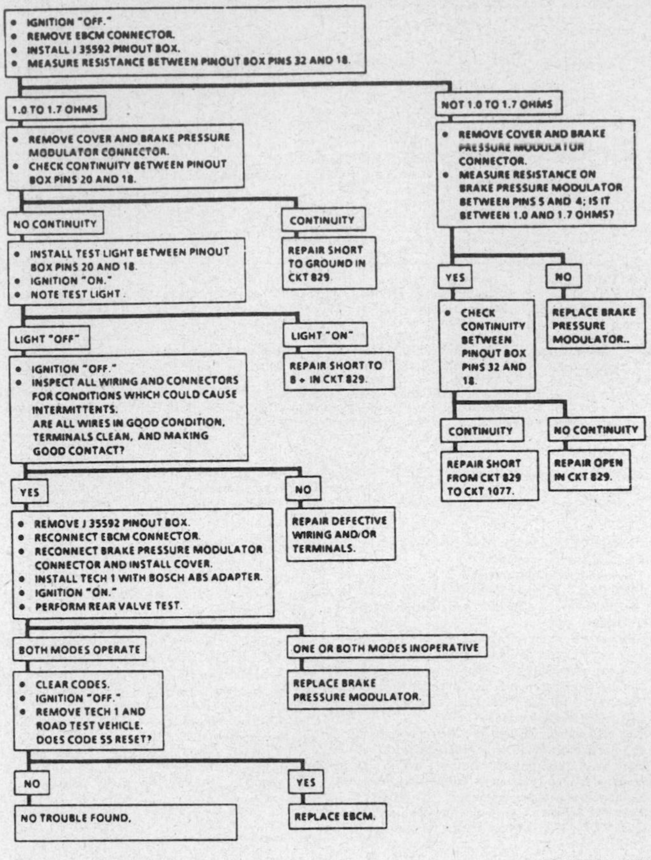
• IGNITION "OFF."
• REMOVE EBCM CONNECTOR.
• INSTALL J 35592 PINOUT BOX.
• MEASURE RESISTANCE BETWEEN PINOUT BOX PINS 32 AND 18.
1.0 TO 1.7 OHMS
NOT 1.0 TO 1.7 OHMS
• REMOVE COVER AND BRAKE PRESSURE MODULATOR CONNECTOR.
• CHECK CONTINUITY BETWEEN PINOUT BOX PINS 20 AND 18.
• REMOVE COVER AND BRAKE PRESSURE MODULATOR CONNECTOR.
• MEASURE RESISTANCE ON BRAKE PRESSURE MODULATOR BETWEEN PINS 5 AND 4; IS IT BETWEEN 1.0 AND 1.7 OHMS?
NO CONTINUITY
CONTINUITY
• INSTALL TEST LIGHT BETWEEN PINOUT BOX PINS 20 AND 18.
• IGNITION "ON."
• NOTE TEST LIGHT.
REPAIR SHORT TO GROUND IN CKT 829.
YES
NO
• CHECK CONTINUITY BETWEEN PINOUT BOX PINS 32 AND 18.
REPLACE BRAKE PRESSURE MODULATOR..
LIGHT "OFF"
LIGHT "ON"
• IGNITION "OFF."
• INSPECT ALL WIRING AND CONNECTORS FOR CONDITIONS WHICH COULD CAUSE INTERMITTENTS.
ARE ALL WIRES IN GOOD CONDITION, TERMINALS CLEAN, AND MAKING GOOD CONTACT?
REPAIR SHORT TO B+ IN CKT 829.
CONTINUITY
NO CONTINUITY
REPAIR SHORT FROM CKT 829 TO CKT 1077.
REPAIR OPEN IN CKT 829.
YES
NO
• REMOVE J 35592 PINOUT BOX.
• RECONNECT EBCM CONNECTOR.
• RECONNECT BRAKE PRESSURE MODULATOR CONNECTOR AND INSTALL COVER.
• INSTALL TECH 1 WITH BOSCH ABS ADAPTER.
• IGNITION "ON."
• PERFORM REAR VALVE TEST.
REPAIR DEFECTIVE WIRING AND/OR TERMINALS.
BOTH MODES OPERATE
ONE OR BOTH MODES INOPERATIVE
• CLEAR CODES.
• IGNITION "OFF."
• REMOVE TECH 1 AND ROAD TEST VEHICLE. DOES CODE 55 RESET?
REPLACE BRAKE PRESSURE MODULATOR.
NO
YES
NO TROUBLE FOUND.
REPLACE EBCM.

GC402920047800BX

Fig. 38 Code 55: Rear Wheels Solenoid Valve Fault. 1992–93 Caprice, Custom Cruiser & Roadmaster

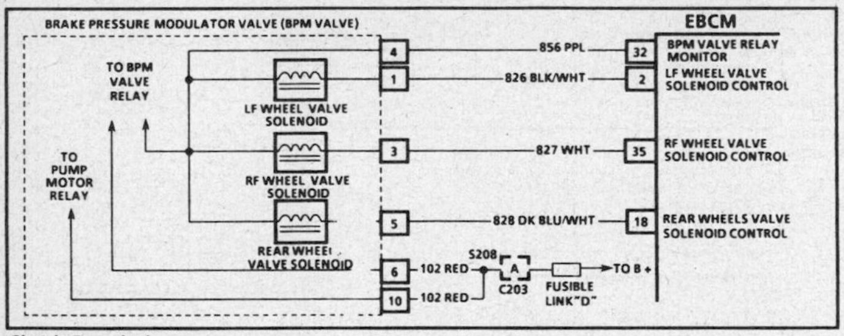
BRAKE PRESSURE MODULATOR VALVE (BPM VALVE)
EBCM
TO BPM VALVE RELAY
TO PUMP MOTOR RELAY
LF WHEEL VALVE SOLENOID
RF WHEEL VALVE SOLENOID
REAR WHEEL VALVE SOLENOID
856 PPL
826 BLK/WHT
827 WHT
828 DK BLU/WHT
102 RED
102 RED
S208
C203
FUSIBLE LINK "D"
TO B+
BPM VALVE RELAY MONITOR
LF WHEEL VALVE SOLENOID CONTROL
RF WHEEL VALVE SOLENOID CONTROL
REAR WHEELS VALVE SOLENOID CONTROL
4
1
3
5
6
10
32
2
35
18

Circuit Description:
With the ignition in "Run," "Bulb Test" or "Start," the EBCM applies voltage to the coil of the BPM valve relay. The EBCM will complete an internal self-check before providing ground to the coil. Once energized, the relay will provide B+ to the valve solenoids.

DTC 55 Will Set When: The expected position of the rear valve solenoid does not match the commanded position from the EBCM (if valve line voltage does not match expected value). Conditions which could cause DTC 55 to set are damage to the rear valve solenoid, an open or short to ground or battery voltage on CKT 828.

Action Taken: If a malfunction is detected which causes a valve DTC 55 to set, antilock braking is disabled and the EBCM turns "ON" the ABS warning lamp for the remainder of the ignition cycle. If the malfunction is intermittent, the EBCM will enable the system at the next ignition cycle and a history DTC 55 will be present.

Important

- The auto test (as described under "ABS Self Diagnostics") is performed once during each ignition cycle when the vehicle reaches approximately 4 mph. This test may be heard and felt while it is taking place and should be considered a normal mode of operation. This test can also be performed by using the Tech 1 in "Misc Tests" mode F4.

DTC Chart Test Description: Number(s) below refer to circled number(s) on the diagnostic chart.

1. This test checks the integrity of CKTs 828 and 856, the rear valve solenoid circuitry internal to the BPM valve and the rear valve solenoid coil.
2. This test checks for a short to ground in CKT 828.
3. This test checks for a short to B+ in CKT 828.
4. This test checks for connector or wiring malfunctions which may cause an intermittent condition.
5. This test uses the Tech 1 to check for proper valve solenoid operation.
6. This test determines whether the DTC was set by an intermittent condition or an EBCM malfunction.
7. This test determines whether the malfunction revealed in Step 1 is due to a malfunctioning BPM valve or a wiring malfunction.
8. This test determines whether the malfunction is an open CKT 828 or a short from CKT 828 to CKT 856.

Diagnostic Aids: All tests which require a connection to Pinout Box Pin 20 are using this pin as ground. This assumes that the integrity of ground CKT 51 has been maintained.

It is important that a thorough inspection of the wiring and connectors be performed prior to road testing the vehicle. This DTC can only be set when the vehicle is in motion. Failure to properly inspect wiring and connectors may result in a misdiagnosis of a faulty BPM valve or EBCM.

If DTCs 41 and 55 are both set the malfunction is likely to be a short to B+ on CKT 828.

If DTCs 45 and 55 are both set the malfunction is likely to be a short to B+ on CKT 826.

GC402940092900AX

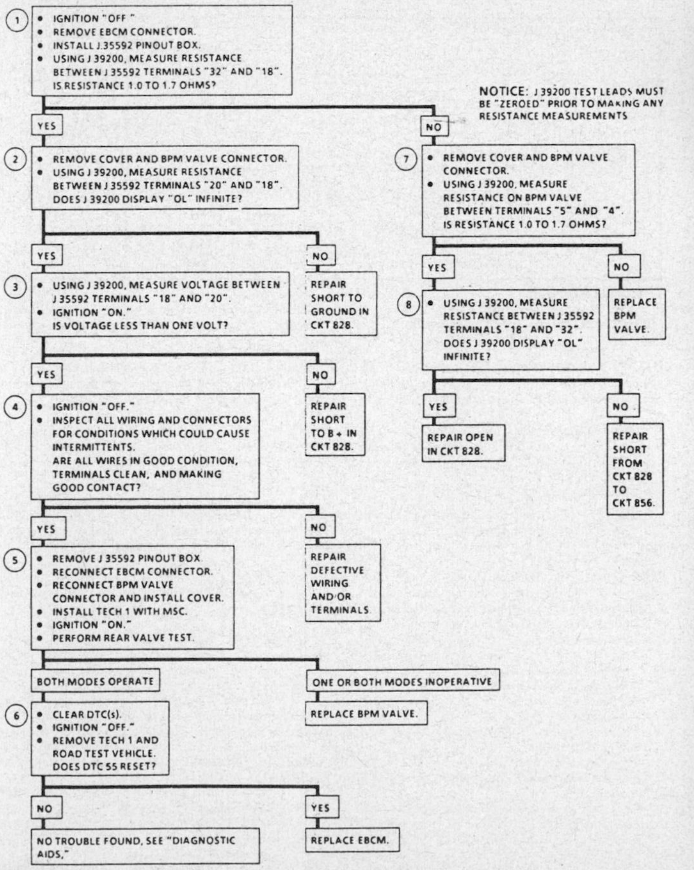
1
• IGNITION "OFF."
• REMOVE EBCM CONNECTOR.
• INSTALL J 35592 PINOUT BOX.
• USING J 39200, MEASURE RESISTANCE BETWEEN J 35592 TERMINALS "32" AND "18". IS RESISTANCE 1.0 TO 1.7 OHMS?
NOTICE: J 39200 TEST LEADS MUST BE "ZEROED" PRIOR TO MAKING ANY RESISTANCE MEASUREMENTS
YES
NO
2
• REMOVE COVER AND BPM VALVE CONNECTOR.
• USING J 39200, MEASURE RESISTANCE BETWEEN J 35592 TERMINALS "20" AND "18". DOES J 39200 DISPLAY "OL" INFINITE?
7
• REMOVE COVER AND BPM VALVE CONNECTOR.
• USING J 39200, MEASURE RESISTANCE ON BPM VALVE BETWEEN TERMINALS "5" AND "4". IS RESISTANCE 1.0 TO 1.7 OHMS?
YES
NO
YES
NO
3
• USING J 39200, MEASURE VOLTAGE BETWEEN J 35592 TERMINALS "18" AND "20".
• IGNITION "ON."
IS VOLTAGE LESS THAN ONE VOLT?
REPAIR SHORT TO GROUND IN CKT 828.
8
• USING J 39200, MEASURE RESISTANCE BETWEEN J 35592 TERMINALS "18" AND "32". DOES J 39200 DISPLAY "OL" INFINITE?
REPLACE BPM VALVE.
YES
NO
YES
NO
4
• IGNITION "OFF."
• INSPECT ALL WIRING AND CONNECTORS FOR CONDITIONS WHICH COULD CAUSE INTERMITTENTS.
ARE ALL WIRES IN GOOD CONDITION, TERMINALS CLEAN, AND MAKING GOOD CONTACT?
REPAIR SHORT TO B+ IN CKT 828.
REPAIR OPEN IN CKT 828.
REPAIR SHORT FROM CKT 828 TO CKT 856.
YES
NO
5
• REMOVE J 35592 PINOUT BOX.
• RECONNECT EBCM CONNECTOR.
• RECONNECT BPM VALVE CONNECTOR AND INSTALL COVER.
• INSTALL TECH 1 WITH MSC.
• IGNITION "ON."
• PERFORM REAR VALVE TEST.
REPAIR DEFECTIVE WIRING AND/OR TERMINALS.
BOTH MODES OPERATE
ONE OR BOTH MODES INOPERATIVE
6
• CLEAR DTC(S).
• IGNITION "OFF."
• REMOVE TECH 1 AND ROAD TEST VEHICLE. DOES DTC 55 RESET?
REPLACE BPM VALVE.
NO
YES
NO TROUBLE FOUND, SEE "DIAGNOSTIC AIDS."
REPLACE EBCM.

Fig. 39 Code 55: Rear Solenoid Valve Fault. 1994 Caprice, Impala SS & Roadmaster

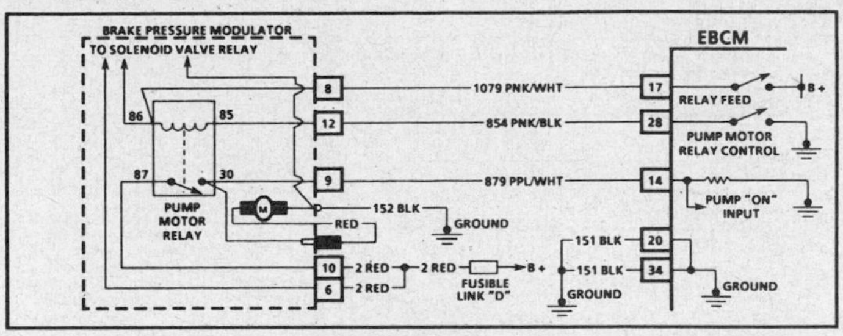
BRAKE PRESSURE MODULATOR
TO SOLENOID VALVE RELAY
EBCM
1079 PNK/WHT
RELAY FEED
B+
854 PNK/BLK
PUMP MOTOR RELAY CONTROL
879 PPL/WHT
PUMP "ON" INPUT
PUMP MOTOR RELAY
152 BLK
GROUND
RED
151 BLK
2 RED
FUSIBLE LINK "D"
GROUND

CODE 61

(Page 1 of 2)
PUMP MOTOR/RELAY
(MOTOR OR RELAY FAULT)

Circuit Description:

The pump motor returns brake fluid to the master cylinder brake hydraulic circuit at the hydraulic modulator, during antilock braking. During normal braking, the pump does not operate. When the vehicle begins to move after start-up, the EBCM will turn "ON" the pump motor and perform a self-check of the pump motor and pump motor electrical circuit. This check may be felt and heard by the driver when the vehicle begins to move. The self-check should be considered normal operation. The pump motor is an integral component of the hydraulic modulator and cannot be serviced separately.

The pump motor relay provides power to the pump motor in the hydraulic modulator. The pump motor relay is located on the hydraulic modulator and may be replaced if it is found to be defective.

Failure Conditions:

Code 61 will set if B+ is present at the pump motor without the pump motor being requested to activate, or if B+ is not present at the pump motor within 60 milliseconds after the pump motor has been requested to activate.

Action Taken:

If a failure is detected which causes a pump motor/relay Code 61 to set antilock braking is disabled and the EBCM turns "ON" the "Antilock" indicator for the remainder of the ignition cycle. If the failure is intermittent, the EBCM will enable the system at the next ignition cycle and a History Code 61 will be present.

Test Description: Number(s) below refer to circled number(s) on the diagnostic chart.

1. Checks for proper resistance of the relay coil.
2. Checks for relay contacts stuck closed.
3. Checks for relay contacts stuck open.
4. Checks the integrity of the circuits internal to the modulator.
5. Checks for an open in the pump "ON" input circuit.
6. Checks for a short to ground in the pump "ON" input circuit.
7. Checks for a short from the pump "ON" input circuit to the relay feed circuit.
8. Checks for an open in the pump motor relay coil switched ground circuit.
9. Checks for a short to ground in the pump motor relay coil switched ground circuit.

GC402920047900AX

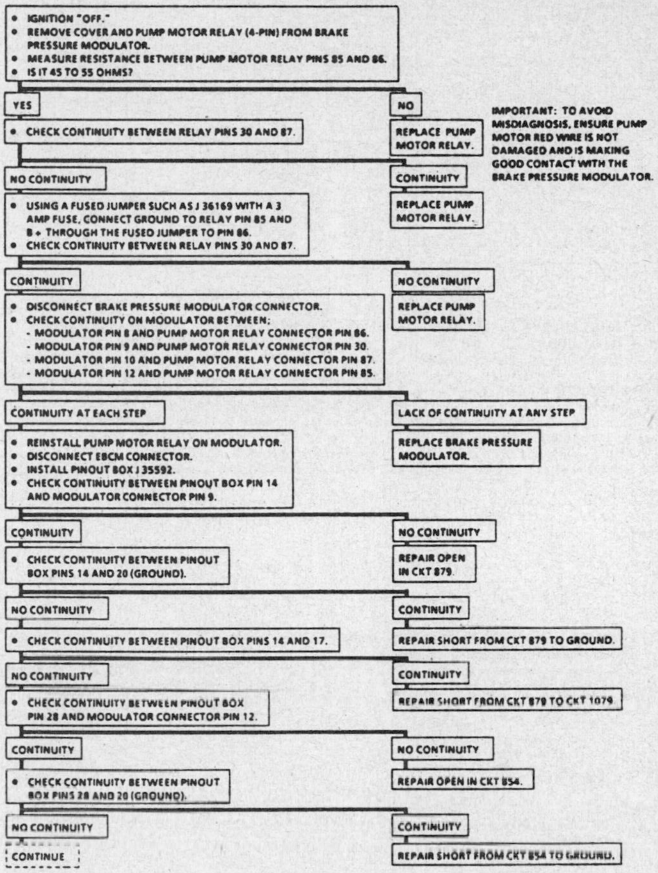
• IGNITION "OFF."
• REMOVE COVER AND PUMP MOTOR RELAY (4-PIN) FROM BRAKE PRESSURE MODULATOR.
• MEASURE RESISTANCE BETWEEN PUMP MOTOR RELAY PINS 85 AND 86.
• IS IT 45 TO 55 OHMS?
YES
NO
REPLACE PUMP MOTOR RELAY.
IMPORTANT: TO AVOID MISDIAGNOSIS, ENSURE PUMP MOTOR RED WIRE IS NOT DAMAGED AND IS MAKING GOOD CONTACT WITH THE BRAKE PRESSURE MODULATOR.
• CHECK CONTINUITY BETWEEN RELAY PINS 30 AND 87.
NO CONTINUITY
CONTINUITY
REPLACE PUMP MOTOR RELAY.
• USING A FUSED JUMPER SUCH AS J 36169 WITH A 3 AMP FUSE, CONNECT GROUND TO RELAY PIN 85 AND B+ THROUGH THE FUSED JUMPER TO PIN 86.
• CHECK CONTINUITY BETWEEN RELAY PINS 30 AND 87.
CONTINUITY
NO CONTINUITY
REPLACE PUMP MOTOR RELAY.
• DISCONNECT BRAKE PRESSURE MODULATOR CONNECTOR.
• CHECK CONTINUITY ON MODULATOR BETWEEN:
- MODULATOR PIN 8 AND PUMP MOTOR RELAY CONNECTOR PIN 86.
- MODULATOR PIN 9 AND PUMP MOTOR RELAY CONNECTOR PIN 30.
- MODULATOR PIN 10 AND PUMP MOTOR RELAY CONNECTOR PIN 87.
- MODULATOR PIN 12 AND PUMP MOTOR RELAY CONNECTOR PIN 85.
CONTINUITY AT EACH STEP
LACK OF CONTINUITY AT ANY STEP
REPLACE BRAKE PRESSURE MODULATOR.
• REINSTALL PUMP MOTOR RELAY ON MODULATOR.
• DISCONNECT EBCM CONNECTOR.
• INSTALL PINOUT BOX J 35592.
• CHECK CONTINUITY BETWEEN PINOUT BOX PIN 14 AND MODULATOR CONNECTOR PIN 9.
CONTINUITY
NO CONTINUITY
REPAIR OPEN IN CKT 879.
• CHECK CONTINUITY BETWEEN PINOUT BOX PINS 14 AND 20 (GROUND).
NO CONTINUITY
CONTINUITY
REPAIR SHORT FROM CKT 879 TO GROUND.
• CHECK CONTINUITY BETWEEN PINOUT BOX PINS 14 AND 17.
NO CONTINUITY
CONTINUITY
REPAIR SHORT FROM CKT 879 TO CKT 1079.
• CHECK CONTINUITY BETWEEN PINOUT BOX PIN 28 AND MODULATOR CONNECTOR PIN 12.
CONTINUITY
NO CONTINUITY
REPAIR OPEN IN CKT 854.
• CHECK CONTINUITY BETWEEN PINOUT BOX PINS 28 AND 20 (GROUND).
NO CONTINUITY
CONTINUITY
REPAIR SHORT FROM CKT 854 TO GROUND.
CONTINUE

Fig. 40 Code 61: Pump Motor Or Relay Fault (Part 1 of 2). 1992–93 Caprice, Custom Cruiser & Roadmaster

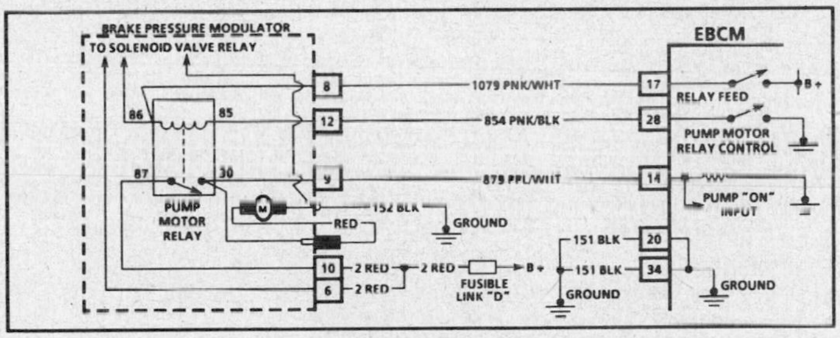
BRAKE PRESSURE MODULATOR
TO SOLENOID VALVE RELAY
EBCM
1079 PNK/WHT
RELAY FEED
B+
854 PNK/BLK
PUMP MOTOR RELAY CONTROL
879 PPL/WHT
PUMP "ON" INPUT
PUMP MOTOR RELAY
152 BLK
GROUND
RED
151 BLK
2 RED
FUSIBLE LINK "D"
GROUND

CODE 61

(Page 2 of 2)
PUMP MOTOR/RELAY
(MOTOR OR RELAY FAULT)

Circuit Description:

The pump motor returns brake fluid to the master cylinder brake hydraulic circuit at the hydraulic modulator, during antilock braking. During normal braking, the pump does not operate. When the vehicle begins to move after start-up, the EBCM will turn "ON" the pump motor and perform a self-check of the pump motor and pump motor electrical circuit. This check may be felt and heard by the driver when the vehicle begins to move. The self-check should be considered normal operation. The pump motor is an integral component of the hydraulic modulator and cannot be serviced separately.

The pump motor relay provides power to the pump motor in the hydraulic modulator. The pump motor relay is located on the hydraulic modulator and may be replaced if it is found to be defective.

Failure Conditions:

Code 61 will set if B+ is present at the pump motor without the pump motor being requested to activate, or if B+ is not present at the pump motor within 60 milliseconds after the pump motor has been requested to activate.

Action Taken:

If a failure is detected which causes a pump motor/relay Code 61 to set antilock braking is disabled and the EBCM turns "ON" the "Antilock" indicator for the remainder of the ignition cycle. If the failure is intermittent, the EBCM will enable the system at the next ignition cycle and a History Code 61 will be present.

Test Description: Number(s) below refer to circled number(s) on the diagnostic chart.

10. Checks for a short from the pump motor relay coil switched ground circuit to the relay feed circuit.
11. Checks for an open in the modulator battery feed circuit.
12. Checks for a short to B+ in the pump "ON" input circuit.
13. Checks for a short to B+ in the pump motor relay coil switched ground circuit.
14. Checks for improper connections which may have set the code.
15. Checks that the pump motor is operational.
16. Checks for a code which set falsely.
17. Checks for a good pump motor ground circuit.

GC402920047900CX

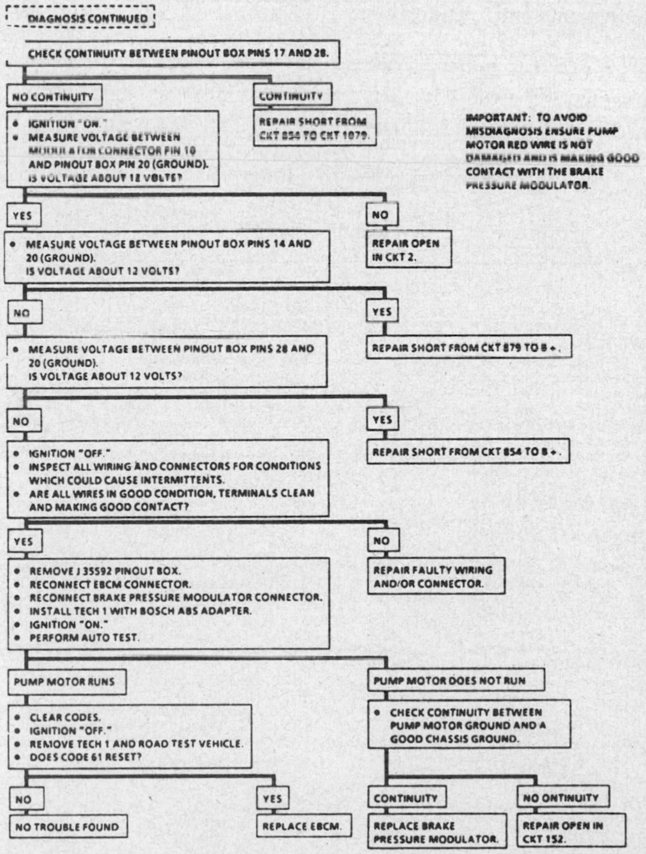
DIAGNOSIS CONTINUED
CHECK CONTINUITY BETWEEN PINOUT BOX PINS 17 AND 28.
NO CONTINUITY
CONTINUITY
REPAIR SHORT FROM CKT 854 TO CKT 1079.
IMPORTANT: TO AVOID MISDIAGNOSIS ENSURE PUMP MOTOR RED WIRE IS NOT DAMAGED AND IS MAKING GOOD CONTACT WITH THE BRAKE PRESSURE MODULATOR.
• IGNITION "ON."
• MEASURE VOLTAGE BETWEEN MODULATOR CONNECTOR PIN 10 AND PINOUT BOX PIN 20 (GROUND). IS VOLTAGE ABOUT 12 VOLTS?
YES
NO
REPAIR OPEN IN CKT 2.
• MEASURE VOLTAGE BETWEEN PINOUT BOX PINS 14 AND 20 (GROUND). IS VOLTAGE ABOUT 12 VOLTS?
NO
YES
REPAIR SHORT FROM CKT 879 TO B+.
• MEASURE VOLTAGE BETWEEN PINOUT BOX PINS 28 AND 20 (GROUND). IS VOLTAGE ABOUT 12 VOLTS?
NO
YES
REPAIR SHORT FROM CKT 854 TO B+.
• IGNITION "OFF."
• INSPECT ALL WIRING AND CONNECTORS FOR CONDITIONS WHICH COULD CAUSE INTERMITTENTS.
• ARE ALL WIRES IN GOOD CONDITION, TERMINALS CLEAN AND MAKING GOOD CONTACT?
YES
NO
REPAIR FAULTY WIRING AND/OR CONNECTOR.
• REMOVE J 35592 PINOUT BOX.
• RECONNECT EBCM CONNECTOR.
• RECONNECT BRAKE PRESSURE MODULATOR CONNECTOR.
• INSTALL TECH 1 WITH BOSCH ABS ADAPTER.
• IGNITION "ON."
• PERFORM AUTO TEST.
PUMP MOTOR RUNS
PUMP MOTOR DOES NOT RUN
• CLEAR CODES.
• IGNITION "OFF."
• REMOVE TECH 1 AND ROAD TEST VEHICLE.
• DOES CODE 61 RESET?
• CHECK CONTINUITY BETWEEN PUMP MOTOR GROUND AND A GOOD CHASSIS GROUND.
NO
YES
CONTINUITY
NO ONTINUITY
NO TROUBLE FOUND
REPLACE EBCM.
REPLACE BRAKE PRESSURE MODULATOR.
REPAIR OPEN IN CKT 152.

GC402920047900DX

Fig. 40 Code 61: Pump Motor Or Relay Fault (Part 2 of 2). 1992–93 Caprice, Custom Cruiser & Roadmaster

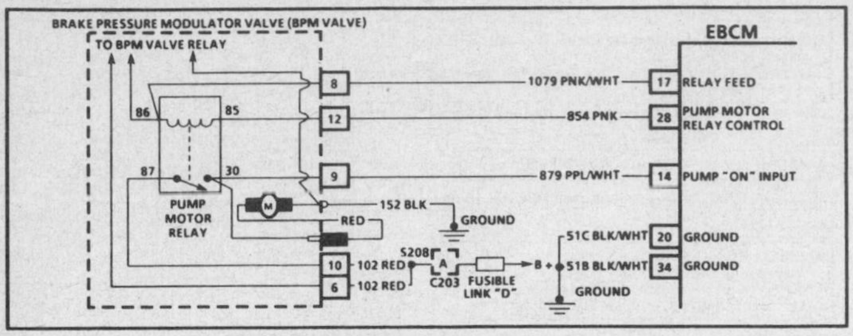

BRAKE PRESSURE MODULATOR VALVE (BPM VALVE)
TO BPM VALVE RELAY
EBCM
86
85
87
30
PUMP MOTOR RELAY
8
12
9
10
6
1079 PNK/WHT
854 PNK
879 PPL/WHT
152 BLK
RED
GROUND
S208
102 RED
102 RED
A
C203
FUSIBLE LINK "D"
B+
51C BLK/WHT
51B BLK/WHT
GROUND
17 RELAY FEED
28 PUMP MOTOR RELAY CONTROL
14 PUMP "ON" INPUT
20 GROUND
34 GROUND

DTC 61

(Page 1 of 2)

BPM VALVE PUMP MOTOR OR PUMP MOTOR RELAY MALFUNCTION

Circuit Description:

The pump motor returns brake fluid to the master cylinder brake hydraulic circuit at the BPM valve during antilock braking. During normal braking, the pump does not operate. When the vehicle begins to move after start-up, the EBCM will turn "ON" the pump motor and perform a self-check of the pump motor and pump motor electrical circuit. This check may be felt and heard by the driver when the vehicle begins to move. The self-check should be considered normal operation. The pump motor is an integral component of the BPM valve and cannot be serviced separately.

The BPM valve pump motor relay provides power to the pump motor in the BPM valve. The BPM valve pump motor relay is located on the BPM valve and may be replaced if it is found to be defective.

DTC 61 Will Set When: B+ is present at the pump motor without the pump motor being requested to activate, or if B+ is not present at the pump motor within 60 milliseconds after the pump motor has been requested to activate.

Action Taken: If a malfunction is detected which causes a pump motor/relay DTC 61 to set, antilock braking is disabled and the EBCM turns "ON" the ABS warning lamp for the remainder of the ignition cycle. If the malfunction is intermittent, the EBCM will enable the system at the next ignition cycle and a history DTC 61 will be present.

DTC Chart Test Description: Number(s) below refer to circled number(s) on the diagnostic chart.

1. Checks for proper resistance of the relay coil.
2. Checks for relay contacts stuck closed.
3. Checks for relay contacts stuck open.
4. Checks the integrity of the circuits internal to the BPM valve.
5. Checks for an open in the pump "ON" input circuit.
6. Checks for an open in the pump motor relay coil switched ground circuit.
7. Checks for a short to ground in the pump "ON" input circuit.

GC402940093001AX

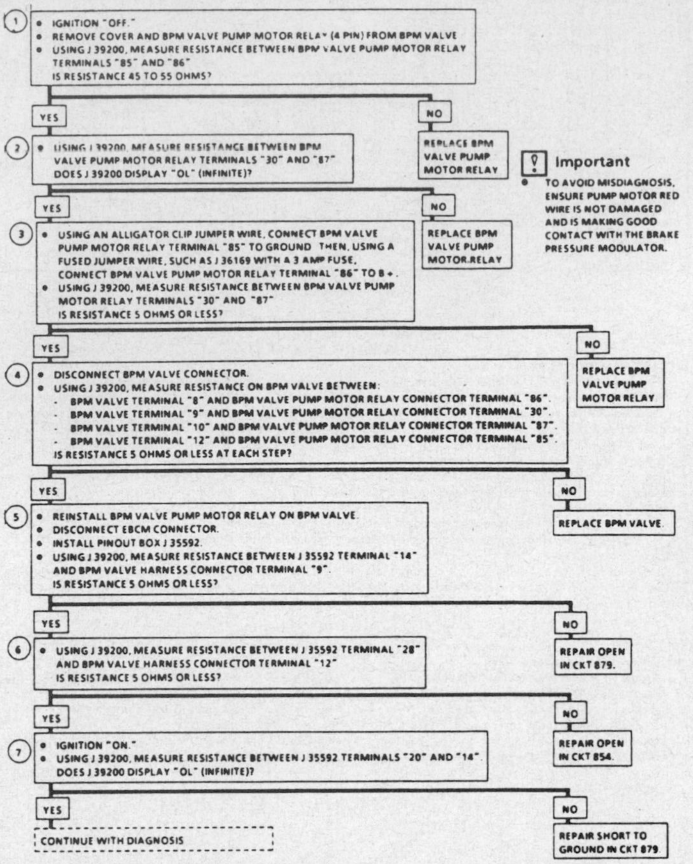

1 • IGNITION "OFF."
• REMOVE COVER AND BPM VALVE PUMP MOTOR RELAY (4 PIN) FROM BPM VALVE
• USING J 39200, MEASURE RESISTANCE BETWEEN BPM VALVE PUMP MOTOR RELAY TERMINALS "85" AND "86"
IS RESISTANCE 45 TO 55 OHMS?
YES
NO
REPLACE BPM VALVE PUMP MOTOR RELAY
2 • USING J 39200, MEASURE RESISTANCE BETWEEN BPM VALVE PUMP MOTOR RELAY TERMINALS "30" AND "87"
DOES J 39200 DISPLAY "OL" (INFINITE)?
Important
• TO AVOID MISDIAGNOSIS, ENSURE PUMP MOTOR RED WIRE IS NOT DAMAGED AND IS MAKING GOOD CONTACT WITH THE BRAKE PRESSURE MODULATOR.
YES
NO
REPLACE BPM VALVE PUMP MOTOR RELAY
3 • USING AN ALLIGATOR CLIP JUMPER WIRE, CONNECT BPM VALVE PUMP MOTOR RELAY TERMINAL "85" TO GROUND. THEN, USING A FUSED JUMPER WIRE, SUCH AS J 36169 WITH A 3 AMP FUSE, CONNECT BPM VALVE PUMP MOTOR RELAY TERMINAL "86" TO B+.
• USING J 39200, MEASURE RESISTANCE BETWEEN BPM VALVE PUMP MOTOR RELAY TERMINALS "30" AND "87"
IS RESISTANCE 5 OHMS OR LESS?
YES
NO
REPLACE BPM VALVE PUMP MOTOR RELAY
4 • DISCONNECT BPM VALVE CONNECTOR.
• USING J 39200, MEASURE RESISTANCE ON BPM VALVE BETWEEN:
- BPM VALVE TERMINAL "8" AND BPM VALVE PUMP MOTOR RELAY CONNECTOR TERMINAL "86".
- BPM VALVE TERMINAL "9" AND BPM VALVE PUMP MOTOR RELAY CONNECTOR TERMINAL "30".
- BPM VALVE TERMINAL "10" AND BPM VALVE PUMP MOTOR RELAY CONNECTOR TERMINAL "87".
- BPM VALVE TERMINAL "12" AND BPM VALVE PUMP MOTOR RELAY CONNECTOR TERMINAL "85".
IS RESISTANCE 5 OHMS OR LESS AT EACH STEP?
YES
NO
REPLACE BPM VALVE.
5 • REINSTALL BPM VALVE PUMP MOTOR RELAY ON BPM VALVE.
• DISCONNECT EBCM CONNECTOR.
• INSTALL PINOUT BOX J 35592.
• USING J 39200, MEASURE RESISTANCE BETWEEN J 35592 TERMINAL "14" AND BPM VALVE HARNESS CONNECTOR TERMINAL "9".
IS RESISTANCE 5 OHMS OR LESS?
YES
NO
REPAIR OPEN IN CKT 879.
6 • USING J 39200, MEASURE RESISTANCE BETWEEN J 35592 TERMINAL "28" AND BPM VALVE HARNESS CONNECTOR TERMINAL "12"
IS RESISTANCE 5 OHMS OR LESS?
YES
NO
REPAIR OPEN IN CKT 854.
7 • IGNITION "ON."
• USING J 39200, MEASURE RESISTANCE BETWEEN J 35592 TERMINALS "20" AND "14".
DOES J 39200 DISPLAY "OL" (INFINITE)?
YES
NO
CONTINUE WITH DIAGNOSIS
REPAIR SHORT TO GROUND IN CKT 879.

GC402940093001BX

Fig. 41 Code 61: Pump Motor Or Relay Fault (Part 1 of 2). 1994 Caprice, Impala SS & Roadmaster

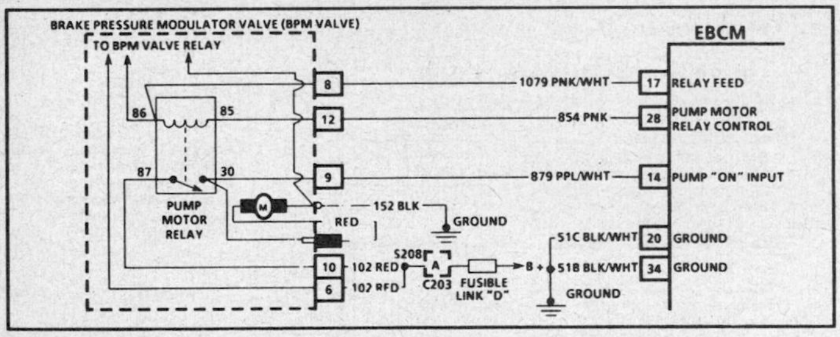

BRAKE PRESSURE MODULATOR VALVE (BPM VALVE)
TO BPM VALVE RELAY
EBCM
86
85
87
30
PUMP MOTOR RELAY
8
12
9
10
6
1079 PNK/WHT
854 PNK
879 PPL/WHT
152 BLK
RED
GROUND
S208
102 RED
102 RED
A
C203
FUSIBLE LINK "D"
B+
51C BLK/WHT
51B BLK/WHT
GROUND
17 RELAY FEED
28 PUMP MOTOR RELAY CONTROL
14 PUMP "ON" INPUT
20 GROUND
34 GROUND

DTC 61

(Page 2 of 2)

BPM VALVE PUMP MOTOR OR PUMP MOTOR RELAY MALFUNCTION

Circuit Description:

The pump motor returns brake fluid to the master cylinder brake hydraulic circuit at the BPM valve during antilock braking. During normal braking, the pump does not operate. When the vehicle begins to move after start-up, the EBCM will turn "ON" the pump motor and perform a self-check of the pump motor and pump motor electrical circuit. This check may be felt and heard by the driver when the vehicle begins to move. The self-check should be considered normal operation. The pump motor is an integral component of the BPM valve and cannot be serviced separately.

The BPM valve pump motor relay provides power to the pump motor in the BPM valve. The BPM valve pump motor relay is located on the BPM valve and may be replaced if it is found to be defective.

DTC 61 Will Set When: B+ is present at the pump motor without the pump motor being requested to activate, or if B+ is not present at the pump motor within 60 milliseconds after the pump motor has been requested to activate.

Action Taken: If a malfunction is detected which causes a BPM valve pump motor/relay DTC 61 to set, antilock braking is disabled and the EBCM turns "ON" the ABS warning lamp for the remainder of the ignition cycle. If the malfunction is intermittent, the EBCM will enable the system at the next ignition cycle and a history DTC 61 will be present.

DTC Chart Test Description: Number(s) below refer to circled number(s) on the diagnostic chart.

8. Checks for a short to ground in the BPM valve pump motor relay coil switched ground circuit.
9. Checks for a short to B+ in the pump "ON" input circuit.
10. Checks for a short to B+ in the BPM valve pump motor relay switched ground circuit.
11. Checks for an open in the BPM valve battery feed circuit.
12. Checks for improper connections which may have set the DTC.
13. Checks that the pump motor is operational.
14. Checks for a DTC which set falsely.
15. Checks for a good pump motor ground circuit.

GC402940093002AX

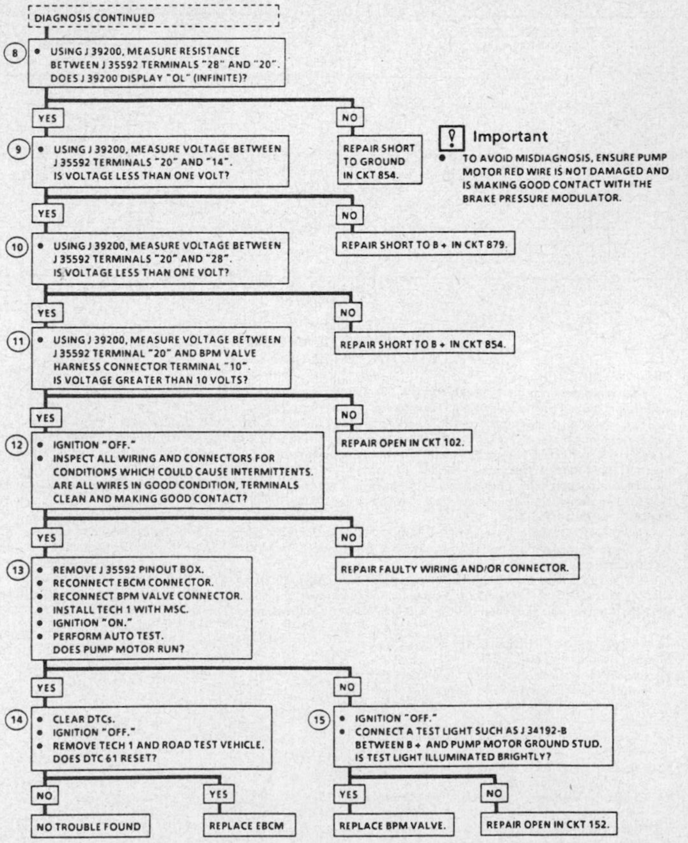

DIAGNOSIS CONTINUED
8 • USING J 39200, MEASURE RESISTANCE BETWEEN J 35592 TERMINALS "28" AND "20".
DOES J 39200 DISPLAY "OL" (INFINITE)?
YES
NO
REPAIR SHORT TO GROUND IN CKT 854.
Important
• TO AVOID MISDIAGNOSIS, ENSURE PUMP MOTOR RED WIRE IS NOT DAMAGED AND IS MAKING GOOD CONTACT WITH THE BRAKE PRESSURE MODULATOR.
9 • USING J 39200, MEASURE VOLTAGE BETWEEN J 35592 TERMINALS "20" AND "14".
IS VOLTAGE LESS THAN ONE VOLT?
YES
NO
REPAIR SHORT TO B+ IN CKT 879.
10 • USING J 39200, MEASURE VOLTAGE BETWEEN J 35592 TERMINALS "20" AND "28".
IS VOLTAGE LESS THAN ONE VOLT?
YES
NO
REPAIR SHORT TO B+ IN CKT 854.
11 • USING J 39200, MEASURE VOLTAGE BETWEEN J 35592 TERMINAL "20" AND BPM VALVE HARNESS CONNECTOR TERMINAL "10".
IS VOLTAGE GREATER THAN 10 VOLTS?
YES
NO
REPAIR OPEN IN CKT 102.
12 • IGNITION "OFF."
• INSPECT ALL WIRING AND CONNECTORS FOR CONDITIONS WHICH COULD CAUSE INTERMITTENTS. ARE ALL WIRES IN GOOD CONDITION, TERMINALS CLEAN AND MAKING GOOD CONTACT?
YES
NO
REPAIR FAULTY WIRING AND/OR CONNECTOR.
13 • REMOVE J 35592 PINOUT BOX.
• RECONNECT EBCM CONNECTOR.
• RECONNECT BPM VALVE CONNECTOR.
• INSTALL TECH 1 WITH MSC.
• IGNITION "ON."
• PERFORM AUTO TEST.
DOES PUMP MOTOR RUN?
YES
NO
14 • CLEAR DTCs.
• IGNITION "OFF."
• REMOVE TECH 1 AND ROAD TEST VEHICLE.
DOES DTC 61 RESET?
15 • IGNITION "OFF."
• CONNECT A TEST LIGHT SUCH AS J 34192-B BETWEEN B+ AND PUMP MOTOR GROUND STUD.
IS TEST LIGHT ILLUMINATED BRIGHTLY?
NO
YES
YES
NO
NO TROUBLE FOUND
REPLACE EBCM
REPLACE BPM VALVE.
REPAIR OPEN IN CKT 152.

GC402940093002BX

Fig. 41 Code 61: Pump Motor Or Relay Fault (Part 2 of 2). 1994 Caprice, Impala SS & Roadmaster

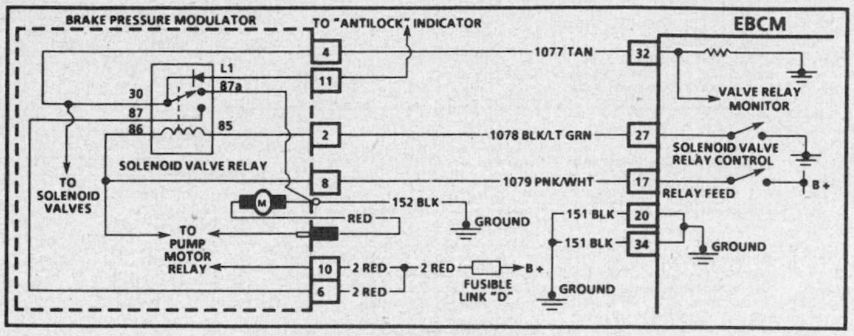
BRAKE PRESSURE MODULATOR
TO "ANTILOCK" INDICATOR
EBCM
L1
87a
30
87
86
85
SOLENOID VALVE RELAY
TO SOLENOID VALVES
TO PUMP MOTOR RELAY
1077 TAN
1078 BLK/LT GRN
1079 PNK/WHT
152 BLK
RED
GROUND
151 BLK
2 RED
FUSIBLE LINK "D"
B+
VALVE RELAY MONITOR
SOLENOID VALVE RELAY CONTROL
RELAY FEED
4
11
2
8
10
6
32
27
17
20
34

CODE 63

(Page 1 of 2)
SOLENOID VALVE RELAY
(RELAY FAULT)

Circuit Description:
The Solenoid Valve Relay has a dual function. With ignition "ON" and the relay coil not energized, the relay provides ground to the "Antilock" indicator causing it to illuminate. This allows illumination of the "Antilock" indicator when the EBCM is disconnected or disabled. With ignition "ON" and the relay coil energized, the relay supplies battery voltage to the solenoid valves. This allows the EBCM to control actuation and position of the solenoid valves by controlling the ground path. CKT 1077 allows the EBCM to monitor the state of the Solenoid Valve Relay to compare with the requested state.

Failure Conditions:
Code 63 will set if the valve relay monitor is at B+ when the EBCM is not requesting it to be, or if the EBCM is requesting the Solenoid Valve Relay be energized and the valve relay monitor voltage is less than 5 volts.

Action Taken:
If a failure is detected which causes a Solenoid Valve Relay Code 63 to set, antilock braking is disabled and the EBCM turns "ON" the "Antilock" indicator for the remainder of the ignition cycle. If the failure is intermittent, the EBCM will enable the system at the next ignition cycle and a History Code 63 will be present.

Test Description: Number(s) below refer to circled number(s) on the diagnostic chart.
1. Checks for proper resistance of the relay coil.
2. Checks for the relay contacts stuck in the normally open position.
3. Checks for the relay contacts stuck in the normally closed position.
4. Checks for integrity of the circuitry internal to the modulator.
5. Checks for a good pump motor ground circuit.
6. Checks for an open in the Valve Relay Monitor circuit.
7. Checks for an open in the Solenoid Valve Relay coil switched ground circuit.
8. Checks for an open in the Relay Feed (coil battery feed) circuit.

GC402920048000AX

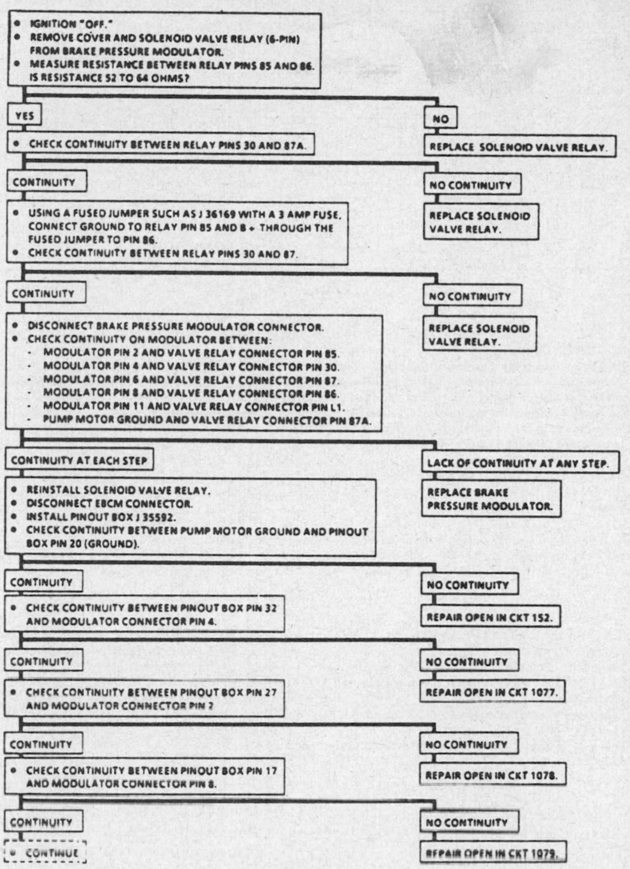
• IGNITION "OFF."
• REMOVE COVER AND SOLENOID VALVE RELAY (6-PIN) FROM BRAKE PRESSURE MODULATOR.
• MEASURE RESISTANCE BETWEEN RELAY PINS 85 AND 86. IS RESISTANCE 52 TO 64 OHMS?
YES
NO
• CHECK CONTINUITY BETWEEN RELAY PINS 30 AND 87A.
REPLACE SOLENOID VALVE RELAY.
CONTINUITY
NO CONTINUITY
• USING A FUSED JUMPER SUCH AS J 36169 WITH A 3 AMP FUSE, CONNECT GROUND TO RELAY PIN 85 AND B+ THROUGH THE FUSED JUMPER TO PIN 86.
• CHECK CONTINUITY BETWEEN RELAY PINS 30 AND 87.
REPLACE SOLENOID VALVE RELAY.
CONTINUITY
NO CONTINUITY
• DISCONNECT BRAKE PRESSURE MODULATOR CONNECTOR.
• CHECK CONTINUITY ON MODULATOR BETWEEN:
- MODULATOR PIN 2 AND VALVE RELAY CONNECTOR PIN 85.
- MODULATOR PIN 4 AND VALVE RELAY CONNECTOR PIN 30.
- MODULATOR PIN 6 AND VALVE RELAY CONNECTOR PIN 87.
- MODULATOR PIN 8 AND VALVE RELAY CONNECTOR PIN 86.
- MODULATOR PIN 11 AND VALVE RELAY CONNECTOR PIN L1.
- PUMP MOTOR GROUND AND VALVE RELAY CONNECTOR PIN 87A.
REPLACE SOLENOID VALVE RELAY.
CONTINUITY AT EACH STEP
LACK OF CONTINUITY AT ANY STEP.
• REINSTALL SOLENOID VALVE RELAY.
• DISCONNECT EBCM CONNECTOR.
• INSTALL PINOUT BOX J 35592.
• CHECK CONTINUITY BETWEEN PUMP MOTOR GROUND AND PINOUT BOX PIN 20 (GROUND).
REPLACE BRAKE PRESSURE MODULATOR.
CONTINUITY
NO CONTINUITY
• CHECK CONTINUITY BETWEEN PINOUT BOX PIN 32 AND MODULATOR CONNECTOR PIN 4.
REPAIR OPEN IN CKT 152.
CONTINUITY
NO CONTINUITY
• CHECK CONTINUITY BETWEEN PINOUT BOX PIN 27 AND MODULATOR CONNECTOR PIN 2
REPAIR OPEN IN CKT 1077.
CONTINUITY
NO CONTINUITY
• CHECK CONTINUITY BETWEEN PINOUT BOX PIN 17 AND MODULATOR CONNECTOR PIN 8.
REPAIR OPEN IN CKT 1078.
CONTINUITY
NO CONTINUITY
• CONTINUE
REPAIR OPEN IN CKT 1079.

GC402920048000BX

Fig. 42 Code 63: Solenoid Valve Relay Fault (Part 1 of 2). 1992–93 Caprice, Custom Cruiser & Roadmaster

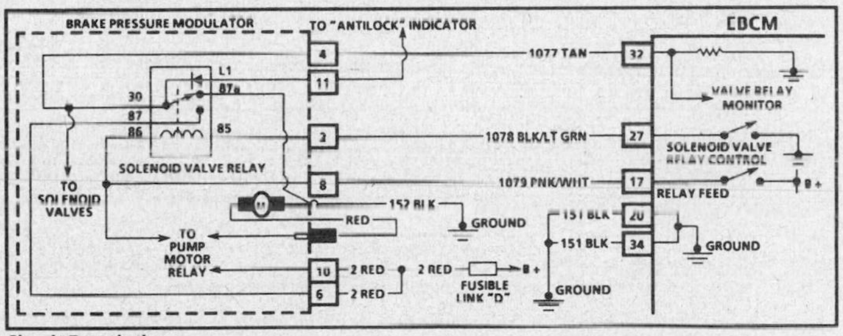
BRAKE PRESSURE MODULATOR
TO "ANTILOCK" INDICATOR
EBCM
L1
87a
30
87
86
85
SOLENOID VALVE RELAY
TO SOLENOID VALVES
TO PUMP MOTOR RELAY
1077 TAN
1078 BLK/LT GRN
1079 PNK/WHT
152 BLK
RED
GROUND
151 BLK
2 RED
FUSIBLE LINK "D"
B+
VALVE RELAY MONITOR
SOLENOID VALVE RELAY CONTROL
RELAY FEED

Circuit Description:
The Solenoid Valve Relay has a dual function. With ignition "ON" and the relay coil not energized, the relay provides ground to the "Antilock" indicator causing it to illuminate. This allows illumination of the "Antilock" indicator when the EBCM is disconnected or disabled. With ignition "ON" and the relay coil energized, the relay supplies battery voltage to the solenoid valves. This allows the EBCM to control actuation and position of the solenoid valves by controlling the ground path. CKT 1077 allows the EBCM to monitor the state of the Solenoid Valve Relay to compare with the requested state.

Failure Conditions:
Code 63 will set if the valve relay monitor is at B+ when the EBCM is not requesting it to be, or if the EBCM is requesting the Solenoid Valve Relay be energized and the valve relay monitor voltage is less than 5 volts.

Action Taken:
If a failure is detected which causes a Solenoid Valve Relay Code 63 to set, antilock braking is disabled and the EBCM turns "ON" the "Antilock" indicator for the remainder of the ignition cycle. If the failure is intermittent, the EBCM will enable the system at the next ignition cycle and a History Code 63 will be present.

Test Description: Number(s) below refer to circled number(s) on the diagnostic chart.
9. Checks for a short to ground in the Valve Relay Monitor circuit.
10. Checks for a short to ground in the Solenoid Valve Relay coil switch ground circuit.
11. Checks for a short to ground in the Relay Feed (coil battery feed) circuit.
12. Checks for a short to B+ in the Valve Relay Monitor circuit.
13. Checks for a short B+ in the Solenoid Valve Relay coil switched ground circuit.
14. Checks for an open in the modulator battery feed circuit.
15. Checks for a short to ground internal to the modulator.
16. Checks for improper connections which may have set the code.
17. Checks for a code which may have set falsely

Diagnostic Aids:

All tests which require a connection to pinout box Pin 20 are using this pin as ground. This assumes the integrity of ground CKT 151 has been maintained.

A disconnected or improperly seated Brake Pressure Modulator connector may set this code.

GC402920048000CX

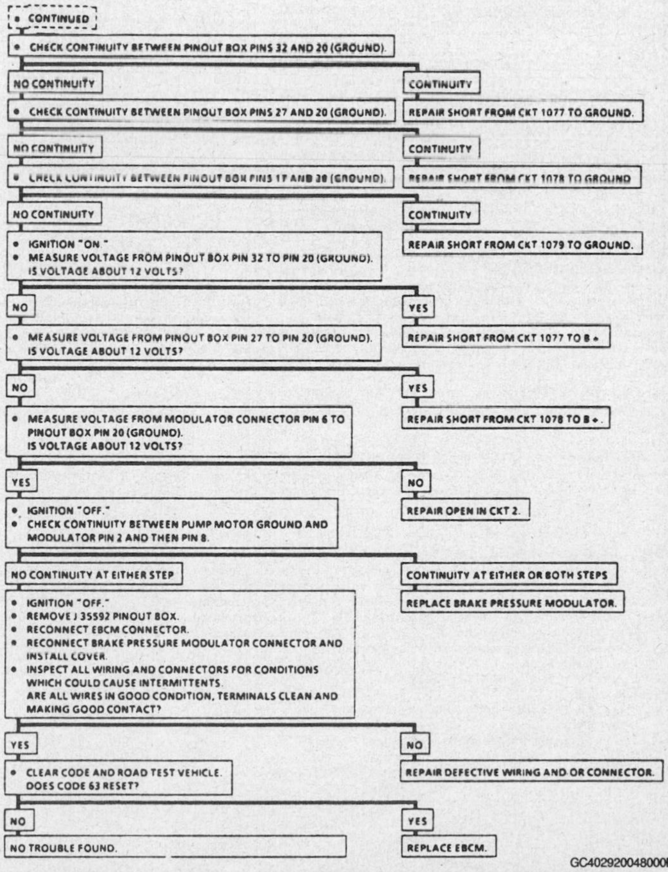
• CONTINUED
• CHECK CONTINUITY BETWEEN PINOUT BOX PINS 32 AND 20 (GROUND).
NO CONTINUITY
CONTINUITY
• CHECK CONTINUITY BETWEEN PINOUT BOX PINS 27 AND 20 (GROUND).
REPAIR SHORT FROM CKT 1077 TO GROUND.
NO CONTINUITY
CONTINUITY
• CHECK CONTINUITY BETWEEN PINOUT BOX PINS 17 AND 20 (GROUND).
REPAIR SHORT FROM CKT 1078 TO GROUND.
NO CONTINUITY
CONTINUITY
• IGNITION "ON."
• MEASURE VOLTAGE FROM PINOUT BOX PIN 32 TO PIN 20 (GROUND). IS VOLTAGE ABOUT 12 VOLTS?
REPAIR SHORT FROM CKT 1079 TO GROUND.
NO
YES
• MEASURE VOLTAGE FROM PINOUT BOX PIN 27 TO PIN 20 (GROUND). IS VOLTAGE ABOUT 12 VOLTS?
REPAIR SHORT FROM CKT 1077 TO B+.
NO
YES
• MEASURE VOLTAGE FROM MODULATOR CONNECTOR PIN 6 TO PINOUT BOX PIN 20 (GROUND). IS VOLTAGE ABOUT 12 VOLTS?
REPAIR SHORT FROM CKT 1078 TO B+.
YES
NO
• IGNITION "OFF."
• CHECK CONTINUITY BETWEEN PUMP MOTOR GROUND AND MODULATOR PIN 2 AND THEN PIN 8.
REPAIR OPEN IN CKT 2.
NO CONTINUITY AT EITHER STEP
CONTINUITY AT EITHER OR BOTH STEPS
REPLACE BRAKE PRESSURE MODULATOR.
• IGNITION "OFF."
• REMOVE J 35592 PINOUT BOX.
• RECONNECT EBCM CONNECTOR.
• RECONNECT BRAKE PRESSURE MODULATOR CONNECTOR AND INSTALL COVER.
• INSPECT ALL WIRING AND CONNECTORS FOR CONDITIONS WHICH COULD CAUSE INTERMITTENTS. ARE ALL WIRES IN GOOD CONDITION, TERMINALS CLEAN AND MAKING GOOD CONTACT?
YES
NO
• CLEAR CODE AND ROAD TEST VEHICLE. DOES CODE 63 RESET?
REPAIR DEFECTIVE WIRING AND OR CONNECTOR.
NO
YES
NO TROUBLE FOUND.
REPLACE EBCM.

GC402920048000DX

Fig. 42 Code 63: Solenoid Valve Relay Fault (Part 2 of 2). 1992–93 Caprice, Custom Cruiser & Roadmaster

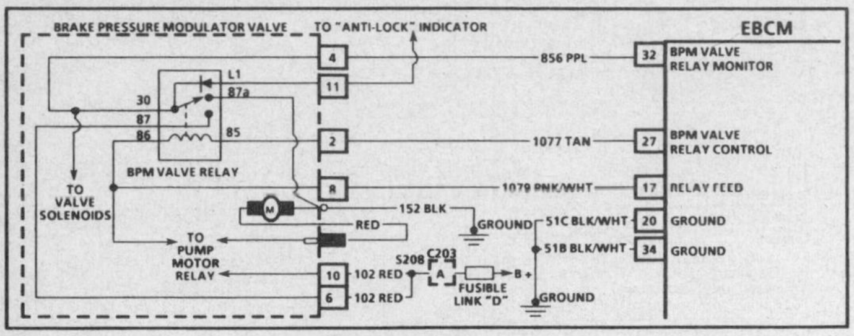
BRAKE PRESSURE MODULATOR VALVE
TO "ANTI-LOCK" INDICATOR
EBCM
856 PPL
32 BPM VALVE RELAY MONITOR
L1
87a
30
87
86
85
1077 TAN
27 BPM VALVE RELAY CONTROL
BPM VALVE RELAY
TO VALVE SOLENOIDS
1079 PNK/WHT
17 RELAY FEED
152 BLK
RED
GROUND
51C BLK/WHT
20 GROUND
51B BLK/WHT
34 GROUND
TO PUMP MOTOR RELAY
S208
C203
102 RED
FUSIBLE LINK "D"
B+
GROUND

DTC 63

(Page 1 of 2)

BPM VALVE RELAY MALFUNCTION

Circuit Description:

The BPM valve relay has a dual function. With ignition "ON" and the relay coil not energized, the relay provides ground to the ABS warning lamp causing it to illuminate. This allows illumination of the ABS warning lamp when the EBCM is disconnected or disabled. With ignition "ON" and the relay coil energized, the relay supplies battery voltage to the valve solenoids. This allows the EBCM to control actuation and position of the valve solenoids by controlling the ground path. CKT 856 allows the EBCM to monitor the state of the BPM valve relay to compare with the requested state.

DTC 63 Will Set When: The BPM valve relay monitor is at B+ when the EBCM is not requesting it to be, or if the EBCM is requesting the BPM valve relay be energized and the BPM valve relay monitor voltage is less than 5 volts.

Action Taken: If a malfunction is detected which causes a BPM valve relay DTC 63 to set, antilock braking is disabled and the EBCM turns "ON" the ABS warning lamp for the remainder of the ignition cycle. If the malfunction is intermittent, the EBCM will enable the system at the next ignition cycle and a history DTC 63 will be present.

DTC Chart Test Description: Number(s) below refer to circled number(s) on the diagnostic chart.

1. Checks for proper resistance of the relay coil.
2. Checks for the relay contacts stuck in the normally open position.
3. Checks for the relay contacts stuck in the normally closed position.
4. Checks for integrity of the circuitry internal to the BPM valve.
5. Checks for a good pump motor ground circuit.
6. Checks for an open in the BPM valve relay monitor circuit.
7. Checks for an open in the BPM valve relay coil switched ground circuit.
8. Checks for an open in the relay feed (coil battery feed) circuit.

GC402940093101AX

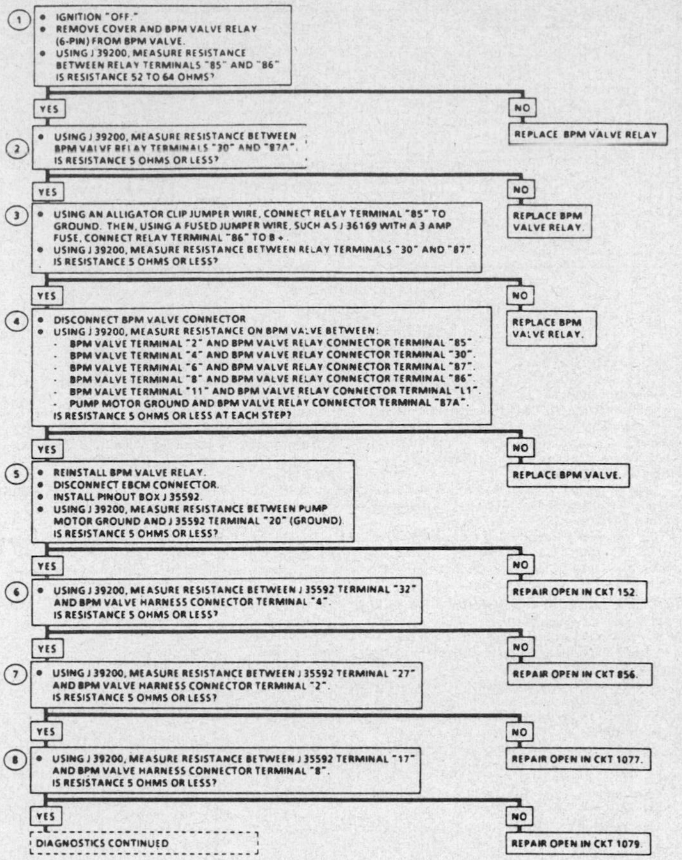
(1) • IGNITION "OFF."
• REMOVE COVER AND BPM VALVE RELAY (6-PIN) FROM BPM VALVE.
• USING J 39200, MEASURE RESISTANCE BETWEEN RELAY TERMINALS "85" AND "86"
IS RESISTANCE 52 TO 64 OHMS?
YES
NO
REPLACE BPM VALVE RELAY
(2) • USING J 39200, MEASURE RESISTANCE BETWEEN BPM VALVE RELAY TERMINALS "30" AND "87A".
IS RESISTANCE 5 OHMS OR LESS?
YES
NO
REPLACE BPM VALVE RELAY.
(3) • USING AN ALLIGATOR CLIP JUMPER WIRE, CONNECT RELAY TERMINAL "85" TO GROUND. THEN, USING A FUSED JUMPER WIRE, SUCH AS J 36169 WITH A 3 AMP FUSE, CONNECT RELAY TERMINAL "86" TO B+.
• USING J 39200, MEASURE RESISTANCE BETWEEN RELAY TERMINALS "30" AND "87".
IS RESISTANCE 5 OHMS OR LESS?
YES
NO
REPLACE BPM VALVE RELAY.
(4) • DISCONNECT BPM VALVE CONNECTOR
• USING J 39200, MEASURE RESISTANCE ON BPM VALVE BETWEEN:
- BPM VALVE TERMINAL "2" AND BPM VALVE RELAY CONNECTOR TERMINAL "85"
- BPM VALVE TERMINAL "4" AND BPM VALVE RELAY CONNECTOR TERMINAL "30".
- BPM VALVE TERMINAL "6" AND BPM VALVE RELAY CONNECTOR TERMINAL "87".
- BPM VALVE TERMINAL "8" AND BPM VALVE RELAY CONNECTOR TERMINAL "86".
- BPM VALVE TERMINAL "11" AND BPM VALVE RELAY CONNECTOR TERMINAL "L1".
- PUMP MOTOR GROUND AND BPM VALVE RELAY CONNECTOR TERMINAL "87A".
IS RESISTANCE 5 OHMS OR LESS AT EACH STEP?
YES
NO
REPLACE BPM VALVE.
(5) • REINSTALL BPM VALVE RELAY.
• DISCONNECT EBCM CONNECTOR.
• INSTALL PINOUT BOX J 35592.
• USING J 39200, MEASURE RESISTANCE BETWEEN PUMP MOTOR GROUND AND J 35592 TERMINAL "20" (GROUND).
IS RESISTANCE 5 OHMS OR LESS?
YES
NO
REPAIR OPEN IN CKT 152.
(6) • USING J 39200, MEASURE RESISTANCE BETWEEN J 35592 TERMINAL "32" AND BPM VALVE HARNESS CONNECTOR TERMINAL "4".
IS RESISTANCE 5 OHMS OR LESS?
YES
NO
REPAIR OPEN IN CKT 856.
(7) • USING J 39200, MEASURE RESISTANCE BETWEEN J 35592 TERMINAL "27" AND BPM VALVE HARNESS CONNECTOR TERMINAL "2".
IS RESISTANCE 5 OHMS OR LESS?
YES
NO
REPAIR OPEN IN CKT 1077.
(8) • USING J 39200, MEASURE RESISTANCE BETWEEN J 35592 TERMINAL "17" AND BPM VALVE HARNESS CONNECTOR TERMINAL "8".
IS RESISTANCE 5 OHMS OR LESS?
YES
NO
REPAIR OPEN IN CKT 1079.
DIAGNOSTICS CONTINUED

GC402940093101BX

Fig. 43 Code 63: BPM Valve Relay Fault (Part 1 of 2). 1994 Caprice, Impala SS & Roadmaster

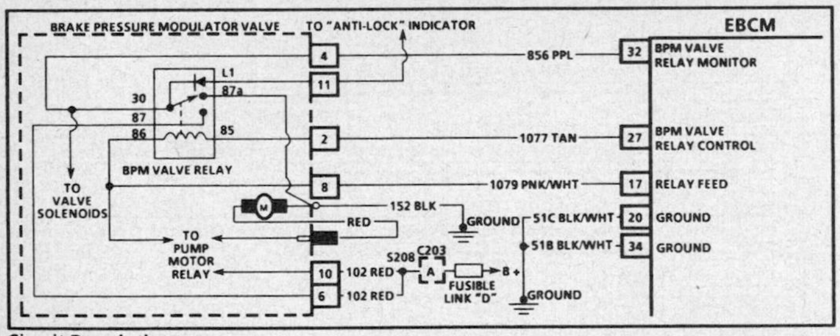
BRAKE PRESSURE MODULATOR VALVE
TO "ANTI-LOCK" INDICATOR
EBCM
856 PPL
32 BPM VALVE RELAY MONITOR
L1
87a
30
87
86
85
1077 TAN
27 BPM VALVE RELAY CONTROL
BPM VALVE RELAY
TO VALVE SOLENOIDS
1079 PNK/WHT
17 RELAY FEED
152 BLK
RED
GROUND
51C BLK/WHT
20 GROUND
51B BLK/WHT
34 GROUND
TO PUMP MOTOR RELAY
S208
C203
102 RED
FUSIBLE LINK "D"
B+
GROUND

Circuit Description:

The BPM valve relay has a dual function. With ignition "ON" and the relay coil not energized, the relay provides ground to the ABS warning lamp causing it to illuminate. This allows illumination of the ABS warning lamp when the EBCM is disconnected or disabled. With ignition "ON" and the relay coil energized, the relay supplies battery voltage to the valve solenoids. This allows the EBCM to control actuation and position of the valve solenoids by controlling the ground path. CKT 856 allows the EBCM to monitor the state of the BPM valve relay to compare with the requested state.

DTC 63 Will Set When: The BPM valve relay monitor is at B+ when the EBCM is not requesting it to be, or if the EBCM is requesting the BPM valve relay be energized and the BPM valve relay monitor voltage is less than 5 volts.

Action Taken: If a malfunction is detected which causes a BPM valve relay DTC 63 to set, antilock braking is disabled and the EBCM turns "ON" the ABS warning lamp for the remainder of the ignition cycle. If the malfunction is intermittent, the EBCM will enable the system at the next ignition cycle and a history DTC 63 will be present.

DTC Chart Test Description: Number(s) below refer to circled number(s) on the diagnostic chart.

9. Checks for a short to ground in the BPM valve relay monitor circuit.
10. Checks for a short to ground in the BPM valve relay coil switched ground circuit.
11. Checks for a short to ground in the relay feed (coil battery feed) circuit.
12. Checks for a short to B+ in the BPM valve relay monitor circuit.
13. Checks for a short B+ in the BPM valve relay coil switched ground circuit.
14. Checks for an open in the BPM valve battery feed circuit.
15. Checks for a short to ground internal to the BPM valve.
16. Checks for improper connections which may have set the DTC.
17. Checks for a DTC which may have set falsely.

Diagnostic Aids: All tests which require a connection to pinout box Pin 20 are using this pin as ground. This assumes the integrity of ground CKT 51 has been maintained.

A disconnected or improperly seated BPM valve connector may set this DTC.

GC402940093102AX

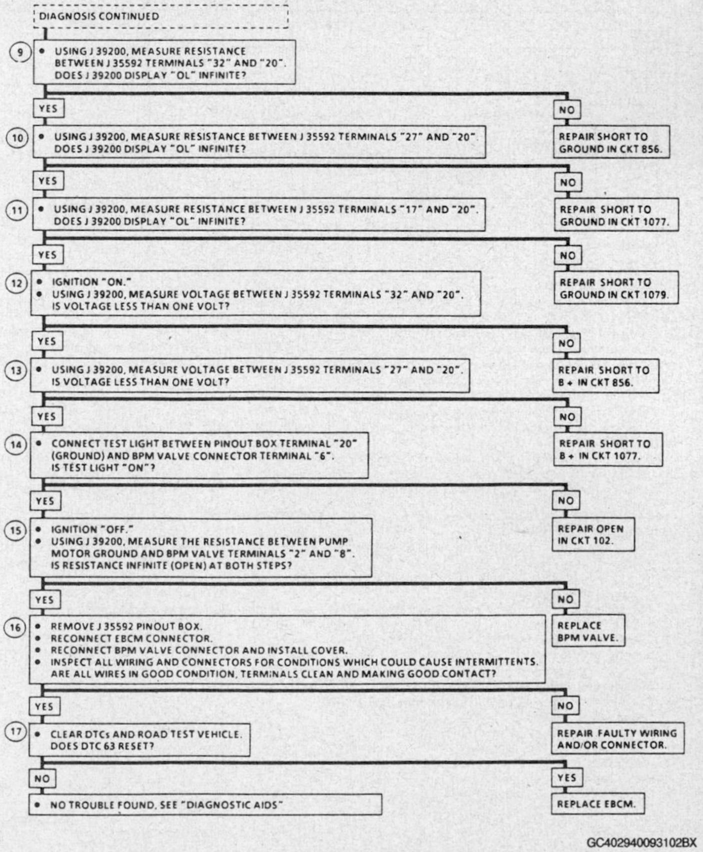
DIAGNOSIS CONTINUED
(9) • USING J 39200, MEASURE RESISTANCE BETWEEN J 35592 TERMINALS "32" AND "20".
DOES J 39200 DISPLAY "OL" INFINITE?
YES
NO
REPAIR SHORT TO GROUND IN CKT 856.
(10) • USING J 39200, MEASURE RESISTANCE BETWEEN J 35592 TERMINALS "27" AND "20".
DOES J 39200 DISPLAY "OL" INFINITE?
YES
NO
REPAIR SHORT TO GROUND IN CKT 1077.
(11) • USING J 39200, MEASURE RESISTANCE BETWEEN J 35592 TERMINALS "17" AND "20".
DOES J 39200 DISPLAY "OL" INFINITE?
YES
NO
REPAIR SHORT TO GROUND IN CKT 1079.
(12) • IGNITION "ON."
• USING J 39200, MEASURE VOLTAGE BETWEEN J 35592 TERMINALS "32" AND "20".
IS VOLTAGE LESS THAN ONE VOLT?
YES
NO
REPAIR SHORT TO B+ IN CKT 856.
(13) • USING J 39200, MEASURE VOLTAGE BETWEEN J 35592 TERMINALS "27" AND "20".
IS VOLTAGE LESS THAN ONE VOLT?
YES
NO
REPAIR SHORT TO B+ IN CKT 1077.
(14) • CONNECT TEST LIGHT BETWEEN PINOUT BOX TERMINAL "20" (GROUND) AND BPM VALVE CONNECTOR TERMINAL "6".
IS TEST LIGHT "ON"?
YES
NO
REPAIR OPEN IN CKT 102.
(15) • IGNITION "OFF."
• USING J 39200, MEASURE THE RESISTANCE BETWEEN PUMP MOTOR GROUND AND BPM VALVE TERMINALS "2" AND "8".
IS RESISTANCE INFINITE (OPEN) AT BOTH STEPS?
YES
NO
REPLACE BPM VALVE.
(16) • REMOVE J 35592 PINOUT BOX.
• RECONNECT EBCM CONNECTOR.
• RECONNECT BPM VALVE CONNECTOR AND INSTALL COVER.
• INSPECT ALL WIRING AND CONNECTORS FOR CONDITIONS WHICH COULD CAUSE INTERMITTENTS.
ARE ALL WIRES IN GOOD CONDITION, TERMINALS CLEAN AND MAKING GOOD CONTACT?
YES
NO
REPAIR FAULTY WIRING AND/OR CONNECTOR.
(17) • CLEAR DTCs AND ROAD TEST VEHICLE.
DOES DTC 63 RESET?
NO
YES
• NO TROUBLE FOUND, SEE "DIAGNOSTIC AIDS"
REPLACE EBCM.

GC402940093102BX

Fig. 43 Code 63: BPM Valve Relay Fault (Part 2 of 2). 1994 Caprice, Impala SS & Roadmaster

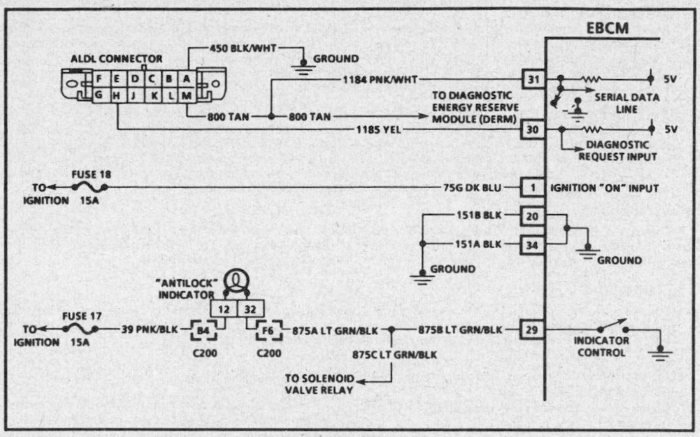
EBCM
ALDL CONNECTOR
450 BLK/WHT
GROUND
1184 PNK/WHT
31
5V
SERIAL DATA LINE
TO DIAGNOSTIC ENERGY RESERVE MODULE (DERM)
800 TAN
800 TAN
1185 YEL
30
5V
DIAGNOSTIC REQUEST INPUT
FUSE 18
TO IGNITION 15A
75G DK BLU
1
IGNITION "ON" INPUT
151B BLK
20
151A BLK
34
GROUND
GROUND
"ANTILOCK" INDICATOR
12
32
FUSE 17
TO IGNITION 15A
39 PNK/BLK
B4
F6
C200
C200
875A LT GRN/BLK
875B LT GRN/BLK
29
INDICATOR CONTROL
875C LT GRN/BLK
TO SOLENOID VALVE RELAY

CODE 71

ELECTRONIC BRAKE CONTROL MODULE (EBCM) (EBCM FAULT)

Circuit Description:

The EBCM has self diagnostics that can detect an internal failure within the module. The EBCM also monitors its supply voltage and the integrity of the EBCM harness connection. When a fault is detected for any of these conditions Code 71 is set.

Action Taken:

If a failure is detected which causes a EBCM Code 71 to set, antilock braking is disabled and the EBCM turns "ON" the "Antilock" indicator for the remainder of the ignition cycle. If the failure is intermittent, the EBCM will enable the system at the next ignition cycle and a History Code 71 will be present.

Test Description: Number(s) below refer to circled number(s) on the diagnostic chart.

1. Checks for additional faults which may be causing Code 71 to set.
2. Checks the integrity of the EBCM ground circuit.
3. Checks for the minimum supply voltage necessary for proper ABS operation.
4. Checks for intermittent connections of the EBCM harness connector and terminals to the EBCM.

GC402920048100AX

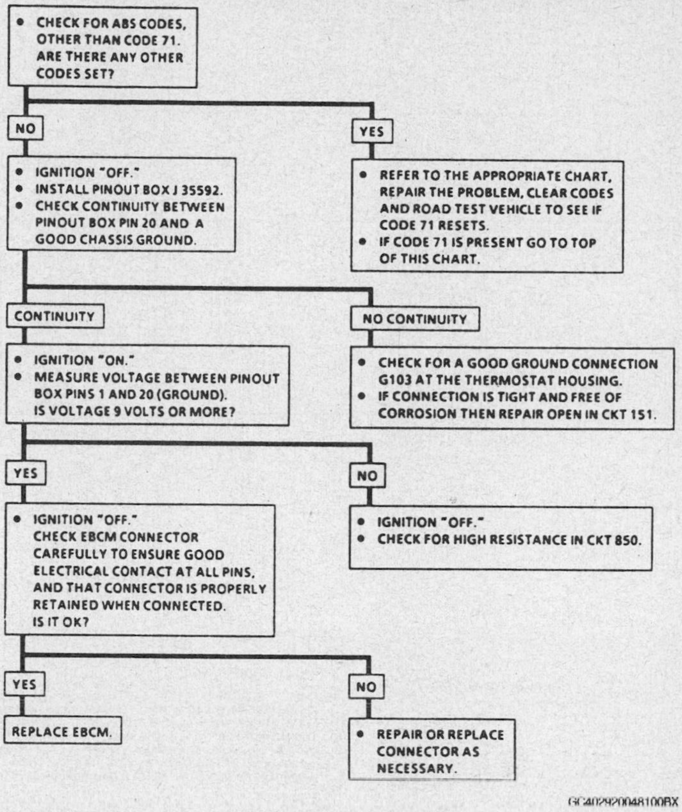
• CHECK FOR ABS CODES, OTHER THAN CODE 71. ARE THERE ANY OTHER CODES SET?
NO
YES
• IGNITION "OFF."
• INSTALL PINOUT BOX J 35592.
• CHECK CONTINUITY BETWEEN PINOUT BOX PIN 20 AND A GOOD CHASSIS GROUND.
• REFER TO THE APPROPRIATE CHART, REPAIR THE PROBLEM, CLEAR CODES AND ROAD TEST VEHICLE TO SEE IF CODE 71 RESETS.
• IF CODE 71 IS PRESENT GO TO TOP OF THIS CHART.
CONTINUITY
NO CONTINUITY
• IGNITION "ON."
• MEASURE VOLTAGE BETWEEN PINOUT BOX PINS 1 AND 20 (GROUND). IS VOLTAGE 9 VOLTS OR MORE?
• CHECK FOR A GOOD GROUND CONNECTION G103 AT THE THERMOSTAT HOUSING.
• IF CONNECTION IS TIGHT AND FREE OF CORROSION THEN REPAIR OPEN IN CKT 151.
YES
NO
• IGNITION "OFF." CHECK EBCM CONNECTOR CAREFULLY TO ENSURE GOOD ELECTRICAL CONTACT AT ALL PINS, AND THAT CONNECTOR IS PROPERLY RETAINED WHEN CONNECTED. IS IT OK?
• IGNITION "OFF."
• CHECK FOR HIGH RESISTANCE IN CKT 850.
YES
NO
REPLACE EBCM.
• REPAIR OR REPLACE CONNECTOR AS NECESSARY.
GC402920048100BX

Fig. 44 Code 71: EBCM Fault. 1992–93 Caprice, Custom Cruiser & Roadmaster

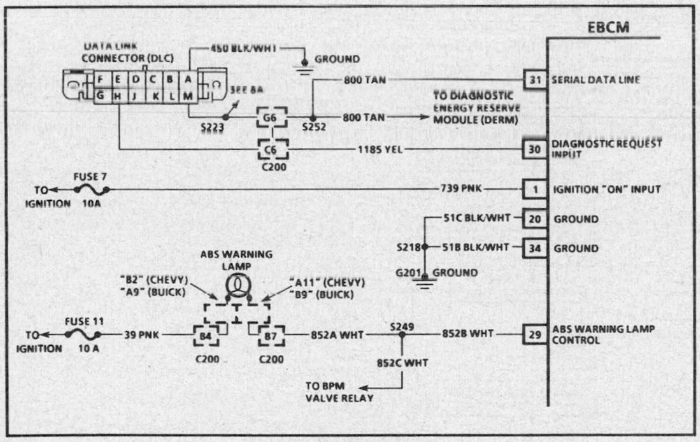
EBCM
DATA LINK CONNECTOR (DLC)
450 BLK/WHT
GROUND
SEE 8A
800 TAN
31
SERIAL DATA LINE
S223
G6
S252
800 TAN
TO DIAGNOSTIC ENERGY RESERVE MODULE (DERM)
C6
C200
1185 YEL
30
DIAGNOSTIC REQUEST INPUT
FUSE 7
TO IGNITION 10A
739 PNK
1
IGNITION "ON" INPUT
51C BLK/WHT
20
GROUND
S218
51B BLK/WHT
34
GROUND
G201
GROUND
ABS WARNING LAMP
"B2" (CHEVY) "A9" (BUICK)
"A11" (CHEVY) "B9" (BUICK)
FUSE 11
TO IGNITION 10 A
39 PNK
B4
B7
852A WHT
S249
852B WHT
29
ABS WARNING LAMP CONTROL
C200
C200
852C WHT
TO BPM VALVE RELAY

DTC 71

EBCM INTERNAL MALFUNCTION (EBCM FAULT)

Circuit Description:

The EBCM has self diagnostics that can detect an internal malfunction within the module. The EBCM also monitors its supply voltage and the integrity of the EBCM harness connection. When a malfunction is detected for any of these conditions DTC 71 is set.

Action Taken: If a malfunction is detected which causes a EBCM DTC 71 to set, antilock braking is disabled and the EBCM turns "ON" the ABS warning lamp for the remainder of the ignition cycle. If the malfunction is intermittent, the EBCM will enable the system at the next ignition cycle and a history DTC 71 will be present.

DTC Chart Test Description: Number(s) below refer to circled number(s) on the diagnostic chart.

1. Checks for additional malfunctions which may be causing DTC 71 to set.
2. Checks the integrity of the EBCM ground circuit.
3. Checks for the minimum supply voltage necessary for proper ABS operation.
4. Checks for intermittent connections of the EBCM harness connector and terminals to the EBCM.

GC402940093200AX

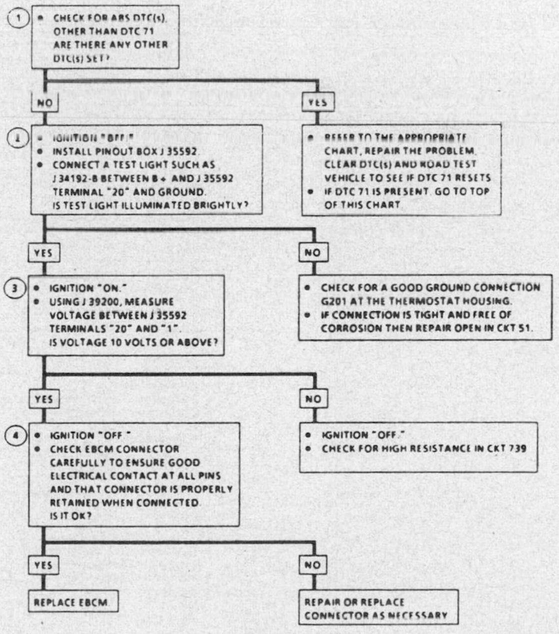
1
• CHECK FOR ABS DTC(s). OTHER THAN DTC 71 ARE THERE ANY OTHER DTC(s) SET?
NO
YES
2
• IGNITION "OFF."
• INSTALL PINOUT BOX J 35592.
• CONNECT A TEST LIGHT SUCH AS J 34192-B BETWEEN B+ AND J 35592 TERMINAL "20" AND GROUND. IS TEST LIGHT ILLUMINATED BRIGHTLY?
• REFER TO THE APPROPRIATE CHART, REPAIR THE PROBLEM. CLEAR DTC(s) AND ROAD TEST VEHICLE TO SEE IF DTC 71 RESETS
• IF DTC 71 IS PRESENT. GO TO TOP OF THIS CHART.
YES
NO
3
• IGNITION "ON."
• USING J 39200, MEASURE VOLTAGE BETWEEN J 35592 TERMINALS "20" AND "1". IS VOLTAGE 10 VOLTS OR ABOVE?
• CHECK FOR A GOOD GROUND CONNECTION G201 AT THE THERMOSTAT HOUSING.
• IF CONNECTION IS TIGHT AND FREE OF CORROSION THEN REPAIR OPEN IN CKT 51.
YES
NO
4
• IGNITION "OFF."
• CHECK EBCM CONNECTOR CAREFULLY TO ENSURE GOOD ELECTRICAL CONTACT AT ALL PINS AND THAT CONNECTOR IS PROPERLY RETAINED WHEN CONNECTED. IS IT OK?
• IGNITION "OFF."
• CHECK FOR HIGH RESISTANCE IN CKT 739
YES
NO
REPLACE EBCM.
REPAIR OR REPLACE CONNECTOR AS NECESSARY
GC402940093200BX

Fig. 45 Code 71: EBCM Fault. 1994 Caprice, Impala SS & Roadmaster

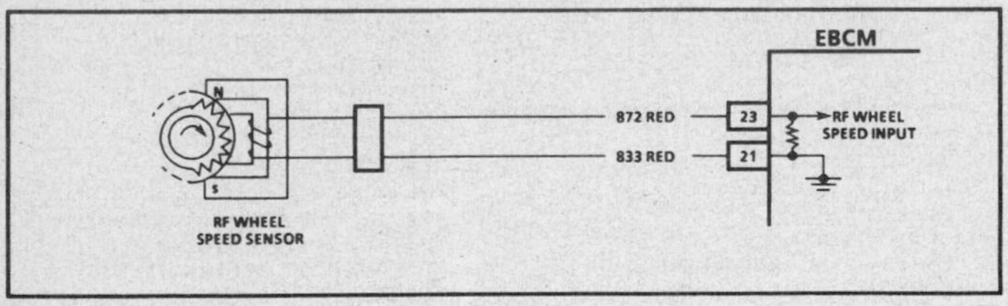
EBCM
872 RED
833 RED
23
21
RF WHEEL SPEED INPUT
N
S
RF WHEEL SPEED SENSOR

GC402920046900AX

Circuit Description:

As each wheel turns, the speed sensor for that wheel creates an AC voltage as the toothed ring rotates by the stationary sensor. The sensor consists of a permanent magnet and coil generating voltage by magnetic induction. The frequency and voltage of the induced signal is proportional to wheel speed.

The EBCM uses the speed sensor signal to calculate vehicle reference speed, individual speed, acceleration and slip values for each wheel which determine when antilock control is required.

Failure Conditions:

The EBCM performs two types of tests on the speed sensors to check continuity and output. Any condition which would result in lack of continuity or output on the right front wheel speed sensor circuit could result in setting Code 21. These conditions include an open, short to ground or short to B+ in CKT 872, an open in CKT 833 or an open across the sensor coil. Conditions which cause a low output from the speed sensor, such as a shorted sensor coil or an improperly installed sensor, will also set a Code 21.

Action Taken:

If a failure is detected which causes a speed sensor Code 21 to set, antilock braking is disabled and the EBCM turns "ON" the "Antilock" indicator for the remainder of the ignition cycle. If the failure is intermittent, the EBCM will enable the system at the next ignition cycle and a history Code 21 will be present.

Important

- The RF wheel speed sensor is located in the RF steering knuckle. In order to prevent electromagnetic interference from disturbing the speed sensor signal, the sensor wires are twisted together 9 times for every foot of wire. If wiring repairs are necessary, refer to "Wiring Repair Procedures"

Test Description: Number(s) below refer to circled number(s) on the diagnostic chart.

1. Checks for a correct resistance reading of the sensor itself.
2. Checks for a short between the wires for the RF wheel speed sensor.
3. Checks for an open, high resistance or short to voltage in the wires between the speed sensor and the EBCM.
4. Checks for a short to ground in CKT 872.
5. Checks for an "Intermittent" in the RF wheel speed sensor circuitry. If no "Intermittent" is found in the wiring, it may be in the sensor itself. Replace the sensor and road test the vehicle. If the code returns, replace the EBCM.

Diagnostic Aids:

Setting of speed sensor fault codes may be caused by improperly mounted sensors or improper wire routing. Verify that the sensor is properly mounted and free of foreign material such as metallic particles, dirt or grease. Verify that sensor wires are properly routed and secure. Improper RF Wheel Speed Sensor wire routing may cause Code 25 and/or Code 35 to set. To aid in troubleshooting intermittent conditions the Tech 1 can be used while test driving the vehicle however, antilock braking will be disabled. Refer to the Tech 1 Brake Cartridge Operators Manual for additional information. If this does not identify the intermittent, wet the speed sensor harness on the underside of the vehicle and road test monitoring wheel speeds with the Tech 1.

GC402920046900BX

NOTE: THIS CODE WILL SET ONLY WHEN AN OFF-BOARD SERIAL DATA DEVICE, SUCH AS THE TECH 1 (T-1) IS ATTEMPTING TO COMMUNICATE WITH THE EBCM. SINCE, BY DEFINITION, THIS CODE MEANS YOU CANNOT COMMUNICATE WITH THE EBCM USING AN OFF-BOARD SERIAL DATA DEVICE, YOU MUST READ AND CLEAR THE CODE USING ALDL FLASH CODE AND CODE CLEARING TECHNIQUES.

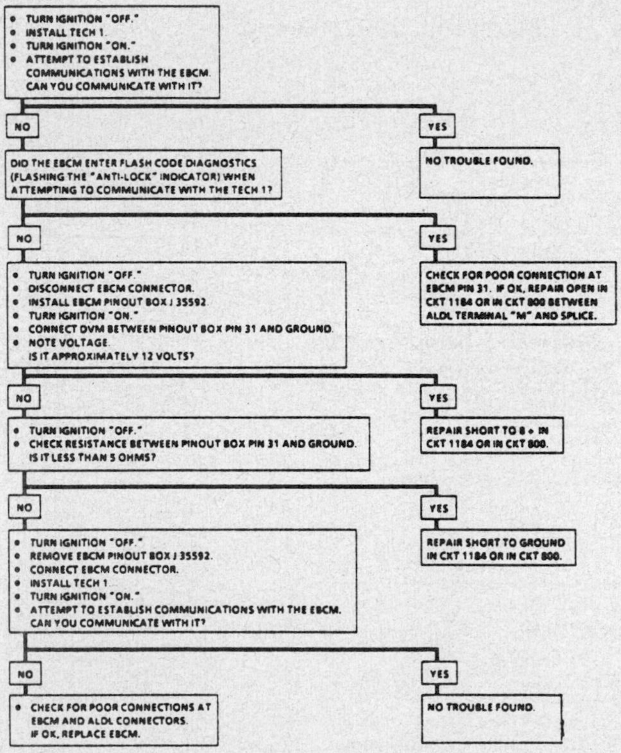
• TURN IGNITION "OFF."
• INSTALL TECH 1.
• TURN IGNITION "ON."
• ATTEMPT TO ESTABLISH COMMUNICATIONS WITH THE EBCM. CAN YOU COMMUNICATE WITH IT?
NO
YES
NO TROUBLE FOUND.
DID THE EBCM ENTER FLASH CODE DIAGNOSTICS (FLASHING THE "ANTI-LOCK" INDICATOR) WHEN ATTEMPTING TO COMMUNICATE WITH THE TECH 1?
NO
YES
CHECK FOR POOR CONNECTION AT EBCM PIN 31. IF OK, REPAIR OPEN IN CKT 1184 OR IN CKT 800 BETWEEN ALDL TERMINAL "M" AND SPLICE.
• TURN IGNITION "OFF."
• DISCONNECT EBCM CONNECTOR.
• INSTALL EBCM PINOUT BOX J 35592.
• TURN IGNITION "ON."
• CONNECT DVM BETWEEN PINOUT BOX PIN 31 AND GROUND.
• NOTE VOLTAGE. IS IT APPROXIMATELY 12 VOLTS?
NO
YES
REPAIR SHORT TO B+ IN CKT 1184 OR IN CKT 800.
• TURN IGNITION "OFF."
• CHECK RESISTANCE BETWEEN PINOUT BOX PIN 31 AND GROUND. IS IT LESS THAN 5 OHMS?
NO
YES
REPAIR SHORT TO GROUND IN CKT 1184 OR IN CKT 800.
• TURN IGNITION "OFF."
• REMOVE EBCM PINOUT BOX J 35592.
• CONNECT EBCM CONNECTOR.
• INSTALL TECH 1.
• TURN IGNITION "ON."
• ATTEMPT TO ESTABLISH COMMUNICATIONS WITH THE EBCM. CAN YOU COMMUNICATE WITH IT?
NO
YES
• CHECK FOR POOR CONNECTIONS AT EBCM AND ALDL CONNECTORS. IF OK, REPLACE EBCM.
NO TROUBLE FOUND.

GC402920048200CX

Fig. 46 Code 72: EBCM Serial Line Data Fault. 1992 Caprice, Custom Cruiser & Roadmaster

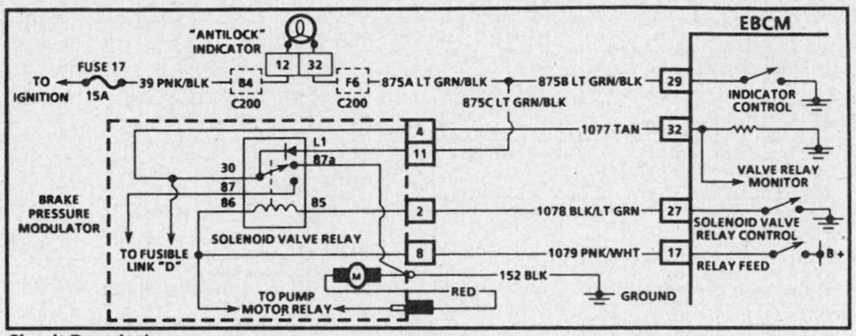
"ANTILOCK" INDICATOR
EBCM
FUSE 17
TO IGNITION
15A
39 PNK/BLK
B4
C200
12
32
F6
C200
875A LT GRN/BLK
875B LT GRN/BLK
875C LT GRN/BLK
29
INDICATOR CONTROL
4
11
1077 TAN
32
VALVE RELAY MONITOR
L1
30
87a
87
86
85
BRAKE PRESSURE MODULATOR
SOLENOID VALVE RELAY
2
1078 BLK/LT GRN
27
SOLENOID VALVE RELAY CONTROL
TO FUSIBLE LINK "D"
8
1079 PNK/WHT
17
RELAY FEED
B+
152 BLK
RED
TO PUMP MOTOR RELAY
GROUND

Circuit Description:

The "Antilock" Indicator is located on the right side of the instrument panel. Battery voltage is applied with ignition in "Run, Bulb Test or Start" through Fuse 17 and CKT 39. The indicator is grounded through CKT 875 and is controlled by the EBCM at Pin "29" and the Modulator at Pin "11" through the Solenoid Valve Relay. The EBCM will supply ground to the indicator for approximately 2 seconds when ignition is first turned "ON." During the first 2 seconds, if no faults are detected, the EBCM will energize the Solenoid Valve Relay. With the relay energized, the ground CKT 875 through the relay will be opened. This allows the indicator to go "OFF" when the EBCM indicator control line at Pin "29" is opened.

Test Description: Number(s) below refer to circled number(s) on the diagnostic chart.

1. Checks for proper battery and/or charging system operation.
2. Checks for an open fuse in the EBCM power feed circuit.
3. Checks for an open in the EBCM power feed circuit.
4. Checks for an open in the EBCM ground circuit.
5. Checks for a possible fault in the Solenoid Valve Relay.
6. Determines whether the fault is in the Solenoid Valve Relay or the EBCM.
7. Checks for a short to ground in the EBCM or the EBCM power feed circuit.
8. Determines whether the short to ground is in the EBCM or the EBCM power feed circuit.
9. Determines whether the short to ground is in the Brake Pressure Modulator or the indicator control circuit.

GC402920048300AX

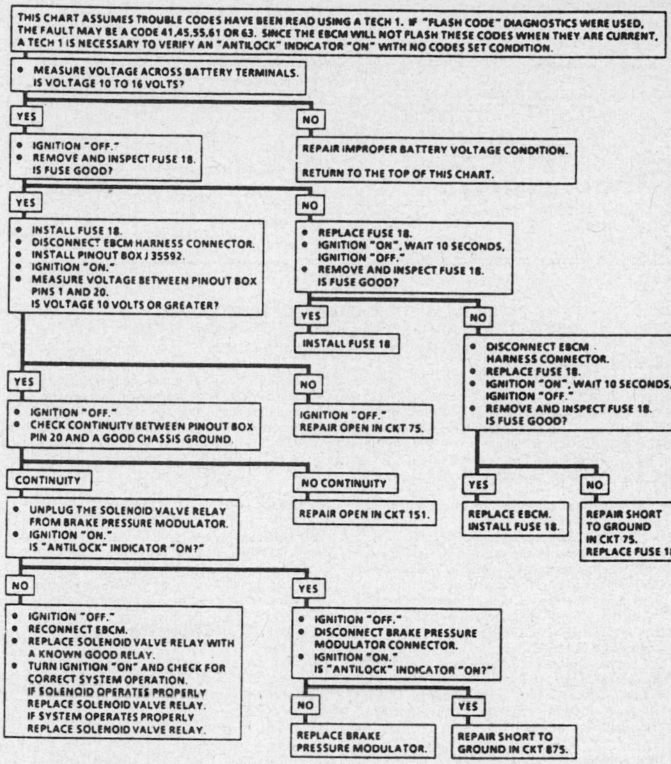
THIS CHART ASSUMES TROUBLE CODES HAVE BEEN READ USING A TECH 1. IF "FLASH CODE" DIAGNOSTICS WERE USED, THE FAULT MAY BE A CODE 41,45,55,61 OR 63. SINCE THE EBCM WILL NOT FLASH THESE CODES WHEN THEY ARE CURRENT, A TECH 1 IS NECESSARY TO VERIFY AN "ANTILOCK" INDICATOR "ON" WITH NO CODES SET CONDITION.
• MEASURE VOLTAGE ACROSS BATTERY TERMINALS. IS VOLTAGE 10 TO 16 VOLTS?
YES
NO
• IGNITION "OFF." • REMOVE AND INSPECT FUSE 18. IS FUSE GOOD?
REPAIR IMPROPER BATTERY VOLTAGE CONDITION. RETURN TO THE TOP OF THIS CHART.
YES
NO
• INSTALL FUSE 18. • DISCONNECT EBCM HARNESS CONNECTOR. • INSTALL PINOUT BOX J 35592. • IGNITION "ON." • MEASURE VOLTAGE BETWEEN PINOUT BOX PINS 1 AND 20. IS VOLTAGE 10 VOLTS OR GREATER?
• REPLACE FUSE 18. • IGNITION "ON", WAIT 10 SECONDS, IGNITION "OFF." • REMOVE AND INSPECT FUSE 18. IS FUSE GOOD?
YES
NO
INSTALL FUSE 18
• DISCONNECT EBCM HARNESS CONNECTOR. • REPLACE FUSE 18. • IGNITION "ON", WAIT 10 SECONDS, IGNITION "OFF." • REMOVE AND INSPECT FUSE 18. IS FUSE GOOD?
YES
NO
• IGNITION "OFF." • CHECK CONTINUITY BETWEEN PINOUT BOX PIN 20 AND A GOOD CHASSIS GROUND.
IGNITION "OFF." REPAIR OPEN IN CKT 75.
CONTINUITY
NO CONTINUITY
YES
NO
• UNPLUG THE SOLENOID VALVE RELAY FROM BRAKE PRESSURE MODULATOR. • IGNITION "ON." IS "ANTILOCK" INDICATOR "ON?"
REPAIR OPEN IN CKT 151.
REPLACE EBCM. INSTALL FUSE 18.
REPAIR SHORT TO GROUND IN CKT 75. REPLACE FUSE 18.
NO
YES
• IGNITION "OFF." • RECONNECT EBCM. • REPLACE SOLENOID VALVE RELAY WITH A KNOWN GOOD RELAY. • TURN IGNITION "ON" AND CHECK FOR CORRECT SYSTEM OPERATION. IF SOLENOID OPERATES PROPERLY REPLACE SOLENOID VALVE RELAY. IF SYSTEM OPERATES PROPERLY REPLACE SOLENOID VALVE RELAY.
• IGNITION "OFF." • DISCONNECT BRAKE PRESSURE MODULATOR CONNECTOR. • IGNITION "ON." IS "ANTILOCK" INDICATOR "ON?"
NO
YES
REPLACE BRAKE PRESSURE MODULATOR.
REPAIR SHORT TO GROUND IN CKT 875.

GC402920048300BX

Fig. 47 Test A: ABS Indicator On w/No Codes Set Or TECH 1 Unable To Receive Data. 1992–93 Caprice, Custom Cruiser & Roadmaster

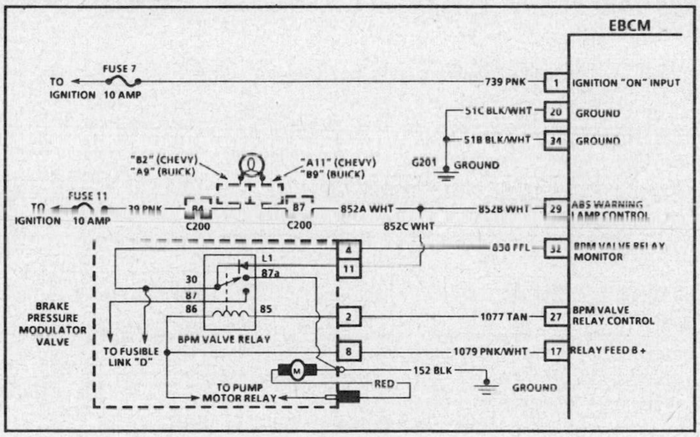
EBCM
FUSE 7
TO IGNITION 10 AMP
739 PNK
1
IGNITION "ON" INPUT
51C BLK/WHT
20
GROUND
51B BLK/WHT
34
GROUND
"B2" (CHEVY) "A9" (BUICK)
"A11" (CHEVY) "B9" (BUICK)
G201
GROUND
FUSE 11
TO IGNITION 10 AMP
39 PNK
B4
C200
B7
C200
852A WHT
852B WHT
852C WHT
29
ABS WARNING LAMP CONTROL
4
11
32
BPM VALVE RELAY MONITOR
L1
30
87a
87
86
85
BRAKE PRESSURE MODULATOR VALVE
2
1077 TAN
27
BPM VALVE RELAY CONTROL
BPM VALVE RELAY
TO FUSIBLE LINK "D"
8
1079 PNK/WHT
17
RELAY FEED B+
152 BLK
RED
GROUND
TO PUMP MOTOR RELAY

CHART A

ABS WARNING LAMP "ON" WITH NO DTCs SET OR WITH TECH 1 UNABLE TO RECEIVE DATA

Circuit Description:

The ABS warning lamp is located on the right side of the instrument panel. Battery voltage is applied with ignition in "Run," "Bulb," or "Start" through Fuse 11 and CKT 39. The ABS warning lamp is grounded through CKT 852 and is controlled by the EBCM at terminal "29" and the BPM valve at terminal "11" through the BPM valve relay. The EBCM will supply ground to the ABS warning lamp for approximately 2 seconds when ignition is first turned "ON." During the first 2 seconds, if no malfunctions are detected, the EBCM will energize the BPM valve relay. With the relay energized, the ground CKT 852 through the relay will be open. This allows the ABS warning lamp to go "OFF" when the EBCM ABS warning lamp control line at terminal "29" is opened.

Chart Test Description: Number(s) below refer to circled number(s) on the diagnostic chart.

1. Checks for proper battery and/or charging system operation.
2. Checks for an open fuse in the EBCM power feed circuit.
3. Checks for an open in the EBCM ground circuit.
4. Checks for an open in the EBCM power feed circuit.
5. Checks for a possible malfunction in the BPM valve relay.
6. Determines whether the malfunction is in the BPM valve relay or the EBCM.
7. Checks for a short to ground in the EBCM or the EBCM power feed circuit.
8. Determines whether the short to ground is in the BPM valve or the ABS warning lamp control circuit.
9. Checks for a short to ground in the ignition "ON" input circuit.
10. Checks for a short to ground in the BPM valve and pump motor relay feed circuitry.
11. Determines whether the short to ground is in the BPM valve or its relay feed circuitry.

GC402940093300AX

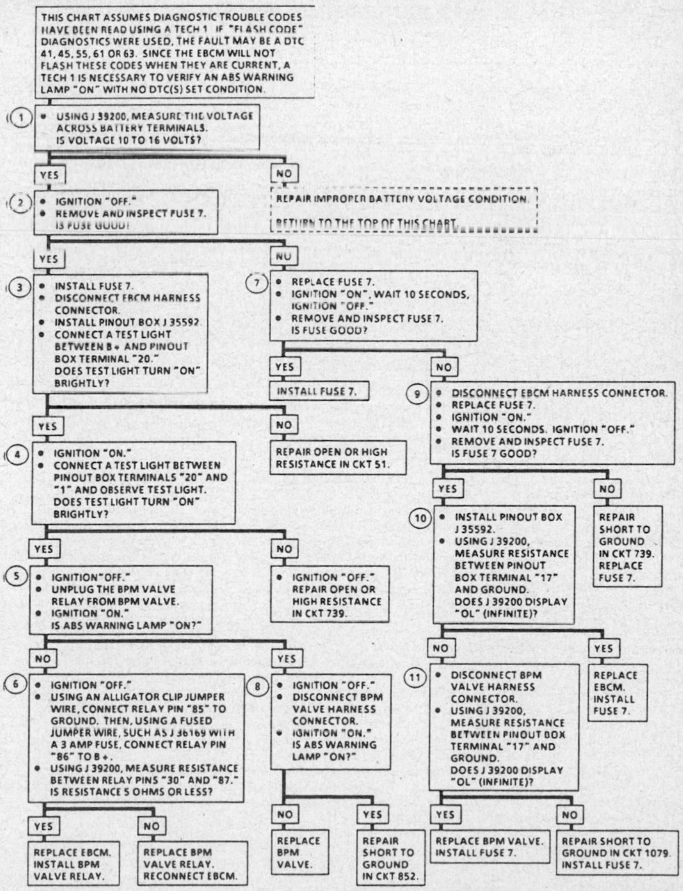
THIS CHART ASSUMES DIAGNOSTIC TROUBLE CODES HAVE BEEN READ USING A TECH 1. IF "FLASH CODE" DIAGNOSTICS WERE USED, THE FAULT MAY BE A DTC 41, 45, 55, 61 OR 63. SINCE THE EBCM WILL NOT FLASH THESE CODES WHEN THEY ARE CURRENT, A TECH 1 IS NECESSARY TO VERIFY AN ABS WARNING LAMP "ON" WITH NO DTC(S) SET CONDITION.
1 • USING J 39200, MEASURE THE VOLTAGE ACROSS BATTERY TERMINALS. IS VOLTAGE 10 TO 16 VOLTS?
YES
NO
2 • IGNITION "OFF." • REMOVE AND INSPECT FUSE 7. IS FUSE GOOD?
REPAIR IMPROPER BATTERY VOLTAGE CONDITION. RETURN TO THE TOP OF THIS CHART.
YES
NO
3 • INSTALL FUSE 7. • DISCONNECT EBCM HARNESS CONNECTOR. • INSTALL PINOUT BOX J 35592. • CONNECT A TEST LIGHT BETWEEN B+ AND PINOUT BOX TERMINAL "20." DOES TEST LIGHT TURN "ON" BRIGHTLY?
7 • REPLACE FUSE 7. • IGNITION "ON", WAIT 10 SECONDS, IGNITION "OFF." • REMOVE AND INSPECT FUSE 7. IS FUSE GOOD?
YES
NO
INSTALL FUSE 7.
9 • DISCONNECT EBCM HARNESS CONNECTOR. • REPLACE FUSE 7. • IGNITION "ON." • WAIT 10 SECONDS. IGNITION "OFF." • REMOVE AND INSPECT FUSE 7. IS FUSE 7 GOOD?
YES
NO
REPAIR OPEN OR HIGH RESISTANCE IN CKT 51.
4 • IGNITION "ON." • CONNECT A TEST LIGHT BETWEEN PINOUT BOX TERMINALS "20" AND "1" AND OBSERVE TEST LIGHT. DOES TEST LIGHT TURN "ON" BRIGHTLY?
YES
NO
10 • INSTALL PINOUT BOX J 35592. • USING J 39200, MEASURE RESISTANCE BETWEEN PINOUT BOX TERMINAL "17" AND GROUND. DOES J 39200 DISPLAY "OL" (INFINITE)?
REPAIR SHORT TO GROUND IN CKT 739. REPLACE FUSE 7.
YES
NO
5 • IGNITION "OFF." • UNPLUG THE BPM VALVE RELAY FROM BPM VALVE. • IGNITION "ON." IS ABS WARNING LAMP "ON?"
• IGNITION "OFF." REPAIR OPEN OR HIGH RESISTANCE IN CKT 739.
NO
YES
NO
YES
6 • IGNITION "OFF." • USING AN ALLIGATOR CLIP JUMPER WIRE, CONNECT RELAY PIN "85" TO GROUND. THEN, USING A FUSED JUMPER WIRE, SUCH AS J 36169 WITH A 3 AMP FUSE, CONNECT RELAY PIN "86" TO B+. • USING J 39200, MEASURE RESISTANCE BETWEEN RELAY PINS "30" AND "87." IS RESISTANCE 5 OHMS OR LESS?
8 • IGNITION "OFF." • DISCONNECT BPM VALVE HARNESS CONNECTOR. • IGNITION "ON." IS ABS WARNING LAMP "ON?"
11 • DISCONNECT BPM VALVE HARNESS CONNECTOR. • USING J 39200, MEASURE RESISTANCE BETWEEN PINOUT BOX TERMINAL "17" AND GROUND. DOES J 39200 DISPLAY "OL" (INFINITE)?
REPLACE EBCM. INSTALL FUSE 7.
YES
NO
NO
YES
YES
NO
REPLACE EBCM. INSTALL BPM VALVE RELAY.
REPLACE BPM VALVE RELAY. RECONNECT EBCM.
REPLACE BPM VALVE.
REPAIR SHORT TO GROUND IN CKT 852.
REPLACE BPM VALVE. INSTALL FUSE 7.
REPAIR SHORT TO GROUND IN CKT 1079. INSTALL FUSE 7.

GC402940093300BX

Fig. 48 Test A: ABS Indicator On w/No Codes Set Or TECH 1 Unable To Receive Data. 1994 Caprice, Impala SS & Roadmaster

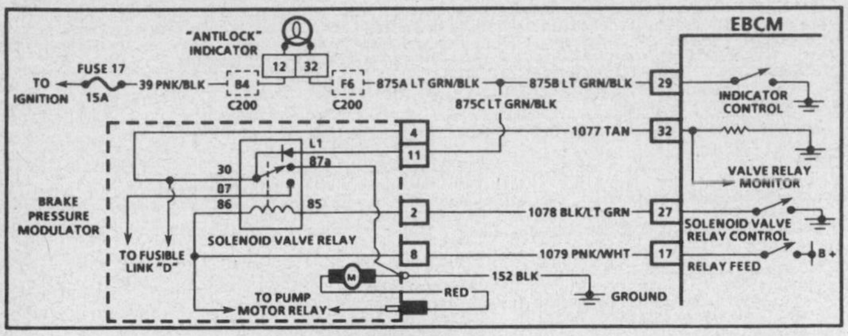
EBCM
"ANTILOCK" INDICATOR
FUSE 17
TO IGNITION 15A
39 PNK/BLK
B4
C200
12
32
F6
C200
875A LT GRN/BLK
875B LT GRN/BLK
29
875C LT GRN/BLK
INDICATOR CONTROL
4
11
1077 TAN
32
L1
87a
30
87
86
85
VALVE RELAY MONITOR
BRAKE PRESSURE MODULATOR
2
1078 BLK/LT GRN
27
SOLENOID VALVE RELAY
SOLENOID VALVE RELAY CONTROL
TO FUSIBLE LINK "D"
8
1079 PNK/WHT
17
RELAY FEED
B+
152 BLK
RED
GROUND
TO PUMP MOTOR RELAY

CHART B

"ANTILOCK" INDICATOR INOPERATIVE OR INDICATOR FLASHES VERY BRIEFLY AT IGNITION "ON" (LESS THAN ONE HALF OF A SECOND)

Circuit Description:

The "Antilock" Indicator is located on the right side of the instrument panel. Battery voltage is applied with ignition in "Run, Bulb Test or Start" through Fuse 17 and CKT 39. The indicator is grounded through CKT 875 and is controlled by the EBCM at Pin "29" and the Hydraulic Modulator at Pin "11" through the Solenoid Valve Relay. The EBCM will supply ground to the indicator for approximately 2 seconds when ignition is first turned "ON." During the first 2 seconds, if no faults are detected, the EBCM will energize the Solenoid Valve Relay. With the relay energized, the ground CKT 875 through the relay will be opened. This allows the indicator to go "OFF" when the EBCM indicator control line at Pin "29" is opened.

Test Description: Number(s) below refer to circled number(s) on the diagnostic chart.

1. Verifies an improperly operating indicator.
2. Determines whether the fault is an inoperative indicator or an improperly operating indicator.
3. Checks for an inoperative Instrument Cluster.
4. Determines whether the fault is in the Instrument Cluster portion of the circuity or in the ABS portion.
5. Checks for a bad bulb.
6. Determines whether the fault is in the wiring, connections, or in the Instrument Cluster printed circuits. (For LTZ only the Instrument Cluster will have different terminals for the "Antilock" indicator.
7. Determines whether the fault is in the wiring, connections, or Solenoid Valve Relay.
8. Determines whether the fault is in the wiring or connections.

Diagnostic Aids:

If indicator failure in "Intermittent," install the Tech 1 diagnostic tool and select any "ABS test mode so the "Antilock" indicator will be turned "ON." While observing the indicator, go through the indicators power and ground circuits wiggling the wiring and connectors. Watch for flickering or failure of the indicator to pin point roblem area.

GC402920048400AX

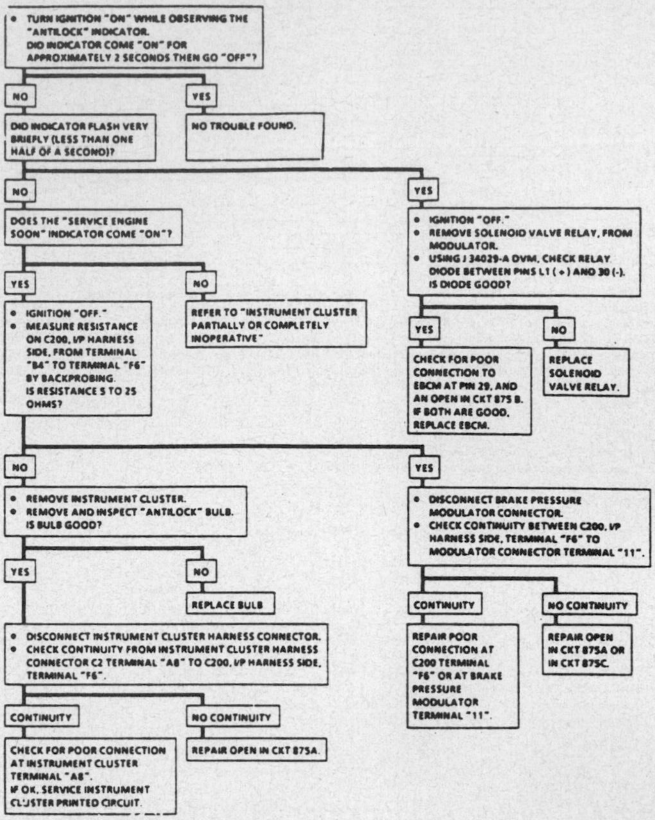
TURN IGNITION "ON" WHILE OBSERVING THE "ANTILOCK" INDICATOR. DID INDICATOR COME "ON" FOR APPROXIMATELY 2 SECONDS THEN GO "OFF"?
NO
YES
DID INDICATOR FLASH VERY BRIEFLY (LESS THAN ONE HALF OF A SECOND)?
NO TROUBLE FOUND.
NO
YES
DOES THE "SERVICE ENGINE SOON" INDICATOR COME "ON"?
IGNITION "OFF." REMOVE SOLENOID VALVE RELAY, FROM MODULATOR. USING J 34029-A DVM, CHECK RELAY DIODE BETWEEN PINS L1 (+) AND 30 (-). IS DIODE GOOD?
YES
NO
IGNITION "OFF." MEASURE RESISTANCE ON C200, I/P HARNESS SIDE, FROM TERMINAL "B4" TO TERMINAL "F6" BY BACKPROBING. IS RESISTANCE 5 TO 25 OHMS?
REFER TO "INSTRUMENT CLUSTER PARTIALLY OR COMPLETELY INOPERATIVE"
YES
NO
CHECK FOR POOR CONNECTION TO EBCM AT PIN 29, AND AN OPEN IN CKT 875 B. IF BOTH ARE GOOD, REPLACE EBCM.
REPLACE SOLENOID VALVE RELAY.
NO
YES
REMOVE INSTRUMENT CLUSTER. REMOVE AND INSPECT "ANTILOCK" BULB. IS BULB GOOD?
DISCONNECT BRAKE PRESSURE MODULATOR CONNECTOR. CHECK CONTINUITY BETWEEN C200, I/P HARNESS SIDE, TERMINAL "F6" TO MODULATOR CONNECTOR TERMINAL "11".
YES
NO
REPLACE BULB
CONTINUITY
NO CONTINUITY
DISCONNECT INSTRUMENT CLUSTER HARNESS CONNECTOR. CHECK CONTINUITY FROM INSTRUMENT CLUSTER HARNESS CONNECTOR C2 TERMINAL "A8" TO C200, I/P HARNESS SIDE, TERMINAL "F6".
REPAIR POOR CONNECTION AT C200 TERMINAL "F6" OR AT BRAKE PRESSURE MODULATOR TERMINAL "11".
REPAIR OPEN IN CKT 875A OR IN CKT 875C.
CONTINUITY
NO CONTINUITY
CHECK FOR POOR CONNECTION AT INSTRUMENT CLUSTER TERMINAL "A8". IF OK, SERVICE INSTRUMENT CLUSTER PRINTED CIRCUIT.
REPAIR OPEN IN CKT 875A.

GC402920048400BX

Fig. 49 Test B: ABS Indicator Inoperative Or Indicator Flashes Very Briefly At Ignition On. 1992–93 Caprice, Custom Cruiser & Roadmaster

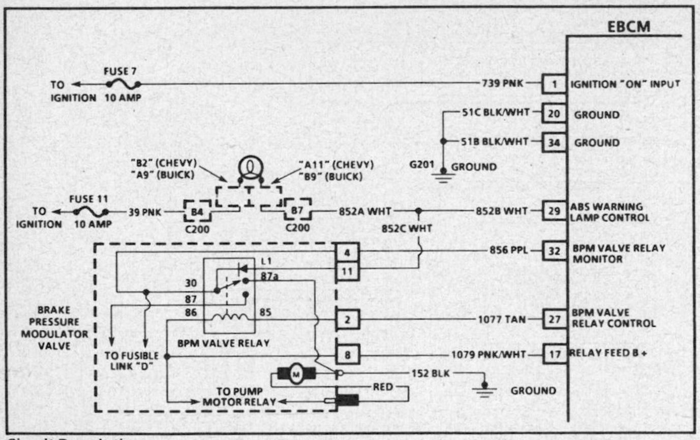
EBCM
FUSE 7
TO IGNITION 10 AMP
739 PNK
1
IGNITION "ON" INPUT
51C BLK/WHT
20
GROUND
51B BLK/WHT
34
GROUND
G201
GROUND
"B2" (CHEVY) "A9" (BUICK)
"A11" (CHEVY) "B9" (BUICK)
FUSE 11
TO IGNITION 10 AMP
39 PNK
B4
C200
B7
C200
852A WHT
852B WHT
29
ABS WARNING LAMP CONTROL
852C WHT
4
856 PPL
32
BPM VALVE RELAY MONITOR
11
L1
87a
30
87
86
85
BRAKE PRESSURE MODULATOR VALVE
2
1077 TAN
27
BPM VALVE RELAY CONTROL
BPM VALVE RELAY
TO FUSIBLE LINK "D"
8
1079 PNK/WHT
17
RELAY FEED B+
152 BLK
RED
GROUND
TO PUMP MOTOR RELAY

Circuit Description:

The ABS warning lamp is located on the right side of the instrument panel. Battery voltage is applied with ignition in "Run, Bulb Test or Start" through Fuse 11 and CKT 39. The ABS warning lamp is grounded through CKT 852 and is controlled by the EBCM at terminal "29" and the BPM valve at terminal "11" through the BPM valve relay. The EBCM will supply ground to the ABS warning lamp for approximately 2 seconds when ignition is first turned "ON." During the first 2 seconds, if no malfunctions are detected, the EBCM will energize the BPM valve relay. With the relay energized, the ground CKT 852 through the relay will be opened. This allows the ABS warning lamp to go "OFF" when the EBCM warning lamp control line at terminal "29" is opened.

Chart Test Description: Number(s) below refer to circled number(s) on the diagnostic chart.

1. Verifies an improperly operating ABS warning lamp.
2. Determines whether the malfunction is an inoperative ABS warning lamp or an improperly operating ABS warning lamp.
3. Checks for an inoperative instrument cluster.
4. Determines whether the malfunction is in the instrument cluster portion of the circuity or in the ABS portion.
5. Checks for a bad bulb.
6. Determines whether the malfunction is in the wiring, connections, or in the instrument cluster printed circuits.
7. Determines whether the malfunction is in the wiring, connections, or BPM valve relay.
8. Determines whether the malfunction is in the wiring or connections.

Diagnostic Aids: If a lamp malfunction is intermittent, install the Tech 1 diagnostic tool and select any ABS test mode so the ABS warning lamp will be turned "ON." While observing the lamp, go through the lamp's power and ground circuits wiggling the wiring and connectors. Watch for flickering or failure of the lamp to pin point problem area.

GC402940091900AX

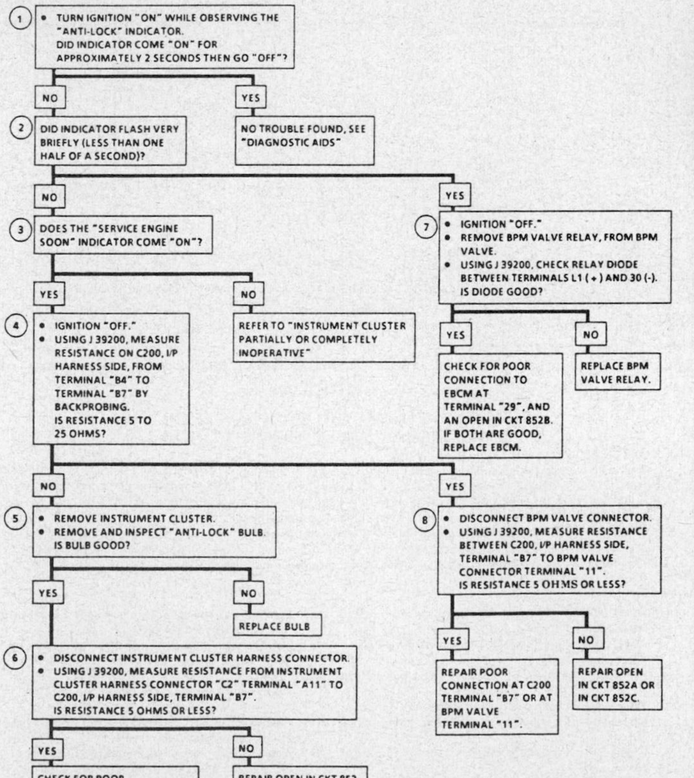
1
TURN IGNITION "ON" WHILE OBSERVING THE "ANTI-LOCK" INDICATOR. DID INDICATOR COME "ON" FOR APPROXIMATELY 2 SECONDS THEN GO "OFF"?
NO
YES
2
DID INDICATOR FLASH VERY BRIEFLY (LESS THAN ONE HALF OF A SECOND)?
NO TROUBLE FOUND, SEE "DIAGNOSTIC AIDS"
NO
YES
3
DOES THE "SERVICE ENGINE SOON" INDICATOR COME "ON"?
7
IGNITION "OFF." REMOVE BPM VALVE RELAY, FROM BPM VALVE. USING J 39200, CHECK RELAY DIODE BETWEEN TERMINALS L1 (+) AND 30 (-). IS DIODE GOOD?
YES
NO
4
IGNITION "OFF." USING J 39200, MEASURE RESISTANCE ON C200, I/P HARNESS SIDE, FROM TERMINAL "B4" TO TERMINAL "B7" BY BACKPROBING. IS RESISTANCE 5 TO 25 OHMS?
REFER TO "INSTRUMENT CLUSTER PARTIALLY OR COMPLETELY INOPERATIVE"
YES
NO
CHECK FOR POOR CONNECTION TO EBCM AT TERMINAL "29", AND AN OPEN IN CKT 852B. IF BOTH ARE GOOD, REPLACE EBCM.
REPLACE BPM VALVE RELAY.
NO
YES
5
REMOVE INSTRUMENT CLUSTER. REMOVE AND INSPECT "ANTI-LOCK" BULB. IS BULB GOOD?
8
DISCONNECT BPM VALVE CONNECTOR. USING J 39200, MEASURE RESISTANCE BETWEEN C200, I/P HARNESS SIDE, TERMINAL "B7" TO BPM VALVE CONNECTOR TERMINAL "11". IS RESISTANCE 5 OHMS OR LESS?
YES
NO
REPLACE BULB
YES
NO
6
DISCONNECT INSTRUMENT CLUSTER HARNESS CONNECTOR. USING J 39200, MEASURE RESISTANCE FROM INSTRUMENT CLUSTER HARNESS CONNECTOR "C2" TERMINAL "A11" TO C200, I/P HARNESS SIDE, TERMINAL "B7". IS RESISTANCE 5 OHMS OR LESS?
REPAIR POOR CONNECTION AT C200 TERMINAL "B7" OR AT BPM VALVE TERMINAL "11".
REPAIR OPEN IN CKT 852A OR IN CKT 852C.
YES
NO
CHECK FOR POOR CONNECTION AT INSTRUMENT CLUSTER TERMINAL "A11" (CHEVY) "B9" (BUICK). IF OK, SERVICE INSTRUMENT CLUSTER PRINTED CIRCUIT.
REPAIR OPEN IN CKT 852.

GC402940091900BX

Fig. 50 Test B: ABS Indicator Inoperative Or Indicator Flashes Very Briefly At Ignition On. 1994 Caprice, Impala SS & Roadmaster

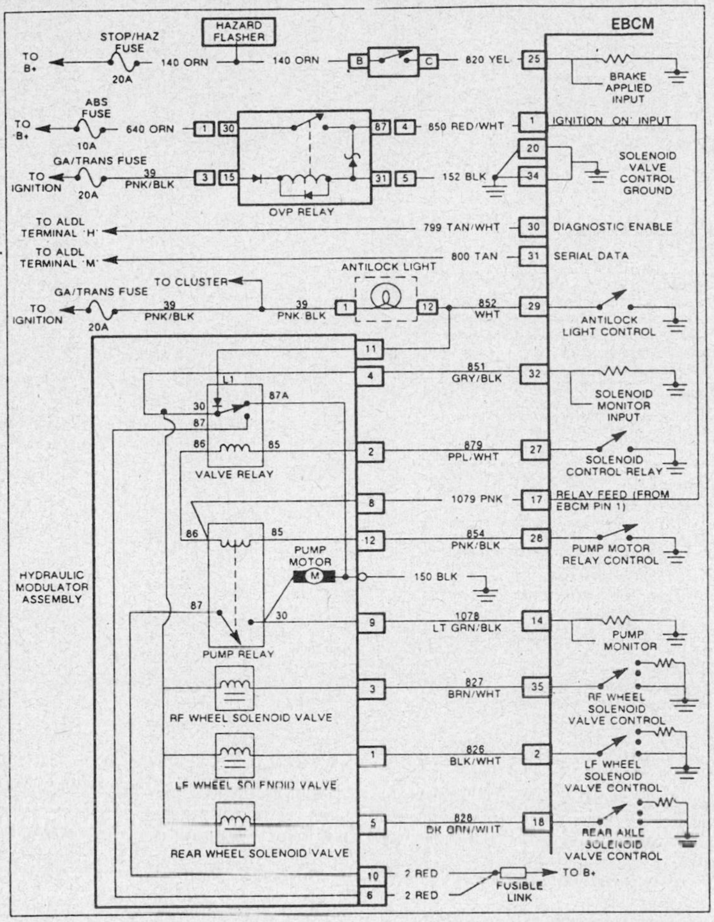
EBCM
STOP/HAZ FUSE 20A
HAZARD FLASHER
140 ORN
820 YEL
BRAKE APPLIED INPUT
ABS FUSE 10A
640 ORN
850 RED/WHT
IGNITION 'ON' INPUT
GA/TRANS FUSE 20A
39 PNK/BLK
152 BLK
SOLENOID VALVE CONTROL GROUND
OVP RELAY
TO ALDL TERMINAL 'H'
799 TAN/WHT
DIAGNOSTIC ENABLE
TO ALDL TERMINAL 'M'
800 TAN
SERIAL DATA
ANTILOCK LIGHT
TO CLUSTER
852 WHT
ANTILOCK LIGHT CONTROL
851 GRY/BLK
SOLENOID MONITOR INPUT
VALVE RELAY
879 PPL/WHT
SOLENOID CONTROL RELAY
1079 PNK
RELAY FEED (FROM EBCM PIN 1)
854 PNK/BLK
PUMP MOTOR RELAY CONTROL
PUMP MOTOR
150 BLK
HYDRAULIC MODULATOR ASSEMBLY
1078 LT GRN/BLK
PUMP MONITOR
PUMP RELAY
827 BRN/WHT
RF WHEEL SOLENOID VALVE CONTROL
RF WHEEL SOLENOID VALVE
826 BLK/WHT
LF WHEEL SOLENOID VALVE CONTROL
LF WHEEL SOLENOID VALVE
828 DK GRN/WHT
REAR AXLE SOLENOID VALVE CONTROL
REAR WHEEL SOLENOID VALVE
2 RED
FUSIBLE LINK
TO B+

GC4029100485010X

Fig. 51 ABS wiring circuit (Part 1 of 2). 1992 Brougham

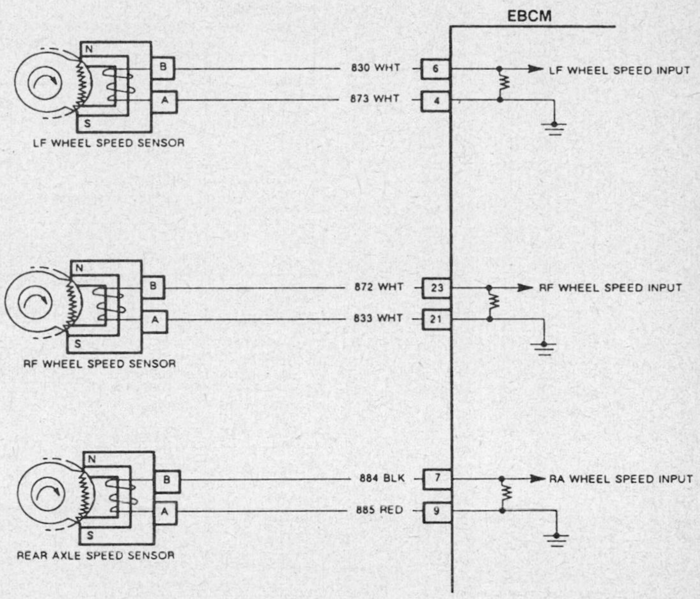
EBCM
830 WHT
873 WHT
LF WHEEL SPEED INPUT
LF WHEEL SPEED SENSOR
872 WHT
833 WHT
RF WHEEL SPEED INPUT
RF WHEEL SPEED SENSOR
884 BLK
885 RED
RA WHEEL SPEED INPUT
REAR AXLE SPEED SENSOR

GC4029100485020X

Fig. 51 ABS wiring circuit (Part 2 of 2). 1992 Brougham

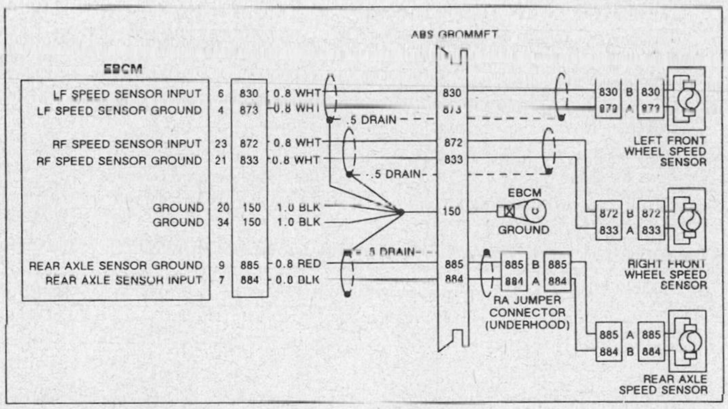
EBCM
ABS GROMMET
LF SPEED SENSOR INPUT
LF SPEED SENSOR GROUND
RF SPEED SENSOR INPUT
RF SPEED SENSOR GROUND
GROUND
REAR AXLE SENSOR GROUND
REAR AXLE SENSOR INPUT
0.8 WHT
.5 DRAIN
1.0 BLK
0.8 RED
0.8 BLK
LEFT FRONT WHEEL SPEED SENSOR
EBCM GROUND
RIGHT FRONT WHEEL SPEED SENSOR
RA JUMPER CONNECTOR (UNDERHOOD)
REAR AXLE SPEED SENSOR

CIRCUIT DESCRIPTION

As each wheel turns, the wheel speed sensor for that wheel creates a small AC voltage as a toothed sensor ring, mounted on the brake rotor (in the front) or differential pinion shaft (in the rear), is passed by the stationary sensor. The sensor consists of a permanent magnet and coil and generates voltage by magnetic induction. The frequency of the wheel speed sensor signal is proportional to wheel speed.

The EBCM uses the wheel speed sensor signal to calculate vehicle reference speeds and individual speed, acceleration and slip values for each wheel. These values are used to determine when antilock control is required.

The EBCM performs two basic types of checks on the wheel speed sensors, these are sensor continuity and sensor output.

TEST CONDITIONS

1. Tested continuously.

FAILURE CONDITIONS

Sensor Output:

1. Drive-away: Speed signal is not detected when vehicle reaches 12 kph or 7.5 mph
   – or –
2. While Driving: Speed signal is lost while vehicle speed is greater than 40 kph or 25 mph
   – or –

Continuity:

3. While Standing: Open circuit is seen while the vehicle is standing still with the ignition on.

ACTION TAKEN

1. Code set
2. ABS switched 'OFF'

NOTES ON CODE 21 CHART

1. This section of the fault tree determines if the code stored is due to a current fault condition. 'Current' wheel speed sensor faults will be detected when the vehicle is driven and reaches a speed of 4 mph (6 kph). If the ABS light turns on, the fault is current. The TECH 1 will indicate ignition cycle since code was set. If the ignition cycle counter is at zero or one the code is current.
2. This section of the fault tree checks for an open or short in the wheel speed sensor wiring or sensor coil.
3. This section of the fault tree checks for conditions which may cause intermittent code setting. Some causes of intermittent wheel speed sensor codes to set are: improper routing or sensor cables next to spark plug wires, cables not retained in brackets, loose fitting or improperly mounted sensors, damaged sensors or toothed rings, poor terminal engagement of connectors, or intermittent shorts or opens in wiring.

GC402910048600AX

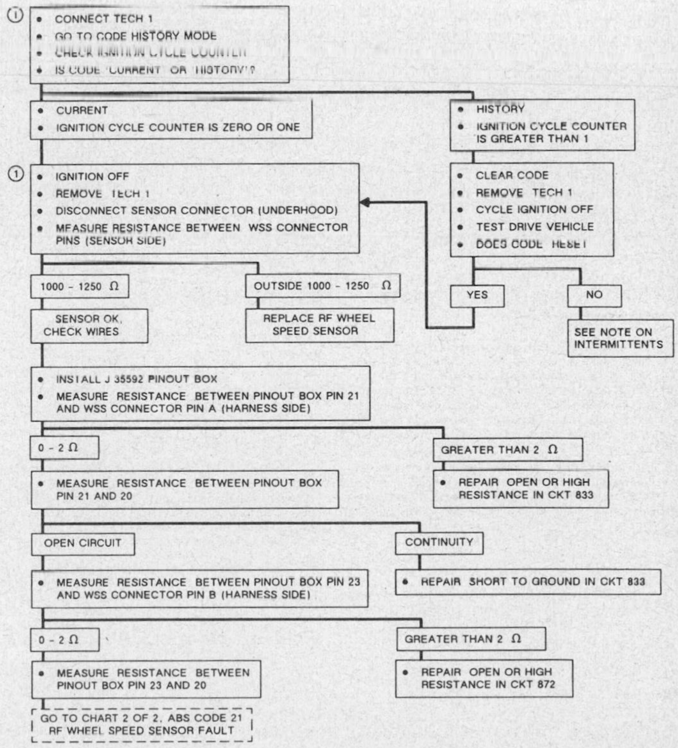
CONNECT TECH 1
GO TO CODE HISTORY MODE
CHECK IGNITION CYCLE COUNTER
IS CODE 'CURRENT' OR 'HISTORY'?
CURRENT
IGNITION CYCLE COUNTER IS ZERO OR ONE
HISTORY
IGNITION CYCLE COUNTER IS GREATER THAN 1
IGNITION OFF
REMOVE TECH 1
DISCONNECT SENSOR CONNECTOR (UNDERHOOD)
MEASURE RESISTANCE BETWEEN WSS CONNECTOR PINS (SENSOR SIDE)
CLEAR CODE
REMOVE TECH 1
CYCLE IGNITION OFF
TEST DRIVE VEHICLE
DOES CODE RESET
1000 - 1250 Ω
OUTSIDE 1000 - 1250 Ω
YES
NO
SENSOR OK, CHECK WIRES
REPLACE RF WHEEL SPEED SENSOR
SEE NOTE ON INTERMITTENTS
INSTALL J 35592 PINOUT BOX
MEASURE RESISTANCE BETWEEN PINOUT BOX PIN 21 AND WSS CONNECTOR PIN A (HARNESS SIDE)
0 - 2 Ω
GREATER THAN 2 Ω
MEASURE RESISTANCE BETWEEN PINOUT BOX PIN 21 AND 20
REPAIR OPEN OR HIGH RESISTANCE IN CKT 833
OPEN CIRCUIT
CONTINUITY
MEASURE RESISTANCE BETWEEN PINOUT BOX PIN 23 AND WSS CONNECTOR PIN B (HARNESS SIDE)
REPAIR SHORT TO GROUND IN CKT 833
0 - 2 Ω
GREATER THAN 2 Ω
MEASURE RESISTANCE BETWEEN PINOUT BOX PIN 23 AND 20
REPAIR OPEN OR HIGH RESISTANCE IN CKT 872
GO TO CHART 2 OF 2, ABS CODE 21 RF WHEEL SPEED SENSOR FAULT

GC402910048600BX

Fig. 52 Code 21: RF Wheel Speed Sensor Fault (Part 1 of 2). 1992 Brougham

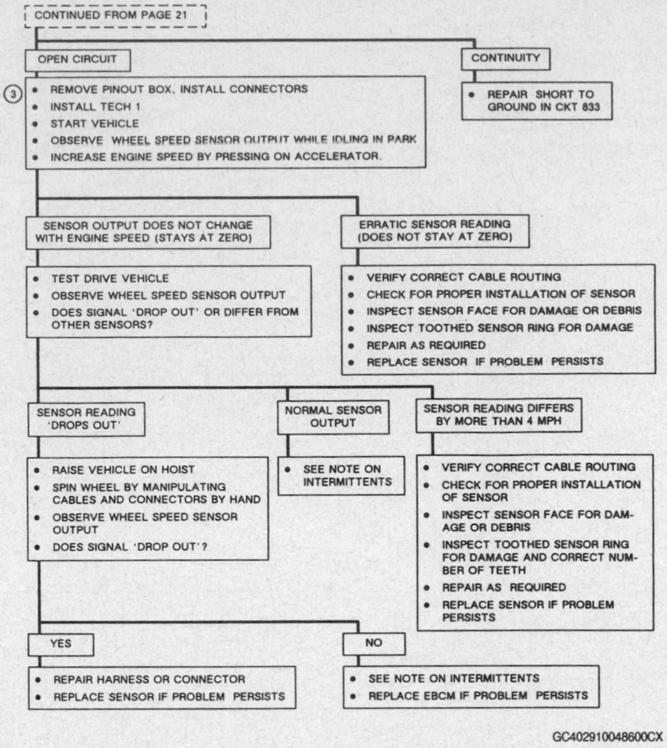
CONTINUED FROM PAGE 21
OPEN CIRCUIT
CONTINUITY
3
• REMOVE PINOUT BOX, INSTALL CONNECTORS
• INSTALL TECH 1
• START VEHICLE
• OBSERVE WHEEL SPEED SENSOR OUTPUT WHILE IDLING IN PARK
• INCREASE ENGINE SPEED BY PRESSING ON ACCELERATOR.
• REPAIR SHORT TO GROUND IN CKT 833
SENSOR OUTPUT DOES NOT CHANGE WITH ENGINE SPEED (STAYS AT ZERO)
ERRATIC SENSOR READING (DOES NOT STAY AT ZERO)
• TEST DRIVE VEHICLE
• OBSERVE WHEEL SPEED SENSOR OUTPUT
• DOES SIGNAL 'DROP OUT' OR DIFFER FROM OTHER SENSORS?
• VERIFY CORRECT CABLE ROUTING
• CHECK FOR PROPER INSTALLATION OF SENSOR
• INSPECT SENSOR FACE FOR DAMAGE OR DEBRIS
• INSPECT TOOTHED SENSOR RING FOR DAMAGE
• REPAIR AS REQUIRED
• REPLACE SENSOR IF PROBLEM PERSISTS
SENSOR READING 'DROPS OUT'
NORMAL SENSOR OUTPUT
SENSOR READING DIFFERS BY MORE THAN 4 MPH
• RAISE VEHICLE ON HOIST
• SPIN WHEEL BY MANIPULATING CABLES AND CONNECTORS BY HAND
• OBSERVE WHEEL SPEED SENSOR OUTPUT
• DOES SIGNAL 'DROP OUT'?
• SEE NOTE ON INTERMITTENTS
• VERIFY CORRECT CABLE ROUTING
• CHECK FOR PROPER INSTALLATION OF SENSOR
• INSPECT SENSOR FACE FOR DAMAGE OR DEBRIS
• INSPECT TOOTHED SENSOR RING FOR DAMAGE AND CORRECT NUMBER OF TEETH
• REPAIR AS REQUIRED
• REPLACE SENSOR IF PROBLEM PERSISTS
YES
NO
• REPAIR HARNESS OR CONNECTOR
• REPLACE SENSOR IF PROBLEM PERSISTS
• SEE NOTE ON INTERMITTENTS
• REPLACE EBCM IF PROBLEM PERSISTS
GC402910048600CX

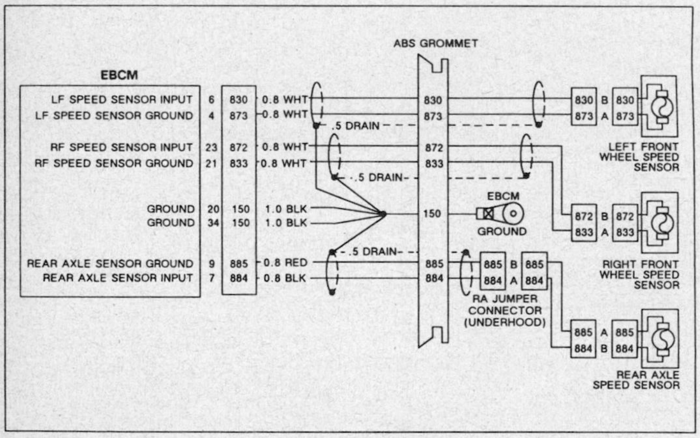
ABS GROMMET
EBCM
LF SPEED SENSOR INPUT 6 830 0.8 WHT
LF SPEED SENSOR GROUND 4 873 0.8 WHT
.5 DRAIN
RF SPEED SENSOR INPUT 23 872 0.8 WHT
RF SPEED SENSOR GROUND 21 833 0.8 WHT
.5 DRAIN
GROUND 20 150 1.0 BLK
GROUND 34 150 1.0 BLK
.5 DRAIN
REAR AXLE SENSOR GROUND 9 885 0.8 RED
REAR AXLE SENSOR INPUT 7 884 0.8 BLK
830
873
872
833
150
885
884
EBCM GROUND
LEFT FRONT WHEEL SPEED SENSOR
RIGHT FRONT WHEEL SPEED SENSOR
RA JUMPER CONNECTOR (UNDERHOOD)
REAR AXLE SPEED SENSOR

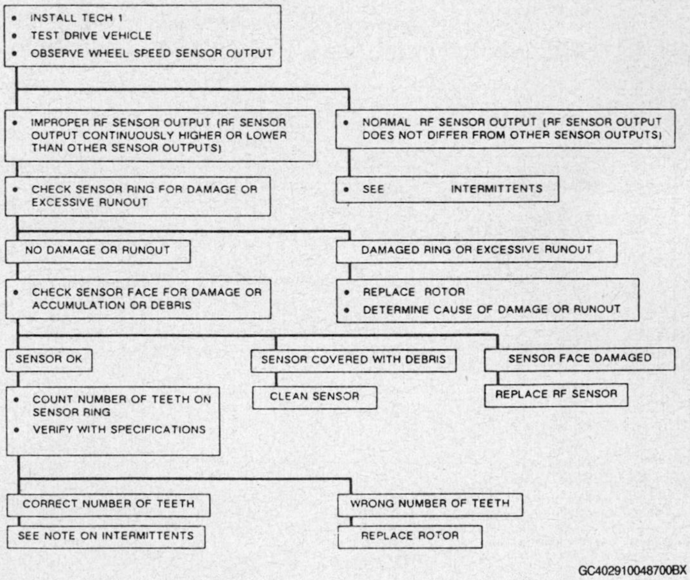
• INSTALL TECH 1
• TEST DRIVE VEHICLE
• OBSERVE WHEEL SPEED SENSOR OUTPUT
• IMPROPER RF SENSOR OUTPUT (RF SENSOR OUTPUT CONTINUOUSLY HIGHER OR LOWER THAN OTHER SENSOR OUTPUTS)
• NORMAL RF SENSOR OUTPUT (RF SENSOR OUTPUT DOES NOT DIFFER FROM OTHER SENSOR OUTPUTS)
• CHECK SENSOR RING FOR DAMAGE OR EXCESSIVE RUNOUT
• SEE INTERMITTENTS
NO DAMAGE OR RUNOUT
DAMAGED RING OR EXCESSIVE RUNOUT
• CHECK SENSOR FACE FOR DAMAGE OR ACCUMULATION OR DEBRIS
• REPLACE ROTOR
• DETERMINE CAUSE OF DAMAGE OR RUNOUT
SENSOR OK
SENSOR COVERED WITH DEBRIS
SENSOR FACE DAMAGED
• COUNT NUMBER OF TEETH ON SENSOR RING
• VERIFY WITH SPECIFICATIONS
CLEAN SENSOR
REPLACE RF SENSOR
CORRECT NUMBER OF TEETH
WRONG NUMBER OF TEETH
SEE NOTE ON INTERMITTENTS
REPLACE ROTOR
GC402910048700BX

ABS CODE 22

RIGHT FRONT TOOTHED WHEEL FREQUENCY ERROR

CIRCUIT DESCRIPTION

As each wheel turns, the wheel speed sensor for that wheel creates a small AC voltage as a toothed sensor ring, mounted on the brake rotor (in the front) or differential pinion shaft (in the rear), is passed by the stationary sensor. The sensor consists of a permanent magnet and coil and generates voltage by magnetic induction. The frequency of the wheel speed sensor signal is proportional to wheel speed.

The EBCM uses the wheel speed sensor signal to calculate vehicle reference speeds and individual speed, acceleration and slip values for each wheel. These values are used to determine when antilock control is required.

TEST CONDITIONS

1. Tested continuously.

FAILURE CONDITIONS

1. While Driving: One wheel is detected at least 30 kph or 19 mph faster than the remaining wheels for an extended period of time.

– or –

One wheel is at least 6 kph or 4 mph less than or greater than the remaining wheels for an extended period of time.

ACTION TAKEN

1. Code set.
2. ABS switched 'OFF'.

Code 22 will set from improper speed signals generated by the toothed ring sensor. Causes of improper speed signal may be caused by incorrect number of teeth on sensor ring, sensor rings which are covered with dirt, grease or metallic particles, or damaged toothed sensor ring.

Code 22 may also set if the mini-spare tire has been previously used or the size of the tires on the vehicle differ from each other. In addition to Code 22, Codes 26 and 36 may also set if the mini-spare tire has been used. If it is known that the spare tire was used, clear codes and test drive the vehicle again, verify that no codes set.

GC402910048700AX

Fig. 52 Code 21: RF Wheel Speed Sensor Fault (Part 2 of 2). 1992 Brougham

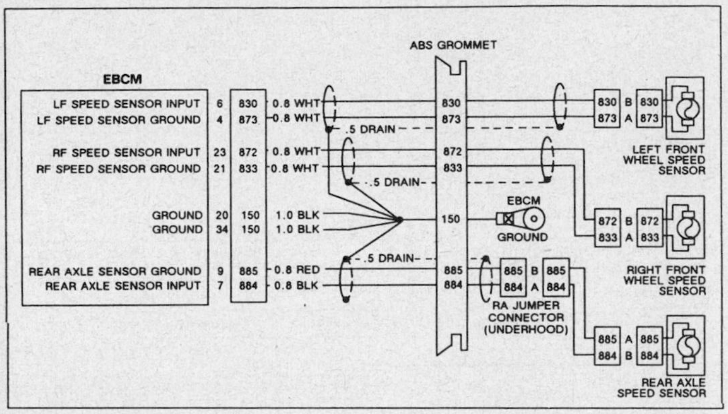
EBCM
ABS GROMMET
LF SPEED SENSOR INPUT 6 830 0.8 WHT
LF SPEED SENSOR GROUND 4 873 0.8 WHT
.5 DRAIN
RF SPEED SENSOR INPUT 23 872 0.8 WHT
RF SPEED SENSOR GROUND 21 833 0.8 WHT
.5 DRAIN
GROUND 20 150 1.0 BLK
GROUND 34 150 1.0 BLK
REAR AXLE SENSOR GROUND 9 885 0.8 RED
REAR AXLE SENSOR INPUT 7 884 0.8 BLK
.5 DRAIN
830
873
872
833
150
885
884
EBCM
GROUND
LEFT FRONT WHEEL SPEED SENSOR
RIGHT FRONT WHEEL SPEED SENSOR
RA JUMPER CONNECTOR (UNDERHOOD)
REAR AXLE SPEED SENSOR

CIRCUIT DESCRIPTION

As each wheel turns, the wheel speed sensor for that wheel creates a small AC voltage as a toothed sensor ring, mounted on the brake rotor (in the front) or differential pinion shaft (in the rear), is passed by the stationary sensor. The sensor consists of a permanent magnet and coil and generates voltage by magnetic induction. The frequency of the wheel speed sensor signal is proportional to wheel speed.

The EBCM uses the wheel speed sensor signal to calculate vehicle reference speeds and individual speed, acceleration and slip values for each wheel. These values are used to determine when antilock control is required.

The EBCM performs two basic types of checks on the wheel speed sensors, these are sensor continuity and sensor output.

TEST CONDITIONS

1. Tested continuously.

FAILURE CONDITIONS

Sensor Output:

1. Drive-away: Speed signal is not detected when vehicle reaches 12 kph or 7.5 mph
   – or –
2. While Driving: Speed signal is lost while vehicle speed is greater than 40 kph or 25 mph
   – or –

Continuity:

3. While Standing: Open circuit is seen while the vehicle is standing still with the ignition on.

ACTION TAKEN

1. Code set
2. ABS switched 'OFF'

NOTES ON CODE 25 CHART

1. This section of the fault tree determines if the code stored is due to a current fault condition. 'Current' wheel speed sensor faults will be detected when the vehicle is driven and reaches a speed of 4 mph (6 kph). If the ABS light turns on, the fault is current. The TECH 1 will indicate ignition cycle since code was set. If the ignition cycle counter is at zero or one the code is current.
2. This section of the fault tree checks for an open or short in the wheel speed sensor wiring or sensor coil.
3. This section of the fault tree checks for conditions which may cause intermittent code setting. Some causes of intermittent wheel speed sensor codes to set are: improper routing or sensor cables next to spark plug wires, cables not retained in brackets, loose fitting or improperly mounted sensors, damaged sensors or toothed rings, poor terminal engagement of connectors, or intermittent shorts or opens in wiring.

GC402910048800AX

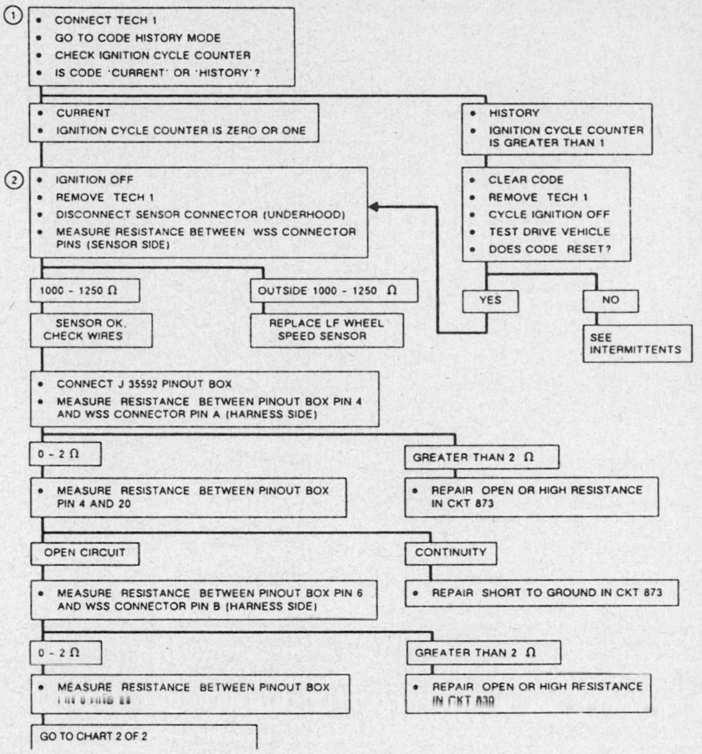
1
CONNECT TECH 1
GO TO CODE HISTORY MODE
CHECK IGNITION CYCLE COUNTER
IS CODE 'CURRENT' OR 'HISTORY'?
CURRENT
IGNITION CYCLE COUNTER IS ZERO OR ONE
HISTORY
IGNITION CYCLE COUNTER IS GREATER THAN 1
2
IGNITION OFF
REMOVE TECH 1
DISCONNECT SENSOR CONNECTOR (UNDERHOOD)
MEASURE RESISTANCE BETWEEN WSS CONNECTOR PINS (SENSOR SIDE)
CLEAR CODE
REMOVE TECH 1
CYCLE IGNITION OFF
TEST DRIVE VEHICLE
DOES CODE RESET?
1000 - 1250 Ω
OUTSIDE 1000 - 1250 Ω
YES
NO
SENSOR OK. CHECK WIRES
REPLACE LF WHEEL SPEED SENSOR
SEE INTERMITTENTS
CONNECT J 35592 PINOUT BOX
MEASURE RESISTANCE BETWEEN PINOUT BOX PIN 4 AND WSS CONNECTOR PIN A (HARNESS SIDE)
0 - 2 Ω
GREATER THAN 2 Ω
MEASURE RESISTANCE BETWEEN PINOUT BOX PIN 4 AND 20
REPAIR OPEN OR HIGH RESISTANCE IN CKT 873
OPEN CIRCUIT
CONTINUITY
MEASURE RESISTANCE BETWEEN PINOUT BOX PIN 6 AND WSS CONNECTOR PIN B (HARNESS SIDE)
REPAIR SHORT TO GROUND IN CKT 873
0 - 2 Ω
GREATER THAN 2 Ω
MEASURE RESISTANCE BETWEEN PINOUT BOX
REPAIR OPEN OR HIGH RESISTANCE IN CKT 830
GO TO CHART 2 OF 2

GC402910048800BX

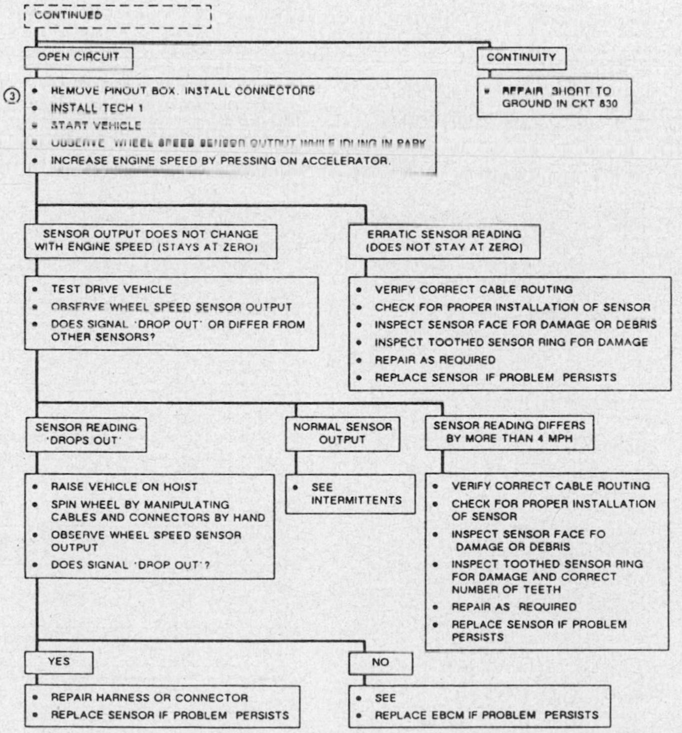
CONTINUED
OPEN CIRCUIT
CONTINUITY
REPAIR SHORT TO GROUND IN CKT 830
3
REMOVE PINOUT BOX. INSTALL CONNECTORS
INSTALL TECH 1
START VEHICLE
OBSERVE WHEEL SPEED SENSOR OUTPUT WHILE IDLING IN PARK
INCREASE ENGINE SPEED BY PRESSING ON ACCELERATOR.
SENSOR OUTPUT DOES NOT CHANGE WITH ENGINE SPEED (STAYS AT ZERO)
ERRATIC SENSOR READING (DOES NOT STAY AT ZERO)
TEST DRIVE VEHICLE
OBSERVE WHEEL SPEED SENSOR OUTPUT
DOES SIGNAL 'DROP OUT' OR DIFFER FROM OTHER SENSORS?
VERIFY CORRECT CABLE ROUTING
CHECK FOR PROPER INSTALLATION OF SENSOR
INSPECT SENSOR FACE FOR DAMAGE OR DEBRIS
INSPECT TOOTHED SENSOR RING FOR DAMAGE
REPAIR AS REQUIRED
REPLACE SENSOR IF PROBLEM PERSISTS
SENSOR READING 'DROPS OUT'
NORMAL SENSOR OUTPUT
SENSOR READING DIFFERS BY MORE THAN 4 MPH
RAISE VEHICLE ON HOIST
SPIN WHEEL BY MANIPULATING CABLES AND CONNECTORS BY HAND
OBSERVE WHEEL SPEED SENSOR OUTPUT
DOES SIGNAL 'DROP OUT'?
SEE INTERMITTENTS
VERIFY CORRECT CABLE ROUTING
CHECK FOR PROPER INSTALLATION OF SENSOR
INSPECT SENSOR FACE FO DAMAGE OR DEBRIS
INSPECT TOOTHED SENSOR RING FOR DAMAGE AND CORRECT NUMBER OF TEETH
REPAIR AS REQUIRED
REPLACE SENSOR IF PROBLEM PERSISTS
YES
NO
REPAIR HARNESS OR CONNECTOR
REPLACE SENSOR IF PROBLEM PERSISTS
SEE
REPLACE EBCM IF PROBLEM PERSISTS

GC402910048800CX

Fig. 54 Code 25: LF Wheel Speed Sensor Fault. 1992 Brougham

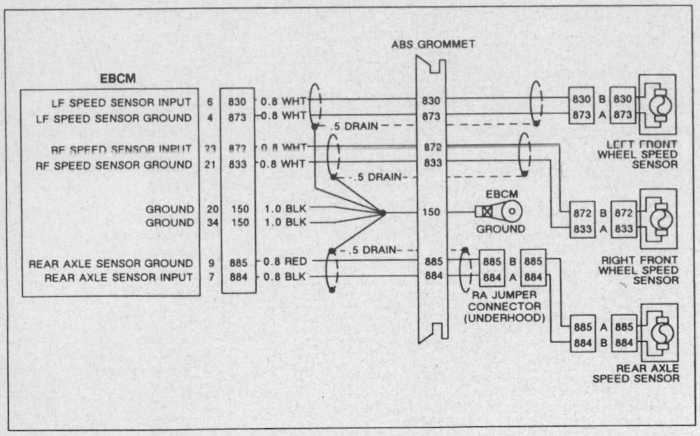
ABS GROMMET
EBCM
LF SPEED SENSOR INPUT 6 830 0.8 WHT
LF SPEED SENSOR GROUND 4 873 0.8 WHT
.5 DRAIN
RF SPEED SENSOR INPUT 23 872 0.8 WHT
RF SPEED SENSOR GROUND 21 833 0.8 WHT
.5 DRAIN
GROUND 20 150 1.0 BLK
GROUND 34 150 1.0 BLK
REAR AXLE SENSOR GROUND 9 885 0.8 RED
REAR AXLE SENSOR INPUT 7 884 0.8 BLK
.5 DRAIN
EBCM GROUND
LEFT FRONT WHEEL SPEED SENSOR
RIGHT FRONT WHEEL SPEED SENSOR
RA JUMPER CONNECTOR (UNDERHOOD)
REAR AXLE SPEED SENSOR

CIRCUIT DESCRIPTION

As each wheel turns, the wheel speed sensor for that wheel creates a small AC voltage as a toothed sensor ring, mounted on the brake rotor (in the front) or differential pinion shaft (in the rear), is passed by the stationary sensor. The sensor consists of a permanent magnet and coil and generates voltage by magnetic induction. The frequency of the wheel speed sensor signal is proportional to wheel speed.

The EBCM uses the wheel speed sensor signal to calculate vehicle reference speeds and individual speed, acceleration and slip values for each wheel. These values are used to determine when antilock control is required.

TEST CONDITIONS

1. Tested continuously.

FAILURE CONDITIONS

1. While Driving: One wheel is detected at least 30 kph or 19 mph faster than the remaining wheels for an extended period of time.

– or –

One wheel is at least 6 kph or 4 mph less than or greater than the remaining wheels for an extended period of time.

ACTION TAKEN

1. Code set.
2. ABS switched 'OFF'.

Code 26 will set from improper speed signals generated by the toothed ring sensor. Causes of improper speed signal may be caused by incorrect number of teeth on sensor ring, sensor rings which are covered with dirt, grease or metallic particles, or damaged toothed sensor ring.

Code 26 may also set if the mini-spare tire has been previously used or the size of the tires on the vehicle differ from each other. In addition to Code 26, Codes 22 and 36 may also set if the mini-spare tire has been used. If it is known that the spare tire was used, clear codes and test drive the vehicle again, verify that no codes set.

GC402910048900AX

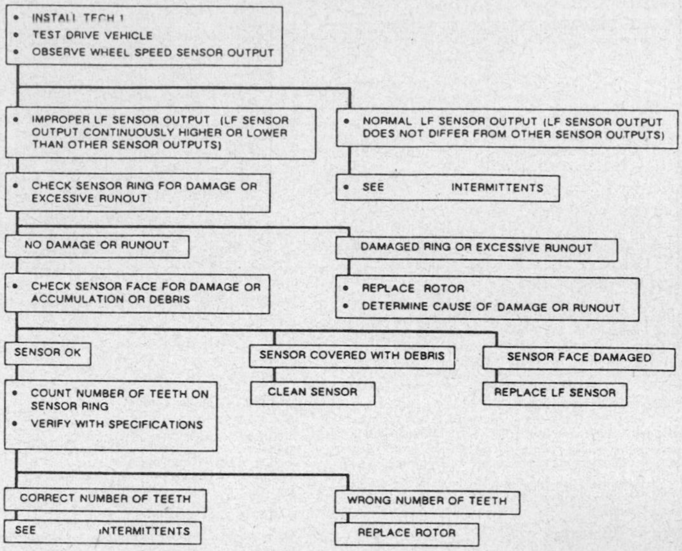
INSTALL TECH 1
TEST DRIVE VEHICLE
OBSERVE WHEEL SPEED SENSOR OUTPUT
IMPROPER LF SENSOR OUTPUT (LF SENSOR OUTPUT CONTINUOUSLY HIGHER OR LOWER THAN OTHER SENSOR OUTPUTS)
NORMAL LF SENSOR OUTPUT (LF SENSOR OUTPUT DOES NOT DIFFER FROM OTHER SENSOR OUTPUTS)
CHECK SENSOR RING FOR DAMAGE OR EXCESSIVE RUNOUT
SEE INTERMITTENTS
NO DAMAGE OR RUNOUT
DAMAGED RING OR EXCESSIVE RUNOUT
CHECK SENSOR FACE FOR DAMAGE OR ACCUMULATION OR DEBRIS
REPLACE ROTOR
DETERMINE CAUSE OF DAMAGE OR RUNOUT
SENSOR OK
SENSOR COVERED WITH DEBRIS
SENSOR FACE DAMAGED
COUNT NUMBER OF TEETH ON SENSOR RING
VERIFY WITH SPECIFICATIONS
CLEAN SENSOR
REPLACE LF SENSOR
CORRECT NUMBER OF TEETH
WRONG NUMBER OF TEETH
SEE INTERMITTENTS
REPLACE ROTOR

GC402910048900BX

Fig. 55 Code 26: LF Toothed Wheel Frequency Error. 1992 Brougham

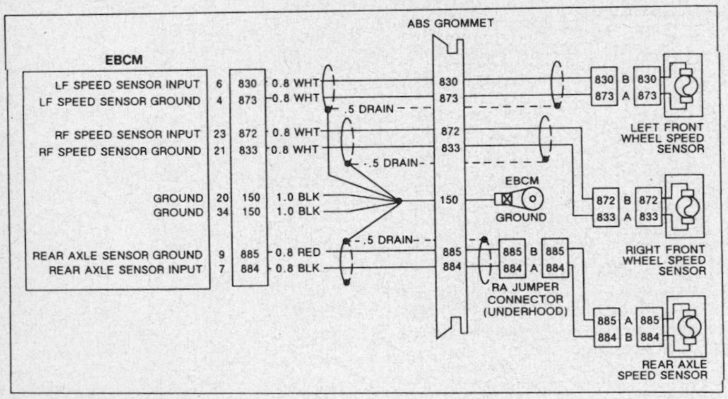
ABS GROMMET
EBCM
LF SPEED SENSOR INPUT 6 830 0.8 WHT
LF SPEED SENSOR GROUND 4 873 0.8 WHT
.5 DRAIN
RF SPEED SENSOR INPUT 23 872 0.8 WHT
RF SPEED SENSOR GROUND 21 833 0.8 WHT
.5 DRAIN
GROUND 20 150 1.0 BLK
GROUND 34 150 1.0 BLK
REAR AXLE SENSOR GROUND 9 885 0.8 RED
REAR AXLE SENSOR INPUT 7 884 0.8 BLK
.5 DRAIN
EBCM GROUND
LEFT FRONT WHEEL SPEED SENSOR
RIGHT FRONT WHEEL SPEED SENSOR
RA JUMPER CONNECTOR (UNDERHOOD)
REAR AXLE SPEED SENSOR

CIRCUIT DESCRIPTION

As each wheel turns, the wheel speed sensor for that wheel creates a small AC voltage as a toothed sensor ring, mounted on the brake rotor (in the front) or differential pinion shaft (in the rear), is passed by the stationary sensor. The sensor consists of a permanent magnet and coil and generates voltage by magnetic induction. The frequency of the wheel speed sensor signal is proportional to wheel speed.

The EBCM uses the wheel speed sensor signal to calculate vehicle reference speeds and individual speed, acceleration and slip values for each wheel. These values are used to determine when antilock control is required.

The EBCM performs two basic types of checks on the wheel speed sensors, these are sensor continuity and sensor output.

TEST CONDITIONS

1. Tested continuously.

FAILURE CONDITIONS

Sensor Output:

1. Drive-away: Speed signal is not detected when vehicle reaches 12 kph or 7.5 mph

– or –

2. While Driving: Speed signal is lost while vehicle speed is greater than 40 kph or 25 mph

– or –

Continuity:

3. While Standing: Open circuit is seen while the vehicle is standing still with the ignition on.

ACTION TAKEN

1. Code set
2. ABS switched 'OFF'

NOTES ON CODE 35 CHART

1. This section of the fault tree determines if the code stored is due to a current fault condition. 'Current' wheel speed sensor faults will be detected when the vehicle is driven and reaches a speed of 4 mph (6 kph). If the ABS light turns on, the fault is current. The TECH 1 will indicate ignition cycle since code was set. If the ignition cycle counter is at zero or one the code is current.
2. This section of the fault tree checks for an open or short in the wheel speed sensor wiring or sensor coil.
3. This section of the fault tree checks for conditions which may cause intermittent code setting. Some causes of intermittent wheel speed sensor codes to set are: improper routing or sensor cables next to spark plug wires, cables not retained in brackets, loose fitting or improperly mounted sensors, damaged sensors or toothed rings, poor terminal engagement of connectors, or intermittent shorts or opens in wiring.

GC402910049000AX

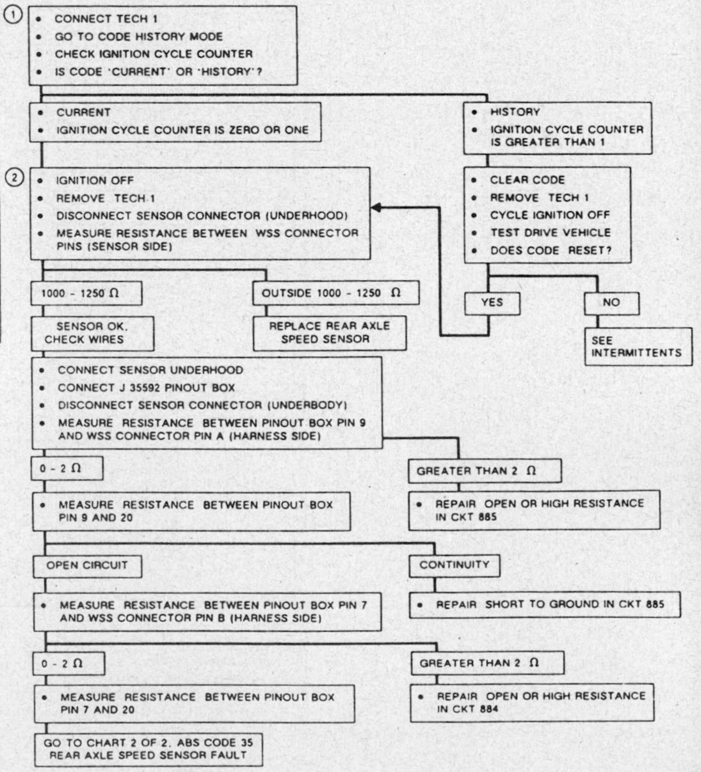
1
CONNECT TECH 1
GO TO CODE HISTORY MODE
CHECK IGNITION CYCLE COUNTER
IS CODE 'CURRENT' OR 'HISTORY'?
CURRENT
IGNITION CYCLE COUNTER IS ZERO OR ONE
HISTORY
IGNITION CYCLE COUNTER IS GREATER THAN 1
2
IGNITION OFF
REMOVE TECH 1
DISCONNECT SENSOR CONNECTOR (UNDERHOOD)
MEASURE RESISTANCE BETWEEN WSS CONNECTOR PINS (SENSOR SIDE)
CLEAR CODE
REMOVE TECH 1
CYCLE IGNITION OFF
TEST DRIVE VEHICLE
DOES CODE RESET?
1000 - 1250 Ω
OUTSIDE 1000 - 1250 Ω
YES
NO
SENSOR OK, CHECK WIRES
REPLACE REAR AXLE SPEED SENSOR
SEE INTERMITTENTS
CONNECT SENSOR UNDERHOOD
CONNECT J 35592 PINOUT BOX
DISCONNECT SENSOR CONNECTOR (UNDERBODY)
MEASURE RESISTANCE BETWEEN PINOUT BOX PIN 9 AND WSS CONNECTOR PIN A (HARNESS SIDE)
0 - 2 Ω
GREATER THAN 2 Ω
MEASURE RESISTANCE BETWEEN PINOUT BOX PIN 9 AND 20
REPAIR OPEN OR HIGH RESISTANCE IN CKT 885
OPEN CIRCUIT
CONTINUITY
MEASURE RESISTANCE BETWEEN PINOUT BOX PIN 7 AND WSS CONNECTOR PIN B (HARNESS SIDE)
REPAIR SHORT TO GROUND IN CKT 885
0 - 2 Ω
GREATER THAN 2 Ω
MEASURE RESISTANCE BETWEEN PINOUT BOX PIN 7 AND 20
REPAIR OPEN OR HIGH RESISTANCE IN CKT 884
GO TO CHART 2 OF 2, ABS CODE 35 REAR AXLE SPEED SENSOR FAULT

GC402910049000BX

Fig. 56 Code 36: LR Wheel Speed Sensor Fault (Part 1 of 2). 1992 Brougham

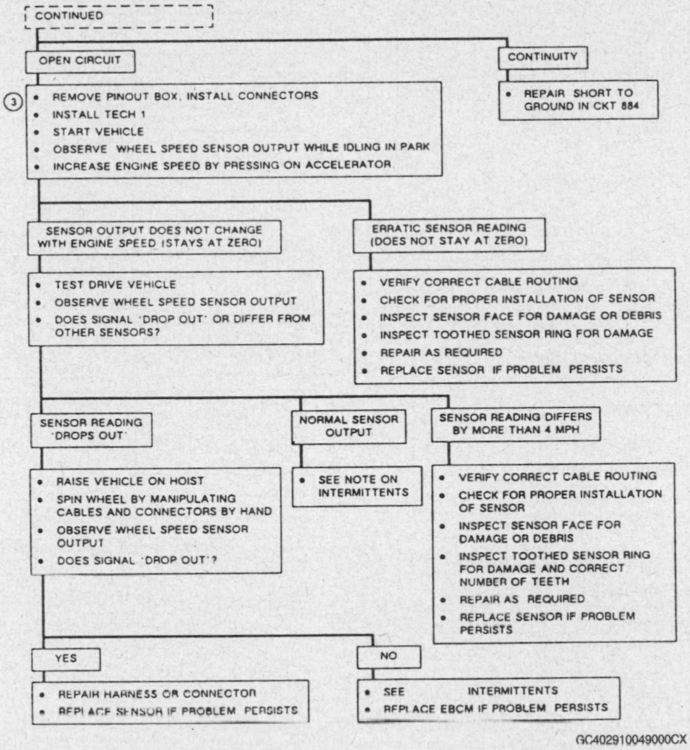
CONTINUED
OPEN CIRCUIT
CONTINUITY
• REPAIR SHORT TO GROUND IN CKT 884
3
• REMOVE PINOUT BOX, INSTALL CONNECTORS
• INSTALL TECH 1
• START VEHICLE
• OBSERVE WHEEL SPEED SENSOR OUTPUT WHILE IDLING IN PARK
• INCREASE ENGINE SPEED BY PRESSING ON ACCELERATOR
SENSOR OUTPUT DOES NOT CHANGE WITH ENGINE SPEED (STAYS AT ZERO)
ERRATIC SENSOR READING (DOES NOT STAY AT ZERO)
• TEST DRIVE VEHICLE
• OBSERVE WHEEL SPEED SENSOR OUTPUT
• DOES SIGNAL 'DROP OUT' OR DIFFER FROM OTHER SENSORS?
• VERIFY CORRECT CABLE ROUTING
• CHECK FOR PROPER INSTALLATION OF SENSOR
• INSPECT SENSOR FACE FOR DAMAGE OR DEBRIS
• INSPECT TOOTHED SENSOR RING FOR DAMAGE
• REPAIR AS REQUIRED
• REPLACE SENSOR IF PROBLEM PERSISTS
SENSOR READING 'DROPS OUT'
NORMAL SENSOR OUTPUT
SENSOR READING DIFFERS BY MORE THAN 4 MPH
• RAISE VEHICLE ON HOIST
• SPIN WHEEL BY MANIPULATING CABLES AND CONNECTORS BY HAND
• OBSERVE WHEEL SPEED SENSOR OUTPUT
• DOES SIGNAL 'DROP OUT'?
• SEE NOTE ON INTERMITTENTS
• VERIFY CORRECT CABLE ROUTING
• CHECK FOR PROPER INSTALLATION OF SENSOR
• INSPECT SENSOR FACE FOR DAMAGE OR DEBRIS
• INSPECT TOOTHED SENSOR RING FOR DAMAGE AND CORRECT NUMBER OF TEETH
• REPAIR AS REQUIRED
• REPLACE SENSOR IF PROBLEM PERSISTS
YES
NO
• REPAIR HARNESS OR CONNECTOR
• REPLACE SENSOR IF PROBLEM PERSISTS
• SEE INTERMITTENTS
• REPLACE EBCM IF PROBLEM PERSISTS
GC402910049000CX

Fig. 56 Code 36: LR Wheel Speed Sensor Fault (Part 2 of 2). 1992 Brougham

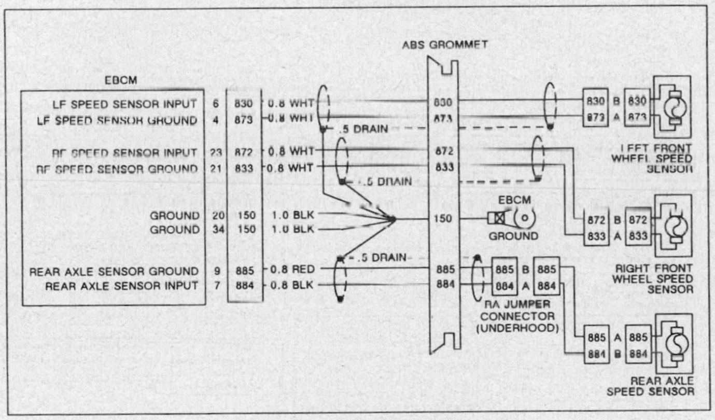
ABS GROMMET
EBCM
LF SPEED SENSOR INPUT 6 830 0.8 WHT
LF SPEED SENSOR GROUND 4 873 0.8 WHT
.5 DRAIN
RF SPEED SENSOR INPUT 23 872 0.8 WHT
RF SPEED SENSOR GROUND 21 833 0.8 WHT
.5 DRAIN
GROUND 20 150 1.0 BLK
GROUND 34 150 1.0 BLK
.5 DRAIN
REAR AXLE SENSOR GROUND 9 885 0.8 RED
REAR AXLE SENSOR INPUT 7 884 0.8 BLK
830
873
872
833
150
885
884
EBCM GROUND
LEFT FRONT WHEEL SPEED SENSOR
RIGHT FRONT WHEEL SPEED SENSOR
RA JUMPER CONNECTOR (UNDERHOOD)
REAR AXLE SPEED SENSOR

ABS CODES 36

REAR AXLE TOOTHED WHEEL FREQUENCY ERROR

CIRCUIT DESCRIPTION

As each wheel turns, the wheel speed sensor for that wheel creates a small AC voltage as a toothed sensor ring, mounted on the brake rotor (in the front) or differential pinion shaft (in the rear), is passed by the stationary sensor. The sensor consists of a permanent magnet and coil and generates voltage by magnetic induction. The frequency of the wheel speed sensor signal is proportional to wheel speed.

The EBCM uses the wheel speed sensor signal to calculate vehicle reference speeds and individual speed, acceleration and slip values for each wheel. These values are used to determine when antilock control is required.

TEST CONDITIONS

1. Tested continuously.

FAILURE CONDITIONS

1. While Driving: One wheel is detected at least 30 kph or 19 mph faster than the remaining wheels for an extended period of time.

- or -

One wheel is at least 6 kph or 4 mph less than or greater than the remaining wheels for an extended period of time.

ACTION TAKEN

1. Code set.
2. ABS switched 'OFF'.

Code 36 will set from improper speed signals generated by the toothed ring sensor. Causes of improper speed signal may be caused by incorrect number of teeth on sensor ring, sensor rings which are covered with dirt, grease or metallic particles, or damaged toothed sensor ring.

Code 36 may also set if the mini-spare tire has been previously used or the size of the tires on the vehicle differ from each other. In addition to Code 36, Codes 22 and 26 may also set if the mini-spare tire has been used. If it is known that the spare tire was used, clear codes and test drive the vehicle again, verify that no codes set.

GC402910049100AX

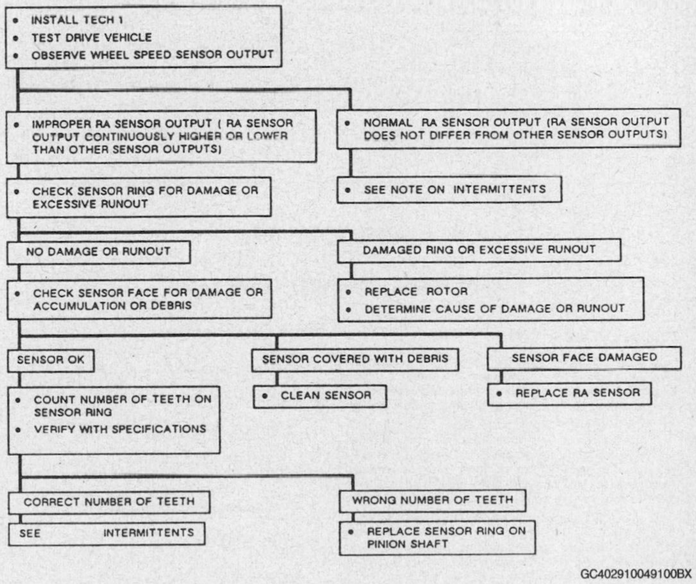
• INSTALL TECH 1
• TEST DRIVE VEHICLE
• OBSERVE WHEEL SPEED SENSOR OUTPUT
• IMPROPER RA SENSOR OUTPUT (RA SENSOR OUTPUT CONTINUOUSLY HIGHER OR LOWER THAN OTHER SENSOR OUTPUTS)
• NORMAL RA SENSOR OUTPUT (RA SENSOR OUTPUT DOES NOT DIFFER FROM OTHER SENSOR OUTPUTS)
• CHECK SENSOR RING FOR DAMAGE OR EXCESSIVE RUNOUT
• SEE NOTE ON INTERMITTENTS
NO DAMAGE OR RUNOUT
DAMAGED RING OR EXCESSIVE RUNOUT
• CHECK SENSOR FACE FOR DAMAGE OR ACCUMULATION OR DEBRIS
• REPLACE ROTOR
• DETERMINE CAUSE OF DAMAGE OR RUNOUT
SENSOR OK
SENSOR COVERED WITH DEBRIS
SENSOR FACE DAMAGED
• COUNT NUMBER OF TEETH ON SENSOR RING
• VERIFY WITH SPECIFICATIONS
• CLEAN SENSOR
• REPLACE RA SENSOR
CORRECT NUMBER OF TEETH
WRONG NUMBER OF TEETH
SEE INTERMITTENTS
• REPLACE SENSOR RING ON PINION SHAFT
GC402910049100BX

Fig. 57 Code 36: Rear Axle Toothed Wheel Frequency Error. 1992 Brougham

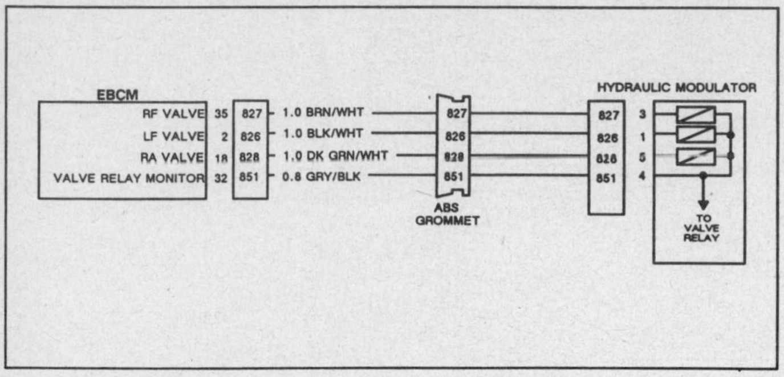
EBCM
RF VALVE 35 827 1.0 BRN/WHT
LF VALVE 2 826 1.0 BLK/WHT
RA VALVE 18 828 1.0 DK GRN/WHT
VALVE RELAY MONITOR 32 851 0.8 GRY/BLK
ABS GROMMET
HYDRAULIC MODULATOR
827 3
826 1
828 5
851 4
TO VALVE RELAY

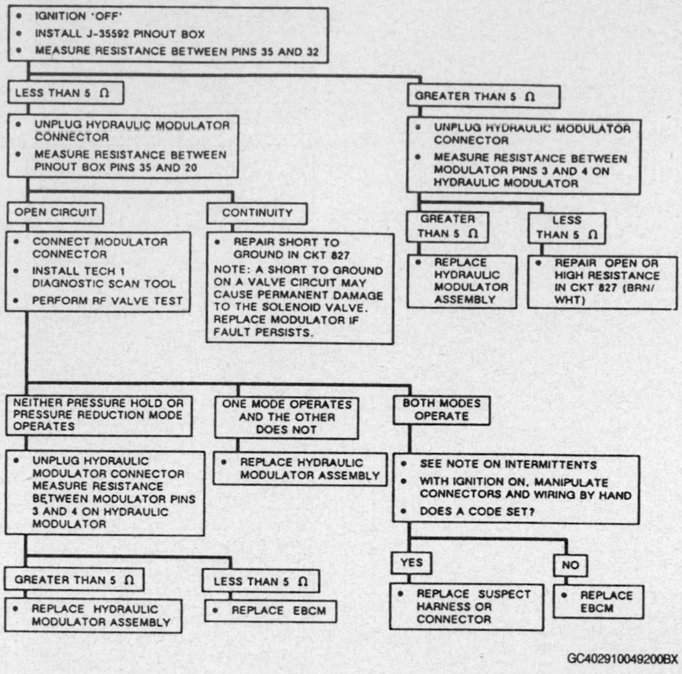
IGNITION 'OFF'
INSTALL J-35592 PINOUT BOX
MEASURE RESISTANCE BETWEEN PINS 35 AND 32
LESS THAN 5 Ω
GREATER THAN 5 Ω
UNPLUG HYDRAULIC MODULATOR CONNECTOR
MEASURE RESISTANCE BETWEEN PINOUT BOX PINS 35 AND 20
UNPLUG HYDRAULIC MODULATOR CONNECTOR
MEASURE RESISTANCE BETWEEN MODULATOR PINS 3 AND 4 ON HYDRAULIC MODULATOR
OPEN CIRCUIT
CONTINUITY
GREATER THAN 5 Ω
LESS THAN 5 Ω
CONNECT MODULATOR CONNECTOR
INSTALL TECH 1 DIAGNOSTIC SCAN TOOL
PERFORM RF VALVE TEST
REPAIR SHORT TO GROUND IN CKT 827
NOTE: A SHORT TO GROUND ON A VALVE CIRCUIT MAY CAUSE PERMANENT DAMAGE TO THE SOLENOID VALVE. REPLACE MODULATOR IF FAULT PERSISTS.
REPLACE HYDRAULIC MODULATOR ASSEMBLY
REPAIR OPEN OR HIGH RESISTANCE IN CKT 827 (BRN/WHT)
NEITHER PRESSURE HOLD OR PRESSURE REDUCTION MODE OPERATES
ONE MODE OPERATES AND THE OTHER DOES NOT
BOTH MODES OPERATE
UNPLUG HYDRAULIC MODULATOR CONNECTOR MEASURE RESISTANCE BETWEEN MODULATOR PINS 3 AND 4 ON HYDRAULIC MODULATOR
REPLACE HYDRAULIC MODULATOR ASSEMBLY
SEE NOTE ON INTERMITTENTS
WITH IGNITION ON, MANIPULATE CONNECTORS AND WIRING BY HAND
DOES A CODE SET?
YES
NO
GREATER THAN 5 Ω
LESS THAN 5 Ω
REPLACE HYDRAULIC MODULATOR ASSEMBLY
REPLACE EBCM
REPLACE SUSPECT HARNESS OR CONNECTOR
REPLACE EBCM
GC402910049200BX

ABS CODE 41

RIGHT FRONT SOLENOID VALVE FAULT

CIRCUIT DESCRIPTION

The right front solenoid valve in the hydraulic modulator may be commanded to three different positions by the EBCM. Valve position is determined by the amount of current which is allowed to flow through the solenoid valve coil.

The solenoid valve circuits receive power through the valve relay on the hydraulic modulator. The valve relay is engaged at key-on and remains engaged throughout the ignition cycle. Solenoid valve lines should have battery voltage available at all times.

When the key is turned to RUN, power is supplied to the EBCM. The EBCM will complete an internal self-check before providing ground to the valve relay. When the valve relay is energized, battery power is supplied to the solenoid valves.

Code 41 will set when the expected position of the right front solenoid valve does not match the commanded position from the EBCM. Conditions which could cause Code 41 to set are damage to the right front solenoid, an open circuit or a short circuit to ground or battery on CKT 827.

TEST CONDITIONS

1. Tested continuously.

FAILURE CONDITIONS

While Standing Or Driving:

1. Valve cannot be activated.

– or –

2. Valve activated in a defective way.

ACTION TAKEN

1. Code Set.
2. ABS switched 'OFF'.

GC402910049200AX

Fig. 58 Code 41: RF Solenoid Valve Fault. 1992 Brougham

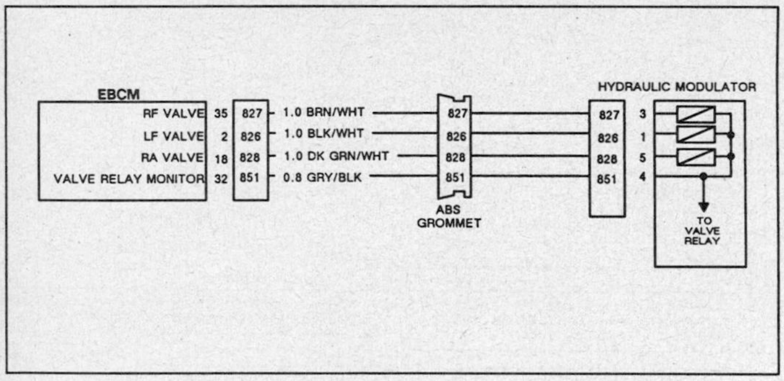
EBCM
RF VALVE 35 827 1.0 BRN/WHT
LF VALVE 2 826 1.0 BLK/WHT
RA VALVE 18 828 1.0 DK GRN/WHT
VALVE RELAY MONITOR 32 851 0.8 GRY/BLK
ABS GROMMET
HYDRAULIC MODULATOR
827 3
826 1
828 5
851 4
TO VALVE RELAY

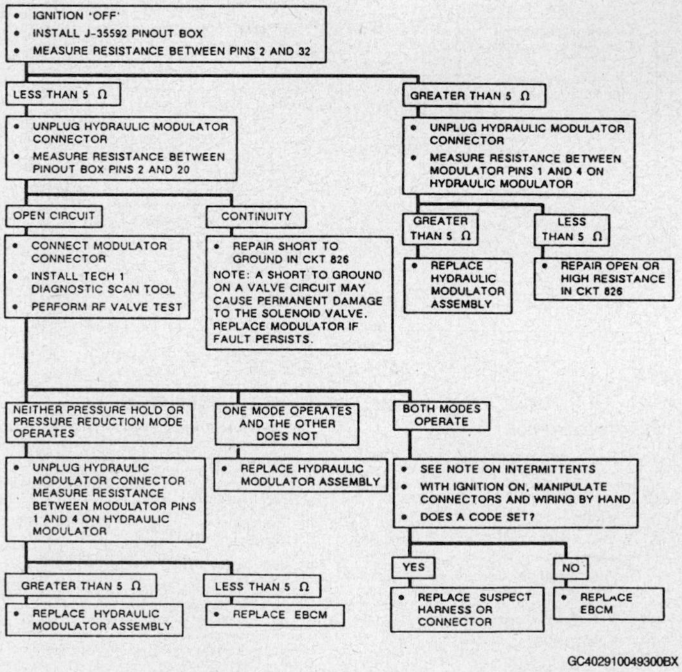
IGNITION 'OFF'
INSTALL J-35592 PINOUT BOX
MEASURE RESISTANCE BETWEEN PINS 2 AND 32
LESS THAN 5 Ω
GREATER THAN 5 Ω
UNPLUG HYDRAULIC MODULATOR CONNECTOR
MEASURE RESISTANCE BETWEEN PINOUT BOX PINS 2 AND 20
UNPLUG HYDRAULIC MODULATOR CONNECTOR
MEASURE RESISTANCE BETWEEN MODULATOR PINS 1 AND 4 ON HYDRAULIC MODULATOR
OPEN CIRCUIT
CONTINUITY
GREATER THAN 5 Ω
LESS THAN 5 Ω
CONNECT MODULATOR CONNECTOR
INSTALL TECH 1 DIAGNOSTIC SCAN TOOL
PERFORM RF VALVE TEST
REPAIR SHORT TO GROUND IN CKT 826
NOTE: A SHORT TO GROUND ON A VALVE CIRCUIT MAY CAUSE PERMANENT DAMAGE TO THE SOLENOID VALVE. REPLACE MODULATOR IF FAULT PERSISTS.
REPLACE HYDRAULIC MODULATOR ASSEMBLY
REPAIR OPEN OR HIGH RESISTANCE IN CKT 826
NEITHER PRESSURE HOLD OR PRESSURE REDUCTION MODE OPERATES
ONE MODE OPERATES AND THE OTHER DOES NOT
BOTH MODES OPERATE
UNPLUG HYDRAULIC MODULATOR CONNECTOR MEASURE RESISTANCE BETWEEN MODULATOR PINS 1 AND 4 ON HYDRAULIC MODULATOR
REPLACE HYDRAULIC MODULATOR ASSEMBLY
SEE NOTE ON INTERMITTENTS
WITH IGNITION ON, MANIPULATE CONNECTORS AND WIRING BY HAND
DOES A CODE SET?
YES
NO
GREATER THAN 5 Ω
LESS THAN 5 Ω
REPLACE HYDRAULIC MODULATOR ASSEMBLY
REPLACE EBCM
REPLACE SUSPECT HARNESS OR CONNECTOR
REPLACE EBCM
GC402910049300BX

ABS CODE 45

LEFT FRONT SOLENOID VALVE FAULT

CIRCUIT DESCRIPTION

The left front solenoid valve in the hydraulic modulator may be commanded to three different positions by the EBCM. Valve position is determined by the amount of current which is allowed to flow through the solenoid valve coil.

The solenoid valve circuits receive power through the valve relay on the hydraulic modulator. The valve relay is engaged at key-on and remains engaged throughout the ignition cycle. Solenoid valve lines should have battery voltage available at all times.

When the key is turned to RUN, power is supplied to the EBCM. The EBCM will complete an internal self-check before providing ground to the valve relay. When the valve relay is energized, battery power is supplied to the solenoid valves.

Code 45 will set when the expected position of the left front solenoid valve does not match the commanded position from the EBCM. Conditions which could cause Code 45 to set are damage to the left front solenoid, an open circuit or a short circuit to ground or battery on CKT 826.

TEST CONDITIONS

1. Tested continuously.

FAILURE CONDITIONS

While Standing Or Driving:

1. Valve cannot be activated.

– or –

2. Valve activated in a defective way.

ACTION TAKEN

1. Code Set.
2. ABS switched 'OFF'.

GC402910049300AX

Fig. 59 Code 45: LF Solenoid Valve Fault. 1992 Brougham

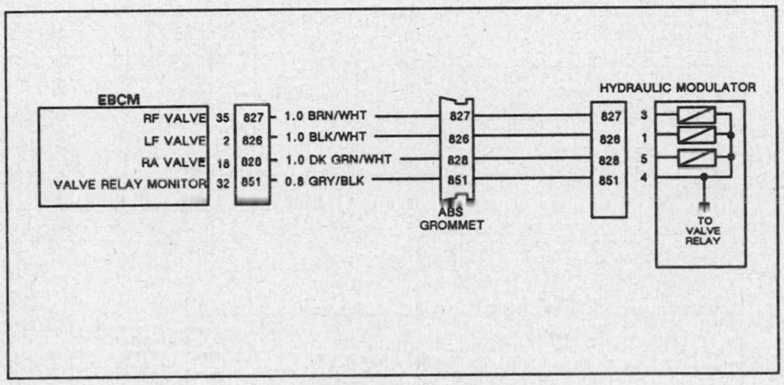
EBCM
RF VALVE
LF VALVE
RA VALVE
VALVE RELAY MONITOR
35
2
18
32
827
826
828
851
1.0 BRN/WHT
1.0 BLK/WHT
1.0 DK GRN/WHT
0.8 GRY/BLK
827
826
828
851
ABS GROMMET
HYDRAULIC MODULATOR
827
826
828
851
3
1
5
4
TO VALVE RELAY

ABS CODE 55

REAR AXLE SOLENOID VALVE FAULT

CIRCUIT DESCRIPTION

The rear axle solenoid valve in the hydraulic modulator may be commanded to three different positions by the EBCM. The rear axle solenoid valve modulates hydraulic brake pressure to both rear wheel circuits. Valve position is determined by the amount of current which is allowed to flow through the solenoid valve coil.

The solenoid valve circuits receive power through the valve relay on the hydraulic modulator. The valve relay is engaged at key on and remains engaged throughout the ignition cycle. Solenoid valve lines should have battery voltage available at all times.

When the key is turned to RUN, power is supplied to the EBCM. The EBCM will complete an internal self-check before providing ground to the valve relay. When the valve relay is energized, battery power is supplied to the solenoid valves.

Code 55 will set when the expected position of the rear axle solenoid valve does not match the commanded position from the EBCM. Conditions which could cause Code 55 to set are damage to the rear axle solenoid, an open circuit or a short circuit to ground or battery on CKT 828.

TEST CONDITIONS

1. Tested continuously.

FAILURE CONDITIONS

While Standing Or Driving:

1. Valve cannot be activated.

- or -

2. Valve activated in a defective way.

ACTION TAKEN

1. Code Set.
2. ABS switched 'OFF'.

GC402910049400AX

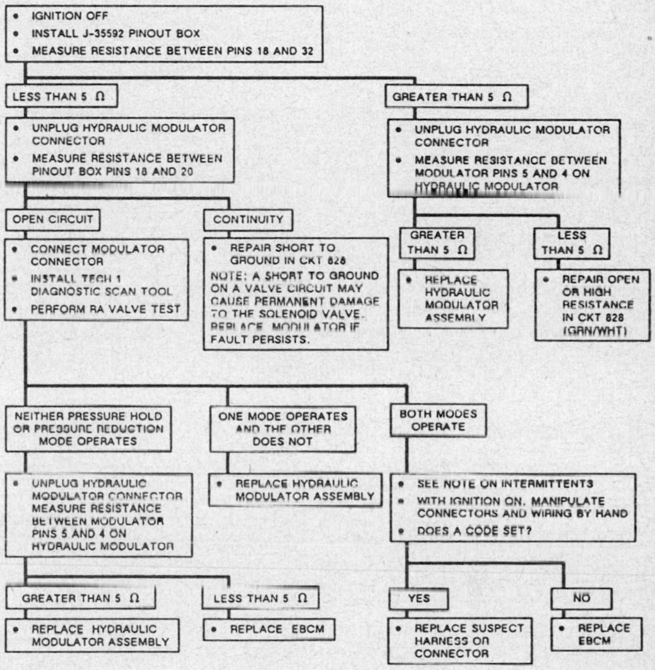
• IGNITION OFF
• INSTALL J-35592 PINOUT BOX
• MEASURE RESISTANCE BETWEEN PINS 18 AND 32
LESS THAN 5 Ω
GREATER THAN 5 Ω
• UNPLUG HYDRAULIC MODULATOR CONNECTOR
• MEASURE RESISTANCE BETWEEN PINOUT BOX PINS 18 AND 20
• UNPLUG HYDRAULIC MODULATOR CONNECTOR
• MEASURE RESISTANCE BETWEEN MODULATOR PINS 5 AND 4 ON HYDRAULIC MODULATOR
OPEN CIRCUIT
CONTINUITY
GREATER THAN 5 Ω
LESS THAN 5 Ω
• CONNECT MODULATOR CONNECTOR
• INSTALL TECH 1 DIAGNOSTIC SCAN TOOL
• PERFORM RA VALVE TEST
• REPAIR SHORT TO GROUND IN CKT 828
NOTE: A SHORT TO GROUND ON A VALVE CIRCUIT MAY CAUSE PERMANENT DAMAGE TO THE SOLENOID VALVE. REPLACE MODULATOR IF FAULT PERSISTS.
• REPLACE HYDRAULIC MODULATOR ASSEMBLY
• REPAIR OPEN OR HIGH RESISTANCE IN CKT 828 (GRN/WHT)
NEITHER PRESSURE HOLD OR PRESSURE REDUCTION MODE OPERATES
ONE MODE OPERATES AND THE OTHER DOES NOT
BOTH MODES OPERATE
• UNPLUG HYDRAULIC MODULATOR CONNECTOR MEASURE RESISTANCE BETWEEN MODULATOR PINS 5 AND 4 ON HYDRAULIC MODULATOR
• REPLACE HYDRAULIC MODULATOR ASSEMBLY
• SEE NOTE ON INTERMITTENTS
• WITH IGNITION ON, MANIPULATE CONNECTORS AND WIRING BY HAND
• DOES A CODE SET?
GREATER THAN 5 Ω
LESS THAN 5 Ω
YES
NO
• REPLACE HYDRAULIC MODULATOR ASSEMBLY
• REPLACE EBCM
• REPLACE SUSPECT HARNESS OR CONNECTOR
• REPLACE EBCM
GC402910049400BX

Fig. 60 Code 55: Rear Axle Solenoid Valve Fault. 1992 Brougham

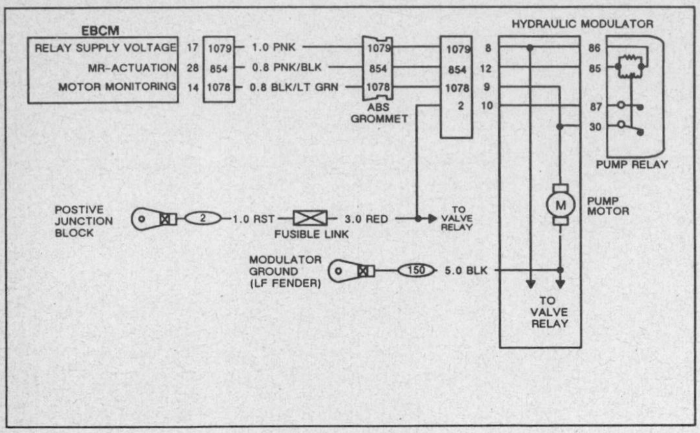
EBCM
RELAY SUPPLY VOLTAGE 17 1079 1.0 PNK
MR-ACTUATION 28 854 0.8 PNK/BLK
MOTOR MONITORING 14 1078 0.8 BLK/LT GRN
ABS GROMMET
HYDRAULIC MODULATOR
1079 8
854 12
1078 9
2 10
86
85
87
30
PUMP RELAY
PUMP MOTOR
M
POSTIVE JUNCTION BLOCK
2
1.0 RST
3.0 RED
FUSIBLE LINK
TO VALVE RELAY
MODULATOR GROUND (LF FENDER)
150
5.0 BLK
TO VALVE RELAY

ABS CODE 61
PUMP MOTOR CIRCUIT FAULT

CIRCUIT DESCRIPTION

The pump motor returns brake fluid to the master cylinder brake circuit at the hydraulic modulator during antilock braking. During normal braking, the pump does not operate. When the vehicle begins to move after start-up, the EBCM will turn on the pump motor and perform a self-check of the pump motor and pump motor circuit. This check may be felt and heard by the driver when the vehicle begins to move. The self-check should be considered normal operation. The pump motor is an integral component of the hydraulic modulator and cannot be serviced separately.

The pump motor relay provides power to the pump motor in the hydraulic modulator. The pump motor relay is located on the hydraulic modulator an may be replaced if it is found to be defective.

TEST CONDITIONS

1. Tested continuously.

FAILURE CONDITIONS

1. Drive Away: Motor voltage is not detected during first drive away after engine start.
2. While driving: Motor relay is energized and motor voltage is not detected.

– or –

3. Voltage at EBCM pin 14 below system voltage

– or –

4. Pump runs continuously

When the pump motor relay is engaged, the motor monitor line should be at battery voltage. With the pump motor relay disengaged, the monitoring line should be at ground. If the commanded position of the pump motor relay and motor monitor line do not agree, Code 61 will set. Some conditions which will cause Code 61 to set are:

- An open circuit on CKTs 854 or 1078
- A short to voltage on CKTs 854 or 1078
- A short to ground on CKTs 854 or 1078
- A defective pump motor relay or pump motor

GC402910049500AX

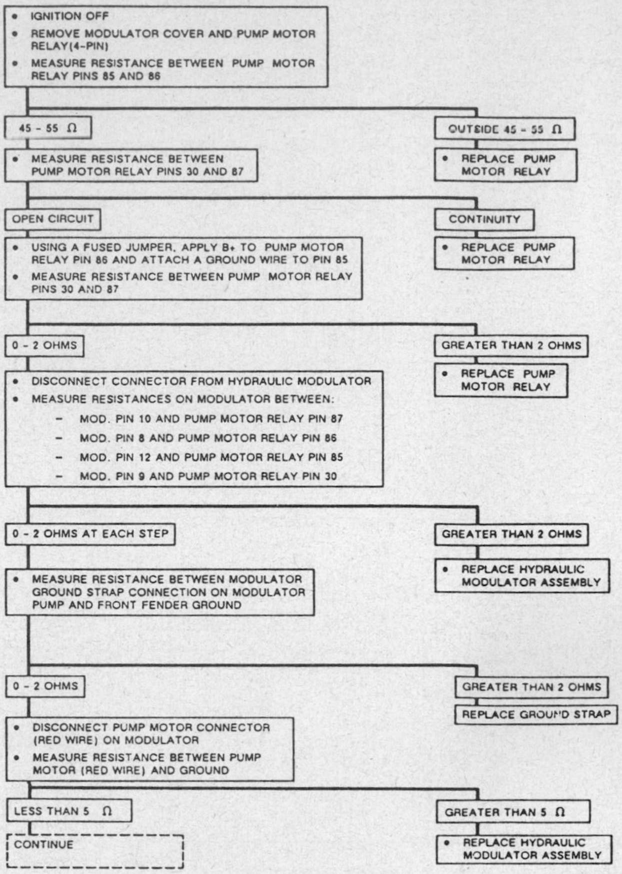
• IGNITION OFF
• REMOVE MODULATOR COVER AND PUMP MOTOR RELAY(4-PIN)
• MEASURE RESISTANCE BETWEEN PUMP MOTOR RELAY PINS 85 AND 86
45 - 55 Ω
OUTSIDE 45 - 55 Ω
• MEASURE RESISTANCE BETWEEN PUMP MOTOR RELAY PINS 30 AND 87
• REPLACE PUMP MOTOR RELAY
OPEN CIRCUIT
CONTINUITY
• USING A FUSED JUMPER, APPLY B+ TO PUMP MOTOR RELAY PIN 86 AND ATTACH A GROUND WIRE TO PIN 85
• MEASURE RESISTANCE BETWEEN PUMP MOTOR RELAY PINS 30 AND 87
• REPLACE PUMP MOTOR RELAY
0 - 2 OHMS
GREATER THAN 2 OHMS
• DISCONNECT CONNECTOR FROM HYDRAULIC MODULATOR
• MEASURE RESISTANCES ON MODULATOR BETWEEN:
– MOD. PIN 10 AND PUMP MOTOR RELAY PIN 87
– MOD. PIN 8 AND PUMP MOTOR RELAY PIN 86
– MOD. PIN 12 AND PUMP MOTOR RELAY PIN 85
– MOD. PIN 9 AND PUMP MOTOR RELAY PIN 30
• REPLACE PUMP MOTOR RELAY
0 - 2 OHMS AT EACH STEP
GREATER THAN 2 OHMS
• MEASURE RESISTANCE BETWEEN MODULATOR GROUND STRAP CONNECTION ON MODULATOR PUMP AND FRONT FENDER GROUND
• REPLACE HYDRAULIC MODULATOR ASSEMBLY
0 - 2 OHMS
GREATER THAN 2 OHMS
REPLACE GROUND STRAP
• DISCONNECT PUMP MOTOR CONNECTOR (RED WIRE) ON MODULATOR
• MEASURE RESISTANCE BETWEEN PUMP MOTOR (RED WIRE) AND GROUND
LESS THAN 5 Ω
GREATER THAN 5 Ω
CONTINUE
• REPLACE HYDRAULIC MODULATOR ASSEMBLY

GC402910049500BX

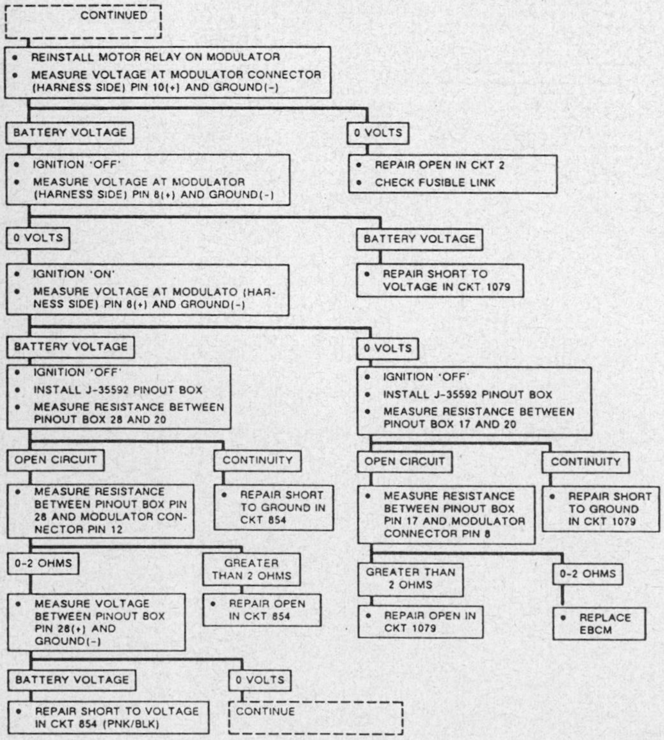
CONTINUED
• REINSTALL MOTOR RELAY ON MODULATOR
• MEASURE VOLTAGE AT MODULATOR CONNECTOR (HARNESS SIDE) PIN 10(+) AND GROUND(-)
BATTERY VOLTAGE
0 VOLTS
• IGNITION 'OFF'
• MEASURE VOLTAGE AT MODULATOR (HARNESS SIDE) PIN 8(+) AND GROUND(-)
• REPAIR OPEN IN CKT 2
• CHECK FUSIBLE LINK
0 VOLTS
BATTERY VOLTAGE
• IGNITION 'ON'
• MEASURE VOLTAGE AT MODULATO (HARNESS SIDE) PIN 8(+) AND GROUND(-)
• REPAIR SHORT TO VOLTAGE IN CKT 1079
BATTERY VOLTAGE
0 VOLTS
• IGNITION 'OFF'
• INSTALL J-35592 PINOUT BOX
• MEASURE RESISTANCE BETWEEN PINOUT BOX 28 AND 20
• IGNITION 'OFF'
• INSTALL J-35592 PINOUT BOX
• MEASURE RESISTANCE BETWEEN PINOUT BOX 17 AND 20
OPEN CIRCUIT
CONTINUITY
OPEN CIRCUIT
CONTINUITY
• MEASURE RESISTANCE BETWEEN PINOUT BOX PIN 28 AND MODULATOR CONNECTOR PIN 12
• REPAIR SHORT TO GROUND IN CKT 854
• MEASURE RESISTANCE BETWEEN PINOUT BOX PIN 17 AND MODULATOR CONNECTOR PIN 8
• REPAIR SHORT TO GROUND IN CKT 1079
0-2 OHMS
GREATER THAN 2 OHMS
GREATER THAN 2 OHMS
0-2 OHMS
• MEASURE VOLTAGE BETWEEN PINOUT BOX PIN 28(+) AND GROUND(-)
• REPAIR OPEN IN CKT 854
• REPAIR OPEN IN CKT 1079
• REPLACE EBCM
BATTERY VOLTAGE
0 VOLTS
• REPAIR SHORT TO VOLTAGE IN CKT 854 (PNK/BLK)
CONTINUE

GC402910049500CX

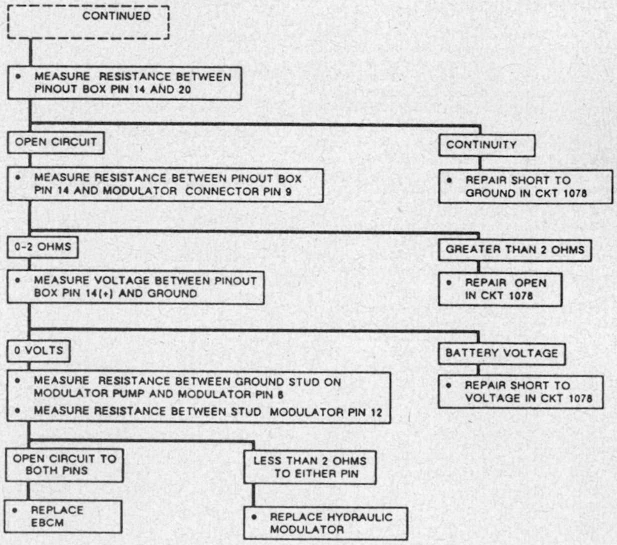
CONTINUED
• MEASURE RESISTANCE BETWEEN PINOUT BOX PIN 14 AND 20
OPEN CIRCUIT
CONTINUITY
• MEASURE RESISTANCE BETWEEN PINOUT BOX PIN 14 AND MODULATOR CONNECTOR PIN 9
• REPAIR SHORT TO GROUND IN CKT 1078
0-2 OHMS
GREATER THAN 2 OHMS
• MEASURE VOLTAGE BETWEEN PINOUT BOX PIN 14(+) AND GROUND
• REPAIR OPEN IN CKT 1078
0 VOLTS
BATTERY VOLTAGE
• MEASURE RESISTANCE BETWEEN GROUND STUD ON MODULATOR PUMP AND MODULATOR PIN 8
• MEASURE RESISTANCE BETWEEN STUD MODULATOR PIN 12
• REPAIR SHORT TO VOLTAGE IN CKT 1078
OPEN CIRCUIT TO BOTH PINS
LESS THAN 2 OHMS TO EITHER PIN
• REPLACE EBCM
• REPLACE HYDRAULIC MODULATOR

GC402910049500DX

Fig. 61 Code 61: Pump Motor Circuit Failure. 1992 Brougham

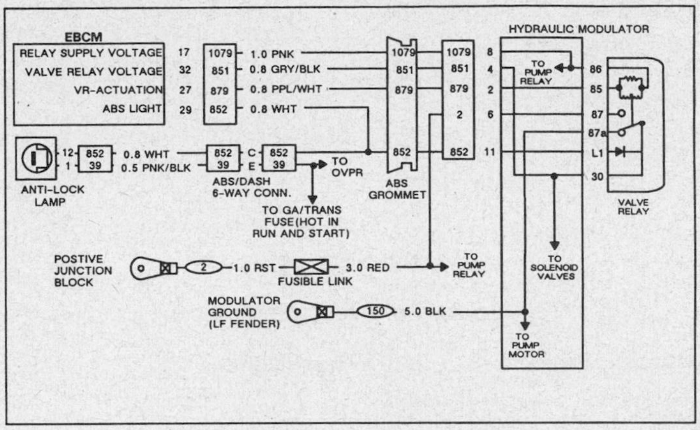
EBCM
RELAY SUPPLY VOLTAGE 17 1079 1.0 PNK
VALVE RELAY VOLTAGE 32 851 0.8 GRY/BLK
VR-ACTUATION 27 879 0.8 PPL/WHT
ABS LIGHT 29 852 0.8 WHT
HYDRAULIC MODULATOR
TO PUMP RELAY
86
85
87
87a
L1
30
VALVE RELAY
12 852 0.8 WHT
1 39 0.5 PNK/BLK
ANTI-LOCK LAMP
ABS/DASH 6-WAY CONN.
TO OVPR
ABS GROMMET
TO GA/TRANS FUSE(HOT IN RUN AND START)
POSTIVE JUNCTION BLOCK
1.0 RST
FUSIBLE LINK
3.0 RED
TO PUMP RELAY
TO SOLENOID VALVES
MODULATOR GROUND (LF FENDER)
150
5.0 BLK
TO PUMP MOTOR

ABS CODE 63
SOLENOID VALVE RELAY FAULT

CIRCUIT DESCRIPTION

The solenoid valve relay provides power to the three solenoid valves in the hydraulic modulator. The solenoid valve relay is located on the hydraulic modulator and may be replaced if it is found to be defective.

The valve relay is engaged during normal system operation. When the ignition is switched to RUN, the EBCM commands the solenoid valve relay on by grounding the valve relay actuation line on CKT 879 (EBCM pin 27). When this ground is provided, the valve relay is energized from the voltage supply line on CKT 1079 (EBCM pin 17). The valve relay switches and battery voltage is provided to the three solenoid valves and the solenoid valve relay feedback line on CKT 851 (EBCM pin 32). The valve relay remains engaged until the ignition is turned off or a failure is detected.

Whenever the solenoid valve relay is not engaged, the ANTILOCK light will turn on. With the ignition on and the solenoid valve relay not engaged, a path to ground exists from the GA/TRANS fuse (20 amps) thru the ANTILOCK light on CKT 39 which turns on the warning light. The ANTILOCK light can also be commanded on by the EBCM on CKT 852 (EBCM pin 29). The EBCM will provide ground on this line and turn on the warning light when a failure is detected.

The pump motor relay is not engaged during normal system operation. When antilock operation is required, the motor relay actuation line on CKT 854 (EBCM pin 28) is pulled to ground. The pump motor relay is engaged by the relay supply voltage line on CKT 1079 (EBCM pin 17). When the relay switches, battery power is provided to the pump motor.

ANTILOCK OPERATION

With the solenoid valve relay engaged, battery power is provided to the three solenoid valves. If antilock operation is required, the EBCM varies the amount of current supplied to the solenoid valves (EBCM pins 2, 18, 35) and the valve is positioned to provide for optimum braking.

TEST CONDITIONS

1. Tested continuously.

FAILURE CONDITIONS

1. While Standing Or Driving: Open circuit is detected
   - or -
2. Relay sticks during initial ignition

ACTION TAKEN

1. Code set.
2. ABS switched 'OFF'.

When the valve relay is engaged, the valve relay feedback line should be at battery voltage. With the valve relay disengaged the feedback line is at ground. If the commanded position of the valve relay and valve relay position indicated by the feedback line do not agree, Code 63 will set. Some conditions which will cause Code 63 to set are:

- An open circuit on CKTs 851 or 879
- A short to voltage on CKTs 851 or 879
- A short to ground on CKTs 851 or 879
- A defective solenoid valve relay
- Open circuit on CKT 1079.

GC402910049600AX

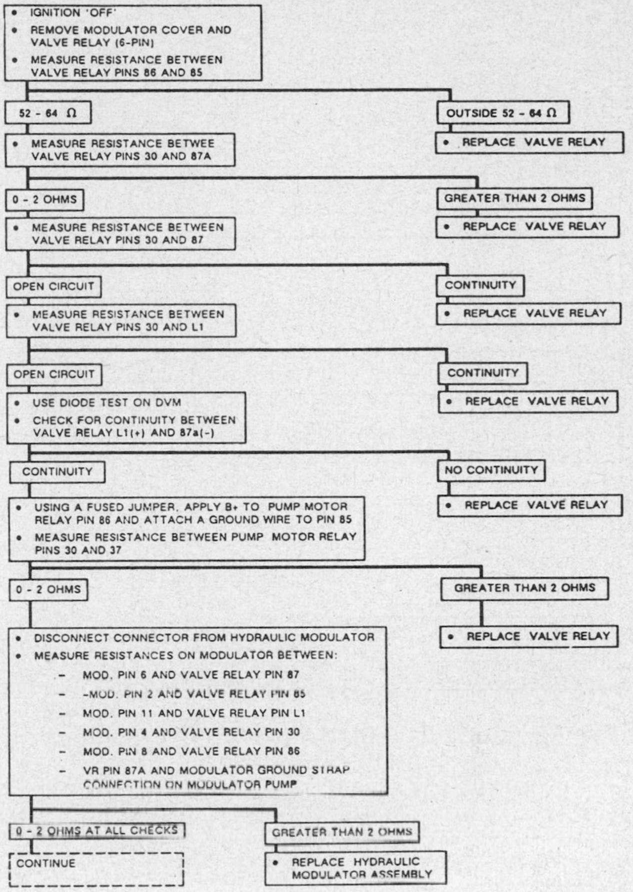
IGNITION 'OFF'
REMOVE MODULATOR COVER AND VALVE RELAY (6-PIN)
MEASURE RESISTANCE BETWEEN VALVE RELAY PINS 86 AND 85
52 - 64 Ω
OUTSIDE 52 - 64 Ω
REPLACE VALVE RELAY
MEASURE RESISTANCE BETWEE VALVE RELAY PINS 30 AND 87A
0 - 2 OHMS
GREATER THAN 2 OHMS
REPLACE VALVE RELAY
MEASURE RESISTANCE BETWEEN VALVE RELAY PINS 30 AND 87
OPEN CIRCUIT
CONTINUITY
REPLACE VALVE RELAY
MEASURE RESISTANCE BETWEEN VALVE RELAY PINS 30 AND L1
OPEN CIRCUIT
CONTINUITY
REPLACE VALVE RELAY
USE DIODE TEST ON DVM
CHECK FOR CONTINUITY BETWEEN VALVE RELAY L1(+) AND 87a(-)
CONTINUITY
NO CONTINUITY
REPLACE VALVE RELAY
USING A FUSED JUMPER, APPLY B+ TO PUMP MOTOR RELAY PIN 86 AND ATTACH A GROUND WIRE TO PIN 85
MEASURE RESISTANCE BETWEEN PUMP MOTOR RELAY PINS 30 AND 37
0 - 2 OHMS
GREATER THAN 2 OHMS
REPLACE VALVE RELAY
DISCONNECT CONNECTOR FROM HYDRAULIC MODULATOR
MEASURE RESISTANCES ON MODULATOR BETWEEN:
– MOD. PIN 6 AND VALVE RELAY PIN 87
– -MOD. PIN 2 AND VALVE RELAY PIN 85
– MOD. PIN 11 AND VALVE RELAY PIN L1
– MOD. PIN 4 AND VALVE RELAY PIN 30
– MOD. PIN 8 AND VALVE RELAY PIN 86
– VR PIN 87A AND MODULATOR GROUND STRAP CONNECTION ON MODULATOR PUMP
0 - 2 OHMS AT ALL CHECKS
GREATER THAN 2 OHMS
CONTINUE
REPLACE HYDRAULIC MODULATOR ASSEMBLY

GC402910049600BX

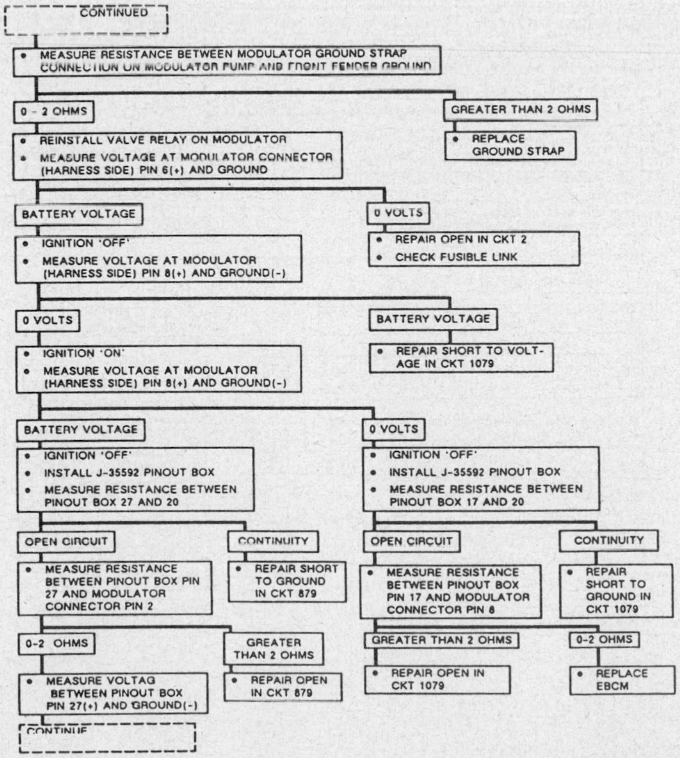
CONTINUED
MEASURE RESISTANCE BETWEEN MODULATOR GROUND STRAP CONNECTION ON MODULATOR PUMP AND FRONT FENDER GROUND
0 - 2 OHMS
GREATER THAN 2 OHMS
REPLACE GROUND STRAP
REINSTALL VALVE RELAY ON MODULATOR
MEASURE VOLTAGE AT MODULATOR CONNECTOR (HARNESS SIDE) PIN 6(+) AND GROUND
BATTERY VOLTAGE
0 VOLTS
REPAIR OPEN IN CKT 2
CHECK FUSIBLE LINK
IGNITION 'OFF'
MEASURE VOLTAGE AT MODULATOR (HARNESS SIDE) PIN 8(+) AND GROUND(-)
0 VOLTS
BATTERY VOLTAGE
REPAIR SHORT TO VOLTAGE IN CKT 1079
IGNITION 'ON'
MEASURE VOLTAGE AT MODULATOR (HARNESS SIDE) PIN 8(+) AND GROUND(-)
BATTERY VOLTAGE
0 VOLTS
IGNITION 'OFF'
INSTALL J-35592 PINOUT BOX
MEASURE RESISTANCE BETWEEN PINOUT BOX 27 AND 20
IGNITION 'OFF'
INSTALL J-35592 PINOUT BOX
MEASURE RESISTANCE BETWEEN PINOUT BOX 17 AND 20
OPEN CIRCUIT
CONTINUITY
OPEN CIRCUIT
CONTINUITY
MEASURE RESISTANCE BETWEEN PINOUT BOX PIN 27 AND MODULATOR CONNECTOR PIN 2
REPAIR SHORT TO GROUND IN CKT 879
MEASURE RESISTANCE BETWEEN PINOUT BOX PIN 17 AND MODULATOR CONNECTOR PIN 8
REPAIR SHORT TO GROUND IN CKT 1079
0-2 OHMS
GREATER THAN 2 OHMS
GREATER THAN 2 OHMS
0-2 OHMS
MEASURE VOLTAG BETWEEN PINOUT BOX PIN 27(+) AND GROUND(-)
REPAIR OPEN IN CKT 879
REPAIR OPEN IN CKT 1079
REPLACE EBCM
CONTINUE

GC402910049600CX

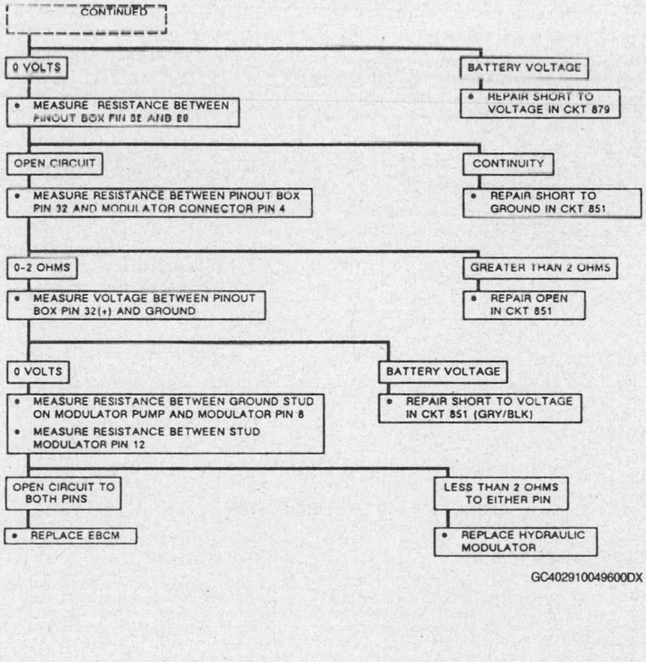
CONTINUED
0 VOLTS
BATTERY VOLTAGE
MEASURE RESISTANCE BETWEEN PINOUT BOX PIN 32 AND 20
REPAIR SHORT TO VOLTAGE IN CKT 879
OPEN CIRCUIT
CONTINUITY
MEASURE RESISTANCE BETWEEN PINOUT BOX PIN 32 AND MODULATOR CONNECTOR PIN 4
REPAIR SHORT TO GROUND IN CKT 851
0-2 OHMS
GREATER THAN 2 OHMS
MEASURE VOLTAGE BETWEEN PINOUT BOX PIN 32(+) AND GROUND
REPAIR OPEN IN CKT 851
0 VOLTS
BATTERY VOLTAGE
MEASURE RESISTANCE BETWEEN GROUND STUD ON MODULATOR PUMP AND MODULATOR PIN 8
MEASURE RESISTANCE BETWEEN STUD MODULATOR PIN 12
REPAIR SHORT TO VOLTAGE IN CKT 851 (GRY/BLK)
OPEN CIRCUIT TO BOTH PINS
LESS THAN 2 OHMS TO EITHER PIN
REPLACE EBCM
REPLACE HYDRAULIC MODULATOR

GC402910049600DX

Fig. 62 Code 63: Solenoid Valve Relay Fault. 1992 Brougham

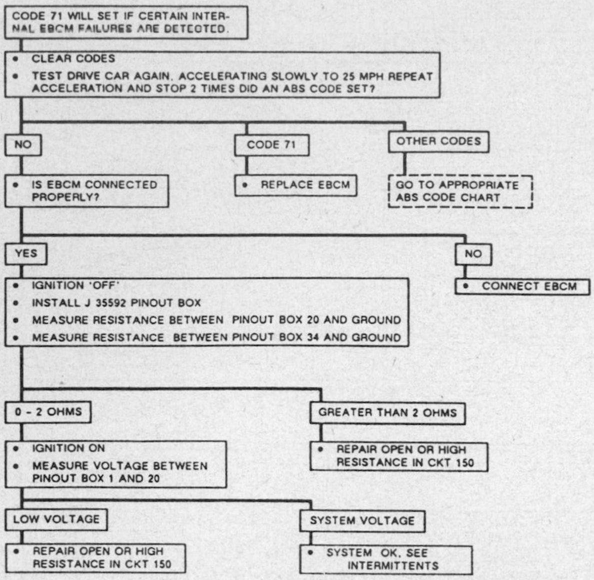
CODE 71 WILL SET IF CERTAIN INTERNAL EBCM FAILURES ARE DETECTED.
• CLEAR CODES
• TEST DRIVE CAR AGAIN. ACCELERATING SLOWLY TO 25 MPH REPEAT ACCELERATION AND STOP 2 TIMES DID AN ABS CODE SET?
NO
CODE 71
OTHER CODES
• IS EBCM CONNECTED PROPERLY?
• REPLACE EBCM
GO TO APPROPRIATE ABS CODE CHART
YES
NO
• IGNITION 'OFF'
• INSTALL J 35592 PINOUT BOX
• MEASURE RESISTANCE BETWEEN PINOUT BOX 20 AND GROUND
• MEASURE RESISTANCE BETWEEN PINOUT BOX 34 AND GROUND
• CONNECT EBCM
0 - 2 OHMS
GREATER THAN 2 OHMS
• IGNITION ON
• MEASURE VOLTAGE BETWEEN PINOUT BOX 1 AND 20
• REPAIR OPEN OR HIGH RESISTANCE IN CKT 150
LOW VOLTAGE
SYSTEM VOLTAGE
• REPAIR OPEN OR HIGH RESISTANCE IN CKT 150
• SYSTEM OK, SEE INTERMITTENTS

GC4029100497000X

Fig. 63 Code 71: EBCM Fault. 1992 Brougham

ABS CODE 72

SERIAL DATA LINK ERROR (TECH 1 ERROR)

CIRCUIT DESCRIPTION

An ABS Code 72 may set when there is a momentary serial data communications error between the EBCM and the TECH 1. This code may set when power to the EBCM is interrupted while the Tech-1 remains powered; such as when the ignition is cycled while the Tech-1 is hooked-up. When this occurs, simply cycle power to the Tech-1 and allow it to reset.

Although it is not an indication of a serious condition this code should be cleared prior to completion of diagnosis.

TEST CONDITIONS

Tested continuously in Diagnostics Mode. (TECH- 1 CONNECTED)

FAILURE CONDITIONS

EBCM receives 3 consecutive invalid messages during diagnostics.

ACTION TAKEN

1. Code set.
2. Transmission from and to TECH- 1 is impossible.

GC4029100498000X

Fig. 64 Code 72: Serial Data Link Error. 1992 Brougham

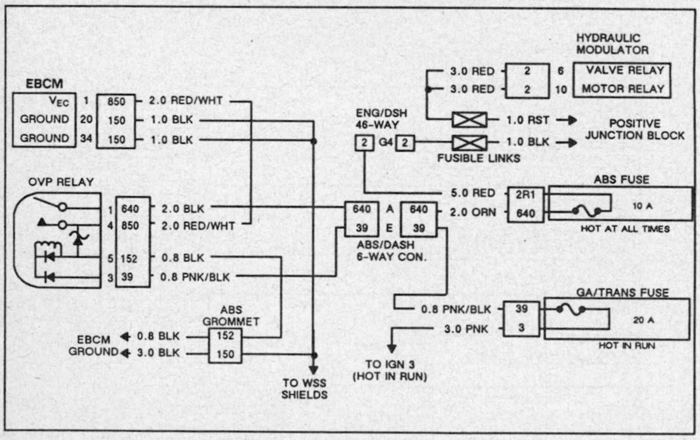
HYDRAULIC MODULATOR
EBCM
V_{EC} 1 850 2.0 RED/WHT
GROUND 20 150 1.0 BLK
GROUND 34 150 1.0 BLK
3.0 RED 2 6 VALVE RELAY
3.0 RED 2 10 MOTOR RELAY
ENG/DSH 46-WAY
2 G4 2
1.0 RST POSITIVE JUNCTION BLOCK
1.0 BLK
FUSIBLE LINKS
OVP RELAY
ABS FUSE
5.0 RED 2R1
2.0 ORN 640
10 A
HOT AT ALL TIMES
1 640 2.0 BLK
4 850 2.0 RED/WHT
5 152 0.8 BLK
3 39 0.8 PNK/BLK
640 A 640
39 E 39
ABS/DASH 6-WAY CON.
GA/TRANS FUSE
0.8 PNK/BLK 39
3.0 PNK 3
20 A
HOT IN RUN
ABS GROMMET
EBCM GROUND 0.8 BLK 152
3.0 BLK 150
TO WSS SHIELDS
TO IGN 3 (HOT IN RUN)

CHART A

NO SYSTEM POWER

CIRCUIT DESCRIPTION

The EBCM receives power from the overvoltage protection relay on CKT 850 (EBCM Pin 1). When the ignition is turned to RUN, the OVP relay is energized by the GA/TRANS fuse; the normally open relay contacts of the OVP relay close. Battery voltage is supplied to the EBCM thru the ABS fuse (10 amp) and CKT 640. If high system voltages occur, the ABS fuse will blow in order to prevent damage to the Antilock Brake System. The OVP relay, is located under the dash, mounted near the EBCM bracket behind the glovebox.

FAILURE CONDITIONS

Intermittent operation of the ANTILOCK light may be caused by intermittent voltage levels which do not correspond to the proper operating range of the Antilock Brake System. Some conditions which may cause a lack of system power are:

- Improper electrical contact of the EBCM connector.
- Low system voltage.
- Improper electrical contact of the vehicle power and ground connections.

GC402910049900AX

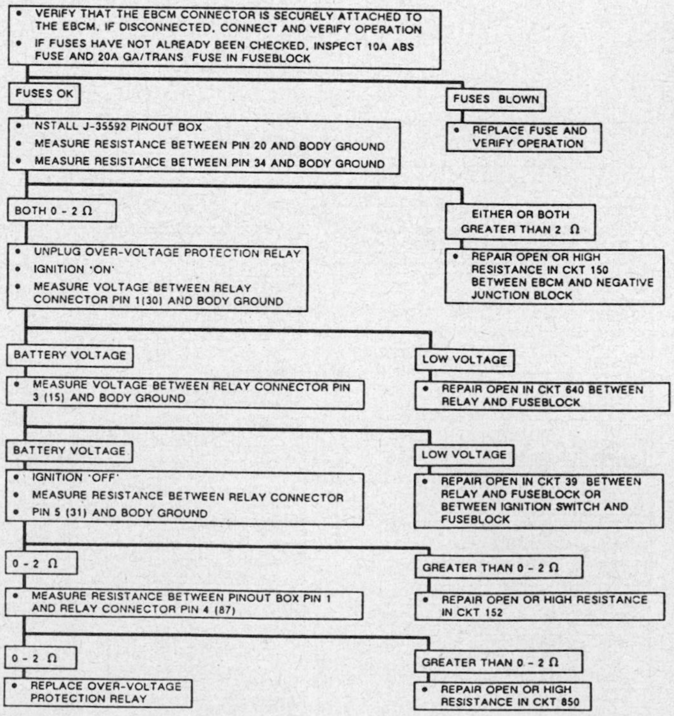
• VERIFY THAT THE EBCM CONNECTOR IS SECURELY ATTACHED TO THE EBCM. IF DISCONNECTED, CONNECT AND VERIFY OPERATION
• IF FUSES HAVE NOT ALREADY BEEN CHECKED, INSPECT 10A ABS FUSE AND 20A GA/TRANS FUSE IN FUSEBLOCK
FUSES OK
FUSES BLOWN
• NSTALL J-35592 PINOUT BOX
• MEASURE RESISTANCE BETWEEN PIN 20 AND BODY GROUND
• MEASURE RESISTANCE BETWEEN PIN 34 AND BODY GROUND
• REPLACE FUSE AND VERIFY OPERATION
BOTH 0 - 2 Ω
EITHER OR BOTH GREATER THAN 2 Ω
• UNPLUG OVER-VOLTAGE PROTECTION RELAY
• IGNITION 'ON'
• MEASURE VOLTAGE BETWEEN RELAY CONNECTOR PIN 1(30) AND BODY GROUND
• REPAIR OPEN OR HIGH RESISTANCE IN CKT 150 BETWEEN EBCM AND NEGATIVE JUNCTION BLOCK
BATTERY VOLTAGE
LOW VOLTAGE
• MEASURE VOLTAGE BETWEEN RELAY CONNECTOR PIN 3 (15) AND BODY GROUND
• REPAIR OPEN IN CKT 640 BETWEEN RELAY AND FUSEBLOCK
BATTERY VOLTAGE
LOW VOLTAGE
• IGNITION 'OFF'
• MEASURE RESISTANCE BETWEEN RELAY CONNECTOR
• PIN 5 (31) AND BODY GROUND
• REPAIR OPEN IN CKT 39 BETWEEN RELAY AND FUSEBLOCK OR BETWEEN IGNITION SWITCH AND FUSEBLOCK
0 - 2 Ω
GREATER THAN 0 - 2 Ω
• MEASURE RESISTANCE BETWEEN PINOUT BOX PIN 1 AND RELAY CONNECTOR PIN 4 (87)
• REPAIR OPEN OR HIGH RESISTANCE IN CKT 152
0 - 2 Ω
GREATER THAN 0 - 2 Ω
• REPLACE OVER-VOLTAGE PROTECTION RELAY
• REPAIR OPEN OR HIGH RESISTANCE IN CKT 850

GC402910049900BX

Fig. 65 Test A: No System Power. 1992 Brougham

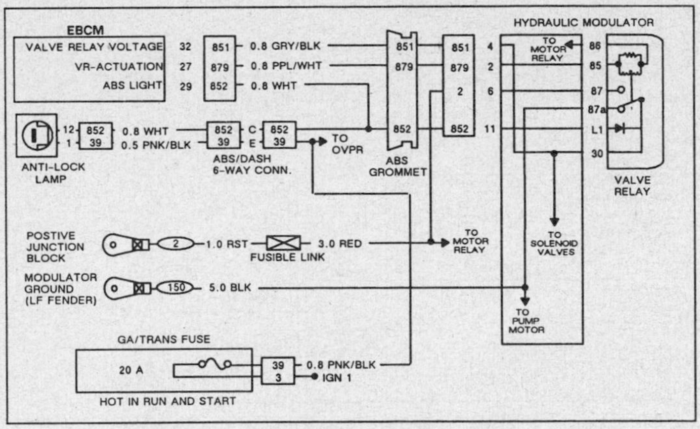
EBCM
VALVE RELAY VOLTAGE
VR-ACTUATION
ABS LIGHT
0.8 GRY/BLK
0.8 PPL/WHT
0.8 WHT
HYDRAULIC MODULATOR
TO MOTOR RELAY
0.8 WHT
0.5 PNK/BLK
TO OVPR
ANTI-LOCK LAMP
ABS/DASH 6-WAY CONN.
ABS GROMMET
VALVE RELAY
POSTIVE JUNCTION BLOCK
1.0 RST
3.0 RED
FUSIBLE LINK
TO MOTOR RELAY
TO SOLENOID VALVES
MODULATOR GROUND (LF FENDER)
5.0 BLK
TO PUMP MOTOR
GA/TRANS FUSE
20 A
0.8 PNK/BLK
IGN 1
HOT IN RUN AND START

CHART B

ABS LIGHT ON, NO CODES SET

CIRCUIT DESCRIPTION

The amber ANTILOCK light is located in the top of the instrument panel. It may be illuminated by the EBCM or a path to ground in the valve relay on the hydraulic modulator.

The ANTILOCK light is powered by the Ignition 1 feed and receives power anytime the ignition switch is turned to RUN or START. Power is provided on CKT 39 through the 20 amp GA/TRANS fuse located in the fuseblock.

Light Operation - Valve Relay Ground

The ANTILOCK light is illuminated anytime the valve relay is not enabled. When the relay is not enabled, the light is grounded through CKT 852 and the valve relay to the modulator ground on the left front fender. During normal operation (no fault conditions found), the valve will switch and the ground will be removed, and the ANTILOCK light will turn off.

Light Operation - EBCM Ground

If the EBCM detects a fault in the ABS, the EBCM can turn on the ANTILOCK light by grounding pin 29. A ground path exists for the light through CKT 852. The EBCM will disable the valve relay when CKT 852 is grounded at pin 29.

FAILURE CONDITIONS

The chart on the next page addresses conditions which result in continuous operation of the ANTILOCK light. If the ANTILOCK light is on and no codes are set, the EBCM should be extracted from the EBCM, the EBCM connector should be checked for proper connection and system power should be checked.

GC402910050000AX

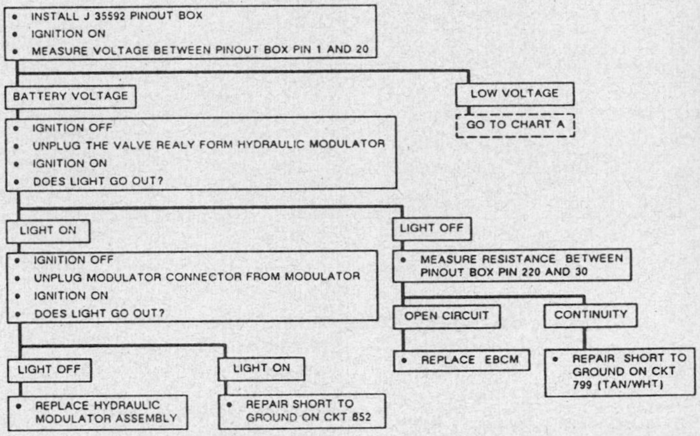
INSTALL J 35592 PINOUT BOX
IGNITION ON
MEASURE VOLTAGE BETWEEN PINOUT BOX PIN 1 AND 20
BATTERY VOLTAGE
LOW VOLTAGE
GO TO CHART A
IGNITION OFF
UNPLUG THE VALVE REALY FORM HYDRAULIC MODULATOR
IGNITION ON
DOES LIGHT GO OUT?
LIGHT ON
LIGHT OFF
IGNITION OFF
UNPLUG MODULATOR CONNECTOR FROM MODULATOR
IGNITION ON
DOES LIGHT GO OUT?
MEASURE RESISTANCE BETWEEN PINOUT BOX PIN 220 AND 30
OPEN CIRCUIT
CONTINUITY
REPLACE EBCM
REPAIR SHORT TO GROUND ON CKT 799 (TAN/WHT)
LIGHT OFF
LIGHT ON
REPLACE HYDRAULIC MODULATOR ASSEMBLY
REPAIR SHORT TO GROUND ON CKT 852

GC402910050000BX

Fig. 66 Test B: ABS Indicator On w/No Codes Set. 1992 Brougham

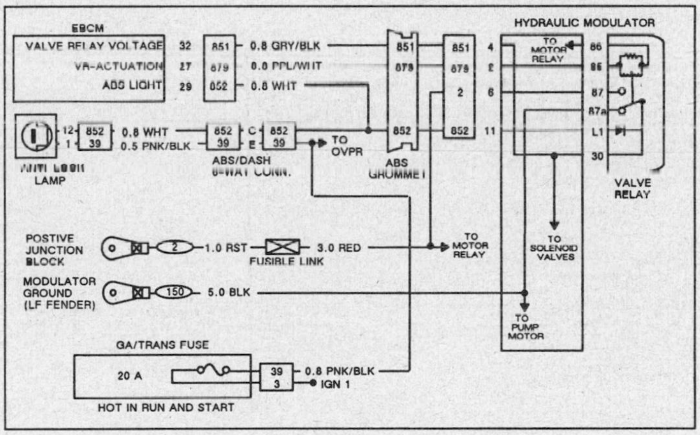
EBCM
VALVE RELAY VOLTAGE
VR-ACTUATION
ABS LIGHT
0.8 GRY/BLK
0.8 WHT
HYDRAULIC MODULATOR
0.8 WHT
0.5 PNK/BLK
TO OVPR
LAMP
ABS/DASH
VALVE RELAY
POSTIVE JUNCTION BLOCK
1.0 RST
3.0 RED
FUSIBLE LINK
TO MOTOR RELAY
TO SOLENOID VALVES
MODULATOR GROUND (LF FENDER)
5.0 BLK
TO PUMP MOTOR
GA/TRANS FUSE
20 A
0.8 PNK/BLK
IGN 1
HOT IN RUN AND START

CHART C

ANTILOCK LIGHT INOPERATIVE AT KEY-ON

CIRCUIT DESCRIPTION

The amber ANTILOCK light is located in the top of the instrument panel. It may be illuminated by the EBCM or a path to ground in the valve relay on the hydraulic modulator.

The ANTILOCK light is powered by the Ignition 1 feed and receives power anytime the ignition switch is turned to RUN or START. Power is provided on CKT 39 through the 20 amp GA/TRANS fuse located in the fuseblock.

Light Operation - Valve Relay Ground

The ANTILOCK light is illuminated anytime the valve relay is not enabled. When the relay is not enabled, the light is grounded through CKT 852 and the valve relay to the modulator ground on the left front fender. During normal operation (no fault conditions found), the valve will switch and the ground will be removed, and the ANTILOCK light will turn off.

Light Operation - EBCM Ground

Whether the valve relay is engaged or not, the EBCM can turn on the ANTILOCK light by grounding pin 29. A ground path exists for the light through CKT 852.

FAILURE CONDITIONS

The chart on the next page addresses conditions which result in no ANTILOCK light operation. As described at the beginning of this section, the ANTILOCK light should illuminate for a minimum of four seconds when the key is moved from OFF to RUN. This chart addresses conditions such as lack of power to the ANTILOCK light which would prevent the light from turning on. This condition could prevent the EBCM from turning on the light in the event of an antilock failure.

GC402910050100AX

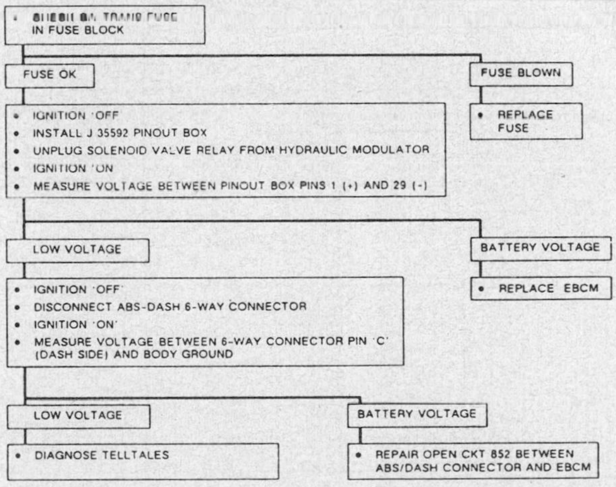
IN FUSE BLOCK
FUSE OK
FUSE BLOWN
REPLACE FUSE
IGNITION 'OFF'
INSTALL J 35592 PINOUT BOX
UNPLUG SOLENOID VALVE RELAY FROM HYDRAULIC MODULATOR
IGNITION 'ON'
MEASURE VOLTAGE BETWEEN PINOUT BOX PINS 1 (+) AND 29 (-)
LOW VOLTAGE
BATTERY VOLTAGE
REPLACE EBCM
IGNITION 'OFF'
DISCONNECT ABS-DASH 6-WAY CONNECTOR
IGNITION 'ON'
MEASURE VOLTAGE BETWEEN 6-WAY CONNECTOR PIN 'C' (DASH SIDE) AND BODY GROUND
LOW VOLTAGE
BATTERY VOLTAGE
DIAGNOSE TELLTALES
REPAIR OPEN CKT 852 BETWEEN ABS/DASH CONNECTOR AND EBCM

GC402910050100BX

Fig. 67 Test C: ABS Indicator Inoperative w/Key On. 1992 Brougham

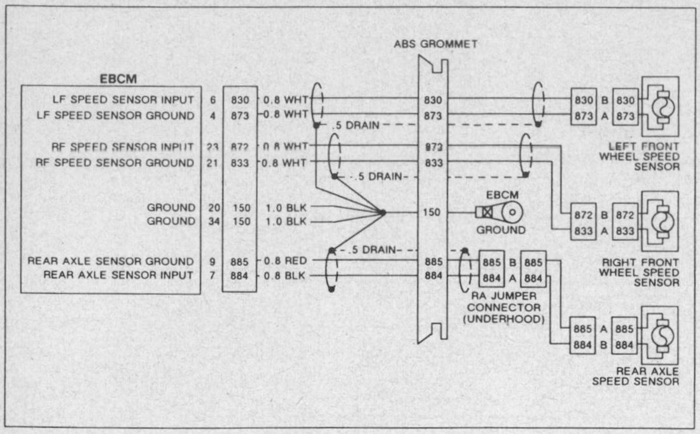
ABS GROMMET
EBCM
LF SPEED SENSOR INPUT 6 830 0.8 WHT
LF SPEED SENSOR GROUND 4 873 0.8 WHT
RF SPEED SENSOR INPUT 23 872 0.8 WHT
RF SPEED SENSOR GROUND 21 833 0.8 WHT
GROUND 20 150 1.0 BLK
GROUND 34 150 1.0 BLK
REAR AXLE SENSOR GROUND 9 885 0.8 RED
REAR AXLE SENSOR INPUT 7 884 0.8 BLK
.5 DRAIN
EBCM GROUND
LEFT FRONT WHEEL SPEED SENSOR
RIGHT FRONT WHEEL SPEED SENSOR
RA JUMPER CONNECTOR (UNDERHOOD)
REAR AXLE SPEED SENSOR

CHART D

VALVE CYCLING (CHATTER) DURING NORMAL STOPS

CIRCUIT DESCRIPTION

As each wheel turns, the wheel speed sensor for that wheel creates a small AC voltage as a toothed sensor ring, mounted on the brake rotor (in the front) or differential pinion shaft (in the rear), is passed by the stationary sensor. The sensor consists of a permanent magnet and coil and generates voltage by magnetic induction. The frequency of the wheel speed sensor signal is proportional to wheel speed.

The EBCM uses the wheel speed sensor signal to calculate vehicle reference speeds and individual speed, acceleration and slip values for each wheel. These values are used to determine when antilock control is required.

The EBCM performs two basic types of checks on the wheel speed sensors, these are sensor continuity and sensor output.

WHEEL SPEED SENSOR CABLES

In order to prevent electromagnetic interference from disturbing the wheel speed sensor signal, the sensor cables are protected with grounded shielding (indicated by dashed lines in the above schematic). This shield surrounds the two individual sensor wires. A black conduit surrounds the wires and shield. When servicing the sensor cables, the sensor wires are accessible by separating the shielding. If the shielding is disturbed, repair as required.

GC402910050200AX

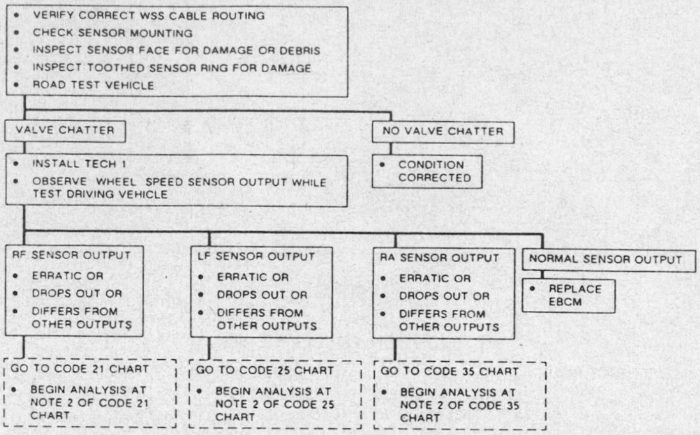
• VERIFY CORRECT WSS CABLE ROUTING
• CHECK SENSOR MOUNTING
• INSPECT SENSOR FACE FOR DAMAGE OR DEBRIS
• INSPECT TOOTHED SENSOR RING FOR DAMAGE
• ROAD TEST VEHICLE
VALVE CHATTER
NO VALVE CHATTER
• INSTALL TECH 1
• OBSERVE WHEEL SPEED SENSOR OUTPUT WHILE TEST DRIVING VEHICLE
• CONDITION CORRECTED
RF SENSOR OUTPUT
• ERRATIC OR
• DROPS OUT OR
• DIFFERS FROM OTHER OUTPUTS
LF SENSOR OUTPUT
• ERRATIC OR
• DROPS OUT OR
• DIFFERS FROM OTHER OUTPUTS
RA SENSOR OUTPUT
• ERRATIC OR
• DROPS OUT OR
• DIFFERS FROM OTHER OUTPUTS
NORMAL SENSOR OUTPUT
• REPLACE EBCM
GO TO CODE 21 CHART
• BEGIN ANALYSIS AT NOTE 2 OF CODE 21 CHART
GO TO CODE 25 CHART
• BEGIN ANALYSIS AT NOTE 2 OF CODE 25 CHART
GO TO CODE 35 CHART
• BEGIN ANALYSIS AT NOTE 2 OF CODE 35 CHART

GC402910050200BX

Fig. 68 Test D: Valve Cycling During Normal Stops. 1992 Brougham

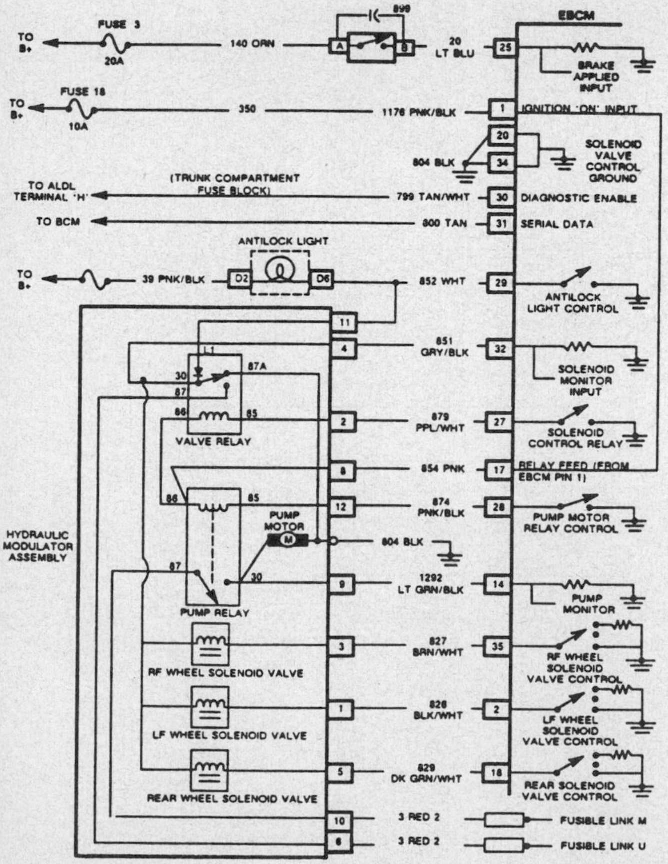
EBCM
TO B+
FUSE 3
20A
140 ORN
20 LT BLU
BRAKE APPLIED INPUT
FUSE 18
10A
350
1176 PNK/BLK
IGNITION "ON" INPUT
804 BLK
SOLENOID VALVE CONTROL GROUND
TO ALDL TERMINAL "H"
(TRUNK COMPARTMENT FUSE BLOCK)
799 TAN/WHT
DIAGNOSTIC ENABLE
TO BCM
800 TAN
SERIAL DATA
ANTILOCK LIGHT
39 PNK/BLK
852 WHT
ANTILOCK LIGHT CONTROL
851 GRY/BLK
SOLENOID MONITOR INPUT
VALVE RELAY
879 PPL/WHT
SOLENOID CONTROL RELAY
854 PNK
RELAY FEED (FROM EBCM PIN 1)
874 PNK/BLK
PUMP MOTOR RELAY CONTROL
PUMP MOTOR
HYDRAULIC MODULATOR ASSEMBLY
1292 LT GRN/BLK
PUMP MONITOR
PUMP RELAY
827 BRN/WHT
RF WHEEL SOLENOID VALVE CONTROL
RF WHEEL SOLENOID VALVE
826 BLK/WHT
LF WHEEL SOLENOID VALVE CONTROL
LF WHEEL SOLENOID VALVE
829 DK GRN/WHT
REAR SOLENOID VALVE CONTROL
REAR WHEEL SOLENOID VALVE
3 RED 2
FUSIBLE LINK M
FUSIBLE LINK U

GC4029200504010X

Fig. 69 ABS wiring circuit (Part 1 of 2). 1992 Eldorado & Seville

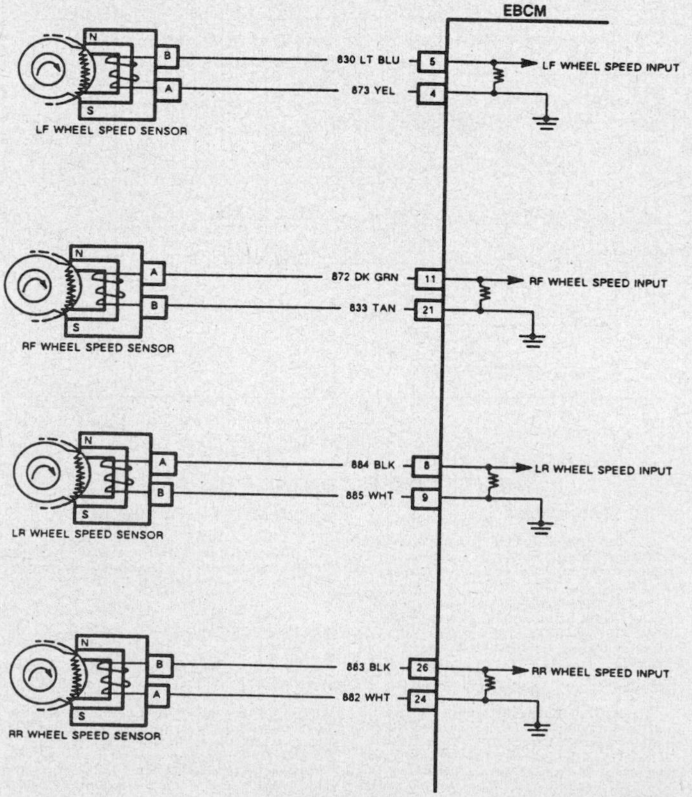
EBCM
830 LT BLU
873 YEL
LF WHEEL SPEED INPUT
LF WHEEL SPEED SENSOR
872 DK GRN
833 TAN
RF WHEEL SPEED INPUT
RF WHEEL SPEED SENSOR
884 BLK
885 WHT
LR WHEEL SPEED INPUT
LR WHEEL SPEED SENSOR
883 BLK
882 WHT
RR WHEEL SPEED INPUT
RR WHEEL SPEED SENSOR

GC4029200504020X

Fig. 69 ABS wiring circuit (Part 2 of 2). 1992 Eldorado & Seville

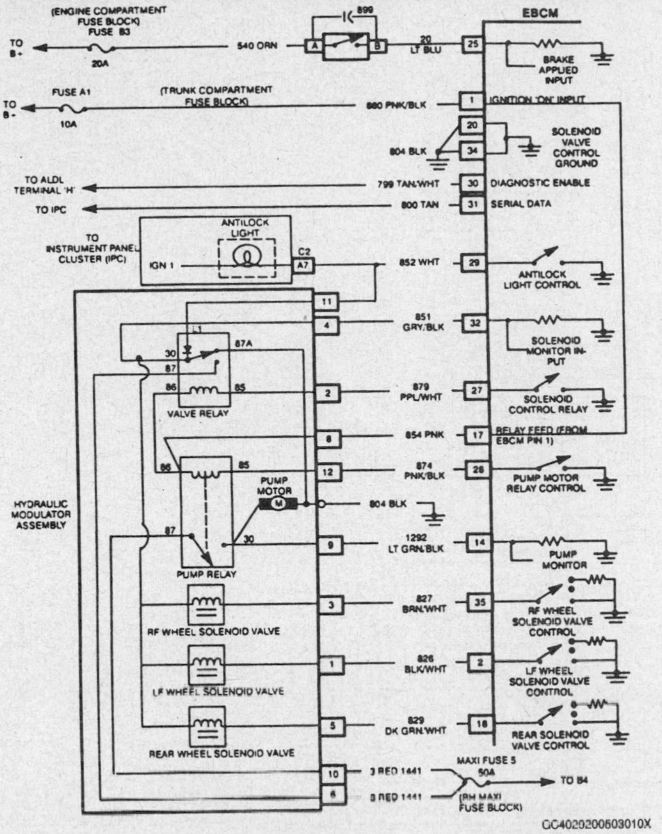
EBCM
(ENGINE COMPARTMENT FUSE BLOCK) FUSE B3
TO B+
20A
540 ORN
899
20 LT BLU
BRAKE APPLIED INPUT
FUSE A1
(TRUNK COMPARTMENT FUSE BLOCK)
TO B-
10A
880 PNK/BLK
IGNITION 'ON' INPUT
804 BLK
SOLENOID VALVE CONTROL GROUND
TO ALDL TERMINAL 'H'
799 TAN/WHT
DIAGNOSTIC ENABLE
TO IPC
800 TAN
SERIAL DATA
TO INSTRUMENT PANEL CLUSTER (IPC)
ANTILOCK LIGHT
IGN 1
C2
852 WHT
ANTILOCK LIGHT CONTROL
851 GRY/BLK
SOLENOID MONITOR INPUT
VALVE RELAY
879 PPL/WHT
SOLENOID CONTROL RELAY
854 PNK
RELAY FEED (FROM EBCM PIN 1)
874 PNK/BLK
PUMP MOTOR RELAY CONTROL
HYDRAULIC MODULATOR ASSEMBLY
PUMP MOTOR
804 BLK
1292 LT GRN/BLK
PUMP MONITOR
PUMP RELAY
827 BRN/WHT
RF WHEEL SOLENOID VALVE CONTROL
RF WHEEL SOLENOID VALVE
826 BLK/WHT
LF WHEEL SOLENOID VALVE CONTROL
LF WHEEL SOLENOID VALVE
829 DK GRN/WHT
REAR SOLENOID VALVE CONTROL
REAR WHEEL SOLENOID VALVE
3 RED 1441
MAXI FUSE 5 50A
TO B4
(RH MAXI FUSE BLOCK)
GC4029200503010X

Fig. 70 ABS wiring circuit (Part 1 of 2). 1992 Riviera, Toronado & Trofeo

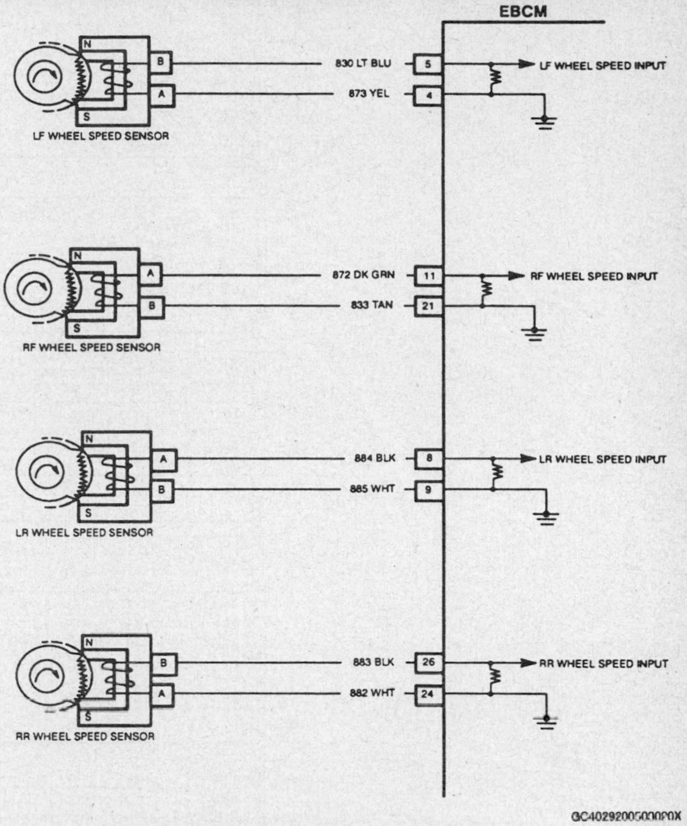
EBCM
830 LT BLU
LF WHEEL SPEED INPUT
873 YEL
LF WHEEL SPEED SENSOR
872 DK GRN
RF WHEEL SPEED INPUT
833 TAN
RF WHEEL SPEED SENSOR
884 BLK
LR WHEEL SPEED INPUT
885 WHT
LR WHEEL SPEED SENSOR
883 BLK
RR WHEEL SPEED INPUT
882 WHT
RR WHEEL SPEED SENSOR

Fig. 70 ABS wiring circuit (Part 2 of 2). 1992 Riviera, Toronado & Trofeo

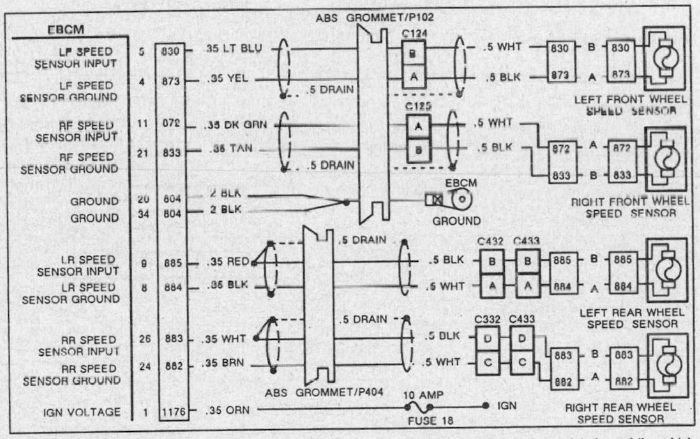
EBCM
ABS GROMMET/P102
LF SPEED SENSOR INPUT
LF SPEED SENSOR GROUND
RF SPEED SENSOR INPUT
RF SPEED SENSOR GROUND
GROUND
GROUND
LR SPEED SENSOR INPUT
LR SPEED SENSOR GROUND
RR SPEED SENSOR INPUT
RR SPEED SENSOR GROUND
IGN VOLTAGE
LEFT FRONT WHEEL SPEED SENSOR
RIGHT FRONT WHEEL SPEED SENSOR
LEFT REAR WHEEL SPEED SENSOR
RIGHT REAR WHEEL SPEED SENSOR
ABS GROMMET/P404
10 AMP FUSE 18
IGN
.5 DRAIN

CIRCUIT DESCRIPTION

As each wheel turns, the wheel speed sensor for that wheel creates a small AC voltage as a toothed sensor ring, mounted in the front integral hub/bearing assembly, is passed by the stationary sensor. The sensor consists of a permanent magnet and coil and generates voltage by magnetic induction. The frequency of the wheel speed sensor signal is proportional to wheel speed.

The EBCM uses the wheel speed sensor signal to calculate vehicle reference speeds and individual speed, acceleration and slip values for each wheel. These values are used to determine when antilock control is required.

The EBCM performs two basic types of checks on the wheel speed sensors, these are sensor continuity and sensor output.

The EBCM will only set one wheel speed sensor fault code at a time, even if multiple faults exist. Detection is prioritized accordingly: LF, RR, LR, RF. Always check for additional stored codes after making repairs.

TEST CONDITIONS

1. Tested continuously.

FAILURE CONDITIONS

Sensor Output:

1. Drive-away: speed signal is not detected when vehicle reaches 12 kph or 7.5 mph.
2. While Driving: speed signal is lost while vehicle speed is greater than 40 kph or 25 mph.

Continuity:

1. While Standing: open circuit is seen while the vehicle is standing still with the ignition on.

ACTION TAKEN

1. Code set.
2. ABS switched 'OFF'.

NOTES ON CODE 21 CHART

1. This section of the fault tree determines if the code stored is due to a current fault condition. 'Current' wheel speed sensor faults may be detected even at vehicle standstill. If the ABS light turns on, the fault is current. The TECH 1 will indicate ignition cycle since code was set. If the ignition cycle counter is at zero, the code is current.
2. This section of the fault tree checks for an open or short in the wheel speed sensor wiring or sensor coil.
3. This section of the fault tree checks for conditions which may cause intermittent code setting. Some causes of intermittent wheel speed sensor codes to set are: improper routing or sensor cables next to spark plug wires, cables not retained in brackets, loose fitting or improperly mounted sensors, damaged sensors or toothed rings, poor terminal engagement of connectors, or intermittent shorts or opens in wiring.

GC402920050500AX

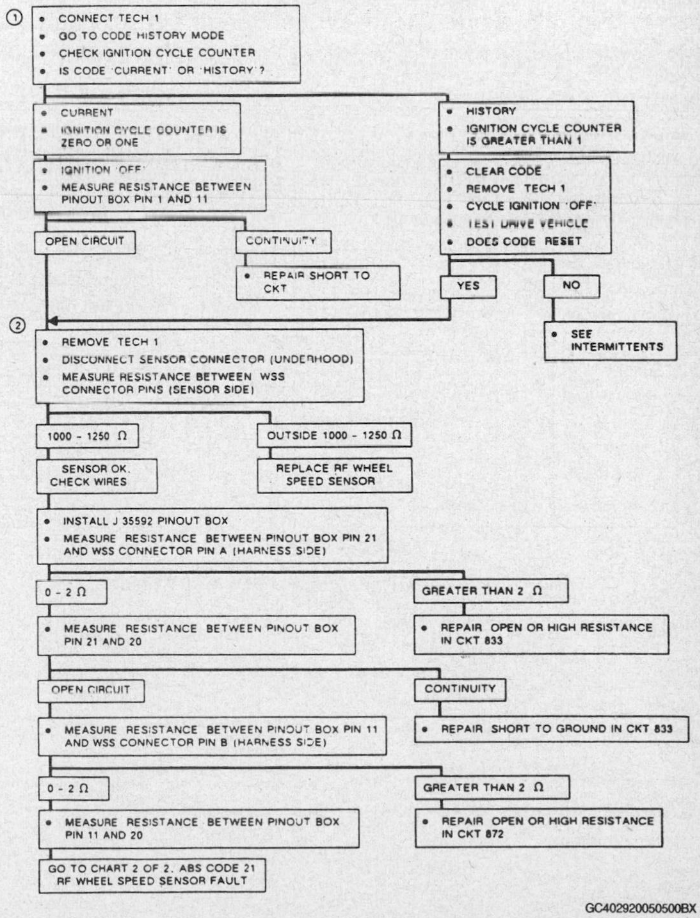
1
CONNECT TECH 1
GO TO CODE HISTORY MODE
CHECK IGNITION CYCLE COUNTER
IS CODE 'CURRENT' OR 'HISTORY'?
CURRENT
IGNITION CYCLE COUNTER IS ZERO OR ONE
HISTORY
IGNITION CYCLE COUNTER IS GREATER THAN 1
IGNITION 'OFF'
MEASURE RESISTANCE BETWEEN PINOUT BOX PIN 1 AND 11
CLEAR CODE
REMOVE TECH 1
CYCLE IGNITION 'OFF'
TEST DRIVE VEHICLE
DOES CODE RESET
OPEN CIRCUIT
CONTINUITY
REPAIR SHORT TO CKT
YES
NO
SEE INTERMITTENTS
2
REMOVE TECH 1
DISCONNECT SENSOR CONNECTOR (UNDERHOOD)
MEASURE RESISTANCE BETWEEN WSS CONNECTOR PINS (SENSOR SIDE)
1000 - 1250 Ω
OUTSIDE 1000 - 1250 Ω
SENSOR OK. CHECK WIRES
REPLACE RF WHEEL SPEED SENSOR
INSTALL J 35592 PINOUT BOX
MEASURE RESISTANCE BETWEEN PINOUT BOX PIN 21 AND WSS CONNECTOR PIN A (HARNESS SIDE)
0 - 2 Ω
GREATER THAN 2 Ω
MEASURE RESISTANCE BETWEEN PINOUT BOX PIN 21 AND 20
REPAIR OPEN OR HIGH RESISTANCE IN CKT 833
OPEN CIRCUIT
CONTINUITY
MEASURE RESISTANCE BETWEEN PINOUT BOX PIN 11 AND WSS CONNECTOR PIN B (HARNESS SIDE)
REPAIR SHORT TO GROUND IN CKT 833
0 - 2 Ω
GREATER THAN 2 Ω
MEASURE RESISTANCE BETWEEN PINOUT BOX PIN 11 AND 20
REPAIR OPEN OR HIGH RESISTANCE IN CKT 872
GO TO CHART 2 OF 2. ABS CODE 21 RF WHEEL SPEED SENSOR FAULT
GC402920050500BX

Fig. 71 Code 21: RF Wheel Speed Sensor Fault (Part 1 of 2). 1992 Eldorado, Seville, Toronado & Trofeo

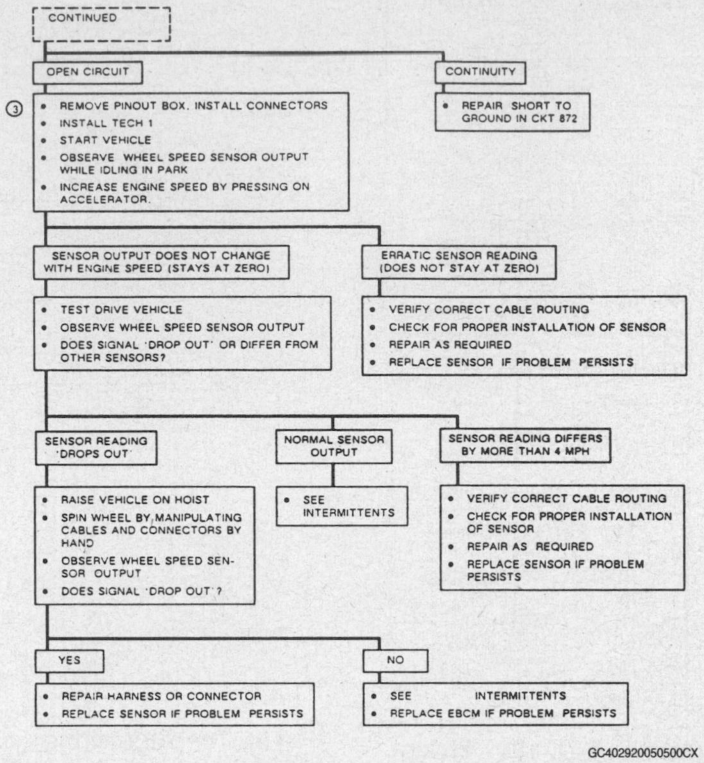
CONTINUED
OPEN CIRCUIT
CONTINUITY
3
• REMOVE PINOUT BOX. INSTALL CONNECTORS
• INSTALL TECH 1
• START VEHICLE
• OBSERVE WHEEL SPEED SENSOR OUTPUT WHILE IDLING IN PARK
• INCREASE ENGINE SPEED BY PRESSING ON ACCELERATOR.
• REPAIR SHORT TO GROUND IN CKT 872
SENSOR OUTPUT DOES NOT CHANGE WITH ENGINE SPEED (STAYS AT ZERO)
ERRATIC SENSOR READING (DOES NOT STAY AT ZERO)
• TEST DRIVE VEHICLE
• OBSERVE WHEEL SPEED SENSOR OUTPUT
• DOES SIGNAL 'DROP OUT' OR DIFFER FROM OTHER SENSORS?
• VERIFY CORRECT CABLE ROUTING
• CHECK FOR PROPER INSTALLATION OF SENSOR
• REPAIR AS REQUIRED
• REPLACE SENSOR IF PROBLEM PERSISTS
SENSOR READING 'DROPS OUT'
NORMAL SENSOR OUTPUT
SENSOR READING DIFFERS BY MORE THAN 4 MPH
• RAISE VEHICLE ON HOIST
• SPIN WHEEL BY MANIPULATING CABLES AND CONNECTORS BY HAND
• OBSERVE WHEEL SPEED SENSOR OUTPUT
• DOES SIGNAL 'DROP OUT'?
• SEE INTERMITTENTS
• VERIFY CORRECT CABLE ROUTING
• CHECK FOR PROPER INSTALLATION OF SENSOR
• REPAIR AS REQUIRED
• REPLACE SENSOR IF PROBLEM PERSISTS
YES
NO
• REPAIR HARNESS OR CONNECTOR
• REPLACE SENSOR IF PROBLEM PERSISTS
• SEE INTERMITTENTS
• REPLACE EBCM IF PROBLEM PERSISTS
GC402920050500CX

Fig. 71 Code 21: RF Wheel Speed Sensor Fault (Part 2 of 2). 1992 Eldorado, Seville, Toronado & Trofeo

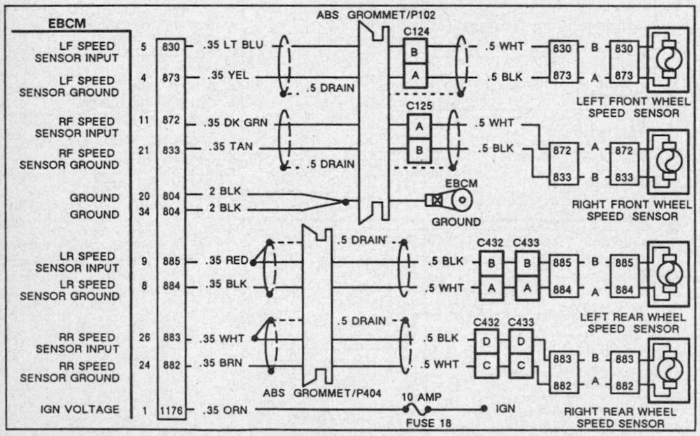
EBCM
ABS GROMMET/P102
LF SPEED SENSOR INPUT
LF SPEED SENSOR GROUND
RF SPEED SENSOR INPUT
RF SPEED SENSOR GROUND
GROUND
GROUND
LR SPEED SENSOR INPUT
LR SPEED SENSOR GROUND
RR SPEED SENSOR INPUT
RR SPEED SENSOR GROUND
IGN VOLTAGE
.35 LT BLU
.35 YEL
.5 DRAIN
.35 DK GRN
.35 TAN
2 BLK
.35 RED
.35 BLK
.35 WHT
.35 BRN
.35 ORN
C124
C125
.5 WHT
.5 BLK
LEFT FRONT WHEEL SPEED SENSOR
RIGHT FRONT WHEEL SPEED SENSOR
EBCM GROUND
C432
C433
LEFT REAR WHEEL SPEED SENSOR
RIGHT REAR WHEEL SPEED SENSOR
ABS GROMMET/P404
10 AMP FUSE 18
IGN

ABS CODE 22

RIGHT FRONT TOOTHED WHEEL FREQUENCY ERROR

CIRCUIT DESCRIPTION

As each wheel turns, the wheel speed sensor for that wheel creates a small AC voltage as a toothed sensor ring, mounted in the front integral hub/bearing assembly, is passed by the stationary sensor. The sensor consists of a permanent magnet and coil and generates voltage by magnetic induction. The frequency of the wheel speed sensor signal is proportional to wheel speed.

The EBCM uses the wheel speed sensor signal to calculate vehicle reference speeds and individual speed, acceleration and slip values for each wheel. These values are used to determine when antilock control is required.

TEST CONDITIONS

1. Tested continuously.

FAILURE CONDITIONS

1. While Driving: one wheel is detected at least 30 kph or 19 mph faster than the remaining wheels for an extended period of time.

or

2. one wheel is at least 6 kph or 4 mph less than or greater than the remaining wheels for an extended period of time.

Causes of improper speed signal may be caused by incorrect number of teeth on sensor ring, sensor rings which are covered with dirt, grease or metallic particles, or damaged toothed sensor ring.

ACTION TAKEN

1. Code set.
2. ABS switched 'OFF'.

GC402920050600AX

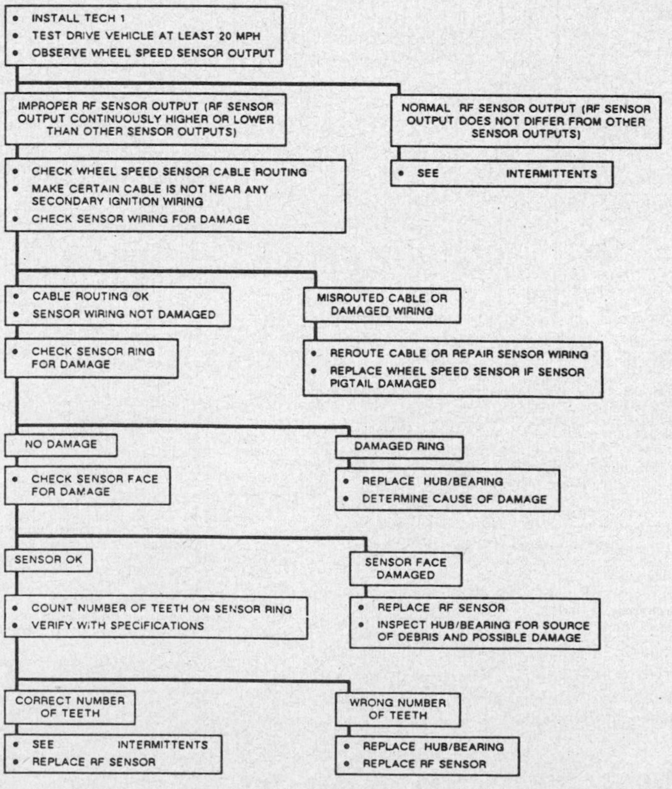
• INSTALL TECH 1
• TEST DRIVE VEHICLE AT LEAST 20 MPH
• OBSERVE WHEEL SPEED SENSOR OUTPUT
IMPROPER RF SENSOR OUTPUT (RF SENSOR OUTPUT CONTINUOUSLY HIGHER OR LOWER THAN OTHER SENSOR OUTPUTS)
NORMAL RF SENSOR OUTPUT (RF SENSOR OUTPUT DOES NOT DIFFER FROM OTHER SENSOR OUTPUTS)
• CHECK WHEEL SPEED SENSOR CABLE ROUTING
• MAKE CERTAIN CABLE IS NOT NEAR ANY SECONDARY IGNITION WIRING
• CHECK SENSOR WIRING FOR DAMAGE
• SEE INTERMITTENTS
• CABLE ROUTING OK
• SENSOR WIRING NOT DAMAGED
MISROUTED CABLE OR DAMAGED WIRING
• CHECK SENSOR RING FOR DAMAGE
• REROUTE CABLE OR REPAIR SENSOR WIRING
• REPLACE WHEEL SPEED SENSOR IF SENSOR PIGTAIL DAMAGED
NO DAMAGE
DAMAGED RING
• CHECK SENSOR FACE FOR DAMAGE
• REPLACE HUB/BEARING
• DETERMINE CAUSE OF DAMAGE
SENSOR OK
SENSOR FACE DAMAGED
• COUNT NUMBER OF TEETH ON SENSOR RING
• VERIFY WITH SPECIFICATIONS
• REPLACE RF SENSOR
• INSPECT HUB/BEARING FOR SOURCE OF DEBRIS AND POSSIBLE DAMAGE
CORRECT NUMBER OF TEETH
WRONG NUMBER OF TEETH
• SEE INTERMITTENTS
• REPLACE RF SENSOR
• REPLACE HUB/BEARING
• REPLACE RF SENSOR
GC402920050600BX

Fig. 72 Code 22: RF Toothed Wheel Frequency Error. 1992 Eldorado, Riviera, Seville, Toronado & Trofeo

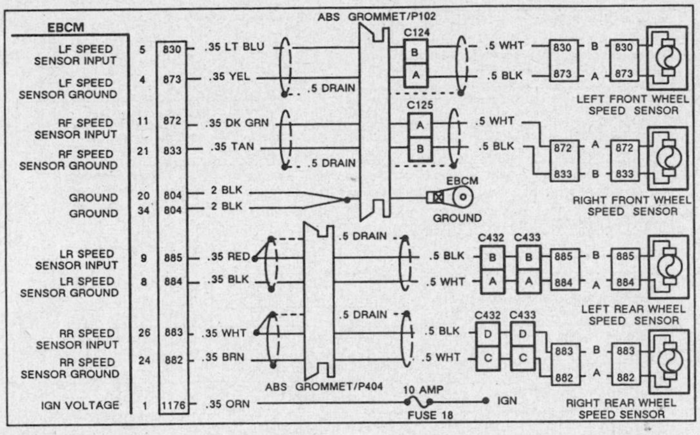
EBCM
ABS GROMMET/P102
LF SPEED SENSOR INPUT
LF SPEED SENSOR GROUND
RF SPEED SENSOR INPUT
RF SPEED SENSOR GROUND
GROUND
GROUND
LR SPEED SENSOR INPUT
LR SPEED SENSOR GROUND
RR SPEED SENSOR INPUT
RR SPEED SENSOR GROUND
IGN VOLTAGE
.35 LT BLU
.35 YEL
.5 DRAIN
.35 DK GRN
.35 TAN
2 BLK
.35 RED
.35 BLK
.35 WHT
.35 BRN
.35 ORN
C124
C125
C432
C433
.5 WHT
.5 BLK
EBCM
GROUND
LEFT FRONT WHEEL SPEED SENSOR
RIGHT FRONT WHEEL SPEED SENSOR
LEFT REAR WHEEL SPEED SENSOR
RIGHT REAR WHEEL SPEED SENSOR
ABS GROMMET/P404
10 AMP
FUSE 18
IGN

CIRCUIT DESCRIPTION

As each wheel turns, the wheel speed sensor for that wheel creates a small AC voltage as a toothed sensor ring, mounted in the front integral hub/bearing assembly, is passed by the stationary sensor. The sensor consists of a permanent magnet and coil and generates voltage by magnetic induction. The frequency of the wheel speed sensor signal is proportional to wheel speed.

The EBCM uses the wheel speed sensor signal to calculate vehicle reference speeds and individual speed, acceleration and slip values for each wheel. These values are used to determine when antilock control is required.

The EBCM performs two basic types of checks on the wheel speed sensors, these are sensor continuity and sensor output.

The EBCM will only set one wheel speed sensor fault code at a time, even if multiple faults exist. Detection is prioritized accordingly: LF, RR, LR, RF. Always check for additional stored codes after making repairs.

TEST CONDITIONS

1. Tested continuously.

FAILURE CONDITIONS

Sensor Output:

1. Drive-away: speed signal is not detected when vehicle reaches 12 kph or 7.5 mph
2. While Driving: speed signal is lost while vehicle speed is greater than 40 kph or 25 mph.

Continuity:

1. While Standing: open circuit is seen while the vehicle is standing still with the ignition on.

ACTION TAKEN

1. Code set.
2. ABS switched 'OFF'.

NOTES ON CODE 25 CHART

1. This section of the fault tree determines if the code stored is due to a current fault condition. 'Current' wheel speed sensor faults may be detected even at vehicle standstill. If the ABS light turns on, the fault is current. The TECH 1 will indicate ignition cycle since code was set. If the ignition cycle counter is at zero, the code is current.
2. This section of the fault tree checks for an open or short in the wheel speed sensor wiring or sensor coil.
3. This section of the fault tree checks for conditions which may cause intermittent code setting. Some causes of intermittent wheel speed sensor codes to set are: improper routing or sensor cables next to spark plug wires, cables not retained in brackets, loose fitting or improperly mounted sensors, damaged sensors or toothed rings, poor terminal engagement of connectors, or intermittent shorts or opens in wiring.

GC402920050700AX

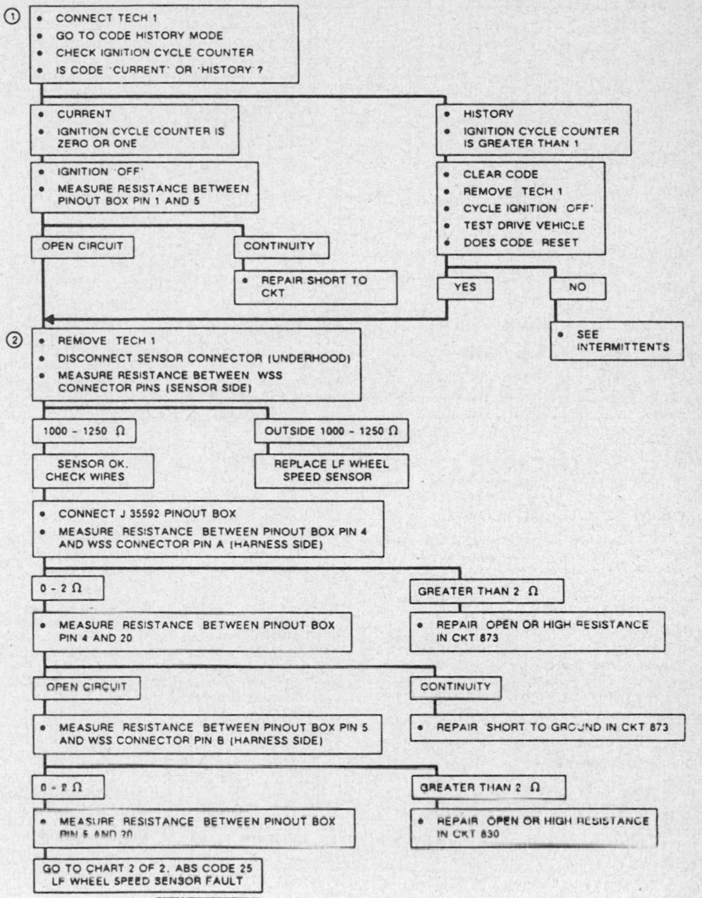
1
CONNECT TECH 1
GO TO CODE HISTORY MODE
CHECK IGNITION CYCLE COUNTER
IS CODE 'CURRENT' OR 'HISTORY'?
CURRENT
IGNITION CYCLE COUNTER IS ZERO OR ONE
HISTORY
IGNITION CYCLE COUNTER IS GREATER THAN 1
IGNITION 'OFF'
MEASURE RESISTANCE BETWEEN PINOUT BOX PIN 1 AND 5
CLEAR CODE
REMOVE TECH 1
CYCLE IGNITION 'OFF'
TEST DRIVE VEHICLE
DOES CODE RESET
OPEN CIRCUIT
CONTINUITY
REPAIR SHORT TO CKT
YES
NO
SEE INTERMITTENTS
2
REMOVE TECH 1
DISCONNECT SENSOR CONNECTOR (UNDERHOOD)
MEASURE RESISTANCE BETWEEN WSS CONNECTOR PINS (SENSOR SIDE)
1000 - 1250 Ω
OUTSIDE 1000 - 1250 Ω
SENSOR OK. CHECK WIRES
REPLACE LF WHEEL SPEED SENSOR
CONNECT J 35592 PINOUT BOX
MEASURE RESISTANCE BETWEEN PINOUT BOX PIN 4 AND WSS CONNECTOR PIN A (HARNESS SIDE)
0 - 2 Ω
GREATER THAN 2 Ω
MEASURE RESISTANCE BETWEEN PINOUT BOX PIN 4 AND 20
REPAIR OPEN OR HIGH RESISTANCE IN CKT 873
OPEN CIRCUIT
CONTINUITY
MEASURE RESISTANCE BETWEEN PINOUT BOX PIN 5 AND WSS CONNECTOR PIN B (HARNESS SIDE)
REPAIR SHORT TO GROUND IN CKT 873
0 - 2 Ω
GREATER THAN 2 Ω
MEASURE RESISTANCE BETWEEN PINOUT BOX PIN 5 AND 20
REPAIR OPEN OR HIGH RESISTANCE IN CKT 830
GO TO CHART 2 OF 2, ABS CODE 25 LF WHEEL SPEED SENSOR FAULT

GC402920050700BX

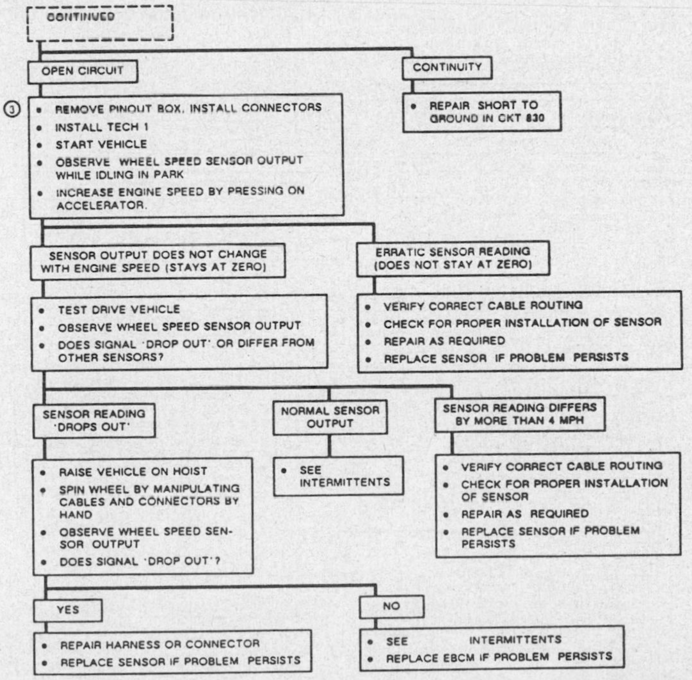
CONTINUED
OPEN CIRCUIT
CONTINUITY
REPAIR SHORT TO GROUND IN CKT 830
3
REMOVE PINOUT BOX, INSTALL CONNECTORS
INSTALL TECH 1
START VEHICLE
OBSERVE WHEEL SPEED SENSOR OUTPUT WHILE IDLING IN PARK
INCREASE ENGINE SPEED BY PRESSING ON ACCELERATOR.
SENSOR OUTPUT DOES NOT CHANGE WITH ENGINE SPEED (STAYS AT ZERO)
ERRATIC SENSOR READING (DOES NOT STAY AT ZERO)
TEST DRIVE VEHICLE
OBSERVE WHEEL SPEED SENSOR OUTPUT
DOES SIGNAL 'DROP OUT' OR DIFFER FROM OTHER SENSORS?
VERIFY CORRECT CABLE ROUTING
CHECK FOR PROPER INSTALLATION OF SENSOR
REPAIR AS REQUIRED
REPLACE SENSOR IF PROBLEM PERSISTS
SENSOR READING 'DROPS OUT'
NORMAL SENSOR OUTPUT
SENSOR READING DIFFERS BY MORE THAN 4 MPH
RAISE VEHICLE ON HOIST
SPIN WHEEL BY MANIPULATING CABLES AND CONNECTORS BY HAND
OBSERVE WHEEL SPEED SENSOR OUTPUT
DOES SIGNAL 'DROP OUT'?
SEE INTERMITTENTS
VERIFY CORRECT CABLE ROUTING
CHECK FOR PROPER INSTALLATION OF SENSOR
REPAIR AS REQUIRED
REPLACE SENSOR IF PROBLEM PERSISTS
YES
NO
REPAIR HARNESS OR CONNECTOR
REPLACE SENSOR IF PROBLEM PERSISTS
SEE INTERMITTENTS
REPLACE EBCM IF PROBLEM PERSISTS

GC402920050700CX

Fig. 73 Code 25: LF Wheel Speed Sensor Fault. 1992 Eldorado, Riviera, Seville, Tornado & Trofeo

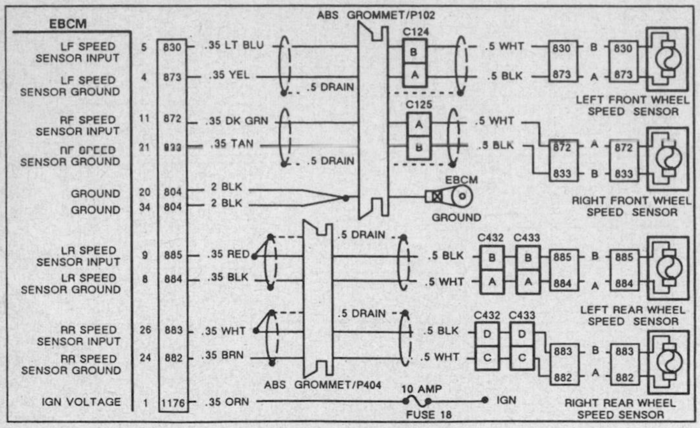
EBCM
LF SPEED SENSOR INPUT
LF SPEED SENSOR GROUND
RF SPEED SENSOR INPUT
RF SPEED SENSOR GROUND
GROUND
GROUND
LR SPEED SENSOR INPUT
LR SPEED SENSOR GROUND
RR SPEED SENSOR INPUT
RR SPEED SENSOR GROUND
IGN VOLTAGE
ABS GROMMET/P102
C124
C125
.35 LT BLU
.35 YEL
.5 DRAIN
.35 DK GRN
.35 TAN
2 BLK
.35 RED
.35 BLK
.35 WHT
.35 BRN
.35 ORN
.5 WHT
.5 BLK
LEFT FRONT WHEEL SPEED SENSOR
RIGHT FRONT WHEEL SPEED SENSOR
EBCM GROUND
C432
C433
LEFT REAR WHEEL SPEED SENSOR
RIGHT REAR WHEEL SPEED SENSOR
ABS GROMMET/P404
10 AMP
FUSE 18
IGN

ABS CODE 26
LEFT FRONT TOOTHED WHEEL FREQUENCY ERROR

CIRCUIT DESCRIPTION

As each wheel turns, the wheel speed sensor for that wheel creates a small AC voltage as a toothed sensor ring, mounted in the front integral hub/bearing assembly, is passed by the stationary sensor. The sensor consists of a permanent magnet and coil and generates voltage by magnetic induction. The frequency of the wheel speed sensor signal is proportional to wheel speed.

The EBCM uses the wheel speed sensor signal to calculate vehicle reference speeds and individual speed, acceleration and slip values for each wheel. These values are used to determine when antilock control is required.

TEST CONDITIONS

1. Tested continuously.

FAILURE CONDITIONS

1. While Driving: one wheel is detected at least 30 kph or 19 mph faster than the remaining wheels for an extended period of time.

   or

2. one wheel is at least 6 kph or 4 mph less than or greater than the remaining wheels for an extended period of time.

Causes of improper speed signal may be caused by incorrect number of teeth on sensor ring, sensor rings which are covered with dirt, grease or metallic particles, or damaged toothed sensor ring.

ACTION TAKEN

1. Code set.
2. ABS switched 'OFF'.

GC402920050800AX

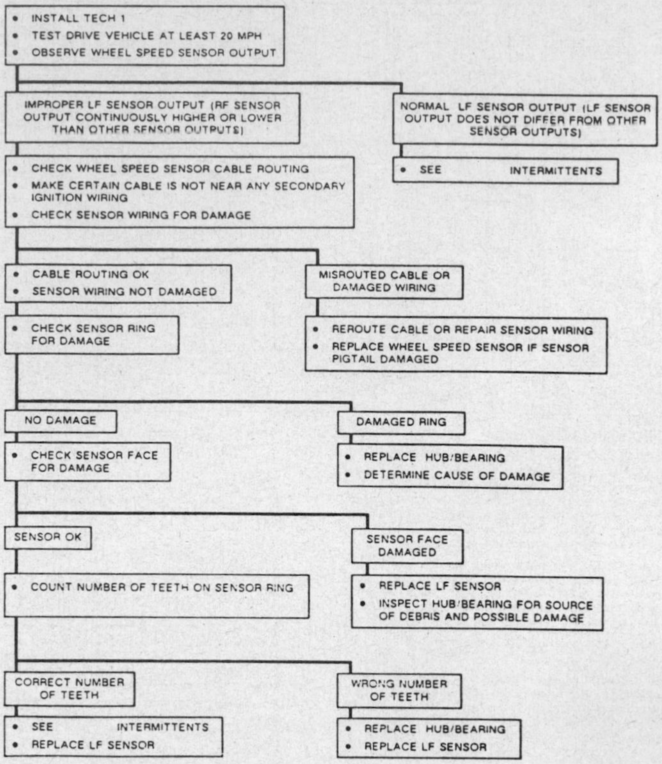
• INSTALL TECH 1
• TEST DRIVE VEHICLE AT LEAST 20 MPH
• OBSERVE WHEEL SPEED SENSOR OUTPUT
IMPROPER LF SENSOR OUTPUT (RF SENSOR OUTPUT CONTINUOUSLY HIGHER OR LOWER THAN OTHER SENSOR OUTPUTS)
NORMAL LF SENSOR OUTPUT (LF SENSOR OUTPUT DOES NOT DIFFER FROM OTHER SENSOR OUTPUTS)
• SEE INTERMITTENTS
• CHECK WHEEL SPEED SENSOR CABLE ROUTING
• MAKE CERTAIN CABLE IS NOT NEAR ANY SECONDARY IGNITION WIRING
• CHECK SENSOR WIRING FOR DAMAGE
• CABLE ROUTING OK
• SENSOR WIRING NOT DAMAGED
MISROUTED CABLE OR DAMAGED WIRING
• CHECK SENSOR RING FOR DAMAGE
• REROUTE CABLE OR REPAIR SENSOR WIRING
• REPLACE WHEEL SPEED SENSOR IF SENSOR PIGTAIL DAMAGED
NO DAMAGE
DAMAGED RING
• CHECK SENSOR FACE FOR DAMAGE
• REPLACE HUB/BEARING
• DETERMINE CAUSE OF DAMAGE
SENSOR OK
SENSOR FACE DAMAGED
• COUNT NUMBER OF TEETH ON SENSOR RING
• REPLACE LF SENSOR
• INSPECT HUB/BEARING FOR SOURCE OF DEBRIS AND POSSIBLE DAMAGE
CORRECT NUMBER OF TEETH
WRONG NUMBER OF TEETH
• SEE INTERMITTENTS
• REPLACE LF SENSOR
• REPLACE HUB/BEARING
• REPLACE LF SENSOR

GC402920050800BX

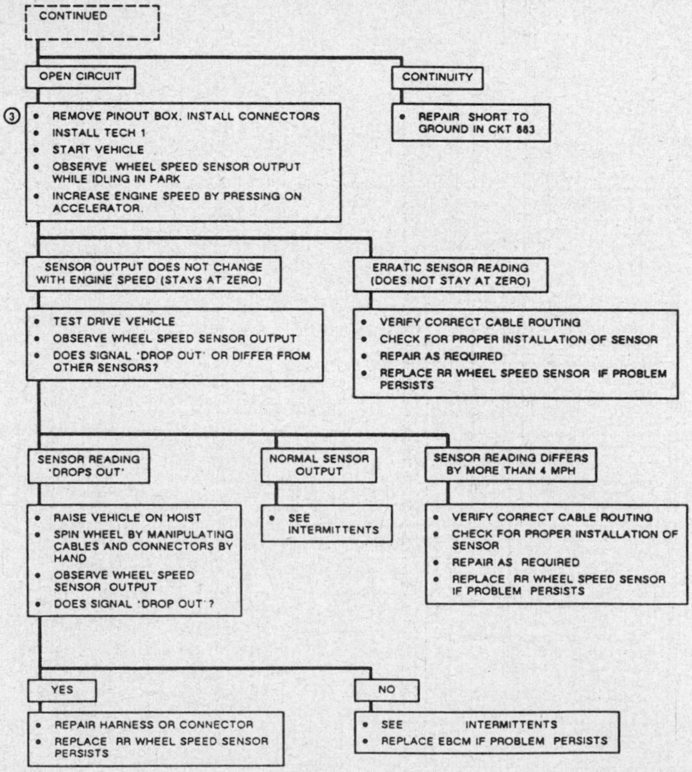
CONTINUED
OPEN CIRCUIT
CONTINUITY
③
• REMOVE PINOUT BOX, INSTALL CONNECTORS
• INSTALL TECH 1
• START VEHICLE
• OBSERVE WHEEL SPEED SENSOR OUTPUT WHILE IDLING IN PARK
• INCREASE ENGINE SPEED BY PRESSING ON ACCELERATOR.
• REPAIR SHORT TO GROUND IN CKT 883
SENSOR OUTPUT DOES NOT CHANGE WITH ENGINE SPEED (STAYS AT ZERO)
ERRATIC SENSOR READING (DOES NOT STAY AT ZERO)
• TEST DRIVE VEHICLE
• OBSERVE WHEEL SPEED SENSOR OUTPUT
• DOES SIGNAL 'DROP OUT' OR DIFFER FROM OTHER SENSORS?
• VERIFY CORRECT CABLE ROUTING
• CHECK FOR PROPER INSTALLATION OF SENSOR
• REPAIR AS REQUIRED
• REPLACE RR WHEEL SPEED SENSOR IF PROBLEM PERSISTS
SENSOR READING 'DROPS OUT'
NORMAL SENSOR OUTPUT
SENSOR READING DIFFERS BY MORE THAN 4 MPH
• RAISE VEHICLE ON HOIST
• SPIN WHEEL BY MANIPULATING CABLES AND CONNECTORS BY HAND
• OBSERVE WHEEL SPEED SENSOR OUTPUT
• DOES SIGNAL 'DROP OUT'?
• SEE INTERMITTENTS
• VERIFY CORRECT CABLE ROUTING
• CHECK FOR PROPER INSTALLATION OF SENSOR
• REPAIR AS REQUIRED
• REPLACE RR WHEEL SPEED SENSOR IF PROBLEM PERSISTS
YES
NO
• REPAIR HARNESS OR CONNECTOR
• REPLACE RR WHEEL SPEED SENSOR PERSISTS
• SEE INTERMITTENTS
• REPLACE EBCM IF PROBLEM PERSISTS

GC402920050900CX

Fig. 74 Code 26: LF Toothed Wheel Frequency Error. 1992 Eldorado, Riviera, Seville, Toronado & Trofeo

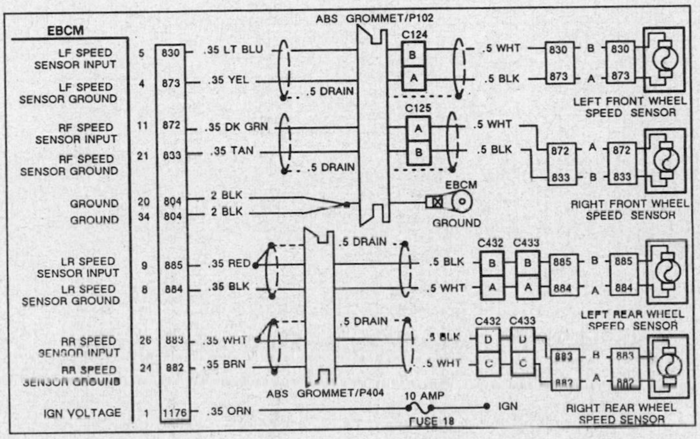
EBCM
ABS GROMMET/P102
LF SPEED SENSOR INPUT 5 830 .35 LT BLU
LF SPEED SENSOR GROUND 4 873 .35 YEL
.5 DRAIN
C124
B
A
.5 WHT
.5 BLK
830
873
LEFT FRONT WHEEL SPEED SENSOR
RF SPEED SENSOR INPUT 11 872 .35 DK GRN
RF SPEED SENSOR GROUND 21 833 .35 TAN
C125
.5 WHT
.5 BLK
872
833
GROUND 20 804 2 BLK
GROUND 34 804 2 BLK
EBCM GROUND
RIGHT FRONT WHEEL SPEED SENSOR
LR SPEED SENSOR INPUT 9 885 .35 RED
LR SPEED SENSOR GROUND 8 884 .35 BLK
C432 C433
885
884
LEFT REAR WHEEL SPEED SENSOR
RR SPEED SENSOR INPUT 26 883 .35 WHT
RR SPEED SENSOR GROUND 24 882 .35 BRN
ABS GROMMET/P404
IGN VOLTAGE 1 1176 .35 ORN
10 AMP
FUSE 18
IGN
RIGHT REAR WHEEL SPEED SENSOR

CIRCUIT DESCRIPTION

As each wheel turns, the wheel speed sensor for that wheel creates a small AC voltage as a toothed sensor ring, mounted in the rear integral hub/bearing assembly, is passed by the stationary sensor. The sensor consists of a permanent magnet and coil and generates voltage by magnetic induction. The frequency of the wheel speed sensor signal is proportional to wheel speed.

The EBCM uses the wheel speed sensor signal to calculate vehicle reference speeds and individual speed, acceleration and slip values for each wheel. These values are used to determine when antilock control is required.

The EBCM performs two basic types of checks on the wheel speed sensors, these are sensor continuity and sensor output.

The EBCM will only set one wheel speed sensor fault code at a time, even if multiple faults exist. Detection is prioritized accordingly: LF, RR, LR, RF. Always check for additional stored codes after making repairs.

TEST CONDITIONS

1. Tested continuously.

FAILURE CONDITIONS

Sensor Output:

1. Drive-away: speed signal is not detected when vehicle reaches 12 kph or 7.5 mph.
2. While Driving: speed signal is lost while vehicle speed is greater than 40 kph or 25 mph.

Continuity:

1. While Standing: open circuit is seen while the vehicle is standing still with the ignition on.

ACTION TAKEN

1. Code set.
2. ABS switched 'OFF'.

NOTES ON CODE 31 CHART

1. This section of the fault tree determines if the code stored is due to a current fault condition. 'Current' wheel speed sensor faults may be detected even at vehicle standstill. If the ABS light turns on, the fault is current. The TECH 1 will indicate ignition cycle since code was set. If the ignition cycle counter is at zero, the code is current.
2. This section of the fault tree checks for an open or short in the wheel speed sensor wiring or sensor coil.
3. This section of the fault tree checks for conditions which may cause intermittent code setting. Some causes of intermittent wheel speed sensor codes to set are: improper routing or sensor cables next to spark plug wires, cables not retained in brackets, loose fitting or improperly mounted sensors, damaged sensors or toothed rings, poor terminal engagement of connectors, or intermittent shorts or opens in wiring.

GC402920050900AX

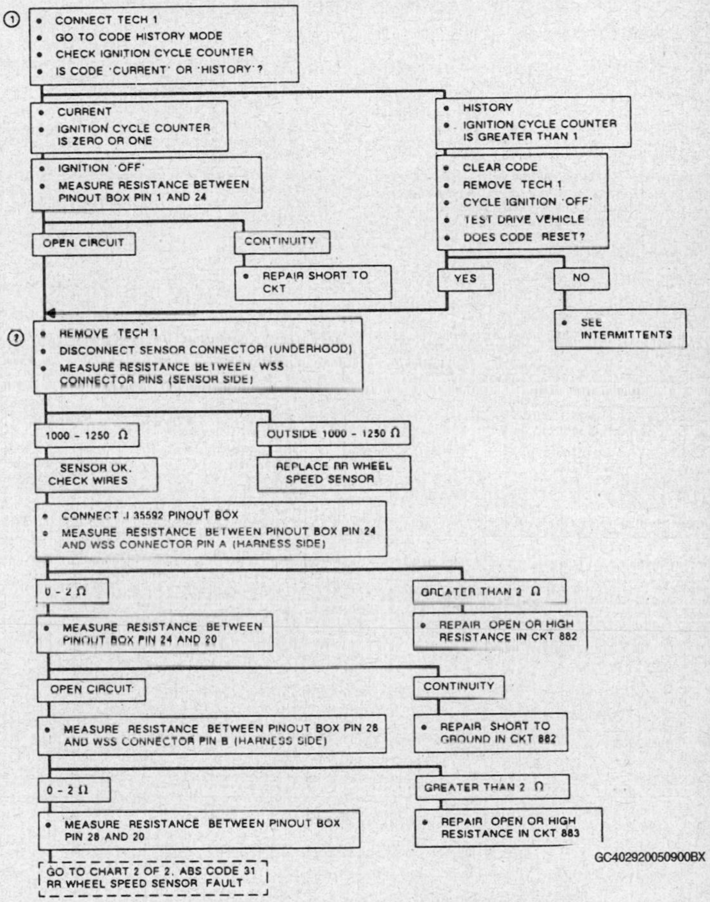
1
• CONNECT TECH 1
• GO TO CODE HISTORY MODE
• CHECK IGNITION CYCLE COUNTER
• IS CODE 'CURRENT' OR 'HISTORY'?
• CURRENT
• IGNITION CYCLE COUNTER IS ZERO OR ONE
• HISTORY
• IGNITION CYCLE COUNTER IS GREATER THAN 1
• IGNITION 'OFF'
• MEASURE RESISTANCE BETWEEN PINOUT BOX PIN 1 AND 24
• CLEAR CODE
• REMOVE TECH 1
• CYCLE IGNITION 'OFF'
• TEST DRIVE VEHICLE
• DOES CODE RESET?
OPEN CIRCUIT
CONTINUITY
• REPAIR SHORT TO CKT
YES
NO
• SEE INTERMITTENTS
2
• REMOVE TECH 1
• DISCONNECT SENSOR CONNECTOR (UNDERHOOD)
• MEASURE RESISTANCE BETWEEN WSS CONNECTOR PINS (SENSOR SIDE)
1000 - 1250 Ω
OUTSIDE 1000 - 1250 Ω
SENSOR OK. CHECK WIRES
REPLACE RR WHEEL SPEED SENSOR
• CONNECT J 35592 PINOUT BOX
• MEASURE RESISTANCE BETWEEN PINOUT BOX PIN 24 AND WSS CONNECTOR PIN A (HARNESS SIDE)
0 - 2 Ω
GREATER THAN 2 Ω
• MEASURE RESISTANCE BETWEEN PINOUT BOX PIN 24 AND 20
• REPAIR OPEN OR HIGH RESISTANCE IN CKT 882
OPEN CIRCUIT
CONTINUITY
• MEASURE RESISTANCE BETWEEN PINOUT BOX PIN 28 AND WSS CONNECTOR PIN B (HARNESS SIDE)
• REPAIR SHORT TO GROUND IN CKT 882
0 - 2 Ω
GREATER THAN 2 Ω
• MEASURE RESISTANCE BETWEEN PINOUT BOX PIN 28 AND 20
• REPAIR OPEN OR HIGH RESISTANCE IN CKT 883
GO TO CHART 2 OF 2, ABS CODE 31 RR WHEEL SPEED SENSOR FAULT
GC402920050900BX

Fig. 75 Code 31: RR Wheel Speed Sensor Fault. 1992 Eldorado, Riviera, Seville, Toronado & Trofeo

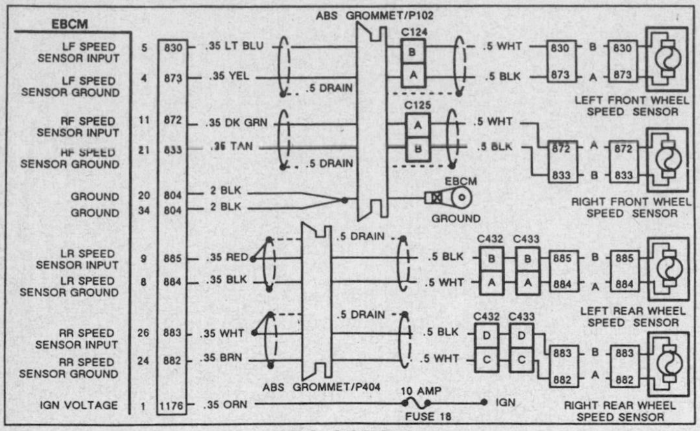
EBCM
LF SPEED SENSOR INPUT 5 830 .35 LT BLU
LF SPEED SENSOR GROUND 4 873 .35 YEL
RF SPEED SENSOR INPUT 11 872 .35 DK GRN
RF SPEED SENSOR GROUND 21 833 .35 TAN
GROUND 20 804 2 BLK
GROUND 34 804 2 BLK
LR SPEED SENSOR INPUT 9 885 .35 RED
LR SPEED SENSOR GROUND 8 884 .35 BLK
RR SPEED SENSOR INPUT 26 883 .35 WHT
RR SPEED SENSOR GROUND 24 882 .35 BRN
IGN VOLTAGE 1 1176 .35 ORN
ABS GROMMET/P102
C124
C125
.5 DRAIN
.5 WHT
.5 BLK
EBCM GROUND
C432 C433
ABS GROMMET/P404
10 AMP FUSE 18
IGN
LEFT FRONT WHEEL SPEED SENSOR
RIGHT FRONT WHEEL SPEED SENSOR
LEFT REAR WHEEL SPEED SENSOR
RIGHT REAR WHEEL SPEED SENSOR

ABS CODE 32

RIGHT REAR TOOTHED WHEEL FREQUENCY ERROR

CIRCUIT DESCRIPTION

As each wheel turns, the wheel speed sensor for that wheel creates a small AC voltage as a toothed sensor ring, mounted in the rear integral hub/bearing assembly, is passed by the stationary sensor. The sensor consists of a permanent magnet and coil and generates voltage by magnetic induction. The frequency of the wheel speed sensor signal is proportional to wheel speed.

The EBCM uses the wheel speed sensor signal to calculate vehicle reference speeds and individual speed, acceleration and slip values for each wheel. These values are used to determine when antilock control is required.

TEST CONDITIONS

1. Tested continuously.

FAILURE CONDITIONS

1. While Driving: one wheel is detected at least 30 kph or 19 mph faster than the remaining wheels for an extended period of time.

   or

2. one wheel is at least 6 kph or 4 mph less than or greater than the remaining wheels for an extended period of time.

Causes of improper speed signal may be caused by incorrect number of teeth on sensor ring, sensor rings which are covered with dirt, grease or metallic particles, or damaged toothed sensor ring.

ACTION TAKEN

1. Code set.
2. ABS switched 'OFF'.

GC402920051000AX

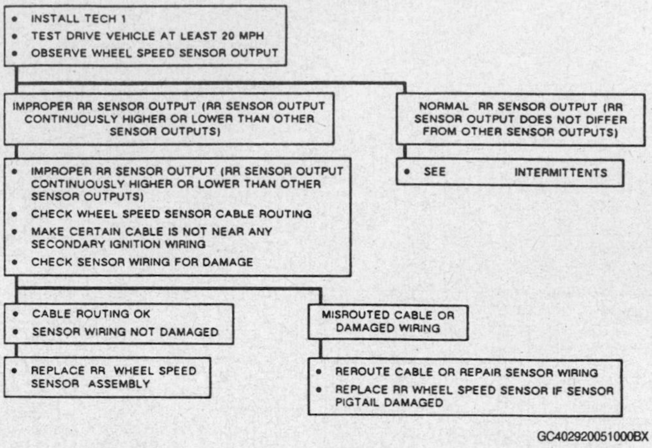
• INSTALL TECH 1
• TEST DRIVE VEHICLE AT LEAST 20 MPH
• OBSERVE WHEEL SPEED SENSOR OUTPUT
IMPROPER RR SENSOR OUTPUT (RR SENSOR OUTPUT CONTINUOUSLY HIGHER OR LOWER THAN OTHER SENSOR OUTPUTS)
NORMAL RR SENSOR OUTPUT (RR SENSOR OUTPUT DOES NOT DIFFER FROM OTHER SENSOR OUTPUTS)
• IMPROPER RR SENSOR OUTPUT (RR SENSOR OUTPUT CONTINUOUSLY HIGHER OR LOWER THAN OTHER SENSOR OUTPUTS)
• CHECK WHEEL SPEED SENSOR CABLE ROUTING
• MAKE CERTAIN CABLE IS NOT NEAR ANY SECONDARY IGNITION WIRING
• CHECK SENSOR WIRING FOR DAMAGE
• SEE INTERMITTENTS
• CABLE ROUTING OK
• SENSOR WIRING NOT DAMAGED
MISROUTED CABLE OR DAMAGED WIRING
• REPLACE RR WHEEL SPEED SENSOR ASSEMBLY
• REROUTE CABLE OR REPAIR SENSOR WIRING
• REPLACE RR WHEEL SPEED SENSOR IF SENSOR PIGTAIL DAMAGED
GC402920051000BX

Fig. 76 Code 32: RR Toothed Wheel Frequency Error. 1992 Eldorado, Riviera, Seville, Toronado & Trofeo

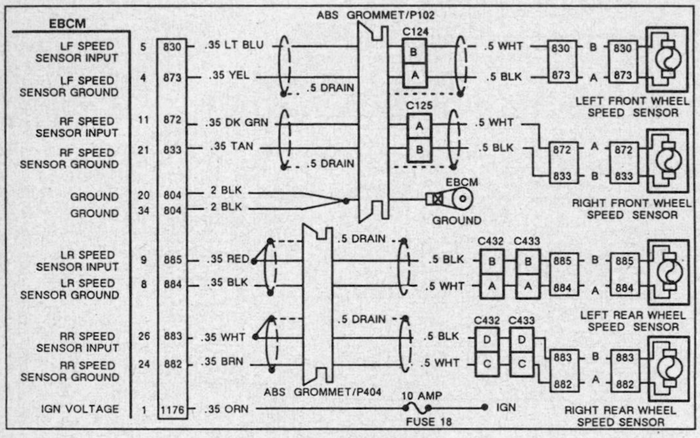
EBCM
LF SPEED SENSOR INPUT 5 830 .35 LT BLU
LF SPEED SENSOR GROUND 4 873 .35 YEL
RF SPEED SENSOR INPUT 11 872 .35 DK GRN
RF SPEED SENSOR GROUND 21 833 .35 TAN
GROUND 20 804 2 BLK
GROUND 34 804 2 BLK
LR SPEED SENSOR INPUT 9 885 .35 RED
LR SPEED SENSOR GROUND 8 884 .35 BLK
RR SPEED SENSOR INPUT 26 883 .35 WHT
RR SPEED SENSOR GROUND 24 882 .35 BRN
IGN VOLTAGE 1 1176 .35 ORN
ABS GROMMET/P102
C124
C125
.5 DRAIN
.5 WHT
.5 BLK
EBCM GROUND
C432 C433
ABS GROMMET/P404
10 AMP FUSE 18
IGN
LEFT FRONT WHEEL SPEED SENSOR
RIGHT FRONT WHEEL SPEED SENSOR
LEFT REAR WHEEL SPEED SENSOR
RIGHT REAR WHEEL SPEED SENSOR

ABS CODE 35

LEFT REAR WHEEL SPEED SENSOR FAULT

CIRCUIT DESCRIPTION

As each wheel turns, the wheel speed sensor for that wheel creates a small AC voltage as a toothed sensor ring, mounted in the rear integral hub/bearing assembly, is passed by the stationary sensor. The sensor consists of a permanent magnet and coil and generates voltage by magnetic induction. The frequency of the wheel speed sensor signal is proportional to wheel speed.

The EBCM uses the wheel speed sensor signal to calculate vehicle reference speeds and individual speed, acceleration and slip values for each wheel. These values are used to determine when antilock control is required.

The EBCM performs two basic types of checks on the wheel speed sensors, these are sensor continuity and sensor output.e

The EBCM will only set one wheel sped sensor fault code at a time, even if multiple faults exist. Detection is prioritized accordingly: LF, RR, LR, RF. Always check for additional stored codes after making repairs.

TEST CONDITIONS

1. Tested continuously.

FAILURE CONDITIONS

Sensor Output:

1. Drive-away: speed signal is not detected when vehicle reaches 12 kph or 7.5 mph.
2. While Driving: speed signal is lost while vehicle speed is greater than 40 kph or 25 mph.

Continuity:

1. While Standing: open circuit is seen while the vehicle is standing still with the ignition on.

ACTION TAKEN

1. Code set.
2. ABS switched 'OFF'.

NOTES ON CODE 35 CHART

1. This section of the fault tree determines if the code stored is due to a current fault condition. 'Current' wheel speed sensor faults may be detected even at vehicle standstill. If the ABS light turns on, the fault is current. The TECH 1 will indicate ignition cycle since code was set. If the ignition cycle counter is at zero, the code is current.
2. This section of the fault tree checks for an open or short in the wheel speed sensor wiring or sensor coil.
3. This section of the fault tree checks for conditions which may cause intermittent code setting. Some causes of intermittent wheel speed sensor codes to set are: improper routing or sensor cables next to spark plug wires, cables not retained in brackets, loose fitting or improperly mounted sensors, damaged sensors or toothed rings, poor terminal engagement of connectors, or intermittent shorts or opens in wiring.

GC402920051100AX

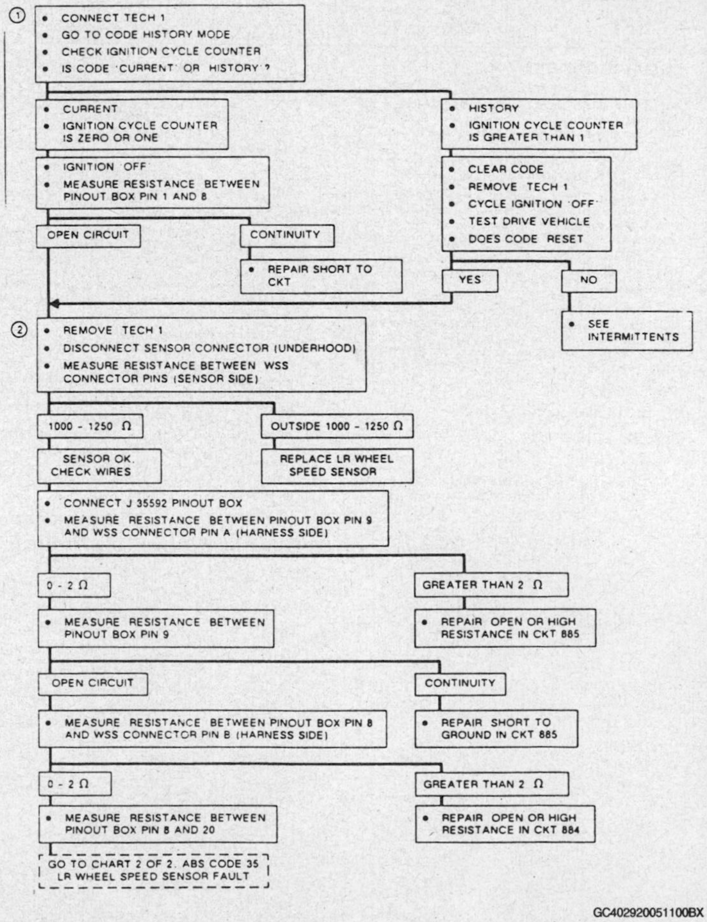
1
• CONNECT TECH 1
• GO TO CODE HISTORY MODE
• CHECK IGNITION CYCLE COUNTER
• IS CODE 'CURRENT' OR 'HISTORY'?
• CURRENT
• IGNITION CYCLE COUNTER IS ZERO OR ONE
• HISTORY
• IGNITION CYCLE COUNTER IS GREATER THAN 1
• IGNITION 'OFF'
• MEASURE RESISTANCE BETWEEN PINOUT BOX PIN 1 AND 8
• CLEAR CODE
• REMOVE TECH 1
• CYCLE IGNITION 'OFF'
• TEST DRIVE VEHICLE
• DOES CODE RESET
OPEN CIRCUIT
CONTINUITY
• REPAIR SHORT TO CKT
YES
NO
• SEE INTERMITTENTS
2
• REMOVE TECH 1
• DISCONNECT SENSOR CONNECTOR (UNDERHOOD)
• MEASURE RESISTANCE BETWEEN WSS CONNECTOR PINS (SENSOR SIDE)
1000 - 1250 Ω
OUTSIDE 1000 - 1250 Ω
SENSOR OK. CHECK WIRES
REPLACE LR WHEEL SPEED SENSOR
• CONNECT J 35592 PINOUT BOX
• MEASURE RESISTANCE BETWEEN PINOUT BOX PIN 9 AND WSS CONNECTOR PIN A (HARNESS SIDE)
0 - 2 Ω
GREATER THAN 2 Ω
• MEASURE RESISTANCE BETWEEN PINOUT BOX PIN 9
• REPAIR OPEN OR HIGH RESISTANCE IN CKT 885
OPEN CIRCUIT
CONTINUITY
• MEASURE RESISTANCE BETWEEN PINOUT BOX PIN 8 AND WSS CONNECTOR PIN B (HARNESS SIDE)
• REPAIR SHORT TO GROUND IN CKT 885
0 - 2 Ω
GREATER THAN 2 Ω
• MEASURE RESISTANCE BETWEEN PINOUT BOX PIN 8 AND 20
• REPAIR OPEN OR HIGH RESISTANCE IN CKT 884
GO TO CHART 2 OF 2. ABS CODE 35 LR WHEEL SPEED SENSOR FAULT
GC402920051100BX

Fig. 77 Code 35: LR Wheel Speed Sensor Fault (Part 1 of 2). 1992 Eldorado, Riviera, Seville, Toronado & Trofeo

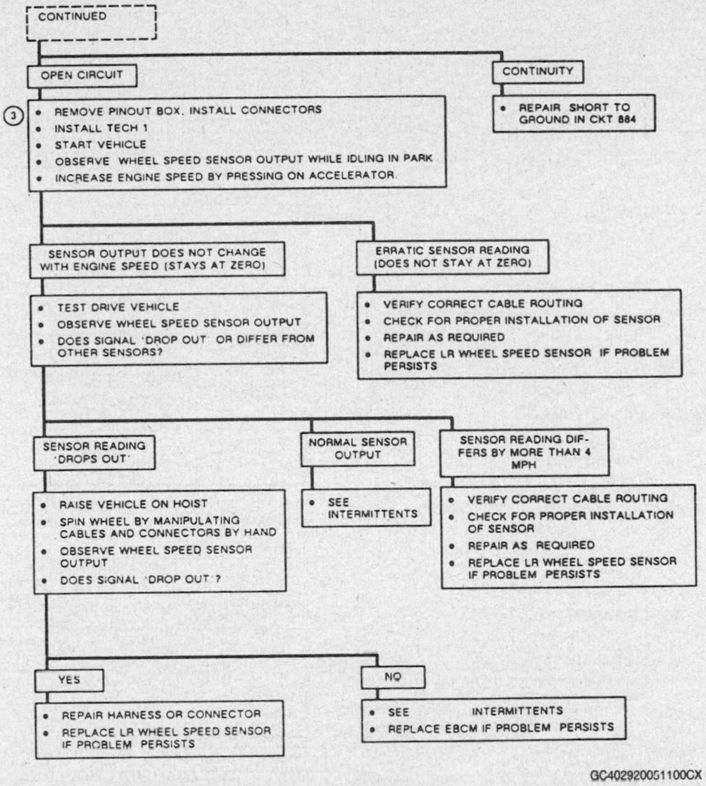
CONTINUED
OPEN CIRCUIT
CONTINUITY
• REPAIR SHORT TO GROUND IN CKT 884
3
• REMOVE PINOUT BOX. INSTALL CONNECTORS
• INSTALL TECH 1
• START VEHICLE
• OBSERVE WHEEL SPEED SENSOR OUTPUT WHILE IDLING IN PARK
• INCREASE ENGINE SPEED BY PRESSING ON ACCELERATOR
SENSOR OUTPUT DOES NOT CHANGE WITH ENGINE SPEED (STAYS AT ZERO)
ERRATIC SENSOR READING (DOES NOT STAY AT ZERO)
• TEST DRIVE VEHICLE
• OBSERVE WHEEL SPEED SENSOR OUTPUT
• DOES SIGNAL 'DROP OUT' OR DIFFER FROM OTHER SENSORS?
• VERIFY CORRECT CABLE ROUTING
• CHECK FOR PROPER INSTALLATION OF SENSOR
• REPAIR AS REQUIRED
• REPLACE LR WHEEL SPEED SENSOR IF PROBLEM PERSISTS
SENSOR READING 'DROPS OUT'
NORMAL SENSOR OUTPUT
SENSOR READING DIFFERS BY MORE THAN 4 MPH
• RAISE VEHICLE ON HOIST
• SPIN WHEEL BY MANIPULATING CABLES AND CONNECTORS BY HAND
• OBSERVE WHEEL SPEED SENSOR OUTPUT
• DOES SIGNAL 'DROP OUT'?
• SEE INTERMITTENTS
• VERIFY CORRECT CABLE ROUTING
• CHECK FOR PROPER INSTALLATION OF SENSOR
• REPAIR AS REQUIRED
• REPLACE LR WHEEL SPEED SENSOR IF PROBLEM PERSISTS
YES
NO
• REPAIR HARNESS OR CONNECTOR
• REPLACE LR WHEEL SPEED SENSOR IF PROBLEM PERSISTS
• SEE INTERMITTENTS
• REPLACE EBCM IF PROBLEM PERSISTS
GC402920051100CX

Fig. 77 Code 35: LR Wheel Speed Sensor Fault (Part 2 of 2). 1992 Eldorado, Riviera, Seville, Toronado & Trofeo

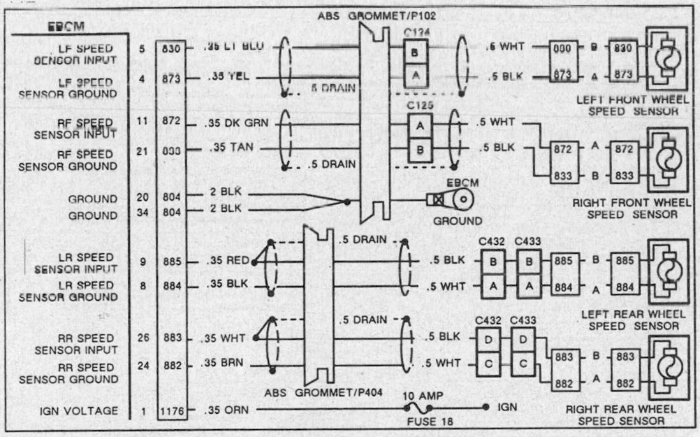
EBCM
ABS GROMMET/P102
LF SPEED SENSOR INPUT
LF SPEED SENSOR GROUND
RF SPEED SENSOR INPUT
RF SPEED SENSOR GROUND
GROUND
GROUND
LR SPEED SENSOR INPUT
LR SPEED SENSOR GROUND
RR SPEED SENSOR INPUT
RR SPEED SENSOR GROUND
IGN VOLTAGE
.35 LT BLU
.35 YEL
.5 DRAIN
.35 DK GRN
.35 TAN
2 BLK
.35 RED
.35 BLK
.35 WHT
.35 BRN
.35 ORN
C124
C125
.6 WHT
.5 BLK
.5 WHT
LEFT FRONT WHEEL SPEED SENSOR
RIGHT FRONT WHEEL SPEED SENSOR
EBCM
GROUND
C432
C433
LEFT REAR WHEEL SPEED SENSOR
RIGHT REAR WHEEL SPEED SENSOR
ABS GROMMET/P404
10 AMP
FUSE 18
IGN

ABS CODE 36

LEFT REAR TOOTHED WHEEL FREQUENCY ERROR

CIRCUIT DESCRIPTION

As each wheel turns, the wheel speed sensor for that wheel creates a small AC voltage as a toothed sensor ring, mounted in the rear integral hub/bearing assembly, is passed by the stationary sensor. The sensor consists of a permanent magnet and coil and generates voltage by magnetic induction. The frequency of the wheel speed sensor signal is proportional to wheel speed.

The EBCM uses the wheel speed sensor signal to calculate vehicle reference speeds and individual speed, acceleration and slip values for each wheel. These values are used to determine when antilock control is required.

TEST CONDITIONS

1. Tested continuously.

FAILURE CONDITIONS

1. While Driving: one wheel is detected at least 30 kph or 19 mph faster than the remaining wheels for an extended period of time.

or

2. one wheel is at least 6 kph or 4 mph less than or greater than the remaining wheels for an extended period of time.

Causes of improper speed signal may be caused by incorrect number of teeth on sensor ring, sensor rings which are covered with dirt, grease or metallic particles, or damaged toothed sensor ring.

ACTION TAKEN

1. Code set.
2. ABS switched 'OFF' after 1 minute.

GC402920051200AX

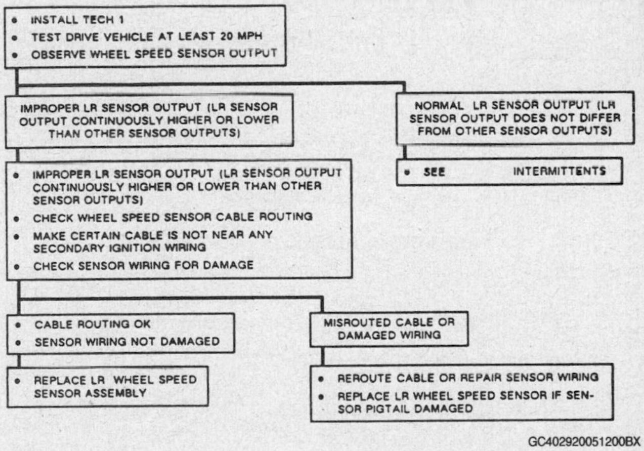
• INSTALL TECH 1
• TEST DRIVE VEHICLE AT LEAST 20 MPH
• OBSERVE WHEEL SPEED SENSOR OUTPUT
IMPROPER LR SENSOR OUTPUT (LR SENSOR OUTPUT CONTINUOUSLY HIGHER OR LOWER THAN OTHER SENSOR OUTPUTS)
NORMAL LR SENSOR OUTPUT (LR SENSOR OUTPUT DOES NOT DIFFER FROM OTHER SENSOR OUTPUTS)
• IMPROPER LR SENSOR OUTPUT (LR SENSOR OUTPUT CONTINUOUSLY HIGHER OR LOWER THAN OTHER SENSOR OUTPUTS)
• CHECK WHEEL SPEED SENSOR CABLE ROUTING
• MAKE CERTAIN CABLE IS NOT NEAR ANY SECONDARY IGNITION WIRING
• CHECK SENSOR WIRING FOR DAMAGE
• SEE INTERMITTENTS
• CABLE ROUTING OK
• SENSOR WIRING NOT DAMAGED
MISROUTED CABLE OR DAMAGED WIRING
• REPLACE LR WHEEL SPEED SENSOR ASSEMBLY
• REROUTE CABLE OR REPAIR SENSOR WIRING
• REPLACE LR WHEEL SPEED SENSOR IF SENSOR PIGTAIL DAMAGED
GC402920051200BX

Fig. 78 Code 36: LR Toothed Wheel Frequency Error. 1992 Eldorado, Riviera, Seville, Toronado & Trofeo

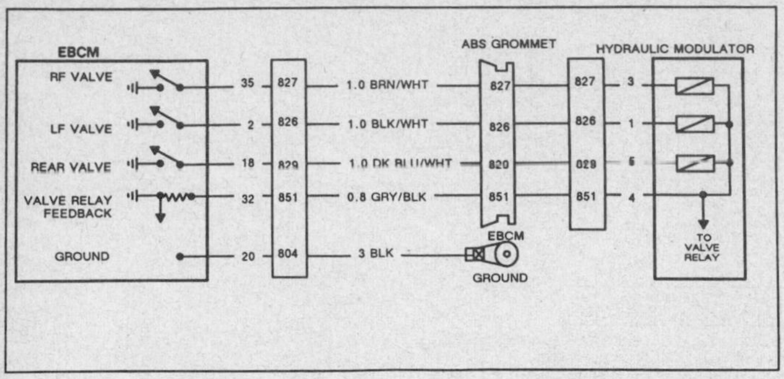
EBCM
RF VALVE
LF VALVE
REAR VALVE
VALVE RELAY FEEDBACK
GROUND
35
2
18
32
20
827
826
829
851
804
1.0 BRN/WHT
1.0 BLK/WHT
1.0 DK BLU/WHT
0.8 GRY/BLK
3 BLK
ABS GROMMET
HYDRAULIC MODULATOR
3
1
5
4
TO VALVE RELAY
EBCM GROUND

ABS CODE 41

RIGHT FRONT SOLENOID VALVE FAULT

CIRCUIT DESCRIPTION

The right front solenoid valve in the hydraulic modulator may be commanded to three different positions by the EBCM. Valve position is determined by the amount of current which is allowed to flow through the solenoid valve coil.

The solenoid valve circuits receive power through the valve relay on the hydraulic modulator. The valve relay is engaged at key-on and remains engaged throughout the ignition cycle. Solenoid valve lines should have battery voltage available at all times.

When the key is turned to RUN, power is supplied to the EBCM. The EBCM will complete an internal self-check before providing ground to the valve relay. When the valve relay is energized, battery power is supplied to the solenoid valves.

TEST CONDITIONS

1. Tested continuously.

FAILURE CONDITIONS

While standing or driving:

1. Valve cannot be activated
   or
2. Valve is activated in a defective way

ACTION TAKEN

1. Code Set.
2. ABS switched 'OFF'.

Code 41 will set when the expected position of the right front solenoid valve does not match the commanded position from the EBCM. Conditions which could cause Code 41 to set are damage to the right front solenoid, an open circuit or a short circuit to ground or battery on CKT 827.

GC402920051300AX

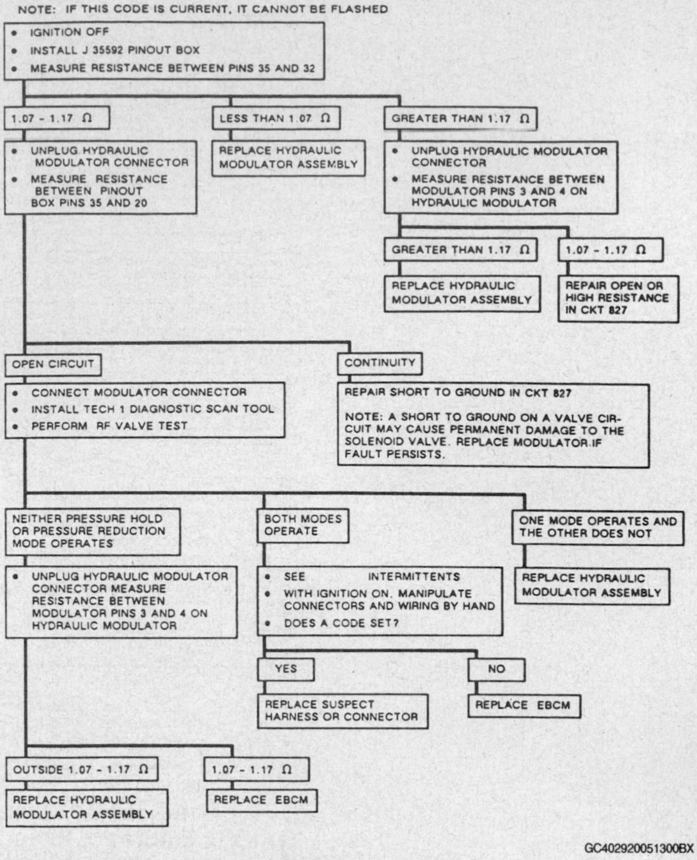
NOTE: IF THIS CODE IS CURRENT, IT CANNOT BE FLASHED
• IGNITION OFF
• INSTALL J 35592 PINOUT BOX
• MEASURE RESISTANCE BETWEEN PINS 35 AND 32
1.07 - 1.17 Ω
LESS THAN 1.07 Ω
GREATER THAN 1.17 Ω
• UNPLUG HYDRAULIC MODULATOR CONNECTOR
• MEASURE RESISTANCE BETWEEN PINOUT BOX PINS 35 AND 20
REPLACE HYDRAULIC MODULATOR ASSEMBLY
• UNPLUG HYDRAULIC MODULATOR CONNECTOR
• MEASURE RESISTANCE BETWEEN MODULATOR PINS 3 AND 4 ON HYDRAULIC MODULATOR
GREATER THAN 1.17 Ω
1.07 - 1.17 Ω
REPLACE HYDRAULIC MODULATOR ASSEMBLY
REPAIR OPEN OR HIGH RESISTANCE IN CKT 827
OPEN CIRCUIT
CONTINUITY
• CONNECT MODULATOR CONNECTOR
• INSTALL TECH 1 DIAGNOSTIC SCAN TOOL
• PERFORM RF VALVE TEST
REPAIR SHORT TO GROUND IN CKT 827
NOTE: A SHORT TO GROUND ON A VALVE CIRCUIT MAY CAUSE PERMANENT DAMAGE TO THE SOLENOID VALVE. REPLACE MODULATOR IF FAULT PERSISTS.
NEITHER PRESSURE HOLD OR PRESSURE REDUCTION MODE OPERATES
BOTH MODES OPERATE
ONE MODE OPERATES AND THE OTHER DOES NOT
• UNPLUG HYDRAULIC MODULATOR CONNECTOR MEASURE RESISTANCE BETWEEN MODULATOR PINS 3 AND 4 ON HYDRAULIC MODULATOR
• SEE INTERMITTENTS
• WITH IGNITION ON, MANIPULATE CONNECTORS AND WIRING BY HAND
• DOES A CODE SET?
REPLACE HYDRAULIC MODULATOR ASSEMBLY
YES
NO
REPLACE SUSPECT HARNESS OR CONNECTOR
REPLACE EBCM
OUTSIDE 1.07 - 1.17 Ω
1.07 - 1.17 Ω
REPLACE HYDRAULIC MODULATOR ASSEMBLY
REPLACE EBCM
GC402920051300BX

Fig. 79 Code 41: RF Solenoid Valve Fault. 1992 Eldorado, Riviera, Seville, Toronado & Trofeo

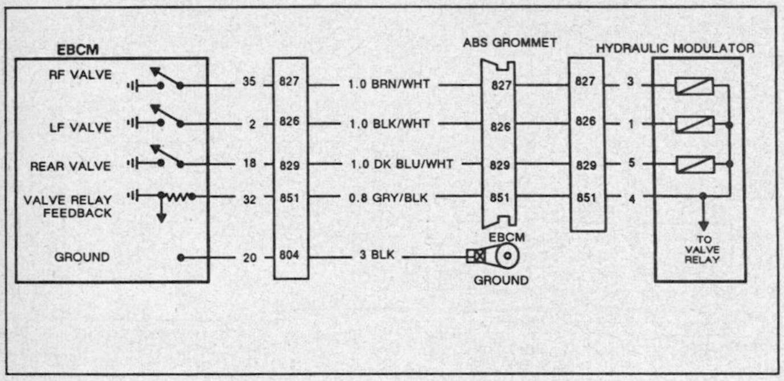
EBCM
RF VALVE
LF VALVE
REAR VALVE
VALVE RELAY FEEDBACK
GROUND
35
2
18
32
20
827
826
829
851
804
1.0 BRN/WHT
1.0 BLK/WHT
1.0 DK BLU/WHT
0.8 GRY/BLK
3 BLK
ABS GROMMET
HYDRAULIC MODULATOR
3
1
5
4
TO VALVE RELAY
EBCM GROUND

ABS CODE 45

LEFT FRONT SOLENOID VALVE FAULT

CIRCUIT DESCRIPTION

The left front solenoid valve in the hydraulic modulator may be commanded to three different positions by the EBCM. Valve position is determined by the amount of current which is allowed to flow through the solenoid valve coil.

The solenoid valve circuits receive power through the valve relay on the hydraulic modulator. The valve relay is engaged at key-on and remains engaged throughout the ignition cycle. Solenoid valve lines should have battery voltage available at all times.

When the key is turned to RUN, power is supplied to the EBCM. The EBCM will complete an internal self-check before providing ground to the valve relay. When the valve relay is energized, battery power is supplied to the solenoid valves.

TEST CONDITIONS

1. Tested continuously.

FAILURE CONDITIONS

While standing or driving:

1. Valve cannot be activated
   or
2. Valve is activated in a defective way

ACTION TAKEN

1. Code Set.
2. ABS switched 'OFF'.

Code 45 will set when the expected position of the left front solenoid valve does not match the commanded position from the EBCM. Conditions which could cause Code 45 to set are damage to the left front solenoid, an open circuit or a short circuit to ground or battery on CKT 826.

GC402920051400AX

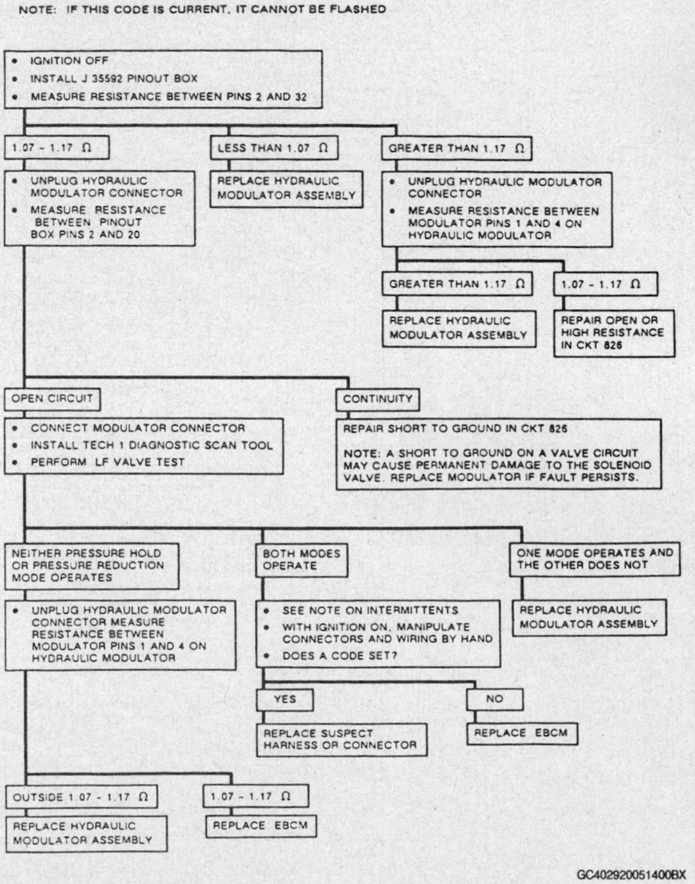
NOTE: IF THIS CODE IS CURRENT, IT CANNOT BE FLASHED
• IGNITION OFF
• INSTALL J 35592 PINOUT BOX
• MEASURE RESISTANCE BETWEEN PINS 2 AND 32
1.07 - 1.17 Ω
LESS THAN 1.07 Ω
GREATER THAN 1.17 Ω
• UNPLUG HYDRAULIC MODULATOR CONNECTOR
• MEASURE RESISTANCE BETWEEN PINOUT BOX PINS 2 AND 20
REPLACE HYDRAULIC MODULATOR ASSEMBLY
• UNPLUG HYDRAULIC MODULATOR CONNECTOR
• MEASURE RESISTANCE BETWEEN MODULATOR PINS 1 AND 4 ON HYDRAULIC MODULATOR
GREATER THAN 1.17 Ω
1.07 - 1.17 Ω
REPLACE HYDRAULIC MODULATOR ASSEMBLY
REPAIR OPEN OR HIGH RESISTANCE IN CKT 826
OPEN CIRCUIT
CONTINUITY
• CONNECT MODULATOR CONNECTOR
• INSTALL TECH 1 DIAGNOSTIC SCAN TOOL
• PERFORM LF VALVE TEST
REPAIR SHORT TO GROUND IN CKT 826
NOTE: A SHORT TO GROUND ON A VALVE CIRCUIT MAY CAUSE PERMANENT DAMAGE TO THE SOLENOID VALVE. REPLACE MODULATOR IF FAULT PERSISTS.
NEITHER PRESSURE HOLD OR PRESSURE REDUCTION MODE OPERATES
BOTH MODES OPERATE
ONE MODE OPERATES AND THE OTHER DOES NOT
• UNPLUG HYDRAULIC MODULATOR CONNECTOR MEASURE RESISTANCE BETWEEN MODULATOR PINS 1 AND 4 ON HYDRAULIC MODULATOR
• SEE NOTE ON INTERMITTENTS
• WITH IGNITION ON, MANIPULATE CONNECTORS AND WIRING BY HAND
• DOES A CODE SET?
REPLACE HYDRAULIC MODULATOR ASSEMBLY
YES
NO
REPLACE SUSPECT HARNESS OR CONNECTOR
REPLACE EBCM
OUTSIDE 1.07 - 1.17 Ω
1.07 - 1.17 Ω
REPLACE HYDRAULIC MODULATOR ASSEMBLY
REPLACE EBCM
GC402920051400BX

Fig. 80 Code 45: LF Solenoid Valve Fault. 1992 Eldorado, Riviera, Seville, Toronado & Trofeo

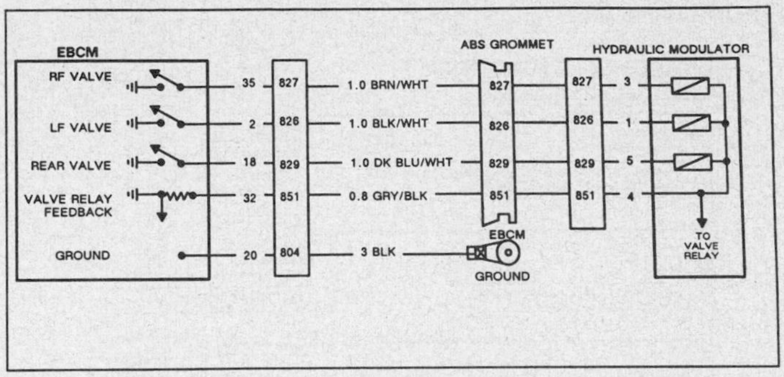

EBCM
RF VALVE
LF VALVE
REAR VALVE
VALVE RELAY FEEDBACK
GROUND
35 — 827 — 1.0 BRN/WHT
2 — 826 — 1.0 BLK/WHT
18 — 829 — 1.0 DK BLU/WHT
32 — 851 — 0.8 GRY/BLK
20 — 804 — 3 BLK
ABS GROMMET
HYDRAULIC MODULATOR
EBCM GROUND
TO VALVE RELAY

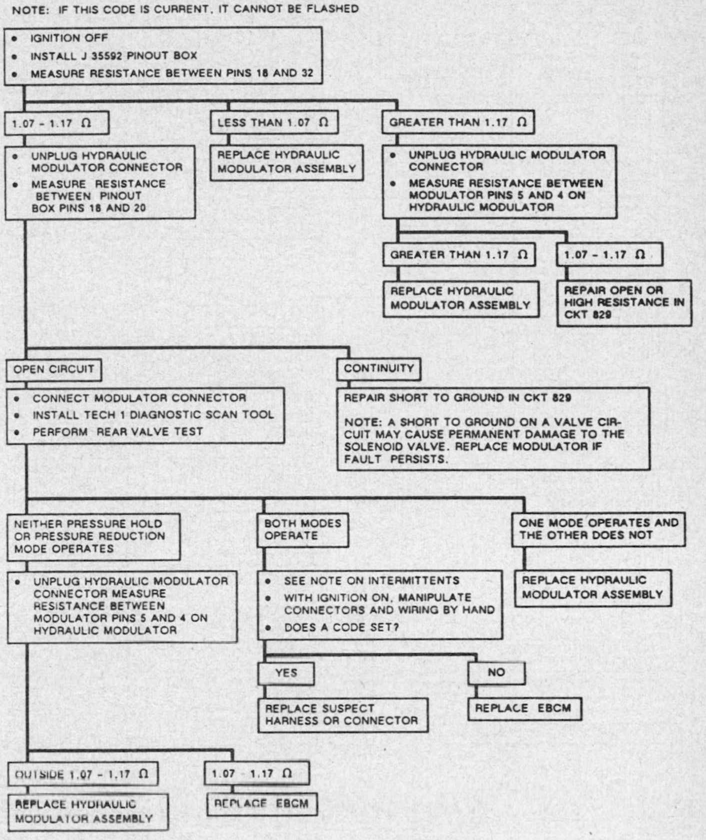

NOTE: IF THIS CODE IS CURRENT, IT CANNOT BE FLASHED
• IGNITION OFF
• INSTALL J 35592 PINOUT BOX
• MEASURE RESISTANCE BETWEEN PINS 18 AND 32
1.07 - 1.17 Ω
LESS THAN 1.07 Ω
GREATER THAN 1.17 Ω
• UNPLUG HYDRAULIC MODULATOR CONNECTOR
• MEASURE RESISTANCE BETWEEN PINOUT BOX PINS 18 AND 20
REPLACE HYDRAULIC MODULATOR ASSEMBLY
• UNPLUG HYDRAULIC MODULATOR CONNECTOR
• MEASURE RESISTANCE BETWEEN MODULATOR PINS 5 AND 4 ON HYDRAULIC MODULATOR
GREATER THAN 1.17 Ω
1.07 - 1.17 Ω
REPLACE HYDRAULIC MODULATOR ASSEMBLY
REPAIR OPEN OR HIGH RESISTANCE IN CKT 829
OPEN CIRCUIT
CONTINUITY
• CONNECT MODULATOR CONNECTOR
• INSTALL TECH 1 DIAGNOSTIC SCAN TOOL
• PERFORM REAR VALVE TEST
REPAIR SHORT TO GROUND IN CKT 829
NOTE: A SHORT TO GROUND ON A VALVE CIRCUIT MAY CAUSE PERMANENT DAMAGE TO THE SOLENOID VALVE. REPLACE MODULATOR IF FAULT PERSISTS.
NEITHER PRESSURE HOLD OR PRESSURE REDUCTION MODE OPERATES
BOTH MODES OPERATE
ONE MODE OPERATES AND THE OTHER DOES NOT
• UNPLUG HYDRAULIC MODULATOR CONNECTOR MEASURE RESISTANCE BETWEEN MODULATOR PINS 5 AND 4 ON HYDRAULIC MODULATOR
• SEE NOTE ON INTERMITTENTS
• WITH IGNITION ON, MANIPULATE CONNECTORS AND WIRING BY HAND
• DOES A CODE SET?
REPLACE HYDRAULIC MODULATOR ASSEMBLY
YES
NO
REPLACE SUSPECT HARNESS OR CONNECTOR
REPLACE EBCM
OUTSIDE 1.07 - 1.17 Ω
1.07 - 1.17 Ω
REPLACE HYDRAULIC MODULATOR ASSEMBLY
REPLACE EBCM

ABS CODE 55

REAR WHEEL SOLENOID VALVE FAULT

CIRCUIT DESCRIPTION

The rear wheels share the same solenoid valve and are connected by a hydraulic plunger internal to the modulator. There are two separate hydraulic lines from the modulator to each rear wheel.

The rear solenoid valve in the hydraulic modulator may be commanded to three different positions by the EBCM. The rear solenoid valve modulates hydraulic brake pressure to both rear wheel circuits. Valve position is determined by the amount of current which is allowed to flow through the solenoid valve coil.

The solenoid valve circuits receive power through the valve relay on the hydraulic modulator. The valve relay is engaged at key-on and remains engaged throughout the ignition cycle. Solenoid valve lines should have battery voltage available at all times.

When the key is turned to RUN, power is supplied to the EBCM. The EBCM will complete an internal self-check before providing ground to the valve relay. When the valve relay is energized, battery power is supplied to the solenoid valves.

Code 55 will set when the expected position of the rear solenoid valve does not match the commanded position from the EBCM. Conditions which could cause Code 55 to set are damage to the rear solenoid, an open circuit or a short circuit to ground or battery on CKT 829.

TEST CONDITIONS

1. Tested continuously.

FAILURE CONDITIONS

While standing or driving:

1. Valve cannot be activated
 or
2. Valve is activated in a defective way.

ACTION TAKEN

1. Code Set.
2. ABS switched 'OFF'.

GC402920051500AX

GC402920051500BX

Fig. 81 Code 55: Rear Solenoid Valve Fault. 1992 Eldorado, Riviera, Seville, Toronado & Trofeo

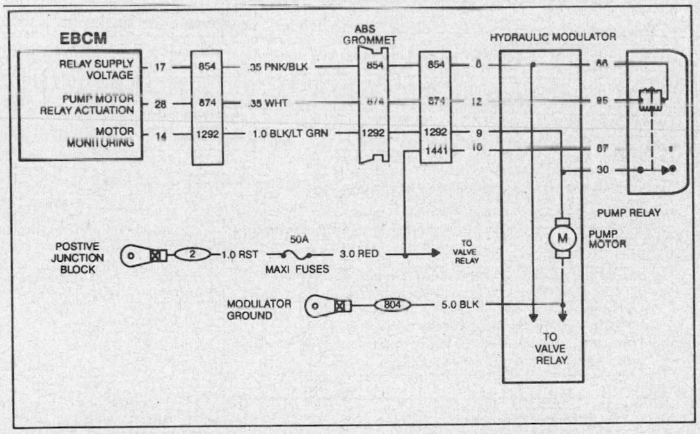

EBCM
RELAY SUPPLY VOLTAGE
PUMP MOTOR RELAY ACTUATION
MOTOR MONITORING
17 — 854 — .35 PNK/BLK
28 — 874 — .35 WHT
14 — 1292 — 1.0 BLK/LT GRN
ABS GROMMET
HYDRAULIC MODULATOR
PUMP RELAY
PUMP MOTOR
POSTIVE JUNCTION BLOCK
1.0 RST
50A
MAXI FUSES
3.0 RED
TO VALVE RELAY
MODULATOR GROUND
804
5.0 BLK
TO VALVE RELAY

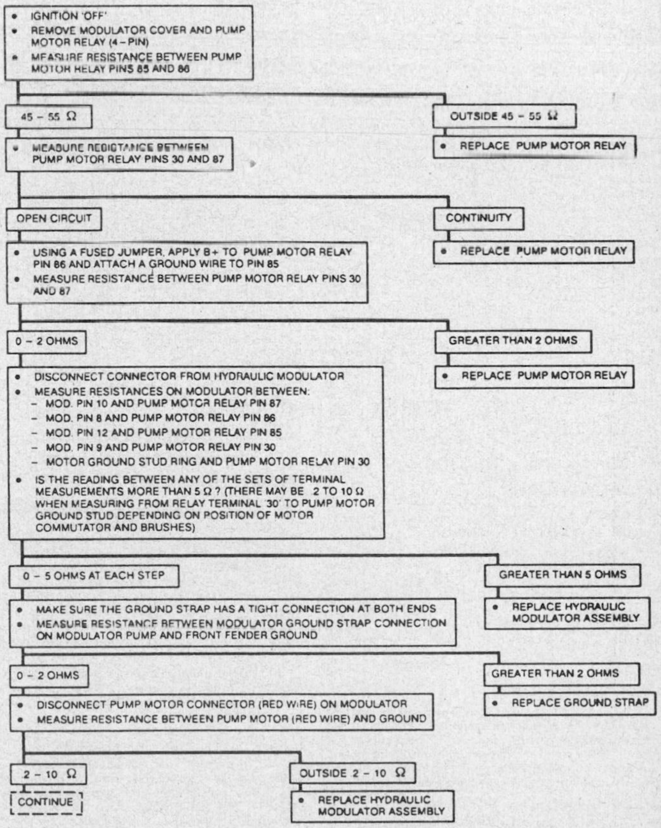

• IGNITION 'OFF'
• REMOVE MODULATOR COVER AND PUMP MOTOR RELAY (4-PIN)
• MEASURE RESISTANCE BETWEEN PUMP MOTOR RELAY PINS 85 AND 86
45 - 55 Ω
OUTSIDE 45 - 55 Ω
• MEASURE RESISTANCE BETWEEN PUMP MOTOR RELAY PINS 30 AND 87
• REPLACE PUMP MOTOR RELAY
OPEN CIRCUIT
CONTINUITY
• USING A FUSED JUMPER, APPLY B+ TO PUMP MOTOR RELAY PIN 86 AND ATTACH A GROUND WIRE TO PIN 85
• MEASURE RESISTANCE BETWEEN PUMP MOTOR RELAY PINS 30 AND 87
• REPLACE PUMP MOTOR RELAY
0 - 2 OHMS
GREATER THAN 2 OHMS
• DISCONNECT CONNECTOR FROM HYDRAULIC MODULATOR
• MEASURE RESISTANCES ON MODULATOR BETWEEN:
– MOD. PIN 10 AND PUMP MOTOR RELAY PIN 87
– MOD. PIN 8 AND PUMP MOTOR RELAY PIN 86
– MOD. PIN 12 AND PUMP MOTOR RELAY PIN 85
– MOD. PIN 9 AND PUMP MOTOR RELAY PIN 30
– MOTOR GROUND STUD RING AND PUMP MOTOR RELAY PIN 30
• IS THE READING BETWEEN ANY OF THE SETS OF TERMINAL MEASUREMENTS MORE THAN 5 Ω ? (THERE MAY BE 2 TO 10 Ω WHEN MEASURING FROM RELAY TERMINAL '30' TO PUMP MOTOR GROUND STUD DEPENDING ON POSITION OF MOTOR COMMUTATOR AND BRUSHES)
• REPLACE PUMP MOTOR RELAY
0 - 5 OHMS AT EACH STEP
GREATER THAN 5 OHMS
• MAKE SURE THE GROUND STRAP HAS A TIGHT CONNECTION AT BOTH ENDS
• MEASURE RESISTANCE BETWEEN MODULATOR GROUND STRAP CONNECTION ON MODULATOR PUMP AND FRONT FENDER GROUND
• REPLACE HYDRAULIC MODULATOR ASSEMBLY
0 - 2 OHMS
GREATER THAN 2 OHMS
• DISCONNECT PUMP MOTOR CONNECTOR (RED WIRE) ON MODULATOR
• MEASURE RESISTANCE BETWEEN PUMP MOTOR (RED WIRE) AND GROUND
• REPLACE GROUND STRAP
2 - 10 Ω
OUTSIDE 2 - 10 Ω
CONTINUE
• REPLACE HYDRAULIC MODULATOR ASSEMBLY

CIRCUIT DESCRIPTION:

The pump motor returns brake fluid to the master cylinder brake circuit at the hydraulic modulator during anti-lock braking. During normal braking, the pump does not operate. When the vehicle begins to move after start-up, the EBCM will turn on the pump motor and perform a self-check of the pump motor and pump motor circuit. This check may be felt and heard by the driver when the vehicle begins to move. The self-check should be considered normal operation. The pump motor is an integral component of the hydraulic modulator and cannot be serviced separately.

The pump motor relay provides power to the pump motor in the hydraulic modulator. The pump motor relay is located on the hydraulic modulator an may be replaced if it is found to be defective.

The pump motor relay is not engaged during normal system operation. When antilock operation is required, the motor relay actuation line on CKT 874 (EBCM pin 28) is pulled to ground. The pump motor relay is engaged by the relay supply voltage line on CKT 854 (EBCM pin 17). When the relay switches, battery power is provided to the pump motor.

TEST CONDITION(S):

1. Tested continuously.

FAILURE CONDITION(S):

1. Drive Away: Motor voltage is not detected during first drive away after engine start.
2. While Driving: Motor relay is energized and motor voltage is not detected.
3. Voltage at EBCM pin 14 below 9 volts.

 OR

4. Pump runs continuously.

ACTION TAKEN:

1. Code set.
2. ABS switched 'OFF'.

When the pump motor relay is engaged, the motor monitor line should be at battery voltage. With the pump motor relay disengaged, the monitoring line should be at ground. If the commanded position of the pump motor relay and motor monitor line do not agree, Code 61 will set. Some conditions which will cause Code 61 to set are:

- An open circuit on CKTs 874 or 1292
- A short to voltage on CKTs 874 or 1292
- A short to ground on CKTs 874 or 1292
- A defective pump motor relay or pump motor

GC402920051600BX

Fig. 82 Code 61: Pump Motor Circuit Fault (Part 1 of 2). 1992 Eldorado & Seville

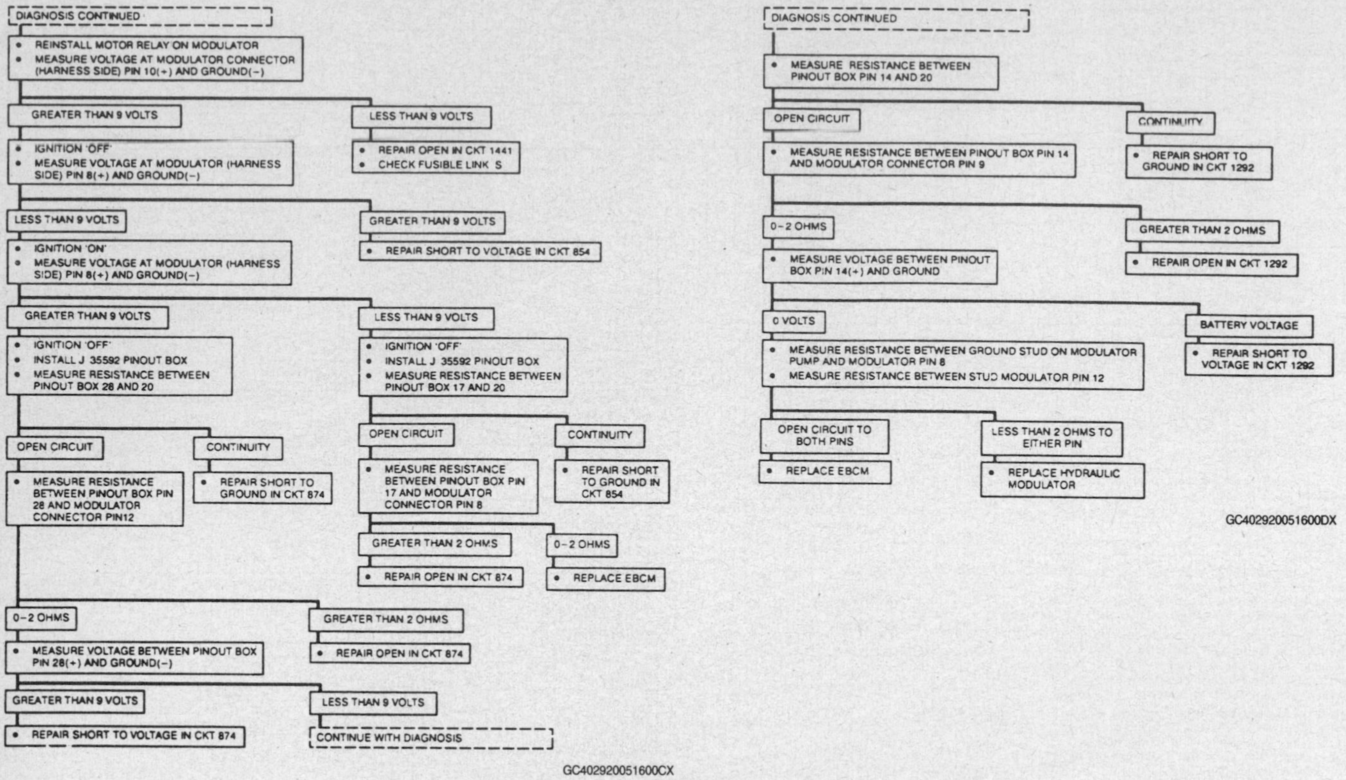
DIAGNOSIS CONTINUED
REINSTALL MOTOR RELAY ON MODULATOR
MEASURE VOLTAGE AT MODULATOR CONNECTOR (HARNESS SIDE) PIN 10(+) AND GROUND(−)
GREATER THAN 9 VOLTS
LESS THAN 9 VOLTS
IGNITION 'OFF'
MEASURE VOLTAGE AT MODULATOR (HARNESS SIDE) PIN 8(+) AND GROUND(−)
REPAIR OPEN IN CKT 1441
CHECK FUSIBLE LINK S
LESS THAN 9 VOLTS
GREATER THAN 9 VOLTS
IGNITION 'ON'
MEASURE VOLTAGE AT MODULATOR (HARNESS SIDE) PIN 8(+) AND GROUND(−)
REPAIR SHORT TO VOLTAGE IN CKT 854
GREATER THAN 9 VOLTS
LESS THAN 9 VOLTS
IGNITION 'OFF'
INSTALL J 35592 PINOUT BOX
MEASURE RESISTANCE BETWEEN PINOUT BOX 28 AND 20
IGNITION 'OFF'
INSTALL J 35592 PINOUT BOX
MEASURE RESISTANCE BETWEEN PINOUT BOX 17 AND 20
OPEN CIRCUIT
CONTINUITY
MEASURE RESISTANCE BETWEEN PINOUT BOX PIN 28 AND MODULATOR CONNECTOR PIN12
REPAIR SHORT TO GROUND IN CKT 874
OPEN CIRCUIT
CONTINUITY
MEASURE RESISTANCE BETWEEN PINOUT BOX PIN 17 AND MODULATOR CONNECTOR PIN 8
REPAIR SHORT TO GROUND IN CKT 854
GREATER THAN 2 OHMS
0–2 OHMS
REPAIR OPEN IN CKT 874
REPLACE EBCM
0–2 OHMS
GREATER THAN 2 OHMS
MEASURE VOLTAGE BETWEEN PINOUT BOX PIN 28(+) AND GROUND(−)
REPAIR OPEN IN CKT 874
GREATER THAN 9 VOLTS
LESS THAN 9 VOLTS
REPAIR SHORT TO VOLTAGE IN CKT 874
CONTINUE WITH DIAGNOSIS
GC402920051600CX
DIAGNOSIS CONTINUED
MEASURE RESISTANCE BETWEEN PINOUT BOX PIN 14 AND 20
OPEN CIRCUIT
CONTINUITY
MEASURE RESISTANCE BETWEEN PINOUT BOX PIN 14 AND MODULATOR CONNECTOR PIN 9
REPAIR SHORT TO GROUND IN CKT 1292
0–2 OHMS
GREATER THAN 2 OHMS
MEASURE VOLTAGE BETWEEN PINOUT BOX PIN 14(+) AND GROUND
REPAIR OPEN IN CKT 1292
0 VOLTS
BATTERY VOLTAGE
MEASURE RESISTANCE BETWEEN GROUND STUD ON MODULATOR PUMP AND MODULATOR PIN 8
MEASURE RESISTANCE BETWEEN STUD MODULATOR PIN 12
REPAIR SHORT TO VOLTAGE IN CKT 1292
OPEN CIRCUIT TO BOTH PINS
LESS THAN 2 OHMS TO EITHER PIN
REPLACE EBCM
REPLACE HYDRAULIC MODULATOR
GC402920051600DX

Fig. 82 Code 61: Pump Motor Circuit Fault (Part 2 of 2). 1992 Eldorado & Seville

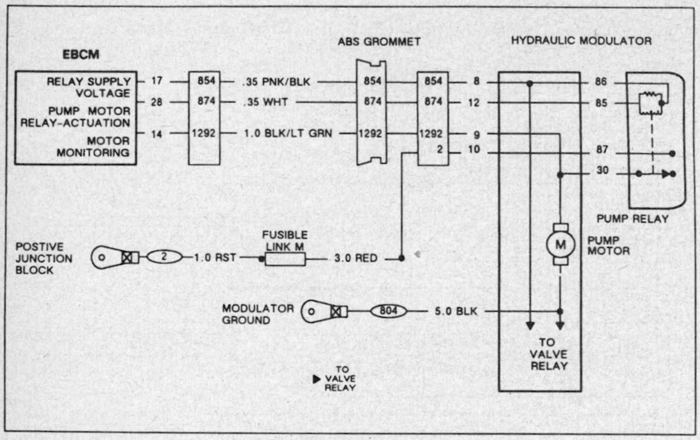
EBCM
ABS GROMMET
HYDRAULIC MODULATOR
RELAY SUPPLY VOLTAGE
PUMP MOTOR RELAY-ACTUATION
MOTOR MONITORING
17
28
14
854
874
1292
.35 PNK/BLK
.35 WHT
1.0 BLK/LT GRN
8
12
9
2
10
86
85
87
30
PUMP RELAY
PUMP MOTOR
POSTIVE JUNCTION BLOCK
1.0 RST
FUSIBLE LINK M
3.0 RED
MODULATOR GROUND
804
5.0 BLK
TO VALVE RELAY
TO VALVE RELAY

ABS CODE 61

PUMP MOTOR CIRCUIT FAULT

TEST CONDITIONS

1. Tested continuously.

FAILURE CONDITIONS

1. Drive Away: motor voltage is not detected during first drive away after engine start.
2. While Driving: motor relay is energized and motor voltage is not detected
   or
3. Voltage at EBCM pin 14 below 9 volts
   or
4. Pump runs continuously.

ACTION TAKEN

1. Code set.
2. ABS switched 'OFF'.

When the pump motor relay is engaged, the motor monitor line should be at battery voltage. With the pump motor relay disengaged, the monitoring line should be at ground. If the commanded position of the pump motor relay and motor monitor line do not agree, Code 61 will set. Some conditions which will cause Code 61 to set are:

- An open circuit on CKTs 874 or 1292
- A short to voltage on CKTs 874 or 1292
- A short to ground on CKTs 874 or 1292
- A defective pump motor relay or pump motor

CIRCUIT DESCRIPTION

The pump motor returns brake fluid to the master cylinder brake circuit at the hydraulic modulator during antilock braking. During normal braking, the pump does not operate. When the vehicle begins to move after start-up, the EBCM will turn on the pump motor and perform a self-check of the pump motor and pump motor circuit. This check may be felt and heard by the driver when the vehicle begins to move. The self-check should be considered normal operation. The pump motor is an integral component of the hydraulic modulator and cannot be serviced separately.

The pump motor relay provides power to the pump motor in the hydraulic modulator. The pump motor relay is located on the hydraulic modulator an may be replaced if it is found to be defective.

The pump motor relay is not engaged during normal system operation. When antilock operation is required, the motor relay actuation line on CKT 874 (EBCM pin 28) is pulled to ground. The pump motor relay is engaged by the relay supply voltage line on CKT 854 (EBCM pin 17). When the relay switches, battery power is provided to the pump motor.

GC402920051700AX

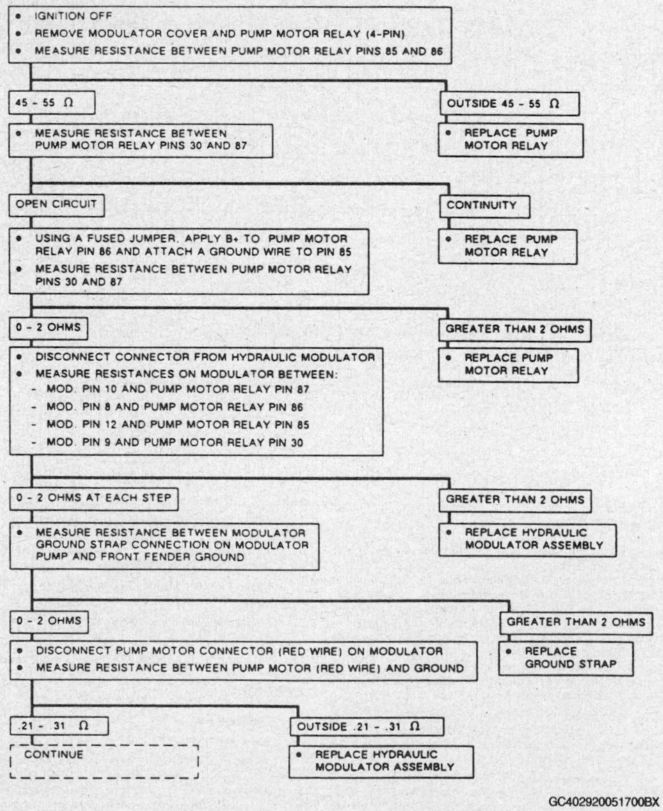
IGNITION OFF
REMOVE MODULATOR COVER AND PUMP MOTOR RELAY (4-PIN)
MEASURE RESISTANCE BETWEEN PUMP MOTOR RELAY PINS 85 AND 86
45 - 55 Ω
OUTSIDE 45 - 55 Ω
MEASURE RESISTANCE BETWEEN PUMP MOTOR RELAY PINS 30 AND 87
REPLACE PUMP MOTOR RELAY
OPEN CIRCUIT
CONTINUITY
USING A FUSED JUMPER, APPLY B+ TO PUMP MOTOR RELAY PIN 86 AND ATTACH A GROUND WIRE TO PIN 85
MEASURE RESISTANCE BETWEEN PUMP MOTOR RELAY PINS 30 AND 87
REPLACE PUMP MOTOR RELAY
0 - 2 OHMS
GREATER THAN 2 OHMS
DISCONNECT CONNECTOR FROM HYDRAULIC MODULATOR
MEASURE RESISTANCES ON MODULATOR BETWEEN:
- MOD. PIN 10 AND PUMP MOTOR RELAY PIN 87
- MOD. PIN 8 AND PUMP MOTOR RELAY PIN 86
- MOD. PIN 12 AND PUMP MOTOR RELAY PIN 85
- MOD. PIN 9 AND PUMP MOTOR RELAY PIN 30
REPLACE PUMP MOTOR RELAY
0 - 2 OHMS AT EACH STEP
GREATER THAN 2 OHMS
MEASURE RESISTANCE BETWEEN MODULATOR GROUND STRAP CONNECTION ON MODULATOR PUMP AND FRONT FENDER GROUND
REPLACE HYDRAULIC MODULATOR ASSEMBLY
0 - 2 OHMS
GREATER THAN 2 OHMS
DISCONNECT PUMP MOTOR CONNECTOR (RED WIRE) ON MODULATOR
MEASURE RESISTANCE BETWEEN PUMP MOTOR (RED WIRE) AND GROUND
REPLACE GROUND STRAP
.21 - .31 Ω
OUTSIDE .21 - .31 Ω
CONTINUE
REPLACE HYDRAULIC MODULATOR ASSEMBLY
GC402920051700BX

Fig. 83 Code 61: Pump Motor Circuit Fault (Part 1 of 2). 1992 Riviera, Toronado & Trofeo

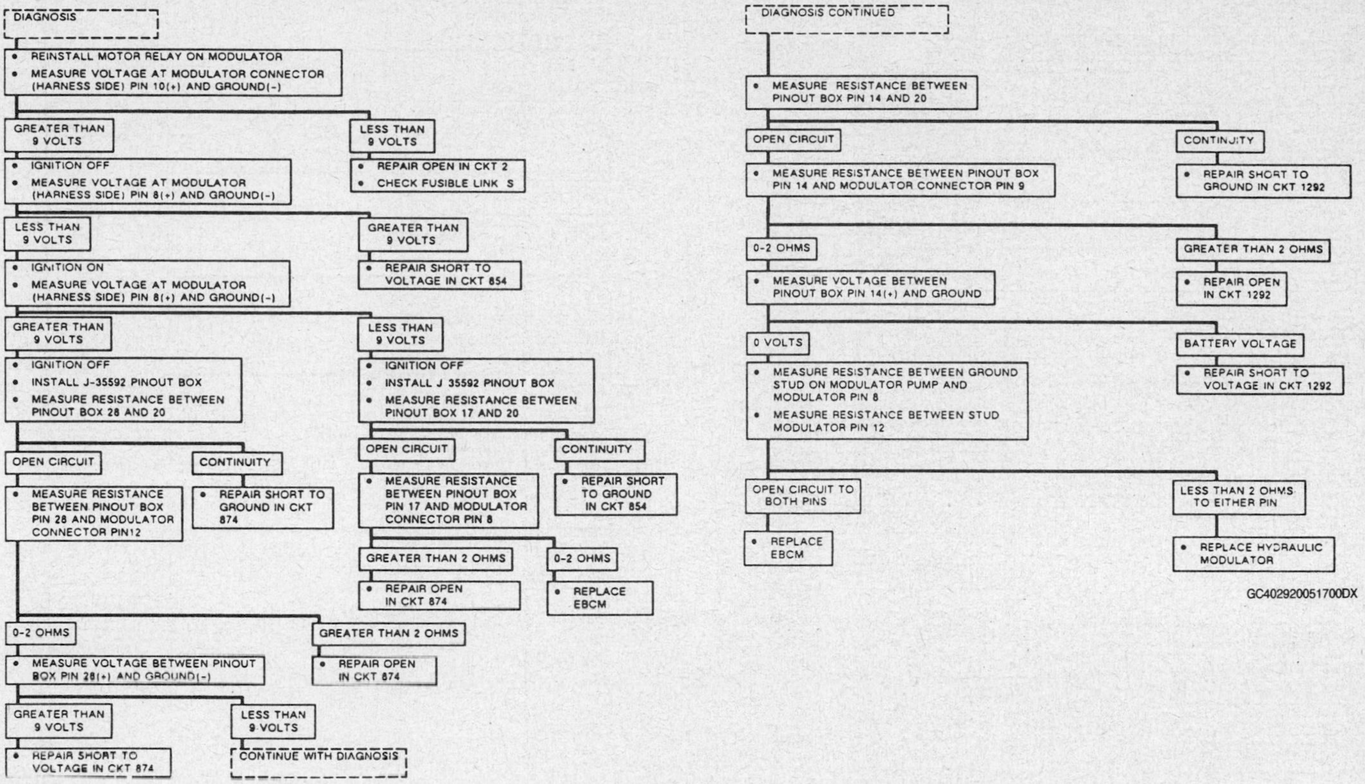

DIAGNOSIS
• REINSTALL MOTOR RELAY ON MODULATOR
• MEASURE VOLTAGE AT MODULATOR CONNECTOR (HARNESS SIDE) PIN 10(+) AND GROUND(-)
GREATER THAN 9 VOLTS
LESS THAN 9 VOLTS
• IGNITION OFF
• MEASURE VOLTAGE AT MODULATOR (HARNESS SIDE) PIN 8(+) AND GROUND(-)
• REPAIR OPEN IN CKT 2
• CHECK FUSIBLE LINK S
LESS THAN 9 VOLTS
GREATER THAN 9 VOLTS
• IGNITION ON
• MEASURE VOLTAGE AT MODULATOR (HARNESS SIDE) PIN 8(+) AND GROUND(-)
• REPAIR SHORT TO VOLTAGE IN CKT 854
GREATER THAN 9 VOLTS
LESS THAN 9 VOLTS
• IGNITION OFF
• INSTALL J-35592 PINOUT BOX
• MEASURE RESISTANCE BETWEEN PINOUT BOX 28 AND 20
• IGNITION OFF
• INSTALL J 35592 PINOUT BOX
• MEASURE RESISTANCE BETWEEN PINOUT BOX 17 AND 20
OPEN CIRCUIT
CONTINUITY
• MEASURE RESISTANCE BETWEEN PINOUT BOX PIN 28 AND MODULATOR CONNECTOR PIN12
• REPAIR SHORT TO GROUND IN CKT 874
OPEN CIRCUIT
CONTINUITY
• MEASURE RESISTANCE BETWEEN PINOUT BOX PIN 17 AND MODULATOR CONNECTOR PIN 8
• REPAIR SHORT TO GROUND IN CKT 854
GREATER THAN 2 OHMS
0-2 OHMS
• REPAIR OPEN IN CKT 874
• REPLACE EBCM
0-2 OHMS
GREATER THAN 2 OHMS
• MEASURE VOLTAGE BETWEEN PINOUT BOX PIN 28(+) AND GROUND(-)
• REPAIR OPEN IN CKT 874
GREATER THAN 9 VOLTS
LESS THAN 9 VOLTS
• REPAIR SHORT TO VOLTAGE IN CKT 874
CONTINUE WITH DIAGNOSIS
DIAGNOSIS CONTINUED
• MEASURE RESISTANCE BETWEEN PINOUT BOX PIN 14 AND 20
OPEN CIRCUIT
CONTINUITY
• MEASURE RESISTANCE BETWEEN PINOUT BOX PIN 14 AND MODULATOR CONNECTOR PIN 9
• REPAIR SHORT TO GROUND IN CKT 1292
0-2 OHMS
GREATER THAN 2 OHMS
• MEASURE VOLTAGE BETWEEN PINOUT BOX PIN 14(+) AND GROUND
• REPAIR OPEN IN CKT 1292
0 VOLTS
BATTERY VOLTAGE
• MEASURE RESISTANCE BETWEEN GROUND STUD ON MODULATOR PUMP AND MODULATOR PIN 8
• MEASURE RESISTANCE BETWEEN STUD MODULATOR PIN 12
• REPAIR SHORT TO VOLTAGE IN CKT 1292
OPEN CIRCUIT TO BOTH PINS
LESS THAN 2 OHMS TO EITHER PIN
• REPLACE EBCM
• REPLACE HYDRAULIC MODULATOR
GC402920051700DX

GC402920051700CX

Fig. 83 Code 61: Pump Motor Circuit Fault (Part 2 of 2). 1992 Riviera, Toronado & Trofeo

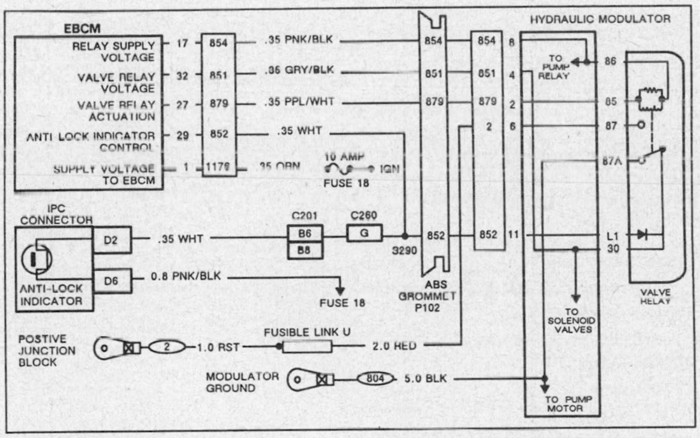

HYDRAULIC MODULATOR
EBCM
RELAY SUPPLY VOLTAGE
VALVE RELAY VOLTAGE
VALVE RELAY ACTUATION
ANTI LOCK INDICATOR CONTROL
SUPPLY VOLTAGE TO EBCM
.35 PNK/BLK
.35 GRY/BLK
.35 PPL/WHT
.35 WHT
.35 ORN
10 AMP
IGN
FUSE 18
TO PUMP RELAY
IPC CONNECTOR
C201
C260
.35 WHT
0.8 PNK/BLK
ANTI-LOCK INDICATOR
FUSE 18
ABS GROMMET P102
TO SOLENOID VALVES
VALVE RELAY
POSTIVE JUNCTION BLOCK
FUSIBLE LINK U
1.0 RST
2.0 RED
MODULATOR GROUND
5.0 BLK
TO PUMP MOTOR

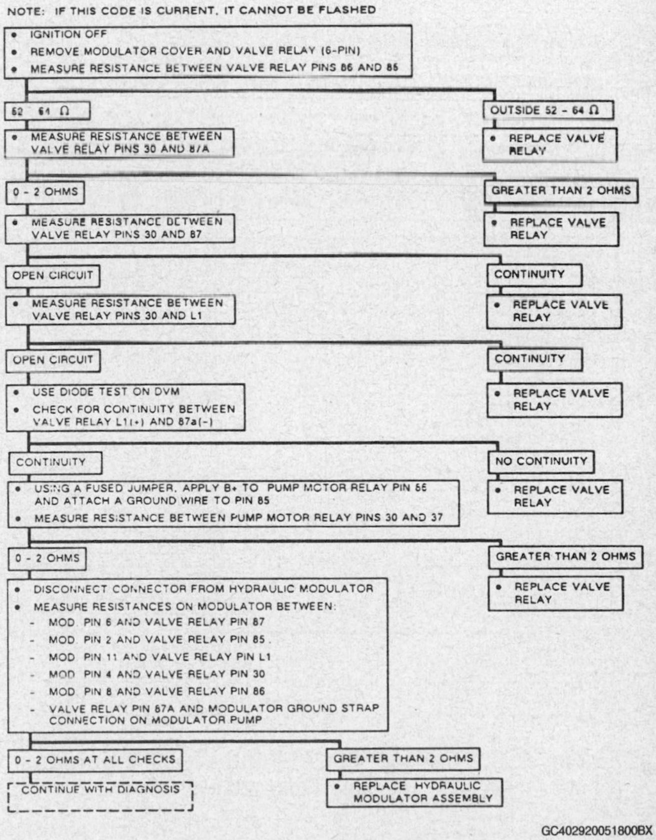

NOTE: IF THIS CODE IS CURRENT, IT CANNOT BE FLASHED
• IGNITION OFF
• REMOVE MODULATOR COVER AND VALVE RELAY (6-PIN)
• MEASURE RESISTANCE BETWEEN VALVE RELAY PINS 86 AND 85
52 - 64 Ω
OUTSIDE 52 - 64 Ω
• MEASURE RESISTANCE BETWEEN VALVE RELAY PINS 30 AND 87A
• REPLACE VALVE RELAY
0 - 2 OHMS
GREATER THAN 2 OHMS
• MEASURE RESISTANCE BETWEEN VALVE RELAY PINS 30 AND 87
• REPLACE VALVE RELAY
OPEN CIRCUIT
CONTINUITY
• MEASURE RESISTANCE BETWEEN VALVE RELAY PINS 30 AND L1
• REPLACE VALVE RELAY
OPEN CIRCUIT
CONTINUITY
• USE DIODE TEST ON DVM
• CHECK FOR CONTINUITY BETWEEN VALVE RELAY L1(+) AND 87a(-)
• REPLACE VALVE RELAY
CONTINUITY
NO CONTINUITY
• USING A FUSED JUMPER, APPLY B+ TO PUMP MOTOR RELAY PIN 86 AND ATTACH A GROUND WIRE TO PIN 85
• MEASURE RESISTANCE BETWEEN PUMP MOTOR RELAY PINS 30 AND 37
• REPLACE VALVE RELAY
0 - 2 OHMS
GREATER THAN 2 OHMS
• DISCONNECT CONNECTOR FROM HYDRAULIC MODULATOR
• MEASURE RESISTANCES ON MODULATOR BETWEEN:
- MOD PIN 6 AND VALVE RELAY PIN 87
- MOD PIN 2 AND VALVE RELAY PIN 85
- MOD PIN 11 AND VALVE RELAY PIN L1
- MOD PIN 4 AND VALVE RELAY PIN 30
- MOD PIN 8 AND VALVE RELAY PIN 86
- VALVE RELAY PIN 87A AND MODULATOR GROUND STRAP CONNECTION ON MODULATOR PUMP
• REPLACE VALVE RELAY
0 - 2 OHMS AT ALL CHECKS
GREATER THAN 2 OHMS
CONTINUE WITH DIAGNOSIS
• REPLACE HYDRAULIC MODULATOR ASSEMBLY
GC402920051800BX

TEST CONDITIONS

1. Tested continuously.

FAILURE CONDITIONS

1. Less than 5 volts at EBCM pin 32,valve relay monitor
   or
2. Voltage at EBCM pin 32, valve relay monitor, remains high, although voltage a EBCM pin 27, valve relay control, is low (valve relay sticks).

ACTION TAKEN

1. ABS switched 'OFF'.
2. Code Set.

When the valve relay is engaged, the valve relay feedback line should be at battery voltage. With the valve relay disengaged the feedback line is at ground. If the commanded position of the valve relay and the position indicated by the feedback line do not agree, Code 63 will set. Some conditions which will cause Code 63 to set are:

- An open circuit on CKTs 851 or 879
- A short to voltage on CKTs 851 or 879
- A short to ground on CKTs 851 or 879
- A defective solenoid valve relay
- Open circuit on CKT 854.

CIRCUIT DESCRIPTION

The solenoid valve relay provides power to the three solenoid valves in the hydraulic modulator. The solenoid valve relay is located on the hydraulic modulator and may be replaced if it is found to be defective.

The valve relay is engaged during normal system operation. When the ignition is switched to RUN, the EBCM commands the solenoid valve relay on by grounding the valve relay actuation line on CKT 879 (EBCM pin 27). When this ground is provided, the valve relay is energized from the voltage supply line on CKT 854 (EBCM pin 17). The valve relay switches and battery voltage is provided to the three solenoid valves and the solenoid valve relay feedback line on CKT 851 (EBCM pin 32). The valve relay remains engaged until the ignition is turned off or a failure is detected.

Whenever the solenoid valve relay is not engaged, the ANTILOCK light will turn on. With the ignition on and the solenoid valve relay not engaged, a path to ground exists from the IGN1–ISO fuse (10 amps) thru the ANTILOCK light on CKT 139 which turns on the warning light. The ANTILOCK light can also be commanded on by the EBCM on CKT 852 (EBCM pin 29). The EBCM will provide ground on this line and turn on the warning light when a failure is detected.

ANTILOCK OPERATION

With the solenoid valve relay engaged, battery power is provided to the three solenoid valves. If antilock operation is required, the EBCM varies the amount of current supplied to the solenoid valves (EBCM pins 2, 18, 35) and the valve is positioned to provide for optimum braking.

GC402920051800AX

Fig. 84 Code 63: Solenoid Valve Relay Fault (Part 1 of 2). 1992 Eldorado, Riviera, Seville, Toronado & Trofeo

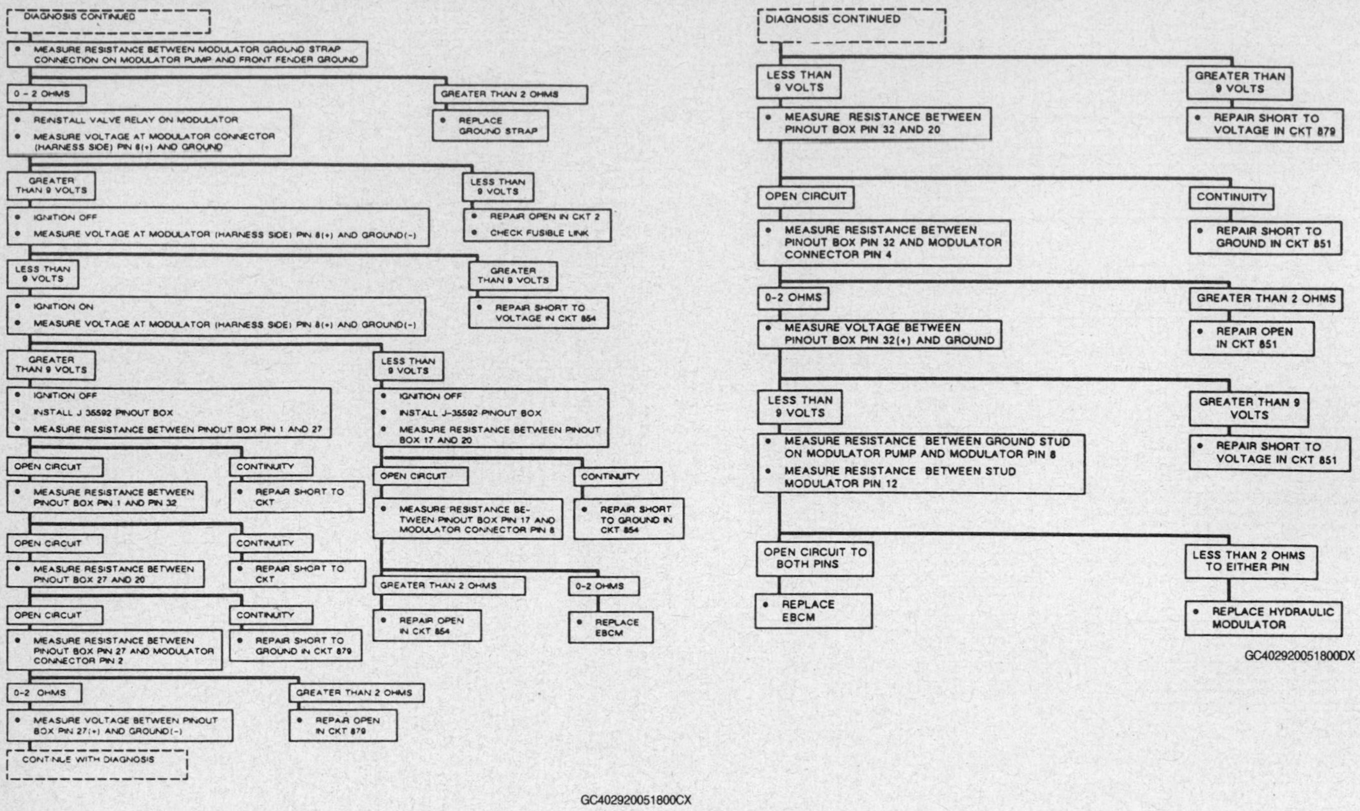
DIAGNOSIS CONTINUED
MEASURE RESISTANCE BETWEEN MODULATOR GROUND STRAP CONNECTION ON MODULATOR PUMP AND FRONT FENDER GROUND
0 – 2 OHMS
GREATER THAN 2 OHMS
REINSTALL VALVE RELAY ON MODULATOR
MEASURE VOLTAGE AT MODULATOR CONNECTOR (HARNESS SIDE) PIN 8(+) AND GROUND
REPLACE GROUND STRAP
GREATER THAN 9 VOLTS
LESS THAN 9 VOLTS
IGNITION OFF
MEASURE VOLTAGE AT MODULATOR (HARNESS SIDE) PIN 8(+) AND GROUND(–)
REPAIR OPEN IN CKT 2
CHECK FUSIBLE LINK
LESS THAN 9 VOLTS
GREATER THAN 9 VOLTS
IGNITION ON
MEASURE VOLTAGE AT MODULATOR (HARNESS SIDE) PIN 8(+) AND GROUND(–)
REPAIR SHORT TO VOLTAGE IN CKT 854
GREATER THAN 9 VOLTS
LESS THAN 9 VOLTS
IGNITION OFF
INSTALL J 35592 PINOUT BOX
MEASURE RESISTANCE BETWEEN PINOUT BOX PIN 1 AND 27
IGNITION OFF
INSTALL J-35592 PINOUT BOX
MEASURE RESISTANCE BETWEEN PINOUT BOX 17 AND 20
OPEN CIRCUIT
CONTINUITY
MEASURE RESISTANCE BETWEEN PINOUT BOX PIN 1 AND PIN 32
REPAIR SHORT TO CKT
OPEN CIRCUIT
CONTINUITY
MEASURE RESISTANCE BETWEEN PINOUT BOX PIN 17 AND MODULATOR CONNECTOR PIN 8
REPAIR SHORT TO GROUND IN CKT 854
OPEN CIRCUIT
CONTINUITY
MEASURE RESISTANCE BETWEEN PINOUT BOX 27 AND 20
REPAIR SHORT TO CKT
GREATER THAN 2 OHMS
0-2 OHMS
REPAIR OPEN IN CKT 854
REPLACE EBCM
OPEN CIRCUIT
CONTINUITY
MEASURE RESISTANCE BETWEEN PINOUT BOX PIN 27 AND MODULATOR CONNECTOR PIN 2
REPAIR SHORT TO GROUND IN CKT 879
0-2 OHMS
GREATER THAN 2 OHMS
MEASURE VOLTAGE BETWEEN PINOUT BOX PIN 27(+) AND GROUND(–)
REPAIR OPEN IN CKT 879
CONTINUE WITH DIAGNOSIS
GC402920051800CX
DIAGNOSIS CONTINUED
LESS THAN 9 VOLTS
GREATER THAN 9 VOLTS
MEASURE RESISTANCE BETWEEN PINOUT BOX PIN 32 AND 20
REPAIR SHORT TO VOLTAGE IN CKT 879
OPEN CIRCUIT
CONTINUITY
MEASURE RESISTANCE BETWEEN PINOUT BOX PIN 32 AND MODULATOR CONNECTOR PIN 4
REPAIR SHORT TO GROUND IN CKT 851
0-2 OHMS
GREATER THAN 2 OHMS
MEASURE VOLTAGE BETWEEN PINOUT BOX PIN 32(+) AND GROUND
REPAIR OPEN IN CKT 851
LESS THAN 9 VOLTS
GREATER THAN 9 VOLTS
MEASURE RESISTANCE BETWEEN GROUND STUD ON MODULATOR PUMP AND MODULATOR PIN 8
MEASURE RESISTANCE BETWEEN STUD MODULATOR PIN 12
REPAIR SHORT TO VOLTAGE IN CKT 851
OPEN CIRCUIT TO BOTH PINS
LESS THAN 2 OHMS TO EITHER PIN
REPLACE EBCM
REPLACE HYDRAULIC MODULATOR
GC402920051800DX

Fig. 84 Code 63: Solenoid Valve Relay Fault (Part 2 of 2). 1992 Eldorado, Riviera, Seville, Toronado & Trofeo

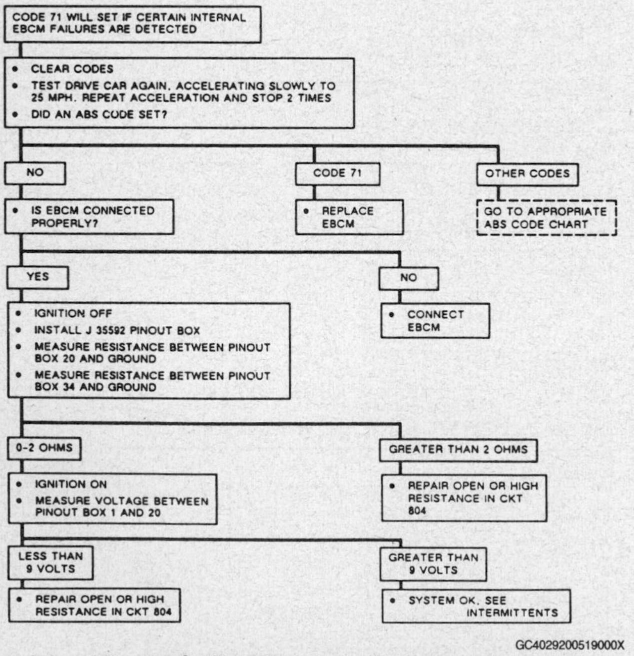
CODE 71 WILL SET IF CERTAIN INTERNAL EBCM FAILURES ARE DETECTED
CLEAR CODES
TEST DRIVE CAR AGAIN, ACCELERATING SLOWLY TO 25 MPH. REPEAT ACCELERATION AND STOP 2 TIMES
DID AN ABS CODE SET?
NO
CODE 71
OTHER CODES
IS EBCM CONNECTED PROPERLY?
REPLACE EBCM
GO TO APPROPRIATE ABS CODE CHART
YES
NO
IGNITION OFF
INSTALL J 35592 PINOUT BOX
MEASURE RESISTANCE BETWEEN PINOUT BOX 20 AND GROUND
MEASURE RESISTANCE BETWEEN PINOUT BOX 34 AND GROUND
CONNECT EBCM
0-2 OHMS
GREATER THAN 2 OHMS
IGNITION ON
MEASURE VOLTAGE BETWEEN PINOUT BOX 1 AND 20
REPAIR OPEN OR HIGH RESISTANCE IN CKT 804
LESS THAN 9 VOLTS
GREATER THAN 9 VOLTS
REPAIR OPEN OR HIGH RESISTANCE IN CKT 804
SYSTEM OK. SEE INTERMITTENTS
GC4029200519000X

Fig. 85 Code 71: EBCM Fault. 1992 Eldorado, Riviera, Seville, Toronado & Trofeo

TEST CONDITIONS

Tested continuously in Diagnostics Mode. (TECH- 1 CONNECTED)

FAILURE CONDITIONS

EBCM receives 3 consecutive invalid message during diagnostics.

ACTION TAKEN

1. Code set.
2. Transmission from and to scan tool is impossible.

CIRCUIT DESCRIPTION

An ABS Code 72 may set when there is a momentary serial data communications error between the EBCM and the TECH 1. This code may set when power to the EBCM is interrupted while the Tech–1 remains powered; such as when the ignition is cycled while the Tech–1 is hooked-up. When this occurs, simply cycle power to the Tech–1 and allow it to reset.

Although it is not an indication of a serious condition, this code should be cleared prior to completion of diagnosis.

GC4029200520000X

Fig. 86 Code 72: Serial Line Data Fault. 1992 Eldorado, Riviera, Seville, Toronado & Trofeo

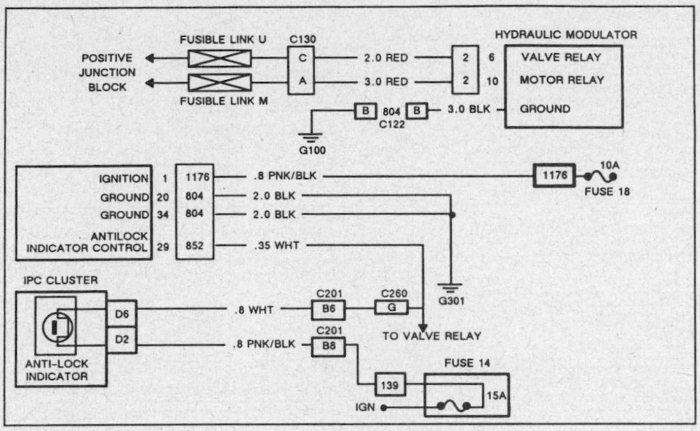
FUSIBLE LINK U
C130
HYDRAULIC MODULATOR
POSITIVE JUNCTION BLOCK
2.0 RED
3.0 RED
VALVE RELAY
MOTOR RELAY
GROUND
FUSIBLE LINK M
804
3.0 BLK
C122
G100
IGNITION
GROUND
GROUND
ANTILOCK INDICATOR CONTROL
1176
804
852
.8 PNK/BLK
2.0 BLK
.35 WHT
10A
FUSE 18
IPC CLUSTER
C201
C260
G301
.8 WHT
.8 PNK/BLK
TO VALVE RELAY
ANTI-LOCK INDICATOR
FUSE 14
139
15A
IGN

CHART A

NO SYSTEM POWER

CIRCUIT DESCRIPTION

The EBCM receives power from ABS/CCR/HW Fuse 7, (located in the interior relay center) on CKT 1176. If high system voltages occur, the EBCM is internally protected by a network of diodes which directs excess voltage to ground.

FAILURE CONDITIONS

Intermittent operation of the ANTILOCK light may be caused by intermittent voltage levels which do not correspond to the proper operating range of the Antilock Brake System. Some conditions which may cause a lack of system power are:

- Improper electrical contact of the EBCM connector.
- Low system voltage.
- Improper electrical contact of the vehicle power and ground connections.

GC402920052100AX

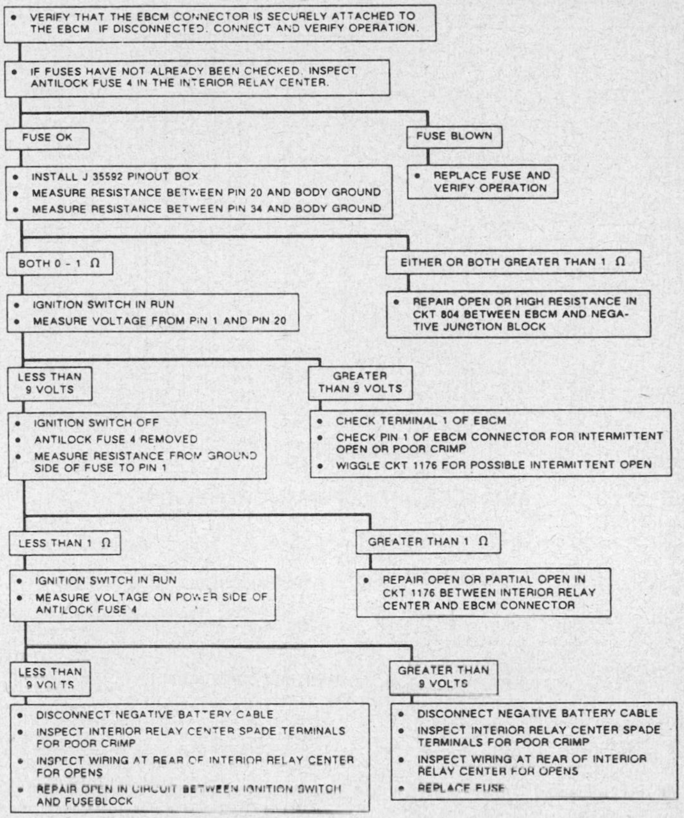
VERIFY THAT THE EBCM CONNECTOR IS SECURELY ATTACHED TO THE EBCM. IF DISCONNECTED, CONNECT AND VERIFY OPERATION.
IF FUSES HAVE NOT ALREADY BEEN CHECKED, INSPECT ANTILOCK FUSE 4 IN THE INTERIOR RELAY CENTER.
FUSE OK
FUSE BLOWN
INSTALL J 35592 PINOUT BOX
MEASURE RESISTANCE BETWEEN PIN 20 AND BODY GROUND
MEASURE RESISTANCE BETWEEN PIN 34 AND BODY GROUND
REPLACE FUSE AND VERIFY OPERATION
BOTH 0 - 1 Ω
EITHER OR BOTH GREATER THAN 1 Ω
IGNITION SWITCH IN RUN
MEASURE VOLTAGE FROM PIN 1 AND PIN 20
REPAIR OPEN OR HIGH RESISTANCE IN CKT 804 BETWEEN EBCM AND NEGATIVE JUNCTION BLOCK
LESS THAN 9 VOLTS
GREATER THAN 9 VOLTS
IGNITION SWITCH OFF
ANTILOCK FUSE 4 REMOVED
MEASURE RESISTANCE FROM GROUND SIDE OF FUSE TO PIN 1
CHECK TERMINAL 1 OF EBCM
CHECK PIN 1 OF EBCM CONNECTOR FOR INTERMITTENT OPEN OR POOR CRIMP
WIGGLE CKT 1176 FOR POSSIBLE INTERMITTENT OPEN
LESS THAN 1 Ω
GREATER THAN 1 Ω
IGNITION SWITCH IN RUN
MEASURE VOLTAGE ON POWER SIDE OF ANTILOCK FUSE 4
REPAIR OPEN OR PARTIAL OPEN IN CKT 1176 BETWEEN INTERIOR RELAY CENTER AND EBCM CONNECTOR
LESS THAN 9 VOLTS
GREATER THAN 9 VOLTS
DISCONNECT NEGATIVE BATTERY CABLE
INSPECT INTERIOR RELAY CENTER SPADE TERMINALS FOR POOR CRIMP
INSPECT WIRING AT REAR OF INTERIOR RELAY CENTER FOR OPENS
REPAIR OPEN IN CIRCUIT BETWEEN IGNITION SWITCH AND FUSEBLOCK
DISCONNECT NEGATIVE BATTERY CABLE
INSPECT INTERIOR RELAY CENTER SPADE TERMINALS FOR POOR CRIMP
INSPECT WIRING AT REAR OF INTERIOR RELAY CENTER FOR OPENS
REPLACE FUSE

GC402920052100BX

Fig. 87 Test A: No System Power. 1992 Eldorado, Riviera, Seville, Toronado & Trofeo

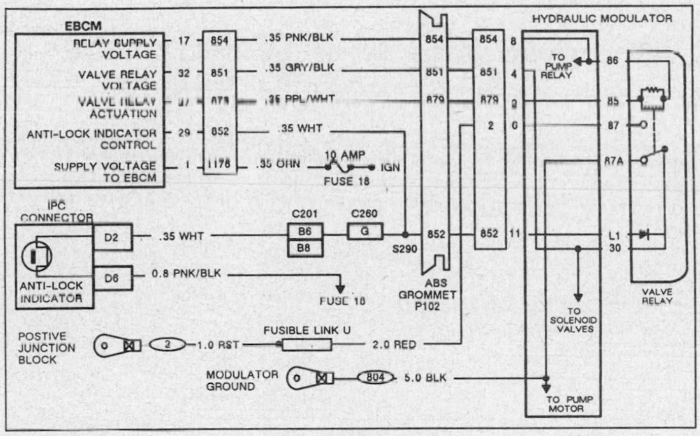
EBCM
HYDRAULIC MODULATOR
RELAY SUPPLY VOLTAGE
VALVE RELAY VOLTAGE
VALVE RELAY ACTUATION
ANTI-LOCK INDICATOR CONTROL
SUPPLY VOLTAGE TO EBCM
.35 PNK/BLK
.35 GRY/BLK
.35 PPL/WHT
.35 WHT
.35 ORN
10 AMP
FUSE 18
IGN
TO PUMP RELAY
IPC CONNECTOR
C201
C260
.35 WHT
0.8 PNK/BLK
ANTI-LOCK INDICATOR
FUSE 18
S290
ABS GROMMET P102
TO SOLENOID VALVES
VALVE RELAY
POSTIVE JUNCTION BLOCK
FUSIBLE LINK U
1.0 RST
2.0 RED
MODULATOR GROUND
5.0 BLK
TO PUMP MOTOR

CHART B

ABS LIGHT ON, NO CODES SET

CIRCUIT DESCRIPTION

The amber ANTILOCK light is located below the instrument panel cluster. It may be illuminated by the EBCM or a path to ground in the valve relay on the hydraulic modulator.

The ANTILOCK light is powered by the Ignition 1 feed and receives power anytime the ignition switch is turned to RUN or START. Power is provided on CKT 39 through the 15 amp Fuse 14 located in the fuse block.

LIGHT OPERATION - VALVE RELAY GROUND

The ANTILOCK light is illuminated anytime the valve relay is not enabled. When the relay is not enabled, the light is grounded through CKT 852 and the valve relay to the modulator ground. During normal operation (no fault conditions found), the valve will switch and the ground will be removed, and the ANTILOCK light will turn off. The ABS light is on whenever the EBCM is disconnected.

LIGHT OPERATION - EBCM GROUND

If the EBCM detects a fault in the ABS, the EBCM can turn on the ANTILOCK light by grounding pin 29. A ground path exists for the light through CKT 852. The EBCM will disable the valve relay when CKT 852 is grounded at pin 29.

NOTE: It is best to check for codes using a TECH-1. It is possible that a valve (Code 41, 45, 55 and 63) may have set. It is **NOT** possible to flash codes when a valve code is present.

FAILURE CONDITIONS

The chart on the next page addresses conditions which result in continuous operation of the ANTILOCK light. If the ANTILOCK light is on and no codes can be extracted from the EBCM, the EBCM connector should be checked for proper connection and system power should be checked.

GC402920052200AX

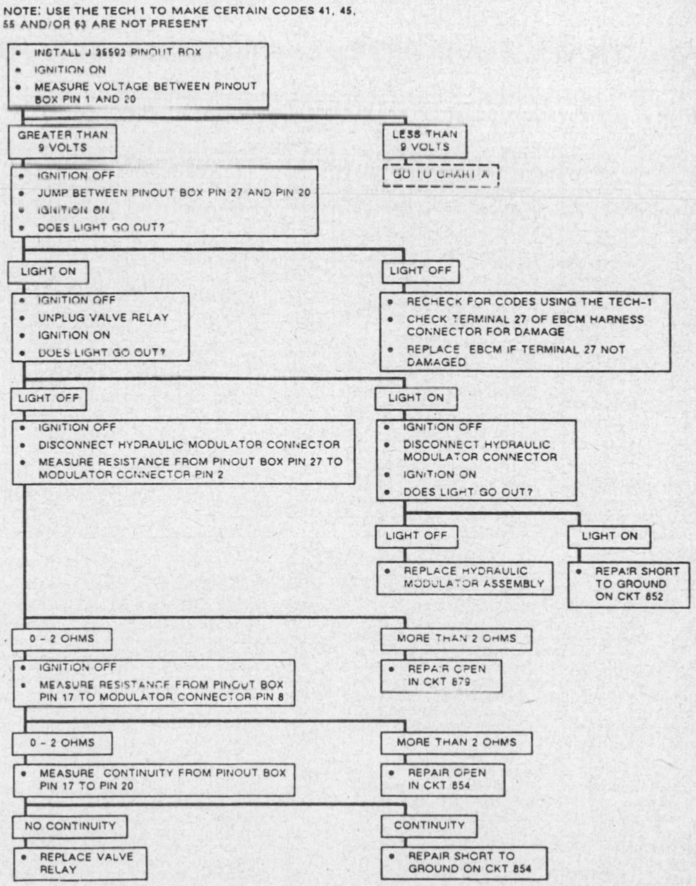
NOTE: USE THE TECH 1 TO MAKE CERTAIN CODES 41, 45, 55 AND/OR 63 ARE NOT PRESENT
INSTALL J 35592 PINOUT BOX
IGNITION ON
MEASURE VOLTAGE BETWEEN PINOUT BOX PIN 1 AND 20
GREATER THAN 9 VOLTS
LESS THAN 9 VOLTS
GO TO CHART A
IGNITION OFF
JUMP BETWEEN PINOUT BOX PIN 27 AND PIN 20
IGNITION ON
DOES LIGHT GO OUT?
LIGHT ON
LIGHT OFF
IGNITION OFF
UNPLUG VALVE RELAY
IGNITION ON
DOES LIGHT GO OUT?
RECHECK FOR CODES USING THE TECH-1
CHECK TERMINAL 27 OF EBCM HARNESS CONNECTOR FOR DAMAGE
REPLACE EBCM IF TERMINAL 27 NOT DAMAGED
LIGHT OFF
LIGHT ON
IGNITION OFF
DISCONNECT HYDRAULIC MODULATOR CONNECTOR
MEASURE RESISTANCE FROM PINOUT BOX PIN 27 TO MODULATOR CONNECTOR PIN 2
IGNITION OFF
DISCONNECT HYDRAULIC MODULATOR CONNECTOR
IGNITION ON
DOES LIGHT GO OUT?
LIGHT OFF
LIGHT ON
REPLACE HYDRAULIC MODULATOR ASSEMBLY
REPAIR SHORT TO GROUND ON CKT 852
0 - 2 OHMS
MORE THAN 2 OHMS
IGNITION OFF
MEASURE RESISTANCE FROM PINOUT BOX PIN 17 TO MODULATOR CONNECTOR PIN 8
REPAIR OPEN IN CKT 879
0 - 2 OHMS
MORE THAN 2 OHMS
MEASURE CONTINUITY FROM PINOUT BOX PIN 17 TO PIN 20
REPAIR OPEN IN CKT 854
NO CONTINUITY
CONTINUITY
REPLACE VALVE RELAY
REPAIR SHORT TO GROUND ON CKT 854

GC402920052200BX

Fig. 88 Test B: ABS Indicator On w/No Codes Set. 1992 Eldorado, Riviera, Seville, Toronado & Trofeo

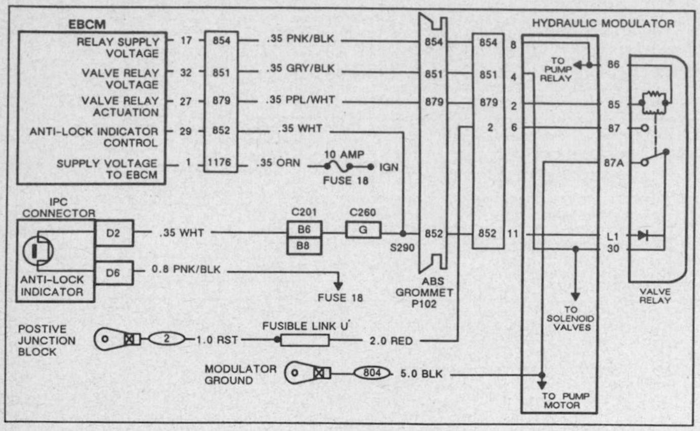
EBCM
RELAY SUPPLY VOLTAGE
VALVE RELAY VOLTAGE
VALVE RELAY ACTUATION
ANTI-LOCK INDICATOR CONTROL
SUPPLY VOLTAGE TO EBCM
17
32
27
29
1
854
851
879
852
1176
.35 PNK/BLK
.35 GRY/BLK
.35 PPL/WHT
.35 WHT
.35 ORN
10 AMP
FUSE 18
IGN
HYDRAULIC MODULATOR
TO PUMP RELAY
86
85
87
87A
L1
30
VALVE RELAY
TO SOLENOID VALVES
TO PUMP MOTOR
IPC CONNECTOR
ANTI-LOCK INDICATOR
D2
D6
.35 WHT
0.8 PNK/BLK
C201
C260
B6
B8
G
S290
FUSE 18
ABS GROMMET P102
POSTIVE JUNCTION BLOCK
FUSIBLE LINK U
1.0 RST
2.0 RED
MODULATOR GROUND
804
5.0 BLK

CHART C

ANTILOCK LIGHT INOPERATIVE AT KEY-ON

CIRCUIT DESCRIPTION

The amber ANTILOCK light is located below the instrument panel cluster. It may be illuminated by the EBCM or a path to ground in the valve relay on the hydraulic modulator.

The ANTILOCK light is powered by the Ignition 1 feed and receives power anytime the ignition switch is turned to RUN or START. Power is provided on CKT 39 through the 15 amp Fuse 14 located in the fuse block.

LIGHT OPERATION - VALVE RELAY GROUND

The ANTILOCK light is illuminated anytime the valve relay is not enabled. When the relay is not enabled, the light is grounded through CKT 852 and the valve relay to the modulator ground. During normal operation (no fault conditions found), the valve will switch and the ground will be removed, and the ANTILOCK light will turn off.

LIGHT OPERATION - EBCM GROUND

Whether the valve relay is engaged or not, the EBCM can turn on the ANTILOCK light by grounding pin 29. A ground path exists for the light through CKT 852.

FAILURE CONDITIONS

The chart on the next page addresses conditions which result in no ANTILOCK light operation; the ABS operates properly. As described at the beginning of this section, the ANTILOCK light should illuminate for a minimum of four seconds when the key is moved from 'OFF' to RUN. This chart addresses conditions such as lack of power to the ANTILOCK light which would prevent the light from turning on. This condition could prevent the EBCM from turning on the light in the event of an antilock failure.

GC402920052300AX

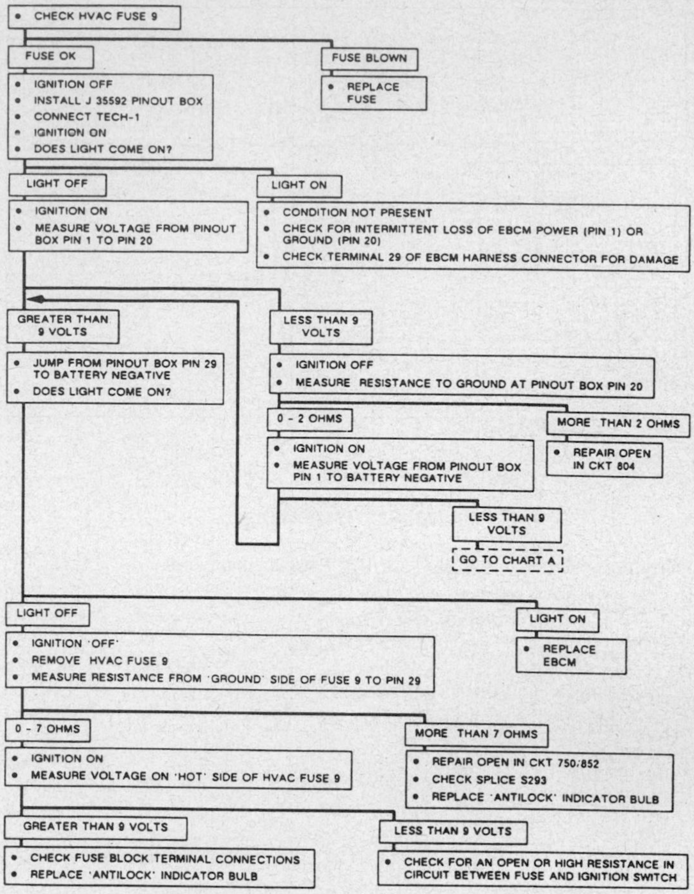
CHECK HVAC FUSE 9
FUSE OK
FUSE BLOWN
REPLACE FUSE
IGNITION OFF
INSTALL J 35592 PINOUT BOX
CONNECT TECH-1
IGNITION ON
DOES LIGHT COME ON?
LIGHT OFF
LIGHT ON
IGNITION ON
MEASURE VOLTAGE FROM PINOUT BOX PIN 1 TO PIN 20
CONDITION NOT PRESENT
CHECK FOR INTERMITTENT LOSS OF EBCM POWER (PIN 1) OR GROUND (PIN 20)
CHECK TERMINAL 29 OF EBCM HARNESS CONNECTOR FOR DAMAGE
GREATER THAN 9 VOLTS
LESS THAN 9 VOLTS
JUMP FROM PINOUT BOX PIN 29 TO BATTERY NEGATIVE
DOES LIGHT COME ON?
IGNITION OFF
MEASURE RESISTANCE TO GROUND AT PINOUT BOX PIN 20
0 - 2 OHMS
MORE THAN 2 OHMS
IGNITION ON
MEASURE VOLTAGE FROM PINOUT BOX PIN 1 TO BATTERY NEGATIVE
REPAIR OPEN IN CKT 804
LESS THAN 9 VOLTS
GO TO CHART A
LIGHT OFF
LIGHT ON
IGNITION 'OFF'
REMOVE HVAC FUSE 9
MEASURE RESISTANCE FROM 'GROUND' SIDE OF FUSE 9 TO PIN 29
REPLACE EBCM
0 - 7 OHMS
MORE THAN 7 OHMS
IGNITION ON
MEASURE VOLTAGE ON 'HOT' SIDE OF HVAC FUSE 9
REPAIR OPEN IN CKT 750/852
CHECK SPLICE S293
REPLACE 'ANTILOCK' INDICATOR BULB
GREATER THAN 9 VOLTS
LESS THAN 9 VOLTS
CHECK FUSE BLOCK TERMINAL CONNECTIONS
REPLACE 'ANTILOCK' INDICATOR BULB
CHECK FOR AN OPEN OR HIGH RESISTANCE IN CIRCUIT BETWEEN FUSE AND IGNITION SWITCH

GC402920052300BX

Fig. 89 Test C: ABS Indicator Inoperative At Key On. 1992 Eldorado, Riviera, Seville, Toronado & Trofeo

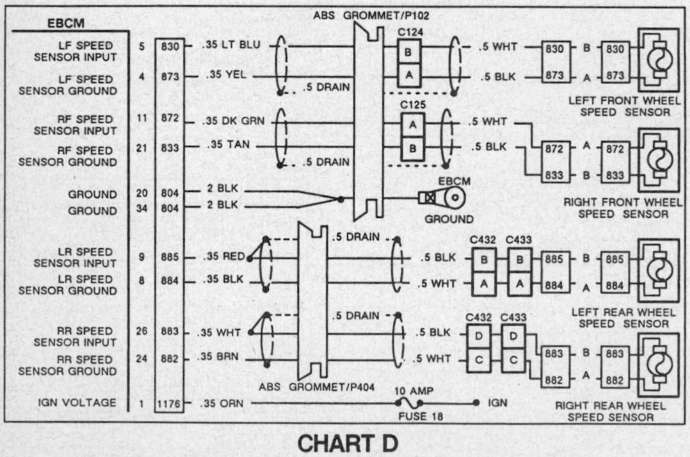
EBCM
LF SPEED SENSOR INPUT
LF SPEED SENSOR GROUND
RF SPEED SENSOR INPUT
RF SPEED SENSOR GROUND
GROUND
GROUND
LR SPEED SENSOR INPUT
LR SPEED SENSOR GROUND
RR SPEED SENSOR INPUT
RR SPEED SENSOR GROUND
IGN VOLTAGE
ABS GROMMET/P102
C124
C125
.35 LT BLU
.35 YEL
.5 DRAIN
.35 DK GRN
.35 TAN
2 BLK
.35 RED
.35 BLK
.35 WHT
.35 BRN
.35 ORN
.5 WHT
.5 BLK
LEFT FRONT WHEEL SPEED SENSOR
RIGHT FRONT WHEEL SPEED SENSOR
EBCM GROUND
C432
C433
LEFT REAR WHEEL SPEED SENSOR
RIGHT REAR WHEEL SPEED SENSOR
ABS GROMMET/P404
10 AMP
FUSE 18
IGN

CHART D

VALVE CYCLING (CHATTER) DURING NORMAL STOPS

CIRCUIT DESCRIPTION

As each wheel turns, the wheel speed sensor for that wheel creates a small AC voltage as a toothed sensor ring, mounted on the front suspension knuckle or in the rear integral hub/bearing assembly, is passed by the stationary sensor. The sensor consists of a permanent magnet and coil and generates voltage by magnetic induction. The frequency of the wheel speed sensor signal is proportional to wheel speed.

The EBCM uses the wheel speed sensor signal to calculate vehicle reference speeds and individual speed, acceleration and slip values for each wheel. These values are used to determine when antilock control is required.

The EBCM performs two basic types of checks on the wheel speed sensors, these are sensor continuity and sensor output.

WHEEL SPEED SENSOR CABLES

In order to prevent electromagnetic interference from disturbing the wheel speed sensor signal, the sensor cables are protected with grounded shielding (indicated by dashed lines in the above schematic). This shield surrounds the two individual sensor wires. A black conduit surrounds the wires and shield. When servicing the sensor cables, the sensor wires are accessible by separating the shielding. If the shielding is disturbed, repair as required.

NOTES ON CHART D

1. The wheel speed sensor output should gradually increase with vehicle speed. There should be no skips or jumps. All four wheel speed sensor outputs should be identical. On a slow down, one of the signals may drop off faster than the others, indicating a lock-up condition or a problem with the speed sensor air gap, wiring, or sensor itself.

GC402920052400AX

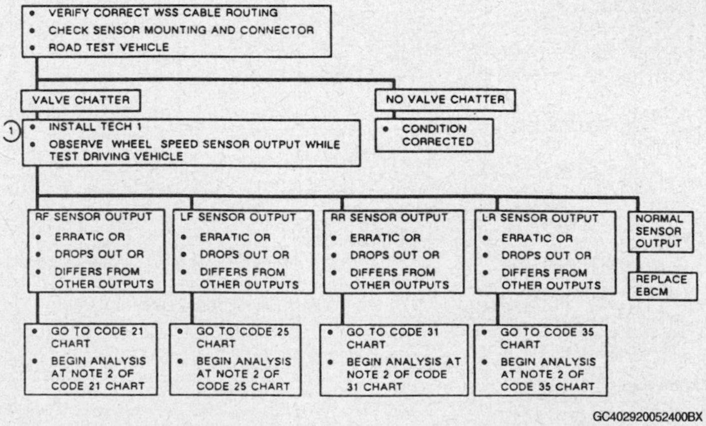
VERIFY CORRECT WSS CABLE ROUTING
CHECK SENSOR MOUNTING AND CONNECTOR
ROAD TEST VEHICLE
VALVE CHATTER
NO VALVE CHATTER
1
INSTALL TECH 1
OBSERVE WHEEL SPEED SENSOR OUTPUT WHILE TEST DRIVING VEHICLE
CONDITION CORRECTED
RF SENSOR OUTPUT
LF SENSOR OUTPUT
RR SENSOR OUTPUT
LR SENSOR OUTPUT
ERRATIC OR
DROPS OUT OR
DIFFERS FROM OTHER OUTPUTS
NORMAL SENSOR OUTPUT
REPLACE EBCM
GO TO CODE 21 CHART
BEGIN ANALYSIS AT NOTE 2 OF CODE 21 CHART
GO TO CODE 25 CHART
BEGIN ANALYSIS AT NOTE 2 OF CODE 25 CHART
GO TO CODE 31 CHART
BEGIN ANALYSIS AT NOTE 2 OF CODE 31 CHART
GO TO CODE 35 CHART
BEGIN ANALYSIS AT NOTE 2 OF CODE 35 CHART

GC402920052400BX

Fig. 90 Test D: Valve Cycling During Normal Stops. 1992 Eldorado, Riviera, Seville, Toronado & Trofeo

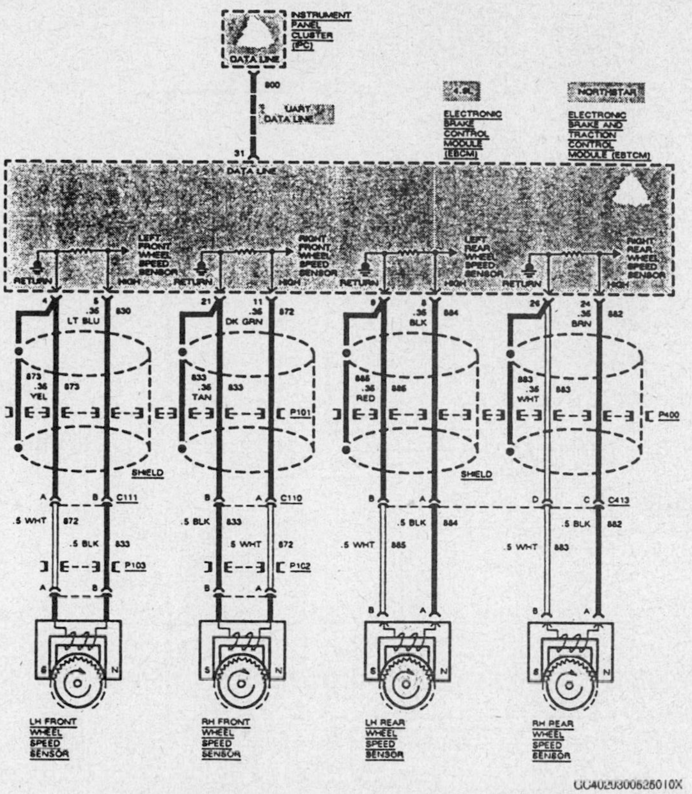
INSTRUMENT PANEL CLUSTER (IPC)
DATA LINE
UART DATA LINE
ELECTRONIC BRAKE CONTROL MODULE (EBCM)
NORTHSTAR
ELECTRONIC BRAKE AND TRACTION CONTROL MODULE (EBTCM)
LEFT FRONT WHEEL SPEED SENSOR
RIGHT FRONT WHEEL SPEED SENSOR
LEFT REAR WHEEL SPEED SENSOR
RIGHT REAR WHEEL SPEED SENSOR
RETURN
HIGH
SHIELD
LH FRONT WHEEL SPEED SENSOR
RH FRONT WHEEL SPEED SENSOR
LH REAR WHEEL SPEED SENSOR
RH REAR WHEEL SPEED SENSOR
GC4020300626010X

Fig. 91 ABS & TCS wiring circuit (Part 1 of 3). 1993-94 DeVille, Eldorado & Seville w/4.6L engine

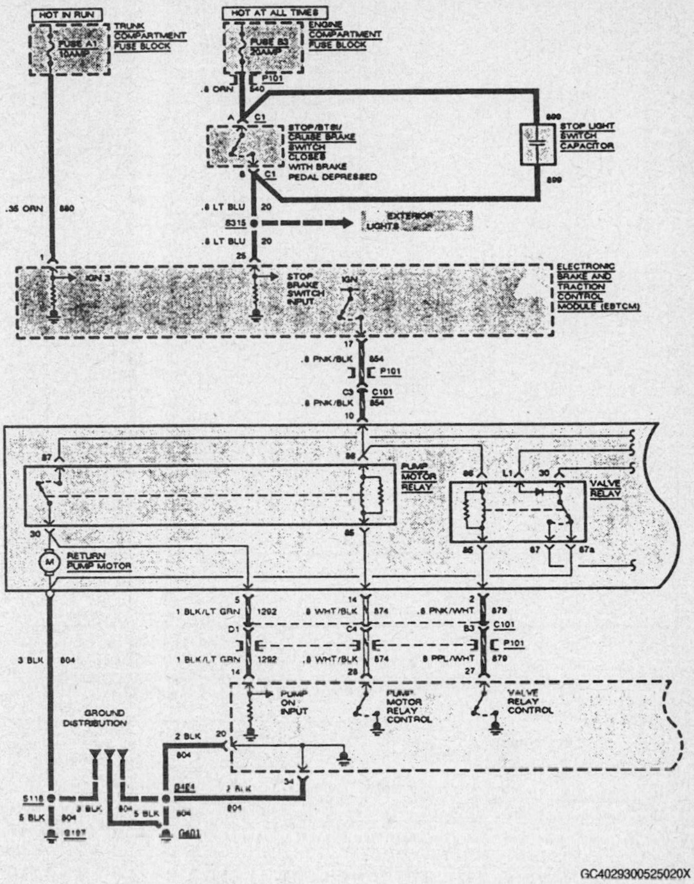
HOT IN RUN
TRUNK COMPARTMENT FUSE BLOCK
HOT AT ALL TIMES
ENGINE COMPARTMENT FUSE BLOCK
STOP/BTSI/ CRUISE BRAKE SWITCH CLOSES WITH BRAKE PEDAL DEPRESSED
STOP LIGHT SWITCH CAPACITOR
EXTERIOR LIGHTS
ELECTRONIC BRAKE AND TRACTION CONTROL MODULE (EBTCM)
STOP BRAKE SWITCH INPUT
PUMP MOTOR RELAY
VALVE RELAY
RETURN PUMP MOTOR
PUMP ON INPUT
PUMP MOTOR RELAY CONTROL
VALVE RELAY CONTROL
GROUND DISTRIBUTION
GC4029300525020X

Fig. 91 ABS & TCS wiring circuit (Part 2 of 3). 1993-94 DeVille, Eldorado & Seville w/4.6L engine

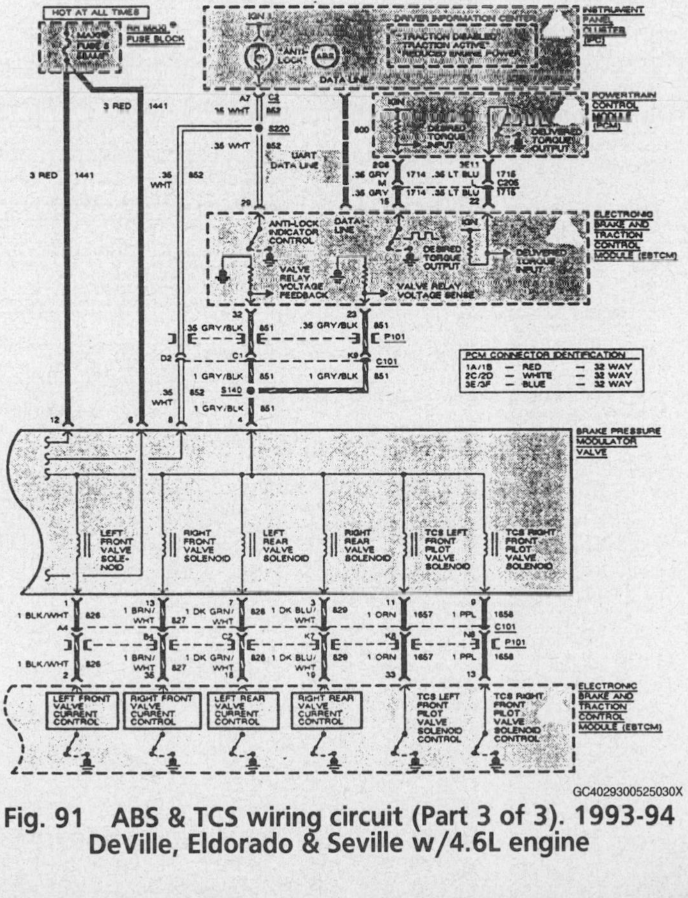
HOT AT ALL TIMES
RH MAXI FUSE BLOCK
INSTRUMENT PANEL CLUSTER (IPC)
DRIVER INFORMATION CENTER
DATA LINE
POWERTRAIN CONTROL MODULE (PCM)
DESIRED TORQUE INPUT
DELIVERED TORQUE OUTPUT
UART DATA LINE
ELECTRONIC BRAKE AND TRACTION CONTROL MODULE (EBTCM)
ANTI-LOCK INDICATOR CONTROL
VALVE RELAY VOLTAGE FEEDBACK
DESIRED TORQUE OUTPUT
DELIVERED TORQUE INPUT
VALVE RELAY VOLTAGE SENSE
PCM CONNECTOR IDENTIFICATION
1A/1B — RED — 32 WAY
2C/2D — WHITE — 32 WAY
3E/3F — BLUE — 32 WAY
BRAKE PRESSURE MODULATOR VALVE
LEFT FRONT VALVE SOLENOID
RIGHT FRONT VALVE SOLENOID
LEFT REAR VALVE SOLENOID
RIGHT REAR VALVE SOLENOID
TCS LEFT FRONT PILOT VALVE SOLENOID
TCS RIGHT FRONT PILOT VALVE SOLENOID
LEFT FRONT VALVE CURRENT CONTROL
RIGHT FRONT VALVE CURRENT CONTROL
LEFT REAR VALVE CURRENT CONTROL
RIGHT REAR VALVE CURRENT CONTROL
TCS LEFT FRONT PILOT VALVE SOLENOID CONTROL
TCS RIGHT FRONT PILOT VALVE SOLENOID CONTROL
GC4029300525030X

Fig. 91 ABS & TCS wiring circuit (Part 3 of 3). 1993-94 DeVille, Eldorado & Seville w/4.6L engine

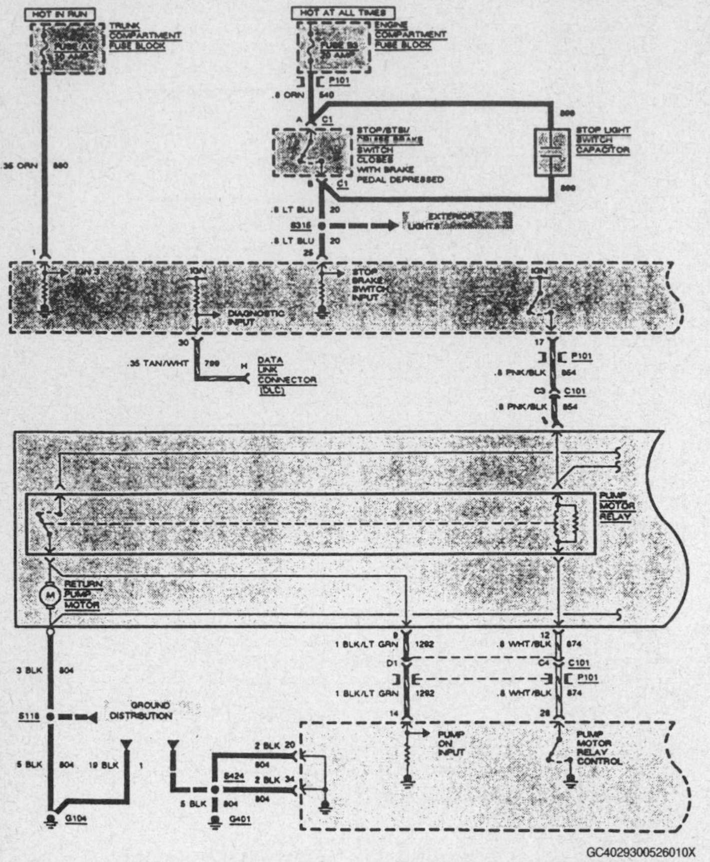
HOT IN RUN
TRUNK COMPARTMENT FUSE BLOCK
HOT AT ALL TIMES
ENGINE COMPARTMENT FUSE BLOCK
STOP/TCC/ CRUISE BRAKE SWITCH CLOSES WITH BRAKE PEDAL DEPRESSED
STOP LIGHT SWITCH CAPACITOR
EXTERIOR LIGHTS
DIAGNOSTIC INPUT
DATA LINK CONNECTOR (DLC)
PUMP MOTOR RELAY
RETURN PUMP MOTOR
GROUND DISTRIBUTION
PUMP ON INPUT
PUMP MOTOR RELAY CONTROL
GC4029300526010X

Fig. 92 ABS & TCS wiring circuit (Part 1 of 2). 1993-94 DeVille, Eldorado & Seville w/4.9L engine

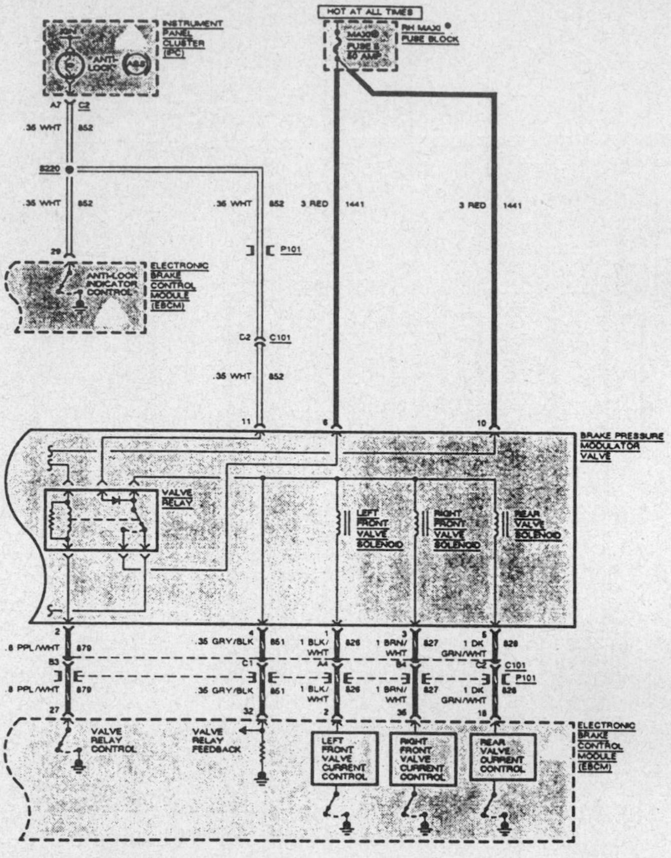
INSTRUMENT PANEL CLUSTER (IPC)
HOT AT ALL TIMES
RH MAXI FUSE BLOCK
ELECTRONIC BRAKE CONTROL MODULE (EBCM)
ANTI-LOCK INDICATOR CONTROL
BRAKE PRESSURE MODULATOR VALVE
VALVE RELAY
LEFT FRONT VALVE SOLENOID
RIGHT FRONT VALVE SOLENOID
REAR VALVE SOLENOID
VALVE RELAY CONTROL
VALVE RELAY FEEDBACK
LEFT FRONT VALVE CURRENT CONTROL
RIGHT FRONT VALVE CURRENT CONTROL
REAR VALVE CURRENT CONTROL
GC4029300526020X

Fig. 92 ABS & TCS wiring circuit (Part 2 of 2). 1993-94 DeVille, Eldorado & Seville w/4.9L engine

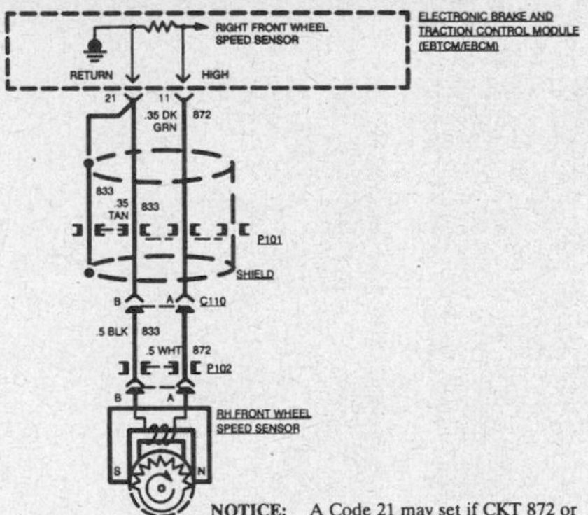
RIGHT FRONT WHEEL SPEED SENSOR
ELECTRONIC BRAKE AND TRACTION CONTROL MODULE (EBTCM/EBCM)
RETURN
HIGH
SHIELD
P101
C110
P102
RH FRONT WHEEL SPEED SENSOR

CIRCUIT DESCRIPTION:

As each wheel turns, the wheel speed sensor for that wheel creates a small AC voltage as a toothed sensor ring, mounted in the front integral hub/bearing assembly, is passed by the stationary sensor. The sensor consists of a permanent magnet and coil and generates voltage by magnetic induction. The frequency of the wheel speed sensor signal is proportional to wheel speed.

The EBTCM/EBCM uses the wheel speed sensor signal to calculate vehicle reference speeds and individual speed, acceleration and slip values for each wheel. These values are used to determine when antilock control is required.

The EBTCM/EBCM will only set one wheel speed sensor fault code at a time, even if multiple faults exist. Detection is prioritized accordingly: LF, RR, LR, RF. Always check for additional stored codes after making repairs.

TEST CONDITION(S):

1. Tested continuously.

FAILURE CONDITION(S):

Sensor Output

1. Drive–away: Speed signal is not detected when vehicle reaches 12 kph or 7.5 mph.
2. While Driving: Speed signal is lost while vehicle speed is greater than 40 kph or 25 mph.

ACTION TAKEN:

1. Code set.
2. ABS/TCS switched 'OFF'.
3. 'ANTILOCK' indicator 'ON'.
4. 'TRACTION DISABLED' message displayed.

Code 31 is set if there is a short to voltage or ground in CKT 882 or 883, or faulty speed sensor. The testing for this fault occurs when the vehicle is in motion, it will not set with the ignition 'ON' and the vehicle at rest.

NOTICE: A Code 21 may set if CKT 872 or 833 lose continuity and the WSS signal is lost while driving. A Code 23 should accompany this code on the subsequent ignition cycle. If both Code 21 and Code 23 are set concurrently, diagnose Code 23 first.

TEST DESCRIPTION: Test numbers refer to circled numbers on the diagnostic chart.

1. Checks if the code resets during a road test.
2. Use the TECH 1 to check for sources of induced electrical noise. Some sources of induced electrical noise which may cause intermittent wheel speed sensor codes to set are: improper routing or sensor cables next to spark plug wires; cables not retained in brackets; loose fitting or improperly mounted sensors; damaged sensors or toothed rings; poor terminal engagement of connectors; or intermittent shorts or opens in wiring; or a loss of sensor circuit shield.
3. Checks for damaged wheel speed sensor circuit shield. The shield is a foil insulator that is wrapped around the wheel speed sensor circuits. Inside the EBTCM/EBCM harness connecter there is an uninsulated drain wire that is attached to the shield and jumped to the wheel speed sensor return line and taken to ground through the EBTCM/EBCM. A shield which has lost its ground through the EBTCM/EBCM leaves the sensor signal circuit susceptible to noise. It may be necessary to disassemble the EBTCM/EBCM connector to check if the drain wire has a poor connection with the wheel speed sensor return connector terminal. The shield can be repaired by redetermining the sensor return line circuit, including the drain wire.
4. Checks for intermittent opens/shorts in wheel speed sensor circuits and cables.

GC4029300527010X

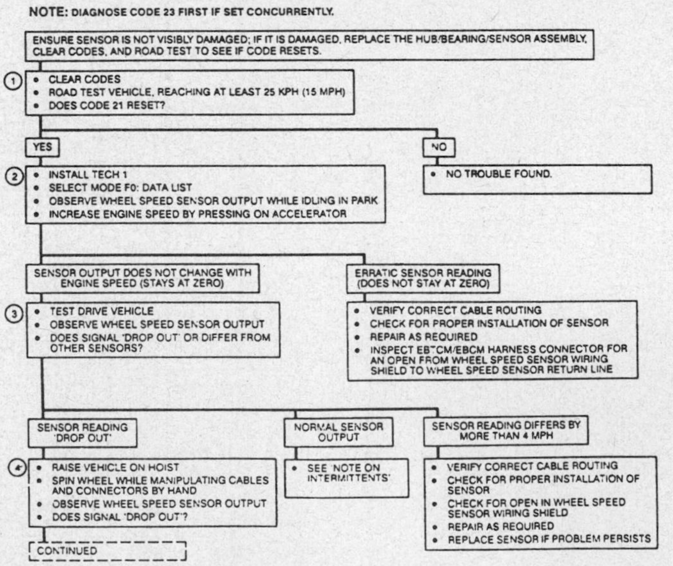
NOTE: DIAGNOSE CODE 23 FIRST IF SET CONCURRENTLY.
ENSURE SENSOR IS NOT VISIBLY DAMAGED; IF IT IS DAMAGED, REPLACE THE HUB/BEARING/SENSOR ASSEMBLY, CLEAR CODES, AND ROAD TEST TO SEE IF CODE RESETS.
1
• CLEAR CODES
• ROAD TEST VEHICLE, REACHING AT LEAST 25 KPH (15 MPH)
• DOES CODE 21 RESET?
YES
NO
• NO TROUBLE FOUND.
2
• INSTALL TECH 1
• SELECT MODE F0: DATA LIST
• OBSERVE WHEEL SPEED SENSOR OUTPUT WHILE IDLING IN PARK
• INCREASE ENGINE SPEED BY PRESSING ON ACCELERATOR
SENSOR OUTPUT DOES NOT CHANGE WITH ENGINE SPEED (STAYS AT ZERO)
ERRATIC SENSOR READING (DOES NOT STAY AT ZERO)
3
• TEST DRIVE VEHICLE
• OBSERVE WHEEL SPEED SENSOR OUTPUT
• DOES SIGNAL 'DROP OUT' OR DIFFER FROM OTHER SENSORS?
• VERIFY CORRECT CABLE ROUTING
• CHECK FOR PROPER INSTALLATION OF SENSOR
• REPAIR AS REQUIRED
• INSPECT EBTCM/EBCM HARNESS CONNECTOR FOR AN OPEN FROM WHEEL SPEED SENSOR WIRING SHIELD TO WHEEL SPEED SENSOR RETURN LINE
SENSOR READING 'DROP OUT'
NORMAL SENSOR OUTPUT
SENSOR READING DIFFERS BY MORE THAN 4 MPH
4
• RAISE VEHICLE ON HOIST
• SPIN WHEEL WHILE MANIPULATING CABLES AND CONNECTORS BY HAND
• OBSERVE WHEEL SPEED SENSOR OUTPUT
• DOES SIGNAL 'DROP OUT'?
• SEE 'NOTE ON INTERMITTENTS'
• VERIFY CORRECT CABLE ROUTING
• CHECK FOR PROPER INSTALLATION OF SENSOR
• CHECK FOR OPEN IN WHEEL SPEED SENSOR WIRING SHIELD
• REPAIR AS REQUIRED
• REPLACE SENSOR IF PROBLEM PERSISTS
CONTINUED
GC4029300527020X

Fig. 93 Code 21: Right Front Wheel Speed Sensor Fault (Part 1 of 2). 1993-94 DeVille, Eldorado & Seville

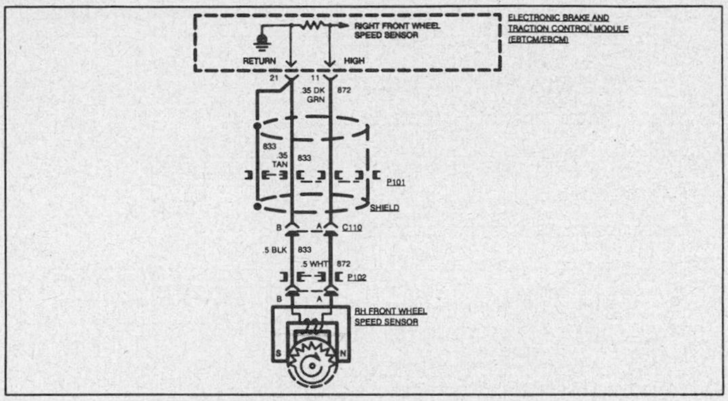
RIGHT FRONT WHEEL SPEED SENSOR
ELECTRONIC BRAKE AND TRACTION CONTROL MODULE (EBTCM/EBCM)
RETURN
HIGH
21
11
.35 DK GRN
872
833
.35 TAN
833
P101
SHIELD
B
A
C110
.5 BLK
833
.5 WHT
872
P102
B
A
RH FRONT WHEEL SPEED SENSOR
S
N

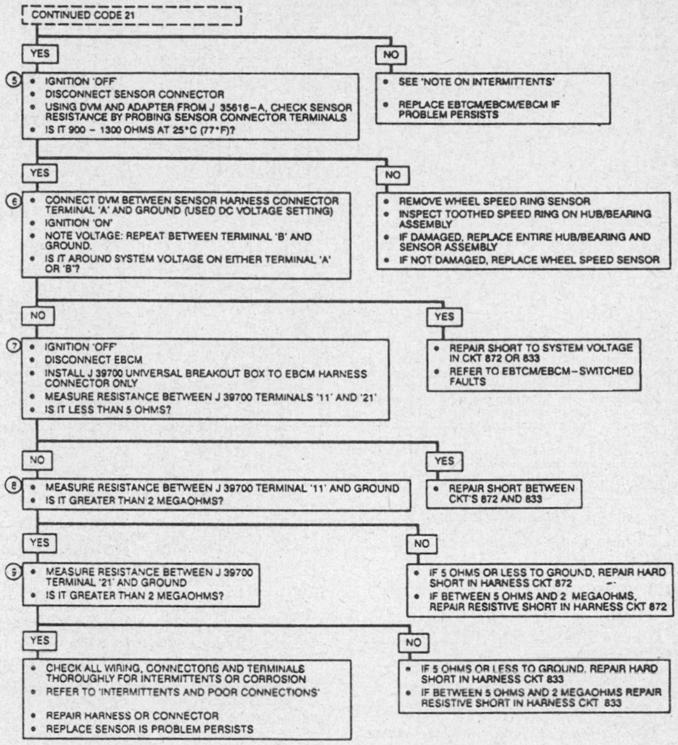
CONTINUED CODE 21
YES
NO
5
• IGNITION 'OFF'
• DISCONNECT SENSOR CONNECTOR
• USING DVM AND ADAPTER FROM J 35616-A, CHECK SENSOR RESISTANCE BY PROBING SENSOR CONNECTOR TERMINALS
• IS IT 900 - 1300 OHMS AT 25°C (77°F)?
• SEE 'NOTE ON INTERMITTENTS'
• REPLACE EBTCM/EBCM/EBCM IF PROBLEM PERSISTS
YES
NO
6
• CONNECT DVM BETWEEN SENSOR HARNESS CONNECTOR TERMINAL 'A' AND GROUND (USED DC VOLTAGE SETTING)
• IGNITION 'ON'
• NOTE VOLTAGE: REPEAT BETWEEN TERMINAL 'B' AND GROUND.
• IS IT AROUND SYSTEM VOLTAGE ON EITHER TERMINAL 'A' OR 'B'?
• REMOVE WHEEL SPEED RING SENSOR
• INSPECT TOOTHED SPEED RING ON HUB/BEARING ASSEMBLY
• IF DAMAGED, REPLACE ENTIRE HUB/BEARING AND SENSOR ASSEMBLY
• IF NOT DAMAGED, REPLACE WHEEL SPEED SENSOR
NO
YES
7
• IGNITION 'OFF'
• DISCONNECT EBCM
• INSTALL J 39700 UNIVERSAL BREAKOUT BOX TO EBCM HARNESS CONNECTOR ONLY
• MEASURE RESISTANCE BETWEEN J 39700 TERMINALS '11' AND '21'
• IS IT LESS THAN 5 OHMS?
• REPAIR SHORT TO SYSTEM VOLTAGE IN CKT 872 OR 833
• REFER TO EBTCM/EBCM-SWITCHED FAULTS
NO
YES
8
• MEASURE RESISTANCE BETWEEN J 39700 TERMINAL '11' AND GROUND
• IS IT GREATER THAN 2 MEGAOHMS?
• REPAIR SHORT BETWEEN CKT'S 872 AND 833
YES
NO
9
• MEASURE RESISTANCE BETWEEN J 39700 TERMINAL '21' AND GROUND
• IS IT GREATER THAN 2 MEGAOHMS?
• IF 5 OHMS OR LESS TO GROUND, REPAIR HARD SHORT IN HARNESS CKT 872
• IF BETWEEN 5 OHMS AND 2 MEGAOHMS, REPAIR RESISTIVE SHORT IN HARNESS CKT 872
YES
NO
• CHECK ALL WIRING, CONNECTORS AND TERMINALS THOROUGHLY FOR INTERMITTENTS OR CORROSION
• REFER TO 'INTERMITTENTS AND POOR CONNECTIONS'
• REPAIR HARNESS OR CONNECTOR
• REPLACE SENSOR IS PROBLEM PERSISTS
• IF 5 OHMS OR LESS TO GROUND, REPAIR HARD SHORT IN HARNESS CKT 833
• IF BETWEEN 5 OHMS AND 2 MEGAOHMS REPAIR RESISTIVE SHORT IN HARNESS CKT 833

GC4029300527040X

DIAGNOSTIC TROUBLE CODE 21

RIGHT FRONT WHEEL SPEED SENSOR FAULT
4 of 4

CIRCUIT DESCRIPTION:

As each wheel turns, the wheel speed sensor for that wheel creates a small AC voltage as a toothed sensor ring, mounted in the front integral hub/bearing assembly, is passed by the stationary sensor. The sensor consists of a permanent magnet and coil and generates voltage by magnetic induction. The frequency of the wheel speed sensor signal is proportional to wheel speed.

The EBTCM/EBCM uses the wheel speed sensor signal to calculate vehicle reference speeds and individual speed, acceleration and slip values for each wheel. These values are used to determine when antilock control is required.

The EBTCM/EBCM will only set one wheel speed sensor fault code at a time, even if multiple faults exist. Detection is prioritized accordingly: LF, RR, LR, RF. Always check for additional stored codes after making repairs.

TEST DESCRIPTION: Test numbers refer to circled numbers on the diagnostic chart.

5. Checks for proper resistance in the sensor itself.
6. Checks for a short to battery in either of the speed sensor circuit wires.
7. Checks for a short between the speed sensor circuit wires.
8. Checks for a short to ground in the speed sensor input circuit wire. The ground may be either a 'hard' short to ground, or a resistive short. A short with a resistance less than 2 megaohms, though not a hard short, can still cause Code 21 to set.
9. Checks wiring and connectors for intermittents.

GC4029300527030X

Fig. 93 Code 21: Right Front Wheel Speed Sensor Fault (Part 2 of 2). 1993-94 DeVille, Eldorado & Seville

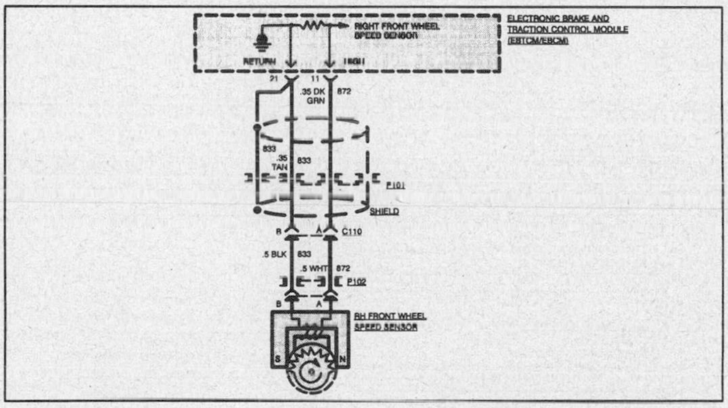
RIGHT FRONT WHEEL SPEED SENSOR
ELECTRONIC BRAKE AND TRACTION CONTROL MODULE (EBTCM/EBCM)
RETURN
HIGH
21
11
.35 DK GRN
872
833
.35 TAN
833
P101
SHIELD
B
A
C110
.5 BLK
833
.5 WHT
872
P102
B
A
RH FRONT WHEEL SPEED SENSOR
S
N

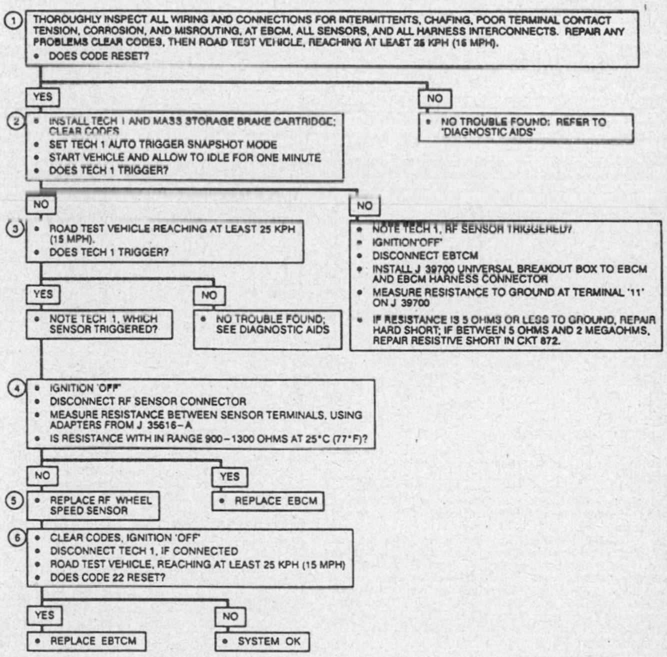
1
THOROUGHLY INSPECT ALL WIRING AND CONNECTIONS FOR INTERMITTENTS, CHAFING, POOR TERMINAL CONTACT TENSION, CORROSION, AND MISROUTING, AT EBCM, ALL SENSORS, AND ALL HARNESS INTERCONNECTS. REPAIR ANY PROBLEMS CLEAR CODES, THEN ROAD TEST VEHICLE, REACHING AT LEAST 25 KPH (15 MPH).
• DOES CODE RESET?
YES
NO
2
• INSTALL TECH 1 AND MASS STORAGE BRAKE CARTRIDGE; CLEAR CODES
• SET TECH 1 AUTO TRIGGER SNAPSHOT MODE
• START VEHICLE AND ALLOW TO IDLE FOR ONE MINUTE
• DOES TECH 1 TRIGGER?
• NO TROUBLE FOUND: REFER TO 'DIAGNOSTIC AIDS'
NO
NO
3
• ROAD TEST VEHICLE REACHING AT LEAST 25 KPH (15 MPH).
• DOES TECH 1 TRIGGER?
• NOTE TECH 1, RF SENSOR TRIGGERED?
• IGNITION 'OFF'
• DISCONNECT EBTCM
• INSTALL J 39700 UNIVERSAL BREAKOUT BOX TO EBCM AND EBCM HARNESS CONNECTOR
• MEASURE RESISTANCE TO GROUND AT TERMINAL '11' ON J 39700
• IF RESISTANCE IS 5 OHMS OR LESS TO GROUND, REPAIR HARD SHORT; IF BETWEEN 5 OHMS AND 2 MEGAOHMS, REPAIR RESISTIVE SHORT IN CKT 872.
YES
NO
• NOTE TECH 1, WHICH SENSOR TRIGGERED?
• NO TROUBLE FOUND; SEE DIAGNOSTIC AIDS
4
• IGNITION 'OFF'
• DISCONNECT RF SENSOR CONNECTOR
• MEASURE RESISTANCE BETWEEN SENSOR TERMINALS, USING ADAPTERS FROM J 35616-A
• IS RESISTANCE WITH IN RANGE 900-1300 OHMS AT 25°C (77°F)?
NO
YES
5
• REPLACE RF WHEEL SPEED SENSOR
• REPLACE EBCM
6
• CLEAR CODES, IGNITION 'OFF'
• DISCONNECT TECH 1, IF CONNECTED
• ROAD TEST VEHICLE, REACHING AT LEAST 25 KPH (15 MPH)
• DOES CODE 22 RESET?
YES
NO
• REPLACE EBTCM
• SYSTEM OK

GC4029300528020X

TEST CONDITION(S):

1. Tested continuously.

FAILURE CONDITION(S):

1. While Driving: The RF wheel is detected at least 30 kph or 19 mph faster than the remaining wheels for an extended period of time.

   OR

   The RF wheel is at least 6 kph or 4 mph less than or greater than the remaining wheels for an extended period of time.

ACTION TAKEN:

1. Code set.
2. ABS/TCS switched 'OFF'.
3. 'ANTILOCK' indicator 'ON'.

TEST DESCRIPTION: Test numbers refer to circled numbers on the diagnostic chart.

1. Checks wiring and connections for problems. It is critical that this step is performed thoroughly, as wiring/connector problems are the most likely cause for this code.
2. Use the TECH 1 to monitor for vehicle electrical/electronic system 'noise' being picked up by the speed sensor circuits.
3. Use the TECH 1 to monitor the wheel speed sensors while the vehicle is operating. If the TECH 1 Auto-Trigger Snapshot mode triggers, the speed sensor or the wiring and/or connectors are going intermittent during the road test.
4. Checks for proper resistance in the sensor itself.
5. Replaces front wheel speed sensor as the likely cause of the triggering intermittent.
6. Use the TECH 1 to monitor the wheel speed sensors while the vehicle is operating. If the TECH 1 Auto-Snapshot mode triggers, the EBCM must be concluding there is a problem with wheel speed sensor frequencies when there is not.
7. Checks for a short to ground in the speed sensor input circuit wires. The circuit to be tested depends on which speed sensor triggered the TECH 1. The ground may be either a 'hard' short to ground, or a resistive short. A short with a resistance less that 2 megaohms, though not a hard short, can still cause Code 22 to set.

DIAGNOSTIC AIDS:

Be sure the speed sensor wiring is properly routed and retained. This will help prevent false signals due to electrical noise being picked up by the wiring.

It is very important that a thorough inspection of the wiring and connectors be performed. Failure to carefully and fully inspect wiring and connectors may result in misdiagnosis, causing part replacement with reappearance of the fault.

Check the toothed wheel for any large grooves, gouges, marks, etc. that might influence the tooth's signal at the wheel speed sensor. Also check for a buildup of foreign material in the gaps between teeth in the toothed wheel; this material may cause this fault.

A worn hub/bearing assembly may cause this fault in extreme cases; the bearing play allows the sensor-to-toothed-ring gap to change excessively. Never reuse a wheel speed sensor once it has been separated from the front hub/bearing assembly.

GC4029300528010X

Fig. 94 Code 22: Right Front Wheel Speed Sensor Frequency Error. 1993-94 DeVille, Eldorado & Seville

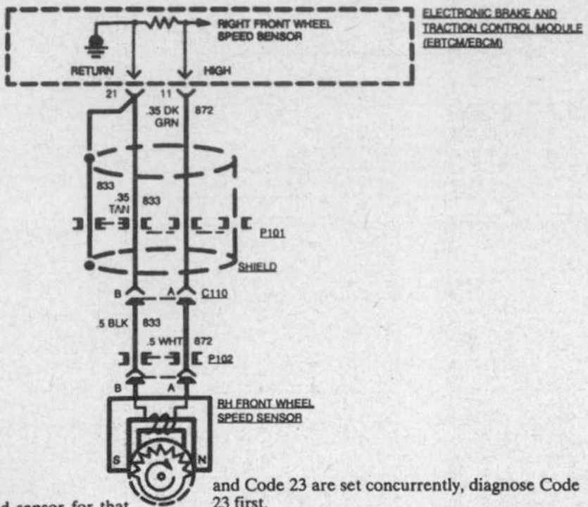
RIGHT FRONT WHEEL SPEED SENSOR
ELECTRONIC BRAKE AND TRACTION CONTROL MODULE (EBTCM/EBCM)
RETURN
HIGH
21
11
.35 DK GRN
872
833
.35 TAN
833
P101
SHIELD
C110
.5 BLK
833
.5 WHT
872
P102
RH FRONT WHEEL SPEED SENSOR
S
N

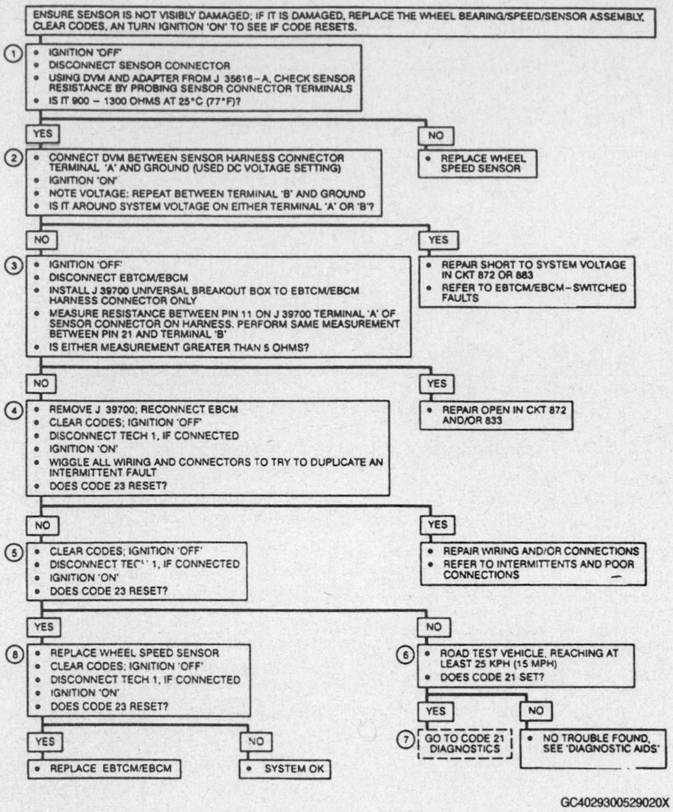
ENSURE SENSOR IS NOT VISIBLY DAMAGED; IF IT IS DAMAGED, REPLACE THE WHEEL BEARING/SPEED/SENSOR ASSEMBLY. CLEAR CODES, AN TURN IGNITION 'ON' TO SEE IF CODE RESETS.
1
• IGNITION 'OFF'
• DISCONNECT SENSOR CONNECTOR
• USING DVM AND ADAPTER FROM J 35616-A, CHECK SENSOR RESISTANCE BY PROBING SENSOR CONNECTOR TERMINALS
• IS IT 900 – 1300 OHMS AT 25°C (77°F)?
YES
NO
• REPLACE WHEEL SPEED SENSOR
2
• CONNECT DVM BETWEEN SENSOR HARNESS CONNECTOR TERMINAL 'A' AND GROUND (USED DC VOLTAGE SETTING)
• IGNITION 'ON'
• NOTE VOLTAGE: REPEAT BETWEEN TERMINAL 'B' AND GROUND
• IS IT AROUND SYSTEM VOLTAGE ON EITHER TERMINAL 'A' OR 'B'?
NO
YES
• REPAIR SHORT TO SYSTEM VOLTAGE IN CKT 872 OR 883
• REFER TO EBTCM/EBCM–SWITCHED FAULTS
3
• IGNITION 'OFF'
• DISCONNECT EBTCM/EBCM
• INSTALL J 39700 UNIVERSAL BREAKOUT BOX TO EBTCM/EBCM HARNESS CONNECTOR ONLY
• MEASURE RESISTANCE BETWEEN PIN 11 ON J 39700 TERMINAL 'A' OF SENSOR CONNECTOR ON HARNESS. PERFORM SAME MEASUREMENT BETWEEN PIN 21 AND TERMINAL 'B'
• IS EITHER MEASUREMENT GREATER THAN 5 OHMS?
NO
YES
• REPAIR OPEN IN CKT 872 AND/OR 833
4
• REMOVE J 39700; RECONNECT EBCM
• CLEAR CODES; IGNITION 'OFF'
• DISCONNECT TECH 1, IF CONNECTED
• IGNITION 'ON'
• WIGGLE ALL WIRING AND CONNECTORS TO TRY TO DUPLICATE AN INTERMITTENT FAULT
• DOES CODE 23 RESET?
NO
YES
• REPAIR WIRING AND/OR CONNECTIONS
• REFER TO INTERMITTENTS AND POOR CONNECTIONS
5
• CLEAR CODES; IGNITION 'OFF'
• DISCONNECT TECH 1, IF CONNECTED
• IGNITION 'ON'
• DOES CODE 23 RESET?
YES
NO
8
• REPLACE WHEEL SPEED SENSOR
• CLEAR CODES; IGNITION 'OFF'
• DISCONNECT TECH 1, IF CONNECTED
• IGNITION 'ON'
• DOES CODE 23 RESET?
6
• ROAD TEST VEHICLE, REACHING AT LEAST 25 KPH (15 MPH)
• DOES CODE 21 SET?
YES
NO
7
GO TO CODE 21 DIAGNOSTICS
• NO TROUBLE FOUND, SEE 'DIAGNOSTIC AIDS'
YES
NO
• REPLACE EBTCM/EBCM
• SYSTEM OK
GC4029300529020X

CIRCUIT DESCRIPTION:

As each wheel turns, the wheel speed sensor for that wheel creates a small AC voltage as a toothed sensor ring, mounted in the front integral hub/bearing assembly, is passed by the stationary sensor. The sensor consists of a permanent magnet and coil and generates voltage by magnetic induction. The frequency of the wheel speed sensor signal is proportional to wheel speed.

The EBTCM/EBCM uses the wheel speed sensor signal to calculate vehicle reference speeds and individual speed, acceleration and slip values for each wheel. These values are used to determine when antilock control is required.

The EBTCM/EBCM will only set one wheel speed sensor fault code at a time, even if multiple faults exist. Detection is prioritized accordingly: LF, RR, LR, RF. Always check for additional stored codes after making repairs.

TEST CONDITION(S):

1. Tested continuously.

FAILURE CONDITION(S):

Continuity

1. While standing: Open circuit is seen while the vehicle is standing still with the ignition 'ON'

ACTION TAKEN:

1. Code set.
2. ABS/TCS switched 'OFF'.
3. 'ANTILOCK' indicator 'ON'.
4. 'TRACTION DISABLED' message displayed. (vehicles with TCS)

Code 23 is set if there is a short to voltage or ground in CKT 872 or 883, or faulty speed sensor. The testing for this fault occurs with the ignition 'ON' and the vehicle at rest.

NOTICE: A Code 21 may set if CKT 872 or 833 lose continuity and the WSS signal is lost while driving. A Code 23 should accompany this code on the subsequent ignition cycle. If both Code 21 and Code 23 are set concurrently, diagnose Code 23 first.

TEST DESCRIPTION: Test numbers refer to circled numbers on the diagnostic chart.

1. Checks for proper resistance in the sensor itself.
2. Checks for a short to battery in either of the speed sensor circuit wires. There should be 5V on CKT 872. If there is, CKT 872 has no hard opens or shorts. The condition may be intermittent.
3. Checks for an open in both the speed sensor circuit wires.
4. Manipulates wiring and connectors, trying to induce an intermittent fault not currently present.
5. This test checks if the code resets on key-up. If so, since Tests 1–4 have validated that the circuitry and components are good, the Wheel Bearing/Speed Sensor assembly may be causing the fault.
6. Checks if the Code 21 sets during a road test.
7. Code 23 sets when the vehicle is at rest: Code 21 sets with a problem in the speed sensor circuitry with the vehicle in motion. If problems are still present, Code 21 would set during the road test, not a 23. If Code 21 sets at this point, Code 21 diagnostics should be used.
8. The wheel speed sensor may be causing an intermittent fault. If Code 23 resets after sensor replacement, the EBTCM/EBCM must be concluding there is a problem present in the speed sensor circuit when there is not.

DIAGNOSTIC AIDS:

Be sure the speed sensor wiring is properly routed and retained. This will help prevent false signals due to electrical noise being picked up by the wiring.

It is very important that a thorough inspection of the wiring and connectors be performed. Failure to carefully and fully inspect wiring and connectors may result in misdiagnosis, causing part replacement with reappearance of the fault.

GC4029300529010X

Fig. 95 Code 23: Right Front Wheel Speed Sensor Continuity Fault. 1993-94 DeVille, Eldorado & Seville

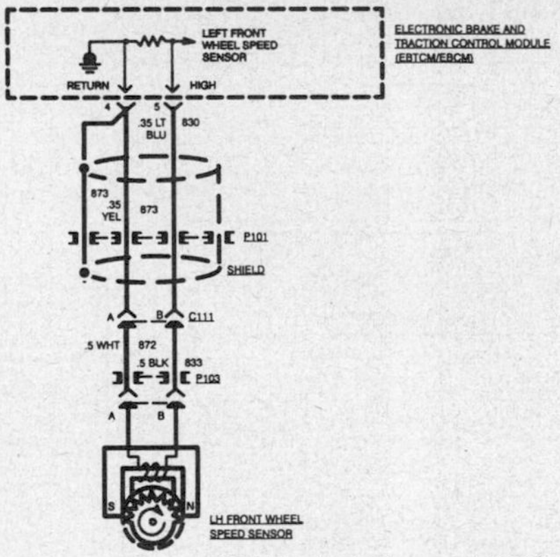
LEFT FRONT WHEEL SPEED SENSOR
ELECTRONIC BRAKE AND TRACTION CONTROL MODULE (EBTCM/EBCM)
RETURN
HIGH
4
5
.35 LT BLU
830
873
.35 YEL
873
P101
SHIELD
C111
.5 WHT
872
.5 BLK
833
P103
LH FRONT WHEEL SPEED SENSOR
S
N

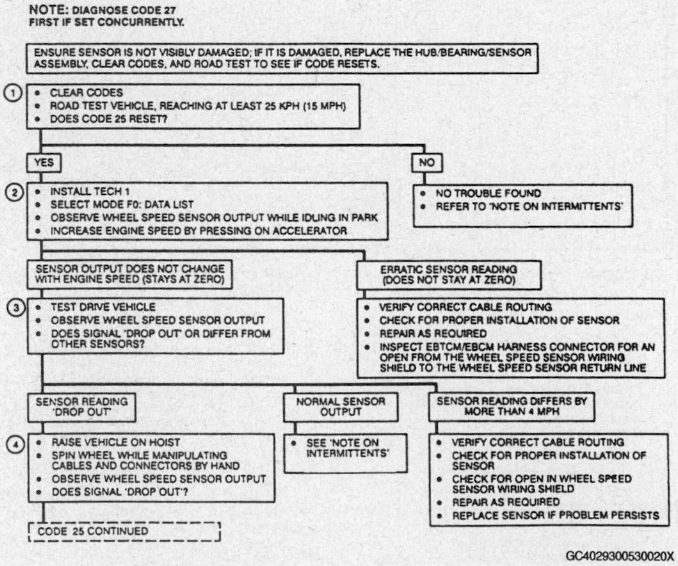
NOTE: DIAGNOSE CODE 27 FIRST IF SET CONCURRENTLY.
ENSURE SENSOR IS NOT VISIBLY DAMAGED; IF IT IS DAMAGED, REPLACE THE HUB/BEARING/SENSOR ASSEMBLY. CLEAR CODES, AND ROAD TEST TO SEE IF CODE RESETS.
1
• CLEAR CODES
• ROAD TEST VEHICLE, REACHING AT LEAST 25 KPH (15 MPH)
• DOES CODE 25 RESET?
YES
NO
• NO TROUBLE FOUND
• REFER TO 'NOTE ON INTERMITTENTS'
2
• INSTALL TECH 1
• SELECT MODE F0: DATA LIST
• OBSERVE WHEEL SPEED SENSOR OUTPUT WHILE IDLING IN PARK
• INCREASE ENGINE SPEED BY PRESSING ON ACCELERATOR
SENSOR OUTPUT DOES NOT CHANGE WITH ENGINE SPEED (STAYS AT ZERO)
ERRATIC SENSOR READING (DOES NOT STAY AT ZERO)
3
• TEST DRIVE VEHICLE
• OBSERVE WHEEL SPEED SENSOR OUTPUT
• DOES SIGNAL 'DROP OUT' OR DIFFER FROM OTHER SENSORS?
• VERIFY CORRECT CABLE ROUTING
• CHECK FOR PROPER INSTALLATION OF SENSOR
• REPAIR AS REQUIRED
• INSPECT EBTCM/EBCM HARNESS CONNECTOR FOR AN OPEN FROM THE WHEEL SPEED SENSOR WIRING SHIELD TO THE WHEEL SPEED SENSOR RETURN LINE
SENSOR READING 'DROP OUT'
NORMAL SENSOR OUTPUT
SENSOR READING DIFFERS BY MORE THAN 4 MPH
4
• RAISE VEHICLE ON HOIST
• SPIN WHEEL WHILE MANIPULATING CABLES AND CONNECTORS BY HAND
• OBSERVE WHEEL SPEED SENSOR OUTPUT
• DOES SIGNAL 'DROP OUT'?
• SEE 'NOTE ON INTERMITTENTS'
• VERIFY CORRECT CABLE ROUTING
• CHECK FOR PROPER INSTALLATION OF SENSOR
• CHECK FOR OPEN IN WHEEL SPEED SENSOR WIRING SHIELD
• REPAIR AS REQUIRED
• REPLACE SENSOR IF PROBLEM PERSISTS
CODE 25 CONTINUED
GC4029300530020X

CIRCUIT DESCRIPTION:

As each wheel turns, the wheel speed sensor for that wheel creates a small AC voltage as a toothed sensor ring, mounted in the front integral hub/bearing assembly, is passed by the stationary sensor. The sensor consists of a permanent magnet and coil and generates voltage by magnetic induction. The frequency of the wheel speed sensor signal is proportional to wheel speed.

The EBTCM/EBCM uses the wheel speed sensor signal to calculate vehicle reference speeds and individual speed, acceleration and slip values for each wheel. These values are used to determine when antilock control is required.

The EBTCM/EBCM will only set one wheel speed sensor fault code at a time, even if multiple faults exist. Detection is prioritized accordingly: LF, RR, LR, RF. Always check for additional stored codes after making repairs.

TEST CONDITION(S):

1. Tested continuously.

FAILURE CONDITION(S):

Sensor Output

1. Drive-away: Speed signal is not detected when vehicle reaches 12 kph or 7.5 mph.

OR

2. While Driving: Speed signal is lost while vehicle speed is greater than 40 kph or 25 mph

ACTION TAKEN:

1. Code set.
2. ABS/TCS switched 'OFF'.
3. 'ANTILOCK' indicator 'ON'.
4. 'TRACTION DISABLED' message displayed. (vehicles with TCS)

Code 25 is set if there is a short to voltage or ground in CKT 830 or 873, or faulty speed sensor. The testing for this fault occurs when vehicle is in motion; it will not set with the ignition 'ON' and the vehicle at rest.

NOTICE: A Code 25 may set if CKT 830 or 873 lose continuity and the WSS signal is lost while driving. A Code 27 should accompany this code on the subsequent ignition cycle. If both Code 25 and Code 27 are set concurrently, diagnose Code 27 first.

TEST DESCRIPTION: Test numbers refer to circled numbers on the diagnostic chart.

1. Checks if the code resets during a road test.
2. Use the TECH 1 to check for sources of induced electrical noise. Some sources of induced electrical noise which may cause intermittent wheel speed sensor codes to set are: improper routing or sensor cables next to spark plug wires; cables not retained in brackets; loose fitting or improperly mounted sensors; damaged sensors or toothed rings; poor terminal engagement of connectors; or intermittent shorts or opens in wiring; or a loss of sensor circuit shield.
3. Checks for damaged wheel speed sensor circuit shield. The shield is a foil insulator that is wrapped around the wheel speed sensor circuits. Inside the EBTCM/EBCM harness connecter there is an uninsulated drain wire that is attached to the shield and jumped to the wheel speed sensor return line and taken to ground through the EBTCM/EBCM. A shield which has lost its ground through the EBTCM/EBCM leaves the sensor signal circuit susceptible to noise. It may be necessary to disassemble the EBTCM/EBCM connector to check if the drain wire has a poor connection with the wheel speed sensor return connector terminal. The shield can be repaired by reterminating the sensor return line circuit, including the drain wire.
4. Checks for intermittent opens/shorts in wheel speed sensor circuits and cables.

GC4029300530010X

Fig. 96 Code 25: Left Front Wheel Speed Sensor Fault (Part 1 of 2). 1993-94 DeVille, Eldorado & Seville

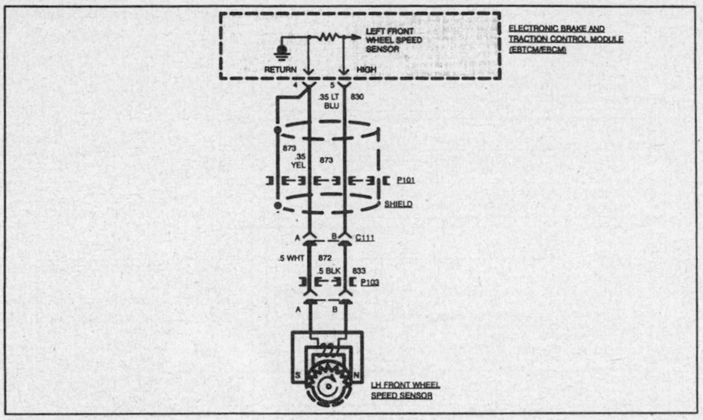
LEFT FRONT WHEEL SPEED SENSOR
ELECTRONIC BRAKE AND TRACTION CONTROL MODULE (EBTCM/EBCM)
RETURN
HIGH
4
5
.35 LT BLU
830
873
.35 YEL
873
P101
SHIELD
A
B
C111
.5 WHT
872
.5 BLK
833
P103
A
B
S
N
LH FRONT WHEEL SPEED SENSOR

CIRCUIT DESCRIPTION:

As each wheel turns, the wheel speed sensor for that wheel creates a small AC voltage as a toothed sensor ring, mounted in the front integral hub/bearing assembly, is passed by the stationary sensor. The sensor consists of a permanent magnet and coil and generates voltage by magnetic induction. The frequency of the wheel speed sensor signal is proportional to wheel speed.

The EBTCM/EBCM uses the wheel speed sensor signal to calculate vehicle reference speeds and individual speed, acceleration and slip values for each wheel. These values are used to determine when antilock control is required.

The EBTCM/EBCM will only set one wheel speed sensor fault code at a time, even if multiple faults exist. Detection is prioritized accordingly: LF, RR, LR, RF. Always check for additional stored codes after making repairs.

TEST DESCRIPTION: Test numbers refer to circled numbers on the diagnostic chart.

5. Checks for proper resistance in the sensor itself.
6. Checks for a short to battery in either of the speed sensor circuit wires.
7. Checks for a short between the speed sensor circuit wires.
8. Checks for a short to ground in the speed sensor input circuit wire. The ground may be either a 'hard' short to ground, or a resistive short. A short with a resistance less than 2 megaohms, though not a hard short, can still cause Code 21 to set.
9. Checks wiring and connectors for intermittents.

GC4029300530030X

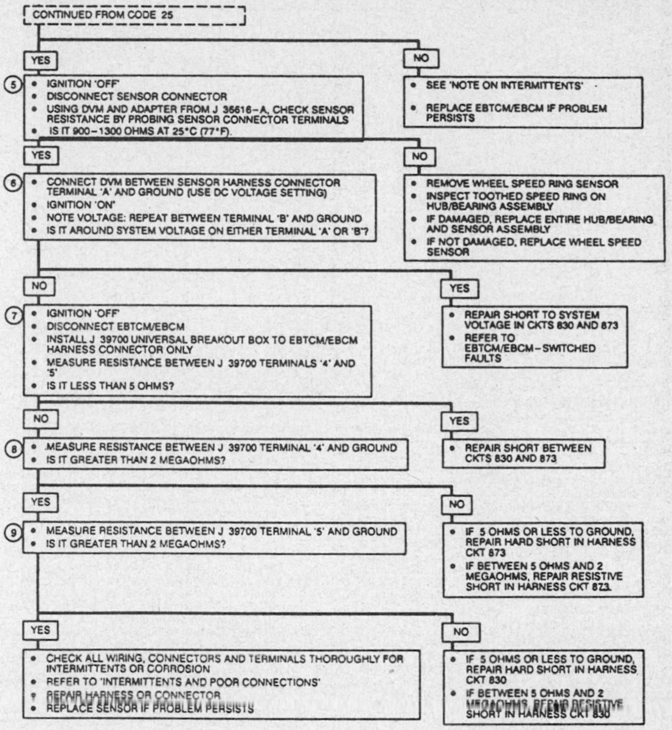
CONTINUED FROM CODE 25
YES
NO
5
• IGNITION 'OFF'
• DISCONNECT SENSOR CONNECTOR
• USING DVM AND ADAPTER FROM J 36616-A, CHECK SENSOR RESISTANCE BY PROBING SENSOR CONNECTOR TERMINALS
• IS IT 900-1300 OHMS AT 25°C (77°F).
• SEE 'NOTE ON INTERMITTENTS'
• REPLACE EBTCM/EBCM IF PROBLEM PERSISTS
YES
NO
6
• CONNECT DVM BETWEEN SENSOR HARNESS CONNECTOR TERMINAL 'A' AND GROUND (USE DC VOLTAGE SETTING)
• IGNITION 'ON'
• NOTE VOLTAGE: REPEAT BETWEEN TERMINAL 'B' AND GROUND
• IS IT AROUND SYSTEM VOLTAGE ON EITHER TERMINAL 'A' OR 'B'?
• REMOVE WHEEL SPEED RING SENSOR
• INSPECT TOOTHED SPEED RING ON HUB/BEARING ASSEMBLY
• IF DAMAGED, REPLACE ENTIRE HUB/BEARING AND SENSOR ASSEMBLY
• IF NOT DAMAGED, REPLACE WHEEL SPEED SENSOR
NO
YES
7
• IGNITION 'OFF'
• DISCONNECT EBTCM/EBCM
• INSTALL J 39700 UNIVERSAL BREAKOUT BOX TO EBTCM/EBCM HARNESS CONNECTOR ONLY
• MEASURE RESISTANCE BETWEEN J 39700 TERMINALS '4' AND '5'
• IS IT LESS THAN 5 OHMS?
• REPAIR SHORT TO SYSTEM VOLTAGE IN CKTS 830 AND 873
• REFER TO EBTCM/EBCM-SWITCHED FAULTS
NO
YES
8
• MEASURE RESISTANCE BETWEEN J 39700 TERMINAL '4' AND GROUND
• IS IT GREATER THAN 2 MEGAOHMS?
• REPAIR SHORT BETWEEN CKTS 830 AND 873
YES
NO
9
• MEASURE RESISTANCE BETWEEN J 39700 TERMINAL '5' AND GROUND
• IS IT GREATER THAN 2 MEGAOHMS?
• IF 5 OHMS OR LESS TO GROUND, REPAIR HARD SHORT IN HARNESS CKT 873
• IF BETWEEN 5 OHMS AND 2 MEGAOHMS, REPAIR RESISTIVE SHORT IN HARNESS CKT 873
YES
NO
• CHECK ALL WIRING, CONNECTORS AND TERMINALS THOROUGHLY FOR INTERMITTENTS OR CORROSION
• REFER TO 'INTERMITTENTS AND POOR CONNECTIONS'
• REPAIR HARNESS OR CONNECTOR
• REPLACE SENSOR IF PROBLEM PERSISTS
• IF 5 OHMS OR LESS TO GROUND, REPAIR HARD SHORT IN HARNESS CKT 830
• IF BETWEEN 5 OHMS AND 2 MEGAOHMS, REPAIR RESISTIVE SHORT IN HARNESS CKT 830

GC4029300530040X

Fig. 96 Code 25: Left Front Wheel Speed Sensor Fault (Part 2 of 2). 1993-94 DeVille, Eldorado & Seville

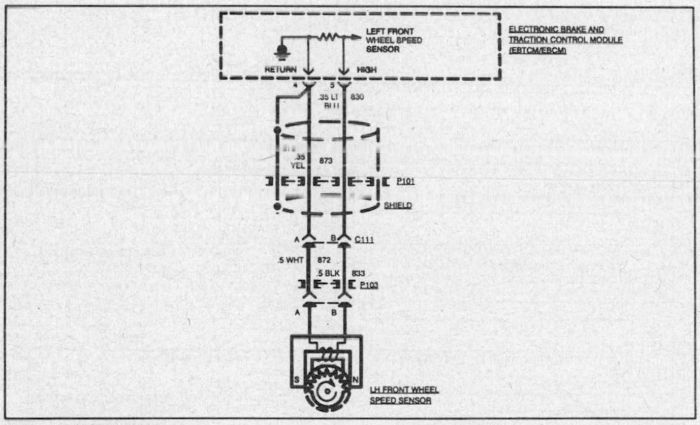
LEFT FRONT WHEEL SPEED SENSOR
ELECTRONIC BRAKE AND TRACTION CONTROL MODULE (EBTCM/EBCM)
RETURN
HIGH
5
830
.35 YEL
873
P101
SHIELD
A
B
C111
.5 WHT
872
.5 BLK
833
P103
A
B
S
N
LH FRONT WHEEL SPEED SENSOR

TEST CONDITION(S):

1. Tested continuously.

FAILURE CONDITION(S):

1. While Driving: The LF wheel is detected at least 30 kph or 19 mph faster than the remaining wheels for an extended period of time.

   OR

   The LF wheel is at least 6 kph or 4 mph less than or greater than the remaining wheels for an extended period of time.

ACTION TAKEN:

1. Code set.
2. ABS switched 'OFF'.
3. 'ANTILOCK' indicator 'ON'.

TEST DESCRIPTION: Test numbers refer to circled numbers on the diagnostic chart.

1. Checks wiring and connections for problems. It is critical that this step is performed thoroughly, as wiring/connector problems are the most likely cause for this code.
2. Use the TECH 1 to monitor for vehicle electrical/electronic system 'noise' being picked up by the speed sensor circuits.
3. Use the TECH 1 to monitor the wheel speed sensors while the vehicle is operating. If the TECH 1 Auto–Trigger Snapshot mode triggers, the speed sensor or the wiring and/or connectors are going intermittent during the road test.
4. Checks for proper resistance in the sensor itself.
5. Replaces front wheel speed sensor as the likely cause of the triggering intermittent.
6. Use the TECH 1 to monitor the wheel speed sensors while the vehicle is operating. If the TECH 1 Auto–Snapshot mode triggers, the EBCM must be concluding there is a problem with wheel speed sensor frequencies when there is not.
7. Checks for a short to ground in the speed sensor input circuit wires. The circuit to be tested depends on which speed sensor triggered the TECH 1. The ground may be either a 'hard' short to ground, or a resistive short. A short with a resistance less that 2 megaohms, though not a hard short, can still cause Code 26 to set.

DIAGNOSTIC AIDS:

Be sure the speed sensor wiring is properly routed and retained. This will help prevent false signals due to electrical noise being picked up by the wiring.

It is very important that a thorough inspection of the wiring and connectors be performed. Failure to carefully and fully inspect wiring and connectors may result in misdiagnosis, causing part replacement with reappearance of the fault.

Check the toothed wheel for any large grooves, gouges, marks, etc. that might influence the tooth's signal at the wheel speed sensor. Also check for a buildup of foreign material in the gaps between teeth in the toothed wheel; this material may cause this fault.

A worn hub/bearing assembly may cause this fault in extreme cases; the bearing play allows the sensor–to–toothed–ring gap to change excessively. Never reuse a wheel speed sensor once it has been separated from the front hub/bearing assembly.

GC4029300531010X

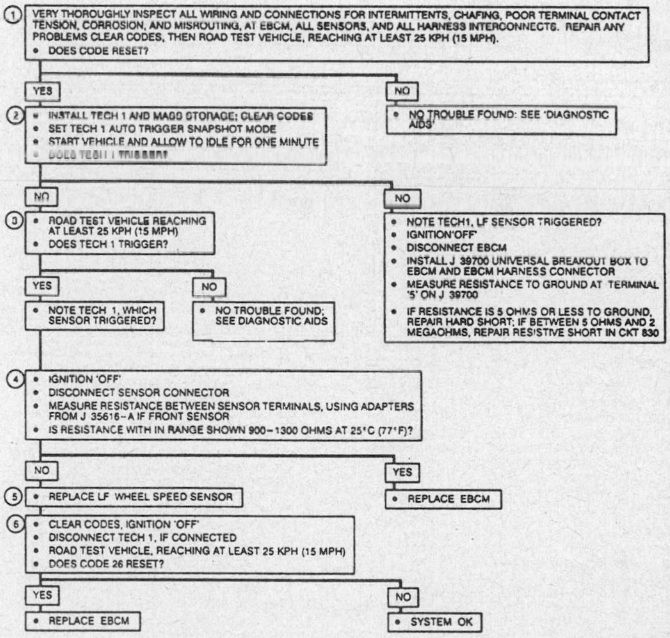
1
VERY THOROUGHLY INSPECT ALL WIRING AND CONNECTIONS FOR INTERMITTENTS, CHAFING, POOR TERMINAL CONTACT TENSION, CORROSION, AND MISROUTING, AT EBCM, ALL SENSORS, AND ALL HARNESS INTERCONNECTS. REPAIR ANY PROBLEMS CLEAR CODES, THEN ROAD TEST VEHICLE, REACHING AT LEAST 25 KPH (15 MPH).
• DOES CODE RESET?
YES
NO
2
• INSTALL TECH 1 AND MASS STORAGE; CLEAR CODES
• SET TECH 1 AUTO TRIGGER SNAPSHOT MODE
• START VEHICLE AND ALLOW TO IDLE FOR ONE MINUTE
• NO TROUBLE FOUND: SEE 'DIAGNOSTIC AIDS'
NO
NO
3
• ROAD TEST VEHICLE REACHING AT LEAST 25 KPH (15 MPH)
• DOES TECH 1 TRIGGER?
• NOTE TECH1, LF SENSOR TRIGGERED?
• IGNITION'OFF'
• DISCONNECT EBCM
• INSTALL J 39700 UNIVERSAL BREAKOUT BOX TO EBCM AND EBCM HARNESS CONNECTOR
• MEASURE RESISTANCE TO GROUND AT TERMINAL '5' ON J 39700
• IF RESISTANCE IS 5 OHMS OR LESS TO GROUND, REPAIR HARD SHORT; IF BETWEEN 5 OHMS AND 2 MEGAOHMS, REPAIR RESISTIVE SHORT IN CKT 830
YES
NO
• NOTE TECH 1, WHICH SENSOR TRIGGERED?
• NO TROUBLE FOUND; SEE DIAGNOSTIC AIDS
4
• IGNITION 'OFF'
• DISCONNECT SENSOR CONNECTOR
• MEASURE RESISTANCE BETWEEN SENSOR TERMINALS, USING ADAPTERS FROM J 35616-A IF FRONT SENSOR
• IS RESISTANCE WITH IN RANGE SHOWN 900-1300 OHMS AT 25°C (77°F)?
NO
YES
5
• REPLACE LF WHEEL SPEED SENSOR
• REPLACE EBCM
6
• CLEAR CODES, IGNITION 'OFF'
• DISCONNECT TECH 1, IF CONNECTED
• ROAD TEST VEHICLE, REACHING AT LEAST 25 KPH (15 MPH)
• DOES CODE 26 RESET?
YES
NO
• REPLACE EBCM
• SYSTEM OK

GC4029300531020X

Fig. 97 Code 26: Left Front Wheel Speed Sensor Frequency Error. 1993-94 DeVille, Eldorado & Seville

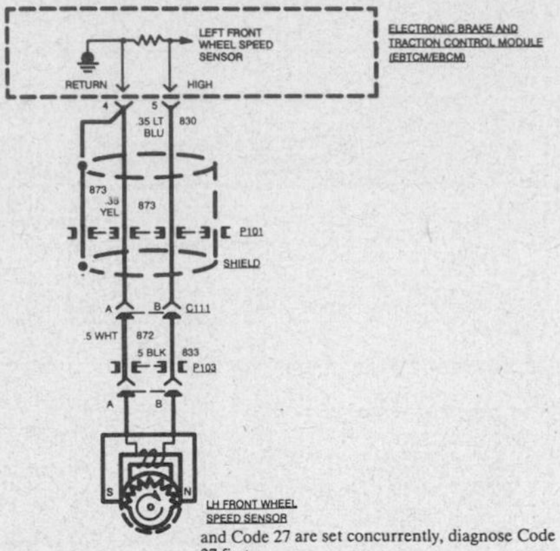
LEFT FRONT WHEEL SPEED SENSOR
ELECTRONIC BRAKE AND TRACTION CONTROL MODULE (EBTCM/EBCM)
RETURN
HIGH
.35 LT BLU
830
873
.35 YEL
873
P101
SHIELD
C111
.5 WHT
872
.5 BLK
833
P103
LH FRONT WHEEL SPEED SENSOR

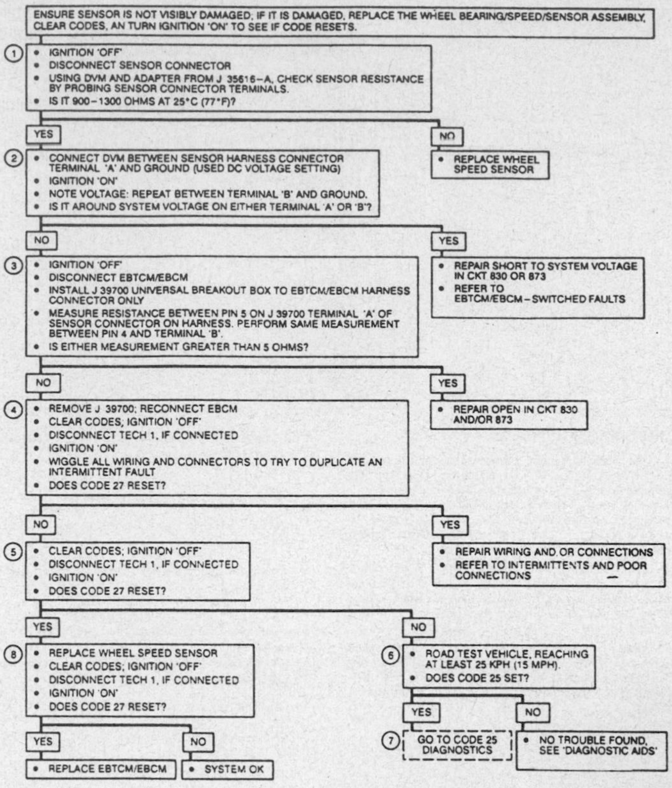
ENSURE SENSOR IS NOT VISIBLY DAMAGED; IF IT IS DAMAGED, REPLACE THE WHEEL BEARING/SPEED/SENSOR ASSEMBLY, CLEAR CODES, AN TURN IGNITION 'ON' TO SEE IF CODE RESETS.
1
• IGNITION 'OFF'
• DISCONNECT SENSOR CONNECTOR
• USING DVM AND ADAPTER FROM J 35616-A, CHECK SENSOR RESISTANCE BY PROBING SENSOR CONNECTOR TERMINALS.
• IS IT 900-1300 OHMS AT 25°C (77°F)?
YES
NO
• REPLACE WHEEL SPEED SENSOR
2
• CONNECT DVM BETWEEN SENSOR HARNESS CONNECTOR TERMINAL 'A' AND GROUND (USED DC VOLTAGE SETTING)
• IGNITION 'ON'
• NOTE VOLTAGE: REPEAT BETWEEN TERMINAL 'B' AND GROUND.
• IS IT AROUND SYSTEM VOLTAGE ON EITHER TERMINAL 'A' OR 'B'?
NO
YES
• REPAIR SHORT TO SYSTEM VOLTAGE IN CKT 830 OR 873
• REFER TO EBTCM/EBCM-SWITCHED FAULTS
3
• IGNITION 'OFF'
• DISCONNECT EBTCM/EBCM
• INSTALL J 39700 UNIVERSAL BREAKOUT BOX TO EBTCM/EBCM HARNESS CONNECTOR ONLY
• MEASURE RESISTANCE BETWEEN PIN 5 ON J 39700 TERMINAL 'A' OF SENSOR CONNECTOR ON HARNESS. PERFORM SAME MEASUREMENT BETWEEN PIN 4 AND TERMINAL 'B'.
• IS EITHER MEASUREMENT GREATER THAN 5 OHMS?
NO
YES
• REPAIR OPEN IN CKT 830 AND/OR 873
4
• REMOVE J 39700; RECONNECT EBCM
• CLEAR CODES, IGNITION 'OFF'
• DISCONNECT TECH 1, IF CONNECTED
• IGNITION 'ON'
• WIGGLE ALL WIRING AND CONNECTORS TO TRY TO DUPLICATE AN INTERMITTENT FAULT
• DOES CODE 27 RESET?
NO
YES
• REPAIR WIRING AND OR CONNECTIONS
• REFER TO INTERMITTENTS AND POOR CONNECTIONS
5
• CLEAR CODES; IGNITION 'OFF'
• DISCONNECT TECH 1, IF CONNECTED
• IGNITION 'ON'
• DOES CODE 27 RESET?
YES
NO
8
• REPLACE WHEEL SPEED SENSOR
• CLEAR CODES; IGNITION 'OFF'
• DISCONNECT TECH 1, IF CONNECTED
• IGNITION 'ON'
• DOES CODE 27 RESET?
6
• ROAD TEST VEHICLE, REACHING AT LEAST 25 KPH (15 MPH).
• DOES CODE 25 SET?
YES
NO
YES
NO
7
GO TO CODE 25 DIAGNOSTICS
• NO TROUBLE FOUND. SEE 'DIAGNOSTIC AIDS'
• REPLACE EBTCM/EBCM
• SYSTEM OK
GC4029300532020X

CIRCUIT DESCRIPTION:

As each wheel turns, the wheel speed sensor for that wheel creates a small AC voltage as a toothed sensor ring, mounted in the front integral hub/bearing assembly, is passed by the stationary sensor. The sensor consists of a permanent magnet and coil and generates voltage by magnetic induction. The frequency of the wheel speed sensor signal is proportional to wheel speed.

The EBTCM/EBCM uses the wheel speed sensor signal to calculate vehicle reference speeds and individual speed, acceleration and slip values for each wheel. These values are used to determine when antilock control is required.

The EBTCM/EBCM will only set one wheel speed sensor fault code at a time, even if multiple faults exist. Detection is prioritized accordingly: LF, RR, LR, RF. Always check for additional stored codes after making repairs.

TEST CONDITION(S):

1. Tested continuously.

FAILURE CONDITION(S):

Continuity

1. While Standing: Open circuit is seen while the vehicle is standing still with the ignition 'ON'.

ACTION TAKEN:

1. Code set.
2. ABS/TCS switched 'OFF'.
3. 'ANTILOCK' indicator 'ON'.
4. 'TRACTION DISABLED' message displayed. (vehicles with TCS)

Code 27 is set if there is a short to voltage or an open in CKT 830 or 873, or faulty speed sensor. The testing for this fault occurs with the ignition 'ON' and the vehicle at rest.

NOTICE: A Code 25 may set CKT 830 or 873 lose continuity and the WSS signal is lost while driving. A Code 27 should accompany this code on the subsequent ignition cycle. If both Code 25 and Code 27 are set concurrently, diagnose Code 27 first.

TEST DESCRIPTION: Test numbers refer to circled numbers on the diagnostic chart.

1. Checks for proper resistance in the sensor itself.
2. Checks for a short to battery in either of the speed sensor circuit wires. There should be 5V on CKT 830. If there is, CKT 830 has no hard opens or shorts. The condition may be intermittent.
3. Checks for an open in both the speed sensor circuit wires.
4. Manipulates wiring and connectors, trying to induce an intermittent fault not currently present.
5. This test checks if the code resets on key-up. If so, since Tests 1-4 have validated that the circuitry and components are good, the Wheel Bearing/Speed Sensor assembly may be causing the fault.
6. Checks if Code 25 sets during a road test.
7. Code 27 sets when the vehicle is at rest: Code 25 sets with a problem in the speed sensor circuitry with the vehicle in motion. If problems are still present, Code 25 would set during the road test, not a 27. If Code 25 sets at this point, Code 25 diagnostics should be used.
8. The wheel speed sensor may be causing an intermittent fault. If Code 27 resets after sensor replacement, the EBTCM/EBCM must be concluding there is a problem present in the speed sensor circuit when there is not.

DIAGNOSTIC AIDS:

Be sure the speed sensor wiring is properly routed and retained. This will help prevent false signals due to electrical noise being picked up by the wiring.

It is very important that a thorough inspection of the wiring and connectors be performed. Failure to carefully and fully inspect wiring and connectors may result in misdiagnosis, causing part replacement with reappearance of the fault.

GC4029300532010X

Fig. 98 Code 27: Left Front Wheel Speed Sensor Continuity Fault. 1993-94 DeVille, Eldorado & Seville

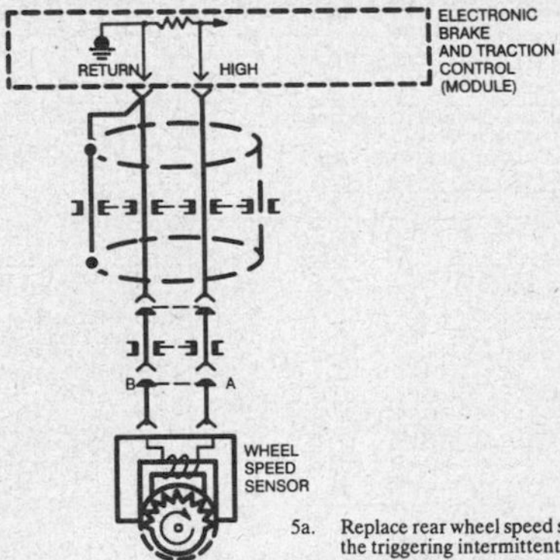
ELECTRONIC BRAKE AND TRACTION CONTROL (MODULE)
RETURN
HIGH
WHEEL SPEED SENSOR

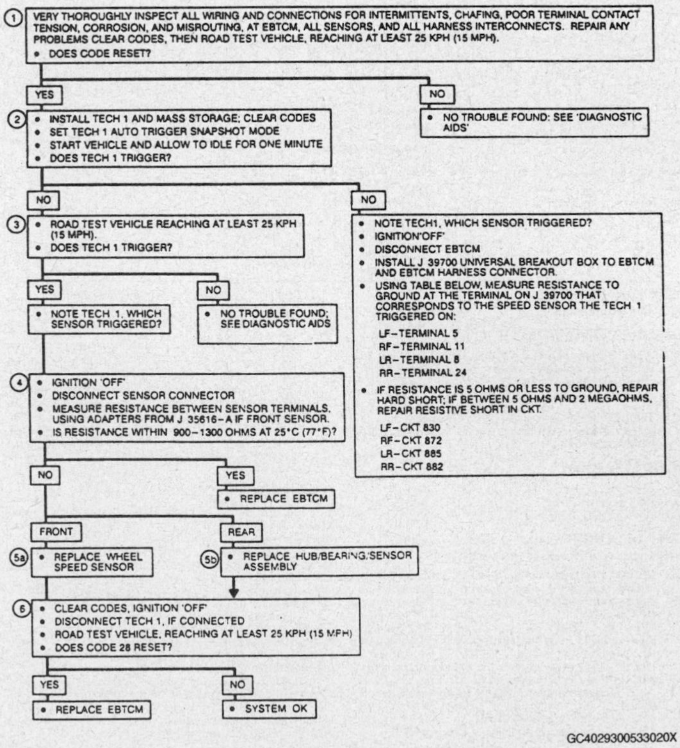
1
VERY THOROUGHLY INSPECT ALL WIRING AND CONNECTIONS FOR INTERMITTENTS, CHAFING, POOR TERMINAL CONTACT TENSION, CORROSION, AND MISROUTING, AT EBTCM, ALL SENSORS, AND ALL HARNESS INTERCONNECTS. REPAIR ANY PROBLEMS CLEAR CODES, THEN ROAD TEST VEHICLE, REACHING AT LEAST 25 KPH (15 MPH).
• DOES CODE RESET?
YES
NO
• NO TROUBLE FOUND: SEE 'DIAGNOSTIC AIDS'
2
• INSTALL TECH 1 AND MASS STORAGE; CLEAR CODES
• SET TECH 1 AUTO TRIGGER SNAPSHOT MODE
• START VEHICLE AND ALLOW TO IDLE FOR ONE MINUTE
• DOES TECH 1 TRIGGER?
NO
NO
3
• ROAD TEST VEHICLE REACHING AT LEAST 25 KPH (15 MPH).
• DOES TECH 1 TRIGGER?
YES
NO
• NOTE TECH 1, WHICH SENSOR TRIGGERED?
• NO TROUBLE FOUND; SEE DIAGNOSTIC AIDS
• NOTE TECH1, WHICH SENSOR TRIGGERED?
• IGNITION 'OFF'
• DISCONNECT EBTCM
• INSTALL J 39700 UNIVERSAL BREAKOUT BOX TO EBTCM AND EBTCM HARNESS CONNECTOR.
• USING TABLE BELOW, MEASURE RESISTANCE TO GROUND AT THE TERMINAL ON J 39700 THAT CORRESPONDS TO THE SPEED SENSOR THE TECH 1 TRIGGERED ON:
LF-TERMINAL 5
RF-TERMINAL 11
LR-TERMINAL 8
RR-TERMINAL 24
• IF RESISTANCE IS 5 OHMS OR LESS TO GROUND, REPAIR HARD SHORT; IF BETWEEN 5 OHMS AND 2 MEGAOHMS, REPAIR RESISTIVE SHORT IN CKT.
LF-CKT 830
RF-CKT 872
LR-CKT 885
RR-CKT 882
4
• IGNITION 'OFF'
• DISCONNECT SENSOR CONNECTOR
• MEASURE RESISTANCE BETWEEN SENSOR TERMINALS, USING ADAPTERS FROM J 35616-A IF FRONT SENSOR.
• IS RESISTANCE WITHIN 900-1300 OHMS AT 25°C (77°F)?
NO
YES
• REPLACE EBTCM
FRONT
REAR
5a
• REPLACE WHEEL SPEED SENSOR
5b
• REPLACE HUB/BEARING/SENSOR ASSEMBLY
6
• CLEAR CODES, IGNITION 'OFF'
• DISCONNECT TECH 1, IF CONNECTED
• ROAD TEST VEHICLE, REACHING AT LEAST 25 KPH (15 MPH)
• DOES CODE 28 RESET?
YES
NO
• REPLACE EBTCM
• SYSTEM OK
GC4029300533020X

TEST CONDITION(S):

1. Tested continuously.

FAILURE CONDITION(S):

1. While Driving: One wheel is detected at least 30 kph or 19 mph faster than the remaining wheels for an extended period of time.

   OR

   One wheel is at least 6 kph or 4 mph less than or greater than the remaining wheels for an extended period of time.

ACTION TAKEN:

1. Code set.
2. ABS/TCS switched 'OFF'.
3. 'ANTILOCK' indicator 'ON'.
4. TRACTION DISABLED' message displayed.

Code 28 is set if the EBTCM cannot specifically identify which wheel speed sensor is causing the frequency error problem. If it can define the specific speed sensor causing the problem, the Sensor Fault code associated with the sensor (21, 25, 31, 35) will be set instead of Code 28.

TEST DESCRIPTION: Test numbers refer to circled numbers on the diagnostic chart.

1. Checks wiring and connections for problems. It is critical that this step is performed thoroughly, as wiring/connector problems are the most likely cause for this code.
2. Use the TECH 1 to monitor for vehicle 'electrical/electronic system 'noise' being picked up by the speed sensor circuits.
3. Use the TECH 1 to monitor the wheel speed sensors while the vehicle is operating. If the TECH 1 Auto-Trigger Snapshot mode triggers, the speed sensor or the wiring and/or connectors are going intermittent during the road test.
4. Checks for proper resistance in the sensor itself.

5a. Replace rear wheel speed sensor as the likely cause of the triggering intermittent.

5b. Replaces front wheel speed sensor as the likely cause of the triggering intermittent.

6. Use the TECH 1 to monitor the wheel speed sensors while the vehicle is operating. If the TECH 1 Auto-Snapshot mode triggers, the EBTCM must be concluding there is a problem with wheel speed sensor frequencies when there is not.
7. Checks for a short to ground in the speed sensor input circuit wires. The circuit to be tested depends on which speed sensor triggered the TECH 1. The ground may be either a 'hard' short to ground, or a resistive short. A short with a resistance less that 2 megaohms, though not a hard short, can still cause Code 28 to set.

DIAGNOSTIC AIDS:

Be sure the speed sensor wiring is properly routed and retained. This will help prevent false signals due to electrical noise being picked up by the wiring.

It is very important that a thorough inspection of the wiring and connectors be performed. Failure to carefully and fully inspect wiring and connectors may result in misdiagnosis, causing part replacement with reappearance of the fault.

Front Speed Sensors Only:

Check the toothed wheel for any large grooves, gouges, marks, etc. that might influence the tooth's signal at the wheel speed sensor. Also check for a buildup of foreign material in the gaps between teeth in the toothed wheel; this material may cause this fault.

A worn hub/bearing assembly may cause this fault in extreme cases; the bearing play allows the sensor-to-toothed-ring gap to change excessively. Never reuse a wheel speed sensor once it has been separated from the front hub/bearing assembly.

GC4029300533010X

Fig. 99 Code 28: Wheel Speed Sensor Frequency Error. 1993-94 DeVille, Eldorado & Seville

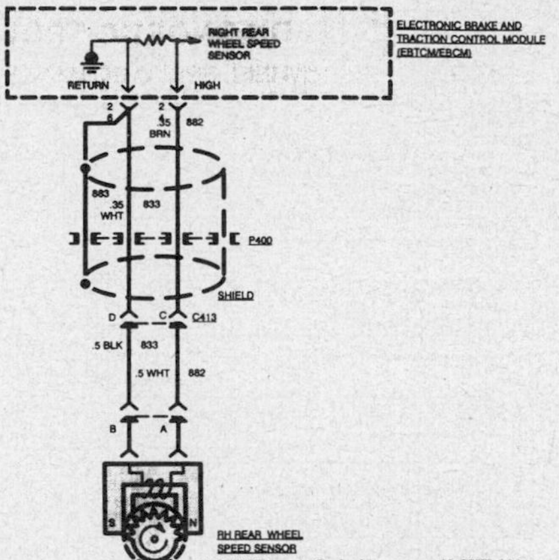
ELECTRONIC BRAKE AND TRACTION CONTROL MODULE (EBTCM/EBCM)
RIGHT REAR WHEEL SPEED SENSOR
RETURN
HIGH
.35 BRN
882
883
.35 WHT
833
P400
SHIELD
C413
.5 BLK
.5 WHT
RH REAR WHEEL SPEED SENSOR

CIRCUIT DESCRIPTION:

As each wheel turns, the wheel speed sensor for that wheel creates a small AC voltage as a toothed sensor ring, mounted in the front integral hub/bearing assembly, is passed by the stationary sensor. The sensor consists of a permanent magnet and coil and generates voltage by magnetic induction. The frequency of the wheel speed sensor signal is proportional to wheel speed.

The EBTCM/EBCM uses the wheel speed sensor signal to calculate vehicle reference speeds and individual speed, acceleration and slip values for each wheel. These values are used to determine when antilock control is required.

The EBTCM/EBCM will only set one wheel speed sensor fault code at a time, even if multiple faults exist. Detection is prioritized accordingly: LF, RR, LR, RF. Always check for additional stored codes after making repairs.

TEST CONDITION(S):

1. Tested continuously.

FAILURE CONDITION(S):

Sensor Output

1. Drive–away: Speed signal is not detected when vehicle reaches 12 kph or 7.5 mph.
2. While Driving: Speed signal is lost while vehicle speed is greater than 40 kph or 25 mph

ACTION TAKEN:

1. Code set.
2. ABS/TCS switched 'OFF'.
3. 'ANTILOCK' indicator 'ON'.
4. 'TRACTION DISABLED' message displayed. (vehicles with TCS)

Code 21 is set if there is a short to voltage or ground in CKT 882 or 883, or faulty speed sensor. The testing for this fault occurs when the vehicle is in motion, it will not set with the ignition 'ON' and the vehicle at rest.

NOTICE: A Code 31 may set if CKT 882 or 883 lose continuity and the WSS signal is lost while driving. A Code 33 should accompany this code on the subsequent ignition cycle. If both Code 31 and Code 33 are set concurrently, diagnose Code 33 first.

TEST DESCRIPTION: Test numbers refer to circled numbers on the diagnostic chart.

1. Checks if the code resets during a road test.
2. Use the TECH 1 to check for sources of induced electrical noise. Some sources of induced electrical noise which may cause intermittent wheel speed sensor codes to set are: improper routing or sensor cables next to spark plug wires; cables not retained in brackets; loose fitting or improperly mounted sensors; damaged sensors or toothed rings; poor terminal engagement of connectors; or intermittent shorts or opens in wiring; or a loss of sensor circuit shield.
3. Checks for damaged wheel speed sensor circuit shield. The shield is a foil insulator that is wrapped around the wheel speed sensor circuits. Inside the EBTCM/EBCM harness connecter there is an uninsulated drain wire that is attached to the shield and jumped to the wheel speed sensor return line and taken to ground through the EBTCM/EBCM. A shield which has lost its ground through the EBTCM/EBCM leaves the sensor signal circuit susceptible to noise. It may be necessary to disassemble the EBTCM/EBCM connector to check if the drain wire has a poor connection with the wheel speed sensor return connector terminal. The shield can be repaired by reterminating the sensor return line circuit, including the drain wire.
4. Checks for intermittent opens/shorts in wheel speed sensor circuits and cables.

GC4029300534010X

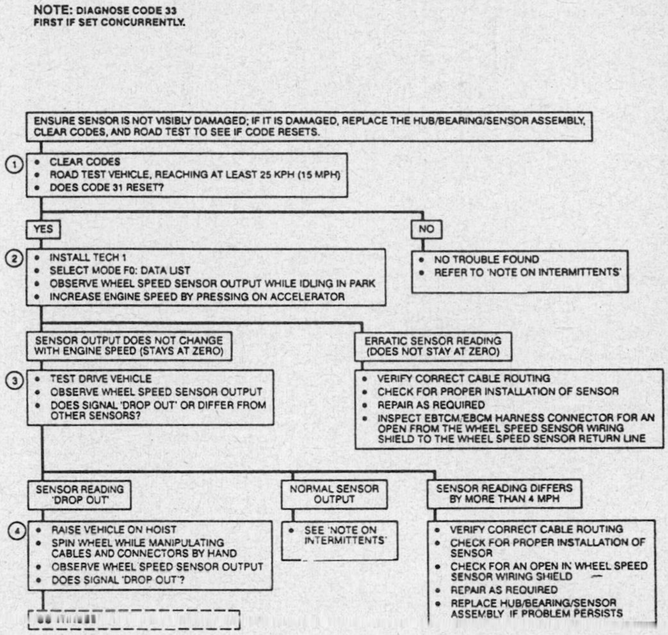
NOTE: DIAGNOSE CODE 33 FIRST IF SET CONCURRENTLY.
ENSURE SENSOR IS NOT VISIBLY DAMAGED; IF IT IS DAMAGED, REPLACE THE HUB/BEARING/SENSOR ASSEMBLY, CLEAR CODES, AND ROAD TEST TO SEE IF CODE RESETS.
1
• CLEAR CODES
• ROAD TEST VEHICLE, REACHING AT LEAST 25 KPH (15 MPH)
• DOES CODE 31 RESET?
YES
NO
• NO TROUBLE FOUND
• REFER TO 'NOTE ON INTERMITTENTS'
2
• INSTALL TECH 1
• SELECT MODE F0: DATA LIST
• OBSERVE WHEEL SPEED SENSOR OUTPUT WHILE IDLING IN PARK
• INCREASE ENGINE SPEED BY PRESSING ON ACCELERATOR
SENSOR OUTPUT DOES NOT CHANGE WITH ENGINE SPEED (STAYS AT ZERO)
ERRATIC SENSOR READING (DOES NOT STAY AT ZERO)
3
• TEST DRIVE VEHICLE
• OBSERVE WHEEL SPEED SENSOR OUTPUT
• DOES SIGNAL 'DROP OUT' OR DIFFER FROM OTHER SENSORS?
• VERIFY CORRECT CABLE ROUTING
• CHECK FOR PROPER INSTALLATION OF SENSOR
• REPAIR AS REQUIRED
• INSPECT EBTCM/EBCM HARNESS CONNECTOR FOR AN OPEN FROM THE WHEEL SPEED SENSOR WIRING SHIELD TO THE WHEEL SPEED SENSOR RETURN LINE
SENSOR READING 'DROP OUT'
NORMAL SENSOR OUTPUT
SENSOR READING DIFFERS BY MORE THAN 4 MPH
4
• RAISE VEHICLE ON HOIST
• SPIN WHEEL WHILE MANIPULATING CABLES AND CONNECTORS BY HAND
• OBSERVE WHEEL SPEED SENSOR OUTPUT
• DOES SIGNAL 'DROP OUT'?
• SEE 'NOTE ON INTERMITTENTS'
• VERIFY CORRECT CABLE ROUTING
• CHECK FOR PROPER INSTALLATION OF SENSOR
• CHECK FOR AN OPEN IN WHEEL SPEED SENSOR WIRING SHIELD
• REPAIR AS REQUIRED
• REPLACE HUB/BEARING/SENSOR ASSEMBLY IF PROBLEM PERSISTS

GC4029300534020X

Fig. 100 Code 31: Right Rear Wheel Speed Sensor Fault (Part 1 of 2). 1993-94 DeVille, Eldorado & Seville

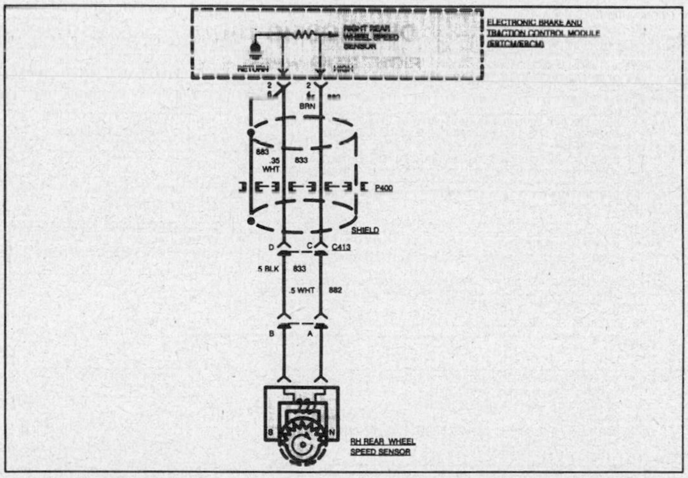
ELECTRONIC BRAKE AND TRACTION CONTROL MODULE (EBTCM/EBCM)
RIGHT REAR WHEEL SPEED SENSOR
RETURN
HIGH
BRN
883
.35 WHT
833
P400
SHIELD
C413
.5 BLK
.5 WHT
882
RH REAR WHEEL SPEED SENSOR

CIRCUIT DESCRIPTION:

As each wheel turns, the wheel speed sensor for that wheel creates a small AC voltage as a toothed sensor ring, mounted in the front integral hub/bearing assembly, is passed by the stationary sensor. The sensor consists of a permanent magnet and coil and generates voltage by magnetic induction. The frequency of the wheel speed sensor signal is proportional to wheel speed.

The EBTCM/EBCM uses the wheel speed sensor signal to calculate vehicle reference speeds and individual speed, acceleration and slip values for each wheel. These values are used to determine when antilock control is required.

The EBTCM/EBCM will only set one wheel speed sensor fault code at a time, even if multiple faults exist. Detection is prioritized accordingly: LF, RR, LR, RF. Always check for additional stored codes after making repairs.

TEST DESCRIPTION: Test numbers refer to circled numbers on the diagnostic chart.

5. Checks for proper resistance in the sensor itself.
6. Checks for a short to battery in either of the speed sensor circuit wires.
7. Checks for a short between the speed sensor circuit wires.
8. Checks for a short to ground in the speed sensor input circuit wire. The ground may be either a 'hard' short to ground, or a resistive short. A short with a resistance less than 2 megaohms, through not a hard short, can still cause Code 21 to set.
9. Checks wiring and connectors for intermittents.

GC4029300534030X

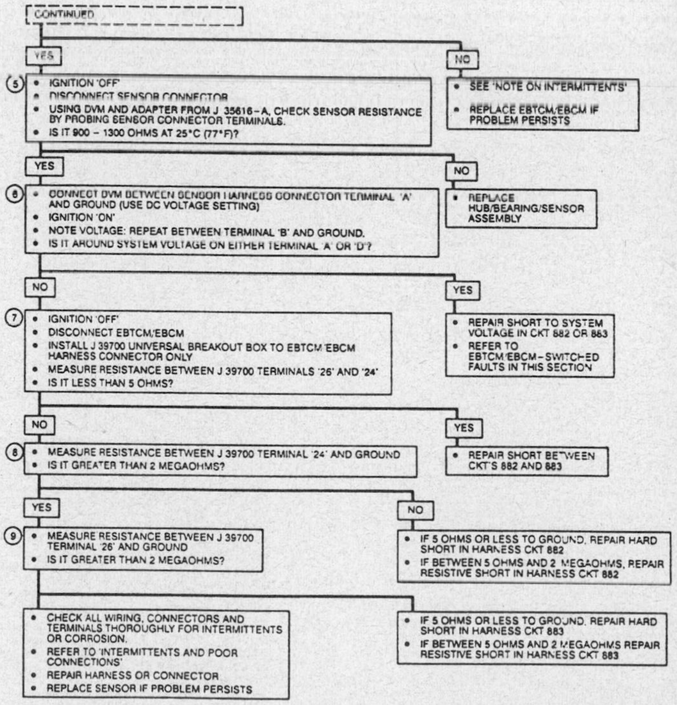
CONTINUED
YES
NO
5
• IGNITION 'OFF'
• DISCONNECT SENSOR CONNECTOR
• USING DVM AND ADAPTER FROM J 35616–A, CHECK SENSOR RESISTANCE BY PROBING SENSOR CONNECTOR TERMINALS.
• IS IT 900 – 1300 OHMS AT 25°C (77°F)?
• SEE 'NOTE ON INTERMITTENTS'
• REPLACE EBTCM/EBCM IF PROBLEM PERSISTS
YES
NO
6
• CONNECT DVM BETWEEN SENSOR HARNESS CONNECTOR TERMINAL 'A' AND GROUND (USE DC VOLTAGE SETTING)
• IGNITION 'ON'
• NOTE VOLTAGE: REPEAT BETWEEN TERMINAL 'B' AND GROUND.
• IS IT AROUND SYSTEM VOLTAGE ON EITHER TERMINAL 'A' OR 'D'?
• REPLACE HUB/BEARING/SENSOR ASSEMBLY
NO
YES
7
• IGNITION 'OFF'
• DISCONNECT EBTCM/EBCM
• INSTALL J 39700 UNIVERSAL BREAKOUT BOX TO EBTCM/EBCM HARNESS CONNECTOR ONLY
• MEASURE RESISTANCE BETWEEN J 39700 TERMINALS '26' AND '24'
• IS IT LESS THAN 5 OHMS?
• REPAIR SHORT TO SYSTEM VOLTAGE IN CKT 882 OR 883
• REFER TO EBTCM/EBCM–SWITCHED FAULTS IN THIS SECTION
NO
YES
8
• MEASURE RESISTANCE BETWEEN J 39700 TERMINAL '24' AND GROUND
• IS IT GREATER THAN 2 MEGAOHMS?
• REPAIR SHORT BETWEEN CKT'S 882 AND 883
YES
NO
9
• MEASURE RESISTANCE BETWEEN J 39700 TERMINAL '26' AND GROUND
• IS IT GREATER THAN 2 MEGAOHMS?
• IF 5 OHMS OR LESS TO GROUND, REPAIR HARD SHORT IN HARNESS CKT 882
• IF BETWEEN 5 OHMS AND 2 MEGAOHMS, REPAIR RESISTIVE SHORT IN HARNESS CKT 882
• CHECK ALL WIRING, CONNECTORS AND TERMINALS THOROUGHLY FOR INTERMITTENTS OR CORROSION.
• REFER TO 'INTERMITTENTS AND POOR CONNECTIONS'
• REPAIR HARNESS OR CONNECTOR
• REPLACE SENSOR IF PROBLEM PERSISTS
• IF 5 OHMS OR LESS TO GROUND, REPAIR HARD SHORT IN HARNESS CKT 883
• IF BETWEEN 5 OHMS AND 2 MEGAOHMS REPAIR RESISTIVE SHORT IN HARNESS CKT 883

GC4029300534040X

Fig. 100 Code 31: Right Rear Wheel Speed Sensor Fault (Part 2 of 2). 1993-94 DeVille, Eldorado & Seville

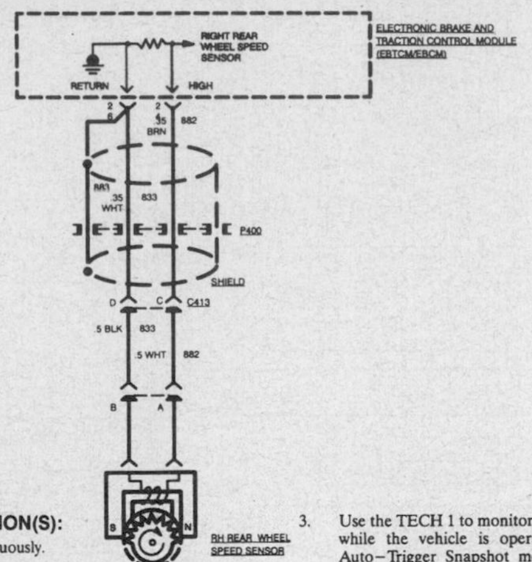
RIGHT REAR WHEEL SPEED SENSOR
ELECTRONIC BRAKE AND TRACTION CONTROL MODULE (EBTCM/EBCM)
RETURN
HIGH
.35 BRN
882
.35 WHT
833
P400
SHIELD
C413
.5 BLK
833
.5 WHT
882
RH REAR WHEEL SPEED SENSOR

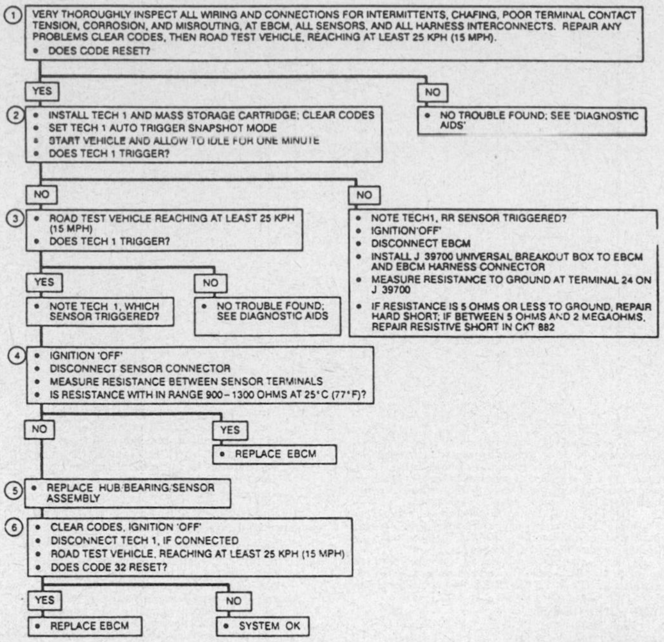
1 VERY THOROUGHLY INSPECT ALL WIRING AND CONNECTIONS FOR INTERMITTENTS, CHAFING, POOR TERMINAL CONTACT TENSION, CORROSION, AND MISROUTING, AT EBCM, ALL SENSORS, AND ALL HARNESS INTERCONNECTS. REPAIR ANY PROBLEMS CLEAR CODES, THEN ROAD TEST VEHICLE, REACHING AT LEAST 25 KPH (15 MPH).
• DOES CODE RESET?
YES
NO
• NO TROUBLE FOUND; SEE 'DIAGNOSTIC AIDS'
2 • INSTALL TECH 1 AND MASS STORAGE CARTRIDGE; CLEAR CODES
• SET TECH 1 AUTO TRIGGER SNAPSHOT MODE
• START VEHICLE AND ALLOW TO IDLE FOR ONE MINUTE
• DOES TECH 1 TRIGGER?
NO
NO
3 • ROAD TEST VEHICLE REACHING AT LEAST 25 KPH (15 MPH)
• DOES TECH 1 TRIGGER?
• NOTE TECH1, RR SENSOR TRIGGERED?
• IGNITION 'OFF'
• DISCONNECT EBCM
• INSTALL J 39700 UNIVERSAL BREAKOUT BOX TO EBCM AND EBCM HARNESS CONNECTOR
• MEASURE RESISTANCE TO GROUND AT TERMINAL 24 ON J 39700
• IF RESISTANCE IS 5 OHMS OR LESS TO GROUND, REPAIR HARD SHORT; IF BETWEEN 5 OHMS AND 2 MEGAOHMS, REPAIR RESISTIVE SHORT IN CKT 882
YES
NO
• NOTE TECH 1, WHICH SENSOR TRIGGERED?
• NO TROUBLE FOUND; SEE DIAGNOSTIC AIDS
4 • IGNITION 'OFF'
• DISCONNECT SENSOR CONNECTOR
• MEASURE RESISTANCE BETWEEN SENSOR TERMINALS
• IS RESISTANCE WITH IN RANGE 900–1300 OHMS AT 25°C (77°F)?
NO
YES
• REPLACE EBCM
5 • REPLACE HUB/BEARING/SENSOR ASSEMBLY
6 • CLEAR CODES, IGNITION 'OFF'
• DISCONNECT TECH 1, IF CONNECTED
• ROAD TEST VEHICLE, REACHING AT LEAST 25 KPH (15 MPH)
• DOES CODE 32 RESET?
YES
NO
• REPLACE EBCM
• SYSTEM OK

GC4029300535020X

TEST CONDITION(S):

1. Tested continuously.

FAILURE CONDITION(S):

1. While Driving: One wheel is detected at least 30 kph or 19 mph faster than the remaining wheels for an extended period of time.

OR

One wheel is at least 6 kph or 4 mph less than or greater than the remaining wheels for an extended period of time.

ACTION TAKEN:

1. Code set.
2. ABS switched 'OFF'.
3. 'ANTILOCK' indicator 'ON'.

TEST DESCRIPTION: Test numbers refer to circled numbers on the diagnostic chart.

1. Checks wiring and connections for problems. It is critical that this step is performed thoroughly, as wiring/connector problems are the most likely cause for this code.
2. Use the TECH 1 to monitor for vehicle electrical/electronic system 'noise' being picked up by the speed sensor circuits.
3. Use the TECH 1 to monitor the wheel speed sensors while the vehicle is operating. If the TECH 1 Auto–Trigger Snapshot mode triggers, the speed sensor or the wiring and/or connectors are going intermittent during the road test.
4. Checks for proper resistance in the sensor itself.
5. Replace rear wheel speed sensor as the likely cause of the triggering intermittent.
6. Use the TECH 1 to monitor the wheel speed sensors while the vehicle is operating. If the TECH 1 Auto–Snapshot mode triggers, the EBTCM/EBCM must be concluding there is a problem with wheel speed sensor frequencies when there is not.
7. Checks for a short to ground in the speed sensor input circuit wires. The circuit to be tested depends on which speed sensor triggered the TECH 1. The ground may be either a 'hard' short to ground, or a resistive short. A short with a resistance less that 2 megaohms, though not a hard short, can still cause Code 32 to set.

DIAGNOSTIC AIDS:

Be sure the speed sensor wiring is properly routed and retained. This will help prevent false signals due to electrical noise being picked up by the wiring.

It is very important that a thorough inspection of the wiring and connectors be performed. Failure to carefully and fully inspect wiring and connectors may result in misdiagnosis, causing part replacement with reappearance of the fault.

GC4029300535010X

Fig. 101 Code 32: Right Rear Wheel Speed Sensor Frequency Error. 1993-94 DeVille, Eldorado & Seville

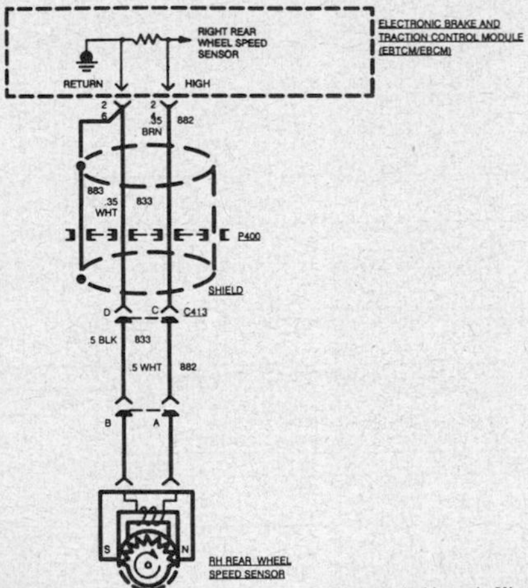
RIGHT REAR WHEEL SPEED SENSOR
ELECTRONIC BRAKE AND TRACTION CONTROL MODULE (EBTCM/EBCM)
RETURN
HIGH
.35 BRN
882
883
.35 WHT
833
P400
SHIELD
C413
.5 BLK
833
.5 WHT
882
RH REAR WHEEL SPEED SENSOR

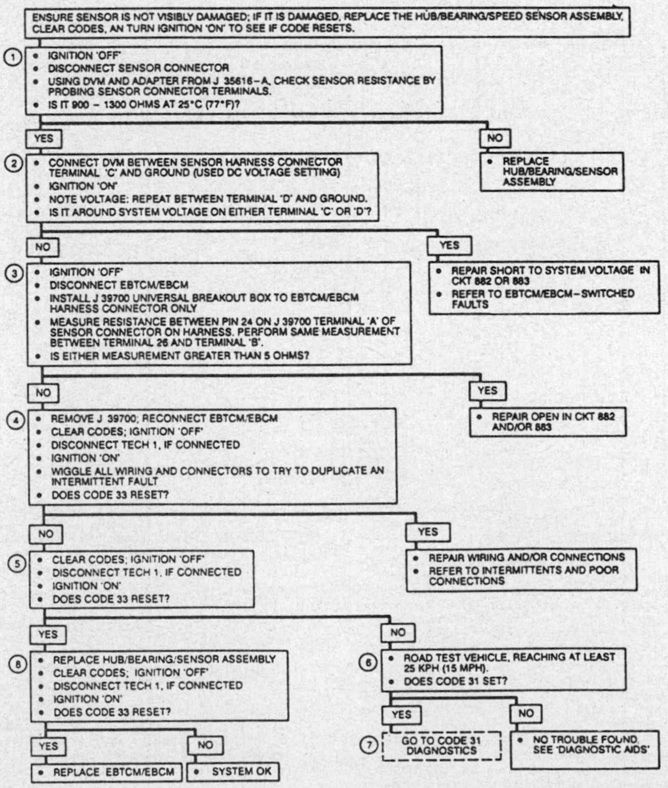
ENSURE SENSOR IS NOT VISIBLY DAMAGED; IF IT IS DAMAGED, REPLACE THE HUB/BEARING/SPEED SENSOR ASSEMBLY, CLEAR CODES, AN TURN IGNITION 'ON' TO SEE IF CODE RESETS.
1 • IGNITION 'OFF'
• DISCONNECT SENSOR CONNECTOR
• USING DVM AND ADAPTER FROM J 35616–A, CHECK SENSOR RESISTANCE BY PROBING SENSOR CONNECTOR TERMINALS.
• IS IT 900 – 1300 OHMS AT 25°C (77°F)?
YES
NO
• REPLACE HUB/BEARING/SENSOR ASSEMBLY
2 • CONNECT DVM BETWEEN SENSOR HARNESS CONNECTOR TERMINAL 'C' AND GROUND (USED DC VOLTAGE SETTING)
• IGNITION 'ON'
• NOTE VOLTAGE: REPEAT BETWEEN TERMINAL 'D' AND GROUND.
• IS IT AROUND SYSTEM VOLTAGE ON EITHER TERMINAL 'C' OR 'D'?
NO
YES
• REPAIR SHORT TO SYSTEM VOLTAGE IN CKT 882 OR 883
• REFER TO EBTCM/EBCM–SWITCHED FAULTS
3 • IGNITION 'OFF'
• DISCONNECT EBTCM/EBCM
• INSTALL J 39700 UNIVERSAL BREAKOUT BOX TO EBTCM/EBCM HARNESS CONNECTOR ONLY
• MEASURE RESISTANCE BETWEEN PIN 24 ON J 39700 TERMINAL 'A' OF SENSOR CONNECTOR ON HARNESS. PERFORM SAME MEASUREMENT BETWEEN TERMINAL 26 AND TERMINAL 'B'.
• IS EITHER MEASUREMENT GREATER THAN 5 OHMS?
NO
YES
• REPAIR OPEN IN CKT 882 AND/OR 883
4 • REMOVE J 39700; RECONNECT EBTCM/EBCM
• CLEAR CODES; IGNITION 'OFF'
• DISCONNECT TECH 1, IF CONNECTED
• IGNITION 'ON'
• WIGGLE ALL WIRING AND CONNECTORS TO TRY TO DUPLICATE AN INTERMITTENT FAULT
• DOES CODE 33 RESET?
NO
YES
• REPAIR WIRING AND/OR CONNECTIONS
• REFER TO INTERMITTENTS AND POOR CONNECTIONS
5 • CLEAR CODES; IGNITION 'OFF'
• DISCONNECT TECH 1, IF CONNECTED
• IGNITION 'ON'
• DOES CODE 33 RESET?
YES
NO
8 • REPLACE HUB/BEARING/SENSOR ASSEMBLY
• CLEAR CODES; IGNITION 'OFF'
• DISCONNECT TECH 1, IF CONNECTED
• IGNITION 'ON'
• DOES CODE 33 RESET?
6 • ROAD TEST VEHICLE, REACHING AT LEAST 25 KPH (15 MPH).
• DOES CODE 31 SET?
YES
NO
7 GO TO CODE 31 DIAGNOSTICS
• NO TROUBLE FOUND, SEE 'DIAGNOSTIC AIDS'
YES
NO
• REPLACE EBTCM/EBCM
• SYSTEM OK

GC4029300536020X

CIRCUIT DESCRIPTION:

As each wheel turns, the wheel speed sensor for that wheel creates a small AC voltage as a toothed sensor ring, mounted in the front integral hub/bearing assembly, is passed by the stationary sensor. The sensor consists of a permanent magnet and coil and generates voltage by magnetic induction. The frequency of the wheel speed sensor signal is proportional to wheel speed.

The EBTCM/EBCM uses the wheel speed sensor signal to calculate vehicle reference speeds and individual speed, acceleration and slip values for each wheel. These values are used to determine when antilock control is required.

The EBTCM/EBCM will only set one wheel speed sensor fault code at a time, even if multiple faults exist. Detection is prioritized accordingly: LF, RR, LR, RF. Always check for additional stored codes after making repairs.

TEST CONDITION(S):

1. Tested continuously.

FAILURE CONDITION(S):

Continuity

1. While standing: Open circuit is seen while the vehicle is standing still with the ignition 'ON'.

ACTION TAKEN:

1. Code set.
2. ABS/TCS switched 'OFF'.
3. 'ANTILOCK' indicator 'ON'.
4. 'TRACTION DISABLED' message displayed. (vehicles with TCS)

Code 33 is set if there is a short to voltage or an open in CKT 882 or 883, or faulty speed sensor. The testing for this fault occurs with the ignition 'ON' and the vehicle at rest.

NOTICE: A Code 31 may set if CKT 882 or 883 lose continuity and the WSS signal is lost while driving. A Code 33 should accompany this code on the subsequent ignition cycle. If both Code 31 and Code 33 are set concurrently, diagnose Code 33 first.

TEST DESCRIPTION: Test numbers refer to circled numbers on the diagnostic chart.

1. Checks for proper resistance in the sensor itself.
2. Checks for a short to battery in either of the speed sensor circuit wires. There should be 5V on CKT 882. If there is, CKT 882 has no hard opens or shorts. The condition may be intermittent.
3. Checks for an open in both the speed sensor circuit wires.
4. Manipulates wiring and connectors, trying to induce an intermittent fault not currently present.
5. This test checks if the code resets on key–up. If so, since Tests 1–4 have validated that the circuitry and components are good, the speed sensor may be causing the fault.
6. Checks if the Code 31 sets during a road test.
7. Code 33 sets when the vehicle is at rest: Code 31 sets with a problem in the speed sensor circuitry with the vehicle in motion. If problems are still present, Code 31 would set during the road test, not a 33. If Code 33 sets at this point, Code 31 diagnostics should be used.
8. The wheel speed sensor may be causing an intermittent fault. If Code 33 resets after sensor replacement, the EBTCM/EBCM must be concluding there is a problem present in the speed sensor circuit when there is not.

DIAGNOSTIC AIDS:

Be sure the speed sensor wiring is properly routed and retained. This will help prevent false signals due to electrical noise being picked up by the wiring.

It is very important that a thorough inspection of the wiring and connectors be performed. Failure to carefully and fully inspect wiring and connectors may result in misdiagnosis, causing part replacement with reappearance of the fault.

GC4029300536010X

Fig. 102 Code 33: Right Rear Wheel Speed Sensor Continuity Fault. 1993-94 DeVille, Eldorado & Seville

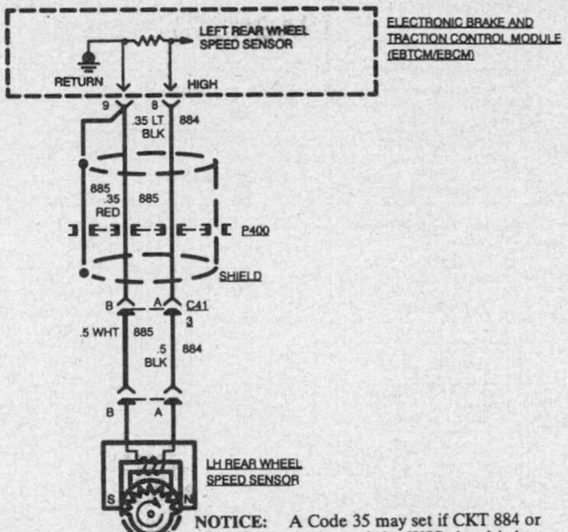
LEFT REAR WHEEL SPEED SENSOR
ELECTRONIC BRAKE AND TRACTION CONTROL MODULE (EBTCM/EBCM)
RETURN
HIGH
9
8
.35 LT BLK
884
885
.35 RED
885
P400
SHIELD
B
A
C41
3
.5 WHT
885
.5 BLK
884
B
A
LH REAR WHEEL SPEED SENSOR
S
N

CIRCUIT DESCRIPTION:

As each wheel turns, the wheel speed sensor for that wheel creates a small AC voltage as a toothed sensor ring, mounted in the front integral hub/bearing assembly, is passed by the stationary sensor. The sensor consists of a permanent magnet and coil and generates voltage by magnetic induction. The frequency of the wheel speed sensor signal is proportional to wheel speed.

The EBTCM/EBCM uses the wheel speed sensor signal to calculate vehicle reference speeds and individual speed, acceleration and slip values for each wheel. These values are used to determine when antilock control is required.

The EBTCM/EBCM will only set one wheel speed sensor fault code at a time, even if multiple faults exist. Detection is prioritized accordingly: LF, RR, LR, RF. Always check for additional stored codes after making repairs.

TEST CONDITION(S):

1. Tested continuously.

FAILURE CONDITION(S):

Sensor Output

1. Drive–away: Speed signal is not detected when vehicle reaches 12 kph or 7.5 mph.
2. While Driving: Speed signal is lost while vehicle speed is greater than 40 kph or 25 mph.

ACTION TAKEN:

1. Code set.
2. ABS/TCS switched 'OFF'.
3. 'ANTILOCK' indicator 'ON'.
4. 'TRACTION DISABLED' message displayed. (vehicles with TCS)

Code 35 is set if there is a short to voltage or ground in CKT 885 or 884, or faulty speed sensor. The testing for this fault occurs when the vehicle is in motion, it will not set with the ignition 'ON' and the vehicle at rest.

NOTICE: A Code 35 may set if CKT 884 or 885 lose continuity and the WSS signal is lost while driving. A Code 37 should accompany this code on the subsequent ignition cycle. If both Code 35 and Code 37 are set concurrently, diagnose Code 37 first.

TEST DESCRIPTION: Test numbers refer to circled numbers on the diagnostic chart.

1. Checks if the code resets during a road test.
2. Use the TECH 1 to check for sources of induced electrical noise. Some sources of induced electrical noise which may cause intermittent wheel speed sensor codes to set are: improper routing or sensor cables next to spark plug wires; cables not retained in brackets; loose fitting or improperly mounted sensors; damaged sensors or toothed rings; poor terminal engagement of connectors; or intermittent shorts or opens in wiring; or a loss of sensor circuit shield.
3. Checks for damaged wheel speed sensor circuit shield. The shield is a foil insulator that is wrapped around the wheel speed sensor circuits. Inside the EBTCM/EBCM harness connecter there is an uninsulated drain wire that is attached to the shield and jumped to the wheel speed sensor return line and taken to ground through the EBTCM/EBCM. A shield which has lost its ground through the EBTCM/EBCM leaves the sensor signal circuit susceptible to noise. It may be necessary to disassemble the EBTCM/EBCM connector to check if the drain wire has a poor connection with the wheel speed sensor return connector terminal. The shield can be repaired by reterminating the sensor return line circuit, including the drain wire.
4. Checks for intermittent opens/shorts in wheel speed sensor circuits and cables

GC4029300537010X

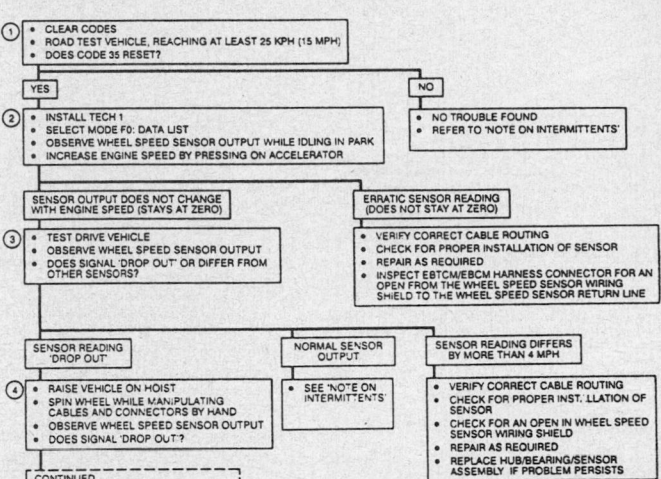

NOTE: DIAGNOSE CODE 37 FIRST IF SET CONCURRENTLY.

(1)
- CLEAR CODES
- ROAD TEST VEHICLE, REACHING AT LEAST 25 KPH (15 MPH)
- DOES CODE 35 RESET?

YES

(2)
- INSTALL TECH 1
- SELECT MODE F0: DATA LIST
- OBSERVE WHEEL SPEED SENSOR OUTPUT WHILE IDLING IN PARK
- INCREASE ENGINE SPEED BY PRESSING ON ACCELERATOR

NO
- NO TROUBLE FOUND
- REFER TO 'NOTE ON INTERMITTENTS'

SENSOR OUTPUT DOES NOT CHANGE WITH ENGINE SPEED (STAYS AT ZERO)

(3)
- TEST DRIVE VEHICLE
- OBSERVE WHEEL SPEED SENSOR OUTPUT
- DOES SIGNAL 'DROP OUT' OR DIFFER FROM OTHER SENSORS?

ERRATIC SENSOR READING (DOES NOT STAY AT ZERO)
- VERIFY CORRECT CABLE ROUTING
- CHECK FOR PROPER INSTALLATION OF SENSOR
- REPAIR AS REQUIRED
- INSPECT EBTCM/EBCM HARNESS CONNECTOR FOR AN OPEN FROM THE WHEEL SPEED SENSOR WIRING SHIELD TO THE WHEEL SPEED SENSOR RETURN LINE

SENSOR READING 'DROP OUT'

(4)
- RAISE VEHICLE ON HOIST
- SPIN WHEEL WHILE MANIPULATING CABLES AND CONNECTORS BY HAND
- OBSERVE WHEEL SPEED SENSOR OUTPUT
- DOES SIGNAL 'DROP OUT'?

CONTINUED

NORMAL SENSOR OUTPUT
- SEE 'NOTE ON INTERMITTENTS'

SENSOR READING DIFFERS BY MORE THAN 4 MPH
- VERIFY CORRECT CABLE ROUTING
- CHECK FOR PROPER INSTALLATION OF SENSOR
- CHECK FOR AN OPEN IN WHEEL SPEED SENSOR WIRING SHIELD
- REPAIR AS REQUIRED
- REPLACE HUB/BEARING/SENSOR ASSEMBLY IF PROBLEM PERSISTS

GC4029300537020X

Fig. 103 Code 35: Left Rear Wheel Speed Sensor Fault (Part 1 of 2). 1993-94 DeVille, Eldorado & Seville

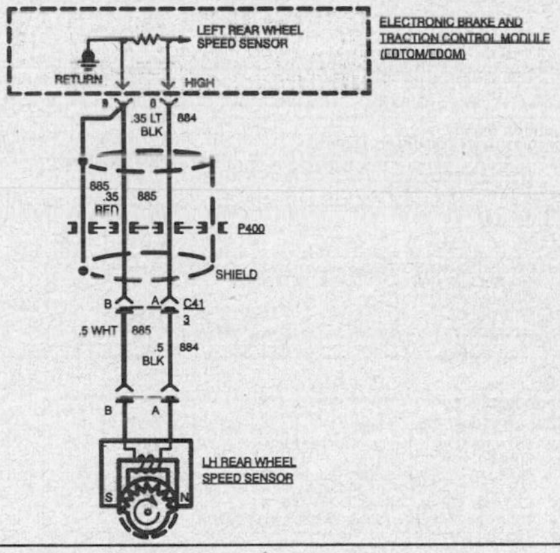
LEFT REAR WHEEL SPEED SENSOR
ELECTRONIC BRAKE AND TRACTION CONTROL MODULE (EBTCM/EBCM)
RETURN
HIGH
9
8
.35 LT BLK
884
885
.35 RED
885
P400
SHIELD
B
A
C41
3
.5 WHT
885
.5 BLK
884
B
A
LH REAR WHEEL SPEED SENSOR
S
N

DIAGNOSTIC TROUBLE CODE 35

LEFT REAR WHEEL SPEED SENSOR FAULT

CIRCUIT DESCRIPTION:

As each wheel turns, the wheel speed sensor for that wheel creates a small AC voltage as a toothed sensor ring, mounted in the front integral hub/bearing assembly, is passed by the stationary sensor. The sensor consists of a permanent magnet and coil and generates voltage by magnetic induction. The frequency of the wheel speed sensor signal is proportional to wheel speed.

The EBTCM/EBCM uses the wheel speed sensor signal to calculate vehicle reference speeds and individual speed, acceleration and slip values for each wheel. These values are used to determine when antilock control is required.

The EBTCM/EBCM will only set one wheel speed sensor fault code at a time, even if multiple faults exist. Detection is prioritized accordingly: LF, RR, LR, RF. Always check for additional stored codes after making repairs.

TEST DESCRIPTION: Test numbers refer to circled numbers on the diagnostic chart.

5. Checks for proper resistance in the sensor itself.
6. Checks for a short to battery in either of the speed sensor circuit wires.
7. Checks for a short between the speed sensor circuit wires.
8. Checks for a short to ground in the speed sensor input circuit wire. The ground may be either a 'hard' short to ground, or a resistive short. A short with a resistance less than 2 megaohms, through not a hard short, can still cause Code 21 to set.
9. Checks wiring and connectors for intermittents.

GC4029300537030X

CONTINUED

YES

(5)
- IGNITION 'OFF'
- DISCONNECT SENSOR CONNECTOR
- USING DVM AND ADAPTER FROM J 35616–A, CHECK SENSOR RESISTANCE BY PROBING SENSOR CONNECTOR TERMINALS.
- IS IT 900 – 1300 OHMS at 25°C (77°F)?

NO
- SEE 'NOTE ON INTERMITTENTS'
- REPLACE EBTCM/EBCM IF PROBLEM PERSISTS

YES

(6)
- CONNECT DVM BETWEEN SENSOR HARNESS CONNECTOR TERMINAL 'A' AND GROUND (USE DC VOLTAGE SETTING)
- IGNITION 'ON'
- NOTE VOLTAGE: REPEAT BETWEEN TERMINAL 'B' AND GROUND
- IS IT AROUND SYSTEM VOLTAGE ON EITHER TERMINAL 'A' OR 'B'?

NO
- REPLACE HUB/BEARING/SENSOR ASSEMBLY

NO

(7)
- IGNITION 'OFF'
- DISCONNECT EBTCM/EBCM
- INSTALL J 39700 UNIVERSAL BREAKOUT BOX TO EBTCM/EBCM HARNESS CONNECTOR ONLY
- MEASURE RESISTANCE BETWEEN J 39700 TERMINALS '8' AND '9'
- IS IT LESS THAN 5 OHMS?

YES
- REPAIR SHORT TO SYSTEM VOLTAGE IN CKT 884 OR 885
- REFER TO EBTCM/EBCM–SWITCHED FAULTS

NO

(8)
- MEASURE RESISTANCE BETWEEN J 39700 TERMINAL '8' AND GROUND
- IS IT GREATER THAN 2 MEGAOHMS?

YES
- REPAIR SHORT BETWEEN CKT S 884 AND 885

YES

(9)
- MEASURE RESISTANCE BETWEEN J 39700 TERMINAL '9' AND GROUND
- IS IT GREATER THAN 2 MEGAOHMS?

NO
- IF 5 OHMS OR LESS TO GROUND, REPAIR HARD SHORT IN HARNESS CKT 884
- IF BETWEEN 5 OHMS AND 2 MEGAOHMS, REPAIR RESISTIVE SHORT IN HARNESS CKT 884

- CHECK ALL WIRING, CONNECTORS AND TERMINALS THOROUGHLY FOR INTERMITTENTS OR CORROSION.
- REFER TO 'INTERMITTENTS AND POOR CONNECTIONS'
- REPAIR HARNESS OR CONNECTOR
- REPLACE SENSOR IF PROBLEM PERSISTS

- IF 5 OHMS OR LESS TO GROUND, REPAIR HARD SHORT IN HARNESS CKT 885
- IF BETWEEN 5 OHMS AND 2 MEGAOHMS REPAIR RESISTIVE SHORT IN HARNESS CKT 885

GC4029300537040X

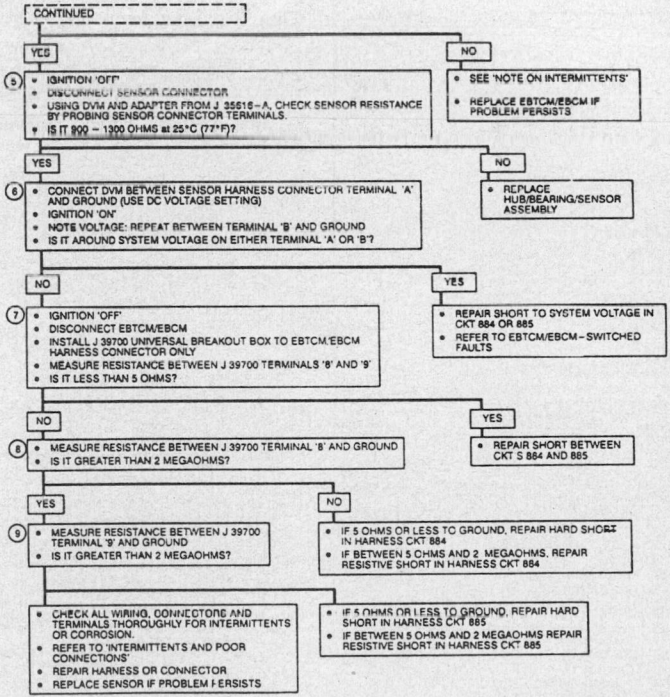

Fig. 103 Code 35: Left Rear Wheel Speed Sensor Fault (Part 2 of 2). 1993-94 DeVille, Eldorado & Seville

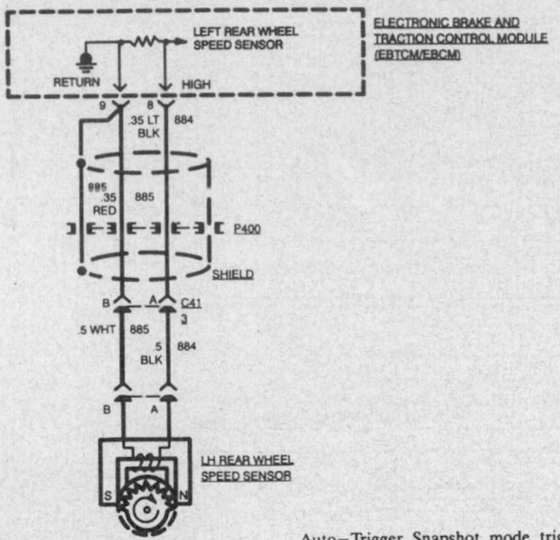

LEFT REAR WHEEL SPEED SENSOR
ELECTRONIC BRAKE AND TRACTION CONTROL MODULE (EBTCM/EBCM)
RETURN
HIGH
9
8
.35 LT BLK
884
885 .35 RED
885
P400
SHIELD
B
A
C41
3
.5 WHT
885
.5 BLK
884
B
A
LH REAR WHEEL SPEED SENSOR
S
N

TEST CONDITION(S):

1. Tested continuously.

FAILURE CONDITION(S):

1. While Driving: One wheel is detected at least 30 kph or 19 mph faster than the remaining wheels for an extended period of time.

OR

One wheel is at least 6 kph or 4 mph less than or greater than the remaining wheels for an extended period of time.

ACTION TAKEN:

1. Code set.
2. ABS switched 'OFF'.
3. 'ANTILOCK' indicator 'ON'.

TEST DESCRIPTION: Test numbers refer to circled numbers on the diagnostic chart.

1. Checks wiring and connections for problems. It is critical that this step is performed thoroughly, as wiring/connector problems are the most likely cause for this code.
2. Use the TECH 1 to monitor for vehicle electrical/electronic system 'noise' being picked up by the speed sensor circuits.
3. Use the TECH 1 to monitor the wheel speed sensors while the vehicle is operating. If the TECH 1 Auto–Trigger Snapshot mode triggers, the speed sensor or the wiring and/or connectors are going intermittent during the road test.
4. Checks for proper resistance in the sensor itself.
5. Replace rear wheel speed sensor as the likely cause of the triggering intermittent.
6. Use the TECH 1 to monitor the wheel speed sensors while the vehicle is operating. If the TECH 1 Auto–Snapshot mode triggers, the EBTCM/EBCM must be concluding there is a problem with wheel speed sensor frequencies when there is not.
7. Checks for a short to ground in the speed sensor input circuit wires. The circuit to be tested depends on which speed sensor triggered the TECH 1. The ground may be either a 'hard' short to ground, or a resistive short. A short with a resistance less that 2 megaohms, though not a hard short, can still cause Code 36 to set.

DIAGNOSTIC AIDS:

Be sure the speed sensor wiring is properly routed and retained. This will help prevent false signals due to electrical noise being picked up by the wiring.

It is very important that a thorough inspection of the wiring and connectors be performed. Failure to carefully and fully inspect wiring and connectors may result in misdiagnosis, causing part replacement with reappearance of the fault.

GC4029300538010X

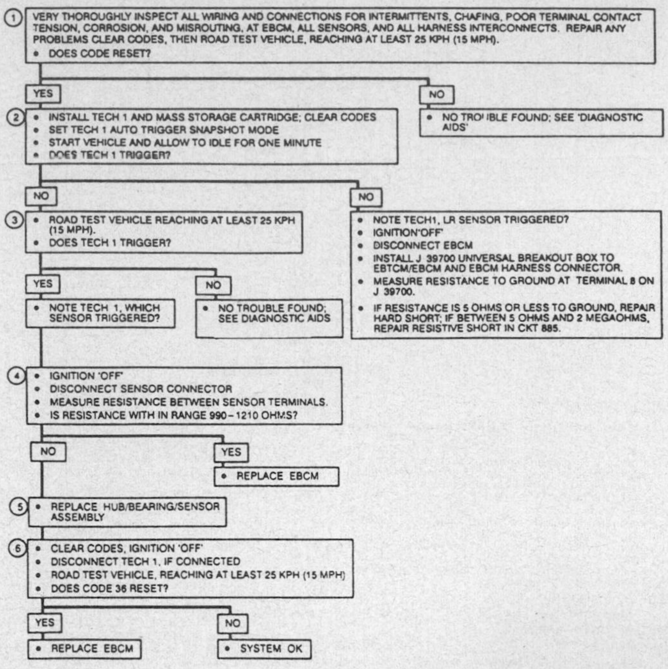

1 VERY THOROUGHLY INSPECT ALL WIRING AND CONNECTIONS FOR INTERMITTENTS, CHAFING, POOR TERMINAL CONTACT TENSION, CORROSION, AND MISROUTING, AT EBCM, ALL SENSORS, AND ALL HARNESS INTERCONNECTS. REPAIR ANY PROBLEMS CLEAR CODES, THEN ROAD TEST VEHICLE, REACHING AT LEAST 25 KPH (15 MPH).
• DOES CODE RESET?
YES
NO
• NO TROUBLE FOUND; SEE 'DIAGNOSTIC AIDS'
2 • INSTALL TECH 1 AND MASS STORAGE CARTRIDGE; CLEAR CODES
• SET TECH 1 AUTO TRIGGER SNAPSHOT MODE
• START VEHICLE AND ALLOW TO IDLE FOR ONE MINUTE
• DOES TECH 1 TRIGGER?
NO
NO
3 • ROAD TEST VEHICLE REACHING AT LEAST 25 KPH (15 MPH).
• DOES TECH 1 TRIGGER?
• NOTE TECH1, LR SENSOR TRIGGERED?
• IGNITION 'OFF'
• DISCONNECT EBCM
• INSTALL J 39700 UNIVERSAL BREAKOUT BOX TO EBTCM/EBCM AND EBCM HARNESS CONNECTOR.
• MEASURE RESISTANCE TO GROUND AT TERMINAL 8 ON J 39700.
• IF RESISTANCE IS 5 OHMS OR LESS TO GROUND, REPAIR HARD SHORT; IF BETWEEN 5 OHMS AND 2 MEGAOHMS, REPAIR RESISTIVE SHORT IN CKT 885.
YES
NO
• NOTE TECH 1, WHICH SENSOR TRIGGERED?
• NO TROUBLE FOUND; SEE DIAGNOSTIC AIDS
4 • IGNITION 'OFF'
• DISCONNECT SENSOR CONNECTOR
• MEASURE RESISTANCE BETWEEN SENSOR TERMINALS.
• IS RESISTANCE WITH IN RANGE 990 - 1210 OHMS?
NO
YES
• REPLACE EBCM
5 • REPLACE HUB/BEARING/SENSOR ASSEMBLY
6 • CLEAR CODES, IGNITION 'OFF'
• DISCONNECT TECH 1, IF CONNECTED
• ROAD TEST VEHICLE, REACHING AT LEAST 25 KPH (15 MPH)
• DOES CODE 36 RESET?
YES
NO
• REPLACE EBCM
• SYSTEM OK

GC4029300538020X

Fig. 104 Code 36: Left Rear Wheel Speed Sensor Frequency Error. 1993-94 DeVille, Eldorado & Seville

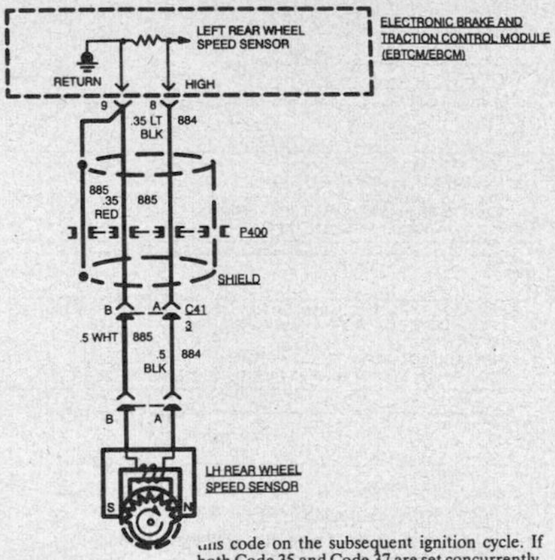

LEFT REAR WHEEL SPEED SENSOR
ELECTRONIC BRAKE AND TRACTION CONTROL MODULE (EBTCM/EBCM)
RETURN
HIGH
9
8
.35 LT BLK
884
885 .35 RED
885
P400
SHIELD
B
A
C41
3
.5 WHT
885
.5 BLK
884
B
A
LH REAR WHEEL SPEED SENSOR
S
N

CIRCUIT DESCRIPTION:

As each wheel turns, the wheel speed sensor for that wheel creates a small AC voltage as a toothed sensor ring, mounted in the front integral hub/bearing assembly, is passed by the stationary sensor. The sensor consists of a permanent magnet and coil and generates voltage by magnetic induction. The frequency of the wheel speed sensor signal is proportional to wheel speed.

The EBTCM/EBCM uses the wheel speed sensor signal to calculate vehicle reference speeds and individual speed, acceleration and slip values for each wheel. These values are used to determine when antilock control is required.

The EBTCM/EBCM will only set one wheel speed sensor fault code at a time, even if multiple faults exist. Detection is prioritized accordingly: LF, RR, LR, RF. Always check for additional stored codes after making repairs.

TEST CONDITION(S):

1. Tested continuously.

FAILURE CONDITION(S):

Continuity

1. While standing: Open circuit is seen while the vehicle is standing still with the ignition 'ON'

ACTION TAKEN:

1. Code set.
2. ABS/TCS switched 'OFF'.
3. 'ANTILOCK' indicator 'ON'.
4. 'TRACTION DISABLED' message displayed. (vehicles with TCS)

Code 37 is set if there is a short to voltage or an open in CKT 885 or 884, or faulty speed sensor. The testing for this fault occurs with the ignition 'ON' and the vehicle at rest.

NOTICE: A Code 35 may set if CKT 884 or 885 lose continuity and the WSS signal is lost while driving. A Code 37 should accompany this code on the subsequent ignition cycle. If both Code 35 and Code 37 are set concurrently, diagnose Code 37 first.

TEST DESCRIPTION: Test numbers refer to circled numbers on the diagnostic chart.

1. Checks for proper resistance in the sensor itself.
2. Checks for a short to battery in either of the speed sensor circuit wires. There should be 5V on CKT 884. If there is, CKT 884 has no hard opens or shorts. The condition may be intermittent.
3. Checks for an open in both the speed sensor circuit wires.
4. Manipulates wiring and connectors, trying to induce an intermittent fault not currently present.
5. This test checks if the code resets on key–up. If so, since Tests 1–4 have validated that the circuitry and components are good, the Speed Sensor may be causing the fault.
6. Checks if the Code 35 sets during a road test.
7. Code 37 sets when the vehicle is at rest: Code 35 sets with a problem in the speed sensor circuitry with the vehicle in motion. If problems are still present, Code 35 would set during the road test, not a 37. If Code 35 sets at this point, Code 35 diagnostics should be used.
8. The wheel speed sensor may be causing an intermittent fault. If Code 37 resets after sensor replacement, the EBTCM/EBCM must be concluding there is a problem present in the speed sensor circuit when there is not.

DIAGNOSTIC AIDS:

Be sure the speed sensor wiring is properly routed and retained. This will help prevent false signals due to electrical noise being picked up by the wiring.

It is very important that a thorough inspection of the wiring and connectors be performed. Failure to carefully and fully inspect wiring and connectors may result in misdiagnosis, causing part replacement with reappearance of the fault.

GC4029300539010X

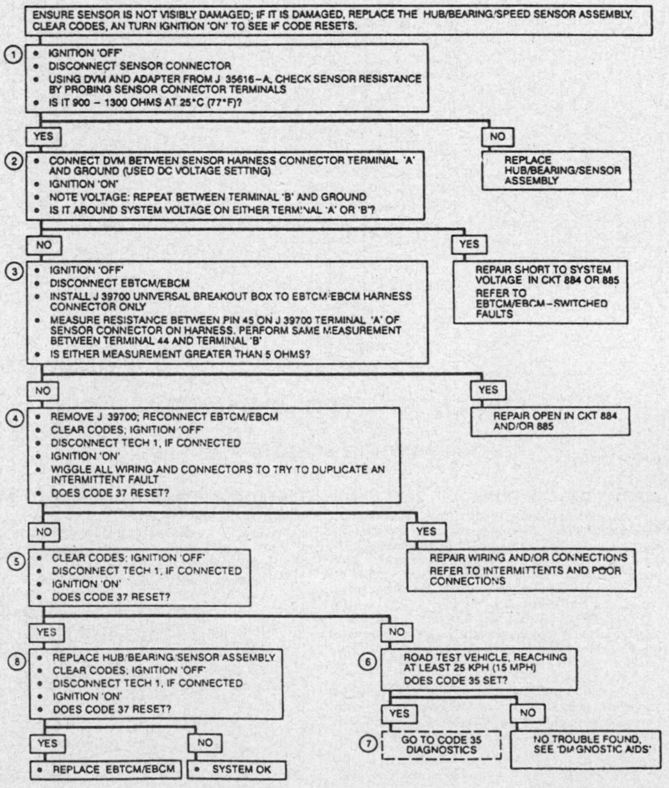

ENSURE SENSOR IS NOT VISIBLY DAMAGED; IF IT IS DAMAGED, REPLACE THE HUB/BEARING/SPEED SENSOR ASSEMBLY, CLEAR CODES, AN TURN IGNITION 'ON' TO SEE IF CODE RESETS.
1 • IGNITION 'OFF'
• DISCONNECT SENSOR CONNECTOR
• USING DVM AND ADAPTER FROM J 35616-A, CHECK SENSOR RESISTANCE BY PROBING SENSOR CONNECTOR TERMINALS
• IS IT 900 - 1300 OHMS AT 25°C (77°F)?
YES
NO
REPLACE HUB/BEARING/SENSOR ASSEMBLY
2 • CONNECT DVM BETWEEN SENSOR HARNESS CONNECTOR TERMINAL 'A' AND GROUND (USED DC VOLTAGE SETTING)
• IGNITION 'ON'
• NOTE VOLTAGE: REPEAT BETWEEN TERMINAL 'B' AND GROUND
• IS IT AROUND SYSTEM VOLTAGE ON EITHER TERMINAL 'A' OR 'B'?
NO
YES
REPAIR SHORT TO SYSTEM VOLTAGE IN CKT 884 OR 885 REFER TO EBTCM/EBCM-SWITCHED FAULTS
3 • IGNITION 'OFF'
• DISCONNECT EBTCM/EBCM
• INSTALL J 39700 UNIVERSAL BREAKOUT BOX TO EBTCM/EBCM HARNESS CONNECTOR ONLY
• MEASURE RESISTANCE BETWEEN PIN 45 ON J 39700 TERMINAL 'A' OF SENSOR CONNECTOR ON HARNESS. PERFORM SAME MEASUREMENT BETWEEN TERMINAL 44 AND TERMINAL 'B'
• IS EITHER MEASUREMENT GREATER THAN 5 OHMS?
NO
YES
REPAIR OPEN IN CKT 884 AND/OR 885
4 • REMOVE J 39700; RECONNECT EBTCM/EBCM
• CLEAR CODES; IGNITION 'OFF'
• DISCONNECT TECH 1, IF CONNECTED
• IGNITION 'ON'
• WIGGLE ALL WIRING AND CONNECTORS TO TRY TO DUPLICATE AN INTERMITTENT FAULT
• DOES CODE 37 RESET?
NO
YES
REPAIR WIRING AND/OR CONNECTIONS REFER TO INTERMITTENTS AND POOR CONNECTIONS
5 • CLEAR CODES; IGNITION 'OFF'
• DISCONNECT TECH 1, IF CONNECTED
• IGNITION 'ON'
• DOES CODE 37 RESET?
YES
NO
8 • REPLACE HUB/BEARING/SENSOR ASSEMBLY
• CLEAR CODES, IGNITION 'OFF'
• DISCONNECT TECH 1, IF CONNECTED
• IGNITION 'ON'
• DOES CODE 37 RESET?
6 ROAD TEST VEHICLE, REACHING AT LEAST 25 KPH (15 MPH)
DOES CODE 35 SET?
YES
NO
7 GO TO CODE 35 DIAGNOSTICS
NO TROUBLE FOUND, SEE 'DIAGNOSTIC AIDS'
YES
NO
• REPLACE EBTCM/EBCM
• SYSTEM OK

GC4029300539020X

Fig. 105 Code 37: Left Rear Wheel Speed Sensor Continuity Fault. 1993-94 DeVille, Eldorado & Seville

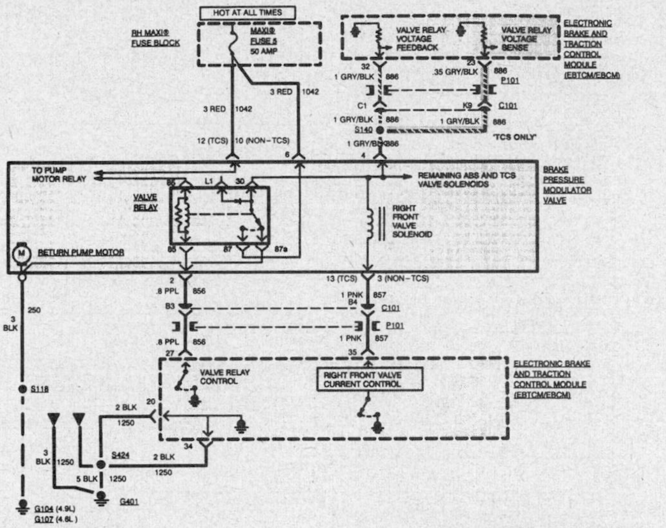

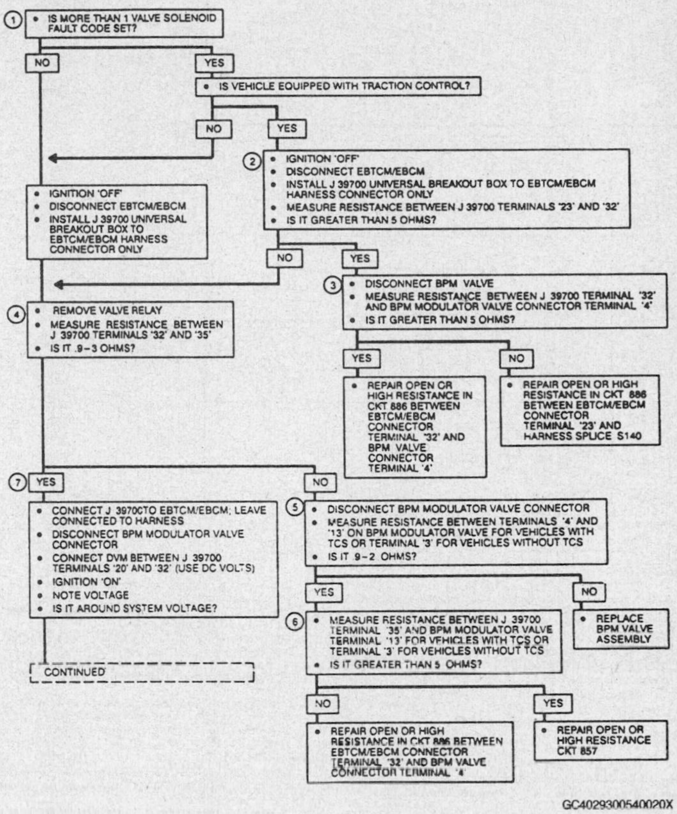
1 • IS MORE THAN 1 VALVE SOLENOID FAULT CODE SET?
NO
YES
• IS VEHICLE EQUIPPED WITH TRACTION CONTROL?
NO
YES
2 • IGNITION 'OFF'
• DISCONNECT EBTCM/EBCM
• INSTALL J 39700 UNIVERSAL BREAKOUT BOX TO EBTCM/EBCM HARNESS CONNECTOR ONLY
• MEASURE RESISTANCE BETWEEN J 39700 TERMINALS '23' AND '32'
• IS IT GREATER THAN 5 OHMS?
• IGNITION 'OFF'
• DISCONNECT EBTCM/EBCM
• INSTALL J 39700 UNIVERSAL BREAKOUT BOX TO EBTCM/EBCM HARNESS CONNECTOR ONLY
NO
YES
3 • DISCONNECT BPM VALVE
• MEASURE RESISTANCE BETWEEN J 39700 TERMINAL '32' AND BPM MODULATOR VALVE CONNECTOR TERMINAL '4'
• IS IT GREATER THAN 5 OHMS?
4 • REMOVE VALVE RELAY
• MEASURE RESISTANCE BETWEEN J 39700 TERMINALS '32' AND '35'
• IS IT .9–3 OHMS?
YES
NO
• REPAIR OPEN OR HIGH RESISTANCE IN CKT 886 BETWEEN EBTCM/EBCM CONNECTOR TERMINAL '32' AND BPM VALVE CONNECTOR TERMINAL '4'
• REPAIR OPEN OR HIGH RESISTANCE IN CKT 886 BETWEEN EBTCM/EBCM CONNECTOR TERMINAL '23' AND HARNESS SPLICE S140
7 YES
NO
• CONNECT J 39700TO EBTCM/EBCM; LEAVE CONNECTED TO HARNESS
• DISCONNECT BPM MODULATOR VALVE CONNECTOR
• CONNECT DVM BETWEEN J 39700 TERMINALS '20' AND '32' (USE DC VOLTS)
• IGNITION 'ON'
• NOTE VOLTAGE
• IS IT AROUND SYSTEM VOLTAGE?
5 • DISCONNECT BPM MODULATOR VALVE CONNECTOR
• MEASURE RESISTANCE BETWEEN TERMINALS '4' AND '13' ON BPM MODULATOR VALVE FOR VEHICLES WITH TCS OR TERMINAL '3' FOR VEHICLES WITHOUT TCS
• IS IT .9–2 OHMS?
YES
NO
6 • MEASURE RESISTANCE BETWEEN J 39700 TERMINAL '35' AND BPM MODULATOR VALVE TERMINAL '13' FOR VEHICLES WITH TCS OR TERMINAL '3' FOR VEHICLES WITHOUT TCS
• IS IT GREATER THAN 5 OHMS?
• REPLACE BPM VALVE ASSEMBLY
CONTINUED
NO
YES
• REPAIR OPEN OR HIGH RESISTANCE IN CKT 886 BETWEEN EBTCM/EBCM CONNECTOR TERMINAL '32' AND BPM VALVE CONNECTOR TERMINAL '4'
• REPAIR OPEN OR HIGH RESISTANCE CKT 857
GC4029300540020X

CIRCUIT DESCRIPTION:

The right front valve solenoid in the BPM Valve may be commanded to three different positions by the EBTCM/EBCM. Valve position is determined by the amount of current which is allowed to flow through the valve solenoid coil.

The valve solenoid circuits receive power through the valve relay on the BPM Valve. The valve relay is engaged at KEY–ON and remains engaged throughout the ignition cycle. Valve solenoid circuits should have battery voltage available at all times.

When the key is turned to RUN, power is supplied to the EBTCM/EBCM. The EBTCM/EBCM will complete an internal self–check before providing ground to the valve relay. When the valve relay is energized, battery power is supplied to the valve solenoids.

TEST CONDITION(S):

1. Tested continuously.

FAILURE CONDITION(S):

While standing or driving:

1. Valve solenoid cannot be activated.

OR

2. Valve solenoid is activated in a defective way.

ACTION TAKEN:

1. Code set.
2. ABS/TCS switched 'OFF'.
3. 'ANTILOCK' indicator 'ON'.
4. 'TRACTION DISABLED' message displayed. (vehicles with TCS)

Code 41 will set when the expected position of the right front valve solenoid does not match the commanded position from the EBTCM/EBCM. Conditions which could cause Code 41 to set are: damage to the right front valve solenoid; an open circuit; or an open circuit to ground or battery on CKT 857.

TEST DESCRIPTION: Test numbers refer to circled numbers on the diagnostic chart.

1. Damage to CKT 886 may result in multiple valve solenoid codes setting.
2. Checks CKT 886 for opens or high resistance from EBTCM/EBCM terminal '23' to '32'.
3. Determines which branch of CKT 886 has an open or high resistance.
4. Checks the integrity of CKTs 886 and 857, the RF ABS Valve Solenoid circuitry internal to the BPM Modulator Valve, and the RF ABS Valve Solenoid coil.
5. Determines whether a problem found in Step 4 is due to an open in CKT 857, 886, or BPM Modulator Valve.
6. Determines whether the problem found in Step 4 is due to an open in CKT 857 or 886.

DIAGNOSTIC AIDS:

All tests using J 39700 Universal Breakout Box terminal '20' are using the terminal as ground. These tests, of course, assume that the ground CKT 1250 terminal '20' is good.

If Codes 41 and 45 are both set, the fault is likely to be an open or high resistance on CKT 886.

If Codes 41 and 55 are both set, the fault is likely to be a short to B+ on CKT 1290.

GC4029300540010X

Fig. 106 Code 41: Right Front ABS Valve Solenoid Fault (Part 1 of 2). 1993-94 DeVille, Eldorado & Seville

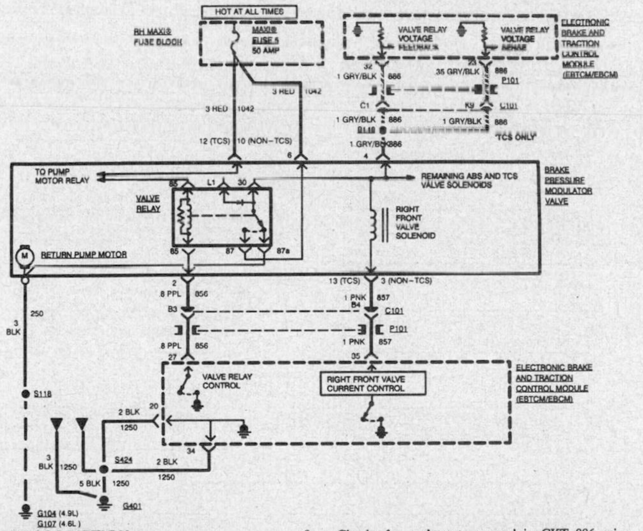

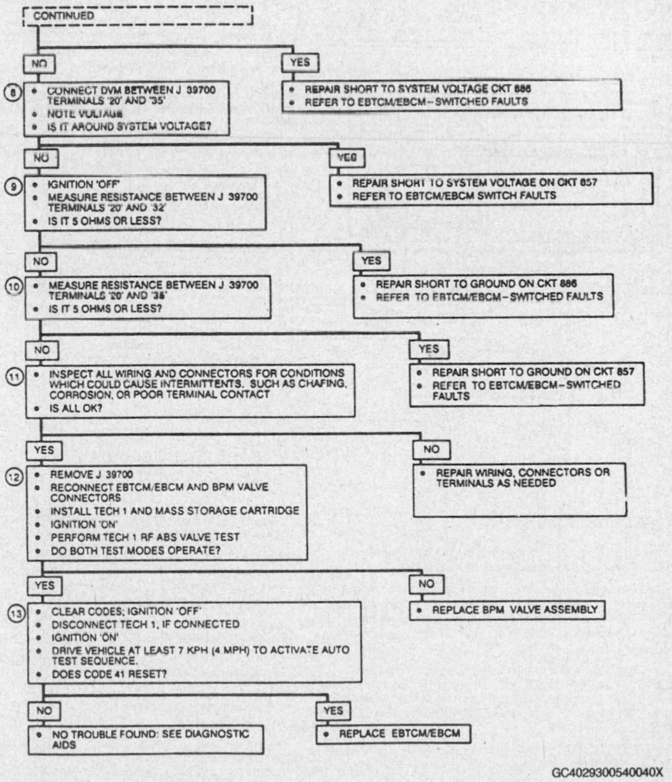
CONTINUED
NO
YES
8 • CONNECT DVM BETWEEN J 39700 TERMINALS '20' AND '35'
• NOTE VOLTAGE
• IS IT AROUND SYSTEM VOLTAGE?
• REPAIR SHORT TO SYSTEM VOLTAGE CKT 886
• REFER TO EBTCM/EBCM–SWITCHED FAULTS
NO
YES
9 • IGNITION 'OFF'
• MEASURE RESISTANCE BETWEEN J 39700 TERMINALS '20' AND '32'
• IS IT 5 OHMS OR LESS?
• REPAIR SHORT TO SYSTEM VOLTAGE ON CKT 857
• REFER TO EBTCM/EBCM SWITCH FAULTS
NO
YES
10 • MEASURE RESISTANCE BETWEEN J 39700 TERMINALS '20' AND '35'
• IS IT 5 OHMS OR LESS?
• REPAIR SHORT TO GROUND ON CKT 886
• REFER TO EBTCM/EBCM–SWITCHED FAULTS
NO
YES
11 • INSPECT ALL WIRING AND CONNECTORS FOR CONDITIONS WHICH COULD CAUSE INTERMITTENTS, SUCH AS CHAFING, CORROSION, OR POOR TERMINAL CONTACT
• IS ALL OK?
• REPAIR SHORT TO GROUND ON CKT 857
• REFER TO EBTCM/EBCM–SWITCHED FAULTS
YES
NO
12 • REMOVE J 39700
• RECONNECT EBTCM/EBCM AND BPM VALVE CONNECTORS
• INSTALL TECH 1 AND MASS STORAGE CARTRIDGE
• IGNITION 'ON'
• PERFORM TECH 1 RF ABS VALVE TEST
• DO BOTH TEST MODES OPERATE?
• REPAIR WIRING, CONNECTORS OR TERMINALS AS NEEDED
YES
NO
13 • CLEAR CODES; IGNITION 'OFF'
• DISCONNECT TECH 1, IF CONNECTED
• IGNITION 'ON'
• DRIVE VEHICLE AT LEAST 7 KPH (4 MPH) TO ACTIVATE AUTO TEST SEQUENCE.
• DOES CODE 41 RESET?
• REPLACE BPM VALVE ASSEMBLY
NO
YES
• NO TROUBLE FOUND: SEE DIAGNOSTIC AIDS
• REPLACE EBTCM/EBCM
GC4029300540040X

CIRCUIT DESCRIPTION:

The right front valve solenoid in the BPM Valve may be commanded to three different positions by the EBTCM/EBCM. Valve position is determined by the amount of current which is allowed to flow through the valve solenoid coil.

The valve solenoid circuits receive power through the valve relay on the BPM Valve. The valve relay is engaged at KEY–ON and remains engaged throughout the ignition cycle. Valve solenoid circuits should have battery voltage available at all times.

When the key is turned to RUN, power is supplied to the EBTCM/EBCM. The EBTCM/EBCM will complete an internal self–check before providing ground to the valve relay. When the valve relay is energized, battery power is supplied to the valve solenoids.

TEST DESCRIPTION: Test numbers refer to circled numbers on the diagnostic chart.

8. Checks for a short to battery in CKT 857 using EBTCM/EBCM terminal '20' as ground.
9. Checks for a short to ground in CKT 886 using EBTCM/EBCM terminal '20' as ground.
10. Checks for a short to ground in CKT 857 using EBTCM/EBCM terminal '20' as ground.
11. Checking wiring and connectors for intermittents.
12. Use the TECH 1 to exercise the RF ABS Valve Solenoid and check it for proper operation.
13. Determines whether the code was set by an intermittent condition or an EBTCM/EBCM fault.

DIAGNOSTIC AIDS:

All tests using J 39700 Universal Breakout Box terminal '20' are using the terminal as ground. These tests, of course, assume that the ground CKT 1250 terminal '20' is good.

If Codes 41 and 45 are both set, the fault is likely to be an open or high resistance on CKT 886.

If Codes 41 and 55 are both set, the fault is likely to be a short to B+ on CKT 1290.

GC4029300540030X

Fig. 106 Code 41: Right Front ABS Valve Solenoid Fault (Part 2 of 2). 1993-94 DeVille, Eldorado & Seville

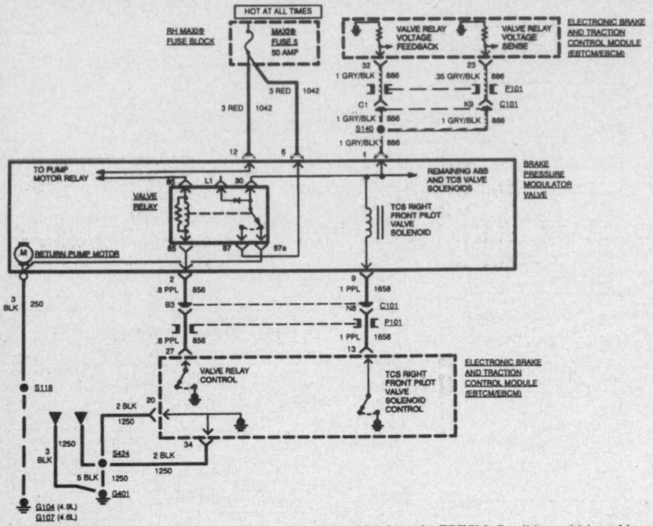
HOT AT ALL TIMES
RH MAXI® FUSE BLOCK
MAXI® FUSE 5 50 AMP
VALVE RELAY VOLTAGE FEEDBACK
VALVE RELAY VOLTAGE SENSE
ELECTRONIC BRAKE AND TRACTION CONTROL MODULE (EBTCM/EBCM)
TO PUMP MOTOR RELAY
VALVE RELAY
RETURN PUMP MOTOR
REMAINING ABS AND TCS VALVE SOLENOIDS
BRAKE PRESSURE MODULATOR VALVE
TCS RIGHT FRONT PILOT VALVE SOLENOID
VALVE RELAY CONTROL
TCS RIGHT FRONT PILOT VALVE SOLENOID CONTROL
ELECTRONIC BRAKE AND TRACTION CONTROL MODULE (EBTCM/EBCM)
S118
S424
G401
G104 (4.9L)
G107 (4.6L)

CIRCUIT DESCRIPTION:

The right front TCS pilot valve in the BPM VALVE may be commanded to close, isolating the master cylinder.

The pilot valve circuits receive power through the valve relay on the BPM Valve. The valve relay is engaged at KEY–ON and remains engaged throughout the ignition cycle. Valve circuits should have battery voltage available at all times.

When the key is turned to RUN, power is supplied to the EBTCM. The EBTCM will complete an internal self–check before providing ground to the valve relay. When the valve relay is energized, battery power is supplied to the pilot valves.

TEST CONDITION(S):

1. Tested continuously.

FAILURE CONDITION(S):

While standing or driving:

1. Valve cannot be activated.

OR

2. Valve is activated in a defective way.

ACTION TAKEN:

1. Code set.
2. ABS/TCS switched 'OFF'.
3. 'ANTILOCK' indicator 'ON'.
4. 'TRACTION DISABLED' message displayed.

Code 44 will set when the expected position of the right front TCS pilot valve does not match the commanded position from the EBTCM. Conditions which could cause Code 44 to set are; damage to the right front TCS pilot valve, an open circuit or a short circuit to ground or battery on CKT 1658.

TEST DESCRIPTION: Test numbers refer to circled numbers on the diagnostic chart.

1. Damage to CKT 886 may result in multiple pilot valve codes setting.
2. Checks CKT 886 for opens or high resistance from EBTCM/EBCM terminal '23' to '32'.
3. Determines which branch of CKT 886 has an open or high resistance.
4. Checks the integrity of CKTs 1658 and 886, the TCS Pilot Valve circuitry internal to the BPM Valve, and the TCS Pilot Valve coil.
5. Determines whether a problem found in Step 4 is due to an open in CKTs 886, 1658 or a faulty BPM Valve.
6. Determines whether the problem found in Step 4 is due to an open in CKT 886 or 1658.

DIAGNOSTIC AIDS:

All tests using J 39700 Universal Breakout Box terminal '20' are using the terminal as ground. These tests, of course, assume that the ground CKT 1250 terminal '20' is good.

If Codes 44 and 48 are both set, the fault is likely to be an open or short in CKT 886.

GC4029300541010X

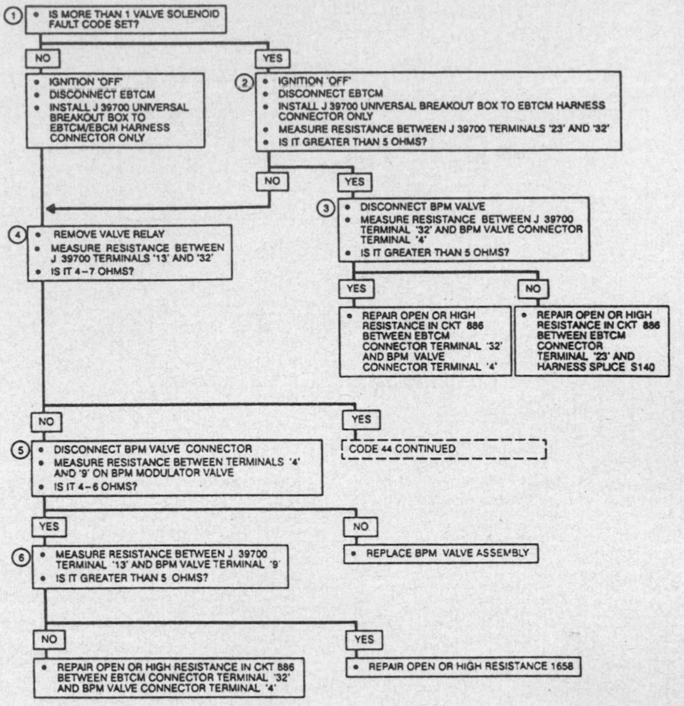
1 • IS MORE THAN 1 VALVE SOLENOID FAULT CODE SET?
NO
YES
• IGNITION 'OFF'
• DISCONNECT EBTCM
• INSTALL J 39700 UNIVERSAL BREAKOUT BOX TO EBTCM/EBCM HARNESS CONNECTOR ONLY
2 • IGNITION 'OFF'
• DISCONNECT EBTCM
• INSTALL J 39700 UNIVERSAL BREAKOUT BOX TO EBTCM HARNESS CONNECTOR ONLY
• MEASURE RESISTANCE BETWEEN J 39700 TERMINALS '23' AND '32'
• IS IT GREATER THAN 5 OHMS?
NO
YES
3 • DISCONNECT BPM VALVE
• MEASURE RESISTANCE BETWEEN J 39700 TERMINAL '32' AND BPM VALVE CONNECTOR TERMINAL '4'
• IS IT GREATER THAN 5 OHMS?
4 • REMOVE VALVE RELAY
• MEASURE RESISTANCE BETWEEN J 39700 TERMINALS '13' AND '32'
• IS IT 4–7 OHMS?
YES
NO
• REPAIR OPEN OR HIGH RESISTANCE IN CKT 886 BETWEEN EBTCM CONNECTOR TERMINAL '32' AND BPM VALVE CONNECTOR TERMINAL '4'
• REPAIR OPEN OR HIGH RESISTANCE IN CKT 886 BETWEEN EBTCM CONNECTOR TERMINAL '23' AND HARNESS SPLICE S140
NO
YES
5 • DISCONNECT BPM VALVE CONNECTOR
• MEASURE RESISTANCE BETWEEN TERMINALS '4' AND '9' ON BPM MODULATOR VALVE
• IS IT 4–6 OHMS?
CODE 44 CONTINUED
YES
NO
6 • MEASURE RESISTANCE BETWEEN J 39700 TERMINAL '13' AND BPM VALVE TERMINAL '9'
• IS IT GREATER THAN 5 OHMS?
• REPLACE BPM VALVE ASSEMBLY
NO
YES
• REPAIR OPEN OR HIGH RESISTANCE IN CKT 886 BETWEEN EBTCM CONNECTOR TERMINAL '32' AND BPM VALVE CONNECTOR TERMINAL '4'
• REPAIR OPEN OR HIGH RESISTANCE 1658

GC4029300541020X

Fig. 107 Code 44: Right Front TCS Pilot Valve Fault (Part 1 of 2). 1993-94 DeVille, Eldorado & Seville

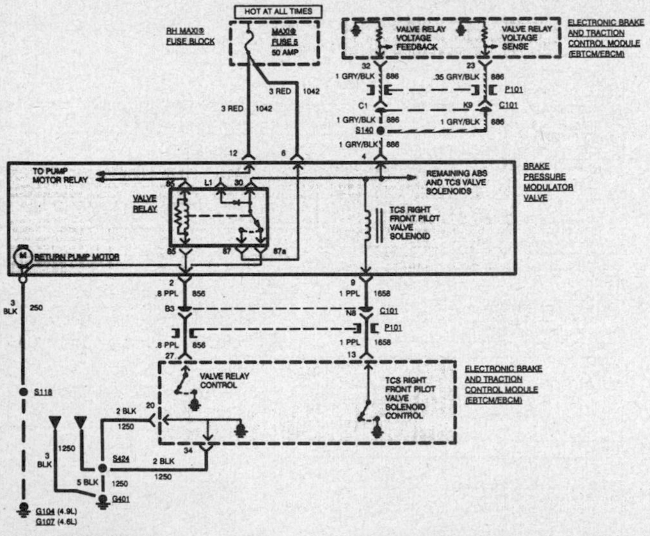
HOT AT ALL TIMES
RH MAXI® FUSE BLOCK
MAXI® FUSE 5 50 AMP
VALVE RELAY VOLTAGE FEEDBACK
VALVE RELAY VOLTAGE SENSE
ELECTRONIC BRAKE AND TRACTION CONTROL MODULE (EBTCM/EBCM)
TO PUMP MOTOR RELAY
VALVE RELAY
RETURN PUMP MOTOR
REMAINING ABS AND TCS VALVE SOLENOIDS
BRAKE PRESSURE MODULATOR VALVE
TCS RIGHT FRONT PILOT VALVE SOLENOID
VALVE RELAY CONTROL
TCS RIGHT FRONT PILOT VALVE SOLENOID CONTROL
ELECTRONIC BRAKE AND TRACTION CONTROL MODULE (EBTCM/EBCM)
S118
S424
G401
G104 (4.9L)
G107 (4.6L)

CIRCUIT DESCRIPTION:

The right front TCS pilot valve in the BPM Valve may be commanded to close, isolating the master cylinder.

The pilot valve circuits receive power through the valve relay on the BPM Valve. The valve relay is engaged at KEY–ON and remains engaged throughout the ignition cycle. Valve circuits should have battery voltage available at all times.

When the key is turned to RUN, power is supplied to the EBTCM. The EBTCM will complete an internal self–check before providing ground to the valve relay. When the valve relay is energized, battery power is supplied to the pilot valves.

TEST DESCRIPTION: Test numbers refer to circled numbers on the diagnostic chart.

7. Checks for a short to battery in CKT 886 using EBTCM terminal '20' as ground.
8. Checks for a short to battery in CKT 1658, using EBTCM terminal '20' as ground.
9. Checks for a short to ground in CKT 886 using EBTCM terminal '20' as ground.
10. Checks for a short to ground in CKT 1658, using EBTCM terminal '20' as ground.
11. Checks for connector or wiring problems which could cause intermittents.
12. Uses the TECH 1 to exercise the TCS pilot valve and check it for proper operation.
13. Determines whether the code was set by an intermittent conditions or an EBTCM fault.

DIAGNOSTIC AIDS:

All tests using J 39700 Universal Breakout Box terminal '20' are using the terminal as ground. These tests, of course, assume that the ground CKT 1250 terminal '20' is good.

If Codes 44 and 48 are both set, the fault is likely to be an open or short in CKT 886.

GC4029300541030X

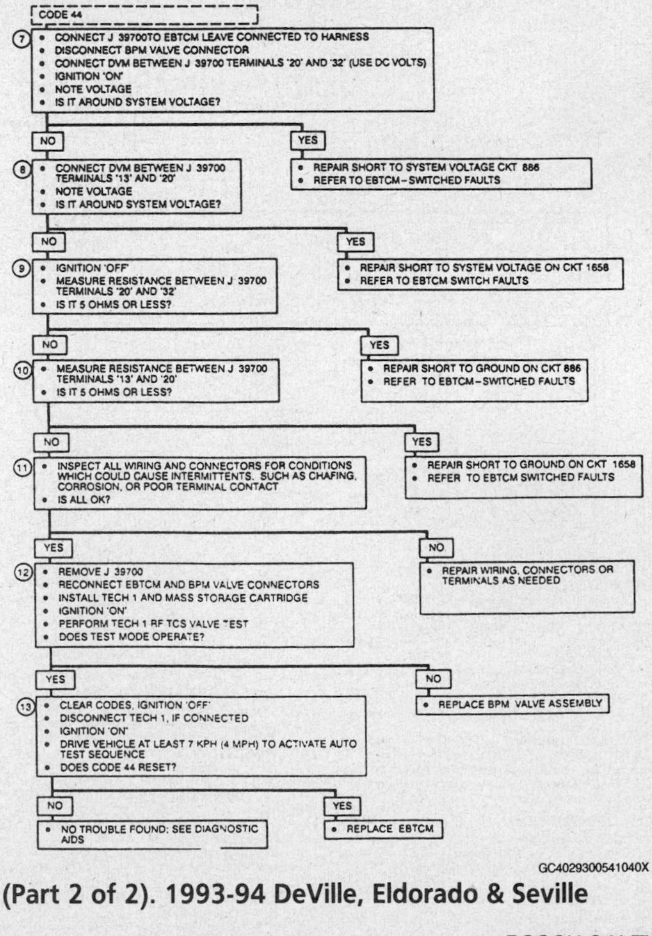
CODE 44
7 • CONNECT J 39700 TO EBTCM LEAVE CONNECTED TO HARNESS
• DISCONNECT BPM VALVE CONNECTOR
• CONNECT DVM BETWEEN J 39700 TERMINALS '20' AND '32' (USE DC VOLTS)
• IGNITION 'ON'
• NOTE VOLTAGE
• IS IT AROUND SYSTEM VOLTAGE?
NO
YES
8 • CONNECT DVM BETWEEN J 39700 TERMINALS '13' AND '20'
• NOTE VOLTAGE
• IS IT AROUND SYSTEM VOLTAGE?
• REPAIR SHORT TO SYSTEM VOLTAGE CKT 886
• REFER TO EBTCM–SWITCHED FAULTS
NO
YES
9 • IGNITION 'OFF'
• MEASURE RESISTANCE BETWEEN J 39700 TERMINALS '20' AND '32'
• IS IT 5 OHMS OR LESS?
• REPAIR SHORT TO SYSTEM VOLTAGE ON CKT 1658
• REFER TO EBTCM SWITCH FAULTS
NO
YES
10 • MEASURE RESISTANCE BETWEEN J 39700 TERMINALS '13' AND '20'
• IS IT 5 OHMS OR LESS?
• REPAIR SHORT TO GROUND ON CKT 886
• REFER TO EBTCM–SWITCHED FAULTS
NO
YES
11 • INSPECT ALL WIRING AND CONNECTORS FOR CONDITIONS WHICH COULD CAUSE INTERMITTENTS. SUCH AS CHAFING, CORROSION, OR POOR TERMINAL CONTACT
• IS ALL OK?
• REPAIR SHORT TO GROUND ON CKT 1658
• REFER TO EBTCM SWITCHED FAULTS
YES
NO
12 • REMOVE J 39700
• RECONNECT EBTCM AND BPM VALVE CONNECTORS
• INSTALL TECH 1 AND MASS STORAGE CARTRIDGE
• IGNITION 'ON'
• PERFORM TECH 1 RF TCS VALVE TEST
• DOES TEST MODE OPERATE?
• REPAIR WIRING, CONNECTORS OR TERMINALS AS NEEDED
YES
NO
13 • CLEAR CODES, IGNITION 'OFF'
• DISCONNECT TECH 1, IF CONNECTED
• IGNITION 'ON'
• DRIVE VEHICLE AT LEAST 7 KPH (4 MPH) TO ACTIVATE AUTO TEST SEQUENCE
• DOES CODE 44 RESET?
• REPLACE BPM VALVE ASSEMBLY
NO
YES
• NO TROUBLE FOUND: SEE DIAGNOSTIC AIDS
• REPLACE EBTCM

GC4029300541040X

Fig. 107 Code 44: Right Front TCS Pilot Valve Fault (Part 2 of 2). 1993-94 DeVille, Eldorado & Seville

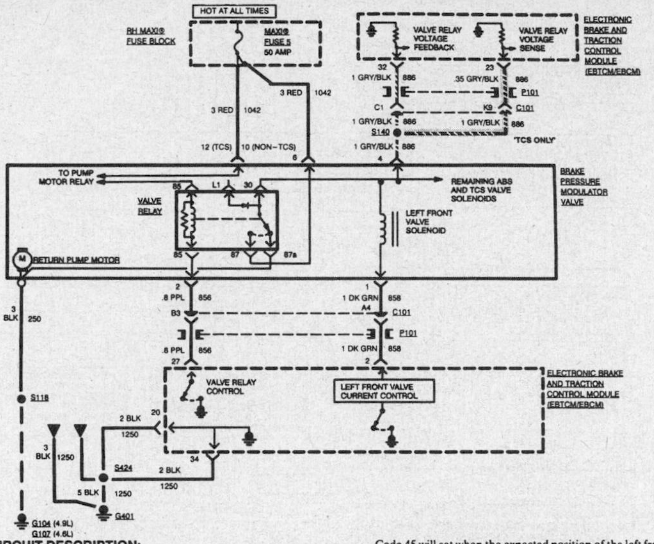
HOT AT ALL TIMES
RH MAXI® FUSE BLOCK
MAXI® FUSE 5 50 AMP
ELECTRONIC BRAKE AND TRACTION CONTROL MODULE (EBTCM/EBCM)
VALVE RELAY VOLTAGE FEEDBACK
VALVE RELAY VOLTAGE SENSE
TCS ONLY
TO PUMP MOTOR RELAY
VALVE RELAY
REMAINING ABS AND TCS VALVE SOLENOIDS
BRAKE PRESSURE MODULATOR VALVE
LEFT FRONT VALVE SOLENOID
RETURN PUMP MOTOR
VALVE RELAY CONTROL
LEFT FRONT VALVE CURRENT CONTROL
G104 (4.9L)
G107 (4.6L)
G401

CIRCUIT DESCRIPTION:

The left front valve solenoid in the BPM Valve may be commanded to three different positions by the EBTCM/EBCM. Valve position is determined by the amount of current which is allowed to flow through the valve solenoid coil.

The valve solenoid circuits receive power through the valve relay on the BPM Valve. The valve relay is engaged at KEY−ON and remains engaged throughout the ignition cycle. Valve solenoid circuits should have battery voltage available at all times.

When the key is turned to RUN, power is supplied to the EBTCM/EBCM. The EBTCM/EBCM will complete an internal self−check before providing ground to the valve relay. When the valve relay is energized, battery power is supplied to the valve solenoids.

TEST CONDITION(S):

1. Tested continuously.

FAILURE CONDITION(S):

While standing or driving:

1. Valve solenoid cannot be activated.

OR

2. Valve solenoid is activated in a defective way.

ACTION TAKEN:

1. Code set.
2. ABS/TCS switched 'OFF'
3. 'ANTILOCK' indicator 'ON'.
4. 'TRACTION DISABLED' message displayed. (vehicles with TCS)

Code 45 will set when the expected position of the left front solenoid valve does not match the commanded position from the EBTCM/EBCM. Conditions which could cause Code 45 to set are: damage to the left front valve solenoid; an open circuit; or a short circuit to ground or battery on CKT 858.

TEST DESCRIPTION: Test numbers refer to circled numbers on the diagnostic chart.

1. Damage to CKT 886 may result in multiple valve solenoid codes setting.
2. Checks CKT 886 for opens or high resistance from EBTCM/EBCM terminal '23' to '32'.
3. Determines which branch of CKT 886 has an open or high resistance.
4. Checks the integrity of CKTs 826 and 886, the LF ABS Valve Solenoid circuitry internal to the BPM Modulator Valve, and the LF ABS Valve Solenoid coil.
5. Determines whether a problem found in Step 4 is due to an open in CKT 858, 886 or a faulty BPM Modulator Valve.
6. Determines whether the problem found in Step 4 is due to an open in CKT 858 or 886.

DIAGNOSTIC AIDS:

All tests using J 39700 Universal Breakout Box terminal '20' are using the terminal as ground. These tests, of course, assume that the ground CKT 1250 terminal '20' is good.

If Codes 41 and 45 are both set, the fault is likely to be an open or high resistance on CKT 886.

GC4029300542010X

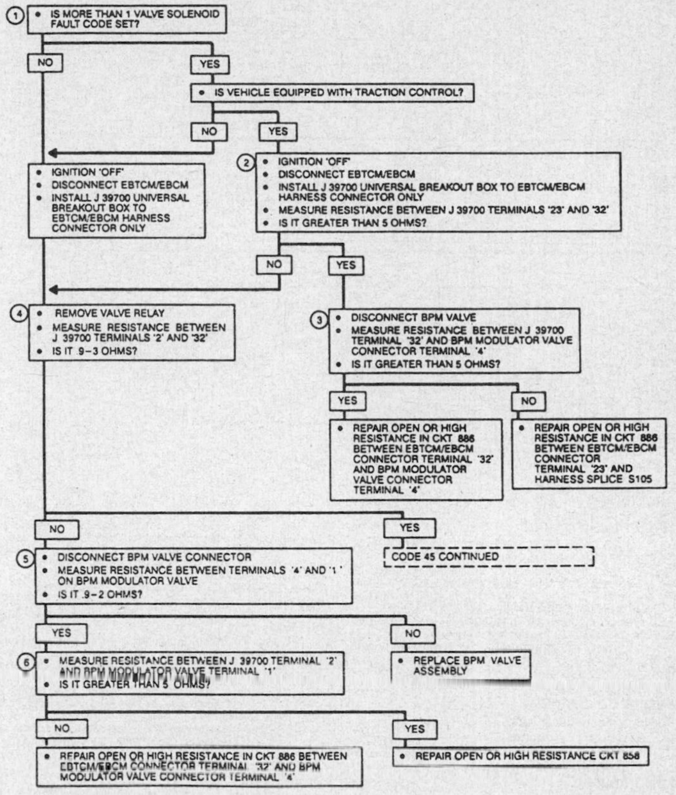
1 • IS MORE THAN 1 VALVE SOLENOID FAULT CODE SET?
NO
YES
• IS VEHICLE EQUIPPED WITH TRACTION CONTROL?
NO
YES
• IGNITION 'OFF'
• DISCONNECT EBTCM/EBCM
• INSTALL J 39700 UNIVERSAL BREAKOUT BOX TO EBTCM/EBCM HARNESS CONNECTOR ONLY
2 • IGNITION 'OFF'
• DISCONNECT EBTCM/EBCM
• INSTALL J 39700 UNIVERSAL BREAKOUT BOX TO EBTCM/EBCM HARNESS CONNECTOR ONLY
• MEASURE RESISTANCE BETWEEN J 39700 TERMINALS '23' AND '32'
• IS IT GREATER THAN 5 OHMS?
NO
YES
4 • REMOVE VALVE RELAY
• MEASURE RESISTANCE BETWEEN J 39700 TERMINALS '2' AND '32'
• IS IT 9−3 OHMS?
3 • DISCONNECT BPM VALVE
• MEASURE RESISTANCE BETWEEN J 39700 TERMINAL '32' AND BPM MODULATOR VALVE CONNECTOR TERMINAL '4'
• IS IT GREATER THAN 5 OHMS?
YES
NO
• REPAIR OPEN OR HIGH RESISTANCE IN CKT 886 BETWEEN EBTCM/EBCM CONNECTOR TERMINAL '32' AND BPM MODULATOR VALVE CONNECTOR TERMINAL '4'
• REPAIR OPEN OR HIGH RESISTANCE IN CKT 886 BETWEEN EBTCM/EBCM CONNECTOR TERMINAL '23' AND HARNESS SPLICE S105
NO
YES
CODE 45 CONTINUED
5 • DISCONNECT BPM VALVE CONNECTOR
• MEASURE RESISTANCE BETWEEN TERMINALS '4' AND '1' ON BPM MODULATOR VALVE
• IS IT .9−2 OHMS?
YES
NO
6 • MEASURE RESISTANCE BETWEEN J 39700 TERMINAL '2' AND BPM MODULATOR VALVE TERMINAL '1'
• IS IT GREATER THAN 5 OHMS?
• REPLACE BPM VALVE ASSEMBLY
NO
YES
• REPAIR OPEN OR HIGH RESISTANCE IN CKT 886 BETWEEN EBTCM/EBCM CONNECTOR TERMINAL '32' AND BPM MODULATOR VALVE CONNECTOR TERMINAL '4'
• REPAIR OPEN OR HIGH RESISTANCE CKT 858

GC4029300542020X

Fig. 108 Code 45: Left Front ABS Valve Solenoid Fault (Part 1 of 2). 1993-94 DeVille, Eldorado & Seville

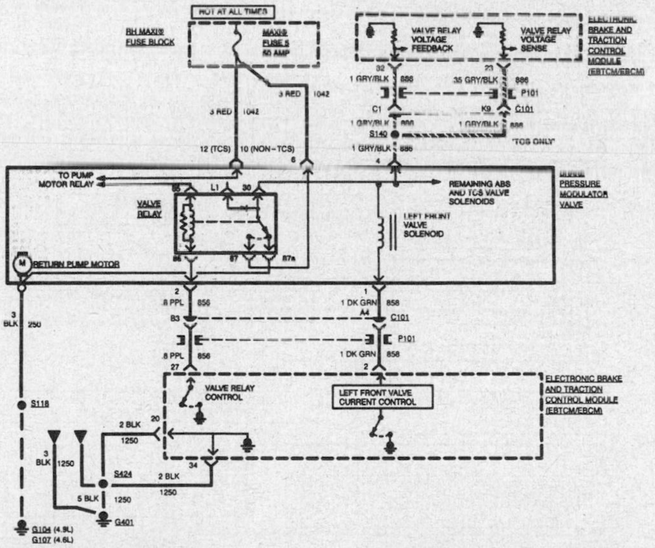
HOT AT ALL TIMES
RH MAXI® FUSE BLOCK
MAXI® FUSE 5 50 AMP
VALVE RELAY VOLTAGE FEEDBACK
VALVE RELAY VOLTAGE SENSE
BRAKE AND TRACTION CONTROL MODULE (EBTCM/EBCM)
TCS ONLY
TO PUMP MOTOR RELAY
VALVE RELAY
REMAINING ABS AND TCS VALVE SOLENOIDS
BRAKE PRESSURE MODULATOR VALVE
LEFT FRONT VALVE SOLENOID
RETURN PUMP MOTOR
VALVE RELAY CONTROL
LEFT FRONT VALVE CURRENT CONTROL
ELECTRONIC BRAKE AND TRACTION CONTROL MODULE (EBTCM/EBCM)
G104 (4.9L)
G107 (4.6L)
G401

CIRCUIT DESCRIPTION:

The left front valve solenoid in the BPM Valve may be commanded to three different positions by the EBTCM/EBCM. Valve position is determined by the amount of current which is allowed to flow through the solenoid valve coil.

The valve solenoid circuits receive power through the valve relay on the BPM Valve. The valve relay is engaged at KEY−ON and remains engaged throughout the ignition cycle. Valve solenoid circuits should have battery voltage available at all times.

When the key is turned to RUN, power is supplied to the EBTCM/EBCM. The EBTCM/EBCM will complete an internal self−check before providing ground to the valve relay. When the valve relay is energized, battery power is supplied to the valve solenoids.

TEST DESCRIPTION: Test numbers refer to circled numbers on the diagnostic chart.

7. Checks for a short to battery in CKT 886 using EBTCM/EBCM terminal '20' as ground.
8. Checks for a short to battery in CKT 858, using EBTCM/EBCM terminal '20' as ground.
9. Checks for a short to ground in CKT 886 using EBTCM/EBCM terminal '20' as ground.
10. Checks for a short to ground in CKT 858, using EBTCM/EBCM terminal '20' as ground.
11. Checks wiring and connectors for intermittents.
12. Uses the TECH 1 to exercise the LF ABS valve solenoid and check it for proper operation.
13. Determines whether the code was set by an intermittent condition or an EBTCM/EBCM fault.

DIAGNOSTIC AIDS:

All tests using J 39700 Universal Breakout Box terminal '20' are using the terminal as ground. These tests, of course, assume that the ground CKT 1250 terminal '20' is good.

If Codes 41 and 45 are both set, the fault is likely to be an open or high resistance on CKT 886.

GC4029300542030X

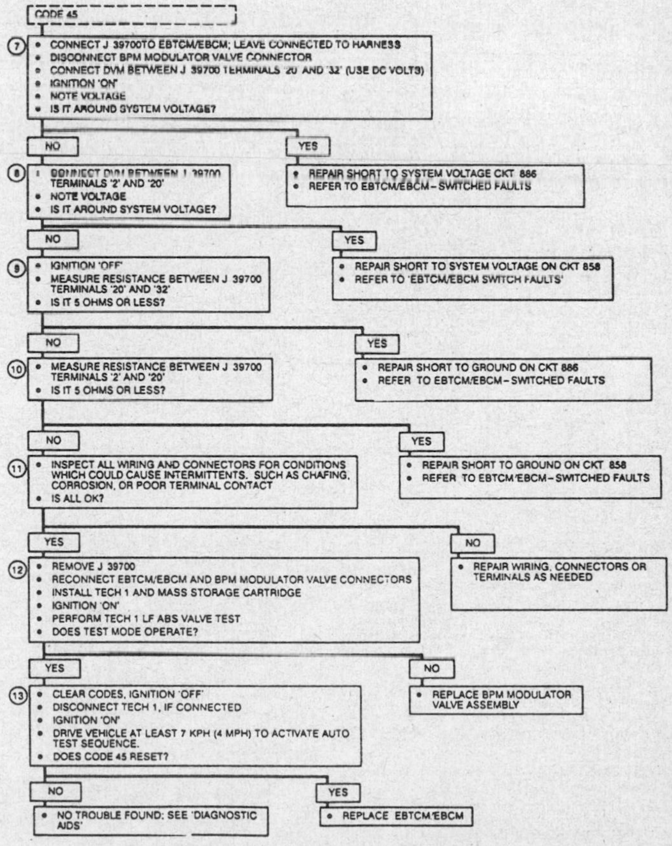
CODE 45
7 • CONNECT J 39700TO EBTCM/EBCM; LEAVE CONNECTED TO HARNESS
• DISCONNECT BPM MODULATOR VALVE CONNECTOR
• CONNECT DVM BETWEEN J 39700 TERMINALS '20' AND '32' (USE DC VOLTS)
• IGNITION 'ON'
• NOTE VOLTAGE
• IS IT AROUND SYSTEM VOLTAGE?
NO
YES
8 • CONNECT DVM BETWEEN J 39700 TERMINALS '2' AND '20'
• NOTE VOLTAGE
• IS IT AROUND SYSTEM VOLTAGE?
• REPAIR SHORT TO SYSTEM VOLTAGE CKT 886
• REFER TO EBTCM/EBCM−SWITCHED FAULTS
NO
YES
9 • IGNITION 'OFF'
• MEASURE RESISTANCE BETWEEN J 39700 TERMINALS '20' AND '32'
• IS IT 5 OHMS OR LESS?
• REPAIR SHORT TO SYSTEM VOLTAGE ON CKT 858
• REFER TO 'EBTCM/EBCM SWITCH FAULTS'
NO
YES
10 • MEASURE RESISTANCE BETWEEN J 39700 TERMINALS '2' AND '20'
• IS IT 5 OHMS OR LESS?
• REPAIR SHORT TO GROUND ON CKT 886
• REFER TO EBTCM/EBCM−SWITCHED FAULTS
NO
YES
11 • INSPECT ALL WIRING AND CONNECTORS FOR CONDITIONS WHICH COULD CAUSE INTERMITTENTS. SUCH AS CHAFING, CORROSION, OR POOR TERMINAL CONTACT
• IS ALL OK?
• REPAIR SHORT TO GROUND ON CKT 858
• REFER TO EBTCM/EBCM−SWITCHED FAULTS
YES
NO
12 • REMOVE J 39700
• RECONNECT EBTCM/EBCM AND BPM MODULATOR VALVE CONNECTORS
• INSTALL TECH 1 AND MASS STORAGE CARTRIDGE
• IGNITION 'ON'
• PERFORM TECH 1 LF ABS VALVE TEST
• DOES TEST MODE OPERATE?
• REPAIR WIRING, CONNECTORS OR TERMINALS AS NEEDED
YES
NO
13 • CLEAR CODES, IGNITION 'OFF'
• DISCONNECT TECH 1, IF CONNECTED
• IGNITION 'ON'
• DRIVE VEHICLE AT LEAST 7 KPH (4 MPH) TO ACTIVATE AUTO TEST SEQUENCE.
• DOES CODE 45 RESET?
• REPLACE BPM MODULATOR VALVE ASSEMBLY
NO
YES
• NO TROUBLE FOUND: SEE 'DIAGNOSTIC AIDS'
• REPLACE EBTCM/EBCM

GC4029300542040X

Fig. 108 Code 45: Left Front ABS Valve Solenoid Fault (Part 2 of 2). 1993-94 DeVille, Eldorado & Seville

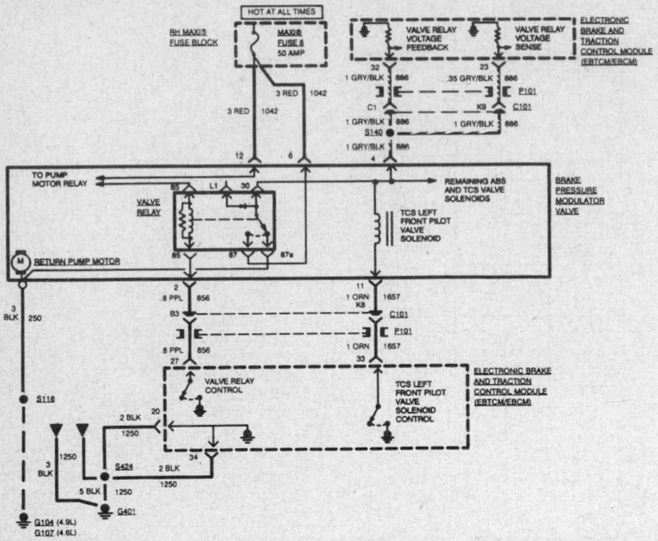
HOT AT ALL TIMES
RH MAXI® FUSE BLOCK
MAXI® FUSE 5 50 AMP
VALVE RELAY VOLTAGE FEEDBACK
VALVE RELAY VOLTAGE SENSE
ELECTRONIC BRAKE AND TRACTION CONTROL MODULE (EBTCM/EBCM)
TO PUMP MOTOR RELAY
VALVE RELAY
REMAINING ABS AND TCS VALVE SOLENOIDS
BRAKE PRESSURE MODULATOR VALVE
TCS LEFT FRONT PILOT VALVE SOLENOID
RETURN PUMP MOTOR
VALVE RELAY CONTROL
TCS LEFT FRONT PILOT VALVE SOLENOID CONTROL
S118
S140
S424
C101
P101
G401
G104 (4.9L)
G107 (4.6L)

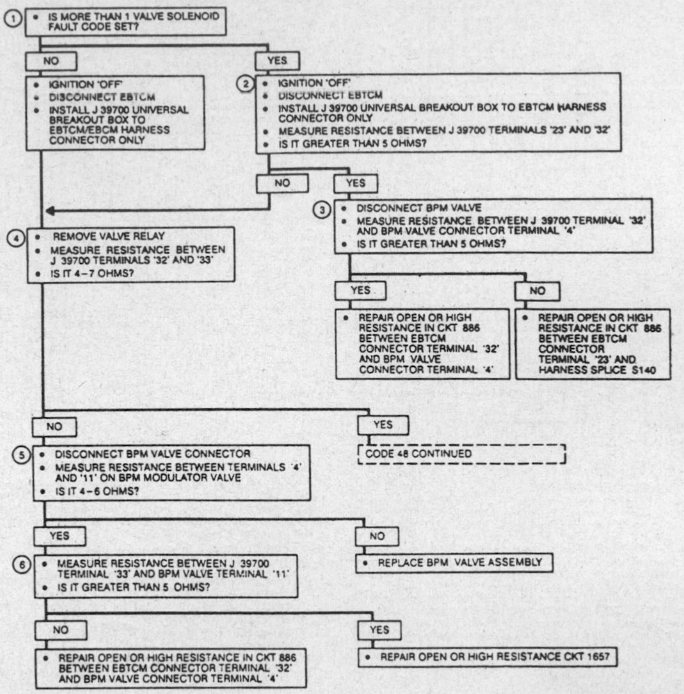
1 IS MORE THAN 1 VALVE SOLENOID FAULT CODE SET?
NO
YES
• IGNITION 'OFF'
• DISCONNECT EBTCM
• INSTALL J 39700 UNIVERSAL BREAKOUT BOX TO EBTCM/EBCM HARNESS CONNECTOR ONLY
2 • IGNITION 'OFF'
• DISCONNECT EBTCM
• INSTALL J 39700 UNIVERSAL BREAKOUT BOX TO EBTCM HARNESS CONNECTOR ONLY
• MEASURE RESISTANCE BETWEEN J 39700 TERMINALS '23' AND '32'
• IS IT GREATER THAN 5 OHMS?
NO
YES
3 • DISCONNECT BPM VALVE
• MEASURE RESISTANCE BETWEEN J 39700 TERMINAL '32' AND BPM VALVE CONNECTOR TERMINAL '4'
• IS IT GREATER THAN 5 OHMS?
4 • REMOVE VALVE RELAY
• MEASURE RESISTANCE BETWEEN J 39700 TERMINALS '32' AND '33'
• IS IT 4–7 OHMS?
YES
NO
• REPAIR OPEN OR HIGH RESISTANCE IN CKT 886 BETWEEN EBTCM CONNECTOR TERMINAL '32' AND BPM VALVE CONNECTOR TERMINAL '4'
• REPAIR OPEN OR HIGH RESISTANCE IN CKT 886 BETWEEN EBTCM CONNECTOR TERMINAL '23' AND HARNESS SPLICE S140
NO
YES
5 • DISCONNECT BPM VALVE CONNECTOR
• MEASURE RESISTANCE BETWEEN TERMINALS '4' AND '11' ON BPM MODULATOR VALVE
• IS IT 4–6 OHMS?
CODE 48 CONTINUED
YES
NO
6 • MEASURE RESISTANCE BETWEEN J 39700 TERMINAL '33' AND BPM VALVE TERMINAL '11'
• IS IT GREATER THAN 5 OHMS?
• REPLACE BPM VALVE ASSEMBLY
NO
YES
• REPAIR OPEN OR HIGH RESISTANCE IN CKT 886 BETWEEN EBTCM CONNECTOR TERMINAL '32' AND BPM VALVE CONNECTOR TERMINAL '4'
• REPAIR OPEN OR HIGH RESISTANCE CKT 1657

GC4029300543020X

CIRCUIT DESCRIPTION:

The left front TCS pilot valve in the BPM Valve may be commanded to close, isolating the master cylinder.

The pilot valve circuits receive power through the valve relay on the BPM Valve. The valve relay is engaged at KEY–ON and remains engaged throughout the ignition cycle. Pilot valve circuits should have battery voltage available at all times.

When the key is turned to RUN, power is supplied to the EBTCM. The EBTCM will complete an internal self–check before providing ground to the valve relay. When the valve relay is energized, battery power is supplied to the pilot valves.

TEST CONDITION(S):

1. Tested continuously.

FAILURE CONDITION(S):

While standing or driving:

1. Valve cannot be activated.

OR

2. Valve is activated in a defective way.

ACTION TAKEN:

1. Code set.
2. ABS/TCS switched 'OFF'.
3. 'ANTILOCK' indicator 'ON'.
4. 'TRACTION DISABLED' message displayed.

Code 48 will set when the expected position of the right front TCS pilot valve does not match the commanded position from the EBTCM. Conditions which could cause Code 48 to set are: damage to the right front TCS pilot valve; an open circuit; or a short circuit to ground or battery on CKT 1657.

TEST DESCRIPTION: Test numbers refer to circled numbers on the diagnostic chart.

1. Damage to CKT 886 may result in multiple valve solenoid codes setting.
2. Checks CKT 886 for opens or high resistance from EBTCM/EBCM terminal '23' to '32'.
3. Determines which branch of CKT 886 has an open or high resistance.
4. Checks the integrity of CKTs 1657 and 886, the TCS Pilot Valve circuitry internal to the BPM Valve, and the TCS Pilot Valve Solenoid coil.
5. Determines whether a problem found in Step 4 is due to an open in CKTs 886, 1657 or a faulty BPM Modulator Valve.
6. Determines whether the problem found in Step 4 is due to an open in CKT 886 or 1657.

DIAGNOSTIC AIDS:

All tests using J 39700 Universal Breakout Box terminal '20' are using the terminal as ground. These tests, of course, assume that the ground CKT 1250 terminal '20' is good.

If Codes 44 and 48 are both set, the fault is likely to be an open or short in CKT 886.

GC4029300543010X

Fig. 109 Code 48: Left Front TCS Pilot Valve Fault (Part 1 of 2). 1993-94 DeVille, Eldorado & Seville

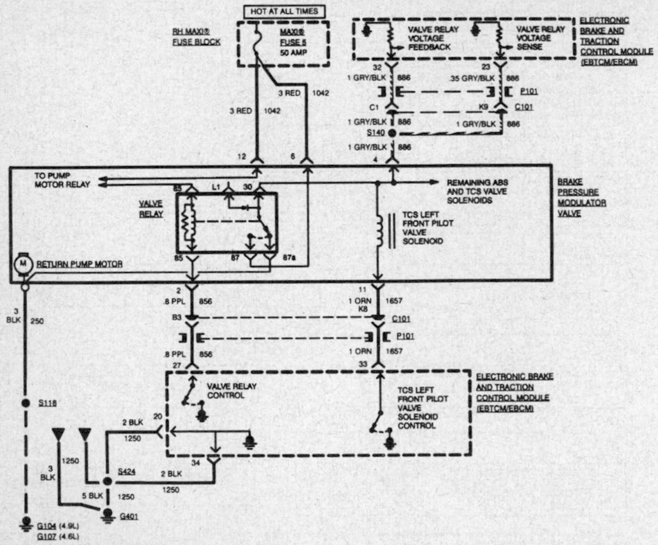
HOT AT ALL TIMES
RH MAXI® FUSE BLOCK
MAXI® FUSE 5 50 AMP
VALVE RELAY VOLTAGE FEEDBACK
VALVE RELAY VOLTAGE SENSE
ELECTRONIC BRAKE AND TRACTION CONTROL MODULE (EBTCM/EBCM)
TO PUMP MOTOR RELAY
VALVE RELAY
REMAINING ABS AND TCS VALVE SOLENOIDS
BRAKE PRESSURE MODULATOR VALVE
TCS LEFT FRONT PILOT VALVE SOLENOID
RETURN PUMP MOTOR
VALVE RELAY CONTROL
TCS LEFT FRONT PILOT VALVE SOLENOID CONTROL
S118
S140
S424
C101
P101
G401
G104 (4.9L)
G107 (4.6L)

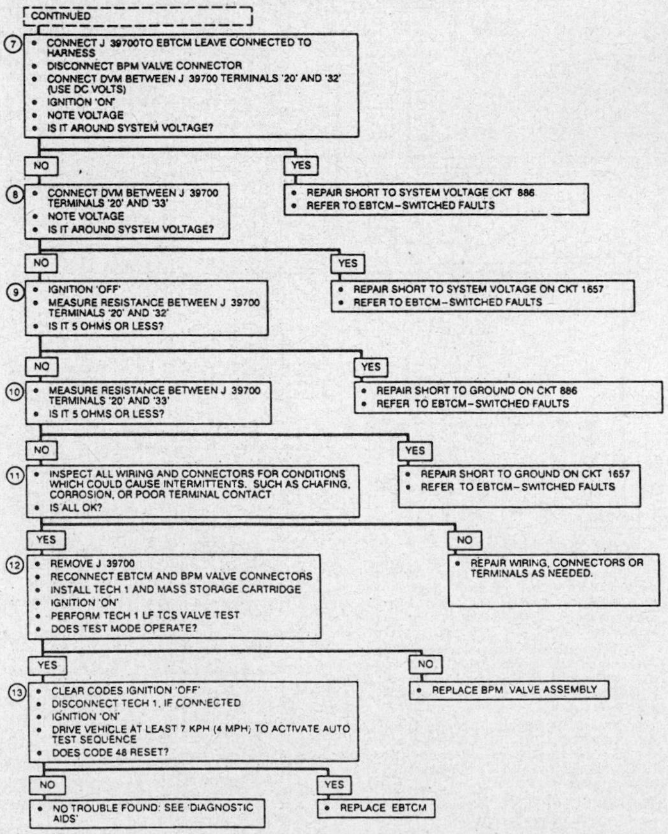
CONTINUED
7 • CONNECT J 39700 TO EBTCM LEAVE CONNECTED TO HARNESS
• DISCONNECT BPM VALVE CONNECTOR
• CONNECT DVM BETWEEN J 39700 TERMINALS '20' AND '32' (USE DC VOLTS)
• IGNITION 'ON'
• NOTE VOLTAGE
• IS IT AROUND SYSTEM VOLTAGE?
NO
YES
8 • CONNECT DVM BETWEEN J 39700 TERMINALS '20' AND '33'
• NOTE VOLTAGE
• IS IT AROUND SYSTEM VOLTAGE?
• REPAIR SHORT TO SYSTEM VOLTAGE CKT 886
• REFER TO EBTCM–SWITCHED FAULTS
NO
YES
9 • IGNITION 'OFF'
• MEASURE RESISTANCE BETWEEN J 39700 TERMINALS '20' AND '32'
• IS IT 5 OHMS OR LESS?
• REPAIR SHORT TO SYSTEM VOLTAGE ON CKT 1657
• REFER TO EBTCM–SWITCHED FAULTS
NO
YES
10 • MEASURE RESISTANCE BETWEEN J 39700 TERMINALS '20' AND '33'
• IS IT 5 OHMS OR LESS?
• REPAIR SHORT TO GROUND ON CKT 886
• REFER TO EBTCM–SWITCHED FAULTS
NO
YES
11 • INSPECT ALL WIRING AND CONNECTORS FOR CONDITIONS WHICH COULD CAUSE INTERMITTENTS. SUCH AS CHAFING, CORROSION, OR POOR TERMINAL CONTACT
• IS ALL OK?
• REPAIR SHORT TO GROUND ON CKT 1657
• REFER TO EBTCM–SWITCHED FAULTS
YES
NO
12 • REMOVE J 39700
• RECONNECT EBTCM AND BPM VALVE CONNECTORS
• INSTALL TECH 1 AND MASS STORAGE CARTRIDGE
• IGNITION 'ON'
• PERFORM TECH 1 LF TCS VALVE TEST
• DOES TEST MODE OPERATE?
• REPAIR WIRING, CONNECTORS OR TERMINALS AS NEEDED.
YES
NO
13 • CLEAR CODES IGNITION 'OFF'
• DISCONNECT TECH 1, IF CONNECTED
• IGNITION 'ON'
• DRIVE VEHICLE AT LEAST 7 KPH (4 MPH) TO ACTIVATE AUTO TEST SEQUENCE
• DOES CODE 48 RESET?
• REPLACE BPM VALVE ASSEMBLY
NO
YES
• NO TROUBLE FOUND: SEE 'DIAGNOSTIC AIDS'
• REPLACE EBTCM

CIRCUIT DESCRIPTION:

The left front TCS pilot valve in the BPM VALVE may be commanded to close, isolating the master cylinder.

The pilot valve circuits receive power through the valve relay on the BPM VALVE. The valve relay is engaged at KEY–ON and remains engaged throughout the ignition cycle. Pilot valve circuits should have battery voltage available at all times.

When the key is turned to RUN, power is supplied to the EBTCM. The EBTCM will complete an internal self–check before providing ground to the valve relay. When the valve relay is energized, battery power is supplied to the pilot valves.

TEST DESCRIPTION: Test numbers refer to circled numbers on the diagnostic chart.

7. Checks for a short to battery in CKT 886 using EBTCM/EBCM terminal '20' as ground.
8. Checks for a short to battery in CKT 1657, using EBTCM terminal '20' as ground.
9. Checks for a short to ground in CKT 886 using EBTCM terminal '20' as ground.
10. Checks for a short to ground in CKT 1657, using EBTCM terminal '20' as ground.
11. Checks for connector or wiring problems which could cause intermittents.
12. Uses the TECH 1 to exercise the TCS pilot valve solenoid and check it for proper operation.
13. Determines whether the code was set by an intermittent conditions or an EBTCM fault.

DIAGNOSTIC AIDS:

All tests using J 39700 Universal Breakout Box terminal '20' are using the terminal as ground. These tests, of course, assume that the ground CKT 1250 terminal '20' is good.

If Codes 44 and 48 are both set, the fault is likely to be an open or short in CKT 886.

GC4029300543030X

GC4029300543040X

Fig. 109 Code 48: Left Front TCS Pilot Valve Fault (Part 2 of 2). 1993-94 DeVille, Eldorado & Seville

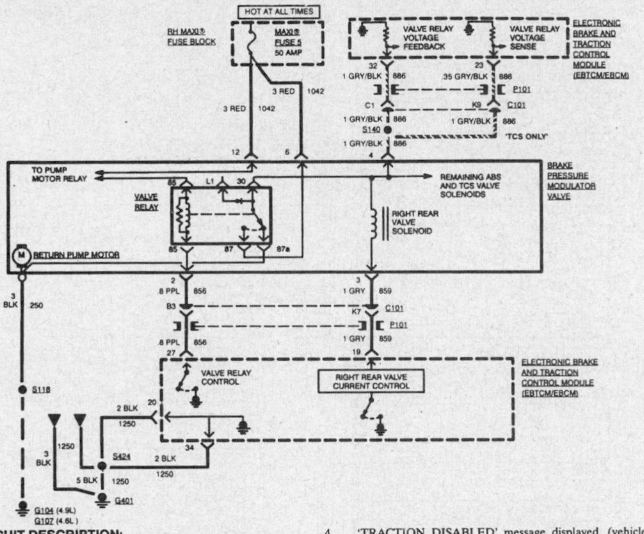

HOT AT ALL TIMES
RH MAXI® FUSE BLOCK
MAXI® FUSE 5 50 AMP
VALVE RELAY VOLTAGE FEEDBACK
VALVE RELAY VOLTAGE SENSE
ELECTRONIC BRAKE AND TRACTION CONTROL MODULE (EBTCM/EBCM)
1 GRY/BLK 886
.35 GRY/BLK 886
P101
C101
3 RED 1042
S140
'TCS ONLY'
TO PUMP MOTOR RELAY
REMAINING ABS AND TCS VALVE SOLENOIDS
BRAKE PRESSURE MODULATOR VALVE
VALVE RELAY
RIGHT REAR VALVE SOLENOID
RETURN PUMP MOTOR
.8 PPL 856
1 GRY 859
3 BLK 250
VALVE RELAY CONTROL
RIGHT REAR VALVE CURRENT CONTROL
S118
2 BLK
1250
S424
5 BLK
G401
G104 (4.9L)
G107 (4.6L)

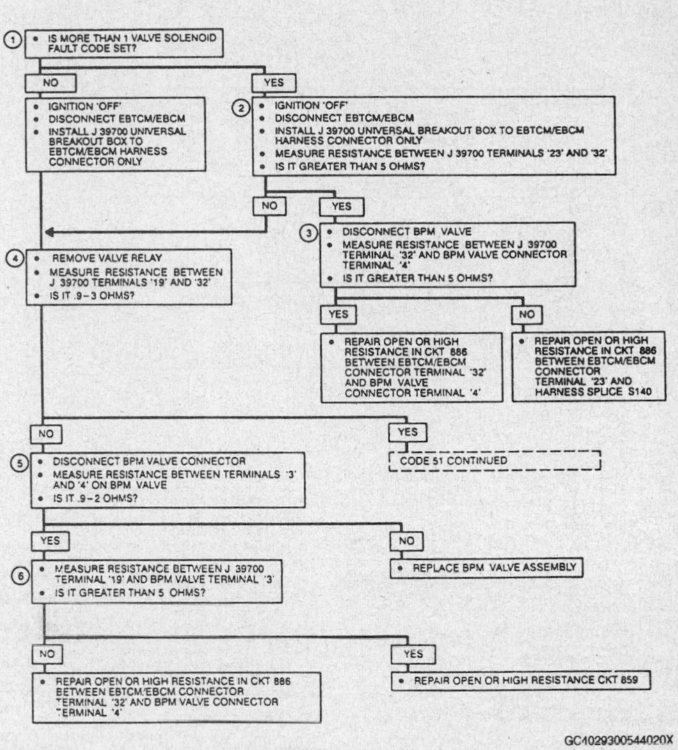

1 • IS MORE THAN 1 VALVE SOLENOID FAULT CODE SET?
NO
YES
• IGNITION 'OFF'
• DISCONNECT EBTCM/EBCM
• INSTALL J 39700 UNIVERSAL BREAKOUT BOX TO EBTCM/EBCM HARNESS CONNECTOR ONLY
2 • IGNITION 'OFF'
• DISCONNECT EBTCM/EBCM
• INSTALL J 39700 UNIVERSAL BREAKOUT BOX TO EBTCM/EBCM HARNESS CONNECTOR ONLY
• MEASURE RESISTANCE BETWEEN J 39700 TERMINALS '23' AND '32'
• IS IT GREATER THAN 5 OHMS?
NO
YES
3 • DISCONNECT BPM VALVE
• MEASURE RESISTANCE BETWEEN J 39700 TERMINAL '32' AND BPM VALVE CONNECTOR TERMINAL '4'
• IS IT GREATER THAN 5 OHMS?
4 • REMOVE VALVE RELAY
• MEASURE RESISTANCE BETWEEN J 39700 TERMINALS '19' AND '32'
• IS IT .9–3 OHMS?
YES
NO
• REPAIR OPEN OR HIGH RESISTANCE IN CKT 886 BETWEEN EBTCM/EBCM CONNECTOR TERMINAL '32' AND BPM VALVE CONNECTOR TERMINAL '4'
• REPAIR OPEN OR HIGH RESISTANCE IN CKT 886 BETWEEN EBTCM/EBCM CONNECTOR TERMINAL '23' AND HARNESS SPLICE S140
NO
YES
CODE 51 CONTINUED
5 • DISCONNECT BPM VALVE CONNECTOR
• MEASURE RESISTANCE BETWEEN TERMINALS '3' AND '4' ON BPM VALVE
• IS IT .9–2 OHMS?
YES
NO
• REPLACE BPM VALVE ASSEMBLY
6 • MEASURE RESISTANCE BETWEEN J 39700 TERMINAL '19' AND BPM VALVE TERMINAL '3'
• IS IT GREATER THAN 5 OHMS?
NO
YES
• REPAIR OPEN OR HIGH RESISTANCE IN CKT 886 BETWEEN EBTCM/EBCM CONNECTOR TERMINAL '32' AND BPM VALVE CONNECTOR TERMINAL '4'
• REPAIR OPEN OR HIGH RESISTANCE CKT 859
GC4029300544020X

CIRCUIT DESCRIPTION:

The right rear valve solenoid in the BPM Valve may be commanded to three different positions by the EBTCM/EBCM. Valve position is determined by the amount of current which is allowed to flow through the valve solenoid coil.

The valve solenoid circuits receive power through the valve relay on the BPM Valve. The valve relay is engaged at KEY−ON and remains engaged throughout the ignition cycle. Valve solenoid circuits should have battery voltage available at all times.

When the key is turned to RUN, power is supplied to the EBTCM/EBCM. The EBTCM/EBCM will complete an internal self−check before providing ground to the valve relay. When the valve relay is energized, battery power is supplied to the valve solenoids.

TEST CONDITION(S):

1. Tested continuously.

FAILURE CONDITION(S):

While standing or driving:

1. Valve solenoid cannot be activated.

OR

2. Valve solenoid is activated in a defective way.

ACTION TAKEN:

1. Code set.
2. ABS/TCS switched 'OFF'.
3. 'ANTILOCK' indicator 'ON'.
4. 'TRACTION DISABLED' message displayed. (vehicles with TCS)

Code 51 will set when the expected position of the right rear valve solenoid does not match the commanded position from the EBTCM/EBCM. Conditions which could cause Code 51 to set are: damage to the right rear valve solenoid; and open circuit; or a short circuit to ground or battery on CKT 859.

TEST DESCRIPTION: Test numbers refer to circled numbers on the diagnostic chart.

1. Damage to CKT 886 may result in multiple valve solenoid codes setting.
2. Checks CKT 886 for opens or high resistance from EBTCM/EBCM terminal '23' to '32'.
3. Determines which branch of CKT 886 has an open or high resistance.
4. Checks the integrity of CKTs 859 and 886, the RR ABS Valve Solenoid circuitry internal to the BPM Valve, and the RR ABS Valve Solenoid coil.
5. Determines whether a problem found in Step 4 is due to an open in CKT 859, 886, or a faulty BPM Valve.
6. Determines whether the problem found in Step 4 is due to an open in CKT 859 or 886.

DIAGNOSTIC AIDS:

All tests using J 39700 Universal Breakout Box terminal '20' are using the terminal as ground. These tests, of course, assume that the ground CKT 1250 terminal '20' is good.

GC4029300544010X

Fig. 110 Code 51: Right Rear ABS Valve Solenoid Fault (Part 1 of 2). 1993-94 DeVille, Eldorado & Seville

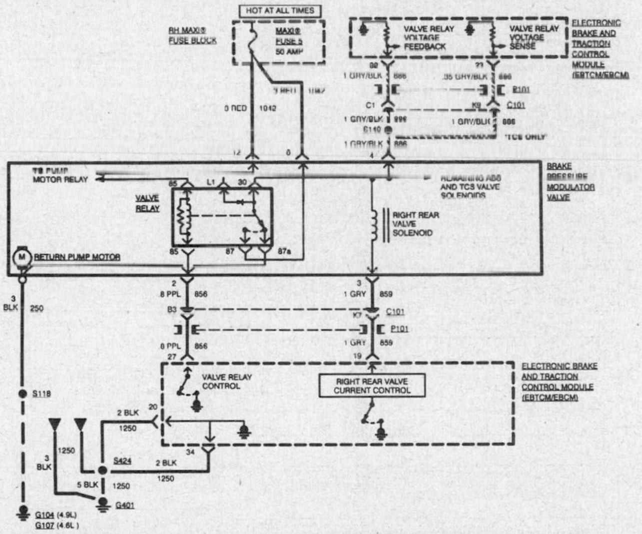

HOT AT ALL TIMES
RH MAXI® FUSE BLOCK
MAXI® FUSE 5 50 AMP
VALVE RELAY VOLTAGE FEEDBACK
VALVE RELAY VOLTAGE SENSE
ELECTRONIC BRAKE AND TRACTION CONTROL MODULE (EBTCM/EBCM)
'TCS ONLY'
TO PUMP MOTOR RELAY
REMAINING ABS AND TCS VALVE SOLENOIDS
BRAKE PRESSURE MODULATOR VALVE
VALVE RELAY
RIGHT REAR VALVE SOLENOID
RETURN PUMP MOTOR
VALVE RELAY CONTROL
RIGHT REAR VALVE CURRENT CONTROL
S118
S424
G401
G104 (4.9L)
G107 (4.6L)

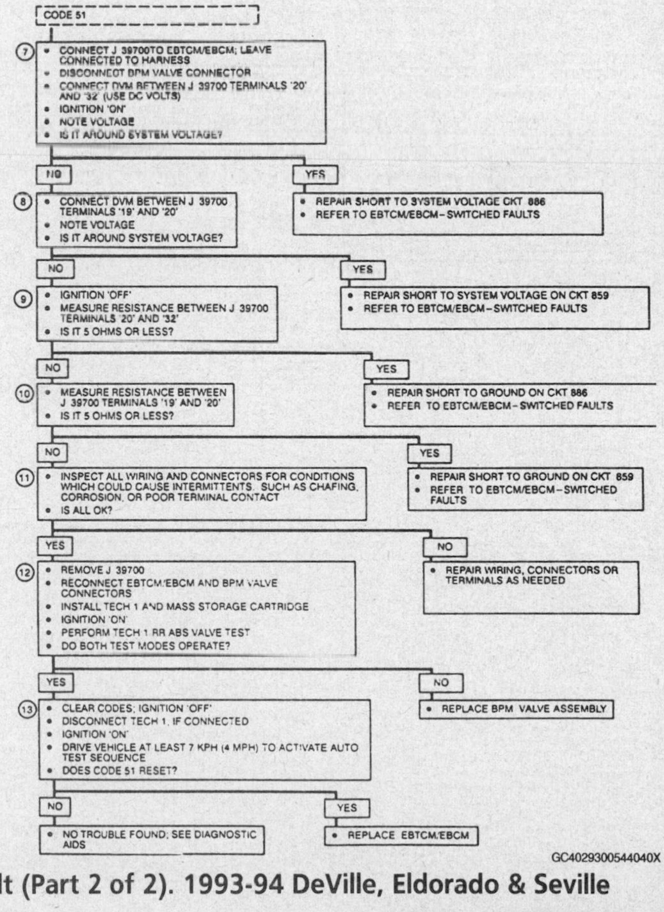

CODE 51
7 • CONNECT J 39700 TO EBTCM/EBCM; LEAVE CONNECTED TO HARNESS
• DISCONNECT BPM VALVE CONNECTOR
• CONNECT DVM BETWEEN J 39700 TERMINALS '20' AND '32' (USE DC VOLTS)
• IGNITION 'ON'
• NOTE VOLTAGE
• IS IT AROUND SYSTEM VOLTAGE?
NO
YES
• REPAIR SHORT TO SYSTEM VOLTAGE CKT 886
• REFER TO EBTCM/EBCM–SWITCHED FAULTS
8 • CONNECT DVM BETWEEN J 39700 TERMINALS '19' AND '20'
• NOTE VOLTAGE
• IS IT AROUND SYSTEM VOLTAGE?
NO
YES
• REPAIR SHORT TO SYSTEM VOLTAGE ON CKT 859
• REFER TO EBTCM/EBCM–SWITCHED FAULTS
9 • IGNITION 'OFF'
• MEASURE RESISTANCE BETWEEN J 39700 TERMINALS '20' AND '32'
• IS IT 5 OHMS OR LESS?
NO
YES
• REPAIR SHORT TO GROUND ON CKT 886
• REFER TO EBTCM/EBCM–SWITCHED FAULTS
10 • MEASURE RESISTANCE BETWEEN J 39700 TERMINALS '19' AND '20'
• IS IT 5 OHMS OR LESS?
NO
YES
• REPAIR SHORT TO GROUND ON CKT 859
• REFER TO EBTCM/EBCM–SWITCHED FAULTS
11 • INSPECT ALL WIRING AND CONNECTORS FOR CONDITIONS WHICH COULD CAUSE INTERMITTENTS, SUCH AS CHAFING, CORROSION, OR POOR TERMINAL CONTACT
• IS ALL OK?
YES
NO
• REPAIR WIRING, CONNECTORS OR TERMINALS AS NEEDED
12 • REMOVE J 39700
• RECONNECT EBTCM/EBCM AND BPM VALVE CONNECTORS
• INSTALL TECH 1 AND MASS STORAGE CARTRIDGE
• IGNITION 'ON'
• PERFORM TECH 1 RR ABS VALVE TEST
• DO BOTH TEST MODES OPERATE?
YES
NO
• REPLACE BPM VALVE ASSEMBLY
13 • CLEAR CODES; IGNITION 'OFF'
• DISCONNECT TECH 1, IF CONNECTED
• IGNITION 'ON'
• DRIVE VEHICLE AT LEAST 7 KPH (4 MPH) TO ACTIVATE AUTO TEST SEQUENCE
• DOES CODE 51 RESET?
NO
YES
• NO TROUBLE FOUND; SEE DIAGNOSTIC AIDS
• REPLACE EBTCM/EBCM
GC4029300544040X

CIRCUIT DESCRIPTION:

The right rear valve solenoid in the BPM Valve may be commanded to three different positions by the EBTCM/EBCM. Valve position is determined by the amount of current which is allowed to flow through the valve solenoid coil.

The valve solenoid circuits receive power through the valve relay on the BPM Valve. The valve relay is engaged at KEY−ON and remains engaged throughout the ignition cycle. Valve solenoid circuits should have battery voltage available at all times.

When the key is turned to RUN, power is supplied to the EBTCM/EBCM. The EBTCM/EBCM will complete an internal self−check before providing ground to the valve relay. When the valve relay is energized, battery power is supplied to the valve solenoids.

TEST DESCRIPTION: Test numbers refer to circled numbers on the diagnostic chart.

7. Checks for a short to battery in CKT 886 using EBTCM/EBCM terminal '20' as ground.
8. Checks for a short to battery in CKT 859, using EBTCM/EBCM terminal '20' as ground.
9. Checks for a short to ground in CKT 886 using EBTCM/EBCM terminal '20' as ground.
10. Checks for a short to ground in CKT 859, using EBTCM/EBCM terminal '20' as ground.
11. Checks wiring and connectors for intermittents.
12. Uses the TECH 1 to exercise the RR ABS valve solenoid and check it for proper operation.
13. Determines whether the code was set by an intermittent conditions or an EBTCM/EBCM fault.

DIAGNOSTIC AIDS:

All tests using J 39700 Universal Breakout Box terminal '20' are using the terminal as ground. These tests, of course, assume that the ground CKT 1250 terminal '20' is good.

GC4029300544030X

Fig. 110 Code 51: Right Rear ABS Valve Solenoid Fault (Part 2 of 2). 1993-94 DeVille, Eldorado & Seville

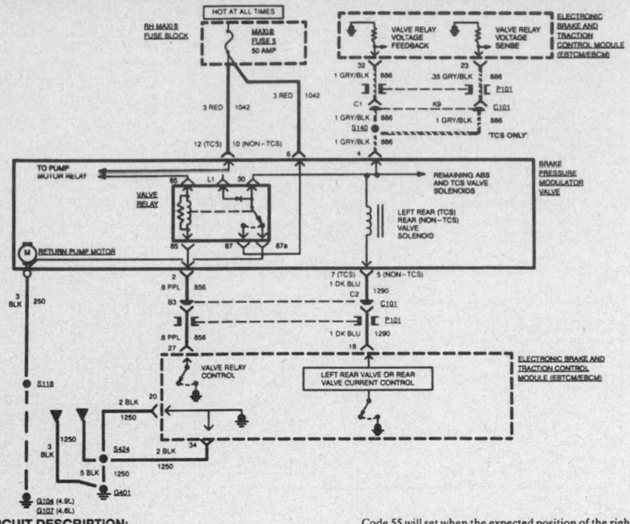
HOT AT ALL TIMES
RH MAXI 3 FUSE BLOCK
MAXI® FUSE 5 50 AMP
VALVE RELAY VOLTAGE FEEDBACK
VALVE RELAY VOLTAGE SENSE
ELECTRONIC BRAKE AND TRACTION CONTROL MODULE (EBTCM/EBCM)
TCS ONLY
TO PUMP MOTOR RELAY
VALVE RELAY
REMAINING ABS AND TCS VALVE SOLENOIDS
BRAKE PRESSURE MODULATOR VALVE
LEFT REAR (TCS) REAR (NON-TCS) VALVE SOLENOID
RETURN PUMP MOTOR
VALVE RELAY CONTROL
LEFT REAR VALVE OR REAR VALVE CURRENT CONTROL
ELECTRONIC BRAKE AND TRACTION CONTROL MODULE (EBTCM/EBCM)
G104 (4.9L)
G107 (4.6L)
G401

CIRCUIT DESCRIPTION:

The left rear valve solenoid (TCS) or rear valve solenoid (non–TCS) in the BPM Valve may be commanded to three different positions by the EBTCM/EBCM. Valve position is determined by the amount of current which is allowed to flow through the valve solenoid coil.

The valve solenoid circuits receive power through the valve relay on the BPM Valve. The valve relay is engaged at KEY–ON and remains engaged throughout the ignition cycle. Valve solenoid circuits should have battery voltage available at all times.

When the key is turned to RUN, power is supplied to the EBTCM/EBCM. The EBTCM/EBCM will complete an internal self–check before providing ground to the valve relay. When the valve relay is energized, battery power is supplied to the valve solenoids.

TEST CONDITION(S):

1. Tested continuously.

FAILURE CONDITION(S):

While standing or driving:

1. Valve solenoid cannot be activated.

OR

2. Valve solenoid is activated in a defective way.

ACTION TAKEN:

1. Code set.
2. ABS/TCS switched 'OFF'.
3. 'ANTILOCK' indicator 'ON'.
4. 'TRACTION DISABLED' message displayed (vehicles with TCS)

Code 55 will set when the expected position of the right rear valve solenoid does not match the commanded position from the EBTCM/EBCM. Conditions which could cause Code 55 to set are: damage to the left rear/rear valve solenoid; an open circuit; or a short circuit to ground or battery on CKT 1290.

TEST DESCRIPTION: Test numbers refer to circled numbers on the diagnostic chart.

1. Damage to CKT 886 may result in multiple valve solenoid codes setting.
2. Checks CKT 886 for opens or high resistance from EBTCM/EBCM terminal '23' to '32'.
3. Determines which branch of CKT 886 has an open or high resistance.
4. Checks the integrity of CKTs 1290 and 886, the LR/Rear ABS Valve Solenoid circuitry internal to the BPM Valve, and the LR/Rear ABS Valve Solenoid coil.
5. Determines whether a problem found in Step 4 is due to an open in CKT 1290, 886, or a faulty BPM Valve.
6. Determines whether the problem found in Step 4 is due to an open in CKT 1290 or 886.

DIAGNOSTIC AIDS:

All tests using J 39700 Universal Breakout Box terminal '20' are using the terminal as ground. These tests, of course, assume that the ground CKT 1250 terminal '20' is good.

If Codes 41 and 55 are both set, the fault is likely to be a short to B+ on 1290.

GC4029300545010X

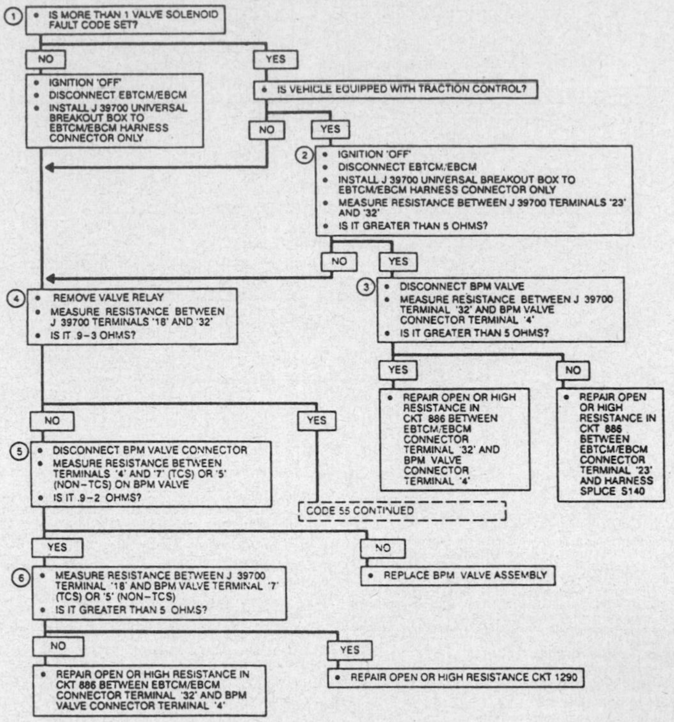
1 • IS MORE THAN 1 VALVE SOLENOID FAULT CODE SET?
NO
YES
• IGNITION 'OFF'
• DISCONNECT EBTCM/EBCM
• INSTALL J 39700 UNIVERSAL BREAKOUT BOX TO EBTCM/EBCM HARNESS CONNECTOR ONLY
• IS VEHICLE EQUIPPED WITH TRACTION CONTROL?
NO
YES
2 • IGNITION 'OFF'
• DISCONNECT EBTCM/EBCM
• INSTALL J 39700 UNIVERSAL BREAKOUT BOX TO EBTCM/EBCM HARNESS CONNECTOR ONLY
• MEASURE RESISTANCE BETWEEN J 39700 TERMINALS '23' AND '32'
• IS IT GREATER THAN 5 OHMS?
NO
YES
3 • DISCONNECT BPM VALVE
• MEASURE RESISTANCE BETWEEN J 39700 TERMINAL '32' AND BPM VALVE CONNECTOR TERMINAL '4'
• IS IT GREATER THAN 5 OHMS?
4 • REMOVE VALVE RELAY
• MEASURE RESISTANCE BETWEEN J 39700 TERMINALS '18' AND '32'
• IS IT .9–3 OHMS?
YES
NO
• REPAIR OPEN OR HIGH RESISTANCE IN CKT 886 BETWEEN EBTCM/EBCM CONNECTOR TERMINAL '32' AND BPM VALVE CONNECTOR TERMINAL '4'
• REPAIR OPEN OR HIGH RESISTANCE IN CKT 886 BETWEEN EBTCM/EBCM CONNECTOR TERMINAL '23' AND HARNESS SPLICE S140
NO
YES
5 • DISCONNECT BPM VALVE CONNECTOR
• MEASURE RESISTANCE BETWEEN TERMINALS '4' AND '7' (TCS) OR '5' (NON–TCS) ON BPM VALVE
• IS IT .9–2 OHMS?
CODE 55 CONTINUED
YES
NO
6 • MEASURE RESISTANCE BETWEEN J 39700 TERMINAL '18' AND BPM VALVE TERMINAL '7' (TCS) OR '5' (NON–TCS)
• IS IT GREATER THAN 5 OHMS?
• REPLACE BPM VALVE ASSEMBLY
NO
YES
• REPAIR OPEN OR HIGH RESISTANCE IN CKT 886 BETWEEN EBTCM/EBCM CONNECTOR TERMINAL '32' AND BPM VALVE CONNECTOR TERMINAL '4'
• REPAIR OPEN OR HIGH RESISTANCE CKT 1290

GC4029300545020X

Fig. 111 Code 55: Left Rear Valve Solenoid Valve (With TCS); Rear Valve Solenoid Valve Fault (Less TCS), (Part 1 of 2). 1993-94 DeVille, Eldorado & Seville

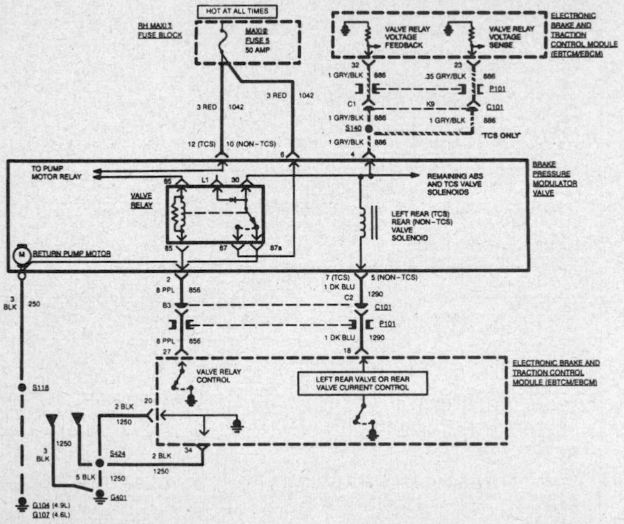
HOT AT ALL TIMES
RH MAXI 3 FUSE BLOCK
MAXI® FUSE 5 50 AMP
VALVE RELAY VOLTAGE FEEDBACK
VALVE RELAY VOLTAGE SENSE
ELECTRONIC BRAKE AND TRACTION CONTROL MODULE (EBTCM/EBCM)
TCS ONLY
TO PUMP MOTOR RELAY
VALVE RELAY
REMAINING ABS AND TCS VALVE SOLENOIDS
BRAKE PRESSURE MODULATOR VALVE
LEFT REAR (TCS) REAR (NON-TCS) VALVE SOLENOID
RETURN PUMP MOTOR
VALVE RELAY CONTROL
LEFT REAR VALVE OR REAR VALVE CURRENT CONTROL
ELECTRONIC BRAKE AND TRACTION CONTROL MODULE (EBTCM/EBCM)
G104 (4.9L)
G107 (4.6L)
G401

CIRCUIT DESCRIPTION:

The left rear valve solenoid (TCS) or rear valve solenoid (non–TCS) in the BPM Valve may be commanded to three different positions by the EBTCM/EBCM. Valve position is determined by the amount of current which is allowed to flow through the valve solenoid coil.

The valve solenoid circuits receive power through the valve relay on the BPM valve. The valve relay is engaged at KEY–ON and remains engaged throughout the ignition cycle. Valve solenoid circuits should have battery voltage available at all times.

When the key is turned to RUN, power is supplied to the EBTCM/EBCM. The EBTCM/EBCM will complete an internal self–check before providing ground to the valve relay. When the valve relay is energized, battery power is supplied to the valve solenoids.

TEST DESCRIPTION: Test numbers refer to circled numbers on the diagnostic chart.

7. Checks for a short to battery in CKT 886 using EBTCM/EBCM terminal '20' as ground.
8. Checks for a short to battery in CKT 1290, using EBTCM/EBCM terminal '20' as ground.
9. Checks for a short to ground in CKT 886 using EBTCM/EBCM terminal '20' as ground.
10. Checks for a short to ground in CKT 1290, using EBTCM/EBCM terminal '20' as ground.
11. Checks wiring and connectors for intermittents.
12. Uses the TECH 1 to exercise the LR (TCS) or rear (non–TCS) ABS valve solenoid and check it for proper operation.
13. Determines whether the code was set by an intermittent conditions or an EBTCM/EBCM fault.

DIAGNOSTIC AIDS:

All tests using J 39700 Universal Breakout Box terminal '20' are using the terminal as ground. These tests, of course, assume that the ground CKT 1250 terminal '20' is good.

If Codes 41 and 55 are both set, the fault is likely to be a short to B+ on CKT 1290.

GC4029300545030X

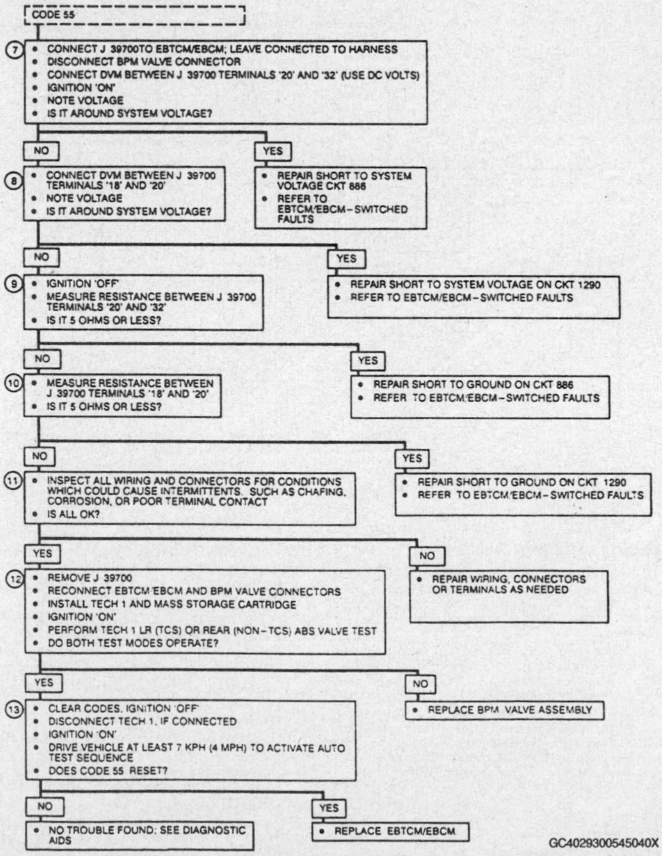
CODE 55
7 • CONNECT J 39700 TO EBTCM/EBCM; LEAVE CONNECTED TO HARNESS
• DISCONNECT BPM VALVE CONNECTOR
• CONNECT DVM BETWEEN J 39700 TERMINALS '20' AND '32' (USE DC VOLTS)
• IGNITION 'ON'
• NOTE VOLTAGE
• IS IT AROUND SYSTEM VOLTAGE?
NO
YES
8 • CONNECT DVM BETWEEN J 39700 TERMINALS '18' AND '20'
• NOTE VOLTAGE
• IS IT AROUND SYSTEM VOLTAGE?
• REPAIR SHORT TO SYSTEM VOLTAGE CKT 886
• REFER TO EBTCM/EBCM–SWITCHED FAULTS
NO
YES
9 • IGNITION 'OFF'
• MEASURE RESISTANCE BETWEEN J 39700 TERMINALS '20' AND '32'
• IS IT 5 OHMS OR LESS?
• REPAIR SHORT TO SYSTEM VOLTAGE ON CKT 1290
• REFER TO EBTCM/EBCM–SWITCHED FAULTS
NO
YES
10 • MEASURE RESISTANCE BETWEEN J 39700 TERMINALS '18' AND '20'
• IS IT 5 OHMS OR LESS?
• REPAIR SHORT TO GROUND ON CKT 886
• REFER TO EBTCM/EBCM–SWITCHED FAULTS
NO
YES
11 • INSPECT ALL WIRING AND CONNECTORS FOR CONDITIONS WHICH COULD CAUSE INTERMITTENTS. SUCH AS CHAFING, CORROSION, OR POOR TERMINAL CONTACT
• IS ALL OK?
• REPAIR SHORT TO GROUND ON CKT 1290
• REFER TO EBTCM/EBCM–SWITCHED FAULTS
YES
NO
12 • REMOVE J 39700
• RECONNECT EBTCM/EBCM AND BPM VALVE CONNECTORS
• INSTALL TECH 1 AND MASS STORAGE CARTRIDGE
• IGNITION 'ON'
• PERFORM TECH 1 LR (TCS) OR REAR (NON–TCS) ABS VALVE TEST
• DO BOTH TEST MODES OPERATE?
• REPAIR WIRING, CONNECTORS OR TERMINALS AS NEEDED
YES
NO
13 • CLEAR CODES. IGNITION 'OFF'
• DISCONNECT TECH 1, IF CONNECTED
• IGNITION 'ON'
• DRIVE VEHICLE AT LEAST 7 KPH (4 MPH) TO ACTIVATE AUTO TEST SEQUENCE
• DOES CODE 55 RESET?
• REPLACE BPM VALVE ASSEMBLY
NO
YES
• NO TROUBLE FOUND: SEE DIAGNOSTIC AIDS
• REPLACE EBTCM/EBCM

GC4029300545040X

Fig. 111 Code 55: Left Rear Valve Solenoid Valve (With TCS); Rear Valve Solenoid Valve Fault (Less TCS), (Part 2 of 2). 1993-94 DeVille, Eldorado & Seville

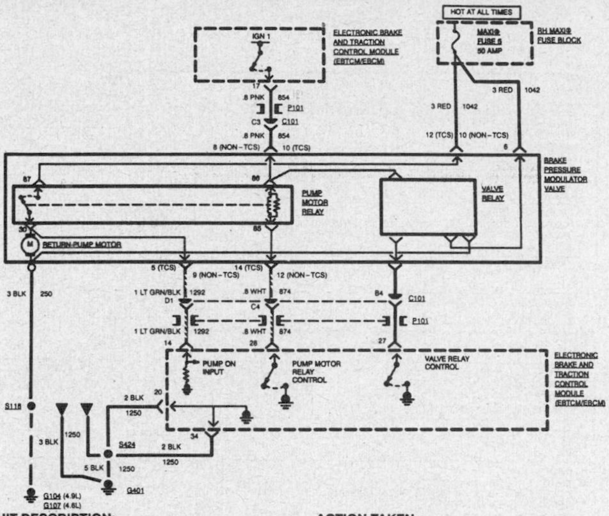

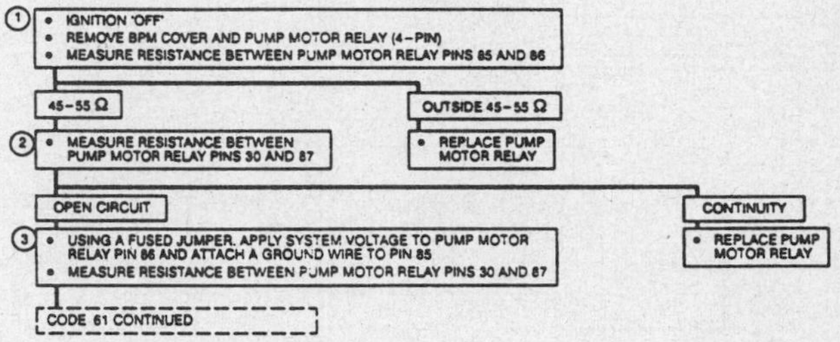

1
• IGNITION 'OFF'
• REMOVE BPM COVER AND PUMP MOTOR RELAY (4-PIN)
• MEASURE RESISTANCE BETWEEN PUMP MOTOR RELAY PINS 85 AND 86
45-55 Ω
OUTSIDE 45-55 Ω
2
• MEASURE RESISTANCE BETWEEN PUMP MOTOR RELAY PINS 30 AND 87
• REPLACE PUMP MOTOR RELAY
OPEN CIRCUIT
CONTINUITY
3
• USING A FUSED JUMPER, APPLY SYSTEM VOLTAGE TO PUMP MOTOR RELAY PIN 86 AND ATTACH A GROUND WIRE TO PIN 85
• MEASURE RESISTANCE BETWEEN PUMP MOTOR RELAY PINS 30 AND 87
• REPLACE PUMP MOTOR RELAY
CODE 61 CONTINUED
GC4029300546020X

CIRCUIT DESCRIPTION:

The pump motor returns brake fluid to the master cylinder brake circuit at the BPM Valve during antilock braking and provides brake fluid pressure to the front wheels during traction control. During normal braking, the pump does not operate. When the vehicle begins to move after start-up, the EBTCM/EBCM will turn on the pump motor and perform a self-check of the pump motor and pump motor circuit. This check may be felt and heard by the driver when the vehicle begins to move. The self-check should be considered normal operation. The pump motor is an integral component of the BPM Valve and cannot be serviced separately.

The pump motor relay provides power to the pump motor in the BPM Valve. The pump motor relay is located on the BPM Valve and may be replaced if it is found to be defective.

The pump motor relay is not engaged during normal system operation. When antilock or traction control operation is required, the motor relay actuation line on CKT 874 (EBTCM/EBCM pin '28') is pulled to ground. The pump motor relay is engaged by the relay supply voltage line on CKT 854 (EBTCM/EBCM pin '17'). When the relay switches, battery power is provided to the pump motor.

TEST CONDITION(S):

1. Tested continuously.

FAILURE CONDITION(S):

1. Drive Away: Motor voltage is not detected during first drive away after engine start.
2. While Driving: Motor relay is energized and motor voltage is not detected.
3. Voltage at EBTCM/EBCM pin '14' below 9 volts.
4. Pump runs continuously.

ACTION TAKEN:

1. Code set.
2. ABS/TCS switched 'OFF'.
3. 'ANTILOCK' indicator 'ON'.
4. 'TRACTION DISABLED' message displayed. (vehicles with TCS)

When the pump motor relay is engaged, the motor monitor line should be at battery voltage. With the pump motor relay disengaged, the monitoring line should be at ground. If the commanded position of the pump motor relay and motor monitor line do not agree, Code 61 will set. Some conditions which will cause Code 61 to set are:

- An open circuit on CKTs 874 or 1292
- A short to voltage on CKTs 874 or 1292
- A short to ground on CKTs 874 or 1292
- A defective pump motor relay or pump motor

TEST DESCRIPTION: Test numbers refer to circled numbers on the diagnostic chart.

1. Checks the pump motor relay coil for proper resistance.
2. Determines if the pump motor relay contacts are stuck closed.
3. Determines if the pump motor relay contacts are stuck open.

DIAGNOSTIC AIDS:

All tests using J 39700 Universal Breakout Box terminal '20' are using the terminal as ground. These tests, of course, assume that the ground CKT 1250 at terminal '20' is good.

It is very important that a through inspection of the wiring and connectors be performed. Failure to carefully and fully inspect wiring and connectors may result in misdiagnosis, causing part replacement with reappearance of the fault.

GC4029300546010X

Fig. 112 Code 61: Pump Motor Or Pump Motor Relay Fault (Part 1 of 3). 1993-94 DeVille, Eldorado & Seville

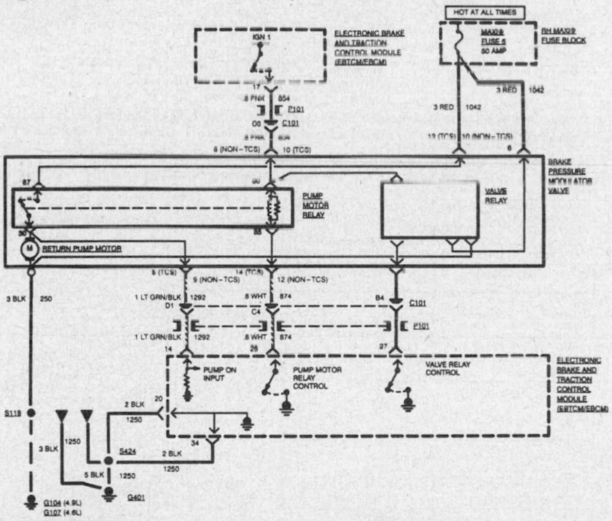

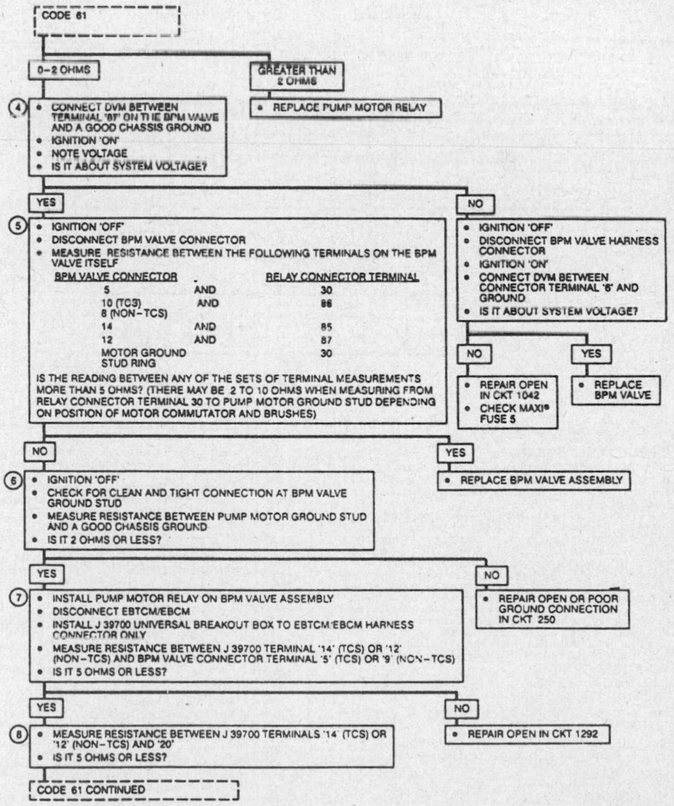

CODE 61
0-2 OHMS
GREATER THAN 2 OHMS
4
• CONNECT DVM BETWEEN TERMINAL '87' ON THE BPM VALVE AND A GOOD CHASSIS GROUND
• IGNITION 'ON'
• NOTE VOLTAGE
• IS IT ABOUT SYSTEM VOLTAGE?
• REPLACE PUMP MOTOR RELAY
YES
NO
5
• IGNITION 'OFF'
• DISCONNECT BPM VALVE CONNECTOR
• MEASURE RESISTANCE BETWEEN THE FOLLOWING TERMINALS ON THE BPM VALVE ITSELF
BPM VALVE CONNECTOR AND RELAY CONNECTOR TERMINAL
5 AND 30
10 (TCS) 8 (NON-TCS) AND 86
14 AND 85
12 AND 87
MOTOR GROUND STUD RING 30
IS THE READING BETWEEN ANY OF THE SETS OF TERMINAL MEASUREMENTS MORE THAN 5 OHMS? (THERE MAY BE 2 TO 10 OHMS WHEN MEASURING FROM RELAY CONNECTOR TERMINAL 30 TO PUMP MOTOR GROUND STUD DEPENDING ON POSITION OF MOTOR COMMUTATOR AND BRUSHES)
• IGNITION 'OFF'
• DISCONNECT BPM VALVE HARNESS CONNECTOR
• IGNITION 'ON'
• CONNECT DVM BETWEEN CONNECTOR TERMINAL '5' AND GROUND
• IS IT ABOUT SYSTEM VOLTAGE?
NO
YES
• REPAIR OPEN IN CKT 1042
• CHECK MAXI® FUSE 5
• REPLACE BPM VALVE
NO
YES
6
• IGNITION 'OFF'
• CHECK FOR CLEAN AND TIGHT CONNECTION AT BPM VALVE GROUND STUD
• MEASURE RESISTANCE BETWEEN PUMP MOTOR GROUND STUD AND A GOOD CHASSIS GROUND
• IS IT 2 OHMS OR LESS?
• REPLACE BPM VALVE ASSEMBLY
YES
NO
7
• INSTALL PUMP MOTOR RELAY ON BPM VALVE ASSEMBLY
• DISCONNECT EBTCM/EBCM
• INSTALL J 39700 UNIVERSAL BREAKOUT BOX TO EBTCM/EBCM HARNESS CONNECTOR ONLY
• MEASURE RESISTANCE BETWEEN J 39700 TERMINAL '14' (TCS) OR '12' (NON-TCS) AND BPM VALVE CONNECTOR TERMINAL '5' (TCS) OR '9' (NON-TCS)
• IS IT 5 OHMS OR LESS?
• REPAIR OPEN OR POOR GROUND CONNECTION IN CKT 250
YES
NO
8
• MEASURE RESISTANCE BETWEEN J 39700 TERMINALS '14' (TCS) OR '12' (NON-TCS) AND '20'
• IS IT 5 OHMS OR LESS?
• REPAIR OPEN IN CKT 1292
CODE 61 CONTINUED
GC4029300546030X

CIRCUIT DESCRIPTION:

The pump motor returns brake fluid to the master cylinder brake circuit at the BPM valve during antilock braking and provides brake fluid pressure to the front wheels during traction control. During normal braking, the pump does not operate. When the vehicle begins to move after start-up, the EBTCM/EBCM will turn on the pump motor and perform a self-check of the pump motor and pump motor circuit. This check may be felt and heard by the driver when the vehicle begins to move. The self-check should be considered normal operation. The pump motor is an integral component of the BPM valve and cannot be serviced separately.

The pump motor relay provides power to the pump motor in the BPM valve. The pump motor relay is located on the BPM valve and may be replaced if it is found to be defective.

The pump motor relay is not engaged during normal system operation. When antilock or traction control operation is required, the motor relay actuation line on CKT 874 (EBTCM/EBCM pin '28') is pulled to ground. The pump motor relay is engaged by the relay supply voltage line on CKT 854 (EBTCM/EBCM pin '17'). When the relay switches, battery power is provided to the pump motor.

TEST DESCRIPTION: Test numbers refer to circled numbers on the diagnostic chart.

4. Checks for an open in power feed CKT 1042.
5. Checks the integrity of the pump motor and pump motor relay circuitry internal to the BPM valve.
6. Checks for a good ground to the BPM valve (CKT 250).
7. Checks for an open in CKT 1292.
8. Checks for a short to ground in CKT 1292.

DIAGNOSTIC AIDS:

All tests using J 39700 Universal Breakout Box terminal '20' are using the terminal as ground. These tests, of course, assume that the ground CKT 1250 at terminal '20' is good.

It is very important that a thorough inspection of the wiring and connectors be performed. Failure to carefully and fully inspect wiring and connectors may result in misdiagnosis, causing part replacement with reappearance of the fault.

GC4029300546040X

Fig. 112 Code 61: Pump Motor Or Pump Motor Relay Fault (Part 2 of 3). 1993-94 DeVille, Eldorado & Seville

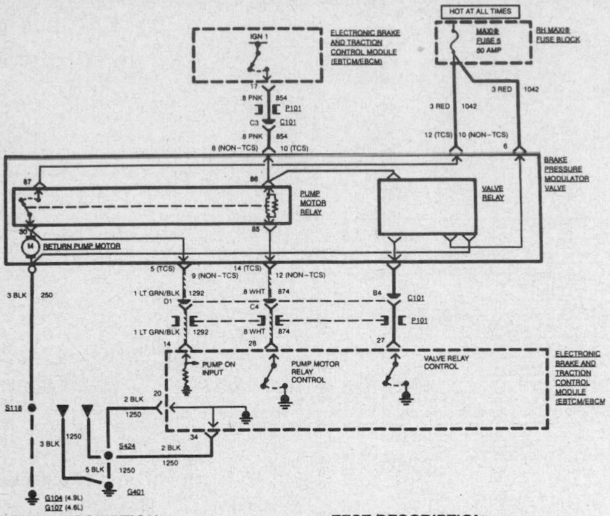
HOT AT ALL TIMES
ELECTRONIC BRAKE AND TRACTION CONTROL MODULE (EBTCM/EBCM)
RH MAXI® FUSE BLOCK
MAXI® FUSE 5 50 AMP
BRAKE PRESSURE MODULATOR VALVE
PUMP MOTOR RELAY
VALVE RELAY
RETURN PUMP MOTOR
PUMP ON INPUT
PUMP MOTOR RELAY CONTROL
VALVE RELAY CONTROL
ELECTRONIC BRAKE AND TRACTION CONTROL MODULE (EBTCM/EBCM)

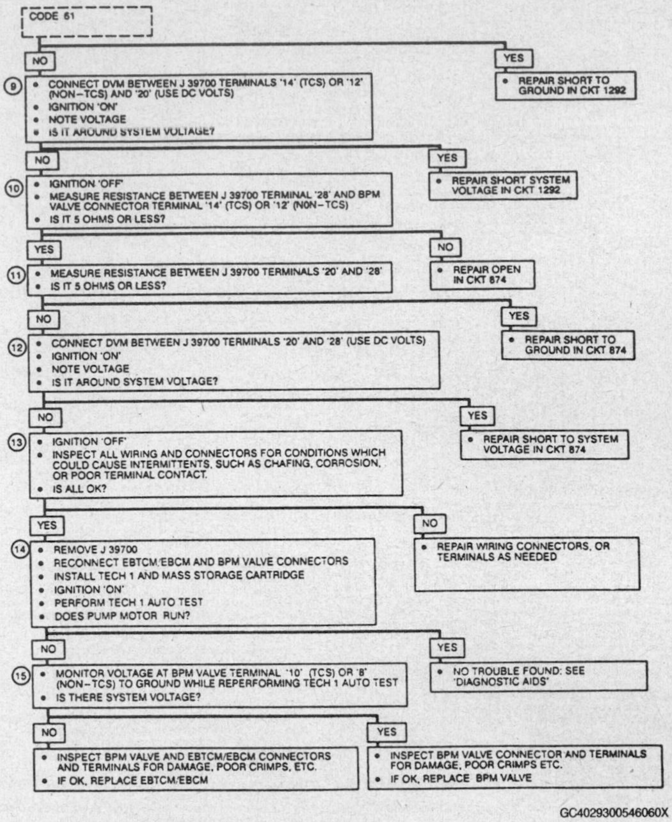
CODE 61
NO
YES
9 • CONNECT DVM BETWEEN J 39700 TERMINALS '14' (TCS) OR '12' (NON–TCS) AND '20' (USE DC VOLTS)
• IGNITION 'ON'
• NOTE VOLTAGE
• IS IT AROUND SYSTEM VOLTAGE?
• REPAIR SHORT TO GROUND IN CKT 1292
NO
YES
10 • IGNITION 'OFF'
• MEASURE RESISTANCE BETWEEN J 39700 TERMINAL '28' AND BPM VALVE CONNECTOR TERMINAL '14' (TCS) OR '12' (NON–TCS)
• IS IT 5 OHMS OR LESS?
• REPAIR SHORT SYSTEM VOLTAGE IN CKT 1292
YES
NO
11 • MEASURE RESISTANCE BETWEEN J 39700 TERMINALS '20' AND '28'
• IS IT 5 OHMS OR LESS?
• REPAIR OPEN IN CKT 874
NO
YES
12 • CONNECT DVM BETWEEN J 39700 TERMINALS '20' AND '28' (USE DC VOLTS)
• IGNITION 'ON'
• NOTE VOLTAGE
• IS IT AROUND SYSTEM VOLTAGE?
• REPAIR SHORT TO GROUND IN CKT 874
NO
YES
13 • IGNITION 'OFF'
• INSPECT ALL WIRING AND CONNECTORS FOR CONDITIONS WHICH COULD CAUSE INTERMITTENTS, SUCH AS CHAFING, CORROSION, OR POOR TERMINAL CONTACT.
• IS ALL OK?
• REPAIR SHORT TO SYSTEM VOLTAGE IN CKT 874
YES
NO
14 • REMOVE J 39700
• RECONNECT EBTCM/EBCM AND BPM VALVE CONNECTORS
• INSTALL TECH 1 AND MASS STORAGE CARTRIDGE
• IGNITION 'ON'
• PERFORM TECH 1 AUTO TEST
• DOES PUMP MOTOR RUN?
• REPAIR WIRING CONNECTORS, OR TERMINALS AS NEEDED
NO
YES
15 • MONITOR VOLTAGE AT BPM VALVE TERMINAL '10' (TCS) OR '8' (NON–TCS) TO GROUND WHILE REPERFORMING TECH 1 AUTO TEST
• IS THERE SYSTEM VOLTAGE?
• NO TROUBLE FOUND: SEE 'DIAGNOSTIC AIDS'
NO
YES
• INSPECT BPM VALVE AND EBTCM/EBCM CONNECTORS AND TERMINALS FOR DAMAGE, POOR CRIMPS, ETC.
• IF OK, REPLACE EBTCM/EBCM
• INSPECT BPM VALVE CONNECTOR AND TERMINALS FOR DAMAGE, POOR CRIMPS ETC.
• IF OK, REPLACE BPM VALVE
GC4029300546060X

CIRCUIT DESCRIPTION:

The pump motor returns brake fluid to the master cylinder brake circuit at the BPM valve during antilock braking and provides brake fluid pressure to the front wheels during traction control. During normal braking, the pump does not operate. When the vehicle begins to move after start–up, the EBTCM/EBCM will turn on the pump motor and perform a self–check of the pump motor and pump motor circuit. This check may be felt and heard by the driver when the vehicle begins to move. The self–check should be considered normal operation. The pump motor is an integral component of the BPM valve and cannot be serviced separately.

The pump motor relay provides power to the pump motor in the BPM valve. The pump motor relay is located on the BPM valve and may be replaced if it is found to be defective.

The pump motor relay is not engaged during normal system operation. When antilock or traction control operation is required, the motor relay actuation line on CKT 874 (EBTCM/EBCM pin '28') is pulled to ground. The pump motor relay is engaged by the relay supply voltage line on CKT 854 (EBTCM/EBCM pin '17'). When the relay switches, battery power is provided to the pump motor.

TEST DESCRIPTION: Test numbers refer to circled numbers on the diagnostic chart.

9. Checks for a short to system voltage in CKT 1292.
10. Checks for an open in CKT 874.
11. Checks for a short to ground on CKT 874.
12. Checks for a short to B+ in CKT 874.
13. Checks wiring and connectors for intermittents.
14. Uses the TECH 1 to check for proper operation of the pump motor and associated circuitry.
15. Determines whether the problem found in Step 13 was due to a faulty EBTCM/EBCM or BPM valve.

DIAGNOSTIC AIDS:

All tests using J 39700 Universal Breakout Box terminal '20' are using the terminal as ground. These tests, of course, assume that the ground CKT 1250 at terminal '20' is good.

It is very important that a thorough inspection of the wiring and connectors be performed. Failure to carefully and fully inspect wiring and connectors may result in misdiagnosis, causing part replacement with reappearance of the fault.

GC4029300546050X

Fig. 112 Code 61: Pump Motor Or Pump Motor Relay Fault (Part 3 of 3). 1993-94 DeVille, Eldorado & Seville

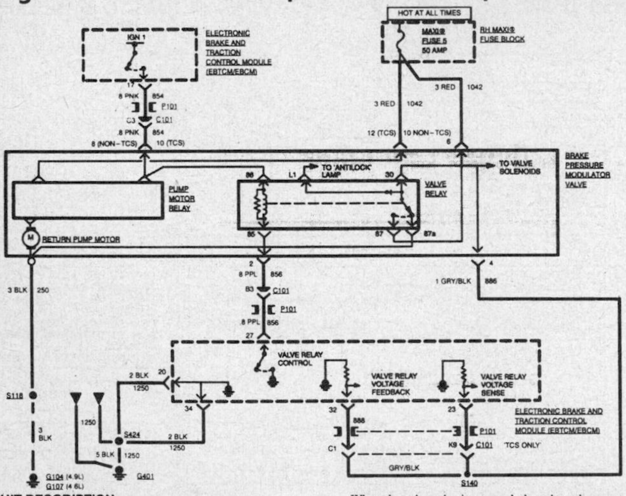
HOT AT ALL TIMES
ELECTRONIC BRAKE AND TRACTION CONTROL MODULE (EBTCM/EBCM)
RH MAXI® FUSE BLOCK
MAXI® FUSE 5 50 AMP
BRAKE PRESSURE MODULATOR VALVE
TO 'ANTILOCK' LAMP
TO VALVE SOLENOIDS
PUMP MOTOR RELAY
VALVE RELAY
RETURN PUMP MOTOR
VALVE RELAY CONTROL
VALVE RELAY VOLTAGE FEEDBACK
VALVE RELAY VOLTAGE SENSE
ELECTRONIC BRAKE AND TRACTION CONTROL MODULE (EBTCM/EBCM)
'TCS ONLY'
GRY/BLK

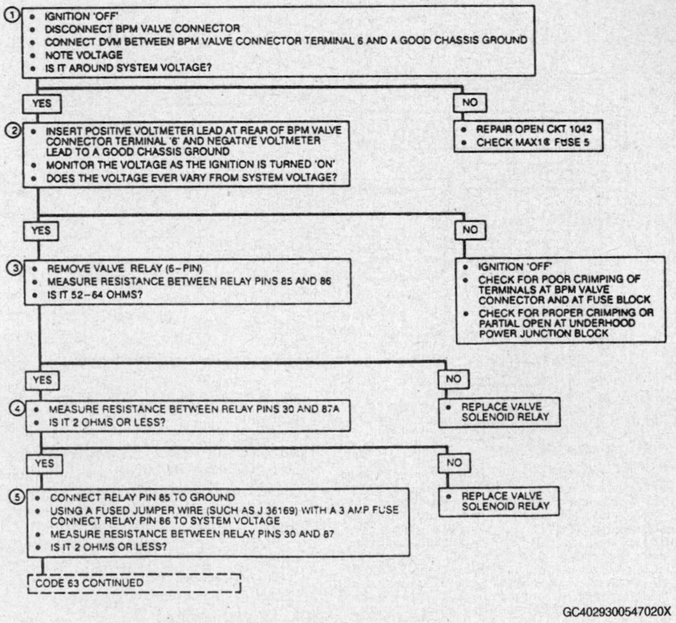
1 • IGNITION 'OFF'
• DISCONNECT BPM VALVE CONNECTOR
• CONNECT DVM BETWEEN BPM VALVE CONNECTOR TERMINAL 6 AND A GOOD CHASSIS GROUND
• NOTE VOLTAGE
• IS IT AROUND SYSTEM VOLTAGE?
YES
NO
• REPAIR OPEN CKT 1042
• CHECK MAX1® FUSE 5
2 • INSERT POSITIVE VOLTMETER LEAD AT REAR OF BPM VALVE CONNECTOR TERMINAL '6' AND NEGATIVE VOLTMETER LEAD TO A GOOD CHASSIS GROUND
• MONITOR THE VOLTAGE AS THE IGNITION IS TURNED 'ON'
• DOES THE VOLTAGE EVER VARY FROM SYSTEM VOLTAGE?
YES
NO
3 • REMOVE VALVE RELAY (6–PIN)
• MEASURE RESISTANCE BETWEEN RELAY PINS 85 AND 86
• IS IT 52–64 OHMS?
• IGNITION 'OFF'
• CHECK FOR POOR CRIMPING OF TERMINALS AT BPM VALVE CONNECTOR AND AT FUSE BLOCK
• CHECK FOR PROPER CRIMPING OR PARTIAL OPEN AT UNDERHOOD POWER JUNCTION BLOCK
YES
NO
4 • MEASURE RESISTANCE BETWEEN RELAY PINS 30 AND 87A
• IS IT 2 OHMS OR LESS?
• REPLACE VALVE SOLENOID RELAY
YES
NO
5 • CONNECT RELAY PIN 85 TO GROUND
• USING A FUSED JUMPER WIRE (SUCH AS J 36169) WITH A 3 AMP FUSE CONNECT RELAY PIN 86 TO SYSTEM VOLTAGE
• MEASURE RESISTANCE BETWEEN RELAY PINS 30 AND 87
• IS IT 2 OHMS OR LESS?
• REPLACE VALVE SOLENOID RELAY
CODE 63 CONTINUED
GC4029300547020X

CIRCUIT DESCRIPTION:

The valve relay provides power to the four ABS valve solenoids and two TCS Pilot Valves (if applicable) in the BPM valve. The valve relay is located on the BPM valve an may be replaced if it is found to be defective.

The valve relay is engaged during normal system operation. When the ignition is switched to RUN, the EBTCM/EBCM commands the valve relay ON by grounding the valve relay actuation line on CKT 856 (EBTCM/EBCM pin '27'). When this ground is provided, the valve relay is energized from the voltage supply line on CKT 854 (EBTCM/EBCM pin '17'). The valve relay switches and battery voltage is provided to the four valve solenoids, the pilot valves and the valve relay voltage sense line on CKT 886 (EBTCM/EBCM pin '23'). The valve relay remains engaged until the ignition is turned OFF or a failure is detected.

The valve relay voltage feedback (EBTCM/EBCM pin '32') provides suppression of voltage spikes created during operation of both front ABS valve solenoids during antilock and traction control.

TEST CONDITION(S):

1. Tested continuously.

FAILURE CONDITION(S):

1. Less than 5 volts at EBTCM/EBCM pin '23', valve relay sense;

OR

2. Voltage at EBTCM/EBCM pin '23', valve relay sense remains high, although voltage at EBTCM/EBCM pin '27', valve relay control, is low (valve relay sticks).

ACTION TAKEN:

1. Code set.
2. ABS/ TCS switched 'OFF'
3. 'ANTILOCK' indicator 'ON'.
4. 'TRACTION DISABLED' message displayed.

When the valve relay is engaged, the valve relay sense line should be at battery voltage. With the valve relay disengaged, the sense line should be at ground. If the commanded position of the valve relay and the position indicated by the sense line do not agree, Code 63 will set. Some conditions which will cause Code 63 to set are:

- An open circuit on CKT 886 or 856.
- A short to voltage on CKT 886 or 856.
- A short to ground on CKT 886 or 856.
- A defective solenoid valve relay.
- Open circuit on CKT 854.
- Loss of voltage to BPM valve terminals '6' and '12' during pump run.

TEST DESCRIPTION: Test numbers refer to circled numbers on the diagnostic chart.

1. Checks for availability of battery voltage to the Valve Relay through Maxi® fuse 5 and CKT 1042.
2. Checks for possible loss of voltage current when system is under load. At Key–ON, system performs the power on Reset Test and cycles the valve relay, checking the current draw of valves.
3. Checks the Valve Relay coil for proper resistance.
4. Checks for the Valve Relay contacts being internally open when in the relay unenergized position.
5. Checks for the Valve Relay contacts being stuck open when in the relay–energized position.

DIAGNOSTIC AIDS:

All tests using J 39700 Universal Breakout Box terminal '20' are using the terminal as ground. These tests, of course, assume that the ground CKT 1250 at terminal '20' is good.

It is very important that a thorough inspection of the wiring and connectors be performed. Failure to carefully and fully inspect wiring and connectors may result in misdiagnosis, causing part replacement with reappearance of the fault.

GC4029300547010X

Fig. 113 Code 63: Valve Relay Fault (Part 1 of 3). 1993-94 DeVille, Eldorado & Seville

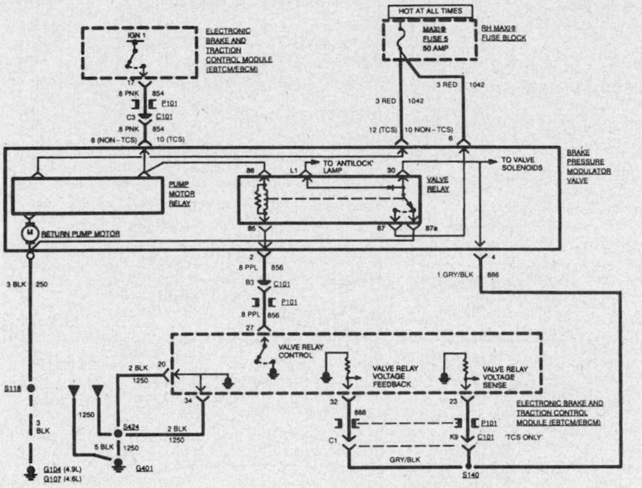
HOT AT ALL TIMES
MAXI® FUSE 5 50 AMP
RH MAXI® FUSE BLOCK
IGN 1
ELECTRONIC BRAKE AND TRACTION CONTROL MODULE (EBTCM/EBCM)
8 PNK 854
P101
C101
8 PNK 854
8 (NON-TCS) 10 (TCS)
3 RED 1042
12 (TCS) 10 NON-TCS)
TO ANTILOCK LAMP
TO VALVE SOLENOIDS
BRAKE PRESSURE MODULATOR VALVE
PUMP MOTOR RELAY
VALVE RELAY
RETURN PUMP MOTOR
8 PPL 856
1 GRY/BLK 886
3 BLK 250
VALVE RELAY CONTROL
VALVE RELAY VOLTAGE FEEDBACK
VALVE RELAY VOLTAGE SENSE
ELECTRONIC BRAKE AND TRACTION CONTROL MODULE (EBTCM/EBCM)
2 BLK 1250
S118
S424
5 BLK 1250
G104 (4.9L)
G107 (4.6L)
G401
GRY/BLK
S140
TCS ONLY

CIRCUIT DESCRIPTION:

The valve relay provides power to the four ABS valve solenoids and two TCS Pilot Valves (if applicable) in the BPM valve. The valve relay is located on the BPM valve an may be replaced if it is found to be defective.

The valve relay is engaged during normal system operation. When the ignition is switched to RUN, the EBTCM/EBCM commands the valve relay ON by grounding the valve relay actuation line on CKT 856 (EBTCM/EBCM pin '27'). When this ground is provided, the valve relay is energized from the voltage supply line on CKT 854 (EBTCM/EBCM pin '17'). The valve relay switches and battery voltage is provided to the four valve solenoids, the pilot valves and the valve relay voltage sense line on CKT 886 (EBTCM/EBCM pin '23'). The valve relay remains engaged until the ignition is turned 'OFF' or a failure is detected.

The valve relay voltage feedback (EBTCM/EBCM pin '32') provides suppression of voltage spikes created during operation of both front ABS valve solenoids during antilock and traction control.

TEST DESCRIPTION:

Test numbers refer to circled numbers on the diagnostic chart.

5. Checks the integrity of the Valve Relay circuitry internal to the BPM valve.
6. Checks for an open in ground CKT 250.
7. Checks for an open in CKT 886.
8. Checks for an open between splice S140 and EBTCM/EBCM terminal '23'.
9. Checks for a short to ground in CKT 886.
10. Checks for a short to system voltage in CKT 886.
11. Checks for an open in CKT 854.
12. Checks for a short to ground in CKT 854.

DIAGNOSTIC AIDS:

All tests using J 39700 Universal Breakout Box terminal '20' are using the terminal as ground. These tests, of course, assume that the ground CKT 1250 at terminal '20' is good.

It is very important that a thorough inspection of the wiring and connectors be performed. Failure to carefully and fully inspect wiring and connectors may result in misdiagnosis, causing part replacement with reappearance of the fault.

GC4029300547030X

CODE 63

YES

(5)
- MEASURE RESISTANCE BETWEEN THE FOLLOWING TERMINALS ON THE BPM VALVE ASSEMBLY ITSELF.

HYDRAULIC BPM VALVE CONNECTOR		RELAY CONNECTOR TERMINAL
2	AND	85
4	AND	30
6	AND	87
MOTOR GROUND STUD RING	AND	87A
10 (TCS) 8 (NON–TCS)	AND	86

IS THE READING BETWEEN ANY OF THE SETS OF TERMINAL MEASUREMENTS MORE THAN 2 OHMS? (THERE MAY BE .2 TO 10 OHMS WHEN MEASURING FROM RELAY CONNECTOR TERMINAL '30' TO PUMP MOTOR GROUND STUD DEPENDING ON POSITION OF MOTOR COMMUTATOR AND BRUSHES)

NO → • REPLACE VALVE RELAY

YES → • REPLACE BPM VALVE

NO

(6)
- DISCONNECT EBTCM/EBCM
- INSTALL J 39700 UNIVERSAL BREAKOUT BOX TO EBTCM/EBCM HARNESS CONNECTOR ONLY
- MEASURE RESISTANCE BETWEEN PUMP MOTOR GROUND STUD AND J 39700 TERMINAL '20'
- IS IT 2 OHMS OR LESS?

NO → • REPAIR OPEN IN CKT 250 TO PUMP MOTOR GROUND STUD

YES

(7)
- INSTALL VALVE SOLENOID RELAY
- MEASURE RESISTANCE BETWEEN BPM VALVE CONNECTOR TERMINAL '4' AND J 39700 TERMINAL '32'
- IS IT 2 OHMS OR LESS?

NO → • REPAIR OPEN IN CKT 886

YES

(8)
- MEASURE RESISTANCE BETWEEN BPM VALVE CONNECTOR TERMINAL '4' AND J 39700 TERMINAL '23'
- IS IT 2 OHMS OR LESS?

NO → • REPAIR OPEN IN CKT 886 BETWEEN TERMINAL '23' SPLICE S140 AND THE EBTCM/EBCM

YES

(9)
- MEASURE RESISTANCE BETWEEN J 39700 TERMINALS '20' AND '32'
- IS IT 5 OHMS OR LESS?

YES → • REPAIR SHORT GROUND IN CKT 886

NO

(10)
- CONNECT DVM BETWEEN J 39700 TERMINALS '20' AND '32' (USE DC VOLTS)
- IGNITION 'ON'
- NOTE VOLTAGE
- IS IT AROUND SYSTEM VOLTAGE?

YES → • REPAIR SHORT TO SYSTEM VOLTAGE ON CKT 886

NO

(11)
- IGNITION 'OFF'
- MEASURE RESISTANCE BETWEEN BPM VALVE CONNECTOR TERMINAL '10' (TCS) OR 8 (NON–TCS) AND J 39700 TERMINAL '17'
- IS IT 5 OHMS OR LESS?

NO → • REPAIR OPEN IN CKT 854

YES

(12)
- MEASURE RESISTANCE BETWEEN J 39700 TERMINALS '17' AND '20'
- IS IT 5 OHMS OR LESS?

CODE 63 CONTINUED

GC4029300547040X

Fig. 113 Code 63: Valve Relay Fault (Part 2 of 3). 1993-94 DeVille, Eldorado & Seville

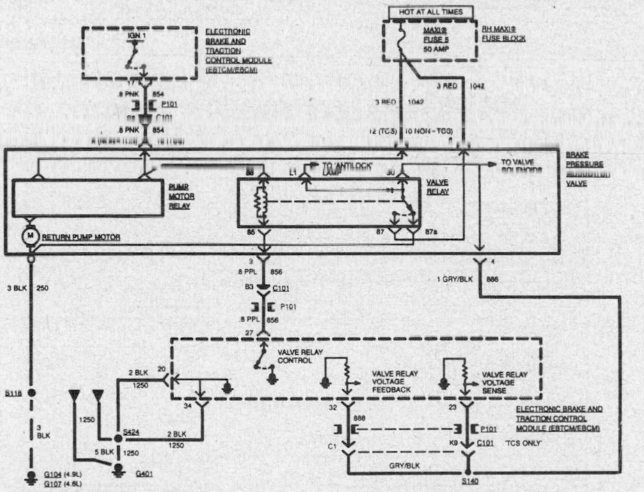
HOT AT ALL TIMES
MAXI® FUSE 5 50 AMP
RH MAXI® FUSE BLOCK
IGN 1
ELECTRONIC BRAKE AND TRACTION CONTROL MODULE (EBTCM/EBCM)
8 PNK 854
P101
C101
3 RED 1042
TO ANTILOCK LAMP
TO VALVE SOLENOIDS
BRAKE PRESSURE MODULATOR VALVE
PUMP MOTOR RELAY
VALVE RELAY
RETURN PUMP MOTOR
8 PPL 856
1 GRY/BLK 886
3 BLK 250
VALVE RELAY CONTROL
VALVE RELAY VOLTAGE FEEDBACK
VALVE RELAY VOLTAGE SENSE
ELECTRONIC BRAKE AND TRACTION CONTROL MODULE (EBTCM/EBCM)
2 BLK 1250
S118
S424
5 BLK 1250
G104 (4.9L)
G107 (4.6L)
G401
GRY/BLK
S140
TCS ONLY

CIRCUIT DESCRIPTION:

The valve relay provides power to the four ABS valve solenoids and two TCS Pilot Valves (if applicable) in the BPM valve. The valve relay is located on the BPM valve an may be replaced if it is found to be defective.

The valve relay is engaged during normal system operation. When the ignition is switched to RUN, the EBTCM/EBCM commands the valve relay ON by grounding the valve relay actuation line on CKT 856 (EBTCM/EBCM pin '27'). When this ground is provided, the valve relay is energized from the voltage supply line on CKT 854 (EBTCM/EBCM pin '17'). The valve relay switches and battery voltage is provided to the four valve solenoids, the pilot valves and the valve relay voltage sense line on CKT 886 (EBTCM/EBCM pin '23'). The valve relay remains engaged until the ignition is turned 'OFF' or a failure is detected.

The valve relay voltage feedback (EBTCM/EBCM pin '32') provides suppression of voltage spikes created during operation of both front ABS valve solenoids during antilock and traction control.

TEST DESCRIPTION:

Test numbers refer to circled numbers on the diagnostic chart.

13. Checks for a short to system voltage in CKT 854.
14. Checks for an open in CKT 856.
15. Checks for a short to ground in CKT 856.
16. Checks for a short to system voltage in CKT 856.
17. Checks wiring and connectors for intermittents.
18. Determines whether the code was set due to an intermittent condition or an EBTCM/EBCM fault.
19. Checks if problem found in step 13 is due to a short to system voltage in CKT 874, 856, or 854.

DIAGNOSTIC AIDS:

All tests using J 39700 Universal Breakout Box terminal '20' are using the terminal as ground. These tests, of course, assume that the ground CKT 1250 at terminal '20' is good.

It is very important that a thorough inspection of the wiring and connectors be performed. Failure to carefully and fully inspect wiring and connectors may result in misdiagnosis, causing part replacement with reappearance of the fault.

GC4029300547050X

CODE 63

YES → • REPAIR SHORT TO GROUND IN CKT 854

NO

(13)
- CONNECT DVM BETWEEN J 39700 TERMINALS '17' AND '20' (USE DC VOLTS)
- IGNITION 'ON'
- NOTE VOLTAGE
- IS IT AROUND SYSTEM VOLTAGE?

YES

(19)
- DISCONNECT VALVE RELAY
- DOES VOLTAGE MEASUREMENT DROP TO 0?

YES → • REPAIR SHORT TO VOLTAGE ON CKT 874

NO

- DISCONNECT PUMP RELAY
- DOES VOLTAGE MEASUREMENT DROP TO 0?

NO → • REPAIR SHORT TO VOLTAGE ON CKT 856

YES → • REPAIR SHORT TO VOLTAGE ON CKT 858

NO

(14)
- IGNITION 'OFF'
- MEASURE RESISTANCE BETWEEN BPM VALVE CONNECTOR TERMINAL '2' AND J 39700 TERMINAL '27'
- IS IT 5 OHMS OR LESS?

NO → • REPAIR OPEN IN CKT 856

YES

(15)
- MEASURE RESISTANCE BETWEEN J 39700 TERMINALS '20' AND '27'
- IS IT 5 OHMS OR LESS?

YES → • REPAIR SHORT TO GROUND IN CKT 856

NO

(16)
- CONNECT DVM BETWEEN J 39700 TERMINALS '20' AND '27'
- IGNITION 'ON'
- NOTE VOLTAGE
- IS IT AROUND SYSTEM VOLTAGE?

YES → • REPAIR SHORT SYSTEM VOLTAGE ON CKT 856

NO

(17)
- IGNITION 'OFF'
- INSPECT ALL WIRING AND CONNECTORS FOR CONDITIONS WHICH COULD CAUSE INTERMITTENTS, SUCH AS CHAFING, CORROSION, OR POOR TERMINAL CONTACT
- IS ALL OK WITH CONNECTIONS AND WIRING?

NO → • REPAIR WIRING AND/OR CONNECTIONS AS NEEDED

YES

(18)
- REMOVE J 39700
- RECONNECT EBTCM/EBCM AND BPM VALVE CONNECTORS
- CLEAR CODES, IGNITION 'OFF'
- DISCONNECT TECH 1, IF CONNECTED
- DRIVE VEHICLE AT LEAST 7 KPH (4 MPH) TO ACTIVATE AUTO TEST SEQUENCE
- DOES CODE 63 RESET?

NO → • NO TROUBLE FOUND; SEE 'DIAGNOSTIC AIDS'

YES → • REPLACE EBTCM/EBCM

GC4029300547060X

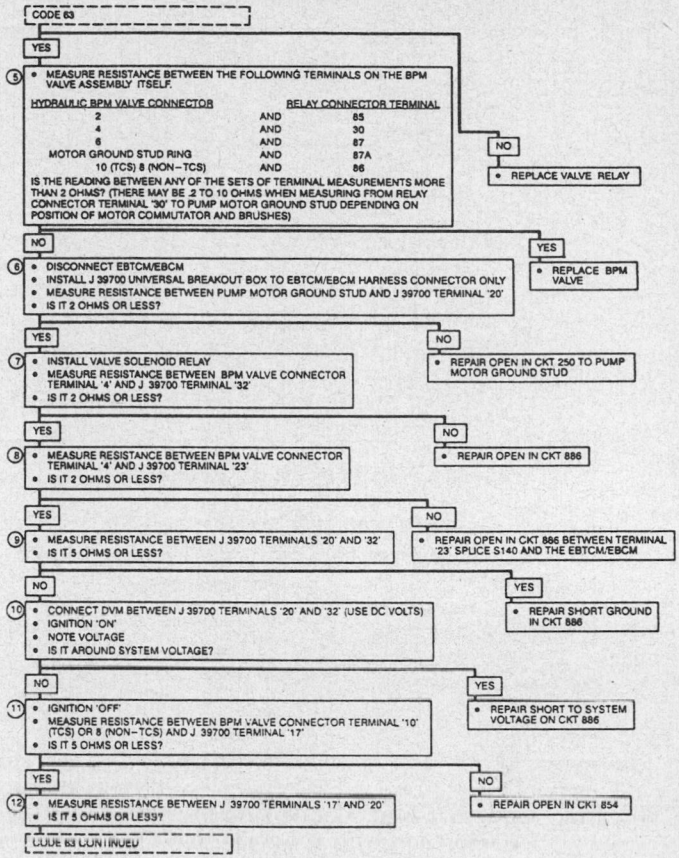

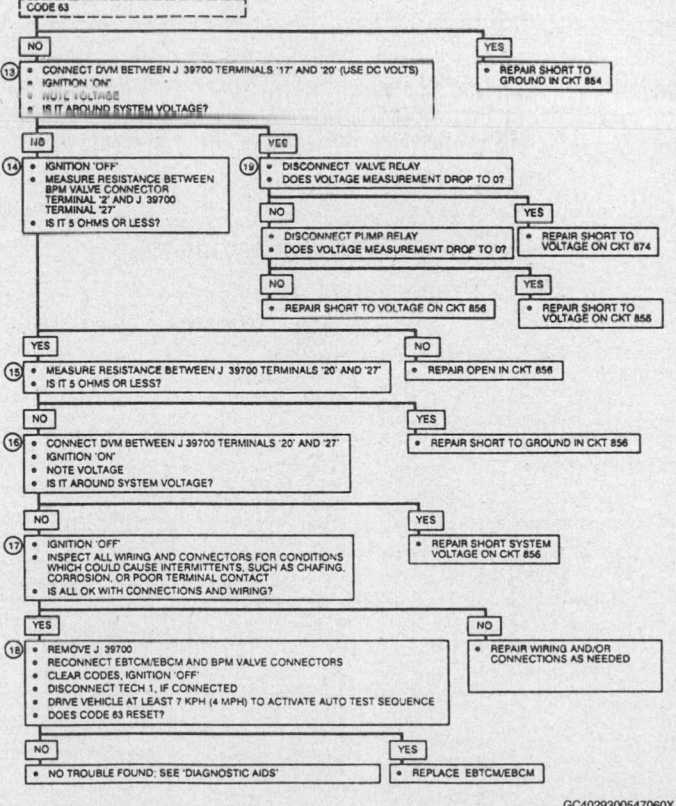

Fig. 113 Code 63: Valve Relay Fault (Part 3 of 3). 1993-94 DeVille, Eldorado & Seville

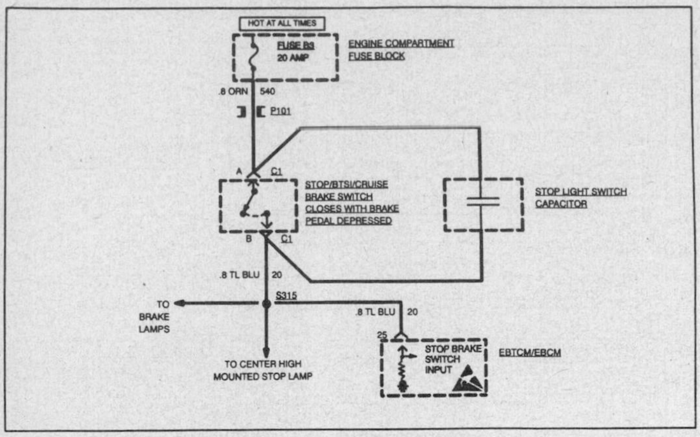
HOT AT ALL TIMES
FUSE B3
20 AMP
ENGINE COMPARTMENT
FUSE BLOCK
.8 ORN 540
P101
A C1
STOP/BTSI/CRUISE
BRAKE SWITCH
CLOSES WITH BRAKE
PEDAL DEPRESSED
B C1
STOP LIGHT SWITCH
CAPACITOR
.8 TL BLU 20
S315
TO
BRAKE
LAMPS
.8 TL BLU 20
25
STOP BRAKE
SWITCH
INPUT
EBTCM/EBCM
TO CENTER HIGH
MOUNTED STOP LAMP

DIAGNOSTIC TROUBLE CODE 67

BRAKE LIGHT SWITCH FAULT

(TRACTION CONTROL EQUIPPED VEHICLES ONLY)

CIRCUIT DESCRIPTION:

The electronic brake control module receives Brake Light Switch status from the PCM via serial data. If fault Code 67 sets, it may be indicative of a loss of switch input to the PCM, check for PCM fault Code PO90 (STOP/BITSI/CRUISE BRAKE SWITCH FAULT CODE) or P106 (BRAKE LIGHT SWITCH FAULT CODE)

TEST CONDITION(S):

1. Tested continuously.

FAILURE CONDITION(S):

1. EBTCM receives failure status of Brake Light Switch from PCM.

ACTION TAKEN:

1. Code set.
2. TCS disabled.
3. 'TRACTION DISABLED' message ON.

GC4029300548000X

Fig. 114 Code 67: Brake Light Switch Fault. 1993-94 DeVille, Eldorado & Seville w/TCS

DIAGNOSTIC TROUBLE CODE 71

ELECTRONIC BRAKE AND TRACTION CONTROL (EBTCM/EBCM) INTERNAL FAULT

CIRCUIT DESCRIPTION:

The EBTCM/EBCM performs various diagnostic checks on itself. If it finds a problem, Code 71 will set.

TEST CONDITION(S):

1. Tested continuously.

FAILURE CONDITION(S):

1. While Standing or Driving: EBTCM/EBCM internal error is detected.

ACTION TAKEN:

1. Code set.
2. ABS and TCS switched 'OFF'.
3. 'ANTILOCK' indicator ON.
4. 'TRACTION DISABLED' message ON. (vehicles with TCS)

TEST DESCRIPTION: Test numbers refer to circled numbers on the diagnostic chart.

1. Checks for good connections from the harness to the EBTCM/EBCM itself.
2. Checks to see if the fault was false. If Code 71 resets, replace the EBTCM/EBCM.

GC4029300549010X

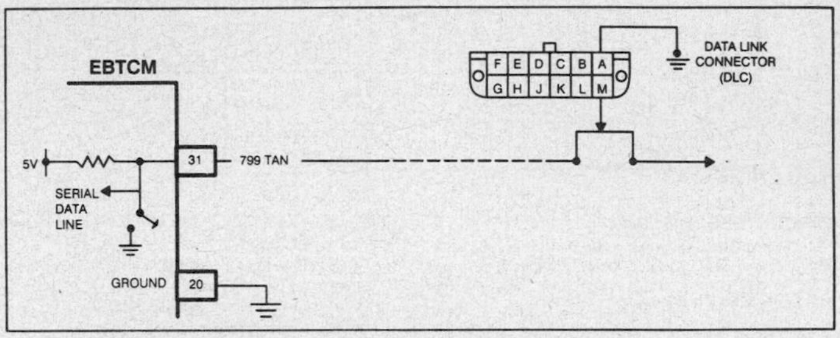
EBTCM
DATA LINK
CONNECTOR
(DLC)
F E D C B A
G H J K L M
5V
31
799 TAN
SERIAL
DATA
LINE
GROUND
20

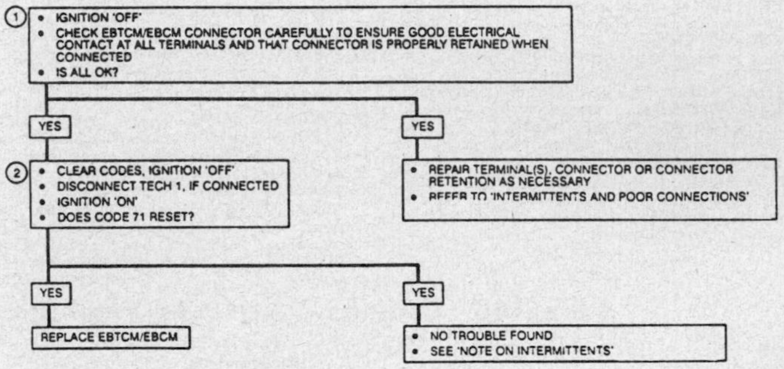
1
IGNITION 'OFF'
CHECK EBTCM/EBCM CONNECTOR CAREFULLY TO ENSURE GOOD ELECTRICAL CONTACT AT ALL TERMINALS AND THAT CONNECTOR IS PROPERLY RETAINED WHEN CONNECTED
IS ALL OK?
YES
YES
2
CLEAR CODES, IGNITION 'OFF'
DISCONNECT TECH 1, IF CONNECTED
IGNITION 'ON'
DOES CODE 71 RESET?
REPAIR TERMINAL(S), CONNECTOR OR CONNECTOR RETENTION AS NECESSARY
REFER TO 'INTERMITTENTS AND POOR CONNECTIONS'
YES
YES
REPLACE EBTCM/EBCM
NO TROUBLE FOUND
SEE 'NOTE ON INTERMITTENTS'

GC4029300549020X

Fig. 115 Code 71: EBTCM/EBCM Internal Fault. 1993-94 DeVille, Eldorado & Seville

DIAGNOSTIC TROUBLE CODE 72

SERIAL DATA LINK FAULT

CIRCUIT DESCRIPTION:

The Serial Data Link is an asynchronous link operating at 8192 bits per second.

Code 72 will set and the 'ANTILOCK' indicator will illuminate if the EBTCM/EBCM does not get polled by the IPC for information, or if it does not see PCM information on the data link.

TEST CONDITION(S):

1. Tested continuously.

FAILURE CONDITION(S):

1. While Standing or Driving: Serial Data communications are lost.

ACTION TAKEN:

1. Code set.
2. ABS and TCS switched 'OFF'.
3. 'ANTILOCK' indicator ON.
4. 'TRACTION DISABLED' message ON (vehicles with TCS).

TEST DESCRIPTION: Test numbers refer to circled numbers on the diagnostic chart.

1. This test checks to see if the off–board device can communicate with the EBTCM/EBCM.
2. This test checks for a short to battery in the serial data circuit.
3. This test checks for a short to ground in the serial data circuit.
4. This test checks for an open in the serial data circuit.
5. This test checks to see if the off–board device can communicate with the EBTCM/EBCM.
6. If the connections at the EBTCM/EBCM and DLC connector are OK, replace the EBTCM/EBCM.

DIAGNOSTIC AIDS:

The problem may be intermittent. Try performing the tests shown while 'wiggling' wiring and connectors; this can often cause the fault to appear.

NOTICE: Diagnostic Trouble Code 72 will never be displayed while serial data fault is current. A current Code 72 will result in a 'NO TCS DATA', and 'TRACTION DISABLED' messages as well as IPC Diagnostic Trouble Code B332 and PCM Code P133.

GC4029300550010X

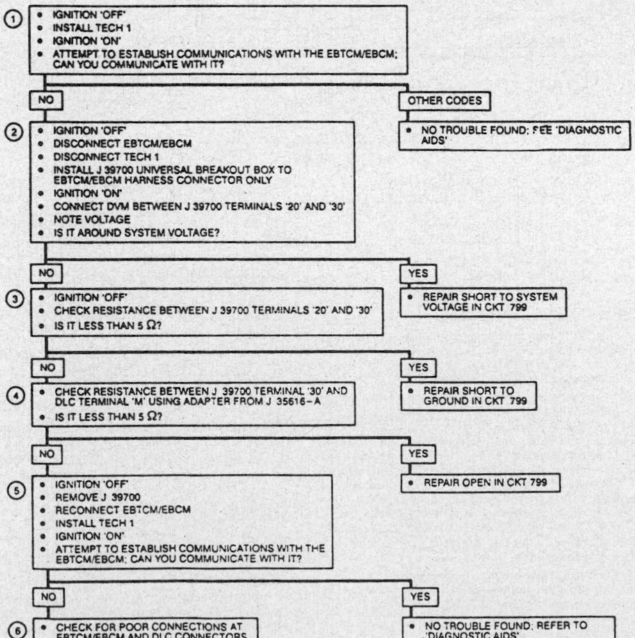
1
IGNITION 'OFF'
INSTALL TECH 1
IGNITION 'ON'
ATTEMPT TO ESTABLISH COMMUNICATIONS WITH THE EBTCM/EBCM; CAN YOU COMMUNICATE WITH IT?
NO
OTHER CODES
2
IGNITION 'OFF'
DISCONNECT EBTCM/EBCM
DISCONNECT TECH 1
INSTALL J 39700 UNIVERSAL BREAKOUT BOX TO EBTCM/EBCM HARNESS CONNECTOR ONLY
IGNITION 'ON'
CONNECT DVM BETWEEN J 39700 TERMINALS '20' AND '30'
NOTE VOLTAGE
IS IT AROUND SYSTEM VOLTAGE?
NO TROUBLE FOUND; SEE 'DIAGNOSTIC AIDS'
NO
YES
3
IGNITION 'OFF'
CHECK RESISTANCE BETWEEN J 39700 TERMINALS '20' AND '30'
IS IT LESS THAN 5 Ω?
REPAIR SHORT TO SYSTEM VOLTAGE IN CKT 799
NO
YES
4
CHECK RESISTANCE BETWEEN J 39700 TERMINAL '30' AND DLC TERMINAL 'M' USING ADAPTER FROM J 35616-A
IS IT LESS THAN 5 Ω?
REPAIR SHORT TO GROUND IN CKT 799
NO
YES
5
IGNITION 'OFF'
REMOVE J 39700
RECONNECT EBTCM/EBCM
INSTALL TECH 1
IGNITION 'ON'
ATTEMPT TO ESTABLISH COMMUNICATIONS WITH THE EBTCM/EBCM; CAN YOU COMMUNICATE WITH IT?
REPAIR OPEN IN CKT 799
NO
YES
6
CHECK FOR POOR CONNECTIONS AT EBTCM/EBCM AND DLC CONNECTORS. IF OK, REPLACE EBTCM/EBCM
NO TROUBLE FOUND, REFER TO 'DIAGNOSTIC AIDS'

Fig. 116 Code 72: Serial Data Link Fault. 1993-94 DeVille, Eldorado & Seville

GC4029300550020X

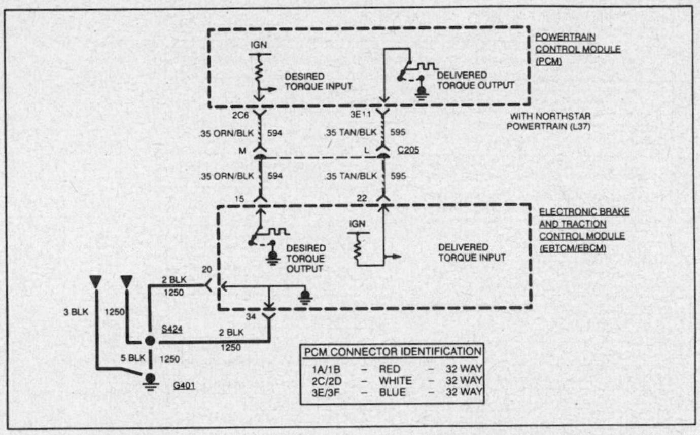
POWERTRAIN CONTROL MODULE (PCM)
IGN
DESIRED TORQUE INPUT
DELIVERED TORQUE OUTPUT
2C6
3E11
WITH NORTHSTAR POWERTRAIN (L37)
.35 ORN/BLK 594
.35 TAN/BLK 595
M
L
C205
.35 ORN/BLK 594
.35 TAN/BLK 595
15
22
ELECTRONIC BRAKE AND TRACTION CONTROL MODULE (EBTCM/EBCM)
IGN
DESIRED TORQUE OUTPUT
DELIVERED TORQUE INPUT
20
2 BLK 1250
3 BLK 1250
S424
2 BLK 1250
34
5 BLK 1250
G401
PCM CONNECTOR IDENTIFICATION
1A/1B – RED – 32 WAY
2C/2D – WHITE – 32 WAY
3E/3F – BLUE – 32 WAY

CIRCUIT DESCRIPTION:

Traction control is simultaneously controlled by the EBTCM on the vehicles equipped with the 4.6L Northstar, and the PCM. The PCM receives a 'DESIRED TORQUE' request via a Pulse Width Modulated (PWM) signal from the EBTCM (CKT 594) requesting the desired torque level for proper traction control system operation. Torque reduction will be indicated if the duty cycle of the PWM signal is between 10% (100 % torque reduction) and 90% (no torque reduction) and at least one (up to five) cylinder is requested to be disabled. The percent duty cycle will indicate the percent torque required. The PCM will selectively disable fuel to certain cylinders to achieve this reduction and communicate the actual torque output back to the EBTCM (CKT 595).

TEST CONDITION(S):

1. Tested continuously.

FAILURE CONDITION(S):

1. While Standing or Driving: PWM interface between EBTCM/EBCM and PCM is lost.

ACTION TAKEN:

1. Code set.
2. 'TRACTION DISABLED' message 'ON'.

A Code 73 may set if either CKT 594 or 595 is open, shorted to ground or shorted to voltage.

If CKT 595, Delivered Torque, is damaged and the EBTCM loses this input, a TCS Diagnostic Code 73 will be set. The PCM monitors the serial data line to see if the traction control has been disabled. If it has, the PCM will not set Code 93.

If CKT 594, Desired Torque is damaged and the PCM loses this input, the PCM monitors the serial data line to see if the traction control has been disabled. If not, the PCM sets a Code 93 and then tells the EBTCM/EBCM, via serial data, that there is a PWM circuit problem and the EBTCM/EBCM sets a Code 73.

TEST DESCRIPTION: Test numbers refer to circled numbers on the diagnostic chart.

1. Checks if the PCM Diagnostic Trouble Code 93 is set. If it is, there is likely a problem with CKT 594.
2. Checks for an open or high resistance in CKT 595.
3. Checks for a short to ground in CKT 595.
4. Checks for a short to voltage in CKT 595.
5. If no problem is found up until this point, CKT 594 should be checked.
6. Checks for an open or high resistance in CKT 594.
7. Checks for a short to ground in CKT 594.
8. Checks for a short to voltage in CKT 594.
9. If CKT 595 has not been checked, proceed to the left hand side of the trouble tree. If it has, continue downward. Problem is intermittent or in one of the controllers.
10. Checks if Code 73 and/or 93 are intermittent. If not, trouble is in either PCM or EBTCM.

DIAGNOSTIC AIDS:

- It is theoretically impossible for only a PCM Code 93 to set. If only a PCM Code 93 is present, either the TCS Code 73 has been cleared or there is a problem with the PCM.
- A Code 73 may set by itself if the PCM PROM has been improperly installed.

GC4029300551010X

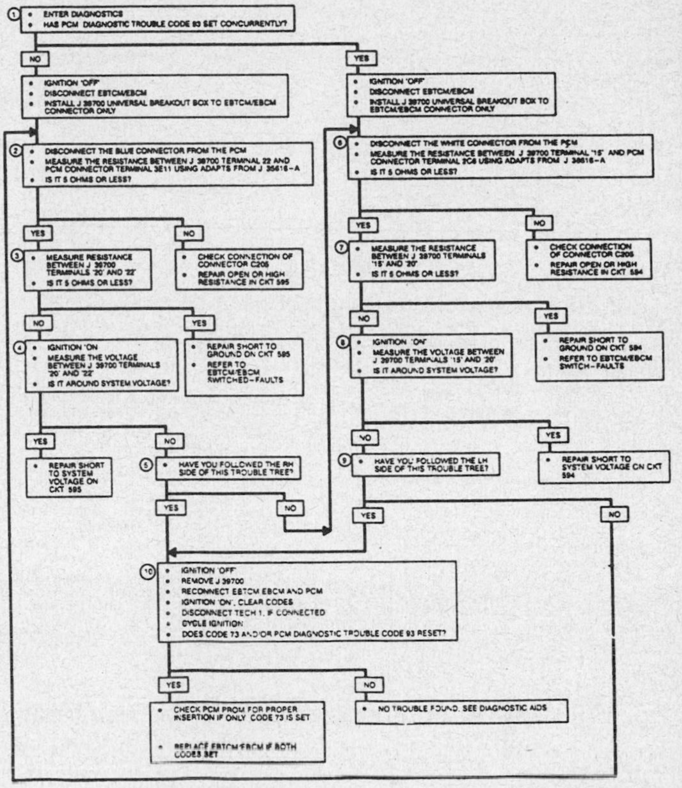
1 • ENTER DIAGNOSTICS
• HAS PCM DIAGNOSTIC TROUBLE CODE 93 SET CONCURRENTLY?
NO
YES
• IGNITION 'OFF'
• DISCONNECT EBTCM/EBCM
• INSTALL J 39700 UNIVERSAL BREAKOUT BOX TO EBTCM/EBCM CONNECTOR ONLY
2 • DISCONNECT THE BLUE CONNECTOR FROM THE PCM
• MEASURE THE RESISTANCE BETWEEN J 39700 TERMINAL 22 AND PCM CONNECTOR TERMINAL 3E11 USING ADAPTS FROM J 35616-A
• IS IT 5 OHMS OR LESS?
3 • MEASURE RESISTANCE BETWEEN J 39700 TERMINALS '20' AND '22'
• IS IT 5 OHMS OR LESS?
• CHECK CONNECTION OF CONNECTOR C205
• REPAIR OPEN OR HIGH RESISTANCE IN CKT 595
4 • IGNITION 'ON'
• MEASURE THE VOLTAGE BETWEEN J 39700 TERMINALS '20' AND '22'
• IS IT AROUND SYSTEM VOLTAGE?
• REPAIR SHORT TO GROUND ON CKT 595
• REFER TO EBTCM/EBCM SWITCHED-FAULTS
• REPAIR SHORT TO SYSTEM VOLTAGE ON CKT 595
5 • HAVE YOU FOLLOWED THE RH SIDE OF THIS TROUBLE TREE?
6 • DISCONNECT THE WHITE CONNECTOR FROM THE PCM
• MEASURE THE RESISTANCE BETWEEN J 39700 TERMINAL '15' AND PCM CONNECTOR TERMINAL 2C6 USING ADAPTS FROM J 35616-A
• IS IT 5 OHMS OR LESS?
7 • MEASURE THE RESISTANCE BETWEEN J 39700 TERMINALS '15' AND '20'
• IS IT 5 OHMS OR LESS?
• CHECK CONNECTION OF CONNECTOR C205
• REPAIR OPEN OR HIGH RESISTANCE IN CKT 594
8 • IGNITION 'ON'
• MEASURE THE VOLTAGE BETWEEN J 39700 TERMINALS '15' AND '20'
• IS IT AROUND SYSTEM VOLTAGE?
• REPAIR SHORT TO GROUND ON CKT 594
• REFER TO EBTCM/EBCM SWITCH-FAULTS
9 • HAVE YOU FOLLOWED THE LH SIDE OF THIS TROUBLE TREE?
• REPAIR SHORT TO SYSTEM VOLTAGE ON CKT 594
10 • IGNITION 'OFF'
• REMOVE J 39700
• RECONNECT EBTCM EBCM AND PCM
• IGNITION 'ON', CLEAR CODES
• DISCONNECT TECH 1, IF CONNECTED
• CYCLE IGNITION
• DOES CODE 73 AND/OR PCM DIAGNOSTIC TROUBLE CODE 93 RESET?
• CHECK PCM PROM FOR PROPER INSERTION IF ONLY CODE 73 IS SET
• REPLACE EBTCM/EBCM IF BOTH CODES SET
• NO TROUBLE FOUND. SEE DIAGNOSTIC AIDS

GC4029300551020X

Fig. 117 Code 73: PCM-EBTCM/EBCM PWM Signal Fault. 1993-94 DeVille, Eldorado & Seville w/4.6L Engine

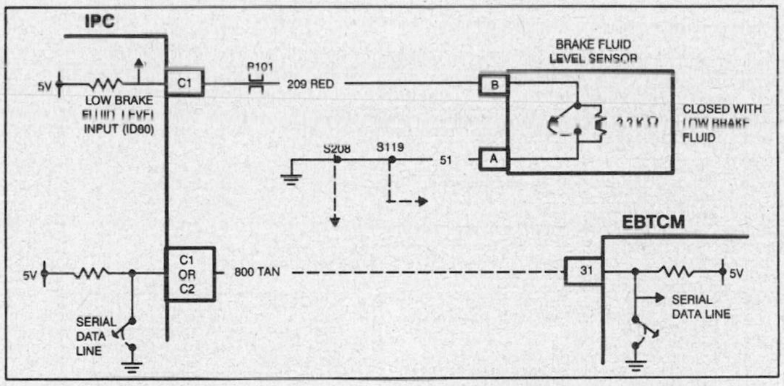
IPC
5V
LOW BRAKE FLUID LEVEL INPUT (ID80)
C1
P101
209 RED
BRAKE FLUID LEVEL SENSOR
B
CLOSED WITH LOW BRAKE FLUID
S208
S119
51
A
EBTCM
5V
C1 OR C2
800 TAN
31
5V
SERIAL DATA LINE
SERIAL DATA LINE

CIRCUIT DESCRIPTION:

The IPC outputs 5 volts on CKT 209 to the brake fluid level sensor. The IPC determines the level of brake fluid by the voltage drop it detects across the sensor circuit. This information is delivered to the EBTCM via the serial data line.

TEST CONDITION(S):

1. Tested continuously.

FAILURE CONDITION(S):

1. While Standing or Driving: Brake fluid falls below acceptable level.
2. Brake fluid level sensor disconnected.
3. Open, short to ground or short to battery on CKT 209.

ACTION TAKEN:

1. Code set.
2. ABS and TCS switched 'OFF'.
3. Red BRAKE warning lamp and 'ANTILOCK' indicator ON.
4. 'TRACTION DISABLED' message ON.

TEST DESCRIPTION: Test numbers refer to circled numbers on the diagnostic chart.

1. Check the brake fluid level in master cylinder reservoir.
2. Check brake fluid level as detected by IPC.
3. Brake fluid level not acceptable. Fill and recheck.
4. Brake fluid level as detected by IPC. See 'DIAGNOSTIC AIDS'.
5. Checks IPC input parameter ID80 with sensor disconnected for a short to ground in CKT 209, or bad sensor.
6. Checks IPC input parameter ID80 with sensor disconnected and connector shorted.
7. IPC detects acceptable brake fluid level. Problem not present.
8. Checks sensor resistor and checks for a short between CKTs 901 and 51.
9. Checks for open in CKTs 209 and 51.

DIAGNOSTIC AIDS:

IPC data parameter ID80 will display the following:

- 3.6–5V – open in sensor circuit.
- 1.5–3.5V – circuit OK. Problem not present.
- 0–1.4V – short between CKTs 209 and 51.

GC4029300552010X

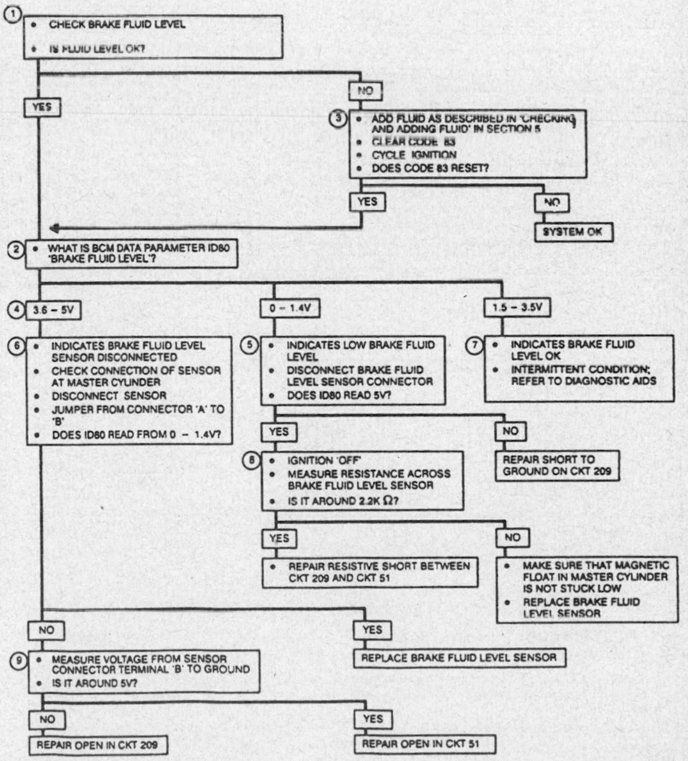
1 • CHECK BRAKE FLUID LEVEL
• IS FLUID LEVEL OK?
YES
NO
3 • ADD FLUID AS DESCRIBED IN 'CHECKING AND ADDING FLUID' IN SECTION 5
• CLEAR CODE 83
• CYCLE IGNITION
• DOES CODE 83 RESET?
SYSTEM OK
2 • WHAT IS BCM DATA PARAMETER ID80 'BRAKE FLUID LEVEL'?
4 3.6 – 5V
0 – 1.4V
1.5 – 3.5V
6 • INDICATES BRAKE FLUID LEVEL SENSOR DISCONNECTED
• CHECK CONNECTION OF SENSOR AT MASTER CYLINDER
• DISCONNECT SENSOR
• JUMPER FROM CONNECTOR 'A' TO 'B'
• DOES ID80 READ FROM 0 – 1.4V?
5 • INDICATES LOW BRAKE FLUID LEVEL
• DISCONNECT BRAKE FLUID LEVEL SENSOR CONNECTOR
• DOES ID80 READ 5V?
7 • INDICATES BRAKE FLUID LEVEL OK
• INTERMITTENT CONDITION; REFER TO DIAGNOSTIC AIDS
8 • IGNITION 'OFF'
• MEASURE RESISTANCE ACROSS BRAKE FLUID LEVEL SENSOR
• IS IT AROUND 2.2K Ω?
REPAIR SHORT TO GROUND ON CKT 209
• REPAIR RESISTIVE SHORT BETWEEN CKT 209 AND CKT 51
• MAKE SURE THAT MAGNETIC FLOAT IN MASTER CYLINDER IS NOT STUCK LOW
• REPLACE BRAKE FLUID LEVEL SENSOR
REPLACE BRAKE FLUID LEVEL SENSOR
9 • MEASURE VOLTAGE FROM SENSOR CONNECTOR TERMINAL 'B' TO GROUND
• IS IT AROUND 5V?
REPAIR OPEN IN CKT 209
REPAIR OPEN IN CKT 51

GC4029300552020X

Fig. 118 Code 83: Low Brake Fluid Level. 1993-94 DeVille, Eldorado & Seville w/TCS

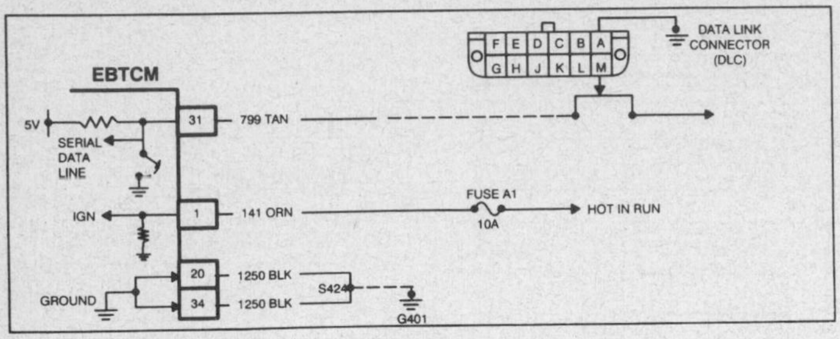
EBTCM
DATA LINK CONNECTOR (DLC)
F E D C B A
G H J K L M
5V
SERIAL DATA LINE
31
799 TAN
IGN
1
141 ORN
FUSE A1
10A
HOT IN RUN
20
34
1250 BLK
1250 BLK
S424
GROUND
G401

CHART A

'ANTILOCK' INDICATOR AND 'TRACTION DISABLED' MESSAGE 'ON', (IF APPLICABLE) NO CODES SET / NO TCS DATA

TEST DESCRIPTION: Test numbers refer to circled numbers on the diagnostic chart.

1. Checks if condition is due to a poor connection at the EBTCM/EBCM. Make sure the connecter is not 'cocked' on module.
2. Verifies that fuse A1 is intact.
3. Checks EBTCM/EBCM ground resistances. Should be less than 5 ohms.
4. Checks EBTCM/EBCM ignition voltage.
5. This step checks for possible open or high resistance in CKT 141 if there is insufficient voltage measured in Step 4. It is assumed a short to ground on CKT 141 would have blown fuse 'A1'.
6. Checks for possible insufficient voltage on power side of fuse 'A1'. This may be due to Maxi® fuse 6 being damaged or an intermittent connection in the ignition switch.
7. Checks for EBTCM/EBCM terminal '1' having a poor solder joint or for being partially backed out.
8. Checks if a loss of serial data communication between EBTCM/EBCM and BCM is due to a damaged CKT 799.
9. If there is no voltage measured in Step 8, there is a possible short to ground on CKT 799. If not, regulated 5V supply from EBTCM/EBCM is lost and EBTCM/EBCM should be replaced.

DIAGNOSTIC AIDS:

BCM Diagnostic Trouble Code B332 and PCM Code P137 should be present. If all of the IPC data line codes are present, refer to 'SYSTEM CHECK'.

GC4029300553010X

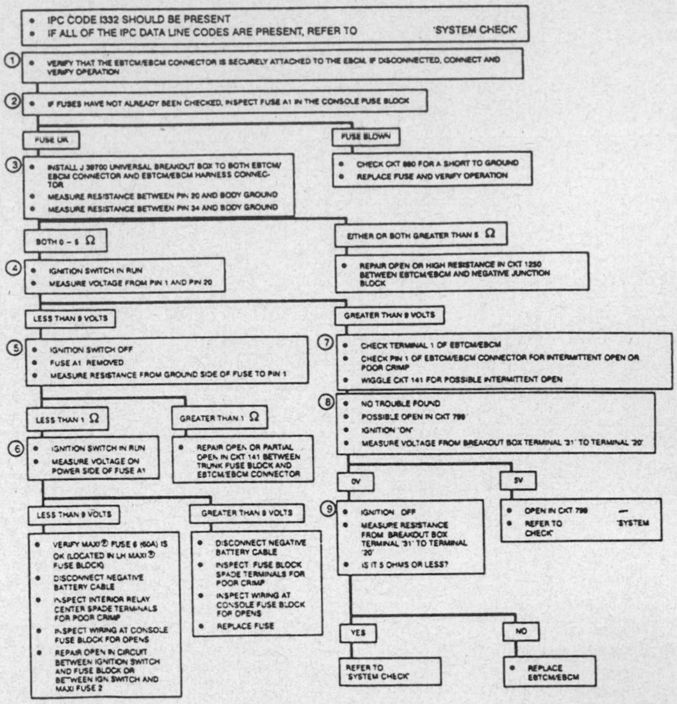
IPC CODE I332 SHOULD BE PRESENT
IF ALL OF THE IPC DATA LINE CODES ARE PRESENT, REFER TO 'SYSTEM CHECK'
1 VERIFY THAT THE EBTCM/EBCM CONNECTOR IS SECURELY ATTACHED TO THE EBCM. IF DISCONNECTED, CONNECT AND VERIFY OPERATION
2 IF FUSES HAVE NOT ALREADY BEEN CHECKED, INSPECT FUSE A1 IN THE CONSOLE FUSE BLOCK
FUSE OK
FUSE BLOWN
CHECK CKT 880 FOR A SHORT TO GROUND
REPLACE FUSE AND VERIFY OPERATION
3 INSTALL J 39700 UNIVERSAL BREAKOUT BOX TO BOTH EBTCM/EBCM CONNECTOR AND EBTCM/EBCM HARNESS CONNECTOR
MEASURE RESISTANCE BETWEEN PIN 20 AND BODY GROUND
MEASURE RESISTANCE BETWEEN PIN 34 AND BODY GROUND
BOTH 0 – 5 Ω
EITHER OR BOTH GREATER THAN 5 Ω
REPAIR OPEN OR HIGH RESISTANCE IN CKT 1250 BETWEEN EBTCM/EBCM AND NEGATIVE JUNCTION BLOCK
4 IGNITION SWITCH IN RUN
MEASURE VOLTAGE FROM PIN 1 AND PIN 20
LESS THAN 9 VOLTS
GREATER THAN 9 VOLTS
5 IGNITION SWITCH OFF
FUSE A1 REMOVED
MEASURE RESISTANCE FROM GROUND SIDE OF FUSE TO PIN 1
7 CHECK TERMINAL 1 OF EBTCM/EBCM
CHECK PIN 1 OF EBTCM/EBCM CONNECTOR FOR INTERMITTENT OPEN OR POOR CRIMP
WIGGLE CKT 141 FOR POSSIBLE INTERMITTENT OPEN
8 NO TROUBLE FOUND
POSSIBLE OPEN IN CKT 799
IGNITION 'ON'
MEASURE VOLTAGE FROM BREAKOUT BOX TERMINAL '31' TO TERMINAL '20'
LESS THAN 1 Ω
GREATER THAN 1 Ω
6 IGNITION SWITCH IN RUN
MEASURE VOLTAGE ON POWER SIDE OF FUSE A1
REPAIR OPEN OR PARTIAL OPEN IN CKT 141 BETWEEN TRUNK FUSE BLOCK AND EBTCM/EBCM CONNECTOR
0V
5V
9 IGNITION OFF
MEASURE RESISTANCE FROM BREAKOUT BOX TERMINAL '31' TO TERMINAL '20'
IS IT 5 OHMS OR LESS?
OPEN IN CKT 799
REFER TO 'SYSTEM CHECK'
LESS THAN 9 VOLTS
GREATER THAN 9 VOLTS
VERIFY MAXI® FUSE 6 (60A) IS OK (LOCATED IN LH MAXI® FUSE BLOCK)
DISCONNECT NEGATIVE BATTERY CABLE
INSPECT INTERIOR RELAY CENTER SPADE TERMINALS FOR POOR CRIMP
INSPECT WIRING AT CONSOLE FUSE BLOCK FOR OPENS
REPAIR OPEN IN CIRCUIT BETWEEN IGNITION SWITCH AND FUSE BLOCK OR BETWEEN IGN SWITCH AND MAXI FUSE 2
DISCONNECT NEGATIVE BATTERY CABLE
INSPECT FUSE BLOCK SPADE TERMINALS FOR POOR CRIMP
INSPECT WIRING AT CONSOLE FUSE BLOCK FOR OPENS
REPLACE FUSE
YES
NO
REFER TO 'SYSTEM CHECK'
REPLACE EBTCM/EBCM

GC4029300553020X

Fig. 119 Test A: Anti-Lock Indicator & Traction Disabled Message On w/No Codes Set Or No TCS Data. 1993-94 DeVille, Eldorado & Seville

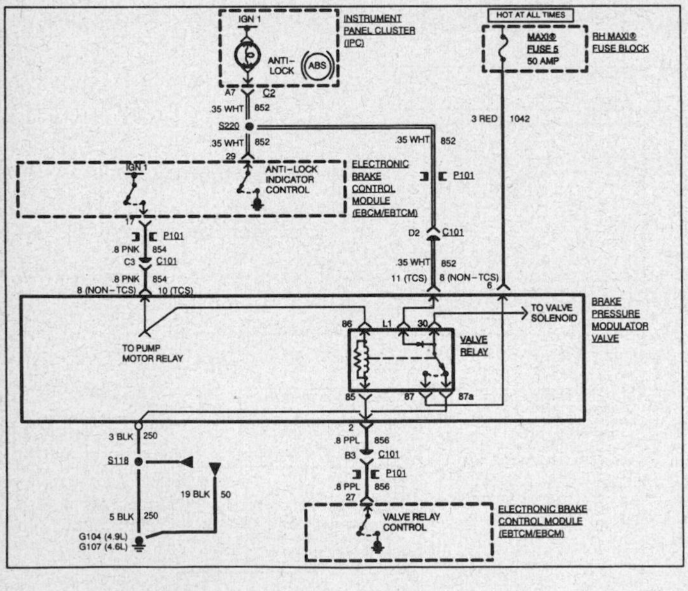
IGN 1
INSTRUMENT PANEL CLUSTER (IPC)
ANTI-LOCK
ABS
HOT AT ALL TIMES
MAXI® FUSE 5 50 AMP
RH MAXI® FUSE BLOCK
A7
C2
.35 WHT 852
S220
3 RED 1042
.35 WHT 852
.35 WHT 852
29
IGN 1
ANTI-LOCK INDICATOR CONTROL
ELECTRONIC BRAKE CONTROL MODULE (EBCM/EBTCM)
P101
17
P101
.8 PNK 854
C3
C101
.8 PNK 854
8 (NON-TCS)
10 (TCS)
D2
C101
.35 WHT 852
11 (TCS)
8 (NON-TCS)
6
TO VALVE SOLENOID
BRAKE PRESSURE MODULATOR VALVE
86
L1
30
VALVE RELAY
TO PUMP MOTOR RELAY
85
87
87a
3 BLK 250
2
.8 PPL 856
B3
C101
S118
P101
19 BLK 50
.8 PPL 856
27
5 BLK 250
VALVE RELAY CONTROL
ELECTRONIC BRAKE CONTROL MODULE (EBTCM/EBCM)
G104 (4.9L)
G107 (4.6L)

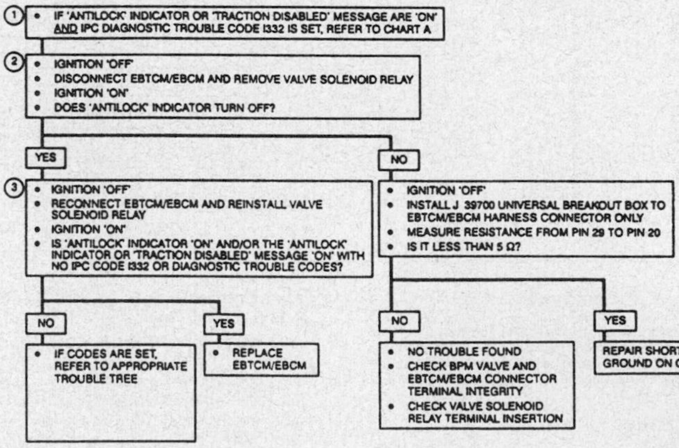
1 IF 'ANTILOCK' INDICATOR OR 'TRACTION DISABLED' MESSAGE ARE 'ON' AND IPC DIAGNOSTIC TROUBLE CODE I332 IS SET, REFER TO CHART A
2 IGNITION 'OFF'
DISCONNECT EBTCM/EBCM AND REMOVE VALVE SOLENOID RELAY
IGNITION 'ON'
DOES 'ANTILOCK' INDICATOR TURN OFF?
YES
NO
3 IGNITION 'OFF'
RECONNECT EBTCM/EBCM AND REINSTALL VALVE SOLENOID RELAY
IGNITION 'ON'
IS 'ANTILOCK' INDICATOR 'ON' AND/OR THE 'ANTILOCK' INDICATOR OR 'TRACTION DISABLED' MESSAGE 'ON' WITH NO IPC CODE I332 OR DIAGNOSTIC TROUBLE CODES?
IGNITION 'OFF'
INSTALL J 39700 UNIVERSAL BREAKOUT BOX TO EBTCM/EBCM HARNESS CONNECTOR ONLY
MEASURE RESISTANCE FROM PIN 29 TO PIN 20
IS IT LESS THAN 5 Ω?
NO
YES
NO
YES
IF CODES ARE SET, REFER TO APPROPRIATE TROUBLE TREE
REPLACE EBTCM/EBCM
NO TROUBLE FOUND
CHECK BPM VALVE AND EBTCM/EBCM CONNECTOR TERMINAL INTEGRITY
CHECK VALVE SOLENOID RELAY TERMINAL INSERTION
REPAIR SHORT TO GROUND ON CKT 852

GC4029300554020X

CHART B

'ANTILOCK' INDICATOR 'ON', NO CODES SET

TEST DESCRIPTION: Test numbers refer to circled numbers on the diagnostic chart.

1. Checks if 'ANTILOCK' indicator is ON due to a loss of communication between the IPC and EBTCM/EBCM.
2. Checks for a short to ground in CKT 852.
3. Final check for diagnostic trouble codes.

DIAGNOSTIC AIDS:

The EBTCM/EBCM controls the 'ANTILOCK' indicator only in instances where serial data communication with the IPC is lost. In all other instances the IPC controls this lamp.

GC4029300554010X

Fig. 120 Test B: Anti-Lock Indicator On w/No Codes Set. 1993-94 DeVille, Eldorado & Seville

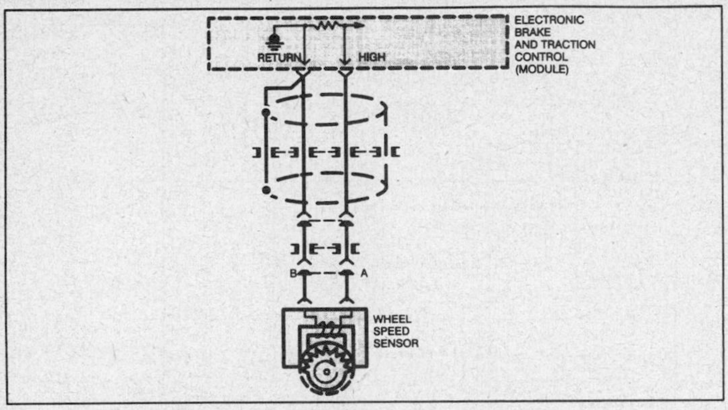
ELECTRONIC BRAKE AND TRACTION CONTROL (MODULE)
RETURN
HIGH
B
A
WHEEL SPEED SENSOR

1. • VERIFY CORRECT WSS CABLE ROUTING
   • CHECK SENSOR MOUNTING AND CONNECTION
   • ROAD TEST VEHICLE

VALVE CHATTER

2. • INSTALL TECH 1
   • OBSERVE WHEEL SPEED SENSOR OUTPUT WHILE TEST DRIVING VEHICLE

- RF SENSOR OUTPUT • ERRATIC OR • DROPS OUT OR • DIFFERS FROM OTHER OUTPUTS → • GO TO CODE 21 CHART • BEGIN ANALYSIS AT NOTE 2 OF CODE 21 CHART
- LF SENSOR OUTPUT • ERRATIC OR • DROPS OUT OR • DIFFERS FROM OTHER OUTPUTS → • GO TO CODE 25 CHART • BEGIN ANALYSIS AT NOTE 2 OF CODE 25 CHART
- RR SENSOR OUTPUT • ERRATIC OR • DROPS OUT OR • DIFFERS FROM OTHER OUTPUTS → • GO TO CODE 31 CHART • BEGIN ANALYSIS AT NOTE 2 OF CODE 31 CHART
- LR SENSOR OUTPUT • ERRATIC OR • DROPS OUT OR • DIFFERS FROM OTHER OUTPUTS → • GO TO CODE 35 CHART • BEGIN ANALYSIS AT NOTE 2 OF CODE 35 CHART
- NORMAL SENSOR OUTPUT → • REPLACE EBTCM /EBCM

NO VALVE CHATTER

- • CONDITION CORRECTED

GC4029300555020X

CHART C

VALVE CYCLING (CHATTER) DURING NORMAL STOPS (UNWANTED ABS MODULATION)

TEST DESCRIPTION: Test numbers refer to circled numbers on the diagnostic chart.

1. Checks if valve activation due to erroneous electrical 'noise' induced onto wheel speed sensor circuits.
2. The wheel speed sensor output should gradually increase with vehicle speed. There should be no skips or jumps. All four wheel speed sensor outputs should be identical. On a slow down, one of the signals may drop off faster than the others, indicating a lock–up condition or a problem with the speed sensor or wiring (corrosion etc.).

GC4029300555010X

Fig. 121 Test C: Valve Cycling (Chatter) During Normal Stops (Unwanted ABS Modulation). 1993-94 DeVille, Eldorado & Seville

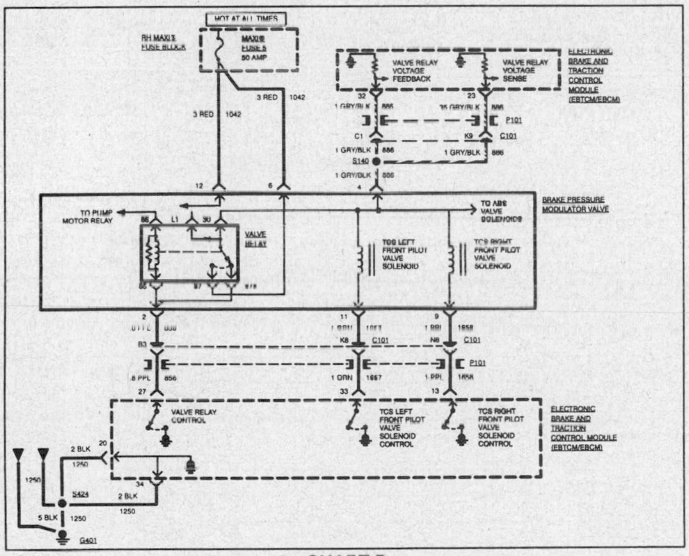
HOT AT ALL TIMES
RH MAXI FUSE BLOCK
MAXI FUSE 5 50 AMP
VALVE RELAY VOLTAGE FEEDBACK
VALVE RELAY VOLTAGE SENSE
ELECTRONIC BRAKE AND TRACTION CONTROL MODULE (EBTCM/EBCM)
TO PUMP MOTOR RELAY
TO ABS VALVE SOLENOIDS
BRAKE PRESSURE MODULATOR VALVE
VALVE RELAY
TCS LEFT FRONT PILOT VALVE SOLENOID
TCS RIGHT FRONT PILOT VALVE SOLENOID
VALVE RELAY CONTROL
TCS LEFT FRONT PILOT VALVE SOLENOID CONTROL
TCS RIGHT FRONT PILOT VALVE SOLENOID CONTROL
G401

NOTE: SOME OF THESE CHECKS WILL CAUSE DIAGNOSTIC TROUBLE CODES TO SET. BE SURE TO VERIFY AUTHENTICITY OF ANY CODES AND CORRECT IF NECESSARY. BE SURE TO CLEAR ANY ERRONEOUS OR CORRECTED CODES.

1. • CLEAR CODES
   • IGNITION 'OFF'
   • DISCONNECT TECH 1
   • RAISE FRONT WHEELS 4" TO 5" ON HOIST
   • IGNITION 'ON', ENGINE 'ON'
   • WITH TRANSMISSION IN DRIVE, ACCELERATE TO 1/2 THROTTLE WHILE AN OBSERVER MONITORS THE DRIVE WHEELS
   • ARE THE FRONT BRAKES MODULATED?

NO

3. • CHECK FLUID LEVEL IN MASTER CYLINDER RESERVOIR
   • CHECK FOR DIRT OR DEBRIS IN RESERVOIR FLUID

LEVEL OK, FLUID NOT DIRTY

4. • POSSIBLE AIR IN SYSTEM
   • BLEED TCS PRIME PIPE AT BPM VALVE
   • PERFORM THE TCS TEST USING THE TECH 1
   ONE OF THE FRONT CALIPER BLEED SCREWS MUST BE 'OPENED'
   • RETEST TRACTION CONTROL OPERATION ON HOIST

LOW

7. • ADD FLUID
   • POSSIBLE AIR IN SYSTEM
   • BLEED TCS PRIME PIPE AT BPM VALVE
   • PERFORM THE TCS TEST USING THE TECH 1
   ONE OF THE FRONT CALIPER BLEED SCREWS MUST BE 'OPENED'
   • RETEST TRACTION CONTROL OPERATION ON HOIST

DIRTY

6. • DISCONNECT TCS PRIME PIPE AT BPM VALVE
   • ALLOW FLUID TO DRAIN FROM RESERVOIR
   • FLUSH RESERVOIR AND TCS PRIME PIPE WITH FRESH BRAKE FLUID
   • RECONNECT TCS PRIME PIPE
   • REFILL
   • POSSIBLE AIR IN SYSTEM
   • BLEED TCS PRIME PIPE AT BPM VALVE
   • PERFORM THE TCS TEST USING THE TECH 1
   ONE OF THE FRONT CALIPER BLEED SCREWS MUST BE 'OPENED'
   • RETEST TRACTION CONTROL OPERATION ON HOIST

YES

2. • SYSTEM IS OPERATING CORRECTLY

GC4029300556020X

CHART D

TRACTION CONTROL OPERATION CHECK (NO DIAGNOSTIC TROUBLE CODES SET)

TEST DESCRIPTION: Test numbers refer to circled numbers on the diagnostic chart.

1. Traction control system should interpret the elevated front wheels as an icy or free spin condition. At 1/2 throttle a properly operating system will allow both front wheels to spin up quickly to about 20–25 MPH and then slow down (but not stop) to about 5–10 MPH and have a jerky appearance. The traction control 'ACTIVE' message should display on the DIC. The pump motor should also be heard.
2. System is building up pressure to the front brake and operating correctly.
3. System is not building up pressure to the front brakes. Possible air or dirt in the system.
4. No dirt in reservoir and the fluid level is OK. Air may still be trapped in system. The TCS hydraulic circuit should be bled using TECH 1 TCS test and bleed procedure outlined in Section 5. One of the front caliper bleed screws must be open to allow air to escape.
5. Fluid level OK. Air may still be trapped in the system. The TCS hydraulic circuit should be bled using TECH 1 TCS test and bleed procedure outlined in Section 5. One of the front caliper bleed screws must be open to allow air to escape.
6. Reservoir TCS prime pipe may be contaminated. Flush pipe and reservoir to remove any debris. Air may still be trapped in system. The TCS hydraulic circuit should be bled using TECH 1 TCS test and bleed procedure outlined in Section 5. One of the front caliper bleed screws must be open to allow air to escape.

DIAGNOSTIC AIDS:

- The Brake Light Switch must be properly adjusted to prevent an erroneous brake application input to the EBTCM/EBCM. Misadjustment may prevent brake intervention during traction control operation. Also, the EBTCM/EBCM receives TCC switch status over serial data from the PCM. If serial data is lost or the switch remains engaged, brake intervention during traction control may be lost. Monitor PCM TCC switch input P171 while cycling brake switch. The input should cycle 'HI' and 'LO'.
- The PCM shall not allow traction control fuel shutoff if:
  - Engine Coolant Temperature less than −40°C
  - Engine Coolant Temperature greater than or equal to 131°C
  - Low Coolant Level Detected
- Cylinders shall be disabled if the engine speed greater than or equal to 600 RPM.
- The PCM can disable traction control for up to 11 ignition cycles if override PS24, Traction Control Disable, is activated. When PS24 is selected, the display will alternate between '– –' for one second and the current state of Traction Control Disable override ('99' for override active and '00' for override not active). Pressing the WARMER button will disable traction control for the next eleven ignition cycles and display '99'. The 'TRACTION DISABLED' message will be displayed for the duration of this override and no TCS diagnostic trouble codes will be set. Pressing the COOLER button will allow normal program control of traction control and display '00'.

GC4029300556010X

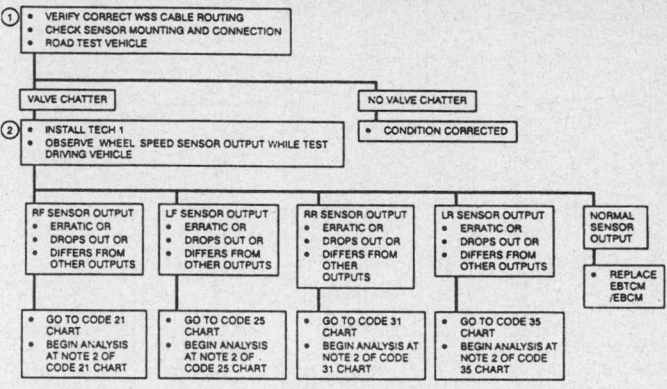

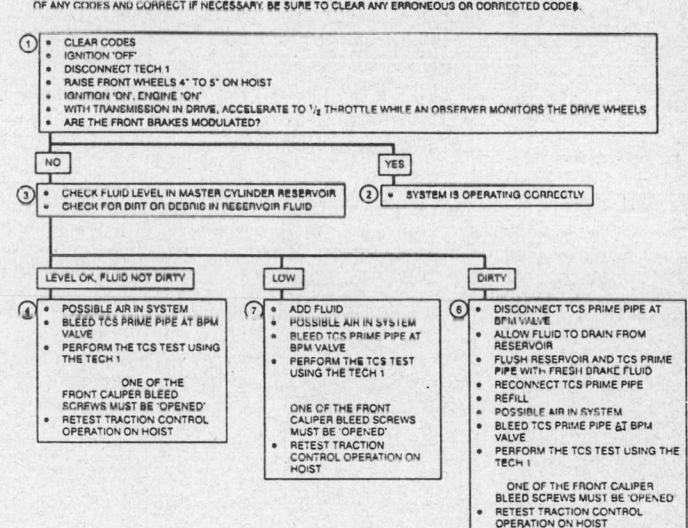

Fig. 122 Test D: Traction Control Operation Check, No DTCs Set. 1993-94 DeVille, Eldorado & Seville

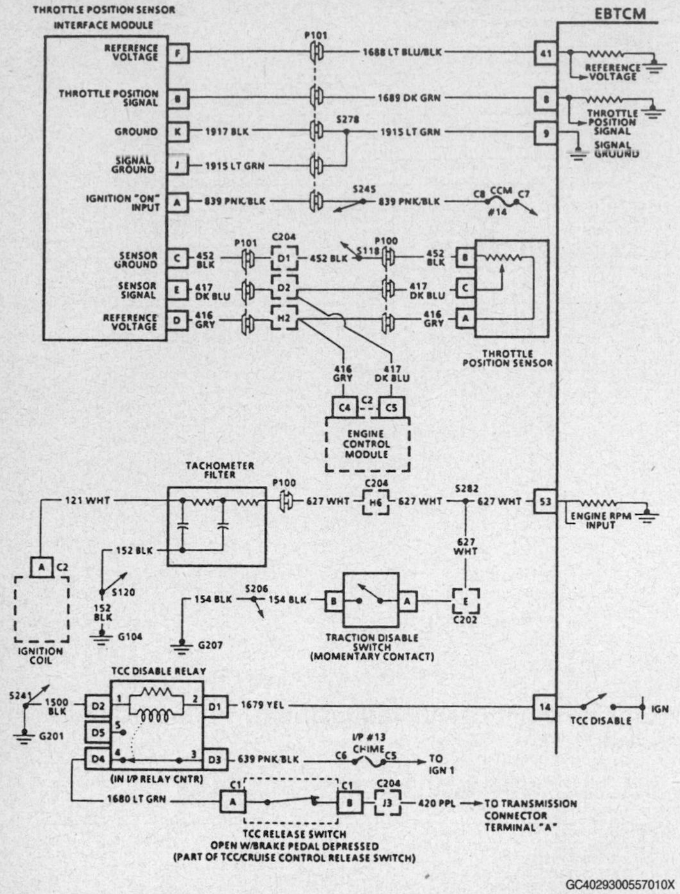
EBTCM
THROTTLE POSITION SENSOR INTERFACE MODULE
REFERENCE VOLTAGE
THROTTLE POSITION SIGNAL
GROUND
SIGNAL GROUND
IGNITION "ON" INPUT
SENSOR GROUND
SENSOR SIGNAL
REFERENCE VOLTAGE
1688 LT BLU/BLK
1689 DK GRN
1917 BLK
1915 LT GRN
839 PNK/BLK
THROTTLE POSITION SENSOR
ENGINE CONTROL MODULE
TACHOMETER FILTER
121 WHT
627 WHT
ENGINE RPM INPUT
IGNITION COIL
TRACTION DISABLE SWITCH (MOMENTARY CONTACT)
TCC DISABLE RELAY
1679 YEL
TCC DISABLE
IGN
(IN I/P RELAY CNTR)
639 PNK/BLK
1680 LT GRN
420 PPL
TO TRANSMISSION CONNECTOR TERMINAL "A"
TCC RELEASE SWITCH OPEN W/BRAKE PEDAL DEPRESSED (PART OF TCC/CRUISE CONTROL RELEASE SWITCH)
GC4029300557010X

Fig. 123 ABS & TCS wiring circuit (Part 1 of 4). 1993 Fleetwood (RWD)

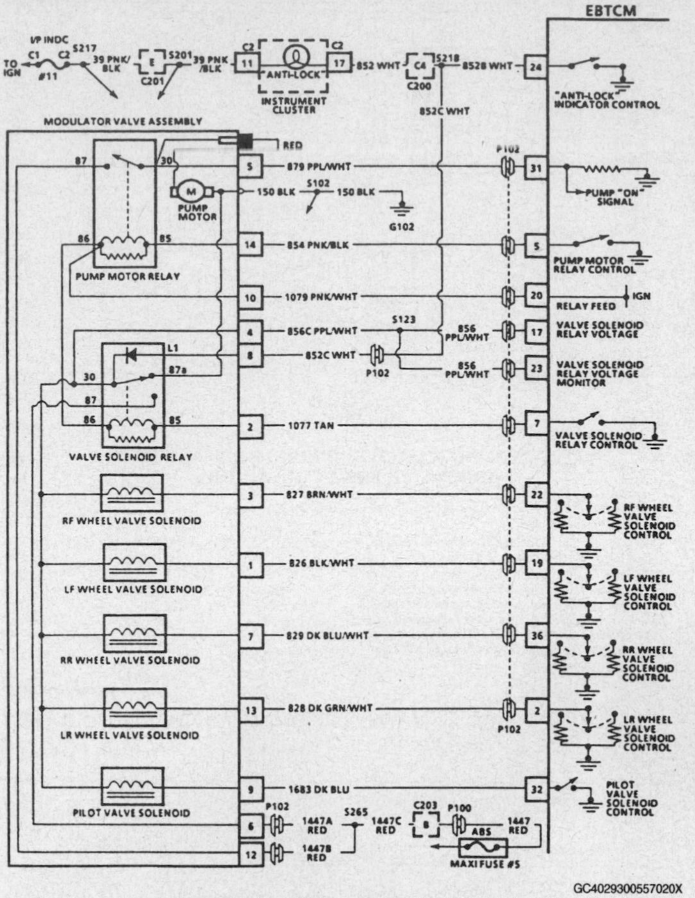
EBTCM
I/P INDC
ANTI-LOCK
INSTRUMENT CLUSTER
852 WHT
852C WHT
"ANTI-LOCK" INDICATOR CONTROL
MODULATOR VALVE ASSEMBLY
RED
879 PPL/WHT
PUMP MOTOR
150 BLK
G102
"PUMP "ON" SIGNAL
PUMP MOTOR RELAY
854 PNK/BLK
PUMP MOTOR RELAY CONTROL
1079 PNK/WHT
RELAY FEED
IGN
856C PPL/WHT
VALVE SOLENOID RELAY VOLTAGE
VALVE SOLENOID RELAY VOLTAGE MONITOR
VALVE SOLENOID RELAY
1077 TAN
VALVE SOLENOID RELAY CONTROL
RF WHEEL VALVE SOLENOID
827 BRN/WHT
RF WHEEL VALVE SOLENOID CONTROL
LF WHEEL VALVE SOLENOID
826 BLK/WHT
LF WHEEL VALVE SOLENOID CONTROL
RR WHEEL VALVE SOLENOID
829 DK BLU/WHT
RR WHEEL VALVE SOLENOID CONTROL
LR WHEEL VALVE SOLENOID
828 DK GRN/WHT
LR WHEEL VALVE SOLENOID CONTROL
PILOT VALVE SOLENOID
1683 DK BLU
PILOT VALVE SOLENOID CONTROL
MAXIFUSE #5
GC4029300557020X

Fig. 123 ABS & TCS wiring circuit (Part 2 of 4). 1993 Fleetwood (RWD)

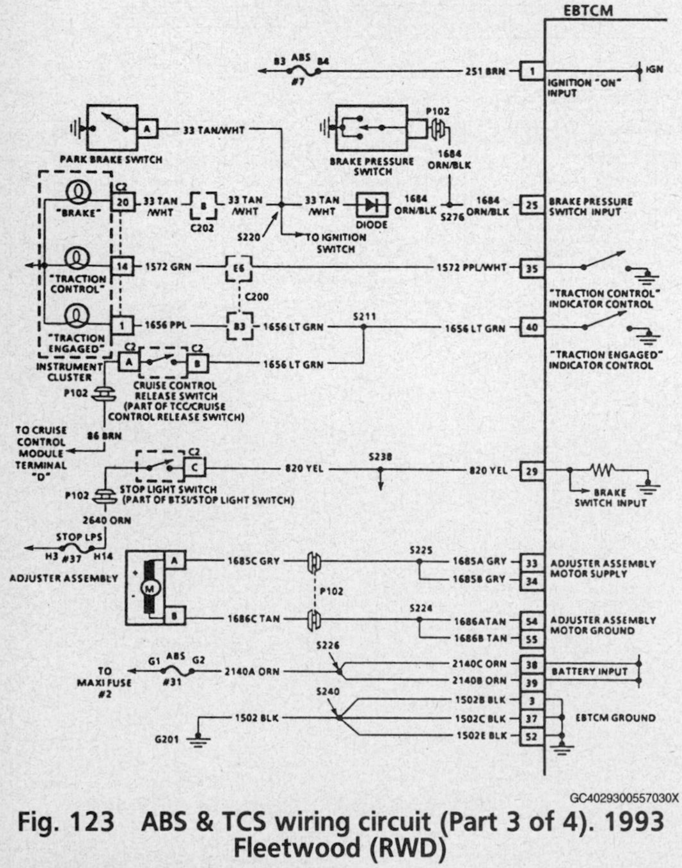
EBTCM
251 BRN
IGNITION "ON" INPUT
IGN
PARK BRAKE SWITCH
33 TAN/WHT
BRAKE PRESSURE SWITCH
1684 ORN/BLK
BRAKE PRESSURE SWITCH INPUT
DIODE
TO IGNITION SWITCH
"BRAKE"
"TRACTION CONTROL"
"TRACTION ENGAGED"
INSTRUMENT CLUSTER
1572 GRN
1572 PPL/WHT
"TRACTION CONTROL" INDICATOR CONTROL
1656 PPL
1656 LT GRN
"TRACTION ENGAGED" INDICATOR CONTROL
CRUISE CONTROL RELEASE SWITCH (PART OF TCC/CRUISE CONTROL RELEASE SWITCH)
TO CRUISE CONTROL MODULE TERMINAL "D"
86 BRN
820 YEL
STOP LIGHT SWITCH (PART OF BTSI/STOP LIGHT SWITCH)
BRAKE SWITCH INPUT
2640 ORN
STOP LPS
ADJUSTER ASSEMBLY
ADJUSTER ASSEMBLY MOTOR SUPPLY
ADJUSTER ASSEMBLY MOTOR GROUND
TO MAXIFUSE #2
2140A ORN
BATTERY INPUT
1502 BLK
EBTCM GROUND
G201
GC4029300557030X

Fig. 123 ABS & TCS wiring circuit (Part 3 of 4). 1993 Fleetwood (RWD)

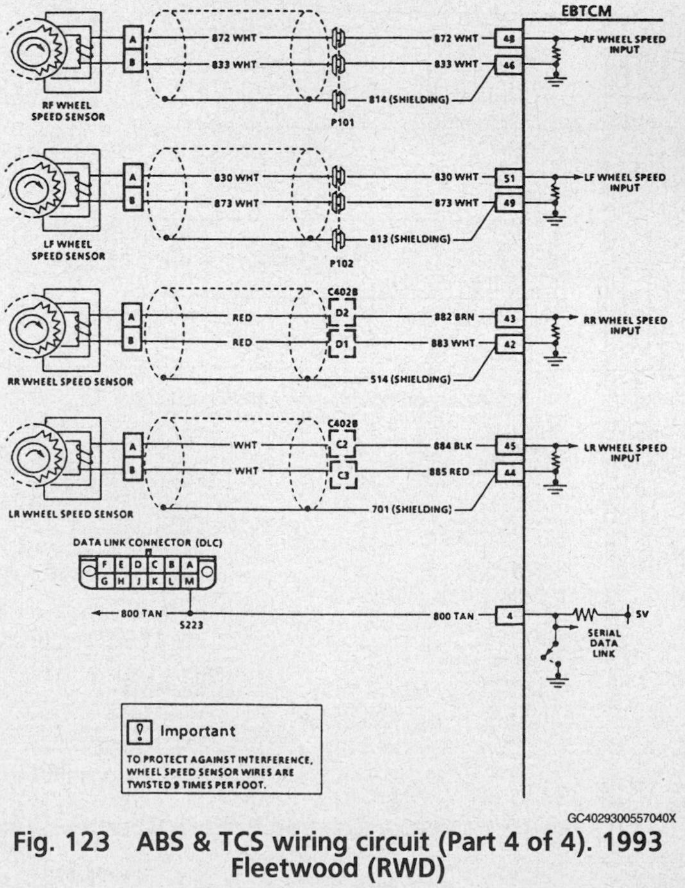
EBTCM
RF WHEEL SPEED SENSOR
872 WHT
833 WHT
814 (SHIELDING)
RF WHEEL SPEED INPUT
LF WHEEL SPEED SENSOR
830 WHT
873 WHT
813 (SHIELDING)
LF WHEEL SPEED INPUT
RR WHEEL SPEED SENSOR
882 BRN
883 WHT
514 (SHIELDING)
RR WHEEL SPEED INPUT
LR WHEEL SPEED SENSOR
884 BLK
885 RED
701 (SHIELDING)
LR WHEEL SPEED INPUT
DATA LINK CONNECTOR (DLC)
800 TAN
SERIAL DATA LINK
5V
Important
TO PROTECT AGAINST INTERFERENCE, WHEEL SPEED SENSOR WIRES ARE TWISTED 9 TIMES PER FOOT.
GC4029300557040X

Fig. 123 ABS & TCS wiring circuit (Part 4 of 4). 1993 Fleetwood (RWD)

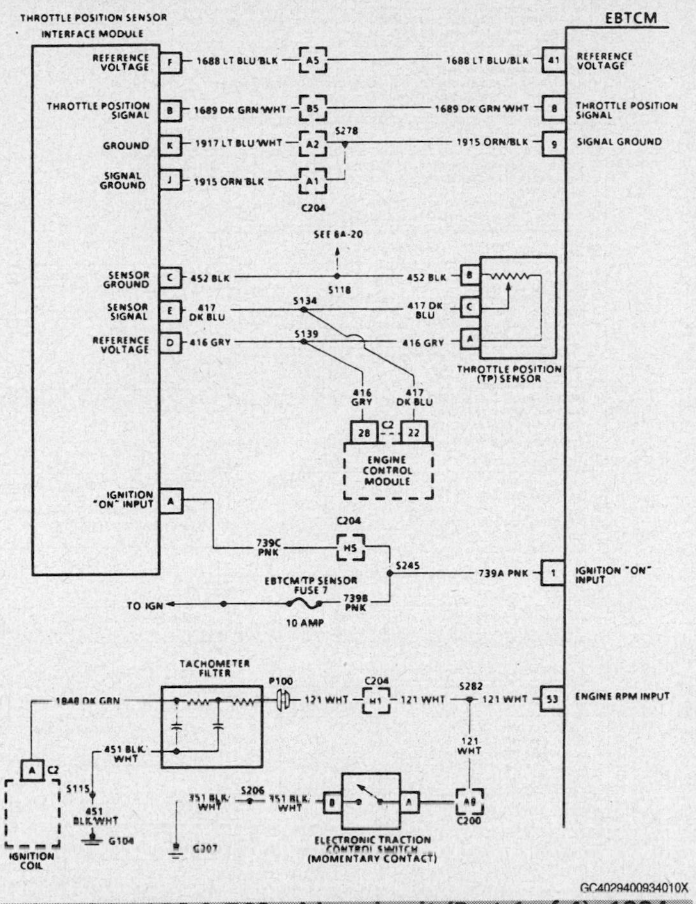
THROTTLE POSITION SENSOR INTERFACE MODULE
EBTCM
REFERENCE VOLTAGE
THROTTLE POSITION SIGNAL
GROUND
SIGNAL GROUND
1688 LT BLU/BLK
1689 DK GRN/WHT
1917 LT BLU/WHT
1915 ORN/BLK
S278
C204
SEE 8A-20
SENSOR GROUND
SENSOR SIGNAL
452 BLK
417 DK BLU
416 GRY
S118
S134
S139
THROTTLE POSITION (TP) SENSOR
ENGINE CONTROL MODULE
IGNITION "ON" INPUT
739C PNK
S245
739A PNK
EBTCM/TP SENSOR FUSE 7
10 AMP
739B PNK
TO IGN
TACHOMETER FILTER
1848 DK GRN
P100
121 WHT
S282
ENGINE RPM INPUT
451 BLK/WHT
S115
G104
IGNITION COIL
351 BLK/WHT
S206
G307
ELECTRONIC TRACTION CONTROL SWITCH (MOMENTARY CONTACT)
C200
GC4029400934010X

Fig. 124 ABS & TCS wiring circuit (Part 1 of 4). 1994 Fleetwood (RWD)

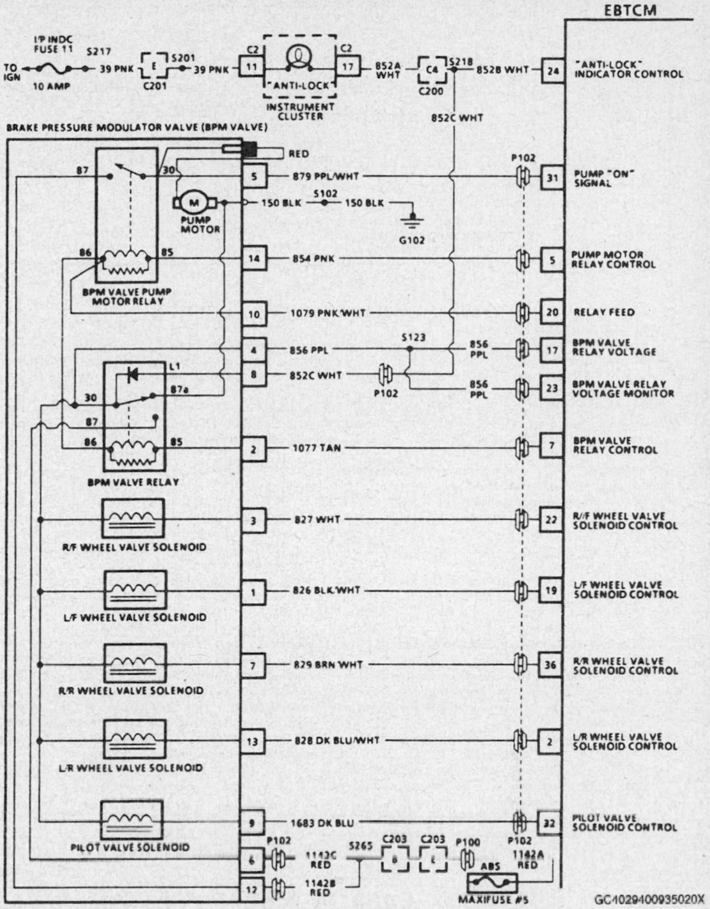
EBTCM
I/P INDC FUSE 11
S217
S201
TO IGN
10 AMP
39 PNK
C201
"ANTI-LOCK"
INSTRUMENT CLUSTER
852A WHT
S218
C200
852B WHT
"ANTI-LOCK" INDICATOR CONTROL
852C WHT
BRAKE PRESSURE MODULATOR VALVE (BPM VALVE)
RED
879 PPL/WHT
P102
PUMP "ON" SIGNAL
PUMP MOTOR
150 BLK
S102
G102
854 PNK
PUMP MOTOR RELAY CONTROL
BPM VALVE PUMP MOTOR RELAY
1079 PNK/WHT
RELAY FEED
856 PPL
S123
BPM VALVE RELAY VOLTAGE
852C WHT
BPM VALVE RELAY VOLTAGE MONITOR
1077 TAN
BPM VALVE RELAY CONTROL
BPM VALVE RELAY
827 WHT
R/F WHEEL VALVE SOLENOID
R/F WHEEL VALVE SOLENOID CONTROL
826 BLK/WHT
L/F WHEEL VALVE SOLENOID
L/F WHEEL VALVE SOLENOID CONTROL
829 BRN/WHT
R/R WHEEL VALVE SOLENOID
R/R WHEEL VALVE SOLENOID CONTROL
828 DK BLU/WHT
L/R WHEEL VALVE SOLENOID
L/R WHEEL VALVE SOLENOID CONTROL
1683 DK BLU
PILOT VALVE SOLENOID
PILOT VALVE SOLENOID CONTROL
1142C RED
1142B RED
S265
C203
P100
ABS
1142A RED
MAXIFUSE #5
GC4029400935020X

Fig. 124 ABS & TCS wiring circuit (Part 2 of 4). 1994 Fleetwood (RWD)

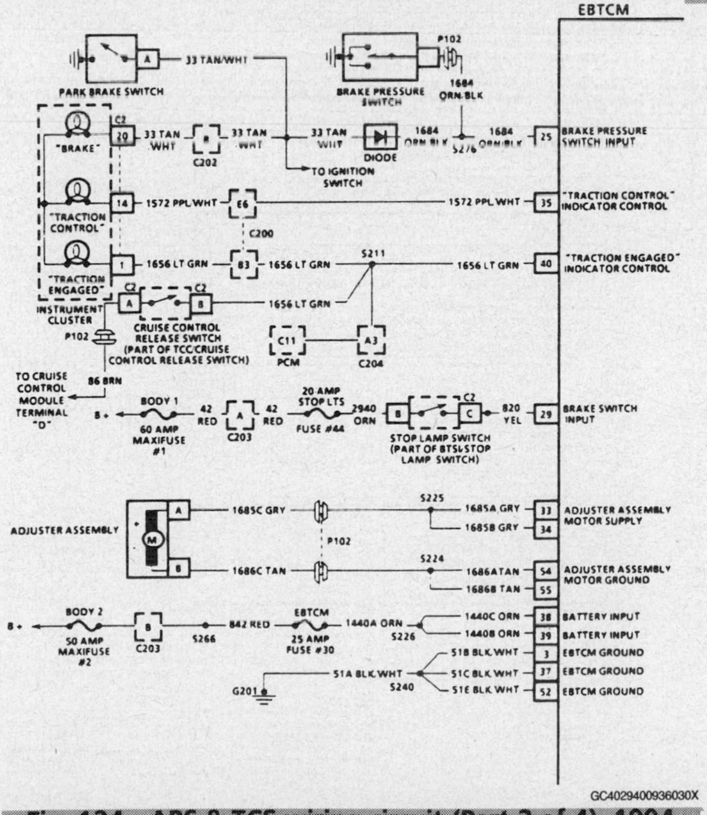
EBTCM
33 TAN/WHT
PARK BRAKE SWITCH
P102
BRAKE PRESSURE SWITCH
1684 ORN/BLK
"BRAKE"
33 TAN WHT
C202
DIODE
S276
BRAKE PRESSURE SWITCH INPUT
TO IGNITION SWITCH
"TRACTION CONTROL"
1572 PPL/WHT
C200
"TRACTION CONTROL" INDICATOR CONTROL
"TRACTION ENGAGED"
1656 LT GRN
S211
"TRACTION ENGAGED" INDICATOR CONTROL
INSTRUMENT CLUSTER
CRUISE CONTROL RELEASE SWITCH (PART OF TCC/CRUISE CONTROL RELEASE SWITCH)
PCM
C204
TO CRUISE CONTROL MODULE TERMINAL "D"
86 BRN
BODY 1
60 AMP MAXIFUSE #1
42 RED
C203
20 AMP STOP LTS
FUSE #44
2940 ORN
STOP LAMP SWITCH (PART OF BTSI/STOP LAMP SWITCH)
820 YEL
BRAKE SWITCH INPUT
ADJUSTER ASSEMBLY
1685C GRY
S225
1685A GRY
1685B GRY
ADJUSTER ASSEMBLY MOTOR SUPPLY
1686C TAN
S224
1686A TAN
1686B TAN
ADJUSTER ASSEMBLY MOTOR GROUND
BODY 2
50 AMP MAXIFUSE #2
S266
842 RED
25 AMP FUSE #30
1440A ORN
S226
1440C ORN
1440B ORN
BATTERY INPUT
51A BLK/WHT
S240
G201
51B BLK/WHT
51C BLK/WHT
51E BLK/WHT
EBTCM GROUND
GC4029400936030X

Fig. 124 ABS & TCS wiring circuit (Part 3 of 4). 1994 Fleetwood (RWD)

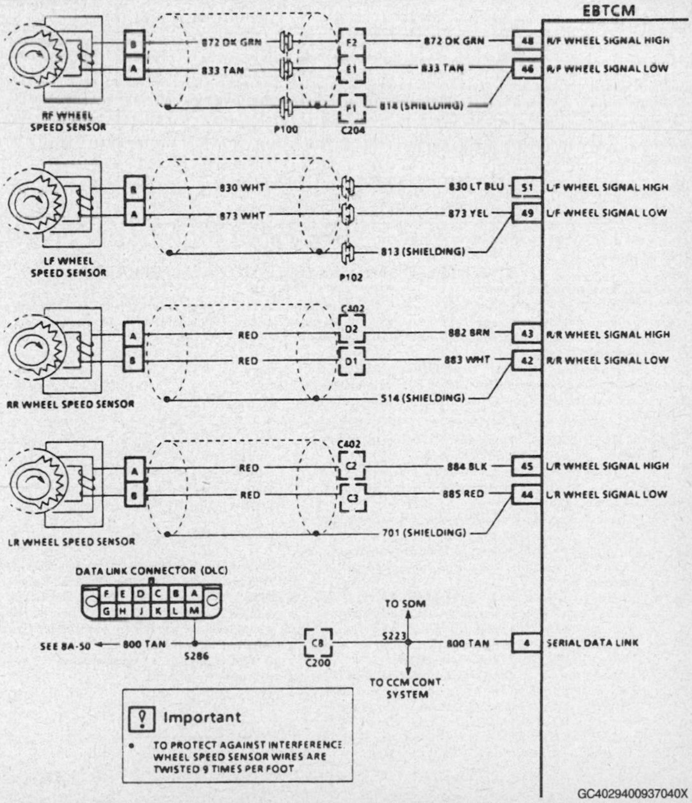
EBTCM
872 DK GRN
833 TAN
814 (SHIELDING)
RF WHEEL SPEED SENSOR
P100
C204
R/F WHEEL SIGNAL HIGH
R/F WHEEL SIGNAL LOW
830 WHT
873 WHT
830 LT BLU
873 YEL
813 (SHIELDING)
LF WHEEL SPEED SENSOR
P102
L/F WHEEL SIGNAL HIGH
L/F WHEEL SIGNAL LOW
RED
C402
882 BRN
883 WHT
514 (SHIELDING)
RR WHEEL SPEED SENSOR
R/R WHEEL SIGNAL HIGH
R/R WHEEL SIGNAL LOW
884 BLK
885 RED
701 (SHIELDING)
LR WHEEL SPEED SENSOR
L/R WHEEL SIGNAL HIGH
L/R WHEEL SIGNAL LOW
DATA LINK CONNECTOR (DLC)
TO SDM
SEE 8A-50
800 TAN
S286
C200
S223
SERIAL DATA LINK
TO CCM CONT. SYSTEM
Important
TO PROTECT AGAINST INTERFERENCE WHEEL SPEED SENSOR WIRES ARE TWISTED 9 TIMES PER FOOT
GC4029400937040X

Fig. 124 ABS & TCS wiring circuit (Part 4 of 4). 1994 Fleetwood (RWD)

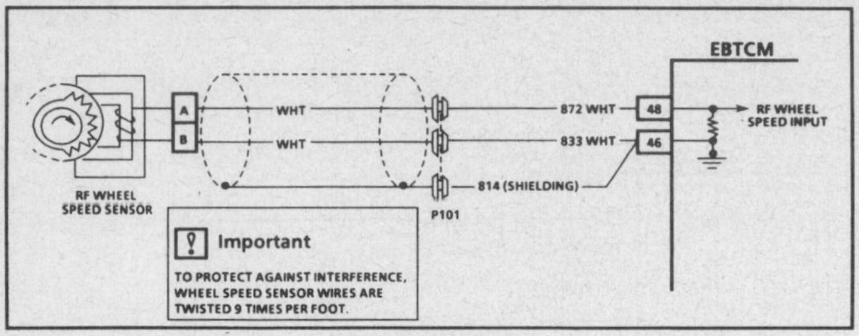
EBTCM
A
B
WHT
WHT
872 WHT
833 WHT
48
46
RF WHEEL SPEED INPUT
814 (SHIELDING)
RF WHEEL SPEED SENSOR
P101
Important
TO PROTECT AGAINST INTERFERENCE, WHEEL SPEED SENSOR WIRES ARE TWISTED 9 TIMES PER FOOT.

DTC 21

RF WHEEL SPEED SENSOR MALFUNCTION

Circuit Description:

The toothed wheel generates a voltage pulse as it moves past the sensor; each tooth-gap-tooth series on the wheel generates these pulses. The frequency of these pulses is used by the EBTCM to determine wheel speed. The amount of voltage generated in each pulse depends on the air gap between the sensor and the toothed wheel, and on wheel speed.

The "ANTI-LOCK" and "TRACTION CONTROL" indicators will be "ON" and DTC 21 is set if there is a short to voltage or ground in CKT 872 or 833, or a malfunctioning speed sensor. The testing for this malfunction occurs when the vehicle is in motion; it will not set with the ignition "ON" and the vehicle at rest.

Test Description: Number(s) below refer to circled number(s) on the diagnostic chart.

1. Checks for proper resistance in the sensor itself.
2. Checks for a short to battery in either of the speed sensor circuit wires.
3. Checks for a short between the speed sensor circuit wires.
4. Checks for a short to ground in the speed sensor input circuit wire. The ground may be either a "hard" short to ground, or a resistive (partial) short. A short with a resistance less than 2 megohms, though not a hard short, can still cause DTC 21 to set.
5. Checks if the DTC resets during a road test. If so, since Tests 1-4 have validated that the circuitry and components are good, intermittent problems are suspected.
6. Checks wiring and connectors for intermittents.
7. Replace the wheel speed sensor, as it is likely the cause of a DTC reset experienced during the road test, since other portions of the circuit have checked out OK. If the DTC resets after sensor replacement, the EBTCM must be concluding there is a problem present in the speed sensor circuit when there is not.

Diagnostic Aids:

Be sure the speed sensor wiring is properly routed and retained. This will help prevent false signals due to electrical noise being picked up by the wiring.

It is very important that a thorough inspection of the wiring and connectors be performed. Failure to carefully and fully inspect wiring and connectors may result in misdiagnosis, causing part replacement with reappearance of the malfunction.

The Tech 1 can also be used to monitor the wheel speeds during a road test. Watch the wheel speeds being displayed on the Tech 1 to see if any of the readings are unusual, such as one sensor varying in speed from the other three, a signal going intermittently high or low, etc. If this does not identify the intermittent, wet the speed sensor harness on the underside of the vehicle and road test monitoring wheel speeds with the Tech 1.

GC4029300558010X

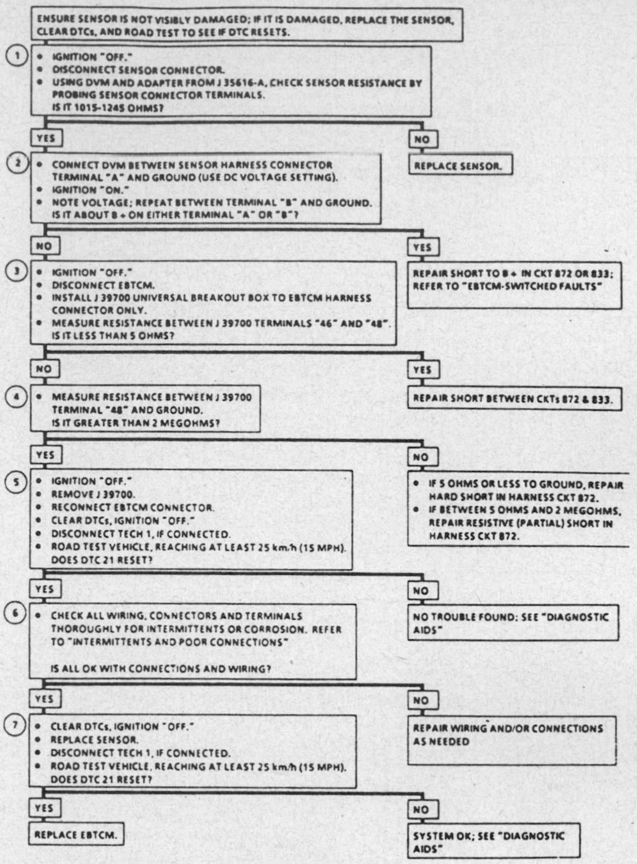
ENSURE SENSOR IS NOT VISIBLY DAMAGED; IF IT IS DAMAGED, REPLACE THE SENSOR, CLEAR DTCs, AND ROAD TEST TO SEE IF DTC RESETS.
1
• IGNITION "OFF."
• DISCONNECT SENSOR CONNECTOR.
• USING DVM AND ADAPTER FROM J 35616-A, CHECK SENSOR RESISTANCE BY PROBING SENSOR CONNECTOR TERMINALS.
IS IT 1015-1245 OHMS?
YES
NO
REPLACE SENSOR.
2
• CONNECT DVM BETWEEN SENSOR HARNESS CONNECTOR TERMINAL "A" AND GROUND (USE DC VOLTAGE SETTING).
• IGNITION "ON."
• NOTE VOLTAGE; REPEAT BETWEEN TERMINAL "B" AND GROUND.
IS IT ABOUT B + ON EITHER TERMINAL "A" OR "B"?
NO
YES
REPAIR SHORT TO B + IN CKT 872 OR 833; REFER TO "EBTCM-SWITCHED FAULTS"
3
• IGNITION "OFF."
• DISCONNECT EBTCM.
• INSTALL J 39700 UNIVERSAL BREAKOUT BOX TO EBTCM HARNESS CONNECTOR ONLY.
• MEASURE RESISTANCE BETWEEN J 39700 TERMINALS "46" AND "48".
IS IT LESS THAN 5 OHMS?
NO
YES
REPAIR SHORT BETWEEN CKTs 872 & 833.
4
• MEASURE RESISTANCE BETWEEN J 39700 TERMINAL "48" AND GROUND.
IS IT GREATER THAN 2 MEGOHMS?
YES
NO
• IF 5 OHMS OR LESS TO GROUND, REPAIR HARD SHORT IN HARNESS CKT 872.
• IF BETWEEN 5 OHMS AND 2 MEGOHMS, REPAIR RESISTIVE (PARTIAL) SHORT IN HARNESS CKT 872.
5
• IGNITION "OFF."
• REMOVE J 39700.
• RECONNECT EBTCM CONNECTOR.
• CLEAR DTCs, IGNITION "OFF."
• DISCONNECT TECH 1, IF CONNECTED.
• ROAD TEST VEHICLE, REACHING AT LEAST 25 km/h (15 MPH).
DOES DTC 21 RESET?
YES
NO
NO TROUBLE FOUND: SEE "DIAGNOSTIC AIDS"
6
• CHECK ALL WIRING, CONNECTORS AND TERMINALS THOROUGHLY FOR INTERMITTENTS OR CORROSION. REFER TO "INTERMITTENTS AND POOR CONNECTIONS"
IS ALL OK WITH CONNECTIONS AND WIRING?
YES
NO
REPAIR WIRING AND/OR CONNECTIONS AS NEEDED
7
• CLEAR DTCs, IGNITION "OFF."
• REPLACE SENSOR.
• DISCONNECT TECH 1, IF CONNECTED.
• ROAD TEST VEHICLE, REACHING AT LEAST 25 km/h (15 MPH).
DOES DTC 21 RESET?
YES
NO
REPLACE EBTCM.
SYSTEM OK; SEE "DIAGNOSTIC AIDS"

GC4029300558020X

Fig. 125 Code 21: Right Front Wheel Speed Sensor Malfunction. 1993-94 Fleetwood (RWD)

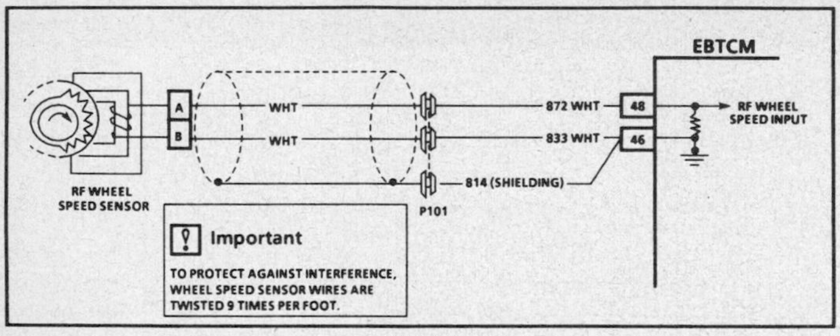
EBTCM
A
B
WHT
WHT
872 WHT
833 WHT
48
46
RF WHEEL SPEED INPUT
814 (SHIELDING)
RF WHEEL SPEED SENSOR
P101
Important
TO PROTECT AGAINST INTERFERENCE, WHEEL SPEED SENSOR WIRES ARE TWISTED 9 TIMES PER FOOT.

DTC 23

RF WHEEL SPEED SENSOR CONTINUITY MALFUNCTION

Circuit Description:

The toothed wheel generates a voltage pulse as it moves past the sensor; each tooth-gap-tooth series on the wheel generates these pulses. The frequency of these pulses is used by the EBTCM to determine wheel speed. The amount of voltage generated in each pulse depends on the air gap between the sensor and the toothed wheel, and on wheel speed.

The "ANTI-LOCK" and "TRACTION CONTROL" indicators will be "ON" and DTC 23 is set if there is a short to voltage or an open in CKT 872 or 833, or a malfunctioning speed sensor. The testing for this malfunction occurs with the ignition "ON" and the vehicle at rest.

Test Description: Number(s) below refer to circled number(s) on the diagnostic chart.

1. Checks for proper resistance in the sensor itself.
2. Checks for a short to battery in either of the speed sensor circuit wires.
3. Checks for an open in both the speed sensor circuit wires.
4. Manipulates wiring and connectors, trying to induce an intermittent malfunction not currently present.
5. This test checks if the DTC resets on key-up. If so, since Tests 1-4 have validated that the circuitry and components are good, the wheel speed sensor may be causing the malfunction.
6. Checks if DTC 21 sets during a road test.
7. DTC 23 sets when the vehicle is at rest; DTC 21 sets with a problem in the speed sensor circuitry with the vehicle in motion. If problems are still present, DTC 21 would set during the road test, not a 23. If the DTC 21 sets at this point, the DTC 21 diagnostics should be used.
8. The wheel speed sensor may be causing an intermittent fault. If DTC 23 resets after sensor replacement, the EBTCM must be concluding there is a problem present in the speed sensor circuit when there is not.

Diagnostic Aids:

Be sure the speed sensor wiring is properly routed and retained. This will help prevent false signals due to electrical noise being picked up by the wiring.

It is very important that a thorough inspection of the wiring and connectors be performed. Failure to carefully and fully inspect wiring and connectors may result in misdiagnosis, causing part replacement with reappearance of the malfunction.

GC4029300559010X

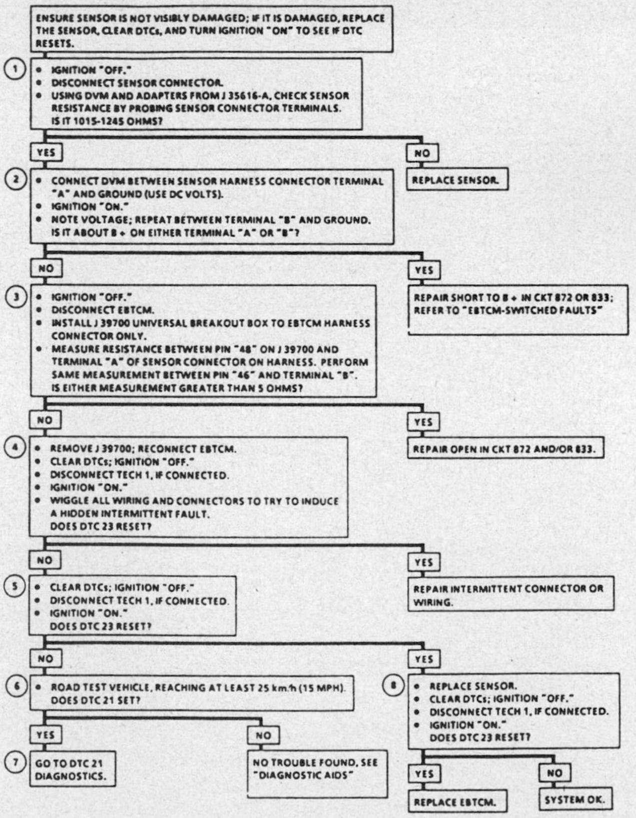
ENSURE SENSOR IS NOT VISIBLY DAMAGED; IF IT IS DAMAGED, REPLACE THE SENSOR, CLEAR DTCs, AND TURN IGNITION "ON" TO SEE IF DTC RESETS.
1
• IGNITION "OFF."
• DISCONNECT SENSOR CONNECTOR.
• USING DVM AND ADAPTERS FROM J 35616-A, CHECK SENSOR RESISTANCE BY PROBING SENSOR CONNECTOR TERMINALS.
IS IT 1015-1245 OHMS?
YES
NO
REPLACE SENSOR.
2
• CONNECT DVM BETWEEN SENSOR HARNESS CONNECTOR TERMINAL "A" AND GROUND (USE DC VOLTS).
• IGNITION "ON."
• NOTE VOLTAGE; REPEAT BETWEEN TERMINAL "B" AND GROUND.
IS IT ABOUT B + ON EITHER TERMINAL "A" OR "B"?
NO
YES
REPAIR SHORT TO B + IN CKT 872 OR 833; REFER TO "EBTCM-SWITCHED FAULTS"
3
• IGNITION "OFF."
• DISCONNECT EBTCM.
• INSTALL J 39700 UNIVERSAL BREAKOUT BOX TO EBTCM HARNESS CONNECTOR ONLY.
• MEASURE RESISTANCE BETWEEN PIN "48" ON J 39700 AND TERMINAL "A" OF SENSOR CONNECTOR ON HARNESS. PERFORM SAME MEASUREMENT BETWEEN PIN "46" AND TERMINAL "B".
IS EITHER MEASUREMENT GREATER THAN 5 OHMS?
NO
YES
REPAIR OPEN IN CKT 872 AND/OR 833.
4
• REMOVE J 39700; RECONNECT EBTCM.
• CLEAR DTCs; IGNITION "OFF."
• DISCONNECT TECH 1, IF CONNECTED.
• IGNITION "ON."
• WIGGLE ALL WIRING AND CONNECTORS TO TRY TO INDUCE A HIDDEN INTERMITTENT FAULT.
DOES DTC 23 RESET?
NO
YES
REPAIR INTERMITTENT CONNECTOR OR WIRING.
5
• CLEAR DTCs; IGNITION "OFF."
• DISCONNECT TECH 1, IF CONNECTED.
• IGNITION "ON."
DOES DTC 23 RESET?
NO
YES
6
• ROAD TEST VEHICLE, REACHING AT LEAST 25 km/h (15 MPH).
DOES DTC 21 SET?
8
• REPLACE SENSOR.
• CLEAR DTCs; IGNITION "OFF."
• DISCONNECT TECH 1, IF CONNECTED.
• IGNITION "ON."
DOES DTC 23 RESET?
YES
NO
7
GO TO DTC 21 DIAGNOSTICS.
NO TROUBLE FOUND, SEE "DIAGNOSTIC AIDS"
YES
NO
REPLACE EBTCM.
SYSTEM OK.

GC4029300559020X

Fig. 126 Code 23: Right Front Wheel Speed Sensor Continuity Malfunction. 1993-94 Fleetwood (RWD)

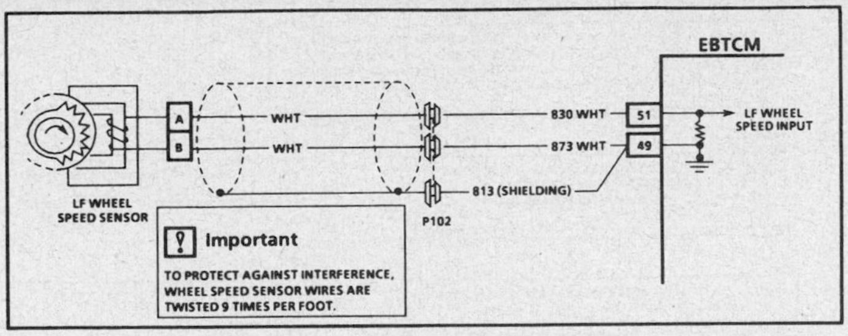
EBTCM
WHT
WHT
830 WHT
873 WHT
51
49
LF WHEEL SPEED INPUT
813 (SHIELDING)
A
B
LF WHEEL SPEED SENSOR
P102
Important
TO PROTECT AGAINST INTERFERENCE, WHEEL SPEED SENSOR WIRES ARE TWISTED 9 TIMES PER FOOT.

DTC 25

LF WHEEL SPEED SENSOR MALFUNCTION

Circuit Description:

The toothed wheel generates a voltage pulse as it moves past the sensor; each tooth-gap-tooth series on the wheel generates these pulses. The frequency of these pulses is used by the EBTCM to determine wheel speed. The amount of voltage generated in each pulse depends on the air gap between the sensor and the toothed wheel, and on wheel speed.

The "ANTI-LOCK" and "TRACTION CONTROL" indicators will be "ON" and DTC 25 is set if there is a short to voltage or ground in CKT 830 or 873, or a malfunctioning speed sensor. The testing for this malfunction occurs when the vehicle is in motion; it will not set with the ignition "ON" and the vehicle at rest.

Test Description: Number(s) below refer to circled number(s) on the diagnostic chart.

1. Checks for proper resistance in the sensor itself.
2. Checks for a short to battery in either of the speed sensor circuit wires.
3. Checks for a short between the speed sensor circuit wires.
4. Checks for a short to ground in the speed sensor input circuit wire. The ground may be either a "hard" short to ground, or a resistive (partial) short. A short with a resistance less than 2 megohms, though not a hard short, can still cause DTC 25 to set.
5. Checks if the DTC resets during a road test. If so, since Tests 1-4 have validated that the circuitry and components are good, intermittent problems are suspected.
6. Checks wiring and connectors for intermittents.
7. Replace the wheel speed sensor, as it is likely the cause of a DTC reset experienced during the road test, since other portions of the circuit have checked out OK. If the DTC resets after sensor replacement, the EBTCM must be concluding there is a problem present in the speed sensor circuit when there is not.

Diagnostic Aids:

Be sure the speed sensor wiring is properly routed and retained. This will help prevent false signals due to electrical noise being picked up by the wiring.

It is very important that a thorough inspection of the wiring and connectors be performed. Failure to carefully and fully inspect wiring and connectors may result in misdiagnosis, causing part replacement with reappearance of the malfunction.

The Tech 1 can also be used to monitor the wheel speeds during a road test. Watch the wheel speeds being displayed on the Tech 1 to see if any of the readings are unusual, such as one sensor varying in speed from the other three, a signal going intermittently high or low, etc. If this does not identify the intermittent, wet the speed sensor harness on the underside of the vehicle and road test monitoring wheel speeds with the Tech 1.

GC4029300560010X

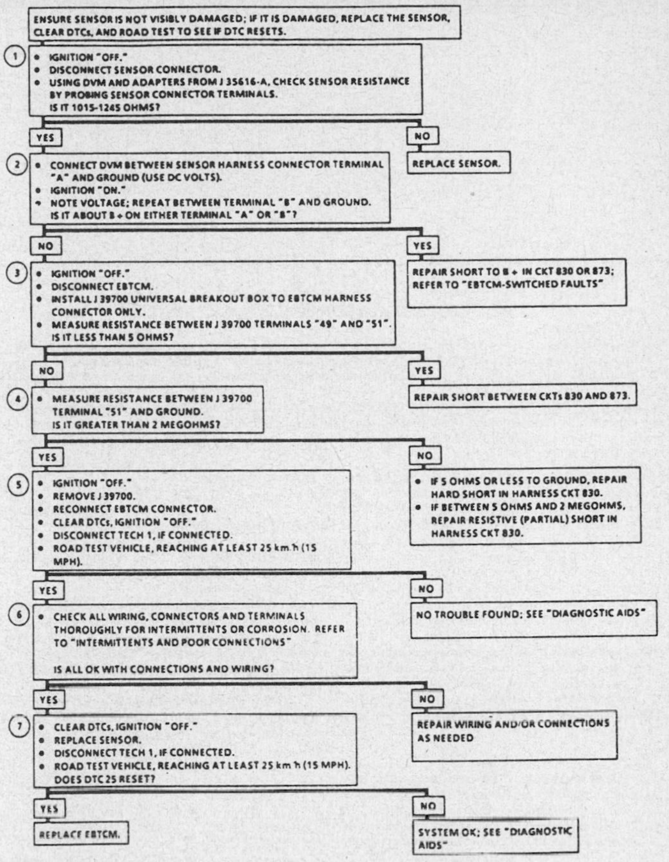
ENSURE SENSOR IS NOT VISIBLY DAMAGED; IF IT IS DAMAGED, REPLACE THE SENSOR, CLEAR DTCs, AND ROAD TEST TO SEE IF DTC RESETS.
1
• IGNITION "OFF."
• DISCONNECT SENSOR CONNECTOR.
• USING DVM AND ADAPTERS FROM J 35616-A, CHECK SENSOR RESISTANCE BY PROBING SENSOR CONNECTOR TERMINALS.
IS IT 1015-1245 OHMS?
YES
NO
REPLACE SENSOR.
2
• CONNECT DVM BETWEEN SENSOR HARNESS CONNECTOR TERMINAL "A" AND GROUND (USE DC VOLTS).
• IGNITION "ON."
• NOTE VOLTAGE; REPEAT BETWEEN TERMINAL "B" AND GROUND.
IS IT ABOUT B+ ON EITHER TERMINAL "A" OR "B"?
NO
YES
REPAIR SHORT TO B+ IN CKT 830 OR 873; REFER TO "EBTCM-SWITCHED FAULTS"
3
• IGNITION "OFF."
• DISCONNECT EBTCM.
• INSTALL J 39700 UNIVERSAL BREAKOUT BOX TO EBTCM HARNESS CONNECTOR ONLY.
• MEASURE RESISTANCE BETWEEN J 39700 TERMINALS "49" AND "51".
IS IT LESS THAN 5 OHMS?
NO
YES
REPAIR SHORT BETWEEN CKTs 830 AND 873.
4
• MEASURE RESISTANCE BETWEEN J 39700 TERMINAL "51" AND GROUND.
IS IT GREATER THAN 2 MEGOHMS?
YES
NO
• IF 5 OHMS OR LESS TO GROUND, REPAIR HARD SHORT IN HARNESS CKT 830.
• IF BETWEEN 5 OHMS AND 2 MEGOHMS, REPAIR RESISTIVE (PARTIAL) SHORT IN HARNESS CKT 830.
5
• IGNITION "OFF."
• REMOVE J 39700.
• RECONNECT EBTCM CONNECTOR.
• CLEAR DTCs, IGNITION "OFF."
• DISCONNECT TECH 1, IF CONNECTED.
• ROAD TEST VEHICLE, REACHING AT LEAST 25 km/h (15 MPH).
YES
NO
NO TROUBLE FOUND; SEE "DIAGNOSTIC AIDS"
6
• CHECK ALL WIRING, CONNECTORS AND TERMINALS THOROUGHLY FOR INTERMITTENTS OR CORROSION. REFER TO "INTERMITTENTS AND POOR CONNECTIONS"
IS ALL OK WITH CONNECTIONS AND WIRING?
YES
NO
REPAIR WIRING AND/OR CONNECTIONS AS NEEDED
7
• CLEAR DTCs, IGNITION "OFF."
• REPLACE SENSOR.
• DISCONNECT TECH 1, IF CONNECTED.
• ROAD TEST VEHICLE, REACHING AT LEAST 25 km/h (15 MPH).
DOES DTC 25 RESET?
YES
REPLACE EBTCM.
NO
SYSTEM OK; SEE "DIAGNOSTIC AIDS"

GC4029300560020X

Fig. 127 Code 25: Left Front Wheel Speed Sensor Malfunction. 1993-94 Fleetwood (RWD)

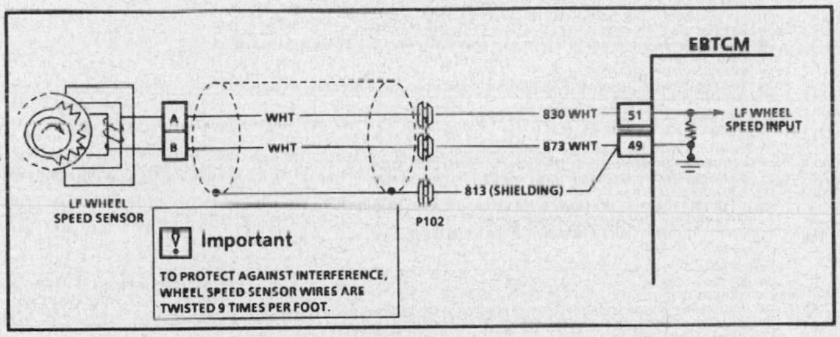
EBTCM
WHT
WHT
830 WHT
873 WHT
51
49
LF WHEEL SPEED INPUT
813 (SHIELDING)
A
B
LF WHEEL SPEED SENSOR
P102
Important
TO PROTECT AGAINST INTERFERENCE, WHEEL SPEED SENSOR WIRES ARE TWISTED 9 TIMES PER FOOT.

DTC 27

LF WHEEL SPEED SENSOR CONTINUITY MALFUNCTION

Circuit Description:

The toothed wheel generates a voltage pulse as it moves past the sensor; each tooth-gap-tooth series on the wheel generates these pulses. The frequency of these pulses is used by the EBTCM to determine wheel speed. The amount of voltage generated in each pulse depends on the air gap between the sensor and the toothed wheel, and on wheel speed.

The "ANTI-LOCK" and "TRACTION CONTROL" indicators will be "ON" and DTC 27 is set if there is a short to voltage or an open in CKT 830 or 873, or a malfunctioning speed sensor. The testing for this malfunction occurs with the ignition "ON" and the vehicle at rest.

Test Description: Number(s) below refer to circled number(s) on the diagnostic chart.

1. Checks for proper resistance in the sensor itself.
2. Checks for a short to battery in either of the speed sensor circuit wires.
3. Checks for an open in both the speed sensor circuit wires.
4. Manipulates wiring and connectors, trying to induce an intermittent malfunction not currently present.
5. This test checks if the DTC resets on key-up. If so, since Tests 1-4 have validated that the circuitry and components are good, the wheel speed sensor may be causing the malfunction.
6. Checks if DTC 25 sets during a road test.
7. DTC 27 sets when the vehicle is at rest; DTC 25 sets with a problem in the speed sensor circuitry with the vehicle in motion. If problems are still present, DTC 25 would set during the road test, not a 27. If the DTC 25 sets at this point, the DTC 25 diagnostics should be used.
8. The wheel speed sensor may be causing an intermittent malfunction. If DTC 27 resets after sensor replacement, the EBTCM must be concluding there is a problem present in the speed sensor circuit when there is not.

Diagnostic Aids:

Be sure the speed sensor wiring is properly routed and retained. This will help prevent false signals due to electrical noise being picked up by the wiring.

It is very important that a thorough inspection of the wiring and connectors be performed. Failure to carefully and fully inspect wiring and connectors may result in misdiagnosis, causing part replacement with reappearance of the malfunction.

GC4029300561010X

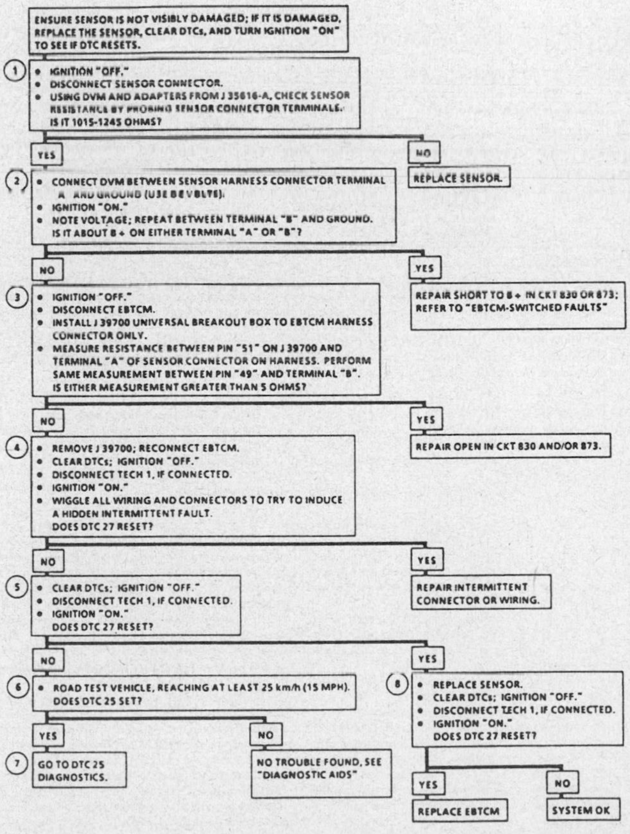
ENSURE SENSOR IS NOT VISIBLY DAMAGED; IF IT IS DAMAGED, REPLACE THE SENSOR, CLEAR DTCs, AND TURN IGNITION "ON" TO SEE IF DTC RESETS.
1
• IGNITION "OFF."
• DISCONNECT SENSOR CONNECTOR.
• USING DVM AND ADAPTERS FROM J 35616-A, CHECK SENSOR RESISTANCE BY PROBING SENSOR CONNECTOR TERMINALS.
IS IT 1015-1245 OHMS?
YES
NO
REPLACE SENSOR.
2
• CONNECT DVM BETWEEN SENSOR HARNESS CONNECTOR TERMINAL "A" AND GROUND (USE DC VOLTS).
• IGNITION "ON."
• NOTE VOLTAGE; REPEAT BETWEEN TERMINAL "B" AND GROUND.
IS IT ABOUT B+ ON EITHER TERMINAL "A" OR "B"?
NO
YES
REPAIR SHORT TO B+ IN CKT 830 OR 873; REFER TO "EBTCM-SWITCHED FAULTS"
3
• IGNITION "OFF."
• DISCONNECT EBTCM.
• INSTALL J 39700 UNIVERSAL BREAKOUT BOX TO EBTCM HARNESS CONNECTOR ONLY.
• MEASURE RESISTANCE BETWEEN PIN "51" ON J 39700 AND TERMINAL "A" OF SENSOR CONNECTOR ON HARNESS. PERFORM SAME MEASUREMENT BETWEEN PIN "49" AND TERMINAL "B".
IS EITHER MEASUREMENT GREATER THAN 5 OHMS?
NO
YES
REPAIR OPEN IN CKT 830 AND/OR 873.
4
• REMOVE J 39700; RECONNECT EBTCM.
• CLEAR DTCs; IGNITION "OFF."
• DISCONNECT TECH 1, IF CONNECTED.
• IGNITION "ON."
• WIGGLE ALL WIRING AND CONNECTORS TO TRY TO INDUCE A HIDDEN INTERMITTENT FAULT.
DOES DTC 27 RESET?
NO
YES
REPAIR INTERMITTENT CONNECTOR OR WIRING.
5
• CLEAR DTCs; IGNITION "OFF."
• DISCONNECT TECH 1, IF CONNECTED.
• IGNITION "ON."
DOES DTC 27 RESET?
NO
YES
6
• ROAD TEST VEHICLE, REACHING AT LEAST 25 km/h (15 MPH).
DOES DTC 25 SET?
8
• REPLACE SENSOR.
• CLEAR DTCs; IGNITION "OFF."
• DISCONNECT TECH 1, IF CONNECTED.
• IGNITION "ON."
DOES DTC 27 RESET?
YES
NO
7
GO TO DTC 25 DIAGNOSTICS.
NO TROUBLE FOUND, SEE "DIAGNOSTIC AIDS"
YES
NO
REPLACE EBTCM
SYSTEM OK

GC4029300561020X

Fig. 128 Code 26: Left Front Wheel Speed Sensor Continuity Malfunction. 1993-94 Fleetwood (RWD)

EBTCM
N
S
WHEEL SPEED INPUT
WHEEL SPEED SENSOR

DTC 28

WHEEL SPEED SENSOR FREQUENCY ERROR

Circuit Description:

The toothed wheel generates a voltage pulse as it moves past the sensor; each tooth-gap-tooth series on the wheel generates these pulses. The frequency of these pulses is used by the EBTCM to determine wheel speed. The amount of voltage generated in each pulse depends on the air gap between the sensor and the toothed wheel, and on wheel speed.

The "ANTI-LOCK" and "TRACTION CONTROL" indicators will be "ON" and DTC 28 is set if the EBTCM cannot specifically identify which wheel speed sensor is causing the frequency error problem. If it can define the specific speed sensor causing the problem, the sensor DTC associated with the sensor (21, 25, 31, 35) will be set instead of DTC 28.

Test Description: Number(s) below refer to circled number(s) on the diagnostic chart.

1. Checks wiring and connections for problems. It is critical that this step is performed thoroughly, as wiring/connector problems are the most likely cause for this DTC being set.
2. Uses the Tech 1 to monitor for vehicle electrical/electronic system "noise" being picked up by the speed sensor circuits.
3. Uses the Tech 1 to monitor the wheel speed sensors while the vehicle is operating. If the Tech 1 auto-trigger snapshot mode triggers, the speed sensor or the wiring and/or connectors are going intermittent during the road test.
4. Checks for proper resistance in the sensor itself.
5. Replaces wheel speed sensor as the likely cause of the triggering intermittent. If DTC resets, replace EBTCM.
6. Checks for a short to ground in the speed sensor input circuit wires. The circuit to be tested depends on which speed sensor triggered the Tech 1. The ground may be either a "hard" short to ground, or a resistive (partial) short. A short with a resistance less than 2 megohms, though not a hard short, can still cause DTC 28 to set.

Diagnostic Aids:

DTC 28 may be set by running the Tech 1 "Auto Test" if the throttle angle readings are not updating while in the data list mode. If this is the case, clear DTCs, disconnect Tech 1, and road test to at least 25 km/h (15 mph) to see if DTC resets.

Rear Speed Sensors Only:

Check the toothed wheel for any large grooves, gouges, marks, etc. that might influence the tooth's signal at the wheel speed sensor. Also check for a buildup of foreign material in the gaps between teeth in the toothed wheel; this material may cause this malfunction.

A worn hub/bearing assembly may cause this fault in extreme cases; the bearing play allows the sensor-to-toothed-ring gap to change excessively.

GC4029300562010X

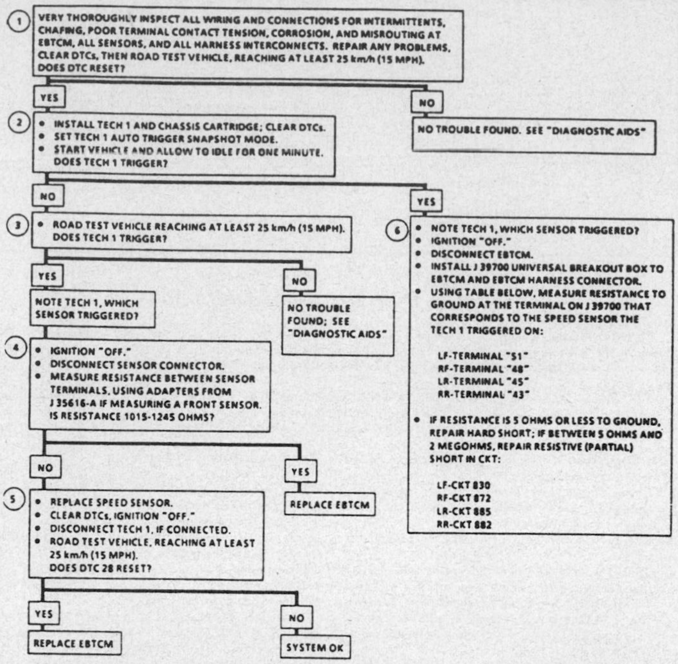
1 VERY THOROUGHLY INSPECT ALL WIRING AND CONNECTIONS FOR INTERMITTENTS, CHAFING, POOR TERMINAL CONTACT TENSION, CORROSION, AND MISROUTING AT EBTCM, ALL SENSORS, AND ALL HARNESS INTERCONNECTS. REPAIR ANY PROBLEMS. CLEAR DTCs, THEN ROAD TEST VEHICLE, REACHING AT LEAST 25 km/h (15 MPH). DOES DTC RESET?
YES
NO
NO TROUBLE FOUND. SEE "DIAGNOSTIC AIDS"
2 • INSTALL TECH 1 AND CHASSIS CARTRIDGE; CLEAR DTCs. • SET TECH 1 AUTO TRIGGER SNAPSHOT MODE. • START VEHICLE AND ALLOW TO IDLE FOR ONE MINUTE. DOES TECH 1 TRIGGER?
NO
YES
3 • ROAD TEST VEHICLE REACHING AT LEAST 25 km/h (15 MPH). DOES TECH 1 TRIGGER?
YES
NO
NOTE TECH 1, WHICH SENSOR TRIGGERED?
NO TROUBLE FOUND; SEE "DIAGNOSTIC AIDS"
4 • IGNITION "OFF." • DISCONNECT SENSOR CONNECTOR. • MEASURE RESISTANCE BETWEEN SENSOR TERMINALS, USING ADAPTERS FROM J 35616-A IF MEASURING A FRONT SENSOR. IS RESISTANCE 1015-1245 OHMS?
NO
YES
REPLACE EBTCM
5 • REPLACE SPEED SENSOR. • CLEAR DTCs, IGNITION "OFF." • DISCONNECT TECH 1, IF CONNECTED. • ROAD TEST VEHICLE, REACHING AT LEAST 25 km/h (15 MPH). DOES DTC 28 RESET?
YES
NO
REPLACE EBTCM
SYSTEM OK
6 • NOTE TECH 1, WHICH SENSOR TRIGGERED? • IGNITION "OFF." • DISCONNECT EBTCM. • INSTALL J 39700 UNIVERSAL BREAKOUT BOX TO EBTCM AND EBTCM HARNESS CONNECTOR. • USING TABLE BELOW, MEASURE RESISTANCE TO GROUND AT THE TERMINAL ON J 39700 THAT CORRESPONDS TO THE SPEED SENSOR THE TECH 1 TRIGGERED ON:
LF-TERMINAL "51"
RF-TERMINAL "48"
LR-TERMINAL "45"
RR-TERMINAL "43"
• IF RESISTANCE IS 5 OHMS OR LESS TO GROUND, REPAIR HARD SHORT; IF BETWEEN 5 OHMS AND 2 MEGOHMS, REPAIR RESISTIVE (PARTIAL) SHORT IN CKT:
LF-CKT 830
RF-CKT 872
LR-CKT 885
RR-CKT 882

GC4029300562020X

Fig. 129 Code 28: Wheel Speed Sensor Frequency Error. 1993-94 Fleetwood (RWD)

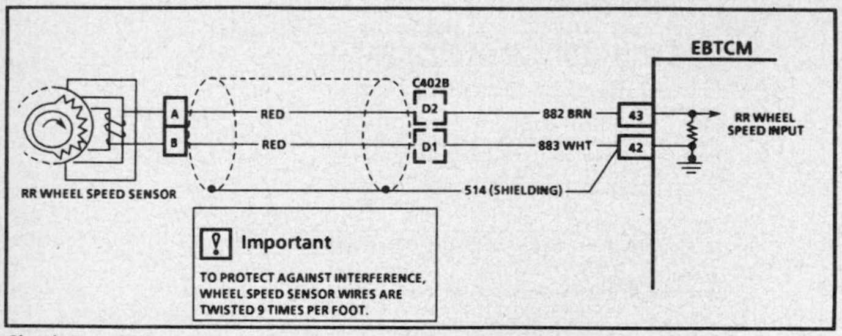
EBTCM
C402B
A
B
RED
RED
D2
D1
882 BRN
883 WHT
43
42
RR WHEEL SPEED INPUT
514 (SHIELDING)
RR WHEEL SPEED SENSOR
Important
TO PROTECT AGAINST INTERFERENCE, WHEEL SPEED SENSOR WIRES ARE TWISTED 9 TIMES PER FOOT.

Circuit Description:

The toothed wheel generates a voltage pulse as it moves past the sensor; each tooth-gap-tooth series on the wheel generates these pulses. The frequency of these pulses is used by the EBTCM to determine wheel speed. The amount of voltage generated in each pulse depends on the air gap between the sensor and the toothed wheel, and on wheel speed.

The "ANTI-LOCK" and "TRACTION CONTROL" indicators will be "ON" and DTC 31 is set if there is a short to voltage or ground in CKT 882 or 883, or a malfunctioning speed sensor. The testing for this malfunction occurs when the vehicle is in motion; it will not set with the ignition "ON" and the vehicle at rest.

Test Description: Number(s) below refer to circled number(s) on the diagnostic chart.

1. Checks for proper resistance in the sensor itself.
2. Checks for a short to battery in either of the speed sensor circuit wires.
3. Checks for a short between the speed sensor circuit wires.
4. Checks for a short to ground in the speed sensor input circuit wire. The ground may be either a "hard" short to ground, or a resistive (partial) short. A short with a resistance less than 2 megohms, though not a hard short, can still cause DTC 31 to set.
5. Checks if the DTC resets during a road test. If so, since Tests 1-4 have validated that all of the circuitry and components are good, intermittent problems are suspected.
6. Checks wiring and connectors for intermittents.
7. Checks for sensor mounting, toothed wheel, and rear wheel bearing problems which may be causing the problem. Check the toothed wheel for any large grooves, gouges, marks, etc. that might influence the tooth's signal at the wheel speed sensor. Also check for a buildup of foreign material in the gaps between teeth in the toothed wheel; this material may cause this malfunction.
8. Replace the speed sensor assembly, as it is likely the cause of a DTC reset experienced during the road test, since other portions of the circuit have checked out OK.

Diagnostic Aids:

A worn hub-bearing assembly may cause this malfunction in extreme cases; the bearing play allows the sensor-to-toothed-ring gap to change excessively.

Be sure the speed sensor wiring is properly routed and retained. This will help prevent false signals due to electrical noise being picked up by the wiring.

It is very important that a thorough inspection of the wiring and connectors be performed. Failure to carefully and fully inspect wiring and connectors may result in misdiagnosis, causing part replacement with reappearance of the malfunction.

The Tech 1 can also be used to monitor the wheel speeds during a road test. Watch the wheel speeds being displayed on the Tech 1 to see if any of the readings are unusual, such as one sensor varying in speed from the other three, a signal going intermittently high or low, etc. If this does not identify the intermittent, wet the speed sensor harness on the underside of the vehicle and road test monitoring wheel speeds with the Tech 1.

GC4029300563010X

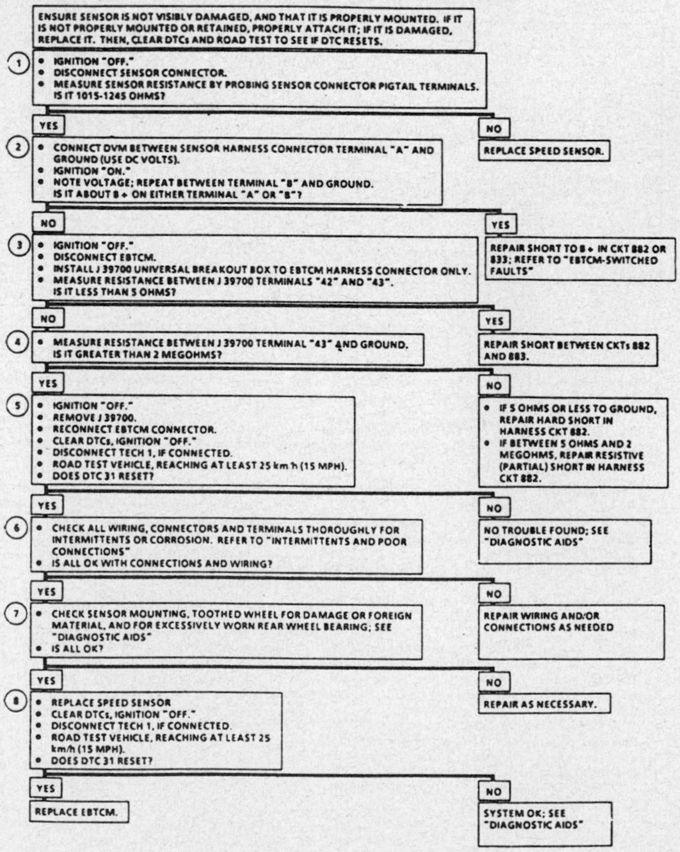
ENSURE SENSOR IS NOT VISIBLY DAMAGED, AND THAT IT IS PROPERLY MOUNTED. IF IT IS NOT PROPERLY MOUNTED OR RETAINED, PROPERLY ATTACH IT; IF IT IS DAMAGED, REPLACE IT. THEN, CLEAR DTCs AND ROAD TEST TO SEE IF DTC RESETS.
1 • IGNITION "OFF." • DISCONNECT SENSOR CONNECTOR. • MEASURE SENSOR RESISTANCE BY PROBING SENSOR CONNECTOR PIGTAIL TERMINALS. IS IT 1015-1245 OHMS?
YES
NO
REPLACE SPEED SENSOR.
2 • CONNECT DVM BETWEEN SENSOR HARNESS CONNECTOR TERMINAL "A" AND GROUND (USE DC VOLTS). • IGNITION "ON." • NOTE VOLTAGE; REPEAT BETWEEN TERMINAL "B" AND GROUND. IS IT ABOUT B+ ON EITHER TERMINAL "A" OR "B"?
NO
YES
REPAIR SHORT TO B+ IN CKT 882 OR 833; REFER TO "EBTCM-SWITCHED FAULTS"
3 • IGNITION "OFF." • DISCONNECT EBTCM. • INSTALL J 39700 UNIVERSAL BREAKOUT BOX TO EBTCM HARNESS CONNECTOR ONLY. • MEASURE RESISTANCE BETWEEN J 39700 TERMINALS "42" AND "43". IS IT LESS THAN 5 OHMS?
NO
YES
REPAIR SHORT BETWEEN CKTs 882 AND 883.
4 • MEASURE RESISTANCE BETWEEN J 39700 TERMINAL "43" AND GROUND. IS IT GREATER THAN 2 MEGOHMS?
YES
NO
• IF 5 OHMS OR LESS TO GROUND, REPAIR HARD SHORT IN HARNESS CKT 882. • IF BETWEEN 5 OHMS AND 2 MEGOHMS, REPAIR RESISTIVE (PARTIAL) SHORT IN HARNESS CKT 882.
5 • IGNITION "OFF." • REMOVE J 39700. • RECONNECT EBTCM CONNECTOR. • CLEAR DTCs, IGNITION "OFF." • DISCONNECT TECH 1, IF CONNECTED. • ROAD TEST VEHICLE, REACHING AT LEAST 25 km/h (15 MPH). • DOES DTC 31 RESET?
YES
NO
NO TROUBLE FOUND; SEE "DIAGNOSTIC AIDS"
6 • CHECK ALL WIRING, CONNECTORS AND TERMINALS THOROUGHLY FOR INTERMITTENTS OR CORROSION. REFER TO "INTERMITTENTS AND POOR CONNECTIONS" • IS ALL OK WITH CONNECTIONS AND WIRING?
YES
NO
REPAIR WIRING AND/OR CONNECTIONS AS NEEDED
7 • CHECK SENSOR MOUNTING, TOOTHED WHEEL FOR DAMAGE OR FOREIGN MATERIAL, AND FOR EXCESSIVELY WORN REAR WHEEL BEARING; SEE "DIAGNOSTIC AIDS" • IS ALL OK?
YES
NO
REPAIR AS NECESSARY.
8 • REPLACE SPEED SENSOR • CLEAR DTCs, IGNITION "OFF." • DISCONNECT TECH 1, IF CONNECTED. • ROAD TEST VEHICLE, REACHING AT LEAST 25 km/h (15 MPH). • DOES DTC 31 RESET?
YES
NO
REPLACE EBTCM.
SYSTEM OK; SEE "DIAGNOSTIC AIDS"

GC4029300563020X

Fig. 130 Code 31: Right Rear Wheel Speed Sensor Malfunction. 1993-94 Fleetwood (RWD)

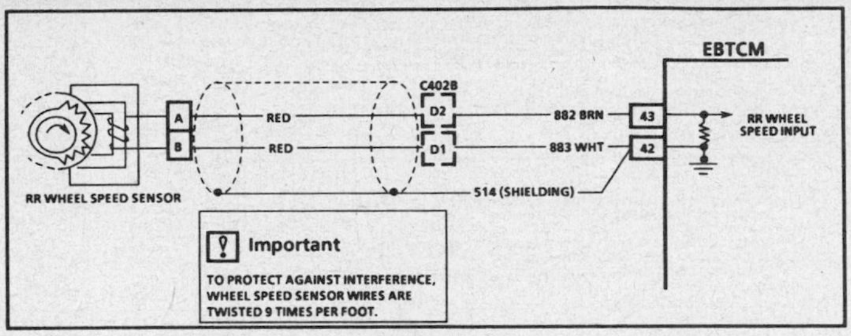
EBTCM
C402B
RED
RED
D2
D1
882 BRN
883 WHT
43
42
RR WHEEL SPEED INPUT
514 (SHIELDING)
A
B
RR WHEEL SPEED SENSOR
Important
TO PROTECT AGAINST INTERFERENCE, WHEEL SPEED SENSOR WIRES ARE TWISTED 9 TIMES PER FOOT.

DTC 33

RR WHEEL SPEED SENSOR CONTINUITY MALFUNCTION

Circuit Description:

The toothed wheel generates a voltage pulse as it moves past the sensor; each tooth-gap-tooth series on the wheel generates these pulses. The frequency of these pulses is used by the EBTCM to determine wheel speed. The amount of voltage generated in each pulse depends on the air gap between the sensor and the toothed wheel, and on wheel speed.

The "ANTI-LOCK" and "TRACTION CONTROL" indicators will be "ON" and DTC 33 is set if there is a short to voltage or an open in CKT 882 or 883, or a malfunctioning speed sensor. The testing for this malfunction occurs with the ignition "ON" and the vehicle at rest.

Test Description: Number(s) below refer to circled number(s) on the diagnostic chart.

1. Checks for proper resistance in the sensor itself.
2. Checks for a short to battery in either of the speed sensor circuit wires.
3. Checks for an open in both the speed sensor circuit wires.
4. Manipulates wiring and connectors, trying to induce an intermittent malfunction not currently present.
5. This test checks if the DTC resets on key-up. If so, since Tests 1-4 have validated that the circuitry and components are good, the speed sensor may be causing the malfunction.
6. Checks if DTC 31 sets during a road test.
7. DTC 33 sets when the vehicle is at rest; DTC 31 sets with a problem in the speed sensor circuitry with the vehicle in motion. If problems are still present, DTC 31 would set during the road test, not a 33. If the DTC 33 sets at this point, the DTC 31 diagnostics should be used.
8. The wheel speed sensor may be causing an intermittent malfunction. If DTC 33 resets after sensor replacement, the EBTCM must be concluding there is a problem present in the speed sensor circuit when there is not.

Diagnostic Aids:

Be sure the speed sensor wiring is properly routed and retained. This will help prevent false signals due to electrical noise being picked up by the wiring.

It is very important that a thorough inspection of the wiring and connectors be performed. Failure to carefully and fully inspect wiring and connectors may result in misdiagnosis, causing part replacement with reappearance of the malfunction.

GC4029300564010X

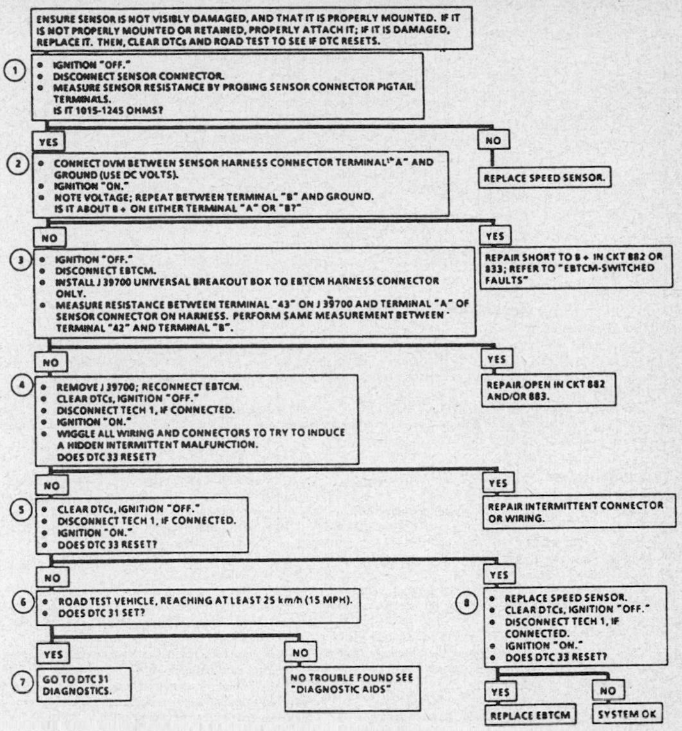
ENSURE SENSOR IS NOT VISIBLY DAMAGED, AND THAT IT IS PROPERLY MOUNTED. IF IT IS NOT PROPERLY MOUNTED OR RETAINED, PROPERLY ATTACH IT; IF IT IS DAMAGED, REPLACE IT. THEN, CLEAR DTCs AND ROAD TEST TO SEE IF DTC RESETS.
1
• IGNITION "OFF." • DISCONNECT SENSOR CONNECTOR. • MEASURE SENSOR RESISTANCE BY PROBING SENSOR CONNECTOR PIGTAIL TERMINALS. IS IT 1015-1245 OHMS?
YES
NO
REPLACE SPEED SENSOR.
2
• CONNECT DVM BETWEEN SENSOR HARNESS CONNECTOR TERMINAL "A" AND GROUND (USE DC VOLTS). • IGNITION "ON." • NOTE VOLTAGE; REPEAT BETWEEN TERMINAL "B" AND GROUND. IS IT ABOUT B+ ON EITHER TERMINAL "A" OR "B?"
NO
YES
REPAIR SHORT TO B+ IN CKT 882 OR 833; REFER TO "EBTCM-SWITCHED FAULTS"
3
• IGNITION "OFF." • DISCONNECT EBTCM. • INSTALL J 39700 UNIVERSAL BREAKOUT BOX TO EBTCM HARNESS CONNECTOR ONLY. • MEASURE RESISTANCE BETWEEN TERMINAL "43" ON J 39700 AND TERMINAL "A" OF SENSOR CONNECTOR ON HARNESS. PERFORM SAME MEASUREMENT BETWEEN TERMINAL "42" AND TERMINAL "B".
NO
YES
REPAIR OPEN IN CKT 882 AND/OR 883.
4
• REMOVE J 39700; RECONNECT EBTCM. • CLEAR DTCs, IGNITION "OFF." • DISCONNECT TECH 1, IF CONNECTED. • IGNITION "ON." • WIGGLE ALL WIRING AND CONNECTORS TO TRY TO INDUCE A HIDDEN INTERMITTENT MALFUNCTION. DOES DTC 33 RESET?
NO
YES
REPAIR INTERMITTENT CONNECTOR OR WIRING.
5
• CLEAR DTCs, IGNITION "OFF." • DISCONNECT TECH 1, IF CONNECTED. • IGNITION "ON." • DOES DTC 33 RESET?
NO
YES
6
• ROAD TEST VEHICLE, REACHING AT LEAST 25 km/h (15 MPH). • DOES DTC 31 SET?
8
• REPLACE SPEED SENSOR. • CLEAR DTCs, IGNITION "OFF." • DISCONNECT TECH 1, IF CONNECTED. • IGNITION "ON." • DOES DTC 33 RESET?
YES
NO
7
GO TO DTC 31 DIAGNOSTICS.
NO TROUBLE FOUND SEE "DIAGNOSTIC AIDS"
YES
NO
REPLACE EBTCM
SYSTEM OK

GC4029300564020X

Fig. 131 Code 33: Right Rear Wheel Speed Sensor Continuity Malfunction. 1993-94 Fleetwood (RWD)

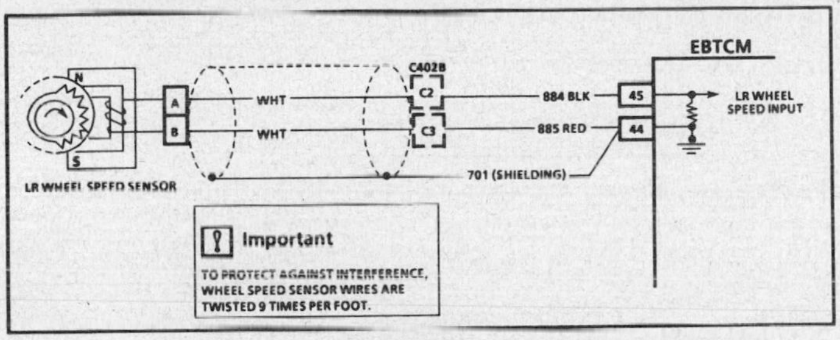
EBTCM
C402B
N
S
WHT
WHT
C2
C3
884 BLK
885 RED
45
44
LR WHEEL SPEED INPUT
701 (SHIELDING)
A
B
LR WHEEL SPEED SENSOR
Important
TO PROTECT AGAINST INTERFERENCE, WHEEL SPEED SENSOR WIRES ARE TWISTED 9 TIMES PER FOOT.

DTC 35

LR WHEEL SPEED SENSOR MALFUNCTION

Circuit Description:

The toothed wheel generates a voltage pulse as it moves past the sensor; each tooth-gap-tooth series on the wheel generates these pulses. The frequency of these pulses is used by the EBTCM to determine wheel speed. The amount of voltage generated in each pulse depends on the air gap between the sensor and the toothed wheel, and on wheel speed.

The "ANTI-LOCK" and "TRACTION CONTROL" indicators will be "ON" and DTC 35 is set if there is a short to voltage or ground in CKT 885 or 884, or a malfunctioning speed sensor. The testing for this malfunction occurs when the vehicle is in motion; it will not set with the ignition "ON" and the vehicle at rest.

Test Description: Number(s) below refer to circled number(s) on the diagnostic chart.

1. Checks for proper resistance in the sensor itself.
2. Checks for a short to battery in either of the speed sensor circuit wires.
3. Checks for a short between the speed sensor circuit wires.
4. Checks for a short to ground in the speed sensor input circuit wire. The ground may be either a "hard" short to ground, or a resistive (partial) short. A short with a resistance less than 2 megohms, though not a hard short, can still cause DTC 35 to set.
5. Checks if the DTC resets during a road test. If so, since Tests 1-4 have validated that all of the circuitry and components are good, intermittent problems are suspected.
6. Checks wiring and connectors for intermittents.
7. Checks for sensor mounting, toothed wheel, and rear wheel bearing problems which may be causing the problem. Check the toothed wheel for any large grooves, gouges, marks, etc. that might influence the tooth's signal at the wheel speed sensor. Also check for a buildup of foreign material in the gaps between teeth in the toothed wheel; this material may cause this malfunction.
8. Replace the speed sensor assembly, as it is likely the cause of a DTC reset experienced during the road test, since other portions of the circuit have checked out OK.

Diagnostic Aids:

A worn hub-bearing assembly may cause this malfunction in extreme cases; the bearing play allows the sensor-to-toothed-ring gap to change excessively.

Be sure the speed sensor wiring is properly routed and retained. This will help prevent false signals due to electrical noise being picked up by the wiring.

It is very important that a thorough inspection of the wiring and connectors be performed. Failure to carefully and fully inspect wiring and connectors may result in misdiagnosis, causing part replacement with reappearance of the malfunction.

The Tech 1 can also be used to monitor the wheel speeds during a road test. Watch the wheel speeds being displayed on the Tech 1 to see if any of the readings are unusual, such as one sensor varying in speed from the other three, a signal going intermittently high or low, etc. If this does not identify the intermittent, wet the speed sensor harness on the underside of the vehicle and road test monitoring wheel speeds with the Tech 1.

GC4029300565010X

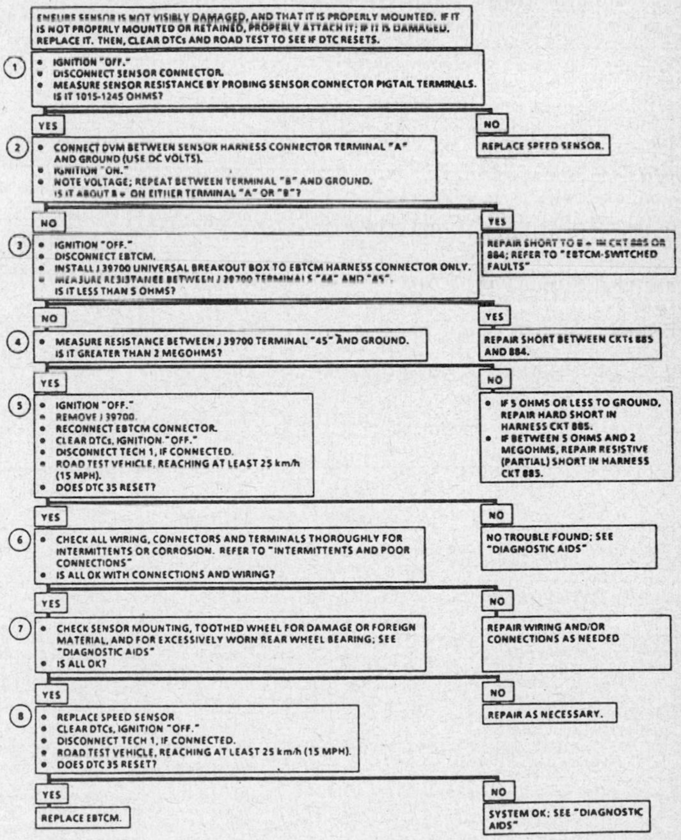
ENSURE SENSOR IS NOT VISIBLY DAMAGED, AND THAT IT IS PROPERLY MOUNTED. IF IT IS NOT PROPERLY MOUNTED OR RETAINED, PROPERLY ATTACH IT; IF IT IS DAMAGED, REPLACE IT. THEN, CLEAR DTCs AND ROAD TEST TO SEE IF DTC RESETS.
1
• IGNITION "OFF." • DISCONNECT SENSOR CONNECTOR. • MEASURE SENSOR RESISTANCE BY PROBING SENSOR CONNECTOR PIGTAIL TERMINALS. IS IT 1015-1245 OHMS?
YES
NO
REPLACE SPEED SENSOR.
2
• CONNECT DVM BETWEEN SENSOR HARNESS CONNECTOR TERMINAL "A" AND GROUND (USE DC VOLTS). • IGNITION "ON." • NOTE VOLTAGE; REPEAT BETWEEN TERMINAL "B" AND GROUND. IS IT ABOUT B+ ON EITHER TERMINAL "A" OR "B"?
NO
YES
REPAIR SHORT TO B+ IN CKT 885 OR 884; REFER TO "EBTCM-SWITCHED FAULTS"
3
• IGNITION "OFF." • DISCONNECT EBTCM. • INSTALL J 39700 UNIVERSAL BREAKOUT BOX TO EBTCM HARNESS CONNECTOR ONLY. • MEASURE RESISTANCE BETWEEN J 39700 TERMINALS "44" AND "45". IS IT LESS THAN 5 OHMS?
NO
YES
REPAIR SHORT BETWEEN CKTs 885 AND 884.
4
• MEASURE RESISTANCE BETWEEN J 39700 TERMINAL "45" AND GROUND. IS IT GREATER THAN 2 MEGOHMS?
YES
NO
• IF 5 OHMS OR LESS TO GROUND, REPAIR HARD SHORT IN HARNESS CKT 885. • IF BETWEEN 5 OHMS AND 2 MEGOHMS, REPAIR RESISTIVE (PARTIAL) SHORT IN HARNESS CKT 885.
5
• IGNITION "OFF." • REMOVE J 39700. • RECONNECT EBTCM CONNECTOR. • CLEAR DTCs, IGNITION "OFF." • DISCONNECT TECH 1, IF CONNECTED. • ROAD TEST VEHICLE, REACHING AT LEAST 25 km/h (15 MPH). • DOES DTC 35 RESET?
YES
NO
NO TROUBLE FOUND; SEE "DIAGNOSTIC AIDS"
6
• CHECK ALL WIRING, CONNECTORS AND TERMINALS THOROUGHLY FOR INTERMITTENTS OR CORROSION. REFER TO "INTERMITTENTS AND POOR CONNECTIONS" • IS ALL OK WITH CONNECTIONS AND WIRING?
YES
NO
REPAIR WIRING AND/OR CONNECTIONS AS NEEDED
7
• CHECK SENSOR MOUNTING, TOOTHED WHEEL FOR DAMAGE OR FOREIGN MATERIAL, AND FOR EXCESSIVELY WORN REAR WHEEL BEARING; SEE "DIAGNOSTIC AIDS" • IS ALL OK?
YES
NO
REPAIR AS NECESSARY.
8
• REPLACE SPEED SENSOR • CLEAR DTCs, IGNITION "OFF." • DISCONNECT TECH 1, IF CONNECTED. • ROAD TEST VEHICLE, REACHING AT LEAST 25 km/h (15 MPH). • DOES DTC 35 RESET?
YES
NO
REPLACE EBTCM.
SYSTEM OK; SEE "DIAGNOSTIC AIDS"

GC4029300565020X

Fig. 132 Code 35: Left Rear Wheel Speed Sensor Malfunction. 1993-94 Fleetwood (RWD)

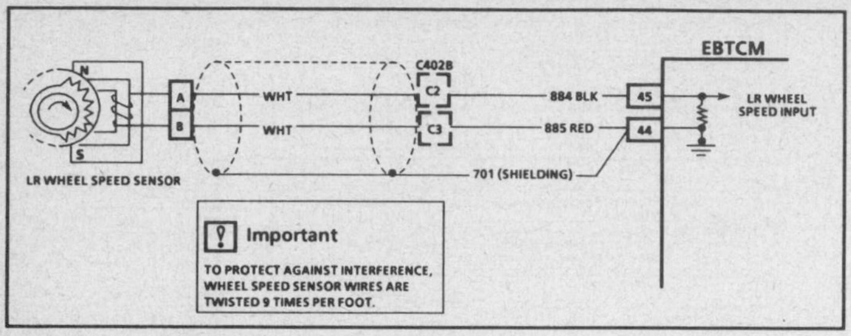

EBTCM
C402B
WHT
WHT
884 BLK
885 RED
45
44
LR WHEEL SPEED INPUT
701 (SHIELDING)
LR WHEEL SPEED SENSOR
Important
TO PROTECT AGAINST INTERFERENCE, WHEEL SPEED SENSOR WIRES ARE TWISTED 9 TIMES PER FOOT.

DTC 37

LR WHEEL SPEED SENSOR CONTINUITY MALFUNCTION

Circuit Description:

The toothed wheel generates a voltage pulse as it moves past the sensor; each tooth-gap-tooth series on the wheel generates these pulses. The frequency of these pulses is used by the EBTCM to determine wheel speed. The amount of voltage generated in each pulse depends on the air gap between the sensor and the toothed wheel, and on wheel speed.

The "ANTI-LOCK" and "TRACTION CONTROL" indicators will be "ON" and DTC 37 is set if there is a short to voltage or an open in CKT 885 or 884, or a malfunctioning speed sensor. The testing for this malfunction occurs with the ignition "ON" and the vehicle at rest.

Test Description: Number(s) below refer to circled number(s) on the diagnostic chart.

1. Checks for proper resistance in the sensor itself.
2. Checks for a short to battery in either of the speed sensor circuit wires.
3. Checks for an open in both the speed sensor circuit wires.
4. Manipulates wiring and connectors, trying to induce an intermittent malfunction not currently present.
5. This test checks if the DTC resets on key-up. If so, since Tests 1-4 have validated that the circuitry and components are good, the speed sensor may be causing the malfunction.
6. Checks if DTC 35 sets during a road test.
7. DTC 37 sets when the vehicle is at rest; DTC 35 sets with a problem in the speed sensor circuitry with the vehicle in motion. If problems are still present, DTC 35 would set during the road test, not a 37. If the DTC 35 sets at this point, the DTC 35 diagnostics should be used.
8. The wheel speed sensor may be causing an intermittent malfunction. If DTC 37 resets after sensor replacement, the EBTCM must be concluding there is a problem present in the speed sensor circuit when there is not.

Diagnostic Aids:

Be sure the speed sensor wiring is properly routed and retained. This will help prevent false signals due to electrical noise being picked up by the wiring.

It is very important that a thorough inspection of the wiring and connectors be performed. Failure to carefully and fully inspect wiring and connectors may result in misdiagnosis, causing part replacement with reappearance of the malfunction.

GC4029300566010X

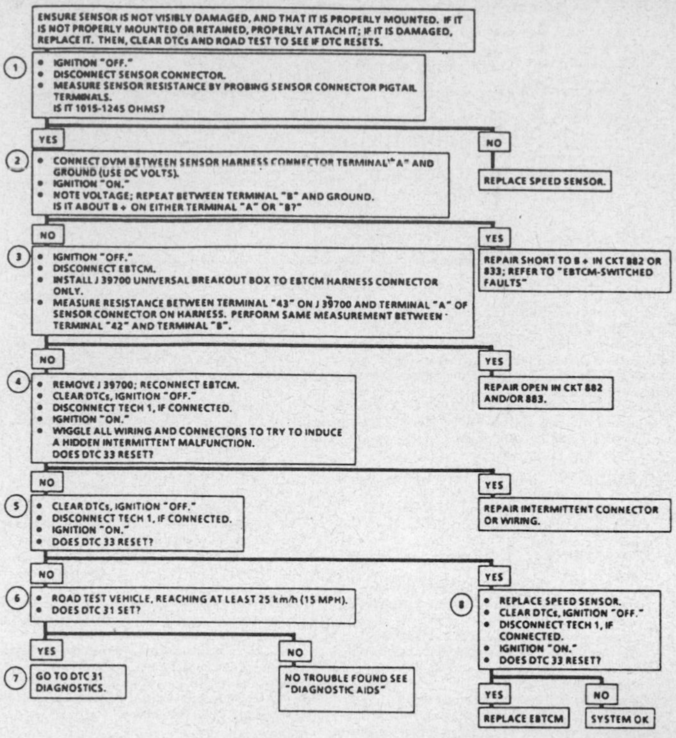

ENSURE SENSOR IS NOT VISIBLY DAMAGED, AND THAT IT IS PROPERLY MOUNTED. IF IT IS NOT PROPERLY MOUNTED OR RETAINED, PROPERLY ATTACH IT; IF IT IS DAMAGED, REPLACE IT. THEN, CLEAR DTCs AND ROAD TEST TO SEE IF DTC RESETS.
1
IGNITION "OFF." DISCONNECT SENSOR CONNECTOR. MEASURE SENSOR RESISTANCE BY PROBING SENSOR CONNECTOR PIGTAIL TERMINALS. IS IT 1015-1245 OHMS?
YES
NO
REPLACE SPEED SENSOR.
2
CONNECT DVM BETWEEN SENSOR HARNESS CONNECTOR TERMINAL "A" AND GROUND (USE DC VOLTS). IGNITION "ON." NOTE VOLTAGE; REPEAT BETWEEN TERMINAL "B" AND GROUND. IS IT ABOUT B+ ON EITHER TERMINAL "A" OR "B"?
NO
YES
REPAIR SHORT TO B+ IN CKT 882 OR 833; REFER TO "EBTCM-SWITCHED FAULTS"
3
IGNITION "OFF." DISCONNECT EBTCM. INSTALL J 39700 UNIVERSAL BREAKOUT BOX TO EBTCM HARNESS CONNECTOR ONLY. MEASURE RESISTANCE BETWEEN TERMINAL "43" ON J 39700 AND TERMINAL "A" OF SENSOR CONNECTOR ON HARNESS. PERFORM SAME MEASUREMENT BETWEEN TERMINAL "42" AND TERMINAL "B".
NO
YES
REPAIR OPEN IN CKT 882 AND/OR 883.
4
REMOVE J 39700; RECONNECT EBTCM. CLEAR DTCs, IGNITION "OFF." DISCONNECT TECH 1, IF CONNECTED. IGNITION "ON." WIGGLE ALL WIRING AND CONNECTORS TO TRY TO INDUCE A HIDDEN INTERMITTENT MALFUNCTION. DOES DTC 33 RESET?
NO
YES
REPAIR INTERMITTENT CONNECTOR OR WIRING.
5
CLEAR DTCs, IGNITION "OFF." DISCONNECT TECH 1, IF CONNECTED. IGNITION "ON." DOES DTC 33 RESET?
NO
YES
6
ROAD TEST VEHICLE, REACHING AT LEAST 25 km/h (15 MPH). DOES DTC 31 SET?
8
REPLACE SPEED SENSOR. CLEAR DTCs, IGNITION "OFF." DISCONNECT TECH 1, IF CONNECTED. IGNITION "ON." DOES DTC 33 RESET?
YES
NO
7
GO TO DTC 31 DIAGNOSTICS.
NO TROUBLE FOUND SEE "DIAGNOSTIC AIDS"
YES
NO
REPLACE EBTCM
SYSTEM OK

GC4029300566020X

Fig. 133 Code 36: Left Rear Wheel Speed Sensor Continuity Malfunction. 1993-94 Fleetwood (RWD)

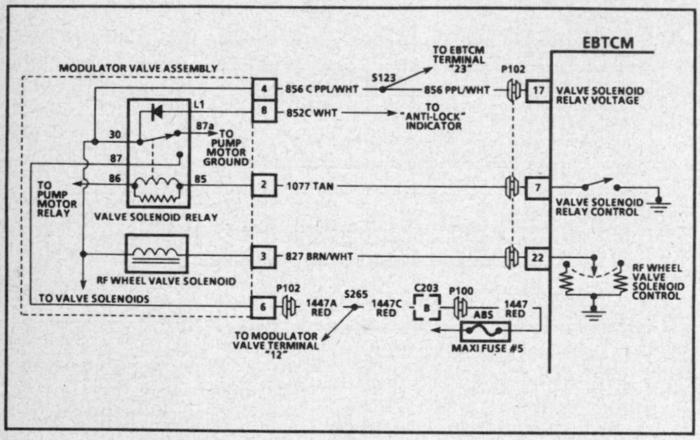

EBTCM
MODULATOR VALVE ASSEMBLY
TO EBTCM TERMINAL "23"
S123
P102
4
856 C PPL/WHT
856 PPL/WHT
17
VALVE SOLENOID RELAY VOLTAGE
8
852C WHT
TO "ANTI-LOCK" INDICATOR
L1
87a
TO PUMP MOTOR GROUND
30
87
86
85
2
1077 TAN
7
VALVE SOLENOID RELAY CONTROL
TO PUMP MOTOR RELAY
VALVE SOLENOID RELAY
3
827 BRN/WHT
22
RF WHEEL VALVE SOLENOID CONTROL
RF WHEEL VALVE SOLENOID
TO VALVE SOLENOIDS
6
P102
1447A RED
S265
1447C RED
C203
P100
ABS
1447 RED
TO MODULATOR VALVE TERMINAL "12"
MAXI FUSE #5

DTC 41

RF VALVE SOLENOID MALFUNCTION

Circuit Description:

The wheel valve solenoid circuits are supplied with battery power when the ignition is "ON." The EBTCM controls the valve functions by permitting one of three levels of current flow (0, 2.5, 5 amps) to the solenoid.

If the EBTCM senses a discrepancy such as an open or ground in the circuit, the valve solenoid relay will turn "OFF," the "ANTI-LOCK" and "TRACTION CONTROL" lights will come "ON," and DTC 41 will set.

Test Description: Number(s) below refer to circled number(s) on the diagnostic chart.

1. Checks the integrity of CKTs 827 and 856, the RF valve solenoid circuitry internal to the modulator valve assembly, and the RF valve solenoid coil.
2. Checks for a short to battery in CKT 827, using EBTCM terminal "3" as ground.
3. Checks for a short to ground in CKT 827, using EBTCM terminal "3" as ground.
4. Checks wiring and connectors for intermittents.
5. Uses the Tech 1 to exercise the RF valve solenoid and check it for proper operation.
6. Determines whether the DTC was set by an intermittent condition or an EBTCM malfunction.
7. Determines whether a problem found in Step 1 is due to an open in CKT 827 or a malfunctioning modulator valve assembly.

Diagnostic Aids:

All tests using J 39700 Universal Breakout Box terminal "3" are using the terminal as ground. These tests, of course, assume that the ground at terminal "3" is good.

If DTCs 41 and 45 are both set the malfunction is likely to be a short to B + on CKT 827.

If DTCs 41 and 55 are both set the malfunction is likely to be a short to B + on CKT 828.

GC4029300567010X

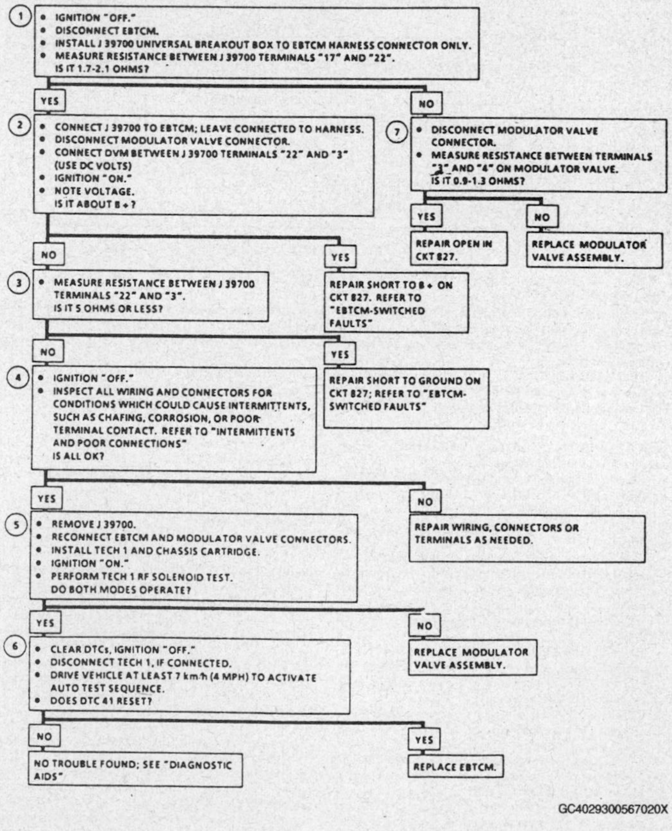

1
IGNITION "OFF." DISCONNECT EBTCM. INSTALL J 39700 UNIVERSAL BREAKOUT BOX TO EBTCM HARNESS CONNECTOR ONLY. MEASURE RESISTANCE BETWEEN J 39700 TERMINALS "17" AND "22". IS IT 1.7-2.1 OHMS?
YES
NO
2
CONNECT J 39700 TO EBTCM; LEAVE CONNECTED TO HARNESS. DISCONNECT MODULATOR VALVE CONNECTOR. CONNECT DVM BETWEEN J 39700 TERMINALS "22" AND "3" (USE DC VOLTS) IGNITION "ON." NOTE VOLTAGE. IS IT ABOUT B+?
7
DISCONNECT MODULATOR VALVE CONNECTOR. MEASURE RESISTANCE BETWEEN TERMINALS "3" AND "4" ON MODULATOR VALVE. IS IT 0.9-1.3 OHMS?
YES
NO
REPAIR OPEN IN CKT 827.
REPLACE MODULATOR VALVE ASSEMBLY.
NO
YES
3
MEASURE RESISTANCE BETWEEN J 39700 TERMINALS "22" AND "3". IS IT 5 OHMS OR LESS?
REPAIR SHORT TO B+ ON CKT 827. REFER TO "EBTCM-SWITCHED FAULTS"
NO
YES
4
IGNITION "OFF." INSPECT ALL WIRING AND CONNECTORS FOR CONDITIONS WHICH COULD CAUSE INTERMITTENTS, SUCH AS CHAFING, CORROSION, OR POOR TERMINAL CONTACT. REFER TO "INTERMITTENTS AND POOR CONNECTIONS" IS ALL OK?
REPAIR SHORT TO GROUND ON CKT 827; REFER TO "EBTCM-SWITCHED FAULTS"
YES
NO
5
REMOVE J 39700. RECONNECT EBTCM AND MODULATOR VALVE CONNECTORS. INSTALL TECH 1 AND CHASSIS CARTRIDGE. IGNITION "ON." PERFORM TECH 1 RF SOLENOID TEST. DO BOTH MODES OPERATE?
REPAIR WIRING, CONNECTORS OR TERMINALS AS NEEDED.
YES
NO
6
CLEAR DTCs, IGNITION "OFF." DISCONNECT TECH 1, IF CONNECTED. DRIVE VEHICLE AT LEAST 7 km/h (4 MPH) TO ACTIVATE AUTO TEST SEQUENCE. DOES DTC 41 RESET?
REPLACE MODULATOR VALVE ASSEMBLY.
NO
YES
NO TROUBLE FOUND; SEE "DIAGNOSTIC AIDS"
REPLACE EBTCM.

GC4029300567020X

Fig. 134 Code 41: Right Front Valve Solenoid Malfunction. 1993-94 Fleetwood (RWD)

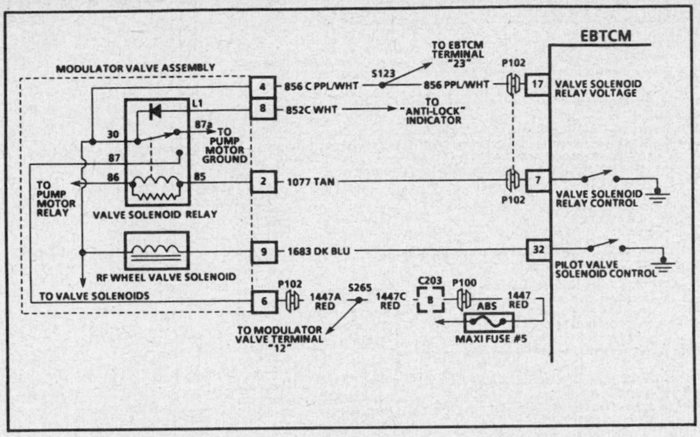

EBTCM
MODULATOR VALVE ASSEMBLY
TO EBTCM TERMINAL "23"
S123
P102
4 856 C PPL/WHT
856 PPL/WHT
17 VALVE SOLENOID RELAY VOLTAGE
8 852C WHT
TO "ANTI-LOCK" INDICATOR
L1
30
87a TO PUMP MOTOR GROUND
87
86
85
TO PUMP MOTOR RELAY
2 1077 TAN
7 VALVE SOLENOID RELAY CONTROL
VALVE SOLENOID RELAY
9 1683 DK BLU
32 PILOT VALVE SOLENOID CONTROL
RF WHEEL VALVE SOLENOID
TO VALVE SOLENOIDS
6 1447A RED
S265
1447C RED
C203
P100
1447 RED
ABS
MAXI FUSE #5
TO MODULATOR VALVE TERMINAL "12"

DTC 44

PILOT VALVE SOLENOID MALFUNCTION

Circuit Description:

The pilot valve solenoid circuit is supplied with battery power when the ignition is "ON." The EBTCM controls the valve by grounding the circuit when necessary.

If the EBTCM senses a discrepancy such as an open or ground in the circuit, the valve solenoid relay will turn "OFF," the "ANTI-LOCK" and "TRACTION CONTROL" lights will come "ON," and DTC 44 will set.

Test Description: Number(s) below refer to circled number(s) on the diagnostic chart.

1. Checks the integrity of CKTs 1683 and 1077, the pilot valve solenoid circuitry internal to the modulator valve assembly, and the pilot valve solenoid coil.
2. Checks for a short to battery in CKT 1683, using EBTCM terminal "3" as ground.
3. Checks for a short to ground in CKT 1683, using EBTCM terminal "3" as ground.
4. Checks for connector or wiring problems which could cause intermittents.
5. Uses the Tech 1 to exercise the pilot valve solenoid and check it for proper operation.
6. Determines whether the DTC was set by an intermittent condition or an EBTCM malfunction.
7. Determines whether a problem found in Step 1 is due to an open in CKT 1683 or a malfunctioning modulator valve assembly.

Diagnostic Aids:

All tests using J 39700 Universal Breakout Box terminal "3" are using the terminal as ground. These tests, of course, assume that the ground at terminal "3" is good.

GC4029300568010X

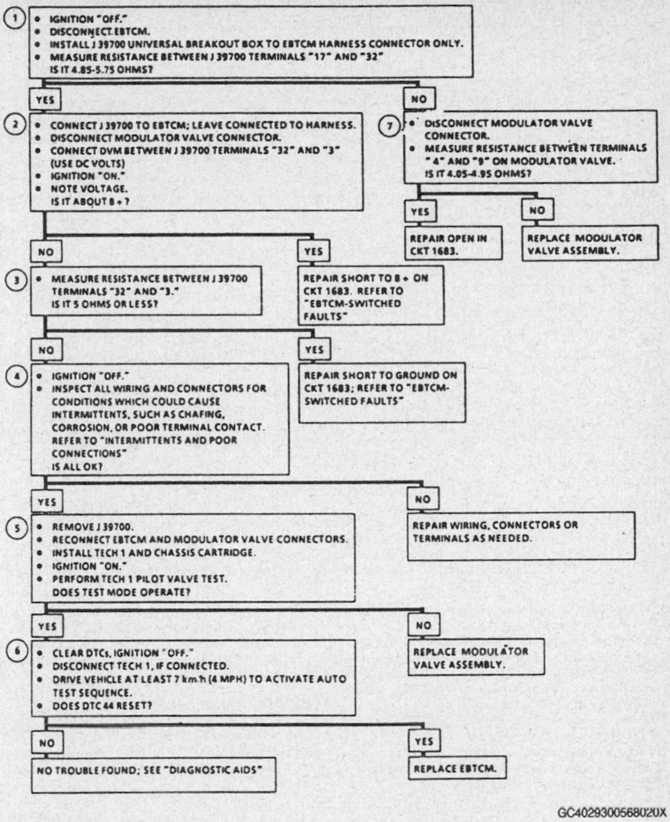

1 • IGNITION "OFF."
• DISCONNECT EBTCM.
• INSTALL J 39700 UNIVERSAL BREAKOUT BOX TO EBTCM HARNESS CONNECTOR ONLY.
• MEASURE RESISTANCE BETWEEN J 39700 TERMINALS "17" AND "32"
IS IT 4.85-5.75 OHMS?
YES
NO
2 • CONNECT J 39700 TO EBTCM; LEAVE CONNECTED TO HARNESS.
• DISCONNECT MODULATOR VALVE CONNECTOR.
• CONNECT DVM BETWEEN J 39700 TERMINALS "32" AND "3" (USE DC VOLTS)
• IGNITION "ON."
• NOTE VOLTAGE.
IS IT ABOUT B+?
7 • DISCONNECT MODULATOR VALVE CONNECTOR.
• MEASURE RESISTANCE BETWEEN TERMINALS "4" AND "9" ON MODULATOR VALVE.
IS IT 4.05-4.95 OHMS?
YES
NO
REPAIR OPEN IN CKT 1683.
REPLACE MODULATOR VALVE ASSEMBLY.
NO
YES
3 • MEASURE RESISTANCE BETWEEN J 39700 TERMINALS "32" AND "3."
IS IT 5 OHMS OR LESS?
REPAIR SHORT TO B+ ON CKT 1683. REFER TO "EBTCM-SWITCHED FAULTS"
NO
YES
4 • IGNITION "OFF."
• INSPECT ALL WIRING AND CONNECTORS FOR CONDITIONS WHICH COULD CAUSE INTERMITTENTS, SUCH AS CHAFING, CORROSION, OR POOR TERMINAL CONTACT. REFER TO "INTERMITTENTS AND POOR CONNECTIONS"
IS ALL OK?
REPAIR SHORT TO GROUND ON CKT 1683; REFER TO "EBTCM-SWITCHED FAULTS"
YES
NO
5 • REMOVE J 39700.
• RECONNECT EBTCM AND MODULATOR VALVE CONNECTORS.
• INSTALL TECH 1 AND CHASSIS CARTRIDGE.
• IGNITION "ON."
• PERFORM TECH 1 PILOT VALVE TEST.
DOES TEST MODE OPERATE?
REPAIR WIRING, CONNECTORS OR TERMINALS AS NEEDED.
YES
NO
6 • CLEAR DTCs, IGNITION "OFF."
• DISCONNECT TECH 1, IF CONNECTED.
• DRIVE VEHICLE AT LEAST 7 km/h (4 MPH) TO ACTIVATE AUTO TEST SEQUENCE.
• DOES DTC 44 RESET?
REPLACE MODULATOR VALVE ASSEMBLY.
NO
YES
NO TROUBLE FOUND; SEE "DIAGNOSTIC AIDS"
REPLACE EBTCM.

GC4029300568020X

Fig. 135 Code 44: Pilot Valve Solenoid Malfunction. 1993-94 Fleetwood (RWD)

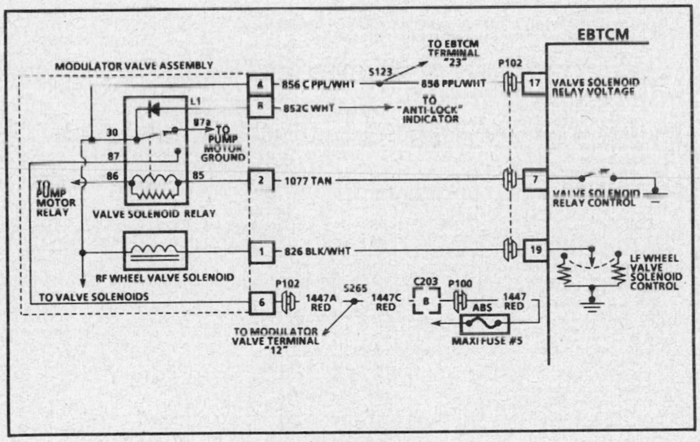

EBTCM
MODULATOR VALVE ASSEMBLY
TO EBTCM TERMINAL "23"
S123
P102
4 856 C PPL/WHT
856 PPL/WHT
17 VALVE SOLENOID RELAY VOLTAGE
8 852C WHT
TO "ANTI-LOCK" INDICATOR
L1
30
87a TO PUMP MOTOR GROUND
87
86
85
TO PUMP MOTOR RELAY
2 1077 TAN
7 VALVE SOLENOID RELAY CONTROL
VALVE SOLENOID RELAY
1 826 BLK/WHT
19 LF WHEEL VALVE SOLENOID CONTROL
RF WHEEL VALVE SOLENOID
TO VALVE SOLENOIDS
6 1447A RED
S265
1447C RED
C203
P100
1447 RED
ABS
MAXI FUSE #5
TO MODULATOR VALVE TERMINAL "12"

DTC 45

LF VALVE SOLENOID MALFUNCTION

Circuit Description:

The wheel valve solenoid circuits are supplied with battery power when the ignition is "ON." The EBTCM controls the valve functions by permitting one of three levels of current flow (0, 2.5, 5 amps) to the solenoid.

If the EBTCM senses a discrepancy such as an open or ground in the circuit, the valve solenoid relay will turn "OFF," the "ANTI-LOCK" and "TRACTION CONTROL" lights will come "ON," and DTC 45 will set.

Test Description: Number(s) below refer to circled number(s) on the diagnostic chart.

1. Checks the integrity of CKTs 826 and 1077, the LF valve solenoid circuitry internal to the modulator valve assembly, and the LF valve solenoid coil.
2. Checks for a short to battery in CKT 826, using EBTCM terminal "3" as ground.
3. Checks for a short to ground in CKT 826, using EBTCM terminal "3" as ground.
4. Checks wiring and connectors for intermittents.
5. Uses the Tech 1 to exercise the LF valve solenoid and check it for proper operation.
6. Determines whether the DTC was set by an intermittent condition or an EBTCM malfunction.
7. Determines whether a problem found in Step 1 is due to an open in CKT 826 or a malfunctioning modulator valve assembly.

Diagnostic Aids:

All tests using J 39700 Universal Breakout Box terminal "3" are using the terminal as ground. These tests, of course, assume that the ground at terminal "3" is good.

If DTCs 41 and 45 are both set, the malfunction is likely to be a short to B+ on CKT 826.

GC4029300569010X

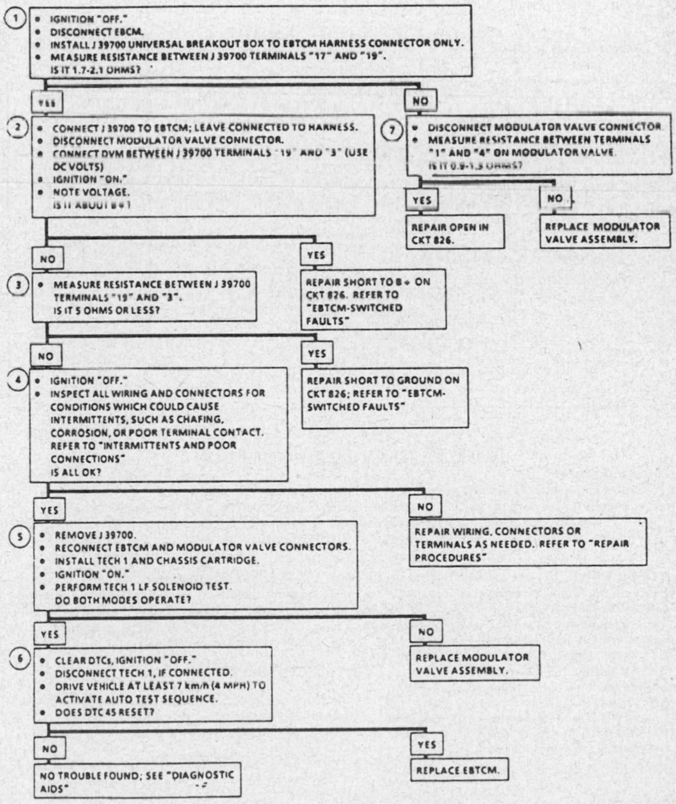

1 • IGNITION "OFF."
• DISCONNECT EBCM.
• INSTALL J 39700 UNIVERSAL BREAKOUT BOX TO EBTCM HARNESS CONNECTOR ONLY.
• MEASURE RESISTANCE BETWEEN J 39700 TERMINALS "17" AND "19".
IS IT 1.7-2.1 OHMS?
NO
2 • CONNECT J 39700 TO EBTCM; LEAVE CONNECTED TO HARNESS.
• DISCONNECT MODULATOR VALVE CONNECTOR.
• NOTE VOLTAGE.
7 • DISCONNECT MODULATOR VALVE CONNECTOR
• MEASURE RESISTANCE BETWEEN TERMINALS "1" AND "4" ON MODULATOR VALVE.
YES
NO
REPAIR OPEN IN CKT 826.
REPLACE MODULATOR VALVE ASSEMBLY.
NO
YES
3 • MEASURE RESISTANCE BETWEEN J 39700 TERMINALS "19" AND "3".
IS IT 5 OHMS OR LESS?
REPAIR SHORT TO B+ ON CKT 826. REFER TO "EBTCM-SWITCHED FAULTS"
NO
YES
4 • IGNITION "OFF."
• INSPECT ALL WIRING AND CONNECTORS FOR CONDITIONS WHICH COULD CAUSE INTERMITTENTS, SUCH AS CHAFING, CORROSION, OR POOR TERMINAL CONTACT. REFER TO "INTERMITTENTS AND POOR CONNECTIONS"
IS ALL OK?
REPAIR SHORT TO GROUND ON CKT 826; REFER TO "EBTCM-SWITCHED FAULTS"
YES
NO
5 • REMOVE J 39700.
• RECONNECT EBTCM AND MODULATOR VALVE CONNECTORS.
• INSTALL TECH 1 AND CHASSIS CARTRIDGE.
• IGNITION "ON."
• PERFORM TECH 1 LF SOLENOID TEST.
DO BOTH MODES OPERATE?
REPAIR WIRING, CONNECTORS OR TERMINALS AS NEEDED. REFER TO "REPAIR PROCEDURES"
YES
NO
6 • CLEAR DTCs, IGNITION "OFF."
• DISCONNECT TECH 1, IF CONNECTED.
• DRIVE VEHICLE AT LEAST 7 km/h (4 MPH) TO ACTIVATE AUTO TEST SEQUENCE.
• DOES DTC 45 RESET?
REPLACE MODULATOR VALVE ASSEMBLY.
NO
YES
NO TROUBLE FOUND; SEE "DIAGNOSTIC AIDS"
REPLACE EBTCM.

GC4029300569020X

Fig. 136 Code 45: Left Front Valve Solenoid Malfunction. 1993-94 Fleetwood (RWD)

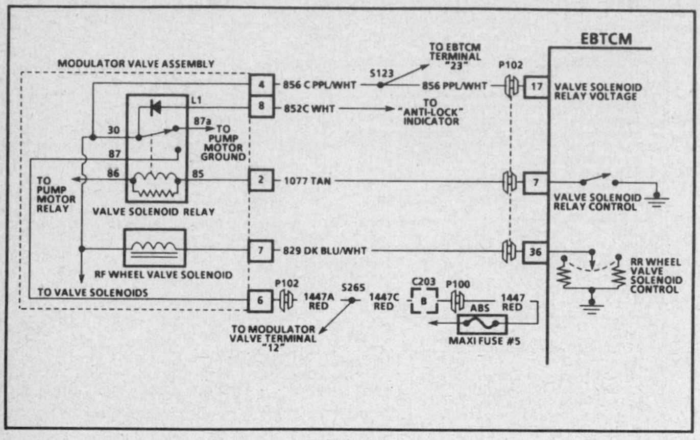
EBTCM
MODULATOR VALVE ASSEMBLY
TO EBTCM TERMINAL "23"
S123
P102
856 C PPL/WHT
856 PPL/WHT
VALVE SOLENOID RELAY VOLTAGE
852C WHT
TO "ANTI-LOCK" INDICATOR
L1
30
87
87a
86
85
TO PUMP MOTOR GROUND
TO PUMP MOTOR RELAY
VALVE SOLENOID RELAY
1077 TAN
VALVE SOLENOID RELAY CONTROL
829 DK BLU/WHT
RR WHEEL VALVE SOLENOID CONTROL
RF WHEEL VALVE SOLENOID
TO VALVE SOLENOIDS
S265
C203
P100
1447A RED
1447C RED
1447 RED
ABS
MAXI FUSE #5
TO MODULATOR VALVE TERMINAL "12"

DTC 51

RR VALVE SOLENOID MALFUNCTION

Circuit Description:

The wheel valve solenoid circuits are supplied with battery power when the ignition is "ON." The EBTCM controls the valve functions by permitting one of three levels of current flow (0, 2.5, 5 amps) to the solenoid.

If the EBTCM senses a discrepancy such as an open or ground in the circuit, the valve solenoid relay will turn "OFF," the "ANTI-LOCK" and "TRACTION CONTROL" lights will come "ON," and DTC 51 will set.

Test Description: Number(s) below refer to circled number(s) on the diagnostic chart.

1. Checks the integrity of CKTs 829 and 856, the RR valve solenoid circuitry internal to the modulator valve assembly, and the RR valve solenoid coil.
2. Checks for a short to battery in CKT 829, using EBTCM terminal "3" as ground.
3. Checks for a short to ground in CKT 829, using EBTCM terminal "3" as ground.
4. Checks wiring and connectors for intermittents.
5. Uses the Tech 1 to exercise the RR valve solenoid and check it for proper operation.
6. Determines whether the DTC was set by an intermittent condition or an EBTCM malfunction.
7. Determines whether a problem found in Step 1 is due to an open in CKT 829 or a malfunctioning modulator valve assembly.

Diagnostic Aids:

All tests using J 39700 Universal Breakout Box terminal "3" are using the terminal as ground. These tests, of course, assume that the ground at terminal "3" is good.

GC4029300570010X

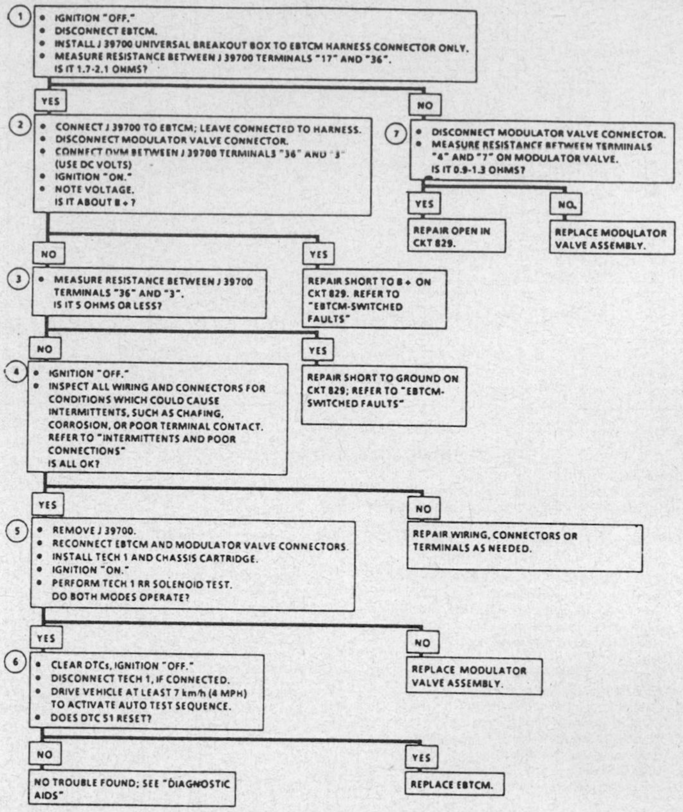
1
• IGNITION "OFF."
• DISCONNECT EBTCM.
• INSTALL J 39700 UNIVERSAL BREAKOUT BOX TO EBTCM HARNESS CONNECTOR ONLY.
• MEASURE RESISTANCE BETWEEN J 39700 TERMINALS "17" AND "36".
IS IT 1.7-2.1 OHMS?
YES
NO
2
• CONNECT J 39700 TO EBTCM; LEAVE CONNECTED TO HARNESS.
• DISCONNECT MODULATOR VALVE CONNECTOR.
• CONNECT DVM BETWEEN J 39700 TERMINALS "36" AND "3"
(USE DC VOLTS)
• IGNITION "ON."
• NOTE VOLTAGE.
IS IT ABOUT B+?
7
• DISCONNECT MODULATOR VALVE CONNECTOR.
• MEASURE RESISTANCE BETWEEN TERMINALS "4" AND "7" ON MODULATOR VALVE.
IS IT 0.9-1.3 OHMS?
YES
NO
REPAIR OPEN IN CKT 829.
REPLACE MODULATOR VALVE ASSEMBLY.
NO
YES
3
• MEASURE RESISTANCE BETWEEN J 39700 TERMINALS "36" AND "3".
IS IT 5 OHMS OR LESS?
REPAIR SHORT TO B+ ON CKT 829. REFER TO "EBTCM-SWITCHED FAULTS"
NO
YES
4
• IGNITION "OFF."
• INSPECT ALL WIRING AND CONNECTORS FOR CONDITIONS WHICH COULD CAUSE INTERMITTENTS, SUCH AS CHAFING, CORROSION, OR POOR TERMINAL CONTACT. REFER TO "INTERMITTENTS AND POOR CONNECTIONS"
IS ALL OK?
REPAIR SHORT TO GROUND ON CKT 829; REFER TO "EBTCM-SWITCHED FAULTS"
YES
NO
5
• REMOVE J 39700.
• RECONNECT EBTCM AND MODULATOR VALVE CONNECTORS.
• INSTALL TECH 1 AND CHASSIS CARTRIDGE.
• IGNITION "ON."
• PERFORM TECH 1 RR SOLENOID TEST.
DO BOTH MODES OPERATE?
REPAIR WIRING, CONNECTORS OR TERMINALS AS NEEDED.
YES
NO
6
• CLEAR DTCs, IGNITION "OFF."
• DISCONNECT TECH 1, IF CONNECTED.
• DRIVE VEHICLE AT LEAST 7 km/h (4 MPH) TO ACTIVATE AUTO TEST SEQUENCE.
• DOES DTC 51 RESET?
REPLACE MODULATOR VALVE ASSEMBLY.
NO
YES
NO TROUBLE FOUND; SEE "DIAGNOSTIC AIDS"
REPLACE EBTCM.

GC4029300570020X

Fig. 137 Code 51: Right Front Valve Solenoid Malfunction. 1993-94 Fleetwood (RWD)

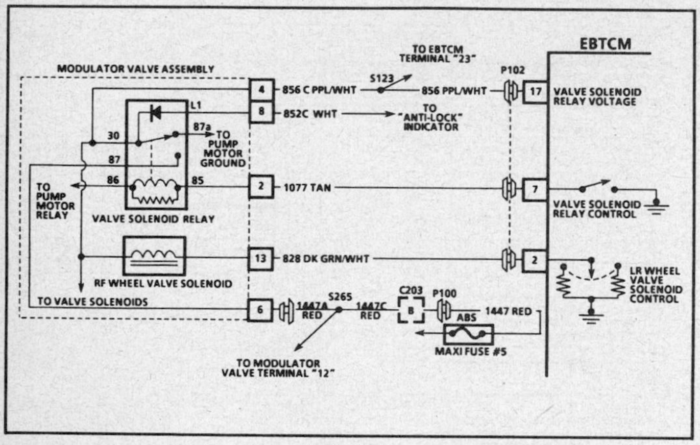
EBTCM
MODULATOR VALVE ASSEMBLY
TO EBTCM TERMINAL "23"
S123
P102
856 C PPL/WHT
856 PPL/WHT
VALVE SOLENOID RELAY VOLTAGE
852C WHT
TO "ANTI-LOCK" INDICATOR
L1
30
87
87a
86
85
TO PUMP MOTOR GROUND
TO PUMP MOTOR RELAY
VALVE SOLENOID RELAY
1077 TAN
VALVE SOLENOID RELAY CONTROL
828 DK GRN/WHT
LR WHEEL VALVE SOLENOID CONTROL
RF WHEEL VALVE SOLENOID
TO VALVE SOLENOIDS
S265
C203
P100
1447A RED
1447C RED
1447 RED
ABS
MAXI FUSE #5
TO MODULATOR VALVE TERMINAL "12"

DTC 55

LR VALVE SOLENOID MALFUNCTION

Circuit Description:

The wheel valve solenoid circuits are supplied with battery power when the ignition is "ON." The EBTCM controls the valve functions by permitting one of three levels of current flow (0, 2.5, 5 amps) to the solenoid.

If the EBTCM senses a discrepancy such as an open or ground in the circuit, the valve solenoid relay will turn "OFF," the "ANTI-LOCK" and "TRACTION CONTROL" lights will come "ON," and DTC 55 will set.

Test Description: Number(s) below refer to circled number(s) on the diagnostic chart.

1. Checks the integrity of CKTs 828 and 856, the LR valve solenoid circuitry internal to the modulator valve assembly, and the LR valve solenoid coil.
2. Checks for a short to battery in CKT 828, using EBTCM terminal "3" as ground.
3. Checks for a short to ground in CKT 828, using EBTCM terminal "3" as ground.
4. Checks wiring and connectors for intermittents.
5. Uses the Tech 1 to exercise the LR valve solenoid and check it for proper operation.
6. Determines whether the DTC was set by an intermittent condition or an EBTCM malfunction.
7. Determines whether a problem found in Step 1 is due to an open in CKT 828 or a malfunctioning modulator valve assembly.

Diagnostic Aids:

All tests using J 39700 Universal Breakout Box terminal "3" are using the terminal as ground. These tests, of course, assume that the ground at terminal "3" is good.

If DTCs 41 and 55 are both set the malfunction is likely to be a short to B+ on CKT 828.

GC4029300571010X

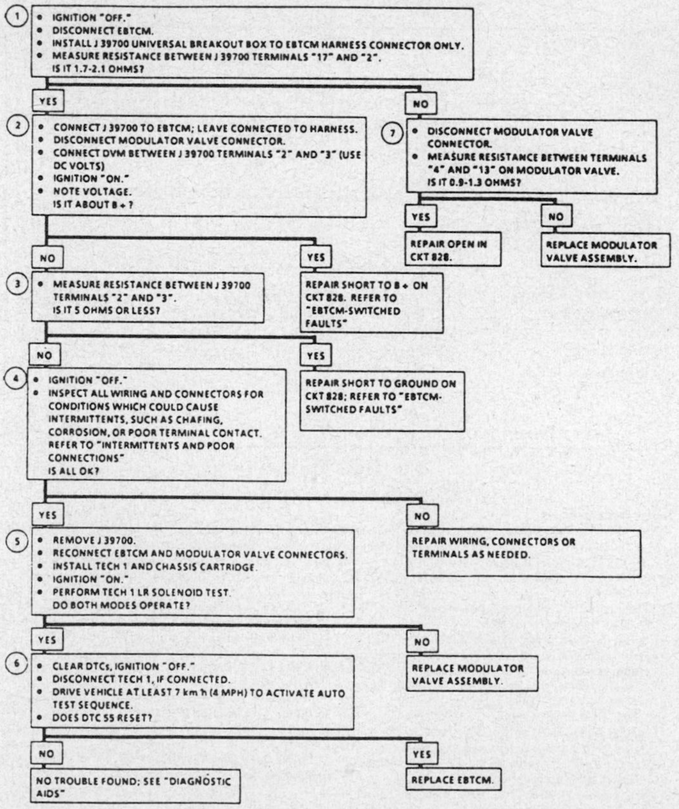
1
• IGNITION "OFF."
• DISCONNECT EBTCM.
• INSTALL J 39700 UNIVERSAL BREAKOUT BOX TO EBTCM HARNESS CONNECTOR ONLY.
• MEASURE RESISTANCE BETWEEN J 39700 TERMINALS "17" AND "2".
IS IT 1.7-2.1 OHMS?
YES
NO
2
• CONNECT J 39700 TO EBTCM; LEAVE CONNECTED TO HARNESS.
• DISCONNECT MODULATOR VALVE CONNECTOR.
• CONNECT DVM BETWEEN J 39700 TERMINALS "2" AND "3" (USE DC VOLTS)
• IGNITION "ON."
• NOTE VOLTAGE.
IS IT ABOUT B+?
7
• DISCONNECT MODULATOR VALVE CONNECTOR.
• MEASURE RESISTANCE BETWEEN TERMINALS "4" AND "13" ON MODULATOR VALVE.
IS IT 0.9-1.3 OHMS?
YES
NO
REPAIR OPEN IN CKT 828.
REPLACE MODULATOR VALVE ASSEMBLY.
NO
YES
3
• MEASURE RESISTANCE BETWEEN J 39700 TERMINALS "2" AND "3".
IS IT 5 OHMS OR LESS?
REPAIR SHORT TO B+ ON CKT 828. REFER TO "EBTCM-SWITCHED FAULTS"
NO
YES
4
• IGNITION "OFF."
• INSPECT ALL WIRING AND CONNECTORS FOR CONDITIONS WHICH COULD CAUSE INTERMITTENTS, SUCH AS CHAFING, CORROSION, OR POOR TERMINAL CONTACT. REFER TO "INTERMITTENTS AND POOR CONNECTIONS"
IS ALL OK?
REPAIR SHORT TO GROUND ON CKT 828; REFER TO "EBTCM-SWITCHED FAULTS"
YES
NO
5
• REMOVE J 39700.
• RECONNECT EBTCM AND MODULATOR VALVE CONNECTORS.
• INSTALL TECH 1 AND CHASSIS CARTRIDGE.
• IGNITION "ON."
• PERFORM TECH 1 LR SOLENOID TEST.
DO BOTH MODES OPERATE?
REPAIR WIRING, CONNECTORS OR TERMINALS AS NEEDED.
YES
NO
6
• CLEAR DTCs, IGNITION "OFF."
• DISCONNECT TECH 1, IF CONNECTED.
• DRIVE VEHICLE AT LEAST 7 km/h (4 MPH) TO ACTIVATE AUTO TEST SEQUENCE.
• DOES DTC 55 RESET?
REPLACE MODULATOR VALVE ASSEMBLY.
NO
YES
NO TROUBLE FOUND; SEE "DIAGNOSTIC AIDS"
REPLACE EBTCM.

GC4029300571020X

Fig. 138 Code 55: Left Rear Valve Solenoid Malfunction. 1993-94 Fleetwood (RWD)

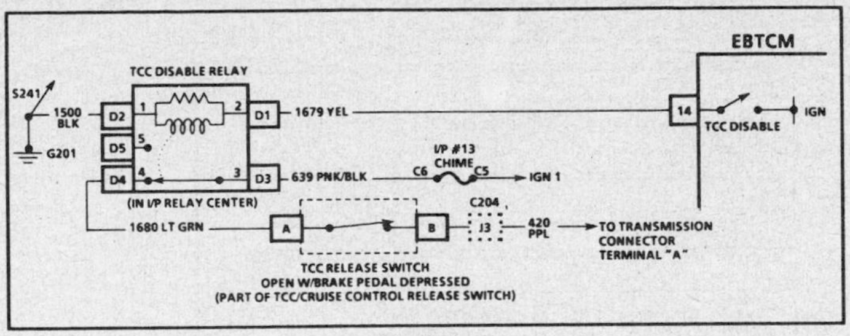
EBTCM
TCC DISABLE RELAY
S241
1500 BLK
G201
D2
D5
D4
D1
D3
1679 YEL
639 PNK/BLK
I/P #13 CHIME
C6
C5
IGN 1
14
TCC DISABLE
IGN
(IN I/P RELAY CENTER)
1680 LT GRN
A
B
C204
J3
420 PPL
TO TRANSMISSION CONNECTOR TERMINAL "A"
TCC RELEASE SWITCH
OPEN W/BRAKE PEDAL DEPRESSED
(PART OF TCC/CRUISE CONTROL RELEASE SWITCH)

DTC 57

TCC DISABLE RELAY OUTPUT MALFUNCTION

Circuit Description:

The TCC disable relay output circuit is used to open the TCC circuit to the automatic transmission when a TCS event occurs. The EBTCM energizes the relay coil by grounding CKT 1679 at EBTCM terminal "14". This opens the switch between contacts "D3" and "D4" of of the TCC disable relay, opening the TCC circuit to the automatic transmission; this has the same effect as the driver depressing the brake pedal, opening the circuit via the TCC release switch.

The "TRACTION CONTROL" lamp will come "ON" and DTC 57 will set if CKT 1679 remains high when the EBTCM requests energization of the relay coil (by grounding EBTCM terminal "14"), which should take the circuit low.

Test Description: Number(s) below refer to circled number(s) on the diagnostic chart.

1. Checks for a blown I/P #13, Chime fuse, which would cause the relay to be inoperative.
2. Checks the relay coil for proper resistance.
3. Checks for a good ground CKT 1500 and G201 connection.
4. Checks for an open in CKT 639, since fuse is OK.
5. Checks for an open in CKT 1679 to ensure relay coil can receive EBTCM ground when needed.
6. Checks for intermittents and poor connections as the cause of the DTC, since the relay, power and ground circuits all check OK. If wiring checks out the EBTCM is either malfunctioning on terminal "14", or is determining there is a problem with the TCC disable output when there is not.
7. Replaces bad fuse found in Step 1 and checks for the fuse blowing again.
8. Checks for a short to ground in CKT 639 causing the fuse to blow.
9. Checks CKTs 1680 and 420 together for a short to ground, since they are connected until the brake pedal is depressed.
10. Checks for internal shorting in the relay itself between power and ground points.
11. Checks for an intermittent short to ground as the cause of the DTC, since all else checks out OK.

Diagnostic Aids:

If the TCC never engages, the fault is likely a short to ground in CKT 1679.

GC4029300572010X

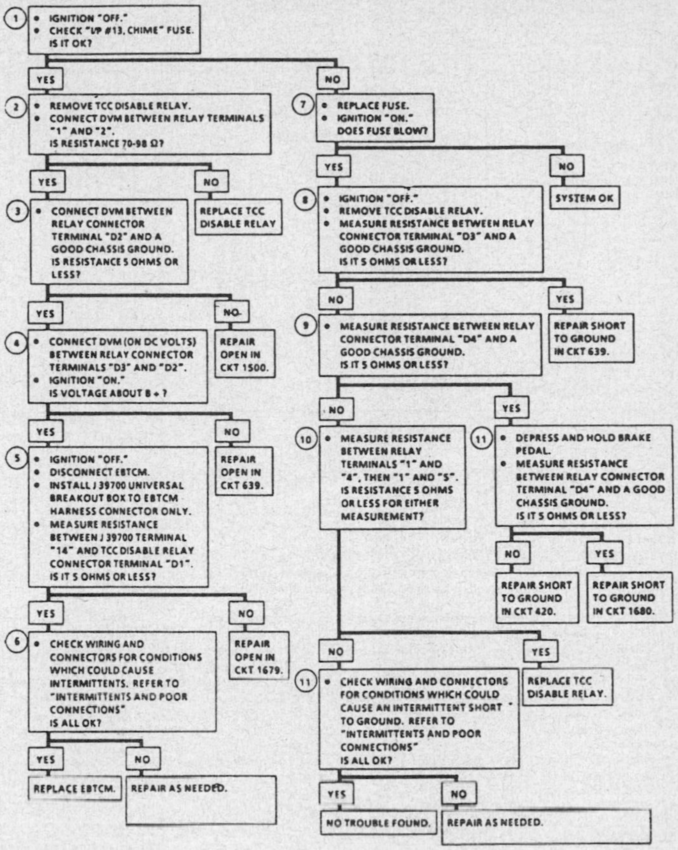
1 • IGNITION "OFF." • CHECK "I/P #13, CHIME" FUSE. IS IT OK?
YES
NO
2 • REMOVE TCC DISABLE RELAY. • CONNECT DVM BETWEEN RELAY TERMINALS "1" AND "2". IS RESISTANCE 70-98 Ω?
7 • REPLACE FUSE. • IGNITION "ON." DOES FUSE BLOW?
YES
NO
YES
NO
REPLACE TCC DISABLE RELAY
SYSTEM OK
3 • CONNECT DVM BETWEEN RELAY CONNECTOR TERMINAL "D2" AND A GOOD CHASSIS GROUND. IS RESISTANCE 5 OHMS OR LESS?
8 • IGNITION "OFF." • REMOVE TCC DISABLE RELAY. • MEASURE RESISTANCE BETWEEN RELAY CONNECTOR TERMINAL "D3" AND A GOOD CHASSIS GROUND. IS IT 5 OHMS OR LESS?
YES
NO
NO
YES
REPAIR OPEN IN CKT 1500.
4 • CONNECT DVM (ON DC VOLTS) BETWEEN RELAY CONNECTOR TERMINALS "D3" AND "D2". • IGNITION "ON." IS VOLTAGE ABOUT B+?
9 • MEASURE RESISTANCE BETWEEN RELAY CONNECTOR TERMINAL "D4" AND A GOOD CHASSIS GROUND. IS IT 5 OHMS OR LESS?
REPAIR SHORT TO GROUND IN CKT 639.
YES
NO
NO
YES
REPAIR OPEN IN CKT 639.
5 • IGNITION "OFF." • DISCONNECT EBTCM. • INSTALL J 39700 UNIVERSAL BREAKOUT BOX TO EBTCM HARNESS CONNECTOR ONLY. • MEASURE RESISTANCE BETWEEN J 39700 TERMINAL "14" AND TCC DISABLE RELAY CONNECTOR TERMINAL "D1". IS IT 5 OHMS OR LESS?
10 • MEASURE RESISTANCE BETWEEN RELAY TERMINALS "1" AND "4", THEN "1" AND "5". IS RESISTANCE 5 OHMS OR LESS FOR EITHER MEASUREMENT?
11 • DEPRESS AND HOLD BRAKE PEDAL. • MEASURE RESISTANCE BETWEEN RELAY CONNECTOR TERMINAL "D4" AND A GOOD CHASSIS GROUND. IS IT 5 OHMS OR LESS?
NO
YES
REPAIR SHORT TO GROUND IN CKT 420.
REPAIR SHORT TO GROUND IN CKT 1680.
YES
NO
REPAIR OPEN IN CKT 1679.
6 • CHECK WIRING AND CONNECTORS FOR CONDITIONS WHICH COULD CAUSE INTERMITTENTS. REFER TO "INTERMITTENTS AND POOR CONNECTIONS" IS ALL OK?
NO
YES
REPLACE TCC DISABLE RELAY.
11 • CHECK WIRING AND CONNECTORS FOR CONDITIONS WHICH COULD CAUSE AN INTERMITTENT SHORT TO GROUND. REFER TO "INTERMITTENTS AND POOR CONNECTIONS" IS ALL OK?
YES
NO
REPLACE EBTCM.
REPAIR AS NEEDED.
YES
NO
NO TROUBLE FOUND.
REPAIR AS NEEDED.

GC402930057202OX

Fig. 139 Code 57: TCC Disable Relay Output Malfunction. 1993-94 Fleetwood (RWD)

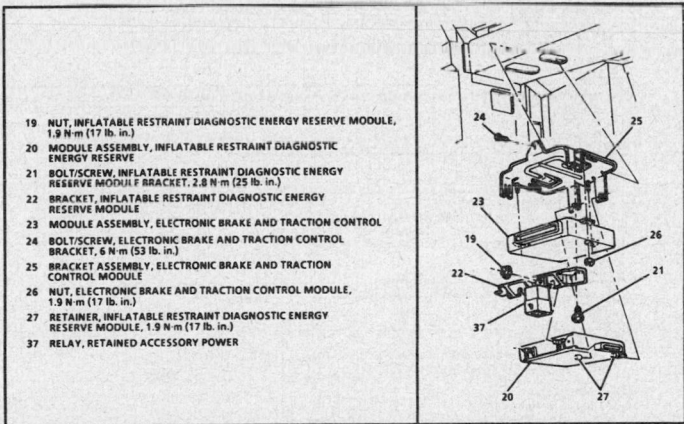

19 NUT, INFLATABLE RESTRAINT DIAGNOSTIC ENERGY RESERVE MODULE, 1.9 N·m (17 lb. in.)
20 MODULE ASSEMBLY, INFLATABLE RESTRAINT DIAGNOSTIC ENERGY RESERVE
21 BOLT/SCREW, INFLATABLE RESTRAINT DIAGNOSTIC ENERGY RESERVE MODULE BRACKET, 2.8 N·m (25 lb. in.)
22 BRACKET, INFLATABLE RESTRAINT DIAGNOSTIC ENERGY RESERVE MODULE
23 MODULE ASSEMBLY, ELECTRONIC BRAKE AND TRACTION CONTROL
24 BOLT/SCREW, ELECTRONIC BRAKE AND TRACTION CONTROL BRACKET, 6 N·m (53 lb. in.)
25 BRACKET ASSEMBLY, ELECTRONIC BRAKE AND TRACTION CONTROL MODULE
26 NUT, ELECTRONIC BRAKE AND TRACTION CONTROL MODULE, 1.9 N·m (17 lb. in.)
27 RETAINER, INFLATABLE RESTRAINT DIAGNOSTIC ENERGY RESERVE MODULE, 1.9 N·m (17 lb. in.)
37 RELAY, RETAINED ACCESSORY POWER

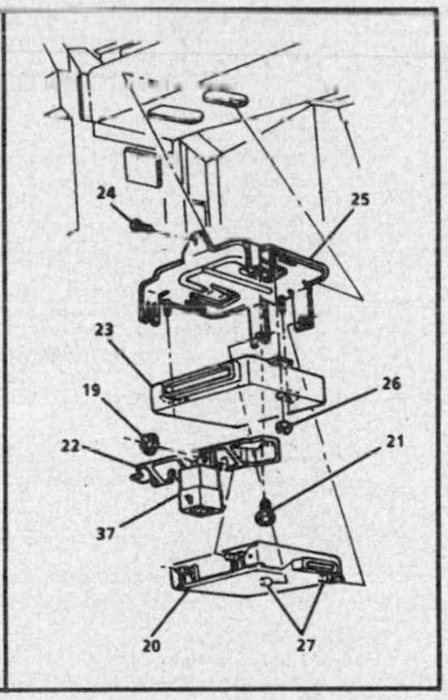
24
25
23
19
26
22
21
37
20
27

DTC 58

EBTCM INTERNAL ADJUSTER ASSEMBLY MALFUNCTION

Circuit Description:

The EBTCM contains a microprocessor for ABS/TCS calculations and functions, as well as a microprocessor for adjuster assembly calculations and functions. If the two microprocessors cannot communicate with each other properly, DTC 58 will set.

Test Description: Number(s) below refer to circled number(s) on the diagnostic chart.

1. Clears DTCs and checks for DTC 58 reset. If the DTC resets, the microprocessor communication problem does exist within the EBTCM.

GC4029300573010X

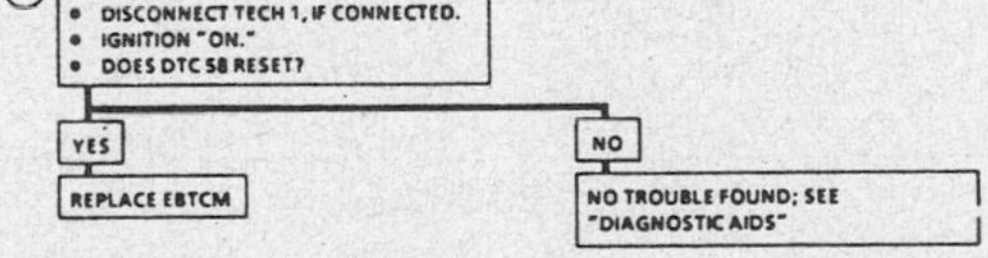
1 • CLEAR DTCs, IGNITION "OFF." • DISCONNECT TECH 1, IF CONNECTED. • IGNITION "ON." • DOES DTC 58 RESET?
YES
NO
REPLACE EBTCM
NO TROUBLE FOUND; SEE "DIAGNOSTIC AIDS"

GC4029300573020X

Fig. 140 Code 58: EBTCM Internal Adjuster Assembly Malfunction. 1993-94 Fleetwood (RWD)

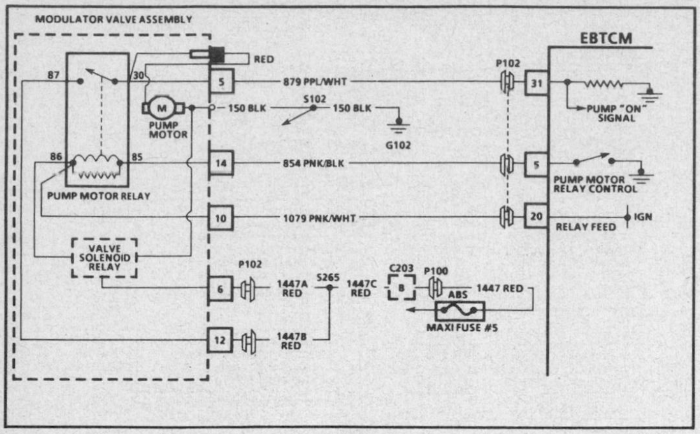

MODULATOR VALVE ASSEMBLY
EBTCM
RED
87
30
5
879 PPL/WHT
P102
31
PUMP MOTOR
150 BLK
S102
150 BLK
PUMP "ON" SIGNAL
G102
86
85
14
854 PNK/BLK
5
PUMP MOTOR RELAY
PUMP MOTOR RELAY CONTROL
10
1079 PNK/WHT
20
RELAY FEED
IGN
VALVE SOLENOID RELAY
P102
6
1447A RED
S265
1447C RED
C203
P100
1447 RED
ABS
MAXI FUSE #5
12
1447B RED

DTC 61

1 of 2

PUMP MOTOR OR PUMP MOTOR RELAY MALFUNCTION

Circuit Description:

When the pump motor relay is grounded by the EBTCM, it closes and provides B+ to operate the pump. Once the motor circuit is energized, a "Pump ON" signal is sensed by the EBTCM through CKT 875 to verify pump operation.

The "ANTI-LOCK" and "TRACTION CONTROL" indicators will be "ON" and DTC 61 will set if B+ is present at the pump motor without pump motor relay activation from the EBTCM, or if B+ is NOT present at the pump motor within 60 milliseconds after the EBTCM requests pump motor relay activation.

Test Description: Number(s) below refer to circled number(s) on the diagnostic chart.

1. Checks the pump motor relay coil for proper resistance.
2. Checks for an open in power feed CKT 1447B.
3. Determines if the pump motor relay contacts are stuck closed.
4. Determines if the pump motor relay contacts are stuck open.
5. Checks the integrity of the pump motor and pump motor relay circuitry internal to the modulator valve assembly.
6. Checks for an open in CKT 879.
7. Checks for a short to ground in CKT 879.
8. Checks for a short to B+ in CKT 879.

Diagnostic Aids:

All tests using J 39700 Universal Breakout Box terminal "3" are using that terminal as ground. These tests, of course, assume that the ground at terminal "3" is good.

It is very important that a thorough inspection of the wiring and connectors be performed. Failure to carefully and fully inspect wiring and connectors may result in misdiagnosis, causing part replacement with reappearance of the malfunction.

GC4029300574010X

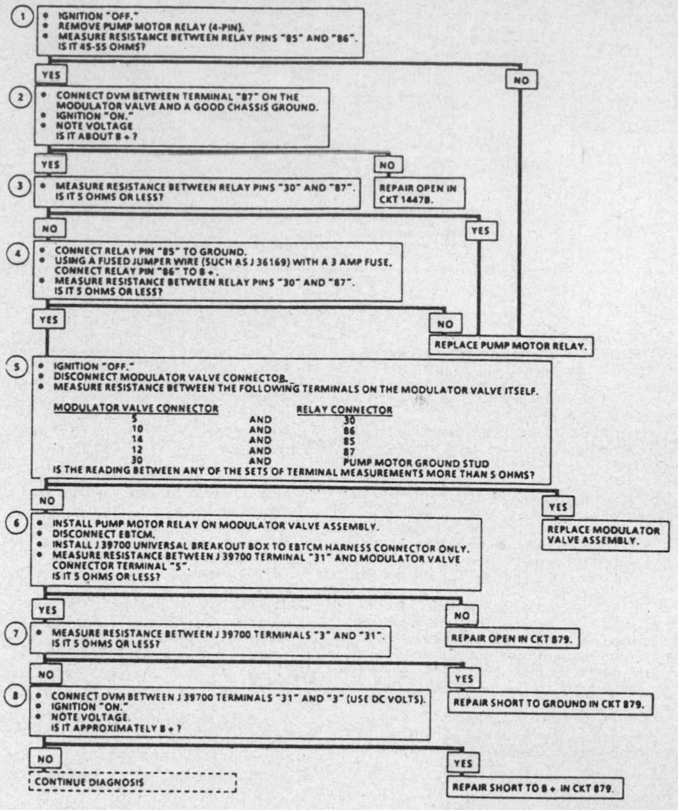

1
IGNITION "OFF."
REMOVE PUMP MOTOR RELAY (4-PIN).
MEASURE RESISTANCE BETWEEN RELAY PINS "85" AND "86".
IS IT 45-55 OHMS?
YES
NO
2
CONNECT DVM BETWEEN TERMINAL "87" ON THE MODULATOR VALVE AND A GOOD CHASSIS GROUND.
IGNITION "ON."
NOTE VOLTAGE
IS IT ABOUT B+?
YES
NO
3
MEASURE RESISTANCE BETWEEN RELAY PINS "30" AND "87".
IS IT 5 OHMS OR LESS?
REPAIR OPEN IN CKT 1447B.
NO
YES
4
CONNECT RELAY PIN "85" TO GROUND.
USING A FUSED JUMPER WIRE (SUCH AS J 36169) WITH A 3 AMP FUSE, CONNECT RELAY PIN "86" TO B+.
MEASURE RESISTANCE BETWEEN RELAY PINS "30" AND "87".
IS IT 5 OHMS OR LESS?
YES
NO
REPLACE PUMP MOTOR RELAY.
5
IGNITION "OFF."
DISCONNECT MODULATOR VALVE CONNECTOR.
MEASURE RESISTANCE BETWEEN THE FOLLOWING TERMINALS ON THE MODULATOR VALVE ITSELF.
MODULATOR VALVE CONNECTOR / RELAY CONNECTOR
5 AND 30
10 AND 86
14 AND 85
12 AND 87
30 AND PUMP MOTOR GROUND STUD
IS THE READING BETWEEN ANY OF THE SETS OF TERMINAL MEASUREMENTS MORE THAN 5 OHMS?
NO
YES
REPLACE MODULATOR VALVE ASSEMBLY.
6
INSTALL PUMP MOTOR RELAY ON MODULATOR VALVE ASSEMBLY.
DISCONNECT EBTCM.
INSTALL J 39700 UNIVERSAL BREAKOUT BOX TO EBTCM HARNESS CONNECTOR ONLY.
MEASURE RESISTANCE BETWEEN J 39700 TERMINAL "31" AND MODULATOR VALVE CONNECTOR TERMINAL "5".
IS IT 5 OHMS OR LESS?
YES
NO
REPAIR OPEN IN CKT 879.
7
MEASURE RESISTANCE BETWEEN J 39700 TERMINALS "3" AND "31".
IS IT 5 OHMS OR LESS?
NO
YES
REPAIR SHORT TO GROUND IN CKT 879.
8
CONNECT DVM BETWEEN J 39700 TERMINALS "31" AND "3" (USE DC VOLTS).
IGNITION "ON."
NOTE VOLTAGE.
IS IT APPROXIMATELY B+?
NO
YES
CONTINUE DIAGNOSIS
REPAIR SHORT TO B+ IN CKT 879.

GC4029300574020X

Fig. 141 Code 61: Pump Motor Or Pump Motor Relay Malfunction (Part 1 of 2). 1993-94 Fleetwood (RWD)

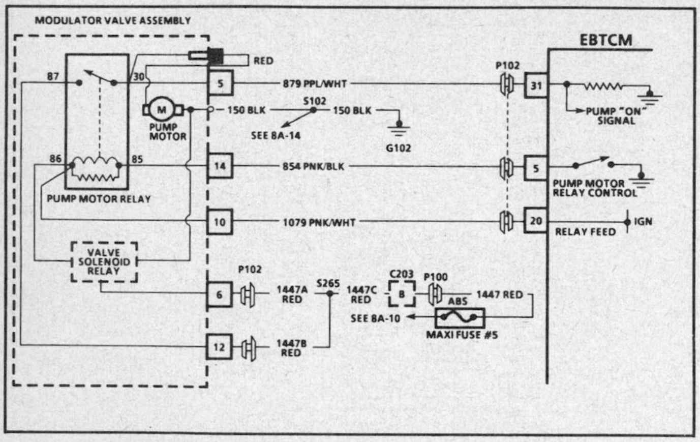

MODULATOR VALVE ASSEMBLY
EBTCM
RED
87
30
5
879 PPL/WHT
P102
31
PUMP MOTOR
150 BLK
S102
150 BLK
SEE 8A-14
PUMP "ON" SIGNAL
G102
86
85
14
854 PNK/BLK
5
PUMP MOTOR RELAY
PUMP MOTOR RELAY CONTROL
10
1079 PNK/WHT
20
RELAY FEED
IGN
VALVE SOLENOID RELAY
P102
6
1447A RED
S265
1447C RED
C203
P100
1447 RED
ABS
SEE 8A-10
MAXI FUSE #5
12
1447B RED

DTC 61

2 of 2

PUMP MOTOR OR PUMP MOTOR RELAY MALFUNCTION

Circuit Description:

When the pump motor relay is grounded by the EBTCM, it closes and provides B+ to operate the pump. Once the motor circuit is energized, a "Pump ON" signal is sensed by the EBTCM through CKT 875 to verify pump operation.

The "ANTI-LOCK" and "TRACTION CONTROL" indicators will be "ON" and DTC 61 will set if B+ is present at the pump motor without pump motor relay activation from the EBTCM, or if B+ is NOT present at the pump motor within 60 milliseconds after the EBTCM requests pump motor relay activation.

Test Description: Number(s) below refer to circled number(s) on the diagnostic chart.

9. Checks for an open in CKT 854.
10. Checks for a short to ground in CKT 854.
11. Checks for a short to B+ in CKT 854.
12. Checks wiring and connectors for intermittents.
13. Uses the Tech 1 to check for proper operation of the pump motor and associated circuitry.
14. Determines whether the problem found in Step 13 was due to a malfunctioning EBTCM or an open in pump motor ground CKT 150.

Diagnostic Aids:

All tests using J 39700 Universal Breakout Box terminal "3" are using that terminal as ground. These tests, of course, assume that the ground at terminal "3" is good.

It is very important that a thorough inspection of the wiring and connectors be performed. Failure to carefully and fully inspect wiring and connectors may result in misdiagnosis, causing part replacement with reappearance of the malfunction.

GC4029300574030X

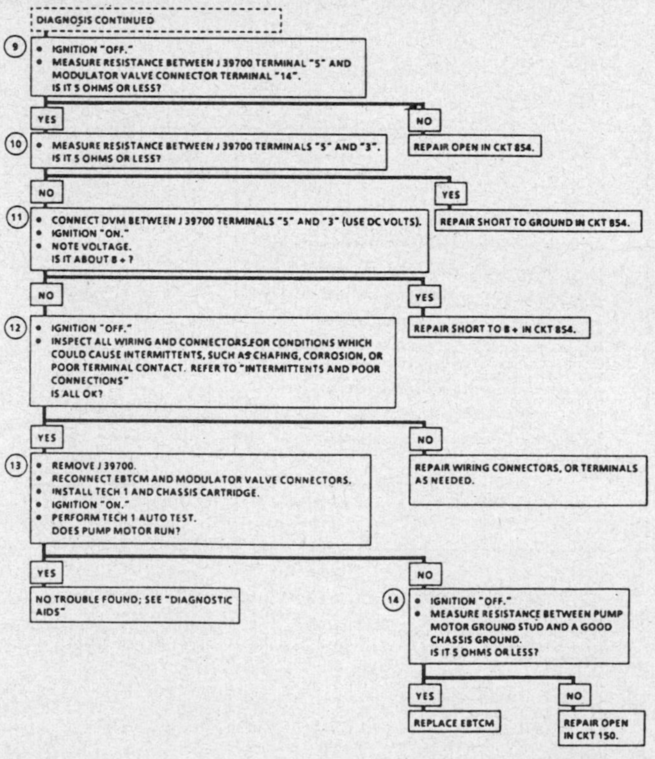

DIAGNOSIS CONTINUED
9
IGNITION "OFF."
MEASURE RESISTANCE BETWEEN J 39700 TERMINAL "5" AND MODULATOR VALVE CONNECTOR TERMINAL "14".
IS IT 5 OHMS OR LESS?
YES
NO
REPAIR OPEN IN CKT 854.
10
MEASURE RESISTANCE BETWEEN J 39700 TERMINALS "5" AND "3".
IS IT 5 OHMS OR LESS?
NO
YES
REPAIR SHORT TO GROUND IN CKT 854.
11
CONNECT DVM BETWEEN J 39700 TERMINALS "5" AND "3" (USE DC VOLTS).
IGNITION "ON."
NOTE VOLTAGE.
IS IT ABOUT B+?
NO
YES
REPAIR SHORT TO B+ IN CKT 854.
12
IGNITION "OFF."
INSPECT ALL WIRING AND CONNECTORS FOR CONDITIONS WHICH COULD CAUSE INTERMITTENTS, SUCH AS CHAFING, CORROSION, OR POOR TERMINAL CONTACT. REFER TO "INTERMITTENTS AND POOR CONNECTIONS"
IS ALL OK?
YES
NO
REPAIR WIRING CONNECTORS, OR TERMINALS AS NEEDED.
13
REMOVE J 39700.
RECONNECT EBTCM AND MODULATOR VALVE CONNECTORS.
INSTALL TECH 1 AND CHASSIS CARTRIDGE.
IGNITION "ON."
PERFORM TECH 1 AUTO TEST.
DOES PUMP MOTOR RUN?
YES
NO
NO TROUBLE FOUND; SEE "DIAGNOSTIC AIDS"
14
IGNITION "OFF."
MEASURE RESISTANCE BETWEEN PUMP MOTOR GROUND STUD AND A GOOD CHASSIS GROUND.
IS IT 5 OHMS OR LESS?
YES
NO
REPLACE EBTCM
REPAIR OPEN IN CKT 150.

GC4029300574040X

Fig. 141 Code 61: Pump Motor Or Pump Motor Relay Malfunction (Part 2 of 2). 1993-94 Fleetwood (RWD)

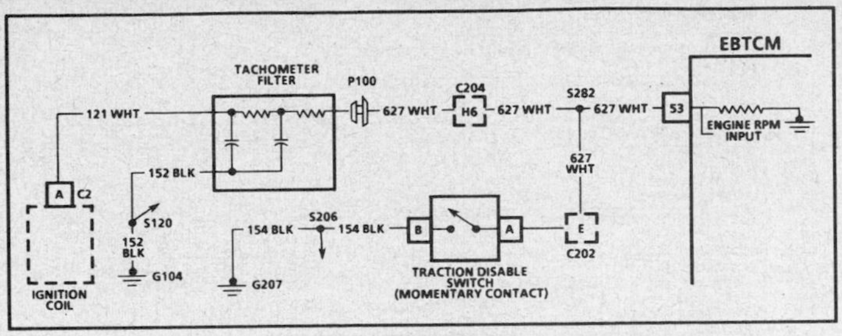
EBTCM
TACHOMETER FILTER
P100
C204
S282
121 WHT
627 WHT
H6
627 WHT
627 WHT
53
ENGINE RPM INPUT
627 WHT
152 BLK
A
C2
S120
152 BLK
G104
IGNITION COIL
S206
154 BLK
154 BLK
B
A
E
C202
G207
TRACTION DISABLE SWITCH (MOMENTARY CONTACT)

DTC 62

RPM SIGNAL MALFUNCTION

Circuit Description:

The RPM signal circuit provides the EBTCM with an indication of engine RPM to help determine TCS control methods and rates when a TCS event takes place.

The "TRACTION CONTROL" indicator will be "ON" and DTC 62 will set if there is a short to ground, short to B+, or an open in CKT 121.

Important

- The "Traction Disable" switch also can set this DTC, since it disables TCS by purposely inducing a momentary "short to ground" malfunction at EBTCM terminal "53". The switch must be held down for at least 2 seconds to do so. Be sure to clear DTCs, turn ignition "OFF," then turn ignition "ON" again to verify the DTC was not set by the owner using the traction disable switch. Review Tech 1 DTC History information for clues as to when the DTC set and how frequently it has set. Also, speak to the customer to determine if traction disable switch use is the cause for this DTC.

Test Description: Number(s) below refer to circled number(s) on the diagnostic chart.

1. Checks for DTC reset after clearing DTCs to ensure a problem really exists, not that the owner used the "Traction Disable" switch.
2. Checks for "Traction Disable" switch stuck closed.
3. Checks for short to ground in CKT 627.
4. Checks for short to B+ in CKT 627.
5. Checks for normal operating voltage of about 5 volts from output side of tachometer filter. If no voltage, CKT 627 is open.

Diagnostic Aids:

Important

- The "Traction Disable" switch also can set this DTC, since it disables TCS by purposely inducing a momentary "short to ground" malfunction at EBTCM terminal "53". The switch must be held down for at least 2 seconds to do so. Be sure to clear DTCs, turn ignition "OFF," then turn ignition "ON" again to verify the DTC was not set by the owner using the "Traction Disable" switch. Review Tech 1 DTC History information for clues as to when the DTC set and how frequently it has set. Also, speak to the customer to determine if "Traction Disable" switch use is the cause for this DTC.

A short to ground in CKT 121 on the ignition system side of the tach filter may cause a no-start or extremely poor driveability condition.

GC4029300575010X

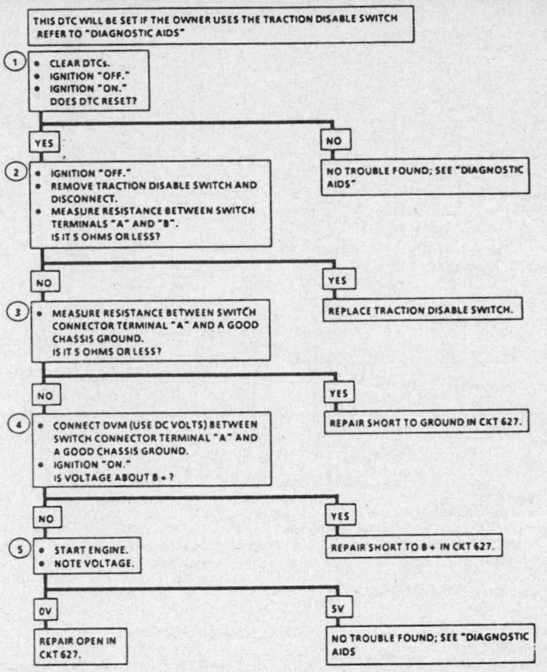
THIS DTC WILL BE SET IF THE OWNER USES THE TRACTION DISABLE SWITCH REFER TO "DIAGNOSTIC AIDS"
1
• CLEAR DTCs.
• IGNITION "OFF."
• IGNITION "ON."
DOES DTC RESET?
YES
NO
NO TROUBLE FOUND; SEE "DIAGNOSTIC AIDS"
2
• IGNITION "OFF."
• REMOVE TRACTION DISABLE SWITCH AND DISCONNECT.
• MEASURE RESISTANCE BETWEEN SWITCH TERMINALS "A" AND "B".
IS IT 5 OHMS OR LESS?
NO
YES
REPLACE TRACTION DISABLE SWITCH.
3
• MEASURE RESISTANCE BETWEEN SWITCH CONNECTOR TERMINAL "A" AND A GOOD CHASSIS GROUND.
IS IT 5 OHMS OR LESS?
NO
YES
REPAIR SHORT TO GROUND IN CKT 627.
4
• CONNECT DVM (USE DC VOLTS) BETWEEN SWITCH CONNECTOR TERMINAL "A" AND A GOOD CHASSIS GROUND.
• IGNITION "ON."
IS VOLTAGE ABOUT B+?
NO
YES
REPAIR SHORT TO B+ IN CKT 627.
5
• START ENGINE.
• NOTE VOLTAGE.
0V
REPAIR OPEN IN CKT 627.
5V
NO TROUBLE FOUND; SEE "DIAGNOSTIC AIDS

GC4029300575020X

Fig. 142 Code 62: RPM Signal Malfunction. 1993-94 Fleetwood (RWD)

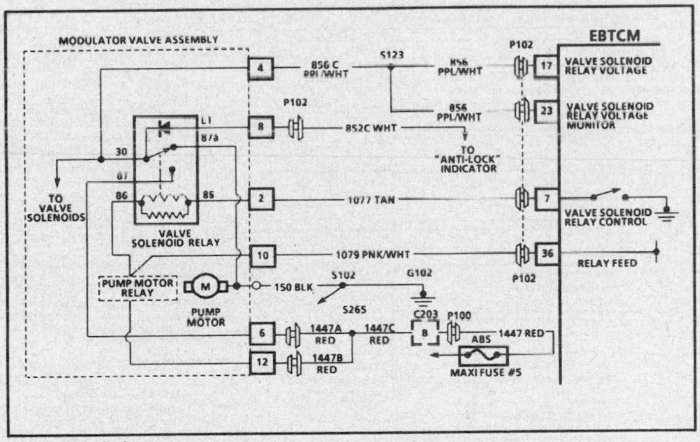
MODULATOR VALVE ASSEMBLY
EBTCM
P102
S123
856 C PPL/WHT
856 PPL/WHT
17
VALVE SOLENOID RELAY VOLTAGE
856 PPL/WHT
23
VALVE SOLENOID RELAY VOLTAGE MONITOR
P102
852C WHT
TO "ANTI-LOCK" INDICATOR
TO VALVE SOLENOIDS
VALVE SOLENOID RELAY
1077 TAN
7
VALVE SOLENOID RELAY CONTROL
1079 PNK/WHT
36
RELAY FEED
PUMP MOTOR RELAY
150 BLK
S102
G102
P102
PUMP MOTOR
S265
C203
P100
1447A RED
1447C RED
1447 RED
ABS
1447B RED
MAXI FUSE #5

Circuit Description:

The valve solenoid relay has two functions. When the ignition is "ON" and the EBTCM is operating, the relay provides voltage to actuate the valve solenoids. However, the valve solenoids do not use this voltage unless the EBTCM provides the ground. The second function of the valve solenoid relay is to provide a ground path for illumination of the "ANTI-LOCK" lamp if the relay loses power or ground.

The "ANTI-LOCK" and "TRACTION CONTROL" indicators will be "ON" and DTC 63 will set if the valve solenoid relay voltage falls to less than 5 volts.

Test Description: Number(s) below refer to circled number(s) on the diagnostic chart.

1. Checks for the availability of battery voltage to the valve solenoid relay through ABS maxifuse #5 and CKT 1447.
2. Checks the valve solenoid relay coil for proper resistance.
3. Checks for the valve solenoid relay contacts being internally open when in the relay-unenergized position.
4. Checks for the valve solenoid relay contacts being stuck open when in the relay-energized position.
5. Checks the integrity of the valve solenoid relay circuitry internal to the modulator valve assembly.
6. Checks for an open in ground CKT 150.
7. Checks for an open in CKT 856.

Diagnostic Aids:

All tests using J 39700 Universal Breakout Box terminal "3" are using that terminal as ground. These tests, of course, assume that the ground at terminal "3" is good.

It is very important that a thorough inspection of the wiring and connectors be performed. Failure to carefully and fully inspect wiring and connectors may result in misdiagnosis, causing part replacement with reappearance of the malfunction.

GC4029300576010X

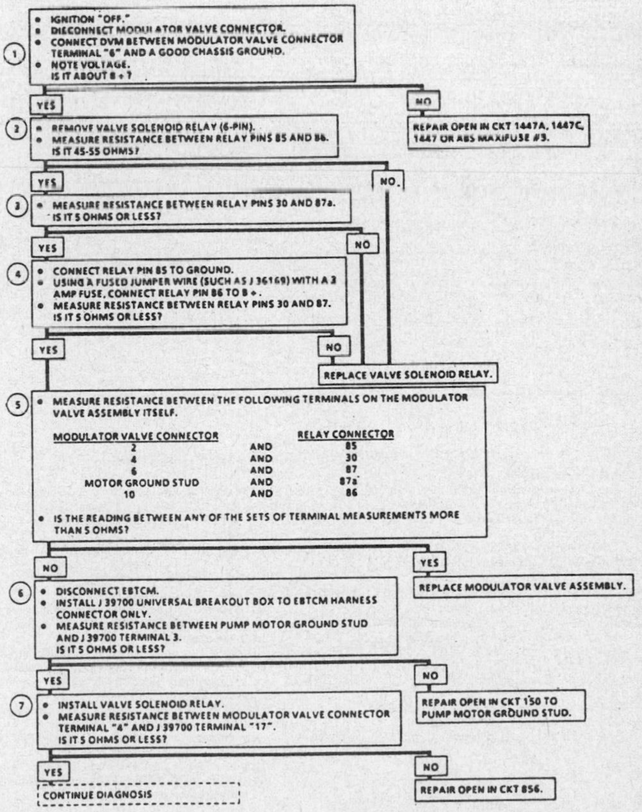
1
• IGNITION "OFF."
• DISCONNECT MODULATOR VALVE CONNECTOR.
• CONNECT DVM BETWEEN MODULATOR VALVE CONNECTOR TERMINAL "6" AND A GOOD CHASSIS GROUND.
• NOTE VOLTAGE.
IS IT ABOUT B+?
YES
NO
REPAIR OPEN IN CKT 1447A, 1447C, 1447 OR ABS MAXIFUSE #5.
2
• REMOVE VALVE SOLENOID RELAY (6-PIN).
• MEASURE RESISTANCE BETWEEN RELAY PINS 85 AND 86.
IS IT 45-55 OHMS?
YES
NO.
3
• MEASURE RESISTANCE BETWEEN RELAY PINS 30 AND 87a.
IS IT 5 OHMS OR LESS?
YES
NO
4
• CONNECT RELAY PIN 85 TO GROUND.
• USING A FUSED JUMPER WIRE (SUCH AS J 36169) WITH A 3 AMP FUSE, CONNECT RELAY PIN 86 TO B+.
• MEASURE RESISTANCE BETWEEN RELAY PINS 30 AND 87.
IS IT 5 OHMS OR LESS?
YES
NO
REPLACE VALVE SOLENOID RELAY.
5
• MEASURE RESISTANCE BETWEEN THE FOLLOWING TERMINALS ON THE MODULATOR VALVE ASSEMBLY ITSELF.
MODULATOR VALVE CONNECTOR — RELAY CONNECTOR
2 AND 85
4 AND 30
6 AND 87
MOTOR GROUND STUD AND 87a
10 AND 86
• IS THE READING BETWEEN ANY OF THE SETS OF TERMINAL MEASUREMENTS MORE THAN 5 OHMS?
NO
YES
REPLACE MODULATOR VALVE ASSEMBLY.
6
• DISCONNECT EBTCM.
• INSTALL J 39700 UNIVERSAL BREAKOUT BOX TO EBTCM HARNESS CONNECTOR ONLY.
• MEASURE RESISTANCE BETWEEN PUMP MOTOR GROUND STUD AND J 39700 TERMINAL 3.
IS IT 5 OHMS OR LESS?
YES
NO
REPAIR OPEN IN CKT 150 TO PUMP MOTOR GROUND STUD.
7
• INSTALL VALVE SOLENOID RELAY.
• MEASURE RESISTANCE BETWEEN MODULATOR VALVE CONNECTOR TERMINAL "4" AND J 39700 TERMINAL "17".
IS IT 5 OHMS OR LESS?
YES
CONTINUE DIAGNOSIS
NO
REPAIR OPEN IN CKT 856.

GC4029300576020X

Fig. 143 Code 63: Valve Solenoid Relay Malfunction (Part 1 of 2). 1993-94 Fleetwood (RWD)

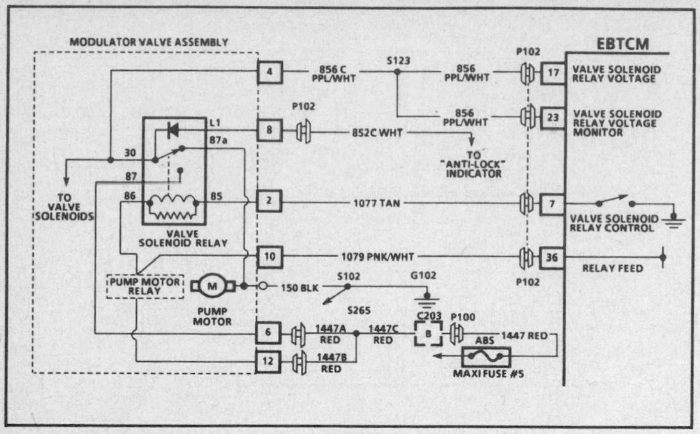

DTC 63

2 of 2

VALVE SOLENOID RELAY MALFUNCTION

Circuit Description:

The valve solenoid relay has two functions. When the ignition is "ON" and the EBTCM is operating, the relay provides voltage to actuate the valve solenoids. However, the valve solenoids do not use this voltage unless the EBTCM provides the ground. The second function of the valve solenoid relay is to provide a ground path for illumination of the "ANTI-LOCK" lamp if the relay loses power or ground.

The "ANTI-LOCK" and "TRACTION CONTROL" indicators will be "ON" and DTC 63 will set if the valve solenoid relay voltage falls to less than 5 volts.

Test Description: Number(s) below refer to circled number(s) on the diagnostic chart.

8. Checks for a short to ground in CKT 856.
9. Checks for a short to B+ in CKT 856.
10. Checks for an open in CKT 1079.
11. Checks for a short to ground in CKT 1079.
12. Checks for an open in CKT 1077.
13. Checks for a short to ground in CKT 1077.
14. Checks wiring and connectors for intermittents.
15. Determines whether the DTC was set due to an intermittent condition or an EBTCM malfunction.

Diagnostic Aids:

All tests using J 39700 Universal Breakout Box terminal "3" are using that terminal as ground. These tests, of course, assume that the ground at terminal "3" is good.

It is very important that a thorough inspection of the wiring and connectors be performed. Failure to carefully and fully inspect wiring and connectors may result in misdiagnosis, causing part replacement with reappearance of the malfunction.

GC4029300576030X

DIAGNOSIS CONTINUED FROM PREVIOUS PAGE.

(8)
- MEASURE RESISTANCE BETWEEN J 39700 TERMINALS "17" AND "3". IS IT 5 OHMS OR LESS?

YES: REPAIR SHORT TO GROUND IN CKT 856.

NO:

(9)
- CONNECT DVM BETWEEN J 39700 TERMINALS "17" AND "3" (USE DC VOLTS).
- IGNITION "ON."
- NOTE VOLTAGE. IS IT ABOUT B+?

YES: REPAIR SHORT TO B+ ON CKT 856.

NO:

(10)
- IGNITION "OFF."
- MEASURE RESISTANCE BETWEEN MODULATOR VALVE CONNECTOR TERMINAL "10" AND J 39700 TERMINAL "20". IS IT 5 OHMS OR LESS?

NO: REPAIR OPEN IN CKT 1079.

YES:

(11)
- MEASURE RESISTANCE BETWEEN J 39700 TERMINALS "20" AND "3". IS IT 5 OHMS OR LESS?

YES: REPAIR SHORT TO GROUND IN CKT 1079.

NO:

(12)
- MEASURE RESISTANCE BETWEEN MODULATOR VALVE CONNECTOR TERMINAL "2" AND J 39700 TERMINAL "7". IS IT 5 OHMS OR LESS?

NO: REPAIR OPEN IN CKT 1077.

(13) YES:
- MEASURE RESISTANCE BETWEEN J 39700 TERMINALS "3" AND "7". IS IT 5 OHMS OR LESS?

YES: REPAIR SHORT TO GROUND IN CKT 1077.

NO:

(14)
- IGNITION "OFF."
- INSPECT ALL WIRING AND CONNECTORS FOR CONDITIONS WHICH COULD CAUSE INTERMITTENTS, SUCH AS CHAFING, CORROSION, OR POOR TERMINAL CONTACT. REFER TO "INTERMITTENTS AND POOR CONNECTIONS"
- IS ALL OK WITH CONNECTIONS AND WIRING?

NO: REPAIR WIRING AND/OR CONNECTIONS AS NEEDED

YES:

(15)
- REMOVE J 39700.
- RECONNECT EBTCM AND MODULATOR VALVE CONNECTORS.
- CLEAR DTCs, IGNITION "OFF."
- DISCONNECT TECH 1, IF CONNECTED.
- DRIVE VEHICLE AT LEAST 7 km/h (4 MPH) TO ACTIVATE AUTO TEST SEQUENCE.
- DOES DTC 63 RESET?

NO: NO TROUBLE FOUND; SEE DIAGNOSTIC AIDS

YES: REPLACE EBTCM

Fig. 143 Code 63: Valve Solenoid Relay Malfunction (Part 2 of 2). 1993-94 Fleetwood (RWD)

GC4029300576040X

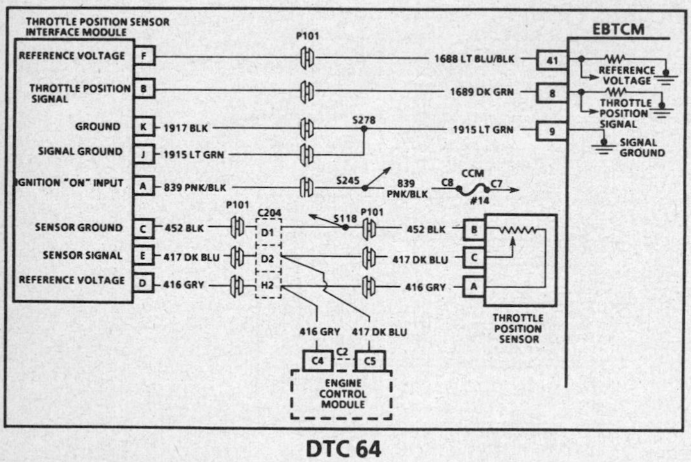

DTC 64

1 of 2

THROTTLE POSITION SIGNAL MALFUNCTION

Circuit Description:

The throttle position signal circuit is used by the EBTCM to monitor the actual throttle position versus desired throttle position to monitor and control engine torque during a TCS event. The throttle position sensor interface module is used to allow EBTCM monitoring of the TP sensor signal without affecting the TP sensor signal to the ECM.

DTC 64 will set if the EBTCM is not receiving reference voltage or a TP sensor signal from the throttle position sensor interface module.

Test Description: Number(s) below refer to circled number(s) on the diagnostic chart.

1. Checks for TP sensor-related ECM DTCs. Many of the same conditions which could cause a TCS DTC 64 will also cause ECM DTCs. The ECM DTCs should be repaired first to eliminate those problems from affecting the TCS DTC 64 condition.
2. Checks for a short to ground in CKT 1689.
3. Checks for an open in CKT 1915.
4. Checks for a short to ground in CKT 1688.
5. Checks for proper voltage in CKT 1688 at the EBTCM connection. (This voltage measurement is only appropriate when the EBTCM is disconnected from the circuit).
6. Checks for proper voltage in CKT 1689 at the EBTCM connection. (This voltage measurement is only appropriate when the EBTCM is disconnected from the circuit).
7. Checks for an additional DTC 64 problem after ground CKT 1915 is repaired.
8. Determines if a problem found in Step 5 is due to a fuse, CKT 839, or CKT 1688.
9. Determines if a problem found in Steps 5 and 13 is due to an open in CKT 1688 or a malfunctioning TP sensor interface module.

GC4029300577010X

(1) IF ECM DTCs 21 OR 22 ARE SET, USE THE ECM DIAGNOSTIC CHARTS TO REPAIR THOSE DTCs. THEN, CLEAR ECM AND TCS DTCs. TURN IGNITION "OFF." DISCONNECT TECH 1, IF CONNECTED. TURN IGNITION "ON." IF TCS DTC 64 RESETS, CONTINUE WITH THIS DIAGNOSTIC CHART.

(2)
- IGNITION "OFF."
- DISCONNECT EBTCM.
- INSTALL J 39700 UNIVERSAL BREAKOUT BOX TO EBTCM HARNESS CONNECTOR ONLY.
- MEASURE RESISTANCE BETWEEN J 39700 TERMINALS "8" AND "3". IS IT 5 OHMS OR LESS?

YES: REPAIR SHORT TO GROUND IN CKT 1689.

NO:

(3)
- MEASURE RESISTANCE BETWEEN J 39700 TERMINALS "9" AND "3". IS IT 5 OHMS OR LESS?

NO:

(7)
- REPAIR OPEN IN CKT 1915.
- CLEAR DTCs, IGNITION "OFF."
- DISCONNECT TECH 1, IF CONNECTED.
- IGNITION "ON."
- DOES DTC 64 RESET?

YES: CONTINUE DIAGNOSTICS AT STEP 4.

NO: SYSTEM OK

YES:

(4)
- MEASURE RESISTANCE BETWEEN J 39700 TERMINALS "41" AND "3". IS IT 5 OHMS OR LESS?

YES: REPAIR SHORT TO GROUND IN CKT 1688.

NO:

(5)
- CONNECT DVM BETWEEN J 39700 TERMINALS "41" AND "3" (USE DC VOLTS).
- IGNITION "ON."
- NOTE VOLTAGE. IS IT ABOUT 10 VOLTS?

YES:

(6)
- CONNECT DVM BETWEEN J 39700 TERMINALS "8" AND "3".
- NOTE VOLTAGE. IS IT ABOUT 9.5 VOLTS?

NO: CONTINUE DIAGNOSIS

YES: NO TROUBLE FOUND; SEE "DIAGNOSTIC AIDS"

NO:

(8)
- IGNITION "OFF."
- DISCONNECT TP SENSOR INTERFACE MODULE.
- CONNECT DVM BETWEEN TP SENSOR INTERFACE MODULE CONNECTOR TERMINAL "A" AND J 39700 TERMINAL "3".
- IGNITION "ON."
- NOTE VOLTAGE. IS IT ABOUT B+?

NO: REPLACE CCM FUSE #14 OR REPAIR OPEN IN CKT 839.

YES:

(9)
- IGNITION "OFF."
- MEASURE RESISTANCE BETWEEN J 39700 TERMINAL "41" AND TP SENSOR INTERFACE MODULE CONNECTOR TERMINAL "F".
- IS IT 5 OHMS OR LESS?

YES: REPLACE TP SENSOR INTERFACE MODULE

NO: REPAIR OPEN IN CKT 1688.

GC4029300577020X

Fig. 144 Code 64: Throttle Position Signal Malfunction (Part 1 of 2). 1993-94 Fleetwood (RWD)

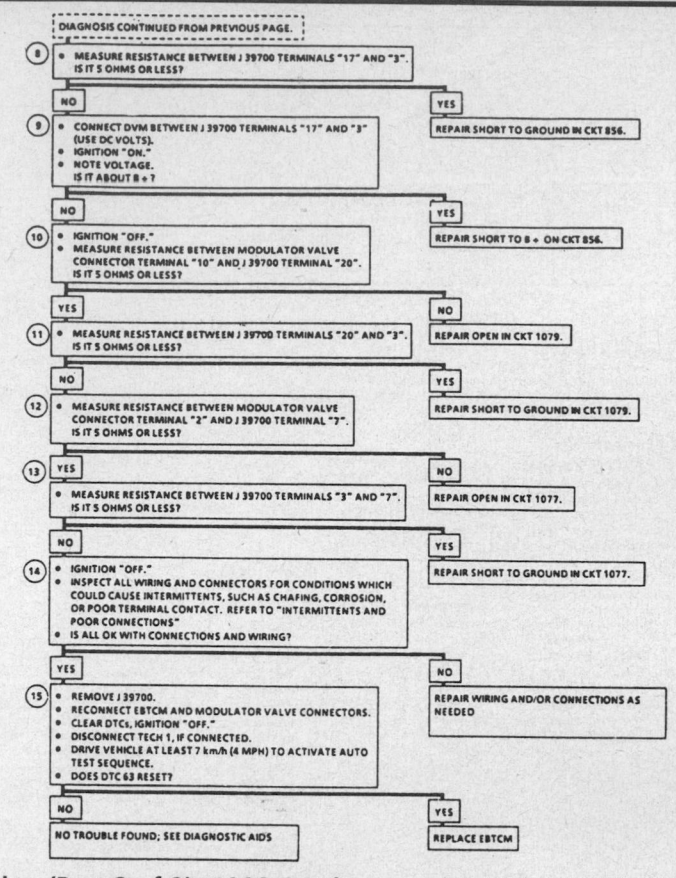

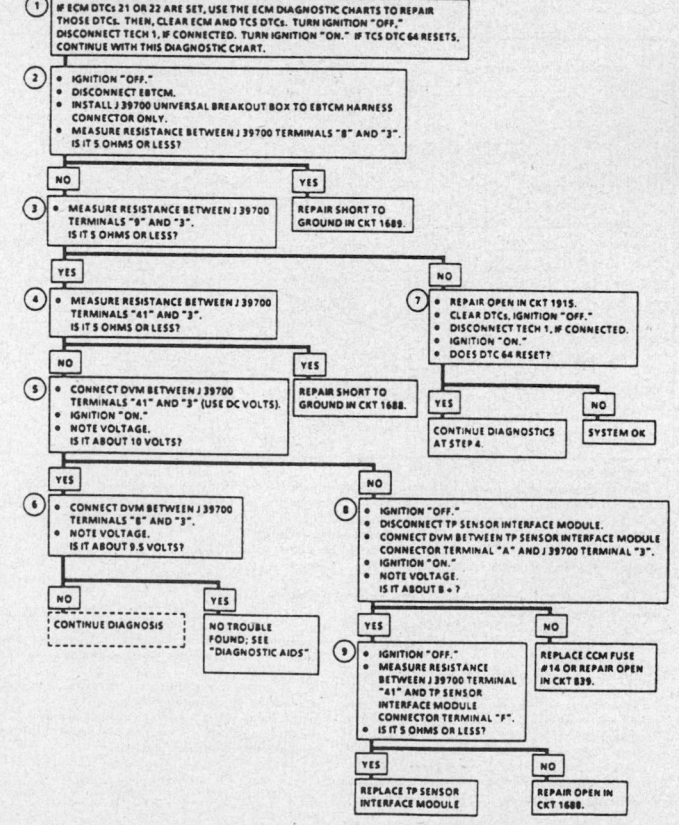

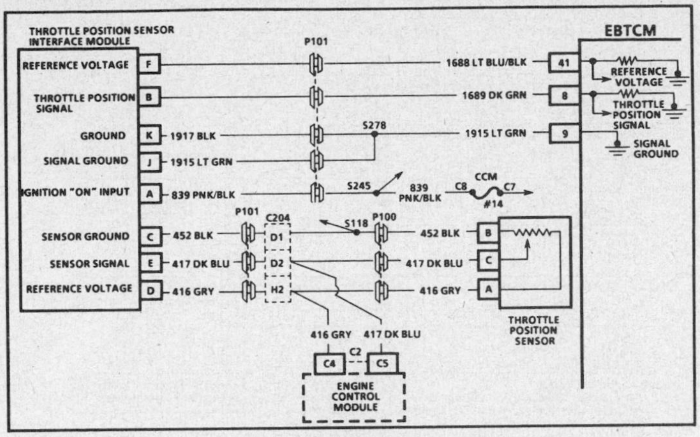

THROTTLE POSITION SENSOR INTERFACE MODULE
EBTCM
P101
REFERENCE VOLTAGE
F
1688 LT BLU/BLK
41
REFERENCE VOLTAGE
THROTTLE POSITION SIGNAL
B
1689 DK GRN
8
THROTTLE POSITION SIGNAL
GROUND
K
1917 BLK
S278
1915 LT GRN
9
SIGNAL GROUND
SIGNAL GROUND
J
1915 LT GRN
IGNITION "ON" INPUT
A
839 PNK/BLK
S245
839 PNK/BLK
C8
CCM
C7
#14
P101
C204
S118
P100
SENSOR GROUND
C
452 BLK
D1
452 BLK
SENSOR SIGNAL
E
417 DK BLU
D2
417 DK BLU
REFERENCE VOLTAGE
D
416 GRY
H2
416 GRY
THROTTLE POSITION SENSOR
416 GRY
417 DK BLU
C2
C4
C5
ENGINE CONTROL MODULE

DTC 64

2 of 2

THROTTLE POSITION SIGNAL MALFUNCTION

Circuit Description:

The throttle position signal circuit is used by the EBTCM to monitor the actual throttle position versus desired throttle position to monitor and control engine torque during a TCS event. The throttle position sensor interface module is used to allow EBTCM monitoring of the TP sensor signal without affecting the TP sensor signal to the ECM.

DTC 64 will set if the EBTCM is not receiving reference voltage or a TP sensor signal from the throttle position sensor interface module.

Test Description: Number(s) below refer to circled number(s) on the diagnostic chart.

10. Checks for an open in CKT 1689.
11. Checks for TP sensor reference voltage from the ECM at the TP sensor interface module connector.
12. Checks for TP sensor signal voltage on CKT 452 at the TP sensor interface module connector.
13. Checks for an open in TP sensor signal ground CKT 416 to the TP sensor interface module connector.
14. Checks for an open in signal ground CKT 1917 to the TP sensor interface module connector.
15. Checks for DTC 64 reset after most system components have checked OK.
16. Replaces TP sensor interface module as likely cause of DTC reset in Step 15. If the DTC resets again, the EBTCM must be concluding there is a problem present when there is not.

Diagnostic Aids:

It is very important that a thorough inspection of the wiring and connectors be performed. Failure to carefully and fully inspect wiring and connectors may result in misdiagnosis, causing part replacement with reappearance of the malfunction.

GC4029300577030X

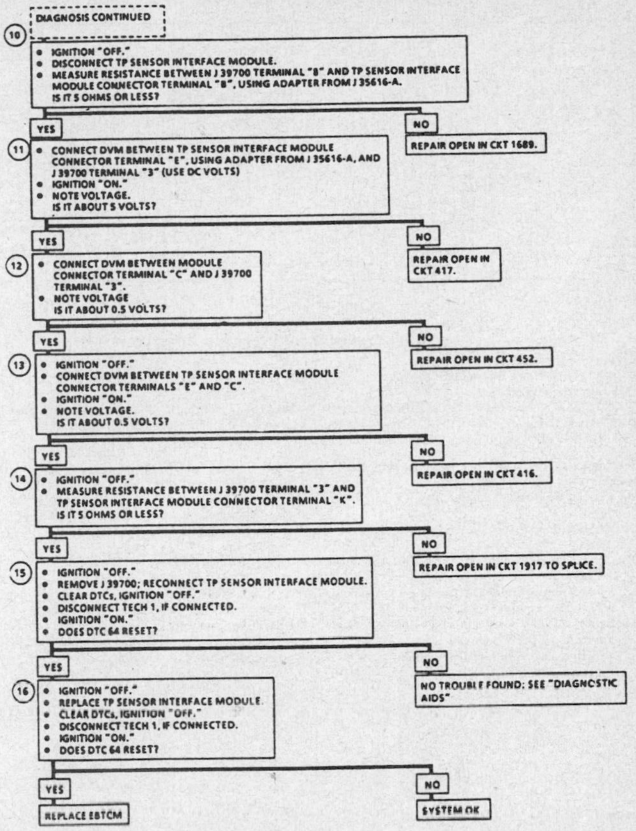

DIAGNOSIS CONTINUED
10
• IGNITION "OFF."
• DISCONNECT TP SENSOR INTERFACE MODULE.
• MEASURE RESISTANCE BETWEEN J 39700 TERMINAL "8" AND TP SENSOR INTERFACE MODULE CONNECTOR TERMINAL "B", USING ADAPTER FROM J 35616-A.
IS IT 5 OHMS OR LESS?
YES
NO
REPAIR OPEN IN CKT 1689.
11
• CONNECT DVM BETWEEN TP SENSOR INTERFACE MODULE CONNECTOR TERMINAL "E", USING ADAPTER FROM J 35616-A, AND J 39700 TERMINAL "3" (USE DC VOLTS)
• IGNITION "ON."
• NOTE VOLTAGE.
IS IT ABOUT 5 VOLTS?
YES
NO
REPAIR OPEN IN CKT 417.
12
• CONNECT DVM BETWEEN MODULE CONNECTOR TERMINAL "C" AND J 39700 TERMINAL "3".
• NOTE VOLTAGE
IS IT ABOUT 0.5 VOLTS?
YES
NO
REPAIR OPEN IN CKT 452.
13
• IGNITION "OFF."
• CONNECT DVM BETWEEN TP SENSOR INTERFACE MODULE CONNECTOR TERMINALS "E" AND "C".
• IGNITION "ON."
• NOTE VOLTAGE.
IS IT ABOUT 0.5 VOLTS?
YES
NO
REPAIR OPEN IN CKT 416.
14
• IGNITION "OFF."
• MEASURE RESISTANCE BETWEEN J 39700 TERMINAL "3" AND TP SENSOR INTERFACE MODULE CONNECTOR TERMINAL "K".
IS IT 5 OHMS OR LESS?
YES
NO
REPAIR OPEN IN CKT 1917 TO SPLICE.
15
• IGNITION "OFF."
• REMOVE J 39700; RECONNECT TP SENSOR INTERFACE MODULE.
• CLEAR DTCs, IGNITION "OFF."
• DISCONNECT TECH 1, IF CONNECTED.
• IGNITION "ON."
• DOES DTC 64 RESET?
YES
NO
NO TROUBLE FOUND; SEE "DIAGNOSTIC AIDS"
16
• IGNITION "OFF."
• REPLACE TP SENSOR INTERFACE MODULE.
• CLEAR DTCs, IGNITION "OFF."
• DISCONNECT TECH 1, IF CONNECTED.
• IGNITION "ON."
• DOES DTC 64 RESET?
YES
NO
REPLACE EBTCM
SYSTEM OK

GC4029300577040X

Fig. 144 Code 64: Throttle Position Signal Malfunction (Part 2 of 2). 1993-94 Fleetwood (RWD)

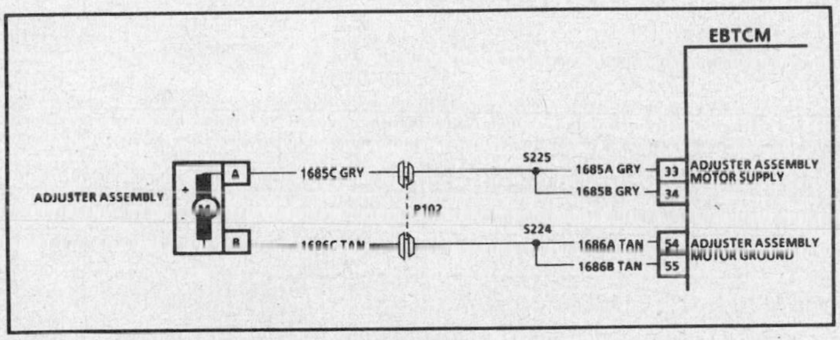

EBTCM
ADJUSTER ASSEMBLY
A
1685C GRY
S225
1685A GRY
33
1685B GRY
34
ADJUSTER ASSEMBLY MOTOR SUPPLY
P102
B
1686C TAN
S224
1686A TAN
54
1686B TAN
55
ADJUSTER ASSEMBLY MOTOR GROUND

DTC 65

1 of 2

ADJUSTER ASSEMBLY MALFUNCTION

Circuit Description:

The adjuster assembly circuit provides both power and ground to the adjuster assembly to help control engine torque during a TCS event.

DTC 65 will set if CKT 1685 or CKT 1686 are shorted to ground, shorted to B+, shorted to each other, or both open at the same time. The TCS system will be disabled for the remainder of the ignition cycle and the "TRACTION CONTROL" lamp will illuminate.

Test Description: Number(s) below refer to circled number(s) on the diagnostic chart.

1. Checks for proper adjuster assembly motor winding resistance.
2. Checks for a poor power feed condition in CKT 2140, which the EBTCM might sense as an open.
3. Checks for open(s) in CKT 1685A and/or 1685B.
4. Checks for open(s) in CKT 1686A and/or 1686B.
5. Checks for a short between CKTs 1685 and 1686.
6. Checks for short(s) to B+ in CKT 1685A and/or 1685B.
7. Repeat Step 1 tests to ensure motor is in "home" position and a correct resistance value can be measured.
8. Sets throttle to a position which enables a special EBTCM monitor. If DTC 65 resets, there is a problem which requires continuing diagnosis.
9. Determines whether wiring or the adjuster assembly are at fault for problems found in Step 7.

Diagnostic Aids:

It is very important that a thorough inspection of the wiring and connectors be performed. Failure to carefully and fully inspect wiring and connectors may result in misdiagnosis, causing part replacement with reappearance of the malfunction.

GC4029300578010X

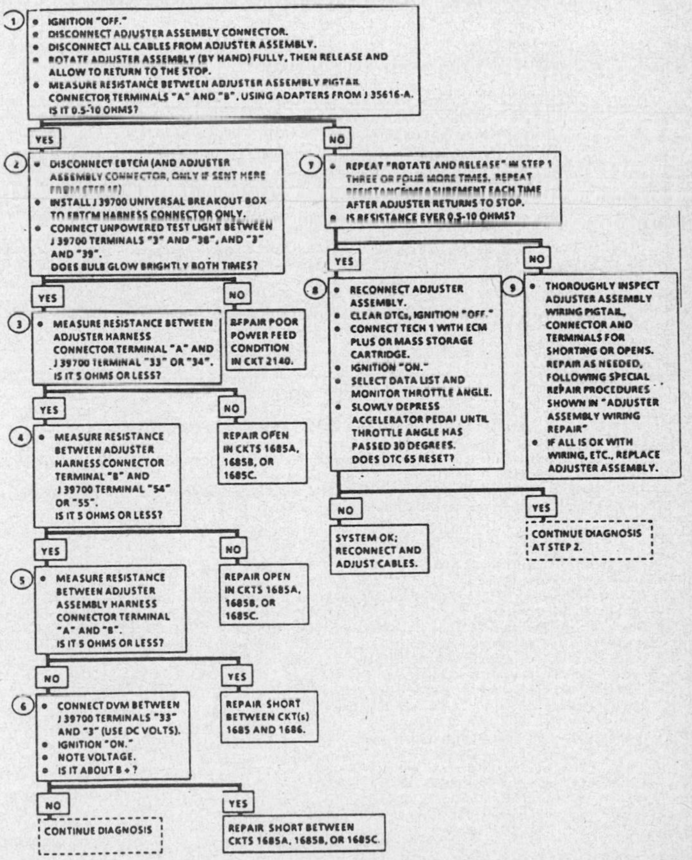

1
• IGNITION "OFF."
• DISCONNECT ADJUSTER ASSEMBLY CONNECTOR.
• DISCONNECT ALL CABLES FROM ADJUSTER ASSEMBLY.
• ROTATE ADJUSTER ASSEMBLY (BY HAND) FULLY, THEN RELEASE AND ALLOW TO RETURN TO THE STOP.
• MEASURE RESISTANCE BETWEEN ADJUSTER ASSEMBLY PIGTAIL CONNECTOR TERMINALS "A" AND "B", USING ADAPTERS FROM J 35616-A.
IS IT 0.5-10 OHMS?
YES
NO
2
• DISCONNECT EBTCM (AND ADJUSTER ASSEMBLY CONNECTOR, ONLY IF SENT HERE FROM STEP 8)
• INSTALL J 39700 UNIVERSAL BREAKOUT BOX TO EBTCM HARNESS CONNECTOR ONLY.
• CONNECT UNPOWERED TEST LIGHT BETWEEN J 39700 TERMINALS "3" AND "38", AND "3" AND "39".
DOES BULB GLOW BRIGHTLY BOTH TIMES?
7
• REPEAT "ROTATE AND RELEASE" IN STEP 1 THREE OR FOUR MORE TIMES. REPEAT RESISTANCE MEASUREMENT EACH TIME AFTER ADJUSTER RETURNS TO STOP.
• IS RESISTANCE EVER 0.5-10 OHMS?
YES
NO
REPAIR POOR POWER FEED CONDITION IN CKT 2140.
3
• MEASURE RESISTANCE BETWEEN ADJUSTER HARNESS CONNECTOR TERMINAL "A" AND J 39700 TERMINAL "33" OR "34".
IS IT 5 OHMS OR LESS?
YES
NO
REPAIR OPEN IN CKTS 1685A, 1685B, OR 1685C.
4
• MEASURE RESISTANCE BETWEEN ADJUSTER HARNESS CONNECTOR TERMINAL "B" AND J 39700 TERMINAL "54" OR "55".
IS IT 5 OHMS OR LESS?
YES
NO
REPAIR OPEN IN CKTS 1685A, 1685B, OR 1685C.
5
• MEASURE RESISTANCE BETWEEN ADJUSTER ASSEMBLY HARNESS CONNECTOR TERMINAL "A" AND "B".
IS IT 5 OHMS OR LESS?
NO
YES
REPAIR SHORT BETWEEN CKT(s) 1685 AND 1686.
6
• CONNECT DVM BETWEEN J 39700 TERMINALS "33" AND "3" (USE DC VOLTS).
• IGNITION "ON."
• NOTE VOLTAGE.
• IS IT ABOUT B+?
NO
YES
CONTINUE DIAGNOSIS
REPAIR SHORT BETWEEN CKTS 1685A, 1685B, OR 1685C.
8
• RECONNECT ADJUSTER ASSEMBLY.
• CLEAR DTCs, IGNITION "OFF."
• CONNECT TECH 1 WITH ECM PLUS OR MASS STORAGE CARTRIDGE.
• IGNITION "ON."
• SELECT DATA LIST AND MONITOR THROTTLE ANGLE.
• SLOWLY DEPRESS ACCELERATOR PEDAL UNTIL THROTTLE ANGLE HAS PASSED 30 DEGREES.
DOES DTC 65 RESET?
9
• THOROUGHLY INSPECT ADJUSTER ASSEMBLY WIRING PIGTAIL, CONNECTOR AND TERMINALS FOR SHORTING OR OPENS. REPAIR AS NEEDED, FOLLOWING SPECIAL REPAIR PROCEDURES SHOWN IN "ADJUSTER ASSEMBLY WIRING REPAIR"
• IF ALL IS OK WITH WIRING, ETC., REPLACE ADJUSTER ASSEMBLY.
NO
YES
SYSTEM OK; RECONNECT AND ADJUST CABLES.
CONTINUE DIAGNOSIS AT STEP 2.

GC4029300578020X

Fig. 145 Code 65: Adjuster Assembly Malfunction (Part 1 of 2). 1993-94 Fleetwood (RWD)

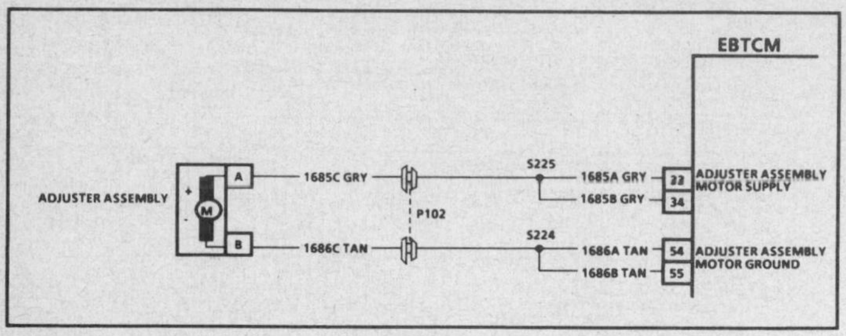
EBTCM
ADJUSTER ASSEMBLY
M
A
B
1685C GRY
1686C TAN
P102
S225
S224
1685A GRY
1685B GRY
1686A TAN
1686B TAN
33
34
54
55
ADJUSTER ASSEMBLY MOTOR SUPPLY
ADJUSTER ASSEMBLY MOTOR GROUND

DTC 65

2 of 2

ADJUSTER ASSEMBLY MALFUNCTION

Circuit Description:

The adjuster assembly circuit provides both power and ground to the adjuster assembly to help control engine torque during a TCS event.

DTC 65 will set if CKT 1685 or CKT 1686 are shorted to ground, shorted to B+, shorted to each other, or both open at the same time. The TCS system will be disabled for the remainder of the ignition cycle and the "TRACTION CONTROL" lamp will illuminate.

Test Description: Number(s) below refer to circled number(s) on the diagnostic chart.

10. Checks for short(s) to B+ in CKT 1686B and/or 1686C.
11. Checks for short(s) to ground in CKT 1685B and/or 1685C.
12. Checks for short(s) to ground in CKT 1686B and/or 1686C.
13. Checks for continued DTC setting after wiring and adjuster assembly inspections.
14. Sets throttle to a position which enables one of the EBTCM's special monitoring systems of the adjuster assembly circuits, checking for a DTC reset. If the DTC resets, the EBTCM is likely malfunctioning.
15. Checks for shorts to B+ or ground that are EBTCM-switched. If you have reached Step 13 for a second time after performing checks for EBTCM-switched malfunctions, the EBTCM is likely malfunctioning for the DTC reset.

Diagnostic Aids:

It is very important that a thorough inspection of the wiring and connectors be performed. Failure to carefully and fully inspect wiring and connectors may result in misdiagnosis, causing part replacement with reappearance of the malfunction.

GC4029300578030X

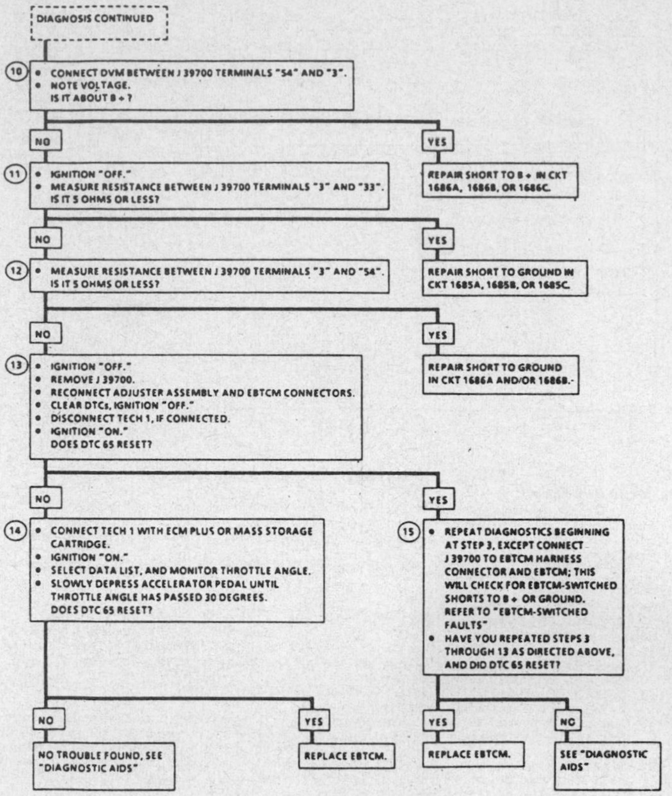
DIAGNOSIS CONTINUED
10
• CONNECT DVM BETWEEN J 39700 TERMINALS "54" AND "3".
• NOTE VOLTAGE.
IS IT ABOUT B + ?
NO
YES
REPAIR SHORT TO B + IN CKT 1686A, 1686B, OR 1686C.
11
• IGNITION "OFF."
• MEASURE RESISTANCE BETWEEN J 39700 TERMINALS "3" AND "33".
IS IT 5 OHMS OR LESS?
NO
YES
REPAIR SHORT TO GROUND IN CKT 1685A, 1685B, OR 1685C.
12
• MEASURE RESISTANCE BETWEEN J 39700 TERMINALS "3" AND "54".
IS IT 5 OHMS OR LESS?
NO
YES
REPAIR SHORT TO GROUND IN CKT 1686A AND/OR 1686B.-
13
• IGNITION "OFF."
• REMOVE J 39700.
• RECONNECT ADJUSTER ASSEMBLY AND EBTCM CONNECTORS.
• CLEAR DTCs, IGNITION "OFF."
• DISCONNECT TECH 1, IF CONNECTED.
• IGNITION "ON."
DOES DTC 65 RESET?
NO
YES
14
• CONNECT TECH 1 WITH ECM PLUS OR MASS STORAGE CARTRIDGE.
• IGNITION "ON."
• SELECT DATA LIST, AND MONITOR THROTTLE ANGLE.
• SLOWLY DEPRESS ACCELERATOR PEDAL UNTIL THROTTLE ANGLE HAS PASSED 30 DEGREES.
DOES DTC 65 RESET?
15
• REPEAT DIAGNOSTICS BEGINNING AT STEP 3, EXCEPT CONNECT J 39700 TO EBTCM HARNESS CONNECTOR AND EBTCM; THIS WILL CHECK FOR EBTCM-SWITCHED SHORTS TO B + OR GROUND. REFER TO "EBTCM-SWITCHED FAULTS"
• HAVE YOU REPEATED STEPS 3 THROUGH 13 AS DIRECTED ABOVE, AND DID DTC 65 RESET?
NO
NO TROUBLE FOUND, SEE "DIAGNOSTIC AIDS"
YES
REPLACE EBTCM.
YES
REPLACE EBTCM.
NO
SEE "DIAGNOSTIC AIDS"

GC4029300578040X

Fig. 145 Code 65: Adjuster Assembly Malfunction (Part 2 of 2). 1993-94 Fleetwood (RWD)

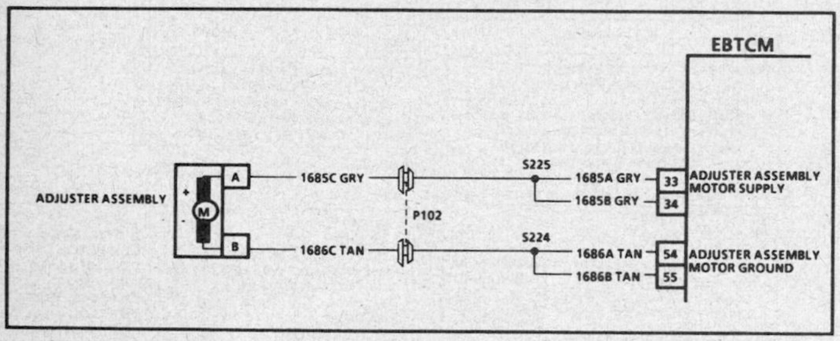
EBTCM
ADJUSTER ASSEMBLY
M
A
B
1685C GRY
1686C TAN
P102
S225
S224
1685A GRY
1685B GRY
1686A TAN
1686B TAN
33
34
54
55
ADJUSTER ASSEMBLY MOTOR SUPPLY
ADJUSTER ASSEMBLY MOTOR GROUND

DTC 66

ADJUSTER ASSEMBLY CONTROL MALFUNCTION

Circuit Description:

The adjuster assembly circuit provides both power and ground to the adjuster assembly to help control engine torque during a TCS event.

DTC 66 will set if, during a TCS event, the EBTCM delivers current greater than 16 amps to the adjuster assembly for more than three seconds without the adjuster assembly reaching its desired position.

Test Description: Number(s) below refer to circled number(s) on the diagnostic chart.

1. Checks to see if TCS DTC 65 is set, since DTC 65 conditions might affect DTC 66.
2. Checks for any mechanical binding of the adjuster assembly, attached cables, and components to which the cables are attached, which could cause excessive load on the adjuster assembly.
3. Since DTC 66 only sets during a TCS event, this check raises the vehicle on a hoist such that the rear wheels will spin while the fronts do not, inducing the system into attempting TCS control. The throttle angle must be greater than 15%, and less than 50%, and the system must attempt TCS control for greater than 3 seconds to ensure that the DTC-setting throttle and timing parameters are met when checking for a DTC 66 reset.

Diagnostic Aids:

It may be helpful to disconnect all cables from the adjuster assembly and move them manually throughout their entire operating range. Also check the components to which the cables are attached for binding.

Important

- After cables are reconnected to the adjuster assembly, perform "Adjustment Procedure-Adjuster Assembly - Accelerator and Cruise Control Cables"

GC4029300579010X

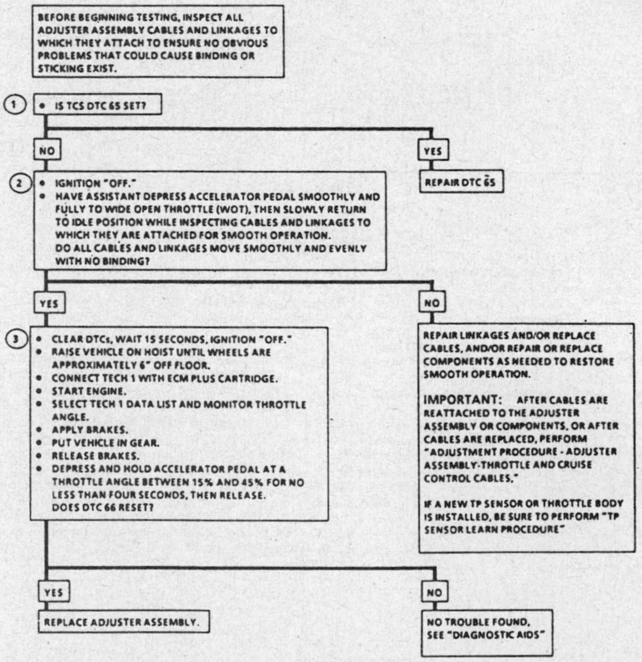
BEFORE BEGINNING TESTING, INSPECT ALL ADJUSTER ASSEMBLY CABLES AND LINKAGES TO WHICH THEY ATTACH TO ENSURE NO OBVIOUS PROBLEMS THAT COULD CAUSE BINDING OR STICKING EXIST.
1
• IS TCS DTC 65 SET?
NO
YES
REPAIR DTC 65
2
• IGNITION "OFF."
• HAVE ASSISTANT DEPRESS ACCELERATOR PEDAL SMOOTHLY AND FULLY TO WIDE OPEN THROTTLE (WOT), THEN SLOWLY RETURN TO IDLE POSITION WHILE INSPECTING CABLES AND LINKAGES TO WHICH THEY ARE ATTACHED FOR SMOOTH OPERATION.
DO ALL CABLES AND LINKAGES MOVE SMOOTHLY AND EVENLY WITH NO BINDING?
YES
NO
REPAIR LINKAGES AND/OR REPLACE CABLES, AND/OR REPAIR OR REPLACE COMPONENTS AS NEEDED TO RESTORE SMOOTH OPERATION.
IMPORTANT: AFTER CABLES ARE REATTACHED TO THE ADJUSTER ASSEMBLY OR COMPONENTS, OR AFTER CABLES ARE REPLACED, PERFORM "ADJUSTMENT PROCEDURE - ADJUSTER ASSEMBLY-THROTTLE AND CRUISE CONTROL CABLES."
IF A NEW TP SENSOR OR THROTTLE BODY IS INSTALLED, BE SURE TO PERFORM "TP SENSOR LEARN PROCEDURE"
3
• CLEAR DTCs, WAIT 15 SECONDS, IGNITION "OFF."
• RAISE VEHICLE ON HOIST UNTIL WHEELS ARE APPROXIMATELY 6" OFF FLOOR.
• CONNECT TECH 1 WITH ECM PLUS CARTRIDGE.
• START ENGINE.
• SELECT TECH 1 DATA LIST AND MONITOR THROTTLE ANGLE.
• APPLY BRAKES.
• PUT VEHICLE IN GEAR.
• RELEASE BRAKES.
• DEPRESS AND HOLD ACCELERATOR PEDAL AT A THROTTLE ANGLE BETWEEN 15% AND 45% FOR NO LESS THAN FOUR SECONDS, THEN RELEASE.
DOES DTC 66 RESET?
YES
REPLACE ADJUSTER ASSEMBLY.
NO
NO TROUBLE FOUND, SEE "DIAGNOSTIC AIDS"

GC4029300579020X

Fig. 146 Code 66: Adjuster Assembly Control Malfunction. 1993-94 Fleetwood (RWD)

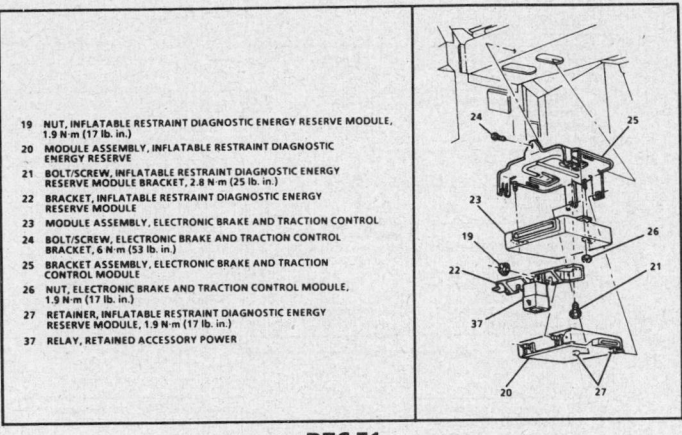

19 NUT, INFLATABLE RESTRAINT DIAGNOSTIC ENERGY RESERVE MODULE, 1.9 N·m (17 lb. in.)
20 MODULE ASSEMBLY, INFLATABLE RESTRAINT DIAGNOSTIC ENERGY RESERVE
21 BOLT/SCREW, INFLATABLE RESTRAINT DIAGNOSTIC ENERGY RESERVE MODULE BRACKET, 2.8 N·m (25 lb. in.)
22 BRACKET, INFLATABLE RESTRAINT DIAGNOSTIC ENERGY RESERVE MODULE
23 MODULE ASSEMBLY, ELECTRONIC BRAKE AND TRACTION CONTROL
24 BOLT/SCREW, ELECTRONIC BRAKE AND TRACTION CONTROL BRACKET, 6 N·m (53 lb. in.)
25 BRACKET ASSEMBLY, ELECTRONIC BRAKE AND TRACTION CONTROL MODULE
26 NUT, ELECTRONIC BRAKE AND TRACTION CONTROL MODULE, 1.9 N·m (17 lb. in.)
27 RETAINER, INFLATABLE RESTRAINT DIAGNOSTIC ENERGY RESERVE MODULE, 1.9 N·m (17 lb. in.)
37 RELAY, RETAINED ACCESSORY POWER

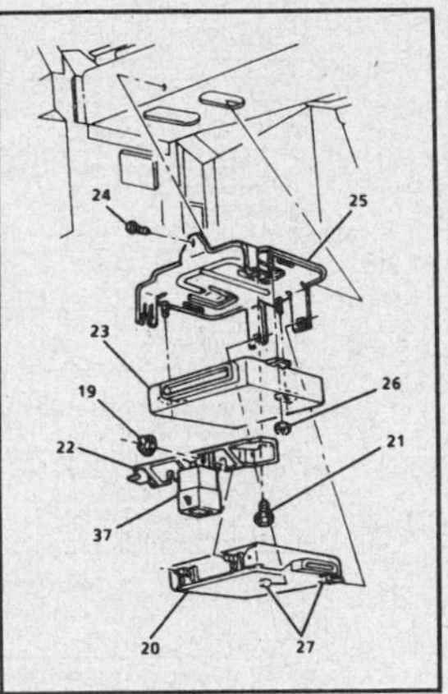
24
25
23
19
26
22
21
37
20
27

DTC 71

EBTCM INTERNAL MALFUNCTION

Circuit Description:

The EBTCM performs various diagnostic checks on itself. If it finds a problem, DTC 71 will set.

Test Description: Number(s) below refer to circled number(s) on the diagnostic chart.

1. Checks for good connections from the harness to the EBTCM itself.
2. Checks to see if the malfunction was false. If DTC 71 resets, replace the EBTCM.

GC4029300580010X

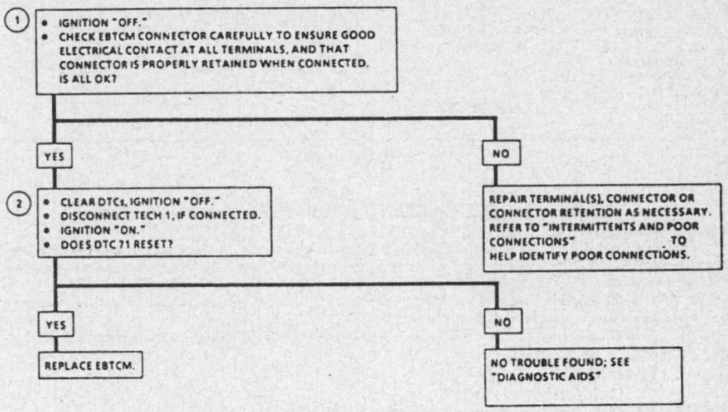
1
IGNITION "OFF."
CHECK EBTCM CONNECTOR CAREFULLY TO ENSURE GOOD ELECTRICAL CONTACT AT ALL TERMINALS, AND THAT CONNECTOR IS PROPERLY RETAINED WHEN CONNECTED. IS ALL OK?
YES
NO
2
CLEAR DTCs, IGNITION "OFF."
DISCONNECT TECH 1, IF CONNECTED.
IGNITION "ON."
DOES DTC 71 RESET?
REPAIR TERMINAL(S), CONNECTOR OR CONNECTOR RETENTION AS NECESSARY. REFER TO "INTERMITTENTS AND POOR CONNECTIONS" . TO HELP IDENTIFY POOR CONNECTIONS.
YES
NO
REPLACE EBTCM.
NO TROUBLE FOUND; SEE "DIAGNOSTIC AIDS"

GC4029300580020X

Fig. 147 Code 71: EBTCM Internal Malfunction. 1993-94 Fleetwood (RWD)

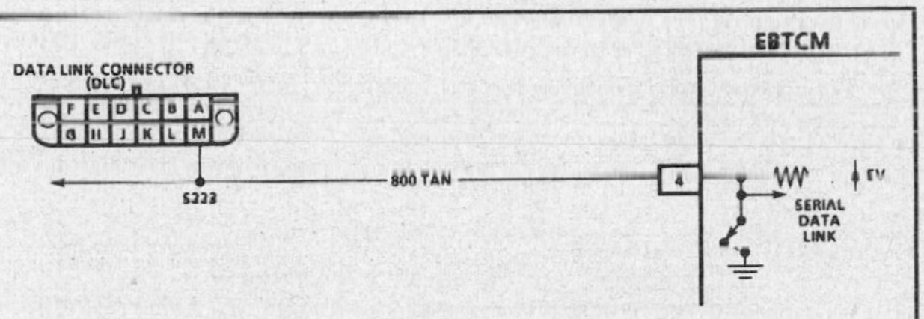
EBTCM
DATA LINK CONNECTOR (DLC)
F E D C B A
G H J K L M
800 TAN
S223
4
SERIAL DATA LINK

DTC 72

SERIAL DATA LINK MALFUNCTION

Circuit Description:

The serial data link is an asynchronous link operating at 8192 bits per second.

DTC 72 will set and the "TRACTION CONTROL" indicator will illuminate if the EBTCM detects three consecutive serial data link messages that are ignored due to errors in transmission.

Test Description: Number(s) below refer to circled number(s) on the diagnostic chart.

1. This test checks to see if the off-board device can communicate with the EBTCM. Automatic control air conditioning DTC display mode can also be used to communicate the the EBTCM. Refer to SECTION 1C for details.
2. This test checks for a short to battery in the ABS/TCS serial data circuit.
3. This test checks for a short to ground in the ABS/TCS serial data circuit.
4. This test checks for an open in the ABS/TCS serial data circuit.
5. This test checks to see if the off-board device can communicate with the EBTCM.
6. If the connections at the EBTCM and DLC connector are OK, replace the EBTCM.

Diagnostic Aids:

The problem may be intermittent. Try performing the tests shown while "wiggling" wiring and connectors; this can often cause the fault to appear.

Automatic control air conditioning DTC 32 will likely be set along with this DTC if the problem is a short to ground or B+ on the serial data circuit.

If ABS/TCS DTC 72 is set and automatic control air conditioning DTC 41 is not, the malfunction is likely to be an open between the EBTCM and the automatic control air conditioning.

GC4029300581010X

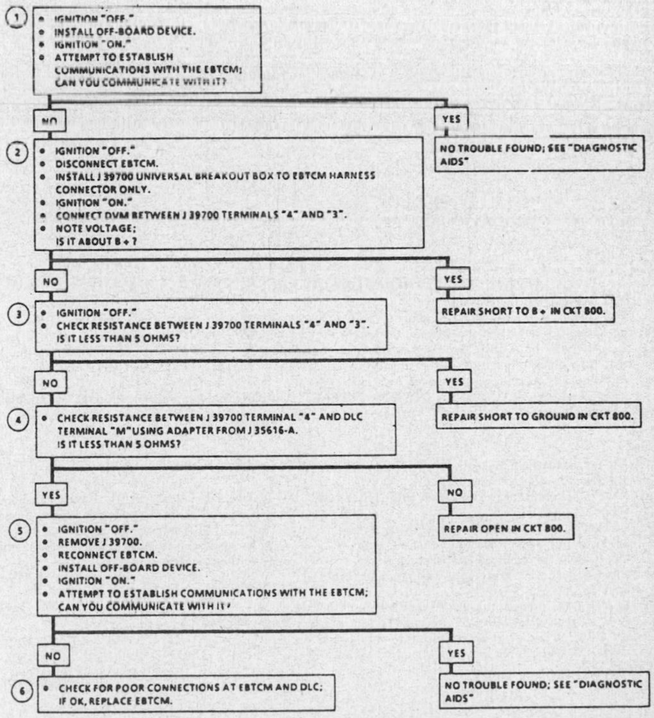
1
IGNITION "OFF."
INSTALL OFF-BOARD DEVICE.
IGNITION "ON."
ATTEMPT TO ESTABLISH COMMUNICATIONS WITH THE EBTCM; CAN YOU COMMUNICATE WITH IT?
NO
YES
NO TROUBLE FOUND; SEE "DIAGNOSTIC AIDS"
2
IGNITION "OFF."
DISCONNECT EBTCM.
INSTALL J 39700 UNIVERSAL BREAKOUT BOX TO EBTCM HARNESS CONNECTOR ONLY.
IGNITION "ON."
CONNECT DVM BETWEEN J 39700 TERMINALS "4" AND "3".
NOTE VOLTAGE; IS IT ABOUT B+?
NO
YES
REPAIR SHORT TO B+ IN CKT 800.
3
IGNITION "OFF."
CHECK RESISTANCE BETWEEN J 39700 TERMINALS "4" AND "3". IS IT LESS THAN 5 OHMS?
NO
YES
REPAIR SHORT TO GROUND IN CKT 800.
4
CHECK RESISTANCE BETWEEN J 39700 TERMINAL "4" AND DLC TERMINAL "M" USING ADAPTER FROM J 35616-A. IS IT LESS THAN 5 OHMS?
YES
NO
REPAIR OPEN IN CKT 800.
5
IGNITION "OFF."
REMOVE J 39700.
RECONNECT EBTCM.
INSTALL OFF-BOARD DEVICE.
IGNITION "ON."
ATTEMPT TO ESTABLISH COMMUNICATIONS WITH THE EBTCM; CAN YOU COMMUNICATE WITH IT?
NO
YES
6
CHECK FOR POOR CONNECTIONS AT EBTCM AND DLC; IF OK, REPLACE EBTCM.
NO TROUBLE FOUND; SEE "DIAGNOSTIC AIDS"

GC4029300581020X

Fig. 148 Code 72: Serial Data Link Malfunction. 1993-94 Fleetwood (RWD)

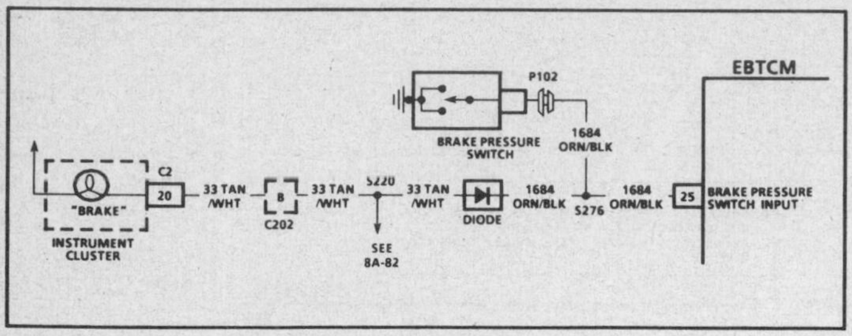
EBTCM
P102
BRAKE PRESSURE SWITCH
1684 ORN/BLK
C2
20
33 TAN /WHT
B
C202
33 TAN /WHT
S220
33 TAN /WHT
DIODE
1684 ORN/BLK
S276
1684 ORN/BLK
25
BRAKE PRESSURE SWITCH INPUT
"BRAKE"
INSTRUMENT CLUSTER
SEE 8A-82

DTC 83

1 of 2

BRAKE FLUID DIFFERENTIAL PRESSURE MALFUNCTION

Circuit Description:

The brake fluid differential pressure circuit monitors the pressure in the brake system. If the pressure becomes significantly different between the two brake hydraulic circuits, as indicated by the brake differential pressure switch, the ABS/TCS system is disabled. This is done to prevent introduction of air into the brake system. The diode is used to prevent disabling ABS/TCS if illumination of the red "BRAKE" warning lamp occurs because of application of the parking brake.

DTC 83 will set and the "ANTI-LOCK" and "TRACTION CONTROL" lamps will illuminate if CKT 1684 is low (grounded).

Test Description: Number(s) below refer to circled number(s) on the diagnostic chart.

1. Checks for proper brake fluid level in the master cylinder reservoir.
2. Checks for illumination of the red "BRAKE" warning lamp for reasons other than parking brake engagement.
3. Checks for brake pressure switch stuck closed.
4. Checks for short from CKT 1684 to chassis ground.
5. Adds fluid, noted to be low in Step 1, then checks for DTC reset.

Diagnostic Aids:

It is very important that a thorough inspection of the wiring and connectors be performed. Failure to carefully and fully inspect wiring and connectors may result in misdiagnosis, causing part replacement with reappearance of the malfunction.

GC4029300582010X

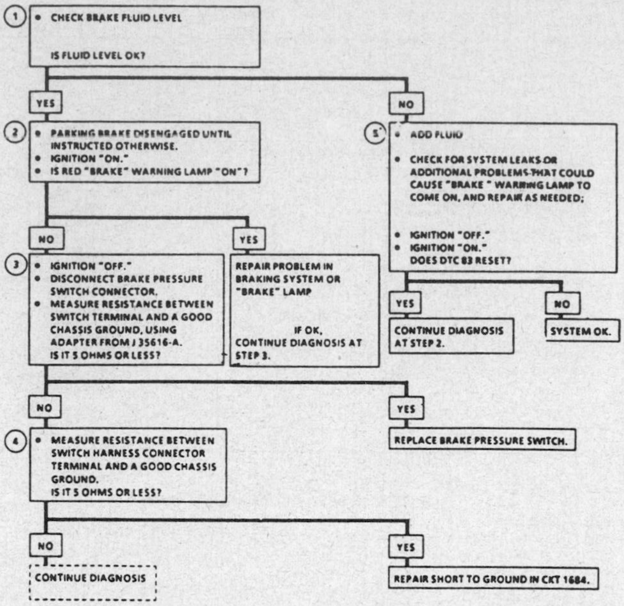
1 • CHECK BRAKE FLUID LEVEL
IS FLUID LEVEL OK?
YES
NO
2 • PARKING BRAKE DISENGAGED UNTIL INSTRUCTED OTHERWISE.
• IGNITION "ON."
• IS RED "BRAKE" WARNING LAMP "ON"?
5 • ADD FLUID
• CHECK FOR SYSTEM LEAKS OR ADDITIONAL PROBLEMS THAT COULD CAUSE "BRAKE" WARNING LAMP TO COME ON, AND REPAIR AS NEEDED;
• IGNITION "OFF."
• IGNITION "ON."
DOES DTC 83 RESET?
NO
YES
3 • IGNITION "OFF."
• DISCONNECT BRAKE PRESSURE SWITCH CONNECTOR.
• MEASURE RESISTANCE BETWEEN SWITCH TERMINAL AND A GOOD CHASSIS GROUND, USING ADAPTER FROM J 35616-A.
IS IT 5 OHMS OR LESS?
REPAIR PROBLEM IN BRAKING SYSTEM OR "BRAKE" LAMP
IF OK, CONTINUE DIAGNOSIS AT STEP 3.
YES
NO
CONTINUE DIAGNOSIS AT STEP 2.
SYSTEM OK.
NO
YES
4 • MEASURE RESISTANCE BETWEEN SWITCH HARNESS CONNECTOR TERMINAL AND A GOOD CHASSIS GROUND.
IS IT 5 OHMS OR LESS?
REPLACE BRAKE PRESSURE SWITCH.
NO
YES
CONTINUE DIAGNOSIS
REPAIR SHORT TO GROUND IN CKT 1684.

GC4029300582020X

Fig. 149 Code 83: Brake Fluid Differential Pressure Malfunction (Part 1 of 2). 1993-94 Fleetwood (RWD)

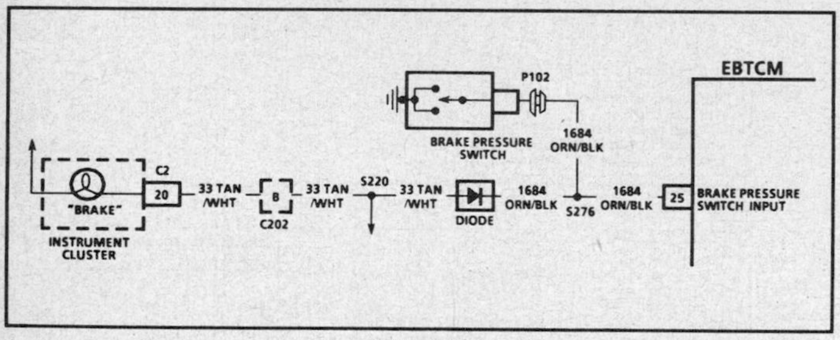
EBTCM
P102
BRAKE PRESSURE SWITCH
1684 ORN/BLK
C2
20
33 TAN /WHT
B
C202
33 TAN /WHT
S220
33 TAN /WHT
DIODE
1684 ORN/BLK
S276
1684 ORN/BLK
25
BRAKE PRESSURE SWITCH INPUT
"BRAKE"
INSTRUMENT CLUSTER

DTC 83

2 of 2

BRAKE FLUID DIFFERENTIAL PRESSURE MALFUNCTION

Circuit Description:

The brake fluid differential pressure circuit monitors the pressure in the brake system. If the pressure becomes significantly different between the two brake hydraulic circuits, as indicated by the brake differential pressure switch, the ABS/TCS system is disabled. This is done to prevent introduction of air into the brake system. The diode is used to prevent disabling ABS/TCS if illumination of the red "BRAKE" warning lamp occurs because of application of the parking brake.

DTC 83 will set and the "ANTI-LOCK" and "TRACTION CONTROL" lamps will illuminate if CKT 1684 is low (grounded).

Test Description: Number(s) below refer to circled number(s) on the diagnostic chart.

6. Checks for continuing DTC reset after checks in Steps 1-4.
7. Checks for DTC reset when parking brake is engaged, likely due to a malfunctioning diode.
8. Checks for parking brake switch stuck closed.
9. Checks for short to ground in parking brake switch CKT 33.
10. Replaces malfunctioning diode found in Step 7 or Step 10, then checks for DTC reset. If DTC resets, the EBTCM is determining there is a problem in CKT 1684 and related circuitry when there is not.

Diagnostic Aids:

It is very important that a thorough inspection of the wiring and connectors be performed. Failure to carefully and fully inspect wiring and connectors may result in misdiagnosis, causing part replacement with reappearance of the malfunction.

GC4029300582030X

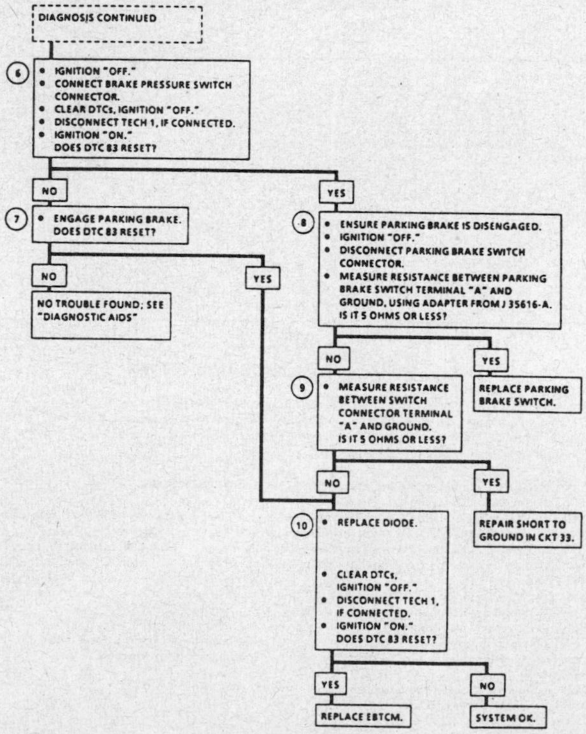
DIAGNOSIS CONTINUED
6 • IGNITION "OFF."
• CONNECT BRAKE PRESSURE SWITCH CONNECTOR.
• CLEAR DTCs, IGNITION "OFF."
• DISCONNECT TECH 1, IF CONNECTED.
• IGNITION "ON."
DOES DTC 83 RESET?
NO
YES
7 • ENGAGE PARKING BRAKE.
DOES DTC 83 RESET?
8 • ENSURE PARKING BRAKE IS DISENGAGED.
• IGNITION "OFF."
• DISCONNECT PARKING BRAKE SWITCH CONNECTOR.
• MEASURE RESISTANCE BETWEEN PARKING BRAKE SWITCH TERMINAL "A" AND GROUND, USING ADAPTER FROM J 35616-A.
IS IT 5 OHMS OR LESS?
NO
YES
NO TROUBLE FOUND; SEE "DIAGNOSTIC AIDS"
NO
YES
9 • MEASURE RESISTANCE BETWEEN SWITCH CONNECTOR TERMINAL "A" AND GROUND.
IS IT 5 OHMS OR LESS?
REPLACE PARKING BRAKE SWITCH.
NO
YES
10 • REPLACE DIODE.
• CLEAR DTCs, IGNITION "OFF."
• DISCONNECT TECH 1, IF CONNECTED.
• IGNITION "ON."
DOES DTC 83 RESET?
REPAIR SHORT TO GROUND IN CKT 33.
YES
NO
REPLACE EBTCM.
SYSTEM OK.

GC4029300582040X

Fig. 149 Code 83: Brake Fluid Differential Pressure Malfunction (Part 2 of 2). 1993-94 Fleetwood (RWD)

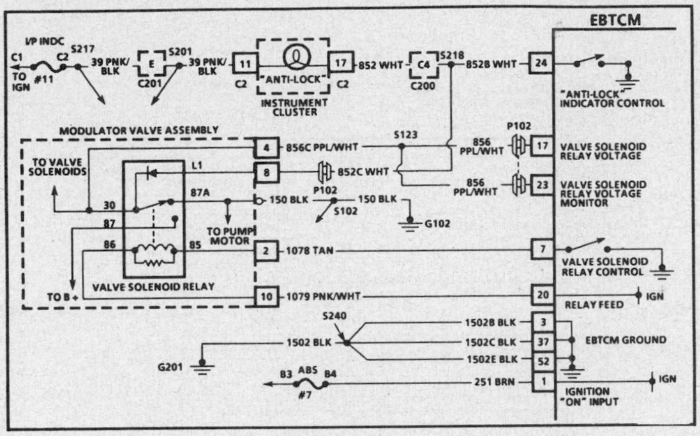
EBTCM
I/P INDC
C1
C2
S217
TO IGN #11
39 PNK/BLK
S201
C201
INSTRUMENT CLUSTER
"ANTI-LOCK"
852 WHT
C4
S218
852B WHT
C200
"ANTI-LOCK" INDICATOR CONTROL
MODULATOR VALVE ASSEMBLY
TO VALVE SOLENOIDS
856C PPL/WHT
S123
P102
856 PPL/WHT
VALVE SOLENOID RELAY VOLTAGE
852C WHT
VALVE SOLENOID RELAY VOLTAGE MONITOR
150 BLK
S102
G102
TO PUMP MOTOR
1078 TAN
VALVE SOLENOID RELAY CONTROL
VALVE SOLENOID RELAY
TO B+
1079 PNK/WHT
RELAY FEED
IGN
S240
1502 BLK
1502B BLK
1502C BLK
1502E BLK
EBTCM GROUND
G201
B3 ABS B4
#7
251 BRN
IGNITION "ON" INPUT

CHART A

"ANTI-LOCK" INDICATOR "ON" WITH NO DTCs SET

Test Description: Number(s) below refer to circled number(s) on the diagnostic chart.

1. This test confirms that a malfunction condition exists.
2. This test determines whether the malfunction is due to a DTC setting condition, an indicator low side circuit malfunction, or an EBTCM supply power malfunction.
3. This test checks whether the malfunction is due to an open fuse.
4. This test checks for an open in the ground feed to the EBTCM.
5. This test checks for an open power feed circuit.
6. This test checks whether the fuse failure is due to a short to ground.

GC4029300583010X

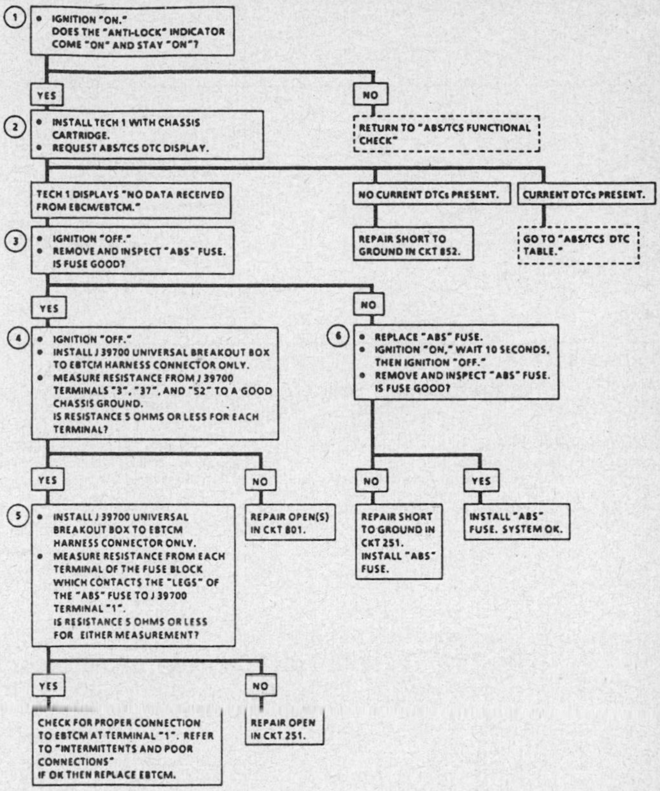
1 • IGNITION "ON."
DOES THE "ANTI-LOCK" INDICATOR COME "ON" AND STAY "ON"?
YES
NO
RETURN TO "ABS/TCS FUNCTIONAL CHECK"
2 • INSTALL TECH 1 WITH CHASSIS CARTRIDGE.
• REQUEST ABS/TCS DTC DISPLAY.
TECH 1 DISPLAYS "NO DATA RECEIVED FROM EBCM/EBTCM."
NO CURRENT DTCs PRESENT.
CURRENT DTCs PRESENT.
REPAIR SHORT TO GROUND IN CKT 852.
GO TO "ABS/TCS DTC TABLE."
3 • IGNITION "OFF."
• REMOVE AND INSPECT "ABS" FUSE.
IS FUSE GOOD?
YES
NO
4 • IGNITION "OFF."
• INSTALL J 39700 UNIVERSAL BREAKOUT BOX TO EBTCM HARNESS CONNECTOR ONLY.
• MEASURE RESISTANCE FROM J 39700 TERMINALS "3", "37", AND "52" TO A GOOD CHASSIS GROUND.
IS RESISTANCE 5 OHMS OR LESS FOR EACH TERMINAL?
6 • REPLACE "ABS" FUSE.
• IGNITION "ON," WAIT 10 SECONDS, THEN IGNITION "OFF."
• REMOVE AND INSPECT "ABS" FUSE.
IS FUSE GOOD?
YES
NO
NO
YES
5 • INSTALL J 39700 UNIVERSAL BREAKOUT BOX TO EBTCM HARNESS CONNECTOR ONLY.
• MEASURE RESISTANCE FROM EACH TERMINAL OF THE FUSE BLOCK WHICH CONTACTS THE "LEGS" OF THE "ABS" FUSE TO J 39700 TERMINAL "1".
IS RESISTANCE 5 OHMS OR LESS FOR EITHER MEASUREMENT?
REPAIR OPEN(S) IN CKT 801.
REPAIR SHORT TO GROUND IN CKT 251.
INSTALL "ABS" FUSE.
INSTALL "ABS" FUSE. SYSTEM OK.
YES
NO
CHECK FOR PROPER CONNECTION TO EBTCM AT TERMINAL "1". REFER TO "INTERMITTENTS AND POOR CONNECTIONS"
IF OK THEN REPLACE EBTCM.
REPAIR OPEN IN CKT 251.

GC4029300583020X

Fig. 150 Test A: Anti-Lock Indicator On w/No Codes Set. 1993-94 Fleetwood (RWD)

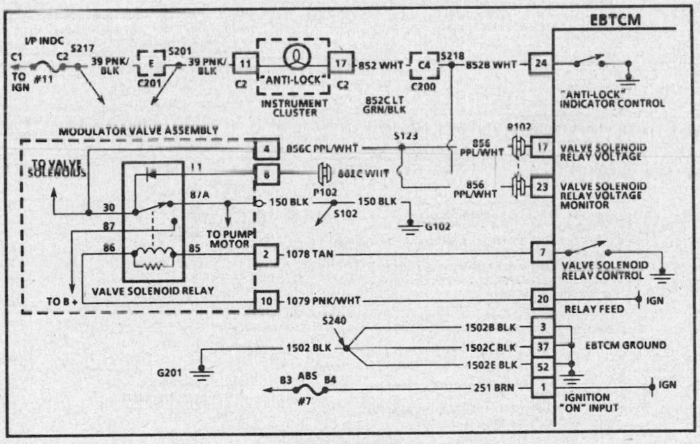
EBTCM
I/P INDC
C1
C2
S217
TO IGN #11
39 PNK/BLK
S201
C201
INSTRUMENT CLUSTER
"ANTI-LOCK"
852 WHT
C4
S218
852B WHT
C200
852C LT GRN/BLK
"ANTI-LOCK" INDICATOR CONTROL
MODULATOR VALVE ASSEMBLY
TO VALVE SOLENOIDS
856C PPL/WHT
S123
856 PPL/WHT
VALVE SOLENOID RELAY VOLTAGE
VALVE SOLENOID RELAY VOLTAGE MONITOR
150 BLK
P102
S102
G102
TO PUMP MOTOR
1078 TAN
VALVE SOLENOID RELAY CONTROL
VALVE SOLENOID RELAY
TO B+
1079 PNK/WHT
RELAY FEED
IGN
S240
1502 BLK
1502B BLK
1502C BLK
1502E BLK
EBTCM GROUND
G201
B3 ABS B4
#7
251 BRN
IGNITION "ON" INPUT

CHART B

"ANTI-LOCK" INDICATOR INOPERATIVE OR FLICKERS BRIEFLY AT IGNITION "ON"

Test Description: Number(s) below refer to circled number(s) on the diagnostic chart.

1. This test confirms that a malfunction condition exists.
2. This test checks the integrity of the indicator bulb.
3. This test checks for an indicator low side circuit open.
4. This test checks for an indicator low side circuit short to B+.
5. This test determines whether the malfunction is due to an EBTCM circuit fault or an open in the instrument cluster.

GC4029300584010X

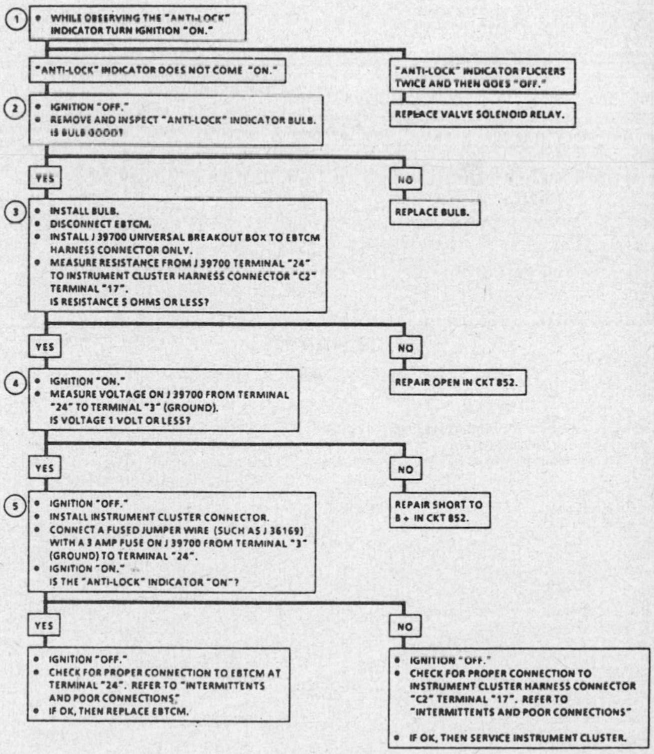
1 • WHILE OBSERVING THE "ANTI-LOCK" INDICATOR TURN IGNITION "ON."
"ANTI-LOCK" INDICATOR DOES NOT COME "ON."
"ANTI-LOCK" INDICATOR FLICKERS TWICE AND THEN GOES "OFF."
REPLACE VALVE SOLENOID RELAY.
2 • IGNITION "OFF."
• REMOVE AND INSPECT "ANTI-LOCK" INDICATOR BULB.
IS BULB GOOD?
YES
NO
REPLACE BULB.
3 • INSTALL BULB.
• DISCONNECT EBTCM.
• INSTALL J 39700 UNIVERSAL BREAKOUT BOX TO EBTCM HARNESS CONNECTOR ONLY.
• MEASURE RESISTANCE FROM J 39700 TERMINAL "24" TO INSTRUMENT CLUSTER HARNESS CONNECTOR "C2" TERMINAL "17".
IS RESISTANCE 5 OHMS OR LESS?
YES
NO
REPAIR OPEN IN CKT 852.
4 • IGNITION "ON."
• MEASURE VOLTAGE ON J 39700 FROM TERMINAL "24" TO TERMINAL "3" (GROUND).
IS VOLTAGE 1 VOLT OR LESS?
YES
NO
REPAIR SHORT TO B+ IN CKT 852.
5 • IGNITION "OFF."
• INSTALL INSTRUMENT CLUSTER CONNECTOR.
• CONNECT A FUSED JUMPER WIRE (SUCH AS J 36169) WITH A 3 AMP FUSE ON J 39700 FROM TERMINAL "3" (GROUND) TO TERMINAL "24".
• IGNITION "ON."
IS THE "ANTI-LOCK" INDICATOR "ON"?
YES
NO
• IGNITION "OFF."
• CHECK FOR PROPER CONNECTION TO EBTCM AT TERMINAL "24". REFER TO "INTERMITTENTS AND POOR CONNECTIONS"
• IF OK, THEN REPLACE EBTCM.
• IGNITION "OFF."
• CHECK FOR PROPER CONNECTION TO INSTRUMENT CLUSTER HARNESS CONNECTOR "C2" TERMINAL "17". REFER TO "INTERMITTENTS AND POOR CONNECTIONS"
• IF OK, THEN SERVICE INSTRUMENT CLUSTER.

GC4029300584020X

Fig. 151 Test B: Anti-Lock Indicator Inoperative Or Flickers Briefly At Ignition. 1993-94 Fleetwood (RWD)

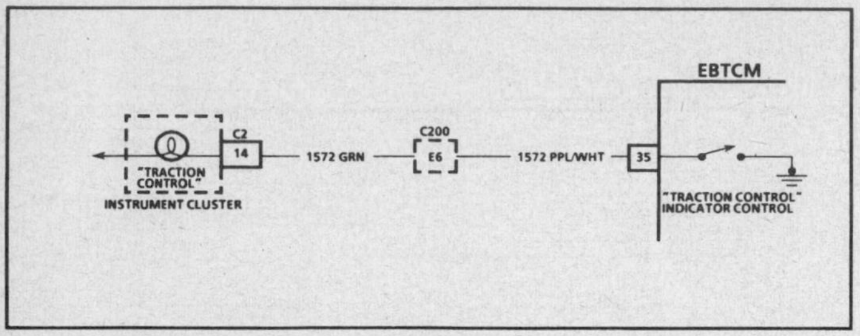
EBTCM
C2
14
"TRACTION CONTROL"
INSTRUMENT CLUSTER
1572 GRN
C200
E6
1572 PPL/WHT
35
"TRACTION CONTROL" INDICATOR CONTROL

CHART C

"TRACTION CONTROL" INDICATOR "ON" WITH NO DTCs SET

Test Description: Number(s) below refer to circled number(s) on the diagnostic chart.

1. This test confirms that a malfunction condition exists.
2. This test checks if the malfunction is due to a DTC-setting condition.
3. This test checks whether the malfunction is due to an indicator low side circuit short to ground or an EBTCM circuit fault.

GC4029300585010X

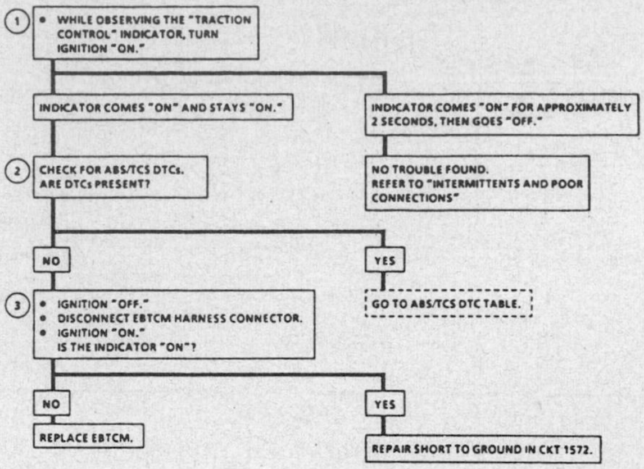
1
• WHILE OBSERVING THE "TRACTION CONTROL" INDICATOR, TURN IGNITION "ON."
INDICATOR COMES "ON" AND STAYS "ON."
INDICATOR COMES "ON" FOR APPROXIMATELY 2 SECONDS, THEN GOES "OFF."
2
CHECK FOR ABS/TCS DTCs. ARE DTCs PRESENT?
NO TROUBLE FOUND. REFER TO "INTERMITTENTS AND POOR CONNECTIONS"
NO
YES
3
• IGNITION "OFF."
• DISCONNECT EBTCM HARNESS CONNECTOR.
• IGNITION "ON." IS THE INDICATOR "ON"?
GO TO ABS/TCS DTC TABLE.
NO
YES
REPLACE EBTCM.
REPAIR SHORT TO GROUND IN CKT 1572.

GC4029300585020X

Fig. 152 Test C: Traction Control Indicator On w/No Codes Set. 1993-94 Fleetwood (RWD)

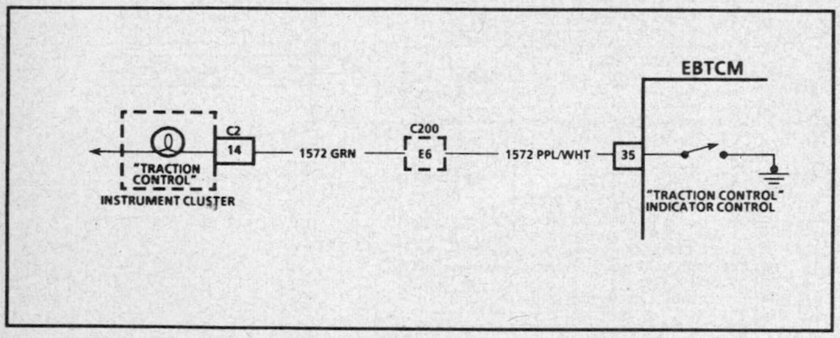
EBTCM
C2
14
"TRACTION CONTROL"
INSTRUMENT CLUSTER
1572 GRN
C200
E6
1572 PPL/WHT
35
"TRACTION CONTROL" INDICATOR CONTROL

CHART D

"TRACTION CONTROL" INDICATOR INOPERATIVE

Test Description: Number(s) below refer to circled number(s) on the diagnostic chart.

1. This test confirms that a malfunction condition exists.
2. This test checks the integrity of the indicator bulb.
3. This test checks for an indicator low side circuit open.
4. This test checks for an indicator low side circuit short to B+.
5. This test determines whether the malfunction is due to an EBTCM circuit malfunction or an open in the instrument cluster.

GC4029300586010X

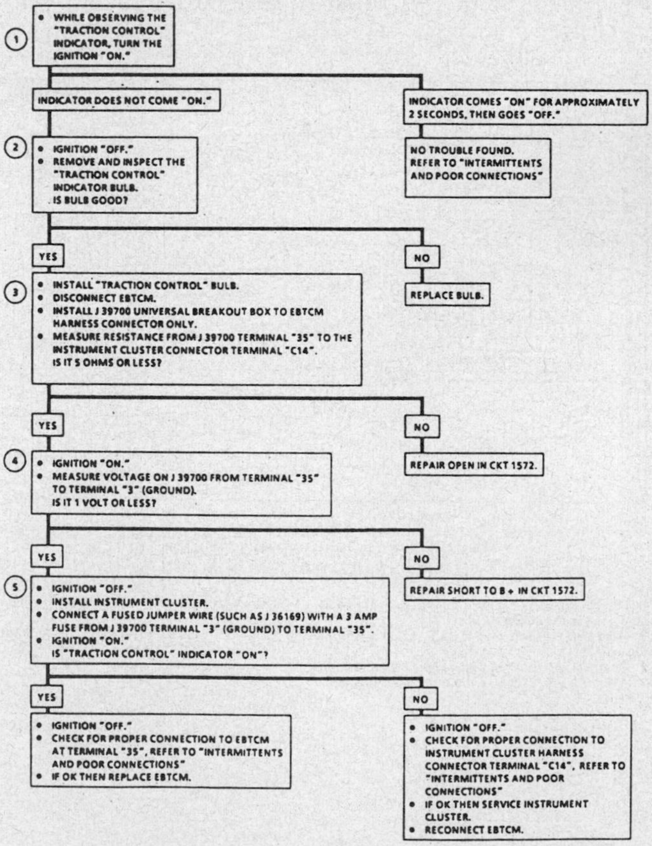
1
• WHILE OBSERVING THE "TRACTION CONTROL" INDICATOR, TURN THE IGNITION "ON."
INDICATOR DOES NOT COME "ON."
INDICATOR COMES "ON" FOR APPROXIMATELY 2 SECONDS, THEN GOES "OFF."
2
• IGNITION "OFF."
• REMOVE AND INSPECT THE "TRACTION CONTROL" INDICATOR BULB. IS BULB GOOD?
NO TROUBLE FOUND. REFER TO "INTERMITTENTS AND POOR CONNECTIONS"
YES
NO
3
• INSTALL "TRACTION CONTROL" BULB.
• DISCONNECT EBTCM.
• INSTALL J 39700 UNIVERSAL BREAKOUT BOX TO EBTCM HARNESS CONNECTOR ONLY.
• MEASURE RESISTANCE FROM J 39700 TERMINAL "35" TO THE INSTRUMENT CLUSTER CONNECTOR TERMINAL "C14". IS IT 5 OHMS OR LESS?
REPLACE BULB.
YES
NO
4
• IGNITION "ON."
• MEASURE VOLTAGE ON J 39700 FROM TERMINAL "35" TO TERMINAL "3" (GROUND). IS IT 1 VOLT OR LESS?
REPAIR OPEN IN CKT 1572.
YES
NO
5
• IGNITION "OFF."
• INSTALL INSTRUMENT CLUSTER.
• CONNECT A FUSED JUMPER WIRE (SUCH AS J 36169) WITH A 3 AMP FUSE FROM J 39700 TERMINAL "3" (GROUND) TO TERMINAL "35".
• IGNITION "ON." IS "TRACTION CONTROL" INDICATOR "ON"?
REPAIR SHORT TO B+ IN CKT 1572.
YES
NO
• IGNITION "OFF."
• CHECK FOR PROPER CONNECTION TO EBTCM AT TERMINAL "35", REFER TO "INTERMITTENTS AND POOR CONNECTIONS"
• IF OK THEN REPLACE EBTCM.
• IGNITION "OFF."
• CHECK FOR PROPER CONNECTION TO INSTRUMENT CLUSTER HARNESS CONNECTOR TERMINAL "C14", REFER TO "INTERMITTENTS AND POOR CONNECTIONS"
• IF OK THEN SERVICE INSTRUMENT CLUSTER.
• RECONNECT EBTCM.

GC4029300586020X

Fig. 153 Test D: Traction Control Indicator Inoperative. 1993-94 Fleetwood (RWD)

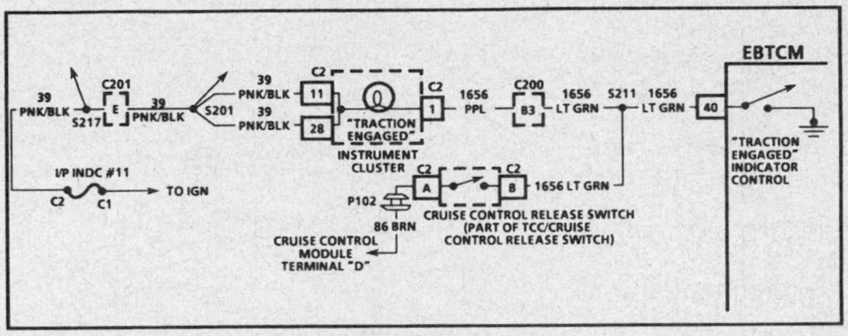
EBTCM
39
PNK/BLK
C201
S217
E
39
PNK/BLK
S201
39
PNK/BLK
39
PNK/BLK
C2
11
28
"TRACTION ENGAGED"
INSTRUMENT CLUSTER
C2
1
1656
PPL
C200
B3
1656
LT GRN
S211
1656
LT GRN
40
"TRACTION ENGAGED" INDICATOR CONTROL
I/P INDC #11
C2
C1
TO IGN
P102
86 BRN
CRUISE CONTROL MODULE TERMINAL "D"
A
B
1656 LT GRN
CRUISE CONTROL RELEASE SWITCH (PART OF TCC/CRUISE CONTROL RELEASE SWITCH)

CHART E

"TRACTION ENGAGED" INDICATOR "ON" WITH NO DTCs SET

Test Description: Number(s) below refer to circled number(s) on the diagnostic chart.

1. This test confirms that a malfunction condition exists.
2. This test checks whether the malfunction is due to a DTC-setting condition.
3. This test determines if the malfunction is due to an indicator low side circuit short to ground.
4. Checks for the indicator remaining "ON" after the bulb check is complete. Since all other portions of the circuit are OK, the EBTCM must be incorrectly commanding the indicator "ON" when it should not.

GC4029300587010X

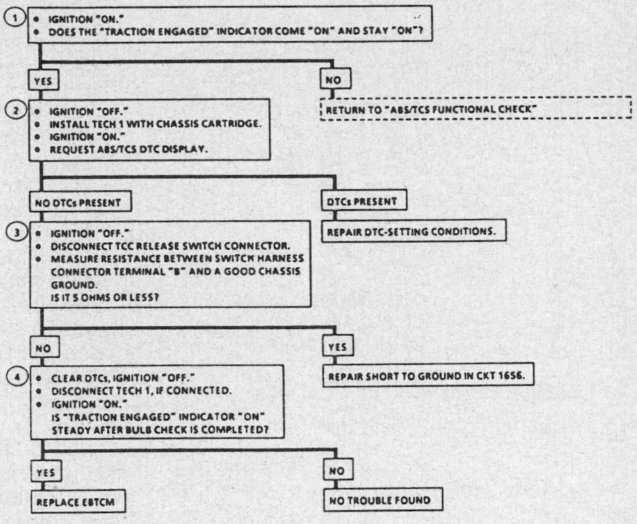
1
• IGNITION "ON."
• DOES THE "TRACTION ENGAGED" INDICATOR COME "ON" AND STAY "ON"?
YES
NO
RETURN TO "ABS/TCS FUNCTIONAL CHECK"
2
• IGNITION "OFF."
• INSTALL TECH 1 WITH CHASSIS CARTRIDGE.
• IGNITION "ON."
• REQUEST ABS/TCS DTC DISPLAY.
NO DTCs PRESENT
DTCs PRESENT
REPAIR DTC-SETTING CONDITIONS.
3
• IGNITION "OFF."
• DISCONNECT TCC RELEASE SWITCH CONNECTOR.
• MEASURE RESISTANCE BETWEEN SWITCH HARNESS CONNECTOR TERMINAL "B" AND A GOOD CHASSIS GROUND.
IS IT 5 OHMS OR LESS?
NO
YES
REPAIR SHORT TO GROUND IN CKT 1656.
4
• CLEAR DTCs, IGNITION "OFF."
• DISCONNECT TECH 1, IF CONNECTED.
• IGNITION "ON."
IS "TRACTION ENGAGED" INDICATOR "ON" STEADY AFTER BULB CHECK IS COMPLETED?
YES
NO
REPLACE EBTCM
NO TROUBLE FOUND

GC4029300587020X

Fig. 154 Test E: Traction Engaged Indicator On w/No Codes Set. 1993-94 Fleetwood (RWD)

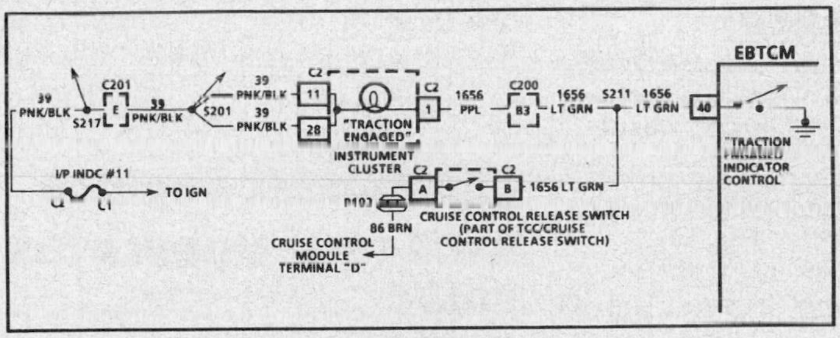
EBTCM
39
PNK/BLK
C201
S217
E
39
PNK/BLK
S201
39
PNK/BLK
39
PNK/BLK
C2
11
28
"TRACTION ENGAGED"
INSTRUMENT CLUSTER
C2
1
1656
PPL
C200
B3
1656
LT GRN
S211
1656
LT GRN
40
INDICATOR CONTROL
I/P INDC #11
TO IGN
P102
86 BRN
CRUISE CONTROL MODULE TERMINAL "D"
A
B
1656 LT GRN
CRUISE CONTROL RELEASE SWITCH (PART OF TCC/CRUISE CONTROL RELEASE SWITCH)

CHART F

"TRACTION ENGAGED" INDICATOR INOPERATIVE WITH NO DTCs SET

Test Description: Number(s) below refer to circled number(s) on the diagnostic chart.

1. Checks for blown "I/P INDC #11" fuse causing inoperative indicator.
2. Replaces fuse, then checks for other indicators fed from CKT 39 as working properly. If not, CKT 39 to the instrument cluster is open.
3. Checks "TRACTION ENGAGED" bulb itself.
4. Checks for open in CKT 1656 between EBTCM and instrument cluster.
5. Checks for short to B+ on CKT 1656 causing inoperative bulb.
6. Checks if problem is within instrument cluster circuitry, due to intermittent wiring or connections, or due to a malfunctioning EBTCM.
7. Checks for short to ground in CKT 39 which blows fuses.
8. Checks for proper "TRACTION ENGAGED" lamp operation after blown fuse replacement.

GC4029300588010X

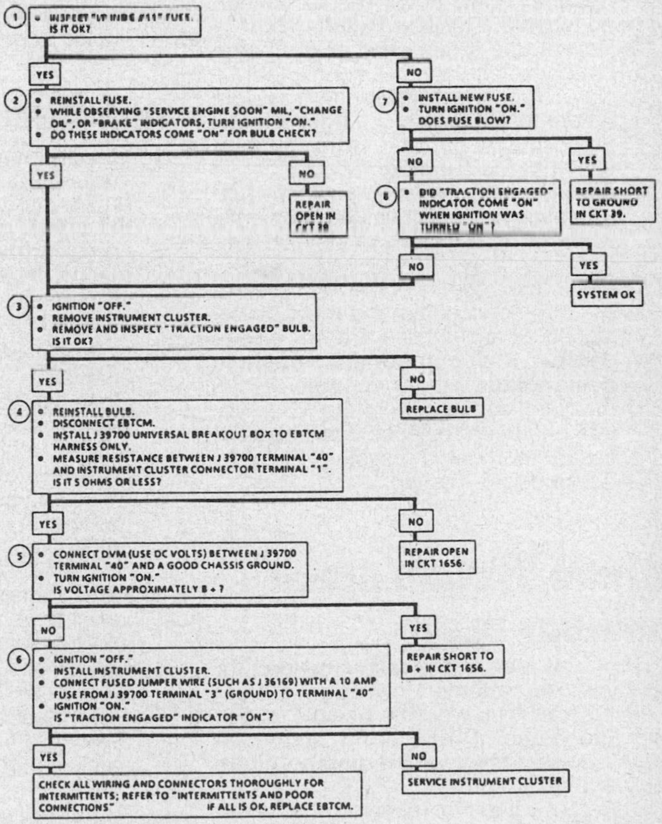
1
IS IT OK?
YES
NO
2
• REINSTALL FUSE.
• WHILE OBSERVING "SERVICE ENGINE SOON" MIL, "CHANGE OIL", OR "BRAKE" INDICATORS, TURN IGNITION "ON."
• DO THESE INDICATORS COME "ON" FOR BULB CHECK?
YES
NO
REPAIR OPEN IN
7
• INSTALL NEW FUSE.
• TURN IGNITION "ON."
DOES FUSE BLOW?
NO
YES
REPAIR SHORT TO GROUND IN CKT 39.
8
• DID "TRACTION ENGAGED" INDICATOR COME "ON" WHEN IGNITION WAS
NO
YES
SYSTEM OK
3
• IGNITION "OFF."
• REMOVE INSTRUMENT CLUSTER.
• REMOVE AND INSPECT "TRACTION ENGAGED" BULB.
IS IT OK?
YES
NO
REPLACE BULB
4
• REINSTALL BULB.
• DISCONNECT EBTCM.
• INSTALL J 39700 UNIVERSAL BREAKOUT BOX TO EBTCM HARNESS ONLY.
• MEASURE RESISTANCE BETWEEN J 39700 TERMINAL "40" AND INSTRUMENT CLUSTER CONNECTOR TERMINAL "1".
IS IT 5 OHMS OR LESS?
YES
NO
REPAIR OPEN IN CKT 1656.
5
• CONNECT DVM (USE DC VOLTS) BETWEEN J 39700 TERMINAL "40" AND A GOOD CHASSIS GROUND.
• TURN IGNITION "ON."
IS VOLTAGE APPROXIMATELY B+?
NO
YES
REPAIR SHORT TO B+ IN CKT 1656.
6
• IGNITION "OFF."
• INSTALL INSTRUMENT CLUSTER.
• CONNECT FUSED JUMPER WIRE (SUCH AS J 36169) WITH A 10 AMP FUSE FROM J 39700 TERMINAL "3" (GROUND) TO TERMINAL "40"
• IGNITION "ON."
IS "TRACTION ENGAGED" INDICATOR "ON"?
YES
NO
CHECK ALL WIRING AND CONNECTORS THOROUGHLY FOR INTERMITTENTS; REFER TO "INTERMITTENTS AND POOR CONNECTIONS" IF ALL IS OK, REPLACE EBTCM.
SERVICE INSTRUMENT CLUSTER

GC4029300588020X

Fig. 155 Test F: Traction Engaged Indicator Inoperative w/No Codes Set. 1993-94 Fleetwood (RWD)

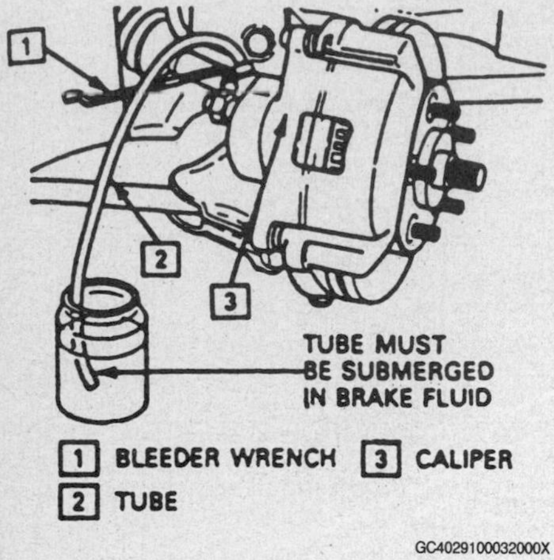
1
2
3
TUBE MUST BE SUBMERGED IN BRAKE FLUID
1 BLEEDER WRENCH
3 CALIPER
2 TUBE
GC4029100032000X

Fig. 156 Bleeding brakes

1. If any welding work is to be done on the vehicle using and arc welder, the EBCM and hydraulic modulator connectors should be disconnected.
2. Hydraulic modulator and EBCM connectors should never be disconnected when the ignition switch is on.
3. Do not use a fast charger to charge battery when battery is connected. Always disconnect battery from system before using a fast charger. **Never disconnect battery from system with engine running.**
4. Always note routing, position and mounting of electrical components, wiring and connectors of the ABS system.
5. Many components of the ABS system are non-serviceable and must be replaced as assemblies. **Do not disassemble any component which is designated non-serviceable.**
6. After any component of the ABS system has been replaced it will be necessary to check the system. Refer to "Diagnosis & Testing."

Brake System Bleed

MANUAL BLEED

Pressure bleeding is recommended for all hydraulic systems. However, if a pressure bleeder is unavailable, use the following procedure. **Brake fluid damages painted surfaces. Immediately clean any spilled fluid.**

1. Remove vacuum reserve by pumping brakes several times with engine off.
2. Fill master cylinder reservoir with clean brake fluid. Check fluid level often during bleeding procedure; do not let reservoir fall below half full.
3. If necessary, bleed master cylinder as follows:
   a. Disconnect master cylinder forward brake line connection until fluid flows from reservoir. Reconnect and tighten brake line.
   b. Instruct an assistant to slowly depress brake pedal one time and hold.
   c. Crack open front brake line connection again, purging air from cylinder.
   d. Retighten connection and slowly release brake pedal.
   e. Wait 15 seconds, then repeat until all air is purged.
   f. Bleed the rearward (nearest the cowl) brake line connection by repeating steps a through e.
4. Loosen, then slightly retighten bleeder valves at all four wheels. Repair any broken, stripped or frozen valves at this time.
5. Proceed to appropriate wheel first and follow set sequence according to "Wheel Bleeding Sequence."
6. Place transparent tube over bleeder valve, then allow tube to hang down into transparent container, **Fig. 156.** Ensure end of tube is submerged in clean brake fluid.
7. Instruct an assistant to slowly depress brake pedal one time and hold.
8. Crack open bleeder valve, purging air from cylinder. Retighten bleeder screw and slowly release pedal.
9. Wait 15 seconds, then repeat steps 7 and 8. Repeat these steps until all air is bled from system.

PRESSURE BLEED

1. Loosen, then slightly retighten bleeder valves at all four wheels. Repair any broken, stripped or frozen valves at this time.
2. Using a diaphragm type pressure bleeder, install suitable bleeder adapter to master cylinder, **Fig. 157.**
3. Charge bleeder ball to 20-25 psi.
4. Connect pressure bleeder line to adapter.
5. Open line valve on pressure bleeder, then depress bleed-off valve on adapter until a small amount of brake fluid is released.
6. Raise and support vehicle.
7. Proceed to appropriate wheel first and follow set sequence according to "Wheel Bleeding Sequence."
8. Place transparent tube over bleeder valve, then allow tube to hang down into transparent container, **Fig. 156.** Ensure end of tube is submerged in clean brake fluid.
9. Open bleeder valve $1/2$ to $3/4$ turn and allow fluid to flow into container until all air is purged from line.

WHEEL BLEED SEQUENCE

Rear wheel drive models: if manual bleeding, RR-LR-RF-LF; if pressure bleeding, bleed front brakes together and rear brakes together.

Front wheel drive models: RR-LF-LR-RF

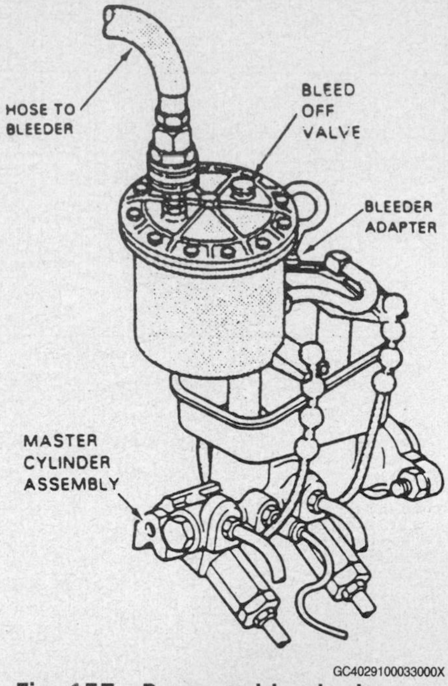
HOSE TO BLEEDER
BLEED OFF VALVE
BLEEDER ADAPTER
MASTER CYLINDER ASSEMBLY
GC4029100033000X

Fig. 157 Pressure bleed adapter installation

HYDRAULIC SYSTEM FLUSH

If brake fluid is old, rusty or contaminated, or whenever new parts are installed in hydraulic system, the system must be flushed. Bleed brakes, allowing at least one quart of clean brake fluid to pass through system. Any rubber parts in hydraulic system which were exposed to contaminated fluid must be replaced.

Component Replace

HYDRAULIC MODULATOR VALVE

Caprice, Impala SS, Custom Cruiser, Roadmaster & Fleetwood (RWD)

1. Disconnect battery ground cable.
2. Disconnect and remove air intake duct and resonator, then position upper coolant hose aside.
3. Disconnect canister purge line at canister and position aside.
4. Remove modulator valve cover attaching screw and cover.
5. Disconnect modulator valve electrical connector and ground wire.
6. Disconnect all hydraulic lines to modulator valve, then plug pipes to prevent loss of fluid and fluid contamination. **Note location of pipes for installation reference.**
7. Remove three modulator valve to bracket attaching nuts, then the modulator valve from vehicle.
8. Reverse procedure to install, perform ABS system check as described in "Diagnosis & Testing." **Ensure brake hydraulic pipes are installed cor-**

rectly. Pipes that are crossed during installation could cause wheel lockup.

Riviera, Toronado & Trofeo & 1992 Eldorado & Seville

1. Disconnect battery ground cable.
2. Drain brake fluid from master cylinder and remove left front radiator brace.
3. Remove air cleaner air intake hose, then the modulator relay cover.
4. Disconnect modulator 12-way connector and ground strap.
5. Disconnect all brake line connections to the modulator.
6. Remove modulator mounting nuts, then the modulator from mounting bracket. **When removing modulator, do not allow and fluid to leak from the modulator onto the vehicle's painted surface.**
7. Remove modulator insulators from modulator.
8. Reverse procedure to install, noting the following:
   a. **Torque** modulator to mounting bracket nuts to 8 ft. lbs.
   b. **Torque** brake lines to modulator fittings to 9 ft. lbs.
   c. Bleed brake system as described in "Hydraulic Brakes."

1993–94 DeVille, Eldorado & Seville

1. Disconnect battery ground cable, then raise and support vehicle and remove left front wheel.
2. Support front of cradle with screw jack, then disconnect Y-pipe from catalytic converter.
3. Remove left front wheel housing splash shields, then disconnect brake lines from BPM valve.
4. Remove brake line bundle from left hand frame rail.
5. Remove bolts from Nos. 1 and 2 body mounts, then loosen No. 3 body mount, then using a screw jack, slowly lower front cradle about 4-5 inches.
6. Remove BPM valve cover (No. 2 Torx), then TCS prime pipe (if equipped).
7. Remove BPM valve ground straps, mounting nuts then BPM valve through wheel housing.
8. Reverse procedure to install noting the following:
   a. Tighten BPM valve mounting nuts to 86 inch lbs.
   b. **When installing ABS/TCS harness, ensure ignition is Off and all connectors are connected.**
   c. **Ensure brake pipes are correctly installed to BPM valve (inlet vs. outlet). If pipes are switched, brake lockup will occur and personal injury may result.**
   d. Tighten BPM valve brake pipes to 13 ft. lbs.
   e. Tighten body mount bolts to 50 ft. lbs.
   f. Tighten exhaust manifold front pipe to catalytic converter bolts to 9 ft. lbs.
   g. Tighten left front wheel nuts to 100 ft. lbs.

ACCELERATOR PEDAL ASSEMBLY

Fleetwood (RWD)

1. Remove left hand sound insulator panel.
2. Disconnect cable from accelerator pedal.
3. Remove bolts/screws and stud attaching pedal to dash panel, then pedal assembly.
4. Reverse procedure to install noting the following:
   a. **Mounting surface between accelerator plate and dash panel must be free of insulation. The floor carpet in pedal area must be positioned to lay flat and be free of wrinkles and bunches.**
   b. Tighten bolts/screws to 25 inch lbs.
   c. **Cable assembly must not be kinked or damaged in nay way during assembly. Throttle must operate smoothly without bind between full and closed throttle.**

ELECTRONIC BRAKE CONTROL MODULE (EBCM)

1. Disconnect battery ground cable.
2. **On wagon models,** remove rear quarter trim panel as follows:
   a. Pull top edge of lefthand side rear quarter trim panel from groove in quarter window garnish molding.
   b. Pull tabs on quarter trim panel from slots in back body pillar and lock pillar trim panel.
   c. Remove bottom edge of quarter trim panel from groove on load floor, then remove panel.
3. **On all models,** disconnect EBCM electrical connector.
4. Remove two EBCM to bracket attaching nuts, then the EBCM from the vehicle.
5. Reverse procedure to install, perform ABS system check as described in "Diagnosis & Testing."

OVER VOLTAGE PROTECTION RELAY (OVP)

Caprice, Impala SS, Custom Cruiser & Roadmaster

1. Disconnect battery ground cable.
2. **On wagon models,** remove left quarter trim panel as described in "Electronic Brake Control Module (EBCM), Replace."
3. **On all models,** disconnect OVP relay from EBCM bracket.
4. Disconnect OVP relay electrical connector, then remove OVP relay from the vehicle.
5. Reverse procedure to install, perform ABS system check as described in "Diagnosis & Testing."

SOLENOID VALVE RELAY & PUMP MOTOR RELAY

1. Disconnect battery ground cable.
2. **On Fleetwood RWD models,** remove air intake duct and resonator assembly, then disconnect radiator upper coolant hose and position out of way.
3. Remove ABS modulator protective cover.
4. Remove relay from modulator.
5. Reverse procedure to install.

LEFT FRONT WHEEL SPEED SENSOR

1. Raise and support vehicle.
2. Disconnect wheel speed sensor harness connector and sensor assembly connector from clip.
3. Disconnect speed sensor connector from harness connector.
4. Remove sensor bracket attaching bolt from frame rail.
5. Disconnect wheel speed sensor assembly harness with grommets from brackets and combination valve brake pipe clip. **Note position of grommets and harness for installation reference.**
6. Remove speed sensor retaining bolt, then the speed sensor from steering knuckle.
7. Reverse procedure to install. **The wheel speed sensors are a tight fit into the knuckle and are to be pushed in by hand. Do not hammer sensor into position. Proper installation of sensor assembly wire into the bracket is critical. Failure to install wire on bracket could cause wire to come in contact with moving parts, causing circuit damage.**

RIGHT FRONT WHEEL SPEED SENSOR

1. Disconnect forward lamp harness wheel speed sensor connector and wheel speed sensor assembly connector from clip.
2. Disconnect forward lamp harness connector from wheel speed sensor connector.
3. Raise and support vehicle.
4. Remove sensor bracket attaching bolt from frame rail.
5. Remove sensor assembly harness with grommets from brackets. **Note position of grommets and harness for assembly reference.**
6. Remove sensor retaining bolt, then the sensor from vehicle.
7. Reverse procedure to install. **The wheel speed sensors are a tight fit into the knuckle and are to be pushed in by hand. Do not hammer sensor into position. Proper installation of sensor assembly wire into the bracket is critical. Failure to install wire on bracket could cause wire to come in contact with moving parts, causing circuit damage.**

REAR AXLE SPEED SENSOR

Caprice, Impala SS, Custom Cruiser, Fleetwood (RWD) & Roadmaster

1. Raise and support vehicle.
2. Unclip sensor assembly connector and differential sensor connector, then separate the connectors.
3. Disconnect speed sensor harness assembly wiring harness with grommets from sensor bracket. **Note position of grommets and harness for installation reference.**
4. Remove sensor attaching bolt, then the sensor from the vehicle.
5. Reverse procedure to install. **The wheel speed sensors are a tight fit into the axle housing and are to be pushed in by hand. Do not hammer sensor into position. Proper installation of sensor assembly wire into the bracket is critical. Failure to install wire on bracket could cause wire to come in contact with moving parts, causing circuit damage.**

REAR WHEEL SPEED SENOR

Eldorado, Riviera, Seville, Toronado & Trofeo

The rear wheel speed sensor is an integral part of the rear bearing assembly. Refer to "Rear Wheel Bearing, Replace" in "Rear Suspension" for replacement procedure. **Do not attempt to remove sensor from bearing assembly.**

Bonneville, Eighty Eight, LeSabre, Ninety Eight, Park Avenue, 1992 DeVille & Fleetwood (FWD) (Teves Type)

NOTE: On Air Bag Equipped Models, Refer To "Air Bag System Precautions" Located In The Front Of This Manual For System Disarming & Arming Procedures.

NOTE: Electrical Symbol & Wire Color Code Identification Located In The Front Of This Manual May Be Used As An Aid When Using Wiring Circuits Found In This Section.

INDEX

PRECAUTIONS

AIR BAG SYSTEMS

Refer to "Air Bag System Precautions" in the front of this manual for system disarming and arming procedures.

DESCRIPTION

Refer to **Fig. 1**, for overview of anti-lock brake system.

The purpose of the anti-lock brake system is to prevent wheel lock-up under heavy braking conditions, on virtually any road surface. When a wheel locking condition exists, the pressure modulator valve (PMV) assembly isolates each wheel hydraulic circuit, then begins modulation of fluid pressure to each wheel according to wheel speed input to the EBCM. The PMV is controlled by the Electronic Brake Control Module (EBCM).

Modulation occurs by means of three ABS modes: pressure hold, pressure reduce and pressure increase. The PMV assembly has two valves per individual hydraulic circuit. These valves work in pairs to achieve the three ABS modes. The ABS system isolates, monitors and controls all wheels simultaneously.

BRAKE WARNING LAMP

The red brake warning lamp is located in the instrument panel. This lamp illuminates to warn driver of conditions which could reduce braking efficiency. Specific conditions causing illumination are the parking brake not fully released, low brake fluid and Bulb Test or Start positions of the ignition switch.

ELECTRONIC BRAKE CONTROL MODULE (EBCM)

The Electronic Brake Control Module (EBCM), is mounted in the passenger compartment and monitors the speed of each wheel and the electrical status of the Pressure Modulator Valve (PMV) assembly. The primary functions of the EBCM are to monitor wheel locking/slipping, control of braking within the anti-lock/traction mode and to monitor the system for proper electrical operation. The EBCM also controls the display of ABS diagnostic codes within the diagnostic mode.

WHEEL SPEED SENSORS

Wheel speed sensors are located at each wheel. The sensor transmits wheel speed information to the EBCM my means of a small AC voltage. This voltage is generated when the toothed sensor ring rotates past a stationary sensor.

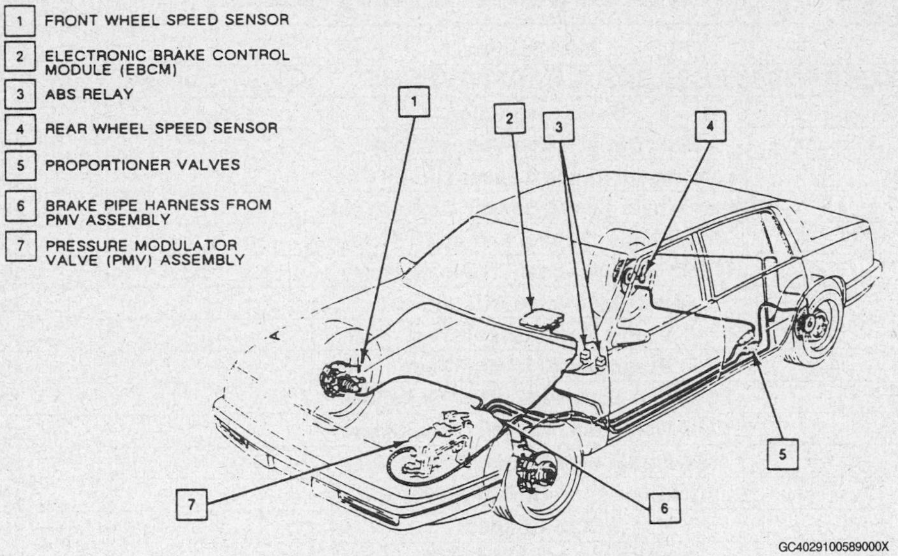

1 FRONT WHEEL SPEED SENSOR
2 ELECTRONIC BRAKE CONTROL MODULE (EBCM)
3 ABS RELAY
4 REAR WHEEL SPEED SENSOR
5 PROPORTIONER VALVES
6 BRAKE PIPE HARNESS FROM PMV ASSEMBLY
7 PRESSURE MODULATOR VALVE (PMV) ASSEMBLY
GC4029100589000X

Fig. 1 Anti-lock brake system overview

TROUBLESHOOTING

Refer to "Diagnostic Procedures" under "Diagnosis & Testing" in this section.

DIAGNOSIS & TESTING

DESCRIPTION

Anti-Lock Warning Lamp

The amber Anti-lock warning lamp is located in the instrument panel cluster. This lamp will illuminate when the EBCM detects a malfunction in the anti-lock brake system. The warning lamp is intended only to warn the driver that a condition has been detected which results in partial or total reduction of the anti-lock brake system. Under this condition full operation of the standard hydraulic braking system is available. If both the red Brake and the amber Anti-Lock brake lights are illuminated, there may be something wrong with the hydraulic brake system, limiting all braking functions.

ABS System Self-Diagnosis Description

In the process of controlling the anti-lock brake system, the Electronic Brake Control Module (EBCM) continually monitors operating conditions for possible malfunctions. By comparing system conditions against standard operating limits, certain circuit and component malfunctions can be detected. A four-digit numerical trouble code is stored in computer memory when a problem is detected by this self-diagnostic system. The trouble codes can later be accessed with a bidirectional scan tool.

To access trouble codes, connect a bi-directional scan tool to the Assembly Line Diagnostic Link (ALDL) connector, then follow manufacturer's instruction for use of the tool. After code have been read, proceed to "Code Diagnosis," if the ABS Functional Test has been performed. After repairs have been made, clear all codes, using the scan tool.

History & Current ABS Codes

The ABS trouble codes which may be stored by the EBCM are not specifically designated as Current or History codes. The Anti-lock lamp may be used to differentiate between Current and History codes.

If the Anti-lock lamp is illuminated prior to entering the ABS diagnostic mode, at least one of the stored codes is current. If the Anti-lock lamp is not illuminated prior to entering the ABS diagnostic mode, none of the stored codes are current.

If more than one code is stored and the Anti-lock lamp was illuminated prior to entering the diagnostic mode, it is impossible to determine which code is Current or History.

Note On Intermittents

Intermittent failures in the anti-lock brake system may be difficult to accurately diagnose. The ABS trouble codes which may be stored by the EBCM are not designated as Current or History codes. These codes can be helpful in diagnosing intermittent conditions.

If an intermittent condition is being diagnosed, the ABS system can be used in the following manner to help isolate the suspected circuit.

1. Display, then clear any ABS trouble codes present in the EBCM.
2. Test Drive Vehicle, attempting to repeat failure condition. A description of driving conditions under which the last failure occurred can be helpful.
3. After duplicating condition, stop the vehicle, then display any trouble codes stored.
4. If no codes were stored, proceed to "Symptom Diagnosis."
5. If a code was stored, check electrical connections and wiring for the following:
   a. Poor mating of connector halves.
   b. Terminals not fully seated in connector halves.
   c. Improperly formed, or damaged terminals. All connector terminals in a problem circuit should be carefully reformed to increase contact tension.
   d. Poor terminal to wire connection. In most cases, this will require removing wire from connector body.
6. If a complaint of intermittent warning lamp operation is encountered, the following circuits to the EBCM should be checked:
   a. Low system voltage. If low voltage is detected at the EBCM, the Anti-lock lamp will illuminate until normal operating voltage is detected.
   b. Low brake fluid. This condition in the Pressure Modulator Valve (PMV) reservoir will cause the Brake and Anti-lock lamps to illuminate. When an acceptable fluid level is registered, the lamps will no longer be illuminated.
7. Any condition which results in interruption of power to the EBCM or hydraulic unit may cause the warning lamps to turn on intermittently. These circuits include the main relay, pump motor relay, fuses and related wiring.

DIAGNOSTIC PROCEDURES

Refer to **Figs. 2 through 42,** for ABS system diagnostic procedures and charts. Refer to **Figs. 63 through 67,** for system wiring diagrams.

Continued on page 32-239

DIAGNOSTIC CHART INDEX

Test	Description	Page No. 32-	Fig. No.
1993-93 MODELS, EXCEPT 1993 LESABRE & PARK AVENUE			
—	Visual Inspection	185	2
Test A	Inlet/Outlet Valve Voltage Test	188	11
Test B	Front Wheel Speed Sensor Circuit Test	189	12
Test C	Rear Wheel Speed Sensor Circuit Test	190	13
Test D	Wheel Speed Signal Erratic Or Noisy	190	14
Test D	Wheel Speed Signal Erratic Or Noisy	191	15
Test E	Inlet/Oulet Valve Circuit Test	192	16
Test F	Pump Motor Circuit Test	193	17
Test F	Pump Motor Circuit Test	194	18
Test G	TCC/Anti-Lock Brake Switch Failure	196	19
Test H	PMV Fluid Level Switch Circuit Test	196	20
Test H	PMV Fluid Level Switch Circuit Test	197	21
Test I	Pump Motor Fault During An ABS Stop	197	22
Test J	EBCM Problem	198	23
Test K	Anti-Lock Indicator Is On & No Codes Are Set/Diagnostic Mode Cannot Be Entered	199	24
Test L	Inlet/Outlet Valve Hydraulic Test	200	25
Test M	Pump Motor Runs Continuously	200	26
Test N	Anti-Lock Indicator Does Not Light	201	27
Test O	Isolation Valve Circuit Failure (1992)	202	28
Test P	Pressure Switch Circuit Failure	203	29
Test Q	Traction Indicator Does Not Light	203	30
Test R	Traction Indicator Is On All The Time & No Codes Are Set	204	31
Test S	Traction Control Engaged Message Does Not Operate (1992 Park Avenue & 98)	204	32
1993-94 LESABRE & PARK AVENUE			
—	Visual Inspection (1993)	185	2
—	Visual Inspection (1994)	186	3
Test 1	Main Relay, EBCM/EBTCM & Pressure Modulator Valve	205	33
Test 2	Pressure Modulator & Valve Control	205	34
Test 3	Wheel Speed Circuit	206	35
Test 4	Pump Motor Circuit	207	36
Test 5	Brake Switch & Hydraulics	208	37
Test 6	Data Line & Anti-Lock Indicator	209	38
Test 7	Anti-Lock Indicator & Main Relay	209	39
Test 8	Brake Warning, Fluid Level Switch & Park Brake Switch	210	40
Test 9	Transaxle Temperature Switch & EBCM/EBTCM Problem	210	41
Test 10	Isolation Valve	211	42
1994 BONNEVILLE, 88 &98			
—	Visual Inspection	186	3
Test A	Diagnostic Mode Cannot Be Entered Or ABS Lamp On w/No Codes Set	212	43
Test B	ABS Lamp Does Not Function	213	44
Test C	Traction Off Lamp Is On Continuously w/No Codes Set	214	45
Test D	Traction Off Lamp Does Not Function	215	46
Test E	Traction Control Switch Lamp Does Not Function Properly	216	47
Codes 21 & 25	Front Wheel Speed Sensor Circuit Test	217	48
Code 31& 35	Rear Wheel Speed Circuit Test	217	49
Code 22, 23, 26, 27, 32, 33, 36, & 37	Wheel Speed Signal Erratic Or Missing	218	50
Code 41, 42, 46, 51, 52, 55 & 56	Inlet/Outlet Valve Circuit Open Or Shorted	219	51
Code 44 & 48	Isolation Valve Circuit Open Or Shorted	220	52
Code 45	Power Interruption Fault	221	53
Code 61	Pump Motor Circuit Test	222	54

Continued

DIAGNOSTIC CHART INDEX—Continued

Test	Description	Page No. 32-	Fig. No.
1994 BONNEVILLE, 88 &98 -Continued			
Code 62	Low Brake Pedal During An ABS Stop	223	55
Code 71	EBCM/EBTCM Internal Fault	223	56
Code 72	Barake Switch Open Or Shorted	224	57
Code 73	Fluid Level Switch Circuit Open Or Shorted	224	58
Code 74	PMV Pressure Switch Circuit Open Or Shorted	225	59
Code 75	PCM Requested TCS To Be Disabled	226	60
Code 76	Data Line Signal Or Circuit Malfunction	226	61
Code 77	Delivered Torque Circuit Fault	227	62

VISUAL INSPECTION

ITEM	INSPECT FOR	CORRECTIVE ACTION
PARKING BRAKE	- FULL RELEASE - PROPER SWITCH FUNCTION IF NECESSARY. UNPLUG SWITCH CONNECTOR TO VERIFY	- OPERATEMANUAL RELEASE LEVER TO VERIFY RELEASE - ADJUST CABLE OR REPAIR RELEASE SYSTEM AS REQUIRED - REPAIR SWITCH AS REQUIRED
MAJOR COMPONENTS - BRAKE FLUID RESERVOIR	- LOW FLUID LEVEL	- ADD FLUID AS REQUIRED DETERMINE CAUSE OF FLUID LOSS AND REPAIR
- PRESSURE MODULATOR VALVE ASSEMBLY (PMV)	- LOW FLUID LEVEL IN RESERVOIR - EXTERNAL LEAKS - PROPER ASSEMBLY	- ADD FLUID AS REQUIRED DETERMINE CAUSE OF FLUID LOSS AND REPAIR - REPAIR LEAKS AS REQUIRED - INSTALL OR POSITION COMPONENTS PROPERLY
IP FUSE BLOCK - FUSE 8 - FUSE 13 - FUSE 19 UNDERHOOD FUSE BLOCK - FUSE 1 - FUSE 2	- OPEN - PROPER ENGAGEMENT	- INSPECT FOR CAUSE OF FAILURE - REPLACE - VERIFY OPERATION
CONNECTORS - MAIN RELAY - PUMP MOTOR RELAY - FLUID LEVEL SENSOR - LF AND RF WHEEL SPEED SENSORS - LR AND RR WHEEL SPEED SENSORS - ELECTRONIC BRAKE CONTROL MODULE (EBCM) - PRESSURE MODULATOR VALVE ASSEMBLY (PMV) CONNECTORS C1 AND C2	- PROPER ENGAGEMENT - LOOSE WIRES OR TERMINALS - CORRODED OR BROKEN EYELETS	- PROPERLY ENGAGE CONNECTOR - REPAIR AS REQUIRED
IF NO PROBLEM IS NOTED IN VISUAL INSPECTION, PROCEED TO FUNCTIONAL CHECK		

GC4029100590000X

Fig. 2 Visual inspection. 1992–93 models

ABS/TCS VISUAL INSPECTION		
ITEM	**INSPECT FOR**	**CORRECTIVE ACTION**
PARKING BRAKE	· FULL RELEASE	· OPERATE MANUAL RELEASE LEVER TO VERIFY RELEASE ADJUST CABLE OR REPAIR RELEASE SYSTEM AS REQUIRED
	PROPER SWITCH FUNCTION WHEN NECESSARY, UNPLUG SWITCH CONNECTOR TO VERIFY	REPAIR SWITCH AS REQUIRED PROCEED TO ABS/TCS FUNCTIONAL TEST
MAJOR COMPONENTS MASTER CYLINDER FLUID RESERVOIR	· LOW FLUID LEVEL	· DETERMINE CAUSE OF FLUID LOSS AND REPAIR ADD FLUID TO MASTER CYLINDER RESERVOIR AS REQUIRED
PRESSURE MODULATOR VALVE (PMV) ASSEMBLY	· LOW FLUID LEVEL IN PMV RESERVOIR	· DETERMINE CAUSE OF FLUID LOSS AND REPAIR ADD FLUID TO MASTER CYLINDER RESERVOIR AS REQUIRED
	· EXTERNAL LEAKS	· REPAIR LEAKS AS REQUIRED
	· PROPER ASSEMBLY	· INSTALL OR POSITION COMPONENTS PROPERLY · PROCEED TO ABS/TCS FUNCTIONAL TEST
IP FUSE BLOCK · FUSE 6 · FUSE 13 · FUSE 19 UNDERHOOD FUSE BLOCK · FUSE 1 · FUSE 2	· OPEN (BLOWN FUSE) · PROPER ENGAGEMENT	· REPLACE · PROCEED TO ABS/TCS FUNCTIONAL TEST
CONNECTORS · MAIN RELAY · PUMP MOTOR RELAY · PMV FLUID LEVEL SWITCH · WHEEL SPEED SENSORS · ELECTRONIC BRAKE (AND TRACTION) CONTROL MODULE (EBCM/EBTCM) · PRESSURE MODULATOR VALVE (PMV) ASSEMBLY CONNECTORS: C1 · VALVE BLOCK CONNECTOR (ROUND) C2 · PUMP MOTOR CONNECTOR (GRY) · MASTER CYLINDER RESERVOIR · CRUISE/SHIFT INTERLOCK/BRAKE SWITCH · VCC/ANTILOCK BRAKE SWITCH · C101, C102, C414 · AUTOMATIC TRANSAXLE (TRACTION CONTROL ONLY)	· PROPER ENGAGEMENT · LOOSE WIRES OR TERMINALS · CORRODED OR BROKEN EYELETS	· PROPERLY ENGAGE CONNECTOR · REPAIR AS REQUIRED · PROCEED TO ABS/TCS FUNCTIONAL TEST
· GROUNDS · G102, G202, G104	· CORRODED/LOOSE WIRES OR BROKEN EYELETS	· REPAIR AS NEEDED
WHEN NO PROBLEM IS NOTED IN VISUAL INSPECTION PROCEED TO ABS/TCS FUNCTIONAL TEST		

GC4029400914000X

Fig. 3 Visual inspection. 1994 models

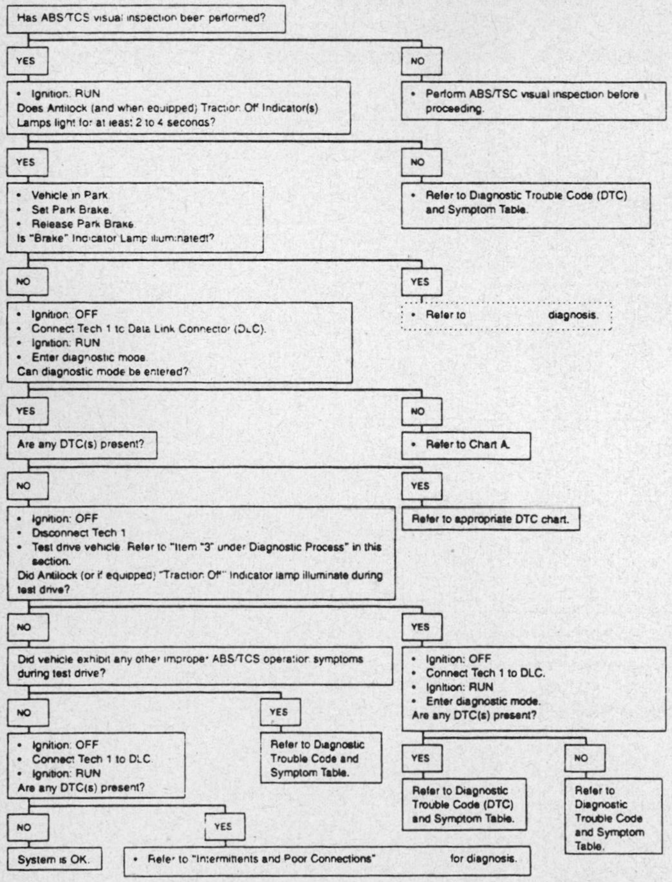
Has ABS/TCS visual inspection beer performed?
YES
NO
• Ignition: RUN
Does Antilock (and when equipped) Traction Off Indicator(s) Lamps light for at least 2 to 4 seconds?
• Perform ABS/TSC visual inspection before proceeding.
YES
NO
• Vehicle in Park
• Set Park Brake.
• Release Park Brake
Is "Brake" Indicator Lamp illuminated?
• Refer to Diagnostic Trouble Code (DTC) and Symptom Table.
NO
YES
• Ignition: OFF
• Connect Tech 1 to Data Link Connector (DLC).
• Ignition: RUN
• Enter diagnostic mode
Can diagnostic mode be entered?
• Refer to diagnosis.
YES
NO
Are any DTC(s) present?
• Refer to Chart A.
NO
YES
• Ignition: OFF
• Disconnect Tech 1
• Test drive vehicle. Refer to "Item "3" under Diagnostic Process" in this section.
Did Antilock (or if equipped) "Traction Off" Indicator lamp illuminate during test drive?
Refer to appropriate DTC chart.
NO
YES
Did vehicle exhibit any other improper ABS/TCS operation symptoms during test drive?
• Ignition: OFF
• Connect Tech 1 to DLC.
• Ignition: RUN
• Enter diagnostic mode.
Are any DTC(s) present?
NO
YES
• Ignition: OFF
• Connect Tech 1 to DLC.
• Ignition: RUN
Are any DTC(s) present?
Refer to Diagnostic Trouble Code and Symptom Table.
YES
NO
Refer to Diagnostic Trouble Code (DTC) and Symptom Table.
Refer to Diagnostic Trouble Code and Symptom Table.
NO
YES
System is OK.
• Refer to "Intermittents and Poor Connections" for diagnosis.

GC4029400913000X

Fig. 5 Functional check. 1994 Bonneville, 88 & 98

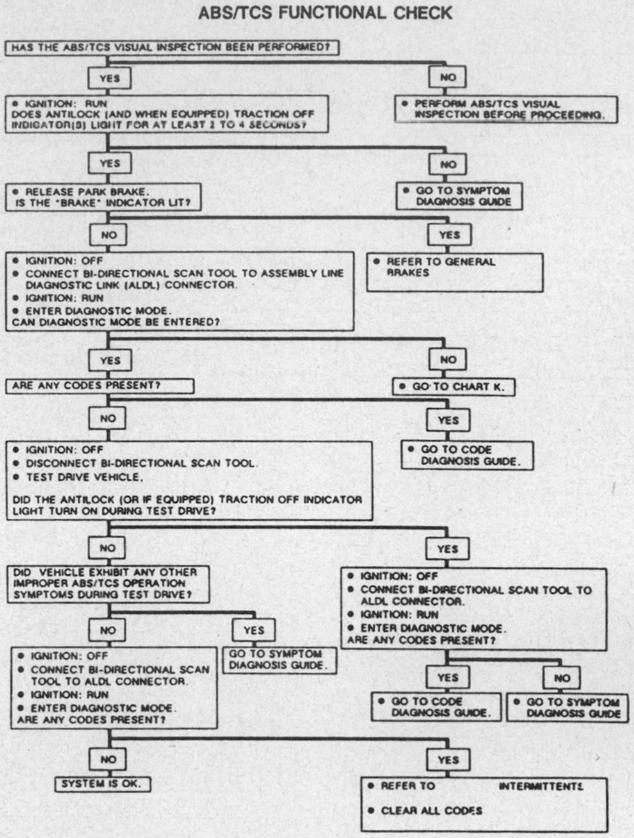
ABS/TCS FUNCTIONAL CHECK
HAS THE ABS/TCS VISUAL INSPECTION BEEN PERFORMED?
YES
NO
• IGNITION: RUN
DOES ANTILOCK (AND WHEN EQUIPPED) TRACTION OFF INDICATOR(S) LIGHT FOR AT LEAST 2 TO 4 SECONDS?
• PERFORM ABS/TCS VISUAL INSPECTION BEFORE PROCEEDING.
YES
NO
• RELEASE PARK BRAKE.
IS THE "BRAKE" INDICATOR LIT?
• GO TO SYMPTOM DIAGNOSIS GUIDE
NO
YES
• IGNITION: OFF
• CONNECT BI-DIRECTIONAL SCAN TOOL TO ASSEMBLY LINE DIAGNOSTIC LINK (ALDL) CONNECTOR.
• IGNITION: RUN
• ENTER DIAGNOSTIC MODE.
CAN DIAGNOSTIC MODE BE ENTERED?
• REFER TO GENERAL BRAKES
YES
NO
ARE ANY CODES PRESENT?
• GO TO CHART K.
NO
YES
• IGNITION: OFF
• DISCONNECT BI-DIRECTIONAL SCAN TOOL.
• TEST DRIVE VEHICLE.
DID THE ANTILOCK (OR IF EQUIPPED) TRACTION OFF INDICATOR LIGHT TURN ON DURING TEST DRIVE?
• GO TO CODE DIAGNOSIS GUIDE.
NO
YES
DID VEHICLE EXHIBIT ANY OTHER IMPROPER ABS/TCS OPERATION SYMPTOMS DURING TEST DRIVE?
• IGNITION: OFF
• CONNECT BI-DIRECTIONAL SCAN TOOL TO ALDL CONNECTOR.
• IGNITION: RUN
• ENTER DIAGNOSTIC MODE.
ARE ANY CODES PRESENT?
NO
YES
• IGNITION: OFF
• CONNECT BI-DIRECTIONAL SCAN TOOL TO ALDL CONNECTOR.
• IGNITION: RUN
• ENTER DIAGNOSTIC MODE.
ARE ANY CODES PRESENT?
GO TO SYMPTOM DIAGNOSIS GUIDE.
YES
NO
• GO TO CODE DIAGNOSIS GUIDE.
• GO TO SYMPTOM DIAGNOSIS GUIDE
NO
YES
SYSTEM IS OK.
• REFER TO INTERMITTENTS
• CLEAR ALL CODES

GC4029100591000X

Fig. 4 Functional check. 1992–93 models

CODE DIAGNOSIS GUIDE

PERFORM THE ABS/TCS FUNCTIONAL CHECK BEFORE PROCEEDING WITH ANY DIAGNOSIS.

CODE	DESCRIPTION	CHART	CODE	DESCRIPTION	CHART
21	RF speed sensor circuit open	B	45	LF inlet valve circuit	A
22	RF speed sensor signal erratic	D	46	LF outlet valve circuit	E
23	RF wheel speed is 0 mph	D	47	LF speed sensor noisy	D
25	LF speed sensor circuit open	B	48	RF isolation valve circuit	O
26	LF speed sensor signal erratic	D	51	RR inlet valve circuit	E
27	LF wheel speed is 0 mph	D	52	RR outlet valve circuit	E
31	RR speed sensor circuit open	C	53	RR speed sensor noisy	D
32	RR speed sensor signal is erratic	D	55	LR inlet valve circuit	E
33	RR wheel speed is 0 mph	D	56	LR outlet valve circuit	E
35	LR speed sensor circuit open	C	57	LR speed sensor noisy	D
36	LR speed sensor signal erratic	D	61	Pump motor test fault	F
37	LR wheel speed is 0 mph	D	62	Pump motor fault in ABS stop	I
41	RF inlet valve circuit	E	71	EBCM problem	J
42	RF outlet valve circuit	E	72	TCC/antilock brake switch circuit	G
43	RF speed sensor noisy	D	73	Fluid level switch circuit	H
44	LF isolation valve circuit	O	74	PMV pressure switch circuit	P

INTERMITTENT "HISTORY" CODES: (Refer to "System Self-Diagnosis" in this section for clarification.)
STORED CODES THAT DO NOT LIGHT THE AMBER "ANTILOCK" INDICATOR ARE INTERMITTENT PROBLEMS. DO NOT USE TROUBLE CODE DIAGNOSIS FOR INTERMITTENT PROBLEMS UNTIL REFERRING TO "NOTE ON INTERMITTENTS" IN THIS SECTION.

MULTIPLE CODES: DIAGNOSE FIRST CODE THAT APPEARS ON BI-DIRECTIONAL SCAN TOOL SCREEN.

CLEARING CODES:
- CLEAR CODES USING A BI-DIRECTIONAL SCAN TOOL.
- CYCLE IGNITION SWITCH.
- AFTER CODES HAVE BEEN CLEARED, REFER TO "ABS/TCS FUNCTIONAL CHECK" CHART IN THIS SECTION TO ASSURE ALL PROBLEMS HAVE BEEN REPAIRED.

GC4029100592000X

Fig. 6 Code diagnosis guide. 1992 models

PERFORM ABS/TCS FUNCTIONAL CHECK BEFORE PROCEEDING WITH ANY DIAGNOSIS.

INTERMITTENT "HISTORY" DIAGNOSTIC TROUBLE CODES:

STORED DIAGNOSTIC TROUBLE CODES THAT DO NOT LIGHT THE AMBER "ANTILOCK" INDICATOR ARE INTERMITTENT PROBLEMS OR HISTORY CODES THAT WERE NOT CLEARED DURING PRIOR SERVICE. DO NOT USE DIAGNOSTIC TROUBLE CODE DIAGNOSIS FOR INTERMITTENT PROBLEMS UNTIL REFERRING TO "INTERMITTENTS AND POOR CONNECTIONS"

MULTIPLE DIAGNOSTIC TROUBLE CODES: DIAGNOSE FIRST DIAGNOSTIC TROUBLE CODE THAT APPEARS ON BI-DIRECTIONAL SCAN TOOL SCREEN.

CLEARING DIAGNOSTIC TROUBLE CODES:

- CLEAR DIAGNOSTIC TROUBLE CODES USING A BI-DIRECTIONAL SCAN TOOL.
- CYCLE IGNITION SWITCH.
- AFTER DIAGNOSTIC TROUBLE CODES HAVE BEEN CLEARED, REFER TO "ABS/TCS FUNCTIONAL CHECK" CHART TO ASSURE ALL PROBLEMS HAVE BEEN REPAIRED.

DTC	DESCRIPTION	CHART	DTC	DESCRIPTION	CHART
21	RF speed sensor circuit open	B	44	LF isolation valve circuit	O
22	RF speed sensor signal erratic	D	45	LF inlet valve circuit	A
23	RF wheel speed is 0 mph	D	46	LF outlet valve circuit	E
25	LF speed sensor circuit open	B	48	RF isolation valve circuit	O
26	LF speed sensor signal erratic	D	51	RR inlet valve circuit	E
27	LF wheel speed is 0 mph	D	52	RR outlet valve circuit	E
31	RR speed sensor circuit open	C	55	LR inlet valve circuit	E
32	RR speed sensor signal is erratic	D	56	LR outlet valve circuit	E
33	RR wheel speed is 0 mph	D	61	Pump motor test fault	F
35	LR speed sensor circuit open	C	62	Pump motor fault in ABS stop	I
36	LR speed sensor signal erratic	D	71	EBCM problem	J
37	LR wheel speed is 0 mph	D	72	TCC/antilock brake switch circuit	G
41	RF inlet valve circuit	E	73	Fluid level switch circuit	H
42	RF outlet valve circuit	E	74	PMV pressure switch circuit	P

GC4029300593000X

Fig. 7 Code diagnosis guide. 1993 models

PERFORM ABS/TCS FUNCTIONAL CHECK BEFORE PROCEEDING WITH ANY DIAGNOSIS.

SYMPTOM	FOR DIAGNOSIS GO TO CHART
Diagnostic mode cannot be entered.	Chart K
ANTILOCK indicator is on all the time and no diagnostic trouble codes are set.	Chart K
ANTILOCK indicator does not light.	Chart N
Poor vehicle tracking during ABS stop (ABS engaged).	Chart L
Brake pedal rises or drops excessively during an ABS stop (ABS engaged).	Chart I
Pressure modulator valve (PMV) assembly pump motor runs continuously.	Chart M
Only TRACTION OFF indicator does not light.	Chart Q
Only TRACTION OFF indicator is on all the time and no diagnostic trouble codes are set.	Chart R
Traction control switch illumination bulb does not operate properly.	Chart S
Brake pedal vibrates (fluctuates) during slow speed (under 16 km/h [10 mph]) braking.	Chart D

GC4029300595000X

Fig. 8 Symptom diagnosis guide. 1993 Bonneville, 88 & 98

CHART	SYMPTOM
A	Diagnostic Mode cannot be entered or "ANTILOCK" Indicator Lamp is "on" constantly with no DTC(s) set
B	"ANTILOCK" Indicator Lamp does not function
C	"TRACTION OFF" Indicator Lamp is "on" constantly with no DTC(s) set
D	"TRACTION OFF" Indicator Lamp does not function
E	"TRACTION ENGAGED" Indicator Lamp does not operate properly
DTC	**DESCRIPTION**
21	RF Wheel Speed Sensor circuit open or shorted
22	RF Wheel Speed Sensor signal erratic
23	RF Wheel Speed Sensor signal missing
25	LF Wheel Speed Sensor circuit open or shorted
26	LF Wheel Speed Sensor signal erratic
27	LF Wheel Speed Sensor signal missing
31	RR Wheel Speed Sensor circuit open or shorted
32	RR Wheel Speed Sensor signal erratic
33	RR Wheel Speed Sensor signal missing
35	LR Wheel Speed Sensor circuit open or shorted
36	LR Wheel Speed Sensor signal erratic
37	LR Wheel Speed Sensor signal missing
41	RF Inlet Valve circuit open or shorted
42	RF Outlet Valve circuit open or shorted
44	LF Isolation Valve circuit open or shorted
45	Power Interruption Fault
46	LF Outlet Valve circuit open or shorted
48	RF Isolation Valve circuit open or shorted
51	RR Inlet Valve circuit open or shorted
52	RR Outlet Valve circuit open or shorted
55	LR Inlet Valve circuit open or shorted
56	LR Outlet Valve circuit open or shorted
61	Pump Motor Circuit Test
62	Low Brake Pedal during an ABS stop
71	EBCM/EBTCM internal failure
72	Brake Switch circuit open or shorted
73	Fluid Level Switch circuit open or shorted
74	Pressure Switch circuit open or shorted
75	PCM requested TCS to be disabled
76	UART SDL circuit or signal malfunction
77	Delivered Torque Circuit open or shorted

GC4029400915000X

Fig. 9 Symptom diagnosis guide. 1994 Bonneville, 88 & 98

- Perform "ABS/TCS Functional Check" before beginning diagnosis.

INTERMITTENT "HISTORY" DIAGNOSTIC TROUBLE CODES:

Stored diagnostic trouble codes that do not light the amber ANTILOCK indicator are intermittent problems or history codes that were not cleared during prior service. Do not use diagnostic trouble code diagnosis for intermittent problems until referring to "intermittents and poor connections"

MULTIPLE DIAGNOSTIC TROUBLE CODES: Diagnose first diagnostic trouble code that appears on bi-directional scan tool screen.

CLEARING DIAGNOSTIC TROUBLE CODES:

- Repair problem.
- Use a bi-directional scan tool to clear codes.
- Cycle ignition switch.
- After clearing diagnostic trouble code, repeat "ABS/TCS Functional Check" to assure all problems have been repaired.

DIAGNOSTIC TROUBLE CODE (DTC) GUIDE

DTC	DIAGNOSIS:
DTC 21, DTC 25, DTC 31, DTC 35	Test F: Wheel Speed Sensor Continuity Test
DTC 23, DTC 27, DTC 33, DTC 37	Test I: Wheel Speed Signal Erratic Or Noisy Test
DTC 22, DTC 26, DTC 32, DTC 36	
DTC 45	Test A: Main Relay Power Test
DTC 41, DTC 42, DTC 46, DTC 51, DTC 52, DTC 55, DTC 56	Test D: Pressure Modulator Valve (PMV) Assembly Continuity Test
DTC 44, DTC 48	Test Z: Isolation Valve Continuity Test
DTC 61	Test J: Pump Motor Circuit Test
DTC 62	Test M: Brake Hydraulic Test
DTC 71	Test Y: EBCM/EBTCM Problem Test
DTC 72	Test O: EBCM/EBTCM Grounded Switch Input Test Note: When DTC 72 and DTC 73 are both set, check wiring (CKT 848) for a short to ground
DTC 73	
DTC 74	Test P: EBCM/EBTCM Open Switch Input Test Note: When DTC 73 and DTC 74 are both set, check wiring (CKT 1659) for a short to ground

DIAGNOSTIC SYMPTOM GUIDE

SYMPTOM	DIAGNOSIS		
	Do 1st	Do 2nd	Do 3rd
Diagnostics cannot be entered.	Data Line Test Q.		
ANTILOCK indicator does not light.	Do Antilock Indicator "OFF" Fault Test S.		
ANTILOCK indicator is on all the time and no diagnostic trouble codes are set.	Check PMV reservoir brake fluid level.	Do Antilock Indicator "ON" Fault Test R.	
Brake pedal rises or drops excessively during an ABS stop (ABS engaged).	Do TCC/Antilock Brake Switch Test L.		
Brake pedal vibrates (fluctuates) during slow speed (under 16 km/h [10 mph]) braking.	Do Wheel Speed Signal Erratic or Noisy Test I.		
Poor vehicle tracking during an ABS stop (ABS engaged).	Do Inlet/Outlet Valve Hydraulic Test BB.		
Pump motor runs continuously.	Do Pump Motor Short Test K.		

GC402930059600AX

Fig. 10 Symptom diagnosis guide (Part 1 of 2). 1993 LeSabre & Park Avenue

DIAGNOSTIC SYMPTOM GUIDE (continued)

SYMPTOM	DIAGNOSIS		
	Do 1st	Do 2nd	Do 3rd
BRAKE indicator is on all the time.	CHECK MECHANICAL BRAKE SYSTEM	Do Brake Warning Short Circuit Test U.	Replace instrument cluster (U23)or information center (UB3), see ⑥ or ⑬, respectively.
BRAKE indicator does not light.	Check BRAKE indicator bulb and wiring (CKT 33) for an open.	Replace instrument cluster (U23)or information center (UB3), see ⑥ or ⑬, respectively.	
BRAKE indicator does not light with park brake applied.	Do Park Brake Switch Test W.		
BRAKE indicator does not light with low brake fluid or during bulb test.	Do Brake Fluid Level Switch Test V.		
Brake pedal is spongy.	CHECK MECHANICAL BRAKE SYSTEM		
BRAKE indicator lights properly, but chime does not sound with park brake applied.	Check wiring (CKT 33) to MFC module for an open		
Only TRACTION OFF indicator does not light.	Check TRACTION OFF indicator and wiring (CKT 1572) for an open.	Replace information center, see ⑬.	Check EBTCM connector for proper terminal contact: If OK, replace EBTCM, see ③.
Only TRACTION OFF indicator is on all the time and no diagnostic trouble codes are set.	Wait 20 minutes. If indicator is now off, system OK. If indicator is still on, continue diagnosis.	Do Transaxle Temperature Switch Test X.	Check wiring (CKT 1572) for a short to ground: If OK, replace EBTCM, see ③.

Important

- Customers may comment that they hear the PMV assembly run at slow speeds (11 km/h [7 mph]). This is simply the ABS system running through its self-test. It is also possible to feel the PMV assembly running through the brake pedal, when it is barely applied, and to hear brake fluid return to the master cylinder. Also, the vehicle may slowly decrease in speed while the PMV modulator valves increase fluid pressure to the wheel cylinders during this test. In both these instances, the driver must be traveling at a very low speed (11 km/h [7 mph]) and have one foot touching the brake pedal (as some two-footed drivers may) to feel the PMV assembly running. These are normal conditions and in no way signify a problem with the ABS system.
- When vehicle is equipped with traction control, any symptom which lights the ANTILOCK indicator also lights the TRACTION OFF indicator. Therefore, when both indicators are lit, follow ANTILOCK indicator diagnosis when no diagnostic trouble codes are set.
- Vehicles with traction control contain a preventive system to avoid brake overheating. During heavy braking conditions, if a traction control mode is entered and the EBTCM determines the brakes are too hot, the EBTCM disables the traction control system and lights only the TRACTION OFF indicator. After a sufficient cooling time, approximately 15-20 minutes, the EBTCM enables traction control system and turns off the indicator. This condition is normal and should not be mistaken as an intermittent system malfunction.

GC402930059600BX

Fig. 10 Symptom diagnosis guide (Part 2 of 2). 1993 LeSabre & Park Avenue

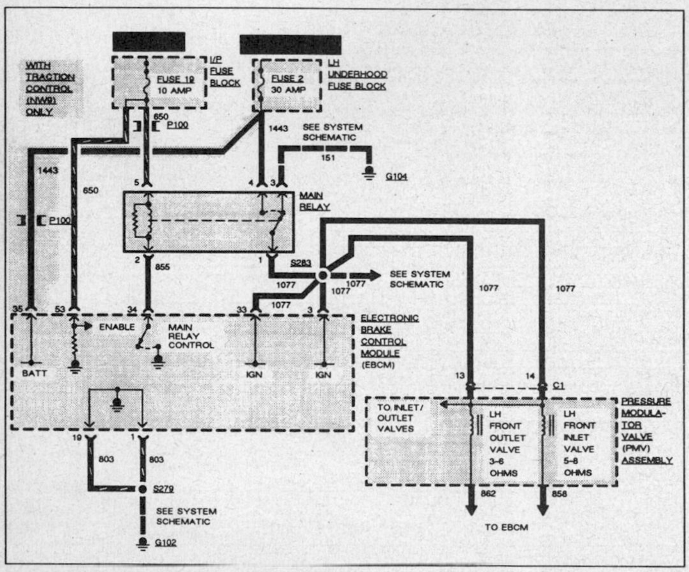
WITH TRACTION CONTROL (NW9) ONLY
FUSE 19 10 AMP
I/P FUSE BLOCK
FUSE 2 30 AMP
LH UNDERHOOD FUSE BLOCK
650
P100
1443
SEE SYSTEM SCHEMATIC
151
G104
MAIN RELAY
855
S283
1077
SEE SYSTEM SCHEMATIC
ENABLE
MAIN RELAY CONTROL
BATT
IGN
IGN
ELECTRONIC BRAKE CONTROL MODULE (EBCM)
C1
TO INLET/ OUTLET VALVES
LH FRONT OUTLET VALVE 3-6 OHMS
LH FRONT INLET VALVE 5-8 OHMS
PRESSURE MODULATOR VALVE (PMV) ASSEMBLY
803
S279
SEE SYSTEM SCHEMATIC
G102
862
858
TO EBCM

CHART A
INLET/OUTLET VALVE VOLTAGE TEST

CIRCUIT OPERATION

When the ignition is first turned to "RUN," the electronic brake control module (EBCM) goes through a self-check lasting 2–4 seconds. During this test the EBCM grounds terminal 34, energizing the main relay. Once the self-check is completed the main relay remains energized. This delivers battery voltage to both the EBCM and the pressure modulator valve (PMV) assembly during vehicle operation. The constant voltage supply allows the vehicle to enter ABS mode without delay. The main relay is de-energized whenever the amber "ANTILOCK" indicator lights due to a system fault, causing the ABS system to shut down.

FAILURE CONDITIONS

Code 45 sets when the ignition switch is at "RUN" and battery voltage is neither detected at the PMV assembly nor EBCM terminal 20, 3 and/or 33. Code 45 also sets when the EBCM detects an open or a short to ground in the LH inlet valve circuit.

Possible Causes

- Open in CKT 650, 855, 858, 1077 or 1443.
- Short to ground in CKT 858, 1077 or 1443.
- Main relay fails "open."

GC402910060200AX

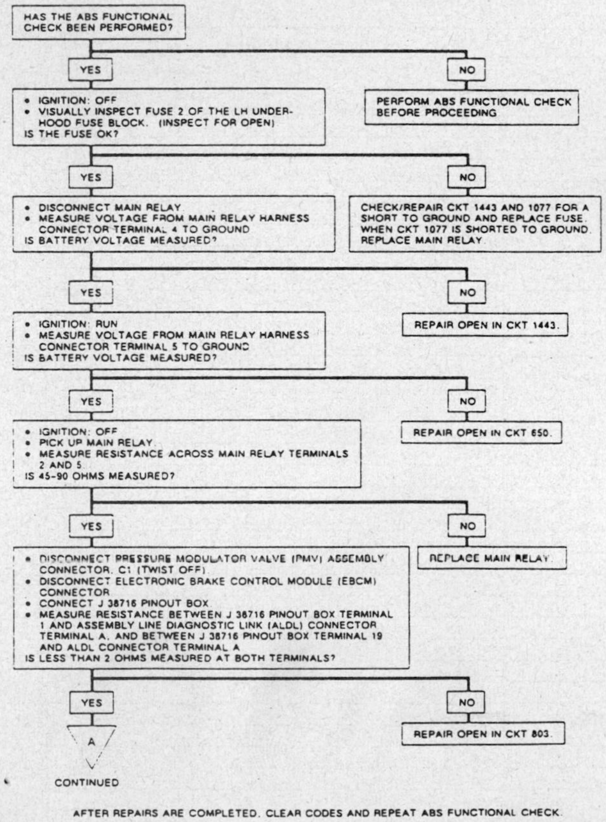
HAS THE ABS FUNCTIONAL CHECK BEEN PERFORMED?
YES
NO
PERFORM ABS FUNCTIONAL CHECK BEFORE PROCEEDING
• IGNITION: OFF
• VISUALLY INSPECT FUSE 2 OF THE LH UNDER-HOOD FUSE BLOCK. (INSPECT FOR OPEN)
IS THE FUSE OK?
YES
NO
CHECK/REPAIR CKT 1443 AND 1077 FOR A SHORT TO GROUND AND REPLACE FUSE. WHEN CKT 1077 IS SHORTED TO GROUND. REPLACE MAIN RELAY.
• DISCONNECT MAIN RELAY.
• MEASURE VOLTAGE FROM MAIN RELAY HARNESS CONNECTOR TERMINAL 4 TO GROUND
IS BATTERY VOLTAGE MEASURED?
YES
NO
REPAIR OPEN IN CKT 1443.
• IGNITION: RUN
• MEASURE VOLTAGE FROM MAIN RELAY HARNESS CONNECTOR TERMINAL 5 TO GROUND
IS BATTERY VOLTAGE MEASURED?
YES
NO
REPAIR OPEN IN CKT 650.
• IGNITION: OFF
• PICK UP MAIN RELAY.
• MEASURE RESISTANCE ACROSS MAIN RELAY TERMINALS 2 AND 5.
IS 45-90 OHMS MEASURED?
YES
NO
REPLACE MAIN RELAY.
• DISCONNECT PRESSURE MODULATOR VALVE (PMV) ASSEMBLY CONNECTOR, C1 (TWIST OFF)
• DISCONNECT ELECTRONIC BRAKE CONTROL MODULE (EBCM) CONNECTOR
• CONNECT J 38716 PINOUT BOX.
• MEASURE RESISTANCE BETWEEN J 38716 PINOUT BOX TERMINAL 1 AND ASSEMBLY LINE DIAGNOSTIC LINK (ALDL) CONNECTOR TERMINAL A, AND BETWEEN J 38716 PINOUT BOX TERMINAL 19 AND ALDL CONNECTOR TERMINAL A
IS LESS THAN 2 OHMS MEASURED AT BOTH TERMINALS?
YES
NO
REPAIR OPEN IN CKT 803.
A
CONTINUED
AFTER REPAIRS ARE COMPLETED, CLEAR CODES AND REPEAT ABS FUNCTIONAL CHECK.

GC402910060200BX

Fig. 11 Test A: Inlet/Outlet Valve Voltage Test (Part 1 of 2). 1992–93 Models Except 1993 LeSabre & Park Avenue

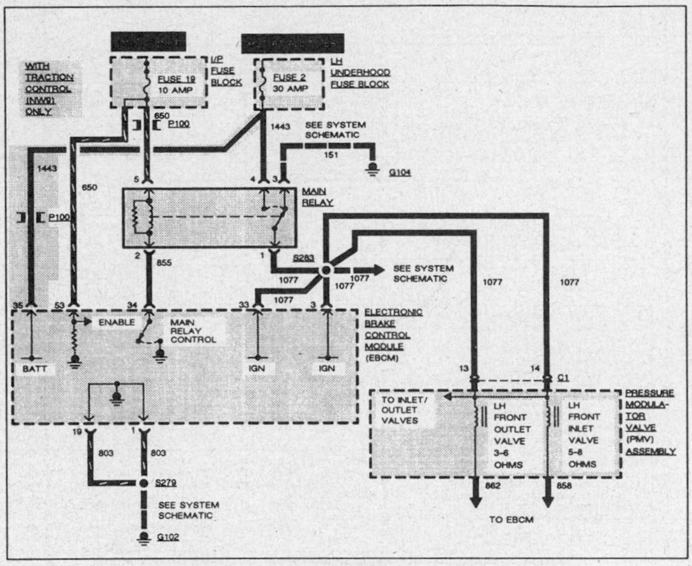

WITH TRACTION CONTROL (NW9) ONLY
FUSE 19 10 AMP
I/P FUSE BLOCK
FUSE 2 30 AMP
LH UNDERHOOD FUSE BLOCK
SEE SYSTEM SCHEMATIC
G104
MAIN RELAY
S283
SEE SYSTEM SCHEMATIC
ENABLE
MAIN RELAY CONTROL
ELECTRONIC BRAKE CONTROL MODULE (EBCM)
BATT
IGN
IGN
C1
TO INLET/ OUTLET VALVES
LH FRONT OUTLET VALVE 3-6 OHMS
LH FRONT INLET VALVE 5-8 OHMS
PRESSURE MODULATOR VALVE (PMV) ASSEMBLY
S279
SEE SYSTEM SCHEMATIC
G102
TO EBCM

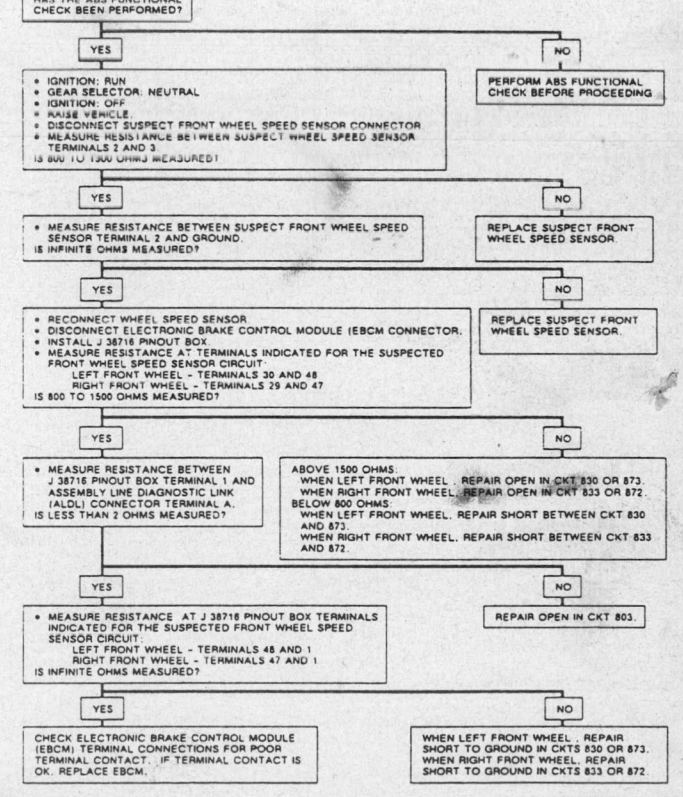

CHART A
INLET/OUTLET VALVE VOLTAGE TEST

CIRCUIT OPERATION

When the ignition is first turned to "RUN," the electronic brake control module (EBCM) goes through a self-check lasting 2–4 seconds. During this test the EBCM grounds terminal 34, energizing the main relay. Once the self-check is completed the main relay remains energized. This delivers battery voltage to both the EBCM and the pressure modulator valve (PMV) assembly during vehicle operation. The constant voltage supply allows the vehicle to enter ABS mode without delay. The main relay is de-energized whenever the amber "ANTILOCK" indicator lights due to a system fault, causing the ABS system to shut down.

FAILURE CONDITIONS

Code 45 sets when the ignition switch is at "RUN" and battery voltage is neither detected at the PMV assembly nor EBCM terminal 20, 3 and/or 33. Code 45 also sets when the EBCM detects an open or a short to ground in the LH inlet valve circuit.

Possible Causes

- Open in CKT 650, 855, 858, 1077 or 1443.
- Short to ground in CKT 858, 1077 or 1443.
- Main relay fails "open."

GC402910060200CX

CONTINUED

(A)

- MEASURE RESISTANCE BETWEEN J 38716 PINOUT BOX TERMINALS 3 AND 1.

IS INFINITE OHMS MEASURED?

- NO: REPAIR CKT 1077 FOR A SHORT TO GROUND.
- YES:
  - RECONNECT MAIN RELAY.
  - IGNITION: RUN
  - MEASURE VOLTAGE BETWEEN J 38716 PINOUT BOX TERMINALS 34 AND 1.

  IS BATTERY VOLTAGE MEASURED?

  - NO: REPAIR OPEN IN CKT 855.
  - YES:
    - PLACE A FUSED JUMPER BETWEEN J 38716 PINOUT BOX TERMINALS 34 AND 1.
    - MEASURE VOLTAGE BETWEEN J 38716 PINOUT BOX TERMINALS 19 AND 3, AND THEN TERMINALS 19 AND 33.

    IS BATTERY VOLTAGE MEASURED AT BOTH TERMINALS 3 AND 33?

    - NO:
      - IGNITION: OFF
      - REMOVE FUSE JUMPER.
      - DISCONNECT MAIN RELAY.
      - CONNECT A FUSED JUMPER BETWEEN MAIN RELAY HARNESS CONNECTOR TERMINALS 4 AND 1.
      - MEASURE VOLTAGE BETWEEN J 38716 PINOUT BOX TERMINALS 19 AND 3, AND THEN TERMINALS 19 AND 33.

      IS BATTERY VOLTAGE MEASURED AT BOTH TERMINALS 3 AND 33?

      - YES: REPLACE MAIN RELAY.
      - NO: REPAIR OPEN IN CKT 1077.
    - YES:
      - MEASURE VOLTAGE BETWEEN PMV ASSEMBLY CONNECTOR, C1, (HARNESS SIDE) TERMINAL 13 AND GROUND, AND TERMINAL 14 AND GROUND.

      IS BATTERY VOLTAGE MEASURED AT BOTH TERMINALS 13 AND 14?

      - NO: REPAIR OPEN IN CKT 1077.
      - YES: GO TO CHART E.

GC402910060200DX

Fig. 11 Test A: Inlet/Outlet Valve Voltage Test (Part 2 of 2). 1992–93 Models Except 1993 LeSabre & Park Avenue

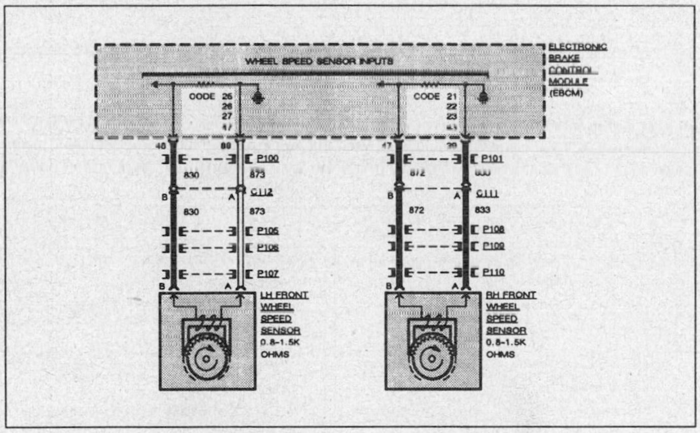

WHEEL SPEED SENSOR INPUTS
ELECTRONIC BRAKE CONTROL MODULE (EBCM)
CODE 26 25 27 47
CODE 21 22 23 43
P100
G112
P105
P106
P107
P101
G111
P108
P109
P110
LH FRONT WHEEL SPEED SENSOR 0.8–1.5K OHMS
RH FRONT WHEEL SPEED SENSOR 0.8–1.5K OHMS

CHART B
FRONT WHEEL SPEED SENSOR CIRCUIT TEST

CIRCUIT OPERATION

As each wheel turns, the wheel speed sensor creates a small AC voltage with a frequency proportional to wheel speed. This magnetically induced voltage is caused by a toothed sensor ring (mounted on the drive axle) passing the wheel speed sensor's stationary pickup coil.

The electronic brake control module (EBCM) uses the wheel speed sensor signal to calculate vehicle reference speeds and individual wheel speed, acceleration and slip values. These values are used to determine when antilock (or when equipped) traction control is required.

WHEEL SPEED SENSOR CABLES

In order to prevent electromagnetic interference from disturbing the wheel speed sensor signal, the cables from the EBCM to each wheel speed sensor are twisted in pairs a minimum of 6 to 9 turns per foot.

When servicing the sensor cables it is important to maintain the original cables' twists (6 to 9 turns per foot).

FAILURE CONDITIONS

The EBCM performs two basic checks on the wheel speed sensors: sensor continuity and sensor output. When the ignition is first turned to "RUN," the EBCM performs the wheel speed sensor continuity check.

Sensor Continuity Check

Any condition which would result in lack of continuity in the front wheel speed sensor circuit could result in a Code 21 or 25 being set. These conditions include an open, a short to ground, or a short between the two wheel speed sensor circuits in the wiring harness between the speed sensor and EBCM. Also an open or short to ground across the wheel speed sensor coil could trigger this code.

GC402910060300AX

HAS THE ABS FUNCTIONAL CHECK BEEN PERFORMED?

- NO: PERFORM ABS FUNCTIONAL CHECK BEFORE PROCEEDING
- YES:
  - IGNITION: RUN
  - GEAR SELECTOR: NEUTRAL
  - IGNITION: OFF
  - RAISE VEHICLE.
  - DISCONNECT SUSPECT FRONT WHEEL SPEED SENSOR CONNECTOR
  - MEASURE RESISTANCE BETWEEN SUSPECT FRONT WHEEL SPEED SENSOR TERMINALS 2 AND 3

  IS 800 TO 1500 OHMS MEASURED?

  - NO: REPLACE SUSPECT FRONT WHEEL SPEED SENSOR.
  - YES:
    - MEASURE RESISTANCE BETWEEN SUSPECT FRONT WHEEL SPEED SENSOR TERMINAL 2 AND GROUND.

    IS INFINITE OHMS MEASURED?

    - NO: REPLACE SUSPECT FRONT WHEEL SPEED SENSOR.
    - YES:
      - RECONNECT WHEEL SPEED SENSOR
      - DISCONNECT ELECTRONIC BRAKE CONTROL MODULE (EBCM CONNECTOR.
      - INSTALL J 38716 PINOUT BOX
      - MEASURE RESISTANCE AT TERMINALS INDICATED FOR THE SUSPECTED FRONT WHEEL SPEED SENSOR CIRCUIT:
        LEFT FRONT WHEEL - TERMINALS 30 AND 48
        RIGHT FRONT WHEEL - TERMINALS 29 AND 47

      IS 800 TO 1500 OHMS MEASURED?

      - NO: ABOVE 1500 OHMS: WHEN LEFT FRONT WHEEL , REPAIR OPEN IN CKT 830 OR 873. WHEN RIGHT FRONT WHEEL, REPAIR OPEN IN CKT 833 OR 872. BELOW 800 OHMS: WHEN LEFT FRONT WHEEL, REPAIR SHORT BETWEEN CKT 830 AND 873. WHEN RIGHT FRONT WHEEL, REPAIR SHORT BETWEEN CKT 833 AND 872.
      - YES:
        - MEASURE RESISTANCE BETWEEN J 38716 PINOUT BOX TERMINAL 1 AND ASSEMBLY LINE DIAGNOSTIC LINK (ALDL) CONNECTOR TERMINAL A.

        IS LESS THAN 2 OHMS MEASURED?

        - NO: REPAIR OPEN IN CKT 803.
        - YES:
          - MEASURE RESISTANCE AT J 38716 PINOUT BOX TERMINALS INDICATED FOR THE SUSPECTED FRONT WHEEL SPEED SENSOR CIRCUIT:
            LEFT FRONT WHEEL - TERMINALS 48 AND 1
            RIGHT FRONT WHEEL - TERMINALS 47 AND 1

          IS INFINITE OHMS MEASURED?

          - YES: CHECK ELECTRONIC BRAKE CONTROL MODULE (EBCM) TERMINAL CONNECTIONS FOR POOR TERMINAL CONTACT. IF TERMINAL CONTACT IS OK, REPLACE EBCM.
          - NO: WHEN LEFT FRONT WHEEL , REPAIR SHORT TO GROUND IN CKTS 830 OR 873. WHEN RIGHT FRONT WHEEL, REPAIR SHORT TO GROUND IN CKTS 833 OR 872.

GC402910060300BX

Fig. 12 Test B: Front Wheel Speed Sensor Circuit Test. 1992–93 Models Except 1993 LeSabre & Park Avenue

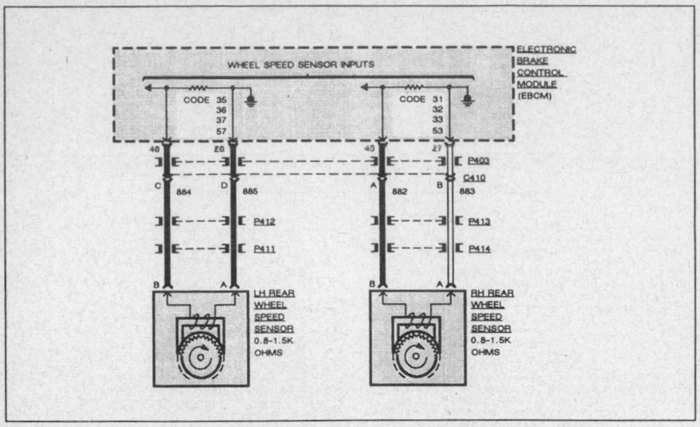
ELECTRONIC BRAKE CONTROL MODULE (EBCM)
WHEEL SPEED SENSOR INPUTS
CODE 35 36 37 57
CODE 31 32 33 53
46 28 45 27
P403
C410
884 885 882 883
P412 P413
P411 P414
LH REAR WHEEL SPEED SENSOR 0.8-1.5K OHMS
RH REAR WHEEL SPEED SENSOR 0.8-1.5K OHMS

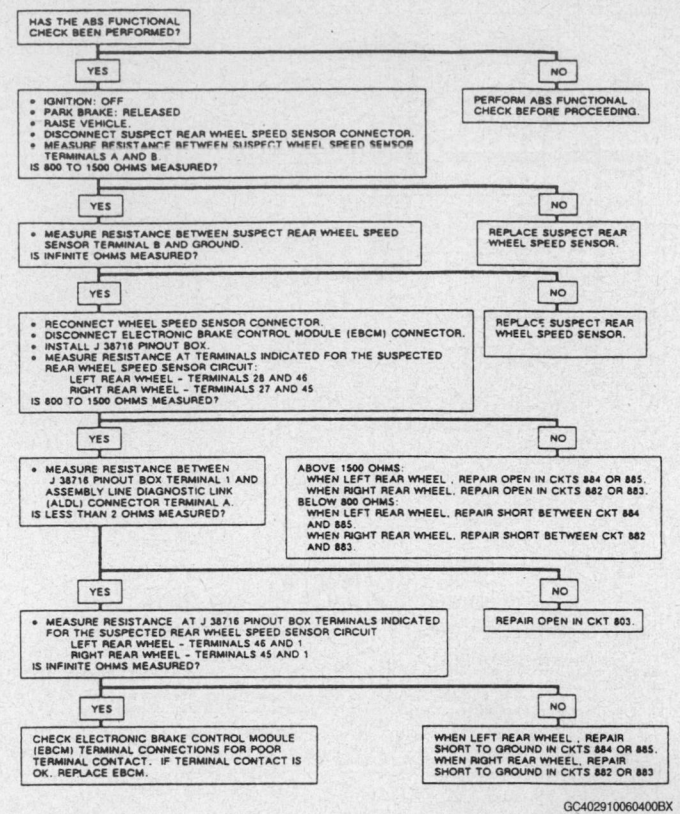

CHART C
REAR WHEEL SPEED SENSOR CIRCUIT TEST

CIRCUIT OPERATION

When each wheel turns, the wheel speed sensor creates a small AC voltage with a frequency proportional to wheel speed. This magnetically induced voltage is caused by a toothed sensor ring passing the wheel speed sensor's stationary pickup coil. Both sensors are part of the hub and bearing assembly.

The electronic brake control module (EBCM) uses the wheel speed sensor signal to calculate vehicle reference speeds and individual wheel speed, acceleration and slip values. These values are used to determine when antilock control is required.

WHEEL SPEED SENSOR CABLES

In order to prevent electromagnetic interference from disturbing the wheel speed sensor signal, the cables from the EBCM to each wheel speed sensor are twisted in pairs a minimum of 6 to 9 turns per foot.

When servicing the sensor cables it is important to maintain the original cables' twists (6 to 9 per foot).

FAILURE CONDITIONS

The EBCM performs two basic checks on the wheel speed sensors: sensor continuity and sensor output. When the ignition is first turned to "RUN," the EBCM performs the wheel speed sensor continuity check.

Sensor Continuity Check

Any condition which would result in lack of continuity in the rear wheel speed sensor circuit could result in a Code 31 or 35 being set. These conditions include an open, a short to ground, or a short between the two wheel speed sensor circuits in the wiring harness between the speed sensor and EBCM. Also an open or short to ground across the wheel speed sensor coil could trigger this code.

GC402910060400AX

HAS THE ABS FUNCTIONAL CHECK BEEN PERFORMED?

- NO: PERFORM ABS FUNCTIONAL CHECK BEFORE PROCEEDING.
- YES:
  - IGNITION: OFF
  - PARK BRAKE: RELEASED
  - RAISE VEHICLE.
  - DISCONNECT SUSPECT REAR WHEEL SPEED SENSOR CONNECTOR.
  - MEASURE RESISTANCE BETWEEN SUSPECT WHEEL SPEED SENSOR TERMINALS A AND B.

  IS 800 TO 1500 OHMS MEASURED?

- NO: REPLACE SUSPECT REAR WHEEL SPEED SENSOR.
- YES:
  - MEASURE RESISTANCE BETWEEN SUSPECT REAR WHEEL SPEED SENSOR TERMINAL B AND GROUND.

  IS INFINITE OHMS MEASURED?

- NO: REPLACE SUSPECT REAR WHEEL SPEED SENSOR.
- YES:
  - RECONNECT WHEEL SPEED SENSOR CONNECTOR.
  - DISCONNECT ELECTRONIC BRAKE CONTROL MODULE (EBCM) CONNECTOR.
  - INSTALL J 38716 PINOUT BOX.
  - MEASURE RESISTANCE AT TERMINALS INDICATED FOR THE SUSPECTED REAR WHEEL SPEED SENSOR CIRCUIT:
    LEFT REAR WHEEL - TERMINALS 28 AND 46
    RIGHT REAR WHEEL - TERMINALS 27 AND 45

  IS 800 TO 1500 OHMS MEASURED?

- NO: ABOVE 1500 OHMS:
  WHEN LEFT REAR WHEEL , REPAIR OPEN IN CKTS 884 OR 885.
  WHEN RIGHT REAR WHEEL, REPAIR OPEN IN CKTS 882 OR 883.
  BELOW 800 OHMS:
  WHEN LEFT REAR WHEEL, REPAIR SHORT BETWEEN CKT 884 AND 885.
  WHEN RIGHT REAR WHEEL, REPAIR SHORT BETWEEN CKT 882 AND 883.
- YES:
  - MEASURE RESISTANCE BETWEEN J 38716 PINOUT BOX TERMINAL 1 AND ASSEMBLY LINE DIAGNOSTIC LINK (ALDL) CONNECTOR TERMINAL A.

  IS LESS THAN 2 OHMS MEASURED?

- NO: REPAIR OPEN IN CKT 803.
- YES:
  - MEASURE RESISTANCE AT J 38716 PINOUT BOX TERMINALS INDICATED FOR THE SUSPECTED REAR WHEEL SPEED SENSOR CIRCUIT
    LEFT REAR WHEEL - TERMINALS 46 AND 1
    RIGHT REAR WHEEL - TERMINALS 45 AND 1

  IS INFINITE OHMS MEASURED?

- YES: CHECK ELECTRONIC BRAKE CONTROL MODULE (EBCM) TERMINAL CONNECTIONS FOR POOR TERMINAL CONTACT. IF TERMINAL CONTACT IS OK, REPLACE EBCM.
- NO: WHEN LEFT REAR WHEEL , REPAIR SHORT TO GROUND IN CKTS 884 OR 885. WHEN RIGHT REAR WHEEL, REPAIR SHORT TO GROUND IN CKTS 882 OR 883

GC402910060400BX

Fig. 13 Test C: Rear Wheel Speed Sensor Circuit Test. 1992–93 Models Except 1993 LeSabre & Park Avenue

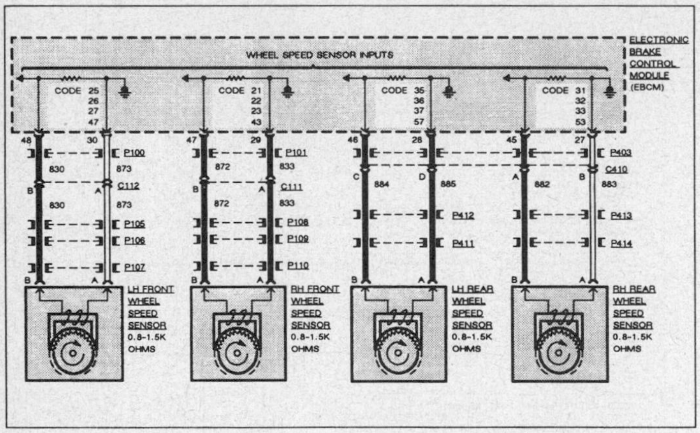
ELECTRONIC BRAKE CONTROL MODULE (EBCM)
WHEEL SPEED SENSOR INPUTS
CODE 25 26 27 47
CODE 21 22 23 43
CODE 35 36 37 57
CODE 31 32 33 53
P100 P101 P403
C112 C111 C410
P105 P108 P412 P413
P106 P109 P411 P414
P107 P110
LH FRONT WHEEL SPEED SENSOR 0.8-1.5K OHMS
RH FRONT WHEEL SPEED SENSOR 0.8-1.5K OHMS
LH REAR WHEEL SPEED SENSOR 0.8-1.5K OHMS
RH REAR WHEEL SPEED SENSOR 0.8-1.5K OHMS

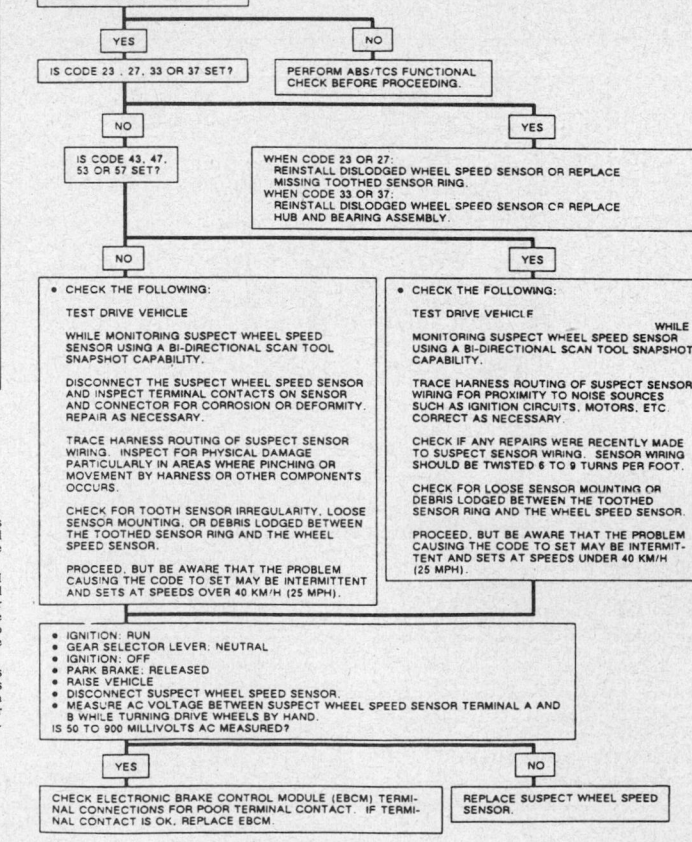

CHART D
WHEEL SPEED SIGNAL ERRATIC OR NOISY

CIRCUIT OPERATION

When each wheel turns, the wheel speed sensor creates a small AC voltage with a frequency proportional to wheel speed. This magnetically induced voltage is caused by a toothed sensor ring passing the wheel speed sensor's stationary pickup coil. The toothed ring sensor is mounted on the drive axle in the front, and in the hub/bearing assembly in the rear.

The electronic brake control module (EBCM) uses the wheel speed sensor signal to calculate vehicle reference speeds, and individual wheel speed, acceleration and slip values. These values are used to determine when antilock control is required. Vehicles equipped with traction control also use front wheel speed sensor signals to determine when traction control is required.

WHEEL SPEED SENSOR CABLES

In order to prevent electromagnetic interference from disturbing the wheel speed sensor signal, the cables from the EBCM to each wheel speed sensor are twisted in pairs a minimum of 6 to 9 turns per foot.

When servicing the sensor cables it is important to maintain the original cables' twists (6 to 9 turns per foot).

FAILURE CONDITIONS

Code 43, 47, 53 or 57 sets when the EBCM detects electromagnetic interference (noise) in a wheel speed sensor signal. Possible interference sources include accessory motors, wiper motors and ignition circuits.

Code 22, 26, 32 or 36 sets when the EBCM determines a wheel speed signal is erratic. A wheel speed signal indicating that a wheel is accelerating or decelerating faster than physically possible is an example of an erratic signal. An intermittent open or short to ground in a wheel speed sensor could also cause the EBCM to set a code.

Code 23, 27, 33 or 37 sets when the EBCM does not see any wheel speed sensor signal, but determines continuity exists in the circuit. This is caused by a dislodged wheel speed sensor, missing toothed sensor ring (front) or defective hub and bearing assembly (rear).

GC402910060500AX

HAS THE ABS/TCS FUNCTIONAL CHECK BEEN PERFORMED?

- NO: PERFORM ABS/TCS FUNCTIONAL CHECK BEFORE PROCEEDING.
- YES: IS CODE 23 , 27, 33 OR 37 SET?

- YES: WHEN CODE 23 OR 27:
  REINSTALL DISLODGED WHEEL SPEED SENSOR OR REPLACE MISSING TOOTHED SENSOR RING.
  WHEN CODE 33 OR 37:
  REINSTALL DISLODGED WHEEL SPEED SENSOR OR REPLACE HUB AND BEARING ASSEMBLY.
- NO: IS CODE 43, 47, 53 OR 57 SET?

- NO:
  - CHECK THE FOLLOWING:

    TEST DRIVE VEHICLE

    WHILE MONITORING SUSPECT WHEEL SPEED SENSOR USING A BI-DIRECTIONAL SCAN TOOL SNAPSHOT CAPABILITY.

    DISCONNECT THE SUSPECT WHEEL SPEED SENSOR AND INSPECT TERMINAL CONTACTS ON SENSOR AND CONNECTOR FOR CORROSION OR DEFORMITY. REPAIR AS NECESSARY.

    TRACE HARNESS ROUTING OF SUSPECT SENSOR WIRING. INSPECT FOR PHYSICAL DAMAGE PARTICULARLY IN AREAS WHERE PINCHING OR MOVEMENT BY HARNESS OR OTHER COMPONENTS OCCURS.

    CHECK FOR TOOTH SENSOR IRREGULARITY, LOOSE SENSOR MOUNTING, OR DEBRIS LODGED BETWEEN THE TOOTHED SENSOR RING AND THE WHEEL SPEED SENSOR.

    PROCEED, BUT BE AWARE THAT THE PROBLEM CAUSING THE CODE TO SET MAY BE INTERMITTENT AND SETS AT SPEEDS OVER 40 KM/H (25 MPH).
- YES:
  - CHECK THE FOLLOWING:

    TEST DRIVE VEHICLE WHILE

    MONITORING SUSPECT WHEEL SPEED SENSOR USING A BI-DIRECTIONAL SCAN TOOL SNAPSHOT CAPABILITY.

    TRACE HARNESS ROUTING OF SUSPECT SENSOR WIRING FOR PROXIMITY TO NOISE SOURCES SUCH AS IGNITION CIRCUITS, MOTORS, ETC. CORRECT AS NECESSARY.

    CHECK IF ANY REPAIRS WERE RECENTLY MADE TO SUSPECT SENSOR WIRING. SENSOR WIRING SHOULD BE TWISTED 6 TO 9 TURNS PER FOOT.

    CHECK FOR LOOSE SENSOR MOUNTING OR DEBRIS LODGED BETWEEN THE TOOTHED SENSOR RING AND THE WHEEL SPEED SENSOR.

    PROCEED, BUT BE AWARE THAT THE PROBLEM CAUSING THE CODE TO SET MAY BE INTERMITTENT AND SETS AT SPEEDS UNDER 40 KM/H (25 MPH).

Both branches then continue to:

- IGNITION: RUN
- GEAR SELECTOR LEVER: NEUTRAL
- IGNITION: OFF
- PARK BRAKE: RELEASED
- RAISE VEHICLE
- DISCONNECT SUSPECT WHEEL SPEED SENSOR.
- MEASURE AC VOLTAGE BETWEEN SUSPECT WHEEL SPEED SENSOR TERMINAL A AND B WHILE TURNING DRIVE WHEELS BY HAND.

IS 50 TO 900 MILLIVOLTS AC MEASURED?

- YES: CHECK ELECTRONIC BRAKE CONTROL MODULE (EBCM) TERMINAL CONNECTIONS FOR POOR TERMINAL CONTACT. IF TERMINAL CONTACT IS OK, REPLACE EBCM.
- NO: REPLACE SUSPECT WHEEL SPEED SENSOR.

GC402910060500BX

Fig. 14 Test D: Wheel Speed Signal Erratic Or Noisy. 1992

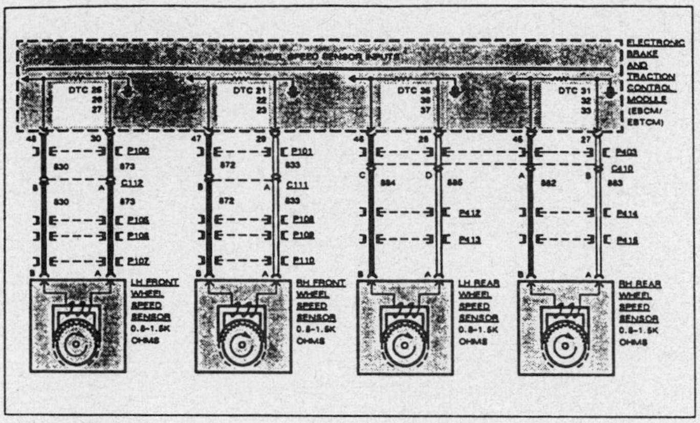
ELECTRONIC BRAKE AND TRACTION CONTROL MODULE (EBCM/EBTCM)
DTC 25 26 27
DTC 21 22 23
DTC 31 32 33
P100
P101
P403
C112
C111
C410
P105
P106
P107
P108
P109
P110
P412
P413
P414
P415
LH FRONT WHEEL SPEED SENSOR 0.8-1.5K OHMS
RH FRONT WHEEL SPEED SENSOR 0.8-1.5K OHMS
LH REAR WHEEL SPEED SENSOR 0.8-1.5K OHMS
RH REAR WHEEL SPEED SENSOR 0.8-1.5K OHMS

CHART D
WHEEL SPEED SIGNAL ERRATIC OR NOISY

CIRCUIT OPERATION

When each wheel turns, the wheel speed sensor creates a small AC voltage with a frequency proportional to wheel speed. This magnetically induced voltage is caused by a toothed sensor ring passing the wheel speed sensor's stationary pickup coil. The toothed ring sensor is mounted on the drive axle in the front, and in the hub/bearing assembly in the rear.

The EBCM/EBTCM uses the wheel speed sensor signal to calculate vehicle reference speeds, and individual wheel speed, acceleration and slip values. These values are used to determine when antilock control is required. Vehicles equipped with traction control also use front wheel speed sensor signals to determine when traction control is required.

WHEEL SPEED SENSOR CABLES

In order to prevent electromagnetic interference from disturbing the wheel speed sensor signal, the cables from the EBCM/EBTCM to each wheel speed sensor are twisted in pairs a minimum of 6 to 9 turns per foot.

When servicing the sensor cables it is important to maintain the original cables' twists (6 to 9 turns per foot).

FAILURE CONDITIONS

DTC 22, DTC 26, DTC 33 or DTC 36 sets when the EBCM/EBTCM detects electromagnetic interference (noise) in a wheel speed sensor signal. Possible interference sources include accessory motors, wiper motors and ignition circuits.

DTC 22, DTC 26, DTC 32 or DTC 36 also sets when the EBCM/EBTCM determines a wheel speed signal is erratic. A wheel speed signal indicating that a wheel is accelerating or decelerating faster than physically possible is an example of an erratic signal. An intermittent open or short to ground in a wheel speed sensor could also cause the EBCM/EBTCM to set a DTC.

DTC 23, DTC 27, DTC 33 or DTC 37 sets when the EBCM/EBTCM does not see any wheel speed sensor signal, but determines continuity exists in the circuit. This is caused by a dislodged wheel speed sensor, missing toothed sensor ring (front) or defective hub and bearing assembly (rear).

An intermittent open or short to ground in a wheel speed sensor (or its circuitry) could cause the pump motor to run inadvertently without setting a DTC. This condition is usually noticed at slow speed driving (under 16 km/h [10 mph]).

GC402930060600AX

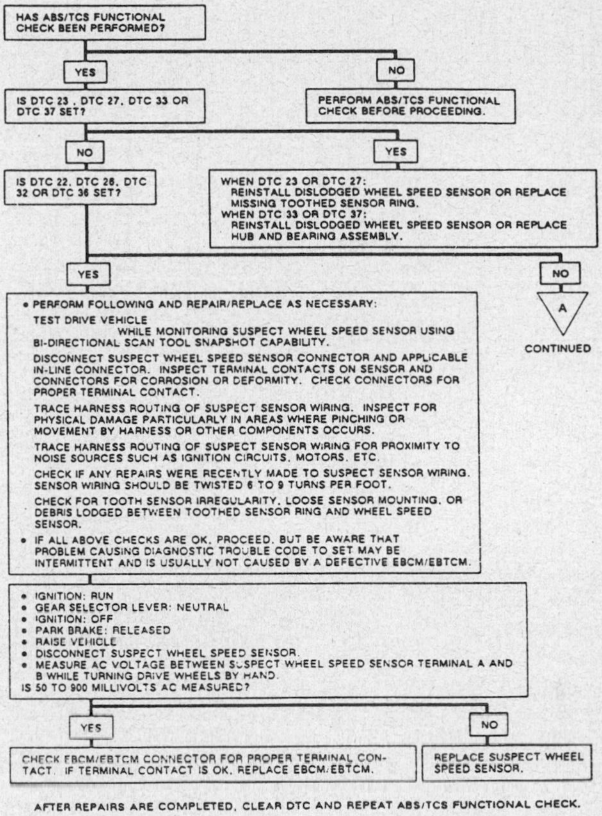
HAS ABS/TCS FUNCTIONAL CHECK BEEN PERFORMED?
YES
NO
IS DTC 23 , DTC 27, DTC 33 OR DTC 37 SET?
PERFORM ABS/TCS FUNCTIONAL CHECK BEFORE PROCEEDING.
NO
YES
IS DTC 22, DTC 26, DTC 32 OR DTC 36 SET?
WHEN DTC 23 OR DTC 27: REINSTALL DISLODGED WHEEL SPEED SENSOR OR REPLACE MISSING TOOTHED SENSOR RING. WHEN DTC 33 OR DTC 37: REINSTALL DISLODGED WHEEL SPEED SENSOR OR REPLACE HUB AND BEARING ASSEMBLY.
YES
NO
A
CONTINUED
• PERFORM FOLLOWING AND REPAIR/REPLACE AS NECESSARY:
TEST DRIVE VEHICLE WHILE MONITORING SUSPECT WHEEL SPEED SENSOR USING BI-DIRECTIONAL SCAN TOOL SNAPSHOT CAPABILITY.
DISCONNECT SUSPECT WHEEL SPEED SENSOR CONNECTOR AND APPLICABLE IN-LINE CONNECTOR. INSPECT TERMINAL CONTACTS ON SENSOR AND CONNECTORS FOR CORROSION OR DEFORMITY. CHECK CONNECTORS FOR PROPER TERMINAL CONTACT.
TRACE HARNESS ROUTING OF SUSPECT SENSOR WIRING. INSPECT FOR PHYSICAL DAMAGE PARTICULARLY IN AREAS WHERE PINCHING OR MOVEMENT BY HARNESS OR OTHER COMPONENTS OCCURS.
TRACE HARNESS ROUTING OF SUSPECT SENSOR WIRING FOR PROXIMITY TO NOISE SOURCES SUCH AS IGNITION CIRCUITS, MOTORS, ETC.
CHECK IF ANY REPAIRS WERE RECENTLY MADE TO SUSPECT SENSOR WIRING. SENSOR WIRING SHOULD BE TWISTED 6 TO 9 TURNS PER FOOT.
CHECK FOR TOOTH SENSOR IRREGULARITY, LOOSE SENSOR MOUNTING, OR DEBRIS LODGED BETWEEN TOOTHED SENSOR RING AND WHEEL SPEED SENSOR.
• IF ALL ABOVE CHECKS ARE OK, PROCEED, BUT BE AWARE THAT PROBLEM CAUSING DIAGNOSTIC TROUBLE CODE TO SET MAY BE INTERMITTENT AND IS USUALLY NOT CAUSED BY A DEFECTIVE EBCM/EBTCM.
• IGNITION: RUN
• GEAR SELECTOR LEVER: NEUTRAL
• IGNITION: OFF
• PARK BRAKE: RELEASED
• RAISE VEHICLE
• DISCONNECT SUSPECT WHEEL SPEED SENSOR.
• MEASURE AC VOLTAGE BETWEEN SUSPECT WHEEL SPEED SENSOR TERMINAL A AND B WHILE TURNING DRIVE WHEELS BY HAND.
IS 50 TO 900 MILLIVOLTS AC MEASURED?
YES
NO
CHECK EBCM/EBTCM CONNECTOR FOR PROPER TERMINAL CONTACT. IF TERMINAL CONTACT IS OK, REPLACE EBCM/EBTCM.
REPLACE SUSPECT WHEEL SPEED SENSOR.
AFTER REPAIRS ARE COMPLETED, CLEAR DTC AND REPEAT ABS/TCS FUNCTIONAL CHECK.

GC402930060600BX

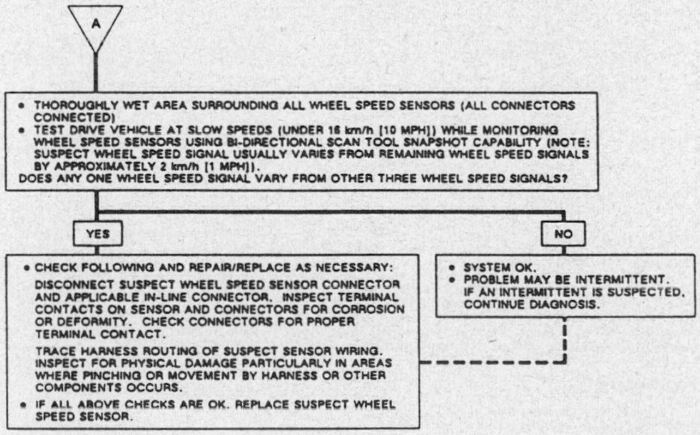
A
• THOROUGHLY WET AREA SURROUNDING ALL WHEEL SPEED SENSORS (ALL CONNECTORS CONNECTED)
• TEST DRIVE VEHICLE AT SLOW SPEEDS (UNDER 16 km/h [10 MPH]) WHILE MONITORING WHEEL SPEED SENSORS USING BI-DIRECTIONAL SCAN TOOL SNAPSHOT CAPABILITY (NOTE: SUSPECT WHEEL SPEED SIGNAL USUALLY VARIES FROM REMAINING WHEEL SPEED SIGNALS BY APPROXIMATELY 2 km/h [1 MPH]).
DOES ANY ONE WHEEL SPEED SIGNAL VARY FROM OTHER THREE WHEEL SPEED SIGNALS?
YES
NO
• CHECK FOLLOWING AND REPAIR/REPLACE AS NECESSARY:
DISCONNECT SUSPECT WHEEL SPEED SENSOR CONNECTOR AND APPLICABLE IN-LINE CONNECTOR. INSPECT TERMINAL CONTACTS ON SENSOR AND CONNECTORS FOR CORROSION OR DEFORMITY. CHECK CONNECTORS FOR PROPER TERMINAL CONTACT.
TRACE HARNESS ROUTING OF SUSPECT SENSOR WIRING. INSPECT FOR PHYSICAL DAMAGE PARTICULARLY IN AREAS WHERE PINCHING OR MOVEMENT BY HARNESS OR OTHER COMPONENTS OCCURS.
• IF ALL ABOVE CHECKS ARE OK, REPLACE SUSPECT WHEEL SPEED SENSOR.
• SYSTEM OK.
• PROBLEM MAY BE INTERMITTENT. IF AN INTERMITTENT IS SUSPECTED, CONTINUE DIAGNOSIS.

GC402930060600CX

Fig. 15 Test D: Wheel Speed Sensor Signal Erratic Or Noisy. 1993 Models Except LeSabre & Park Avenue

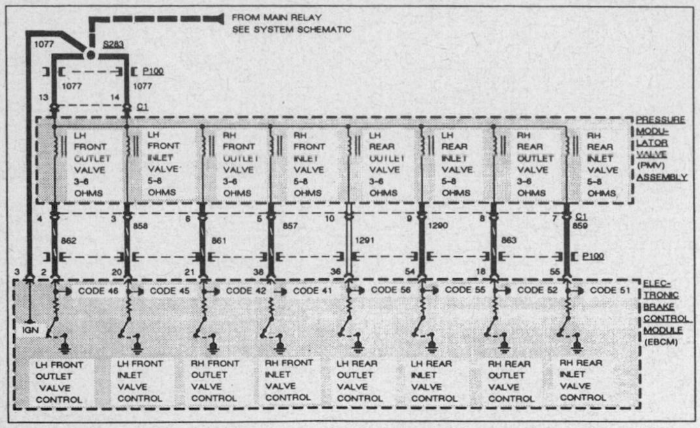
FROM MAIN RELAY
SEE SYSTEM SCHEMATIC
1077
S283
P100
C1
PRESSURE MODULATOR VALVE (PMV) ASSEMBLY
LH FRONT OUTLET VALVE 3-6 OHMS
LH FRONT INLET VALVE 5-8 OHMS
RH FRONT OUTLET VALVE 3-6 OHMS
RH FRONT INLET VALVE 5-8 OHMS
LH REAR OUTLET VALVE 3-6 OHMS
LH REAR INLET VALVE 5-8 OHMS
RH REAR OUTLET VALVE 3-6 OHMS
RH REAR INLET VALVE 5-8 OHMS
862
858
861
857
1291
1290
863
859
CODE 46
CODE 45
CODE 42
CODE 41
CODE 56
CODE 55
CODE 52
CODE 51
ELECTRONIC BRAKE CONTROL MODULE (EBCM)
IGN
LH FRONT OUTLET VALVE CONTROL
LH FRONT INLET VALVE CONTROL
RH FRONT OUTLET VALVE CONTROL
RH FRONT INLET VALVE CONTROL
LH REAR OUTLET VALVE CONTROL
LH REAR INLET VALVE CONTROL
RH REAR OUTLET VALVE CONTROL
RH REAR INLET VALVE CONTROL

CIRCUIT OPERATION

Inlet Valves

Voltage is applied to the normally open inlet valves whenever the main relay is energized. An inlet valve closes when the electronic brake control module (EBCM) supplies a ground path at the inlet valve control terminal. The EBCM closes an inlet valve for short periods to maintain (hold) or reduce pressure at a particular wheel.

Outlet Valves

The normally closed outlet valves operate similarly to the inlet valves, except that when the EBCM grounds an outlet valve, the valve opens instead of closes. The EBCM opens an outlet valve for short periods to reduce pressure at a particular wheel.

VALVE MODES

Pressure Increase

The pressure increase position is the operating valve position for normal (non-ABS) braking and traction control mode (when equipped). The EBCM does not energize either valve, leaving the inlet valve open and the outlet valve closed.

Pressure Hold

The pressure hold position occurs when the EBCM first notices an abnormal hydraulic pressure increase. This signifies an impending wheel lockup condition. The EBCM closes the corresponding inlet valve in an attempt to avoid any additional hydraulic pressure increase (avoiding an ABS braking condition).

Pressure Reduce

During a wheel lockup condition, the EBCM close the inlet valve while pulsing open the outlet valve. This decreases hydraulic pressure at a specific wheel without decreasing overall system pressure. The reduced hydraulic pressure allows greater wheel spin, eliminating the wheel lockup condition.

Test Description

This test checks for proper inlet and outlet valve operation. The wheel brake behavior must be checked to verify the valves hydraulic effectiveness. This is accomplished using the TECH 1 to actuate the valves.

Failure Conditions

Code 41, 42, 45, 46, 51, 52, 55, or 56 sets when the electronic brake control module (EBCM) detects an open or short to ground in the respective inlet or outlet valve circuit.

GC402910060700AX

HAS THE ABS FUNCTIONAL CHECK BEEN PERFORMED?

- YES:
  - IGNITION: OFF
  - DISCONNECT PRESSURE MODULATOR VALVE (PMV) ASSEMBLY VALVE CONNECTOR, C1.
  - MEASURE RESISTANCE BETWEEN CONNECTOR C1, (PMV ASSEMBLY SIDE) TERMINAL 14 AND PMV ASSEMBLY CASING.

  IS INFINITE OHMS MEASURED?
- NO: PERFORM ABS FUNCTIONAL CHECK BEFORE PROCEEDING.

IS INFINITE OHMS MEASURED?

- YES:
  - MEASURE RESISTANCE AT CONNECTOR, C1, (PMV ASSEMBLY SIDE) BETWEEN TERMINAL 14 AND THE SUSPECT VALVE TERMINAL. REFER TO CHART.
- NO: REPLACE PMV ASSEMBLY.

CODE/VALVE	SUSPECT TERMINAL	CORRECT RESISTANCE
45/LH FRONT INLET	3	5 TO 8 OHMS
41/RH FRONT INLET	5	
55/LH REAR INLET	9	
51/RH REAR INLET	7	
46/LH FRONT OUTLET	4	3 TO 6 OHMS
42/RH FRONT OUTLET	6	
56/LH REAR OUTLET	10	
52/RH REAR OUTLET	8	

IS THE CORRECT RESISTANCE MEASURED?

- YES: A — CONTINUED
- NO: REPLACE PMV ASSEMBLY.

GC402910060700BX

Fig. 16 Test E: Inlet/Oulet Valve Circuit Test (Part 1 of 2). 1992–93 Models Except 1993 LeSabre & Park Avenue

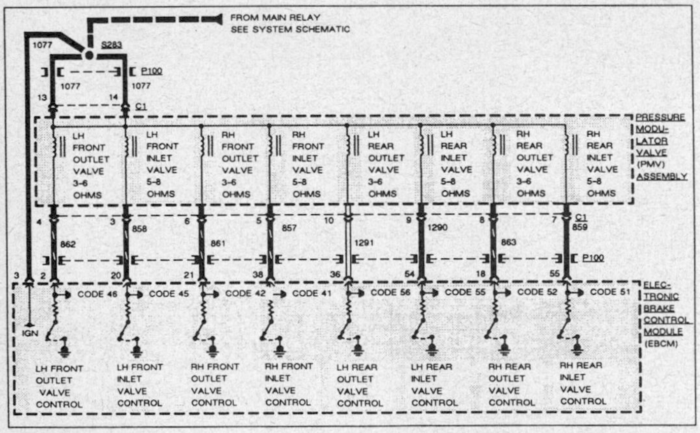
FROM MAIN RELAY
SEE SYSTEM SCHEMATIC
1077
S283
P100
C1
PRESSURE MODULATOR VALVE (PMV) ASSEMBLY
LH FRONT OUTLET VALVE 3-6 OHMS
LH FRONT INLET VALVE 5-8 OHMS
RH FRONT OUTLET VALVE 3-6 OHMS
RH FRONT INLET VALVE 5-8 OHMS
LH REAR OUTLET VALVE 3-6 OHMS
LH REAR INLET VALVE 5-8 OHMS
RH REAR OUTLET VALVE 3-6 OHMS
RH REAR INLET VALVE 5-8 OHMS
862
858
861
857
1291
1290
863
859
CODE 46
CODE 45
CODE 42
CODE 41
CODE 56
CODE 55
CODE 52
CODE 51
ELECTRONIC BRAKE CONTROL MODULE (EBCM)
IGN
LH FRONT OUTLET VALVE CONTROL
LH FRONT INLET VALVE CONTROL
RH FRONT OUTLET VALVE CONTROL
RH FRONT INLET VALVE CONTROL
LH REAR OUTLET VALVE CONTROL
LH REAR INLET VALVE CONTROL
RH REAR OUTLET VALVE CONTROL
RH REAR INLET VALVE CONTROL

CIRCUIT OPERATION

Inlet Valves

Voltage is applied to the normally open inlet valves whenever the main relay is energized. An inlet valve closes when the electronic brake control module (EBCM) supplies a ground path at the inlet valve control terminal. The EBCM closes an inlet valve for short periods to maintain (hold) or reduce pressure at a particular wheel.

Outlet Valves

The normally closed outlet valves operate similarly to the inlet valves, except that when the EBCM grounds an outlet valve, the valve opens instead of closes. The EBCM opens an outlet valve for short periods to reduce pressure at a particular wheel.

VALVE MODES

Pressure Increase

The pressure increase position is the operating valve position for normal (non-ABS) braking and traction control mode (when equipped). The EBCM does not energize either valve, leaving the inlet valve open and the outlet valve closed.

Pressure Hold

The pressure hold position occurs when the EBCM first notices an abnormal hydraulic pressure increase. This signifies an impending wheel lockup condition. The EBCM closes the corresponding inlet valve in an attempt to avoid any additional hydraulic pressure increase (avoiding an ABS braking condition).

Pressure Reduce

During a wheel lockup condition, the EBCM close the inlet valve while pulsing open the outlet valve. This decreases hydraulic pressure at a specific wheel without decreasing overall system pressure. The reduced hydraulic pressure allows greater wheel spin, eliminating the wheel lockup condition.

Test Description

This test checks for proper inlet and outlet valve operation. The wheel brake behavior must be checked to verify the valves hydraulic effectiveness. This is accomplished using the TECH 1 to actuate the valves.

Failure Conditions

Code 41, 42, 45, 46, 51, 52, 55, or 56 sets when the electronic brake control module (EBCM) detects an open or short to ground in the respective inlet or outlet valve circuit.

GC402910060700CX

CONTINUED

A

- RECONNECT PMV ASSEMBLY CONNECTOR, C1.
- DISCONNECT ELECTRONIC BRAKE CONTROL MODULE (EBCM) CONNECTOR.
- INSTALL J 38716 PINOUT BOX.
- MEASURE RESISTANCE BETWEEN J 38716 PINOUT BOX TERMINAL 3 AND THE SUSPECT VALVE. REFER TO CHART.

CODE/VALVE	J 38716 TERMINAL	CORRECT RESISTANCE
45/LH FRONT INLET	20	5 TO 8 OHMS
41/RH FRONT INLET	38	
55/LH REAR INLET	54	
51/RH REAR INLET	55	
46/LH FRONT OUTLET	2	3 TO 6 OHMS
42/RH FRONT OUTLET	21	
56/LH REAR OUTLET	36	
52/RH REAR OUTLET	18	

IS RESISTANCE MEASURED LESS THAN 10 OHMS?

- YES:
  - MEASURE RESISTANCE BETWEEN J 38716 PINOUT BOX TERMINAL 1 AND ASSEMBLY LINE DIAGNOSTIC LINK (ALDL) CONNECTOR TERMINAL A.

  IS LESS THAN 2 OHMS MEASURED?
- NO: REPAIR OPEN IN SUSPECT VALVE CIRCUIT BETWEEN PRESSURE MODULATOR VALVE (PMV) ASSEMBLY AND ELECTRONIC BRAKE CONTROL MODULE (EBCM).

IS LESS THAN 2 OHMS MEASURED?

- YES:
  - DISCONNECT MAIN RELAY.
  - MEASURE RESISTANCE BETWEEN J 38716 PINOUT BOX TERMINAL 1 AND THE SUSPECT VALVE. REFER TO CHART.
- NO: REPAIR OPEN IN CKT 803.

CODE/VALVE	J 38716 TERMINAL	CORRECT RESISTANCE
45/LH FRONT INLET	20	INFINITE OHMS
41/RH FRONT INLET	38	
55/LH REAR INLET	54	
51/RH REAR INLET	55	
46/LH FRONT OUTLET	2	
42/RH FRONT OUTLET	21	
56/LH REAR OUTLET	36	
52/RH REAR OUTLET	18	

IS INFINITE OHMS MEASURED?

- YES: GO TO CHART L. WHEN NO PROBLEM IS FOUND, CHECK ELECTRONIC BRAKE CONTROL MODULE (EBCM) TERMINAL CONNECTIONS FOR POOR TERMINAL CONTACT. IF TERMINAL CONTACT IS OK, REPLACE EBCM.
- NO: REPAIR SHORT TO GROUND IN SUSPECT VALVE CIRCUIT BETWEEN PRESSURE MODULATOR VALVE (PMV) ASSEMBLY AND ELECTRONIC BRAKE CONTROL MODULE (EBCM).

GC402910060700DX

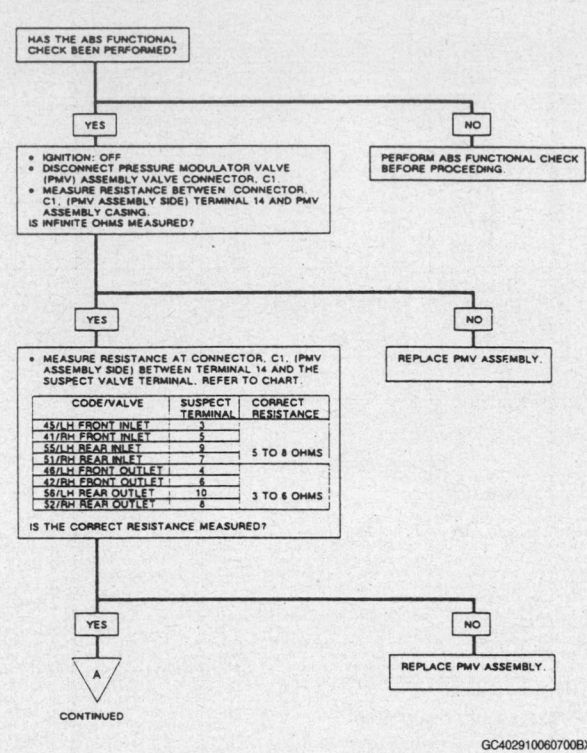

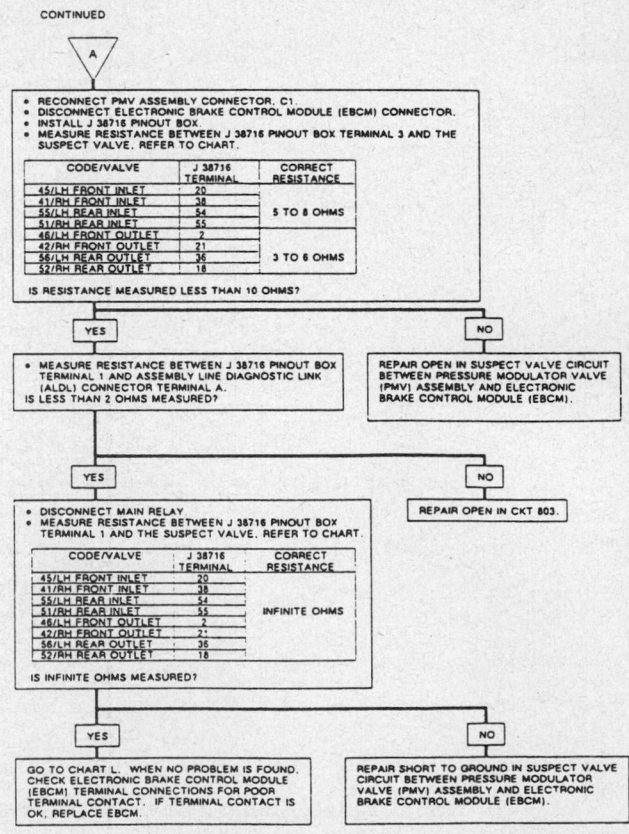

Fig. 16 Test E: Inlet/Oulet Valve Circuit Test (Part 2 of 2). 1992–93 Models Except 1993 LeSabre & Park Avenue

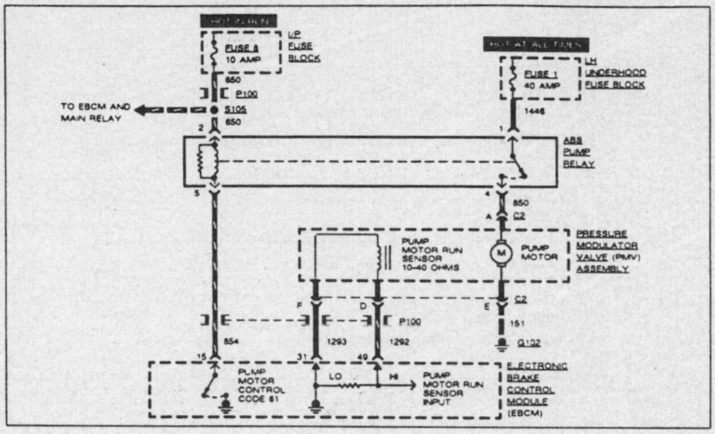
HOT IN RUN
FUSE 8
10 AMP
I/P FUSE BLOCK
HOT AT ALL TIMES
FUSE 1
40 AMP
LH UNDERHOOD FUSE BLOCK
TO EBCM AND MAIN RELAY
S105
P100
ABS PUMP RELAY
PUMP MOTOR RUN SENSOR 10-40 OHMS
PUMP MOTOR
PRESSURE MODULATOR VALVE (PMV) ASSEMBLY
C2
G102
PUMP MOTOR CONTROL CODE 61
LO
HI
PUMP MOTOR RUN SENSOR INPUT
ELECTRONIC BRAKE CONTROL MODULE (EBCM)

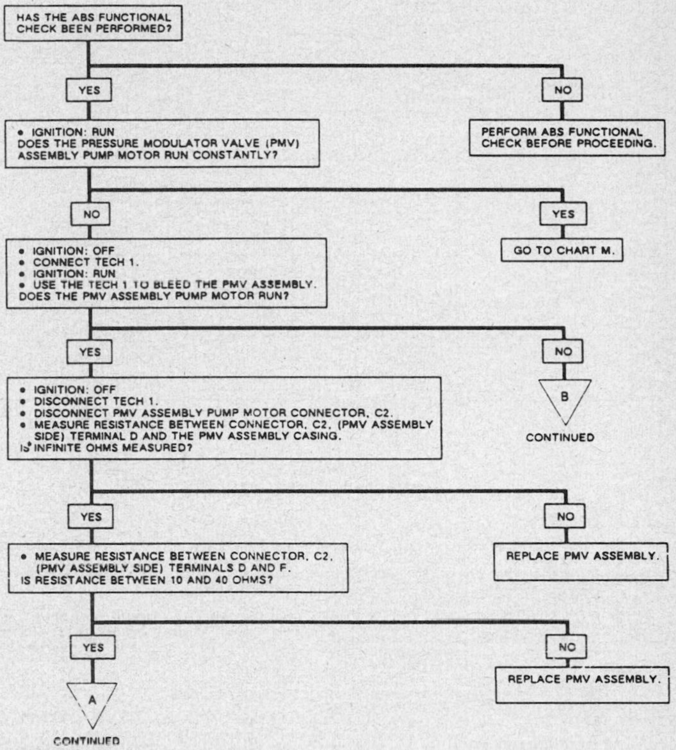
HAS THE ABS FUNCTIONAL CHECK BEEN PERFORMED?
YES
NO
PERFORM ABS FUNCTIONAL CHECK BEFORE PROCEEDING.
• IGNITION: RUN
DOES THE PRESSURE MODULATOR VALVE (PMV) ASSEMBLY PUMP MOTOR RUN CONSTANTLY?
NO
YES
GO TO CHART M.
• IGNITION: OFF
• CONNECT TECH 1.
• IGNITION: RUN
• USE THE TECH 1 TO BLEED THE PMV ASSEMBLY.
DOES THE PMV ASSEMBLY PUMP MOTOR RUN?
YES
NO
B
CONTINUED
• IGNITION: OFF
• DISCONNECT TECH 1.
• DISCONNECT PMV ASSEMBLY PUMP MOTOR CONNECTOR, C2.
• MEASURE RESISTANCE BETWEEN CONNECTOR, C2, (PMV ASSEMBLY SIDE) TERMINAL D AND THE PMV ASSEMBLY CASING.
IS INFINITE OHMS MEASURED?
YES
NO
REPLACE PMV ASSEMBLY.
• MEASURE RESISTANCE BETWEEN CONNECTOR, C2, (PMV ASSEMBLY SIDE) TERMINALS D AND F.
IS RESISTANCE BETWEEN 10 AND 40 OHMS?
YES
NO
REPLACE PMV ASSEMBLY.
A
CONTINUED

AFTER REPAIRS ARE COMPLETED, CLEAR CODES AND REPEAT ABS FUNCTIONAL CHECK

CHART F
PUMP MOTOR CIRCUIT TEST

CIRCUIT OPERATION

When the electronic brake control module (EBCM) grounds terminal 15, the pump relay contacts close applying voltage to the pressure modulator valve (PMV) assembly's pump motor. The EBCM turns on the pump motor during most ABS braking conditions. When the pump motor runs, the PMV assembly reservoir is replenished and fluid pressure is applied to the master cylinder. This causes the brake pedal to rise gradually. The pump motor runs until the brake pedal sufficiently rises to close the VCC/antilock brake switch. The EBCM monitors pump motor operation via the pump motor run sensor. When the pump is operating, voltage is induced into the sensor's coil and the EBCM monitors this voltage at terminals 49 and 31.

FAILURE CONDITIONS

When the EBCM grounds terminal 15, Code 61 sets when the EBCM determines the voltage between EBCM terminals 31 and 49 is not between 500–800 mV AC. The EBCM recognizes this condition only during ABS braking requiring pump motor operation, and during the EBCM self-check which occurs when the vehicle reaches 11 km/h (7 mph). Therefore, be sure to test drive vehicle, clearing the code to assure correct diagnosis.

Code 61 also sets when the pump motor runs all the time (i.e. EBCM sees proper voltage between terminals 31 and 49 without grounding terminal 15). Refer to Chart M for diagnosing a continuous running pump motor.

Possible Causes

- Open in CKT 151, 650, 850, 854, 1292, 1293 or 1446.
- Short to ground in CKT 850, 854, 1292, 1293 or 1446.
- ABS pump relay fails "open" or "engaged."

GC402910060801AX

GC402910060001BX

Fig. 17 Test F: Pump Motor Circuit Test (Part 1 of 3). 1992 DeVille & Fleetwood (FWD)

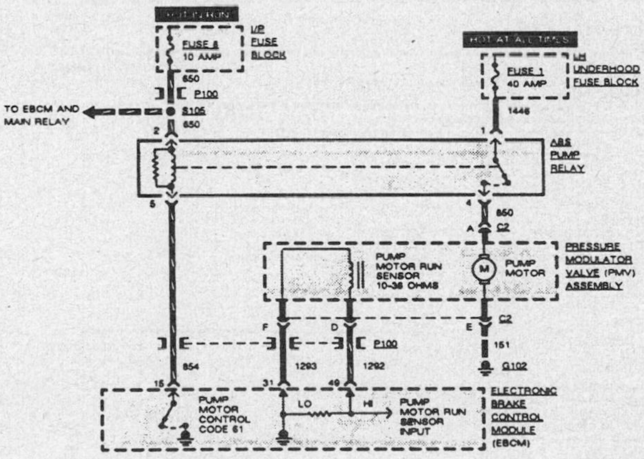
HOT IN RUN
FUSE 8
10 AMP
I/P FUSE BLOCK
HOT AT ALL TIMES
FUSE 1
40 AMP
LH UNDERHOOD FUSE BLOCK
TO EBCM AND MAIN RELAY
S105
P100
ABS PUMP RELAY
PUMP MOTOR RUN SENSOR 10-38 OHMS
PUMP MOTOR
PRESSURE MODULATOR VALVE (PMV) ASSEMBLY
C2
G102
PUMP MOTOR CONTROL CODE 61
LO
HI
PUMP MOTOR RUN SENSOR INPUT
ELECTRONIC BRAKE CONTROL MODULE (EBCM)

GC402910060802CX

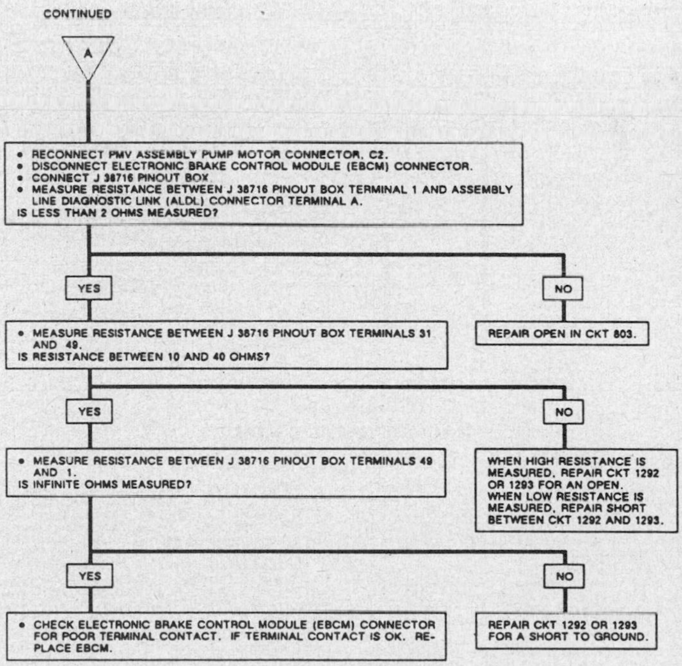
CONTINUED
A
• RECONNECT PMV ASSEMBLY PUMP MOTOR CONNECTOR, C2.
• DISCONNECT ELECTRONIC BRAKE CONTROL MODULE (EBCM) CONNECTOR.
• CONNECT J 38716 PINOUT BOX.
• MEASURE RESISTANCE BETWEEN J 38716 PINOUT BOX TERMINAL 1 AND ASSEMBLY LINE DIAGNOSTIC LINK (ALDL) CONNECTOR TERMINAL A.
IS LESS THAN 2 OHMS MEASURED?
YES
NO
REPAIR OPEN IN CKT 803.
• MEASURE RESISTANCE BETWEEN J 38716 PINOUT BOX TERMINALS 31 AND 49.
IS RESISTANCE BETWEEN 10 AND 40 OHMS?
YES
NO
WHEN HIGH RESISTANCE IS MEASURED, REPAIR CKT 1292 OR 1293 FOR AN OPEN. WHEN LOW RESISTANCE IS MEASURED, REPAIR SHORT BETWEEN CKT 1292 AND 1293.
• MEASURE RESISTANCE BETWEEN J 38716 PINOUT BOX TERMINALS 49 AND 1.
IS INFINITE OHMS MEASURED?
YES
NO
REPAIR CKT 1292 OR 1293 FOR A SHORT TO GROUND.
• CHECK ELECTRONIC BRAKE CONTROL MODULE (EBCM) CONNECTOR FOR POOR TERMINAL CONTACT. IF TERMINAL CONTACT IS OK, REPLACE EBCM.

AFTER REPAIRS ARE COMPLETED, CLEAR CODES AND REPEAT ABS FUNCTIONAL CHECK.

GC402910060802DX

Fig. 17 Test F: Pump Motor Circuit Test (Part 2 of 3). 1992 DeVille & Fleetwood (FWD)

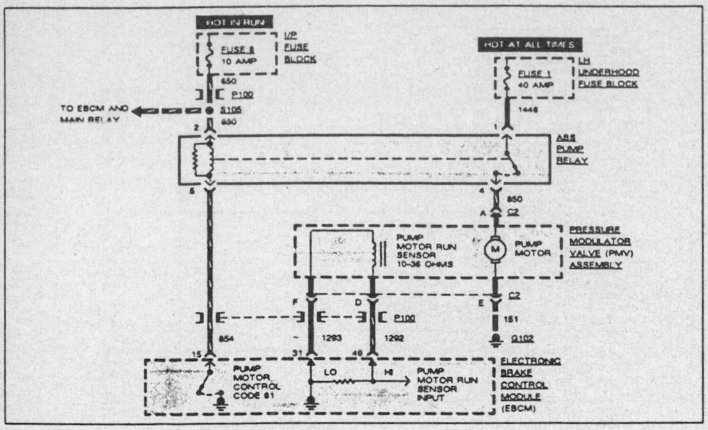
HOT IN RUN
FUSE 8
10 AMP
I/P FUSE BLOCK
HOT AT ALL TIMES
FUSE 1
40 AMP
LH UNDERHOOD FUSE BLOCK
650
P100
TO EBCM AND MAIN RELAY
S105
1446
ABS PUMP RELAY
850
C2
PUMP MOTOR RUN SENSOR 10-36 OHMS
PUMP MOTOR
PRESSURE MODULATOR VALVE (PMV) ASSEMBLY
854
1293
1292
151
G102
PUMP MOTOR CONTROL CODE 61
LO
HI
PUMP MOTOR RUN SENSOR INPUT
ELECTRONIC BRAKE CONTROL MODULE (EBCM)

CHART F
PUMP MOTOR CIRCUIT TEST

CIRCUIT OPERATION

When the electronic brake control module (EBCM) grounds terminal 15, the pump relay contacts close applying voltage to the pressure modulator valve (PMV) assembly's pump motor. The EBCM turns on the pump motor during most ABS braking conditions. When the pump motor runs, the PMV assembly reservoir is replenished and fluid pressure is applied to the master cylinder. This causes the brake pedal to rise gradually. The pump motor runs until the brake pedal sufficiently rises to close the VCC/antilock brake switch. The EBCM monitors pump motor operation via the pump motor run sensor. When the pump is operating, voltage is induced into the sensor's coil and the EBCM monitors this voltage at terminals 49 and 31.

FAILURE CONDITIONS

When the EBCM grounds terminal 15, Code 61 sets when the EBCM determines the voltage between EBCM terminals 31 and 49 is not between 500–800 mV AC. The EBCM recognizes this condition only during ABS braking requiring pump motor operation, and during the EBCM self-check which occurs when the vehicle reaches 11 km/h (7 mph). Therefore, be sure to test drive vehicle, after clearing the code to assure correct diagnosis.

Code 61 also sets when the pump motor runs all the time (i.e. EBCM sees proper voltage between terminals 31 and 49 without grounding terminal 15). Refer to Chart M for diagnosing a continuous running pump motor.

Possible Causes

- Open in CKT 151, 650, 850, 854, 1292, 1293 or 1446.
- Short to ground in CKT 850, 854, 1292, 1293 or 1446.
- ABS pump relay fails "open" or "engaged."

GC402910060803EX

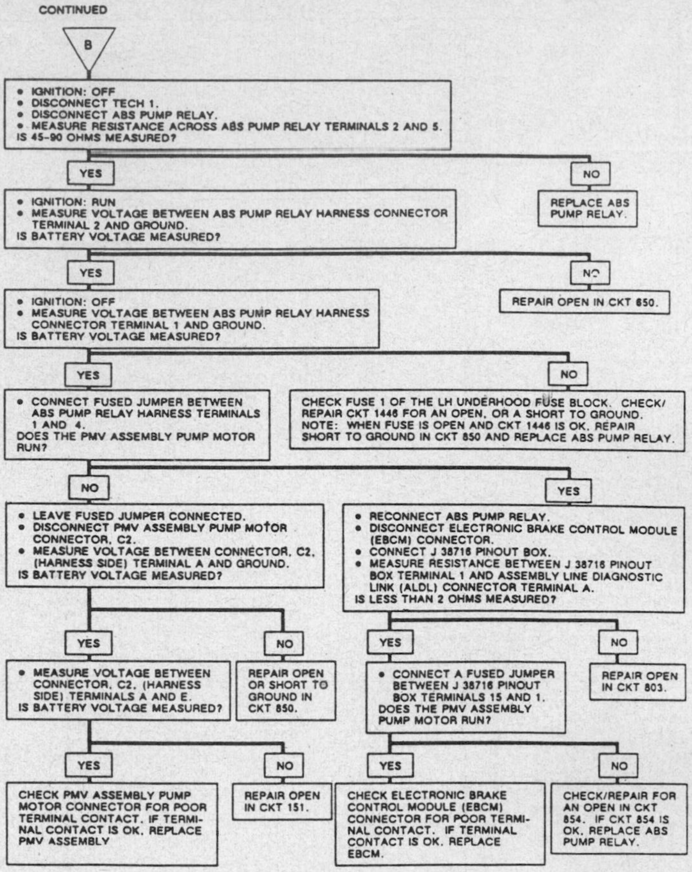
CONTINUED
B
• IGNITION: OFF
• DISCONNECT TECH 1.
• DISCONNECT ABS PUMP RELAY.
• MEASURE RESISTANCE ACROSS ABS PUMP RELAY TERMINALS 2 AND 5.
IS 45–90 OHMS MEASURED?
YES
NO
REPLACE ABS PUMP RELAY.
• IGNITION: RUN
• MEASURE VOLTAGE BETWEEN ABS PUMP RELAY HARNESS CONNECTOR TERMINAL 2 AND GROUND.
IS BATTERY VOLTAGE MEASURED?
YES
NO
REPAIR OPEN IN CKT 650.
• IGNITION: OFF
• MEASURE VOLTAGE BETWEEN ABS PUMP RELAY HARNESS CONNECTOR TERMINAL 1 AND GROUND.
IS BATTERY VOLTAGE MEASURED?
YES
NO
CHECK FUSE 1 OF THE LH UNDERHOOD FUSE BLOCK. CHECK/REPAIR CKT 1446 FOR AN OPEN, OR A SHORT TO GROUND. NOTE: WHEN FUSE IS OPEN AND CKT 1446 IS OK, REPAIR SHORT TO GROUND IN CKT 850 AND REPLACE ABS PUMP RELAY.
• CONNECT FUSED JUMPER BETWEEN ABS PUMP RELAY HARNESS TERMINALS 1 AND 4.
DOES THE PMV ASSEMBLY PUMP MOTOR RUN?
NO
YES
• LEAVE FUSED JUMPER CONNECTED.
• DISCONNECT PMV ASSEMBLY PUMP MOTOR CONNECTOR, C2.
• MEASURE VOLTAGE BETWEEN CONNECTOR, C2, (HARNESS SIDE) TERMINAL A AND GROUND.
IS BATTERY VOLTAGE MEASURED?
• RECONNECT ABS PUMP RELAY.
• DISCONNECT ELECTRONIC BRAKE CONTROL MODULE (EBCM) CONNECTOR.
• CONNECT J 38716 PINOUT BOX.
• MEASURE RESISTANCE BETWEEN J 38716 PINOUT BOX TERMINAL 1 AND ASSEMBLY LINE DIAGNOSTIC LINK (ALDL) CONNECTOR TERMINAL A.
IS LESS THAN 2 OHMS MEASURED?
YES
NO
YES
NO
• MEASURE VOLTAGE BETWEEN CONNECTOR, C2, (HARNESS SIDE) TERMINALS A AND E.
IS BATTERY VOLTAGE MEASURED?
REPAIR OPEN OR SHORT TO GROUND IN CKT 850.
• CONNECT A FUSED JUMPER BETWEEN J 38716 PINOUT BOX TERMINALS 15 AND 1.
DOES THE PMV ASSEMBLY PUMP MOTOR RUN?
REPAIR OPEN IN CKT 803.
YES
NO
YES
NO
CHECK PMV ASSEMBLY PUMP MOTOR CONNECTOR FOR POOR TERMINAL CONTACT. IF TERMINAL CONTACT IS OK, REPLACE PMV ASSEMBLY
REPAIR OPEN IN CKT 151.
CHECK ELECTRONIC BRAKE CONTROL MODULE (EBCM) CONNECTOR FOR POOR TERMINAL CONTACT. IF TERMINAL CONTACT IS OK, REPLACE EBCM.
CHECK/REPAIR FOR AN OPEN IN CKT 854. IF CKT 854 IS OK, REPLACE ABS PUMP RELAY.

GC402910060803FX

Fig. 17 Test F: Pump Motor Circuit Test (Part 3 of 3). 1992 DeVille & Fleetwood (FWD)

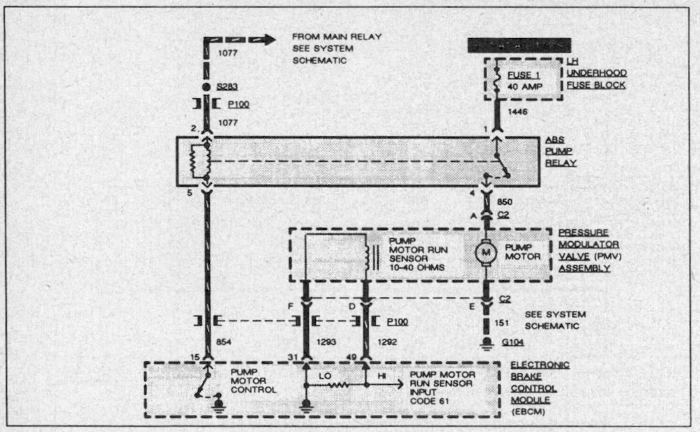
FROM MAIN RELAY SEE SYSTEM SCHEMATIC
1077
S283
P100
FUSE 1
40 AMP
LH UNDERHOOD FUSE BLOCK
1446
ABS PUMP RELAY
850
C2
PUMP MOTOR RUN SENSOR 10-40 OHMS
PUMP MOTOR
PRESSURE MODULATOR VALVE (PMV) ASSEMBLY
SEE SYSTEM SCHEMATIC
151
G104
854
1293
1292
PUMP MOTOR CONTROL
LO
HI
PUMP MOTOR RUN SENSOR INPUT CODE 61
ELECTRONIC BRAKE CONTROL MODULE (EBCM)

CHART F
PUMP MOTOR CIRCUIT TEST

CIRCUIT OPERATION

When the electronic brake control module (EBCM) grounds terminal 15, the pump relay contacts close applying voltage to the pressure modulator valve (PMV) assembly's pump motor. The EBCM turns on the pump motor during most ABS braking conditions (and when equipped) during all traction control conditions.

When the pump motor runs during ABS braking, the PMV assembly reservoir is replenished and fluid pressure is applied to the master cylinder. This causes the brake pedal to rise gradually. The pump motor runs until the brake pedal sufficiently rises to close the TCC/antilock brake switch.

During traction control mode, after the front hydraulic brake circuits are isolated, the pump motor runs to increase brake fluid pressure in these circuits. The increased pressure is directed to the slipping wheel through the PMV assembly's front inlet and outlet valves. This causes the brakes to be applied, reducing wheel spin at the slipping wheel. Traction control is disabled as soon as the brakes are manually applied.

The EBCM monitors pump motor operation via the pump motor run sensor. When the pump is operating, voltage is induced into the sensor's coil and the EBCM monitors this voltage at terminals 49 and 31.

FAILURE CONDITIONS

When the EBCM grounds terminal 15, Code 61 sets when the EBCM determines the voltage between EBCM terminals 31 and 49 is not between 500–800 mV AC. The EBCM recognizes this condition only during ABS braking requiring pump motor operation, traction control mode (when equipped), and during the EBCM self-check which occurs when the vehicle reaches 11 km/h (7 mph). Therefore, be sure to test drive vehicle, refer to "Test Driving Complaint Vehicles" in this section, after clearing the code to assure correct diagnosis.

Code 61 also sets when the pump motor runs all the time (i.e. EBCM sees proper voltage between terminals 31 and 49 without grounding terminal 15). Refer to Chart M for diagnosing a continuous running pump motor.

Possible Causes

- Open in CKT 151, 850, 854, 1077, 1292, 1293 or 1446.
- Short to ground in CKT 850, 854, 1292, 1293 or 1446.
- ABS pump relay fails "open" or "engaged."

GC402920060900AX

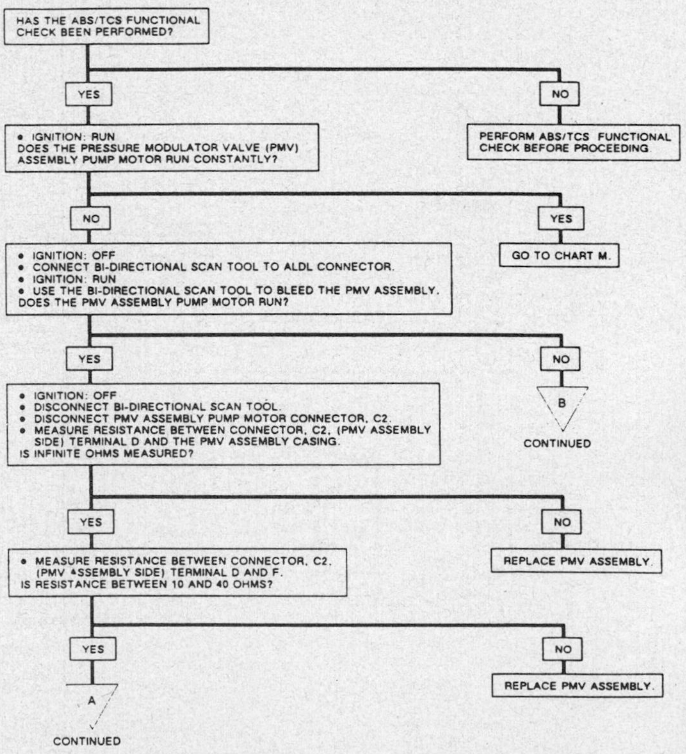
HAS THE ABS/TCS FUNCTIONAL CHECK BEEN PERFORMED?
YES
NO
PERFORM ABS/TCS FUNCTIONAL CHECK BEFORE PROCEEDING.
• IGNITION: RUN
DOES THE PRESSURE MODULATOR VALVE (PMV) ASSEMBLY PUMP MOTOR RUN CONSTANTLY?
NO
YES
GO TO CHART M.
• IGNITION: OFF
• CONNECT BI-DIRECTIONAL SCAN TOOL TO ALDL CONNECTOR.
• IGNITION: RUN
• USE THE BI-DIRECTIONAL SCAN TOOL TO BLEED THE PMV ASSEMBLY.
DOES THE PMV ASSEMBLY PUMP MOTOR RUN?
YES
NO
B
CONTINUED
• IGNITION: OFF
• DISCONNECT BI-DIRECTIONAL SCAN TOOL.
• DISCONNECT PMV ASSEMBLY PUMP MOTOR CONNECTOR, C2.
• MEASURE RESISTANCE BETWEEN CONNECTOR, C2, (PMV ASSEMBLY SIDE) TERMINAL D AND THE PMV ASSEMBLY CASING.
IS INFINITE OHMS MEASURED?
YES
NO
REPLACE PMV ASSEMBLY.
• MEASURE RESISTANCE BETWEEN CONNECTOR, C2, (PMV ASSEMBLY SIDE) TERMINAL D AND F.
IS RESISTANCE BETWEEN 10 AND 40 OHMS?
YES
NO
REPLACE PMV ASSEMBLY.
A
CONTINUED

AFTER REPAIRS ARE COMPLETED, CLEAR CODES AND REPEAT ABS/TCS FUNCTIONAL CHECK.

GC402920060900BX

Fig. 18 Test F: Pump Motor Circuit Test (Part 1 of 3). 1992–93 Models Except 1993 LeSabre & Park Avenue

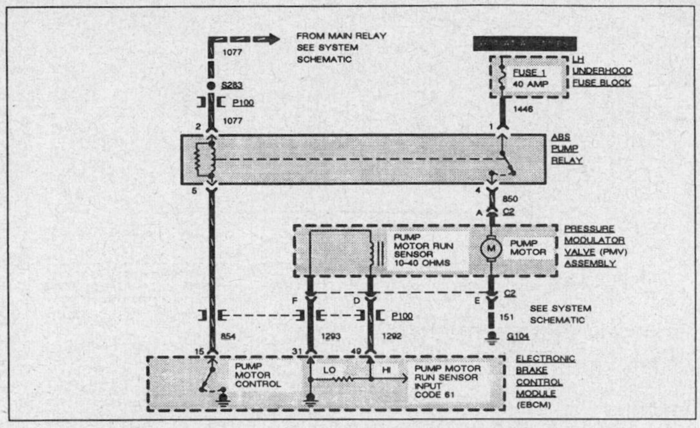
FROM MAIN RELAY
SEE SYSTEM
SCHEMATIC
1077
S283
P100
1077
LH
UNDERHOOD
FUSE BLOCK
FUSE 1
40 AMP
1446
ABS
PUMP
RELAY
850
C2
PUMP
MOTOR RUN
SENSOR
10-40 OHMS
PUMP
MOTOR
PRESSURE
MODULATOR
VALVE (PMV)
ASSEMBLY
C2
SEE SYSTEM
SCHEMATIC
151
G104
P100
854
1293
1292
PUMP
MOTOR
CONTROL
LO
HI
PUMP MOTOR
RUN SENSOR
INPUT
CODE 61
ELECTRONIC
BRAKE
CONTROL
MODULE
(EBCM)

CIRCUIT OPERATION

When the electronic brake control module (EBCM) grounds terminal 15, the pump relay contacts close applying voltage to the pressure modulator valve (PMV) assembly's pump motor. The EBCM turns on the pump motor during most ABS braking conditions (and when equipped) during all traction control conditions.

When the pump motor runs during ABS braking, the PMV assembly reservoir is replenished and fluid pressure is applied to the master cylinder. This causes the brake pedal to rise gradually. The pump motor runs until the brake pedal sufficiently rises to close the TCC/antilock brake switch.

During traction control mode, after the front hydraulic brake circuits are isolated, the pump motor runs to increase brake fluid pressure in these circuits. The increased pressure is directed to the slipping wheel through the PMV assembly's front inlet and outlet valves. This causes the brakes to be applied, reducing wheel spin at the slipping wheel. Traction control is disabled as soon as the brakes are manually applied.

The EBCM monitors pump motor operation via the pump motor run sensor. When the pump is operating, voltage is induced into the sensor's coil and the EBCM monitors this voltage at terminals 49 and 31.

FAILURE CONDITIONS

When the EBCM grounds terminal 15, Code 61 sets when the EBCM determines the voltage between EBCM terminals 31 and 49 is not between 500–800 mV AC. The EBCM recognizes this condition only during ABS braking requiring pump motor operation, traction control mode (when equipped), and during the EBCM self-check which occurs when the vehicle reaches 11 km/h (7 mph). Therefore, be sure to test drive vehicle, refer to "Test Driving Complaint Vehicles" in this section, after clearing the code to assure correct diagnosis.

Code 61 also sets when the pump motor runs all the time (i.e. EBCM sees proper voltage between terminals 31 and 49 without grounding terminal 15). Refer to Chart M for diagnosing a continuous running pump motor.

Possible Causes

- Open in CKT 151, 850, 854, 1077, 1292, 1293 or 1446.
- Short to ground in CKT 850, 854, 1292, 1293 or 1446.
- ABS pump relay fails "open" or "engaged."

GC402920060900CX

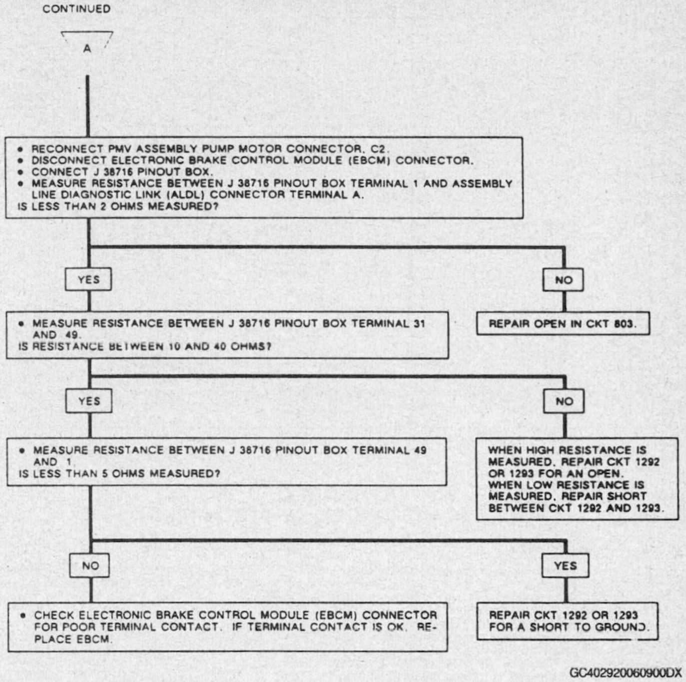
CONTINUED
A
• RECONNECT PMV ASSEMBLY PUMP MOTOR CONNECTOR, C2.
• DISCONNECT ELECTRONIC BRAKE CONTROL MODULE (EBCM) CONNECTOR.
• CONNECT J 38716 PINOUT BOX.
• MEASURE RESISTANCE BETWEEN J 38716 PINOUT BOX TERMINAL 1 AND ASSEMBLY LINE DIAGNOSTIC LINK (ALDL) CONNECTOR TERMINAL A.
IS LESS THAN 2 OHMS MEASURED?
YES
NO
• MEASURE RESISTANCE BETWEEN J 38716 PINOUT BOX TERMINAL 31 AND 49.
IS RESISTANCE BETWEEN 10 AND 40 OHMS?
REPAIR OPEN IN CKT 803.
YES
NO
• MEASURE RESISTANCE BETWEEN J 38716 PINOUT BOX TERMINAL 49 AND 1.
IS LESS THAN 5 OHMS MEASURED?
WHEN HIGH RESISTANCE IS MEASURED, REPAIR CKT 1292 OR 1293 FOR AN OPEN. WHEN LOW RESISTANCE IS MEASURED, REPAIR SHORT BETWEEN CKT 1292 AND 1293.
NO
YES
• CHECK ELECTRONIC BRAKE CONTROL MODULE (EBCM) CONNECTOR FOR POOR TERMINAL CONTACT. IF TERMINAL CONTACT IS OK, REPLACE EBCM.
REPAIR CKT 1292 OR 1293 FOR A SHORT TO GROUND.
GC402920060900DX

DUMMY00000000001

Fig. 18 Test F: Pump Motor Circuit Test (Part 2 of 3). 1992–93 Models Except 1993 LeSabre & Park Avenue

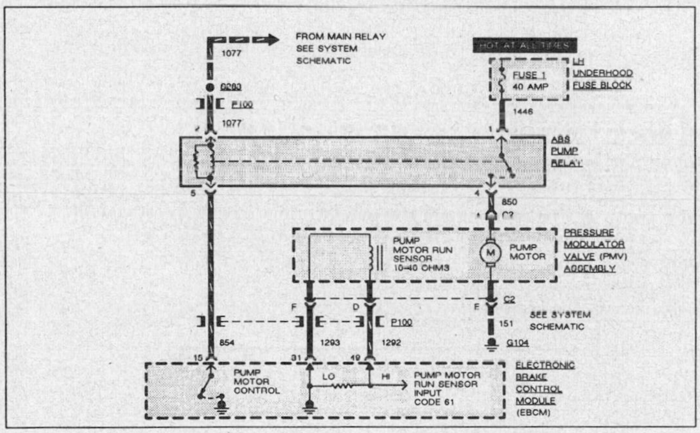
FROM MAIN RELAY
SEE SYSTEM
SCHEMATIC
HOT AT ALL TIMES
1077
S283
P100
1077
LH
UNDERHOOD
FUSE BLOCK
FUSE 1
40 AMP
1446
ABS
PUMP
RELAY
850
C2
PUMP
MOTOR RUN
SENSOR
10-40 OHMS
PUMP
MOTOR
PRESSURE
MODULATOR
VALVE (PMV)
ASSEMBLY
C2
SEE SYSTEM
SCHEMATIC
151
G104
P100
854
1293
1292
PUMP
MOTOR
CONTROL
LO
HI
PUMP MOTOR
RUN SENSOR
INPUT
CODE 61
ELECTRONIC
BRAKE
CONTROL
MODULE
(EBCM)

CIRCUIT OPERATION

When the electronic brake control module (EBCM) grounds terminal 15, the pump relay contacts close applying voltage to the pressure modulator valve (PMV) assembly's pump motor. The EBCM turns on the pump motor during most ABS braking conditions (and when equipped) during all traction control conditions.

When the pump motor runs during ABS braking, the PMV assembly reservoir is replenished and fluid pressure is applied to the master cylinder. This causes the brake pedal to rise gradually. The pump motor runs until the brake pedal sufficiently rises to close the TCC/antilock brake switch.

During traction control mode, after the front hydraulic brake circuits are isolated, the pump motor runs to increase brake fluid pressure in these circuits. The increased pressure is directed to the slipping wheel through the PMV assembly's front inlet and outlet valves. This causes the brakes to be applied, reducing wheel spin at the slipping wheel. Traction control is disabled as soon as the brakes are manually applied.

The EBCM monitors pump motor operation via the pump motor run sensor. When the pump is operating, voltage is induced into the sensor's coil and the EBCM monitors this voltage at terminals 49 and 31.

FAILURE CONDITIONS

When the EBCM grounds terminal 15, Code 61 sets when the EBCM determines the voltage between EBCM terminals 31 and 49 is not between 500–800 mV AC. The EBCM recognizes this condition only during ABS braking requiring pump motor operation, traction control mode (when equipped), and during the EBCM self-check which occurs when the vehicle reaches 11 km/h (7 mph). Therefore, be sure to test drive vehicle, refer to "Test Driving Complaint Vehicles" in this section, after clearing the code to assure correct diagnosis.

Code 61 also sets when the pump motor runs all the time (i.e. EBCM sees proper voltage between terminals 31 and 49 without grounding terminal 15). Refer to Chart M for diagnosing a continuous running pump motor.

Possible Causes

- Open in CKT 151, 850, 854, 1077, 1292, 1293 or 1446.
- Short to ground in CKT 850, 854, 1292, 1293 or 1446.
- ABS pump relay fails "open" or "engaged."

GC402920060900EX

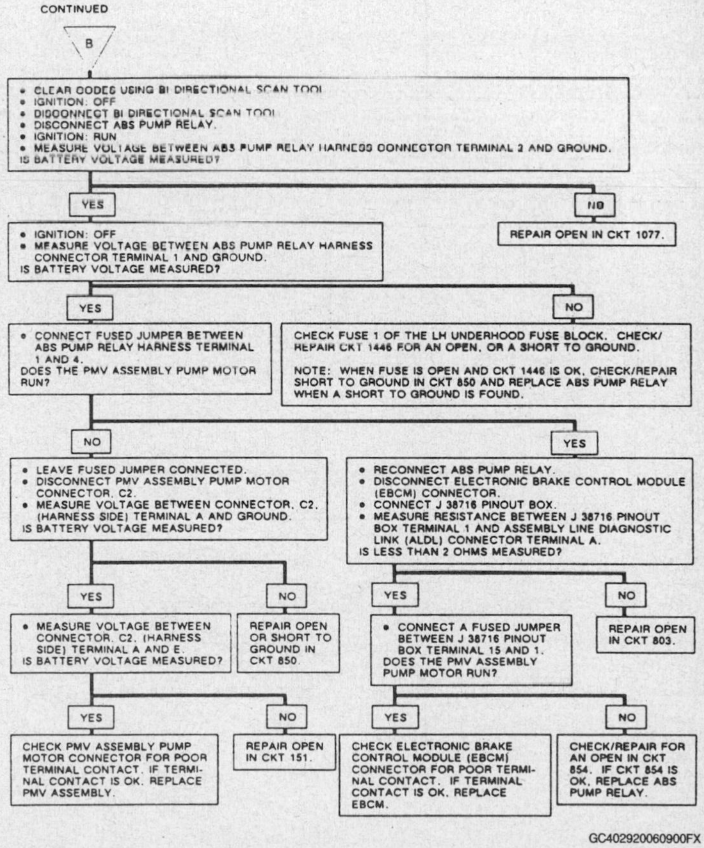
CONTINUED
B
• CLEAR CODES USING BI DIRECTIONAL SCAN TOOL.
• IGNITION: OFF
• DISCONNECT BI DIRECTIONAL SCAN TOOL.
• DISCONNECT ABS PUMP RELAY.
• IGNITION: RUN
• MEASURE VOLTAGE BETWEEN ABS PUMP RELAY HARNESS CONNECTOR TERMINAL 2 AND GROUND.
IS BATTERY VOLTAGE MEASURED?
YES
NO
• IGNITION: OFF
• MEASURE VOLTAGE BETWEEN ABS PUMP RELAY HARNESS CONNECTOR TERMINAL 1 AND GROUND.
IS BATTERY VOLTAGE MEASURED?
REPAIR OPEN IN CKT 1077.
YES
NO
• CONNECT FUSED JUMPER BETWEEN ABS PUMP RELAY HARNESS TERMINAL 1 AND 4.
DOES THE PMV ASSEMBLY PUMP MOTOR RUN?
CHECK FUSE 1 OF THE LH UNDERHOOD FUSE BLOCK. CHECK/REPAIR CKT 1446 FOR AN OPEN, OR A SHORT TO GROUND.
NOTE: WHEN FUSE IS OPEN AND CKT 1446 IS OK, CHECK/REPAIR SHORT TO GROUND IN CKT 850 AND REPLACE ABS PUMP RELAY WHEN A SHORT TO GROUND IS FOUND.
NO
YES
• LEAVE FUSED JUMPER CONNECTED.
• DISCONNECT PMV ASSEMBLY PUMP MOTOR CONNECTOR, C2.
• MEASURE VOLTAGE BETWEEN CONNECTOR, C2, (HARNESS SIDE) TERMINAL A AND GROUND.
IS BATTERY VOLTAGE MEASURED?
• RECONNECT ABS PUMP RELAY.
• DISCONNECT ELECTRONIC BRAKE CONTROL MODULE (EBCM) CONNECTOR.
• CONNECT J 38716 PINOUT BOX.
• MEASURE RESISTANCE BETWEEN J 38716 PINOUT BOX TERMINAL 1 AND ASSEMBLY LINE DIAGNOSTIC LINK (ALDL) CONNECTOR TERMINAL A.
IS LESS THAN 2 OHMS MEASURED?
YES
NO
YES
NO
• MEASURE VOLTAGE BETWEEN CONNECTOR, C2, (HARNESS SIDE) TERMINAL A AND E.
IS BATTERY VOLTAGE MEASURED?
REPAIR OPEN OR SHORT TO GROUND IN CKT 850.
• CONNECT A FUSED JUMPER BETWEEN J 38716 PINOUT BOX TERMINAL 15 AND 1.
DOES THE PMV ASSEMBLY PUMP MOTOR RUN?
REPAIR OPEN IN CKT 803.
YES
NO
YES
NO
CHECK PMV ASSEMBLY PUMP MOTOR CONNECTOR FOR POOR TERMINAL CONTACT. IF TERMINAL CONTACT IS OK, REPLACE PMV ASSEMBLY.
REPAIR OPEN IN CKT 151.
CHECK ELECTRONIC BRAKE CONTROL MODULE (EBCM) CONNECTOR FOR POOR TERMINAL CONTACT. IF TERMINAL CONTACT IS OK, REPLACE EBCM.
CHECK/REPAIR FOR AN OPEN IN CKT 854. IF CKT 854 IS OK, REPLACE ABS PUMP RELAY.
GC402920060900FX

Fig. 18 Test F: Pump Motor Circuit Test (Part 3 of 3). 1992–93 Models Except 1993 LeSabre & Park Avenue

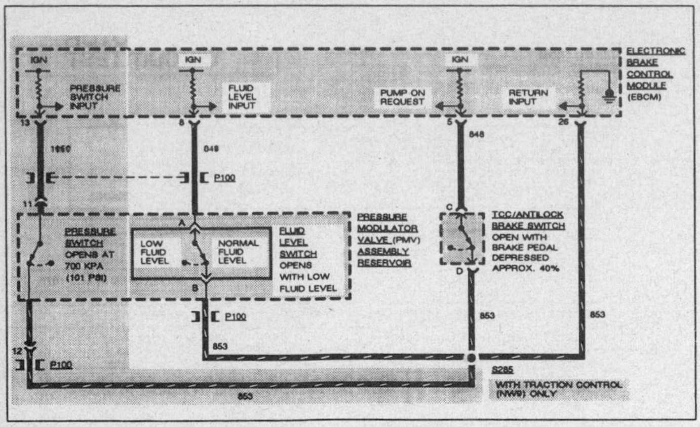
ELECTRONIC BRAKE CONTROL MODULE (EBCM)
IGN
PRESSURE SWITCH INPUT
FLUID LEVEL INPUT
PUMP ON REQUEST
RETURN INPUT
848
853
P100
PRESSURE SWITCH OPENS AT 700 KPA (101 PSI)
LOW FLUID LEVEL
NORMAL FLUID LEVEL
FLUID LEVEL SWITCH OPENS WITH LOW FLUID LEVEL
PRESSURE MODULATOR VALVE (PMV) ASSEMBLY RESERVOIR
TCC/ANTILOCK BRAKE SWITCH OPEN WITH BRAKE PEDAL DEPRESSED APPROX. 40%
S285
WITH TRACTION CONTROL (NW9) ONLY

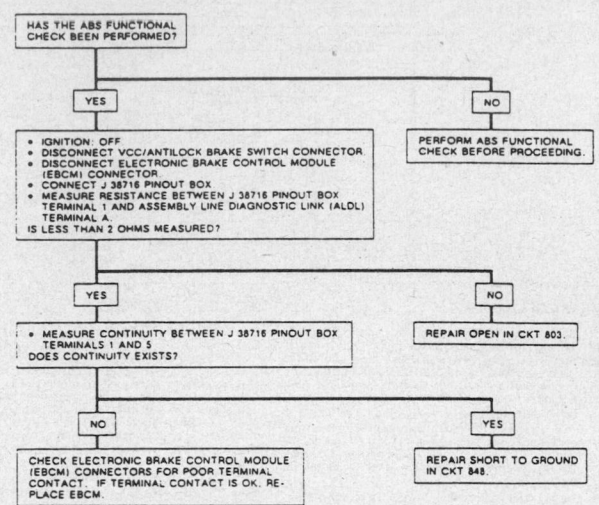

CHART G
TCC/ANTILOCK BRAKE SWITCH TEST

CIRCUIT OPERATION

The electronic brake control module (EBCM) monitors brake pedal position using the TCC/antilock brake switch. The switch is normally closed. It opens when the brake pedal is depressed approximately 40% down. During most ABS braking conditions the EBCM turns on the pump motor, replenishing the PMV assembly reservoir and applying fluid pressure to the master cylinder. This causes the brake pedal to gradually rise. The EBCM turns off the pump motor when brake pedal height sufficiently rises to close the TCC/antilock brake switch.

FAILURE CONDITIONS

Code 72 sets when the EBCM detects the TCC/antilock brake switch CKT 848 is shorted to ground.

GC402910061000AX

HAS THE ABS FUNCTIONAL CHECK BEEN PERFORMED?

NO: PERFORM ABS FUNCTIONAL CHECK BEFORE PROCEEDING.

YES:
- IGNITION: OFF
- DISCONNECT VCC/ANTILOCK BRAKE SWITCH CONNECTOR.
- DISCONNECT ELECTRONIC BRAKE CONTROL MODULE (EBCM) CONNECTOR.
- CONNECT J 38716 PINOUT BOX.
- MEASURE RESISTANCE BETWEEN J 38716 PINOUT BOX TERMINAL 1 AND ASSEMBLY LINE DIAGNOSTIC LINK (ALDL) TERMINAL A.

IS LESS THAN 2 OHMS MEASURED?

NO: REPAIR OPEN IN CKT 803.

YES:
- MEASURE CONTINUITY BETWEEN J 38716 PINOUT BOX TERMINALS 1 AND 5

DOES CONTINUITY EXISTS?

YES: REPAIR SHORT TO GROUND IN CKT 848.

NO: CHECK ELECTRONIC BRAKE CONTROL MODULE (EBCM) CONNECTORS FOR POOR TERMINAL CONTACT. IF TERMINAL CONTACT IS OK, REPLACE EBCM.

AFTER REPAIRS ARE COMPLETED, CLEAR CODES AND REPEAT ABS FUNCTIONAL CHECK.

GC402910061000BX

Fig. 19 Test G: TCC/Anti-Lock Brake Switch Failure. 1992–93 Models Except 1993 LeSabre & Park Avenue

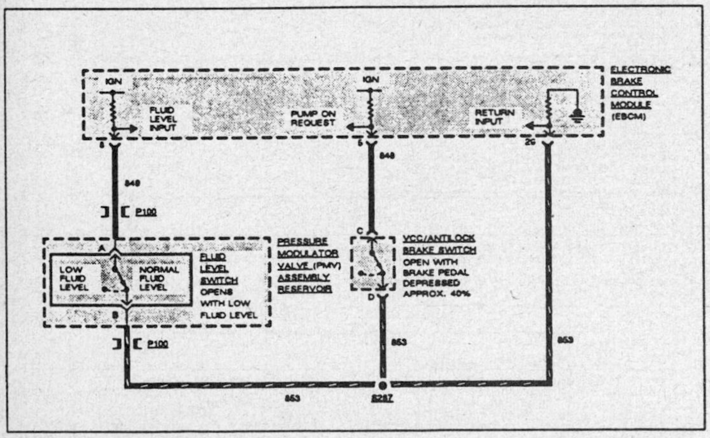
ELECTRONIC BRAKE CONTROL MODULE (EBCM)
IGN
FLUID LEVEL INPUT
PUMP ON REQUEST
RETURN INPUT
848
849
853
P100
LOW FLUID LEVEL
NORMAL FLUID LEVEL
FLUID LEVEL SWITCH OPENS WITH LOW FLUID LEVEL
PRESSURE MODULATOR VALVE (PMV) ASSEMBLY RESERVOIR
VCC/ANTILOCK BRAKE SWITCH OPEN WITH BRAKE PEDAL DEPRESSED APPROX. 40%
S287

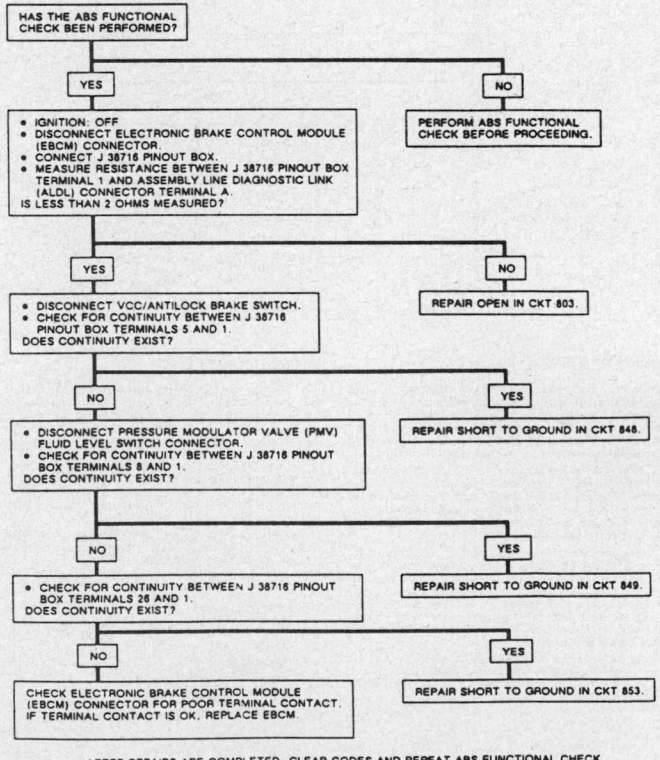

CHART H
PMV FLUID LEVEL SWITCH CIRCUIT TEST

CIRCUIT OPERATION

The pressure modulator valve (PMV) fluid level switch alerts the electronic brake control module (EBCM) to a low brake fluid condition in the PMV reservoir. The fluid level switch is located in the PMV assembly's reservoir. The fluid level switch is normally closed when the reservoir contains sufficient fluid. When fluid level is low, the switch opens, causing the EBCM to turn on the "ANTILOCK" indicator.

FAILURE CONDITIONS

Code 73 will set when the EBCM detects a short to ground in the PMV fluid level switch circuitry. These include: CKT 848, 849, and 853.

GC402910061100AX

HAS THE ABS FUNCTIONAL CHECK BEEN PERFORMED?

NO: PERFORM ABS FUNCTIONAL CHECK BEFORE PROCEEDING.

YES:
- IGNITION: OFF
- DISCONNECT ELECTRONIC BRAKE CONTROL MODULE (EBCM) CONNECTOR.
- CONNECT J 38716 PINOUT BOX.
- MEASURE RESISTANCE BETWEEN J 38716 PINOUT BOX TERMINAL 1 AND ASSEMBLY LINE DIAGNOSTIC LINK (ALDL) CONNECTOR TERMINAL A.

IS LESS THAN 2 OHMS MEASURED?

NO: REPAIR OPEN IN CKT 803.

YES:
- DISCONNECT VCC/ANTILOCK BRAKE SWITCH.
- CHECK FOR CONTINUITY BETWEEN J 38716 PINOUT BOX TERMINALS 5 AND 1.

DOES CONTINUITY EXIST?

YES: REPAIR SHORT TO GROUND IN CKT 848.

NO:
- DISCONNECT PRESSURE MODULATOR VALVE (PMV) FLUID LEVEL SWITCH CONNECTOR.
- CHECK FOR CONTINUITY BETWEEN J 38716 PINOUT BOX TERMINALS 8 AND 1.

DOES CONTINUITY EXIST?

YES: REPAIR SHORT TO GROUND IN CKT 849.

NO:
- CHECK FOR CONTINUITY BETWEEN J 38716 PINOUT BOX TERMINALS 26 AND 1.

DOES CONTINUITY EXIST?

YES: REPAIR SHORT TO GROUND IN CKT 853.

NO: CHECK ELECTRONIC BRAKE CONTROL MODULE (EBCM) CONNECTOR FOR POOR TERMINAL CONTACT. IF TERMINAL CONTACT IS OK, REPLACE EBCM.

AFTER REPAIRS ARE COMPLETED, CLEAR CODES AND REPEAT ABS FUNCTIONAL CHECK.

GC402910061100BX

Fig. 20 Test H: PMV Fluid Level Switch Circuit Test. 1992 DeVille & Fleetwood (FWD)

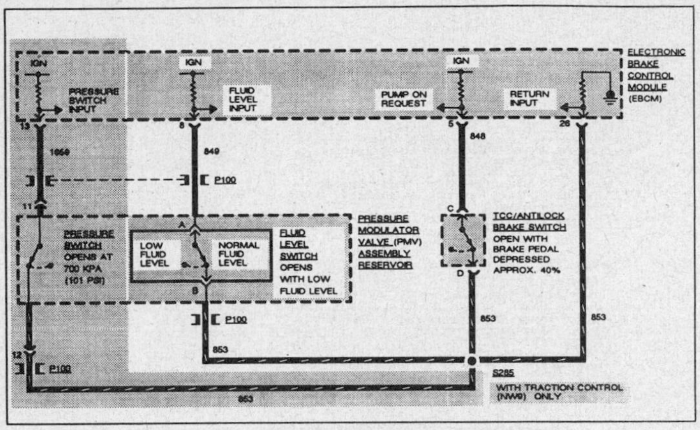
IGN
PRESSURE SWITCH INPUT
FLUID LEVEL INPUT
PUMP ON REQUEST
RETURN INPUT
ELECTRONIC BRAKE CONTROL MODULE (EBCM)
1659
849
848
P100
PRESSURE SWITCH OPENS AT 700 KPA (101 PSI)
LOW FLUID LEVEL
NORMAL FLUID LEVEL
FLUID LEVEL SWITCH OPENS WITH LOW FLUID LEVEL
PRESSURE MODULATOR VALVE (PMV) ASSEMBLY RESERVOIR
TCC/ANTILOCK BRAKE SWITCH OPEN WITH BRAKE PEDAL DEPRESSED APPROX. 40%
853
S285
WITH TRACTION CONTROL (NW9) ONLY

CHART H
PMV FLUID LEVEL SWITCH CIRCUIT TEST

CIRCUIT OPERATION

The pressure modulator valve (PMV) fluid level switch alerts the electronic brake control module (EBCM) to a low brake fluid condition in the PMV reservoir. The fluid level switch is located in the PMV assembly's reservoir. The fluid level switch is normally closed when the reservoir contains sufficient fluid. When fluid level is low, the switch opens, causing the EBCM to turn on the "ANTILOCK" indicator.

FAILURE CONDITIONS

Code 73 sets when the EBCM detects a short to ground in the PMV fluid level switch circuitry. These include: CKT 848, 849, 853 and 1659.

GC402920061200AX

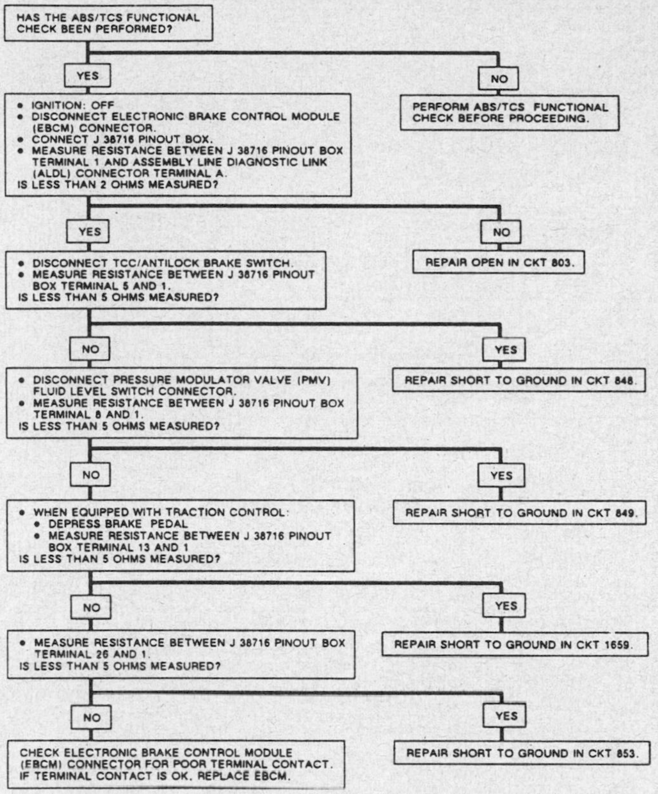
HAS THE ABS/TCS FUNCTIONAL CHECK BEEN PERFORMED?
YES
NO
PERFORM ABS/TCS FUNCTIONAL CHECK BEFORE PROCEEDING.
• IGNITION: OFF
• DISCONNECT ELECTRONIC BRAKE CONTROL MODULE (EBCM) CONNECTOR.
• CONNECT J 38716 PINOUT BOX.
• MEASURE RESISTANCE BETWEEN J 38716 PINOUT BOX TERMINAL 1 AND ASSEMBLY LINE DIAGNOSTIC LINK (ALDL) CONNECTOR TERMINAL A.
IS LESS THAN 2 OHMS MEASURED?
YES
NO
REPAIR OPEN IN CKT 803.
• DISCONNECT TCC/ANTILOCK BRAKE SWITCH.
• MEASURE RESISTANCE BETWEEN J 38716 PINOUT BOX TERMINAL 5 AND 1.
IS LESS THAN 5 OHMS MEASURED?
NO
YES
REPAIR SHORT TO GROUND IN CKT 848.
• DISCONNECT PRESSURE MODULATOR VALVE (PMV) FLUID LEVEL SWITCH CONNECTOR.
• MEASURE RESISTANCE BETWEEN J 38716 PINOUT BOX TERMINAL 8 AND 1.
IS LESS THAN 5 OHMS MEASURED?
NO
YES
REPAIR SHORT TO GROUND IN CKT 849.
• WHEN EQUIPPED WITH TRACTION CONTROL:
• DEPRESS BRAKE PEDAL
• MEASURE RESISTANCE BETWEEN J 38716 PINOUT BOX TERMINAL 13 AND 1
IS LESS THAN 5 OHMS MEASURED?
NO
YES
REPAIR SHORT TO GROUND IN CKT 1659.
• MEASURE RESISTANCE BETWEEN J 38716 PINOUT BOX TERMINAL 26 AND 1.
IS LESS THAN 5 OHMS MEASURED?
NO
YES
CHECK ELECTRONIC BRAKE CONTROL MODULE (EBCM) CONNECTOR FOR POOR TERMINAL CONTACT. IF TERMINAL CONTACT IS OK, REPLACE EBCM.
REPAIR SHORT TO GROUND IN CKT 853.

GC402920061200BX

Fig. 21 Test H: PMV Fluid Level Switch Circuit Test. 1992–93 Models Except 1993 LeSabre & Park Avenue

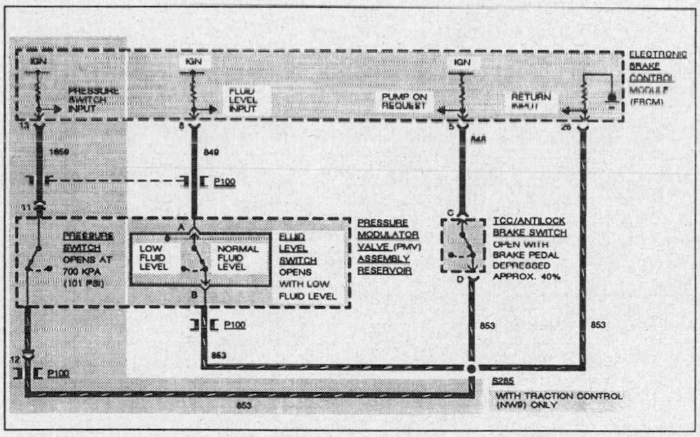
IGN
PRESSURE SWITCH INPUT
FLUID LEVEL INPUT
PUMP ON REQUEST
RETURN INPUT
ELECTRONIC BRAKE CONTROL MODULE (EBCM)
1659
849
848
P100
PRESSURE SWITCH OPENS AT 700 KPA (101 PSI)
LOW FLUID LEVEL
NORMAL FLUID LEVEL
FLUID LEVEL SWITCH OPENS WITH LOW FLUID LEVEL
PRESSURE MODULATOR VALVE (PMV) ASSEMBLY RESERVOIR
TCC/ANTILOCK BRAKE SWITCH OPEN WITH BRAKE PEDAL DEPRESSED APPROX. 40%
853
S285
WITH TRACTION CONTROL (NW9) ONLY

CHART I
PUMP MOTOR FAULT DURING AN ABS STOP

CIRCUIT OPERATION

The electronic brake control module (EBCM) monitors brake pedal position using the TCC/antilock brake switch. The normally closed switch opens when the brake pedal is depressed approximately 40% down. The EBCM also monitors pump motor operation using a pump motor run sensor.

During most ABS braking conditions the EBCM turns on the pump motor, replenishing the PMV assembly reservoir and applying fluid pressure to the master cylinder. This causes the brake pedal to gradually rise. The EBCM turns off the pump motor when brake pedal height sufficiently rises to close the TCC/antilock brake switch.

FAILURE CONDITIONS

During ABS braking, Code 62 sets when the EBCM determines the pump is working, and brake pedal height has not sufficiently risen to close the TCC/antilock brake switch after 3 seconds.

This code usually indicates a hydraulic problem. Some possible causes include air in the brake lines or a pump motor mechanical failure. Non-hydraulic causes for Code 62 include an open 848 or 853 CKT or a misadjusted/defective TCC/antilock brake switch.

GC402910061300AX

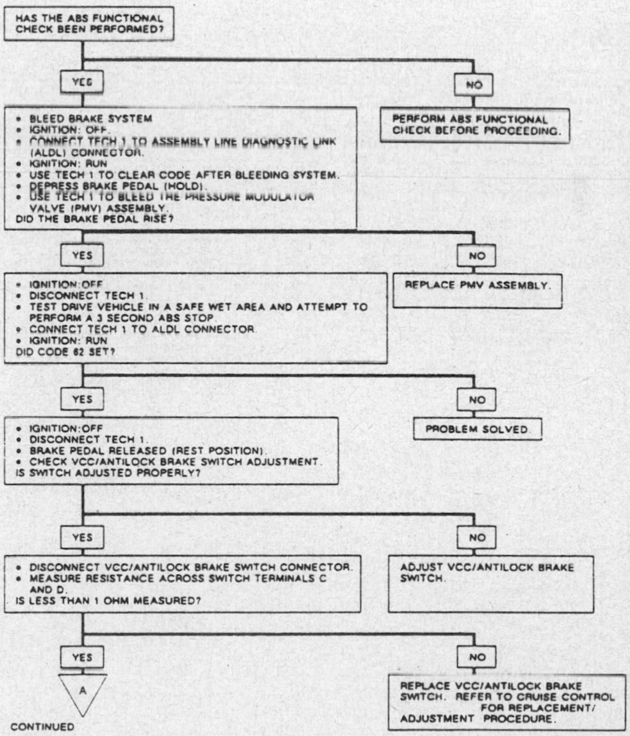
HAS THE ABS FUNCTIONAL CHECK BEEN PERFORMED?
YES
NO
PERFORM ABS FUNCTIONAL CHECK BEFORE PROCEEDING.
• BLEED BRAKE SYSTEM
• IGNITION: OFF.
• CONNECT TECH 1 TO ASSEMBLY LINE DIAGNOSTIC LINK (ALDL) CONNECTOR.
• IGNITION: RUN
• USE TECH 1 TO CLEAR CODE AFTER BLEEDING SYSTEM.
• DEPRESS BRAKE PEDAL (HOLD).
• USE TECH 1 TO BLEED THE PRESSURE MODULATOR VALVE (PMV) ASSEMBLY.
DID THE BRAKE PEDAL RISE?
YES
NO
REPLACE PMV ASSEMBLY.
• IGNITION:OFF
• DISCONNECT TECH 1.
• TEST DRIVE VEHICLE IN A SAFE WET AREA AND ATTEMPT TO PERFORM A 3 SECOND ABS STOP.
• CONNECT TECH 1 TO ALDL CONNECTOR.
• IGNITION: RUN
DID CODE 62 SET?
YES
NO
PROBLEM SOLVED.
• IGNITION:OFF
• DISCONNECT TECH 1.
• BRAKE PEDAL RELEASED (REST POSITION).
• CHECK VCC/ANTILOCK BRAKE SWITCH ADJUSTMENT.
IS SWITCH ADJUSTED PROPERLY?
YES
NO
ADJUST VCC/ANTILOCK BRAKE SWITCH.
• DISCONNECT VCC/ANTILOCK BRAKE SWITCH CONNECTOR.
• MEASURE RESISTANCE ACROSS SWITCH TERMINALS C AND D.
IS LESS THAN 1 OHM MEASURED?
YES
NO
A
CONTINUED
REPLACE VCC/ANTILOCK BRAKE SWITCH. REFER TO CRUISE CONTROL FOR REPLACEMENT/ ADJUSTMENT PROCEDURE.

GC402910061300BX

Fig. 22 Test I: Pump Motor Fault During An ABS Stop (Part 1 of 2). 1992–93 Models Except 1993 LeSabre & Park Avenue

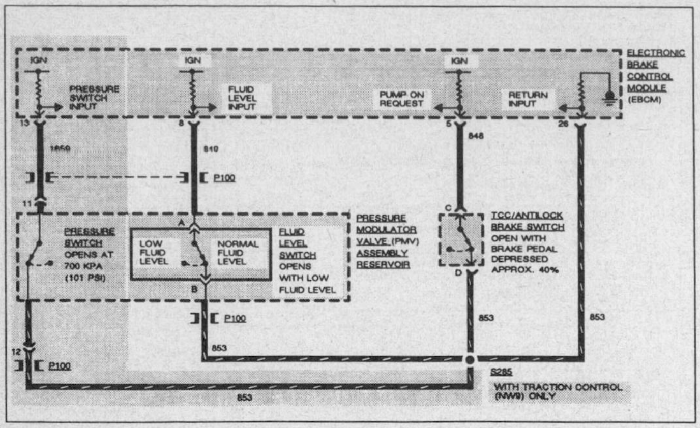

IGN
IGN
IGN
PRESSURE SWITCH INPUT
FLUID LEVEL INPUT
PUMP ON REQUEST
RETURN INPUT
ELECTRONIC BRAKE CONTROL MODULE (EBCM)
13
8
5
26
810
848
P100
11
A
C
PRESSURE SWITCH OPENS AT 700 KPA (101 PSI)
LOW FLUID LEVEL
NORMAL FLUID LEVEL
FLUID LEVEL SWITCH OPENS WITH LOW FLUID LEVEL
PRESSURE MODULATOR VALVE (PMV) ASSEMBLY RESERVOIR
TCC/ANTILOCK BRAKE SWITCH OPEN WITH BRAKE PEDAL DEPRESSED APPROX. 40%
B
D
P100
853
853
853
12
P100
S285
WITH TRACTION CONTROL (NW9) ONLY
853

CHART I
PUMP MOTOR FAULT
DURING AN ABS STOP

CIRCUIT OPERATION

The electronic brake control module (EBCM) monitors brake pedal position using the TCC/antilock brake switch. The normally closed switch opens when the brake pedal is depressed approximately 40% down. The EBCM also monitors pump motor operation using a pump motor run sensor.

During most ABS braking conditions the EBCM turns on the pump motor, replenishing the PMV assembly reservoir and applying fluid pressure to the master cylinder. This causes the brake pedal to gradually rise. The EBCM turns off the pump motor when brake pedal height sufficiently rises to close the TCC/antilock brake switch.

FAILURE CONDITIONS

During ABS braking, Code 62 sets when the EBCM determines the pump is working, and brake pedal height has not sufficiently risen to close the TCC/antilock brake switch after 3 seconds.

This code usually indicates a hydraulic problem. Some possible causes include air in the brake lines or a pump motor mechanical failure. Non-hydraulic causes for Code 62 include an open 848 or 853 CKT or a misadjusted/defective TCC/antilock brake switch.

GC402910061300CX

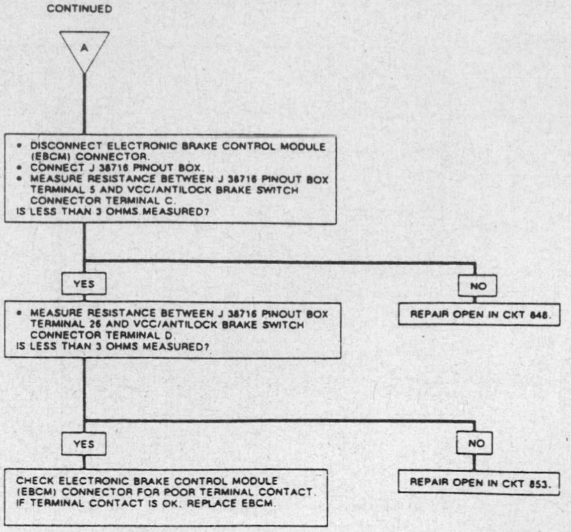

CONTINUED
A
• DISCONNECT ELECTRONIC BRAKE CONTROL MODULE (EBCM) CONNECTOR.
• CONNECT J 38716 PINOUT BOX.
• MEASURE RESISTANCE BETWEEN J 38716 PINOUT BOX TERMINAL 5 AND VCC/ANTILOCK BRAKE SWITCH CONNECTOR TERMINAL C.
IS LESS THAN 3 OHMS MEASURED?
YES
NO
• MEASURE RESISTANCE BETWEEN J 38716 PINOUT BOX TERMINAL 26 AND VCC/ANTILOCK BRAKE SWITCH CONNECTOR TERMINAL D.
IS LESS THAN 3 OHMS MEASURED?
REPAIR OPEN IN CKT 848.
YES
NO
CHECK ELECTRONIC BRAKE CONTROL MODULE (EBCM) CONNECTOR FOR POOR TERMINAL CONTACT. IF TERMINAL CONTACT IS OK, REPLACE EBCM.
REPAIR OPEN IN CKT 853.

AFTER REPAIRS ARE COMPLETED, CLEAR CODES AND REPEAT ABS FUNCTIONAL CHECK.

GC402910061300DX

Fig. 22 Test I: Pump Motor Fault During An ABS Stop (Part 2 of 2). 1992–93 Models Except 1993 LeSabre & Park Avenue

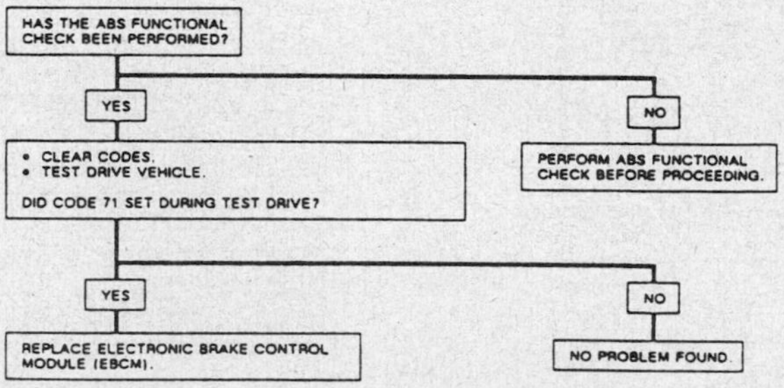

HAS THE ABS FUNCTIONAL CHECK BEEN PERFORMED?
YES
NO
• CLEAR CODES.
• TEST DRIVE VEHICLE.
DID CODE 71 SET DURING TEST DRIVE?
PERFORM ABS FUNCTIONAL CHECK BEFORE PROCEEDING.
YES
NO
REPLACE ELECTRONIC BRAKE CONTROL MODULE (EBCM).
NO PROBLEM FOUND.

AFTER REPAIRS ARE COMPLETED, CLEAR CODES AND REPEAT ABS FUNCTIONAL CHECK.

GC4029100614000X

Fig. 23 Test J: EBCM Problem. 1992–93 Models Except 1993 LeSabre & Park Avenue

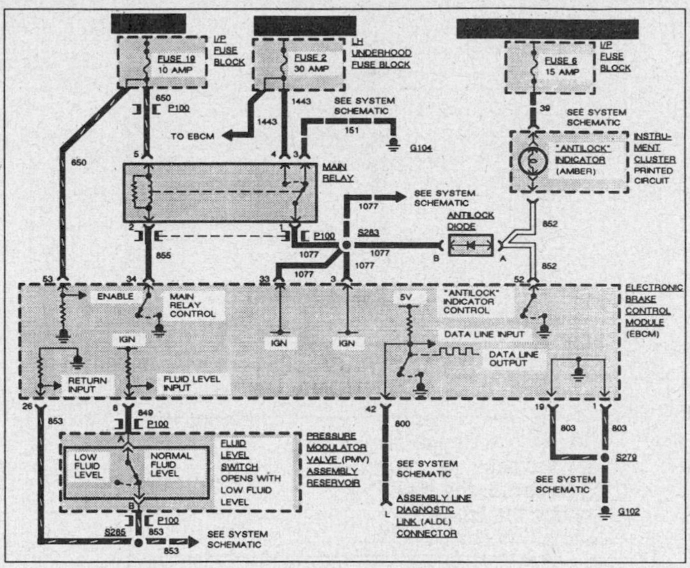

FUSE 19 10 AMP
I/P FUSE BLOCK
FUSE 2 30 AMP
LH UNDERHOOD FUSE BLOCK
FUSE 6 15 AMP
I/P FUSE BLOCK
650
P100
TO EBCM
1443
SEE SYSTEM SCHEMATIC
151
G104
39
SEE SYSTEM SCHEMATIC
"ANTILOCK" INDICATOR (AMBER)
INSTRU-MENT CLUSTER PRINTED CIRCUIT
MAIN RELAY
1077
SEE SYSTEM SCHEMATIC
ANTILOCK DIODE
852
S283
855
ENABLE
MAIN RELAY CONTROL
"ANTILOCK" INDICATOR CONTROL
5V
IGN
DATA LINE INPUT
DATA LINE OUTPUT
RETURN INPUT
FLUID LEVEL INPUT
ELECTRONIC BRAKE CONTROL MODULE (EBCM)
849
853
800
803
LOW FLUID LEVEL
NORMAL FLUID LEVEL
FLUID LEVEL SWITCH OPENS WITH LOW FLUID LEVEL
PRESSURE MODULATOR VALVE (PMV) ASSEMBLY RESERVOIR
SEE SYSTEM SCHEMATIC
S279
G102
ASSEMBLY LINE DIAGNOSTIC LINK (ALDL) CONNECTOR
S285

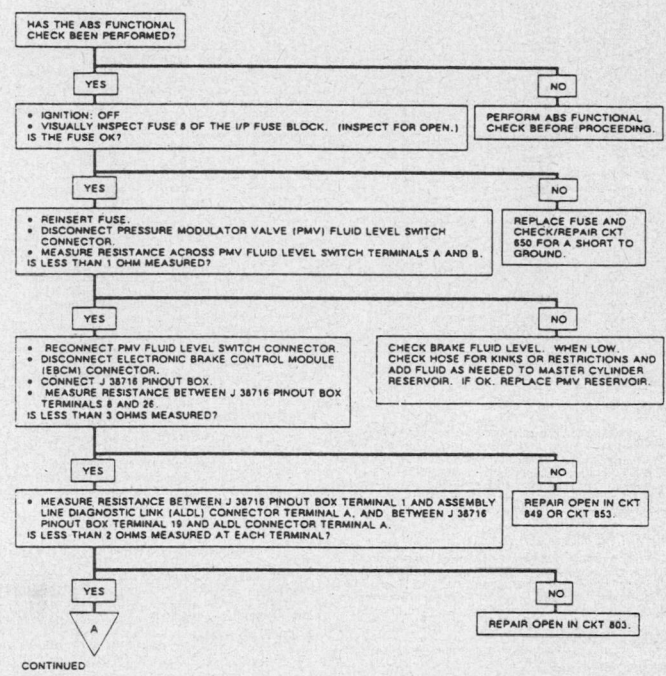

CHART K
"ANTILOCK" INDICATOR IS ON AND NO CODES ARE SET/ DIAGNOSTIC MODE CANNOT BE ENTERED

CIRCUIT OPERATION

When the ignition is first turned to "RUN," the electronic brake control module (EBCM) goes through a self-test lasting 2–4 seconds. During this test, the EBCM grounds terminal 52 causing the amber "ANTILOCK" indicator to light. This serves as an indicator bulb test.

When a low fluid condition exists, the EBCM turns on the amber "ANTILOCK" indicator but does not set a code. A low fluid level condition usually lights the red "BRAKE" indicator since the master cylinder supplies the PMV reservoir. However, restrictions or air in the hose could cause a low fluid condition in the PMV reservoir without lighting the red "BRAKE" indicator.

FAILURE CONDITIONS

Possible Causes

- Open in CKT 650, 800, 803, 849 or 853.
- Low brake fluid level or open PMV fluid level switch.
- Short to ground in CKT 650, 800 or 852.

GC402910061500AX

- HAS THE ABS FUNCTIONAL CHECK BEEN PERFORMED?
  - NO: PERFORM ABS FUNCTIONAL CHECK BEFORE PROCEEDING.
  - YES:
- • IGNITION: OFF
  • VISUALLY INSPECT FUSE 8 OF THE I/P FUSE BLOCK. (INSPECT FOR OPEN.)
  IS THE FUSE OK?
  - NO: REPLACE FUSE AND CHECK/REPAIR CKT 650 FOR A SHORT TO GROUND.
  - YES:
- • REINSERT FUSE.
  • DISCONNECT PRESSURE MODULATOR VALVE (PMV) FLUID LEVEL SWITCH CONNECTOR.
  • MEASURE RESISTANCE ACROSS PMV FLUID LEVEL SWITCH TERMINALS A AND B.
  IS LESS THAN 1 OHM MEASURED?
  - NO: CHECK BRAKE FLUID LEVEL. WHEN LOW, CHECK HOSE FOR KINKS OR RESTRICTIONS AND ADD FLUID AS NEEDED TO MASTER CYLINDER RESERVOIR. IF OK, REPLACE PMV RESERVOIR.
  - YES:
- • RECONNECT PMV FLUID LEVEL SWITCH CONNECTOR.
  • DISCONNECT ELECTRONIC BRAKE CONTROL MODULE (EBCM) CONNECTOR.
  • CONNECT J 38716 PINOUT BOX.
  • MEASURE RESISTANCE BETWEEN J 38716 PINOUT BOX TERMINALS 8 AND 26.
  IS LESS THAN 3 OHMS MEASURED?
  - NO: REPAIR OPEN IN CKT 849 OR CKT 853.
  - YES:
- • MEASURE RESISTANCE BETWEEN J 38716 PINOUT BOX TERMINAL 1 AND ASSEMBLY LINE DIAGNOSTIC LINK (ALDL) CONNECTOR TERMINAL A, AND BETWEEN J 38716 PINOUT BOX TERMINAL 19 AND ALDL CONNECTOR TERMINAL A.
  IS LESS THAN 2 OHMS MEASURED AT EACH TERMINAL?
  - NO: REPAIR OPEN IN CKT 803.
  - YES: A

CONTINUED

AFTER REPAIRS ARE COMPLETED, CLEAR CODES AND REPEAT ABS FUNCTIONAL CHECK.

GC402910061500BX

Fig. 24 Test K: Anti-Lock Indicator Is On & No Codes Are Set/Diagnostic Mode Cannot Be Entered (Part 1 of 2). 1992–93 Models Except 1993 LeSabre & Park Avenue

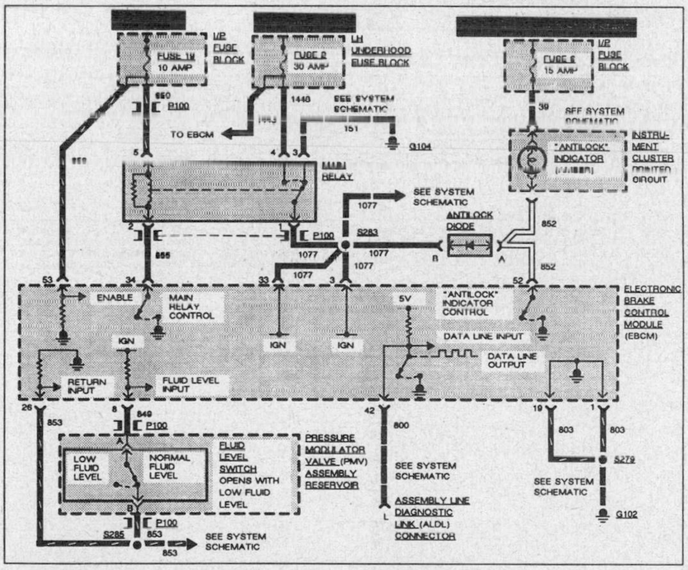

FUSE 19 10 AMP
I/P FUSE BLOCK
FUSE 2 30 AMP
LH UNDERHOOD FUSE BLOCK
FUSE 6 15 AMP
I/P FUSE BLOCK

CIRCUIT OPERATION

When the ignition is first turned to "RUN," the electronic brake control module (EBCM) goes through a self-test lasting 2–4 seconds. During this test, the EBCM grounds terminal 52 causing the amber "ANTILOCK" indicator to light. This serves as an indicator bulb test.

When a low fluid condition exists, the EBCM turns on the amber "ANTILOCK" indicator but does not set a code. A low fluid level condition usually lights the red "BRAKE" indicator since the master cylinder supplies the PMV reservoir. However, restrictions or air in the hose could cause a low fluid condition in the PMV reservoir without lighting the red "BRAKE" indicator.

FAILURE CONDITIONS

Possible Causes

- Open in CKT 650, 800, 803, 849 or 853.
- Low brake fluid level or open PMV fluid level switch.
- Short to ground in CKT 650, 800 or 852.

GC402910061500CX

CONTINUED

A

- • IGNITION: RUN
  • MEASURE VOLTAGE BETWEEN J38716 PINOUT BOX TERMINALS 53 AND 1.
  IS BATTERY VOLTAGE MEASURED?
  - NO: REPAIR OPEN IN CKT 650.
  - YES:
- • IGNITION: OFF
  • DISCONNECT MAIN RELAY.
  • IGNITION: RUN
  • MEASURE VOLTAGE BETWEEN J 38716 PINOUT TERMINALS 52 AND 1.
  IS BATTERY VOLTAGE MEASURED?
  - NO: REPAIR CKT 852 FOR A SHORT TO GROUND.
  - YES:
- • IGNITION: OFF
  • MEASURE RESISTANCE BETWEEN J38716 PINOUT BOX TERMINALS 42 AND 1.
  IS INFINITE OHMS MEASURED?
  - NO: REPAIR CKT 800 FOR A SHORT TO GROUND.
  - YES:
- • MEASURE RESISTANCE BETWEEN J38716 PINOUT BOX TERMINAL 42 AND THE ASSEMBLY LINE DIAGNOSTIC LINK (ALDL) CONNECTOR TERMINAL L.
  IS LESS THAN 1 OHM MEASURED?
  - NO: REPAIR OPEN IN CKT 800.
  - YES: CHECK ELECTRONIC BRAKE CONTROL MODULE (EBCM) CONNECTOR FOR POOR TERMINAL CONTACT. IF TERMINAL CONTACT IS OK, REPLACE EBCM.

AFTER REPAIRS ARE COMPLETED, CLEAR CODES AND REPEAT ABS FUNCTIONAL CHECK.

GC402910061500DX

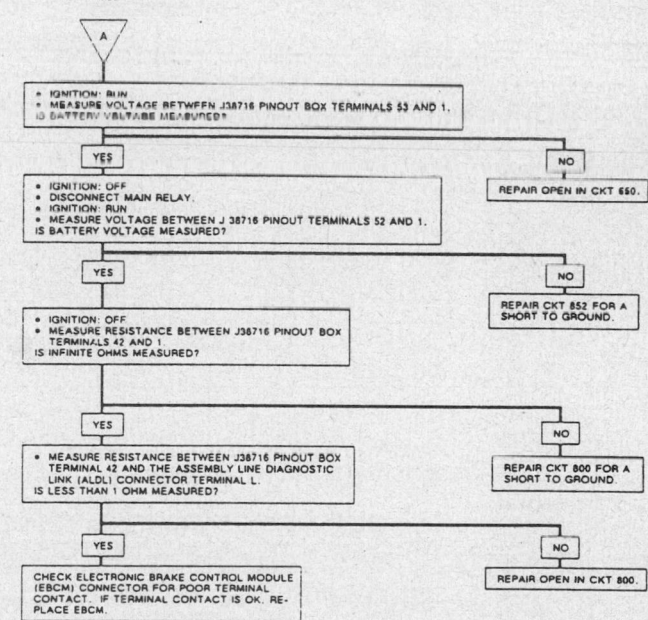

Fig. 24 Test K: Anti-Lock Indicator Is On & No Codes Are Set/Diagnostic Mode Cannot Be Entered (Part 2 of 2). 1992–93 Models Except 1993 LeSabre & Park Avenue

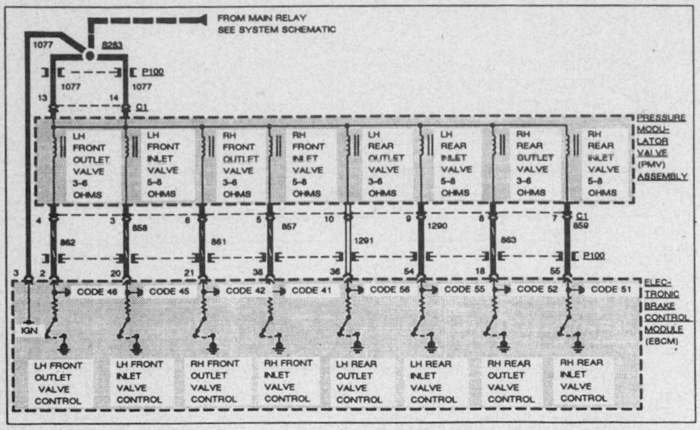
FROM MAIN RELAY
SEE SYSTEM SCHEMATIC
PRESSURE MODULATOR VALVE (PMV) ASSEMBLY
LH FRONT OUTLET VALVE 3-6 OHMS
LH FRONT INLET VALVE 5-8 OHMS
RH FRONT OUTLET VALVE 3-6 OHMS
RH FRONT INLET VALVE 5-8 OHMS
LH REAR OUTLET VALVE 3-6 OHMS
LH REAR INLET VALVE 5-8 OHMS
RH REAR OUTLET VALVE 3-6 OHMS
RH REAR INLET VALVE 5-8 OHMS
CODE 46
CODE 45
CODE 42
CODE 41
CODE 56
CODE 55
CODE 52
CODE 51
ELECTRONIC BRAKE CONTROL MODULE (EBCM)
LH FRONT OUTLET VALVE CONTROL
LH FRONT INLET VALVE CONTROL
RH FRONT OUTLET VALVE CONTROL
RH FRONT INLET VALVE CONTROL
LH REAR OUTLET VALVE CONTROL
LH REAR INLET VALVE CONTROL
RH REAR OUTLET VALVE CONTROL
RH REAR INLET VALVE CONTROL

CIRCUIT OPERATION

Inlet Valves

Voltage is applied to the normally open inlet valves whenever the main relay is energized. An inlet valve closes when the electronic brake control module (EBCM) supplies a ground path at the inlet valve control terminal. The EBCM closes an inlet valve for short periods to maintain (hold) or reduce pressure at a particular wheel.

Outlet Valves

The normally closed outlet valves operate similarly to the inlet valves, except that when the EBCM grounds an outlet valve, the valve opens instead of closes. The EBCM opens an outlet valve for short periods to reduce pressure at a particular wheel.

VALVE MODES

Pressure Increase

The pressure increase position is the operating valve position for normal (non-ABS) braking and traction control mode (when equipped). The EBCM does not energize either valve, leaving the inlet valve open and the outlet valve closed.

Pressure Hold

The pressure hold position occurs when the EBCM first notices an abnormal hydraulic pressure increase. This signifies an impending wheel lockup condition. The EBCM closes the corresponding inlet valve in an attempt to avoid any additional hydraulic pressure increase (avoiding an ABS braking condition).

Pressure Reduce

During a wheel lockup condition, the EBCM close the inlet valve while pulsing open the outlet valve. This decreases hydraulic pressure at a specific wheel without decreasing overall system pressure. The reduced hydraulic pressure allows greater wheel spin, eliminating the wheel lockup condition.

Test Description

This test checks for proper inlet and outlet valve operation. The wheel brake behavior must be checked to verify the valves hydraulic effectiveness. This is accomplished using the TECH 1 to actuate the valves.

GC402910061600AX

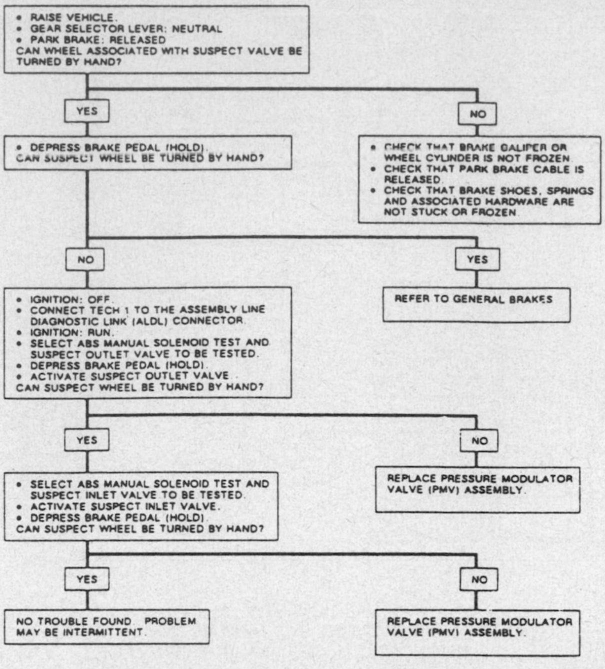
• RAISE VEHICLE.
• GEAR SELECTOR LEVER: NEUTRAL
• PARK BRAKE: RELEASED
CAN WHEEL ASSOCIATED WITH SUSPECT VALVE BE TURNED BY HAND?
YES
NO
• DEPRESS BRAKE PEDAL (HOLD).
CAN SUSPECT WHEEL BE TURNED BY HAND?
• CHECK THAT BRAKE CALIPER OR WHEEL CYLINDER IS NOT FROZEN.
• CHECK THAT PARK BRAKE CABLE IS RELEASED.
• CHECK THAT BRAKE SHOES, SPRINGS AND ASSOCIATED HARDWARE ARE NOT STUCK OR FROZEN.
NO
YES
• IGNITION: OFF.
• CONNECT TECH 1 TO THE ASSEMBLY LINE DIAGNOSTIC LINK (ALDL) CONNECTOR.
• IGNITION: RUN.
• SELECT ABS MANUAL SOLENOID TEST AND SUSPECT OUTLET VALVE TO BE TESTED.
• DEPRESS BRAKE PEDAL (HOLD).
• ACTIVATE SUSPECT OUTLET VALVE.
CAN SUSPECT WHEEL BE TURNED BY HAND?
REFER TO GENERAL BRAKES
YES
NO
• SELECT ABS MANUAL SOLENOID TEST AND SUSPECT INLET VALVE TO BE TESTED.
• ACTIVATE SUSPECT INLET VALVE.
• DEPRESS BRAKE PEDAL (HOLD).
CAN SUSPECT WHEEL BE TURNED BY HAND?
REPLACE PRESSURE MODULATOR VALVE (PMV) ASSEMBLY.
YES
NO
NO TROUBLE FOUND. PROBLEM MAY BE INTERMITTENT.
REPLACE PRESSURE MODULATOR VALVE (PMV) ASSEMBLY.

NOTE: TO PREVENT OVERHEATING OF INLET/OUTLET VALVES. SCAN TOOL WILL ONLY ALLOW VALVES TO BE ENERGIZED FOR A MAXIMUM OF 20 SECONDS. A MINIMUM OF 30 SECONDS MUST ELAPSE BEFORE VALVES CAN BE RE-ENERGIZED.

AFTER REPAIRS ARE COMPLETED, CLEAR CODES AND REPEAT ABS FUNCTIONAL CHECK.

GC402910061600BX

Fig. 25 Test L: Inlet/Outlet Valve Hydraulic Test. 1992–93 Models Except 1993 LeSabre & Park Avenue

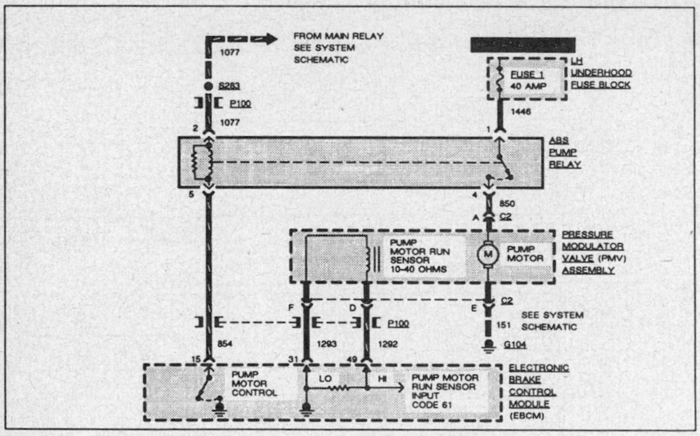
FROM MAIN RELAY
SEE SYSTEM SCHEMATIC
FUSE 1 40 AMP
LH UNDERHOOD FUSE BLOCK
ABS PUMP RELAY
PUMP MOTOR RUN SENSOR 10-40 OHMS
PUMP MOTOR
PRESSURE MODULATOR VALVE (PMV) ASSEMBLY
SEE SYSTEM SCHEMATIC
PUMP MOTOR CONTROL
PUMP MOTOR RUN SENSOR INPUT CODE 61
ELECTRONIC BRAKE CONTROL MODULE (EBCM)

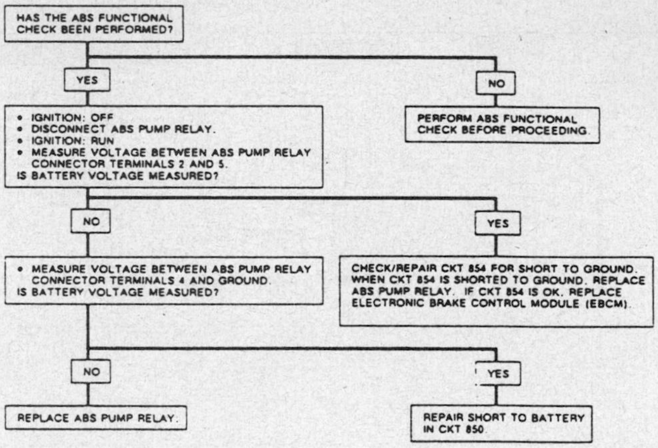
HAS THE ABS FUNCTIONAL CHECK BEEN PERFORMED?
YES
NO
• IGNITION: OFF
• DISCONNECT ABS PUMP RELAY.
• IGNITION: RUN
• MEASURE VOLTAGE BETWEEN ABS PUMP RELAY CONNECTOR TERMINALS 2 AND 5.
IS BATTERY VOLTAGE MEASURED?
PERFORM ABS FUNCTIONAL CHECK BEFORE PROCEEDING.
NO
YES
• MEASURE VOLTAGE BETWEEN ABS PUMP RELAY CONNECTOR TERMINALS 4 AND GROUND.
IS BATTERY VOLTAGE MEASURED?
CHECK/REPAIR CKT 854 FOR SHORT TO GROUND. WHEN CKT 854 IS SHORTED TO GROUND, REPLACE ABS PUMP RELAY. IF CKT 854 IS OK, REPLACE ELECTRONIC BRAKE CONTROL MODULE (EBCM).
NO
YES
REPLACE ABS PUMP RELAY.
REPAIR SHORT TO BATTERY IN CKT 850.

CHART M
PUMP MOTOR RUNS CONTINUOUSLY

CIRCUIT OPERATION

When the electronic brake control module (EBCM) grounds terminal 15, the ABS pump relay is energized. The pump relay contacts close, applying voltage to the pressure modulator valve (PMV) assembly's pump motor.

During most ABS braking conditions, the EBCM turns on the pump motor while monitoring the TCC/antilock brake switch to determine brake pedal position. The switch opens when the brake pedal is depressed approximately 40% down. The motor restores the master cylinder's fluid pressure, causing the brake pedal to gradually rise. The pump motor continues to run until the brake pedal sufficiently rises to close the TCC/antilock brake switch.

During traction control mode (when equipped), after the front hydraulic brake circuits are isolated, the pump motor runs to increase brake fluid pressure in these circuits. The increased pressure is directed to the slipping wheel through the PMV assembly's front inlet and outlet valves. This causes the brakes to be applied, reducing wheel spin at the slipping wheel. Traction control is disabled as soon as the brakes are manually applied.

The EBCM monitors pump motor operation via the pump motor run sensor. When the pump is operating, voltage is induced into the sensor's coil and the EBCM monitors this voltage at terminals 49 and 31.

FAILURE CONDITIONS

A continuously running pump motor occurs when CKT 854 is shorted to ground, the pump relay fails "engaged," or CKT 850 is shorted to a battery source. This condition illuminates the amber "ANTILOCK" indicator and sets Code 61.

GC402910061700AX

AFTER REPAIRS ARE COMPLETED, CLEAR CODES AND REPEAT ABS FUNCTIONAL CHECK.

GC402910061700BX

Fig. 26 Test M: Pump Motor Runs Continuously. 1992–93 Models Except 1993 LeSabre & Park Avenue

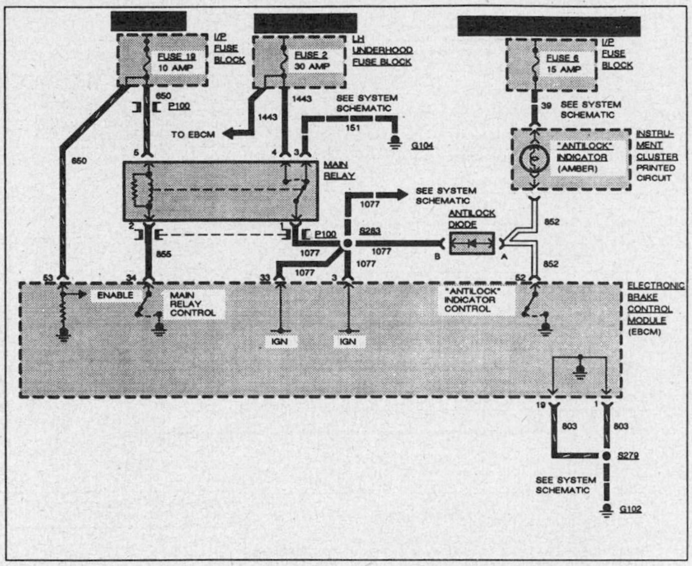

FUSE 19
10 AMP
I/P FUSE BLOCK
FUSE 2
30 AMP
LH UNDERHOOD FUSE BLOCK
FUSE 8
15 AMP
I/P FUSE BLOCK
SEE SYSTEM SCHEMATIC
TO EBCM
G104
"ANTILOCK" INDICATOR (AMBER)
INSTRUMENT CLUSTER PRINTED CIRCUIT
MAIN RELAY
ANTILOCK DIODE
P100
S283
ENABLE
MAIN RELAY CONTROL
"ANTILOCK" INDICATOR CONTROL
ELECTRONIC BRAKE CONTROL MODULE (EBCM)
IGN
S279
G102

CIRCUIT OPERATION

When the ignition switch is first turned to "RUN" the electronic brake control module (EBCM) goes through a self-test lasting 2–4 seconds. During this test, the EBCM grounds terminal 52, causing the amber "ANTILOCK" indicator to light. This serves as an indicator bulb test. The EBCM also grounds terminal 34, energizing the main relay. This removes the indicator ground path provided through the antilock diode and the main relay contacts.

When the self-test is completed (and no faults are detected) the EBCM removes the ground at terminal 52, turning off the indicator. The main relay remains energized.

When the EBCM detects a fault, it grounds terminal 52 causing the amber "ANTILOCK" indicator to light. (Note: The EBCM will also de-energize the main relay creating a redundant ground path.)

When the EBCM is disabled for any reason (i.e. open Fuse 19), the main relay is de-energized. This provides an "ANTILOCK" indicator ground path through the antilock diode and main relay contacts, and causes the indicator to light with no codes being set.

FAILURE CONDITIONS

Possible Causes

- Open in CKT 151, 852 or 1077.
- Open bulb.
- Short to voltage in CKT 852.
- Open or shorted antilock diode.
- Main relay fails "engaged."
- Short to ground in CKT 855.

GC402910061800AX

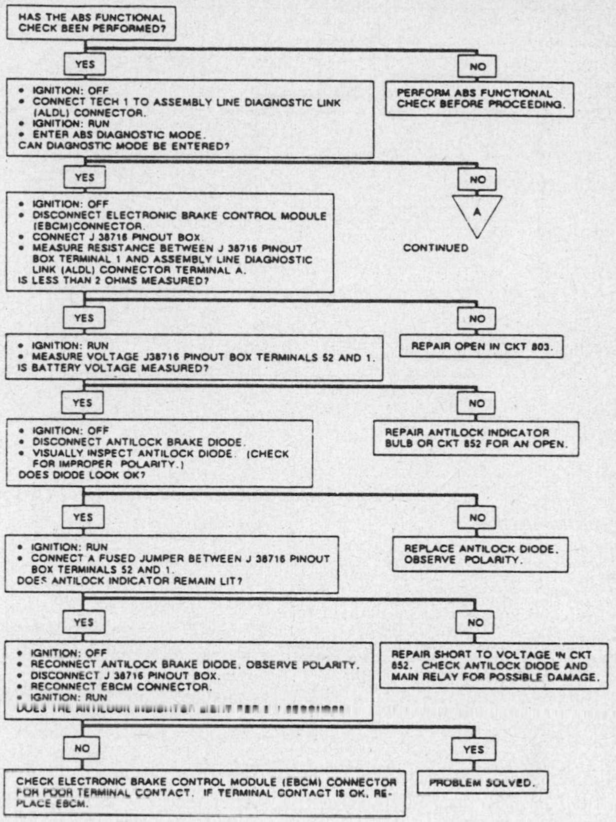

HAS THE ABS FUNCTIONAL CHECK BEEN PERFORMED?
YES
NO
PERFORM ABS FUNCTIONAL CHECK BEFORE PROCEEDING.
• IGNITION: OFF • CONNECT TECH 1 TO ASSEMBLY LINE DIAGNOSTIC LINK (ALDL) CONNECTOR. • IGNITION: RUN • ENTER ABS DIAGNOSTIC MODE. CAN DIAGNOSTIC MODE BE ENTERED?
YES
NO
A
CONTINUED
• IGNITION: OFF • DISCONNECT ELECTRONIC BRAKE CONTROL MODULE (EBCM)CONNECTOR. • CONNECT J 38716 PINOUT BOX. • MEASURE RESISTANCE BETWEEN J 38716 PINOUT BOX TERMINAL 1 AND ASSEMBLY LINE DIAGNOSTIC LINK (ALDL) CONNECTOR TERMINAL A. IS LESS THAN 2 OHMS MEASURED?
YES
NO
REPAIR OPEN IN CKT 803.
• IGNITION: RUN • MEASURE VOLTAGE J38716 PINOUT BOX TERMINALS 52 AND 1. IS BATTERY VOLTAGE MEASURED?
YES
NO
REPAIR ANTILOCK INDICATOR BULB OR CKT 852 FOR AN OPEN.
• IGNITION: OFF • DISCONNECT ANTILOCK BRAKE DIODE. • VISUALLY INSPECT ANTILOCK DIODE. (CHECK FOR IMPROPER POLARITY.) DOES DIODE LOOK OK?
YES
NO
REPLACE ANTILOCK DIODE. OBSERVE POLARITY.
• IGNITION: RUN • CONNECT A FUSED JUMPER BETWEEN J 38716 PINOUT BOX TERMINALS 52 AND 1. DOES ANTILOCK INDICATOR REMAIN LIT?
YES
NO
REPAIR SHORT TO VOLTAGE IN CKT 852. CHECK ANTILOCK DIODE AND MAIN RELAY FOR POSSIBLE DAMAGE.
• IGNITION: OFF • RECONNECT ANTILOCK BRAKE DIODE. OBSERVE POLARITY. • DISCONNECT J 38716 PINOUT BOX. • RECONNECT EBCM CONNECTOR. • IGNITION: RUN
NO
YES
CHECK ELECTRONIC BRAKE CONTROL MODULE (EBCM) CONNECTOR FOR POOR TERMINAL CONTACT. IF TERMINAL CONTACT IS OK, REPLACE EBCM.
PROBLEM SOLVED.

GC402910061800BX

Fig. 27 Test N: Anti-Lock Indicator Does Not Light (Part 1 of 2). 1992–93 Models Except 1993 LeSabre & Park Avenue

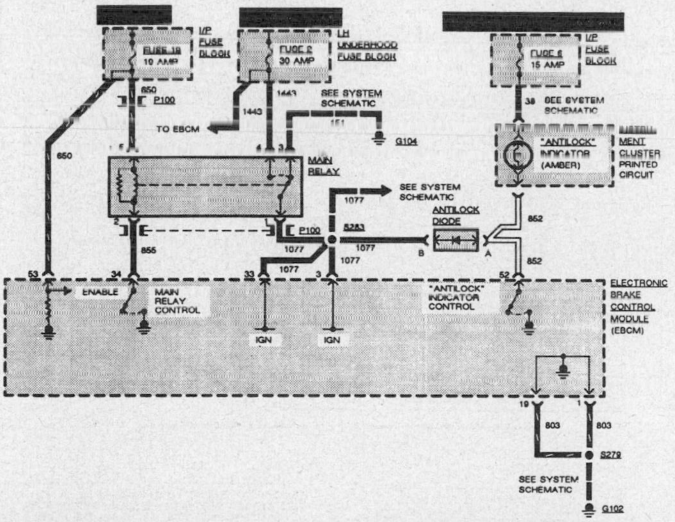

FUSE 19
10 AMP
I/P FUSE BLOCK
FUSE 2
30 AMP
LH UNDERHOOD FUSE BLOCK
FUSE 8
15 AMP
I/P FUSE BLOCK
SEE SYSTEM SCHEMATIC
TO EBCM
G104
"ANTILOCK" INDICATOR (AMBER)
MENT CLUSTER PRINTED CIRCUIT
MAIN RELAY
ANTILOCK DIODE
P100
S283
ENABLE
MAIN RELAY CONTROL
"ANTILOCK" INDICATOR CONTROL
ELECTRONIC BRAKE CONTROL MODULE (EBCM)
IGN
S279
G102

CIRCUIT OPERATION

When the ignition switch is first turned to "RUN" the electronic brake control module (EBCM) goes through a self-test lasting 2–4 seconds. During this test, the EBCM grounds terminal 52, causing the amber "ANTILOCK" indicator to light. This serves as an indicator bulb test. The EBCM also grounds terminal 34, energizing the main relay. This removes the indicator ground path provided through the antilock diode and the main relay contacts.

When the self-test is completed (and no faults are detected) the EBCM removes the ground at terminal 52, turning off the indicator. The main relay remains energized.

When the EBCM detects a fault, it grounds terminal 52 causing the amber "ANTILOCK" indicator to light. (Note: The EBCM will also de-energize the main relay creating a redundant ground path.)

When the EBCM is disabled for any reason (i.e. open Fuse 19), the main relay is de-energized. This provides an "ANTILOCK" indicator ground path through the antilock diode and main relay contacts, and causes the indicator to light with no codes being set.

FAILURE CONDITIONS

Possible Causes

- Open in CKT 151, 852 or 1077.
- Open bulb.
- Short to voltage in CKT 852.
- Open or shorted antilock diode.
- Main relay fails "engaged."
- Short to ground in CKT 855.

GC402910061800CX

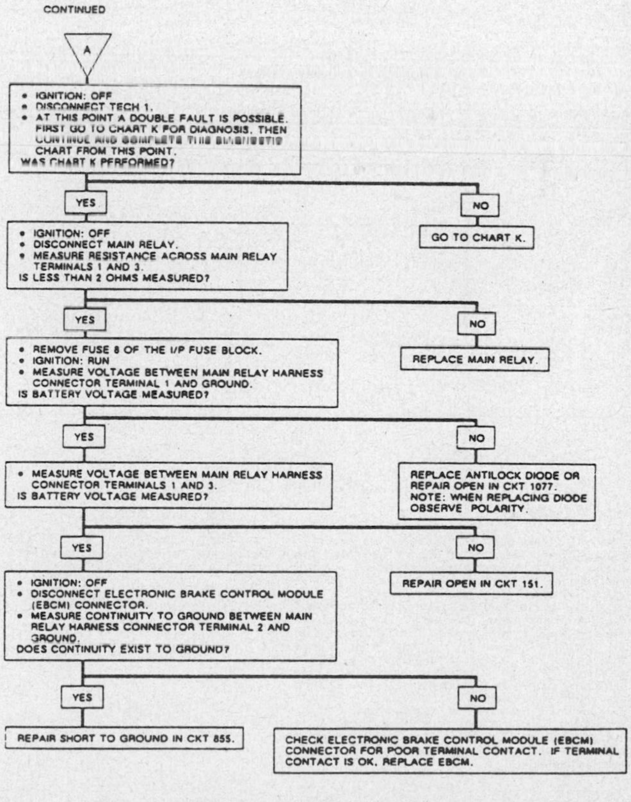

CONTINUED
A
• IGNITION: OFF • DISCONNECT TECH 1. • AT THIS POINT A DOUBLE FAULT IS POSSIBLE. FIRST GO TO CHART K FOR DIAGNOSIS. THEN CONTINUE AND COMPLETE THIS DIAGNOSTIC CHART FROM THIS POINT. WAS CHART K PERFORMED?
YES
NO
GO TO CHART K.
• IGNITION: OFF • DISCONNECT MAIN RELAY. • MEASURE RESISTANCE ACROSS MAIN RELAY TERMINALS 1 AND 3. IS LESS THAN 2 OHMS MEASURED?
YES
NO
REPLACE MAIN RELAY.
• REMOVE FUSE 8 OF THE I/P FUSE BLOCK. • IGNITION: RUN • MEASURE VOLTAGE BETWEEN MAIN RELAY HARNESS CONNECTOR TERMINAL 1 AND GROUND. IS BATTERY VOLTAGE MEASURED?
YES
NO
REPLACE ANTILOCK DIODE OR REPAIR OPEN IN CKT 1077. NOTE: WHEN REPLACING DIODE OBSERVE POLARITY.
• MEASURE VOLTAGE BETWEEN MAIN RELAY HARNESS CONNECTOR TERMINALS 1 AND 3. IS BATTERY VOLTAGE MEASURED?
YES
NO
REPAIR OPEN IN CKT 151.
• IGNITION: OFF • DISCONNECT ELECTRONIC BRAKE CONTROL MODULE (EBCM) CONNECTOR. • MEASURE CONTINUITY TO GROUND BETWEEN MAIN RELAY HARNESS CONNECTOR TERMINAL 2 AND GROUND. DOES CONTINUITY EXIST TO GROUND?
YES
NO
REPAIR SHORT TO GROUND IN CKT 855.
CHECK ELECTRONIC BRAKE CONTROL MODULE (EBCM) CONNECTOR FOR POOR TERMINAL CONTACT. IF TERMINAL CONTACT IS OK, REPLACE EBCM.
AFTER REPAIRS ARE COMPLETED, CLEAR CODES AND REPEAT ABS FUNCTIONAL CHECK.

GC402910061800DX

Fig. 27 Test N: Anti-Lock Indicator Does Not Light (Part 2 of 2). 1992–93 Models Except 1993 LeSabre & Park Avenue

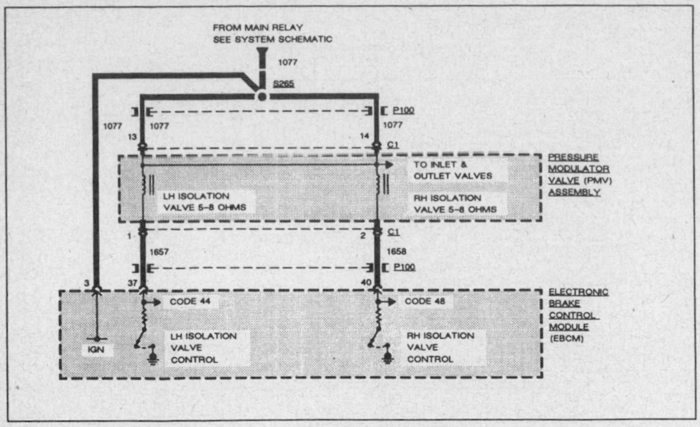
FROM MAIN RELAY
SEE SYSTEM SCHEMATIC
1077
S265
P100
1077
13
14
C1
TO INLET &
OUTLET VALVES
PRESSURE
MODULATOR
VALVE (PMV)
ASSEMBLY
LH ISOLATION
VALVE 5–8 OHMS
RH ISOLATION
VALVE 5–8 OHMS
1
2
1657
1658
3
37
40
CODE 44
CODE 48
ELECTRONIC
BRAKE
CONTROL
MODULE
(EBCM)
IGN
LH ISOLATION
VALVE
CONTROL
RH ISOLATION
VALVE
CONTROL

CHART O
ISOLATION VALVE CIRCUIT FAILURE

CIRCUIT OPERATION

Voltage is applied to the normally open isolation valves whenever the main relay is energized. An isolation valve closes when the electronic brake control module (EBCM) supplies a ground path at the isolation valve control terminal. The EBCM closes an isolation valve when the EBCM detects wheel slip in a drive wheel and vehicle speed is below 40 km/h (25 mph).

The isolation valves are closed only during traction control operations, and are not used during any antilock or normal braking conditions. The isolation valves separate (isolate) the front brake hydraulic circuits from the master cylinder and rear brake hydraulic circuits. Once the front brake hydraulic circuits are isolated, pressure can be applied to the front wheels without affecting any other brake hydraulic circuit.

FAILURE CONDITIONS

Code 44 or 48 sets when the electronic brake control module (EBCM) detects an open or short to ground in the respective isolation valve circuit.

GC402920059701AX

HAS THE ABS AND TRACTION CONTROL FUNCTIONAL CHECKS BEEN PERFORMED?

- NO: PERFORM BOTH THE ABS AND TRACTION CONTROL FUNCTIONAL CHECKS BEFORE PROCEEDING.
- YES:
  - IGNITION: OFF
  - DISCONNECT POWER MODULATOR VALVE (PMV) ASSEMBLY
  - MEASURE RESISTANCE BETWEEN PRESSURE MODULATOR (PMV) VALVE ASSEMBLY (ASSEMBLY HALF) TERMINAL 14 AND GROUND.

  IS LESS THAN 10 OHMS MEASURED?

- YES: REPLACE PRESSURE MODULATOR VALVE (PMV) ASSEMBLY.
- NO:
  - MEASURE RESISTANCE AT PRESSURE MODULATOR VALVE CONNECTOR (ASSEMBLY HALF) BETWEEN TERMINAL 14 AND THE SUSPECT VALVE TERMINAL. REFER TO CHART.

CODE/VALVE	SUSPECT TERMINAL	CORRECT RESISTANCE
44/LH ISOLATION	37	5 TO 8 OHMS
48/RH ISOLATION	40	

IS THE CORRECT RESISTANCE MEASURED?

- NO: REPLACE PRESSURE MODULATOR VALVE (PMV) ASSEMBLY.
- YES:
  - IGNITION: OFF
  - DISCONNECT ELECTRONIC BRAKE CONTROL MODULE (EBCM).
  - INSTALL J 38716 PINOUT BOX.
  - POWER MODULATOR VALVE ASSEMBLY RECONNECTED.
  - MEASURE RESISTANCE BETWEEN J 38716 PINOUT BOX TERMINAL 3 AND THE SUSPECT ISOLATION VALVE TERMINAL. REFER TO CHART.

CODE/VALVE	J 38716 TERMINAL
44/LH ISOLATION	37
48/RH ISOLATION	40

IS RESISTANCE MEASURED LESS THAN 10 OHMS?

- NO: REPAIR OPEN IN SUSPECT ISOLATION VALVE SOLENOID CIRCUIT BETWEEN PRESSURE MODULATOR VALVE (PMV) ASSEBMLY AND THE ELECTRONIC BRAKE CONTROL MODULE (EBCM). REFER TO SCHEMATIC.
- YES: A

CONTINUED

GC402920059701BX

Fig. 28 Test O: Isolation Valve Circuit Failure (Part 1 of 2). 1992

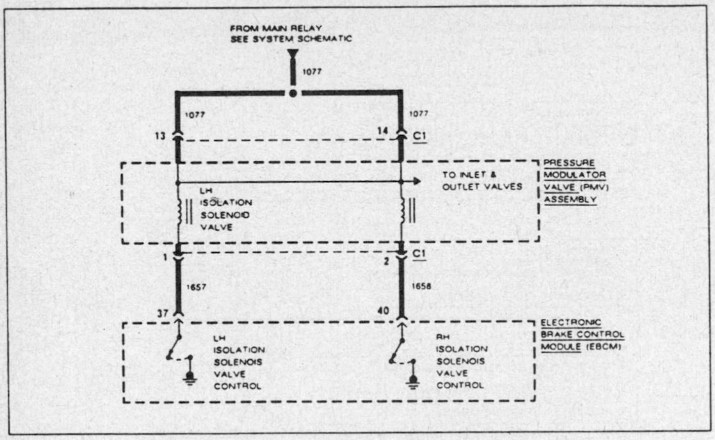
FROM MAIN RELAY
SEE SYSTEM SCHEMATIC
1077
1077
1077
13
14
C1
TO INLET &
OUTLET VALVES
PRESSURE
MODULATOR
VALVE (PMV)
ASSEMBLY
LH
ISOLATION
SOLENOID
VALVE
1
2
C1
1657
1658
37
40
ELECTRONIC
BRAKE CONTROL
MODULE (EBCM)
LH
ISOLATION
SOLENOIS
VALVE
CONTROL
RH
ISOLATION
SOLENOIS
VALVE
CONTROL

CHART O
ISOLATION VALVE CIRCUIT FAILURE

CIRCUIT OPERATION

The normally open isolation valves are located in the pressure modulator valve (PMV) assembly. the isolation valves are used only during traction control operations, the valves are not used during any antilock or braking functions. The isolation valves purpose is to separate or isolate the front wheel brake hydraulic circuits and the master cylinder. This allows the electronic brake control module (EBCM) to regulate brake hydraulic pressure to the front driven wheels during traction control operations without effect on the rear wheels. Voltage is applied to the isolation valves whenever the main relay is energized. The isolation valves will close when the EBCM energizes the isolation valve solenoids by supplying a ground path at the EBCM's isolation valve control terminals. The EBCM will energize the isolation valves when the EBCM detects wheel slip in a driven wheel and vehicle speed is below 20 km/h (12 mph).

FAILURE CONDITIONS

Code 44 and 48 will set if the electronic brake control module (EBCM) detects an open or short to ground in the respective isolation valve circuit.

GC402920059702AX

A

- MEASURE RESISTANCE BETWEEN J 38716 PINOUT BOX TERMINAL 1 AND THE SUSPECT ISOLATION VALVE. REFER TO CHART

CODE/VALVE	J 38716 TERMINAL
44/LH ISOLATION	13
48/RH ISOLATION	14

IS LESS THAN 10 OHMS MEASURED?

- NO: CHECK EBCM TERMINALS FOR GOOD TERMINAL CONTACT. IF TERMINAL CONTACT IS GOOD, REPLACE EBCM.
- YES: REPAIR SHORT TO GROUND IN ISOLATION VALVE CIRCUIT BETWEEN PRESSURE MODULATOR VALVE (PMV) ASSEMBLY AND THE ELECTRONIC BRAKE CONTROL MODULE (EBCM).

GC402920059702BX

Fig. 28 Test O: Isolation Valve Circuit Failure (Part 2 of 2). 1992

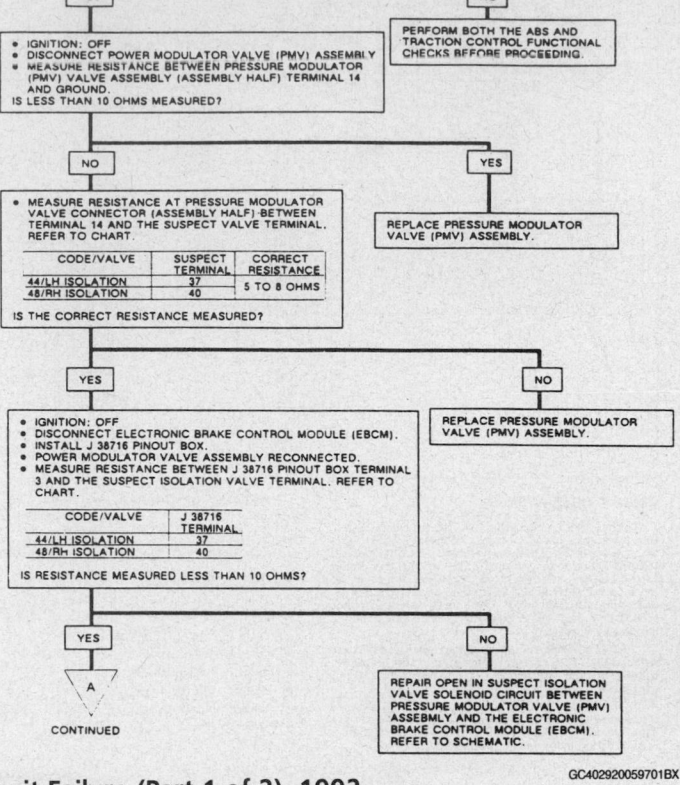

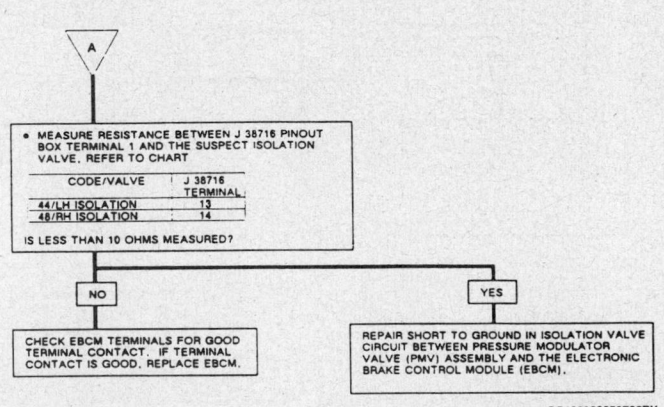

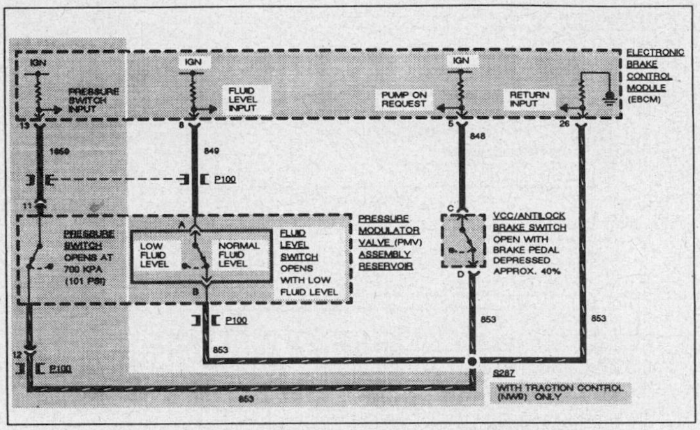
ELECTRONIC BRAKE CONTROL MODULE (EBCM)
IGN
PRESSURE SWITCH INPUT
FLUID LEVEL INPUT
PUMP ON REQUEST
RETURN INPUT
1659
849
848
P100
PRESSURE SWITCH OPENS AT 700 KPA (101 PSI)
LOW FLUID LEVEL
NORMAL FLUID LEVEL
FLUID LEVEL SWITCH OPENS WITH LOW FLUID LEVEL
PRESSURE MODULATOR VALVE (PMV) ASSEMBLY RESERVOIR
VCC/ANTILOCK BRAKE SWITCH OPEN WITH BRAKE PEDAL DEPRESSED APPROX. 40%
853
S287
WITH TRACTION CONTROL (NW9) ONLY

CHART P
PRESSURE SWITCH CIRCUIT FAILURE

CIRCUIT OPERATION

The pressure switch monitors primary brake system pressure. The normally closed switch opens when the brakes are applied (pressure exceeds 700 kPa [101 psi]). If the brakes are manually applied during traction control mode, the PMV pressure switch input, along with the brake switch input, signal the electronic brake control module (EBCM) to disable traction control and allow manual braking. The pressure switch is part of the pressure modulator valve (PMV) assembly and is not serviceable.

FAILURE CONDITIONS

Code 74 sets when the electronic brake control module (EBCM) detects an open or short to ground in the PMV pressure switch circuitry.

Possible Causes

- Open in CKT 853 or 1659.
- Short to ground in CKT 1659 with the brakes applied.
- Failed PMV pressure switch.

GC402920059800AX

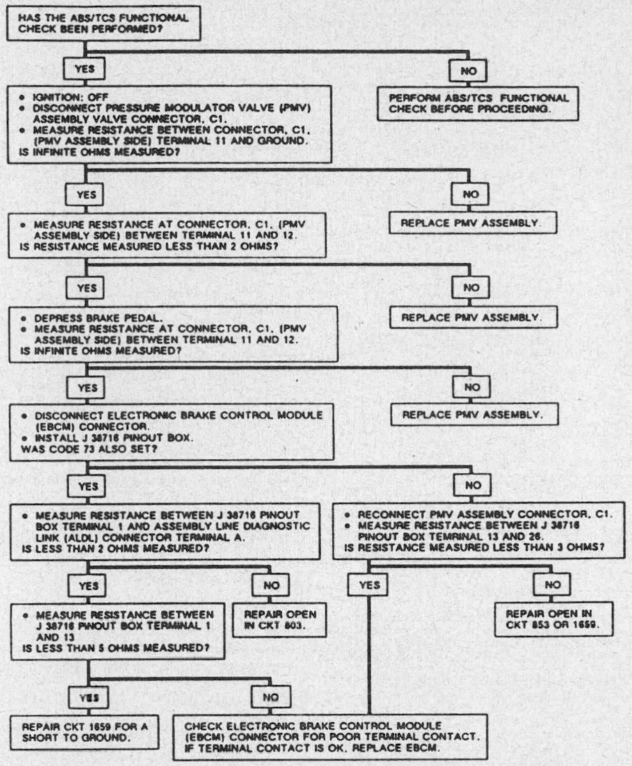
HAS THE ABS/TCS FUNCTIONAL CHECK BEEN PERFORMED?
YES
NO
PERFORM ABS/TCS FUNCTIONAL CHECK BEFORE PROCEEDING.
• IGNITION: OFF
• DISCONNECT PRESSURE MODULATOR VALVE (PMV) ASSEMBLY VALVE CONNECTOR, C1.
• MEASURE RESISTANCE BETWEEN CONNECTOR, C1, (PMV ASSEMBLY SIDE) TERMINAL 11 AND GROUND.
IS INFINITE OHMS MEASURED?
REPLACE PMV ASSEMBLY.
• MEASURE RESISTANCE AT CONNECTOR, C1, (PMV ASSEMBLY SIDE) BETWEEN TERMINAL 11 AND 12.
IS RESISTANCE MEASURED LESS THAN 2 OHMS?
• DEPRESS BRAKE PEDAL.
• MEASURE RESISTANCE AT CONNECTOR, C1, (PMV ASSEMBLY SIDE) BETWEEN TERMINAL 11 AND 12.
IS INFINITE OHMS MEASURED?
• DISCONNECT ELECTRONIC BRAKE CONTROL MODULE (EBCM) CONNECTOR.
• INSTALL J 38716 PINOUT BOX.
WAS CODE 73 ALSO SET?
• MEASURE RESISTANCE BETWEEN J 38716 PINOUT BOX TERMINAL 1 AND ASSEMBLY LINE DIAGNOSTIC LINK (ALDL) CONNECTOR TERMINAL A.
IS LESS THAN 2 OHMS MEASURED?
• RECONNECT PMV ASSEMBLY CONNECTOR, C1.
• MEASURE RESISTANCE BETWEEN J 38716 PINOUT BOX TERMINAL 13 AND 26.
IS RESISTANCE MEASURED LESS THAN 3 OHMS?
• MEASURE RESISTANCE BETWEEN J 38716 PINOUT BOX TERMINAL 1 AND 13
IS LESS THAN 5 OHMS MEASURED?
REPAIR OPEN IN CKT 803.
REPAIR OPEN IN CKT 853 OR 1659.
REPAIR CKT 1659 FOR A SHORT TO GROUND.
CHECK ELECTRONIC BRAKE CONTROL MODULE (EBCM) CONNECTOR FOR POOR TERMINAL CONTACT. IF TERMINAL CONTACT IS OK, REPLACE EBCM.

GC402920059800BX

Fig. 29 Test P: Pressure Switch Circuit Failure. 1992–93 Models Except 1993 LeSabre & Park Avenue

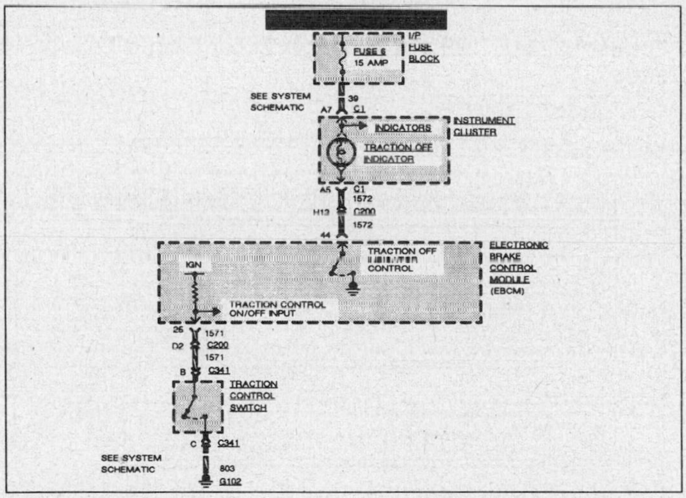
I/P FUSE BLOCK
FUSE 6 15 AMP
SEE SYSTEM SCHEMATIC
INSTRUMENT CLUSTER
INDICATORS
TRACTION OFF INDICATOR
1572
C200
ELECTRONIC BRAKE CONTROL MODULE (EBCM)
TRACTION OFF INDICATOR CONTROL
IGN
TRACTION CONTROL ON/OFF INPUT
1571
C341
TRACTION CONTROL SWITCH
803
G102

CIRCUIT OPERATION

When the ignition is first turned to "RUN," the electronic brake control module (EBCM) goes through a self-test. During this test, the EBCM grounds both the "ANTILOCK" and "TRACTION OFF" indicators for approximately 2 to 4 seconds. This acts as a bulb test for the indicators.

Traction Control Switch

Located in the console center trim plate, the switch allows the driver to select the traction control mode (on/off). When the traction control system is turned off, the "TRACTION OFF" indicator remains illuminated.

Transaxle Temperature Switch (with Traction Control)

The EBCM monitors transaxle temperature through the transaxle temperature switch. When the transaxle becomes hot, about 160°C (320°F), the normally closed switch opens signaling the EBCM to disable the traction control system and turn on the "TRACTION OFF" indicator. This allows the brakes and transaxle to cool down. As the transaxle cools to 149°C (300°F) the transaxle temperature switch closes.

The EBCM keeps the "TRACTION OFF" indicator on and the system disabled for an additional three to five minutes to allow for sufficient cooling.

When performing tests on this system, if the transaxle temperature switch is disconnected, and the ignition is turned to "RUN" the traction control system is disabled for three to five minutes.

FAILURE CONDITIONS

Possible Causes

- Open in CKT 803, 1571 or 1572.
- Open bulb.
- Faulty traction control switch.

Important

- When vehicle is equipped with traction control, any symptom which lights the "ANTILOCK" indicator also lights the "TRACTION OFF" indicator. Therefore, when both indicators are lit, follow "ANTILOCK" indicator diagnosis when no codes are set.

GC402910059900AX

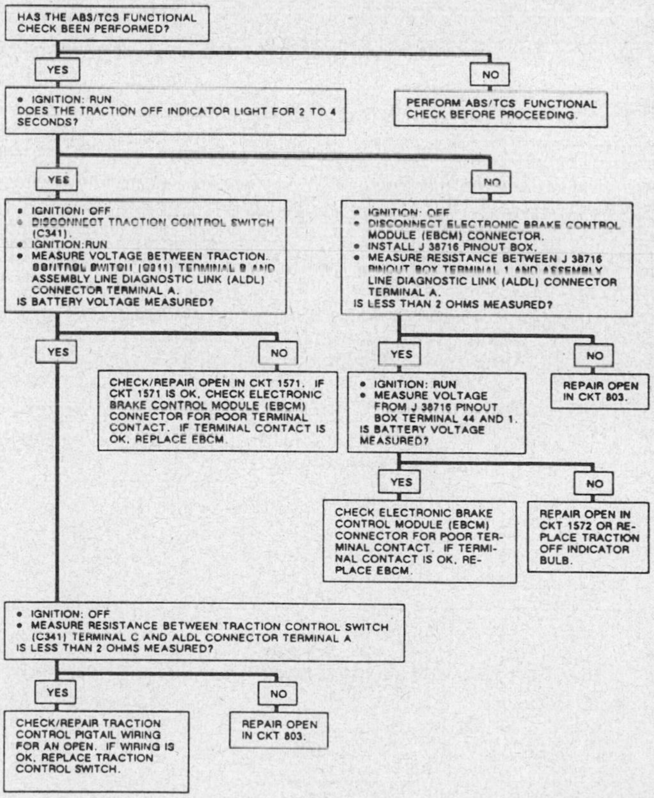
HAS THE ABS/TCS FUNCTIONAL CHECK BEEN PERFORMED?
YES
NO
PERFORM ABS/TCS FUNCTIONAL CHECK BEFORE PROCEEDING.
• IGNITION: RUN
DOES THE TRACTION OFF INDICATOR LIGHT FOR 2 TO 4 SECONDS?
• IGNITION: OFF
• DISCONNECT TRACTION CONTROL SWITCH (C341).
• IGNITION: RUN
• MEASURE VOLTAGE BETWEEN TRACTION CONTROL SWITCH (C341) TERMINAL B AND ASSEMBLY LINE DIAGNOSTIC LINK (ALDL) CONNECTOR TERMINAL A.
IS BATTERY VOLTAGE MEASURED?
• IGNITION: OFF
• DISCONNECT ELECTRONIC BRAKE CONTROL MODULE (EBCM) CONNECTOR.
• INSTALL J 38716 PINOUT BOX.
• MEASURE RESISTANCE BETWEEN J 38716 PINOUT BOX TERMINAL 1 AND ASSEMBLY LINE DIAGNOSTIC LINK (ALDL) CONNECTOR TERMINAL A.
IS LESS THAN 2 OHMS MEASURED?
CHECK/REPAIR OPEN IN CKT 1571. IF CKT 1571 IS OK, CHECK ELECTRONIC BRAKE CONTROL MODULE (EBCM) CONNECTOR FOR POOR TERMINAL CONTACT. IF TERMINAL CONTACT IS OK, REPLACE EBCM.
• IGNITION: RUN
• MEASURE VOLTAGE FROM J 38716 PINOUT BOX TERMINAL 44 AND 1.
IS BATTERY VOLTAGE MEASURED?
REPAIR OPEN IN CKT 803.
CHECK ELECTRONIC BRAKE CONTROL MODULE (EBCM) CONNECTOR FOR POOR TERMINAL CONTACT. IF TERMINAL CONTACT IS OK, REPLACE EBCM.
REPAIR OPEN IN CKT 1572 OR REPLACE TRACTION OFF INDICATOR BULB.
• IGNITION: OFF
• MEASURE RESISTANCE BETWEEN TRACTION CONTROL SWITCH (C341) TERMINAL C AND ALDL CONNECTOR TERMINAL A
IS LESS THAN 2 OHMS MEASURED?
CHECK/REPAIR TRACTION CONTROL PIGTAIL WIRING FOR AN OPEN. IF WIRING IS OK, REPLACE TRACTION CONTROL SWITCH.
REPAIR OPEN IN CKT 803.

GC402910059900BX

Fig. 30 Test Q: Traction Indicator Does Not Light. 1992–93 Models Except 1993 LeSabre & Park Avenue

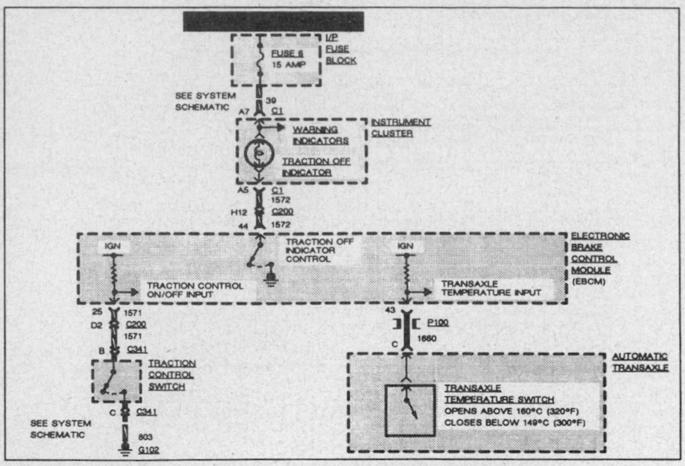
I/P FUSE BLOCK
FUSE 6 15 AMP
SEE SYSTEM SCHEMATIC
39
A7 C1
INSTRUMENT CLUSTER
WARNING INDICATORS
TRACTION OFF INDICATOR
A5 C1
1572
H12 C200
1572
44
ELECTRONIC BRAKE CONTROL MODULE (EBCM)
IGN
TRACTION OFF INDICATOR CONTROL
IGN
TRACTION CONTROL ON/OFF INPUT
TRANSAXLE TEMPERATURE INPUT
25 1571
D2 C200
1571
B C341
TRACTION CONTROL SWITCH
C C341
SEE SYSTEM SCHEMATIC
803
G102
43
P100
1660
C
AUTOMATIC TRANSAXLE
TRANSAXLE TEMPERATURE SWITCH
OPENS ABOVE 160°C (320°F)
CLOSES BELOW 149°C (300°F)

CIRCUIT OPERATION

When the ignition is first turned to "RUN," the electronic brake control module (EBCM) goes through a self-test. During this test, the EBCM grounds both the "ANTILOCK" and "TRACTION OFF" indicators for approximately 2 to 4 seconds. This acts as a bulb test for the indicators.

Traction Control Switch

Located in the console center trim plate, the switch allows the driver to select the traction control mode (on/off). When the traction control system is turned off, the "TRACTION OFF" indicator remains illuminated.

Transaxle Temperature Switch (with Traction Control)

The EBCM monitors transaxle temperature through the transaxle temperature switch. When the transaxle becomes hot, about 160°C (320°F), the normally closed switch opens signaling the EBCM to disable the traction control system and turn on the "TRACTION OFF" indicator. This allows the brakes and transaxle to cool down. As the transaxle cools to 149°C (300°F) the transaxle temperature switch closes. The EBCM keeps the "TRACTION OFF" indicator on and the system disabled for an additional three to five minutes to allow for sufficient cooling.

When performing tests on this system, if the transaxle temperature switch is disconnected, and the ignition is turned to "RUN" the traction control system is disabled for three to five minutes.

FAILURE CONDITIONS

Possible Causes

- Short to ground in CKT 1571 or 1572.
- Open in CKT 1660.
- Faulty traction control switch or transaxle temperature switch.

Important

- When vehicle is equipped with traction control, any symptom which lights the "ANTILOCK" indicator also lights the "TRACTION OFF" indicator. Therefore, when both indicators are lit, follow "ANTILOCK" indicator diagnosis when no codes are set.

GC402910060000AX

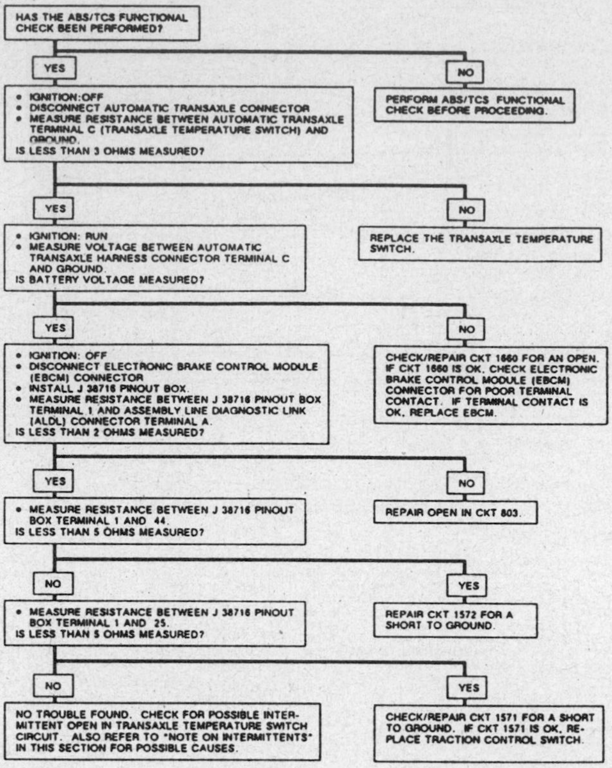
HAS THE ABS/TCS FUNCTIONAL CHECK BEEN PERFORMED?
YES
NO
PERFORM ABS/TCS FUNCTIONAL CHECK BEFORE PROCEEDING.
• IGNITION: OFF
• DISCONNECT AUTOMATIC TRANSAXLE CONNECTOR
• MEASURE RESISTANCE BETWEEN AUTOMATIC TRANSAXLE TERMINAL C (TRANSAXLE TEMPERATURE SWITCH) AND GROUND.
IS LESS THAN 3 OHMS MEASURED?
YES
NO
REPLACE THE TRANSAXLE TEMPERATURE SWITCH.
• IGNITION: RUN
• MEASURE VOLTAGE BETWEEN AUTOMATIC TRANSAXLE HARNESS CONNECTOR TERMINAL C AND GROUND.
IS BATTERY VOLTAGE MEASURED?
YES
NO
CHECK/REPAIR CKT 1660 FOR AN OPEN. IF CKT 1660 IS OK, CHECK ELECTRONIC BRAKE CONTROL MODULE (EBCM) CONNECTOR FOR POOR TERMINAL CONTACT. IF TERMINAL CONTACT IS OK, REPLACE EBCM.
• IGNITION: OFF
• DISCONNECT ELECTRONIC BRAKE CONTROL MODULE (EBCM) CONNECTOR
• INSTALL J 38716 PINOUT BOX.
• MEASURE RESISTANCE BETWEEN J 38716 PINOUT BOX TERMINAL 1 AND ASSEMBLY LINE DIAGNOSTIC LINK (ALDL) CONNECTOR TERMINAL A.
IS LESS THAN 2 OHMS MEASURED?
YES
NO
REPAIR OPEN IN CKT 803.
• MEASURE RESISTANCE BETWEEN J 38716 PINOUT BOX TERMINAL 1 AND 44.
IS LESS THAN 5 OHMS MEASURED?
NO
YES
REPAIR CKT 1572 FOR A SHORT TO GROUND.
• MEASURE RESISTANCE BETWEEN J 38716 PINOUT BOX TERMINAL 1 AND 25.
IS LESS THAN 5 OHMS MEASURED?
NO
YES
NO TROUBLE FOUND. CHECK FOR POSSIBLE INTERMITTENT OPEN IN TRANSAXLE TEMPERATURE SWITCH CIRCUIT. ALSO REFER TO "NOTE ON INTERMITTENTS" IN THIS SECTION FOR POSSIBLE CAUSES.
CHECK/REPAIR CKT 1571 FOR A SHORT TO GROUND. IF CKT 1571 IS OK, REPLACE TRACTION CONTROL SWITCH.

GC402910060000BX

Fig. 31 Test R: Traction Indicator Is On All The Time & No Codes Are Set. 1992–93 Models Except 1993 LeSabre & Park Avenue

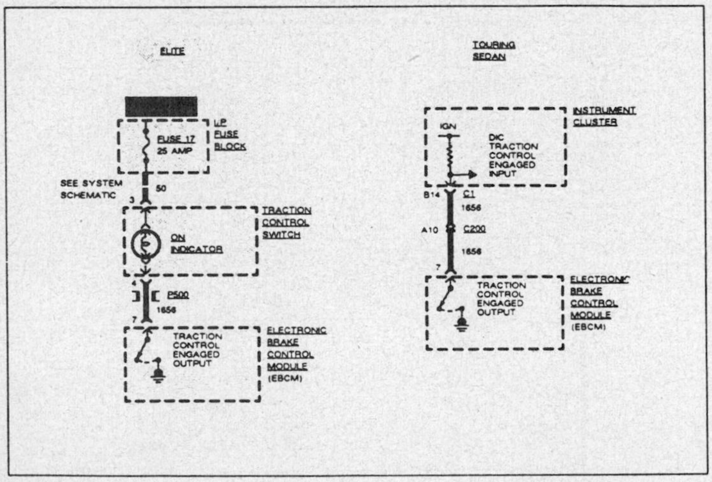
ELITE
I/P FUSE BLOCK
FUSE 17 25 AMP
SEE SYSTEM SCHEMATIC
3
50
TRACTION CONTROL SWITCH
ON INDICATOR
P500
1656
7
TRACTION CONTROL ENGAGED OUTPUT
ELECTRONIC BRAKE CONTROL MODULE (EBCM)
TOURING SEDAN
INSTRUMENT CLUSTER
IGN
DIC TRACTION CONTROL ENGAGED INPUT
B14 C1
1656
A10 C200
1656
7
TRACTION CONTROL ENGAGED OUTPUT
ELECTRONIC BRAKE CONTROL MODULE (EBCM)

CHART S
TRACTION ENGAGED MESSAGE/BULB DOES NOT OPERATE PROPERLY

CIRCUIT OPERATION

When the electronic brake control module (EBCM) is operating in the traction control mode, the EBCM's traction control engaged output (terminal 7) closes, grounding either the instrument cluster's DIC traction control engaged input (Touring Sedan) or the traction control switch LED (Elite). The EBCM grounds this terminal to alert the driver that the traction control system (TCS) is operating.

GC402920060100AX

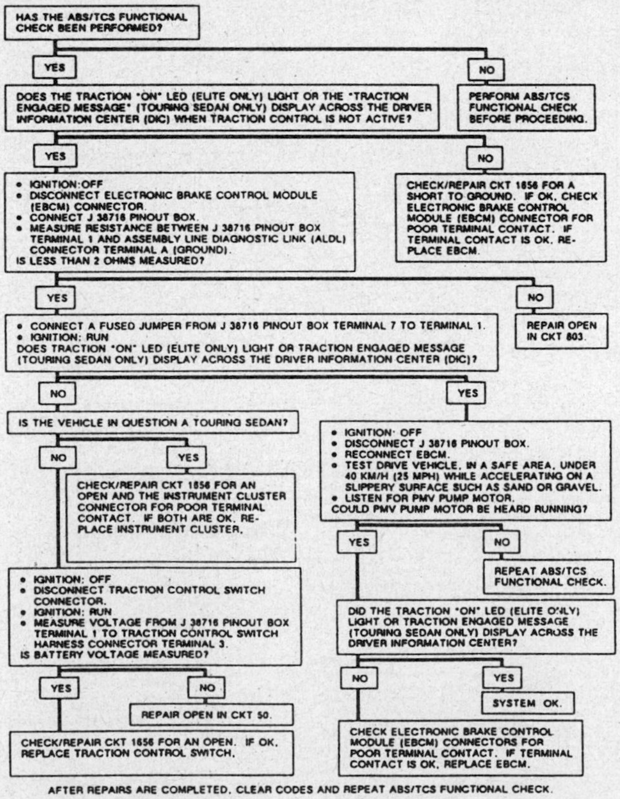
HAS THE ABS/TCS FUNCTIONAL CHECK BEEN PERFORMED?
YES
NO
PERFORM ABS/TCS FUNCTIONAL CHECK BEFORE PROCEEDING.
DOES THE TRACTION "ON" LED (ELITE ONLY) LIGHT OR THE "TRACTION ENGAGED MESSAGE" (TOURING SEDAN ONLY) DISPLAY ACROSS THE DRIVER INFORMATION CENTER (DIC) WHEN TRACTION CONTROL IS NOT ACTIVE?
YES
NO
CHECK/REPAIR CKT 1656 FOR A SHORT TO GROUND. IF OK, CHECK ELECTRONIC BRAKE CONTROL MODULE (EBCM) CONNECTOR FOR POOR TERMINAL CONTACT. IF TERMINAL CONTACT IS OK, REPLACE EBCM.
• IGNITION: OFF
• DISCONNECT ELECTRONIC BRAKE CONTROL MODULE (EBCM) CONNECTOR.
• CONNECT J 38716 PINOUT BOX.
• MEASURE RESISTANCE BETWEEN J 38716 PINOUT BOX TERMINAL 1 AND ASSEMBLY LINE DIAGNOSTIC LINK (ALDL) CONNECTOR TERMINAL A (GROUND).
IS LESS THAN 2 OHMS MEASURED?
YES
NO
REPAIR OPEN IN CKT 803.
• CONNECT A FUSED JUMPER FROM J 38716 PINOUT BOX TERMINAL 7 TO TERMINAL 1.
• IGNITION: RUN
DOES TRACTION "ON" LED (ELITE ONLY) LIGHT OR TRACTION ENGAGED MESSAGE (TOURING SEDAN ONLY) DISPLAY ACROSS THE DRIVER INFORMATION CENTER (DIC)?
NO
YES
IS THE VEHICLE IN QUESTION A TOURING SEDAN?
NO
YES
CHECK/REPAIR CKT 1656 FOR AN OPEN AND THE INSTRUMENT CLUSTER CONNECTOR FOR POOR TERMINAL CONTACT. IF BOTH ARE OK, REPLACE INSTRUMENT CLUSTER.
• IGNITION: OFF
• DISCONNECT J 38716 PINOUT BOX.
• RECONNECT EBCM.
• TEST DRIVE VEHICLE, IN A SAFE AREA, UNDER 40 KM/H (25 MPH) WHILE ACCELERATING ON A SLIPPERY SURFACE SUCH AS SAND OR GRAVEL.
• LISTEN FOR PMV PUMP MOTOR.
COULD PMV PUMP MOTOR BE HEARD RUNNING?
YES
NO
REPEAT ABS/TCS FUNCTIONAL CHECK.
• IGNITION: OFF
• DISCONNECT TRACTION CONTROL SWITCH CONNECTOR.
• IGNITION: RUN
• MEASURE VOLTAGE FROM J 38716 PINOUT BOX TERMINAL 1 TO TRACTION CONTROL SWITCH HARNESS CONNECTOR TERMINAL 3.
IS BATTERY VOLTAGE MEASURED?
YES
NO
REPAIR OPEN IN CKT 50.
CHECK/REPAIR CKT 1656 FOR AN OPEN. IF OK, REPLACE TRACTION CONTROL SWITCH.
DID THE TRACTION "ON" LED (ELITE ONLY) LIGHT OR TRACTION ENGAGED MESSAGE (TOURING SEDAN ONLY) DISPLAY ACROSS THE DRIVER INFORMATION CENTER?
NO
YES
SYSTEM OK.
CHECK ELECTRONIC BRAKE CONTROL MODULE (EBCM) CONNECTORS FOR POOR TERMINAL CONTACT. IF TERMINAL CONTACT IS OK, REPLACE EBCM.
AFTER REPAIRS ARE COMPLETED, CLEAR CODES AND REPEAT ABS/TCS FUNCTIONAL CHECK.

GC402920060100BX

Fig. 32 Test S: Traction Control Engaged Message Does Not Operate. 1992 98 & Park Ave.

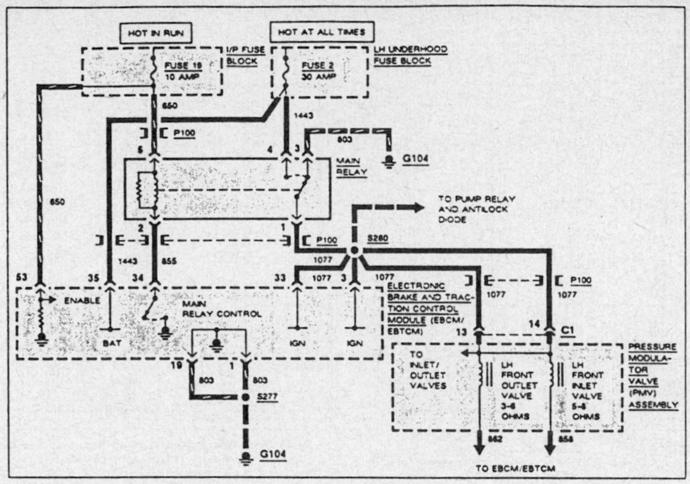
HOT IN RUN
HOT AT ALL TIMES
I/P FUSE BLOCK
FUSE 18 10 AMP
FUSE 2 30 AMP
LH UNDERHOOD FUSE BLOCK
MAIN RELAY
G104
TO PUMP RELAY AND ANTILOCK DIODE
S280
P100
ENABLE
MAIN RELAY CONTROL
BAT
IGN
ELECTRONIC BRAKE AND TRACTION CONTROL MODULE (EBCM/EBTCM)
C1
TO INLET/OUTLET VALVES
LH FRONT OUTLET VALVE 3-6 OHMS
LH FRONT INLET VALVE 5-8 OHMS
PRESSURE MODULATOR VALVE (PMV) ASSEMBLY
S277
TO EBCM/EBTCM

OPERATION:

When the ignition switch is first turned to RUN, EBCM/EBTCM goes through a self-check lasting 2–4 seconds. During this test, the EBCM/EBTCM grounds terminal 34, energizing the main relay. Once the self-check is completed, the main relay remains energized and delivers battery voltage to both the EBCM/EBTCM and the pressure modulator valve (PMV) assembly during vehicle operation. The constant voltage supply allows the vehicle to enter ABS mode without delay. The main relay is de-energized whenever the amber ANTILOCK indicator lights due to a system fault, causing the ABS system to shut down.

DTC 45 sets when the ignition switch is at run and battery voltage is detected at neither the PMV assembly nor EBCM/EBTCM terminals 20, 3 and/or 33. DTC 45 also sets when the EBCM/EBTCM detects an open or a short to ground in the LH inlet valve circuit.

POSSIBLE CAUSES:

- Open CKT 650, 855, 858, 1077 or 1443.
- Short to ground in CKT 858, 1077 or 1443.
- Main relay fails "open."

GC4029300619010X

Fig. 33 Test 1: Main Relay, EBCM/EBTCM & Pressure Modulator Valve (Part 1 of 3). 1993–94 LeSabre & Park Avenue

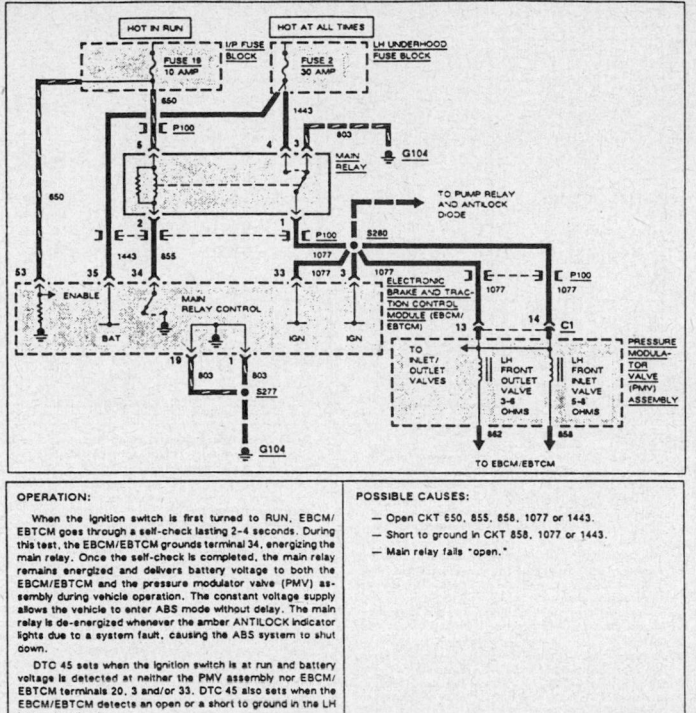

A: MAIN RELAY POWER TEST

- Make sure "ABS/TCS Functional Check" is performed before proceeding.
- Ignition switch: OFF
- Main relay: disconnected

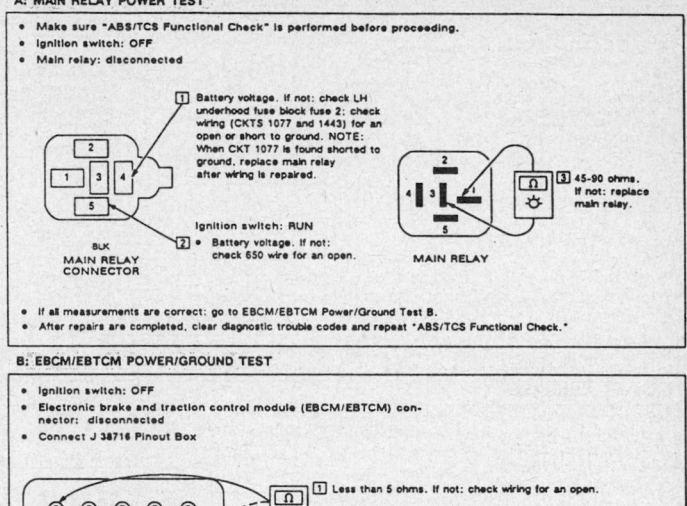

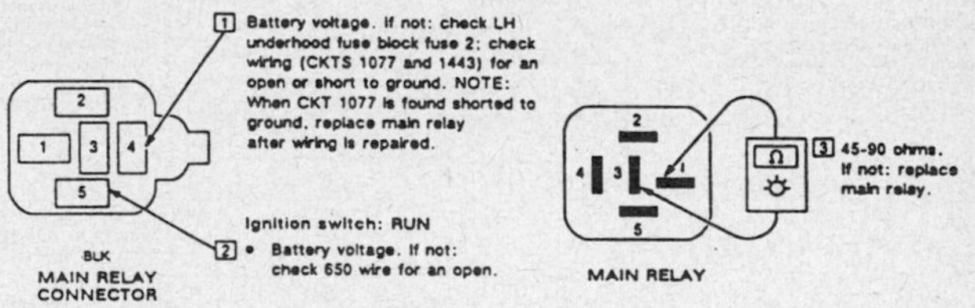
1 Battery voltage. If not: check LH underhood fuse block fuse 2; check wiring (CKTS 1077 and 1443) for an open or short to ground. NOTE: When CKT 1077 is found shorted to ground, replace main relay after wiring is repaired.
Ignition switch: RUN
2 • Battery voltage. If not: check 650 wire for an open.
BLK
MAIN RELAY CONNECTOR
MAIN RELAY
3 45-90 ohms. If not: replace main relay.

- If all measurements are correct: go to EBCM/EBTCM Power/Ground Test B.
- After repairs are completed, clear diagnostic trouble codes and repeat "ABS/TCS Functional Check."

B: EBCM/EBTCM POWER/GROUND TEST

- Ignition switch: OFF
- Electronic brake and traction control module (EBCM/EBTCM) connector: disconnected
- Connect J 38716 Pinout Box

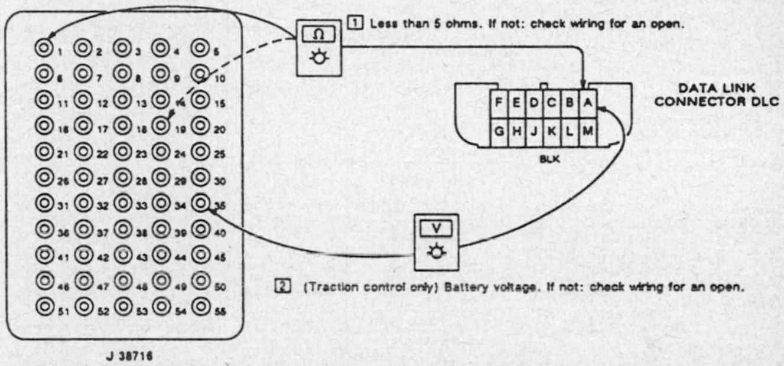
1 Less than 5 ohms. If not: check wiring for an open.
DATA LINK CONNECTOR DLC
BLK
2 (Traction control only) Battery voltage. If not: check wiring for an open.
J 38716

- If all measurements are correct: go to EBCM/EBTCM Power/Ground Test B1.

GC4029300619020X

Fig. 33 Test 1: Main Relay, EBCM/EBTCM & Pressure Modulator Valve (Part 2 of 3). 1993–94 LeSabre & Park Avenue

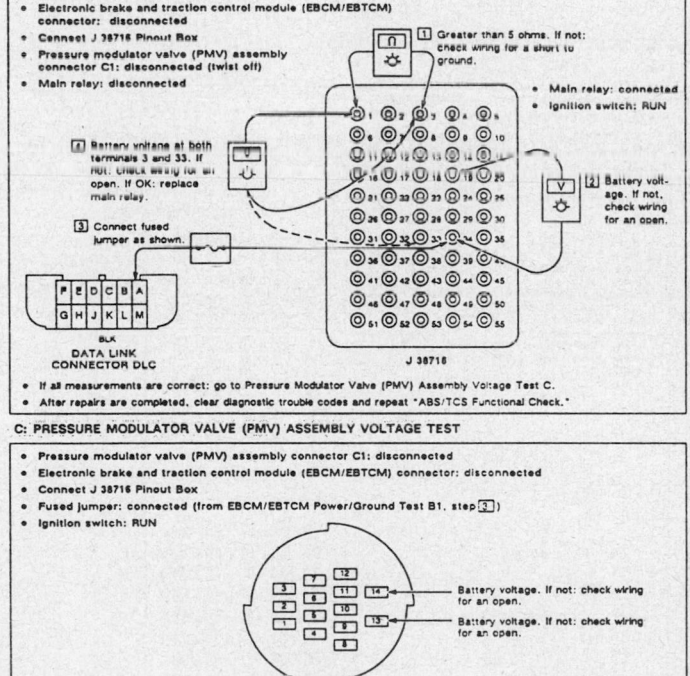

B1: EBCM/EBTCM POWER/GROUND TEST

- Ignition switch: OFF
- Electronic brake and traction control module (EBCM/EBTCM) connector: disconnected
- Connect J 38716 Pinout Box
- Pressure modulator valve (PMV) assembly connector C1: disconnected (twist off)
- Main relay: disconnected

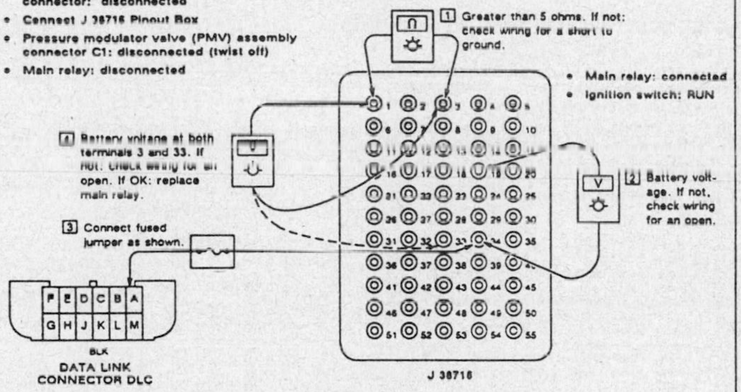
1 Greater than 5 ohms. If not: check wiring for a short to ground.
• Main relay: connected
• Ignition switch: RUN
4 Battery voltage at both terminals 3 and 33. If not: check wiring for an open. If OK: replace main relay.
2 Battery voltage. If not, check wiring for an open.
3 Connect fused jumper as shown.
BLK
DATA LINK CONNECTOR DLC
J 38716

- If all measurements are correct: go to Pressure Modulator Valve (PMV) Assembly Voltage Test C.
- After repairs are completed, clear diagnostic trouble codes and repeat "ABS/TCS Functional Check."

C: PRESSURE MODULATOR VALVE (PMV) ASSEMBLY VOLTAGE TEST

- Pressure modulator valve (PMV) assembly connector C1: disconnected
- Electronic brake and traction control module (EBCM/EBTCM) connector: disconnected
- Connect J 38716 Pinout Box
- Fused jumper: connected (from EBCM/EBTCM Power/Ground Test B1, step 3)
- Ignition switch: RUN

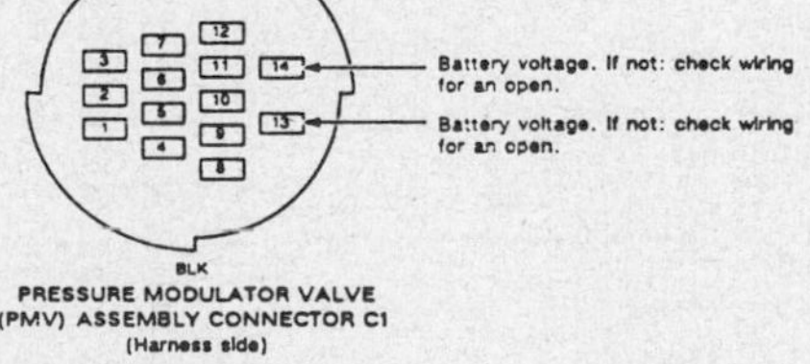
Battery voltage. If not: check wiring for an open.
Battery voltage. If not: check wiring for an open.
BLK
PRESSURE MODULATOR VALVE (PMV) ASSEMBLY CONNECTOR C1
(Harness side)

- If both measurements are correct: remove fused jumper and go to Pressure Modulator Valve (PMV) Assembly Continuity Test D.
- After repairs are completed, clear diagnostic trouble codes and repeat "ABS/TCS Functional Check."

GC4029300619030X

Fig. 33 Test 1: Main Relay, EBCM/EBTCM & Pressure Modulator Valve (Part 3 of 3). 1993–94 LeSabre & Park Avenue

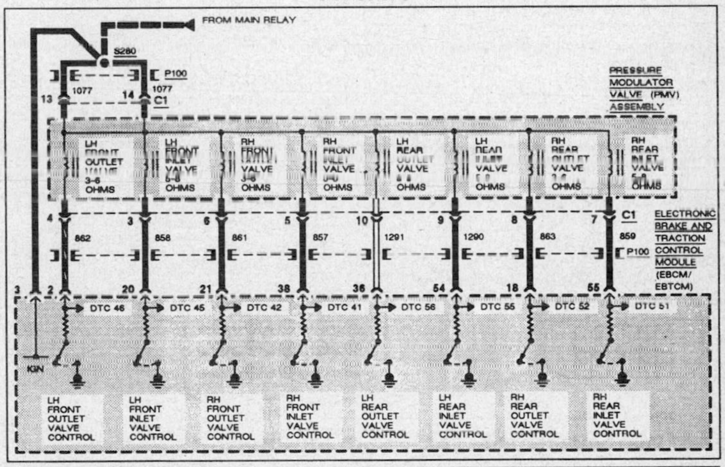
FROM MAIN RELAY
S280
P100
C1
PRESSURE MODULATOR VALVE (PMV) ASSEMBLY
ELECTRONIC BRAKE AND TRACTION CONTROL MODULE (EBCM/EBTCM)
DTC 46
DTC 45
DTC 42
DTC 41
DTC 56
DTC 55
DTC 52
DTC 51
IGN
LH FRONT OUTLET VALVE CONTROL
LH FRONT INLET VALVE CONTROL
RH FRONT OUTLET VALVE CONTROL
RH FRONT INLET VALVE CONTROL
LH REAR OUTLET VALVE CONTROL
LH REAR INLET VALVE CONTROL
RH REAR OUTLET VALVE CONTROL
RH REAR INLET VALVE CONTROL

OPERATION:

INLET/OUTLET VALVES

- Voltage is applied to the normally open inlet valves whenever the main relay is energized. An inlet valve closes when the EBCM/EBTCM supplies a ground path at the inlet valve control terminal. The EBCM/EBTCM closes an inlet valve for short periods to maintain (hold) or reduce pressure at a particular wheel.
- The normally closed outlet valves operate similarly to the inlet valves, except that when the EBCM/EBTCM grounds an outlet valve, the valve opens instead of closes. The EBCM/EBTCM opens an outlet valve for short periods to reduce pressure at a particular wheel.

VALVE MODES

- The pressure increase position is the operating valve position for normal (non-ABS) braking and traction control mode (when equipped). The EBCM/EBTCM does not energize either valve, leaving the inlet valve open and the outlet valve closed.
- The pressure hold position occurs when the EBCM/EBTCM first notices an abnormal hydraulic pressure increase. This signifies an impending wheel lockup condition. The EBCM/EBTCM closes the corresponding inlet valve to avoid any additional hydraulic pressure increase (avoiding an ABS braking condition).
- During a wheel lockup condition, the EBCM/EBTCM closes the inlet valve while pulsing open the outlet valve. This decreases hydraulic pressure at a specific wheel without decreasing overall system pressure. The reduced hydraulic pressure allows greater wheel spin, eliminating the wheel lockup condition.
- DTC 41, 42, 45, 46, 51, 52, 55, or 56 sets when the (EBCM/EBTCM) detects an open or short to ground in the respective inlet or outlet valve circuit.

POSSIBLE CAUSES:

- Open in CKT 857, 858, 859, 861, 862, 863, 1290 or 1291.
- Short to ground in CKT 857, 858, 859, 861, 862, 863, 1290 or 1291.

GC4029300620010X

Fig. 34 Test 2: Pressure Modulator & Valve Control (Part 1 of 2). 1993–94 LeSabre & Park Avenue

D: PRESSURE MODULATOR VALVE (PMV) ASSEMBLY CONTINUITY TEST

- Make sure "ABS/TCS Functional Check" is performed before proceeding.
- Ignition switch: OFF
- Pressure modulator valve (PMV) assembly connector C1: disconnected

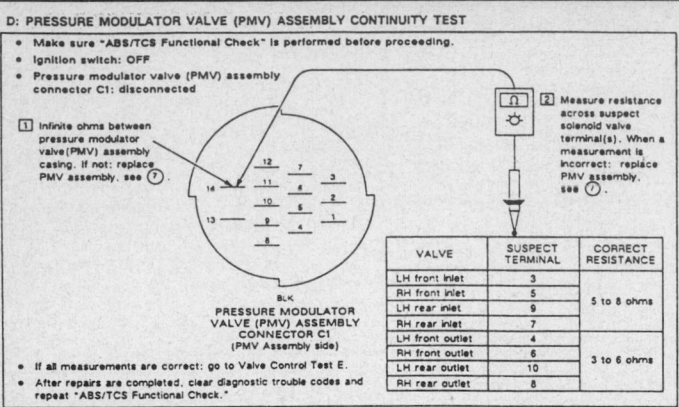

[1] Infinite ohms between pressure modulator valve (PMV) assembly casing. If not: replace PMV assembly, see (7).

[2] Measure resistance across suspect solenoid valve terminal(s). When a measurement is incorrect: replace PMV assembly, see (7).

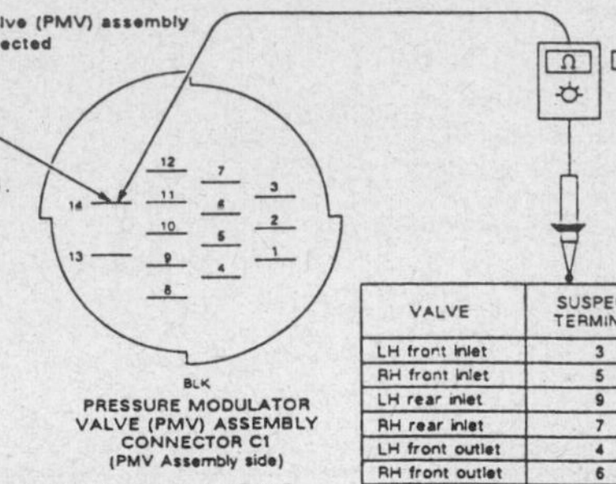

12
7
14
11
6
3
10
5
2
13
9
4
1
8
BLK
PRESSURE MODULATOR
VALVE (PMV) ASSEMBLY
CONNECTOR C1
(PMV Assembly side)

VALVE	SUSPECT TERMINAL	CORRECT RESISTANCE
LH front inlet	3	5 to 8 ohms
RH front inlet	5	
LH rear inlet	9	
RH rear inlet	7	
LH front outlet	4	3 to 6 ohms
RH front outlet	6	
LH rear outlet	10	
RH rear outlet	8	

- If all measurements are correct: go to Valve Control Test E.
- After repairs are completed, clear diagnostic trouble codes and repeat "ABS/TCS Functional Check."

E: VALVE CONTROL TEST

- Ignition switch: OFF
- Pressure modulator valve (PMV) assembly connector C1: connected
- (EBCM/EBTCM) connector: disconnected
- Connect J 38716 Pinout Box
- Main relay: disconnected

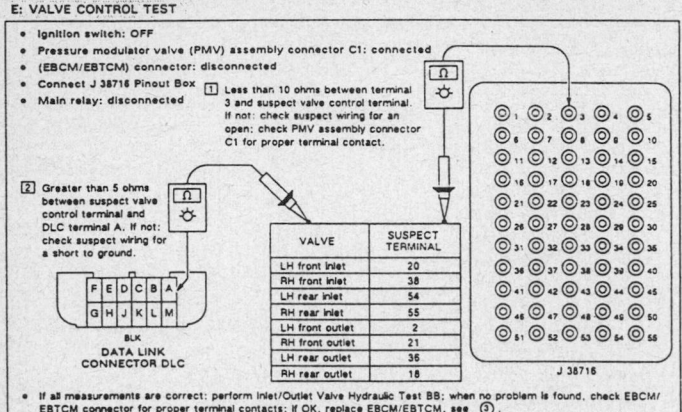

[1] Less than 10 ohms between terminal 3 and suspect valve control terminal. If not: check suspect wiring for an open; check PMV assembly connector C1 for proper terminal contact.

[2] Greater than 5 ohms between suspect valve control terminal and DLC terminal A. If not: check suspect wiring for a short to ground.

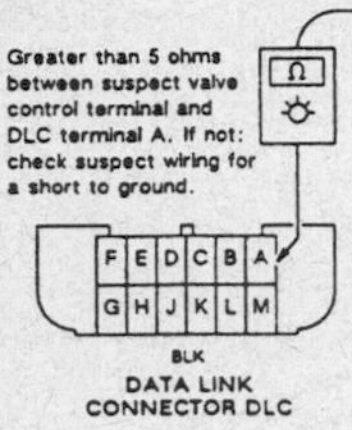

F E D C B A
G H J K L M
BLK
DATA LINK
CONNECTOR DLC

VALVE	SUSPECT TERMINAL
LH front inlet	20
RH front inlet	38
LH rear inlet	54
RH rear inlet	55
LH front outlet	2
RH front outlet	21
LH rear outlet	36
RH rear outlet	18

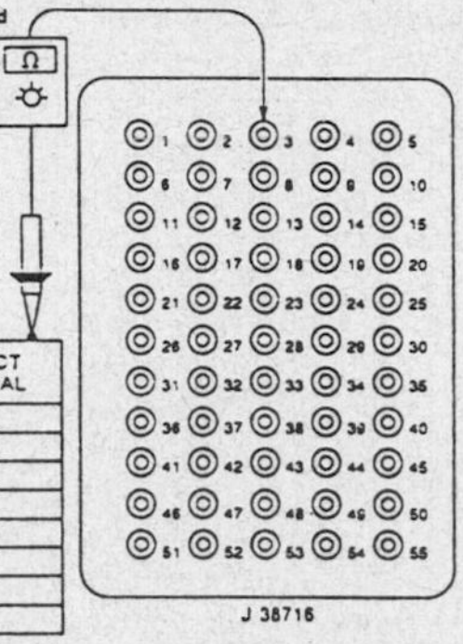

J 38716

- If all measurements are correct: perform Inlet/Outlet Valve Hydraulic Test BB; when no problem is found, check EBCM/EBTCM connector for proper terminal contacts: If OK, replace EBCM/EBTCM, see (3).
- After repairs are completed, clear diagnostic trouble codes and repeat "ABS/TCS Functional Check."

GC4029300620020X

Fig. 34 Test 2: Pressure Modulator & Valve Control (Part 2 of 2). 1993–94 LeSabre & Park Avenue

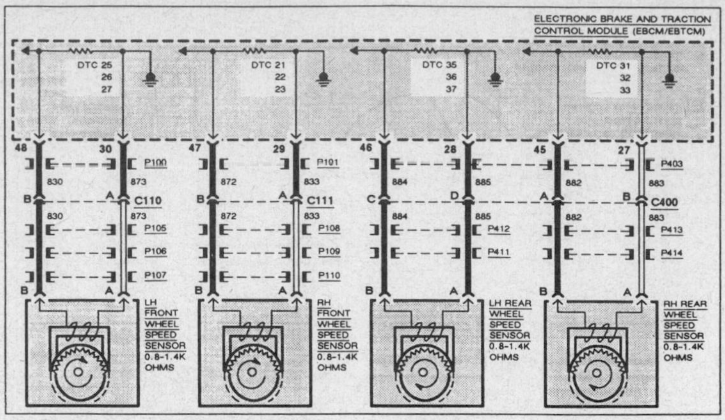

ELECTRONIC BRAKE AND TRACTION CONTROL MODULE (EBCM/EBTCM)
DTC 25
26
27
DTC 21
22
23
DTC 35
36
37
DTC 31
32
33
48
30
47
29
46
28
45
27
P100
P101
P403
830
873
872
833
884
885
882
883
C110
C111
C400
P105
P108
P412
P413
P106
P109
P411
P414
P107
P110
LH FRONT WHEEL SPEED SENSOR 0.8-1.4K OHMS
RH FRONT WHEEL SPEED SENSOR 0.8-1.4K OHMS
LH REAR WHEEL SPEED SENSOR 0.8-1.4K OHMS
RH REAR WHEEL SPEED SENSOR 0.8-1.4K OHMS

OPERATION:

- When each wheel turns, the wheel speed sensor creates a small AC voltage with a frequency proportional to wheel speed. This magnetically induced voltage is caused by a toothed sensor ring passing the wheel speed sensor's stationary pickup coil. The toothed sensor ring is mounted on the drive axle in the front, and the hub/bearing assembly in the rear.
- The EBCM/EBTCM uses the wheel speed sensor signal to calculate vehicle reference speeds, and individual wheel speed, acceleration and slip values. These values are used to determine when antilock control is required. Vehicles equipped with traction control also use front wheel speed sensor signals to determine when traction control is required.
- To prevent electromagnetic interference from disturbing the wheel speed sensor signal, the cables from the EBCM/EBTCM to each wheel speed sensor are twisted in pairs a minimum of 6 to 9 turns per foot . When servicing the sensor cables, it is important to maintain the original cables' twists (6 to 9 turns per foot).
- DTC 22, 26, 32,or 36 sets when the EBCM/EBTCM determines that a wheel speed signal is erratic. A wheel speed signal indicating that a wheel is accelerating or decelerating faster than physically possible is an example of an erratic signal. An intermittent open or short to ground in a wheel speed sensor could also cause the EBCM/EBTCM to set a diagnostic trouble code. DTC 22, 26, 32 or 36 also sets when the EBCM/EBTCM detects electromagnetic interference (noise) in a wheel speed sensor signal. Possible interference sources include accessory motors, wiper motors and ignition circuits.
- DTC 23, 27, 33 or 37 sets when the EBCM/EBTCM does not see any wheel speed sensor signal, but determines that continuity exists in the circuit. This is caused by a dislodged wheel speed sensor, missing toothed sensor ring (front) or defective hub and bearing assembly (rear).
- Any condition which would result in lack of continuity in a wheel speed sensor circuit could result in DTC 21 or 25 (front) or 31 or 35 (rear) being set. These conditions include an open, a short to ground, or a short between the two wheel speed sensor circuits in the wiring harness between the speed sensor and EBCM/EBTCM. Also, an open or short to ground across the wheel speed sensor coil could trigger this diagnostic trouble code.

POSSIBLE CAUSES:

— Faulty or dislodged wheel speed sensor.
— Missing or irregular toothed sensor ring.
— Open or short to ground in wheel speed sensor circuit.
— Short between wheel speed sensor circuits.
— Erratic wheel speed signal.
— Defective hub and bearing assembly.
— Intermittent open or short to ground in wheel speed sensor circuit.
— Noise interference in wheel speed sensor signal.
— Improperly twisted sensor cable.

GC4029300621010X

Fig. 35 Test 3: Wheel Speed Circuit (Part 1 of 4). 1993–94 LeSabre & Park Avenue

F: WHEEL SPEED SENSOR CONTINUITY TEST

- Make sure "ABS/TCS Functional Check" is performed before proceeding.
- Raise vehicle
- Ignition switch: RUN
- Gear selector lever: NEUTRAL
- Ignition switch: OFF
- Park brake: released
- Make measurements at suspect wheel speed sensor (connector disconnected).

[1] 800-1500 ohms. If not: replace suspect wheel speed sensor.
- Rear wheel speed sensor, see (12).
- Front wheel speed sensor, see (10).

[2] Greater than 5 ohms. If not: replace suspect wheel speed sensor.
- Rear wheel speed sensor, see (12).
- Front wheel speed sensor, see (10).

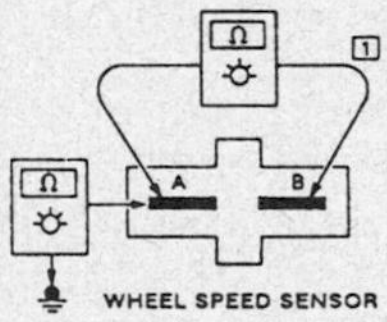

A
B
WHEEL SPEED SENSOR

- If all measurements are correct: go to EBCM/EBTCM/Wheel Speed Circuit Input Test H.
- After repairs are completed, clear diagnostic trouble codes and repeat "ABS/TCS Functional Check."

G: WHEEL SPEED SENSOR OUTPUT TEST

- Raise vehicle
- Ignition switch: RUN
- Gear selector lever: NEUTRAL
- Ignition switch: OFF
- Park brake: released
- Make measurements at suspect wheel speed sensor (connector disconnected).

[1] 50-900 mvAC while turning wheel by hand.
If measurement is incorrect: replace suspect wheel speed sensor.
- Rear wheel speed sensors, see (12).
- Front wheel speed sensors, see (10).

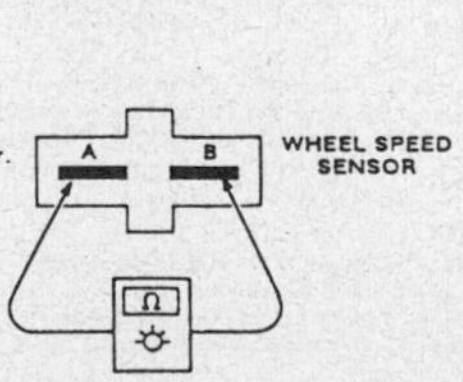

A
B
WHEEL SPEED
SENSOR

- If all measurements are correct: check EBCM/EBTCM connector for proper terminal contact: If OK, replace EBCM/EBTCM, see (3).
- After repairs are completed, clear diagnostic trouble codes and repeat "ABS/TCS Functional Check."

GC4029300621020X

Fig. 35 Test 3: Wheel Speed Circuit (Part 2 of 4). 1993–94 LeSabre & Park Avenue

H: EBCM/EBTCM/WHEEL SPEED CIRCUIT INPUT TEST

- Ignition switch: OFF
- Suspect wheel speed sensor connector: connected
- EBCM/EBTCM connector: disconnected
- Connect J 38716 Pinout Box
- Do steps [1] and [2] at suspect wheel speed sensor terminals
- Example shown is for LH rear wheel speed circuit; other wheels similar.

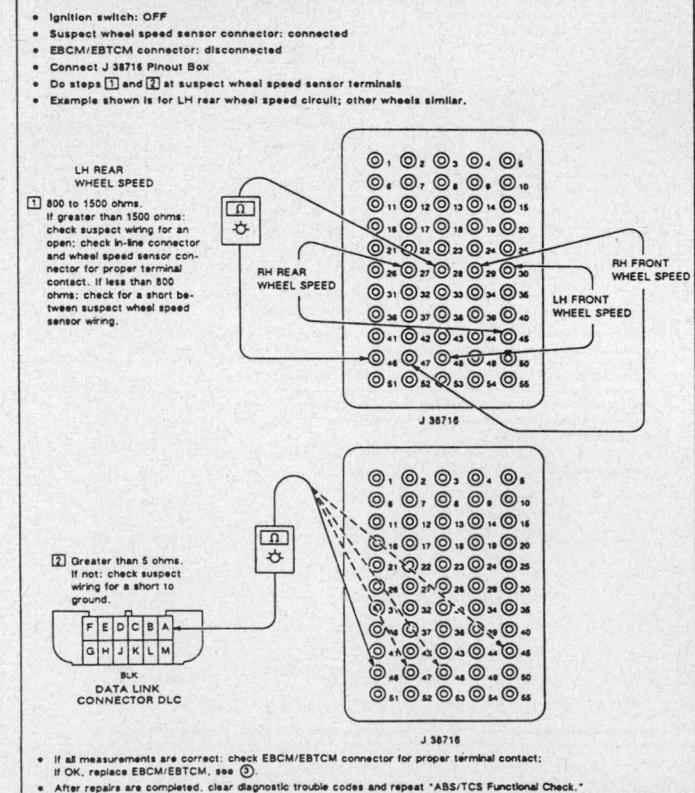

LH REAR WHEEL SPEED

[1] 800 to 1500 ohms.
If greater than 1500 ohms: check suspect wiring for an open; check in-line connector and wheel speed sensor connector for proper terminal contact. If less than 800 ohms: check for a short between suspect wheel speed sensor wiring.

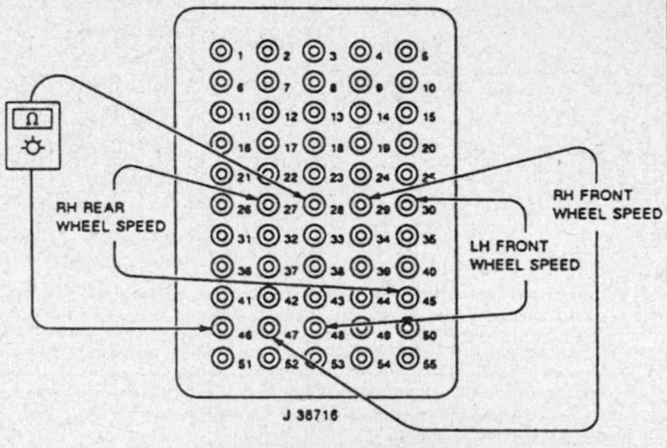

RH REAR
WHEEL SPEED
RH FRONT
WHEEL SPEED
LH FRONT
WHEEL SPEED
J 38716

[2] Greater than 5 ohms.
If not: check suspect wiring for a short to ground.

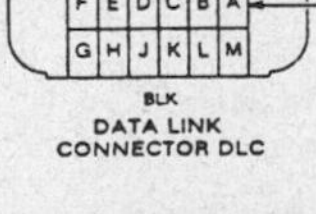

F E D C B A
G H J K L M
BLK
DATA LINK
CONNECTOR DLC

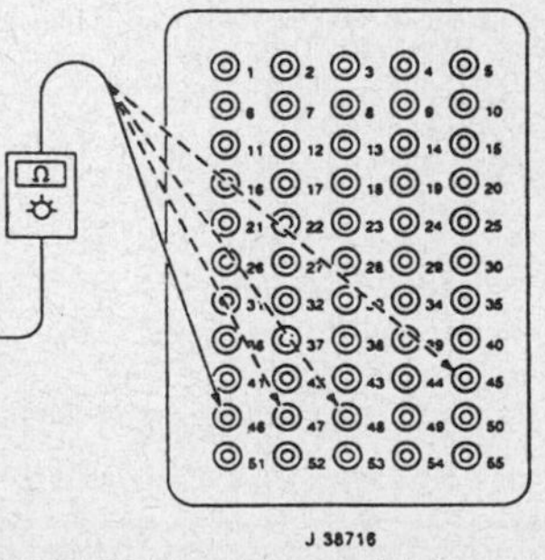

J 38716

- If all measurements are correct: check EBCM/EBTCM connector for proper terminal contact; If OK, replace EBCM/EBTCM, see (3).
- After repairs are completed, clear diagnostic trouble codes and repeat "ABS/TCS Functional Check."

GC4029300621030X

Fig. 35 Test 3: Wheel Speed Circuit (Part 3 of 4). 1993–94 LeSabre & Park Avenue

I: WHEEL SPEED SIGNAL ERRATIC OR NOISY TEST

- Make sure "ABS/TCS Functional Check" is performed before proceeding.

Is DTC 23, DTC 27, DTC 33 or DTC 37 set?

YES → When DTC 23 or DTC 27:
Reinstall dislodged wheel speed sensor or replace missing toothed sensor ring.

When DTC 33 or DTC 37:
Reinstall dislodged wheel speed sensor or replace hub and bearing assembly.

NO → **Is DTC 22, DTC 26, DTC 32 or DTC 36 set?**

YES →
- CHECK FOLLOWING AND REPAIR/REPLACE AS NECESSARY, BUT BE AWARE THAT PROBLEM CAUSING DTC TO SET MAY BE INTERMITTENT AND IS USUALLY NOT CAUSED BY A DEFECTIVE EBCM/EBTCM:

  Test drive vehicle while monitoring suspect wheel speed sensor using bi-directional scan tool snapshot capability.

  Disconnect suspect wheel speed sensor connector and applicable in-line connector and inspect terminal contacts on sensor and connector for corrosion or deformity.

  Trace harness routing of suspect sensor wiring. Inspect for physical damage, particularly in areas where pinching or movement by harness or other component occurs.

  Trace harness routing of suspect sensor wiring for proximity to noise sources such as ignition circuits, motors, etc.

  Check if any repairs were recently made to suspect sensor wiring. Sensor wiring should be twisted 6 to 9 turns per foot.

  Check for toothed sensor ring irregularity, loose sensor mounting, or debris lodged between the toothed sensor ring and the wheel speed sensor.

NO →
- Thoroughly wet area surrounding all wheel speed sensors (all connectors connected).
- Test drive vehicle at slow speeds (under 16 km/h [10 mph]) while monitoring wheel speed sensors using bi-directional scan tool snapshot capability (Note: suspect wheel speed signal usually varies from remaining wheel speed signals by approximately 2 km/h [1 mph]).

  Does any one wheel speed signal vary from other three wheel speed signals?

  NO →
  - System OK.
  - Problem may be intermittent. If an intermittent is suspected, continue diagnosis.

  YES →
  - CHECK FOLLOWING AND REPAIR/REPLACE AS NECESSARY:
    Disconnect suspect wheel speed sensor connector and applicable in-line connector. Inspect terminal contacts on sensor and connectors for corrosion or deformity. Check connectors for proper terminal contact.
    Trace harness routing of suspect sensor wiring. Inspect for physical damage, particularly in areas where pinching or movement by harness or other component occurs.
  - If all above checks are OK, replace suspect wheel speed sensor, see (10) (front) or (12) (rear).

- If all checks and measurements are correct: go to Wheel Speed Sensor Output Test Q.
- After repairs are completed, clear diagnostic trouble codes and repeat "ABS/TCS Functional Check."

GC4029300621040X

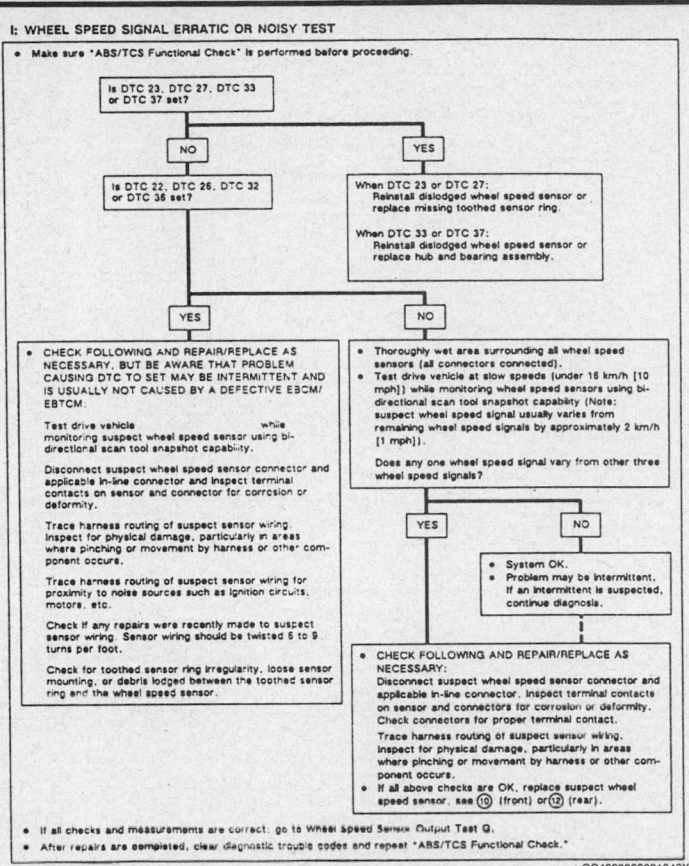

Fig. 35 Test 3: Wheel Speed Circuit (Part 4 of 4). 1993–94 LeSabre & Park Avenue

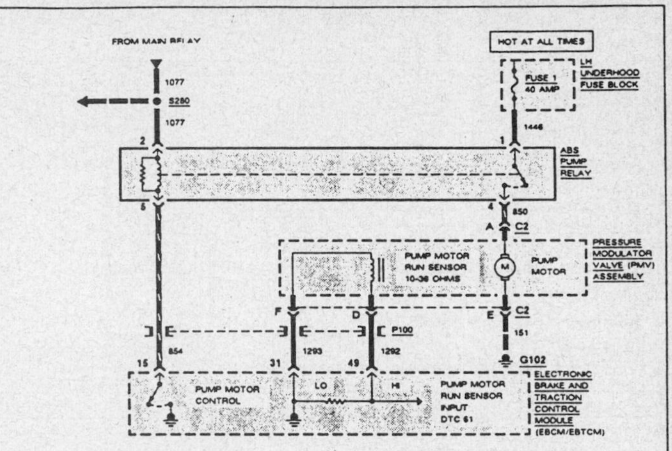
FROM MAIN RELAY
1077
S280
1077
2
5
HOT AT ALL TIMES
FUSE 1
40 AMP
LH
UNDERHOOD
FUSE BLOCK
1446
1
ABS
PUMP
RELAY
4
850
A
C2
PUMP MOTOR
RUN SENSOR
10-36 OHMS
M
PUMP
MOTOR
PRESSURE
MODULATOR
VALVE (PMV)
ASSEMBLY
F
D
E
C2
P100
151
854
1293
1292
G102
15
31
49
PUMP MOTOR
CONTROL
LO
HI
PUMP MOTOR
RUN SENSOR
INPUT
DTC 61
ELECTRONIC
BRAKE AND
TRACTION
CONTROL
MODULE
(EBCM/EBTCM)

OPERATION:
- When EBCM/EBTCM grounds terminal 15, the ABS pump relay is energized. The pump relay contacts close, applying voltage to the pressure modulator valve (PMV) assembly's pump motor. The EBCM/EBTCM turns on the pump motor during most ABS braking conditions and, when equipped, during all traction control conditions.
- During most ABS braking conditions, the EBCM/EBTCM turns on the pump motor while monitoring the TCC/antilock brake switch to determine brake pedal position. The switch opens when the brake pedal is depressed approximately 40%. The motor restores the master cylinder's fluid pressure, causing the brake pedal to gradually rise. The pump motor continues to run until the brake pedal sufficiently rises to close the TCC/antilock brake switch.
- During traction control mode (when equipped), after the front hydraulic brake circuits are isolated, the pump motor runs to increase brake fluid pressure in these circuits. The increased pressure is directed to the slipping wheel through the PMV assembly's front inlet and outlet valves. This causes the brakes to be applied, reducing wheel spin at the slipping wheel. Traction control is disabled as soon as the brakes are manually applied.
- When the EBCM/EBTCM grounds terminal 15, DTC 61 sets when the EBCM/EBTCM determines that the voltage between EBCM/EBTCM terminals 31 and 49 is not between 500-800 mVAC. The EBCM/EBTCM recognizes this condition only during ABS braking requiring pump motor operation, traction control mode (when equipped), and during the EBCM/EBTCM self-check which occurs when the vehicle reaches 11 km/h (7 mph). Therefore, be sure to test drive vehicle;
  after clearing the diagnostic trouble code to assure correct diagnosis.
- DTC 61 also sets when the pump motor runs all the time (i.e., EBCM/EBTCM sees proper voltage between terminals 31 and 49 without grounding terminal 15).

POSSIBLE CAUSES:
- — Open in CKT 151, 850, 854, 1077, 1292, 1293 or 1446.
- — Short to ground in CKT 850, 854, 1292, 1293 or 1446.
- — ABS pump relay fails "open" or "engaged."

GC4029300622010X

Fig. 36 Test 4: Pump Motor Circuit (Part 1 of 3). 1993–94 LeSabre & Park Avenue

J: PUMP MOTOR CIRCUIT TEST

- Make sure "ABS/TCS Functional/Check" is performed before proceeding.
- Ignition switch: OFF
- Connect bi-directional scan tool to data link connector DLC.
- Ignition switch: RUN
- Command bi-directional scan tool to bleed pressure modulator valve (PMV) assembly.
  - If pump motor runs: turn ignition switch OFF, disconnect bi-directional scan tool and go to step [5].
  - If pump motor does not run: clear diagnostic trouble codes, turn ignition switch OFF, disconnect bi-directional scan tool and go to step [1].

- Ignition switch: OFF
- ABS pump relay connector: disconnected
- Ignition switch: RUN

[1] Battery voltage. If not: check wiring for an open.

[2] Battery voltage. If not: check LH underhood fuse block fuse 1: check wiring (CKTS 850 and 1446) for an open or short to ground. NOTE: When CKT 850 is found shorted to ground, replace ABS pump relay after wiring is repaired.

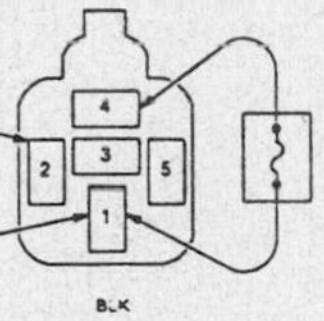
4
2
3
5
1

BLK
ABS PUMP RELAY

[3] Pump motor runs. If motor does not run: go to step [4].
If motor runs: reconnect ABS pump relay and go to Pump Motor Circuit Test J1.

- Ignition switch: OFF
- Pressure modulator valve (PMV) assembly connector C2: disconnected

[5] Battery voltage.
If not: check wiring for an open. If measurement is correct: check PMV connector C2 for proper terminal contact; If OK, replace pressure modulator valve (PMV) assembly, see (7).

[4] Battery voltage with jumper still in place from step [3].
If not: check wiring for an open or short to ground.

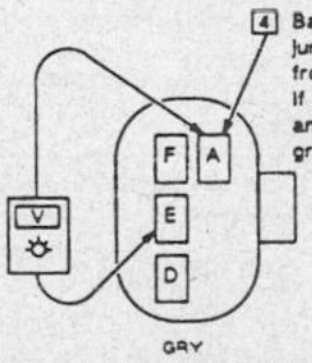
V
F
A
E
D

GRY
PRESSURE MODULATOR VALVE (PMV) ASSEMBLY CONNECTOR C2 (Harness side)

[6] Infinite ohms between pressure modulator valve (PMV) assembly casing. If not: replace PMV assembly, see (7).

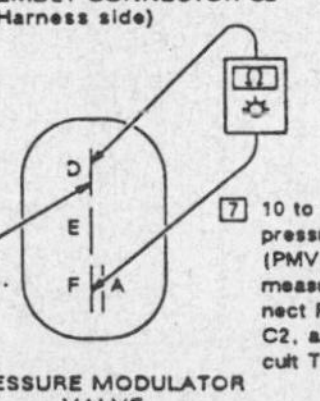
Ω
D
E
F
A

[7] 10 to 40 ohms. If not: replace pressure modulator valve (PMV) assembly, see (7). If measurement is correct: reconnect PMV assembly connector C2, and go to Pump Motor Circuit Test J1.

PRESSURE MODULATOR VALVE (PMV Assembly side)

GC4029300622020X

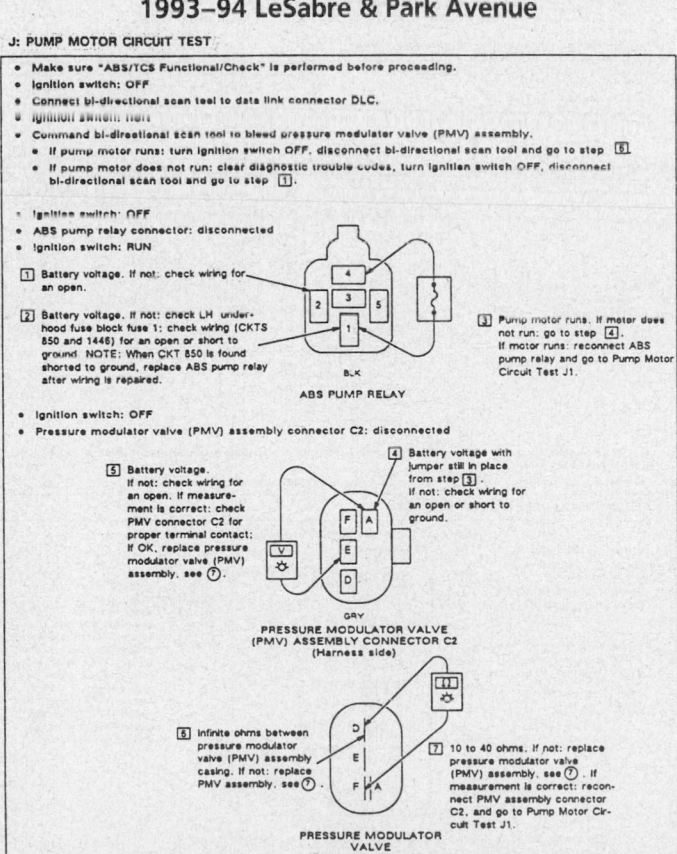

Fig. 36 Test 4: Pump Motor Circuit (Part 2 of 3). 1993–94 LeSabre & Park Avenue

J1: PUMP MOTOR CIRCUIT TEST

- Ignition switch: OFF
- EBCM/EBTCM connector: disconnected
- Connect J 38716 Pinout Box

[1] Less than 5 ohms. If not: check wiring for an open.

- Disconnect fused jumper.
- Ignition switch: OFF

[3] Greater than 5 ohms. If not: check wiring CKTS 1292 and 1293 for a short to ground.

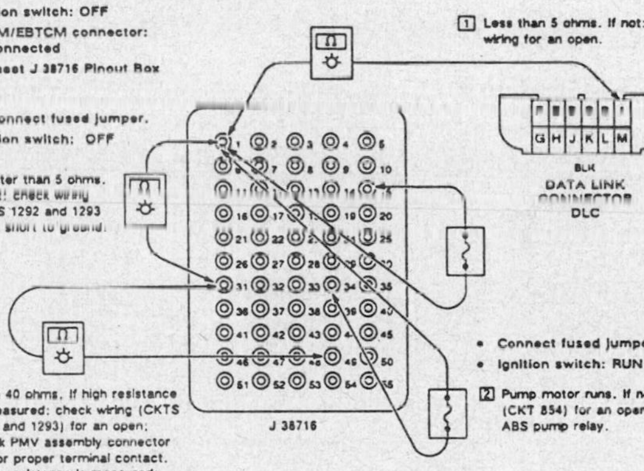
Ω
G H J K L M
BLK
DATA LINK
CONNECTOR
DLC
J 38716

- Connect fused jumpers as shown
- Ignition switch: RUN

[2] Pump motor runs. If not: check wiring (CKT 854) for an open: If OK, replace ABS pump relay.

[4] 10 to 40 ohms. If high resistance is measured: check wiring (CKTS 1292 and 1293) for an open; check PMV assembly connector C2 for proper terminal contact. If low resistance is measured: check for a short between wiring.

- If all measurements are correct: check EBCM/EBTCM connector for proper terminal contact; If OK, replace EBCM/EBTCM, see (3).
- After repairs are completed, clear diagnostic trouble codes and repeat "ABS/TCS Functional Check."

K: PUMP MOTOR SHORT TEST

- Make sure "ABS/TCS Functional Check" is performed before proceeding.
- Ignition switch: OFF
- ABS pump relay connector: disconnected
- Ignition switch: RUN

[1] 0 volts. If not: check wiring (CKT 854) for a short to ground. If wiring is shorted to ground, replace ABS pump relay: If wiring is OK, check EBCM/EBTCM connector for proper terminal contact: If OK, replace EBCM/EBTCM, see (3).

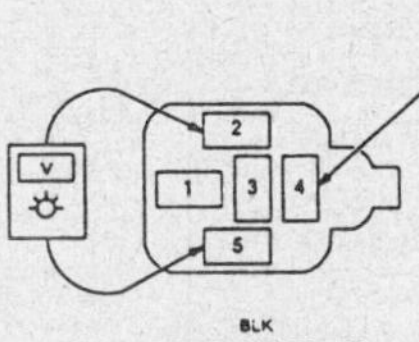
V
2
1
3
4
5

[2] 0 volts. If not: check wiring for a short to battery.

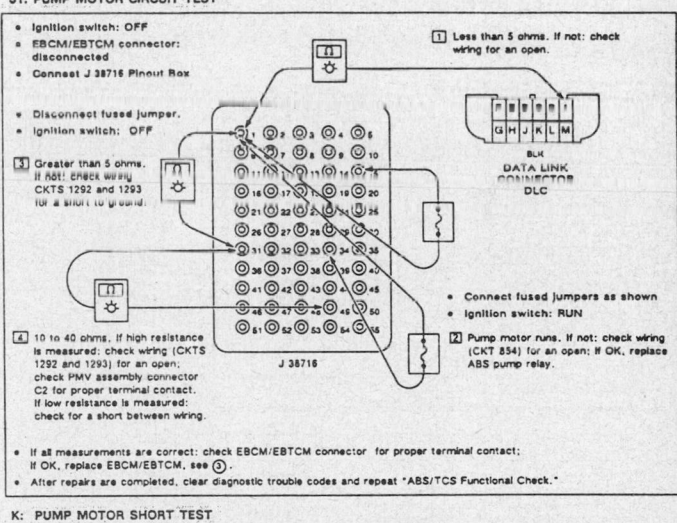

BLK
ABS PUMP RELAY CONNECTOR

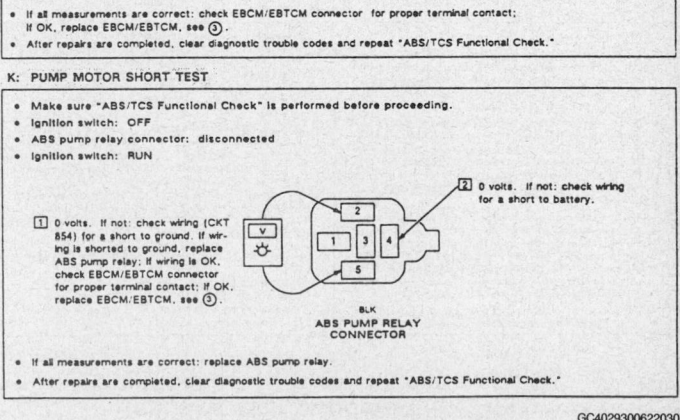

- If all measurements are correct: replace ABS pump relay.
- After repairs are completed, clear diagnostic trouble codes and repeat "ABS/TCS Functional Check."

GC4029300622030X

Fig. 36 Test 4: Pump Motor Circuit (Part 3 of 3). 1993–94 LeSabre & Park Avenue

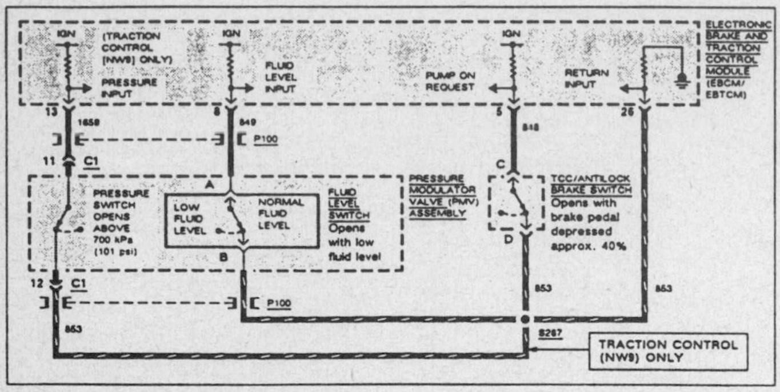

IGN
(TRACTION CONTROL [NW9] ONLY)
PRESSURE INPUT
IGN
FLUID LEVEL INPUT
IGN
PUMP ON REQUEST
RETURN INPUT
ELECTRONIC BRAKE AND TRACTION CONTROL MODULE (EBCM/EBTCM)
1659
849
848
P100
C1
PRESSURE SWITCH OPENS ABOVE 700 kPa (101 psi)
LOW FLUID LEVEL
NORMAL FLUID LEVEL
FLUID LEVEL SWITCH Opens with low fluid level
PRESSURE MODULATOR VALVE (PMV) ASSEMBLY
TCC/ANTILOCK BRAKE SWITCH Opens with brake pedal depressed approx. 40%
853
S267
TRACTION CONTROL (NW9) ONLY

OPERATION:

- The EBCM/EBTCM monitors brake pedal position using the TCC/antilock brake switch. The normally closed switch opens when the brake pedal is depressed approximately 40%. The EBCM/EBTCM also monitors pump motor operation using a pump motor run sensor.
- During most ABS braking conditions the EBCM/EBTCM turns on the pump motor, replenishing the PMV assembly reservoir and applying fluid pressure to the master cylinder. This causes the brake pedal to gradually rise. The EBCM/EBTCM turns off the pump motor when brake pedal height rises sufficiently to close the TCC/antilock brake switch.
- During ABS braking, DTC 62 sets when the EBCM/EBTCM determines the pump is working, and brake pedal height has not risen sufficiently to close the TCC/antilock brake switch after 3 seconds.

POSSIBLE CAUSES:

- Air in the brake lines.
- Pump motor mechanical failure.
- Open in CKT 848 or 853.
- Misadjusted/defective TCC/antilock brake switch.

L: TCC/ANTILOCK BRAKE SWITCH TEST

- Ignition switch: OFF
- Brake pedal: released (rest position)
- TCC/antilock brake switch connector: disconnected

[1] Less than 1 ohm. If not: check switch adjustment; replace if necessary, see (4).

[2] Brake pedal: fully depressed

- Infinite ohms. If not: check switch adjustment; replace if necessary, see (4).

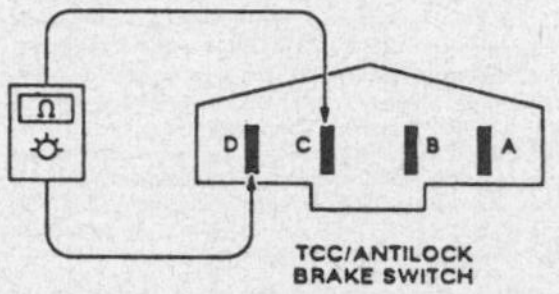

D
C
B
A
TCC/ANTILOCK BRAKE SWITCH

- If both measurements are correct and DTC 62 is set: reconnect TCC/antilock brake switch connector and go to Pump On Request Circuit Test N.
- After repairs are completed, clear diagnostic trouble codes and repeat "ABS/TCS Functional Check."

GC4029300623010X

Fig. 37 Test 5: Brake Switch & Hydraulics (Part 1 of 4). 1993–94 LeSabre & Park Avenue

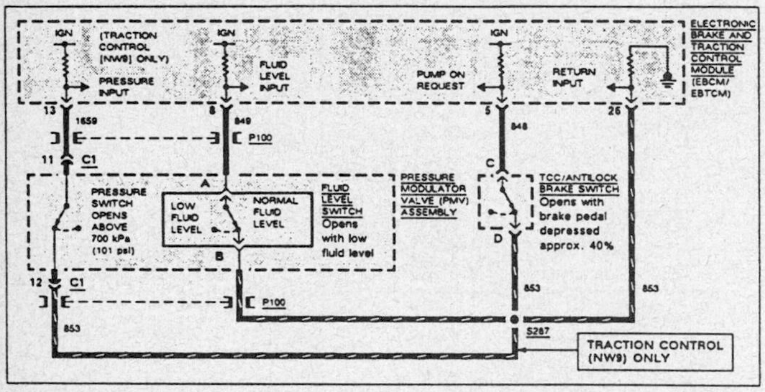

IGN
(TRACTION CONTROL [NW9] ONLY)
PRESSURE INPUT
IGN
FLUID LEVEL INPUT
IGN
PUMP ON REQUEST
RETURN INPUT
ELECTRONIC BRAKE AND TRACTION CONTROL MODULE (EBCM/EBTCM)
1659
849
848
P100
C1
PRESSURE SWITCH OPENS ABOVE 700 kPa (101 psi)
LOW FLUID LEVEL
NORMAL FLUID LEVEL
FLUID LEVEL SWITCH Opens with low fluid level
PRESSURE MODULATOR VALVE (PMV) ASSEMBLY
TCC/ANTILOCK BRAKE SWITCH Opens with brake pedal depressed approx. 40%
853
S267
TRACTION CONTROL (NW9) ONLY

OPERATION:

- The EBCM/EBTCM monitors brake pedal position using the TCC/antilock brake switch. The normally closed switch opens when the brake pedal is depressed approximately 40%. The EBCM/EBTCM also monitors pump motor operation using a pump motor run sensor.
- During most ABS braking condition, the EBCM/EBTCM turns on the pump motor, replenishing the PMV assembly reservoir and applying fluid pressure to the master cylinder. This causes the brake pedal to gradually rise. The EBCM/EBTCM turns off the pump motor when brake pedal height rises sufficiently to close the TCC/antilock brake switch.
- The pressure modulator valve (PMV) fluid level switch alerts the EBCM/EBTCM to a low brake fluid condition in the PMV reservoir. The fluid level switch is located in the PMV assembly's reservoir. The fluid level switch is normally closed when the reservoir contains sufficient fluid. When fluid level is low, the switch opens, causing the EBCM/EBTCM to turn on the ANTILOCK indicator.
- The pressure switch monitors primary brake system pressure. The normally closed switch opens when the brakes are applied (pressure exceeds 700 kPa [101 psi]). If the brakes are manually applied during traction control mode, the PMV pressure switch input, along with the brake switch input, signal EBCM/EBTCM to disable traction control and allow manual braking. The pressure switch is part of the pressure modulator valve (PMV) assembly and is not serviceable.
- DTC 72 sets when the EBCM/EBTCM detects that the TCC/antilock brake switch CKT 848 is shorted to ground.
- DTC 73 sets when the EBCM detects a short to ground in the PMV fluid level switch circuitry. These include CKTS 848, 849, 853 and 1659.
- DTC 74 sets when the EBCM/EBTCM detects an open or short to ground in the PMV pressure switch circuitry.

POSSIBLE CAUSES:

- Short to ground in CKT 848 with TCC/antilock brake switch open.
- Short to ground in CKT 848, 849, 853 or 1659.
- Open in CKT 853 or 1659.
- Short to ground in CKT 1659 with brake pedal depressed.
- Failed PMV pressure switch.

GC4029300623030X

Fig. 37 Test 5: Brake Switch & Hydraulics (Part 3 of 4). 1993–94 LeSabre & Park Avenue

M: BRAKE HYDRAULIC TEST

- Make sure "ABS/TCS Functional Check" is performed before proceeding.
  - Bleed brake system, see (1) or (2).
  - Ignition switch: OFF
  - Connect bi-directional scan tool to data link connector DLC.
  - Ignition switch: RUN
  - Use bi-directional scan tool to clear diagnostic trouble code after bleeding system.
  - Depress brake pedal (hold).
  - Use bi-directional scan tool to bleed pressure modulator valve (PMV) assembly

  Did brake pedal rise?

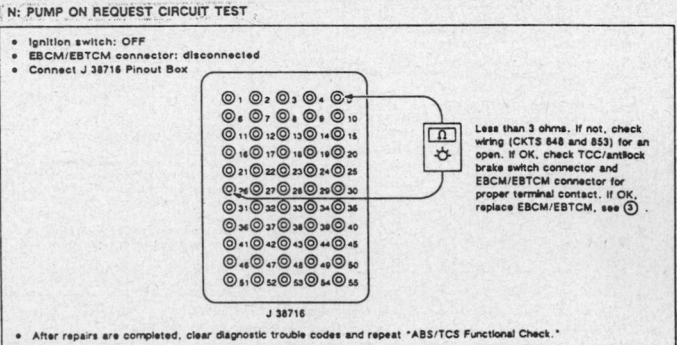

YES:

- Ignition switch: OFF
- Disconnect bi-directional scan tool.
- Test drive vehicle in a safe wet area and attempt to perform a 3 second ABS stop.
- Connect bi-directional scan tool to DLC.
- Ignition switch: RUN

Did DTC 62 set?

- **YES:**
  - Ignition switch: OFF
  - Disconnect bi-directional scan tool.
  - Go to TCC/Antilock Brake Switch Test L.
- **NO:** Problem solved.

NO: Replace PMV assembly, see (7).

- After repairs are completed, clear diagnostic trouble codes and repeat "ABS/TCS Functional Check."

N: PUMP ON REQUEST CIRCUIT TEST

- Ignition switch: OFF
- EBCM/EBTCM connector: disconnected
- Connect J 38716 Pinout Box

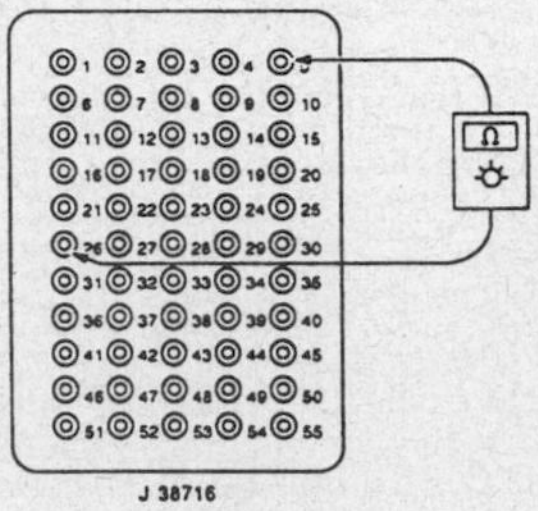

J 38716

Less than 3 ohms. If not, check wiring (CKTS 848 and 853) for an open. If OK, check TCC/antilock brake switch connector and EBCM/EBTCM connector for proper terminal contact. If OK, replace EBCM/EBTCM, see (3).

- After repairs are completed, clear diagnostic trouble codes and repeat "ABS/TCS Functional Check."

GC4029300623020X

Fig. 37 Test 5: Brake Switch & Hydraulics (Part 2 of 4). 1993–94 LeSabre & Park Avenue

O: EBCM/EBTCM GROUNDED SWITCH INPUT TEST

- Make sure "ABS/TCS Functional Check" is performed before proceeding.
- Ignition switch: OFF
- EBCM/EBTCM connector: disconnected
- Connect J 38716 Pinout Box
- TCC/antilock brake switch connector: disconnected
- Pressure modulator valve (PMV) fluid level switch: disconnected
- PMV assembly connector, C1: disconnected (traction control [NW9] only)

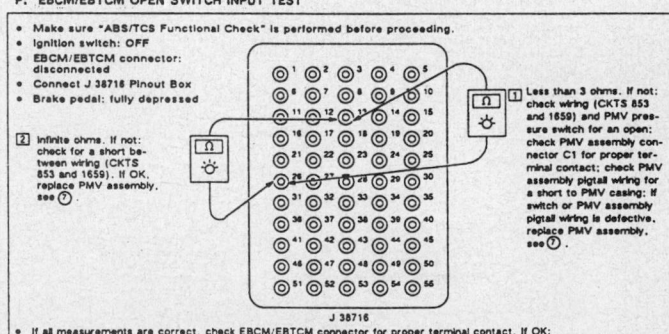

[1] Less than 5 ohms between data link connector DLC terminal A. If not: check wiring for an open.

[3] Greater than 5 ohms. If not: check wiring for a short to ground.

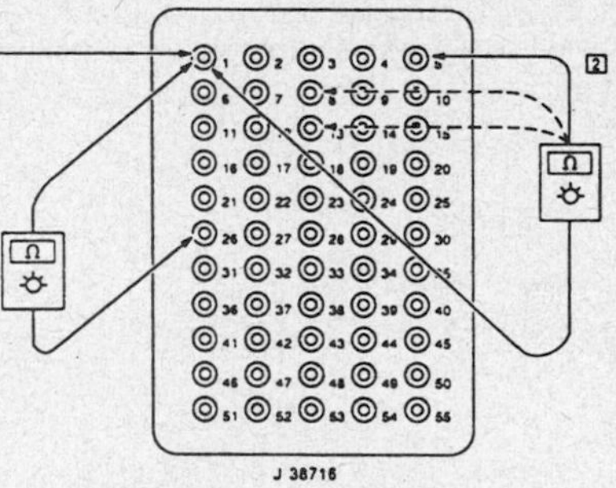

J 38716

[2] Greater than 5 ohms. If not: check wiring (see schematic) for a short to ground.

- If all measurements are correct: check EBCM/EBTCM connector for proper terminal contact. If OK: replace EBCM/EBTCM, see (3).
- After repairs are completed, clear diagnostic trouble codes and repeat "ABS/TCS Functional Check."

P: EBCM/EBTCM OPEN SWITCH INPUT TEST

- Make sure "ABS/TCS Functional Check" is performed before proceeding.
- Ignition switch: OFF
- EBCM/EBTCM connector: disconnected
- Connect J 38716 Pinout Box
- Brake pedal: fully depressed

[2] Infinite ohms. If not: check for a short between wiring (CKTS 853 and 1659). If OK, replace PMV assembly, see (7).

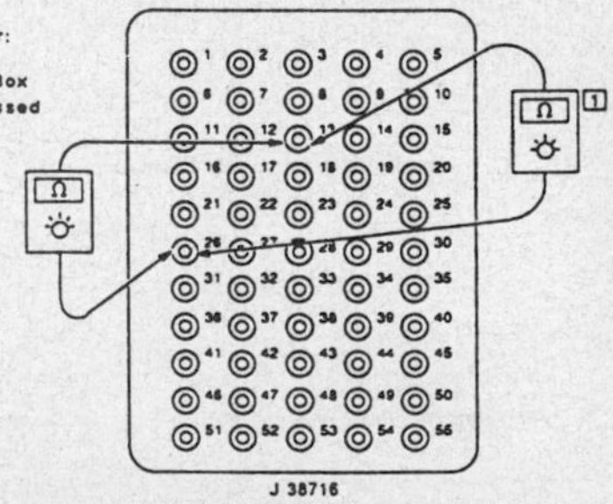

J 38716

[1] Less than 3 ohms. If not: check wiring (CKTS 853 and 1659) and PMV pressure switch for an open: check PMV assembly connector C1 for proper terminal contact; check PMV assembly pigtail wiring for a short to PMV casing: If switch or PMV assembly pigtail wiring is defective, replace PMV assembly, see (7).

- If all measurements are correct, check EBCM/EBTCM connector for proper terminal contact. If OK: replace EBCM/EBTCM, see (3).
- After repairs are completed, clear diagnostic trouble codes and repeat "ABS/TCS Functional Check."

GC4029300623040X

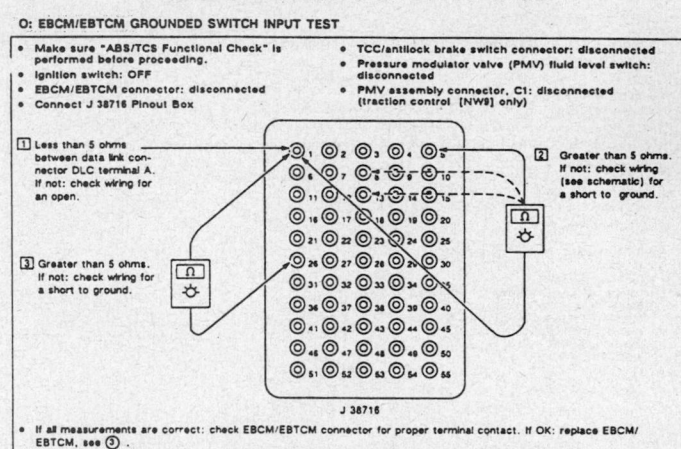

Fig. 37 Test 5: Brake Switch & Hydraulics (Part 4 of 4). 1993–94 LeSabre & Park Avenue

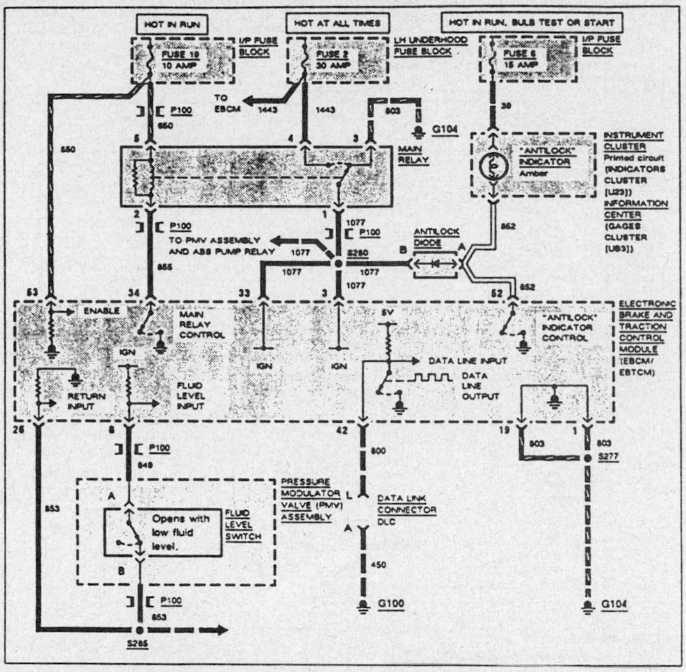

HOT IN RUN
HOT AT ALL TIMES
HOT IN RUN, BULB TEST OR START
I/P FUSE BLOCK
FUSE 19 10 AMP
LH UNDERHOOD FUSE BLOCK
FUSE 2 30 AMP
FUSE 6 15 AMP
TO EBCM
MAIN RELAY
G104
INSTRUMENT CLUSTER
"ANTILOCK" INDICATOR Amber
TO PMV ASSEMBLY AND ABS PUMP RELAY
ANTILOCK DIODE
S280
ELECTRONIC BRAKE AND TRACTION CONTROL MODULE (EBCM/EBTCM)
ENABLE
MAIN RELAY CONTROL
"ANTILOCK" INDICATOR CONTROL
DATA LINE INPUT
DATA LINE OUTPUT
RETURN INPUT
FLUID LEVEL INPUT
PRESSURE MODULATOR VALVE (PMV) ASSEMBLY
Opens with low fluid level.
FLUID LEVEL SWITCH
DATA LINK CONNECTOR DLC
S277
G100
S285

OPERATION:

- When the ignition switch is first turned to RUN, the EBCM/EBTCM goes through a self-test lasting 2-4 seconds. During this test, the EBCM/EBTCM grounds terminal 52, causing the amber ANTILOCK indicator to light. This serves as an indicator bulb test.
- When a low fluid condition exists, the EBCM/EBTCM turns on the amber ANTILOCK indicator but does not set a code. A low fluid level condition usually lights the red BRAKE indicator since the master cylinder supplies the PMV reservoir. However, restrictions or air in the hose could cause a low fluid condition in the PMV reservoir without lighting the red BRAKE indicator.

POSSIBLE CAUSES:

- — Open in CKT 650, 800, 803, 849 or 853.
- — Low brake fluid level or open PMV fluid level switch.
- — Short to ground in CKT 650, 800 or 852.

GC4029300624010X

Fig. 38 Test 6: Data Line & Anti-Lock Indicator (Part 1 of 2). 1993–94 LeSabre & Park Avenue

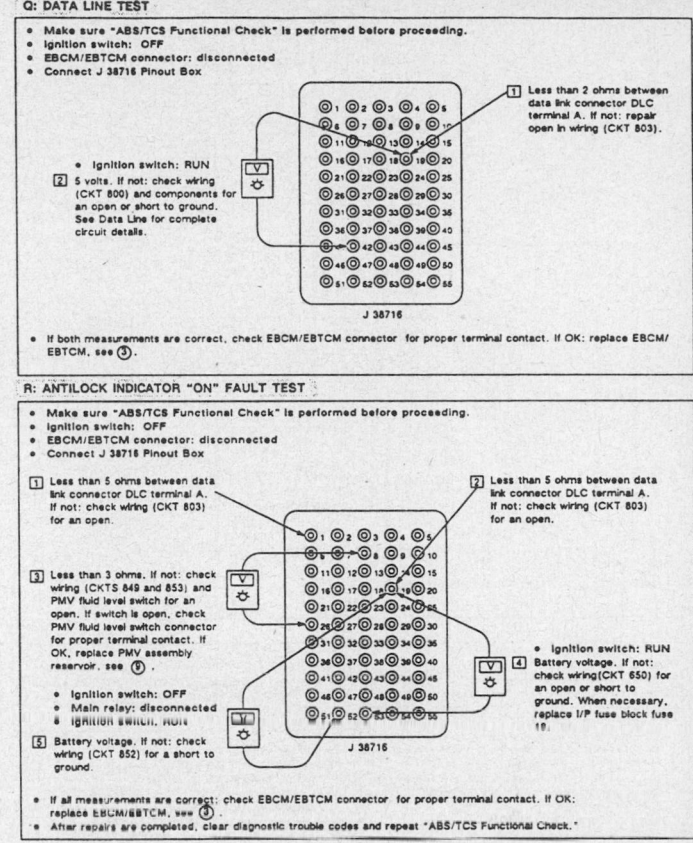

Q: DATA LINE TEST

- Make sure "ABS/TCS Functional Check" is performed before proceeding.
- Ignition switch: OFF
- EBCM/EBTCM connector: disconnected
- Connect J 38716 Pinout Box

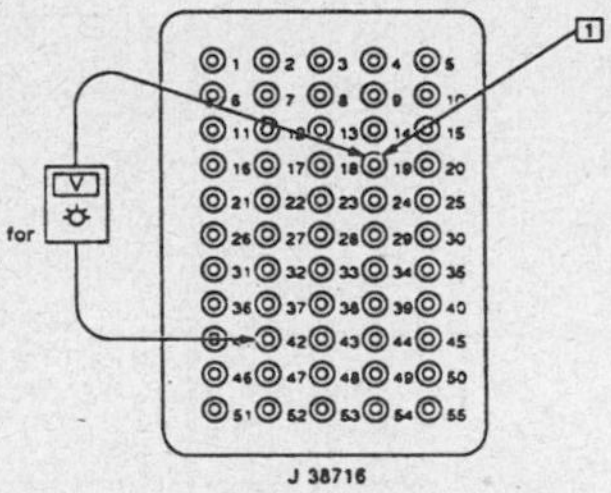

J 38716

1 Less than 2 ohms between data link connector DLC terminal A. If not: repair open in wiring (CKT 803).

- Ignition switch: RUN

2 5 volts. If not: check wiring (CKT 800) and components for an open or short to ground. See Data Line for complete circuit details.

- If both measurements are correct, check EBCM/EBTCM connector for proper terminal contact. If OK: replace EBCM/EBTCM, see (3).

R: ANTILOCK INDICATOR "ON" FAULT TEST

- Make sure "ABS/TCS Functional Check" is performed before proceeding.
- Ignition switch: OFF
- EBCM/EBTCM connector: disconnected
- Connect J 38716 Pinout Box

1 Less than 5 ohms between data link connector DLC terminal A. If not: check wiring (CKT 803) for an open.

2 Less than 5 ohms between data link connector DLC terminal A. If not: check wiring (CKT 803) for an open.

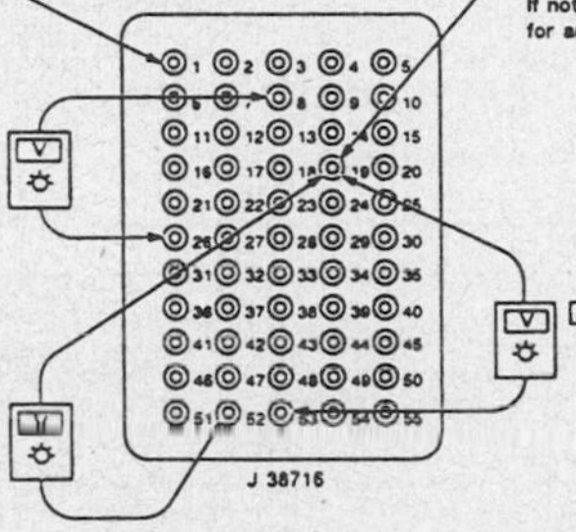

J 38716

3 Less than 3 ohms. If not: check wiring (CKTS 849 and 853) and PMV fluid level switch for an open. If switch is open, check PMV fluid level switch connector for proper terminal contact. If OK, replace PMV assembly reservoir, see (9).

- Ignition switch: RUN

4 Battery voltage. If not: check wiring(CKT 650) for an open or short to ground. When necessary, replace I/P fuse block fuse 19.

- Ignition switch: OFF
- Main relay: disconnected
- Ignition switch: RUN

5 Battery voltage. If not: check wiring (CKT 852) for a short to ground.

- If all measurements are correct: check EBCM/EBTCM connector for proper terminal contact. If OK: replace EBCM/EBTCM, see (3).
- After repairs are completed, clear diagnostic trouble codes and repeat "ABS/TCS Functional Check."

GC4029300624020X

Fig. 38 Test 6: Data Line & Anti-Lock Indicator (Part 2 of 2). 1993–94 LeSabre & Park Avenue

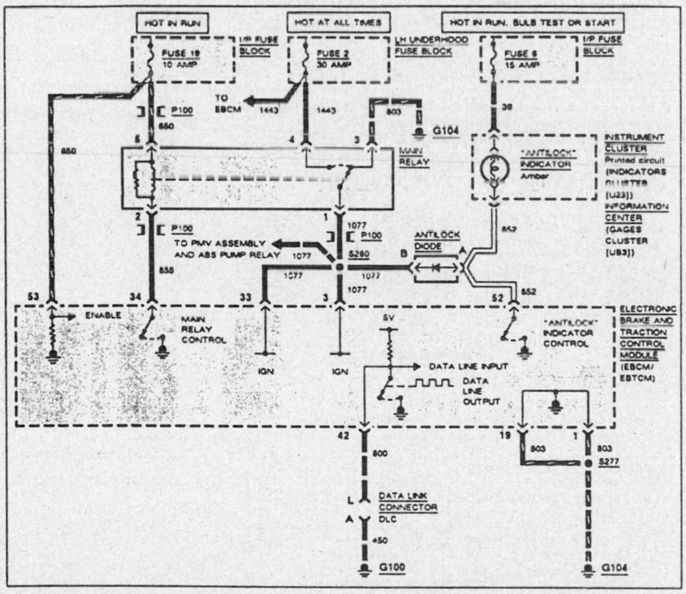

HOT IN RUN
HOT AT ALL TIMES
HOT IN RUN, BULB TEST OR START
I/P FUSE BLOCK
FUSE 19 10 AMP
LH UNDERHOOD FUSE BLOCK
FUSE 2 30 AMP
FUSE 6 15 AMP
TO EBCM
MAIN RELAY
G104
INSTRUMENT CLUSTER
"ANTILOCK" INDICATOR Amber
TO PMV ASSEMBLY AND ABS PUMP RELAY
ANTILOCK DIODE
S280
ELECTRONIC BRAKE AND TRACTION CONTROL MODULE (EBCM/EBTCM)
ENABLE
MAIN RELAY CONTROL
"ANTILOCK" INDICATOR CONTROL
DATA LINE INPUT
DATA LINE OUTPUT
DATA LINK CONNECTOR DLC
S277
G100

OPERATION:

- When the ignition switch is first turned to RUN, the EBCM/EBTCM goes through a self-test lasting 2-4 seconds. During this test, the EBCM/EBTCM grounds terminal 52, causing the amber ANTILOCK indicator to light. This serves as an indicator bulb test. The EBCM/EBTCM also grounds terminal 34, energizing the main relay. This removes the indicator ground path provided through the antilock diode and the main relay contacts.
- When the self-test is completed (and no faults are detected), the EBCM/EBTCM removes the ground at terminal 52, turning off the indicator. The main relay remains energized.
- When the EBCM/EBTCM detects a fault, it grounds terminal 52, causing the amber ANTILOCK indicator to light. (Note: The EBCM/EBTCM also de-energizes the main relay, creating a redundant ground path.)
- When the EBCM/EBTCM is disabled for any reason (i. e., open fuse 19), the main relay is de-energized. This provides an ANTILOCK indicator ground path through the antilock diode and main relay contacts, and causes the indicator to light with no codes being set.

POSSIBLE CAUSES:

- — Open in CKT 803, 852 or 1077.
- — Open bulb.
- — Short to voltage in CKT 852.
- — Open or shorted antilock diode.
- — Main relay fails "engaged."
- — Short to ground in CKT 855.

GC4029300625010X

Fig. 39 Test 7: Anti-Lock Indicator & Main Relay (Part 1 of 2). 1993–94 LeSabre & Park Avenue

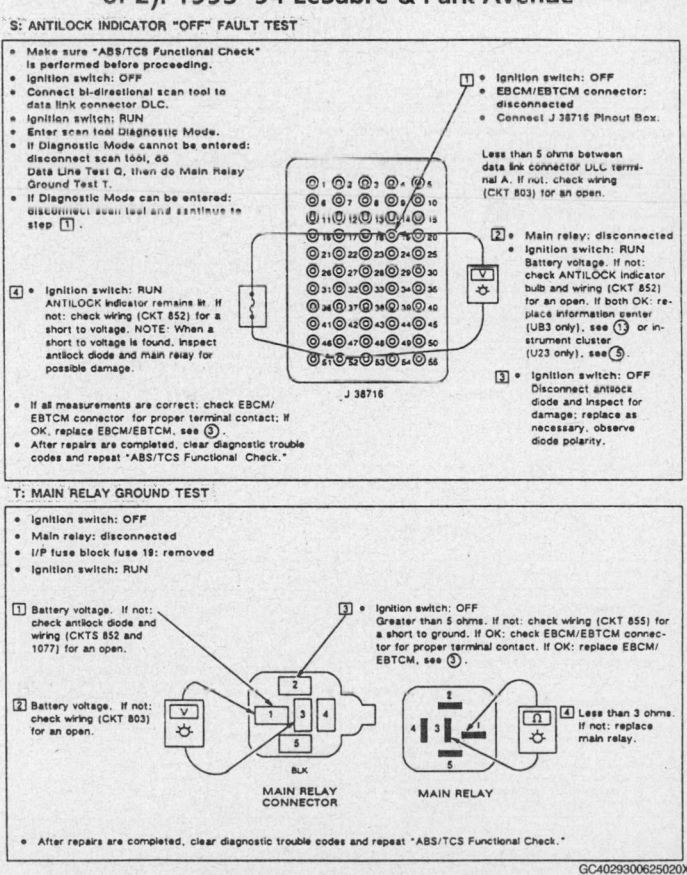

S: ANTILOCK INDICATOR "OFF" FAULT TEST

- Make sure "ABS/TCS Functional Check" is performed before proceeding.
- Ignition switch: OFF
- Connect bi-directional scan tool to data link connector DLC.
- Ignition switch: RUN
- Enter scan tool Diagnostic Mode.
- If Diagnostic Mode cannot be entered: disconnect scan tool, do Data Line Test Q, then do Main Relay Ground Test T.
- If Diagnostic Mode can be entered: disconnect scan tool and continue to step 1.

1
- Ignition switch: OFF
- EBCM/EBTCM connector: disconnected
- Connect J 38716 Pinout Box.

Less than 5 ohms between data link connector DLC terminal A. If not: check wiring (CKT 803) for an open.

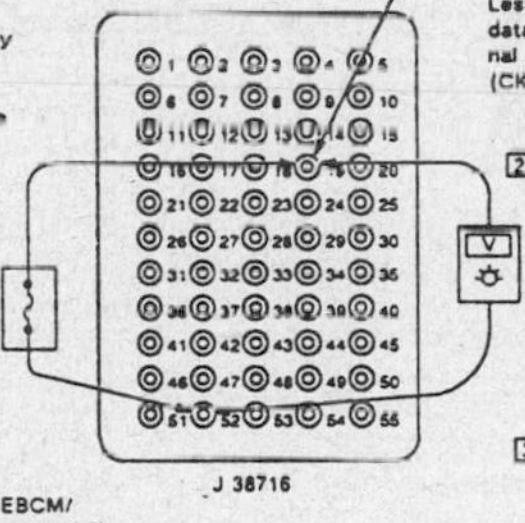

J 38716

2
- Main relay: disconnected
- Ignition switch: RUN

Battery voltage. If not: check ANTILOCK indicator bulb and wiring (CKT 852) for an open. If both OK: replace information center (UB3 only), see (13) or instrument cluster (U23 only), see (5).

3
- Ignition switch: OFF

Disconnect antilock diode and inspect for damage; replace as necessary, observe diode polarity.

4
- Ignition switch: RUN

ANTILOCK indicator remains lit. If not: check wiring (CKT 852) for a short to voltage. NOTE: When a short to voltage is found, inspect antilock diode and main relay for possible damage.

- If all measurements are correct: check EBCM/EBTCM connector for proper terminal contact; If OK, replace EBCM/EBTCM, see (3).
- After repairs are completed, clear diagnostic trouble codes and repeat "ABS/TCS Functional Check."

T: MAIN RELAY GROUND TEST

- Ignition switch: OFF
- Main relay: disconnected
- I/P fuse block fuse 19: removed
- Ignition switch: RUN

1 Battery voltage. If not: check antilock diode and wiring (CKTS 852 and 1077) for an open.

2 Battery voltage. If not: check wiring (CKT 803) for an open.

3
- Ignition switch: OFF

Greater than 5 ohms. If not: check wiring (CKT 855) for a short to ground. If OK: check EBCM/EBTCM connector for proper terminal contact. If OK: replace EBCM/EBTCM, see (3).

4 Less than 3 ohms. If not: replace main relay.

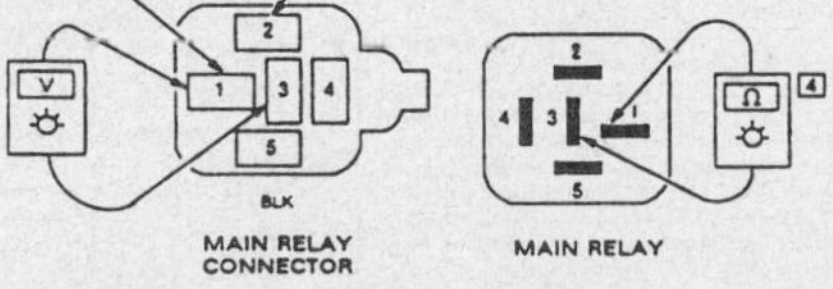

BLK
MAIN RELAY CONNECTOR
MAIN RELAY

- After repairs are completed, clear diagnostic trouble codes and repeat "ABS/TCS Functional Check."

GC4029300625020X

Fig. 39 Test 7: Anti-Lock Indicator & Main Relay (Part 2 of 2). 1993–94 LeSabre & Park Avenue

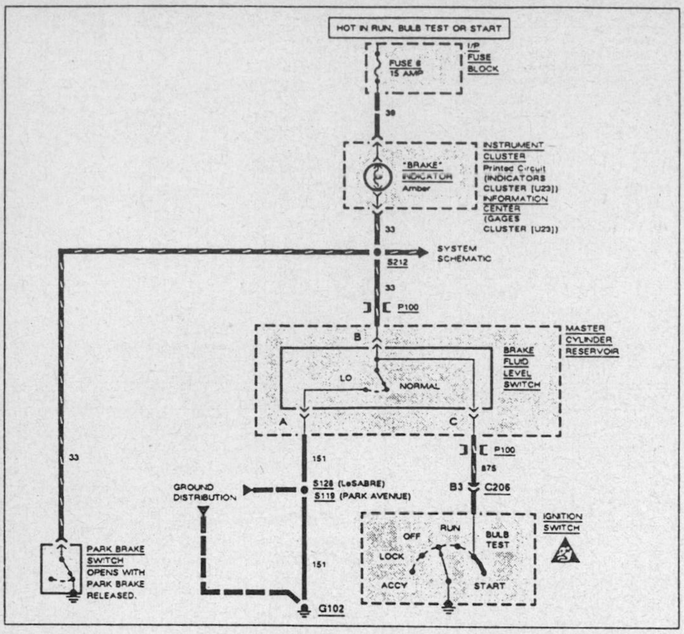
HOT IN RUN, BULB TEST OR START
FUSE 6
15 AMP
I/P
FUSE
BLOCK
39
INSTRUMENT
CLUSTER
Printed Circuit
(INDICATORS
CLUSTER [U23])
INFORMATION
CENTER
(GAGES
CLUSTER [U23])
"BRAKE"
INDICATOR
Amber
33
SYSTEM
SCHEMATIC
S212
33
P100
MASTER
CYLINDER
RESERVOIR
BRAKE
FLUID
LEVEL
SWITCH
LO
NORMAL
B
A
C
151
P100
875
B3
C206
S128 (LeSABRE)
S119 (PARK AVENUE)
GROUND
DISTRIBUTION
33
IGNITION
SWITCH
RUN
OFF
BULB
TEST
LOCK
ACCY
START
151
PARK BRAKE
SWITCH
OPENS WITH
PARK BRAKE
RELEASED.
G102

OPERATION:

The BRAKE indicator illuminates to alert the driver to either a brake system condition, which reduces braking ability, or a park brake, which is not fully released. Specific conditions which cause the BRAKE indicator to illuminate include:

— Park brake not fully released. When park brake is applied or not fully released, the park brake switch grounds the BRAKE indicator, causing the indicator to light.
— Low brake fluid level. The brake fluid level switch in the master cylinder reservoir grounds the BRAKE indicator when low brake fluid is detected.
— Ignition switch in START or BULB TEST position.

Important

A lit BRAKE indicator may indicate a hydraulic system fault, possibly causing reduced braking ability.

POSSIBLE CAUSES:

— Open in CKT 33, 151 or 875.
— Short to ground in CKT 33 or 875.
— Failed ignition switch.
— Failed/misadjusted park brake switch.
— Failed brake fluid level switch/master cylinder reservoir.

GC4029300626010X

Fig. 40 Test 8: Brake Warning, Fluid Level Switch & Park Brake Switch (Part 1 of 2). 1993–94 LeSabre & Park Avenue

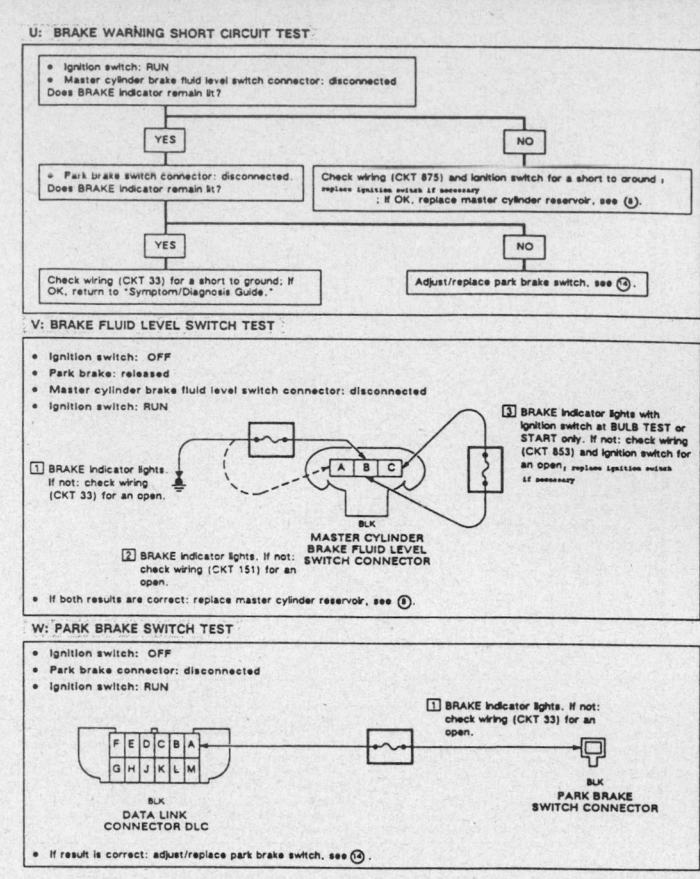

U: BRAKE WARNING SHORT CIRCUIT TEST

- Ignition switch: RUN
- Master cylinder brake fluid level switch connector: disconnected

Does BRAKE indicator remain lit?

YES:
- Park brake switch connector: disconnected.

Does BRAKE indicator remain lit?

YES: Check wiring (CKT 33) for a short to ground; if OK, return to "Symptom/Diagnosis Guide."

NO: Adjust/replace park brake switch, see (14).

NO: Check wiring (CKT 875) and ignition switch for a short to ground ; replace ignition switch if necessary ; If OK, replace master cylinder reservoir, see (8).

V: BRAKE FLUID LEVEL SWITCH TEST

- Ignition switch: OFF
- Park brake: released
- Master cylinder brake fluid level switch connector: disconnected
- Ignition switch: RUN

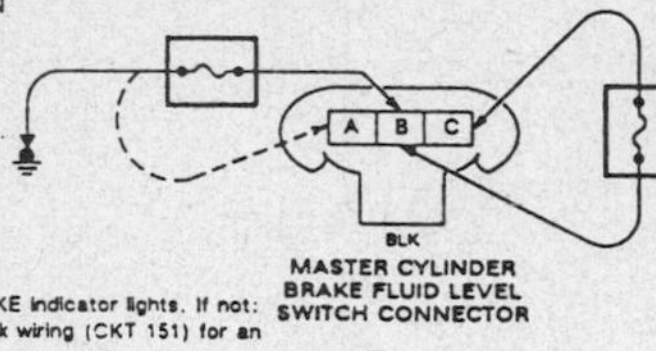
A
B
C
BLK
MASTER CYLINDER
BRAKE FLUID LEVEL
SWITCH CONNECTOR

1. BRAKE indicator lights. If not: check wiring (CKT 33) for an open.
2. BRAKE indicator lights. If not: check wiring (CKT 151) for an open.
3. BRAKE indicator lights with ignition switch at BULB TEST or START only. If not: check wiring (CKT 853) and ignition switch for an open, replace ignition switch if necessary

- If both results are correct: replace master cylinder reservoir, see (8).

W: PARK BRAKE SWITCH TEST

- Ignition switch: OFF
- Park brake connector: disconnected
- Ignition switch: RUN

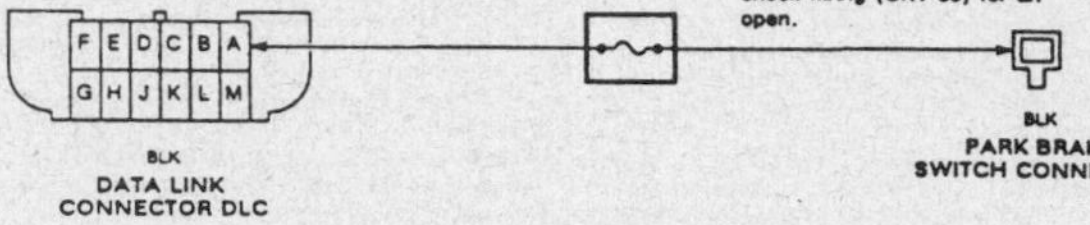
F E D C B A
G H J K L M
BLK
DATA LINK
CONNECTOR DLC
BLK
PARK BRAKE
SWITCH CONNECTOR

1. BRAKE indicator lights. If not: check wiring (CKT 33) for an open.

- If result is correct: adjust/replace park brake switch, see (14).

GC4029300626020X

Fig. 40 Test 8: Brake Warning, Fluid Level Switch & Park Brake Switch (Part 2 of 2). 1993–94 LeSabre & Park Avenue

IMPORTANT: When performing tests on system, if transaxle temperature switch is disconnected with ignition switch in RUN, the traction control system is disabled for approximately 3-5 minutes. The TRACTION OFF indicator remains lit during this time period.

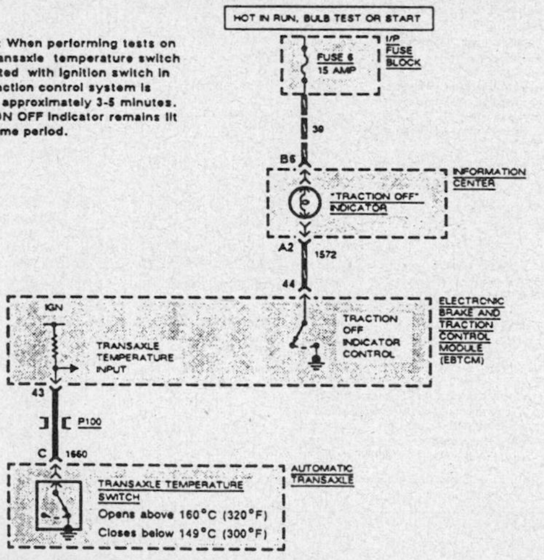
HOT IN RUN, BULB TEST OR START
FUSE 6
15 AMP
I/P
FUSE
BLOCK
39
B6
INFORMATION
CENTER
"TRACTION OFF"
INDICATOR
A2
1572
44
IGN
TRANSAXLE
TEMPERATURE
INPUT
TRACTION
OFF
INDICATOR
CONTROL
ELECTRONIC
BRAKE AND
TRACTION
CONTROL
MODULE
(EBTCM)
43
P100
C
1660
AUTOMATIC
TRANSAXLE
TRANSAXLE TEMPERATURE
SWITCH
Opens above 160°C (320°F)
Closes below 149°C (300°F)

OPERATION:

- When the ignition switch is first turned to RUN, the EBTCM goes through a self test. During this test, the EBTCM grounds both the ANTILOCK and TRACTION OFF indicators for approximately 2 to 4 seconds. This acts as a bulb test for the indicators.

  The EBTCM monitors transaxle temperature through the transaxle temperature switch. When the transaxle becomes hot, about 160°C (320°F), the normally closed switch opens, signaling the EBTCM to disable the traction control system and turn on the TRACTION OFF indicator. This allows the brakes and transaxle to cool down. As the transaxle cools to 149°C (300°F), the transaxle temperature switch closes. The EBTCM keeps the TRACTION OFF indicator on and the system disabled for an additional three to five minutes to allow for sufficient cooling.

POSSIBLE CAUSES:

Important

- When vehicle is equipped with traction control, any symptom which lights the ANTILOCK indicator also lights the TRACTION OFF indicator. Therefore, when both indicators are lit, follow ANTILOCK indicator diagnosis when no codes are set.

— Short to ground in CKT 1572.
— Open in CKT 1660.
— Faulty transaxle temperature switch.

GC4029300627010X

Fig. 41 Test 9: Transaxle Temperature Switch & EBCM/EBTCM Problem (Part 1 of 2). 1993–94 LeSabre & Park Avenue

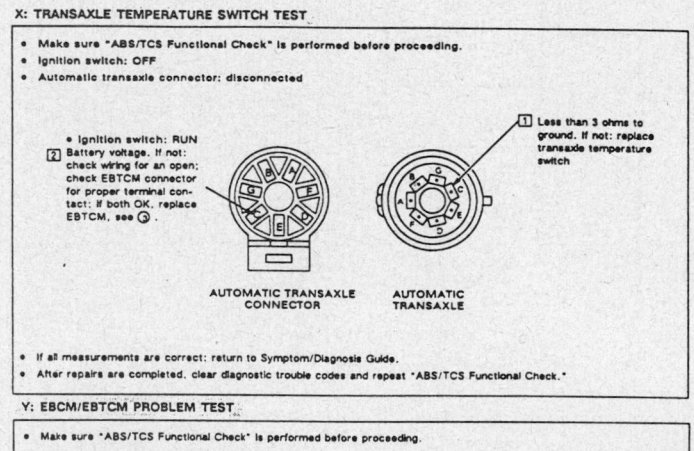

X: TRANSAXLE TEMPERATURE SWITCH TEST

- Make sure "ABS/TCS Functional Check" is performed before proceeding.
- Ignition switch: OFF
- Automatic transaxle connector: disconnected

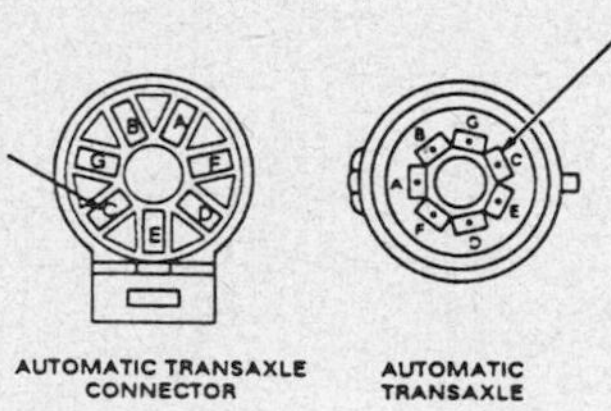
B
A
G
F
C
D
E
AUTOMATIC TRANSAXLE
CONNECTOR
AUTOMATIC
TRANSAXLE

1. Less than 3 ohms to ground. If not: replace transaxle temperature switch
2. • Ignition switch: RUN
   Battery voltage. If not: check wiring for an open; check EBTCM connector for proper terminal contact; if both OK, replace EBTCM, see (3).

- If all measurements are correct: return to Symptom/Diagnosis Guide.
- After repairs are completed, clear diagnostic trouble codes and repeat "ABS/TCS Functional Check."

Y: EBCM/EBTCM PROBLEM TEST

- Make sure "ABS/TCS Functional Check" is performed before proceeding.

- Clear diagnostic trouble codes.
- Test drive vehicle.

Did DTC 71 set during test drive?

YES: Replace EBCM/EBTCM, see (3)

NO: No problem found. Problem may be intermittent, see "Notes on Intermittents."

- After repairs are completed, clear diagnostic trouble codes and repeat "ABS/TCS Functional Check."

GC4029300627020X

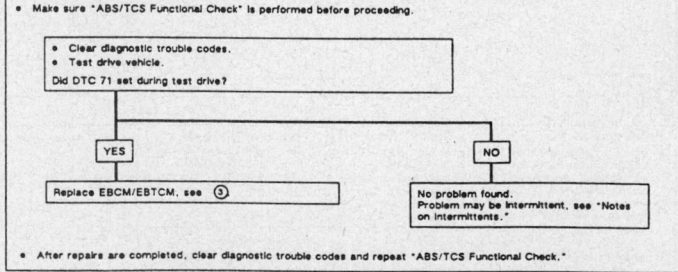

Fig. 41 Test 9: Transaxle Temperature Switch & EBCM/EBTCM Problem (Part 2 of 2). 1993–94 LeSabre & Park Avenue

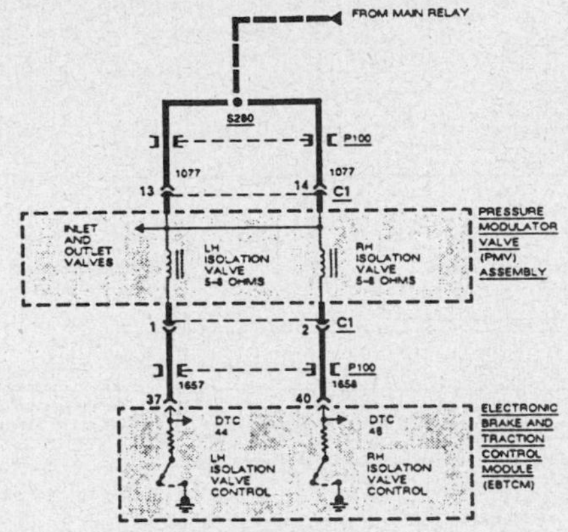
FROM MAIN RELAY
S280
P100
1077
1077
13
14
C1
INLET AND OUTLET VALVES
LH ISOLATION VALVE 5-8 OHMS
RH ISOLATION VALVE 5-8 OHMS
PRESSURE MODULATOR VALVE (PMV) ASSEMBLY
1
2
C1
P100
1657
1658
37
40
DTC 44
DTC 48
LH ISOLATION VALVE CONTROL
RH ISOLATION VALVE CONTROL
ELECTRONIC BRAKE AND TRACTION CONTROL MODULE (EBTCM)

OPERATION:

- Voltage is applied to the normally open isolation valves whenever the main relay is energized. An isolation valve closes when the EBTCM supplies a ground path at the isolation valve control terminal. The EBTCM closes an isolation valve when the EBTCM detects wheel slip in a drive wheel and vehicle speed is below 40 km/h (25 mph).
- The isolation valves are closed only during traction control operations, and are not used during any antilock or normal braking conditions. The isolation valves separate (isolate) the front brake hydraulic circuits from the master cylinder and rear brake hydraulic circuits. Once the front brake hydraulic circuits are isolated, pressure can be applied to the front wheels without affecting any other brake hydraulic circuit.
- DTC 44 or 48 sets when the EBTCM detects an open or short to ground in the respective isolation valve circuit.

POSSIBLE CAUSES:

— Open in CKT 1077, 1657 or 1658.
— Short to ground in CKT 1657 or 1658.
— Faulty pressure modulator valve (PMV) assembly.

GC4029300628010X

Fig. 42 Test 10: Isolation Valve (Part 1 of 3). 1993–94 LeSabre & Park Avenue

Z: ISOLATION VALVE CONTINUITY TEST

- Make sure "ABS/TCS Functional Check" is performed before proceeding.
- Ignition switch: OFF
- Pressure modulator valve (PMV) assembly connector C1: disconnected

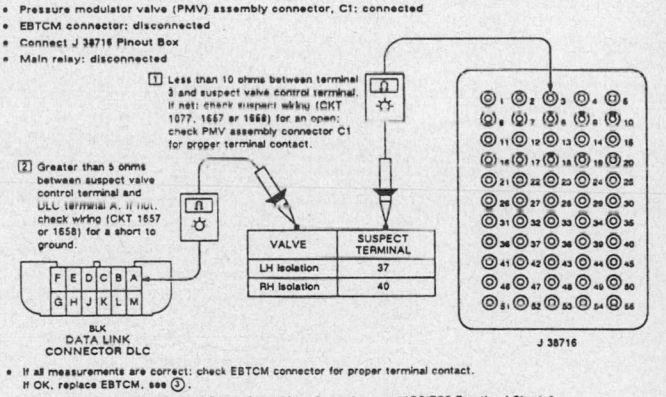

[1] Infinite ohms between pressure modulator valve (PMV) assembly casing. If not: replace PMV assembly, see ⑦.

[2] Measure resistance across suspect solenoid valve terminal(s). When a measurement is incorrect: replace PMV assembly, see ⑦.

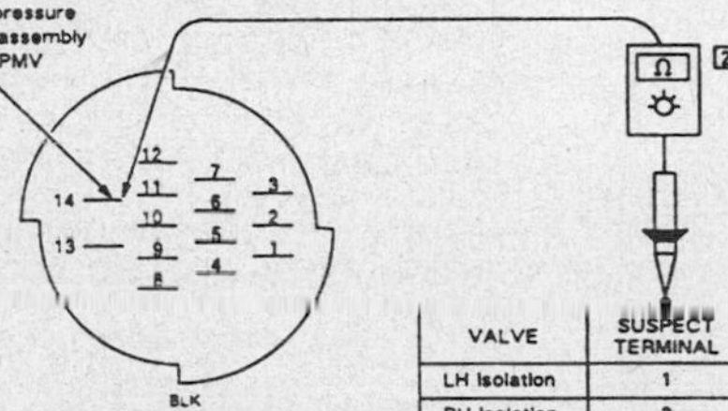
12
11
10
9
8
7
6
5
4
3
2
1
14
13
BLK
PRESSURE MODULATOR VALVE (PMV) ASSEMBLY CONNECTOR C1
(PMV Assembly half)

VALVE	SUSPECT TERMINAL	CORRECT RESISTANCE
LH Isolation	1	5 to 8 ohms
RH Isolation	2	

- If all measurements are correct, go to Isolation Valve Control Test AA
- After repairs are completed, clear diagnostic trouble codes and repeat "ABS/TCS Functional Check."

AA: ISOLATION VALVE CONTROL TEST

- Ignition switch: OFF
- Pressure modulator valve (PMV) assembly connector, C1: connected
- EBTCM connector: disconnected
- Connect J 38716 Pinout Box
- Main relay: disconnected

[1] Less than 10 ohms between terminal 3 and suspect valve control terminal. If not: check suspect wiring (CKT 1077, 1657 or 1658) for an open; check PMV assembly connector C1 for proper terminal contact.

[2] Greater than 5 ohms between suspect valve control terminal and DLC terminal A. If not, check wiring (CKT 1657 or 1658) for a short to ground.

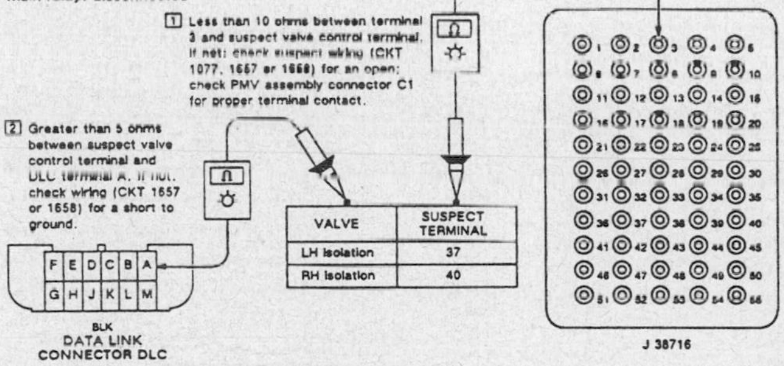
F E D C B A
G H J K L M
BLK
DATA LINK CONNECTOR DLC
J 38716

VALVE	SUSPECT TERMINAL
LH Isolation	37
RH Isolation	40

- If all measurements are correct: check EBTCM connector for proper terminal contact. If OK, replace EBTCM, see ③.
- After repairs are completed, clear diagnostic trouble codes and repeat "ABS/TCS Functional Check."

GC4029300628020X

Fig. 42 Test 10: Isolation Valve (Part 2 of 3). 1993–94 LeSabre & Park Avenue

BB: INLET/OUTLET VALVE HYDRAULIC TEST

NOTE: To prevent overheating of inlet/outlet valves, the bi-directional scan tool only allows valves to be energized for a maximum of 20 seconds. A minimum of 30 seconds must elapse before valves can be re-energized.

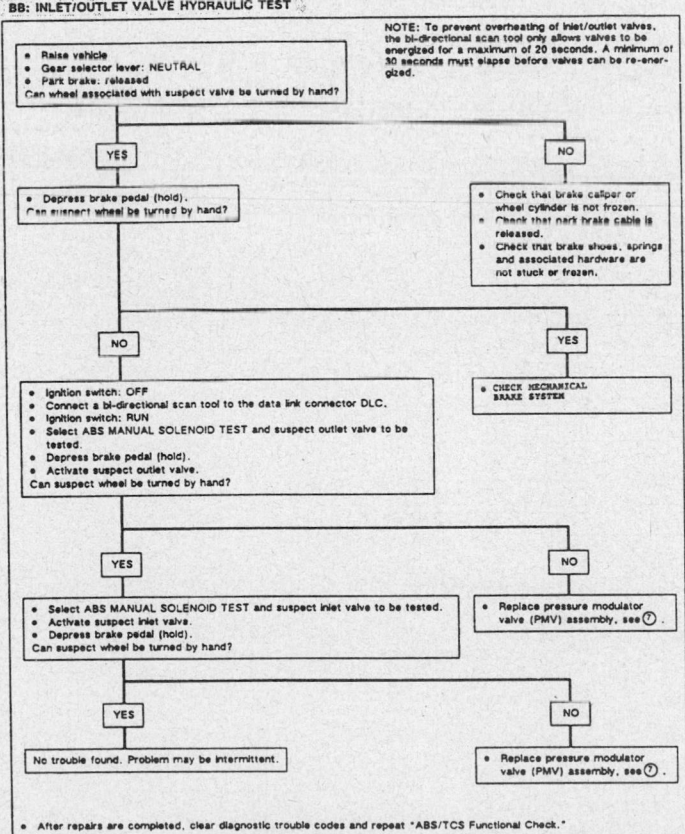

- Raise vehicle
- Gear selector lever: NEUTRAL
- Park brake: released

Can wheel associated with suspect valve be turned by hand?

YES:

- Depress brake pedal (hold).

Can suspect wheel be turned by hand?

YES:

- CHECK MECHANICAL BRAKE SYSTEM

NO:

- Ignition switch: OFF
- Connect a bi-directional scan tool to the data link connector DLC.
- Ignition switch: RUN
- Select ABS MANUAL SOLENOID TEST and suspect outlet valve to be tested.
- Depress brake pedal (hold).
- Activate suspect outlet valve.

Can suspect wheel be turned by hand?

YES:

- Select ABS MANUAL SOLENOID TEST and suspect inlet valve to be tested.
- Activate suspect inlet valve.
- Depress brake pedal (hold).

Can suspect wheel be turned by hand?

YES: No trouble found. Problem may be intermittent.

NO:

- Replace pressure modulator valve (PMV) assembly, see ⑦.

NO:

- Replace pressure modulator valve (PMV) assembly, see ⑦.

NO:

- Check that brake caliper or wheel cylinder is not frozen.
- Check that park brake cable is released.
- Check that brake shoes, springs and associated hardware are not stuck or frozen.

- After repairs are completed, clear diagnostic trouble codes and repeat "ABS/TCS Functional Check."

GC4029300628030X

Fig. 42 Test 10: Isolation Valve (Part 3 of 3). 1993–94 LeSabre & Park Avenue

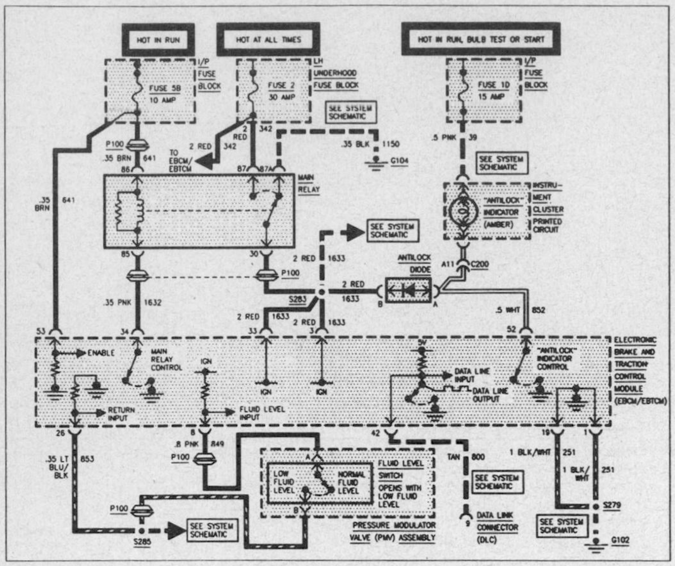
HOT IN RUN
HOT AT ALL TIMES
HOT IN RUN, BULB TEST OR START
FUSE 5B 10 AMP
I/P FUSE BLOCK
FUSE 2 30 AMP
LH UNDERHOOD FUSE BLOCK
FUSE 10 15 AMP
SEE SYSTEM SCHEMATIC
MAIN RELAY
"ANTILOCK" INDICATOR (AMBER)
INSTRUMENT CLUSTER PRINTED CIRCUIT
ANTILOCK DIODE
ELECTRONIC BRAKE AND TRACTION CONTROL MODULE (EBCM/EBTCM)
ENABLE
MAIN RELAY CONTROL
RETURN INPUT
FLUID LEVEL INPUT
DATA LINE INPUT
DATA LINE OUTPUT
"ANTILOCK" INDICATOR CONTROL
LOW FLUID LEVEL
NORMAL FLUID LEVEL
FLUID LEVEL SWITCH OPENS WITH LOW FLUID LEVEL
PRESSURE MODULATOR VALVE (PMV) ASSEMBLY
DATA LINK CONNECTOR (DLC)

CHART A

DIAGNOSTIC MODE CANNOT BE ENTERED OR "ANTILOCK" INDICATOR LAMP IS ON CONTINUOUSLY WITH NO DTC(s) SET

CIRCUIT OPERATION

When the ignition is first turned to "RUN," the EBCM/EBTCM goes through a self-test lasting 2-4 seconds. During this test, the EBCM/EBTCM grounds terminal 52 causing the amber "ANTILOCK" indicator to light. This serves as an indicator bulb test.

When a low fluid condition exists, the EBCM/EBTCM turns on the amber "ANTILOCK" indicator but does not set a DTC. A low fluid level condition usually lights the red "BRAKE" indicator since the master cylinder supplies the PMV reservoir. However, restrictions or air in the hose could cause a low fluid condition in the PMV reservoir without lighting the red "BRAKE" indicator.

FAILURE CONDITIONS

Possible Causes

- Open in CKT 641, 800, 251, 849 or 853.
- Low brake fluid level or open PMV fluid level switch.
- Short to ground in CKT 641, 800 or 852.
- Wrong scan tool adapter being used.

GC402940089300AX

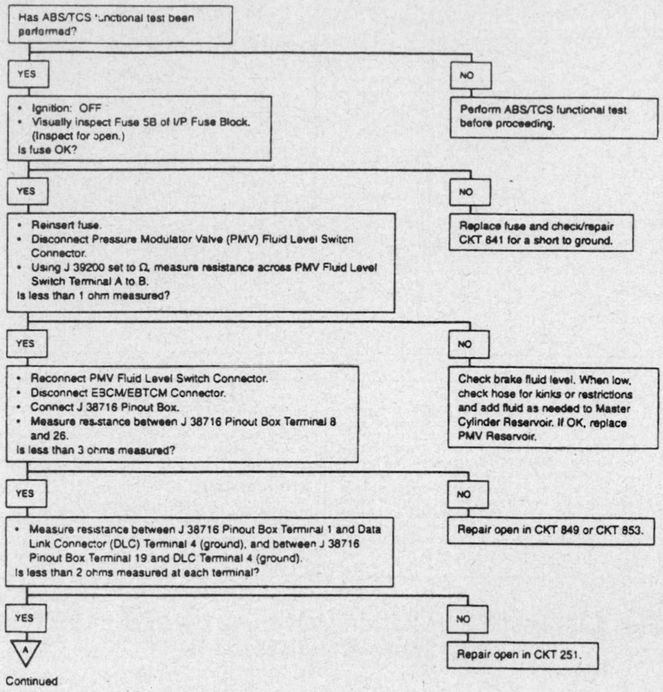
Has ABS/TCS functional test been performed?
YES
NO
Perform ABS/TCS functional test before proceeding.
• Ignition: OFF
• Visually inspect Fuse 5B of I/P Fuse Block. (Inspect for open.)
Is fuse OK?
YES
NO
Replace fuse and check/repair CKT 641 for a short to ground.
• Reinsert fuse.
• Disconnect Pressure Modulator Valve (PMV) Fluid Level Switch Connector.
• Using J 39200 set to Ω, measure resistance across PMV Fluid Level Switch Terminal A to B.
Is less than 1 ohm measured?
YES
NO
Check brake fluid level. When low, check hose for kinks or restrictions and add fluid as needed to Master Cylinder Reservoir. If OK, replace PMV Reservoir.
• Reconnect PMV Fluid Level Switch Connector.
• Disconnect EBCM/EBTCM Connector.
• Connect J 38716 Pinout Box.
• Measure resistance between J 38716 Pinout Box Terminal 8 and 26.
Is less than 3 ohms measured?
YES
NO
Repair open in CKT 849 or CKT 853.
• Measure resistance between J 38716 Pinout Box Terminal 1 and Data Link Connector (DLC) Terminal 4 (ground), and between J 38716 Pinout Box Terminal 19 and DLC Terminal 4 (ground).
Is less than 2 ohms measured at each terminal?
YES
NO
Repair open in CKT 251.
A
Continued

GC402940089300BX

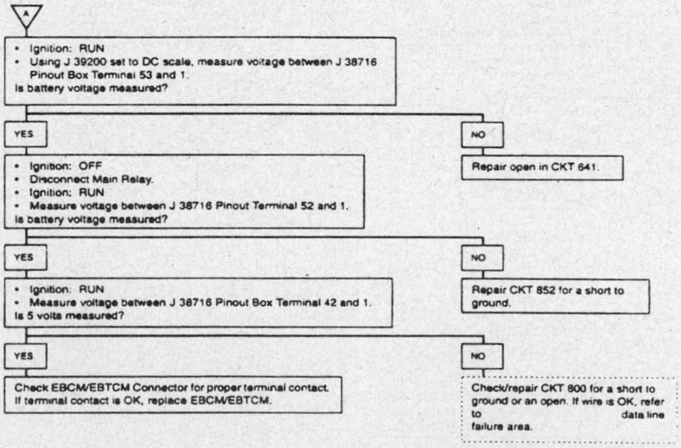
A
• Ignition: RUN
• Using J 39200 set to DC scale, measure voltage between J 38716 Pinout Box Terminal 53 and 1.
Is battery voltage measured?
YES
NO
Repair open in CKT 641.
• Ignition: OFF
• Disconnect Main Relay.
• Ignition: RUN
• Measure voltage between J 38716 Pinout Terminal 52 and 1.
Is battery voltage measured?
YES
NO
Repair CKT 852 for a short to ground.
• Ignition: RUN
• Measure voltage between J 38716 Pinout Box Terminal 42 and 1.
Is 5 volts measured?
YES
NO
Check EBCM/EBTCM Connector for proper terminal contact. If terminal contact is OK, replace EBCM/EBTCM.
Check/repair CKT 800 for a short to ground or an open. If wire is OK, refer to data line failure area.

GC402940089300CX

Fig. 43 Test A: Diagnostic Mode Cannot Be Entered Or ABS Lamp On w/No Codes Set. 1994 Bonneville, 88 & 98

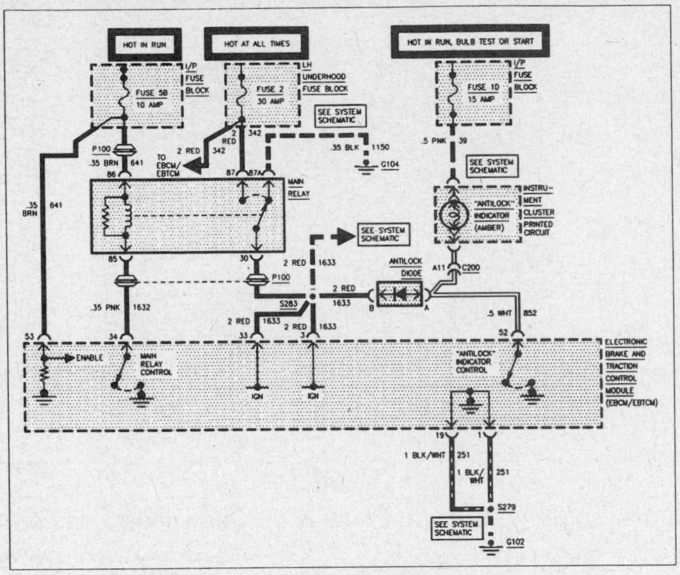
HOT IN RUN
HOT AT ALL TIMES
HOT IN RUN, BULB TEST OR START
I/P FUSE BLOCK
FUSE 5B 10 AMP
FUSE 2 30 AMP
LH UNDERHOOD FUSE BLOCK
SEE SYSTEM SCHEMATIC
FUSE 10 15 AMP
I/P FUSE BLOCK
MAIN RELAY
"ANTILOCK" INDICATOR (AMBER)
INSTRUMENT CLUSTER PRINTED CIRCUIT
ANTILOCK DIODE
ENABLE
MAIN RELAY CONTROL
IGN
"ANTILOCK" INDICATOR CONTROL
ELECTRONIC BRAKE AND TRACTION CONTROL MODULE (EBCM/EBTCM)
TO EBCM/EBTCM
P100
C200
S283
S279
G104
G102

CHART B

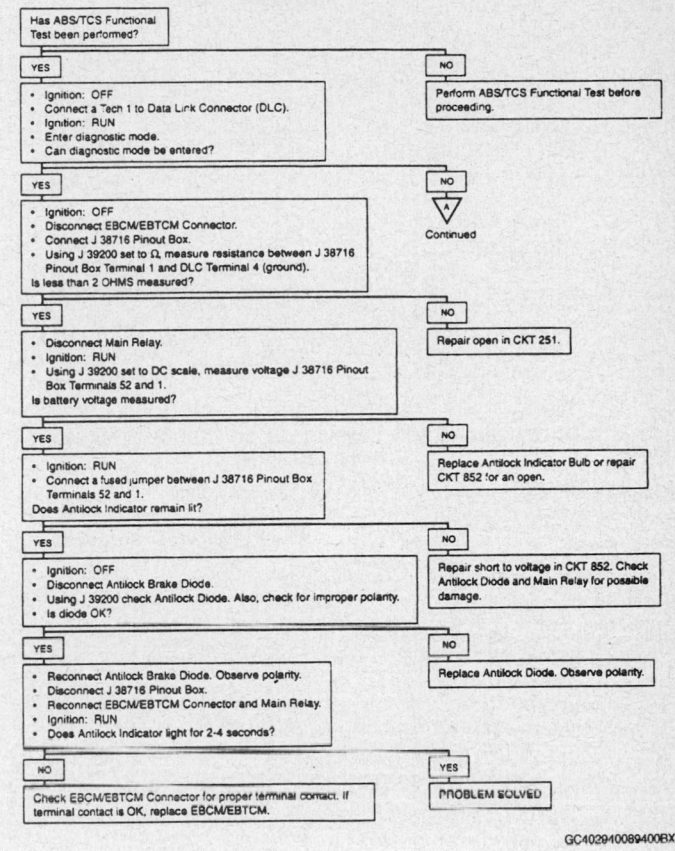

"ANTILOCK" INDICATOR LAMP DOES NOT FUNCTION

CIRCUIT OPERATION

When the ignition switch is first turned to "RUN" the EBCM/EBTCM goes through a self-test lasting 2-4 seconds. During this test, the EBCM/EBTCM grounds terminal 52, causing the amber "ANTILOCK" indicator to light. This serves as an indicator bulb test. The EBCM/EBTCM also grounds terminal 34, energizing the main relay. This removes the indicator ground path provided through the antilock diode and the main relay contacts.

When the self-test is completed (and no faults detected) the EBCM/EBTCM removes the ground at terminal 52, turning off the indicator. The main relay remains energized.

When the EBCM/EBTCM detects a fault, it grounds terminal 52 causing the amber "ANTILOCK" indicator to light. (Note: The EBCM/EBTCM also de-energizes the main relay creating a redundant ground path.)

When the EBCM/EBTCM is disabled for any reason (i.e. open Fuse 5B), the main relay is de-energized. This provides an "ANTILOCK" indicator ground path through the antilock diode and main relay contacts, and causes the indicator to light with no DTC being set.

FAILURE CONDITIONS

Possible Causes

- Open in CKT 251, 852 or 1633.
- Open bulb.
- Short to voltage in CKT 852.
- Open or shorted antilock diode.
- Main relay fails "engaged."
- Short to ground in CKT 1632.

GC402940089400AX

Has ABS/TCS Functional Test been performed?

- NO: Perform ABS/TCS Functional Test before proceeding.
- YES:
  - Ignition: OFF
  - Connect a Tech 1 to Data Link Connector (DLC).
  - Ignition: RUN
  - Enter diagnostic mode.
  - Can diagnostic mode be entered?

- NO: (A) Continued
- YES:
  - Ignition: OFF
  - Disconnect EBCM/EBTCM Connector.
  - Connect J 38716 Pinout Box.
  - Using J 39200 set to Ω, measure resistance between J 38716 Pinout Box Terminal 1 and DLC Terminal 4 (ground).
  - Is less than 2 OHMS measured?

- NO: Repair open in CKT 251.
- YES:
  - Disconnect Main Relay.
  - Ignition: RUN
  - Using J 39200 set to DC scale, measure voltage J 38716 Pinout Box Terminals 52 and 1.
  - Is battery voltage measured?

- NO: Replace Antilock Indicator Bulb or repair CKT 852 for an open.
- YES:
  - Ignition: RUN
  - Connect a fused jumper between J 38716 Pinout Box Terminals 52 and 1.
  - Does Antilock Indicator remain lit?

- NO: Repair short to voltage in CKT 852. Check Antilock Diode and Main Relay for possible damage.
- YES:
  - Ignition: OFF
  - Disconnect Antilock Brake Diode.
  - Using J 39200 check Antilock Diode. Also, check for improper polarity.
  - Is diode OK?

- NO: Replace Antilock Diode. Observe polarity.
- YES:
  - Reconnect Antilock Brake Diode. Observe polarity.
  - Disconnect J 38716 Pinout Box.
  - Reconnect EBCM/EBTCM Connector and Main Relay.
  - Ignition: RUN
  - Does Antilock Indicator light for 2-4 seconds?

- NO: Check EBCM/EBTCM Connector for proper terminal contact. If terminal contact is OK, replace EBCM/EBTCM.
- YES: PROBLEM SOLVED

GC402940089400BX

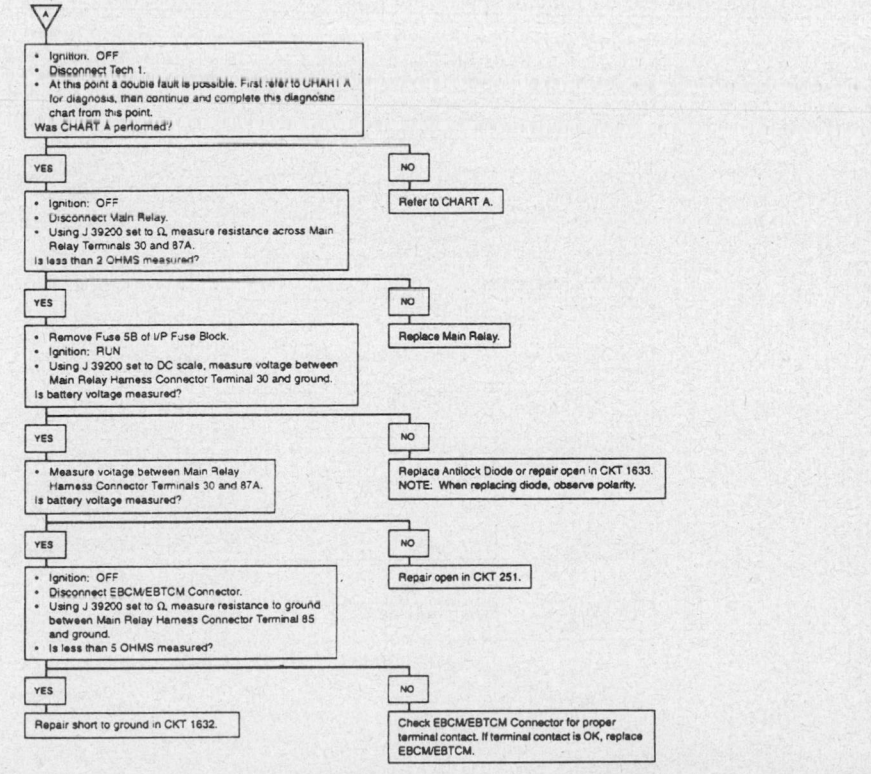

(A)

- Ignition: OFF
- Disconnect Tech 1.
- At this point a double fault is possible. First refer to CHART A for diagnosis, then continue and complete this diagnostic chart from this point.
- Was CHART A performed?

- NO: Refer to CHART A.
- YES:
  - Ignition: OFF
  - Disconnect Main Relay.
  - Using J 39200 set to Ω, measure resistance across Main Relay Terminals 30 and 87A.
  - Is less than 2 OHMS measured?

- NO: Replace Main Relay.
- YES:
  - Remove Fuse 5B of I/P Fuse Block.
  - Ignition: RUN
  - Using J 39200 set to DC scale, measure voltage between Main Relay Harness Connector Terminal 30 and ground.
  - Is battery voltage measured?

- NO: Replace Antilock Diode or repair open in CKT 1633. NOTE: When replacing diode, observe polarity.
- YES:
  - Measure voltage between Main Relay Harness Connector Terminals 30 and 87A.
  - Is battery voltage measured?

- NO: Repair open in CKT 251.
- YES:
  - Ignition: OFF
  - Disconnect EBCM/EBTCM Connector.
  - Using J 39200 set to Ω, measure resistance to ground between Main Relay Harness Connector Terminal 85 and ground.
  - Is less than 5 OHMS measured?

- NO: Check EBCM/EBTCM Connector for proper terminal contact. If terminal contact is OK, replace EBCM/EBTCM.
- YES: Repair short to ground in CKT 1632.

GC402940089400CX

Fig. 44 Test B: ABS Lamp Does Not Function. 1994 Bonneville, 88 & 98

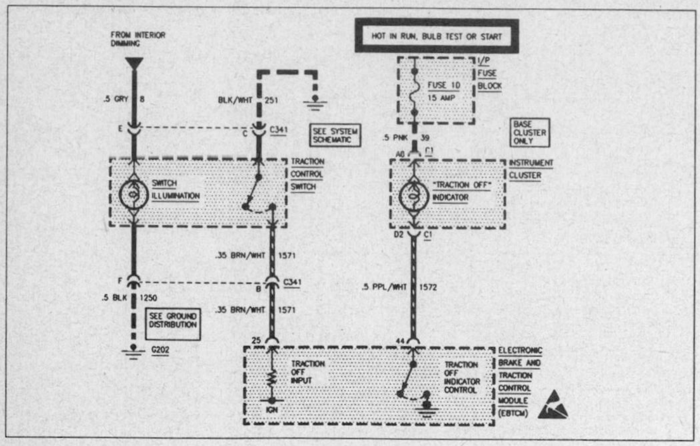
FROM INTERIOR DIMMING
HOT IN RUN, BULB TEST OR START
I/P FUSE BLOCK
FUSE 10 15 AMP
SEE SYSTEM SCHEMATIC
BASE CLUSTER ONLY
SWITCH ILLUMINATION
TRACTION CONTROL SWITCH
"TRACTION OFF" INDICATOR
INSTRUMENT CLUSTER
SEE GROUND DISTRIBUTION
G202
TRACTION OFF INPUT
TRACTION OFF INDICATOR CONTROL
ELECTRONIC BRAKE AND TRACTION CONTROL MODULE (EBTCM)

CHART C

"TRACTION OFF" INDICATOR LAMP IS ON CONTINUOUSLY AND NO DTC(s) SET

CIRCUIT OPERATION

When the ignition is first turned to "RUN," the EBTCM goes through a self-test. During this test, the EBTCM grounds both the "ANTILOCK" and "TRACTION OFF" indicators for approximately 2 to 4 seconds. This acts as a bulb test for the indicators.

Traction Control Switch

Located in the center console trim plate, the switch allows the driver to select the traction control mode (on/off). When the traction control system is turned off, the "TRACTION OFF" indicator remains illuminated.

Transaxle Temperature

The EBTCM monitors transaxle temperature through information provided by the PCM. When the transaxle becomes hot, about 160°C(320°F), the EBTCM disables the traction control system and turns on the "TRACTION OFF" indicator. This allows the brakes and transaxle to cool down. When the transaxle cools to 149°C (300°F) the EBTCM keeps the "TRACTION OFF" indicator on and the system disabled for an additional three to five minutes to allow for sufficient cooling.

FAILURE CONDITIONS

Possible Causes

- Short to ground in CKT 1571 or 1572.
- Faulty traction control switch.
- Faulty EBTCM

Important

- When the vehicle is equipped with traction control, any symptom which lights the "ANTILOCK" indicator also lights the "TRACTION OFF" indicator. Therefore, when both indicators are lit, follow "ANTILOCK" indicator diagnosis when no diagnostic trouble codes are set.

GC402940089500AX

Bonneville

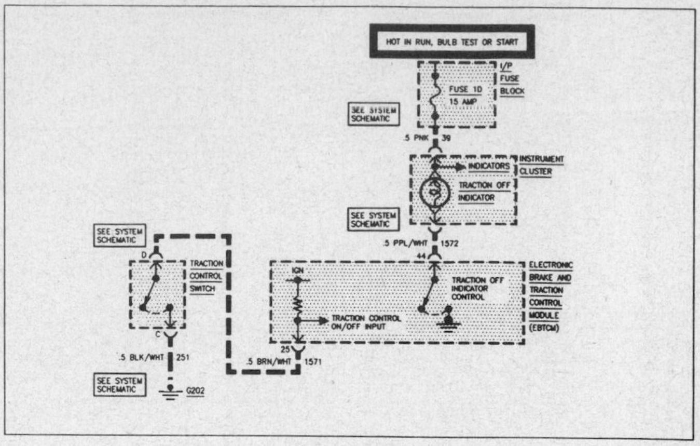
HOT IN RUN, BULB TEST OR START
I/P FUSE BLOCK
FUSE 10 15 AMP
SEE SYSTEM SCHEMATIC
INDICATORS
INSTRUMENT CLUSTER
TRACTION OFF INDICATOR
TRACTION CONTROL SWITCH
TRACTION OFF INDICATOR CONTROL
TRACTION CONTROL ON/OFF INPUT
ELECTRONIC BRAKE AND TRACTION CONTROL MODULE (EBTCM)
G202

CHART C

"TRACTION OFF" INDICATOR LAMP IS ON CONTINUOUSLY AND NO DTC(s) SET

CIRCUIT OPERATION

When the ignition is first turned to "RUN," the EBTCM goes through a self-test. During this test, the EBTCM grounds both the "ANTILOCK" and "TRACTION OFF" indicators for approximately 2 to 4 seconds. This acts as a bulb test for the indicators.

Traction Control Switch

Located in the instrument panel center trim plate, the switch allows the driver to select the traction control mode (on/off). When the traction control system is turned off, the "TRACTION OFF" indicator remains illuminated.

Transaxle Temperature

The EBTCM monitors transaxle temperature through information provided by the PCM. When the transaxle becomes hot, about 160°C (320°F), the EBTCM disables the traction control system and turns on the "TRACTION OFF" indicator. This allows the brakes and transaxle to cool down. When the transaxle cools to 149°C (300°F) the EBTCM keeps the "TRACTION OFF" indicator on and the system disabled for an additional three to five minutes to allow for sufficient cooling.

FAILURE CONDITIONS

Possible Causes

- Short to ground in CKT 1571 or 1572.
- Faulty traction control switch.
- Faulty EBTCM

Important

- When the vehicle is equipped with traction control, any symptom which lights the "ANTILOCK" indicator also lights the "TRACTION OFF" indicator. Therefore, when both indicators are lit, follow "ANTILOCK" indicator diagnosis when no diagnostic trouble codes are set.

GC402940089500BX

88 & 98

Has ABS/TCS Functional Test been performed?

- NO: Perform ABS/TCS Functional Test before proceeding.
- YES:
  - Ignition: OFF
  - Disconnect EBTCM Connector.
  - Install J 38716 Pinout Box.
  - Using J 39200 set to Ω, measure resistance between J 38716 Pinout Box Terminal 1 and Data Link Connector (DLC) Terminal 4 (ground).

  Is less than 2 OHMS measured?

  - NO: Repair open in CKT 251.
  - YES:
    - Measure resistance between J 38716 Pinout Box Terminal 1 and 44.

    Is less than 5 OHMS measured?

    - YES:
      - Check CKT 1572 for short to ground.
      - Is short to ground present?
        - YES: Repair CKT 1572
        - NO: Replace EBTCM.
    - NO:
      - Measure resistance between J 38716 Pinout Box Terminal 1 and 25.

      Is less than 5 OHMS measured?

      - NO: No trouble found. Refer to "INTERMITTENTS AND POOR CONNECTIONS"
      - YES: Check/repair CKT 1571 for a short to ground. If CKT 1571 is OK, replace Traction Control Switch.

GC402940089500CX

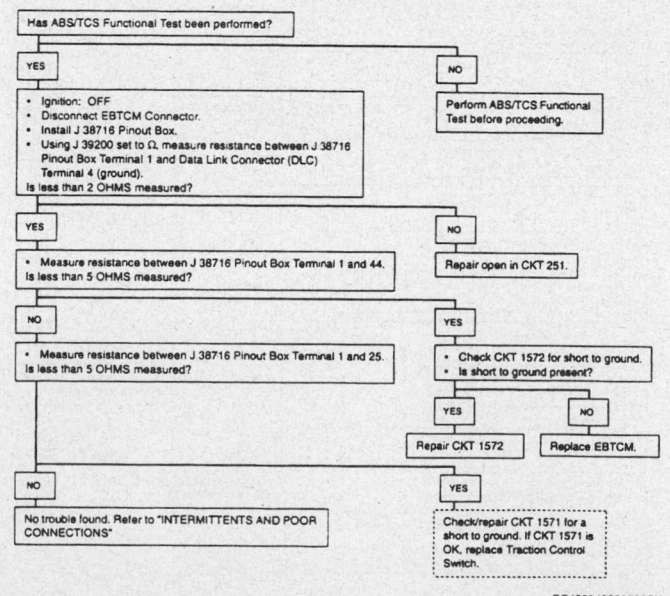

Fig. 45 Test C: Traction Off Lamp Is On Continuously w/No Codes Set. 1994 Bonneville, 88 & 98

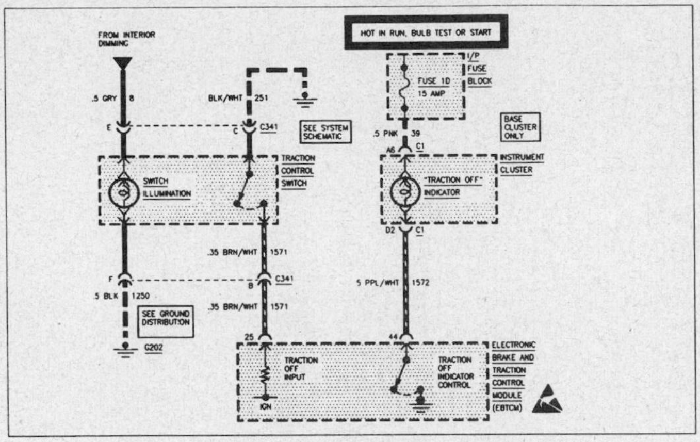
HOT IN RUN, BULB TEST OR START
FROM INTERIOR DIMMING
I/P FUSE BLOCK
FUSE 10 15 AMP
BASE CLUSTER ONLY
SEE SYSTEM SCHEMATIC
TRACTION CONTROL SWITCH
SWITCH ILLUMINATION
INSTRUMENT CLUSTER
"TRACTION OFF" INDICATOR
SEE GROUND DISTRIBUTION
G202
ELECTRONIC BRAKE AND TRACTION CONTROL MODULE (EBTCM)
TRACTION OFF INPUT
TRACTION OFF INDICATOR CONTROL

CHART D

"TRACTION OFF" INDICATOR LAMP DOES NOT FUNCTION

CIRCUIT OPERATION

When the ignition is first turned to "RUN," the EBTCM goes through a self-test. During this test, the EBCM grounds both the "ANTILOCK" and "TRACTION OFF" indicators for approximately 2 to 4 seconds. This acts as a bulb test for the indicators.

Traction Control Switch

Located in the center console trim plate, the switch allows the driver to select the traction control mode (on/off). When the traction control system is turned off, the "TRACTION OFF" indicator remains illuminated.

FAILURE CONDITIONS

Possible Causes

- Open in CKT 251, 1571 or 1572.
- Open bulb.
- Faulty traction control switch.

Important

- When the vehicle is equipped with traction control, any symptom which lights the "ANTILOCK" indicator also lights the "TRACTION OFF" indicator. Therefore, when both indicators are lit, follow "ANTILOCK" indicator diagnosis when no diagnostic trouble codes are set.

GC40294008960OAX

Bonneville

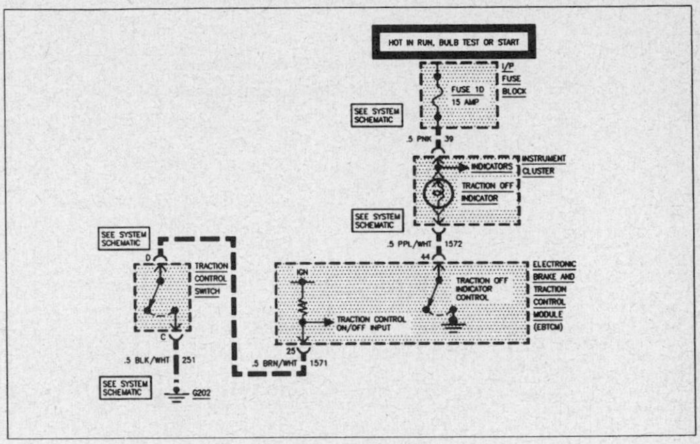
HOT IN RUN, BULB TEST OR START
I/P FUSE BLOCK
FUSE 10 15 AMP
SEE SYSTEM SCHEMATIC
INSTRUMENT CLUSTER
INDICATORS
TRACTION OFF INDICATOR
TRACTION CONTROL SWITCH
ELECTRONIC BRAKE AND TRACTION CONTROL MODULE (EBTCM)
TRACTION OFF INDICATOR CONTROL
TRACTION CONTROL ON/OFF INPUT
G202

CHART D

"TRACTION OFF" INDICATOR LAMP DOES NOT FUNCTION

CIRCUIT OPERATION

When the ignition is first turned to "RUN," the EBTCM goes through a self-test. During this test, the EBCM grounds both the "ANTILOCK" and "TRACTION OFF" indicators for approximately 2 to 4 seconds. This acts as a bulb test for the indicators.

Traction Control Switch

Located in the instrument panel center trim plate, the switch allows the driver to select the traction control mode (on/off). When the traction control system is turned off, the "TRACTION OFF" indicator remains illuminated.

FAILURE CONDITIONS

Possible Causes

- Open in CKT 251, 1571 or 1572.
- Open bulb.
- Faulty traction control switch.

Important

- When the vehicle is equipped with traction control, any symptom which lights the "ANTILOCK" indicator also lights the "TRACTION OFF" indicator. Therefore, when both indicators are lit, follow "ANTILOCK" indicator diagnosis when no diagnostic trouble codes are set.

GC40294008960OBX

88 & 98

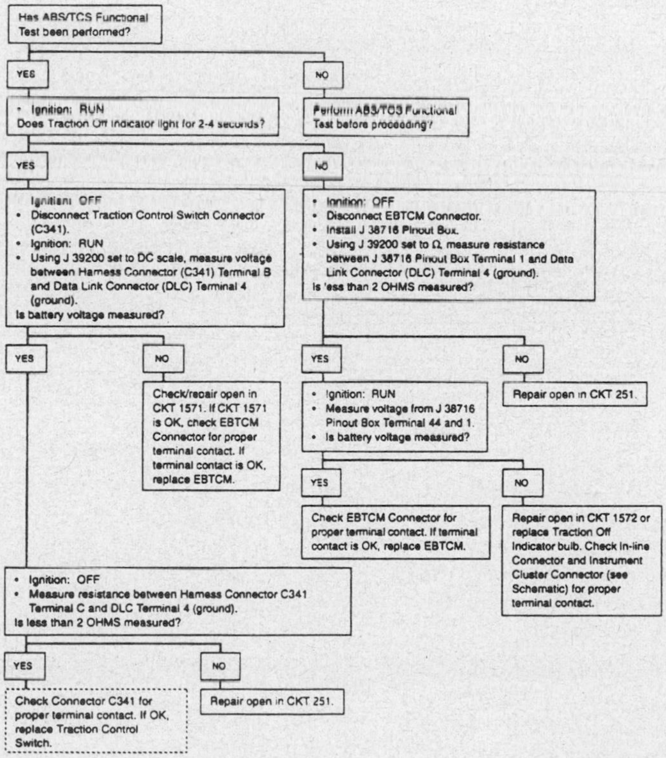
Has ABS/TCS Functional Test been performed?
YES
NO
• Ignition: RUN
Does Traction Off indicator light for 2-4 seconds?
Perform ABS/TCS Functional Test before proceeding?
YES
NO
• Ignition: OFF
• Disconnect Traction Control Switch Connector (C341).
• Ignition: RUN
• Using J 39200 set to DC scale, measure voltage between Harness Connector (C341) Terminal B and Data Link Connector (DLC) Terminal 4 (ground).
Is battery voltage measured?
• Ignition: OFF
• Disconnect EBTCM Connector.
• Install J 38716 Pinout Box.
• Using J 39200 set to Ω, measure resistance between J 38716 Pinout Box Terminal 1 and Data Link Connector (DLC) Terminal 4 (ground).
Is less than 2 OHMS measured?
YES
NO
YES
NO
Check/repair open in CKT 1571. If CKT 1571 is OK, check EBTCM Connector for proper terminal contact. If terminal contact is OK, replace EBTCM.
• Ignition: RUN
• Measure voltage from J 38716 Pinout Box Terminal 44 and 1.
• Is battery voltage measured?
Repair open in CKT 251.
YES
NO
Check EBTCM Connector for proper terminal contact. If terminal contact is OK, replace EBTCM.
Repair open in CKT 1572 or replace Traction Off Indicator bulb. Check In-line Connector and Instrument Cluster Connector (see Schematic) for proper terminal contact.
• Ignition: OFF
• Measure resistance between Harness Connector C341 Terminal C and DLC Terminal 4 (ground).
Is less than 2 OHMS measured?
YES
NO
Check Connector C341 for proper terminal contact. If OK, replace Traction Control Switch.
Repair open in CKT 251.

GC40294008960OCX

Fig. 46 Test D: Traction Off Lamp Does Not Function. 1994 Bonneville, 88 & 98

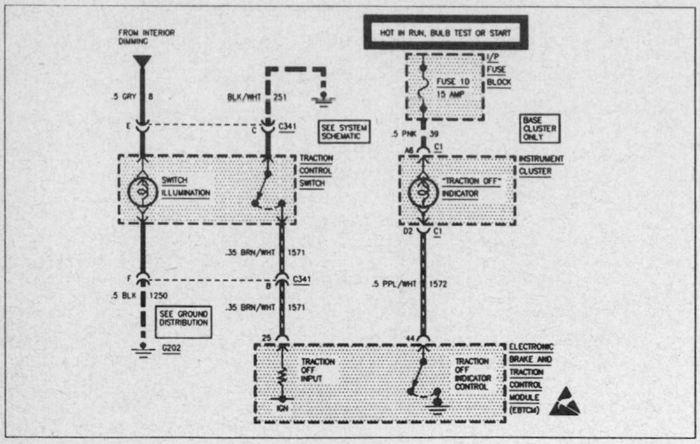
FROM INTERIOR DIMMING
HOT IN RUN, BULB TEST OR START
I/P FUSE BLOCK
FUSE 1D 15 AMP
.5 GRY 8
BLK/WHT 251
E
C
C341
SEE SYSTEM SCHEMATIC
.5 PNK 39
BASE CLUSTER ONLY
A6 C1
TRACTION CONTROL SWITCH
SWITCH ILLUMINATION
INSTRUMENT CLUSTER
"TRACTION OFF" INDICATOR
D2 C1
.35 BRN/WHT 1571
F
B
C341
.5 BLK 1250
.5 PPL/WHT 1572
SEE GROUND DISTRIBUTION
.35 BRN/WHT 1571
G202
25
44
TRACTION OFF INPUT
IGN
TRACTION OFF INDICATOR CONTROL
ELECTRONIC BRAKE AND TRACTION CONTROL MODULE (EBTCM)

CHART E

TRACTION CONTROL SWITCH LAMP DOES NOT OPERATE PROPERLY

CIRCUIT OPERATION

The traction control switch illumination bulb is on whenever the key is in the RUN, BULB TEST, or START position. It is not serviced seperately from the traction control switch. The traction control switch illumination is not illuminated when there is an ABS or TCS system failure.

GC402940089700AX

Bonneville

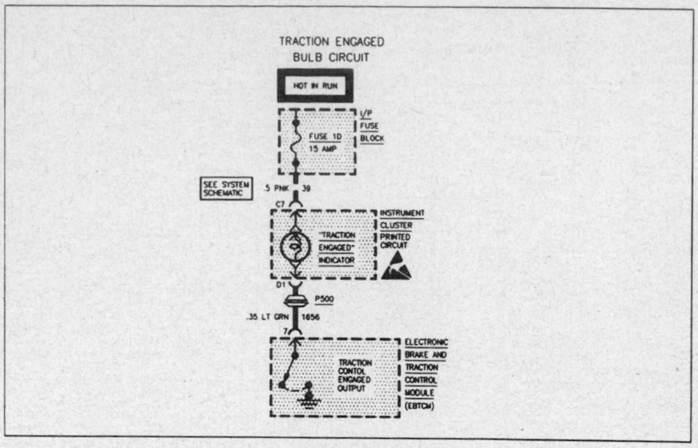
TRACTION ENGAGED BULB CIRCUIT
HOT IN RUN
I/P FUSE BLOCK
FUSE 1D 15 AMP
SEE SYSTEM SCHEMATIC
.5 PNK 39
C7
"TRACTION ENGAGED" INDICATOR
INSTRUMENT CLUSTER PRINTED CIRCUIT
D1
P500
.35 LT GRN 1656
7
TRACTION CONTOL ENGAGED OUTPUT
ELECTRONIC BRAKE AND TRACTION CONTROL MODULE (EBTCM)

CHART E

"TRACTION ENGAGED" INDICATOR LAMP DOES NOT OPERATE PROPERLY

CIRCUIT OPERATION

When the EBTCM is operating in the traction control mode, the EBTCM's traction control engaged output (terminal 7) closes, grounding either the instrument cluster's DIC traction control engaged input or the traction control switch LED. The EBTCM grounds this terminal to alert the driver that the traction control system (TCS) is operating.

GC402940089700BX

88 & 98

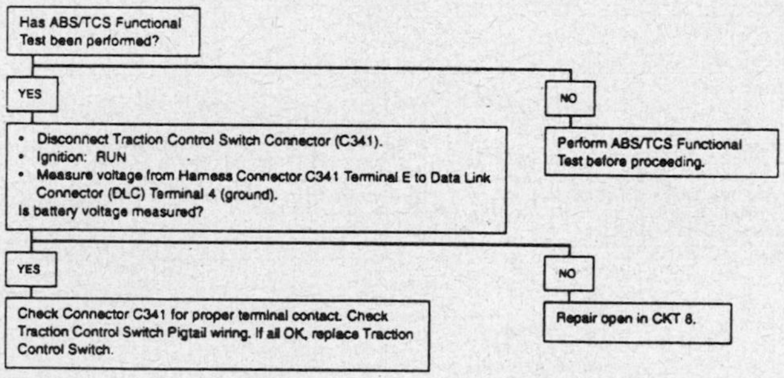
Has ABS/TCS Functional Test been performed?
YES
NO
• Disconnect Traction Control Switch Connector (C341).
• Ignition: RUN
• Measure voltage from Harness Connector C341 Terminal E to Data Link Connector (DLC) Terminal 4 (ground).
Is battery voltage measured?
Perform ABS/TCS Functional Test before proceeding.
YES
NO
Check Connector C341 for proper terminal contact. Check Traction Control Switch Pigtail wiring. If all OK, replace Traction Control Switch.
Repair open in CKT 8.

GC402940089700CX

Fig. 47 Test E: Traction Control Switch Lamp Does Not Function Properly. 1994 Bonneville, 88 & 98

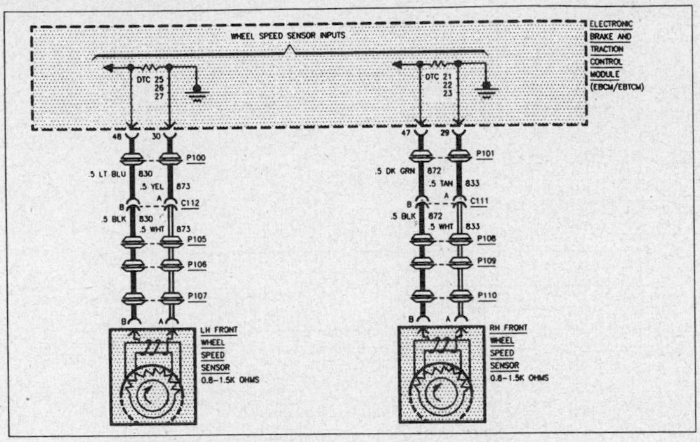
ELECTRONIC BRAKE AND TRACTION CONTROL MODULE (EBCM/EBTCM)
WHEEL SPEED SENSOR INPUTS
DTC 25 26 27
DTC 21 22 23
P100
P101
C112
C111
P105
P106
P107
P108
P109
P110
LH FRONT WHEEL SPEED SENSOR 0.8–1.5K OHMS
RH FRONT WHEEL SPEED SENSOR 0.8–1.5K OHMS

DTC(s) 21, 25

FRONT WHEEL SPEED SENSOR CIRCUIT TEST

CIRCUIT OPERATION

As each wheel turns, the wheel speed sensor creates an AC voltage with a frequency proportional to wheel speed. This magnetically induced voltage is caused by a toothed sensor ring (mounted on the drive axle) passing the wheel speed sensor's stationary pickup coil.

The EBCM/EBTCM uses the wheel speed sensor signal to calculate vehicle reference speeds and individual wheel speed, acceleration and slip values. These values are used to determine when antilock (or when equipped) traction control is required.

WHEEL SPEED SENSOR CABLES

In order to prevent electromagnetic interference from disturbing the wheel speed sensor signal, the cables from the EBCM/EBTCM to each wheel speed sensor are twisted in pairs a minimum of 6 to 9 turns per foot.

When servicing the sensor cables it is important to maintain the original cable's twists (6 to 9 turns per foot).

FAILURE CONDITIONS

The EBCM/EBTCM performs two basic checks on the wheel speed sensors: sensor continuity and sensor output. When the ignition is first turned to "RUN," the EBCM/EBTCM performs the wheel speed sensor continuity check.

Sensor Continuity Check

Any condition which would result in lack of continuity in the front wheel speed sensor circuit could result in a DTC 21 or 25 being set. These conditions include an open, a short to ground, or a short between the two wheel speed sensor circuits in the wiring harness between the speed sensor and EBCM/EBTCM. Also an open or short to ground across the wheel speed sensor coil could trigger this code.

GC402940089800AX

Has ABS/TCS functional test been performed?

NO: Perform ABS/TCS functional test before proceeding.

YES:
- Ignition: OFF
- Raise vehicle.
- Disconnect suspect front Wheel Speed Sensor Connector.
- Check connector for proper terminal contact.
- Using J 39200 set to Ω, measure resistance between suspect Wheel Speed Sensor Terminal A and B.

Is 800 to 1500 ohms measured?

NO: Replace suspect front Wheel Speed Sensor.

YES:
- Measure resistance between suspect front Wheel Speed Sensor Terminal B and ground.

Is infinite ohms measured?

NO: Replace suspect front Wheel Speed Sensor.

YES:
- Reconnect Wheel Speed Sensor.
- Disconnect Wheel Speed Sensor Jumper Harness.
- Check connector for proper terminal contact.
- Measure resistance between Jumper Harness Terminals A and B (sensor side).

Is 800 to 1500 ohms measured?

NO: Replace suspect front Wheel Speed Sensor Jumper Harness.

YES:
- Reconnect Wheel Speed Sensor Jumper Harness.
- Disconnect EBCM/EBTCM Connector.
- Check connector for proper terminal contact.
- Install J 38716 Pinout Box.
- Measure resistance between terminals indicated for suspected front Wheel Speed Sensor Circuit:
  - Left Front Wheel - Terminals 30 and 48
  - Right Front Wheel - Terminals 29 and 47

Is 800 to 1500 ohms measured?

NO: Above 1500 ohms (remember to check in-line connector [see schematic] and Wheel Speed Sensor Connector for proper terminal contact):
When left front wheel, repair open in CKT 830 or 873.
When right front wheel, repair open in CKT 833 or 872.
Below 800 ohms:
When left front wheel, repair short between CKT 830 and 873.
When right front wheel, repair short between CKT 833 and 872.

YES:
- Measure resistance between J 38716 Pinout Box Terminal 1 and Data Link Connector (DLC) Terminal 4 (ground).

Is less than 5 ohms measured?

NO: Repair open in CKT 251.

YES:
- Measure resistance at J 38716 Pinout Box Terminals indicated for suspected front Wheel Speed Sensor Circuit:
  - Left Front Wheel - Terminal 48 and 1
  - Right Front Wheel - Terminal 47 and 1

Is less than 5 ohms measured?

NO: Check EBCM/EBTCM Connector for proper terminal contact. If terminal contact is OK, reconnect EBCM/EBTCM, clear DTC and test drive vehicle. If DTC resets, replace EBTCM. If DTC does not reset, refer to Intermittants and Poor Connections.

YES: When left front wheel, repair short to ground in CKT 830 or 873. When right front wheel, repair short to ground in CKT 872 or 833.

GC402940089800BX

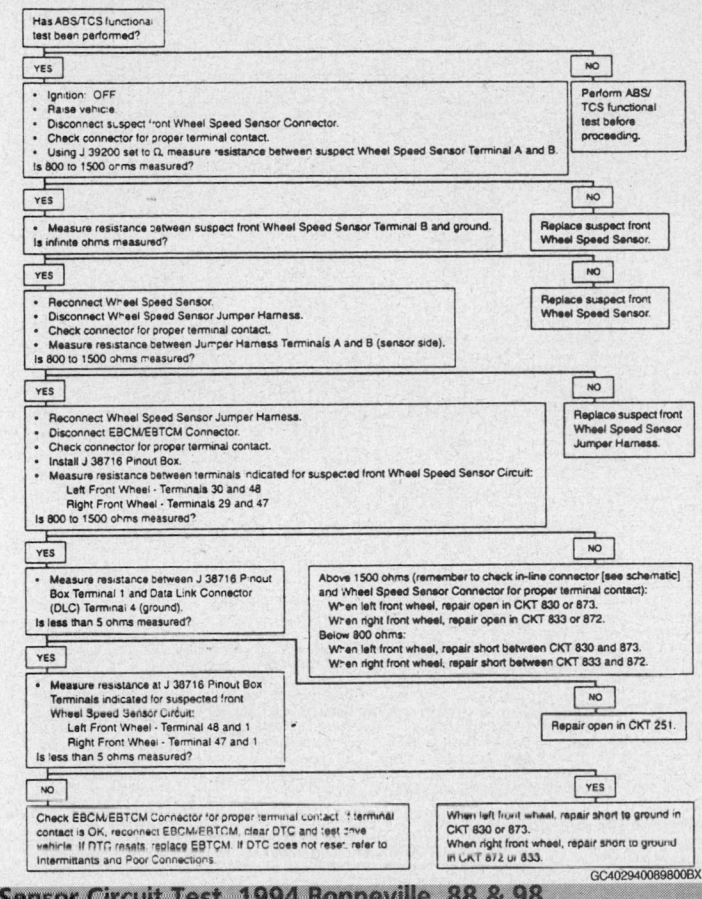

Fig. 48 Code 21 & 25: Front Wheel Speed Sensor Circuit Test. 1994 Bonneville, 88 & 98

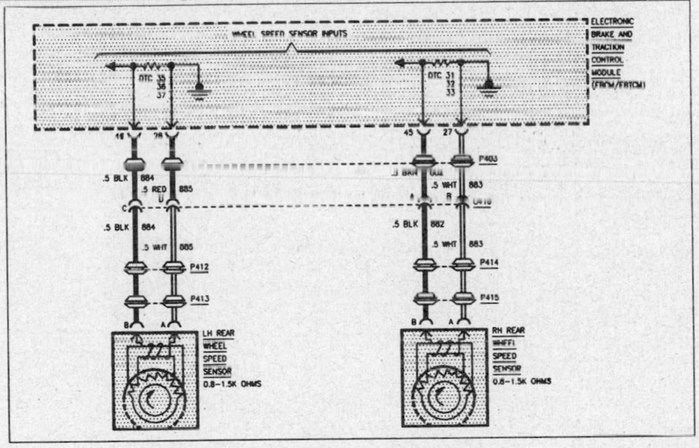
ELECTRONIC BRAKE AND TRACTION CONTROL MODULE (EBCM/EBTCM)
WHEEL SPEED SENSOR INPUTS
P403
P412
P413
P414
P415
LH REAR WHEEL SPEED SENSOR 0.8–1.5K OHMS
RH REAR WHEEL SPEED SENSOR 0.8–1.5K OHMS

DTC(s) 31, 35

REAR WHEEL SPEED SENSOR CIRCUIT OPEN OR SHORTED

CIRCUIT OPERATION

When each wheel turns, the wheel speed sensor creates a small AC voltage with a frequency proportional to wheel speed. This magnetically induced voltage is caused by a toothed sensor ring passing the wheel speed sensor's stationary pickup coil. Both sensors are part of the hub and bearing assembly.

The EBCM/EBTCM uses the wheel speed sensor signal to calculate vehicle reference speeds and individual wheel speed, acceleration and slip values. These values are used to determine when antilock traction control is required.

WHEEL SPEED SENSOR CABLES

In order to prevent electromagnetic interference from disturbing the wheel speed sensor signal, the cables from the EBCM/EBTCM to each wheel speed sensor are twisted in pairs a minimum of 6 to 9 turns per foot.

When servicing the sensor cables it is important to maintain the original cable's twists (6 to 9 turns per foot).

FAILURE CONDITIONS

The EBCM/EBTCM performs two basic checks on the wheel speed sensors: sensor continuity and sensor output. When the ignition is first turned to "RUN," the EBCM/EBTCM performs the wheel speed sensor continuity check.

Sensor Continuity Check

Any condition which would result in lack of continuity in the rear wheel speed sensor circuit could result in a DTC 31 or 35 being set. These conditions include an open, a short to ground, or a short between the two wheel speed sensor circuits in the wiring harness between the speed sensor and EBCM/EBTCM. Also an open or short to ground across the wheel speed sensor coil could trigger this DTC.

GC402940089900AX

Has ABS/TCS functional test been performed?

NO: Perform ABS/TCS functional test before proceeding.

YES:
- Ignition: OFF
- Park Brake: RELEASED
- Raise vehicle.
- Disconnect suspect rear Wheel Speed Sensor Connector at wheel.
- Check connector for proper terminal contact.
- Using J 39200 set to Ω, measure resistance between suspect Wheel Speed Sensor Terminal A and B.

Is 800 to 1500 ohms measured?

NO: Replace suspect rear Wheel Speed Sensor.

YES:
- Measure resistance between suspect rear Wheel Speed Sensor Terminal B and ground.

Is infinite ohms measured?

NO: Replace suspect rear Wheel Speed Sensor.

YES:
- Reconnect Wheel Speed Sensor.
- Disconnect Wheel Speed Jumper Harness.
- Check connector for proper terminal contact.
- Measure resistance between Jumper Harness Terminals A and B if right side Wheel Speed Sensor is suspect or Terminals D and C if left side Wheel Speed Sensor is suspect.

Is 800 to 1500 ohms measured?

NO: Replace Wheel Speed Sensor Jumper Harness.

YES:
- Reconnect Wheel Speed Sensor Jumper Harness.
- Disconnect EBCM/EBTCM Connector.
- Check connector for proper terminal contact.
- Install J 38716 Pinout Box.
- Measure resistance between terminals indicated for suspected rear Wheel Speed Sensor Circuit:
  - Left Rear Wheel - Terminals 28 and 46
  - Right Rear Wheel - Terminals 27 and 45

Is 800 to 1500 ohms measured?

NO: Above 1500 ohms (remember to check in-line connector [see schematic] and Wheel Speed Sensor Connector for proper terminal contact):
When left rear wheel, repair open in CKT 884 or 885.
When right rear wheel, repair open in CKT 882 or 883.
Below 800 ohms:
When left rear wheel, repair short between CKT 884 and 885.
When right rear wheel, repair short between CKT 882 and 883.

YES:
- Measure resistance between J 38716 Pinout Box Terminal 1 and Data Link Connector (DLC) Terminal A (ground).

Is less than 5 ohms measured?

NO: Repair open in CKT 251.

YES:
- Measure resistance at J 38716 Pinout Box Terminals indicated for suspected rear Wheel Speed Sensor Circuit:
  - Left Rear Wheel - Terminal 46 and 1
  - Right Rear Wheel - Terminal 45 and 1

Is less than 5 ohms measured?

NO: Check EBCM/EBTCM Connector for proper terminal contact. If terminal contact is OK, reconnect EBCM/EBTCM, clear DTC and test drive vehicle. If DTC resets, replace EBTCM. If DTC does not reset, refer to Intermittants and Poor Connections in this section.

YES: When left rear wheel, repair short to ground in CKT 884 or 885. When right rear wheel, repair short to ground in CKT 882 or 883.

GC402940089900BX

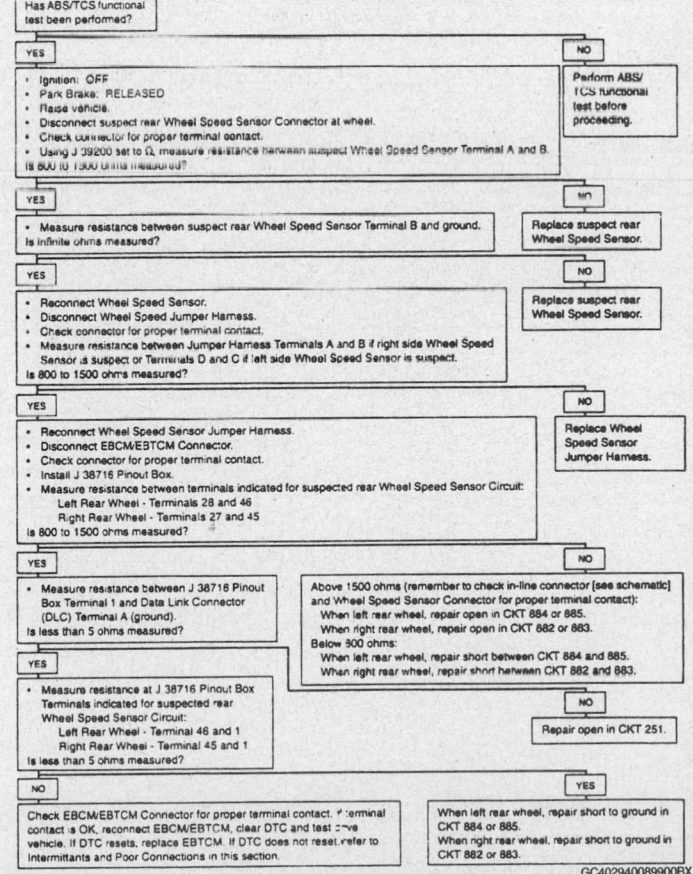

Fig. 49 Code 31 & 35: Rear Wheel Speed Circuit Test. 1994 Bonneville, 88 & 98

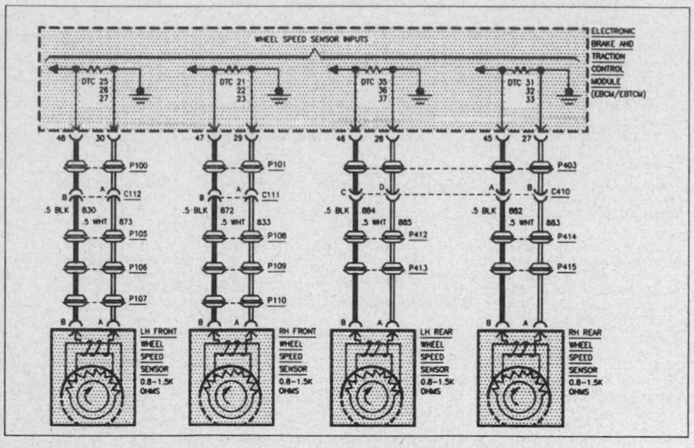
WHEEL SPEED SENSOR INPUTS
ELECTRONIC BRAKE AND TRACTION CONTROL MODULE (EBCM/EBTCM)
DTC 25 26 27
DTC 21 22 23
DTC 35 36 37
DTC 31 32 33
P100
P101
P403
C112
C111
C410
P105
P108
P412
P414
P106
P109
P413
P415
P107
P110
LH FRONT WHEEL SPEED SENSOR 0.8–1.5K OHMS
RH FRONT WHEEL SPEED SENSOR 0.8–1.5K OHMS
LH REAR WHEEL SPEED SENSOR 0.8–1.5K OHMS
RH REAR WHEEL SPEED SENSOR 0.8–1.5K OHMS

DTC(s) 22, 23, 26, 27, 32, 33, 36, 37

WHEEL SPEED SIGNAL ERRATIC OR MISSING

CIRCUIT OPERATION

When each wheel turns, the wheel speed sensor creates a small AC voltage with a frequency proportional to wheel speed. This magnetically induced voltage is caused by a toothed sensor ring passing the wheel speed sensor's stationary pickup coil. The toothed ring sensor is mounted on the drive axle in the front, and in the hub/bearing assembly in the rear.

The EBCM/EBTCM uses the wheel speed sensor signal to calculate vehicle reference speeds, and individual wheel speed, acceleration and slip values. These values are used to determine when antilock control is required. Vehicles equipped with traction control also use front wheel speed sensor signals to determine when traction control is required.

WHEEL SPEED SENSOR CABLES

In order to prevent electromagnetic interference from disturbing the wheel speed sensor signal, the cables from the EBCM/EBTCM to each wheel speed sensor are twisted in pairs a minimum of 6 to 9 turns per foot.

When servicing the sensor cables it is important to maintain the original cables' twist (6 to 9 turns per foot).

FAILURE CONDITIONS

DTC 22, DTC 26, DTC 33 or DTC 36 sets when the EBCM/EBTCM detects electromagnetic interference (noise) in a wheel speed sensor signal. Possible interference sources include accessory motors, wiper motors, ignition circuits and any add-on or "After Market" equipment.

DTC 22, DTC 26, DTC 32 or DTC 36 also sets when the EBCM/EBTCM determines a wheel speed signal is erratic. A wheel speed signal indicating that a wheel is accelerating or decelerating faster than physically possible is an example of an erratic signal. An intermittent open or short to ground in a wheel speed sensor could also cause the EBCM/EBTCM to set a DTC.

DTC 23, DTC 27, DTC 33, or DTC 37 sets when the EBCM/EBTCM does not see any wheel speed sensor signal, but determines continuity exists in the circuit. This is cause by a dislodged wheel speed sensor, missing toothed sensor ring (front) or defective hub and bearing assembly (rear).

GC402940090000AX

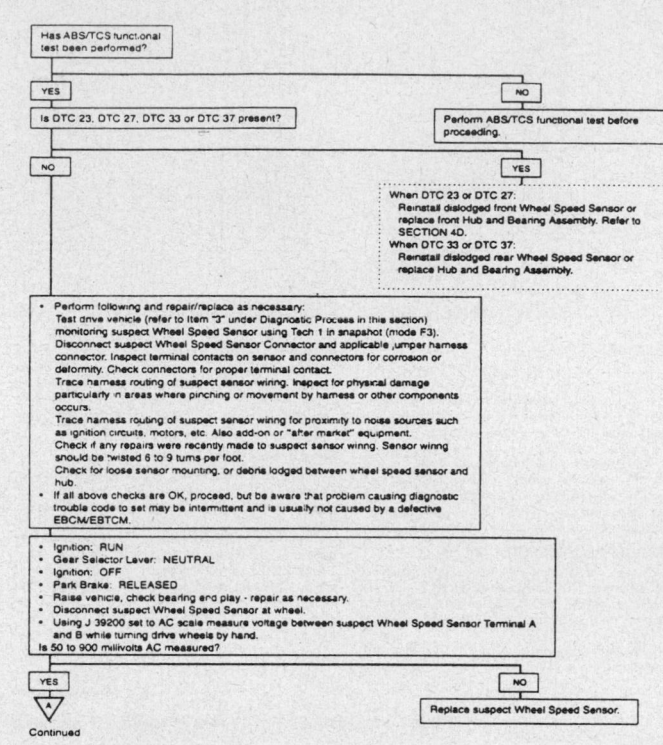

Has ABS/TCS functional test been performed?

YES

Is DTC 23, DTC 27, DTC 33 or DTC 37 present?

NO

Perform ABS/TCS functional test before proceeding.

(DTC present?) YES

When DTC 23 or DTC 27:
Reinstall dislodged front Wheel Speed Sensor or replace front Hub and Bearing Assembly. Refer to SECTION 4D.
When DTC 33 or DTC 37:
Reinstall dislodged rear Wheel Speed Sensor or replace Hub and Bearing Assembly.

(DTC present?) NO

- Perform following and repair/replace as necessary:
  Test drive vehicle (refer to Item "3" under Diagnostic Process in this section) monitoring suspect Wheel Speed Sensor using Tech 1 in snapshot (mode F3).
  Disconnect suspect Wheel Speed Sensor Connector and applicable jumper harness connector. Inspect terminal contacts on sensor and connectors for corrosion or deformity. Check connectors for proper terminal contact.
  Trace harness routing of suspect sensor wiring. Inspect for physical damage particularly in areas where pinching or movement by harness or other components occurs.
  Trace harness routing of suspect sensor wiring for proximity to noise sources such as ignition circuits, motors, etc. Also add-on or "after market" equipment.
  Check if any repairs were recently made to suspect sensor wiring. Sensor wiring should be twisted 6 to 9 turns per foot.
  Check for loose sensor mounting, or debris lodged between wheel speed sensor and hub.
- If all above checks are OK, proceed, but be aware that problem causing diagnostic trouble code to set may be intermittent and is usually not caused by a defective EBCM/EBTCM.

- Ignition: RUN
- Gear Selector Lever: NEUTRAL
- Ignition: OFF
- Park Brake: RELEASED
- Raise vehicle, check bearing end play - repair as necessary.
- Disconnect suspect Wheel Speed Sensor at wheel.
- Using J 39200 set to AC scale measure voltage between suspect Wheel Speed Sensor Terminal A and B while turning drive wheels by hand.

Is 50 to 900 milivolts AC measured?

YES → A Continued

NO → Replace suspect Wheel Speed Sensor.

GC402940090000BX

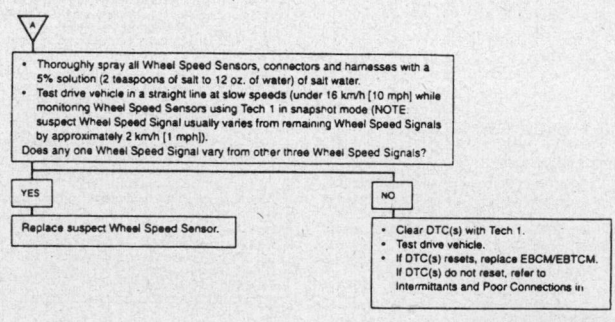

A

- Thoroughly spray all Wheel Speed Sensors, connectors and harnesses with a 5% solution (2 teaspoons of salt to 12 oz. of water) of salt water.
- Test drive vehicle in a straight line at slow speeds (under 16 km/h [10 mph] while monitoring Wheel Speed Sensors using Tech 1 in snapshot mode (NOTE: suspect Wheel Speed Signal usually varies from remaining Wheel Speed Signals by approximately 2 km/h [1 mph]).

Does any one Wheel Speed Signal vary from other three Wheel Speed Signals?

YES → Replace suspect Wheel Speed Sensor.

NO →
- Clear DTC(s) with Tech 1.
- Test drive vehicle.
- If DTC(s) resets, replace EBCM/EBTCM.
  If DTC(s) do not reset, refer to Intermittants and Poor Connections in

GC402940090000CX

Fig. 50 Code 22, 23, 26, 27, 32, 33, 36 & 37: Wheel Speed Signal Erratic Or Missing. 1994 Bonneville, 88 & 98

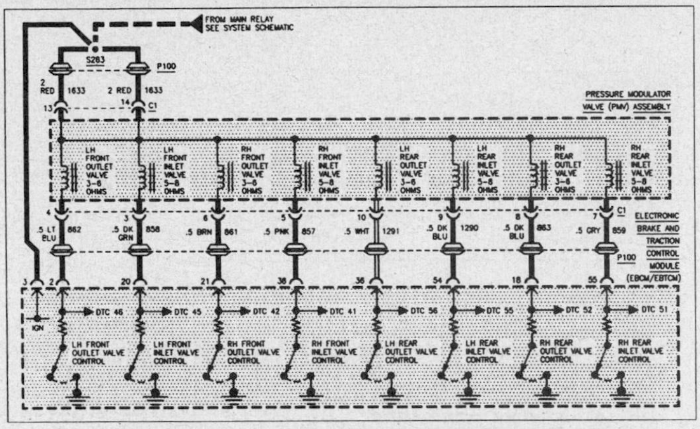
FROM MAIN RELAY SEE SYSTEM SCHEMATIC
S283
P100
C1
PRESSURE MODULATOR VALVE (PMV) ASSEMBLY
LH FRONT OUTLET VALVE 3-6 OHMS
LH FRONT INLET VALVE 5-8 OHMS
RH FRONT OUTLET VALVE 3-6 OHMS
RH FRONT INLET VALVE 5-8 OHMS
LH REAR OUTLET VALVE 3-6 OHMS
LH REAR INLET VALVE 5-8 OHMS
RH REAR OUTLET VALVE 3-6 OHMS
RH REAR INLET VALVE 5-8 OHMS
ELECTRONIC BRAKE AND TRACTION CONTROL MODULE (EBCM/EBTCM)
DTC 46
DTC 45
DTC 42
DTC 41
DTC 56
DTC 55
DTC 52
DTC 51
LH FRONT OUTLET VALVE CONTROL
LH FRONT INLET VALVE CONTROL
RH FRONT OUTLET VALVE CONTROL
RH FRONT INLET VALVE CONTROL
LH REAR OUTLET VALVE CONTROL
LH REAR INLET VALVE CONTROL
RH REAR OUTLET VALVE CONTROL
RH REAR INLET VALVE CONTROL

DTC(s) 41, 42, 45, 46, 51, 52, 55, 56
INLET/OUTLET VALVE CIRCUIT OPEN OR SHORTED

CIRCUIT OPERATION

Inlet Valves

Voltage is applied to the normally open inlet valves whenever the main relay is energized. An inlet valve closes when the EBCM/EBTCM supplies a ground path at the inlet valve control terminal. The EBCM/EBTCM closes an inlet valve for short periods to maintain (hold) or reduce pressure at a particular wheel.

Outlet Valves

The normally closed outlet valves operate similarly to the inlet valves, except that when the EBCM/EBTCM grounds an outlet valve, the valve opens instead of closes. The EBCM/EBTCM opens an outlet valve for short periods to reduce pressure at a particular wheel.

VALVE MODES

Pressure Increase

The pressure increase position is the operating valve position for normal (non-ABS) braking and traction control mode (when equipped). The EBCM/EBTCM does not energize either valve, leaving the inlet valve open and the outlet valve closed.

Pressure Hold

The pressure hold position occurs when the EBCM/EBTCM first notices an impending wheel lockup condition. This signifies and over abundance of hydraulic brake pressure at the locking wheel. The EBCM/EBTCM closes the corresponding inlet valve in an attempt to avoid any additional hydraulic pressure increase at the wheel.

Pressure Reduce

During a wheel lockup condition, the EBCM/EBTCM closes the inlet valve while pulsing open the outlet valve. This decreases hydraulic pressure at a specific wheel without decreasing overall system pressure. The reduced hydraulic pressure allows greater wheel spin, eliminating the wheel lockup condition.

Test Description

This test checks for proper inlet and outlet valve operation. The wheel brake behavior must be checked to verify the valves hydraulic effectiveness. This is accomplished using a Tech 1 to actuate the valves.

Failure conditions

DTC 41, 42, 45, 46, 51, 52, 55, or 56 sets when the EBCM/EBTCM detects an open or short to ground in the respective inlet or outlet valve circuit.

GC102940090200AX

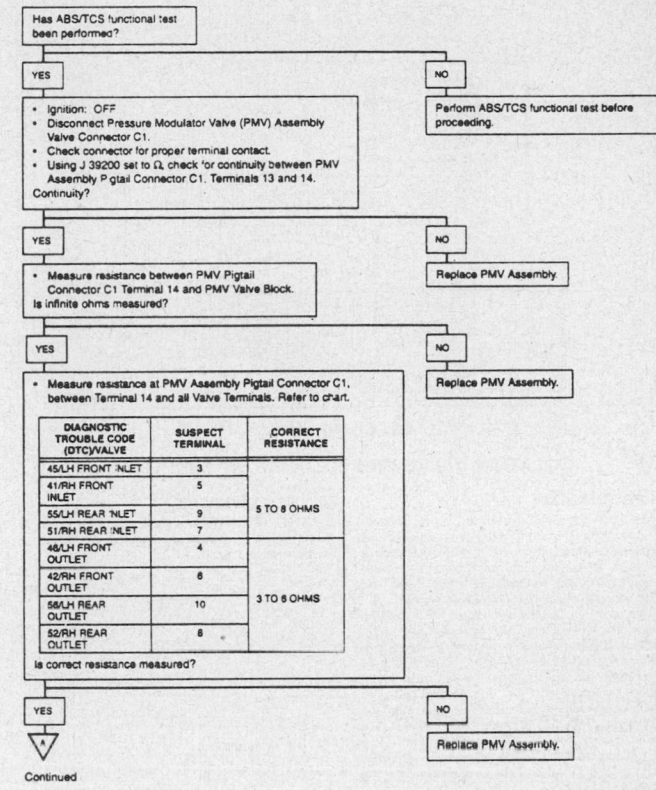

Has ABS/TCS functional test been performed?

NO: Perform ABS/TCS functional test before proceeding.

YES:
- Ignition: OFF
- Disconnect Pressure Modulator Valve (PMV) Assembly Valve Connector C1.
- Check connector for proper terminal contact.
- Using J 39200 set to Ω, check for continuity between PMV Assembly Pigtail Connector C1, Terminals 13 and 14.

Continuity?

NO: Replace PMV Assembly.

YES:
- Measure resistance between PMV Pigtail Connector C1 Terminal 14 and PMV Valve Block.

Is infinite ohms measured?

NO: Replace PMV Assembly.

YES:
- Measure resistance at PMV Assembly Pigtail Connector C1, between Terminal 14 and all Valve Terminals. Refer to chart.

DIAGNOSTIC TROUBLE CODE (DTC)/VALVE	SUSPECT TERMINAL	CORRECT RESISTANCE
45/LH FRONT INLET	3	5 TO 8 OHMS
41/RH FRONT INLET	5	
55/LH REAR INLET	9	
51/RH REAR INLET	7	
46/LH FRONT OUTLET	4	3 TO 6 OHMS
42/RH FRONT OUTLET	6	
56/LH REAR OUTLET	10	
52/RH REAR OUTLET	8	

Is correct resistance measured?

NO: Replace PMV Assembly.

YES: A

Continued

GC102010000200BX

A

- Reconnect PMV Assembly Valve Connector C1.
- Disconnect EBCM/EBTCM Connector.
- Install J 38716 Pinout Box.
- Measure resistance between J 38716 Pinout Box Terminal 3 and all Valve Terminals. Refer to Chart.

DIAGNOSTIC TROUBLE CODE (DTC)/VALVE	J 38716 TERMINAL	CORRECT RESISTANCE
45/LH FRONT INLET	20	5 TO 8 OHMS
41/RH FRONT INLET	38	
55/LH REAR INLET	54	
51/RH REAR INLET	55	
46/LH FRONT OUTLET	2	3 TO 6 OHMS
42/RH FRONT OUTLET	21	
56/LH REAR OUTLET	36	
52/RH REAR OUTLET	18	

Is resistance measured less than 10 ohms?

NO: Repair open in Suspect Valve Circuit between Pressure Modulator Valve (PVM) Assembly and EBCM/EBTCM.

YES:
- Measure resistance between J 38716 Pinout Box Terminal 1 and Data Link Connector (DLC) Terminal 4 (ground).

Is less than 5 ohms measured?

NO: Repair open in CKT 251.

YES:
- Disconnect Main Relay.
- Measure resistance between J 38716 Pinout Box Terminal 1 and all Valve Terminals. Refer to Chart.

DIAGNOSTIC TROUBLE CODE (DTC)/VALVE	J 38716 TERMINAL	CORRECT RESISTANCE
45/LH FRONT INLET	20	INFINITE OHMS
41/RH FRONT INLET	38	
55/LH REAR INLET	54	
51/RH REAR INLET	55	
46/LH FRONT OUTLET	2	
42/RH FRONT OUTLET	21	
56/LH REAR OUTLET	36	
52/RH REAR OUTLET	18	

Is infinite ohms measured?

NO: Repair short to ground in suspect valve circuit between PMV Assembly and EBCM/EBTCM.

YES:
- Reinstall main relay.
- IGNITION: RUN
- Using J 39200 set to DC scale, measure voltage between Pinout Box Terminal 1 and suspect valve terminal.

Is more than 2 volts measured?

YES: Repair short to battery in suspect valve circuit.

NO:
- If diagnosing DTC 45, return to DTC 45 chart.

If not, Check EBCM/EBTCM connector for proper terminal contact. If terminal contact is OK, replace EBCM/EBTCM.

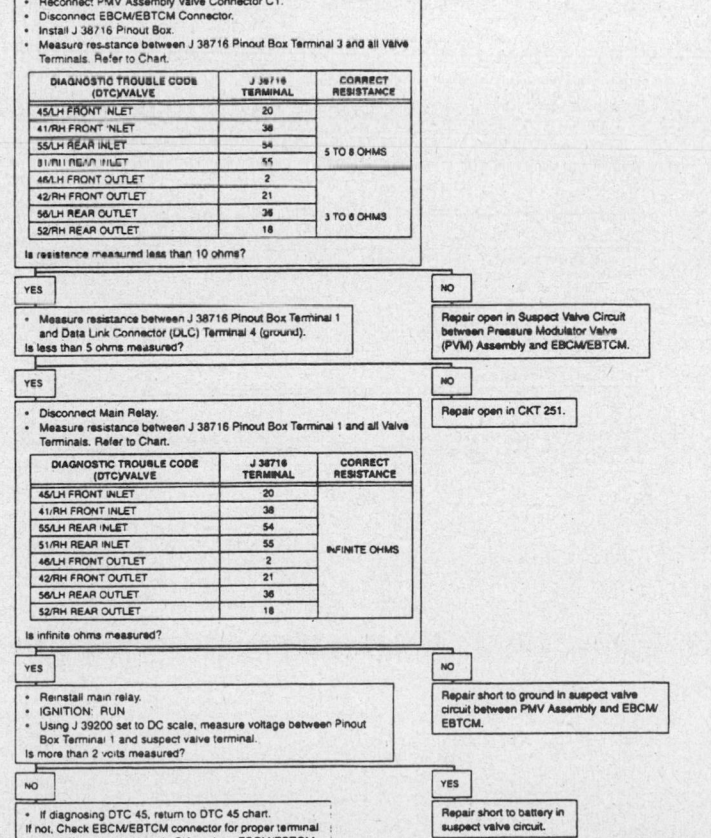

GC402940090200CX

Fig. 51 Code 41, 42, 46, 51, 52, 55 & 56: Inlet/Outlet Valve Circuit Open Or Shorted. 1994 Bonneville, 88 & 98

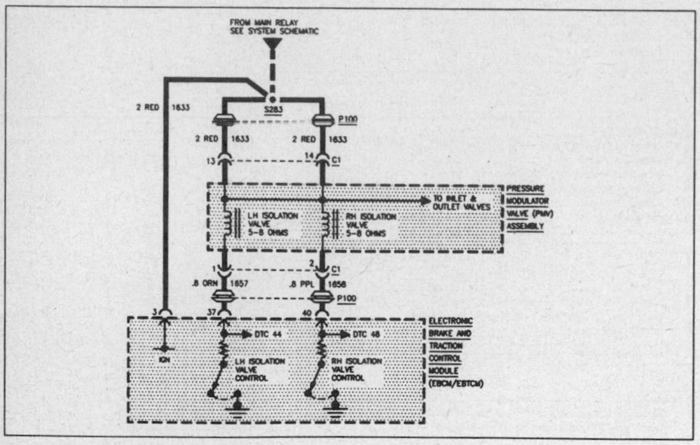
FROM MAIN RELAY
SEE SYSTEM SCHEMATIC
2 RED 1633
S283
P100
2 RED 1633
2 RED 1633
13
14
C1
PRESSURE
MODULATOR
VALVE (PMV)
ASSEMBLY
TO INLET &
OUTLET VALVES
LH ISOLATION
VALVE
5–8 OHMS
RH ISOLATION
VALVE
5–8 OHMS
1
2
C1
.8 ORN 1657
.8 PPL 1658
P100
3
37
40
ELECTRONIC
BRAKE AND
TRACTION
CONTROL
MODULE
(EBCM/EBTCM)
DTC 44
DTC 48
IGN
LH ISOLATION
VALVE
CONTROL
RH ISOLATION
VALVE
CONTROL

DTC(s) 44, 48

ISOLATION VALVE CIRCUIT OPEN OR SHORTED

CIRCUIT OPERATION

Voltage is applied to the normally open isolation valves whenever the main relay is energized. An isolation valve closes when the EBTCM supplies a ground path at the isolation valve control terminal. The EBTCM closes an isolation valve when the EBTCM detects wheel slip in a drive wheel.

The isolation valves are closed only during traction control operations, and are not used during antilock or normal braking conditions. The isolation valves separate (isolate) the front brake hydraulic circuits from the master cylinder and rear brake hydraulic circuits. Once the front brake hydraulic circuits are isolated, pressure can be applied to the front wheels without affecting any other brake hydraulic circuit. The EBTCM turns on the PMV motor to apply pressure, and begins cycling the PMV assembly inlet and outlet valves to modulate pressure.

FAILURE CONDITIONS

DTC 44 or DTC 48 sets when the EBTCM detects an open or short to ground in the respective isolation valve circuit.

GC402940090300AX

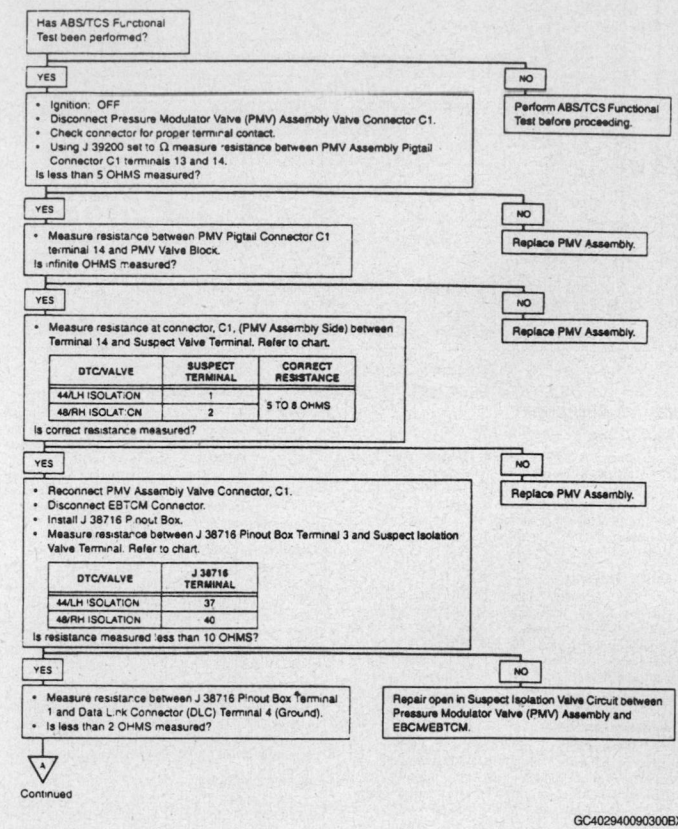

Has ABS/TCS Functional Test been performed?

NO: Perform ABS/TCS Functional Test before proceeding.

YES:
- Ignition: OFF
- Disconnect Pressure Modulator Valve (PMV) Assembly Valve Connector C1.
- Check connector for proper terminal contact.
- Using J 39200 set to Ω measure resistance between PMV Assembly Pigtail Connector C1 terminals 13 and 14.

Is less than 5 OHMS measured?

NO: Replace PMV Assembly.

YES:
- Measure resistance between PMV Pigtail Connector C1 terminal 14 and PMV Valve Block.

Is infinite OHMS measured?

NO: Replace PMV Assembly.

YES:
- Measure resistance at connector, C1, (PMV Assembly Side) between Terminal 14 and Suspect Valve Terminal. Refer to chart.

DTC/VALVE	SUSPECT TERMINAL	CORRECT RESISTANCE
44/LH ISOLATION	1	5 TO 8 OHMS
48/RH ISOLATION	2	

Is correct resistance measured?

NO: Replace PMV Assembly.

YES:
- Reconnect PMV Assembly Valve Connector, C1.
- Disconnect EBTCM Connector.
- Install J 38716 Pinout Box.
- Measure resistance between J 38716 Pinout Box Terminal 3 and Suspect Isolation Valve Terminal. Refer to chart.

DTC/VALVE	J 38716 TERMINAL
44/LH ISOLATION	37
48/RH ISOLATION	40

Is resistance measured less than 10 OHMS?

NO: Repair open in Suspect Isolation Valve Circuit between Pressure Modulator Valve (PMV) Assembly and EBCM/EBTCM.

YES:
- Measure resistance between J 38716 Pinout Box Terminal 1 and Data Link Connector (DLC) Terminal 4 (Ground).
- Is less than 2 OHMS measured?

A Continued

GC402940090300BX

A

NO: Repair open in CKT 251.

YES:
- Disconnect Main Relay.
- Measure resistance between J 38716 Pinout Box Terminal 1 and Suspect Isolation Valve Terminal. Refer to chart.

DTC/VALVE	J 38716 TERMINAL
44/LH ISOLATION	37
48/RH ISOLATION	40

Is less than 5 OHMS measured?

NO: Check EBTCM Connector for proper terminal contact. If terminal contact is OK, replace EBTCM.

YES: Repair short to ground in Suspect Isolation Valve Circuit between Pressure Modulator Valve (PMV) Assembly and EBTCM.

GC402940090300CX

Fig. 52 Code 44 & 48: Isolation Valve Circuit Open Or Shorted. 1994 Bonneville, 88 & 98

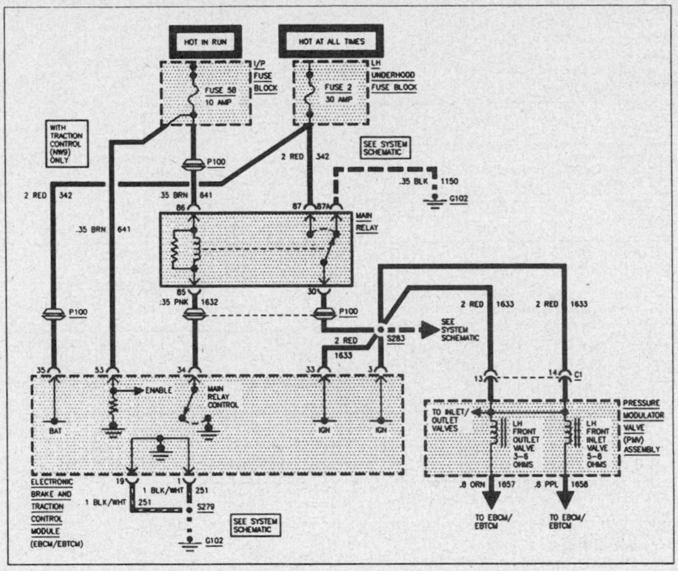
HOT IN RUN
HOT AT ALL TIMES
FUSE 5B 10 AMP
I/P FUSE BLOCK
FUSE 2 30 AMP
LH UNDERHOOD FUSE BLOCK
WITH TRACTION CONTROL (NW9) ONLY
SEE SYSTEM SCHEMATIC
MAIN RELAY
P100
G102
S283
S279
ENABLE
MAIN RELAY CONTROL
BAT
IGN
TO INLET/OUTLET VALVES
LH FRONT OUTLET VALVE 3-6 OHMS
LH FRONT INLET VALVE 5-8 OHMS
PRESSURE MODULATOR VALVE (PMV) ASSEMBLY
TO EBCM/EBTCM
ELECTRONIC BRAKE AND TRACTION CONTROL MODULE (EBCM/EBTCM)

DTC 45

POWER INTERRUPTION FAULT

CIRCUIT OPERATION

When the ignition is first turned to "RUN," the EBCM/EBTCM goes through a self-check lasting 2-4 seconds. During this test the EBCM/EBTCM grounds terminal 34, energizing the main relay. Once the self-check is completed the main relay remains energized. This delivers battery voltage to both the EBCM/EBTCM and the pressure modulator valve (PMV) assembly during vehicle operation. The constant voltage supply allows the vehicle to enter ABS mode without delay. The main relay is de energized whenever the amber "ANTILOCK" indicator lights due to a system fault, causing the ABS system to shut down.

FAILURE CONDITION

DTC 45 sets when the ignition switch is at "RUN" and battery voltage is neither detected at the PMV assembly nor EBCM/EBTCM terminal 20, 3 and/or 33. Code 45 also sets when the EBCM/EBTCM detects an open or a short to ground in the LH inlet valve circuit.

Possible Causes

- Open in CKT 641, 1632, 858, 1633, or 342.
- Short to ground in CKT 858, 1633, or 342.
- Main relay fails "open."

DIAGNOSTIC AIDS

DTC 45 may also set when the vehicle is hot (running for a minimum of 30 minutes) check PMV valve resistance and main relay coil resistance when vehicle is hot.

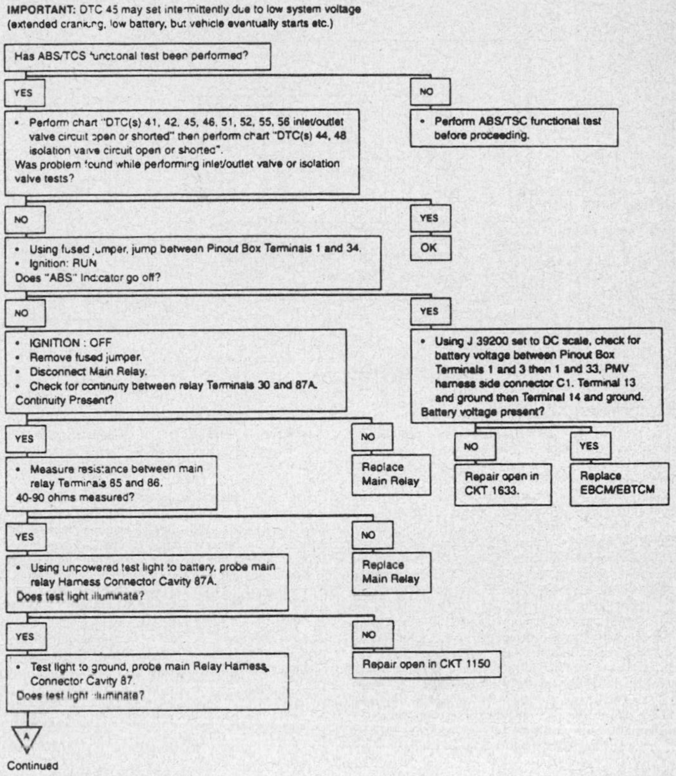
IMPORTANT: DTC 45 may set intermittently due to low system voltage (extended cranking, low battery, but vehicle eventually starts etc.)
Has ABS/TCS functional test been performed?
YES
NO
• Perform ABS/TSC functional test before proceeding.
• Perform chart "DTC(s) 41, 42, 45, 46, 51, 52, 55, 56 inlet/outlet valve circuit open or shorted" then perform chart "DTC(s) 44, 48 isolation valve circuit open or shorted".
Was problem found while performing inlet/outlet valve or isolation valve tests?
NO
YES
OK
• Using fused jumper, jump between Pinout Box Terminals 1 and 34.
• Ignition: RUN
Does "ABS" Indicator go off?
NO
YES
• IGNITION : OFF
• Remove fused jumper.
• Disconnect Main Relay.
• Check for continuity between relay Terminals 30 and 87A.
Continuity Present?
• Using J 39200 set to DC scale, check for battery voltage between Pinout Box Terminals 1 and 3 then 1 and 33, PMV harness side connector C1. Terminal 13 and ground then Terminal 14 and ground.
Battery voltage present?
YES
NO
Replace Main Relay
NO
YES
Repair open in CKT 1633.
Replace EBCM/EBTCM
• Measure resistance between main relay Terminals 85 and 86.
40-90 ohms measured?
YES
NO
Replace Main Relay
• Using unpowered test light to battery, probe main relay Harness Connector Cavity 87A.
Does test light illuminate?
YES
NO
Repair open in CKT 1150
• Test light to ground, probe main Relay Harness Connector Cavity 87.
Does test light illuminate?
A
Continued

GC402940090100BX

GC402940090100AX

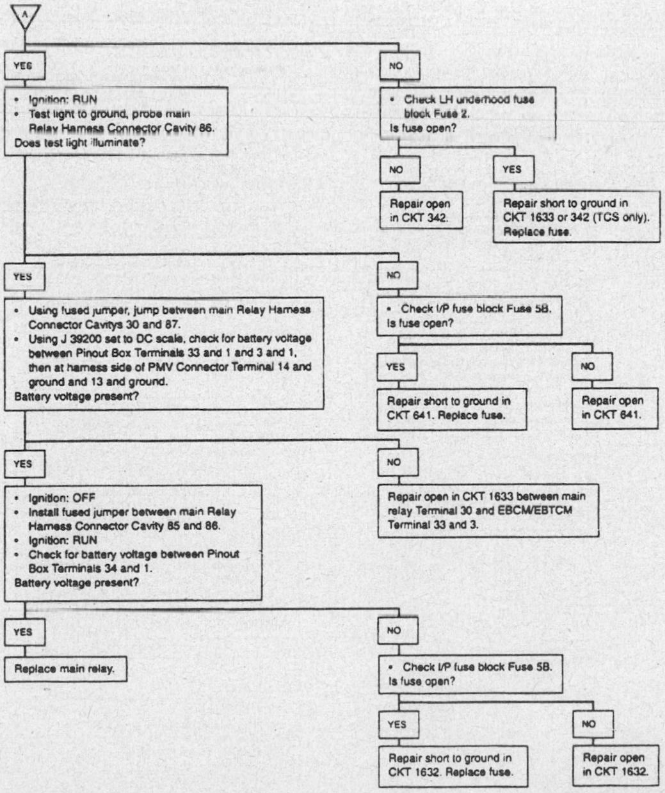
A
YES
NO
• Ignition: RUN
• Test light to ground, probe main Relay Harness Connector Cavity 86.
Does test light illuminate?
• Check LH underhood fuse block Fuse 2.
Is fuse open?
NO
YES
Repair open in CKT 342.
Repair short to ground in CKT 1633 or 342 (TCS only). Replace fuse.
YES
NO
• Using fused jumper, jump between main Relay Harness Connector Cavitys 30 and 87.
• Using J 39200 set to DC scale, check for battery voltage between Pinout Box Terminals 33 and 1 and 3 and 1, then at harness side of PMV Connector Terminal 14 and ground and 13 and ground.
Battery voltage present?
• Check I/P fuse block Fuse 5B.
Is fuse open?
YES
NO
Repair short to ground in CKT 641. Replace fuse.
Repair open in CKT 641.
YES
NO
• Ignition: OFF
• Install fused jumper between main Relay Harness Connector Cavity 85 and 86.
• Ignition: RUN
• Check for battery voltage between Pinout Box Terminals 34 and 1.
Battery voltage present?
Repair open in CKT 1633 between main relay Terminal 30 and EBCM/EBTCM Terminal 33 and 3.
YES
NO
Replace main relay.
• Check I/P fuse block Fuse 5B.
Is fuse open?
YES
NO
Repair short to ground in CKT 1632. Replace fuse.
Repair open in CKT 1632.

GC402940090100CX

Fig. 53 Code 45: Power Interruption Fault. 1994 Bonneville, 88 & 98

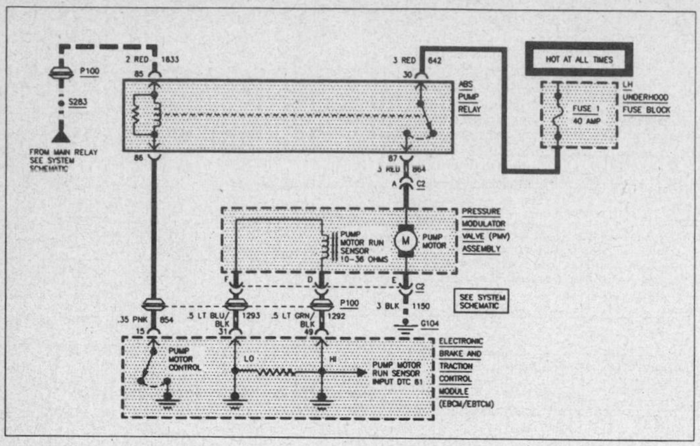
P100
S283
FROM MAIN RELAY SEE SYSTEM SCHEMATIC
2 RED 1833
85
86
3 RED 642
30
ABS PUMP RELAY
HOT AT ALL TIMES
FUSE 1 40 AMP
LH UNDERHOOD FUSE BLOCK
87
3 RED 864
A C2
PUMP MOTOR RUN SENSOR 10-36 OHMS
M
PUMP MOTOR
PRESSURE MODULATOR VALVE (PMV) ASSEMBLY
F
D
E C2
P100
3 BLK 1150
G104
SEE SYSTEM SCHEMATIC
.35 PNK 854
.5 LT BLU/BLK 1293
.5 LT GRN/BLK 1292
15
31
49
PUMP MOTOR CONTROL
LO
HI
PUMP MOTOR RUN SENSOR INPUT DTC 61
ELECTRONIC BRAKE AND TRACTION CONTROL MODULE (EBCM/EBTCM)

DTC 61

PUMP MOTOR CIRCUIT TEST

CIRCUIT OPERATION

When the EBCM/EBTCM grounds terminal 15, the pump relay contacts close applying voltage to the pressure modulator valve (PMV) assembly's pump motor. The EBCM/EBTCM turns on the pump motor during most ABS braking conditions (and when equipped) during all traction control conditions.

When the pump motor runs during ABS braking, the PMV assembly reservoir is replenished and fluid pressure is applied to the master cylinder. This causes the brake pedal to rise gradually. The pump motor runs until the brake pedal sufficiently rises to close the TCC/antilock brake switch.

During traction control mode, after the front hydraulic circuits are isolated, the pump motor runs to increase brake fluid pressure in these circuits. The increased pressure is directed to the slipping wheel through the PMV assembly's front inlet and outlet valves. This causes the brakes to be applied, reducing wheel spin at the slipping wheel. Traction control is disabled as soon as the brakes are manually applied.

The EBCM/EBTCM monitors pump motor operation via the pump motor run sensor. When the pump is operating, voltage is induced into the sensor's coil and the EBCM/EBTCM monitors this voltage at terminals 49 and 31.

FAILURE CONDITIONS

When the EBCM/EBTCM grounds terminal 15, DTC 61 sets when the EBCM/EBTCM determines the frequency between EBCM/EBTCM terminals 31 and 49 is not between 70-150 Hz. The EBCM/EBTCM recognizes this condition only during ABS braking requiring pump motor operation, traction control mode (when equipped), and during the EBCM/EBTCM self-check which occurs when the vehicle reaches 11 km/h (7 mph). Therefore, be sure to test drive vehicle, refer to Item 3 under diagnostic process in this section, after clearing the DTC to assure correct diagnosis.

DTC 61 also sets when the pump motor runs all the time (i.e. EBCM/EBTCM sees proper voltage between terminals 31 and 49 without grounding terminal 15). Refer to Chart F for diagnosing a continuous running pump motor.

Possible Causes

- Open in CKT 1150, 864, 854, 1633, 1292, 1293 or 1446.
- Short to ground in CKT 864, 854, 1292, 1293, or 642.
- ABS pump relay fails "open" or "engaged."

GC402940090400AX

IMPORTANT
DTC 61 usually sets while the vehicle is moving during the system "Self Test"

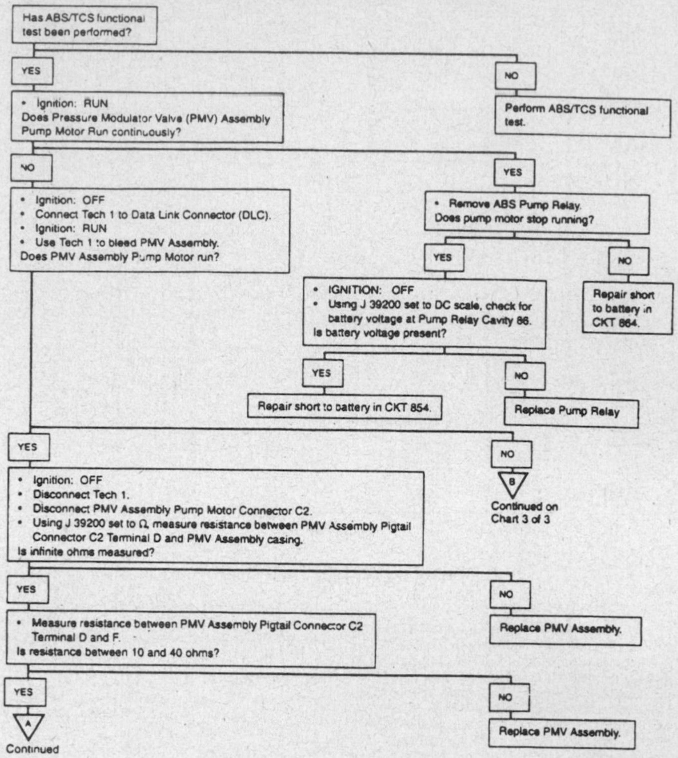
Has ABS/TCS functional test been performed?
YES
NO
Perform ABS/TCS functional test.
• Ignition: RUN
Does Pressure Modulator Valve (PMV) Assembly Pump Motor Run continuously?
NO
YES
• Ignition: OFF
• Connect Tech 1 to Data Link Connector (DLC).
• Ignition: RUN
• Use Tech 1 to bleed PMV Assembly.
Does PMV Assembly Pump Motor run?
• Remove ABS Pump Relay.
Does pump motor stop running?
YES
NO
• IGNITION: OFF
• Using J 39200 set to DC scale, check for battery voltage at Pump Relay Cavity 86.
Is battery voltage present?
Repair short to battery in CKT 864.
YES
NO
Repair short to battery in CKT 854.
Replace Pump Relay
YES
NO
Continued on Chart 3 of 3
• Ignition: OFF
• Disconnect Tech 1.
• Disconnect PMV Assembly Pump Motor Connector C2.
• Using J 39200 set to Ω, measure resistance between PMV Assembly Pigtail Connector C2 Terminal D and PMV Assembly casing.
Is infinite ohms measured?
YES
NO
Replace PMV Assembly.
• Measure resistance between PMV Assembly Pigtail Connector C2 Terminal D and F.
Is resistance between 10 and 40 ohms?
YES
NO
Replace PMV Assembly.
Continued

GC402940090400BX

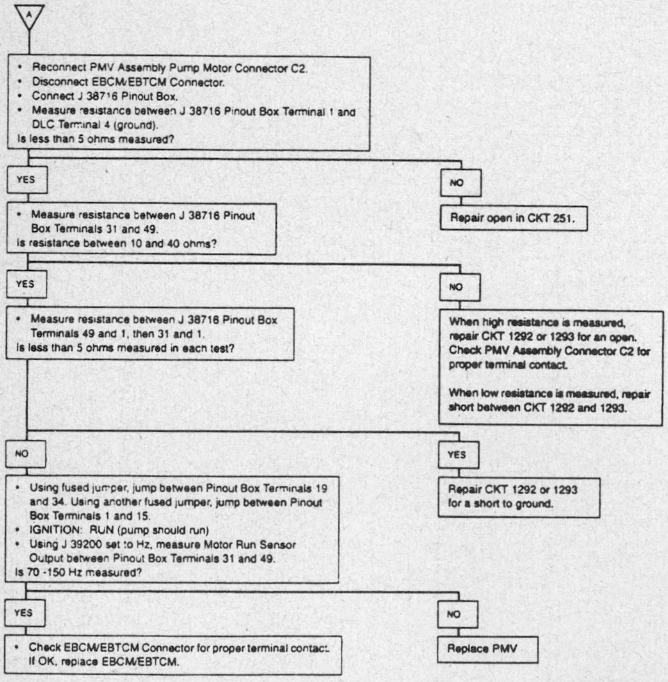
A
• Reconnect PMV Assembly Pump Motor Connector C2.
• Disconnect EBCM/EBTCM Connector.
• Connect J 38716 Pinout Box.
• Measure resistance between J 38716 Pinout Box Terminal 1 and DLC Terminal 4 (ground).
Is less than 5 ohms measured?
YES
NO
Repair open in CKT 251.
• Measure resistance between J 38716 Pinout Box Terminals 31 and 49.
Is resistance between 10 and 40 ohms?
YES
NO
When high resistance is measured, repair CKT 1292 or 1293 for an open. Check PMV Assembly Connector C2 for proper terminal contact.
When low resistance is measured, repair short between CKT 1292 and 1293.
• Measure resistance between J 38716 Pinout Box Terminals 49 and 1, then 31 and 1.
Is less than 5 ohms measured in each test?
NO
YES
Repair CKT 1292 or 1293 for a short to ground.
• Using fused jumper, jump between Pinout Box Terminals 19 and 34. Using another fused jumper, jump between Pinout Box Terminals 1 and 15.
• IGNITION: RUN (pump should run)
• Using J 39200 set to Hz, measure Motor Run Sensor Output between Pinout Box Terminals 31 and 49.
Is 70 -150 Hz measured?
YES
NO
• Check EBCM/EBTCM Connector for proper terminal contact. If OK, replace EBCM/EBTCM.
Replace PMV

GC402940090400CX

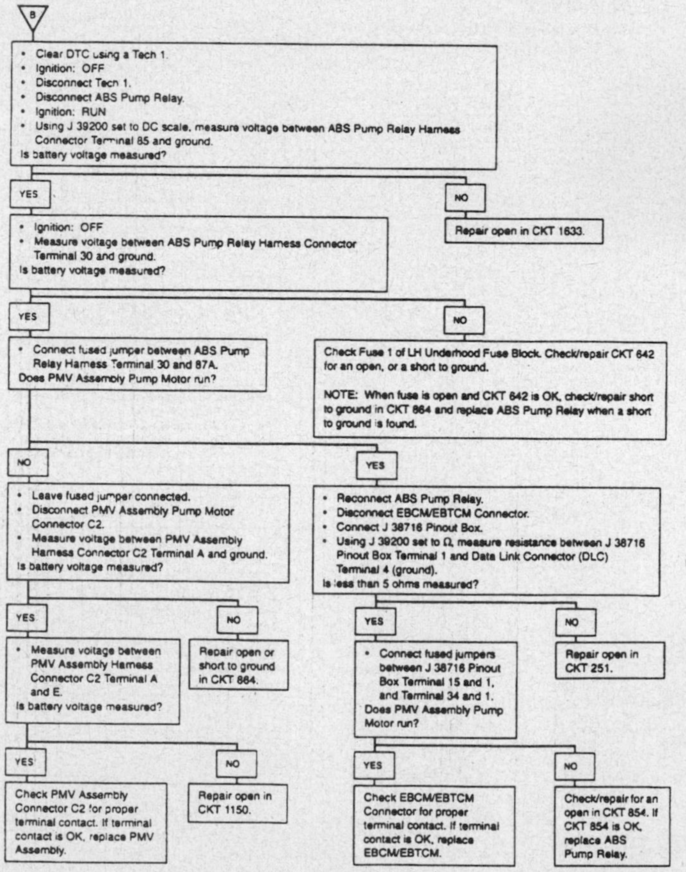
B
• Clear DTC using a Tech 1.
• Ignition: OFF
• Disconnect Tech 1.
• Disconnect ABS Pump Relay.
• Ignition: RUN
• Using J 39200 set to DC scale, measure voltage between ABS Pump Relay Harness Connector Terminal 85 and ground.
Is battery voltage measured?
YES
NO
Repair open in CKT 1633.
• Ignition: OFF
• Measure voltage between ABS Pump Relay Harness Connector Terminal 30 and ground.
Is battery voltage measured?
YES
NO
• Connect fused jumper between ABS Pump Relay Harness Terminal 30 and 87A.
Does PMV Assembly Pump Motor run?
Check Fuse 1 of LH Underhood Fuse Block. Check/repair CKT 642 for an open, or a short to ground.
NOTE: When fuse is open and CKT 642 is OK, check/repair short to ground in CKT 864 and replace ABS Pump Relay when a short to ground is found.
NO
YES
• Leave fused jumper connected.
• Disconnect PMV Assembly Pump Motor Connector C2.
• Measure voltage between PMV Assembly Harness Connector C2 Terminal A and ground.
Is battery voltage measured?
• Reconnect ABS Pump Relay.
• Disconnect EBCM/EBTCM Connector.
• Connect J 38716 Pinout Box.
• Using J 39200 set to Ω, measure resistance between J 38716 Pinout Box Terminal 1 and Data Link Connector (DLC) Terminal 4 (ground).
Is less than 5 ohms measured?
YES
NO
Repair open or short to ground in CKT 864.
YES
NO
Repair open in CKT 251.
• Measure voltage between PMV Assembly Harness Connector C2 Terminal A and E.
Is battery voltage measured?
• Connect fused jumpers between J 38716 Pinout Box Terminal 15 and 1, and Terminal 34 and 1.
Does PMV Assembly Pump Motor run?
YES
NO
Check PMV Assembly Connector C2 for proper terminal contact. If terminal contact is OK, replace PMV Assembly.
Repair open in CKT 1150.
YES
NO
Check EBCM/EBTCM Connector for proper terminal contact. If terminal contact is OK, replace EBCM/EBTCM.
Check/repair for an open in CKT 854. If CKT 854 is OK, replace ABS Pump Relay.

GC402940090400DX

Fig. 54 Code 61: Pump Motor Circuit Test. 1994 Bonneville, 88 & 98

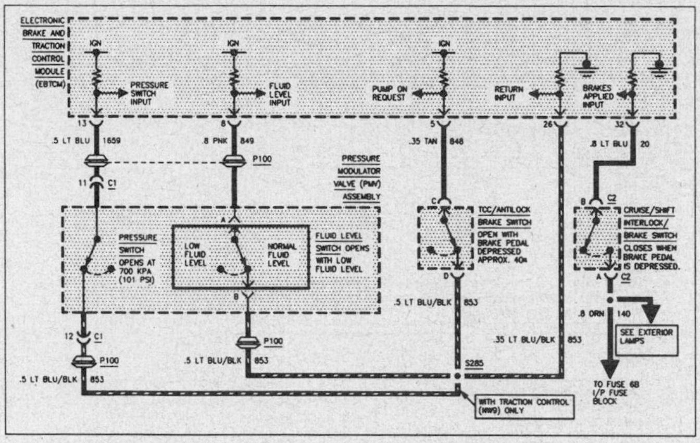
ELECTRONIC BRAKE AND TRACTION CONTROL MODULE (EBTCM)
IGN
PRESSURE SWITCH INPUT
FLUID LEVEL INPUT
PUMP ON REQUEST
RETURN INPUT
BRAKES APPLIED INPUT
13
8
5
26
32
.5 LT BLU 1659
.8 PNK 849
.35 TAN 848
.8 LT BLU 20
P100
11 C1
PRESSURE MODULATOR VALVE (PMV) ASSEMBLY
PRESSURE SWITCH
OPENS AT 700 KPA (101 PSI)
LOW FLUID LEVEL
NORMAL FLUID LEVEL
FLUID LEVEL SWITCH OPENS WITH LOW FLUID LEVEL
TCC/ANTILOCK BRAKE SWITCH
OPEN WITH BRAKE PEDAL DEPRESSED APPROX. 40%
CRUISE/SHIFT INTERLOCK/ BRAKE SWITCH
CLOSES WHEN BRAKE PEDAL IS DEPRESSED.
C2
.5 LT BLU/BLK 853
.8 ORN 140
SEE EXTERIOR LAMPS
12 C1
.35 LT BLU/BLK 853
S285
TO FUSE 6B I/P FUSE BLOCK
WITH TRACTION CONTROL (NW9) ONLY

DTC 62

LOW BRAKE PEDAL DURING AN ABS STOP

CIRCUIT OPERATION

The EBCM/EBTCM monitors brake pedal position using the TCC/antilock brake switch. The normally closed switch opens when the brake pedal is depressed approximately 40% down. The EBCM/EBTCM also monitors pump motor operation using a pump motor run sensor.

During most ABS braking conditions the EBCM turns on the pump motor, replenishing the PMV assembly reservoir and applying fluid pressure to the master cylinder. This causes the brake pedal to gradually rise. The EBCM/EBTCM turns off the pump motor when the brake pedal height sufficiently rises to close the TCC/antilock brake switch.

FAILURE CONDITIONS

During ABS braking, DTC 62 sets when the EBCM/EBTCM determines the pump is working, and brake pedal height has not sufficiently risen to close the TCC/antilock brake switch after 3 seconds.

This DTC may indicate a hydraulic problem. Some possible causes include air in the brake lines or a pump motor mechanical failure. Non-hydraulic causes for DTC 62 include an open 848 or 853 CKT or a misadjusted/defective TCC/antilock brake switch.

GC402940090500AX

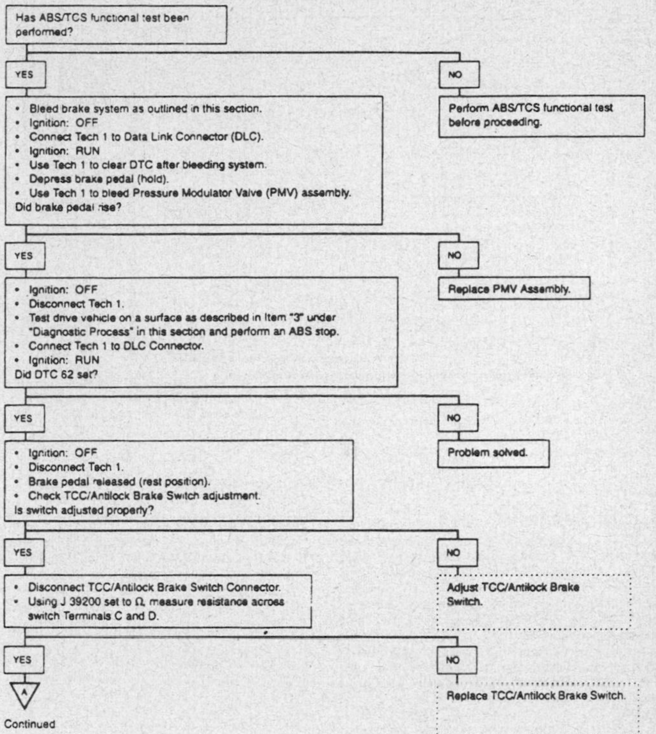
Has ABS/TCS functional test been performed?
YES
NO
• Bleed brake system as outlined in this section.
• Ignition: OFF
• Connect Tech 1 to Data Link Connector (DLC).
• Ignition: RUN
• Use Tech 1 to clear DTC after bleeding system.
• Depress brake pedal (hold).
• Use Tech 1 to bleed Pressure Modulator Valve (PMV) assembly.
Did brake pedal rise?
Perform ABS/TCS functional test before proceeding.
YES
NO
• Ignition: OFF
• Disconnect Tech 1.
• Test drive vehicle on a surface as described in Item "3" under "Diagnostic Process" in this section and perform an ABS stop.
• Connect Tech 1 to DLC Connector.
• Ignition: RUN
Did DTC 62 set?
Replace PMV Assembly.
YES
NO
• Ignition: OFF
• Disconnect Tech 1.
• Brake pedal released (rest position).
• Check TCC/Antilock Brake Switch adjustment.
Is switch adjusted properly?
Problem solved.
YES
NO
• Disconnect TCC/Antilock Brake Switch Connector.
• Using J 39200 set to Ω, measure resistance across switch Terminals C and D.
Adjust TCC/Antilock Brake Switch.
YES
NO
A
Continued
Replace TCC/Antilock Brake Switch.

GC402940090500BX

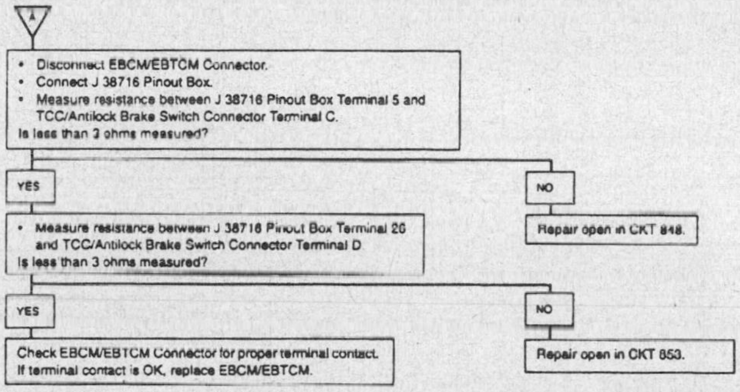
A
• Disconnect EBCM/EBTCM Connector.
• Connect J 38716 Pinout Box.
• Measure resistance between J 38716 Pinout Box Terminal 5 and TCC/Antilock Brake Switch Connector Terminal C.
Is less than 3 ohms measured?
YES
NO
• Measure resistance between J 38716 Pinout Box Terminal 26 and TCC/Antilock Brake Switch Connector Terminal D.
Is less than 3 ohms measured?
Repair open in CKT 848.
YES
NO
Check EBCM/EBTCM Connector for proper terminal contact. If terminal contact is OK, replace EBCM/EBTCM.
Repair open in CKT 853.

GC402940090500CX

Fig. 55 Code 62: Low Brake Pedal During An ABS Stop. 1994 Bonneville, 88 & 98

DTC 71

EBCM/EBTCM INTERNAL MALFUNCTION

DTC 71 indicates that a failure has occurred within the EBCM/EBTCM. DTC 71 can occur intermittently, due to interference, therefore clear the code and test drive the vehicle before replacing the EBCM/EBTCM.

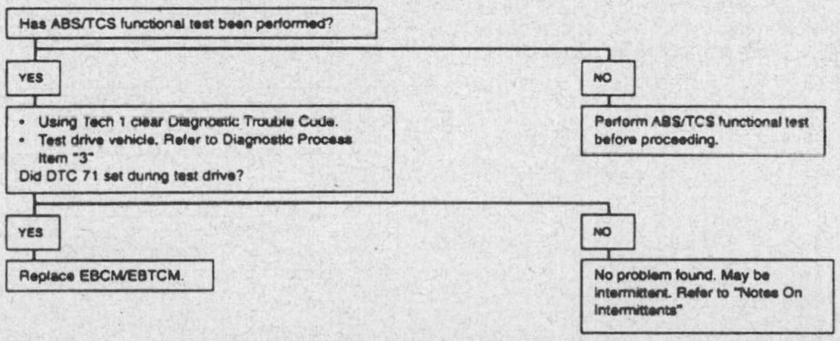
Has ABS/TCS functional test been performed?
YES
NO
• Using Tech 1 clear Diagnostic Trouble Code.
• Test drive vehicle. Refer to Diagnostic Process Item "3"
Did DTC 71 set during test drive?
Perform ABS/TCS functional test before proceeding.
YES
NO
Replace EBCM/EBTCM.
No problem found. May be intermittent. Refer to "Notes On Intermittents"

GC4029400906000X

Fig. 56 Code 71: EBCM/EBTCM Internal Fault. 1994 Bonneville, 88 & 98

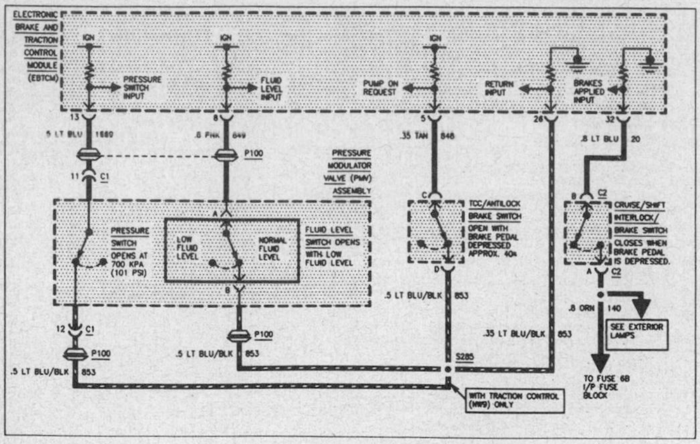
ELECTRONIC BRAKE AND TRACTION CONTROL MODULE (EBTCM)
IGN
PRESSURE SWITCH INPUT
FLUID LEVEL INPUT
PUMP ON REQUEST
RETURN INPUT
BRAKES APPLIED INPUT
.5 LT BLU 1659
.8 PNK 849
.35 TAN 848
.8 LT BLU 20
P100
PRESSURE MODULATOR VALVE (PMV) ASSEMBLY
C1
PRESSURE SWITCH OPENS AT 700 KPA (101 PSI)
LOW FLUID LEVEL
NORMAL FLUID LEVEL
FLUID LEVEL SWITCH OPENS WITH LOW FLUID LEVEL
TCC/ANTILOCK BRAKE SWITCH OPEN WITH BRAKE PEDAL DEPRESSED APPROX. 40%
CRUISE/SHIFT INTERLOCK/ BRAKE SWITCH CLOSES WHEN BRAKE PEDAL IS DEPRESSED.
C2
.5 LT BLU/BLK 853
.8 ORN 140
SEE EXTERIOR LAMPS
.35 LT BLU/BLK 853
S285
TO FUSE 6B I/P FUSE BLOCK
WITH TRACTION CONTROL (NW9) ONLY

DTC 72

BRAKE SWITCH OPEN OR SHORTED

CIRCUIT OPERATION

The electronic brake control module EBCM/EBTCM monitors brake pedal position using the brake travel switch. The switch is normally closed. It opens when the brake pedal is depressed approximately 40% down. During most ABS braking conditions the EBCM/EBTCM turns on the pump motor, replenishing the PMV assembly reservoir and applying fluid pressure to the master cylinder. This causes the brake pedal to gradually rise. The EBCM/EBTCM turns off the pump motor when brake pedal height sufficiently rises to close the brake travel switch.

FAILURE CONDITIONS

DTC 72 sets when the EBCM/EBTCM detects the brake travel switch CKT 848 is shorted to ground (with the brake pedal depressed) or open.

GC402940090700AX

Has ABS/TCS functional test been performed?

- NO: Perform ABS/TCS functional test before proceeding.
- YES:
  - Ignition: OFF
  - Disconnect Brake Travel Switch Connector.
  - Disconnect EBCM/EBTCM Connector.
  - Connect J 38716 Pinout Box.
  - Using J 39200 set to Ω, measure resistance between J 38716 Pinout Box Terminal 1 and Data Link Connector (DLC) Terminal 4 (ground).

  Is less than 5 ohms measured?
  - NO: Repair open in CKT 251.
  - YES:
    - Measure resistance between J 38716 Pinout Box Terminal 1 and 5.

    Is less than 5 ohms measured?
    - YES: Repair short to ground in CKT 848.
    - NO:
      - Measure resistance between Pinout Box Terminals 1 and 26.
      - Is less than 5 Ω measured?
      - NO: Repair short to ground in CKT 853.
      - YES: Check EBCM/EBTCM Connector for proper terminal contact. If terminal contact is OK, replace EBCM/EBTCM.

GC402940090700BX

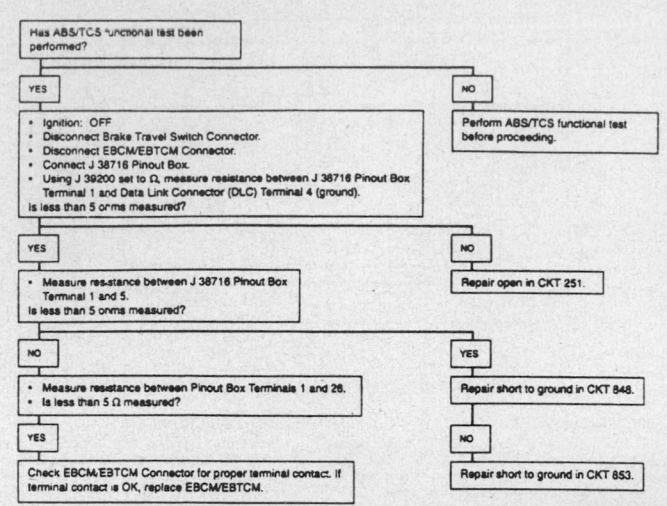

Fig. 57 Code 72: Brake Switch Open Or Shorted. 1994 Bonneville, 88 & 98

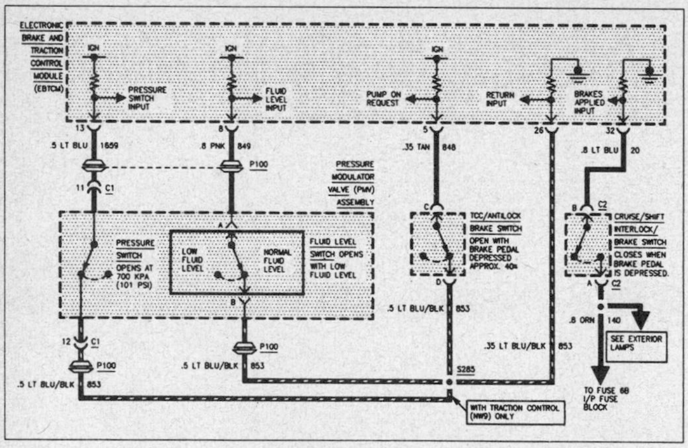
ELECTRONIC BRAKE AND TRACTION CONTROL MODULE (EBTCM)
IGN
PRESSURE SWITCH INPUT
FLUID LEVEL INPUT
PUMP ON REQUEST
RETURN INPUT
BRAKES APPLIED INPUT
.5 LT BLU 1659
.8 PNK 849
.35 TAN 848
.8 LT BLU 20
P100
PRESSURE MODULATOR VALVE (PMV) ASSEMBLY
C1
PRESSURE SWITCH OPENS AT 700 KPA (101 PSI)
LOW FLUID LEVEL
NORMAL FLUID LEVEL
FLUID LEVEL SWITCH OPENS WITH LOW FLUID LEVEL
TCC/ANTILOCK BRAKE SWITCH OPEN WITH BRAKE PEDAL DEPRESSED APPROX. 40%
CRUISE/SHIFT INTERLOCK/ BRAKE SWITCH CLOSES WHEN BRAKE PEDAL IS DEPRESSED.
C2
.5 LT BLU/BLK 853
.8 ORN 140
SEE EXTERIOR LAMPS
.35 LT BLU/BLK 853
S285
TO FUSE 6B I/P FUSE BLOCK
WITH TRACTION CONTROL (NW9) ONLY

DTC 73

FLUID LEVEL SWITCH CIRCUIT OPEN OR SHORTED

CIRCUIT OPERATION

The pressure modulator valve (PMV) fluid level switch alerts the EBCM/EBTCM to a low brake fluid condition in the PMV reservoir. The fluid level switch is located in the PMV assembly's reservoir. The fluid level switch is normally closed when the reservoir contains sufficient fluid. When fluid level is low, the switch opens, causing the EBCM/EBTCM to turn on the "ANTILOCK" indicator.

FAILURE CONDITIONS

DTC 73 sets when the EBCM/EBTCM detects a short to ground in the PMV fluid level switch circuitry. These include: CKT 848, 849, 853, and 1659. DTC 73 will also set if an open exists in CKT 251.

GC402940090800AX

Has ABS/TCS functional test been performed?

- NO: Perform ABS/TCS functional test before proceeding.
- YES:
  - Ignition: OFF
  - Disconnect EBCM/EBTCM Connector.
  - Connect J 38716 Pinout Box.
  - Using J 39200 set to Ω, measure resistance between J 38716 Pinout Box Terminal 1 and Data Link Connector (DLC) Terminal A (ground).

  Is less than 5 ohms measured?
  - NO: Repair open in CKT 251.
  - YES:
    - Disconnect Brake Travel Switch.
    - Measure resistance between J 38716 Pinout Box Terminal 5 and 1.

    Is less than 5 ohms measured?
    - YES: Repair short to ground in CKT 848.
    - NO:
      - Disconnect Pressure Modulator Valve (PMV) Fluid Level Switch Connector.
      - Measure resistance between J 38716 Pinout Box Terminal 8 and 1.

      Is less than 5 ohms measured?
      - YES: Repair short to ground in CKT 849.
      - NO:
        - When equipped with Traction Control:
          Depress Brake Pedal.
          Measure resistance between J 38716 Pinout Box Terminal 13 and 1.

        Is less than 5 ohms measured?
        - YES: Repair short to ground in CKT 1659.
        - NO:
          - Measure resistance between J 38716 Pinout Box Terminal 26 and 1.

          Is less than 5 ohms measured?
          - YES: Repair short to ground in CKT 853.
          - NO: Check EBCM/EBTCM Connector for proper terminal contact. If terminal contact is OK, replace EBCM/EBTCM.

GC402940090800BX

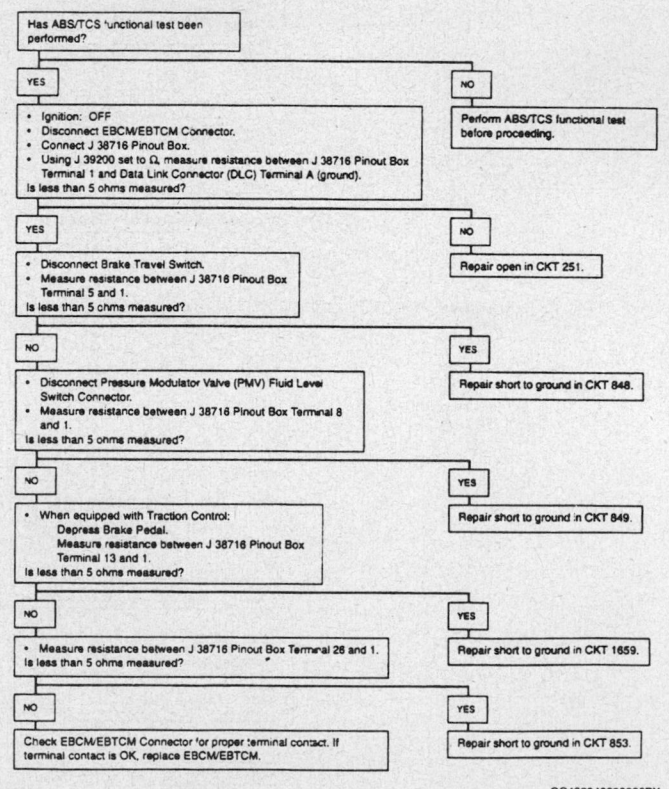

Fig. 58 Code 73: Fluid Level Switch Circuit Open Or Shorted. 1994 Bonneville, 88 & 98

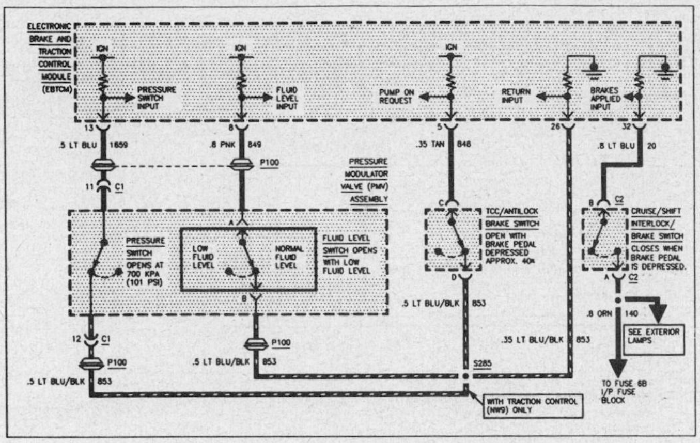
ELECTRONIC BRAKE AND TRACTION CONTROL MODULE (EBTCM)
IGN
PRESSURE SWITCH INPUT
FLUID LEVEL INPUT
PUMP ON REQUEST
RETURN INPUT
BRAKES APPLIED INPUT
13
8
5
26
32
.5 LT BLU 1659
.8 PNK 849
.35 TAN 848
.8 LT BLU 20
P100
11 C1
PRESSURE MODULATOR VALVE (PMV) ASSEMBLY
PRESSURE SWITCH OPENS AT 700 KPA (101 PSI)
LOW FLUID LEVEL
NORMAL FLUID LEVEL
FLUID LEVEL SWITCH OPENS WITH LOW FLUID LEVEL
TCC/ANTILOCK BRAKE SWITCH OPEN WITH BRAKE PEDAL DEPRESSED APPROX. 40%
CRUISE/SHIFT INTERLOCK/ BRAKE SWITCH CLOSES WHEN BRAKE PEDAL IS DEPRESSED.
C2
.5 LT BLU/BLK 853
.8 ORN 140
SEE EXTERIOR LAMPS
.35 LT BLU/BLK 853
12 C1
S285
TO FUSE 6B I/P FUSE BLOCK
WITH TRACTION CONTROL (NW9) ONLY

DTC 74

PMV PRESSURE SWITCH CIRCUIT OPEN OR SHORTED

CIRCUIT OPERATION

The pressure switch monitors primary brake system pressure. The normally closed switch opens when the brakes are applied and pressure exceeds 700 kPa (101 psi). If the brakes are manually applied during traction control mode, the PMV pressure switch input, along with the brake switch input, signal the EBTCM to disable traction control and allow manual braking. The pressure switch is part of the pressure modulator valve (PMV) assembly and is not serviceable.

FAILURE CONDITIONS

DTC 74 sets when the EBTCM detects an open or short to ground in the PMV pressure switch circuitry.

Possible Causes

- Open in CKT 853 or 1659.
- Short to ground in CKT 1659 with the brakes applied.
- Failed PMV pressure switch.

GC402940090900AX

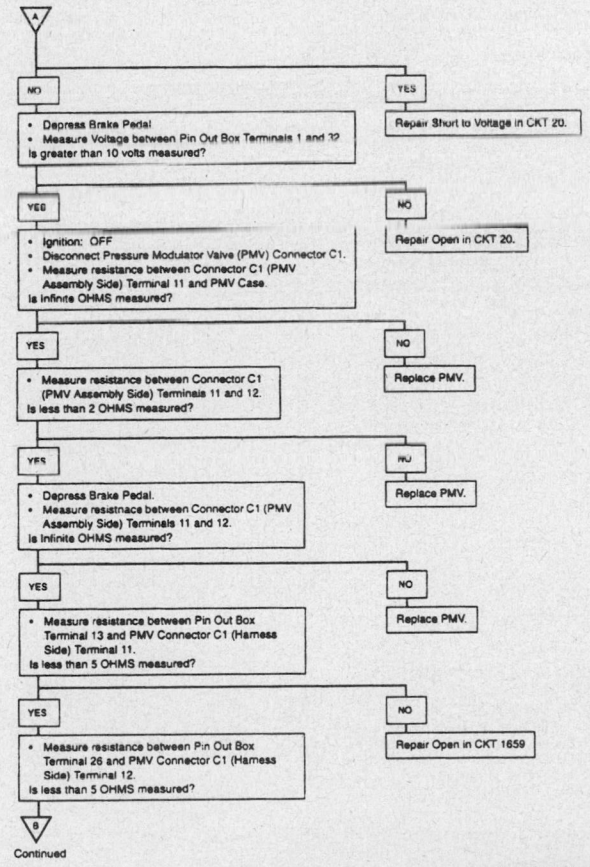

Has ABS/TCS Functional Test been performed?

- NO: Perform ABS/TCS Functional Test.
- YES:
  - Ignition: OFF
  - Inspect I/P Fuse Block Fuse 6B.
  - Is Fuse 6B open?

- YES: Repair Short to Ground in CKT 140 or CKT 20. Replace Fuse.
- NO:
  - Disconnect Brake Switch Connector (Grey Connector).
  - Using J 39200 set to DC scale measure voltage between DLC Terminal 4 and Brake Switch Connector (Harness Side) Terminal A.
  - Is greater than 10 volts measured?

- NO: Repair Open in CKT 140.
- YES:
  - Depress Brake Pedal.
  - Using J 39200 set to Ω measure resistance between Brake Switch Terminals A and B.
  - Is less than 2 OHMS measured?

- NO: Replace Brake Switch.
- YES:
  - Check for proper terminal contact on Brake Switch Connector.
  - Reconnect Brake Switch Connector.
  - Check for proper Brake Switch Adjustment (refer to SECTION 5).
  - Is Brake Switch Adjusted Properly?

- NO: Adjust Brake Switch. Refer to SECTION 5.
- YES:
  - Disconnect EBTCM Connector.
  - Install J 38716 Pin Out Box.
  - Measure resistance between Pin Out Box Terminal 1 and DLC Terminal 4.
  - Is less than 5 OHMS measured?

- NO: Repair Open in CKT 251.
- YES:
  - Ignition: ON
  - Using J 39200 set to DC scale, measure voltage between Pin Out Box Terminals 1 and 32.
  - Is greater than 2 volts measured?

(A) Continued

GC402940090900BX

(A)

- YES: Repair Short to Voltage in CKT 20.
- NO:
  - Depress Brake Pedal.
  - Measure Voltage between Pin Out Box Terminals 1 and 32.
  - Is greater than 10 volts measured?

- NO: Repair Open in CKT 20.
- YES:
  - Ignition: OFF
  - Disconnect Pressure Modulator Valve (PMV) Connector C1.
  - Measure resistance between Connector C1 (PMV Assembly Side) Terminal 11 and PMV Case.
  - Is infinite OHMS measured?

- NO: Replace PMV.
- YES:
  - Measure resistance between Connector C1 (PMV Assembly Side) Terminals 11 and 12.
  - Is less than 2 OHMS measured?

- NO: Replace PMV.
- YES:
  - Depress Brake Pedal.
  - Measure resistnace between Connector C1 (PMV Assembly Side) Terminals 11 and 12.
  - Is infinite OHMS measured?

- NO: Replace PMV.
- YES:
  - Measure resistance between Pin Out Box Terminal 13 and PMV Connector C1 (Harness Side) Terminal 11.
  - Is less than 5 OHMS measured?

- NO: Repair Open in CKT 1659
- YES:
  - Measure resistance between Pin Out Box Terminal 26 and PMV Connector C1 (Harness Side) Terminal 12.
  - Is less than 5 OHMS measured?

(B) Continued

GC402940090900CX

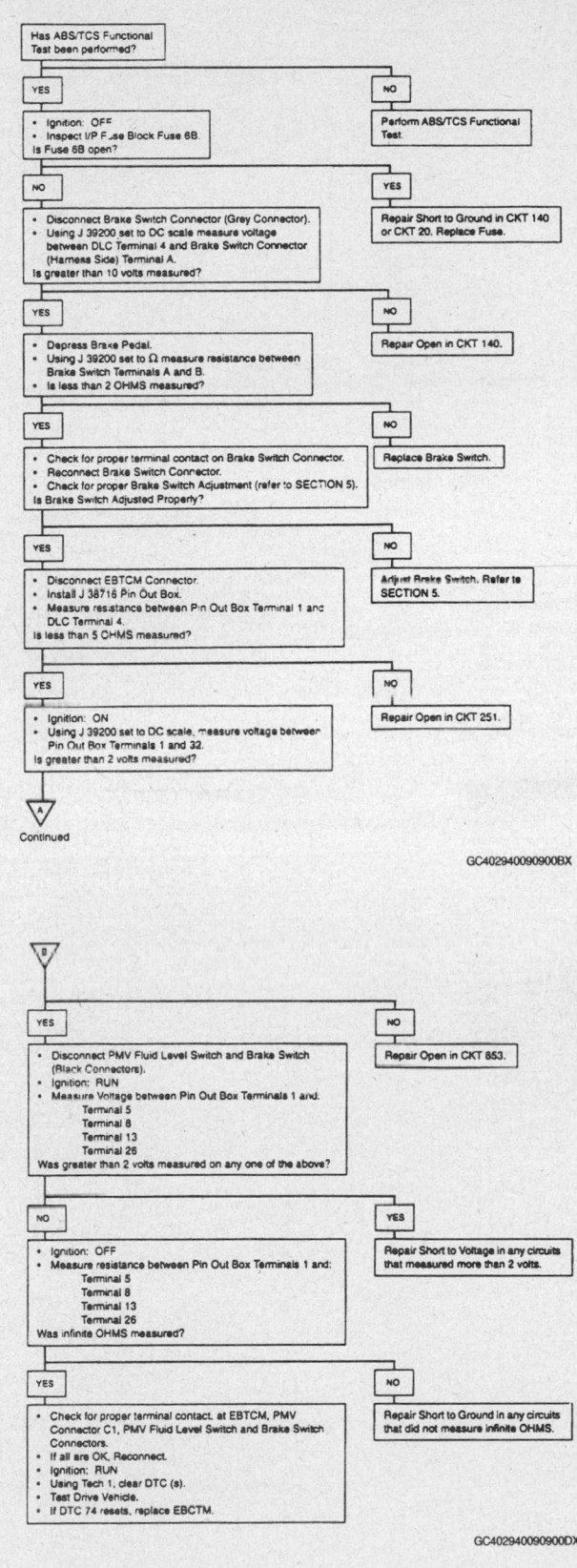

(B)

- NO: Repair Open in CKT 853.
- YES:
  - Disconnect PMV Fluid Level Switch and Brake Switch (Black Connectors).
  - Ignition: RUN
  - Measure Voltage between Pin Out Box Terminals 1 and:
    - Terminal 5
    - Terminal 8
    - Terminal 13
    - Terminal 26
  - Was greater than 2 volts measured on any one of the above?

- YES: Repair Short to Voltage in any circuits that measured more than 2 volts.
- NO:
  - Ignition: OFF
  - Measure resistance between Pin Out Box Terminals 1 and:
    - Terminal 5
    - Terminal 8
    - Terminal 13
    - Terminal 26
  - Was infinite OHMS measured?

- NO: Repair Short to Ground in any circuits that did not measure infinite OHMS.
- YES:
  - Check for proper terminal contact. at EBTCM, PMV Connector C1, PMV Fluid Level Switch and Brake Switch Connectors.
  - If all are OK, Reconnect.
  - Ignition: RUN
  - Using Tech 1, clear DTC (s).
  - Test Drive Vehicle.
  - If DTC 74 resets, replace EBCTM.

GC402940090900DX

Fig. 59 Code 74: PMV Pressure Switch Circuit Open Or Shorted. 1994 Bonneville, 88 & 98

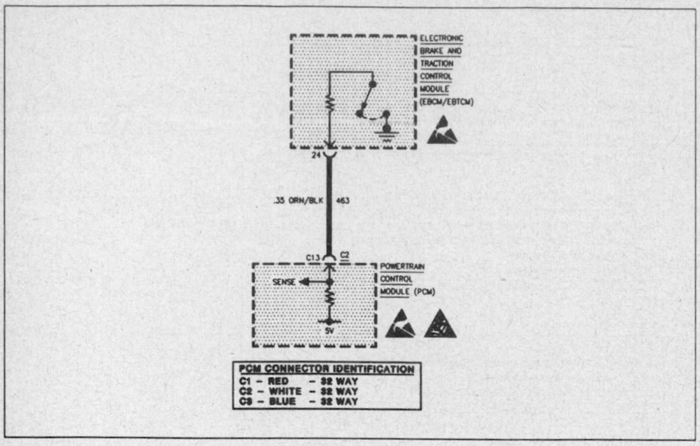
ELECTRONIC
BRAKE AND
TRACTION
CONTROL
MODULE
(EBCM/EBTCM)
24
.35 ORN/BLK
463
C13
C2
SENSE
POWERTRAIN
CONTROL
MODULE (PCM)
5V
PCM CONNECTOR IDENTIFICATION
C1 – RED – 32 WAY
C2 – WHITE – 32 WAY
C3 – BLUE – 32 WAY

DTC 75

PCM REQUESTED TCS TO BE DISABLED

CIRCUIT OPERATION

When excessive wheel spin is detected by the EBTCM, it will request the PCM to reduce engine torque via a high speed pulse width modulated (PWM) signal on circuit 463.

FAILURE CONDITIONS

Important

If PCM code 1571 is not present, no fault exists with the ABS/TCS system.

DTC 75 sets when the EBTCM receives a serial data message from the PCM to disable traction control. DTC 75 sets under the two following conditions:

1. EBTCM to PMC communications.
   - CKT 463 or CKT 800 open or shorted
2. PCM drivability conditions to include PCM codes P0101, P0341, P0342, P1350, P1361, P1623, P1630, P0131, P0132, P0171 and P0172.

GC402940091000AX

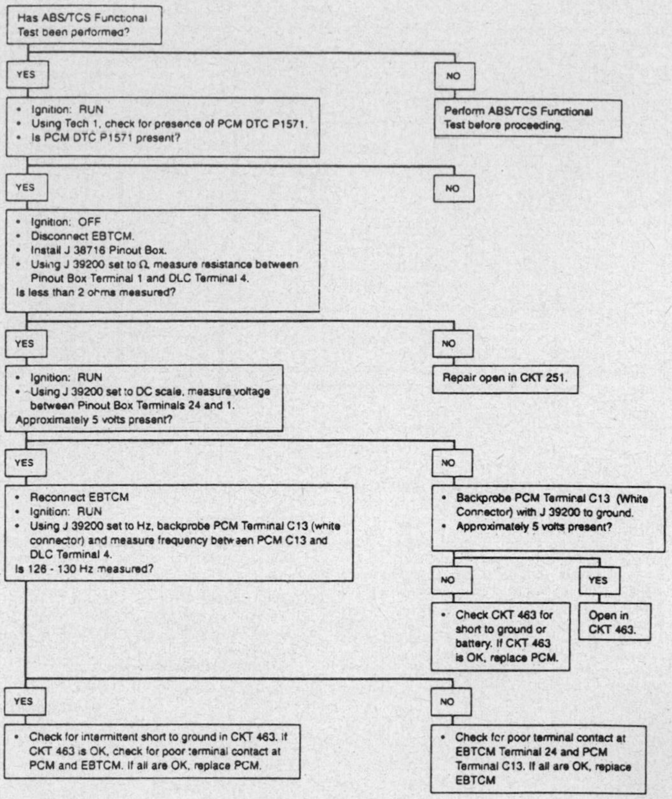
Has ABS/TCS Functional Test been performed?
YES
NO
• Ignition: RUN
• Using Tech 1, check for presence of PCM DTC P1571.
• Is PCM DTC P1571 present?
Perform ABS/TCS Functional Test before proceeding.
YES
NO
• Ignition: OFF
• Disconnect EBTCM.
• Install J 38716 Pinout Box.
• Using J 39200 set to Ω, measure resistance between Pinout Box Terminal 1 and DLC Terminal 4.
Is less than 2 ohms measured?
YES
NO
• Ignition: RUN
• Using J 39200 set to DC scale, measure voltage between Pinout Box Terminals 24 and 1.
Approximately 5 volts present?
Repair open in CKT 251.
YES
NO
• Reconnect EBTCM
• Ignition: RUN
• Using J 39200 set to Hz, backprobe PCM Terminal C13 (white connector) and measure frequency between PCM C13 and DLC Terminal 4.
Is 128 - 130 Hz measured?
• Backprobe PCM Terminal C13 (White Connector) with J 39200 to ground.
• Approximately 5 volts present?
NO
YES
• Check CKT 463 for short to ground or battery. If CKT 463 is OK, replace PCM.
Open in CKT 463.
YES
NO
• Check for intermittent short to ground in CKT 463. If CKT 463 is OK, check for poor terminal contact at PCM and EBTCM. If all are OK, replace PCM.
• Check for poor terminal contact at EBTCM Terminal 24 and PCM Terminal C13. If all are OK, replace EBTCM

GC402940091000BX

Fig. 60 Code 75: PCM Requested TCS To Be Disabled. 1994 Bonneville, 88 & 98

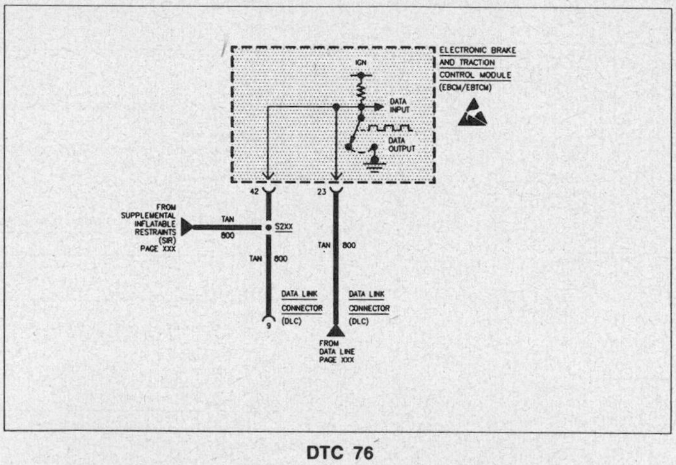
ELECTRONIC BRAKE
AND TRACTION
CONTROL MODULE
(EBCM/EBTCM)
IGN
DATA
INPUT
DATA
OUTPUT
42
23
FROM
SUPPLEMENTAL
INFLATABLE
RESTRAINTS
(SIR)
PAGE XXX
TAN
800
S2XX
TAN 800
TAN 800
DATA LINK
CONNECTOR
(DLC)
9
DATA LINK
CONNECTOR
(DLC)
FROM
DATA LINE
PAGE XXX

DTC 76

DATA LINE SIGNAL OR CIRCUIT MALFUNCTION

CIRCUIT OPERATION

The EBTCM shares specific serial data information supplied on the data line. The data line also allows the use of a bi-directional scan tool such as a Tech 1.

FAILURE CONDITIONS

A current DTC 76 cannot be read with a Tech 1 due to the loss of serial data communications. After data line communications are restored, DTC 76 will be stored in memory. Refer to data line diagnosis.

GC4029400911000X

Fig. 61 Code 76: Data Line Signal Or Circuit Malfunction. 1994 Bonneville, 88 & 98

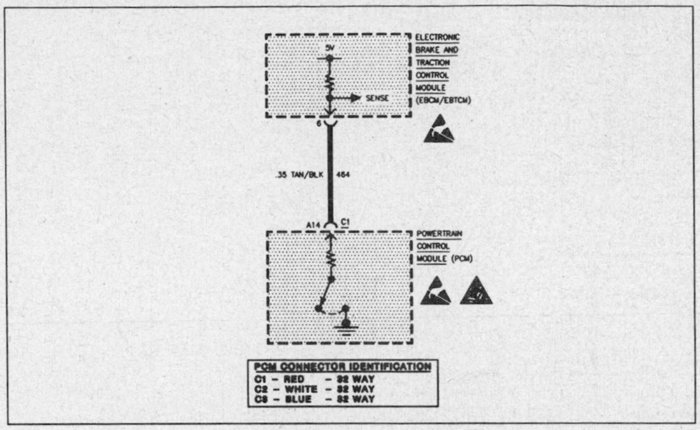

ELECTRONIC BRAKE AND TRACTION CONTROL MODULE (EBCM/EBTCM)
5V
SENSE
6
.35 TAN/BLK 464
A14 C1
POWERTRAIN CONTROL MODULE (PCM)
PCM CONNECTOR IDENTIFICATION
C1 – RED – 32 WAY
C2 – WHITE – 32 WAY
C3 – BLUE – 32 WAY

DTC 77

DELIVERED TORQUE CIRCUIT FAULT

CIRCUIT OPERATION

The PCM provides the EBTCM information on engine torque output via a high speed pulse width modulated (PWM) signal on circuit 464. This information is provided so the EBTCM can determine if engine torque management is required during a wheel slip condition.

FAILURE CONDITIONS

If the EBTCM determines there is a signal/circuit malfunction in circuit 464, the "TRACTION OFF" telltale will be illuminated and DTC 77 will set.

GC402940091200AX

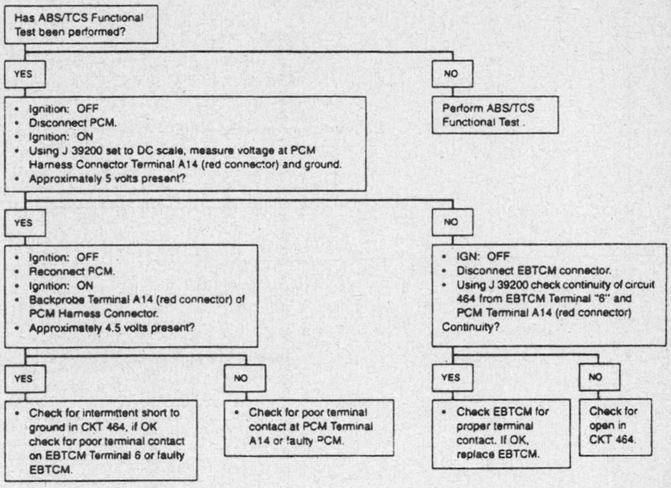

Has ABS/TCS Functional Test been performed?
YES
NO
Perform ABS/TCS Functional Test.
• Ignition: OFF
• Disconnect PCM.
• Ignition: ON
• Using J 39200 set to DC scale, measure voltage at PCM Harness Connector Terminal A14 (red connector) and ground.
• Approximately 5 volts present?
YES
NO
• Ignition: OFF
• Reconnect PCM.
• Ignition: ON
• Backprobe Terminal A14 (red connector) of PCM Harness Connector.
• Approximately 4.5 volts present?
• IGN: OFF
• Disconnect EBTCM connector.
• Using J 39200 check continuity of circuit 464 from EBTCM Terminal "6" and PCM Terminal A14 (red connector) Continuity?
YES
NO
YES
NO
• Check for intermittent short to ground in CKT 464, if OK check for poor terminal contact on EBTCM Terminal 6 or faulty EBTCM.
• Check for poor terminal contact at PCM Terminal A14 or faulty PCM.
• Check EBTCM for proper terminal contact. If OK, replace EBTCM.
Check for open in CKT 464.

GC402940091200BX

Fig. 62 Code 77: Delivered Torque Circuit Fault. 1994 Bonneville, 88 & 98

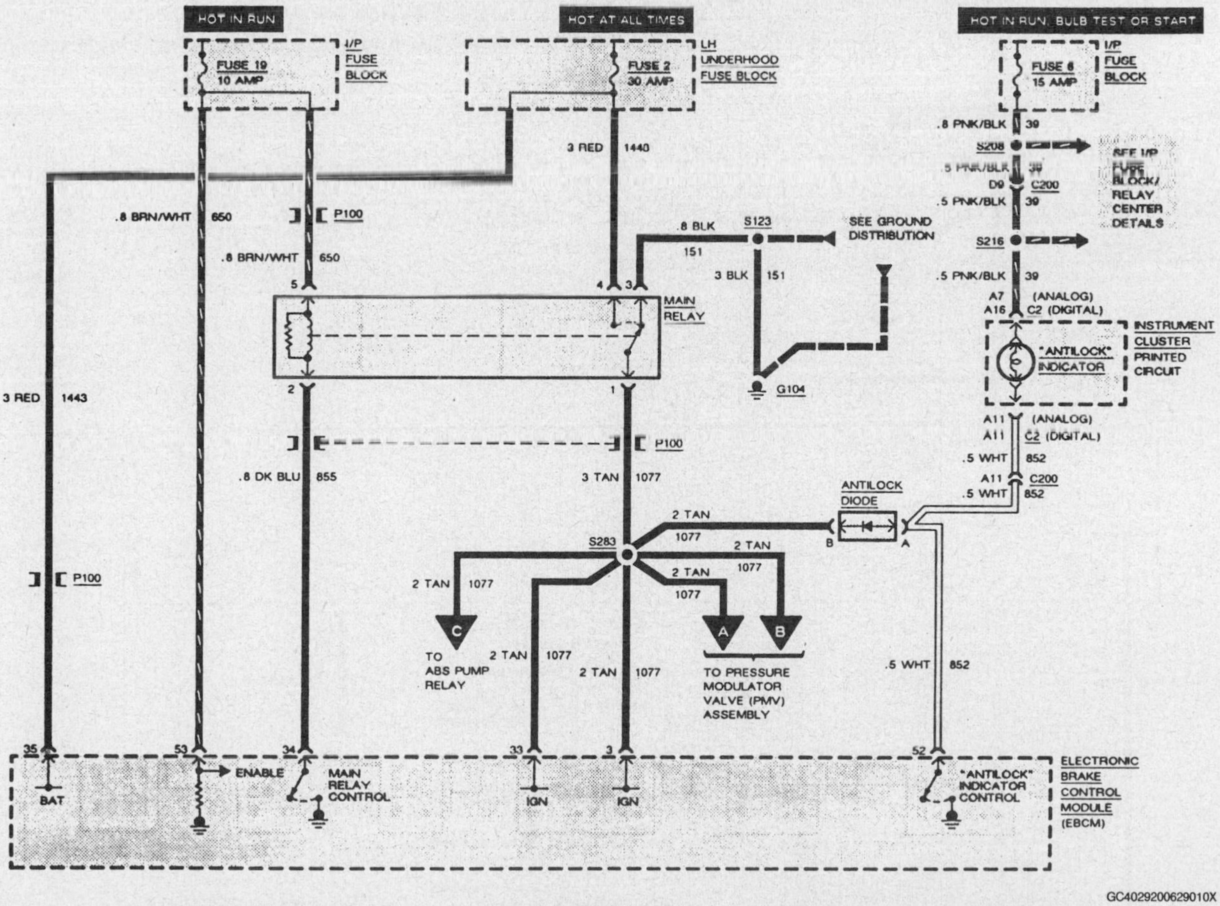

HOT IN RUN
HOT AT ALL TIMES
HOT IN RUN, BULB TEST OR START
FUSE 19 10 AMP
I/P FUSE BLOCK
FUSE 2 30 AMP
LH UNDERHOOD FUSE BLOCK
FUSE 6 15 AMP
I/P FUSE BLOCK
.8 PNK/BLK 39
S208
SEE I/P FUSE BLOCK/ RELAY CENTER DETAILS
.5 PNK/BLK 39
D9 C200
.5 PNK/BLK 39
3 RED 1440
.8 BRN/WHT 650
P100
.8 BRN/WHT 650
.8 BLK 151
S123
SEE GROUND DISTRIBUTION
S216
3 BLK 151
.5 PNK/BLK 39
A7 (ANALOG)
A16 C2 (DIGITAL)
MAIN RELAY
INSTRUMENT CLUSTER PRINTED CIRCUIT
"ANTILOCK" INDICATOR
G104
3 RED 1443
P100
A11 (ANALOG)
A11 C2 (DIGITAL)
.5 WHT 852
A11 C200
.5 WHT 852
.8 DK BLU 855
3 TAN 1077
ANTILOCK DIODE
2 TAN 1077
S283
2 TAN 1077
2 TAN 1077
2 TAN 1077
P100
TO ABS PUMP RELAY
2 TAN 1077
2 TAN 1077
TO PRESSURE MODULATOR VALVE (PMV) ASSEMBLY
.5 WHT 852
35
53
34
33
3
52
BAT
ENABLE
MAIN RELAY CONTROL
IGN
IGN
"ANTILOCK" INDICATOR CONTROL
ELECTRONIC BRAKE CONTROL MODULE (EBCM)

GC4029200629010X

Fig. 63 ABS wiring circuit (Part 1 of 5). 1992–93 Bonneville, 88 & LeSabre

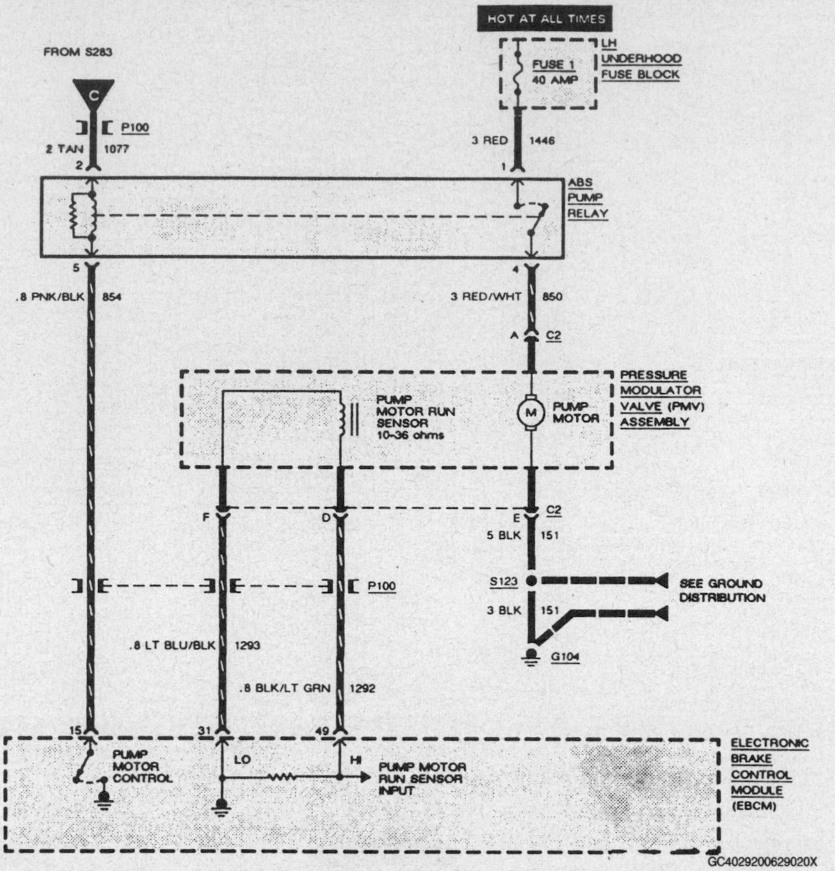
HOT AT ALL TIMES
LH UNDERHOOD FUSE BLOCK
FUSE 1 40 AMP
FROM S283
P100
2 TAN 1077
3 RED 1446
ABS PUMP RELAY
.8 PNK/BLK 854
3 RED/WHT 850
C2
PRESSURE MODULATOR VALVE (PMV) ASSEMBLY
PUMP MOTOR RUN SENSOR 10-36 ohms
PUMP MOTOR
5 BLK 151
S123
SEE GROUND DISTRIBUTION
3 BLK 151
G104
.8 LT BLU/BLK 1293
.8 BLK/LT GRN 1292
PUMP MOTOR CONTROL
LO
HI
PUMP MOTOR RUN SENSOR INPUT
ELECTRONIC BRAKE CONTROL MODULE (EBCM)
GC4029200629020X

Fig. 63 ABS wiring circuit (Part 2 of 5). 1992–93 Bonneville, 88 & LeSabre

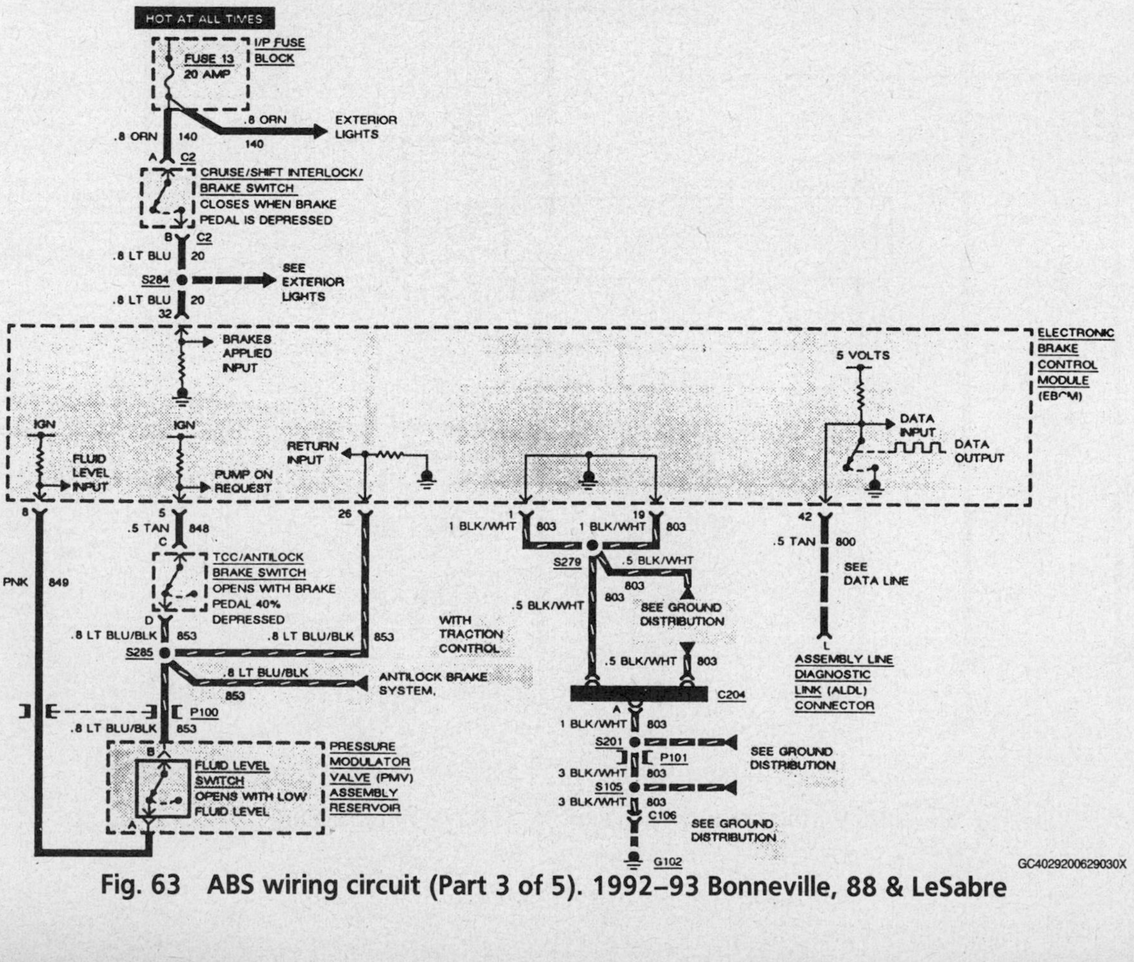
HOT AT ALL TIMES
I/P FUSE BLOCK
FUSE 13 20 AMP
.8 ORN 140
EXTERIOR LIGHTS
CRUISE/SHIFT INTERLOCK/ BRAKE SWITCH CLOSES WHEN BRAKE PEDAL IS DEPRESSED
.8 LT BLU 20
S284
SEE EXTERIOR LIGHTS
BRAKES APPLIED INPUT
ELECTRONIC BRAKE CONTROL MODULE (EBCM)
5 VOLTS
IGN
FLUID LEVEL INPUT
PUMP ON REQUEST
RETURN INPUT
DATA INPUT
DATA OUTPUT
.5 TAN 848
1 BLK/WHT 803
.5 TAN 800
SEE DATA LINE
TCC/ANTILOCK BRAKE SWITCH OPENS WITH BRAKE PEDAL 40% DEPRESSED
.8 PNK 849
S279
.5 BLK/WHT
SEE GROUND DISTRIBUTION
.8 LT BLU/BLK 853
S285
WITH TRACTION CONTROL
ANTILOCK BRAKE SYSTEM.
C204
ASSEMBLY LINE DIAGNOSTIC LINK (ALDL) CONNECTOR
P100
FLUID LEVEL SWITCH OPENS WITH LOW FLUID LEVEL
PRESSURE MODULATOR VALVE (PMV) ASSEMBLY RESERVOIR
S201
P101
3 BLK/WHT 803
S105
C106
G102
GC4029200629030X

Fig. 63 ABS wiring circuit (Part 3 of 5). 1992–93 Bonneville, 88 & LeSabre

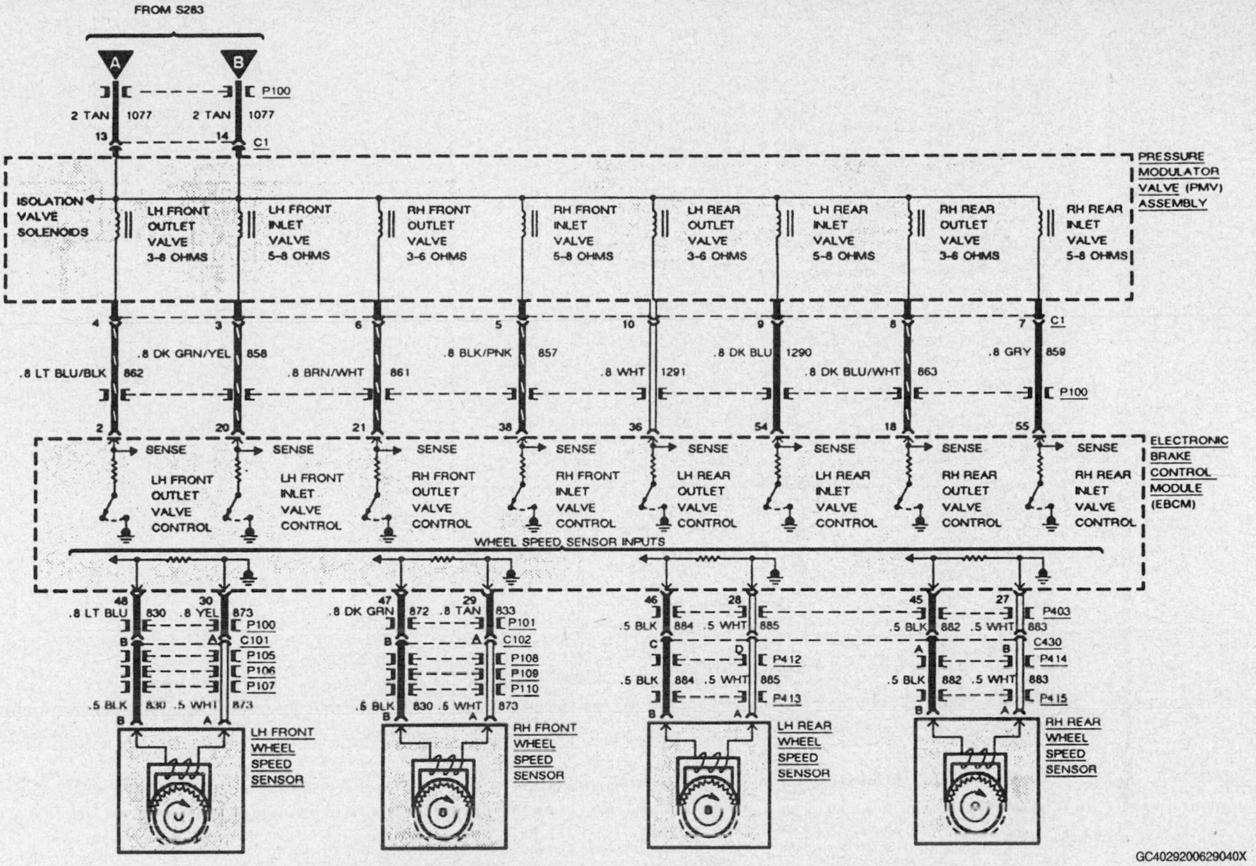
FROM S283
A
B
P100
2 TAN 1077
2 TAN 1077
C1
PRESSURE MODULATOR VALVE (PMV) ASSEMBLY
ISOLATION VALVE SOLENOIDS
LH FRONT OUTLET VALVE 3-6 OHMS
LH FRONT INLET VALVE 5-8 OHMS
RH FRONT OUTLET VALVE 3-6 OHMS
RH FRONT INLET VALVE 5-8 OHMS
LH REAR OUTLET VALVE 3-6 OHMS
LH REAR INLET VALVE 5-8 OHMS
RH REAR OUTLET VALVE 3-6 OHMS
RH REAR INLET VALVE 5-8 OHMS
.8 LT BLU/BLK 862
.8 DK GRN/YEL 858
.8 BRN/WHT 861
.8 BLK/PNK 857
.8 WHT 1291
.8 DK BLU 1290
.8 DK BLU/WHT 863
.8 GRY 859
SENSE
LH FRONT OUTLET VALVE CONTROL
LH FRONT INLET VALVE CONTROL
RH FRONT OUTLET VALVE CONTROL
RH FRONT INLET VALVE CONTROL
LH REAR OUTLET VALVE CONTROL
LH REAR INLET VALVE CONTROL
RH REAR OUTLET VALVE CONTROL
RH REAR INLET VALVE CONTROL
ELECTRONIC BRAKE CONTROL MODULE (EBCM)
WHEEL SPEED SENSOR INPUTS
.8 LT BLU 830 .8 YEL 873
.8 DK GRN 872 .8 TAN 833
.5 BLK 884 .5 WHT 885
.5 BLK 882 .5 WHT 883
P100 C101 P105 P106 P107
P101 C102 P108 P109 P110
P412 P413
P403 C430 P414 P415
.5 BLK 830 .5 WHT 873
LH FRONT WHEEL SPEED SENSOR
RH FRONT WHEEL SPEED SENSOR
LH REAR WHEEL SPEED SENSOR
RH REAR WHEEL SPEED SENSOR
GC4029200629040X

Fig. 63 ABS wiring circuit (Part 4 of 5). 1992–93 Bonneville, 88 & LeSabre

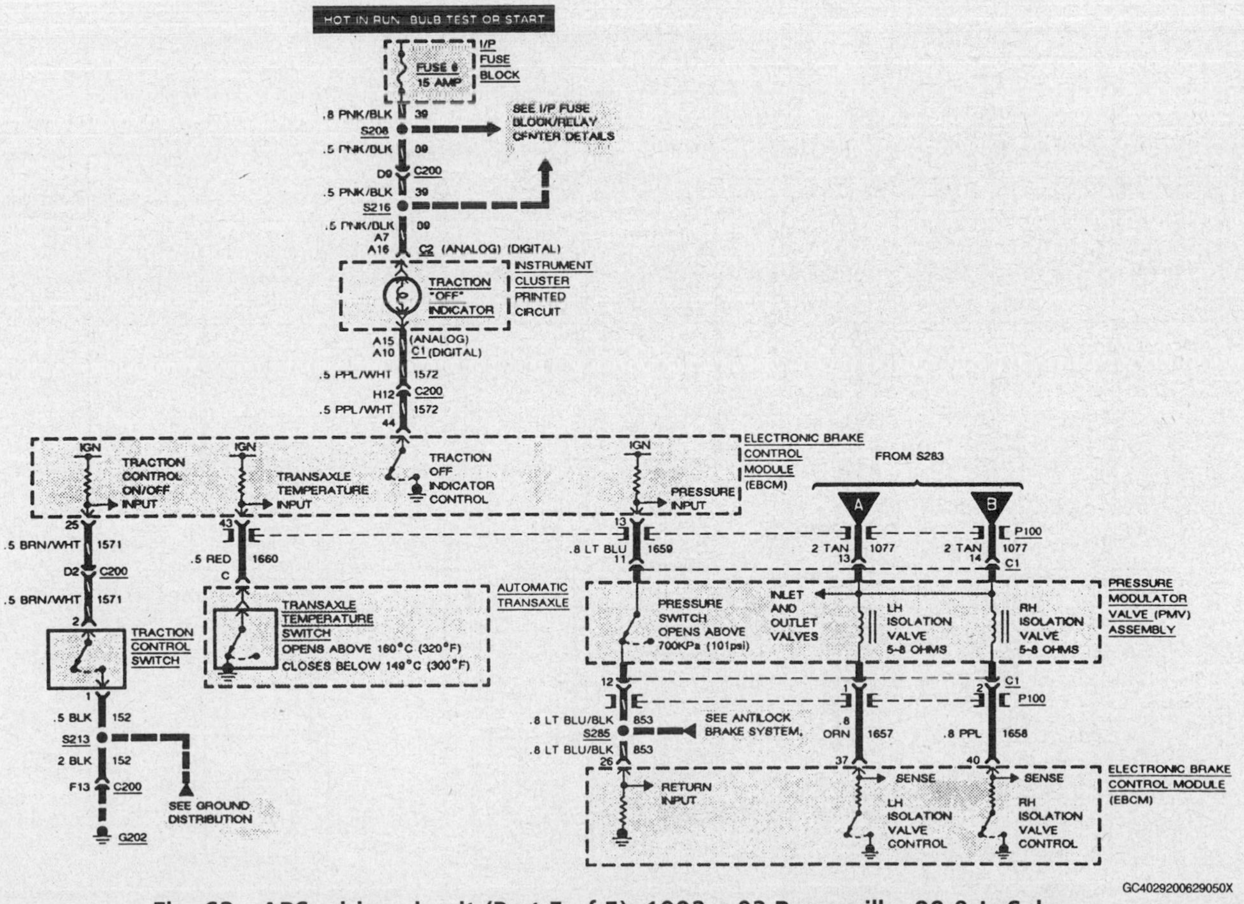
HOT IN RUN, BULB TEST OR START
FUSE 8 15 AMP
I/P FUSE BLOCK
.8 PNK/BLK 39
S208
.5 PNK/BLK 39
SEE I/P FUSE BLOCK/RELAY CENTER DETAILS
C200
S216
C2 (ANALOG) (DIGITAL)
TRACTION "OFF" INDICATOR
INSTRUMENT CLUSTER PRINTED CIRCUIT
C1 (DIGITAL)
.5 PPL/WHT 1572
ELECTRONIC BRAKE CONTROL MODULE (EBCM)
IGN
TRACTION CONTROL ON/OFF INPUT
TRANSAXLE TEMPERATURE INPUT
TRACTION OFF INDICATOR CONTROL
PRESSURE INPUT
FROM S283
.5 BRN/WHT 1571
.5 RED 1660
.8 LT BLU 1659
2 TAN 1077
P100
C1
AUTOMATIC TRANSAXLE
TRACTION CONTROL SWITCH
TRANSAXLE TEMPERATURE SWITCH OPENS ABOVE 160°C (320°F) CLOSES BELOW 149°C (300°F)
PRESSURE SWITCH OPENS ABOVE 700KPa (101psi)
INLET AND OUTLET VALVES
LH ISOLATION VALVE 5-8 OHMS
RH ISOLATION VALVE 5-8 OHMS
PRESSURE MODULATOR VALVE (PMV) ASSEMBLY
.5 BLK 152
S213
2 BLK 152
SEE GROUND DISTRIBUTION
G202
.8 LT BLU/BLK 853
S285
SEE ANTILOCK BRAKE SYSTEM.
.8 ORN 1657
.8 PPL 1658
RETURN INPUT
SENSE
LH ISOLATION VALVE CONTROL
RH ISOLATION VALVE CONTROL
ELECTRONIC BRAKE CONTROL MODULE (EBCM)
GC4029200629050X

Fig. 63 ABS wiring circuit (Part 5 of 5). 1992—93 Bonneville, 88 & LeSabre

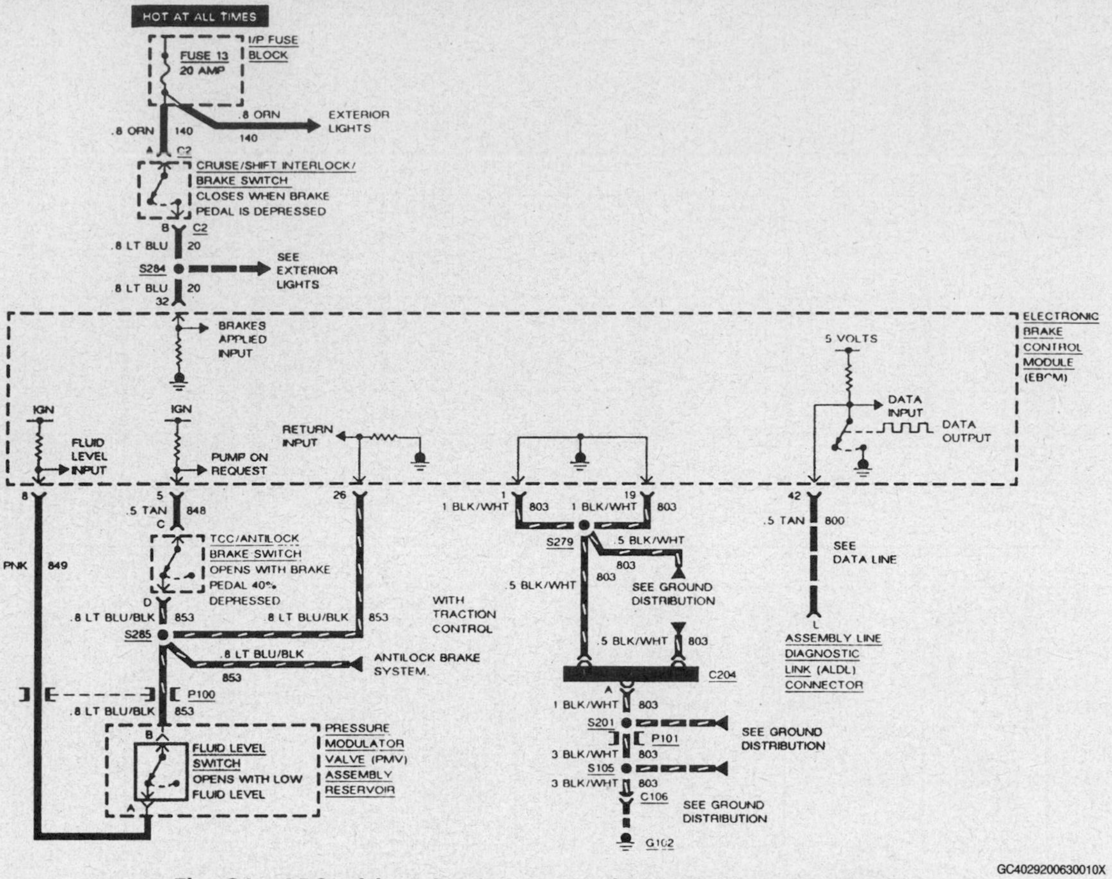
HOT AT ALL TIMES
FUSE 13
20 AMP
I/P FUSE BLOCK
.8 ORN
140
EXTERIOR LIGHTS
C2
CRUISE/SHIFT INTERLOCK/
BRAKE SWITCH
CLOSES WHEN BRAKE
PEDAL IS DEPRESSED
.8 LT BLU
20
S284
SEE EXTERIOR LIGHTS
BRAKES APPLIED INPUT
ELECTRONIC BRAKE CONTROL MODULE (EBCM)
5 VOLTS
DATA INPUT
DATA OUTPUT
IGN
FLUID LEVEL INPUT
PUMP ON REQUEST
RETURN INPUT
.5 TAN
848
TCC/ANTILOCK
BRAKE SWITCH
OPENS WITH BRAKE
PEDAL 40%
DEPRESSED
.8 PNK
849
.8 LT BLU/BLK
853
S285
WITH TRACTION CONTROL
ANTILOCK BRAKE SYSTEM
P100
FLUID LEVEL SWITCH
OPENS WITH LOW FLUID LEVEL
PRESSURE MODULATOR VALVE (PMV) ASSEMBLY RESERVOIR
1 BLK/WHT
803
S279
.5 BLK/WHT
SEE GROUND DISTRIBUTION
C204
S201
P101
3 BLK/WHT
S105
C106
G102
.5 TAN
800
SEE DATA LINE
ASSEMBLY LINE DIAGNOSTIC LINK (ALDL) CONNECTOR
GC4029200630010X

Fig. 64 ABS wiring circuit (Part 1 of 3). 1992 98 & Park Ave.

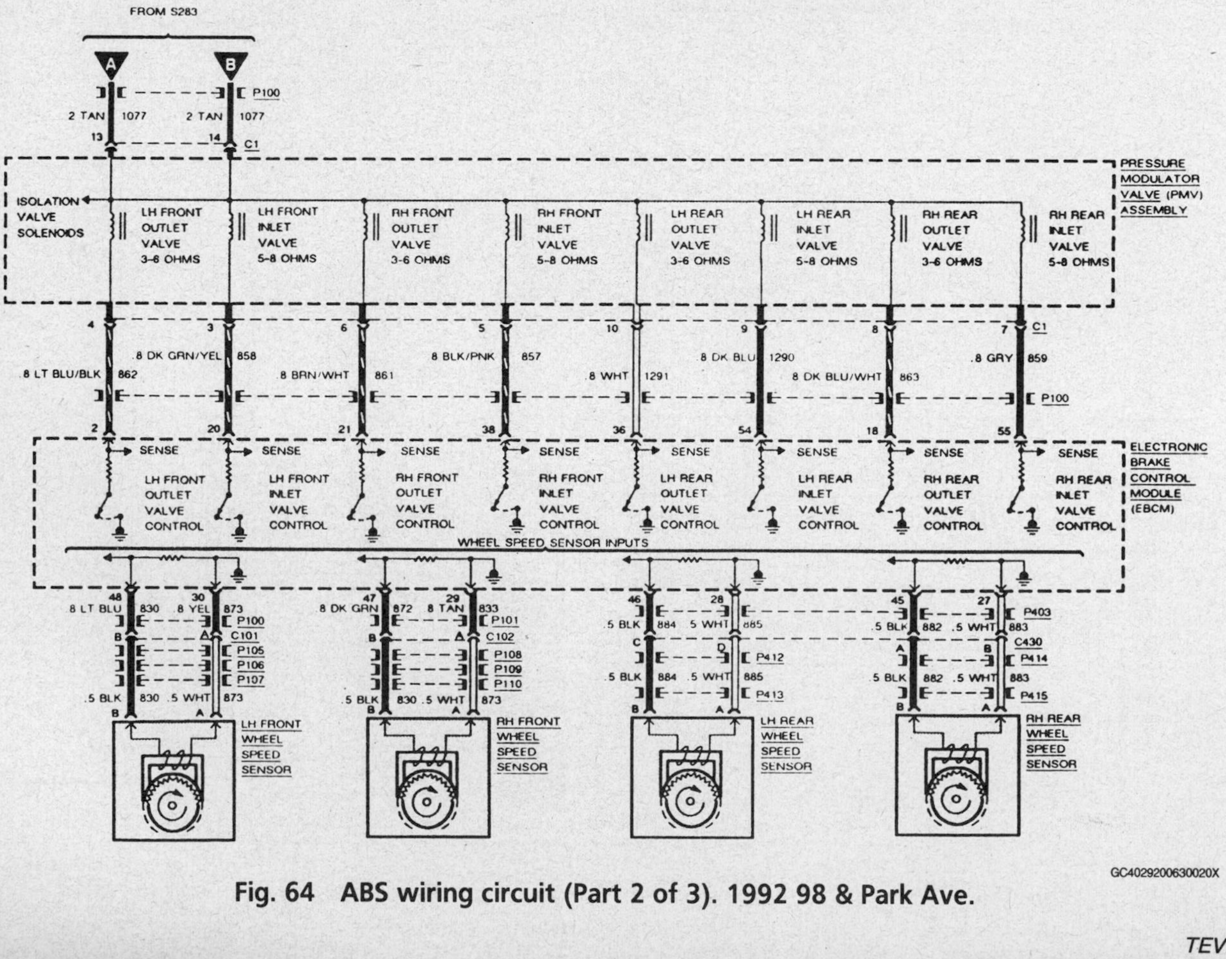
FROM S283
P100
2 TAN
1077
C1
ISOLATION VALVE SOLENOIDS
LH FRONT OUTLET VALVE 3-6 OHMS
LH FRONT INLET VALVE 5-8 OHMS
RH FRONT OUTLET VALVE 3-6 OHMS
RH FRONT INLET VALVE 5-8 OHMS
LH REAR OUTLET VALVE 3-6 OHMS
LH REAR INLET VALVE 5-8 OHMS
RH REAR OUTLET VALVE 3-6 OHMS
RH REAR INLET VALVE 5-8 OHMS
PRESSURE MODULATOR VALVE (PMV) ASSEMBLY
.8 LT BLU/BLK 862
.8 DK GRN/YEL 858
.8 BRN/WHT 861
.8 BLK/PNK 857
.8 WHT 1291
.8 DK BLU 1290
.8 DK BLU/WHT 863
.8 GRY 859
SENSE
LH FRONT OUTLET VALVE CONTROL
LH FRONT INLET VALVE CONTROL
RH FRONT OUTLET VALVE CONTROL
RH FRONT INLET VALVE CONTROL
LH REAR OUTLET VALVE CONTROL
LH REAR INLET VALVE CONTROL
RH REAR OUTLET VALVE CONTROL
RH REAR INLET VALVE CONTROL
ELECTRONIC BRAKE CONTROL MODULE (EBCM)
WHEEL SPEED SENSOR INPUTS
.8 LT BLU 830
.8 YEL 873
C101
P105
P106
P107
.8 DK GRN 872
.8 TAN 833
P101
C102
P108
P109
P110
.5 BLK 884
.5 WHT 885
P412
P413
.5 BLK 882
.5 WHT 883
P403
C430
P414
P415
LH FRONT WHEEL SPEED SENSOR
RH FRONT WHEEL SPEED SENSOR
LH REAR WHEEL SPEED SENSOR
RH REAR WHEEL SPEED SENSOR
GC4029200630020X

Fig. 64 ABS wiring circuit (Part 2 of 3). 1992 98 & Park Ave.

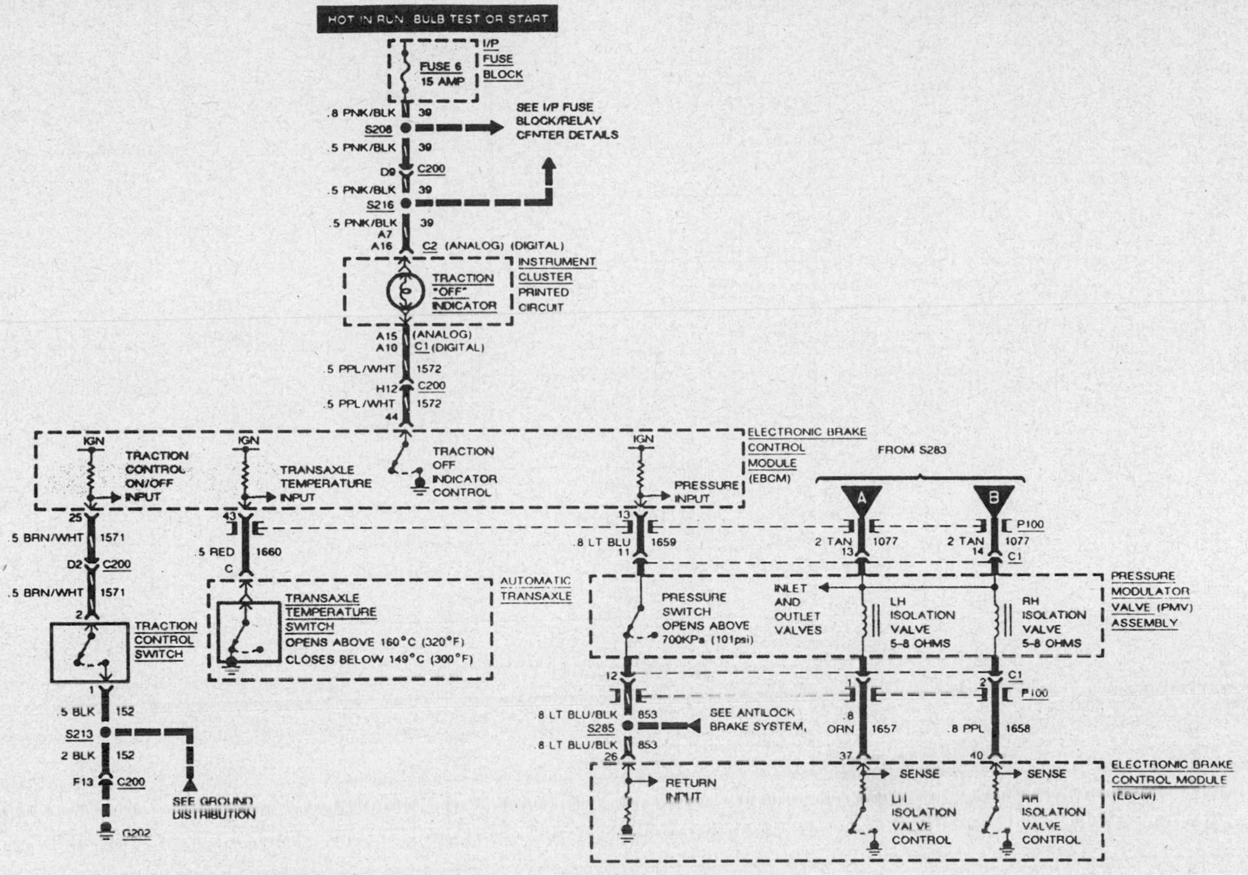

GC4029200630030X

Fig. 64 ABS wiring circuit (Part 3 of 3). 1992 98 & Park Ave.

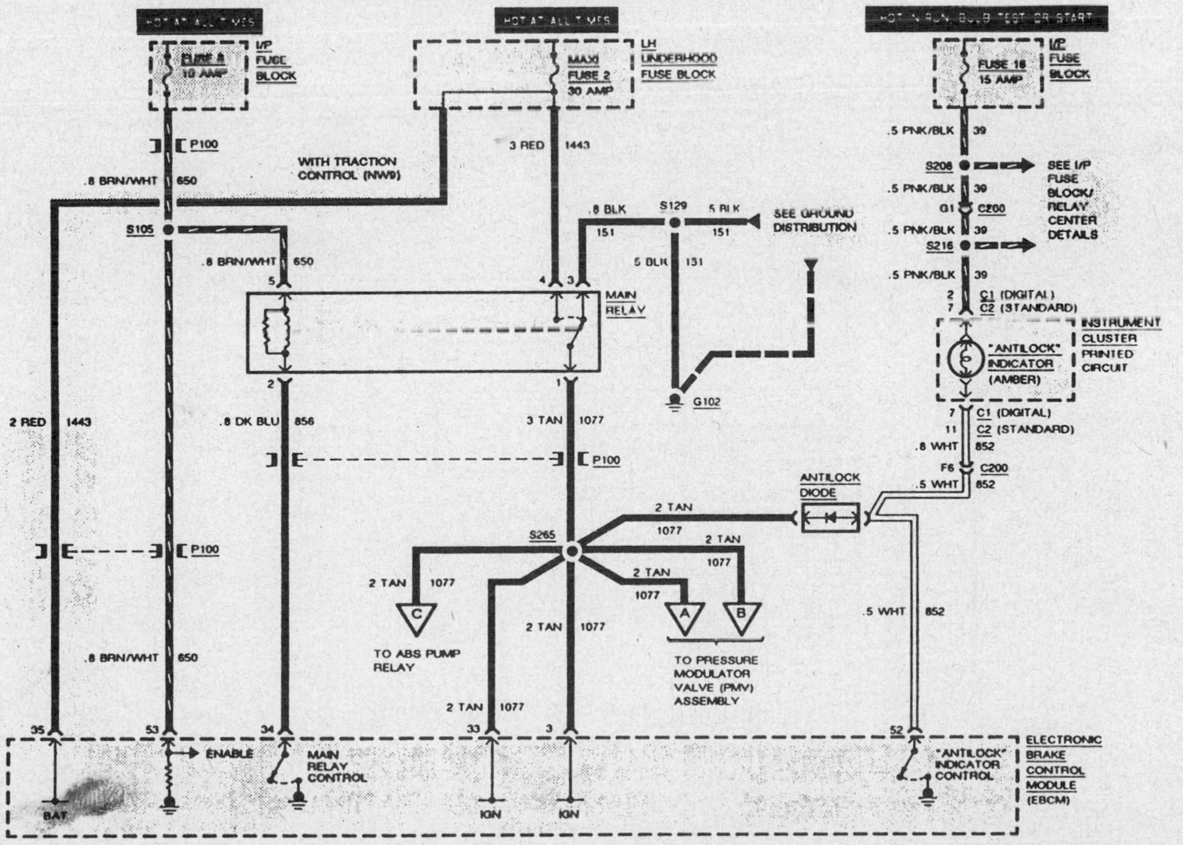

GC4029200631010X

Fig. 65 ABS wiring circuit (Part 1 of 5). 1992 DeVille & Fleetwood (FWD)

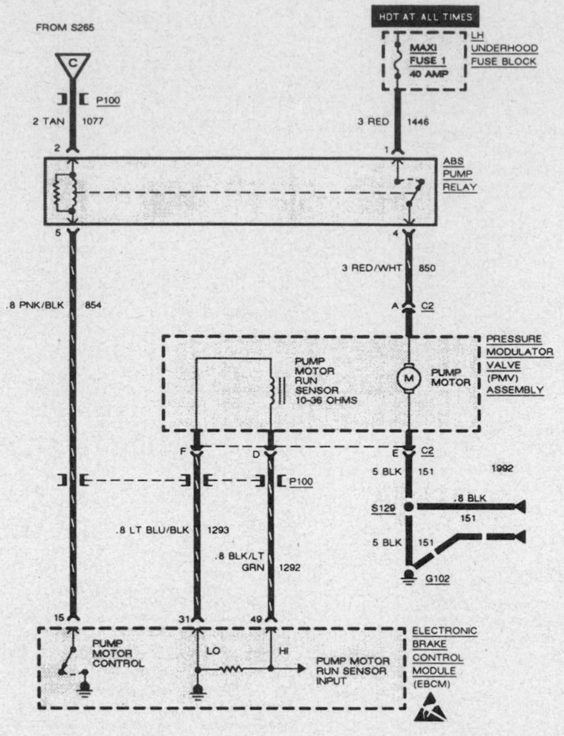
HOT AT ALL TIMES
FROM S265
C
P100
2 TAN 1077
MAXI FUSE 1 40 AMP
LH UNDERHOOD FUSE BLOCK
3 RED 1446
ABS PUMP RELAY
.8 PNK/BLK 854
3 RED/WHT 850
C2
PUMP MOTOR RUN SENSOR 10-36 OHMS
PUMP MOTOR
PRESSURE MODULATOR VALVE (PMV) ASSEMBLY
5 BLK 151
1992
.8 BLK
151
S129
5 BLK 151
G102
.8 LT BLU/BLK 1293
.8 BLK/LT GRN 1292
PUMP MOTOR CONTROL
LO
HI
PUMP MOTOR RUN SENSOR INPUT
ELECTRONIC BRAKE CONTROL MODULE (EBCM)

GC4029200631020X

Fig. 65 ABS wiring circuit (Part 2 of 5). 1992 DeVille & Fleetwood (FWD)

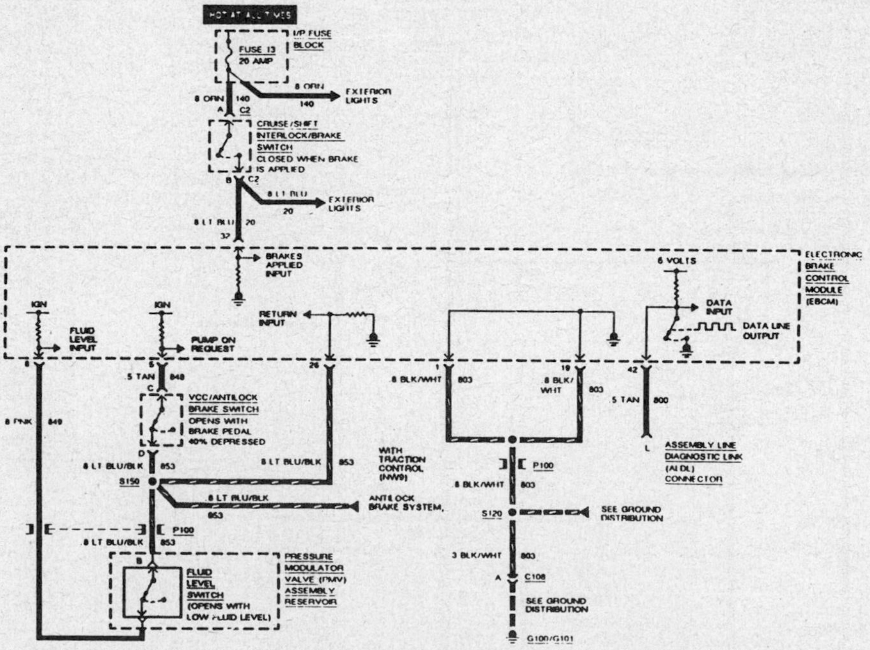
HOT AT ALL TIMES
FUSE 13 20 AMP
I/P FUSE BLOCK
8 ORN 140
EXTERIOR LIGHTS
C2
CRUISE/SHIFT INTERLOCK/BRAKE SWITCH CLOSED WHEN BRAKE IS APPLIED
EXTERIOR LIGHTS
BRAKES APPLIED INPUT
ELECTRONIC BRAKE CONTROL MODULE (EBCM)
6 VOLTS
DATA INPUT
DATA LINE OUTPUT
IGN
FLUID LEVEL INPUT
PUMP ON REQUEST
RETURN INPUT
VCC/ANTILOCK BRAKE SWITCH OPENS WITH BRAKE PEDAL 40% DEPRESSED
WITH TRACTION CONTROL
ANTILOCK BRAKE SYSTEM,
S150
P100
S120
SEE GROUND DISTRIBUTION
C108
G100/G101
ASSEMBLY LINE DIAGNOSTIC LINK (ALDL) CONNECTOR
PRESSURE MODULATOR VALVE (PMV) ASSEMBLY RESERVOIR
FLUID LEVEL SWITCH (OPENS WITH LOW FLUID LEVEL)

GC4029200631030X

Fig. 65 ABS wiring circuit (Part 3 of 5). 1992 DeVille & Fleetwood (FWD)

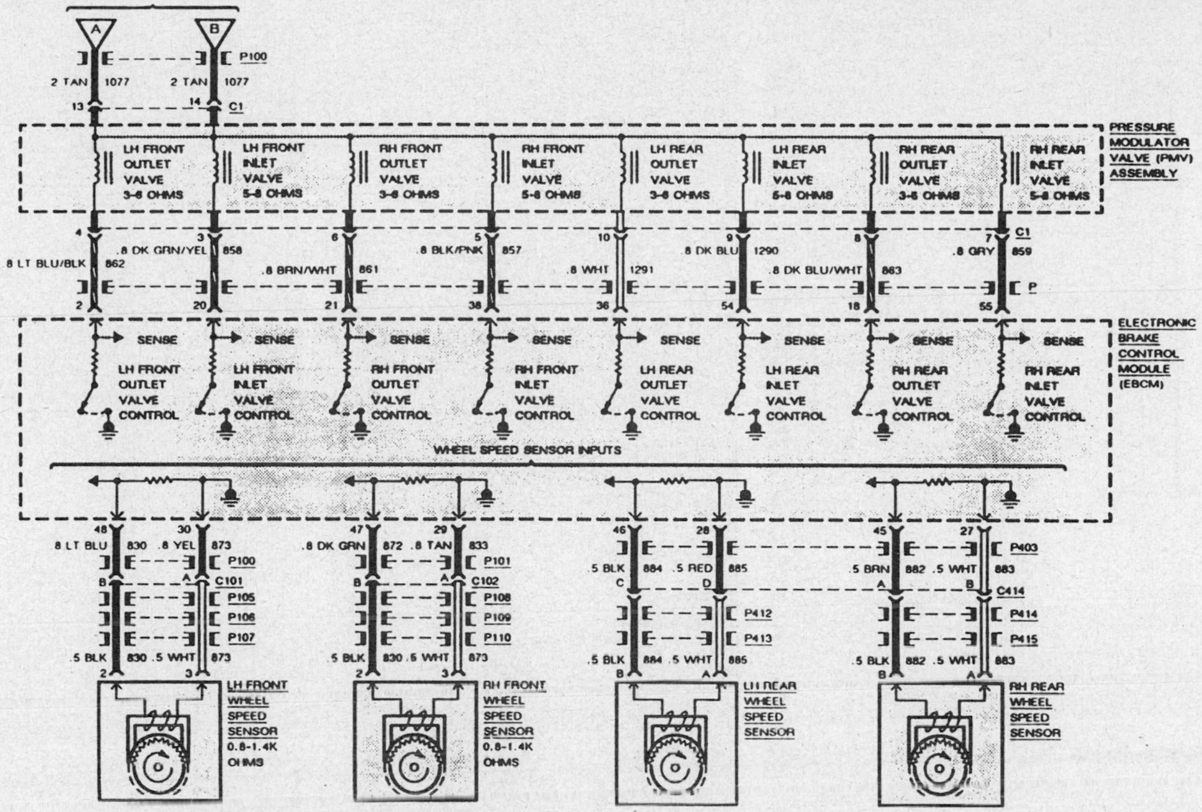

P100
2 TAN 1077
C1
LH FRONT OUTLET VALVE 3-6 OHMS
LH FRONT INLET VALVE 5-8 OHMS
RH FRONT OUTLET VALVE 3-6 OHMS
RH FRONT INLET VALVE 5-8 OHMS
LH REAR OUTLET VALVE 3-6 OHMS
LH REAR INLET VALVE 5-8 OHMS
RH REAR OUTLET VALVE 3-6 OHMS
RH REAR INLET VALVE 5-8 OHMS
PRESSURE MODULATOR VALVE (PMV) ASSEMBLY
.8 LT BLU/BLK 862
.8 DK GRN/YEL 858
.8 BRN/WHT 861
.8 BLK/PNK 857
.8 WHT 1291
.8 DK BLU 1290
.8 DK BLU/WHT 863
.8 GRY 859
SENSE
LH FRONT OUTLET VALVE CONTROL
LH FRONT INLET VALVE CONTROL
RH FRONT OUTLET VALVE CONTROL
RH FRONT INLET VALVE CONTROL
LH REAR OUTLET VALVE CONTROL
LH REAR INLET VALVE CONTROL
RH REAR OUTLET VALVE CONTROL
RH REAR INLET VALVE CONTROL
ELECTRONIC BRAKE CONTROL MODULE (EBCM)
WHEEL SPEED SENSOR INPUTS
.8 LT BLU 830
.8 YEL 873
.8 DK GRN 872
.8 TAN 833
.5 BLK 884
.5 RED 885
.5 BRN 882
.5 WHT 883
P100 C101 P105 P106 P107
P101 C102 P108 P109 P110
P412 P413
P403 C414 P414 P415
LH FRONT WHEEL SPEED SENSOR 0.8-1.4K OHMS
RH FRONT WHEEL SPEED SENSOR 0.8-1.4K OHMS
LH REAR WHEEL SPEED SENSOR
RH REAR WHEEL SPEED SENSOR

GC4029200631040X

Fig. 65 ABS wiring circuit (Part 4 of 5). 1992 DeVille & Fleetwood (FWD)

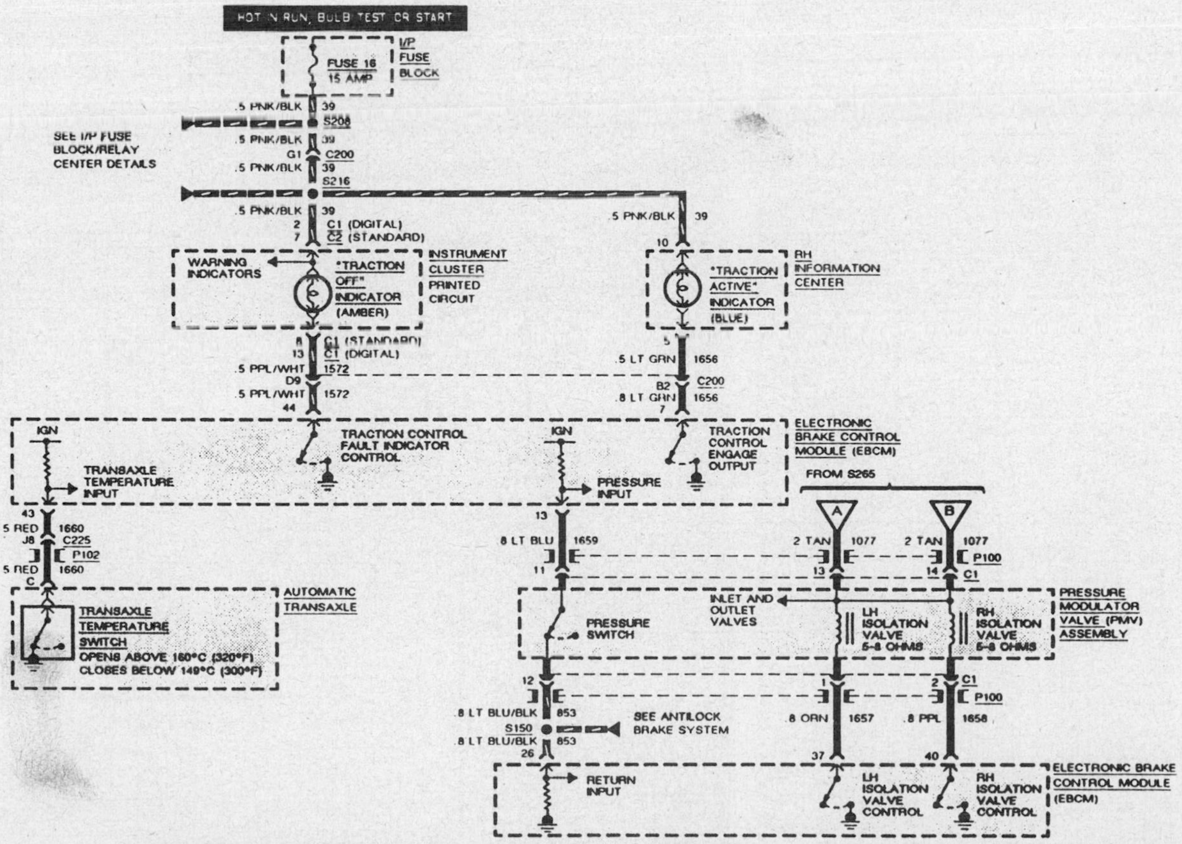

HOT IN RUN, BULB TEST OR START
FUSE 16 15 AMP
I/P FUSE BLOCK
.5 PNK/BLK 39
S208
SEE I/P FUSE BLOCK/RELAY CENTER DETAILS
C200
S216
C1 (DIGITAL)
C2 (STANDARD)
WARNING INDICATORS
"TRACTION OFF" INDICATOR (AMBER)
INSTRUMENT CLUSTER PRINTED CIRCUIT
"TRACTION ACTIVE" INDICATOR (BLUE)
RH INFORMATION CENTER
.5 PPL/WHT 1572
.5 LT GRN 1656
.8 LT GRN 1656
IGN
TRANSAXLE TEMPERATURE INPUT
TRACTION CONTROL FAULT INDICATOR CONTROL
PRESSURE INPUT
TRACTION CONTROL ENGAGE OUTPUT
ELECTRONIC BRAKE CONTROL MODULE (EBCM)
FROM S265
.5 RED 1660
C225
P102
.8 LT BLU 1659
2 TAN 1077
P100
C1
AUTOMATIC TRANSAXLE
TRANSAXLE TEMPERATURE SWITCH
OPENS ABOVE 160°C (320°F)
CLOSES BELOW 149°C (300°F)
INLET AND OUTLET VALVES
PRESSURE SWITCH
LH ISOLATION VALVE 5-8 OHMS
RH ISOLATION VALVE 5-8 OHMS
PRESSURE MODULATOR VALVE (PMV) ASSEMBLY
.8 LT BLU/BLK 853
S150
SEE ANTILOCK BRAKE SYSTEM
.8 ORN 1657
.8 PPL 1658
RETURN INPUT
LH ISOLATION VALVE CONTROL
RH ISOLATION VALVE CONTROL
ELECTRONIC BRAKE CONTROL MODULE (EBCM)

GC4029200631050X

Fig. 65 ABS wiring circuit (Part 5 of 5). 1992 DeVille & Fleetwood (FWD)

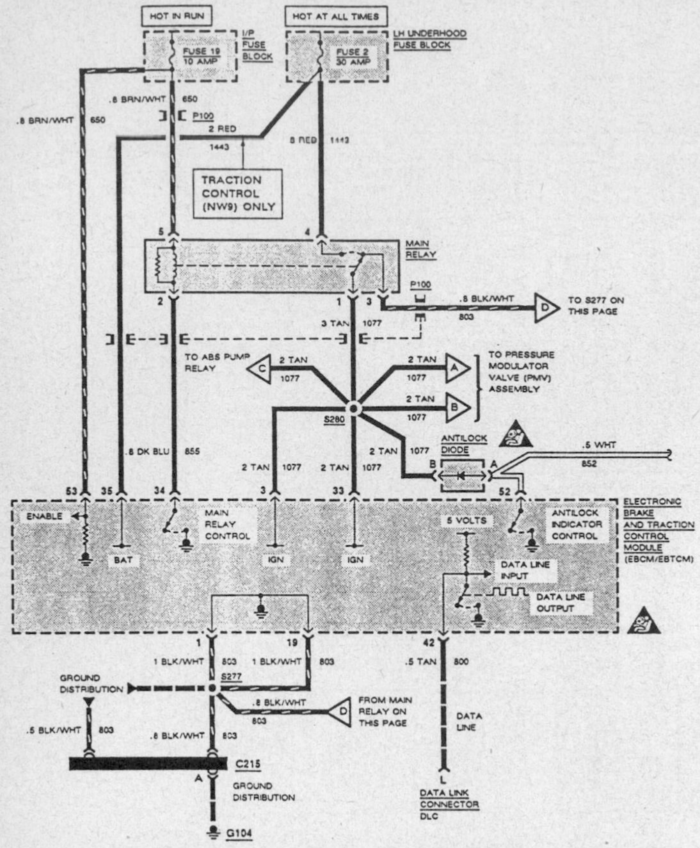
HOT IN RUN
HOT AT ALL TIMES
I/P FUSE BLOCK
FUSE 19 10 AMP
LH UNDERHOOD FUSE BLOCK
FUSE 2 30 AMP
TRACTION CONTROL (NW9) ONLY
MAIN RELAY
TO S277 ON THIS PAGE
TO ABS PUMP RELAY
TO PRESSURE MODULATOR VALVE (PMV) ASSEMBLY
S280
ANTILOCK DIODE
ENABLE
MAIN RELAY CONTROL
BAT
IGN
5 VOLTS
ANTILOCK INDICATOR CONTROL
DATA LINE INPUT
DATA LINE OUTPUT
ELECTRONIC BRAKE AND TRACTION CONTROL MODULE (EBCM/EBTCM)
GROUND DISTRIBUTION
S277
FROM MAIN RELAY ON THIS PAGE
DATA LINE
C215
G104
DATA LINK CONNECTOR DLC

Fig. 71 ABS wiring circuit (Part 1 of 6). 1993 LeSabre & Park Avenue

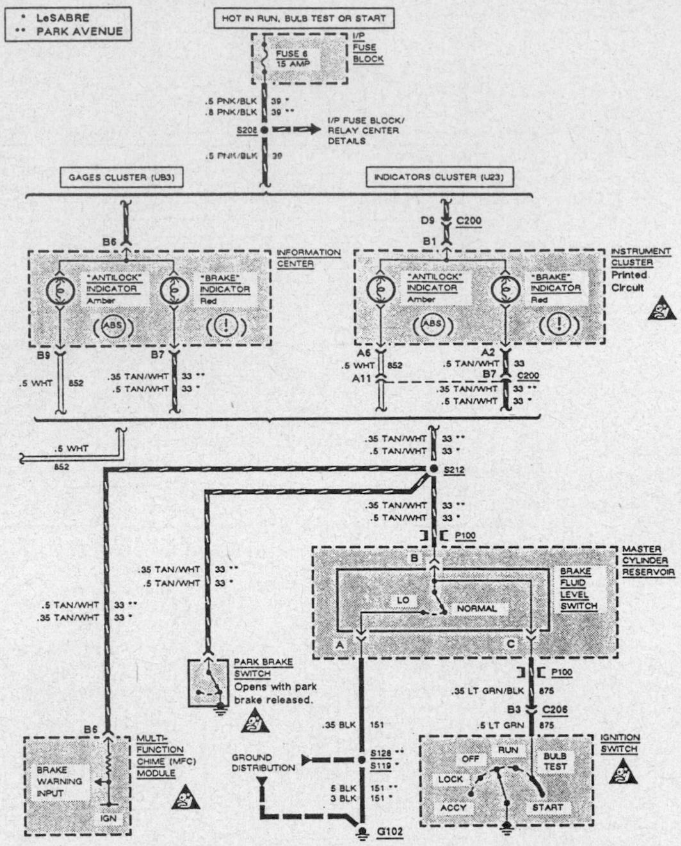
* LeSABRE
** PARK AVENUE
HOT IN RUN, BULB TEST OR START
FUSE 6 15 AMP
I/P FUSE BLOCK
S208
I/P FUSE BLOCK/RELAY CENTER DETAILS
GAGES CLUSTER (UB3)
INDICATORS CLUSTER (U23)
C200
"ANTILOCK" INDICATOR Amber
"BRAKE" INDICATOR Red
INFORMATION CENTER
INSTRUMENT CLUSTER Printed Circuit
S212
P100
MASTER CYLINDER RESERVOIR
BRAKE FLUID LEVEL SWITCH
LO
NORMAL
PARK BRAKE SWITCH
Opens with park brake released.
MULTI-FUNCTION CHIME (MFC) MODULE
BRAKE WARNING INPUT
IGN
GROUND DISTRIBUTION
S128 **
S119 *
G102
C206
IGNITION SWITCH
OFF
RUN
BULB TEST
LOCK
ACCY
START

Fig. 71 ABS wiring circuit (Part 2 of 6). 1993 LeSabre & Park Avenue

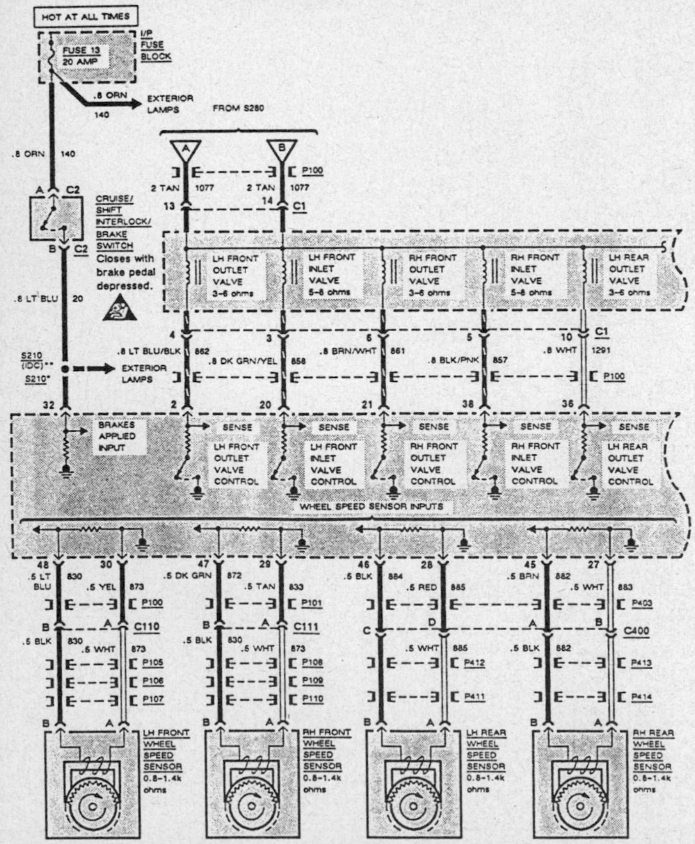
HOT AT ALL TIMES
FUSE 13 20 AMP
I/P FUSE BLOCK
EXTERIOR LAMPS
FROM S280
CRUISE/SHIFT INTERLOCK/BRAKE SWITCH
Closes with brake pedal depressed.
LH FRONT OUTLET VALVE 3-6 ohms
LH FRONT INLET VALVE 5-8 ohms
RH FRONT OUTLET VALVE 3-6 ohms
RH FRONT INLET VALVE 5-8 ohms
LH REAR OUTLET VALVE 3-6 ohms
BRAKES APPLIED INPUT
SENSE
LH FRONT OUTLET VALVE CONTROL
LH FRONT INLET VALVE CONTROL
RH FRONT OUTLET VALVE CONTROL
RH FRONT INLET VALVE CONTROL
LH REAR OUTLET VALVE CONTROL
WHEEL SPEED SENSOR INPUTS
LH FRONT WHEEL SPEED SENSOR 0.8-1.4k ohms
RH FRONT WHEEL SPEED SENSOR 0.8-1.4k ohms
LH REAR WHEEL SPEED SENSOR 0.8-1.4k ohms
RH REAR WHEEL SPEED SENSOR 0.8-1.4k ohms

Fig. 71 ABS wiring circuit (Part 3 of 6). 1993 LeSabre & Park Avenue

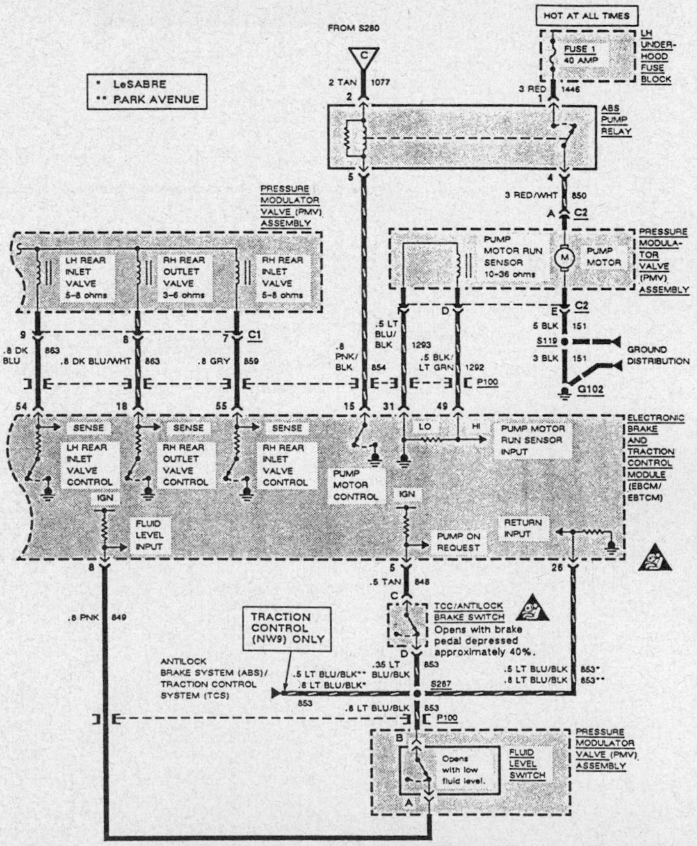
FROM S280
HOT AT ALL TIMES
FUSE 1 40 AMP
LH UNDER-HOOD FUSE BLOCK
* LeSABRE
** PARK AVENUE
ABS PUMP RELAY
PRESSURE MODULATOR VALVE (PMV) ASSEMBLY
LH REAR INLET VALVE 5-8 ohms
RH REAR OUTLET VALVE 3-6 ohms
RH REAR INLET VALVE 5-8 ohms
PUMP MOTOR RUN SENSOR 10-36 ohms
PUMP MOTOR
GROUND DISTRIBUTION
G102
SENSE
LH REAR INLET VALVE CONTROL
RH REAR OUTLET VALVE CONTROL
RH REAR INLET VALVE CONTROL
PUMP MOTOR CONTROL
PUMP MOTOR RUN SENSOR INPUT
ELECTRONIC BRAKE AND TRACTION CONTROL MODULE (EBCM/EBTCM)
FLUID LEVEL INPUT
PUMP ON REQUEST
RETURN INPUT
TRACTION CONTROL (NW9) ONLY
TCC/ANTILOCK BRAKE SWITCH
Opens with brake pedal depressed approximately 40%.
ANTILOCK BRAKE SYSTEM (ABS)/TRACTION CONTROL SYSTEM (TCS)
S267
FLUID LEVEL SWITCH
Opens with low fluid level.

Fig. 71 ABS wiring circuit (Part 4 of 6). 1993 LeSabre & Park Avenue

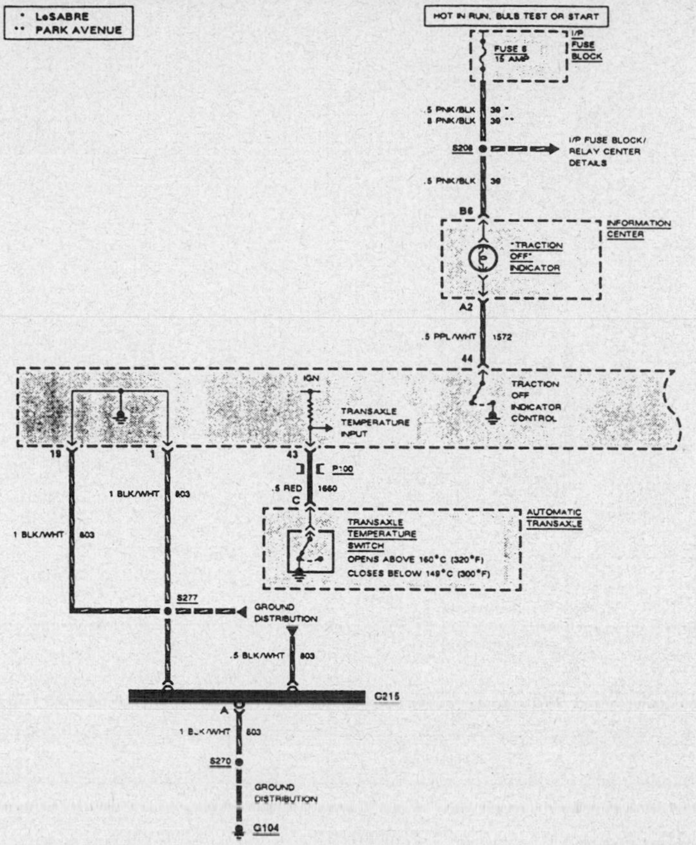

* LeSABRE
** PARK AVENUE
HOT IN RUN, BULB TEST OR START
FUSE 6 15 AMP
I/P FUSE BLOCK
I/P FUSE BLOCK/ RELAY CENTER DETAILS
INFORMATION CENTER
"TRACTION OFF" INDICATOR
TRACTION OFF INDICATOR CONTROL
TRANSAXLE TEMPERATURE INPUT
AUTOMATIC TRANSAXLE
TRANSAXLE TEMPERATURE SWITCH
OPENS ABOVE 160°C (320°F)
CLOSES BELOW 149°C (300°F)
GROUND DISTRIBUTION
C215
G104

GC4029300632050X

Fig. 66 ABS wiring circuit (Part 5 of 6). 1993 LeSabre & Park Avenue

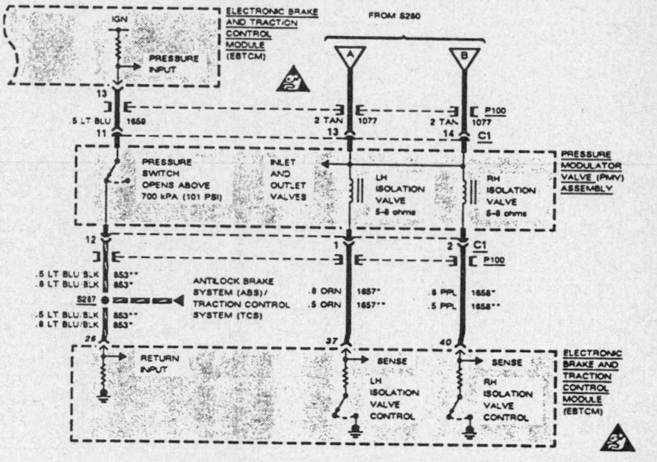

ELECTRONIC BRAKE AND TRACTION CONTROL MODULE (EBTCM)
FROM S250
PRESSURE INPUT
PRESSURE SWITCH OPENS ABOVE 700 kPA (101 PSI)
INLET AND OUTLET VALVES
LH ISOLATION VALVE
RH ISOLATION VALVE
PRESSURE MODULATOR VALVE (PMV) ASSEMBLY
ANTILOCK BRAKE SYSTEM (ABS)/ TRACTION CONTROL SYSTEM (TCS)
RETURN INPUT
SENSE
LH ISOLATION VALVE CONTROL
RH ISOLATION VALVE CONTROL

GC4029300632060X

Fig. 66 ABS wiring circuit (Part 6 of 6). 1993 LeSabre & Park Avenue

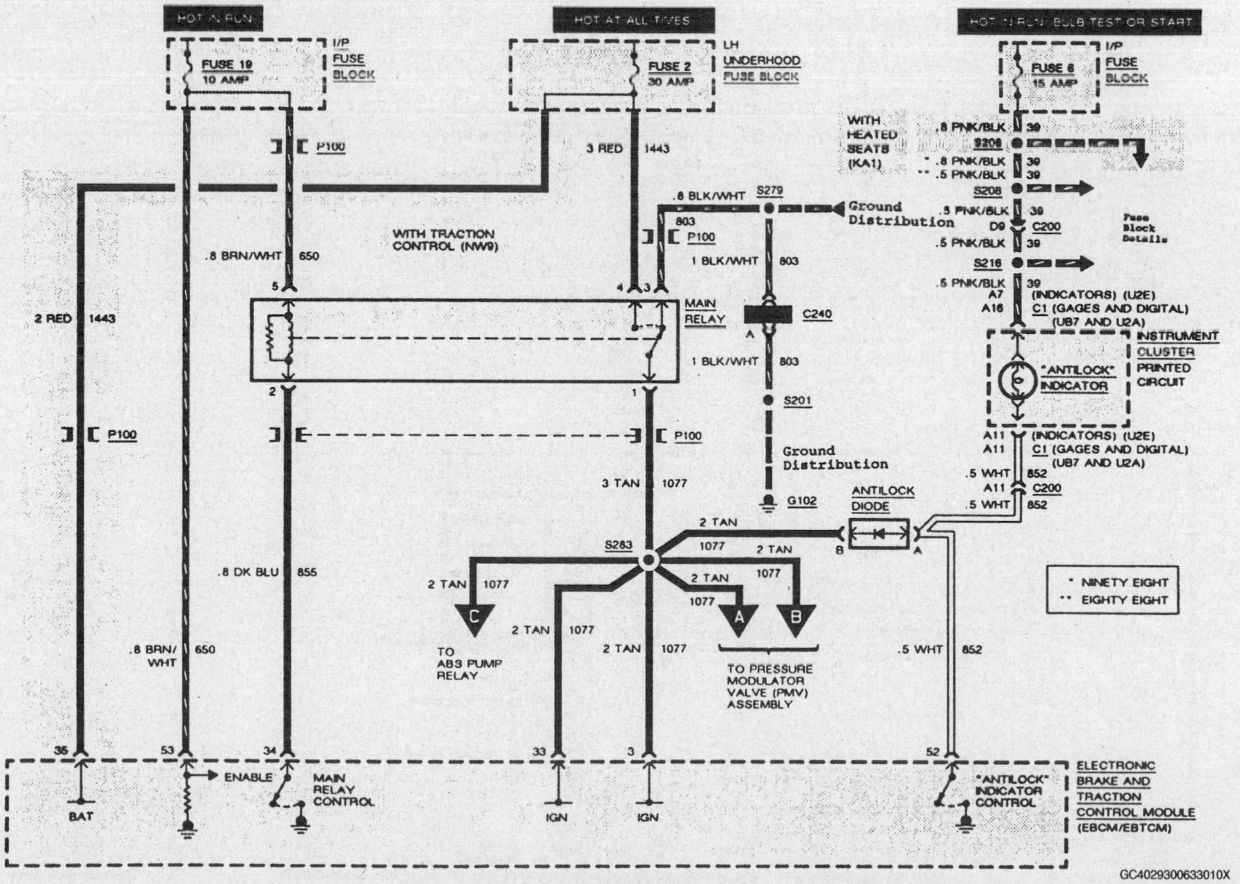

HOT IN RUN
HOT AT ALL TIMES
HOT IN RUN, BULB TEST OR START
FUSE 19 10 AMP
I/P FUSE BLOCK
FUSE 2 30 AMP
LH UNDERHOOD FUSE BLOCK
FUSE 6 15 AMP
WITH HEATED SEATS (KA1)
Ground Distribution
Fuse Block Details
WITH TRACTION CONTROL (NW9)
MAIN RELAY
(INDICATORS) (U2E)
(GAGES AND DIGITAL) (UB7 AND U2A)
INSTRUMENT CLUSTER PRINTED CIRCUIT
"ANTILOCK" INDICATOR
ANTILOCK DIODE
* NINETY EIGHT
** EIGHTY EIGHT
TO ABS PUMP RELAY
TO PRESSURE MODULATOR VALVE (PMV) ASSEMBLY
ENABLE
MAIN RELAY CONTROL
BAT
IGN
"ANTILOCK" INDICATOR CONTROL
ELECTRONIC BRAKE AND TRACTION CONTROL MODULE (EBCM/EBTCM)

GC4029300633010X

Fig. 67 ABS wiring circuit (Part 1 of 7). 1993 88 & 98

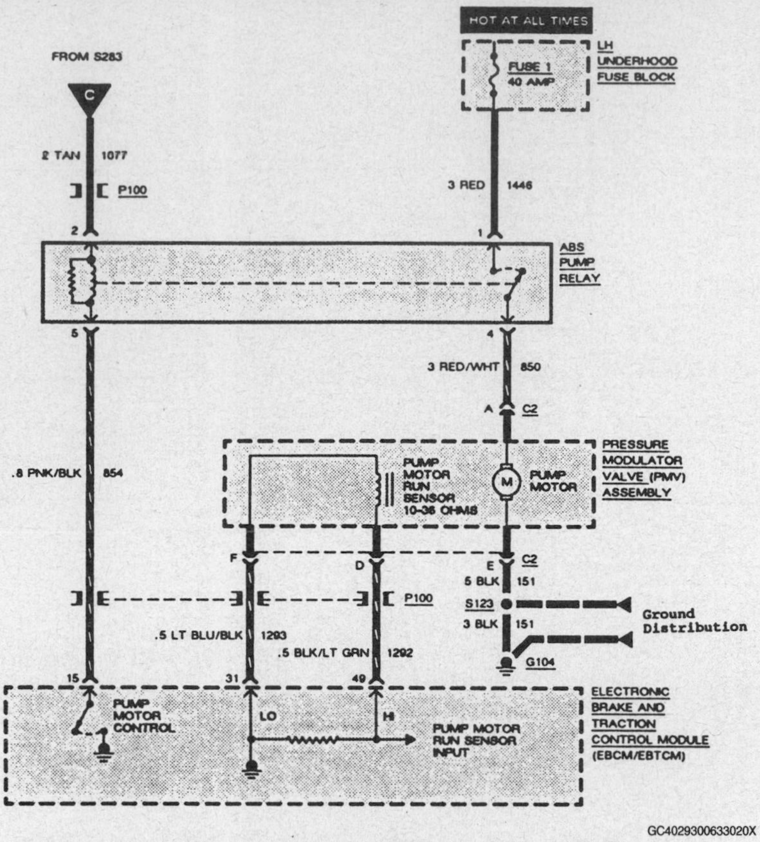
HOT AT ALL TIMES
FUSE 1
40 AMP
LH
UNDERHOOD
FUSE BLOCK
FROM S283
C
2 TAN
1077
P100
3 RED
1446
ABS
PUMP
RELAY
3 RED/WHT
850
C2
.8 PNK/BLK
854
PUMP
MOTOR
RUN
SENSOR
10-36 OHMS
PUMP
MOTOR
PRESSURE
MODULATOR
VALVE (PMV)
ASSEMBLY
5 BLK
151
S123
3 BLK
151
Ground
Distribution
G104
.5 LT BLU/BLK
1293
.5 BLK/LT GRN
1292
PUMP
MOTOR
CONTROL
LO
HI
PUMP MOTOR
RUN SENSOR
INPUT
ELECTRONIC
BRAKE AND
TRACTION
CONTROL MODULE
(EBCM/EBTCM)
GC4029300633020X

Fig. 67 ABS wiring circuit (Part 2 of 7). 1993 88 & 98

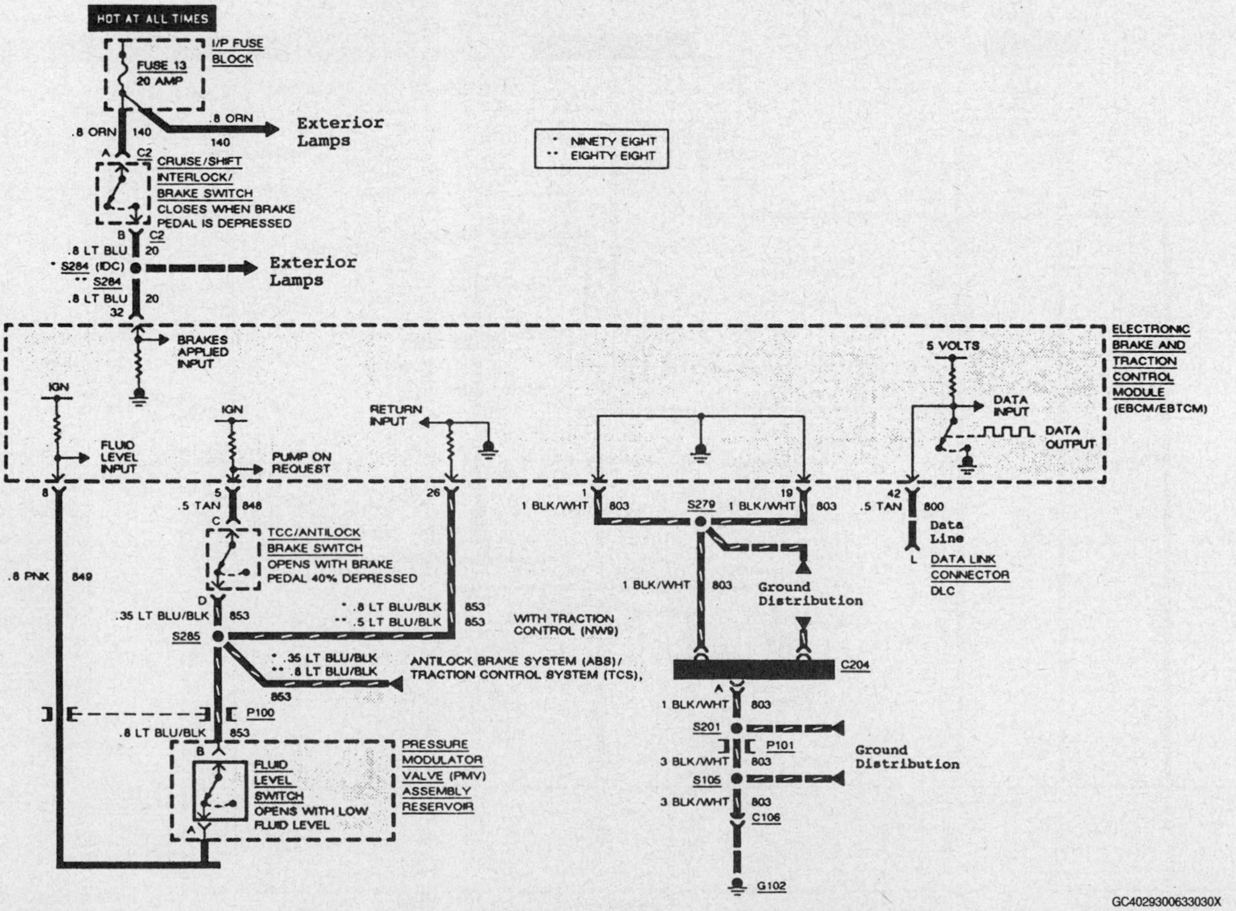
HOT AT ALL TIMES
FUSE 13
20 AMP
I/P FUSE
BLOCK
.8 ORN
140
Exterior
Lamps
* NINETY EIGHT
** EIGHTY EIGHT
CRUISE/SHIFT
INTERLOCK/
BRAKE SWITCH
CLOSES WHEN BRAKE
PEDAL IS DEPRESSED
.8 LT BLU
20
* S284 (IDC)
** S284
BRAKES
APPLIED
INPUT
IGN
FLUID
LEVEL
INPUT
PUMP ON
REQUEST
RETURN
INPUT
5 VOLTS
DATA
INPUT
DATA
OUTPUT
ELECTRONIC
BRAKE AND
TRACTION
CONTROL
MODULE
(EBCM/EBTCM)
.5 TAN
848
TCC/ANTILOCK
BRAKE SWITCH
OPENS WITH BRAKE
PEDAL 40% DEPRESSED
.8 PNK
849
.35 LT BLU/BLK
853
* .8 LT BLU/BLK
** .5 LT BLU/BLK
WITH TRACTION
CONTROL (NW9)
S285
* .35 LT BLU/BLK
** .8 LT BLU/BLK
ANTILOCK BRAKE SYSTEM (ABS)/
TRACTION CONTROL SYSTEM (TCS),
P100
.8 LT BLU/BLK
FLUID
LEVEL
SWITCH
OPENS WITH LOW
FLUID LEVEL
PRESSURE
MODULATOR
VALVE (PMV)
ASSEMBLY
RESERVOIR
1 BLK/WHT
803
S279
.5 TAN
800
Data
Line
DATA LINK
CONNECTOR
DLC
Ground
Distribution
C204
S201
P101
3 BLK/WHT
S105
C106
G102
GC4029300633030X

Fig. 67 ABS wiring circuit (Part 3 of 7). 1993 88 & 98

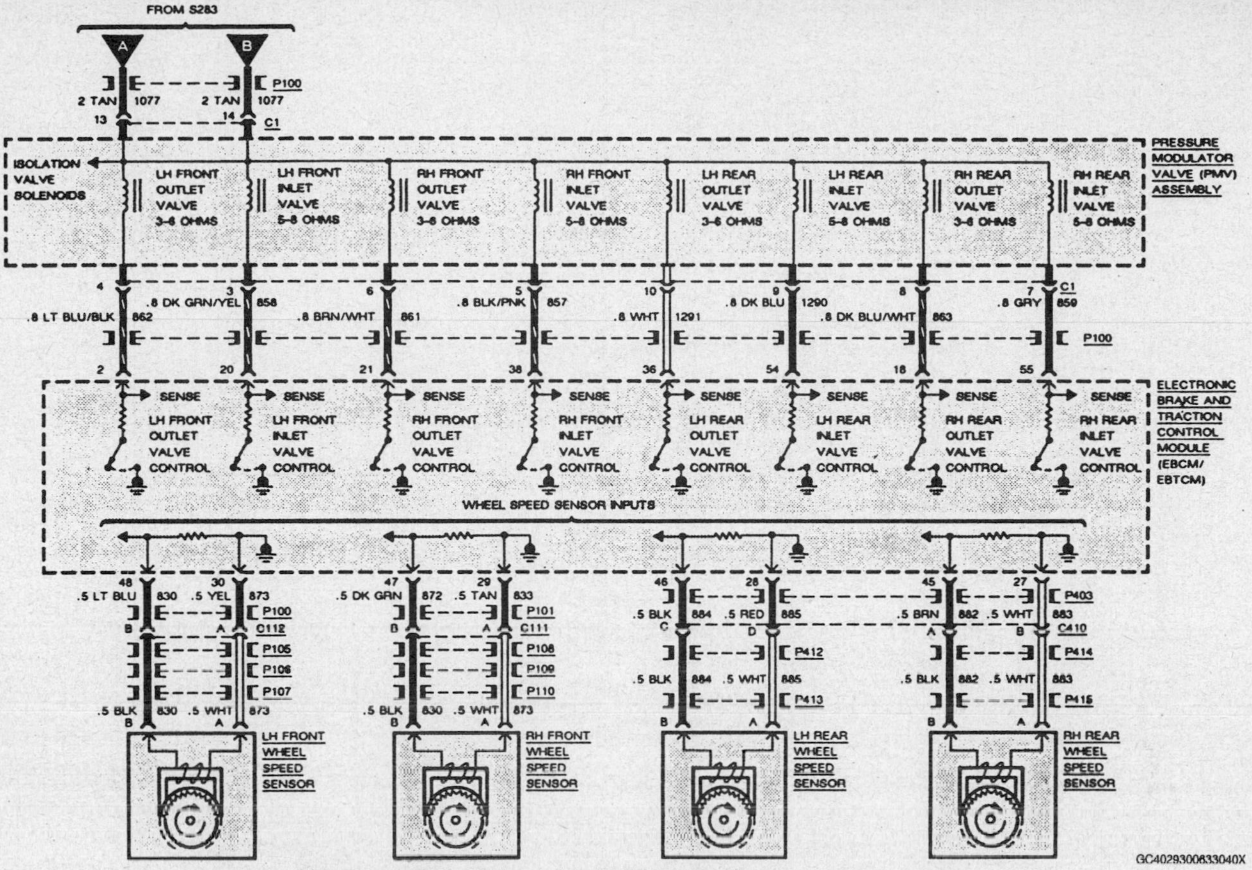
FROM S283
A
B
2 TAN 1077
2 TAN 1077
P100
C1
ISOLATION VALVE SOLENOIDS
LH FRONT OUTLET VALVE 3-6 OHMS
LH FRONT INLET VALVE 5-8 OHMS
RH FRONT OUTLET VALVE 3-6 OHMS
RH FRONT INLET VALVE 5-8 OHMS
LH REAR OUTLET VALVE 3-6 OHMS
LH REAR INLET VALVE 5-8 OHMS
RH REAR OUTLET VALVE 3-6 OHMS
RH REAR INLET VALVE 5-8 OHMS
PRESSURE MODULATOR VALVE (PMV) ASSEMBLY
.8 LT BLU/BLK 862
.8 DK GRN/YEL 858
.8 BRN/WHT 861
.8 BLK/PNK 857
.8 WHT 1291
.8 DK BLU 1290
.8 DK BLU/WHT 863
.8 GRY 859
SENSE
LH FRONT OUTLET VALVE CONTROL
LH FRONT INLET VALVE CONTROL
RH FRONT OUTLET VALVE CONTROL
RH FRONT INLET VALVE CONTROL
LH REAR OUTLET VALVE CONTROL
LH REAR INLET VALVE CONTROL
RH REAR OUTLET VALVE CONTROL
RH REAR INLET VALVE CONTROL
ELECTRONIC BRAKE AND TRACTION CONTROL MODULE (EBCM/ EBTCM)
WHEEL SPEED SENSOR INPUTS
.5 LT BLU 830
.5 YEL 873
.5 DK GRN 872
.5 TAN 833
.5 BLK 884
.5 RED 885
.5 BRN 882
.5 WHT 883
P100
C112
P105
P106
P107
P101
C111
P108
P109
P110
P403
C410
P412
P413
P414
P415
.5 BLK 830
.5 WHT 873
LH FRONT WHEEL SPEED SENSOR
RH FRONT WHEEL SPEED SENSOR
LH REAR WHEEL SPEED SENSOR
RH REAR WHEEL SPEED SENSOR
GC4029300633040X

Fig. 67 ABS wiring circuit (Part 4 of 7). 1993 88 & 98

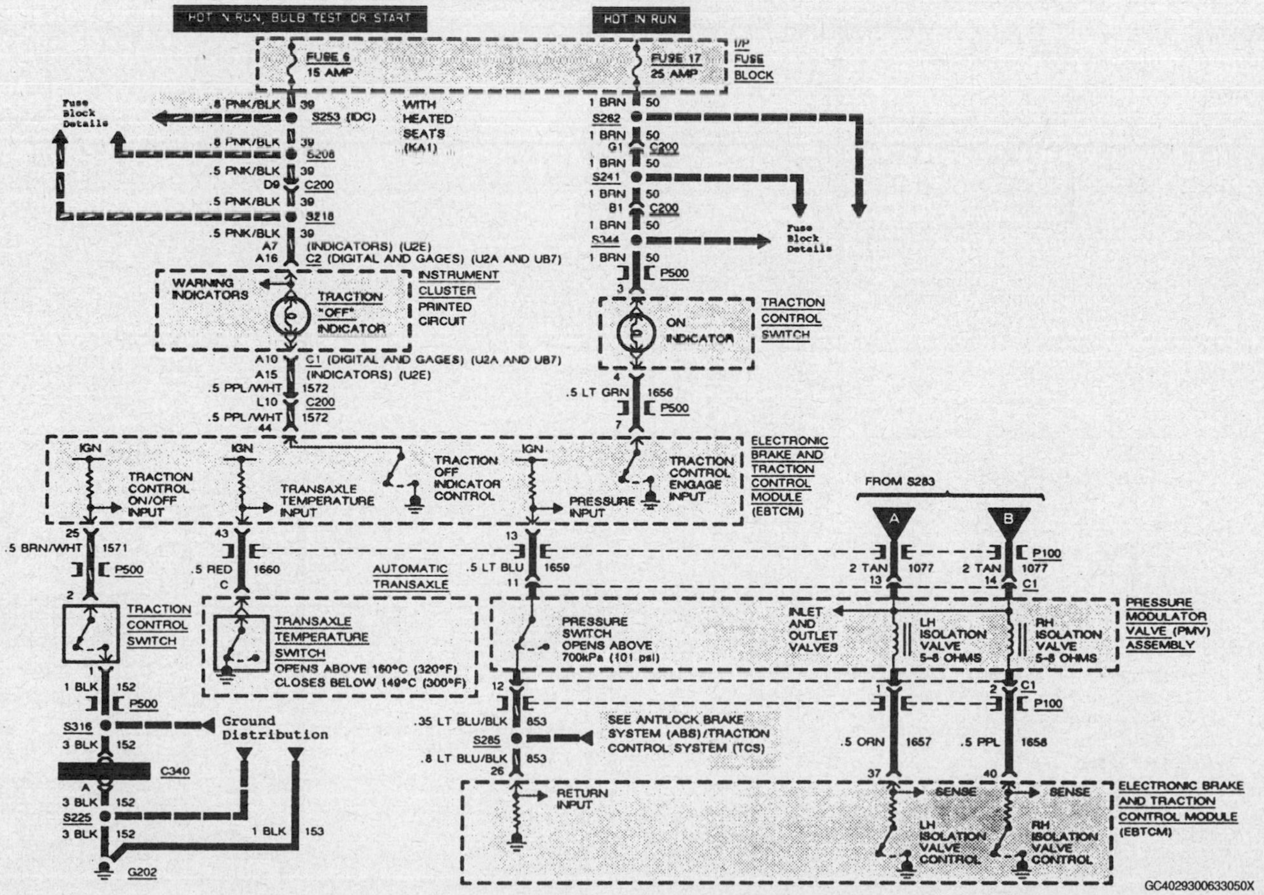
HOT IN RUN, BULB TEST OR START
HOT IN RUN
FUSE 6 15 AMP
FUSE 17 25 AMP
I/P FUSE BLOCK
Fuse Block Details
.8 PNK/BLK 39
S253 (IDC)
WITH HEATED SEATS (KA1)
S208
.5 PNK/BLK 39
C200
S218
(INDICATORS) (U2E)
C2 (DIGITAL AND GAGES) (U2A AND UB7)
WARNING INDICATORS
TRACTION "OFF" INDICATOR
INSTRUMENT CLUSTER PRINTED CIRCUIT
C1 (DIGITAL AND GAGES) (U2A AND UB7)
.5 PPL/WHT 1572
1 BRN 50
S262
S241
S344
P500
ON INDICATOR
TRACTION CONTROL SWITCH
.5 LT GRN 1656
IGN
TRACTION CONTROL ON/OFF INPUT
TRANSAXLE TEMPERATURE INPUT
TRACTION OFF INDICATOR CONTROL
PRESSURE INPUT
TRACTION CONTROL ENGAGE INPUT
ELECTRONIC BRAKE AND TRACTION CONTROL MODULE (EBTCM)
.5 BRN/WHT 1571
.5 RED 1660
.5 LT BLU 1659
AUTOMATIC TRANSAXLE
TRACTION CONTROL SWITCH
TRANSAXLE TEMPERATURE SWITCH OPENS ABOVE 160°C (320°F) CLOSES BELOW 149°C (300°F)
PRESSURE SWITCH OPENS ABOVE 700kPa (101 psi)
FROM S283
2 TAN 1077
P100
C1
INLET AND OUTLET VALVES
LH ISOLATION VALVE 5-8 OHMS
RH ISOLATION VALVE 5-8 OHMS
PRESSURE MODULATOR VALVE (PMV) ASSEMBLY
1 BLK 152
S316
Ground Distribution
3 BLK 152
C340
S225
1 BLK 153
G202
.35 LT BLU/BLK 853
S285
.8 LT BLU/BLK 853
SEE ANTILOCK BRAKE SYSTEM (ABS)/TRACTION CONTROL SYSTEM (TCS)
.5 ORN 1657
.5 PPL 1658
RETURN INPUT
SENSE
LH ISOLATION VALVE CONTROL
RH ISOLATION VALVE CONTROL
ELECTRONIC BRAKE AND TRACTION CONTROL MODULE (EBTCM)
GC4029300633050X

Fig. 67 ABS wiring circuit (Part 5 of 7). 1993 98 Elite Series w/TCS

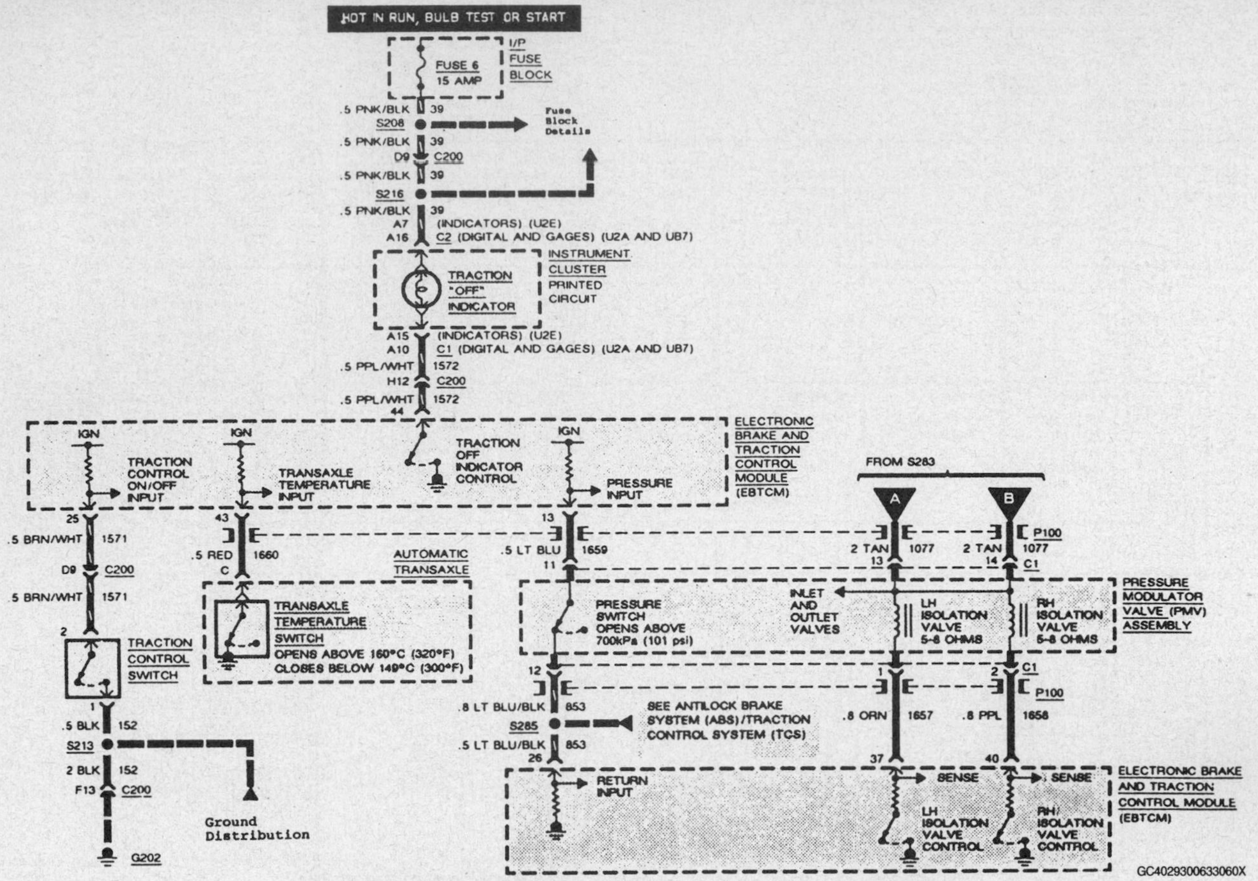
HOT IN RUN, BULB TEST OR START
FUSE 6
15 AMP
I/P
FUSE
BLOCK
.5 PNK/BLK 39
S208
Fuse Block Details
.5 PNK/BLK 39
D9 C200
.5 PNK/BLK 39
S216
.5 PNK/BLK 39
A7 (INDICATORS) (U2E)
A16 C2 (DIGITAL AND GAGES) (U2A AND UB7)
TRACTION
"OFF"
INDICATOR
INSTRUMENT
CLUSTER
PRINTED
CIRCUIT
A15 (INDICATORS) (U2E)
A10 C1 (DIGITAL AND GAGES) (U2A AND UB7)
.5 PPL/WHT 1572
H12 C200
.5 PPL/WHT 1572
44
IGN
TRACTION
CONTROL
ON/OFF
INPUT
TRANSAXLE
TEMPERATURE
INPUT
TRACTION
OFF
INDICATOR
CONTROL
PRESSURE
INPUT
ELECTRONIC
BRAKE AND
TRACTION
CONTROL
MODULE
(EBTCM)
FROM S283
A
B
25
.5 BRN/WHT 1571
D9 C200
.5 BRN/WHT 1571
43
.5 RED 1660
C
AUTOMATIC
TRANSAXLE
13
.5 LT BLU 1659
11
2 TAN 1077
13
2 TAN 1077
14
P100
C1
TRACTION
CONTROL
SWITCH
TRANSAXLE
TEMPERATURE
SWITCH
OPENS ABOVE 160°C (320°F)
CLOSES BELOW 149°C (300°F)
PRESSURE
SWITCH
OPENS ABOVE
700kPa (101 psi)
INLET
AND
OUTLET
VALVES
LH
ISOLATION
VALVE
5-8 OHMS
RH
ISOLATION
VALVE
5-8 OHMS
PRESSURE
MODULATOR
VALVE (PMV)
ASSEMBLY
12
.8 LT BLU/BLK 853
S285
SEE ANTILOCK BRAKE
SYSTEM (ABS)/TRACTION
CONTROL SYSTEM (TCS)
.5 LT BLU/BLK 853
26
.8 ORN 1657
.8 PPL 1658
37
40
.5 BLK 152
S213
2 BLK 152
F13 C200
Ground
Distribution
G202
RETURN
INPUT
SENSE
LH
ISOLATION
VALVE
CONTROL
RH
ISOLATION
VALVE
CONTROL
GC4029300633060X

Fig. 67 ABS wiring circuit (Part 6 of 7). 1993 88 w/TCS

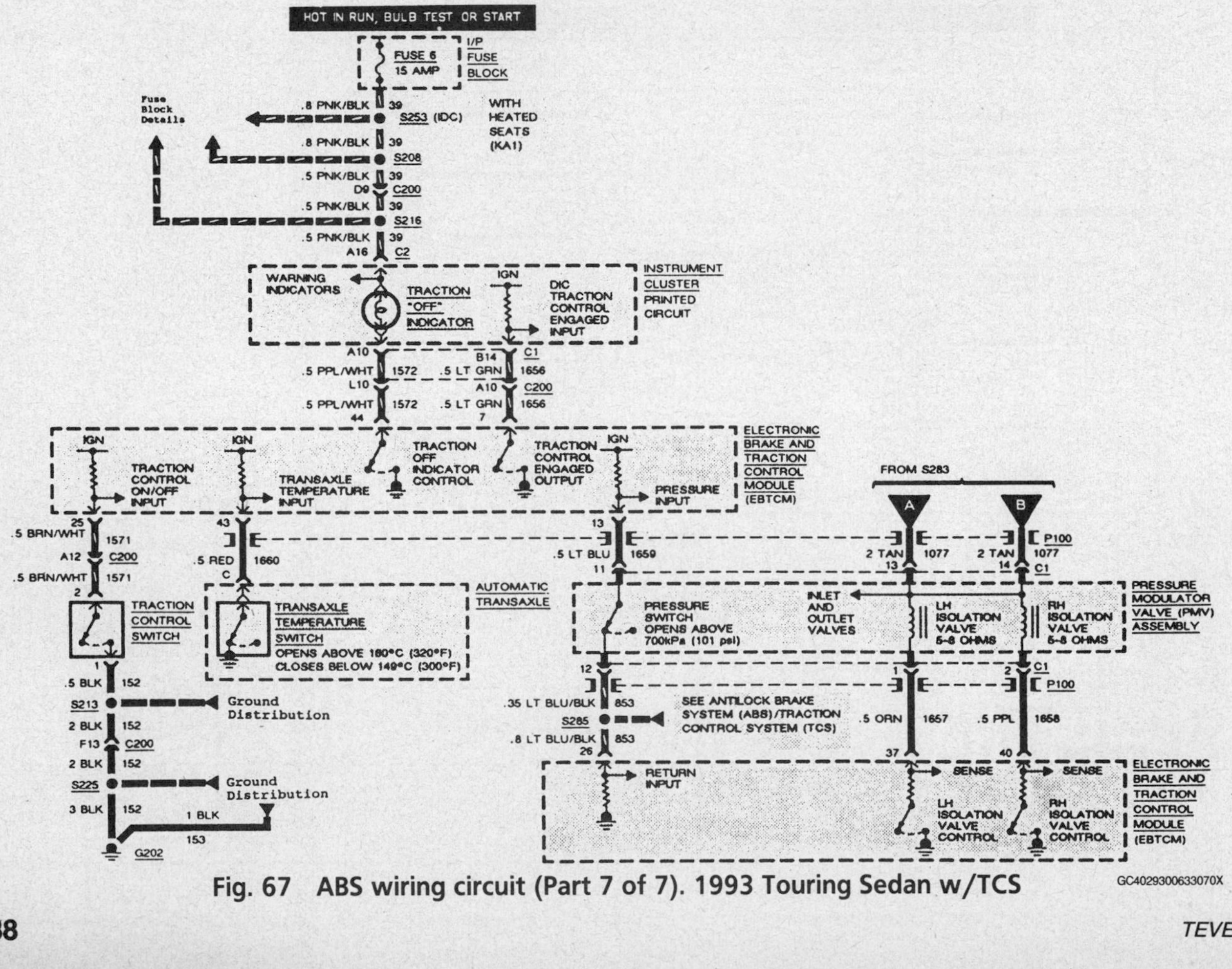
HOT IN RUN, BULB TEST OR START
FUSE 6
15 AMP
I/P
FUSE
BLOCK
Fuse Block Details
.8 PNK/BLK 39
S253 (IDC)
WITH
HEATED
SEATS
(KA1)
.8 PNK/BLK 39
S208
.5 PNK/BLK 39
D9 C200
.5 PNK/BLK 39
S216
.5 PNK/BLK 39
A16 C2
WARNING
INDICATORS
TRACTION
"OFF"
INDICATOR
IGN
DIC
TRACTION
CONTROL
ENGAGED
INPUT
INSTRUMENT
CLUSTER
PRINTED
CIRCUIT
A10
B14 C1
.5 PPL/WHT 1572
.5 LT GRN 1656
L10
A10 C200
.5 PPL/WHT 1572
.5 LT GRN 1656
44
7
TRACTION
CONTROL
ON/OFF
INPUT
TRANSAXLE
TEMPERATURE
INPUT
TRACTION
OFF
INDICATOR
CONTROL
TRACTION
CONTROL
ENGAGED
OUTPUT
PRESSURE
INPUT
ELECTRONIC
BRAKE AND
TRACTION
CONTROL
MODULE
(EBTCM)
FROM S283
A
B
25
.5 BRN/WHT 1571
A12 C200
.5 BRN/WHT 1571
43
.5 RED 1660
C
13
.5 LT BLU 1659
11
2 TAN 1077
2 TAN 1077
P100
C1
AUTOMATIC
TRANSAXLE
TRACTION
CONTROL
SWITCH
TRANSAXLE
TEMPERATURE
SWITCH
OPENS ABOVE 160°C (320°F)
CLOSES BELOW 149°C (300°F)
PRESSURE
SWITCH
OPENS ABOVE
700kPa (101 psi)
INLET
AND
OUTLET
VALVES
LH
ISOLATION
VALVE
5-8 OHMS
RH
ISOLATION
VALVE
5-8 OHMS
PRESSURE
MODULATOR
VALVE (PMV)
ASSEMBLY
.5 BLK 152
S213
Ground
Distribution
2 BLK 152
F13 C200
2 BLK 152
S225
Ground
Distribution
3 BLK 152
1 BLK
153
G202
.35 LT BLU/BLK 853
S285
SEE ANTILOCK BRAKE
SYSTEM (ABS)/TRACTION
CONTROL SYSTEM (TCS)
.8 LT BLU/BLK 853
26
.5 ORN 1657
.5 PPL 1658
37
40
RETURN
INPUT
SENSE
LH
ISOLATION
VALVE
CONTROL
RH
ISOLATION
VALVE
CONTROL
GC4029300633070X

Fig. 67 ABS wiring circuit (Part 7 of 7). 1993 Touring Sedan w/TCS

(1) FILLING AND MANUAL BLEEDING PROCEDURE

NOTICE:
- The reservoir must be properly filled to insure correct operating conditions. However, brake fluid addition is not usually necessary unless there is a leak, indicated by the BRAKE warning indicator, or the system is being serviced.
- Use only Delco Supreme 11 Brake Fluid or equivalent DOT 3 brake fluid from a clean, sealed container.
- Thoroughly clean master cylinder reservoir cover before removal to avoid getting dirt in reservoir.

[1] Fill master cylinder reservoir to proper level with brake fluid and keep at least one-half full of fluid during bleeding operation.
- Have an assistant press brake pedal during bleeding operation.
- IMPORTANT: Master cylinder reservoir cap must be installed before pressing on brake pedal during bleeding operation. This prevents the reservoir from spraying brake fluid.
- If master cylinder is known or suspected to have air in the bore, continue to step [2]; otherwise go to step [9].

[2] Loosen forward (secondary) brake pipe connection at master cylinder.
[3] Allow brake fluid to flow from connector port. Maintain reservoir fluid level.
[4] Tighten forward brake pipe connection at master cylinder.
[5] Depress brake pedal slowly one time and hold. Loosen forward brake pipe connection at master cylinder to purge air from bore. Tighten connection and then release brake pedal slowly. Wait 15 seconds. Repeat sequence, including 15 second wait, until all air is removed from bore.
[6] Tighten forward brake pipe connection to 15 N•M (11 LB-FT).
[7] After all air has been removed at forward connection, repeat steps [2] through [6] to bleed master cylinder at rear primary connection.
[8] If it is known that calipers and wheel cylinders do not contain any air, then it is not necessary to bleed them; otherwise, continue to step [9].
[9] If all the wheel circuits must be bled, use the following sequence: RH rear, LH rear, RH front, LH front.
[10] Raise vehicle and suitable support.
[11] Remove bleeder valve cap and place proper size box-end wrench, J 28434, or J 21472 over caliper/cylinder bleeder valve. Attach a transparent tube to bleeder valve and allow tube to hang submerged in a transparent container, partially filled with clean brake fluid.
[12] Depress brake pedal slowly one time and hold. Loosen bleeder valve to purge air from caliper/cylinder. Tighten bleeder valve and slowly release pedal. Wait 15 seconds. Repeat sequence, including 15 second wait until all air is removed. It may be necessay to repeat sequence 10 or more times to remove all air. Rapid pedal pumping pushes master cylinder secondary piston down the bore in a manner that makes it difficult to bleed system.
[13] Tighten wheel cylinder bleeder valves to 7 N•M (62 LB-IN).
- Tighten caliper bleeder valve to 13 N•M (10 LB-FT).

[14] Install bleeder valve caps.
[15] Lower vehicle.
[16] Fill master cylinder to proper level.
[17] Check brake pedal for "sponginess."
- Repeat entire bleeding procedure to correct "sponginess."

(2) FILLING AND PRESSURE BLEEDING PROCEDURE

NOTICE:
- The reservoir must be properly filled to insure correct operating conditions. However, brake fluid addition is not usually necessary unless there is a leak, indicated by the BRAKE indicator, or the system is being serviced.
- Use only Delco Supreme 11 Brake Fluid or equivalent DOT 3 brake fluid from a clean, sealed container.
- Thoroughly clean master cylinder reservoir cover before removal to avoid getting dirt in reservoir.

NOTICE: Pressure bleeding equipment must be of the diaphragm type. It must have a rubber diaphragm between the air supply and the brake fluid to prevent air, moisture, oil and other contaminants from entering the hydraulic system.

Important: The correct master cylinder bleeder adapter must be used to avoid possible damage to the master cylinder reservoirs.

[1] Fill master cylinder reservoir to proper level with brake fluid.
[2] Install J 35589 to master cylinder.
[3] Charge J 29532 to 140–172 kPa (20–25 psi).
[4] Connect J 29532 hose to adapter and open the line valve.
[5] Raise vehicle and suitably support.
[6] If all the wheel circuits must be bled, use the following sequence: RH rear, LH rear, RH front, LH front.
[7] Remove bleeder valve cap and place proper size box-end wrench, J 28434, or J 21472 over caliper/cylinder bleeder valve. Attach a transparent tube to bleeder valve and allow tube to hang submerged in a transparent container, partially filled with clean brake fluid.
[8] Loosen bleeder valve at least ¾ turn, and allow fluid to flow until no air is seen in fluid.
[9] Tighten wheel cylinder bleeder valves to 7 N•M (62 LB-FT).
- Tighten caliper bleeder valve to 13 N•M (10 LB-FT).

[10] Repeat steps [7] through [9] until all calipers/cylinders have been bled. Then install bleeder valve caps.
[11] Lower vehicle.
[12] Check brake pedal for "sponginess."
- Repeat entire bleeding procedure to correct "sponginess."

[13] Remove J 29532 and J 35589.
[14] Fill master cylinder to proper level.

GC4029300634000X

Fig. 68 Procedures 1 & 2, bleeding brakes & filling & pressure bleeding brakes.

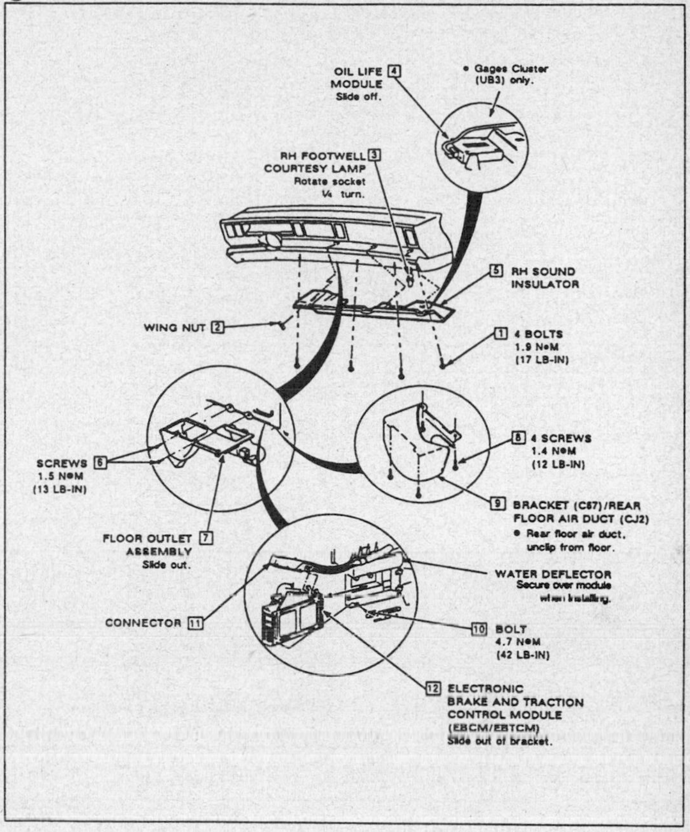

(3) ELECTRONIC BRAKE AND TRACTION CONTROL MODULE (EBCM/EBTCM), REPLACE
OIL LIFE [4] MODULE Slide off.
• Gages Cluster (UB3) only.
RH FOOTWELL [3] COURTESY LAMP Rotate socket ¼ turn.
[5] RH SOUND INSULATOR
WING NUT [2]
[1] 4 BOLTS 1.9 N•M (17 LB-IN)
SCREWS [6] 1.5 N•M (13 LB-IN)
[8] 4 SCREWS 1.4 N•M (12 LB-IN)
[9] BRACKET (C67)/REAR FLOOR AIR DUCT (CJ2)
• Rear floor air duct, unclip from floor.
FLOOR OUTLET [7] ASSEMBLY Slide out.
WATER DEFLECTOR Secure over module when installing.
CONNECTOR [11]
[10] BOLT 4.7 N•M (42 LB-IN)
[12] ELECTRONIC BRAKE AND TRACTION CONTROL MODULE (EBCM/EBTCM) Slide out of bracket.

GC4029300635000X

Fig. 69 Procedure 3. 1993-94 LeSabre & Park Avenue

SYSTEM SERVICE

Brake System Bleed

Refer to **Fig. 68** for procedure.

Component Replace

1993-94 LESABRE & PARK AVENUE

Refer to **Figs. 69 through 76** for replacement and adjustment procedures.

EXCEPT 1993-94 LESABRE & PARK AVENUE

ELECTRONIC BRAKE CONTROL MODULE (EBCM)

Ignition switch must be in the Off position prior to disconnecting or connecting the EBCM.

1. Remove right and left sound insulators.
2. Disconnect floor outlet, then remove bolt retaining EBCM, **Fig. 77.**
3. Slide EBCM toward accelerator pedal just far enough to expose connector.
4. Disconnect EBCM harness connector, then remove EBCM.
5. Reverse procedure to install. **Torque** EBCM retaining bolt to 19 inch lbs.

WHEEL SPEED SENSORS

Front

Wheel speed sensor is non-adjustable. Left and right speed sensors are not interchangeable.

Proper installation of speed sensor cables is critical. Failure to route cables properly could cause system malfunction due to over stressing or abrasion. Refer to **Fig. 78,** for proper routing of cables.

1. Open hood, then disconnect wheel speed sensor connector, **Fig. 78.**
2. Cut strap retaining sensor lead, then raise and support vehicle.
3. Remove sensor lead from brackets, sensor retaining bolt, then the sensor.
4. Inspect sensor face for build up of metallic particles, dirt, grease, or other contaminants. Clean as needed.
5. Inspect sensor face for damage. Replace sensor if damage causes improper operation.
6. If sensor is removed or replaced, coat sensor body with anti-corrosion compound where the sensor contacts knuckle.
7. Reverse procedure to install. **Torque** sensor retaining bolt to 7 ft. lbs.

Rear

Refer to **Figs. 79 and 80,** during removal and installation procedure.

1. Remove hub and bearing assembly.
2. Clean area surrounding sensor housing/interface area.
3. Remove Torx type screws securing sensor, then the sensor. **Do not allow dirt or other contaminants to enter sensor housing.**
4. **Do not add lubricant to bearing through sensor housing opening.** This bearing is lubricated for life of vehicle.
5. **Do not clean grease from toothed sensor ring.** Grease does not effect operation of sensor.
6. Reverse procedure to install. Ensure O-ring is not torn or missing. **Torque** Torx screws to 33 inch lbs.

WHEEL SPEED SENSOR RINGS

Front

For front wheel speed sensor ring replacement procedure, refer to "Drive Axle, Replace."

Rear

For rear wheel speed sensor ring replacement procedure, refer to "Hub & Bearing, Replace."

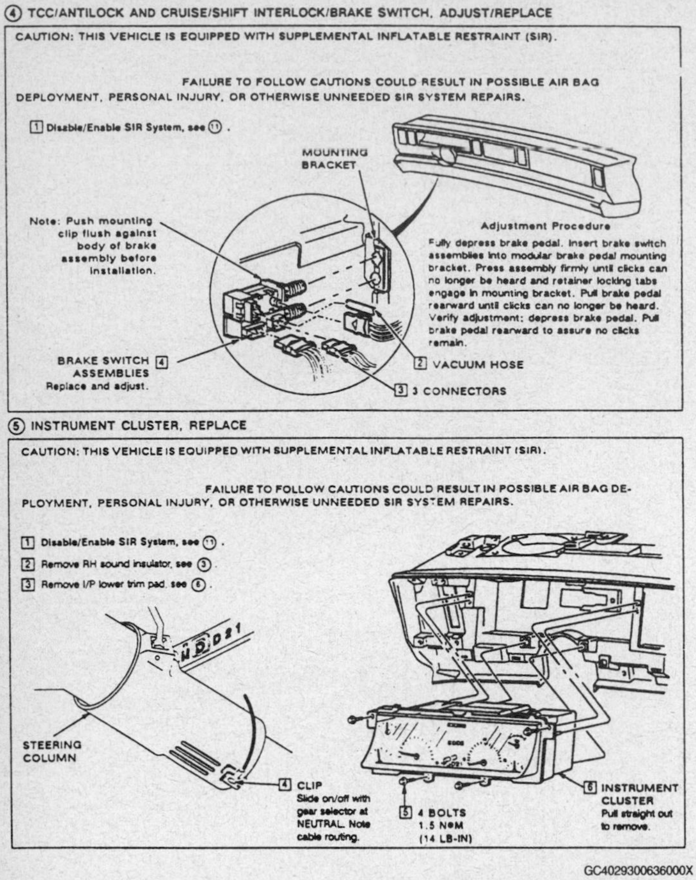

④ TCC/ANTILOCK AND CRUISE/SHIFT INTERLOCK/BRAKE SWITCH, ADJUST/REPLACE
CAUTION: THIS VEHICLE IS EQUIPPED WITH SUPPLEMENTAL INFLATABLE RESTRAINT (SIR).
FAILURE TO FOLLOW CAUTIONS COULD RESULT IN POSSIBLE AIR BAG DEPLOYMENT, PERSONAL INJURY, OR OTHERWISE UNNEEDED SIR SYSTEM REPAIRS.
1 Disable/Enable SIR System, see ⑪.
MOUNTING BRACKET
Note: Push mounting clip flush against body of brake assembly before installation.
Adjustment Procedure
Fully depress brake pedal. Insert brake switch assemblies into modular brake pedal mounting bracket. Press assembly firmly until clicks can no longer be heard and retainer locking tabs engage in mounting bracket. Pull brake pedal rearward until clicks can no longer be heard. Verify adjustment: depress brake pedal. Pull brake pedal rearward to assure no clicks remain.
BRAKE SWITCH 4 ASSEMBLIES Replace and adjust.
2 VACUUM HOSE
3 3 CONNECTORS
⑤ INSTRUMENT CLUSTER, REPLACE
CAUTION: THIS VEHICLE IS EQUIPPED WITH SUPPLEMENTAL INFLATABLE RESTRAINT (SIR).
FAILURE TO FOLLOW CAUTIONS COULD RESULT IN POSSIBLE AIR BAG DEPLOYMENT, PERSONAL INJURY, OR OTHERWISE UNNEEDED SIR SYSTEM REPAIRS.
1 Disable/Enable SIR System, see ⑪.
2 Remove RH sound insulator, see ③.
3 Remove I/P lower trim pad, see ⑥.
STEERING COLUMN
4 CLIP Slide on/off with gear selector at NEUTRAL. Note cable routing.
5 4 BOLTS 1.5 N•M (14 LB-IN)
6 INSTRUMENT CLUSTER Pull straight out to remove.
GC4029300636000X

Fig. 70 Procedures 4 & 5. 1993-94 LeSabre & Park Avenue

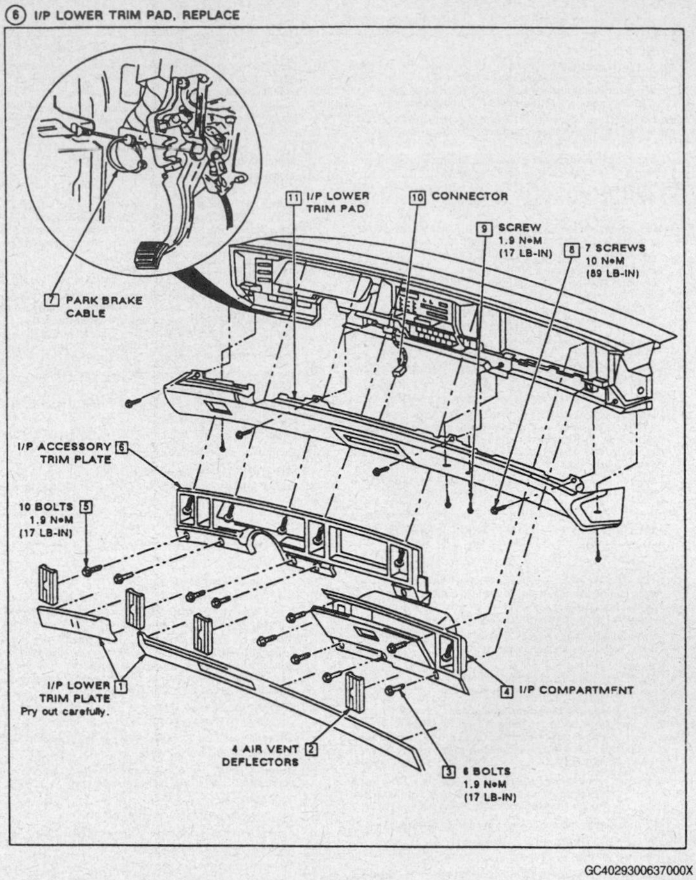

⑥ I/P LOWER TRIM PAD, REPLACE
11 I/P LOWER TRIM PAD
10 CONNECTOR
9 SCREW 1.9 N•M (17 LB-IN)
8 7 SCREWS 10 N•M (89 LB-IN)
7 PARK BRAKE CABLE
I/P ACCESSORY 6 TRIM PLATE
10 BOLTS 5 1.9 N•M (17 LB-IN)
I/P LOWER 1 TRIM PLATE Pry out carefully.
4 AIR VENT 2 DEFLECTORS
4 I/P COMPARTMENT
3 6 BOLTS 1.9 N•M (17 LB-IN)
GC4029300637000X

Fig. 71 Procedure 6. 1993-94 LeSabre & Park Avenue

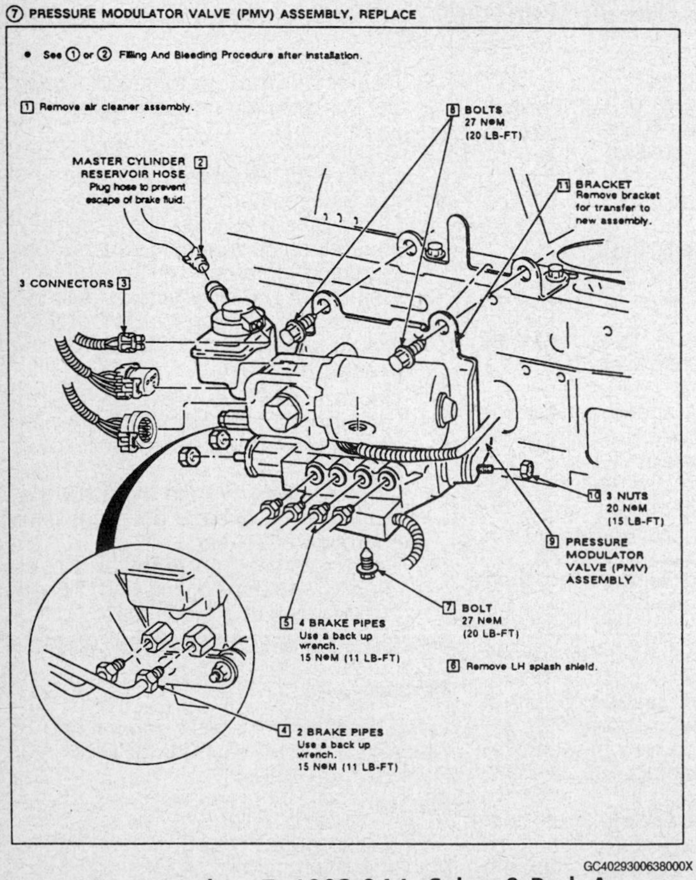

⑦ PRESSURE MODULATOR VALVE (PMV) ASSEMBLY, REPLACE
• See ① or ② Filling And Bleeding Procedure after installation.
1 Remove air cleaner assembly.
8 BOLTS 27 N•M (20 LB-FT)
MASTER CYLINDER 2 RESERVOIR HOSE Plug hose to prevent escape of brake fluid.
11 BRACKET Remove bracket for transfer to new assembly.
3 CONNECTORS 3
10 3 NUTS 20 N•M (15 LB-FT)
9 PRESSURE MODULATOR VALVE (PMV) ASSEMBLY
7 BOLT 27 N•M (20 LB-FT)
5 4 BRAKE PIPES Use a back up wrench. 15 N•M (11 LB-FT)
6 Remove LH splash shield.
4 2 BRAKE PIPES Use a back up wrench. 15 N•M (11 LB-FT)
GC4029300638000X

Fig. 72 Procedure 7. 1993-94 LeSabre & Park Avenue

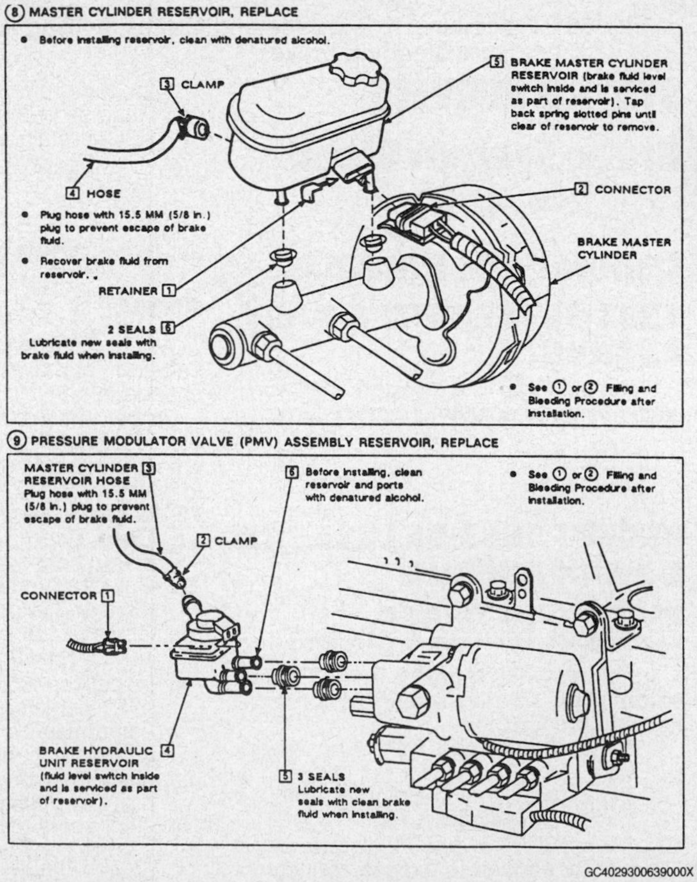

⑧ MASTER CYLINDER RESERVOIR, REPLACE
• Before installing reservoir, clean with denatured alcohol.
3 CLAMP
5 BRAKE MASTER CYLINDER RESERVOIR (brake fluid level switch inside and is serviced as part of reservoir). Tap back spring slotted pins until clear of reservoir to remove.
4 HOSE
• Plug hose with 15.5 MM (5/8 in.) plug to prevent escape of brake fluid.
• Recover brake fluid from reservoir.
2 CONNECTOR
BRAKE MASTER CYLINDER
RETAINER 1
2 SEALS 6 Lubricate new seals with brake fluid when installing.
• See ① or ② Filling and Bleeding Procedure after installation.
⑨ PRESSURE MODULATOR VALVE (PMV) ASSEMBLY RESERVOIR, REPLACE
MASTER CYLINDER 3 RESERVOIR HOSE Plug hose with 15.5 MM (5/8 in.) plug to prevent escape of brake fluid.
6 Before installing, clean reservoir and ports with denatured alcohol.
• See ① or ② Filling and Bleeding Procedure after installation.
2 CLAMP
CONNECTOR 1
BRAKE HYDRAULIC 4 UNIT RESERVOIR (fluid level switch inside and is serviced as part of reservoir).
5 3 SEALS Lubricate new seals with clean brake fluid when installing.
GC4029300639000X

Fig. 73 Procedures 8 & 9. 1993-94 LeSabre & Park Avenue

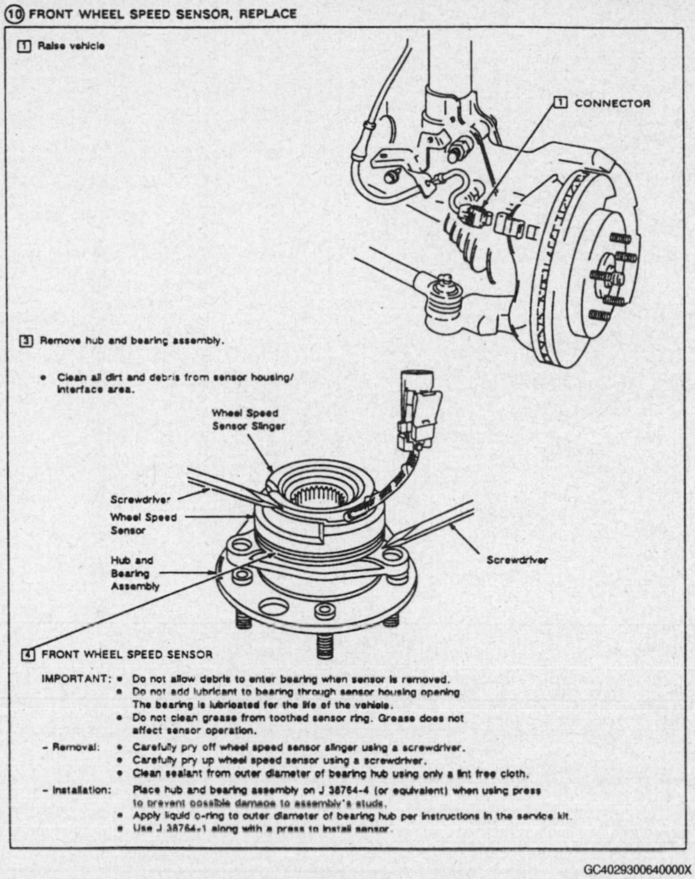
10 FRONT WHEEL SPEED SENSOR, REPLACE
1 Raise vehicle
1 CONNECTOR
3 Remove hub and bearing assembly.
• Clean all dirt and debris from sensor housing/interface area.
Wheel Speed Sensor Slinger
Screwdriver
Wheel Speed Sensor
Hub and Bearing Assembly
Screwdriver
4 FRONT WHEEL SPEED SENSOR
IMPORTANT: • Do not allow debris to enter bearing when sensor is removed.
• Do not add lubricant to bearing through sensor housing opening The bearing is lubricated for the life of the vehicle.
• Do not clean grease from toothed sensor ring. Grease does not affect sensor operation.
- Removal: • Carefully pry off wheel speed sensor slinger using a screwdriver.
• Carefully pry up wheel speed sensor using a screwdriver.
• Clean sealant from outer diameter of bearing hub using only a lint free cloth.
- Installation: Place hub and bearing assembly on J 38764-4 (or equivalent) when using press to prevent possible damage to assembly's studs.
• Apply liquid o-ring to outer diameter of bearing hub per instructions in the service kit.
• Use J 38764-1 along with a press to install sensor.
GC4029300640000X

Fig. 74 Procedure 10. 1993-94 LeSabre & Park Avenue

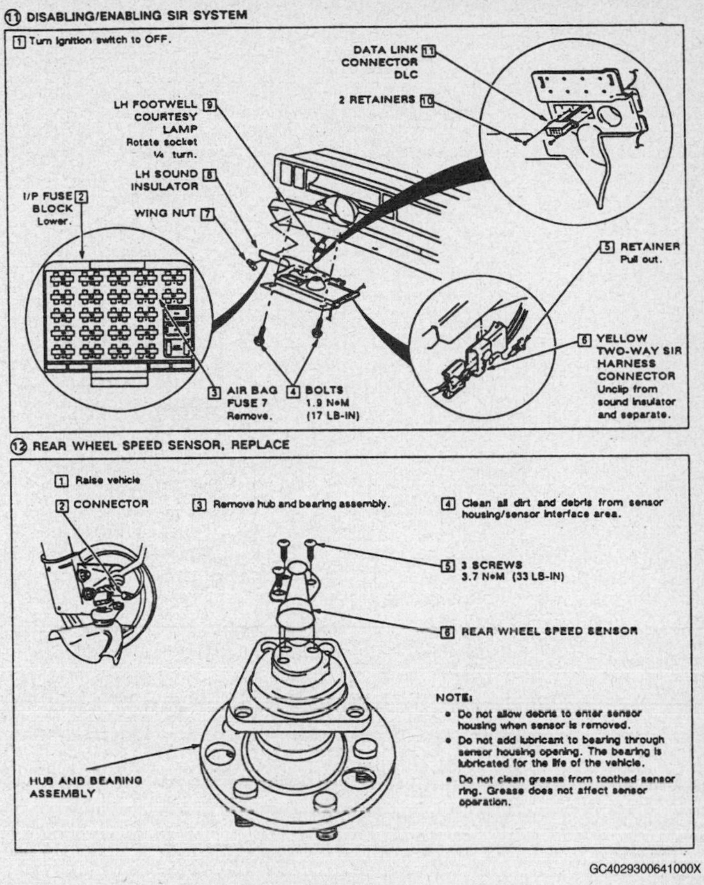
11 DISABLING/ENABLING SIR SYSTEM
1 Turn ignition switch to OFF.
DATA LINK CONNECTOR DLC 11
2 RETAINERS 10
LH FOOTWELL COURTESY LAMP 9 Rotate socket ¼ turn.
LH SOUND INSULATOR 8
I/P FUSE BLOCK 2 Lower.
WING NUT 7
5 RETAINER Pull out.
6 YELLOW TWO-WAY SIR HARNESS CONNECTOR Unclip from sound insulator and separate.
3 AIR BAG FUSE 7 Remove.
4 BOLTS 1.9 N•M (17 LB-IN)
12 REAR WHEEL SPEED SENSOR, REPLACE
1 Raise vehicle
2 CONNECTOR
3 Remove hub and bearing assembly.
4 Clean all dirt and debris from sensor housing/sensor interface area.
5 3 SCREWS 3.7 N•M (33 LB-IN)
6 REAR WHEEL SPEED SENSOR
NOTE:
• Do not allow debris to enter sensor housing when sensor is removed.
• Do not add lubricant to bearing through sensor housing opening. The bearing is lubricated for the life of the vehicle.
• Do not clean grease from toothed sensor ring. Grease does not affect sensor operation.
HUB AND BEARING ASSEMBLY
GC4029300641000X

Fig. 75 Procedures 11 & 12. 1993-94 LeSabre & Park Avenue

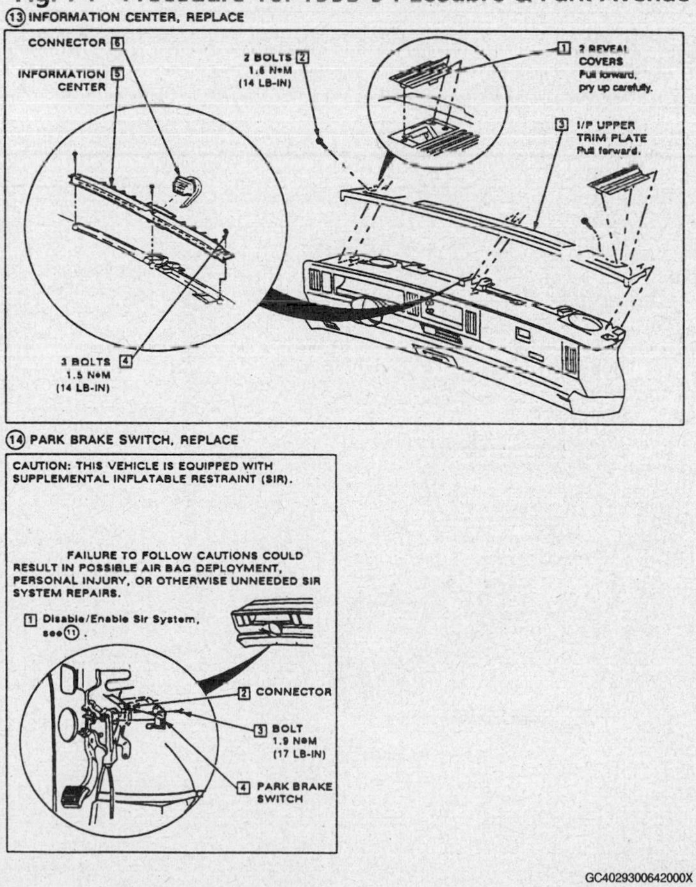
13 INFORMATION CENTER, REPLACE
CONNECTOR 6
INFORMATION CENTER 5
2 BOLTS 2 1.6 N•M (14 LB-IN)
1 2 REVEAL COVERS Pull forward, pry up carefully.
3 I/P UPPER TRIM PLATE Pull forward.
3 BOLTS 4 1.5 N•M (14 LB-IN)
14 PARK BRAKE SWITCH, REPLACE
CAUTION: THIS VEHICLE IS EQUIPPED WITH SUPPLEMENTAL INFLATABLE RESTRAINT (SIR).
FAILURE TO FOLLOW CAUTIONS COULD RESULT IN POSSIBLE AIR BAG DEPLOYMENT, PERSONAL INJURY, OR OTHERWISE UNNEEDED SIR SYSTEM REPAIRS.
1 Disable/Enable Sir System, see 11.
2 CONNECTOR
3 BOLT 1.9 N•M (17 LB-IN)
4 PARK BRAKE SWITCH
GC4029300642000X

Fig. 76 Procedures 13 & 14. 1993-94 LeSabre & Park Avenue

PRESSURE MODULATOR VALVE (PMV)

1. Disconnect battery ground cable and the air cleaner assembly.
2. Disconnect fluid level switch, pump motor and valve block electrical connectors from the PMV.
3. Clamp PMV reservoir hose, disconnect reservoir hose, then plug using a ⁵⁄₈ inch plug.
4. Remove primary and secondary hoses, then the brake pipes from PMV assembly, **Fig. 81.**
5. Raise and support vehicle, then remove lower PMV assembly bolt.
6. Lower vehicle, remove upper PMV assembly bolts, then the PMV assembly.
7. Reverse procedure to install, noting the following:
   a. **Torque** upper and lower PMV assembly bolts to 20 ft. lbs.
   b. **Torque** brake pipes to 11 ft. lbs.
   c. **Torque** battery cable to 13 ft. lbs.

PROPORTIONER VALVE

1. Raise and support vehicle, then clean proportioner valve and brake pipe connections to avoid system contamination.
2. Remove lines from proportioner valve.
3. Remove proportioner valve.
4. Reverse procedure to install. **Torque** proportioner valve fittings to 11 ft. lbs.

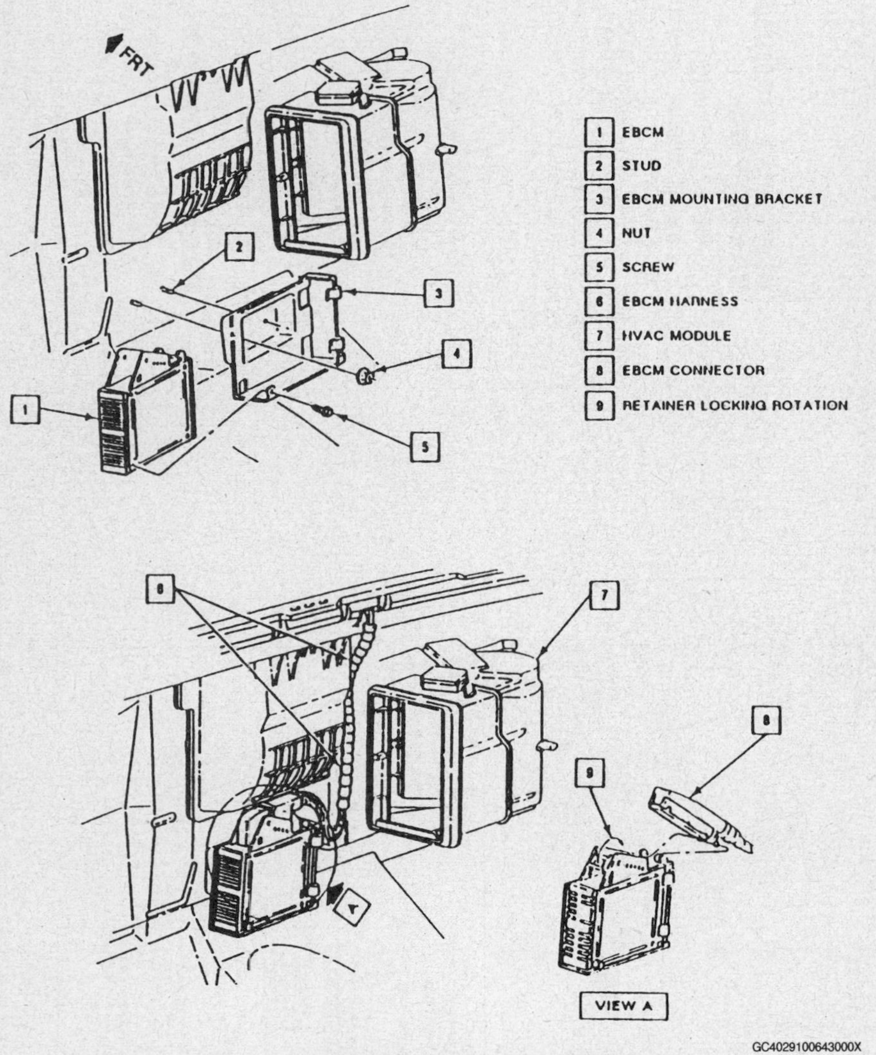
FRT
1 EBCM
2 STUD
3 EBCM MOUNTING BRACKET
4 NUT
5 SCREW
6 EBCM HARNESS
7 HVAC MODULE
8 EBCM CONNECTOR
9 RETAINER LOCKING ROTATION
A
VIEW A
GC4029100643000X

Fig. 77 EBCM mounting bolt locations

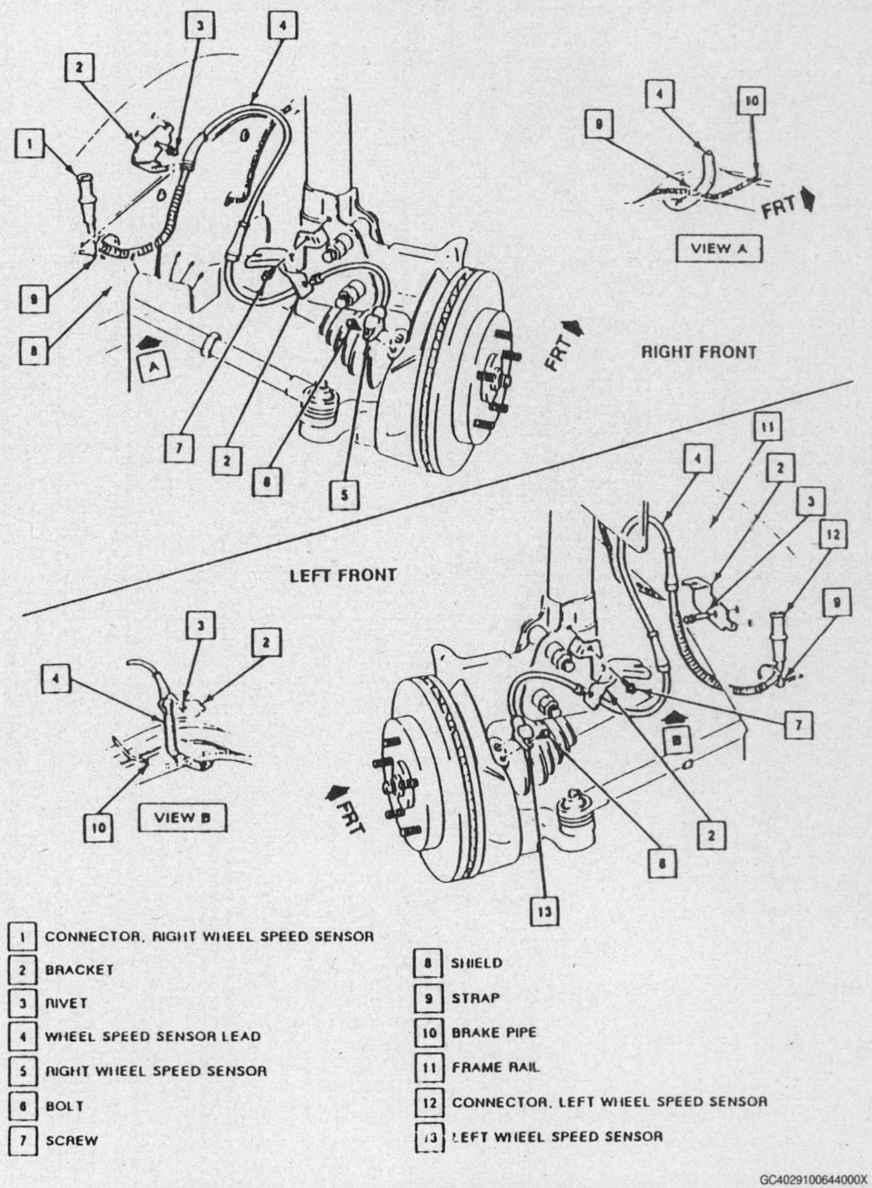
RIGHT FRONT
VIEW A
FRT
LEFT FRONT
VIEW B
A
B
1 CONNECTOR, RIGHT WHEEL SPEED SENSOR
2 BRACKET
3 RIVET
4 WHEEL SPEED SENSOR LEAD
5 RIGHT WHEEL SPEED SENSOR
6 BOLT
7 SCREW
8 SHIELD
9 STRAP
10 BRAKE PIPE
11 FRAME RAIL
12 CONNECTOR, LEFT WHEEL SPEED SENSOR
13 LEFT WHEEL SPEED SENSOR
GC4029100644000X

Fig. 78 Front wheel speed sensor replace

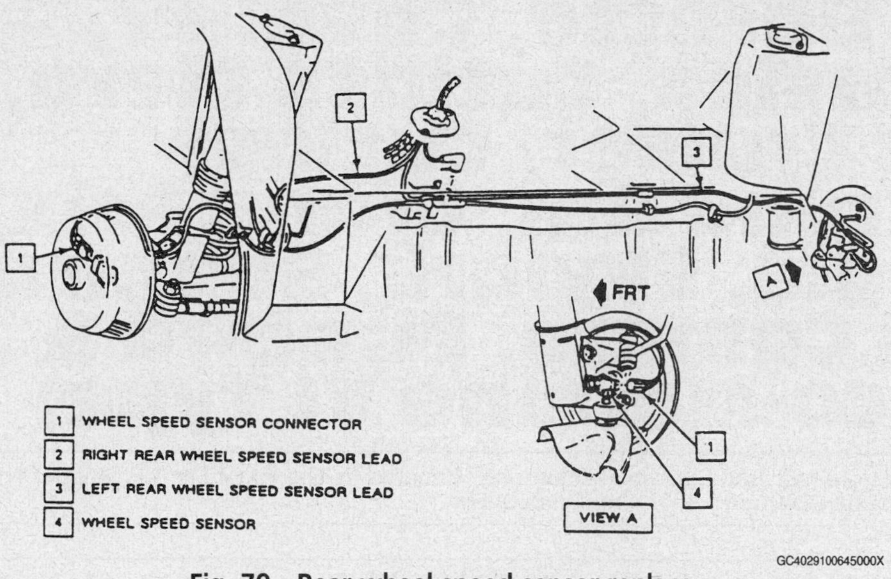
1 WHEEL SPEED SENSOR CONNECTOR
2 RIGHT REAR WHEEL SPEED SENSOR LEAD
3 LEFT REAR WHEEL SPEED SENSOR LEAD
4 WHEEL SPEED SENSOR
FRT
VIEW A
GC4029100645000X

Fig. 79 Rear wheel speed sensor replace

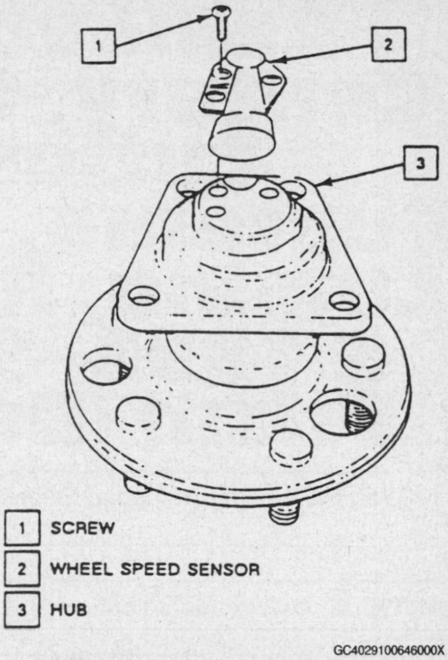
1 SCREW
2 WHEEL SPEED SENSOR
3 HUB
GC4029100646000X

Fig. 80 Rear wheel sensor alignment

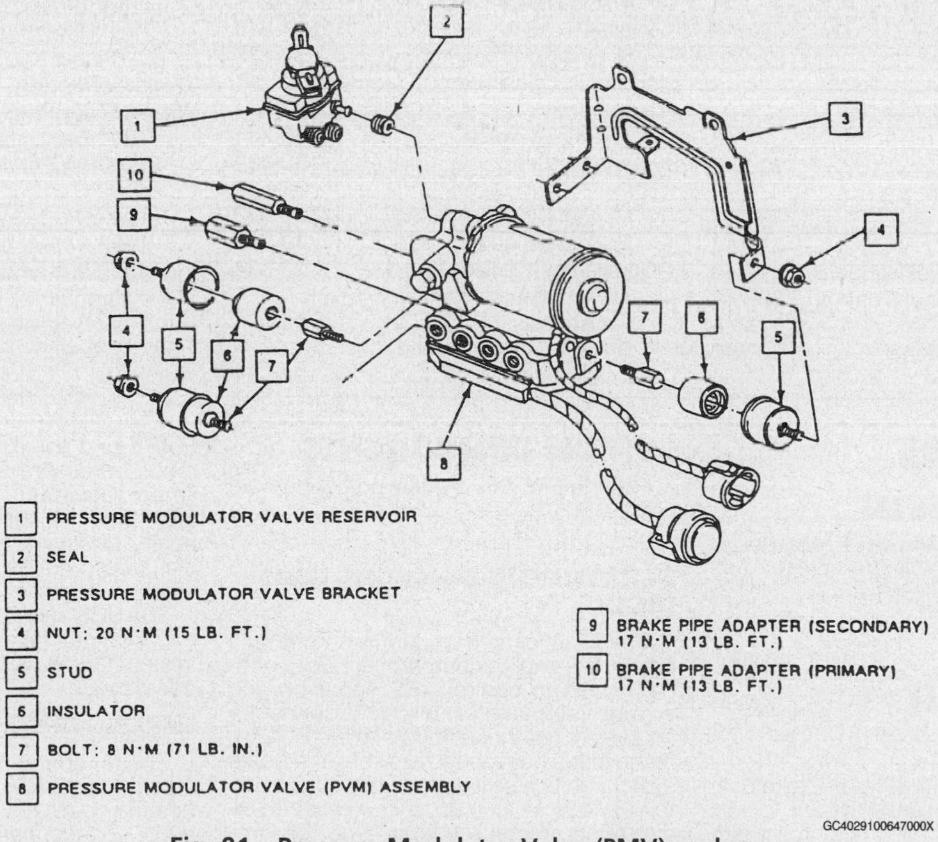
1 PRESSURE MODULATOR VALVE RESERVOIR
2 SEAL
3 PRESSURE MODULATOR VALVE BRACKET
4 NUT: 20 N·M (15 LB. FT.)
5 STUD
6 INSULATOR
7 BOLT: 8 N·M (71 LB. IN.)
8 PRESSURE MODULATOR VALVE (PVM) ASSEMBLY
9 BRAKE PIPE ADAPTER (SECONDARY) 17 N·M (13 LB. FT.)
10 BRAKE PIPE ADAPTER (PRIMARY) 17 N·M (13 LB. FT.)
GC4029100647000X

Fig. 81 Pressure Modulator Valve (PMV) replace

Achieva, Beretta, Cavalier, Century, Corsica, Cutlass Ciera, Cutlass Cruiser, Cutlass Supreme, Grand Am, Grand Prix, Lumina, Regal, Skylark, Sunbird & 1993–94 Camaro, Firebird & Prizm (Delco-Moraine VI Type)

NOTE: On Air Bag Equipped Models, Refer To "Air Bag System Precautions" Located In The Front Of This Manual For System Disarming & Arming Procedures.

NOTE: Wire Code Identification And Symbol Identification Located In The Front Of This Manual Can Be Used As An Aid When Using Wiring Circuits Found In This Section.

INDEX

PRECAUTIONS

AIR BAG SYSTEMS

Refer to "Air Bag System Precautions" in the front of this manual for system disarming and arming procedures.

DESCRIPTION

SYSTEM

The function of the Anti-Lock Brake System (ABS) is to minimize wheel lockup during heavy braking on most road surfaces. The system performs this function by monitoring wheel speed and controlling the brake fluid pressure to each front wheel and both rear wheels during braking. This allows the driver to retain directional stability and better steering capability.

SYSTEM COMPONENTS

Refer to **Fig. 1** for system component locations.

ELECTRONIC CONTROL UNIT (ECU)

The ECU located on the rear righthand side of the engine compartment uses various inputs to control ABS operation and provide information to the ALDL connector for system diagnosis. Inputs to the ECU include four wheel speed sensors, the brake switch, ignition switch and unswitched battery voltage. ECU outputs include three bidirectional motor controls, two Electromagnetic Brakes (EMB), two solenoids, system enable relay and serial data link.

The ECU using signals from the wheel sensors, monitors the speed of each wheel. If any wheel begins to approach a lock-up condition and the brake switch is "ON," the ECU will control the motors, EMB's and solenoids to reduce brake hydraulic pressure to that wheel. Once the wheel regains traction, brake pressure is increased until the wheel begins to lock-up again. This cycle will repeat until the vehicle stops, the brake is released, or no wheels approach a lock-up condition.

The ECU monitors itself, each input and each output for proper operation. If any system fault is detected, the ECU will store a fault code.

WHEEL SPEED SENSORS

These sensors located on the front steering knuckles and under the wheel bearing dust caps on the rear wheels, send a low voltage signal to the ECU. This signal is produced by rotating a toothed ring around the sensor pole piece, which produces a magnetic field that increases and decreases in magnitude.

HYDRAULIC MODULATOR

The hydraulic modulator located on the

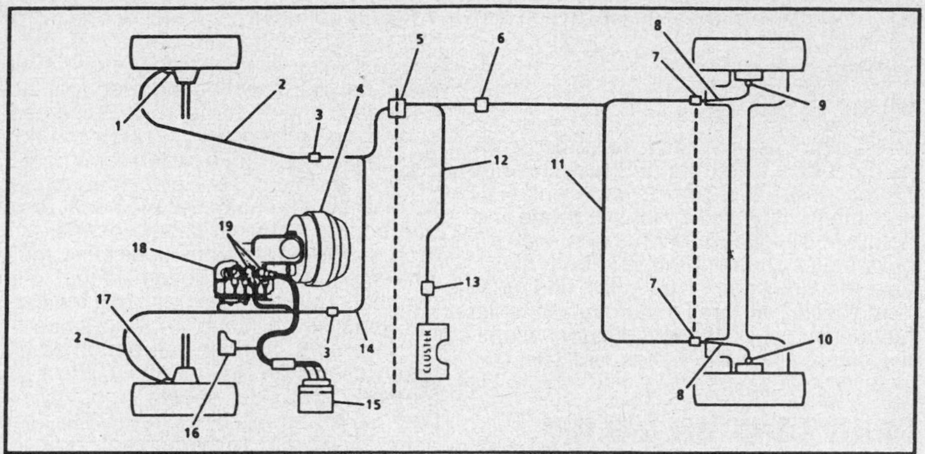
CLUSTER

1	RIGHT FRONT WHEEL SPEED SENSOR	11	BODY HARNESS
2	ABS JUMPER HARNESS	12	I/P CONNECTOR
3	FORWARD LAMP TO FRONT WHEEL SPEED SENSOR	13	LAMP DRIVER MODULE
4	MASTER CYLINDER	14	FORWARD LAMP HARNESS
5	FORWARD LAMP TO I/P CONNECTOR	15	ELECTRONIC BRAKE CONTROL MODULE
6	BODY TO I/P CONNECTOR	16	ABS RELAY IN LH CONVIENCE CENTER
7	REAR BODY PASS THRU CONNECTOR	17	LEFT FRONT WHEEL SPEED SENSOR
8	ABS JUMPER HARNESS	18	ABS HYDRAULIC MODULATOR ASSEMBLY
9	RIGHT REAR WHEEL SPEED SENSOR	19	ISOLATION SOLENOIDS
10	LEFT REAR WHEEL SPEED SENSOR		

GC4029100640000A

Fig. 1 Typical ABS system components (locations may differ slightly)

front lefthand side of the engine compartment controls hydraulic brake pressure during ABS operation. The modulator contains three motors, two solenoids and two Electromagnetic Brakes EMB's. The modulator acts on signals it receives from the ECU.

ABS WARNING LIGHT (AMBER)

The ABS warning light operates on a signal it receives from the ECU. If the ECU detects a fault that does not interfere immediately with ABS operation, the ABS warning lamp will flash. However, ABS operation will continue. If the ECU detects a fault that does interfere with ABS operation, the ABS warning lamp will stay lit and ABS operation will be suspended until the fault is repaired. In any case, the warning lamp is indicating that the system be serviced as soon as possible.

BRAKE WARNING LAMP (RED)

This warning lamp can be activated by a low brake fluid condition, a closed parking brake switch, a bulb test switch section of the ignition switch is closed or under the control of the ECU when certain ABS codes are set.

TROUBLESHOOTING

Refer to "Diagnosis & Testing" to properly troubleshoot and diagnose system errors.

DIAGNOSIS & TESTING System Testing

This system contains a sophisticated onboard diagnostics that can by accessed with a bidirectional "SCAN" tool. **To properly diagnose the ABS system a GM TECH 1 bidirectional scan tool or suitable equivalent is necessary.** The scan tool can be used to identify system faults as specifically as possible including whether or not the fault is intermittent. The scan tool can also be used to monitor the input and output signals of the ABS Module, manually control system components and perform automated functional tests. Using the scan tool, allows for accurate fault confirmation and repair verification.

DIAGNOSTIC PROCEDURE

Refer to **Figs. 2 through 21** for wiring diagrams and connector pin identification.

In order to properly diagnose and repair this system the following steps should be followed in order. Failure to follow the procedure in order could result in loss of diagnostic data.

1. Connect GM TECH 1 or suitable equivalent to ALDL connector, then read all current and history diagnostic codes. Refer to **Fig. 21** for scan tool operation. **Be sure to note which codes are current code failures. Do not clear codes unless directed to do so.**
2. Read "CODE HISTORY" data, note diagnostic codes stored and their frequency of failure. Ensure to note the last failure code entered and the conditions present when the failure occurred. This last failure code should be the starting point for diagnosis and repair.
3. Before beginning service on this system, perform the following preliminary inspection:
   a. Check master cylinder for proper brake fluid level.
   b. Inspect hydraulic modulator for any leaks or wiring damage.
   c. Inspect brakes at all four wheels to ensure that no drag exists and that brakes are operating normally.
   d. Check wheel bearings for any excessive wear or damage.
   e. Inspect wheel speed sensors for correct air gap, solid sensor attachment, damaged toothed ring or damaged wiring. Refer to "Wheel Sensors, Replace."
   f. Check CV joint for proper operation and alignment.
4. When plugged into the ALDL connector the TECH 1 scan tool can display ABS data, display and clear ABS trouble codes, control ABS components, perform diagnostic testing for intermittent conditions. The TECH 1 uses five different test modes to aid in diagnosis. Use the following TECH 1 diagnostic modes when servicing this system:
   a. **MODE F0: DATA LIST:** In this mode the SCAN tool continuously monitors wheel speed data, brake switch status and other inputs and outputs.
   b. **MODE F1: CODE HISTORY:** In this mode, fault code history data is displayed. This includes how many ignition cycles since the fault code occurred and other ABS information.
   c. **MODE F2: TROUBLE CODES:** In this mode both current and history codes can be displayed or cleared.
   d. **MODE F3: ABS SNAPSHOT:** In this mode, SCAN tool captures ABS data before and after a fault occurrence or a forced manual trigger.
   e. **MODE F4: ABS TESTS:** In this mode, SCAN tool performs hydraulic modulator functional tests to assist in problem isolation during troubleshooting.
5. "On all models with 24 pin EBCM connector" refer to **Figs. 22 through 28** for diagnostic circuit check and warning lamp diagnosis. Refer to **Figs. 29 through 93** on 1992 models and **Figs. 94 through 222** on 1993-94 models, for ABS system code diagnosis and repair.
6. "On all models with 32 pin EBCM connector except Prizm" refer to **Figs. 223 through 236** for diagnostic circuit

check and warning lamp diagnosis. Refer to **Figs. 237** through **292**for ABS system code diagnosis and repair.

7. "On Prizm models with 32 pin EBCM connector" refer to **Figs. 294** for diagnostic circuit and **Figs. 297 through 301** for check lamp and warning lamp diagnosis. Refer to **Figs. 302** through **352** for ABS system code diagnosis and repair.
8. If no codes are present, or mechanical component failure codes are present, perform automated modulator test using the SCAN tool to isolate the cause of the problem. If the failure is intermittent and not reproducible, test drive vehicle while using the automatic snapshot feature of the SCAN tool. Perform normal acceleration, stopping and turning maneuvers. If this does not reproduce the fault, perform an ABS stop from approximately 30-50 mph while triggering an ABS code. If failure still will not reproduce, use enhanced diagnostic information found in CODE HISTORY to determine whether or not this failure should be further diagnosed.
9. Once all failures have been corrected, clear ABS codes.

Component Testing

Component testing can only be accomplished by using a TECH 1 scan tool or suitable equivalent.

AUTOMATED SELF-DIAGNOSING MODULATOR

If a mechanical modulator fault is suspected, rough ABS performance is indicated, or if any modulator service has been performed, this test should be run to verify the repair has corrected the problem and the displacement pistons are returned to their top most position. The scan tool will prompt for replies to changes in brake pedal position. These pedal changes are a result of modular component control in a specific order that allows component faults to be determined. It is important, when testing the rear channel, that each reply to the scan tool questions be carefully considered. During rear channel testing, pedal movement will be felt as a bump, which is much different than the movement felt in the front channels.

ABS AUTOMATED MOTOR PACK

This test should be performed to identify a potential problem in the motor pack assembly. If a problem exists, the results of the motor pack test will be indicated by the scan tool. If the motor is found to be defective, the motor pack is not serviceable and must be replaced as an assembly.

HYDRAULIC FUNCTIONAL CONTROL

This test is used to verify, ABS hold and ABS release functions. Raise and support the vehicle, then allow scan tool to perform the entire test.

MOTOR PACK FUNCTIONAL

The motor pack must be separated from the modulator to perform this test. Refer to "Motor Assembly" in "Component Replacement." The scan tool will rotate the motors first in one direction, then the other. If any motor does not rotate in both directions, the motor pack is defective and must be replaced. If all three motors rotate, try to rotate each gear on the modulator assembly, refer to "No Gear Movement Test."

GEAR TENSION RELIEF SEQUENCE

When the displacement cylinder pistons are in their top most position, each motor has prevailing torque due to the force necessary to hold each piston at the top of its travel. This torque results in gear tension or force on each gear that makes motor pack separation difficult. To avoid injury or damaging the aluminum gears, this sequence will briefly reverse each motor to eliminate the prevailing torque.

ENABLE RELAY

This test monitors the voltage at the EBCM while turning the enable relay on and off. When the relay is commanded "ON," the voltage should be equal to battery voltage. When relay is commanded "OFF, " the voltage should drop below five volts. Voltage will not drop to zero when relay contacts are open due to capacitors within the EBCM. If voltage drops below five volts, the relay is working properly.

VOLTAGE (BATTERY) LOAD

This ABS system can draw a significant amount of voltage when in operation. This test turns on many of the ABS system components to load test the vehicle electrical system. If low voltage faults or intermittent EBCM operation are occurring while this test is being performed. This test will allow monitoring of two separate power circuits for ABS (ignition and battery). If only one of these inputs drops below 10 volts during testing, a high resistance may be present in that power feed circuit.

ABS & RED BRAKE WARNING LAMP CONTROL

This test allows a functional test of the ABS warning light circuit, lamp driver module and brake warning light circuit.

ABS VERSION

This selection allows the display of the EEPROM identification, date code, sequence number and calibration identification.

MOTOR

In this test the motor can be turned on manually for up to five seconds at a current of 10 amps forward or 6 amps reverse. To verify correct front motor operation, the test must be done with engine off and all vacuum reverse depleted. Depress brake pedal as you would during a normal stop. "Release" one of the motors. Brake pedal should move smoothly towards the floor. Rough or jumpy brake pedal movement indicates an intermittent electrical connections within the motor. As the pedal drops, the feedback current should momentarily drop to only a few amps (indicating motor movement), and then become equal to the command current (6 amps), this indicates the motor is no longer moving since the displacement cylinder has bottomed out. With foot still on brake, "Apply" the same motor. Brake pedal should smoothly rise back up to the top of its travel. The feedback current should momentarily drop to a few amps then quickly increase to the command current (10 amps) as the displacement cylinder reaches the top of its travel and the motor stops moving. The rear motor is tested in the same manner, except there will only be a slight pedal drop and slight pedal rise.

If the brake pedal does not move in both directions and no trouble codes are set indicating an electrical problem, monitor the feedback current. If the feedback current is always only a few amps, the motor is free spinning. In either case, the motor pack must be separated from the hydraulic modulator to identify an ESB, motor, gear or ball screw problem.

SOLENOIDS

To functionally test the solenoids, select one front channel at a time. "Release" the motor for the channel and solenoid that is being tested. With foot off the brake pedal, turn "ON" the solenoid. Depress the brake, pedal should be very high and firm. If the pedal goes nearly to the floor, the solenoid is not closing or the check valve is leaking. Leaving brake pedal depressed, turn off the solenoid. The brake pedal should drop as the solenoid is being turned off. If the brake pedal does not drop and the motor is running, the solenoid is stuck on or off. To verify whether the solenoid is stuck on or off, depress the brake pedal and "apply the motor for the channel that is being tested. If the brake pedal rises, the solenoid is stuck open or the check valve is leaking. If the pedal drops suddenly, the solenoid is stuck closed.

If when depressing the brake pedal, the pedal slowly sinks to the floor or the pedal rose during the "apply," swap the two solenoids. Be sure to install the electrical connectors so that the left and right front channels are correct. Repeat the test for the other channel (different check valve but the same solenoid). If the solenoid does not check out (pedal also sank or rose during the second test), the solenoid is leaking and should be replaced. If the solenoid does check out, retest the first channel. If the brake pedal should rise or fall, indicating a leaking check valve, the ABS hydraulic modulator would have to be replaced.

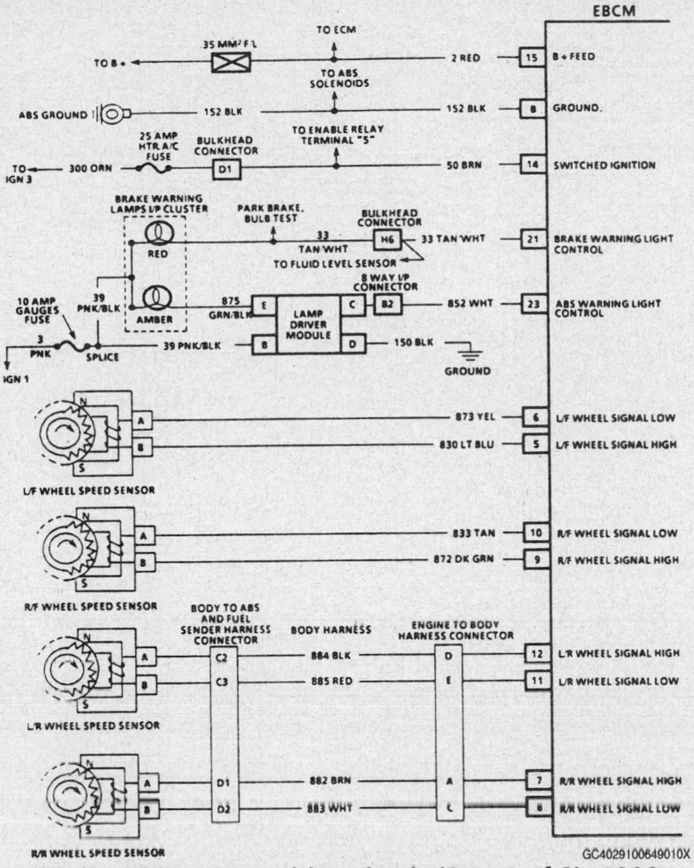

EBCM
TO ECM
35 MM² F.L
TO B+
2 RED
15 B+FEED
TO ABS SOLENOIDS
ABS GROUND
152 BLK
8 GROUND
25 AMP HTR A/C FUSE
BULKHEAD CONNECTOR
TO ENABLE RELAY TERMINAL "5"
TO IGN 3
300 ORN
D1
50 BRN
14 SWITCHED IGNITION
BRAKE WARNING LAMPS I/P CLUSTER
PARK BRAKE, BULB TEST
BULKHEAD CONNECTOR
RED
33 TAN/WHT
H6
21 BRAKE WARNING LIGHT CONTROL
TO FLUID LEVEL SENSOR
8 WAY I/P CONNECTOR
10 AMP GAUGES FUSE
39 PNK/BLK
AMBER
875 GRN/BLK
LAMP DRIVER MODULE
B2
852 WHT
23 ABS WARNING LIGHT CONTROL
3 PNK
SPLICE
39 PNK/BLK
150 BLK
GROUND
IGN 1
873 YEL
6 L/F WHEEL SIGNAL LOW
830 LT BLU
5 L/F WHEEL SIGNAL HIGH
L/F WHEEL SPEED SENSOR
833 TAN
10 R/F WHEEL SIGNAL LOW
872 DK GRN
9 R/F WHEEL SIGNAL HIGH
R/F WHEEL SPEED SENSOR
BODY TO ABS AND FUEL SENDER HARNESS CONNECTOR
BODY HARNESS
ENGINE TO BODY HARNESS CONNECTOR
884 BLK
12 L/R WHEEL SIGNAL HIGH
885 RED
11 L/R WHEEL SIGNAL LOW
L/R WHEEL SPEED SENSOR
882 BRN
7 R/R WHEEL SIGNAL HIGH
883 WHT
8 R/R WHEEL SIGNAL LOW
R/R WHEEL SPEED SENSOR
GC4029100649010X

Fig. 2 ABS system wiring circuit (Part 1 of 2). 1992 Achieva, Calais, Grand Am & Skylark

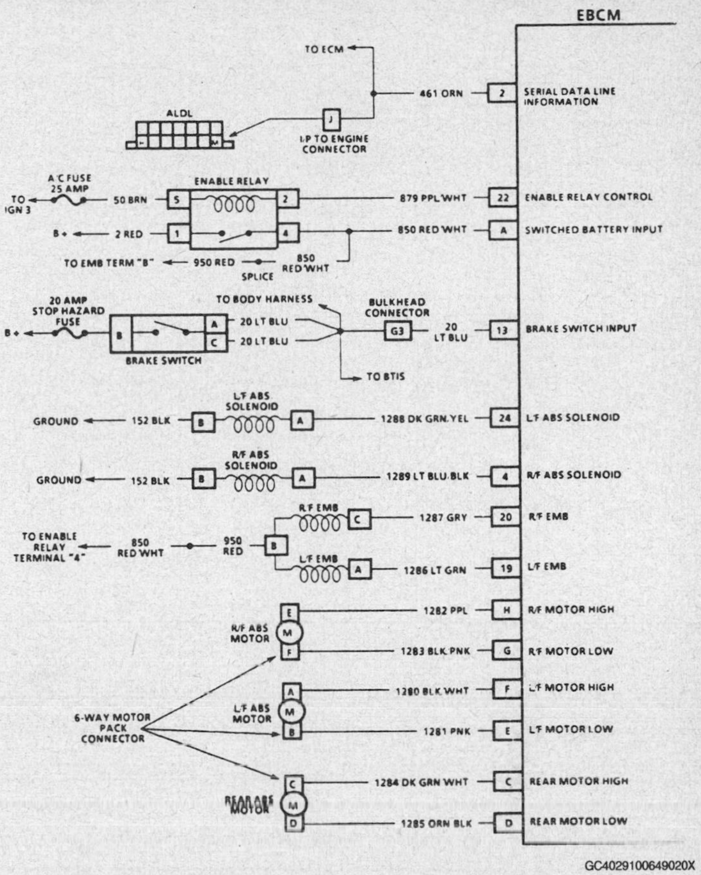

EBCM
TO ECM
461 ORN
2 SERIAL DATA LINE INFORMATION
ALDL
I/P TO ENGINE CONNECTOR
A/C FUSE 25 AMP
ENABLE RELAY
TO IGN 3
50 BRN
879 PPL/WHT
22 ENABLE RELAY CONTROL
B+
2 RED
850 RED/WHT
A SWITCHED BATTERY INPUT
TO EMB TERM "B"
950 RED
SPLICE
850 RED/WHT
20 AMP STOP HAZARD FUSE
TO BODY HARNESS
BULKHEAD CONNECTOR
20 LT BLU
G3
13 BRAKE SWITCH INPUT
BRAKE SWITCH
TO BTIS
L/F ABS SOLENOID
GROUND
152 BLK
1288 DK GRN/YEL
24 L/F ABS SOLENOID
R/F ABS SOLENOID
1289 LT BLU/BLK
4 R/F ABS SOLENOID
R/F EMB
1287 GRY
20 R/F EMB
TO ENABLE RELAY TERMINAL "4"
850 RED/WHT
950 RED
L/F EMB
1286 LT GRN
19 L/F EMB
1282 PPL
H R/F MOTOR HIGH
R/F ABS MOTOR
1283 BLK/PNK
G R/F MOTOR LOW
1280 BLK/WHT
F L/F MOTOR HIGH
L/F ABS MOTOR
6-WAY MOTOR PACK CONNECTOR
1281 PNK
E L/F MOTOR LOW
1284 DK GRN/WHT
C REAR MOTOR HIGH
REAR ABS MOTOR
1285 ORN/BLK
D REAR MOTOR LOW
GC4029100649020X

Fig. 2 ABS system wiring circuit (Part 2 of 2). 1992 Achieva, Calais, Grand Am & Skylark

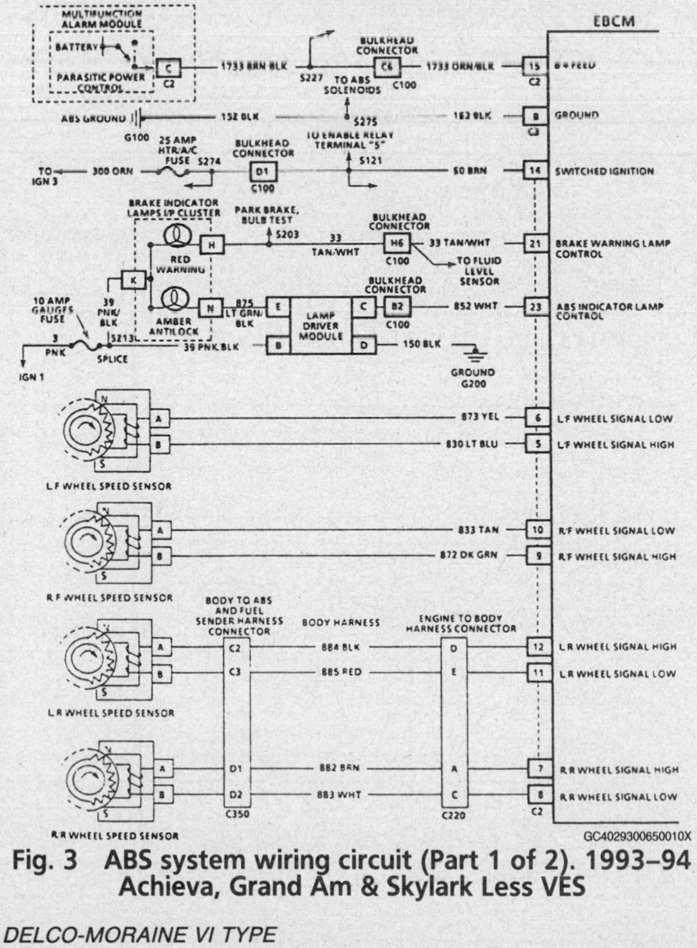

MULTIFUNCTION ALARM MODULE
BATTERY
PARASITIC POWER CONTROL
EBCM
1733 BRN/BLK
S227
BULKHEAD CONNECTOR
C6
1733 ORN/BLK
15 B+FEED
TO ABS SOLENOIDS
C100
ABS GROUND
152 BLK
S275
8 GROUND
G100
25 AMP HTR/A/C FUSE
S274
BULKHEAD CONNECTOR
TO ENABLE RELAY TERMINAL "5"
S121
TO IGN 3
300 ORN
D1
50 BRN
14 SWITCHED IGNITION
BRAKE INDICATOR LAMPS I/P CLUSTER
PARK BRAKE, BULB TEST
S203
33 TAN/WHT
BULKHEAD CONNECTOR
H6
21 BRAKE WARNING LAMP CONTROL
RED WARNING
TO FLUID LEVEL SENSOR
10 AMP GAUGES FUSE
39 PNK/BLK
AMBER ANTILOCK
875 LT GRN/BLK
LAMP DRIVER MODULE
B2
852 WHT
23 ABS INDICATOR LAMP CONTROL
S213
3 PNK
SPLICE
39 PNK/BLK
150 BLK
GROUND G200
IGN 1
873 YEL
6 L/F WHEEL SIGNAL LOW
830 LT BLU
5 L/F WHEEL SIGNAL HIGH
L/F WHEEL SPEED SENSOR
833 TAN
10 R/F WHEEL SIGNAL LOW
872 DK GRN
9 R/F WHEEL SIGNAL HIGH
R/F WHEEL SPEED SENSOR
BODY TO ABS AND FUEL SENDER HARNESS CONNECTOR
BODY HARNESS
ENGINE TO BODY HARNESS CONNECTOR
884 BLK
12 L/R WHEEL SIGNAL HIGH
885 RED
11 L/R WHEEL SIGNAL LOW
L/R WHEEL SPEED SENSOR
882 BRN
7 R/R WHEEL SIGNAL HIGH
883 WHT
8 R/R WHEEL SIGNAL LOW
C350
C220
R/R WHEEL SPEED SENSOR
GC4029300650010X

Fig. 3 ABS system wiring circuit (Part 1 of 2). 1993–94 Achieva, Grand Am & Skylark Less VES

NO GEAR MOVEMENT

If all three motors release, the motor pack appears to be satisfactory. Rotate each gear on the ABS hydraulic modulator assembly by hand. The front gears (non-center) should be able to rotate approximately 12¼ turns from lock to lock and the rear gear should turn approximately 7¼ turns. If the front gear will not freely turn at least 12 turns or the rear gear will not freely turn at least 7 turns, replace hydraulic modulator assembly.

Continued on page 32-530

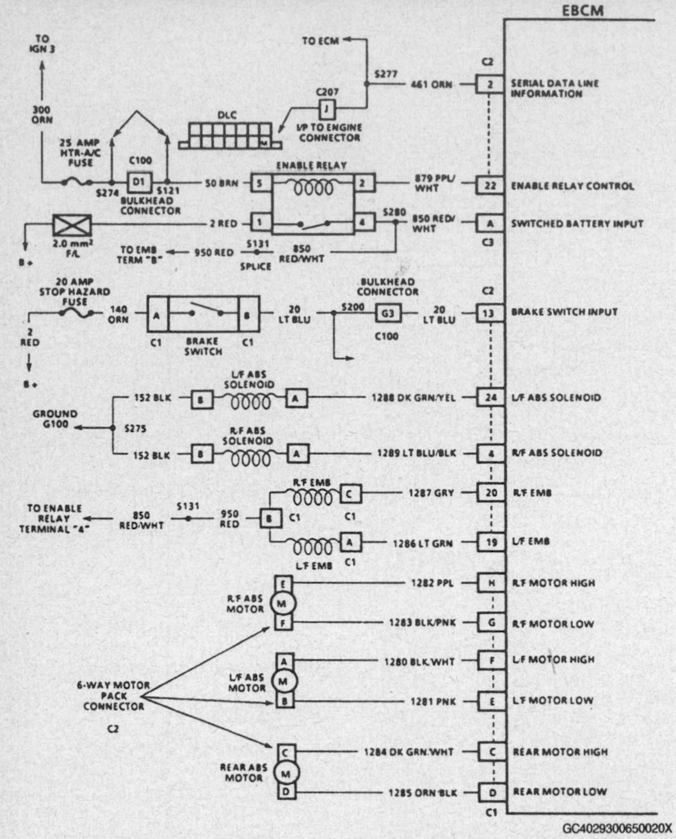
EBCM
SERIAL DATA LINE INFORMATION
ENABLE RELAY CONTROL
SWITCHED BATTERY INPUT
BRAKE SWITCH INPUT
L/F ABS SOLENOID
R/F ABS SOLENOID
R/F EMB
L/F EMB
R/F MOTOR HIGH
R/F MOTOR LOW
L/F MOTOR HIGH
L/F MOTOR LOW
REAR MOTOR HIGH
REAR MOTOR LOW
ENABLE RELAY
BRAKE SWITCH
6-WAY MOTOR PACK CONNECTOR
GC4029300650020X

Fig. 3 ABS system wiring circuit (Part 2 of 2). 1993–94 Achieva, Grand Am & Skylark Less VES

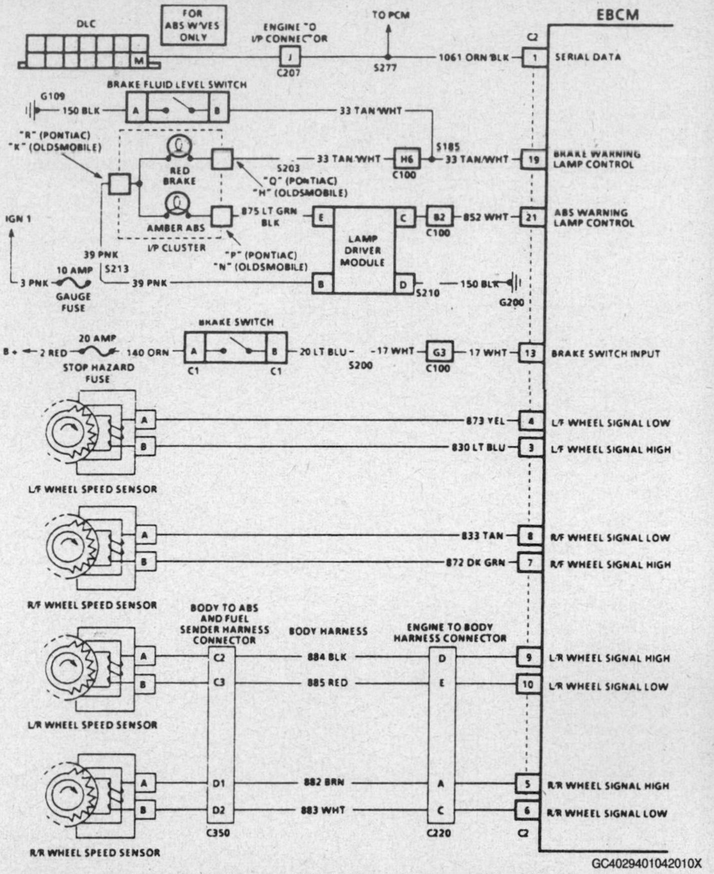
EBCM
SERIAL DATA
BRAKE WARNING LAMP CONTROL
ABS WARNING LAMP CONTROL
BRAKE SWITCH INPUT
L/F WHEEL SIGNAL LOW
L/F WHEEL SIGNAL HIGH
R/F WHEEL SIGNAL LOW
R/F WHEEL SIGNAL HIGH
L/R WHEEL SIGNAL HIGH
L/R WHEEL SIGNAL LOW
R/R WHEEL SIGNAL HIGH
R/R WHEEL SIGNAL LOW
BRAKE FLUID LEVEL SWITCH
LAMP DRIVER MODULE
L/F WHEEL SPEED SENSOR
R/F WHEEL SPEED SENSOR
L/R WHEEL SPEED SENSOR
R/R WHEEL SPEED SENSOR
GC4029401042010X

Fig. 4 ABS system wiring circuit (Part 1 of 2). 1994 Achieva, Grand Am & Skylark w/VES

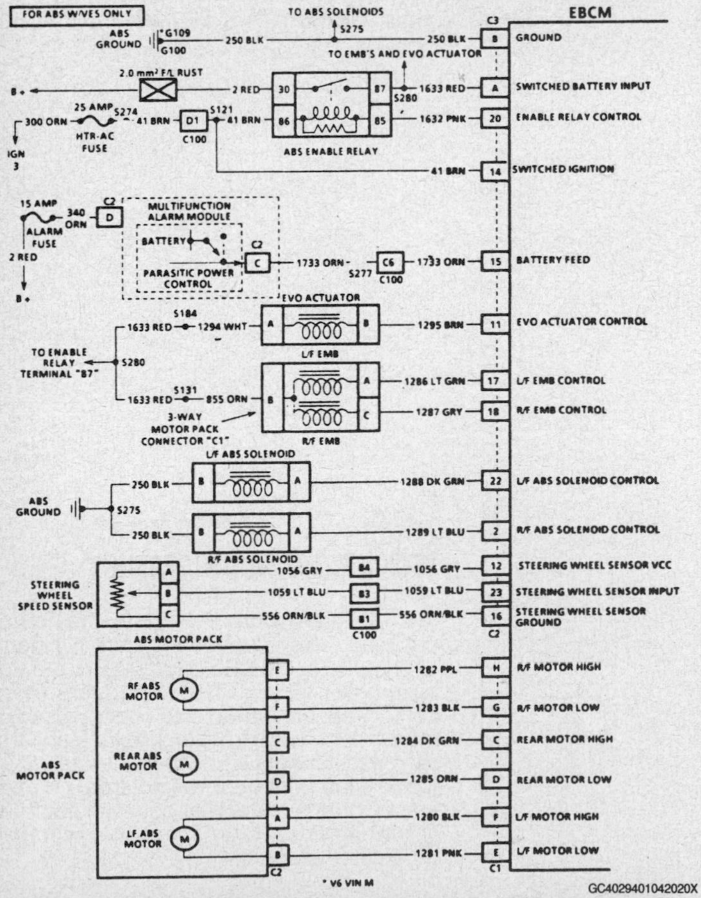
FOR ABS W/VES ONLY
EBCM
GROUND
SWITCHED BATTERY INPUT
ENABLE RELAY CONTROL
SWITCHED IGNITION
BATTERY FEED
EVO ACTUATOR CONTROL
L/F EMB CONTROL
R/F EMB CONTROL
L/F ABS SOLENOID CONTROL
R/F ABS SOLENOID CONTROL
STEERING WHEEL SENSOR VCC
STEERING WHEEL SENSOR INPUT
STEERING WHEEL SENSOR GROUND
R/F MOTOR HIGH
R/F MOTOR LOW
REAR MOTOR HIGH
REAR MOTOR LOW
L/F MOTOR HIGH
L/F MOTOR LOW
ABS ENABLE RELAY
MULTIFUNCTION ALARM MODULE
ABS MOTOR PACK
* V6 VIN M
GC4029401042020X

Fig. 4 ABS system wiring circuit (Part 2 of 2). 1994 Achieva, Grand Am & Skylark w/VES

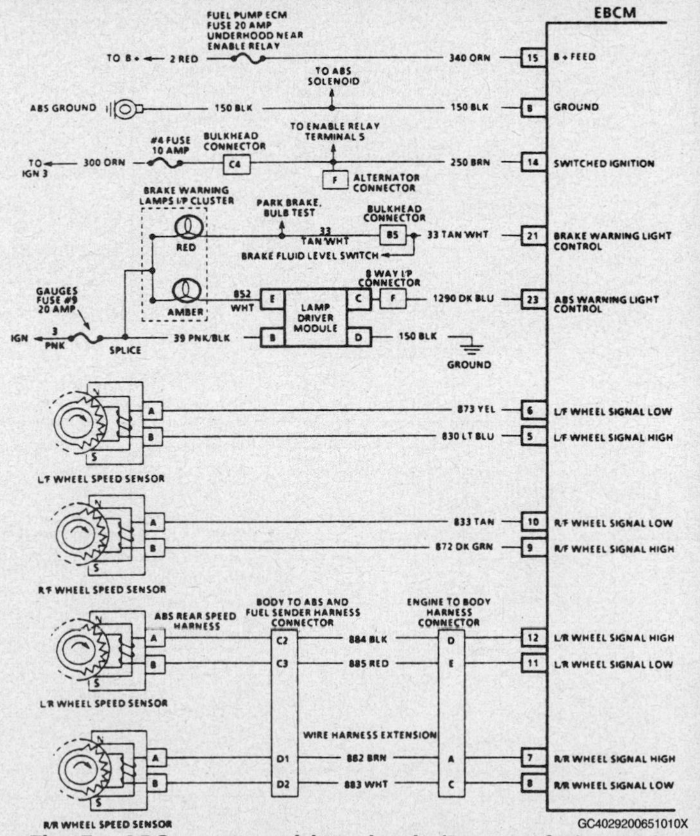
EBCM
B + FEED
GROUND
SWITCHED IGNITION
BRAKE WARNING LIGHT CONTROL
ABS WARNING LIGHT CONTROL
L/F WHEEL SIGNAL LOW
L/F WHEEL SIGNAL HIGH
R/F WHEEL SIGNAL LOW
R/F WHEEL SIGNAL HIGH
L/R WHEEL SIGNAL HIGH
L/R WHEEL SIGNAL LOW
R/R WHEEL SIGNAL HIGH
R/R WHEEL SIGNAL LOW
LAMP DRIVER MODULE
L/F WHEEL SPEED SENSOR
R/F WHEEL SPEED SENSOR
L/R WHEEL SPEED SENSOR
R/R WHEEL SPEED SENSOR
GC4029200651010X

Fig. 5 ABS system wiring circuit (Part 1 of 2). 1992 Beretta & Corsica

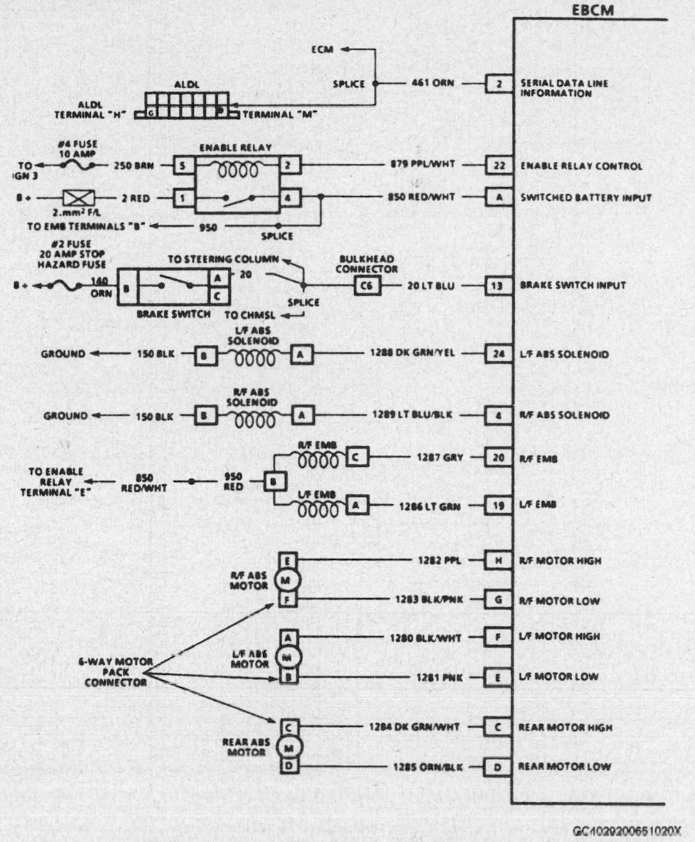
EBCM
ECM
SPLICE
461 ORN
SERIAL DATA LINE INFORMATION
ALDL
ALDL TERMINAL "H"
TERMINAL "M"
ENABLE RELAY
879 PPL/WHT
ENABLE RELAY CONTROL
850 RED/WHT
SWITCHED BATTERY INPUT
TO EMB TERMINALS "B"
BULKHEAD CONNECTOR
20 LT BLU
BRAKE SWITCH INPUT
BRAKE SWITCH
TO CHMSL
GROUND
150 BLK
L/F ABS SOLENOID
1288 DK GRN/YEL
R/F ABS SOLENOID
1289 LT BLU/BLK
R/F EMB
1287 GRY
L/F EMB
1286 LT GRN
TO ENABLE RELAY TERMINAL "E"
R/F ABS MOTOR
1282 PPL
R/F MOTOR HIGH
1283 BLK/PNK
R/F MOTOR LOW
L/F ABS MOTOR
1280 BLK/WHT
L/F MOTOR HIGH
1281 PNK
L/F MOTOR LOW
6-WAY MOTOR PACK CONNECTOR
REAR ABS MOTOR
1284 DK GRN/WHT
REAR MOTOR HIGH
1285 ORN/BLK
REAR MOTOR LOW

Fig. 5 ABS system wiring circuit (Part 2 of 2). 1992 Beretta & Corsica

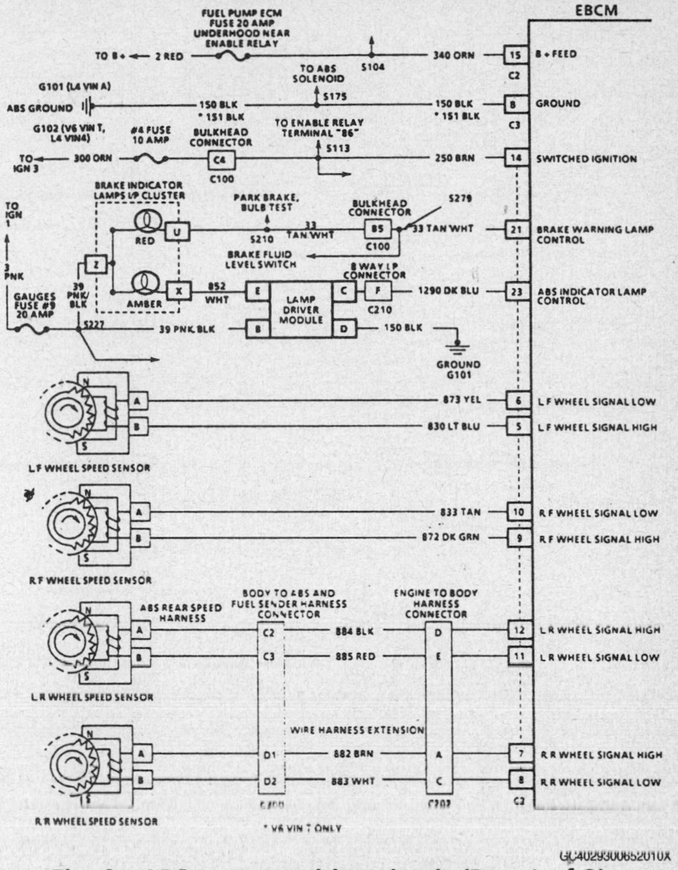
EBCM
FUEL PUMP ECM FUSE 20 AMP UNDERHOOD NEAR ENABLE RELAY
340 ORN
B+FEED
ABS GROUND
150 BLK
GROUND
300 ORN
250 BRN
SWITCHED IGNITION
BRAKE INDICATOR LAMPS I/P CLUSTER
PARK BRAKE, BULB TEST
33 TAN WHT
BRAKE WARNING LAMP CONTROL
BRAKE FLUID LEVEL SWITCH
LAMP DRIVER MODULE
1290 DK BLU
ABS INDICATOR LAMP CONTROL
GROUND G101
873 YEL
L F WHEEL SIGNAL LOW
830 LT BLU
L F WHEEL SIGNAL HIGH
L/F WHEEL SPEED SENSOR
833 TAN
R F WHEEL SIGNAL LOW
872 DK GRN
R F WHEEL SIGNAL HIGH
R/F WHEEL SPEED SENSOR
884 BLK
L R WHEEL SIGNAL HIGH
885 RED
L R WHEEL SIGNAL LOW
L R WHEEL SPEED SENSOR
WIRE HARNESS EXTENSION
882 BRN
R R WHEEL SIGNAL HIGH
883 WHT
R R WHEEL SIGNAL LOW
R R WHEEL SPEED SENSOR
* V6 VIN T ONLY

Fig. 6 ABS system wiring circuit (Part 1 of 2). 1993–94 Beretta & Corsica

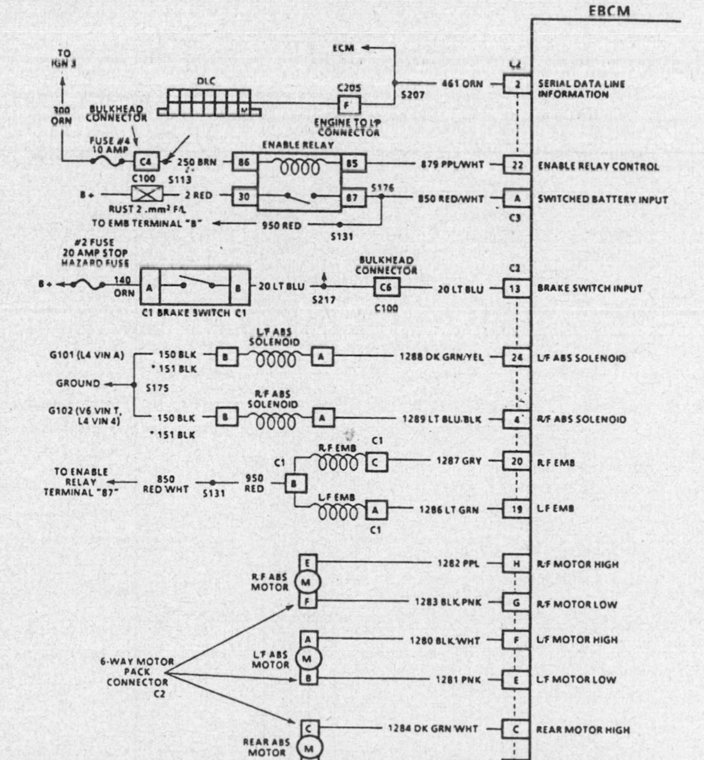
EBCM
ECM
DLC
461 ORN
SERIAL DATA LINE INFORMATION
ENABLE RELAY
879 PPL/WHT
ENABLE RELAY CONTROL
850 RED/WHT
SWITCHED BATTERY INPUT
TO EMB TERMINAL "B"
950 RED
20 LT BLU
BRAKE SWITCH INPUT
BRAKE SWITCH
1288 DK GRN/YEL
L/F ABS SOLENOID
1289 LT BLU/BLK
R/F ABS SOLENOID
1287 GRY
R F EMB
1286 LT GRN
L F EMB
TO ENABLE RELAY TERMINAL "87"
1282 PPL
R/F MOTOR HIGH
1283 BLK PNK
R/F MOTOR LOW
1280 BLK/WHT
L/F MOTOR HIGH
1281 PNK
L/F MOTOR LOW
6-WAY MOTOR PACK CONNECTOR
1284 DK GRN WHT
REAR MOTOR HIGH
1285 ORN BLK
REAR MOTOR LOW
* V6 VIN T ONLY

Fig. 6 ABS system wiring circuit (Part 2 of 2). 1993–94 Beretta & Corsica

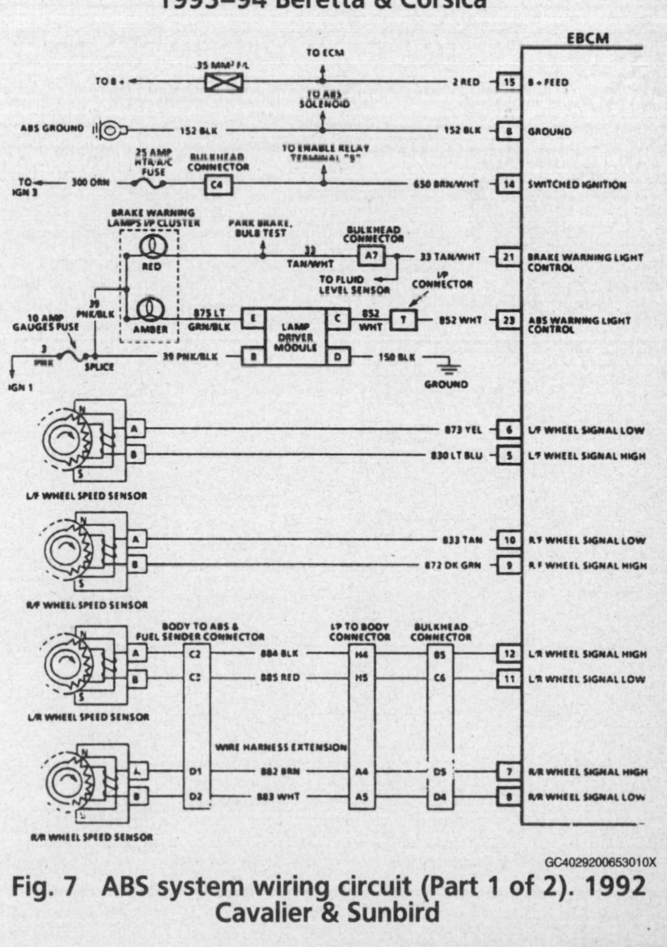
EBCM
TO ECM
2 RED
B+FEED
ABS GROUND
152 BLK
GROUND
650 BRN/WHT
SWITCHED IGNITION
BRAKE WARNING LAMPS I/P CLUSTER
PARK BRAKE, BULB TEST
33 TAN/WHT
BRAKE WARNING LIGHT CONTROL
LAMP DRIVER MODULE
852 WHT
ABS WARNING LIGHT CONTROL
873 YEL
L/F WHEEL SIGNAL LOW
830 LT BLU
L/F WHEEL SIGNAL HIGH
L/F WHEEL SPEED SENSOR
833 TAN
R/F WHEEL SIGNAL LOW
872 DK GRN
R/F WHEEL SIGNAL HIGH
R/F WHEEL SPEED SENSOR
884 BLK
L/R WHEEL SIGNAL HIGH
885 RED
L/R WHEEL SIGNAL LOW
L/R WHEEL SPEED SENSOR
WIRE HARNESS EXTENSION
882 BRN
R/R WHEEL SIGNAL HIGH
883 WHT
R/R WHEEL SIGNAL LOW
R/R WHEEL SPEED SENSOR

Fig. 7 ABS system wiring circuit (Part 1 of 2). 1992 Cavalier & Sunbird

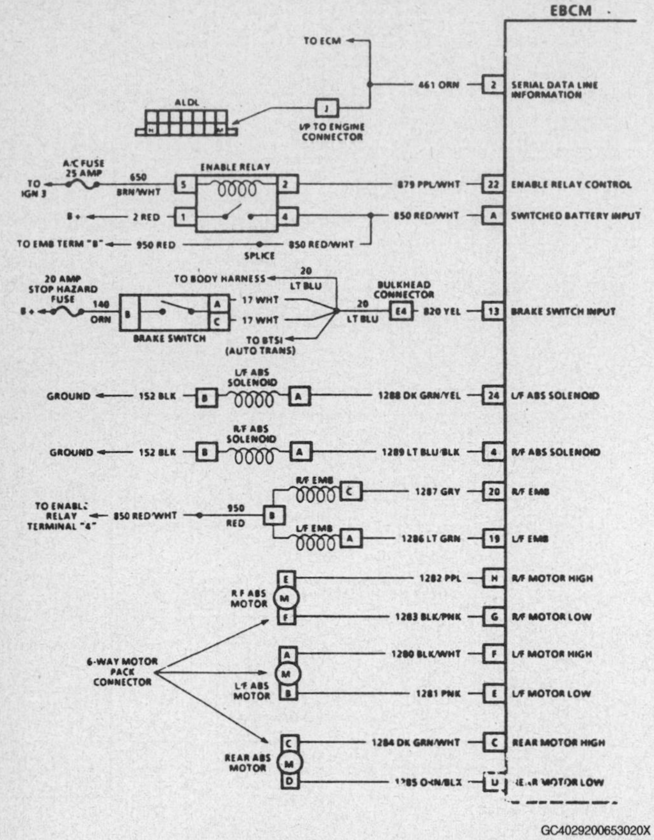
EBCM
TO ECM
ALDL
461 ORN
SERIAL DATA LINE INFORMATION
I/P TO ENGINE CONNECTOR
A/C FUSE 25 AMP
TO IGN 3
650 BRN/WHT
ENABLE RELAY
879 PPL/WHT
ENABLE RELAY CONTROL
B+
2 RED
850 RED/WHT
SWITCHED BATTERY INPUT
TO EMB TERM "B"
950 RED
SPLICE
20 AMP STOP HAZARD FUSE
TO BODY HARNESS
20 LT BLU
17 WHT
BULKHEAD CONNECTOR
820 YEL
BRAKE SWITCH INPUT
BRAKE SWITCH
TO BTSI (AUTO TRANS)
L/F ABS SOLENOID
GROUND
152 BLK
1288 DK GRN/YEL
L/F ABS SOLENOID
R/F ABS SOLENOID
1289 LT BLU/BLK
R/F ABS SOLENOID
R/F EMB
1287 GRY
TO ENABLE RELAY TERMINAL "4"
850 RED/WHT
950 RED
L/F EMB
1286 LT GRN
1282 PPL
R/F MOTOR HIGH
R/F ABS MOTOR
1283 BLK/PNK
R/F MOTOR LOW
6-WAY MOTOR PACK CONNECTOR
1280 BLK/WHT
L/F MOTOR HIGH
L/F ABS MOTOR
1281 PNK
L/F MOTOR LOW
1284 DK GRN/WHT
REAR MOTOR HIGH
REAR ABS MOTOR
REAR MOTOR LOW
GC4029200653020X

Fig. 7 ABS system wiring circuit (Part 2 of 2). 1992 Cavalier & Sunbird

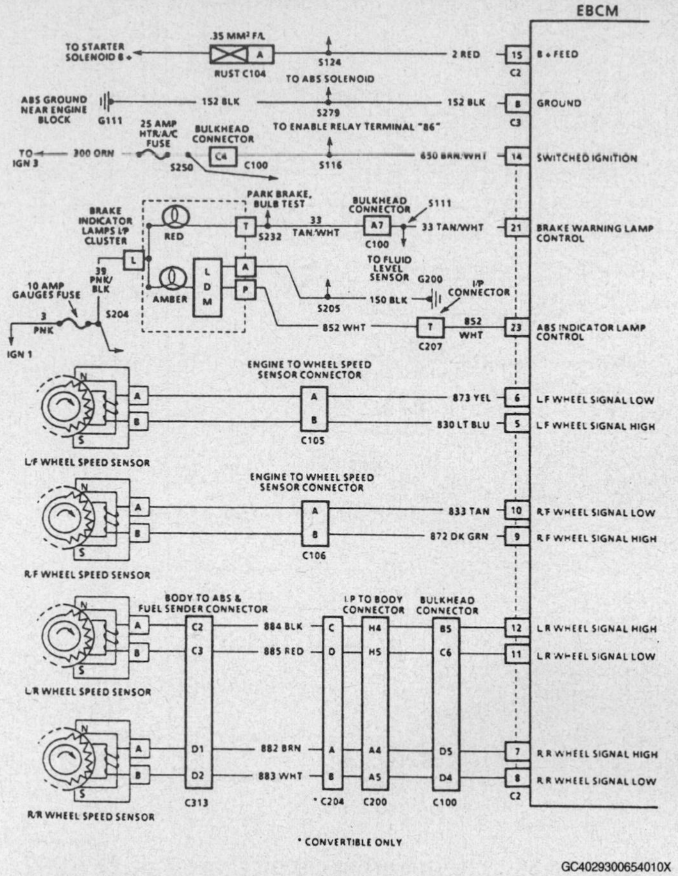
EBCM
TO STARTER SOLENOID B+
.35 MM² F/L
RUST C104
S124
2 RED
B+FEED
TO ABS SOLENOID
ABS GROUND NEAR ENGINE BLOCK
G111
152 BLK
S279
GROUND
25 AMP HTR/A/C FUSE
BULKHEAD CONNECTOR
TO ENABLE RELAY TERMINAL "86"
TO IGN 3
300 ORN
S250
C100
S116
650 BRN/WHT
SWITCHED IGNITION
BRAKE INDICATOR LAMPS I/P CLUSTER
RED
PARK BRAKE, BULB TEST
S232
33 TAN/WHT
S111
BRAKE WARNING LAMP CONTROL
TO FLUID LEVEL SENSOR
G200
I/P CONNECTOR
10 AMP GAUGES FUSE
39 PNK/BLK
AMBER
LDM
S205
150 BLK
3 PNK
S204
852 WHT
C207
ABS INDICATOR LAMP CONTROL
IGN 1
ENGINE TO WHEEL SPEED SENSOR CONNECTOR
873 YEL
L/F WHEEL SIGNAL LOW
830 LT BLU
L/F WHEEL SIGNAL HIGH
C105
L/F WHEEL SPEED SENSOR
833 TAN
R/F WHEEL SIGNAL LOW
872 DK GRN
R/F WHEEL SIGNAL HIGH
C106
R/F WHEEL SPEED SENSOR
BODY TO ABS & FUEL SENDER CONNECTOR
I/P TO BODY CONNECTOR
BULKHEAD CONNECTOR
884 BLK
L/R WHEEL SIGNAL HIGH
885 RED
L/R WHEEL SIGNAL LOW
L/R WHEEL SPEED SENSOR
882 BRN
R/R WHEEL SIGNAL HIGH
883 WHT
R/R WHEEL SIGNAL LOW
C313
*C204
C200
C100
R/R WHEEL SPEED SENSOR
* CONVERTIBLE ONLY
GC4029300654010X

Fig. 8 ABS system wiring circuit (Part 1 of 2). 1993–94 Cavalier

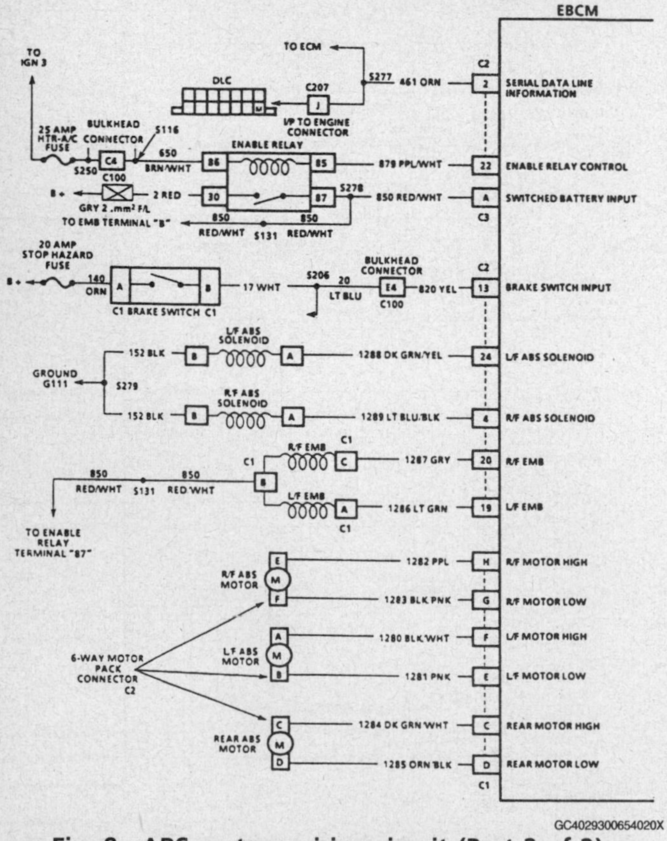
EBCM
TO IGN 3
TO ECM
DLC
C207
S277
461 ORN
SERIAL DATA LINE INFORMATION
I/P TO ENGINE CONNECTOR
25 AMP HTR-A/C FUSE
BULKHEAD CONNECTOR
S116
650 BRN/WHT
ENABLE RELAY
879 PPL/WHT
ENABLE RELAY CONTROL
S250
C100
B+
GRY 2 .mm² F/L
2 RED
S278
850 RED/WHT
SWITCHED BATTERY INPUT
TO EMB TERMINAL "B"
S131
20 AMP STOP HAZARD FUSE
140 ORN
C1 BRAKE SWITCH C1
17 WHT
S206
20 LT BLU
820 YEL
BRAKE SWITCH INPUT
L/F ABS SOLENOID
152 BLK
1288 DK GRN/YEL
L/F ABS SOLENOID
GROUND G111
S279
R/F ABS SOLENOID
1289 LT BLU/BLK
R/F ABS SOLENOID
R/F EMB
1287 GRY
850 RED/WHT
L/F EMB
1286 LT GRN
TO ENABLE RELAY TERMINAL "87"
1282 PPL
R/F MOTOR HIGH
R/F ABS MOTOR
1283 BLK PNK
R/F MOTOR LOW
6-WAY MOTOR PACK CONNECTOR C2
1280 BLK/WHT
L/F MOTOR HIGH
L/F ABS MOTOR
1281 PNK
L/F MOTOR LOW
1284 DK GRN WHT
REAR MOTOR HIGH
REAR ABS MOTOR
1285 ORN BLK
REAR MOTOR LOW
GC4029300654020X

Fig. 8 ABS system wiring circuit (Part 2 of 2). 1993–94 Cavalier

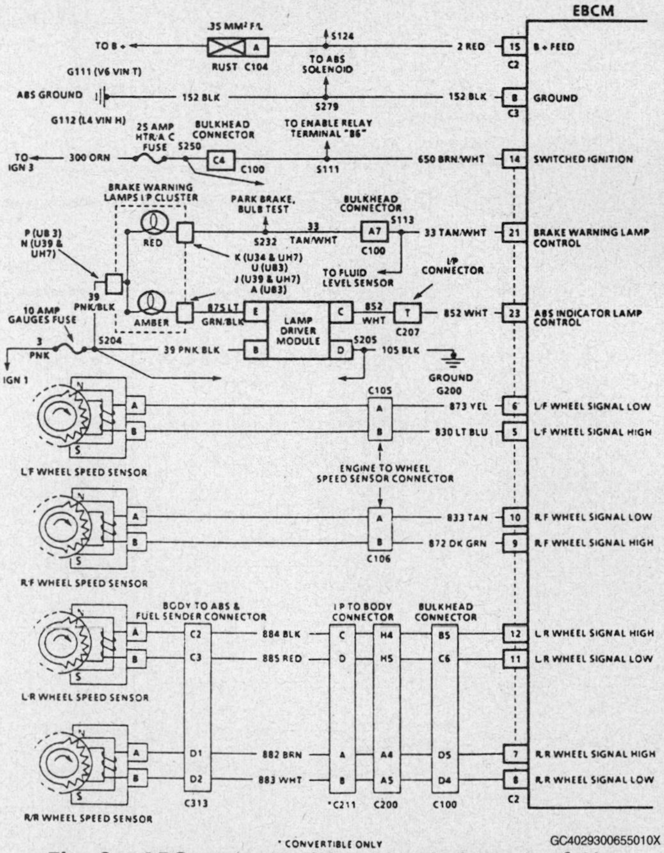
EBCM
TO B+
.35 MM² F/L
RUST C104
S124
2 RED
B+FEED
G111 (V6 VIN T)
TO ABS SOLENOID
ABS GROUND
152 BLK
S279
GROUND
G112 (L4 VIN H)
25 AMP HTR/A C FUSE
BULKHEAD CONNECTOR
TO ENABLE RELAY TERMINAL "86"
TO IGN 3
300 ORN
S250
C100
S111
650 BRN/WHT
SWITCHED IGNITION
BRAKE WARNING LAMPS I/P CLUSTER
PARK BRAKE, BULB TEST
RED
S232
33 TAN/WHT
S113
BRAKE WARNING LAMP CONTROL
P (UB 3)
N (U39 & UH7)
K (U34 & UH7)
U (UB3)
J (U39 & UH7)
A (UB3)
TO FLUID LEVEL SENSOR
I/P CONNECTOR
10 AMP GAUGES FUSE
39 PNK/BLK
AMBER
875 LT GRN/BLK
LAMP DRIVER MODULE
852 WHT
C207
ABS INDICATOR LAMP CONTROL
S204
39 PNK BLK
S205
105 BLK
GROUND G200
IGN 1
C105
873 YEL
L/F WHEEL SIGNAL LOW
830 LT BLU
L/F WHEEL SIGNAL HIGH
L/F WHEEL SPEED SENSOR
ENGINE TO WHEEL SPEED SENSOR CONNECTOR
833 TAN
R/F WHEEL SIGNAL LOW
872 DK GRN
R/F WHEEL SIGNAL HIGH
C106
R/F WHEEL SPEED SENSOR
BODY TO ABS & FUEL SENDER CONNECTOR
I/P TO BODY CONNECTOR
BULKHEAD CONNECTOR
884 BLK
L/R WHEEL SIGNAL HIGH
885 RED
L/R WHEEL SIGNAL LOW
L/R WHEEL SPEED SENSOR
882 BRN
R/R WHEEL SIGNAL HIGH
883 WHT
R/R WHEEL SIGNAL LOW
C313
*C211
C200
C100
R/R WHEEL SPEED SENSOR
* CONVERTIBLE ONLY
GC4029300655010X

Fig. 9 ABS system wiring circuit (Part 1 of 2). 1993–94 Sunbird

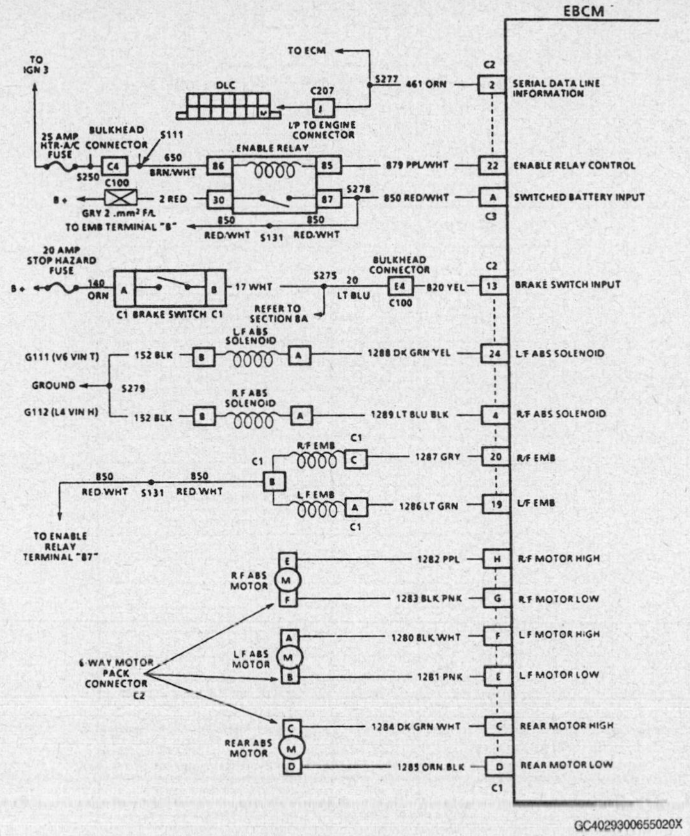
EBCM
TO ECM
TO IGN 3
DLC
C207
L/P TO ENGINE CONNECTOR
25 AMP HTR-A/C FUSE
BULKHEAD CONNECTOR
S111
ENABLE RELAY
S277 461 ORN
SERIAL DATA LINE INFORMATION
879 PPL/WHT
ENABLE RELAY CONTROL
850 RED/WHT
SWITCHED BATTERY INPUT
TO EMB TERMINAL "B"
20 AMP STOP HAZARD FUSE
C1 BRAKE SWITCH C1
REFER TO SECTION 8A
BULKHEAD CONNECTOR
820 YEL
BRAKE SWITCH INPUT
L/F ABS SOLENOID
1288 DK GRN/YEL
L/F ABS SOLENOID
G111 (V6 VIN T)
GROUND
G112 (L4 VIN H)
R/F ABS SOLENOID
1289 LT BLU BLK
R/F ABS SOLENOID
R/F EMB
1287 GRY
R/F EMB
L/F EMB
1286 LT GRN
L/F EMB
TO ENABLE RELAY TERMINAL "87"
R/F ABS MOTOR
1282 PPL
R/F MOTOR HIGH
1283 BLK PNK
R/F MOTOR LOW
L/F ABS MOTOR
1280 BLK/WHT
L/F MOTOR HIGH
6 WAY MOTOR PACK CONNECTOR C2
1281 PNK
L/F MOTOR LOW
REAR ABS MOTOR
1284 DK GRN WHT
REAR MOTOR HIGH
1285 ORN BLK
REAR MOTOR LOW
GC4029300655020X

Fig. 9 ABS system wiring circuit (Part 2 of 2). 1993–94 Sunbird

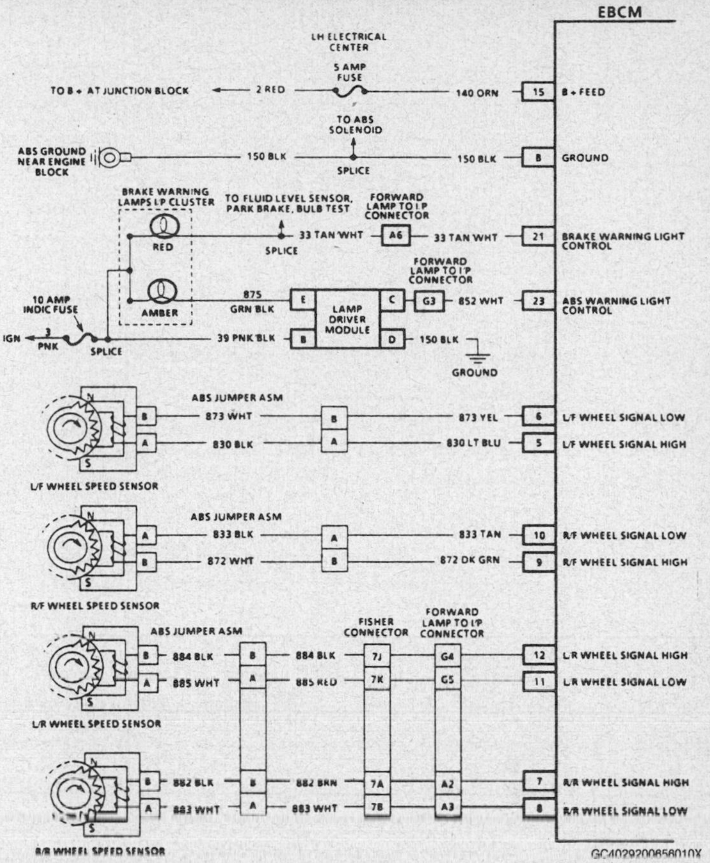
EBCM
LH ELECTRICAL CENTER
5 AMP FUSE
TO B+ AT JUNCTION BLOCK
2 RED
140 ORN
B+ FEED
TO ABS SOLENOID
ABS GROUND NEAR ENGINE BLOCK
150 BLK
SPLICE
GROUND
BRAKE WARNING LAMPS I/P CLUSTER
TO FLUID LEVEL SENSOR, PARK BRAKE, BULB TEST
FORWARD LAMP TO I/P CONNECTOR
RED
33 TAN WHT
BRAKE WARNING LIGHT CONTROL
AMBER
LAMP DRIVER MODULE
852 WHT
ABS WARNING LIGHT CONTROL
10 AMP INDIC FUSE
IGN
39 PNK/BLK
GROUND
ABS JUMPER ASM
873 WHT
830 BLK
873 YEL
830 LT BLU
L/F WHEEL SIGNAL LOW
L/F WHEEL SIGNAL HIGH
L/F WHEEL SPEED SENSOR
833 BLK
872 WHT
833 TAN
872 DK GRN
R/F WHEEL SIGNAL LOW
R/F WHEEL SIGNAL HIGH
R/F WHEEL SPEED SENSOR
FISHER CONNECTOR
884 BLK
885 WHT
885 RED
L/R WHEEL SIGNAL HIGH
L/R WHEEL SIGNAL LOW
L/R WHEEL SPEED SENSOR
882 BLK
883 WHT
882 BRN
R/R WHEEL SIGNAL HIGH
R/R WHEEL SIGNAL LOW
R/R WHEEL SPEED SENSOR
GC4029200656010X

Fig. 10 ABS system wiring circuit (Part 1 of 2). 1992–93 Cutlass Supreme, Grand Prix, Lumina & Regal

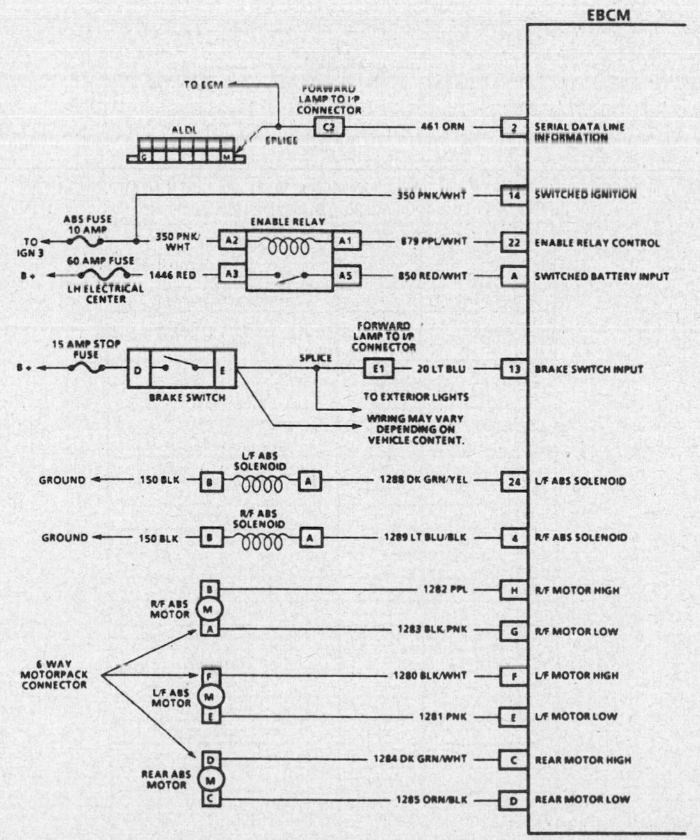
EBCM
TO ECM
FORWARD LAMP TO I/P CONNECTOR
ALDL
SPLICE
461 ORN
SERIAL DATA LINE INFORMATION
350 PNK/WHT
SWITCHED IGNITION
ABS FUSE 10 AMP
TO IGN 3
ENABLE RELAY
879 PPL/WHT
ENABLE RELAY CONTROL
60 AMP FUSE
LH ELECTRICAL CENTER
1446 RED
850 RED/WHT
SWITCHED BATTERY INPUT
15 AMP STOP FUSE
BRAKE SWITCH
20 LT BLU
BRAKE SWITCH INPUT
TO EXTERIOR LIGHTS
WIRING MAY VARY DEPENDING ON VEHICLE CONTENT.
GROUND
150 BLK
L/F ABS SOLENOID
1288 DK GRN/YEL
R/F ABS SOLENOID
1289 LT BLU/BLK
1282 PPL
R/F MOTOR HIGH
R/F ABS MOTOR
1283 BLK PNK
R/F MOTOR LOW
6 WAY MOTORPACK CONNECTOR
1280 BLK/WHT
L/F MOTOR HIGH
L/F ABS MOTOR
1281 PNK
L/F MOTOR LOW
1284 DK GRN/WHT
REAR MOTOR HIGH
REAR ABS MOTOR
1285 ORN/BLK
REAR MOTOR LOW
GC4029200656020X

Fig. 10 ABS system wiring circuit (Part 2 of 2). 1992–93 Cutlass Supreme, Grand Prix, Lumina & Regal

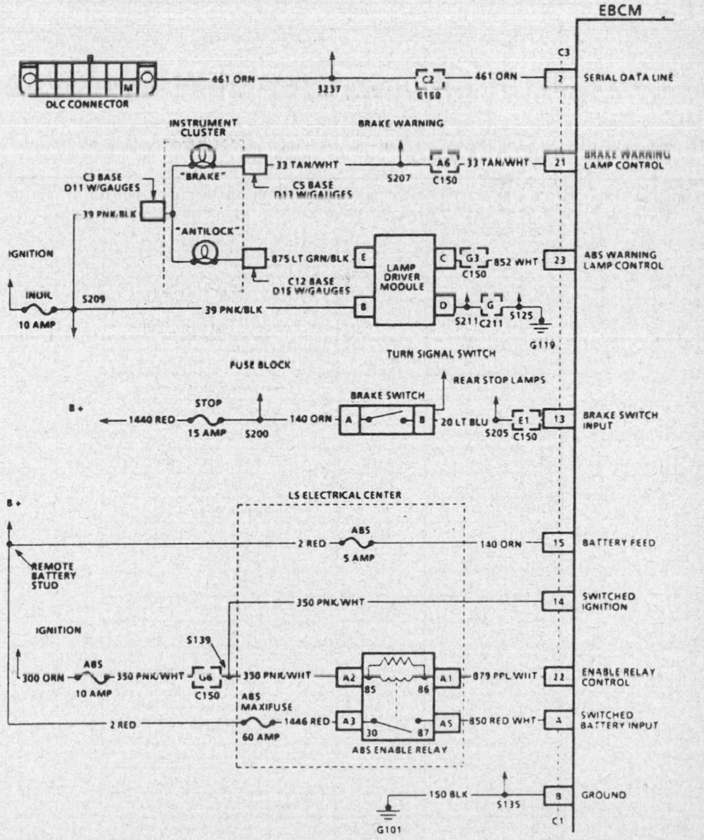
EBCM
DLC CONNECTOR
461 ORN
S237
SERIAL DATA LINE
INSTRUMENT CLUSTER
BRAKE WARNING
"BRAKE"
33 TAN/WHT
S207
BRAKE WARNING LAMP CONTROL
"ANTILOCK"
IGNITION
875 LT GRN/BLK
LAMP DRIVER MODULE
852 WHT
ABS WARNING LAMP CONTROL
10 AMP
39 PNK/BLK
G119
FUSE BLOCK
TURN SIGNAL SWITCH
REAR STOP LAMPS
BRAKE SWITCH
STOP 15 AMP
1440 RED
140 ORN
20 LT BLU
BRAKE SWITCH INPUT
LS ELECTRICAL CENTER
REMOTE BATTERY STUD
2 RED
ABS 5 AMP
BATTERY FEED
350 PNK/WHT
SWITCHED IGNITION
300 ORN
ABS MAXIFUSE 60 AMP
1446 RED
879 PPL WHT
ENABLE RELAY CONTROL
850 RED WHT
SWITCHED BATTERY INPUT
ABS ENABLE RELAY
150 BLK
GROUND
G101
GC4029400950010X

Fig. 11 ABS system wiring circuit (Part 1 of 2). 1994 Cutlass Supreme, Lumina & Regal

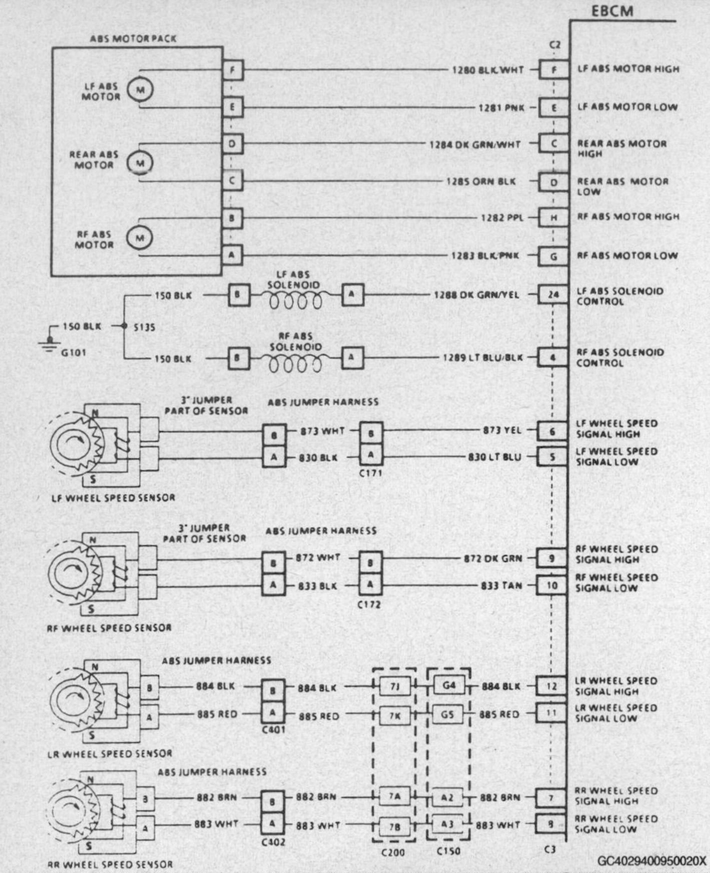
EBCM
ABS MOTOR PACK
LF ABS MOTOR
REAR ABS MOTOR
RF ABS MOTOR
C2
1280 BLK/WHT
LF ABS MOTOR HIGH
1281 PNK
LF ABS MOTOR LOW
1284 DK GRN/WHT
REAR ABS MOTOR HIGH
1285 ORN BLK
REAR ABS MOTOR LOW
1282 PPL
RF ABS MOTOR HIGH
1283 BLK/PNK
RF ABS MOTOR LOW
150 BLK
LF ABS SOLENOID
1288 DK GRN/YEL
LF ABS SOLENOID CONTROL
150 BLK
S135
G101
RF ABS SOLENOID
1289 LT BLU/BLK
RF ABS SOLENOID CONTROL
3" JUMPER PART OF SENSOR
ABS JUMPER HARNESS
873 WHT
873 YEL
LF WHEEL SPEED SIGNAL HIGH
830 BLK
830 LT BLU
LF WHEEL SPEED SIGNAL LOW
C171
LF WHEEL SPEED SENSOR
872 WHT
872 DK GRN
RF WHEEL SPEED SIGNAL HIGH
833 BLK
833 TAN
RF WHEEL SPEED SIGNAL LOW
C172
RF WHEEL SPEED SENSOR
884 BLK
LR WHEEL SPEED SIGNAL HIGH
885 RED
LR WHEEL SPEED SIGNAL LOW
C401
LR WHEEL SPEED SENSOR
882 BRN
RR WHEEL SPEED SIGNAL HIGH
883 WHT
RR WHEEL SPEED SIGNAL LOW
C402
C200
C150
C3
RR WHEEL SPEED SENSOR
GC4029400950020X

Fig. 11 ABS system wiring circuit (Part 2 of 2). 1994 Cutlass Supreme, Lumina & Regal

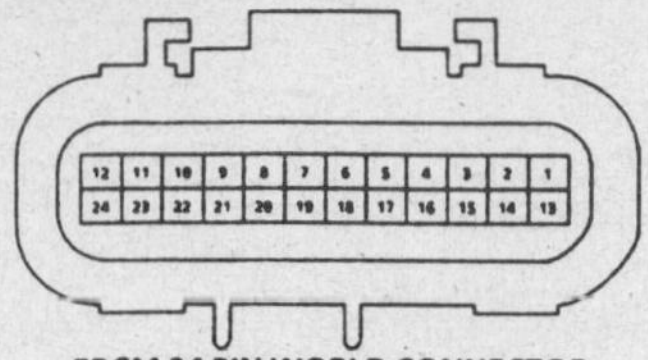
12 11 10 9 8 7 6 5 4 3 2 1
24 23 22 21 20 19 18 17 16 15 14 13

EBCM 24 PIN WORLD CONNECTOR

PIN	CIRCUIT NO.	COLOR	CIRCUIT
1	799	TAN/WHT	NOT USED
2	461	ORN	SERIAL DATA LINE
3	OPEN		NOT USED
4	1289	LT BLU/BLK	R/F ABS SOLENOID
5	830	LT BLU	L/F WHEEL SIGNAL HIGH
6	873	YEL	L/F WHEEL SIGNAL LOW
7	882	BRN	R/R WHEEL SIGNAL HIGH
8	883	WHT	R/R WHEEL SIGNAL LOW
9	872	DK GRN	R/F WHEEL SIGNAL HIGH
10	833	TAN	R/F WHEEL SIGNAL LOW
11	885	RED	L/R WHEEL SIGNAL LOW
12	884	BLK	L/R WHEEL SIGNAL HIGH
13	20	LT BLU	BRAKE SWITCH INPUT
14	50	BRN	SWITCH IGNITION
15	2	RED	B + FEED
16	OPEN		NOT USED
17	OPEN		NOT USED
18	VENT TUBE	BLK	VENT TUBE
19	1286	LT GRN	L/F EMB
20	1287	GRY	R/F EMB
21	33	TAN/WHT	BRAKE TELLTALE
22	879	PPL/WHT	ENABLE RELAY CONTROL
23	852	WHT	ABS WARNING LIGHT CONTROL
24	1288	DK GRN/YEL	L/F ABS SOLENOID

GC4029100657000X

Fig. 12 ECU 24-pin connector. 1992 Achieva, Calais, Grand Am & Skylark

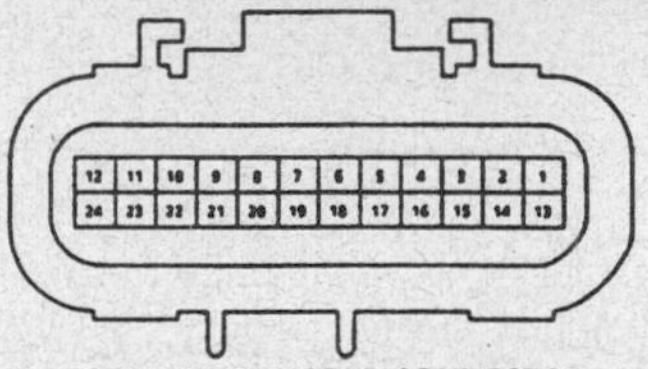
12 11 10 9 8 7 6 5 4 3 2 1
24 23 22 21 20 19 18 17 16 15 14 13

EBCM 24 PIN WORLD CONNECTOR

PIN	CIRCUIT NO.	COLOR	CIRCUIT
1	OPEN		NOT USED
2	461	ORN	SERIAL DATA LINE
3	OPEN		NOT USED
4	1289	LT BLU/BLK	R/F ABS SOLENOID
5	830	LT BLU	L/F WHEEL SIGNAL HIGH
6	873	YEL	L/F WHEEL SIGNAL LOW
7	882	BRN	R/R WHEEL SIGNAL HIGH
8	883	WHT	R/R WHEEL SIGNAL LOW
9	872	DK GRN	R/F WHEEL SIGNAL HIGH
10	833	TAN	R/F WHEEL SIGNAL LOW
11	885	RED	L/R WHEEL SIGNAL LOW
12	884	BLK	L/R WHEEL SIGNAL HIGH
13	20	LT BLU	BRAKE SWITCH INPUT
14	50	BRN	SWITCH IGNITION
15	1733	ORN/BLK	B + FEED
16	OPEN		NOT USED
17	OPEN		NOT USED
18	VENT TUBE	BLK	VENT TUBE
19	1286	LT GRN	L/F EMB
20	1287	GRY	R/F EMB
21	33	TAN/WHT	BRAKE WARNING LAMP CONTROL
22	879	PPL/WHT	ENABLE RELAY CONTROL
23	852	WHT	ABS INDICATOR LAMP CONTROL
24	1288	DK GRN/YEL	L/F ABS SOLENOID

GC4029300658000X

Fig. 13 ECU 24-pin connector. 1993–94 Achieva, Grand Am & Skylark Less VES

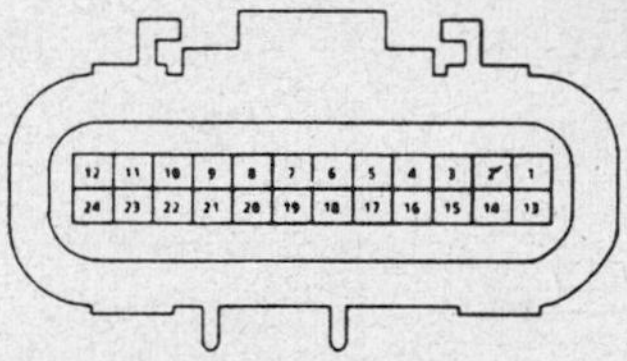
12 11 10 9 8 7 6 5 4 3 2 1
24 23 22 21 20 19 18 17 16 15 14 13

24-WAY EBCM HARNESS CONNECTOR (ABS WITH VES)

PIN	CIRCUIT NO.	COLOR	CIRCUIT
1	1061	ORN/BLK	SERIAL DATA
2	1289	LT BLU	R/F ABS SOLENOID CONTROL
3	830	LT BLU	L/F WHEEL SIGNAL HIGH
4	873	YEL	L/F WHEEL SIGNAL LOW
5	882	BRN	R/R WHEEL SIGNAL HIGH
6	883	WHT	R/R WHEEL SIGNAL LOW
7	872	DK GRN	R/F WHEEL SIGNAL HIGH
8	833	TAN	R/F WHEEL SIGNAL LOW
9	884	BLK	L/R WHEEL SIGNAL HIGH
10	885	RED	L/R WHEEL SIGNAL LOW
11	1295	BRN	EVO ACTUATOR CONTROL
12	1056	GRY	STEERING WHEEL SENSOR VCC
13	17	WHT	BRAKE SWITCH INPUT
14	41	BRN	SWITCHED IGNITION
15	1733	ORN	BATTERY FEED
16	556	ORN/BLK	STEERING WHEEL SENSOR GROUND
17	1286	LT GRN	L/F EMB CONTROL
18	1287	GRY	R/F EMB CONTROL
19	33	TAN/WHT	BRAKE WARNING LAMP CONTROL
20	1632	PNK	ENABLE RELAY CONTROL
21	852	WHT	ABS WARNING LAMP CONTROL
22	1288	DK GRN	L/F ABS SOLENOID CONTROL
23	1059	LT BLU	STEERING WHEEL SENSOR INPUT
24	VENT TUBE	BLK	VENT TUBE

GC4029401043000X

Fig. 14 ECU 24-pin connector. 1994 Achieva, Grand Am & Skylark w/VES

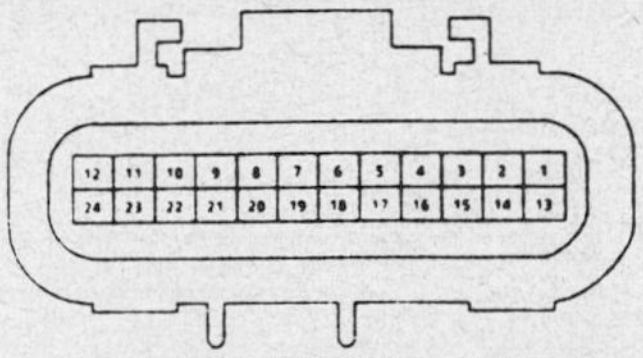

EBCM 24 PIN WORLD CONNECTOR

PIN	CIRCUIT NO.	COLOR	CIRCUIT
1	799	TAN/WHT	NOT USED
2	461	ORN	SERIAL DATA LINE
3	OPEN		NOT USED
4	1289	LT BLU/BLK	R/F ABS SOLENOID
5	830	LT BLU	L/F WHEEL SIGNAL HIGH
6	873	YEL	L/F WHEEL SIGNAL LOW
7	882	BRN	R/R WHEEL SIGNAL HIGH
8	883	WHT	R/R WHEEL SIGNAL LOW
9	872	DK GRN	R/F WHEEL SIGNAL HIGH
10	833	TAN	R/F WHEEL SIGNAL LOW
11	885	RED	L/R WHEEL SIGNAL LOW
12	884	BLK	L/R WHEEL SIGNAL HIGH
13	20	LT BLU	BRAKE SWITCH INPUT
14	250	BRN	SWITCH IGNITION
15	340	ORN	B + FEED
16	OPEN		NOT USED
17	OPEN		NOT USED
18	VENT TUBE	BLK	VENT TUBE
19	1286	LT GRN	L/F EMB
20	1287	GRY	R/F EMB
21	33	TAN/WHT	BRAKE TELLTALE
22	879	PPL/WHT	ENABLE RELAY CONTROL
23	1290	DK BLU	ABS WARNING LIGHT CONTROL
24	1288	DK GRN/YEL	L/F ABS SOLENOID

GC4029200659000X

Fig. 15 ECU 24-pin connector. 1992 Beretta & Corsica

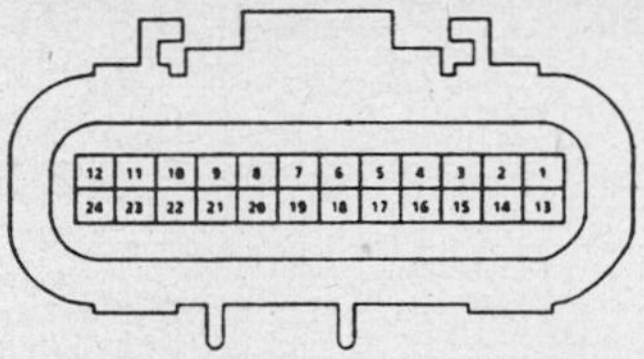

EBCM 24 PIN WORLD CONNECTOR

PIN	CIRCUIT NO.	COLOR	CIRCUIT
1	OPEN		NOT USED
2	461	ORN	SERIAL DATA LINE
3	OPEN		NOT USED
4	1289	LT BLU/BLK	R/F ABS SOLENOID
5	830	LT BLU	L/F WHEEL SIGNAL HIGH
6	873	YEL	L/F WHEEL SIGNAL LOW
7	882	BRN	R/R WHEEL SIGNAL HIGH
8	883	WHT	R/R WHEEL SIGNAL LOW
9	872	DK GRN	R/F WHEEL SIGNAL HIGH
10	833	TAN	R/F WHEEL SIGNAL LOW
11	885	RED	L/R WHEEL SIGNAL LOW
12	884	BLK	L/R WHEEL SIGNAL HIGH
13	20	LT BLU	BRAKE SWITCH INPUT
14	250	BRN	SWITCHED IGNITION
15	340	ORN	B + FEED
16	OPEN		NOT USED
17	OPEN		NOT USED
18	VENT TUBE	BLK	VENT TUBE
19	1286	LT GRN	L/F EMB
20	1287	GRY	R/F EMB
21	33	TAN/WHT	BRAKE WARNING LAMP CONTROL
22	879	PPL/WHT	ENABLE RELAY CONTROL
23	1290	DK BLU	ABS INDICATOR LAMP CONTROL
24	1288	DK GRN/YEL	L/F ABS SOLENOID

GC4029300660000X

Fig. 16 ECU 24-pin connector. 1993–94 Beretta & Corsica

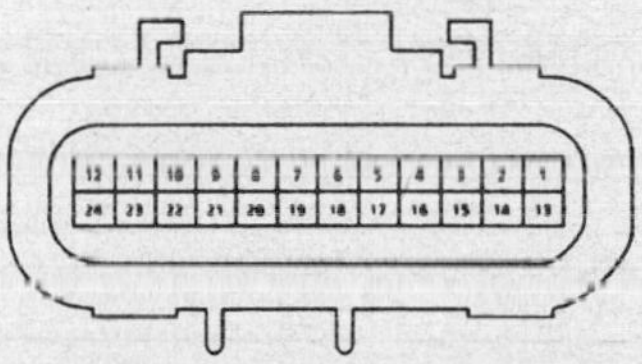

EBCM 24 PIN WORLD CONNECTOR

PIN	CIRCUIT NO.	COLOR	CIRCUIT
1	OPEN		NOT USED
2	461	ORN	SERIAL DATA LINE
3	OPEN		NOT USED
4	1289	LT BLU/BLK	R/F ABS SOLENOID
5	830	LT BLU	L/F WHEEL SIGNAL HIGH
6	873	YEL	L/F WHEEL SIGNAL LOW
7	882	BRN	R/R WHEEL SIGNAL HIGH
8	883	WHT	R/R WHEEL SIGNAL LOW
9	872	DK GRN	R/F WHEEL SIGNAL HIGH
10	833	TAN	R/F WHEEL SIGNAL LOW
11	885	RED	L/R WHEEL SIGNAL LOW
12	884	BLK	L/R WHEEL SIGNAL HIGH
13	820	YEL	BRAKE SWITCH INPUT
14	650	BRN/WHT	SWITCH IGNITION
15	2	RED	B + FEED
16	OPEN		NOT USED
17	OPEN		NOT USED
18	VENT TUBE	BLK	VENT TUBE
19	1286	LT GRN	L/F EMB
20	1287	GRY	R/F EMB
21	33	TAN/WHT	BRAKE WARNING LAMP CONTROL
22	879	PPL/WHT	ENABLE RELAY CONTROL
23	852	WHT	ABS WARNING LAMP CONTROL
24	1288	DK GRN/YEL	L/F ABS SOLENOID

GC4029200661000X

Fig. 17 ECU 24-pin connector. Cavalier & Sunbird

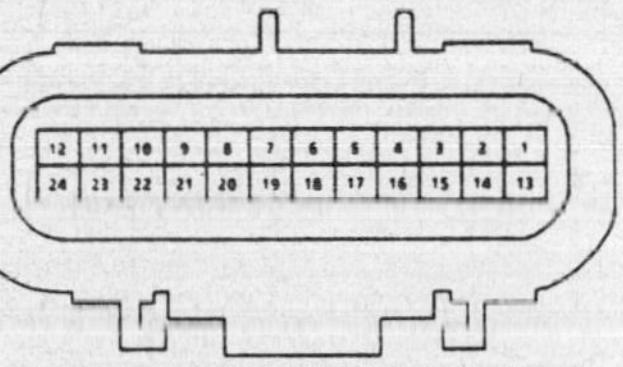

EBCM 24 PIN WORLD CONNECTOR

PIN	CIRCUIT NO.	COLOR	CIRCUIT
1	PLUGGED		NOT USED
2	461	ORN	SERIAL DATA LINE
3	PLUGGED		NOT USED
4	1289	LT BLU/BLK	R/F ABS SOLENOID
5	830	LT BLU	L/F WHEEL SIGNAL HIGH
6	873	YEL	L/F WHEEL SIGNAL LOW
7	882	BRN	R/R WHEEL SIGNAL HIGH
8	883	WHT	R/R WHEEL SIGNAL LOW
9	872	DK GRN	R/F WHEEL SIGNAL HIGH
10	833	TAN	R/F WHEEL SIGNAL LOW
11	885	RED	L/R WHEEL SIGNAL LOW
12	884	BLK	L/R WHEEL SIGNAL HIGH
13	20	LT BLU	BRAKE SWITCH INPUT
14	350	PNK/WHT	SWITCH IGNITION
15	140	ORN	B + FEED
16	PLUGGED		NOT USED
17	PLUGGED		NOT USED
18	VENT TUBE	BLK	VENT TUBE
19	PLUGGED		NOT USED
20	PLUGGED		NOT USED
21	33	TAN/WHT	BRAKE TELLTALE
22	879	PPL/WHT	ENABLE RELAY CONTROL
23	852	WHT	ABS WARNING LIGHT CONTROL
24	1288	DK GRN/YEL	L/F ABS SOLENOID

GC4029200662000X

Fig. 18 ECU 24-pin connector. 1992–1993 Grand Prix & 1992–94 Cutlass Supreme, Lumina, Regal

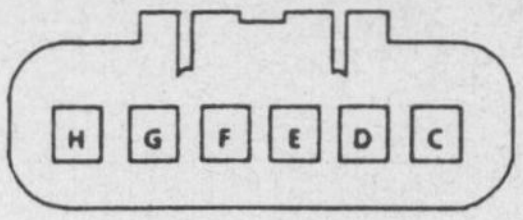
H
G
F
E
D
C

6 WAY EBCM CONNECTOR

PIN	CIRCUIT NO.	COLOR	CIRCUIT
C	1284	DK GRN/WHT	REAR MOTOR HIGH
D	1285	ORN/BLK	REAR MOTOR LOW
E	1281	PNK	L/F MOTOR LOW
F	1280	BLK/WHT	L/F MOTOR HIGH
G	1283	BLK/PNK	R/F MOTOR LOW
H	1282	PPL	R/F MOTOR HIGH

GC4029100663000X

Fig. 19 ECU 6-pin connector

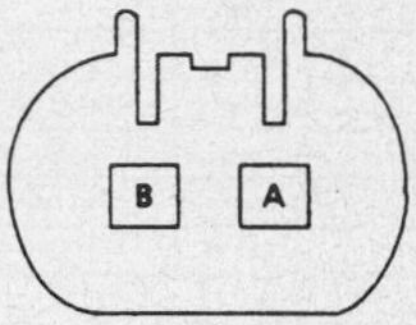
B
A

2 WAY EBCM CONNECTOR

PIN	CIRCUIT NO.	COLOR	CIRCUIT
A	850	RED/WHT	SWITCHED BATTERY INPUT
B	150	BLK	GROUND

GC4029100664000X

Fig. 20 ECU 2-pin connector

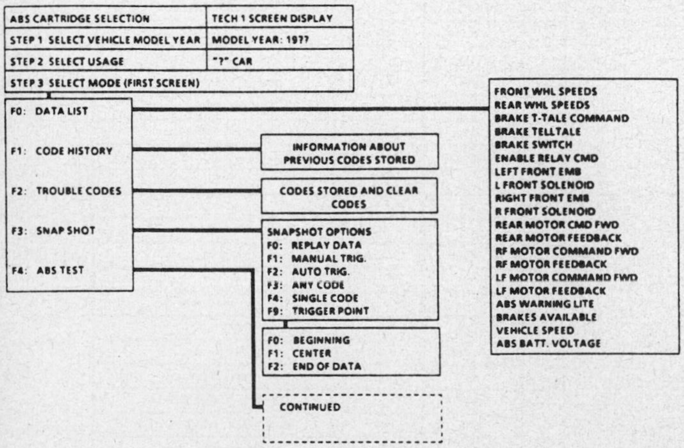
ABS CARTRIDGE SELECTION
TECH 1 SCREEN DISPLAY
STEP 1 SELECT VEHICLE MODEL YEAR
MODEL YEAR: 19??
STEP 2 SELECT USAGE
"?" CAR
STEP 3 SELECT MODE (FIRST SCREEN)
F0: DATA LIST
F1: CODE HISTORY
F2: TROUBLE CODES
F3: SNAP SHOT
F4: ABS TEST
INFORMATION ABOUT PREVIOUS CODES STORED
CODES STORED AND CLEAR CODES
SNAPSHOT OPTIONS
F0: REPLAY DATA
F1: MANUAL TRIG.
F2: AUTO TRIG.
F3: ANY CODE
F4: SINGLE CODE
F9: TRIGGER POINT
F0: BEGINNING
F1: CENTER
F2: END OF DATA
CONTINUED
FRONT WHL SPEEDS
REAR WHL SPEEDS
BRAKE T-TALE COMMAND
BRAKE TELLTALE
BRAKE SWITCH
ENABLE RELAY CMD
LEFT FRONT EMB
L FRONT SOLENOID
RIGHT FRONT EMB
R FRONT SOLENOID
REAR MOTOR CMD FWD
REAR MOTOR FEEDBACK
RF MOTOR COMMAND FWD
RF MOTOR FEEDBACK
LF MOTOR COMMAND FWD
LF MOTOR FEEDBACK
ABS WARNING LITE
BRAKES AVAILABLE
VEHICLE SPEED
ABS BATT. VOLTAGE

GC4029100665010X

Fig. 21 TECH 1 scan tool operation (Part 1 of 3)

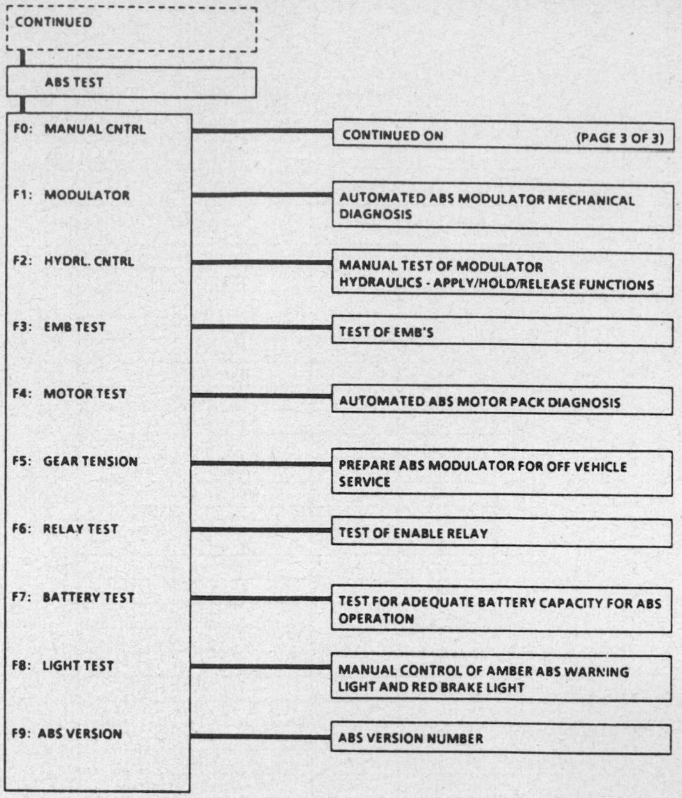
CONTINUED
ABS TEST
F0: MANUAL CNTRL
F1: MODULATOR
F2: HYDRL. CNTRL
F3: EMB TEST
F4: MOTOR TEST
F5: GEAR TENSION
F6: RELAY TEST
F7: BATTERY TEST
F8: LIGHT TEST
F9: ABS VERSION
CONTINUED ON (PAGE 3 OF 3)
AUTOMATED ABS MODULATOR MECHANICAL DIAGNOSIS
MANUAL TEST OF MODULATOR HYDRAULICS - APPLY/HOLD/RELEASE FUNCTIONS
TEST OF EMB'S
AUTOMATED ABS MOTOR PACK DIAGNOSIS
PREPARE ABS MODULATOR FOR OFF VEHICLE SERVICE
TEST OF ENABLE RELAY
TEST FOR ADEQUATE BATTERY CAPACITY FOR ABS OPERATION
MANUAL CONTROL OF AMBER ABS WARNING LIGHT AND RED BRAKE LIGHT
ABS VERSION NUMBER

GC4029100665020X

Fig. 21 TECH 1 scan tool operation (Part 2 of 3)

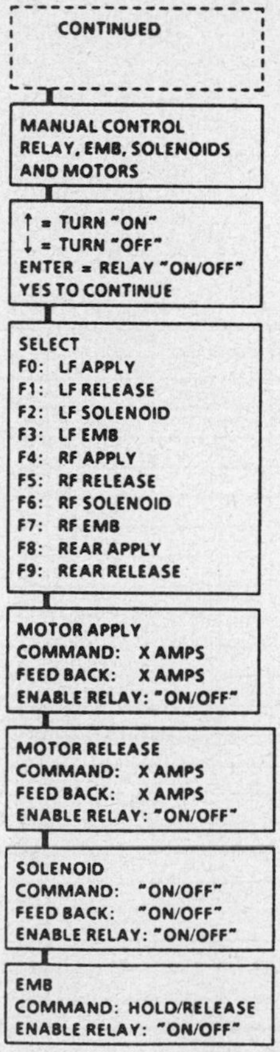
CONTINUED
MANUAL CONTROL RELAY, EMB, SOLENOIDS AND MOTORS
↑ = TURN "ON"
↓ = TURN "OFF"
ENTER = RELAY "ON/OFF"
YES TO CONTINUE
SELECT
F0: LF APPLY
F1: LF RELEASE
F2: LF SOLENOID
F3: LF EMB
F4: RF APPLY
F5: RF RELEASE
F6: RF SOLENOID
F7: RF EMB
F8: REAR APPLY
F9: REAR RELEASE
MOTOR APPLY
COMMAND: X AMPS
FEED BACK: X AMPS
ENABLE RELAY: "ON/OFF"
MOTOR RELEASE
COMMAND: X AMPS
FEED BACK: X AMPS
ENABLE RELAY: "ON/OFF"
SOLENOID
COMMAND: "ON/OFF"
FEED BACK: "ON/OFF"
ENABLE RELAY: "ON/OFF"
EMB
COMMAND: HOLD/RELEASE
ENABLE RELAY: "ON/OFF"

GC4029100665030X

Fig. 21 TECH 1 scan tool operation (Part 3 of 3)

DIAGNOSTIC CIRCUIT CHECK

The Diagnostic Circuit Check is an organized approach to identifying a problem created by an Antilock Brake System (ABS) malfunction. It must be the starting point for any ABS complaint diagnosis, because it directs the Service Technician to the next logical step in diagnosing the complaint.

The "Scan" Data listed in the table may be used after completing the Diagnostic Circuit Check and finding the on-board diagnostics functioning properly and no trouble codes displayed.

A "SCAN" TOOL THAT DISPLAYS FAULTY DATA SHOULD NOT BE USED, AND THE PROBLEM SHOULD BE REPORTED TO THE MANUFACTURER. THE USE OF A FAULTY "SCAN" TOOL CAN RESULT IN MISDIAGNOSIS AND UNNECESSARY PARTS REPLACEMENT.

Only the parameters listed below are used in this manual for diagnosing. If a "Scan" reads other parameters, the values are not recommended by General Motors for use in diagnosing.

"SCAN" DATA

"SCAN" Position	Units Displayed
Front WHL Speeds	MPH/KPH
Rear WHL Speeds	MPH/KPH
Brake T-TALE CMD	ON/OFF
Brake Tell-TALE	ON/OFF/CIRCUIT OPEN
Brake Switch	ON/OFF/CIRCUIT OPEN
Enable Relay CMD	ON/OFF
R Front Solenoid	ON/OFF
Right Front EMB	RELEASE/HOLD
L Front Solenoid	ON/OFF
Left Front EMB	RELEASE/HOLD
Rear Motor CMD FWD/REV	AMPS
Rear Motor FDBK	AMPS
RF Motor Command FWD/REV	AMPS
RF Motor Feedbac	AMPS
LF Motor Command FWD/REV	AMPS
LF Motor Feedbac	AMPS
ABS Warning Lite	ON/OFF/FLASHING
Brakes Available	ANTILOCK/BASE BRAKES
Vehicle Speed	MPH/KPH
ABS BATT Voltage	VOLTS

GC402920066600AX

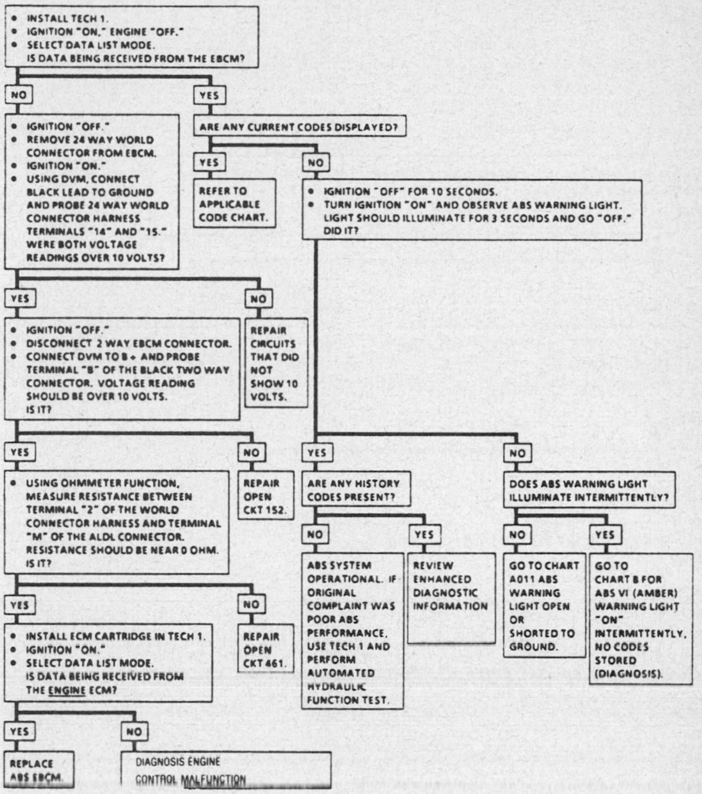
INSTALL TECH 1.
IGNITION "ON," ENGINE "OFF."
SELECT DATA LIST MODE. IS DATA BEING RECEIVED FROM THE EBCM?
NO
YES
IGNITION "OFF." REMOVE 24 WAY WORLD CONNECTOR FROM EBCM. IGNITION "ON." USING DVM, CONNECT BLACK LEAD TO GROUND AND PROBE 24 WAY WORLD CONNECTOR HARNESS TERMINALS "14" AND "15." WERE BOTH VOLTAGE READINGS OVER 10 VOLTS?
ARE ANY CURRENT CODES DISPLAYED?
REFER TO APPLICABLE CODE CHART.
IGNITION "OFF" FOR 10 SECONDS. TURN IGNITION "ON" AND OBSERVE ABS WARNING LIGHT. LIGHT SHOULD ILLUMINATE FOR 3 SECONDS AND GO "OFF." DID IT?
IGNITION "OFF." DISCONNECT 2 WAY EBCM CONNECTOR. CONNECT DVM TO B+ AND PROBE TERMINAL "B" OF THE BLACK TWO WAY CONNECTOR. VOLTAGE READING SHOULD BE OVER 10 VOLTS. IS IT?
REPAIR CIRCUITS THAT DID NOT SHOW 10 VOLTS.
USING OHMMETER FUNCTION, MEASURE RESISTANCE BETWEEN TERMINAL "2" OF THE WORLD CONNECTOR HARNESS AND TERMINAL "M" OF THE ALDL CONNECTOR. RESISTANCE SHOULD BE NEAR 0 OHM. IS IT?
REPAIR OPEN CKT 152.
ARE ANY HISTORY CODES PRESENT?
DOES ABS WARNING LIGHT ILLUMINATE INTERMITTENTLY?
ABS SYSTEM OPERATIONAL. IF ORIGINAL COMPLAINT WAS POOR ABS PERFORMANCE, USE TECH 1 AND PERFORM AUTOMATED HYDRAULIC FUNCTION TEST.
REVIEW ENHANCED DIAGNOSTIC INFORMATION
GO TO CHART A011 ABS WARNING LIGHT OPEN OR SHORTED TO GROUND.
GO TO CHART B FOR ABS VI (AMBER) WARNING LIGHT "ON" INTERMITTENTLY, NO CODES STORED (DIAGNOSIS).
INSTALL ECM CARTRIDGE IN TECH 1. IGNITION "ON." SELECT DATA LIST MODE. IS DATA BEING RECEIVED FROM THE ENGINE ECM?
REPAIR OPEN CKT 461.
REPLACE ABS EBCM.
DIAGNOSIS ENGINE CONTROL MALFUNCTION

GC402920066800BX

Fig. 22 Diagnostic Circuit Check. 1992 Models & 1993–94 Beretta, Cavalier, Corsica & Sunbird

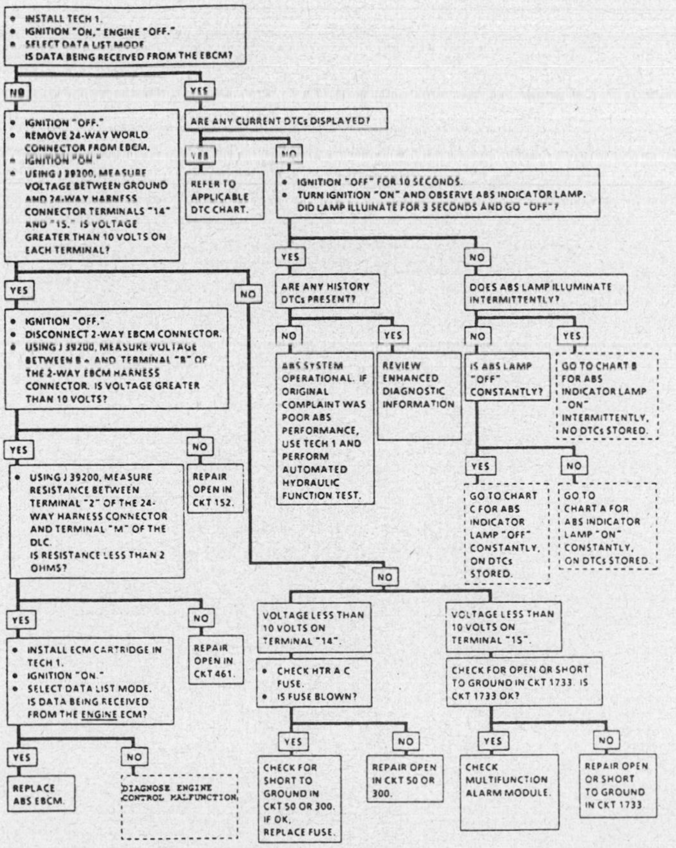
INSTALL TECH 1. IGNITION "ON," ENGINE "OFF." SELECT DATA LIST MODE. IS DATA BEING RECEIVED FROM THE EBCM?
NO
YES
IGNITION "OFF." REMOVE 24-WAY WORLD CONNECTOR FROM EBCM. IGNITION "ON." USING J 39200, MEASURE VOLTAGE BETWEEN GROUND AND 24-WAY HARNESS CONNECTOR TERMINALS "14" AND "15." IS VOLTAGE GREATER THAN 10 VOLTS ON EACH TERMINAL?
ARE ANY CURRENT DTCs DISPLAYED?
REFER TO APPLICABLE DTC CHART.
IGNITION "OFF" FOR 10 SECONDS. TURN IGNITION "ON" AND OBSERVE ABS INDICATOR LAMP. DID LAMP ILLUMINATE FOR 3 SECONDS AND GO "OFF"?
ARE ANY HISTORY DTCs PRESENT?
DOES ABS LAMP ILLUMINATE INTERMITTENTLY?
IGNITION "OFF." DISCONNECT 2-WAY EBCM CONNECTOR. USING J 39200, MEASURE VOLTAGE BETWEEN B+ AND TERMINAL "B" OF THE 2-WAY EBCM HARNESS CONNECTOR. IS VOLTAGE GREATER THAN 10 VOLTS?
ABS SYSTEM OPERATIONAL. IF ORIGINAL COMPLAINT WAS POOR ABS PERFORMANCE, USE TECH 1 AND PERFORM AUTOMATED HYDRAULIC FUNCTION TEST.
REVIEW ENHANCED DIAGNOSTIC INFORMATION
IS ABS LAMP "OFF" CONSTANTLY?
GO TO CHART B FOR ABS INDICATOR LAMP "ON" INTERMITTENTLY, NO DTCs STORED.
USING J 39200, MEASURE RESISTANCE BETWEEN TERMINAL "2" OF THE 24-WAY HARNESS CONNECTOR AND TERMINAL "M" OF THE DLC. IS RESISTANCE LESS THAN 2 OHMS?
REPAIR OPEN IN CKT 152.
GO TO CHART C FOR ABS INDICATOR LAMP "OFF" CONSTANTLY, ON DTCs STORED.
GO TO CHART A FOR ABS INDICATOR LAMP "ON" CONSTANTLY, ON DTCs STORED.
VOLTAGE LESS THAN 10 VOLTS ON TERMINAL "14".
VOLTAGE LESS THAN 10 VOLTS ON TERMINAL "15".
INSTALL ECM CARTRIDGE IN TECH 1. IGNITION "ON." SELECT DATA LIST MODE. IS DATA BEING RECEIVED FROM THE ENGINE ECM?
REPAIR OPEN IN CKT 461.
CHECK HTR A C FUSE. IS FUSE BLOWN?
CHECK FOR OPEN OR SHORT TO GROUND IN CKT 1733. IS CKT 1733 OK?
REPLACE ABS EBCM.
DIAGNOSE ENGINE CONTROL MALFUNCTION.
CHECK FOR SHORT TO GROUND IN CKT 50 OR 300. IF OK, REPLACE FUSE.
REPAIR OPEN IN CKT 50 OR 300.
CHECK MULTIFUNCTION ALARM MODULE.
REPAIR OPEN OR SHORT TO GROUND IN CKT 1733

GC4029300667000X

Fig. 23 Diagnostic Circuit Check. 1993–94 Achieva, Grand Am & Skylark

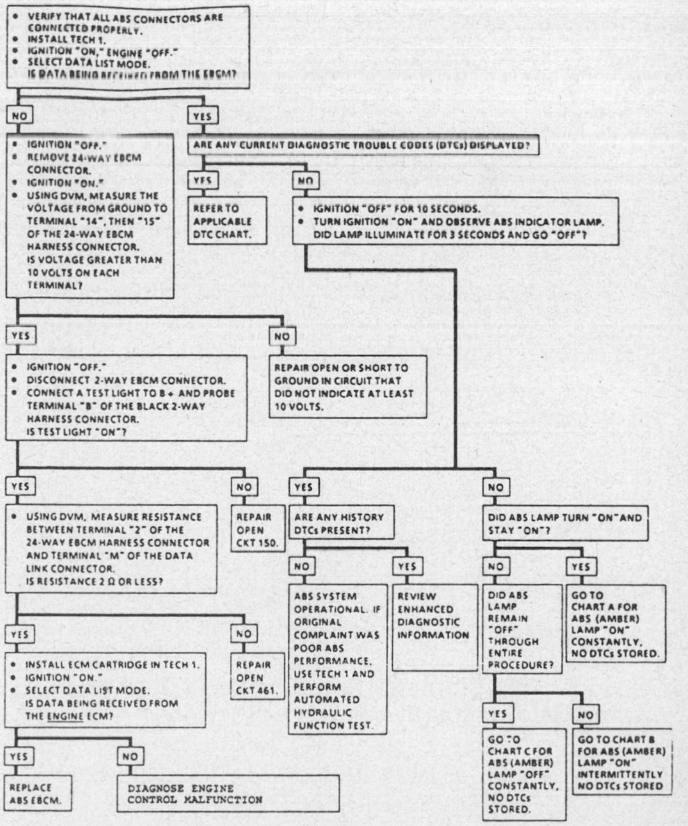
VERIFY THAT ALL ABS CONNECTORS ARE CONNECTED PROPERLY. INSTALL TECH 1. IGNITION "ON," ENGINE "OFF." SELECT DATA LIST MODE. IS DATA BEING RECEIVED FROM THE EBCM?
NO
YES
IGNITION "OFF." REMOVE 24-WAY EBCM CONNECTOR. IGNITION "ON." USING DVM, MEASURE THE VOLTAGE FROM GROUND TO TERMINAL "14", THEN "15" OF THE 24-WAY EBCM HARNESS CONNECTOR. IS VOLTAGE GREATER THAN 10 VOLTS ON EACH TERMINAL?
ARE ANY CURRENT DIAGNOSTIC TROUBLE CODES (DTCs) DISPLAYED?
REFER TO APPLICABLE DTC CHART.
IGNITION "OFF" FOR 10 SECONDS. TURN IGNITION "ON" AND OBSERVE ABS INDICATOR LAMP. DID LAMP ILLUMINATE FOR 3 SECONDS AND GO "OFF"?
IGNITION "OFF." DISCONNECT 2-WAY EBCM CONNECTOR. CONNECT A TEST LIGHT TO B+ AND PROBE TERMINAL "B" OF THE BLACK 2-WAY HARNESS CONNECTOR. IS TEST LIGHT "ON"?
REPAIR OPEN OR SHORT TO GROUND IN CIRCUIT THAT DID NOT INDICATE AT LEAST 10 VOLTS.
USING DVM, MEASURE RESISTANCE BETWEEN TERMINAL "2" OF THE 24-WAY EBCM HARNESS CONNECTOR AND TERMINAL "M" OF THE DATA LINK CONNECTOR. IS RESISTANCE 2 Ω OR LESS?
REPAIR OPEN CKT 150.
ARE ANY HISTORY DTCs PRESENT?
DID ABS LAMP TURN "ON" AND STAY "ON"?
ABS SYSTEM OPERATIONAL. IF ORIGINAL COMPLAINT WAS POOR ABS PERFORMANCE, USE TECH 1 AND PERFORM AUTOMATED HYDRAULIC FUNCTION TEST.
REVIEW ENHANCED DIAGNOSTIC INFORMATION
DID ABS LAMP REMAIN "OFF" THROUGH ENTIRE PROCEDURE?
GO TO CHART A FOR ABS (AMBER) LAMP "ON" CONSTANTLY, NO DTCs STORED.
INSTALL ECM CARTRIDGE IN TECH 1. IGNITION "ON." SELECT DATA LIST MODE. IS DATA BEING RECEIVED FROM THE ENGINE ECM?
REPAIR OPEN CKT 461.
GO TO CHART C FOR ABS (AMBER) LAMP "OFF" CONSTANTLY, NO DTCs STORED.
GO TO CHART B FOR ABS (AMBER) LAMP "ON" INTERMITTENTLY NO DTCs STORED
REPLACE ABS EBCM.
DIAGNOSE ENGINE CONTROL MALFUNCTION

GC4029300668000X

Fig. 24 Diagnostic Circuit Check. 1993 Grand Prix, 1993–94 Cutlass Supreme, Lumina & Regal

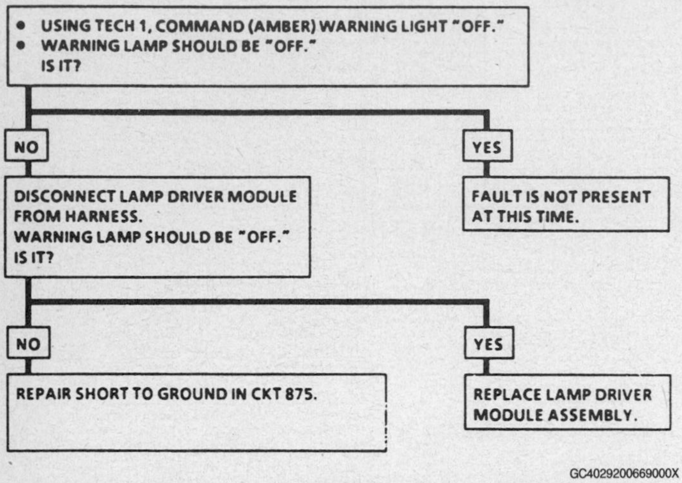
• USING TECH 1, COMMAND (AMBER) WARNING LIGHT "OFF."
• WARNING LAMP SHOULD BE "OFF."
IS IT?
NO
YES
DISCONNECT LAMP DRIVER MODULE FROM HARNESS.
WARNING LAMP SHOULD BE "OFF."
IS IT?
FAULT IS NOT PRESENT AT THIS TIME.
NO
YES
REPAIR SHORT TO GROUND IN CKT 875.
REPLACE LAMP DRIVER MODULE ASSEMBLY.
GC4029200669000X

Fig. 25 ABS Warning Lamp Diagnosis, ABS warning lamp on constantly w/no codes stored. 1992

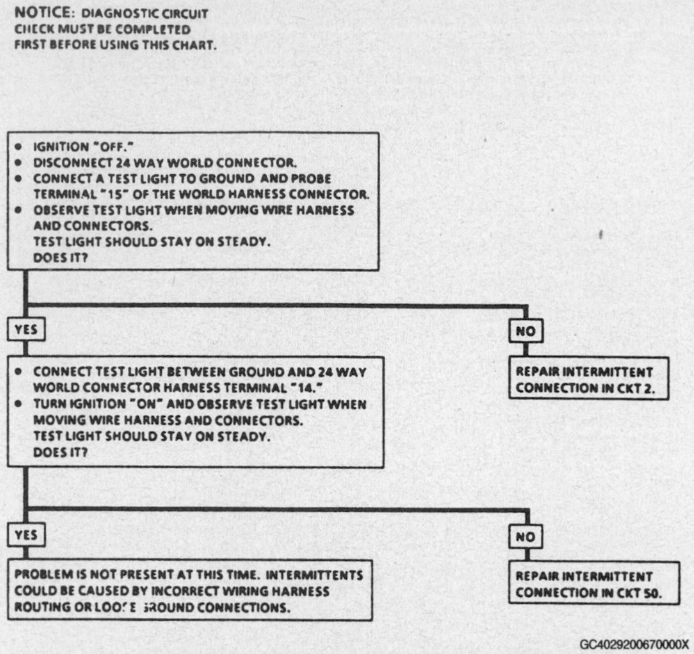
NOTICE: DIAGNOSTIC CIRCUIT CHECK MUST BE COMPLETED FIRST BEFORE USING THIS CHART.
• IGNITION "OFF."
• DISCONNECT 24 WAY WORLD CONNECTOR.
• CONNECT A TEST LIGHT TO GROUND AND PROBE TERMINAL "15" OF THE WORLD HARNESS CONNECTOR.
• OBSERVE TEST LIGHT WHEN MOVING WIRE HARNESS AND CONNECTORS.
TEST LIGHT SHOULD STAY ON STEADY.
DOES IT?
YES
NO
• CONNECT TEST LIGHT BETWEEN GROUND AND 24 WAY WORLD CONNECTOR HARNESS TERMINAL "14."
• TURN IGNITION "ON" AND OBSERVE TEST LIGHT WHEN MOVING WIRE HARNESS AND CONNECTORS.
TEST LIGHT SHOULD STAY ON STEADY.
DOES IT?
REPAIR INTERMITTENT CONNECTION IN CKT 2.
YES
NO
PROBLEM IS NOT PRESENT AT THIS TIME. INTERMITTENTS COULD BE CAUSED BY INCORRECT WIRING HARNESS ROUTING OR LOO: E 3ROUND CONNECTIONS.
REPAIR INTERMITTENT CONNECTION IN CKT 50.
GC4029200670000X

Fig. 26 ABS Warning Lamp Diagnosis, ABS warning lamp on intermittently w/no codes stored. 1992

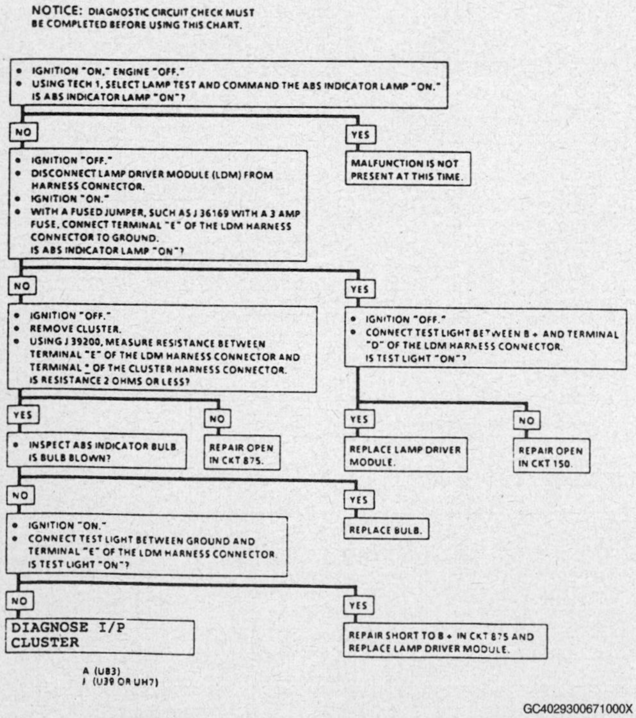
NOTICE: DIAGNOSTIC CIRCUIT CHECK MUST BE COMPLETED BEFORE USING THIS CHART.
• IGNITION "ON," ENGINE "OFF."
• USING TECH 1, SELECT LAMP TEST AND COMMAND THE ABS INDICATOR LAMP "ON."
IS ABS INDICATOR LAMP "ON"?
NO
YES
• IGNITION "OFF."
• DISCONNECT LAMP DRIVER MODULE (LDM) FROM HARNESS CONNECTOR.
• IGNITION "ON."
• WITH A FUSED JUMPER, SUCH AS J 36169 WITH A 3 AMP FUSE, CONNECT TERMINAL "E" OF THE LDM HARNESS CONNECTOR TO GROUND.
IS ABS INDICATOR LAMP "ON"?
MALFUNCTION IS NOT PRESENT AT THIS TIME.
NO
YES
• IGNITION "OFF."
• REMOVE CLUSTER.
• USING J 39200, MEASURE RESISTANCE BETWEEN TERMINAL "E" OF THE LDM HARNESS CONNECTOR AND TERMINAL * OF THE CLUSTER HARNESS CONNECTOR.
IS RESISTANCE 2 OHMS OR LESS?
• IGNITION "OFF."
• CONNECT TEST LIGHT BETWEEN B + AND TERMINAL "D" OF THE LDM HARNESS CONNECTOR.
IS TEST LIGHT "ON"?
YES
NO
YES
NO
• INSPECT ABS INDICATOR BULB. IS BULB BLOWN?
REPAIR OPEN IN CKT 875.
REPLACE LAMP DRIVER MODULE.
REPAIR OPEN IN CKT 150.
NO
YES
• IGNITION "ON."
• CONNECT TEST LIGHT BETWEEN GROUND AND TERMINAL "E" OF THE LDM HARNESS CONNECTOR.
IS TEST LIGHT "ON"?
REPLACE BULB.
NO
YES
DIAGNOSE I/P CLUSTER
REPAIR SHORT TO B + IN CKT 875 AND REPLACE LAMP DRIVER MODULE.
A (UB3)
I (U39 OR UH7)
GC4029300671000X

Fig. 27 ABS Warning Lamp Diagnosis, ABS Warning Lamp Off Constantly w/No Codes Stored. 1993–94

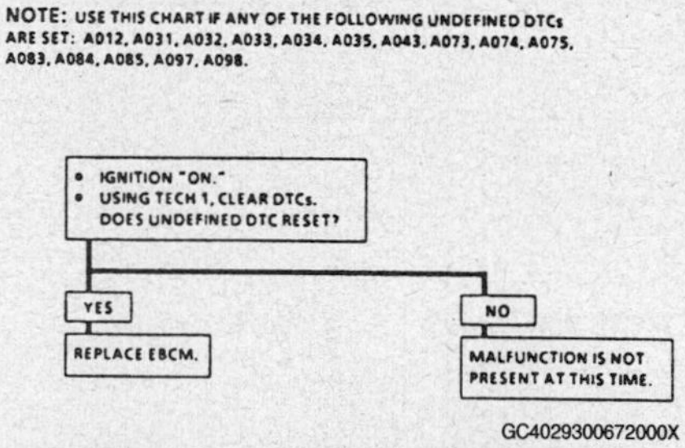
NOTE: USE THIS CHART IF ANY OF THE FOLLOWING UNDEFINED DTCs ARE SET: A012, A031, A032, A033, A034, A035, A043, A073, A074, A075, A083, A084, A085, A097, A098.
• IGNITION "ON."
• USING TECH 1, CLEAR DTCs.
DOES UNDEFINED DTC RESET?
YES
NO
REPLACE EBCM.
MALFUNCTION IS NOT PRESENT AT THIS TIME.
GC4029300672000X

Fig. 28 Tech 1 Displays Undefined DTCs. 1993–94

DIAGNOSTIC CHART INDEX

Test/Code	Description	Page No. 32-	Fig. No.
1992 MODELS			
Code A011	ABS Warning Light Open Or Shorted To Ground	264	29
Code A013	ABS Warning Light Circuit Shorted To Battery	266	30
Code A014	Enable Relay Contacts Open Or Fuse Open	267	31
Code A015	Enable Relay Contacts Shorted To Battery	268	32
Code A016	Enable Relay Coil Circuit Open	269	33
Code A017	Enable Relay Coil Circuit Shorted To Ground	270	34
Code A018	Enable Relay Coil Circuit Shorted To Battery Positive Or Coil Has Zero Ohms	271	35
Code A021	Left Front Wheel Speed — 0	272	36
Code A022	Right Front Wheel Speed — 0	274	37
Code A023	Left Rear Wheel Speed — 0	276	38
Code A024	Right Rear Wheel Speed — 0	278	39
Code A025	Excessive Left Front Wheel Acceleration	280	40
Code A026	Excessive Right Front Wheel Acceleration	282	41
Code A027	Excessive Left Rear Wheel Acceleration	284	42
Code A028	Excessive Right Rear Wheel Acceleration	286	43
Code A031	Two Wheel Speed Sensors Open	288	44
Code A031	Two Wheel Speed Sensors Open	290	45
Code A032	LH Front Wheel Speed Sensor Shorted To Battery Or Ground	291	46
Code A033	RH Front Wheel Speed Sensor Shorted To Battery Or Ground	291	47
Code A034	LH Rear Wheel Speed Sensor Shorted To Battery Or Ground	292	48
Code A035	RH Rear Wheel Speed Sensor Shorted To Battery Or Ground	292	49
Code A036	System Voltage Is Low	293	50
Code A037	System Voltage Is High	294	51
Code A038	Left Front EMB Will Not Hold Motor	294	52
Code A041	Right Front EMB Will Not Hold Motor	295	53
Code A042	Rear Axle ESB Will Not Hold Motor	296	54
Code A044	Left Front EMB Will Not Release Motor Or Gears Frozen	296	55
Code A044	Left Front EMB Will Not Release Motor Or Gears Frozen	297	56
Code A045	Right Front EMB Will Not Release Motor Or Gears Frozen	297	57
Code A045	Right Front EMB Will Not Release Motor Or Gears Frozen	298	58
Code A046	Rear Axle ESB Will Not Release Motor Or Gears Frozen	298	59
Code A047	Left Front Nut Failure, Motor Free Spins	299	60
Code A048	Right Front Nut Failure, Motor Free Spins	299	61
Code A051	Rear Axle Nut Failure, Motor Free Spins	300	62
Code A051	Rear Axle Nut Failure, Motor Free Spins	301	63
Code A052	Left Front Channel In Release Too Long	301	64
Code A053	Right Front Channel In Release Too Long	302	65
Code A054	Rear Axle In Release Too Long	302	66
Code A055	Motor Driver Interface MDI Fault Detected	303	67
Code A056	Left Front Motor Circuit Open	304	68
Code A057	Left Front Motor Circuit Shorted To Ground	304	69
Code A058	Left Front Motor Circuit Shorted To Battery	305	70
Code A061	Right Front Motor Circuit Open	305	71
Code A062	Right Front Motor Circuit Shorted To Ground	306	72
Code A063	Right Front Motor Circuit Shorted To Battery	306	73
Code A065	Rear Axle Motor Circuit Shorted To Ground	307	74

Continued

DIAGNOSTIC CHART INDEX-Continued

Test/Code	Description	Page No. 32-	Fig. No.
1992 MODELS -Continued			
Code A066	Rear Axle Motor Circuit Shorted To Battery	307	75
Code A067	Left Front EMB Release Circuit Open Or Shorted To Ground	308	76
Code A068	Left Front EMB Release Circuit Shorted To Battery Or Driver Open	308	77
Code A071	Right Front EMB Release Circuit Open Or Shorted To Ground	309	78
Code A072	Right Front EMB Release Circuit Shorted To Battery Or Driver Open	309	79
Code A076	Left Front Solenoid Circuit Open Or Shorted To Battery	310	80
Code A077	Left Front Solenoid Shorted To Ground Or Driver Open	310	81
Code A078	Right Front Solenoid Circuit Open Or Shorted To Battery	311	82
Code A081	Right Front Solenoid Shorted To Ground Or Driver Open	312	83
Code A082	Calibration Memory Failure	313	84
Code A086	ABS Enable Red Brake Telltale	314	85
Code A087	Red Brake Telltale Circuit open	315	86
Code A088	Red Brake Telltale Circuit Shorted To Battery Or Driver Open	316	87
Code A091	Open Brake Switch Contacts, Decel Detection	317	88
Code A092	Open Brake Switch Contacts	318	89
Code A093	Test 91 Or 92 Failed Last Or Current Ignition Cycle	319	90
Code A094	Brake Switch Contacts Or Brake Switch Input Shorted To Battery	320	91
Code A095	Brake Switch Circuit Open	321	92
Code A096	Brake Lights Open, Brake Light Grounds Open, CHMSL Open During 4-Way Flasher Operation	322	93
1993-94 CAVALIER & SUNBIRD. BERETTA & CORSCIA, ACHIEVA, GRAND AM & SKYLARK			
Code A011	ABS Warning Light Open Or Shorted To Ground	323	94
Code A014	Enable Relay Contacts Or Fuse Open	326	98
Code A014	Enable Relay Contacts Or Fuse Open	326	99
Code A014	Enable Relay Contacts Or Fuse Open	327	100
Code A015	Enable Relay Contacts Shorted To Battery	329	103
Code A016	Enable Relay Coil Circuit Open	331	105
Code A017	Enable Relay Coil Circuit Shorted To Ground	332	107
Code A018	Enable Relay Coil Circuit Shorted To Battery Or Coil Shorted	334	109
Code A021	Left Front Wheel Speed—0	335	111
Code A021	Left Front Wheel Speed—0	337	112
Code A022	Right Front Wheel Speed—0 (Less VES)	339	115
Code A022	Right Front Wheel Speed—0 (With VES)	341	116
Code A023	Left Rear Wheel Speed—0 (Less VES)	342	118
Code A023	Left Rear Wheel Speed—0 (With VES)	344	119
Code A024	Right Rear Wheel Speed—0 (Less VES)	346	121
Code A024	Right Rear Wheel Speed—0 (With VES)	347	122
Code A025	Left Front Excessive Wheel Speed Variation	349	124
Code A026	Right Front Excessive Wheel Speed Variation	352	126
Code A027	Left Rear Excessive Wheel Speed Variation	354	128
Code A028	Right Rear Excessive Wheel Speed Variation	357	130
Code A032	Left Front Wheel Speed Sensor Circuit Open Or Shorted To Ground/Battery (With VES)	360	133
Code A033	Right Front Wheel Speed Sensor Circuit Open Or Shorted To Ground/Battery (With VES)	363	135

Continued

DIAGNOSTIC CHART INDEX-Continued

Test/Code	Description	Page No. 32-	Fig. No.
1993-94 CAVALIER & SUNBIRD. BERETTA & CORSCIA, ACHIEVA, GRAND AM & SKYLARK -Continued			
Code A034	Left Rear Wheel Speed Sensor Circuit Open Or Shorted To Ground/Battery (With VES)	365	137
Code A035	Right Rear Wheel Speed Sensor Circuit Open Or Shorted To Ground/Battery (With VES)	368	139
Code A036	Low System Voltage	370	141
Code A037	High System Voltage	372	143
Code A038	Left Front EMB Will Not Hold Motor	373	145
Code A041	Right Front EMB Will Not Hold Motor	374	147
Code A042	Rear Axle ESB Will Not Hold Motor	375	149
Code A043	VES Steering Wheel Speed Sensor Circuit Fault	377	151
Code A044	Left Front Channel Will Not Move	378	152
Code A045	Right Front Channel Will Not Move	380	154
Code A046	Rear Axle Channel Will Not Move	381	136
Code A047	Left Front Motor Free Spins	382	158
Code A048	Right Front Motor Free Spins	384	161
Code A051	Rear Axle Motor Free Spins	386	164
Code A052	Left Front Channel Release Too Long	389	167
Code A053	Right Front Channel Release Too Long	390	169
Code A054	Rear Axle Channel Release Too Long	391	171
Code A055	EBCM Failure	392	173
Code A056	Left Front Motor Circuit Open	393	175
Code A057	Left Front Motor Circuit Shorted To Ground	394	177
Code A058	Left Front Motor Circuit Shorted To Battery Or Motor Shorted	395	179
Code A061	Right Front Motor Circuit Open	396	181
Code A062	Right Front Motor Circuit Shorted To Ground	397	183
Code A063	Right Front Motor Circuit Shorted To Battery Or Motor Shorted	398	185
Code A064	Rear Axle Motor Circuit Open	399	187
Code A065	Rear Axle Motor Circuit Shorted To Ground	400	189
Code A066	Rear Axle Motor Circuit Shorted To Battery Or Motor Shorted	401	191
Code A067	Left Front EMB Circuit Open Or Shorted To Ground	402	193
Code A068	Left Front EMB Circuit Shorted To Battery Or Driver Open	402	194
Code A071	Right Front EMB Circuit Open Or Shorted To Ground	403	195
Code A072	Right Front EMB Circuit Shorted To Battery Or Driver Open	404	196
Code A073	VO Actuator Circuit Shorted To Battery Or Solenoid Shorted	405	197
Code A076	Left Front Solenoid Circuit Open Or Shorted To Battery	405	198
Code A077	Left front Solenoid Circuit Shorted To Ground Or Driver Open	406	200
Code A078	Right Front Solenoid Circuit Open Or Shorted To Battery	407	202
Code A081	Right Front Solenoid Circuit Open Or Shorted To Ground Or Driver Open	408	204
Code A082	Calibration Memory Failure	409	206
Code A086	Red Brake Warning Lamp Activated By ABS	410	207
Code A087	Red Brake Warning Lamp Circuit Open	411	209
Code A088	Red Brake Warning Lamp Circuit Shorted To Battery	413	211
Code A091	Open Brake Switch Contacts During Acceleration	414	213
Code A092	Open Brake Switch Contacts When ABS Required	416	215
Code A093	DTCs A091 Or A092 Set In Current Or Previous Ignition Cycle	417	217

Continued

DIAGNOSTIC CHART INDEX-Continued

Test/Code	Description	Page No. 32-	Fig. No.
1993-94 CAVALIER & SUNBIRD. BERETTA & CORSCIA, ACHIEVA, GRAND AM & SKYLARK -Continued			
Code A094	Brake Switch Contacts Always Closed	418	218
Code A095	Brake Switch Circuit Open	419	220
Code A096	Brake Lamp Circuit Open	421	222
1993 GRAND PRIX, 1993-94 CUTLASS SUPREME, LUMINA & REGAL			
Code A011	ABS Warning Light Open Or Shorted To Ground	324	95
Code A013	ABS Warning Light Circuit Shorted To Battery (1993)	324	96
Code A013	ABS Warning Light Circuit Shorted To Battery (1994)	325	97
Code A014	Enable Relay Contacts Or Fuse Open (1993)	327	101
Code A014	Enable Relay Contacts Circuit Open (1994)	328	102
Code A015	Enable Relay Contacts Shorted To Battery Or Always Closed	330	04
Code A016	Enable Relay Coil Circuit Open	332	106
Code A017	Enable Relay Coil Circuit Shorted To Ground	333	108
Code A018	Enable Relay Coil Circuit Shorted To Battery	335	110
Code A021	Left Front Wheel Speed—0 (1993)	337	113
Code A021	Left Front Wheel Speed—0 (1994)	338	114
Code A022	Right Front Wheel Speed—0	341	117
Code A023	Left Rear Wheel Speed—0	345	120
Code A024	Right Rear Wheel Speed—0	348	123
Code A025	Left Front Excessive Wheel Speed Variation	351	125
Code A026	Right Front Excessive Wheel Speed Variation	353	127
Code A027	Left Rear Excessive Wheel Speed Variation	356	129
Code A028	Right Rear Excessive Wheel Speed Variation	358	131
Code A031	Two Wheel Speeds—0	359	132
Code A032	Left Front Wheel Sensor Shorted To Battery Or Ground	362	134
Code A033	Right Front Wheel Sensor Shorted To Battery Or Ground	364	136
Code A034	Left Rear Wheel Sensor Shorted To Battery Or Ground	367	138
Code A035	Right Rear Wheel Sensor Shorted To Battery Or Ground	369	140
Code A036	Low System Voltage	371	142
Code A037	High System Voltage (1993)	372	143
Code A037	High System Voltage (1994)	373	144
Code A038	Left Front ESB Will Not Hold Motor	374	146
Code A041	Right Front ESB Will Not Hold Motor	375	148
Code A042	Right Front ESB Will Not Hold Motor	376	150
Code A044	Left Front Channel Will Not Move	379	153
Code A045	Right Front Channel Will Not Move	381	155
Code A046	Rear Axle Channel Will Not Move (1993)	381	156
Code A046	Rear Channel Will Not Move (1994)	382	157
Code A047	Left Front Motor Free Spins (1993)	383	159
Code A047	Left Front Motor Free Spins (1994)	383	160
Code A048	Right Front Motor Free Spins (1993)	385	162
Code A048	Right Front ABS Motor Free Spins (1994)	386	163
Code A051	Rear Axle Motor Free Spins (1993)	387	165
Code A051	Rear Axle Motor Free Spins (1994)	388	166
Code A052	Left Front Channel Release Too Long (1993)	389	167
Code A052	Left Front Channel Release Too Long (1994)	389	168
Code A053	Right Front Channel Release Too Long (1993)	390	169
Code A053	Right Front Channel Release Too Long (1994)	390	170
Code A054	Rear Axle Channel In Release Too Long (1993)	391	171

Continued

DIAGNOSTIC CHART INDEX-Continued

Continued

DIAGNOSTIC CHART INDEX-Continued

Test/Code	Description	Page No. 32-	Fig. No.
1993-94 CAMARO & FIREBIRD &1994 CENTURY, CUTLASS CIERA , CUTLASS CRUISER & GRAND PRIX -Continued			
Code A035	RR Wheel Speed Sensor Circuit Open Or Shorted To Gnd/Batt	449	254
Code A036	Low System Voltage	451	255
Code A037	High System Voltage	453	256
Code A038	Left Front ESB Will Not Hold Motor	454	257
Code A041	Right Front ESB Will Not Hold Motor	455	258
Code A042	Rear ESB Will Not hold Motor	456	259
Code A044	Left Front Channel Will Not Move	457	260
Code A045	Right Front Channel Will Not Move	458	261
Code A046	Rear Channel Will Not Move	459	262
Code A047	Left Front ABS Motor Free Spins	460	263
Code A048	Right Front ABS Motor Free Spins	461	264
Code A051	Rear ABS Motor Free Spins	463	265
Code A052	Left Front Channel In Release Too Long	464	266
Code A053	Right Front Channel In Release Too Long	465	267
Code A054	Rear Channel In Release Too Long	466	268
Code A055	EBCM internal Fault	467	269
Code A056	Left Front ABS Motor Circuit Open	468	270
Code A057	Left Front ABS Motor Circuit Shorted To Ground	469	271
Code A058	Left Front ABS Motor Circuit Shorted To Battery	470	272
Code A061	Right Front ABS Motor Circuit Open	471	273
Code A062	Right Front ABS Motor Circuit Shorted To Ground	472	274
Code A063	Right Front ABS Motor Circuit Shorted To Battery	473	275
Code A064	Rear ABS Motor Circuit Open	474	276
Code A065	Rear ABS Motor Circuit Shorted To Ground	475	277
Code A066	Rear ABS Motor Circuit Shorted To Battery	476	278
Code A076	Left Front Solenoid Circuit Open Or Shorted To Battery	477	279
Code A077	Left Front Solenoid Circuit Shorted To Ground	478	280
Code A078	Right Front Solenoid Circuit Open Or Shorted To Battery	479	281
Code A081	Left Front Solenoid Circuit Shorted To Ground	480	282
Code A082	Calibration Fault	481	283
Code A086	EBCM Turned On The Brake Warning Lamp	482	284
Code A087	Red Brake Warning Lamp Circuit Open	483	285
Code A088	Red Brake Warning Lamp Circuit Shorted To Battery	484	286
Code A091	Open Brake Switch During Deceleration	485	287
Code A092	Open Brake Switch When ABS Was Required	486	288
Code A093	DTC 91 or 92 Set In Current Or Previous Ignition Cycle	487	289
Code A094	Brake Switch Contacts Always Closed	488	290
Code A095	Brake Switch Circuit Open	489	291
Code A096	Brake Lamps Circuit Open	490	292

Continued

DIAGNOSTIC CHART INDEX-Continued

Test/Code	Description	Page No. 32-	Fig. No.
1993-94 PRIZM			
Code A014	ABS Enable Contact Circuit Open	494	302
Code A015	ABS Enable Circuit Shorted To Battery Or Always Closed	497	303
Code A016	ABS Enable Relay Coil Circuit Open	497	304
Code A017	ABS Enable Relay Coil Shorted To Ground	498	305
Code A018	ABS Enable Relay Coil Circuit Shorted To Battery	498	306
Code A021	Left Front Wheel Speed 0 or Unreasonable	499	307
Code A022	Right Front Wheel Speed 0 or Unreasonable	500	308
Code A023	Left Rear Wheel Speed 0 Or Unreasonable	502	309
Code A024	Right Rear Wheel Speed 0 Or Unreasonable	503	310
Code A025	Left Front Wheel Excessive Wheel Speed Variation	505	311
Code A026	Right Front Wheel Excessive Wheel Speed Variation	506	312
Code A027	Left Rear Excessive Wheel Speed Variation	508	313
Code A028	Right Rear Excessive Wheel Speed Variation	509	314
Code 036	Low System Voltage	511	315
Code A037	High System Voltage	511	316
Code A038	Left Front EBS Will Not Hold Motor	512	317
Code A041	Right Front EBS Will Not Hold Motor	512	318
Code A042	Rear EBS Will Not Hold Motor	513	319
Code A044	Left Front Channel Will Not Move	513	320
Code A045	Right Front Channel Will Not Move	514	321
Code A046	Rear Channel Will Not Move	514	322
Code A047	Left Front Motor Spins Free	515	323
Code A048	Right Front Motor Spins Free	516	324
Code A051	Rear Motor Spins Free	517	325
Code A052	Left Front Channel In Release Too Long	518	326
Code A053	Right Front Channel In Release Too Long	518	327
Code A054	Rear Channel In Release Too Long	519	328
Code A055	EBCM Malfunction	520	329
Code A056	Left Front Motor Circuit Open	520	330
Code A057	Left Front Motor Circuit Shorted To Ground	521	331
Code A058	Left Front Motor Circuit Shorted To Battery	521	332
Code A061	Right Front Motor Circuit Open	522	333
Code A062	Right Front Motor Circuit Shorted To Ground	522	334
Code A063	Right Front Motor Circuit Shorted To Battery	523	335
Code A064	Rear Motor Circuit Open	523	336
Code A065	Rear Motor Shorted To Ground	524	337
Code A066	Rear Motor Circuit Shorted To Battery	524	338
Code A076	Left Front Solenoid Circuit Open Or Shorted To Battery	525	339
Code A077	Left Front Solenoid Circuit Shorted To Ground	525	340
Code A078	Right Front Solenoid Circuit Shorted To Ground	526	341
Code A081	Right Front Solenoid Circuit Shorted To Ground	526	342
Code A082	Calibration Malfunction	527	343
Code A086	EBCM Turned On The Red Brake Warning Lamp	527	344
Code A087	Red Brake Warning Lamp Circuit Shorted Open	528	345
Code A088	Red Brake Warning Lamp Circuit Shorted To Battery	529	346
Code A091	Open Brake Switch During Deceleration	530	347

Continued

DIAGNOSTIC CHART INDEX-Continued

Test/Code	Description	Page No. 32-	Fig. No.
1993-94 PRIZM -Continued			
Code A092	Open Brake Switch When ABS Required	530	349
Code A093	Code A091 Or A092 Set In Current Or Previous Ignition Cycle	531	349
Code A094	Brake Switch Contacts Always Closed	531	350
Code A095	Brake Circuit Open	531	351
Code A096	Rear Brake Lamp Circuit Open	532	352

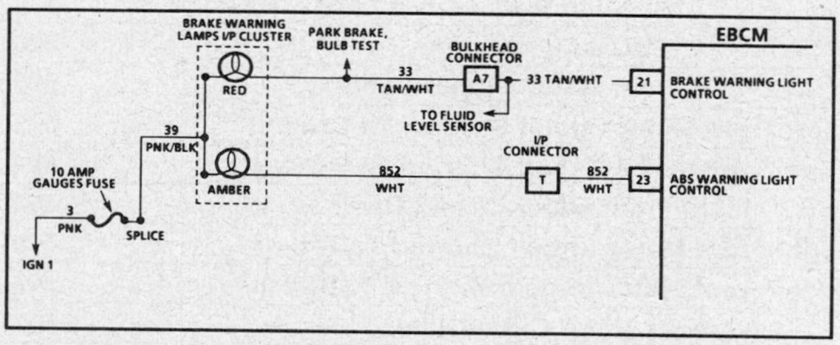

BRAKE WARNING LAMPS I/P CLUSTER
PARK BRAKE, BULB TEST
EBCM
BULKHEAD CONNECTOR
33
TAN/WHT
A7
33 TAN/WHT
21
BRAKE WARNING LIGHT CONTROL
RED
TO FLUID LEVEL SENSOR
39
PNK/BLK
I/P CONNECTOR
10 AMP GAUGES FUSE
852
WHT
T
852
WHT
23
ABS WARNING LIGHT CONTROL
AMBER
3
PNK
SPLICE
IGN 1

GC402910067300AX

Cavalier & Sunbird

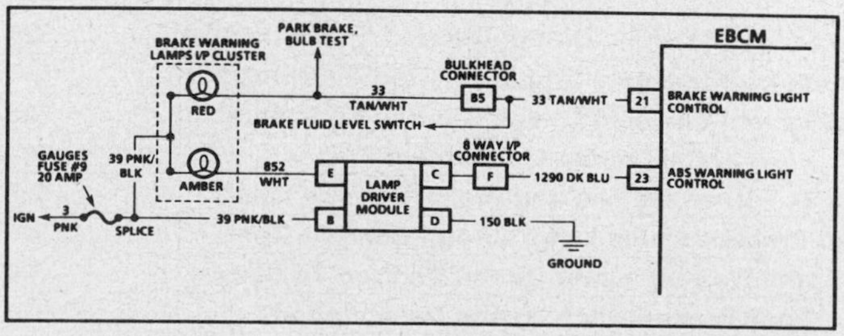

PARK BRAKE, BULB TEST
BRAKE WARNING LAMPS I/P CLUSTER
EBCM
BULKHEAD CONNECTOR
33
TAN/WHT
B5
33 TAN/WHT
21
BRAKE WARNING LIGHT CONTROL
RED
BRAKE FLUID LEVEL SWITCH
8 WAY I/P CONNECTOR
GAUGES FUSE #9 20 AMP
39 PNK/BLK
852
WHT
E
LAMP DRIVER MODULE
C
F
1290 DK BLU
23
ABS WARNING LIGHT CONTROL
AMBER
IGN
3
PNK
SPLICE
39 PNK/BLK
B
D
150 BLK
GROUND

GC402910067300BX

Beretta & Corsica

Fig. 29 Code A011: ABS Warning Light Open Or Shorted to Ground (Part 1 of 2). 1992

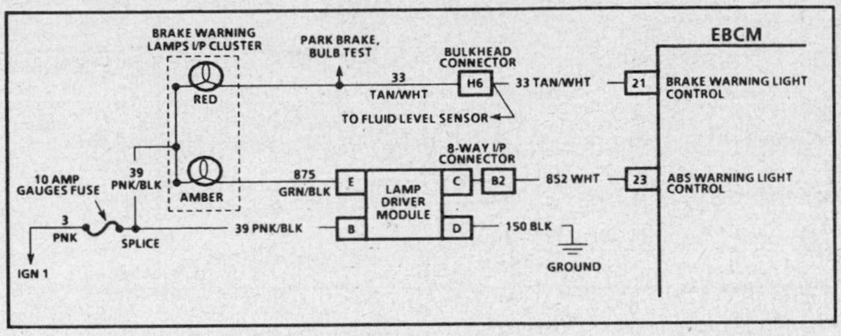
BRAKE WARNING LAMPS I/P CLUSTER
PARK BRAKE, BULB TEST
BULKHEAD CONNECTOR
EBCM
RED
33 TAN/WHT
H6
33 TAN/WHT
21
BRAKE WARNING LIGHT CONTROL
TO FLUID LEVEL SENSOR
8-WAY I/P CONNECTOR
10 AMP GAUGES FUSE
39 PNK/BLK
AMBER
875 GRN/BLK
LAMP DRIVER MODULE
B2
852 WHT
23
ABS WARNING LIGHT CONTROL
3 PNK
SPLICE
39 PNK/BLK
150 BLK
GROUND
IGN 1

GC402910067300CX

Achieva, Calais & Grand Am

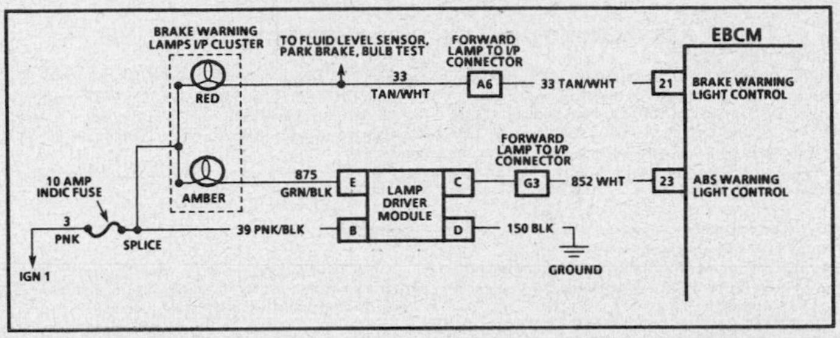
BRAKE WARNING LAMPS I/P CLUSTER
TO FLUID LEVEL SENSOR, PARK BRAKE, BULB TEST
FORWARD LAMP TO I/P CONNECTOR
EBCM
RED
33 TAN/WHT
A6
33 TAN/WHT
21
BRAKE WARNING LIGHT CONTROL
FORWARD LAMP TO I/P CONNECTOR
10 AMP INDIC FUSE
AMBER
875 GRN/BLK
LAMP DRIVER MODULE
G3
852 WHT
23
ABS WARNING LIGHT CONTROL
3 PNK
SPLICE
39 PNK/BLK
150 BLK
GROUND
IGN 1

GC402910067300DX

Cutlass Supreme, Grand Prix, Lumina & Regal

ABS WARNING LIGHT CIRCUIT OPEN OR SHORTED TO GROUND

Circuit Description:

This code checks the state of the ABS warning light to identify a situation in which the driver could not be warned of a system fault by the ABS warning light, or the warning light is always "ON." The Lamp Driver Module (LDM) turns the ABS warning light "ON," unless the EBCM provides ground to turn it "OFF." Because of the circuitry in the LDM, only external faults can be detected. As a result, the ABS warning light itself is not diagnosable, only the control line to the EBCM can be diagnosed. In the event of an open CKT 852, the ABS warning light will be on at all times, due to the loss of ground at the LDM input. If the control line is shorted to ground, the ABS warning light is kept "OFF," due to the LDM input being grounded.

Test Description: Number(s) below refer to circled number(s) on the diagnostic chart.

1. Checks to see if ABS light functions properly. Normal operation would indicate that the problem is not present.
2. This step determines if any other codes are present or if A018 is set falsely.
3. This step insures that the circuitry from the EBCM to the lamp driver module is complete.
4. This step insures that the ignition circuit to the lamp driver module is functional. An open indicator fuse or open CKT 3, 39, or 875 would result in inoperative indicator lights.
5. Isolates the cause of the ABS lamp remaining "OFF," by disconnecting the 24 way world connector, CKT 852 should be open and cause the ABS lamp to be "ON."

Diagnostic Aids:

An "Intermittent" problem may be caused by a poor connection, rubbed through wire insulation, or a wire that is broken inside the insulation.

The light test function of the "Scan" tool may be used to command the light "ON" while looking for an intermittent problem in the warning light circuitry.

The frequency of the problem can be checked by using the enhanced diagnostic function of the "Scan" tool.

Any circuitry that is suspected as causing the intermittent complaint should be thoroughly checked for backed out terminals, improper mating, broken locks, improperly formed or damaged terminals, poor terminal to wiring connections or physical damage to the wiring harness.

GC402910067300EX

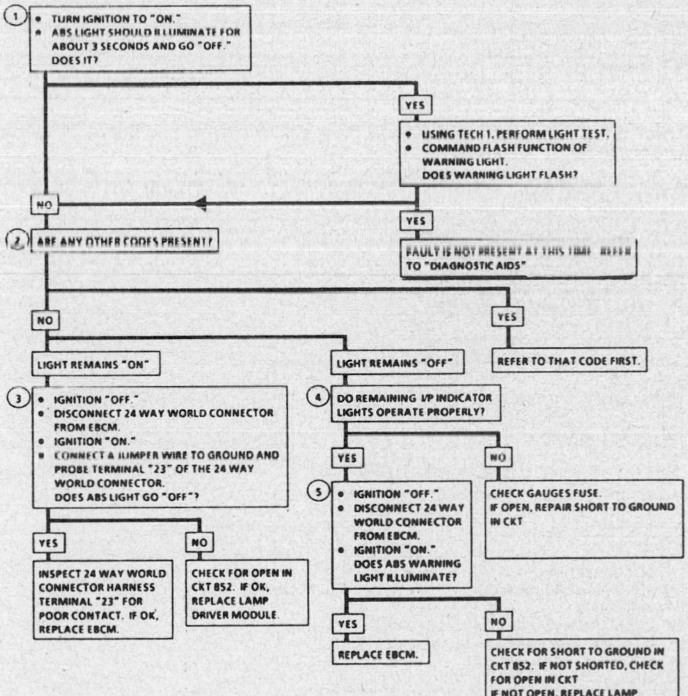
1 • TURN IGNITION TO "ON."
• ABS LIGHT SHOULD ILLUMINATE FOR ABOUT 3 SECONDS AND GO "OFF." DOES IT?
YES
• USING TECH 1, PERFORM LIGHT TEST.
• COMMAND FLASH FUNCTION OF WARNING LIGHT. DOES WARNING LIGHT FLASH?
NO
YES
2 ARE ANY OTHER CODES PRESENT?
FAULT IS NOT PRESENT AT THIS TIME. REFER TO "DIAGNOSTIC AIDS"
NO
YES
LIGHT REMAINS "ON"
LIGHT REMAINS "OFF"
REFER TO THAT CODE FIRST.
3 • IGNITION "OFF."
• DISCONNECT 24 WAY WORLD CONNECTOR FROM EBCM.
• IGNITION "ON."
• CONNECT A JUMPER WIRE TO GROUND AND PROBE TERMINAL "23" OF THE 24 WAY WORLD CONNECTOR. DOES ABS LIGHT GO "OFF"?
4 DO REMAINING I/P INDICATOR LIGHTS OPERATE PROPERLY?
YES
NO
5 • IGNITION "OFF."
• DISCONNECT 24 WAY WORLD CONNECTOR FROM EBCM.
• IGNITION "ON." DOES ABS WARNING LIGHT ILLUMINATE?
CHECK GAUGES FUSE. IF OPEN, REPAIR SHORT TO GROUND IN CKT
YES
NO
INSPECT 24 WAY WORLD CONNECTOR HARNESS TERMINAL "23" FOR POOR CONTACT. IF OK, REPLACE EBCM.
CHECK FOR OPEN IN CKT 852. IF OK, REPLACE LAMP DRIVER MODULE.
YES
NO
REPLACE EBCM.
CHECK FOR SHORT TO GROUND IN CKT 852. IF NOT SHORTED, CHECK FOR OPEN IN CKT
IF NOT OPEN, REPLACE LAMP DRIVER MODULE.

GC402910067300FX

Fig. 29 Code A011: ABS Warning Light Open Or Shorted to Ground (Part 2 of 2). 1992

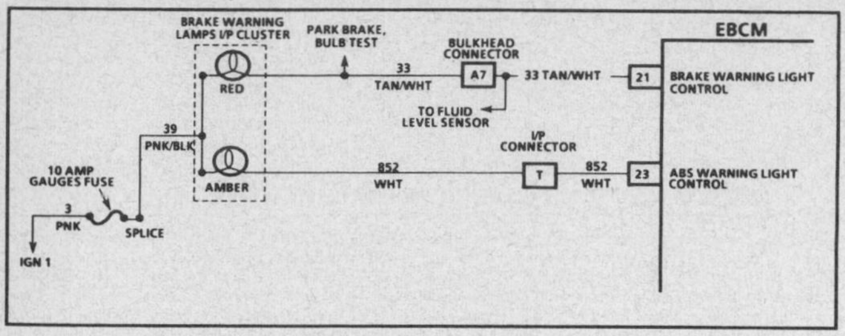
BRAKE WARNING LAMPS I/P CLUSTER
PARK BRAKE, BULB TEST
BULKHEAD CONNECTOR
EBCM
RED
33
TAN/WHT
A7
33 TAN/WHT
21
BRAKE WARNING LIGHT CONTROL
TO FLUID LEVEL SENSOR
39
PNK/BLK
I/P CONNECTOR
10 AMP GAUGES FUSE
AMBER
852
WHT
T
852
WHT
23
ABS WARNING LIGHT CONTROL
3
PNK
SPLICE
IGN 1

GC402910067400AX

Cavalier & Sunbird

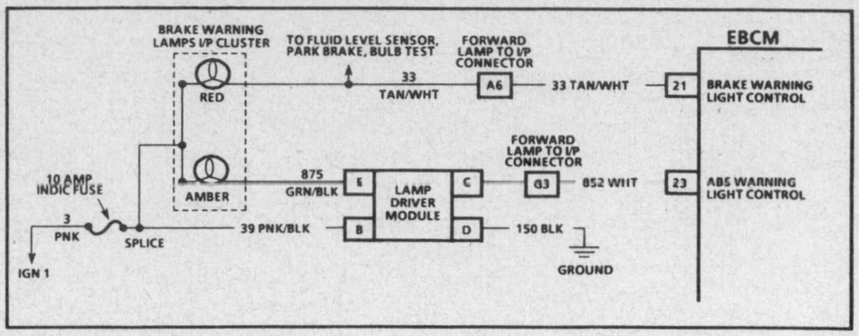
BRAKE WARNING LAMPS I/P CLUSTER
TO FLUID LEVEL SENSOR, PARK BRAKE, BULB TEST
FORWARD LAMP TO I/P CONNECTOR
EBCM
RED
33
TAN/WHT
A6
33 TAN/WHT
21
BRAKE WARNING LIGHT CONTROL
FORWARD LAMP TO I/P CONNECTOR
10 AMP INDIC FUSE
AMBER
875
GRN/BLK
E
LAMP DRIVER MODULE
C
G3
852 WHT
23
ABS WARNING LIGHT CONTROL
3
PNK
SPLICE
39 PNK/BLK
B
D
150 BLK
GROUND
IGN 1

GC402910067400DX

Cutlass Supreme, Grand Prix, Lumina & Regal

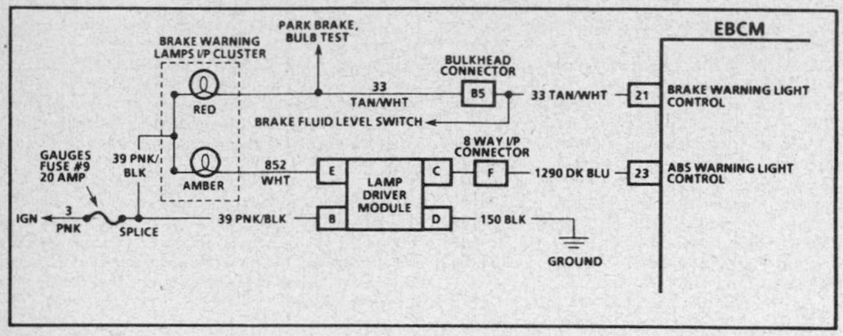
PARK BRAKE, BULB TEST
BRAKE WARNING LAMPS I/P CLUSTER
EBCM
BULKHEAD CONNECTOR
RED
33
TAN/WHT
B5
33 TAN/WHT
21
BRAKE WARNING LIGHT CONTROL
BRAKE FLUID LEVEL SWITCH
8 WAY I/P CONNECTOR
GAUGES FUSE #9 20 AMP
39 PNK/BLK
AMBER
852
WHT
E
LAMP DRIVER MODULE
C
F
1290 DK BLU
23
ABS WARNING LIGHT CONTROL
IGN
3
PNK
SPLICE
39 PNK/BLK
B
D
150 BLK
GROUND

GC402910067400BX

Beretta & Corsica

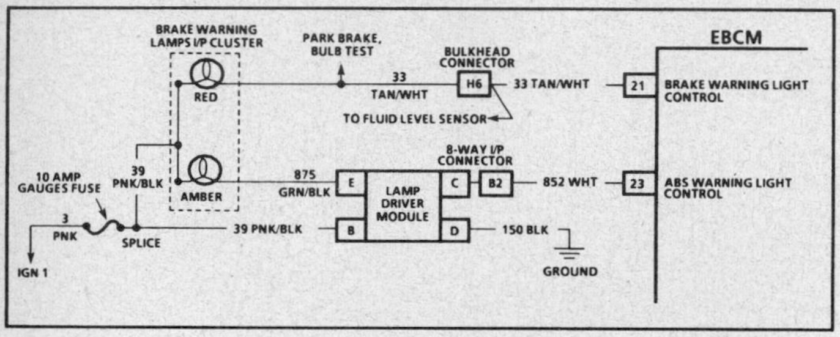
BRAKE WARNING LAMPS I/P CLUSTER
PARK BRAKE, BULB TEST
BULKHEAD CONNECTOR
EBCM
RED
33
TAN/WHT
H6
33 TAN/WHT
21
BRAKE WARNING LIGHT CONTROL
TO FLUID LEVEL SENSOR
8-WAY I/P CONNECTOR
10 AMP GAUGES FUSE
39
PNK/BLK
AMBER
875
GRN/BLK
E
LAMP DRIVER MODULE
C
B2
852 WHT
23
ABS WARNING LIGHT CONTROL
3
PNK
SPLICE
39 PNK/BLK
B
D
150 BLK
GROUND
IGN 1

GC402910067400CX

Achieva, Calais & Grand Am

ABS WARNING LIGHT CIRCUIT SHORTED TO BATTERY

Circuit Description:

This code checks the state of the ABS warning light to identify a situation in which the driver could not be warned of a system fault by the ABS warning light. The Lamp Driver Module (LDM) turns the ABS warning light "ON," unless the EBCM provides ground to turn it "OFF." Because of the circuitry in the LDM which is part of the I/P cluster, only external faults can be detected. As a result, the ABS warning light itself is not diagnosable, only the control line to the EBCM can be diagnosed.

If the ABS warning light control line is shorted to battery or the EBCM control circuit is open, the Electronic Brake Control Module (EBCM) is not able to turn "OFF" the ABS warning light.

Test Description: Number(s) below refer to circled number(s) on the diagnostic chart.

1. Checks to see if ABS light functions properly. Normal operation would indicate that the problem is not present.
2. After the ignition is turned to the "OFF" position, voltage to the lamp driver module should be interrupted. A light that remains "ON" would indicate that voltage to this circuit is from a point other than ignition.
3. After removing the 10 amp gauges fuse, voltage on CKT 852 will be eliminated. If voltage is still present, it would indicate that a short to voltage is present between the lamp driver module and EBCM.

Diagnostic Aids:

An "Intermittent" problem may be caused by a poor connection, rubbed through wire insulation or a wire that is broken inside the insulation.

Code A013 must be currently set before it should be addressed. If Code A013 is set as a history code, proceed to those codes that are currently set before attempting to repair a Code A013 fault.

The frequency of the problem can be checked by using the enhanced diagnostic function of the "Scan" tool

Any circuitry that is suspected as causing the "Intermittent" complaint should be thoroughly checked for backed out terminals, improper mating, broken locks, improperly formed or damaged terminals, poor terminal to wiring connections or physical damage to the wiring harness.

GC402910067400EX

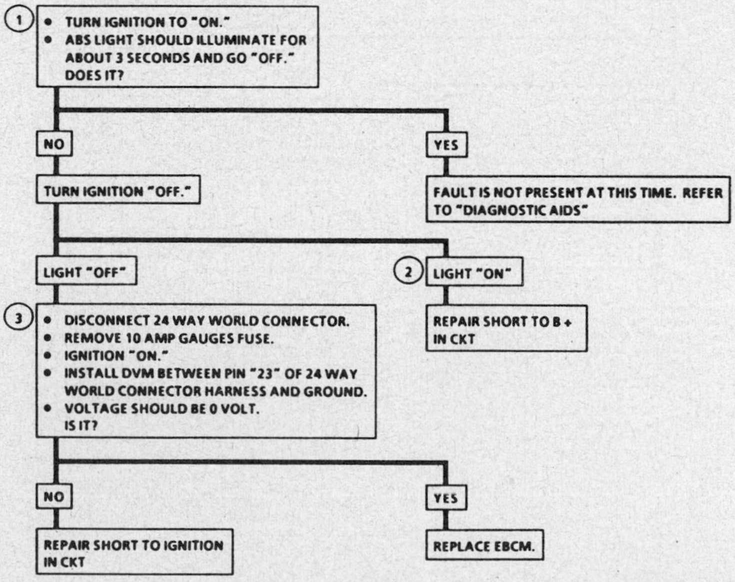
1
• TURN IGNITION TO "ON."
• ABS LIGHT SHOULD ILLUMINATE FOR ABOUT 3 SECONDS AND GO "OFF." DOES IT?
NO
YES
TURN IGNITION "OFF."
FAULT IS NOT PRESENT AT THIS TIME. REFER TO "DIAGNOSTIC AIDS"
LIGHT "OFF"
2
LIGHT "ON"
3
• DISCONNECT 24 WAY WORLD CONNECTOR.
• REMOVE 10 AMP GAUGES FUSE.
• IGNITION "ON."
• INSTALL DVM BETWEEN PIN "23" OF 24 WAY WORLD CONNECTOR HARNESS AND GROUND.
• VOLTAGE SHOULD BE 0 VOLT. IS IT?
REPAIR SHORT TO B + IN CKT
NO
YES
REPAIR SHORT TO IGNITION IN CKT
REPLACE EBCM.

GC402910067400FX

Fig. 30 Code A013: ABS Warning Light Circuit Shorted To Battery. 1992

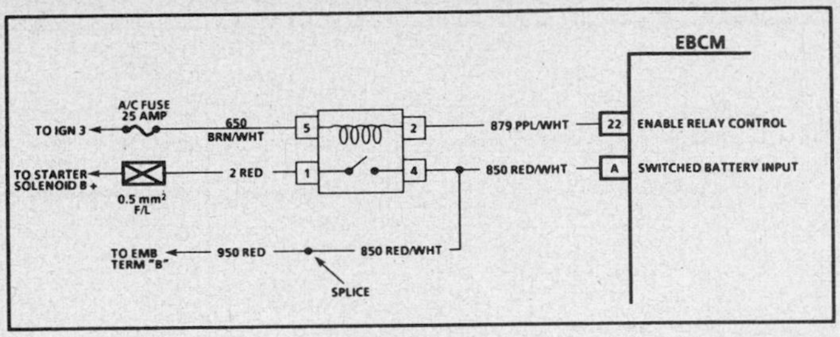
EBCM
A/C FUSE
25 AMP
TO IGN 3
650
BRN/WHT
5
2
879 PPL/WHT
22
ENABLE RELAY CONTROL
TO STARTER SOLENOID B +
2 RED
1
4
850 RED/WHT
A
SWITCHED BATTERY INPUT
0.5 mm²
F/L
TO EMB TERM "B"
950 RED
850 RED/WHT
SPLICE

GC402910067500AX

Cavalier & Sunbird

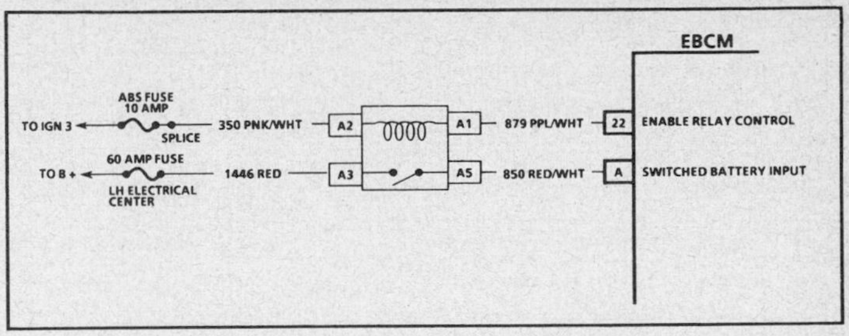
EBCM
ABS FUSE
10 AMP
TO IGN 3
SPLICE
350 PNK/WHT
A2
A1
879 PPL/WHT
22
ENABLE RELAY CONTROL
60 AMP FUSE
TO B +
LH ELECTRICAL CENTER
1446 RED
A3
A5
850 RED/WHT
A
SWITCHED BATTERY INPUT

GC402910067500DX

Cutlass Supreme, Grand Prix, Lumina & Regal

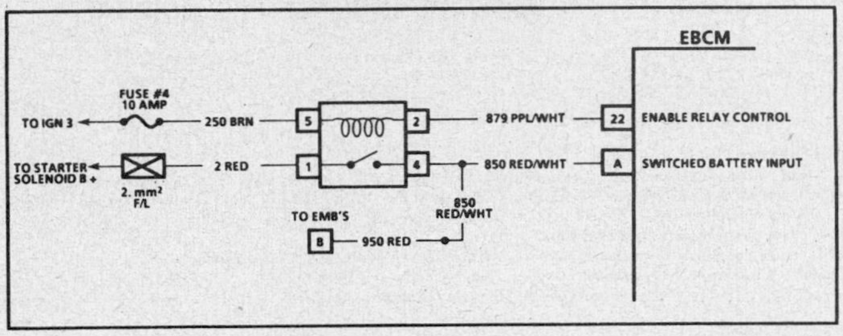
EBCM
FUSE #4
10 AMP
TO IGN 3
250 BRN
5
2
879 PPL/WHT
22
ENABLE RELAY CONTROL
TO STARTER SOLENOID B +
2 RED
1
4
850 RED/WHT
A
SWITCHED BATTERY INPUT
2. mm²
F/L
850
RED/WHT
TO EMB'S
B
950 RED

GC402910067500BX

Beretta & Corsica

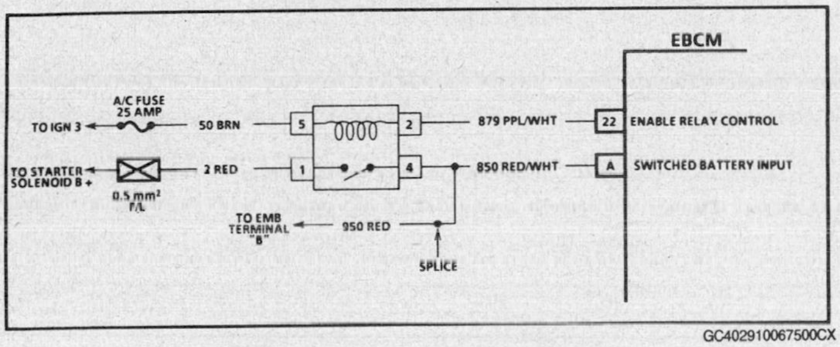
EBCM
A/C FUSE
25 AMP
TO IGN 3
50 BRN
5
2
879 PPL/WHT
22
ENABLE RELAY CONTROL
TO STARTER SOLENOID B +
2 RED
1
4
850 RED/WHT
A
SWITCHED BATTERY INPUT
0.5 mm²
F/L
TO EMB TERMINAL "B"
950 RED
SPLICE

GC402910067500CX

Achieva, Calais & Grand Am

Circuit Description:

Ignition voltage is supplied through terminal "5" of the ABS enable relay. The EBCM then is able to energize the pull-in coil by completing the ground circuit at Pin "22" of the EBCM. The magnetic field created closes the enable relay contacts and allows battery voltage and current to be supplied to the EMB's and EBCM, which supplies power to the motors and solenoids.

This test monitors the availability of current/voltage to the motors, solenoids and EMB's. This fault indicates voltage is not available and would therefore not allow ABS operation if required.

Test Description: Number(s) below refer to circled number(s) on the diagnostic chart.

1. This step would indicate that the EBCM is sensing battery voltage present through the relay contacts at terminal "A." This shows that the relay and circuitry is functional.
2. This insures that battery voltage is available to terminals "1" and "5" of the relay.
3. This step checks to make sure that the pull-in coil of the enable relay has continuity.
4. This checks the ability of the EBCM to energize the enable relay. An open circuit in the EBCM or CKT 879 would not allow the enable relay to be energized.
5. This step checks for an open CKT 850 between the enable relay and EBCM.

Diagnostic Aids:

An "Intermittent" problem may be caused by a poor connection, rubbed through wire insulation, or a wire that is broken inside the insulation.

The frequency of the problem can be checked by using the enhanced diagnostic function of the "Scan" tool as described in the "General Information," found in this section.

Any circuitry that is suspected as causing the "Intermittent" complaint should be thoroughly checked for backed out terminals, improper mating, broken locks, improperly formed or damaged terminals, poor terminal to wiring connections or physical damage to the wiring harness.

VIBRATION, TEMPERATURE EFFECTS:

Check for vibration effects by performing the relay test function of the "Scan" tool. With the relay test commanded "ON," lightly tap the top and sides of the relay while monitoring relay voltage. If the relay voltage changes significantly, replace the relay.

If test 14 only fails when the vehicle is initially started in cold ambient conditions (temperature less than 32°F - 0°C), replace the relay.

GC402910067500EX

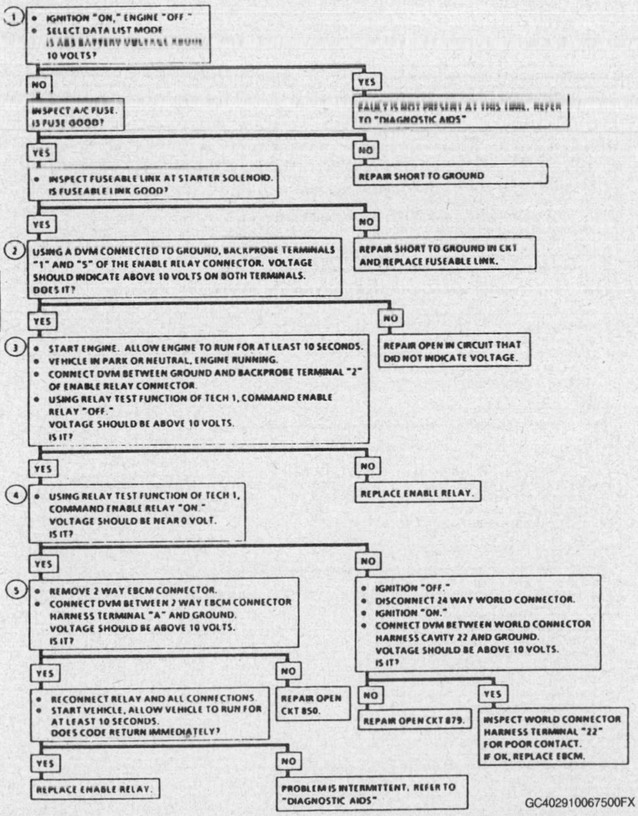
1
• IGNITION "ON," ENGINE "OFF."
• SELECT DATA LIST MODE
IS ABS BATTERY VOLTAGE ABOVE
10 VOLTS?
NO
YES
INSPECT A/C FUSE.
IS FUSE GOOD?
FAULT IS NOT PRESENT AT THIS TIME. REFER TO "DIAGNOSTIC AIDS"
YES
NO
• INSPECT FUSEABLE LINK AT STARTER SOLENOID.
IS FUSEABLE LINK GOOD?
REPAIR SHORT TO GROUND
YES
NO
2
USING A DVM CONNECTED TO GROUND, BACKPROBE TERMINALS "1" AND "5" OF THE ENABLE RELAY CONNECTOR. VOLTAGE SHOULD INDICATE ABOVE 10 VOLTS ON BOTH TERMINALS. DOES IT?
REPAIR SHORT TO GROUND IN CKT AND REPLACE FUSEABLE LINK.
YES
NO
3
• START ENGINE. ALLOW ENGINE TO RUN FOR AT LEAST 10 SECONDS.
• VEHICLE IN PARK OR NEUTRAL, ENGINE RUNNING.
• CONNECT DVM BETWEEN GROUND AND BACKPROBE TERMINAL "2" OF ENABLE RELAY CONNECTOR.
• USING RELAY TEST FUNCTION OF TECH 1, COMMAND ENABLE RELAY "OFF."
VOLTAGE SHOULD BE ABOVE 10 VOLTS.
IS IT?
REPAIR OPEN IN CIRCUIT THAT DID NOT INDICATE VOLTAGE.
YES
NO
4
• USING RELAY TEST FUNCTION OF TECH 1, COMMAND ENABLE RELAY "ON."
VOLTAGE SHOULD BE NEAR 0 VOLT.
IS IT?
REPLACE ENABLE RELAY.
YES
NO
5
• REMOVE 2 WAY EBCM CONNECTOR.
• CONNECT DVM BETWEEN 2 WAY EBCM CONNECTOR HARNESS TERMINAL "A" AND GROUND.
VOLTAGE SHOULD BE ABOVE 10 VOLTS.
IS IT?
• IGNITION "OFF."
• DISCONNECT 24 WAY WORLD CONNECTOR.
• IGNITION "ON."
• CONNECT DVM BETWEEN WORLD CONNECTOR HARNESS CAVITY 22 AND GROUND.
VOLTAGE SHOULD BE ABOVE 10 VOLTS.
IS IT?
YES
NO
NO
YES
• RECONNECT RELAY AND ALL CONNECTIONS.
• START VEHICLE, ALLOW VEHICLE TO RUN FOR AT LEAST 10 SECONDS.
DOES CODE RETURN IMMEDIATELY?
REPAIR OPEN CKT 850.
REPAIR OPEN CKT 879.
INSPECT WORLD CONNECTOR HARNESS TERMINAL "22" FOR POOR CONTACT.
IF OK, REPLACE EBCM.
YES
NO
REPLACE ENABLE RELAY.
PROBLEM IS INTERMITTENT. REFER TO "DIAGNOSTIC AIDS"

GC402910067500FX

Fig. 31 Code A014: Enable Relay Contacts Open Or Fuse Open. 1992

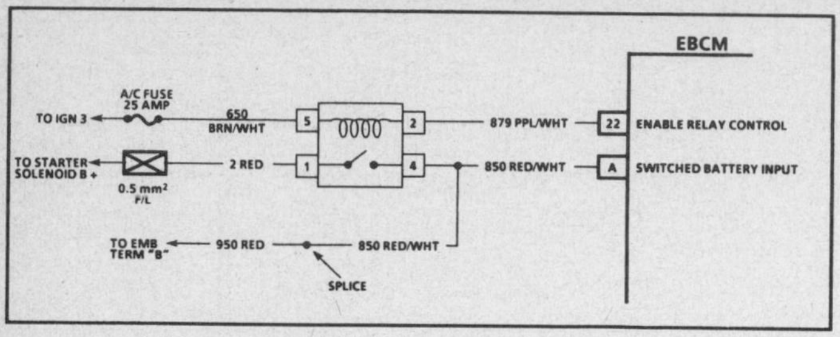
EBCM
A/C FUSE 25 AMP
TO IGN 3
650 BRN/WHT
TO STARTER SOLENOID B+
0.5 mm² F/L
2 RED
879 PPL/WHT
850 RED/WHT
22 ENABLE RELAY CONTROL
A SWITCHED BATTERY INPUT
TO EMB TERM "B"
950 RED
850 RED/WHT
SPLICE

GC402910067600AX

Cavalier & Sunbird

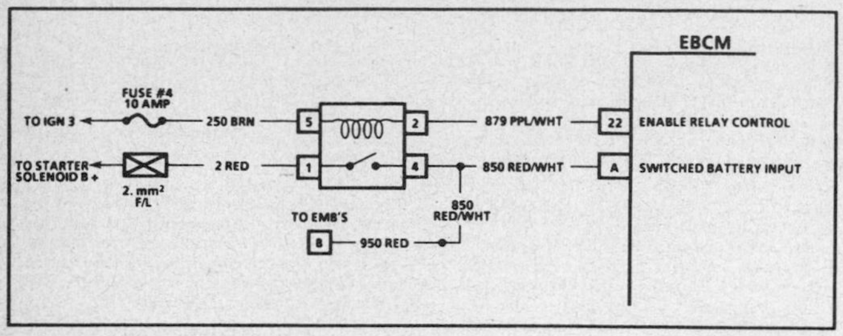
EBCM
FUSE #4 10 AMP
TO IGN 3
250 BRN
TO STARTER SOLENOID B+
2. mm² F/L
2 RED
879 PPL/WHT
850 RED/WHT
22 ENABLE RELAY CONTROL
A SWITCHED BATTERY INPUT
850 RED/WHT
TO EMB'S
B
950 RED

GC402910067600BX

Beretta & Corsica

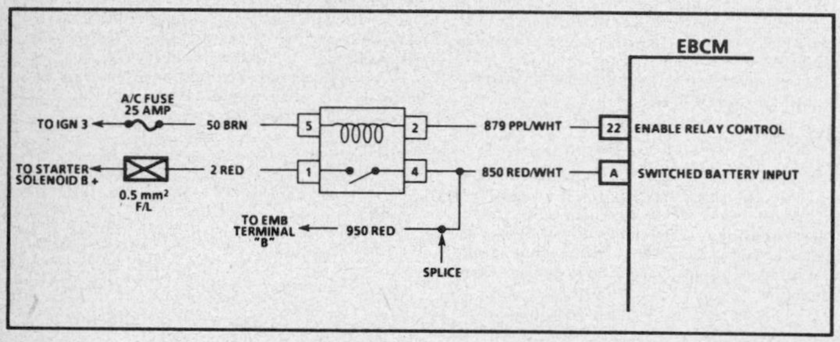
EBCM
A/C FUSE 25 AMP
TO IGN 3
50 BRN
TO STARTER SOLENOID B+
0.5 mm² F/L
2 RED
879 PPL/WHT
850 RED/WHT
22 ENABLE RELAY CONTROL
A SWITCHED BATTERY INPUT
TO EMB TERMINAL "B"
950 RED
SPLICE

GC402910067600CX

Achieva, Calais & Grand Am

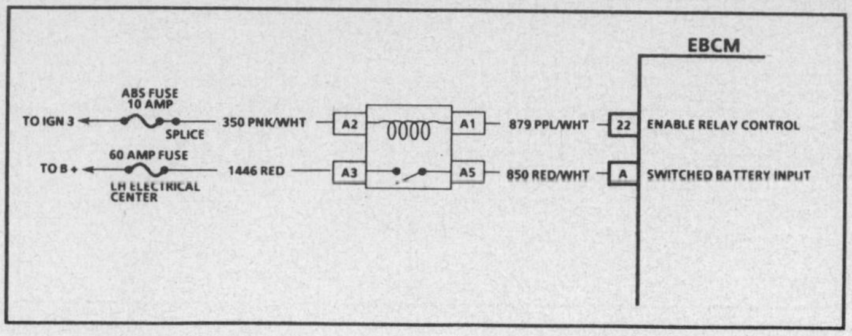
EBCM
ABS FUSE 10 AMP
TO IGN 3
SPLICE
350 PNK/WHT
60 AMP FUSE
TO B+
LH ELECTRICAL CENTER
1446 RED
A2
A1
A3
A5
879 PPL/WHT
850 RED/WHT
22 ENABLE RELAY CONTROL
A SWITCHED BATTERY INPUT

GC402910067600DX

Cutlass Supreme, Grand Prix, Lumina & Regal

Circuit Description:

Ignition voltage is supplied through terminal "A2" of the ABS enable relay. The EBCM then is able to energize the pull-in coil by completing the ground circuit at Pin "22" of the EBCM. The magnetic field created closes the enable relay contacts and allows battery voltage and current to be supplied to the EBCM, which supplies power to the motors and solenoids.

This code determines if the enable relay is energized when it should not be. This fault would not allow the enable relay to remove power to the ABS system. If a second fault were to occur that requires the enable relay to be turned "OFF," that fault cannot be removed if the relay cannot be controlled.

Test Description: Number(s) below refer to circled number(s) on the diagnostic chart.

1. This step indicates that the EBCM is capable of controlling the enable relay as commanded.
2. This step checks for a possible short to battery voltage in CKT 850.
3. This step insures that the EBCM and also CKT 879 are not shorted to ground. A short to ground in either case would cause the enable relay to be energized constantly.

Diagnostic Aids:

An "Intermittent" problem may be caused by a poor connection, rubbed through wire insulation, or a wire that is broken inside the insulation.

The frequency of the problem can be checked by using the enhanced diagnostic function of the "Scan" tool.

Any circuitry, that is suspected as causing the intermittent complaint, should be thoroughly checked for backed out terminals, improper mating, broken locks, improperly formed or damaged terminals, poor terminal to wiring connections or physical damage to the wiring harness.

GC402910067600EX

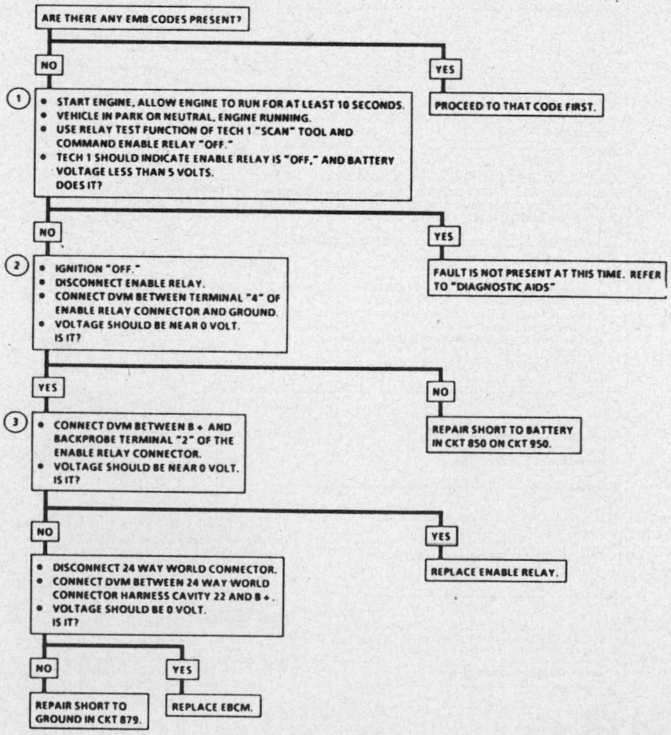
ARE THERE ANY EMB CODES PRESENT?
NO
YES
PROCEED TO THAT CODE FIRST.
1
• START ENGINE, ALLOW ENGINE TO RUN FOR AT LEAST 10 SECONDS.
• VEHICLE IN PARK OR NEUTRAL, ENGINE RUNNING.
• USE RELAY TEST FUNCTION OF TECH 1 "SCAN" TOOL AND COMMAND ENABLE RELAY "OFF."
• TECH 1 SHOULD INDICATE ENABLE RELAY IS "OFF," AND BATTERY VOLTAGE LESS THAN 5 VOLTS. DOES IT?
NO
YES
FAULT IS NOT PRESENT AT THIS TIME. REFER TO "DIAGNOSTIC AIDS"
2
• IGNITION "OFF."
• DISCONNECT ENABLE RELAY.
• CONNECT DVM BETWEEN TERMINAL "4" OF ENABLE RELAY CONNECTOR AND GROUND.
• VOLTAGE SHOULD BE NEAR 0 VOLT. IS IT?
YES
NO
REPAIR SHORT TO BATTERY IN CKT 850 ON CKT 950.
3
• CONNECT DVM BETWEEN B+ AND BACKPROBE TERMINAL "2" OF THE ENABLE RELAY CONNECTOR.
• VOLTAGE SHOULD BE NEAR 0 VOLT. IS IT?
NO
YES
REPLACE ENABLE RELAY.
• DISCONNECT 24 WAY WORLD CONNECTOR.
• CONNECT DVM BETWEEN 24 WAY WORLD CONNECTOR HARNESS CAVITY 22 AND B+.
• VOLTAGE SHOULD BE 0 VOLT. IS IT?
NO
YES
REPAIR SHORT TO GROUND IN CKT 879.
REPLACE EBCM.

GC402910067600FX

Fig. 32 Code A015: Enable Relay Contacts Shorted To Battery. 1992

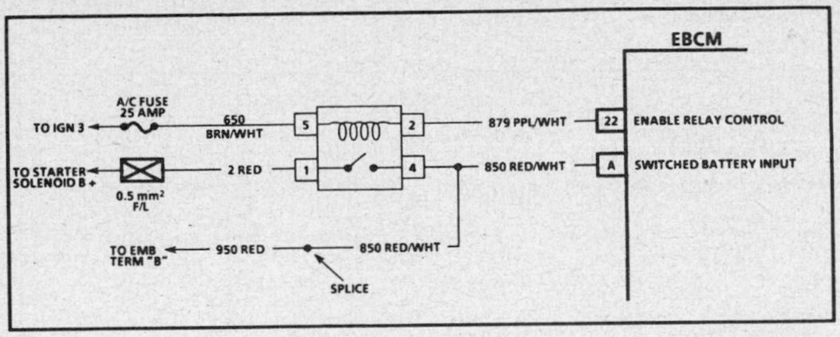
EBCM
A/C FUSE 25 AMP
TO IGN 3
650 BRN/WHT
5
2
879 PPL/WHT
22
ENABLE RELAY CONTROL
TO STARTER SOLENOID B +
0.5 mm² F/L
2 RED
1
4
850 RED/WHT
A
SWITCHED BATTERY INPUT
TO EMB TERM "B"
950 RED
850 RED/WHT
SPLICE

GC402910067700AX

Cavalier & Sunbird

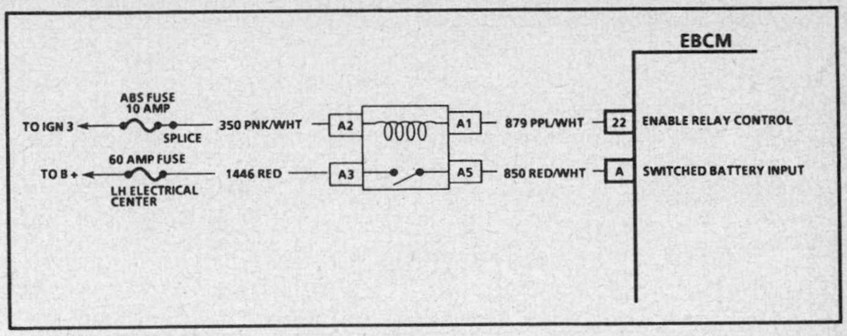
EBCM
ABS FUSE 10 AMP
TO IGN 3
SPLICE
350 PNK/WHT
A2
A1
879 PPL/WHT
22
ENABLE RELAY CONTROL
60 AMP FUSE
TO B +
LH ELECTRICAL CENTER
1446 RED
A3
A5
850 RED/WHT
A
SWITCHED BATTERY INPUT

GC402910067700DX

Cutlass Supreme, Grand Prix, Lumina & Regal

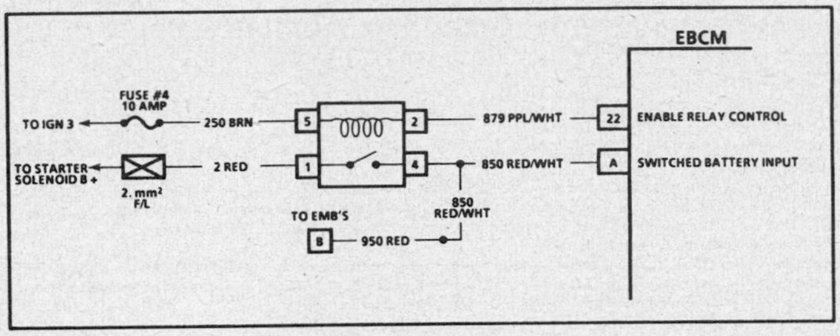
EBCM
FUSE #4 10 AMP
TO IGN 3
250 BRN
5
2
879 PPL/WHT
22
ENABLE RELAY CONTROL
TO STARTER SOLENOID B +
2. mm² F/L
2 RED
1
4
850 RED/WHT
A
SWITCHED BATTERY INPUT
TO EMB'S
850 RED/WHT
B
950 RED

GC402910067700BX

Beretta & Corsica

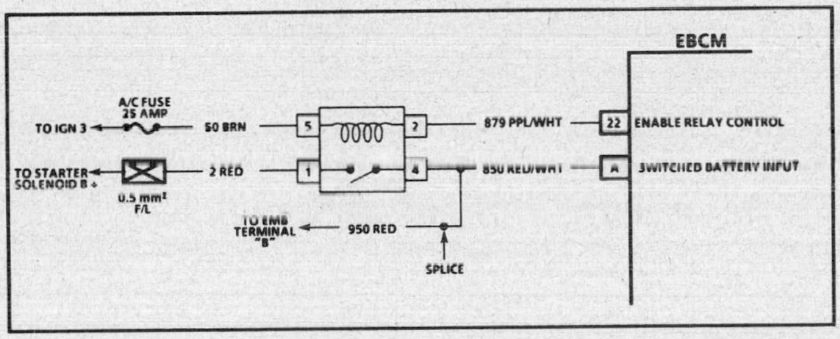
EBCM
A/C FUSE 25 AMP
TO IGN 3
50 BRN
5
2
879 PPL/WHT
22
ENABLE RELAY CONTROL
TO STARTER SOLENOID B +
0.5 mm² F/L
2 RED
1
4
850 RED/WHT
A
SWITCHED BATTERY INPUT
TO EMB TERMINAL "B"
950 RED
SPLICE

GC402910067700CX

Achieva, Calais & Grand Am

Circuit Description:

Ignition voltage is supplied through terminal "5" of the ABS enable relay. The EBCM then is able to energize the pull-in coil by completing the ground circuit at Pin "22" of the EBCM. The magnetic field created closes the enable relay contacts and allows battery voltage and current to be supplied to the EMB's and EBCM, which supplies power to the motors and solenoids.

This code detects opens in the enable relay coil circuit. An open in this circuit will not allow the enable relay to be energized, thus preventing voltage/current to the motors, EMB's and solenoids.

Test Description: Number(s) below refer to circled number(s) on the diagnostic chart.

1. This step indicates the EBCM is capable of controlling the enable relay as commanded.
2. This step checks to insure that voltage is available to the pull-in coil of the enable relay.
3. This step insures that there is continuity through the pull-in coil of the enable relay.

Diagnostic Aids:

An "Intermittent" problem may be caused by a poor connection, rubbed through wire insulation, or a wire that is broken inside the insulation.

The frequency of the problem can be checked by using the enhanced diagnostic function of the "Scan" tool.

If the frequency of the problem is high, but is currently intermittent, check for high coil resistance by measuring between relay terminals 5 and 2 using a DVM. If resistance shows greater than 100 ohms, replace the relay.

Any circuitry, that is suspected as causing the intermittent complaint, should be thoroughly checked for backed out terminals, improper mating, broken locks, improperly formed or damaged terminals, poor terminal to wiring connections or physical damage to the wiring harness.

GC402910067700EX

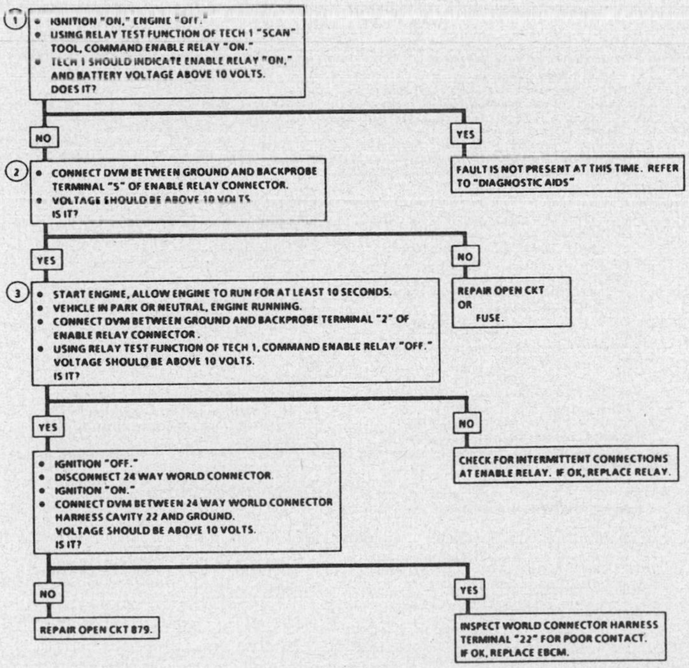
1
• IGNITION "ON," ENGINE "OFF."
• USING RELAY TEST FUNCTION OF TECH 1 "SCAN" TOOL, COMMAND ENABLE RELAY "ON."
• TECH 1 SHOULD INDICATE ENABLE RELAY "ON," AND BATTERY VOLTAGE ABOVE 10 VOLTS.
DOES IT?
NO
YES
FAULT IS NOT PRESENT AT THIS TIME. REFER TO "DIAGNOSTIC AIDS"
2
• CONNECT DVM BETWEEN GROUND AND BACKPROBE TERMINAL "5" OF ENABLE RELAY CONNECTOR.
• VOLTAGE SHOULD BE ABOVE 10 VOLTS.
IS IT?
YES
NO
REPAIR OPEN CKT OR FUSE.
3
• START ENGINE, ALLOW ENGINE TO RUN FOR AT LEAST 10 SECONDS.
• VEHICLE IN PARK OR NEUTRAL, ENGINE RUNNING.
• CONNECT DVM BETWEEN GROUND AND BACKPROBE TERMINAL "2" OF ENABLE RELAY CONNECTOR.
• USING RELAY TEST FUNCTION OF TECH 1, COMMAND ENABLE RELAY "OFF."
VOLTAGE SHOULD BE ABOVE 10 VOLTS.
IS IT?
YES
NO
CHECK FOR INTERMITTENT CONNECTIONS AT ENABLE RELAY. IF OK, REPLACE RELAY.
• IGNITION "OFF."
• DISCONNECT 24 WAY WORLD CONNECTOR.
• IGNITION "ON."
• CONNECT DVM BETWEEN 24 WAY WORLD CONNECTOR HARNESS CAVITY 22 AND GROUND.
VOLTAGE SHOULD BE ABOVE 10 VOLTS.
IS IT?
NO
YES
REPAIR OPEN CKT 879.
INSPECT WORLD CONNECTOR HARNESS TERMINAL "22" FOR POOR CONTACT. IF OK, REPLACE EBCM.

GC402910067700FX

Fig. 33 Code A016: Enable Relay Coil Circuit Open. 1992

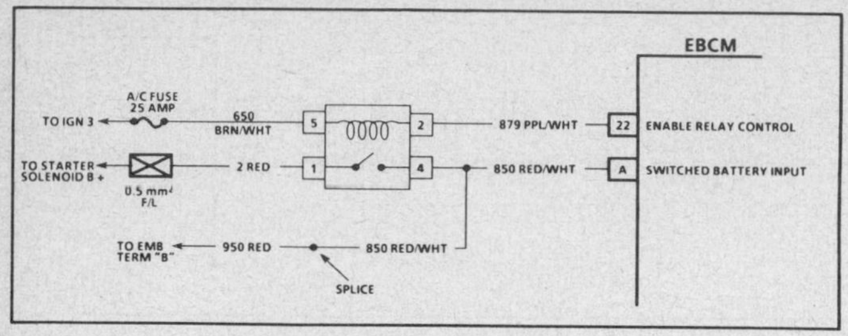
EBCM
A/C FUSE 25 AMP
TO IGN 3
650 BRN/WHT
879 PPL/WHT
22
ENABLE RELAY CONTROL
TO STARTER SOLENOID B+
2 RED
0.5 mm² F/L
850 RED/WHT
A
SWITCHED BATTERY INPUT
TO EMB TERM "B"
950 RED
850 RED/WHT
SPLICE

GC402910067800AX

Cavalier & Sunbird

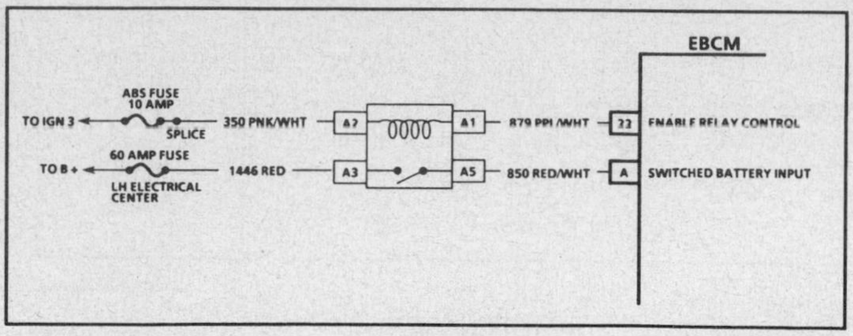
EBCM
ABS FUSE 10 AMP
TO IGN 3
SPLICE
350 PNK/WHT
A2
A1
879 PPL/WHT
22
ENABLE RELAY CONTROL
60 AMP FUSE
TO B+
LH ELECTRICAL CENTER
1446 RED
A3
A5
850 RED/WHT
A
SWITCHED BATTERY INPUT

GC402910067800DX

Cutlass Supreme, Grand Prix, Lumina & Regal

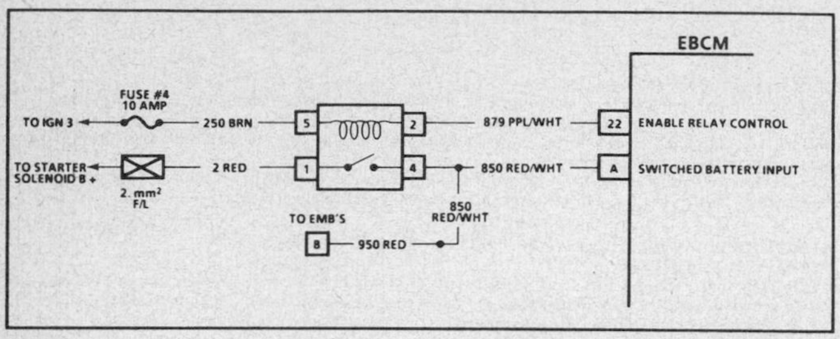
EBCM
FUSE #4 10 AMP
TO IGN 3
250 BRN
879 PPL/WHT
22
ENABLE RELAY CONTROL
TO STARTER SOLENOID B+
2 RED
2. mm² F/L
850 RED/WHT
A
SWITCHED BATTERY INPUT
TO EMB'S
850 RED/WHT
B
950 RED

GC402910067800BX

Beretta & Corsica

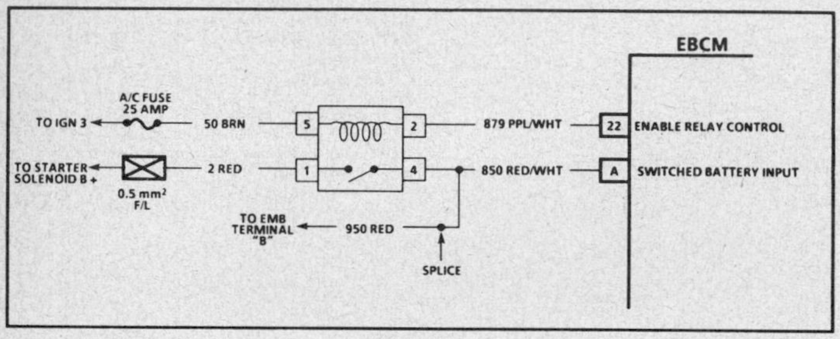
EBCM
A/C FUSE 25 AMP
TO IGN 3
50 BRN
879 PPL/WHT
22
ENABLE RELAY CONTROL
TO STARTER SOLENOID B+
2 RED
0.5 mm² F/L
850 RED/WHT
A
SWITCHED BATTERY INPUT
TO EMB TERMINAL "B"
950 RED
SPLICE

GC402910067800CX

Achieva, Calais & Grand Am

Circuit Description:

Ignition voltage is supplied through terminal "5" of the ABS enable relay. The EBCM then is able to energize the pull-in coil by completing the ground circuit at Pin "22" of the EBCM. The magnetic field created closes the enable relay contacts and allows battery voltage and current to be supplied to the EMB's and EBCM, which supplies voltage to the motors and solenoids.

This code determines if the enable relay is energized when it should not be. This fault would not allow the enable relay to remove power to the ABS system. If a second fault were to occur that requires the enable relay to be turned "OFF," that fault cannot be removed if the relay cannot be controlled.

Test Description: Number(s) below refer to circled number(s) on the diagnostic chart.

1. This step indicates that the EBCM is capable of controlling the enable relay as commanded.
2. This checks to insure that the enable relay or control CKT 879 are not shorted to ground.
3. This step checks to see if the EBCM is internally shorted to ground. A grounded Pin "22" would cause the enable relay to be energized any time the ignition was in the "ON" position.

Diagnostic Aids:

An "Intermittent" problem may be caused by a poor connection, rubbed through wire insulation, or a wire that is broken inside the insulation.

The frequency of the problem can be checked by using the enhanced diagnostic function of the "Scan" tool.

Any circuitry, that is suspected as causing the intermittent complaint, should be thoroughly checked for backed out terminals, improper mating, broken locks, improperly formed or damaged terminals, poor terminal to wiring connections or physical damage to the wiring harness.

GC402910067800EX

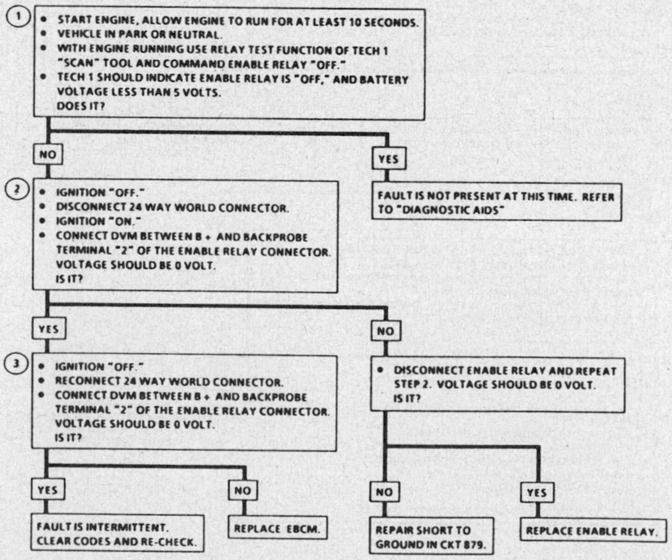
1
• START ENGINE, ALLOW ENGINE TO RUN FOR AT LEAST 10 SECONDS.
• VEHICLE IN PARK OR NEUTRAL.
• WITH ENGINE RUNNING USE RELAY TEST FUNCTION OF TECH 1 "SCAN" TOOL AND COMMAND ENABLE RELAY "OFF."
• TECH 1 SHOULD INDICATE ENABLE RELAY IS "OFF," AND BATTERY VOLTAGE LESS THAN 5 VOLTS. DOES IT?
NO
YES
FAULT IS NOT PRESENT AT THIS TIME. REFER TO "DIAGNOSTIC AIDS"
2
• IGNITION "OFF."
• DISCONNECT 24 WAY WORLD CONNECTOR.
• IGNITION "ON."
• CONNECT DVM BETWEEN B+ AND BACKPROBE TERMINAL "2" OF THE ENABLE RELAY CONNECTOR. VOLTAGE SHOULD BE 0 VOLT. IS IT?
YES
NO
3
• IGNITION "OFF."
• RECONNECT 24 WAY WORLD CONNECTOR.
• CONNECT DVM BETWEEN B+ AND BACKPROBE TERMINAL "2" OF THE ENABLE RELAY CONNECTOR. VOLTAGE SHOULD BE 0 VOLT. IS IT?
• DISCONNECT ENABLE RELAY AND REPEAT STEP 2. VOLTAGE SHOULD BE 0 VOLT. IS IT?
YES
NO
NO
YES
FAULT IS INTERMITTENT. CLEAR CODES AND RE-CHECK.
REPLACE EBCM.
REPAIR SHORT TO GROUND IN CKT 879.
REPLACE ENABLE RELAY.

GC402910067800FX

Fig. 34 Code A017: Enable Relay Coil Circuit Shorted To Ground. 1992

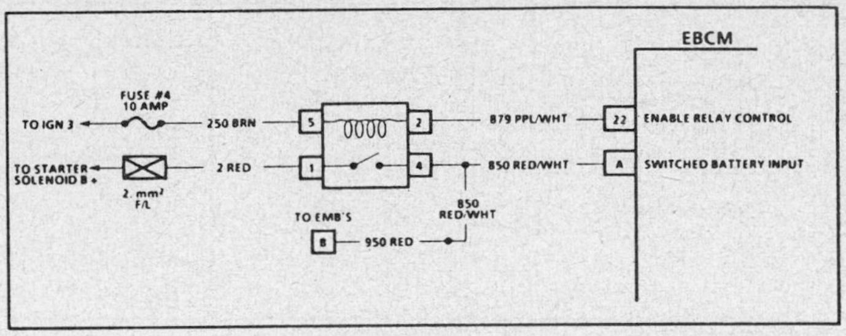
EBCM
FUSE #4
10 AMP
TO IGN 3
250 BRN
5
2
879 PPL/WHT
22
ENABLE RELAY CONTROL
TO STARTER SOLENOID B+
2 RED
1
4
850 RED/WHT
A
SWITCHED BATTERY INPUT
2. mm²
F/L
TO EMB'S
850
RED/WHT
B
950 RED

GC402910067900AX

Cavalier & Sunbird

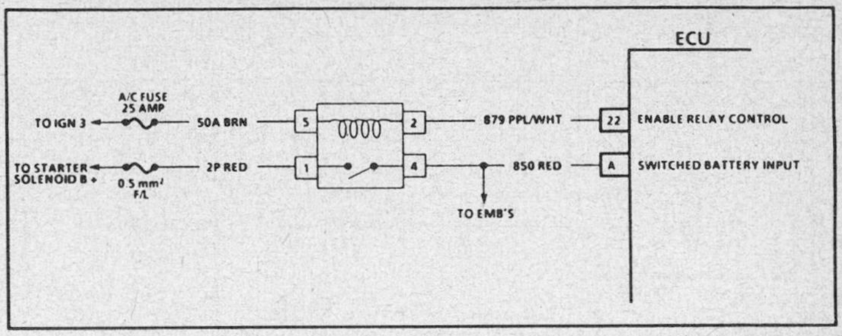
ECU
A/C FUSE
25 AMP
TO IGN 3
50A BRN
5
2
879 PPL/WHT
22
ENABLE RELAY CONTROL
TO STARTER SOLENOID B+
0.5 mm²
F/L
2P RED
1
4
850 RED
A
SWITCHED BATTERY INPUT
TO EMB'S

GC402910067900FX

Cutlass Supreme, Grand Prix, Lumina & Regal

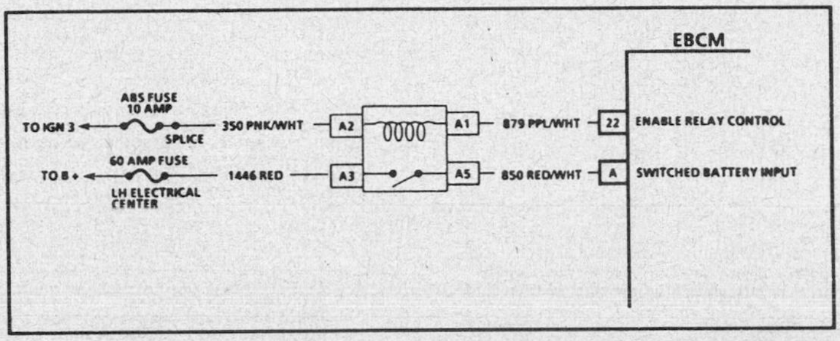
EBCM
ABS FUSE
10 AMP
TO IGN 3
SPLICE
350 PNK/WHT
A2
A1
879 PPL/WHT
22
ENABLE RELAY CONTROL
60 AMP FUSE
TO B+
1446 RED
A3
A5
850 RED/WHT
A
SWITCHED BATTERY INPUT
LH ELECTRICAL CENTER

GC402910067900BX

Beretta & Corsica

Circuit Description:

Ignition voltage is supplied through terminal "5" of the ABS enable relay. The EBCM then is able to energize the pull-in coil by completing the ground circuit at Pin "22" of the EBCM. The magnetic field created closes the enable relay contacts and allows battery voltage and current to be supplied to the EMB's and EBCM, which supplies voltage to the motors and solenoids.

This code monitors the availability of current/voltage to the motors, solenoids and EMB's. A fault of the type specified above would not allow voltage to be available to the motors, solenoids and EMB's and would, therefore, not allow ABS operation if required.

Test Description: Number(s) below refer to circled number(s) on the diagnostic chart.

1. This step indicates that the EBCM is capable of controlling the enable relay as commanded.
2. With the enable relay removed, voltage should not be available at cavity 2. Any voltage at this point would indicate that CKT 879 was shorted to a voltage source.
3. This step checks for an open Quad-Driver in the EBCM.

Diagnostic Aids:

An "Intermittent" problem may be caused by a poor connection, rubbed through wire insulation, or a wire that is broken inside the insulation.

The frequency of the problem can be checked by using the enhanced diagnostic function of the "Scan" tool

Any circuitry, that is suspected as causing the intermittent complaint, should be thoroughly checked for backed out terminals, improper mating, broken locks, improperly formed or damaged terminals, poor terminal to wiring connections or physical damage to the wiring harness.

GC402910067900CX

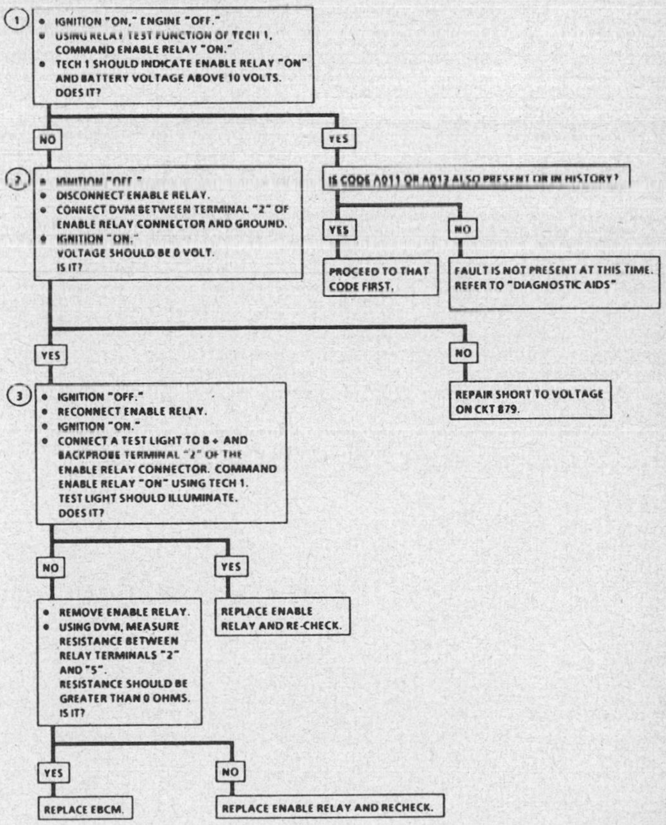
1
• IGNITION "ON," ENGINE "OFF."
• USING RELAY TEST FUNCTION OF TECH 1, COMMAND ENABLE RELAY "ON."
• TECH 1 SHOULD INDICATE ENABLE RELAY "ON" AND BATTERY VOLTAGE ABOVE 10 VOLTS. DOES IT?
NO
YES
IS CODE A011 OR A013 ALSO PRESENT OR IN HISTORY?
YES
NO
PROCEED TO THAT CODE FIRST.
FAULT IS NOT PRESENT AT THIS TIME. REFER TO "DIAGNOSTIC AIDS"
2
• IGNITION "OFF."
• DISCONNECT ENABLE RELAY.
• CONNECT DVM BETWEEN TERMINAL "2" OF ENABLE RELAY CONNECTOR AND GROUND.
• IGNITION "ON." VOLTAGE SHOULD BE 0 VOLT. IS IT?
YES
NO
REPAIR SHORT TO VOLTAGE ON CKT 879.
3
• IGNITION "OFF."
• RECONNECT ENABLE RELAY.
• IGNITION "ON."
• CONNECT A TEST LIGHT TO B+ AND BACKPROBE TERMINAL "2" OF THE ENABLE RELAY CONNECTOR. COMMAND ENABLE RELAY "ON" USING TECH 1. TEST LIGHT SHOULD ILLUMINATE. DOES IT?
NO
YES
REPLACE ENABLE RELAY AND RE-CHECK.
• REMOVE ENABLE RELAY.
• USING DVM, MEASURE RESISTANCE BETWEEN RELAY TERMINALS "2" AND "5". RESISTANCE SHOULD BE GREATER THAN 0 OHMS. IS IT?
YES
NO
REPLACE EBCM.
REPLACE ENABLE RELAY AND RECHECK.

GC402910067900DX

Fig. 35 Code A018: Enable Relay Coil Circuit Shorted To Battery Positive Or Coil Has Zero Ohms. 1992

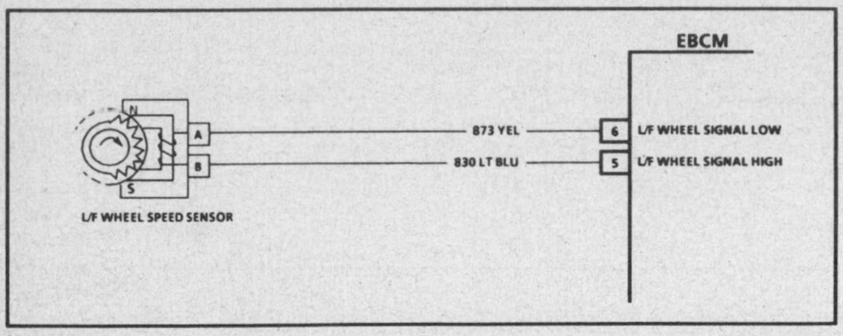
EBCM
873 YEL
830 LT BLU
6 L/F WHEEL SIGNAL LOW
5 L/F WHEEL SIGNAL HIGH
N
S
A
B
L/F WHEEL SPEED SENSOR

GC402910068000AX

Except Cutlass Supreme, Grand Prix, Lumina & Regal

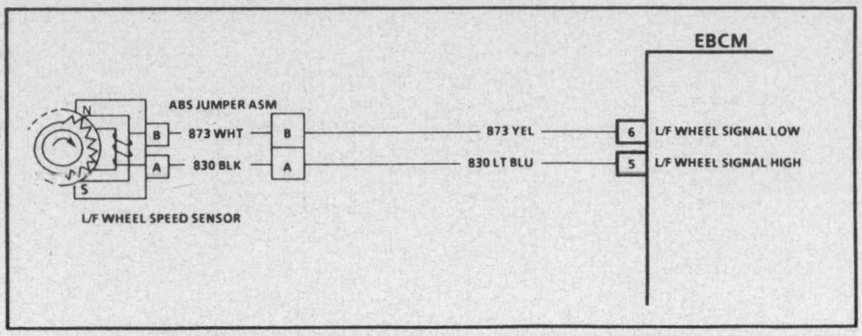
EBCM
ABS JUMPER ASM
873 WHT
830 BLK
873 YEL
830 LT BLU
6 L/F WHEEL SIGNAL LOW
5 L/F WHEEL SIGNAL HIGH
N
S
A
B
L/F WHEEL SPEED SENSOR

GC402910068000BX

Cutlass Supreme, Grand Prix, Lumina & Regal

Circuit Description:

As a toothed ring passes by the wheel speed sensor, changes in the electromagnetic field cause the wheel speed sensor to produce a sinusoidal (AC) voltage signal whose frequency is proportional to wheel speed. The magnitude of this signal is directly related to wheel speed and the proximity of the wheel speed sensor to the toothed ring, often referred to as the air gap.

The code detects opens, shorts to ground, and shorts to battery that cause a wheel speed of 0 mph to be calculated by the ABS EBCM. The conditions present to fail this test are: (1) Three (3) wheels are rotating at least 5 mph, and (2) The fourth wheel is 0 mph.

Test Description: Number(s) below refer to circled number(s) on the diagnostic chart.

1. This test verifies whether the fault is currently present.
2. This step is designed to identify a wheel speed sensor or circuitry that is damaged and visibly apparent.
3. This test checks to see that the wheel speed sensor is within proper resistance values.
4. This insures that the wheel speed sensor is not shorted to ground.

Diagnostic Aids:

An "Intermittent" problem may be caused by a poor connection, rubbed through wire insulation, or a wire that is broken inside the insulation.

The frequency of the problem can be checked by using the enhanced diagnostic function of the "Scan" tool

If the customers comments reflect that the ABS Amber warning light is "ON" only during moist environmental changes, (rain, snow, vehicle wash) all wheel speed sensor circuitry should be thoroughly inspected for signs of water intrusion. Use the following procedure. Spray down the suspected area with 5% salt water solution (two teaspoons of salt to 12 oz. of water). Start vehicle, allow vehicle to run for 10 seconds. If code returns immediately, replace suspected harness.

Any circuitry, that is suspected as causing the intermittent complaint, should be thoroughly checked for backed out terminals, improper mating, broken locks, improperly formed or damaged terminals, poor terminal to wiring connections or physical damage to the wiring harness.

GC402910068000CX

IMPORTANT: WHEEL SPEED SENSOR INTERMITTENT PROBLEMS MAY BE DIFFICULT TO LOCATE. CARE SHOULD BE TAKEN NOT TO DISTURB ANY ELECTRICAL CONNECTIONS PRIOR TO AN INDICATED STEP OF THIS CHART. THIS WILL INSURE THAT AN INTERMITTENT CONNECTION WILL NOT BE CORRECTED BEFORE THE SOURCE OF THE PROBLEM IS FOUND.

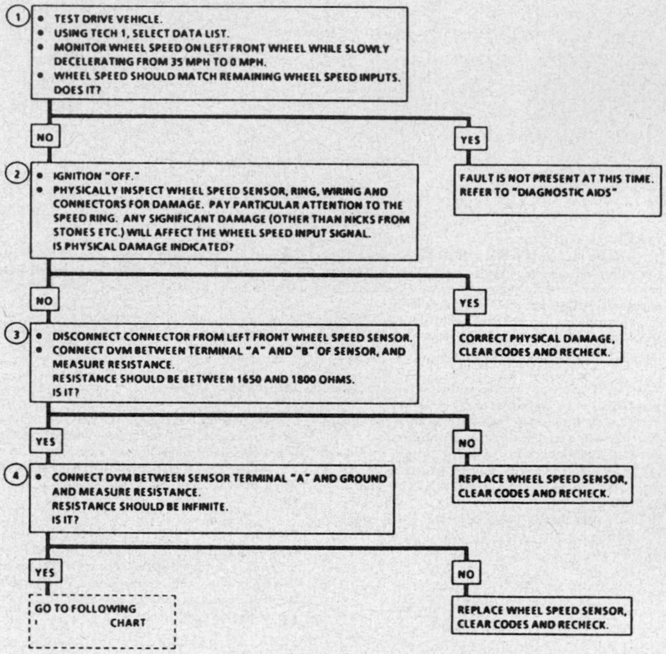
1
• TEST DRIVE VEHICLE.
• USING TECH 1, SELECT DATA LIST.
• MONITOR WHEEL SPEED ON LEFT FRONT WHEEL WHILE SLOWLY DECELERATING FROM 35 MPH TO 0 MPH.
• WHEEL SPEED SHOULD MATCH REMAINING WHEEL SPEED INPUTS. DOES IT?
NO
YES
FAULT IS NOT PRESENT AT THIS TIME. REFER TO "DIAGNOSTIC AIDS"
2
• IGNITION "OFF."
• PHYSICALLY INSPECT WHEEL SPEED SENSOR, RING, WIRING AND CONNECTORS FOR DAMAGE. PAY PARTICULAR ATTENTION TO THE SPEED RING. ANY SIGNIFICANT DAMAGE (OTHER THAN NICKS FROM STONES ETC.) WILL AFFECT THE WHEEL SPEED INPUT SIGNAL. IS PHYSICAL DAMAGE INDICATED?
NO
YES
CORRECT PHYSICAL DAMAGE, CLEAR CODES AND RECHECK.
3
• DISCONNECT CONNECTOR FROM LEFT FRONT WHEEL SPEED SENSOR.
• CONNECT DVM BETWEEN TERMINAL "A" AND "B" OF SENSOR, AND MEASURE RESISTANCE. RESISTANCE SHOULD BE BETWEEN 1650 AND 1800 OHMS. IS IT?
YES
NO
REPLACE WHEEL SPEED SENSOR, CLEAR CODES AND RECHECK.
4
• CONNECT DVM BETWEEN SENSOR TERMINAL "A" AND GROUND AND MEASURE RESISTANCE. RESISTANCE SHOULD BE INFINITE. IS IT?
YES
NO
GO TO FOLLOWING CHART
REPLACE WHEEL SPEED SENSOR, CLEAR CODES AND RECHECK.

GC402910068000DX

Fig. 36 Code A021: Left Front Wheel Speed = 0 (Part 1 of 2). 1992

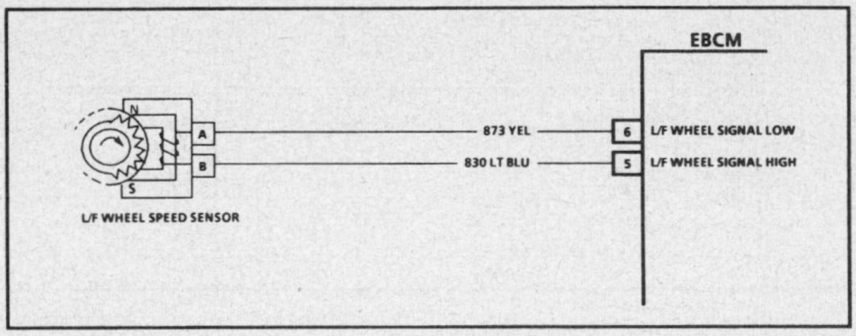
EBCM
N
S
A
B
873 YEL
830 LT BLU
6
5
L/F WHEEL SIGNAL LOW
L/F WHEEL SIGNAL HIGH
L/F WHEEL SPEED SENSOR

GC402910068000EX

Except Cutlass Supreme, Grand Prix, Lumina & Regal

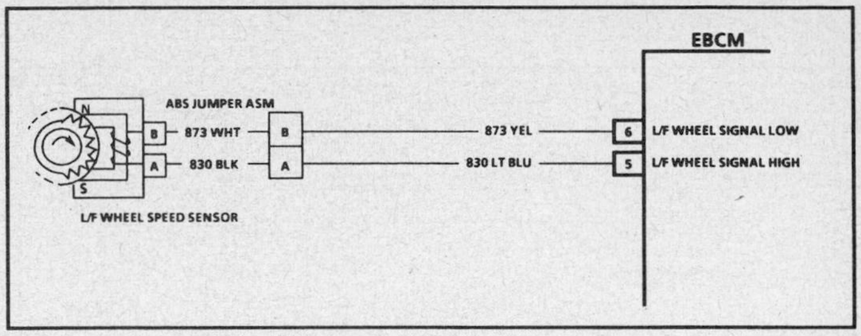
EBCM
ABS JUMPER ASM
N
S
B
A
873 WHT
830 BLK
873 YEL
830 LT BLU
6
5
L/F WHEEL SIGNAL LOW
L/F WHEEL SIGNAL HIGH
L/F WHEEL SPEED SENSOR

GC402910068000FX

Cutlass Supreme, Grand Prix, Lumina & Regal

Circuit Description:

As a toothed ring passes by the wheel speed sensor, changes in the electromagnetic field cause the wheel speed sensor to produce a sinusoidal (AC) voltage signal whose frequency is proportional to wheel speed. The magnitude of this signal is directly related to wheel speed and the proximity of the wheel speed sensor to the toothed ring often referred to as the air gap.

This code detects opens, shorts to ground, and shorts to battery that cause a wheel speed of 0 mph to be calculated by the ABS EBCM. The conditions present to fail this test are: (1) Three (3) wheels are rotating at least 5 mph, and (2) The fourth wheel is 0 mph.

Test Description: Number(s) below refer to circled number(s) on the diagnostic chart.

5. This step checks to see if the wheel speed sensor circuitry is shorted to voltage.
6. This step insures that the wheel speed sensor circuitry resistance is within the proper value.
7. This checks for an open in the wheel signal low circuit.
8. This checks for an open in the wheel signal high circuit.
9. This step insures that Code A021 was not set due to a poor connection between the world connector and EBCM.

Diagnostic Aids:

An "Intermittent" problem may be caused by a poor connection, rubbed through wire insulation, or a wire that is broken inside the insulation.

The frequency of the problem can be checked by using the enhanced diagnostic function of the "Scan" tool.

If the customers comments reflect that the ABS Amber warning light is "ON" only during moist environmental changes, (rain, snow, vehicle wash) all wheel speed sensor circuitry should be thoroughly inspected for signs of water intrusion. Use the following procedure. Spray down the suspected area with 5% salt water solution (two teaspoons of salt to 12 oz. of water). Start vehicle, allow vehicle to run for 10 seconds. If code returns immediately, replace suspected harness.

Any circuitry, that is suspected as causing the intermittent complaint, should be thoroughly checked for backed out terminals, improper mating, broken locks, improperly formed or damaged terminals, poor terminal to wiring connections or physical damage to the wiring harness.

GC402910068000GX

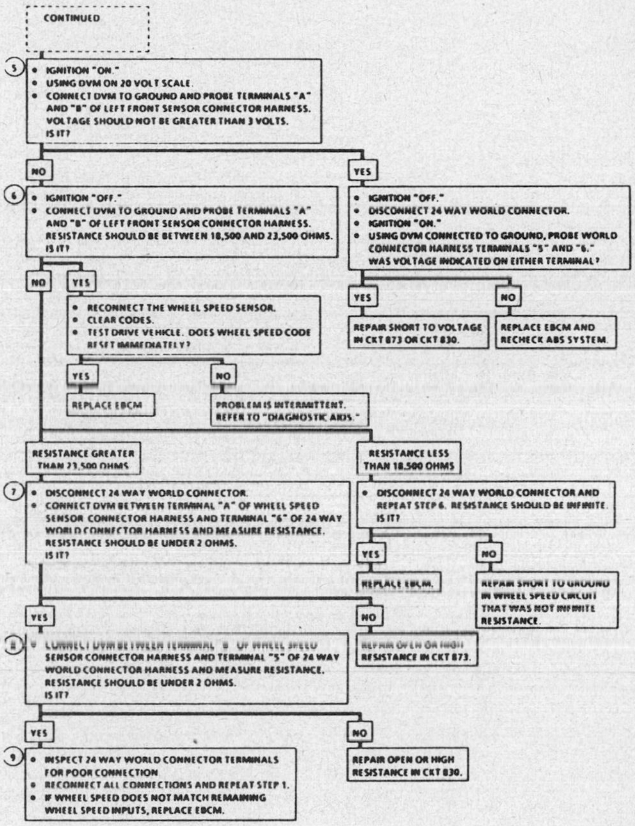
CONTINUED
5
• IGNITION "ON."
• USING DVM ON 20 VOLT SCALE.
• CONNECT DVM TO GROUND AND PROBE TERMINALS "A" AND "B" OF LEFT FRONT SENSOR CONNECTOR HARNESS. VOLTAGE SHOULD NOT BE GREATER THAN 3 VOLTS. IS IT?
NO
YES
6
• IGNITION "OFF."
• CONNECT DVM TO GROUND AND PROBE TERMINALS "A" AND "B" OF LEFT FRONT SENSOR CONNECTOR HARNESS. RESISTANCE SHOULD BE BETWEEN 18,500 AND 23,500 OHMS. IS IT?
• IGNITION "OFF."
• DISCONNECT 24 WAY WORLD CONNECTOR.
• IGNITION "ON."
• USING DVM CONNECTED TO GROUND, PROBE WORLD CONNECTOR HARNESS TERMINALS "5" AND "6." WAS VOLTAGE INDICATED ON EITHER TERMINAL?
NO
YES
• RECONNECT THE WHEEL SPEED SENSOR.
• CLEAR CODES.
• TEST DRIVE VEHICLE. DOES WHEEL SPEED CODE RESET IMMEDIATELY?
YES
NO
REPAIR SHORT TO VOLTAGE IN CKT 873 OR CKT 830.
REPLACE EBCM AND RECHECK ABS SYSTEM.
YES
NO
REPLACE EBCM
PROBLEM IS INTERMITTENT. REFER TO "DIAGNOSTIC AIDS."
RESISTANCE GREATER THAN 23,500 OHMS
RESISTANCE LESS THAN 18,500 OHMS
7
• DISCONNECT 24 WAY WORLD CONNECTOR.
• CONNECT DVM BETWEEN TERMINAL "A" OF WHEEL SPEED SENSOR CONNECTOR HARNESS AND TERMINAL "6" OF 24 WAY WORLD CONNECTOR HARNESS AND MEASURE RESISTANCE. RESISTANCE SHOULD BE UNDER 2 OHMS. IS IT?
• DISCONNECT 24 WAY WORLD CONNECTOR AND REPEAT STEP 6. RESISTANCE SHOULD BE INFINITE. IS IT?
YES
NO
REPLACE EBCM.
REPAIR SHORT TO GROUND IN WHEEL SPEED CIRCUIT THAT WAS NOT INFINITE RESISTANCE.
YES
NO
8
• CONNECT DVM BETWEEN TERMINAL "B" OF WHEEL SPEED SENSOR CONNECTOR HARNESS AND TERMINAL "5" OF 24 WAY WORLD CONNECTOR HARNESS AND MEASURE RESISTANCE. RESISTANCE SHOULD BE UNDER 2 OHMS. IS IT?
REPAIR OPEN OR HIGH RESISTANCE IN CKT 873.
YES
NO
9
• INSPECT 24 WAY WORLD CONNECTOR TERMINALS FOR POOR CONNECTION
• RECONNECT ALL CONNECTIONS AND REPEAT STEP 1.
• IF WHEEL SPEED DOES NOT MATCH REMAINING WHEEL SPEED INPUTS, REPLACE EBCM.
REPAIR OPEN OR HIGH RESISTANCE IN CKT 830.

GC402910068000HX

Fig. 36 Code A021: Left Front Wheel Speed = 0 (Part 2 of 2). 1992

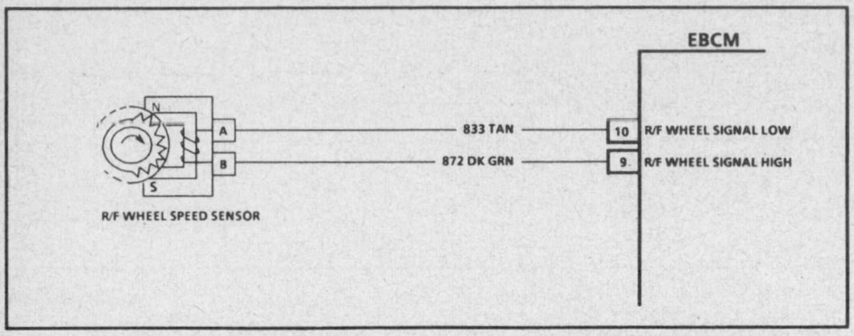
EBCM
A
B
N
S
833 TAN
872 DK GRN
10
9
R/F WHEEL SIGNAL LOW
R/F WHEEL SIGNAL HIGH
R/F WHEEL SPEED SENSOR

GC402910068100AX

Except Cutlass Supreme, Grand Prix, Lumina & Regal

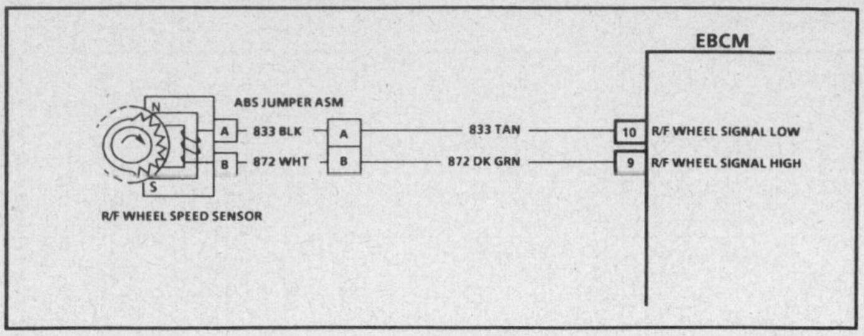
EBCM
ABS JUMPER ASM
N
S
A
B
833 BLK
872 WHT
833 TAN
872 DK GRN
10
9
R/F WHEEL SIGNAL LOW
R/F WHEEL SIGNAL HIGH
R/F WHEEL SPEED SENSOR

GC402910068100BX

Cutlass Supreme, Grand Prix, Lumina & Regal

Circuit Description:

As a toothed ring passes by the wheel speed sensor, changes in the electromagnetic field cause the wheel speed sensor to produce a sinusoidal (AC) voltage signal whose frequency is proportional to wheel speed. The magnitude of this signal is directly related to wheel speed and the proximity of the wheel speed sensor to the toothed ring, often referred to as the air gap.

This code detects opens, shorts to ground, and shorts to battery that cause a wheel speed of 0 mph to be calculated by the ABS EBCM. The conditions present to fail this test are: (1) Three (3) wheels are rotating at least 5 mph, and (2) The fourth wheel is 0 mph.

Test Description: Number(s) below refer to circled number(s) on the diagnostic chart.

1. This test verifies whether the fault is currently present.
2. This step is designed to identify a wheel speed sensor or circuitry that is damaged and visibly apparent.
3. This test checks to see that the wheel speed sensor is within proper resistance values.
4. This insures that the wheel speed sensor is not shorted to ground.

Diagnostic Aids:

An "Intermittent" problem may be caused by a poor connection, rubbed through wire insulation, or a wire that is broken inside the insulation.

The frequency of the problem can be checked by using the enhanced diagnostic function of the "Scan" tool.

If the customers comments reflect that the ABS Amber warning light is on only during moist environmental changes, (rain, snow, vehicle wash) all wheel speed sensor circuitry should be thoroughly inspected for signs of water intrusion. Use the following procedure. Spray down the suspected area with 5% salt water solution (two teaspoons of salt to 12 oz. of water). Start vehicle, allow vehicle to run for 10 seconds. If code returns immediately, replace suspected harness.

Any circuitry, that is suspected as causing the intermittent complaint, should be thoroughly checked for backed out terminals, improper mating, broken locks, improperly formed or damaged terminals, poor terminal to wiring connections or physical damage to the wiring harness.

GC402910068100CX

IMPORTANT: WHEEL SPEED SENSOR INTERMITTENT PROBLEMS MAY BE DIFFICULT TO LOCATE. CARE SHOULD BE TAKEN NOT TO DISTURB ANY ELECTRICAL CONNECTIONS PRIOR TO AN INDICATED STEP OF THIS CHART. THIS WILL INSURE THAT AN INTERMITTENT CONNECTION WILL NOT BE CORRECTED BEFORE THE SOURCE OF THE PROBLEM IS FOUND.

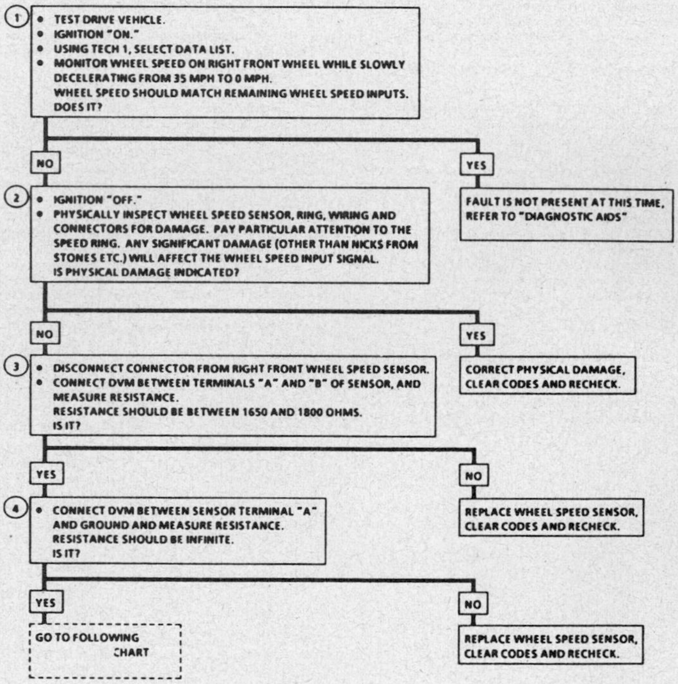
1
• TEST DRIVE VEHICLE.
• IGNITION "ON."
• USING TECH 1, SELECT DATA LIST.
• MONITOR WHEEL SPEED ON RIGHT FRONT WHEEL WHILE SLOWLY DECELERATING FROM 35 MPH TO 0 MPH.
WHEEL SPEED SHOULD MATCH REMAINING WHEEL SPEED INPUTS.
DOES IT?
NO
YES
FAULT IS NOT PRESENT AT THIS TIME, REFER TO "DIAGNOSTIC AIDS"
2
• IGNITION "OFF."
• PHYSICALLY INSPECT WHEEL SPEED SENSOR, RING, WIRING AND CONNECTORS FOR DAMAGE. PAY PARTICULAR ATTENTION TO THE SPEED RING. ANY SIGNIFICANT DAMAGE (OTHER THAN NICKS FROM STONES ETC.) WILL AFFECT THE WHEEL SPEED INPUT SIGNAL.
IS PHYSICAL DAMAGE INDICATED?
NO
YES
CORRECT PHYSICAL DAMAGE, CLEAR CODES AND RECHECK.
3
• DISCONNECT CONNECTOR FROM RIGHT FRONT WHEEL SPEED SENSOR.
• CONNECT DVM BETWEEN TERMINALS "A" AND "B" OF SENSOR, AND MEASURE RESISTANCE.
RESISTANCE SHOULD BE BETWEEN 1650 AND 1800 OHMS.
IS IT?
YES
NO
REPLACE WHEEL SPEED SENSOR, CLEAR CODES AND RECHECK.
4
• CONNECT DVM BETWEEN SENSOR TERMINAL "A" AND GROUND AND MEASURE RESISTANCE.
RESISTANCE SHOULD BE INFINITE.
IS IT?
YES
NO
GO TO FOLLOWING CHART
REPLACE WHEEL SPEED SENSOR, CLEAR CODES AND RECHECK.

GC402910068100DX

Fig. 37 Code A022: Right Front Wheel Speed = 0 (Part 1 of 2). 1992

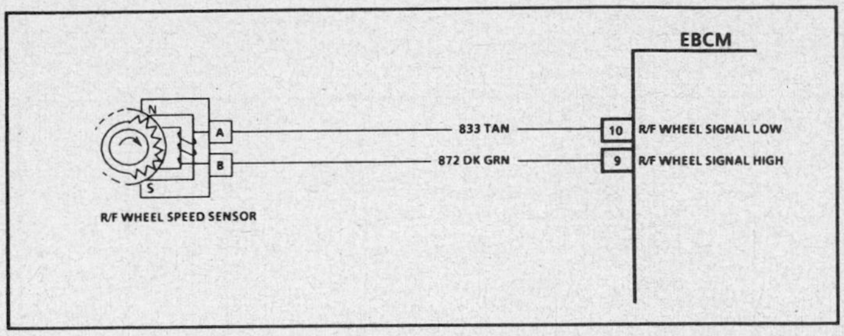
EBCM
N
A
B
S
833 TAN
872 DK GRN
10
9
R/F WHEEL SIGNAL LOW
R/F WHEEL SIGNAL HIGH
R/F WHEEL SPEED SENSOR

GC402910068100EX

Except Cutlass Supreme, Grand Prix, Lumina & Regal

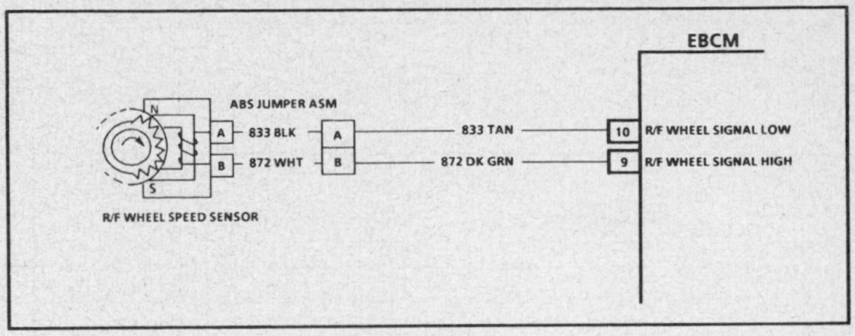
EBCM
ABS JUMPER ASM
N
A
B
S
833 BLK
872 WHT
833 TAN
872 DK GRN
10
9
R/F WHEEL SIGNAL LOW
R/F WHEEL SIGNAL HIGH
R/F WHEEL SPEED SENSOR

GC402910068100FX

Cutlass Supreme, Grand Prix, Lumina & Regal

Circuit Description:

As a toothed ring passes by the wheel speed sensor, changes in the electromagnetic field cause the wheel speed sensor to produce a sinusoidal (AC) voltage signal whose frequency is proportional to wheel speed. The magnitude of this signal is directly related to wheel speed and the proximity of the wheel speed sensor to the toothed ring, often referred to as the air gap.

This code detects opens, shorts to ground, and shorts to battery that cause a wheel speed of 0 mph to be calculated by the ABS EBCM. The conditions present to fail this test are: (1) Three (3) wheels are rotating at least 5 mph, and (2) The fourth wheel is 0 mph.

Test Description: Number(s) below refer to circled number(s) on the diagnostic chart.

5. This step checks to see if the wheel speed sensor circuitry is shorted to voltage.
6. This step insures that the wheel speed sensor circuitry resistance is within the proper value.
7. This checks for an open in the wheel signal low circuit.
8. This checks for an open in the wheel signal high circuit.
9. This step insures that Code A022 was not set due to a poor connection between the world connector and EBCM.

Diagnostic Aids:

An "Intermittent" problem may be caused by a poor connection, rubbed through wire insulation, or a wire that is broken inside the insulation.

The frequency of the problem can be checked by using the enhanced diagnostic function of the "Scan" tool.

If the customers comments reflect that the ABS Amber warning light is "ON" only during moist environmental changes, (rain, snow, vehicle wash) all wheel speed sensor circuitry should be thoroughly inspected for signs of water intrusion. Use the following procedure. Spray down the suspected area with 5% salt water solution (two teaspoons of salt to 12 oz. of water). Start vehicle, allow vehicle to run for 10 seconds. If code returns immediately, replace suspected harness.

Any circuitry, that is suspected as causing the intermittent complaint, should be thoroughly checked for backed out terminals, improper mating, broken locks, improperly formed or damaged terminals, poor terminal to wiring connections or physical damage to the wiring harness.

GC402910068100GX

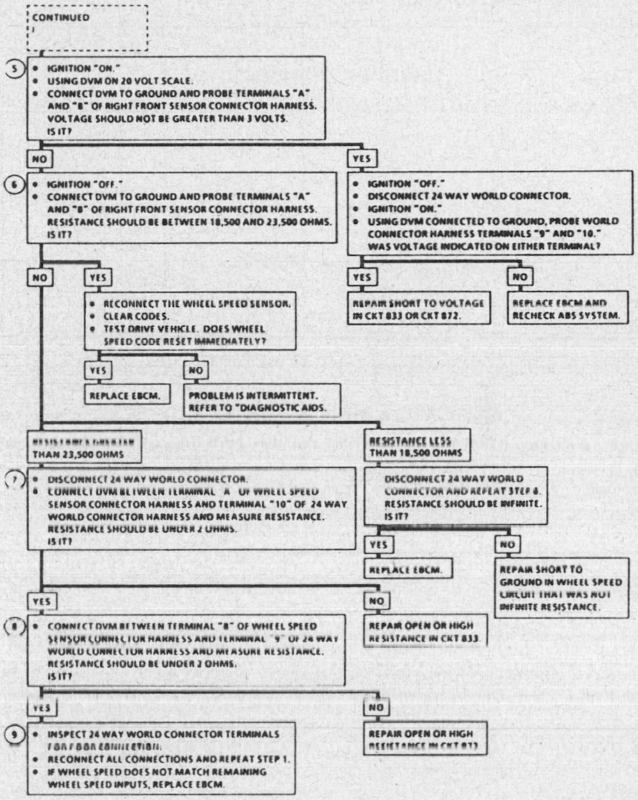
CONTINUED
5
• IGNITION "ON."
• USING DVM ON 20 VOLT SCALE.
• CONNECT DVM TO GROUND AND PROBE TERMINALS "A" AND "B" OF RIGHT FRONT SENSOR CONNECTOR HARNESS. VOLTAGE SHOULD NOT BE GREATER THAN 3 VOLTS. IS IT?
NO
YES
6
• IGNITION "OFF."
• CONNECT DVM TO GROUND AND PROBE TERMINALS "A" AND "B" OF RIGHT FRONT SENSOR CONNECTOR HARNESS. RESISTANCE SHOULD BE BETWEEN 18,500 AND 23,500 OHMS. IS IT?
• IGNITION "OFF."
• DISCONNECT 24 WAY WORLD CONNECTOR.
• IGNITION "ON."
• USING DVM CONNECTED TO GROUND, PROBE WORLD CONNECTOR HARNESS TERMINALS "9" AND "10." WAS VOLTAGE INDICATED ON EITHER TERMINAL?
NO
YES
YES
NO
• RECONNECT THE WHEEL SPEED SENSOR.
• CLEAR CODES.
• TEST DRIVE VEHICLE. DOES WHEEL SPEED CODE RESET IMMEDIATELY?
REPAIR SHORT TO VOLTAGE IN CKT 833 OR CKT 872.
REPLACE EBCM AND RECHECK ABS SYSTEM.
YES
NO
REPLACE EBCM.
PROBLEM IS INTERMITTENT. REFER TO "DIAGNOSTIC AIDS.
THAN 23,500 OHMS
RESISTANCE LESS THAN 18,500 OHMS
7
• DISCONNECT 24 WAY WORLD CONNECTOR.
SENSOR CONNECTOR HARNESS AND TERMINAL "10" OF 24 WAY WORLD CONNECTOR HARNESS AND MEASURE RESISTANCE.
IS IT?
DISCONNECT 24 WAY WORLD CONNECTOR AND REPEAT STEP 6. RESISTANCE SHOULD BE INFINITE. IS IT?
YES
NO
REPLACE EBCM.
REPAIR SHORT TO GROUND IN WHEEL SPEED INFINITE RESISTANCE.
YES
NO
8
• CONNECT DVM BETWEEN TERMINAL "B" OF WHEEL SPEED
WORLD CONNECTOR HARNESS AND MEASURE RESISTANCE.
RESISTANCE SHOULD BE UNDER 2 OHMS.
IS IT?
REPAIR OPEN OR HIGH RESISTANCE IN CKT 833.
YES
NO
9
• INSPECT 24 WAY WORLD CONNECTOR TERMINALS
• RECONNECT ALL CONNECTIONS AND REPEAT STEP 1.
• IF WHEEL SPEED DOES NOT MATCH REMAINING WHEEL SPEED INPUTS, REPLACE EBCM.
REPAIR OPEN OR HIGH

GC402910068100HX

Fig. 37 Code A022: Right Front Wheel Speed = 0 (Part 2 of 2). 1992

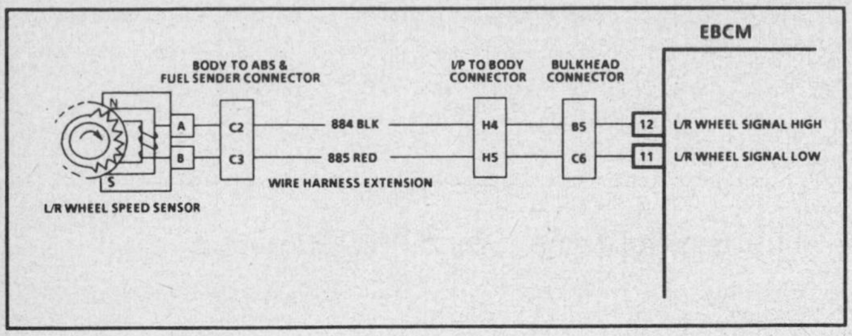
EBCM
BODY TO ABS & FUEL SENDER CONNECTOR
I/P TO BODY CONNECTOR
BULKHEAD CONNECTOR
N
A
B
S
C2
C3
884 BLK
885 RED
H4
H5
B5
C6
12
11
L/R WHEEL SIGNAL HIGH
L/R WHEEL SIGNAL LOW
WIRE HARNESS EXTENSION
L/R WHEEL SPEED SENSOR

GC402910068200AX

Cavalier & Sunbird

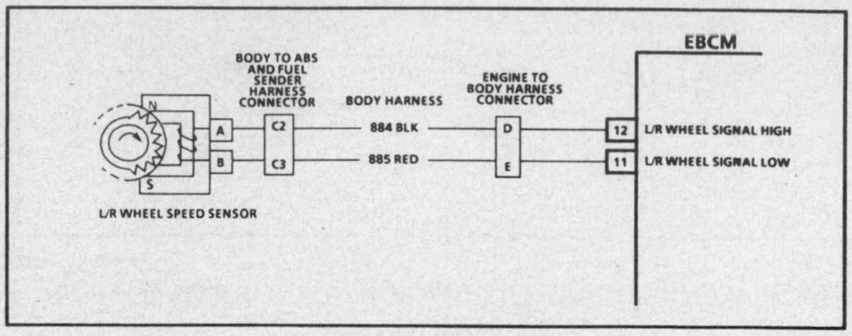
EBCM
BODY TO ABS AND FUEL SENDER HARNESS CONNECTOR
BODY HARNESS
ENGINE TO BODY HARNESS CONNECTOR
N
A
B
S
C2
C3
884 BLK
885 RED
D
E
12
11
L/R WHEEL SIGNAL HIGH
L/R WHEEL SIGNAL LOW
L/R WHEEL SPEED SENSOR

GC402910068200BX

Beretta & Corsica

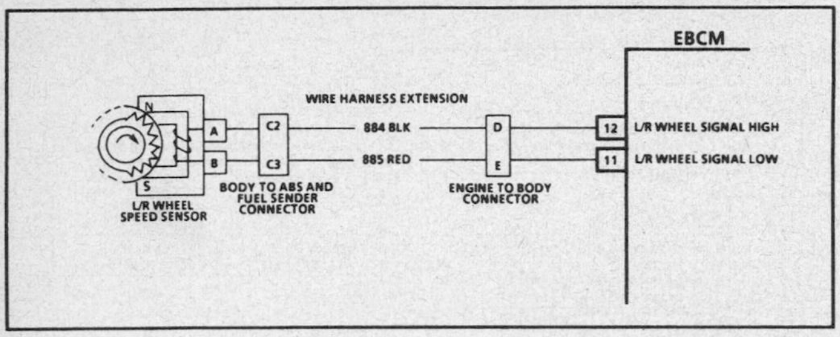
EBCM
WIRE HARNESS EXTENSION
N
A
B
S
C2
C3
884 BLK
885 RED
D
E
12
11
L/R WHEEL SIGNAL HIGH
L/R WHEEL SIGNAL LOW
L/R WHEEL SPEED SENSOR
BODY TO ABS AND FUEL SENDER CONNECTOR
ENGINE TO BODY CONNECTOR

GC402910068200CX

Achieva, Calais & Grand Am

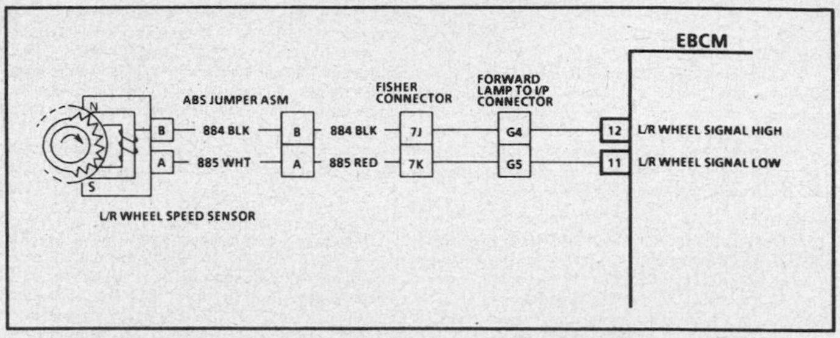
EBCM
ABS JUMPER ASM
FISHER CONNECTOR
FORWARD LAMP TO I/P CONNECTOR
N
B
A
S
884 BLK
885 WHT
884 BLK
885 RED
7J
7K
G4
G5
12
11
L/R WHEEL SIGNAL HIGH
L/R WHEEL SIGNAL LOW
L/R WHEEL SPEED SENSOR

GC402910068200DX

Cutlass Supreme, Grand Prix, Lumina & Regal

IMPORTANT: WHEEL SPEED SENSOR INTERMITTENT PROBLEMS MAY BE DIFFICULT TO LOCATE. CARE SHOULD BE TAKEN NOT TO DISTURB ANY ELECTRICAL CONNECTIONS PRIOR TO AN INDICATED STEP OF THIS CHART. THIS WILL INSURE THAT AN INTERMITTENT CONNECTION WILL NOT BE CORRECTED BEFORE THE SOURCE OF THE PROBLEM IS FOUND.

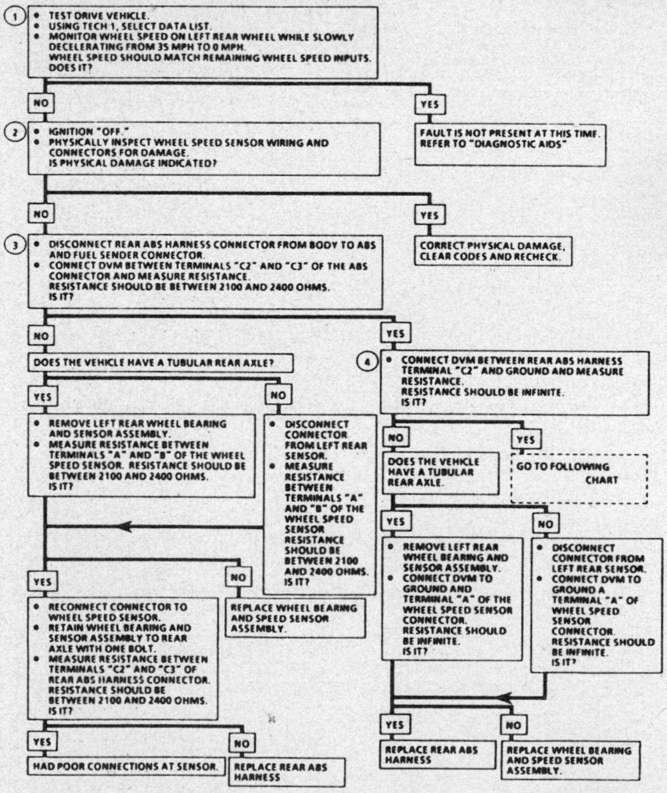
1
• TEST DRIVE VEHICLE.
• USING TECH 1, SELECT DATA LIST.
• MONITOR WHEEL SPEED ON LEFT REAR WHEEL WHILE SLOWLY DECELERATING FROM 35 MPH TO 0 MPH.
WHEEL SPEED SHOULD MATCH REMAINING WHEEL SPEED INPUTS. DOES IT?
NO
YES
FAULT IS NOT PRESENT AT THIS TIME. REFER TO "DIAGNOSTIC AIDS"
2
• IGNITION "OFF."
• PHYSICALLY INSPECT WHEEL SPEED SENSOR WIRING AND CONNECTORS FOR DAMAGE.
IS PHYSICAL DAMAGE INDICATED?
NO
YES
CORRECT PHYSICAL DAMAGE, CLEAR CODES AND RECHECK.
3
• DISCONNECT REAR ABS HARNESS CONNECTOR FROM BODY TO ABS AND FUEL SENDER CONNECTOR.
• CONNECT DVM BETWEEN TERMINALS "C2" AND "C3" OF THE ABS CONNECTOR AND MEASURE RESISTANCE.
RESISTANCE SHOULD BE BETWEEN 2100 AND 2400 OHMS. IS IT?
NO
YES
DOES THE VEHICLE HAVE A TUBULAR REAR AXLE?
YES
NO
• REMOVE LEFT REAR WHEEL BEARING AND SENSOR ASSEMBLY.
• MEASURE RESISTANCE BETWEEN TERMINALS "A" AND "B" OF THE WHEEL SPEED SENSOR. RESISTANCE SHOULD BE BETWEEN 2100 AND 2400 OHMS. IS IT?
• DISCONNECT CONNECTOR FROM LEFT REAR SENSOR.
• MEASURE RESISTANCE BETWEEN TERMINALS "A" AND "B" OF THE WHEEL SPEED SENSOR RESISTANCE SHOULD BE BETWEEN 2100 AND 2400 OHMS. IS IT?
YES
NO
• RECONNECT CONNECTOR TO WHEEL SPEED SENSOR.
• RETAIN WHEEL BEARING AND SENSOR ASSEMBLY TO REAR AXLE WITH ONE BOLT.
• MEASURE RESISTANCE BETWEEN TERMINALS "C2" AND "C3" OF REAR ABS HARNESS CONNECTOR. RESISTANCE SHOULD BE BETWEEN 2100 AND 2400 OHMS. IS IT?
REPLACE WHEEL BEARING AND SPEED SENSOR ASSEMBLY.
YES
NO
HAD POOR CONNECTIONS AT SENSOR.
REPLACE REAR ABS HARNESS
4
• CONNECT DVM BETWEEN REAR ABS HARNESS TERMINAL "C2" AND GROUND AND MEASURE RESISTANCE.
RESISTANCE SHOULD BE INFINITE. IS IT?
NO
YES
DOES THE VEHICLE HAVE A TUBULAR REAR AXLE.
GO TO FOLLOWING CHART
YES
NO
• REMOVE LEFT REAR WHEEL BEARING AND SENSOR ASSEMBLY.
• CONNECT DVM TO GROUND AND TERMINAL "A" OF THE WHEEL SPEED SENSOR CONNECTOR.
RESISTANCE SHOULD BE INFINITE. IS IT?
• DISCONNECT CONNECTOR FROM LEFT REAR SENSOR.
• CONNECT DVM TO GROUND A TERMINAL "A" OF WHEEL SPEED SENSOR CONNECTOR.
RESISTANCE SHOULD BE INFINITE. IS IT?
YES
NO
REPLACE REAR ABS HARNESS
REPLACE WHEEL BEARING AND SPEED SENSOR ASSEMBLY.

GC402910068200FX

Circuit Description:

As a toothed ring passes by the wheel speed sensor, changes in the electromagnetic field cause the wheel speed sensor to produce a sinusoidal (AC) voltage signal whose frequency is proportional to wheel speed. The magnitude of this signal is directly related to wheel speed and the proximity of the wheel speed sensor to the toothed ring, often referred to as the air gap.

This code detects opens, shorts to ground, and shorts to battery that cause a wheel speed of 0 mph to be calculated by the ABS EBCM. The conditions present to fail this test are: (1) Three (3) wheels are rotating at least 5 mph, (2) The fourth wheel is 0 mph.

Test Description: Number(s) below refer to circled number(s) on the diagnostic chart.

1. This test verifies whether the fault is currently present.
2. This step is designed to identify a wheel speed sensor or circuitry that is damaged and visibly apparent.
3. This test checks to see that the wheel speed sensor is within proper resistance values.
4. This insures that the wheel speed sensor is not shorted to ground.

Diagnostic Aids:

An "Intermittent" problem may be caused by a poor connection, rubbed through wire insulation, or a wire that is broken inside the insulation.

The frequency of the problem can be checked by using the enhanced diagnostic function of the "Scan" tool.

If the customers comments reflect that the ABS Amber warning light is "ON" only during moist environmental changes, (rain, snow, vehicle wash) all wheel speed senor circuitry should be thoroughly inspected for signs of water intrusion. Use the following procedure. Spray down the suspected area with 5% salt water solution (two teaspoons of salt to 12 oz. of water). Start vehicle, allow vehicle to run for 10 seconds. If code returns immediately, replace suspected harness.

Any circuitry, that is suspected as causing the intermittent complaint, should be thoroughly checked for backed out terminals, improper mating, broken locks, improperly formed or damaged terminals, poor terminal to wiring connections or physical damage to the wiring harness.

GC402910068200EX

Fig. 38 Code A023: Left Rear Wheel Speed = 0 (Part 1 of 2). 1992

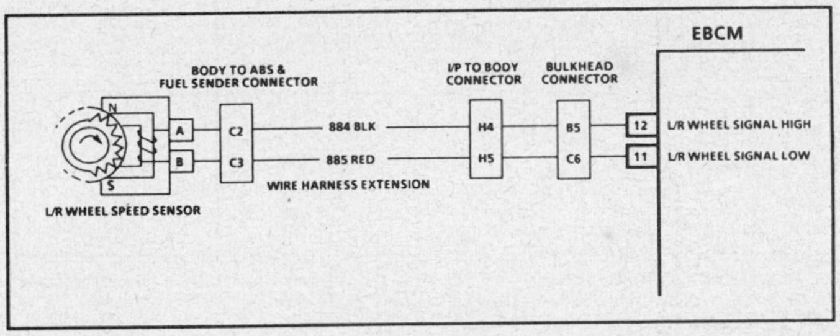
EBCM
BODY TO ABS & FUEL SENDER CONNECTOR
I/P TO BODY CONNECTOR
BULKHEAD CONNECTOR
884 BLK
885 RED
WIRE HARNESS EXTENSION
L/R WHEEL SIGNAL HIGH
L/R WHEEL SIGNAL LOW
L/R WHEEL SPEED SENSOR

GC402910068200GX

Cavalier & Sunbird

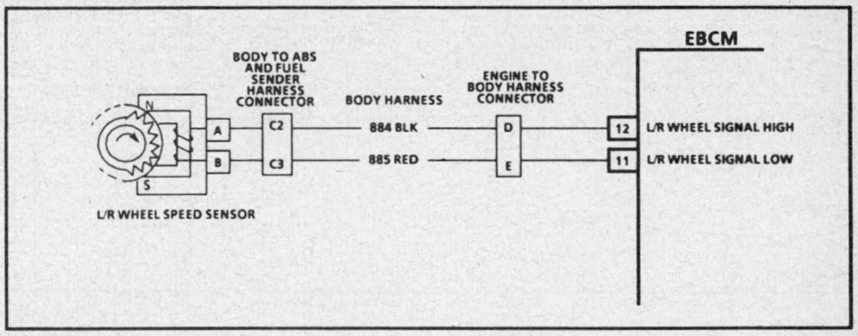
EBCM
BODY TO ABS AND FUEL SENDER HARNESS CONNECTOR
BODY HARNESS
ENGINE TO BODY HARNESS CONNECTOR
884 BLK
885 RED
L/R WHEEL SIGNAL HIGH
L/R WHEEL SIGNAL LOW
L/R WHEEL SPEED SENSOR

GC402910068200HX

Beretta & Corsica

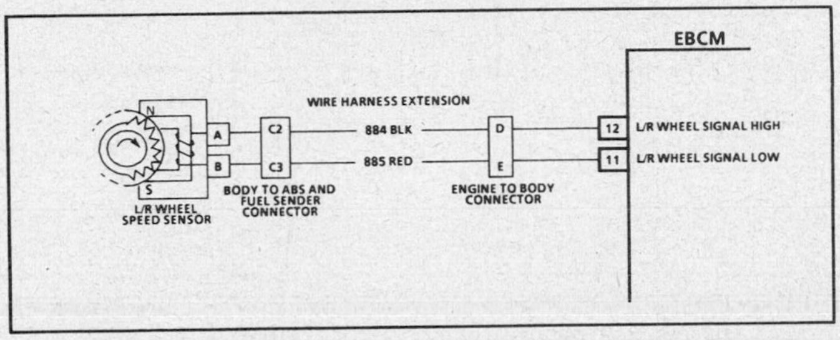
EBCM
WIRE HARNESS EXTENSION
884 BLK
885 RED
L/R WHEEL SIGNAL HIGH
L/R WHEEL SIGNAL LOW
L/R WHEEL SPEED SENSOR
BODY TO ABS AND FUEL SENDER CONNECTOR
ENGINE TO BODY CONNECTOR

GC402910068200IX

Achieva, Calais & Grand Am

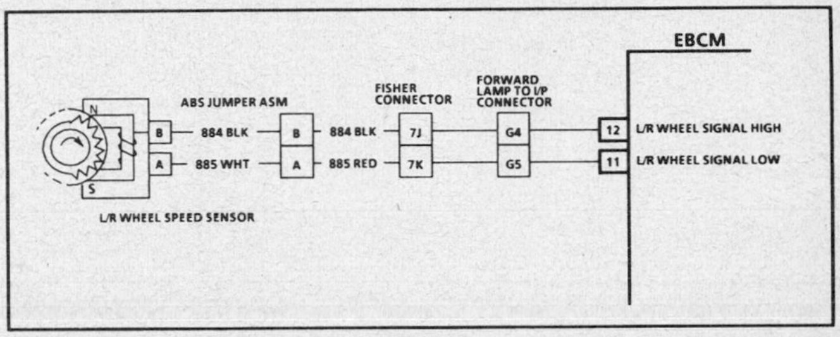
EBCM
ABS JUMPER ASM
FISHER CONNECTOR
FORWARD LAMP TO I/P CONNECTOR
884 BLK
885 WHT
884 BLK
885 RED
L/R WHEEL SIGNAL HIGH
L/R WHEEL SIGNAL LOW
L/R WHEEL SPEED SENSOR

GC402910068200JX

Cutlass Supreme, Grand Prix, Lumina & Regal

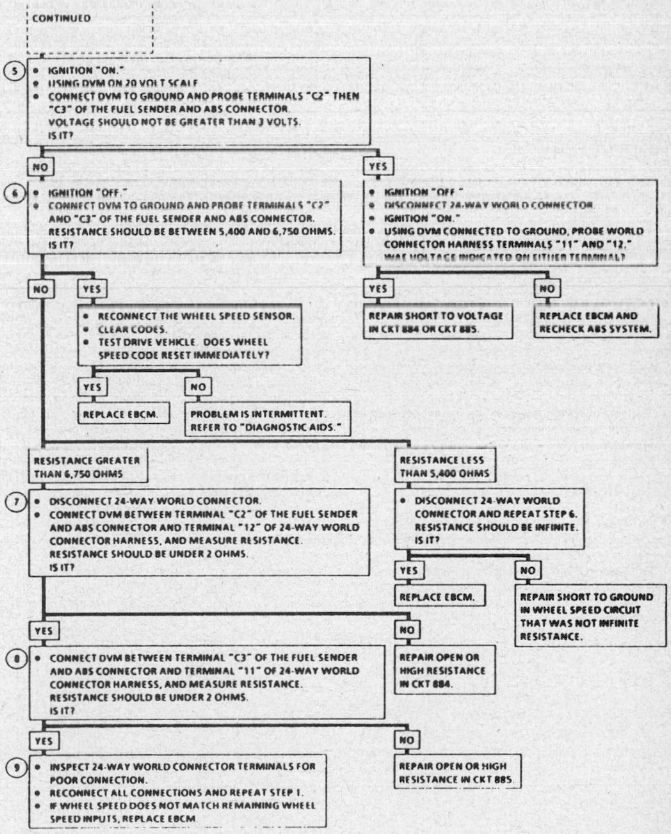
CONTINUED
5 • IGNITION "ON." • USING DVM ON 20 VOLT SCALE • CONNECT DVM TO GROUND AND PROBE TERMINALS "C2" THEN "C3" OF THE FUEL SENDER AND ABS CONNECTOR. VOLTAGE SHOULD NOT BE GREATER THAN 3 VOLTS. IS IT?
NO
YES
6 • IGNITION "OFF." • CONNECT DVM TO GROUND AND PROBE TERMINALS "C2" AND "C3" OF THE FUEL SENDER AND ABS CONNECTOR. RESISTANCE SHOULD BE BETWEEN 5,400 AND 6,750 OHMS. IS IT?
• IGNITION "OFF." • DISCONNECT 24-WAY WORLD CONNECTOR. • IGNITION "ON." • USING DVM CONNECTED TO GROUND, PROBE WORLD CONNECTOR HARNESS TERMINALS "11" AND "12." WAS VOLTAGE INDICATED ON EITHER TERMINAL?
NO
YES
YES
NO
• RECONNECT THE WHEEL SPEED SENSOR. • CLEAR CODES. • TEST DRIVE VEHICLE. DOES WHEEL SPEED CODE RESET IMMEDIATELY?
REPAIR SHORT TO VOLTAGE IN CKT 884 OR CKT 885.
REPLACE EBCM AND RECHECK ABS SYSTEM.
YES
NO
REPLACE EBCM.
PROBLEM IS INTERMITTENT. REFER TO "DIAGNOSTIC AIDS."
RESISTANCE GREATER THAN 6,750 OHMS
RESISTANCE LESS THAN 5,400 OHMS
7 • DISCONNECT 24-WAY WORLD CONNECTOR. • CONNECT DVM BETWEEN TERMINAL "C2" OF THE FUEL SENDER AND ABS CONNECTOR AND TERMINAL "12" OF 24-WAY WORLD CONNECTOR HARNESS, AND MEASURE RESISTANCE. RESISTANCE SHOULD BE UNDER 2 OHMS. IS IT?
• DISCONNECT 24-WAY WORLD CONNECTOR AND REPEAT STEP 6. RESISTANCE SHOULD BE INFINITE. IS IT?
YES
NO
REPLACE EBCM.
REPAIR SHORT TO GROUND IN WHEEL SPEED CIRCUIT THAT WAS NOT INFINITE RESISTANCE.
YES
NO
8 • CONNECT DVM BETWEEN TERMINAL "C3" OF THE FUEL SENDER AND ABS CONNECTOR AND TERMINAL "11" OF 24-WAY WORLD CONNECTOR HARNESS, AND MEASURE RESISTANCE. RESISTANCE SHOULD BE UNDER 2 OHMS. IS IT?
REPAIR OPEN OR HIGH RESISTANCE IN CKT 884.
YES
NO
9 • INSPECT 24-WAY WORLD CONNECTOR TERMINALS FOR POOR CONNECTION. • RECONNECT ALL CONNECTIONS AND REPEAT STEP 1. • IF WHEEL SPEED DOES NOT MATCH REMAINING WHEEL SPEED INPUTS, REPLACE EBCM
REPAIR OPEN OR HIGH RESISTANCE IN CKT 885.

GC402910068200LX

Circuit Description:

As a toothed ring passes by the wheel speed sensor, changes in the electromagnetic field cause the wheel speed sensor to produce a sinusoidal (AC) voltage signal whose frequency is proportional to wheel speed. The magnitude of this signal is directly related to wheel speed and the proximity of the wheel speed sensor to the toothed ring, often referred to as the air gap.

This code detects opens, shorts to ground, and shorts to battery that cause a wheel speed of 0 mph to be calculated by the ABS EBCM. The conditions present to fail this test are: (1) Three (3) wheels are rotating at least 5 mph, and (2) The fourth wheel is 0 mph.

Test Description: Number(s) below refer to circled number(s) on the diagnostic chart.

5. This step checks to see if the wheel speed sensor circuitry is shorted to voltage.
6. This step insures that the wheel speed sensor circuitry resistance is within the proper value.
7. This checks for an open in the wheel signal high circuit.
8. This checks for an open in the wheel signal low circuit.
9. This step insures that Code A023 was not set due to a poor connection between the world connector and EBCM.

Diagnostic Aids:

An "Intermittent" problem may be caused by a poor connection, rubbed through wire insulation, or a wire that is broken inside the insulation.

The frequency of the problem can be checked by using the enhanced diagnostic function of the "Scan" tool.

If the customers comments reflect that the ABS Amber warning light is "ON" only during moist environmental changes, (rain, snow, vehicle wash) all wheel speed sensor circuitry should be thoroughly inspected for signs of water intrusion. Use the following procedure. Spray down the suspected area with 5% salt water solution (two teaspoons of salt to 12 oz. of water). Start vehicle, allow vehicle to run for 10 seconds. If code returns immediately, replace suspected harness.

Any circuitry, that is suspected as causing the intermittent complaint, should be thoroughly checked for backed out terminals, improper mating, broken locks, improperly formed or damaged terminals, poor terminal to wiring connections or physical damage to the wiring harness.

GC402910068200KX

Fig. 38 Code A023: Left Rear Wheel Speed = 0 (Part 2 of 2). 1992

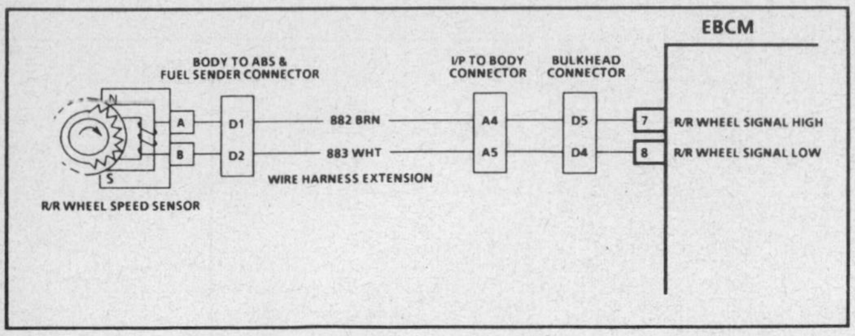
EBCM
BODY TO ABS & FUEL SENDER CONNECTOR
I/P TO BODY CONNECTOR
BULKHEAD CONNECTOR
N
S
A
B
D1
D2
882 BRN
883 WHT
A4
A5
D5
D4
7
8
R/R WHEEL SIGNAL HIGH
R/R WHEEL SIGNAL LOW
WIRE HARNESS EXTENSION
R/R WHEEL SPEED SENSOR

GC402910068300AX

Cavalier & Sunbird

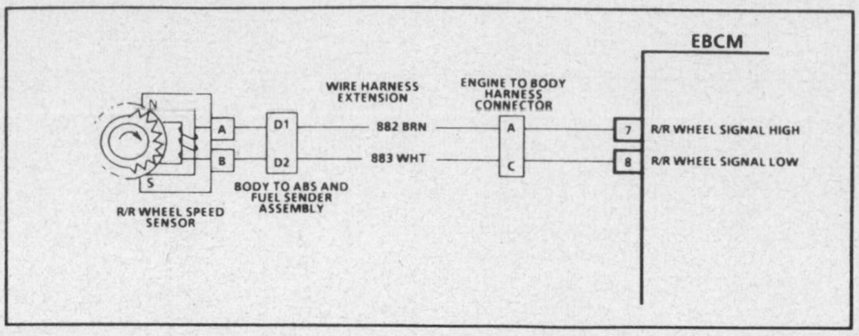
EBCM
WIRE HARNESS EXTENSION
ENGINE TO BODY HARNESS CONNECTOR
N
S
A
B
D1
D2
882 BRN
883 WHT
A
C
7
8
R/R WHEEL SIGNAL HIGH
R/R WHEEL SIGNAL LOW
BODY TO ABS AND FUEL SENDER ASSEMBLY
R/R WHEEL SPEED SENSOR

GC402910068300BX

Beretta & Corsica

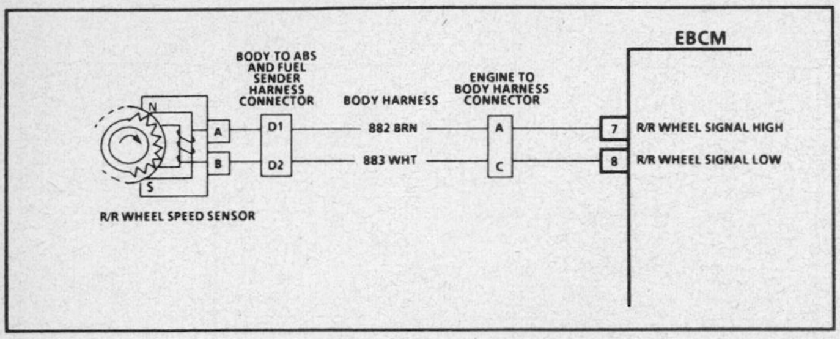
EBCM
BODY TO ABS AND FUEL SENDER HARNESS CONNECTOR
BODY HARNESS
ENGINE TO BODY HARNESS CONNECTOR
N
S
A
B
D1
D2
882 BRN
883 WHT
A
C
7
8
R/R WHEEL SIGNAL HIGH
R/R WHEEL SIGNAL LOW
R/R WHEEL SPEED SENSOR

GC402910068300CX

Achieva, Calais & Grand Am

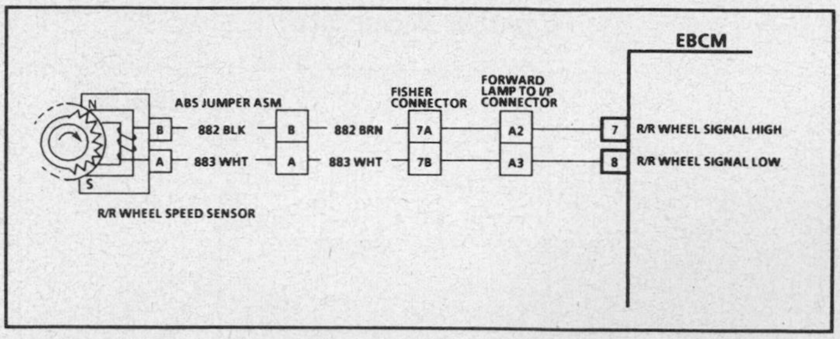
EBCM
ABS JUMPER ASM
FISHER CONNECTOR
FORWARD LAMP TO I/P CONNECTOR
N
S
B
A
882 BLK
883 WHT
882 BRN
883 WHT
7A
7B
A2
A3
7
8
R/R WHEEL SIGNAL HIGH
R/R WHEEL SIGNAL LOW
R/R WHEEL SPEED SENSOR

GC402910068300DX

Cutlass Supreme, Grand Prix, Lumina & Regal

Circuit Description:

As a toothed ring passes by the wheel speed sensor, changes in the electromagnetic field cause the wheel speed sensor to produce a sinusoidal (AC) voltage signal whose frequency is proportional to wheel speed. The magnitude of this signal is directly related to wheel speed and the proximity of the wheel speed sensor to the toothed ring, often referred to as the air gap.

This code detects opens, shorts to ground, and shorts to battery that cause a wheel speed of 0 mph to be calculated by the ABS EBCM. The conditions present to fail this test are: (1) Three (3) wheels are rotating at least 5 mph, and (2) The fourth wheel is 0 mph.

Test Description: Number(s) below refer to circled number(s) on the diagnostic chart.

1. This test verifies whether the fault is currently present.
2. This step is designed to identify a wheel speed sensor or circuitry that is damaged and visibly apparent.
3. This test checks to see that the wheel speed sensor is within proper resistance values.
4. This insures that the wheel speed sensor is not shorted to ground.

Diagnostic Aids:

An "Intermittent" problem may be caused by a poor connection, rubbed through wire insulation, or a wire that is broken inside the insulation.

The frequency of the problem can be checked by using the enhanced diagnostic function of the "Scan" tool.

If the customers comments reflect that the ABS Amber warning light is on only during moist environmental changes, (rain, snow, vehicle wash) all wheel speed sensor circuitry should be thoroughly inspected for water intrusion. Use the following procedure. Spray down the suspected area with 5% salt water solution (two teaspoons of salt to 12 oz. of water). Start vehicle, allow vehicle to run for 10 seconds. If code returns immediately, replace suspected harness.

Any circuitry, that is suspected as causing the intermittent complaint, should be thoroughly checked for backed out terminals, improper mating, broken locks, improperly formed or damaged terminals, poor terminal to wiring connections or physical damage to the wiring harness.

GC402910068300EX

IMPORTANT: WHEEL SPEED SENSOR INTERMITTENT PROBLEMS MAY BE DIFFICULT TO LOCATE. CARE SHOULD BE TAKEN NOT TO DISTURB ANY ELECTRICAL CONNECTIONS PRIOR TO AN INDICATED STEP OF THIS CHART. THIS WILL INSURE THAT AN INTERMITTENT CONNECTION WILL NOT BE CORRECTED BEFORE THE SOURCE OF THE PROBLEM IS FOUND.

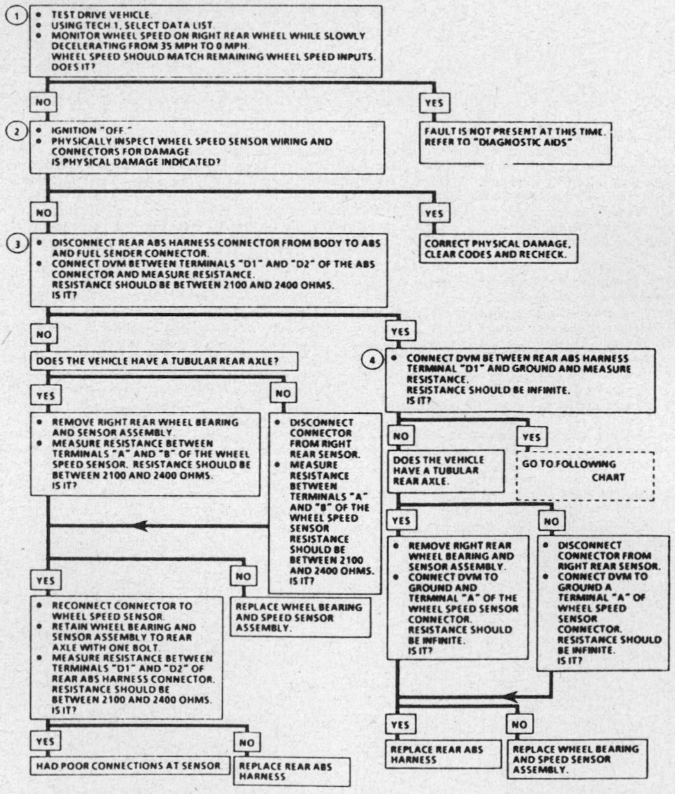
1
• TEST DRIVE VEHICLE.
• USING TECH 1, SELECT DATA LIST.
• MONITOR WHEEL SPEED ON RIGHT REAR WHEEL WHILE SLOWLY DECELERATING FROM 35 MPH TO 0 MPH. WHEEL SPEED SHOULD MATCH REMAINING WHEEL SPEED INPUTS. DOES IT?
NO
YES
FAULT IS NOT PRESENT AT THIS TIME. REFER TO "DIAGNOSTIC AIDS"
2
• IGNITION "OFF."
• PHYSICALLY INSPECT WHEEL SPEED SENSOR WIRING AND CONNECTORS FOR DAMAGE IS PHYSICAL DAMAGE INDICATED?
NO
YES
CORRECT PHYSICAL DAMAGE, CLEAR CODES AND RECHECK.
3
• DISCONNECT REAR ABS HARNESS CONNECTOR FROM BODY TO ABS AND FUEL SENDER CONNECTOR.
• CONNECT DVM BETWEEN TERMINALS "D1" AND "D2" OF THE ABS CONNECTOR AND MEASURE RESISTANCE. RESISTANCE SHOULD BE BETWEEN 2100 AND 2400 OHMS. IS IT?
NO
YES
DOES THE VEHICLE HAVE A TUBULAR REAR AXLE?
4
• CONNECT DVM BETWEEN REAR ABS HARNESS TERMINAL "D1" AND GROUND AND MEASURE RESISTANCE. RESISTANCE SHOULD BE INFINITE. IS IT?
YES
NO
• REMOVE RIGHT REAR WHEEL BEARING AND SENSOR ASSEMBLY.
• MEASURE RESISTANCE BETWEEN TERMINALS "A" AND "B" OF THE WHEEL SPEED SENSOR. RESISTANCE SHOULD BE BETWEEN 2100 AND 2400 OHMS. IS IT?
• DISCONNECT CONNECTOR FROM RIGHT REAR SENSOR.
• MEASURE RESISTANCE BETWEEN TERMINALS "A" AND "B" OF THE WHEEL SPEED SENSOR RESISTANCE SHOULD BE BETWEEN 2100 AND 2400 OHMS. IS IT?
NO
YES
DOES THE VEHICLE HAVE A TUBULAR REAR AXLE.
GO TO FOLLOWING CHART
YES
NO
• REMOVE RIGHT REAR WHEEL BEARING AND SENSOR ASSEMBLY.
• CONNECT DVM TO GROUND AND TERMINAL "A" OF THE WHEEL SPEED SENSOR CONNECTOR. RESISTANCE SHOULD BE INFINITE. IS IT?
• DISCONNECT CONNECTOR FROM RIGHT REAR SENSOR.
• CONNECT DVM TO GROUND A TERMINAL "A" OF WHEEL SPEED SENSOR CONNECTOR. RESISTANCE SHOULD BE INFINITE. IS IT?
YES
NO
• RECONNECT CONNECTOR TO WHEEL SPEED SENSOR.
• RETAIN WHEEL BEARING AND SENSOR ASSEMBLY TO REAR AXLE WITH ONE BOLT.
• MEASURE RESISTANCE BETWEEN TERMINALS "D1" AND "D2" OF REAR ABS HARNESS CONNECTOR. RESISTANCE SHOULD BE BETWEEN 2100 AND 2400 OHMS. IS IT?
REPLACE WHEEL BEARING AND SPEED SENSOR ASSEMBLY.
YES
NO
REPLACE REAR ABS HARNESS
REPLACE WHEEL BEARING AND SPEED SENSOR ASSEMBLY.
YES
NO
HAD POOR CONNECTIONS AT SENSOR
REPLACE REAR ABS HARNESS

GC402910068300FX

Fig. 39 Code A024: Right Rear Wheel Speed = 0 (Part 1 of 2). 1992

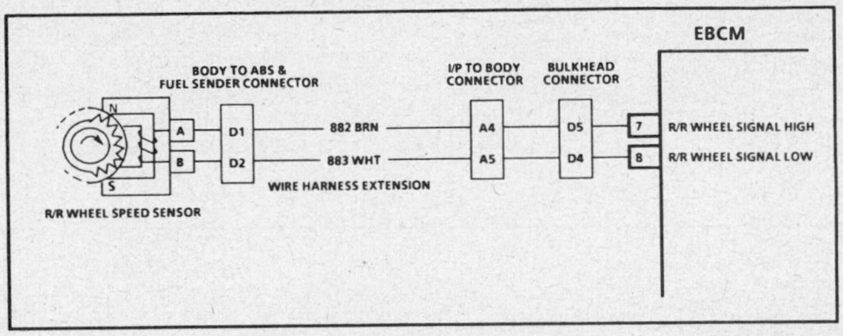
EBCM
BODY TO ABS & FUEL SENDER CONNECTOR
I/P TO BODY CONNECTOR
BULKHEAD CONNECTOR
N
S
A
B
D1
D2
882 BRN
883 WHT
A4
A5
D5
D4
7
8
R/R WHEEL SIGNAL HIGH
R/R WHEEL SIGNAL LOW
WIRE HARNESS EXTENSION
R/R WHEEL SPEED SENSOR

GC402910068300GX

Cavalier & Sunbird

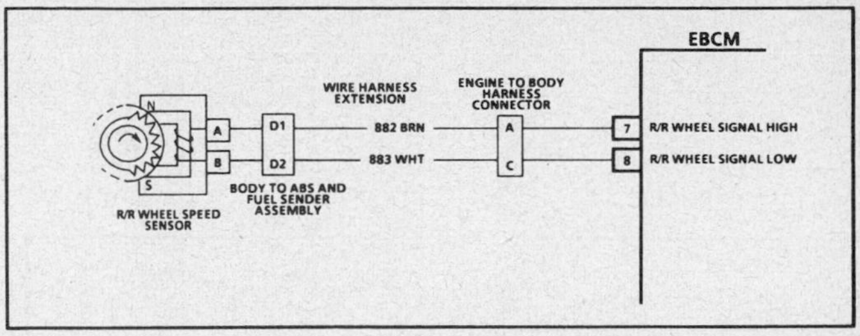
EBCM
WIRE HARNESS EXTENSION
ENGINE TO BODY HARNESS CONNECTOR
N
S
A
B
D1
D2
882 BRN
883 WHT
A
C
7
8
R/R WHEEL SIGNAL HIGH
R/R WHEEL SIGNAL LOW
BODY TO ABS AND FUEL SENDER ASSEMBLY
R/R WHEEL SPEED SENSOR

GC402910068300HX

Beretta & Corsica

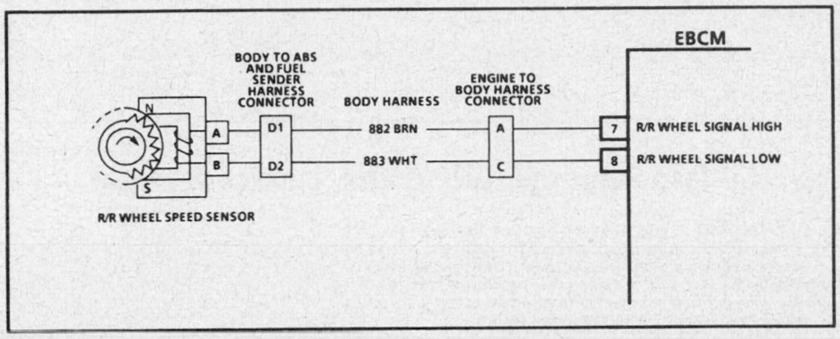
EBCM
BODY TO ABS AND FUEL SENDER HARNESS CONNECTOR
BODY HARNESS
ENGINE TO BODY HARNESS CONNECTOR
N
S
A
B
D1
D2
882 BRN
883 WHT
A
C
7
8
R/R WHEEL SIGNAL HIGH
R/R WHEEL SIGNAL LOW
R/R WHEEL SPEED SENSOR

GC402910068300IX

Achieva, Calais & Grand Am

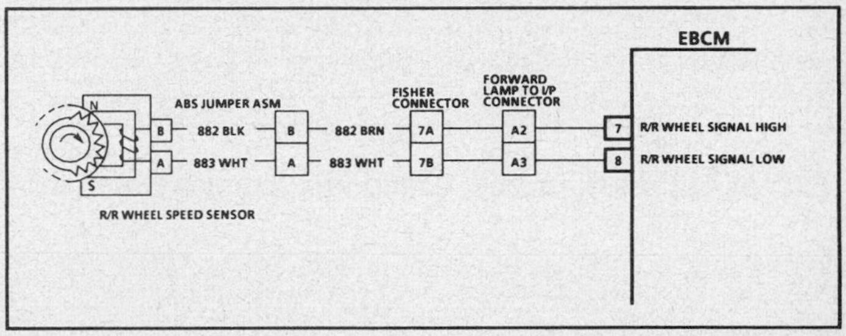
EBCM
ABS JUMPER ASM
FISHER CONNECTOR
FORWARD LAMP TO I/P CONNECTOR
N
S
B
A
882 BLK
883 WHT
882 BRN
883 WHT
7A
7B
A2
A3
7
8
R/R WHEEL SIGNAL HIGH
R/R WHEEL SIGNAL LOW
R/R WHEEL SPEED SENSOR

GC402910068300JX

Cutlass Supreme, Grand Prix, Lumina & Regal

Circuit Description:

As a toothed ring passes by the wheel speed sensor, changes in the electromagnetic field cause the wheel speed sensor to produce a sinusoidal (AC) voltage signal whose frequency is proportional to wheel speed. The magnitude of this signal is directly related to wheel speed and the proximity of the wheel speed sensor to the toothed ring, often referred to as the air gap.

This code detects opens, shorts to ground, and shorts to battery that cause a wheel speed of 0 mph to be calculated by the ABS EBCM. The conditions present to fail this test are: (1) Three (3) wheels are rotating at least 5 mph, and (2) The fourth wheel is 0 mph.

Test Description: Number(s) below refer to circled number(s) on the diagnostic chart.

5. This step checks to see if the wheel speed sensor circuitry is shorted to voltage.
6. This step insures that the wheel speed sensor circuitry resistance is within the proper value.
7. This checks for an open in the wheel signal high circuit.
8. This checks for an open in the wheel signal low circuit.
9. This step insures that Code A024 was not set due to a poor connection between the world connector and EBCM.

Diagnostic Aids:

An "Intermittent" problem may be caused by a poor connection, rubbed through wire insulation, or a wire that is broken inside the insulation.

The frequency of the problem can be checked by using the enhanced diagnostic function of the "Scan" tool.

If the customers comments reflect that the ABS Amber warning light is on only during moist environmental changes, (rain, snow, vehicle wash) all wheel speed sensor circuitry should be thoroughly inspected for water intrusion. Use the following procedure. Spray down the suspected area with 5% salt water solution (two teaspoons of salt to 12 oz. of water). Start vehicle, allow vehicle to run for 10 seconds. If code returns immediately, replace suspected harness.

Any circuitry, that is suspected as causing the intermittent complaint, should be thoroughly checked for backed out terminals, improper mating, broken locks, improperly formed or damaged terminals, poor terminal to wiring connections or physical damage to the wiring harness.

GC402910068300KX

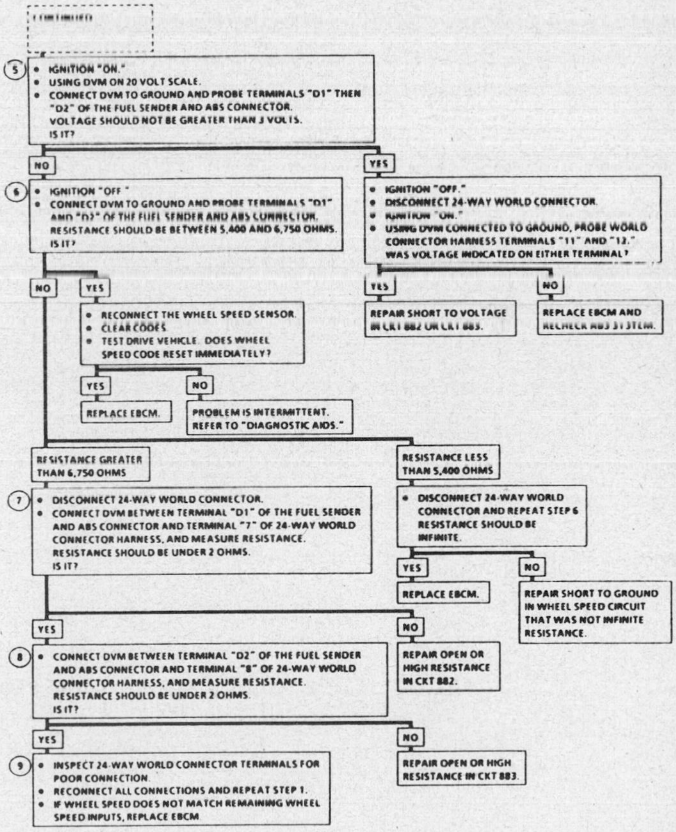
5
• IGNITION "ON."
• USING DVM ON 20 VOLT SCALE.
• CONNECT DVM TO GROUND AND PROBE TERMINALS "D1" THEN "D2" OF THE FUEL SENDER AND ABS CONNECTOR. VOLTAGE SHOULD NOT BE GREATER THAN 3 VOLTS. IS IT?
NO
YES
6
• IGNITION "OFF."
• CONNECT DVM TO GROUND AND PROBE TERMINALS "D1" AND "D2" OF THE FUEL SENDER AND ABS CONNECTOR. RESISTANCE SHOULD BE BETWEEN 5,400 AND 6,750 OHMS. IS IT?
• IGNITION "OFF."
• DISCONNECT 24-WAY WORLD CONNECTOR.
• IGNITION "ON."
• USING DVM CONNECTED TO GROUND, PROBE WORLD CONNECTOR HARNESS TERMINALS "11" AND "12." WAS VOLTAGE INDICATED ON EITHER TERMINAL?
NO
YES
YES
NO
• RECONNECT THE WHEEL SPEED SENSOR.
• CLEAR CODES
• TEST DRIVE VEHICLE. DOES WHEEL SPEED CODE RESET IMMEDIATELY?
REPAIR SHORT TO VOLTAGE IN CKT 882 OR CKT 883.
REPLACE EBCM AND RECHECK ABS SYSTEM.
YES
NO
REPLACE EBCM.
PROBLEM IS INTERMITTENT. REFER TO "DIAGNOSTIC AIDS."
RESISTANCE GREATER THAN 6,750 OHMS
RESISTANCE LESS THAN 5,400 OHMS
7
• DISCONNECT 24-WAY WORLD CONNECTOR.
• CONNECT DVM BETWEEN TERMINAL "D1" OF THE FUEL SENDER AND ABS CONNECTOR AND TERMINAL "7" OF 24-WAY WORLD CONNECTOR HARNESS, AND MEASURE RESISTANCE. RESISTANCE SHOULD BE UNDER 2 OHMS. IS IT?
• DISCONNECT 24-WAY WORLD CONNECTOR AND REPEAT STEP 6 RESISTANCE SHOULD BE INFINITE.
YES
NO
REPLACE EBCM.
REPAIR SHORT TO GROUND IN WHEEL SPEED CIRCUIT THAT WAS NOT INFINITE RESISTANCE.
YES
NO
8
• CONNECT DVM BETWEEN TERMINAL "D2" OF THE FUEL SENDER AND ABS CONNECTOR AND TERMINAL "8" OF 24-WAY WORLD CONNECTOR HARNESS, AND MEASURE RESISTANCE. RESISTANCE SHOULD BE UNDER 2 OHMS. IS IT?
REPAIR OPEN OR HIGH RESISTANCE IN CKT 882.
YES
NO
9
• INSPECT 24-WAY WORLD CONNECTOR TERMINALS FOR POOR CONNECTION.
• RECONNECT ALL CONNECTIONS AND REPEAT STEP 1.
• IF WHEEL SPEED DOES NOT MATCH REMAINING WHEEL SPEED INPUTS, REPLACE EBCM
REPAIR OPEN OR HIGH RESISTANCE IN CKT 883.

GC402910068300LX

Fig. 39 Code A024: Right Rear Wheel Speed = 0 (Part 2 of 2). 1992

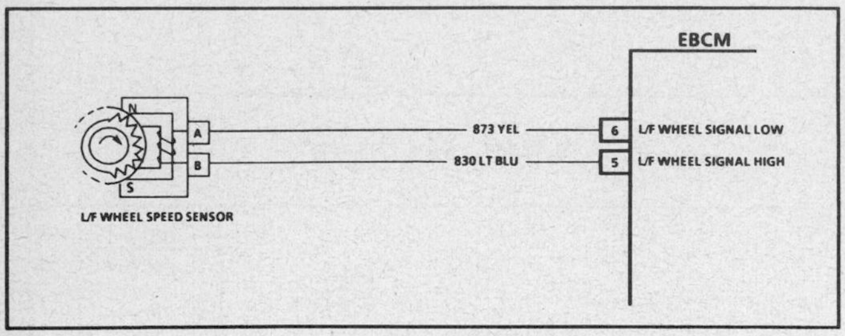
EBCM
A
B
N
S
873 YEL
830 LT BLU
6
5
L/F WHEEL SIGNAL LOW
L/F WHEEL SIGNAL HIGH
L/F WHEEL SPEED SENSOR

GC402910068400AX

Except Cutlass Supreme, Grand Prix, Lumina & Regal

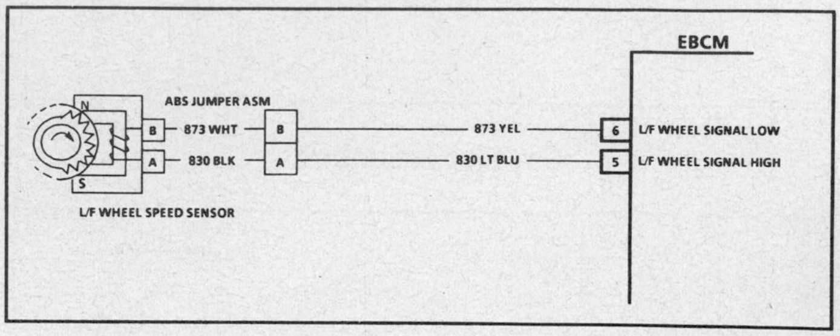
EBCM
ABS JUMPER ASM
N
S
B
A
873 WHT
830 BLK
B
A
873 YEL
830 LT BLU
6
5
L/F WHEEL SIGNAL LOW
L/F WHEEL SIGNAL HIGH
L/F WHEEL SPEED SENSOR

GC402910068400BX

Cutlass Supreme, Grand Prix, Lumina & Regal

Circuit Description:

As a toothed ring passes by the wheel speed sensor, changes in the electromagnetic field cause the wheel speed sensor to produce a sinusoidal (AC) voltage signal whose frequency is proportional to wheel speed. The magnitude of this signal is directly related to wheel speed and the proximity of the wheel speed sensor to the toothed ring, often referred to as the air gap.

This code detects opens, shorts to ground, and shorts to battery that cause intermittent wheel speed operation. Also detected is any sudden change in wheel speed determined to the unreasonable.

Test Description: Number(s) below refer to circled number(s) on the diagnostic chart.

1. This test verifies whether the fault is currently present.
2. This step is designed to identify a wheel speed sensor or circuitry that is damaged and visibly apparent.
3. This test checks to see that the wheel speed sensor circuitry is within proper resistance value.
4. This insure that the wheel speed sensor is not shorted to ground.

Diagnostic Aids:

An "Intermittent" problem may be caused by a poor connection, rubbed through wire insulation, or a wire that is broken inside the insulation.

The frequency of the problem can be checked by using the enhanced diagnostic function of the "Scan" tool.

If the customer's comments reflect that the ABS Amber warning light is on only during moist environmental changes, (rain, snow, vehicle wash) all wheel speed sensor circuitry should be thoroughly inspected for water intrusion. Use the following procedure. Spray down the suspected area with 5% salt water solution (two teaspoons of salt to 12 oz. of water). Start vehicle, allow vehicle to run for 10 seconds. If code returns immediately, replace suspected harness.

Any circuitry, that is suspected as causing the intermittent complaint, should be thoroughly checked for backed out terminals, improper mating, broken locks, improperly formed or damaged terminals, poor terminal to wiring connections or physical damage to the wiring harness.

A careful visual inspection of the toothed ring, CV joint, bearing and wheel speed sensor for physical damage should also be performed. If code sets at the same mph every time and wheel speed variation is noted above this mph on the Tech 1, the speed ring is most likely damaged. This can occur at any speed.

GC402910068400CX

IMPORTANT: WHEEL SPEED SENSOR INTERMITTENT PROBLEMS MAY BE DIFFICULT TO LOCATE. CARE SHOULD BE TAKEN NOT TO DISTURB ANY ELECTRICAL CONNECTIONS PRIOR TO AN INDICATED STEP OF THIS CHART. THIS WILL INSURE THAT AN INTERMITTENT CONNECTION WILL NOT BE CORRECTED BEFORE THE SOURCE OF THE PROBLEM IS FOUND.

(1)
- TEST DRIVE VEHICLE.
- USING TECH 1, SELECT DATA LIST.
- MONITOR WHEEL SPEED ON LEFT FRONT WHEEL WHILE SLOWLY DECELERATING FROM 35 MPH TO 0 MPH.
- WHEEL SPEED SHOULD MATCH REMAINING WHEEL SPEED INPUTS. DOES IT?

YES: FAULT IS NOT PRESENT AT THIS TIME. REFER TO "DIAGNOSTIC AIDS"

NO:

(2)
- IGNITION "OFF."
- PHYSICALLY INSPECT WHEEL SPEED SENSOR, RING, WIRING AND CONNECTORS FOR DAMAGE. PAY PARTICULAR ATTENTION TO THE SPEED RING. ANY SIGNIFICANT DAMAGE (OTHER THAN NICKS FROM STONES ETC.) WILL AFFECT THE WHEEL SPEED INPUT SIGNAL. IS PHYSICAL DAMAGE INDICATED?

YES: CORRECT PHYSICAL DAMAGE, CLEAR CODES AND RECHECK.

NO:

(3)
- DISCONNECT CONNECTOR FROM LEFT FRONT WHEEL SPEED SENSOR.
- CONNECT DVM BETWEEN TERMINAL "A" AND "B" OF SENSOR, AND MEASURE RESISTANCE. RESISTANCE SHOULD BE BETWEEN 1650 AND 1800 OHMS. IS IT?

NO: REPLACE WHEEL SPEED SENSOR, CLEAR CODES AND RECHECK.

YES:

(4)
- CONNECT DVM BETWEEN SENSOR TERMINAL "A" AND GROUND AND MEASURE RESISTANCE. RESISTANCE SHOULD BE INFINITE. IS IT?

NO: REPLACE WHEEL SPEED SENSOR, CLEAR CODES AND RECHECK.

YES: GO TO FOLLOWING CHART

GC402910068400DX

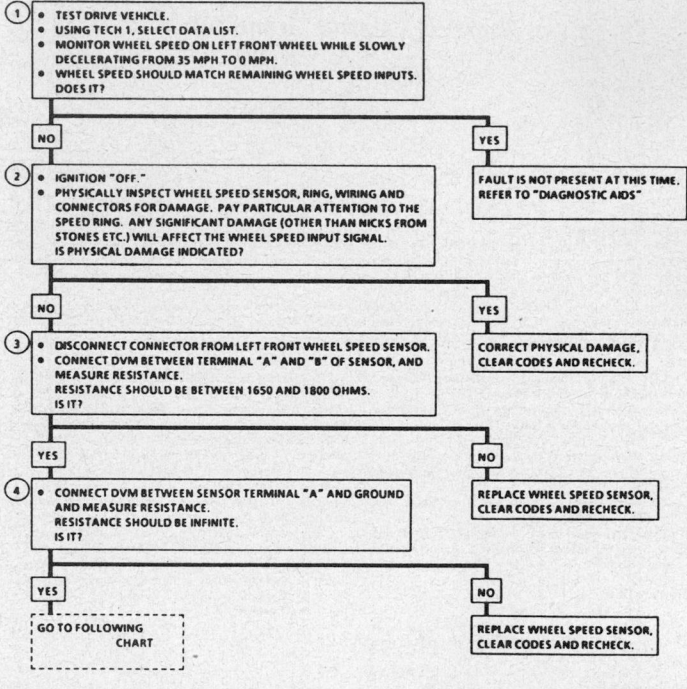

Fig. 40 Code A025: Excessive Left Front Wheel Acceleration (Part 1 of 2). 1992

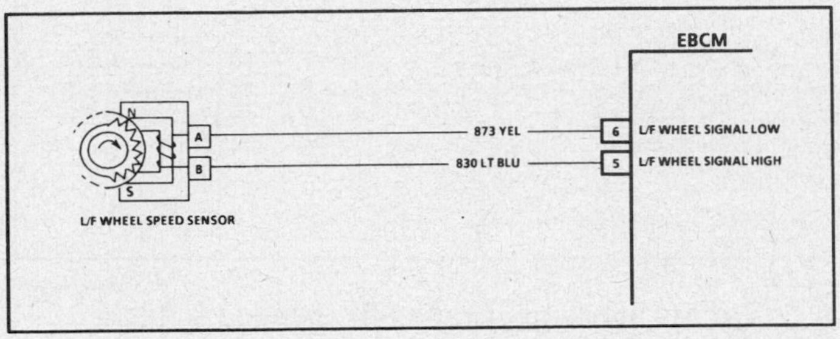
EBCM
N
S
A
B
873 YEL
830 LT BLU
6
5
L/F WHEEL SIGNAL LOW
L/F WHEEL SIGNAL HIGH
L/F WHEEL SPEED SENSOR

GC402910068400EX

Except Cutlass Supreme, Grand Prix, Lumina & Regal

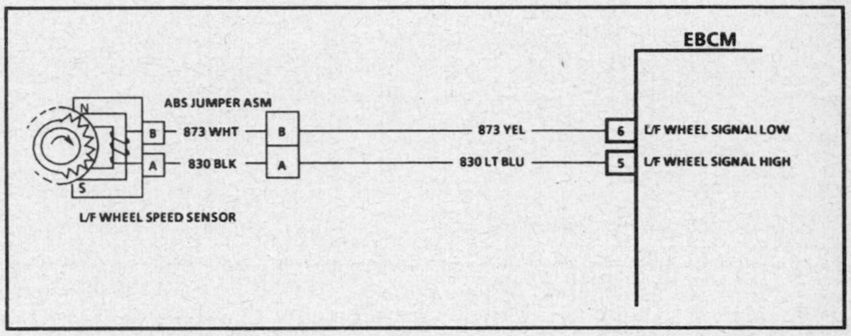
EBCM
ABS JUMPER ASM
N
S
B
A
873 WHT
830 BLK
873 YEL
830 LT BLU
6
5
L/F WHEEL SIGNAL LOW
L/F WHEEL SIGNAL HIGH
L/F WHEEL SPEED SENSOR

GC402910068400FX

Cutlass Supreme, Grand Prix, Lumina & Regal

Circuit Description:

As a toothed ring passes by the wheel speed sensor, changes in the electromagnetic field cause the wheel speed sensor to produce a sinusoidal (AC) voltage signal whose frequency is proportional to wheel speed. The magnitude of this signal is directly related to wheel speed and the proximity of the wheel speed sensor to the toothed ring, often referred to as the air gap.

This code detects opens or a low output condition that cause intermittent wheel speed operational. Also detected is any sudden change in wheel speed determined to be unreasonable.

Test Description: Number(s) below refer to circled number(s) on the diagnostic chart.

6. This step insures that the wheel speed sensor circuitry resistance is within the proper value.
7. This checks for an open in the wheel signal high circuit.
8. This checks for an open in the wheel signal low circuit.
9. This step insures that Code A025 was not set due to a poor connection between the world connector and EBCM.

Diagnostic Aids:

An "Intermittent" problem may be caused by a poor connection, rubbed through wire insulation, or a wire that is broken inside the insulation.

The frequency of the problem can be checked by using the enhanced diagnostic function of the Tech 1 "Scan" tool.

If the customers comments reflect that the ABS Amber warning lamp is "ON" only during moist environmental changes, (rain, snow, vehicle wash) all wheel speed sensor circuitry should be thoroughly inspected for signs of water intrusion. If code is not current clear codes and simulate the effects of water intrusion. Use the following procedure. Spray down the suspected area with a 5% salt water solution (two teaspoons of salt to 12 oz. of water). Start vehicle, allow vehicle to run for 10 seconds. If code returns immediately, replace suspected harness.

Any circuitry, that is suspected as causing the intermittent complaint, should be thoroughly checked for backed out terminals, improper mating, broken locks, improperly formed or damaged terminals, poor terminal to wiring connections or physical damage to the wiring harness.

A careful visual inspection of the toothed ring, CV joint, bearing and wheel speed sensor for physical damage should also be performed. If code sets at the same mph every time and wheel speed variation is noted above this mph on the Tech 1, the speed ring is most likely damaged. This can occur at any speed.

GC402910068400GX

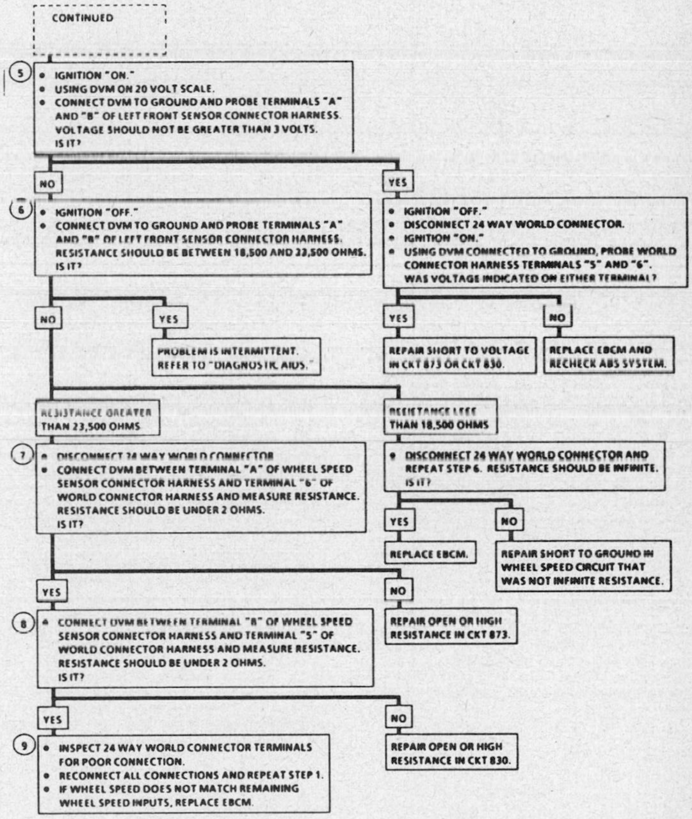
CONTINUED
5
• IGNITION "ON."
• USING DVM ON 20 VOLT SCALE.
• CONNECT DVM TO GROUND AND PROBE TERMINALS "A" AND "B" OF LEFT FRONT SENSOR CONNECTOR HARNESS. VOLTAGE SHOULD NOT BE GREATER THAN 3 VOLTS. IS IT?
NO
YES
6
• IGNITION "OFF."
• CONNECT DVM TO GROUND AND PROBE TERMINALS "A" AND "B" OF LEFT FRONT SENSOR CONNECTOR HARNESS. RESISTANCE SHOULD BE BETWEEN 18,500 AND 23,500 OHMS. IS IT?
• IGNITION "OFF."
• DISCONNECT 24 WAY WORLD CONNECTOR.
• IGNITION "ON."
• USING DVM CONNECTED TO GROUND, PROBE WORLD CONNECTOR HARNESS TERMINALS "5" AND "6". WAS VOLTAGE INDICATED ON EITHER TERMINAL?
NO
YES
PROBLEM IS INTERMITTENT. REFER TO "DIAGNOSTIC AIDS."
YES
NO
REPAIR SHORT TO VOLTAGE IN CKT 873 OR CKT 830.
REPLACE EBCM AND RECHECK ABS SYSTEM.
RESISTANCE GREATER THAN 23,500 OHMS
RESISTANCE LESS THAN 18,500 OHMS
7
• DISCONNECT 24 WAY WORLD CONNECTOR
• CONNECT DVM BETWEEN TERMINAL "A" OF WHEEL SPEED SENSOR CONNECTOR HARNESS AND TERMINAL "6" OF WORLD CONNECTOR HARNESS AND MEASURE RESISTANCE. RESISTANCE SHOULD BE UNDER 2 OHMS. IS IT?
• DISCONNECT 24 WAY WORLD CONNECTOR AND REPEAT STEP 6. RESISTANCE SHOULD BE INFINITE. IS IT?
YES
NO
REPLACE EBCM.
REPAIR SHORT TO GROUND IN WHEEL SPEED CIRCUIT THAT WAS NOT INFINITE RESISTANCE.
YES
NO
8
• CONNECT DVM BETWEEN TERMINAL "B" OF WHEEL SPEED SENSOR CONNECTOR HARNESS AND TERMINAL "5" OF WORLD CONNECTOR HARNESS AND MEASURE RESISTANCE. RESISTANCE SHOULD BE UNDER 2 OHMS. IS IT?
REPAIR OPEN OR HIGH RESISTANCE IN CKT 873.
YES
NO
9
• INSPECT 24 WAY WORLD CONNECTOR TERMINALS FOR POOR CONNECTION.
• RECONNECT ALL CONNECTIONS AND REPEAT STEP 1.
• IF WHEEL SPEED DOES NOT MATCH REMAINING WHEEL SPEED INPUTS, REPLACE EBCM.
REPAIR OPEN OR HIGH RESISTANCE IN CKT 830.

GC402910068400HX

Fig. 40 Code A025: Excessive Left Front Wheel Acceleration (Part 2 of 2). 1992

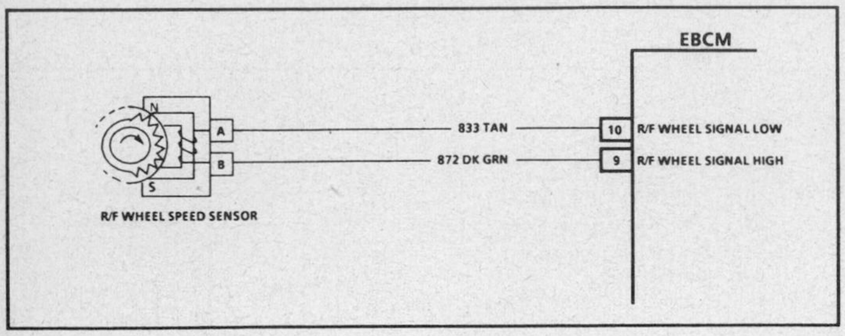
EBCM
N
A
B
S
833 TAN
872 DK GRN
10
9
R/F WHEEL SIGNAL LOW
R/F WHEEL SIGNAL HIGH
R/F WHEEL SPEED SENSOR

GC402910068500AX

Except Cutlass Supreme, Grand Prix, Lumina & Regal

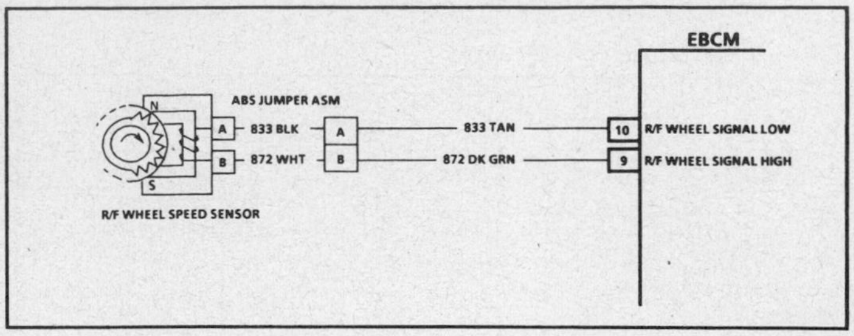
EBCM
ABS JUMPER ASM
N
A
B
S
833 BLK
872 WHT
A
B
833 TAN
872 DK GRN
10
9
R/F WHEEL SIGNAL LOW
R/F WHEEL SIGNAL HIGH
R/F WHEEL SPEED SENSOR

GC402910068500BX

Cutlass Supreme, Grand Prix, Lumina & Regal

IMPORTANT: WHEEL SPEED SENSOR INTERMITTENT PROBLEMS MAY BE DIFFICULT TO LOCATE. CARE SHOULD BE TAKEN NOT TO DISTURB ANY ELECTRICAL CONNECTIONS PRIOR TO AN INDICATED STEP OF THIS CHART. THIS WILL INSURE THAT AN INTERMITTENT CONNECTION WILL NOT BE CORRECTED BEFORE THE SOURCE OF THE PROBLEM IS FOUND.

Circuit Description:

As a toothed ring passes by the wheel speed sensor, changes in the electromagnetic field cause the wheel speed sensor to produce a sinusoidal (AC) voltage signal whose frequency is proportional to wheel speed. The magnitude of this signal is directly related to wheel speed and the proximity of the wheel speed sensor to the toothed ring, often referred to as the air gap.

This code detects opens, shorts to ground, and shorts to battery that cause intermittent wheel speed operation. Also detected is any sudden change in wheel speed determined to be unreasonable.

Test Description: Number(s) below refer to circled number(s) on the diagnostic chart.

1. This test verifies whether the fault is currently present.
2. This step is designed to identify a wheel speed sensor or circuitry that is damaged and visibly apparent.
3. This test checks to see that the wheel speed sensor circuitry is within proper resistance value.
4. This insures that the wheel speed sensor is not shorted to ground.

Diagnostic Aids:

An "Intermittent" problem may be caused by a poor connection, rubbed through wire insulation, or a wire that is broken inside the insulation.

The frequency of the problem can be checked by using the enhanced diagnostic function of the "Scan" tool.

If the customers comments reflect that the ABS Amber warning light is on only during moist environmental changes, (rain, snow, vehicle wash) all wheel speed sensor circuitry should be thoroughly inspected for water intrusion. Use the following procedure. Spray down the suspected area with 5% salt water solution (two teaspoons of salt to 12 oz. of water). Start vehicle, allow vehicle to run for 10 seconds. If code returns immediately, replace suspected harness.

Any circuitry, that is suspected as causing the intermittent complaint, should be thoroughly checked for backed out terminals, improper mating, broken locks, improperly formed or damaged terminals, poor terminal to wiring connections or physical damage to the wiring harness.

A careful visual inspection of the toothed ring, CV joint, bearing and wheel speed sensor for physical damage should also be performed. If code sets at the same mph every time and wheel speed variation is noted above this mph on the Tech 1, the speed ring is most likely damaged. This can occur at any speed.

GC402910068500CX

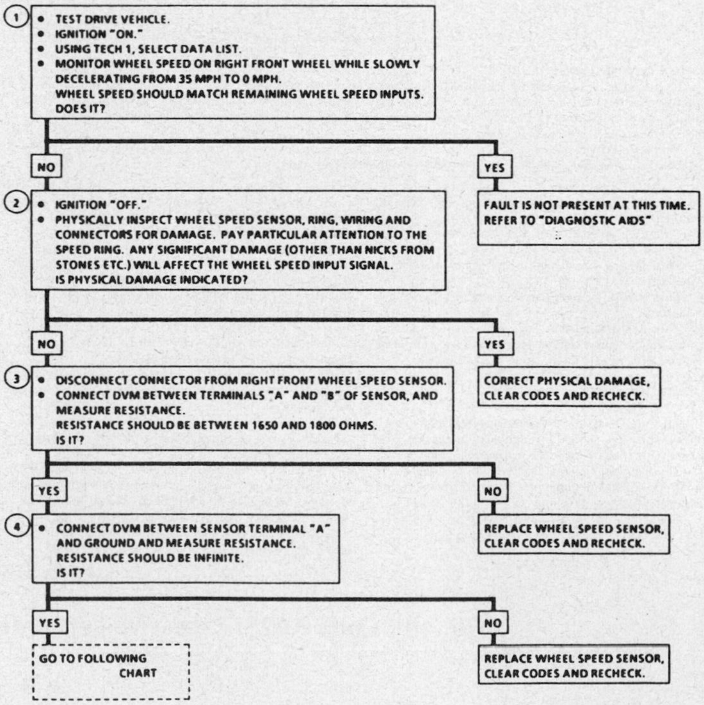
1
• TEST DRIVE VEHICLE.
• IGNITION "ON."
• USING TECH 1, SELECT DATA LIST.
• MONITOR WHEEL SPEED ON RIGHT FRONT WHEEL WHILE SLOWLY DECELERATING FROM 35 MPH TO 0 MPH.
WHEEL SPEED SHOULD MATCH REMAINING WHEEL SPEED INPUTS.
DOES IT?
NO
YES
2
• IGNITION "OFF."
• PHYSICALLY INSPECT WHEEL SPEED SENSOR, RING, WIRING AND CONNECTORS FOR DAMAGE. PAY PARTICULAR ATTENTION TO THE SPEED RING. ANY SIGNIFICANT DAMAGE (OTHER THAN NICKS FROM STONES ETC.) WILL AFFECT THE WHEEL SPEED INPUT SIGNAL.
IS PHYSICAL DAMAGE INDICATED?
FAULT IS NOT PRESENT AT THIS TIME. REFER TO "DIAGNOSTIC AIDS"
NO
YES
3
• DISCONNECT CONNECTOR FROM RIGHT FRONT WHEEL SPEED SENSOR.
• CONNECT DVM BETWEEN TERMINALS "A" AND "B" OF SENSOR, AND MEASURE RESISTANCE.
RESISTANCE SHOULD BE BETWEEN 1650 AND 1800 OHMS.
IS IT?
CORRECT PHYSICAL DAMAGE, CLEAR CODES AND RECHECK.
YES
NO
4
• CONNECT DVM BETWEEN SENSOR TERMINAL "A" AND GROUND AND MEASURE RESISTANCE.
RESISTANCE SHOULD BE INFINITE.
IS IT?
REPLACE WHEEL SPEED SENSOR, CLEAR CODES AND RECHECK.
YES
NO
GO TO FOLLOWING CHART
REPLACE WHEEL SPEED SENSOR, CLEAR CODES AND RECHECK.

GC402910068500DX

Fig. 41 Code A026: Excessive Right Front Wheel Acceleration (Part 1 of 2). 1992

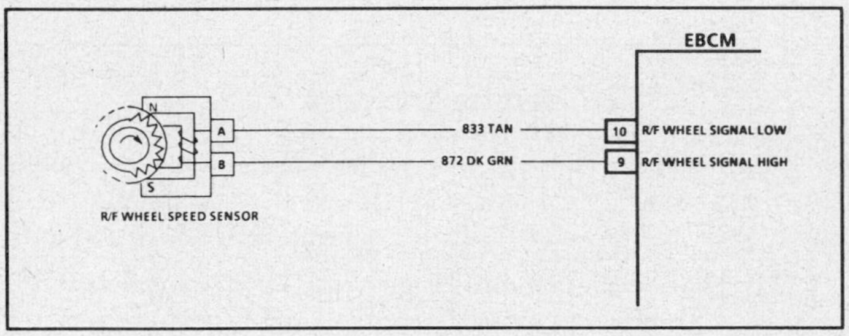
EBCM
N
S
A
B
833 TAN
872 DK GRN
10
9
R/F WHEEL SIGNAL LOW
R/F WHEEL SIGNAL HIGH
R/F WHEEL SPEED SENSOR

GC402910068500EX

Except Cutlass Supreme, Grand Prix, Lumina & Regal

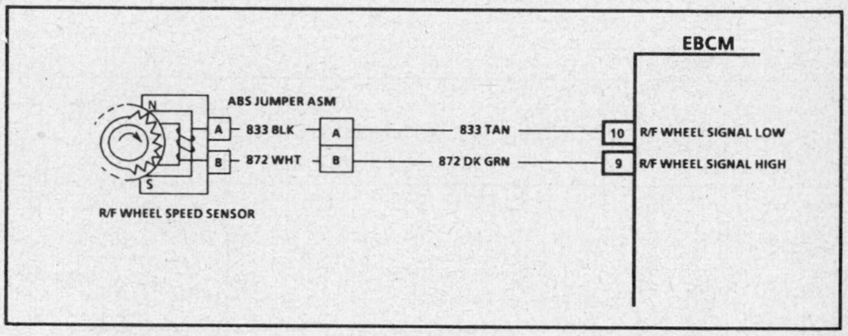
EBCM
ABS JUMPER ASM
N
S
A
B
833 BLK
872 WHT
A
B
833 TAN
872 DK GRN
10
9
R/F WHEEL SIGNAL LOW
R/F WHEEL SIGNAL HIGH
R/F WHEEL SPEED SENSOR

GC402910068500FX

Cutlass Supreme, Grand Prix, Lumina & Regal

Circuit Description:

As a toothed ring passes by the wheel speed sensor, changes in the electromagnetic field cause the wheel speed sensor to produce a sinusoidal (AC) voltage signal whose frequency is proportional to wheel speed. The magnitude of this signal is directly related to wheel speed and the proximity of the wheel speed sensor to the toothed ring, often referred to as the air gap.

This code detects opens or a low output condition that cause intermittent wheel speed operation. Also detected is any sudden change in wheel speed determined to be unreasonable.

Test Description: Number(s) below refer to circled number(s) on the diagnostic chart.

6. This step insures that the wheel speed sensor circuitry is not internally shorted.
7. This checks for an open in the wheel signal low circuit.
8. This checks for an open in the wheel signal high circuit.
9. This step insures that Code A026 was not set due to a poor connection between the world connector and EBCM.

Diagnostic Aids:

An "Intermittent" problem may be caused by a poor connection, rubbed through wire insulation, or a wire that is broken inside the insulation.

The frequency of the problem can be checked by using the enhanced diagnostic function of the "Scan" tool.

If the customers comments reflect that the ABS Amber warning lamp is "ON" only during moist environmental changes, (rain, snow, vehicle wash) all wheel speed sensor circuitry should be thoroughly inspected for signs of water intrusion. If code is not current clear codes and simulate the effects of water intrusion. Use the following procedure. Spray down the suspected area with a 5% salt water solution (two teaspoons of salt to 12 oz. of water). Start vehicle, allow vehicle to run for 10 seconds. If code returns immediately, replace suspected harness.

Any circuitry, that is suspected as causing the intermittent complaint, should be thoroughly checked for backed out terminals, improper mating, broken locks, improperly formed or damaged terminals, poor terminal to wiring connections or physical damage to the wiring harness.

A careful visual inspection of the toothed ring, CV joint, bearing and wheel speed sensor for physical damage should also be performed. If code sets at the same mph every time and wheel speed variation is noted above this mph on the Tech 1, the speed ring is most likely damaged. This can occur at any speed.

GC402910068500GX

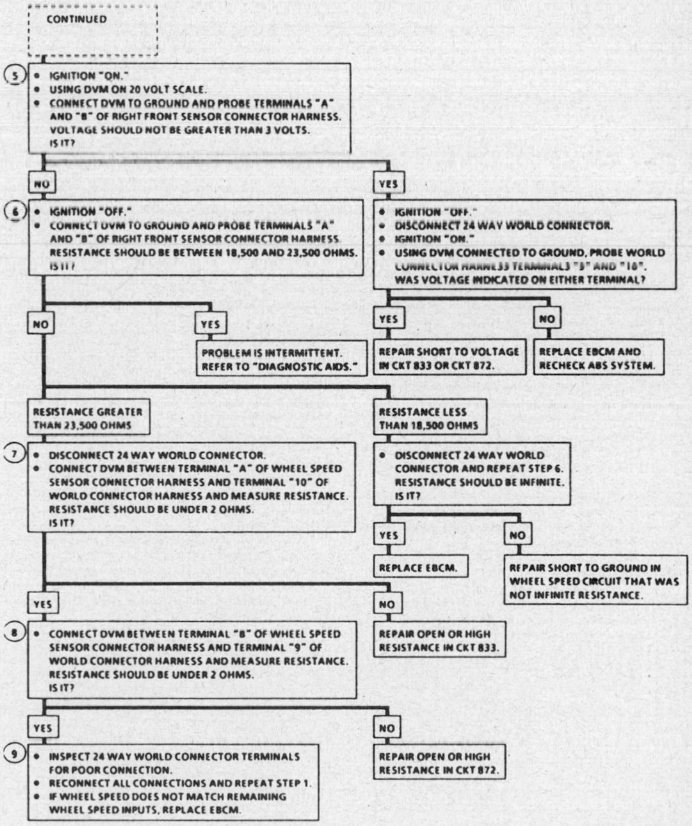
CONTINUED
5
• IGNITION "ON."
• USING DVM ON 20 VOLT SCALE.
• CONNECT DVM TO GROUND AND PROBE TERMINALS "A" AND "B" OF RIGHT FRONT SENSOR CONNECTOR HARNESS. VOLTAGE SHOULD NOT BE GREATER THAN 3 VOLTS. IS IT?
NO
YES
6
• IGNITION "OFF."
• CONNECT DVM TO GROUND AND PROBE TERMINALS "A" AND "B" OF RIGHT FRONT SENSOR CONNECTOR HARNESS. RESISTANCE SHOULD BE BETWEEN 18,500 AND 23,500 OHMS. IS IT?
• IGNITION "OFF."
• DISCONNECT 24 WAY WORLD CONNECTOR.
• IGNITION "ON."
• USING DVM CONNECTED TO GROUND, PROBE WORLD CONNECTOR HARNESS TERMINALS "9" AND "10". WAS VOLTAGE INDICATED ON EITHER TERMINAL?
NO
YES
PROBLEM IS INTERMITTENT. REFER TO "DIAGNOSTIC AIDS."
YES
NO
REPAIR SHORT TO VOLTAGE IN CKT 833 OR CKT 872.
REPLACE EBCM AND RECHECK ABS SYSTEM.
RESISTANCE GREATER THAN 23,500 OHMS
RESISTANCE LESS THAN 18,500 OHMS
7
• DISCONNECT 24 WAY WORLD CONNECTOR.
• CONNECT DVM BETWEEN TERMINAL "A" OF WHEEL SPEED SENSOR CONNECTOR HARNESS AND TERMINAL "10" OF WORLD CONNECTOR HARNESS AND MEASURE RESISTANCE. RESISTANCE SHOULD BE UNDER 2 OHMS. IS IT?
• DISCONNECT 24 WAY WORLD CONNECTOR AND REPEAT STEP 6. RESISTANCE SHOULD BE INFINITE. IS IT?
YES
NO
REPLACE EBCM.
REPAIR SHORT TO GROUND IN WHEEL SPEED CIRCUIT THAT WAS NOT INFINITE RESISTANCE.
YES
NO
8
• CONNECT DVM BETWEEN TERMINAL "B" OF WHEEL SPEED SENSOR CONNECTOR HARNESS AND TERMINAL "9" OF WORLD CONNECTOR HARNESS AND MEASURE RESISTANCE. RESISTANCE SHOULD BE UNDER 2 OHMS. IS IT?
REPAIR OPEN OR HIGH RESISTANCE IN CKT 833.
YES
NO
9
• INSPECT 24 WAY WORLD CONNECTOR TERMINALS FOR POOR CONNECTION.
• RECONNECT ALL CONNECTIONS AND REPEAT STEP 1.
• IF WHEEL SPEED DOES NOT MATCH REMAINING WHEEL SPEED INPUTS, REPLACE EBCM.
REPAIR OPEN OR HIGH RESISTANCE IN CKT 872.

GC402910068500HX

Fig. 41 Code A026: Excessive Right Front Wheel Acceleration (Part 2 of 2). 1992

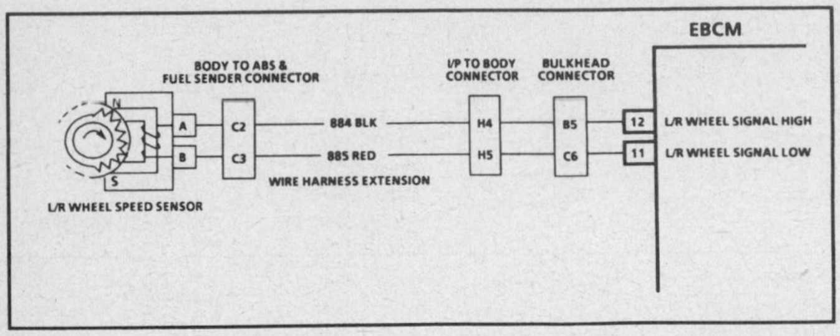
EBCM
BODY TO ABS & FUEL SENDER CONNECTOR
I/P TO BODY CONNECTOR
BULKHEAD CONNECTOR
N
S
A
B
C2
C3
884 BLK
885 RED
H4
H5
B5
C6
12
11
L/R WHEEL SIGNAL HIGH
L/R WHEEL SIGNAL LOW
WIRE HARNESS EXTENSION
L/R WHEEL SPEED SENSOR

GC402910068600AX

Cavalier & Sunbird

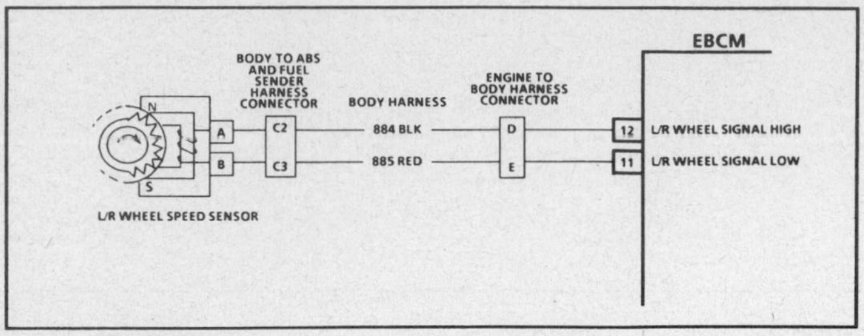
EBCM
BODY TO ABS AND FUEL SENDER HARNESS CONNECTOR
BODY HARNESS
ENGINE TO BODY HARNESS CONNECTOR
N
S
A
B
C2
C3
884 BLK
885 RED
D
E
12
11
L/R WHEEL SIGNAL HIGH
L/R WHEEL SIGNAL LOW
L/R WHEEL SPEED SENSOR

GC402910068600BX

Beretta & Corsica

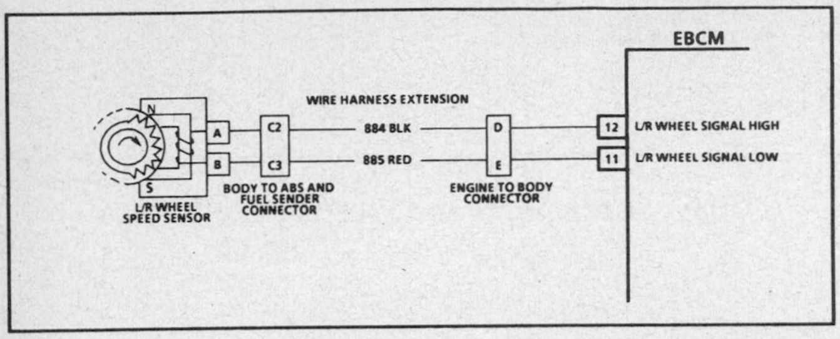
EBCM
WIRE HARNESS EXTENSION
N
S
A
B
C2
C3
884 BLK
885 RED
D
E
12
11
L/R WHEEL SIGNAL HIGH
L/R WHEEL SIGNAL LOW
L/R WHEEL SPEED SENSOR
BODY TO ABS AND FUEL SENDER CONNECTOR
ENGINE TO BODY CONNECTOR

GC402910068600CX

Achieva, Calais & Grand Am

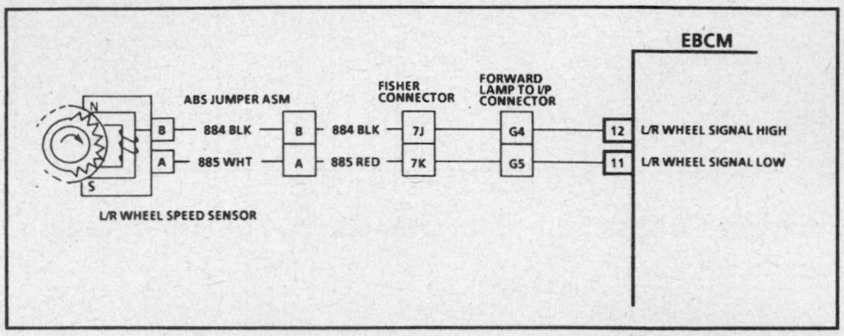
EBCM
ABS JUMPER ASM
FISHER CONNECTOR
FORWARD LAMP TO I/P CONNECTOR
N
S
B
A
884 BLK
885 WHT
884 BLK
885 RED
7J
7K
G4
G5
12
11
L/R WHEEL SIGNAL HIGH
L/R WHEEL SIGNAL LOW
L/R WHEEL SPEED SENSOR

GC402910068600DX

Cutlass Supreme, Grand Prix, Lumina & Regal

Circuit Description:

As a toothed ring passes by the wheel speed sensor, changes in the electromagnetic field cause the wheel speed sensor to produce a sinusoidal (AC) voltage signal whose frequency is proportional to wheel speed. The magnitude of this signal is directly related to wheel speed and the proximity of the wheel speed sensor to the toothed ring, often referred to as the air gap.

This code detects opens, shorts to ground, and shorts to battery that cause intermittent wheel speed operation. Also detected is any sudden change in wheel speed determined to be unreasonable.

Test Description: Number(s) below refer to circled number(s) on the diagnostic chart.

1. This test verifies whether the fault is currently present.
2. This step is designed to identify a wheel speed sensor or circuitry that is damaged and visibly apparent.
3. This test checks to see that the wheel speed sensor circuitry is within proper resistance value.
4. This insures that the wheel speed sensor is not shorted to ground.

Diagnostic Aids:

An "Intermittent" problem may be caused by a poor connection, rubbed through wire insulation, or a wire that is broken inside the insulation.

The frequency of the problem can be checked by using the enhanced diagnostic function of the "Scan" tool.

If the customers comments reflect that the ABS Amber warning light is on only during moist environmental changes, (rain, snow, vehicle wash) all wheel speed sensor circuitry should be thoroughly inspected for water intrusion. Use the following procedure. Spray down the suspected area with 5% salt water solution (two teaspoons of salt to 12 oz. of water). Start vehicle, allow vehicle to run for 10 seconds. If code returns immediately, replace suspected harness.

Any circuitry, that is suspected as causing the intermittent complaint, should be thoroughly checked for backed out terminals, improper mating, broken locks, improperly formed or damaged terminals, poor terminal to wiring connections or physical damage to the wiring harness.

Excessive end play can cause this code to set. Check integral bearing for excessive axial end play

GC402910068600EX

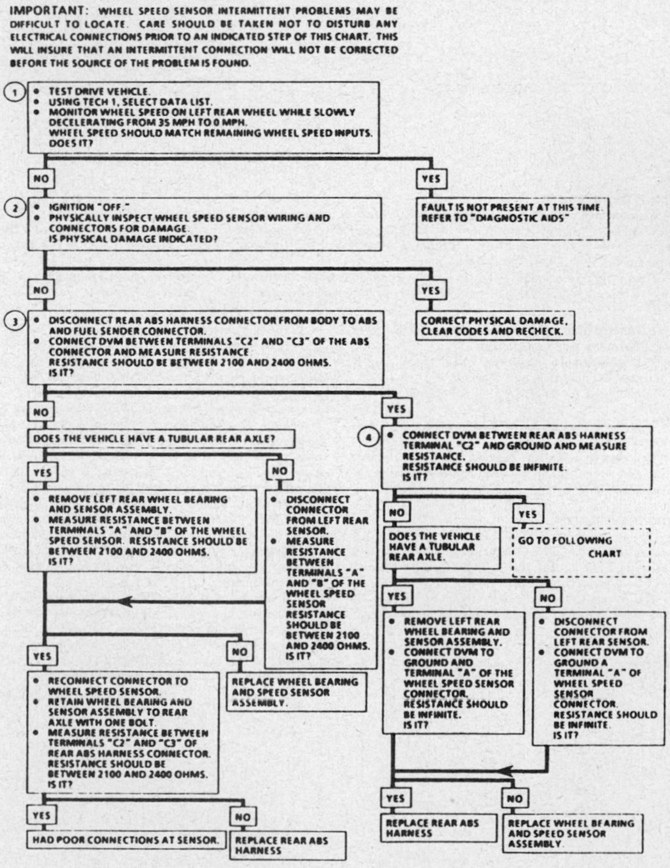
IMPORTANT: WHEEL SPEED SENSOR INTERMITTENT PROBLEMS MAY BE DIFFICULT TO LOCATE. CARE SHOULD BE TAKEN NOT TO DISTURB ANY ELECTRICAL CONNECTIONS PRIOR TO AN INDICATED STEP OF THIS CHART. THIS WILL INSURE THAT AN INTERMITTENT CONNECTION WILL NOT BE CORRECTED BEFORE THE SOURCE OF THE PROBLEM IS FOUND.
1
• TEST DRIVE VEHICLE.
• USING TECH 1, SELECT DATA LIST.
• MONITOR WHEEL SPEED ON LEFT REAR WHEEL WHILE SLOWLY DECELERATING FROM 35 MPH TO 0 MPH.
WHEEL SPEED SHOULD MATCH REMAINING WHEEL SPEED INPUTS.
DOES IT?
NO
YES
FAULT IS NOT PRESENT AT THIS TIME. REFER TO "DIAGNOSTIC AIDS"
2
• IGNITION "OFF."
• PHYSICALLY INSPECT WHEEL SPEED SENSOR WIRING AND CONNECTORS FOR DAMAGE.
IS PHYSICAL DAMAGE INDICATED?
NO
YES
CORRECT PHYSICAL DAMAGE, CLEAR CODES AND RECHECK.
3
• DISCONNECT REAR ABS HARNESS CONNECTOR FROM BODY TO ABS AND FUEL SENDER CONNECTOR.
• CONNECT DVM BETWEEN TERMINALS "C2" AND "C3" OF THE ABS CONNECTOR AND MEASURE RESISTANCE
RESISTANCE SHOULD BE BETWEEN 2100 AND 2400 OHMS.
IS IT?
NO
DOES THE VEHICLE HAVE A TUBULAR REAR AXLE?
YES
• REMOVE LEFT REAR WHEEL BEARING AND SENSOR ASSEMBLY.
• MEASURE RESISTANCE BETWEEN TERMINALS "A" AND "B" OF THE WHEEL SPEED SENSOR. RESISTANCE SHOULD BE BETWEEN 2100 AND 2400 OHMS.
IS IT?
NO
• DISCONNECT CONNECTOR FROM LEFT REAR SENSOR.
• MEASURE RESISTANCE BETWEEN TERMINALS "A" AND "B" OF THE WHEEL SPEED SENSOR RESISTANCE SHOULD BE BETWEEN 2100 AND 2400 OHMS.
IS IT?
YES
• RECONNECT CONNECTOR TO WHEEL SPEED SENSOR.
• RETAIN WHEEL BEARING AND SENSOR ASSEMBLY TO REAR AXLE WITH ONE BOLT.
• MEASURE RESISTANCE BETWEEN TERMINALS "C2" AND "C3" OF REAR ABS HARNESS CONNECTOR. RESISTANCE SHOULD BE BETWEEN 2100 AND 2400 OHMS.
IS IT?
NO
REPLACE WHEEL BEARING AND SPEED SENSOR ASSEMBLY.
YES
HAD POOR CONNECTIONS AT SENSOR.
NO
REPLACE REAR ABS HARNESS
YES
4
• CONNECT DVM BETWEEN REAR ABS HARNESS TERMINAL "C2" AND GROUND AND MEASURE RESISTANCE.
RESISTANCE SHOULD BE INFINITE.
IS IT?
NO
DOES THE VEHICLE HAVE A TUBULAR REAR AXLE.
YES
GO TO FOLLOWING CHART
YES
• REMOVE LEFT REAR WHEEL BEARING AND SENSOR ASSEMBLY.
• CONNECT DVM TO GROUND AND TERMINAL "A" OF THE WHEEL SPEED SENSOR CONNECTOR.
RESISTANCE SHOULD BE INFINITE.
IS IT?
NO
• DISCONNECT CONNECTOR FROM LEFT REAR SENSOR.
• CONNECT DVM TO GROUND A TERMINAL "A" OF WHEEL SPEED SENSOR CONNECTOR.
RESISTANCE SHOULD BE INFINITE.
IS IT?
YES
REPLACE REAR ABS HARNESS
NO
REPLACE WHEEL BEARING AND SPEED SENSOR ASSEMBLY.

GC402910068600FX

Fig. 42 Code A027: Excessive Left Rear Wheel Acceleration (Part 1 of 2). 1992

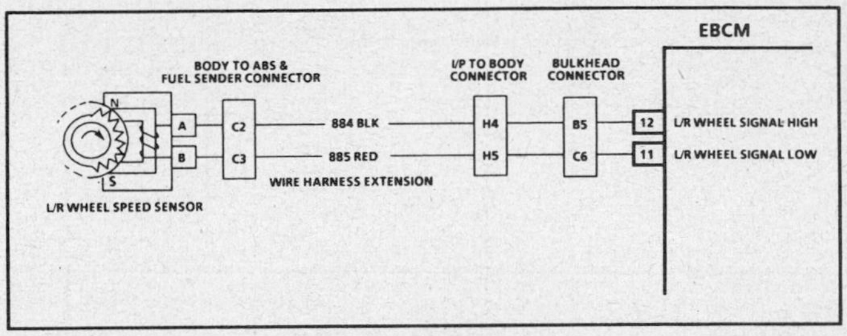
EBCM
BODY TO ABS & FUEL SENDER CONNECTOR
I/P TO BODY CONNECTOR
BULKHEAD CONNECTOR
884 BLK
885 RED
12 L/R WHEEL SIGNAL HIGH
11 L/R WHEEL SIGNAL LOW
WIRE HARNESS EXTENSION
L/R WHEEL SPEED SENSOR

GC402910068600GX

Cavalier & Sunbird

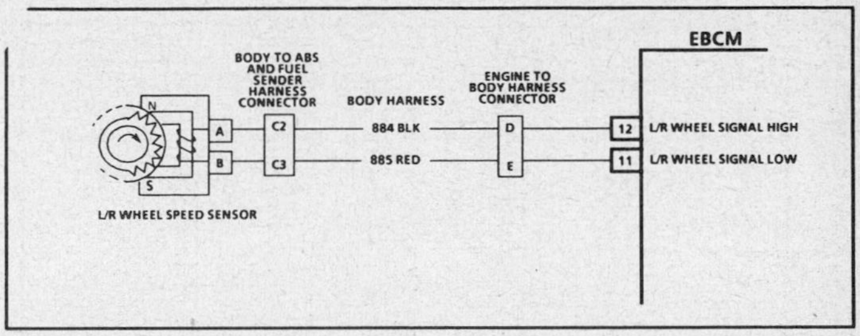
EBCM
BODY TO ABS AND FUEL SENDER HARNESS CONNECTOR
BODY HARNESS
ENGINE TO BODY HARNESS CONNECTOR
884 BLK
885 RED
12 L/R WHEEL SIGNAL HIGH
11 L/R WHEEL SIGNAL LOW
L/R WHEEL SPEED SENSOR

GC402910068600HX

Beretta & Corsica

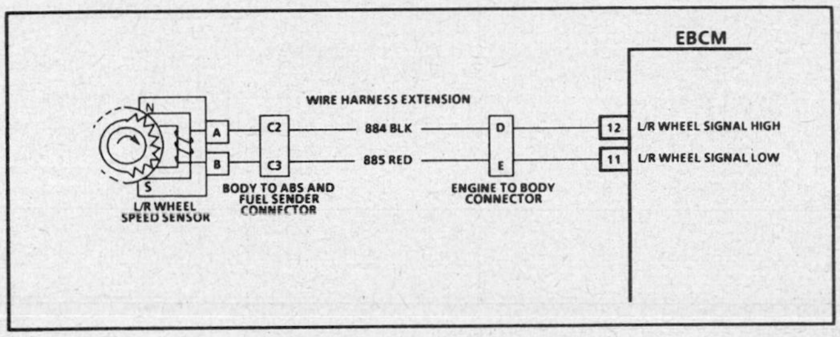
EBCM
WIRE HARNESS EXTENSION
884 BLK
885 RED
12 L/R WHEEL SIGNAL HIGH
11 L/R WHEEL SIGNAL LOW
L/R WHEEL SPEED SENSOR
BODY TO ABS AND FUEL SENDER CONNECTOR
ENGINE TO BODY CONNECTOR

GC402910068600IX

Achieva, Calais & Grand Am

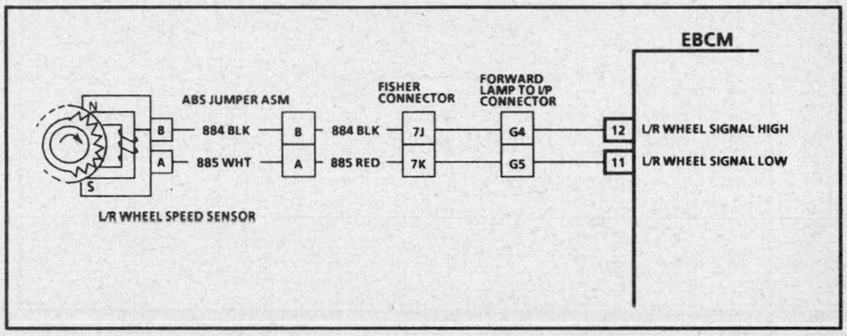
EBCM
ABS JUMPER ASM
FISHER CONNECTOR
FORWARD LAMP TO I/P CONNECTOR
884 BLK
885 WHT
885 RED
12 L/R WHEEL SIGNAL HIGH
11 L/R WHEEL SIGNAL LOW
L/R WHEEL SPEED SENSOR

GC402910068600JX

Cutlass Supreme, Grand Prix, Lumina & Regal

Circuit Description:

As a toothed ring passes by the wheel speed sensor, changes in the electromagnetic field cause the wheel speed sensor to produce a sinusoidal (AC) voltage signal whose frequency is proportional to wheel speed. The magnitude of this signal is directly related to wheel speed and the proximity of the wheel speed sensor to the toothed ring, often referred to as the air gap.

This code detects opens, shorts to ground, and shorts to battery that cause intermittent wheel speed operation. Also detected is any sudden change in wheel speed determined to be unreasonable.

Test Description: Number(s) below refer to circled number(s) on the diagnostic chart.

5. This step checks to see if the wheel speed sensor circuitry is shorted to voltage.
6. This step insures that the wheel speed sensor circuitry resistance is within the proper value.
7. This checks for an open in the wheel signal high circuit.
8. This checks for an open in the wheel signal low circuit.
9. This step insures that Code A027 was not set due to a poor connection between the world connector and EBCM.

Diagnostic Aids:

An "Intermittent" problem may be caused by a poor connection, rubbed through wire insulation, or a wire that is broken inside the insulation.

The frequency of the problem can be checked by using the enhanced diagnostic function of the "Scan" tool.

If the customers comments reflect that the ABS Amber warning light is on only during moist environmental changes, (rain, snow, vehicle wash) all wheel speed sensor circuitry should be thoroughly inspected for water intrusion. Use the following procedure. Spray down the suspected area with 5% salt water solution (two teaspoons of salt to 12 oz. of water). Start vehicle, allow vehicle to run for 10 seconds. If code returns immediately, replace suspected harness.

Any circuitry, that is suspected as causing the intermittent complaint, should be thoroughly checked for backed out terminals, improper mating, broken locks, improperly formed or damaged terminals, poor terminal to wiring connections or physical damage to the wiring harness.

Excessive end play can cause this code to set. Check integral bearing for excessive axial end play.

GC402910068600KX

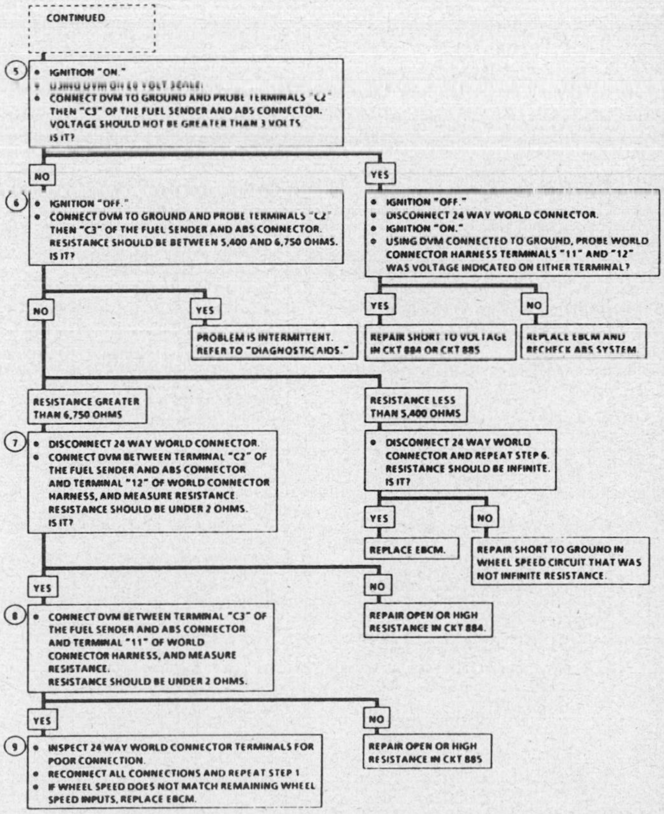
CONTINUED
5 • IGNITION "ON."
• CONNECT DVM TO GROUND AND PROBE TERMINALS "C2" THEN "C3" OF THE FUEL SENDER AND ABS CONNECTOR. VOLTAGE SHOULD NOT BE GREATER THAN 3 VOLTS IS IT?
NO
YES
6 • IGNITION "OFF." • CONNECT DVM TO GROUND AND PROBE TERMINALS "C2" THEN "C3" OF THE FUEL SENDER AND ABS CONNECTOR. RESISTANCE SHOULD BE BETWEEN 5,400 AND 6,750 OHMS. IS IT?
• IGNITION "OFF." • DISCONNECT 24 WAY WORLD CONNECTOR. • IGNITION "ON." • USING DVM CONNECTED TO GROUND, PROBE WORLD CONNECTOR HARNESS TERMINALS "11" AND "12" WAS VOLTAGE INDICATED ON EITHER TERMINAL?
PROBLEM IS INTERMITTENT. REFER TO "DIAGNOSTIC AIDS."
REPAIR SHORT TO VOLTAGE IN CKT 884 OR CKT 885
REPLACE EBCM AND RECHECK ABS SYSTEM
RESISTANCE GREATER THAN 6,750 OHMS
RESISTANCE LESS THAN 5,400 OHMS
7 • DISCONNECT 24 WAY WORLD CONNECTOR. • CONNECT DVM BETWEEN TERMINAL "C2" OF THE FUEL SENDER AND ABS CONNECTOR AND TERMINAL "12" OF WORLD CONNECTOR HARNESS, AND MEASURE RESISTANCE. RESISTANCE SHOULD BE UNDER 2 OHMS. IS IT?
• DISCONNECT 24 WAY WORLD CONNECTOR AND REPEAT STEP 6. RESISTANCE SHOULD BE INFINITE. IS IT?
REPLACE EBCM.
REPAIR SHORT TO GROUND IN WHEEL SPEED CIRCUIT THAT WAS NOT INFINITE RESISTANCE.
REPAIR OPEN OR HIGH RESISTANCE IN CKT 884.
8 • CONNECT DVM BETWEEN TERMINAL "C3" OF THE FUEL SENDER AND ABS CONNECTOR AND TERMINAL "11" OF WORLD CONNECTOR HARNESS, AND MEASURE RESISTANCE. RESISTANCE SHOULD BE UNDER 2 OHMS.
REPAIR OPEN OR HIGH RESISTANCE IN CKT 885
9 • INSPECT 24 WAY WORLD CONNECTOR TERMINALS FOR POOR CONNECTION. • RECONNECT ALL CONNECTIONS AND REPEAT STEP 1 • IF WHEEL SPEED DOES NOT MATCH REMAINING WHEEL SPEED INPUTS, REPLACE EBCM.

GC402910068600LX

Fig. 42 Code A027: Excessive Left Rear Wheel Acceleration (Part 2 of 2). 1992

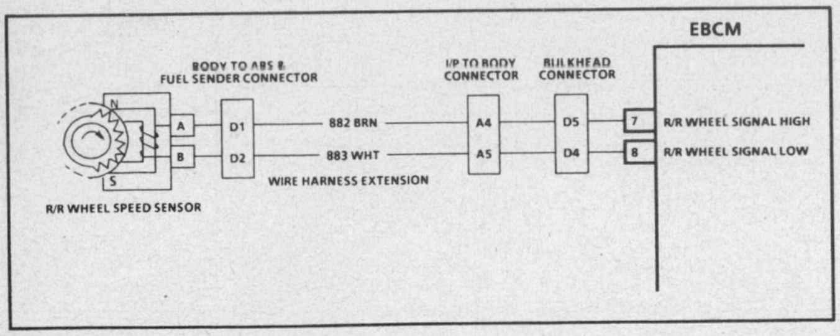
EBCM
BODY TO ABS & FUEL SENDER CONNECTOR
I/P TO BODY CONNECTOR
BULKHEAD CONNECTOR
882 BRN
883 WHT
WIRE HARNESS EXTENSION
R/R WHEEL SIGNAL HIGH
R/R WHEEL SIGNAL LOW
R/R WHEEL SPEED SENSOR

GC402910068700AX

Cavalier & Sunbird

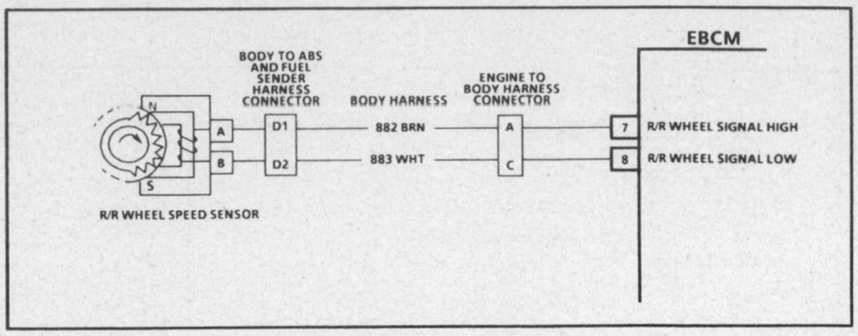
EBCM
BODY TO ABS AND FUEL SENDER HARNESS CONNECTOR
BODY HARNESS
ENGINE TO BODY HARNESS CONNECTOR
882 BRN
883 WHT
R/R WHEEL SIGNAL HIGH
R/R WHEEL SIGNAL LOW
R/R WHEEL SPEED SENSOR

GC402910068700BX

Beretta & Corsica

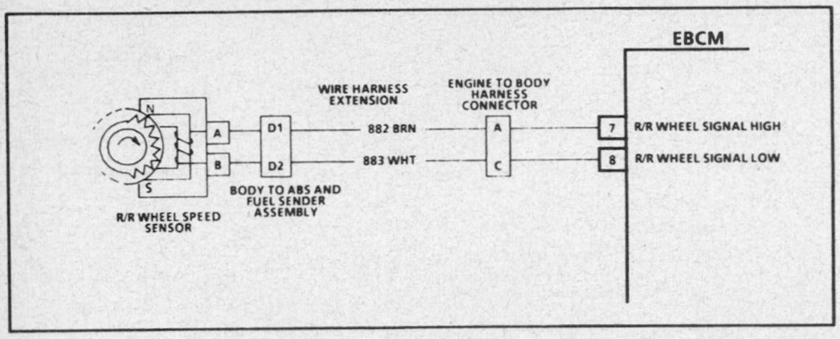
EBCM
WIRE HARNESS EXTENSION
ENGINE TO BODY HARNESS CONNECTOR
882 BRN
883 WHT
R/R WHEEL SIGNAL HIGH
R/R WHEEL SIGNAL LOW
BODY TO ABS AND FUEL SENDER ASSEMBLY
R/R WHEEL SPEED SENSOR

GC402910068700CX

Achieva, Calais & Grand Am

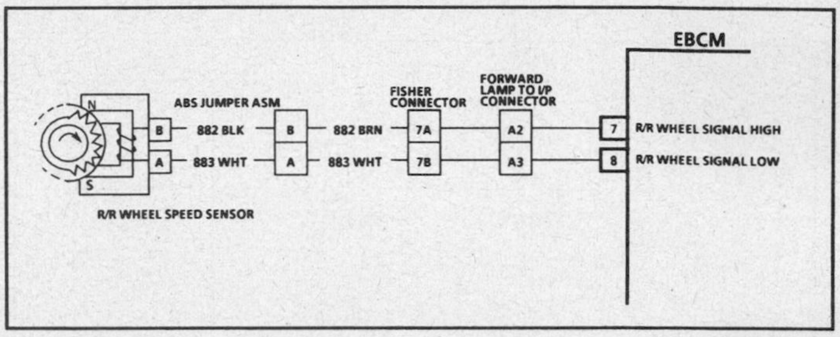
EBCM
ABS JUMPER ASM
FISHER CONNECTOR
FORWARD LAMP TO I/P CONNECTOR
882 BLK
883 WHT
882 BRN
883 WHT
R/R WHEEL SIGNAL HIGH
R/R WHEEL SIGNAL LOW
R/R WHEEL SPEED SENSOR

GC402910068700DX

Cutlass Supreme, Grand Prix, Lumina & Regal

Circuit Description:

As a toothed ring passes by the wheel speed sensor, changes in the electromagnetic field cause the wheel speed sensor to produce a sinusoidal (AC) voltage signal whose frequency is proportional to wheel speed. The magnitude of this signal is directly related to wheel speed and the proximity of the wheel speed sensor to the toothed ring, often referred to as the air gap.

This code detects opens, shorts to ground, and shorts to battery that cause intermittent wheel speed operation. Also detected is any sudden change in wheel speed determined to be unreasonable.

Test Description: Number(s) below refer to circled number(s) on the diagnostic chart.

1. This test verifies whether the fault is currently present.
2. This step is designed to identify a wheel speed sensor or circuitry that is damaged and visibly apparent.
3. This test checks to see that the wheel speed sensor circuitry is within proper resistance value.
4. This insures that the wheel speed sensor is not shorted to ground.

Diagnostic Aids:

An "Intermittent" problem may be caused by a poor connection, rubbed through wire insulation, or a wire that is broken inside the insulation.

The frequency of the problem can be checked by using the enhanced diagnostic function of the "Scan" tool.

If the customers comments reflect that the ABS Amber warning light is on only during moist environmental changes, (rain, snow, vehicle wash) all wheel speed sensor circuitry should be thoroughly inspected for water intrusion. Use the following procedure. Spray down the suspected area with 5% salt water solution (two teaspoons of salt to 12 oz. of water). Start vehicle, allow vehicle to run for 10 seconds. If code returns immediately, replace suspected harness.

Any circuitry, that is suspected as causing the intermittent complaint, should be thoroughly checked for backed out terminals, improper mating, broken locks, improperly formed or damaged terminals, poor terminal to wiring connections or physical damage to the wiring harness.

Excessive end play can cause this code to set. Check integral bearing for excessive axial end play.

GC402910068700EX

IMPORTANT: WHEEL SPEED SENSOR INTERMITTENT PROBLEMS MAY BE DIFFICULT TO LOCATE. CARE SHOULD BE TAKEN NOT TO DISTURB ANY ELECTRICAL CONNECTIONS PRIOR TO AN INDICATED STEP OF THIS CHART. THIS WILL INSURE THAT AN INTERMITTENT CONNECTION WILL NOT BE CORRECTED BEFORE THE SOURCE OF THE PROBLEM IS FOUND.

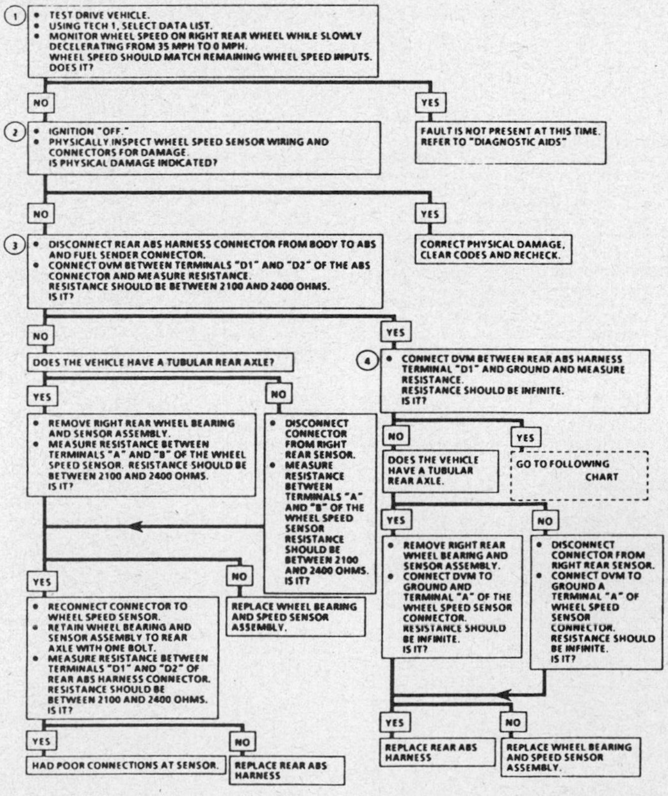
1
• TEST DRIVE VEHICLE.
• USING TECH 1, SELECT DATA LIST.
• MONITOR WHEEL SPEED ON RIGHT REAR WHEEL WHILE SLOWLY DECELERATING FROM 35 MPH TO 0 MPH. WHEEL SPEED SHOULD MATCH REMAINING WHEEL SPEED INPUTS. DOES IT?
NO
YES
FAULT IS NOT PRESENT AT THIS TIME. REFER TO "DIAGNOSTIC AIDS"
2
• IGNITION "OFF."
• PHYSICALLY INSPECT WHEEL SPEED SENSOR WIRING AND CONNECTORS FOR DAMAGE. IS PHYSICAL DAMAGE INDICATED?
NO
YES
CORRECT PHYSICAL DAMAGE, CLEAR CODES AND RECHECK.
3
• DISCONNECT REAR ABS HARNESS CONNECTOR FROM BODY TO ABS AND FUEL SENDER CONNECTOR.
• CONNECT DVM BETWEEN TERMINALS "D1" AND "D2" OF THE ABS CONNECTOR AND MEASURE RESISTANCE. RESISTANCE SHOULD BE BETWEEN 2100 AND 2400 OHMS. IS IT?
NO
YES
DOES THE VEHICLE HAVE A TUBULAR REAR AXLE?
4
• CONNECT DVM BETWEEN REAR ABS HARNESS TERMINAL "D1" AND GROUND AND MEASURE RESISTANCE. RESISTANCE SHOULD BE INFINITE. IS IT?
YES
NO
• REMOVE RIGHT REAR WHEEL BEARING AND SENSOR ASSEMBLY.
• MEASURE RESISTANCE BETWEEN TERMINALS "A" AND "B" OF THE WHEEL SPEED SENSOR. RESISTANCE SHOULD BE BETWEEN 2100 AND 2400 OHMS. IS IT?
• DISCONNECT CONNECTOR FROM RIGHT REAR SENSOR.
• MEASURE RESISTANCE BETWEEN TERMINALS "A" AND "B" OF THE WHEEL SPEED SENSOR RESISTANCE SHOULD BE BETWEEN 2100 AND 2400 OHMS. IS IT?
NO
YES
DOES THE VEHICLE HAVE A TUBULAR REAR AXLE.
GO TO FOLLOWING CHART
YES
NO
• REMOVE RIGHT REAR WHEEL BEARING AND SENSOR ASSEMBLY.
• CONNECT DVM TO GROUND AND TERMINAL "A" OF THE WHEEL SPEED SENSOR CONNECTOR. RESISTANCE SHOULD BE INFINITE. IS IT?
• DISCONNECT CONNECTOR FROM RIGHT REAR SENSOR.
• CONNECT DVM TO GROUND A TERMINAL "A" OF WHEEL SPEED SENSOR CONNECTOR. RESISTANCE SHOULD BE INFINITE. IS IT?
YES
NO
• RECONNECT CONNECTOR TO WHEEL SPEED SENSOR.
• RETAIN WHEEL BEARING AND SENSOR ASSEMBLY TO REAR AXLE WITH ONE BOLT.
• MEASURE RESISTANCE BETWEEN TERMINALS "D1" AND "D2" OF REAR ABS HARNESS CONNECTOR. RESISTANCE SHOULD BE BETWEEN 2100 AND 2400 OHMS. IS IT?
REPLACE WHEEL BEARING AND SPEED SENSOR ASSEMBLY.
YES
NO
REPLACE REAR ABS HARNESS
REPLACE WHEEL BEARING AND SPEED SENSOR ASSEMBLY.
YES
NO
HAD POOR CONNECTIONS AT SENSOR.
REPLACE REAR ABS HARNESS

GC402910068700FX

Fig. 43 Code A028: Excessive Right Rear Wheel Acceleration (Part 1 of 2). 1992

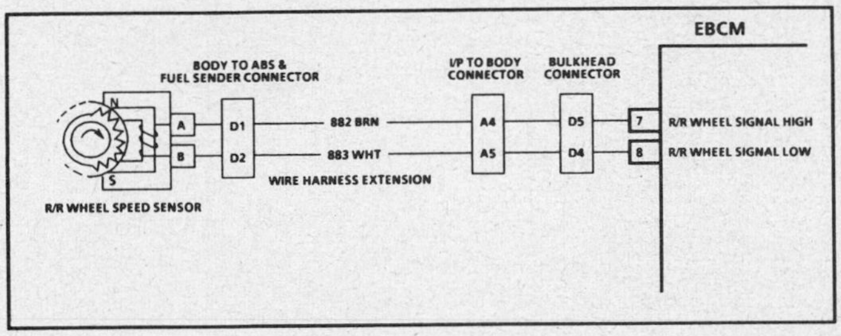
EBCM
BODY TO ABS &
FUEL SENDER CONNECTOR
I/P TO BODY
CONNECTOR
BULKHEAD
CONNECTOR
N
S
A
B
D1
D2
882 BRN
883 WHT
A4
A5
D5
D4
7
8
R/R WHEEL SIGNAL HIGH
R/R WHEEL SIGNAL LOW
WIRE HARNESS EXTENSION
R/R WHEEL SPEED SENSOR

GC402910068700GX

Cavalier & Sunbird

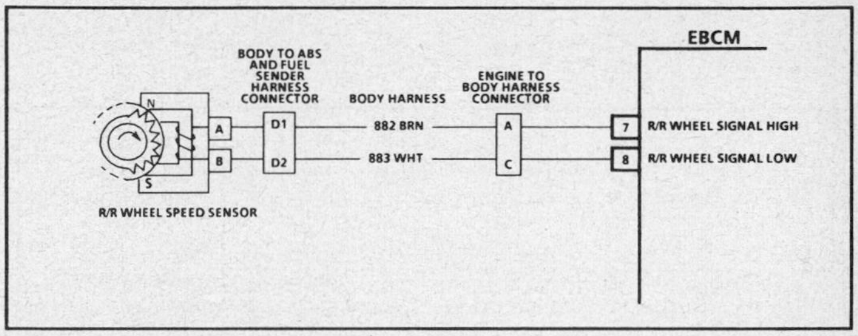
EBCM
BODY TO ABS
AND FUEL
SENDER
HARNESS
CONNECTOR
BODY HARNESS
ENGINE TO
BODY HARNESS
CONNECTOR
N
S
A
B
D1
D2
882 BRN
883 WHT
A
C
7
8
R/R WHEEL SIGNAL HIGH
R/R WHEEL SIGNAL LOW
R/R WHEEL SPEED SENSOR

GC402910068700HX

Beretta & Corsica

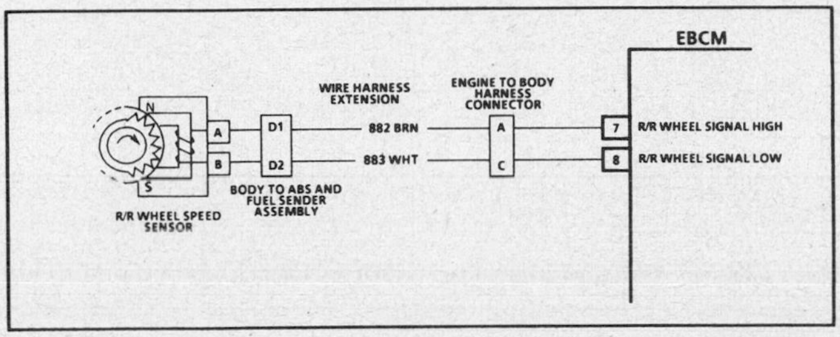
EBCM
WIRE HARNESS
EXTENSION
ENGINE TO BODY
HARNESS
CONNECTOR
N
S
A
B
D1
D2
882 BRN
883 WHT
A
C
7
8
R/R WHEEL SIGNAL HIGH
R/R WHEEL SIGNAL LOW
BODY TO ABS AND
FUEL SENDER
ASSEMBLY
R/R WHEEL SPEED
SENSOR

GC402910068700IX

Achieva, Calais & Grand Am

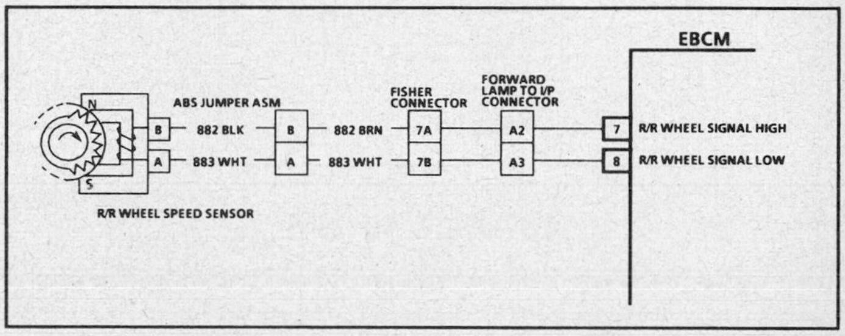
EBCM
ABS JUMPER ASM
FISHER
CONNECTOR
FORWARD
LAMP TO I/P
CONNECTOR
N
S
B
A
882 BLK
883 WHT
B
A
882 BRN
883 WHT
7A
7B
A2
A3
7
8
R/R WHEEL SIGNAL HIGH
R/R WHEEL SIGNAL LOW
R/R WHEEL SPEED SENSOR

GC402910068700JX

Cutlass Supreme, Grand Prix, Lumina & Regal

Circuit Description:

As a toothed ring passes by the wheel speed sensor, changes in the electromagnetic field cause the wheel speed sensor to produce a sinusoidal (AC) voltage signal whose frequency is proportional to wheel speed. The magnitude of this signal is directly related to wheel speed and the proximity of the wheel speed sensor to the toothed ring, often referred to as the air gap.

This code detects opens, shorts to ground, and shorts to battery that cause intermittent wheel speed operation. Also detected is any sudden change in wheel speed determined to be unreasonable.

Test Description: Number(s) below refer to circled number(s) on the diagnostic chart.

5. This step checks to see if the wheel speed sensor circuitry is shorted to voltage.
6. This step insures that the wheel speed sensor circuitry resistance is within proper value.
7. This checks for an open in the wheel signal high circuit.
8. This checks for an open in the wheel signal low circuit.
9. This step insures that Code A028 was not set due to a poor connection between the world connector and EBCM.

Diagnostic Aids:

An "Intermittent" problem may be caused by a poor connection, rubbed through wire insulation, or a wire that is broken inside the insulation.

The frequency of the problem can be checked by using the enhanced diagnostic function of the "Scan" tool.

If the customers comments reflect that the ABS Amber warning light is on only during moist environmental changes, (rain, snow, vehicle wash) all wheel speed sensor circuitry should be thoroughly inspected for water intrusion. Use the following procedure. Spray down the suspected area with 5% salt water solution (two teaspoons of salt to 12 oz. of water). Start vehicle, allow vehicle to run for 10 seconds. If code returns immediately, replace suspected harness.

Any circuitry, that is suspected as causing the intermittent complaint, should be thoroughly checked for backed out terminals, improper mating, broken locks, improperly formed or damaged terminals, poor terminal to wiring connections or physical damage to the wiring harness.

Excessive end play can cause this code to set. Check integral bearing for excessive axial end play.

GC402910068700KX

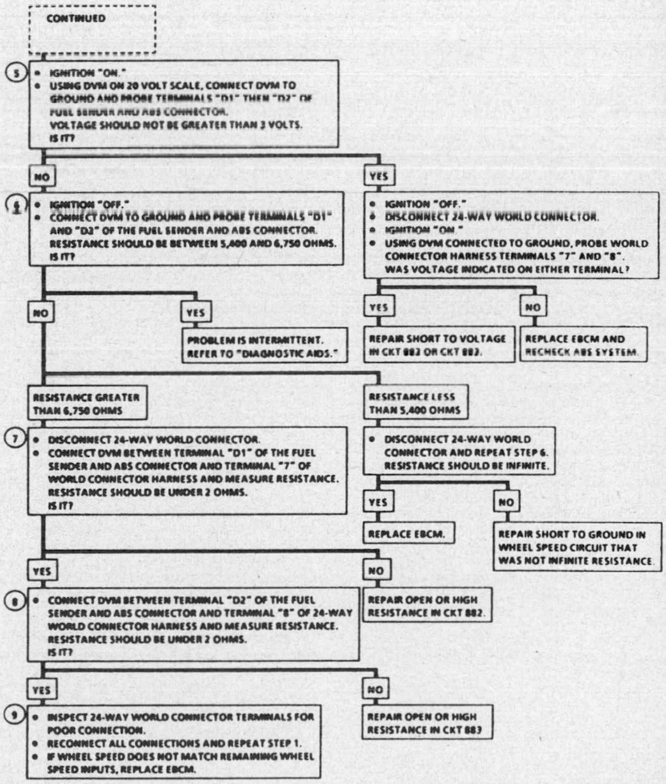
CONTINUED
5
• IGNITION "ON."
• USING DVM ON 20 VOLT SCALE, CONNECT DVM TO GROUND AND PROBE TERMINALS "D1" THEN "D2" OF FUEL SENDER AND ABS CONNECTOR.
VOLTAGE SHOULD NOT BE GREATER THAN 3 VOLTS.
IS IT?
NO
YES
6
• IGNITION "OFF."
• CONNECT DVM TO GROUND AND PROBE TERMINALS "D1" AND "D2" OF THE FUEL SENDER AND ABS CONNECTOR.
RESISTANCE SHOULD BE BETWEEN 5,400 AND 6,750 OHMS.
IS IT?
• IGNITION "OFF."
• DISCONNECT 24-WAY WORLD CONNECTOR.
• IGNITION "ON."
• USING DVM CONNECTED TO GROUND, PROBE WORLD CONNECTOR HARNESS TERMINALS "7" AND "8".
WAS VOLTAGE INDICATED ON EITHER TERMINAL?
NO
YES
PROBLEM IS INTERMITTENT.
REFER TO "DIAGNOSTIC AIDS."
YES
NO
REPAIR SHORT TO VOLTAGE IN CKT 882 OR CKT 883.
REPLACE EBCM AND RECHECK ABS SYSTEM.
RESISTANCE GREATER THAN 6,750 OHMS
RESISTANCE LESS THAN 5,400 OHMS
7
• DISCONNECT 24-WAY WORLD CONNECTOR.
• CONNECT DVM BETWEEN TERMINAL "D1" OF THE FUEL SENDER AND ABS CONNECTOR AND TERMINAL "7" OF WORLD CONNECTOR HARNESS AND MEASURE RESISTANCE.
RESISTANCE SHOULD BE UNDER 2 OHMS.
IS IT?
• DISCONNECT 24-WAY WORLD CONNECTOR AND REPEAT STEP 6.
RESISTANCE SHOULD BE INFINITE.
YES
NO
REPLACE EBCM.
REPAIR SHORT TO GROUND IN WHEEL SPEED CIRCUIT THAT WAS NOT INFINITE RESISTANCE.
YES
NO
8
• CONNECT DVM BETWEEN TERMINAL "D2" OF THE FUEL SENDER AND ABS CONNECTOR AND TERMINAL "8" OF 24-WAY WORLD CONNECTOR HARNESS AND MEASURE RESISTANCE.
RESISTANCE SHOULD BE UNDER 2 OHMS.
IS IT?
REPAIR OPEN OR HIGH RESISTANCE IN CKT 882.
YES
NO
9
• INSPECT 24-WAY WORLD CONNECTOR TERMINALS FOR POOR CONNECTION.
• RECONNECT ALL CONNECTIONS AND REPEAT STEP 1.
• IF WHEEL SPEED DOES NOT MATCH REMAINING WHEEL SPEED INPUTS, REPLACE EBCM.
REPAIR OPEN OR HIGH RESISTANCE IN CKT 883

GC402910068700LX

Fig. 43 Code A028: Excessive Right Rear Wheel Acceleration (Part 2 of 2). 1992

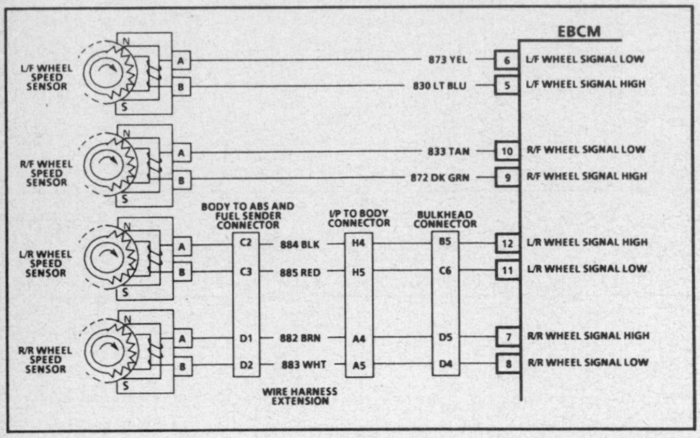
EBCM
L/F WHEEL SPEED SENSOR
R/F WHEEL SPEED SENSOR
L/R WHEEL SPEED SENSOR
R/R WHEEL SPEED SENSOR
873 YEL
830 LT BLU
833 TAN
872 DK GRN
884 BLK
885 RED
882 BRN
883 WHT
BODY TO ABS AND FUEL SENDER CONNECTOR
I/P TO BODY CONNECTOR
BULKHEAD CONNECTOR
WIRE HARNESS EXTENSION
L/F WHEEL SIGNAL LOW
L/F WHEEL SIGNAL HIGH
R/F WHEEL SIGNAL LOW
R/F WHEEL SIGNAL HIGH
L/R WHEEL SIGNAL HIGH
L/R WHEEL SIGNAL LOW
R/R WHEEL SIGNAL HIGH
R/R WHEEL SIGNAL LOW
GC402910068800AX

Cavalier & Sunbird

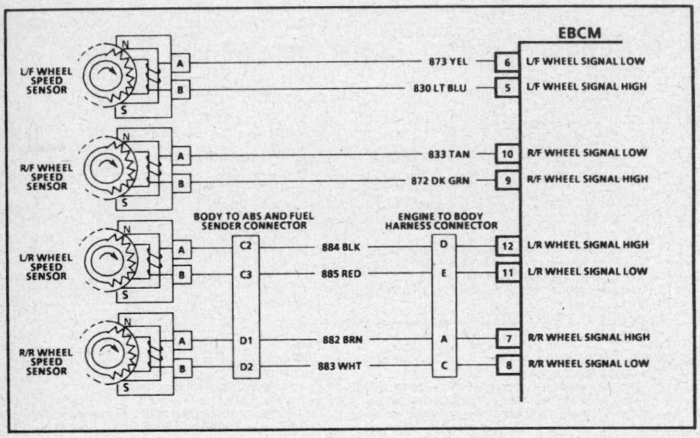
EBCM
L/F WHEEL SPEED SENSOR
R/F WHEEL SPEED SENSOR
L/R WHEEL SPEED SENSOR
R/R WHEEL SPEED SENSOR
873 YEL
830 LT BLU
833 TAN
872 DK GRN
884 BLK
885 RED
882 BRN
883 WHT
BODY TO ABS AND FUEL SENDER CONNECTOR
ENGINE TO BODY HARNESS CONNECTOR
L/F WHEEL SIGNAL LOW
L/F WHEEL SIGNAL HIGH
R/F WHEEL SIGNAL LOW
R/F WHEEL SIGNAL HIGH
L/R WHEEL SIGNAL HIGH
L/R WHEEL SIGNAL LOW
R/R WHEEL SIGNAL HIGH
R/R WHEEL SIGNAL LOW
GC402910068800CX

Achieva, Calais & Grand Am

Circuit Description:

As a toothed ring passes by the wheel speed sensor, changes in the electromagnetic field cause the wheel speed sensor to produce a sinusoidal (AC) voltage signal whose frequency is proportional to wheel speed. The magnitude of this signal is directly related to wheel speed and the proximity of the wheel speed sensor to the toothed ring, often referred to as the air gap.

This code is designed to detect two open wheel speed sensors in any combination. This test exists due to a condition that may exist that does not allow the driver to be informed by the ABS warning light of non-functioning ABS. If one wheel speed sensor is open, the driver is informed. If a second fails, the driver is no longer informed without this test and ABS is not available. By requiring the two operating wheels to be within 7 mph, a false code is prevented during spin-ups while still allowing for detection when the stowaway spare tire is used.

Test Description: Number(s) below refer to circled number(s) on the diagnostic chart.

1. This test verifies whether the fault is currently present.
2. This step is designed to identify a wheel speed sensor or circuitry that is damaged and visibly apparent.
3. This step identifies if the cause of the problem is common to the rear wheel sensor circuitry.
4. Because both rear sensors are common to the extension harness, the 4 way connectors and harness should be inspected.
5. This test checks to see that the wheel speed sensor is within proper resistance values.
6. This insures that the wheel speed sensor is not shorted to ground.

Diagnostic Aids:

A false Code A031 may be set as a result of vehicle operation while on a hoist or a lifted condition or stuck in mud or snow, when the vehicle is in gear.

An "Intermittent" problem may be caused by a poor connection, rubbed through wire insulation, or a wire that is broken inside the insulation.

The frequency of the problem can be checked by using the enhanced diagnostic function of the "Scan" tool.

GC402910068800EX

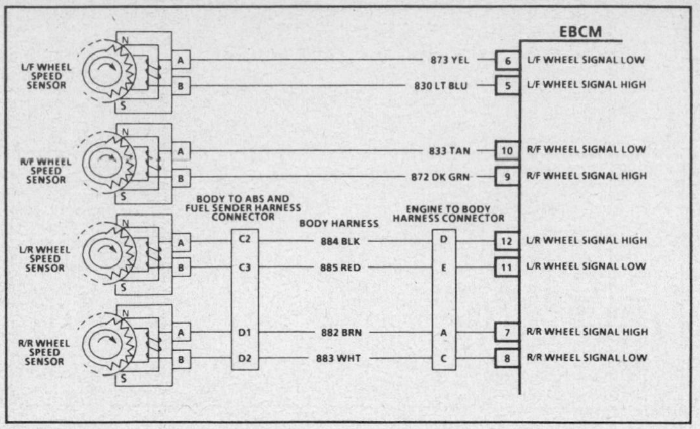
EBCM
L/F WHEEL SPEED SENSOR
R/F WHEEL SPEED SENSOR
L/R WHEEL SPEED SENSOR
R/R WHEEL SPEED SENSOR
873 YEL
830 LT BLU
833 TAN
872 DK GRN
BODY TO ABS AND FUEL SENDER HARNESS CONNECTOR
BODY HARNESS
ENGINE TO BODY HARNESS CONNECTOR
884 BLK
885 RED
882 BRN
883 WHT
L/F WHEEL SIGNAL LOW
L/F WHEEL SIGNAL HIGH
R/F WHEEL SIGNAL LOW
R/F WHEEL SIGNAL HIGH
L/R WHEEL SIGNAL HIGH
L/R WHEEL SIGNAL LOW
R/R WHEEL SIGNAL HIGH
R/R WHEEL SIGNAL LOW
GC402910068800BX

Beretta & Corsica

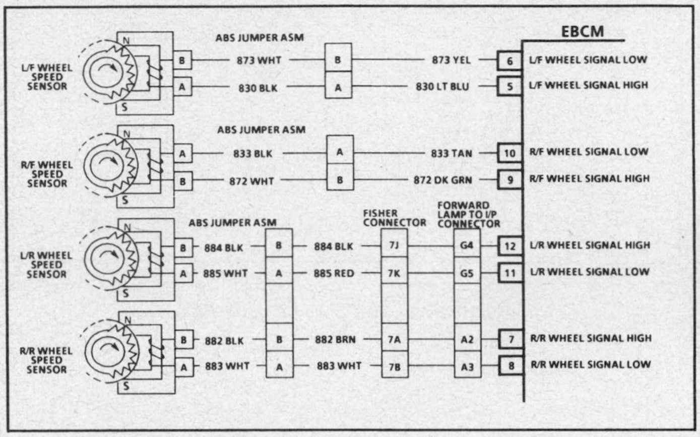
EBCM
L/F WHEEL SPEED SENSOR
R/F WHEEL SPEED SENSOR
L/R WHEEL SPEED SENSOR
R/R WHEEL SPEED SENSOR
ABS JUMPER ASM
873 WHT
830 BLK
833 BLK
872 WHT
884 BLK
885 WHT
882 BLK
883 WHT
873 YEL
830 LT BLU
833 TAN
872 DK GRN
884 BLK
885 RED
882 BRN
883 WHT
FISHER CONNECTOR
FORWARD LAMP TO I/P CONNECTOR
L/F WHEEL SIGNAL LOW
L/F WHEEL SIGNAL HIGH
R/F WHEEL SIGNAL LOW
R/F WHEEL SIGNAL HIGH
L/R WHEEL SIGNAL HIGH
L/R WHEEL SIGNAL LOW
R/R WHEEL SIGNAL HIGH
R/R WHEEL SIGNAL LOW
GC402910068800DX

Cutlass Supreme, Grand Prix, Lumina & Regal

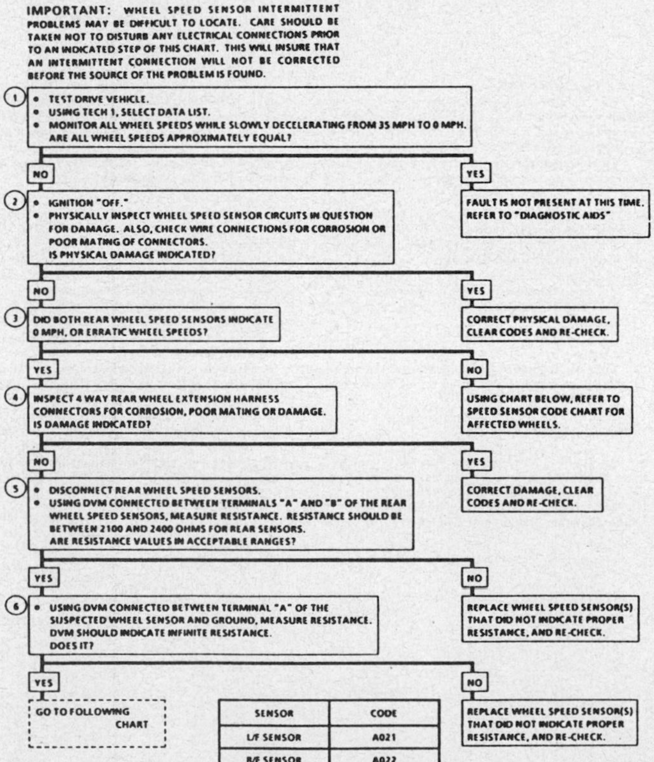
IMPORTANT: WHEEL SPEED SENSOR INTERMITTENT PROBLEMS MAY BE DIFFICULT TO LOCATE. CARE SHOULD BE TAKEN NOT TO DISTURB ANY ELECTRICAL CONNECTIONS PRIOR TO AN INDICATED STEP OF THIS CHART. THIS WILL INSURE THAT AN INTERMITTENT CONNECTION WILL NOT BE CORRECTED BEFORE THE SOURCE OF THE PROBLEM IS FOUND.
1 • TEST DRIVE VEHICLE. • USING TECH 1, SELECT DATA LIST. • MONITOR ALL WHEEL SPEEDS WHILE SLOWLY DECELERATING FROM 35 MPH TO 0 MPH. ARE ALL WHEEL SPEEDS APPROXIMATELY EQUAL?
NO
YES
FAULT IS NOT PRESENT AT THIS TIME. REFER TO "DIAGNOSTIC AIDS"
2 • IGNITION "OFF." • PHYSICALLY INSPECT WHEEL SPEED SENSOR CIRCUITS IN QUESTION FOR DAMAGE. ALSO, CHECK WIRE CONNECTIONS FOR CORROSION OR POOR MATING OF CONNECTORS. IS PHYSICAL DAMAGE INDICATED?
NO
YES
CORRECT PHYSICAL DAMAGE, CLEAR CODES AND RE-CHECK.
3 DID BOTH REAR WHEEL SPEED SENSORS INDICATE 0 MPH, OR ERRATIC WHEEL SPEEDS?
YES
NO
USING CHART BELOW, REFER TO SPEED SENSOR CODE CHART FOR AFFECTED WHEELS.
4 INSPECT 4 WAY REAR WHEEL EXTENSION HARNESS CONNECTORS FOR CORROSION, POOR MATING OR DAMAGE. IS DAMAGE INDICATED?
NO
YES
CORRECT DAMAGE, CLEAR CODES AND RE-CHECK.
5 • DISCONNECT REAR WHEEL SPEED SENSORS. • USING DVM CONNECTED BETWEEN TERMINALS "A" AND "B" OF THE REAR WHEEL SPEED SENSORS, MEASURE RESISTANCE. RESISTANCE SHOULD BE BETWEEN 2100 AND 2400 OHMS FOR REAR SENSORS. ARE RESISTANCE VALUES IN ACCEPTABLE RANGES?
YES
NO
REPLACE WHEEL SPEED SENSOR(S) THAT DID NOT INDICATE PROPER RESISTANCE, AND RE-CHECK.
6 • USING DVM CONNECTED BETWEEN TERMINAL "A" OF THE SUSPECTED WHEEL SENSOR AND GROUND, MEASURE RESISTANCE. DVM SHOULD INDICATE INFINITE RESISTANCE. DOES IT?
YES
NO
GO TO FOLLOWING CHART
REPLACE WHEEL SPEED SENSOR(S) THAT DID NOT INDICATE PROPER RESISTANCE, AND RE-CHECK.

SENSOR	CODE
L/F SENSOR	A021
R/F SENSOR	A022
L/R SENSOR	A023
R/R SENSOR	A024

GC402910068800FX

Fig. 44 Code A031: Two Wheel Speed Sensors Open (Part 1 of 2). Less tubular rear axle. 1992

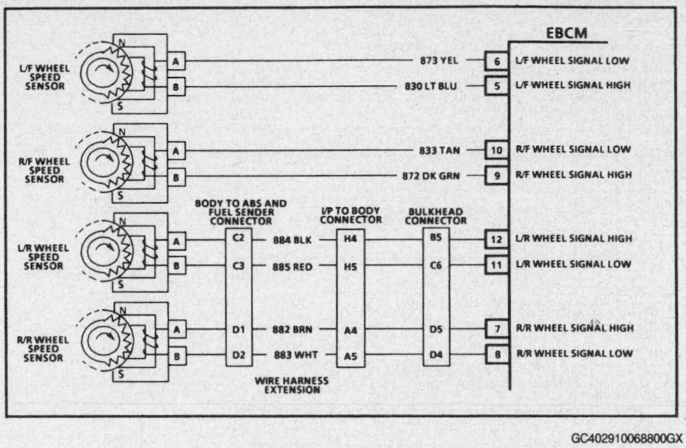
EBCM
L/F WHEEL SPEED SENSOR
R/F WHEEL SPEED SENSOR
L/R WHEEL SPEED SENSOR
R/R WHEEL SPEED SENSOR
873 YEL
830 LT BLU
833 TAN
872 DK GRN
884 BLK
885 RED
882 BRN
883 WHT
BODY TO ABS AND FUEL SENDER CONNECTOR
I/P TO BODY CONNECTOR
BULKHEAD CONNECTOR
WIRE HARNESS EXTENSION
L/F WHEEL SIGNAL LOW
L/F WHEEL SIGNAL HIGH
R/F WHEEL SIGNAL LOW
R/F WHEEL SIGNAL HIGH
L/R WHEEL SIGNAL HIGH
L/R WHEEL SIGNAL LOW
R/R WHEEL SIGNAL HIGH
R/R WHEEL SIGNAL LOW
GC402910068800GX

Cavalier & Sunbird

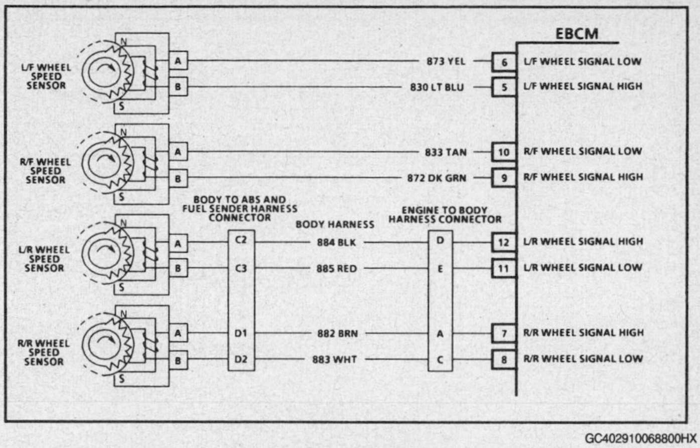
EBCM
L/F WHEEL SPEED SENSOR
R/F WHEEL SPEED SENSOR
L/R WHEEL SPEED SENSOR
R/R WHEEL SPEED SENSOR
873 YEL
830 LT BLU
833 TAN
872 DK GRN
884 BLK
885 RED
882 BRN
883 WHT
BODY TO ABS AND FUEL SENDER HARNESS CONNECTOR
BODY HARNESS
ENGINE TO BODY HARNESS CONNECTOR
L/F WHEEL SIGNAL LOW
L/F WHEEL SIGNAL HIGH
R/F WHEEL SIGNAL LOW
R/F WHEEL SIGNAL HIGH
L/R WHEEL SIGNAL HIGH
L/R WHEEL SIGNAL LOW
R/R WHEEL SIGNAL HIGH
R/R WHEEL SIGNAL LOW
GC402910068800HX

Beretta & Corsica

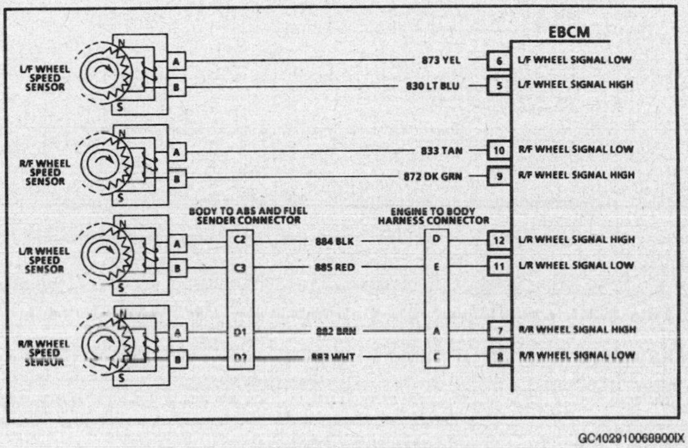
EBCM
L/F WHEEL SPEED SENSOR
R/F WHEEL SPEED SENSOR
L/R WHEEL SPEED SENSOR
R/R WHEEL SPEED SENSOR
873 YEL
830 LT BLU
833 TAN
872 DK GRN
884 BLK
885 RED
882 BRN
883 WHT
BODY TO ABS AND FUEL SENDER CONNECTOR
ENGINE TO BODY HARNESS CONNECTOR
L/F WHEEL SIGNAL LOW
L/F WHEEL SIGNAL HIGH
R/F WHEEL SIGNAL LOW
R/F WHEEL SIGNAL HIGH
L/R WHEEL SIGNAL HIGH
L/R WHEEL SIGNAL LOW
R/R WHEEL SIGNAL HIGH
R/R WHEEL SIGNAL LOW
GC402910068800IX

Achieva, Calais & Grand Am

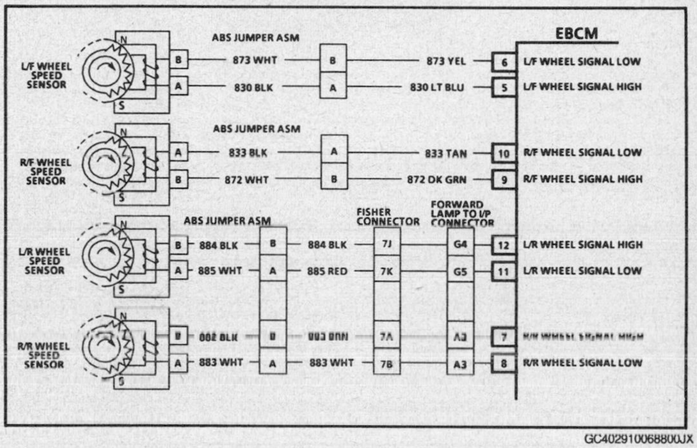
EBCM
ABS JUMPER ASM
L/F WHEEL SPEED SENSOR
R/F WHEEL SPEED SENSOR
L/R WHEEL SPEED SENSOR
R/R WHEEL SPEED SENSOR
873 WHT
830 BLK
833 BLK
872 WHT
873 YEL
830 LT BLU
833 TAN
872 DK GRN
884 BLK
885 WHT
885 RED
883 WHT
FISHER CONNECTOR
FORWARD LAMP TO I/P CONNECTOR
L/F WHEEL SIGNAL LOW
L/F WHEEL SIGNAL HIGH
R/F WHEEL SIGNAL LOW
R/F WHEEL SIGNAL HIGH
L/R WHEEL SIGNAL HIGH
L/R WHEEL SIGNAL LOW
R/R WHEEL SIGNAL LOW
GC402910068800JX

Cutlass Supreme, Grand Prix, Lumina & Regal

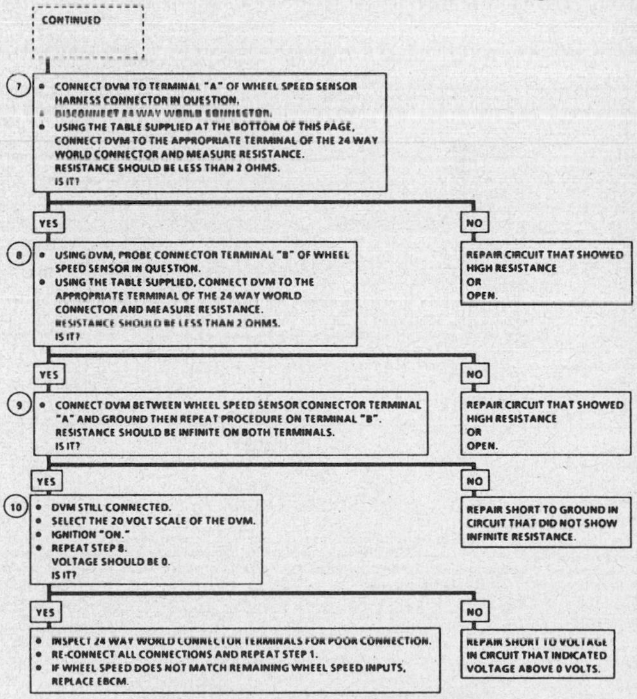
CONTINUED
7
CONNECT DVM TO TERMINAL "A" OF WHEEL SPEED SENSOR HARNESS CONNECTOR IN QUESTION.
DISCONNECT 24 WAY WORLD CONNECTOR.
USING THE TABLE SUPPLIED AT THE BOTTOM OF THIS PAGE, CONNECT DVM TO THE APPROPRIATE TERMINAL OF THE 24 WAY WORLD CONNECTOR AND MEASURE RESISTANCE.
RESISTANCE SHOULD BE LESS THAN 2 OHMS.
IS IT?
YES
NO
8
USING DVM, PROBE CONNECTOR TERMINAL "B" OF WHEEL SPEED SENSOR IN QUESTION.
USING THE TABLE SUPPLIED, CONNECT DVM TO THE APPROPRIATE TERMINAL OF THE 24 WAY WORLD CONNECTOR AND MEASURE RESISTANCE.
RESISTANCE SHOULD BE LESS THAN 2 OHMS.
IS IT?
REPAIR CIRCUIT THAT SHOWED HIGH RESISTANCE OR OPEN.
YES
NO
9
CONNECT DVM BETWEEN WHEEL SPEED SENSOR CONNECTOR TERMINAL "A" AND GROUND THEN REPEAT PROCEDURE ON TERMINAL "B".
RESISTANCE SHOULD BE INFINITE ON BOTH TERMINALS.
IS IT?
REPAIR CIRCUIT THAT SHOWED HIGH RESISTANCE OR OPEN.
YES
NO
10
DVM STILL CONNECTED.
SELECT THE 20 VOLT SCALE OF THE DVM.
IGNITION "ON."
REPEAT STEP 8.
VOLTAGE SHOULD BE 0.
IS IT?
REPAIR SHORT TO GROUND IN CIRCUIT THAT DID NOT SHOW INFINITE RESISTANCE.
YES
NO
INSPECT 24 WAY WORLD CONNECTOR TERMINALS FOR POOR CONNECTION.
RE-CONNECT ALL CONNECTIONS AND REPEAT STEP 1.
IF WHEEL SPEED DOES NOT MATCH REMAINING WHEEL SPEED INPUTS, REPLACE EBCM.
REPAIR SHORT TO VOLTAGE IN CIRCUIT THAT INDICATED VOLTAGE ABOVE 0 VOLTS.

SENSOR TERMINAL	24 WAY WORLD CONNECTOR	CIRCUIT NUMBER
L/R WHEEL A	PIN 12	884
L/R WHEEL B	PIN 11	885
R/R WHEEL A	PIN 7	882
R/R WHEEL B	PIN 8	883

GC402910068800LX

Circuit Description:

As a toothed ring passes by the wheel speed sensor, changes in the electromagnetic field cause the wheel speed sensor to produce a sinusoidal (AC) voltage signal whose frequency is proportional to wheel speed. The magnitude of this signal is directly related to wheel speed and the proximity of the wheel speed sensor to the toothed ring, often referred to as the air gap.

This code is designed to detect two open wheel speed sensors in any combination. This test exists due to a condition that may exist that does not allow the driver to be informed by the ABS warning light of non-functioning ABS. If one wheel speed sensor is open, the driver is informed. If a second fails, the driver is no longer informed without this test and ABS is not available. By requiring the two operating wheels to be within 7 mph, a false code is prevented during spin-ups while still allowing for detection when the stowaway spare tire is used.

Test Description: Number(s) below refer to circled number(s) on the diagnostic chart.

7. This step checks for an open in the wheel speed sensor circuitry of one side of the sensor.
8. This step checks for an open on the other side of the sensor in question.
9. This step checks for a short to ground in the wheel speed sensor circuitry.
10. This insures that the circuitry is not shorted to voltage.

Diagnostic Aids:

A false Code A031 may be set as a result of vehicle operation while on a hoist or a lifted condition, or stuck in mud or snow when the vehicle is in gear.

An "Intermittent" problem may be caused by a poor connection, rubbed through wire insulation, or a wire that is broken inside the insulation.

The frequency of the problem can be checked by using the enhanced diagnostic function of the "Scan" tool.

GC402910068800KX

Fig. 44 Code A031: Two Wheel Speed Sensors Open (Part 2 of 2). Less tubular rear axle. 1992

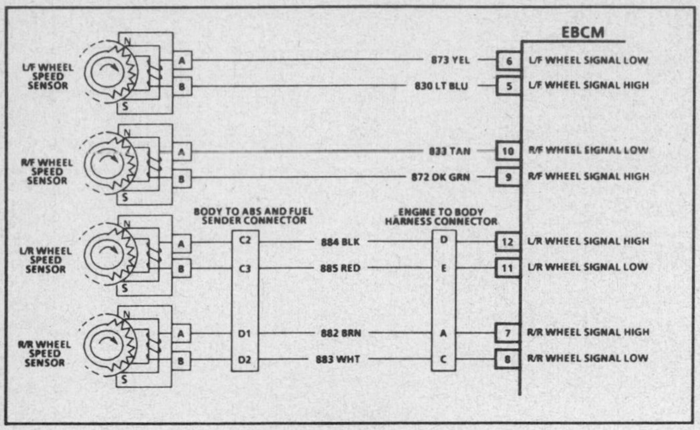
EBCM
L/F WHEEL SPEED SENSOR
873 YEL
6
L/F WHEEL SIGNAL LOW
830 LT BLU
5
L/F WHEEL SIGNAL HIGH
R/F WHEEL SPEED SENSOR
833 TAN
10
R/F WHEEL SIGNAL LOW
872 DK GRN
9
R/F WHEEL SIGNAL HIGH
BODY TO ABS AND FUEL SENDER CONNECTOR
ENGINE TO BODY HARNESS CONNECTOR
L/R WHEEL SPEED SENSOR
C2
884 BLK
D
12
L/R WHEEL SIGNAL HIGH
C3
885 RED
E
11
L/R WHEEL SIGNAL LOW
R/R WHEEL SPEED SENSOR
D1
882 BRN
A
7
R/R WHEEL SIGNAL HIGH
D2
883 WHT
C
8
R/R WHEEL SIGNAL LOW

CODE A031

(Page 1 of 2)
TWO WHEEL SPEEDS = 0
(TUBULAR REAR AXLE)

Circuit Description:

As a toothed ring passes by the wheel speed sensor, changes in the electromagnetic field cause the wheel speed sensor to produce a sinusoidal (AC) voltage signal whose frequency is proportional to wheel speed. The magnitude of this signal is directly related to wheel speed and the proximity of the wheel speed sensor to the toothed ring, often referred to as the air gap.

This code is designed to detect two open wheel speed sensors in any combination. This test exists due to a condition that may exist that does not allow the driver to be informed by the ABS warning light of non-functioning ABS. If one wheel speed sensor is open, the driver is informed. If a second fails, the driver is no longer informed without this test and ABS is not available. By requiring the two operating wheels to be within 7 mph, a false code is prevented during spin-ups while still allowing for detection when the stowaway spare tire is used.

Test Description: Number(s) below refer to circled number(s) on the diagnostic chart.

1. This test verifies whether the fault is currently present.
2. This step is designed to identify a wheel speed sensor or circuitry that is damaged and visibly apparent.
3. This step identifies if the cause of the problem is common to the rear wheel sensor circuitry.
4. Because both rear sensors are common to the extension harness, the 4 way connectors and harness should be inspected.
5. This test checks to see that the wheel speed sensor is within proper resistance values.
6. This insures that the wheel speed sensor is not shorted to ground.

Diagnostic Aids:

A false Code A031 may be set as a result of vehicle operation while on a hoist or a lifted condition or stuck in mud or snow, when the vehicle is in gear.

An "Intermittent" problem may be caused by a poor connection, rubbed through wire insulation, or a wire that is broken inside the insulation.

The frequency of the problem can be checked by using the enhanced diagnostic function of the "Scan" tool, as described in the "General Information."

GC402910068900AX

IMPORTANT: WHEEL SPEED SENSOR INTERMITTENT PROBLEMS MAY BE DIFFICULT TO LOCATE. CARE SHOULD BE TAKEN NOT TO DISTURB ANY ELECTRICAL CONNECTIONS PRIOR TO AN INDICATED STEP OF THIS CHART. THIS WILL INSURE THAT AN INTERMITTENT CONNECTION WILL NOT BE CORRECTED BEFORE THE SOURCE OF THE PROBLEM IS FOUND.

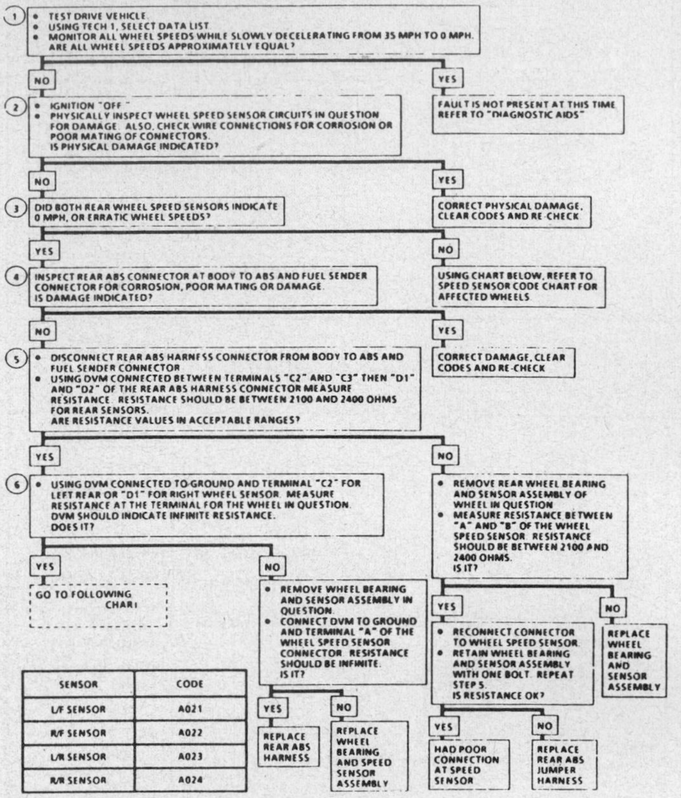
1
• TEST DRIVE VEHICLE.
• USING TECH 1, SELECT DATA LIST.
• MONITOR ALL WHEEL SPEEDS WHILE SLOWLY DECELERATING FROM 35 MPH TO 0 MPH. ARE ALL WHEEL SPEEDS APPROXIMATELY EQUAL?
NO
YES
FAULT IS NOT PRESENT AT THIS TIME REFER TO "DIAGNOSTIC AIDS"
2
• IGNITION "OFF"
• PHYSICALLY INSPECT WHEEL SPEED SENSOR CIRCUITS IN QUESTION FOR DAMAGE. ALSO, CHECK WIRE CONNECTIONS FOR CORROSION OR POOR MATING OF CONNECTORS. IS PHYSICAL DAMAGE INDICATED?
NO
YES
CORRECT PHYSICAL DAMAGE, CLEAR CODES AND RE-CHECK
3
DID BOTH REAR WHEEL SPEED SENSORS INDICATE 0 MPH, OR ERRATIC WHEEL SPEEDS?
YES
NO
USING CHART BELOW, REFER TO SPEED SENSOR CODE CHART FOR AFFECTED WHEELS.
4
INSPECT REAR ABS CONNECTOR AT BODY TO ABS AND FUEL SENDER CONNECTOR FOR CORROSION, POOR MATING OR DAMAGE. IS DAMAGE INDICATED?
NO
YES
CORRECT DAMAGE, CLEAR CODES AND RE-CHECK
5
• DISCONNECT REAR ABS HARNESS CONNECTOR FROM BODY TO ABS AND FUEL SENDER CONNECTOR
• USING DVM CONNECTED BETWEEN TERMINALS "C2" AND "C3" THEN "D1" AND "D2" OF THE REAR ABS HARNESS CONNECTOR MEASURE RESISTANCE. RESISTANCE SHOULD BE BETWEEN 2100 AND 2400 OHMS FOR REAR SENSORS. ARE RESISTANCE VALUES IN ACCEPTABLE RANGES?
YES
NO
6
• USING DVM CONNECTED TO GROUND AND TERMINAL "C2" FOR LEFT REAR OR "D1" FOR RIGHT WHEEL SENSOR. MEASURE RESISTANCE AT THE TERMINAL FOR THE WHEEL IN QUESTION. DVM SHOULD INDICATE INFINITE RESISTANCE. DOES IT?
• REMOVE REAR WHEEL BEARING AND SENSOR ASSEMBLY OF WHEEL IN QUESTION
• MEASURE RESISTANCE BETWEEN "A" AND "B" OF THE WHEEL SPEED SENSOR. RESISTANCE SHOULD BE BETWEEN 2100 AND 2400 OHMS. IS IT?
YES
NO
GO TO FOLLOWING CHART
• REMOVE WHEEL BEARING AND SENSOR ASSEMBLY IN QUESTION.
• CONNECT DVM TO GROUND AND TERMINAL "A" OF THE WHEEL SPEED SENSOR CONNECTOR. RESISTANCE SHOULD BE INFINITE. IS IT?
YES
NO
• RECONNECT CONNECTOR TO WHEEL SPEED SENSOR.
• RETAIN WHEEL BEARING AND SENSOR ASSEMBLY WITH ONE BOLT. REPEAT STEP 5. IS RESISTANCE OK?
REPLACE WHEEL BEARING AND SENSOR ASSEMBLY
YES
NO
REPLACE REAR ABS HARNESS
REPLACE WHEEL BEARING AND SPEED SENSOR ASSEMBLY
YES
NO
HAD POOR CONNECTION AT SPEED SENSOR
REPLACE REAR ABS JUMPER HARNESS

SENSOR	CODE
L/F SENSOR	A021
R/F SENSOR	A022
L/R SENSOR	A023
R/R SENSOR	A024

GC402910068900BX

Fig. 45 Code A031: Two Wheel Speed Sensors Open (Part 1 of 2). With tubular rear axle. 1992

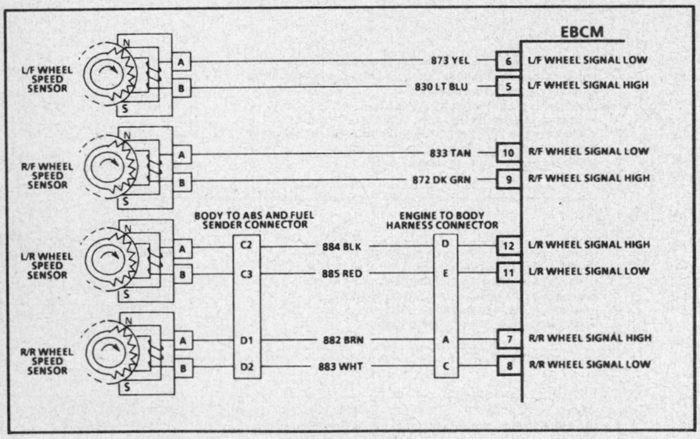
EBCM
L/F WHEEL SPEED SENSOR
873 YEL
6
L/F WHEEL SIGNAL LOW
830 LT BLU
5
L/F WHEEL SIGNAL HIGH
R/F WHEEL SPEED SENSOR
833 TAN
10
R/F WHEEL SIGNAL LOW
872 DK GRN
9
R/F WHEEL SIGNAL HIGH
BODY TO ABS AND FUEL SENDER CONNECTOR
ENGINE TO BODY HARNESS CONNECTOR
L/R WHEEL SPEED SENSOR
C2
884 BLK
D
12
L/R WHEEL SIGNAL HIGH
C3
885 RED
E
11
L/R WHEEL SIGNAL LOW
R/R WHEEL SPEED SENSOR
D1
882 BRN
A
7
R/R WHEEL SIGNAL HIGH
D2
883 WHT
C
8
R/R WHEEL SIGNAL LOW

CODE A031

(Page 2 of 2)
TWO WHEEL SPEEDS = 0
(TUBULAR REAR AXLE)

Circuit Description:

As a toothed ring passes by the wheel speed sensor, changes in the electromagnetic field cause the wheel speed sensor to produce a sinusoidal (AC) voltage signal whose frequency is proportional to wheel speed. The magnitude of this signal is directly related to wheel speed and the proximity of the wheel speed sensor to the toothed ring, often referred to as the air gap.

This code is designed to detect two open wheel speed sensors in any combination. This test exists due to a condition that may exist that does not allow the driver to be informed by the ABS warning light of non-functioning ABS. If one wheel speed sensor is open, the driver is informed. If a second fails, the driver is no longer informed without this test and ABS is not available. By requiring the two operating wheels to be within 7 mph, a false code is prevented during spin-ups while still allowing for detection when the stowaway spare tire is used.

Test Description: Number(s) below refer to circled number(s) on the diagnostic chart.

7. This step checks for an open in the wheel speed sensor circuitry of one side of the sensor.
8. This step checks for an open on the other side of the sensor in question.
9. This step checks for a short to ground in the wheel speed sensor circuitry.
10. This insures that the circuitry is not shorted to voltage.

Diagnostic Aids:

A false Code A031 may be set as a result of vehicle operation while on a hoist or a lifted condition, or stuck in mud or snow when the vehicle is in gear.

An "Intermittent" problem may be caused by a poor connection, rubbed through wire insulation, or a wire that is broken inside the insulation.

The frequency of the problem can be checked by using the enhanced diagnostic function of the "Scan" tool.

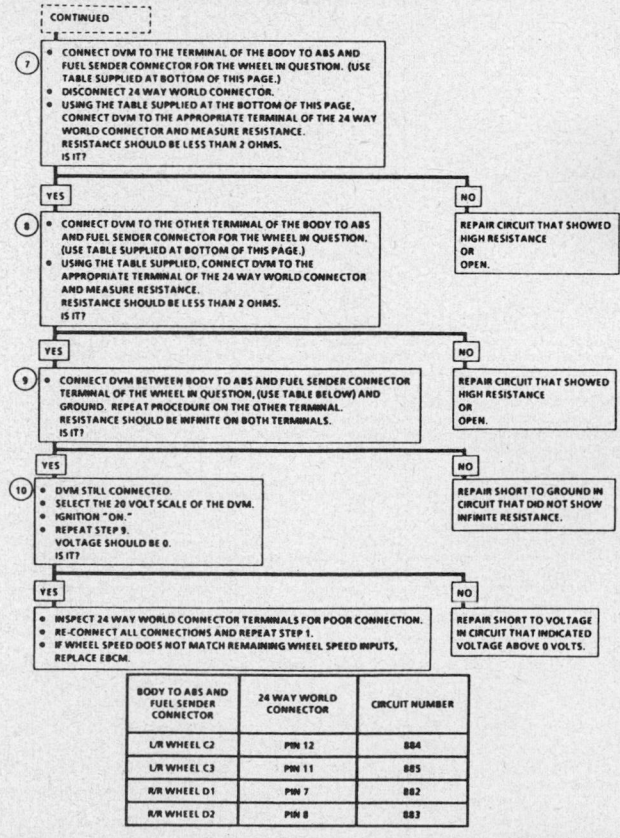

GC402910068900CX

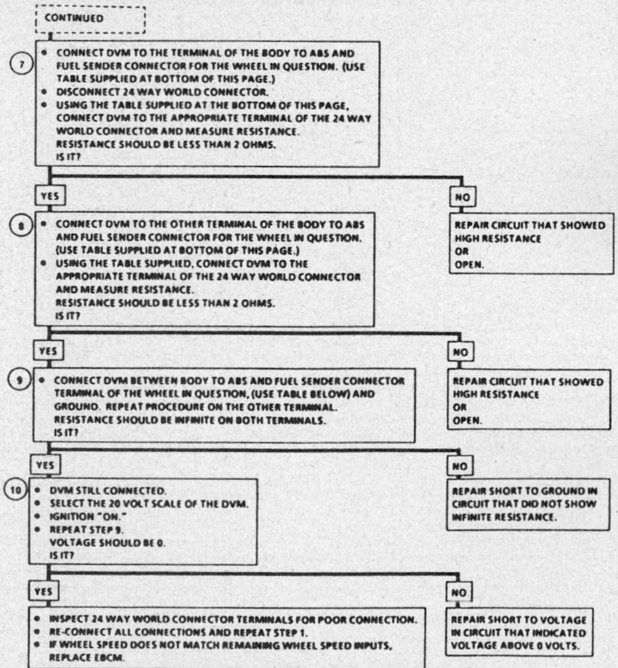
CONTINUED
7
• CONNECT DVM TO THE TERMINAL OF THE BODY TO ABS AND FUEL SENDER CONNECTOR FOR THE WHEEL IN QUESTION. (USE TABLE SUPPLIED AT BOTTOM OF THIS PAGE.)
• DISCONNECT 24 WAY WORLD CONNECTOR.
• USING THE TABLE SUPPLIED AT THE BOTTOM OF THIS PAGE, CONNECT DVM TO THE APPROPRIATE TERMINAL OF THE 24 WAY WORLD CONNECTOR AND MEASURE RESISTANCE. RESISTANCE SHOULD BE LESS THAN 2 OHMS. IS IT?
YES
NO
8
• CONNECT DVM TO THE OTHER TERMINAL OF THE BODY TO ABS AND FUEL SENDER CONNECTOR FOR THE WHEEL IN QUESTION. (USE TABLE SUPPLIED AT BOTTOM OF THIS PAGE.)
• USING THE TABLE SUPPLIED, CONNECT DVM TO THE APPROPRIATE TERMINAL OF THE 24 WAY WORLD CONNECTOR AND MEASURE RESISTANCE. RESISTANCE SHOULD BE LESS THAN 2 OHMS. IS IT?
REPAIR CIRCUIT THAT SHOWED HIGH RESISTANCE OR OPEN.
YES
NO
9
• CONNECT DVM BETWEEN BODY TO ABS AND FUEL SENDER CONNECTOR TERMINAL OF THE WHEEL IN QUESTION, (USE TABLE BELOW) AND GROUND. REPEAT PROCEDURE ON THE OTHER TERMINAL. RESISTANCE SHOULD BE INFINITE ON BOTH TERMINALS. IS IT?
REPAIR CIRCUIT THAT SHOWED HIGH RESISTANCE OR OPEN.
YES
NO
10
• DVM STILL CONNECTED.
• SELECT THE 20 VOLT SCALE OF THE DVM.
• IGNITION "ON."
• REPEAT STEP 9. VOLTAGE SHOULD BE 0. IS IT?
REPAIR SHORT TO GROUND IN CIRCUIT THAT DID NOT SHOW INFINITE RESISTANCE.
YES
NO
• INSPECT 24 WAY WORLD CONNECTOR TERMINALS FOR POOR CONNECTION.
• RE-CONNECT ALL CONNECTIONS AND REPEAT STEP 1.
• IF WHEEL SPEED DOES NOT MATCH REMAINING WHEEL SPEED INPUTS, REPLACE EBCM.
REPAIR SHORT TO VOLTAGE IN CIRCUIT THAT INDICATED VOLTAGE ABOVE 0 VOLTS.

BODY TO ABS AND FUEL SENDER CONNECTOR	24 WAY WORLD CONNECTOR	CIRCUIT NUMBER
L/R WHEEL C2	PIN 12	884
L/R WHEEL C3	PIN 11	885
R/R WHEEL D1	PIN 7	882
R/R WHEEL D2	PIN 8	883

GC402910068900DX

Fig. 45 Code A031: Two Wheel Speed Sensors Open (Part 2 of 2). With tubular rear axle. 1992

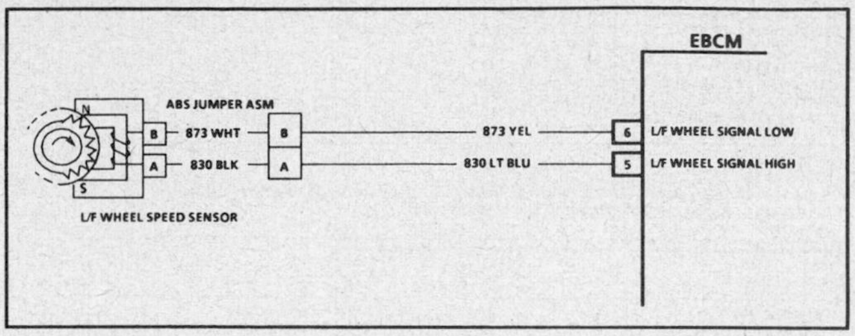
EBCM
ABS JUMPER ASM
N
S
B
A
873 WHT
830 BLK
B
A
873 YEL
830 LT BLU
6
5
L/F WHEEL SIGNAL LOW
L/F WHEEL SIGNAL HIGH
L/F WHEEL SPEED SENSOR

CODE A032

LEFT FRONT WHEEL SENSOR SHORTED TO BATTERY OR GROUND

Circuit Description:

As a toothed ring passes by the wheel speed sensor, changes in the electromagnetic field cause the wheel speed sensor to produce a sinusoidal (AC) voltage signal whose frequency is proportional to wheel speed. The magnitude of this signal is directly related to wheel speed and the proximity of the wheel speed sensor to the toothed ring often referred to as the air gap.

This code detects shorts to ground, and shorts to battery in the wheel speed circuitry sensed by ABS EBCM.

Test Description: Number(s) below refer to circled number(s) on the diagnostic chart.

1. This test helps to identify whether the code is due to a short to battery or short to ground.
2. This insures that the wheel speed sensor is not shorted to ground.
3. This step checks to see if wheel speed sensor circuitry is shorted to voltage.
4. This insures that the wheel speed sensor circuitry has good continuity.
5. This checks for short to ground in wheel speed sensor wiring.
6. This checks for short to voltage in wheel speed sensor wiring.

Diagnostic Aids:

An "Intermittent" problem may be caused by a poor connection, rubbed through wire insulation, or a wire that is broken inside the insulation.

The frequency of the problem can be checked by using the enhanced diagnostic function of the "Scan" tool

If the customers comments reflect that the ABS Amber warning lamp is "ON" only during moist environmental changes, (rain, snow, vehicle wash) all wheel speed sensor circuitry should be thoroughly inspected for signs of water intrusion. If code is not current clear codes and simulate the effects of water intrusion. Use the following procedure. Spray down the suspected area with a 5% salt water solution (two teaspoons of salt to 12 oz. of water). Start vehicle, allow vehicle to run for 10 seconds. If code returns immediately, replace suspected harness.

Any circuitry, that is suspected as causing the intermittent complaint, should be thoroughly checked for backed out terminals, improper mating, broken locks, improperly formed or damaged terminals, poor terminal to wiring connections or physical damage to the wiring harness.

GC402910069000AX

IMPORTANT: WHEEL SPEED SENSOR INTERMITTENT PROBLEMS MAY BE DIFFICULT TO LOCATE. CARE SHOULD BE TAKEN NOT TO DISTURB ANY ELECTRICAL CONNECTIONS PRIOR TO AN INDICATED STEP OF THIS CHART. THIS WILL INSURE THAT AN INTERMITTENT CONNECTION WILL NOT BE CORRECTED BEFORE THE SOURCE OF THE PROBLEM IS FOUND.

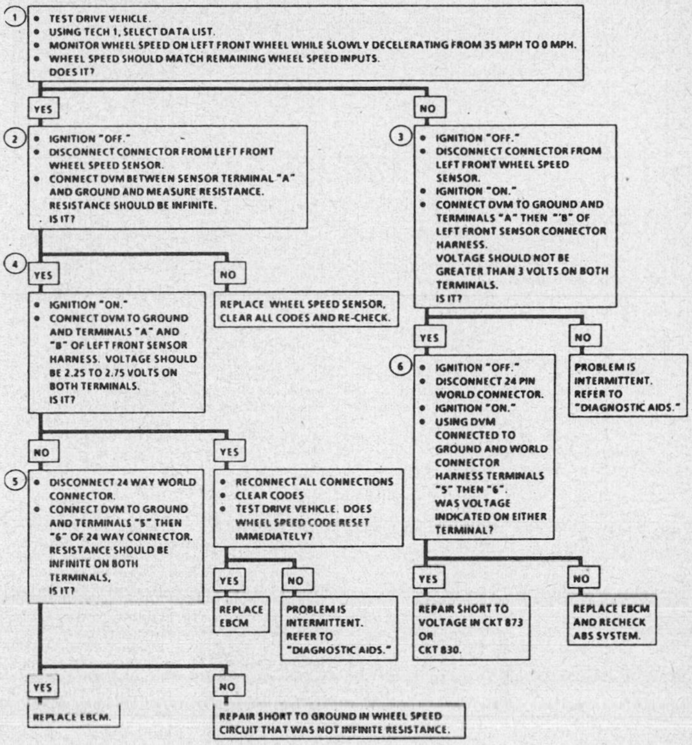
1
• TEST DRIVE VEHICLE.
• USING TECH 1, SELECT DATA LIST.
• MONITOR WHEEL SPEED ON LEFT FRONT WHEEL WHILE SLOWLY DECELERATING FROM 35 MPH TO 0 MPH.
• WHEEL SPEED SHOULD MATCH REMAINING WHEEL SPEED INPUTS.
DOES IT?
YES
NO
2
• IGNITION "OFF."
• DISCONNECT CONNECTOR FROM LEFT FRONT WHEEL SPEED SENSOR.
• CONNECT DVM BETWEEN SENSOR TERMINAL "A" AND GROUND AND MEASURE RESISTANCE. RESISTANCE SHOULD BE INFINITE.
IS IT?
3
• IGNITION "OFF."
• DISCONNECT CONNECTOR FROM LEFT FRONT WHEEL SPEED SENSOR.
• IGNITION "ON."
• CONNECT DVM TO GROUND AND TERMINALS "A" THEN "B" OF LEFT FRONT SENSOR CONNECTOR HARNESS.
VOLTAGE SHOULD NOT BE GREATER THAN 3 VOLTS ON BOTH TERMINALS.
IS IT?
4
YES
NO
• IGNITION "ON."
• CONNECT DVM TO GROUND AND TERMINALS "A" AND "B" OF LEFT FRONT SENSOR HARNESS. VOLTAGE SHOULD BE 2.25 TO 2.75 VOLTS ON BOTH TERMINALS.
IS IT?
REPLACE WHEEL SPEED SENSOR, CLEAR ALL CODES AND RE-CHECK.
YES
NO
6
• IGNITION "OFF."
• DISCONNECT 24 PIN WORLD CONNECTOR.
• IGNITION "ON."
• USING DVM CONNECTED TO GROUND AND WORLD CONNECTOR HARNESS TERMINALS "5" THEN "6".
WAS VOLTAGE INDICATED ON EITHER TERMINAL?
PROBLEM IS INTERMITTENT. REFER TO "DIAGNOSTIC AIDS."
NO
YES
5
• DISCONNECT 24 WAY WORLD CONNECTOR.
• CONNECT DVM TO GROUND AND TERMINALS "5" THEN "6" OF 24 WAY CONNECTOR. RESISTANCE SHOULD BE INFINITE ON BOTH TERMINALS.
IS IT?
• RECONNECT ALL CONNECTIONS
• CLEAR CODES
• TEST DRIVE VEHICLE. DOES WHEEL SPEED CODE RESET IMMEDIATELY?
YES
NO
REPLACE EBCM
PROBLEM IS INTERMITTENT. REFER TO "DIAGNOSTIC AIDS."
YES
NO
REPAIR SHORT TO VOLTAGE IN CKT 873 OR CKT 830.
REPLACE EBCM AND RECHECK ABS SYSTEM.
YES
NO
REPLACE EBCM.
REPAIR SHORT TO GROUND IN WHEEL SPEED CIRCUIT THAT WAS NOT INFINITE RESISTANCE.

GC402910069000BX

Fig. 46 Code A032: LH Front Wheel Speed Sensor Shorted To Battery Or Ground. 1992 Cutlass Supreme, Grand Prix, Lumina & Regal

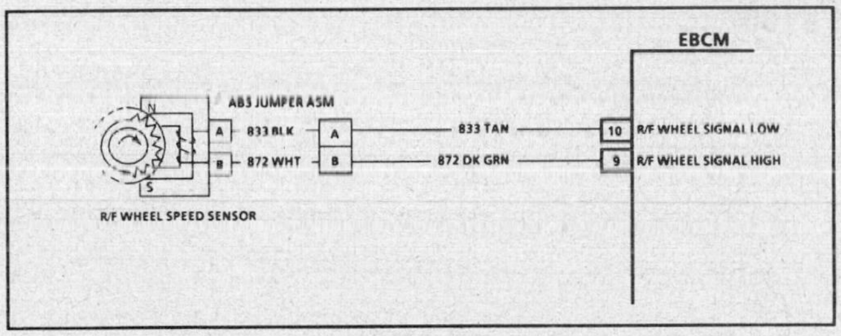
EBCM
ABS JUMPER ASM
N
S
A
B
833 BLK
872 WHT
A
B
833 TAN
872 DK GRN
10
9
R/F WHEEL SIGNAL LOW
R/F WHEEL SIGNAL HIGH
R/F WHEEL SPEED SENSOR

CODE A033

RIGHT FRONT WHEEL SENSOR SHORTED TO BATTERY OR GROUND

Circuit Description:

As a toothed ring passes by the wheel speed sensor, changes in the electromagnetic field cause the wheel speed sensor to produce a sinusoidal (AC) voltage signal whose frequency is proportional to wheel speed. The magnitude of this signal is directly related to wheel speed and the proximity of the wheel speed sensor to the toothed ring, often referred to as the air gap.

This code detects shorts to ground, and shorts to battery in the wheel speed circuitry sensed by the ABS EBCM.

Test Description: Number(s) below refer to circled number(s) on the diagnostic chart.

1. This test helps identify whether the code is due to a short to battery or short to ground.
2. This insures that the wheel speed sensor is not shorted to ground.
3. This step checks to see if wheel speed sensor circuitry is shorted to voltage.
4. This insures that the wheel speed sensor circuitry has good continuity.
5. This checks for short to ground in wheel speed sensor wiring.
6. This checks for short to voltage in wheel speed sensor wiring.

Diagnostic Aids:

An "Intermittent" problem may be caused by a poor connection, rubbed through wire insulation, or a wire that is broken inside the insulation.

The frequency of the problem can be checked by using the enhanced diagnostic function of the "Scan" tool

If the customers comments reflect that the ABS Amber warning lamp is "ON" only during moist environmental changes, (rain, snow, vehicle wash) all wheel speed sensor circuitry should be thoroughly inspected for signs of water intrusion. If code is not current clear codes and simulate the effects of water intrusion. Use the following procedure. Spray down the suspected area with a 5% salt water solution (two teaspoons of salt to 12 oz. of water). Start vehicle, allow vehicle to run for 10 seconds. If code returns immediately, replace suspected harness.

Any circuitry, that is suspected as causing the intermittent complaint, should be thoroughly checked for backed out terminals, improper mating, broken locks, improperly formed or damaged terminals, poor terminal to wiring connections or physical damage to the wiring harness.

GC402910069100AX

IMPORTANT: WHEEL SPEED SENSOR INTERMITTENT PROBLEMS MAY BE DIFFICULT TO LOCATE. CARE SHOULD BE TAKEN NOT TO DISTURB ANY ELECTRICAL CONNECTIONS PRIOR TO AN INDICATED STEP OF THIS CHART. THIS WILL INSURE THAT AN INTERMITTENT CONNECTION WILL NOT BE CORRECTED BEFORE THE SOURCE OF THE PROBLEM IS FOUND.

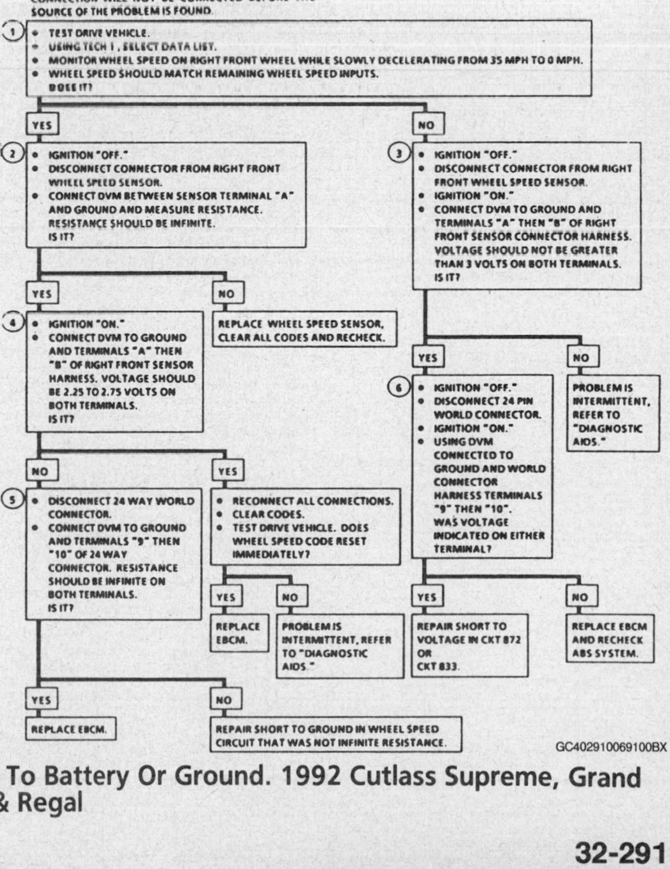
1
• TEST DRIVE VEHICLE.
• USING TECH 1, SELECT DATA LIST.
• MONITOR WHEEL SPEED ON RIGHT FRONT WHEEL WHILE SLOWLY DECELERATING FROM 35 MPH TO 0 MPH.
• WHEEL SPEED SHOULD MATCH REMAINING WHEEL SPEED INPUTS.
DOES IT?
YES
NO
2
• IGNITION "OFF."
• DISCONNECT CONNECTOR FROM RIGHT FRONT WHEEL SPEED SENSOR.
• CONNECT DVM BETWEEN SENSOR TERMINAL "A" AND GROUND AND MEASURE RESISTANCE. RESISTANCE SHOULD BE INFINITE.
IS IT?
3
• IGNITION "OFF."
• DISCONNECT CONNECTOR FROM RIGHT FRONT WHEEL SPEED SENSOR.
• IGNITION "ON."
• CONNECT DVM TO GROUND AND TERMINALS "A" THEN "B" OF RIGHT FRONT SENSOR CONNECTOR HARNESS. VOLTAGE SHOULD NOT BE GREATER THAN 3 VOLTS ON BOTH TERMINALS.
IS IT?
YES
NO
4
• IGNITION "ON."
• CONNECT DVM TO GROUND AND TERMINALS "A" THEN "B" OF RIGHT FRONT SENSOR HARNESS. VOLTAGE SHOULD BE 2.25 TO 2.75 VOLTS ON BOTH TERMINALS.
IS IT?
REPLACE WHEEL SPEED SENSOR, CLEAR ALL CODES AND RECHECK.
YES
NO
6
• IGNITION "OFF."
• DISCONNECT 24 PIN WORLD CONNECTOR.
• IGNITION "ON."
• USING DVM CONNECTED TO GROUND AND WORLD CONNECTOR HARNESS TERMINALS "9" THEN "10".
WAS VOLTAGE INDICATED ON EITHER TERMINAL?
PROBLEM IS INTERMITTENT, REFER TO "DIAGNOSTIC AIDS."
NO
YES
5
• DISCONNECT 24 WAY WORLD CONNECTOR.
• CONNECT DVM TO GROUND AND TERMINALS "9" THEN "10" OF 24 WAY CONNECTOR. RESISTANCE SHOULD BE INFINITE ON BOTH TERMINALS.
IS IT?
• RECONNECT ALL CONNECTIONS.
• CLEAR CODES.
• TEST DRIVE VEHICLE. DOES WHEEL SPEED CODE RESET IMMEDIATELY?
YES
NO
REPLACE EBCM.
PROBLEM IS INTERMITTENT, REFER TO "DIAGNOSTIC AIDS."
YES
NO
REPAIR SHORT TO VOLTAGE IN CKT 872 OR CKT 833.
REPLACE EBCM AND RECHECK ABS SYSTEM.
YES
NO
REPLACE EBCM.
REPAIR SHORT TO GROUND IN WHEEL SPEED CIRCUIT THAT WAS NOT INFINITE RESISTANCE.

GC402910069100BX

Fig. 47 Code A033: RH Front Wheel Speed Sensor Shorted To Battery Or Ground. 1992 Cutlass Supreme, Grand Prix, Lumina & Regal

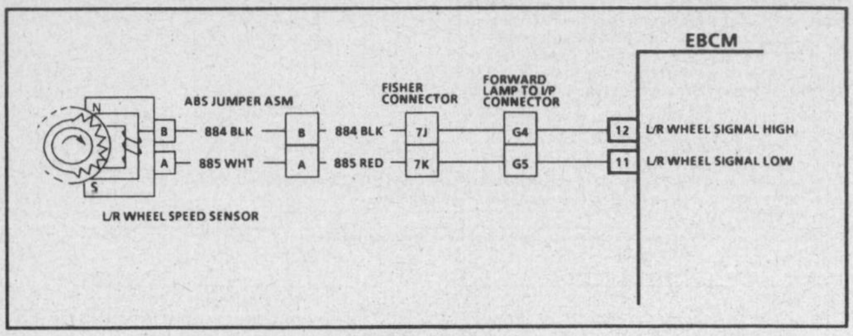
EBCM
ABS JUMPER ASM
FISHER CONNECTOR
FORWARD LAMP TO I/P CONNECTOR
N
B
884 BLK
B
884 BLK
7J
G4
12
L/R WHEEL SIGNAL HIGH
A
885 WHT
A
885 RED
7K
G5
11
L/R WHEEL SIGNAL LOW
S
L/R WHEEL SPEED SENSOR

CODE A034

LEFT REAR WHEEL SENSOR SHORTED TO BATTERY OR GROUND

Circuit Description:

As a toothed ring passes by the wheel speed sensor, changes in the electromagnetic field cause the wheel speed sensor to produce a sinusoidal (AC) voltage signal whose frequency is proportional to wheel speed. The magnitude of this signal is directly related to wheel speed and the proximity of the wheel speed sensor to the toothed ring, often referred to as the air gap.

This code detects opens, shorts to ground, and shorts to battery in the wheel speed circuitry sensed by the ABS EBCM.

Test Description: Number(s) below refer to circled number(s) on the diagnostic chart.

1. This test helps to identify whether the code is due to a short to battery or short to ground.
2. This insures that the wheel speed sensor is not shorted to ground.
3. This step checks to see if wheel speed sensor circuitry is shorted to voltage.
4. This insures that the wheel speed sensor circuitry has good continuity.
5. This checks for short to ground in wheel speed sensor wiring.
6. This checks for short to voltage in wheel speed sensor wiring.

Diagnostic Aids:

An "Intermittent" problem may be caused by a poor connection, rubbed through wire insulation, or a wire that is broken inside the insulation.

The frequency of the problem can be checked by using the enhanced diagnostic function of the "Scan" tool

If the customers comments reflect that the ABS Amber warning lamp is "ON" only during moist environmental changes, (rain, snow, vehicle wash) all wheel speed sensor circuitry should be thoroughly inspected for signs of water intrusion. If code is not current clear codes and simulate the effects of water intrusion. Use the following procedure. Spray down the suspected area with a 5% salt water solution (two teaspoons of salt to 12 oz. of water). Start vehicle, allow vehicle to run for 10 seconds. If code returns immediately, replace suspected harness.

Any circuitry, that is suspected as causing the intermittent complaint, should be thoroughly checked for backed out terminals, improper mating, broken locks, improperly formed or damaged terminals, poor terminal to wiring connections or physical damage to the wiring harness.

GC402910069200AX

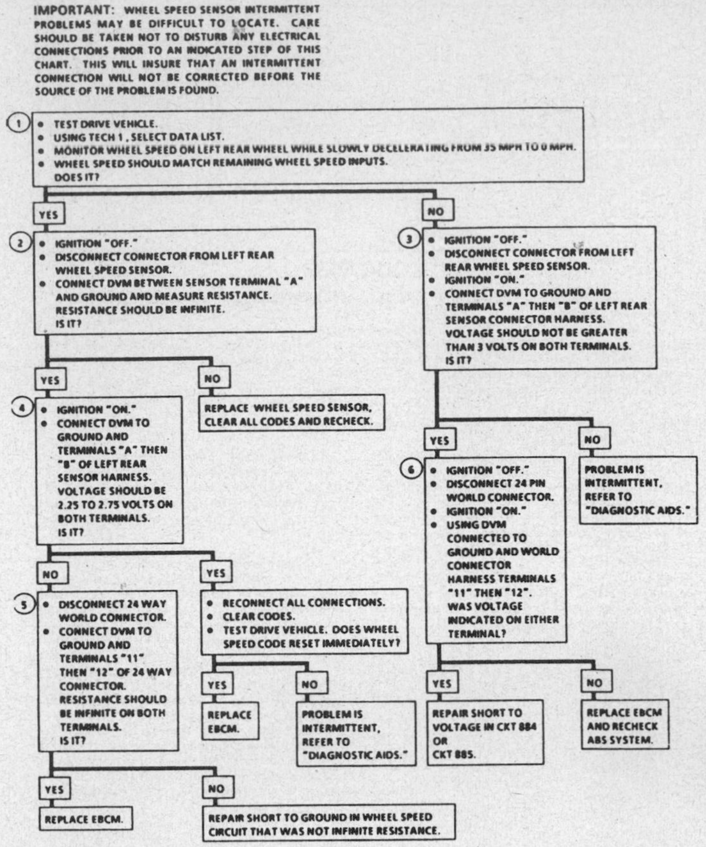
IMPORTANT: WHEEL SPEED SENSOR INTERMITTENT PROBLEMS MAY BE DIFFICULT TO LOCATE. CARE SHOULD BE TAKEN NOT TO DISTURB ANY ELECTRICAL CONNECTIONS PRIOR TO AN INDICATED STEP OF THIS CHART. THIS WILL INSURE THAT AN INTERMITTENT CONNECTION WILL NOT BE CORRECTED BEFORE THE SOURCE OF THE PROBLEM IS FOUND.
1 • TEST DRIVE VEHICLE. • USING TECH 1, SELECT DATA LIST. • MONITOR WHEEL SPEED ON LEFT REAR WHEEL WHILE SLOWLY DECELERATING FROM 35 MPH TO 0 MPH. • WHEEL SPEED SHOULD MATCH REMAINING WHEEL SPEED INPUTS. DOES IT?
YES
NO
2 • IGNITION "OFF." • DISCONNECT CONNECTOR FROM LEFT REAR WHEEL SPEED SENSOR. • CONNECT DVM BETWEEN SENSOR TERMINAL "A" AND GROUND AND MEASURE RESISTANCE. RESISTANCE SHOULD BE INFINITE. IS IT?
3 • IGNITION "OFF." • DISCONNECT CONNECTOR FROM LEFT REAR WHEEL SPEED SENSOR. • IGNITION "ON." • CONNECT DVM TO GROUND AND TERMINALS "A" THEN "B" OF LEFT REAR SENSOR CONNECTOR HARNESS. VOLTAGE SHOULD NOT BE GREATER THAN 3 VOLTS ON BOTH TERMINALS. IS IT?
YES
NO
REPLACE WHEEL SPEED SENSOR, CLEAR ALL CODES AND RECHECK.
4 • IGNITION "ON." • CONNECT DVM TO GROUND AND TERMINALS "A" THEN "B" OF LEFT REAR SENSOR HARNESS. VOLTAGE SHOULD BE 2.25 TO 2.75 VOLTS ON BOTH TERMINALS. IS IT?
YES
NO
6 • IGNITION "OFF." • DISCONNECT 24 PIN WORLD CONNECTOR. • IGNITION "ON." • USING DVM CONNECTED TO GROUND AND WORLD CONNECTOR HARNESS TERMINALS "11" THEN "12". WAS VOLTAGE INDICATED ON EITHER TERMINAL?
PROBLEM IS INTERMITTENT, REFER TO "DIAGNOSTIC AIDS."
NO
YES
5 • DISCONNECT 24 WAY WORLD CONNECTOR. • CONNECT DVM TO GROUND AND TERMINALS "11" THEN "12" OF 24 WAY CONNECTOR. RESISTANCE SHOULD BE INFINITE ON BOTH TERMINALS. IS IT?
• RECONNECT ALL CONNECTIONS. • CLEAR CODES. • TEST DRIVE VEHICLE. DOES WHEEL SPEED CODE RESET IMMEDIATELY?
YES
NO
YES
NO
REPLACE EBCM.
PROBLEM IS INTERMITTENT, REFER TO "DIAGNOSTIC AIDS."
REPAIR SHORT TO VOLTAGE IN CKT 884 OR CKT 885.
REPLACE EBCM AND RECHECK ABS SYSTEM.
YES
NO
REPLACE EBCM.
REPAIR SHORT TO GROUND IN WHEEL SPEED CIRCUIT THAT WAS NOT INFINITE RESISTANCE.

GC402910069200BX

Fig. 48 Code A034: LH Rear Wheel Speed Sensor Shorted To Battery Or Ground. 1992 Cutlass Supreme, Grand Prix, Lumina & Regal

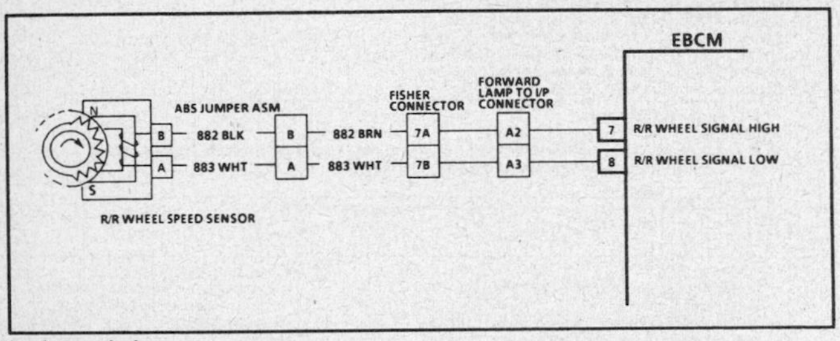
EBCM
ABS JUMPER ASM
FISHER CONNECTOR
FORWARD LAMP TO I/P CONNECTOR
N
B
882 BLK
B
882 BRN
7A
A2
7
R/R WHEEL SIGNAL HIGH
A
883 WHT
A
883 WHT
7B
A3
8
R/R WHEEL SIGNAL LOW
S
R/R WHEEL SPEED SENSOR

Circuit Description:

As a toothed ring passes by the wheel speed sensor, changes in the electromagnetic field cause the wheel speed sensor to produce a sinusoidal (AC) voltage signal whose frequency is proportional to wheel speed. The magnitude of this signal is directly related to wheel speed and the proximity of the wheel speed sensor to the toothed ring, often referred to as the air gap.

This code detects opens, shorts to ground, and shorts to battery in the wheel speed circuitry sensed by the ABS EBCM.

Test Description: Number(s) below refer to circled number(s) on the diagnostic chart.

1. This helps to identify whether the code is due to a short to battery or short to ground.
2. This insures that the wheel speed sensor is not shorted to ground.
3. This step checks to see if wheel speed sensor circuitry is shorted to voltage.
4. This insures that the wheel speed sensor circuitry has good continuity.
5. This checks for short to ground in wheel speed sensor wiring.
6. This checks for short to voltage in wheel speed sensor wiring.

Diagnostic Aids:

An "Intermittent" problem may be caused by a poor connection, rubbed through wire insulation, or a wire that is broken inside the insulation.

The frequency of the problem can be checked by using the enhanced diagnostic function of the "Scan" tool

If the customers comments reflect that the ABS Amber warning lamp is "ON" only during moist environmental changes, (rain, snow, vehicle wash) all wheel speed sensor circuitry should be thoroughly inspected for signs of water intrusion. If code is not current clear codes and simulate the effects of water intrusion. Use the following procedure. Spray down the suspected area with a 5% salt water solution (two teaspoons of salt to 12 oz. of water). Start vehicle, allow vehicle to run for 10 seconds. If code returns immediately, replace suspected harness.

Any circuitry, that is suspected as causing the intermittent complaint, should be thoroughly checked for backed out terminals, improper mating, broken locks, improperly formed or damaged terminals, poor terminal to wiring connections or physical damage to the wiring harness.

GC402910069300AX

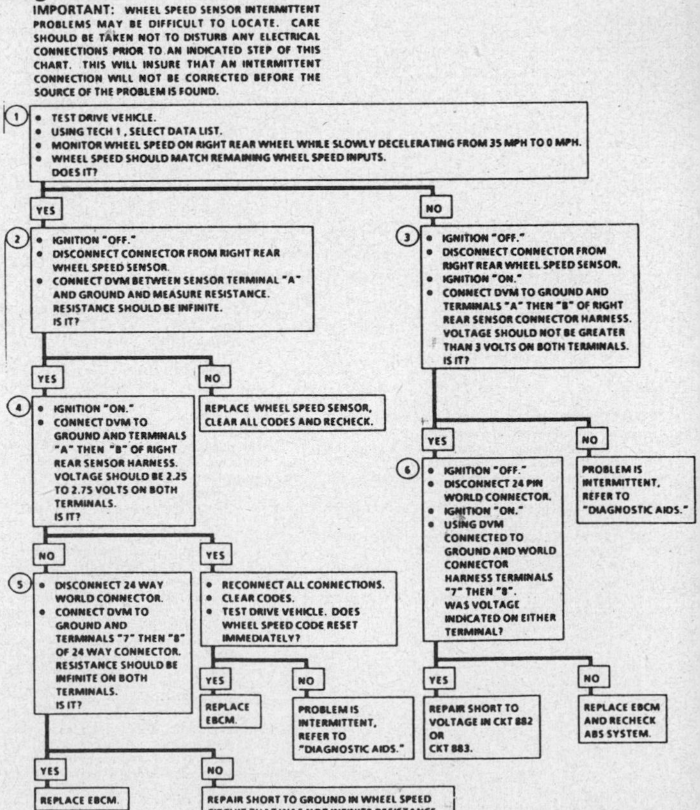
IMPORTANT: WHEEL SPEED SENSOR INTERMITTENT PROBLEMS MAY BE DIFFICULT TO LOCATE. CARE SHOULD BE TAKEN NOT TO DISTURB ANY ELECTRICAL CONNECTIONS PRIOR TO AN INDICATED STEP OF THIS CHART. THIS WILL INSURE THAT AN INTERMITTENT CONNECTION WILL NOT BE CORRECTED BEFORE THE SOURCE OF THE PROBLEM IS FOUND.
1 • TEST DRIVE VEHICLE. • USING TECH 1, SELECT DATA LIST. • MONITOR WHEEL SPEED ON RIGHT REAR WHEEL WHILE SLOWLY DECELERATING FROM 35 MPH TO 0 MPH. • WHEEL SPEED SHOULD MATCH REMAINING WHEEL SPEED INPUTS. DOES IT?
YES
NO
2 • IGNITION "OFF." • DISCONNECT CONNECTOR FROM RIGHT REAR WHEEL SPEED SENSOR. • CONNECT DVM BETWEEN SENSOR TERMINAL "A" AND GROUND AND MEASURE RESISTANCE. RESISTANCE SHOULD BE INFINITE. IS IT?
3 • IGNITION "OFF." • DISCONNECT CONNECTOR FROM RIGHT REAR WHEEL SPEED SENSOR. • IGNITION "ON." • CONNECT DVM TO GROUND AND TERMINALS "A" THEN "B" OF RIGHT REAR SENSOR CONNECTOR HARNESS. VOLTAGE SHOULD NOT BE GREATER THAN 3 VOLTS ON BOTH TERMINALS. IS IT?
YES
NO
REPLACE WHEEL SPEED SENSOR, CLEAR ALL CODES AND RECHECK.
4 • IGNITION "ON." • CONNECT DVM TO GROUND AND TERMINALS "A" THEN "B" OF RIGHT REAR SENSOR HARNESS. VOLTAGE SHOULD BE 2.25 TO 2.75 VOLTS ON BOTH TERMINALS. IS IT?
YES
NO
6 • IGNITION "OFF." • DISCONNECT 24 PIN WORLD CONNECTOR. • IGNITION "ON." • USING DVM CONNECTED TO GROUND AND WORLD CONNECTOR HARNESS TERMINALS "7" THEN "8". WAS VOLTAGE INDICATED ON EITHER TERMINAL?
PROBLEM IS INTERMITTENT, REFER TO "DIAGNOSTIC AIDS."
NO
YES
5 • DISCONNECT 24 WAY WORLD CONNECTOR. • CONNECT DVM TO GROUND AND TERMINALS "7" THEN "8" OF 24 WAY CONNECTOR. RESISTANCE SHOULD BE INFINITE ON BOTH TERMINALS. IS IT?
• RECONNECT ALL CONNECTIONS. • CLEAR CODES. • TEST DRIVE VEHICLE. DOES WHEEL SPEED CODE RESET IMMEDIATELY?
YES
NO
YES
NO
REPLACE EBCM.
PROBLEM IS INTERMITTENT, REFER TO "DIAGNOSTIC AIDS."
REPAIR SHORT TO VOLTAGE IN CKT 882 OR CKT 883.
REPLACE EBCM AND RECHECK ABS SYSTEM.
YES
NO
REPLACE EBCM.
REPAIR SHORT TO GROUND IN WHEEL SPEED CIRCUIT THAT WAS NOT INFINITE RESISTANCE.

GC402910069300BX

Fig. 49 Code A035: RH Rear Wheel Speed Sensor Shorted To Battery Or Ground. 1992 Cutlass Supreme, Grand Prix, Lumina & Regal

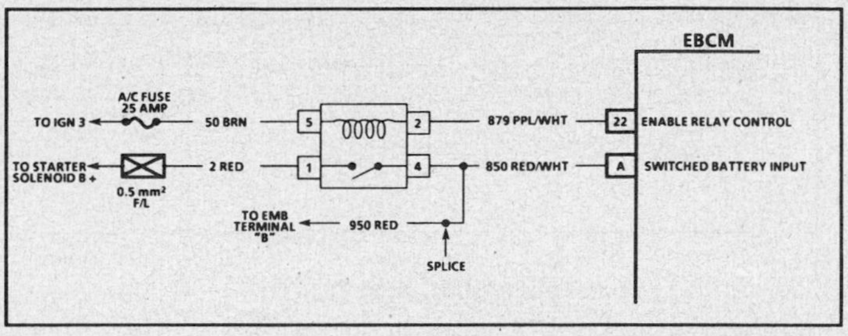
EBCM
A/C FUSE
25 AMP
TO IGN 3
50 BRN
5
2
879 PPL/WHT
22
ENABLE RELAY CONTROL
TO STARTER SOLENOID B+
2 RED
1
4
850 RED/WHT
A
SWITCHED BATTERY INPUT
0.5 mm²
F/L
TO EMB TERMINAL "B"
950 RED
SPLICE

GC402910069400BX

Beretta & Corsica

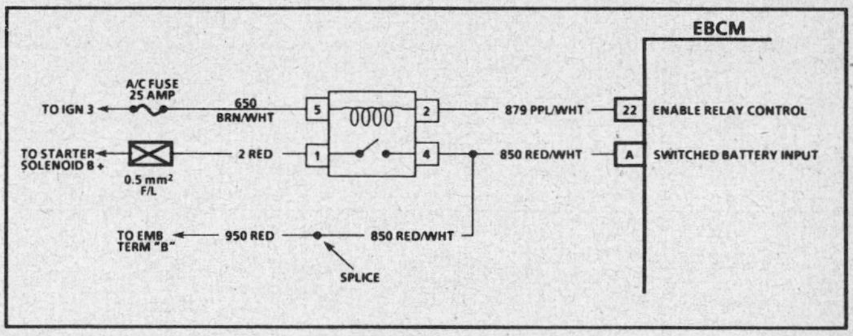
EBCM
A/C FUSE
25 AMP
TO IGN 3
650
BRN/WHT
5
2
879 PPL/WHT
22
ENABLE RELAY CONTROL
TO STARTER SOLENOID B+
2 RED
1
4
850 RED/WHT
A
SWITCHED BATTERY INPUT
0.5 mm²
F/L
TO EMB TERM "B"
950 RED
850 RED/WHT
SPLICE

GC402910069400AX

Cavalier & Sunbird

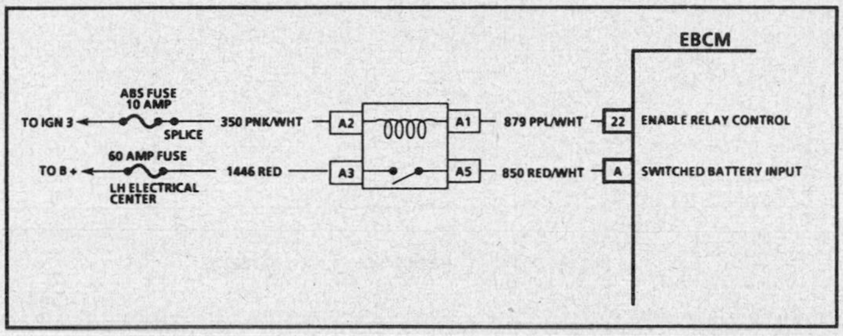
EBCM
ABS FUSE
10 AMP
TO IGN 3
SPLICE
350 PNK/WHT
A2
A1
879 PPL/WHT
22
ENABLE RELAY CONTROL
60 AMP FUSE
TO B+
1446 RED
A3
A5
850 RED/WHT
A
SWITCHED BATTERY INPUT
LH ELECTRICAL CENTER

GC402910069400DX

Cutlass Supreme, Grand Prix, Lumina & Regal

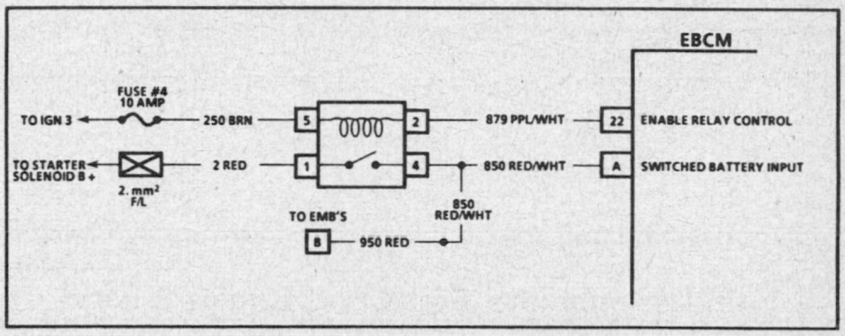
EBCM
FUSE #4
10 AMP
TO IGN 3
250 BRN
5
2
879 PPL/WHT
22
ENABLE RELAY CONTROL
TO STARTER SOLENOID B+
2 RED
1
4
850 RED/WHT
A
SWITCHED BATTERY INPUT
2. mm²
F/L
TO EMB'S
850
RED/WHT
B
950 RED

GC402910069400CX

Achieva, Calais & Grand Am

Circuit Description:

This code is used to monitor the voltage level available to the ABS EBCM. If the voltage drops below 11 volts, full performance of the ABS system cannot be guaranteed. During ABS operation, there are several current requirements that will cause battery voltage to drop. Because of this, voltage is monitored prior to ABS to indicate good charging system condition and also during ABS when voltage may drop significantly. If voltage falls below a level that will provide adequate ABS performance, Code A036 will result.

Test Description: Number(s) below refer to circled number(s) on the diagnostic chart.

1. This test checks to see what voltage is readily available at terminal "A" of the EBCM. If voltage is representative of good charging system condition, a fault is not present.
2. This step isolates the EBCM to check the condition of the circuitry and charging system.
3. This step isolates the low voltage condition to high circuit resistance, or improper charging system operation.

Diagnostic Aids:

An "Intermittent" problem may be caused by a poor connection, rubbed through wire insulation, or a wire that is broken inside the insulation.

The frequency of the problem can be checked by using the enhanced diagnostic function of the "Scan" tool.

Any circuitry, that is suspected as causing the intermittent complaint, should be thoroughly checked for backed out terminals, improper mating, broken locks, improperly formed or damaged terminals, poor terminal to wiring connections or physical damage to the wiring harness.

While performing a voltage load test, if it is noted that only ignition voltage drops below acceptable voltage levels, CKT 650 should be checked for high resistance or an open condition.

GC402910069400EX

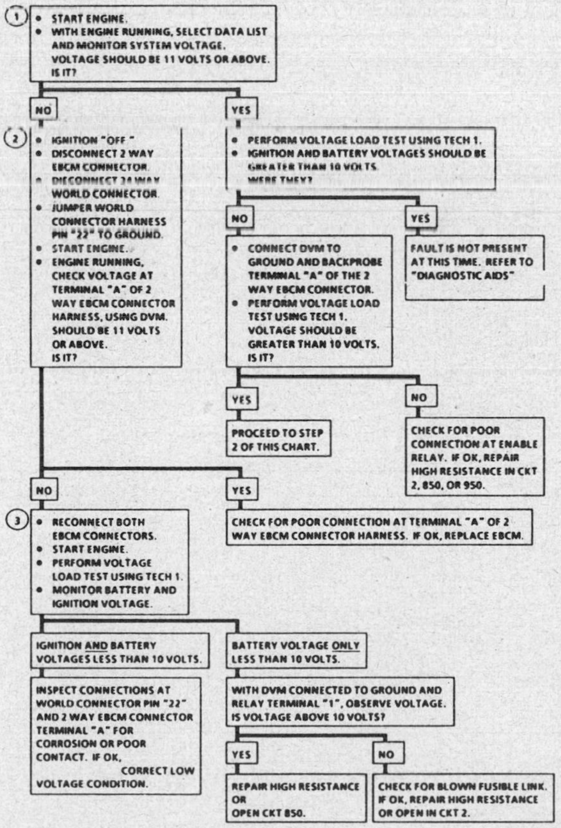
1
• START ENGINE.
• WITH ENGINE RUNNING, SELECT DATA LIST AND MONITOR SYSTEM VOLTAGE. VOLTAGE SHOULD BE 11 VOLTS OR ABOVE. IS IT?
NO
YES
2
• IGNITION "OFF"
• DISCONNECT 2 WAY EBCM CONNECTOR.
• DISCONNECT 24 WAY WORLD CONNECTOR.
• JUMPER WORLD CONNECTOR HARNESS PIN "22" TO GROUND.
• START ENGINE.
• ENGINE RUNNING, CHECK VOLTAGE AT TERMINAL "A" OF 2 WAY EBCM CONNECTOR HARNESS, USING DVM. SHOULD BE 11 VOLTS OR ABOVE. IS IT?
• PERFORM VOLTAGE LOAD TEST USING TECH 1.
• IGNITION AND BATTERY VOLTAGES SHOULD BE GREATER THAN 10 VOLTS. WERE THEY?
NO
YES
• CONNECT DVM TO GROUND AND BACKPROBE TERMINAL "A" OF THE 2 WAY EBCM CONNECTOR.
• PERFORM VOLTAGE LOAD TEST USING TECH 1. VOLTAGE SHOULD BE GREATER THAN 10 VOLTS. IS IT?
FAULT IS NOT PRESENT AT THIS TIME. REFER TO "DIAGNOSTIC AIDS"
YES
NO
PROCEED TO STEP 2 OF THIS CHART.
CHECK FOR POOR CONNECTION AT ENABLE RELAY. IF OK, REPAIR HIGH RESISTANCE IN CKT 2, 850, OR 950.
NO
YES
3
• RECONNECT BOTH EBCM CONNECTORS.
• START ENGINE.
• PERFORM VOLTAGE LOAD TEST USING TECH 1.
• MONITOR BATTERY AND IGNITION VOLTAGE.
CHECK FOR POOR CONNECTION AT TERMINAL "A" OF 2 WAY EBCM CONNECTOR HARNESS. IF OK, REPLACE EBCM.
IGNITION AND BATTERY VOLTAGES LESS THAN 10 VOLTS.
BATTERY VOLTAGE ONLY LESS THAN 10 VOLTS.
INSPECT CONNECTIONS AT WORLD CONNECTOR PIN "22" AND 2 WAY EBCM CONNECTOR TERMINAL "A" FOR CORROSION OR POOR CONTACT. IF OK, CORRECT LOW VOLTAGE CONDITION.
WITH DVM CONNECTED TO GROUND AND RELAY TERMINAL "1", OBSERVE VOLTAGE. IS VOLTAGE ABOVE 10 VOLTS?
YES
NO
REPAIR HIGH RESISTANCE OR OPEN CKT 850.
CHECK FOR BLOWN FUSIBLE LINK. IF OK, REPAIR HIGH RESISTANCE OR OPEN IN CKT 2.

GC402910069400FX

Fig. 50 Code A036: System Voltage Is Low. 1992

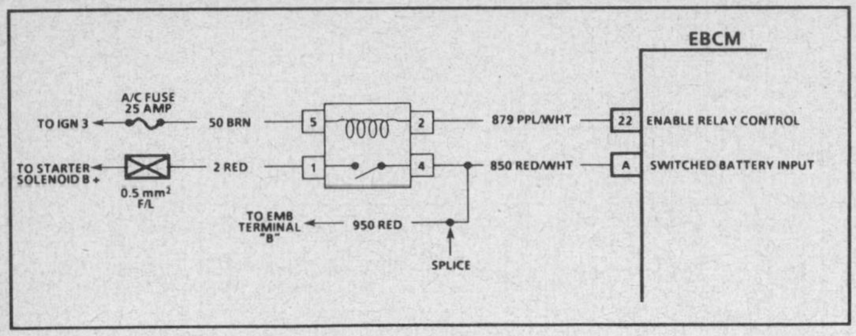
EBCM
A/C FUSE 25 AMP
TO IGN 3
50 BRN
5
2
879 PPL/WHT
22
ENABLE RELAY CONTROL
TO STARTER SOLENOID B+
2 RED
1
4
850 RED/WHT
A
SWITCHED BATTERY INPUT
0.5 mm² F/L
TO EMB TERMINAL "B"
950 RED
SPLICE

GC402910069500BX

Beretta & Corsica

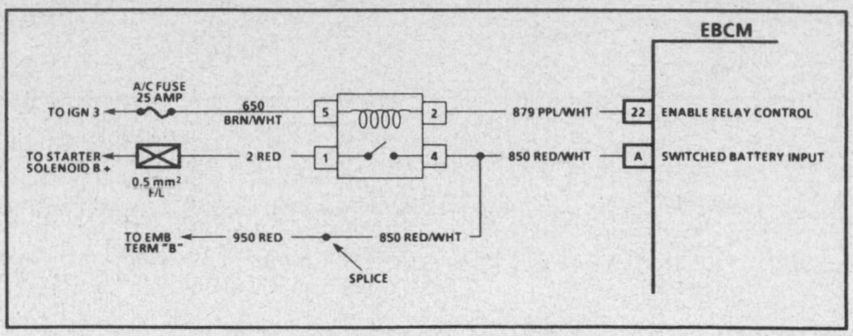
EBCM
A/C FUSE 25 AMP
TO IGN 3
650 BRN/WHT
5
2
879 PPL/WHT
22
ENABLE RELAY CONTROL
TO STARTER SOLENOID B+
2 RED
1
4
850 RED/WHT
A
SWITCHED BATTERY INPUT
0.5 mm² F/L
TO EMB TERM "B"
950 RED
850 RED/WHT
SPLICE

GC402910069500AX

Cavalier & Sunbird

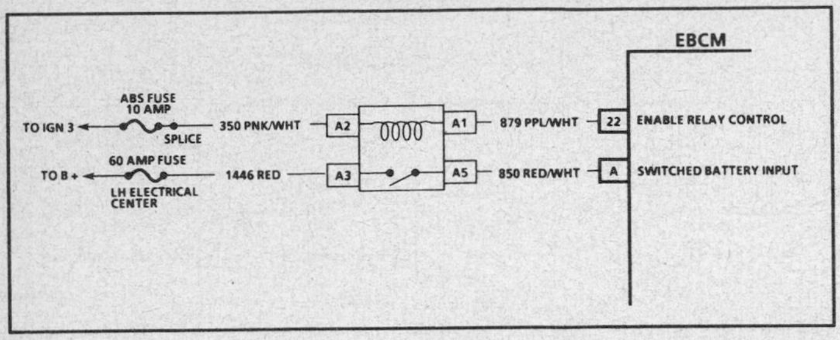
EBCM
ABS FUSE 10 AMP
TO IGN 3
SPLICE
350 PNK/WHT
A2
A1
879 PPL/WHT
22
ENABLE RELAY CONTROL
60 AMP FUSE
TO B+
LH ELECTRICAL CENTER
1446 RED
A3
A5
850 RED/WHT
A
SWITCHED BATTERY INPUT

GC402910069500DX

Cutlass Supreme, Grand Prix, Lumina & Regal

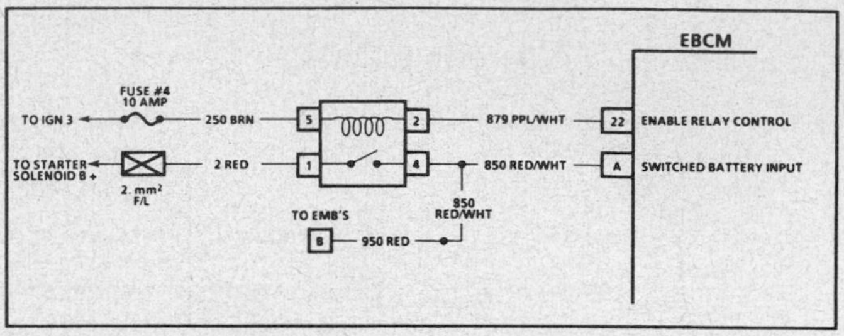
EBCM
FUSE #4 10 AMP
TO IGN 3
250 BRN
5
2
879 PPL/WHT
22
ENABLE RELAY CONTROL
TO STARTER SOLENOID B+
2 RED
1
4
850 RED/WHT
A
SWITCHED BATTERY INPUT
2. mm² F/L
TO EMB'S
850 RED/WHT
B
950 RED

GC402910069500CX

Achieva, Calais & Grand Am

Circuit Description:
This code is designed to detect high vehicle voltage levels prior to any required motor movement (initialization or ABS). If excessive voltage exists, demagnetization of the motor magnets may occur, which would eventually affect or eliminate ABS performance.

Test Description: Number(s) below refer to circled number(s) on the diagnostic chart.

1. This step checks the voltage level being received by the EBCM. If high voltage is present, a charging system problem is indicated.

Diagnostic Aids:

An "Intermittent" problem may be caused by a poor connection, rubbed through wire insulation, or a wire that is broken inside the insulation.

The frequency of the problem can be checked by using the enhanced diagnostic function of the "Scan" tool.

Any circuitry, that is suspected as causing the intermittent complaint, should be thoroughly checked for backed out terminals, improper mating, broken locks, improperly formed or damaged terminals, poor terminal to wiring connections or physical damage to the wiring harness.

GC402910069500EX

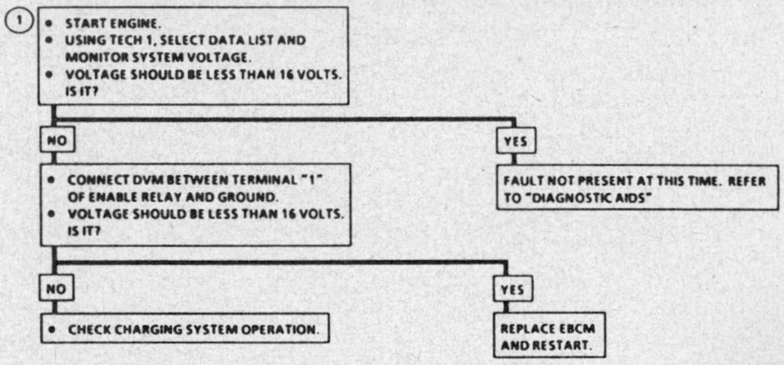
1
• START ENGINE.
• USING TECH 1, SELECT DATA LIST AND MONITOR SYSTEM VOLTAGE.
• VOLTAGE SHOULD BE LESS THAN 16 VOLTS. IS IT?
NO
YES
• CONNECT DVM BETWEEN TERMINAL "1" OF ENABLE RELAY AND GROUND.
• VOLTAGE SHOULD BE LESS THAN 16 VOLTS. IS IT?
FAULT NOT PRESENT AT THIS TIME. REFER TO "DIAGNOSTIC AIDS"
NO
YES
• CHECK CHARGING SYSTEM OPERATION.
REPLACE EBCM AND RESTART.

GC402910069500FX

Fig. 51 Code A037: System Voltage Is High. 1992

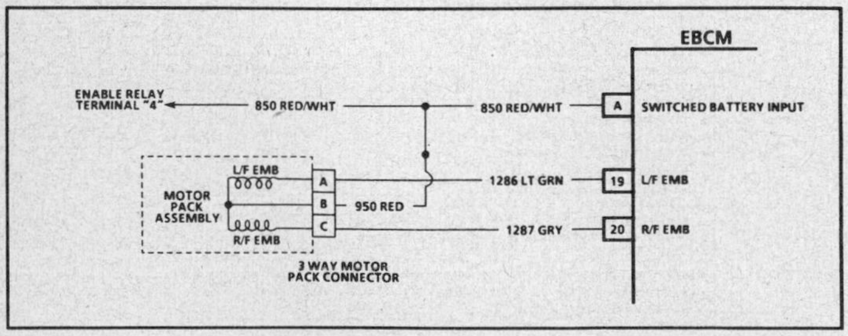
EBCM
ENABLE RELAY TERMINAL "4"
850 RED/WHT
850 RED/WHT
A
SWITCHED BATTERY INPUT
L/F EMB
MOTOR PACK ASSEMBLY
A
B
C
950 RED
1286 LT GRN
19
L/F EMB
R/F EMB
1287 GRY
20
R/F EMB
3 WAY MOTOR PACK CONNECTOR

GC402910069600AX

Except Cutlass Supreme, Grand Prix, Lumina & Regal

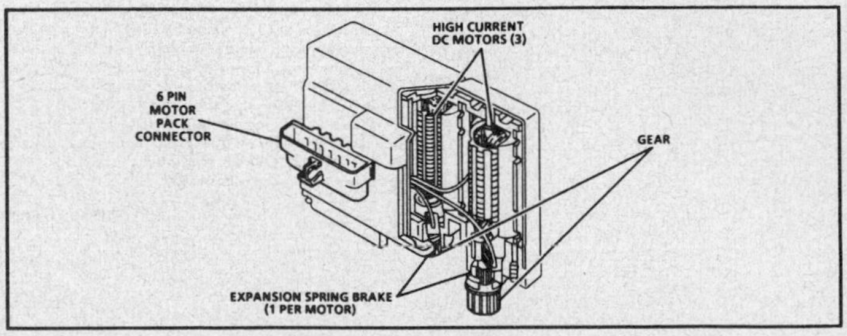
HIGH CURRENT DC MOTORS (3)
6 PIN MOTOR PACK CONNECTOR
GEAR
EXPANSION SPRING BRAKE (1 PER MOTOR)

GC402910069600BX

Cutlass Supreme, Grand Prix, Lumina & Regal

Fig. 52 Code A038: Left Front EMB Will Not Hold Motor (Part 1 of 2). 1992

NOTICE: TESTING EMB WITH JUMPER WIRES TO VOLTAGE OR GROUND WILL DESTROY THE EMB.

Circuit Description:

Current is supplied to the EMB's through terminal "B" of the three way motor pack connector. When a release of the EMB is commanded, the EBCM grounds the EMB input and allows the EMB to be energized to release the motor.

This code is designed to detect slipping EMB's during initialization. When the release is commanded during initialization, the EMB is not energized and should hold the motor, resulting in sensed current of the motor being equal to commanded current (motor is at stall). If the motor is moving, sensed current will be less than stall current.

Test Description: Number(s) below refer to circled number(s) on the diagnostic chart.

1. This functionally checks the ability of the EMB to hold the motor. If the brake pedal moves during this test, it would indicate the EMB is slipping.
2. This step is used to release the tension of the motor pack prior to removal.

Diagnostic Aids:

An "Intermittent" fault in this code may result from a mechanical part of the system that sticks, binds, or slips.

The frequency of the problem can be checked by using the enhanced diagnostic function of the "Scan tool

Depending on the frequency of the failure, a physical inspection of the mechanical parts suspected may be necessary.

The static modulator test function of the Tech 1 or T-100 may be used to locate an intermittent problem associated with the EMB.

NOTICE: This test may fail if low voltage (10 volts or less) was present when initialization occurred. Ensure battery/charging system is functioning properly.

GC402910069600CX

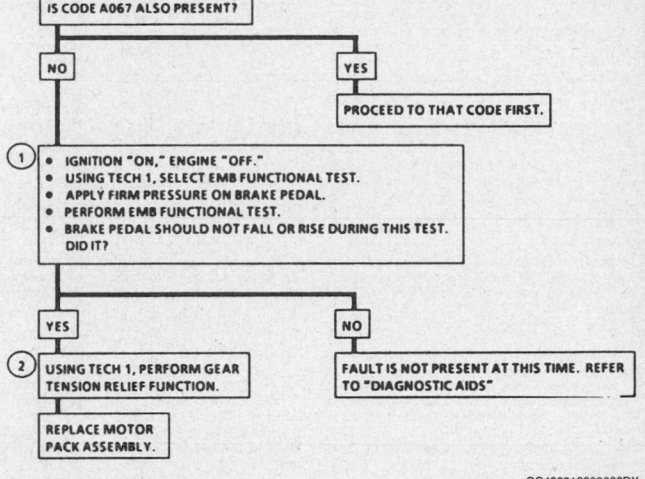

IS CODE A067 ALSO PRESENT?

- NO → (1)
- YES → PROCEED TO THAT CODE FIRST.

(1)
- IGNITION "ON," ENGINE "OFF."
- USING TECH 1, SELECT EMB FUNCTIONAL TEST.
- APPLY FIRM PRESSURE ON BRAKE PEDAL.
- PERFORM EMB FUNCTIONAL TEST.
- BRAKE PEDAL SHOULD NOT FALL OR RISE DURING THIS TEST. DID IT?

- YES → (2) USING TECH 1, PERFORM GEAR TENSION RELIEF FUNCTION. → REPLACE MOTOR PACK ASSEMBLY.
- NO → FAULT IS NOT PRESENT AT THIS TIME. REFER TO "DIAGNOSTIC AIDS"

GC402910069600DX

Fig. 52 Code A038: Left Front EMB Will Not Hold Motor (Part 2 of 2). 1992

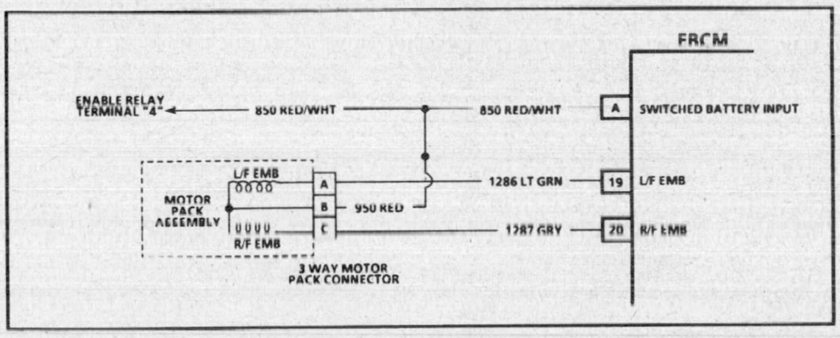
EBCM
ENABLE RELAY TERMINAL "4"
850 RED/WHT
850 RED/WHT
A
SWITCHED BATTERY INPUT
L/F EMB
MOTOR PACK ASSEMBLY
A
B
C
950 RED
1286 LT GRN
19
L/F EMB
1287 GRY
20
R/F EMB
R/F EMB
3 WAY MOTOR PACK CONNECTOR

GC402910069700AX

Except Cutlass Supreme, Grand Prix, Lumina & Regal

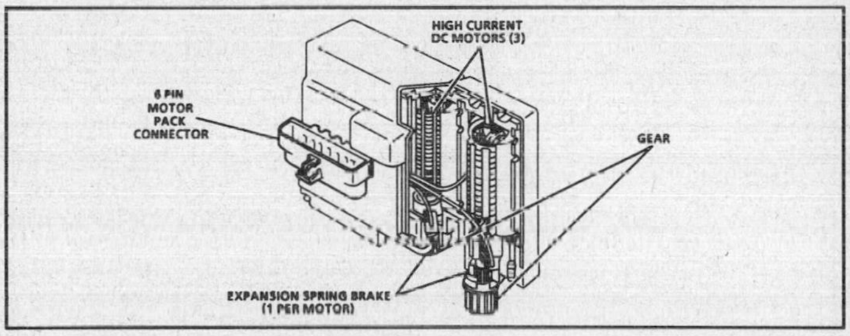
HIGH CURRENT DC MOTORS (3)
6 PIN MOTOR PACK CONNECTOR
GEAR
EXPANSION SPRING BRAKE (1 PER MOTOR)

GC402910069700BX

Cutlass Supreme, Grand Prix, Lumina & Regal

Circuit Description:

Current is supplied to the EMB's through terminal "B" of the three way motor pack connector. When a release of the EMB is commanded, the EBCM grounds the EMB input and allows the EMB to be energized to release the motor.

This code is designed to detect slipping EMB's during initialization. When the release is commanded during initialization, the EMB is not energized and should hold the motor, resulting in sensed current of the motor being equal to commanded current (motor is at stall). If the motor is moving, sensed current will be less than stall current.

Test Description: Number(s) below refer to circled number(s) on the diagnostic chart.

1. This functionally checks the ability of the EMB to hold the motor. If the brake pedal moves during this test, it would indicate the EMB is slipping.
2. This step is used to release the tension of the motor pack prior to removal.

Diagnostic Aids:

An "Intermittent" fault in this code may result from a mechanical part of the system that sticks, binds, or slips.

The frequency of the problem can be checked by using the enhanced diagnostic function of the "Scan" tool

Depending on the frequency of the failure, a physical inspection of the mechanical parts suspected may be necessary.

The static modulator test function of the Tech 1 or T-100 may be used to locate an intermittent problem associated with the EMB.

NOTICE: This code may fail if low voltage (10 volts or less) was present when initialization occurred. Ensure battery/charging system is functioning properly.

GC402910069700CX

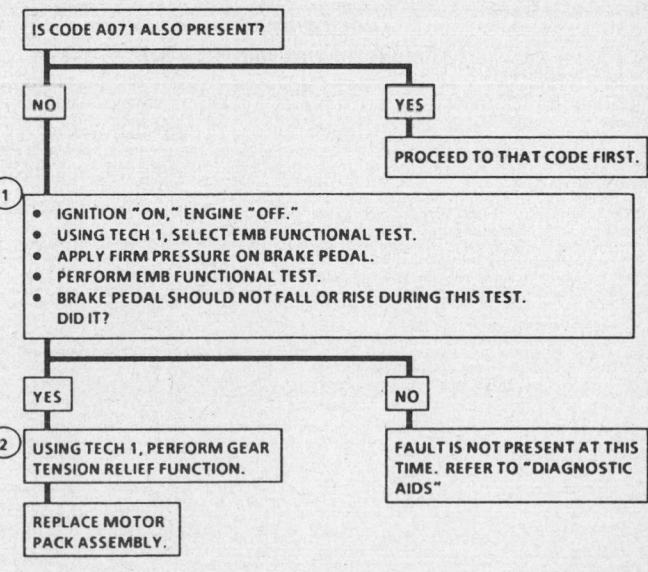

IS CODE A071 ALSO PRESENT?

- NO → (1)
- YES → PROCEED TO THAT CODE FIRST.

(1)
- IGNITION "ON," ENGINE "OFF."
- USING TECH 1, SELECT EMB FUNCTIONAL TEST.
- APPLY FIRM PRESSURE ON BRAKE PEDAL.
- PERFORM EMB FUNCTIONAL TEST.
- BRAKE PEDAL SHOULD NOT FALL OR RISE DURING THIS TEST. DID IT?

- YES → (2) USING TECH 1, PERFORM GEAR TENSION RELIEF FUNCTION. → REPLACE MOTOR PACK ASSEMBLY.
- NO → FAULT IS NOT PRESENT AT THIS TIME. REFER TO "DIAGNOSTIC AIDS"

GC402910069700DX

Fig. 53 Code A041: Right Front EMB Will Not Hold Motor. 1992

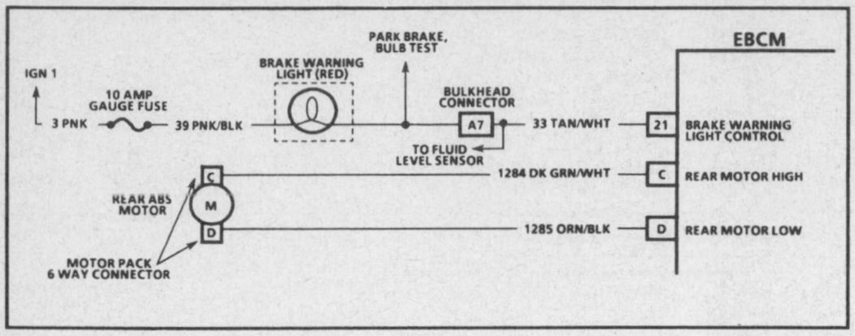
EBCM
PARK BRAKE, BULB TEST
BRAKE WARNING LIGHT (RED)
IGN 1
10 AMP GAUGE FUSE
3 PNK
39 PNK/BLK
BULKHEAD CONNECTOR
A7
33 TAN/WHT
21
BRAKE WARNING LIGHT CONTROL
TO FLUID LEVEL SENSOR
1284 DK GRN/WHT
C
REAR MOTOR HIGH
REAR ABS MOTOR
M
D
1285 ORN/BLK
REAR MOTOR LOW
MOTOR PACK 6 WAY CONNECTOR

GC402910069800AX

Except Cutlass Supreme, Grand Prix, Lumina & Regal

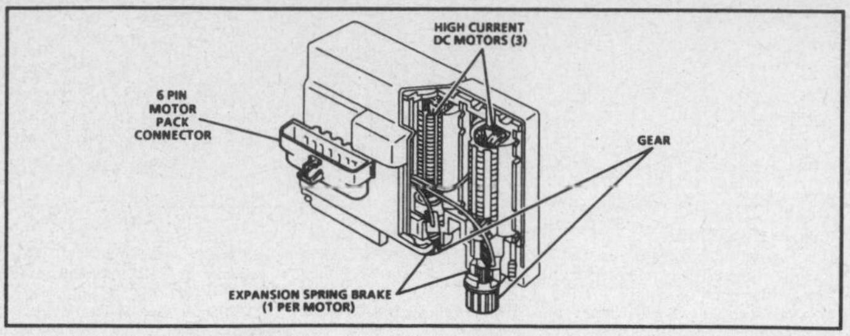
HIGH CURRENT DC MOTORS (3)
6 PIN MOTOR PACK CONNECTOR
GEAR
EXPANSION SPRING BRAKE (1 PER MOTOR)

GC402910069800BX

Cutlass Supreme, Grand Prix, Lumina & Regal

Circuit Description:

This code is designed to detect a slipping rear axle ESB. During initialization and braking, the rear motor is re-homed. If the ESB slips, the motor/piston will move. During the next key on initialization, a re-home of the motor verifies the motor/piston remained at the home position. If motor movement is detected, the ESB must be slipping.

Test Description: Number(s) below refer to circled number(s) on the diagnostic chart.

1. This step checks the rear axle ESB. A broken or defective ESB would result in the rear piston being back driven by hydraulic pressure, and wheel movement would result.
2. This step is used to release the tension of the motor pack prior to removal.

Diagnostic Aids:

An "Intermittent" fault in this code may result from a mechanical part of the system that sticks, binds, or slips.

The frequency of the problem can be checked by using the enhanced diagnostic function of the "Scan" tool

Depending on the frequency of the failure, a physical inspection of the mechanical parts suspected may be necessary.

The static modulator test function of the Tech 1 or T-100 may be used to locate an intermittent problem associated with the ESB.

GC402910069800CX

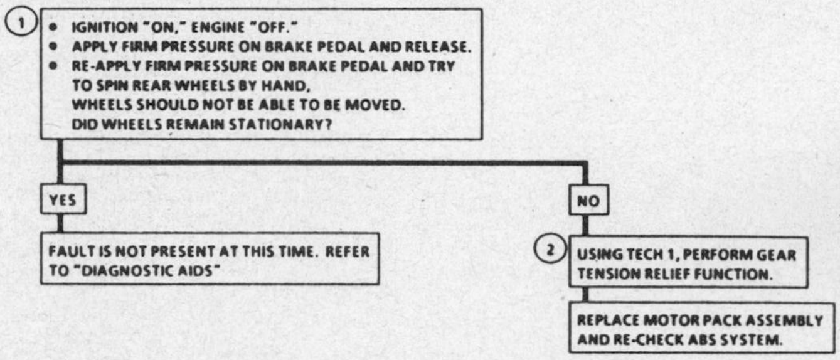
1
• IGNITION "ON," ENGINE "OFF."
• APPLY FIRM PRESSURE ON BRAKE PEDAL AND RELEASE.
• RE-APPLY FIRM PRESSURE ON BRAKE PEDAL AND TRY TO SPIN REAR WHEELS BY HAND.
WHEELS SHOULD NOT BE ABLE TO BE MOVED.
DID WHEELS REMAIN STATIONARY?
YES
NO
FAULT IS NOT PRESENT AT THIS TIME. REFER TO "DIAGNOSTIC AIDS"
2
USING TECH 1, PERFORM GEAR TENSION RELIEF FUNCTION.
REPLACE MOTOR PACK ASSEMBLY AND RE-CHECK ABS SYSTEM.

GC402910069800DX

Fig. 54 Code A042: Rear Axle ESB Will Not Hold Motor. 1992

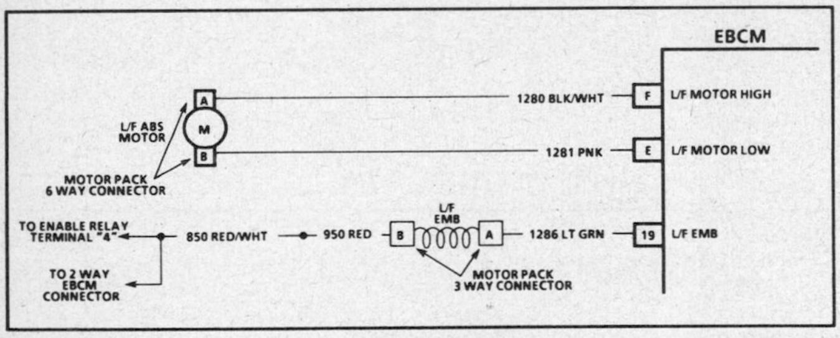
EBCM
1280 BLK/WHT
F
L/F MOTOR HIGH
L/F ABS MOTOR
A
M
B
1281 PNK
E
L/F MOTOR LOW
MOTOR PACK 6 WAY CONNECTOR
TO ENABLE RELAY TERMINAL "4"
850 RED/WHT
950 RED
L/F EMB
1286 LT GRN
19
L/F EMB
TO 2 WAY EBCM CONNECTOR
MOTOR PACK 3 WAY CONNECTOR

CODE A044

LEFT FRONT CHANNEL WILL NOT MOVE

Circuit Description:

Current is supplied to the EMB through terminal "B" of the three way motor pack connector. When a release of the EMB is commanded, the EBCM grounds the EMB input and allows the EMB to be energized to release the motor.

This code is designed to detect non-actuating EMB, stuck motor or a seized hydraulic modulator. When the release is commanded during initialization, the EMB should release the motor, resulting in sensed current being less than commanded current (motor is spinning freely). If the motor is not moving, sensed current will be equal to stall current.

Test Description: Number(s) below refer to circled number(s) on the diagnostic chart.

1. This step checks for motor movement while also positioning the brake pedal at the top of its travel.
2. This procedure functionally checks to see if the EMB is capable of releasing.
3. This step identifies a short to voltage in the EMB control circuitry.
4. This step is used to release the tension of the motor pack prior to removal.
5. This step serves to isolate the fault to either the motor pack assembly or ABS hydraulic modulator.

Diagnostic Aids:

An "Intermittent" fault in this code may result from a mechanical part of the system that sticks, binds, or slips.

The frequency of the problem can be checked by using the enhanced diagnostic function of the "Scan" tool

Code A044 may set after modulator disassembly if the modulator pistons are positioned at the bottom of their bore.

Any circuitry, that is suspected as causing the intermittent complaint, should be thoroughly checked for backed out terminals, improper mating, broken locks, improperly formed or damaged terminals, poor terminal to wiring connections or physical damage to the wiring harness.

NOTICE: This code may fail if low voltage (10 volts or less) was present when initialization occurred. Ensure battery/charging system is functioning properly.

GC402910069900AX

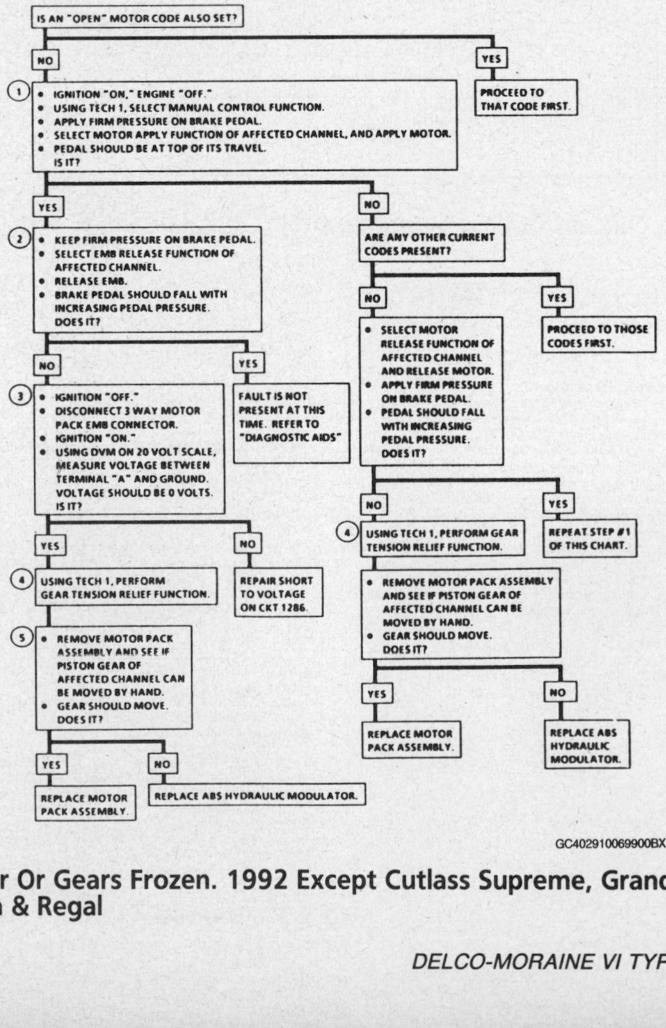
IS AN "OPEN" MOTOR CODE ALSO SET?
NO
YES
PROCEED TO THAT CODE FIRST.
1
• IGNITION "ON," ENGINE "OFF."
• USING TECH 1, SELECT MANUAL CONTROL FUNCTION.
• APPLY FIRM PRESSURE ON BRAKE PEDAL.
• SELECT MOTOR APPLY FUNCTION OF AFFECTED CHANNEL, AND APPLY MOTOR.
• PEDAL SHOULD BE AT TOP OF ITS TRAVEL.
IS IT?
YES
NO
2
• KEEP FIRM PRESSURE ON BRAKE PEDAL.
• SELECT EMB RELEASE FUNCTION OF AFFECTED CHANNEL.
• RELEASE EMB.
• BRAKE PEDAL SHOULD FALL WITH INCREASING PEDAL PRESSURE.
DOES IT?
ARE ANY OTHER CURRENT CODES PRESENT?
NO
YES
PROCEED TO THOSE CODES FIRST.
• SELECT MOTOR RELEASE FUNCTION OF AFFECTED CHANNEL AND RELEASE MOTOR.
• APPLY FIRM PRESSURE ON BRAKE PEDAL.
• PEDAL SHOULD FALL WITH INCREASING PEDAL PRESSURE.
DOES IT?
NO
YES
FAULT IS NOT PRESENT AT THIS TIME. REFER TO "DIAGNOSTIC AIDS"
3
• IGNITION "OFF."
• DISCONNECT 3 WAY MOTOR PACK EMB CONNECTOR.
• IGNITION "ON."
• USING DVM ON 20 VOLT SCALE, MEASURE VOLTAGE BETWEEN TERMINAL "A" AND GROUND.
VOLTAGE SHOULD BE 0 VOLTS.
IS IT?
NO
YES
4
USING TECH 1, PERFORM GEAR TENSION RELIEF FUNCTION.
REPEAT STEP #1 OF THIS CHART.
YES
NO
4
USING TECH 1, PERFORM GEAR TENSION RELIEF FUNCTION.
REPAIR SHORT TO VOLTAGE ON CKT 1286.
• REMOVE MOTOR PACK ASSEMBLY AND SEE IF PISTON GEAR OF AFFECTED CHANNEL CAN BE MOVED BY HAND.
• GEAR SHOULD MOVE.
DOES IT?
5
• REMOVE MOTOR PACK ASSEMBLY AND SEE IF PISTON GEAR OF AFFECTED CHANNEL CAN BE MOVED BY HAND.
• GEAR SHOULD MOVE.
DOES IT?
YES
NO
REPLACE MOTOR PACK ASSEMBLY.
REPLACE ABS HYDRAULIC MODULATOR.
YES
NO
REPLACE MOTOR PACK ASSEMBLY.
REPLACE ABS HYDRAULIC MODULATOR.

GC402910069900BX

Fig. 55 Code A044: Left Front EMB Will Not Release Motor Or Gears Frozen. 1992 Except Cutlass Supreme, Grand Prix, Lumina & Regal

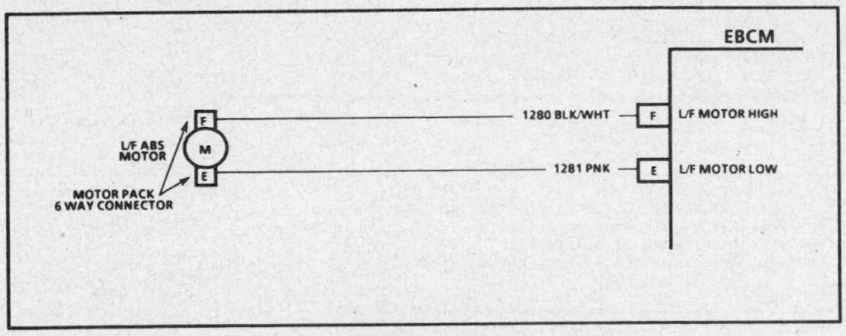
EBCM
L/F ABS MOTOR
M
F
E
MOTOR PACK 6 WAY CONNECTOR
1280 BLK/WHT
F
L/F MOTOR HIGH
1281 PNK
E
L/F MOTOR LOW

CODE A044

LEFT FRONT CHANNEL WILL NOT MOVE

Circuit Description:

This code is designed to detect bound-up ESB, a stuck motor, or a seized hydraulic modulator. When the release is commanded during initialization, the ESB should release the motor, resulting in sensed current being less than commanded current (motor is spinning freely). If the motor is not moving, sensed current will be equal to stall current.

Test Description: Number(s) below refer to circled number(s) on the diagnostic chart.

1. This step checks for motor movement.
2. This step is used to release the tension of the motor pack prior to removal.
3. This step serves to isolate the fault to either the motor pack assembly or ABS hydraulic modulator.

Diagnostic Aids:

An "Intermittent" fault in this code may result from a mechanical part of the system that sticks, binds, or slips.

The frequency of the problem can be checked by using the enhanced diagnostic function of the "Scan" tool

Code A044 may set after modulator disassembly if the modulator pistons are positioned at the bottom of their bore.

Any circuitry, that is suspected as causing the intermittent complaint, should be thoroughly checked for backed out terminals, improper mating, broken locks, improperly formed or damaged terminals, poor terminal to wiring connections or physical damage to the wiring harness.

GC40291007000AX

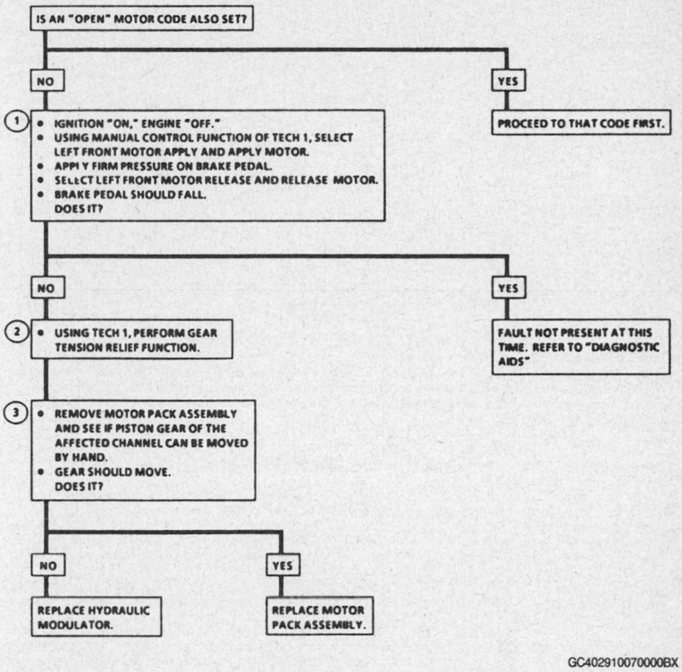
IS AN "OPEN" MOTOR CODE ALSO SET?
NO
YES
PROCEED TO THAT CODE FIRST.
1
• IGNITION "ON," ENGINE "OFF."
• USING MANUAL CONTROL FUNCTION OF TECH 1, SELECT LEFT FRONT MOTOR APPLY AND APPLY MOTOR.
• APPLY FIRM PRESSURE ON BRAKE PEDAL.
• SELECT LEFT FRONT MOTOR RELEASE AND RELEASE MOTOR.
• BRAKE PEDAL SHOULD FALL.
DOES IT?
NO
YES
FAULT NOT PRESENT AT THIS TIME. REFER TO "DIAGNOSTIC AIDS"
2
• USING TECH 1, PERFORM GEAR TENSION RELIEF FUNCTION.
3
• REMOVE MOTOR PACK ASSEMBLY AND SEE IF PISTON GEAR OF THE AFFECTED CHANNEL CAN BE MOVED BY HAND.
• GEAR SHOULD MOVE.
DOES IT?
NO
YES
REPLACE HYDRAULIC MODULATOR.
REPLACE MOTOR PACK ASSEMBLY.
GC402910070000BX

Fig. 56 Code A044: Left Front EMB Will Not Release Motor Or Gears Frozen. 1992 Cutlass Supreme, Grand Prix, Lumina & Regal

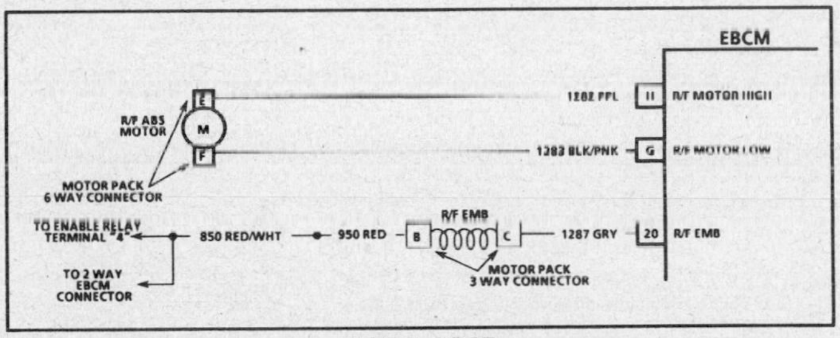
EBCM
R/F ABS MOTOR
M
E
F
MOTOR PACK 6 WAY CONNECTOR
1282 PPL
H
R/F MOTOR HIGH
1283 BLK/PNK
G
R/F MOTOR LOW
TO ENABLE RELAY TERMINAL "4"
850 RED/WHT
950 RED
B
R/F EMB
C
1287 GRY
20
R/F EMB
MOTOR PACK 3 WAY CONNECTOR
TO 2 WAY EBCM CONNECTOR

CODE A045

RIGHT FRONT CHANNEL WILL NOT MOVE

Circuit Description:

Current is supplied to the EMB through terminal "B" of the three way motor pack connector. When a release of the EMB is commanded, the EBCM grounds the EMB input and allows the EMB to be energized to release the motor.

This code is designed to detect non-actuating EMB, stuck motor or a seized hydraulic modulator. When the release is commanded during initialization, the EMB should release the motor, resulting in sensed current being less than commanded current (motor is spinning freely). If the motor is not moving, sensed current will be equal to stall current.

Test Description: Number(s) below refer to circled number(s) on the diagnostic chart.

1. This step checks for motor movement while also positioning the brake pedal at the top of its travel.
2. This procedure functionally checks to see if the EMB is capable of releasing.
3. This step is used to release the tension of the motor pack prior to removal.
4. This step serves to isolate the fault to either the motor pack assembly or ABS hydraulic modulator.

Diagnostic Aids:

An "Intermittent" fault in this code may result from a mechanical part of the system that sticks, binds, or slips.

The frequency of the problem can be checked by using the enhanced diagnostic function of the "Scan" tool

Code A045 may set after modulator disassembly if the modulator pistons are positioned at the bottom of their bore.

Any circuitry, that is suspected as causing the intermittent complaint, should be thoroughly checked for backed out terminals, improper mating, broken locks, improperly formed or damaged terminals, poor terminal to wiring connections or physical damage to the wiring harness.

NOTICE: This code may fail if low voltage (10 volts or less) was present when initialization occurred. Ensure battery/charging system is functioning properly.

GC402910070100AX

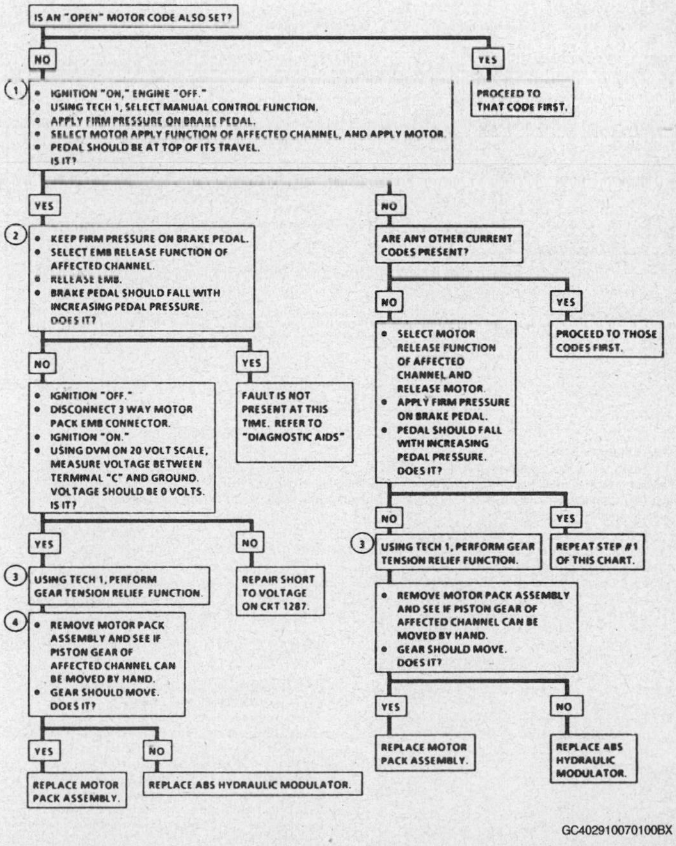
IS AN "OPEN" MOTOR CODE ALSO SET?
NO
YES
PROCEED TO THAT CODE FIRST.
1
• IGNITION "ON," ENGINE "OFF."
• USING TECH 1, SELECT MANUAL CONTROL FUNCTION.
• APPLY FIRM PRESSURE ON BRAKE PEDAL.
• SELECT MOTOR APPLY FUNCTION OF AFFECTED CHANNEL, AND APPLY MOTOR.
• PEDAL SHOULD BE AT TOP OF ITS TRAVEL.
IS IT?
YES
NO
2
• KEEP FIRM PRESSURE ON BRAKE PEDAL.
• SELECT EMB RELEASE FUNCTION OF AFFECTED CHANNEL.
• RELEASE EMB.
• BRAKE PEDAL SHOULD FALL WITH INCREASING PEDAL PRESSURE.
DOES IT?
ARE ANY OTHER CURRENT CODES PRESENT?
NO
YES
PROCEED TO THOSE CODES FIRST.
• SELECT MOTOR RELEASE FUNCTION OF AFFECTED CHANNEL AND RELEASE MOTOR.
• APPLY FIRM PRESSURE ON BRAKE PEDAL.
• PEDAL SHOULD FALL WITH INCREASING PEDAL PRESSURE.
DOES IT?
NO
YES
FAULT IS NOT PRESENT AT THIS TIME. REFER TO "DIAGNOSTIC AIDS"
• IGNITION "OFF."
• DISCONNECT 3 WAY MOTOR PACK EMB CONNECTOR.
• IGNITION "ON."
• USING DVM ON 20 VOLT SCALE, MEASURE VOLTAGE BETWEEN TERMINAL "C" AND GROUND. VOLTAGE SHOULD BE 0 VOLTS.
IS IT?
NO
YES
3
USING TECH 1, PERFORM GEAR TENSION RELIEF FUNCTION.
REPEAT STEP #1 OF THIS CHART.
YES
NO
REPAIR SHORT TO VOLTAGE ON CKT 1287.
3
USING TECH 1, PERFORM GEAR TENSION RELIEF FUNCTION.
• REMOVE MOTOR PACK ASSEMBLY AND SEE IF PISTON GEAR OF AFFECTED CHANNEL CAN BE MOVED BY HAND.
• GEAR SHOULD MOVE.
DOES IT?
4
• REMOVE MOTOR PACK ASSEMBLY AND SEE IF PISTON GEAR OF AFFECTED CHANNEL CAN BE MOVED BY HAND.
• GEAR SHOULD MOVE.
DOES IT?
YES
NO
REPLACE MOTOR PACK ASSEMBLY.
REPLACE ABS HYDRAULIC MODULATOR.
YES
NO
REPLACE MOTOR PACK ASSEMBLY.
REPLACE ABS HYDRAULIC MODULATOR.
GC402910070100BX

Fig. 57 Code A045: Right Front EMB Will Not Release Motor Or Gears Frozen. 1992 Except Cutlass Supreme, Grand Prix, Lumina & Regal

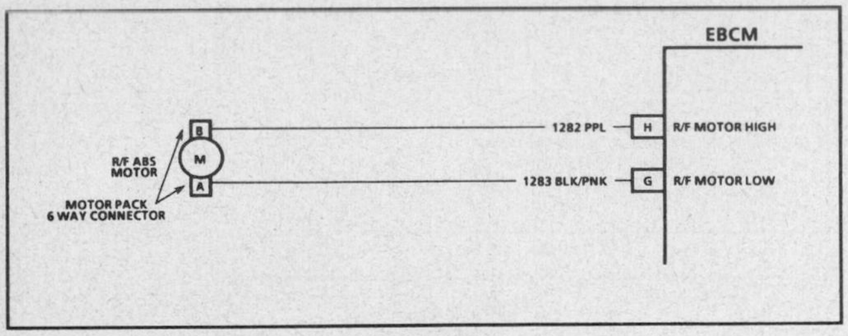
EBCM
1282 PPL
H
R/F MOTOR HIGH
1283 BLK/PNK
G
R/F MOTOR LOW
B
M
A
R/F ABS MOTOR
MOTOR PACK 6 WAY CONNECTOR

CODE A045

RIGHT FRONT CHANNEL WILL NOT MOVE

Circuit Description:

This code is designed to detect bound-up ESB, a stuck motor, or a seized hydraulic modulator. When the release is commanded during initialization, the ESB should release the motor, resulting in sensed current being less than commanded current (motor is spinning freely). If the motor is not moving, sensed current will be equal to stall current.

Test Description: Number(s) below refer to circled number(s) on the diagnostic chart.

1. This step checks for motor movement.
2. This step is used to release the tension of the motor pack prior to removal.
3. This step serves to isolate the fault to either the motor pack assembly or ABS hydraulic modulator.

Diagnostic Aids:

An "Intermittent" fault in this code may result from a mechanical part of the system that sticks, binds, or slips.

The frequency of the problem can be checked by using the enhanced diagnostic function of the "Scan" tool

Code A045 may set after modulator disassembly if the modulator pistons are positioned at the bottom of their bore.

Any circuitry, that is suspected as causing the intermittent complaint, should be thoroughly checked for backed out terminals, improper mating, broken locks, improperly formed or damaged terminals, poor terminal to wiring connections or physical damage to the wiring harness.

GC402910070200AX

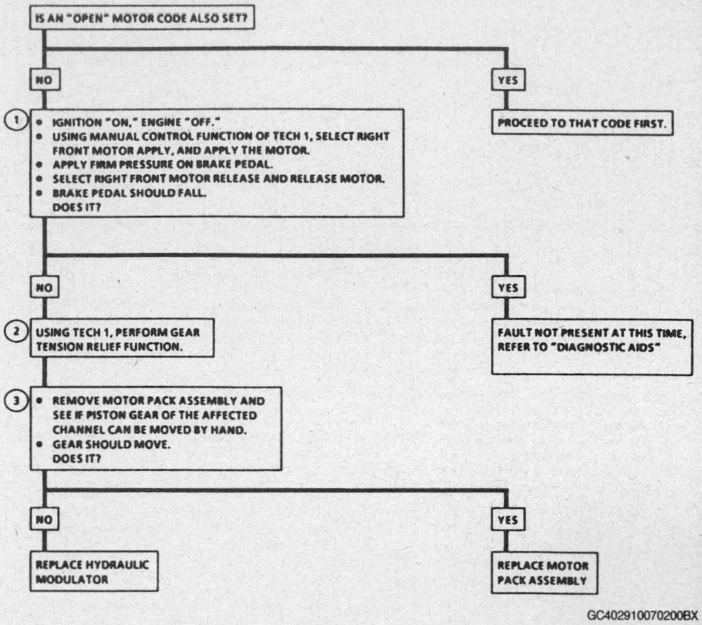
IS AN "OPEN" MOTOR CODE ALSO SET?
NO
YES
PROCEED TO THAT CODE FIRST.
1
• IGNITION "ON," ENGINE "OFF."
• USING MANUAL CONTROL FUNCTION OF TECH 1, SELECT RIGHT FRONT MOTOR APPLY, AND APPLY THE MOTOR.
• APPLY FIRM PRESSURE ON BRAKE PEDAL.
• SELECT RIGHT FRONT MOTOR RELEASE AND RELEASE MOTOR.
• BRAKE PEDAL SHOULD FALL. DOES IT?
NO
YES
2
USING TECH 1, PERFORM GEAR TENSION RELIEF FUNCTION.
FAULT NOT PRESENT AT THIS TIME, REFER TO "DIAGNOSTIC AIDS"
3
• REMOVE MOTOR PACK ASSEMBLY AND SEE IF PISTON GEAR OF THE AFFECTED CHANNEL CAN BE MOVED BY HAND.
• GEAR SHOULD MOVE. DOES IT?
NO
YES
REPLACE HYDRAULIC MODULATOR
REPLACE MOTOR PACK ASSEMBLY

GC402910070200BX

Fig. 58 Code A045: Right Front EMB Will Not Release Motor Or Gears Frozen. 1992 Cutlass Supreme, Grand Prix, Lumina & Regal

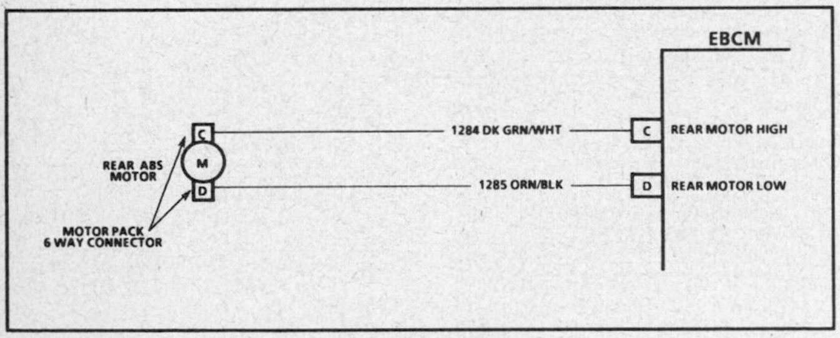
EBCM
1284 DK GRN/WHT
C
REAR MOTOR HIGH
1285 ORN/BLK
D
REAR MOTOR LOW
C
M
D
REAR ABS MOTOR
MOTOR PACK 6 WAY CONNECTOR

CODE A046

REAR AXLE CHANNEL WILL NOT MOVE

Circuit Description:

This code is designed to detect bound-up ESB's, stuck motor or a seized hydraulic modulator. When the release is commanded during initialization, the ESB should release the motor, resulting in sensed current being less than commanded current (motor is spinning freely). If the motor is not moving, sensed current will be equal to stall current.

Test Description: Number(s) below refer to circled number(s) on the diagnostic chart.

1. This checks the ability of the motor to move, applying hydraulic pressure to the wheel cylinders. A frozen piston or gear would result in no apply of rear brakes and a wheel that freely spins.
2. This step checks to see that the motor can also move to the release position. If a motor were not able to release hydraulic pressure, the wheel would not spin.
3. This step is used to release the tension of the motor pack prior to removal.
4. Isolation of the faulty component is identified in this step.

Diagnostic Aids:

An "Intermittent" fault in this code may result from a mechanical part of the system that sticks or binds.

The frequency of the problem can be checked by using the enhanced diagnostic function of the Tech 1 "Scan" tool

Code A046 may set after modulator disassembly if the modulator pistons are positioned at the bottom of their bore.

Depending on the frequency of the failure, a physical inspection of the mechanical parts suspected may be necessary.

Any circuitry, that is suspected as causing the intermittent complaint, should be thoroughly checked for backed out terminals, improper mating, broken locks, improperly formed or damaged terminals, poor terminal to wiring connections or physical damage to the wiring harness.

GC402910070300AX

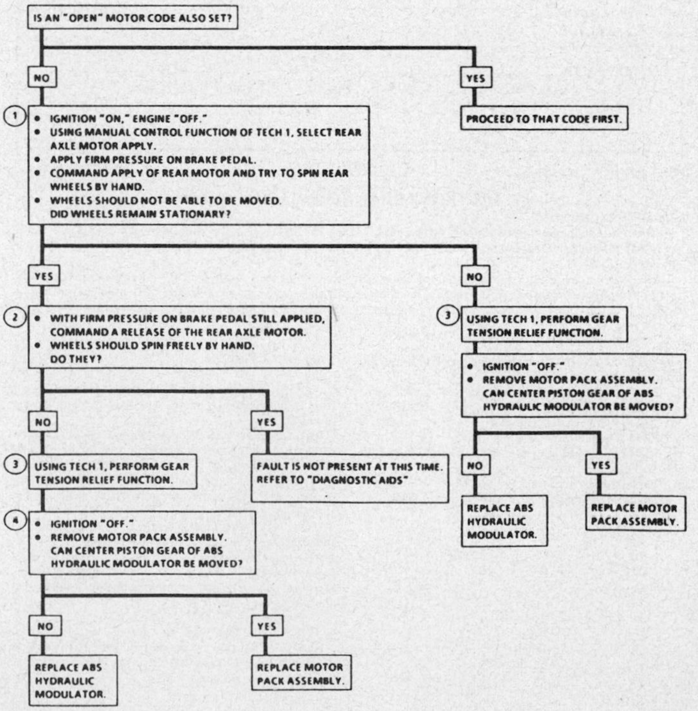
IS AN "OPEN" MOTOR CODE ALSO SET?
NO
YES
PROCEED TO THAT CODE FIRST.
1
• IGNITION "ON," ENGINE "OFF."
• USING MANUAL CONTROL FUNCTION OF TECH 1, SELECT REAR AXLE MOTOR APPLY.
• APPLY FIRM PRESSURE ON BRAKE PEDAL.
• COMMAND APPLY OF REAR MOTOR AND TRY TO SPIN REAR WHEELS BY HAND.
• WHEELS SHOULD NOT BE ABLE TO BE MOVED. DID WHEELS REMAIN STATIONARY?
YES
NO
2
• WITH FIRM PRESSURE ON BRAKE PEDAL STILL APPLIED, COMMAND A RELEASE OF THE REAR AXLE MOTOR.
• WHEELS SHOULD SPIN FREELY BY HAND. DO THEY?
3
USING TECH 1, PERFORM GEAR TENSION RELIEF FUNCTION.
• IGNITION "OFF."
• REMOVE MOTOR PACK ASSEMBLY. CAN CENTER PISTON GEAR OF ABS HYDRAULIC MODULATOR BE MOVED?
NO
YES
NO
YES
REPLACE ABS HYDRAULIC MODULATOR.
REPLACE MOTOR PACK ASSEMBLY.
3
USING TECH 1, PERFORM GEAR TENSION RELIEF FUNCTION.
FAULT IS NOT PRESENT AT THIS TIME. REFER TO "DIAGNOSTIC AIDS"
4
• IGNITION "OFF."
• REMOVE MOTOR PACK ASSEMBLY. CAN CENTER PISTON GEAR OF ABS HYDRAULIC MODULATOR BE MOVED?
NO
YES
REPLACE ABS HYDRAULIC MODULATOR.
REPLACE MOTOR PACK ASSEMBLY.

GC402910070300BX

Fig. 59 Code A046: Rear Axle ESB Will Not Release Motor Or Gears Frozen. 1992

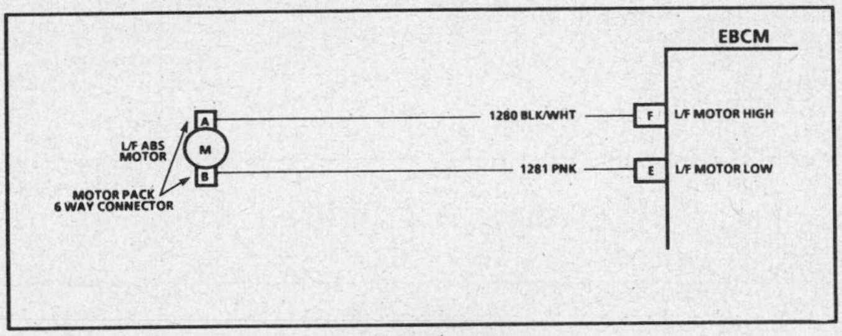

EBCM
L/F ABS MOTOR
M
A
B
MOTOR PACK 6 WAY CONNECTOR
1280 BLK/WHT
F
L/F MOTOR HIGH
1281 PNK
E
L/F MOTOR LOW

CODE A047

LEFT FRONT MOTOR FREE SPINS

Circuit Description:
This code is designed to detect a stripped nut or gear assembly during initialization. During the homing sequence, the piston should reach the top of the bore resulting in a stalled motor. If this does not occur, the motor must be spinning with little or no resistance, indicating a nut/screw or gear failure.

Test Description: Number(s) below refer to circled number(s) on the diagnostic chart.

1. This step positions the motor at the bottom of its travel.
2. This checks to see if the nut or gear is stripped. If either were stripped, the hydraulic pressure applied from the master cylinder would not be able to be overcome by the hydraulic ball screw, resulting in a brake pedal that would not rise.
3. During a full apply, once the ball screw reaches the top of its travel, the motor should stall. If the motor continues to run, an indication of a stripped nut or gear is present.
4. This step is used to release the tension of the motor pack prior to removal.

Diagnostic Aids:

An "Intermittent" fault in this code may result from a mechanical part of the system that sticks, binds, or slips.

The frequency of the problem can be checked by using the enhanced diagnostic function of the "Scan" tool

If code only fails once and Code A056 also fails see Code A056. If intermittent and enhanced diagnostics shows this code fails during ABS, see Code A056.

Depending on the frequency of the failure, a physical inspection of the mechanical parts suspected may be necessary.

GC402910070400AX

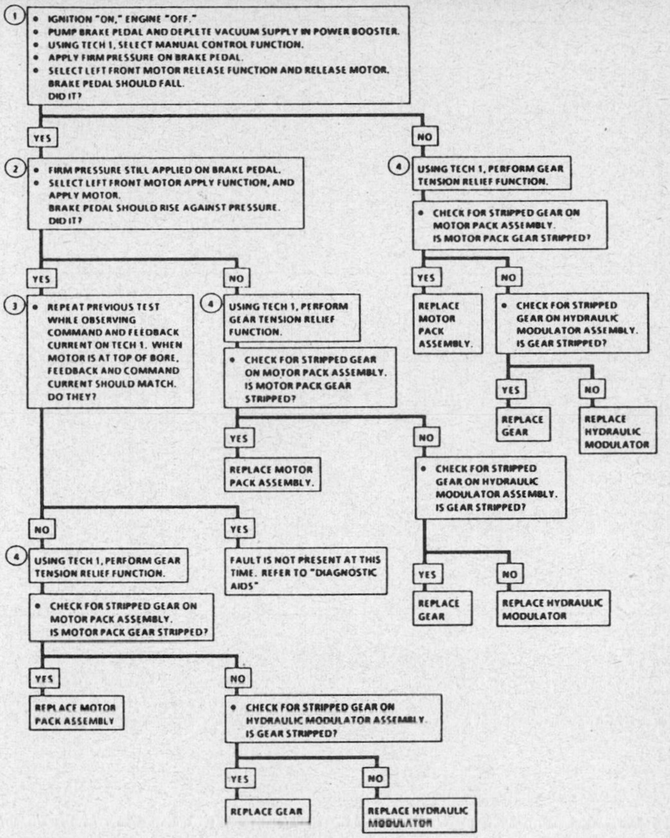

1
• IGNITION "ON," ENGINE "OFF."
• PUMP BRAKE PEDAL AND DEPLETE VACUUM SUPPLY IN POWER BOOSTER.
• USING TECH 1, SELECT MANUAL CONTROL FUNCTION.
• APPLY FIRM PRESSURE ON BRAKE PEDAL.
• SELECT LEFT FRONT MOTOR RELEASE FUNCTION AND RELEASE MOTOR. BRAKE PEDAL SHOULD FALL. DID IT?
YES
NO
2
• FIRM PRESSURE STILL APPLIED ON BRAKE PEDAL.
• SELECT LEFT FRONT MOTOR APPLY FUNCTION, AND APPLY MOTOR. BRAKE PEDAL SHOULD RISE AGAINST PRESSURE. DID IT?
4
USING TECH 1, PERFORM GEAR TENSION RELIEF FUNCTION.
• CHECK FOR STRIPPED GEAR ON MOTOR PACK ASSEMBLY. IS MOTOR PACK GEAR STRIPPED?
YES
NO
3
• REPEAT PREVIOUS TEST WHILE OBSERVING COMMAND AND FEEDBACK CURRENT ON TECH 1. WHEN MOTOR IS AT TOP OF BORE, FEEDBACK AND COMMAND CURRENT SHOULD MATCH. DO THEY?
4
USING TECH 1, PERFORM GEAR TENSION RELIEF FUNCTION.
• CHECK FOR STRIPPED GEAR ON MOTOR PACK ASSEMBLY. IS MOTOR PACK GEAR STRIPPED?
REPLACE MOTOR PACK ASSEMBLY.
• CHECK FOR STRIPPED GEAR ON HYDRAULIC MODULATOR ASSEMBLY. IS GEAR STRIPPED?
REPLACE GEAR
REPLACE HYDRAULIC MODULATOR
REPLACE MOTOR PACK ASSEMBLY.
• CHECK FOR STRIPPED GEAR ON HYDRAULIC MODULATOR ASSEMBLY. IS GEAR STRIPPED?
FAULT IS NOT PRESENT AT THIS TIME. REFER TO "DIAGNOSTIC AIDS"
4
USING TECH 1, PERFORM GEAR TENSION RELIEF FUNCTION.
• CHECK FOR STRIPPED GEAR ON MOTOR PACK ASSEMBLY. IS MOTOR PACK GEAR STRIPPED?
REPLACE GEAR
REPLACE HYDRAULIC MODULATOR
REPLACE MOTOR PACK ASSEMBLY
• CHECK FOR STRIPPED GEAR ON HYDRAULIC MODULATOR ASSEMBLY. IS GEAR STRIPPED?
REPLACE GEAR
REPLACE HYDRAULIC MODULATOR

GC402910070400BX

Fig. 60 Code A047: Left Front Nut Failure, Motor Free Spins. 1992

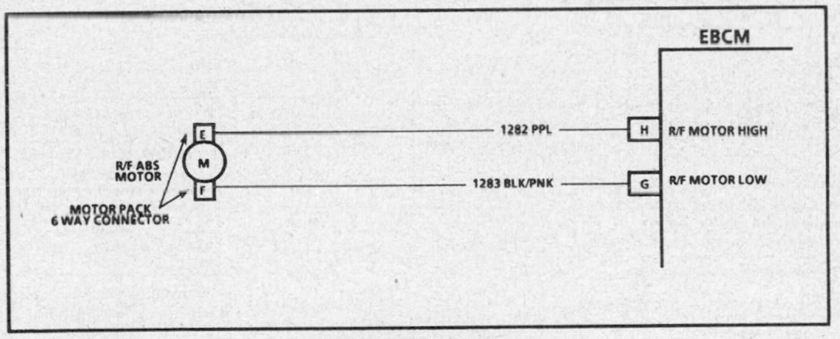

EBCM
R/F ABS MOTOR
M
E
F
MOTOR PACK 6 WAY CONNECTOR
1282 PPL
H
R/F MOTOR HIGH
1283 BLK/PNK
G
R/F MOTOR LOW

CODE A048

RIGHT FRONT MOTOR FREE SPINS

Circuit Description:
This code is designed to detect a stripped nut or gear assembly during initialization. During the homing sequence, the piston should reach the top of the bore resulting in a stalled motor. If this does not occur, the motor must be spinning with little or no resistance, indicating a nut/screw or gear failure.

Test Description: Number(s) below refer to circled number(s) on the diagnostic chart.

1. This step positions the motor at the bottom of its travel.
2. This checks to see if the nut or gear is stripped. If either were stripped, the hydraulic pressure applied from the master cylinder would not be able to be overcome by the hydraulic ball screw, resulting in a bake pedal that would not rise.
3. During a full apply, once the ball screw reaches the top of its travel, the motor should stall. If the motor continues to run, an indication of a stripped nut or gear is present.
4. This step is used to release the tension of the motor pack prior to removal.

Diagnostic Aids:

An "Intermittent" fault in this code may result from a mechanical part of the system that sticks, binds, or slips.

The frequency of the problem can be checked by using the enhanced diagnostic function of the "Scan" tool

If code only fails once and Code A061 also fails see Code A061. If intermittent and enhanced diagnostics shows this code fails during ABS, see Code A061.

Depending on the frequency of the failure, a physical inspection of the mechanical parts suspected may be necessary.

GC402910070500AX

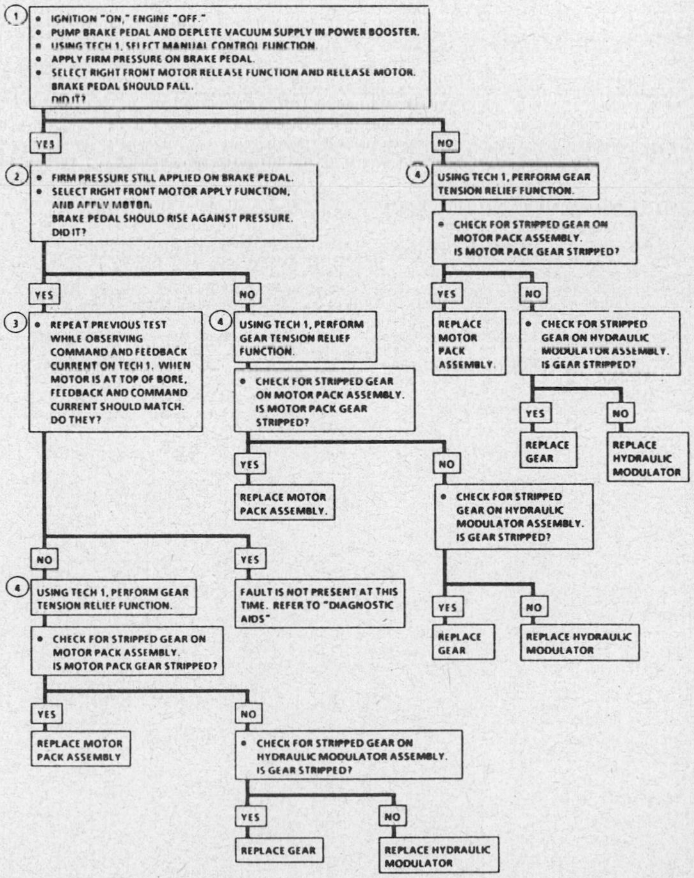

1
• IGNITION "ON," ENGINE "OFF."
• PUMP BRAKE PEDAL AND DEPLETE VACUUM SUPPLY IN POWER BOOSTER.
• USING TECH 1, SELECT MANUAL CONTROL FUNCTION.
• APPLY FIRM PRESSURE ON BRAKE PEDAL.
• SELECT RIGHT FRONT MOTOR RELEASE FUNCTION AND RELEASE MOTOR. BRAKE PEDAL SHOULD FALL. DID IT?
YES
NO
2
• FIRM PRESSURE STILL APPLIED ON BRAKE PEDAL.
• SELECT RIGHT FRONT MOTOR APPLY FUNCTION, AND APPLY MOTOR. BRAKE PEDAL SHOULD RISE AGAINST PRESSURE. DID IT?
4
USING TECH 1, PERFORM GEAR TENSION RELIEF FUNCTION.
• CHECK FOR STRIPPED GEAR ON MOTOR PACK ASSEMBLY. IS MOTOR PACK GEAR STRIPPED?
3
• REPEAT PREVIOUS TEST WHILE OBSERVING COMMAND AND FEEDBACK CURRENT ON TECH 1. WHEN MOTOR IS AT TOP OF BORE, FEEDBACK AND COMMAND CURRENT SHOULD MATCH. DO THEY?
4
USING TECH 1, PERFORM GEAR TENSION RELIEF FUNCTION.
• CHECK FOR STRIPPED GEAR ON MOTOR PACK ASSEMBLY. IS MOTOR PACK GEAR STRIPPED?
REPLACE MOTOR PACK ASSEMBLY.
• CHECK FOR STRIPPED GEAR ON HYDRAULIC MODULATOR ASSEMBLY. IS GEAR STRIPPED?
REPLACE GEAR
REPLACE HYDRAULIC MODULATOR
REPLACE MOTOR PACK ASSEMBLY.
• CHECK FOR STRIPPED GEAR ON HYDRAULIC MODULATOR ASSEMBLY. IS GEAR STRIPPED?
FAULT IS NOT PRESENT AT THIS TIME. REFER TO "DIAGNOSTIC AIDS"
4
USING TECH 1, PERFORM GEAR TENSION RELIEF FUNCTION.
• CHECK FOR STRIPPED GEAR ON MOTOR PACK ASSEMBLY. IS MOTOR PACK GEAR STRIPPED?
REPLACE GEAR
REPLACE HYDRAULIC MODULATOR
REPLACE MOTOR PACK ASSEMBLY
• CHECK FOR STRIPPED GEAR ON HYDRAULIC MODULATOR ASSEMBLY. IS GEAR STRIPPED?
REPLACE GEAR
REPLACE HYDRAULIC MODULATOR

GC402910070500BX

Fig. 61 Code A048: Right Front Nut Failure, Motor Free Spins. 1992

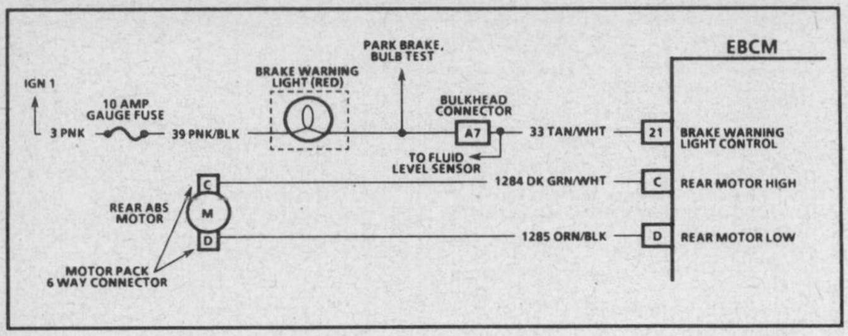
EBCM
IGN 1
PARK BRAKE, BULB TEST
BRAKE WARNING LIGHT (RED)
10 AMP GAUGE FUSE
3 PNK
39 PNK/BLK
BULKHEAD CONNECTOR
A7
33 TAN/WHT
21
BRAKE WARNING LIGHT CONTROL
TO FLUID LEVEL SENSOR
1284 DK GRN/WHT
C
REAR MOTOR HIGH
REAR ABS MOTOR
M
D
1285 ORN/BLK
REAR MOTOR LOW
MOTOR PACK 6 WAY CONNECTOR

GC402910070600AX

Cavalier & Sunbird

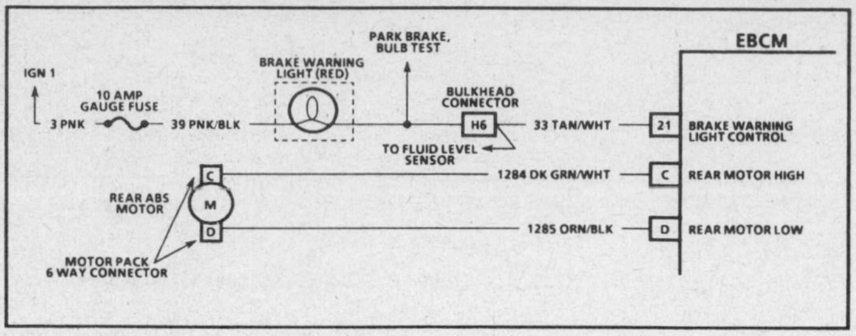
EBCM
IGN 1
PARK BRAKE, BULB TEST
BRAKE WARNING LIGHT (RED)
10 AMP GAUGE FUSE
3 PNK
39 PNK/BLK
BULKHEAD CONNECTOR
H6
33 TAN/WHT
21
BRAKE WARNING LIGHT CONTROL
TO FLUID LEVEL SENSOR
1284 DK GRN/WHT
C
REAR MOTOR HIGH
REAR ABS MOTOR
M
D
1285 ORN/BLK
REAR MOTOR LOW
MOTOR PACK 6 WAY CONNECTOR

GC402910070600BX

Beretta & Corsica

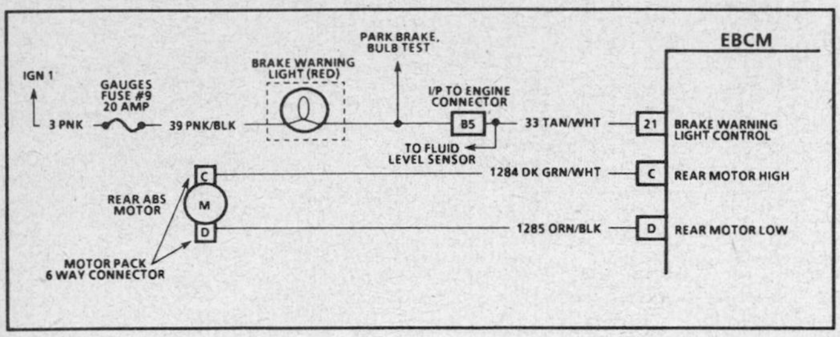
EBCM
IGN 1
PARK BRAKE, BULB TEST
BRAKE WARNING LIGHT (RED)
GAUGES FUSE #9 20 AMP
3 PNK
39 PNK/BLK
I/P TO ENGINE CONNECTOR
B5
33 TAN/WHT
21
BRAKE WARNING LIGHT CONTROL
TO FLUID LEVEL SENSOR
1284 DK GRN/WHT
C
REAR MOTOR HIGH
REAR ABS MOTOR
M
D
1285 ORN/BLK
REAR MOTOR LOW
MOTOR PACK 6 WAY CONNECTOR

GC402910070600CX

Achieva, Calais & Grand Am

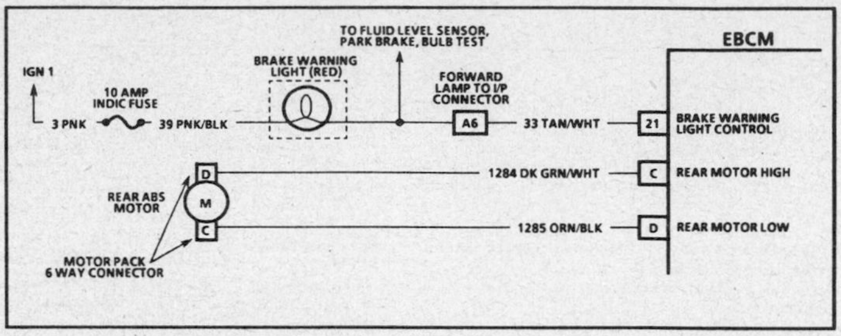
EBCM
IGN 1
TO FLUID LEVEL SENSOR, PARK BRAKE, BULB TEST
BRAKE WARNING LIGHT (RED)
10 AMP INDIC FUSE
3 PNK
39 PNK/BLK
FORWARD LAMP TO I/P CONNECTOR
A6
33 TAN/WHT
21
BRAKE WARNING LIGHT CONTROL
1284 DK GRN/WHT
C
REAR MOTOR HIGH
REAR ABS MOTOR
M
D
1285 ORN/BLK
REAR MOTOR LOW
MOTOR PACK 6 WAY CONNECTOR

GC402910070600DX

Cutlass Supreme, Grand Prix, Lumina & Regal

Circuit Description:

This code is designed to detect a stripped nut or gear assembly during initialization. During the homing sequence, the piston should reach the top of the bore resulting in a stalled motor. If this does not occur, the motor must be spinning with little or no resistance, indicating a nut/screw or gear failure.

Test Description: Number(s) below refer to circled number(s) on the diagnostic chart.

1. This step checks for a slipping nut or gear if either were to slip, it would result in a lack of hydraulic pressure being applied at the rear wheels, causing the wheels to be able to be moved.
2. During a full apply, once the ball screw reaches the top of its travel, the motor should stall. If the motor continues to run, an indication of a stripped nut or gear is present.
3. This step is used to release the tension of the motor pack prior to removal.

Diagnostic Aids:

An "Intermittent" fault in this code may result from a mechanical part of the system that sticks, binds, or slips.

The frequency of the problem can be checked by using the enhanced diagnostic function of the "Scan" tool

If code only fails once and Code A064 also fails, see Code A064. If intermittent and enhanced diagnostics show this code fails during ABS, see Code A064.

Depending on the frequency of the failure, a physical inspection of the mechanical parts suspected may be necessary.

GC402910070600EX

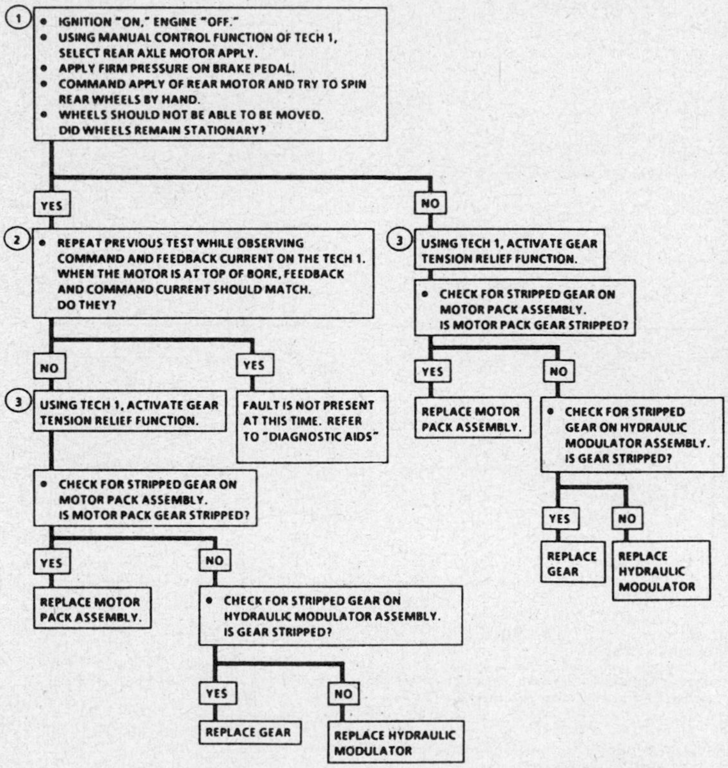
1
IGNITION "ON," ENGINE "OFF."
USING MANUAL CONTROL FUNCTION OF TECH 1, SELECT REAR AXLE MOTOR APPLY.
APPLY FIRM PRESSURE ON BRAKE PEDAL.
COMMAND APPLY OF REAR MOTOR AND TRY TO SPIN REAR WHEELS BY HAND.
WHEELS SHOULD NOT BE ABLE TO BE MOVED.
DID WHEELS REMAIN STATIONARY?
YES
NO
2
REPEAT PREVIOUS TEST WHILE OBSERVING COMMAND AND FEEDBACK CURRENT ON THE TECH 1. WHEN THE MOTOR IS AT TOP OF BORE, FEEDBACK AND COMMAND CURRENT SHOULD MATCH. DO THEY?
3
USING TECH 1, ACTIVATE GEAR TENSION RELIEF FUNCTION.
CHECK FOR STRIPPED GEAR ON MOTOR PACK ASSEMBLY. IS MOTOR PACK GEAR STRIPPED?
NO
YES
3
USING TECH 1, ACTIVATE GEAR TENSION RELIEF FUNCTION.
FAULT IS NOT PRESENT AT THIS TIME. REFER TO "DIAGNOSTIC AIDS"
YES
NO
REPLACE MOTOR PACK ASSEMBLY.
CHECK FOR STRIPPED GEAR ON HYDRAULIC MODULATOR ASSEMBLY. IS GEAR STRIPPED?
CHECK FOR STRIPPED GEAR ON MOTOR PACK ASSEMBLY. IS MOTOR PACK GEAR STRIPPED?
YES
NO
REPLACE GEAR
REPLACE HYDRAULIC MODULATOR
YES
NO
REPLACE MOTOR PACK ASSEMBLY.
CHECK FOR STRIPPED GEAR ON HYDRAULIC MODULATOR ASSEMBLY. IS GEAR STRIPPED?
YES
NO
REPLACE GEAR
REPLACE HYDRAULIC MODULATOR

GC402910070600FX

Fig. 62 Code A051: Rear Axle Nut Failure, Motor Free Spins. 1992

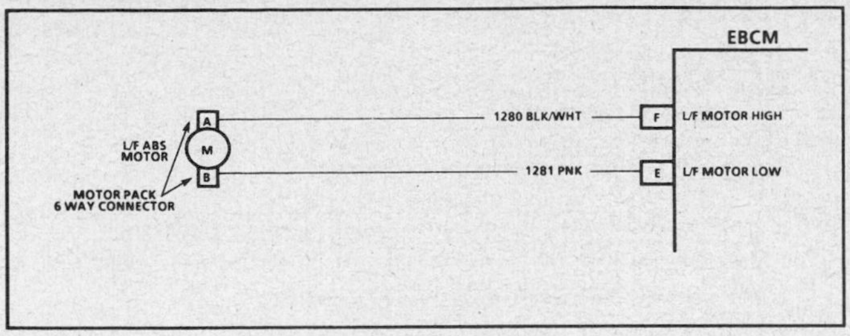
EBCM
L/F ABS MOTOR
M
A
B
MOTOR PACK 6 WAY CONNECTOR
1280 BLK/WHT
1281 PNK
F
E
L/F MOTOR HIGH
L/F MOTOR LOW

CODE A052

LEFT FRONT CHANNEL IN RELEASE TOO LONG

Circuit Description:

This code will diagnose a motor that is energized longer than expected. This could occur if a wheel speed sensor is faulty, the motor does not turn, the left front solenoid mechanically fails open, or the motor wires are crossed.

Test Description: Number(s) below refer to circled number(s) on the diagnostic chart.

1. This step identifies a problem in a wheel speed sensor that may cause the system to be in release too long.
2. This step identifies a motor fault as being failed or wired incorrectly.
3. This step checks for a solenoid that may have mechanically failed open.
4. If Step 3 has failed, this serves to isolate the cause of the hydraulic problem, to either the solenoid or the ABS hydraulic modulator assembly.
5. This step is used to release the tension of the motor pack.

Diagnostic Aids:

An "Intermittent" problem may be caused by a mechanical part of the system that sticks or binds.

The frequency of the problem can be checked by using the enhanced diagnostic function of the "Scan" tool

Code A052 may fail if on ice and steering wheel is turned to lock during braking. Using "scan" tool perform Hydraulic test to ensure total brake system is functional.

Any circuitry, that is suspected as causing the intermittent complaint, should be thoroughly checked for backed out terminals, improper mating, broken locks, improperly formed or damaged terminals, poor terminal to wiring connections or physical damage to the wiring harness.

GC402910070700AX

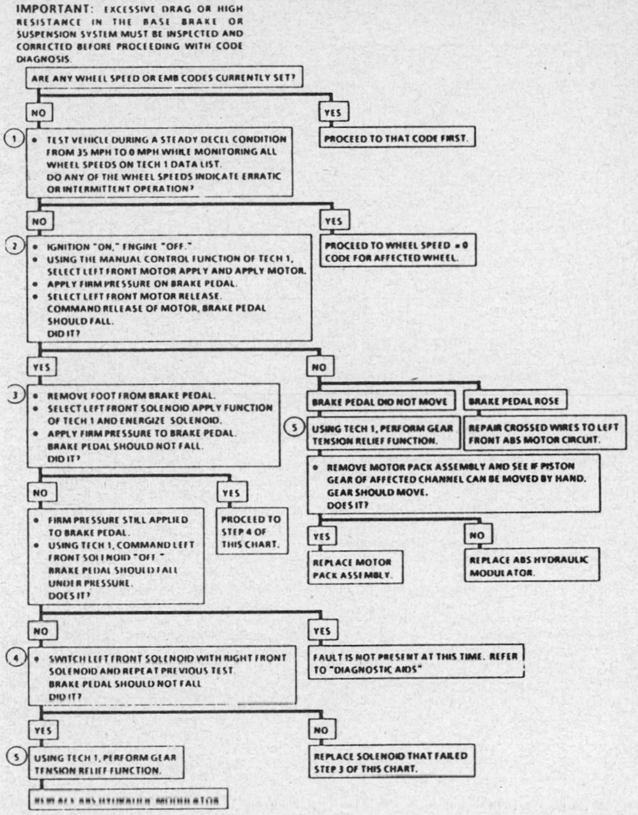
IMPORTANT: EXCESSIVE DRAG OR HIGH RESISTANCE IN THE BASE BRAKE OR SUSPENSION SYSTEM MUST BE INSPECTED AND CORRECTED BEFORE PROCEEDING WITH CODE DIAGNOSIS.
ARE ANY WHEEL SPEED OR EMB CODES CURRENTLY SET?
NO
YES
PROCEED TO THAT CODE FIRST.
1
• TEST VEHICLE DURING A STEADY DECEL CONDITION FROM 35 MPH TO 0 MPH WHILE MONITORING ALL WHEEL SPEEDS ON TECH 1 DATA LIST. DO ANY OF THE WHEEL SPEEDS INDICATE ERRATIC OR INTERMITTENT OPERATION?
NO
YES
PROCEED TO WHEEL SPEED = 0 CODE FOR AFFECTED WHEEL.
2
• IGNITION "ON," ENGINE "OFF."
• USING THE MANUAL CONTROL FUNCTION OF TECH 1, SELECT LEFT FRONT MOTOR APPLY AND APPLY MOTOR.
• APPLY FIRM PRESSURE ON BRAKE PEDAL.
• SELECT LEFT FRONT MOTOR RELEASE. COMMAND RELEASE OF MOTOR, BRAKE PEDAL SHOULD FALL. DID IT?
YES
NO
BRAKE PEDAL DID NOT MOVE
BRAKE PEDAL ROSE
3
• REMOVE FOOT FROM BRAKE PEDAL.
• SELECT LEFT FRONT SOLENOID APPLY FUNCTION OF TECH 1 AND ENERGIZE SOLENOID.
• APPLY FIRM PRESSURE TO BRAKE PEDAL. BRAKE PEDAL SHOULD NOT FALL. DID IT?
5
USING TECH 1, PERFORM GEAR TENSION RELIEF FUNCTION.
REPAIR CROSSED WIRES TO LEFT FRONT ABS MOTOR CIRCUIT.
• REMOVE MOTOR PACK ASSEMBLY AND SEE IF PISTON GEAR OF AFFECTED CHANNEL CAN BE MOVED BY HAND. GEAR SHOULD MOVE. DOES IT?
NO
YES
• FIRM PRESSURE STILL APPLIED TO BRAKE PEDAL.
• USING TECH 1, COMMAND LEFT FRONT SOLENOID "OFF." BRAKE PEDAL SHOULD FALL UNDER PRESSURE. DOES IT?
PROCEED TO STEP 4 OF THIS CHART.
YES
NO
REPLACE MOTOR PACK ASSEMBLY.
REPLACE ABS HYDRAULIC MODULATOR.
NO
YES
4
• SWITCH LEFT FRONT SOLENOID WITH RIGHT FRONT SOLENOID AND REPEAT PREVIOUS TEST. BRAKE PEDAL SHOULD NOT FALL. DID IT?
FAULT IS NOT PRESENT AT THIS TIME. REFER TO "DIAGNOSTIC AIDS"
YES
NO
5
USING TECH 1, PERFORM GEAR TENSION RELIEF FUNCTION.
REPLACE SOLENOID THAT FAILED STEP 3 OF THIS CHART.

GC402910070700BX

Fig. 63 Code A052: Left Front Channel In Release Too Long. 1992

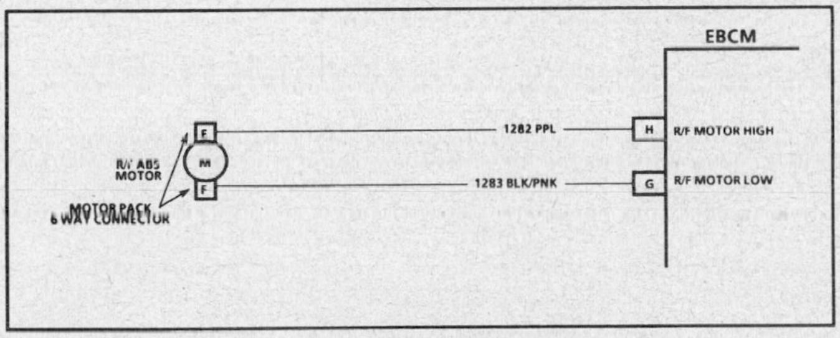
EBCM
R/F ABS MOTOR
M
E
F
MOTOR PACK 6 WAY CONNECTOR
1282 PPL
1283 BLK/PNK
H
G
R/F MOTOR HIGH
R/F MOTOR LOW

CODE A053

RIGHT FRONT CHANNEL IN RELEASE TOO LONG

Circuit Description:

This code will diagnose a motor that is energized longer than expected. This could occur if a wheel speed sensor is faulty, the motor does not turn, the right front solenoid mechanically fails open, or the motor wires are crossed.

Test Description: Number(s) below refer to circled number(s) on the diagnostic chart.

1. This step identifies a problem in a wheel speed sensor that may cause the system to be in release too long.
2. This step identifies a motor fault as being failed or wired incorrectly.
3. This step checks for a solenoid that may have mechanically failed open.
4. If Step 3 has failed, this serves to isolate the cause of the hydraulic problem, to either the solenoid or the ABS hydraulic modulator assembly.
5. This step is used to release the tension of the motor pack prior to removal.

Diagnostic Aids:

An "Intermittent" problem may be caused by a mechanical part of the system that sticks or binds.

The frequency of the problem can be checked by using the enhanced diagnostic function of the "Scan" tool

Code A053 may fail on ice if steering wheel is turned to lock during braking. Using "Scan" tool perform Hydraulic test to ensure total brake system is functional.

Any circuitry, that is suspected as causing the intermittent complaint, should be thoroughly checked for backed out terminals, improper mating, broken locks, improperly formed or damaged terminals, poor terminal to wiring connections or physical damage to the wiring harness.

GC402910070800AX

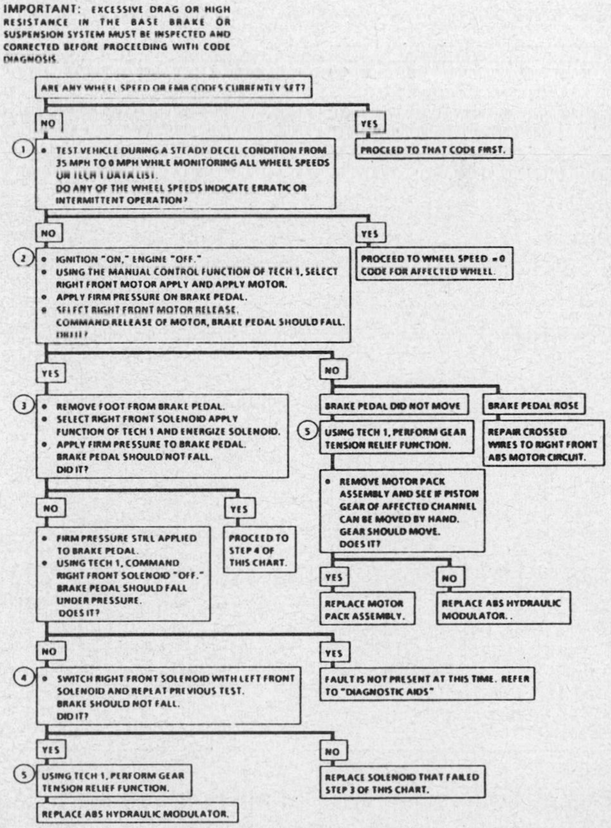
IMPORTANT: EXCESSIVE DRAG OR HIGH RESISTANCE IN THE BASE BRAKE OR SUSPENSION SYSTEM MUST BE INSPECTED AND CORRECTED BEFORE PROCEEDING WITH CODE DIAGNOSIS.
ARE ANY WHEEL SPEED OR EMB CODES CURRENTLY SET?
NO
YES
PROCEED TO THAT CODE FIRST.
1
• TEST VEHICLE DURING A STEADY DECEL CONDITION FROM 35 MPH TO 0 MPH WHILE MONITORING ALL WHEEL SPEEDS ON TECH 1 DATA LIST. DO ANY OF THE WHEEL SPEEDS INDICATE ERRATIC OR INTERMITTENT OPERATION?
NO
YES
PROCEED TO WHEEL SPEED = 0 CODE FOR AFFECTED WHEEL.
2
• IGNITION "ON," ENGINE "OFF."
• USING THE MANUAL CONTROL FUNCTION OF TECH 1, SELECT RIGHT FRONT MOTOR APPLY AND APPLY MOTOR.
• APPLY FIRM PRESSURE ON BRAKE PEDAL.
• SELECT RIGHT FRONT MOTOR RELEASE. COMMAND RELEASE OF MOTOR, BRAKE PEDAL SHOULD FALL.
YES
NO
BRAKE PEDAL DID NOT MOVE
BRAKE PEDAL ROSE
3
• REMOVE FOOT FROM BRAKE PEDAL.
• SELECT RIGHT FRONT SOLENOID APPLY FUNCTION OF TECH 1 AND ENERGIZE SOLENOID.
• APPLY FIRM PRESSURE TO BRAKE PEDAL. BRAKE PEDAL SHOULD NOT FALL. DID IT?
5
USING TECH 1, PERFORM GEAR TENSION RELIEF FUNCTION.
REPAIR CROSSED WIRES TO RIGHT FRONT ABS MOTOR CIRCUIT.
• REMOVE MOTOR PACK ASSEMBLY AND SEE IF PISTON GEAR OF AFFECTED CHANNEL CAN BE MOVED BY HAND. GEAR SHOULD MOVE. DOES IT?
NO
YES
• FIRM PRESSURE STILL APPLIED TO BRAKE PEDAL.
• USING TECH 1, COMMAND RIGHT FRONT SOLENOID "OFF." BRAKE PEDAL SHOULD FALL UNDER PRESSURE. DOES IT?
PROCEED TO STEP 4 OF THIS CHART.
YES
NO
REPLACE MOTOR PACK ASSEMBLY.
REPLACE ABS HYDRAULIC MODULATOR..
NO
YES
4
• SWITCH RIGHT FRONT SOLENOID WITH LEFT FRONT SOLENOID AND REPEAT PREVIOUS TEST. BRAKE SHOULD NOT FALL. DID IT?
FAULT IS NOT PRESENT AT THIS TIME. REFER TO "DIAGNOSTIC AIDS"
YES
NO
5
USING TECH 1, PERFORM GEAR TENSION RELIEF FUNCTION.
REPLACE SOLENOID THAT FAILED STEP 3 OF THIS CHART.
REPLACE ABS HYDRAULIC MODULATOR.

GC402910070800BX

Fig. 64 Code A053: Right Front Channel In Release Too Long. 1992

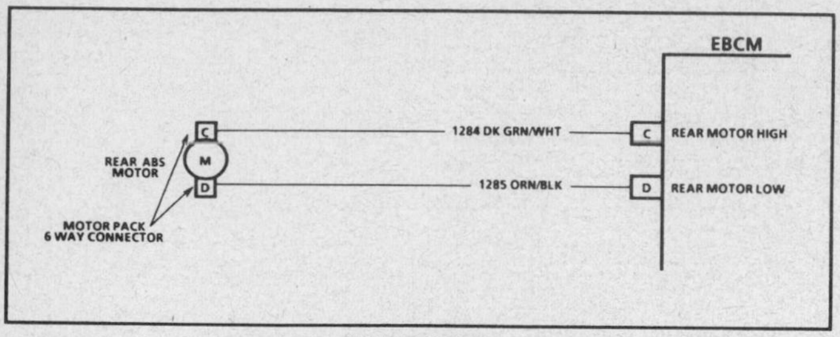
EBCM
REAR ABS MOTOR
M
C
D
MOTOR PACK 6 WAY CONNECTOR
1284 DK GRN/WHT
1285 ORN/BLK
C REAR MOTOR HIGH
D REAR MOTOR LOW

CODE A054

REAR AXLE IN RELEASE TOO LONG

Circuit Description:

This code will diagnose a motor that is energized longer than expected. This could occur if a wheel speed sensor is faulty, the motor does not turn, or the motor wires are crossed.

Test Description: Numbers below refer to circled numbers on the diagnostic chart.

1. This step identifies a problem in a wheel speed sensor that may cause the system to be in release too long.
2. This checks for a wheel that may stick or bind because of a mechanical fault.
3. This checks to see if the motor is capable of moving and applying the hydraulic piston for the rear wheels.
4. This step insures that the motor wiring is not crossed.
5. This step is used to release the tension of the motor pack prior to removal.
6. This isolates the fault of a "no-apply" situation to either the motor pack or ABS hydraulic modulator assembly.

Diagnostic Aids:

An "Intermittent" problem may be caused by a mechanical part of the system that sticks or binds.

The frequency of the problem can be checked by using the enhanced diagnostic function of the "Scan" tool

Using "Scan" tool perform hydraulic test to ensure total brake system is functional.

Any circuitry, that is suspected as causing the intermittent complaint, should be thoroughly checked for backed out terminals, improper mating, broken locks, improperly formed or damaged terminals, poor terminal to wiring connections or physical damage to the wiring harness.

GC402910070900AX

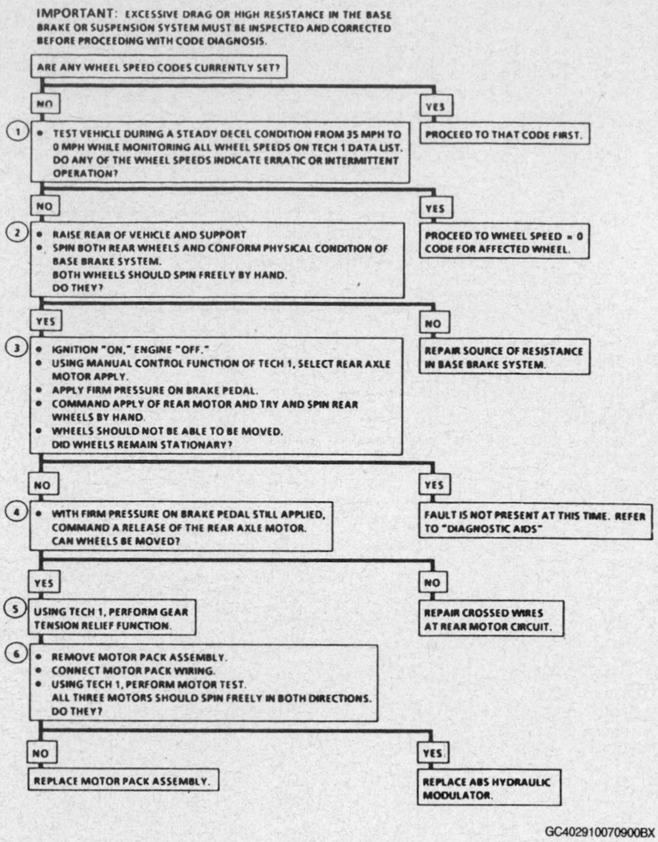
IMPORTANT: EXCESSIVE DRAG OR HIGH RESISTANCE IN THE BASE BRAKE OR SUSPENSION SYSTEM MUST BE INSPECTED AND CORRECTED BEFORE PROCEEDING WITH CODE DIAGNOSIS.
ARE ANY WHEEL SPEED CODES CURRENTLY SET?
NO
YES
PROCEED TO THAT CODE FIRST.
1
• TEST VEHICLE DURING A STEADY DECEL CONDITION FROM 35 MPH TO 0 MPH WHILE MONITORING ALL WHEEL SPEEDS ON TECH 1 DATA LIST. DO ANY OF THE WHEEL SPEEDS INDICATE ERRATIC OR INTERMITTENT OPERATION?
NO
YES
PROCEED TO WHEEL SPEED = 0 CODE FOR AFFECTED WHEEL.
2
• RAISE REAR OF VEHICLE AND SUPPORT
• SPIN BOTH REAR WHEELS AND CONFORM PHYSICAL CONDITION OF BASE BRAKE SYSTEM.
BOTH WHEELS SHOULD SPIN FREELY BY HAND.
DO THEY?
YES
NO
REPAIR SOURCE OF RESISTANCE IN BASE BRAKE SYSTEM.
3
• IGNITION "ON," ENGINE "OFF."
• USING MANUAL CONTROL FUNCTION OF TECH 1, SELECT REAR AXLE MOTOR APPLY.
• APPLY FIRM PRESSURE ON BRAKE PEDAL.
• COMMAND APPLY OF REAR MOTOR AND TRY AND SPIN REAR WHEELS BY HAND.
• WHEELS SHOULD NOT BE ABLE TO BE MOVED.
DID WHEELS REMAIN STATIONARY?
NO
YES
FAULT IS NOT PRESENT AT THIS TIME. REFER TO "DIAGNOSTIC AIDS"
4
• WITH FIRM PRESSURE ON BRAKE PEDAL STILL APPLIED, COMMAND A RELEASE OF THE REAR AXLE MOTOR. CAN WHEELS BE MOVED?
YES
NO
REPAIR CROSSED WIRES AT REAR MOTOR CIRCUIT.
5
USING TECH 1, PERFORM GEAR TENSION RELIEF FUNCTION.
6
• REMOVE MOTOR PACK ASSEMBLY.
• CONNECT MOTOR PACK WIRING.
• USING TECH 1, PERFORM MOTOR TEST.
ALL THREE MOTORS SHOULD SPIN FREELY IN BOTH DIRECTIONS.
DO THEY?
NO
YES
REPLACE MOTOR PACK ASSEMBLY.
REPLACE ABS HYDRAULIC MODULATOR.

GC402910070900BX

Fig. 65 Code A054: Rear Axle In Release Too Long. 1992

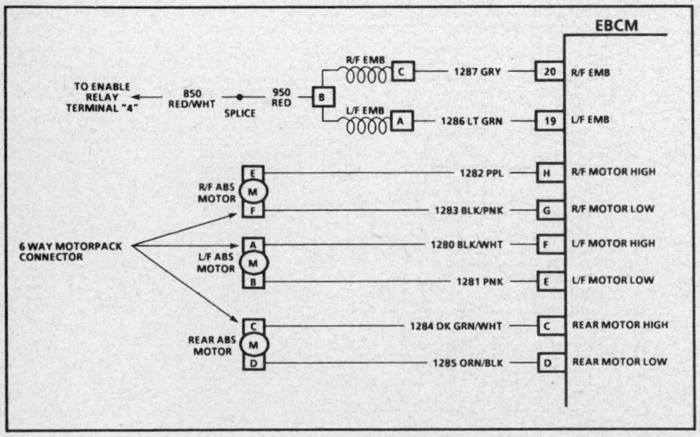
EBCM
TO ENABLE RELAY TERMINAL "4"
850 RED/WHT
SPLICE
950 RED
B
R/F EMB
C
1287 GRY
20 R/F EMB
L/F EMB
A
1286 LT GRN
19 L/F EMB
R/F ABS MOTOR
E
F
1282 PPL
H R/F MOTOR HIGH
1283 BLK/PNK
G R/F MOTOR LOW
6 WAY MOTORPACK CONNECTOR
L/F ABS MOTOR
A
B
1280 BLK/WHT
F L/F MOTOR HIGH
1281 PNK
E L/F MOTOR LOW
REAR ABS MOTOR
C
D
1284 DK GRN/WHT
C REAR MOTOR HIGH
1285 ORN/BLK
D REAR MOTOR LOW

GC402910071000AX

Except Cutlass Supreme, Grand Prix, Lumina & Regal

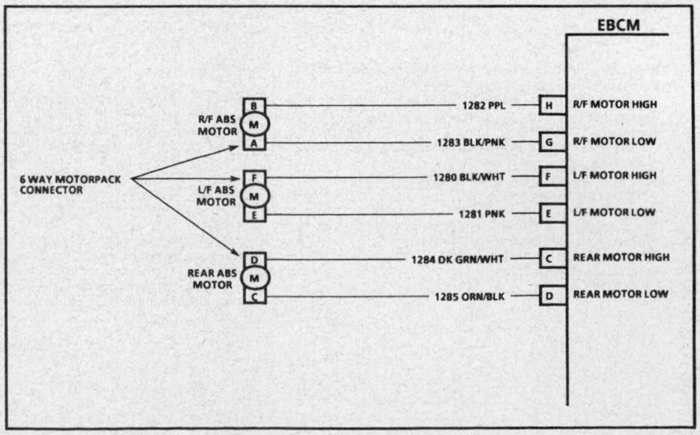
EBCM
R/F ABS MOTOR
B
A
1282 PPL
H R/F MOTOR HIGH
1283 BLK/PNK
G R/F MOTOR LOW
6 WAY MOTORPACK CONNECTOR
L/F ABS MOTOR
F
E
1280 BLK/WHT
F L/F MOTOR HIGH
1281 PNK
E L/F MOTOR LOW
REAR ABS MOTOR
D
C
1284 DK GRN/WHT
C REAR MOTOR HIGH
1285 ORN/BLK
D REAR MOTOR LOW

GC402910071000BX

Cutlass Supreme, Grand Prix, Lumina & Regal

Fig. 66 Code A055: Motor Driver Interface MDI Fault Detected (Part 1 of 2). 1992

Circuit Description:
This code identifies a fault detected by the MDI custom IC. It also ensures the cause of the fault is not a result of a problem with the enable relay under a Code A055 failure. The MDI fault tests will be run to identify which circuit has failed, and may also cause additional codes to set to pinpoint the problem circuit.

Test Description: Number(s) below refer to circled number(s) on the diagnostic chart.

1. This insures that the Code A055 fault was not set due to a motor or EMB fault.
2. This checks to see if the fault is still present.
3. This step insures that Code A055 was not due to poor terminal contact at the motor pack connector.

Diagnostic Aids:

An "Intermittent" problem may be caused by a poor connection, rubbed through wire insulation, or a wire that is broken inside the insulation.

The frequency of the problem can be checked by using the enhanced diagnostic function of the "Scan" tool.

Any circuitry, that is suspected as causing the intermittent complaint, should be thoroughly checked for backed out terminals, improper mating, broken locks, improperly formed or damaged terminals, poor terminal to wiring connections or physical damage to the wiring harness.

GC402910071000CX

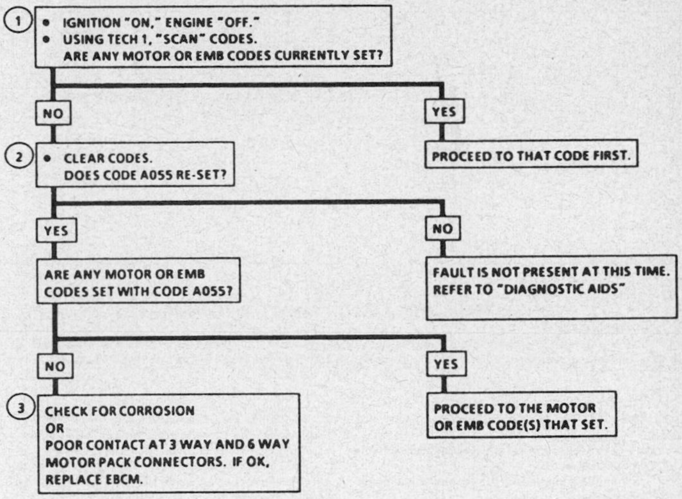

1
• IGNITION "ON," ENGINE "OFF."
• USING TECH 1, "SCAN" CODES.
ARE ANY MOTOR OR EMB CODES CURRENTLY SET?
NO
YES
PROCEED TO THAT CODE FIRST.
2
• CLEAR CODES.
DOES CODE A055 RE-SET?
YES
NO
ARE ANY MOTOR OR EMB CODES SET WITH CODE A055?
FAULT IS NOT PRESENT AT THIS TIME. REFER TO "DIAGNOSTIC AIDS"
NO
YES
3
CHECK FOR CORROSION OR POOR CONTACT AT 3 WAY AND 6 WAY MOTOR PACK CONNECTORS. IF OK, REPLACE EBCM.
PROCEED TO THE MOTOR OR EMB CODE(S) THAT SET.

GC402910071000DX

Fig. 66 Code A055: Motor Driver Interface MDI Fault Detected (Part 2 of 2). 1992

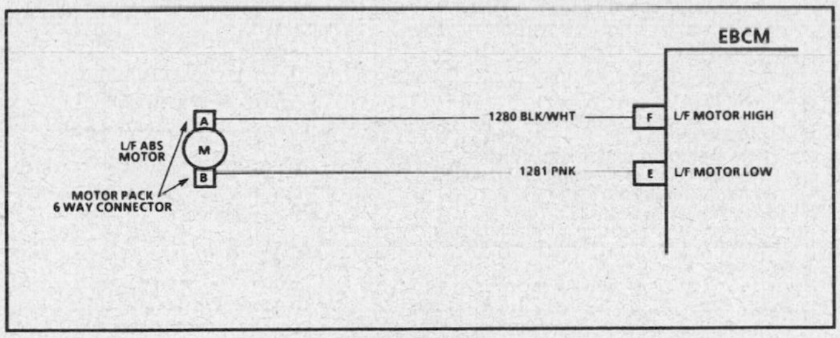

EBCM
L/F ABS MOTOR
M
A
B
MOTOR PACK 6 WAY CONNECTOR
1280 BLK/WHT
1281 PNK
F
E
L/F MOTOR HIGH
L/F MOTOR LOW

CODE A056

LEFT FRONT MOTOR CIRCUIT OPEN

Circuit Description:
This code identifies a motor that cannot be energized due to an open in its circuitry. This fault will not allow proper front ABS operation.

Test Description: Number(s) below refer to circled number(s) on the diagnostic chart.

1. This step checks for proper resistance of the motor.
2. This step is used to release the tension of the motor pack prior to removal.
3. This step checks for an open in the motor "high" circuitry.
4. This step checks for an open in the motor "low" circuitry.

Diagnostic Aids:

Using Tech 1, select manual control function, and exercise motor movement of affected channel in both directions while applying light pressure on the brake pedal.

If erratic or "jumpy" brake pedal movement is detected while performing an "apply" or "release" function of the motor, an intermittent fault may be indicated.

An "Intermittent" problem may be caused by a poor connection, rubbed through wire insulation, or a wire that is broken inside the insulation.

If the fault is not current, wiggle the wires of the affected channel and check if the code resets. This will help to pinpoint an intermittent problem in the motor circuitry or connections.

The frequency of the problem can be checked by using the enhanced diagnostic function of the "Scan" tool

Any circuitry, that is suspected as causing the intermittent complaint, should be thoroughly checked for backed out terminals, improper mating, broken locks, improperly formed or damaged terminals, poor terminal to wiring connections or physical damage to the wiring harness.

GC402910071100AX

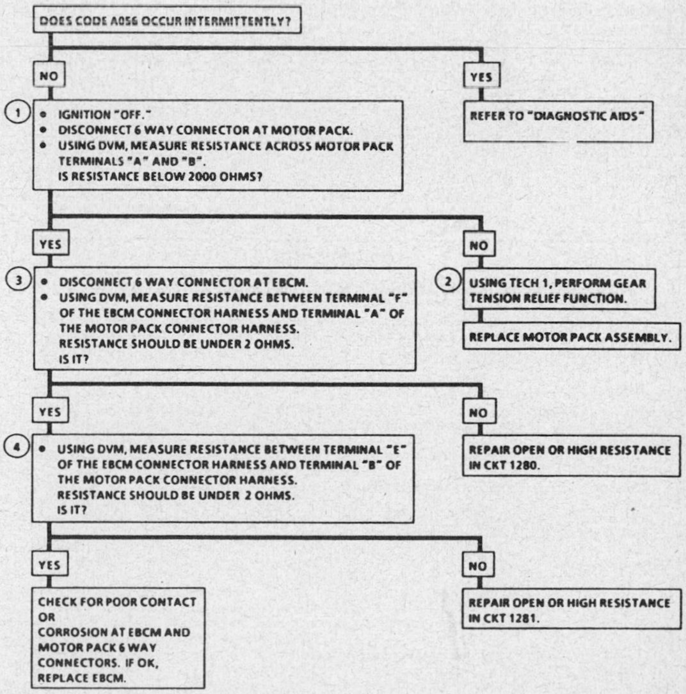

DOES CODE A056 OCCUR INTERMITTENTLY?
NO
YES
REFER TO "DIAGNOSTIC AIDS"
1
• IGNITION "OFF."
• DISCONNECT 6 WAY CONNECTOR AT MOTOR PACK.
• USING DVM, MEASURE RESISTANCE ACROSS MOTOR PACK TERMINALS "A" AND "B".
IS RESISTANCE BELOW 2000 OHMS?
YES
NO
2
USING TECH 1, PERFORM GEAR TENSION RELIEF FUNCTION.
REPLACE MOTOR PACK ASSEMBLY.
3
• DISCONNECT 6 WAY CONNECTOR AT EBCM.
• USING DVM, MEASURE RESISTANCE BETWEEN TERMINAL "F" OF THE EBCM CONNECTOR HARNESS AND TERMINAL "A" OF THE MOTOR PACK CONNECTOR HARNESS.
RESISTANCE SHOULD BE UNDER 2 OHMS.
IS IT?
YES
NO
REPAIR OPEN OR HIGH RESISTANCE IN CKT 1280.
4
• USING DVM, MEASURE RESISTANCE BETWEEN TERMINAL "E" OF THE EBCM CONNECTOR HARNESS AND TERMINAL "B" OF THE MOTOR PACK CONNECTOR HARNESS.
RESISTANCE SHOULD BE UNDER 2 OHMS.
IS IT?
YES
NO
CHECK FOR POOR CONTACT OR CORROSION AT EBCM AND MOTOR PACK 6 WAY CONNECTORS. IF OK, REPLACE EBCM.
REPAIR OPEN OR HIGH RESISTANCE IN CKT 1281.

GC402910071100BX

Fig. 67 Code A056: Left Front Motor Circuit Open. 1992

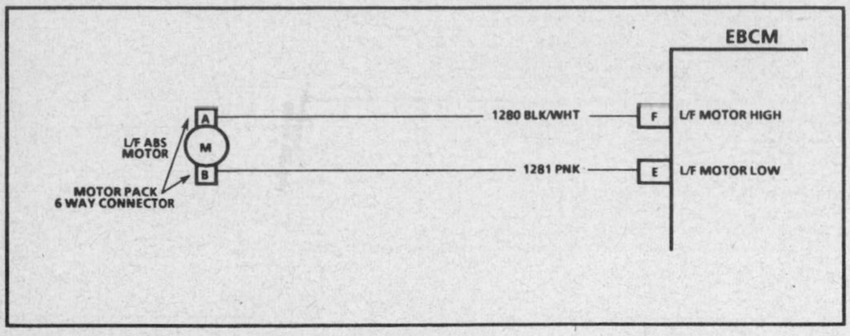
EBCM
L/F ABS MOTOR
M
A
B
MOTOR PACK 6 WAY CONNECTOR
1280 BLK/WHT
1281 PNK
F
E
L/F MOTOR HIGH
L/F MOTOR LOW

CODE A057

LEFT FRONT MOTOR CIRCUIT SHORTED TO GROUND

Circuit Description:

This code identifies a motor circuit that is shorted to ground. This fault will not allow the motor to be controlled at the commanded current rate or will cause the driver circuit to allow current directly to ground.

Test Description: Number(s) below refer to circled number(s) on the diagnostic chart.

1. This step checks for a short to ground in the motor "high" circuitry.
2. This step checks for a short to ground in the motor "low" circuitry.
3. This step checks for a motor that is internally shorted to ground.
4. This step is used to release the tension of the motor pack prior to removal.

Diagnostic Aids:

Using Tech 1, select manual control function, and exercise motor movement of affected channel in both directions while applying light pressure on the brake pedal.

If erratic or "jumpy" brake pedal movement is detected while performing an "apply" or "release" function of the motor, an intermittent fault may be indicated.

An "Intermittent" problem may be caused by a poor connection, rubbed through wire insulation, or a wire that is broken inside the insulation.

If the fault is not current, wiggle the wires of the affected channel and check if the code resets. This will help to pinpoint an intermittent problem in the motor circuitry or connections.

The frequency of the problem can be checked by using the enhanced diagnostic function of the Tech 1 "Scan" tool

Any circuitry, that is suspected as causing the intermittent complaint, should be thoroughly checked for backed out terminals, improper mating, broken locks, improperly formed or damaged terminals, poor terminal to wiring connections or physical damage to the wiring harness.

GC402910071200AX

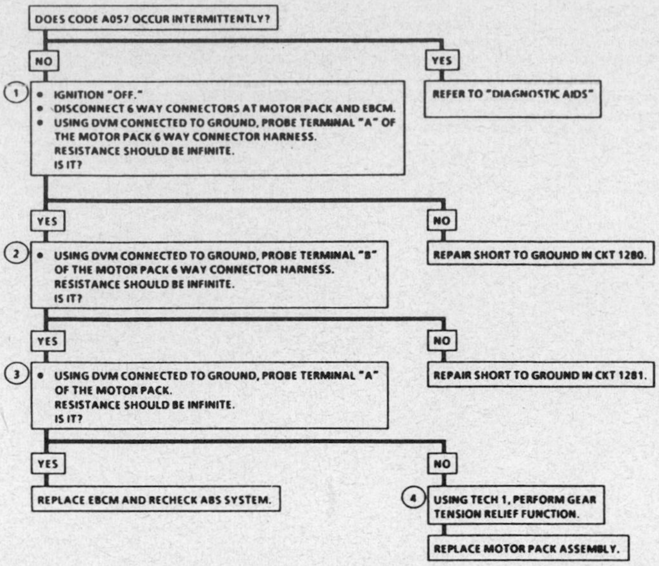
DOES CODE A057 OCCUR INTERMITTENTLY?
NO
YES
1
• IGNITION "OFF."
• DISCONNECT 6 WAY CONNECTORS AT MOTOR PACK AND EBCM.
• USING DVM CONNECTED TO GROUND, PROBE TERMINAL "A" OF THE MOTOR PACK 6 WAY CONNECTOR HARNESS. RESISTANCE SHOULD BE INFINITE. IS IT?
REFER TO "DIAGNOSTIC AIDS"
YES
NO
2
• USING DVM CONNECTED TO GROUND, PROBE TERMINAL "B" OF THE MOTOR PACK 6 WAY CONNECTOR HARNESS. RESISTANCE SHOULD BE INFINITE. IS IT?
REPAIR SHORT TO GROUND IN CKT 1280.
YES
NO
3
• USING DVM CONNECTED TO GROUND, PROBE TERMINAL "A" OF THE MOTOR PACK. RESISTANCE SHOULD BE INFINITE. IS IT?
REPAIR SHORT TO GROUND IN CKT 1281.
YES
NO
REPLACE EBCM AND RECHECK ABS SYSTEM.
4
USING TECH 1, PERFORM GEAR TENSION RELIEF FUNCTION.
REPLACE MOTOR PACK ASSEMBLY.

GC402910071200BX

Fig. 68 Code A057: Left Front Motor Circuit Shorted To Ground. 1992

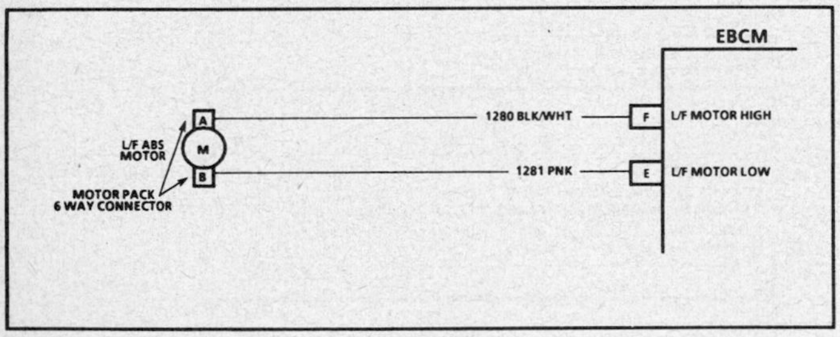
EBCM
L/F ABS MOTOR
M
A
B
MOTOR PACK 6 WAY CONNECTOR
1280 BLK/WHT
1281 PNK
F
E
L/F MOTOR HIGH
L/F MOTOR LOW

CODE A058

LEFT FRONT MOTOR CIRCUIT SHORTED TO BATTERY OR MOTOR SHORTED

Circuit Description:

This code identifies a motor circuit that is shorted to battery or a motor that has low or no resistance. This fault will not allow the motor to be controlled at the commanded current rate or will cause the motor to turn in the opposite direction, or not at all.

Test Description: Number(s) below refer to circled number(s) on the diagnostic chart.

1. This step checks for a short to voltage in the motor "high" circuitry.
2. This step checks for a short to voltage in the motor "low" circuitry.
3. This step checks for a motor that is internally shorted.
4. This step is used to release the tension of the motor pack prior to removal.

Diagnostic Aids:

Using Tech 1, select manual control function, and exercise motor movement of affected channel in both directions while applying light pressure on the brake pedal.

If erratic or "jumpy" brake pedal movement is detected while performing an "apply" or "release" function of the motor, an intermittent fault may be indicated.

An "Intermittent" problem may be caused by a poor connection, rubbed through wire insulation, or a wire that is broken inside the insulation.

If the fault is not current, wiggle the wires of the affected channel and check if the code resets. This will help to pinpoint an intermittent problem in the motor circuitry or connections.

The frequency of the problem can be checked by using the enhanced diagnostic function of the "Scan" tool

Code A038 sets as a current code and A058 is an infrequent history code, see Code A038 diagnostics.

Any circuitry, that is suspected as causing the intermittent complaint, should be thoroughly checked for backed out terminals, improper mating, broken locks, improperly formed or damaged terminals, poor terminal to wiring connections or physical damage to the wiring harness.

GC402910071300AX

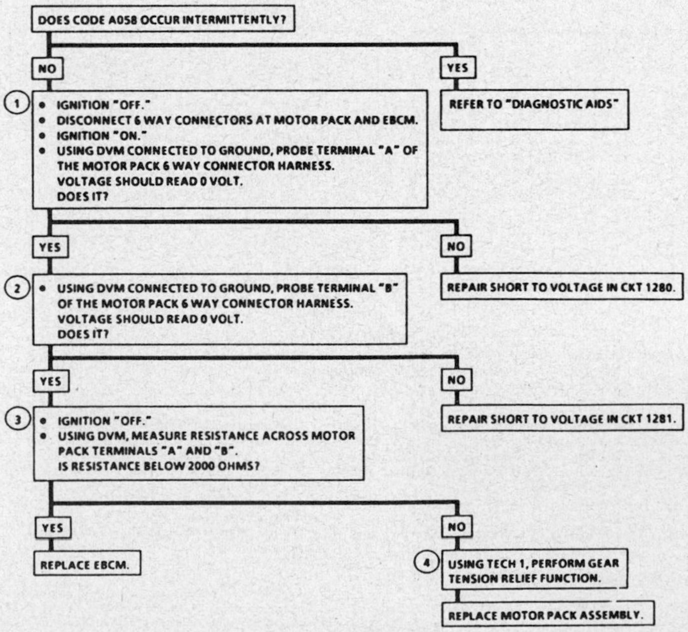
DOES CODE A058 OCCUR INTERMITTENTLY?
NO
YES
1
• IGNITION "OFF."
• DISCONNECT 6 WAY CONNECTORS AT MOTOR PACK AND EBCM.
• IGNITION "ON."
• USING DVM CONNECTED TO GROUND, PROBE TERMINAL "A" OF THE MOTOR PACK 6 WAY CONNECTOR HARNESS. VOLTAGE SHOULD READ 0 VOLT. DOES IT?
REFER TO "DIAGNOSTIC AIDS"
YES
NO
2
• USING DVM CONNECTED TO GROUND, PROBE TERMINAL "B" OF THE MOTOR PACK 6 WAY CONNECTOR HARNESS. VOLTAGE SHOULD READ 0 VOLT. DOES IT?
REPAIR SHORT TO VOLTAGE IN CKT 1280.
YES
NO
3
• IGNITION "OFF."
• USING DVM, MEASURE RESISTANCE ACROSS MOTOR PACK TERMINALS "A" AND "B". IS RESISTANCE BELOW 2000 OHMS?
REPAIR SHORT TO VOLTAGE IN CKT 1281.
YES
NO
REPLACE EBCM.
4
USING TECH 1, PERFORM GEAR TENSION RELIEF FUNCTION.
REPLACE MOTOR PACK ASSEMBLY.

GC402910071300BX

Fig. 69 Code A058: Left Front Motor Circuit Shorted To Battery. 1992

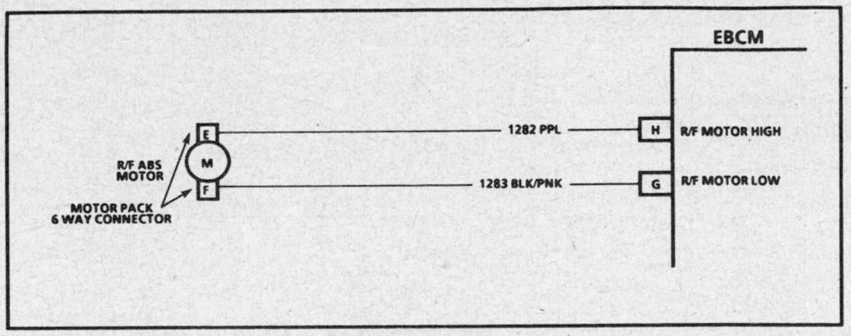
EBCM
1282 PPL
H
R/F MOTOR HIGH
R/F ABS MOTOR
M
E
F
MOTOR PACK 6 WAY CONNECTOR
1283 BLK/PNK
G
R/F MOTOR LOW

CODE A061

RIGHT FRONT MOTOR CIRCUIT OPEN

Circuit Description:

This code identifies a motor that cannot be energized due to an open in its circuitry. This fault will not allow proper front ABS operation.

Test Description: Number(s) below refer to circled number(s) on the diagnostic chart.

1. This step checks for proper resistance of the motor.
2. This step is used to release the tension of the motor pack prior to removal.
3. This step checks for an open in the motor "high" circuitry.
4. This step checks for an open in the motor "low" circuitry.

Diagnostic Aids:

Using Tech 1, select manual control function, and exercise motor movement of affected channel in both directions while applying light pressure on the brake pedal.

If erratic or "jumpy" brake pedal movement is detected while performing an "apply" or "release" function of the motor, an intermittent fault may be indicated.

An "Intermittent" problem may be caused by a poor connection, rubbed through wire insulation, or a wire that is broken inside the insulation.

If the fault is not current, wiggle the wires of the affected channel and check if the code resets. This will help to pinpoint an intermittent problem in the motor circuitry or connections.

The frequency of the problem can be checked by using the enhanced diagnostic function of the "Scan" tool

Any circuitry, that is suspected as causing the intermittent complaint, should be thoroughly checked for backed out terminals, improper mating, broken locks, improperly formed or damaged terminals, poor terminal to wiring connections or physical damage to the wiring harness.

GC402910071400AX

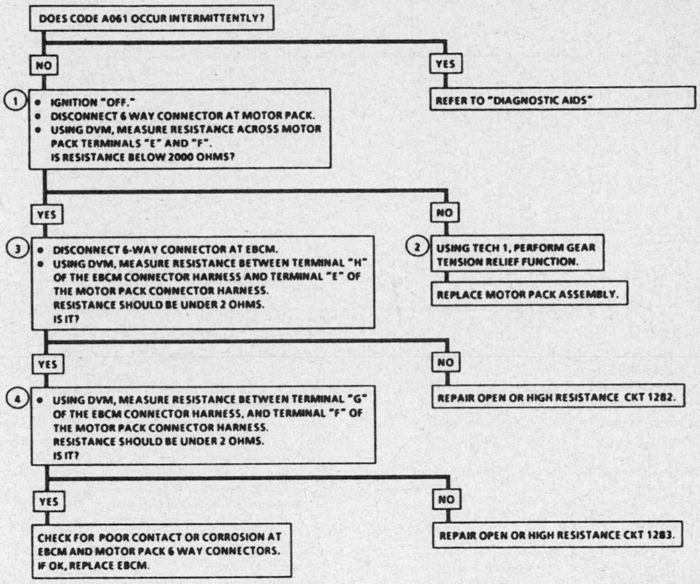
DOES CODE A061 OCCUR INTERMITTENTLY?
NO
YES
REFER TO "DIAGNOSTIC AIDS"
1
• IGNITION "OFF."
• DISCONNECT 6 WAY CONNECTOR AT MOTOR PACK.
• USING DVM, MEASURE RESISTANCE ACROSS MOTOR PACK TERMINALS "E" AND "F".
IS RESISTANCE BELOW 2000 OHMS?
YES
NO
3
• DISCONNECT 6-WAY CONNECTOR AT EBCM.
• USING DVM, MEASURE RESISTANCE BETWEEN TERMINAL "H" OF THE EBCM CONNECTOR HARNESS AND TERMINAL "E" OF THE MOTOR PACK CONNECTOR HARNESS.
RESISTANCE SHOULD BE UNDER 2 OHMS.
IS IT?
2
USING TECH 1, PERFORM GEAR TENSION RELIEF FUNCTION.
REPLACE MOTOR PACK ASSEMBLY.
YES
NO
4
• USING DVM, MEASURE RESISTANCE BETWEEN TERMINAL "G" OF THE EBCM CONNECTOR HARNESS, AND TERMINAL "F" OF THE MOTOR PACK CONNECTOR HARNESS.
RESISTANCE SHOULD BE UNDER 2 OHMS.
IS IT?
REPAIR OPEN OR HIGH RESISTANCE CKT 1282.
YES
NO
CHECK FOR POOR CONTACT OR CORROSION AT EBCM AND MOTOR PACK 6 WAY CONNECTORS.
IF OK, REPLACE EBCM.
REPAIR OPEN OR HIGH RESISTANCE CKT 1283.

GC402910071400AX

Fig. 70 Code A061: Right Front Motor Circuit Open. 1992

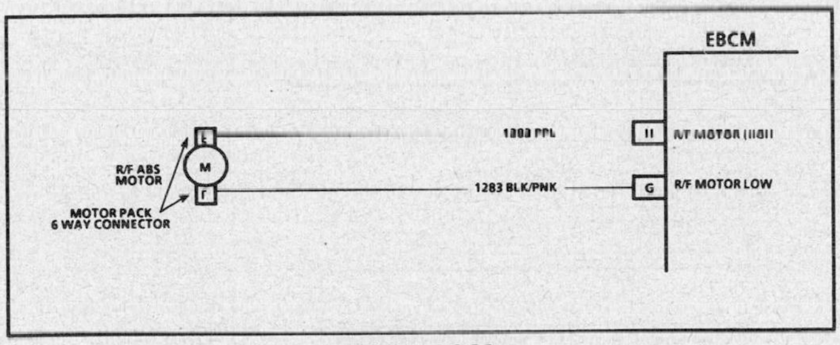
EBCM
R/F ABS MOTOR
M
E
F
MOTOR PACK 6 WAY CONNECTOR
1283 BLK/PNK
G
R/F MOTOR LOW

CODE A062

RIGHT FRONT MOTOR CIRCUIT SHORTED TO GROUND

Circuit Description:

This code identifies a motor circuit that is shorted to ground. This fault will not allow the motor to be controlled at the commanded current rate or will cause the motor driver circuit to allow current directly to ground.

Test Description: Number(s) below refer to circled number(s) on the diagnostic chart.

1. This step checks for a short to ground in the motor "high" circuitry.
2. This step checks for a short to ground in the motor "low" circuitry.
3. This step checks for a motor that is internally shorted to ground.
4. This step is used to release the tension of the motor pack prior to removal.

Diagnostic Aids:

Using Tech 1, select manual control function, and exercise motor movement of affected channel in both directions while applying light pressure on the brake pedal.

If erratic or "jumpy" brake pedal movement is detected while performing an "apply" or "release" function of the motor, an intermittent fault may be indicated.

An "Intermittent" problem may be caused by a poor connection, rubbed through wire insulation, or a wire that is broken inside the insulation.

If the fault is not current, wiggle the wires of the affected channel and check if the code resets. This will help to pinpoint an intermittent problem in the motor circuitry or connections.

The frequency of the problem can be checked by using the enhanced diagnostic function of the "Scan" tool

Any circuitry, that is suspected as causing the intermittent complaint, should be thoroughly checked for backed out terminals, improper mating, broken locks, improperly formed or damaged terminals, poor terminal to wiring connections or physical damage to the wiring harness.

GC402910071500AX

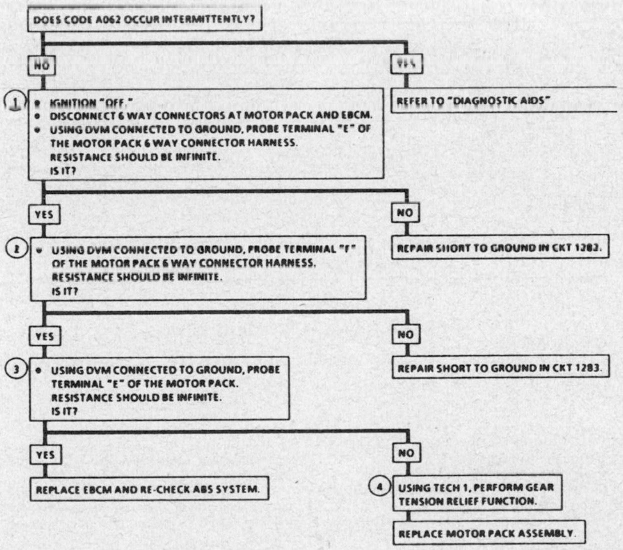
DOES CODE A062 OCCUR INTERMITTENTLY?
NO
REFER TO "DIAGNOSTIC AIDS"
1
• IGNITION "OFF."
• DISCONNECT 6 WAY CONNECTORS AT MOTOR PACK AND EBCM.
• USING DVM CONNECTED TO GROUND, PROBE TERMINAL "E" OF THE MOTOR PACK 6 WAY CONNECTOR HARNESS.
RESISTANCE SHOULD BE INFINITE.
IS IT?
YES
NO
2
• USING DVM CONNECTED TO GROUND, PROBE TERMINAL "F" OF THE MOTOR PACK 6 WAY CONNECTOR HARNESS.
RESISTANCE SHOULD BE INFINITE.
IS IT?
REPAIR SHORT TO GROUND IN CKT 1282.
YES
NO
3
• USING DVM CONNECTED TO GROUND, PROBE TERMINAL "E" OF THE MOTOR PACK.
RESISTANCE SHOULD BE INFINITE.
IS IT?
REPAIR SHORT TO GROUND IN CKT 1283.
YES
NO
REPLACE EBCM AND RE-CHECK ABS SYSTEM.
4
USING TECH 1, PERFORM GEAR TENSION RELIEF FUNCTION.
REPLACE MOTOR PACK ASSEMBLY.

GC402910071500BX

Fig. 71 Code A062: Right Front Motor Circuit Shorted To Ground. 1992

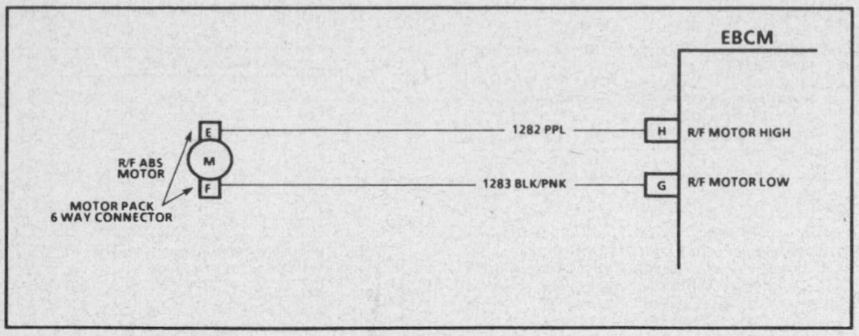
EBCM
R/F ABS MOTOR
M
E
F
MOTOR PACK 6 WAY CONNECTOR
1282 PPL
1283 BLK/PNK
H
G
R/F MOTOR HIGH
R/F MOTOR LOW

CODE A063

RIGHT FRONT MOTOR CIRCUIT SHORTED TO BATTERY OR MOTOR SHORTED

Circuit Description:

This code identifies a motor circuit that is shorted to battery or a motor that has low or no resistance. This fault will not allow the motor to be controlled at the commanded current rate or will cause the motor to turn in the opposite direction or not at all.

Test Description: Number(s) below refer to circled number(s) on the diagnostic chart.

1. This step checks for a short to voltage in the motor "high" circuitry.
2. This step checks for a short to voltage in the motor "low" circuitry.
3. This step checks for a motor that is internally shorted.
4. This test is used to release the tension of the motor pack prior to removal.

Diagnostic Aids:

Using Tech 1, select manual control function, and exercise motor movement of affected channel in both directions while applying light pressure on the brake pedal.

If erratic or "jumpy" brake pedal movement is detected while performing an "apply" or "release" function of the motor, an intermittent fault may be indicated.

An "Intermittent" problem may be caused by a poor connection, rubbed through wire insulation, or a wire that is broken inside the insulation.

If the fault is not current, wiggle the wires of the affected channel and check if the code resets. This will help to pinpoint an intermittent problem in the motor circuitry or connections.

The frequency of the problem can be checked by using the enhanced diagnostic function of the Tech 1 "Scan" tool.

If Code A041 sets as a current code and A063 is infrequent history code, see Code A041 for diagnosis.

Any circuitry, that is suspected as causing the intermittent complaint, should be thoroughly checked for backed out terminals, improper mating, broken locks, improperly formed or damaged terminals, poor terminal to wiring connections or physical damage to the wiring harness.

GC402910071600AX

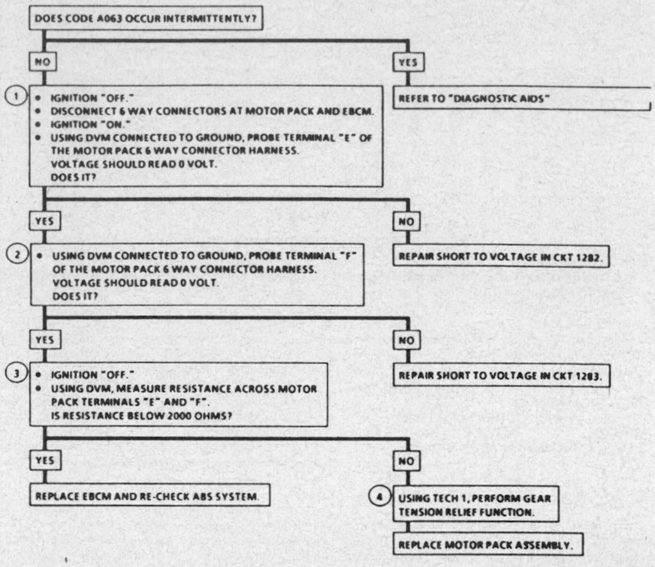
DOES CODE A063 OCCUR INTERMITTENTLY?
NO
YES
REFER TO "DIAGNOSTIC AIDS"
1
• IGNITION "OFF."
• DISCONNECT 6 WAY CONNECTORS AT MOTOR PACK AND EBCM.
• IGNITION "ON."
• USING DVM CONNECTED TO GROUND, PROBE TERMINAL "E" OF THE MOTOR PACK 6 WAY CONNECTOR HARNESS.
VOLTAGE SHOULD READ 0 VOLT.
DOES IT?
YES
NO
REPAIR SHORT TO VOLTAGE IN CKT 1282.
2
• USING DVM CONNECTED TO GROUND, PROBE TERMINAL "F" OF THE MOTOR PACK 6 WAY CONNECTOR HARNESS.
VOLTAGE SHOULD READ 0 VOLT.
DOES IT?
YES
NO
REPAIR SHORT TO VOLTAGE IN CKT 1283.
3
• IGNITION "OFF."
• USING DVM, MEASURE RESISTANCE ACROSS MOTOR PACK TERMINALS "E" AND "F".
IS RESISTANCE BELOW 2000 OHMS?
YES
NO
REPLACE EBCM AND RE-CHECK ABS SYSTEM.
4
USING TECH 1, PERFORM GEAR TENSION RELIEF FUNCTION.
REPLACE MOTOR PACK ASSEMBLY.

GC402910071600BX

Fig. 72 Code A063: Right Front Motor Circuit Shorted To Battery. 1992

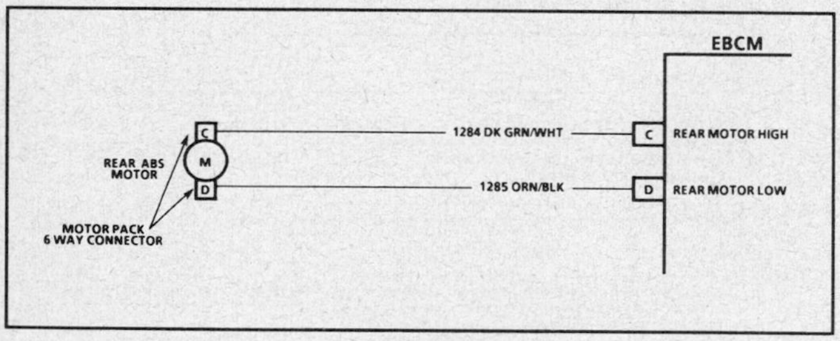
EBCM
REAR ABS MOTOR
M
C
D
MOTOR PACK 6 WAY CONNECTOR
1284 DK GRN/WHT
1285 ORN/BLK
C
D
REAR MOTOR HIGH
REAR MOTOR LOW

CODE A064

REAR AXLE MOTOR CIRCUIT OPEN

Circuit Description:

This code identifies a motor that cannot be energized due to an open in its circuitry. This fault will not allow proper rear ABS operation.

Test Description: Number(s) below refer to circled number(s) on the diagnostic chart.

1. This checks for an open circuit in the motor.
2. This step is used to release the tension of the motor pack prior to removal.
3. This step checks for an open in the motor "high" circuitry.
4. This step checks for an open in the motor "low" circuitry.

Diagnostic Aids:

Using Tech 1, select manual control function, and exercise motor movement of affected channel in both directions while applying light pressure on the brake pedal.

If erratic or "jumpy" brake pedal movement is detected while performing an "apply" or "release" function of the motor, an intermittent fault may be indicated.

An "Intermittent" problem may be caused by a poor connection, rubbed through wire insulation, or a wire that is broken inside the insulation.

If the fault is not current, wiggle the wires of the affected channel and check if the code resets. This will help to pinpoint an intermittent problem in the motor circuitry or connections.

The frequency of the problem can be checked by using the enhanced diagnostic function of the "Scan" tool.

Any circuitry, that is suspected as causing the intermittent complaint, should be thoroughly checked for backed out terminals, improper mating, broken locks, improperly formed or damaged terminals, poor terminal to wiring connections or physical damage to the wiring harness.

GC402910071700AX

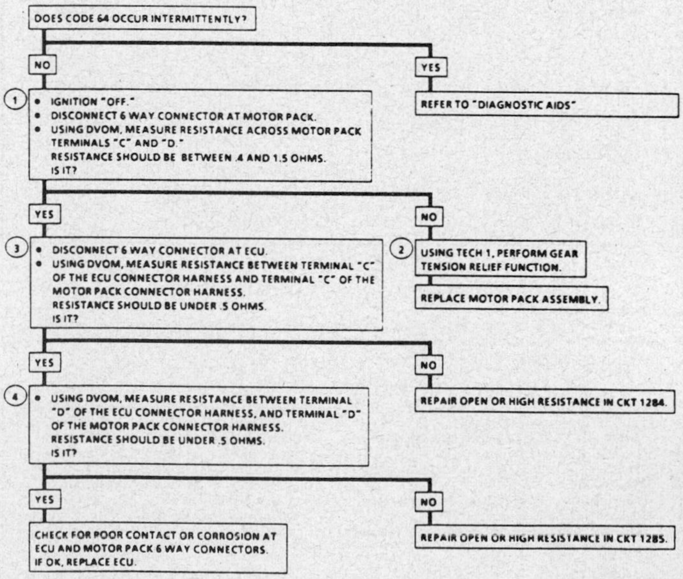
DOES CODE 64 OCCUR INTERMITTENTLY?
NO
YES
REFER TO "DIAGNOSTIC AIDS"
1
• IGNITION "OFF."
• DISCONNECT 6 WAY CONNECTOR AT MOTOR PACK.
• USING DVOM, MEASURE RESISTANCE ACROSS MOTOR PACK TERMINALS "C" AND "D."
RESISTANCE SHOULD BE BETWEEN .4 AND 1.5 OHMS.
IS IT?
YES
NO
2
USING TECH 1, PERFORM GEAR TENSION RELIEF FUNCTION.
REPLACE MOTOR PACK ASSEMBLY.
3
• DISCONNECT 6 WAY CONNECTOR AT ECU.
• USING DVOM, MEASURE RESISTANCE BETWEEN TERMINAL "C" OF THE ECU CONNECTOR HARNESS AND TERMINAL "C" OF THE MOTOR PACK CONNECTOR HARNESS.
RESISTANCE SHOULD BE UNDER .5 OHMS.
IS IT?
YES
NO
REPAIR OPEN OR HIGH RESISTANCE IN CKT 1284.
4
• USING DVOM, MEASURE RESISTANCE BETWEEN TERMINAL "D" OF THE ECU CONNECTOR HARNESS, AND TERMINAL "D" OF THE MOTOR PACK CONNECTOR HARNESS.
RESISTANCE SHOULD BE UNDER .5 OHMS.
IS IT?
YES
NO
CHECK FOR POOR CONTACT OR CORROSION AT ECU AND MOTOR PACK 6 WAY CONNECTORS.
IF OK, REPLACE ECU.
REPAIR OPEN OR HIGH RESISTANCE IN CKT 1285.

GC402910071700BX

Fig. 73 Code A064: Rear Axle Motor Circuit Open. 1992

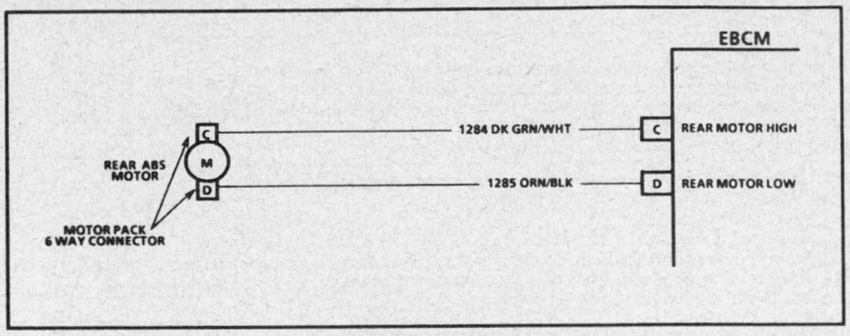
EBCM
1284 DK GRN/WHT
C
REAR MOTOR HIGH
1285 ORN/BLK
D
REAR MOTOR LOW
REAR ABS MOTOR
M
MOTOR PACK 6 WAY CONNECTOR

CODE A065

REAR AXLE MOTOR CIRCUIT SHORTED TO GROUND

Circuit Description:

This code identifies a motor circuit that is shorted to ground. This fault will not allow the motor to be controlled at the commanded current rate or will cause the driver circuit to allow current directly to ground.

Test Description: Number(s) below refer to circled number(s) on the diagnostic chart.

1. This step checks for a short to ground in the motor "high" circuitry.
2. This step checks for a short to ground in the motor "low" circuitry.
3. This step checks for a motor that is internally shorted to ground.
4. This step is used to release the tension of the motor pack prior to removal.

Diagnostic Aids:

Using Tech 1, select manual control function, and exercise motor movement of affected channel in both directions while applying light pressure on the brake pedal.

If erratic or "jumpy" brake pedal movement is detected while performing an "apply" or "release" function of the motor, an intermittent fault may be indicated.

An "Intermittent" problem may be caused by a poor connection, rubbed through wire insulation, or a wire that is broken inside the insulation.

If the fault is not current, wiggle the wires of the affected channel and check if the code resets. This will help to pinpoint an intermittent problem in the motor circuitry or connections.

The frequency of the problem can be checked by using the enhanced diagnostic function of the "Scan" tool

Any circuitry, that is suspected as causing the intermittent complaint, should be thoroughly checked for backed out terminals, improper mating, broken locks, improperly formed or damaged terminals, poor terminal to wiring connections or physical damage to the wiring harness.

GC402910071800AX

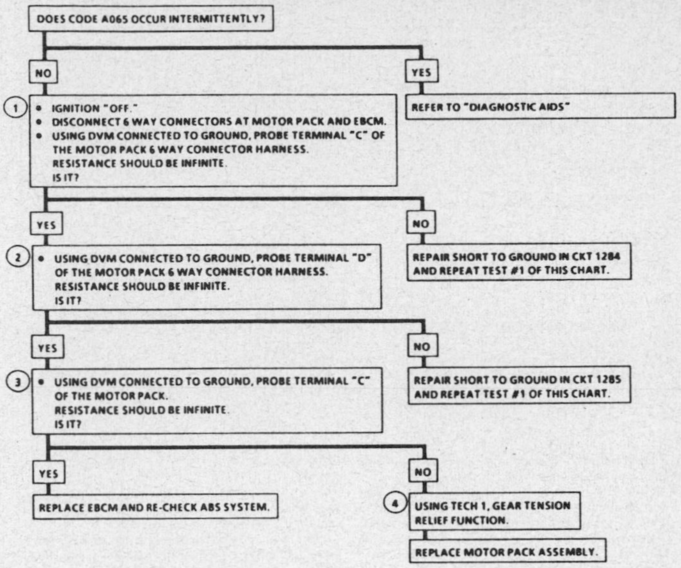
DOES CODE A065 OCCUR INTERMITTENTLY?
NO
YES
REFER TO "DIAGNOSTIC AIDS"
1
• IGNITION "OFF."
• DISCONNECT 6 WAY CONNECTORS AT MOTOR PACK AND EBCM.
• USING DVM CONNECTED TO GROUND, PROBE TERMINAL "C" OF THE MOTOR PACK 6 WAY CONNECTOR HARNESS. RESISTANCE SHOULD BE INFINITE.
IS IT?
YES
NO
REPAIR SHORT TO GROUND IN CKT 1284 AND REPEAT TEST #1 OF THIS CHART.
2
• USING DVM CONNECTED TO GROUND, PROBE TERMINAL "D" OF THE MOTOR PACK 6 WAY CONNECTOR HARNESS. RESISTANCE SHOULD BE INFINITE.
IS IT?
YES
NO
REPAIR SHORT TO GROUND IN CKT 1285 AND REPEAT TEST #1 OF THIS CHART.
3
• USING DVM CONNECTED TO GROUND, PROBE TERMINAL "C" OF THE MOTOR PACK. RESISTANCE SHOULD BE INFINITE.
IS IT?
YES
NO
REPLACE EBCM AND RE-CHECK ABS SYSTEM.
4
USING TECH 1, GEAR TENSION RELIEF FUNCTION.
REPLACE MOTOR PACK ASSEMBLY.

GC402910071800BX

Fig. 74 Code A065: Rear Axle Motor Circuit Shorted To Ground. 1992

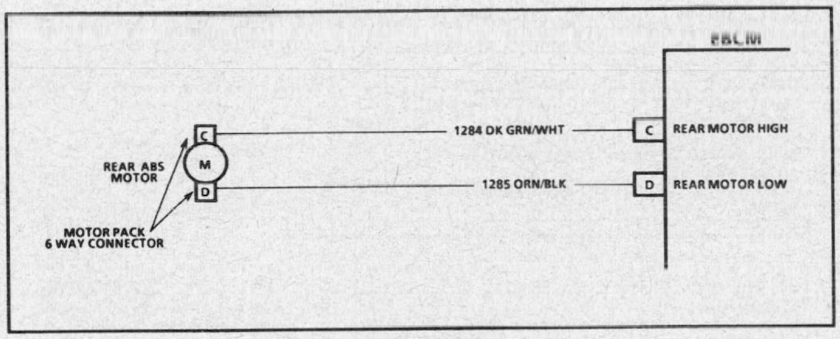
EBCM
1284 DK GRN/WHT
C
REAR MOTOR HIGH
1285 ORN/BLK
D
REAR MOTOR LOW
REAR ABS MOTOR
M
MOTOR PACK 6 WAY CONNECTOR

CODE A066

REAR AXLE MOTOR CIRCUIT SHORTED TO BATTERY OR MOTOR SHORTED

Circuit Description:

This code identifies a motor circuit that is shorted to battery or a motor that has low or zero resistance. This fault will not allow the motor to be controlled at the commanded current rate or will cause the motor to turn in the opposite direction or not turn at all.

Test Description: Number(s) below refer to circled number(s) on the diagnostic chart.

1. This step checks for a short to voltage in the motor "high" circuitry.
2. This step checks for a short to voltage in the motor "low" circuitry.
3. This step checks for a motor that is internally shorted.
4. This step is used to release the tension of the motor pack prior to removal.

Diagnostic Aids:

Using Tech 1, select manual control function, and exercise motor movement of affected channel in both directions while applying light pressure on the brake pedal.

If erratic or "jumpy" brake pedal movement is detected while performing an "apply" or "release" function of the motor, an intermittent fault may be indicated.

An "Intermittent" problem may be caused by a poor connection, rubbed through wire insulation, or a wire that is broken inside the insulation.

If the fault is not current, wiggle the wires of the affected channel and check if the code resets. This will help to pinpoint an intermittent problem in the motor circuitry or connections.

The frequency of the problem can be checked by using the enhanced diagnostic function of the "Scan" tool

If Code A042 sets as current code and A066 is infrequent history code, see Code A042 diagnostics.

Any circuitry, that is suspected as causing the intermittent complaint, should be thoroughly checked for backed out terminals, improper mating, broken locks, improperly formed or damaged terminals, poor terminal to wiring connections or physical damage to the wiring harness.

GC402910071900AX

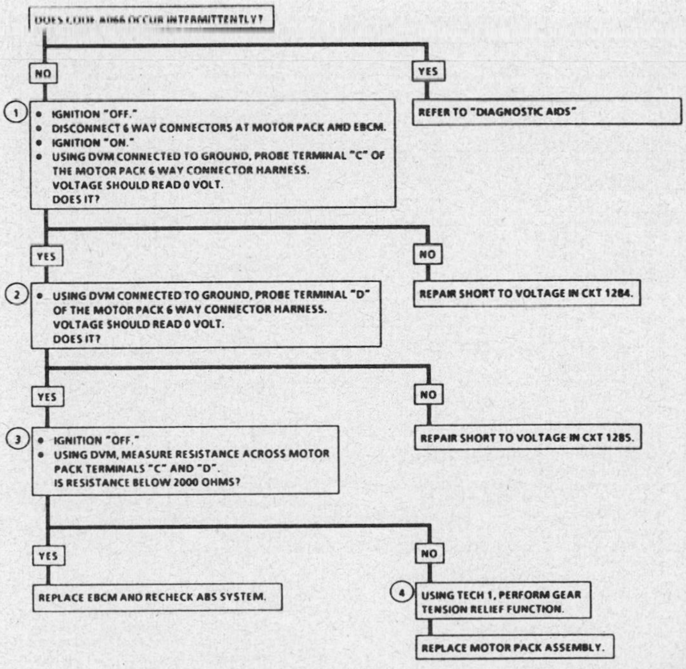
DOES CODE A066 OCCUR INTERMITTENTLY?
NO
YES
REFER TO "DIAGNOSTIC AIDS"
1
• IGNITION "OFF."
• DISCONNECT 6 WAY CONNECTORS AT MOTOR PACK AND EBCM.
• IGNITION "ON."
• USING DVM CONNECTED TO GROUND, PROBE TERMINAL "C" OF THE MOTOR PACK 6 WAY CONNECTOR HARNESS. VOLTAGE SHOULD READ 0 VOLT.
DOES IT?
YES
NO
REPAIR SHORT TO VOLTAGE IN CKT 1284.
2
• USING DVM CONNECTED TO GROUND, PROBE TERMINAL "D" OF THE MOTOR PACK 6 WAY CONNECTOR HARNESS. VOLTAGE SHOULD READ 0 VOLT.
DOES IT?
YES
NO
REPAIR SHORT TO VOLTAGE IN CKT 1285.
3
• IGNITION "OFF."
• USING DVM, MEASURE RESISTANCE ACROSS MOTOR PACK TERMINALS "C" AND "D".
IS RESISTANCE BELOW 2000 OHMS?
YES
NO
REPLACE EBCM AND RECHECK ABS SYSTEM.
4
USING TECH 1, PERFORM GEAR TENSION RELIEF FUNCTION.
REPLACE MOTOR PACK ASSEMBLY.

GC402910071900BX

Fig. 75 Code A066: Rear Axle Motor Circuit Shorted To Battery. 1992

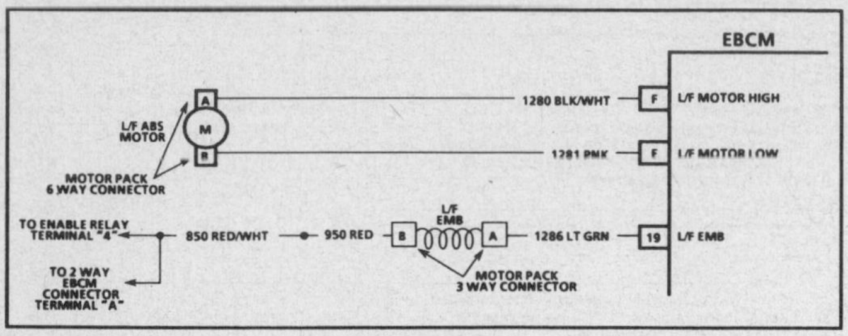
EBCM
1280 BLK/WHT
F
L/F MOTOR HIGH
A
M
B
L/F ABS MOTOR
1281 PNK
F
L/F MOTOR LOW
MOTOR PACK 6 WAY CONNECTOR
TO ENABLE RELAY TERMINAL "4"
850 RED/WHT
950 RED
B
L/F EMB
A
1286 LT GRN
19
L/F EMB
TO 2 WAY EBCM CONNECTOR TERMINAL "A"
MOTOR PACK 3 WAY CONNECTOR

CODE A067

LEFT FRONT EMB RELEASE CIRCUIT OPEN OR SHORTED TO GROUND

Circuit Description:

This code is designed to detect shorts to ground and opens in the EMB release circuit.

A short to ground between the EMB and the ABS EBCM will cause the EMB to be energized indefinitely at an uncontrolled current, causing the EMB to damage itself. To remove the effects of the fault, the enable relay must be turned "OFF," eliminating power to the EMB as well as the ABS system.

Test Description: Number(s) below refer to circled number(s) on the diagnostic chart.

1. This step checks for a short to ground in the EMB control circuitry.
2. This step insures that the EMB is not internally shorted or open.
3. This step checks to see if CKT 850/950 has continuity to the EMB connector.
4. This step looks for an open in the EMB control circuitry.
5. This step is used to release the tension of the motor pack prior to removal.

Diagnostic Aids:

An "Intermittent" problem may be caused by a poor connection, rubbed through wire insulation, or a wire that is broken inside the insulation.

The frequency of the problem can be checked by using the enhanced diagnostic function of the "Scan" tool

Any circuitry, that is suspected as causing the intermittent complaint, should be thoroughly checked for backed out terminals, improper mating, broken locks, improperly formed or damaged terminals, poor terminal to wiring connections or physical damage to the wiring harness.

GC402910072000AX

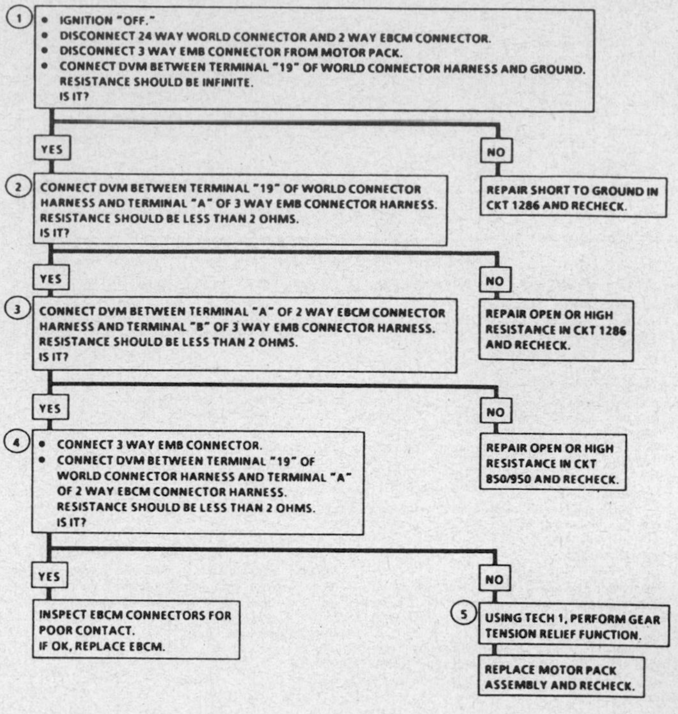
1
• IGNITION "OFF."
• DISCONNECT 24 WAY WORLD CONNECTOR AND 2 WAY EBCM CONNECTOR.
• DISCONNECT 3 WAY EMB CONNECTOR FROM MOTOR PACK.
• CONNECT DVM BETWEEN TERMINAL "19" OF WORLD CONNECTOR HARNESS AND GROUND. RESISTANCE SHOULD BE INFINITE. IS IT?
YES
NO
REPAIR SHORT TO GROUND IN CKT 1286 AND RECHECK.
2
CONNECT DVM BETWEEN TERMINAL "19" OF WORLD CONNECTOR HARNESS AND TERMINAL "A" OF 3 WAY EMB CONNECTOR HARNESS. RESISTANCE SHOULD BE LESS THAN 2 OHMS. IS IT?
YES
NO
REPAIR OPEN OR HIGH RESISTANCE IN CKT 1286 AND RECHECK.
3
CONNECT DVM BETWEEN TERMINAL "A" OF 2 WAY EBCM CONNECTOR HARNESS AND TERMINAL "B" OF 3 WAY EMB CONNECTOR HARNESS. RESISTANCE SHOULD BE LESS THAN 2 OHMS. IS IT?
YES
NO
REPAIR OPEN OR HIGH RESISTANCE IN CKT 850/950 AND RECHECK.
4
• CONNECT 3 WAY EMB CONNECTOR.
• CONNECT DVM BETWEEN TERMINAL "19" OF WORLD CONNECTOR HARNESS AND TERMINAL "A" OF 2 WAY EBCM CONNECTOR HARNESS. RESISTANCE SHOULD BE LESS THAN 2 OHMS. IS IT?
YES
NO
INSPECT EBCM CONNECTORS FOR POOR CONTACT. IF OK, REPLACE EBCM.
5
USING TECH 1, PERFORM GEAR TENSION RELIEF FUNCTION.
REPLACE MOTOR PACK ASSEMBLY AND RECHECK.

GC402910072000BX

Fig. 76 Code A067: Left Front EMB Release Circuit Open Or Shorted To Ground. 1992 Except Cutlass Supreme, Grand Prix, Lumina & Regal

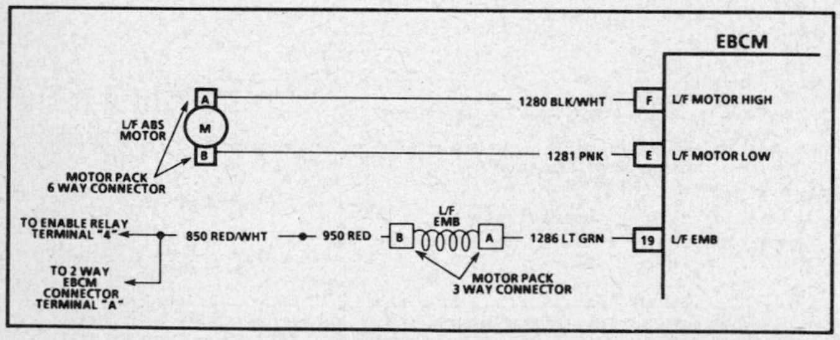
EBCM
1280 BLK/WHT
F
L/F MOTOR HIGH
A
M
B
L/F ABS MOTOR
1281 PNK
E
L/F MOTOR LOW
MOTOR PACK 6 WAY CONNECTOR
TO ENABLE RELAY TERMINAL "4"
850 RED/WHT
950 RED
B
L/F EMB
A
1286 LT GRN
19
L/F EMB
TO 2 WAY EBCM CONNECTOR TERMINAL "A"
MOTOR PACK 3 WAY CONNECTOR

CODE A068

LEFT FRONT EMB CIRCUIT SHORTED TO BATTERY OR EMB SHORTED

Circuit Description:

This code is designed to detect shorts to battery and shorts in the EMB release circuit. These faults will not allow the EMB to be energized when needed.

Test Description: Number(s) below refer to circled number(s) on the diagnostic chart.

1. This step checks to see if the fault is currently present.
2. This step identifies a short to voltage in the EMB control circuitry.
3. This step checks for an EMB that has lower than normal resistance.
4. This step is used to release the tension of the motor pack prior to removal.

Diagnostic Aids:

An "Intermittent" problem may be caused by a poor connection, rubbed through wire insulation, or a wire that is broken inside the insulation.

The frequency of the problem can be checked by using the enhanced diagnostic function of the "Scan" tool

Any circuitry, that is suspected as causing the intermittent complaint, should be thoroughly checked for backed out terminals, improper mating, broken locks, improperly formed or damaged terminals, poor terminal to wiring connections or physical damage to the wiring harness.

GC402910072100AX

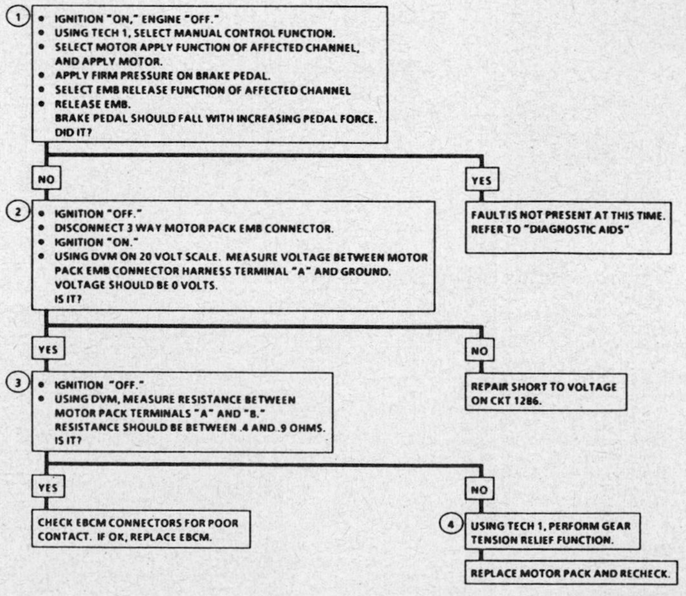
1
• IGNITION "ON," ENGINE "OFF."
• USING TECH 1, SELECT MANUAL CONTROL FUNCTION.
• SELECT MOTOR APPLY FUNCTION OF AFFECTED CHANNEL, AND APPLY MOTOR.
• APPLY FIRM PRESSURE ON BRAKE PEDAL.
• SELECT EMB RELEASE FUNCTION OF AFFECTED CHANNEL
• RELEASE EMB. BRAKE PEDAL SHOULD FALL WITH INCREASING PEDAL FORCE. DID IT?
NO
YES
FAULT IS NOT PRESENT AT THIS TIME. REFER TO "DIAGNOSTIC AIDS"
2
• IGNITION "OFF."
• DISCONNECT 3 WAY MOTOR PACK EMB CONNECTOR.
• IGNITION "ON."
• USING DVM ON 20 VOLT SCALE. MEASURE VOLTAGE BETWEEN MOTOR PACK EMB CONNECTOR HARNESS TERMINAL "A" AND GROUND. VOLTAGE SHOULD BE 0 VOLTS. IS IT?
YES
NO
REPAIR SHORT TO VOLTAGE ON CKT 1286.
3
• IGNITION "OFF."
• USING DVM, MEASURE RESISTANCE BETWEEN MOTOR PACK TERMINALS "A" AND "B." RESISTANCE SHOULD BE BETWEEN .4 AND .9 OHMS. IS IT?
YES
NO
CHECK EBCM CONNECTORS FOR POOR CONTACT. IF OK, REPLACE EBCM.
4
USING TECH 1, PERFORM GEAR TENSION RELIEF FUNCTION.
REPLACE MOTOR PACK AND RECHECK.

GC402910072100BX

Fig. 77 Code A068: Left Front EMB Release Circuit Shorted To Battery Or Driver Open. 1992 Except Cutlass Supreme, Grand Prix, Lumina & Regal

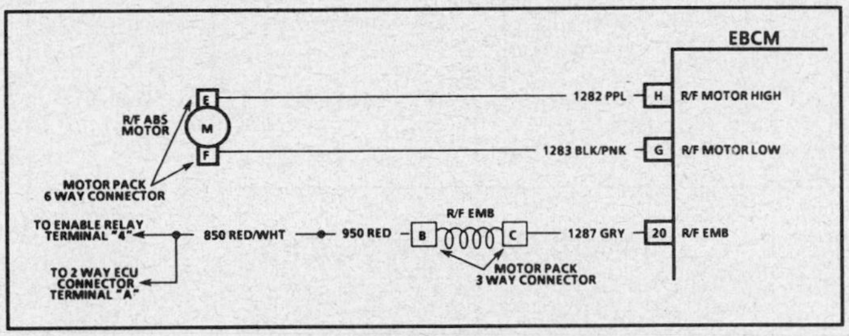
EBCM
1282 PPL
H
R/F MOTOR HIGH
R/F ABS MOTOR
M
E
F
1283 BLK/PNK
G
R/F MOTOR LOW
MOTOR PACK 6 WAY CONNECTOR
R/F EMB
TO ENABLE RELAY TERMINAL "4"
850 RED/WHT
950 RED
B
C
1287 GRY
20
R/F EMB
TO 2 WAY ECU CONNECTOR TERMINAL "A"
MOTOR PACK 3 WAY CONNECTOR

CODE A071

RIGHT FRONT EMB CIRCUIT OPEN OR SHORTED TO GROUND

Circuit Description:

This code is designed to detect shorts to ground and opens in the EMB release circuit.

A short to ground between the EMB and the ABS EBCM will cause the EMB to be energized indefinitely at an uncontrolled current causing the EMB to damage itself.

Test Description: Number(s) below refer to circled number(s) on the diagnostic chart.

1. This step checks for a short to ground in the EMB control circuitry.
2. This step insures that the EMB is not internally shorted or open.
3. This step checks to see if CKT 850/950 has continuity to the EMB connector.
4. This step looks for an open in the EMB control circuitry.
5. This step is used to release the tension of the motor pack prior to removal.

Diagnostic Aids:

An "Intermittent" problem may be caused by a poor connection, rubbed through wire insulation, or a wire that is broken inside the insulation.

The frequency of the problem can be checked by using the enhanced diagnostic function of the "Scan" tool

Any circuitry, that is suspected as causing the intermittent complaint, should be thoroughly checked for backed out terminals, improper mating, broken locks, improperly formed or damaged terminals, poor terminal to wiring connections or physical damage to the wiring harness.

GC402910072200AX

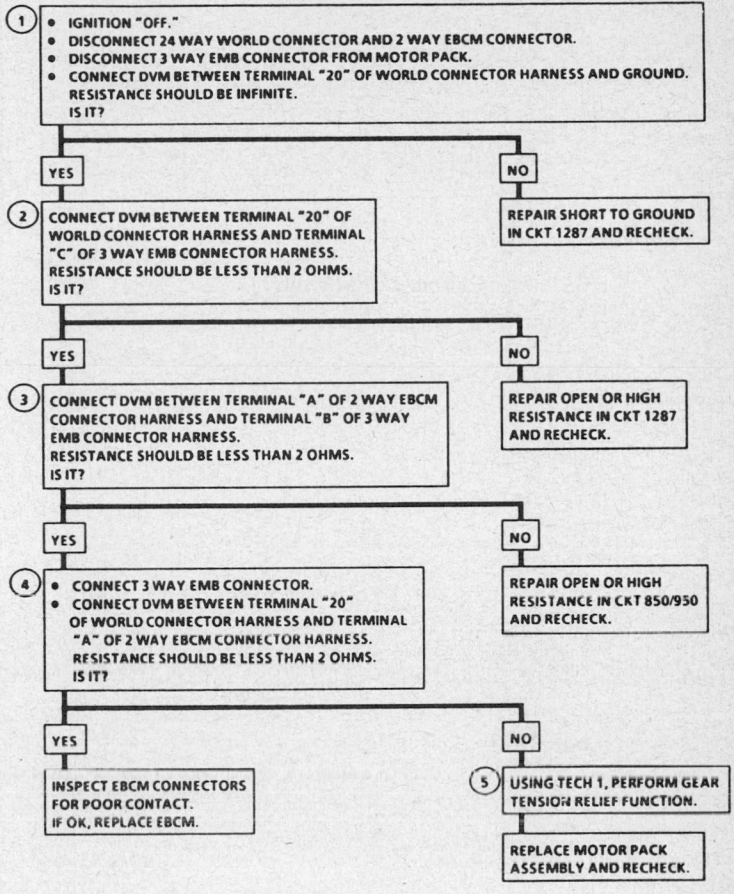

(1)
- IGNITION "OFF."
- DISCONNECT 24 WAY WORLD CONNECTOR AND 2 WAY EBCM CONNECTOR.
- DISCONNECT 3 WAY EMB CONNECTOR FROM MOTOR PACK.
- CONNECT DVM BETWEEN TERMINAL "20" OF WORLD CONNECTOR HARNESS AND GROUND. RESISTANCE SHOULD BE INFINITE.

IS IT?

NO: REPAIR SHORT TO GROUND IN CKT 1287 AND RECHECK.

YES: (2) CONNECT DVM BETWEEN TERMINAL "20" OF WORLD CONNECTOR HARNESS AND TERMINAL "C" OF 3 WAY EMB CONNECTOR HARNESS. RESISTANCE SHOULD BE LESS THAN 2 OHMS. IS IT?

NO: REPAIR OPEN OR HIGH RESISTANCE IN CKT 1287 AND RECHECK.

YES: (3) CONNECT DVM BETWEEN TERMINAL "A" OF 2 WAY EBCM CONNECTOR HARNESS AND TERMINAL "B" OF 3 WAY EMB CONNECTOR HARNESS. RESISTANCE SHOULD BE LESS THAN 2 OHMS. IS IT?

NO: REPAIR OPEN OR HIGH RESISTANCE IN CKT 850/950 AND RECHECK.

YES: (4)
- CONNECT 3 WAY EMB CONNECTOR.
- CONNECT DVM BETWEEN TERMINAL "20" OF WORLD CONNECTOR HARNESS AND TERMINAL "A" OF 2 WAY EBCM CONNECTOR HARNESS. RESISTANCE SHOULD BE LESS THAN 2 OHMS.

IS IT?

YES: INSPECT EBCM CONNECTORS FOR POOR CONTACT. IF OK, REPLACE EBCM.

NO: (5) USING TECH 1, PERFORM GEAR TENSION RELIEF FUNCTION. → REPLACE MOTOR PACK ASSEMBLY AND RECHECK.

GC402910072200BX

Fig. 78 Code A071: Right Front EMB Release Circuit Open Or Shorted To Ground. 1992 Except Cutlass Supreme, Grand Prix, Lumina & Regal

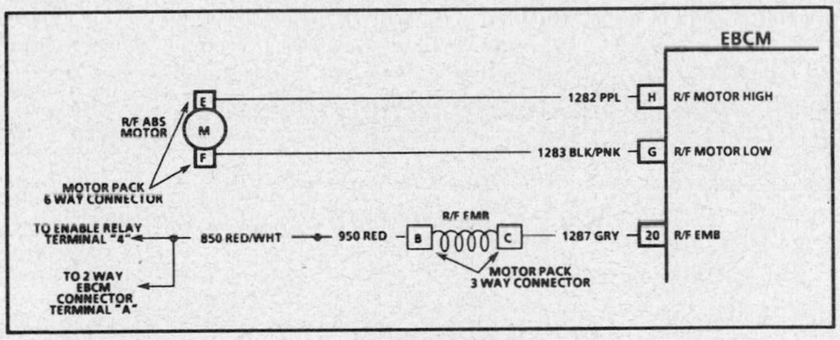
EBCM
1282 PPL
H
R/F MOTOR HIGH
R/F ABS MOTOR
M
E
F
1283 BLK/PNK
G
R/F MOTOR LOW
MOTOR PACK 6 WAY CONNECTOR
R/F EMB
TO ENABLE RELAY TERMINAL "4"
850 RED/WHT
950 RED
B
C
1287 GRY
20
R/F EMB
TO 2 WAY EBCM CONNECTOR TERMINAL "A"
MOTOR PACK 3 WAY CONNECTOR

CODE A072

RIGHT FRONT EMB CIRCUIT SHORTED TO BATTERY OR EMB SHORTED

Circuit Description:

This code is designed to detect shorts to battery and shorts in the EMB release circuit. These faults will not allow the EMB to be energized when needed.

Test Description: Number(s) below refer to circled number(s) on the diagnostic chart.

1. This step checks to see if the fault is currently present.
2. This step identifies a short to voltage in the EMB control circuitry.
3. This step checks for an EMB that has lower than normal resistance.
4. This step is used to release the tension of the motor pack prior to removal.

Diagnostic Aids:

An "Intermittent" problem may be caused by a poor connection, rubbed through wire insulation, or a wire that is broken inside the insulation.

The frequency of the problem can be checked by using the enhanced diagnostic function of the "Scan" tool

Any circuitry, that is suspected as causing the intermittent complaint, should be thoroughly checked for backed out terminals, improper mating, broken locks, improperly formed or damaged terminals, poor terminal to wiring connections or physical damage to the wiring harness.

GC402910072300AX

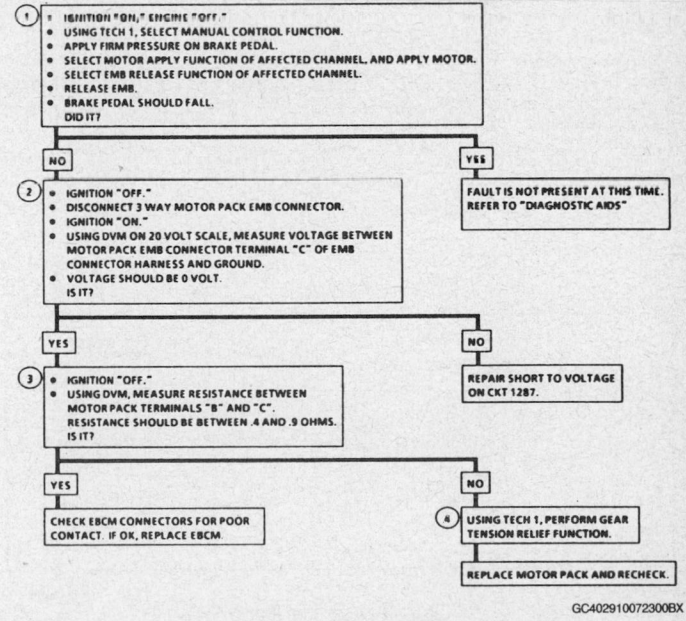

(1)
- IGNITION "ON," ENGINE "OFF."
- USING TECH 1, SELECT MANUAL CONTROL FUNCTION.
- APPLY FIRM PRESSURE ON BRAKE PEDAL.
- SELECT MOTOR APPLY FUNCTION OF AFFECTED CHANNEL, AND APPLY MOTOR.
- SELECT EMB RELEASE FUNCTION OF AFFECTED CHANNEL.
- RELEASE EMB.
- BRAKE PEDAL SHOULD FALL.

DID IT?

YES: FAULT IS NOT PRESENT AT THIS TIME. REFER TO "DIAGNOSTIC AIDS"

NO: (2)
- IGNITION "OFF."
- DISCONNECT 3 WAY MOTOR PACK EMB CONNECTOR.
- IGNITION "ON."
- USING DVM ON 20 VOLT SCALE, MEASURE VOLTAGE BETWEEN MOTOR PACK EMB CONNECTOR TERMINAL "C" OF EMB CONNECTOR HARNESS AND GROUND.
- VOLTAGE SHOULD BE 0 VOLT.

IS IT?

NO: REPAIR SHORT TO VOLTAGE ON CKT 1287.

YES: (3)
- IGNITION "OFF."
- USING DVM, MEASURE RESISTANCE BETWEEN MOTOR PACK TERMINALS "B" AND "C". RESISTANCE SHOULD BE BETWEEN .4 AND .9 OHMS.

IS IT?

YES: CHECK EBCM CONNECTORS FOR POOR CONTACT. IF OK, REPLACE EBCM.

NO: (4) USING TECH 1, PERFORM GEAR TENSION RELIEF FUNCTION. → REPLACE MOTOR PACK AND RECHECK.

GC402910072300BX

Fig. 79 Code A072: Right Front EMB Release Circuit Shorted To Battery Or Driver Open. 1992 Except Cutlass Supreme, Grand Prix, Lumina & Regal

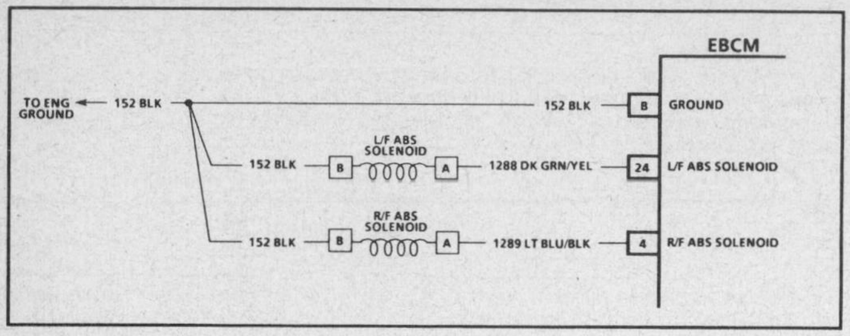
EBCM
TO ENG GROUND
152 BLK
152 BLK
B
GROUND
L/F ABS SOLENOID
152 BLK
B
A
1288 DK GRN/YEL
24
L/F ABS SOLENOID
R/F ABS SOLENOID
152 BLK
B
A
1289 LT BLU/BLK
4
R/F ABS SOLENOID

GC402910072400AX

Cavalier & Sunbird

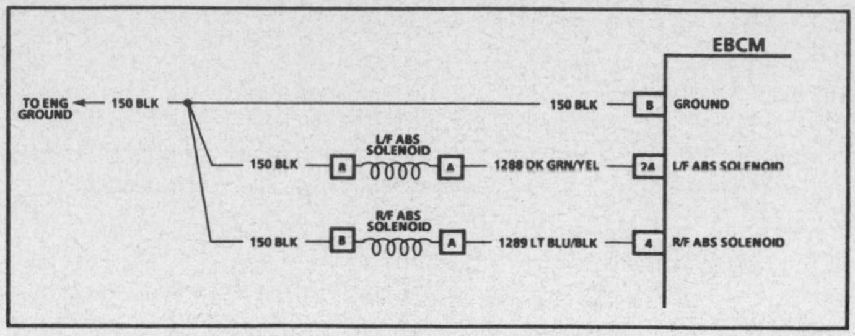
EBCM
TO ENG GROUND
150 BLK
150 BLK
B
GROUND
L/F ABS SOLENOID
150 BLK
B
A
1288 DK GRN/YEL
24
L/F ABS SOLENOID
R/F ABS SOLENOID
150 BLK
B
A
1289 LT BLU/BLK
4
R/F ABS SOLENOID

GC402910072400BX

Except Cavalier & Sunbird

Circuit Description:

This code identifies a solenoid that cannot be energized due to an open in its circuitry, or a solenoid that is always energized due to a short to battery in its circuitry between the driver and the solenoid. An open will not allow proper ABS operation, but the short to battery simply turns "ON" the solenoid. A path for base brakes is still allowed once the motor re-homes and the check valve is lifted off its seat during key on initialization.

Test Description: Number(s) below refer to circled number(s) on the diagnostic chart.

1. This checks for a short to voltage in the control circuitry of the solenoid.
2. This checks for an open in the control circuit of the solenoid.
3. This step identifies an open in the solenoid or ground circuit.
4. This step checks for a possible intermittent problem in the solenoid circuitry due to poor terminal contact.

Diagnostic Aids:

An "Intermittent" problem may be caused by a poor connection, rubbed through wire insulation, or a wire that is broken inside the insulation.

The frequency of the problem can be checked by using the enhanced diagnostic function of the "Scan" tool.

Any circuitry, that is suspected as causing the intermittent complaint, should be thoroughly checked for backed out terminals, improper mating, broken locks, improperly formed or damaged terminals, poor terminal to wiring connections or physical damage to the wiring harness.

GC402910072400CX

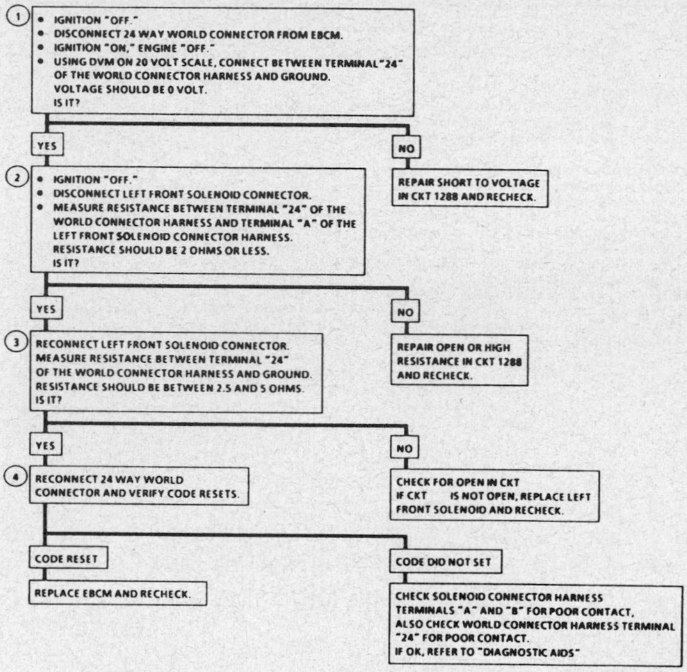
1
• IGNITION "OFF."
• DISCONNECT 24 WAY WORLD CONNECTOR FROM EBCM.
• IGNITION "ON," ENGINE "OFF."
• USING DVM ON 20 VOLT SCALE, CONNECT BETWEEN TERMINAL "24" OF THE WORLD CONNECTOR HARNESS AND GROUND. VOLTAGE SHOULD BE 0 VOLT. IS IT?
YES
NO
REPAIR SHORT TO VOLTAGE IN CKT 1288 AND RECHECK.
2
• IGNITION "OFF."
• DISCONNECT LEFT FRONT SOLENOID CONNECTOR.
• MEASURE RESISTANCE BETWEEN TERMINAL "24" OF THE WORLD CONNECTOR HARNESS AND TERMINAL "A" OF THE LEFT FRONT SOLENOID CONNECTOR HARNESS. RESISTANCE SHOULD BE 2 OHMS OR LESS. IS IT?
YES
NO
REPAIR OPEN OR HIGH RESISTANCE IN CKT 1288 AND RECHECK.
3
RECONNECT LEFT FRONT SOLENOID CONNECTOR. MEASURE RESISTANCE BETWEEN TERMINAL "24" OF THE WORLD CONNECTOR HARNESS AND GROUND. RESISTANCE SHOULD BE BETWEEN 2.5 AND 5 OHMS. IS IT?
YES
NO
CHECK FOR OPEN IN CKT IF CKT IS NOT OPEN, REPLACE LEFT FRONT SOLENOID AND RECHECK.
4
RECONNECT 24 WAY WORLD CONNECTOR AND VERIFY CODE RESETS.
CODE RESET
REPLACE EBCM AND RECHECK.
CODE DID NOT SET
CHECK SOLENOID CONNECTOR HARNESS TERMINALS "A" AND "B" FOR POOR CONTACT, ALSO CHECK WORLD CONNECTOR HARNESS TERMINAL "24" FOR POOR CONTACT. IF OK, REFER TO "DIAGNOSTIC AIDS"

GC402910072400DX

Fig. 80 Code A076: Left Front Solenoid Circuit Open Or Shorted To Battery. 1992

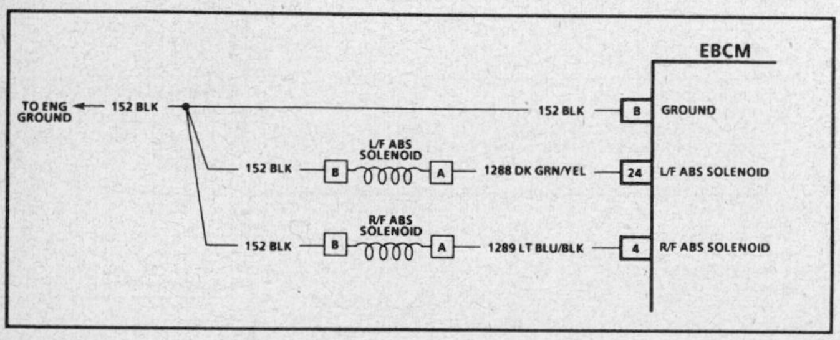
EBCM
TO ENG GROUND
152 BLK
152 BLK
B
GROUND
L/F ABS SOLENOID
152 BLK
B
A
1288 DK GRN/YEL
24
L/F ABS SOLENOID
R/F ABS SOLENOID
152 BLK
B
A
1289 LT BLU/BLK
4
R/F ABS SOLENOID

GC402910072500AX

Cavalier & Sunbird

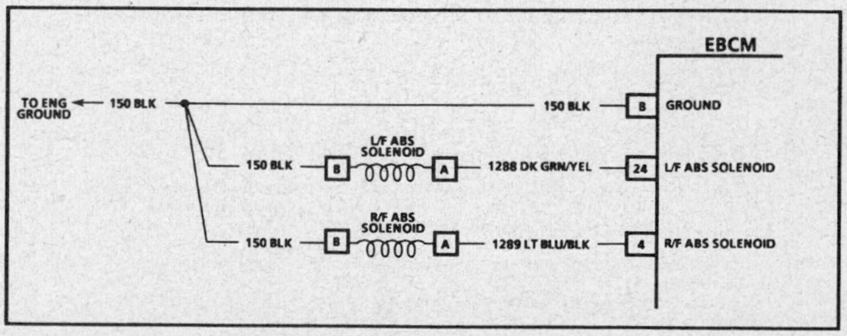
EBCM
TO ENG GROUND
150 BLK
150 BLK
B
GROUND
L/F ABS SOLENOID
150 BLK
B
A
1288 DK GRN/YEL
24
L/F ABS SOLENOID
R/F ABS SOLENOID
150 BLK
B
A
1289 LT BLU/BLK
4
R/F ABS SOLENOID

GC402910072500BX

Except Cavalier & Sunbird

Fig. 81 Code A077: Left Front Solenoid Shorted To Ground Or Driver Open (Part 1 of 2). 1992

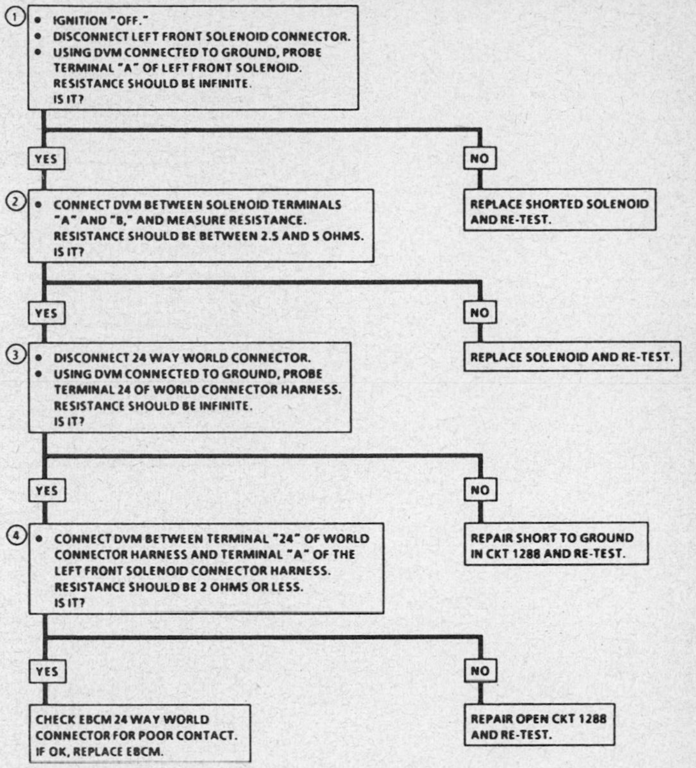

1
• IGNITION "OFF."
• DISCONNECT LEFT FRONT SOLENOID CONNECTOR.
• USING DVM CONNECTED TO GROUND, PROBE TERMINAL "A" OF LEFT FRONT SOLENOID. RESISTANCE SHOULD BE INFINITE. IS IT?
YES
NO
REPLACE SHORTED SOLENOID AND RE-TEST.
2
• CONNECT DVM BETWEEN SOLENOID TERMINALS "A" AND "B," AND MEASURE RESISTANCE. RESISTANCE SHOULD BE BETWEEN 2.5 AND 5 OHMS. IS IT?
YES
NO
REPLACE SOLENOID AND RE-TEST.
3
• DISCONNECT 24 WAY WORLD CONNECTOR.
• USING DVM CONNECTED TO GROUND, PROBE TERMINAL 24 OF WORLD CONNECTOR HARNESS. RESISTANCE SHOULD BE INFINITE. IS IT?
YES
NO
REPAIR SHORT TO GROUND IN CKT 1288 AND RE-TEST.
4
• CONNECT DVM BETWEEN TERMINAL "24" OF WORLD CONNECTOR HARNESS AND TERMINAL "A" OF THE LEFT FRONT SOLENOID CONNECTOR HARNESS. RESISTANCE SHOULD BE 2 OHMS OR LESS. IS IT?
YES
NO
CHECK EBCM 24 WAY WORLD CONNECTOR FOR POOR CONTACT. IF OK, REPLACE EBCM.
REPAIR OPEN CKT 1288 AND RE-TEST.

GC402010072600DX

Circuit Description:

This code identifies a solenoid that cannot be energized due to an open in its driver circuitry, or a short to ground between the solenoid driver and the solenoid. These faults can affect ABS operation since the flow of brake fluid to the wheel cylinder cannot be stopped, making ABS operation for that channel impossible.

Test Description: Number(s) below refer to circled number(s) on the diagnostic chart.

1. This step checks for a solenoid that is internally shorted to ground.
2. This step checks for a solenoid that is not within proper resistance values.
3. This step indicates if a short to ground exists in the solenoid circuitry.
4. This checks for an open control circuit to the EBCM.

Diagnostic Aids:

An "Intermittent" problem may be caused by a poor connection, rubbed through wire insulation, or a wire that is broken inside the insulation.

The frequency of the problem can be checked by using the enhanced diagnostic function of the Tech 1 "Scan" tool.

Any circuitry, that is suspected as causing the intermittent complaint, should be thoroughly checked for backed out terminals, improper mating, broken locks, improperly formed or damaged terminals, poor terminal to wiring connections or physical damage to the wiring harness.

GC402910072500CX

Fig. 81 Code A077: Left Front Solenoid Shorted To Ground Or Driver Open (Part 2 of 2). 1992

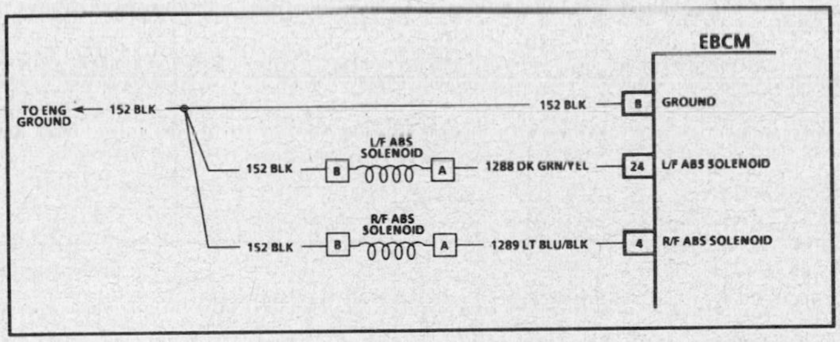

EBCM
TO ENG GROUND
152 BLK
152 BLK
B
GROUND
L/F ABS SOLENOID
152 BLK
B
A
1288 DK GRN/YEL
24
L/F ABS SOLENOID
R/F ABS SOLENOID
152 BLK
B
A
1289 LT BLU/BLK
4
R/F ABS SOLENOID

GC402910072600AX

Cavalier & Sunbird

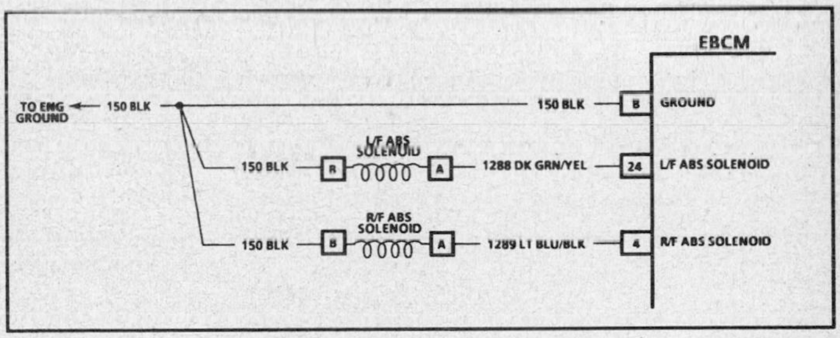

EBCM
TO ENG GROUND
150 BLK
150 BLK
B
GROUND
L/F ABS SOLENOID
150 BLK
B
A
1288 DK GRN/YEL
24
L/F ABS SOLENOID
R/F ABS SOLENOID
150 BLK
B
A
1289 LT BLU/BLK
4
R/F ABS SOLENOID

GC402910072600BX

Except Cavalier & Sunbird

Circuit Description:

This code identifies a solenoid that cannot be energized due to an open in its circuitry, or a solenoid that is always energized due to a short to battery in its circuitry between the driver and the solenoid. An open will not allow proper ABS operation, but the short to battery simply turns "ON" the solenoid. A path for base brakes is still allowed once the motor re-homes and the check ball is lifted off its seat during key on initialization.

Test Description: Number(s) below refer to circled number(s) on the diagnostic chart.

1. This checks for a short to voltage in the control circuitry of the solenoid.
2. This checks for an open in the control circuit of the solenoid.
3. This step identifies an open in the solenoid or ground circuit.
4. This step checks for a possible intermittent problem in the solenoid circuitry due to poor terminal contact.

Diagnostic Aids:

An "Intermittent" problem may be caused by a poor connection, rubbed through wire insulation, or a wire that is broken inside the insulation.

The frequency of the problem can be checked by using the enhanced diagnostic function of the "Scan" tool.

Any circuitry, that is suspected as causing the intermittent complaint, should be thoroughly checked for backed out terminals, improper mating, broken locks, improperly formed or damaged terminals, poor terminal to wiring connections or physical damage to the wiring harness.

GC402910072600CX

Fig. 82 Code A078: Right Front Solenoid Circuit Open Or Shorted To Battery (Part 1 of 2). 1992

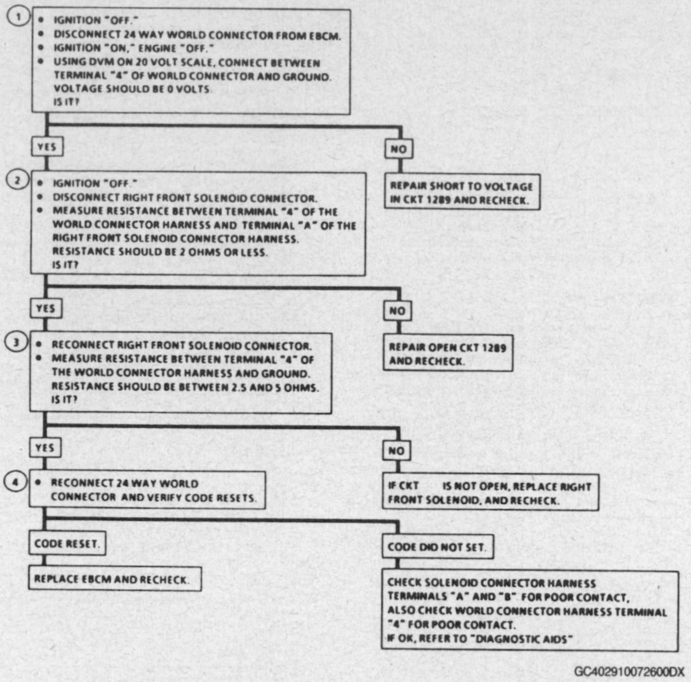
1
• IGNITION "OFF."
• DISCONNECT 24 WAY WORLD CONNECTOR FROM EBCM.
• IGNITION "ON," ENGINE "OFF."
• USING DVM ON 20 VOLT SCALE, CONNECT BETWEEN TERMINAL "4" OF WORLD CONNECTOR AND GROUND. VOLTAGE SHOULD BE 0 VOLTS. IS IT?
YES
NO
REPAIR SHORT TO VOLTAGE IN CKT 1289 AND RECHECK.
2
• IGNITION "OFF."
• DISCONNECT RIGHT FRONT SOLENOID CONNECTOR.
• MEASURE RESISTANCE BETWEEN TERMINAL "4" OF THE WORLD CONNECTOR HARNESS AND TERMINAL "A" OF THE RIGHT FRONT SOLENOID CONNECTOR HARNESS. RESISTANCE SHOULD BE 2 OHMS OR LESS. IS IT?
YES
NO
REPAIR OPEN CKT 1289 AND RECHECK.
3
• RECONNECT RIGHT FRONT SOLENOID CONNECTOR.
• MEASURE RESISTANCE BETWEEN TERMINAL "4" OF THE WORLD CONNECTOR HARNESS AND GROUND. RESISTANCE SHOULD BE BETWEEN 2.5 AND 5 OHMS. IS IT?
YES
NO
IF CKT IS NOT OPEN, REPLACE RIGHT FRONT SOLENOID, AND RECHECK.
4
• RECONNECT 24 WAY WORLD CONNECTOR AND VERIFY CODE RESETS.
CODE RESET.
CODE DID NOT SET.
REPLACE EBCM AND RECHECK.
CHECK SOLENOID CONNECTOR HARNESS TERMINALS "A" AND "B" FOR POOR CONTACT, ALSO CHECK WORLD CONNECTOR HARNESS TERMINAL "4" FOR POOR CONTACT. IF OK, REFER TO "DIAGNOSTIC AIDS"
GC402910072600DX

Fig. 82 Code A078: Right Front Solenoid Circuit Open Or Shorted To Battery (Part 2 of 2). 1992

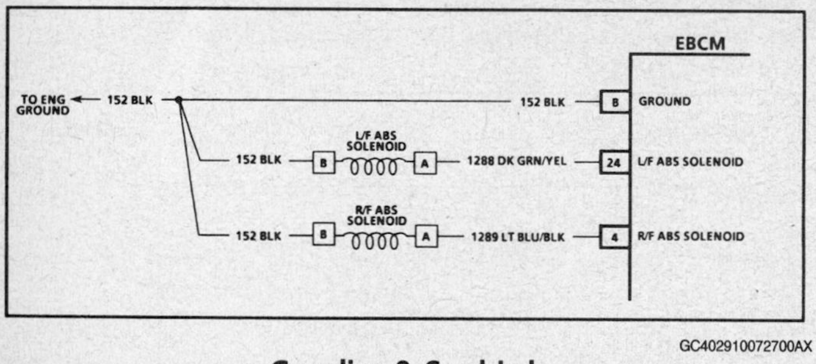
EBCM
TO ENG GROUND
152 BLK
152 BLK
B
GROUND
L/F ABS SOLENOID
152 BLK
B
A
1288 DK GRN/YEL
24
L/F ABS SOLENOID
R/F ABS SOLENOID
152 BLK
B
A
1289 LT BLU/BLK
4
R/F ABS SOLENOID
GC402910072700AX

Cavalier & Sunbird

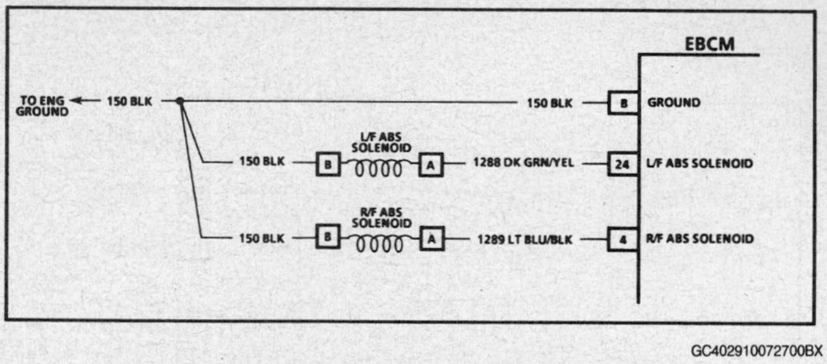
EBCM
TO ENG GROUND
150 BLK
150 BLK
B
GROUND
L/F ABS SOLENOID
150 BLK
B
A
1288 DK GRN/YEL
24
L/F ABS SOLENOID
R/F ABS SOLENOID
150 BLK
B
A
1289 LT BLU/BLK
4
R/F ABS SOLENOID
GC402910072700BX

Except Cavalier & Sunbird

Circuit Description:

This code identifies a solenoid that cannot be energized due to an open in its driver circuitry, or a short to ground between the solenoid driver and the solenoid. These faults can affect ABS operation since the flow of brake fluid to the wheel cylinder cannot be stopped, making ABS operation for that channel impossible.

Test Description: Number(s) below refer to circled number(s) on the diagnostic chart.

1. This step checks for a solenoid that is internally shorted to ground.
2. This step checks for a solenoid that is not within proper resistance values.
3. This step indicates if a short to ground exists in the solenoid circuitry.
4. This checks for an open control circuit to the EBCM.

Diagnostic Aids:

An "Intermittent" problem may be caused by a poor connection, rubbed through wire insulation, or a wire that is broken inside the insulation.

The frequency of the problem can be checked by using the enhanced diagnostic function of the "Scan" tool.

Any circuitry, that is suspected as causing the intermittent complaint, should be thoroughly checked for backed out terminals, improper mating, broken locks, improperly formed or damaged terminals, poor terminal to wiring connections or physical damage to the wiring harness.

GC402910072700CX

Fig. 83 Code A081: Right Front Solenoid Shorted To Ground Or Driver Open (Part 1 of 2). 1992

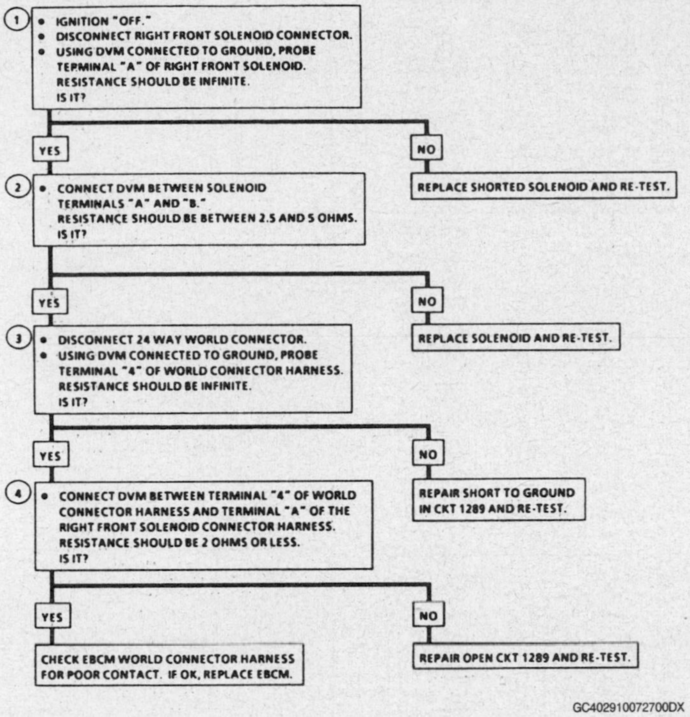
1
• IGNITION "OFF."
• DISCONNECT RIGHT FRONT SOLENOID CONNECTOR.
• USING DVM CONNECTED TO GROUND, PROBE TERMINAL "A" OF RIGHT FRONT SOLENOID. RESISTANCE SHOULD BE INFINITE. IS IT?
YES
NO
REPLACE SHORTED SOLENOID AND RE-TEST.
2
• CONNECT DVM BETWEEN SOLENOID TERMINALS "A" AND "B." RESISTANCE SHOULD BE BETWEEN 2.5 AND 5 OHMS. IS IT?
YES
NO
REPLACE SOLENOID AND RE-TEST.
3
• DISCONNECT 24 WAY WORLD CONNECTOR.
• USING DVM CONNECTED TO GROUND, PROBE TERMINAL "4" OF WORLD CONNECTOR HARNESS. RESISTANCE SHOULD BE INFINITE. IS IT?
YES
NO
REPAIR SHORT TO GROUND IN CKT 1289 AND RE-TEST.
4
• CONNECT DVM BETWEEN TERMINAL "4" OF WORLD CONNECTOR HARNESS AND TERMINAL "A" OF THE RIGHT FRONT SOLENOID CONNECTOR HARNESS. RESISTANCE SHOULD BE 2 OHMS OR LESS. IS IT?
YES
NO
CHECK EBCM WORLD CONNECTOR HARNESS FOR POOR CONTACT. IF OK, REPLACE EBCM.
REPAIR OPEN CKT 1289 AND RE-TEST.
GC402910072700DX

Fig. 83 Code A081: Right Front Solenoid Shorted To Ground Or Driver Open (Part 2 of 2). 1992

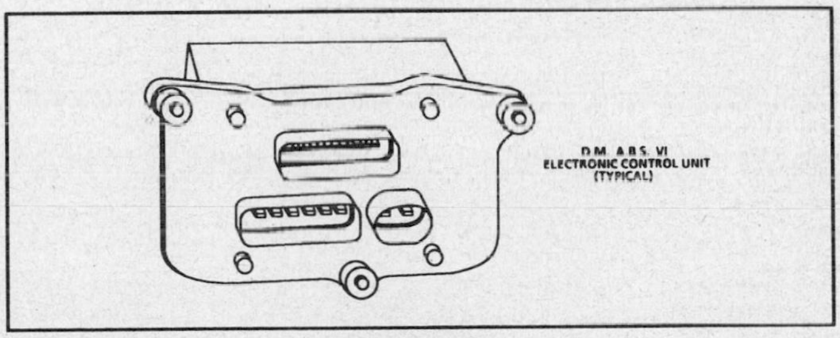
DM ABS VI
ELECTRONIC CONTROL UNIT
(TYPICAL)

CODE A082

CALIBRATION MEMORY FAILURE

Circuit Description:

This code allows the EBCM to check for a calibration failure by comparing the calibration value to a known value stored in the EEPROM.

This test is also used as a security measure to prevent improper use of calibrations or changes to these calibrations that may alter the designed function of ABS.

Test Description: Number(s) below refer to circled number(s) on the diagnostic chart.

1. This step checks to see if the fault is present during diagnosis. If present, the EBCM is not functioning correctly and must be replaced.

IMPORTANT: At the time of printing, 1992 vehicles with ABS-VI were not being field reprogrammed to correct this failure. A service bulletin will be issued when EEPROM reprogramming is authorized.

Diagnostic Aids:

An intermittent Code A082 may be caused by a bad cell in the EEPROM that is sensitive to temperature changes. If Code A082 failed more than once, but is intermittent, replace EBCM.

The frequency of the problem can be checked by using the enhanced diagnostic function of the "Scan" tool

GC402910072800AX

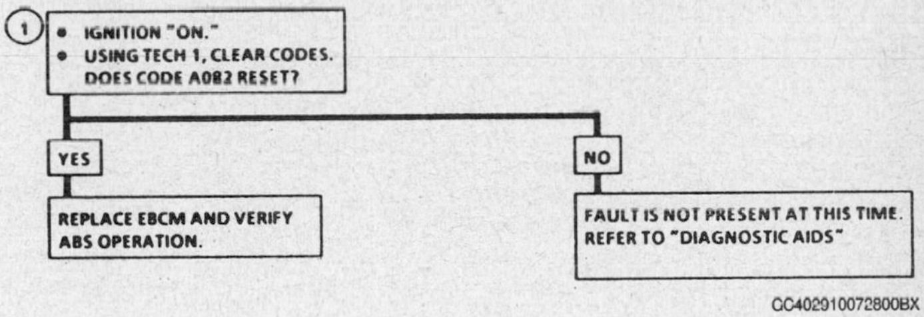
1
• IGNITION "ON."
• USING TECH 1, CLEAR CODES. DOES CODE A082 RESET?
YES
NO
REPLACE EBCM AND VERIFY ABS OPERATION.
FAULT IS NOT PRESENT AT THIS TIME. REFER TO "DIAGNOSTIC AIDS"
GC402910072800BX

Fig. 84 Code A082: Calibration Memory Failure. 1992

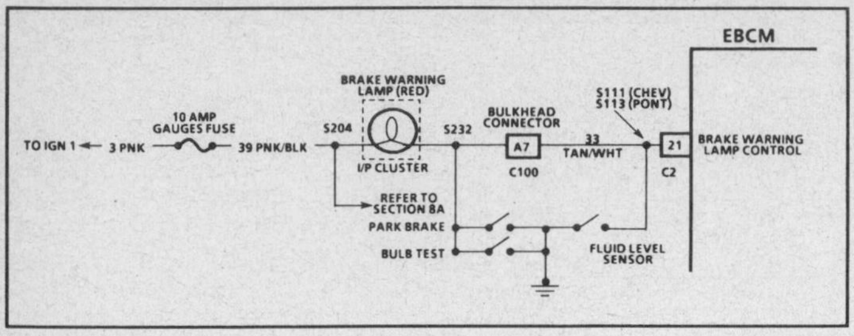
EBCM
BRAKE WARNING LAMP (RED)
10 AMP GAUGES FUSE
TO IGN 1 ← 3 PNK
39 PNK/BLK
S204
S232
BULKHEAD CONNECTOR
A7
C100
S111 (CHEV)
S113 (PONT)
33 TAN/WHT
21
C2
BRAKE WARNING LAMP CONTROL
I/P CLUSTER
REFER TO SECTION 8A
PARK BRAKE
BULB TEST
FLUID LEVEL SENSOR

GC402910072900AX

Cavalier & Sunbird

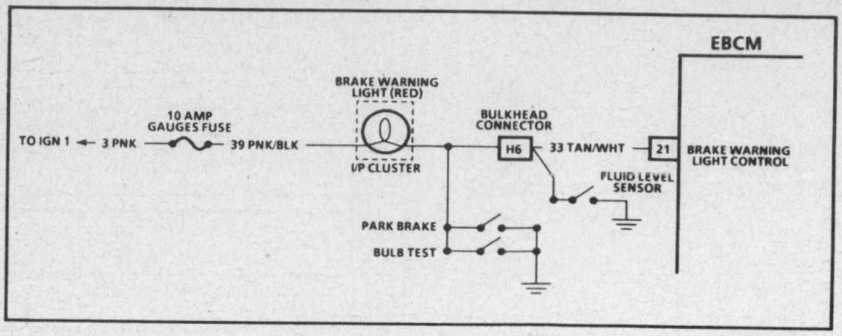
EBCM
BRAKE WARNING LIGHT (RED)
10 AMP GAUGES FUSE
TO IGN 1 ← 3 PNK
39 PNK/BLK
BULKHEAD CONNECTOR
H6
33 TAN/WHT
21
BRAKE WARNING LIGHT CONTROL
I/P CLUSTER
FLUID LEVEL SENSOR
PARK BRAKE
BULB TEST

GC402910072900BX

Beretta & Corsica

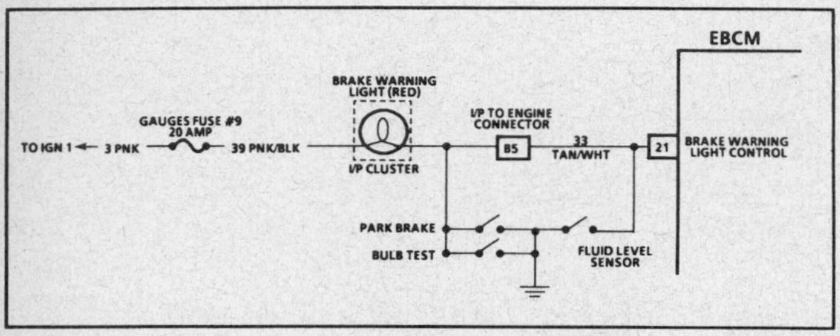
EBCM
BRAKE WARNING LIGHT (RED)
GAUGES FUSE #9 20 AMP
TO IGN 1 ← 3 PNK
39 PNK/BLK
I/P TO ENGINE CONNECTOR
B5
33 TAN/WHT
21
BRAKE WARNING LIGHT CONTROL
I/P CLUSTER
PARK BRAKE
BULB TEST
FLUID LEVEL SENSOR

GC402910072900CX

Achieva, Calais & Grand Am

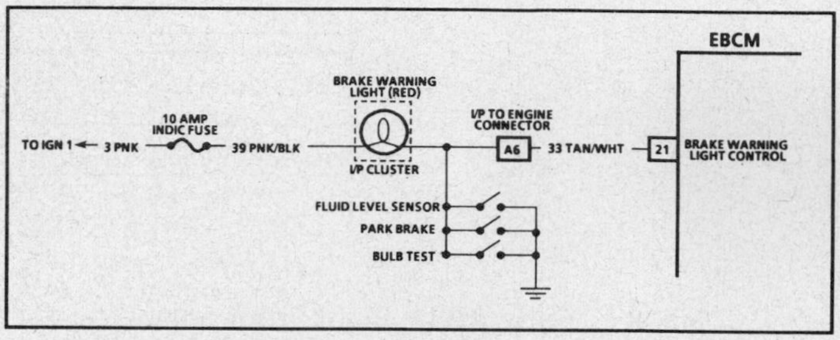
EBCM
BRAKE WARNING LIGHT (RED)
10 AMP INDIC FUSE
TO IGN 1 ← 3 PNK
39 PNK/BLK
I/P TO ENGINE CONNECTOR
A6
33 TAN/WHT
21
BRAKE WARNING LIGHT CONTROL
I/P CLUSTER
FLUID LEVEL SENSOR
PARK BRAKE
BULB TEST

GC402910072900DX

Cutlass Supreme, Grand Prix, Lumina & Regal

Circuit Description:

This code is provided as an information only test, and reflects the status of the command issued by the ABS EBCM to illuminate the red brake warning light. If another diagnostic code issues a command to illuminate the red brake warning light, Code A086 will be stored in EEPROM as a history code at the conclusion of the ignition cycle.

Test Description: Number(s) below refer to circled number(s) on the diagnostic chart.

1. This step serves to identify if a code other than Code A086 commanded the red brake warning light "ON."

Diagnostic Aids:

Any ABS mechanical code that issues a command to illuminate the red brake warning light will also result in Code A086 being stored in EEPROM during shut down. These codes are: A038, A041, A042, A045, A046, A047, A048 and A051. If the motors are not in their home position, certain electrical codes will also command the red brake warning light "ON." These codes are: A014, A018, A055, A056, A057, A0587, A061, A062, A063, A064, A065, A066, A067, A068, A071 and A072.

If any of these codes are indicated along with Code A086, they must be corrected prior to addressing a Code A086 fault.

GC402910072900EX

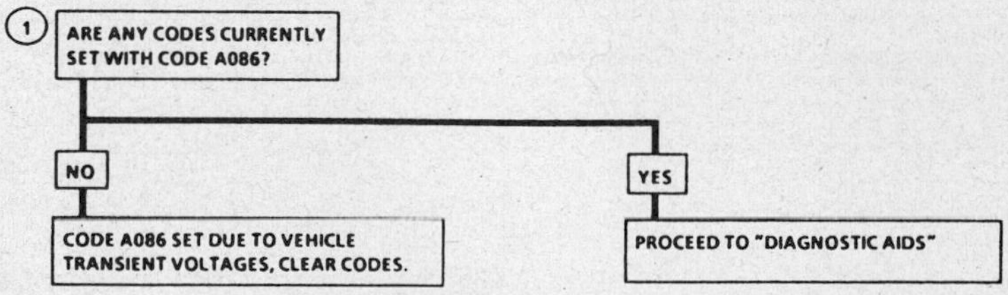
1
ARE ANY CODES CURRENTLY SET WITH CODE A086?
NO
YES
CODE A086 SET DUE TO VEHICLE TRANSIENT VOLTAGES, CLEAR CODES.
PROCEED TO "DIAGNOSTIC AIDS"

GC402910072900FX

Fig. 85 Code A086: ABS Enable Red Brake Telltale. 1992

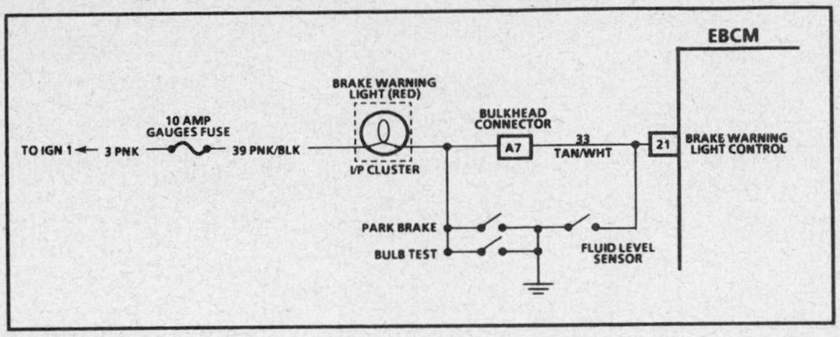
EBCM
BRAKE WARNING LIGHT (RED)
10 AMP GAUGES FUSE
BULKHEAD CONNECTOR
TO IGN 1 ← 3 PNK
39 PNK/BLK
I/P CLUSTER
A7
33 TAN/WHT
21
BRAKE WARNING LIGHT CONTROL
PARK BRAKE
BULB TEST
FLUID LEVEL SENSOR

GC402910073000AX

Cavalier & Sunbird

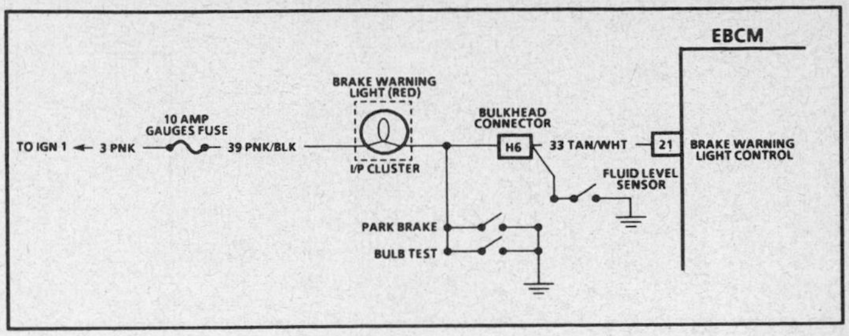
EBCM
BRAKE WARNING LIGHT (RED)
10 AMP GAUGES FUSE
BULKHEAD CONNECTOR
TO IGN 1 ← 3 PNK
39 PNK/BLK
I/P CLUSTER
H6
33 TAN/WHT
21
BRAKE WARNING LIGHT CONTROL
FLUID LEVEL SENSOR
PARK BRAKE
BULB TEST

GC402910073000BX

Beretta & Corsica

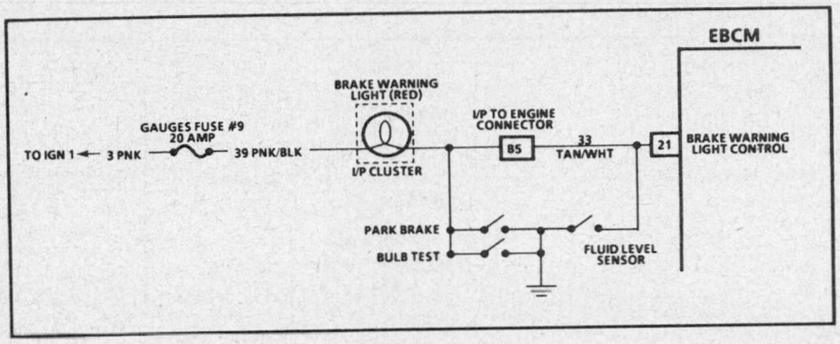
EBCM
BRAKE WARNING LIGHT (RED)
GAUGES FUSE #9 20 AMP
I/P TO ENGINE CONNECTOR
TO IGN 1 ← 3 PNK
39 PNK/BLK
I/P CLUSTER
B5
33 TAN/WHT
21
BRAKE WARNING LIGHT CONTROL
PARK BRAKE
BULB TEST
FLUID LEVEL SENSOR

GC402910073000CX

Achieva, Calais & Grand Am

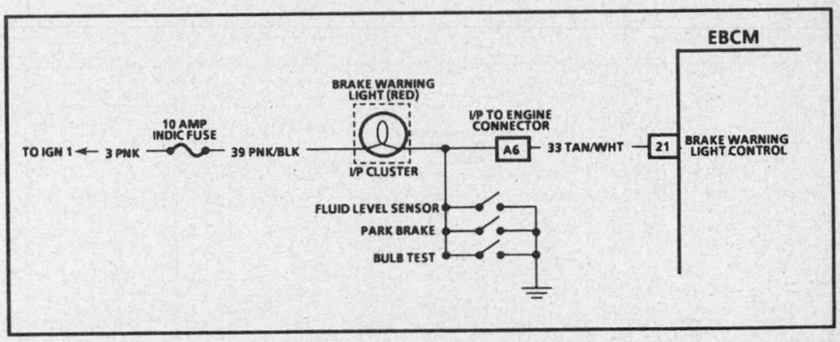
EBCM
BRAKE WARNING LIGHT (RED)
10 AMP INDIC FUSE
I/P TO ENGINE CONNECTOR
TO IGN 1 ← 3 PNK
39 PNK/BLK
I/P CLUSTER
A6
33 TAN/WHT
21
BRAKE WARNING LIGHT CONTROL
FLUID LEVEL SENSOR
PARK BRAKE
BULB TEST

GC402910073000DX

Cutlass Supreme, Grand Prix, Lumina & Regal

Circuit Description:

This code is used to verify the EBCM has continuity to the brake warning light in case the EBCM must turn it "ON." This will only occur if an ABS fault is detected that may degrade base brake operation.

Because ABS is not the only device controlling the brake warning light (parking brake and low fluid sensor may also turn "ON" the light) a short to ground in this circuit cannot be detected.

Test Description: Number(s) below refer to circled number(s) on the diagnostic chart.

1. This step identifies if the fault is currently present.
2. This step indicates if the EBCM and circuitry has the ability to complete the ground to the brake warning light and illuminate it.
3. Because the brake warning light has current supplied to it through the 10 amp gauge fuse, this step would indicate if the ignition circuit is complete to the I/P cluster.
4. This step isolates if the open circuit is due to a EBCM failure or open circuitry to the brake warning light.

Diagnostic Aids:

An "Intermittent" problem may be caused by a poor connection, rubbed through wire insulation, or a wire that is broken inside the insulation.

The frequency of the problem can be checked by using the enhanced diagnostic function of the Tech 1 "Scan" tool.

If a Tech 1 or T-100 are not available the parking brake handle may be lifted to verify proper light operation and continuity of CKTs 3 and 39.

Any circuitry, that is suspected as causing the intermittent complaint, should be thoroughly checked for backed out terminals, improper mating, broken locks, improperly formed or damaged terminals, poor terminal to wiring connections or physical damage to the wiring harness.

GC402910073000EX

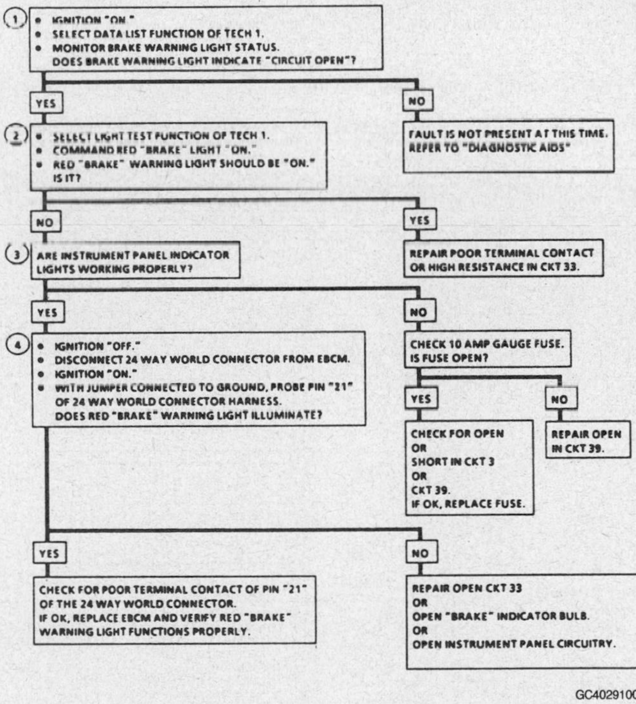
1
• IGNITION "ON."
• SELECT DATA LIST FUNCTION OF TECH 1.
• MONITOR BRAKE WARNING LIGHT STATUS.
DOES BRAKE WARNING LIGHT INDICATE "CIRCUIT OPEN"?
YES
NO
FAULT IS NOT PRESENT AT THIS TIME. REFER TO "DIAGNOSTIC AIDS"
2
• SELECT LIGHT TEST FUNCTION OF TECH 1.
• COMMAND RED "BRAKE" LIGHT "ON."
• RED "BRAKE" WARNING LIGHT SHOULD BE "ON." IS IT?
NO
YES
REPAIR POOR TERMINAL CONTACT OR HIGH RESISTANCE IN CKT 33.
3
ARE INSTRUMENT PANEL INDICATOR LIGHTS WORKING PROPERLY?
YES
NO
CHECK 10 AMP GAUGE FUSE. IS FUSE OPEN?
YES
NO
CHECK FOR OPEN OR SHORT IN CKT 3 OR CKT 39. IF OK, REPLACE FUSE.
REPAIR OPEN IN CKT 39.
4
• IGNITION "OFF."
• DISCONNECT 24 WAY WORLD CONNECTOR FROM EBCM.
• IGNITION "ON."
• WITH JUMPER CONNECTED TO GROUND, PROBE PIN "21" OF 24 WAY WORLD CONNECTOR HARNESS.
DOES RED "BRAKE" WARNING LIGHT ILLUMINATE?
YES
NO
CHECK FOR POOR TERMINAL CONTACT OF PIN "21" OF THE 24 WAY WORLD CONNECTOR. IF OK, REPLACE EBCM AND VERIFY RED "BRAKE" WARNING LIGHT FUNCTIONS PROPERLY.
REPAIR OPEN CKT 33 OR OPEN "BRAKE" INDICATOR BULB. OR OPEN INSTRUMENT PANEL CIRCUITRY.

GC402910073000FX

Fig. 86 Code A087: Red Brake Telltale Circuit open. 1992

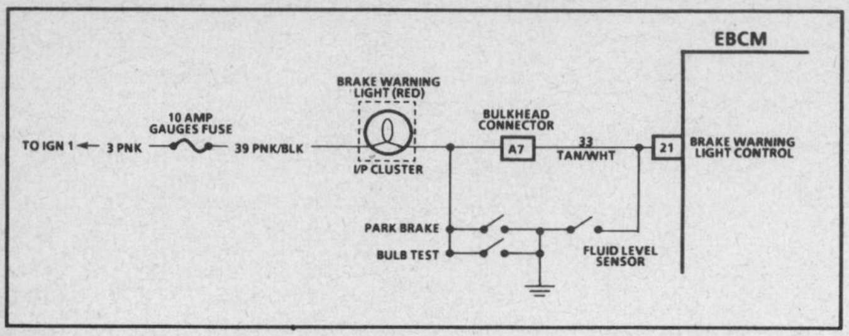
EBCM
BRAKE WARNING LIGHT (RED)
10 AMP GAUGES FUSE
TO IGN 1 3 PNK
39 PNK/BLK
I/P CLUSTER
BULKHEAD CONNECTOR
A7
33 TAN/WHT
21
BRAKE WARNING LIGHT CONTROL
PARK BRAKE
BULB TEST
FLUID LEVEL SENSOR

GC402910073100AX

Cavalier & Sunbird

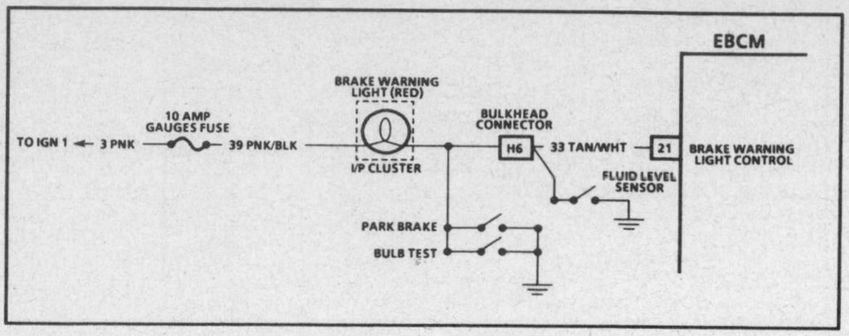
EBCM
BRAKE WARNING LIGHT (RED)
10 AMP GAUGES FUSE
TO IGN 1 3 PNK
39 PNK/BLK
I/P CLUSTER
BULKHEAD CONNECTOR
H6
33 TAN/WHT
21
BRAKE WARNING LIGHT CONTROL
FLUID LEVEL SENSOR
PARK BRAKE
BULB TEST

GC402910073100BX

Beretta & Corsica

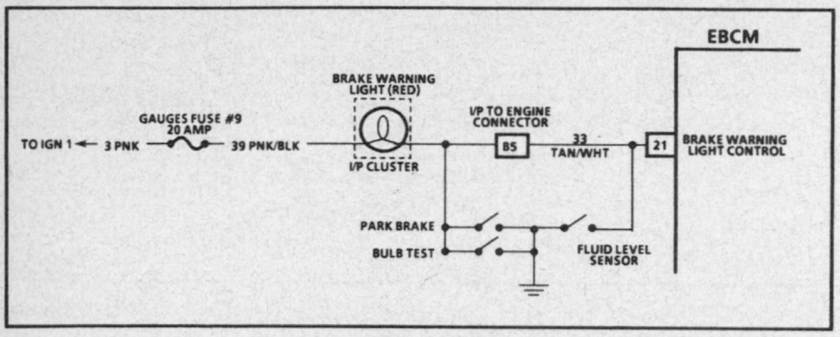
EBCM
BRAKE WARNING LIGHT (RED)
GAUGES FUSE #9 20 AMP
TO IGN 1 3 PNK
39 PNK/BLK
I/P CLUSTER
I/P TO ENGINE CONNECTOR
B5
33 TAN/WHT
21
BRAKE WARNING LIGHT CONTROL
PARK BRAKE
BULB TEST
FLUID LEVEL SENSOR

GC402910073100CX

Achieva, Calais & Grand Am

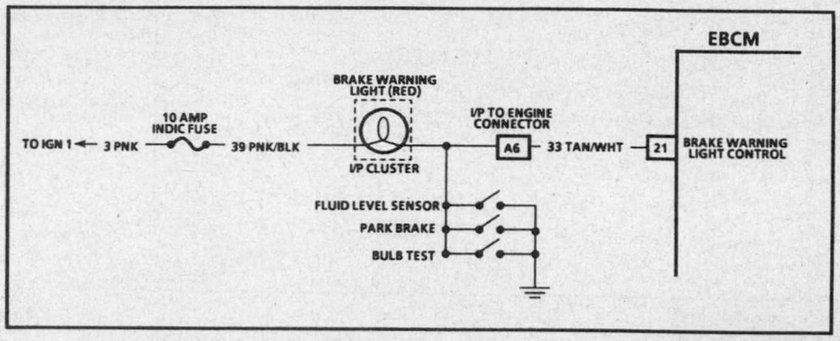
EBCM
BRAKE WARNING LIGHT (RED)
10 AMP INDIC FUSE
TO IGN 1 3 PNK
39 PNK/BLK
I/P CLUSTER
I/P TO ENGINE CONNECTOR
A6
33 TAN/WHT
21
BRAKE WARNING LIGHT CONTROL
FLUID LEVEL SENSOR
PARK BRAKE
BULB TEST

GC402910073100DX

Cutlass Supreme, Grand Prix, Lumina & Regal

Circuit Description:

This code identifies a short to battery between the EBCM and the RED brake warning light, or an open driver that does not allow the RED brake warning light to be illuminated by the EBCM. This will only occur if an ABS fault is detected that may degrade base brake operation.

Test Description: Number(s) below refer to circled number(s) on the diagnostic chart.

1. This step identifies if the ground circuit to the Red brake warning light is being completed by a source other than the EBCM.
2. This step identifies if the fault is currently present.
3. By removing the 10 amp gauge fuse, the voltage source is eliminated. This test indicates if voltage is being supplied from a source other than the gauge fuse.

Diagnostic Aids:

An "Intermittent" problem may be caused by a poor connection, rubbed through wire insulation, or a wire that is broken inside the insulation.

The frequency of the problem can be checked by using the enhanced diagnostic function of the "Scan" tool.

Any circuitry, that is suspected as causing the intermittent complaint, should be thoroughly checked for backed out terminals, improper mating, broken locks, improperly formed or damaged terminals, poor terminal to wiring connections or physical damage to the wiring harness.

GC402910073100EX

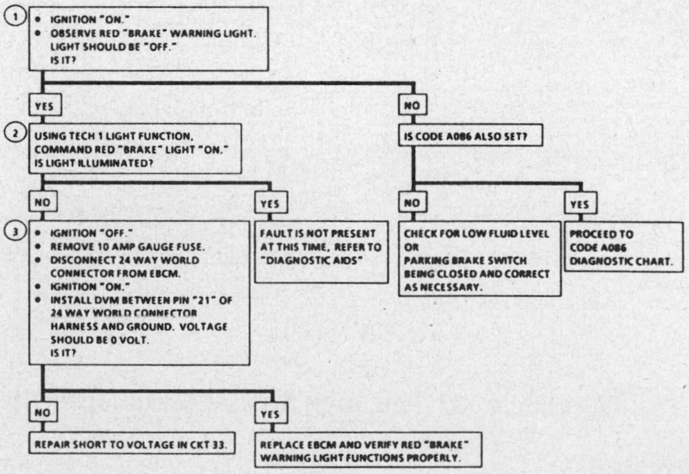
1
• IGNITION "ON."
• OBSERVE RED "BRAKE" WARNING LIGHT. LIGHT SHOULD BE "OFF." IS IT?
YES
NO
2
USING TECH 1 LIGHT FUNCTION, COMMAND RED "BRAKE" LIGHT "ON." IS LIGHT ILLUMINATED?
IS CODE A086 ALSO SET?
NO
YES
NO
YES
3
• IGNITION "OFF."
• REMOVE 10 AMP GAUGE FUSE.
• DISCONNECT 24 WAY WORLD CONNECTOR FROM EBCM.
• IGNITION "ON."
• INSTALL DVM BETWEEN PIN "21" OF 24 WAY WORLD CONNECTOR HARNESS AND GROUND. VOLTAGE SHOULD BE 0 VOLT. IS IT?
FAULT IS NOT PRESENT AT THIS TIME, REFER TO "DIAGNOSTIC AIDS"
CHECK FOR LOW FLUID LEVEL OR PARKING BRAKE SWITCH BEING CLOSED AND CORRECT AS NECESSARY.
PROCEED TO CODE A086 DIAGNOSTIC CHART.
NO
YES
REPAIR SHORT TO VOLTAGE IN CKT 33.
REPLACE EBCM AND VERIFY RED "BRAKE" WARNING LIGHT FUNCTIONS PROPERLY.

GC402910073100FX

Fig. 87 Code A088: Red Brake Telltale Circuit Shorted To Battery Or Driver Open. 1992

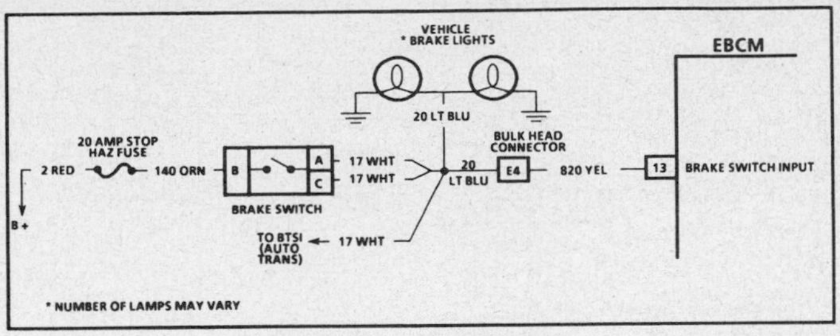
VEHICLE
* BRAKE LIGHTS
EBCM
20 LT BLU
20 AMP STOP
HAZ FUSE
BULK HEAD
CONNECTOR
2 RED
140 ORN
B
A
C
17 WHT
17 WHT
20
LT BLU
E4
820 YEL
13
BRAKE SWITCH INPUT
BRAKE SWITCH
B+
TO BTSI
(AUTO
TRANS)
17 WHT
* NUMBER OF LAMPS MAY VARY

GC402910073200AX

Cavalier & Sunbird

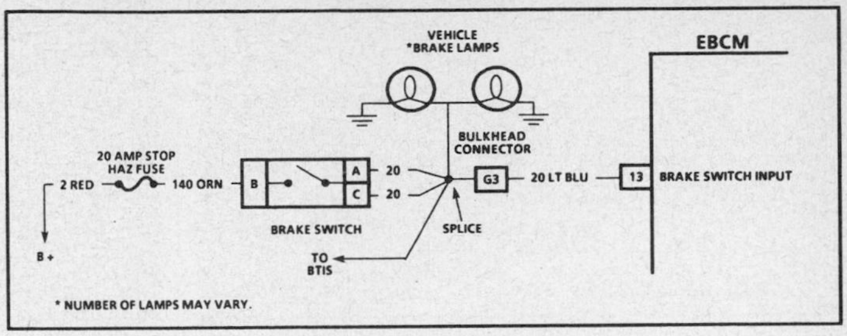
VEHICLE
*BRAKE LAMPS
EBCM
BULKHEAD
CONNECTOR
20 AMP STOP
HAZ FUSE
2 RED
140 ORN
B
A
C
20
20
G3
20 LT BLU
13
BRAKE SWITCH INPUT
BRAKE SWITCH
SPLICE
B+
TO
BTIS
* NUMBER OF LAMPS MAY VARY.

GC402910073200BX

Beretta & Corsica

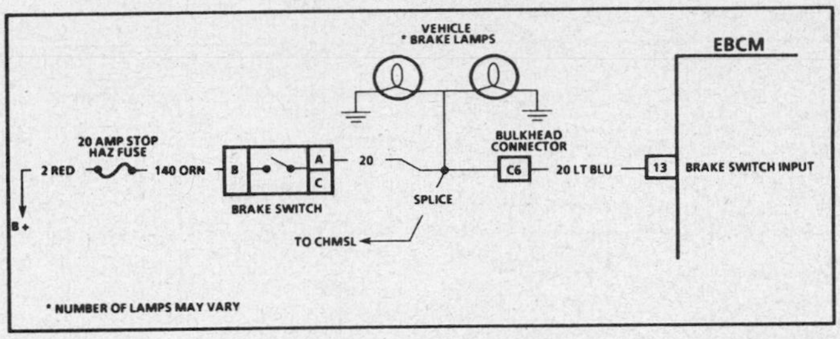
VEHICLE
* BRAKE LAMPS
EBCM
20 AMP STOP
HAZ FUSE
BULKHEAD
CONNECTOR
2 RED
140 ORN
B
A
C
20
C6
20 LT BLU
13
BRAKE SWITCH INPUT
BRAKE SWITCH
SPLICE
B+
TO CHMSL
* NUMBER OF LAMPS MAY VARY

GC402910073200CX

Achieva, Calais & Grand Am

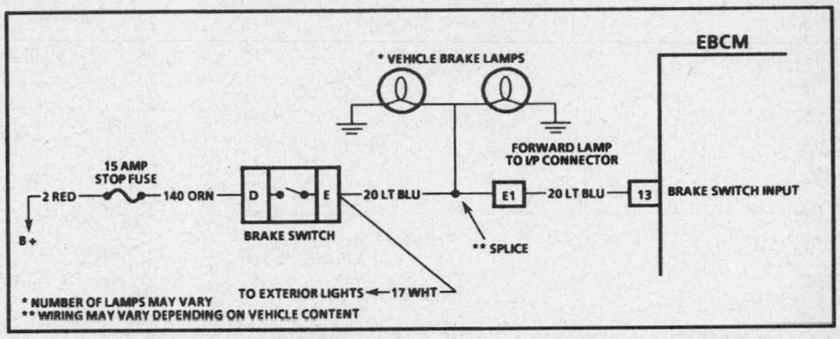
EBCM
* VEHICLE BRAKE LAMPS
FORWARD LAMP
TO I/P CONNECTOR
15 AMP
STOP FUSE
2 RED
140 ORN
D
E
20 LT BLU
E1
20 LT BLU
13
BRAKE SWITCH INPUT
B+
BRAKE SWITCH
** SPLICE
* NUMBER OF LAMPS MAY VARY
TO EXTERIOR LIGHTS
17 WHT
** WIRING MAY VARY DEPENDING ON VEHICLE CONTENT

GC402910073200DX

Cutlass Supreme, Grand Prix, Lumina & Regal

Circuit Description:
This code is used to detect an open brake switch in the non-ABS mode. The EBCM looks for decel rates that would indicate braking action and verifies this assumption by requiring several repeats of this detection method. In each case, ABS will not be available since no brake switch is seen.

Test Description: Number(s) below refer to circled number(s) on the diagnostic chart.

1. This step indicates if the brake switch signal is being received by the EBCM.
2. This step indicates if an open circuit exists in the brake switch or brake lamp circuitry.
3. This step isolates the open circuit to either the brake switch input circuitry, or the EBCM.

Diagnostic Aids:

An "Intermittent" problem may be caused by a poor connection, rubbed through wire insulation, or a wire that is broken inside the insulation.

The frequency of the problem can be checked by using the enhanced diagnostic function of the "Scan" tool.

Any circuitry, that is suspected as causing the intermittent complaint, should be thoroughly checked for backed out terminals, improper mating, broken locks, improperly formed or damaged terminals, poor terminal to wiring connections or physical damage to the wiring harness.

GC402910073200EX

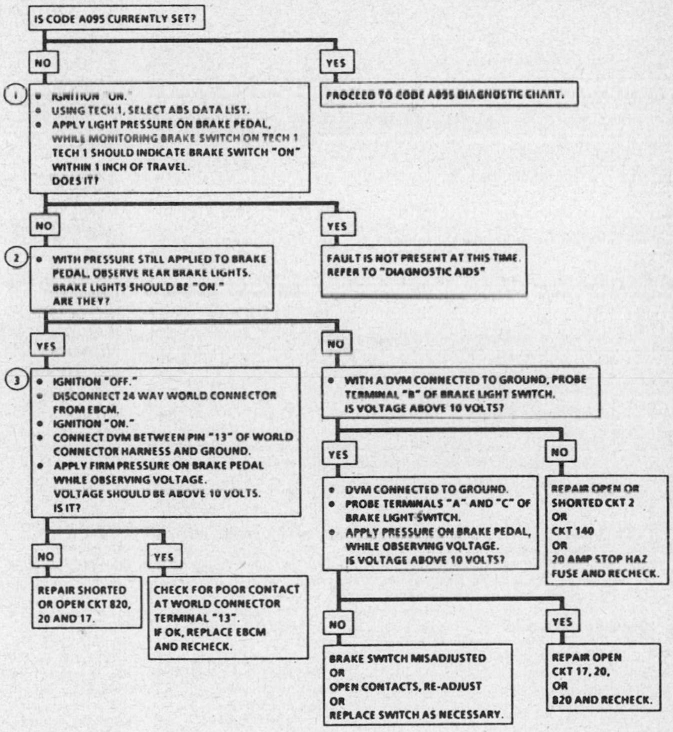
IS CODE A095 CURRENTLY SET?
NO
YES
PROCEED TO CODE A095 DIAGNOSTIC CHART.
1
• IGNITION "ON."
• USING TECH 1, SELECT ABS DATA LIST.
• APPLY LIGHT PRESSURE ON BRAKE PEDAL, WHILE MONITORING BRAKE SWITCH ON TECH 1
TECH 1 SHOULD INDICATE BRAKE SWITCH "ON" WITHIN 1 INCH OF TRAVEL.
DOES IT?
NO
YES
FAULT IS NOT PRESENT AT THIS TIME. REFER TO "DIAGNOSTIC AIDS"
2
• WITH PRESSURE STILL APPLIED TO BRAKE PEDAL, OBSERVE REAR BRAKE LIGHTS.
BRAKE LIGHTS SHOULD BE "ON."
ARE THEY?
YES
NO
3
• IGNITION "OFF."
• DISCONNECT 24 WAY WORLD CONNECTOR FROM EBCM.
• IGNITION "ON."
• CONNECT DVM BETWEEN PIN "13" OF WORLD CONNECTOR HARNESS AND GROUND.
• APPLY FIRM PRESSURE ON BRAKE PEDAL WHILE OBSERVING VOLTAGE.
VOLTAGE SHOULD BE ABOVE 10 VOLTS.
IS IT?
• WITH A DVM CONNECTED TO GROUND, PROBE TERMINAL "B" OF BRAKE LIGHT SWITCH.
IS VOLTAGE ABOVE 10 VOLTS?
YES
NO
• DVM CONNECTED TO GROUND.
• PROBE TERMINALS "A" AND "C" OF BRAKE LIGHT SWITCH.
• APPLY PRESSURE ON BRAKE PEDAL, WHILE OBSERVING VOLTAGE.
IS VOLTAGE ABOVE 10 VOLTS?
REPAIR OPEN OR SHORTED CKT 2 OR CKT 140 OR 20 AMP STOP HAZ FUSE AND RECHECK.
NO
YES
REPAIR SHORTED OR OPEN CKT 820, 20 AND 17.
CHECK FOR POOR CONTACT AT WORLD CONNECTOR TERMINAL "13".
IF OK, REPLACE EBCM AND RECHECK.
NO
YES
BRAKE SWITCH MISADJUSTED OR OPEN CONTACTS, RE-ADJUST OR REPLACE SWITCH AS NECESSARY.
REPAIR OPEN CKT 17, 20, OR 820 AND RECHECK.

GC402910073200FX

Fig. 88 Code A091: Open Brake Switch Contacts, Deceleration Detection. 1992

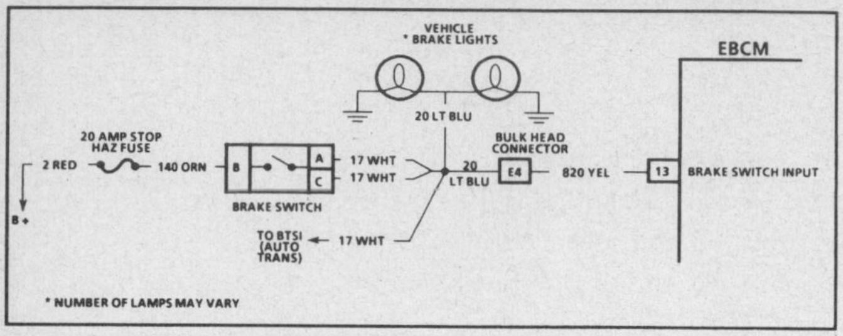
VEHICLE
* BRAKE LIGHTS
EBCM
20 LT BLU
20 AMP STOP
HAZ FUSE
BULK HEAD
CONNECTOR
2 RED
140 ORN
B
A
C
17 WHT
17 WHT
20
LT BLU
E4
820 YEL
13
BRAKE SWITCH INPUT
B+
BRAKE SWITCH
TO BTSI
(AUTO
TRANS)
17 WHT
* NUMBER OF LAMPS MAY VARY

GC402910073300AX

Cavalier & Sunbird

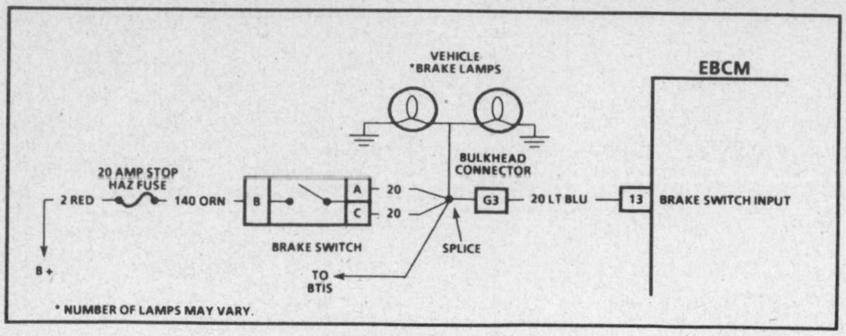
VEHICLE
*BRAKE LAMPS
EBCM
BULKHEAD
CONNECTOR
20 AMP STOP
HAZ FUSE
2 RED
140 ORN
B
A
C
20
20
G3
20 LT BLU
13
BRAKE SWITCH INPUT
BRAKE SWITCH
SPLICE
B+
TO
BTIS
* NUMBER OF LAMPS MAY VARY.

GC402910073300BX

Beretta & Corsica

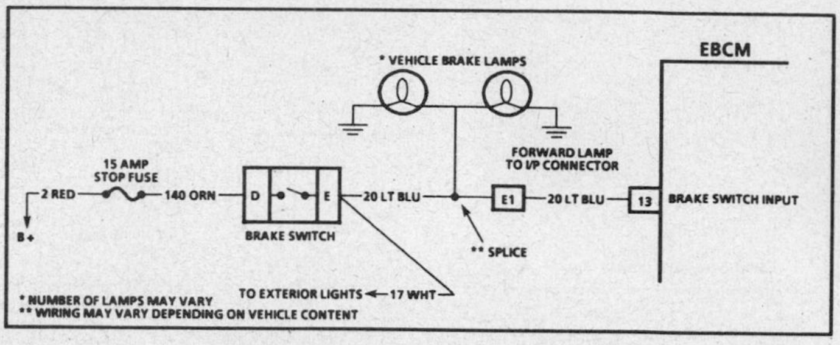
* VEHICLE BRAKE LAMPS
EBCM
FORWARD LAMP
TO I/P CONNECTOR
15 AMP
STOP FUSE
2 RED
140 ORN
D
E
20 LT BLU
E1
20 LT BLU
13
BRAKE SWITCH INPUT
B+
BRAKE SWITCH
** SPLICE
TO EXTERIOR LIGHTS
17 WHT
* NUMBER OF LAMPS MAY VARY
** WIRING MAY VARY DEPENDING ON VEHICLE CONTENT

GC402910073300DX

Cutlass Supreme, Grand Prix, Lumina & Regal

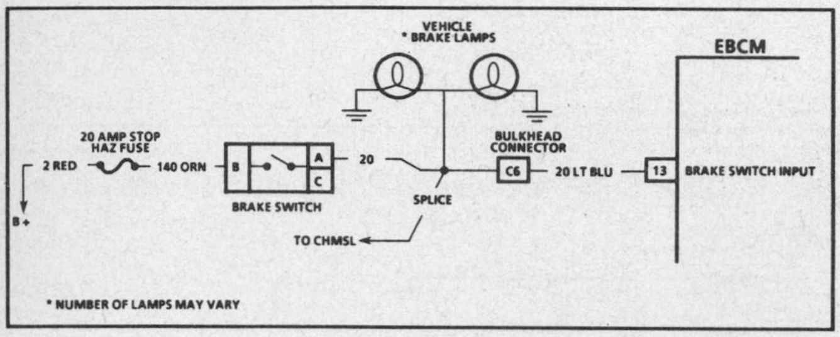
VEHICLE
* BRAKE LAMPS
EBCM
20 AMP STOP
HAZ FUSE
BULKHEAD
CONNECTOR
2 RED
140 ORN
B
A
C
20
C6
20 LT BLU
13
BRAKE SWITCH INPUT
B+
BRAKE SWITCH
SPLICE
TO CHMSL
* NUMBER OF LAMPS MAY VARY

GC402910073300CX

Achieva, Calais & Grand Am

Circuit Description:

This code is designed to detect a stripped nut or gear assembly during initialization. During the homing sequence, the piston should reach the top of the bore resulting in a stalled motor. If this does not occur, the motor must be spinning with little or no resistance, indicating a nut/screw or gear failure.

Test Description: Number(s) below refer to circled number(s) on the diagnostic chart.

1. This step checks for a slipping nut or gear if either were to slip, it would result in a lack of hydraulic pressure being applied at the rear wheels, causing the wheels to be able to be moved.
2. During a full apply, once the ball screw reaches the top of its travel, the motor should stall. If the motor continues to run, an indication of a stripped nut or gear is present.
3. This step is used to release the tension of the motor pack prior to removal.

Diagnostic Aids:

An "Intermittent" fault in this code may result from a mechanical part of the system that sticks, binds, or slips.

The frequency of the problem can be checked by using the enhanced diagnostic function of the "Scan" tool

If code only fails once and Code A064 also fails, see Code A064. If intermittent and enhanced diagnostics show this code fails during ABS, see Code A064.

Depending on the frequency of the failure, a physical inspection of the mechanical parts suspected may be necessary.

GC402910070600EX

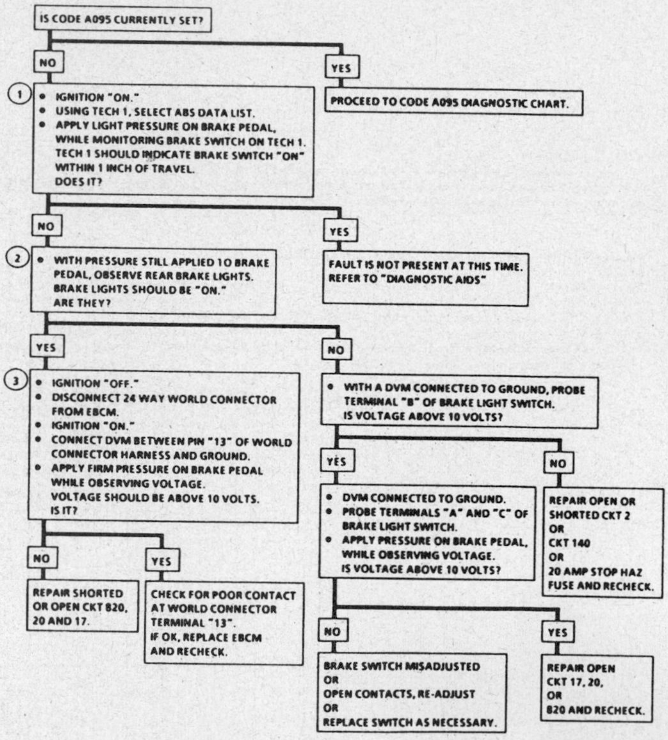
IS CODE A095 CURRENTLY SET?
NO
YES
PROCEED TO CODE A095 DIAGNOSTIC CHART.
1
• IGNITION "ON."
• USING TECH 1, SELECT ABS DATA LIST.
• APPLY LIGHT PRESSURE ON BRAKE PEDAL, WHILE MONITORING BRAKE SWITCH ON TECH 1. TECH 1 SHOULD INDICATE BRAKE SWITCH "ON" WITHIN 1 INCH OF TRAVEL.
DOES IT?
NO
YES
FAULT IS NOT PRESENT AT THIS TIME. REFER TO "DIAGNOSTIC AIDS"
2
• WITH PRESSURE STILL APPLIED TO BRAKE PEDAL, OBSERVE REAR BRAKE LIGHTS. BRAKE LIGHTS SHOULD BE "ON."
ARE THEY?
YES
NO
3
• IGNITION "OFF."
• DISCONNECT 24 WAY WORLD CONNECTOR FROM EBCM.
• IGNITION "ON."
• CONNECT DVM BETWEEN PIN "13" OF WORLD CONNECTOR HARNESS AND GROUND.
• APPLY FIRM PRESSURE ON BRAKE PEDAL WHILE OBSERVING VOLTAGE.
VOLTAGE SHOULD BE ABOVE 10 VOLTS.
IS IT?
• WITH A DVM CONNECTED TO GROUND, PROBE TERMINAL "B" OF BRAKE LIGHT SWITCH.
IS VOLTAGE ABOVE 10 VOLTS?
YES
NO
• DVM CONNECTED TO GROUND.
• PROBE TERMINALS "A" AND "C" OF BRAKE LIGHT SWITCH.
• APPLY PRESSURE ON BRAKE PEDAL, WHILE OBSERVING VOLTAGE.
IS VOLTAGE ABOVE 10 VOLTS?
REPAIR OPEN OR SHORTED CKT 2 OR CKT 140 OR 20 AMP STOP HAZ FUSE AND RECHECK.
NO
YES
REPAIR SHORTED OR OPEN CKT 820, 20 AND 17.
CHECK FOR POOR CONTACT AT WORLD CONNECTOR TERMINAL "13".
IF OK, REPLACE EBCM AND RECHECK.
NO
YES
BRAKE SWITCH MISADJUSTED OR OPEN CONTACTS, RE-ADJUST OR REPLACE SWITCH AS NECESSARY.
REPAIR OPEN CKT 17, 20, OR 820 AND RECHECK.

GC402910073300FX

Fig. 89 Code A092: Open Brake Switch Contacts. 1992

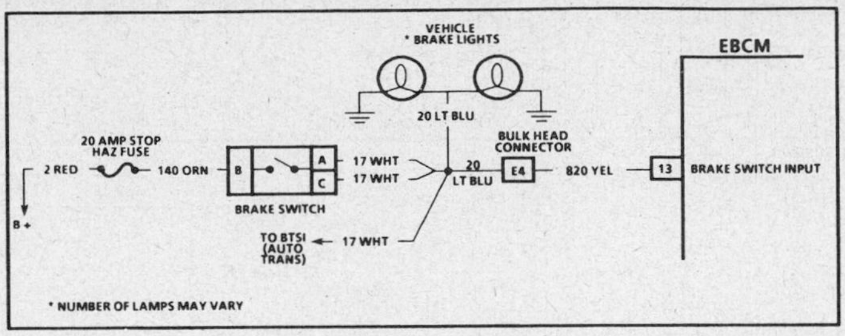
VEHICLE
* BRAKE LIGHTS
EBCM
20 LT BLU
20 AMP STOP
HAZ FUSE
2 RED
140 ORN
B
A
C
17 WHT
17 WHT
BULK HEAD
CONNECTOR
20
LT BLU
E4
820 YEL
13
BRAKE SWITCH INPUT
BRAKE SWITCH
B+
TO BTSI
(AUTO
TRANS)
17 WHT
* NUMBER OF LAMPS MAY VARY

GC402910073400AX

Cavalier & Sunbird

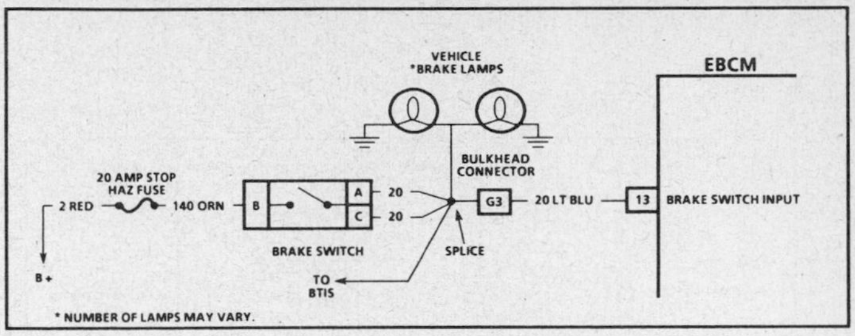
VEHICLE
*BRAKE LAMPS
EBCM
BULKHEAD
CONNECTOR
20 AMP STOP
HAZ FUSE
2 RED
140 ORN
B
A
C
20
20
G3
20 LT BLU
13
BRAKE SWITCH INPUT
BRAKE SWITCH
SPLICE
B+
TO
BTIS
* NUMBER OF LAMPS MAY VARY.

GC402910073400BX

Beretta & Corsica

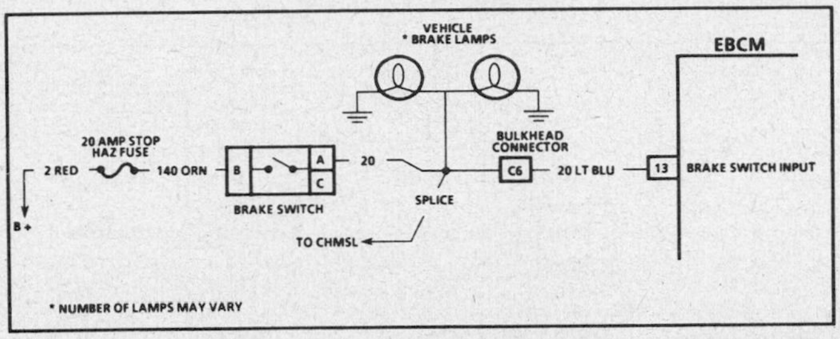
VEHICLE
* BRAKE LAMPS
EBCM
BULKHEAD
CONNECTOR
20 AMP STOP
HAZ FUSE
2 RED
140 ORN
B
A
C
20
C6
20 LT BLU
13
BRAKE SWITCH INPUT
BRAKE SWITCH
SPLICE
B+
TO CHMSL
* NUMBER OF LAMPS MAY VARY

GC402910073400CX

Achieva, Calais & Grand Am

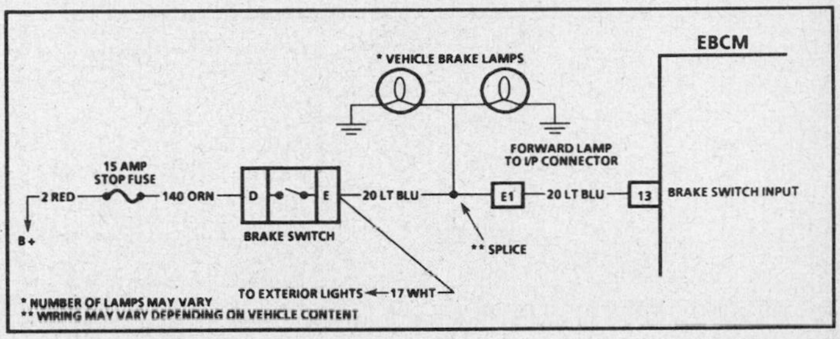
EBCM
* VEHICLE BRAKE LAMPS
FORWARD LAMP
TO I/P CONNECTOR
15 AMP
STOP FUSE
2 RED
140 ORN
D
E
20 LT BLU
E1
20 LT BLU
13
BRAKE SWITCH INPUT
BRAKE SWITCH
B+
** SPLICE
TO EXTERIOR LIGHTS
17 WHT
* NUMBER OF LAMPS MAY VARY
** WIRING MAY VARY DEPENDING ON VEHICLE CONTENT

GC402910073400DX

Cutlass Supreme, Grand Prix, Lumina & Regal

Circuit Description:

This code is the second portion of Codes A091 and A092. If Codes A091 or A092 failed during the last ignition cycle, Code A093 becomes a current failure during the next ignition cycle, keeping ABS disabled until a brake switch "ON" state is seen. When a change is seen during an ignition cycle in which Code A093 is a current failure, Code A091 or A092 will clear itself at the end of the current ignition cycle, and ABS will enable itself at the start of the next ignition cycle. Code A093 alone indicates Codes A091 or A092 failed previously, but is intermittent, or has been corrected.

Test Description: Number(s) below refer to circled number(s) on the diagnostic chart.

1. This step indicates which code (either A091 or A092) caused Code A093 to set.
2. This insures that the code that set is repaired so that Code A093 can be cleared.

Diagnostic Aids:

An "Intermittent" problem may be caused by a poor connection, rubbed through wire insulation, or a wire that is broken inside the insulation.

The frequency of the problem can be checked by using the enhanced diagnostic function of the "Scan" tool.

Any circuitry, that is suspected as causing the intermittent complaint, should be thoroughly checked for backed out terminals, improper mating, broken locks, improperly formed or damaged terminals, poor terminal to wiring connections or physical damage to the wiring harness.

Also, verify proper brake switch operation using the data list of the "Scan" tool. As the brake is applied, the data list should display the brake switch "ON" within 1 inch of travel.

GC402910073400EX

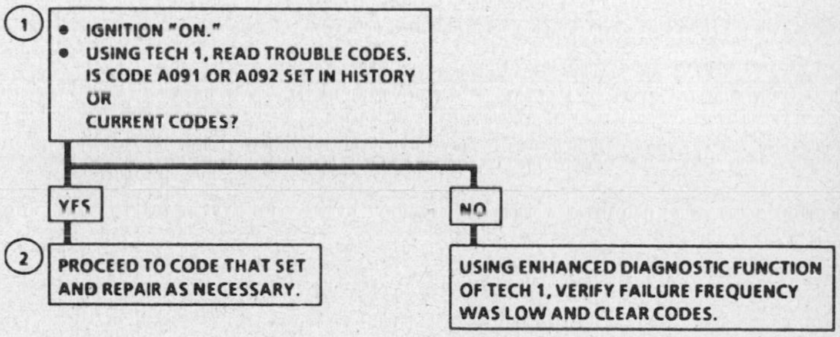
1
• IGNITION "ON."
• USING TECH 1, READ TROUBLE CODES.
IS CODE A091 OR A092 SET IN HISTORY
OR
CURRENT CODES?
YES
NO
2
PROCEED TO CODE THAT SET
AND REPAIR AS NECESSARY.
USING ENHANCED DIAGNOSTIC FUNCTION
OF TECH 1, VERIFY FAILURE FREQUENCY
WAS LOW AND CLEAR CODES.

GC402910073400FX

Fig. 90 Code A093: Test 91 Or 92 Failed Last Or Current Ignition Cycle. 1992

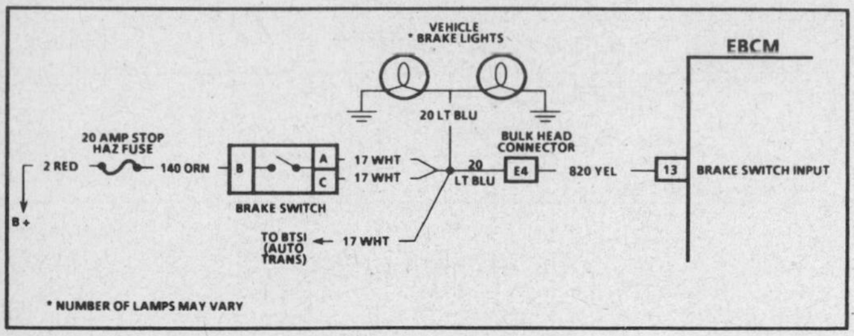
VEHICLE
* BRAKE LIGHTS
EBCM
20 LT BLU
20 AMP STOP
HAZ FUSE
2 RED
140 ORN
B
A
C
17 WHT
17 WHT
20
LT BLU
BULK HEAD
CONNECTOR
E4
820 YEL
13
BRAKE SWITCH INPUT
B+
BRAKE SWITCH
TO BTSI
(AUTO
TRANS)
17 WHT
* NUMBER OF LAMPS MAY VARY

GC402910073500AX

Cavalier & Sunbird

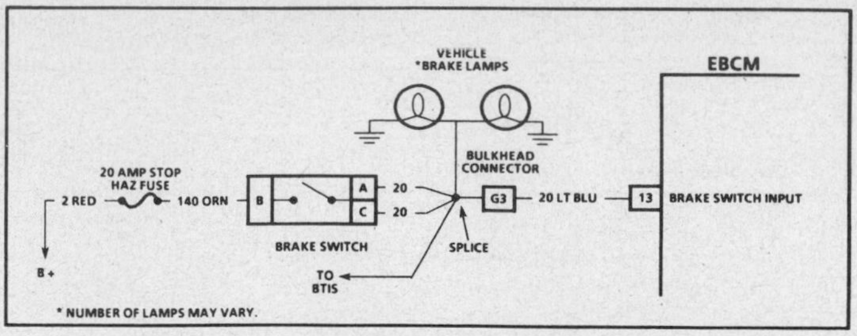
VEHICLE
*BRAKE LAMPS
EBCM
20 AMP STOP
HAZ FUSE
2 RED
140 ORN
B
A
C
20
20
BULKHEAD
CONNECTOR
G3
20 LT BLU
13
BRAKE SWITCH INPUT
B+
BRAKE SWITCH
SPLICE
TO
BTIS
* NUMBER OF LAMPS MAY VARY.

GC402910073500BX

Beretta & Corsica

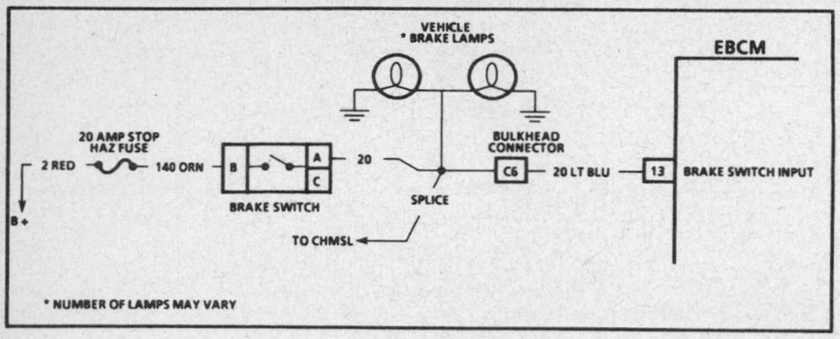
VEHICLE
* BRAKE LAMPS
EBCM
20 AMP STOP
HAZ FUSE
2 RED
140 ORN
B
A
C
20
BULKHEAD
CONNECTOR
C6
20 LT BLU
13
BRAKE SWITCH INPUT
B+
BRAKE SWITCH
SPLICE
TO CHMSL
* NUMBER OF LAMPS MAY VARY

GC402910073500CX

Achieva, Calais & Grand Am

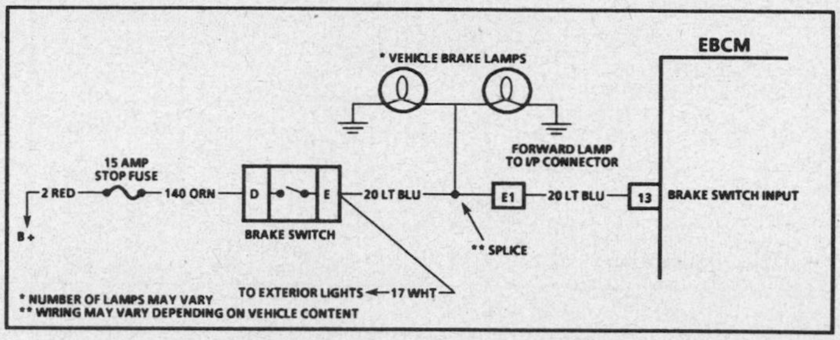
* VEHICLE BRAKE LAMPS
EBCM
FORWARD LAMP
TO I/P CONNECTOR
15 AMP
STOP FUSE
2 RED
140 ORN
D
E
20 LT BLU
E1
20 LT BLU
13
BRAKE SWITCH INPUT
B+
BRAKE SWITCH
** SPLICE
TO EXTERIOR LIGHTS
17 WHT
* NUMBER OF LAMPS MAY VARY
** WIRING MAY VARY DEPENDING ON VEHICLE CONTENT

GC402910073500DX

Cutlass Supreme, Grand Prix, Lumina & Regal

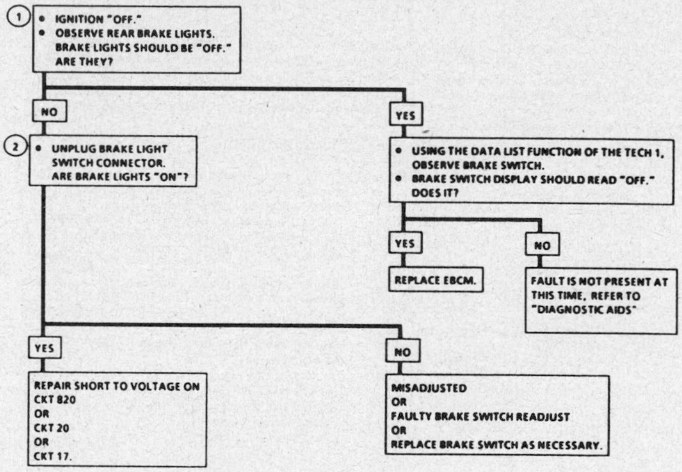
1
• IGNITION "OFF."
• OBSERVE REAR BRAKE LIGHTS. BRAKE LIGHTS SHOULD BE "OFF." ARE THEY?
NO
YES
2
• UNPLUG BRAKE LIGHT SWITCH CONNECTOR. ARE BRAKE LIGHTS "ON"?
• USING THE DATA LIST FUNCTION OF THE TECH 1, OBSERVE BRAKE SWITCH.
• BRAKE SWITCH DISPLAY SHOULD READ "OFF." DOES IT?
YES
NO
REPLACE EBCM.
FAULT IS NOT PRESENT AT THIS TIME, REFER TO "DIAGNOSTIC AIDS"
YES
NO
REPAIR SHORT TO VOLTAGE ON CKT 820 OR CKT 20 OR CKT 17.
MISADJUSTED OR FAULTY BRAKE SWITCH READJUST OR REPLACE BRAKE SWITCH AS NECESSARY.

GC402910073500FX

Circuit Description:

This code is run to determine the proper operation of the brake switch. This is important because ABS is activated when the brake switch is "ON" and turned "OFF" when the brake is "OFF." If the brake switch is always "ON," ABS operation will always be requested resulting in potential modulator cycling on rough roads. Additionally, this failure will most likely result in a dead battery (due to the brake lights staying "ON") if the driver is not informed of this fault.

Test Description: Number(s) below refer to circled number(s) on the diagnostic chart.

1. This checks if the fault is currently present.
2. This step isolates the cause of the fault to either a faulty or misadjusted brake switch, or a short to voltage in the brake switch circuitry.

Diagnostic Aids:

An "Intermittent" problem may be caused by a poor connection, rubbed through wire insulation, or a wire that is broken inside the insulation.

The frequency of the problem can be checked by using the enhanced diagnostic function of the "Scan" tool.

Any circuitry, that is suspected as causing the intermittent complaint, should be thoroughly checked for backed out terminals, improper mating, broken locks, improperly formed or damaged terminals, poor terminal to wiring connections or physical damage to the wiring harness.

GC402910073500EX

Fig. 91 Code A094: Brake Switch Contacts Or Brake Switch Input Shorted To Battery. 1992

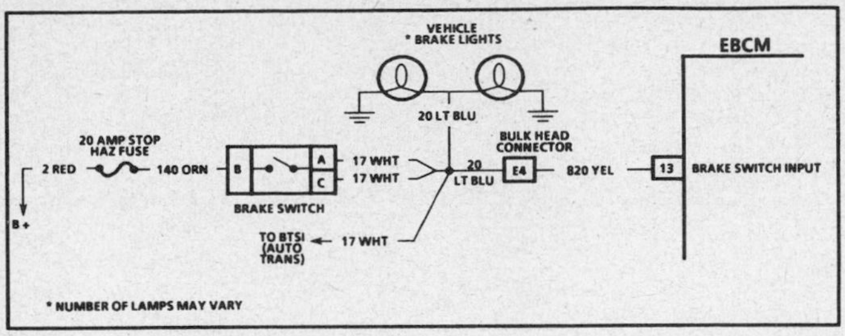
VEHICLE
* BRAKE LIGHTS
EBCM
20 LT BLU
20 AMP STOP HAZ FUSE
2 RED
140 ORN
B
A
C
17 WHT
17 WHT
20 LT BLU
BULK HEAD CONNECTOR
E4
820 YEL
13
BRAKE SWITCH INPUT
BRAKE SWITCH
B+
TO BTSI (AUTO TRANS)
17 WHT
* NUMBER OF LAMPS MAY VARY

GC402910073600AX

Cavalier & Sunbird

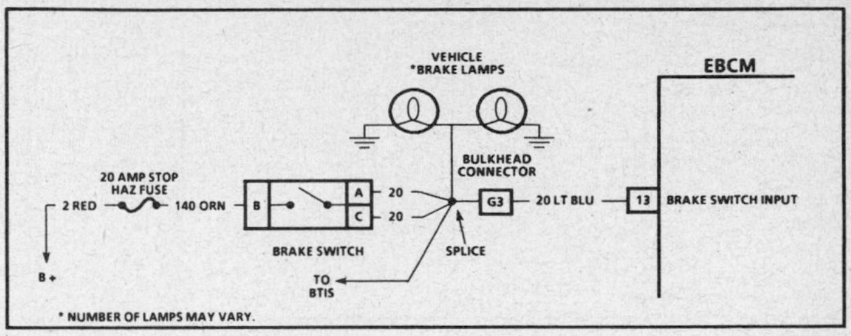
VEHICLE
*BRAKE LAMPS
EBCM
BULKHEAD CONNECTOR
20 AMP STOP HAZ FUSE
2 RED
140 ORN
B
A
C
20
20
G3
20 LT BLU
13
BRAKE SWITCH INPUT
BRAKE SWITCH
SPLICE
B+
TO BTIS
* NUMBER OF LAMPS MAY VARY.

GC402910073600BX

Beretta & Corsica

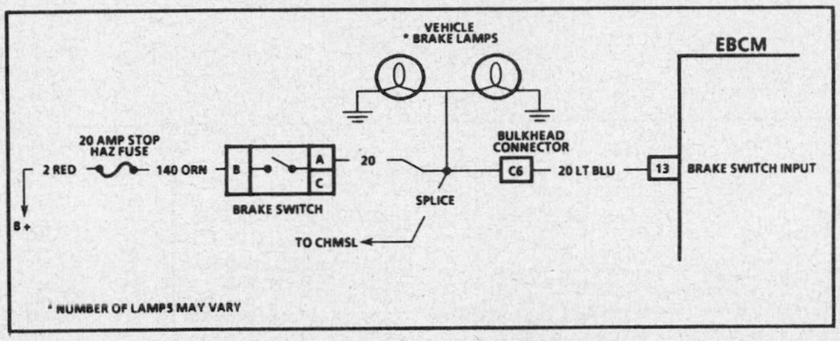
VEHICLE
* BRAKE LAMPS
EBCM
BULKHEAD CONNECTOR
20 AMP STOP HAZ FUSE
2 RED
140 ORN
B
A
C
20
C6
20 LT BLU
13
BRAKE SWITCH INPUT
BRAKE SWITCH
SPLICE
B+
TO CHMSL
* NUMBER OF LAMPS MAY VARY

GC402910073600CX

Achieva, Calais & Grand Am

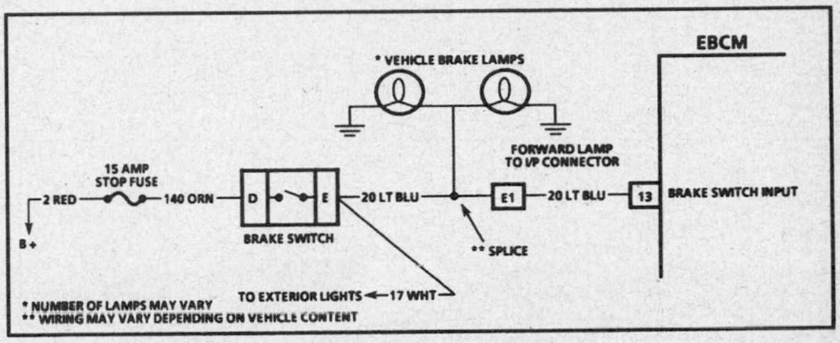
* VEHICLE BRAKE LAMPS
EBCM
FORWARD LAMP TO I/P CONNECTOR
15 AMP STOP FUSE
2 RED
140 ORN
D
E
20 LT BLU
E1
20 LT BLU
13
BRAKE SWITCH INPUT
BRAKE SWITCH
** SPLICE
B+
TO EXTERIOR LIGHTS
17 WHT
* NUMBER OF LAMPS MAY VARY
** WIRING MAY VARY DEPENDING ON VEHICLE CONTENT

GC402910073600DX

Cutlass Supreme, Grand Prix, Lumina & Regal

Circuit Description:

This code is used to identify open brake switch circuitry that prevents the brake switch input to the EBCM from changing states when the brake is applied. This code is used in conjunction with Codes A091 and A092 to determine the cause of an open brake switch fault.

Test Description: Number(s) below refer to circled number(s) on the diagnostic chart.

1. This step is used to confirm that an open in the brake switch circuitry currently exists.
2. This step indicates if the brake switch signal is being received by the EBCM.
3. This step indicates if an open circuit exists in the brake switch or brake light circuitry.
4. This step isolates the open circuit to either the brake switch input circuitry,or the EBCM.

Diagnostic Aids:

An "Intermittent" problem may be caused by a poor connection, rubbed through wire insulation, or a wire that is broken inside the insulation.

The frequency of the problem can be checked by using the enhanced diagnostic function of the "Scan" tool.

Any circuitry, that is suspected as causing the intermittent complaint, should be thoroughly checked for backed out terminals, improper mating, broken locks, improperly formed or damaged terminals, poor terminal to wiring connections or physical damage to the wiring harness.

GC402910073600EX

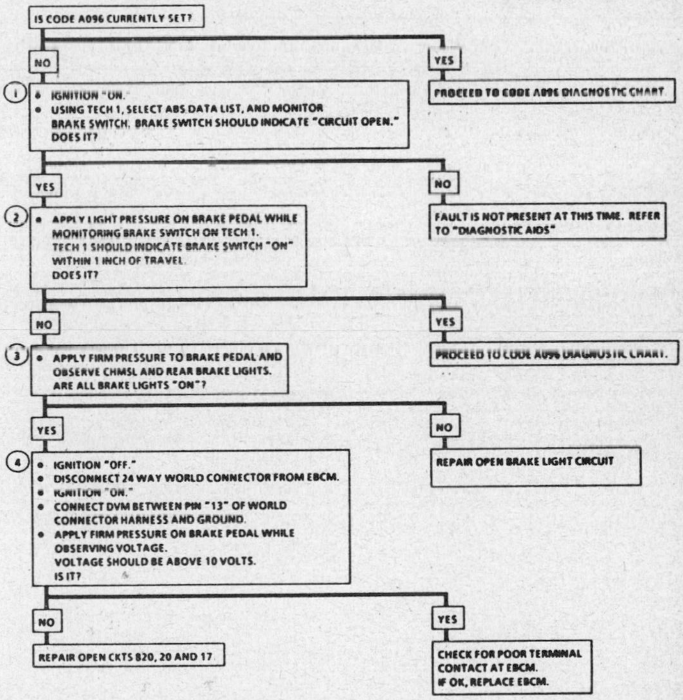
IS CODE A096 CURRENTLY SET?
NO
YES
PROCEED TO CODE A096 DIAGNOSTIC CHART
1
• IGNITION "ON."
• USING TECH 1, SELECT ABS DATA LIST, AND MONITOR BRAKE SWITCH. BRAKE SWITCH SHOULD INDICATE "CIRCUIT OPEN." DOES IT?
YES
NO
FAULT IS NOT PRESENT AT THIS TIME. REFER TO "DIAGNOSTIC AIDS"
2
• APPLY LIGHT PRESSURE ON BRAKE PEDAL WHILE MONITORING BRAKE SWITCH ON TECH 1. TECH 1 SHOULD INDICATE BRAKE SWITCH "ON" WITHIN 1 INCH OF TRAVEL. DOES IT?
NO
YES
PROCEED TO CODE A096 DIAGNOSTIC CHART.
3
• APPLY FIRM PRESSURE TO BRAKE PEDAL AND OBSERVE CHMSL AND REAR BRAKE LIGHTS. ARE ALL BRAKE LIGHTS "ON"?
YES
NO
REPAIR OPEN BRAKE LIGHT CIRCUIT
4
• IGNITION "OFF."
• DISCONNECT 24 WAY WORLD CONNECTOR FROM EBCM.
• IGNITION "ON."
• CONNECT DVM BETWEEN PIN "13" OF WORLD CONNECTOR HARNESS AND GROUND.
• APPLY FIRM PRESSURE ON BRAKE PEDAL WHILE OBSERVING VOLTAGE. VOLTAGE SHOULD BE ABOVE 10 VOLTS. IS IT?
NO
YES
REPAIR OPEN CKTS 820, 20 AND 17.
CHECK FOR POOR TERMINAL CONTACT AT EBCM. IF OK, REPLACE EBCM.

GC402910073600FX

Fig. 92 Code A095: Brake Switch Circuit Open. 1992

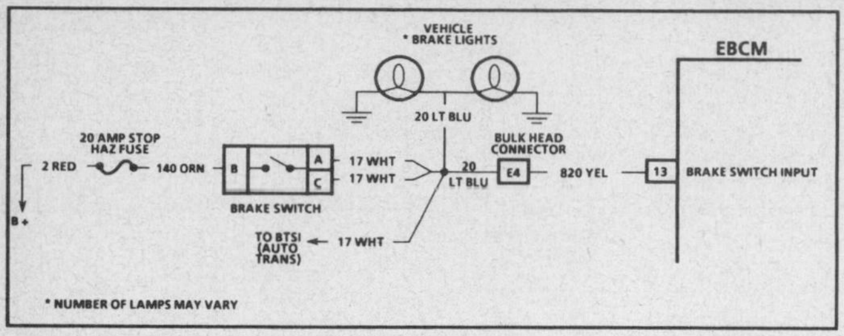
VEHICLE
* BRAKE LIGHTS
EBCM
20 LT BLU
20 AMP STOP
HAZ FUSE
2 RED
140 ORN
B
A
C
17 WHT
17 WHT
20
LT BLU
BULK HEAD
CONNECTOR
E4
820 YEL
13
BRAKE SWITCH INPUT
BRAKE SWITCH
B+
TO BTSI
(AUTO
TRANS)
17 WHT
* NUMBER OF LAMPS MAY VARY

GC402910073700AX

Cavalier & Sunbird

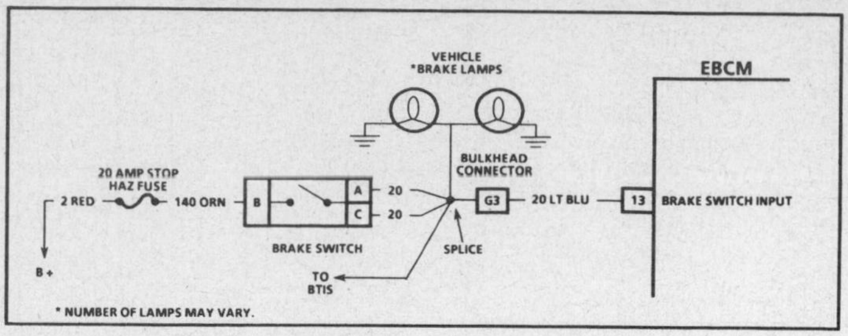
VEHICLE
*BRAKE LAMPS
EBCM
BULKHEAD
CONNECTOR
20 AMP STOP
HAZ FUSE
2 RED
140 ORN
B
A
C
20
20
G3
20 LT BLU
13
BRAKE SWITCH INPUT
BRAKE SWITCH
SPLICE
B+
TO
BTIS
* NUMBER OF LAMPS MAY VARY.

GC402910073700BX

Beretta & Corsica

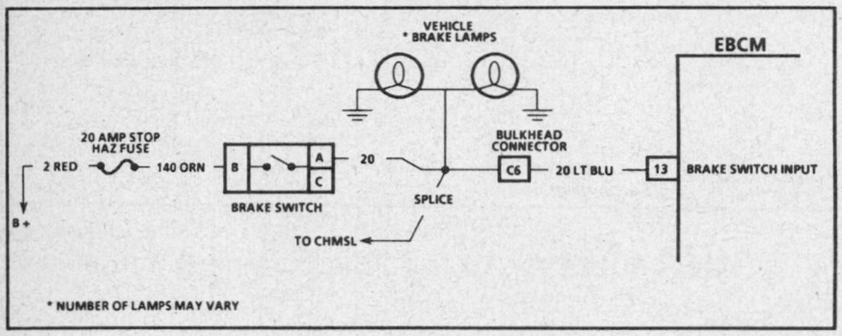
VEHICLE
* BRAKE LAMPS
EBCM
20 AMP STOP
HAZ FUSE
2 RED
140 ORN
B
A
C
20
BULKHEAD
CONNECTOR
C6
20 LT BLU
13
BRAKE SWITCH INPUT
BRAKE SWITCH
SPLICE
B+
TO CHMSL
* NUMBER OF LAMPS MAY VARY

GC402910073700CX

Achieva, Calais & Grand Am

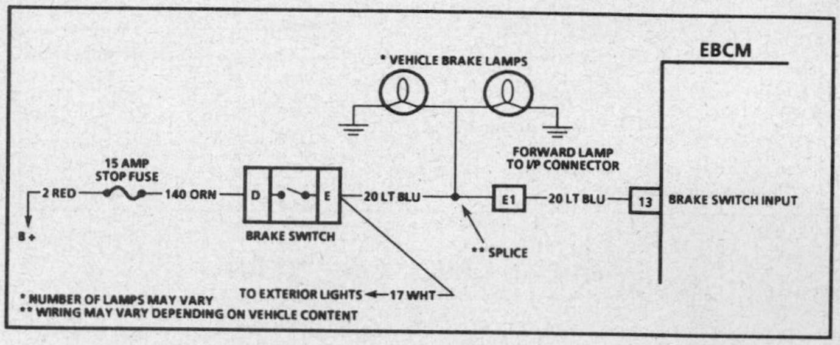
* VEHICLE BRAKE LAMPS
EBCM
15 AMP
STOP FUSE
2 RED
140 ORN
D
E
20 LT BLU
FORWARD LAMP
TO I/P CONNECTOR
E1
20 LT BLU
13
BRAKE SWITCH INPUT
BRAKE SWITCH
** SPLICE
B+
TO EXTERIOR LIGHTS
17 WHT
* NUMBER OF LAMPS MAY VARY
** WIRING MAY VARY DEPENDING ON VEHICLE CONTENT

GC402910073700DX

Cutlass Supreme, Grand Prix, Lumina & Regal

Circuit Description:

This code is designed to isolate the cause of a Code A095 failure and indicate to the driver ABS is still available. If Code A095 fails with Code A096, the brake lights are open, the brake light grounds are open, or the Center High Mounted Stop Light (CHMSL) circuit is open during 4 way flasher use. The presence of battery voltage at the brake switch input indicates a valid brake switch input is still available.

Test Description: Number(s) below refer to circled number(s) on the diagnostic chart.

1. As a result of a failure of an additional brake switch circuit code, this code may be set. To insure proper diagnosis, any additional brake switch codes must be repaired first.
2. This step identifies if the fault is currently present in the brake circuit.

Diagnostic Aids:

An "Intermittent" problem may be caused by a poor connection, rubbed through wire insulation, or a wire that is broken inside the insulation.

The frequency of the problem can be checked by using the enhanced diagnostic function of the "Scan" tool.

Any circuitry, that is suspected as causing the intermittent complaint, should be thoroughly checked for backed out terminals, improper mating, broken locks, improperly formed or damaged terminals, poor terminal to wiring connections or physical damage to the wiring harness.

GC402910073700EX

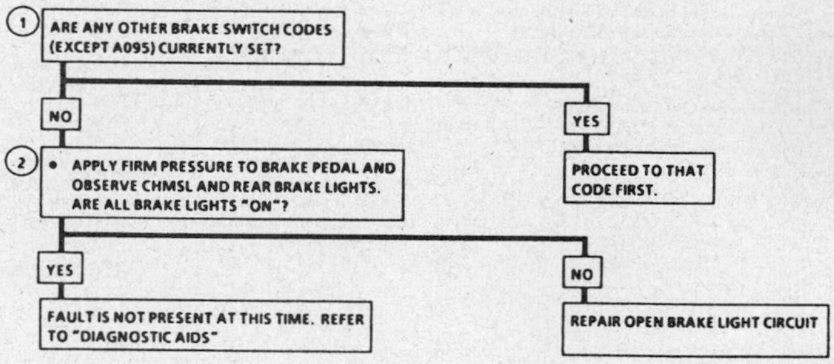
1
ARE ANY OTHER BRAKE SWITCH CODES
(EXCEPT A095) CURRENTLY SET?
NO
YES
2
• APPLY FIRM PRESSURE TO BRAKE PEDAL AND
OBSERVE CHMSL AND REAR BRAKE LIGHTS.
ARE ALL BRAKE LIGHTS "ON"?
PROCEED TO THAT
CODE FIRST.
YES
NO
FAULT IS NOT PRESENT AT THIS TIME. REFER
TO "DIAGNOSTIC AIDS"
REPAIR OPEN BRAKE LIGHT CIRCUIT

GC402910073700FX

Fig. 93 Code A096: Brake Lights Open, Brake Light Grounds Open, CHMSL Open During 4-Way Flasher Operation. 1992

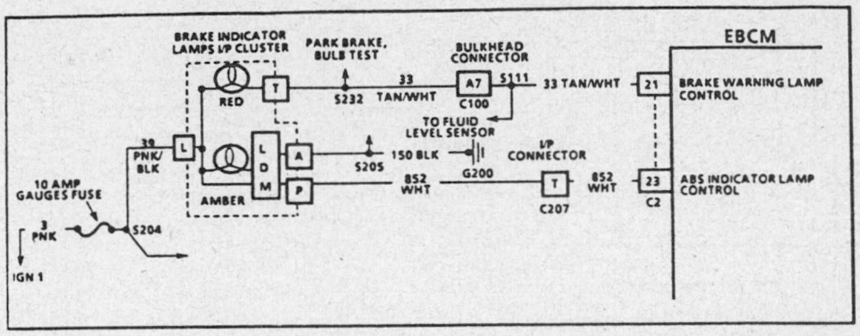
BRAKE INDICATOR LAMPS I/P CLUSTER
PARK BRAKE, BULB TEST
BULKHEAD CONNECTOR
EBCM
RED
S232
33 TAN/WHT
A7
C100
S111
33 TAN/WHT
21
BRAKE WARNING LAMP CONTROL
TO FLUID LEVEL SENSOR
39 PNK/BLK
150 BLK
I/P CONNECTOR
S205
852 WHT
G200
C207
852 WHT
23
C2
ABS INDICATOR LAMP CONTROL
AMBER
10 AMP GAUGES FUSE
3 PNK
S204
IGN 1

GC402930073800AX

Cavalier

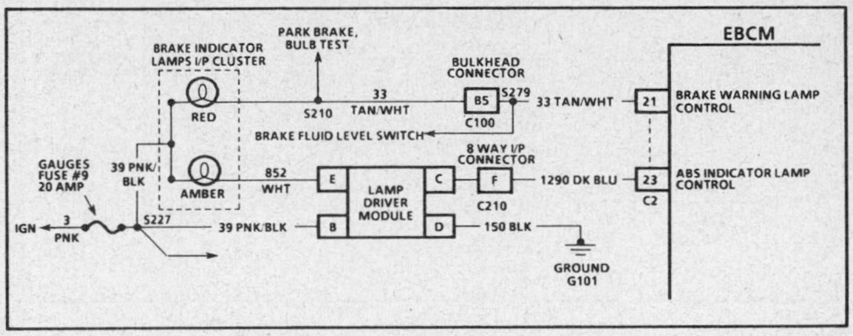
PARK BRAKE, BULB TEST
BRAKE INDICATOR LAMPS I/P CLUSTER
BULKHEAD CONNECTOR
EBCM
RED
33
S210
TAN/WHT
B5
S279
C100
33 TAN/WHT
21
BRAKE WARNING LAMP CONTROL
BRAKE FLUID LEVEL SWITCH
8 WAY I/P CONNECTOR
GAUGES FUSE #9 20 AMP
39 PNK/BLK
AMBER
852 WHT
LAMP DRIVER MODULE
C210
1290 DK BLU
23
C2
ABS INDICATOR LAMP CONTROL
IGN
3 PNK
S227
39 PNK/BLK
150 BLK
GROUND G101

GC402930073800BX

Sunbird

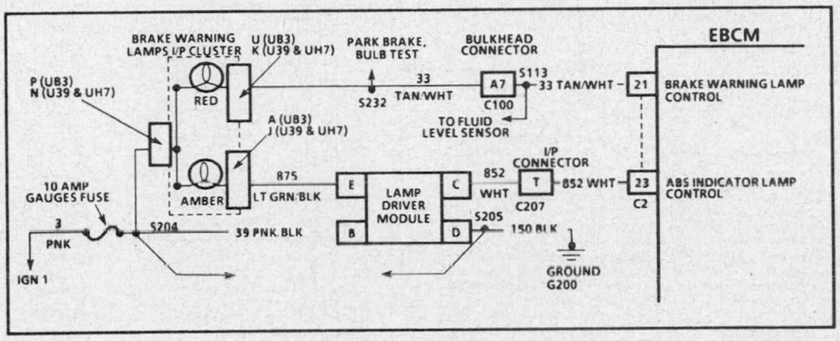
BRAKE WARNING LAMPS I/P CLUSTER
U (UB3) K (U39 & UH7)
PARK BRAKE, BULB TEST
BULKHEAD CONNECTOR
EBCM
P (UB3) N (U39 & UH7)
RED
S232
33 TAN/WHT
A7
S113
C100
33 TAN/WHT
21
BRAKE WARNING LAMP CONTROL
A (UB3) J (U39 & UH7)
TO FLUID LEVEL SENSOR
I/P CONNECTOR
10 AMP GAUGES FUSE
AMBER
875 LT GRN/BLK
LAMP DRIVER MODULE
852 WHT
C207
852 WHT
23
C2
ABS INDICATOR LAMP CONTROL
3 PNK
S204
39 PNK BLK
S205
150 BLK
GROUND G200
IGN 1

GC402930073800CX

Beretta & Corsica

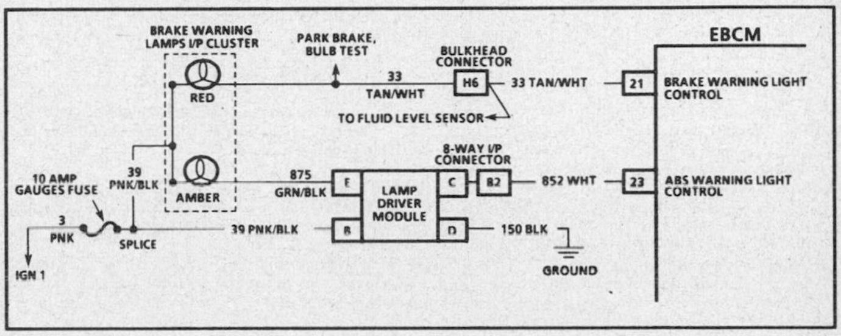
BRAKE WARNING LAMPS I/P CLUSTER
PARK BRAKE, BULB TEST
BULKHEAD CONNECTOR
EBCM
RED
33 TAN/WHT
H6
33 TAN/WHT
21
BRAKE WARNING LIGHT CONTROL
TO FLUID LEVEL SENSOR
8-WAY I/P CONNECTOR
10 AMP GAUGES FUSE
39 PNK/BLK
AMBER
875 GRN/BLK
LAMP DRIVER MODULE
B2
852 WHT
23
ABS WARNING LIGHT CONTROL
3 PNK
SPLICE
39 PNK/BLK
150 BLK
GROUND
IGN 1

GC402930073800DX

Achieva, Grand Am & Skylark

Circuit Description:

This test checks the state of the ABS indicator lamp to identify a situation in which the driver could not be warned of a system malfunction by the ABS indicator lamp, or the indicator lamp is always "ON." The Lamp Driver Module (LDM) turns the ABS indicator lamp "ON," unless the EBCM provides ground to turn it "OFF." Because of the circuitry in the LDM, only external malfunctions can be detected. As a result, the ABS indicator lamp itself is not diagnosable, only the control line to the EBCM can be diagnosed. In the event of an open CKT 1290, the ABS indicator lamp will be "ON" at all times, due to the loss of ground at the LDM input. If the control line is shorted to ground, the ABS indicator lamp is kept "OFF," due to the LDM input being grounded.

Failure Condition:

DTC A011 can be set only during the three second bulb check or when the ABS indicator lamp is commanded "ON." If the EBCM can not control the ABS indicator lamp for two seconds, a malfunction exists.

Action Taken:

A malfunction DTC is stored, however, ABS is not disabled.

Test Description: Number(s) below refer to circled number(s) on the diagnostic chart.

1. Checks to see if ABS indicator lamp functions properly. Normal operation would indicate that the malfunction is not present.
2. This step ensures that the circuitry from the EBCM to the lamp driver module is complete.
3. This step ensures that the ignition circuit to the lamp driver module is functional. An open gauge fuse or open CKT 3 or 39 would result in inoperative indicator lamps.
4. Isolates the cause of the ABS lamp remaining "OFF," by disconnecting the 24-way world connector, CKT 1290 should be open and cause the ABS lamp to be "ON."

Diagnostic Aids:

An "Intermittent" malfunction may be caused by a poor connection, rubbed through wire insulation, or a wire that is broken inside the insulation.

The lamp test function of the Tech 1 may be used to command the lamp "ON" while looking for an intermittent malfunction in the indicator lamp circuitry.

The frequency of the malfunction can be checked by using the enhanced diagnostic function of the Tech 1.

Any circuitry that is suspected as causing the intermittent complaint should be thoroughly checked for backed out terminals, improper mating, broken locks, improperly formed or damaged terminals, poor terminal to wiring connections or physical damage to the wiring harness.

GC402930073800EX

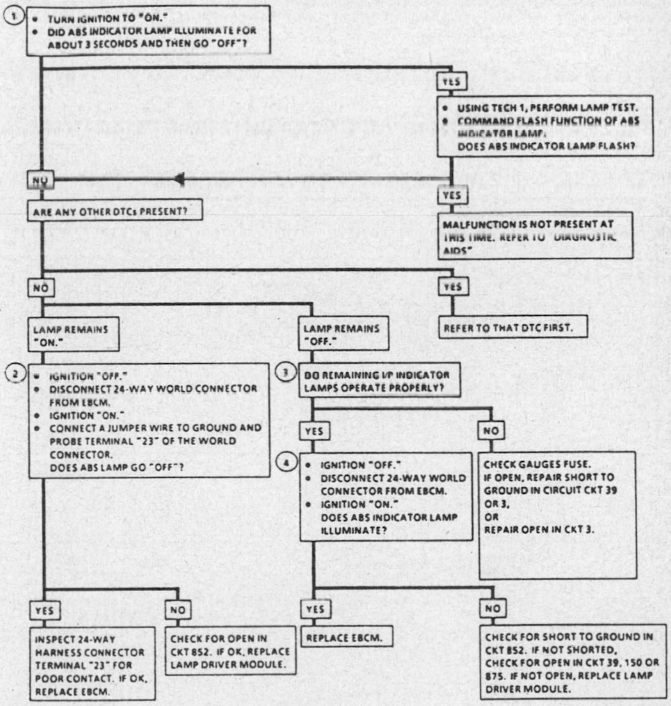
1
• TURN IGNITION TO "ON."
• DID ABS INDICATOR LAMP ILLUMINATE FOR ABOUT 3 SECONDS AND THEN GO "OFF"?
YES
• USING TECH 1, PERFORM LAMP TEST.
• COMMAND FLASH FUNCTION OF ABS INDICATOR LAMP.
DOES ABS INDICATOR LAMP FLASH?
NO
YES
ARE ANY OTHER DTCs PRESENT?
MALFUNCTION IS NOT PRESENT AT THIS TIME. REFER TO DIAGNOSTIC AIDS"
NO
YES
LAMP REMAINS "ON."
LAMP REMAINS "OFF."
REFER TO THAT DTC FIRST.
2
• IGNITION "OFF."
• DISCONNECT 24-WAY WORLD CONNECTOR FROM EBCM.
• IGNITION "ON."
• CONNECT A JUMPER WIRE TO GROUND AND PROBE TERMINAL "23" OF THE WORLD CONNECTOR.
DOES ABS LAMP GO "OFF"?
3
DO REMAINING I/P INDICATOR LAMPS OPERATE PROPERLY?
YES
NO
4
• IGNITION "OFF."
• DISCONNECT 24-WAY WORLD CONNECTOR FROM EBCM.
• IGNITION "ON."
DOES ABS INDICATOR LAMP ILLUMINATE?
CHECK GAUGES FUSE.
IF OPEN, REPAIR SHORT TO GROUND IN CIRCUIT CKT 39 OR 3,
OR
REPAIR OPEN IN CKT 3.
YES
NO
YES
NO
INSPECT 24-WAY HARNESS CONNECTOR TERMINAL "23" FOR POOR CONTACT. IF OK, REPLACE EBCM.
CHECK FOR OPEN IN CKT 852. IF OK, REPLACE LAMP DRIVER MODULE.
REPLACE EBCM.
CHECK FOR SHORT TO GROUND IN CKT 852. IF NOT SHORTED, CHECK FOR OPEN IN CKT 39, 150 OR 875. IF NOT OPEN, REPLACE LAMP DRIVER MODULE.

GC402930073800FX

Fig. 94 Code A011: ABS Warning Light Open Or Shorted To Ground. 1993–94 Cavalier, Sunbird, Beretta, Corsica & Achieva, Grand Am & Skylark Less VES

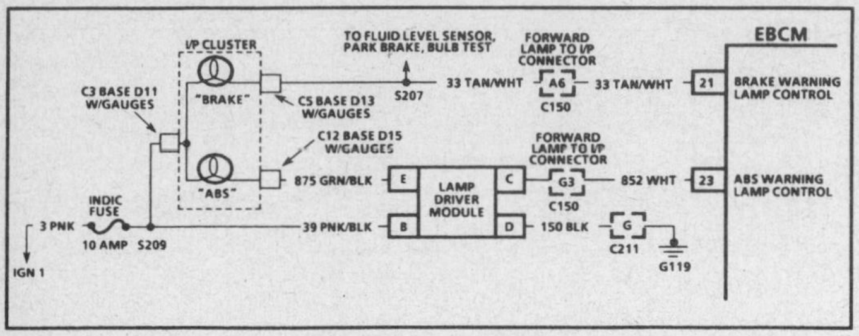
I/P CLUSTER
"BRAKE"
"ABS"
C3 BASE D11 W/GAUGES
C5 BASE D13 W/GAUGES
C12 BASE D15 W/GAUGES
TO FLUID LEVEL SENSOR, PARK BRAKE, BULB TEST
S207
33 TAN/WHT
FORWARD LAMP TO I/P CONNECTOR
A6
C150
G3
875 GRN/BLK
LAMP DRIVER MODULE
852 WHT
150 BLK
C211
G119
39 PNK/BLK
INDIC FUSE
3 PNK
10 AMP
S209
IGN 1
EBCM
21
BRAKE WARNING LAMP CONTROL
23
ABS WARNING LAMP CONTROL

DTC 11

ABS WARNING LAMP CIRCUIT OPEN OR SHORTED TO GROUND

Circuit Description:
This DTC checks the state of the ABS warning lamp to identify a situation in which the driver could not be warned of a system malfunction by the ABS warning lamp, or the warning lamp is always "ON." The Lamp Driver Module (LDM) turns the ABS warning lamp "ON," unless the EBCM provides ground to turn it "OFF." Because of the circuitry in the LDM, only external malfunctions can be detected. As a result, the ABS warning lamp itself is not diagnosable, only the control line to the EBCM can be diagnosed. In the event of an open CKT 852, the ABS warning lamp will be "ON" at all times, due to the loss of ground at the LDM input. If the control line is shorted to ground, the ABS warning lamp is kept "OFF," due to the LDM input being grounded.

DTC Will Set When: DTC 11 can be set only during the three second bulb check or when the ABS warning lamp is commanded "ON." If the EBCM cannot control the ABS warning lamp for two seconds, a malfunction exists.

Action Taken: A malfunction DTC is stored; however, ABS is not disabled.

DTC Chart Test Description: Number(s) below refer to circled number(s) on the diagnostic chart.

1. Checks to see if ABS lamp functions properly. Normal operation would indicate that the problem is not present.
2. Determines if any other DTCs are present or if DTC 18 is set falsely.
3. Ensures that the circuitry from the EBCM to the lamp driver module is complete.
4. Ensures that the ignition circuit to the lamp driver module is functional. An open indicator fuse or open CKT 3, 39 or 875 would result in inoperative indicator lamp.
5. Isolates the cause of the ABS lamp remaining "OFF," by disconnecting the 24-way EBCM connector, CKT 852 should be open and cause the ABS lamp to be "ON."
6. Determines whether the lamp remains "ON" due to a lamp driver malfunction or an open in CKT 852.
7. Determines if the "INDIC" fuse or CKT 3 is open, causing the I/P indicator lamps to remain "OFF."
8. Checks for an open in CKT 39 which supplies voltage to the lamp driver module.
9. Isolates the cause of the lamp remaining "OFF" to a short to ground in CKT 852 or a malfunctioning lamp driver module.

Diagnostic Aids: An "Intermittent" malfunction may be caused by a poor connection, rubbed through wire insulation, or a wire that is broken inside the insulation.

The lamp test function of the Tech 1 may be used to command the lamp "ON" while looking for an intermittent malfunction in the ABS warning lamp circuitry.

The frequency of the malfunction can be checked by using the enhanced diagnostic function of the Tech 1.

Any circuitry that is suspected as causing the intermittent complaint should be thoroughly checked for backed out terminals, improper mating, broken locks, improperly formed or damaged terminals, poor terminal to wiring connections or physical damage to the wiring harness.

GC402930073900AA

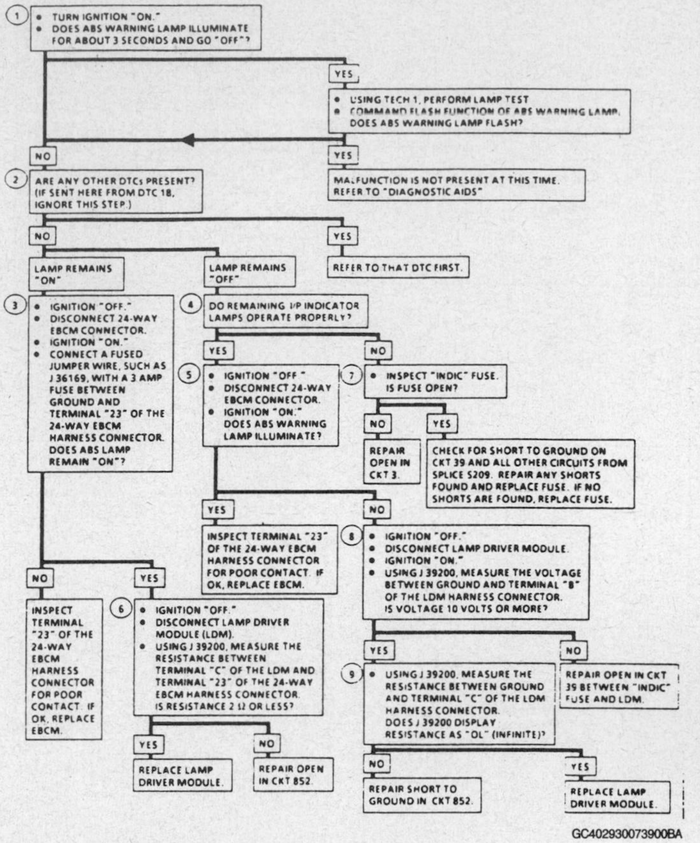
1 • TURN IGNITION "ON." • DOES ABS WARNING LAMP ILLUMINATE FOR ABOUT 3 SECONDS AND GO "OFF"?
YES
• USING TECH 1, PERFORM LAMP TEST • COMMAND FLASH FUNCTION OF ABS WARNING LAMP. DOES ABS WARNING LAMP FLASH?
NO
YES
MALFUNCTION IS NOT PRESENT AT THIS TIME. REFER TO "DIAGNOSTIC AIDS"
2 ARE ANY OTHER DTCs PRESENT? (IF SENT HERE FROM DTC 18, IGNORE THIS STEP.)
NO
YES
REFER TO THAT DTC FIRST.
LAMP REMAINS "ON"
LAMP REMAINS "OFF"
3 • IGNITION "OFF." • DISCONNECT 24-WAY EBCM CONNECTOR. • IGNITION "ON." • CONNECT A FUSED JUMPER WIRE, SUCH AS J 36169, WITH A 3 AMP FUSE BETWEEN GROUND AND TERMINAL "23" OF THE 24-WAY HARNESS CONNECTOR. DOES ABS LAMP REMAIN "ON"?
4 DO REMAINING I/P INDICATOR LAMPS OPERATE PROPERLY?
YES
NO
5 • IGNITION "OFF." • DISCONNECT 24-WAY EBCM CONNECTOR. • IGNITION "ON." DOES ABS WARNING LAMP ILLUMINATE?
7 • INSPECT "INDIC" FUSE. IS FUSE OPEN?
NO
YES
REPAIR OPEN IN CKT 3.
CHECK FOR SHORT TO GROUND ON CKT 39 AND ALL OTHER CIRCUITS FROM SPLICE S209. REPAIR ANY SHORTS FOUND AND REPLACE FUSE. IF NO SHORTS ARE FOUND, REPLACE FUSE.
YES
NO
INSPECT TERMINAL "23" OF THE 24-WAY EBCM HARNESS CONNECTOR FOR POOR CONTACT. IF OK, REPLACE EBCM.
8 • IGNITION "OFF." • DISCONNECT LAMP DRIVER MODULE. • IGNITION "ON." • USING J 39200, MEASURE THE VOLTAGE BETWEEN GROUND AND TERMINAL "B" OF THE LDM HARNESS CONNECTOR. IS VOLTAGE 10 VOLTS OR MORE?
NO
YES
INSPECT TERMINAL "23" OF THE 24-WAY EBCM HARNESS CONNECTOR FOR POOR CONTACT. IF OK, REPLACE EBCM.
6 • IGNITION "OFF." • DISCONNECT LAMP DRIVER MODULE (LDM). • USING J 39200, MEASURE THE RESISTANCE BETWEEN TERMINAL "C" OF THE LDM AND TERMINAL "23" OF THE 24-WAY EBCM HARNESS CONNECTOR. IS RESISTANCE 2 Ω OR LESS?
YES
NO
9 • USING J 39200, MEASURE THE RESISTANCE BETWEEN GROUND AND TERMINAL "C" OF THE LDM HARNESS CONNECTOR. DOES J 39200 DISPLAY RESISTANCE AS "OL" (INFINITE)?
REPAIR OPEN IN CKT 39 BETWEEN "INDIC" FUSE AND LDM.
YES
NO
REPLACE LAMP DRIVER MODULE.
REPAIR OPEN IN CKT 852.
NO
YES
REPAIR SHORT TO GROUND IN CKT 852.
REPLACE LAMP DRIVER MODULE.

GC402930073900BA

Fig. 95 Code A011: ABS Warning Light Open Or Shorted To Ground. 1993 Grand Prix, 1993–94 Cutlass Supreme, Lumina & Regal

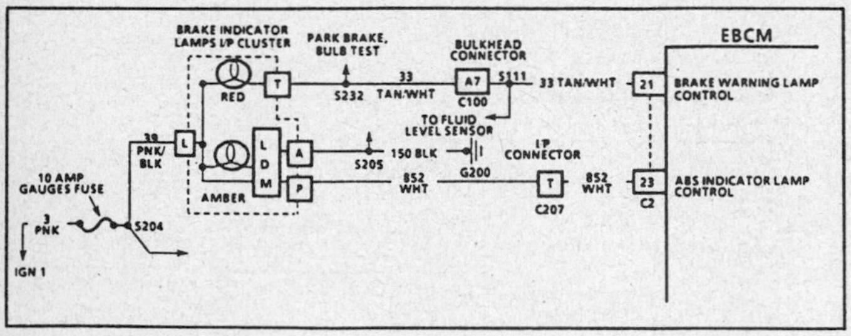
BRAKE INDICATOR LAMPS I/P CLUSTER
PARK BRAKE, BULB TEST
BULKHEAD CONNECTOR
EBCM
RED
AMBER
S232
33 TAN/WHT
A7
S111
C100
TO FLUID LEVEL SENSOR
S205
150 BLK
G200
I/P CONNECTOR
852 WHT
C207
BRAKE WARNING LAMP CONTROL
ABS INDICATOR LAMP CONTROL
10 AMP GAUGES FUSE
3 PNK
S204
IGN 1

GC402930074000AX

Cavalier

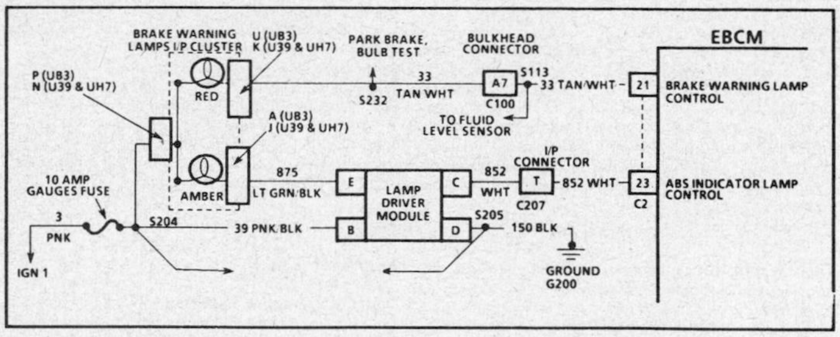
BRAKE WARNING LAMPS I/P CLUSTER
PARK BRAKE, BULB TEST
BULKHEAD CONNECTOR
EBCM
S232
33 TAN WHT
A7
S113
C100
TO FLUID LEVEL SENSOR
RED
AMBER
875 LT GRN/BLK
LAMP DRIVER MODULE
852 WHT
I/P CONNECTOR
C207
S205
150 BLK
GROUND G200
39 PNK/BLK
S204
10 AMP GAUGES FUSE
3 PNK
IGN 1
BRAKE WARNING LAMP CONTROL
ABS INDICATOR LAMP CONTROL

GC402930074000BX

Sunbird

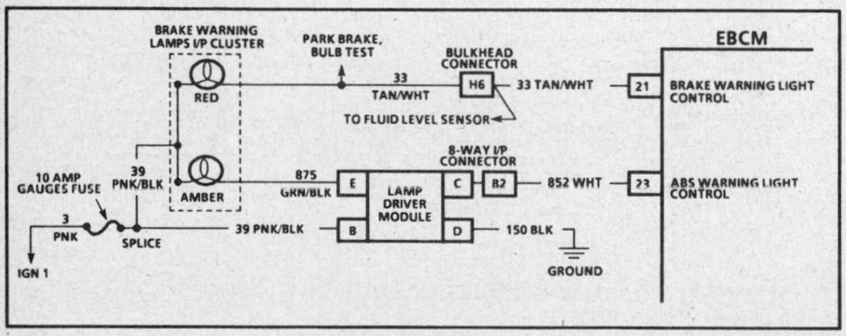
BRAKE WARNING LAMPS I/P CLUSTER
PARK BRAKE, BULB TEST
BULKHEAD CONNECTOR
EBCM
RED
33 TAN/WHT
H6
TO FLUID LEVEL SENSOR
BRAKE WARNING LIGHT CONTROL
8-WAY I/P CONNECTOR
AMBER
875 GRN/BLK
LAMP DRIVER MODULE
852 WHT
ABS WARNING LIGHT CONTROL
10 AMP GAUGES FUSE
39 PNK/BLK
SPLICE
150 BLK
GROUND
3 PNK
IGN 1

GC402930074000CX

Beretta & Corsica

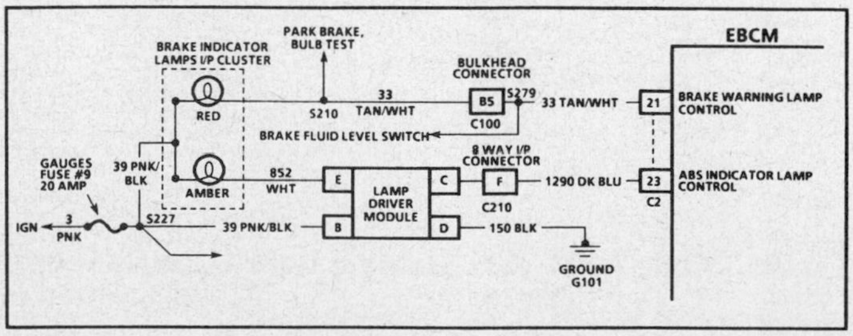
BRAKE INDICATOR LAMPS I/P CLUSTER
PARK BRAKE, BULB TEST
BULKHEAD CONNECTOR
EBCM
RED
S210
33 TAN/WHT
B5
S279
C100
BRAKE FLUID LEVEL SWITCH
BRAKE WARNING LAMP CONTROL
8 WAY I/P CONNECTOR
AMBER
852 WHT
LAMP DRIVER MODULE
1290 DK BLU
C210
ABS INDICATOR LAMP CONTROL
GAUGES FUSE #9 20 AMP
39 PNK/BLK
S227
150 BLK
GROUND G101
IGN
3 PNK

GC402930074000DX

Achieva, Grand Am & Skylark

Fig. 96 Code A013: ABS Warning Light Circuit Shorted To Battery (Part 1 of 2). 1993 Cutlass Supreme, Grand Prix, Lumina, Regal & 1993-94 Cavalier, Sunbird, Beretta, Corsica & Achieva, Grand Am & Skylark Less VES

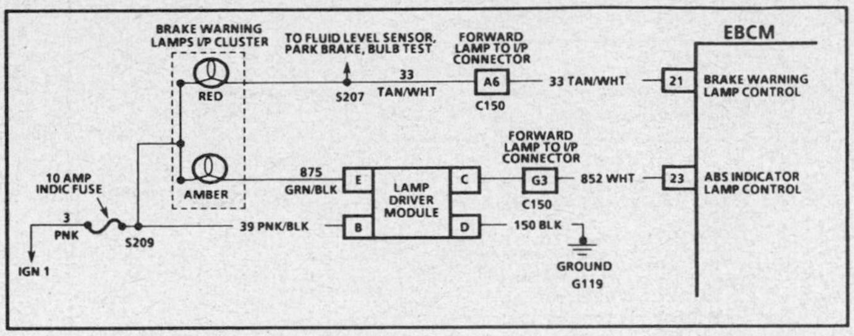
BRAKE WARNING LAMPS I/P CLUSTER
TO FLUID LEVEL SENSOR, PARK BRAKE, BULB TEST
FORWARD LAMP TO I/P CONNECTOR
EBCM
33
S207
TAN/WHT
A6
33 TAN/WHT
21
BRAKE WARNING LAMP CONTROL
C150
RED
FORWARD LAMP TO I/P CONNECTOR
10 AMP INDIC FUSE
875 GRN/BLK
E
LAMP DRIVER MODULE
C
G3
852 WHT
23
ABS INDICATOR LAMP CONTROL
AMBER
C150
3 PNK
S209
39 PNK/BLK
B
D
150 BLK
IGN 1
GROUND G119

GC402930074000EX

Cutlass Supreme, Grand Prix, Lumina & Regal

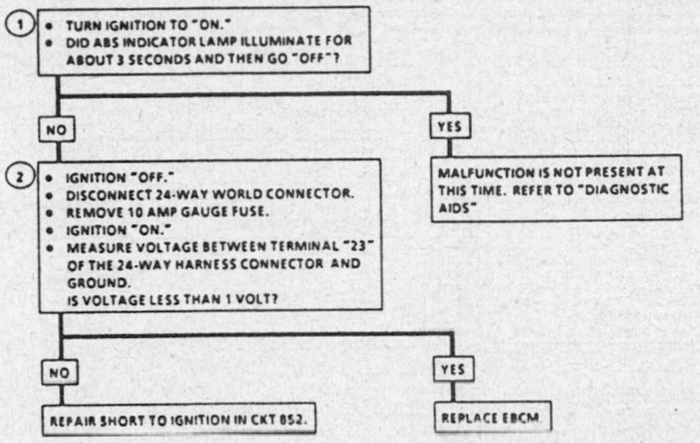
1
• TURN IGNITION TO "ON."
• DID ABS INDICATOR LAMP ILLUMINATE FOR ABOUT 3 SECONDS AND THEN GO "OFF"?
NO
YES
MALFUNCTION IS NOT PRESENT AT THIS TIME. REFER TO "DIAGNOSTIC AIDS"
2
• IGNITION "OFF."
• DISCONNECT 24-WAY WORLD CONNECTOR.
• REMOVE 10 AMP GAUGE FUSE.
• IGNITION "ON."
• MEASURE VOLTAGE BETWEEN TERMINAL "23" OF THE 24-WAY HARNESS CONNECTOR AND GROUND.
IS VOLTAGE LESS THAN 1 VOLT?
NO
YES
REPAIR SHORT TO IGNITION IN CKT 852.
REPLACE EBCM

GC402930074000GX

Circuit Description:

This test checks the state of the ABS indicator lamp to identify a situation in which the driver could not be warned of a system malfunction by the ABS indicator lamp. The Lamp Driver Module (LDM) turns the ABS indicator lamp "ON," unless the EBCM provides ground to turn it "OFF." Because of the circuitry internal to the LDM, only external malfunctions can be detected. As a result, the ABS indicator lamp itself is not diagnosable, only the control line to the EBCM can be diagnosed.

If the ABS indicator lamp control line is shorted to battery or the EBCM control circuit is open, the Electronic Brake Control Module (EBCM) is not able to turn "OFF" the ABS indicator lamp.

Failure Condition:

DTC A013 can be set anytime the EBCM commands the ABS indicator lamp "OFF." If the EBCM can not control the ABS indicator lamp for two seconds, a malfunction exists.

Action Taken:

A malfunction DTC is stored, however, ABS is not disabled.

Test Description: Number(s) below refer to circled number(s) on the diagnostic chart.

1. Checks to see if ABS lamp functions properly. Normal operation would indicate that the problem is not present.
2. After removing the 10 amp gauge fuse, voltage on CKT 852 will be eliminated. If voltage is still present, it would indicate that a short to voltage is present between the lamp driver module and EBCM.

Diagnostic Aids:

An "Intermittent" malfunction may be caused by a poor connection, rubbed through wire insulation or a wire that is broken inside the insulation.

DTC 13 must be currently set before it should be addressed. If DTC 13 is set as a history DTC, proceed to those DTCs that are currently set before attempting to repair a DTC 13 malfunction.

The frequency of the malfunction can be checked by using the enhanced diagnostic function of the Tech 1

Any circuitry that is suspected as causing the "Intermittent" complaint should be thoroughly checked for backed out terminals, improper mating, broken locks, improperly formed or damaged terminals, poor terminal to wiring connections or physical damage to the wiring harness.

GC402930074000FX

Fig. 96 Code A013: ABS Warning Light Circuit Shorted To Battery (Part 2 of 2). 1993 Cutlass Supreme, Grand Prix, Lumina, Regal & 1993-94 Cavalier, Sunbird, Beretta, Corsica & Achieva, Grand Am & Skylark Less VES

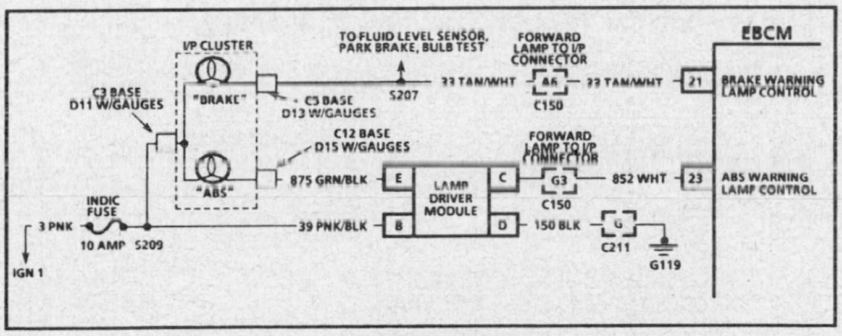
I/P CLUSTER
TO FLUID LEVEL SENSOR, PARK BRAKE, BULB TEST
FORWARD LAMP TO I/P CONNECTOR
EBCM
33 TAN/WHT
A6
33 TAN/WHT
21
BRAKE WARNING LAMP CONTROL
C3 BASE D11 W/GAUGES
"BRAKE"
C5 BASE D13 W/GAUGES
S207
C150
C12 BASE D15 W/GAUGES
FORWARD LAMP TO I/P CONNECTOR
875 GRN/BLK
E
LAMP DRIVER MODULE
C
G3
852 WHT
23
ABS WARNING LAMP CONTROL
"ABS"
INDIC FUSE
C150
3 PNK
10 AMP
S209
39 PNK/BLK
B
D
150 BLK
C211
G119
IGN 1

DTC 13

ABS WARNING LAMP CIRCUIT SHORTED TO BATTERY

Circuit Description:

This DTC checks the state of the ABS warning lamp to identify a situation in which the driver could not be warned of a system malfunction by the ABS warning lamp. The Lamp Driver Module (LDM) turns the ABS warning lamp "ON," unless the EBCM provides ground to turn it "OFF." Because of the circuitry internal to the LDM, only external malfunctions can be detected. As a result, the ABS warning lamp itself is not diagnosable, only the control line to the EBCM can be diagnosed.

If the ABS warning lamp control line is shorted to battery or the EBCM control circuit is open, the Electronic Brake Control Module (EBCM) is not able to turn "OFF" the ABS warning lamp.

DTC Will Set When: DTC 13 can be set anytime the EBCM commands the ABS indicator lamp "OFF." If the EBCM cannot control the ABS warning lamp for two seconds, a malfunction exists.

Action Taken: A malfunction DTC is stored; however, ABS is not disabled.

DTC Chart Test Description: Number(s) below refer to circled number(s) on the diagnostic chart.

1. Checks to see if ABS lamp functions properly. Normal operation would indicate that the problem is not present.
2. After removing the 10 amp indicator fuse, voltage on CKT 852 will be eliminated. If voltage is still present, it would indicate that a short to voltage is present between the lamp driver module and EBCM.

Diagnostic Aids: An "Intermittent" malfunction may be caused by a poor connection, rubbed through wire insulation or a wire that is broken inside the insulation.

DTC 13 must be currently set before it should be addressed. If DTC 13 is set as a history DTC, proceed to those DTCs that are currently set before attempting to repair a DTC 13 malfunction.

The frequency of the malfunction can be checked by using the enhanced diagnostic function of the Tech 1

Any circuitry that is suspected as causing the "Intermittent" complaint should be thoroughly checked for backed out terminals, improper mating, broken locks, improperly formed or damaged terminals, poor terminal to wiring connections or physical damage to the wiring harness.

GC402940093800AX

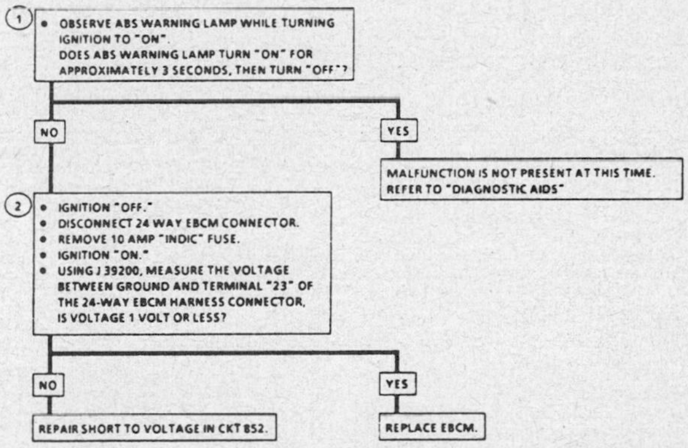
1
• OBSERVE ABS WARNING LAMP WHILE TURNING IGNITION TO "ON".
DOES ABS WARNING LAMP TURN "ON" FOR APPROXIMATELY 3 SECONDS, THEN TURN "OFF"?
NO
YES
MALFUNCTION IS NOT PRESENT AT THIS TIME. REFER TO "DIAGNOSTIC AIDS"
2
• IGNITION "OFF."
• DISCONNECT 24 WAY EBCM CONNECTOR.
• REMOVE 10 AMP "INDIC" FUSE.
• IGNITION "ON."
• USING J 39200, MEASURE THE VOLTAGE BETWEEN GROUND AND TERMINAL "23" OF THE 24-WAY EBCM HARNESS CONNECTOR.
IS VOLTAGE 1 VOLT OR LESS?
NO
YES
REPAIR SHORT TO VOLTAGE IN CKT 852.
REPLACE EBCM.

GC402940093800BX

Fig. 97 Code A013: ABS Warning Light Circuit Shorted To Battery. 1994 Cutlass Supreme, Lumina & Regal

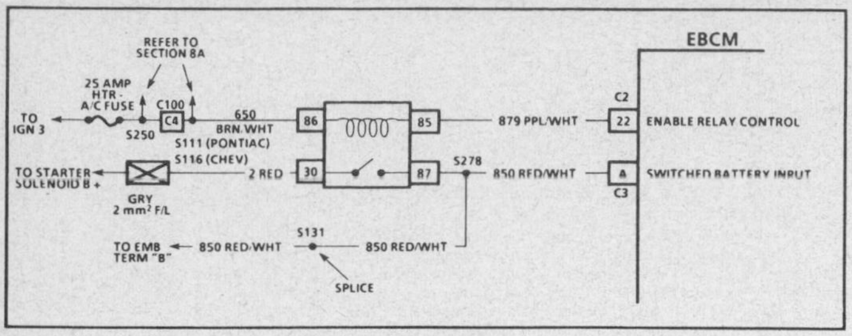
EBCM
REFER TO SECTION 8A
25 AMP HTR-A/C FUSE
C100
TO IGN 3
C4
S250
650 BRN/WHT
S111 (PONTIAC)
S116 (CHEV)
86
85
879 PPL/WHT
C2
22
ENABLE RELAY CONTROL
TO STARTER SOLENOID B+
GRY 2 mm² F/L
2 RED
30
87
S278
850 RED/WHT
A
C3
SWITCHED BATTERY INPUT
S131
TO EMB TERM "B"
850 RED/WHT
850 RED/WHT
SPLICE

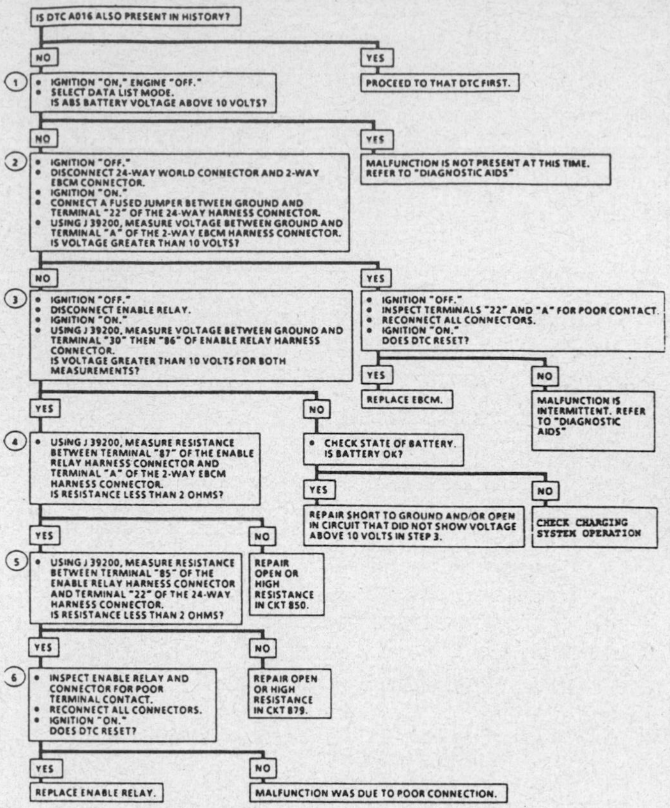
IS DTC A016 ALSO PRESENT IN HISTORY?
NO
YES
PROCEED TO THAT DTC FIRST.
1 • IGNITION "ON," ENGINE "OFF."
• SELECT DATA LIST MODE.
IS ABS BATTERY VOLTAGE ABOVE 10 VOLTS?
NO
YES
MALFUNCTION IS NOT PRESENT AT THIS TIME. REFER TO "DIAGNOSTIC AIDS"
2 • IGNITION "OFF."
• DISCONNECT 24-WAY WORLD CONNECTOR AND 2-WAY EBCM CONNECTOR.
• IGNITION "ON."
• CONNECT A FUSED JUMPER BETWEEN GROUND AND TERMINAL "22" OF THE 24-WAY HARNESS CONNECTOR.
• USING J 39200, MEASURE VOLTAGE BETWEEN GROUND AND TERMINAL "A" OF THE 2-WAY EBCM HARNESS CONNECTOR.
IS VOLTAGE GREATER THAN 10 VOLTS?
NO
YES
• IGNITION "OFF."
• INSPECT TERMINALS "22" AND "A" FOR POOR CONTACT.
• RECONNECT ALL CONNECTORS.
• IGNITION "ON."
DOES DTC RESET?
YES
NO
REPLACE EBCM.
MALFUNCTION IS INTERMITTENT. REFER TO "DIAGNOSTIC AIDS"
3 • IGNITION "OFF."
DISCONNECT ENABLE RELAY.
• IGNITION "ON."
• USING J 39200, MEASURE VOLTAGE BETWEEN GROUND AND TERMINAL "30" THEN "86" OF ENABLE RELAY HARNESS CONNECTOR.
IS VOLTAGE GREATER THAN 10 VOLTS FOR BOTH MEASUREMENTS?
YES
NO
4 • USING J 39200, MEASURE RESISTANCE BETWEEN TERMINAL "87" OF THE ENABLE RELAY HARNESS CONNECTOR AND TERMINAL "A" OF THE 2-WAY EBCM HARNESS CONNECTOR.
IS RESISTANCE LESS THAN 2 OHMS?
• CHECK STATE OF BATTERY.
IS BATTERY OK?
YES
NO
REPAIR SHORT TO GROUND AND/OR OPEN IN CIRCUIT THAT DID NOT SHOW VOLTAGE ABOVE 10 VOLTS IN STEP 3.
CHECK CHARGING SYSTEM OPERATION
YES
NO
5 • USING J 39200, MEASURE RESISTANCE BETWEEN TERMINAL "85" OF THE ENABLE RELAY HARNESS CONNECTOR AND TERMINAL "22" OF THE 24-WAY HARNESS CONNECTOR.
IS RESISTANCE LESS THAN 2 OHMS?
REPAIR OPEN OR HIGH RESISTANCE IN CKT 850.
YES
NO
6 • INSPECT ENABLE RELAY AND CONNECTOR FOR POOR TERMINAL CONTACT.
• RECONNECT ALL CONNECTORS.
• IGNITION "ON."
DOES DTC RESET?
REPAIR OPEN OR HIGH RESISTANCE IN CKT 879.
YES
NO
REPLACE ENABLE RELAY.
MALFUNCTION WAS DUE TO POOR CONNECTION.

THIS CHART ASSUMES THAT A CURRENT DTC IS STORED INDICATING THAT THIS MALFUNCTION IS PRESENT.

GC402930074100BX

DTC A014

ENABLE RELAY CONTACTS OR FUSE OPEN

Circuit Description:

Ignition voltage is supplied through terminal "86" of the ABS enable relay. The EBCM then is able to energize the pull-in coil by completing the ground circuit at Pin "22" of the EBCM. The magnetic field created closes the enable relay contacts and allows battery voltage and current to be supplied to the EMBs and EBCM, which supplies power to the motors and solenoids.

Failure Condition:

DTC A014 can be set anytime after the EBCM commands the enable relay "ON" (the relay is first commanded "ON" during the three second bulb check). This test monitors the availability of current/voltage to the motors, solenoids and EMBs. This malfunction indicates voltage is not available and would therefore not allow ABS operation if required.

Action Taken

A malfunction DTC is stored, ABS is disabled and the ABS indicator lamp is turned "ON."

Test Description: Number(s) below refer to circled number(s) on the diagnostic chart.

1. This step would indicate that the EBCM is sensing battery voltage present through the relay contacts at terminal "A." This shows that the relay and circuitry is functional.
2. This step ensures the enable relay and related circuitry are operating properly.
3. This ensures that battery voltage is available to terminals "30" and "86" of the relay.
4. This step checks for an open in CKT 850 between the enable relay and EBCM.
5. This step checks for an open in CKT 879 between enable relay and EBCM.
6. This test ensures malfunction was not due to poor harness connections.

Diagnostic Aids:

An "Intermittent" malfunction may be caused by a poor connection, rubbed through wire insulation, or a wire that is broken inside the insulation.

The frequency of the malfunction can be checked by using the enhanced diagnostic function of the Tech 1 as described in "Enhanced Diagnostics," found in this section.

Any circuitry that is suspected as causing the "Intermittent" complaint should be thoroughly checked for backed out terminals, improper mating, broken locks, improperly formed or damaged terminals, poor terminal to wiring connections or physical damage to the wiring harness.

VIBRATION, TEMPERATURE EFFECTS:

Check for vibration effects by performing the relay test function of the Tech 1. With the relay commanded "ON," lightly tap the top and sides of the relay while monitoring relay voltage. If the relay voltage changes significantly, replace the relay.

If test 14 only fails when the vehicle is initially started in cold ambient conditions (temperature less than 32°F - 0°C), replace the relay.

GC402930074100AX

Fig. 98 Code A014: Enable Relay Contacts Or Fuse Open. 1993–94 Cavalier & Sunbird

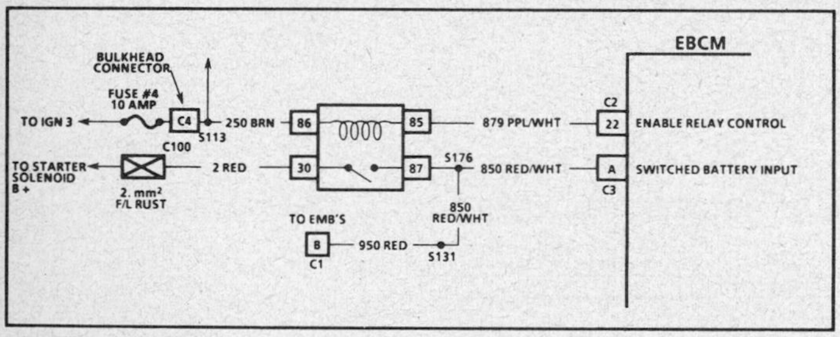
EBCM
BULKHEAD CONNECTOR
FUSE #4 10 AMP
TO IGN 3
C4
C100
S113
250 BRN
86
85
879 PPL/WHT
C2
22
ENABLE RELAY CONTROL
TO STARTER SOLENOID B+
2. mm² F/L RUST
2 RED
30
87
S176
850 RED/WHT
A
C3
SWITCHED BATTERY INPUT
850 RED/WHT
TO EMB'S
B
C1
950 RED
S131

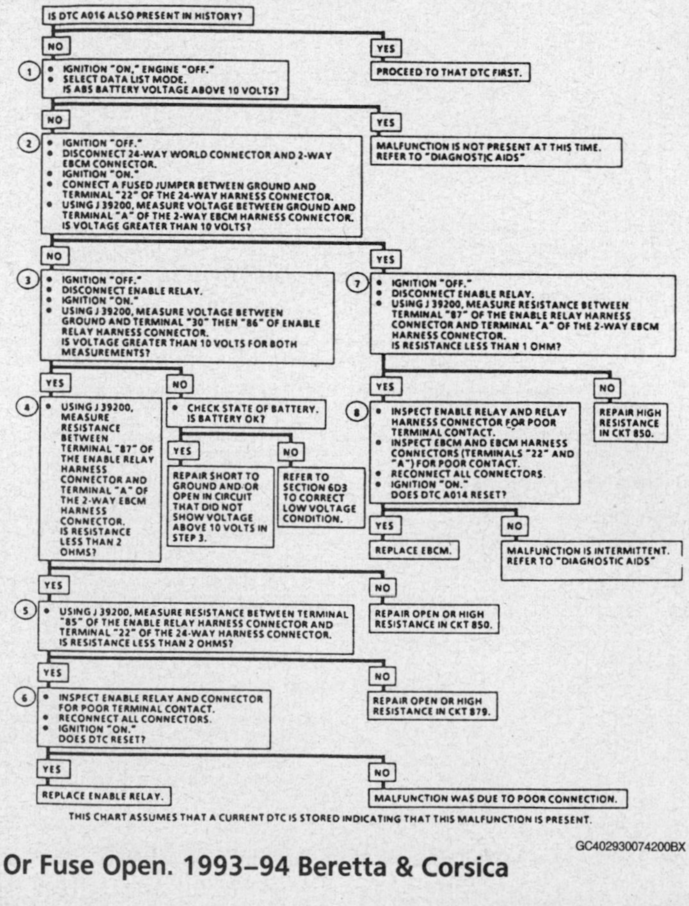
IS DTC A016 ALSO PRESENT IN HISTORY?
NO
YES
PROCEED TO THAT DTC FIRST.
1 • IGNITION "ON," ENGINE "OFF."
• SELECT DATA LIST MODE.
IS ABS BATTERY VOLTAGE ABOVE 10 VOLTS?
NO
YES
MALFUNCTION IS NOT PRESENT AT THIS TIME. REFER TO "DIAGNOSTIC AIDS"
2 • IGNITION "OFF."
• DISCONNECT 24-WAY WORLD CONNECTOR AND 2-WAY EBCM CONNECTOR.
• IGNITION "ON."
• CONNECT A FUSED JUMPER BETWEEN GROUND AND TERMINAL "22" OF THE 24-WAY HARNESS CONNECTOR.
• USING J 39200, MEASURE VOLTAGE BETWEEN GROUND AND TERMINAL "A" OF THE 2-WAY EBCM HARNESS CONNECTOR.
IS VOLTAGE GREATER THAN 10 VOLTS?
NO
YES
3 • IGNITION "OFF."
• DISCONNECT ENABLE RELAY.
• IGNITION "ON."
• USING J 39200, MEASURE VOLTAGE BETWEEN GROUND AND TERMINAL "30" THEN "86" OF ENABLE RELAY HARNESS CONNECTOR.
IS VOLTAGE GREATER THAN 10 VOLTS FOR BOTH MEASUREMENTS?
7 • IGNITION "OFF."
• DISCONNECT ENABLE RELAY.
• USING J 39200, MEASURE RESISTANCE BETWEEN TERMINAL "87" OF THE ENABLE RELAY HARNESS CONNECTOR AND TERMINAL "A" OF THE 2-WAY EBCM HARNESS CONNECTOR.
IS RESISTANCE LESS THAN 1 OHM?
YES
NO
YES
NO
4 • USING J 39200, MEASURE RESISTANCE BETWEEN TERMINAL "87" OF THE ENABLE RELAY HARNESS CONNECTOR AND TERMINAL "A" OF THE 2-WAY EBCM HARNESS CONNECTOR.
IS RESISTANCE LESS THAN 2 OHMS?
• CHECK STATE OF BATTERY.
IS BATTERY OK?
YES
NO
REPAIR SHORT TO GROUND AND/OR OPEN IN CIRCUIT THAT DID NOT SHOW VOLTAGE ABOVE 10 VOLTS IN STEP 3.
REFER TO SECTION 6D3 TO CORRECT LOW VOLTAGE CONDITION.
8 • INSPECT ENABLE RELAY AND RELAY HARNESS CONNECTOR FOR POOR TERMINAL CONTACT.
• INSPECT EBCM AND EBCM HARNESS CONNECTORS (TERMINALS "22" AND "A") FOR POOR CONTACT.
• RECONNECT ALL CONNECTORS.
• IGNITION "ON."
DOES DTC A014 RESET?
REPAIR HIGH RESISTANCE IN CKT 850.
YES
NO
REPLACE EBCM.
MALFUNCTION IS INTERMITTENT. REFER TO "DIAGNOSTIC AIDS"
YES
NO
5 • USING J 39200, MEASURE RESISTANCE BETWEEN TERMINAL "85" OF THE ENABLE RELAY HARNESS CONNECTOR AND TERMINAL "22" OF THE 24-WAY HARNESS CONNECTOR.
IS RESISTANCE LESS THAN 2 OHMS?
REPAIR OPEN OR HIGH RESISTANCE IN CKT 850.
YES
NO
6 • INSPECT ENABLE RELAY AND CONNECTOR FOR POOR TERMINAL CONTACT.
• RECONNECT ALL CONNECTORS.
• IGNITION "ON."
DOES DTC RESET?
REPAIR OPEN OR HIGH RESISTANCE IN CKT 879.
YES
NO
REPLACE ENABLE RELAY.
MALFUNCTION WAS DUE TO POOR CONNECTION.

THIS CHART ASSUMES THAT A CURRENT DTC IS STORED INDICATING THAT THIS MALFUNCTION IS PRESENT.

GC402930074200BX

Circuit Description:

Ignition voltage is supplied through terminal "86" of the ABS enable relay. The EBCM then is able to energize the pull-in coil by completing the ground circuit at Pin "22" of the EBCM. The magnetic field created closes the enable relay contacts and allows battery voltage and current to be supplied to the EMBs and EBCM, which supplies power to the motors and solenoids.

Failure Condition:

DTC A014 can be set anytime after the EBCM commands the enable relay "ON" (the relay is first commanded "ON" during the three second bulb check). This test monitors the availability of current/voltage to the motors, solenoids and EMBs. This malfunction indicates voltage is not available and would therefore not allow ABS operation if required.

Action Taken:

A malfunction DTC is stored, ABS is disabled and the ABS indicator lamp is turned "ON."

Test Description: Number(s) below refer to circled number(s) on the diagnostic chart.

1. This step would indicate that the EBCM is sensing battery voltage present through the relay contacts at terminal "A." This shows that the relay and circuitry is functional.
2. This step ensures voltage is available at terminal "A".
3. This ensures that battery voltage is available to terminals "30" and "86" of the relay.
4. This step checks for an open in CKT 850 between the enable relay and EBCM.
5. This step checks for an open in CKT 879 between enable relay and EBCM.
6. This test ensures malfunction was not due to poor harness connections.
7. This step checks for high resistance in the switched battery input circuitry.
8. This step checks for an intermittent malfunction.

Diagnostic Aids:

An "Intermittent" malfunction may be caused by a poor connection, rubbed through wire insulation, or a wire that is broken inside the insulation.

The frequency of the malfunction can be checked by using the enhanced diagnostic function of the Tech 1.

Any circuitry that is suspected as causing the "Intermittent" complaint should be thoroughly checked for backed out terminals, improper mating, broken locks, improperly formed or damaged terminals, poor terminal to wiring connections or physical damage to the wiring harness.

VIBRATION, TEMPERATURE EFFECTS:

Check for vibration effects by performing the relay test function of the Tech 1. With the relay commanded "ON," lightly tap the top and sides of the relay while monitoring relay voltage. If the relay voltage changes significantly, replace the relay.

If test 14 only fails when the vehicle is initially started in cold ambient conditions (temperature less than 32°F - 0°C), replace the relay.

GC402930074200AX

Fig. 99 Code A014: Enable Relay Contacts Or Fuse Open. 1993–94 Beretta & Corsica

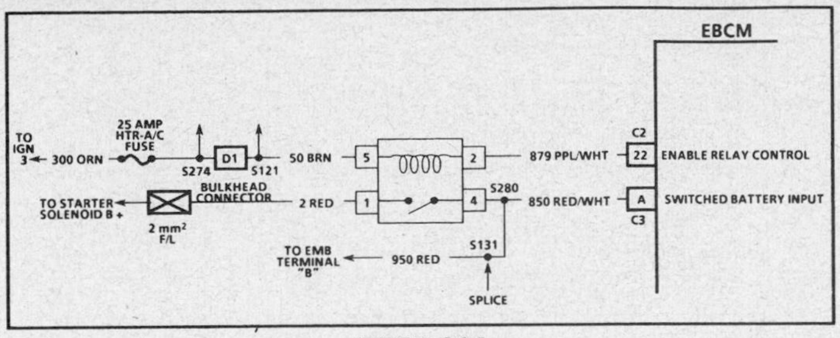
EBCM
TO IGN 3
25 AMP HTR-A/C FUSE
300 ORN
S274
D1
S121
50 BRN
5
2
879 PPL/WHT
C2
22
ENABLE RELAY CONTROL
TO STARTER SOLENOID B+
BULKHEAD CONNECTOR
2 mm² F/L
2 RED
1
4
S280
850 RED/WHT
A
SWITCHED BATTERY INPUT
C3
TO EMB TERMINAL "B"
950 RED
S131
SPLICE

DTC A014

ENABLE RELAY CONTACTS OR FUSE OPEN

Circuit Description:

Ignition voltage is supplied through terminal "5" of the ABS enable relay. The EBCM then is able to energize the pull-in coil by completing the ground circuit at Pin "22" of the EBCM. The magnetic field created closes the enable relay contacts and allows battery voltage and current to be supplied to the EMBs and EBCM, which supplies power to the motors and solenoids.

Failure Condition:

DTC A014 can be set anytime after the EBCM commands the enable relay "ON" (the relay is first commanded "ON" during the three second bulb check). This test monitors the availability of current/voltage to the motors, solenoids and EMBs. This malfunction indicates voltage is not available and would therefore not allow ABS operation if required.

Action Taken:

A malfunction DTC is stored, ABS is disabled and the ABS indicator lamp is turned "ON."

Test Description: Number(s) below refer to circled number(s) on the diagnostic chart.

1. This step would indicate that the EBCM is sensing battery voltage present through the relay contacts at terminal "A." This shows that the relay and circuitry is functional.
2. This step ensures the enable relay and related circuitry are operating properly.
3. This ensures that battery voltage is available to terminals "1" and "5" of the relay.
4. This step checks for an open in CKT 850 between the enable relay and EBCM.
5. This step checks for an open in CKT 879 between enable relay and EBCM.
6. This test ensures malfunction was not due to poor harness connections.

Diagnostic Aids:

An "Intermittent" malfunction may be caused by a poor connection, rubbed through wire insulation, or a wire that is broken inside the insulation.

The frequency of the malfunction can be checked by using the enhanced diagnostic function of the Tech 1.

Any circuitry that is suspected as causing the "Intermittent" complaint should be thoroughly checked for backed out terminals, improper mating, broken locks, improperly formed or damaged terminals, poor terminal to wiring connections or physical damage to the wiring harness.

VIBRATION, TEMPERATURE EFFECTS:

Check for vibration effects by performing the relay test function of the Tech 1. With the relay commanded "ON," lightly tap the top and sides of the relay while monitoring relay voltage. If the relay voltage changes significantly, replace the relay.

If test 14 only fails when the vehicle is initially started in cold ambient conditions (temperature less than 32°F - 0°C), replace the relay.

GC402930074300AX

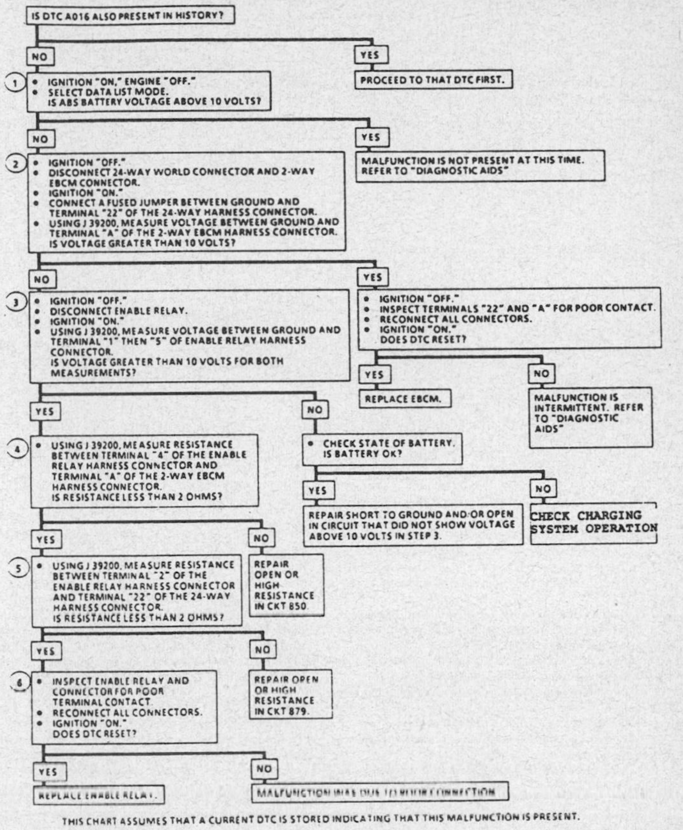
IS DTC A016 ALSO PRESENT IN HISTORY?
NO
YES
PROCEED TO THAT DTC FIRST.
1
• IGNITION "ON," ENGINE "OFF."
• SELECT DATA LIST MODE.
IS ABS BATTERY VOLTAGE ABOVE 10 VOLTS?
NO
YES
MALFUNCTION IS NOT PRESENT AT THIS TIME. REFER TO "DIAGNOSTIC AIDS"
2
• IGNITION "OFF."
• DISCONNECT 24-WAY WORLD CONNECTOR AND 2-WAY EBCM CONNECTOR.
• IGNITION "ON."
• CONNECT A FUSED JUMPER BETWEEN GROUND AND TERMINAL "22" OF THE 24-WAY HARNESS CONNECTOR.
• USING J 39200, MEASURE VOLTAGE BETWEEN GROUND AND TERMINAL "A" OF THE 2-WAY EBCM HARNESS CONNECTOR.
IS VOLTAGE GREATER THAN 10 VOLTS?
NO
YES
• IGNITION "OFF."
• INSPECT TERMINALS "22" AND "A" FOR POOR CONTACT.
• RECONNECT ALL CONNECTORS.
• IGNITION "ON."
DOES DTC RESET?
YES
REPLACE EBCM.
NO
MALFUNCTION IS INTERMITTENT. REFER TO "DIAGNOSTIC AIDS"
3
• IGNITION "OFF."
• DISCONNECT ENABLE RELAY.
• IGNITION "ON."
• USING J 39200, MEASURE VOLTAGE BETWEEN GROUND AND TERMINAL "1" THEN "5" OF ENABLE RELAY HARNESS CONNECTOR.
IS VOLTAGE GREATER THAN 10 VOLTS FOR BOTH MEASUREMENTS?
YES
NO
• CHECK STATE OF BATTERY.
IS BATTERY OK?
YES
REPAIR SHORT TO GROUND AND/OR OPEN IN CIRCUIT THAT DID NOT SHOW VOLTAGE ABOVE 10 VOLTS IN STEP 3.
NO
CHECK CHARGING SYSTEM OPERATION
4
• USING J 39200, MEASURE RESISTANCE BETWEEN TERMINAL "4" OF THE ENABLE RELAY HARNESS CONNECTOR AND TERMINAL "A" OF THE 2-WAY EBCM HARNESS CONNECTOR.
IS RESISTANCE LESS THAN 2 OHMS?
YES
NO
REPAIR OPEN OR HIGH RESISTANCE IN CKT 850.
5
• USING J 39200, MEASURE RESISTANCE BETWEEN TERMINAL "2" OF THE ENABLE RELAY HARNESS CONNECTOR AND TERMINAL "22" OF THE 24-WAY HARNESS CONNECTOR.
IS RESISTANCE LESS THAN 2 OHMS?
YES
NO
REPAIR OPEN OR HIGH RESISTANCE IN CKT 879.
6
• INSPECT ENABLE RELAY AND CONNECTOR FOR POOR TERMINAL CONTACT.
• RECONNECT ALL CONNECTORS.
• IGNITION "ON."
DOES DTC RESET?
YES
REPLACE ENABLE RELAY.
NO
MALFUNCTION WAS DUE TO POOR CONNECTION
THIS CHART ASSUMES THAT A CURRENT DTC IS STORED INDICATING THAT THIS MALFUNCTION IS PRESENT.

GC402930074300BX

Fig. 100 Code A014: Enable Relay Contacts Or Fuse Open. 1993–94 Achieva, Grand Am & Skylark Less VES

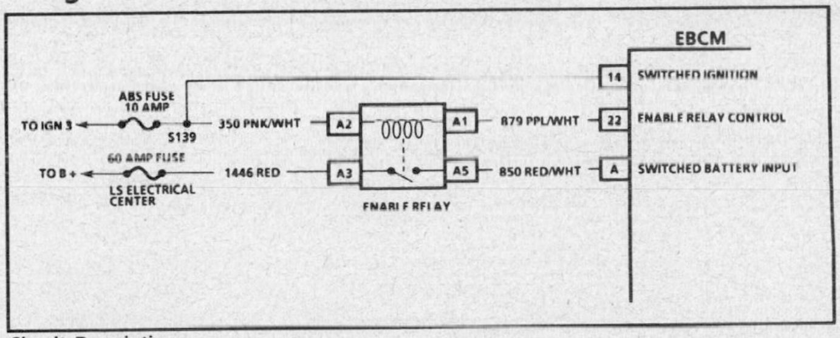
EBCM
ABS FUSE 10 AMP
TO IGN 3
S139
350 PNK/WHT
A2
A1
879 PPL/WHT
14
SWITCHED IGNITION
22
ENABLE RELAY CONTROL
60 AMP FUSE
TO B+
LS ELECTRICAL CENTER
1446 RED
A3
A5
850 RED/WHT
A
SWITCHED BATTERY INPUT
ENABLE RELAY

Circuit Description:

Ignition voltage is supplied through terminal "A2" of the ABS enable relay. The EBCM then is able to energize the pull in coil by completing the ground circuit at terminal "22" of the EBCM. The magnetic field created closes the enable relay contacts and allows battery voltage and current to be supplied to the EBCM, which supplies power to the motors and solenoids.

Failure Condition:

DTC A014 can be set anytime after the EBCM commands the enable relay "ON" (the relay is first commanded "ON" during the three second bulb check). This test monitors the availability of current/voltage to the motors and solenoids. This malfunction indicates voltage is not available and would therefore not allow ABS operation if required.

Action Taken:

A malfunction DTC is stored, ABS is disabled and the ABS indicator lamp is turned "ON."

Test Description: Number(s) below refer to circled number(s) on the diagnostic chart.

1. This step checks to see if DTC A016 is also set as current or history. If DTC A016 is also set, proceed to that chart first.
2. This step verifies that the malfunction is currently present.
3. This step verifies that voltage is available at the relay coil and at the relay switch.
4. This step checks to see if a malfunctioning EBCM is the cause of DTC A014 being set.
5. This step checks for an open in the switched battery input circuit.
6. This step checks for an open in the relay control circuit.
7. This step determines whether the malfunction is intermittent or caused by a malfunctioning relay.
8. This step determines if the low voltage condition was caused by an open in the voltage feed circuits to the relay or by a vehicle charging system malfunction.
9. This step checks for a possible intermittent malfunction.

Diagnostic Aids:

An "Intermittent" problem may be caused by a poor connection, rubbed through wire insulation, or a wire that is broken inside the insulation.

The frequency of the problem can be checked by using the enhanced diagnostic function of the Tech 1.

Any circuitry that is suspected as causing the "Intermittent" complaint should be thoroughly checked for backed out terminals, improper mating, broken locks, improperly formed or damaged terminals, poor terminal to wiring connections or physical damage to the wiring harness.

VIBRATION, TEMPERATURE EFFECTS:

Check for vibration effects by performing the relay test function of the Tech 1. With the relay commanded "ON," lightly tap the top and sides of the relay while monitoring relay voltage. If the relay voltage changes significantly, replace the relay.

If DTC A014 only sets when the vehicle is initially started in cold ambient conditions (temperature less than 32°F-0°C), replace the relay.

GC402930074400AX

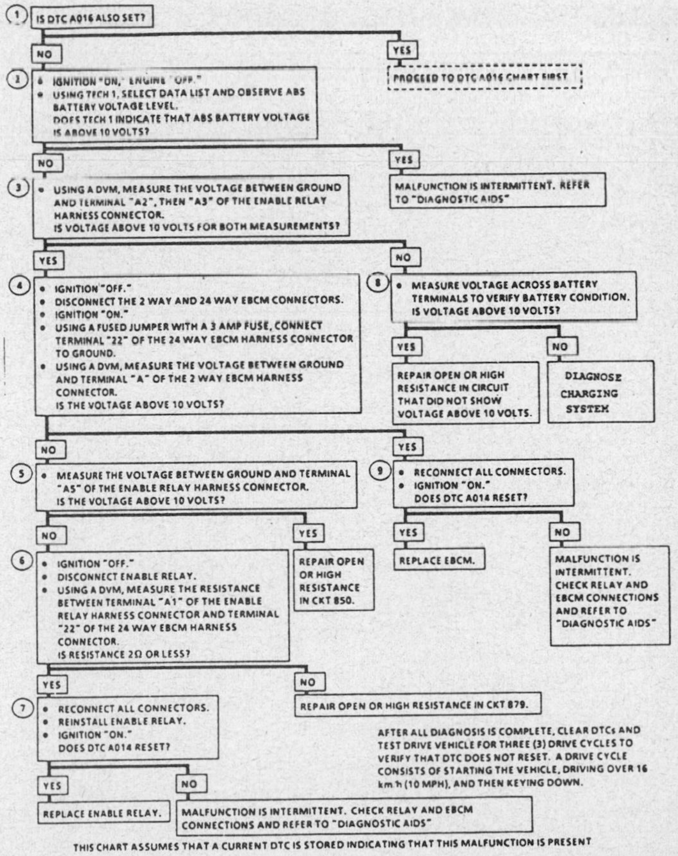
1
IS DTC A016 ALSO SET?
NO
YES
PROCEED TO DTC A016 CHART FIRST
2
• IGNITION "ON," ENGINE "OFF."
• USING TECH 1, SELECT DATA LIST AND OBSERVE ABS BATTERY VOLTAGE LEVEL.
DOES TECH 1 INDICATE THAT ABS BATTERY VOLTAGE IS ABOVE 10 VOLTS?
NO
YES
MALFUNCTION IS INTERMITTENT. REFER TO "DIAGNOSTIC AIDS"
3
• USING A DVM, MEASURE THE VOLTAGE BETWEEN GROUND AND TERMINAL "A2", THEN "A3" OF THE ENABLE RELAY HARNESS CONNECTOR.
IS VOLTAGE ABOVE 10 VOLTS FOR BOTH MEASUREMENTS?
YES
NO
8
• MEASURE VOLTAGE ACROSS BATTERY TERMINALS TO VERIFY BATTERY CONDITION.
IS VOLTAGE ABOVE 10 VOLTS?
YES
REPAIR OPEN OR HIGH RESISTANCE IN CIRCUIT THAT DID NOT SHOW VOLTAGE ABOVE 10 VOLTS.
NO
DIAGNOSE CHARGING SYSTEM
4
• IGNITION "OFF."
• DISCONNECT THE 2 WAY AND 24 WAY EBCM CONNECTORS.
• IGNITION "ON."
• USING A FUSED JUMPER WITH A 3 AMP FUSE, CONNECT TERMINAL "22" OF THE 24 WAY EBCM HARNESS CONNECTOR TO GROUND.
• USING A DVM, MEASURE THE VOLTAGE BETWEEN GROUND AND TERMINAL "A" OF THE 2 WAY EBCM HARNESS CONNECTOR.
IS THE VOLTAGE ABOVE 10 VOLTS?
NO
YES
9
• RECONNECT ALL CONNECTORS.
• IGNITION "ON."
DOES DTC A014 RESET?
YES
REPLACE EBCM.
NO
MALFUNCTION IS INTERMITTENT. CHECK RELAY AND EBCM CONNECTIONS AND REFER TO "DIAGNOSTIC AIDS"
5
• MEASURE THE VOLTAGE BETWEEN GROUND AND TERMINAL "A5" OF THE ENABLE RELAY HARNESS CONNECTOR.
IS THE VOLTAGE ABOVE 10 VOLTS?
NO
YES
REPAIR OPEN OR HIGH RESISTANCE IN CKT 850.
6
• IGNITION "OFF."
• DISCONNECT ENABLE RELAY.
• USING A DVM, MEASURE THE RESISTANCE BETWEEN TERMINAL "A1" OF THE ENABLE RELAY HARNESS CONNECTOR AND TERMINAL "22" OF THE 24 WAY EBCM HARNESS CONNECTOR.
IS RESISTANCE 2Ω OR LESS?
YES
NO
REPAIR OPEN OR HIGH RESISTANCE IN CKT 879.
7
• RECONNECT ALL CONNECTORS.
• REINSTALL ENABLE RELAY.
• IGNITION "ON."
DOES DTC A014 RESET?
YES
REPLACE ENABLE RELAY.
NO
MALFUNCTION IS INTERMITTENT. CHECK RELAY AND EBCM CONNECTIONS AND REFER TO "DIAGNOSTIC AIDS"
AFTER ALL DIAGNOSIS IS COMPLETE, CLEAR DTCs AND TEST DRIVE VEHICLE FOR THREE (3) DRIVE CYCLES TO VERIFY THAT DTC DOES NOT RESET. A DRIVE CYCLE CONSISTS OF STARTING THE VEHICLE, DRIVING OVER 16 km/h (10 MPH), AND THEN KEYING DOWN.
THIS CHART ASSUMES THAT A CURRENT DTC IS STORED INDICATING THAT THIS MALFUNCTION IS PRESENT

GC402930074400BX

Fig. 101 Code A014: Enable Relay Contacts Or Fuse Open. 1993 Cutlass Supreme, Grand Prix, Lumina & Regal

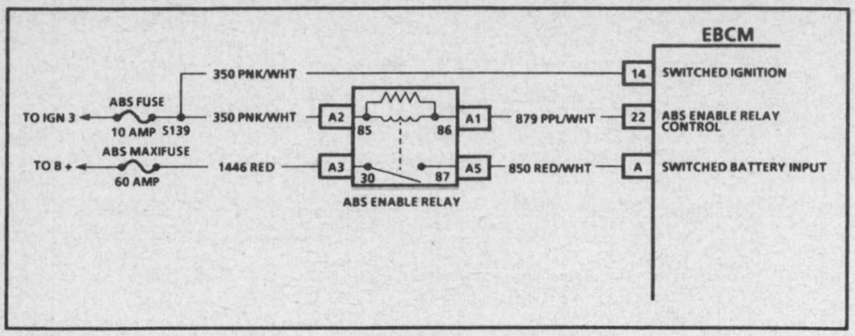
EBCM
350 PNK/WHT
14 SWITCHED IGNITION
ABS FUSE
TO IGN 3
10 AMP S139
350 PNK/WHT
A2
85
86
A1
879 PPL/WHT
22
ABS ENABLE RELAY CONTROL
ABS MAXIFUSE
TO B +
60 AMP
1446 RED
A3
30
87
A5
850 RED/WHT
A
SWITCHED BATTERY INPUT
ABS ENABLE RELAY

DTC 14

(Page 1 of 3)

ABS ENABLE RELAY CONTACT CIRCUIT OPEN

Circuit Description:

Ignition voltage is supplied through terminal "A2" of the ABS enable relay. The EBCM then is able to energize the pull-in coil by completing the ground circuit at terminal "22" of the EBCM. The magnetic field created closes the ABS enable relay contacts and allows battery voltage and current to be supplied to the EBCM, which supplies power to the motors and solenoids.

DTC Will Set When: DTC 14 can be set anytime after the EBCM commands the ABS enable relay "ON" (the relay is first commanded "ON" during the three second bulb check). This test monitors the availability of current/voltage to the motors and solenoids. This malfunction indicates voltage is not available and would therefore not allow ABS operation if required.

Action Taken: A malfunction DTC is stored, ABS is disabled and the ABS warning lamp is turned "ON."

DTC Chart Test Description: Number(s) below refer to circled number(s) on the diagnostic chart.

1. Checks to see if DTC 16 is also set as current or history. If DTC 16 is also set, proceed to that chart first.
2. Verifies that the malfunction is currently present.
3. Verifies that the relay can be turned "ON" and provide voltage to the EBCM.
4. Checks for high resistance in the switched battery circuit from the relay to the EBCM.
5. Checks for high resistance in the switched battery circuit from the battery to the relay.
6. Verifies the condition of the ABS enable relay.
7. Checks for poor terminal contact or corrosion at the connectors.
8. Determines if the EBCM is the cause of the malfunction.

Diagnostic Aids: An "Intermittent" problem may be caused by a poor connection, rubbed through wire insulation, or a wire that is broken inside the insulation.

The frequency of the problem can be checked by using the enhanced diagnostic function of the Tech 1

Any circuitry that is suspected as causing the "Intermittent" complaint should be thoroughly checked for backed out terminals, improper mating, broken locks, improperly formed or damaged terminals, poor terminal to wiring connections or physical damage to the wiring harness.

VIBRATION, TEMPERATURE EFFECTS:

Check for vibration effects by performing the relay test function of the Tech 1. With the relay test commanded "ON," lightly tap the top and sides of the relay while monitoring relay voltage. If the relay voltage changes significantly, replace the relay.

If DTC 14 only sets when the vehicle is initially started in cold ambient conditions (temperature less than 32°F-0°C), replace the relay.

GC402940093901AX

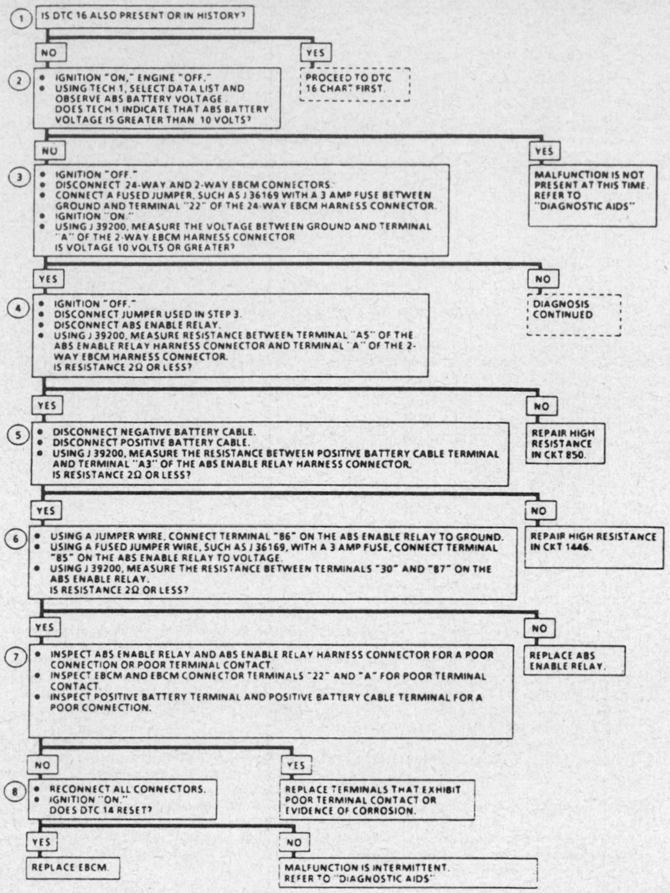
1 IS DTC 16 ALSO PRESENT OR IN HISTORY?
NO
YES
PROCEED TO DTC 16 CHART FIRST.
2 • IGNITION "ON," ENGINE "OFF."
• USING TECH 1, SELECT DATA LIST AND OBSERVE ABS BATTERY VOLTAGE. DOES TECH 1 INDICATE THAT ABS BATTERY VOLTAGE IS GREATER THAN 10 VOLTS?
NO
YES
MALFUNCTION IS NOT PRESENT AT THIS TIME. REFER TO "DIAGNOSTIC AIDS"
3 • IGNITION "OFF."
• DISCONNECT 24-WAY AND 2-WAY EBCM CONNECTORS.
• CONNECT A FUSED JUMPER, SUCH AS J 36169 WITH A 3 AMP FUSE BETWEEN GROUND AND TERMINAL "22" OF THE 24-WAY EBCM HARNESS CONNECTOR.
• IGNITION "ON."
• USING J 39200, MEASURE THE VOLTAGE BETWEEN GROUND AND TERMINAL "A" OF THE 2-WAY EBCM HARNESS CONNECTOR IS VOLTAGE 10 VOLTS OR GREATER?
YES
NO
DIAGNOSIS CONTINUED
4 • IGNITION "OFF."
• DISCONNECT JUMPER USED IN STEP 3.
• DISCONNECT ABS ENABLE RELAY.
• USING J 39200, MEASURE RESISTANCE BETWEEN TERMINAL "A5" OF THE ABS ENABLE RELAY HARNESS CONNECTOR AND TERMINAL "A" OF THE 2-WAY EBCM HARNESS CONNECTOR. IS RESISTANCE 2Ω OR LESS?
YES
NO
REPAIR HIGH RESISTANCE IN CKT 850.
5 • DISCONNECT NEGATIVE BATTERY CABLE.
• DISCONNECT POSITIVE BATTERY CABLE.
• USING J 39200, MEASURE THE RESISTANCE BETWEEN POSITIVE BATTERY CABLE TERMINAL AND TERMINAL "A3" OF THE ABS ENABLE RELAY HARNESS CONNECTOR. IS RESISTANCE 2Ω OR LESS?
YES
NO
REPAIR HIGH RESISTANCE IN CKT 1446.
6 • USING A JUMPER WIRE, CONNECT TERMINAL "86" ON THE ABS ENABLE RELAY TO GROUND.
• USING A FUSED JUMPER WIRE, SUCH AS J 36169, WITH A 3 AMP FUSE, CONNECT TERMINAL "85" ON THE ABS ENABLE RELAY TO VOLTAGE.
• USING J 39200, MEASURE THE RESISTANCE BETWEEN TERMINALS "30" AND "87" ON THE ABS ENABLE RELAY. IS RESISTANCE 2Ω OR LESS?
YES
NO
REPLACE ABS ENABLE RELAY.
7 • INSPECT ABS ENABLE RELAY AND ABS ENABLE RELAY HARNESS CONNECTOR FOR A POOR CONNECTION OR POOR TERMINAL CONTACT.
• INSPECT EBCM AND EBCM CONNECTOR TERMINALS "22" AND "A" FOR POOR TERMINAL CONTACT.
• INSPECT POSITIVE BATTERY TERMINAL AND POSITIVE BATTERY CABLE TERMINAL FOR A POOR CONNECTION.
NO
YES
REPLACE TERMINALS THAT EXHIBIT POOR TERMINAL CONTACT OR EVIDENCE OF CORROSION.
8 • RECONNECT ALL CONNECTORS.
• IGNITION "ON." DOES DTC 14 RESET?
YES
NO
REPLACE EBCM.
MALFUNCTION IS INTERMITTENT. REFER TO "DIAGNOSTIC AIDS"

GC402940093901BX

Fig. 102 Code A014: Enable Relay Contacts Circuit Open (Part 1 of 3). 1994 Cutlass Supreme, Lumina & Regal

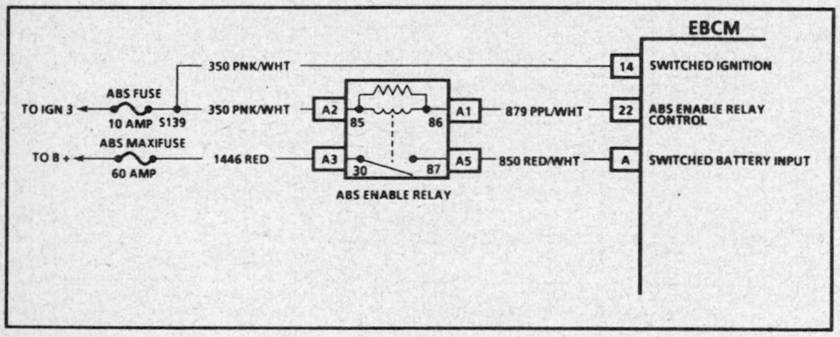
EBCM
350 PNK/WHT
14 SWITCHED IGNITION
ABS FUSE
TO IGN 3
10 AMP S139
350 PNK/WHT
A2
85
86
A1
879 PPL/WHT
22
ABS ENABLE RELAY CONTROL
ABS MAXIFUSE
TO B +
60 AMP
1446 RED
A3
30
87
A5
850 RED/WHT
A
SWITCHED BATTERY INPUT
ABS ENABLE RELAY

DTC 14

(Page 2 of 3)

ABS ENABLE RELAY CONTACT CIRCUIT OPEN

Circuit Description:

Ignition voltage is supplied through terminal "A2" of the ABS enable relay. The EBCM then is able to energize the pull-in coil by completing the ground circuit at terminal "22" of the EBCM. The magnetic field created closes the ABS enable relay contacts and allows battery voltage and current to be supplied to the EBCM, which supplies power to the motors and solenoids.

DTC Will Set When: DTC 14 can be set anytime after the EBCM commands the ABS enable relay "ON" (the relay is first commanded "ON" during the three second bulb check). This test monitors the availability of current/voltage to the motors and solenoids. This malfunction indicates voltage is not available and would therefore not allow ABS operation if required.

Action Taken: A malfunction DTC is stored, ABS is disabled and the ABS warning lamp is turned "ON."

DTC Chart Test Description: Number(s) below refer to circled number(s) on the diagnostic chart.

9. Checks for high resistance in the entire relay coil circuit.
10. Verifies proper battery condition.
11. Verifies proper voltage is available at the ABS enable relay.
12. Checks for an open in the switched battery circuit from the relay to the EBCM.
13. Verifies the condition of the ABS enable relay.

Diagnostic Aids: An "Intermittent" problem may be caused by a poor connection, rubbed through wire insulation, or a wire that is broken inside the insulation.

The frequency of the problem can be checked by using the enhanced diagnostic function of the Tech 1

Any circuitry that is suspected as causing the "Intermittent" complaint should be thoroughly checked for backed out terminals, improper mating, broken locks, improperly formed or damaged terminals, poor terminal to wiring connections or physical damage to the wiring harness.

VIBRATION, TEMPERATURE EFFECTS:

Check for vibration effects by performing the relay test function of the Tech 1. With the relay test commanded "ON," lightly tap the top and sides of the relay while monitoring relay voltage. If the relay voltage changes significantly, replace the relay.

If DTC 14 only sets when the vehicle is initially started in cold ambient conditions (temperature less than 32°F-0°C), replace the relay.

GC402940093902AX

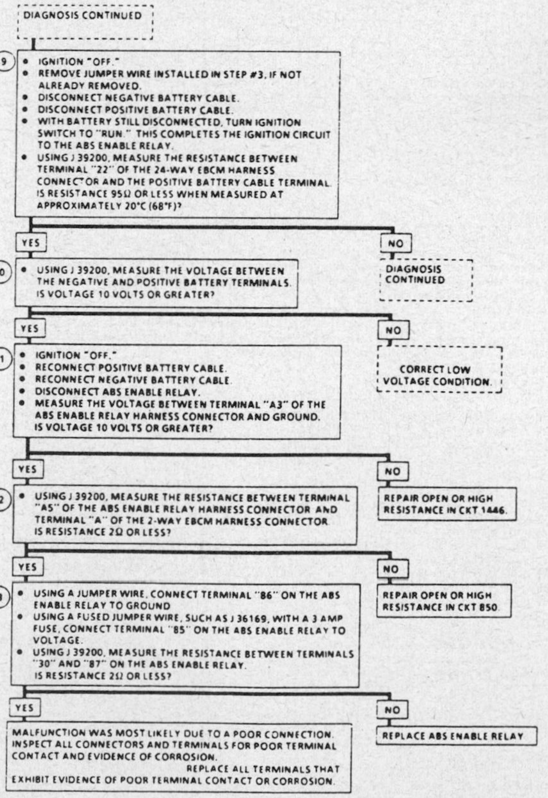
DIAGNOSIS CONTINUED
9 • IGNITION "OFF."
• REMOVE JUMPER WIRE INSTALLED IN STEP #3, IF NOT ALREADY REMOVED.
• DISCONNECT NEGATIVE BATTERY CABLE.
• DISCONNECT POSITIVE BATTERY CABLE.
• WITH BATTERY STILL DISCONNECTED, TURN IGNITION SWITCH TO "RUN." THIS COMPLETES THE IGNITION CIRCUIT TO THE ABS ENABLE RELAY.
• USING J 39200, MEASURE THE RESISTANCE BETWEEN TERMINAL "22" OF THE 24-WAY EBCM HARNESS CONNECTOR AND THE POSITIVE BATTERY CABLE TERMINAL. IS RESISTANCE 95Ω OR LESS WHEN MEASURED AT APPROXIMATELY 20°C (68°F)?
YES
NO
DIAGNOSIS CONTINUED
10 • USING J 39200, MEASURE THE VOLTAGE BETWEEN THE NEGATIVE AND POSITIVE BATTERY TERMINALS. IS VOLTAGE 10 VOLTS OR GREATER?
YES
NO
CORRECT LOW VOLTAGE CONDITION.
11 • IGNITION "OFF."
• RECONNECT POSITIVE BATTERY CABLE.
• RECONNECT NEGATIVE BATTERY CABLE.
• DISCONNECT ABS ENABLE RELAY.
• MEASURE THE VOLTAGE BETWEEN TERMINAL "A3" OF THE ABS ENABLE RELAY HARNESS CONNECTOR AND GROUND. IS VOLTAGE 10 VOLTS OR GREATER?
YES
NO
REPAIR OPEN OR HIGH RESISTANCE IN CKT 1446.
12 • USING J 39200, MEASURE THE RESISTANCE BETWEEN TERMINAL "A5" OF THE ABS ENABLE RELAY HARNESS CONNECTOR AND TERMINAL "A" OF THE 2-WAY EBCM HARNESS CONNECTOR IS RESISTANCE 2Ω OR LESS?
YES
NO
REPAIR OPEN OR HIGH RESISTANCE IN CKT 850.
13 • USING A JUMPER WIRE, CONNECT TERMINAL "86" ON THE ABS ENABLE RELAY TO GROUND
• USING A FUSED JUMPER WIRE, SUCH AS J 36169, WITH A 3 AMP FUSE, CONNECT TERMINAL "85" ON THE ABS ENABLE RELAY TO VOLTAGE.
• USING J 39200, MEASURE THE RESISTANCE BETWEEN TERMINALS "30" AND "87" ON THE ABS ENABLE RELAY. IS RESISTANCE 2Ω OR LESS?
YES
NO
MALFUNCTION WAS MOST LIKELY DUE TO A POOR CONNECTION. INSPECT ALL CONNECTORS AND TERMINALS FOR POOR TERMINAL CONTACT AND EVIDENCE OF CORROSION. REPLACE ALL TERMINALS THAT EXHIBIT EVIDENCE OF POOR TERMINAL CONTACT OR CORROSION.
REPLACE ABS ENABLE RELAY

GC402940093902BX

Fig. 102 Code A014: Enable Relay Contacts Circuit Open (Part 2 of 3). 1994 Cutlass Supreme, Lumina & Regal

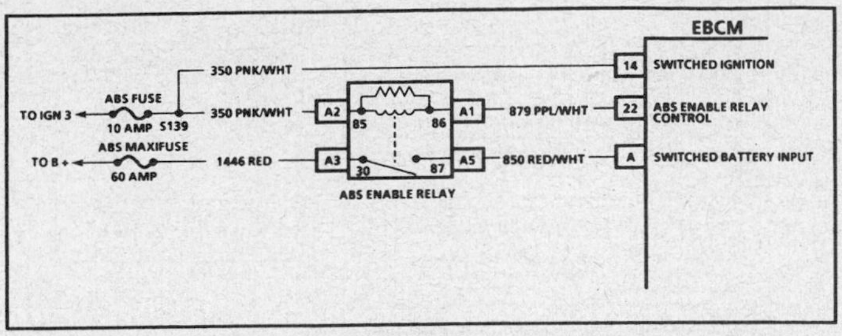
EBCM
350 PNK/WHT
14 SWITCHED IGNITION
ABS FUSE
TO IGN 3
10 AMP S139
350 PNK/WHT
A2 85 86 A1
879 PPL/WHT
22 ABS ENABLE RELAY CONTROL
ABS MAXIFUSE
TO B+
60 AMP
1446 RED
A3 30 87 A5
850 RED/WHT
A SWITCHED BATTERY INPUT
ABS ENABLE RELAY

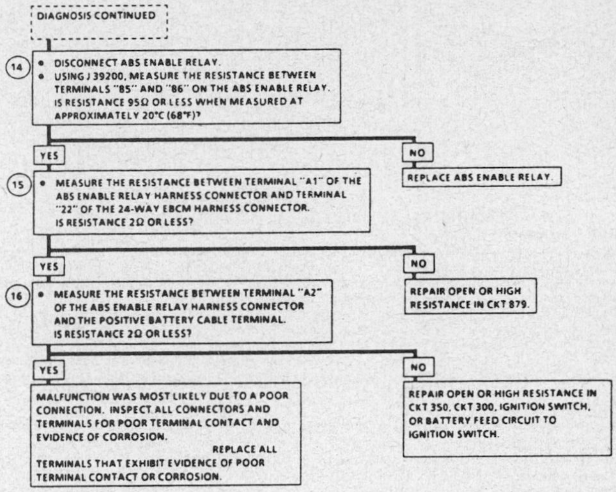
DIAGNOSIS CONTINUED
14 • DISCONNECT ABS ENABLE RELAY.
• USING J 39200, MEASURE THE RESISTANCE BETWEEN TERMINALS "85" AND "86" ON THE ABS ENABLE RELAY. IS RESISTANCE 95Ω OR LESS WHEN MEASURED AT APPROXIMATELY 20°C (68°F)?
YES
NO
REPLACE ABS ENABLE RELAY.
15 • MEASURE THE RESISTANCE BETWEEN TERMINAL "A1" OF THE ABS ENABLE RELAY HARNESS CONNECTOR AND TERMINAL "22" OF THE 24-WAY EBCM HARNESS CONNECTOR. IS RESISTANCE 2Ω OR LESS?
YES
NO
REPAIR OPEN OR HIGH RESISTANCE IN CKT 879.
16 • MEASURE THE RESISTANCE BETWEEN TERMINAL "A2" OF THE ABS ENABLE RELAY HARNESS CONNECTOR AND THE POSITIVE BATTERY CABLE TERMINAL. IS RESISTANCE 2Ω OR LESS?
YES
NO
MALFUNCTION WAS MOST LIKELY DUE TO A POOR CONNECTION. INSPECT ALL CONNECTORS AND TERMINALS FOR POOR TERMINAL CONTACT AND EVIDENCE OF CORROSION. REPLACE ALL TERMINALS THAT EXHIBIT EVIDENCE OF POOR TERMINAL CONTACT OR CORROSION.
REPAIR OPEN OR HIGH RESISTANCE IN CKT 350, CKT 300, IGNITION SWITCH, OR BATTERY FEED CIRCUIT TO IGNITION SWITCH.

GC402940093903BX

DTC 14

(Page 3 of 3)

ABS ENABLE RELAY CONTACT CIRCUIT OPEN

Circuit Description:

Ignition voltage is supplied through terminal "A2" of the ABS enable relay. The EBCM then is able to energize the pull-in coil by completing the ground circuit at terminal "22" of the EBCM. The magnetic field created closes the ABS enable relay contacts and allows battery voltage and current to be supplied to the EBCM, which supplies power to the motors and solenoids.

DTC Will Set When: DTC 14 can be set anytime after the EBCM commands the ABS enable relay "ON" (the relay is first commanded "ON" during the three second bulb check). This test monitors the availability of current/voltage to the motors and solenoids. This malfunction indicates voltage is not available and would therefore not allow ABS operation if required.

Action Taken: A malfunction DTC is stored, ABS is disabled and the ABS warning lamp is turned "ON."

DTC Chart Test Description: Number(s) below refer to circled number(s) on the diagnostic chart.

14. Checks for proper resistance of the relay coil.
15. Checks for high resistance in the ABS enable relay control circuit between the relay and the EBCM.
16. Checks for high resistance in the ABS enable relay control circuit between the battery and the relay.

Diagnostic Aids: An "Intermittent" problem may be caused by a poor connection, rubbed through wire insulation, or a wire that is broken inside the insulation.

The frequency of the problem can be checked by using the enhanced diagnostic function of the Tech 1.

Any circuitry that is suspected as causing the "Intermittent" complaint should be thoroughly checked for backed out terminals, improper mating, broken locks, improperly formed or damaged terminals, poor terminal to wiring connections or physical damage to the wiring harness.

VIBRATION, TEMPERATURE EFFECTS:

Check for vibration effects by performing the relay test function of the Tech 1. With the relay test commanded "ON," lightly tap the top and sides of the relay while monitoring relay voltage. If the relay voltage changes significantly, replace the relay.

If DTC 14 only sets when the vehicle is initially started in cold ambient conditions (temperature less than 32°F-0°C), replace the relay.

GC402940093903AX

Fig. 102 Code A014: Enable Relay Contacts Circuit Open (Part 3 of 3). 1994 Cutlass Supreme, Lumina & Regal

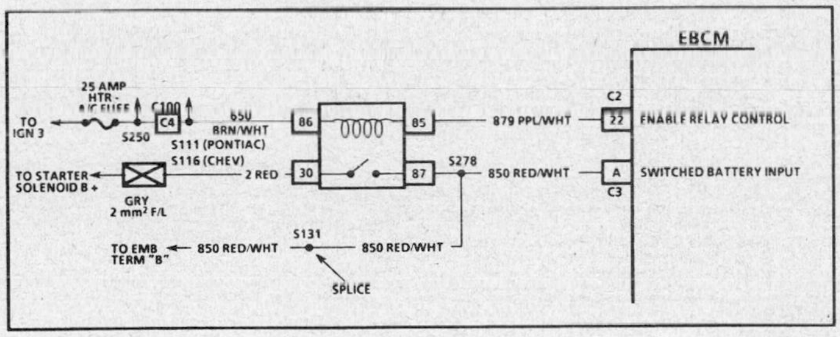
EBCM
25 AMP HTR-A/C FUSE
C100
TO IGN 3
S250
C4
850 BRN/WHT
S111 (PONTIAC)
S116 (CHEV)
86 85
879 PPL/WHT
C2
22 ENABLE RELAY CONTROL
TO STARTER SOLENOID B+
GRY 2 mm² F/L
2 RED
30 87
S278
850 RED/WHT
A SWITCHED BATTERY INPUT
C3
TO EMB TERM "B"
850 RED/WHT
S131
850 RED/WHT
SPLICE

GC402930074500AX

Cavalier & Sunbird

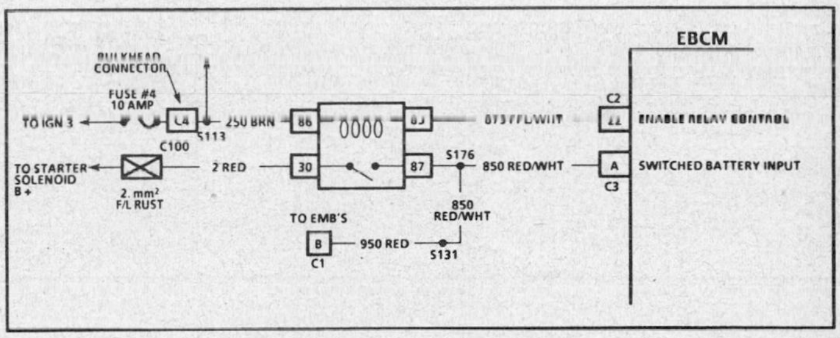
EBCM
BULKHEAD CONNECTOR
FUSE #4 10 AMP
TO IGN 3
C4
250 BRN
S113
C100
86
C2
TO STARTER SOLENOID B+
2 RED
30 87
S176
850 RED/WHT
A SWITCHED BATTERY INPUT
C3
2 mm² F/L RUST
TO EMB'S
850 RED/WHT
B 950 RED
C1
S131

GC402930074500BX

Beretta & Corsica

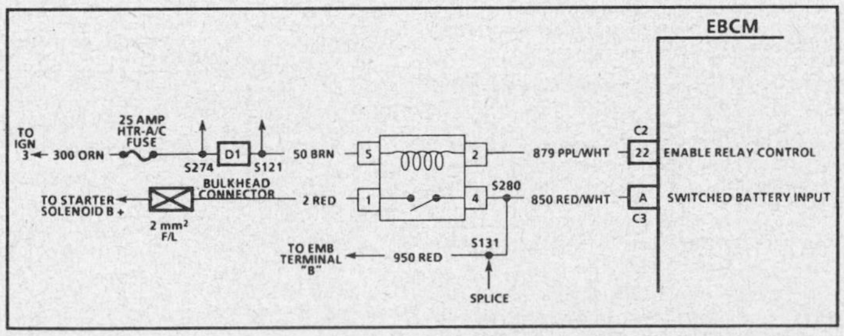
EBCM
TO IGN 3
300 ORN
25 AMP HTR-A/C FUSE
S274
D1
S121
50 BRN
5 2
879 PPL/WHT
C2
22 ENABLE RELAY CONTROL
BULKHEAD CONNECTOR
TO STARTER SOLENOID B+
2 mm² F/L
2 RED
1 4
S280
850 RED/WHT
A SWITCHED BATTERY INPUT
C3
TO EMB TERMINAL "B"
950 RED
S131
SPLICE

GC402930074500CX

Achieva, Grand Am & Skylark

Fig. 103 Code A015: Enable Relay Contacts Shorted to Battery (Part 1 of 2). 1993-94 Cavalier, Sunbird, Beretta, Corsica & Achieva, Grand Am & Skylark Less VES

DTC A015

ENABLE RELAY CONTACTS SHORTED TO BATTERY

Circuit Description:

Ignition voltage is supplied through terminal "86" of the ABS enable relay. The EBCM then is able to energize the pull-in coil by completing the ground circuit at Pin "22" of the EBCM. The magnetic field created closes the enable relay contacts and allows battery voltage and current to be supplied to the EMBs and EBCM, which supplies power to the motors and solenoids.

Failure Condition:

DTC A015 can be set only before the EBCM commands the relay "ON." This test determines if the enable relay is energized when it should not be. This malfunction would not allow the enable relay to remove power to the ABS system. If a second malfunction were to occur that requires the enable relay to be turned "OFF," that malfunction can not be removed if the relay can not be controlled. The malfunction must be present for three consecutive drive cycles before the DTC is set.

Action Taken:

A malfunction DTC is stored. ABS is not disabled; however, the ABS indicator lamp will flash to indicate a malfunction exists.

Test Description: Number(s) below refer to circled number(s) on the diagnostic chart.

1. This step indicates that the EBCM is capable of controlling the enable relay as commanded.
2. This step checks for voltage at terminal "A" of the 2-way EBCM harness connector. If voltage is present, the malfunction exists in the enable relay and/or its circuitry.
3. This test checks for a short to ground in the enable relay control circuit.
4. This step checks for a short to voltage in CKT 850.
5. This step identifies if the EBCM is malfunctioning.

Diagnostic Aids:

An "Intermittent" malfunction may be caused by a poor connection, rubbed through wire insulation, or a wire that is broken inside the insulation.

The frequency of the malfunction can be checked by using the enhanced diagnostic function of the Tech 1.

Any circuitry, that is suspected as causing the intermittent complaint, should be thoroughly checked for backed out terminals, improper mating, broken locks, improperly formed or damaged terminals, poor terminal to wiring connections or physical damage to the wiring harness.

GC402930074500DX

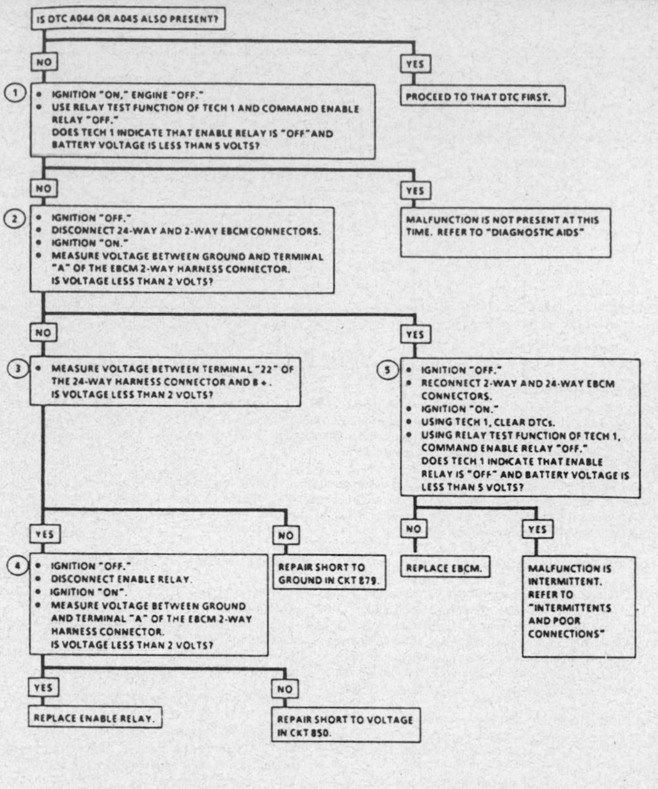
IS DTC A044 OR A045 ALSO PRESENT?
NO
YES
1
• IGNITION "ON," ENGINE "OFF."
• USE RELAY TEST FUNCTION OF TECH 1 AND COMMAND ENABLE RELAY "OFF."
DOES TECH 1 INDICATE THAT ENABLE RELAY IS "OFF" AND BATTERY VOLTAGE IS LESS THAN 5 VOLTS?
PROCEED TO THAT DTC FIRST.
NO
YES
2
• IGNITION "OFF."
• DISCONNECT 24-WAY AND 2-WAY EBCM CONNECTORS.
• IGNITION "ON."
• MEASURE VOLTAGE BETWEEN GROUND AND TERMINAL "A" OF THE EBCM 2-WAY HARNESS CONNECTOR.
IS VOLTAGE LESS THAN 2 VOLTS?
MALFUNCTION IS NOT PRESENT AT THIS TIME. REFER TO "DIAGNOSTIC AIDS"
NO
YES
3
• MEASURE VOLTAGE BETWEEN TERMINAL "22" OF THE 24-WAY HARNESS CONNECTOR AND B+.
IS VOLTAGE LESS THAN 2 VOLTS?
5
• IGNITION "OFF."
• RECONNECT 2-WAY AND 24-WAY EBCM CONNECTORS.
• IGNITION "ON."
• USING TECH 1, CLEAR DTCs.
• USING RELAY TEST FUNCTION OF TECH 1, COMMAND ENABLE RELAY "OFF."
DOES TECH 1 INDICATE THAT ENABLE RELAY IS "OFF" AND BATTERY VOLTAGE IS LESS THAN 5 VOLTS?
YES
NO
NO
YES
4
• IGNITION "OFF."
• DISCONNECT ENABLE RELAY.
• IGNITION "ON".
• MEASURE VOLTAGE BETWEEN GROUND AND TERMINAL "A" OF THE EBCM 2-WAY HARNESS CONNECTOR.
IS VOLTAGE LESS THAN 2 VOLTS?
REPAIR SHORT TO GROUND IN CKT 879.
REPLACE EBCM.
MALFUNCTION IS INTERMITTENT. REFER TO "INTERMITTENTS AND POOR CONNECTIONS"
YES
NO
REPLACE ENABLE RELAY.
REPAIR SHORT TO VOLTAGE IN CKT 850.

THIS CHART ASSUMES THAT A CURRENT DTC IS STORED INDICATING THAT THIS MALFUNCTION IS PRESENT.

GC402930074500EX

Fig. 103 Code A015: Enable Relay Contacts Shorted to Battery (Part 2 of 2). 1993-94 Cavalier, Sunbird, Beretta, Corsica & Achieva, Grand Am & Skylark Less VES

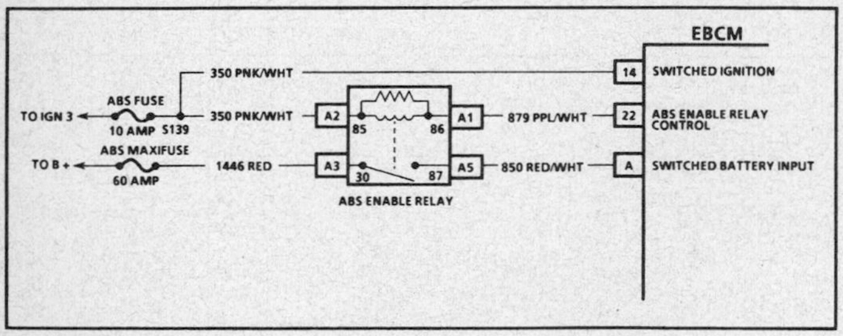
EBCM
350 PNK/WHT
14
SWITCHED IGNITION
ABS FUSE
TO IGN 3
10 AMP S139
350 PNK/WHT
A2
85
86
A1
879 PPL/WHT
22
ABS ENABLE RELAY CONTROL
ABS MAXIFUSE
TO B+
60 AMP
1446 RED
A3
30
87
A5
850 RED/WHT
A
SWITCHED BATTERY INPUT
ABS ENABLE RELAY

DTC 15

ABS RLY CONTACT CKT SHORT TO BATT OR ALWAYS CLOSED

Circuit Description:

Ignition voltage is supplied through terminal "A2" of the ABS enable relay. The EBCM then is able to energize the pull-in coil by completing the ground circuit at terminal "22" of the EBCM. The magnetic field created closes the ABS enable relay contacts and allows battery voltage and current to be supplied to the EBCM, which supplies power to the motors and solenoids.

DTC Will Set When: DTC 15 can be set only before the EBCM commands the relay "ON." This test determines if the ABS enable relay is energized when it should not be. This malfunction would not allow the ABS enable relay to remove power to the ABS system. If a second malfunction were to occur that requires the ABS enable relay to be turned "OFF," that malfunction cannot be removed if the relay cannot be controlled. The malfunction must be present for three consecutive drive cycles before the DTC is set.

Action Taken: A malfunction DTC is stored. ABS is not disabled; however, the ABS warning lamp will flash to indicate a malfunction exists.

DTC Chart Test Description: Number(s) below refer to circled number(s) on the diagnostic chart.

1. Checks to see if other DTCs are set.
2. Indicates that the EBCM is capable of controlling the ABS enable relay as commanded.
3. Checks for a possible short to battery voltage in CKT 850.
4. Determines whether the short to voltage is in CKT 850 due to a malfunctioning relay.
5. Checks for a possible intermittent in wiring or connectors.

Diagnostic Aids: An "Intermittent" malfunction may be caused by a poor connection, rubbed through wire insulation, or a wire that is broken inside the insulation.

The frequency of the malfunction can be checked by using the enhanced diagnostic function of the Tech 1.

Any circuitry, that is suspected as causing the intermittent complaint, should be thoroughly checked for backed out terminals, improper mating, broken locks, improperly formed or damaged terminals, poor terminal to wiring connections or physical damage to the wiring harness.

GC402930074600AA

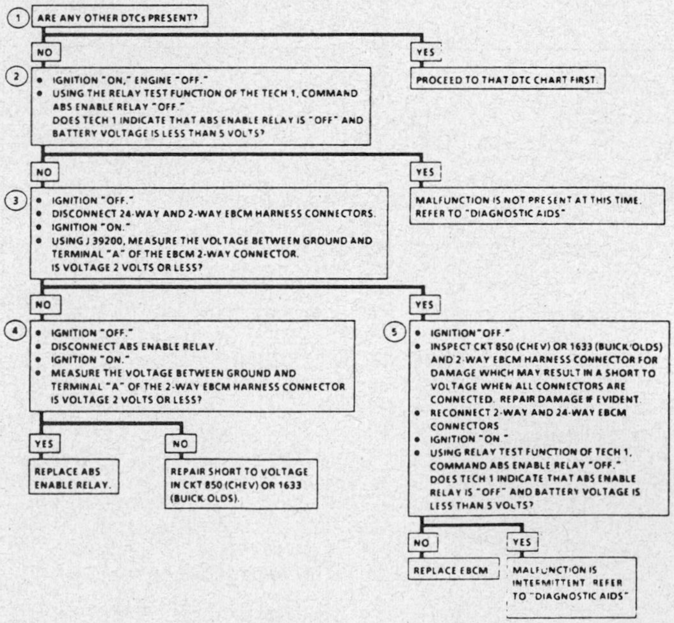
1
ARE ANY OTHER DTCs PRESENT?
NO
YES
2
• IGNITION "ON," ENGINE "OFF."
• USING THE RELAY TEST FUNCTION OF THE TECH 1, COMMAND ABS ENABLE RELAY "OFF."
DOES TECH 1 INDICATE THAT ABS ENABLE RELAY IS "OFF" AND BATTERY VOLTAGE IS LESS THAN 5 VOLTS?
PROCEED TO THAT DTC CHART FIRST.
NO
YES
3
• IGNITION "OFF."
• DISCONNECT 24-WAY AND 2-WAY EBCM HARNESS CONNECTORS.
• IGNITION "ON."
• USING J 39200, MEASURE THE VOLTAGE BETWEEN GROUND AND TERMINAL "A" OF THE EBCM 2-WAY CONNECTOR.
IS VOLTAGE 2 VOLTS OR LESS?
MALFUNCTION IS NOT PRESENT AT THIS TIME. REFER TO "DIAGNOSTIC AIDS"
NO
YES
4
• IGNITION "OFF."
• DISCONNECT ABS ENABLE RELAY.
• IGNITION "ON."
• MEASURE THE VOLTAGE BETWEEN GROUND AND TERMINAL "A" OF THE 2-WAY EBCM HARNESS CONNECTOR
IS VOLTAGE 2 VOLTS OR LESS?
5
• IGNITION "OFF."
• INSPECT CKT 850 (CHEV) OR 1633 (BUICK/OLDS) AND 2-WAY EBCM HARNESS CONNECTOR FOR DAMAGE WHICH MAY RESULT IN A SHORT TO VOLTAGE WHEN ALL CONNECTORS ARE CONNECTED. REPAIR DAMAGE IF EVIDENT.
• RECONNECT 2-WAY AND 24-WAY EBCM CONNECTORS
• IGNITION "ON."
• USING RELAY TEST FUNCTION OF TECH 1, COMMAND ABS ENABLE RELAY "OFF."
DOES TECH 1 INDICATE THAT ABS ENABLE RELAY IS "OFF" AND BATTERY VOLTAGE IS LESS THAN 5 VOLTS?
YES
NO
REPLACE ABS ENABLE RELAY.
REPAIR SHORT TO VOLTAGE IN CKT 850 (CHEV) OR 1633 (BUICK OLDS).
NO
YES
REPLACE EBCM
MALFUNCTION IS INTERMITTENT. REFER TO "DIAGNOSTIC AIDS"

GC402930074600BA

Fig. 104 Code A015: Enable Relay Contacts Shorted To Battery Or Always Closed. 1993 Grand Prix, 1993–94 Cutlass Supreme, Lumina & Regal

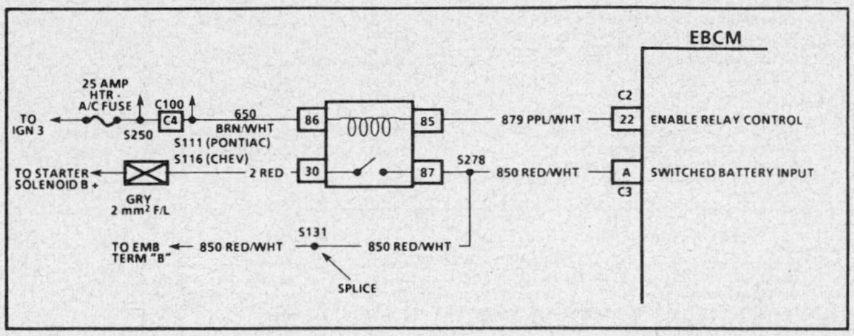

EBCM
25 AMP HTR-A/C FUSE
C100
C4
TO IGN 3
S250
650 BRN/WHT
S111 (PONTIAC)
S116 (CHEV)
86
85
30
87
879 PPL/WHT
C2
22
ENABLE RELAY CONTROL
TO STARTER SOLENOID B+
GRY 2 mm² F/L
2 RED
S278
850 RED/WHT
A
C3
SWITCHED BATTERY INPUT
S131
TO EMB TERM "B"
850 RED/WHT
850 RED/WHT
SPLICE

GC402930074700AX

Cavalier & Sunbird

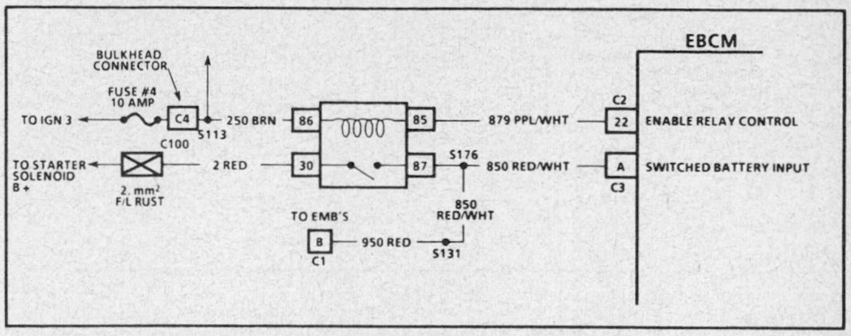

EBCM
BULKHEAD CONNECTOR
FUSE #4 10 AMP
TO IGN 3
C4
S113
C100
250 BRN
86
85
30
87
879 PPL/WHT
C2
22
ENABLE RELAY CONTROL
TO STARTER SOLENOID B+
2 mm² F/L RUST
2 RED
S176
850 RED/WHT
A
C3
SWITCHED BATTERY INPUT
TO EMB'S
850 RED/WHT
B
C1
950 RED
S131

GC402930074700BX

Beretta & Corsica

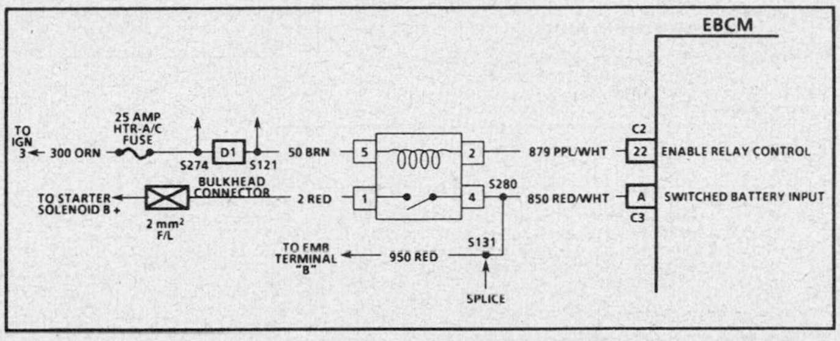

EBCM
25 AMP HTR-A/C FUSE
TO IGN 3
300 ORN
D1
S274
S121
50 BRN
BULKHEAD CONNECTOR
5
2
1
4
879 PPL/WHT
C2
22
ENABLE RELAY CONTROL
TO STARTER SOLENOID B+
2 mm² F/L
2 RED
S280
850 RED/WHT
A
C3
SWITCHED BATTERY INPUT
TO EMB TERMINAL "B"
950 RED
S131
SPLICE

GC402930074700CX

Achieva, Grand Am & Skylark

DTC A016

ENABLE RELAY COIL CIRCUIT OPEN

Circuit Description:

Ignition voltage is supplied through terminal "86" of the ABS enable relay. The EBCM then is able to energize the pull in coil by completing the ground circuit at Pin "22" of the EBCM. The magnetic field created closes the enable relay contacts and allows battery voltage and current to be supplied to the EMBs and EBCM, which supplies power to the motors and solenoids.

Failure Condition:

DTC A016 can be set only after DTC A014 has been set. This test detects an open in the enable relay coil circuit. An open in this circuit will not allow the enable relay to be energized thus preventing voltage/current to the motors, EMBs and solenoids. If this malfunction is present and the ignition is turned "OFF" before 5 km/h (3 mph) is reached, DTC A014 is set alone.

Action Taken:

A malfunction DTC is stored, ABS is disabled and the ABS indicator lamp is turned "ON."

Test Description: Number(s) below refer to circled number(s) on the diagnostic chart.

1. This step indicates if the EBCM is capable of controlling the enable relay as commanded.
2. This step ensures that there is continuity through the pull-in coil of the enable relay.
3. This step checks to ensure that voltage is available to the pull-in coil of the enable relay.
4. This step checks continuity in CKT 879.
5. This step ensures DTC was not set due to a poor connection.

Diagnostic Aids:

An "Intermittent" malfunction may be caused by a poor connection, rubbed through wire insulation, or a wire that is broken inside the insulation.

The frequency of the malfunction can be checked by using the enhanced diagnostic function of the Tech 1.

If the frequency of the malfunction is high, but is currently intermittent, check for high coil resistance by measuring resistance between relay terminals "86" and "85". If resistance is greater than 100 ohms, replace the relay.

Any circuitry, that is suspected as causing the intermittent complaint, should be thoroughly checked for backed out terminals, improper mating, broken locks, improperly formed or damaged terminals, poor terminal to wiring connections or physical damage to the wiring harness.

GC402930074700DX

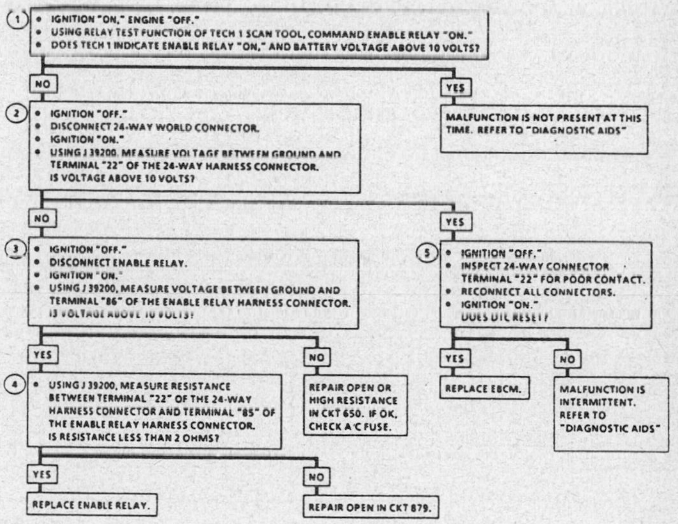

1
• IGNITION "ON," ENGINE "OFF."
• USING RELAY TEST FUNCTION OF TECH 1 SCAN TOOL, COMMAND ENABLE RELAY "ON."
• DOES TECH 1 INDICATE ENABLE RELAY "ON," AND BATTERY VOLTAGE ABOVE 10 VOLTS?
NO
YES
MALFUNCTION IS NOT PRESENT AT THIS TIME. REFER TO "DIAGNOSTIC AIDS"
2
• IGNITION "OFF."
• DISCONNECT 24-WAY WORLD CONNECTOR.
• IGNITION "ON."
• USING J 39200, MEASURE VOLTAGE BETWEEN GROUND AND TERMINAL "22" OF THE 24-WAY HARNESS CONNECTOR. IS VOLTAGE ABOVE 10 VOLTS?
NO
YES
3
• IGNITION "OFF."
• DISCONNECT ENABLE RELAY.
• IGNITION "ON."
• USING J 39200, MEASURE VOLTAGE BETWEEN GROUND AND TERMINAL "86" OF THE ENABLE RELAY HARNESS CONNECTOR. IS VOLTAGE ABOVE 10 VOLTS?
5
• IGNITION "OFF."
• INSPECT 24-WAY CONNECTOR TERMINAL "22" FOR POOR CONTACT.
• RECONNECT ALL CONNECTORS.
• IGNITION "ON."
DOES DTC RESET?
YES
NO
YES
NO
4
• USING J 39200, MEASURE RESISTANCE BETWEEN TERMINAL "22" OF THE 24-WAY HARNESS CONNECTOR AND TERMINAL "85" OF THE ENABLE RELAY HARNESS CONNECTOR. IS RESISTANCE LESS THAN 2 OHMS?
REPAIR OPEN OR HIGH RESISTANCE IN CKT 650. IF OK, CHECK A/C FUSE.
REPLACE EBCM.
MALFUNCTION IS INTERMITTENT. REFER TO "DIAGNOSTIC AIDS"
YES
NO
REPLACE ENABLE RELAY.
REPAIR OPEN IN CKT 879.

AFTER DIAGNOSIS IS COMPLETE, CLEAR DTCs AND TEST DRIVE VEHICLE FOR THREE (3) DRIVE CYCLES TO VERIFY DTC DOES NOT RESET. A DRIVE CYCLE CONSISTS OF STARTING THE VEHICLE, DRIVING OVER 16 km/h (10 MPH) AND THEN KEYING DOWN.

GC402930074700EX

Fig. 105 Code A016: Enable Relay Coil Circuit Open. 1993–94 Cavalier, Sunbird, Beretta, Corsica & Achieva, Grand Am & Skylark Less VES

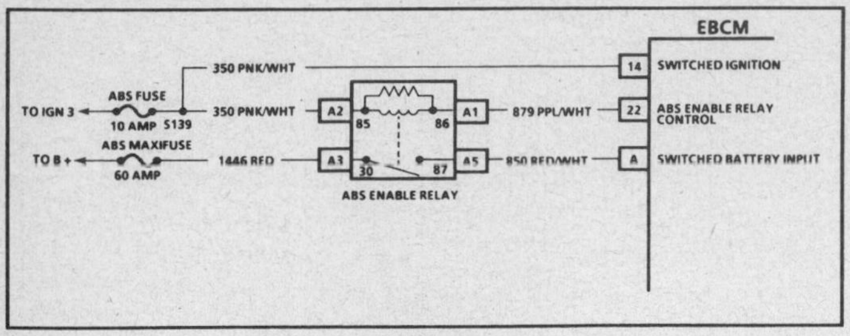
EBCM
350 PNK/WHT
14 SWITCHED IGNITION
ABS FUSE
TO IGN 3
10 AMP S139
350 PNK/WHT
A2 85 86 A1
879 PPL/WHT
22 ABS ENABLE RELAY CONTROL
ABS MAXIFUSE
TO B+
60 AMP
1446 RED
A3 30 87 A5
850 RED/WHT
A SWITCHED BATTERY INPUT
ABS ENABLE RELAY

DTC 16

ABS ENABLE RELAY COIL CIRCUIT OPEN

Circuit Description:

Ignition voltage is supplied through terminal "A2" of the ABS enable relay. The EBCM then is able to energize the pull-in coil by completing the ground circuit at terminal "22" of the EBCM. The magnetic field created closes the ABS enable relay contacts and allows battery voltage and current to be supplied to the EBCM, which supplies power to the motors and solenoids.

DTC Will Set When: DTC 16 can be set only after DTC 14 has been set. This test detects an open in the ABS enable relay coil circuit. An open in this circuit will not allow the ABS enable relay to be energized thus preventing voltage/current to the motors and solenoids. If this malfunction is present and the ignition is turned "OFF" before 5 km/h (3 mph) is reached, DTC 14 is set alone.

Action Taken: A malfunction DTC is stored, ABS is disabled and the ABS warning lamp is turned "ON."

DTC Chart Test Description: Number(s) below refer to circled number(s) on the diagnostic chart.

1. Indicates the EBCM is capable of controlling the ABS enable relay as commanded.
2. Checks to ensure that voltage is available to the pull-in coil of the enable relay.
3. Ensures that there is continuity through the pull-in coil of the enable relay.
4. Verifies the integrity of the relay control circuit.
5. Ensures malfunction was not due to poor terminal contact.

Diagnostic Aids: An "Intermittent" malfunction may be caused by a poor connection, rubbed through wire insulation, or a wire that is broken inside the insulation.

The frequency of the malfunction can be checked by using the enhanced diagnostic function of the Tech 1.

If the frequency of the malfunction is high, but is currently intermittent, check for high coil resistance by measuring between relay terminals "A1" and "A2" using a J 39200. If resistance shows greater than 100Ω, replace the relay.

Any circuitry, that is suspected as causing the intermittent complaint, should be thoroughly checked for backed out terminals, improper mating, broken locks, improperly formed or damaged terminals, poor terminal to wiring connections or physical damage to the wiring harness.

GC402930074800AA

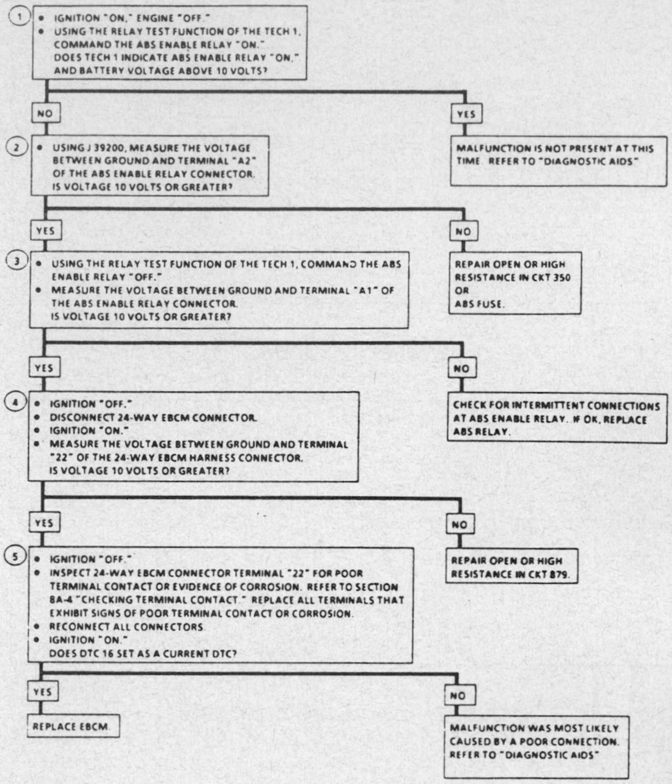
1
• IGNITION "ON," ENGINE "OFF."
• USING THE RELAY TEST FUNCTION OF THE TECH 1, COMMAND THE ABS ENABLE RELAY "ON."
DOES TECH 1 INDICATE ABS ENABLE RELAY "ON." AND BATTERY VOLTAGE ABOVE 10 VOLTS?
NO
YES
MALFUNCTION IS NOT PRESENT AT THIS TIME. REFER TO "DIAGNOSTIC AIDS"
2
• USING J 39200, MEASURE THE VOLTAGE BETWEEN GROUND AND TERMINAL "A2" OF THE ABS ENABLE RELAY CONNECTOR.
IS VOLTAGE 10 VOLTS OR GREATER?
YES
NO
REPAIR OPEN OR HIGH RESISTANCE IN CKT 350 OR ABS FUSE.
3
• USING THE RELAY TEST FUNCTION OF THE TECH 1, COMMAND THE ABS ENABLE RELAY "OFF."
• MEASURE THE VOLTAGE BETWEEN GROUND AND TERMINAL "A1" OF THE ABS ENABLE RELAY CONNECTOR.
IS VOLTAGE 10 VOLTS OR GREATER?
YES
NO
CHECK FOR INTERMITTENT CONNECTIONS AT ABS ENABLE RELAY. IF OK, REPLACE ABS RELAY.
4
• IGNITION "OFF."
• DISCONNECT 24-WAY EBCM CONNECTOR.
• IGNITION "ON."
• MEASURE THE VOLTAGE BETWEEN GROUND AND TERMINAL "22" OF THE 24-WAY EBCM HARNESS CONNECTOR.
IS VOLTAGE 10 VOLTS OR GREATER?
YES
NO
REPAIR OPEN OR HIGH RESISTANCE IN CKT 879.
5
• IGNITION "OFF."
• INSPECT 24-WAY EBCM CONNECTOR TERMINAL "22" FOR POOR TERMINAL CONTACT OR EVIDENCE OF CORROSION. REFER TO SECTION 8A-4 "CHECKING TERMINAL CONTACT." REPLACE ALL TERMINALS THAT EXHIBIT SIGNS OF POOR TERMINAL CONTACT OR CORROSION.
• RECONNECT ALL CONNECTORS.
• IGNITION "ON."
DOES DTC 16 SET AS A CURRENT DTC?
YES
NO
REPLACE EBCM.
MALFUNCTION WAS MOST LIKELY CAUSED BY A POOR CONNECTION. REFER TO "DIAGNOSTIC AIDS"

GC402930074800BA

Fig. 106 Code A016: Enable Relay Coil Circuit Open. 1993 Grand Prix, 1993–94 Cutlass Supreme, Lumina & Regal

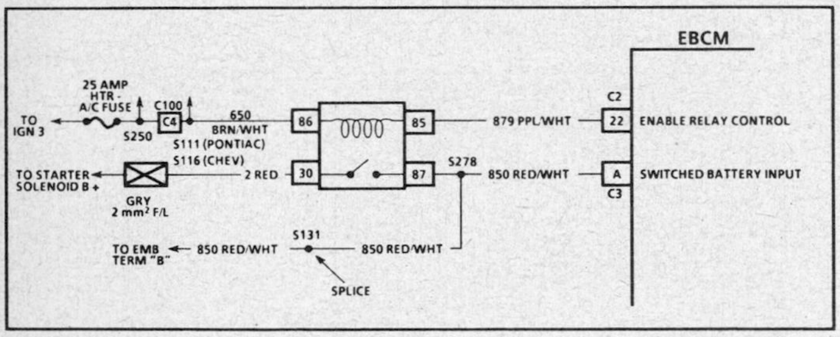
EBCM
25 AMP HTR-A/C FUSE
C100
C4
TO IGN 3
S250
650 BRN/WHT
S111 (PONTIAC)
S116 (CHEV)
86 85
879 PPL/WHT
C2
22 ENABLE RELAY CONTROL
TO STARTER SOLENOID B+
GRY 2 mm² F/L
2 RED
30 87
S278
850 RED/WHT
A SWITCHED BATTERY INPUT
C3
TO EMB TERM "B"
850 RED/WHT
S131
850 RED/WHT
SPLICE

GC402930074900AX

Cavalier & Sunbird

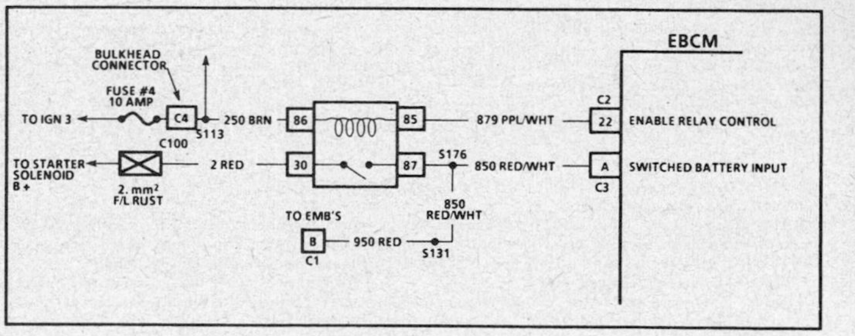
EBCM
BULKHEAD CONNECTOR
FUSE #4 10 AMP
TO IGN 3
C4
C100
250 BRN
S113
86 85
879 PPL/WHT
C2
22 ENABLE RELAY CONTROL
TO STARTER SOLENOID B+
2 mm² F/L RUST
2 RED
30 87
S176
850 RED/WHT
A SWITCHED BATTERY INPUT
C3
850 RED/WHT
TO EMB'S
B C1
950 RED
S131

GC402930074900BX

Beretta & Corsica

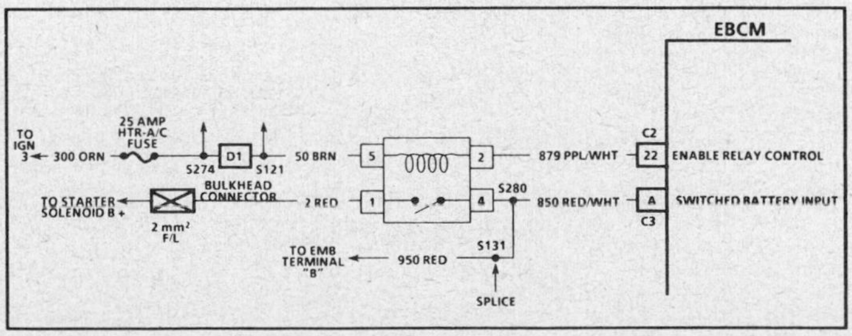
EBCM
25 AMP HTR-A/C FUSE
TO IGN 3
300 ORN
S274
D1
S121
50 BRN
5 2
879 PPL/WHT
C2
22 ENABLE RELAY CONTROL
BULKHEAD CONNECTOR
TO STARTER SOLENOID B+
2 mm² F/L
2 RED
1 4
S280
850 RED/WHT
A SWITCHED BATTERY INPUT
C3
TO EMB TERMINAL "B"
950 RED
S131
SPLICE

GC402930074900CX

Achieva, Grand Am & Skylark

Fig. 107 Code A017: Enable Relay Coil Circuit Shorted To Ground (Part 1 of 2). 1993-94 Cavalier, Sunbird, Beretta, Corsica & Achieva, Grand Am & Skylark Less VES

DTC A017

ENABLE RELAY COIL CIRCUIT SHORTED TO GROUND

Circuit Description:

Ignition voltage is supplied through terminal "86" of the ABS enable relay. The EBCM then is able to energize the pull-in coil by completing the ground circuit at Pin "22" of the EBCM. The magnetic field created closes the enable relay contacts and allows battery voltage and current to be supplied to the EMBs and EBCM, which supplies voltage to the motors and solenoids.

Failure Condition:

DTC A017 can be set before the EBCM commands the enable relay "ON." This test determines if the enable relay is energized when it should not be. This malfunction would not allow the enable relay to remove power to the ABS system. If a second malfunction were to occur that requires the enable relay to be turned "OFF," that malfunction can not be removed if the relay can not be controlled.

Action Taken:

A malfunction DTC is stored. ABS is not disabled; however the ABS indicator lamp flashes to indicate a malfunction exists.

Test Description: Number(s) below refer to circled number(s) on the diagnostic chart.

1. This step indicates if the EBCM is capable of controlling the enable relay as commanded.
2. This checks to ensure the enable relay or control CKT 879 are not shorted to ground.
3. This step ensures DTC was not set due to a poor connection.

Diagnostic Aids:

An "Intermittent" malfunction may be caused by a poor connection, rubbed through wire insulation, or a wire that is broken inside the insulation.

The frequency of the malfunction can be checked by using the enhanced diagnostic function of the Tech 1.

Any circuitry, that is suspected as causing the intermittent complaint, should be thoroughly checked for backed out terminals, improper mating, broken locks, improperly formed or damaged terminals, poor terminal to wiring connections or physical damage to the wiring harness.

GC402930074900DX

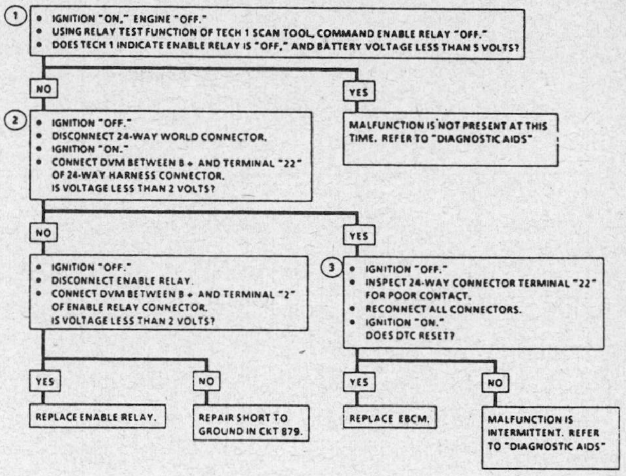
1 • IGNITION "ON," ENGINE "OFF."
• USING RELAY TEST FUNCTION OF TECH 1 SCAN TOOL, COMMAND ENABLE RELAY "OFF."
• DOES TECH 1 INDICATE ENABLE RELAY IS "OFF," AND BATTERY VOLTAGE LESS THAN 5 VOLTS?
NO
YES
2 • IGNITION "OFF."
• DISCONNECT 24-WAY WORLD CONNECTOR.
• IGNITION "ON."
• CONNECT DVM BETWEEN B + AND TERMINAL "22" OF 24-WAY HARNESS CONNECTOR.
IS VOLTAGE LESS THAN 2 VOLTS?
MALFUNCTION IS NOT PRESENT AT THIS TIME. REFER TO "DIAGNOSTIC AIDS"
NO
YES
• IGNITION "OFF."
• DISCONNECT ENABLE RELAY.
• CONNECT DVM BETWEEN B + AND TERMINAL "2" OF ENABLE RELAY CONNECTOR.
IS VOLTAGE LESS THAN 2 VOLTS?
3 • IGNITION "OFF."
• INSPECT 24-WAY CONNECTOR TERMINAL "22" FOR POOR CONTACT.
• RECONNECT ALL CONNECTORS.
• IGNITION "ON."
DOES DTC RESET?
YES
NO
YES
NO
REPLACE ENABLE RELAY.
REPAIR SHORT TO GROUND IN CKT 879.
REPLACE EBCM.
MALFUNCTION IS INTERMITTENT. REFER TO "DIAGNOSTIC AIDS"

GC402930074900EX

Fig. 107 Code A017: Enable Relay Coil Circuit Shorted To Ground (Part 2 of 2). 1993-94 Cavalier, Sunbird, Beretta, Corsica & Achieva, Grand Am & Skylark Less VES

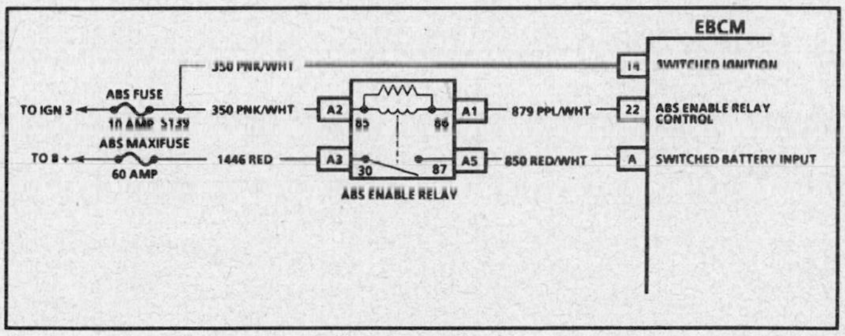
EBCM
350 PNK/WHT
14 SWITCHED IGNITION
ABS FUSE
TO IGN 3
10 AMP S139
350 PNK/WHT
A2
85
86
A1
879 PPL/WHT
22 ABS ENABLE RELAY CONTROL
ABS MAXIFUSE
TO B +
60 AMP
1446 RED
A3
30
87
A5
850 RED/WHT
A SWITCHED BATTERY INPUT
ABS ENABLE RELAY

DTC 17

ABS ENABLE RELAY COIL CIRCUIT SHORTED TO GND

Circuit Description:

Ignition voltage is supplied through terminal "A2" of the ABS enable relay. The EBCM then is able to energize the pull-in coil by completing the ground circuit at terminal "22" of the EBCM. The magnetic field created closes the ABS enable relay contacts and allows battery voltage and current to be supplied to the EBCM, which supplies voltage to the motors and solenoids.

DTC Will Set When: DTC 17 can be set before the EBCM commands the ABS enable relay "ON." This test determines if the ABS enable relay is energized when it should not be. This malfunction would not allow the ABS enable relay to remove power to the ABS system. If a second malfunction were to occur that requires the ABS enable relay to be turned "OFF," that malfunction cannot be removed if the relay cannot be controlled.

Action Taken: A malfunction DTC is stored. ABS is not disabled; however the ABS warning lamp is flashed to indicate a malfunction exists.

DTC Chart Test Description: Number(s) below refer to circled number(s) on the diagnostic chart.

1. Indicates that the EBCM is capable of controlling the ABS enable relay as commanded.
2. Checks to ensure that the ABS enable relay or control CKT 879 are not shorted to ground.
3. Checks to see if the EBCM is internally shorted to ground. A grounded terminal "22" would cause the ABS enable relay to be energized anytime the ignition was in the "ON" position.
4. Checks for a short to ground in control CKT 879 or a defective relay.

Diagnostic Aids: An "Intermittent" malfunction may be caused by a poor connection, rubbed through wire insulation, or a wire that is broken inside the insulation.

The frequency of the malfunction can be checked by using the enhanced diagnostic function of the Tech 1

Any circuitry, that is suspected as causing the intermittent complaint, should be thoroughly checked for backed out terminals, improper mating, broken locks, improperly formed or damaged terminals, poor terminal to wiring connections or physical damage to the wiring harness.

GC402930075000AA

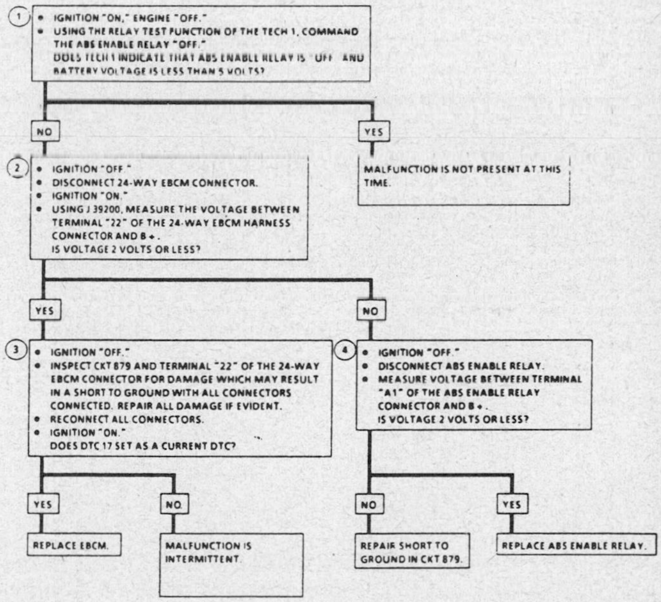
1 • IGNITION "ON," ENGINE "OFF."
• USING THE RELAY TEST FUNCTION OF THE TECH 1, COMMAND THE ABS ENABLE RELAY "OFF."
DOES TECH 1 INDICATE THAT ABS ENABLE RELAY IS "OFF" AND BATTERY VOLTAGE IS LESS THAN 5 VOLTS?
NO
YES
2 • IGNITION "OFF."
• DISCONNECT 24-WAY EBCM CONNECTOR.
• IGNITION "ON."
• USING J 39200, MEASURE THE VOLTAGE BETWEEN TERMINAL "22" OF THE 24-WAY EBCM HARNESS CONNECTOR AND B +.
IS VOLTAGE 2 VOLTS OR LESS?
MALFUNCTION IS NOT PRESENT AT THIS TIME.
YES
NO
3 • IGNITION "OFF."
• INSPECT CKT 879 AND TERMINAL "22" OF THE 24-WAY EBCM CONNECTOR FOR DAMAGE WHICH MAY RESULT IN A SHORT TO GROUND WITH ALL CONNECTORS CONNECTED. REPAIR ALL DAMAGE IF EVIDENT.
• RECONNECT ALL CONNECTORS.
• IGNITION "ON."
DOES DTC 17 SET AS A CURRENT DTC?
4 • IGNITION "OFF."
• DISCONNECT ABS ENABLE RELAY.
• MEASURE VOLTAGE BETWEEN TERMINAL "A1" OF THE ABS ENABLE RELAY CONNECTOR AND B +.
IS VOLTAGE 2 VOLTS OR LESS?
YES
NO
NO
YES
REPLACE EBCM.
MALFUNCTION IS INTERMITTENT.
REPAIR SHORT TO GROUND IN CKT 879.
REPLACE ABS ENABLE RELAY.

GC402930075000BA

Fig. 108 Code A017: Enable Relay Coil Circuit Shorted To Ground. 1993 Grand Prix, 1993–94 Cutlass Supreme, Lumina & Regal

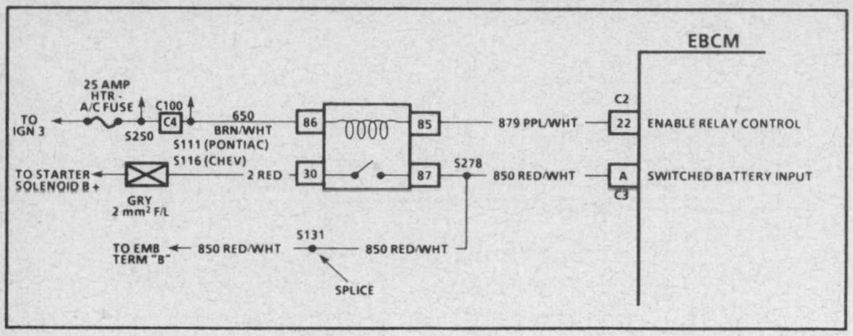
EBCM
25 AMP
HTR-
A/C FUSE
C100
TO
IGN 3
C4
S250
650
BRN/WHT
S111 (PONTIAC)
S116 (CHEV)
86
85
C2
879 PPL/WHT
22
ENABLE RELAY CONTROL
TO STARTER
SOLENOID B+
GRY
2 mm² F/L
2 RED
30
87
S278
850 RED/WHT
A
C3
SWITCHED BATTERY INPUT
S131
TO EMB
TERM "B"
850 RED/WHT
850 RED/WHT
SPLICE

GC402930075100AX

Cavalier & Sunbird

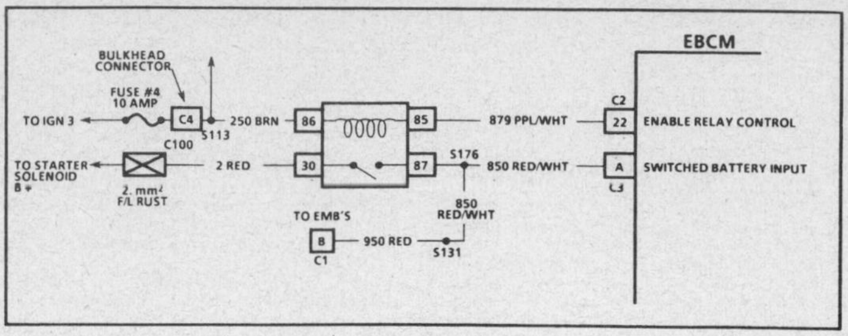
EBCM
BULKHEAD
CONNECTOR
FUSE #4
10 AMP
TO IGN 3
C4
S113
250 BRN
86
85
879 PPL/WHT
C2
22
ENABLE RELAY CONTROL
C100
TO STARTER
SOLENOID
B+
2 RED
30
87
S176
850 RED/WHT
A
C3
SWITCHED BATTERY INPUT
2. mm²
F/L RUST
TO EMB'S
850
RED/WHT
B
C1
950 RED
S131

GC402930075100BX

Beretta & Corsica

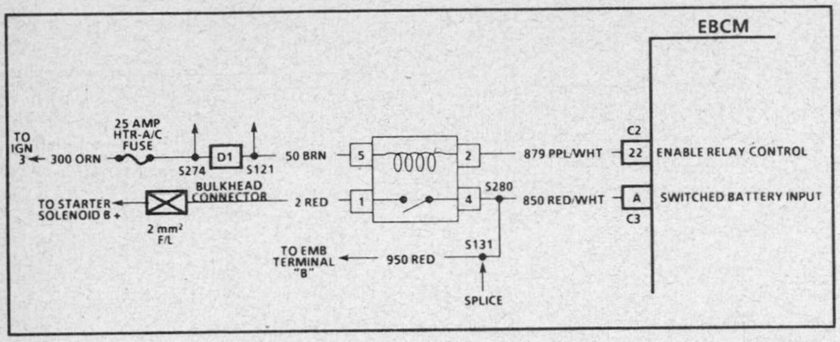
EBCM
TO
IGN
3
300 ORN
25 AMP
HTR-A/C
FUSE
D1
S274
S121
50 BRN
5
2
C2
879 PPL/WHT
22
ENABLE RELAY CONTROL
BULKHEAD
CONNECTOR
TO STARTER
SOLENOID B+
2 mm²
F/L
2 RED
1
4
S280
850 RED/WHT
A
C3
SWITCHED BATTERY INPUT
TO EMB
TERMINAL
"B"
950 RED
S131
SPLICE

GC402930075100CX

Achieva, Grand Am & Skylark

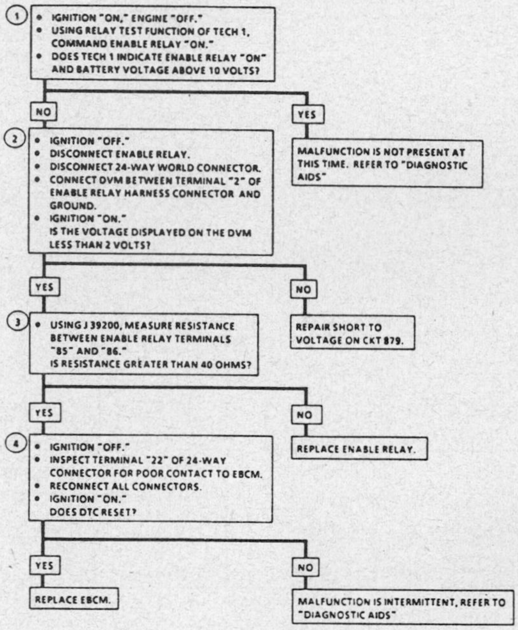
1
• IGNITION "ON," ENGINE "OFF."
• USING RELAY TEST FUNCTION OF TECH 1, COMMAND ENABLE RELAY "ON."
• DOES TECH 1 INDICATE ENABLE RELAY "ON" AND BATTERY VOLTAGE ABOVE 10 VOLTS?
NO
YES
MALFUNCTION IS NOT PRESENT AT THIS TIME. REFER TO "DIAGNOSTIC AIDS"
2
• IGNITION "OFF."
• DISCONNECT ENABLE RELAY.
• DISCONNECT 24-WAY WORLD CONNECTOR.
• CONNECT DVM BETWEEN TERMINAL "2" OF ENABLE RELAY HARNESS CONNECTOR AND GROUND.
• IGNITION "ON."
IS THE VOLTAGE DISPLAYED ON THE DVM LESS THAN 2 VOLTS?
YES
NO
REPAIR SHORT TO VOLTAGE ON CKT 879.
3
• USING J 39200, MEASURE RESISTANCE BETWEEN ENABLE RELAY TERMINALS "85" AND "86."
IS RESISTANCE GREATER THAN 40 OHMS?
YES
NO
REPLACE ENABLE RELAY.
4
• IGNITION "OFF."
• INSPECT TERMINAL "22" OF 24-WAY CONNECTOR FOR POOR CONTACT TO EBCM.
• RECONNECT ALL CONNECTORS.
• IGNITION "ON."
DOES DTC RESET?
YES
NO
REPLACE EBCM.
MALFUNCTION IS INTERMITTENT, REFER TO "DIAGNOSTIC AIDS"

GC402930075100EX

DTC A018

ENABLE RELAY COIL CIRCUIT SHORTED TO BATTERY OR COIL SHORTED

Circuit Description:

Ignition voltage is supplied through terminal "86" of the ABS enable relay. The EBCM then is able to energize the pull-in coil by completing the ground circuit at Pin "22" of the EBCM. The magnetic field created closes the enable relay contacts and allows battery voltage and current to be supplied to the EMBs and EBCM, which supplies voltage to the motors and solenoids.

Failure Condition:

DTC A018 can be set after the EBCM commands the enable relay "ON." This test monitors the availability of current/voltage to the motors, solenoids and EMBs. A malfunction of this type will not allow voltage to be available to the motors, solenoids and EMBs; therefore, ABS operation would not be allowed if required.

Action Taken:

A malfunction DTC is stored, ABS is disabled and the ABS indicator lamp is turned "ON."

Test Description: Number(s) below refer to circled number(s) on the diagnostic chart.

1. This step indicates if the EBCM is capable of controlling the enable relay as commanded.
2. With the enable relay removed, voltage should not be available at terminal "85". Any voltage at this point would indicate that CKT 879 was shorted to a voltage source.
3. This step checks for a shorted coil.
4. This ensures malfunction was not due to a poor connection.

Diagnostic Aids:

An "Intermittent" malfunction may be caused by a poor connection, rubbed through wire insulation, or a wire that is broken inside the insulation.

The frequency of the malfunction can be checked by using the enhanced diagnostic function of the Tech 1.

Any circuitry, that is suspected as causing the intermittent complaint, should be thoroughly checked for backed out terminals, improper mating, broken locks, improperly formed or damaged terminals, poor terminal to wiring connections or physical damage to the wiring harness.

GC402930075100DX

DUMMY00000000001

Fig. 109 Code A018: Enable Relay Coil Circuit Shorted To Battery Or Coil Shorted. 1993–94 Cavalier, Sunbird, Beretta, Corsica & Achieva, Grand Am & Skylark Less VES

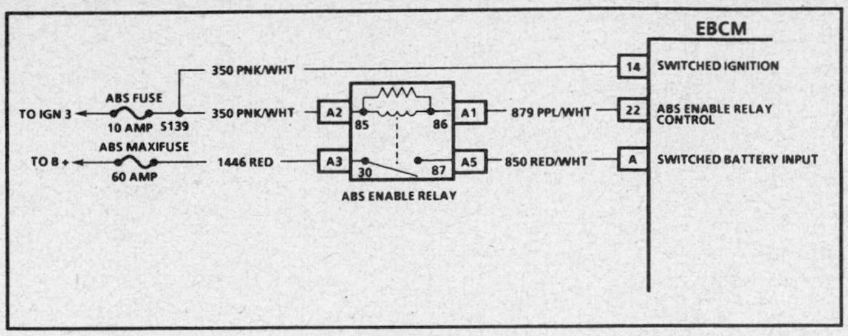
EBCM
350 PNK/WHT
14 SWITCHED IGNITION
ABS FUSE
TO IGN 3
10 AMP S139
350 PNK/WHT
A2
85
86
A1
879 PPL/WHT
22 ABS ENABLE RELAY CONTROL
ABS MAXIFUSE
TO B+
60 AMP
1446 RED
A3
30
87
A5
850 RED/WHT
A SWITCHED BATTERY INPUT
ABS ENABLE RELAY

DTC 18

ABS ENABLE RELAY COIL CIRCUIT SHORTED TO BATT

Circuit Description:

Ignition voltage is supplied through terminal "A2" of the ABS enable relay. The EBCM then is able to energize the pull-in coil by completing the ground circuit at terminal "22" of the EBCM. The magnetic field created closes the ABS enable relay contacts and allows battery voltage and current to be supplied to the EBCM, which supplies voltage to the motors and solenoids.

DTC Will Set When: DTC 18 can be set after the EBCM commands the enable relay "ON." This test monitors the availability of current/voltage to the motors and solenoids. A malfunction of this type will not allow voltage to be available to the motors and solenoids; therefore, ABS operation would not be allowed if required.

Action Taken: A malfunction DTC is stored, ABS is disabled and the ABS warning lamp is turned "ON."

DTC Chart Test Description: Number(s) below refer to circled number(s) on the diagnostic chart.

1. Indicates that the EBCM is capable of controlling the ABS enable relay as commanded.
2. Checks for a short to voltage on the relay control circuit.
3. Verifies that the relay coil has the appropriate resistance.
4. Verifies that the relay contacts are not failed closed.
5. Checks for possible poor terminal contact at the EBCM.

Diagnostic Aids: An "Intermittent" malfunction may be caused by a poor connection, rubbed through wire insulation, or a wire that is broken inside the insulation.

The frequency of the malfunction can be checked by using the enhanced diagnostic function of the Tech 1.

Any circuitry, that is suspected as causing the intermittent complaint, should be thoroughly checked for backed out terminals, improper mating, broken locks, improperly formed or damaged terminals, poor terminal to wiring connections or physical damage to the wiring harness.

GC402930075200AA

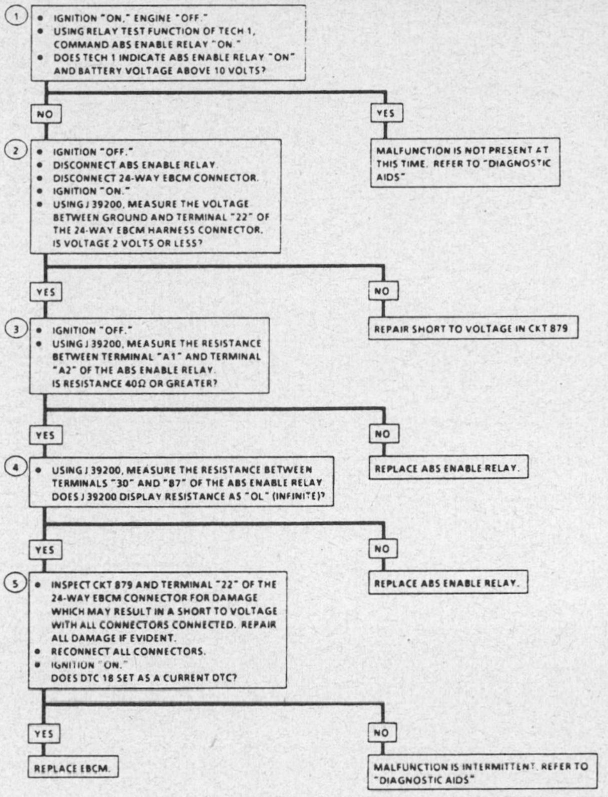
1
• IGNITION "ON," ENGINE "OFF."
• USING RELAY TEST FUNCTION OF TECH 1, COMMAND ABS ENABLE RELAY "ON."
• DOES TECH 1 INDICATE ABS ENABLE RELAY "ON" AND BATTERY VOLTAGE ABOVE 10 VOLTS?
NO
YES
MALFUNCTION IS NOT PRESENT AT THIS TIME. REFER TO "DIAGNOSTIC AIDS"
2
• IGNITION "OFF."
• DISCONNECT ABS ENABLE RELAY.
• DISCONNECT 24-WAY EBCM CONNECTOR.
• IGNITION "ON."
• USING J 39200, MEASURE THE VOLTAGE BETWEEN GROUND AND TERMINAL "22" OF THE 24-WAY EBCM HARNESS CONNECTOR. IS VOLTAGE 2 VOLTS OR LESS?
YES
NO
REPAIR SHORT TO VOLTAGE IN CKT 879
3
• IGNITION "OFF."
• USING J 39200, MEASURE THE RESISTANCE BETWEEN TERMINAL "A1" AND TERMINAL "A2" OF THE ABS ENABLE RELAY. IS RESISTANCE 40Ω OR GREATER?
YES
NO
REPLACE ABS ENABLE RELAY.
4
• USING J 39200, MEASURE THE RESISTANCE BETWEEN TERMINALS "30" AND "87" OF THE ABS ENABLE RELAY. DOES J 39200 DISPLAY RESISTANCE AS "OL" (INFINITE)?
YES
NO
REPLACE ABS ENABLE RELAY.
5
• INSPECT CKT 879 AND TERMINAL "22" OF THE 24-WAY EBCM CONNECTOR FOR DAMAGE WHICH MAY RESULT IN A SHORT TO VOLTAGE WITH ALL CONNECTORS CONNECTED. REPAIR ALL DAMAGE IF EVIDENT.
• RECONNECT ALL CONNECTORS.
• IGNITION "ON."
DOES DTC 18 SET AS A CURRENT DTC?
YES
NO
REPLACE EBCM.
MALFUNCTION IS INTERMITTENT. REFER TO "DIAGNOSTIC AIDS"

GC402930075200BA

DUMMY00000000001

Fig. 110 Code A018: Enable Relay Coil Circuit Shorted To Battery. 1993 Grand Prix, 1993–94 Cutlass Supreme, Lumina & Regal

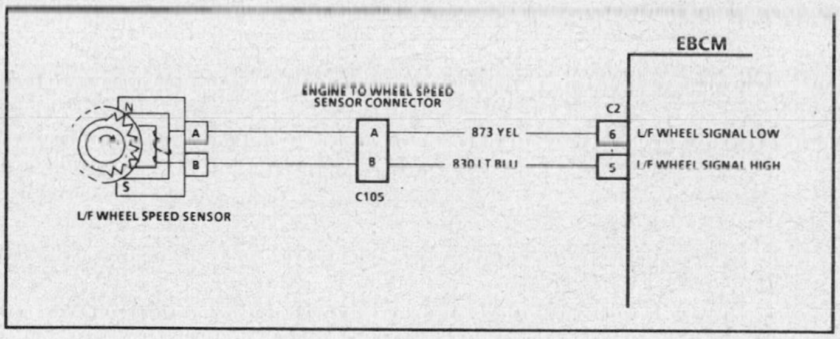
EBCM
ENGINE TO WHEEL SPEED SENSOR CONNECTOR
N
S
A
B
C105
C2
873 YEL
830 LT BLU
6 L/F WHEEL SIGNAL LOW
5 L/F WHEEL SIGNAL HIGH
L/F WHEEL SPEED SENSOR

GC402930075300AX

Cavalier & Sunbird

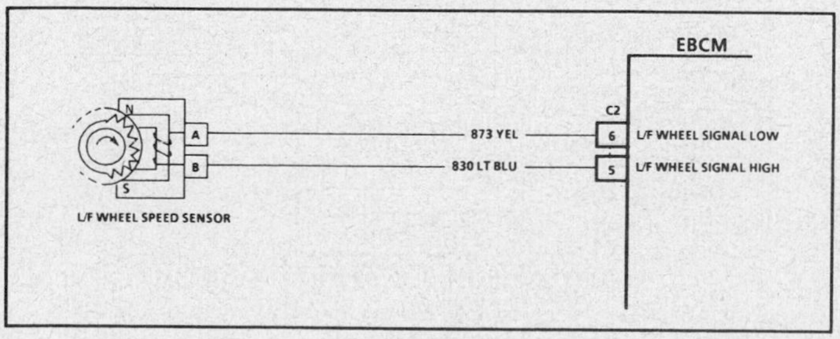
EBCM
N
S
A
B
C2
873 YEL
830 LT BLU
6 L/F WHEEL SIGNAL LOW
5 L/F WHEEL SIGNAL HIGH
L/F WHEEL SPEED SENSOR

GC402930075300BX

Achieva, Beretta, Corsica, Grand Am & Skylark

DTC A021

LEFT FRONT WHEEL SPEED = 0

Circuit Description:

As a toothed ring passes by the wheel speed sensor, changes in the electromagnetic field cause the wheel speed sensor to produce a sinusoidal (AC) voltage signal whose frequency is proportional to wheel speed. The magnitude of this signal is directly related to wheel speed and the proximity of the wheel speed sensor to the toothed ring, often referred to as the air gap.

Failure Condition:

DTC A021 can be set when the vehicle is not in an ABS stop. If the left front wheel speed is less than 1/2 of the vehicle's reference speed and the vehicle's reference speed is greater than 8 km/h (5 mph), a malfunction exists.

Action Taken:

A malfunction DTC is stored, ABS is disabled and the ABS indicator lamp is turned "ON."

Test Description: Number(s) below refer to circled number(s) on the diagnostic chart.

1. This test verifies whether the malfunction is currently present.
2. This step will identify a wheel speed sensor or circuitry that is damaged and visibly apparent.
3. This test checks wheel speed sensor for proper resistance values.
4. This test ensures the wheel speed sensor and sensor ring generate the proper voltage.
5. This step ensures the wheel speed sensor is not shorted to ground.

Diagnostic Aids:

An "Intermittent" malfunction may be caused by a poor connection, rubbed through wire insulation, or a wire that is broken inside the insulation.

The frequency of the malfunction can be checked by using the enhanced diagnostic function of the Tech 1.

If the customer's comments reflect that the ABS amber indicator lamp is "ON" only during moist environmental changes, (rain, snow, vehicle wash) all wheel speed sensor circuitry should be thoroughly inspected for signs of water intrusion. Use the following procedure. Spray down the suspected area with 5% salt water solution (two teaspoons of salt to 12 oz. of water). Start vehicle, allow vehicle to run for 10 seconds. If DTC returns immediately, replace suspected harness.

Any circuitry, that is suspected as causing the intermittent complaint, should be thoroughly checked for backed out terminals, improper mating, broken locks, improperly formed or damaged terminals, poor terminal to wiring connections or physical damage to the wiring harness.

When measuring wheel speed sensor resistance, ensure vehicle is at room temperature. Wheel speed sensor resistance will vary with temperature.

When replacing a wheel speed sensor, inspect the sensor terminals and harness connector for corrosion and/or water intrusion. If evidence of corrosion or water intrusion exists, replace wheel speed sensor harness.

GC402930075300CX

DUMMY00000000001

Fig. 111 Code A021: Left Front Wheel Speed = 0. 1993–94 Cavalier, Sunbird, Beretta, Corsica & Achieva, Grand Am & Skylark Less VES (Part 1 of 2)

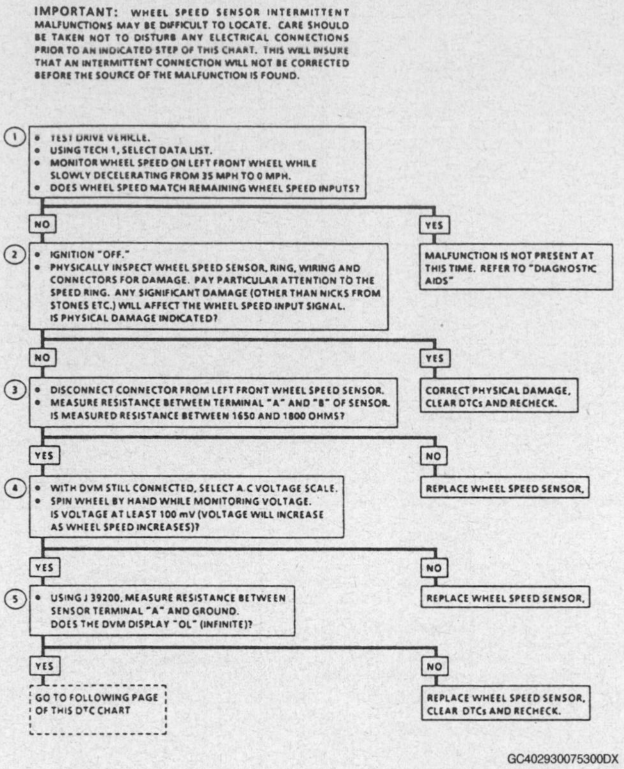
IMPORTANT: WHEEL SPEED SENSOR INTERMITTENT MALFUNCTIONS MAY BE DIFFICULT TO LOCATE. CARE SHOULD BE TAKEN NOT TO DISTURB ANY ELECTRICAL CONNECTIONS PRIOR TO AN INDICATED STEP OF THIS CHART. THIS WILL INSURE THAT AN INTERMITTENT CONNECTION WILL NOT BE CORRECTED BEFORE THE SOURCE OF THE MALFUNCTION IS FOUND.
1
• TEST DRIVE VEHICLE.
• USING TECH 1, SELECT DATA LIST.
• MONITOR WHEEL SPEED ON LEFT FRONT WHEEL WHILE SLOWLY DECELERATING FROM 35 MPH TO 0 MPH.
• DOES WHEEL SPEED MATCH REMAINING WHEEL SPEED INPUTS?
NO
YES
MALFUNCTION IS NOT PRESENT AT THIS TIME. REFER TO "DIAGNOSTIC AIDS"
2
• IGNITION "OFF."
• PHYSICALLY INSPECT WHEEL SPEED SENSOR, RING, WIRING AND CONNECTORS FOR DAMAGE. PAY PARTICULAR ATTENTION TO THE SPEED RING. ANY SIGNIFICANT DAMAGE (OTHER THAN NICKS FROM STONES ETC.) WILL AFFECT THE WHEEL SPEED INPUT SIGNAL. IS PHYSICAL DAMAGE INDICATED?
NO
YES
CORRECT PHYSICAL DAMAGE, CLEAR DTCs AND RECHECK.
3
• DISCONNECT CONNECTOR FROM LEFT FRONT WHEEL SPEED SENSOR.
• MEASURE RESISTANCE BETWEEN TERMINAL "A" AND "B" OF SENSOR. IS MEASURED RESISTANCE BETWEEN 1650 AND 1800 OHMS?
YES
NO
REPLACE WHEEL SPEED SENSOR.
4
• WITH DVM STILL CONNECTED, SELECT A.C VOLTAGE SCALE.
• SPIN WHEEL BY HAND WHILE MONITORING VOLTAGE. IS VOLTAGE AT LEAST 100 mV (VOLTAGE WILL INCREASE AS WHEEL SPEED INCREASES)?
YES
NO
REPLACE WHEEL SPEED SENSOR.
5
• USING J 39200, MEASURE RESISTANCE BETWEEN SENSOR TERMINAL "A" AND GROUND. DOES THE DVM DISPLAY "OL" (INFINITE)?
YES
NO
GO TO FOLLOWING PAGE OF THIS DTC CHART
REPLACE WHEEL SPEED SENSOR, CLEAR DTCs AND RECHECK.
GC402930075300DX

DTC A021

LEFT FRONT WHEEL SPEED = 0

Circuit Description:

As a toothed ring passes by the wheel speed sensor, changes in the electromagnetic field cause the wheel speed sensor to produce a sinusoidal (AC) voltage signal whose frequency is proportional to wheel speed. The magnitude of this signal is directly related to wheel speed and the proximity of the wheel speed sensor to the toothed ring often referred to as the air gap.

Failure Condition:

DTC A021 can be set when the vehicle is not in an ABS stop. If the left front wheel speed is less than 1/2 of the vehicle's reference speed and the vehicle's reference speed is greater than 8 km/h (5 mph), a malfunction exists.

Action Taken:

A malfunction DTC is stored, ABS is disabled and the ABS indicator lamp is turned "ON."

Test Description: Number(s) below refer to circled number(s) on the diagnostic chart.

6. This step checks for proper voltages at speed sensor harness connector.
7. This test ensures that the wheel speed sensor circuitry is not internally shorted.
8. This checks for an open in the wheel signal low circuit.
9. This checks for an open in the wheel signal high circuit.
10. This test checks for a short to ground in both high and low wheel signal circuits.
11. This step ensures that DTC A021 was not set due to a poor connection between the world connector and EBCM.

Diagnostic Aids:

An "Intermittent" malfunction may be caused by a poor connection, rubbed through wire insulation, or a wire that is broken inside the insulation.

The frequency of the malfunction can be checked by using the enhanced diagnostic function of the Tech 1.

If the customer's comments reflect that the ABS amber indicator lamp is "ON" only during moist environmental changes, (rain, snow, vehicle wash) all wheel speed sensor circuitry should be thoroughly inspected for signs of water intrusion. Use the following procedure. Spray down the suspected area with 5% salt water solution (two teaspoons of salt to 12 oz. of water). Start vehicle, allow vehicle to run for 10 seconds. If DTC returns immediately, replace suspected harness.

Any circuitry, that is suspected as causing the intermittent complaint, should be thoroughly checked for backed out terminals, improper mating, broken locks, improperly formed or damaged terminals, poor terminal to wiring connections or physical damage to the wiring harness.

When measuring wheel speed sensor resistance, ensure vehicle is at room temperature. Wheel speed sensor resistance will vary with temperature.

When replacing a wheel speed sensor, inspect the sensor terminals and harness connector for corrosion and/or water intrusion. If evidence of corrosion or water intrusion exists, replace wheel speed sensor harness.

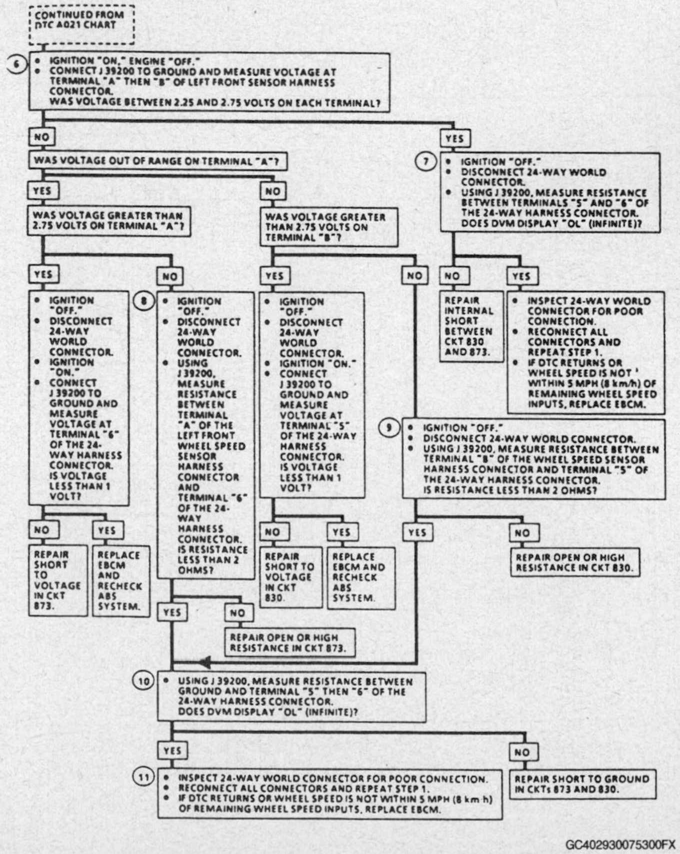
CONTINUED FROM DTC A021 CHART
6
• IGNITION "ON," ENGINE "OFF."
• CONNECT J 39200 TO GROUND AND MEASURE VOLTAGE AT TERMINAL "A" THEN "B" OF LEFT FRONT SENSOR HARNESS CONNECTOR. WAS VOLTAGE BETWEEN 2.25 AND 2.75 VOLTS ON EACH TERMINAL?
NO
YES
WAS VOLTAGE OUT OF RANGE ON TERMINAL "A"?
7
• IGNITION "OFF."
• DISCONNECT 24-WAY WORLD CONNECTOR.
• USING J 39200, MEASURE RESISTANCE BETWEEN TERMINALS "5" AND "6" OF THE 24-WAY HARNESS CONNECTOR. DOES DVM DISPLAY "OL" (INFINITE)?
YES
NO
WAS VOLTAGE GREATER THAN 2.75 VOLTS ON TERMINAL "A"?
WAS VOLTAGE GREATER THAN 2.75 VOLTS ON TERMINAL "B"?
YES
NO
YES
NO
NO
YES
• IGNITION "OFF."
• DISCONNECT 24-WAY WORLD CONNECTOR.
• IGNITION "ON."
• CONNECT J 39200 TO GROUND AND MEASURE VOLTAGE AT TERMINAL "6" OF THE 24-WAY HARNESS CONNECTOR. IS VOLTAGE LESS THAN 1 VOLT?
8
• IGNITION "OFF."
• DISCONNECT 24-WAY WORLD CONNECTOR.
• USING J 39200, MEASURE RESISTANCE BETWEEN TERMINAL "A" OF THE LEFT FRONT WHEEL SPEED SENSOR HARNESS CONNECTOR AND TERMINAL "6" OF THE 24-WAY HARNESS CONNECTOR. IS RESISTANCE LESS THAN 2 OHMS?
• IGNITION "OFF."
• DISCONNECT 24-WAY WORLD CONNECTOR.
• IGNITION "ON."
• CONNECT J 39200 TO GROUND AND MEASURE VOLTAGE AT TERMINAL "5" OF THE 24-WAY HARNESS CONNECTOR. IS VOLTAGE LESS THAN 1 VOLT?
REPAIR INTERNAL SHORT BETWEEN CKT 830 AND 873.
• INSPECT 24-WAY WORLD CONNECTOR FOR POOR CONNECTION.
• RECONNECT ALL CONNECTORS AND REPEAT STEP 1.
• IF DTC RETURNS OR WHEEL SPEED IS NOT WITHIN 5 MPH (8 km/h) OF REMAINING WHEEL SPEED INPUTS, REPLACE EBCM.
9
• IGNITION "OFF."
• DISCONNECT 24-WAY WORLD CONNECTOR.
• USING J 39200, MEASURE RESISTANCE BETWEEN TERMINAL "B" OF THE WHEEL SPEED SENSOR HARNESS CONNECTOR AND TERMINAL "5" OF THE 24-WAY HARNESS CONNECTOR. IS RESISTANCE LESS THAN 2 OHMS?
NO
YES
NO
YES
YES
NO
REPAIR SHORT TO VOLTAGE IN CKT 873.
REPLACE EBCM AND RECHECK ABS SYSTEM.
REPAIR SHORT TO VOLTAGE IN CKT 830.
REPLACE EBCM AND RECHECK ABS SYSTEM.
REPAIR OPEN OR HIGH RESISTANCE IN CKT 830.
YES
NO
REPAIR OPEN OR HIGH RESISTANCE IN CKT 873.
10
• USING J 39200, MEASURE RESISTANCE BETWEEN GROUND AND TERMINAL "5" THEN "6" OF THE 24-WAY HARNESS CONNECTOR. DOES DVM DISPLAY "OL" (INFINITE)?
YES
NO
11
• INSPECT 24-WAY WORLD CONNECTOR FOR POOR CONNECTION.
• RECONNECT ALL CONNECTORS AND REPEAT STEP 1.
• IF DTC RETURNS OR WHEEL SPEED IS NOT WITHIN 5 MPH (8 km/h) OF REMAINING WHEEL SPEED INPUTS, REPLACE EBCM.
REPAIR SHORT TO GROUND IN CKTs 873 AND 830.
GC402930075300FX

Fig. 111 Code A021: Left Front Wheel Speed = 0. 1993–94 Cavalier, Sunbird, Beretta, Corsica & Achieva, Grand Am & Skylark Less VES (Part 2 of 2)

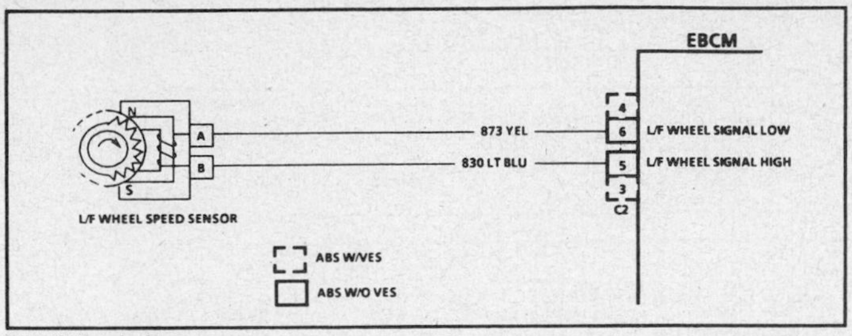
EBCM
873 YEL
830 LT BLU
A
B
N
S
4
6
5
3
C2
L/F WHEEL SIGNAL LOW
L/F WHEEL SIGNAL HIGH
L/F WHEEL SPEED SENSOR
ABS W/VES
ABS W/O VES

Circuit Description:
As a toothed ring passes by the wheel speed sensor, changes in the electromagnetic field cause the wheel speed sensor to produce a sinusoidal (AC) voltage signal whose frequency is proportional to wheel speed. The magnitude of this signal is directly related to wheel speed and the proximity of the wheel speed sensor to the toothed ring, often referred to as the air gap.

DTC Will Set When: DTC 21 can be set when the vehicle is not in an ABS stop. A malfunction exists if the left front wheel speed = 0 and the vehicle speed is greater than 8 km/h (5 mph).

Action Taken: A malfunction DTC is stored, ABS/VES is disabled and the ABS warning lamp is turned "ON."

DTC Chart Test Description: Number(s) below refer to circled number(s) on the diagnostic chart.

1. Identifies if a wheel speed sensor or circuitry is damaged and visibly apparent.
2. Tests wheel speed sensor for proper resistance values.
3. Ensures the wheel speed sensor and toothed ring generate the proper voltage.
4. Ensures wheel speed sensor high and low circuits are not shorted together.
5. Ensures malfunction is not due to physical damage of the wheel speed sensor circuitry.

Diagnostic Aids: An "Intermittent" malfunction is most likely caused by a poor connection, rubbed through wire insulation, or a wire that is broken inside the insulation.

The frequency of the malfunction can be checked by using the enhanced diagnostic function of the Tech 1.

If the customer's comments reflect that the ABS amber warning lamp is "ON" only during moist environmental changes, (rain, snow, vehicle wash) all wheel speed sensor circuitry should be thoroughly inspected for signs of water intrusion. Use the following procedure. Spray down the suspected area with 5% salt water solution (two teaspoons of salt to 12 oz. of water). Drive vehicle above 24 km/h (15 mph) for at least 30 seconds. If DTC returns immediately, replace suspected harness.

Any circuitry, that is suspected as causing the intermittent complaint, should be thoroughly checked for backed out terminals, improper mating, broken locks, improperly formed or damaged terminals, poor terminal to wiring connections or physical damage to the wiring harness.

Resistance of the wheel speed sensor will increase with an increase in sensor temperature.

When replacing a wheel speed sensor, inspect the sensor terminals and harness connector for corrosion and/or water intrusion. If evidence of corrosion or water intrusion exists, replace wheel speed sensor harness. Refer to "On-Vehicle Service" in this section.

If wheel speed sensor harness shows evidence of water intrusion, inspect wheel speed sensor for water intrusion. If water intrusion is evident, replace wheel speed sensor.

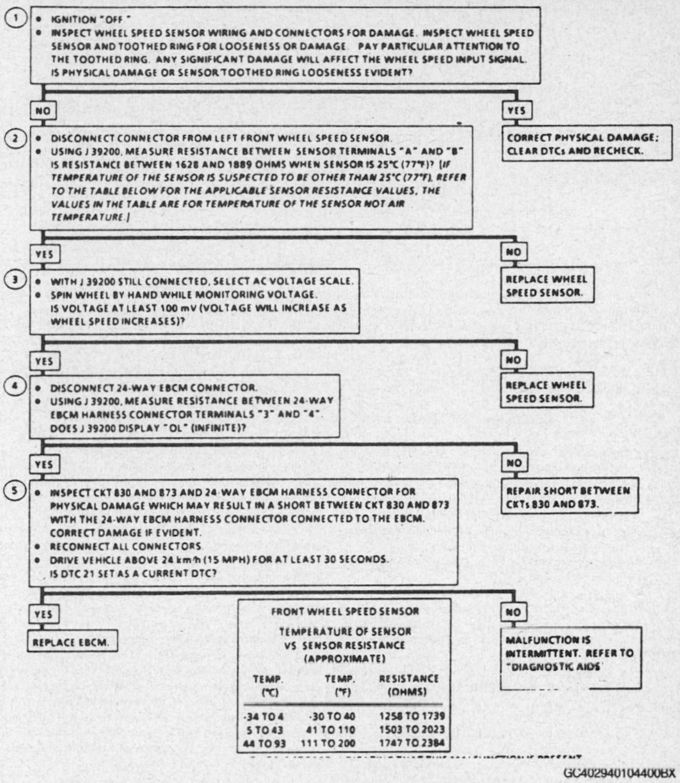
1
• IGNITION "OFF."
• INSPECT WHEEL SPEED SENSOR WIRING AND CONNECTORS FOR DAMAGE. INSPECT WHEEL SPEED SENSOR AND TOOTHED RING FOR LOOSENESS OR DAMAGE. PAY PARTICULAR ATTENTION TO THE TOOTHED RING. ANY SIGNIFICANT DAMAGE WILL AFFECT THE WHEEL SPEED INPUT SIGNAL.
IS PHYSICAL DAMAGE OR SENSOR TOOTHED RING LOOSENESS EVIDENT?
NO
YES
CORRECT PHYSICAL DAMAGE; CLEAR DTCs AND RECHECK.
2
• DISCONNECT CONNECTOR FROM LEFT FRONT WHEEL SPEED SENSOR.
• USING J 39200, MEASURE RESISTANCE BETWEEN SENSOR TERMINALS "A" AND "B"
IS RESISTANCE BETWEEN 1628 AND 1889 OHMS WHEN SENSOR IS 25°C (77°F)? [IF TEMPERATURE OF THE SENSOR IS SUSPECTED TO BE OTHER THAN 25°C (77°F), REFER TO THE TABLE BELOW FOR THE APPLICABLE SENSOR RESISTANCE VALUES, THE VALUES IN THE TABLE ARE FOR TEMPERATURE OF THE SENSOR NOT AIR TEMPERATURE.]
YES
NO
REPLACE WHEEL SPEED SENSOR.
3
• WITH J 39200 STILL CONNECTED, SELECT AC VOLTAGE SCALE.
• SPIN WHEEL BY HAND WHILE MONITORING VOLTAGE.
IS VOLTAGE AT LEAST 100 mV (VOLTAGE WILL INCREASE AS WHEEL SPEED INCREASES)?
YES
NO
REPLACE WHEEL SPEED SENSOR.
4
• DISCONNECT 24-WAY EBCM CONNECTOR.
• USING J 39200, MEASURE RESISTANCE BETWEEN 24-WAY EBCM HARNESS CONNECTOR TERMINALS "3" AND "4".
DOES J 39200 DISPLAY "OL" (INFINITE)?
YES
NO
REPAIR SHORT BETWEEN CKTs 830 AND 873.
5
• INSPECT CKT 830 AND 873 AND 24-WAY EBCM HARNESS CONNECTOR FOR PHYSICAL DAMAGE WHICH MAY RESULT IN A SHORT BETWEEN CKT 830 AND 873 WITH THE 24-WAY EBCM HARNESS CONNECTOR CONNECTED TO THE EBCM. CORRECT DAMAGE IF EVIDENT.
• RECONNECT ALL CONNECTORS.
• DRIVE VEHICLE ABOVE 24 km/h (15 MPH) FOR AT LEAST 30 SECONDS.
IS DTC 21 SET AS A CURRENT DTC?
YES
REPLACE EBCM.
NO
MALFUNCTION IS INTERMITTENT. REFER TO "DIAGNOSTIC AIDS"
GC402940104400BX

FRONT WHEEL SPEED SENSOR
TEMPERATURE OF SENSOR VS SENSOR RESISTANCE (APPROXIMATE)

TEMP. (°C)	TEMP. (°F)	RESISTANCE (OHMS)
-34 TO 4	-30 TO 40	1258 TO 1739
5 TO 43	41 TO 110	1503 TO 2023
44 TO 93	111 TO 200	1747 TO 2384

Fig. 112 Code A021: Left Front Wheel Speed = 0. 1994 Achieva, Grand Am & Skylark w/VES

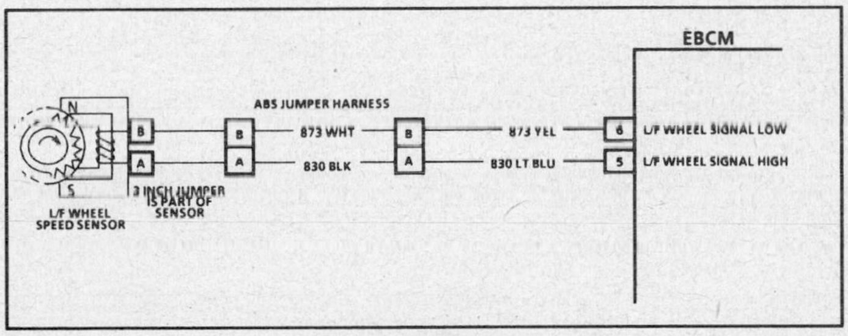
EBCM
ABS JUMPER HARNESS
873 WHT
830 BLK
873 YEL
830 LT BLU
B
A
N
S
6
5
L/F WHEEL SIGNAL LOW
L/F WHEEL SIGNAL HIGH
3 INCH JUMPER IS PART OF SENSOR
L/F WHEEL SPEED SENSOR

DTC A021

(Page 1 of 2)

LEFT FRONT WHEEL SPEED = 0

Circuit Description:
As a toothed ring passes by the wheel speed sensor, changes in the electromagnetic field cause the wheel speed sensor to produce a sinusoidal (AC) voltage signal whose frequency is proportional to wheel speed. The magnitude of this signal is directly related to wheel speed and the proximity of the wheel speed sensor to the toothed ring, often referred to as the air gap.

Failure Condition:
DTC A021 can be set when the vehicle is not in an ABS stop. If the left front wheel speed = 0 and the vehicle's reference speed is greater than 8 km/h (5 mph), a malfunction exists.

Action Taken:
A malfunction DTC is stored, ABS is disabled and the ABS indicator lamp is turned "ON."

Test Description: Number(s) below refer to circled number(s) on the diagnostic chart.

1. This determines if DTC A032 is present.
2. This test verifies whether the malfunction is currently present.
3. This step is designed to identify a wheel speed sensor or circuitry that is damaged and visibly apparent.
4. This test checks to see that the wheel speed sensor is within proper resistance values.
5. This step verifies that the wheel speed sensor can generate an appropriate output signal.
6. This test checks for proper output voltage from the EBCM.

Diagnostic Aids:

An "Intermittent" malfunction may be caused by a poor connection, rubbed through wire insulation, or a wire that is broken inside the insulation.

The frequency of the malfunction can be checked by using the enhanced diagnostic function of the Tech 1, as described in "Tech 1 Diagnostics" found in this section.

If the customers comments reflect that the ABS indicator lamp is "ON" only during moist environmental changes (rain, snow, vehicle wash), all wheel speed sensor circuitry should be thoroughly inspected for signs of water intrusion. If DTC is not current, clear DTCs and simulate the effects of water intrusion. Use the following procedure. Spray down the suspected area with a 5% salt water solution (two teaspoons of salt to 12 oz. of water). Start vehicle, allow vehicle to run for 10 seconds. If DTC returns immediately, replace suspected harness.

Any circuitry, that is suspected as causing the intermittent complaint, should be thoroughly checked for backed out terminals, improper mating, broken locks, improperly formed or damaged terminals, poor terminal to wiring connections or physical damage to the wiring harness.

When measuring wheel speed sensor resistance, insure vehicle is at room temperature. Wheel speed sensor resistance will vary with temperature.

When replacing a wheel speed sensor, inspect the sensor terminals and harness connector for corrosion and/or water intrusion. If evidence of corrosion or water intrusion exists, replace wheel speed sensor harness. Refer to "On-Vehicle Service" in this section.

IMPORTANT: WHEEL SPEED SENSOR INTERMITTENT PROBLEMS MAY BE DIFFICULT TO LOCATE. CARE SHOULD BE TAKEN NOT TO DISTURB ANY ELECTRICAL CONNECTIONS PRIOR TO AN INDICATED STEP OF THIS CHART. THIS WILL INSURE THAT AN INTERMITTENT CONNECTION WILL NOT BE CORRECTED BEFORE THE SOURCE OF THE PROBLEM IS FOUND.

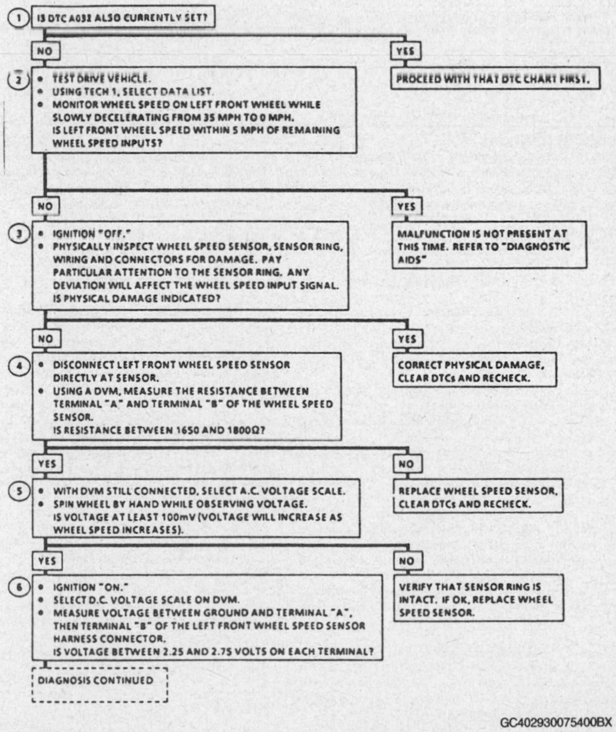
1
IS DTC A032 ALSO CURRENTLY SET?
NO
YES
PROCEED WITH THAT DTC CHART FIRST.
2
• TEST DRIVE VEHICLE.
• USING TECH 1, SELECT DATA LIST.
• MONITOR WHEEL SPEED ON LEFT FRONT WHEEL WHILE SLOWLY DECELERATING FROM 35 MPH TO 0 MPH.
IS LEFT FRONT WHEEL SPEED WITHIN 5 MPH OF REMAINING WHEEL SPEED INPUTS?
NO
YES
MALFUNCTION IS NOT PRESENT AT THIS TIME. REFER TO "DIAGNOSTIC AIDS"
3
• IGNITION "OFF."
• PHYSICALLY INSPECT WHEEL SPEED SENSOR, SENSOR RING, WIRING AND CONNECTORS FOR DAMAGE. PAY PARTICULAR ATTENTION TO THE SENSOR RING. ANY DEVIATION WILL AFFECT THE WHEEL SPEED INPUT SIGNAL.
IS PHYSICAL DAMAGE INDICATED?
NO
YES
CORRECT PHYSICAL DAMAGE, CLEAR DTCs AND RECHECK.
4
• DISCONNECT LEFT FRONT WHEEL SPEED SENSOR DIRECTLY AT SENSOR.
• USING A DVM, MEASURE THE RESISTANCE BETWEEN TERMINAL "A" AND TERMINAL "B" OF THE WHEEL SPEED SENSOR.
IS RESISTANCE BETWEEN 1650 AND 1800Ω?
YES
NO
REPLACE WHEEL SPEED SENSOR, CLEAR DTCs AND RECHECK.
5
• WITH DVM STILL CONNECTED, SELECT A.C. VOLTAGE SCALE.
• SPIN WHEEL BY HAND WHILE OBSERVING VOLTAGE.
IS VOLTAGE AT LEAST 100mV (VOLTAGE WILL INCREASE AS WHEEL SPEED INCREASES).
YES
NO
VERIFY THAT SENSOR RING IS INTACT. IF OK, REPLACE WHEEL SPEED SENSOR.
6
• IGNITION "ON."
• SELECT D.C. VOLTAGE SCALE ON DVM.
• MEASURE VOLTAGE BETWEEN GROUND AND TERMINAL "A", THEN TERMINAL "B" OF THE LEFT FRONT WHEEL SPEED SENSOR HARNESS CONNECTOR.
IS VOLTAGE BETWEEN 2.25 AND 2.75 VOLTS ON EACH TERMINAL?
DIAGNOSIS CONTINUED
GC402930075400BX

Fig. 113 Code A021: Left Front Wheel Speed = 0. 1993 Cutlass Supreme, Grand Prix, Lumina & Regal

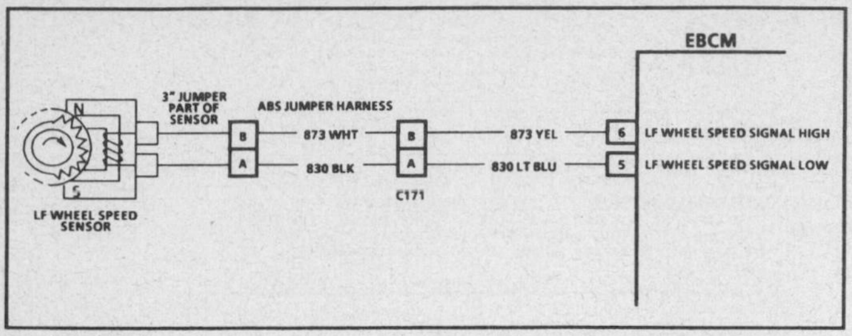

EBCM
3" JUMPER PART OF SENSOR
ABS JUMPER HARNESS
N
S
B
A
873 WHT
830 BLK
B
A
C171
873 YEL
830 LT BLU
6
5
LF WHEEL SPEED SIGNAL HIGH
LF WHEEL SPEED SIGNAL LOW
LF WHEEL SPEED SENSOR

Circuit Description:

As a toothed ring passes by the wheel speed sensor, changes in the electromagnetic field cause the wheel speed sensor to produce a sinusoidal (AC) voltage signal whose frequency is proportional to wheel speed. The magnitude of this signal is directly related to wheel speed and the proximity of the wheel speed sensor to the toothed ring, often referred to as the air gap.

DTC Will Set When: DTC 21 can be set when the vehicle is not in an ABS stop. If the left front wheel speed = 0 and the vehicle's reference speed is greater than 8 km/h (5 mph), a malfunction exists.

Action Taken: A malfunction DTC is stored, ABS is disabled and the ABS warning lamp is turned "ON."

DTC Chart Test Description: Number(s) below refer to circled number(s) on the diagnostic chart.

1. Determines if DTC 32 is present.
2. Designed to identify a wheel speed sensor or circuitry that is damaged and visibly apparent.
3. Checks to see that the wheel speed sensor is within proper resistance values.
4. Verifies that the wheel speed sensor can generate an appropriate output signal.

Diagnostic Aids: An "Intermittent" malfunction may be caused by a poor connection, rubbed through wire insulation, or a wire that is broken inside the insulation.

The frequency of the malfunction can be checked by using the enhanced diagnostic function of the Tech 1

If the customer's comments reflect that the ABS warning lamp is "ON" only during moist environmental changes (rain, snow, vehicle wash), all wheel speed sensor circuitry should be thoroughly inspected for signs of water intrusion. If DTC is not current, clear DTCs and simulate the effects of water intrusion. Use the following procedure. Spray down the suspected area with a 5% salt water solution (two teaspoons of salt to 12 oz. of water). Test drive vehicle over various road surfaces (bumps, turns, etc.) above 24 km/h (15 mph) for at least 30 seconds. If DTC returns replace suspected harness.

Any circuitry, that is suspected as causing the intermittent complaint, should be thoroughly checked for backed out terminals, improper mating, broken locks, improperly formed or damaged terminals, poor terminal to wiring connections or physical damage to the wiring harness.

Resistance of the wheel speed sensor will increase with an increase in sensor temperature.

When replacing a wheel speed sensor, inspect the sensor terminals and harness connector for corrosion and/or water intrusion. If evidence of corrosion or water intrusion exists, replace wheel speed sensor jumper harness. Likewise, if replacing a wheel speed sensor jumper harness, inspect sensor terminals. If evidence of corrosion or water intrusion exists, replace wheel speed sensor.

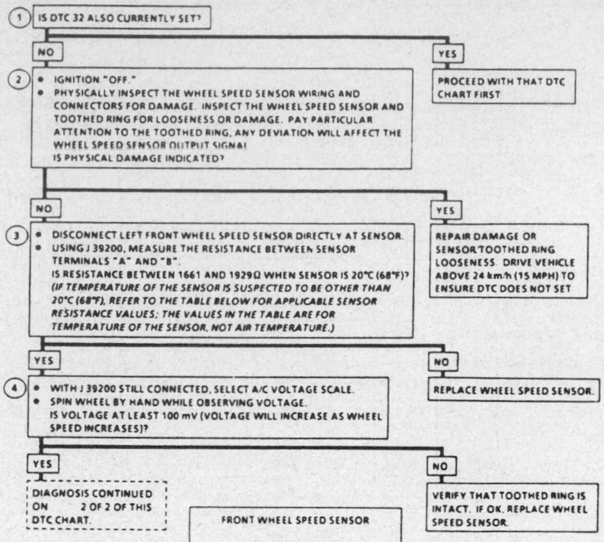

1 IS DTC 32 ALSO CURRENTLY SET?
NO
YES
PROCEED WITH THAT DTC CHART FIRST
2 • IGNITION "OFF."
• PHYSICALLY INSPECT THE WHEEL SPEED SENSOR WIRING AND CONNECTORS FOR DAMAGE. INSPECT THE WHEEL SPEED SENSOR AND TOOTHED RING FOR LOOSENESS OR DAMAGE. PAY PARTICULAR ATTENTION TO THE TOOTHED RING, ANY DEVIATION WILL AFFECT THE WHEEL SPEED SENSOR OUTPUT SIGNAL
IS PHYSICAL DAMAGE INDICATED?
NO
YES
REPAIR DAMAGE OR SENSOR/TOOTHED RING LOOSENESS. DRIVE VEHICLE ABOVE 24 km/h (15 MPH) TO ENSURE DTC DOES NOT SET
3 • DISCONNECT LEFT FRONT WHEEL SPEED SENSOR DIRECTLY AT SENSOR.
• USING J 39200, MEASURE THE RESISTANCE BETWEEN SENSOR TERMINALS "A" AND "B".
IS RESISTANCE BETWEEN 1661 AND 1929Ω WHEN SENSOR IS 20°C (68°F)?
(IF TEMPERATURE OF THE SENSOR IS SUSPECTED TO BE OTHER THAN 20°C (68°F), REFER TO THE TABLE BELOW FOR APPLICABLE SENSOR RESISTANCE VALUES; THE VALUES IN THE TABLE ARE FOR TEMPERATURE OF THE SENSOR, NOT AIR TEMPERATURE.)
YES
NO
REPLACE WHEEL SPEED SENSOR.
4 • WITH J 39200 STILL CONNECTED, SELECT A/C VOLTAGE SCALE.
• SPIN WHEEL BY HAND WHILE OBSERVING VOLTAGE.
IS VOLTAGE AT LEAST 100 mV (VOLTAGE WILL INCREASE AS WHEEL SPEED INCREASES)?
YES
NO
DIAGNOSIS CONTINUED ON 2 OF 2 OF THIS DTC CHART.
VERIFY THAT TOOTHED RING IS INTACT. IF OK, REPLACE WHEEL SPEED SENSOR.

FRONT WHEEL SPEED SENSOR

TEMPERATURE OF SENSOR VS. SENSOR RESISTANCE (APPROXIMATE)

TEMP. (°C)	TEMP. (°F)	RESISTANCE (OHMS)
-34 TO 4	-30 TO 40	1309 TO 1808
5 TO 43	41 TO 110	1557 TO 2103
44 TO 93	111 TO 200	1811 TO 2482

GC402940094001BX

Fig. 114 Code A021: Left Front Wheel Speed = 0 (Part 1 of 2). 1994 Cutlass Supreme, Lumina & Regal

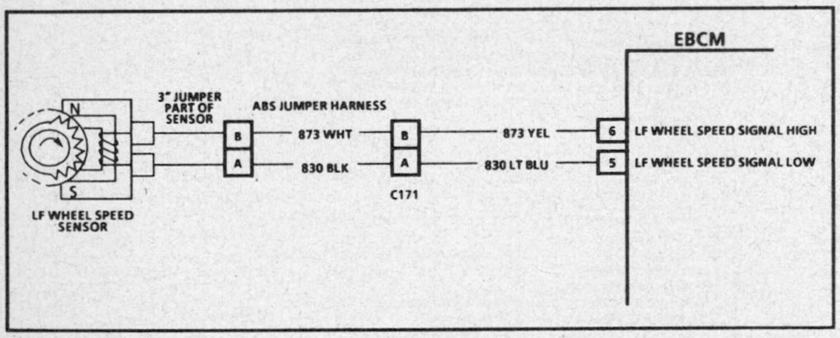

EBCM
3" JUMPER PART OF SENSOR
ABS JUMPER HARNESS
N
S
B
A
873 WHT
830 BLK
B
A
C171
873 YEL
830 LT BLU
6
5
LF WHEEL SPEED SIGNAL HIGH
LF WHEEL SPEED SIGNAL LOW
LF WHEEL SPEED SENSOR

Circuit Description:

As a toothed ring passes by the wheel speed sensor, changes in the electromagnetic field cause the wheel speed sensor to produce a sinusoidal (AC) voltage signal whose frequency is proportional to wheel speed. The magnitude of this signal is directly related to wheel speed and the proximity of the wheel speed sensor to the toothed ring often referred to as the air gap.

DTC Will Set When: DTC 21 can be set when the vehicle is not in an ABS stop. If the left front wheel speed = 0 and the vehicle's reference speed is greater than 8 km/h (5 mph), a malfunction exists.

Action Taken: A malfunction DTC is stored, ABS is disabled and the ABS warning lamp is turned "ON."

DTC Chart Test Description: Number(s) below refer to circled number(s) on the diagnostic chart.

5. Checks for proper output voltage from the EBCM.
6. Checks for an open in the wheel speed sensor high circuit.
7. Ensures malfunction was not due to physical damage of the circuitry.
8. Ensures that wheel speed sensor circuitry is not shorted.
9. Ensures malfunction was not due to physical damage of the circuitry.
10. Checks for an open in the wheel speed sensor low circuit.

Diagnostic Aids: An "Intermittent" malfunction may be caused by a poor connection, rubbed through wire insulation, or a wire that is broken inside the insulation.

The frequency of the malfunction can be checked by using the enhanced diagnostic function of the Tech 1

If the customer's comments reflect that the ABS warning lamp is "ON" only during moist environmental changes (rain, snow, vehicle wash), all wheel speed sensor circuitry should be thoroughly inspected for signs of water intrusion. If DTC is not current, clear DTCs and simulate the effects of water intrusion. Use the following procedure. Spray down the suspected area with a 5% salt water solution (two teaspoons of salt to 12 oz. of water). Test drive vehicle over various road surfaces (bumps, turns, etc.) above 24 km/h (15 mph) for at least 30 seconds. If DTC returns replace suspected harness.

Any circuitry, that is suspected as causing the intermittent complaint, should be thoroughly checked for backed out terminals, improper mating, broken locks, improperly formed or damaged terminals, poor terminal to wiring connections or physical damage to the wiring harness.

Resistance of the wheel speed sensor will increase with an increase in sensor temperature.

When replacing a wheel speed sensor, inspect the sensor terminals and harness connector for corrosion and/or water intrusion. If evidence of corrosion or water intrusion exists, replace wheel speed sensor jumper harness. Likewise, if replacing a wheel speed sensor jumper harness, inspect sensor terminals. If evidence of corrosion or water intrusion exits, replace wheel speed sensor.

GC402940094002AX

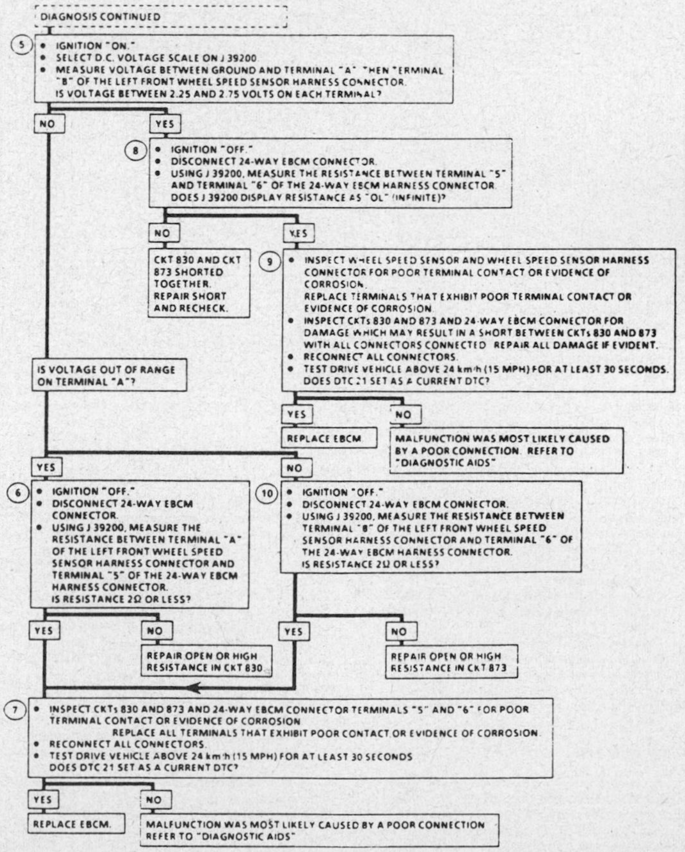

DIAGNOSIS CONTINUED
5 • IGNITION "ON."
• SELECT D.C. VOLTAGE SCALE ON J 39200
• MEASURE VOLTAGE BETWEEN GROUND AND TERMINAL "A" THEN TERMINAL "B" OF THE LEFT FRONT WHEEL SPEED SENSOR HARNESS CONNECTOR.
IS VOLTAGE BETWEEN 2.25 AND 2.75 VOLTS ON EACH TERMINAL?
NO
YES
8 • IGNITION "OFF."
• DISCONNECT 24-WAY EBCM CONNECTOR.
• USING J 39200, MEASURE THE RESISTANCE BETWEEN TERMINAL "5" AND TERMINAL "6" OF THE 24-WAY EBCM HARNESS CONNECTOR.
DOES J 39200 DISPLAY RESISTANCE AS "OL" (INFINITE)?
NO
YES
CKT 830 AND CKT 873 SHORTED TOGETHER. REPAIR SHORT AND RECHECK.
9 • INSPECT WHEEL SPEED SENSOR AND WHEEL SPEED SENSOR HARNESS CONNECTOR FOR POOR TERMINAL CONTACT OR EVIDENCE OF CORROSION.
REPLACE TERMINALS THAT EXHIBIT POOR TERMINAL CONTACT OR EVIDENCE OF CORROSION.
• INSPECT CKTs 830 AND 873 AND 24-WAY EBCM CONNECTOR FOR DAMAGE WHICH MAY RESULT IN A SHORT BETWEEN CKTs 830 AND 873 WITH ALL CONNECTORS CONNECTED. REPAIR ALL DAMAGE IF EVIDENT.
• RECONNECT ALL CONNECTORS.
• TEST DRIVE VEHICLE ABOVE 24 km/h (15 MPH) FOR AT LEAST 30 SECONDS.
DOES DTC 21 SET AS A CURRENT DTC?
IS VOLTAGE OUT OF RANGE ON TERMINAL "A"?
YES
NO
REPLACE EBCM.
MALFUNCTION WAS MOST LIKELY CAUSED BY A POOR CONNECTION. REFER TO "DIAGNOSTIC AIDS"
YES
NO
6 • IGNITION "OFF."
• DISCONNECT 24-WAY EBCM CONNECTOR.
• USING J 39200, MEASURE THE RESISTANCE BETWEEN TERMINAL "A" OF THE LEFT FRONT WHEEL SPEED SENSOR HARNESS CONNECTOR AND TERMINAL "5" OF THE 24-WAY EBCM HARNESS CONNECTOR.
IS RESISTANCE 2Ω OR LESS?
10 • IGNITION "OFF."
• DISCONNECT 24-WAY EBCM CONNECTOR.
• USING J 39200, MEASURE THE RESISTANCE BETWEEN TERMINAL "B" OF THE LEFT FRONT WHEEL SPEED SENSOR HARNESS CONNECTOR AND TERMINAL "6" OF THE 24-WAY EBCM HARNESS CONNECTOR.
IS RESISTANCE 2Ω OR LESS?
YES
NO
REPAIR OPEN OR HIGH RESISTANCE IN CKT 830
YES
NO
REPAIR OPEN OR HIGH RESISTANCE IN CKT 873
7 • INSPECT CKTs 830 AND 873 AND 24-WAY EBCM CONNECTOR TERMINALS "5" AND "6" FOR POOR TERMINAL CONTACT OR EVIDENCE OF CORROSION
REPLACE ALL TERMINALS THAT EXHIBIT POOR CONTACT OR EVIDENCE OF CORROSION.
• RECONNECT ALL CONNECTORS.
• TEST DRIVE VEHICLE ABOVE 24 km/h (15 MPH) FOR AT LEAST 30 SECONDS
DOES DTC 21 SET AS A CURRENT DTC?
YES
NO
REPLACE EBCM.
MALFUNCTION WAS MOST LIKELY CAUSED BY A POOR CONNECTION REFER TO "DIAGNOSTIC AIDS"

GC402940094002BX

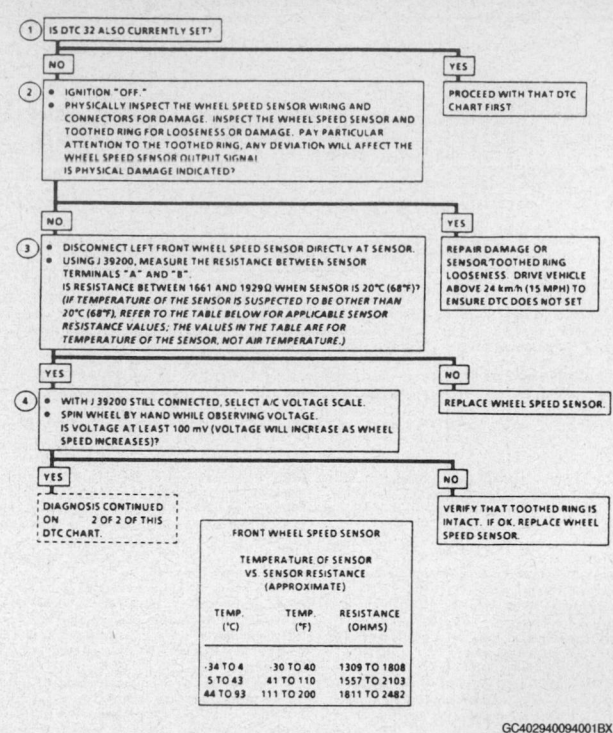

Fig. 114 Code A021: Left Front Wheel Speed = 0 (Part 2 of 2). 1993 Grand Prix, 1993–94 Cutlass Supreme, Lumina & Regal

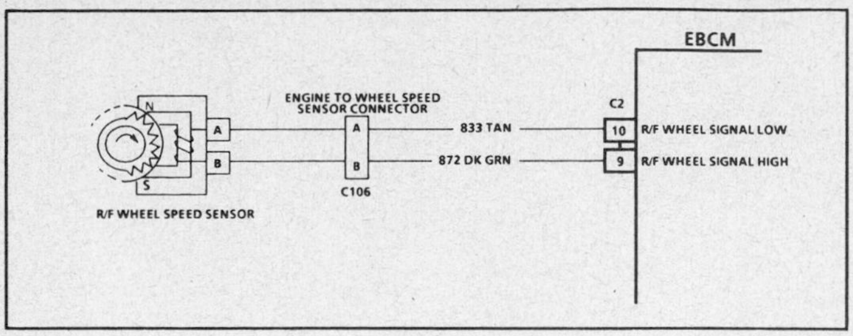
EBCM
ENGINE TO WHEEL SPEED SENSOR CONNECTOR
N
A
B
S
C106
833 TAN
872 DK GRN
C2
10 R/F WHEEL SIGNAL LOW
9 R/F WHEEL SIGNAL HIGH
R/F WHEEL SPEED SENSOR

GC402930075500AX

Cavalier & Sunbird

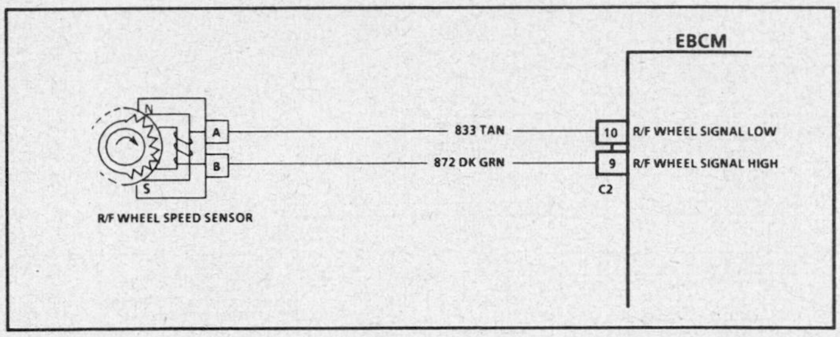
EBCM
N
A
B
S
833 TAN
872 DK GRN
10 R/F WHEEL SIGNAL LOW
9 R/F WHEEL SIGNAL HIGH
C2
R/F WHEEL SPEED SENSOR

GC402930075500BX

Achieva, Beretta, Corsica, Grand Am & Skylark

RIGHT FRONT WHEEL SPEED = 0

Circuit Description:

As a toothed ring passes by the wheel speed sensor, changes in the electromagnetic field cause the wheel speed sensor to produce a sinusoidal (AC) voltage signal whose frequency is proportional to wheel speed. The magnitude of this signal is directly related to wheel speed and the proximity of the wheel speed sensor to the toothed ring, often referred to as the air gap.

Failure Condition:

DTC A022 can be set when the vehicle is not in an ABS stop. If the right front wheel speed is less than 1/2 of the vehicle's reference speed and the vehicle's reference speed is greater than 8 km/h (5 mph), a malfunction exists.

Action Taken:

A malfunction DTC is stored, ABS is disabled and the ABS indicator lamp is turned "ON."

Test Description: Number(s) below refer to circled number(s) on the diagnostic chart.

1. This test verifies whether the malfunction is currently present.
2. This step will identify a wheel speed sensor or circuitry that is damaged and visibly apparent.
3. This test checks wheel speed sensor for proper resistance values.
4. This test ensures the wheel speed sensor and sensor ring generate the proper voltage.
5. This step ensures the wheel speed sensor is not shorted to ground.

Diagnostic Aids:

An "Intermittent" malfunction may be caused by a poor connection, rubbed through wire insulation, or a wire that is broken inside the insulation.

The frequency of the malfunction can be checked by using the enhanced diagnostic function of the Tech 1.

If the customer's comments reflect that the ABS amber indicator lamp is "ON" only during moist environmental changes, (rain, snow, vehicle wash) all wheel speed sensor circuitry should be thoroughly inspected for signs of water intrusion. Use the following procedure. Spray down the suspected area with 5% salt water solution (two teaspoons of salt to 12 oz. of water). Start vehicle, allow vehicle to run for 10 seconds. If DTC returns immediately, replace suspected harness.

Any circuitry, that is suspected as causing the intermittent complaint, should be thoroughly checked for backed out terminals, improper mating, broken locks, improperly formed or damaged terminals, poor terminal to wiring connections or physical damage to the wiring harness.

When measuring wheel speed sensor resistance, ensure vehicle is at room temperature. Wheel speed sensor resistance will vary with temperature.

When replacing a wheel speed sensor, inspect the sensor terminals and harness connector for corrosion and/or water intrusion. If evidence of corrosion or water intrusion exists, replace wheel speed sensor harness.

GC402930075500CX

IMPORTANT: WHEEL SPEED SENSOR INTERMITTENT MALFUNCTIONS MAY BE DIFFICULT TO LOCATE. CARE SHOULD BE TAKEN NOT TO DISTURB ANY ELECTRICAL CONNECTIONS PRIOR TO AN INDICATED STEP OF THIS CHART. THIS WILL INSURE THAT AN INTERMITTENT CONNECTION WILL NOT BE CORRECTED BEFORE THE SOURCE OF THE MALFUNCTION IS FOUND.

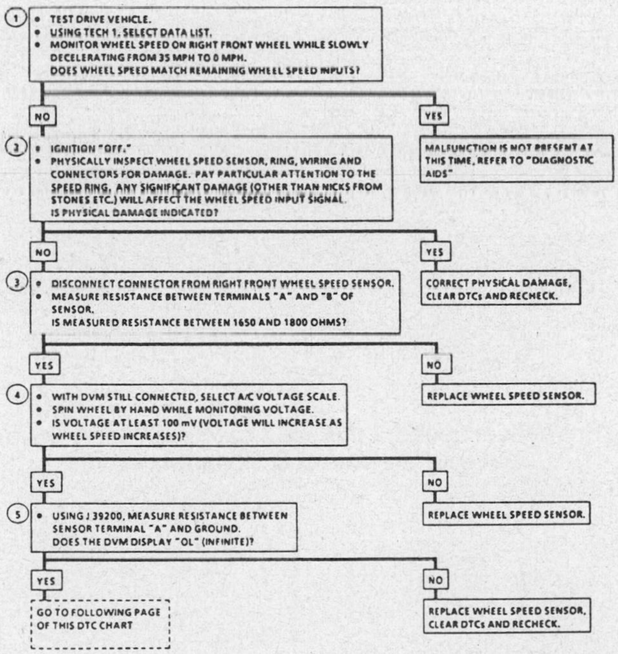
1
• TEST DRIVE VEHICLE.
• USING TECH 1, SELECT DATA LIST.
• MONITOR WHEEL SPEED ON RIGHT FRONT WHEEL WHILE SLOWLY DECELERATING FROM 35 MPH TO 0 MPH.
DOES WHEEL SPEED MATCH REMAINING WHEEL SPEED INPUTS?
NO
YES
MALFUNCTION IS NOT PRESENT AT THIS TIME, REFER TO "DIAGNOSTIC AIDS"
2
• IGNITION "OFF."
• PHYSICALLY INSPECT WHEEL SPEED SENSOR, RING, WIRING AND CONNECTORS FOR DAMAGE. PAY PARTICULAR ATTENTION TO THE SPEED RING. ANY SIGNIFICANT DAMAGE (OTHER THAN NICKS FROM STONES ETC.) WILL AFFECT THE WHEEL SPEED INPUT SIGNAL.
IS PHYSICAL DAMAGE INDICATED?
NO
YES
CORRECT PHYSICAL DAMAGE, CLEAR DTCs AND RECHECK.
3
• DISCONNECT CONNECTOR FROM RIGHT FRONT WHEEL SPEED SENSOR.
• MEASURE RESISTANCE BETWEEN TERMINALS "A" AND "B" OF SENSOR.
IS MEASURED RESISTANCE BETWEEN 1650 AND 1800 OHMS?
YES
NO
REPLACE WHEEL SPEED SENSOR.
4
• WITH DVM STILL CONNECTED, SELECT A/C VOLTAGE SCALE.
• SPIN WHEEL BY HAND WHILE MONITORING VOLTAGE.
• IS VOLTAGE AT LEAST 100 mV (VOLTAGE WILL INCREASE AS WHEEL SPEED INCREASES)?
YES
NO
REPLACE WHEEL SPEED SENSOR.
5
• USING J 39200, MEASURE RESISTANCE BETWEEN SENSOR TERMINAL "A" AND GROUND.
DOES THE DVM DISPLAY "OL" (INFINITE)?
YES
NO
GO TO FOLLOWING PAGE OF THIS DTC CHART
REPLACE WHEEL SPEED SENSOR, CLEAR DTCs AND RECHECK.

GC402930075500DX

Fig. 115 Code A022: Right Front Wheel Speed = 0 (Part 1 of 2). 1993–94 Cavalier, Sunbird, Beretta, Corsica & Achieva, Grand Am & Skylark Less VES

DTC A022

RIGHT FRONT WHEEL SPEED = 0

Circuit Description:

As a toothed ring passes by the wheel speed sensor, changes in the electromagnetic field cause the wheel speed sensor to produce a sinusoidal (AC) voltage signal whose frequency is proportional to wheel speed. The magnitude of this signal is directly related to wheel speed and the proximity of the wheel speed sensor to the toothed ring, often referred to as the air gap.

Failure Condition:

DTC A022 can be set when the vehicle is not in an ABS stop. If the right front wheel speed is less than 1/2 of the vehicle's reference speed and the vehicle's reference speed is greater than 8 km/h (5 mph), a malfunction exists.

Action Taken:

A malfunction DTC is stored, ABS is disabled and the ABS indicator lamp is turned "ON."

Test Description: Number(s) below refer to circled number(s) on the diagnostic chart.

6. This step checks for proper voltages at speed sensor harness connector.
7. This test ensures that the wheel and speed sensor circuitry is not internally shorted.
8. This checks for an open in the wheel signal low circuit.
9. This checks for an open in the wheel signal high circuit.
10. This test checks for a short to ground in both high and low wheel signal circuits.
11. This step ensures that DTC A022 was not set due to a poor connection between the world connector and EBCM.

Diagnostic Aids:

An "Intermittent" malfunction may be caused by a poor connection, rubbed through wire insulation, or a wire that is broken inside the insulation.

The frequency of the malfunction can be checked by using the enhanced diagnostic function of the Tech 1

If the customer's comments reflect that the ABS amber indicator lamp is "ON" only during moist environmental changes, (rain, snow, vehicle wash) all wheel speed sensor circuitry should be thoroughly inspected for signs of water intrusion. Use the following procedure. Spray down the suspected area with 5% salt water solution (two teaspoons of salt to 12 oz. of water). Start vehicle, allow vehicle to run for 10 seconds. If DTC returns immediately, replace suspected harness.

Any circuitry, that is suspected as causing the intermittent complaint, should be thoroughly checked for backed out terminals, improper mating, broken locks, improperly formed or damaged terminals, poor terminal to wiring connections or physical damage to the wiring harness.

When measuring wheel speed sensor resistance, ensure vehicle is at room temperature. Wheel speed sensor resistance will vary with temperature.

When replacing a wheel speed sensor, inspect the sensor terminals and harness connector for corrosion and/or water intrusion. If evidence of corrosion or water intrusion exists, replace wheel speed sensor harness.

GC402930075500EX

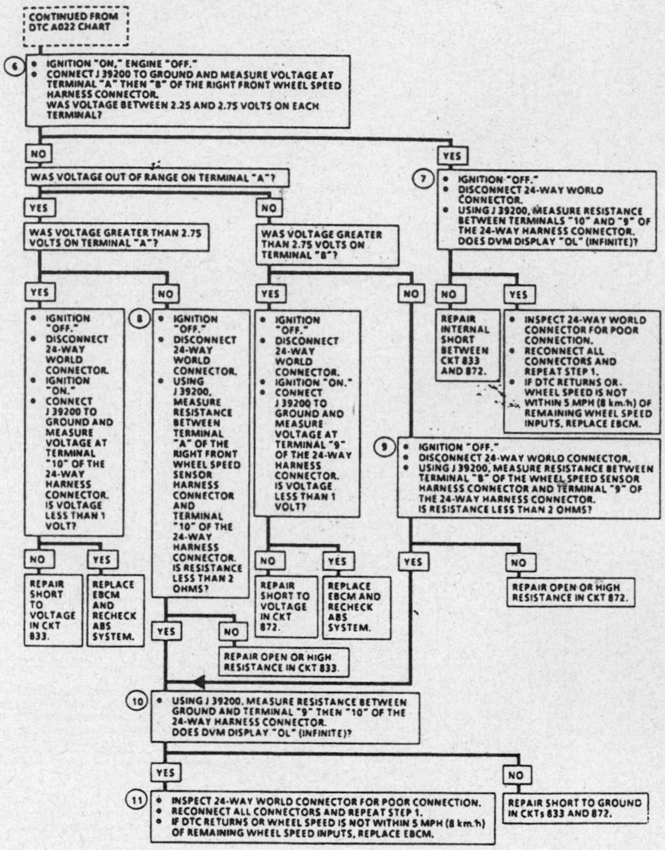
CONTINUED FROM DTC A022 CHART
6
• IGNITION "ON," ENGINE "OFF."
• CONNECT J 39200 TO GROUND AND MEASURE VOLTAGE AT TERMINAL "A" THEN "B" OF THE RIGHT FRONT WHEEL SPEED HARNESS CONNECTOR. WAS VOLTAGE BETWEEN 2.25 AND 2.75 VOLTS ON EACH TERMINAL?
NO
YES
WAS VOLTAGE OUT OF RANGE ON TERMINAL "A"?
7
• IGNITION "OFF."
• DISCONNECT 24-WAY WORLD CONNECTOR.
• USING J 39200, MEASURE RESISTANCE BETWEEN TERMINALS "10" AND "9" OF THE 24-WAY HARNESS CONNECTOR. DOES DVM DISPLAY "OL" (INFINITE)?
WAS VOLTAGE GREATER THAN 2.75 VOLTS ON TERMINAL "A"?
WAS VOLTAGE GREATER THAN 2.75 VOLTS ON TERMINAL "B"?
REPAIR INTERNAL SHORT BETWEEN CKT 833 AND 872.
• INSPECT 24-WAY WORLD CONNECTOR FOR POOR CONNECTION.
• RECONNECT ALL CONNECTORS AND REPEAT STEP 1.
• IF DTC RETURNS OR. WHEEL SPEED IS NOT WITHIN 5 MPH (8 km/h) OF REMAINING WHEEL SPEED INPUTS, REPLACE EBCM.
• IGNITION "OFF."
• DISCONNECT 24-WAY WORLD CONNECTOR.
• IGNITION "ON."
• CONNECT J 39200 TO GROUND AND MEASURE VOLTAGE AT TERMINAL "10" OF THE 24-WAY HARNESS CONNECTOR. IS VOLTAGE LESS THAN 1 VOLT?
8
• IGNITION "OFF."
• DISCONNECT 24-WAY WORLD CONNECTOR.
• USING J 39200, MEASURE RESISTANCE BETWEEN TERMINAL "A" OF THE RIGHT FRONT WHEEL SPEED SENSOR HARNESS CONNECTOR AND TERMINAL "10" OF THE 24-WAY HARNESS CONNECTOR. IS RESISTANCE LESS THAN 2 OHMS?
• IGNITION "OFF."
• DISCONNECT 24-WAY WORLD CONNECTOR.
• IGNITION "ON."
• CONNECT J 39200 TO GROUND AND MEASURE VOLTAGE AT TERMINAL "9" OF THE 24-WAY HARNESS CONNECTOR. IS VOLTAGE LESS THAN 1 VOLT?
9
• IGNITION "OFF."
• DISCONNECT 24-WAY WORLD CONNECTOR.
• USING J 39200, MEASURE RESISTANCE BETWEEN TERMINAL "B" OF THE WHEEL SPEED SENSOR HARNESS CONNECTOR AND TERMINAL "9" OF THE 24-WAY HARNESS CONNECTOR. IS RESISTANCE LESS THAN 2 OHMS?
REPAIR SHORT TO VOLTAGE IN CKT 833.
REPLACE EBCM AND RECHECK ABS SYSTEM.
REPAIR SHORT TO VOLTAGE IN CKT 872.
REPLACE EBCM AND RECHECK ABS SYSTEM.
REPAIR OPEN OR HIGH RESISTANCE IN CKT 872.
REPAIR OPEN OR HIGH RESISTANCE IN CKT 833.
10
• USING J 39200, MEASURE RESISTANCE BETWEEN GROUND AND TERMINAL "9" THEN "10" OF THE 24-WAY HARNESS CONNECTOR. DOES DVM DISPLAY "OL" (INFINITE)?
11
• INSPECT 24-WAY WORLD CONNECTOR FOR POOR CONNECTION.
• RECONNECT ALL CONNECTORS AND REPEAT STEP 1.
• IF DTC RETURNS OR WHEEL SPEED IS NOT WITHIN 5 MPH (8 km/h) OF REMAINING WHEEL SPEED INPUTS, REPLACE EBCM.
REPAIR SHORT TO GROUND IN CKTs 833 AND 872.

GC402930075500FX

Fig. 115 Code A022: Right Front Wheel Speed = 0 (Part 2 of 2). 1993–94 Cavalier, Sunbird, Beretta, Corsica & Achieva, Grand Am & Skylark Less VES

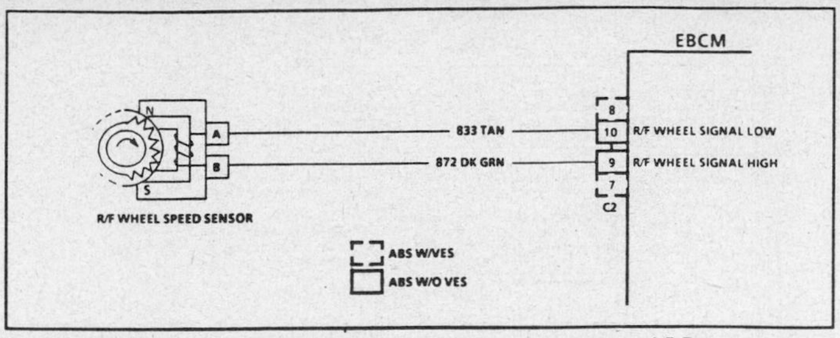
EBCM
833 TAN
872 DK GRN
8
10
9
7
C2
R/F WHEEL SIGNAL LOW
R/F WHEEL SIGNAL HIGH
N
A
B
S
R/F WHEEL SPEED SENSOR
ABS W/VES
ABS W/O VES

Circuit Description:
As a toothed ring passes by the wheel speed sensor, changes in the electromagnetic field cause the wheel speed sensor to produce a sinusoidal (AC) voltage signal whose frequency is proportional to wheel speed. The magnitude of this signal is directly related to wheel speed and the proximity of the wheel speed sensor to the toothed ring, often referred to as the air gap.

DTC Will Set When: DTC 22 can be set when the vehicle is not in an ABS stop. A malfunction exists if the right front wheel speed = 0 and the vehicle speed is greater than 8 km/h (5 mph).

Action Taken: A malfunction DTC is stored, ABS/VES is disabled and the ABS warning lamp is turned "ON."

DTC Chart Test Description: Number(s) below refer to circled number(s) on the diagnostic chart.
1. Identifies if a wheel speed sensor or circuitry is damaged and visibly apparent.
2. Tests wheel speed sensor for proper resistance values.
3. Ensures wheel speed sensor and toothed ring generate the proper voltage.
4. Ensures wheel speed sensor high and low circuits are not shorted together.
5. Ensures malfunction is not due to physical damage of the wheel speed sensor circuitry.

Diagnostic Aids: An "Intermittent" malfunction is most likely caused by a poor connection, rubbed through wire insulation, or a wire that is broken inside the insulation.

The frequency of the malfunction can be checked by using the enhanced diagnostic function of the Tech 1.

If the customer's comments reflect that the ABS amber warning lamp is "ON" only during moist environmental changes, (rain, snow, vehicle wash) all wheel speed sensor circuitry should be thoroughly inspected for signs of water intrusion. Use the following procedure. Spray down the suspected area with 5% salt water solution (two teaspoons of salt to 12 oz. of water). Drive vehicle above 24 km/h (15 mph) for at least 30 seconds. If DTC returns immediately, replace suspected harness.

Any circuitry, that is suspected as causing the intermittent complaint, should be thoroughly checked for backed out terminals, improper mating, broken locks, improperly formed or damaged terminals, poor terminal to wiring connections or physical damage to the wiring harness.

Resistance of the wheel speed sensor will increase with an increase in sensor temperature.

When replacing a wheel speed sensor, inspect the sensor terminals and harness connector for corrosion and/or water intrusion. If evidence of corrosion or water intrusion exists, replace wheel speed sensor harness. Refer to "On-Vehicle Service" in this section.

If wheel speed sensor harness shows evidence of water intrusion, inspect wheel speed sensor for water intrusion. If water intrusion is evident, replace wheel speed sensor.

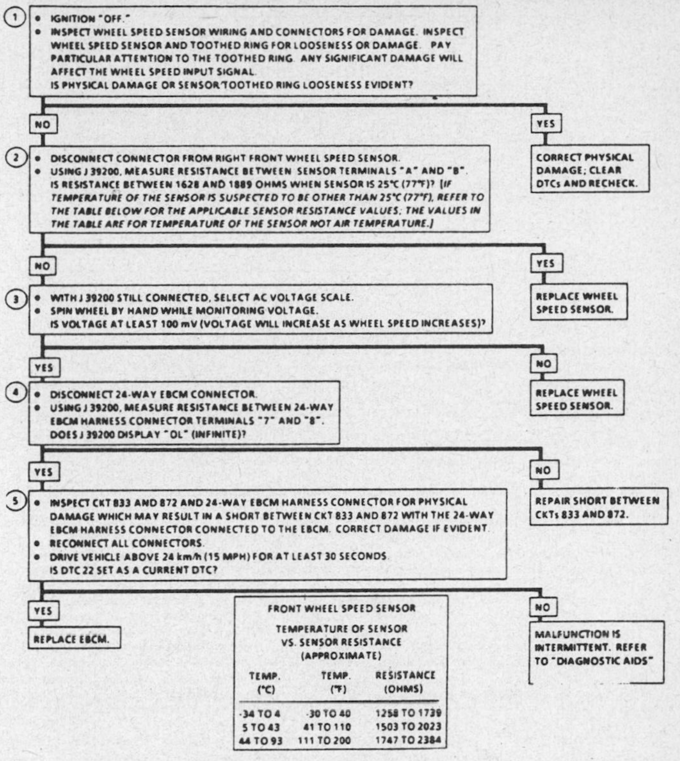
1
• IGNITION "OFF."
• INSPECT WHEEL SPEED SENSOR WIRING AND CONNECTORS FOR DAMAGE. INSPECT WHEEL SPEED SENSOR AND TOOTHED RING FOR LOOSENESS OR DAMAGE. PAY PARTICULAR ATTENTION TO THE TOOTHED RING. ANY SIGNIFICANT DAMAGE WILL AFFECT THE WHEEL SPEED INPUT SIGNAL.
IS PHYSICAL DAMAGE OR SENSOR/TOOTHED RING LOOSENESS EVIDENT?
NO
YES
CORRECT PHYSICAL DAMAGE; CLEAR DTCs AND RECHECK.
2
• DISCONNECT CONNECTOR FROM RIGHT FRONT WHEEL SPEED SENSOR.
• USING J 39200, MEASURE RESISTANCE BETWEEN SENSOR TERMINALS "A" AND "B".
IS RESISTANCE BETWEEN 1628 AND 1889 OHMS WHEN SENSOR IS 25°C (77°F)? [IF TEMPERATURE OF THE SENSOR IS SUSPECTED TO BE OTHER THAN 25°C (77°F), REFER TO THE TABLE BELOW FOR THE APPLICABLE SENSOR RESISTANCE VALUES; THE VALUES IN THE TABLE ARE FOR TEMPERATURE OF THE SENSOR NOT AIR TEMPERATURE.]
NO
YES
REPLACE WHEEL SPEED SENSOR.
3
• WITH J 39200 STILL CONNECTED, SELECT AC VOLTAGE SCALE.
• SPIN WHEEL BY HAND WHILE MONITORING VOLTAGE.
IS VOLTAGE AT LEAST 100 mV (VOLTAGE WILL INCREASE AS WHEEL SPEED INCREASES)?
YES
NO
REPLACE WHEEL SPEED SENSOR.
4
• DISCONNECT 24-WAY EBCM CONNECTOR.
• USING J 39200, MEASURE RESISTANCE BETWEEN 24-WAY EBCM HARNESS CONNECTOR TERMINALS "7" AND "8".
DOES J 39200 DISPLAY "OL" (INFINITE)?
YES
NO
REPAIR SHORT BETWEEN CKTs 833 AND 872.
5
• INSPECT CKT 833 AND 872 AND 24-WAY EBCM HARNESS CONNECTOR FOR PHYSICAL DAMAGE WHICH MAY RESULT IN A SHORT BETWEEN CKT 833 AND 872 WITH THE 24-WAY EBCM HARNESS CONNECTOR CONNECTED TO THE EBCM. CORRECT DAMAGE IF EVIDENT.
• RECONNECT ALL CONNECTORS.
• DRIVE VEHICLE ABOVE 24 km/h (15 MPH) FOR AT LEAST 30 SECONDS.
IS DTC 22 SET AS A CURRENT DTC?
YES
REPLACE EBCM.
NO
MALFUNCTION IS INTERMITTENT. REFER TO "DIAGNOSTIC AIDS"
FRONT WHEEL SPEED SENSOR
TEMPERATURE OF SENSOR VS. SENSOR RESISTANCE (APPROXIMATE)
TEMP. (°C) | TEMP. (°F) | RESISTANCE (OHMS)
-34 TO 4 | -30 TO 40 | 1258 TO 1739
5 TO 43 | 41 TO 110 | 1503 TO 2023
44 TO 93 | 111 TO 200 | 1747 TO 2384
GC402940104500BX

Fig. 116 Code A022: Right Front Wheel Speed = 0. 1994 Achieva, Grand Am & Skylark w/VES

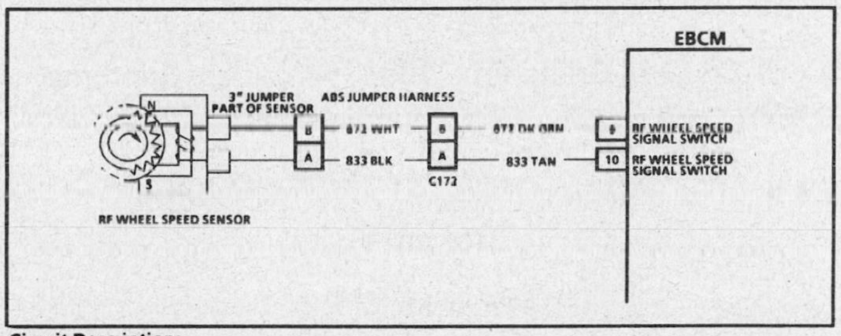
EBCM
3" JUMPER PART OF SENSOR
ABS JUMPER HARNESS
N
S
B
A
833 BLK
C172
833 TAN
10
RF WHEEL SPEED SIGNAL SWITCH
RF WHEEL SPEED SIGNAL SWITCH
RF WHEEL SPEED SENSOR

Circuit Description:
As a toothed ring passes by the wheel speed sensor, changes in the electromagnetic field cause the wheel speed sensor to produce a sinusoidal (AC) voltage signal whose frequency is proportional to wheel speed. The magnitude of this signal is directly related to wheel speed and the proximity of the wheel speed sensor to the toothed ring, often referred to as the air gap.

DTC Will Set When: DTC 22 can be set when the vehicle is not in an ABS stop. If the right front wheel speed = 0 and the vehicle's reference speed is greater than 8 km/h (5 mph), a malfunction exists.

Action Taken: A malfunction DTC is stored, ABS is disabled and the ABS warning lamp is turned "ON."

DTC Chart Test Description: Number(s) below refer to circled number(s) on the diagnostic chart.
1. Determines if DTC 33 is present.
2. Designed to identify a wheel speed sensor or circuitry that is damaged and visibly apparent.
3. Checks to see that the wheel speed sensor is within proper resistance values.
4. Verifies that the wheel speed sensor can generate an appropriate output signal.

Diagnostic Aids: An "Intermittent" malfunction may be caused by a poor connection, rubbed through wire insulation, or a wire that is broken inside the insulation.

The frequency of the malfunction can be checked by using the enhanced diagnostic function of the Tech 1.

If the customer's comments reflect that the ABS warning lamp is "ON" only during moist environmental changes (rain, snow, vehicle wash), all wheel speed sensor circuitry should be thoroughly inspected for signs of water intrusion. If DTC is not current, clear DTCs and simulate the effects of water intrusion. Use the following procedure. Spray down the suspected area with a 5% salt water solution (two teaspoons of salt to 12 oz. of water). Test drive vehicle over various road surfaces (bumps, turns, etc.) above 24 km/h (15 mph) for at least 30 seconds. If DTC returns replace suspected harness.

Any circuitry, that is suspected as causing the intermittent complaint, should be thoroughly checked for backed out terminals, improper mating, broken locks, improperly formed or damaged terminals, poor terminal to wiring connections or physical damage to the wiring harness.

Resistance of the wheel speed sensor will increase with an increase in sensor temperature.

When replacing a wheel speed sensor, inspect the sensor terminals and harness connector for corrosion and/or water intrusion. If evidence of corrosion or water intrusion exists, replace wheel speed sensor jumper harness. Likewise, if replacing a wheel speed sensor jumper harness, inspect sensor terminals. If evidence of corrosion or water intrusion exists, replace wheel speed sensor.

GC402930075601AA

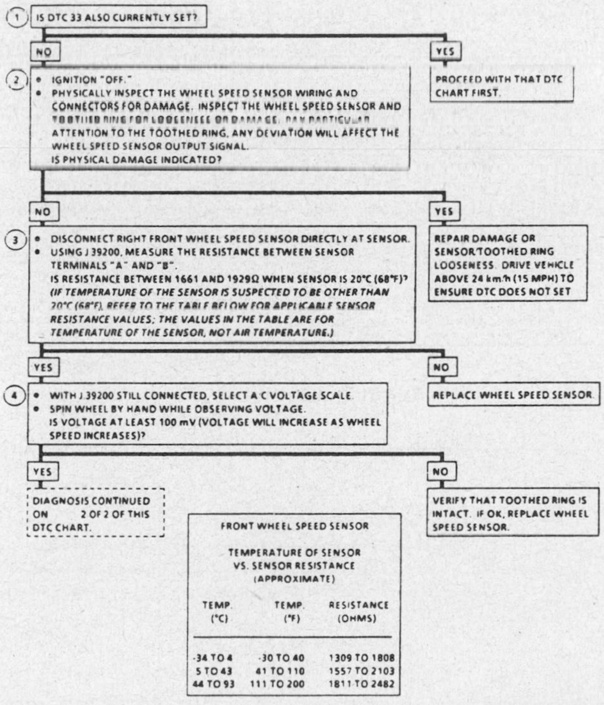
1
IS DTC 33 ALSO CURRENTLY SET?
NO
YES
PROCEED WITH THAT DTC CHART FIRST.
2
• IGNITION "OFF."
• PHYSICALLY INSPECT THE WHEEL SPEED SENSOR WIRING AND CONNECTORS FOR DAMAGE. INSPECT THE WHEEL SPEED SENSOR AND TOOTHED RING FOR LOOSENESS OR DAMAGE. PAY PARTICULAR ATTENTION TO THE TOOTHED RING, ANY DEVIATION WILL AFFECT THE WHEEL SPEED SENSOR OUTPUT SIGNAL.
IS PHYSICAL DAMAGE INDICATED?
NO
YES
REPAIR DAMAGE OR SENSOR/TOOTHED RING LOOSENESS. DRIVE VEHICLE ABOVE 24 km/h (15 MPH) TO ENSURE DTC DOES NOT SET
3
• DISCONNECT RIGHT FRONT WHEEL SPEED SENSOR DIRECTLY AT SENSOR.
• USING J 39200, MEASURE THE RESISTANCE BETWEEN SENSOR TERMINALS "A" AND "B".
IS RESISTANCE BETWEEN 1661 AND 1929Ω WHEN SENSOR IS 20°C (68°F)? (IF TEMPERATURE OF THE SENSOR IS SUSPECTED TO BE OTHER THAN 20°C (68°F), REFER TO THE TABLE BELOW FOR APPLICABLE SENSOR RESISTANCE VALUES; THE VALUES IN THE TABLE ARE FOR TEMPERATURE OF THE SENSOR, NOT AIR TEMPERATURE.)
YES
NO
REPLACE WHEEL SPEED SENSOR.
4
• WITH J 39200 STILL CONNECTED, SELECT A/C VOLTAGE SCALE.
• SPIN WHEEL BY HAND WHILE OBSERVING VOLTAGE.
IS VOLTAGE AT LEAST 100 mV (VOLTAGE WILL INCREASE AS WHEEL SPEED INCREASES)?
YES
DIAGNOSIS CONTINUED ON 2 OF 2 OF THIS DTC CHART.
NO
VERIFY THAT TOOTHED RING IS INTACT. IF OK, REPLACE WHEEL SPEED SENSOR.
FRONT WHEEL SPEED SENSOR
TEMPERATURE OF SENSOR VS. SENSOR RESISTANCE (APPROXIMATE)
TEMP. (°C) | TEMP. (°F) | RESISTANCE (OHMS)
-34 TO 4 | -30 TO 40 | 1309 TO 1808
5 TO 43 | 41 TO 110 | 1557 TO 2103
44 TO 93 | 111 TO 200 | 1811 TO 2482
GC402930075601BA

Fig. 117 Code A022: Right Front Wheel Speed = 0 (Part 1 of 2). 1993 Grand Prix, 1993–94 Cutlass Supreme, Lumina & Regal

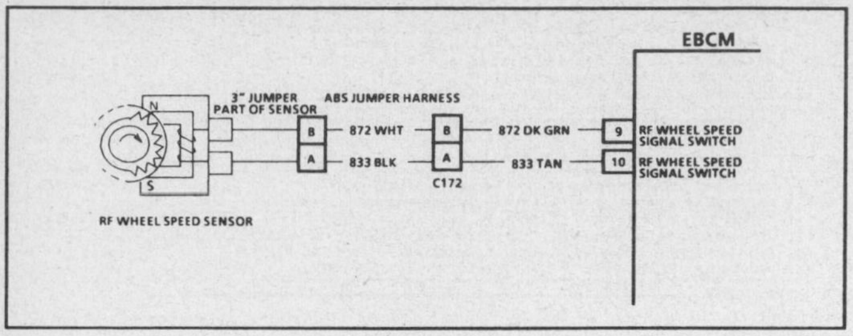
EBCM
3" JUMPER PART OF SENSOR
ABS JUMPER HARNESS
872 WHT
872 DK GRN
833 BLK
833 TAN
C172
RF WHEEL SPEED SIGNAL SWITCH
RF WHEEL SPEED SIGNAL SWITCH
RF WHEEL SPEED SENSOR

DTC 22

(Page 2 of 2)

RIGHT FRONT WHEEL SPEED = 0

Circuit Description:

As a toothed ring passes by the wheel speed sensor, changes in the electromagnetic field cause the wheel speed sensor to produce a sinusoidal (AC) voltage signal whose frequency is proportional to wheel speed. The magnitude of this signal is directly related to wheel speed and the proximity of the wheel speed sensor to the toothed ring, often referred to as the air gap.

DTC Will Set When: DTC 22 can be set when the vehicle is not in an ABS stop. If the right front wheel speed = 0 and the vehicle's reference speed is greater than 8 km/h (5 mph), a malfunction exists.

Action Taken: A malfunction DTC is stored, ABS is disabled and the ABS warning lamp is turned "ON."

DTC Chart Test Description: Number(s) below refer to circled number(s) on the diagnostic chart.

5. Checks for proper output voltage from the EBCM.
6. Checks for an open in the wheel speed sensor low circuit.
7. Ensures malfunction was not due to physical damage of the circuitry.
8. Ensures that wheel speed sensor circuitry is not shorted.
9. Ensures malfunction was not due to physical damage of the circuitry.
10. This checks for an open in the wheel speed sensor high circuit.

Diagnostic Aids: An "Intermittent" malfunction may be caused by a poor connection, rubbed through wire insulation, or a wire that is broken inside the insulation.

The frequency of the malfunction can be checked by using the enhanced diagnostic function of the Tech 1.

If the customer's comments reflect that the ABS warning lamp is "ON" only during moist environmental changes (rain, snow, vehicle wash), all wheel speed sensor circuitry should be thoroughly inspected for signs of water intrusion. If DTC is not current, clear DTCs and simulate the effects of water intrusion. Use the following procedure. Spray down the suspected area with a 5% salt water solution (two teaspoons of salt to 12 oz. of water). Test drive vehicle over various road surfaces (bumps, turns, etc.) above 24 km/h (15 mph) for at least 30 seconds. If DTC returns replace suspected harness.

Any circuitry, that is suspected as causing the intermittent complaint, should be thoroughly checked for backed out terminals, improper mating, broken locks, improperly formed or damaged terminals, poor terminal to wiring connections or physical damage to the wiring harness.

Resistance of the wheel speed sensor will increase with an increase in sensor temperature.

When replacing a wheel speed sensor, inspect the sensor terminals and harness connector for corrosion and/or water intrusion. If evidence of corrosion or water intrusion exists, replace wheel speed sensor jumper harness. Likewise, if replacing a wheel speed sensor jumper harness, inspect sensor terminals. If evidence of corrosion or water intrusion exists, replace wheel speed sensor.

GC402930075602AA

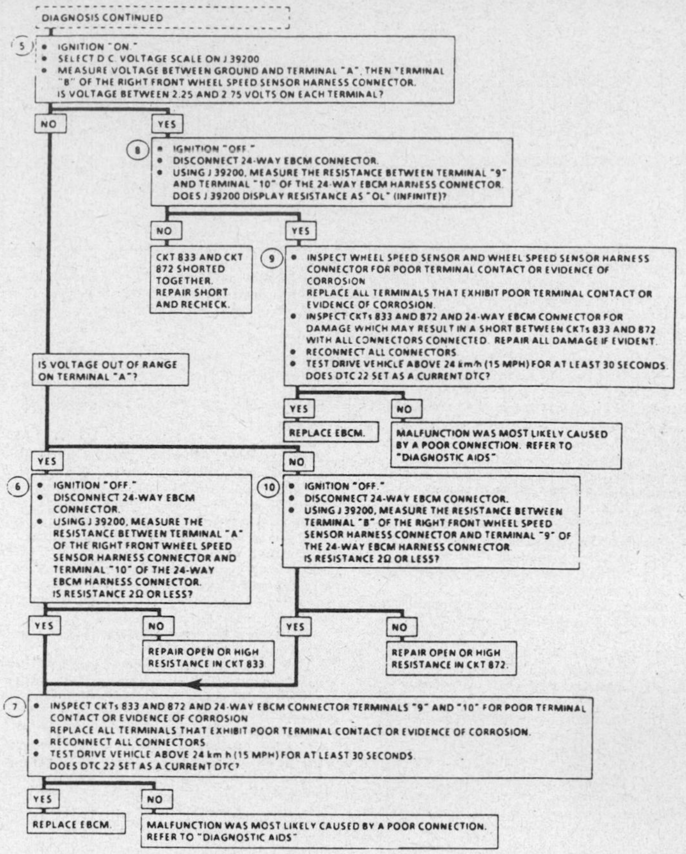
DIAGNOSIS CONTINUED
5
• IGNITION "ON."
• SELECT D.C. VOLTAGE SCALE ON J 39200
• MEASURE VOLTAGE BETWEEN GROUND AND TERMINAL "A", THEN TERMINAL "B" OF THE RIGHT FRONT WHEEL SPEED SENSOR HARNESS CONNECTOR.
IS VOLTAGE BETWEEN 2.25 AND 2.75 VOLTS ON EACH TERMINAL?
NO
YES
8
• IGNITION "OFF."
• DISCONNECT 24-WAY EBCM CONNECTOR.
• USING J 39200, MEASURE THE RESISTANCE BETWEEN TERMINAL "9" AND TERMINAL "10" OF THE 24-WAY EBCM HARNESS CONNECTOR.
DOES J 39200 DISPLAY RESISTANCE AS "OL" (INFINITE)?
NO
YES
CKT 833 AND CKT 872 SHORTED TOGETHER. REPAIR SHORT AND RECHECK.
9
• INSPECT WHEEL SPEED SENSOR AND WHEEL SPEED SENSOR HARNESS CONNECTOR FOR POOR TERMINAL CONTACT OR EVIDENCE OF CORROSION
REPLACE ALL TERMINALS THAT EXHIBIT POOR TERMINAL CONTACT OR EVIDENCE OF CORROSION.
• INSPECT CKTs 833 AND 872 AND 24-WAY EBCM CONNECTOR FOR DAMAGE WHICH MAY RESULT IN A SHORT BETWEEN CKTs 833 AND 872 WITH ALL CONNECTORS CONNECTED. REPAIR ALL DAMAGE IF EVIDENT.
• RECONNECT ALL CONNECTORS.
• TEST DRIVE VEHICLE ABOVE 24 km/h (15 MPH) FOR AT LEAST 30 SECONDS.
DOES DTC 22 SET AS A CURRENT DTC?
IS VOLTAGE OUT OF RANGE ON TERMINAL "A"?
YES
NO
REPLACE EBCM.
MALFUNCTION WAS MOST LIKELY CAUSED BY A POOR CONNECTION. REFER TO "DIAGNOSTIC AIDS"
YES
NO
6
• IGNITION "OFF."
• DISCONNECT 24-WAY EBCM CONNECTOR.
• USING J 39200, MEASURE THE RESISTANCE BETWEEN TERMINAL "A" OF THE RIGHT FRONT WHEEL SPEED SENSOR HARNESS CONNECTOR AND TERMINAL "10" OF THE 24-WAY EBCM HARNESS CONNECTOR.
IS RESISTANCE 2Ω OR LESS?
10
• IGNITION "OFF."
• DISCONNECT 24-WAY EBCM CONNECTOR.
• USING J 39200, MEASURE THE RESISTANCE BETWEEN TERMINAL "B" OF THE RIGHT FRONT WHEEL SPEED SENSOR HARNESS CONNECTOR AND TERMINAL "9" OF THE 24-WAY EBCM HARNESS CONNECTOR.
IS RESISTANCE 2Ω OR LESS?
YES
NO
REPAIR OPEN OR HIGH RESISTANCE IN CKT 833
YES
NO
REPAIR OPEN OR HIGH RESISTANCE IN CKT 872.
7
• INSPECT CKTs 833 AND 872 AND 24-WAY EBCM CONNECTOR TERMINALS "9" AND "10" FOR POOR TERMINAL CONTACT OR EVIDENCE OF CORROSION
REPLACE ALL TERMINALS THAT EXHIBIT POOR TERMINAL CONTACT OR EVIDENCE OF CORROSION.
• RECONNECT ALL CONNECTORS.
• TEST DRIVE VEHICLE ABOVE 24 km/h (15 MPH) FOR AT LEAST 30 SECONDS.
DOES DTC 22 SET AS A CURRENT DTC?
YES
NO
REPLACE EBCM.
MALFUNCTION WAS MOST LIKELY CAUSED BY A POOR CONNECTION. REFER TO "DIAGNOSTIC AIDS"

GC402930075602BA

Fig. 117 Code A022: Right Front Wheel Speed = 0 (Part 2 of 2). 1993 Grand Prix, 1993–94 Cutlass Supreme, Lumina & Regal

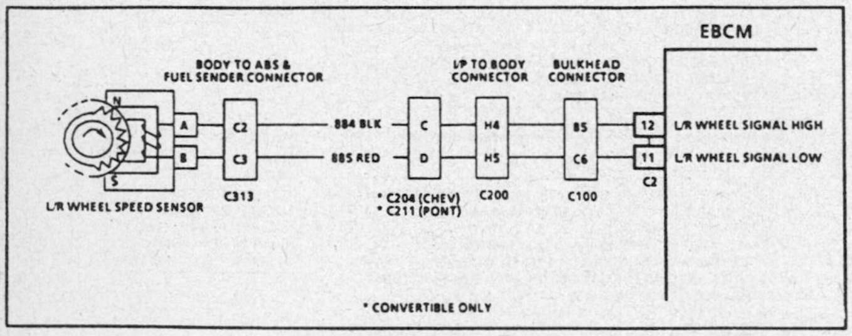
EBCM
BODY TO ABS & FUEL SENDER CONNECTOR
I/P TO BODY CONNECTOR
BULKHEAD CONNECTOR
884 BLK
885 RED
12 L/R WHEEL SIGNAL HIGH
11 L/R WHEEL SIGNAL LOW
C313
* C204 (CHEV)
* C211 (PONT)
C200
C100
L/R WHEEL SPEED SENSOR
* CONVERTIBLE ONLY

GC402930075700AX

Cavalier & Sunbird

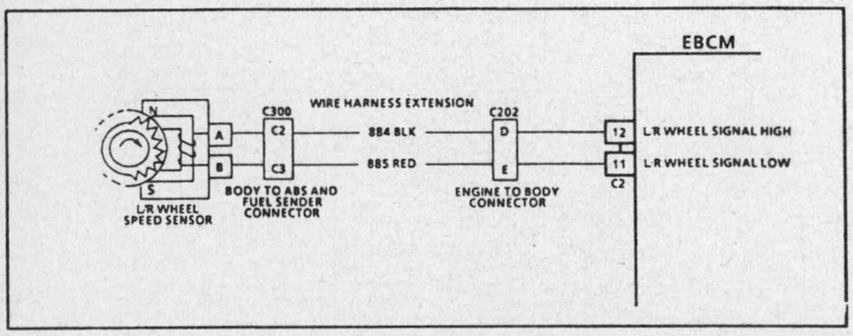
EBCM
WIRE HARNESS EXTENSION
C300
C202
884 BLK
885 RED
12 L/R WHEEL SIGNAL HIGH
11 L/R WHEEL SIGNAL LOW
BODY TO ABS AND FUEL SENDER CONNECTOR
ENGINE TO BODY CONNECTOR
L/R WHEEL SPEED SENSOR

GC402930075700BX

Achieva, Beretta, Corsica, Grand Am & Skylark

DTC A023

LEFT REAR WHEEL SPEED = 0

Circuit Description:

As a toothed ring passes by the wheel speed sensor, changes in the electromagnetic field cause the wheel speed sensor to produce a sinusoidal (AC) voltage signal whose frequency is proportional to wheel speed. The magnitude of this signal is directly related to wheel speed and the proximity of the wheel speed sensor to the toothed ring, often referred to as the air gap.

Failure Condition:

DTC A023 can be set when the vehicle is not in an ABS stop. If the left rear wheel speed = 0 and the vehicle's reference speed is greater than 8 km/h (5 mph), a malfunction exists.

Action Taken:

A malfunction DTC is stored, ABS is disabled and the ABS indicator lamp is turned "ON."

Test Description: Number(s) below refer to circled number(s) on the diagnostic chart.

1. This determines if DTC A034 is present.
2. This test verifies whether the malfunction is currently present.
3. This step is designed to identify a wheel speed sensor or circuitry that is damaged and visibly apparent.
4. This test checks to see that the wheel speed sensor is within proper resistance values.
5. This step verifies that the wheel speed sensor can generate an appropriate output signal.
6. This test checks for proper output voltage from the EBCM.

Diagnostic Aids:

An "Intermittent" malfunction may be caused by a poor connection, rubbed through wire insulation, or a wire that is broken inside the insulation.

The frequency of the malfunction can be checked by using the enhanced diagnostic function of the Tech 1.

If the customers comments reflect that the ABS indicator lamp is "ON" only during moist environmental changes (rain, snow, vehicle wash), all wheel speed senor circuitry should be thoroughly inspected for signs of water intrusion. If DTC is not current, clear DTCs and simulate the effects of water intrusion. Use the following procedure. Spray down the suspected area with a 5% salt water solution (two teaspoons of salt to 12 oz. of water). Start vehicle, allow vehicle to run for 10 seconds. If DTC returns immediately, replace suspected harness.

Any circuitry, that is suspected as causing the intermittent complaint, should be thoroughly checked for backed out terminals, improper mating, broken locks, improperly formed or damaged terminals, poor terminal to wiring connections or physical damage to the wiring harness.

When measuring wheel speed sensor resistance, insure vehicle is at room temperature. Wheel speed sensor resistance will vary with temperature.

When replacing a wheel speed sensor, inspect the sensor terminals and harness connector for corrosion and/or water intrusion. If evidence of corrosion or water intrusion exists, replace wheel speed sensor harness.

GC402930075700CX

Fig. 118 Code A023: Left Rear Wheel Speed = 0 (Part 1 of 2). 1993–94 Cavalier, Sunbird, Beretta, Corsica & Achieva, Grand Am & Skylark Less VES

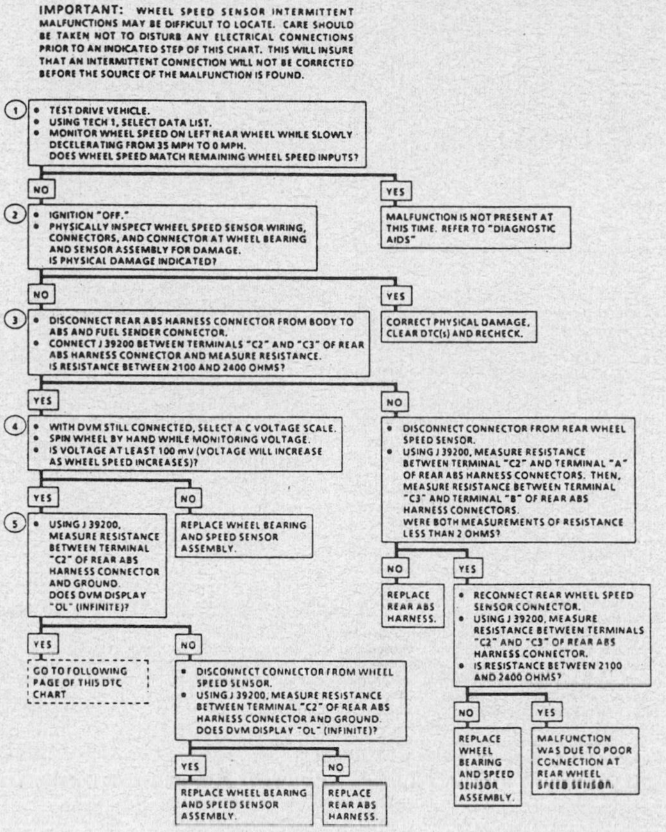
IMPORTANT: WHEEL SPEED SENSOR INTERMITTENT MALFUNCTIONS MAY BE DIFFICULT TO LOCATE. CARE SHOULD BE TAKEN NOT TO DISTURB ANY ELECTRICAL CONNECTIONS PRIOR TO AN INDICATED STEP OF THIS CHART. THIS WILL INSURE THAT AN INTERMITTENT CONNECTION WILL NOT BE CORRECTED BEFORE THE SOURCE OF THE MALFUNCTION IS FOUND.
1
• TEST DRIVE VEHICLE. • USING TECH 1, SELECT DATA LIST. • MONITOR WHEEL SPEED ON LEFT REAR WHEEL WHILE SLOWLY DECELERATING FROM 35 MPH TO 0 MPH. DOES WHEEL SPEED MATCH REMAINING WHEEL SPEED INPUTS?
NO
YES
MALFUNCTION IS NOT PRESENT AT THIS TIME. REFER TO "DIAGNOSTIC AIDS"
2
• IGNITION "OFF." • PHYSICALLY INSPECT WHEEL SPEED SENSOR WIRING, CONNECTORS, AND CONNECTOR AT WHEEL BEARING AND SENSOR ASSEMBLY FOR DAMAGE. IS PHYSICAL DAMAGE INDICATED?
NO
YES
CORRECT PHYSICAL DAMAGE. CLEAR DTC(s) AND RECHECK.
3
• DISCONNECT REAR ABS HARNESS CONNECTOR FROM BODY TO ABS AND FUEL SENDER CONNECTOR. • CONNECT J 39200 BETWEEN TERMINALS "C2" AND "C3" OF REAR ABS HARNESS CONNECTOR AND MEASURE RESISTANCE. IS RESISTANCE BETWEEN 2100 AND 2400 OHMS?
YES
NO
4
• WITH DVM STILL CONNECTED, SELECT A C VOLTAGE SCALE. • SPIN WHEEL BY HAND WHILE MONITORING VOLTAGE. • IS VOLTAGE AT LEAST 100 mV (VOLTAGE WILL INCREASE AS WHEEL SPEED INCREASES)?
• DISCONNECT CONNECTOR FROM REAR WHEEL SPEED SENSOR. • USING J 39200, MEASURE RESISTANCE BETWEEN TERMINAL "C2" AND TERMINAL "A" OF REAR ABS HARNESS CONNECTORS. THEN, MEASURE RESISTANCE BETWEEN TERMINAL "C3" AND TERMINAL "B" OF REAR ABS HARNESS CONNECTORS. WERE BOTH MEASUREMENTS OF RESISTANCE LESS THAN 2 OHMS?
YES
NO
5
• USING J 39200, MEASURE RESISTANCE BETWEEN TERMINAL "C2" OF REAR ABS HARNESS CONNECTOR AND GROUND. DOES DVM DISPLAY "OL" (INFINITE)?
REPLACE WHEEL BEARING AND SPEED SENSOR ASSEMBLY.
NO
YES
REPLACE REAR ABS HARNESS.
• RECONNECT REAR WHEEL SPEED SENSOR CONNECTOR. • USING J 39200, MEASURE RESISTANCE BETWEEN TERMINALS "C2" AND "C3" OF REAR ABS HARNESS CONNECTOR. • IS RESISTANCE BETWEEN 2100 AND 2400 OHMS?
YES
NO
GO TO FOLLOWING PAGE OF THIS DTC CHART
• DISCONNECT CONNECTOR FROM WHEEL SPEED SENSOR. • USING J 39200, MEASURE RESISTANCE BETWEEN TERMINAL "C2" OF REAR ABS HARNESS CONNECTOR AND GROUND. DOES DVM DISPLAY "OL" (INFINITE)?
NO
YES
REPLACE WHEEL BEARING AND SPEED SENSOR ASSEMBLY.
MALFUNCTION WAS DUE TO POOR CONNECTION AT REAR WHEEL SPEED SENSOR.
YES
NO
REPLACE WHEEL BEARING AND SPEED SENSOR ASSEMBLY.
REPLACE REAR ABS HARNESS.

GC402930075700DX

LEFT REAR WHEEL SPEED = 0

Circuit Description:

As a toothed ring passes by the wheel speed sensor, changes in the electromagnetic field cause the wheel speed sensor to produce a sinusoidal (AC) voltage signal whose frequency is proportional to wheel speed. The magnitude of this signal is directly related to wheel speed and the proximity of the wheel speed sensor to the toothed ring, often referred to as the air gap.

Failure Condition:

DTC A023 can be set when the vehicle is not in an ABS stop. If the left rear wheel speed is less than 1/2 of the vehicle's reference speed and the vehicle's reference speed is greater than 8 km/h (5 mph), a malfunction exists.

Action Taken:

A malfunction DTC is stored. ABS is disabled and the ABS indicator lamp is turned "ON."

Test Description: Number(s) below refer to circled number(s) on the diagnostic chart.

6. This step checks for proper voltages at body to ABS and fuel sender harness connector.
7. This test ensures that the wheel speed sensor circuitry is not internally shorted.
8. This checks for an open in the wheel signal high circuit.
9. This checks for an open in the wheel signal low circuit.
10. This test checks for a short to ground in both high and low wheel signal circuits.
11. This step ensures that DTC A023 was not set due to a poor connection between the world connector and EBCM.

Diagnostic Aids:

An "Intermittent" malfunction may be caused by a poor connection, rubbed through wire insulation, or a wire that is broken inside the insulation.

The frequency of the malfunction can be checked by using the enhanced diagnostic function of the Tech 1

If the customer's comments reflect that the ABS amber indicator lamp is "ON" only during moist environmental changes, (rain, snow, vehicle wash) all wheel speed sensor circuitry should be thoroughly inspected for signs of water intrusion. Use the following procedure. Spray down the suspected area with 5% salt water solution (two teaspoons of salt to 12 oz. of water). Start vehicle, allow vehicle to run for 10 seconds. If DTC returns immediately, replace suspected harness.

Any circuitry, that is suspected as causing the intermittent complaint, should be thoroughly checked for backed out terminals, improper mating, broken locks, improperly formed or damaged terminals, poor terminal to wiring connections or physical damage to the wiring harness.

When measuring wheel speed sensor resistance, ensure vehicle is at room temperature. Wheel speed sensor resistance will vary with temperature.

When replacing a wheel speed sensor, inspect the sensor terminals and harness connector for corrosion and/or water intrusion. If evidence of corrosion or water intrusion exists, replace wheel speed sensor harness.

GC402930075700EX

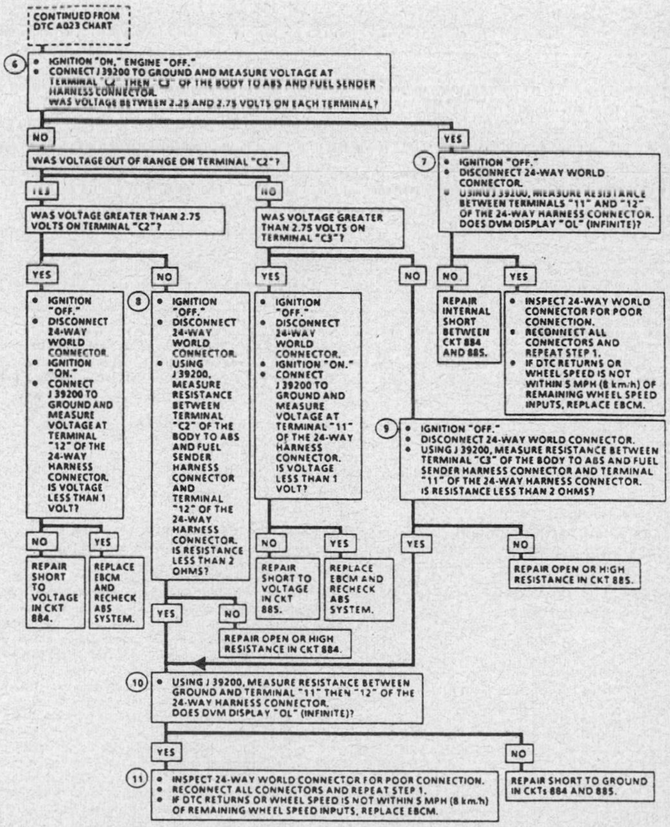
CONTINUED FROM DTC A023 CHART
6
• IGNITION "ON," ENGINE "OFF." • CONNECT J 39200 TO GROUND AND MEASURE VOLTAGE AT TERMINAL "C2" THEN "C3" OF THE BODY TO ABS AND FUEL SENDER HARNESS CONNECTOR. WAS VOLTAGE BETWEEN 2.25 AND 2.75 VOLTS ON EACH TERMINAL?
NO
YES
WAS VOLTAGE OUT OF RANGE ON TERMINAL "C2"?
7
• IGNITION "OFF." • DISCONNECT 24-WAY WORLD CONNECTOR. • USING J 39200, MEASURE RESISTANCE BETWEEN TERMINALS "11" AND "12" OF THE 24-WAY WORLD CONNECTOR. DOES DVM DISPLAY "OL" (INFINITE)?
YES
NO
WAS VOLTAGE GREATER THAN 2.75 VOLTS ON TERMINAL "C2"?
WAS VOLTAGE GREATER THAN 2.75 VOLTS ON TERMINAL "C3"?
NO
YES
REPAIR INTERNAL SHORT BETWEEN CKT 884 AND 885.
• INSPECT 24-WAY WORLD CONNECTOR FOR POOR CONNECTION. • RECONNECT ALL CONNECTORS AND REPEAT STEP 1. • IF DTC RETURNS OR WHEEL SPEED IS NOT WITHIN 5 MPH (8 km/h) OF REMAINING WHEEL SPEED INPUTS, REPLACE EBCM.
YES
NO
YES
NO
• IGNITION "OFF." • DISCONNECT 24-WAY WORLD CONNECTOR. • IGNITION "ON." • CONNECT J 39200 TO GROUND AND MEASURE VOLTAGE AT TERMINAL "12" OF THE 24-WAY HARNESS CONNECTOR. IS VOLTAGE LESS THAN 1 VOLT?
8
• IGNITION "OFF." • DISCONNECT 24-WAY WORLD CONNECTOR. • USING J 39200, MEASURE RESISTANCE BETWEEN TERMINAL "C2" OF THE BODY TO ABS AND FUEL SENDER HARNESS CONNECTOR AND TERMINAL "12" OF THE 24-WAY HARNESS CONNECTOR. IS RESISTANCE LESS THAN 2 OHMS?
• IGNITION "OFF." • DISCONNECT 24-WAY WORLD CONNECTOR. • IGNITION "ON." • CONNECT J 39200 TO GROUND AND MEASURE VOLTAGE AT TERMINAL "11" OF THE 24-WAY HARNESS CONNECTOR. IS VOLTAGE LESS THAN 1 VOLT?
9
• IGNITION "OFF." • DISCONNECT 24-WAY WORLD CONNECTOR. • USING J 39200, MEASURE RESISTANCE BETWEEN TERMINAL "C3" OF THE BODY TO ABS AND FUEL SENDER HARNESS CONNECTOR AND TERMINAL "11" OF THE 24-WAY HARNESS CONNECTOR. IS RESISTANCE LESS THAN 2 OHMS?
NO
YES
NO
YES
YES
NO
REPAIR SHORT TO VOLTAGE IN CKT 884.
REPLACE EBCM AND RECHECK ABS SYSTEM.
REPAIR SHORT TO VOLTAGE IN CKT 885.
REPLACE EBCM AND RECHECK ABS SYSTEM.
REPAIR OPEN OR HIGH RESISTANCE IN CKT 885.
YES
NO
REPAIR OPEN OR HIGH RESISTANCE IN CKT 884.
10
• USING J 39200, MEASURE RESISTANCE BETWEEN GROUND AND TERMINAL "11" THEN "12" OF THE 24-WAY HARNESS CONNECTOR. DOES DVM DISPLAY "OL" (INFINITE)?
YES
NO
11
• INSPECT 24-WAY WORLD CONNECTOR FOR POOR CONNECTION. • RECONNECT ALL CONNECTORS AND REPEAT STEP 1. • IF DTC RETURNS OR WHEEL SPEED IS NOT WITHIN 5 MPH (8 km/h) OF REMAINING WHEEL SPEED INPUTS, REPLACE EBCM.
REPAIR SHORT TO GROUND IN CKTs 884 AND 885.

GC402930075700FX

Fig. 118 Code A023: Left Rear Wheel Speed = 0 (Part 2 of 2). 1993–94 Cavalier, Sunbird, Beretta, Corsica & Achieva, Grand Am & Skylark Less VES

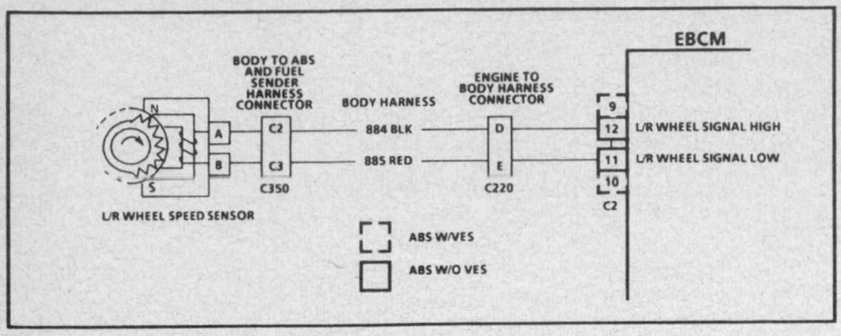
EBCM
BODY TO ABS AND FUEL SENDER HARNESS CONNECTOR
BODY HARNESS
ENGINE TO BODY HARNESS CONNECTOR
884 BLK
885 RED
L/R WHEEL SIGNAL HIGH
L/R WHEEL SIGNAL LOW
C350
C220
C2
L/R WHEEL SPEED SENSOR
ABS W/VES
ABS W/O VES

Circuit Description:
As a toothed ring passes by the wheel speed sensor, changes in the electromagnetic field cause the wheel speed sensor to produce a sinusoidal (AC) voltage signal whose frequency is proportional to wheel speed. The magnitude of this signal is directly related to wheel speed and the proximity of the wheel speed sensor to the toothed ring, often referred to as the air gap.

DTC Will Set When: DTC 23 can be set when the vehicle is not in an ABS stop. A malfunction exists if the left rear wheel speed = 0 and the vehicle speed is greater than 8 km/h (5 mph).

Action Taken: A malfunction DTC is stored, ABS/VES is disabled and the ABS warning lamp is turned "ON."

DTC Chart Test Description: Number(s) below refer to circled number(s) on the diagnostic chart.
1. Identifies if wheel speed sensor circuitry is damaged and visibly apparent.
2. Tests wheel speed sensor and rear ABS harness for proper resistance values.
3. Checks for a short between circuits in the rear ABS harness.
4. Tests wheel speed sensor for proper resistance values.

Diagnostic Aids: An "Intermittent" malfunction is most likely caused by a poor connection, rubbed through wire insulation, or a wire that is broken inside the insulation.

The frequency of the malfunction can be checked by using the enhanced diagnostic function of the Tech 1.

If the customer's comments reflect that the ABS amber warning lamp is "ON" only during moist environmental changes, (rain, snow, vehicle wash) all wheel speed sensor circuitry should be thoroughly inspected for signs of water intrusion. Use the following procedure. Spray down the suspected area with 5% salt water solution (two teaspoons of salt to 12 oz. of water). Drive vehicle above 24 km/h (15 mph) for at least 30 seconds. If DTC returns immediately, replace suspected harness.

Any circuitry, that is suspected as causing the intermittent complaint, should be thoroughly checked for backed out terminals, improper mating, broken locks, improperly formed or damaged terminals, poor terminal to wiring connections or physical damage to the wiring harness.

Resistance of the wheel speed sensor will increase with an increase in sensor temperature.

When replacing a wheel speed sensor, inspect the sensor terminals and harness connector for corrosion and/or water intrusion. If evidence of corrosion or water intrusion exists, replace wheel speed sensor harness. Refer to "On-Vehicle Service" in this section.

If wheel speed sensor harness shows evidence of water intrusion, inspect wheel speed sensor for water intrusion. If water intrusion is evident, replace wheel speed sensor.

GC402940104601AX

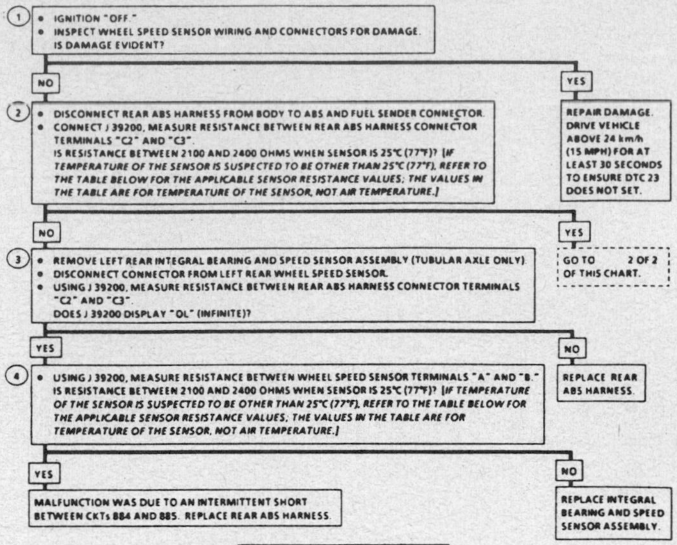
1 • IGNITION "OFF."
• INSPECT WHEEL SPEED SENSOR WIRING AND CONNECTORS FOR DAMAGE. IS DAMAGE EVIDENT?
NO
YES
2 • DISCONNECT REAR ABS HARNESS FROM BODY TO ABS AND FUEL SENDER CONNECTOR.
• CONNECT J 39200, MEASURE RESISTANCE BETWEEN REAR ABS HARNESS CONNECTOR TERMINALS "C2" AND "C3".
IS RESISTANCE BETWEEN 2100 AND 2400 OHMS WHEN SENSOR IS 25°C (77°F)? [IF TEMPERATURE OF THE SENSOR IS SUSPECTED TO BE OTHER THAN 25°C (77°F), REFER TO THE TABLE BELOW FOR THE APPLICABLE SENSOR RESISTANCE VALUES; THE VALUES IN THE TABLE ARE FOR TEMPERATURE OF THE SENSOR, NOT AIR TEMPERATURE.]
REPAIR DAMAGE. DRIVE VEHICLE ABOVE 24 km/h (15 MPH) FOR AT LEAST 30 SECONDS TO ENSURE DTC 23 DOES NOT SET.
NO
YES
3 • REMOVE LEFT REAR INTEGRAL BEARING AND SPEED SENSOR ASSEMBLY (TUBULAR AXLE ONLY).
• DISCONNECT CONNECTOR FROM LEFT REAR WHEEL SPEED SENSOR.
• USING J 39200, MEASURE RESISTANCE BETWEEN REAR ABS HARNESS CONNECTOR TERMINALS "C2" AND "C3".
DOES J 39200 DISPLAY "OL" (INFINITE)?
GO TO 2 OF 2 OF THIS CHART.
YES
NO
4 • USING J 39200, MEASURE RESISTANCE BETWEEN WHEEL SPEED SENSOR TERMINALS "A" AND "B." IS RESISTANCE BETWEEN 2100 AND 2400 OHMS WHEN SENSOR IS 25°C (77°F)? [IF TEMPERATURE OF THE SENSOR IS SUSPECTED TO BE OTHER THAN 25°C (77°F), REFER TO THE TABLE BELOW FOR THE APPLICABLE SENSOR RESISTANCE VALUES; THE VALUES IN THE TABLE ARE FOR TEMPERATURE OF THE SENSOR, NOT AIR TEMPERATURE.]
REPLACE REAR ABS HARNESS.
YES
NO
MALFUNCTION WAS DUE TO AN INTERMITTENT SHORT BETWEEN CKTs 884 AND 885. REPLACE REAR ABS HARNESS.
REPLACE INTEGRAL BEARING AND SPEED SENSOR ASSEMBLY.

REAR WHEEL SPEED SENSOR

TEMPERATURE OF SENSOR VS. SENSOR RESISTANCE (APPROXIMATE)

TEMP. (°C)	TEMP. (°F)	RESISTANCE (OHMS)
-34 TO 4	-30 TO 40	1623 TO 2210
5 TO 43	41 TO 110	1939 TO 2570
44 TO 93	111 TO 200	2254 TO 3029

GC402940104601BX

Fig. 119 Code A023: Left Rear Wheel Speed = 0 (Part 1 of 2). 1994 Achieva, Grand Am & Skylark w/VES

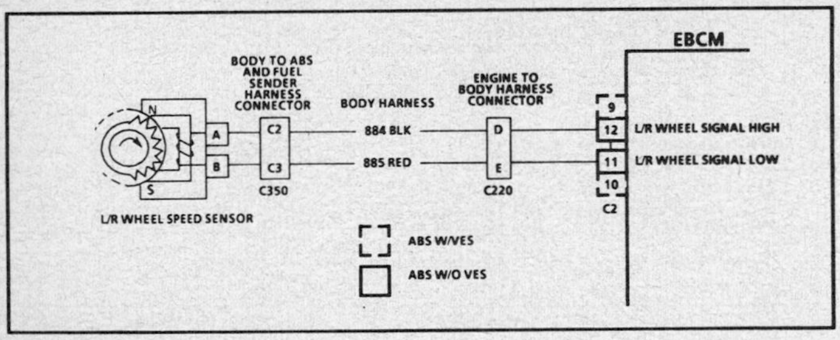
EBCM
BODY TO ABS AND FUEL SENDER HARNESS CONNECTOR
BODY HARNESS
ENGINE TO BODY HARNESS CONNECTOR
884 BLK
885 RED
L/R WHEEL SIGNAL HIGH
L/R WHEEL SIGNAL LOW
C350
C220
C2
L/R WHEEL SPEED SENSOR
ABS W/VES
ABS W/O VES

Circuit Description:
As a toothed ring passes by the wheel speed sensor, changes in the electromagnetic field cause the wheel speed sensor to produce a sinusoidal (AC) voltage signal whose frequency is proportional to wheel speed. The magnitude of this signal is directly related to wheel speed and the proximity of the wheel speed sensor to the toothed ring, often referred to as the air gap.

DTC Will Set When: DTC 23 can be set when the vehicle is not in an ABS stop. A malfunction exists if the left rear wheel speed = 0 and the vehicle speed is greater than 8 km/h (5 mph).

Action Taken: A malfunction DTC is stored, ABS/VES is disabled and the ABS warning lamp is turned "ON."

DTC Chart Test Description: Number(s) below refer to circled number(s) on the diagnostic chart.
5. Ensures wheel speed sensor and toothed ring generate the proper voltage.
6. Ensures wheel speed sensor high and low circuits are not shorted together.
7. Ensures malfunction is not due to physical damage of the wheel speed sensor circuitry.

Diagnostic Aids: An "Intermittent" malfunction is most likely caused by a poor connection, rubbed through wire insulation, or a wire that is broken inside the insulation.

The frequency of the malfunction can be checked by using the enhanced diagnostic function of the Tech 1.

If the customer's comments reflect that the ABS amber warning lamp is "ON" only during moist environmental changes, (rain, snow, vehicle wash) all wheel speed sensor circuitry should be thoroughly inspected for signs of water intrusion. Use the following procedure. Spray down the suspected area with 5% salt water solution (two teaspoons of salt to 12 oz. of water). Drive vehicle above 24 km/h (15 mph) for at least 30 seconds. If DTC returns immediately, replace suspected harness.

Any circuitry, that is suspected as causing the intermittent complaint, should be thoroughly checked for backed out terminals, improper mating, broken locks, improperly formed or damaged terminals, poor terminal to wiring connections or physical damage to the wiring harness.

Resistance of the wheel speed sensor will increase with an increase in sensor temperature.

When replacing a wheel speed sensor, inspect the sensor terminals and harness connector for corrosion and/or water intrusion. If evidence of corrosion or water intrusion exists, replace wheel speed sensor harness. Refer to "On-Vehicle Service" in this section.

If wheel speed sensor harness shows evidence of water intrusion, inspect wheel speed sensor for water intrusion. If water intrusion is evident, replace wheel speed sensor.

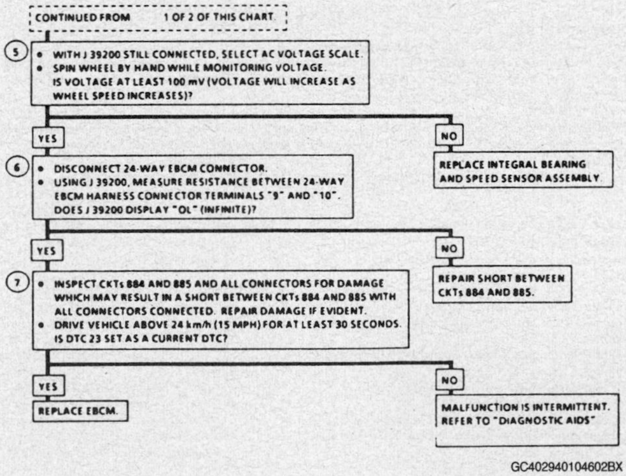
CONTINUED FROM 1 OF 2 OF THIS CHART.
5 • WITH J 39200 STILL CONNECTED, SELECT AC VOLTAGE SCALE.
• SPIN WHEEL BY HAND WHILE MONITORING VOLTAGE.
IS VOLTAGE AT LEAST 100 mV (VOLTAGE WILL INCREASE AS WHEEL SPEED INCREASES)?
YES
NO
REPLACE INTEGRAL BEARING AND SPEED SENSOR ASSEMBLY.
6 • DISCONNECT 24-WAY EBCM CONNECTOR.
• USING J 39200, MEASURE RESISTANCE BETWEEN 24-WAY EBCM HARNESS CONNECTOR TERMINALS "9" AND "10".
DOES J 39200 DISPLAY "OL" (INFINITE)?
YES
NO
REPAIR SHORT BETWEEN CKTs 884 AND 885.
7 • INSPECT CKTs 884 AND 885 AND ALL CONNECTORS FOR DAMAGE WHICH MAY RESULT IN A SHORT BETWEEN CKTs 884 AND 885 WITH ALL CONNECTORS CONNECTED. REPAIR DAMAGE IF EVIDENT.
• DRIVE VEHICLE ABOVE 24 km/h (15 MPH) FOR AT LEAST 30 SECONDS. IS DTC 23 SET AS A CURRENT DTC?
YES
NO
REPLACE EBCM.
MALFUNCTION IS INTERMITTENT. REFER TO "DIAGNOSTIC AIDS"

GC402940104602BX

Fig. 119 Code A023: Left Rear Wheel Speed = 0 (Part 2 of 2). 1994 Achieva, Grand Am & Skylark w/VES

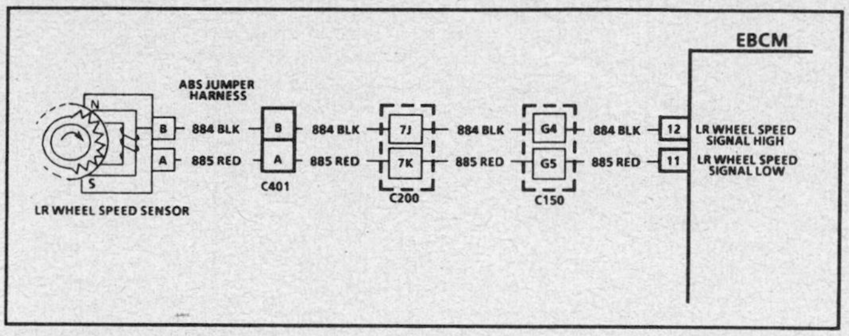

EBCM
ABS JUMPER HARNESS
884 BLK
885 RED
C401
C200
C150
LR WHEEL SPEED SIGNAL HIGH
LR WHEEL SPEED SIGNAL LOW
LR WHEEL SPEED SENSOR

Circuit Description:
As a toothed ring passes by the wheel speed sensor, changes in the electromagnetic field cause the wheel speed sensor to produce a sinusoidal (AC) voltage signal whose frequency is proportional to wheel speed. The magnitude of this signal is directly related to wheel speed and the proximity of the wheel speed sensor to the toothed ring, often referred to as the air gap.

DTC Will Set When: DTC 23 can be set when the vehicle is not in an ABS stop. If the left rear wheel speed = 0 and the vehicle's reference speed is greater than 8 km/h (5 mph), a malfunction exists.

Action Taken: A malfunction DTC is stored, ABS is disabled and the ABS warning lamp is turned "ON."

DTC Chart Test Description: Number(s) below refer to circled number(s) on the diagnostic chart.
1. Determines if DTC 34 is present.
2. Designed to identify a wheel speed sensor or circuitry that is damaged and visibly apparent.
3. Checks to see that the wheel speed sensor is within proper resistance values.
4. Verifies that the wheel speed sensor can generate an appropriate output signal.

Diagnostic Aids: An "Intermittent" malfunction may be caused by a poor connection, rubbed through wire insulation, or a wire that is broken inside the insulation.

The frequency of the malfunction can be checked by using the enhanced diagnostic function of the Tech 1.

If the customer's comments reflect that the ABS warning lamp is "ON" only during moist environmental changes (rain, snow, vehicle wash), all wheel speed sensor circuitry should be thoroughly inspected for signs of water intrusion. If DTC is not current, clear DTCs and simulate the effects of water intrusion. Use the following procedure. Spray down the suspected area with a 5% salt water solution (two teaspoons of salt to 12 oz. of water). Test drive vehicle over various road surfaces (bumps, turns, etc.) above 24 km/h (15 mph) for at least 30 seconds. If DTC returns replace suspected harness.

Any circuitry, that is suspected as causing the intermittent complaint, should be thoroughly checked for backed out terminals, improper mating, broken locks, improperly formed or damaged terminals, poor terminal to wiring connections or physical damage to the wiring harness.

Resistance of the wheel speed sensor will increase with an increase in sensor temperature.

When replacing a wheel speed sensor, inspect the sensor terminals and harness connector for corrosion and/or water intrusion. If evidence of corrosion or water intrusion exists, replace wheel speed sensor jumper harness. Likewise, if replacing a wheel speed sensor jumper harness, inspect sensor terminals. If evidence of corrosion or water intrusion exists, replace wheel speed sensor.

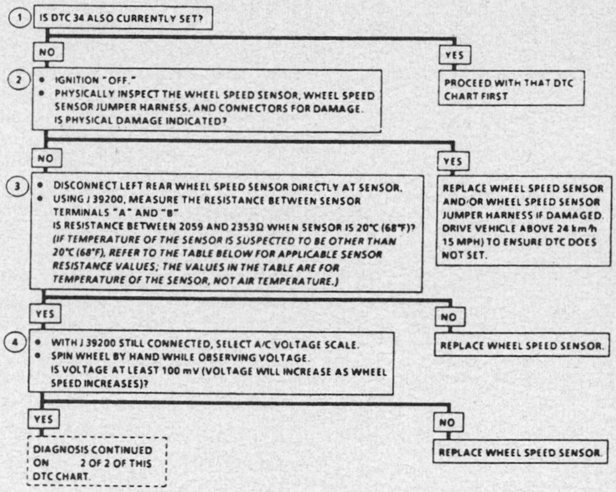

1 IS DTC 34 ALSO CURRENTLY SET?
NO
YES
PROCEED WITH THAT DTC CHART FIRST
2 • IGNITION "OFF."
• PHYSICALLY INSPECT THE WHEEL SPEED SENSOR, WHEEL SPEED SENSOR JUMPER HARNESS, AND CONNECTORS FOR DAMAGE.
IS PHYSICAL DAMAGE INDICATED?
NO
YES
REPLACE WHEEL SPEED SENSOR AND/OR WHEEL SPEED SENSOR JUMPER HARNESS IF DAMAGED. DRIVE VEHICLE ABOVE 24 km/h 15 MPH) TO ENSURE DTC DOES NOT SET.
3 • DISCONNECT LEFT REAR WHEEL SPEED SENSOR DIRECTLY AT SENSOR.
• USING J 39200, MEASURE THE RESISTANCE BETWEEN SENSOR TERMINALS "A" AND "B"
IS RESISTANCE BETWEEN 2059 AND 2353Ω WHEN SENSOR IS 20°C (68°F)? (IF TEMPERATURE OF THE SENSOR IS SUSPECTED TO BE OTHER THAN 20°C (68°F), REFER TO THE TABLE BELOW FOR APPLICABLE SENSOR RESISTANCE VALUES; THE VALUES IN THE TABLE ARE FOR TEMPERATURE OF THE SENSOR, NOT AIR TEMPERATURE.)
YES
NO
REPLACE WHEEL SPEED SENSOR.
4 • WITH J 39200 STILL CONNECTED, SELECT A/C VOLTAGE SCALE.
• SPIN WHEEL BY HAND WHILE OBSERVING VOLTAGE.
IS VOLTAGE AT LEAST 100 mV (VOLTAGE WILL INCREASE AS WHEEL SPEED INCREASES)?
YES
NO
REPLACE WHEEL SPEED SENSOR.
DIAGNOSIS CONTINUED ON 2 OF 2 OF THIS DTC CHART.

REAR WHEEL SPEED SENSOR

TEMPERATURE OF SENSOR VS. SENSOR RESISTANCE (APPROXIMATE)

TEMP. (°C)	TEMP. (°F)	RESISTANCE (OHMS)
-34 TO 4	-30 TO 40	1622 TO 2205
5 TO 43	41 TO 110	1930 TO 2566
44 TO 93	111 TO 200	2245 TO 3028

GC40930075001AA

Fig. 120 Code A023: Left Rear Wheel Speed = 0 (Part 1 of 2). 1993 Grand Prix, 1993–94 Cutlass Supreme, Lumina & Regal

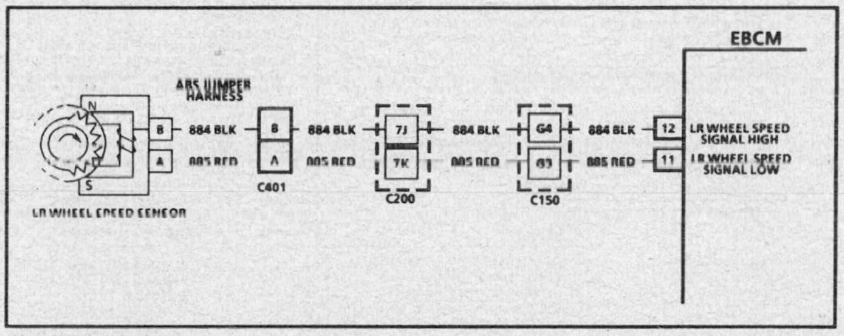

EBCM
ABS JUMPER HARNESS
884 BLK
885 RED
C401
C200
C150
LR WHEEL SPEED SIGNAL HIGH
LR WHEEL SPEED SIGNAL LOW

Circuit Description:
As a toothed ring passes by the wheel speed sensor, changes in the electromagnetic field cause the wheel speed sensor to produce a sinusoidal (AC) voltage signal whose frequency is proportional to wheel speed. The magnitude of this signal is directly related to wheel speed and the proximity of the wheel speed sensor to the toothed ring, often referred to as the air gap.

DTC Will Set When: DTC 23 can be set when the vehicle is not in an ABS stop. If the left rear wheel speed = 0 and the vehicle's reference speed is greater than 8 km/h (5 mph), a malfunction exists.

Action Taken: A malfunction DTC is stored, ABS is disabled and the ABS warning lamp is turned "ON."

DTC Chart Test Description: Number(s) below refer to circled number(s) on the diagnostic chart.
5. Checks for proper output voltage from the EBCM.
6. Checks for an open in the wheel speed sensor low circuit.
7. Ensures malfunction was not due to physical damage of the circuitry.
8. Ensures that wheel speed sensor circuitry is not shorted.
9. Ensures malfunction was not due to physical damage of the circuitry.
10. Checks for an incorrect or malfunctioning hub and bearing assembly.
11. Checks for an open in the wheel speed sensor high circuit.

Diagnostic Aids: An "Intermittent" malfunction may be caused by a poor connection, rubbed through wire insulation, or a wire that is broken inside the insulation.

The frequency of the malfunction can be checked by using the enhanced diagnostic function of the Tech 1.

If the customer's comments reflect that the ABS warning lamp is "ON" only during moist environmental changes (rain, snow, vehicle wash), all wheel speed sensor circuitry should be thoroughly inspected for signs of water intrusion. If DTC is not current, clear DTCs and simulate the effects of water intrusion. Use the following procedure. Spray down the suspected area with a 5% salt water solution (two teaspoons of salt to 12 oz. of water). Test drive vehicle over various road surfaces (bumps, turns, etc.) above 24 km/h (15 mph) for at least 30 seconds. If DTC returns replace suspected harness.

Any circuitry, that is suspected as causing the intermittent complaint, should be thoroughly checked for backed out terminals, improper mating, broken locks, improperly formed or damaged terminals, poor terminal to wiring connections or physical damage to the wiring harness.

Resistance of the wheel speed sensor will increase with an increase in sensor temperature.

When replacing a wheel speed sensor, inspect the sensor terminals and harness connector for corrosion and/or water intrusion. If evidence of corrosion or water intrusion exists, replace wheel speed sensor jumper harness. Likewise, if replacing a wheel speed sensor jumper harness, inspect sensor terminals. If evidence of corrosion or water intrusion exists, replace wheel speed sensor.

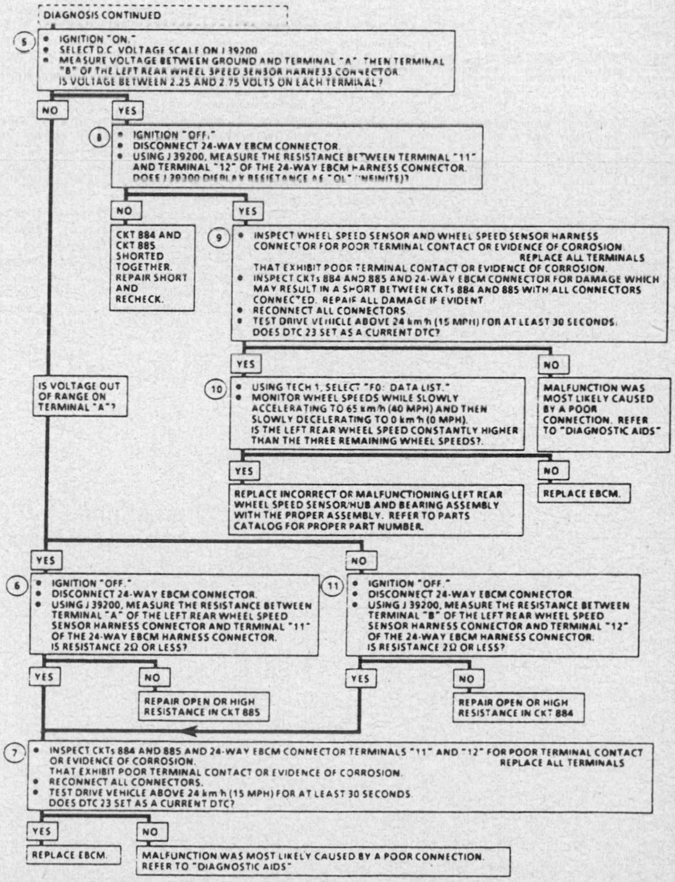

DIAGNOSIS CONTINUED
5 • IGNITION "ON."
• SELECT D.C. VOLTAGE SCALE ON J 39200
• MEASURE VOLTAGE BETWEEN GROUND AND TERMINAL "A" THEN TERMINAL "B" OF THE LEFT REAR WHEEL SPEED SENSOR HARNESS CONNECTOR.
IS VOLTAGE BETWEEN 2.25 AND 2.75 VOLTS ON EACH TERMINAL?
NO
YES
8 • IGNITION "OFF."
• DISCONNECT 24-WAY EBCM CONNECTOR.
• USING J 39200, MEASURE THE RESISTANCE BETWEEN TERMINAL "11" AND TERMINAL "12" OF THE 24-WAY EBCM HARNESS CONNECTOR.
NO
YES
CKT 884 AND CKT 885 SHORTED TOGETHER. REPAIR SHORT AND RECHECK.
9 • INSPECT WHEEL SPEED SENSOR AND WHEEL SPEED SENSOR HARNESS CONNECTOR FOR POOR TERMINAL CONTACT OR EVIDENCE OF CORROSION. REPLACE ALL TERMINALS THAT EXHIBIT POOR TERMINAL CONTACT OR EVIDENCE OF CORROSION.
• INSPECT CKTs 884 AND 885 AND 24-WAY EBCM CONNECTOR FOR DAMAGE WHICH MAY RESULT IN A SHORT BETWEEN CKTs 884 AND 885 WITH ALL CONNECTORS CONNECTED. REPAIR ALL DAMAGE IF EVIDENT.
• RECONNECT ALL CONNECTORS.
• TEST DRIVE VEHICLE ABOVE 24 km/h (15 MPH) FOR AT LEAST 30 SECONDS.
DOES DTC 23 SET AS A CURRENT DTC?
YES
NO
MALFUNCTION WAS MOST LIKELY CAUSED BY A POOR CONNECTION. REFER TO "DIAGNOSTIC AIDS"
IS VOLTAGE OUT OF RANGE ON TERMINAL "A"?
10 • USING TECH 1, SELECT "F0: DATA LIST."
• MONITOR WHEEL SPEEDS WHILE SLOWLY ACCELERATING TO 65 km/h (40 MPH) AND THEN SLOWLY DECELERATING TO 0 km/h (0 MPH).
IS THE LEFT REAR WHEEL SPEED CONSTANTLY HIGHER THAN THE THREE REMAINING WHEEL SPEEDS?.
YES
NO
REPLACE INCORRECT OR MALFUNCTIONING LEFT REAR WHEEL SPEED SENSOR/HUB AND BEARING ASSEMBLY WITH THE PROPER ASSEMBLY. REFER TO PARTS CATALOG FOR PROPER PART NUMBER.
REPLACE EBCM.
YES
NO
6 • IGNITION "OFF."
• DISCONNECT 24-WAY EBCM CONNECTOR.
• USING J 39200, MEASURE THE RESISTANCE BETWEEN TERMINAL "A" OF THE LEFT REAR WHEEL SPEED SENSOR HARNESS CONNECTOR AND TERMINAL "11" OF THE 24-WAY EBCM HARNESS CONNECTOR.
IS RESISTANCE 2Ω OR LESS?
11 • IGNITION "OFF."
• DISCONNECT 24-WAY EBCM CONNECTOR.
• USING J 39200, MEASURE THE RESISTANCE BETWEEN TERMINAL "B" OF THE LEFT REAR WHEEL SPEED SENSOR HARNESS CONNECTOR AND TERMINAL "12" OF THE 24-WAY EBCM HARNESS CONNECTOR.
IS RESISTANCE 2Ω OR LESS?
YES
NO
REPAIR OPEN OR HIGH RESISTANCE IN CKT 885
YES
NO
REPAIR OPEN OR HIGH RESISTANCE IN CKT 884
7 • INSPECT CKTs 884 AND 885 AND 24-WAY EBCM CONNECTOR TERMINALS "11" AND "12" FOR POOR TERMINAL CONTACT OR EVIDENCE OF CORROSION. REPLACE ALL TERMINALS THAT EXHIBIT POOR TERMINAL CONTACT OR EVIDENCE OF CORROSION.
• RECONNECT ALL CONNECTORS.
• TEST DRIVE VEHICLE ABOVE 24 km/h (15 MPH) FOR AT LEAST 30 SECONDS.
DOES DTC 23 SET AS A CURRENT DTC?
YES
NO
REPLACE EBCM.
MALFUNCTION WAS MOST LIKELY CAUSED BY A POOR CONNECTION. REFER TO "DIAGNOSTIC AIDS"

GC402930075802AA

Fig. 120 Code A023: Left Rear Wheel Speed = 0 (Part 2 of 2). 1993 Grand Prix, 1993–94 Cutlass Supreme, Lumina & Regal

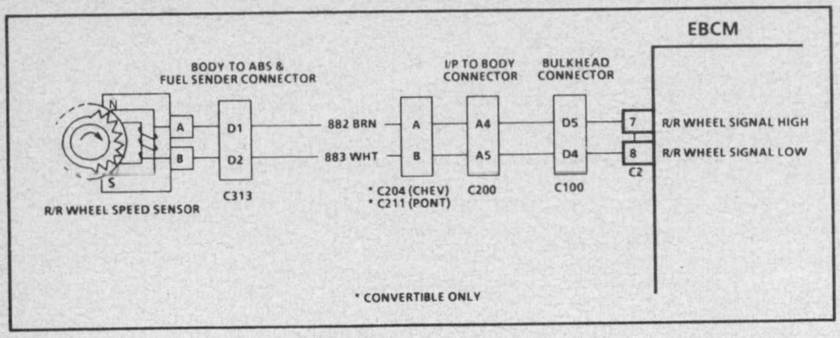
EBCM
BODY TO ABS & FUEL SENDER CONNECTOR
I/P TO BODY CONNECTOR
BULKHEAD CONNECTOR
N
S
A
B
D1
D2
882 BRN
883 WHT
A
B
A4
A5
D5
D4
7
8
R/R WHEEL SIGNAL HIGH
R/R WHEEL SIGNAL LOW
C2
C313
* C204 (CHEV)
* C211 (PONT)
C200
C100
R/R WHEEL SPEED SENSOR
* CONVERTIBLE ONLY
GC402930075900AX

Cavalier & Sunbird

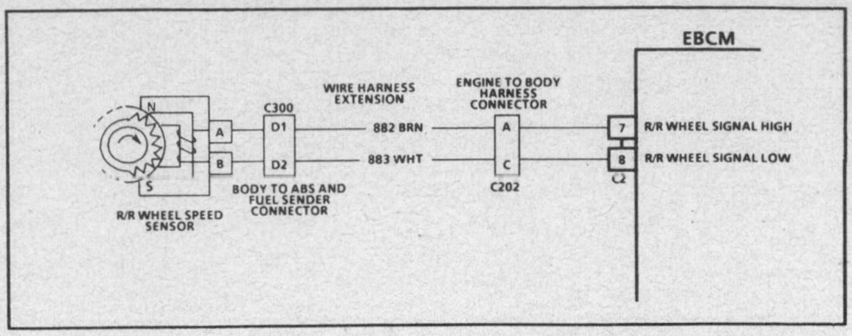
EBCM
WIRE HARNESS EXTENSION
ENGINE TO BODY HARNESS CONNECTOR
C300
N
S
A
B
D1
D2
882 BRN
883 WHT
A
C
7
8
R/R WHEEL SIGNAL HIGH
R/R WHEEL SIGNAL LOW
C2
C202
BODY TO ABS AND FUEL SENDER CONNECTOR
R/R WHEEL SPEED SENSOR
GC402930075900BX

Achieva, Beretta, Corsica, Grand Am & Skylark

DTC A024

(Page 1 of 2)

RIGHT REAR WHEEL SPEED = 0

Circuit Description:

As a toothed ring passes by the wheel speed sensor, changes in the electromagnetic field cause the wheel speed sensor to produce a sinusoidal (AC) voltage signal whose frequency is proportional to wheel speed. The magnitude of this signal is directly related to wheel speed and the proximity of the wheel speed sensor to the toothed ring, often referred to as the air gap.

Failure Condition:

DTC A024 can be set when the vehicle is not in an ABS stop. If the right rear wheel speed is less than 1/2 of the vehicle's reference speed and the vehicle's reference speed is greater than 8 km/h (5 mph), a malfunction exists.

Action Taken:

A malfunction DTC is stored, ABS is disabled and the ABS indicator lamp is turned "ON."

Test Description: Number(s) below refer to circled number(s) on the diagnostic chart.

1. This test verifies whether the malfunction is currently present.
2. This step will identify a wheel speed sensor or circuitry that is damaged and visibly apparent.
3. This test checks wheel speed sensor for proper resistance values.
4. This test ensures the wheel speed sensor and sensor ring generate the proper voltage.
5. This step ensures the wheel speed sensor is not shorted to ground.

Diagnostic Aids:

An "Intermittent" malfunction may be caused by a poor connection, rubbed through wire insulation, or a wire that is broken inside the insulation.

The frequency of the malfunction can be checked by using the enhanced diagnostic function of the Tech 1.

If the customer's comments reflect that the ABS amber indicator lamp is "ON" only during moist environmental changes, (rain, snow, vehicle wash) all wheel speed sensor circuitry should be thoroughly inspected for water intrusion. Use the following procedure. Spray down the suspected area with 5% salt water solution (two teaspoons of salt to 12 oz. of water). Start vehicle, allow vehicle to run for 10 seconds. If DTC returns immediately, replace suspected harness.

Any circuitry, that is suspected as causing the intermittent complaint, should be thoroughly checked for backed out terminals, improper mating, broken locks, improperly formed or damaged terminals, poor terminal to wiring connections or physical damage to the wiring harness.

When measuring wheel speed sensor resistance, ensure vehicle is at room temperature. Wheel speed sensor resistance will vary with temperature.

When replacing a wheel speed sensor, inspect the sensor terminals and harness connector for corrosion and/or water intrusion. If evidence of corrosion or water intrusion exists, replace wheel speed sensor harness.

GC402930075900CX

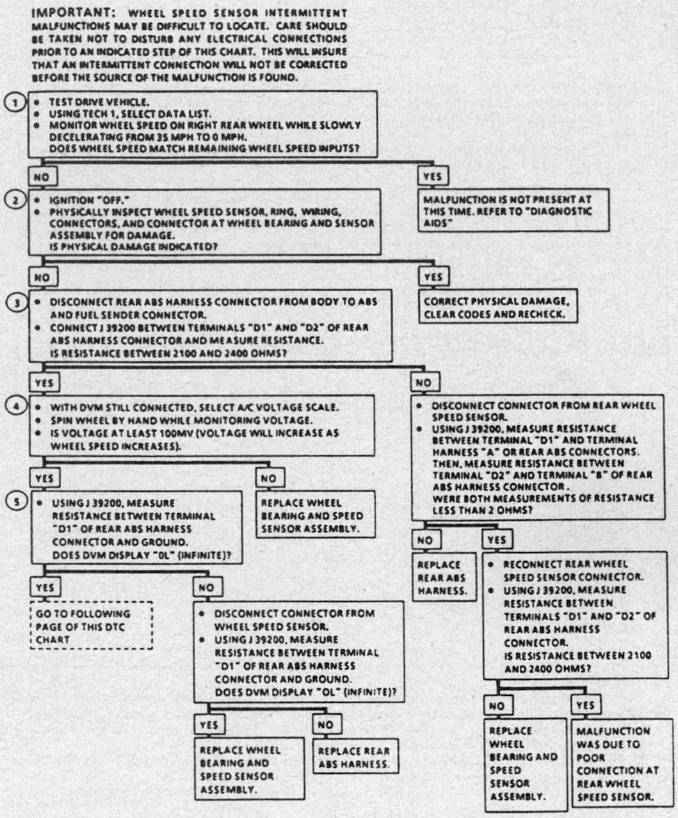
IMPORTANT: WHEEL SPEED SENSOR INTERMITTENT MALFUNCTIONS MAY BE DIFFICULT TO LOCATE. CARE SHOULD BE TAKEN NOT TO DISTURB ANY ELECTRICAL CONNECTIONS PRIOR TO AN INDICATED STEP OF THIS CHART. THIS WILL INSURE THAT AN INTERMITTENT CONNECTION WILL NOT BE CORRECTED BEFORE THE SOURCE OF THE MALFUNCTION IS FOUND.
1
• TEST DRIVE VEHICLE. • USING TECH 1, SELECT DATA LIST. • MONITOR WHEEL SPEED ON RIGHT REAR WHEEL WHILE SLOWLY DECELERATING FROM 35 MPH TO 0 MPH. DOES WHEEL SPEED MATCH REMAINING WHEEL SPEED INPUTS?
NO
YES
MALFUNCTION IS NOT PRESENT AT THIS TIME. REFER TO "DIAGNOSTIC AIDS"
2
• IGNITION "OFF." • PHYSICALLY INSPECT WHEEL SPEED SENSOR, RING, WIRING, CONNECTORS, AND CONNECTOR AT WHEEL BEARING AND SENSOR ASSEMBLY FOR DAMAGE. IS PHYSICAL DAMAGE INDICATED?
NO
YES
CORRECT PHYSICAL DAMAGE, CLEAR CODES AND RECHECK.
3
• DISCONNECT REAR ABS HARNESS CONNECTOR FROM BODY TO ABS AND FUEL SENDER CONNECTOR. • CONNECT J 39200 BETWEEN TERMINALS "D1" AND "D2" OF REAR ABS HARNESS CONNECTOR AND MEASURE RESISTANCE. IS RESISTANCE BETWEEN 2100 AND 2400 OHMS?
YES
NO
4
• WITH DVM STILL CONNECTED, SELECT A/C VOLTAGE SCALE. • SPIN WHEEL BY HAND WHILE MONITORING VOLTAGE. • IS VOLTAGE AT LEAST 100MV (VOLTAGE WILL INCREASE AS WHEEL SPEED INCREASES).
• DISCONNECT CONNECTOR FROM REAR WHEEL SPEED SENSOR. • USING J 39200, MEASURE RESISTANCE BETWEEN TERMINAL "D1" AND TERMINAL HARNESS "A" OR REAR ABS CONNECTORS. THEN, MEASURE RESISTANCE BETWEEN TERMINAL "D2" AND TERMINAL "B" OF REAR ABS HARNESS CONNECTOR. WERE BOTH MEASUREMENTS OF RESISTANCE LESS THAN 2 OHMS?
YES
NO
REPLACE WHEEL BEARING AND SPEED SENSOR ASSEMBLY.
5
• USING J 39200, MEASURE RESISTANCE BETWEEN TERMINAL "D1" OF REAR ABS HARNESS CONNECTOR AND GROUND. DOES DVM DISPLAY "OL" (INFINITE)?
NO
YES
REPLACE REAR ABS HARNESS.
• RECONNECT REAR WHEEL SPEED SENSOR CONNECTOR. • USING J 39200, MEASURE RESISTANCE BETWEEN TERMINALS "D1" AND "D2" OF REAR ABS HARNESS CONNECTOR. IS RESISTANCE BETWEEN 2100 AND 2400 OHMS?
YES
NO
GO TO FOLLOWING PAGE OF THIS DTC CHART
• DISCONNECT CONNECTOR FROM WHEEL SPEED SENSOR. • USING J 39200, MEASURE RESISTANCE BETWEEN TERMINAL "D1" OF REAR ABS HARNESS CONNECTOR AND GROUND. DOES DVM DISPLAY "OL" (INFINITE)?
YES
NO
REPLACE WHEEL BEARING AND SPEED SENSOR ASSEMBLY.
REPLACE REAR ABS HARNESS.
NO
YES
REPLACE WHEEL BEARING AND SPEED SENSOR ASSEMBLY.
MALFUNCTION WAS DUE TO POOR CONNECTION AT REAR WHEEL SPEED SENSOR.
GC402930075900DX

Fig. 121 Code A024: Right Rear Wheel Speed = 0 (Part 1 of 2). 1993–94 Cavalier, Sunbird, Beretta, Corsica & Achieva, Grand Am & Skylark Less VES

DTC A024

RIGHT REAR WHEEL SPEED = 0

Circuit Description:
As a toothed ring passes by the wheel speed sensor, changes in the electromagnetic field cause the wheel speed sensor to produce a sinusoidal (AC) voltage signal whose frequency is proportional to wheel speed. The magnitude of this signal is directly related to wheel speed and the proximity of the wheel speed sensor to the toothed ring, often referred to as the air gap.

Failure Condition:
DTC A024 can be set when the vehicle is not in an ABS stop. If the right rear wheel speed is less than 1/2 of the vehicle's reference speed and the vehicle's reference speed is greater than 8 km/h (5 mph), a malfunction exists.

Action Taken:
A malfunction DTC is stored, ABS is disabled and the ABS indicator lamp is turned "ON."

Test Description: Number(s) below refer to circled number(s) on the diagnostic chart.

6. This step checks for proper voltages at body to ABS and fuel sender harness connector.
7. This test ensures that the wheel speed sensor circuitry is not internally shorted.
8. This checks for an open in the wheel signal high circuit.
9. This checks for an open in the wheel signal low circuit.
10. This test checks for a short to ground in both high and low wheel signal circuits.
11. This step ensures that DTC A024 was not set due to a poor connection between the world connector and EBCM.

Diagnostic Aids:

An "Intermittent" malfunction may be caused by a poor connection, rubbed through wire insulation, or a wire that is broken inside the insulation.

The frequency of the malfunction can be checked by using the enhanced diagnostic function of the Tech 1.

If the customer's comments reflect that the ABS amber indicator lamp is "ON" only during moist environmental changes, (rain, snow, vehicle wash) all wheel speed sensor circuitry should be thoroughly inspected for water intrusion. Use the following procedure. Spray down the suspected area with 5% salt water solution (two teaspoons of salt to 12 oz. of water). Start vehicle, allow vehicle to run for 10 seconds. If DTC returns immediately, replace suspected harness.

Any circuitry, that is suspected as causing the intermittent complaint, should be thoroughly checked for backed out terminals, improper mating, broken locks, improperly formed or damaged terminals, poor terminal to wiring connections or physical damage to the wiring harness.

When measuring wheel speed sensor resistance, ensure vehicle is at room temperature. Wheel speed sensor resistance will vary with temperature.

When replacing a wheel speed sensor, inspect the sensor terminals and harness connector for corrosion and/or water intrusion. If evidence of corrosion or water intrusion exists, replace wheel speed sensor harness.

GC402930075900EX

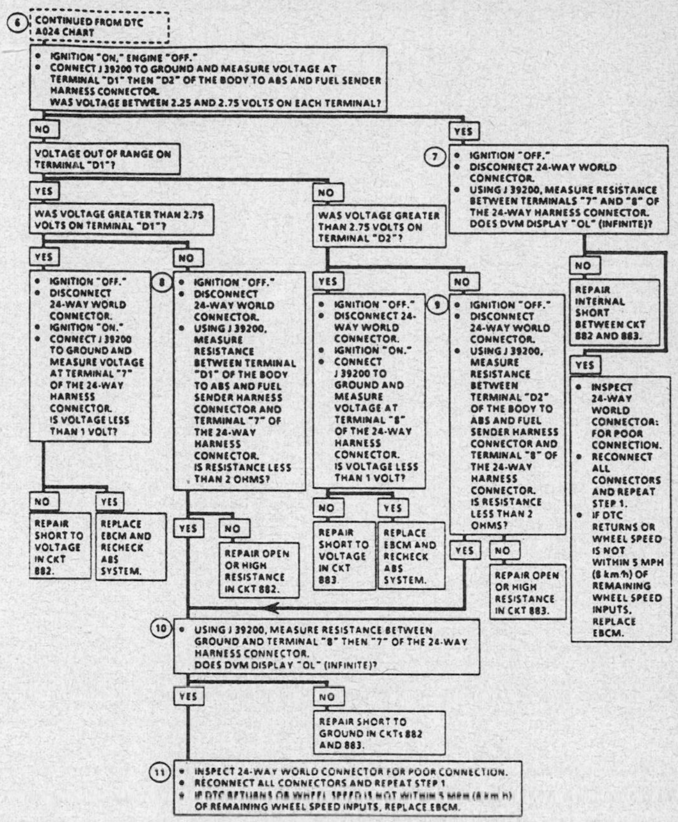
6
CONTINUED FROM DTC A024 CHART
• IGNITION "ON," ENGINE "OFF."
• CONNECT J 39200 TO GROUND AND MEASURE VOLTAGE AT TERMINAL "D1" THEN "D2" OF THE BODY TO ABS AND FUEL SENDER HARNESS CONNECTOR.
WAS VOLTAGE BETWEEN 2.25 AND 2.75 VOLTS ON EACH TERMINAL?
NO
VOLTAGE OUT OF RANGE ON TERMINAL "D1"?
YES
WAS VOLTAGE GREATER THAN 2.75 VOLTS ON TERMINAL "D1"?
YES
• IGNITION "OFF."
• DISCONNECT 24-WAY WORLD CONNECTOR.
• IGNITION "ON."
• CONNECT J 39200 TO GROUND AND MEASURE VOLTAGE AT TERMINAL "7" OF THE 24-WAY HARNESS CONNECTOR.
IS VOLTAGE LESS THAN 1 VOLT?
NO
REPAIR SHORT TO VOLTAGE IN CKT 882.
YES
REPLACE EBCM AND RECHECK ABS SYSTEM.
NO
8
• IGNITION "OFF."
• DISCONNECT 24-WAY WORLD CONNECTOR.
• USING J 39200, MEASURE RESISTANCE BETWEEN TERMINAL "D1" OF THE BODY TO ABS AND FUEL SENDER HARNESS CONNECTOR AND TERMINAL "7" OF THE 24-WAY HARNESS CONNECTOR.
IS RESISTANCE LESS THAN 2 OHMS?
YES
NO
REPAIR OPEN OR HIGH RESISTANCE IN CKT 882.
NO
WAS VOLTAGE GREATER THAN 2.75 VOLTS ON TERMINAL "D2"?
YES
• IGNITION "OFF."
• DISCONNECT 24-WAY WORLD CONNECTOR.
• IGNITION "ON."
• CONNECT J 39200 TO GROUND AND MEASURE VOLTAGE AT TERMINAL "8" OF THE 24-WAY HARNESS CONNECTOR.
IS VOLTAGE LESS THAN 1 VOLT?
NO
REPAIR SHORT TO VOLTAGE IN CKT 883.
YES
REPLACE EBCM AND RECHECK ABS SYSTEM.
NO
9
• IGNITION "OFF."
• DISCONNECT 24-WAY WORLD CONNECTOR.
• USING J 39200, MEASURE RESISTANCE BETWEEN TERMINAL "D2" OF THE BODY TO ABS AND FUEL SENDER HARNESS CONNECTOR AND TERMINAL "8" OF THE 24-WAY HARNESS CONNECTOR.
IS RESISTANCE LESS THAN 2 OHMS?
YES
NO
REPAIR OPEN OR HIGH RESISTANCE IN CKT 883.
YES
7
• IGNITION "OFF."
• DISCONNECT 24-WAY WORLD CONNECTOR.
• USING J 39200, MEASURE RESISTANCE BETWEEN TERMINALS "7" AND "8" OF THE 24-WAY HARNESS CONNECTOR.
DOES DVM DISPLAY "OL" (INFINITE)?
NO
REPAIR INTERNAL SHORT BETWEEN CKT 882 AND 883.
YES
• INSPECT 24-WAY WORLD CONNECTOR: FOR POOR CONNECTION.
• RECONNECT ALL CONNECTORS AND REPEAT STEP 1.
• IF DTC RETURNS OR WHEEL SPEED IS NOT WITHIN 5 MPH (8 km/h) OF REMAINING WHEEL SPEED INPUTS, REPLACE EBCM.
10
• USING J 39200, MEASURE RESISTANCE BETWEEN GROUND AND TERMINAL "8" THEN "7" OF THE 24-WAY HARNESS CONNECTOR.
DOES DVM DISPLAY "OL" (INFINITE)?
YES
NO
REPAIR SHORT TO GROUND IN CKTs 882 AND 883.
11
• INSPECT 24-WAY WORLD CONNECTOR FOR POOR CONNECTION.
• RECONNECT ALL CONNECTORS AND REPEAT STEP 1
• IF DTC RETURNS OR WHEEL SPEED IS NOT WITHIN 5 MPH (8 km/h) OF REMAINING WHEEL SPEED INPUTS, REPLACE EBCM.

Fig. 121 Code A024: Right Rear Wheel Speed = 0 (Part 2 of 2). 1993–94 Cavalier, Sunbird, Beretta, Corsica & Achieva, Grand Am & Skylark Less VES

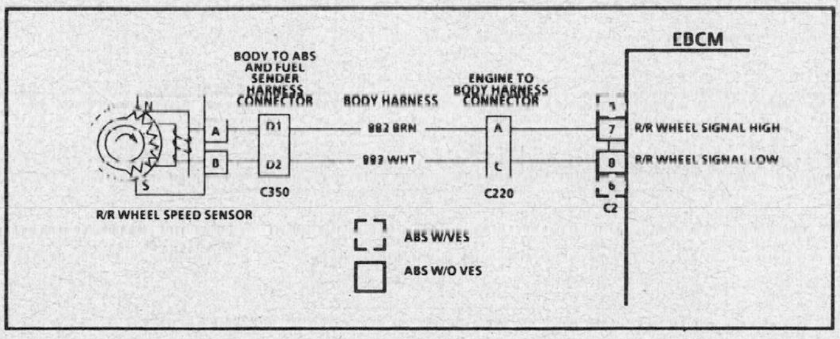
EBCM
BODY TO ABS AND FUEL SENDER HARNESS CONNECTOR
BODY HARNESS
ENGINE TO BODY HARNESS CONNECTOR
A
B
S
D1
D2
C350
882 BRN
883 WHT
A
C
C220
7
8
6
C2
R/R WHEEL SIGNAL HIGH
R/R WHEEL SIGNAL LOW
R/R WHEEL SPEED SENSOR
ABS W/VES
ABS W/O VES

Circuit Description:
As a toothed ring passes by the wheel speed sensor, changes in the electromagnetic field cause the wheel speed sensor to produce a sinusoidal (AC) voltage signal whose frequency is proportional to wheel speed. The magnitude of this signal is directly related to wheel speed and the proximity of the wheel speed sensor to the toothed ring, often referred to as the air gap.

DTC Will Set When: DTC 24 can be set when the vehicle is not in an ABS stop. A malfunction exists if the right rear wheel speed = 0 and the vehicle speed is greater than 8 km/h (5 mph).

Action Taken: A malfunction DTC is stored, ABS/VES is disabled and the ABS warning lamp is turned "ON."

DTC Chart Test Description: Number(s) below refer to circled number(s) on the diagnostic chart.

1. Identifies if wheel speed sensor circuitry is damaged and visibly apparent.
2. Tests wheel speed sensor and rear ABS harness for proper resistance values.
3. Checks for a short between circuits in the rear ABS harness.
4. Tests wheel speed sensor for proper resistance values.

Diagnostic Aids: An "Intermittent" malfunction is most likely caused by a poor connection, rubbed through wire insulation, or a wire that is broken inside the insulation.

The frequency of the malfunction can be checked by using the enhanced diagnostic function of the Tech 1.

If the customer's comments reflect that the ABS amber warning lamp is "ON" only during moist environmental changes, (rain, snow, vehicle wash) all wheel speed sensor circuitry should be thoroughly inspected for water intrusion. Use the following procedure. Spray down the suspected area with 5% salt water solution (two teaspoons of salt to 12 oz. of water). Drive vehicle above 24 km/h (15 mph) for at least 30 seconds. If DTC returns immediately, replace suspected harness.

Any circuitry, that is suspected as causing the intermittent complaint, should be thoroughly checked for backed out terminals, improper mating, broken locks, improperly formed or damaged terminals, poor terminal to wiring connections or physical damage to the wiring harness.

Resistance of the wheel speed sensor will increase with an increase in sensor temperature.

When replacing a wheel speed sensor, inspect the sensor terminals and harness connector for corrosion and/or water intrusion. If evidence of corrosion or water intrusion exists, replace wheel speed sensor harness. Refer to "On-Vehicle Service" in this section.

If wheel speed sensor harness shows evidence of water intrusion, inspect wheel speed sensor for water intrusion. If water intrusion is evident, replace wheel speed sensor.

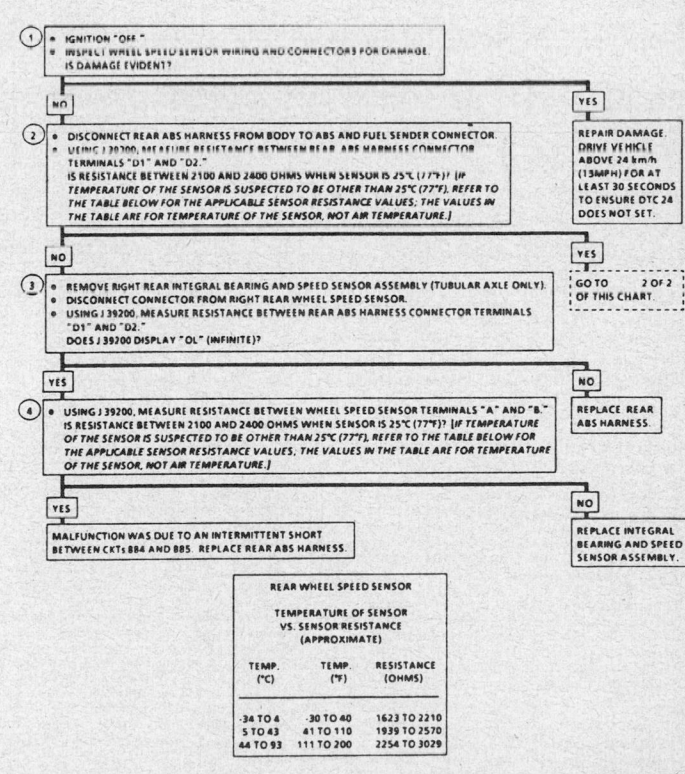

GC402940104701AX

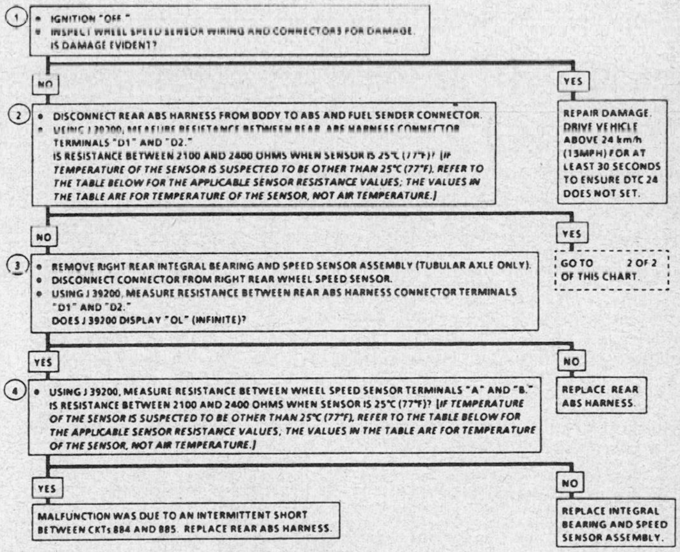
1
• IGNITION "OFF."
• INSPECT WHEEL SPEED SENSOR WIRING AND CONNECTORS FOR DAMAGE.
IS DAMAGE EVIDENT?
NO
2
• DISCONNECT REAR ABS HARNESS FROM BODY TO ABS AND FUEL SENDER CONNECTOR.
• USING J 39200, MEASURE RESISTANCE BETWEEN REAR ABS HARNESS CONNECTOR TERMINALS "D1" AND "D2."
IS RESISTANCE BETWEEN 2100 AND 2400 OHMS WHEN SENSOR IS 25°C (77°F)? [IF TEMPERATURE OF THE SENSOR IS SUSPECTED TO BE OTHER THAN 25°C (77°F), REFER TO THE TABLE BELOW FOR THE APPLICABLE SENSOR RESISTANCE VALUES; THE VALUES IN THE TABLE ARE FOR TEMPERATURE OF THE SENSOR, NOT AIR TEMPERATURE.]
YES
REPAIR DAMAGE. DRIVE VEHICLE ABOVE 24 km/h (15MPH) FOR AT LEAST 30 SECONDS TO ENSURE DTC 24 DOES NOT SET.
NO
3
• REMOVE RIGHT REAR INTEGRAL BEARING AND SPEED SENSOR ASSEMBLY (TUBULAR AXLE ONLY).
• DISCONNECT CONNECTOR FROM RIGHT REAR WHEEL SPEED SENSOR.
• USING J 39200, MEASURE RESISTANCE BETWEEN REAR ABS HARNESS CONNECTOR TERMINALS "D1" AND "D2."
DOES J 39200 DISPLAY "OL" (INFINITE)?
YES
GO TO 2 OF 2 OF THIS CHART.
YES
4
• USING J 39200, MEASURE RESISTANCE BETWEEN WHEEL SPEED SENSOR TERMINALS "A" AND "B."
IS RESISTANCE BETWEEN 2100 AND 2400 OHMS WHEN SENSOR IS 25°C (77°F)? [IF TEMPERATURE OF THE SENSOR IS SUSPECTED TO BE OTHER THAN 25°C (77°F), REFER TO THE TABLE BELOW FOR THE APPLICABLE SENSOR RESISTANCE VALUES; THE VALUES IN THE TABLE ARE FOR TEMPERATURE OF THE SENSOR, NOT AIR TEMPERATURE.]
NO
REPLACE REAR ABS HARNESS.
YES
MALFUNCTION WAS DUE TO AN INTERMITTENT SHORT BETWEEN CKTs 884 AND 885. REPLACE REAR ABS HARNESS.
NO
REPLACE INTEGRAL BEARING AND SPEED SENSOR ASSEMBLY.

REAR WHEEL SPEED SENSOR

TEMPERATURE OF SENSOR VS. SENSOR RESISTANCE (APPROXIMATE)

TEMP. (°C)	TEMP. (°F)	RESISTANCE (OHMS)
-34 TO 4	-30 TO 40	1623 TO 2210
5 TO 43	41 TO 110	1939 TO 2570
44 TO 93	111 TO 200	2254 TO 3029

GC402940104701BX

Fig. 122 Code A024: Right Rear Wheel Speed = 0 (Part 1 of 2). 1994 Achieva, Grand Am & Skylark w/VES

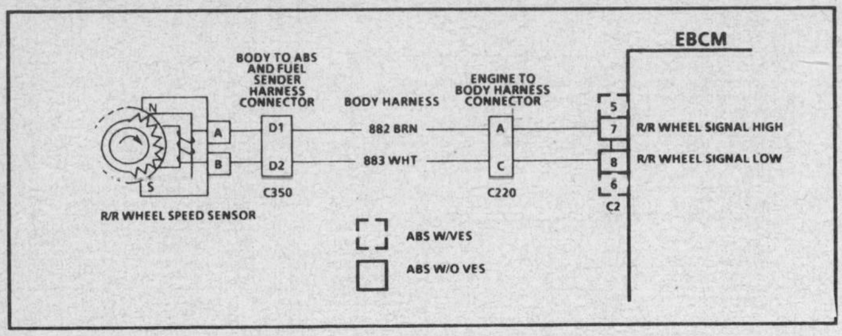
EBCM
BODY TO ABS AND FUEL SENDER HARNESS CONNECTOR
BODY HARNESS
ENGINE TO BODY HARNESS CONNECTOR
N
S
A
B
D1
D2
882 BRN
883 WHT
A
C
5
7
8
6
R/R WHEEL SIGNAL HIGH
R/R WHEEL SIGNAL LOW
C350
C220
C2
R/R WHEEL SPEED SENSOR
ABS W/VES
ABS W/O VES

Circuit Description:
As a toothed ring passes by the wheel speed sensor, changes in the electromagnetic field cause the wheel speed sensor to produce a sinusoidal (AC) voltage signal whose frequency is proportional to wheel speed. The magnitude of this signal is directly related to wheel speed and the proximity of the wheel speed sensor to the toothed ring, often referred to as the air gap.

DTC Will Set When: DTC 24 can be set when the vehicle is not in an ABS stop. A malfunction exists if the right rear wheel speed = 0 and the vehicle speed is greater than 8 km/h (5 mph).

Action Taken: A malfunction DTC is stored, ABS/VES is disabled and the ABS warning lamp is turned "ON."

DTC Chart Test Description: Number(s) below refer to circled number(s) on the diagnostic chart.
5. Ensures wheel speed sensor and toothed ring generate the proper voltage.
6. Ensures wheel speed sensor high and low circuits are not shorted together.
7. Ensures malfunction is not due to physical damage of the wheel speed sensor circuitry.

Diagnostic Aids: An "Intermittent" malfunction is most likely caused by a poor connection, rubbed through wire insulation, or a wire that is broken inside the insulation.

The frequency of the malfunction can be checked by using the enhanced diagnostic function of the Tech 1

If the customer's comments reflect that the ABS amber warning lamp is "ON" only during moist environmental changes, (rain, snow, vehicle wash) all wheel speed sensor circuitry should be thoroughly inspected for water intrusion. Use the following procedure. Spray down the suspected area with 5% salt water solution (two teaspoons of salt to 12 oz. of water). Drive vehicle above 24 km/h (15 mph) for at least 30 seconds. If DTC returns immediately, replace suspected harness.

Any circuitry, that is suspected as causing the intermittent complaint, should be thoroughly checked for backed out terminals, improper mating, broken locks, improperly formed or damaged terminals, poor terminal to wiring connections or physical damage to the wiring harness.

Resistance of the wheel speed sensor will increase with an increase in sensor temperature.

When replacing a wheel speed sensor, inspect the sensor terminals and harness connector for corrosion and/or water intrusion. If evidence of corrosion or water intrusion exists, replace wheel speed sensor harness. Refer to "On-Vehicle Service" in this section.

If wheel speed sensor harness shows evidence of water intrusion, inspect wheel speed sensor for water intrusion. If water intrusion is evident, replace wheel speed sensor.

GC402940104702AX

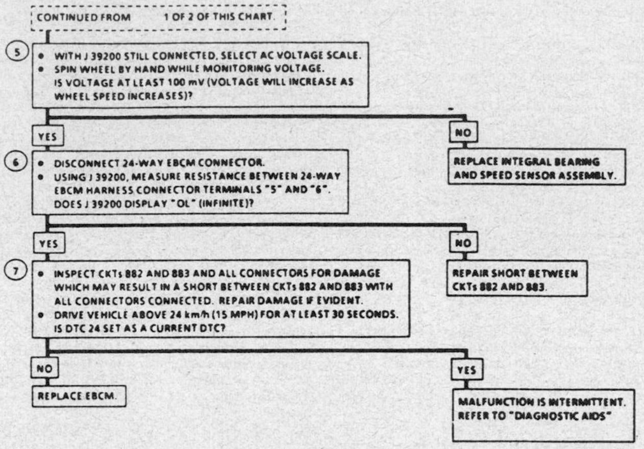
CONTINUED FROM 1 OF 2 OF THIS CHART.
5
• WITH J 39200 STILL CONNECTED, SELECT AC VOLTAGE SCALE.
• SPIN WHEEL BY HAND WHILE MONITORING VOLTAGE.
IS VOLTAGE AT LEAST 100 mV (VOLTAGE WILL INCREASE AS WHEEL SPEED INCREASES)?
YES
NO
REPLACE INTEGRAL BEARING AND SPEED SENSOR ASSEMBLY.
6
• DISCONNECT 24-WAY EBCM CONNECTOR.
• USING J 39200, MEASURE RESISTANCE BETWEEN 24-WAY EBCM HARNESS CONNECTOR TERMINALS "5" AND "6".
DOES J 39200 DISPLAY "OL" (INFINITE)?
YES
NO
REPAIR SHORT BETWEEN CKTs 882 AND 883.
7
• INSPECT CKTs 882 AND 883 AND ALL CONNECTORS FOR DAMAGE WHICH MAY RESULT IN A SHORT BETWEEN CKTs 882 AND 883 WITH ALL CONNECTORS CONNECTED. REPAIR DAMAGE IF EVIDENT.
• DRIVE VEHICLE ABOVE 24 km/h (15 MPH) FOR AT LEAST 30 SECONDS.
IS DTC 24 SET AS A CURRENT DTC?
NO
REPLACE EBCM.
YES
MALFUNCTION IS INTERMITTENT. REFER TO "DIAGNOSTIC AIDS"

GC402940104702BX

Fig. 122 Code A024: Right Rear Wheel Speed = 0 (Part 2 of 2). 1994 Achieva, Grand Am & Skylark w/VES

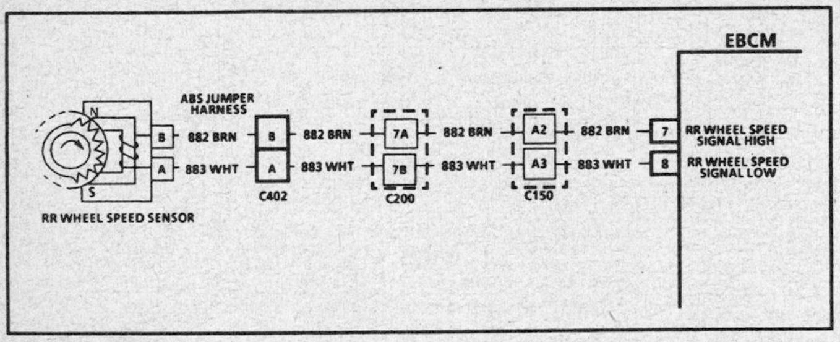
EBCM
ABS JUMPER HARNESS
N
S
B
A
882 BRN
883 WHT
B
A
C402
882 BRN
883 WHT
7A
7B
C200
882 BRN
883 WHT
A2
A3
C150
882 BRN
883 WHT
7
8
RR WHEEL SPEED SIGNAL HIGH
RR WHEEL SPEED SIGNAL LOW
RR WHEEL SPEED SENSOR

Circuit Description:
As a toothed ring passes by the wheel speed sensor, changes in the electromagnetic field cause the wheel speed sensor to produce a sinusoidal (AC) voltage signal whose frequency is proportional to wheel speed. The magnitude of this signal is directly related to wheel speed and the proximity of the wheel speed sensor to the toothed ring, often referred to as the air gap.

DTC Will Set When: DTC 24 can be set when the vehicle is not in an ABS stop. If the right rear wheel speed = 0 and the vehicle's reference speed is greater than 8 km/h (5 mph), a malfunction exists.

Action Taken: A malfunction DTC is stored, ABS is disabled and the ABS warning lamp is turned "ON."

DTC Chart Test Description: Number(s) below refer to circled number(s) on the diagnostic chart.
1. Determines if DTC 35 is present.
2. Designed to identify a wheel speed sensor or circuitry that is damaged and visibly apparent.
3. Checks to see that the wheel speed sensor is within proper resistance values.
4. Verifies that the wheel speed sensor can generate an appropriate output signal.

Diagnostic Aids: An "Intermittent" malfunction may be caused by a poor connection, rubbed through wire insulation, or a wire that is broken inside the insulation.

The frequency of the malfunction can be checked by using the enhanced diagnostic function of the Tech 1

If the customer's comments reflect that the ABS warning lamp is "ON" only during moist environmental changes (rain, snow, vehicle wash), all wheel speed sensor circuitry should be thoroughly inspected for signs of water intrusion. If DTC is not current, clear DTCs and simulate the effects of water intrusion. Use the following procedure. Spray down the suspected area with a 5% salt water solution (two teaspoons of salt to 12 oz. of water). Test drive vehicle over various road surfaces (bumps, turns, etc.) above 24 km/h (15 mph) for at least 30 seconds. If DTC returns replace suspected harness.

Any circuitry, that is suspected as causing the intermittent complaint, should be thoroughly checked for backed out terminals, improper mating, broken locks, improperly formed or damaged terminals, poor terminal to wiring connections or physical damage to the wiring harness.

Resistance of the wheel speed sensor will increase with an increase in sensor temperature.

When replacing a wheel speed sensor, inspect the sensor terminals and harness connector for corrosion and/or water intrusion. If evidence of corrosion or water intrusion exists, replace wheel speed sensor jumper harness. Likewise, if replacing a wheel speed sensor jumper harness, inspect sensor terminals. If evidence of corrosion or water intrusion exists, replace wheel speed sensor.

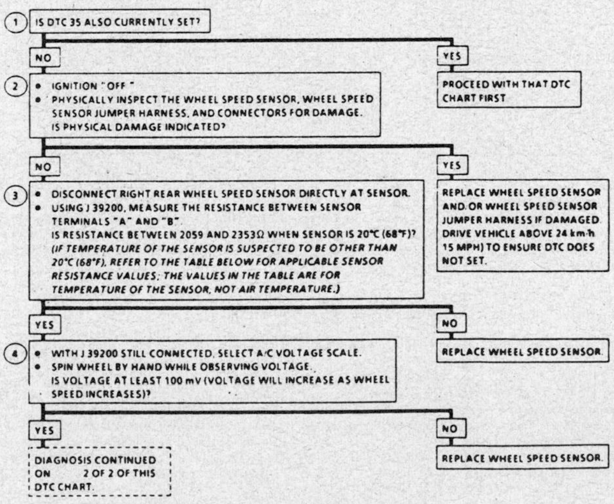
1
IS DTC 35 ALSO CURRENTLY SET?
NO
YES
PROCEED WITH THAT DTC CHART FIRST
2
• IGNITION "OFF"
• PHYSICALLY INSPECT THE WHEEL SPEED SENSOR, WHEEL SPEED SENSOR JUMPER HARNESS, AND CONNECTORS FOR DAMAGE.
IS PHYSICAL DAMAGE INDICATED?
NO
YES
REPLACE WHEEL SPEED SENSOR AND/OR WHEEL SPEED SENSOR JUMPER HARNESS IF DAMAGED. DRIVE VEHICLE ABOVE 24 km/h 15 MPH) TO ENSURE DTC DOES NOT SET.
3
• DISCONNECT RIGHT REAR WHEEL SPEED SENSOR DIRECTLY AT SENSOR.
• USING J 39200, MEASURE THE RESISTANCE BETWEEN SENSOR TERMINALS "A" AND "B".
IS RESISTANCE BETWEEN 2059 AND 2353Ω WHEN SENSOR IS 20°C (68°F)?
(IF TEMPERATURE OF THE SENSOR IS SUSPECTED TO BE OTHER THAN 20°C (68°F), REFER TO THE TABLE BELOW FOR APPLICABLE SENSOR RESISTANCE VALUES; THE VALUES IN THE TABLE ARE FOR TEMPERATURE OF THE SENSOR, NOT AIR TEMPERATURE.)
YES
NO
REPLACE WHEEL SPEED SENSOR.
4
• WITH J 39200 STILL CONNECTED, SELECT A/C VOLTAGE SCALE.
• SPIN WHEEL BY HAND WHILE OBSERVING VOLTAGE.
IS VOLTAGE AT LEAST 100 mV (VOLTAGE WILL INCREASE AS WHEEL SPEED INCREASES)?
YES
NO
REPLACE WHEEL SPEED SENSOR.
DIAGNOSIS CONTINUED ON 2 OF 2 OF THIS DTC CHART.

REAR WHEEL SPEED SENSOR

TEMPERATURE OF SENSOR VS. SENSOR RESISTANCE (APPROXIMATE)

TEMP. (°C)	TEMP. (°F)	RESISTANCE (OHMS)
-34 TO 4	-30 TO 40	1622 TO 2205
5 TO 43	41 TO 110	1930 TO 2566
44 TO 93	111 TO 200	2245 TO 3028

GC402930076001BA

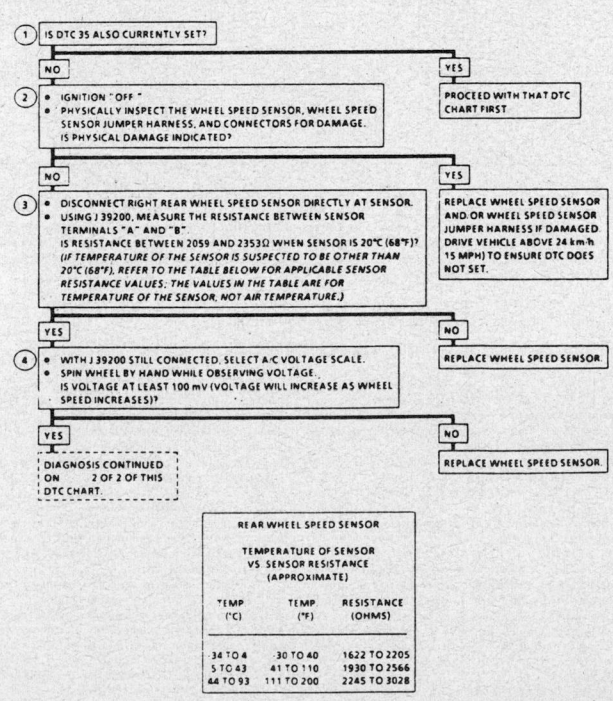

Fig. 123 Code A024: Right Rear Wheel Speed = 0 (Part 1 of 2). 1993 Grand Prix, 1993–94 Cutlass Supreme, Lumina & Regal

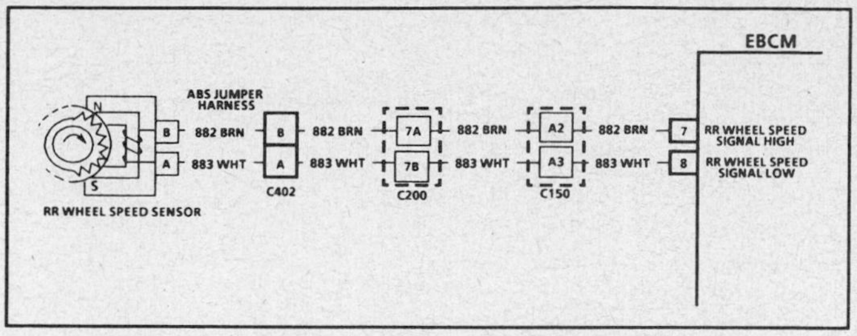
EBCM
ABS JUMPER HARNESS
N
S
B 882 BRN
A 883 WHT
B 882 BRN
A 883 WHT
C402
7A 882 BRN
7B 883 WHT
C200
A2 882 BRN
A3 883 WHT
C150
7 RR WHEEL SPEED SIGNAL HIGH
8 RR WHEEL SPEED SIGNAL LOW
RR WHEEL SPEED SENSOR

DTC 24

(Page 2 of 2)

RIGHT REAR WHEEL SPEED = 0

Circuit Description:

As a toothed ring passes by the wheel speed sensor, changes in the electromagnetic field cause the wheel speed sensor to produce a sinusoidal (AC) voltage signal whose frequency is proportional to wheel speed. The magnitude of this signal is directly related to wheel speed and the proximity of the wheel speed sensor to the toothed ring, often referred to as the air gap.

DTC Will Set When: DTC 24 can be set when the vehicle is not in an ABS stop. If the right rear wheel speed = 0 and the vehicle's reference speed is greater than 8 km/h (5 mph), a malfunction exists.

Action Taken: A malfunction DTC is stored, ABS is disabled and the ABS warning lamp is turned "ON."

DTC Chart Test Description: Number(s) below refer to circled number(s) on the diagnostic chart.

5. Checks for proper output voltage from the EBCM.
6. Checks for an open in the wheel speed sensor low circuit.
7. Ensures malfunction was not due to physical damage of the circuitry.
8. Ensures that wheel speed sensor circuitry is not shorted.
9. Ensures malfunction was not due to physical damage of the circuitry.
10. Checks for an incorrect or malfunctioning hub and bearing assembly.
11. This checks for an open in the wheel speed sensor high circuit.

Diagnostic Aids: An "Intermittent" malfunction may be caused by a poor connection, rubbed through wire insulation, or a wire that is broken inside the insulation.

The frequency of the malfunction can be checked by using the enhanced diagnostic function of the Tech 1.

If the customer's comments reflect that the ABS warning lamp is "ON" only during moist environmental changes (rain, snow, vehicle wash), all wheel speed sensor circuitry should be thoroughly inspected for signs of water intrusion. If DTC is not current, clear DTCs and simulate the effects of water intrusion. Use the following procedure. Spray down the suspected area with a 5% salt water solution (two teaspoons of salt to 12 oz. of water). Test drive vehicle over various road surfaces (bumps, turns, etc.) above 24 km/h (15 mph) for at least 30 seconds. If DTC returns replace suspected harness.

Any circuitry, that is suspected as causing the intermittent complaint, should be thoroughly checked for backed out terminals, improper mating, broken locks, improperly formed or damaged terminals, poor terminal to wiring connections or physical damage to the wiring harness.

Resistance of the wheel speed sensor will increase with an increase in sensor temperature.

When replacing a wheel speed sensor, inspect the sensor terminals and harness connector for corrosion and/or water intrusion. If evidence of corrosion or water intrusion exists, replace wheel speed sensor jumper harness. Likewise, if replacing a wheel speed sensor jumper harness, inspect sensor terminals. If evidence of corrosion or water intrusion exists, replace wheel speed sensor.

GC402930076002AA

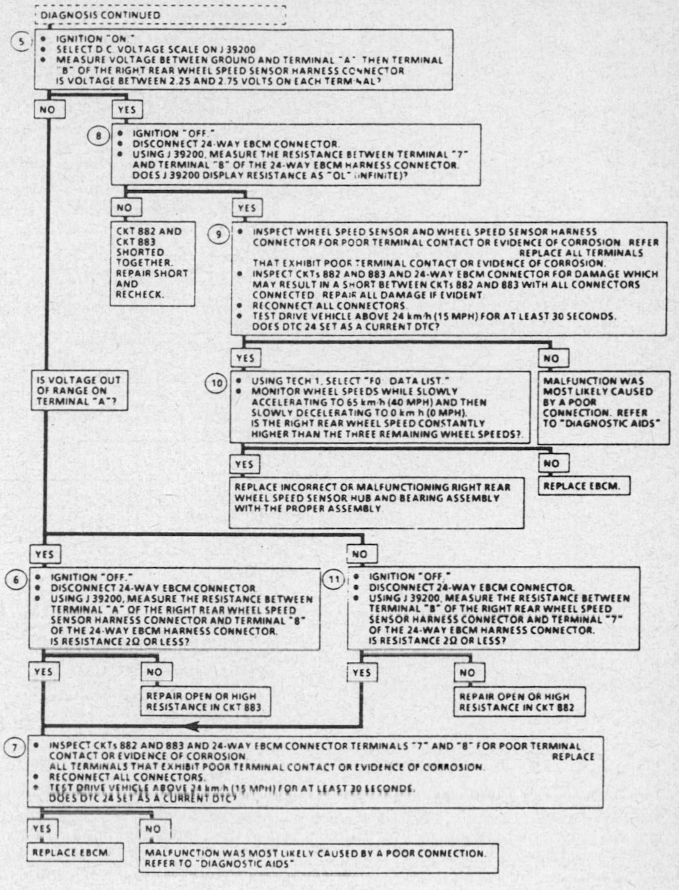
DIAGNOSIS CONTINUED
5
• IGNITION "ON."
• SELECT D.C. VOLTAGE SCALE ON J 39200
• MEASURE VOLTAGE BETWEEN GROUND AND TERMINAL "A" THEN TERMINAL "B" OF THE RIGHT REAR WHEEL SPEED SENSOR HARNESS CONNECTOR
IS VOLTAGE BETWEEN 2.25 AND 2.75 VOLTS ON EACH TERMINAL?
NO
YES
8
• IGNITION "OFF."
• DISCONNECT 24-WAY EBCM CONNECTOR.
• USING J 39200, MEASURE THE RESISTANCE BETWEEN TERMINAL "7" AND TERMINAL "8" OF THE 24-WAY EBCM HARNESS CONNECTOR.
DOES J 39200 DISPLAY RESISTANCE AS "OL" (INFINITE)?
NO
YES
CKT 882 AND CKT 883 SHORTED TOGETHER. REPAIR SHORT AND RECHECK.
9
• INSPECT WHEEL SPEED SENSOR AND WHEEL SPEED SENSOR HARNESS CONNECTOR FOR POOR TERMINAL CONTACT OR EVIDENCE OF CORROSION. REFER
REPLACE ALL TERMINALS THAT EXHIBIT POOR TERMINAL CONTACT OR EVIDENCE OF CORROSION.
• INSPECT CKTs 882 AND 883 AND 24-WAY EBCM CONNECTOR FOR DAMAGE WHICH MAY RESULT IN A SHORT BETWEEN CKTs 882 AND 883 WITH ALL CONNECTORS CONNECTED. REPAIR ALL DAMAGE IF EVIDENT.
• RECONNECT ALL CONNECTORS.
• TEST DRIVE VEHICLE ABOVE 24 km/h (15 MPH) FOR AT LEAST 30 SECONDS.
DOES DTC 24 SET AS A CURRENT DTC?
YES
NO
IS VOLTAGE OUT OF RANGE ON TERMINAL "A"?
10
• USING TECH 1, SELECT "F0: DATA LIST."
• MONITOR WHEEL SPEEDS WHILE SLOWLY ACCELERATING TO 65 km/h (40 MPH) AND THEN SLOWLY DECELERATING TO 0 km/h (0 MPH).
IS THE RIGHT REAR WHEEL SPEED CONSTANTLY HIGHER THAN THE THREE REMAINING WHEEL SPEEDS?.
MALFUNCTION WAS MOST LIKELY CAUSED BY A POOR CONNECTION. REFER TO "DIAGNOSTIC AIDS"
YES
NO
REPLACE INCORRECT OR MALFUNCTIONING RIGHT REAR WHEEL SPEED SENSOR HUB AND BEARING ASSEMBLY WITH THE PROPER ASSEMBLY.
REPLACE EBCM.
YES
NO
6
• IGNITION "OFF."
• DISCONNECT 24-WAY EBCM CONNECTOR.
• USING J 39200, MEASURE THE RESISTANCE BETWEEN TERMINAL "A" OF THE RIGHT REAR WHEEL SPEED SENSOR HARNESS CONNECTOR AND TERMINAL "8" OF THE 24-WAY EBCM HARNESS CONNECTOR.
IS RESISTANCE 2Ω OR LESS?
11
• IGNITION "OFF."
• DISCONNECT 24-WAY EBCM CONNECTOR.
• USING J 39200, MEASURE THE RESISTANCE BETWEEN TERMINAL "B" OF THE RIGHT REAR WHEEL SPEED SENSOR HARNESS CONNECTOR AND TERMINAL "7" OF THE 24-WAY EBCM HARNESS CONNECTOR.
IS RESISTANCE 2Ω OR LESS?
YES
NO
REPAIR OPEN OR HIGH RESISTANCE IN CKT 883.
YES
NO
REPAIR OPEN OR HIGH RESISTANCE IN CKT 882.
7
• INSPECT CKTs 882 AND 883 AND 24-WAY EBCM CONNECTOR TERMINALS "7" AND "8" FOR POOR TERMINAL CONTACT OR EVIDENCE OF CORROSION. REPLACE ALL TERMINALS THAT EXHIBIT POOR TERMINAL CONTACT OR EVIDENCE OF CORROSION.
• RECONNECT ALL CONNECTORS.
• TEST DRIVE VEHICLE ABOVE 24 km/h (15 MPH) FOR AT LEAST 30 SECONDS.
DOES DTC 24 SET AS A CURRENT DTC?
YES
NO
REPLACE EBCM.
MALFUNCTION WAS MOST LIKELY CAUSED BY A POOR CONNECTION. REFER TO "DIAGNOSTIC AIDS"

GC402930076002BA

Fig. 123 Code A024: Right Rear Wheel Speed = 0 (Part 2 of 2). 1993 Grand Prix, 1993–94 Cutlass Supreme, Lumina & Regal

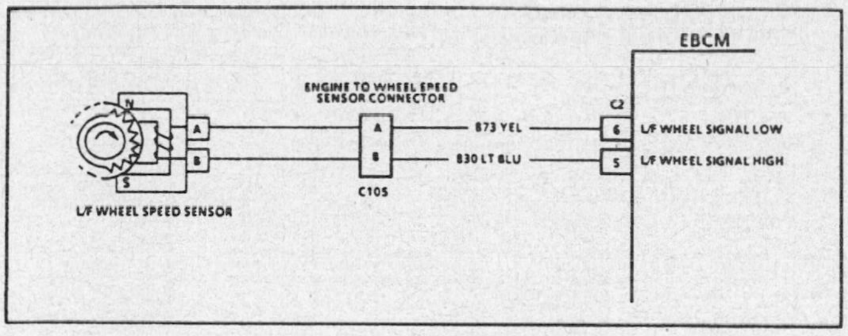
EBCM
ENGINE TO WHEEL SPEED SENSOR CONNECTOR
C2
N
S
A
B
873 YEL
830 LT BLU
C105
6 L/F WHEEL SIGNAL LOW
5 L/F WHEEL SIGNAL HIGH
L/F WHEEL SPEED SENSOR

GC402930076100AX

Cavalier & Sunbird

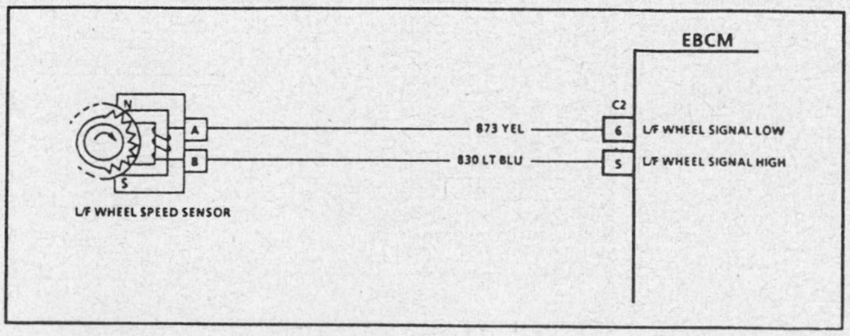
EBCM
C2
N
S
A
B
873 YEL
830 LT BLU
6 L/F WHEEL SIGNAL LOW
5 L/F WHEEL SIGNAL HIGH
L/F WHEEL SPEED SENSOR

GC402930076100BX

Achieva, Beretta, Corsica, Grand Am & Skylark

DTC A025

LEFT FRONT EXCESSIVE WHEEL SPEED VARIATION

Circuit Description:

As a toothed ring passes by the wheel speed sensor, changes in the electromagnetic field cause the wheel speed sensor to produce a sinusoidal (AC) voltage signal whose frequency is proportional to wheel speed. The magnitude of this signal is directly related to wheel speed and the proximity of the wheel speed sensor to the toothed ring, often referred to as the air gap.

Failure Condition:

DTC A025 can be set when the brake is "OFF." The purpose of this test is to detect a situation in which the left front wheel acceleration or deceleration is beyond specified limits.

Action Taken:

A malfunction DTC is stored, ABS is disabled and the ABS indicator lamp is turned "ON."

Test Description: Number(s) below refer to circled number(s) on the diagnostic chart.

1. This test verifies whether the malfunction is currently present.
2. This step will identify a wheel speed sensor or circuitry that is damaged and visibly apparent.
3. This test checks wheel speed sensor for proper resistance values.
4. This test ensures the wheel speed sensor and sensor ring generate the proper voltage.
5. This step ensures the wheel speed sensor is not shorted to ground.

Diagnostic Aids:

An "Intermittent" malfunction may be caused by a poor connection, rubbed through wire insulation, or a wire that is broken inside the insulation.

The frequency of the malfunction can be checked by using the enhanced diagnostic function of the Tech 1.

If the customer's comments reflect that the ABS amber indicator lamp is "ON" only during moist environmental changes, (rain, snow, vehicle wash) all wheel speed sensor circuitry should be thoroughly inspected for water intrusion. Use the following procedure. Spray down the suspected area with 5% salt water solution (two teaspoons of salt to 12 oz. of water). Start vehicle, allow vehicle to run for 10 seconds. If DTC returns immediately, replace suspected harness.

Any circuitry, that is suspected as causing the intermittent complaint, should be thoroughly checked for backed out terminals, improper mating, broken locks, improperly formed or damaged terminals, poor terminal to wiring connections or physical damage to the wiring harness.

A careful visual inspection of the toothed ring, CV joint, bearing and wheel speed sensor for physical damage should also be performed. If DTC sets at the same mph every time and wheel speed variation is noted above this mph on the Tech 1, the speed ring is most likely damaged. This can occur at any speed.

When measuring wheel speed sensor resistance, ensure vehicle is at room temperature. Wheel speed sensor resistance will vary with temperature.

When replacing a wheel speed sensor, inspect the sensor terminals and harness connector for corrosion and/or water intrusion. If evidence of corrosion or water instrusion exists, replace wheel speed sensor harness.

GC402930076100CX

Fig. 124 Code A025: Left Front Excessive Wheel Speed Variation (Part 1 Of 2). 1993–94 Cavalier, Sunbird, Beretta, Corsica & Achieva, Grand Am & Skylark Less VES

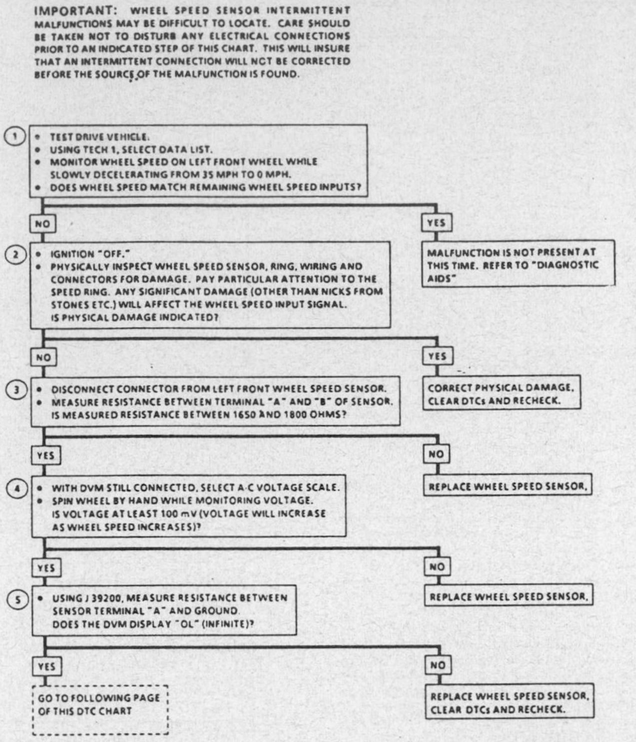
IMPORTANT: WHEEL SPEED SENSOR INTERMITTENT MALFUNCTIONS MAY BE DIFFICULT TO LOCATE. CARE SHOULD BE TAKEN NOT TO DISTURB ANY ELECTRICAL CONNECTIONS PRIOR TO AN INDICATED STEP OF THIS CHART. THIS WILL INSURE THAT AN INTERMITTENT CONNECTION WILL NOT BE CORRECTED BEFORE THE SOURCE OF THE MALFUNCTION IS FOUND.
1
• TEST DRIVE VEHICLE.
• USING TECH 1, SELECT DATA LIST.
• MONITOR WHEEL SPEED ON LEFT FRONT WHEEL WHILE SLOWLY DECELERATING FROM 35 MPH TO 0 MPH.
• DOES WHEEL SPEED MATCH REMAINING WHEEL SPEED INPUTS?
NO
YES
MALFUNCTION IS NOT PRESENT AT THIS TIME. REFER TO "DIAGNOSTIC AIDS"
2
• IGNITION "OFF."
• PHYSICALLY INSPECT WHEEL SPEED SENSOR, RING, WIRING AND CONNECTORS FOR DAMAGE. PAY PARTICULAR ATTENTION TO THE SPEED RING. ANY SIGNIFICANT DAMAGE (OTHER THAN NICKS FROM STONES ETC.) WILL AFFECT THE WHEEL SPEED INPUT SIGNAL. IS PHYSICAL DAMAGE INDICATED?
NO
YES
CORRECT PHYSICAL DAMAGE, CLEAR DTCs AND RECHECK.
3
• DISCONNECT CONNECTOR FROM LEFT FRONT WHEEL SPEED SENSOR.
• MEASURE RESISTANCE BETWEEN TERMINAL "A" AND "B" OF SENSOR. IS MEASURED RESISTANCE BETWEEN 1650 AND 1800 OHMS?
YES
NO
REPLACE WHEEL SPEED SENSOR.
4
• WITH DVM STILL CONNECTED, SELECT A/C VOLTAGE SCALE.
• SPIN WHEEL BY HAND WHILE MONITORING VOLTAGE. IS VOLTAGE AT LEAST 100 mV (VOLTAGE WILL INCREASE AS WHEEL SPEED INCREASES)?
YES
NO
REPLACE WHEEL SPEED SENSOR.
5
• USING J 39200, MEASURE RESISTANCE BETWEEN SENSOR TERMINAL "A" AND GROUND. DOES THE DVM DISPLAY "OL" (INFINITE)?
YES
NO
GO TO FOLLOWING PAGE OF THIS DTC CHART
REPLACE WHEEL SPEED SENSOR, CLEAR DTCs AND RECHECK.

GC402930076100DX

DTC A025

LEFT FRONT EXCESSIVE WHEEL SPEED VARIATION

Circuit Description:

As a toothed ring passes by the wheel speed sensor, changes in the electromagnetic field cause the wheel speed sensor to produce a sinusoidal (AC) voltage signal whose frequency is proportional to wheel speed. The magnitude of this signal is directly related to wheel speed and the proximity of the wheel speed sensor to the toothed ring, often referred to as the air gap.

Failure Condition:

DTC A025 can be set when the brake is "OFF." The purpose of this test is to detect a situation in which the left front wheel acceleration or deceleration is beyond specified limits.

Action Taken:

A malfunction DTC is stored, ABS is disabled and the ABS indicator lamp is turned "ON."

Test Description: Number(s) below refer to circled number(s) on the diagnostic chart.

6. This step checks for proper voltages at speed sensor harness connector.
7. This test ensures that the wheel speed sensor circuitry is not internally shorted.
8. This checks for an open in the wheel signal low circuit.
9. This checks for an open in the wheel signal high circuit.
10. This test checks for a short to ground in both high and low wheel signal circuits.
11. This step ensures that DTC A025 was not set due to a poor connection between the world connector and EBCM.

Diagnostic Aids:

An "Intermittent" malfunction may be caused by a poor connection, rubbed through wire insulation, or a wire that is broken inside the insulation.

The frequency of the malfunction can be checked by using the enhanced diagnostic function of the Tech 1.

If the customer's comments reflect that the ABS amber indicator lamp is "ON" only during moist environmental changes, (rain, snow, vehicle wash) all wheel speed sensor circuitry should be thoroughly inspected for water intrusion. Use the following procedure. Spray down the suspected area with 5% salt water solution (two teaspoons of salt to 12 oz. of water). Start vehicle, allow vehicle to run for 10 seconds. If DTC returns immediately, replace suspected harness.

Any circuitry, that is suspected as causing the intermittent complaint, should be thoroughly checked for backed out terminals, improper mating, broken locks, improperly formed or damaged terminals, poor terminal to wiring connections or physical damage to the wiring harness.

A careful visual inspection of the toothed ring, CV joint, bearing and wheel speed sensor for physical damage should also be performed. If DTC sets at the same mph every time and wheel speed variation is noted above this mph on the Tech 1, the speed ring is most likely damaged. This can occur at any speed.

When measuring wheel speed sensor resistance, ensure vehicle is at room temperature. Wheel speed sensor resistance will vary with temperature.

When replacing a wheel speed sensor, inspect the sensor terminals and harness connector for corrosion and/or water intrusion. If evidence of corrosion or water intrusion exists, replace wheel speed sensor harness.

GC402930076100EX

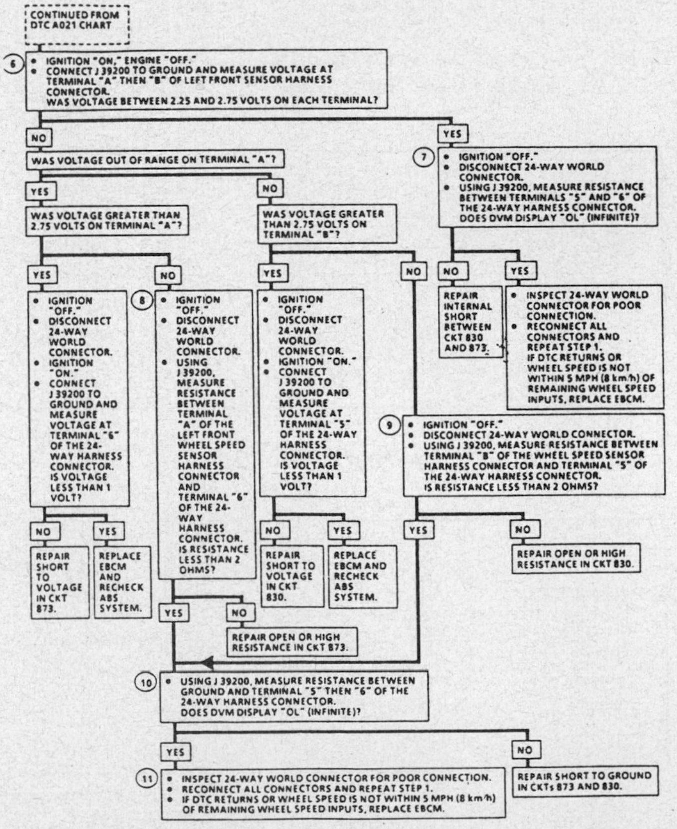
CONTINUED FROM DTC A021 CHART
6
• IGNITION "ON," ENGINE "OFF."
• CONNECT J 39200 TO GROUND AND MEASURE VOLTAGE AT TERMINAL "A" THEN "B" OF LEFT FRONT SENSOR HARNESS CONNECTOR. WAS VOLTAGE BETWEEN 2.25 AND 2.75 VOLTS ON EACH TERMINAL?
NO
YES
WAS VOLTAGE OUT OF RANGE ON TERMINAL "A"?
YES
NO
WAS VOLTAGE GREATER THAN 2.75 VOLTS ON TERMINAL "A"?
WAS VOLTAGE GREATER THAN 2.75 VOLTS ON TERMINAL "B"?
7
• IGNITION "OFF."
• DISCONNECT 24-WAY WORLD CONNECTOR.
• USING J 39200, MEASURE RESISTANCE BETWEEN TERMINALS "5" AND "6" OF THE 24-WAY HARNESS CONNECTOR. DOES DVM DISPLAY "OL" (INFINITE)?
YES
NO
YES
NO
NO
YES
• IGNITION "OFF."
• DISCONNECT 24-WAY WORLD CONNECTOR.
• IGNITION "ON."
• CONNECT J 39200 TO GROUND AND MEASURE VOLTAGE AT TERMINAL "6" OF THE 24-WAY HARNESS CONNECTOR. IS VOLTAGE LESS THAN 1 VOLT?
8
• IGNITION "OFF."
• DISCONNECT 24-WAY WORLD CONNECTOR.
• USING J 39200, MEASURE RESISTANCE BETWEEN TERMINAL "A" OF THE LEFT FRONT WHEEL SPEED SENSOR HARNESS CONNECTOR AND TERMINAL "6" OF THE 24-WAY HARNESS CONNECTOR. IS RESISTANCE LESS THAN 2 OHMS?
• IGNITION "OFF."
• DISCONNECT 24-WAY WORLD CONNECTOR.
• IGNITION "ON."
• CONNECT J 39200 TO GROUND AND MEASURE VOLTAGE AT TERMINAL "5" OF THE 24-WAY HARNESS CONNECTOR. IS VOLTAGE LESS THAN 1 VOLT?
REPAIR INTERNAL SHORT BETWEEN CKT 830 AND 873.
• INSPECT 24-WAY WORLD CONNECTOR FOR POOR CONNECTION.
• RECONNECT ALL CONNECTORS AND REPEAT STEP 1. IF DTC RETURNS OR WHEEL SPEED IS NOT WITHIN 5 MPH (8 km/h) OF REMAINING WHEEL SPEED INPUTS, REPLACE EBCM.
9
• IGNITION "OFF."
• DISCONNECT 24-WAY WORLD CONNECTOR.
• USING J 39200, MEASURE RESISTANCE BETWEEN TERMINAL "B" OF THE WHEEL SPEED SENSOR HARNESS CONNECTOR AND TERMINAL "5" OF THE 24-WAY HARNESS CONNECTOR. IS RESISTANCE LESS THAN 2 OHMS?
NO
YES
NO
YES
YES
NO
REPAIR SHORT TO VOLTAGE IN CKT 873.
REPLACE EBCM AND RECHECK ABS SYSTEM.
REPAIR SHORT TO VOLTAGE IN CKT 830.
REPLACE EBCM AND RECHECK ABS SYSTEM.
REPAIR OPEN OR HIGH RESISTANCE IN CKT 830.
YES
NO
REPAIR OPEN OR HIGH RESISTANCE IN CKT 873.
10
• USING J 39200, MEASURE RESISTANCE BETWEEN GROUND AND TERMINAL "5" THEN "6" OF THE 24-WAY HARNESS CONNECTOR. DOES DVM DISPLAY "OL" (INFINITE)?
YES
NO
11
• INSPECT 24-WAY WORLD CONNECTOR FOR POOR CONNECTION.
• RECONNECT ALL CONNECTORS AND REPEAT STEP 1.
• IF DTC RETURNS OR WHEEL SPEED IS NOT WITHIN 5 MPH (8 km/h) OF REMAINING WHEEL SPEED INPUTS, REPLACE EBCM.
REPAIR SHORT TO GROUND IN CKTs 873 AND 830.

GC402930076100FX

Fig. 124 Code A025: Left Front Excessive Wheel Speed Variation (Part 2 Of 2). 1993–94 Cavalier, Sunbird, Beretta, Corsica & Achieva, Grand Am & Skylark Less VES

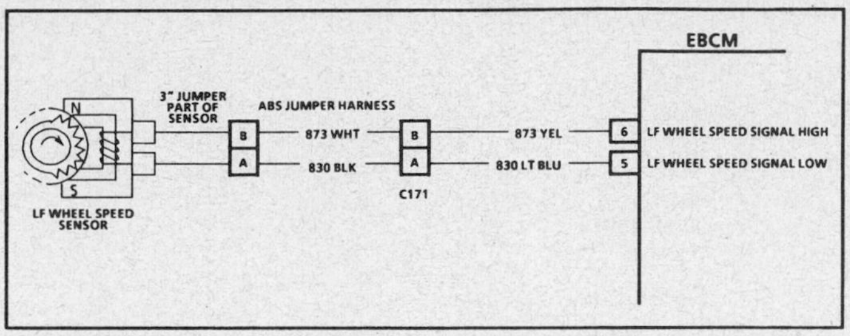
EBCM
3" JUMPER PART OF SENSOR
ABS JUMPER HARNESS
873 WHT
830 BLK
873 YEL
830 LT BLU
C171
LF WHEEL SPEED SIGNAL HIGH
LF WHEEL SPEED SIGNAL LOW
LF WHEEL SPEED SENSOR

Circuit Description:
As a toothed ring passes by the wheel speed sensor, changes in the electromagnetic field cause the wheel speed sensor to produce a sinusoidal (AC) voltage signal whose frequency is proportional to wheel speed. The magnitude of this signal is directly related to wheel speed and the proximity of the wheel speed sensor to the toothed ring, often referred to as the air gap.

DTC Will Set When: DTC 25 can be set when the brake is "OFF." The purpose of this test is to detect a situation in which the left front wheel acceleration or deceleration is beyond specified limits.

Action Taken: A malfunction DTC is stored, ABS is disabled and the ABS warning lamp is turned "ON."

DTC Chart Test Description: Number(s) below refer to circled number(s) on the diagnostic chart.
1. Determines if DTC 32 is present.
2. Designed to identify a wheel speed sensor or circuitry that is damaged and visibly apparent.
3. Checks to see that the wheel speed sensor is within proper resistance values.
4. Verifies that the wheel speed sensor can generate an appropriate output signal.

Diagnostic Aids: An "Intermittent" malfunction may be caused by a poor connection, rubbed through wire insulation, or a wire that is broken inside the insulation.

The frequency of the malfunction can be checked by using the enhanced diagnostic function of the Tech 1.

If the customer's comments reflect that the ABS warning lamp is "ON" only during moist environmental changes (rain, snow, vehicle wash), all wheel speed sensor circuitry should be thoroughly inspected for signs of water intrusion. If DTC is not current, clear DTCs and simulate the effects of water intrusion. Use the following procedure. Spray down the suspected area with a 5% salt water solution (two teaspoons of salt to 12 oz. of water). Test drive vehicle over various road surfaces (bumps, turns, etc.) above 24 km/h (15 mph) for at least 30 seconds. If DTC returns replace suspected harness.

Any circuitry, that is suspected as causing the intermittent complaint, should be thoroughly checked for backed out terminals, improper mating, broken locks, improperly formed or damaged terminals, poor terminal to wiring connections or physical damage to the wiring harness.

Resistance of the wheel speed sensor will increase with an increase in sensor temperature.

When replacing a wheel speed sensor, inspect the sensor terminals and harness connector for corrosion and/or water intrusion. If evidence of corrosion or water intrusion exists, replace wheel speed sensor jumper harness. Likewise, if replacing a wheel speed sensor jumper harness, inspect sensor terminals. If evidence of corrosion or water intrusion exists, replace wheel speed sensor.

GC402930076201AA

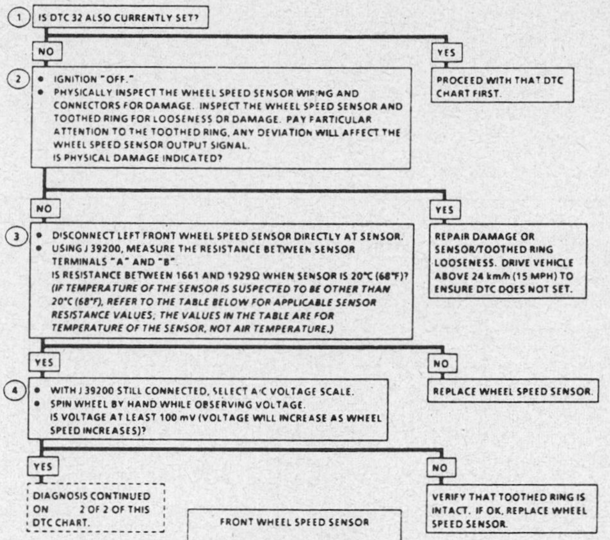
1 IS DTC 32 ALSO CURRENTLY SET?
NO
YES
PROCEED WITH THAT DTC CHART FIRST.
2 • IGNITION "OFF."
• PHYSICALLY INSPECT THE WHEEL SPEED SENSOR WIRING AND CONNECTORS FOR DAMAGE. INSPECT THE WHEEL SPEED SENSOR AND TOOTHED RING FOR LOOSENESS OR DAMAGE. PAY PARTICULAR ATTENTION TO THE TOOTHED RING, ANY DEVIATION WILL AFFECT THE WHEEL SPEED SENSOR OUTPUT SIGNAL.
IS PHYSICAL DAMAGE INDICATED?
NO
YES
REPAIR DAMAGE OR SENSOR/TOOTHED RING LOOSENESS. DRIVE VEHICLE ABOVE 24 km/h (15 MPH) TO ENSURE DTC DOES NOT SET.
3 • DISCONNECT LEFT FRONT WHEEL SPEED SENSOR DIRECTLY AT SENSOR.
• USING J 39200, MEASURE THE RESISTANCE BETWEEN SENSOR TERMINALS "A" AND "B".
IS RESISTANCE BETWEEN 1661 AND 1929Ω WHEN SENSOR IS 20°C (68°F)? (IF TEMPERATURE OF THE SENSOR IS SUSPECTED TO BE OTHER THAN 20°C (68°F), REFER TO THE TABLE BELOW FOR APPLICABLE SENSOR RESISTANCE VALUES. THE VALUES IN THE TABLE ARE FOR TEMPERATURE OF THE SENSOR, NOT AIR TEMPERATURE.)
YES
NO
REPLACE WHEEL SPEED SENSOR.
4 • WITH J 39200 STILL CONNECTED, SELECT A/C VOLTAGE SCALE.
• SPIN WHEEL BY HAND WHILE OBSERVING VOLTAGE.
IS VOLTAGE AT LEAST 100 mV (VOLTAGE WILL INCREASE AS WHEEL SPEED INCREASES)?
YES
NO
DIAGNOSIS CONTINUED ON 2 OF 2 OF THIS DTC CHART.
VERIFY THAT TOOTHED RING IS INTACT. IF OK, REPLACE WHEEL SPEED SENSOR.

FRONT WHEEL SPEED SENSOR

TEMPERATURE OF SENSOR VS. SENSOR RESISTANCE (APPROXIMATE)

TEMP. (°C)	TEMP. (°F)	RESISTANCE (OHMS)
-34 TO 4	-30 TO 40	1309 TO 1808
5 TO 43	41 TO 110	1557 TO 2103
44 TO 93	111 TO 200	1811 TO 2482

GC402930076201BA

Fig. 125 Code A025: Left Front Excessive Wheel Speed Variation (Part 1 of 2). 1993 Grand Prix, 1993–94 Cutlass Supreme, Lumina & Regal

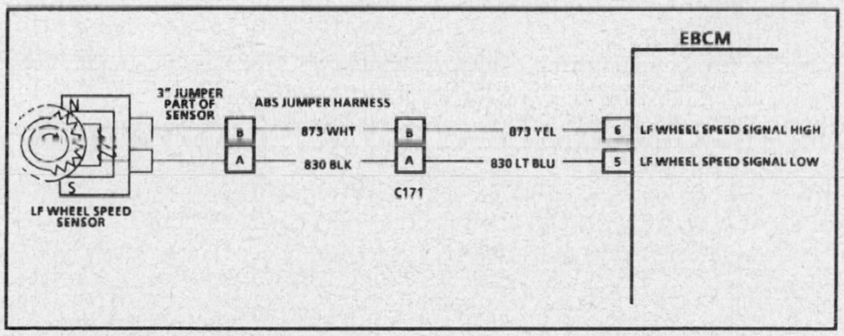
EBCM
3" JUMPER PART OF SENSOR
ABS JUMPER HARNESS
873 WHT
830 BLK
873 YEL
830 LT BLU
C171
LF WHEEL SPEED SIGNAL HIGH
LF WHEEL SPEED SIGNAL LOW
LF WHEEL SPEED SENSOR

Circuit Description:
As a toothed ring passes by the wheel speed sensor, changes in the electromagnetic field cause the wheel speed sensor to produce a sinusoidal (AC) voltage signal whose frequency is proportional to wheel speed. The magnitude of this signal is directly related to wheel speed and the proximity of the wheel speed sensor to the toothed ring, often referred to as the air gap.

DTC Will Set When: DTC 25 can be set when the brake is "OFF." The purpose of this test is to detect a situation in which the left front wheel acceleration or deceleration is beyond specified limits.

Action Taken: A malfunction DTC is stored, ABS is disabled and the ABS warning lamp is turned "ON."

DTC Chart Test Description: Number(s) below refer to circled number(s) on the diagnostic chart.
5. Checks for proper output voltage from the EBCM.
6. Checks for an open in the wheel speed sensor low circuit.
7. Ensures malfunction was not due to physical damage of the circuitry.
8. Ensures that wheel speed sensor circuitry is not shorted.
9. Ensures malfunction was not due to physical damage of the circuitry.
10. Checks for an open in the wheel speed sensor high circuit.

Diagnostic Aids: An "Intermittent" malfunction may be caused by a poor connection, rubbed through wire insulation, or a wire that is broken inside the insulation.

The frequency of the malfunction can be checked by using the enhanced diagnostic function of the Tech 1.

If the customer's comments reflect that the ABS warning lamp is "ON" only during moist environmental changes (rain, snow, vehicle wash), all wheel speed sensor circuitry should be thoroughly inspected for signs of water intrusion. If DTC is not current, clear DTCs and simulate the effects of water intrusion. Use the following procedure. Spray down the suspected area with a 5% salt water solution (two teaspoons of salt to 12 oz. of water). Test drive vehicle over various road surfaces (bumps, turns, etc.) above 24 km/h (15 mph) for at least 30 seconds. If DTC returns replace suspected harness.

Any circuitry, that is suspected as causing the intermittent complaint, should be thoroughly checked for backed out terminals, improper mating, broken locks, improperly formed or damaged terminals, poor terminal to wiring connections or physical damage to the wiring harness.

Resistance of the wheel speed sensor will increase with an increase in sensor temperature.

When replacing a wheel speed sensor, inspect the sensor terminals and harness connector for corrosion and/or water intrusion. If evidence of corrosion or water intrusion exists, replace wheel speed sensor jumper harness. Likewise, if replacing a wheel speed sensor jumper harness, inspect sensor terminals. If evidence of corrosion or water intrusion exists, replace wheel speed sensor.

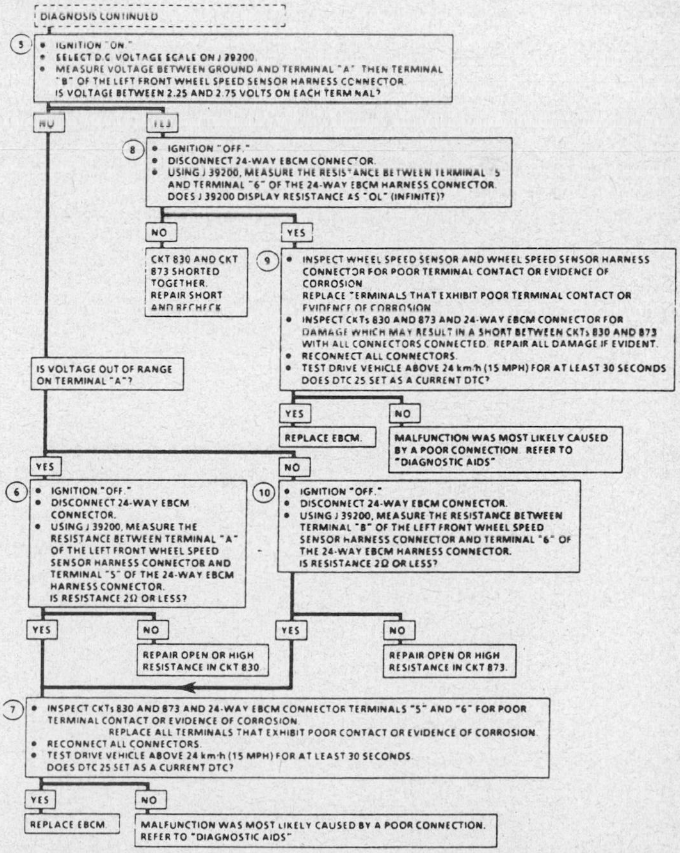
DIAGNOSIS CONTINUED
5 • IGNITION "ON."
• SELECT D.C VOLTAGE SCALE ON J 39200.
• MEASURE VOLTAGE BETWEEN GROUND AND TERMINAL "A" THEN TERMINAL "B" OF THE LEFT FRONT WHEEL SPEED SENSOR HARNESS CONNECTOR.
IS VOLTAGE BETWEEN 2.25 AND 2.75 VOLTS ON EACH TERMINAL?
NO
YES
8 • IGNITION "OFF."
• DISCONNECT 24-WAY EBCM CONNECTOR.
• USING J 39200, MEASURE THE RESISTANCE BETWEEN TERMINAL "5 AND TERMINAL "6" OF THE 24-WAY EBCM HARNESS CONNECTOR.
DOES J 39200 DISPLAY RESISTANCE AS "OL" (INFINITE)?
NO
YES
CKT 830 AND CKT 873 SHORTED TOGETHER. REPAIR SHORT AND RECHECK
9 • INSPECT WHEEL SPEED SENSOR AND WHEEL SPEED SENSOR HARNESS CONNECTOR FOR POOR TERMINAL CONTACT OR EVIDENCE OF CORROSION
REPLACE TERMINALS THAT EXHIBIT POOR TERMINAL CONTACT OR EVIDENCE OF CORROSION
• INSPECT CKTs 830 AND 873 AND 24-WAY EBCM CONNECTOR FOR DAMAGE WHICH MAY RESULT IN A SHORT BETWEEN CKTs 830 AND 873 WITH ALL CONNECTORS CONNECTED. REPAIR ALL DAMAGE IF EVIDENT.
• RECONNECT ALL CONNECTORS.
• TEST DRIVE VEHICLE ABOVE 24 km/h (15 MPH) FOR AT LEAST 30 SECONDS
DOES DTC 25 SET AS A CURRENT DTC?
IS VOLTAGE OUT OF RANGE ON TERMINAL "A"?
YES
NO
REPLACE EBCM.
MALFUNCTION WAS MOST LIKELY CAUSED BY A POOR CONNECTION. REFER TO "DIAGNOSTIC AIDS"
YES
NO
6 • IGNITION "OFF."
• DISCONNECT 24-WAY EBCM CONNECTOR.
• USING J 39200, MEASURE THE RESISTANCE BETWEEN TERMINAL "A" OF THE LEFT FRONT WHEEL SPEED SENSOR HARNESS CONNECTOR AND TERMINAL "5" OF THE 24-WAY EBCM HARNESS CONNECTOR.
IS RESISTANCE 2Ω OR LESS?
10 • IGNITION "OFF."
• DISCONNECT 24-WAY EBCM CONNECTOR.
• USING J 39200, MEASURE THE RESISTANCE BETWEEN TERMINAL "B" OF THE LEFT FRONT WHEEL SPEED SENSOR HARNESS CONNECTOR AND TERMINAL "6" OF THE 24-WAY EBCM HARNESS CONNECTOR.
IS RESISTANCE 2Ω OR LESS?
YES
NO
REPAIR OPEN OR HIGH RESISTANCE IN CKT 830.
YES
NO
REPAIR OPEN OR HIGH RESISTANCE IN CKT 873.
7 • INSPECT CKTs 830 AND 873 AND 24-WAY EBCM CONNECTOR TERMINALS "5" AND "6" FOR POOR TERMINAL CONTACT OR EVIDENCE OF CORROSION.
REPLACE ALL TERMINALS THAT EXHIBIT POOR CONTACT OR EVIDENCE OF CORROSION.
• RECONNECT ALL CONNECTORS.
• TEST DRIVE VEHICLE ABOVE 24 km/h (15 MPH) FOR AT LEAST 30 SECONDS.
DOES DTC 25 SET AS A CURRENT DTC?
YES
NO
REPLACE EBCM.
MALFUNCTION WAS MOST LIKELY CAUSED BY A POOR CONNECTION. REFER TO "DIAGNOSTIC AIDS"

Fig. 125 Code A025: Left Front Excessive Wheel Speed Variation (Part 2 of 2). 1993 Grand Prix, 1993–94 Cutlass Supreme, Lumina & Regal

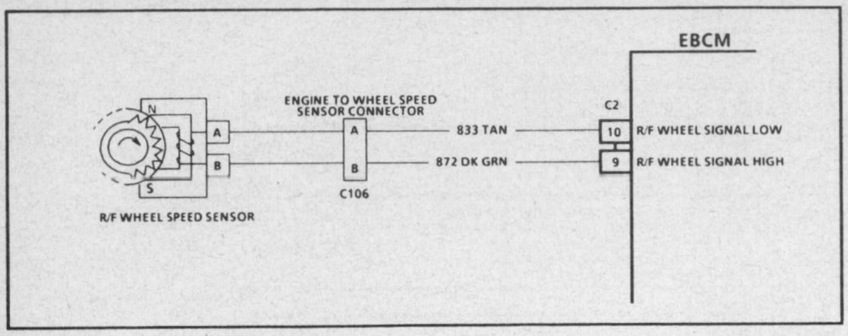
EBCM
ENGINE TO WHEEL SPEED SENSOR CONNECTOR
C2
N
A
B
S
833 TAN
872 DK GRN
10
9
R/F WHEEL SIGNAL LOW
R/F WHEEL SIGNAL HIGH
C106
R/F WHEEL SPEED SENSOR

GC402930076300AX

Cavalier & Sunbird

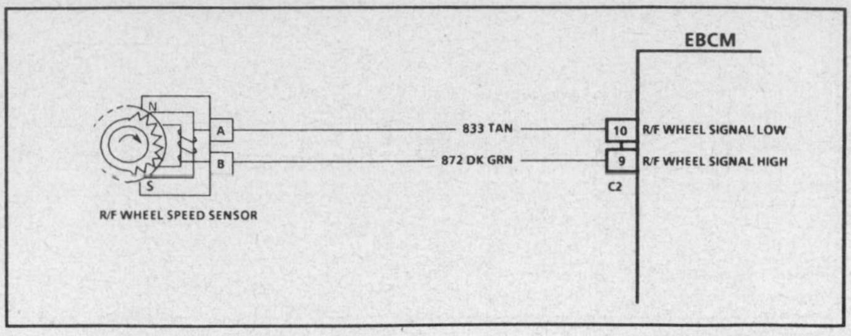
EBCM
N
A
B
S
833 TAN
872 DK GRN
10
9
C2
R/F WHEEL SIGNAL LOW
R/F WHEEL SIGNAL HIGH
R/F WHEEL SPEED SENSOR

GC402930076300BX

Achieva, Beretta, Corsica, Grand Am & Skylark

DTC A026

(Page 1 of 2)

RIGHT FRONT EXCESSIVE WHEEL SPEED VARIATION

Circuit Description:

As a toothed ring passes by the wheel speed sensor, changes in the electromagnetic field cause the wheel speed sensor to produce a sinusoidal (AC) voltage signal whose frequency is proportional to wheel speed. The magnitude of this signal is directly related to wheel speed and the proximity of the wheel speed sensor to the toothed ring, often referred to as the air gap.

Failure Condition:

DTC A026 can be set when the brake is "OFF." The purpose of this test is to detect a situation in which the right front wheel acceleration or deceleration is beyond specified limits.

Action Taken:

A malfunction DTC is stored, ABS is disabled and the ABS indicator lamp is turned "ON."

Test Description: Number(s) below refer to circled number(s) on the diagnostic chart.

1. This test verifies whether the malfunction is currently present.
2. This step will identify a wheel speed sensor or circuitry that is damaged and visibly apparent.
3. This test checks wheel speed sensor for proper resistance values.
4. This test ensures the wheel speed sensor and sensor ring generate the proper voltage.
5. This step ensures the wheel speed sensor is not shorted to ground.

Diagnostic Aids:

An "Intermittent" malfunction may be caused by a poor connection, rubbed through wire insulation, or a wire that is broken inside the insulation.

The frequency of the malfunction can be checked by using the enhanced diagnostic function of the Tech 1.

If the customer's comments reflect that the ABS amber indicator lamp is "ON" only during moist environmental changes, (rain, snow, vehicle wash) all wheel speed sensor circuitry should be thoroughly inspected for water intrusion. Use the following procedure. Spray down the suspected area with 5% salt water solution (two teaspoons of salt to 12 oz. of water). Start vehicle, allow vehicle to run for 10 seconds. If DTC returns immediately, replace suspected harness.

Any circuitry, that is suspected as causing the intermittent complaint, should be thoroughly checked for backed out terminals, improper mating, broken locks, improperly formed or damaged terminals, poor terminal to wiring connections or physical damage to the wiring harness.

A careful visual inspection of the toothed ring, CV joint, bearing and wheel speed sensor for physical damage should also be performed. If DTC sets at the same mph every time and wheel speed variation is noted above this mph on the Tech 1, the speed ring is most likely damaged. This can occur at any speed.

When measuring wheel speed sensor resistance, ensure vehicle is at room temperature. Wheel speed sensor resistance will vary with temperature.

When replacing a wheel speed sensor, inspect the sensor terminals and harness connector for corrosion and/or water intrusion. If evidence of corrosion or water intrusion exists, replace wheel speed sensor harness.

GC402930076300CX

IMPORTANT: WHEEL SPEED SENSOR INTERMITTENT MALFUNCTIONS MAY BE DIFFICULT TO LOCATE. CARE SHOULD BE TAKEN NOT TO DISTURB ANY ELECTRICAL CONNECTIONS PRIOR TO AN INDICATED STEP OF THIS CHART. THIS WILL INSURE THAT AN INTERMITTENT CONNECTION WILL NOT BE CORRECTED BEFORE THE SOURCE OF THE MALFUNCTION IS FOUND.

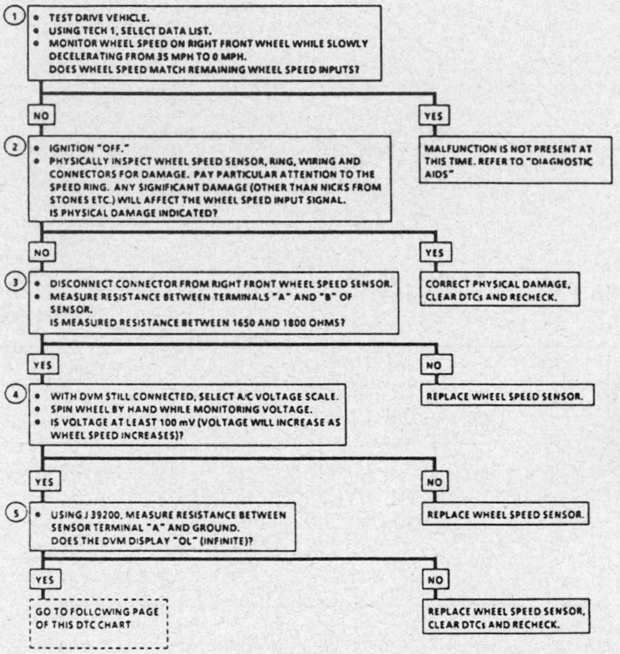
1
• TEST DRIVE VEHICLE.
• USING TECH 1, SELECT DATA LIST.
• MONITOR WHEEL SPEED ON RIGHT FRONT WHEEL WHILE SLOWLY DECELERATING FROM 35 MPH TO 0 MPH.
DOES WHEEL SPEED MATCH REMAINING WHEEL SPEED INPUTS?
NO
YES
MALFUNCTION IS NOT PRESENT AT THIS TIME. REFER TO "DIAGNOSTIC AIDS"
2
• IGNITION "OFF."
• PHYSICALLY INSPECT WHEEL SPEED SENSOR, RING, WIRING AND CONNECTORS FOR DAMAGE. PAY PARTICULAR ATTENTION TO THE SPEED RING. ANY SIGNIFICANT DAMAGE (OTHER THAN NICKS FROM STONES ETC.) WILL AFFECT THE WHEEL SPEED INPUT SIGNAL.
IS PHYSICAL DAMAGE INDICATED?
NO
YES
CORRECT PHYSICAL DAMAGE, CLEAR DTCs AND RECHECK.
3
• DISCONNECT CONNECTOR FROM RIGHT FRONT WHEEL SPEED SENSOR.
• MEASURE RESISTANCE BETWEEN TERMINALS "A" AND "B" OF SENSOR.
IS MEASURED RESISTANCE BETWEEN 1650 AND 1800 OHMS?
YES
NO
REPLACE WHEEL SPEED SENSOR.
4
• WITH DVM STILL CONNECTED, SELECT A/C VOLTAGE SCALE.
• SPIN WHEEL BY HAND WHILE MONITORING VOLTAGE.
• IS VOLTAGE AT LEAST 100 mV (VOLTAGE WILL INCREASE AS WHEEL SPEED INCREASES)?
YES
NO
REPLACE WHEEL SPEED SENSOR.
5
• USING J 39200, MEASURE RESISTANCE BETWEEN SENSOR TERMINAL "A" AND GROUND.
DOES THE DVM DISPLAY "OL" (INFINITE)?
YES
NO
GO TO FOLLOWING PAGE OF THIS DTC CHART
REPLACE WHEEL SPEED SENSOR, CLEAR DTCs AND RECHECK.

GC402930076300DX

Fig. 126 Code A026: Right Front Excessive Wheel Speed Variation (Part 1 of 2). 1993–94 Cavalier, Sunbird, Beretta, Corsica & Achieva, Grand Am & Skylark Less VES

DTC A026

RIGHT FRONT EXCESSIVE WHEEL SPEED VARIATION

Circuit Description:

As a toothed ring passes by the wheel speed sensor, changes in the electromagnetic field cause the wheel speed sensor to produce a sinusoidal (AC) voltage signal whose frequency is proportional to wheel speed. The magnitude of this signal is directly related to wheel speed and the proximity of the wheel speed sensor to the toothed ring, often referred to as the air gap.

Failure Condition:

DTC A026 can be set when the brake is "OFF." The purpose of this test is to detect a situation in which the right front wheel acceleration or deceleration is beyond specified limits.

Action Taken:

A malfunction DTC is stored, ABS is disabled and the ABS indicator lamp is turned "ON."

Test Description: Number(s) below refer to circled number(s) on the diagnostic chart.

6. This step checks for proper voltages at speed sensor harness connector.
7. This test ensures that the wheel speed sensor circuitry is not internally shorted.
8. This checks for an open in the wheel signal low circuit.
9. This checks for an open in the wheel signal high circuit.
10. This test checks for a short to ground in both high and low wheel signal circuits.
11. This step ensures that DTC A026 was not set due to a poor connection between the world connector and EBCM.

Diagnostic Aids:

An "Intermittent" malfunction may be caused by a poor connection, rubbed through wire insulation, or a wire that is broken inside the insulation.

The frequency of the malfunction can be checked by using the enhanced diagnostic function of the Tech 1

If the customer's comments reflect that the ABS amber indicator lamp is "ON" only during moist environmental changes, (rain, snow, vehicle wash) all wheel speed sensor circuitry should be thoroughly inspected for water intrusion. Use the following procedure. Spray down the suspected area with 5% salt water solution (two teaspoons of salt to 12 oz. of water). Start vehicle, allow vehicle to run for 10 seconds. If DTC returns immediately, replace suspected harness.

Any circuitry, that is suspected as causing the intermittent complaint, should be thoroughly checked for backed out terminals, improper mating, broken locks, improperly formed or damaged terminals, poor terminal to wiring connections or physical damage to the wiring harness.

A careful visual inspection of the toothed ring, CV joint, bearing and wheel speed sensor for physical damage should also be performed. If DTC sets at the same mph every time and wheel speed variation is noted above this mph on the Tech 1, the speed ring is most likely damaged. This can occur at any speed.

When measuring wheel speed sensor resistance, ensure vehicle is at room temperature. Wheel speed sensor resistance will vary with temperature.

When replacing a wheel speed sensor, inspect the sensor terminals and harness connector for corrosion and/or water intrusion. If evidence or corrosion or water intrusion exists, replace wheel speed sensor harness.

GC402930076300EX

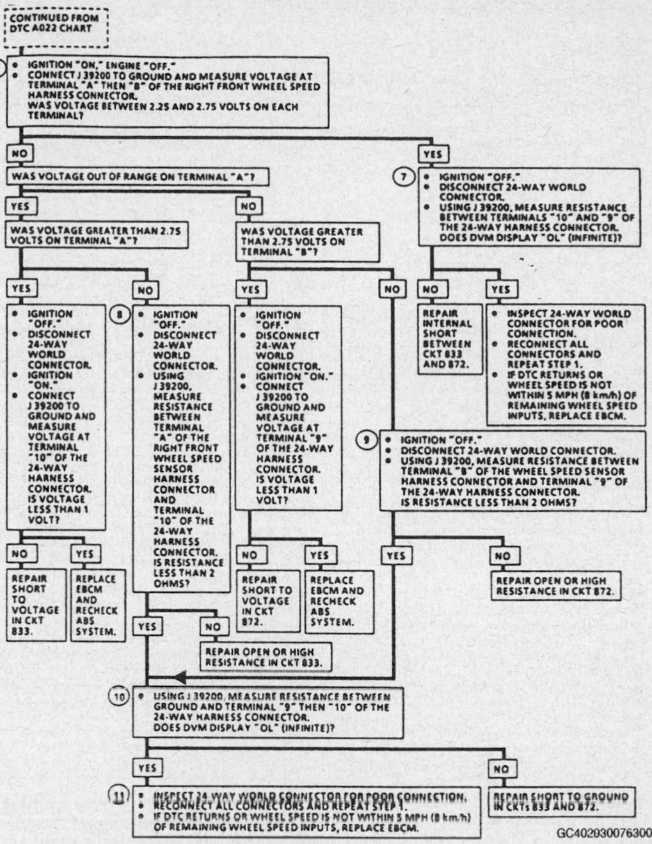
CONTINUED FROM DTC A022 CHART
6
• IGNITION "ON," ENGINE "OFF."
• CONNECT J 39200 TO GROUND AND MEASURE VOLTAGE AT TERMINAL "A" THEN "B" OF THE RIGHT FRONT WHEEL SPEED HARNESS CONNECTOR.
WAS VOLTAGE BETWEEN 2.25 AND 2.75 VOLTS ON EACH TERMINAL?
NO
YES
WAS VOLTAGE OUT OF RANGE ON TERMINAL "A"?
7
• IGNITION "OFF."
• DISCONNECT 24-WAY WORLD CONNECTOR.
• USING J 39200, MEASURE RESISTANCE BETWEEN TERMINALS "10" AND "9" OF THE 24-WAY HARNESS CONNECTOR.
DOES DVM DISPLAY "OL" (INFINITE)?
WAS VOLTAGE GREATER THAN 2.75 VOLTS ON TERMINAL "A"?
WAS VOLTAGE GREATER THAN 2.75 VOLTS ON TERMINAL "B"?
• IGNITION "OFF."
• DISCONNECT 24-WAY WORLD CONNECTOR.
• IGNITION "ON."
• CONNECT J 39200 TO GROUND AND MEASURE VOLTAGE AT TERMINAL "10" OF THE 24-WAY HARNESS CONNECTOR.
IS VOLTAGE LESS THAN 1 VOLT?
8
• IGNITION "OFF."
• DISCONNECT 24-WAY WORLD CONNECTOR.
• USING J 39200, MEASURE RESISTANCE BETWEEN TERMINAL "A" OF THE RIGHT FRONT WHEEL SPEED SENSOR HARNESS CONNECTOR AND TERMINAL "10" OF THE 24-WAY HARNESS CONNECTOR.
IS RESISTANCE LESS THAN 2 OHMS?
• IGNITION "OFF."
• DISCONNECT 24-WAY WORLD CONNECTOR.
• IGNITION "ON."
• CONNECT J 39200 TO GROUND AND MEASURE VOLTAGE AT TERMINAL "9" OF THE 24-WAY HARNESS CONNECTOR.
IS VOLTAGE LESS THAN 1 VOLT?
REPAIR INTERNAL SHORT BETWEEN CKT 833 AND 872.
• INSPECT 24-WAY WORLD CONNECTOR FOR POOR CONNECTION.
• RECONNECT ALL CONNECTORS AND REPEAT STEP 1.
• IF DTC RETURNS OR WHEEL SPEED IS NOT WITHIN 5 MPH (8 km/h) OF REMAINING WHEEL SPEED INPUTS, REPLACE EBCM.
9
• IGNITION "OFF."
• DISCONNECT 24-WAY WORLD CONNECTOR.
• USING J 39200, MEASURE RESISTANCE BETWEEN TERMINAL "B" OF THE WHEEL SPEED SENSOR HARNESS CONNECTOR AND TERMINAL "9" OF THE 24-WAY HARNESS CONNECTOR.
IS RESISTANCE LESS THAN 2 OHMS?
REPAIR SHORT TO VOLTAGE IN CKT 833.
REPLACE EBCM AND RECHECK ABS SYSTEM.
REPAIR SHORT TO VOLTAGE IN CKT 872.
REPLACE EBCM AND RECHECK ABS SYSTEM.
REPAIR OPEN OR HIGH RESISTANCE IN CKT 872.
REPAIR OPEN OR HIGH RESISTANCE IN CKT 833.
10
• USING J 39200, MEASURE RESISTANCE BETWEEN GROUND AND TERMINAL "9" THEN "10" OF THE 24-WAY HARNESS CONNECTOR.
DOES DVM DISPLAY "OL" (INFINITE)?
11
• INSPECT 24-WAY WORLD CONNECTOR FOR POOR CONNECTION.
• RECONNECT ALL CONNECTORS AND REPEAT STEP 1.
• IF DTC RETURNS OR WHEEL SPEED IS NOT WITHIN 5 MPH (8 km/h) OF REMAINING WHEEL SPEED INPUTS, REPLACE EBCM.
REPAIR SHORT TO GROUND IN CKTs 833 AND 872.

GC402930076300FX

Fig. 126 Code A026: Right Front Excessive Wheel Speed Variation (Part 2 of 2). 1993–94 Cavalier, Sunbird, Beretta, Corsica & Achieva, Grand Am & Skylark Less VES

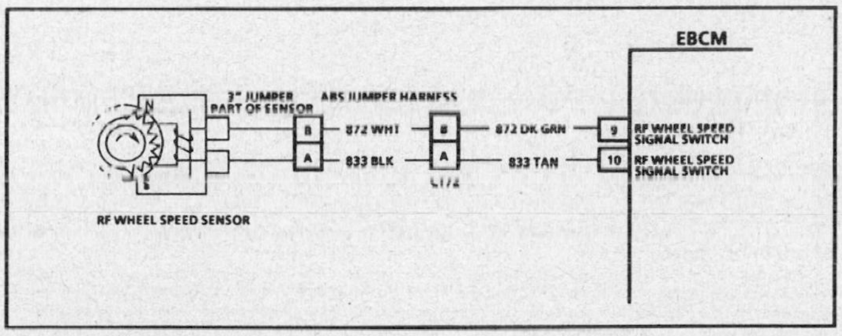
EBCM
3" JUMPER PART OF SENSOR
ABS JUMPER HARNESS
872 WHT
833 BLK
872 DK GRN
833 TAN
9 RF WHEEL SPEED SIGNAL SWITCH
10 RF WHEEL SPEED SIGNAL SWITCH
RF WHEEL SPEED SENSOR

Circuit Description:

As a toothed ring passes by the wheel speed sensor, changes in the electromagnetic field cause the wheel speed sensor to produce a sinusoidal (AC) voltage signal whose frequency is proportional to wheel speed. The magnitude of this signal is directly related to wheel speed and the proximity of the wheel speed sensor to the toothed ring, often referred to as the air gap.

DTC Will Set When: DTC 26 can be set when the brake is "OFF." The purpose of this test is to detect a situation in which the right front wheel acceleration or deceleration is beyond specified limits.

Action Taken: A malfunction DTC is stored, ABS is disabled and the ABS warning lamp is turned "ON."

DTC Chart Test Description: Number(s) below refer to circled number(s) on the diagnostic chart.

1. Determines if DTC 33 is present.
2. Designed to identify a wheel speed sensor or circuitry that is damaged and visibly apparent.
3. Checks to see that the wheel speed sensor is within proper resistance values.
4. Verifies that the wheel speed sensor can generate an appropriate output signal.

Diagnostic Aids: An "Intermittent" malfunction may be caused by a poor connection, rubbed through wire insulation, or a wire that is broken inside the insulation.

The frequency of the malfunction can be checked by using the enhanced diagnostic function of the Tech 1

If the customer's comments reflect that the ABS warning lamp is "ON" only during moist environmental changes (rain, snow, vehicle wash), all wheel speed sensor circuitry should be thoroughly inspected for signs of water intrusion. If DTC is not current, clear DTCs and simulate the effects of water intrusion. Use the following procedure. Spray down the suspected area with a 5% salt water solution (two teaspoons of salt to 12 oz. of water). Test drive vehicle over various road surfaces (bumps, turns, etc.) above 24 km/h (15 mph) for at least 30 seconds. If DTC returns replace suspected harness.

Any circuitry, that is suspected as causing the intermittent complaint, should be thoroughly checked for backed out terminals, improper mating, broken locks, improperly formed or damaged terminals, poor terminal to wiring connections or physical damage to the wiring harness.

Resistance of the wheel speed sensor will increase with an increase in sensor temperature.

When replacing a wheel speed sensor, inspect the sensor terminals and harness connector for corrosion and/or water intrusion. If evidence of corrosion or water intrusion exists, replace wheel speed sensor jumper harness. Likewise, if replacing a wheel speed sensor jumper harness, inspect sensor terminals. If evidence of corrosion or water intrusion exists, replace wheel speed sensor.

GC402930076401AA

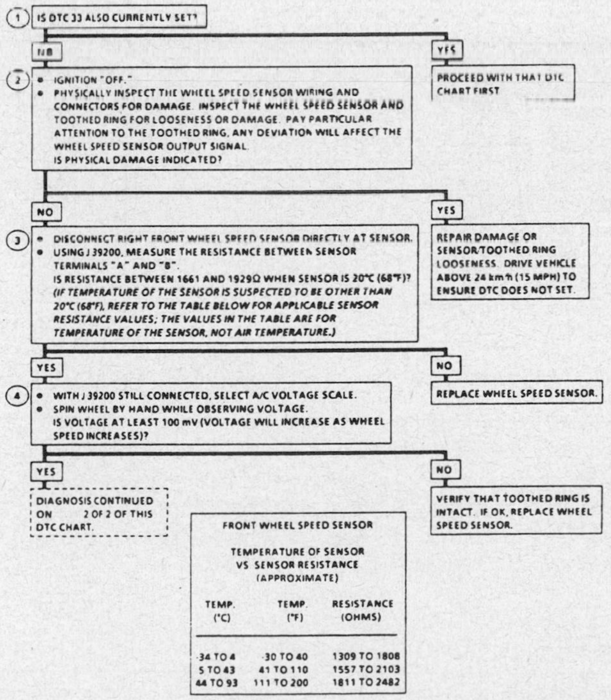
1
IS DTC 33 ALSO CURRENTLY SET?
NB
YES
PROCEED WITH THAT DTC CHART FIRST
2
• IGNITION "OFF."
• PHYSICALLY INSPECT THE WHEEL SPEED SENSOR WIRING AND CONNECTORS FOR DAMAGE. INSPECT THE WHEEL SPEED SENSOR AND TOOTHED RING FOR LOOSENESS OR DAMAGE. PAY PARTICULAR ATTENTION TO THE TOOTHED RING, ANY DEVIATION WILL AFFECT THE WHEEL SPEED SENSOR OUTPUT SIGNAL.
IS PHYSICAL DAMAGE INDICATED?
NO
YES
REPAIR DAMAGE OR SENSOR/TOOTHED RING LOOSENESS. DRIVE VEHICLE ABOVE 24 km/h (15 MPH) TO ENSURE DTC DOES NOT SET.
3
• DISCONNECT RIGHT FRONT WHEEL SPEED SENSOR DIRECTLY AT SENSOR.
• USING J 39200, MEASURE THE RESISTANCE BETWEEN SENSOR TERMINALS "A" AND "B".
IS RESISTANCE BETWEEN 1661 AND 1929Ω WHEN SENSOR IS 20°C (68°F)?
(IF TEMPERATURE OF THE SENSOR IS SUSPECTED TO BE OTHER THAN 20°C (68°F), REFER TO THE TABLE BELOW FOR APPLICABLE SENSOR RESISTANCE VALUES; THE VALUES IN THE TABLE ARE FOR TEMPERATURE OF THE SENSOR, NOT AIR TEMPERATURE.)
YES
NO
REPLACE WHEEL SPEED SENSOR.
4
• WITH J 39200 STILL CONNECTED, SELECT A/C VOLTAGE SCALE.
• SPIN WHEEL BY HAND WHILE OBSERVING VOLTAGE.
IS VOLTAGE AT LEAST 100 mV (VOLTAGE WILL INCREASE AS WHEEL SPEED INCREASES)?
YES
NO
DIAGNOSIS CONTINUED ON 2 OF 2 OF THIS DTC CHART.
VERIFY THAT TOOTHED RING IS INTACT. IF OK, REPLACE WHEEL SPEED SENSOR.
FRONT WHEEL SPEED SENSOR
TEMPERATURE OF SENSOR VS SENSOR RESISTANCE (APPROXIMATE)
TEMP. (°C) TEMP. (°F) RESISTANCE (OHMS)
-34 TO 4 -30 TO 40 1309 TO 1808
5 TO 43 41 TO 110 1557 TO 2103
44 TO 93 111 TO 200 1811 TO 2482

GC402930076401BA

Fig. 127 Code A026: Right Front Excessive Wheel Speed Variation (Part 1 of 2). 1993 Grand Prix, 1993–94 Cutlass Supreme, Lumina & Regal

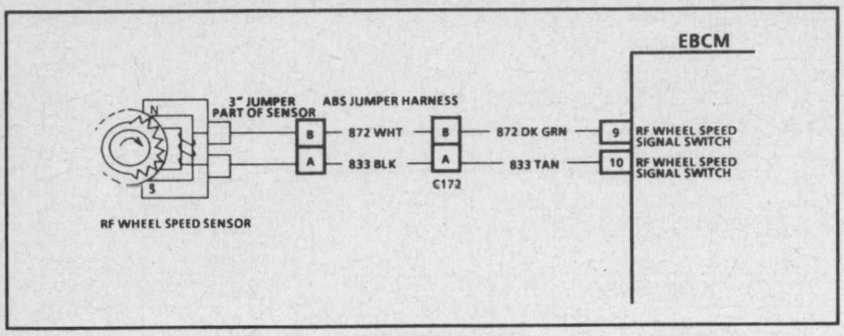

EBCM
3" JUMPER PART OF SENSOR
ABS JUMPER HARNESS
N
S
B
A
872 WHT
833 BLK
B
A
C172
872 DK GRN
833 TAN
9
10
RF WHEEL SPEED SIGNAL SWITCH
RF WHEEL SPEED SIGNAL SWITCH
RF WHEEL SPEED SENSOR

DTC 26

(Page 2 of 2)

RIGHT FRONT EXCESSIVE WHEEL SPEED VARIATION

Circuit Description:

As a toothed ring passes by the wheel speed sensor, changes in the electromagnetic field cause the wheel speed sensor to produce a sinusoidal (AC) voltage signal whose frequency is proportional to wheel speed. The magnitude of this signal is directly related to wheel speed and the proximity of the wheel speed sensor to the toothed ring, often referred to as the air gap.

DTC Will Set When: DTC 26 can be set when the brake is "OFF." The purpose of this test is to detect a situation in which the right front wheel acceleration or deceleration is beyond specified limits.

Action Taken: A malfunction DTC is stored, ABS is disabled and the ABS warning lamp is turned "ON."

DTC Chart Test Description: Number(s) below refer to circled number(s) on the diagnostic chart.

5. Checks for proper output voltage from the EBCM.
6. Checks for an open in the wheel speed sensor low circuit.
7. Ensures malfunction was not due to physical damage of the circuitry.
8. Ensures that wheel speed sensor circuitry is not shorted.
9. Ensures malfunction was not due to physical damage of the circuitry.
10. Checks for an open in the wheel speed sensor high circuit.

Diagnostic Aids: An "Intermittent" malfunction may be caused by a poor connection, rubbed through wire insulation, or a wire that is broken inside the insulation.

The frequency of the malfunction can be checked by using the enhanced diagnostic function of the Tech 1

If the customer's comments reflect that the ABS warning lamp is "ON" only during moist environmental changes (rain, snow, vehicle wash), all wheel speed sensor circuitry should be thoroughly inspected for signs of water intrusion. If DTC is not current, clear DTCs and simulate the effects of water intrusion. Use the following procedure. Spray down the suspected area with a 5% salt water solution (two teaspoons of salt to 12 oz. of water). Test drive vehicle over various road surfaces (bumps, turns, etc.) above 24 km/h (15 mph) for at least 30 seconds. If DTC returns replace suspected harness.

Any circuitry, that is suspected as causing the intermittent complaint, should be thoroughly checked for backed out terminals, improper mating, broken locks, improperly formed or damaged terminals, poor terminal to wiring connections or physical damage to the wiring harness.

Resistance of the wheel speed sensor will increase with an increase in sensor temperature.

When replacing a wheel speed sensor, inspect the sensor terminals and harness connector for corrosion and/or water intrusion. If evidence of corrosion or water intrusion exists, replace wheel speed sensor jumper harness. Likewise, if replacing a wheel speed sensor jumper harness, inspect sensor terminals. If evidence of corrosion or water intrusion exists, replace wheel speed sensor.

GC402930076402AA

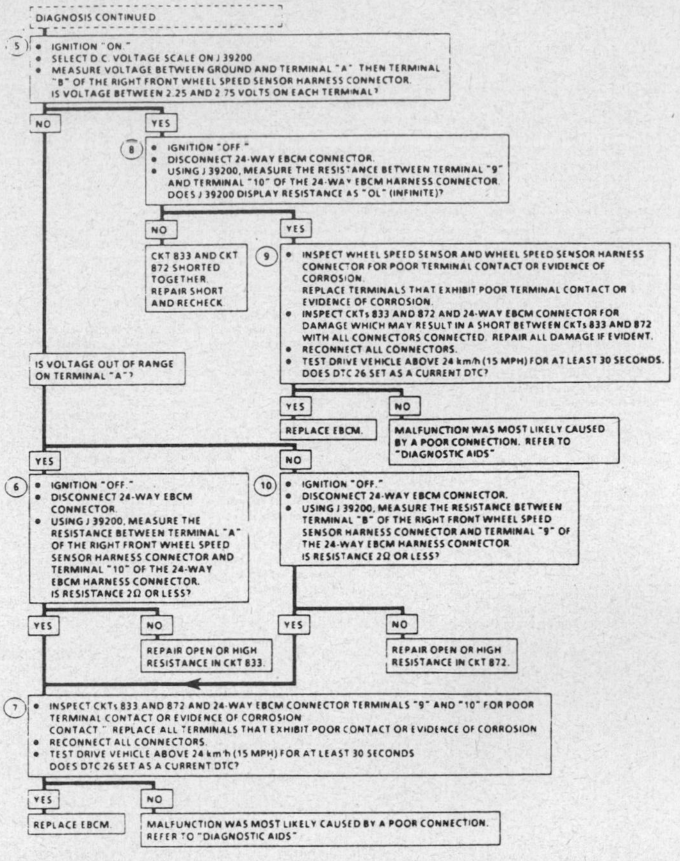

DIAGNOSIS CONTINUED
5
• IGNITION "ON."
• SELECT D.C. VOLTAGE SCALE ON J 39200
• MEASURE VOLTAGE BETWEEN GROUND AND TERMINAL "A" THEN TERMINAL "B" OF THE RIGHT FRONT WHEEL SPEED SENSOR HARNESS CONNECTOR.
IS VOLTAGE BETWEEN 2.25 AND 2.75 VOLTS ON EACH TERMINAL?
NO
YES
8
• IGNITION "OFF."
• DISCONNECT 24-WAY EBCM CONNECTOR.
• USING J 39200, MEASURE THE RESISTANCE BETWEEN TERMINAL "9" AND TERMINAL "10" OF THE 24-WAY EBCM HARNESS CONNECTOR.
DOES J 39200 DISPLAY RESISTANCE AS "OL" (INFINITE)?
NO
YES
CKT 833 AND CKT 872 SHORTED TOGETHER. REPAIR SHORT AND RECHECK.
9
• INSPECT WHEEL SPEED SENSOR AND WHEEL SPEED SENSOR HARNESS CONNECTOR FOR POOR TERMINAL CONTACT OR EVIDENCE OF CORROSION.
REPLACE TERMINALS THAT EXHIBIT POOR TERMINAL CONTACT OR EVIDENCE OF CORROSION.
• INSPECT CKTs 833 AND 872 AND 24-WAY EBCM CONNECTOR FOR DAMAGE WHICH MAY RESULT IN A SHORT BETWEEN CKTs 833 AND 872 WITH ALL CONNECTORS CONNECTED. REPAIR ALL DAMAGE IF EVIDENT.
• RECONNECT ALL CONNECTORS.
• TEST DRIVE VEHICLE ABOVE 24 km/h (15 MPH) FOR AT LEAST 30 SECONDS.
DOES DTC 26 SET AS A CURRENT DTC?
IS VOLTAGE OUT OF RANGE ON TERMINAL "A"?
YES
NO
REPLACE EBCM.
MALFUNCTION WAS MOST LIKELY CAUSED BY A POOR CONNECTION. REFER TO "DIAGNOSTIC AIDS"
YES
NO
6
• IGNITION "OFF."
• DISCONNECT 24-WAY EBCM CONNECTOR.
• USING J 39200, MEASURE THE RESISTANCE BETWEEN TERMINAL "A" OF THE RIGHT FRONT WHEEL SPEED SENSOR HARNESS CONNECTOR AND TERMINAL "10" OF THE 24-WAY EBCM HARNESS CONNECTOR.
IS RESISTANCE 2Ω OR LESS?
10
• IGNITION "OFF."
• DISCONNECT 24-WAY EBCM CONNECTOR.
• USING J 39200, MEASURE THE RESISTANCE BETWEEN TERMINAL "B" OF THE RIGHT FRONT WHEEL SPEED SENSOR HARNESS CONNECTOR AND TERMINAL "9" OF THE 24-WAY EBCM HARNESS CONNECTOR.
IS RESISTANCE 2Ω OR LESS?
YES
NO
YES
NO
REPAIR OPEN OR HIGH RESISTANCE IN CKT 833.
REPAIR OPEN OR HIGH RESISTANCE IN CKT 872.
7
• INSPECT CKTs 833 AND 872 AND 24-WAY EBCM CONNECTOR TERMINALS "9" AND "10" FOR POOR TERMINAL CONTACT OR EVIDENCE OF CORROSION
CONTACT. REPLACE ALL TERMINALS THAT EXHIBIT POOR CONTACT OR EVIDENCE OF CORROSION
• RECONNECT ALL CONNECTORS.
• TEST DRIVE VEHICLE ABOVE 24 km/h (15 MPH) FOR AT LEAST 30 SECONDS
DOES DTC 26 SET AS A CURRENT DTC?
YES
NO
REPLACE EBCM.
MALFUNCTION WAS MOST LIKELY CAUSED BY A POOR CONNECTION. REFER TO "DIAGNOSTIC AIDS"

GC402930076402BA

Fig. 127 Code A026: Right Front Excessive Wheel Speed Variation (Part 2 of 2). 1993 Grand Prix, 1993–94 Cutlass Supreme, Lumina & Regal

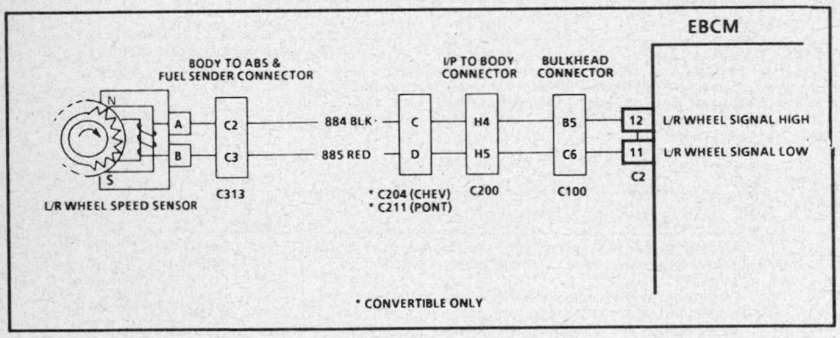

EBCM
BODY TO ABS & FUEL SENDER CONNECTOR
I/P TO BODY CONNECTOR
BULKHEAD CONNECTOR
N
S
A
B
C2
C3
884 BLK
885 RED
C
D
H4
H5
B5
C6
12
11
C2
L/R WHEEL SIGNAL HIGH
L/R WHEEL SIGNAL LOW
C313
* C204 (CHEV)
* C211 (PONT)
C200
C100
L/R WHEEL SPEED SENSOR
* CONVERTIBLE ONLY

GC402930076500AX

Cavalier & Sunbird

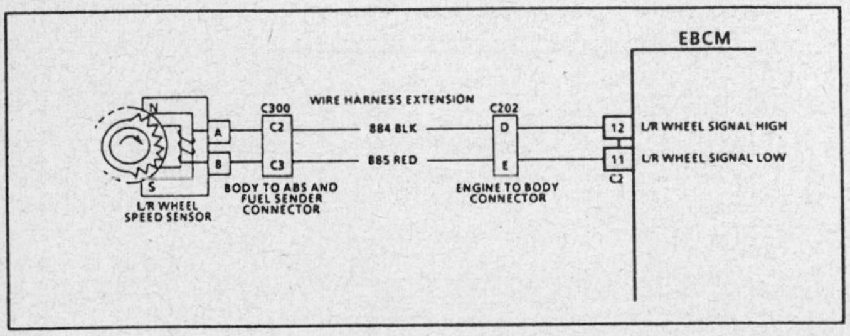

EBCM
WIRE HARNESS EXTENSION
C300
C202
N
S
A
B
C2
C3
884 BLK
885 RED
D
E
12
11
C2
L/R WHEEL SIGNAL HIGH
L/R WHEEL SIGNAL LOW
L/R WHEEL SPEED SENSOR
BODY TO ABS AND FUEL SENDER CONNECTOR
ENGINE TO BODY CONNECTOR

GC402930076500BX

Achieva, Beretta, Corsica, Grand Am & Skylark

DTC A027

LEFT REAR EXCESSIVE WHEEL SPEED VARIATION

Circuit Description:

As a toothed ring passes by the wheel speed sensor, changes in the electromagnetic field cause the wheel speed sensor to produce a sinusoidal (AC) voltage signal whose frequency is proportional to wheel speed. The magnitude of this signal is directly related to wheel speed and the proximity of the wheel speed sensor to the toothed ring, often referred to as the air gap.

Failure Condition:

DTC A027 can be set when the brake is "OFF." The purpose of this test is to detect a situation in which the left rear wheel acceleration or deceleration is beyond specified limits.

Action Taken:

A malfunction DTC is stored, ABS is disabled and the ABS indicator lamp is turned "ON."

Test Description: Number(s) below refer to circled number(s) on the diagnostic chart.

1. This test verifies whether the malfunction is currently present.
2. This step will identify a wheel speed sensor or circuitry that is damaged and visibly apparent.
3. This test checks wheel speed sensor for proper resistance values.
4. This test ensures the wheel speed sensor and sensor ring generate the proper voltage.
5. This step ensures the wheel speed sensor is not shorted to ground.

Diagnostic Aids:

An "Intermittent" malfunction may be caused by a poor connection, rubbed through wire insulation, or a wire that is broken inside the insulation.

The frequency of the malfunction can be checked by using the enhanced diagnostic function of the Tech 1

If the customer's comments reflect that the ABS amber indicator lamp is "ON" only during moist environmental changes, (rain, snow, vehicle wash) all wheel speed sensor circuitry should be thoroughly inspected for water intrusion. Use the following procedure. Spray down the suspected area with 5% salt water solution (two teaspoons of salt to 12 oz. of water). Start vehicle, allow vehicle to run for 10 seconds. If DTC returns immediately, replace suspected harness.

Any circuitry, that is suspected as causing the intermittent complaint, should be thoroughly checked for backed out terminals, improper mating, broken locks, improperly formed or damaged terminals, poor terminal to wiring connections or physical damage to the wiring harness.

Excessive end play can cause this DTC to set. Check integral bearing for excessive axial end play.

When measuring wheel speed sensor resistance, ensure vehicle is at room temperature. Wheel speed sensor resistance will vary with temperature.

When replacing a wheel speed sensor, inspect the sensor terminals and harness connector for corrosion and/or water intrusion. If evidence of corrosion or water intrusion exists, replace wheel speed sensor harness.

GC402930076500CX

Fig. 128 Code A027: Left Rear Excessive Wheel Speed Variation (Part 1 of 2). 1993–94 Cavalier, Sunbird, Beretta, Corsica & Achieva, Grand Am & Skylark Less VES

IMPORTANT: WHEEL SPEED SENSOR INTERMITTENT MALFUNCTIONS MAY BE DIFFICULT TO LOCATE. CARE SHOULD BE TAKEN NOT TO DISTURB ANY ELECTRICAL CONNECTIONS PRIOR TO AN INDICATED STEP OF THIS CHART. THIS WILL INSURE THAT AN INTERMITTENT CONNECTION WILL NOT BE CORRECTED BEFORE THE SOURCE OF THE MALFUNCTION IS FOUND.

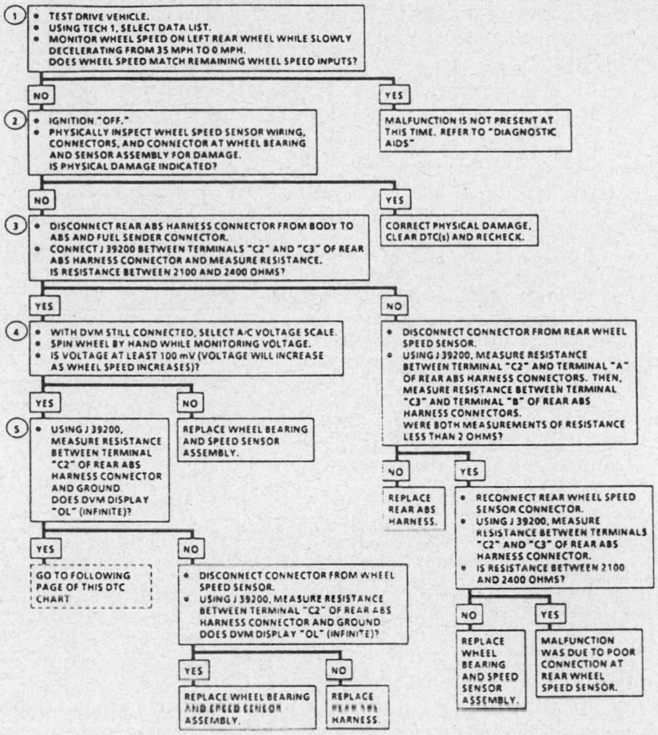
1 • TEST DRIVE VEHICLE.
• USING TECH 1, SELECT DATA LIST.
• MONITOR WHEEL SPEED ON LEFT REAR WHEEL WHILE SLOWLY DECELERATING FROM 35 MPH TO 0 MPH. DOES WHEEL SPEED MATCH REMAINING WHEEL SPEED INPUTS?
NO
YES
MALFUNCTION IS NOT PRESENT AT THIS TIME. REFER TO "DIAGNOSTIC AIDS"
2 • IGNITION "OFF."
• PHYSICALLY INSPECT WHEEL SPEED SENSOR WIRING, CONNECTORS, AND CONNECTOR AT WHEEL BEARING AND SENSOR ASSEMBLY FOR DAMAGE. IS PHYSICAL DAMAGE INDICATED?
NO
YES
CORRECT PHYSICAL DAMAGE, CLEAR DTC(s) AND RECHECK.
3 • DISCONNECT REAR ABS HARNESS CONNECTOR FROM BODY TO ABS AND FUEL SENDER CONNECTOR.
• CONNECT J 39200 BETWEEN TERMINALS "C2" AND "C3" OF REAR ABS HARNESS CONNECTOR AND MEASURE RESISTANCE. IS RESISTANCE BETWEEN 2100 AND 2400 OHMS?
YES
NO
4 • WITH DVM STILL CONNECTED, SELECT A/C VOLTAGE SCALE.
• SPIN WHEEL BY HAND WHILE MONITORING VOLTAGE.
• IS VOLTAGE AT LEAST 100 mV (VOLTAGE WILL INCREASE AS WHEEL SPEED INCREASES)?
• DISCONNECT CONNECTOR FROM REAR WHEEL SPEED SENSOR.
• USING J 39200, MEASURE RESISTANCE BETWEEN TERMINAL "C2" AND TERMINAL "A" OF REAR ABS HARNESS CONNECTORS. THEN, MEASURE RESISTANCE BETWEEN TERMINAL "C3" AND TERMINAL "B" OF REAR ABS HARNESS CONNECTORS. WERE BOTH MEASUREMENTS OF RESISTANCE LESS THAN 2 OHMS?
YES
NO
5 • USING J 39200, MEASURE RESISTANCE BETWEEN TERMINAL "C2" OF REAR ABS HARNESS CONNECTOR AND GROUND DOES DVM DISPLAY "OL" (INFINITE)?
REPLACE WHEEL BEARING AND SPEED SENSOR ASSEMBLY.
NO
YES
REPLACE REAR ABS HARNESS.
• RECONNECT REAR WHEEL SPEED SENSOR CONNECTOR.
• USING J 39200, MEASURE RESISTANCE BETWEEN TERMINALS "C2" AND "C3" OF REAR ABS HARNESS CONNECTOR.
• IS RESISTANCE BETWEEN 2100 AND 2400 OHMS?
YES
NO
GO TO FOLLOWING PAGE OF THIS DTC CHART
• DISCONNECT CONNECTOR FROM WHEEL SPEED SENSOR.
• USING J 39200, MEASURE RESISTANCE BETWEEN TERMINAL "C2" OF REAR ABS HARNESS CONNECTOR AND GROUND DOES DVM DISPLAY "OL" (INFINITE)?
NO
YES
REPLACE WHEEL BEARING AND SPEED SENSOR ASSEMBLY.
MALFUNCTION WAS DUE TO POOR CONNECTION AT REAR WHEEL SPEED SENSOR.
YES
NO
REPLACE WHEEL BEARING AND SPEED SENSOR ASSEMBLY.
REPLACE REAR ABS HARNESS.

GC402930076500DX

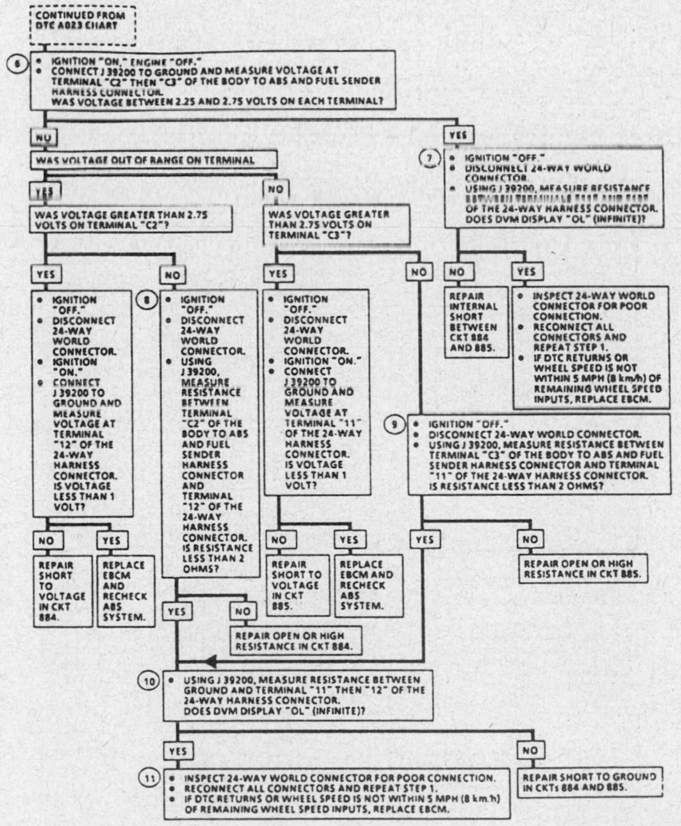
CONTINUED FROM DTC A023 CHART
6 • IGNITION "ON," ENGINE "OFF."
• CONNECT J 39200 TO GROUND AND MEASURE VOLTAGE AT TERMINAL "C2" THEN "C3" OF THE BODY TO ABS AND FUEL SENDER HARNESS CONNECTOR. WAS VOLTAGE BETWEEN 2.25 AND 2.75 VOLTS ON EACH TERMINAL?
NO
YES
WAS VOLTAGE OUT OF RANGE ON TERMINAL
7 • IGNITION "OFF."
• DISCONNECT 24-WAY WORLD CONNECTOR.
• USING J 39200, MEASURE RESISTANCE OF THE 24-WAY HARNESS CONNECTOR. DOES DVM DISPLAY "OL" (INFINITE)?
YES
NO
WAS VOLTAGE GREATER THAN 2.75 VOLTS ON TERMINAL "C2"?
WAS VOLTAGE GREATER THAN 2.75 VOLTS ON TERMINAL "C3"?
NO
YES
REPAIR INTERNAL SHORT BETWEEN CKT 884 AND 885.
• INSPECT 24-WAY WORLD CONNECTOR FOR POOR CONNECTION.
• RECONNECT ALL CONNECTORS AND REPEAT STEP 1.
• IF DTC RETURNS OR WHEEL SPEED IS NOT WITHIN 5 MPH (8 km/h) OF REMAINING WHEEL SPEED INPUTS, REPLACE EBCM.
YES
NO
YES
NO
• IGNITION "OFF."
• DISCONNECT 24-WAY WORLD CONNECTOR.
• IGNITION "ON."
• CONNECT J 39200 TO GROUND AND MEASURE VOLTAGE AT TERMINAL "12" OF THE 24-WAY HARNESS CONNECTOR. IS VOLTAGE LESS THAN 1 VOLT?
8 • IGNITION "OFF."
• DISCONNECT 24-WAY WORLD CONNECTOR.
• USING J 39200, MEASURE RESISTANCE BETWEEN TERMINAL "C2" OF THE BODY TO ABS AND FUEL SENDER HARNESS CONNECTOR AND TERMINAL "12" OF THE 24-WAY HARNESS CONNECTOR. IS RESISTANCE LESS THAN 2 OHMS?
• IGNITION "OFF."
• DISCONNECT 24-WAY WORLD CONNECTOR.
• IGNITION "ON."
• CONNECT J 39200 TO GROUND AND MEASURE VOLTAGE AT TERMINAL "11" OF THE 24-WAY HARNESS CONNECTOR. IS VOLTAGE LESS THAN 1 VOLT?
9 • IGNITION "OFF."
• DISCONNECT 24-WAY WORLD CONNECTOR.
• USING J 39200, MEASURE RESISTANCE BETWEEN TERMINAL "C3" OF THE BODY TO ABS AND FUEL SENDER HARNESS CONNECTOR AND TERMINAL "11" OF THE 24-WAY HARNESS CONNECTOR. IS RESISTANCE LESS THAN 2 OHMS?
NO
YES
NO
YES
YES
NO
REPAIR SHORT TO VOLTAGE IN CKT 884.
REPLACE EBCM AND RECHECK ABS SYSTEM.
REPAIR SHORT TO VOLTAGE IN CKT 885.
REPLACE EBCM AND RECHECK ABS SYSTEM.
REPAIR OPEN OR HIGH RESISTANCE IN CKT 885.
YES
NO
REPAIR OPEN OR HIGH RESISTANCE IN CKT 884.
10 • USING J 39200, MEASURE RESISTANCE BETWEEN GROUND AND TERMINAL "11" THEN "12" OF THE 24-WAY HARNESS CONNECTOR. DOES DVM DISPLAY "OL" (INFINITE)?
YES
NO
11 • INSPECT 24-WAY WORLD CONNECTOR FOR POOR CONNECTION.
• RECONNECT ALL CONNECTORS AND REPEAT STEP 1.
• IF DTC RETURNS OR WHEEL SPEED IS NOT WITHIN 5 MPH (8 km/h) OF REMAINING WHEEL SPEED INPUTS, REPLACE EBCM.
REPAIR SHORT TO GROUND IN CKTs 884 AND 885.

GC402930076500EX

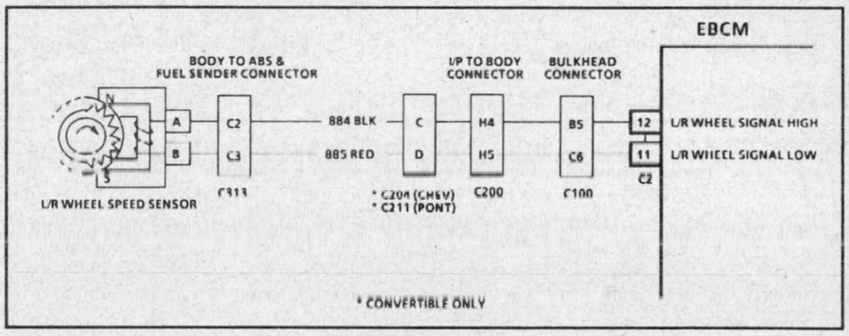
EBCM
BODY TO ABS & FUEL SENDER CONNECTOR
I/P TO BODY CONNECTOR
BULKHEAD CONNECTOR
A
B
C2
C3
884 BLK
885 RED
C
D
H4
H5
B5
C6
12
11
L/R WHEEL SIGNAL HIGH
L/R WHEEL SIGNAL LOW
C2
C313
* C204 (CHEV)
* C211 (PONT)
C200
C100
L/R WHEEL SPEED SENSOR
* CONVERTIBLE ONLY

DTC A027

LEFT REAR EXCESSIVE WHEEL SPEED VARIATION

Circuit Description:

As a toothed ring passes by the wheel speed sensor, changes in the electromagnetic field cause the wheel speed sensor to produce a sinusoidal (AC) voltage signal whose frequency is proportional to wheel speed. The magnitude of this signal is directly related to wheel speed and the proximity of the wheel speed sensor to the toothed ring, often referred to as the air gap.

Failure Condition:

DTC A027 can be set when the brake is "OFF." The purpose of this test is to detect a situation in which the left rear wheel acceleration or deceleration is beyond specified limits.

Action Taken:

A malfunction DTC is stored, ABS is disabled and the ABS indicator lamp is turned "ON."

Test Description: Number(s) below refer to circled number(s) on the diagnostic chart.

6. This step checks for proper voltages at body to ABS and fuel sender harness connector.
7. This test ensures that the wheel speed sensor circuitry is not internally shorted.
8. This checks for an open in the wheel signal high circuit.
9. This checks for an open in the wheel signal low circuit.
10. This test checks for a short to ground in both high and low wheel signal circuits.
11. This step ensures that DTC A027 was not set due to a poor connection between the world connector and EBCM.

Diagnostic Aids:

An "Intermittent" malfunction may be caused by a poor connection, rubbed through wire insulation, or a wire that is broken inside the insulation.

The frequency of the malfunction can be checked by using the enhanced diagnostic function of the Tech 1, as described in "Enhanced Diagnostics," found in this section.

If the customer's comments reflect that the ABS amber indicator lamp is "ON" only during moist environmental changes, (rain, snow, vehicle wash) all wheel speed sensor circuitry should be thoroughly inspected for water intrusion. Use the following procedure. Spray down the suspected area with 5% salt water solution (two teaspoons of salt to 12 oz. of water). Start vehicle, allow vehicle to run for 10 seconds. If DTC returns immediately, replace suspected harness.

Any circuitry, that is suspected as causing the intermittent complaint, should be thoroughly checked for backed out terminals, improper mating, broken locks, improperly formed or damaged terminals, poor terminal to wiring connections or physical damage to the wiring harness.

Excessive end play can cause this DTC to set. Check integral bearing for excessive axial end play.

When measuring wheel speed sensor resistance, ensure vehicle is at room temperature. Wheel speed sensor resistance will vary with temperature.

When replacing a wheel speed sensor, inspect the sensor terminals and harness connector for corrosion and/or water intrusion. If evidence of corrosion or water intrusion exists, replace wheel speed sensor harness.

GC402930076500FX

Fig. 128 Code A027: Left Rear Excessive Wheel Speed Variation (Part 2 of 2). 1993–94 Cavalier, Sunbird, Beretta, Corsica & Achieva, Grand Am & Skylark Less VES

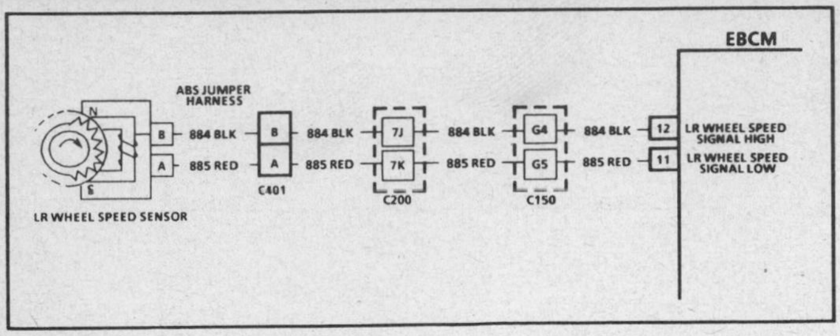
EBCM
ABS JUMPER HARNESS
B 884 BLK B 884 BLK 7J 884 BLK G4 884 BLK 12 LR WHEEL SPEED SIGNAL HIGH
A 885 RED A 885 RED 7K 885 RED G5 885 RED 11 LR WHEEL SPEED SIGNAL LOW
N
S
C401
C200
C150
LR WHEEL SPEED SENSOR

Circuit Description:

As a toothed ring passes by the wheel speed sensor, changes in the electromagnetic field cause the wheel speed sensor to produce a sinusoidal (AC) voltage signal whose frequency is proportional to wheel speed. The magnitude of this signal is directly related to wheel speed and the proximity of the wheel speed sensor to the toothed ring, often referred to as the air gap.

DTC Will Set When: DTC 27 can be set when the brake is "OFF." The purpose of this test is to detect a situation in which the left rear wheel acceleration or deceleration is beyond specified limits.

Action Taken: A malfunction DTC is stored, ABS is disabled and the ABS warning lamp is turned "ON."

DTC Chart Test Description: Number(s) below refer to circled number(s) on the diagnostic chart.

1. Determines if DTC 34 is present.
2. Designed to identify a wheel speed sensor or circuitry that is damaged and visibly apparent.
3. Checks to see that the wheel speed sensor is within proper resistance values.
4. Verifies that the wheel speed sensor can generate an appropriate output signal.

Diagnostic Aids: An "Intermittent" malfunction may be caused by a poor connection, rubbed through wire insulation, or a wire that is broken inside the insulation.

The frequency of the malfunction can be checked by using the enhanced diagnostic function of the Tech 1

If the customer's comments reflect that the ABS warning lamp is "ON" only during moist environmental changes (rain, snow, vehicle wash), all wheel speed sensor circuitry should be thoroughly inspected for signs of water intrusion. If DTC is not current, clear DTCs and simulate the effects of water intrusion. Use the following procedure. Spray down the suspected area with a 5% salt water solution (two teaspoons of salt to 12 oz. of water). Test drive vehicle over various road surfaces (bumps, turns, etc.) above 24 km/h (15 mph) for at least 30 seconds. If DTC returns replace suspected harness.

Any circuitry, that is suspected as causing the intermittent complaint, should be thoroughly checked for backed out terminals, improper mating, broken locks, improperly formed or damaged terminals, poor terminal to wiring connections or physical damage to the wiring harness.

Resistance of the wheel speed sensor will increase with an increase in sensor temperature.

When replacing a wheel speed sensor, inspect the sensor terminals and harness connector for corrosion and/or water intrusion. If evidence of corrosion or water intrusion exists, replace wheel speed sensor jumper harness. Likewise, if replacing a wheel speed sensor jumper harness, inspect sensor terminals. If evidence of corrosion or water intrusion exists, replace wheel speed sensor.

GC402930076601AA

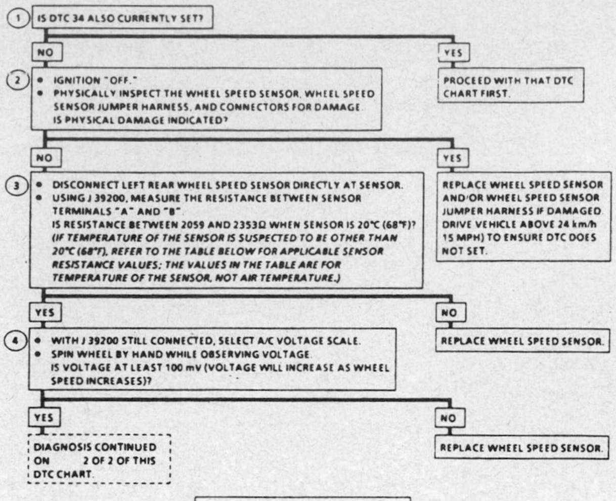
1 IS DTC 34 ALSO CURRENTLY SET?
NO
YES
PROCEED WITH THAT DTC CHART FIRST.
2 • IGNITION "OFF." • PHYSICALLY INSPECT THE WHEEL SPEED SENSOR, WHEEL SPEED SENSOR JUMPER HARNESS, AND CONNECTORS FOR DAMAGE. IS PHYSICAL DAMAGE INDICATED?
NO
YES
REPLACE WHEEL SPEED SENSOR AND/OR WHEEL SPEED SENSOR JUMPER HARNESS IF DAMAGED. DRIVE VEHICLE ABOVE 24 km/h 15 MPH) TO ENSURE DTC DOES NOT SET.
3 • DISCONNECT LEFT REAR WHEEL SPEED SENSOR DIRECTLY AT SENSOR. • USING J 39200, MEASURE THE RESISTANCE BETWEEN SENSOR TERMINALS "A" AND "B". IS RESISTANCE BETWEEN 2059 AND 2353Ω WHEN SENSOR IS 20°C (68°F)? (IF TEMPERATURE OF THE SENSOR IS SUSPECTED TO BE OTHER THAN 20°C (68°F), REFER TO THE TABLE BELOW FOR APPLICABLE SENSOR RESISTANCE VALUES; THE VALUES IN THE TABLE ARE FOR TEMPERATURE OF THE SENSOR, NOT AIR TEMPERATURE.)
YES
NO
REPLACE WHEEL SPEED SENSOR.
4 • WITH J 39200 STILL CONNECTED, SELECT A/C VOLTAGE SCALE. • SPIN WHEEL BY HAND WHILE OBSERVING VOLTAGE. IS VOLTAGE AT LEAST 100 mV (VOLTAGE WILL INCREASE AS WHEEL SPEED INCREASES)?
YES
NO
DIAGNOSIS CONTINUED ON 2 OF 2 OF THIS DTC CHART.
REPLACE WHEEL SPEED SENSOR.

REAR WHEEL SPEED SENSOR

TEMPERATURE OF SENSOR VS SENSOR RESISTANCE (APPROXIMATE)

TEMP. (°C)	TEMP. (°F)	RESISTANCE (OHMS)
-34 TO 4	-30 TO 40	1622 TO 2205
5 TO 43	41 TO 110	1930 TO 2566
44 TO 93	111 TO 200	2245 TO 3028

GC402930076601BA

Fig. 129 Code A027: Left Rear Excessive Wheel Speed Variation (Part 1 of 2). 1993 Grand Prix, 1993–94 Cutlass Supreme, Lumina & Regal

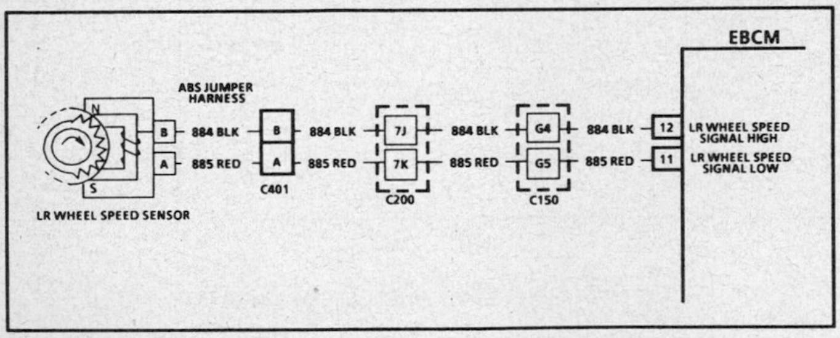
EBCM
ABS JUMPER HARNESS
B 884 BLK B 884 BLK 7J 884 BLK G4 884 BLK 12 LR WHEEL SPEED SIGNAL HIGH
A 885 RED A 885 RED 7K 885 RED G5 885 RED 11 LR WHEEL SPEED SIGNAL LOW
N
S
C401
C200
C150
LR WHEEL SPEED SENSOR

Circuit Description:

As a toothed ring passes by the wheel speed sensor, changes in the electromagnetic field cause the wheel speed sensor to produce a sinusoidal (AC) voltage signal whose frequency is proportional to wheel speed. The magnitude of this signal is directly related to wheel speed and the proximity of the wheel speed sensor to the toothed ring, often referred to as the air gap.

DTC Will Set When: DTC 27 can be set when the brake is "OFF." The purpose of this test is to detect a situation in which the left rear wheel acceleration or deceleration is beyond specified limits.

Action Taken: A malfunction DTC is stored, ABS is disabled and the ABS warning lamp is turned "ON."

DTC Chart Test Description: Number(s) below refer to circled number(s) on the diagnostic chart.

5. Checks for proper output voltage from the EBCM.
6. Checks for an open in the wheel speed sensor low circuit.
7. Ensures malfunction was not due to physical damage of the circuitry.
8. Ensures that wheel speed sensor circuitry is not shorted.
9. Ensures malfunction was not due to physical damage of the circuitry.
10. Checks for an open in the wheel speed sensor high circuit.

Diagnostic Aids: An "Intermittent" malfunction may be caused by a poor connection, rubbed through wire insulation, or a wire that is broken inside the insulation.

The frequency of the malfunction can be checked by using the enhanced diagnostic function of the Tech 1

If the customer's comments reflect that the ABS warning lamp is "ON" only during moist environmental changes (rain, snow, vehicle wash), all wheel speed sensor circuitry should be thoroughly inspected for signs of water intrusion. If DTC is not current, clear DTCs and simulate the effects of water intrusion. Use the following procedure. Spray down the suspected area with a 5% salt water solution (two teaspoons of salt to 12 oz. of water). Test drive vehicle over various road surfaces (bumps, turns, etc.) above 24 km/h (15 mph) for at least 30 seconds. If DTC returns replace suspected harness.

Any circuitry, that is suspected as causing the intermittent complaint, should be thoroughly checked for backed out terminals, improper mating, broken locks, improperly formed or damaged terminals, poor terminal to wiring connections or physical damage to the wiring harness.

Resistance of the wheel speed sensor will increase with an increase in sensor temperature.

When replacing a wheel speed sensor, inspect the sensor terminals and harness connector for corrosion and/or water intrusion. If evidence of corrosion or water intrusion exists, replace wheel speed sensor jumper harness. Likewise, if replacing a wheel speed sensor jumper harness, inspect sensor terminals. If evidence of corrosion or water intrusion exists, replace wheel speed sensor. Refer to "On-Vehicle Service" in this section.

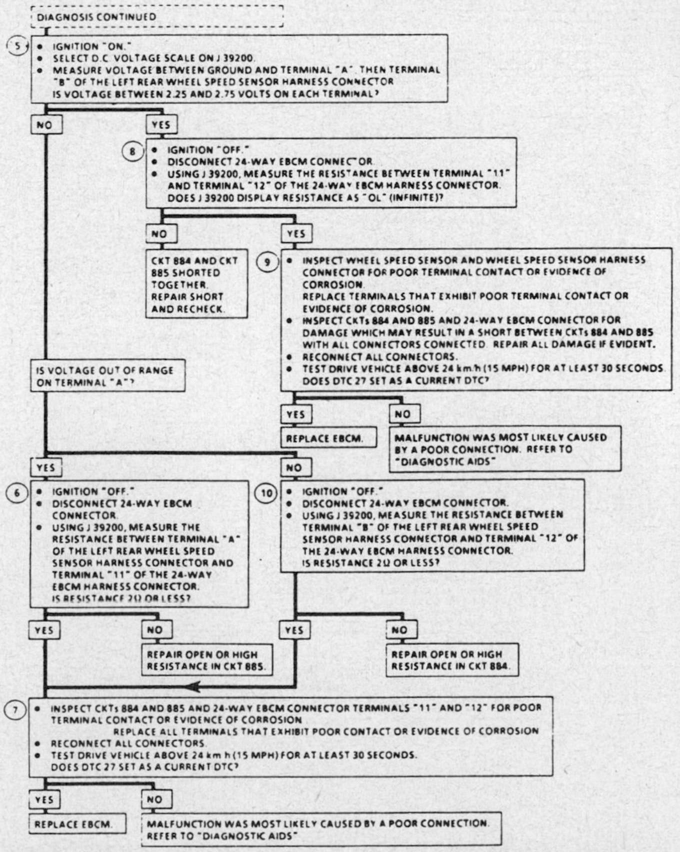
DIAGNOSIS CONTINUED
5 • IGNITION "ON." • SELECT D.C. VOLTAGE SCALE ON J 39200. • MEASURE VOLTAGE BETWEEN GROUND AND TERMINAL "A", THEN TERMINAL "B" OF THE LEFT REAR WHEEL SPEED SENSOR HARNESS CONNECTOR IS VOLTAGE BETWEEN 2.25 AND 2.75 VOLTS ON EACH TERMINAL?
NO
YES
8 • IGNITION "OFF." • DISCONNECT 24-WAY EBCM CONNECTOR. • USING J 39200, MEASURE THE RESISTANCE BETWEEN TERMINAL "11" AND TERMINAL "12" OF THE 24-WAY EBCM HARNESS CONNECTOR. DOES J 39200 DISPLAY RESISTANCE AS "OL" (INFINITE)?
NO
YES
CKT 884 AND CKT 885 SHORTED TOGETHER. REPAIR SHORT AND RECHECK.
9 • INSPECT WHEEL SPEED SENSOR AND WHEEL SPEED SENSOR HARNESS CONNECTOR FOR POOR TERMINAL CONTACT OR EVIDENCE OF CORROSION. REPLACE TERMINALS THAT EXHIBIT POOR TERMINAL CONTACT OR EVIDENCE OF CORROSION. • INSPECT CKTs 884 AND 885 AND 24-WAY EBCM CONNECTOR FOR DAMAGE WHICH MAY RESULT IN A SHORT BETWEEN CKTs 884 AND 885 WITH ALL CONNECTORS CONNECTED. REPAIR ALL DAMAGE IF EVIDENT. • RECONNECT ALL CONNECTORS. • TEST DRIVE VEHICLE ABOVE 24 km/h (15 MPH) FOR AT LEAST 30 SECONDS. DOES DTC 27 SET AS A CURRENT DTC?
IS VOLTAGE OUT OF RANGE ON TERMINAL "A"?
YES
NO
REPLACE EBCM.
MALFUNCTION WAS MOST LIKELY CAUSED BY A POOR CONNECTION. REFER TO "DIAGNOSTIC AIDS"
YES
NO
6 • IGNITION "OFF." • DISCONNECT 24-WAY EBCM CONNECTOR. • USING J 39200, MEASURE THE RESISTANCE BETWEEN TERMINAL "A" OF THE LEFT REAR WHEEL SPEED SENSOR HARNESS CONNECTOR AND TERMINAL "11" OF THE 24-WAY EBCM HARNESS CONNECTOR. IS RESISTANCE 2Ω OR LESS?
10 • IGNITION "OFF." • DISCONNECT 24-WAY EBCM CONNECTOR. • USING J 39200, MEASURE THE RESISTANCE BETWEEN TERMINAL "B" OF THE LEFT REAR WHEEL SPEED SENSOR HARNESS CONNECTOR AND TERMINAL "12" OF THE 24-WAY EBCM HARNESS CONNECTOR. IS RESISTANCE 2Ω OR LESS?
YES
NO
YES
NO
REPAIR OPEN OR HIGH RESISTANCE IN CKT 885.
REPAIR OPEN OR HIGH RESISTANCE IN CKT 884.
7 • INSPECT CKTs 884 AND 885 AND 24-WAY EBCM CONNECTOR TERMINALS "11" AND "12" FOR POOR TERMINAL CONTACT OR EVIDENCE OF CORROSION. REPLACE ALL TERMINALS THAT EXHIBIT POOR CONTACT OR EVIDENCE OF CORROSION • RECONNECT ALL CONNECTORS. • TEST DRIVE VEHICLE ABOVE 24 km/h (15 MPH) FOR AT LEAST 30 SECONDS. DOES DTC 27 SET AS A CURRENT DTC?
YES
NO
REPLACE EBCM.
MALFUNCTION WAS MOST LIKELY CAUSED BY A POOR CONNECTION. REFER TO "DIAGNOSTIC AIDS"

Fig. 129 Code A027: Left Rear Excessive Wheel Speed Variation (Part 2 of 2). 1993 Grand Prix, 1993–94 Cutlass Supreme, Lumina & Regal

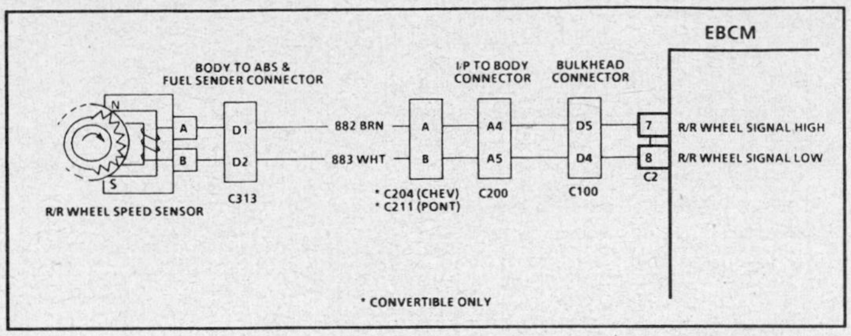
EBCM
BODY TO ABS & FUEL SENDER CONNECTOR
I/P TO BODY CONNECTOR
BULKHEAD CONNECTOR
882 BRN
883 WHT
R/R WHEEL SIGNAL HIGH
R/R WHEEL SIGNAL LOW
C313
* C204 (CHEV)
* C211 (PONT)
C200
C100
C2
R/R WHEEL SPEED SENSOR
* CONVERTIBLE ONLY

GC402930076700AX

Cavalier & Sunbird

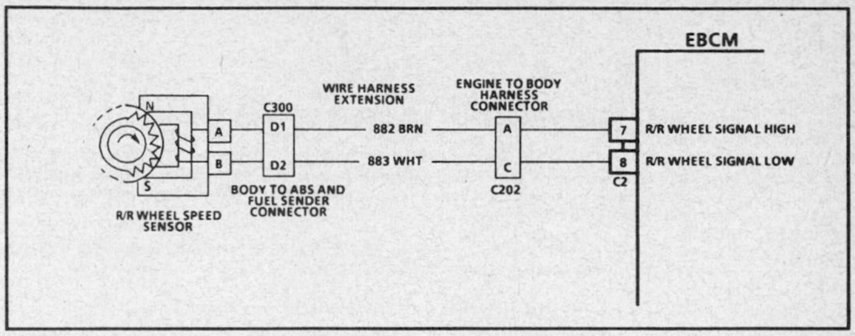
EBCM
WIRE HARNESS EXTENSION
ENGINE TO BODY HARNESS CONNECTOR
C300
882 BRN
883 WHT
R/R WHEEL SIGNAL HIGH
R/R WHEEL SIGNAL LOW
C202
C2
BODY TO ABS AND FUEL SENDER CONNECTOR
R/R WHEEL SPEED SENSOR

GC402930076700BX

Achieva, Beretta, Corsica, Grand Am & Skylark

DTC A028

RIGHT REAR EXCESSIVE WHEEL SPEED VARIATION

Circuit Description:

As a toothed ring passes by the wheel speed sensor, changes in the electromagnetic field cause the wheel speed sensor to produce a sinusoidal (AC) voltage signal whose frequency is proportional to wheel speed. The magnitude of this signal is directly related to wheel speed and the proximity of the wheel speed sensor to the toothed ring, often referred to as the air gap.

Failure Condition:

DTC A028 can be set when the brake is "OFF." The purpose of this test is to detect a situation in which the right rear wheel acceleration or deceleration is beyond specified limits.

Action Taken:

A malfunction DTC is stored, ABS is disabled and the ABS indicator lamp is turned "ON."

Test Description: Number(s) below refer to circled number(s) on the diagnostic chart.

1. This test verifies whether the malfunction is currently present.
2. This step will identify a wheel speed sensor or circuitry that is damaged and visibly apparent.
3. This test checks wheel speed sensor for proper resistance values.
4. This test ensures the wheel speed sensor and sensor ring generate the proper voltage.
5. This step ensures the wheel speed sensor is not shorted to ground.

Diagnostic Aids:

An "Intermittent" malfunction may be caused by a poor connection, rubbed through wire insulation, or a wire that is broken inside the insulation.

The frequency of the malfunction can be checked by using the enhanced diagnostic function of the Tech 1.

If the customer's comments reflect that the ABS amber indicator lamp is "ON" only during moist environmental changes, (rain, snow, vehicle wash) all wheel speed sensor circuitry should be thoroughly inspected for water intrusion. Use the following procedure. Spray down the suspected area with 5% salt water solution (two teaspoons of salt to 12 oz. of water). Start vehicle, allow vehicle to run for 10 seconds. If DTC returns immediately, replace suspected harness.

Any circuitry, that is suspected as causing the intermittent complaint, should be thoroughly checked for backed out terminals, improper mating, broken locks, improperly formed or damaged terminals, poor terminal to wiring connections or physical damage to the wiring harness.

Excessive end play can cause this DTC to set. Check integral bearing for excessive axial end play,

When measuring wheel speed sensor resistance, ensure vehicle is at room temperature. Wheel speed sensor resistance will vary with temperature.

When replacing a wheel speed sensor, inspect the sensor terminals and harness connector for corrosion and/or water intrusion. If evidence of corrosion or water intrusion exists, replace wheel speed sensor harness.

GC402930076700CX

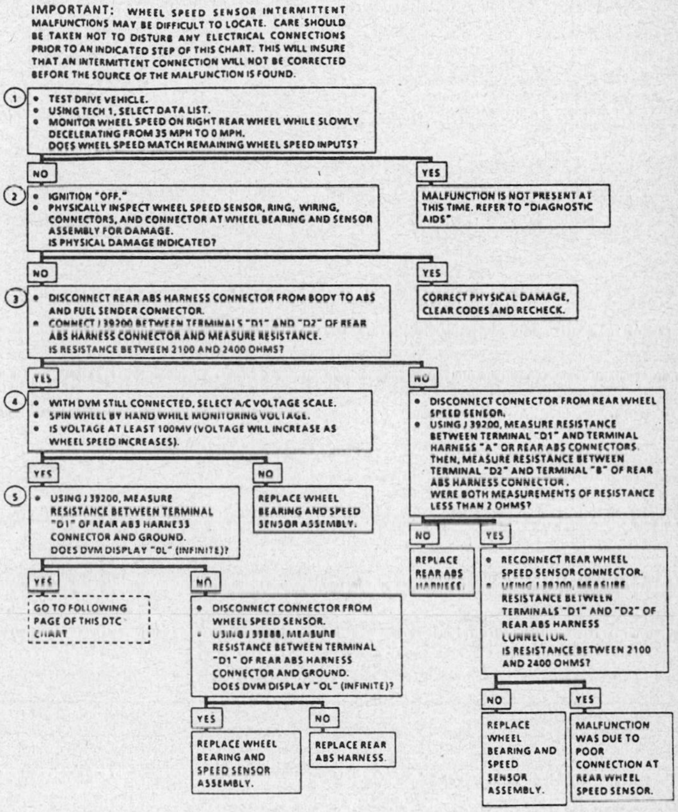
IMPORTANT: WHEEL SPEED SENSOR INTERMITTENT MALFUNCTIONS MAY BE DIFFICULT TO LOCATE. CARE SHOULD BE TAKEN NOT TO DISTURB ANY ELECTRICAL CONNECTIONS PRIOR TO AN INDICATED STEP OF THIS CHART. THIS WILL INSURE THAT AN INTERMITTENT CONNECTION WILL NOT BE CORRECTED BEFORE THE SOURCE OF THE MALFUNCTION IS FOUND.
1 • TEST DRIVE VEHICLE. • USING TECH 1, SELECT DATA LIST. • MONITOR WHEEL SPEED ON RIGHT REAR WHEEL WHILE SLOWLY DECELERATING FROM 35 MPH TO 0 MPH. DOES WHEEL SPEED MATCH REMAINING WHEEL SPEED INPUTS?
NO
YES
MALFUNCTION IS NOT PRESENT AT THIS TIME. REFER TO "DIAGNOSTIC AIDS"
2 • IGNITION "OFF." • PHYSICALLY INSPECT WHEEL SPEED SENSOR, RING, WIRING, CONNECTORS, AND CONNECTOR AT WHEEL BEARING AND SENSOR ASSEMBLY FOR DAMAGE. IS PHYSICAL DAMAGE INDICATED?
NO
YES
CORRECT PHYSICAL DAMAGE, CLEAR CODES AND RECHECK.
3 • DISCONNECT REAR ABS HARNESS CONNECTOR FROM BODY TO ABS AND FUEL SENDER CONNECTOR. • CONNECT J 39200 BETWEEN TERMINALS "D1" AND "D2" OF REAR ABS HARNESS CONNECTOR AND MEASURE RESISTANCE. IS RESISTANCE BETWEEN 2100 AND 2400 OHMS?
YES
NO
4 • WITH DVM STILL CONNECTED, SELECT A/C VOLTAGE SCALE. • SPIN WHEEL BY HAND WHILE MONITORING VOLTAGE. • IS VOLTAGE AT LEAST 100MV (VOLTAGE WILL INCREASE AS WHEEL SPEED INCREASES).
• DISCONNECT CONNECTOR FROM REAR WHEEL SPEED SENSOR. • USING J 39200, MEASURE RESISTANCE BETWEEN TERMINAL "D1" AND TERMINAL HARNESS "A" OR REAR ABS CONNECTORS. THEN, MEASURE RESISTANCE BETWEEN TERMINAL "D2" AND TERMINAL "B" OF REAR ABS HARNESS CONNECTOR. WERE BOTH MEASUREMENTS OF RESISTANCE LESS THAN 2 OHMS?
YES
NO
REPLACE WHEEL BEARING AND SPEED SENSOR ASSEMBLY.
5 • USING J 39200, MEASURE RESISTANCE BETWEEN TERMINAL "D1" OF REAR ABS HARNESS CONNECTOR AND GROUND. DOES DVM DISPLAY "OL" (INFINITE)?
NO
YES
REPLACE REAR ABS HARNESS.
• RECONNECT REAR WHEEL SPEED SENSOR CONNECTOR. • USING J 39200, MEASURE RESISTANCE BETWEEN TERMINALS "D1" AND "D2" OF REAR ABS HARNESS CONNECTOR. IS RESISTANCE BETWEEN 2100 AND 2400 OHMS?
YES
NO
GO TO FOLLOWING PAGE OF THIS DTC CHART
• DISCONNECT CONNECTOR FROM WHEEL SPEED SENSOR. • USING J 39200, MEASURE RESISTANCE BETWEEN TERMINAL "D1" OF REAR ABS HARNESS CONNECTOR AND GROUND. DOES DVM DISPLAY "OL" (INFINITE)?
YES
NO
REPLACE WHEEL BEARING AND SPEED SENSOR ASSEMBLY.
REPLACE REAR ABS HARNESS.
NO
YES
REPLACE WHEEL BEARING AND SPEED SENSOR ASSEMBLY.
MALFUNCTION WAS DUE TO POOR CONNECTION AT REAR WHEEL SPEED SENSOR.

GC402930076700DX

Fig. 130 Code A028: Right Rear Excessive Wheel Speed Variation (Part 1 of 2). 1993–94 Cavalier, Sunbird, Beretta, Corsica & Achieva, Grand Am & Skylark Less VES

DTC A028

RIGHT REAR EXCESSIVE WHEEL SPEED VARIATION

Circuit Description:

As a toothed ring passes by the wheel speed sensor, changes in the electromagnetic field cause the wheel speed sensor to produce a sinusoidal (AC) voltage signal whose frequency is proportional to wheel speed. The magnitude of this signal is directly related to wheel speed and the proximity of the wheel speed sensor to the toothed ring, often referred to as the air gap.

Failure Condition:

DTC A028 can be set when the brake is "OFF." The purpose of this test is to detect a situation in which the right rear wheel acceleration or deceleration is beyond specified limits.

Action Taken:

A malfunction DTC is stored, ABS is disabled and the ABS indicator lamp is turned "ON."

Test Description: Number(s) below refer to circled number(s) on the diagnostic chart.

6. This step checks for proper voltages at body to ABS and fuel sender harness connector.
7. This test ensures that the wheel speed sensor circuitry is not internally shorted.
8. This checks for an open in the wheel signal high circuit.
9. This checks for an open in the wheel signal low circuit.
10. This test checks for a short to ground in both high and low wheel signal circuits.
11. This step ensures that DTC A028 was not set due to a poor connection between the world connector and EBCM.

Diagnostic Aids:

An "Intermittent" malfunction may be caused by a poor connection, rubbed through wire insulation, or a wire that is broken inside the insulation.

The frequency of the malfunction can be checked by using the enhanced diagnostic function of the Tech 1

If the customer's comments reflect that the ABS amber indicator lamp is "ON" only during moist environmental changes, (rain, snow, vehicle wash) all wheel speed sensor circuitry should be thoroughly inspected for water intrusion. Use the following procedure. Spray down the suspected area with 5% salt water solution (two teaspoons of salt to 12 oz. of water). Start vehicle, allow vehicle to run for 10 seconds. If DTC returns immediately, replace suspected harness.

Any circuitry, that is suspected as causing the intermittent complaint, should be thoroughly checked for backed out terminals, improper mating, broken locks, improperly formed or damaged terminals, poor terminal to wiring connections or physical damage to the wiring harness.

Excessive end play can cause this DTC to set. Check integral bearing for excessive axial end play

When measuring wheel speed sensor resistance, ensure vehicle is at room temperature. Wheel speed sensor resistance will vary with temperature.

When replacing a wheel speed sensor, inspect the sensor terminals and harness connector for corrosion and/or water intrusion. If evidence of corrosion or water intrusion exists, replace wheel speed sensor harness.

GC402930076700EX

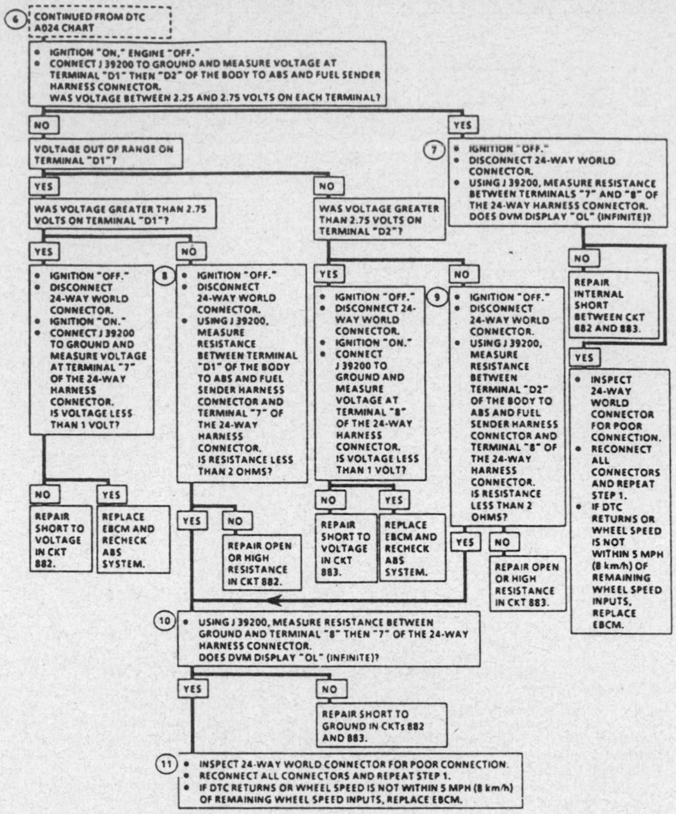
6
CONTINUED FROM DTC A024 CHART
• IGNITION "ON," ENGINE "OFF."
• CONNECT J 39200 TO GROUND AND MEASURE VOLTAGE AT TERMINAL "D1" THEN "D2" OF THE BODY TO ABS AND FUEL SENDER HARNESS CONNECTOR.
WAS VOLTAGE BETWEEN 2.25 AND 2.75 VOLTS ON EACH TERMINAL?
NO
YES
VOLTAGE OUT OF RANGE ON TERMINAL "D1"?
7
• IGNITION "OFF."
• DISCONNECT 24-WAY WORLD CONNECTOR.
• USING J 39200, MEASURE RESISTANCE BETWEEN TERMINALS "7" AND "8" OF THE 24-WAY HARNESS CONNECTOR.
DOES DVM DISPLAY "OL" (INFINITE)?
YES
NO
WAS VOLTAGE GREATER THAN 2.75 VOLTS ON TERMINAL "D1"?
WAS VOLTAGE GREATER THAN 2.75 VOLTS ON TERMINAL "D2"?
NO
REPAIR INTERNAL SHORT BETWEEN CKT 882 AND 883.
YES
• INSPECT 24-WAY WORLD CONNECTOR FOR POOR CONNECTION.
• RECONNECT ALL CONNECTORS AND REPEAT STEP 1.
• IF DTC RETURNS OR WHEEL SPEED IS NOT WITHIN 5 MPH (8 km/h) OF REMAINING WHEEL SPEED INPUTS, REPLACE EBCM.
YES
NO
• IGNITION "OFF."
• DISCONNECT 24-WAY WORLD CONNECTOR.
• IGNITION "ON."
• CONNECT J 39200 TO GROUND AND MEASURE VOLTAGE AT TERMINAL "7" OF THE 24-WAY HARNESS CONNECTOR.
IS VOLTAGE LESS THAN 1 VOLT?
8
• IGNITION "OFF."
• DISCONNECT 24-WAY WORLD CONNECTOR.
• USING J 39200, MEASURE RESISTANCE BETWEEN TERMINAL "D1" OF THE BODY TO ABS AND FUEL SENDER HARNESS CONNECTOR AND TERMINAL "7" OF THE 24-WAY HARNESS CONNECTOR.
IS RESISTANCE LESS THAN 2 OHMS?
YES
NO
• IGNITION "OFF."
• DISCONNECT 24-WAY WORLD CONNECTOR.
• IGNITION "ON."
• CONNECT J 39200 TO GROUND AND MEASURE VOLTAGE AT TERMINAL "8" OF THE 24-WAY HARNESS CONNECTOR.
IS VOLTAGE LESS THAN 1 VOLT?
9
• IGNITION "OFF."
• DISCONNECT 24-WAY WORLD CONNECTOR.
• USING J 39200, MEASURE RESISTANCE BETWEEN TERMINAL "D2" OF THE BODY TO ABS AND FUEL SENDER HARNESS CONNECTOR AND TERMINAL "8" OF THE 24-WAY HARNESS CONNECTOR.
IS RESISTANCE LESS THAN 2 OHMS?
NO
YES
REPAIR SHORT TO VOLTAGE IN CKT 882.
REPLACE EBCM AND RECHECK ABS SYSTEM.
YES
NO
REPAIR OPEN OR HIGH RESISTANCE IN CKT 882.
NO
YES
REPAIR SHORT TO VOLTAGE IN CKT 883.
REPLACE EBCM AND RECHECK ABS SYSTEM.
YES
NO
REPAIR OPEN OR HIGH RESISTANCE IN CKT 883.
10
• USING J 39200, MEASURE RESISTANCE BETWEEN GROUND AND TERMINAL "8" THEN "7" OF THE 24-WAY HARNESS CONNECTOR.
DOES DVM DISPLAY "OL" (INFINITE)?
YES
NO
REPAIR SHORT TO GROUND IN CKTs 882 AND 883.
11
• INSPECT 24-WAY WORLD CONNECTOR FOR POOR CONNECTION.
• RECONNECT ALL CONNECTORS AND REPEAT STEP 1.
• IF DTC RETURNS OR WHEEL SPEED IS NOT WITHIN 5 MPH (8 km/h) OF REMAINING WHEEL SPEED INPUTS, REPLACE EBCM.

GC402930076700FX

Fig. 130 Code A028: Right Rear Excessive Wheel Speed Variation (Part 2 of 2). 1993–94 Cavalier, Sunbird, Beretta, Corsica & Achieva, Grand Am & Skylark Less VES

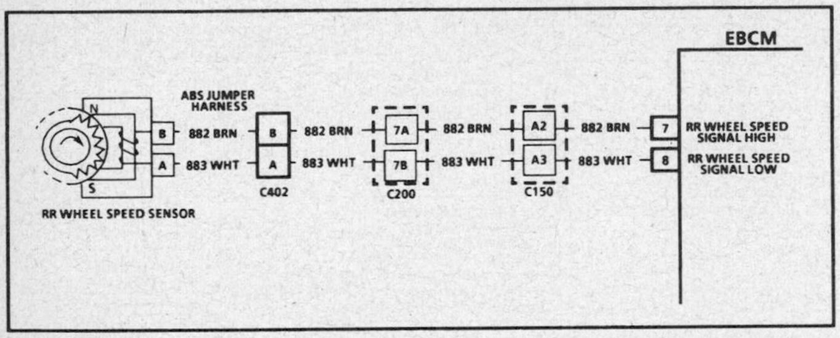
EBCM
ABS JUMPER HARNESS
N
S
B
A
882 BRN
883 WHT
B
A
C402
882 BRN
883 WHT
7A
7B
C200
882 BRN
883 WHT
A2
A3
C150
882 BRN
883 WHT
7
8
RR WHEEL SPEED SIGNAL HIGH
RR WHEEL SPEED SIGNAL LOW
RR WHEEL SPEED SENSOR

Circuit Description:

As a toothed ring passes by the wheel speed sensor, changes in the electromagnetic field cause the wheel speed sensor to produce a sinusoidal (AC) voltage signal whose frequency is proportional to wheel speed. The magnitude of this signal is directly related to wheel speed and the proximity of the wheel speed sensor to the toothed ring, often referred to as the air gap.

DTC Will Set When: DTC 28 can be set when the brake is "OFF." The purpose of this test is to detect a situation in which the right rear wheel acceleration or deceleration is beyond specified limits.

Action Taken: A malfunction DTC is stored, ABS is disabled and the ABS warning lamp is turned "ON."

DTC Chart Test Description: Number(s) below refer to circled number(s) on the diagnostic chart.

1. Determines if DTC 35 is present.
2. Designed to identify a wheel speed sensor or circuitry that is damaged and visibly apparent.
3. Checks to see that the wheel speed sensor is within proper resistance values.
4. Verifies that the wheel speed sensor can generate an appropriate output signal.

Diagnostic Aids: An "Intermittent" malfunction may be caused by a poor connection, rubbed through wire insulation, or a wire that is broken inside the insulation.

The frequency of the malfunction can be checked by using the enhanced diagnostic function of the Tech 1

If the customer's comments reflect that the ABS warning lamp is "ON" only during moist environmental changes (rain, snow, vehicle wash), all wheel speed sensor circuitry should be thoroughly inspected for signs of water intrusion. If DTC is not current, clear DTCs and simulate the effects of water intrusion. Use the following procedure. Spray down the suspected area with a 5% salt water solution (two teaspoons of salt to 12 oz. of water). Test drive vehicle over various road surfaces (bumps, turns, etc.) above 24 km/h (15 mph) for at least 30 seconds. If DTC returns replace suspected harness.

Any circuitry, that is suspected as causing the intermittent complaint, should be thoroughly checked for backed out terminals, improper mating, broken locks, improperly formed or damaged terminals, poor terminal to wiring connections or physical damage to the wiring harness.

Resistance of the wheel speed sensor will increase with an increase in sensor temperature.

When replacing a wheel speed sensor, inspect the sensor terminals and harness connector for corrosion and/or water intrusion. If evidence of corrosion or water intrusion exists, replace wheel speed sensor jumper harness. Likewise, if replacing a wheel speed sensor jumper harness, inspect sensor terminals. If evidence of corrosion or water intrusion exists, replace wheel speed sensor.

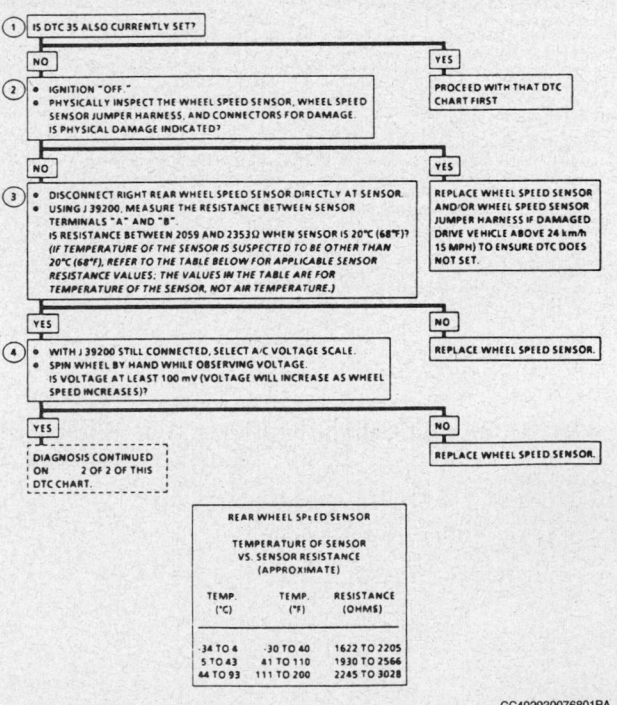

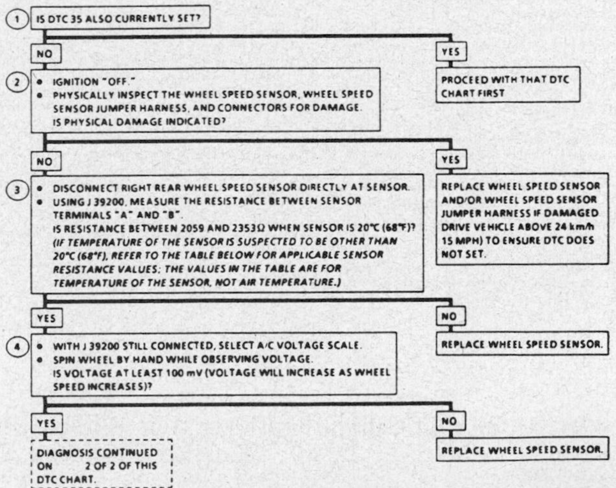
1
IS DTC 35 ALSO CURRENTLY SET?
NO
YES
PROCEED WITH THAT DTC CHART FIRST
2
• IGNITION "OFF."
• PHYSICALLY INSPECT THE WHEEL SPEED SENSOR, WHEEL SPEED SENSOR JUMPER HARNESS, AND CONNECTORS FOR DAMAGE.
IS PHYSICAL DAMAGE INDICATED?
NO
YES
REPLACE WHEEL SPEED SENSOR AND/OR WHEEL SPEED SENSOR JUMPER HARNESS IF DAMAGED DRIVE VEHICLE ABOVE 24 km/h 15 MPH) TO ENSURE DTC DOES NOT SET.
3
• DISCONNECT RIGHT REAR WHEEL SPEED SENSOR DIRECTLY AT SENSOR.
• USING J 39200, MEASURE THE RESISTANCE BETWEEN SENSOR TERMINALS "A" AND "B".
IS RESISTANCE BETWEEN 2059 AND 2353Ω WHEN SENSOR IS 20°C (68°F)?
(IF TEMPERATURE OF THE SENSOR IS SUSPECTED TO BE OTHER THAN 20°C (68°F), REFER TO THE TABLE BELOW FOR APPLICABLE SENSOR RESISTANCE VALUES; THE VALUES IN THE TABLE ARE FOR TEMPERATURE OF THE SENSOR, NOT AIR TEMPERATURE.)
YES
NO
REPLACE WHEEL SPEED SENSOR.
4
• WITH J 39200 STILL CONNECTED, SELECT A/C VOLTAGE SCALE.
• SPIN WHEEL BY HAND WHILE OBSERVING VOLTAGE.
IS VOLTAGE AT LEAST 100 mV (VOLTAGE WILL INCREASE AS WHEEL SPEED INCREASES)?
YES
NO
DIAGNOSIS CONTINUED ON 2 OF 2 OF THIS DTC CHART.
REPLACE WHEEL SPEED SENSOR.

REAR WHEEL SPEED SENSOR

TEMPERATURE OF SENSOR VS. SENSOR RESISTANCE (APPROXIMATE)

TEMP. (°C)	TEMP. (°F)	RESISTANCE (OHMS)
-34 TO 4	-30 TO 40	1622 TO 2205
5 TO 43	41 TO 110	1930 TO 2566
44 TO 93	111 TO 200	2245 TO 3028

GC402930076801BA

GC402930076801AA

Fig. 131 Code A028: Right Rear Excessive Wheel Speed Variation (Part 1 of 2). 1993 Grand Prix, 1993–94 Cutlass Supreme, Lumina & Regal

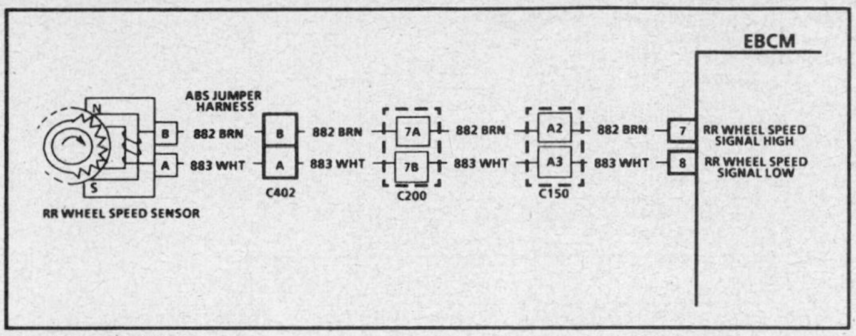
EBCM
ABS JUMPER HARNESS
B
A
N
S
882 BRN
883 WHT
C402
7A
7B
C200
A2
A3
C150
7
8
RR WHEEL SPEED SIGNAL HIGH
RR WHEEL SPEED SIGNAL LOW
RR WHEEL SPEED SENSOR

Circuit Description:
As a toothed ring passes by the wheel speed sensor, changes in the electromagnetic field cause the wheel speed sensor to produce a sinusoidal (AC) voltage signal whose frequency is proportional to wheel speed. The magnitude of this signal is directly related to wheel speed and the proximity of the wheel speed sensor to the toothed ring, often referred to as the air gap.

DTC Will Set When: DTC 28 can be set when the brake is "OFF." The purpose of this test is to detect a situation in which the right rear wheel acceleration or deceleration is beyond specified limits.

Action Taken: A malfunction DTC is stored, ABS is disabled and the ABS warning lamp is turned "ON."

DTC Chart Test Description: Number(s) below refer to circled number(s) on the diagnostic chart.
5. Checks for proper output voltage from the EBCM.
6. Checks for an open in the wheel speed sensor low circuit.
7. Ensures malfunction was not due to physical damage of the circuitry.
8. Ensures that wheel speed sensor circuitry is not shorted.
9. Ensures malfunction was not due to physical damage of the circuitry.
10. Checks for an open in the wheel speed sensor high circuit.

Diagnostic Aids: An "Intermittent" malfunction may be caused by a poor connection, rubbed through wire insulation, or a wire that is broken inside the insulation.

The frequency of the malfunction can be checked by using the enhanced diagnostic function of the Tech 1

If the customer's comments reflect that the ABS warning lamp is "ON" only during moist environmental changes (rain, snow, vehicle wash), all wheel speed sensor circuitry should be thoroughly inspected for signs of water intrusion. If DTC is not current, clear DTCs and simulate the effects of water intrusion. Use the following procedure. Spray down the suspected area with a 5% salt water solution (two teaspoons of salt to 12 oz. of water). Test drive vehicle over various road surfaces (bumps, turns, etc.) above 24 km/h (15 mph) for at least 30 seconds. If DTC returns replace suspected harness.

Any circuitry, that is suspected as causing the intermittent complaint, should be thoroughly checked for backed out terminals, improper mating, broken locks, improperly formed or damaged terminals, poor terminal to wiring connections or physical damage to the wiring harness.

Resistance of the wheel speed sensor will increase with an increase in sensor temperature.

When replacing a wheel speed sensor, inspect the sensor terminals and harness connector for corrosion and/or water intrusion. If evidence of corrosion or water intrusion exists, replace wheel speed sensor jumper harness. Likewise, if replacing a wheel speed sensor jumper harness, inspect sensor terminals. If evidence of corrosion or water intrusion exists, replace wheel speed sensor.

GC402930076802AA

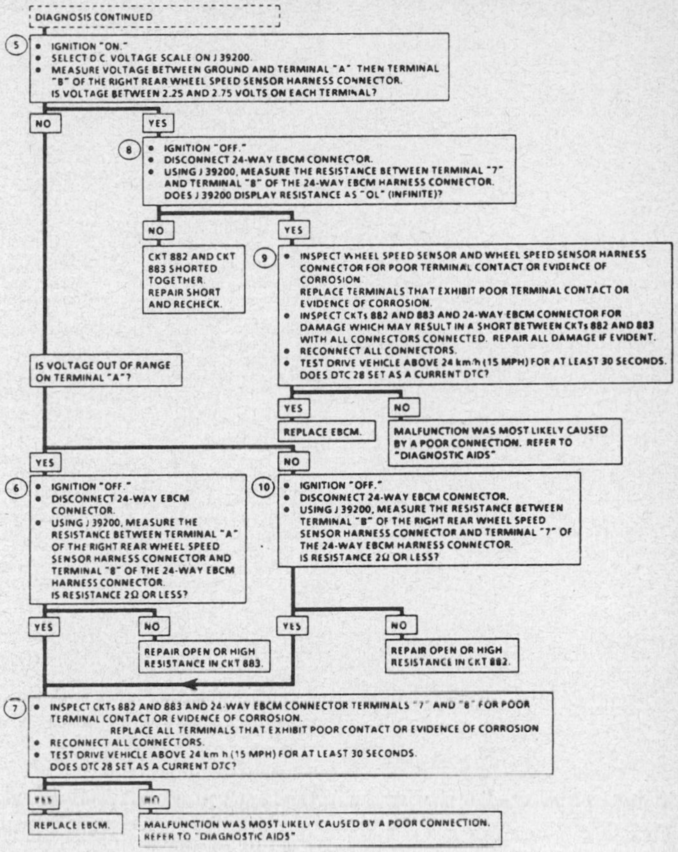
DIAGNOSIS CONTINUED
5
• IGNITION "ON."
• SELECT D.C. VOLTAGE SCALE ON J 39200.
• MEASURE VOLTAGE BETWEEN GROUND AND TERMINAL "A" THEN TERMINAL "B" OF THE RIGHT REAR WHEEL SPEED SENSOR HARNESS CONNECTOR.
IS VOLTAGE BETWEEN 2.25 AND 2.75 VOLTS ON EACH TERMINAL?
NO
YES
8
• IGNITION "OFF."
• DISCONNECT 24-WAY EBCM CONNECTOR.
• USING J 39200, MEASURE THE RESISTANCE BETWEEN TERMINAL "7" AND TERMINAL "8" OF THE 24-WAY EBCM HARNESS CONNECTOR.
DOES J 39200 DISPLAY RESISTANCE AS "OL" (INFINITE)?
NO
YES
CKT 882 AND CKT 883 SHORTED TOGETHER. REPAIR SHORT AND RECHECK.
9
• INSPECT WHEEL SPEED SENSOR AND WHEEL SPEED SENSOR HARNESS CONNECTOR FOR POOR TERMINAL CONTACT OR EVIDENCE OF CORROSION.
REPLACE TERMINALS THAT EXHIBIT POOR TERMINAL CONTACT OR EVIDENCE OF CORROSION.
• INSPECT CKTs 882 AND 883 AND 24-WAY EBCM CONNECTOR FOR DAMAGE WHICH MAY RESULT IN A SHORT BETWEEN CKTs 882 AND 883 WITH ALL CONNECTORS CONNECTED. REPAIR ALL DAMAGE IF EVIDENT.
• RECONNECT ALL CONNECTORS.
• TEST DRIVE VEHICLE ABOVE 24 km/h (15 MPH) FOR AT LEAST 30 SECONDS.
DOES DTC 28 SET AS A CURRENT DTC?
IS VOLTAGE OUT OF RANGE ON TERMINAL "A"?
YES
NO
REPLACE EBCM.
MALFUNCTION WAS MOST LIKELY CAUSED BY A POOR CONNECTION. REFER TO "DIAGNOSTIC AIDS"
YES
NO
6
• IGNITION "OFF."
• DISCONNECT 24-WAY EBCM CONNECTOR.
• USING J 39200, MEASURE THE RESISTANCE BETWEEN TERMINAL "A" OF THE RIGHT REAR WHEEL SPEED SENSOR HARNESS CONNECTOR AND TERMINAL "8" OF THE 24-WAY EBCM HARNESS CONNECTOR.
IS RESISTANCE 2Ω OR LESS?
10
• IGNITION "OFF."
• DISCONNECT 24-WAY EBCM CONNECTOR.
• USING J 39200, MEASURE THE RESISTANCE BETWEEN TERMINAL "B" OF THE RIGHT REAR WHEEL SPEED SENSOR HARNESS CONNECTOR AND TERMINAL "7" OF THE 24-WAY EBCM HARNESS CONNECTOR.
IS RESISTANCE 2Ω OR LESS?
YES
NO
REPAIR OPEN OR HIGH RESISTANCE IN CKT 883.
YES
NO
REPAIR OPEN OR HIGH RESISTANCE IN CKT 882.
7
• INSPECT CKTs 882 AND 883 AND 24-WAY EBCM CONNECTOR TERMINALS "7" AND "8" FOR POOR TERMINAL CONTACT OR EVIDENCE OF CORROSION.
REPLACE ALL TERMINALS THAT EXHIBIT POOR CONTACT OR EVIDENCE OF CORROSION
• RECONNECT ALL CONNECTORS.
• TEST DRIVE VEHICLE ABOVE 24 km/h (15 MPH) FOR AT LEAST 30 SECONDS.
DOES DTC 28 SET AS A CURRENT DTC?
YES
NO
REPLACE EBCM.
MALFUNCTION WAS MOST LIKELY CAUSED BY A POOR CONNECTION. REFER TO "DIAGNOSTIC AIDS"

GC402930076802BA

Fig. 131 Code A028: Right Rear Excessive Wheel Speed Variation (Part 2 of 2). 1993 Grand Prix, 1993–94 Cutlass Supreme, Lumina & Regal

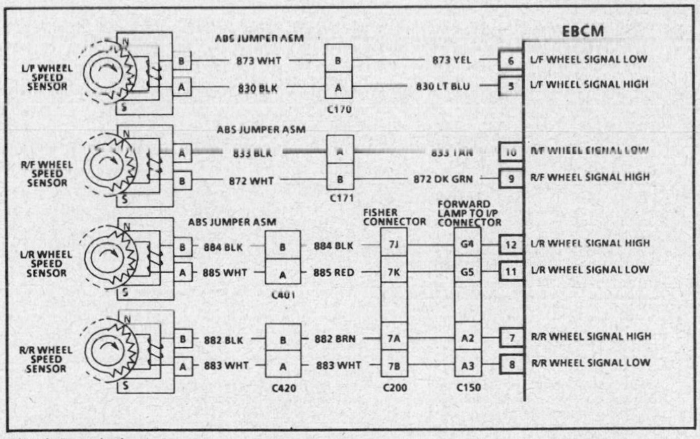
EBCM
ABS JUMPER ASM
L/F WHEEL SPEED SENSOR
873 WHT
830 BLK
C170
873 YEL
830 LT BLU
6
5
L/F WHEEL SIGNAL LOW
L/F WHEEL SIGNAL HIGH
ABS JUMPER ASM
R/F WHEEL SPEED SENSOR
833 BLK
872 WHT
C171
833 TAN
872 DK GRN
10
9
R/F WHEEL SIGNAL LOW
R/F WHEEL SIGNAL HIGH
ABS JUMPER ASM
FISHER CONNECTOR
FORWARD LAMP TO I/P CONNECTOR
L/R WHEEL SPEED SENSOR
884 BLK
885 WHT
C401
884 BLK
885 RED
7J
7K
G4
G5
12
11
L/R WHEEL SIGNAL HIGH
L/R WHEEL SIGNAL LOW
R/R WHEEL SPEED SENSOR
882 BLK
883 WHT
C420
882 BRN
883 WHT
7A
7B
C200
A2
A3
C150
7
8
R/R WHEEL SIGNAL HIGH
R/R WHEEL SIGNAL LOW

Circuit Description:
As a toothed ring passes by the wheel speed sensor, changes in the electromagnetic field cause the wheel speed sensor to produce a sinusoidal (AC) voltage signal whose frequency is proportional to wheel speed. The magnitude of this signal is directly related to wheel speed and the proximity of the wheel speed sensor to the toothed ring, often referred to as the air gap.

This DTC is designed to detect two open wheel speed sensors in any combination. This DTC exists due to a condition that may exist that does not allow the driver to be informed by the ABS indicator lamp of non-functioning ABS. If one wheel speed sensor is open, the driver is informed. If a second fails, the driver is no longer informed without this DTC and ABS is not available. By requiring the two operating wheels to be within 7 mph, a false DTC is prevented during spin-ups while still allowing for detection when the stowaway spare tire is used.

Test Description: Number(s) below refer to circled number(s) on the diagnostic chart.
1. This test verifies whether the malfunction is currently present.
2. This step is designed to identify a wheel speed sensor or circuitry that is damaged and visibly apparent.
3. This step identifies if the cause of the malfunction is common to the rear wheel sensor circuitry.
4. This test checks to see if connectors at pass thru are connected properly.
5. This test checks to see that the wheel speed sensor is within proper resistance values.

Diagnostic Aids:

A false DTC A031 may be set as a result of vehicle operation while on a hoist or a lifted condition or stuck in mud or snow, when the vehicle is in gear.

An "Intermittent" malfunction may be caused by a poor connection, rubbed through wire insulation, or a wire that is broken inside the insulation.

The frequency of the malfunction can be checked by using the enhanced diagnostic function of the Tech 1, as described in the "Tech 1 Diagnostics" found in this section.

GC402930076900AX

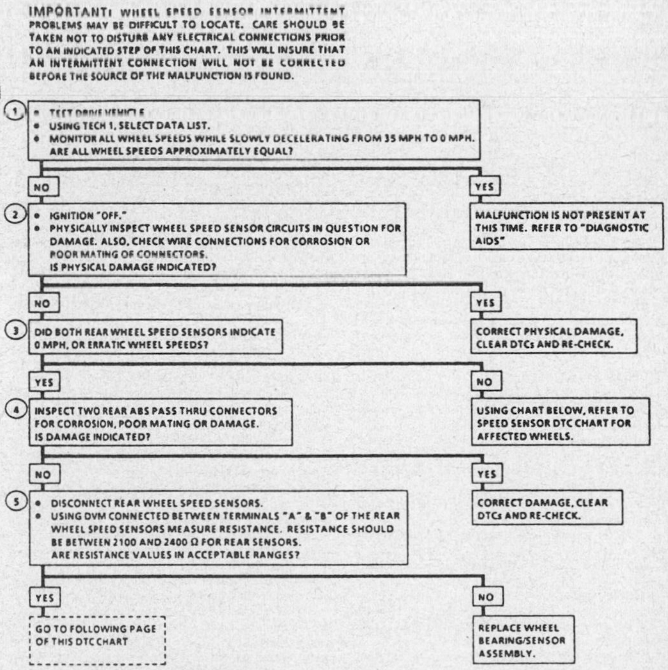
IMPORTANT: WHEEL SPEED SENSOR INTERMITTENT PROBLEMS MAY BE DIFFICULT TO LOCATE. CARE SHOULD BE TAKEN NOT TO DISTURB ANY ELECTRICAL CONNECTIONS PRIOR TO AN INDICATED STEP OF THIS CHART. THIS WILL INSURE THAT AN INTERMITTENT CONNECTION WILL NOT BE CORRECTED BEFORE THE SOURCE OF THE MALFUNCTION IS FOUND.
1
• TEST DRIVE VEHICLE.
• USING TECH 1, SELECT DATA LIST.
• MONITOR ALL WHEEL SPEEDS WHILE SLOWLY DECELERATING FROM 35 MPH TO 0 MPH.
ARE ALL WHEEL SPEEDS APPROXIMATELY EQUAL?
NO
YES
2
• IGNITION "OFF."
• PHYSICALLY INSPECT WHEEL SPEED SENSOR CIRCUITS IN QUESTION FOR DAMAGE. ALSO, CHECK WIRE CONNECTIONS FOR CORROSION OR POOR MATING OF CONNECTORS.
IS PHYSICAL DAMAGE INDICATED?
MALFUNCTION IS NOT PRESENT AT THIS TIME. REFER TO "DIAGNOSTIC AIDS"
NO
YES
3
DID BOTH REAR WHEEL SPEED SENSORS INDICATE 0 MPH, OR ERRATIC WHEEL SPEEDS?
CORRECT PHYSICAL DAMAGE, CLEAR DTCs AND RE-CHECK.
YES
NO
4
INSPECT TWO REAR ABS PASS THRU CONNECTORS FOR CORROSION, POOR MATING OR DAMAGE.
IS DAMAGE INDICATED?
USING CHART BELOW, REFER TO SPEED SENSOR DTC CHART FOR AFFECTED WHEELS.
NO
YES
5
• DISCONNECT REAR WHEEL SPEED SENSORS.
• USING DVM CONNECTED BETWEEN TERMINALS "A" & "B" OF THE REAR WHEEL SPEED SENSORS MEASURE RESISTANCE. RESISTANCE SHOULD BE BETWEEN 2100 AND 2400 Ω FOR REAR SENSORS.
ARE RESISTANCE VALUES IN ACCEPTABLE RANGES?
CORRECT DAMAGE, CLEAR DTCs AND RE-CHECK.
YES
NO
GO TO FOLLOWING PAGE OF THIS DTC CHART
REPLACE WHEEL BEARING/SENSOR ASSEMBLY.

SENSOR	DTC
L/F SENSOR	A021
R/F SENSOR	A022
L/R SENSOR	A023
R/R SENSOR	A024

GC402930076900BX

Fig. 132 Code A031: Two Wheel Speeds = 0 (Part 1 of 2). 1993 Cutlass Supreme, Grand Prix, Lumina & Regal

DTC A031

(Page 2 of 2)
TWO WHEEL SPEEDS = 0

Circuit Description:

As a toothed ring passes by the wheel speed sensor, changes in the electromagnetic field cause the wheel speed sensor to produce a sinusoidal (AC) voltage signal whose frequency is proportional to wheel speed. The magnitude of this signal is directly related to wheel speed and the proximity of the wheel speed sensor to the toothed ring, often referred to as the air gap.

This DTC is designed to detect two open wheel speed sensors in any combination. This DTC exists due to a condition that may exist that does not allow the driver to be informed by the ABS indicator lamp of non-functioning ABS. If one wheel speed sensor is open, the driver is informed. If a second fails, the driver is no longer informed without this DTC and ABS is not available. By requiring the two operating wheels to be within 7 mph, a false DTC is prevented during spin-ups while still allowing for detection when the stowaway spare tire is used.

Test Description: Number(s) below refer to circled number(s) on the diagnostic chart.

6. This step checks for an open in the wheel speed sensor circuitry of one side of the sensor.
7. This step checks for an open on the other side of the sensor in question.
8. This insures that the circuitry is not shorted to voltage.

Diagnostic Aids:

A false DTC A031 may be set as a result of vehicle operation while on a hoist or a lifted condition, or stuck in mud or snow when the vehicle is in gear.

An "Intermittent" malfunction may be caused by a poor connection, rubbed through wire insulation, or a wire that is broken inside the insulation.

The frequency of the malfunction can be checked by using the enhanced diagnostic function of the Tech 1 as described in the "Tech 1 Diagnostics," found in this section.

GC402930076900CX

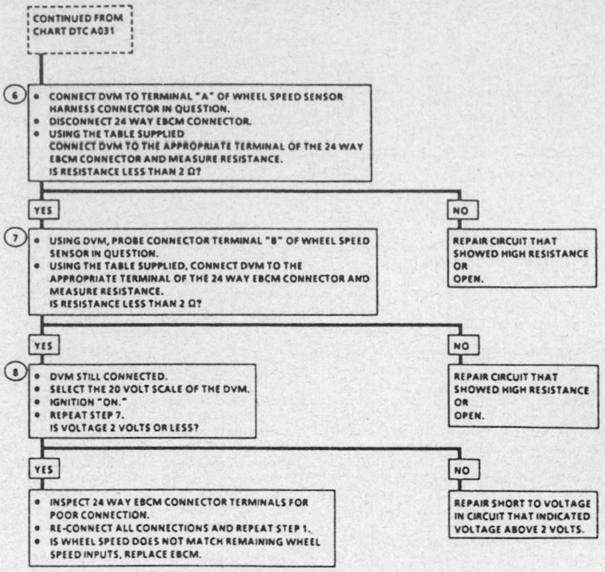
CONTINUED FROM CHART DTC A031
6
• CONNECT DVM TO TERMINAL "A" OF WHEEL SPEED SENSOR HARNESS CONNECTOR IN QUESTION.
• DISCONNECT 24 WAY EBCM CONNECTOR.
• USING THE TABLE SUPPLIED CONNECT DVM TO THE APPROPRIATE TERMINAL OF THE 24 WAY EBCM CONNECTOR AND MEASURE RESISTANCE. IS RESISTANCE LESS THAN 2 Ω?
YES
NO
REPAIR CIRCUIT THAT SHOWED HIGH RESISTANCE OR OPEN.
7
• USING DVM, PROBE CONNECTOR TERMINAL "B" OF WHEEL SPEED SENSOR IN QUESTION.
• USING THE TABLE SUPPLIED, CONNECT DVM TO THE APPROPRIATE TERMINAL OF THE 24 WAY EBCM CONNECTOR AND MEASURE RESISTANCE. IS RESISTANCE LESS THAN 2 Ω?
YES
NO
REPAIR CIRCUIT THAT SHOWED HIGH RESISTANCE OR OPEN.
8
• DVM STILL CONNECTED.
• SELECT THE 20 VOLT SCALE OF THE DVM.
• IGNITION "ON."
• REPEAT STEP 7. IS VOLTAGE 2 VOLTS OR LESS?
YES
NO
REPAIR SHORT TO VOLTAGE IN CIRCUIT THAT INDICATED VOLTAGE ABOVE 2 VOLTS.
• INSPECT 24 WAY EBCM CONNECTOR TERMINALS FOR POOR CONNECTION.
• RE-CONNECT ALL CONNECTIONS AND REPEAT STEP 1.
• IS WHEEL SPEED DOES NOT MATCH REMAINING WHEEL SPEED INPUTS, REPLACE EBCM.

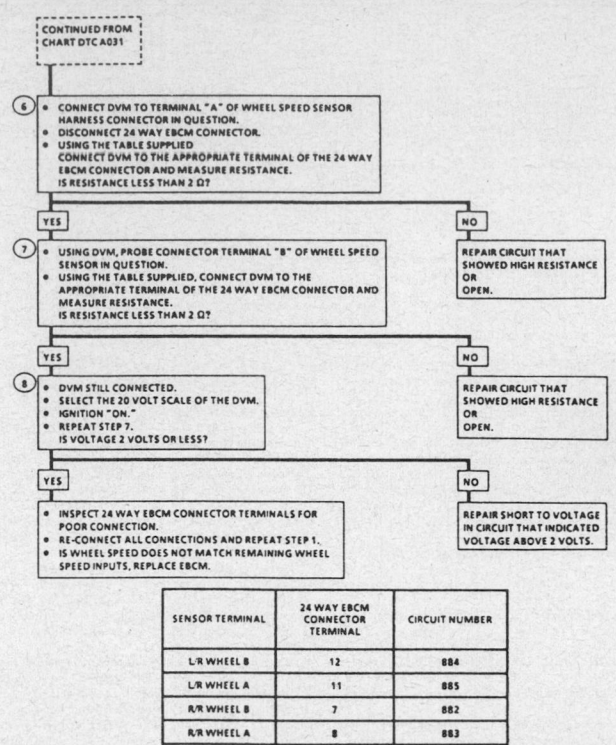

SENSOR TERMINAL	24 WAY EBCM CONNECTOR TERMINAL	CIRCUIT NUMBER
L/R WHEEL B	12	884
L/R WHEEL A	11	885
R/R WHEEL B	7	882
R/R WHEEL A	8	883

GC402930076900DX

Fig. 132 Code A031: Two Wheel Speeds = 0 (Part 2 of 2). 1993 Cutlass Supreme, Grand Prix, Lumina & Regal

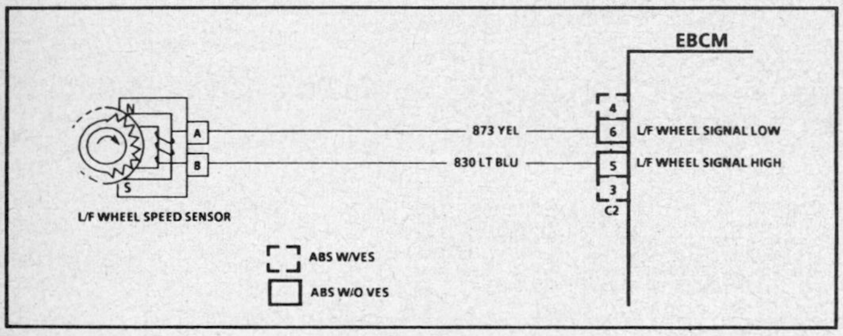
EBCM
873 YEL
830 LT BLU
L/F WHEEL SIGNAL LOW
L/F WHEEL SIGNAL HIGH
N
A
B
S
4
6
5
3
C2
L/F WHEEL SPEED SENSOR
ABS W/VES
ABS W/O VES

DTC 32

(Page 1 of 3)
LEFT FRONT WHEEL SPEED SENSOR CIRCUIT OPEN OR SHORTED TO GROUND/BATTERY (FOR ABS WITH VES ONLY)

Circuit Description:

As a toothed ring passes by the wheel speed sensor, changes in the electromagnetic field cause the wheel speed sensor to produce a sinusoidal (AC) voltage signal whose frequency is proportional to wheel speed. The magnitude of this signal is directly related to wheel speed and the proximity of the wheel speed sensor to the toothed ring, often referred to as the air gap.

DTC Will Set When: DTC 32 can be set anytime after the ABS enable relay has been commanded "ON." The relay is commanded "ON" during the three second bulb check.

Action Taken: A malfunction DTC is stored, ABS/VES is disabled and the ABS warning lamp is turned "ON."

DTC Chart Test Description: Number(s) below refer to circled number(s) on the diagnostic chart.

1. Checks wheel speed sensor circuitry for proper resistance values.
2. Checks for a short to ground in the wheel speed sensor circuitry.
3. Checks for a short to voltage in the wheel speed sensor circuitry.
4. Ensures malfunction was not due to physical damage of the circuitry.
5. Checks for a short to voltage in the wheel signal low circuit.
6. Checks for a short to voltage in the wheel signal high circuit.

Diagnostic Aids: An "Intermittent" malfunction is most likely caused by a poor connection, rubbed through wire insulation, or a wire that is broken inside the insulation.

The frequency of the malfunction can be checked by using the enhanced diagnostic function of the Tech 1.

If the customer's comments reflect that the ABS amber warning lamp is "ON" only during moist environmental changes, (rain, snow, vehicle wash) all wheel speed sensor circuitry should be thoroughly inspected for signs of water intrusion. Use the following procedure. Spray down the suspected area with 5% salt water solution (two teaspoons of salt to 12 oz. of water). Drive vehicle above 24 km/h (15 mph) for at least 30 seconds. If DTC returns immediately, replace suspected harness.

Any circuitry, that is suspected as causing the intermittent complaint, should be thoroughly checked for backed out terminals, improper mating, broken locks, improperly formed or damaged terminals, poor terminal to wiring connections or physical damage to the wiring harness.

Resistance of the wheel speed sensor will increase with an increase in sensor temperature.

When replacing a wheel speed sensor, inspect the sensor terminals and harness connector for corrosion and/or water intrusion. If evidence of corrosion or water intrusion exists, replace wheel speed sensor harness. Refer to "On-Vehicle Service" in this section.

If wheel speed sensor harness shows evidence of water intrusion, inspect wheel speed sensor for water intrusion. If water intrusion is evident, replace wheel speed sensor.

GC402940104801AX

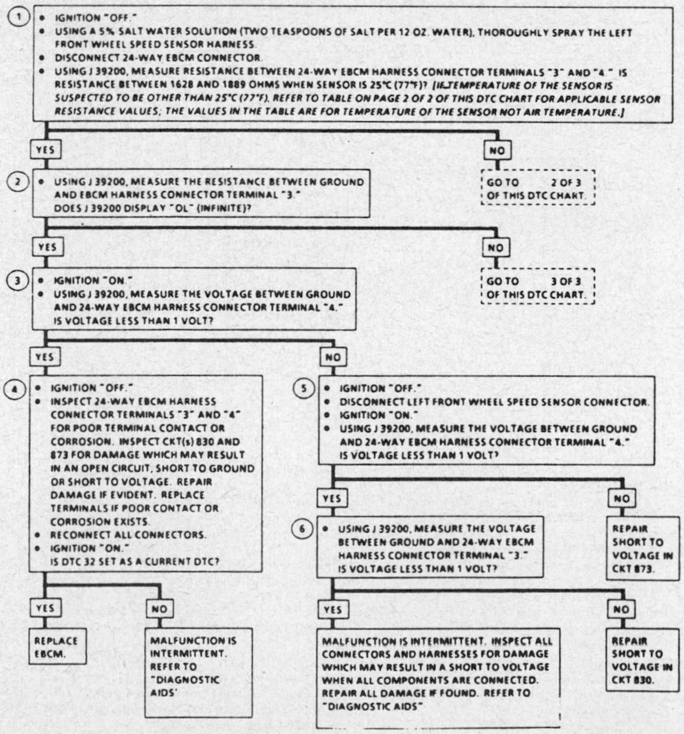
1
• IGNITION "OFF."
• USING A 5% SALT WATER SOLUTION (TWO TEASPOONS OF SALT PER 12 OZ. WATER), THOROUGHLY SPRAY THE LEFT FRONT WHEEL SPEED SENSOR HARNESS.
• DISCONNECT 24-WAY EBCM CONNECTOR.
• USING J 39200, MEASURE RESISTANCE BETWEEN 24-WAY EBCM HARNESS CONNECTOR TERMINALS "3" AND "4." IS RESISTANCE BETWEEN 1628 AND 1889 OHMS WHEN SENSOR IS 25°C (77°F)? [IF TEMPERATURE OF THE SENSOR IS SUSPECTED TO BE OTHER THAN 25°C (77°F), REFER TO TABLE ON PAGE 2 OF 2 OF THIS DTC CHART FOR APPLICABLE SENSOR RESISTANCE VALUES; THE VALUES IN THE TABLE ARE FOR TEMPERATURE OF THE SENSOR NOT AIR TEMPERATURE.]
YES
NO
GO TO 2 OF 3 OF THIS DTC CHART.
2
• USING J 39200, MEASURE THE RESISTANCE BETWEEN GROUND AND EBCM HARNESS CONNECTOR TERMINAL "3." DOES J 39200 DISPLAY "OL" (INFINITE)?
YES
NO
GO TO 3 OF 3 OF THIS DTC CHART.
3
• IGNITION "ON."
• USING J 39200, MEASURE THE VOLTAGE BETWEEN GROUND AND 24-WAY EBCM HARNESS CONNECTOR TERMINAL "4." IS VOLTAGE LESS THAN 1 VOLT?
YES
NO
4
• IGNITION "OFF."
• INSPECT 24-WAY EBCM HARNESS CONNECTOR TERMINALS "3" AND "4" FOR POOR TERMINAL CONTACT OR CORROSION. INSPECT CKT(s) 830 AND 873 FOR DAMAGE WHICH MAY RESULT IN AN OPEN CIRCUIT, SHORT TO GROUND OR SHORT TO VOLTAGE. REPAIR DAMAGE IF EVIDENT. REPLACE TERMINALS IF POOR CONTACT OR CORROSION EXISTS.
• RECONNECT ALL CONNECTORS.
• IGNITION "ON." IS DTC 32 SET AS A CURRENT DTC?
YES
NO
REPLACE EBCM.
MALFUNCTION IS INTERMITTENT. REFER TO "DIAGNOSTIC AIDS"
5
• IGNITION "OFF."
• DISCONNECT LEFT FRONT WHEEL SPEED SENSOR CONNECTOR.
• IGNITION "ON."
• USING J 39200, MEASURE THE VOLTAGE BETWEEN GROUND AND 24-WAY EBCM HARNESS CONNECTOR TERMINAL "4." IS VOLTAGE LESS THAN 1 VOLT?
YES
NO
REPAIR SHORT TO VOLTAGE IN CKT 873.
6
• USING J 39200, MEASURE THE VOLTAGE BETWEEN GROUND AND 24-WAY EBCM HARNESS CONNECTOR TERMINAL "3." IS VOLTAGE LESS THAN 1 VOLT?
YES
NO
MALFUNCTION IS INTERMITTENT. INSPECT ALL CONNECTORS AND HARNESSES FOR DAMAGE WHICH MAY RESULT IN A SHORT TO VOLTAGE WHEN ALL COMPONENTS ARE CONNECTED. REPAIR ALL DAMAGE IF FOUND. REFER TO "DIAGNOSTIC AIDS"
REPAIR SHORT TO VOLTAGE IN CKT 830.

GC402940104801BX

Fig. 133 Code A032: Left Front Wheel Speed Sensor Circuit Open Or Shorted To Ground/Battery (Part 1 of 3). 1994 Achieva, Grand Am & Skylark w/VES

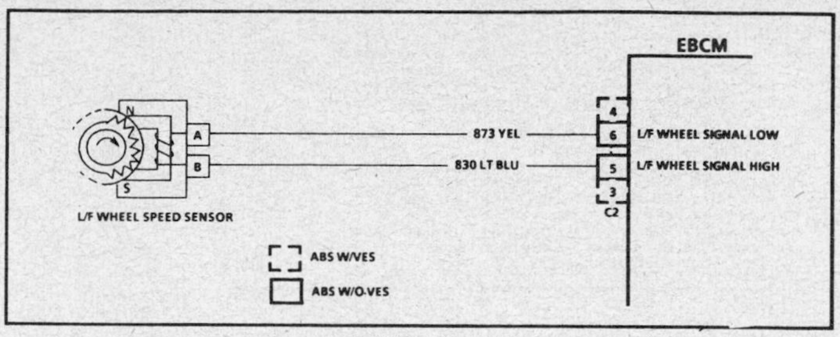
EBCM
A
B
N
S
873 YEL
830 LT BLU
4
6
5
3
C2
L/F WHEEL SIGNAL LOW
L/F WHEEL SIGNAL HIGH
L/F WHEEL SPEED SENSOR
ABS W/VES
ABS W/O-VES

DTC 32

Circuit Description:
As a toothed ring passes by the wheel speed sensor, changes in the electromagnetic field cause the wheel speed sensor to produce a sinusoidal (AC) voltage signal whose frequency is proportional to wheel speed. The magnitude of this signal is directly related to wheel speed and the proximity of the wheel speed sensor to the toothed ring, often referred to as the air gap.

DTC Will Set When: DTC 32 can be set anytime after the ABS enable relay has been commanded "ON." The relay is commanded "ON" during the three second bulb check.

Action Taken: A malfunction DTC is stored, ABS/VES is disabled and the ABS warning lamp is turned "ON."

DTC Chart Test Description: Number(s) below refer to circled number(s) on the diagnostic chart.

7. Checks for high resistance in the wheel signal low circuit.
8. Checks for high resistance in the wheel signal high circuit.
9. Checks for proper resistance of the wheel speed sensor.

Diagnostic Aids: An "Intermittent" malfunction is most likely caused by a poor connection, rubbed through wire insulation, or a wire that is broken inside the insulation.

The frequency of the malfunction can be checked by using the enhanced diagnostic function of the Tech 1.

If the customer's comments reflect that the ABS amber warning lamp is "ON" only during moist environmental changes, (rain, snow, vehicle wash) all wheel speed sensor circuitry should be thoroughly inspected for signs of water intrusion. Use the following procedure. Spray down the suspected area with 5% salt water solution (two teaspoons of salt to 12 oz. of water). Drive vehicle above 24 km/h (15 mph) for at least 30 seconds. If DTC returns immediately, replace suspected harness.

Any circuitry, that is suspected as causing the intermittent complaint, should be thoroughly checked for backed out terminals, improper mating, broken locks, improperly formed or damaged terminals, poor terminal to wiring connections or physical damage to the wiring harness.

Resistance of the wheel speed sensor will increase with an increase in sensor temperature.

When replacing a wheel speed sensor, inspect the sensor terminals and harness connector for corrosion and/or water intrusion. If evidence of corrosion or water intrusion exists, replace wheel speed sensor harness. Refer to "On-Vehicle Service" in this section.

If wheel speed sensor harness shows evidence of water intrusion, inspect wheel speed sensor for water intrusion. If water intrusion is evident, replace wheel speed sensor.

GC402940104802BX

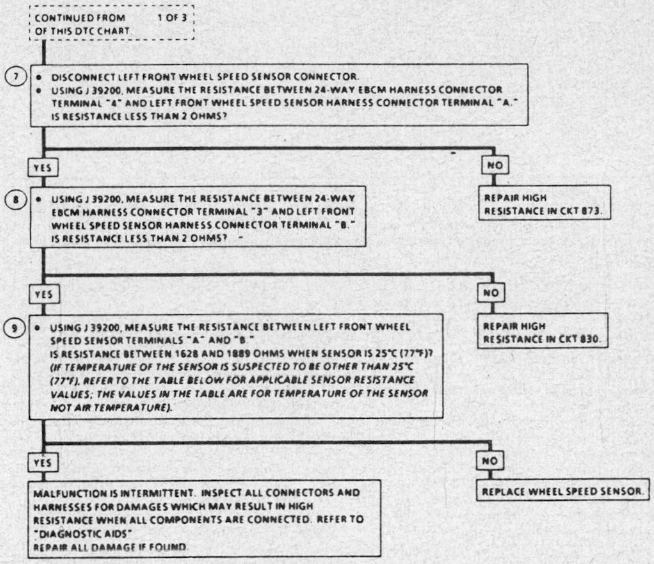
CONTINUED FROM 1 OF 3 OF THIS DTC CHART.
7
• DISCONNECT LEFT FRONT WHEEL SPEED SENSOR CONNECTOR.
• USING J 39200, MEASURE THE RESISTANCE BETWEEN 24-WAY EBCM HARNESS CONNECTOR TERMINAL "4" AND LEFT FRONT WHEEL SPEED SENSOR HARNESS CONNECTOR TERMINAL "A." IS RESISTANCE LESS THAN 2 OHMS?
YES
NO
REPAIR HIGH RESISTANCE IN CKT 873.
8
• USING J 39200, MEASURE THE RESISTANCE BETWEEN 24-WAY EBCM HARNESS CONNECTOR TERMINAL "3" AND LEFT FRONT WHEEL SPEED SENSOR HARNESS CONNECTOR TERMINAL "B." IS RESISTANCE LESS THAN 2 OHMS?
YES
NO
REPAIR HIGH RESISTANCE IN CKT 830.
9
• USING J 39200, MEASURE THE RESISTANCE BETWEEN LEFT FRONT WHEEL SPEED SENSOR TERMINALS "A" AND "B." IS RESISTANCE BETWEEN 1628 AND 1889 OHMS WHEN SENSOR IS 25°C (77°F)? (IF TEMPERATURE OF THE SENSOR IS SUSPECTED TO BE OTHER THAN 25°C (77°F), REFER TO THE TABLE BELOW FOR APPLICABLE SENSOR RESISTANCE VALUES; THE VALUES IN THE TABLE ARE FOR TEMPERATURE OF THE SENSOR NOT AIR TEMPERATURE).
YES
NO
MALFUNCTION IS INTERMITTENT. INSPECT ALL CONNECTORS AND HARNESSES FOR DAMAGES WHICH MAY RESULT IN HIGH RESISTANCE WHEN ALL COMPONENTS ARE CONNECTED. REFER TO "DIAGNOSTIC AIDS" REPAIR ALL DAMAGE IF FOUND.
REPLACE WHEEL SPEED SENSOR.

FRONT WHEEL SPEED SENSOR

TEMPERATURE OF SENSOR VS. SENSOR RESISTANCE (APPROXIMATE)

TEMP. (°C)	TEMP. (°F)	RESISTANCE (OHMS)
[illegible]	-30 TO 40	1258 TO 1739
5 TO 43	41 TO 110	1503 TO 2023
44 TO 93	111 TO 200	1747 TO 2384

GC402940104802AX

Fig. 133 Code A032: Left Front Wheel Speed Sensor Circuit Open Or Shorted To Ground/Battery (Part 2 of 3). 1994 Achieva, Grand Am & Skylark w/VES

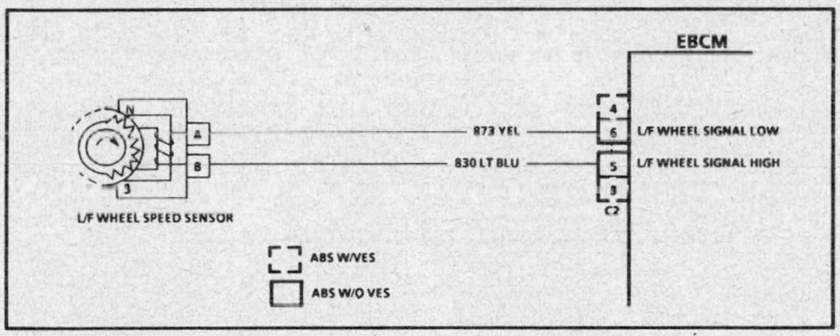
EBCM
A
B
N
S
873 YEL
830 LT BLU
4
6
5
3
C2
L/F WHEEL SIGNAL LOW
L/F WHEEL SIGNAL HIGH
L/F WHEEL SPEED SENSOR
ABS W/VES
ABS W/O VES

Circuit Description:
As a toothed ring passes by the wheel speed sensor, changes in the electromagnetic field cause the wheel speed sensor to produce a sinusoidal (AC) voltage signal whose frequency is proportional to wheel speed. The magnitude of this signal is directly related to wheel speed and the proximity of the wheel speed sensor to the toothed ring, often referred to as the air gap.

DTC Will Set When: DTC 32 can be set anytime after the ABS enable relay has been commanded "ON." The relay is commanded "ON" during the three second bulb check.

Action Taken: A malfunction DTC is stored, ABS/VES is disabled and the ABS warning lamp is turned "ON."

DTC Chart Test Description: Number(s) below refer to circled number(s) on the diagnostic chart.

10. Checks for a short to ground in either of the wheel signal high or low circuits.
11. Checks for a short to ground in the wheel speed sensor.

Diagnostic Aids: An "Intermittent" malfunction is most likely caused by a poor connection, rubbed through wire insulation, or a wire that is broken inside the insulation.

The frequency of the malfunction can be checked by using the enhanced diagnostic function of the Tech 1.

If the customer's comments reflect that the ABS amber warning lamp is "ON" only during moist environmental changes, (rain, snow, vehicle wash) all wheel speed sensor circuitry should be thoroughly inspected for signs of water intrusion. Use the following procedure. Spray down the suspected area with 5% salt water solution (two teaspoons of salt to 12 oz. of water). Drive vehicle above 24 km/h (15 mph) for at least 30 seconds. If DTC returns immediately, replace suspected harness.

Any circuitry, that is suspected as causing the intermittent complaint, should be thoroughly checked for backed out terminals, improper mating, broken locks, improperly formed or damaged terminals, poor terminal to wiring connections or physical damage to the wiring harness.

Resistance of the wheel speed sensor will increase with an increase in sensor temperature.

When replacing a wheel speed sensor, inspect the sensor terminals and harness connector for corrosion and/or water intrusion. If evidence of corrosion or water intrusion exists, replace wheel speed sensor harness. Refer to "On-Vehicle Service" in this section.

If wheel speed sensor harness shows evidence of water intrusion, inspect wheel speed sensor for water intrusion. If water intrusion is evident, replace wheel speed sensor.

GC402940104803AX

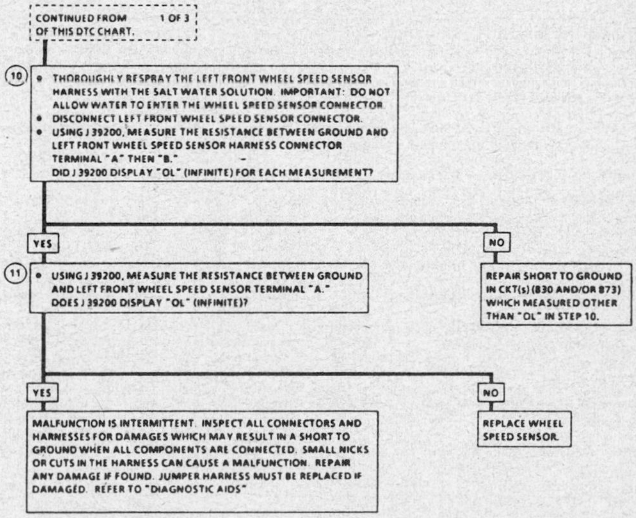
CONTINUED FROM 1 OF 3 OF THIS DTC CHART.
10
• THOROUGHLY RESPRAY THE LEFT FRONT WHEEL SPEED SENSOR HARNESS WITH THE SALT WATER SOLUTION. IMPORTANT: DO NOT ALLOW WATER TO ENTER THE WHEEL SPEED SENSOR CONNECTOR
• DISCONNECT LEFT FRONT WHEEL SPEED SENSOR CONNECTOR.
• USING J 39200, MEASURE THE RESISTANCE BETWEEN GROUND AND LEFT FRONT WHEEL SPEED SENSOR HARNESS CONNECTOR TERMINAL "A" THEN "B." DID J 39200 DISPLAY "OL" (INFINITE) FOR EACH MEASUREMENT?
YES
NO
REPAIR SHORT TO GROUND IN CKT(s) (830 AND/OR 873) WHICH MEASURED OTHER THAN "OL" IN STEP 10.
11
• USING J 39200, MEASURE THE RESISTANCE BETWEEN GROUND AND LEFT FRONT WHEEL SPEED SENSOR TERMINAL "A." DOES J 39200 DISPLAY "OL" (INFINITE)?
YES
NO
MALFUNCTION IS INTERMITTENT. INSPECT ALL CONNECTORS AND HARNESSES FOR DAMAGES WHICH MAY RESULT IN A SHORT TO GROUND WHEN ALL COMPONENTS ARE CONNECTED. SMALL NICKS OR CUTS IN THE HARNESS CAN CAUSE A MALFUNCTION. REPAIR ANY DAMAGE IF FOUND. JUMPER HARNESS MUST BE REPLACED IF DAMAGED. REFER TO "DIAGNOSTIC AIDS"
REPLACE WHEEL SPEED SENSOR.

GC402940104803BX

Fig. 133 Code A032: Left Front Wheel Speed Sensor Circuit Open Or Shorted To Ground/Battery (Part 3 of 3). 1994 Achieva, Grand Am & Skylark w/VES

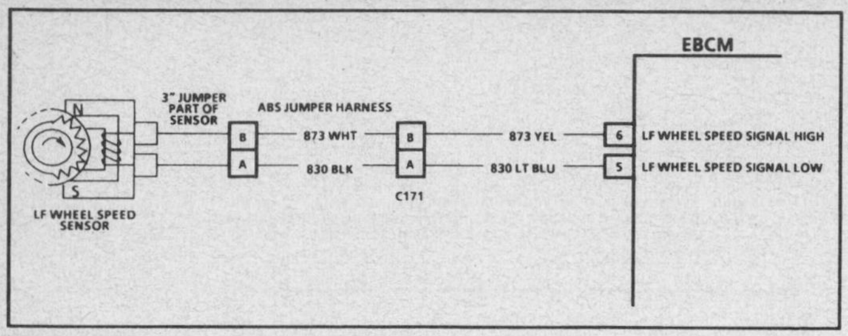
EBCM
3" JUMPER PART OF SENSOR
ABS JUMPER HARNESS
N
S
B
A
873 WHT
830 BLK
B
A
C171
873 YEL
830 LT BLU
6
5
LF WHEEL SPEED SIGNAL HIGH
LF WHEEL SPEED SIGNAL LOW
LF WHEEL SPEED SENSOR

Circuit Description:
As a toothed ring passes by the wheel speed sensor, changes in the electromagnetic field cause the wheel speed sensor to produce a sinusoidal (AC) voltage signal whose frequency is proportional to wheel speed. The magnitude of this signal is directly related to wheel speed and the proximity of the wheel speed sensor to the toothed ring often referred to as the air gap.

DTC Will Set When: DTC 32 can be set anytime after initialization. If either of the left front wheel speed circuits are shorted to voltage or ground, a malfunction exists.

Action Taken: A malfunction DTC is stored, ABS is disabled and the ABS warning lamp is turned "ON."

DTC Chart Test Description: Number(s) below refer to circled number(s) on the diagnostic chart.
1. Checks for short to ground in wheel speed sensor wiring circuitry.
2. Checks for short to voltage in wheel speed sensor wiring circuitry.
3. Checks for short to voltage in CKT 830.
4. Checks for short to voltage in CKT 873.
5. Checks for short to ground in CKT 830.

Diagnostic Aids: An "Intermittent" malfunction may be caused by a poor connection, rubbed through wire insulation, or a wire that is broken inside the insulation.

The frequency of the malfunction can be checked by using the enhanced diagnostic function of the Tech 1.

If the customer's comments reflect that the ABS warning lamp is "ON" only during moist environmental changes (rain, snow, vehicle wash), all wheel speed sensor circuitry should be thoroughly inspected for signs of water intrusion. If DTC is not current, clear DTCs and simulate the effects of water intrusion. Use the following procedure. Spray down the suspected area with a 5% salt water solution (two teaspoons of salt to 12 oz. of water). Test drive vehicle over various road surfaces (bumps, turns, etc.) above 24 km/h (15 mph) for at least 30 seconds. If DTC returns replace suspected harness.

Any circuitry, that is suspected as causing the intermittent complaint, should be thoroughly checked for backed out terminals, improper mating, broken locks, improperly formed or damaged terminals, poor terminal to wiring connections or physical damage to the wiring harness.

Resistance of the wheel speed sensor will increase with an increase in sensor temperature.

When replacing a wheel speed sensor, inspect the sensor terminals and harness connector for corrosion and/or water intrusion. If evidence of corrosion or water intrusion exists, replace wheel speed sensor jumper harness. Likewise, if replacing a wheel speed sensor jumper harness, inspect sensor terminals. If evidence of corrosion or water intrusion exists, replace wheel speed sensor.

GC402930077001AA

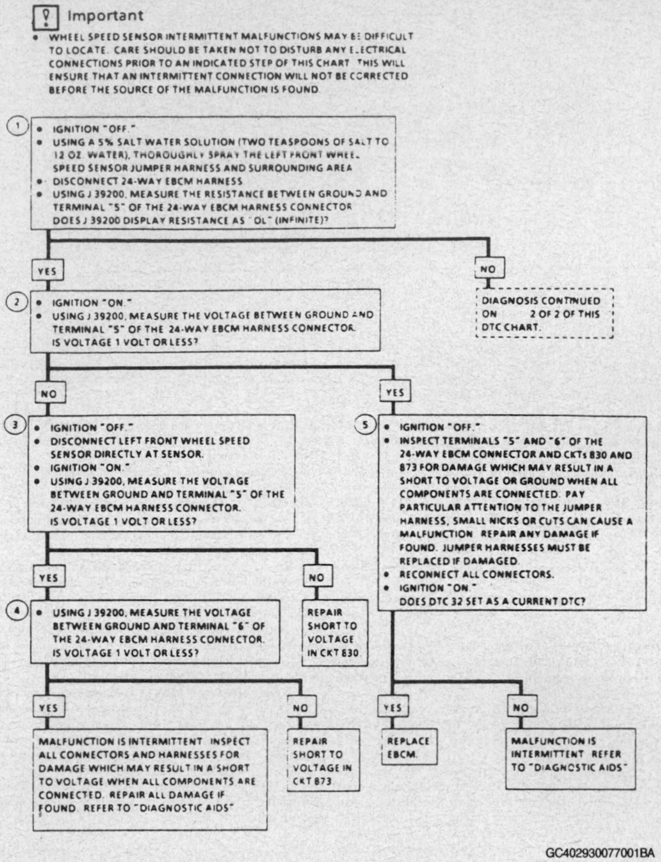
Important
• WHEEL SPEED SENSOR INTERMITTENT MALFUNCTIONS MAY BE DIFFICULT TO LOCATE. CARE SHOULD BE TAKEN NOT TO DISTURB ANY ELECTRICAL CONNECTIONS PRIOR TO AN INDICATED STEP OF THIS CHART. THIS WILL ENSURE THAT AN INTERMITTENT CONNECTION WILL NOT BE CORRECTED BEFORE THE SOURCE OF THE MALFUNCTION IS FOUND.
1
• IGNITION "OFF."
• USING A 5% SALT WATER SOLUTION (TWO TEASPOONS OF SALT TO 12 OZ. WATER), THOROUGHLY SPRAY THE LEFT FRONT WHEEL SPEED SENSOR JUMPER HARNESS AND SURROUNDING AREA.
• DISCONNECT 24-WAY EBCM HARNESS.
• USING J 39200, MEASURE THE RESISTANCE BETWEEN GROUND AND TERMINAL "5" OF THE 24-WAY EBCM HARNESS CONNECTOR. DOES J 39200 DISPLAY RESISTANCE AS "OL" (INFINITE)?
YES
NO
DIAGNOSIS CONTINUED ON 2 OF 2 OF THIS DTC CHART.
2
• IGNITION "ON."
• USING J 39200, MEASURE THE VOLTAGE BETWEEN GROUND AND TERMINAL "5" OF THE 24-WAY EBCM HARNESS CONNECTOR. IS VOLTAGE 1 VOLT OR LESS?
NO
YES
3
• IGNITION "OFF."
• DISCONNECT LEFT FRONT WHEEL SPEED SENSOR DIRECTLY AT SENSOR.
• IGNITION "ON."
• USING J 39200, MEASURE THE VOLTAGE BETWEEN GROUND AND TERMINAL "5" OF THE 24-WAY EBCM HARNESS CONNECTOR. IS VOLTAGE 1 VOLT OR LESS?
5
• IGNITION "OFF."
• INSPECT TERMINALS "5" AND "6" OF THE 24-WAY EBCM CONNECTOR AND CKTs 830 AND 873 FOR DAMAGE WHICH MAY RESULT IN A SHORT TO VOLTAGE OR GROUND WHEN ALL COMPONENTS ARE CONNECTED. PAY PARTICULAR ATTENTION TO THE JUMPER HARNESS, SMALL NICKS OR CUTS CAN CAUSE A MALFUNCTION. REPAIR ANY DAMAGE IF FOUND. JUMPER HARNESSES MUST BE REPLACED IF DAMAGED.
• RECONNECT ALL CONNECTORS.
• IGNITION "ON."
DOES DTC 32 SET AS A CURRENT DTC?
YES
NO
REPAIR SHORT TO VOLTAGE IN CKT 830
4
• USING J 39200, MEASURE THE VOLTAGE BETWEEN GROUND AND TERMINAL "6" OF THE 24-WAY EBCM HARNESS CONNECTOR. IS VOLTAGE 1 VOLT OR LESS?
YES
NO
YES
NO
MALFUNCTION IS INTERMITTENT. INSPECT ALL CONNECTORS AND HARNESSES FOR DAMAGE WHICH MAY RESULT IN A SHORT TO VOLTAGE WHEN ALL COMPONENTS ARE CONNECTED. REPAIR ALL DAMAGE IF FOUND. REFER TO "DIAGNOSTIC AIDS"
REPAIR SHORT TO VOLTAGE IN CKT 873.
REPLACE EBCM.
MALFUNCTION IS INTERMITTENT. REFER TO "DIAGNOSTIC AIDS"
GC402930077001BA

Fig. 134 Code A032: Left Front Wheel Sensor Shorted To Battery Or Ground (1 of 2). 1993 Grand Prix, 1993–94 Cutlass Supreme, Lumina & Regal

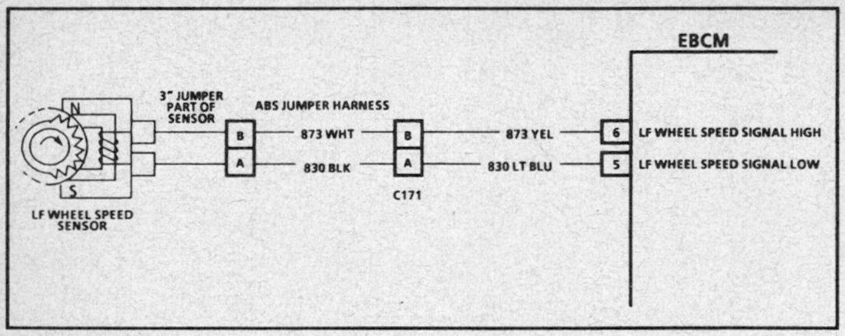
EBCM
3" JUMPER PART OF SENSOR
ABS JUMPER HARNESS
N
S
B
A
873 WHT
830 BLK
B
A
C171
873 YEL
830 LT BLU
6
5
LF WHEEL SPEED SIGNAL HIGH
LF WHEEL SPEED SIGNAL LOW
LF WHEEL SPEED SENSOR

Circuit Description:
As a toothed ring passes by the wheel speed sensor, changes in the electromagnetic field cause the wheel speed sensor to produce a sinusoidal (AC) voltage signal whose frequency is proportional to wheel speed. The magnitude of this signal is directly related to wheel speed and the proximity of the wheel speed sensor to the toothed ring often referred to as the air gap.

DTC Will Set When: DTC 32 can be set anytime after initialization. If either of the left front wheel speed circuits are shorted to voltage or ground, a malfunction exists.

Action Taken: A malfunction DTC is stored, ABS is disabled and the ABS warning lamp is turned "ON."

DTC Chart Test Description: Number(s) below refer to circled number(s) on the diagnostic chart.
6. Checks for short to ground in CKT 830.
7. Checks for short to ground in CKT 873.
8. Checks for short to ground in wheel speed sensor jumper harness.
9. Checks for proper resistance in wheel speed sensor.

Diagnostic Aids: An "Intermittent" malfunction may be caused by a poor connection, rubbed through wire insulation, or a wire that is broken inside the insulation.

The frequency of the malfunction can be checked by using the enhanced diagnostic function of the Tech 1.

If the customer's comments reflect that the ABS warning lamp is "ON" only during moist environmental changes (rain, snow, vehicle wash), all wheel speed sensor circuitry should be thoroughly inspected for signs of water intrusion. If DTC is not current, clear DTCs and simulate the effects of water intrusion. Use the following procedure. Spray down the suspected area with a 5% salt water solution (two teaspoons of salt to 12 oz. of water). Test drive vehicle over various road surfaces (bumps, turns, etc.) above 24 km/h (15 mph) for at least 30 seconds. If DTC returns replace suspected harness.

Any circuitry, that is suspected as causing the intermittent complaint, should be thoroughly checked for backed out terminals, improper mating, broken locks, improperly formed or damaged terminals, poor terminal to wiring connections or physical damage to the wiring harness.

Resistance of the wheel speed sensor will increase with an increase in sensor temperature.

When replacing a wheel speed sensor, inspect the sensor terminals and harness connector for corrosion and/or water intrusion. If evidence of corrosion or water intrusion exists, replace wheel speed sensor jumper harness. Likewise, if replacing a wheel speed sensor jumper harness, inspect sensor terminals. If evidence of corrosion or water intrusion exists, replace wheel speed sensor.

GC402930077002AA

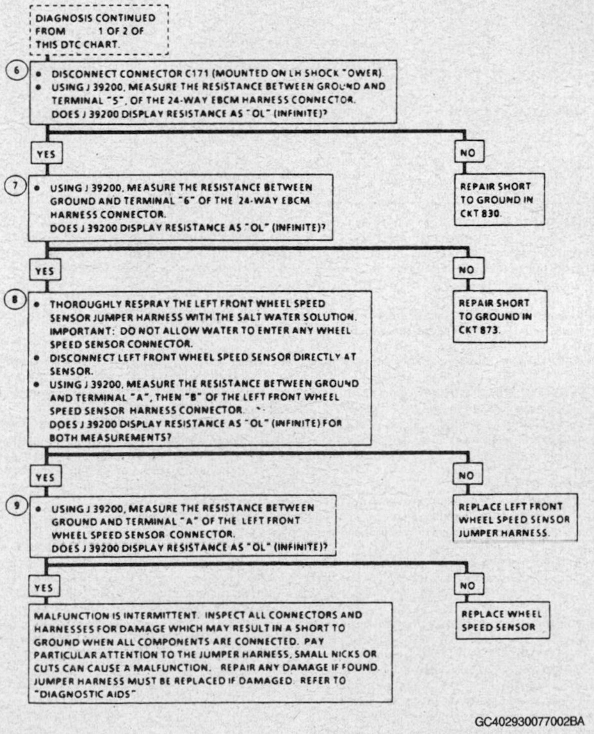
DIAGNOSIS CONTINUED FROM 1 OF 2 OF THIS DTC CHART.
6
• DISCONNECT CONNECTOR C171 (MOUNTED ON LH SHOCK TOWER).
• USING J 39200, MEASURE THE RESISTANCE BETWEEN GROUND AND TERMINAL "5", OF THE 24-WAY EBCM HARNESS CONNECTOR. DOES J 39200 DISPLAY RESISTANCE AS "OL" (INFINITE)?
YES
NO
7
• USING J 39200, MEASURE THE RESISTANCE BETWEEN GROUND AND TERMINAL "6" OF THE 24-WAY EBCM HARNESS CONNECTOR. DOES J 39200 DISPLAY RESISTANCE AS "OL" (INFINITE)?
REPAIR SHORT TO GROUND IN CKT 830.
YES
NO
8
• THOROUGHLY RESPRAY THE LEFT FRONT WHEEL SPEED SENSOR JUMPER HARNESS WITH THE SALT WATER SOLUTION. IMPORTANT: DO NOT ALLOW WATER TO ENTER ANY WHEEL SPEED SENSOR CONNECTOR.
• DISCONNECT LEFT FRONT WHEEL SPEED SENSOR DIRECTLY AT SENSOR.
• USING J 39200, MEASURE THE RESISTANCE BETWEEN GROUND AND TERMINAL "A", THEN "B" OF THE LEFT FRONT WHEEL SPEED SENSOR HARNESS CONNECTOR. DOES J 39200 DISPLAY RESISTANCE AS "OL" (INFINITE) FOR BOTH MEASUREMENTS?
REPAIR SHORT TO GROUND IN CKT 873.
YES
NO
9
• USING J 39200, MEASURE THE RESISTANCE BETWEEN GROUND AND TERMINAL "A" OF THE LEFT FRONT WHEEL SPEED SENSOR CONNECTOR. DOES J 39200 DISPLAY RESISTANCE AS "OL" (INFINITE)?
REPLACE LEFT FRONT WHEEL SPEED SENSOR JUMPER HARNESS.
YES
NO
MALFUNCTION IS INTERMITTENT. INSPECT ALL CONNECTORS AND HARNESSES FOR DAMAGE WHICH MAY RESULT IN A SHORT TO GROUND WHEN ALL COMPONENTS ARE CONNECTED. PAY PARTICULAR ATTENTION TO THE JUMPER HARNESS, SMALL NICKS OR CUTS CAN CAUSE A MALFUNCTION. REPAIR ANY DAMAGE IF FOUND. JUMPER HARNESS MUST BE REPLACED IF DAMAGED. REFER TO "DIAGNOSTIC AIDS"
REPLACE WHEEL SPEED SENSOR
GC402930077002BA

Fig. 134 Code A032: Left Front Wheel Sensor Shorted To Battery Or Ground (2 of 2). 1993 Grand Prix, 1993–94 Cutlass Supreme, Lumina & Regal

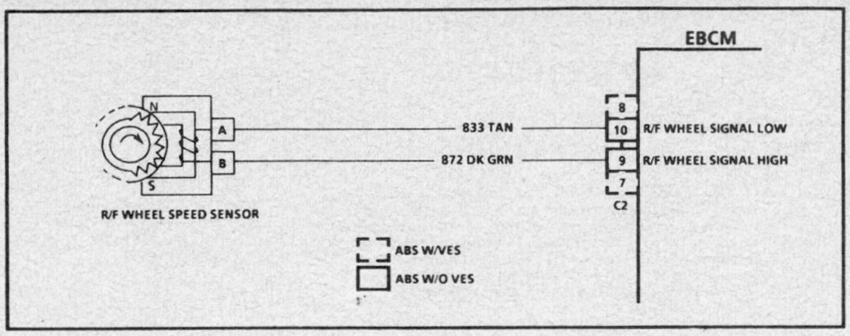
EBCM
N
A
B
S
833 TAN
872 DK GRN
8
10
9
7
C2
R/F WHEEL SIGNAL LOW
R/F WHEEL SIGNAL HIGH
R/F WHEEL SPEED SENSOR
ABS W/VES
ABS W/O VES

Circuit Description:
As a toothed ring passes by the wheel speed sensor, changes in the electromagnetic field cause the wheel speed sensor to produce a sinusoidal (AC) voltage signal whose frequency is proportional to wheel speed. The magnitude of this signal is directly related to wheel speed and the proximity of the wheel speed sensor to the toothed ring, often referred to as the air gap.

DTC Will Set When: DTC 33 can be set anytime after the ABS enable relay has been commanded "ON." The relay is commanded "ON" during the three second bulb check.

Action Taken: A malfunction DTC is stored, ABS/VES is disabled and the ABS warning lamp is turned "ON."

DTC Chart Test Description: Number(s) below refer to circled number(s) on the diagnostic chart.

1. Checks wheel speed sensor circuitry for proper resistance values.
2. Checks for a short to ground in the wheel speed sensor circuitry.
3. Checks for a short to voltage in the wheel speed sensor circuitry.
4. Ensures malfunction was not due to physical damage of the circuitry.
5. Checks for a short to voltage in the wheel signal low circuit.
6. Checks for a short to voltage in the wheel signal high circuit.

Diagnostic Aids: An "Intermittent" malfunction is most likely caused by a poor connection, rubbed through wire insulation, or a wire that is broken inside the insulation.

The frequency of the malfunction can be checked by using the enhanced diagnostic function of the Tech 1

If the customer's comments reflect that the ABS amber warning lamp is "ON" only during moist environmental changes, (rain, snow, vehicle wash) all wheel speed sensor circuitry should be thoroughly inspected for signs of water intrusion. Use the following procedure. Spray down the suspected area with 5% salt water solution (two teaspoons of salt to 12 oz. of water). Drive vehicle above 24 km/h (15 mph) for at least 30 seconds. If DTC returns immediately, replace suspected harness.

Any circuitry, that is suspected as causing the intermittent complaint, should be thoroughly checked for backed out terminals, improper mating, broken locks, improperly formed or damaged terminals, poor terminal to wiring connections or physical damage to the wiring harness.

Resistance of the wheel speed sensor will increase with an increase in sensor temperature.

When replacing a wheel speed sensor, inspect the sensor terminals and harness connector for corrosion and/or water intrusion. If evidence of corrosion or water intrusion exists, replace wheel speed sensor harness. Refer to "On-Vehicle Service" in this section.

If wheel speed sensor harness shows evidence of water intrusion, inspect wheel speed sensor for water intrusion. If water intrusion is evident, replace wheel speed sensor.

GC402940104901AX

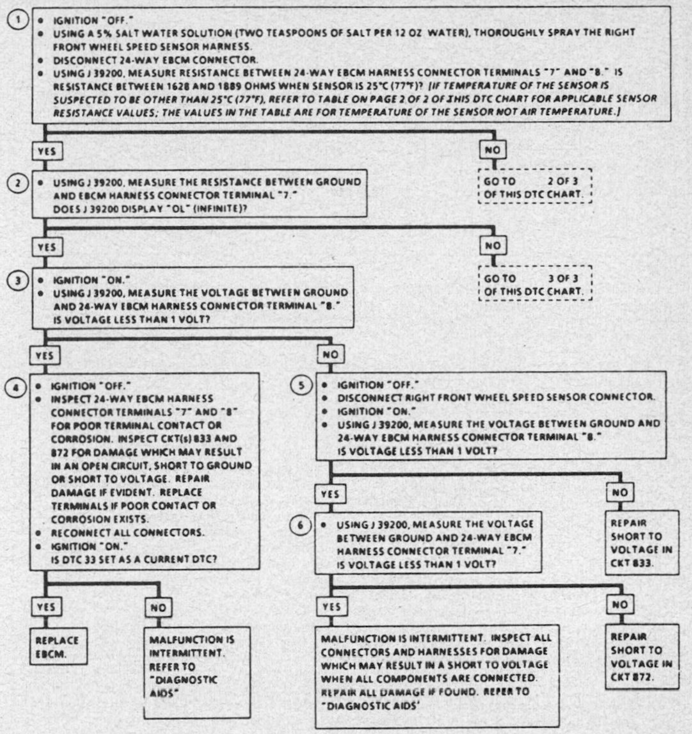
1
• IGNITION "OFF."
• USING A 5% SALT WATER SOLUTION (TWO TEASPOONS OF SALT PER 12 OZ WATER), THOROUGHLY SPRAY THE RIGHT FRONT WHEEL SPEED SENSOR HARNESS.
• DISCONNECT 24-WAY EBCM CONNECTOR.
• USING J 39200, MEASURE RESISTANCE BETWEEN 24-WAY EBCM HARNESS CONNECTOR TERMINALS "7" AND "8." IS RESISTANCE BETWEEN 1628 AND 1889 OHMS WHEN SENSOR IS 25°C (77°F)? (IF TEMPERATURE OF THE SENSOR IS SUSPECTED TO BE OTHER THAN 25°C (77°F), REFER TO TABLE ON PAGE 2 OF 2 OF THIS DTC CHART FOR APPLICABLE SENSOR RESISTANCE VALUES; THE VALUES IN THE TABLE ARE FOR TEMPERATURE OF THE SENSOR NOT AIR TEMPERATURE.)
YES
NO
GO TO 2 OF 3 OF THIS DTC CHART.
2
• USING J 39200, MEASURE THE RESISTANCE BETWEEN GROUND AND EBCM HARNESS CONNECTOR TERMINAL "7." DOES J 39200 DISPLAY "OL" (INFINITE)?
YES
NO
GO TO 3 OF 3 OF THIS DTC CHART.
3
• IGNITION "ON."
• USING J 39200, MEASURE THE VOLTAGE BETWEEN GROUND AND 24-WAY EBCM HARNESS CONNECTOR TERMINAL "8." IS VOLTAGE LESS THAN 1 VOLT?
YES
NO
4
• IGNITION "OFF."
• INSPECT 24-WAY EBCM HARNESS CONNECTOR TERMINALS "7" AND "8" FOR POOR TERMINAL CONTACT OR CORROSION. INSPECT CKT(s) 833 AND 872 FOR DAMAGE WHICH MAY RESULT IN AN OPEN CIRCUIT, SHORT TO GROUND OR SHORT TO VOLTAGE. REPAIR DAMAGE IF EVIDENT. REPLACE TERMINALS IF POOR CONTACT OR CORROSION EXISTS.
• RECONNECT ALL CONNECTORS.
• IGNITION "ON." IS DTC 33 SET AS A CURRENT DTC?
YES
NO
REPLACE EBCM.
MALFUNCTION IS INTERMITTENT. REFER TO "DIAGNOSTIC AIDS"
5
• IGNITION "OFF."
• DISCONNECT RIGHT FRONT WHEEL SPEED SENSOR CONNECTOR.
• IGNITION "ON."
• USING J 39200, MEASURE THE VOLTAGE BETWEEN GROUND AND 24-WAY EBCM HARNESS CONNECTOR TERMINAL "8." IS VOLTAGE LESS THAN 1 VOLT?
YES
NO
REPAIR SHORT TO VOLTAGE IN CKT 833.
6
• USING J 39200, MEASURE THE VOLTAGE BETWEEN GROUND AND 24-WAY EBCM HARNESS CONNECTOR TERMINAL "7." IS VOLTAGE LESS THAN 1 VOLT?
YES
NO
MALFUNCTION IS INTERMITTENT. INSPECT ALL CONNECTORS AND HARNESSES FOR DAMAGE WHICH MAY RESULT IN A SHORT TO VOLTAGE WHEN ALL COMPONENTS ARE CONNECTED. REPAIR ALL DAMAGE IF FOUND. REFER TO "DIAGNOSTIC AIDS"
REPAIR SHORT TO VOLTAGE IN CKT 872.

GC402940104901BX

Fig. 135 Code A033: Right Front Wheel Speed Sensor Circuit Open Or Shorted To Ground/Battery (Part 1 of 3). 1994 Achieva, Grand Am & Skylark w/VES

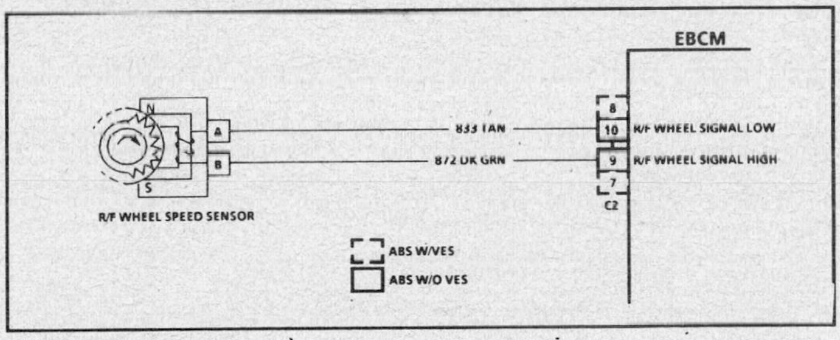
EBCM
N
A
B
S
833 TAN
872 DK GRN
8
10
9
7
C2
R/F WHEEL SIGNAL LOW
R/F WHEEL SIGNAL HIGH
R/F WHEEL SPEED SENSOR
ABS W/VES
ABS W/O VES

Circuit Description:
As a toothed ring passes by the wheel speed sensor, changes in the electromagnetic field cause the wheel speed sensor to produce a sinusoidal (AC) voltage signal whose frequency is proportional to wheel speed. The magnitude of this signal is directly related to wheel speed and the proximity of the wheel speed sensor to the toothed ring, often referred to as the air gap.

DTC Will Set When: DTC 33 can be set anytime after the ABS enable relay has been commanded "ON." The relay is commanded "ON" during the three second bulb check.

Action Taken: A malfunction DTC is stored, ABS/VES is disabled and the ABS warning lamp is turned "ON."

DTC Chart Test Description: Number(s) below refer to circled number(s) on the diagnostic chart.

7. Checks for high resistance in the wheel signal low circuit.
8. Checks for high resistance in the wheel signal high circuit.
9. Checks for proper resistance of the wheel speed sensor.

Diagnostic Aids: An "Intermittent" malfunction is most likely caused by a poor connection, rubbed through wire insulation, or a wire that is broken inside the insulation.

The frequency of the malfunction can be checked by using the enhanced diagnostic function of the Tech 1

If the customer's comments reflect that the ABS amber warning lamp is "ON" only during moist environmental changes, (rain, snow, vehicle wash) all wheel speed sensor circuitry should be thoroughly inspected for signs of water intrusion. Use the following procedure. Spray down the suspected area with 5% salt water solution (two teaspoons of salt to 12 oz. of water). Drive vehicle above 24 km/h (15 mph) for at least 30 seconds. If DTC returns immediately, replace suspected harness.

Any circuitry, that is suspected as causing the intermittent complaint, should be thoroughly checked for backed out terminals, improper mating, broken locks, improperly formed or damaged terminals, poor terminal to wiring connections or physical damage to the wiring harness.

Resistance of the wheel speed sensor will increase with an increase in sensor temperature.

When replacing a wheel speed sensor, inspect the sensor terminals and harness connector for corrosion and/or water intrusion. If evidence of corrosion or water intrusion exists, replace wheel speed sensor harness. Refer to "On-Vehicle Service" in this section.

If wheel speed sensor harness shows evidence of water intrusion, inspect wheel speed sensor for water intrusion. If water intrusion is evident, replace wheel speed sensor.

GC402940104902AX

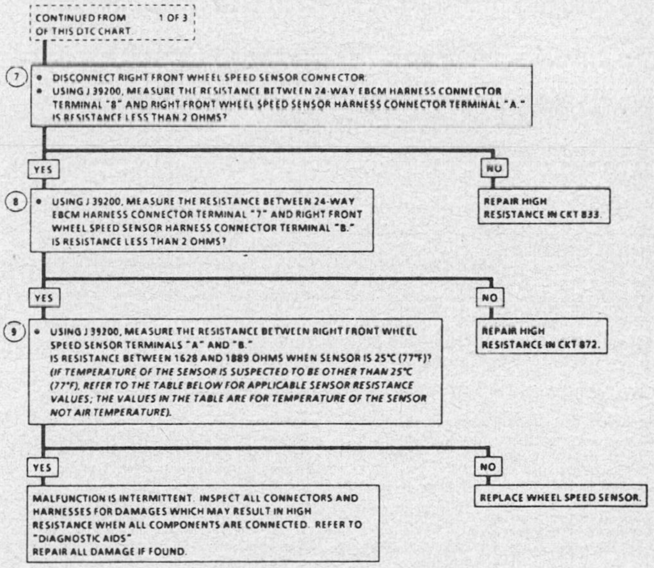
CONTINUED FROM 1 OF 3 OF THIS DTC CHART
7
• DISCONNECT RIGHT FRONT WHEEL SPEED SENSOR CONNECTOR.
• USING J 39200, MEASURE THE RESISTANCE BETWEEN 24-WAY EBCM HARNESS CONNECTOR TERMINAL "8" AND RIGHT FRONT WHEEL SPEED SENSOR HARNESS CONNECTOR TERMINAL "A." IS RESISTANCE LESS THAN 2 OHMS?
YES
NO
REPAIR HIGH RESISTANCE IN CKT 833.
8
• USING J 39200, MEASURE THE RESISTANCE BETWEEN 24-WAY EBCM HARNESS CONNECTOR TERMINAL "7" AND RIGHT FRONT WHEEL SPEED SENSOR HARNESS CONNECTOR TERMINAL "B." IS RESISTANCE LESS THAN 2 OHMS?
YES
NO
REPAIR HIGH RESISTANCE IN CKT 872.
9
• USING J 39200, MEASURE THE RESISTANCE BETWEEN RIGHT FRONT WHEEL SPEED SENSOR TERMINALS "A" AND "B." IS RESISTANCE BETWEEN 1628 AND 1889 OHMS WHEN SENSOR IS 25°C (77°F)? (IF TEMPERATURE OF THE SENSOR IS SUSPECTED TO BE OTHER THAN 25°C (77°F), REFER TO THE TABLE BELOW FOR APPLICABLE SENSOR RESISTANCE VALUES; THE VALUES IN THE TABLE ARE FOR TEMPERATURE OF THE SENSOR NOT AIR TEMPERATURE).
YES
NO
MALFUNCTION IS INTERMITTENT. INSPECT ALL CONNECTORS AND HARNESSES FOR DAMAGES WHICH MAY RESULT IN HIGH RESISTANCE WHEN ALL COMPONENTS ARE CONNECTED. REFER TO "DIAGNOSTIC AIDS" REPAIR ALL DAMAGE IF FOUND.
REPLACE WHEEL SPEED SENSOR.

FRONT WHEEL SPEED SENSOR

TEMPERATURE OF SENSOR VS. SENSOR RESISTANCE (APPROXIMATE)

TEMP. (°C)	TEMP. (°F)	RESISTANCE (OHMS)
-34 TO 4	-30 TO 40	1258 TO 1739
5 TO 43	41 TO 110	1503 TO 2023
44 TO 93	111 TO 200	1747 TO 2384

GC402940104902BX

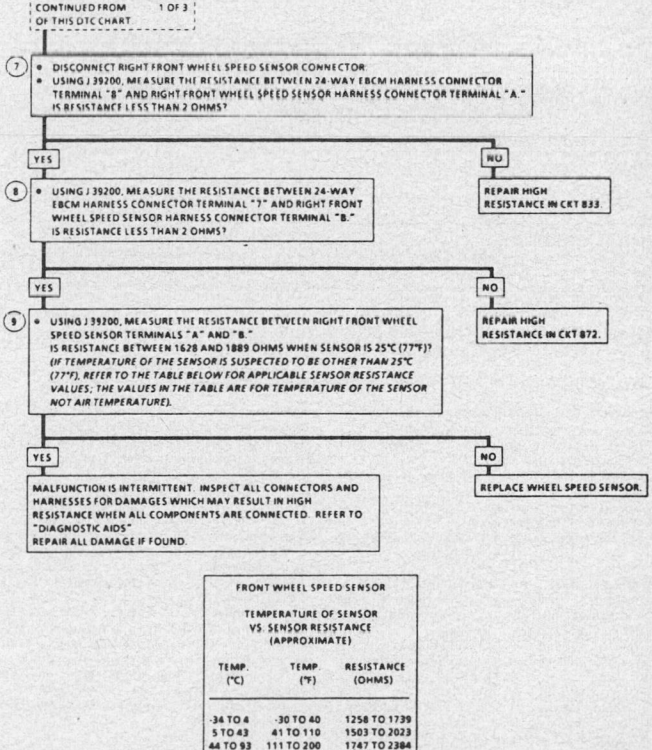

Fig. 135 Code A033: Right Front Wheel Speed Sensor Circuit Open Or Shorted To Ground/Battery (Part 2 of 3). 1994 Achieva, Grand Am & Skylark w/VES

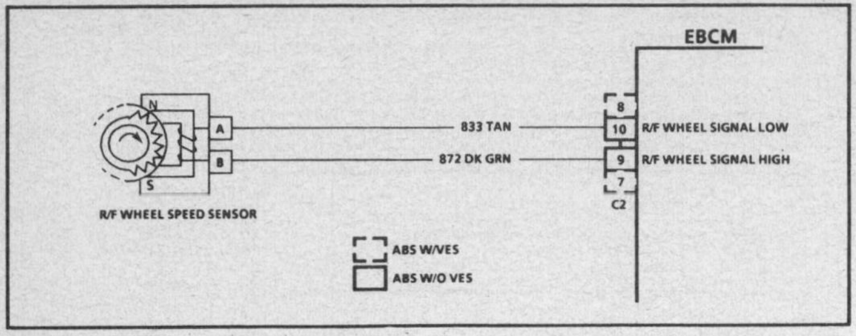
EBCM
N
A
B
S
833 TAN
872 DK GRN
8
10
9
7
C2
R/F WHEEL SIGNAL LOW
R/F WHEEL SIGNAL HIGH
R/F WHEEL SPEED SENSOR
ABS W/VES
ABS W/O VES

Circuit Description:
As a toothed ring passes by the wheel speed sensor, changes in the electromagnetic field cause the wheel speed sensor to produce a sinusoidal (AC) voltage signal whose frequency is proportional to wheel speed. The magnitude of this signal is directly related to wheel speed and the proximity of the wheel speed sensor to the toothed ring, often referred to as the air gap.

DTC Will Set When: DTC 33 can be set anytime after the ABS enable relay has been commanded "ON." The relay is commanded "ON" during the three second bulb check.

Action Taken: A malfunction DTC is stored, ABS/VES is disabled and the ABS warning lamp is turned "ON."

DTC Chart Test Description: Number(s) below refer to circled number(s) on the diagnostic chart.
10. Checks for a short to ground in either of the wheel signal high or low circuits.
11. Checks for a short to ground in the wheel speed sensor.

Diagnostic Aids: An "Intermittent" malfunction is most likely caused by a poor connection, rubbed through wire insulation, or a wire that is broken inside the insulation.

The frequency of the malfunction can be checked by using the enhanced diagnostic function of the Tech 1.

If the customer's comments reflect that the ABS amber warning lamp is "ON" only during moist environmental changes, (rain, snow, vehicle wash) all wheel speed sensor circuitry should be thoroughly inspected for signs of water intrusion. Use the following procedure. Spray down the suspected area with 5% salt water solution (two teaspoons of salt to 12 oz. of water). Drive vehicle above 24 km/h (15 mph) for at least 30 seconds. If DTC returns immediately, replace suspected harness.

Any circuitry, that is suspected as causing the intermittent complaint, should be thoroughly checked for backed out terminals, improper mating, broken locks, improperly formed or damaged terminals, poor terminal to wiring connections or physical damage to the wiring harness.

Resistance of the wheel speed sensor will increase with an increase in sensor temperature.

When replacing a wheel speed sensor, inspect the sensor terminals and harness connector for corrosion and/or water intrusion. If evidence of corrosion or water intrusion exists, replace wheel speed sensor harness. Refer to "On-Vehicle Service" in this section.

If wheel speed sensor harness shows evidence of water intrusion, inspect wheel speed sensor for water intrusion. If water intrusion is evident, replace wheel speed sensor.

GC402940104903AX

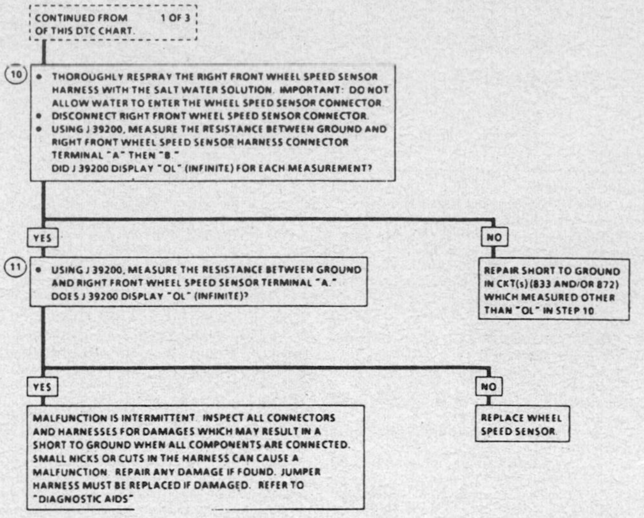
CONTINUED FROM 1 OF 3 OF THIS DTC CHART.
10
• THOROUGHLY RESPRAY THE RIGHT FRONT WHEEL SPEED SENSOR HARNESS WITH THE SALT WATER SOLUTION. IMPORTANT: DO NOT ALLOW WATER TO ENTER THE WHEEL SPEED SENSOR CONNECTOR.
• DISCONNECT RIGHT FRONT WHEEL SPEED SENSOR CONNECTOR.
• USING J 39200, MEASURE THE RESISTANCE BETWEEN GROUND AND RIGHT FRONT WHEEL SPEED SENSOR HARNESS CONNECTOR TERMINAL "A" THEN "B."
DID J 39200 DISPLAY "OL" (INFINITE) FOR EACH MEASUREMENT?
YES
NO
11
• USING J 39200, MEASURE THE RESISTANCE BETWEEN GROUND AND RIGHT FRONT WHEEL SPEED SENSOR TERMINAL "A."
DOES J 39200 DISPLAY "OL" (INFINITE)?
REPAIR SHORT TO GROUND IN CKT(s) (833 AND/OR 872) WHICH MEASURED OTHER THAN "OL" IN STEP 10
YES
NO
MALFUNCTION IS INTERMITTENT. INSPECT ALL CONNECTORS AND HARNESSES FOR DAMAGES WHICH MAY RESULT IN A SHORT TO GROUND WHEN ALL COMPONENTS ARE CONNECTED. SMALL NICKS OR CUTS IN THE HARNESS CAN CAUSE A MALFUNCTION. REPAIR ANY DAMAGE IF FOUND. JUMPER HARNESS MUST BE REPLACED IF DAMAGED. REFER TO "DIAGNOSTIC AIDS"
REPLACE WHEEL SPEED SENSOR.

GC402940104903BX

Fig. 135 Code A033: Right Front Wheel Speed Sensor Circuit Open Or Shorted To Ground/Battery (Part 3 of 3). 1994 Achieva, Grand Am & Skylark w/VES

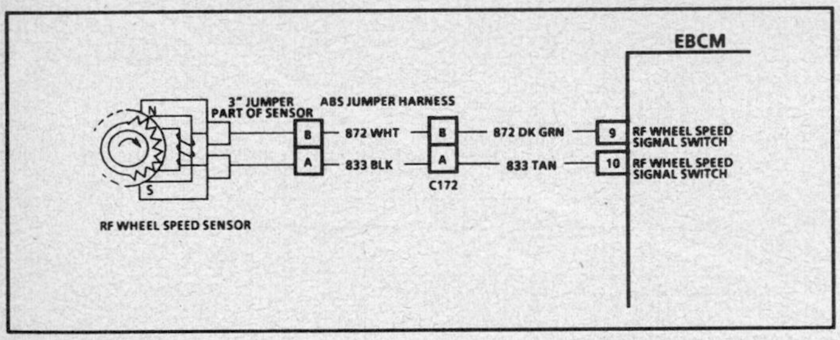
EBCM
3" JUMPER PART OF SENSOR
ABS JUMPER HARNESS
N
S
B
A
872 WHT
833 BLK
B
A
C172
872 DK GRN
833 TAN
9
10
RF WHEEL SPEED SIGNAL SWITCH
RF WHEEL SPEED SIGNAL SWITCH
RF WHEEL SPEED SENSOR

Circuit Description:
As a toothed ring passes by the wheel speed sensor, changes in the electromagnetic field cause the wheel speed sensor to produce a sinusoidal (AC) voltage signal whose frequency is proportional to wheel speed. The magnitude of this signal is directly related to wheel speed and the proximity of the wheel speed sensor to the toothed ring, often referred to as the air gap.

DTC Will Set When: DTC 33 can be set anytime after initialization. If either of the right front wheel speed circuits are shorted to voltage or ground, a malfunction exists.

Action Taken: A malfunction DTC is stored, ABS is disabled and the ABS warning lamp is turned "ON."

DTC Chart Test Description: Number(s) below refer to circled number(s) on the diagnostic chart.
1. Checks for short to ground in wheel speed sensor wiring circuitry.
2. Checks for short to voltage in wheel speed sensor wiring circuitry.
3. Checks for short to voltage in CKT 872.
4. Checks for short to voltage in CKT 833.
5. Checks for short to ground or voltage in CKTs 872 or 833.

Diagnostic Aids: An "Intermittent" malfunction may be caused by a poor connection, rubbed through wire insulation, or a wire that is broken inside the insulation.

The frequency of the malfunction can be checked by using the enhanced diagnostic function of the Tech 1.

If the customer's comments reflect that the ABS warning lamp is "ON" only during moist environmental changes (rain, snow, vehicle wash), all wheel speed sensor circuitry should be thoroughly inspected for signs of water intrusion. If DTC is not current, clear DTCs and simulate the effects of water intrusion. Use the following procedure. Spray down the suspected area with a 5% salt water solution (two teaspoons of salt to 12 oz. of water). Test drive vehicle over various road surfaces (bumps, turns, etc.) above 24 km/h (15 mph) for at least 30 seconds. If DTC returns replace suspected harness.

Any circuitry, that is suspected as causing the intermittent complaint, should be thoroughly checked for backed out terminals, improper mating, broken locks, improperly formed or damaged terminals, poor terminal to wiring connections or physical damage to the wiring harness.

Resistance of the wheel speed sensor will increase with an increase in sensor temperature.

When replacing a wheel speed sensor, inspect the sensor terminals and harness connector for corrosion and/or water intrusion. If evidence of corrosion or water intrusion exists, replace wheel speed sensor jumper harness. Likewise, if replacing a wheel speed sensor jumper harness, inspect sensor terminals. If evidence of corrosion or water intrusion exists, replace wheel speed sensor.

GC402930077101AA

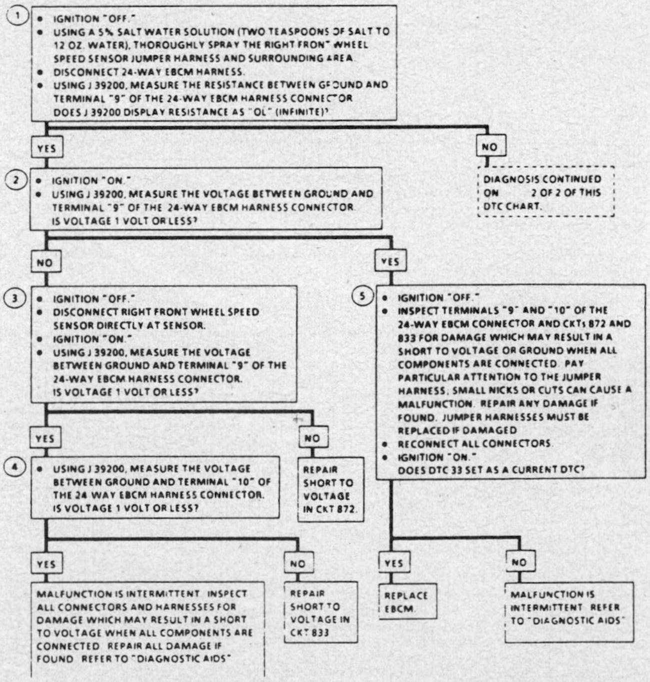
1
• IGNITION "OFF."
• USING A 5% SALT WATER SOLUTION (TWO TEASPOONS OF SALT TO 12 OZ. WATER), THOROUGHLY SPRAY THE RIGHT FRONT WHEEL SPEED SENSOR JUMPER HARNESS AND SURROUNDING AREA.
• DISCONNECT 24-WAY EBCM HARNESS.
• USING J 39200, MEASURE THE RESISTANCE BETWEEN GROUND AND TERMINAL "9" OF THE 24-WAY EBCM HARNESS CONNECTOR.
DOES J 39200 DISPLAY RESISTANCE AS "OL" (INFINITE)?
YES
NO
2
• IGNITION "ON."
• USING J 39200, MEASURE THE VOLTAGE BETWEEN GROUND AND TERMINAL "9" OF THE 24-WAY EBCM HARNESS CONNECTOR.
IS VOLTAGE 1 VOLT OR LESS?
DIAGNOSIS CONTINUED ON 2 OF 2 OF THIS DTC CHART.
NO
YES
3
• IGNITION "OFF."
• DISCONNECT RIGHT FRONT WHEEL SPEED SENSOR DIRECTLY AT SENSOR.
• IGNITION "ON."
• USING J 39200, MEASURE THE VOLTAGE BETWEEN GROUND AND TERMINAL "9" OF THE 24-WAY EBCM HARNESS CONNECTOR.
IS VOLTAGE 1 VOLT OR LESS?
5
• IGNITION "OFF."
• INSPECT TERMINALS "9" AND "10" OF THE 24-WAY EBCM CONNECTOR AND CKTs 872 AND 833 FOR DAMAGE WHICH MAY RESULT IN A SHORT TO VOLTAGE OR GROUND WHEN ALL COMPONENTS ARE CONNECTED. PAY PARTICULAR ATTENTION TO THE JUMPER HARNESS. SMALL NICKS OR CUTS CAN CAUSE A MALFUNCTION. REPAIR ANY DAMAGE IF FOUND. JUMPER HARNESSES MUST BE REPLACED IF DAMAGED.
• RECONNECT ALL CONNECTORS.
• IGNITION "ON."
DOES DTC 33 SET AS A CURRENT DTC?
YES
NO
REPAIR SHORT TO VOLTAGE IN CKT 872.
4
• USING J 39200, MEASURE THE VOLTAGE BETWEEN GROUND AND TERMINAL "10" OF THE 24 WAY EBCM HARNESS CONNECTOR.
IS VOLTAGE 1 VOLT OR LESS?
YES
NO
YES
NO
MALFUNCTION IS INTERMITTENT. INSPECT ALL CONNECTORS AND HARNESSES FOR DAMAGE WHICH MAY RESULT IN A SHORT TO VOLTAGE WHEN ALL COMPONENTS ARE CONNECTED. REPAIR ALL DAMAGE IF FOUND. REFER TO "DIAGNOSTIC AIDS"
REPAIR SHORT TO VOLTAGE IN CKT 833
REPLACE EBCM.
MALFUNCTION IS INTERMITTENT. REFER TO "DIAGNOSTIC AIDS"

GC402930077101BA

Fig. 136 Code A033: Right Front Wheel Sensor Shorted To Battery Or Ground (Part 1 of 2). 1993 Grand Prix, 1993–94 Cutlass Supreme, Lumina & Regal

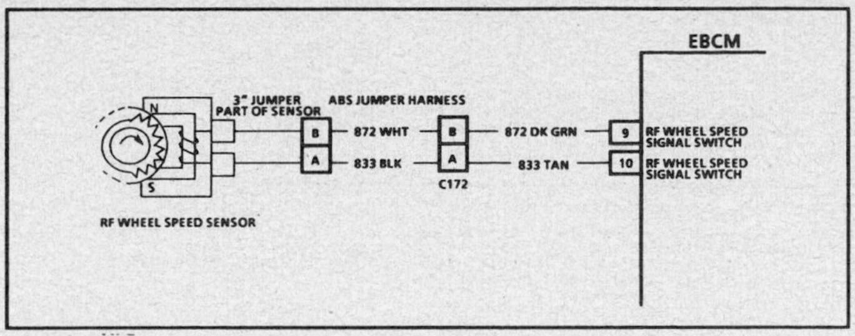

EBCM
3" JUMPER PART OF SENSOR
ABS JUMPER HARNESS
N
S
B
A
872 WHT
833 BLK
B
A
C172
872 DK GRN
833 TAN
9
10
RF WHEEL SPEED SIGNAL SWITCH
RF WHEEL SPEED SIGNAL SWITCH
RF WHEEL SPEED SENSOR

Circuit Description:
As a toothed ring passes by the wheel speed sensor, changes in the electromagnetic field cause the wheel speed sensor to produce a sinusoidal (AC) voltage signal whose frequency is proportional to wheel speed. The magnitude of this signal is directly related to wheel speed and the proximity of the wheel speed sensor to the toothed ring, often referred to as the air gap.

DTC Will Set When: DTC 33 can be set anytime after initialization. If either of the right front wheel speed circuits are shorted to voltage or ground, a malfunction exists.

Action Taken: A malfunction DTC is stored, ABS is disabled and the ABS warning lamp is turned "ON."

DTC Chart Test Description: Number(s) below refer to circled number(s) on the diagnostic chart.
6. Checks for short to ground in CKT 872.
7. Checks for short to ground in CKT 833.
8. Checks for short to ground in wheel speed sensor jumper harness.
9. Checks for proper resistance in wheel speed sensor circuitry.

Diagnostic Aids: An "Intermittent" malfunction may be caused by a poor connection, rubbed through wire insulation, or a wire that is broken inside the insulation.

The frequency of the malfunction can be checked by using the enhanced diagnostic function of the Tech 1.

If the customer's comments reflect that the ABS warning lamp is "ON" only during moist environmental changes (rain, snow, vehicle wash), all wheel speed sensor circuitry should be thoroughly inspected for signs of water intrusion. If DTC is not current, clear DTCs and simulate the effects of water intrusion. Use the following procedure. Spray down the suspected area with a 5% salt water solution (two teaspoons of salt to 12 oz. of water). Test drive vehicle over various road surfaces (bumps, turns, etc.) above 24 km/h (15 mph) for at least 30 seconds. If DTC returns replace suspected harness.

Any circuitry, that is suspected as causing the intermittent complaint, should be thoroughly checked for backed out terminals, improper mating, broken locks, improperly formed or damaged terminals, poor terminal to wiring connections or physical damage to the wiring harness.

Resistance of the wheel speed sensor will increase with an increase in sensor temperature.

When replacing a wheel speed sensor, inspect the sensor terminals and harness connector for corrosion and/or water intrusion. If evidence of corrosion or water intrusion exists, replace wheel speed sensor jumper harness. Likewise, if replacing a wheel speed sensor jumper harness, inspect sensor terminals. If evidence of corrosion or water intrusion exists, replace wheel speed sensor.

GC402930077102AA

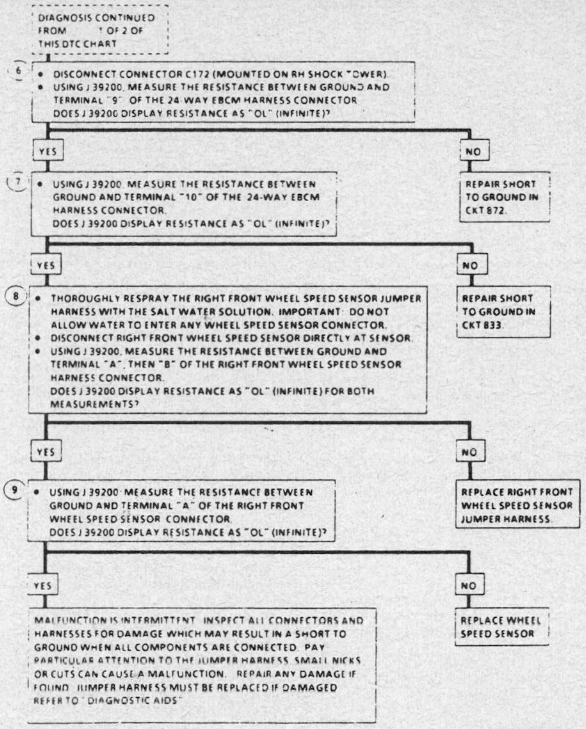

DIAGNOSIS CONTINUED FROM 1 OF 2 OF THIS DTC CHART
6
• DISCONNECT CONNECTOR C172 (MOUNTED ON RH SHOCK TOWER).
• USING J 39200, MEASURE THE RESISTANCE BETWEEN GROUND AND TERMINAL "9" OF THE 24-WAY EBCM HARNESS CONNECTOR
DOES J 39200 DISPLAY RESISTANCE AS "OL" (INFINITE)?
YES
NO
REPAIR SHORT TO GROUND IN CKT 872.
7
• USING J 39200 MEASURE THE RESISTANCE BETWEEN GROUND AND TERMINAL "10" OF THE 24-WAY EBCM HARNESS CONNECTOR.
DOES J 39200 DISPLAY RESISTANCE AS "OL" (INFINITE)?
YES
NO
REPAIR SHORT TO GROUND IN CKT 833.
8
• THOROUGHLY RESPRAY THE RIGHT FRONT WHEEL SPEED SENSOR JUMPER HARNESS WITH THE SALT WATER SOLUTION. IMPORTANT: DO NOT ALLOW WATER TO ENTER ANY WHEEL SPEED SENSOR CONNECTOR.
• DISCONNECT RIGHT FRONT WHEEL SPEED SENSOR DIRECTLY AT SENSOR.
• USING J 39200, MEASURE THE RESISTANCE BETWEEN GROUND AND TERMINAL "A", THEN "B" OF THE RIGHT FRONT WHEEL SPEED SENSOR HARNESS CONNECTOR.
DOES J 39200 DISPLAY RESISTANCE AS "OL" (INFINITE) FOR BOTH MEASUREMENTS?
YES
NO
REPLACE RIGHT FRONT WHEEL SPEED SENSOR JUMPER HARNESS.
9
• USING J 39200 MEASURE THE RESISTANCE BETWEEN GROUND AND TERMINAL "A" OF THE RIGHT FRONT WHEEL SPEED SENSOR CONNECTOR.
DOES J 39200 DISPLAY RESISTANCE AS "OL" (INFINITE)?
YES
NO
REPLACE WHEEL SPEED SENSOR
MALFUNCTION IS INTERMITTENT. INSPECT ALL CONNECTORS AND HARNESSES FOR DAMAGE WHICH MAY RESULT IN A SHORT TO GROUND WHEN ALL COMPONENTS ARE CONNECTED. PAY PARTICULAR ATTENTION TO THE JUMPER HARNESS. SMALL NICKS OR CUTS CAN CAUSE A MALFUNCTION. REPAIR ANY DAMAGE IF FOUND. JUMPER HARNESS MUST BE REPLACED IF DAMAGED. REFER TO "DIAGNOSTIC AIDS"

GC402930077102BA

Fig. 136 Code A033: Right Front Wheel Sensor Shorted To Battery Or Ground (Part 2 of 2). 1993 Grand Prix, 1993–94 Cutlass Supreme, Lumina & Regal

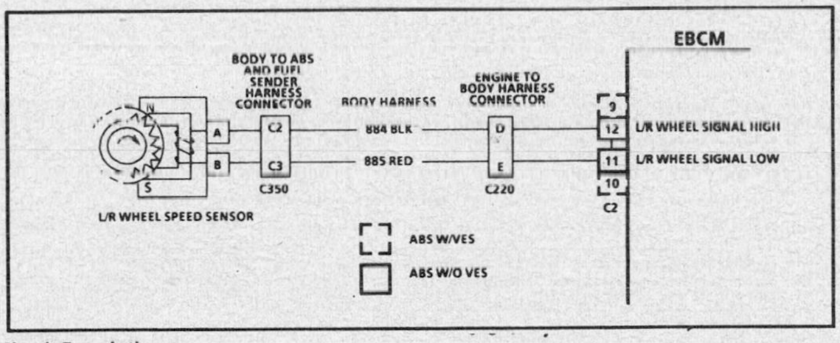

EBCM
BODY TO ABS AND FUEL SENDER HARNESS CONNECTOR
BODY HARNESS
ENGINE TO BODY HARNESS CONNECTOR
N
S
A
B
C2
C3
C350
884 BLK
885 RED
D
E
C220
9
12
11
10
C2
L/R WHEEL SIGNAL HIGH
L/R WHEEL SIGNAL LOW
L/R WHEEL SPEED SENSOR
ABS W/VES
ABS W/O VES

Circuit Description:
As a toothed ring passes by the wheel speed sensor, changes in the electromagnetic field cause the wheel speed sensor to produce a sinusoidal (AC) voltage signal whose frequency is proportional to wheel speed. The magnitude of this signal is directly related to wheel speed and the proximity of the wheel speed sensor to the toothed ring, often referred to as the air gap.

DTC Will Set When: DTC 34 can be set anytime after the ABS enable relay has been commanded "ON." The relay is commanded "ON" during the three second bulb check.

Action Taken: A malfunction DTC is stored, ABS/VES is disabled and the ABS warning lamp is turned "ON."

DTC Chart Test Description: Number(s) below refer to circled number(s) on the diagnostic chart.
1. Checks wheel speed sensor circuitry for proper resistance values.
2. Checks for a short to ground in the wheel speed sensor circuitry.
3. Checks for a short to voltage in the wheel speed sensor circuitry.
4. Ensures malfunction was not due to physical damage of the circuitry.
5. Checks for a short to voltage in the wheel signal low circuit.
6. Checks for a short to voltage in the wheel signal high circuit.

Diagnostic Aids: An "Intermittent" malfunction is most likely caused by a poor connection, rubbed through wire insulation, or a wire that is broken inside the insulation.

The frequency of the malfunction can be checked by using the enhanced diagnostic function of the Tech 1.

If the customer's comments reflect that the ABS amber warning lamp is "ON" only during moist environmental changes, (rain, snow, vehicle wash) all wheel speed sensor circuitry should be thoroughly inspected for signs of water intrusion. Use the following procedure. Spray down the suspected area with 5% salt water solution (two teaspoons of salt to 12 oz. of water). Drive vehicle above 24 km/h (15 mph) for at least 30 seconds. If DTC returns immediately, replace suspected harness.

Any circuitry, that is suspected as causing the intermittent complaint, should be thoroughly checked for backed out terminals, improper mating, broken locks, improperly formed or damaged terminals, poor terminal to wiring connections or physical damage to the wiring harness.

Resistance of the wheel speed sensor will increase with an increase in sensor temperature.

When replacing a wheel speed sensor, inspect the sensor terminals and harness connector for corrosion and/or water intrusion. If evidence of corrosion or water intrusion exists, replace wheel speed sensor harness. Refer to "On-Vehicle Service" in this section.

If wheel speed sensor harness shows evidence of water intrusion, inspect wheel speed sensor for water intrusion. If water intrusion is evident, replace wheel speed sensor.

GC402940105001AX

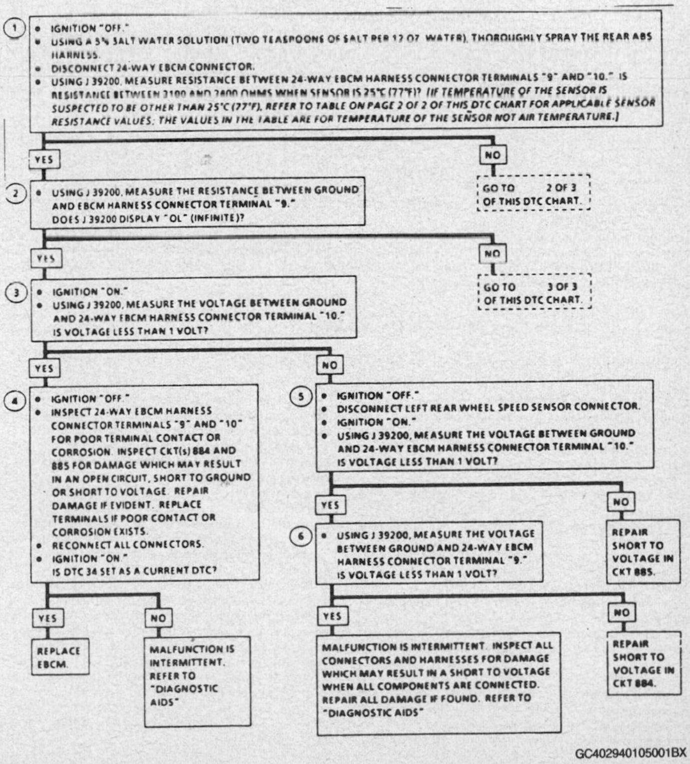

1
• IGNITION "OFF."
• USING A 5% SALT WATER SOLUTION (TWO TEASPOONS OF SALT PER 12 OZ. WATER), THOROUGHLY SPRAY THE REAR ABS HARNESS.
• DISCONNECT 24-WAY EBCM CONNECTOR.
• USING J 39200, MEASURE RESISTANCE BETWEEN 24-WAY EBCM HARNESS CONNECTOR TERMINALS "9" AND "10." IS RESISTANCE BETWEEN 3100 AND 3400 OHMS WHEN SENSOR IS 25°C (77°F)? [IF TEMPERATURE OF THE SENSOR IS SUSPECTED TO BE OTHER THAN 25°C (77°F), REFER TO TABLE ON PAGE 2 OF 2 OF THIS DTC CHART FOR APPLICABLE SENSOR RESISTANCE VALUES. THE VALUES IN THE TABLE ARE FOR TEMPERATURE OF THE SENSOR NOT AIR TEMPERATURE.]
YES
NO
GO TO 2 OF 3 OF THIS DTC CHART.
2
• USING J 39200, MEASURE THE RESISTANCE BETWEEN GROUND AND EBCM HARNESS CONNECTOR TERMINAL "9."
DOES J 39200 DISPLAY "OL" (INFINITE)?
YES
NO
GO TO 3 OF 3 OF THIS DTC CHART.
3
• IGNITION "ON."
• USING J 39200, MEASURE THE VOLTAGE BETWEEN GROUND AND 24-WAY EBCM HARNESS CONNECTOR TERMINAL "10."
IS VOLTAGE LESS THAN 1 VOLT?
YES
NO
4
• IGNITION "OFF."
• INSPECT 24-WAY EBCM HARNESS CONNECTOR TERMINALS "9" AND "10" FOR POOR TERMINAL CONTACT OR CORROSION. INSPECT CKT(s) 884 AND 885 FOR DAMAGE WHICH MAY RESULT IN AN OPEN CIRCUIT, SHORT TO GROUND OR SHORT TO VOLTAGE. REPAIR DAMAGE IF EVIDENT. REPLACE TERMINALS IF POOR CONTACT OR CORROSION EXISTS.
• RECONNECT ALL CONNECTORS.
• IGNITION "ON."
IS DTC 34 SET AS A CURRENT DTC?
5
• IGNITION "OFF."
• DISCONNECT LEFT REAR WHEEL SPEED SENSOR CONNECTOR.
• IGNITION "ON."
• USING J 39200, MEASURE THE VOLTAGE BETWEEN GROUND AND 24-WAY EBCM HARNESS CONNECTOR TERMINAL "10."
IS VOLTAGE LESS THAN 1 VOLT?
YES
NO
REPAIR SHORT TO VOLTAGE IN CKT 885.
6
• USING J 39200, MEASURE THE VOLTAGE BETWEEN GROUND AND 24-WAY EBCM HARNESS CONNECTOR TERMINAL "9."
IS VOLTAGE LESS THAN 1 VOLT?
YES
NO
REPAIR SHORT TO VOLTAGE IN CKT 884.
YES
NO
REPLACE EBCM.
MALFUNCTION IS INTERMITTENT. REFER TO "DIAGNOSTIC AIDS"
MALFUNCTION IS INTERMITTENT. INSPECT ALL CONNECTORS AND HARNESSES FOR DAMAGE WHICH MAY RESULT IN A SHORT TO VOLTAGE WHEN ALL COMPONENTS ARE CONNECTED. REPAIR ALL DAMAGE IF FOUND. REFER TO "DIAGNOSTIC AIDS"

GC402940105001BX

Fig. 137 Code A034: Left Rear Wheel Speed Sensor Circuit Open Or Shorted To Ground/Battery (Part 1 of 3). 1994 Achieva, Grand Am & Skylark w/VES

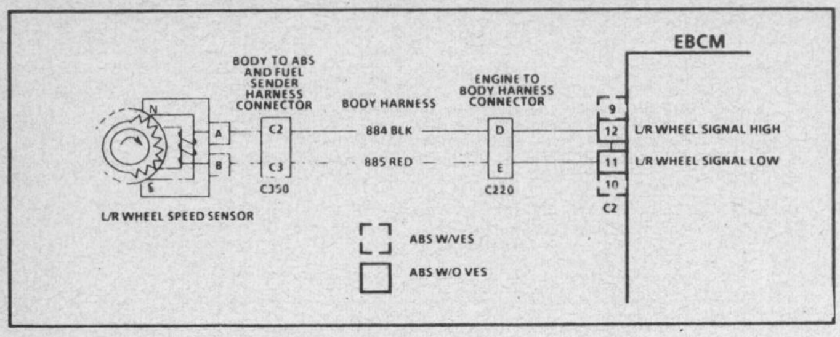
EBCM
BODY TO ABS AND FUEL SENDER HARNESS CONNECTOR
ENGINE TO BODY HARNESS CONNECTOR
BODY HARNESS
N
A
B
S
C2
C3
C350
884 BLK
885 RED
D
E
C220
9
12
11
10
C2
L/R WHEEL SIGNAL HIGH
L/R WHEEL SIGNAL LOW
L/R WHEEL SPEED SENSOR
ABS W/VES
ABS W/O VES

Circuit Description:
As a toothed ring passes by the wheel speed sensor, changes in the electromagnetic field cause the wheel speed sensor to produce a sinusoidal (AC) voltage signal whose frequency is proportional to wheel speed. The magnitude of this signal is directly related to wheel speed and the proximity of the wheel speed sensor to the toothed ring, often referred to as the air gap.

DTC Will Set When: DTC 34 can be set anytime after the ABS enable relay has been commanded "ON." The relay is commanded "ON" during the three second bulb check.

Action Taken: A malfunction DTC is stored, ABS/VES is disabled and the ABS warning lamp is turned "ON."

DTC Chart Test Description: Number(s) below refer to circled number(s) on the diagnostic chart.
7. Checks for high resistance in the wheel signal high circuit.
8. Checks for high resistance in the wheel signal low circuit.
9. Checks for proper resistance of the wheel speed sensor.

Diagnostic Aids: An "Intermittent" malfunction is most likely caused by a poor connection, rubbed through wire insulation, or a wire that is broken inside the insulation.

The frequency of the malfunction can be checked by using the enhanced diagnostic function of the Tech 1.

If the customer's comments reflect that the ABS amber warning lamp is "ON" only during moist environmental changes, (rain, snow, vehicle wash) all wheel speed sensor circuitry should be thoroughly inspected for signs of water intrusion. Use the following procedure. Spray down the suspected area with 5% salt water solution (two teaspoons of salt to 12 oz. of water). Drive vehicle above 24 km/h (15 mph) for at least 30 seconds. If DTC returns immediately, replace suspected harness.

Any circuitry, that is suspected as causing the intermittent complaint, should be thoroughly checked for backed out terminals, improper mating, broken locks, improperly formed or damaged terminals, poor terminal to wiring connections or physical damage to the wiring harness.

Resistance of the wheel speed sensor will increase with an increase in sensor temperature.

When replacing a wheel speed sensor, inspect the sensor terminals and harness connector for corrosion and/or water intrusion. If evidence of corrosion or water intrusion exists, replace wheel speed sensor harness. Refer to "On-Vehicle Service" in this section.

If wheel speed sensor harness shows evidence of water intrusion, inspect wheel speed sensor for water intrusion. If water intrusion is evident, replace wheel speed sensor.

GC402940105002AX

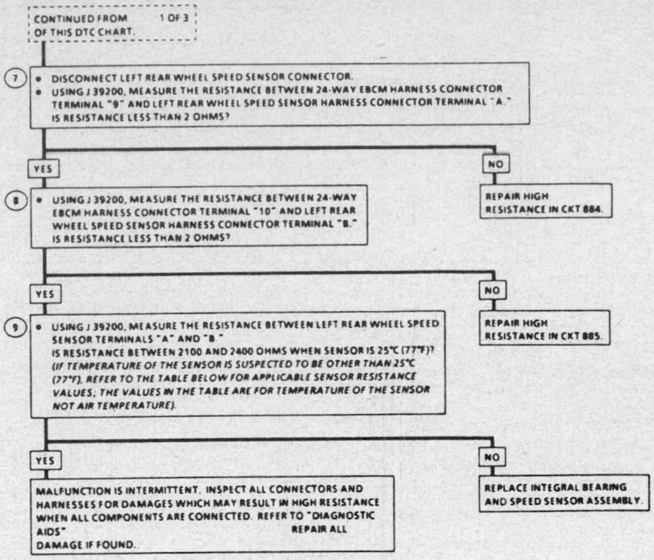
CONTINUED FROM 1 OF 3 OF THIS DTC CHART.
7
• DISCONNECT LEFT REAR WHEEL SPEED SENSOR CONNECTOR.
• USING J 39200, MEASURE THE RESISTANCE BETWEEN 24-WAY EBCM HARNESS CONNECTOR TERMINAL "9" AND LEFT REAR WHEEL SPEED SENSOR HARNESS CONNECTOR TERMINAL "A."
IS RESISTANCE LESS THAN 2 OHMS?
YES
NO
REPAIR HIGH RESISTANCE IN CKT 884.
8
• USING J 39200, MEASURE THE RESISTANCE BETWEEN 24-WAY EBCM HARNESS CONNECTOR TERMINAL "10" AND LEFT REAR WHEEL SPEED SENSOR HARNESS CONNECTOR TERMINAL "B."
IS RESISTANCE LESS THAN 2 OHMS?
YES
NO
REPAIR HIGH RESISTANCE IN CKT 885.
9
• USING J 39200, MEASURE THE RESISTANCE BETWEEN LEFT REAR WHEEL SPEED SENSOR TERMINALS "A" AND "B."
IS RESISTANCE BETWEEN 2100 AND 2400 OHMS WHEN SENSOR IS 25°C (77°F)?
(IF TEMPERATURE OF THE SENSOR IS SUSPECTED TO BE OTHER THAN 25°C (77°F), REFER TO THE TABLE BELOW FOR APPLICABLE SENSOR RESISTANCE VALUES; THE VALUES IN THE TABLE ARE FOR TEMPERATURE OF THE SENSOR NOT AIR TEMPERATURE).
YES
NO
MALFUNCTION IS INTERMITTENT. INSPECT ALL CONNECTORS AND HARNESSES FOR DAMAGES WHICH MAY RESULT IN HIGH RESISTANCE WHEN ALL COMPONENTS ARE CONNECTED. REFER TO "DIAGNOSTIC AIDS" REPAIR ALL DAMAGE IF FOUND.
REPLACE INTEGRAL BEARING AND SPEED SENSOR ASSEMBLY.

REAR WHEEL SPEED SENSOR

TEMPERATURE OF SENSOR VS. SENSOR RESISTANCE (APPROXIMATE)

TEMP. (°C)	TEMP. (°F)	RESISTANCE (OHMS)
-34 TO 4	-30 TO 40	1623 TO 2210
5 TO 43	41 TO 110	1939 TO 2570
44 TO 93	111 TO 200	2254 TO 3029

GC402940105002BX

Fig. 137 Code A034: Left Rear Wheel Speed Sensor Circuit Open Or Shorted To Ground/Battery (Part 2 of 3). 1994 Achieva, Grand Am & Skylark w/VES

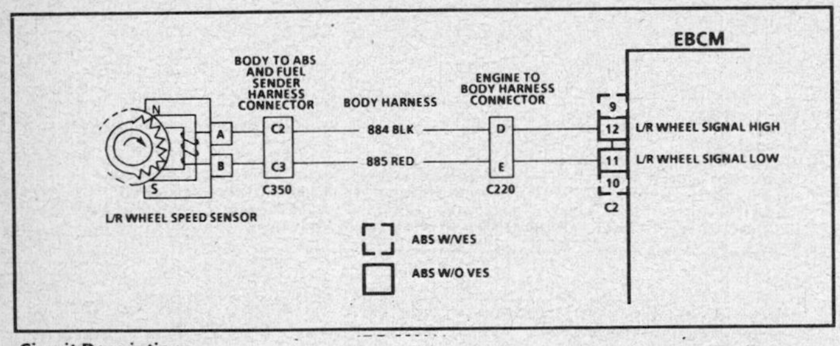
EBCM
BODY TO ABS AND FUEL SENDER HARNESS CONNECTOR
ENGINE TO BODY HARNESS CONNECTOR
BODY HARNESS
N
A
B
S
C2
C3
C350
884 BLK
885 RED
D
E
C220
9
12
11
10
C2
L/R WHEEL SIGNAL HIGH
L/R WHEEL SIGNAL LOW
L/R WHEEL SPEED SENSOR
ABS W/VES
ABS W/O VES

Circuit Description:
As a toothed ring passes by the wheel speed sensor, changes in the electromagnetic field cause the wheel speed sensor to produce a sinusoidal (AC) voltage signal whose frequency is proportional to wheel speed. The magnitude of this signal is directly related to wheel speed and the proximity of the wheel speed sensor to the toothed ring, often referred to as the air gap.

DTC Will Set When: DTC 34 can be set anytime after the ABS enable relay has been commanded "ON." The relay is commanded "ON" during the three second bulb check.

Action Taken: A malfunction DTC is stored, ABS/VES is disabled and the ABS warning lamp is turned "ON."

DTC Chart Test Description: Number(s) below refer to circled number(s) on the diagnostic chart.
10. Checks for a short to ground in the wheel signal high circuit.
11. Checks for a short to ground in the wheel signal low circuit.
12. Checks for a short to ground in the rear ABS harness.
13. Checks for a short to ground in the wheel speed sensor.

Diagnostic Aids: An "Intermittent" malfunction is most likely caused by a poor connection, rubbed through wire insulation, or a wire that is broken inside the insulation.

The frequency of the malfunction can be checked by using the enhanced diagnostic function of the Tech 1.

If the customer's comments reflect that the ABS amber warning lamp is "ON" only during moist environmental changes, (rain, snow, vehicle wash) all wheel speed sensor circuitry should be thoroughly inspected for signs of water intrusion. Use the following procedure. Spray down the suspected area with 5% salt water solution (two teaspoons of salt to 12 oz. of water). Drive vehicle above 24 km/h (15 mph) for at least 30 seconds. If DTC returns immediately, replace suspected harness.

Any circuitry, that is suspected as causing the intermittent complaint, should be thoroughly checked for backed out terminals, improper mating, broken locks, improperly formed or damaged terminals, poor terminal to wiring connections or physical damage to the wiring harness.

Resistance of the wheel speed sensor will increase with an increase in sensor temperature.

When replacing a wheel speed sensor, inspect the sensor terminals and harness connector for corrosion and/or water intrusion. If evidence of corrosion or water intrusion exists, replace wheel speed sensor harness. Refer to "On-Vehicle Service" in this section.

If wheel speed sensor harness shows evidence of water intrusion, inspect wheel speed sensor for water intrusion. If water intrusion is evident, replace wheel speed sensor.

GC402940105003AX

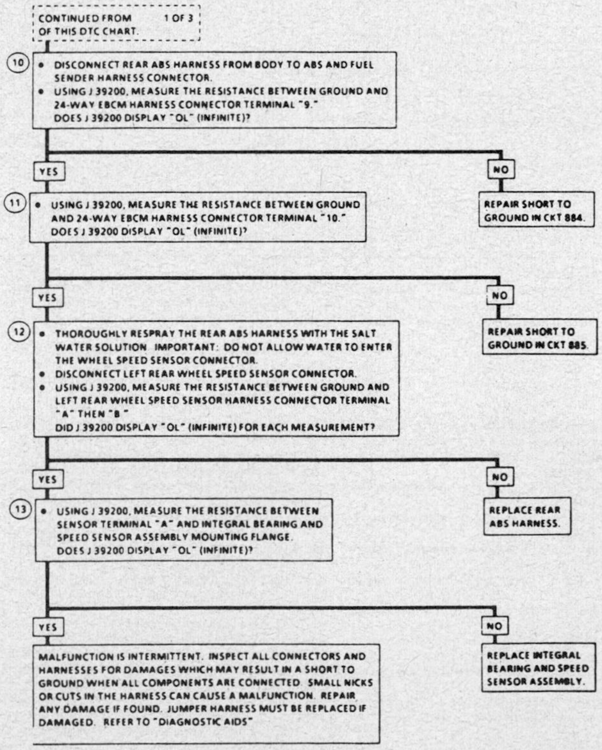
CONTINUED FROM 1 OF 3 OF THIS DTC CHART.
10
• DISCONNECT REAR ABS HARNESS FROM BODY TO ABS AND FUEL SENDER HARNESS CONNECTOR.
• USING J 39200, MEASURE THE RESISTANCE BETWEEN GROUND AND 24-WAY EBCM HARNESS CONNECTOR TERMINAL "9."
DOES J 39200 DISPLAY "OL" (INFINITE)?
YES
NO
REPAIR SHORT TO GROUND IN CKT 884.
11
• USING J 39200, MEASURE THE RESISTANCE BETWEEN GROUND AND 24-WAY EBCM HARNESS CONNECTOR TERMINAL "10."
DOES J 39200 DISPLAY "OL" (INFINITE)?
YES
NO
REPAIR SHORT TO GROUND IN CKT 885.
12
• THOROUGHLY RESPRAY THE REAR ABS HARNESS WITH THE SALT WATER SOLUTION. IMPORTANT: DO NOT ALLOW WATER TO ENTER THE WHEEL SPEED SENSOR CONNECTOR.
• DISCONNECT LEFT REAR WHEEL SPEED SENSOR CONNECTOR.
• USING J 39200, MEASURE THE RESISTANCE BETWEEN GROUND AND LEFT REAR WHEEL SPEED SENSOR HARNESS CONNECTOR TERMINAL "A" THEN "B."
DID J 39200 DISPLAY "OL" (INFINITE) FOR EACH MEASUREMENT?
YES
NO
REPLACE REAR ABS HARNESS.
13
• USING J 39200, MEASURE THE RESISTANCE BETWEEN SENSOR TERMINAL "A" AND INTEGRAL BEARING AND SPEED SENSOR ASSEMBLY MOUNTING FLANGE.
DOES J 39200 DISPLAY "OL" (INFINITE)?
YES
NO
MALFUNCTION IS INTERMITTENT. INSPECT ALL CONNECTORS AND HARNESSES FOR DAMAGES WHICH MAY RESULT IN A SHORT TO GROUND WHEN ALL COMPONENTS ARE CONNECTED. SMALL NICKS OR CUTS IN THE HARNESS CAN CAUSE A MALFUNCTION. REPAIR ANY DAMAGE IF FOUND. JUMPER HARNESS MUST BE REPLACED IF DAMAGED. REFER TO "DIAGNOSTIC AIDS"
REPLACE INTEGRAL BEARING AND SPEED SENSOR ASSEMBLY.

GC402940105003BX

Fig. 137 Code A034: Left Rear Wheel Speed Sensor Circuit Open Or Shorted To Ground/Battery (Part 3 of 3). 1994 Achieva, Grand Am & Skylark w/VES

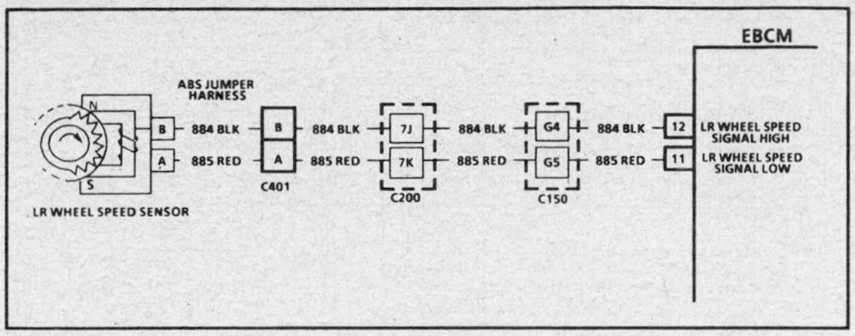
EBCM
ABS JUMPER HARNESS
B 884 BLK
A 885 RED
C401
7J
7K
C200
G4
G5
C150
12 LR WHEEL SPEED SIGNAL HIGH
11 LR WHEEL SPEED SIGNAL LOW
LR WHEEL SPEED SENSOR

Circuit Description:
As a toothed ring passes by the wheel speed sensor, changes in the electromagnetic field cause the wheel speed sensor to produce a sinusoidal (AC) voltage signal whose frequency is proportional to wheel speed. The magnitude of this signal is directly related to wheel speed and the proximity of the wheel speed sensor to the toothed ring, often referred to as the air gap.

DTC Will Set When: DTC 34 can be set anytime after initialization. If either of the left rear wheel speed circuits are shorted to voltage or ground, a malfunction exists.

Action Taken: A malfunction DTC is stored, ABS is disabled and the ABS warning lamp is turned "ON."

DTC Chart Test Description: Number(s) below refer to circled number(s) on the diagnostic chart.

1. Checks for short to ground in wheel speed sensor wiring circuitry.
2. Checks for short to voltage in wheel speed sensor wiring circuitry.
3. Checks for short to voltage in CKT 885.
4. Checks for short to voltage in CKT 884.
5. Checks for short to ground or voltage in CKTs 885 or 884.

Diagnostic Aids: An "Intermittent" malfunction may be caused by a poor connection, rubbed through wire insulation, or a wire that is broken inside the insulation.

The frequency of the malfunction can be checked by using the enhanced diagnostic function of the Tech 1

If the customer's comments reflect that the ABS warning lamp is "ON" only during moist environmental changes (rain, snow, vehicle wash), all wheel speed sensor circuitry should be thoroughly inspected for signs of water intrusion. If DTC is not current, clear DTCs and simulate the effects of water intrusion. Use the following procedure; spray down the suspected area with a 5% salt water solution (two teaspoons of salt to 12 oz. of water). Test drive vehicle over various road surfaces (bumps, turns, etc.) above 24 km/h (15 mph) for at least 30 seconds. If DTC returns replace suspected harness.

Any circuitry, that is suspected as causing the intermittent complaint, should be thoroughly checked for backed out terminals, improper mating, broken locks, improperly formed or damaged terminals, poor terminal to wiring connections or physical damage to the wiring harness.

Resistance of the wheel speed sensor will increase with an increase in sensor temperature.

When replacing a wheel speed sensor, inspect the sensor terminals and harness connector for corrosion and/or water intrusion. If evidence of corrosion or water intrusion exists, replace wheel speed sensor jumper harness. Likewise, if replacing a wheel speed sensor jumper harness, inspect sensor terminals. If evidence of corrosion or water intrusion exists, replace wheel speed sensor.

GC402930077201AA

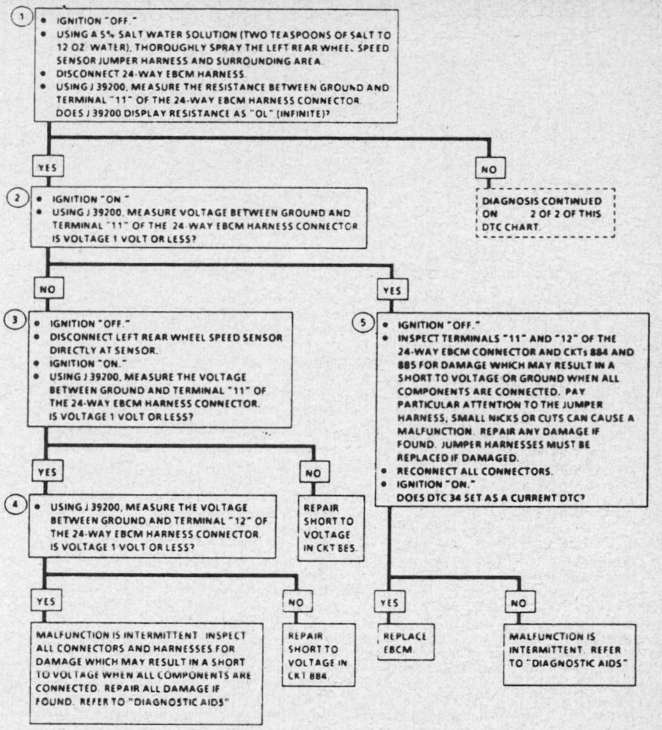
1
IGNITION "OFF."
USING A 5% SALT WATER SOLUTION (TWO TEASPOONS OF SALT TO 12 OZ WATER), THOROUGHLY SPRAY THE LEFT REAR WHEEL SPEED SENSOR JUMPER HARNESS AND SURROUNDING AREA.
DISCONNECT 24-WAY EBCM HARNESS.
USING J 39200, MEASURE THE RESISTANCE BETWEEN GROUND AND TERMINAL "11" OF THE 24-WAY EBCM HARNESS CONNECTOR.
DOES J 39200 DISPLAY RESISTANCE AS "OL" (INFINITE)?
YES
NO
DIAGNOSIS CONTINUED ON 2 OF 2 OF THIS DTC CHART.
2
IGNITION "ON."
USING J 39200, MEASURE VOLTAGE BETWEEN GROUND AND TERMINAL "11" OF THE 24-WAY EBCM HARNESS CONNECTOR.
IS VOLTAGE 1 VOLT OR LESS?
NO
YES
3
IGNITION "OFF."
DISCONNECT LEFT REAR WHEEL SPEED SENSOR DIRECTLY AT SENSOR.
IGNITION "ON."
USING J 39200, MEASURE THE VOLTAGE BETWEEN GROUND AND TERMINAL "11" OF THE 24-WAY EBCM HARNESS CONNECTOR.
IS VOLTAGE 1 VOLT OR LESS?
5
IGNITION "OFF."
INSPECT TERMINALS "11" AND "12" OF THE 24-WAY EBCM CONNECTOR AND CKTs 884 AND 885 FOR DAMAGE WHICH MAY RESULT IN A SHORT TO VOLTAGE OR GROUND WHEN ALL COMPONENTS ARE CONNECTED. PAY PARTICULAR ATTENTION TO THE JUMPER HARNESS, SMALL NICKS OR CUTS CAN CAUSE A MALFUNCTION. REPAIR ANY DAMAGE IF FOUND. JUMPER HARNESSES MUST BE REPLACED IF DAMAGED.
RECONNECT ALL CONNECTORS.
IGNITION "ON."
DOES DTC 34 SET AS A CURRENT DTC?
YES
NO
4
USING J 39200, MEASURE THE VOLTAGE BETWEEN GROUND AND TERMINAL "12" OF THE 24-WAY EBCM HARNESS CONNECTOR.
IS VOLTAGE 1 VOLT OR LESS?
REPAIR SHORT TO VOLTAGE IN CKT 885.
YES
NO
YES
NO
MALFUNCTION IS INTERMITTENT. INSPECT ALL CONNECTORS AND HARNESSES FOR DAMAGE WHICH MAY RESULT IN A SHORT TO VOLTAGE WHEN ALL COMPONENTS ARE CONNECTED. REPAIR ALL DAMAGE IF FOUND. REFER TO "DIAGNOSTIC AIDS"
REPAIR SHORT TO VOLTAGE IN CKT 884.
REPLACE EBCM.
MALFUNCTION IS INTERMITTENT. REFER TO "DIAGNOSTIC AIDS"

GC402930077201BA

Fig. 138 Code A034: Left Rear Wheel Sensor Shorted To Battery Or Ground (Part 1 of 2). 1993 Grand Prix, 1993–94 Cutlass Supreme, Lumina & Regal

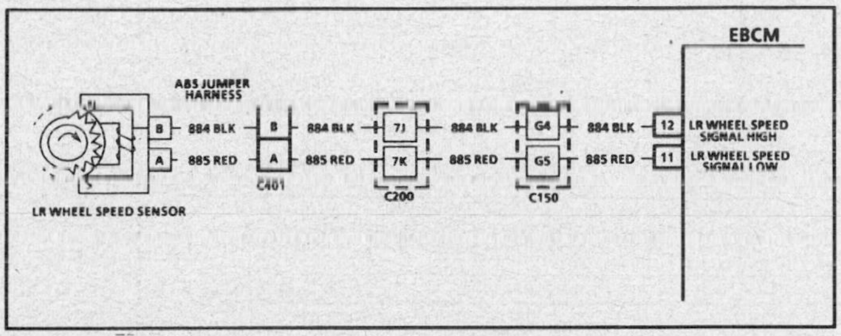
EBCM
ABS JUMPER HARNESS
B 884 BLK
A 885 RED
C401
7J
7K
C200
G4
G5
C150
12 LR WHEEL SPEED SIGNAL HIGH
11 LR WHEEL SPEED SIGNAL LOW
LR WHEEL SPEED SENSOR

Circuit Description:
As a toothed ring passes by the wheel speed sensor, changes in the electromagnetic field cause the wheel speed sensor to produce a sinusoidal (AC) voltage signal whose frequency is proportional to wheel speed. The magnitude of this signal is directly related to wheel speed and the proximity of the wheel speed sensor to the toothed ring, often referred to as the air gap.

DTC Will Set When: DTC 34 can be set anytime after initialization. If either of the left rear wheel speed circuits are shorted to voltage or ground, a malfunction exists.

Action Taken: A malfunction DTC is stored, ABS is disabled and the ABS warning lamp is turned "ON."

DTC Chart Test Description: Number(s) below refer to circled number(s) on the diagnostic chart.

6. Checks for short to ground in CKT 885.
7. Checks for short to ground in CKT 884.
8. Checks for short to ground in wheel speed sensor jumper harness.
9. Checks for proper resistance in wheel speed sensor circuitry.

Diagnostic Aids: An "Intermittent" malfunction may be caused by a poor connection, rubbed through wire insulation, or a wire that is broken inside the insulation.

The frequency of the malfunction can be checked by using the enhanced diagnostic function of the Tech 1

If the customer's comments reflect that the ABS warning lamp is "ON" only during moist environmental changes (rain, snow, vehicle wash), all wheel speed sensor circuitry should be thoroughly inspected for signs of water intrusion. If DTC is not current, clear DTCs and simulate the effects of water intrusion. Use the following procedure. Spray down the suspected area with a 5% salt water solution (two teaspoons of salt to 12 oz. of water). Test drive vehicle over various road surfaces (bumps, turns, etc.) above 24 km/h (15 mph) for at least 30 seconds. If DTC returns replace suspected harness.

Any circuitry, that is suspected as causing the intermittent complaint, should be thoroughly checked for backed out terminals, improper mating, broken locks, improperly formed or damaged terminals, poor terminal to wiring connections or physical damage to the wiring harness.

Resistance of the wheel speed sensor will increase with an increase in sensor temperature.

When replacing a wheel speed sensor, inspect the sensor terminals and harness connector for corrosion and/or water intrusion. If evidence of corrosion or water intrusion exists, replace wheel speed sensor jumper harness. Likewise, if replacing a wheel speed sensor jumper harness, inspect sensor terminals. If evidence of corrosion or water intrusion exists, replace wheel speed sensor.

GC402930077202AA

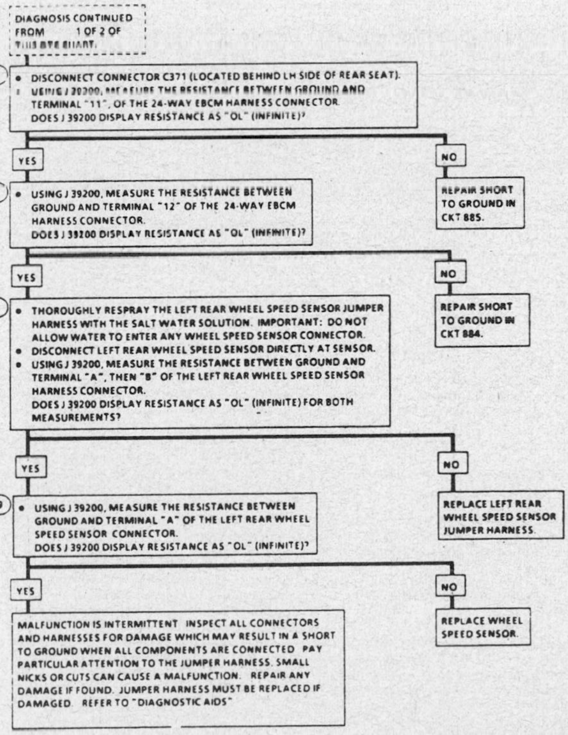
DIAGNOSIS CONTINUED FROM 1 OF 2 OF
6
DISCONNECT CONNECTOR C371 (LOCATED BEHIND LH SIDE OF REAR SEAT).
TERMINAL "11", OF THE 24-WAY EBCM HARNESS CONNECTOR.
DOES J 39200 DISPLAY RESISTANCE AS "OL" (INFINITE)?
YES
NO
7
USING J 39200, MEASURE THE RESISTANCE BETWEEN GROUND AND TERMINAL "12" OF THE 24-WAY EBCM HARNESS CONNECTOR.
DOES J 39200 DISPLAY RESISTANCE AS "OL" (INFINITE)?
REPAIR SHORT TO GROUND IN CKT 885.
YES
NO
8
THOROUGHLY RESPRAY THE LEFT REAR WHEEL SPEED SENSOR JUMPER HARNESS WITH THE SALT WATER SOLUTION. IMPORTANT: DO NOT ALLOW WATER TO ENTER ANY WHEEL SPEED SENSOR CONNECTOR.
DISCONNECT LEFT REAR WHEEL SPEED SENSOR DIRECTLY AT SENSOR.
USING J 39200, MEASURE THE RESISTANCE BETWEEN GROUND AND TERMINAL "A", THEN "B" OF THE LEFT REAR WHEEL SPEED SENSOR HARNESS CONNECTOR.
DOES J 39200 DISPLAY RESISTANCE AS "OL" (INFINITE) FOR BOTH MEASUREMENTS?
REPAIR SHORT TO GROUND IN CKT 884.
YES
NO
9
USING J 39200, MEASURE THE RESISTANCE BETWEEN GROUND AND TERMINAL "A" OF THE LEFT REAR WHEEL SPEED SENSOR CONNECTOR.
DOES J 39200 DISPLAY RESISTANCE AS "OL" (INFINITE)?
REPLACE LEFT REAR WHEEL SPEED SENSOR JUMPER HARNESS.
YES
NO
MALFUNCTION IS INTERMITTENT. INSPECT ALL CONNECTORS AND HARNESSES FOR DAMAGE WHICH MAY RESULT IN A SHORT TO GROUND WHEN ALL COMPONENTS ARE CONNECTED. PAY PARTICULAR ATTENTION TO THE JUMPER HARNESS. SMALL NICKS OR CUTS CAN CAUSE A MALFUNCTION. REPAIR ANY DAMAGE IF FOUND. JUMPER HARNESS MUST BE REPLACED IF DAMAGED. REFER TO "DIAGNOSTIC AIDS"
REPLACE WHEEL SPEED SENSOR.

GC402930077202BA

Fig. 138 Code A034: Left Rear Wheel Sensor Shorted To Battery Or Ground (Part 2 of 2). 1993 Grand Prix, 1993–94 Cutlass Supreme, Lumina & Regal

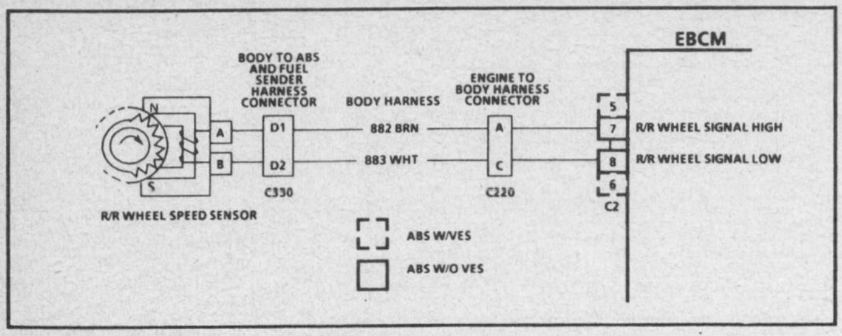
EBCM
BODY TO ABS AND FUEL SENDER HARNESS CONNECTOR
BODY HARNESS
ENGINE TO BODY HARNESS CONNECTOR
N
S
A
B
D1
D2
882 BRN
883 WHT
A
C
5
7
8
6
R/R WHEEL SIGNAL HIGH
R/R WHEEL SIGNAL LOW
C350
C220
C2
R/R WHEEL SPEED SENSOR
ABS W/VES
ABS W/O VES

Circuit Description:
As a toothed ring passes by the wheel speed sensor, changes in the electromagnetic field cause the wheel speed sensor to produce a sinusoidal (AC) voltage signal whose frequency is proportional to wheel speed. The magnitude of this signal is directly related to wheel speed and the proximity of the wheel speed sensor to the toothed ring, often referred to as the air gap.

DTC Will Set When: DTC 35 can be set anytime after the ABS enable relay has been commanded "ON." The relay is commanded "ON" during the three second bulb check.

Action Taken: A malfunction DTC is stored, ABS/VES is disabled and the ABS warning lamp is turned "ON."

DTC Chart Test Description: Number(s) below refer to circled number(s) on the diagnostic chart.

1. Checks wheel speed sensor circuitry for proper resistance values.
2. Checks for a short to ground in the wheel speed sensor circuitry.
3. Checks for a short to voltage in the wheel speed sensor circuitry.
4. Ensures malfunction was not due to physical damage of the circuitry.
5. Checks for a short to voltage in the wheel signal low circuit.
6. Checks for a short to voltage in the wheel signal high circuit.

Diagnostic Aids: An "Intermittent" malfunction is most likely caused by a poor connection, rubbed through wire insulation, or a wire that is broken inside the insulation.

The frequency of the malfunction can be checked by using the enhanced diagnostic function of the Tech 1

If the customer's comments reflect that the ABS amber warning lamp is "ON" only during moist environmental changes, (rain, snow, vehicle wash) all wheel speed sensor circuitry should be thoroughly inspected for signs of water intrusion. Use the following procedure. Spray down the suspected area with 5% salt water solution (two teaspoons of salt to 12 oz. of water). Drive vehicle above 24 km/h (15 mph) for at least 30 seconds. If DTC returns immediately, replace suspected harness.

Any circuitry, that is suspected as causing the intermittent complaint, should be thoroughly checked for backed out terminals, improper mating, broken locks, improperly formed or damaged terminals, poor terminal to wiring connections or physical damage to the wiring harness.

Resistance of the wheel speed sensor will increase with an increase in sensor temperature.

When replacing a wheel speed sensor, inspect the sensor terminals and harness connector for corrosion and/or water intrusion. If evidence of corrosion or water intrusion exists, replace wheel speed sensor harness. Refer to "On-Vehicle Service" in this section.

If wheel speed sensor harness shows evidence of water intrusion, inspect wheel speed sensor for water intrusion. If water intrusion is evident, replace wheel speed sensor.

GC402940105101AX

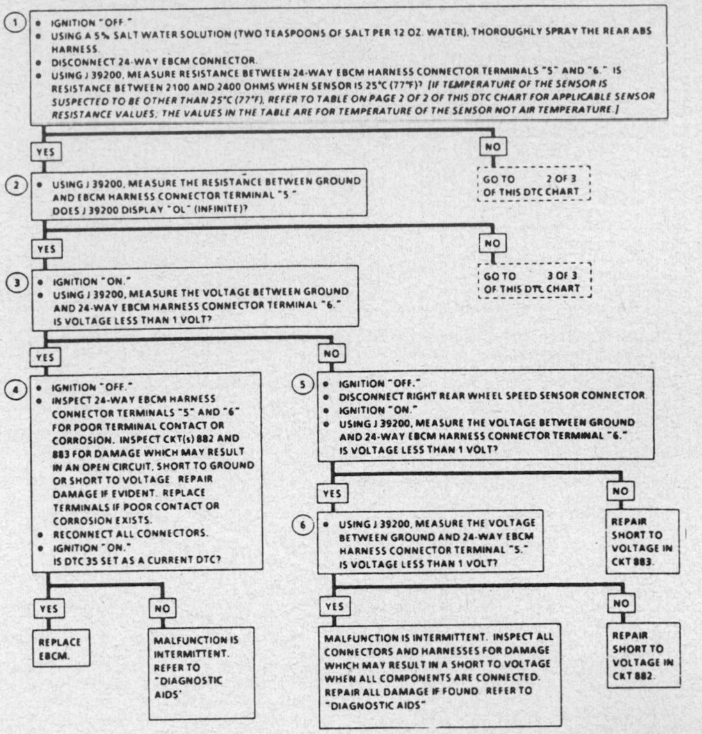
1
• IGNITION "OFF."
• USING A 5% SALT WATER SOLUTION (TWO TEASPOONS OF SALT PER 12 OZ. WATER), THOROUGHLY SPRAY THE REAR ABS HARNESS.
• DISCONNECT 24-WAY EBCM CONNECTOR.
• USING J 39200, MEASURE RESISTANCE BETWEEN 24-WAY EBCM HARNESS CONNECTOR TERMINALS "5" AND "6." IS RESISTANCE BETWEEN 2100 AND 2400 OHMS WHEN SENSOR IS 25°C (77°F)? [IF TEMPERATURE OF THE SENSOR IS SUSPECTED TO BE OTHER THAN 25°C (77°F), REFER TO TABLE ON PAGE 2 OF 2 OF THIS DTC CHART FOR APPLICABLE SENSOR RESISTANCE VALUES; THE VALUES IN THE TABLE ARE FOR TEMPERATURE OF THE SENSOR NOT AIR TEMPERATURE.]
YES
NO
GO TO 2 OF 3 OF THIS DTC CHART
2
• USING J 39200, MEASURE THE RESISTANCE BETWEEN GROUND AND EBCM HARNESS CONNECTOR TERMINAL "5." DOES J 39200 DISPLAY "OL" (INFINITE)?
YES
NO
GO TO 3 OF 3 OF THIS DTC CHART
3
• IGNITION "ON."
• USING J 39200, MEASURE THE VOLTAGE BETWEEN GROUND AND 24-WAY EBCM HARNESS CONNECTOR TERMINAL "6." IS VOLTAGE LESS THAN 1 VOLT?
YES
NO
4
• IGNITION "OFF."
• INSPECT 24-WAY EBCM HARNESS CONNECTOR TERMINALS "5" AND "6" FOR POOR TERMINAL CONTACT OR CORROSION. INSPECT CKT(s) 882 AND 883 FOR DAMAGE WHICH MAY RESULT IN AN OPEN CIRCUIT, SHORT TO GROUND OR SHORT TO VOLTAGE. REPAIR DAMAGE IF EVIDENT. REPLACE TERMINALS IF POOR CONTACT OR CORROSION EXISTS.
• RECONNECT ALL CONNECTORS.
• IGNITION "ON." IS DTC 35 SET AS A CURRENT DTC?
5
• IGNITION "OFF."
• DISCONNECT RIGHT REAR WHEEL SPEED SENSOR CONNECTOR.
• IGNITION "ON."
• USING J 39200, MEASURE THE VOLTAGE BETWEEN GROUND AND 24-WAY EBCM HARNESS CONNECTOR TERMINAL "6." IS VOLTAGE LESS THAN 1 VOLT?
YES
NO
6
• USING J 39200, MEASURE THE VOLTAGE BETWEEN GROUND AND 24-WAY EBCM HARNESS CONNECTOR TERMINAL "5." IS VOLTAGE LESS THAN 1 VOLT?
REPAIR SHORT TO VOLTAGE IN CKT 883.
YES
NO
REPLACE EBCM.
MALFUNCTION IS INTERMITTENT. REFER TO "DIAGNOSTIC AIDS"
YES
NO
MALFUNCTION IS INTERMITTENT. INSPECT ALL CONNECTORS AND HARNESSES FOR DAMAGE WHICH MAY RESULT IN A SHORT TO VOLTAGE WHEN ALL COMPONENTS ARE CONNECTED. REPAIR ALL DAMAGE IF FOUND. REFER TO "DIAGNOSTIC AIDS"
REPAIR SHORT TO VOLTAGE IN CKT 882.

GC402940105101BX

Fig. 139 Code A035: Right Rear Wheel Speed Sensor Circuit Open Or Shorted To Ground/Battery (Part 1 of 3). 1994 Achieva, Grand Am & Skylark w/VES

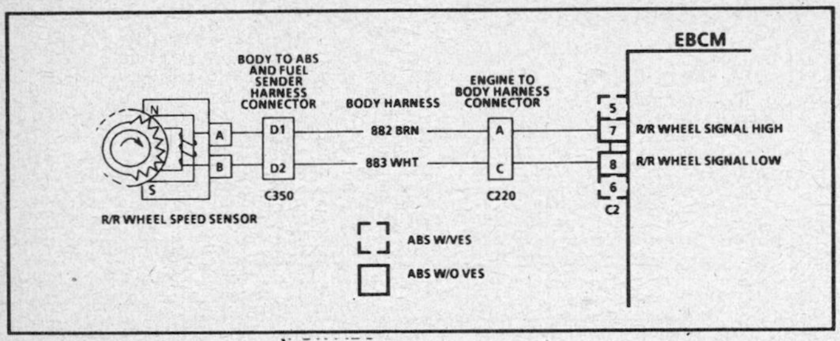
EBCM
BODY TO ABS AND FUEL SENDER HARNESS CONNECTOR
BODY HARNESS
ENGINE TO BODY HARNESS CONNECTOR
N
S
A
B
D1
D2
882 BRN
883 WHT
A
C
5
7
8
6
R/R WHEEL SIGNAL HIGH
R/R WHEEL SIGNAL LOW
C350
C220
C2
R/R WHEEL SPEED SENSOR
ABS W/VES
ABS W/O VES

Circuit Description:
As a toothed ring passes by the wheel speed sensor, changes in the electromagnetic field cause the wheel speed sensor to produce a sinusoidal (AC) voltage signal whose frequency is proportional to wheel speed. The magnitude of this signal is directly related to wheel speed and the proximity of the wheel speed sensor to the toothed ring, often referred to as the air gap.

DTC Will Set When: DTC 35 can be set anytime after the ABS enable relay has been commanded "ON." The relay is commanded "ON" during the three second bulb check.

Action Taken: A malfunction DTC is stored, ABS/VES is disabled and the ABS warning lamp is turned "ON."

DTC Chart Test Description: Number(s) below refer to circled number(s) on the diagnostic chart.

7. Checks for high resistance in the wheel signal high circuit.
8. Checks for high resistance in the wheel signal low circuit.
9. Checks for proper resistance of the wheel speed sensor.

Diagnostic Aids: An "Intermittent" malfunction is most likely caused by a poor connection, rubbed through wire insulation, or a wire that is broken inside the insulation.

The frequency of the malfunction can be checked by using the enhanced diagnostic function of the Tech 1.

If the customer's comments reflect that the ABS amber warning lamp is "ON" only during moist environmental changes, (rain, snow, vehicle wash) all wheel speed sensor circuitry should be thoroughly inspected for signs of water intrusion. Use the following procedure. Spray down the suspected area with 5% salt water solution (two teaspoons of salt to 12 oz. of water). Drive vehicle above 24 km/h (15 mph) for at least 30 seconds. If DTC returns immediately, replace suspected harness.

Any circuitry, that is suspected as causing the intermittent complaint, should be thoroughly checked for backed out terminals, improper mating, broken locks, improperly formed or damaged terminals, poor terminal to wiring connections or physical damage to the wiring harness.

Resistance of the wheel speed sensor will increase with an increase in sensor temperature.

When replacing a wheel speed sensor, inspect the sensor terminals and harness connector for corrosion and/or water intrusion. If evidence of corrosion or water intrusion exists, replace wheel speed sensor harness. Refer to "On-Vehicle Service" in this section.

If wheel speed sensor harness shows evidence of water intrusion, inspect wheel speed sensor for water intrusion. If water intrusion is evident, replace wheel speed sensor.

GC402940105102AX

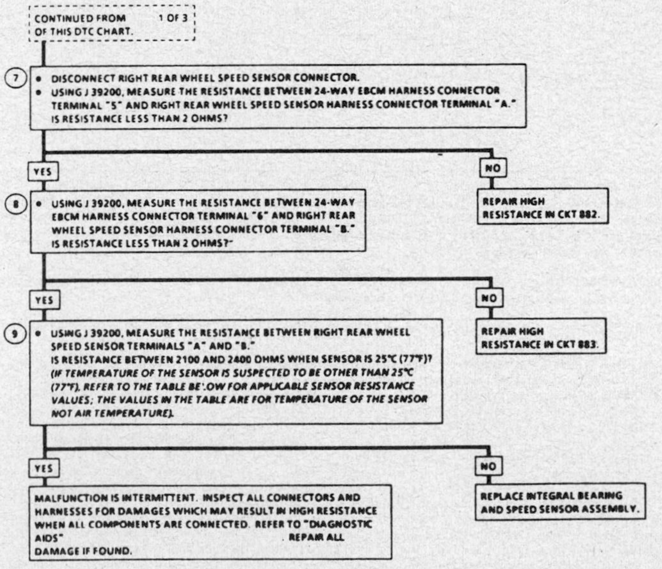
CONTINUED FROM 1 OF 3 OF THIS DTC CHART.
7
• DISCONNECT RIGHT REAR WHEEL SPEED SENSOR CONNECTOR.
• USING J 39200, MEASURE THE RESISTANCE BETWEEN 24-WAY EBCM HARNESS CONNECTOR TERMINAL "5" AND RIGHT REAR WHEEL SPEED SENSOR HARNESS CONNECTOR TERMINAL "A." IS RESISTANCE LESS THAN 2 OHMS?
YES
NO
REPAIR HIGH RESISTANCE IN CKT 882.
8
• USING J 39200, MEASURE THE RESISTANCE BETWEEN 24-WAY EBCM HARNESS CONNECTOR TERMINAL "6" AND RIGHT REAR WHEEL SPEED SENSOR HARNESS CONNECTOR TERMINAL "B." IS RESISTANCE LESS THAN 2 OHMS?
YES
NO
REPAIR HIGH RESISTANCE IN CKT 883.
9
• USING J 39200, MEASURE THE RESISTANCE BETWEEN RIGHT REAR WHEEL SPEED SENSOR TERMINALS "A" AND "B." IS RESISTANCE BETWEEN 2100 AND 2400 OHMS WHEN SENSOR IS 25°C (77°F)? (IF TEMPERATURE OF THE SENSOR IS SUSPECTED TO BE OTHER THAN 25°C (77°F), REFER TO THE TABLE BELOW FOR APPLICABLE SENSOR RESISTANCE VALUES; THE VALUES IN THE TABLE ARE FOR TEMPERATURE OF THE SENSOR NOT AIR TEMPERATURE).
YES
NO
MALFUNCTION IS INTERMITTENT. INSPECT ALL CONNECTORS AND HARNESSES FOR DAMAGES WHICH MAY RESULT IN HIGH RESISTANCE WHEN ALL COMPONENTS ARE CONNECTED. REFER TO "DIAGNOSTIC AIDS". REPAIR ALL DAMAGE IF FOUND.
REPLACE INTEGRAL BEARING AND SPEED SENSOR ASSEMBLY.

REAR WHEEL SPEED SENSOR

TEMPERATURE OF SENSOR VS. SENSOR RESISTANCE (APPROXIMATE)

TEMP. (°C)	TEMP. (°F)	RESISTANCE (OHMS)
-34 TO 4	-30 TO 40	1623 TO 2210
5 TO 43	41 TO 110	1939 TO 2570
44 TO 93	111 TO 200	2254 TO 3029

GC402940105102BX

Fig. 139 Code A035: Right Rear Wheel Speed Sensor Circuit Open Or Shorted To Ground/Battery (Part 2 of 3). 1994 Achieva, Grand Am & Skylark w/VES

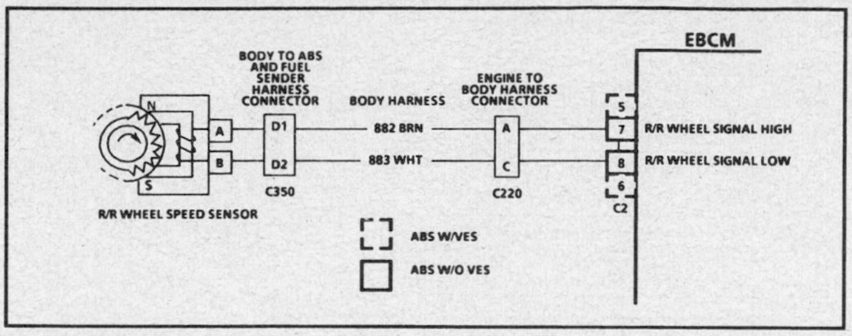
EBCM
BODY TO ABS AND FUEL SENDER HARNESS CONNECTOR
BODY HARNESS
ENGINE TO BODY HARNESS CONNECTOR
882 BRN
883 WHT
R/R WHEEL SIGNAL HIGH
R/R WHEEL SIGNAL LOW
C350
C220
C2
R/R WHEEL SPEED SENSOR
ABS W/VES
ABS W/O VES

Circuit Description:
As a toothed ring passes by the wheel speed sensor, changes in the electromagnetic field cause the wheel speed sensor to produce a sinusoidal (AC) voltage signal whose frequency is proportional to wheel speed. The magnitude of this signal is directly related to wheel speed and the proximity of the wheel speed sensor to the toothed ring, often referred to as the air gap.

DTC Will Set When: DTC 35 can be set anytime after the ABS enable relay has been commanded "ON." The relay is commanded "ON" during the three second bulb check.

Action Taken: A malfunction DTC is stored, ABS/VES is disabled and the ABS warning lamp is turned "ON."

DTC Chart Test Description: Number(s) below refer to circled number(s) on the diagnostic chart.
10. Checks for a short to ground in the wheel signal high circuit.
11. Checks for a short to ground in the wheel signal low circuit.
12. Checks for a short to ground in the rear ABS harness.
13. Checks for a short to ground in the wheel speed sensor.

Diagnostic Aids: An "Intermittent" malfunction is most likely caused by a poor connection, rubbed through wire insulation, or a wire that is broken inside the insulation.

The frequency of the malfunction can be checked by using the enhanced diagnostic function of the Tech 1

If the customer's comments reflect that the ABS amber warning lamp is "ON" only during moist environmental changes, (rain, snow, vehicle wash) all wheel speed sensor circuitry should be thoroughly inspected for signs of water intrusion. Use the following procedure. Spray down the suspected area with 5% salt water solution (two teaspoons of salt to 12 oz. of water). Drive vehicle above 24 km/h (15 mph) for at least 30 seconds. If DTC returns immediately, replace suspected harness.

Any circuitry, that is suspected as causing the intermittent complaint, should be thoroughly checked for backed out terminals, improper mating, broken locks, improperly formed or damaged terminals, poor terminal to wiring connections or physical damage to the wiring harness.

Resistance of the wheel speed sensor will increase with an increase in sensor temperature.

When replacing a wheel speed sensor, inspect the sensor terminals and harness connector for corrosion and/or water intrusion. If evidence of corrosion or water intrusion exists, replace wheel speed sensor harness. Refer to "On-Vehicle Service" in this section.

If wheel speed sensor harness shows evidence of water intrusion, inspect wheel speed sensor for water intrusion. If water intrusion is evident, replace wheel speed sensor.

GC402940105103AX

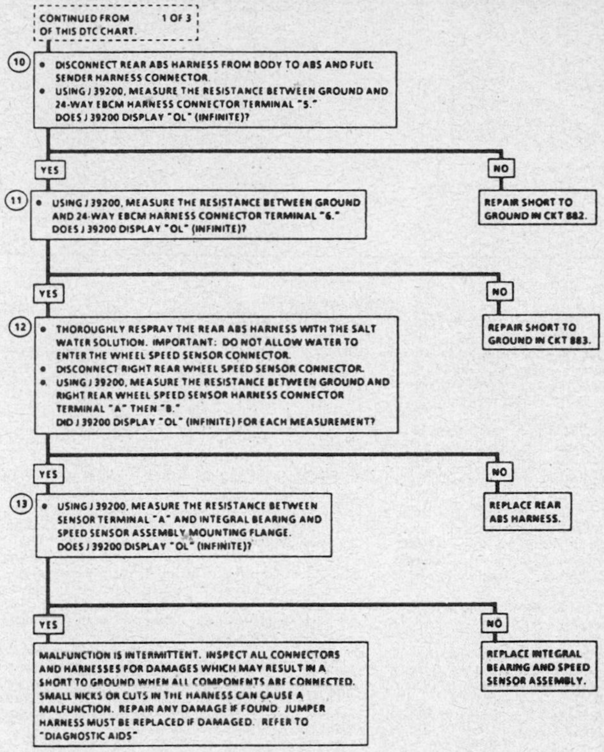
CONTINUED FROM 1 OF 3 OF THIS DTC CHART.
10
• DISCONNECT REAR ABS HARNESS FROM BODY TO ABS AND FUEL SENDER HARNESS CONNECTOR.
• USING J 39200, MEASURE THE RESISTANCE BETWEEN GROUND AND 24-WAY EBCM HARNESS CONNECTOR TERMINAL "5." DOES J 39200 DISPLAY "OL" (INFINITE)?
YES
NO
REPAIR SHORT TO GROUND IN CKT 882.
11
• USING J 39200, MEASURE THE RESISTANCE BETWEEN GROUND AND 24-WAY EBCM HARNESS CONNECTOR TERMINAL "6." DOES J 39200 DISPLAY "OL" (INFINITE)?
YES
NO
REPAIR SHORT TO GROUND IN CKT 883.
12
• THOROUGHLY RESPRAY THE REAR ABS HARNESS WITH THE SALT WATER SOLUTION. IMPORTANT: DO NOT ALLOW WATER TO ENTER THE WHEEL SPEED SENSOR CONNECTOR.
• DISCONNECT RIGHT REAR WHEEL SPEED SENSOR CONNECTOR.
• USING J 39200, MEASURE THE RESISTANCE BETWEEN GROUND AND RIGHT REAR WHEEL SPEED SENSOR HARNESS CONNECTOR TERMINAL "A" THEN "B." DID J 39200 DISPLAY "OL" (INFINITE) FOR EACH MEASUREMENT?
YES
NO
REPLACE REAR ABS HARNESS.
13
• USING J 39200, MEASURE THE RESISTANCE BETWEEN SENSOR TERMINAL "A" AND INTEGRAL BEARING AND SPEED SENSOR ASSEMBLY MOUNTING FLANGE. DOES J 39200 DISPLAY "OL" (INFINITE)?
YES
NO
MALFUNCTION IS INTERMITTENT. INSPECT ALL CONNECTORS AND HARNESSES FOR DAMAGES WHICH MAY RESULT IN A SHORT TO GROUND WHEN ALL COMPONENTS ARE CONNECTED. SMALL NICKS OR CUTS IN THE HARNESS CAN CAUSE A MALFUNCTION. REPAIR ANY DAMAGE IF FOUND. JUMPER HARNESS MUST BE REPLACED IF DAMAGED. REFER TO "DIAGNOSTIC AIDS"
REPLACE INTEGRAL BEARING AND SPEED SENSOR ASSEMBLY.

GC402940105103BX

Fig. 139 Code A035: Right Rear Wheel Speed Sensor Circuit Open Or Shorted To Ground/Battery (Part 3 of 3). 1994 Achieva, Grand Am & Skylark w/VES

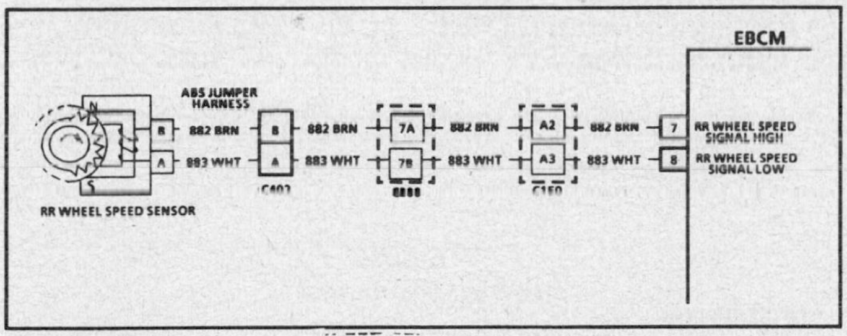
EBCM
ABS JUMPER HARNESS
882 BRN
883 WHT
RR WHEEL SPEED SIGNAL HIGH
RR WHEEL SPEED SIGNAL LOW
RR WHEEL SPEED SENSOR

Circuit Description:
As a toothed ring passes by the wheel speed sensor, changes in the electromagnetic field cause the wheel speed sensor to produce a sinusoidal (AC) voltage signal whose frequency is proportional to wheel speed. The magnitude of this signal is directly related to wheel speed and the proximity of the wheel speed sensor to the toothed ring, often referred to as the air gap.

DTC Will Set When: DTC 35 can be set anytime after initialization. If either of the right rear wheel speed circuits are shorted to voltage or ground, a malfunction exists.

Action Taken: A malfunction DTC is stored, ABS is disabled and the ABS warning lamp is turned "ON."

DTC Chart Test Description: Number(s) below refer to circled number(s) on the diagnostic chart.
1. Checks for short to ground in wheel speed sensor wiring circuitry.
2. Checks for short to voltage in wheel speed sensor wiring circuitry.
3. Checks for short to voltage in CKT 882.
4. Checks for short to voltage in CKT 883.
5. Checks for short to ground or voltage in CKTs 882 or 883.

Diagnostic Aids: An "Intermittent" malfunction may be caused by a poor connection, rubbed through wire insulation, or a wire that is broken inside the insulation.

The frequency of the malfunction can be checked by using the enhanced diagnostic function of the Tech 1

If the customer's comments reflect that the ABS warning lamp is "ON" only during moist environmental changes (rain, snow, vehicle wash), all wheel speed sensor circuitry should be thoroughly inspected for signs of water intrusion. If DTC is not current, clear DTCs and simulate the effects of water intrusion. Use the following procedure; spray down the suspected area with a 5% salt water solution (two teaspoons of salt to 12 oz. of water). Test drive vehicle over various road surfaces (bumps, turns, etc.) above 24 km/h (15 mph) for at least 30 seconds. If DTC returns replace suspected harness.

Any circuitry, that is suspected as causing the intermittent complaint, should be thoroughly checked for backed out terminals, improper mating, broken locks, improperly formed or damaged terminals, poor terminal to wiring connections or physical damage to the wiring harness.

Resistance of the wheel speed sensor will increase with an increase in sensor temperature.

When replacing a wheel speed sensor, inspect the sensor terminals and harness connector for corrosion and/or water intrusion. If evidence of corrosion or water intrusion exists, replace wheel speed sensor jumper harness. Likewise, if replacing a wheel speed sensor jumper harness, inspect sensor terminals. If evidence of corrosion or water intrusion exists, replace wheel speed sensor.

GC402930077301AA

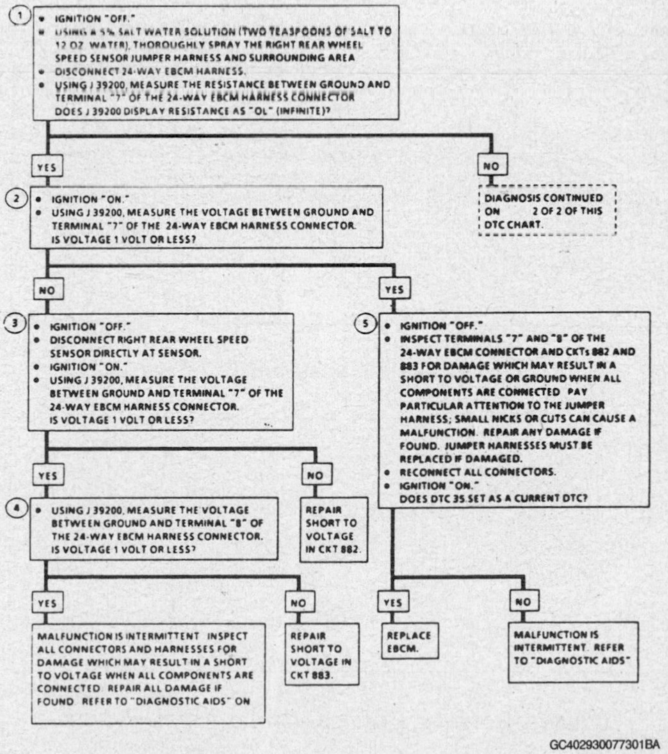
1
• IGNITION "OFF."
• USING A 5% SALT WATER SOLUTION (TWO TEASPOONS OF SALT TO 12 OZ. WATER), THOROUGHLY SPRAY THE RIGHT REAR WHEEL SPEED SENSOR JUMPER HARNESS AND SURROUNDING AREA
• DISCONNECT 24-WAY EBCM HARNESS.
• USING J 39200, MEASURE THE RESISTANCE BETWEEN GROUND AND TERMINAL "7" OF THE 24-WAY EBCM HARNESS CONNECTOR DOES J 39200 DISPLAY RESISTANCE AS "OL" (INFINITE)?
YES
NO
DIAGNOSIS CONTINUED ON 2 OF 2 OF THIS DTC CHART.
2
• IGNITION "ON."
• USING J 39200, MEASURE THE VOLTAGE BETWEEN GROUND AND TERMINAL "7" OF THE 24-WAY EBCM HARNESS CONNECTOR. IS VOLTAGE 1 VOLT OR LESS?
NO
YES
3
• IGNITION "OFF."
• DISCONNECT RIGHT REAR WHEEL SPEED SENSOR DIRECTLY AT SENSOR.
• IGNITION "ON."
• USING J 39200, MEASURE THE VOLTAGE BETWEEN GROUND AND TERMINAL "7" OF THE 24-WAY EBCM HARNESS CONNECTOR. IS VOLTAGE 1 VOLT OR LESS?
5
• IGNITION "OFF."
• INSPECT TERMINALS "7" AND "8" OF THE 24-WAY EBCM CONNECTOR AND CKTs 882 AND 883 FOR DAMAGE WHICH MAY RESULT IN A SHORT TO VOLTAGE OR GROUND WHEN ALL COMPONENTS ARE CONNECTED PAY PARTICULAR ATTENTION TO THE JUMPER HARNESS; SMALL NICKS OR CUTS CAN CAUSE A MALFUNCTION. REPAIR ANY DAMAGE IF FOUND. JUMPER HARNESSES MUST BE REPLACED IF DAMAGED.
• RECONNECT ALL CONNECTORS.
• IGNITION "ON." DOES DTC 35 SET AS A CURRENT DTC?
YES
NO
REPAIR SHORT TO VOLTAGE IN CKT 882.
4
• USING J 39200, MEASURE THE VOLTAGE BETWEEN GROUND AND TERMINAL "8" OF THE 24-WAY EBCM HARNESS CONNECTOR. IS VOLTAGE 1 VOLT OR LESS?
YES
NO
YES
NO
MALFUNCTION IS INTERMITTENT INSPECT ALL CONNECTORS AND HARNESSES FOR DAMAGE WHICH MAY RESULT IN A SHORT TO VOLTAGE WHEN ALL COMPONENTS ARE CONNECTED REPAIR ALL DAMAGE IF FOUND REFER TO "DIAGNOSTIC AIDS" ON
REPAIR SHORT TO VOLTAGE IN CKT 883.
REPLACE EBCM.
MALFUNCTION IS INTERMITTENT. REFER TO "DIAGNOSTIC AIDS"

GC402930077301BA

Fig. 140 Code A035: Right Rear Wheel Sensor Shorted To Battery Or Ground (Part 1 of 2). 1993 Grand Prix, 1993–94 Cutlass Supreme, Lumina & Regal

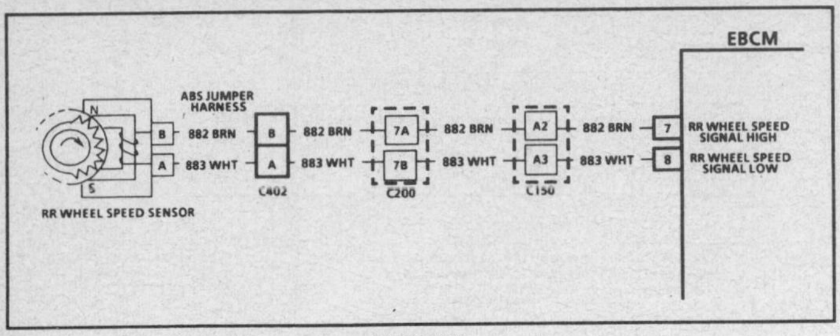
EBCM
ABS JUMPER HARNESS
N
S
B
A
882 BRN
883 WHT
C402
7A
7B
C200
A2
A3
C150
7
8
RR WHEEL SPEED SIGNAL HIGH
RR WHEEL SPEED SIGNAL LOW
RR WHEEL SPEED SENSOR

DTC 35

(Page 2 of 2)

RIGHT REAR WHEEL SPEED SENSOR CKT SHORT TO GND/BAT

Circuit Description:

As a toothed ring passes by the wheel speed sensor, changes in the electromagnetic field cause the wheel speed sensor to produce a sinusoidal (AC) voltage signal whose frequency is proportional to wheel speed. The magnitude of this signal is directly related to wheel speed and the proximity of the wheel speed sensor to the toothed ring, often referred to as the air gap.

DTC Will Set When: DTC 35 can be set anytime after initialization. If either of the right rear wheel speed circuits are shorted to voltage or ground, a malfunction exists.

Action Taken: A malfunction DTC is stored, ABS is disabled and the ABS warning lamp is turned "ON."

DTC Chart Test Description: Number(s) below refer to circled number(s) on the diagnostic chart.

6. Checks for short to ground in CKT 882.
7. Checks for short to ground in CKT 883.
8. Checks for short to ground in wheel speed sensor jumper harness.
9. Checks for proper resistance in wheel speed sensor circuitry.

Diagnostic Aids: An "Intermittent" malfunction may be caused by a poor connection, rubbed through wire insulation, or a wire that is broken inside the insulation.

The frequency of the malfunction can be checked by using the enhanced diagnostic function of the Tech 1

If the customer's comments reflect that the ABS warning lamp is "ON" only during moist environmental changes (rain, snow, vehicle wash), all wheel speed sensor circuitry should be thoroughly inspected for signs of water intrusion. If DTC is not current, clear DTCs and simulate the effects of water intrusion. Use the following procedure. Spray down the suspected area with a 5% salt water solution (two teaspoons of salt to 12 oz. of water). Start vehicle, allow vehicle to run for 10 seconds. If DTC returns immediately, replace suspected harness.

Any circuitry, that is suspected as causing the intermittent complaint, should be thoroughly checked for backed out terminals, improper mating, broken locks, improperly formed or damaged terminals, poor terminal to wiring connections or physical damage to the wiring harness.

When replacing a wheel speed sensor, inspect the sensor terminals and harness connector for corrosion and/or water intrusion. If evidence of corrosion or water intrusion exists, replace wheel speed sensor harness. If evidence of corrosion or water intrusion exists, replace wheel speed sensor.

GC402930077302AA

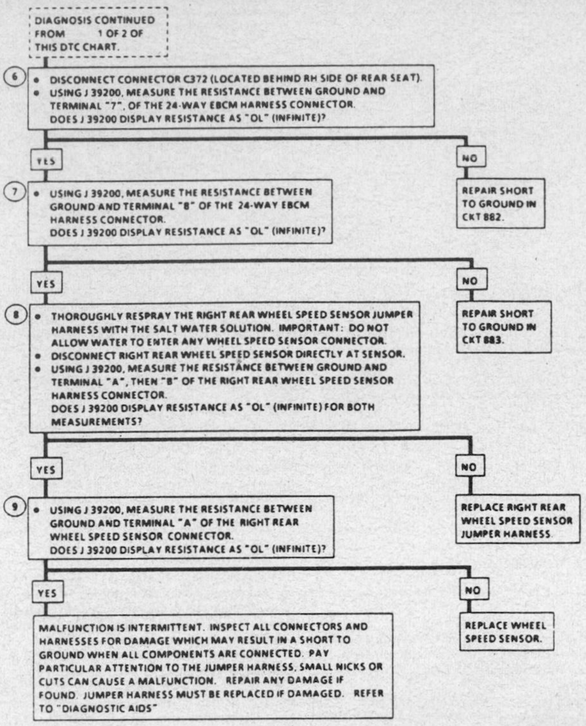
DIAGNOSIS CONTINUED FROM 1 OF 2 OF THIS DTC CHART.
6
• DISCONNECT CONNECTOR C372 (LOCATED BEHIND RH SIDE OF REAR SEAT).
• USING J 39200, MEASURE THE RESISTANCE BETWEEN GROUND AND TERMINAL "7", OF THE 24-WAY EBCM HARNESS CONNECTOR.
DOES J 39200 DISPLAY RESISTANCE AS "OL" (INFINITE)?
YES
NO
REPAIR SHORT TO GROUND IN CKT 882.
7
• USING J 39200, MEASURE THE RESISTANCE BETWEEN GROUND AND TERMINAL "B" OF THE 24-WAY EBCM HARNESS CONNECTOR.
DOES J 39200 DISPLAY RESISTANCE AS "OL" (INFINITE)?
YES
NO
REPAIR SHORT TO GROUND IN CKT 883.
8
• THOROUGHLY RESPRAY THE RIGHT REAR WHEEL SPEED SENSOR JUMPER HARNESS WITH THE SALT WATER SOLUTION. IMPORTANT: DO NOT ALLOW WATER TO ENTER ANY WHEEL SPEED SENSOR CONNECTOR.
• DISCONNECT RIGHT REAR WHEEL SPEED SENSOR DIRECTLY AT SENSOR.
• USING J 39200, MEASURE THE RESISTANCE BETWEEN GROUND AND TERMINAL "A", THEN "B" OF THE RIGHT REAR WHEEL SPEED SENSOR HARNESS CONNECTOR.
DOES J 39200 DISPLAY RESISTANCE AS "OL" (INFINITE) FOR BOTH MEASUREMENTS?
YES
NO
REPLACE RIGHT REAR WHEEL SPEED SENSOR JUMPER HARNESS.
9
• USING J 39200, MEASURE THE RESISTANCE BETWEEN GROUND AND TERMINAL "A" OF THE RIGHT REAR WHEEL SPEED SENSOR CONNECTOR.
DOES J 39200 DISPLAY RESISTANCE AS "OL" (INFINITE)?
YES
NO
REPLACE WHEEL SPEED SENSOR.
MALFUNCTION IS INTERMITTENT. INSPECT ALL CONNECTORS AND HARNESSES FOR DAMAGE WHICH MAY RESULT IN A SHORT TO GROUND WHEN ALL COMPONENTS ARE CONNECTED. PAY PARTICULAR ATTENTION TO THE JUMPER HARNESS, SMALL NICKS OR CUTS CAN CAUSE A MALFUNCTION. REPAIR ANY DAMAGE IF FOUND. JUMPER HARNESS MUST BE REPLACED IF DAMAGED. REFER TO "DIAGNOSTIC AIDS"

GC402930077302BA

Fig. 140 Code A035: Right Rear Wheel Sensor Shorted To Battery Or Ground (Part 2 of 2). 1993 Grand Prix, 1993–94 Cutlass Supreme, Lumina & Regal

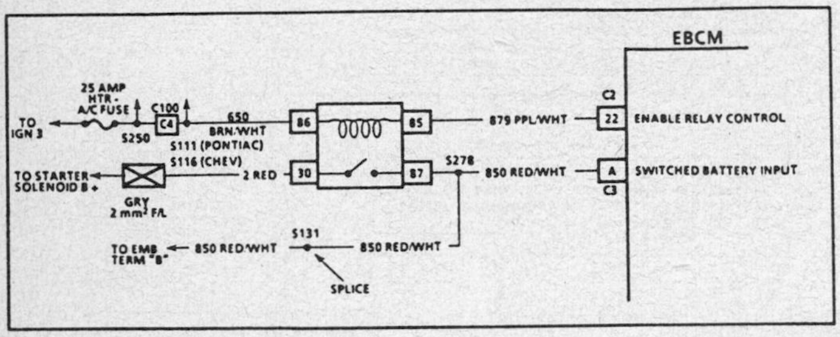
EBCM
25 AMP HTR-A/C FUSE
TO IGN 3
S250
C100
C4
650 BRN/WHT
S111 (PONTIAC)
S116 (CHEV)
86
85
30
87
879 PPL/WHT
C2
22
ENABLE RELAY CONTROL
TO STARTER SOLENOID B+
GRY 2 mm² F/L
2 RED
S278
850 RED/WHT
A
C3
SWITCHED BATTERY INPUT
S131
TO EMB TERM "B"
SPLICE

GC402930077400AX

Cavalier & Sunbird

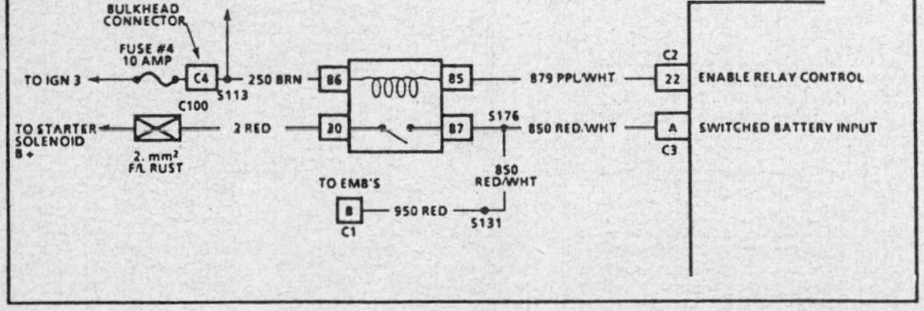
EBCM
BULKHEAD CONNECTOR
FUSE #4 10 AMP
TO IGN 3
C4
S113
C100
250 BRN
86
85
879 PPL/WHT
C2
22
ENABLE RELAY CONTROL
TO STARTER SOLENOID B+
2. mm² F/L RUST
2 RED
30
87
S176
850 RED/WHT
A
C3
SWITCHED BATTERY INPUT
TO EMB'S
B
C1
950 RED
S131
850 RED/WHT

GC402930077400BX

Achieva, Beretta, Corsica, Grand Am & Skylark

DTC A036

LOW SYSTEM VOLTAGE

Circuit Description:

This DTC is used to monitor the voltage level available to the ABS EBCM. If the voltage drops below 11 volts, full performance of the ABS system cannot be guaranteed. During ABS operation, there are several current requirements that will cause battery voltage to drop. Because of this, voltage is monitored prior to ABS to indicate good charging system condition and also during ABS when voltage may drop significantly.

Failure Condition:

DTC A036 can only be set if the vehicle's speed is greater than 5 km/h (3 mph). If the switched battery voltage is less than 11.2 volts non-ABS or less than 9.6 volts ABS, a malfunction exists.

Action Taken:

A malfunction DTC is stored, ABS is disabled and the ABS indicator lamp is turned "ON."

Test Description: Number(s) below refer to circled number(s) on the diagnostic chart.

1. This test checks to see what voltage is readily available at terminal "A" of the EBCM. If voltage is representative of good charging system condition, a malfunction is not present.
2. This step isolates the EBCM to check the condition of the circuitry and charging system.
3. This step isolates the low voltage condition to high circuit resistance, or improper charging system operation.

Diagnostic Aids:

An "Intermittent" malfunction may be caused by a poor connection, rubbed through wire insulation, or a wire that is broken inside the insulation.

The frequency of the malfunction can be checked by using the enhanced diagnostic function of the Tech 1

Any circuitry, that is suspected as causing the intermittent complaint, should be thoroughly checked for backed out terminals, improper mating, broken locks, improperly formed or damaged terminals, poor terminal to wiring connections or physical damage to the wiring harness.

While performing a voltage load test, if it is noted that only ignition voltage drops below acceptable voltage levels, CKT 650 should be checked for high resistance or an open condition.

GC402930077400CX

Fig. 141 Code A036: Low System Voltage (Part 1 of 2). 1993-94 Cavalier, Sunbird, Beretta, Corsica & Achieva, Grand Am & Skylark Less VES

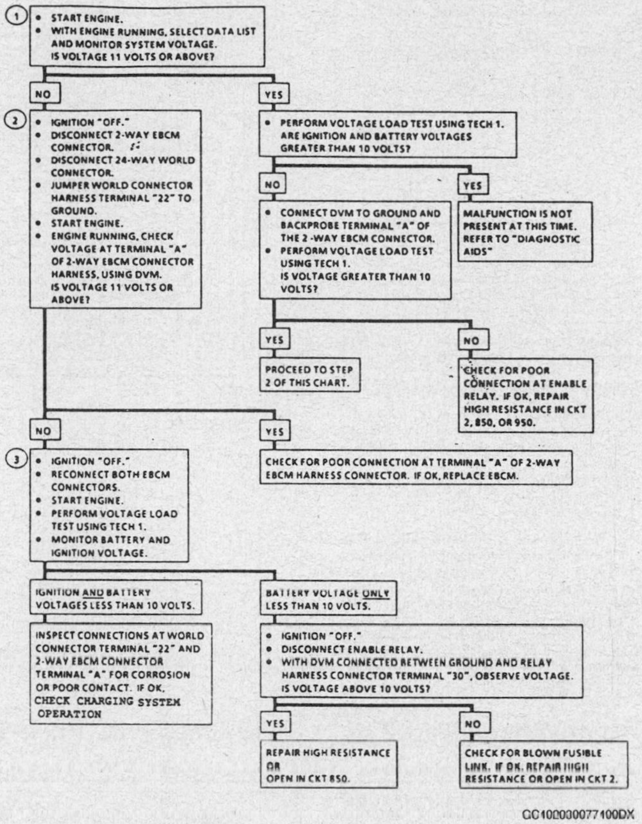
1
• START ENGINE.
• WITH ENGINE RUNNING, SELECT DATA LIST AND MONITOR SYSTEM VOLTAGE. IS VOLTAGE 11 VOLTS OR ABOVE?
NO
YES
2
• IGNITION "OFF."
• DISCONNECT 2-WAY EBCM CONNECTOR.
• DISCONNECT 24-WAY WORLD CONNECTOR.
• JUMPER WORLD CONNECTOR HARNESS TERMINAL "22" TO GROUND.
• START ENGINE.
• ENGINE RUNNING, CHECK VOLTAGE AT TERMINAL "A" OF 2-WAY EBCM CONNECTOR HARNESS, USING DVM. IS VOLTAGE 11 VOLTS OR ABOVE?
• PERFORM VOLTAGE LOAD TEST USING TECH 1. ARE IGNITION AND BATTERY VOLTAGES GREATER THAN 10 VOLTS?
NO
YES
• CONNECT DVM TO GROUND AND BACKPROBE TERMINAL "A" OF THE 2-WAY EBCM CONNECTOR.
• PERFORM VOLTAGE LOAD TEST USING TECH 1. IS VOLTAGE GREATER THAN 10 VOLTS?
MALFUNCTION IS NOT PRESENT AT THIS TIME. REFER TO "DIAGNOSTIC AIDS"
YES
NO
PROCEED TO STEP 2 OF THIS CHART.
CHECK FOR POOR CONNECTION AT ENABLE RELAY. IF OK, REPAIR HIGH RESISTANCE IN CKT 2, 850, OR 950.
NO
YES
3
• IGNITION "OFF."
• RECONNECT BOTH EBCM CONNECTORS.
• START ENGINE.
• PERFORM VOLTAGE LOAD TEST USING TECH 1.
• MONITOR BATTERY AND IGNITION VOLTAGE.
CHECK FOR POOR CONNECTION AT TERMINAL "A" OF 2-WAY EBCM HARNESS CONNECTOR. IF OK, REPLACE EBCM.
IGNITION AND BATTERY VOLTAGES LESS THAN 10 VOLTS.
BATTERY VOLTAGE ONLY LESS THAN 10 VOLTS.
INSPECT CONNECTIONS AT WORLD CONNECTOR TERMINAL "22" AND 2-WAY EBCM CONNECTOR TERMINAL "A" FOR CORROSION OR POOR CONTACT. IF OK, CHECK CHARGING SYSTEM OPERATION
• IGNITION "OFF."
• DISCONNECT ENABLE RELAY.
• WITH DVM CONNECTED BETWEEN GROUND AND RELAY HARNESS CONNECTOR TERMINAL "30", OBSERVE VOLTAGE. IS VOLTAGE ABOVE 10 VOLTS?
YES
NO
REPAIR HIGH RESISTANCE OR OPEN IN CKT 850.
CHECK FOR BLOWN FUSIBLE LINK. IF OK, REPAIR HIGH RESISTANCE OR OPEN IN CKT 2.
GC1020030077100DX

Fig. 141 Code A036: Low System Voltage (Part 2 of 2). 1993-94 Cavalier, Sunbird, Beretta, Corsica & Achieva, Grand Am & Skylark Less VES

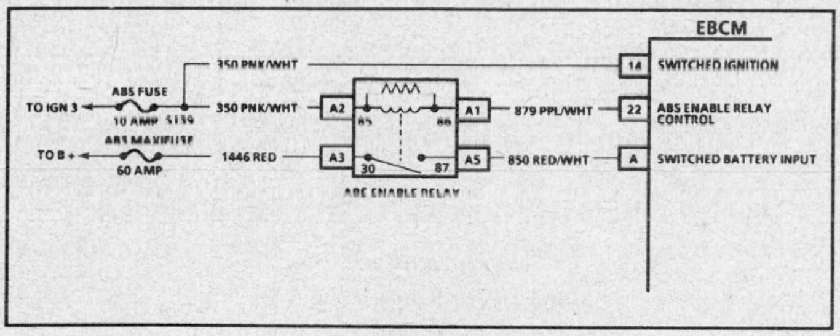
EBCM
350 PNK/WHT
14 SWITCHED IGNITION
ABS FUSE
TO IGN 3
10 AMP 5139
350 PNK/WHT
A2
85
86
A1
879 PPL/WHT
22 ABS ENABLE RELAY CONTROL
ABS MAXIFUSE
TO B+
60 AMP
1446 RED
A3
30
87
A5
850 RED/WHT
A SWITCHED BATTERY INPUT
ABS ENABLE RELAY

DTC 36

(Page 1 of 2)

LOW SYSTEM VOLTAGE

Circuit Description:

This DTC is used to monitor the voltage level available to the EBCM controller. If the voltage drops below 11 volts, full performance of the ABS system cannot be guaranteed. During ABS operation, there are several current requirements that will cause battery voltage to drop. Because of this, voltage is monitored prior to ABS to indicate good charging system condition and also during ABS when voltage may drop significantly.

DTC Will Set When: DTC 36 can only be set if the vehicle's speed is greater than 5 km/h (3 mph). If the switched battery voltage is less than 11.2 volts non-ABS or less than 9.6 volts ABS, a malfunction exists.

Action Taken: A malfunction DTC is stored, ABS is disabled and the ABS warning lamp is turned "ON."

DTC Chart Test Description: Number(s) below refer to circled number(s) on the diagnostic chart.

1. Checks to see what voltage is readily available at terminal "A" of the EBCM. If voltage is representative of good charging system condition, a malfunction is not present.
2. Isolates the condition to high circuit resistance, or improper charging system operation.
3. Isolates which circuit is the source of the high resistance condition.
4. Checks for high resistance in CKTs 1446 or 2.

Diagnostic Aids: An "Intermittent" malfunction may be caused by a poor connection, rubbed through wire insulation, or a wire that is broken inside the insulation.

The frequency of the malfunction can be checked by using the enhanced diagnostic function of the Tech 1

Any circuitry, that is suspected as causing the intermittent complaint, should be thoroughly checked for backed out terminals, improper mating, broken locks, improperly formed or damaged terminals, poor terminal to wiring connections or physical damage to the wiring harness.

While performing a voltage load test, if it is noted that only ignition voltage drops below acceptable voltage levels, CKT 350 should be checked for high resistance or an open condition.

GC402930077501AA

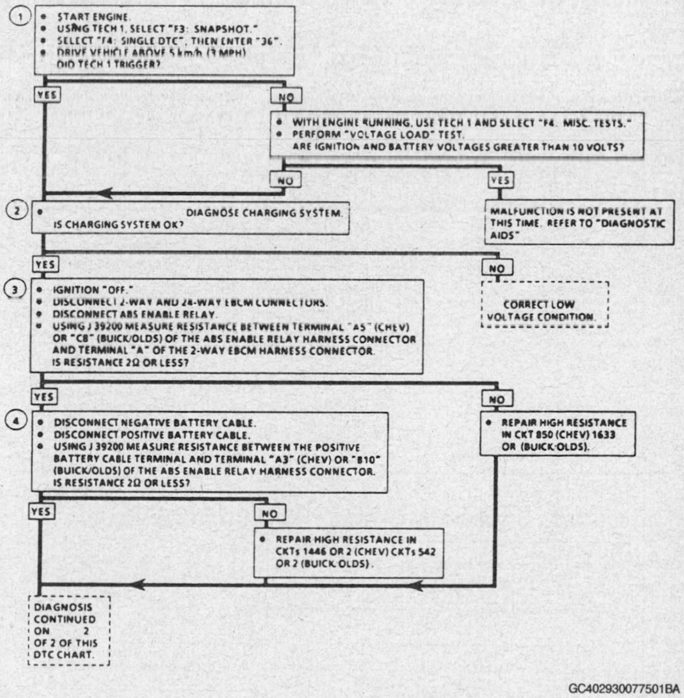
1
• START ENGINE.
• USING TECH 1, SELECT "F3: SNAPSHOT."
• SELECT "F4: SINGLE DTC"; THEN ENTER "36".
• DRIVE VEHICLE ABOVE 5 km/h (3 MPH) DID TECH 1 TRIGGER?
YES
NO
• WITH ENGINE RUNNING, USE TECH 1 AND SELECT "F4: MISC. TESTS."
• PERFORM "VOLTAGE LOAD" TEST. ARE IGNITION AND BATTERY VOLTAGES GREATER THAN 10 VOLTS?
NO
YES
2
• DIAGNOSE CHARGING SYSTEM. IS CHARGING SYSTEM OK?
MALFUNCTION IS NOT PRESENT AT THIS TIME. REFER TO "DIAGNOSTIC AIDS"
YES
NO
CORRECT LOW VOLTAGE CONDITION.
3
• IGNITION "OFF."
• DISCONNECT 2-WAY AND 24-WAY EBCM CONNECTORS.
• DISCONNECT ABS ENABLE RELAY.
• USING J 39200 MEASURE RESISTANCE BETWEEN TERMINAL "A5" (CHEV) OR "C8" (BUICK/OLDS) OF THE ABS ENABLE RELAY HARNESS CONNECTOR AND TERMINAL "A" OF THE 2-WAY EBCM HARNESS CONNECTOR. IS RESISTANCE 2Ω OR LESS?
YES
NO
4
• DISCONNECT NEGATIVE BATTERY CABLE.
• DISCONNECT POSITIVE BATTERY CABLE.
• USING J 39200 MEASURE RESISTANCE BETWEEN THE POSITIVE BATTERY CABLE TERMINAL AND TERMINAL "A3" (CHEV) OR "B10" (BUICK/OLDS) OF THE ABS ENABLE RELAY HARNESS CONNECTOR. IS RESISTANCE 2Ω OR LESS?
• REPAIR HIGH RESISTANCE IN CKT 850 (CHEV) 1633 OR (BUICK-OLDS).
YES
NO
• REPAIR HIGH RESISTANCE IN CKTs 1446 OR 2 (CHEV) CKTs 542 OR 2 (BUICK OLDS).
DIAGNOSIS CONTINUED ON 2 OF 2 OF THIS DTC CHART.
GC402930077501BA

Fig. 142 Code A036: Low System Voltage (Part 1 of 2). 1993 Grand Prix, 1993–94 Cutlass Supreme, Lumina & Regal

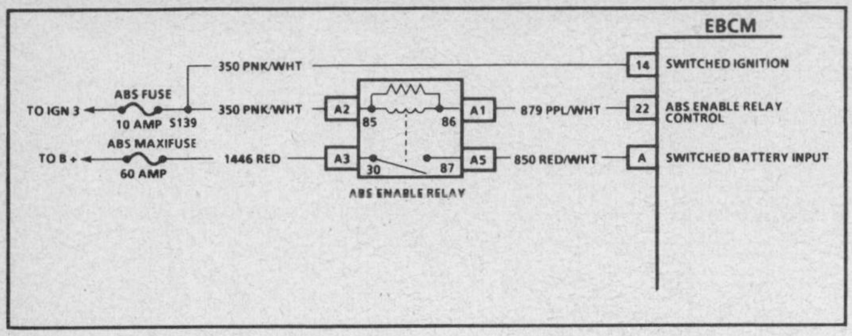
EBCM
350 PNK/WHT
14 SWITCHED IGNITION
ABS FUSE
TO IGN 3
10 AMP S139
350 PNK/WHT
A2
85
86
A1
879 PPL/WHT
22 ABS ENABLE RELAY CONTROL
ABS MAXIFUSE
TO B+
60 AMP
1446 RED
A3
30
87
A5
850 RED/WHT
A SWITCHED BATTERY INPUT
ABS ENABLE RELAY

Circuit Description:
This DTC is used to monitor the voltage level available to the EBCM controller. If the voltage drops below 11 volts, full performance of the ABS system cannot be guaranteed. During ABS operation, there are several current requirements that will cause battery voltage to drop. Because of this, voltage is monitored prior to ABS to indicate good charging system condition and also during ABS when voltage may drop significantly.

DTC Will Set When: DTC 36 can only be set if the vehicle's speed is greater than 5 km/h (3 mph). If the switched battery voltage is less than 11.2 volts non-ABS or less than 9.6 volts ABS, a malfunction exists.

Action Taken: A malfunction DTC is stored, ABS is disabled and the ABS warning lamp is turned "ON."

DTC Chart Test Description: Number(s) below refer to circled number(s) on the diagnostic chart.
5. Checks for high resistance in CKT 350.
6. Checks for high resistance in the ignition feed fuse circuit.
7. Checks for malfunctioning EBCM.

Diagnostic Aids: An "Intermittent" malfunction may be caused by a poor connection, rubbed through wire insulation, or a wire that is broken inside the insulation.

The frequency of the malfunction can be checked by using the enhanced diagnostic function of the Tech 1

Any circuitry, that is suspected as causing the intermittent complaint, should be thoroughly checked for backed out terminals, improper mating, broken locks, improperly formed or damaged terminals, poor terminal to wiring connections or physical damage to the wiring harness.

While performing a voltage load test, if it is noted that only ignition voltage drops below acceptable voltage levels, CKT 350 should be checked for high resistance or an open condition.

GC402930077502AA

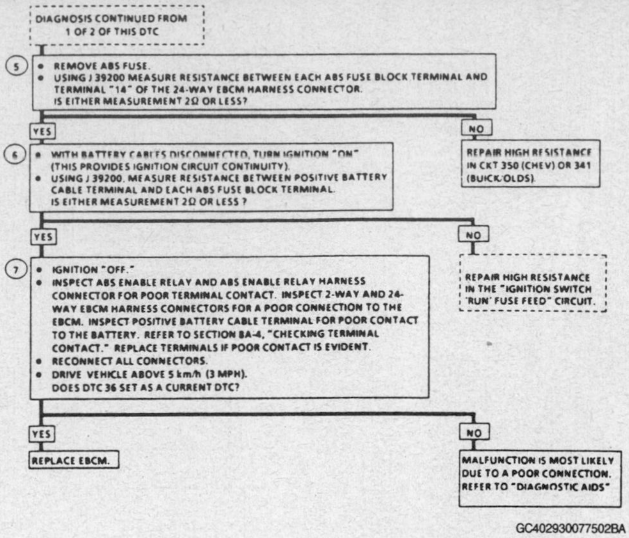
DIAGNOSIS CONTINUED FROM 1 OF 2 OF THIS DTC
5
• REMOVE ABS FUSE.
• USING J 39200 MEASURE RESISTANCE BETWEEN EACH ABS FUSE BLOCK TERMINAL AND TERMINAL "14" OF THE 24-WAY EBCM HARNESS CONNECTOR.
IS EITHER MEASUREMENT 2Ω OR LESS?
YES
NO
REPAIR HIGH RESISTANCE IN CKT 350 (CHEV) OR 341 (BUICK/OLDS).
6
• WITH BATTERY CABLES DISCONNECTED, TURN IGNITION "ON" (THIS PROVIDES IGNITION CIRCUIT CONTINUITY).
• USING J 39200, MEASURE RESISTANCE BETWEEN POSITIVE BATTERY CABLE TERMINAL AND EACH ABS FUSE BLOCK TERMINAL.
IS EITHER MEASUREMENT 2Ω OR LESS ?
YES
NO
REPAIR HIGH RESISTANCE IN THE "IGNITION SWITCH 'RUN' FUSE FEED" CIRCUIT.
7
• IGNITION "OFF."
• INSPECT ABS ENABLE RELAY AND ABS ENABLE RELAY HARNESS CONNECTOR FOR POOR TERMINAL CONTACT. INSPECT 2-WAY AND 24-WAY EBCM HARNESS CONNECTORS FOR A POOR CONNECTION TO THE EBCM. INSPECT POSITIVE BATTERY CABLE TERMINAL FOR POOR CONTACT TO THE BATTERY. REFER TO SECTION 8A-4, "CHECKING TERMINAL CONTACT." REPLACE TERMINALS IF POOR CONTACT IS EVIDENT.
• RECONNECT ALL CONNECTORS.
• DRIVE VEHICLE ABOVE 5 km/h (3 MPH).
DOES DTC 36 SET AS A CURRENT DTC?
YES
REPLACE EBCM.
NO
MALFUNCTION IS MOST LIKELY DUE TO A POOR CONNECTION. REFER TO "DIAGNOSTIC AIDS"

GC402930077502BA

Fig. 142 Code A036: Low System Voltage (Part 2 of 2). 1993 Grand Prix, 1993–94 Cutlass Supreme, Lumina & Regal

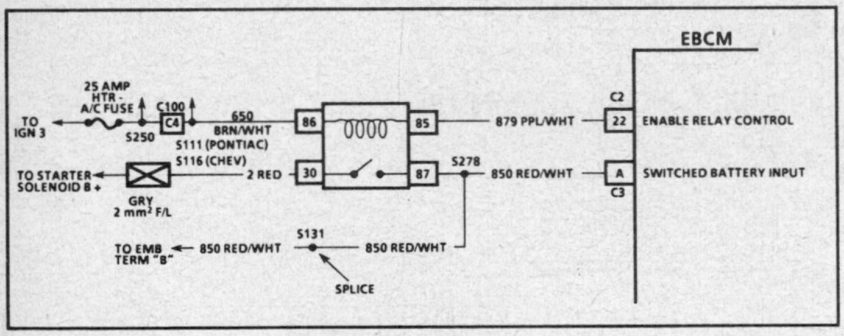
EBCM
25 AMP HTR-A/C FUSE
C100
TO IGN 3
C4
S250
650 BRN/WHT
S111 (PONTIAC)
S116 (CHEV)
86
85
879 PPL/WHT
C2
22 ENABLE RELAY CONTROL
TO STARTER SOLENOID B+
GRY 2 mm² F/L
2 RED
30
87
S278
850 RED/WHT
A SWITCHED BATTERY INPUT
C3
S131
TO EMB TERM "B"
850 RED/WHT
850 RED/WHT
SPLICE

GC402930077600AX

Cavalier & Sunbird

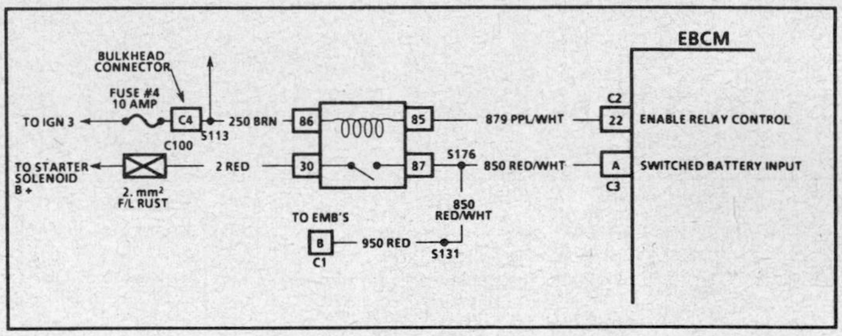
EBCM
BULKHEAD CONNECTOR
FUSE #4 10 AMP
TO IGN 3
C4
S113
C100
250 BRN
86
85
879 PPL/WHT
C2
22 ENABLE RELAY CONTROL
TO STARTER SOLENOID B+
2 mm² F/L RUST
2 RED
30
87
S176
850 RED/WHT
A SWITCHED BATTERY INPUT
C3
TO EMB'S
850 RED/WHT
B
950 RED
C1
S131

GC402930077600BX

Achieva, Beretta, Corsica, Grand Am & Skylark

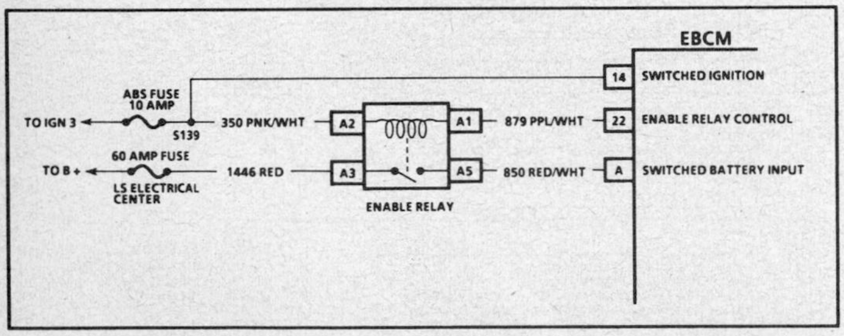
EBCM
14 SWITCHED IGNITION
ABS FUSE 10 AMP
TO IGN 3
S139
350 PNK/WHT
A2
A1
879 PPL/WHT
22 ENABLE RELAY CONTROL
60 AMP FUSE
TO B+
1446 RED
LS ELECTRICAL CENTER
A3
A5
850 RED/WHT
A SWITCHED BATTERY INPUT
ENABLE RELAY

GC402930077600CX

Cutlass Supreme, Grand Prix, Lumina & Regal

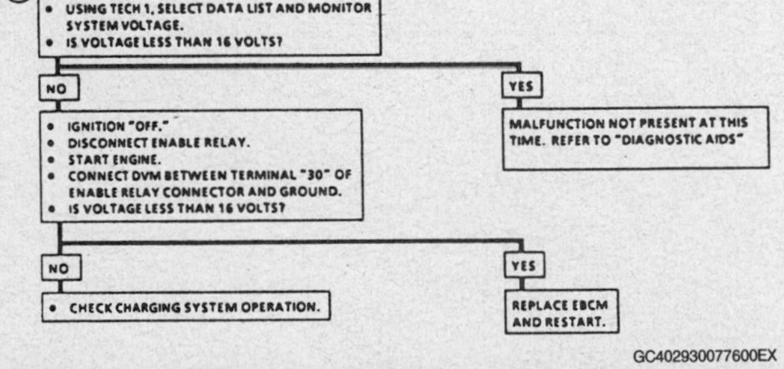
1
• START ENGINE.
• USING TECH 1, SELECT DATA LIST AND MONITOR SYSTEM VOLTAGE.
• IS VOLTAGE LESS THAN 16 VOLTS?
NO
YES
MALFUNCTION NOT PRESENT AT THIS TIME. REFER TO "DIAGNOSTIC AIDS"
• IGNITION "OFF."
• DISCONNECT ENABLE RELAY.
• START ENGINE.
• CONNECT DVM BETWEEN TERMINAL "30" OF ENABLE RELAY CONNECTOR AND GROUND.
• IS VOLTAGE LESS THAN 16 VOLTS?
NO
• CHECK CHARGING SYSTEM OPERATION.
YES
REPLACE EBCM AND RESTART.

GC402930077600EX

DTC A037

HIGH SYSTEM VOLTAGE

Circuit Description:
This DTC is designed to detect high vehicle voltage levels prior to any required motor movement (initialization or ABS). If excessive voltage exists, demagnetization of the motor magnets may occur, which would eventually affect or eliminate ABS performance.

Failure Condition:
DTC A037 can only be set if the vehicle's speed is greater than 5 km/h (3 mph). If the switched battery voltage is greater than 17 volts, a malfunction exists.

Action Taken:
A malfunction DTC is stored, ABS is disabled and the ABS indicator lamp is turned "ON."

Test Description: Number(s) below refer to circled number(s) on the diagnostic chart.
1. This step checks the voltage level being received by the EBCM. If high voltage is present, a charging system problem is indicated.

Diagnostic Aids:

An "Intermittent" malfunction may be caused by a poor connection, rubbed through wire insulation, or a wire that is broken inside the insulation.

The frequency of the malfunction can be checked by using the enhanced diagnostic function of the Tech 1 tool.

Any circuitry, that is suspected as causing the intermittent complaint, should be thoroughly checked for backed out terminals, improper mating, broken locks, improperly formed or damaged terminals, poor terminal to wiring connections or physical damage to the wiring harness.

GC402930077600DX

Fig. 143 Code A037: High System Voltage. 1993 Cutlass Supreme, Grand Prix, Lumina, Regal & 1993–94 Cavalier, Sunbird, Beretta, Corsica & Achieva, Grand Am & Skylark Less VES

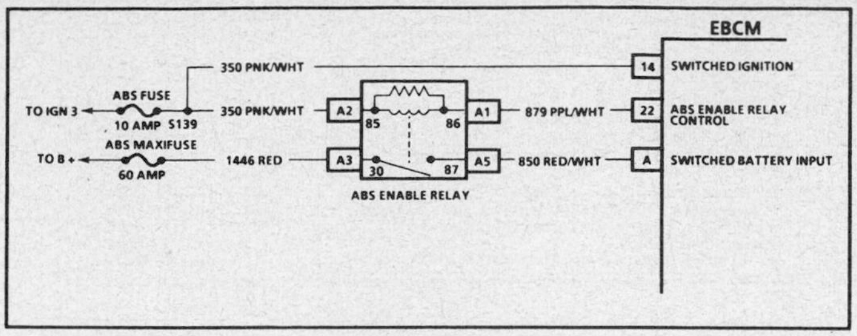
EBCM
350 PNK/WHT
14 SWITCHED IGNITION
ABS FUSE
TO IGN 3
10 AMP S139
350 PNK/WHT
A2
85
86
A1
879 PPL/WHT
22 ABS ENABLE RELAY CONTROL
ABS MAXIFUSE
TO B+
60 AMP
1446 RED
A3
30
87
A5
850 RED/WHT
A SWITCHED BATTERY INPUT
ABS ENABLE RELAY

DTC 37

HIGH SYSTEM VOLTAGE

Circuit Description:

This DTC is designed to detect high vehicle voltage levels prior to any required motor movement (initialization or ABS). If excessive voltage exists, demagnetization of the motor magnets may occur, which would eventually affect or eliminate ABS performance.

DTC Will Set When: DTC 37 can only be set if the vehicle's speed is greater than 5 km/h (3 mph). If the switched battery voltage is greater than 17 volts, a malfunction exists.

Action Taken: A malfunction DTC is stored, ABS is disabled and the ABS warning lamp is turned "ON."

DTC Chart Test Description: Number(s) below refer to circled number(s) on the diagnostic chart.

1. Checks the voltage level being received by the EBCM.
2. Checks to see if high voltage condition is due to charging system malfunction.
3. Checks for poor terminal contact which may cause an intermittent malfunction or a malfunctioning EBCM.

Diagnostic Aids: An "Intermittent" malfunction may be caused by a poor connection, rubbed through wire insulation, or a wire that is broken inside the insulation.

The frequency of the malfunction can be checked by using the enhanced diagnostic function of the Tech 1.

Any circuitry, that is suspected as causing the intermittent complaint, should be thoroughly checked for backed out terminals, improper mating, broken locks, improperly formed or damaged terminals, poor terminal to wiring connections or physical damage to the wiring harness.

GC402940094100AX

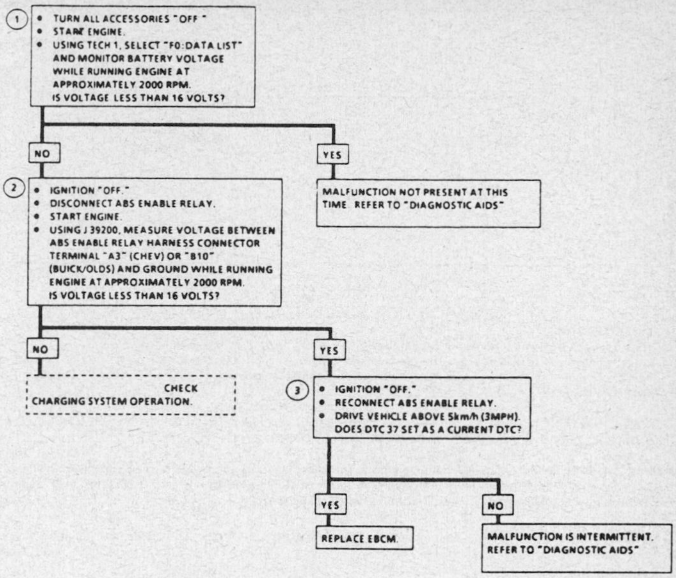
1
TURN ALL ACCESSORIES "OFF."
START ENGINE.
USING TECH 1, SELECT "F0: DATA LIST" AND MONITOR BATTERY VOLTAGE WHILE RUNNING ENGINE AT APPROXIMATELY 2000 RPM.
IS VOLTAGE LESS THAN 16 VOLTS?
NO
YES
MALFUNCTION NOT PRESENT AT THIS TIME. REFER TO "DIAGNOSTIC AIDS"
2
IGNITION "OFF."
DISCONNECT ABS ENABLE RELAY.
START ENGINE.
USING J 39200, MEASURE VOLTAGE BETWEEN ABS ENABLE RELAY HARNESS CONNECTOR TERMINAL "A3" (CHEV) OR "B10" (BUICK/OLDS) AND GROUND WHILE RUNNING ENGINE AT APPROXIMATELY 2000 RPM.
IS VOLTAGE LESS THAN 16 VOLTS?
NO
YES
CHECK CHARGING SYSTEM OPERATION.
3
IGNITION "OFF."
RECONNECT ABS ENABLE RELAY.
DRIVE VEHICLE ABOVE 5km/h (3MPH).
DOES DTC 37 SET AS A CURRENT DTC?
YES
NO
REPLACE EBCM.
MALFUNCTION IS INTERMITTENT. REFER TO "DIAGNOSTIC AIDS"

GC402940094100BX

Fig. 144 Code A037: High System Voltage. 1994 Cutlass Supreme, Lumina & Regal

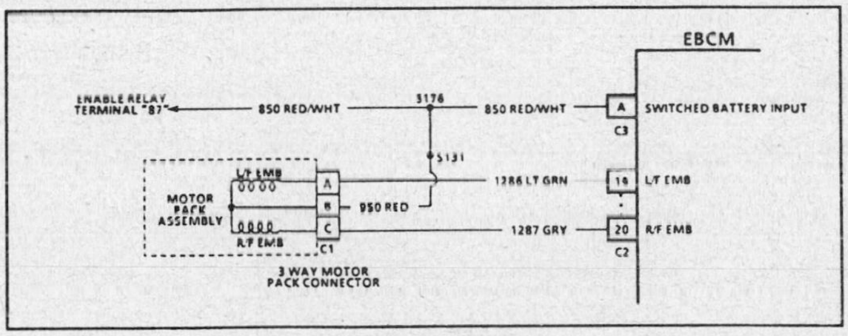
EBCM
ENABLE RELAY TERMINAL "87"
850 RED/WHT
S176
850 RED/WHT
A SWITCHED BATTERY INPUT
C3
S131
L/F EMB
A
1286 LT GRN
19 L/F EMB
MOTOR PACK ASSEMBLY
B
950 RED
C
1287 GRY
20 R/F EMB
C2
R/F EMB
C1
3 WAY MOTOR PACK CONNECTOR

DTC A038

LEFT FRONT EMB WILL NOT HOLD MOTOR

Circuit Description:

Current is supplied to the EMBs through terminal "B" of the three way motor pack connector. When a release of the EMB is commanded, the EBCM grounds the EMB input and allows the EMB to be energized to release the motor.

This DTC is designed to detect slipping EMBs during initialization. When the release is commanded during initialization, the EMB is not energized and should hold the motor, resulting in sensed current of the motor being equal to commanded current (motor is at stall). If the motor is moving, sensed current will be less than stall current.

Failure Condition:

DTC A038 can be set during initialization. DTC A086 is always set with A038.

Action Taken:

If an EMB can not hold a motor in the home position, the motor may be backdriven when the brake pedal is applied causing the brake pedal to drop. A malfunction DTC is stored, ABS is disabled and the ABS indicator lamp is turned "ON."

Test Description: Number(s) below refer to circled number(s) on the diagnostic chart.

1. This step ensures motor circuits are in the proper connector cavity.
2. This functionally checks the ability of the EMB to hold the motor. If the brake pedal moves during this test, it would indicate the EMB is slipping.
3. This step is used to release the tension of the motor pack prior to removal.

Diagnostic Aids:

An "Intermittent" malfunction in this DTC may result from a mechanical part of the system that sticks, binds, or slips.

The frequency of the malfunction can be checked by using the enhanced diagnostic function of the Tech 1.

The static modulator test function of the Tech 1 may be used to locate an intermittent malfunction associated with the EMB.

NOTICE: This test may fail if low voltage (10 volts or less) was present when initialization occurred. Ensure battery/charging system is functioning properly.

GC402930077700AX

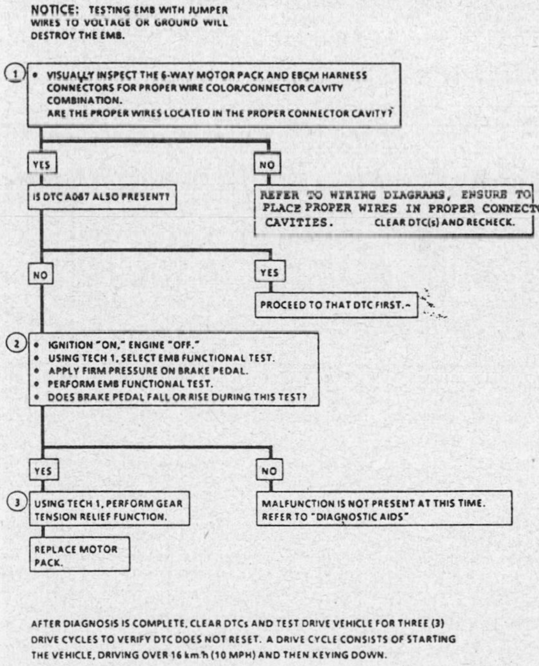
NOTICE: TESTING EMB WITH JUMPER WIRES TO VOLTAGE OR GROUND WILL DESTROY THE EMB.
1
VISUALLY INSPECT THE 6-WAY MOTOR PACK AND EBCM HARNESS CONNECTORS FOR PROPER WIRE COLOR/CONNECTOR CAVITY COMBINATION.
ARE THE PROPER WIRES LOCATED IN THE PROPER CONNECTOR CAVITY?
YES
NO
IS DTC A067 ALSO PRESENT?
REFER TO WIRING DIAGRAMS, ENSURE TO PLACE PROPER WIRES IN PROPER CONNECTOR CAVITIES. CLEAR DTC(s) AND RECHECK.
NO
YES
PROCEED TO THAT DTC FIRST.
2
IGNITION "ON," ENGINE "OFF."
USING TECH 1, SELECT EMB FUNCTIONAL TEST.
APPLY FIRM PRESSURE ON BRAKE PEDAL.
PERFORM EMB FUNCTIONAL TEST.
DOES BRAKE PEDAL FALL OR RISE DURING THIS TEST?
YES
NO
3
USING TECH 1, PERFORM GEAR TENSION RELIEF FUNCTION.
MALFUNCTION IS NOT PRESENT AT THIS TIME. REFER TO "DIAGNOSTIC AIDS"
REPLACE MOTOR PACK.
AFTER DIAGNOSIS IS COMPLETE, CLEAR DTCs AND TEST DRIVE VEHICLE FOR THREE (3) DRIVE CYCLES TO VERIFY DTC DOES NOT RESET. A DRIVE CYCLE CONSISTS OF STARTING THE VEHICLE, DRIVING OVER 16 km/h (10 MPH) AND THEN KEYING DOWN.

GC402930077700BX

Fig. 145 Code A038: Left Front EMB Will Not Hold Motor. 1993–94 Cavalier, Sunbird, Beretta, Corsica & Achieva, Grand Am & Skylark Less VES

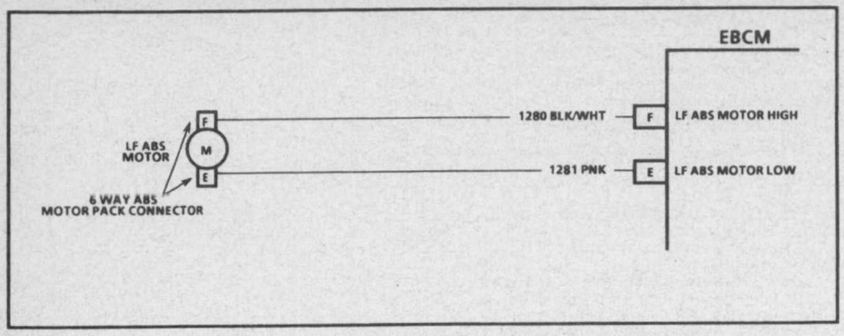
EBCM
1280 BLK/WHT
F
LF ABS MOTOR HIGH
LF ABS MOTOR
M
F
E
1281 PNK
E
LF ABS MOTOR LOW
6 WAY ABS
MOTOR PACK CONNECTOR

DTC 38

LEFT FRONT ESB WILL NOT HOLD MOTOR

Circuit Description:

This DTC is designed to detect a slipping left front ESB. During initialization and braking, the left front motor is rehomed. If the ESB slips, the motor/piston will move. During the next key "ON" initialization, a rehome of the motor verifies the motor/piston remained at the home position. If motor movement is detected, the ESB must be slipping.

DTC Will Set When: DTC 38 can be set during initialization. If the EBCM detects that the ESB could not hold the piston in the home position, a malfunction exists. DTC 86 is always set with DTC 38.

Action Taken: If an ESB cannot hold a piston in the home position, the piston may be backdriven when the brake pedal is applied, causing the brake pedal to drop. A malfunction DTC is stored, ABS is disabled, and the ABS warning lamp and the red "BRAKE" warning lamp are turned "ON."

DTC Chart Test Description: Number(s) below refer to circled number(s) on the diagnostic chart.

1. Checks the left front ESB. A broken or defective ESB would result in the left front piston being backdriven by hydraulic pressure and pedal movement would result.
2. Ensures that the proper motor circuits are located in the proper connector cavities.
3. Checks for high resistance in the motor "HIGH" circuitry.
4. Checks for high resistance in the motor "LOW" circuitry.
5. Checks for proper resistance of the motor windings.
6. Checks for poor terminal contact or corrosion in the connectors.
7. Checks for a malfunctioning EBCM.

Diagnostic Aids: An "Intermittent" malfunction in this DTC may result from a mechanical part of the system that sticks, binds, or slips.

The frequency of the malfunction can be checked by using the enhanced diagnostic function of the Tech 1.

The static modulator test function of the Tech 1 or T-100 may be used to locate an intermittent malfunction associated with the ESB.

GC402930077800AA

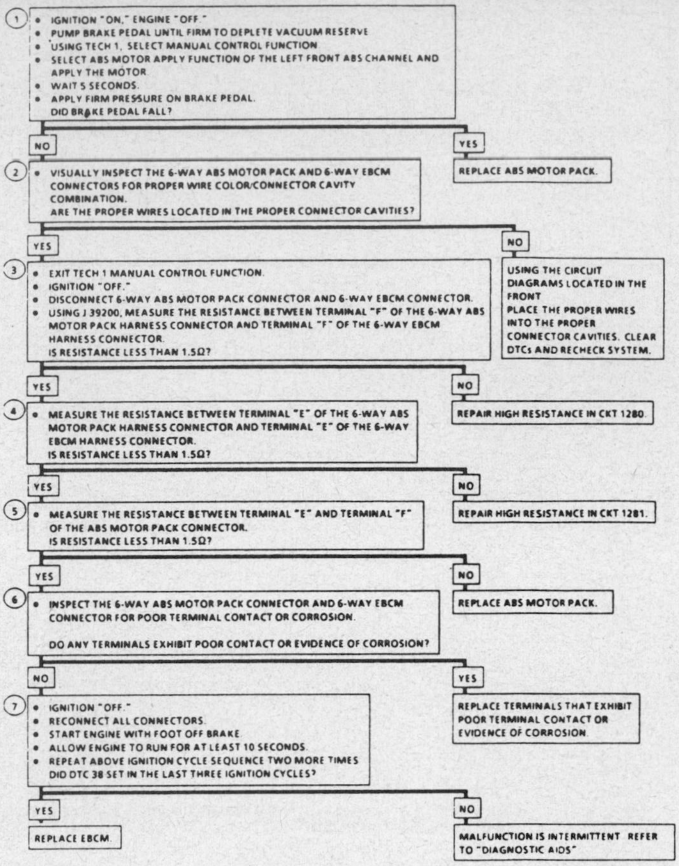
1
• IGNITION "ON," ENGINE "OFF."
• PUMP BRAKE PEDAL UNTIL FIRM TO DEPLETE VACUUM RESERVE
• USING TECH 1, SELECT MANUAL CONTROL FUNCTION
• SELECT ABS MOTOR APPLY FUNCTION OF THE LEFT FRONT ABS CHANNEL AND APPLY THE MOTOR
• WAIT 5 SECONDS.
• APPLY FIRM PRESSURE ON BRAKE PEDAL.
DID BRAKE PEDAL FALL?
NO
YES
REPLACE ABS MOTOR PACK.
2
• VISUALLY INSPECT THE 6-WAY ABS MOTOR PACK AND 6-WAY EBCM CONNECTORS FOR PROPER WIRE COLOR/CONNECTOR CAVITY COMBINATION.
ARE THE PROPER WIRES LOCATED IN THE PROPER CONNECTOR CAVITIES?
YES
NO
USING THE CIRCUIT DIAGRAMS LOCATED IN THE FRONT
PLACE THE PROPER WIRES INTO THE PROPER CONNECTOR CAVITIES. CLEAR DTCs AND RECHECK SYSTEM.
3
• EXIT TECH 1 MANUAL CONTROL FUNCTION.
• IGNITION "OFF."
• DISCONNECT 6-WAY ABS MOTOR PACK CONNECTOR AND 6-WAY EBCM CONNECTOR.
• USING J 39200, MEASURE THE RESISTANCE BETWEEN TERMINAL "F" OF THE 6-WAY ABS MOTOR PACK HARNESS CONNECTOR AND TERMINAL "F" OF THE 6-WAY EBCM HARNESS CONNECTOR.
IS RESISTANCE LESS THAN 1.5Ω?
YES
NO
REPAIR HIGH RESISTANCE IN CKT 1280.
4
• MEASURE THE RESISTANCE BETWEEN TERMINAL "E" OF THE 6-WAY ABS MOTOR PACK HARNESS CONNECTOR AND TERMINAL "E" OF THE 6-WAY EBCM HARNESS CONNECTOR.
IS RESISTANCE LESS THAN 1.5Ω?
YES
NO
REPAIR HIGH RESISTANCE IN CKT 1281.
5
• MEASURE THE RESISTANCE BETWEEN TERMINAL "E" AND TERMINAL "F" OF THE ABS MOTOR PACK CONNECTOR.
IS RESISTANCE LESS THAN 1.5Ω?
YES
NO
REPLACE ABS MOTOR PACK.
6
• INSPECT THE 6-WAY ABS MOTOR PACK CONNECTOR AND 6-WAY EBCM CONNECTOR FOR POOR TERMINAL CONTACT OR CORROSION.
DO ANY TERMINALS EXHIBIT POOR CONTACT OR EVIDENCE OF CORROSION?
NO
YES
REPLACE TERMINALS THAT EXHIBIT POOR TERMINAL CONTACT OR EVIDENCE OF CORROSION.
7
• IGNITION "OFF."
• RECONNECT ALL CONNECTORS.
• START ENGINE WITH FOOT OFF BRAKE.
• ALLOW ENGINE TO RUN FOR AT LEAST 10 SECONDS.
• REPEAT ABOVE IGNITION CYCLE SEQUENCE TWO MORE TIMES
DID DTC 38 SET IN THE LAST THREE IGNITION CYCLES?
YES
NO
REPLACE EBCM.
MALFUNCTION IS INTERMITTENT REFER TO "DIAGNOSTIC AIDS"

GC402930077800BA

Fig. 146 Code A038: Left Front ESB Will Not Hold Motor. 1993 Grand Prix, 1993–94 Cutlass Supreme, Lumina & Regal

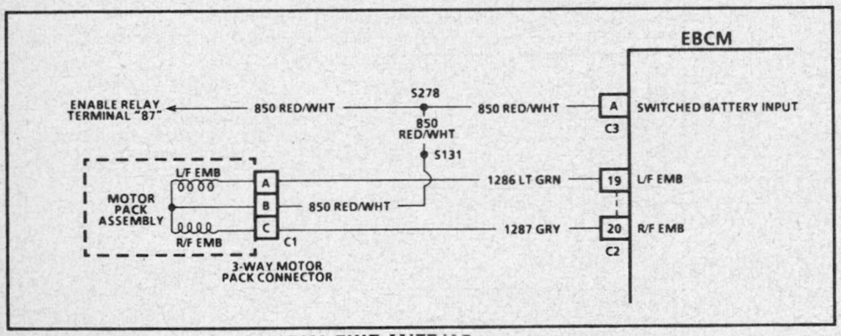
EBCM
ENABLE RELAY TERMINAL "87"
850 RED/WHT
S278
850 RED/WHT
A
SWITCHED BATTERY INPUT
C3
850 RED/WHT
S131
L/F EMB
MOTOR PACK ASSEMBLY
R/F EMB
A
B
C
C1
1286 LT GRN
19
L/F EMB
850 RED/WHT
1287 GRY
20
R/F EMB
C2
3-WAY MOTOR PACK CONNECTOR

NOTICE: TESTING END WITH JUMPER WIRES TO VOLTAGE OR GROUND WILL DESTROY THE EMB.

Circuit Description:

Current is supplied to the EMBs through terminal "B" of the three way motor pack connector. When a release of the EMB is commanded, the EBCM grounds the EMB input and allows the EMB to be energized to release the motor.

This DTC is designed to detect slipping EMBs during initialization. When the release is commanded during initialization, the EMB is not energized and should hold the motor, resulting in sensed current of the motor being equal to commanded current (motor is at stall). If the motor is moving, sensed current will be less than stall current.

Failure Condition:

DTC A041 can be set during initialization. DTC A086 is always set with DTC A041.

Action Taken:

If an EMB can not hold a motor in the home position, the motor may be backdriven when the brake pedal is applied causing the brake pedal to fall. A malfunction DTC is stored, ABS is disabled and the ABS indicator lamp is turned "ON."

Test Description: Number(s) below refer to circled number(s) on the diagnostic chart.

1. This step ensures motor circuits are in the proper connector cavity.
2. This functionally checks the ability of the EMB to hold the motor. If the brake pedal moves during this test, it would indicate the EMB is slipping.
3. This step is used to release the tension of the motor pack prior to removal.

Diagnostic Aids:

An "Intermittent" malfunction in this DTC may result from a mechanical part of the system that sticks, binds, or slips.

The frequency of the malfunction can be checked by using the enhanced diagnostic function of the Tech 1 tool as described in "Enhanced Diagnostics" found in this section.

The static modulator test function of the Tech 1 may be used to locate an intermittent malfunction associated with the EMB.

NOTICE: This DTC may fail if low voltage (10 volts or less) was present when initialization occurred. Ensure battery/charging system is functioning properly.

GC402930077900AX

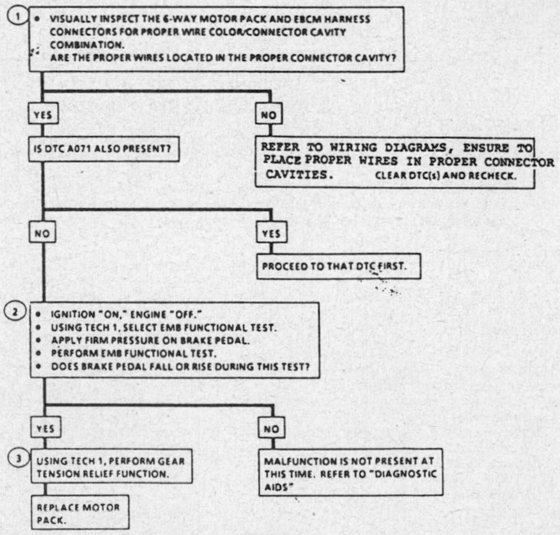
1
• VISUALLY INSPECT THE 6-WAY MOTOR PACK AND EBCM HARNESS CONNECTORS FOR PROPER WIRE COLOR/CONNECTOR CAVITY COMBINATION.
ARE THE PROPER WIRES LOCATED IN THE PROPER CONNECTOR CAVITY?
YES
NO
IS DTC A071 ALSO PRESENT?
REFER TO WIRING DIAGRAMS, ENSURE TO PLACE PROPER WIRES IN PROPER CONNECTOR CAVITIES. CLEAR DTC(s) AND RECHECK.
NO
YES
PROCEED TO THAT DTC FIRST.
2
• IGNITION "ON," ENGINE "OFF."
• USING TECH 1, SELECT EMB FUNCTIONAL TEST.
• APPLY FIRM PRESSURE ON BRAKE PEDAL.
• PERFORM EMB FUNCTIONAL TEST.
• DOES BRAKE PEDAL FALL OR RISE DURING THIS TEST?
YES
NO
3
USING TECH 1, PERFORM GEAR TENSION RELIEF FUNCTION.
MALFUNCTION IS NOT PRESENT AT THIS TIME. REFER TO "DIAGNOSTIC AIDS"
REPLACE MOTOR PACK.

* AFTER DIAGNOSIS IS COMPLETE, CLEAR DTCs AND TEST DRIVE VEHICLE FOR THREE (3) DRIVE CYCLES TO VERIFY DTC DOES NOT RESET. A DRIVE CYCLE CONSISTS OF STARTING THE VEHICLE, DRIVING OVER 16 km.h (10 MPH) AND THEN KEYING DOWN.

GC402930077900BX

Fig. 147 Code A041: Right Front EMB Will Not Hold Motor. 1993–94 Cavalier, Sunbird, Beretta, Corsica & Achieva, Grand Am & Skylark Less VES

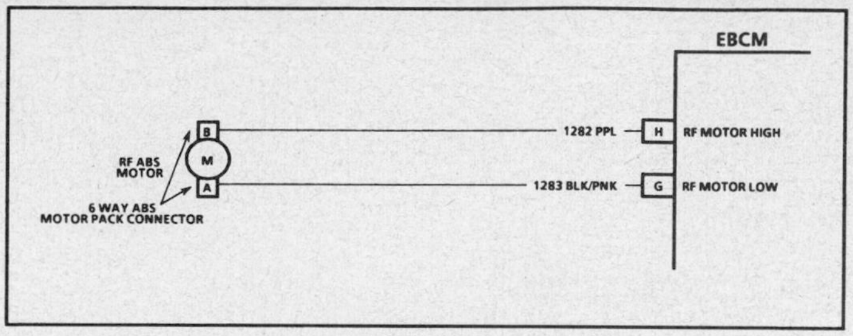
EBCM
RF ABS MOTOR
B
M
A
6 WAY ABS MOTOR PACK CONNECTOR
1282 PPL
H
RF MOTOR HIGH
1283 BLK/PNK
G
RF MOTOR LOW

DTC 41

RIGHT FRONT ESB WILL NOT HOLD MOTOR

Circuit Description:

This DTC is designed to detect a slipping right front ESB. During initialization and braking, the right front motor is rehomed. If the ESB slips, the motor/piston will move. During the next key "ON" initialization, a rehome of the motor verifies the motor/piston remained at the home position. If motor movement is detected, the ESB must be slipping.

DTC Will Set When: DTC 41 can be set during initialization. If the EBCM detects that the ESB could not hold the piston in the home position, a malfunction exists. DTC 86 is always set with DTC 41.

Action Taken: If an ESB cannot hold a piston in the home position, the piston may be backdriven when the brake pedal is applied, causing the brake pedal to drop. A malfunction DTC is stored, ABS is disabled, and the ABS warning lamp and the red "BRAKE" warning lamp are turned "ON."

DTC Chart Test Description: Number(s) below refer to circled number(s) on the diagnostic chart.

1. Checks the right front ESB. A broken or defective ESB would result in the right front piston being backdriven by hydraulic pressure, and pedal movement would result.
2. Ensures that the proper motor circuits are located in the proper connector cavities.
3. Checks for high resistance in the motor "HIGH" circuitry.
4. Checks for high resistance in the motor "LOW" circuitry.
5. Checks for proper resistance of the motor windings.
6. Checks for poor terminal contact or corrosion in the connectors.
7. Checks for a malfunctioning EBCM.

Diagnostic Aids: An "Intermittent" malfunction in this DTC may result from a mechanical part of the system that sticks, binds, or slips.

The frequency of the malfunction can be checked by using the enhanced diagnostic function of the Tech 1

The static modulator test function of the Tech 1 or T-100 may be used to locate an intermittent malfunction associated with the ESB.

GC402930078000AA

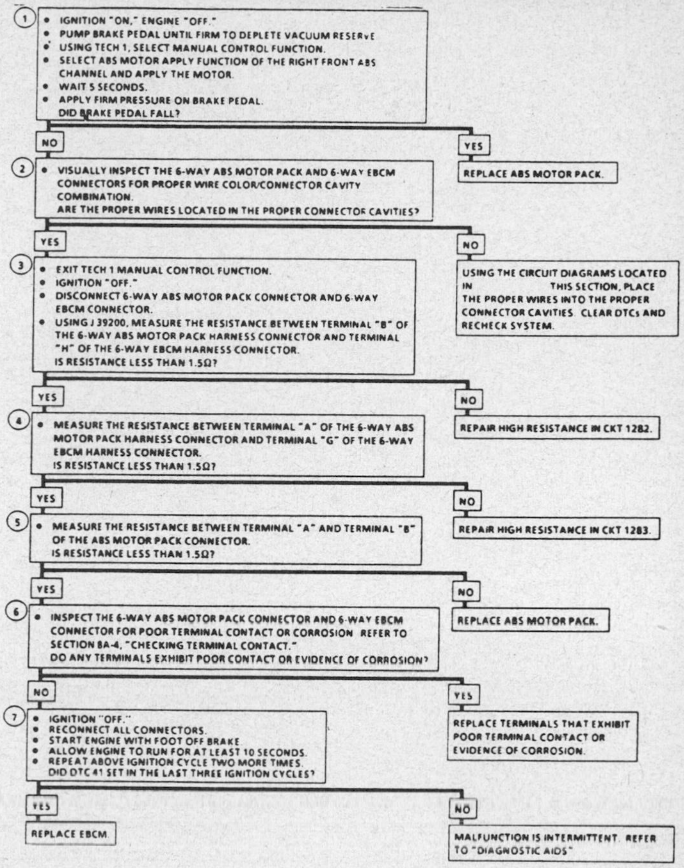
1
IGNITION "ON," ENGINE "OFF."
PUMP BRAKE PEDAL UNTIL FIRM TO DEPLETE VACUUM RESERVE
USING TECH 1, SELECT MANUAL CONTROL FUNCTION.
SELECT ABS MOTOR APPLY FUNCTION OF THE RIGHT FRONT ABS CHANNEL AND APPLY THE MOTOR.
WAIT 5 SECONDS.
APPLY FIRM PRESSURE ON BRAKE PEDAL.
DID BRAKE PEDAL FALL?
NO
YES
REPLACE ABS MOTOR PACK.
2
VISUALLY INSPECT THE 6-WAY ABS MOTOR PACK AND 6-WAY EBCM CONNECTORS FOR PROPER WIRE COLOR/CONNECTOR CAVITY COMBINATION.
ARE THE PROPER WIRES LOCATED IN THE PROPER CONNECTOR CAVITIES?
YES
NO
USING THE CIRCUIT DIAGRAMS LOCATED IN THIS SECTION, PLACE THE PROPER WIRES INTO THE PROPER CONNECTOR CAVITIES. CLEAR DTCs AND RECHECK SYSTEM.
3
EXIT TECH 1 MANUAL CONTROL FUNCTION.
IGNITION "OFF."
DISCONNECT 6-WAY ABS MOTOR PACK CONNECTOR AND 6-WAY EBCM CONNECTOR.
USING J 39200, MEASURE THE RESISTANCE BETWEEN TERMINAL "B" OF THE 6-WAY ABS MOTOR PACK HARNESS CONNECTOR AND TERMINAL "H" OF THE 6-WAY EBCM HARNESS CONNECTOR.
IS RESISTANCE LESS THAN 1.5Ω?
YES
NO
REPAIR HIGH RESISTANCE IN CKT 1282.
4
MEASURE THE RESISTANCE BETWEEN TERMINAL "A" OF THE 6-WAY ABS MOTOR PACK HARNESS CONNECTOR AND TERMINAL "G" OF THE 6-WAY EBCM HARNESS CONNECTOR.
IS RESISTANCE LESS THAN 1.5Ω?
YES
NO
REPAIR HIGH RESISTANCE IN CKT 1283.
5
MEASURE THE RESISTANCE BETWEEN TERMINAL "A" AND TERMINAL "B" OF THE ABS MOTOR PACK CONNECTOR.
IS RESISTANCE LESS THAN 1.5Ω?
YES
NO
REPLACE ABS MOTOR PACK.
6
INSPECT THE 6-WAY ABS MOTOR PACK CONNECTOR AND 6-WAY EBCM CONNECTOR FOR POOR TERMINAL CONTACT OR CORROSION REFER TO SECTION 8A-4, "CHECKING TERMINAL CONTACT."
DO ANY TERMINALS EXHIBIT POOR CONTACT OR EVIDENCE OF CORROSION?
NO
YES
REPLACE TERMINALS THAT EXHIBIT POOR TERMINAL CONTACT OR EVIDENCE OF CORROSION.
7
IGNITION "OFF."
RECONNECT ALL CONNECTORS.
START ENGINE WITH FOOT OFF BRAKE
ALLOW ENGINE TO RUN FOR AT LEAST 10 SECONDS.
REPEAT ABOVE IGNITION CYCLE TWO MORE TIMES.
DID DTC 41 SET IN THE LAST THREE IGNITION CYCLES?
YES
REPLACE EBCM.
NO
MALFUNCTION IS INTERMITTENT. REFER TO "DIAGNOSTIC AIDS"

GC402930078000BA

Fig. 148 Code A041: Right Front ESB Will Not Hold Motor. 1993 Grand Prix, 1993–94 Cutlass Supreme, Lumina & Regal

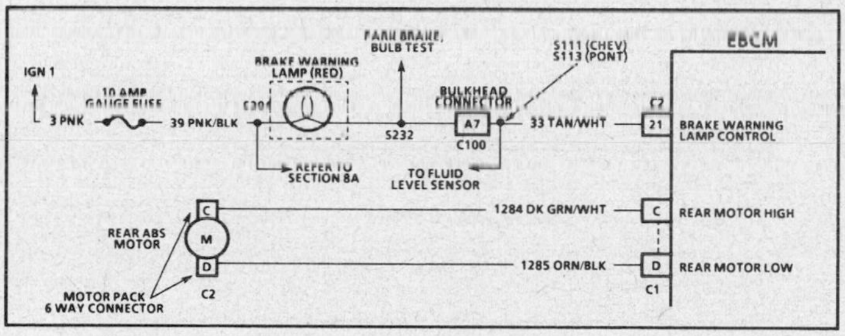
EBCM
IGN 1
3 PNK
10 AMP GAUGE FUSE
39 PNK/BLK
BRAKE WARNING LAMP (RED)
PARK BRAKE, BULB TEST
S232
REFER TO SECTION 8A
BULKHEAD CONNECTOR
A7
C100
TO FLUID LEVEL SENSOR
S111 (CHEV)
S113 (PONT)
33 TAN/WHT
C2
21
BRAKE WARNING LAMP CONTROL
REAR ABS MOTOR
C
M
D
1284 DK GRN/WHT
REAR MOTOR HIGH
1285 ORN/BLK
REAR MOTOR LOW
C1
MOTOR PACK 6 WAY CONNECTOR

GC402930078100AX

Cavalier & Sunbird

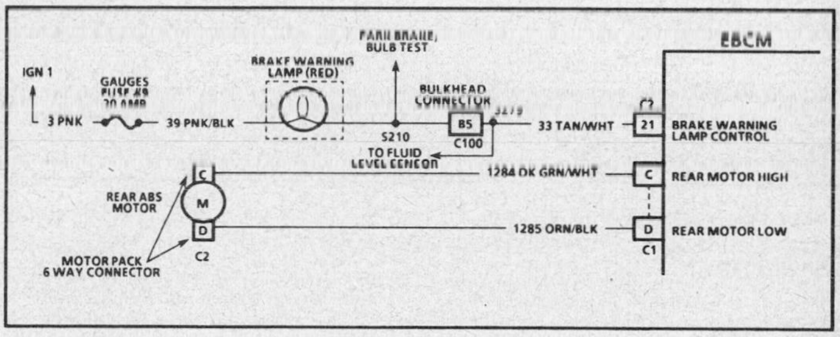
EBCM
IGN 1
3 PNK
GAUGES FUSE 20 AMP
39 PNK/BLK
BRAKE WARNING LAMP (RED)
PARK BRAKE, BULB TEST
BULKHEAD CONNECTOR
B5
S210
C100
TO FLUID LEVEL SENSOR
33 TAN/WHT
C2
21
BRAKE WARNING LAMP CONTROL
REAR ABS MOTOR
C
M
D
1284 DK GRN/WHT
REAR MOTOR HIGH
1285 ORN/BLK
REAR MOTOR LOW
C1
MOTOR PACK 6 WAY CONNECTOR

GC402930078100BX

Beretta & Corsica

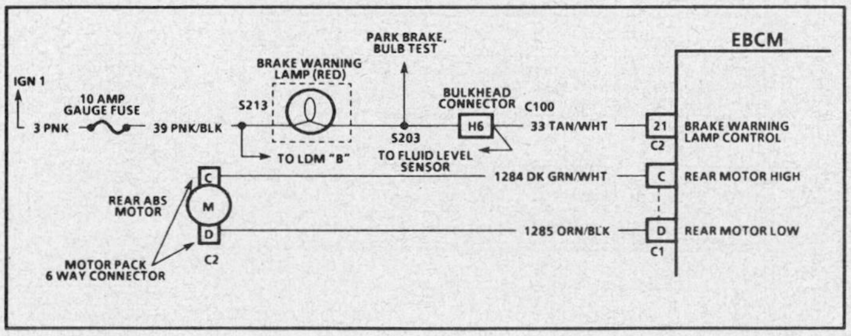
EBCM
IGN 1
3 PNK
10 AMP GAUGE FUSE
39 PNK/BLK
S213
BRAKE WARNING LAMP (RED)
PARK BRAKE, BULB TEST
S203
TO LDM "B"
BULKHEAD CONNECTOR
C100
H6
TO FLUID LEVEL SENSOR
33 TAN/WHT
21
C2
BRAKE WARNING LAMP CONTROL
REAR ABS MOTOR
C
M
D
1284 DK GRN/WHT
REAR MOTOR HIGH
1285 ORN/BLK
REAR MOTOR LOW
C1
MOTOR PACK 6 WAY CONNECTOR

GC402930078100CX

Achieva, Grand Am & Skylark

DTC A042

REAR AXLE ESB WILL NOT HOLD MOTOR

Circuit Description:

This DTC is designed to detect a slipping rear axle ESB. During initialization and braking, the rear motor is re-homed. If the ESB slips, the motor/piston will move. During the next key on initialization, a re-home of the motor verifies the motor/piston remained at the home position. If motor movement is detected, the ESB must be slipping.

Failure Condition:

DTC A042 can be set during initialization. DTC A086 is always set with A042.

Action Taken:

If an ESB can not hold a motor in the home position, the motor may be backdriven when the brake pedal is applied causing the brake pedal to drop. A malfunction DTC is stored, ABS is disabled and the ABS indicator lamp is turned "ON."

Test Description: Number(s) below refer to circled number(s) on the diagnostic chart.

1. This step ensures motor circuits are in the proper connector cavity.
2. This step checks the rear axle ESB. A broken or defective ESB would result in the rear piston being back driven by hydraulic pressure, and wheel movement would result.
3. This step is used to release the tension of the motor pack prior to removal.

Diagnostic Aids:

An "Intermittent" malfunction in this DTC may result from a mechanical part of the system that sticks, binds, or slips.

The frequency of the malfunction can be checked by using the enhanced diagnostic function of the Tech 1

The static modulator test function of the Tech 1 may be used to locate an intermittent malfunction associated with the ESB.

GC402930078100DX

Fig. 149 Code A042: Rear Axle ESB Will Not Hold Motor (Part 1 of 2). 1993-94 Cavalier, Sunbird, Beretta, Corsica & Achieva, Grand Am & Skylark Less VES

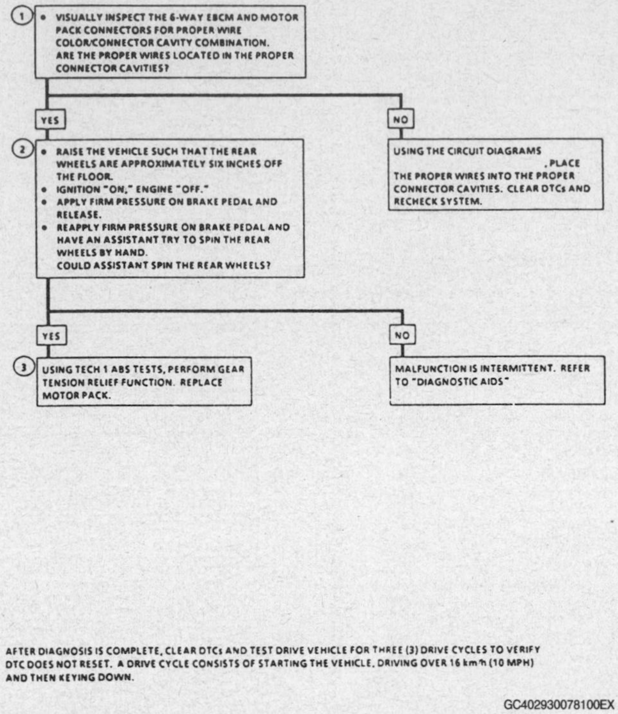
1 • VISUALLY INSPECT THE 6-WAY EBCM AND MOTOR PACK CONNECTORS FOR PROPER WIRE COLOR/CONNECTOR CAVITY COMBINATION. ARE THE PROPER WIRES LOCATED IN THE PROPER CONNECTOR CAVITIES?
YES
NO
2 • RAISE THE VEHICLE SUCH THAT THE REAR WHEELS ARE APPROXIMATELY SIX INCHES OFF THE FLOOR.
• IGNITION "ON," ENGINE "OFF."
• APPLY FIRM PRESSURE ON BRAKE PEDAL AND RELEASE.
• REAPPLY FIRM PRESSURE ON BRAKE PEDAL AND HAVE AN ASSISTANT TRY TO SPIN THE REAR WHEELS BY HAND. COULD ASSISTANT SPIN THE REAR WHEELS?
USING THE CIRCUIT DIAGRAMS , PLACE THE PROPER WIRES INTO THE PROPER CONNECTOR CAVITIES. CLEAR DTCs AND RECHECK SYSTEM.
YES
NO
3 USING TECH 1 ABS TESTS, PERFORM GEAR TENSION RELIEF FUNCTION. REPLACE MOTOR PACK.
MALFUNCTION IS INTERMITTENT. REFER TO "DIAGNOSTIC AIDS"
AFTER DIAGNOSIS IS COMPLETE, CLEAR DTCs AND TEST DRIVE VEHICLE FOR THREE (3) DRIVE CYCLES TO VERIFY DTC DOES NOT RESET. A DRIVE CYCLE CONSISTS OF STARTING THE VEHICLE, DRIVING OVER 16 km/h (10 MPH) AND THEN KEYING DOWN.
GC402930078100EX

Fig. 149 Code A042: Rear Axle ESB Will Not Hold Motor (Part 2 of 2). 1993-94 Cavalier, Sunbird, Beretta, Corsica & Achieva, Grand Am & Skylark Less VES

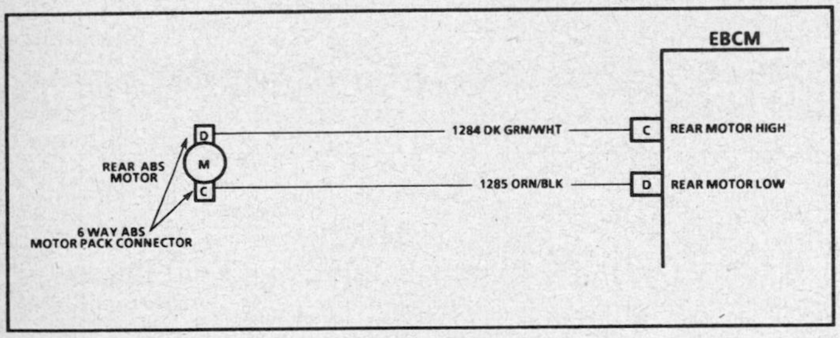
EBCM
1284 DK GRN/WHT
C
REAR MOTOR HIGH
1285 ORN/BLK
D
REAR MOTOR LOW
REAR ABS MOTOR
M
D
C
6 WAY ABS MOTOR PACK CONNECTOR

DTC 42

REAR ESB WILL NOT HOLD MOTOR

Circuit Description:

This DTC is designed to detect a slipping rear axle ESB. During initialization and braking, the rear motor is rehomed. If the ESB slips, the motor/piston will move. During the next key "ON" initialization, a rehome of the motor verifies the motor/piston remained at the home position. If motor movement is detected, the ESB must be slipping.

DTC Will Set When: DTC 42 can be set during initialization. If the EBCM detects that the ESB could not hold the piston in the home position, a malfunction exists. DTC 86 is always set with DTC 42.

Action Taken: If an ESB cannot hold a piston in the home position, the piston may be backdriven when the brake pedal is applied, causing the brake pedal to drop. A malfunction DTC is stored, ABS is disabled, and the ABS warning lamp and the red "BRAKE" warning lamp are turned "ON."

DTC Chart Test Description: Number(s) below refer to circled number(s) on the diagnostic chart.

1. Checks the rear axle ESB. A broken or defective ESB would result in the rear axle pistons being backdriven by hydraulic pressure and wheel movement would result.
2. Ensures that the proper motor circuits are located in the proper connector cavities.
3. Checks for high resistance in the motor "HIGH" circuitry.
4. Checks for high resistance in the motor "LOW" circuitry.
5. Checks for proper resistance of the motor windings.
6. Checks for poor terminal contact or corrosion in the connectors.
7. Checks for a malfunctioning EBCM.

Diagnostic Aids: An "Intermittent" malfunction in this DTC may result from a mechanical part of the system that sticks, binds, or slips.

The frequency of the malfunction can be checked by using the enhanced diagnostic function of the Tech 1

The static modulator test function of the Tech 1 or T-100 may be used to locate an intermittent malfunction associated with the ESB.

GC402930078200AA

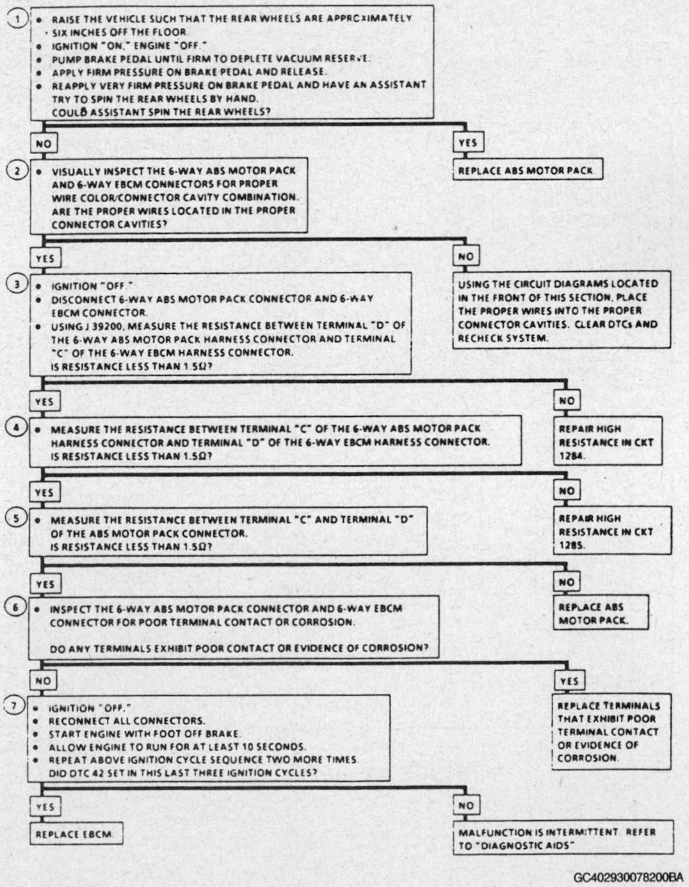
1 • RAISE THE VEHICLE SUCH THAT THE REAR WHEELS ARE APPROXIMATELY SIX INCHES OFF THE FLOOR.
• IGNITION "ON," ENGINE "OFF."
• PUMP BRAKE PEDAL UNTIL FIRM TO DEPLETE VACUUM RESERVE.
• APPLY FIRM PRESSURE ON BRAKE PEDAL AND RELEASE.
• REAPPLY VERY FIRM PRESSURE ON BRAKE PEDAL AND HAVE AN ASSISTANT TRY TO SPIN THE REAR WHEELS BY HAND. COULD ASSISTANT SPIN THE REAR WHEELS?
NO
YES
REPLACE ABS MOTOR PACK.
2 • VISUALLY INSPECT THE 6-WAY ABS MOTOR PACK AND 6-WAY EBCM CONNECTORS FOR PROPER WIRE COLOR/CONNECTOR CAVITY COMBINATION. ARE THE PROPER WIRES LOCATED IN THE PROPER CONNECTOR CAVITIES?
YES
NO
3 • IGNITION "OFF."
• DISCONNECT 6-WAY ABS MOTOR PACK CONNECTOR AND 6-WAY EBCM CONNECTOR.
• USING J 39200, MEASURE THE RESISTANCE BETWEEN TERMINAL "D" OF THE 6-WAY ABS MOTOR PACK HARNESS CONNECTOR AND TERMINAL "C" OF THE 6-WAY EBCM HARNESS CONNECTOR. IS RESISTANCE LESS THAN 1.5Ω?
USING THE CIRCUIT DIAGRAMS LOCATED IN THE FRONT OF THIS SECTION, PLACE THE PROPER WIRES INTO THE PROPER CONNECTOR CAVITIES. CLEAR DTCs AND RECHECK SYSTEM.
YES
NO
4 • MEASURE THE RESISTANCE BETWEEN TERMINAL "C" OF THE 6-WAY ABS MOTOR PACK HARNESS CONNECTOR AND TERMINAL "D" OF THE 6-WAY EBCM HARNESS CONNECTOR. IS RESISTANCE LESS THAN 1.5Ω?
REPAIR HIGH RESISTANCE IN CKT 1284.
YES
NO
5 • MEASURE THE RESISTANCE BETWEEN TERMINAL "C" AND TERMINAL "D" OF THE ABS MOTOR PACK CONNECTOR. IS RESISTANCE LESS THAN 1.5Ω?
REPAIR HIGH RESISTANCE IN CKT 1285.
YES
NO
6 • INSPECT THE 6-WAY ABS MOTOR PACK CONNECTOR AND 6-WAY EBCM CONNECTOR FOR POOR TERMINAL CONTACT OR CORROSION.
DO ANY TERMINALS EXHIBIT POOR CONTACT OR EVIDENCE OF CORROSION?
REPLACE ABS MOTOR PACK.
NO
YES
7 • IGNITION "OFF."
• RECONNECT ALL CONNECTORS.
• START ENGINE WITH FOOT OFF BRAKE.
• ALLOW ENGINE TO RUN FOR AT LEAST 10 SECONDS.
• REPEAT ABOVE IGNITION CYCLE SEQUENCE TWO MORE TIMES. DID DTC 42 SET IN THIS LAST THREE IGNITION CYCLES?
REPLACE TERMINALS THAT EXHIBIT POOR TERMINAL CONTACT OR EVIDENCE OF CORROSION.
YES
NO
REPLACE EBCM.
MALFUNCTION IS INTERMITTENT. REFER TO "DIAGNOSTIC AIDS"
GC402930078200BA

Fig. 150 Code A042: Right Front ESB Will Not Hold Motor. 1993 Grand Prix, 1993–94 Cutlass Supreme, Lumina & Regal

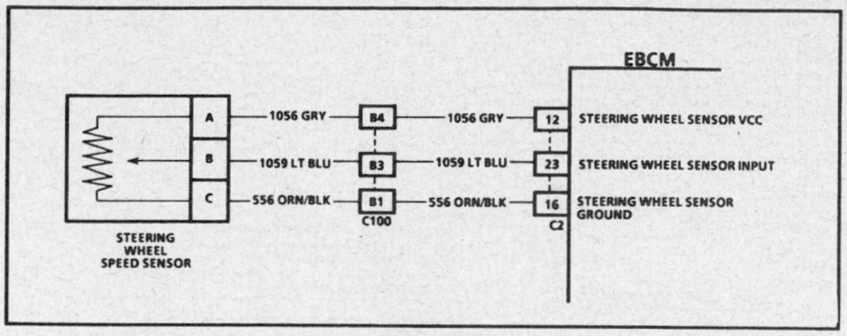
EBCM
A
B
C
1056 GRY
1059 LT BLU
556 ORN/BLK
B4
B3
B1
C100
12
23
16
C2
STEERING WHEEL SENSOR VCC
STEERING WHEEL SENSOR INPUT
STEERING WHEEL SENSOR GROUND
STEERING WHEEL SPEED SENSOR

DTC 43

(Page 1 of 3)
VES STEERING WHEEL SPEED SENSOR CIRCUIT MALFUNCTION (FOR ABS WITH VES ONLY)

Circuit Description:

A 5 volt reference is supplied to the steering wheel speed sensor through EBCM terminal "12" to sensor terminal "A". Steering wheel position input to the EBCM is provided through steering wheel speed sensor terminal "B" to EBCM terminal "23". Steering wheel speed sensor ground is provided through EBCM terminal "16".

DTC Will Set When: DTC 43 can be set anytime. A malfunction exists if the steering wheel speed sensor voltage is: less than .4 volt, greater than 4.67 volts or changes by more than 2 volts in 8 msec.

Action Taken: A malfunction DTC is stored, VES is disabled and power steering returns to full assist.

DTC Chart Test Description: Number(s) below refer to circled number(s) on the diagnostic chart.

1. Checks steering wheel speed sensor input to the EBCM.
2. Checks for a short between the steering wheel sensor input and ground circuits.
3. Checks for a short between the steering wheel sensor VCC and ground circuits.
4. Checks for a short to ground in the steering wheel sensor input circuit.
5. Checks for a short to ground in the steering wheel sensor VCC circuit.
6. Checks for high resistance in the steering wheel sensor VCC circuit.
7. Checks for high resistance in the steering wheel sensor input circuit.
8. Checks for poor terminal contact.
9. Checks for proper voltage output of the EBCM.
10. Ensures malfunction was not due to physical damage of the steering wheel speed sensor circuits.

Diagnostic Aids: An "Intermittent" malfunction is most likely caused by a poor connection, rubbed through wire insulation, or a wire that is broken inside the insulation.

The frequency of the malfunction can be checked by using the enhanced diagnostic function of the Tech 1

Any circuitry, that is suspected as causing the intermittent malfunction, should be thoroughly checked for backed out terminals, improper mating, broken locks, improperly formed or damaged terminals, poor terminal to wiring connections or physical damage to the wiring harness.

GC402940105201AX

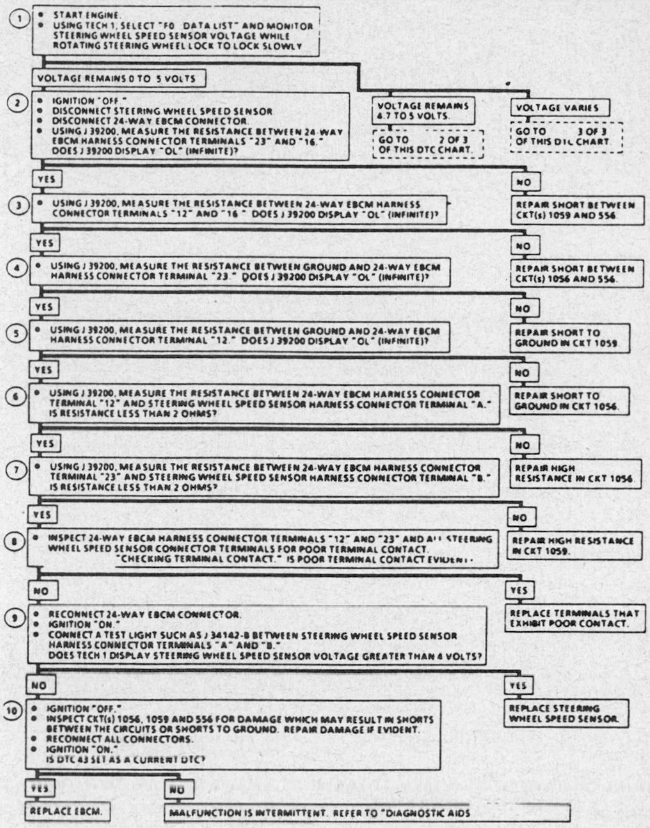
1
• START ENGINE.
• USING TECH 1, SELECT "F0 DATA LIST" AND MONITOR STEERING WHEEL SPEED SENSOR VOLTAGE WHILE ROTATING STEERING WHEEL LOCK TO LOCK SLOWLY
VOLTAGE REMAINS 0 TO 5 VOLTS
VOLTAGE REMAINS 4.7 TO 5 VOLTS.
GO TO 2 OF 3 OF THIS DTC CHART.
VOLTAGE VARIES
GO TO 3 OF 3 OF THIS DTC CHART.
2
• IGNITION "OFF."
• DISCONNECT STEERING WHEEL SPEED SENSOR
• DISCONNECT 24-WAY EBCM CONNECTOR.
• USING J 39200, MEASURE THE RESISTANCE BETWEEN 24-WAY EBCM HARNESS CONNECTOR TERMINALS "23" AND "16." DOES J 39200 DISPLAY "OL" (INFINITE)?
YES
NO
REPAIR SHORT BETWEEN CKT(s) 1059 AND 556.
3
• USING J 39200, MEASURE THE RESISTANCE BETWEEN 24-WAY EBCM HARNESS CONNECTOR TERMINALS "12" AND "16" DOES J 39200 DISPLAY "OL" (INFINITE)?
YES
NO
REPAIR SHORT BETWEEN CKT(s) 1056 AND 556.
4
• USING J 39200, MEASURE THE RESISTANCE BETWEEN GROUND AND 24-WAY EBCM HARNESS CONNECTOR TERMINAL "23." DOES J 39200 DISPLAY "OL" (INFINITE)?
YES
NO
REPAIR SHORT TO GROUND IN CKT 1059.
5
• USING J 39200, MEASURE THE RESISTANCE BETWEEN GROUND AND 24-WAY EBCM HARNESS CONNECTOR TERMINAL "12." DOES J 39200 DISPLAY "OL" (INFINITE)?
YES
NO
REPAIR SHORT TO GROUND IN CKT 1056.
6
• USING J 39200, MEASURE THE RESISTANCE BETWEEN 24-WAY EBCM HARNESS CONNECTOR TERMINAL "12" AND STEERING WHEEL SPEED SENSOR HARNESS CONNECTOR TERMINAL "A." IS RESISTANCE LESS THAN 2 OHMS?
YES
NO
REPAIR HIGH RESISTANCE IN CKT 1056.
7
• USING J 39200, MEASURE THE RESISTANCE BETWEEN 24-WAY EBCM HARNESS CONNECTOR TERMINAL "23" AND STEERING WHEEL SPEED SENSOR HARNESS CONNECTOR TERMINAL "B." IS RESISTANCE LESS THAN 2 OHMS?
YES
NO
REPAIR HIGH RESISTANCE IN CKT 1059.
8
• INSPECT 24-WAY EBCM HARNESS CONNECTOR TERMINALS "12" AND "23" AND ALL STEERING WHEEL SPEED SENSOR CONNECTOR TERMINALS FOR POOR TERMINAL CONTACT.
"CHECKING TERMINAL CONTACT." IS POOR TERMINAL CONTACT EVIDENT?
NO
YES
REPLACE TERMINALS THAT EXHIBIT POOR CONTACT.
9
• RECONNECT 24-WAY EBCM CONNECTOR.
• IGNITION "ON."
• CONNECT A TEST LIGHT SUCH AS J 34142-B BETWEEN STEERING WHEEL SPEED SENSOR HARNESS CONNECTOR TERMINALS "A" AND "B."
DOES TECH 1 DISPLAY STEERING WHEEL SPEED SENSOR VOLTAGE GREATER THAN 4 VOLTS?
NO
YES
REPLACE STEERING WHEEL SPEED SENSOR.
10
• IGNITION "OFF."
• INSPECT CKT(s) 1056, 1059 AND 556 FOR DAMAGE WHICH MAY RESULT IN SHORTS BETWEEN THE CIRCUITS OR SHORTS TO GROUND. REPAIR DAMAGE IF EVIDENT.
• RECONNECT ALL CONNECTORS.
• IGNITION "ON."
IS DTC 43 SET AS A CURRENT DTC?
YES
NO
REPLACE EBCM.
MALFUNCTION IS INTERMITTENT. REFER TO "DIAGNOSTIC AIDS

GC402940105201BX

Fig. 151 Code A043: VES Steering Wheel Speed Sensor Circuit Fault (Part 1 of 3). 1994 Achieva, Grand Am & Skylark w/VES

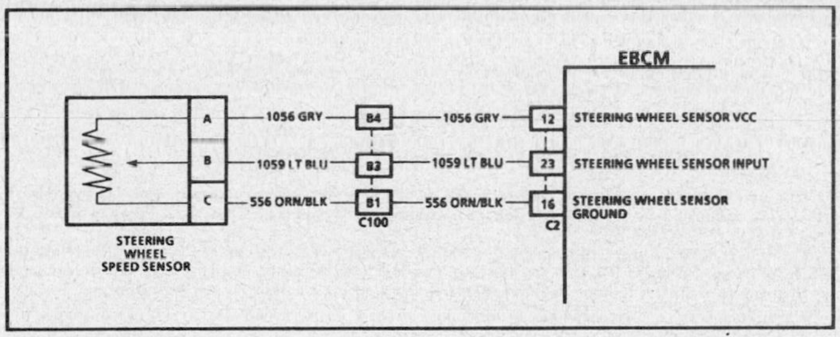
EBCM
A
B
C
1056 GRY
1059 LT BLU
556 ORN/BLK
B4
B3
B1
C100
12
23
16
C2
STEERING WHEEL SENSOR VCC
STEERING WHEEL SENSOR INPUT
STEERING WHEEL SENSOR GROUND
STEERING WHEEL SPEED SENSOR

Circuit Description:

A 5 volt reference is supplied to the steering wheel speed sensor through EBCM terminal "12" to sensor terminal "A". Steering wheel position input to the EBCM is provided through steering wheel speed sensor terminal "B" to EBCM terminal "23". Steering wheel speed sensor ground is provided through EBCM terminal "16".

DTC Will Set When: DTC 43 can be set anytime. A malfunction exists if the steering wheel speed sensor voltage is: less than .4 volt, greater than 4.67 volts or changes by more than 2 volts in 8 msec.

Action Taken: A malfunction DTC is stored, VES is disabled and power steering returns to full assist.

DTC Chart Test Description: Number(s) below refer to circled number(s) on the diagnostic chart.

11. Checks for proper voltage with the steering wheel speed sensor disconnected.
12. Checks for high resistance in the steering wheel sensor ground.
13. Isolates high resistance to the EBCM or the ground circuit.
14. Ensures open ground was not due to a short to battery.
15. Ensures malfunction was not due to circuit damage or poor terminal contact.
16. Checks for a short to B+ in the steering wheel sensor input circuit.
17. Ensures malfunction was not due to physical damage of the circuitry.

Diagnostic Aids: An "Intermittent" malfunction is most likely caused by a poor connection, rubbed through wire insulation, or a wire that is broken inside the insulation.

The frequency of the malfunction can be checked by using the enhanced diagnostic function of the Tech 1

Any circuitry, that is suspected as causing the intermittent malfunction, should be thoroughly checked for backed out terminals, improper mating, broken locks, improperly formed or damaged terminals, poor terminal to wiring connections or physical damage to the wiring harness.

GC402940105202AX

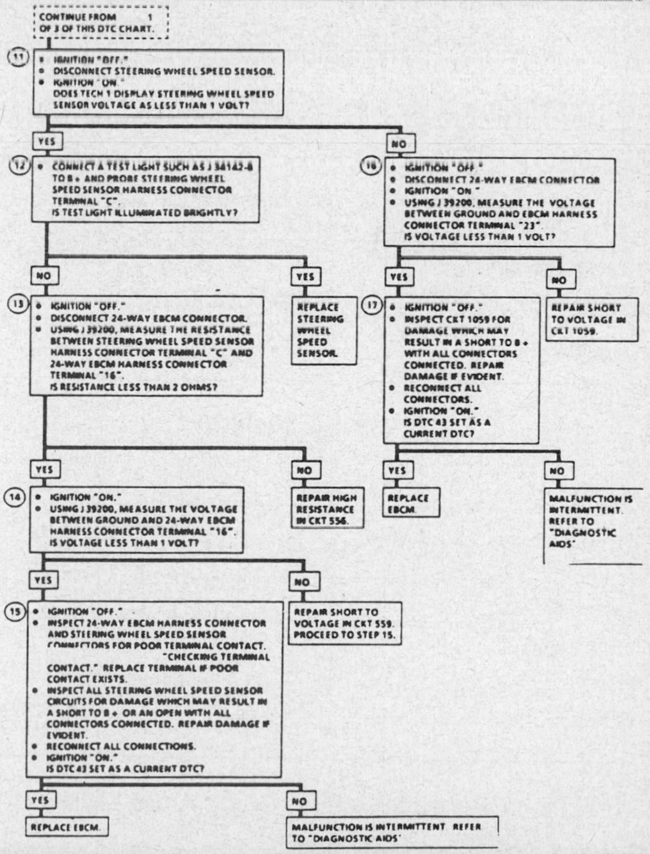
CONTINUE FROM 1 OF 3 OF THIS DTC CHART.
11
• IGNITION "OFF."
• DISCONNECT STEERING WHEEL SPEED SENSOR.
• IGNITION "ON."
DOES TECH 1 DISPLAY STEERING WHEEL SPEED SENSOR VOLTAGE AS LESS THAN 1 VOLT?
YES
NO
12
• CONNECT A TEST LIGHT SUCH AS J 34142-B TO B+ AND PROBE STEERING WHEEL SPEED SENSOR HARNESS CONNECTOR TERMINAL "C".
IS TEST LIGHT ILLUMINATED BRIGHTLY?
16
• IGNITION "OFF."
• DISCONNECT 24-WAY EBCM CONNECTOR
• IGNITION "ON."
• USING J 39200, MEASURE THE VOLTAGE BETWEEN GROUND AND EBCM HARNESS CONNECTOR TERMINAL "23".
IS VOLTAGE LESS THAN 1 VOLT?
NO
YES
REPLACE STEERING WHEEL SPEED SENSOR.
13
• IGNITION "OFF."
• DISCONNECT 24-WAY EBCM CONNECTOR.
• USING J 39200, MEASURE THE RESISTANCE BETWEEN STEERING WHEEL SPEED SENSOR HARNESS CONNECTOR TERMINAL "C" AND 24-WAY EBCM HARNESS CONNECTOR TERMINAL "16".
IS RESISTANCE LESS THAN 2 OHMS?
YES
NO
REPAIR SHORT TO VOLTAGE IN CKT 1059.
17
• IGNITION "OFF."
• INSPECT CKT 1059 FOR DAMAGE WHICH MAY RESULT IN A SHORT TO B+ WITH ALL CONNECTORS CONNECTED. REPAIR DAMAGE IF EVIDENT.
• RECONNECT ALL CONNECTORS.
• IGNITION "ON."
IS DTC 43 SET AS A CURRENT DTC?
YES
NO
REPAIR HIGH RESISTANCE IN CKT 556.
YES
NO
REPLACE EBCM.
MALFUNCTION IS INTERMITTENT. REFER TO "DIAGNOSTIC AIDS"
14
• IGNITION "ON."
• USING J 39200, MEASURE THE VOLTAGE BETWEEN GROUND AND 24-WAY EBCM HARNESS CONNECTOR TERMINAL "16".
IS VOLTAGE LESS THAN 1 VOLT?
YES
NO
REPAIR SHORT TO VOLTAGE IN CKT 559. PROCEED TO STEP 15.
15
• IGNITION "OFF."
• INSPECT 24-WAY EBCM HARNESS CONNECTOR AND STEERING WHEEL SPEED SENSOR CONNECTORS FOR POOR TERMINAL CONTACT.
"CHECKING TERMINAL CONTACT." REPLACE TERMINAL IF POOR CONTACT EXISTS.
• INSPECT ALL STEERING WHEEL SPEED SENSOR CIRCUITS FOR DAMAGE WHICH MAY RESULT IN A SHORT TO B+ OR AN OPEN WITH ALL CONNECTORS CONNECTED. REPAIR DAMAGE IF EVIDENT.
• RECONNECT ALL CONNECTIONS.
• IGNITION "ON."
IS DTC 43 SET AS A CURRENT DTC?
YES
NO
REPLACE EBCM.
MALFUNCTION IS INTERMITTENT. REFER TO "DIAGNOSTIC AIDS"

Fig. 151 Code A043: VES Steering Wheel Speed Sensor Circuit Fault (Part 2 of 3). 1994 Achieva, Grand Am & Skylark w/VES

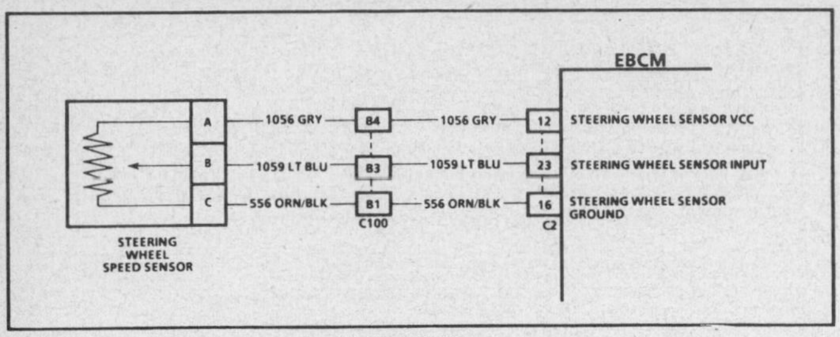
EBCM
A
B
C
1056 GRY
1059 LT BLU
556 ORN/BLK
B4
B3
B1
C100
12
23
16
C2
STEERING WHEEL SENSOR VCC
STEERING WHEEL SENSOR INPUT
STEERING WHEEL SENSOR GROUND
STEERING WHEEL SPEED SENSOR

DTC 43

(Page 3 of 3)

VES STEERING WHEEL SPEED SENSOR CIRCUIT MALFUNCTION (FOR ABS WITH VES ONLY)

Circuit Description:

A 5 volt reference is supplied to the steering wheel speed sensor through EBCM terminal "12" to sensor terminal "A". Steering wheel position input to the EBCM is provided through steering wheel speed sensor terminal "B" to EBCM terminal "23". Steering wheel speed sensor ground is provided through EBCM terminal "16".

DTC Will Set When: DTC 43 can be set anytime. A malfunction exists if the steering wheel speed sensor voltage is: less than .4 volt, greater than 4.67 volts or changes by more than 2 volts in 8 msec.

Action Taken: A malfunction DTC is stored, VES is disabled and power steering returns to full assist.

DTC Chart Test Description: Number(s) below refer to circled number(s) on the diagnostic chart.

18. Checks for proper voltage with the steering wheel speed sensor connected.
19. Checks for proper voltage with the steering wheel speed sensor disconnected.
20. Checks for a short to voltage in the steering wheel sensor VCC circuit.
21. Ensures malfunction was not due to physical damage of the circuitry.
22. Checks for a short between the steering wheel sensor VCC and input circuits.
23. Checks for proper resistance of the steering wheel speed sensor.
24. Ensures malfunction was not due to physical damage of the circuits.
25. Checks for an open resistor in the steering wheel speed sensor.

Diagnostic Aids: An "Intermittent" malfunction is most likely caused by a poor connection, rubbed through wire insulation, or a wire that is broken inside the insulation.

The frequency of the malfunction can be checked by using the enhanced diagnostic function of the Tech 1

Any circuitry, that is suspected as causing the intermittent malfunction, should be thoroughly checked for backed out terminals, improper mating, broken locks, improperly formed or damaged terminals, poor terminal to wiring connections or physical damage to the wiring harness.

GC402940105203AX

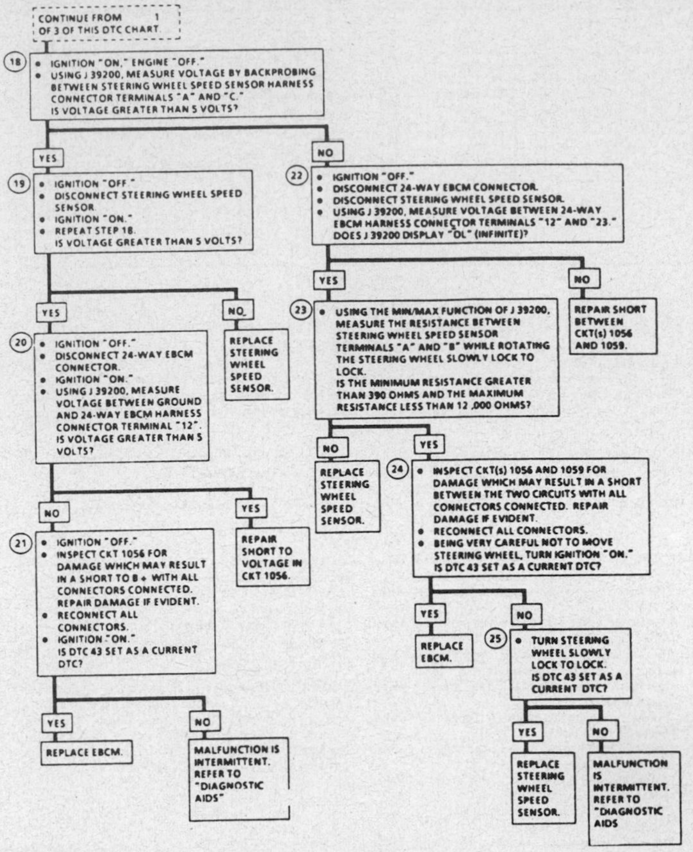
CONTINUE FROM 1 OF 3 OF THIS DTC CHART.
18
• IGNITION "ON," ENGINE "OFF."
• USING J 39200, MEASURE VOLTAGE BY BACKPROBING BETWEEN STEERING WHEEL SPEED SENSOR HARNESS CONNECTOR TERMINALS "A" AND "C."
IS VOLTAGE GREATER THAN 5 VOLTS?
YES
NO
19
• IGNITION "OFF."
• DISCONNECT STEERING WHEEL SPEED SENSOR.
• IGNITION "ON."
• REPEAT STEP 18.
IS VOLTAGE GREATER THAN 5 VOLTS?
22
• IGNITION "OFF."
• DISCONNECT 24-WAY EBCM CONNECTOR.
• DISCONNECT STEERING WHEEL SPEED SENSOR.
• USING J 39200, MEASURE VOLTAGE BETWEEN 24-WAY EBCM HARNESS CONNECTOR TERMINALS "12" AND "23."
DOES J 39200 DISPLAY "OL" (INFINITE)?
YES
NO
REPLACE STEERING WHEEL SPEED SENSOR.
20
• IGNITION "OFF."
• DISCONNECT 24-WAY EBCM CONNECTOR.
• IGNITION "ON."
• USING J 39200, MEASURE VOLTAGE BETWEEN GROUND AND 24-WAY EBCM HARNESS CONNECTOR TERMINAL "12".
IS VOLTAGE GREATER THAN 5 VOLTS?
23
• USING THE MIN/MAX FUNCTION OF J 39200, MEASURE THE RESISTANCE BETWEEN STEERING WHEEL SPEED SENSOR TERMINALS "A" AND "B" WHILE ROTATING THE STEERING WHEEL SLOWLY LOCK TO LOCK.
IS THE MINIMUM RESISTANCE GREATER THAN 390 OHMS AND THE MAXIMUM RESISTANCE LESS THAN 12,000 OHMS?
REPAIR SHORT BETWEEN CKT(s) 1056 AND 1059.
REPLACE STEERING WHEEL SPEED SENSOR.
24
• INSPECT CKT(s) 1056 AND 1059 FOR DAMAGE WHICH MAY RESULT IN A SHORT BETWEEN THE TWO CIRCUITS WITH ALL CONNECTORS CONNECTED. REPAIR DAMAGE IF EVIDENT.
• RECONNECT ALL CONNECTORS.
• BEING VERY CAREFUL NOT TO MOVE STEERING WHEEL, TURN IGNITION "ON."
IS DTC 43 SET AS A CURRENT DTC?
REPAIR SHORT TO VOLTAGE IN CKT 1056.
21
• IGNITION "OFF."
• INSPECT CKT 1056 FOR DAMAGE WHICH MAY RESULT IN A SHORT TO B+ WITH ALL CONNECTORS CONNECTED. REPAIR DAMAGE IF EVIDENT.
• RECONNECT ALL CONNECTORS.
• IGNITION "ON."
IS DTC 43 SET AS A CURRENT DTC?
REPLACE EBCM.
25
• TURN STEERING WHEEL SLOWLY LOCK TO LOCK.
IS DTC 43 SET AS A CURRENT DTC?
REPLACE EBCM.
MALFUNCTION IS INTERMITTENT. REFER TO "DIAGNOSTIC AIDS"
REPLACE STEERING WHEEL SPEED SENSOR.
MALFUNCTION IS INTERMITTENT. REFER TO "DIAGNOSTIC AIDS"

GC402940105203BX

Fig. 151 Code A043: VES Steering Wheel Speed Sensor Circuit Fault (Part 3 of 3). 1994 Achieva, Grand Am & Skylark w/VES

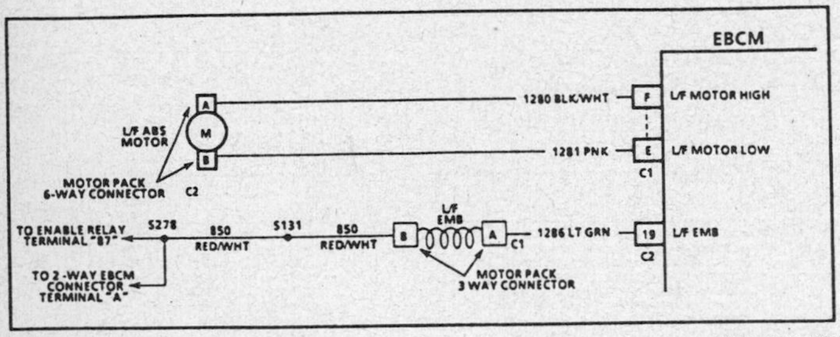
EBCM
L/F ABS MOTOR
M
A
B
1280 BLK/WHT
1281 PNK
F
E
C1
L/F MOTOR HIGH
L/F MOTOR LOW
MOTOR PACK 6-WAY CONNECTOR
C2
TO ENABLE RELAY TERMINAL "87"
S278
850 RED/WHT
S131
850 RED/WHT
L/F EMB
1286 LT GRN
19
L/F EMB
MOTOR PACK 3 WAY CONNECTOR
TO 2-WAY EBCM CONNECTOR TERMINAL "A"

GC402930078300AX

Cavalier & Sunbird

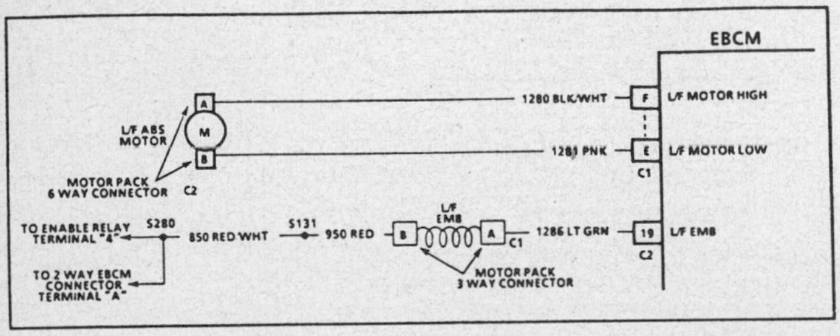
EBCM
L/F ABS MOTOR
1280 BLK/WHT
1281 PNK
L/F MOTOR HIGH
L/F MOTOR LOW
MOTOR PACK 6 WAY CONNECTOR
C2
C1
TO ENABLE RELAY TERMINAL "4"
S280
850 RED WHT
S131
950 RED
L/F EMB
1286 LT GRN
19
L/F EMB
MOTOR PACK 3 WAY CONNECTOR
TO 2 WAY EBCM CONNECTOR TERMINAL "A"

GC402930078300BX

Achieva, Beretta, Corsica, Grand Am & Skylark

DTC A044

LEFT FRONT CHANNEL WILL NOT MOVE

Circuit Description:

Current is supplied to the EMB through terminal "B" of the three way motor pack connector. When a release of the EMB is commanded, the EBCM grounds the EMB input and allows the EMB to be energized to release the motor.

This DTC is designed to detect non-actuating EMB, stuck motor or a seized hydraulic modulator. When the release is commanded during initialization, the EMB should release the motor, resulting in sensed current being less than commanded current (motor is spinning freely). If the motor is not moving, sensed current will be equal to stall current.

Failure Condition:

DTC A044 can be set at 5 km/h (3 mph). If the EBCM detects a condition in which it cannot move the motor in either direction, a malfunction exists.

Action Taken:

This malfunction indicates the channel can not be moved properly. A malfunction DTC is stored, ABS is disabled and the ABS indicator lamp is turned "ON."

Test Description: Number(s) below refer to circled number(s) on the diagnostic chart.

1. This step ensures motor circuits are in the proper connector cavity.
2. This step checks for motor movement during release.
3. This procedure compares feedback current to command current during apply.
4. This step checks to see if hydraulic modulator is functioning properly.
5. This step checks if motor can apply properly under load.
6. This step serves to isolate the malfunction to either the EBCM or a short between CKTs 1280 and 1281.

Diagnostic Aids:

An "Intermittent" malfunction in this DTC may result from a mechanical part of the system that sticks, binds, or slips.

The frequency of the malfunction can be checked by using the enhanced diagnostic function of the Tech 1

DTC A044 may set after modulator disassembly if the modulator pistons are positioned at the bottom of their bore.

Any circuitry, that is suspected as causing the intermittent complaint, should be thoroughly checked for backed out terminals, improper mating, broken locks, improperly formed or damaged terminals, poor terminal to wiring connections or physical damage to the wiring harness.

NOTICE: This DTC may fail if low voltage (10 volts or less) was present when initialization occurred. Ensure battery/charging system is functioning properly.

GC402930078300CX

Fig. 152 Code A044: Left Front Channel Will Not Move (Part 1 of 2). 1993-94 Cavalier, Sunbird, Beretta, Corsica & Achieva, Grand Am & Skylark Less VES

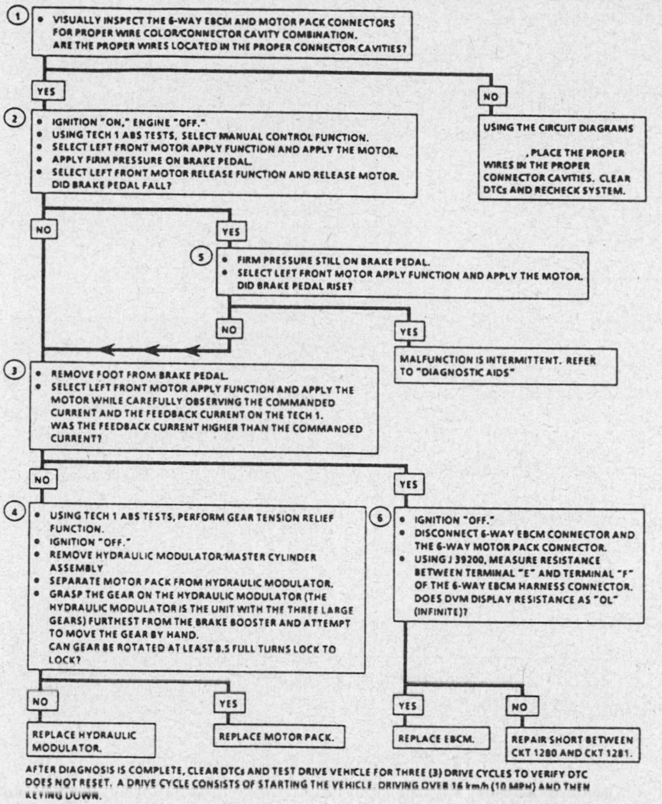
1
VISUALLY INSPECT THE 6-WAY EBCM AND MOTOR PACK CONNECTORS FOR PROPER WIRE COLOR/CONNECTOR CAVITY COMBINATION. ARE THE PROPER WIRES LOCATED IN THE PROPER CONNECTOR CAVITIES?
YES
NO
USING THE CIRCUIT DIAGRAMS , PLACE THE PROPER WIRES IN THE PROPER CONNECTOR CAVITIES. CLEAR DTCs AND RECHECK SYSTEM.
2
IGNITION "ON," ENGINE "OFF."
USING TECH 1 ABS TESTS, SELECT MANUAL CONTROL FUNCTION.
SELECT LEFT FRONT MOTOR APPLY FUNCTION AND APPLY THE MOTOR.
APPLY FIRM PRESSURE ON BRAKE PEDAL.
SELECT LEFT FRONT MOTOR RELEASE FUNCTION AND RELEASE MOTOR. DID BRAKE PEDAL FALL?
NO
YES
5
FIRM PRESSURE STILL ON BRAKE PEDAL.
SELECT LEFT FRONT MOTOR APPLY FUNCTION AND APPLY THE MOTOR. DID BRAKE PEDAL RISE?
NO
YES
MALFUNCTION IS INTERMITTENT. REFER TO "DIAGNOSTIC AIDS"
3
REMOVE FOOT FROM BRAKE PEDAL.
SELECT LEFT FRONT MOTOR APPLY FUNCTION AND APPLY THE MOTOR WHILE CAREFULLY OBSERVING THE COMMANDED CURRENT AND THE FEEDBACK CURRENT ON THE TECH 1. WAS THE FEEDBACK CURRENT HIGHER THAN THE COMMANDED CURRENT?
NO
YES
4
USING TECH 1 ABS TESTS, PERFORM GEAR TENSION RELIEF FUNCTION.
IGNITION "OFF."
REMOVE HYDRAULIC MODULATOR/MASTER CYLINDER ASSEMBLY
SEPARATE MOTOR PACK FROM HYDRAULIC MODULATOR.
GRASP THE GEAR ON THE HYDRAULIC MODULATOR (THE HYDRAULIC MODULATOR IS THE UNIT WITH THE THREE LARGE GEARS) FURTHEST FROM THE BRAKE BOOSTER AND ATTEMPT TO MOVE THE GEAR BY HAND. CAN GEAR BE ROTATED AT LEAST 8.5 FULL TURNS LOCK TO LOCK?
6
IGNITION "OFF."
DISCONNECT 6-WAY EBCM CONNECTOR AND THE 6-WAY MOTOR PACK CONNECTOR.
USING J 39200, MEASURE RESISTANCE BETWEEN TERMINAL "E" AND TERMINAL "F" OF THE 6-WAY EBCM HARNESS CONNECTOR. DOES DVM DISPLAY RESISTANCE AS "OL" (INFINITE)?
NO
YES
YES
NO
REPLACE HYDRAULIC MODULATOR.
REPLACE MOTOR PACK.
REPLACE EBCM.
REPAIR SHORT BETWEEN CKT 1280 AND CKT 1281.
AFTER DIAGNOSIS IS COMPLETE, CLEAR DTCs AND TEST DRIVE VEHICLE FOR THREE (3) DRIVE CYCLES TO VERIFY DTC DOES NOT RESET. A DRIVE CYCLE CONSISTS OF STARTING THE VEHICLE, DRIVING OVER 16 km/h (10 MPH) AND THEN KEYING DOWN.

GC402930078300DX

Fig. 152 Code A044: Left Front Channel Will Not Move (Part 2 of 2). 1993-94 Cavalier, Sunbird, Beretta, Corsica & Achieva, Grand Am & Skylark Less VES

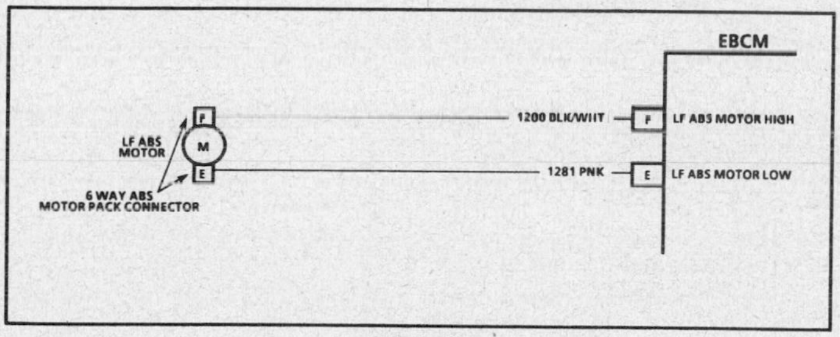
EBCM
F
M
E
LF ABS MOTOR
6 WAY ABS MOTOR PACK CONNECTOR
1280 BLK/WHT
F
LF ABS MOTOR HIGH
1281 PNK
E
LF ABS MOTOR LOW

DTC 44

LEFT FRONT CHANNEL WILL NOT MOVE

Circuit Description:

This DTC is designed to detect bound-up ESB, a stuck ABS motor, or a seized hydraulic modulator. When the release is commanded during initialization, the ESB should release the ABS motor, resulting in sensed current being less than commanded current (motor is spinning freely). If the ABS motor is not moving, sensed current will be equal to stall current.

DTC Will Set When: DTC 44 can be set during normal operation. If the EBCM detects a condition in which it cannot move the ABS motor in either direction, a malfunction exists.

Action Taken: This malfunction indicates the channel cannot be moved properly. A malfunction DTC is stored, ABS is disabled and the ABS warning lamp is turned "ON."

DTC Chart Test Description: Number(s) below refer to circled number(s) on the diagnostic chart.

1. Ensures that proper motor circuits are located in the proper connector cavities.
2. Checks for proper ABS motor movement during apply and release commands from the Tech 1.
3. Compares EBCM command current to ABS motor feedback current.
4. Checks for short between CKTs 1280 and 1281.
5. Checks for an ABS motor that is internally shorted.
6. Determines if the malfunction is caused by a defective EBCM or by a short circuit.
7. Verifies that the ABS motor can actually apply when commanded.
8. Checks for proper hydraulic modulator gear and piston movement.

Diagnostic Aids: An "Intermittent" malfunction in this DTC may result from a mechanical part of the system that sticks, binds, or slips.

The frequency of the malfunction can be checked by using the enhanced diagnostic function of the Tech 1.

DTC 44 may set after modulator disassembly if the modulator pistons are positioned at the bottom of their bore.

Any circuitry, that is suspected as causing the intermittent complaint, should be thoroughly checked for backed out terminals, improper mating, broken locks, improperly formed or damaged terminals, poor terminal to wiring connections or physical damage to the wiring harness.

GC402930078400AA

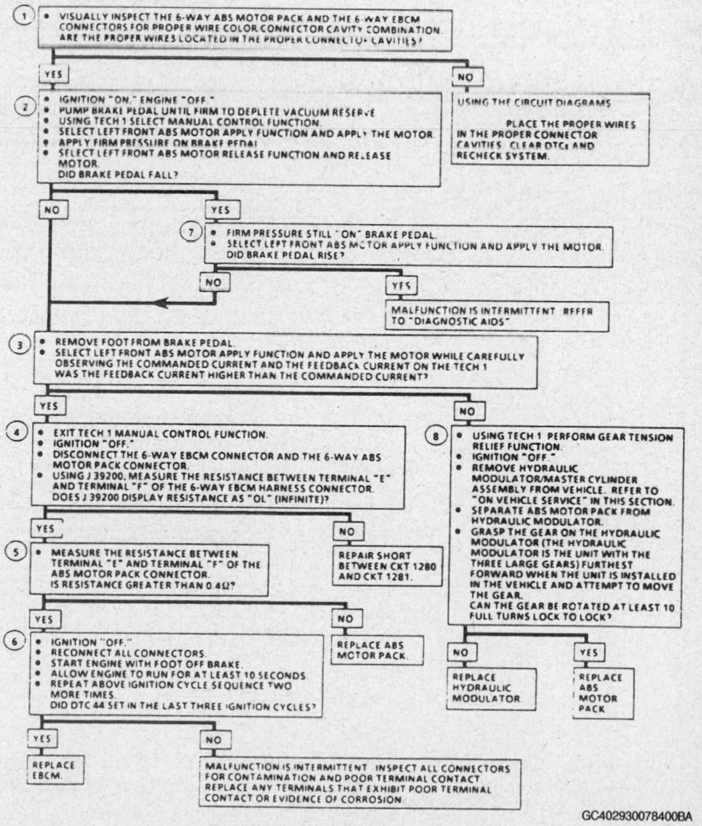
1
VISUALLY INSPECT THE 6-WAY ABS MOTOR PACK AND THE 6-WAY EBCM CONNECTORS FOR PROPER WIRE COLOR CONNECTOR CAVITY COMBINATION. ARE THE PROPER WIRES LOCATED IN THE PROPER CONNECTOR CAVITIES?
YES
NO
USING THE CIRCUIT DIAGRAMS PLACE THE PROPER WIRES IN THE PROPER CONNECTOR CAVITIES. CLEAR DTCs AND RECHECK SYSTEM.
2
IGNITION "ON," ENGINE "OFF."
PUMP BRAKE PEDAL UNTIL FIRM TO DEPLETE VACUUM RESERVE
USING TECH 1 SELECT MANUAL CONTROL FUNCTION.
SELECT LEFT FRONT ABS MOTOR APPLY FUNCTION AND APPLY THE MOTOR.
APPLY FIRM PRESSURE ON BRAKE PEDAL
SELECT LEFT FRONT ABS MOTOR RELEASE FUNCTION AND RELEASE MOTOR. DID BRAKE PEDAL FALL?
NO
YES
7
FIRM PRESSURE STILL "ON" BRAKE PEDAL.
SELECT LEFT FRONT ABS MOTOR APPLY FUNCTION AND APPLY THE MOTOR. DID BRAKE PEDAL RISE?
NO
YES
MALFUNCTION IS INTERMITTENT. REFER TO "DIAGNOSTIC AIDS"
3
REMOVE FOOT FROM BRAKE PEDAL.
SELECT LEFT FRONT ABS MOTOR APPLY FUNCTION AND APPLY THE MOTOR WHILE CAREFULLY OBSERVING THE COMMANDED CURRENT AND THE FEEDBACK CURRENT ON THE TECH 1 WAS THE FEEDBACK CURRENT HIGHER THAN THE COMMANDED CURRENT?
YES
NO
4
EXIT TECH 1 MANUAL CONTROL FUNCTION.
IGNITION "OFF."
DISCONNECT THE 6-WAY EBCM CONNECTOR AND THE 6-WAY ABS MOTOR PACK CONNECTOR.
USING J 39200, MEASURE THE RESISTANCE BETWEEN TERMINAL "E" AND TERMINAL "F" OF THE 6-WAY EBCM HARNESS CONNECTOR. DOES J 39200 DISPLAY RESISTANCE AS "OL" (INFINITE)?
8
USING TECH 1 PERFORM GEAR TENSION RELIEF FUNCTION.
IGNITION "OFF."
REMOVE HYDRAULIC MODULATOR/MASTER CYLINDER ASSEMBLY FROM VEHICLE. REFER TO "ON VEHICLE SERVICE" IN THIS SECTION.
SEPARATE ABS MOTOR PACK FROM HYDRAULIC MODULATOR.
GRASP THE GEAR ON THE HYDRAULIC MODULATOR (THE HYDRAULIC MODULATOR IS THE UNIT WITH THE THREE LARGE GEARS) FURTHEST FORWARD WHEN THE UNIT IS INSTALLED IN THE VEHICLE AND ATTEMPT TO MOVE THE GEAR. CAN THE GEAR BE ROTATED AT LEAST 10 FULL TURNS LOCK TO LOCK?
YES
NO
REPAIR SHORT BETWEEN CKT 1280 AND CKT 1281.
5
MEASURE THE RESISTANCE BETWEEN TERMINAL "E" AND TERMINAL "F" OF THE ABS MOTOR PACK CONNECTOR. IS RESISTANCE GREATER THAN 0.4Ω?
YES
NO
REPLACE ABS MOTOR PACK.
NO
YES
REPLACE HYDRAULIC MODULATOR
REPLACE ABS MOTOR PACK
6
IGNITION "OFF."
RECONNECT ALL CONNECTORS.
START ENGINE WITH FOOT OFF BRAKE.
ALLOW ENGINE TO RUN FOR AT LEAST 10 SECONDS.
REPEAT ABOVE IGNITION CYCLE SEQUENCE TWO MORE TIMES. DID DTC 44 SET IN THE LAST THREE IGNITION CYCLES?
YES
NO
REPLACE EBCM.
MALFUNCTION IS INTERMITTENT. INSPECT ALL CONNECTORS FOR CONTAMINATION AND POOR TERMINAL CONTACT. REPLACE ANY TERMINALS THAT EXHIBIT POOR TERMINAL CONTACT OR EVIDENCE OF CORROSION.

GC402930078400BA

Fig. 153 Code A044: Left Front Channel Will Not Move. 1993 Grand Prix, 1993–94 Cutlass Supreme, Lumina & Regal

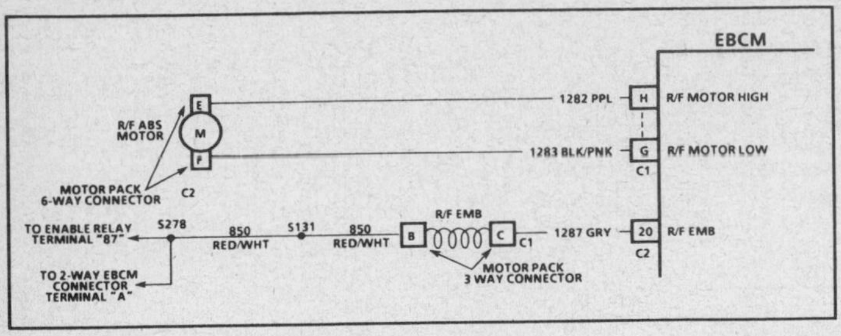
EBCM
1282 PPL
H
R/F MOTOR HIGH
R/F ABS MOTOR
E
M
F
1283 BLK/PNK
G
R/F MOTOR LOW
C1
MOTOR PACK 6-WAY CONNECTOR
C2
R/F EMB
TO ENABLE RELAY TERMINAL "87"
S278
850 RED/WHT
S131
850 RED/WHT
B
C
C1
1287 GRY
20
R/F EMB
C2
MOTOR PACK 3 WAY CONNECTOR
TO 2-WAY EBCM CONNECTOR TERMINAL "A"

GC402930078500AX

Cavalier & Sunbird

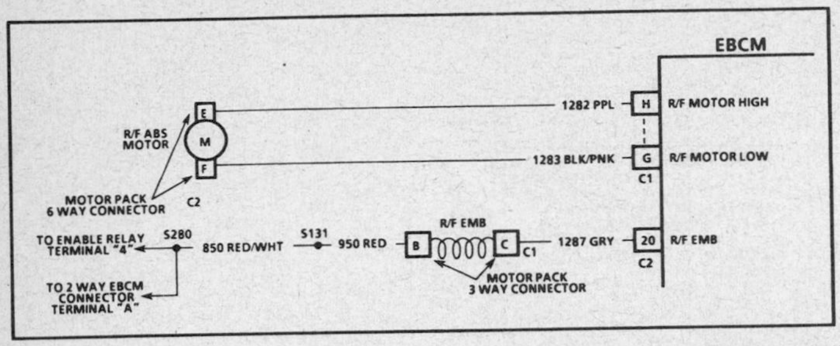
EBCM
1282 PPL
H
R/F MOTOR HIGH
R/F ABS MOTOR
E
M
F
1283 BLK/PNK
G
R/F MOTOR LOW
C1
MOTOR PACK 6 WAY CONNECTOR
C2
R/F EMB
TO ENABLE RELAY TERMINAL "4"
S280
850 RED/WHT
S131
950 RED
B
C
C1
1287 GRY
20
R/F EMB
C2
MOTOR PACK 3 WAY CONNECTOR
TO 2 WAY EBCM CONNECTOR TERMINAL "A"

GC402930078500BX

Achieva, Beretta, Corsica, Grand Am & Skylark

DTC A045

RIGHT FRONT CHANNEL WILL NOT MOVE

Circuit Description:

Current is supplied to the EMB through terminal "B" of the three way motor pack connector. When a release of the EMB is commanded, the EBCM grounds the EMB input and allows the EMB to be energized to release the motor.

This DTC is designed to detect non-actuating EMB, stuck motor or a seized hydraulic modulator. When the release is commanded during initialization, the EMB should release the motor, resulting in sensed current being less than commanded current (motor is spinning freely). If the motor is not moving, sensed current will be equal to stall current.

Failure Condition:

DTC A045 can be set at 5 km/h (3 mph). If the EBCM detects a condition in which it cannot move the motor in either direction, a malfunction exists.

Action Taken:

This malfunction indicates the channel can not be moved properly. A malfunction DTC is stored, ABS is disabled and the ABS indicator lamp is turned "ON."

Test Description: Number(s) below refer to circled number(s) on the diagnostic chart

1. This step ensures motor circuits are in the proper connector cavity.
2. This step checks for the motor movement during release.
3. This procedure compares feedback current to command current during apply.
4. This step checks to see if hydraulic modulator is functioning properly.
5. This step checks if motor can apply properly under load.
6. This step serves to isolate the malfunction to either the EBCM or a short between CKTs 1282 and 1283.

Diagnostic Aids:

An "Intermittent" malfunction in this DTC may result from a mechanical part of the system that sticks, binds, or slips.

The frequency of the malfunction can be checked by using the enhanced diagnostic function of the Tech 1.

DTC A045 may set after modulator disassembly if the modulator pistons are positioned at the bottom of their bore.

Any circuitry, that is suspected as causing the intermittent complaint, should be thoroughly checked for backed out terminals, improper mating, broken locks, improperly formed or damaged terminals, poor terminal to wiring connections or physical damage to the wiring harness.

NOTICE: This DTC may fail if low voltage (10 volts or less) was present when initialization occurred. Ensure battery/charging system is functioning properly.

GC402930078500CX

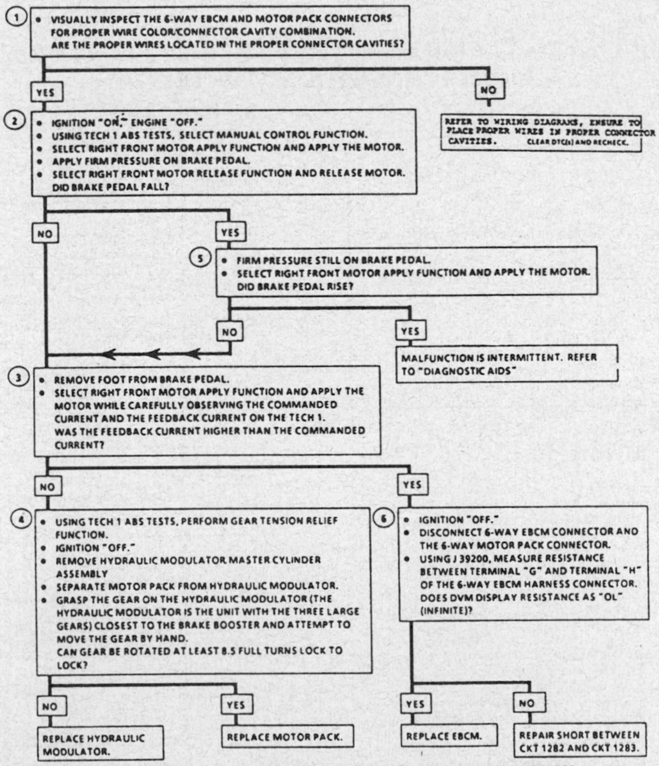
1
• VISUALLY INSPECT THE 6-WAY EBCM AND MOTOR PACK CONNECTORS FOR PROPER WIRE COLOR/CONNECTOR CAVITY COMBINATION.
ARE THE PROPER WIRES LOCATED IN THE PROPER CONNECTOR CAVITIES?
YES
NO
REFER TO WIRING DIAGRAMS, ENSURE TO PLACE PROPER WIRES IN PROPER CONNECTOR CAVITIES. CLEAR DTC(s) AND RECHECK.
2
• IGNITION "ON," ENGINE "OFF."
• USING TECH 1 ABS TESTS, SELECT MANUAL CONTROL FUNCTION.
• SELECT RIGHT FRONT MOTOR APPLY FUNCTION AND APPLY THE MOTOR.
• APPLY FIRM PRESSURE ON BRAKE PEDAL.
• SELECT RIGHT FRONT MOTOR RELEASE FUNCTION AND RELEASE MOTOR.
DID BRAKE PEDAL FALL?
NO
YES
5
• FIRM PRESSURE STILL ON BRAKE PEDAL.
• SELECT RIGHT FRONT MOTOR APPLY FUNCTION AND APPLY THE MOTOR.
DID BRAKE PEDAL RISE?
NO
YES
MALFUNCTION IS INTERMITTENT. REFER TO "DIAGNOSTIC AIDS"
3
• REMOVE FOOT FROM BRAKE PEDAL.
• SELECT RIGHT FRONT MOTOR APPLY FUNCTION AND APPLY THE MOTOR WHILE CAREFULLY OBSERVING THE COMMANDED CURRENT AND THE FEEDBACK CURRENT ON THE TECH 1.
WAS THE FEEDBACK CURRENT HIGHER THAN THE COMMANDED CURRENT?
NO
YES
4
• USING TECH 1 ABS TESTS, PERFORM GEAR TENSION RELIEF FUNCTION.
• IGNITION "OFF."
• REMOVE HYDRAULIC MODULATOR MASTER CYLINDER ASSEMBLY
• SEPARATE MOTOR PACK FROM HYDRAULIC MODULATOR.
• GRASP THE GEAR ON THE HYDRAULIC MODULATOR (THE HYDRAULIC MODULATOR IS THE UNIT WITH THE THREE LARGE GEARS) CLOSEST TO THE BRAKE BOOSTER AND ATTEMPT TO MOVE THE GEAR BY HAND.
CAN GEAR BE ROTATED AT LEAST 8.5 FULL TURNS LOCK TO LOCK?
6
• IGNITION "OFF."
• DISCONNECT 6-WAY EBCM CONNECTOR AND THE 6-WAY MOTOR PACK CONNECTOR.
• USING J 39200, MEASURE RESISTANCE BETWEEN TERMINAL "G" AND TERMINAL "H" OF THE 6-WAY EBCM HARNESS CONNECTOR.
DOES DVM DISPLAY RESISTANCE AS "OL" (INFINITE)?
NO
YES
YES
NO
REPLACE HYDRAULIC MODULATOR.
REPLACE MOTOR PACK.
REPLACE EBCM.
REPAIR SHORT BETWEEN CKT 1282 AND CKT 1283.

AFTER DIAGNOSIS IS COMPLETE, CLEAR DTCs AND TEST DRIVE VEHICLE FOR THREE (3) DRIVE CYCLES TO VERIFY DTC DOES NOT RESET. A DRIVE CYCLE CONSISTS OF STARTING THE VEHICLE, DRIVING OVER 16 km/h (10 MPH) AND THEN KEYING DOWN.

GC402930078500DX

Fig. 154 Code A045: Right Front Channel Will Not Move. 1993–94 Cavalier, Sunbird, Beretta, Corsica & Achieva, Grand Am & Skylark Less VES

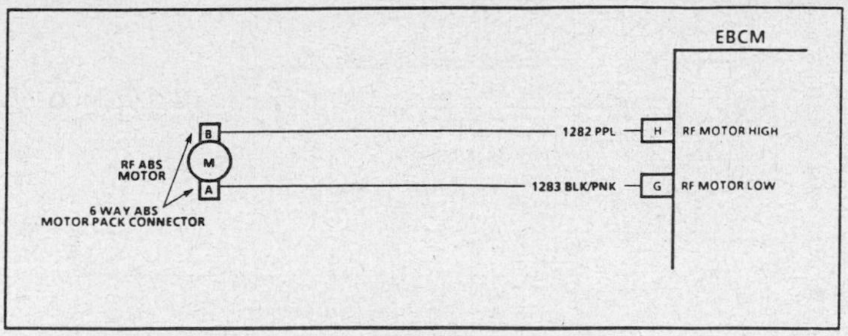
EBCM
RF ABS MOTOR
M
B
A
6 WAY ABS MOTOR PACK CONNECTOR
1282 PPL
H
RF MOTOR HIGH
1283 BLK/PNK
G
RF MOTOR LOW

DTC 45

RIGHT FRONT CHANNEL WILL NOT MOVE

Circuit Description:

This DTC is designed to detect bound-up ESB, a stuck ABS motor, or a seized hydraulic modulator. When the release is commanded during initialization, the ESB should release the ABS motor, resulting in sensed current being less than commanded current (motor is spinning freely). If the ABS motor is not moving, sensed current will be equal to stall current.

DTC Will Set When: DTC 45 can be set during normal operation. If the EBCM detects a condition in which it cannot move the ABS motor in either direction, a malfunction exists.

Action Taken: This malfunction indicates the channel cannot be moved properly. A malfunction DTC is stored, ABS is disabled and the ABS warning lamp is turned "ON."

DTC Chart Test Description: Number(s) below refer to circled number(s) on the diagnostic chart.

1. Ensures that proper motor circuits are located in the proper connector cavities.
2. Checks for proper ABS motor movement during apply and release commands from the Tech 1.
3. Compares EBCM command current to ABS motor feedback current.
4. Checks for short between CKT 1282 and CKT 1283.
5. Checks for an ABS motor that is internally shorted.
6. Checks to see if malfunction is due to poor terminal contact or the EBCM.
7. Verifies that the motor can actually apply when commanded.
8. Checks for proper hydraulic modulator gear and piston movement.

Diagnostic Aids: An "Intermittent" malfunction in this DTC may result from a mechanical part of the system that sticks, binds, or slips.

The frequency of the malfunction can be checked by using the enhanced diagnostic function of the Tech 1.

DTC 45 may set after modulator disassembly if the modulator pistons are positioned at the bottom of their bore.

Any circuitry, that is suspected as causing the intermittent complaint, should be thoroughly checked for backed out terminals, improper mating, broken locks, improperly formed or damaged terminals, poor terminal to wiring connections or physical damage to the wiring harness.

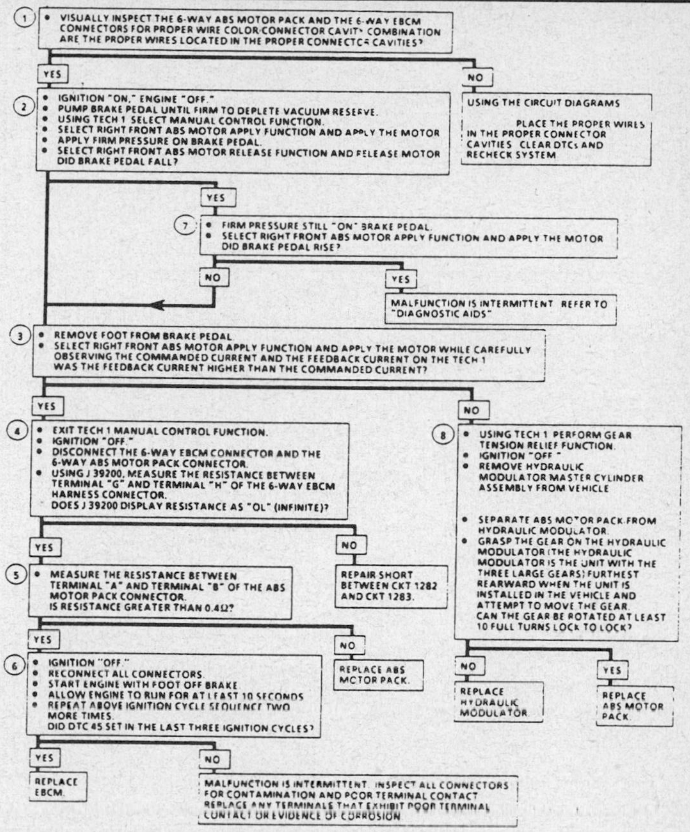
1
• VISUALLY INSPECT THE 6-WAY ABS MOTOR PACK AND THE 6-WAY EBCM CONNECTORS FOR PROPER WIRE COLOR/CONNECTOR CAVITY COMBINATION ARE THE PROPER WIRES LOCATED IN THE PROPER CONNECTOR CAVITIES?
YES
NO
USING THE CIRCUIT DIAGRAMS PLACE THE PROPER WIRES IN THE PROPER CONNECTOR CAVITIES. CLEAR DTCs AND RECHECK SYSTEM.
2
• IGNITION "ON," ENGINE "OFF."
• PUMP BRAKE PEDAL UNTIL FIRM TO DEPLETE VACUUM RESERVE.
• USING TECH 1 SELECT MANUAL CONTROL FUNCTION.
• SELECT RIGHT FRONT ABS MOTOR APPLY FUNCTION AND APPLY THE MOTOR
• APPLY FIRM PRESSURE ON BRAKE PEDAL.
• SELECT RIGHT FRONT ABS MOTOR RELEASE FUNCTION AND RELEASE MOTOR DID BRAKE PEDAL FALL?
YES
7
• FIRM PRESSURE STILL "ON" BRAKE PEDAL.
• SELECT RIGHT FRONT ABS MOTOR APPLY FUNCTION AND APPLY THE MOTOR DID BRAKE PEDAL RISE?
NO
YES
MALFUNCTION IS INTERMITTENT. REFER TO "DIAGNOSTIC AIDS"
3
• REMOVE FOOT FROM BRAKE PEDAL.
• SELECT RIGHT FRONT ABS MOTOR APPLY FUNCTION AND APPLY THE MOTOR WHILE CAREFULLY OBSERVING THE COMMANDED CURRENT AND THE FEEDBACK CURRENT ON THE TECH 1 WAS THE FEEDBACK CURRENT HIGHER THAN THE COMMANDED CURRENT?
YES
NO
4
• EXIT TECH 1 MANUAL CONTROL FUNCTION.
• IGNITION "OFF."
• DISCONNECT THE 6-WAY EBCM CONNECTOR AND THE 6-WAY ABS MOTOR PACK CONNECTOR.
• USING J 39200, MEASURE THE RESISTANCE BETWEEN TERMINAL "G" AND TERMINAL "H" OF THE 6-WAY EBCM HARNESS CONNECTOR. DOES J 39200 DISPLAY RESISTANCE AS "OL" (INFINITE)?
8
• USING TECH 1 PERFORM GEAR TENSION RELIEF FUNCTION.
• IGNITION "OFF."
• REMOVE HYDRAULIC MODULATOR MASTER CYLINDER ASSEMBLY FROM VEHICLE.
• SEPARATE ABS MOTOR PACK FROM HYDRAULIC MODULATOR.
• GRASP THE GEAR ON THE HYDRAULIC MODULATOR (THE HYDRAULIC MODULATOR IS THE UNIT WITH THE THREE LARGE GEARS) FURTHEST REARWARD WHEN THE UNIT IS INSTALLED IN THE VEHICLE AND ATTEMPT TO MOVE THE GEAR. CAN THE GEAR BE ROTATED AT LEAST 10 FULL TURNS LOCK TO LOCK?
YES
NO
5
• MEASURE THE RESISTANCE BETWEEN TERMINAL "A" AND TERMINAL "B" OF THE ABS MOTOR PACK CONNECTOR. IS RESISTANCE GREATER THAN 0.4Ω?
REPAIR SHORT BETWEEN CKT 1282 AND CKT 1283.
YES
NO
6
• IGNITION "OFF."
• RECONNECT ALL CONNECTORS.
• START ENGINE WITH FOOT OFF BRAKE.
• ALLOW ENGINE TO RUN FOR AT LEAST 10 SECONDS.
• REPEAT ABOVE IGNITION CYCLE SEQUENCE TWO MORE TIMES. DID DTC 45 SET IN THE LAST THREE IGNITION CYCLES?
REPLACE ABS MOTOR PACK.
NO
YES
REPLACE HYDRAULIC MODULATOR
REPLACE ABS MOTOR PACK
YES
NO
REPLACE EBCM.
MALFUNCTION IS INTERMITTENT. INSPECT ALL CONNECTORS FOR CONTAMINATION AND POOR TERMINAL CONTACT. REPLACE ANY TERMINALS THAT EXHIBIT POOR TERMINAL CONTACT OR EVIDENCE OF CORROSION.

GC402930078600BA

Fig. 155 Code A045: Right Front Channel Will Not Move. 1993 Grand Prix, 1993–94 Cutlass Supreme, Lumina & Regal

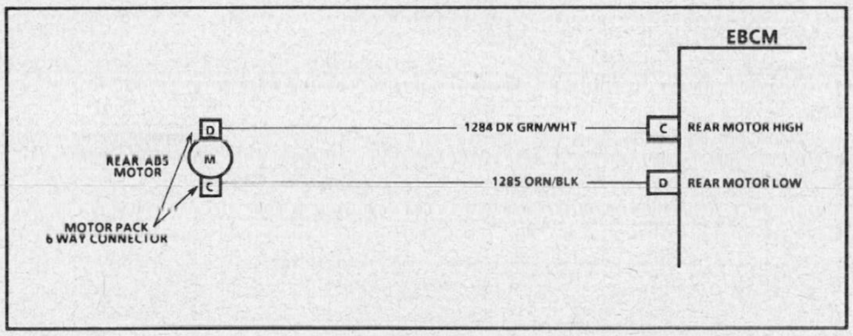
EBCM
REAR ABS MOTOR
M
D
C
MOTOR PACK 6 WAY CONNECTOR
1284 DK GRN/WHT
C
REAR MOTOR HIGH
1285 ORN/BLK
D
REAR MOTOR LOW

DTC A046

REAR AXLE CHANNEL WILL NOT MOVE

Circuit Description:

This DTC is designed to detect bound-up ESB, a stuck motor, or a seized hydraulic modulator. When the release is commanded during initialization, the ESB should release the motor, resulting in sensed current being less than commanded current (motor is spinning freely). If the motor is not moving, sensed current will be equal to stall current.

Failure Condition:

DTC A046 can be set during normal operation. If the EBCM detects a condition in which it cannot move the motor in either direction, a malfunction exists.

Action Taken:

This malfunction indicates the channel cannot be moved properly. A malfunction DTC is stored, ABS is disabled and the ABS indicator lamp is turned "ON."

Test Description: Number(s) below refer to circled number(s) on the diagnostic chart.

1. This step insures that proper motor circuits are located in the proper connector cavities.
2. This step checks for proper motor movement during apply and release commands from the Tech 1.
3. This step compares EBCM command current to motor feedback current.
4. This step checks for proper hydraulic modulator gear and piston movement.
5. This step verifies that the motor can actually apply when commanded.
6. This test determines if the malfunction is caused by a defective EBCM or by a short circuit.

Diagnostic Aids:

An "Intermittent" malfunction in this DTC may result from a mechanical part of the system that sticks or binds.

The frequency of the malfunction can be checked by using the enhanced diagnostic function of the Tech 1, as described in "Tech 1 Diagnostics" found in this section. DTC A046 may set after modulator disassembly if the modulator pistons are positioned at the bottom of their bore.

Depending on the frequency of the malfunction, a physical inspection of the mechanical parts suspected may be necessary.

Any circuitry, that is suspected as causing the intermittent complaint, should be thoroughly checked for backed out terminals, improper mating, broken locks, improperly formed or damaged terminals, poor terminal to wiring connections or physical damage to the wiring harness.

GC402930078700AX

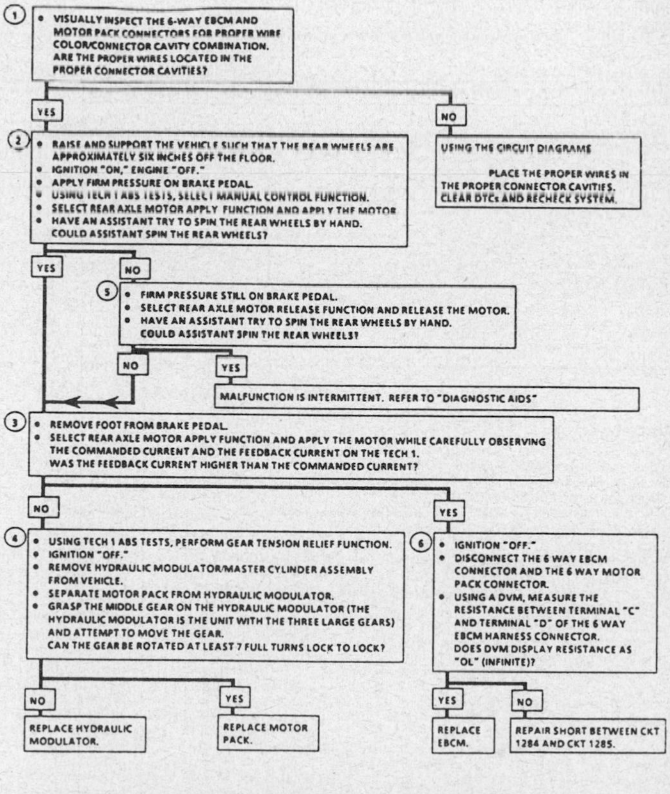
1
• VISUALLY INSPECT THE 6-WAY EBCM AND MOTOR PACK CONNECTORS FOR PROPER WIRE COLOR/CONNECTOR CAVITY COMBINATION. ARE THE PROPER WIRES LOCATED IN THE PROPER CONNECTOR CAVITIES?
YES
NO
USING THE CIRCUIT DIAGRAMS PLACE THE PROPER WIRES IN THE PROPER CONNECTOR CAVITIES. CLEAR DTCs AND RECHECK SYSTEM.
2
• RAISE AND SUPPORT THE VEHICLE SUCH THAT THE REAR WHEELS ARE APPROXIMATELY SIX INCHES OFF THE FLOOR.
• IGNITION "ON," ENGINE "OFF."
• APPLY FIRM PRESSURE ON BRAKE PEDAL.
• USING TECH 1 ABS TESTS, SELECT MANUAL CONTROL FUNCTION.
• SELECT REAR AXLE MOTOR APPLY FUNCTION AND APPLY THE MOTOR
• HAVE AN ASSISTANT TRY TO SPIN THE REAR WHEELS BY HAND. COULD ASSISTANT SPIN THE REAR WHEELS?
YES
NO
5
• FIRM PRESSURE STILL ON BRAKE PEDAL.
• SELECT REAR AXLE MOTOR RELEASE FUNCTION AND RELEASE THE MOTOR.
• HAVE AN ASSISTANT TRY TO SPIN THE REAR WHEELS BY HAND. COULD ASSISTANT SPIN THE REAR WHEELS?
NO
YES
MALFUNCTION IS INTERMITTENT. REFER TO "DIAGNOSTIC AIDS"
3
• REMOVE FOOT FROM BRAKE PEDAL.
• SELECT REAR AXLE MOTOR APPLY FUNCTION AND APPLY THE MOTOR WHILE CAREFULLY OBSERVING THE COMMANDED CURRENT AND THE FEEDBACK CURRENT ON THE TECH 1. WAS THE FEEDBACK CURRENT HIGHER THAN THE COMMANDED CURRENT?
NO
YES
4
• USING TECH 1 ABS TESTS, PERFORM GEAR TENSION RELIEF FUNCTION.
• IGNITION "OFF."
• REMOVE HYDRAULIC MODULATOR/MASTER CYLINDER ASSEMBLY FROM VEHICLE.
• SEPARATE MOTOR PACK FROM HYDRAULIC MODULATOR.
• GRASP THE MIDDLE GEAR ON THE HYDRAULIC MODULATOR (THE HYDRAULIC MODULATOR IS THE UNIT WITH THE THREE LARGE GEARS) AND ATTEMPT TO MOVE THE GEAR. CAN THE GEAR BE ROTATED AT LEAST 7 FULL TURNS LOCK TO LOCK?
6
• IGNITION "OFF."
• DISCONNECT THE 6 WAY EBCM CONNECTOR AND THE 6 WAY MOTOR PACK CONNECTOR.
• USING A DVM, MEASURE THE RESISTANCE BETWEEN TERMINAL "C" AND TERMINAL "D" OF THE 6 WAY EBCM HARNESS CONNECTOR. DOES DVM DISPLAY RESISTANCE AS "OL" (INFINITE)?
NO
YES
YES
NO
REPLACE HYDRAULIC MODULATOR.
REPLACE MOTOR PACK.
REPLACE EBCM.
REPAIR SHORT BETWEEN CKT 1284 AND CKT 1285.

AFTER ALL DIAGNOSIS IS COMPLETE, CLEAR DTCs AND TEST DRIVE VEHICLE FOR THREE (3) DRIVE CYCLES TO VERIFY THAT DTC DOES NOT RESET. A DRIVE CYCLE CONSISTS OF STARTING THE VEHICLE, DRIVING OVER 16 KM/H (10 MPH), AND THEN KEYING DOWN.

GC402930078700BX

Fig. 156 Code A046: Rear Axle Channel Will Not Move. 1993 Cutlass Supreme, Grand Prix, Lumina, Regal & 1993–94 Cavalier, Sunbird, Beretta, Corsica & Achieva, Grand Am & Skylark Less VES

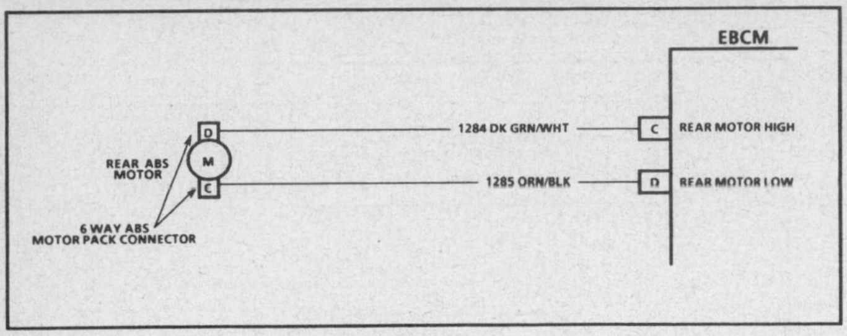
EBCM
1284 DK GRN/WHT
C
REAR MOTOR HIGH
1285 ORN/BLK
D
REAR MOTOR LOW
D
M
C
REAR ABS MOTOR
6 WAY ABS MOTOR PACK CONNECTOR

DTC 46

REAR CHANNEL WILL NOT MOVE

Circuit Description:

This DTC is designed to detect bound-up ESB, a stuck ABS motor, or a seized hydraulic modulator. When the release is commanded during initialization, the ESB should release the ABS motor, resulting in sensed current being less than commanded current (motor is spinning freely). If the ABS motor is not moving, sensed current will be equal to stall current.

DTC Will Set When: DTC 46 can be set during normal operation. If the EBCM detects a condition in which it cannot move the ABS motor in either direction, a malfunction exists.

Action Taken: This malfunction indicates the channel cannot be moved properly. A malfunction DTC is stored, ABS is disabled and the ABS warning lamp is turned "ON."

DTC Chart Test Description: Number(s) below refer to circled number(s) on the diagnostic chart.

1. Ensures that proper motor circuits are located in the proper connector cavities.
2. Checks for proper motor movement during apply and release commands from the Tech 1.
3. Compares EBCM command current to ABS motor feedback current.
4. Checks for short between CKT 1284 and CKT 1285.
5. Checks for an ABS motor that is internally shorted.
6. Checks to see if malfunction is due to poor terminal contact or the EBCM.
7. Verifies that the motor can actually release when commanded.
8. Checks for proper hydraulic modulator gear and piston movement.

Diagnostic Aids: An "Intermittent" malfunction in this DTC may result from a mechanical part of the system that sticks or binds.

The frequency of the malfunction can be checked by using the enhanced diagnostic function of the Tech 1

DTC 46 may set after modulator disassembly if the modulator pistons are positioned at the bottom of their bore.

Depending on the frequency of the malfunction, a physical inspection of the mechanical parts suspected may be necessary.

Any circuitry, that is suspected as causing the intermittent complaint, should be thoroughly checked for backed out terminals, improper mating, broken locks, improperly formed or damaged terminals, poor terminal to wiring connections or physical damage to the wiring harness.

GC402940094200AX

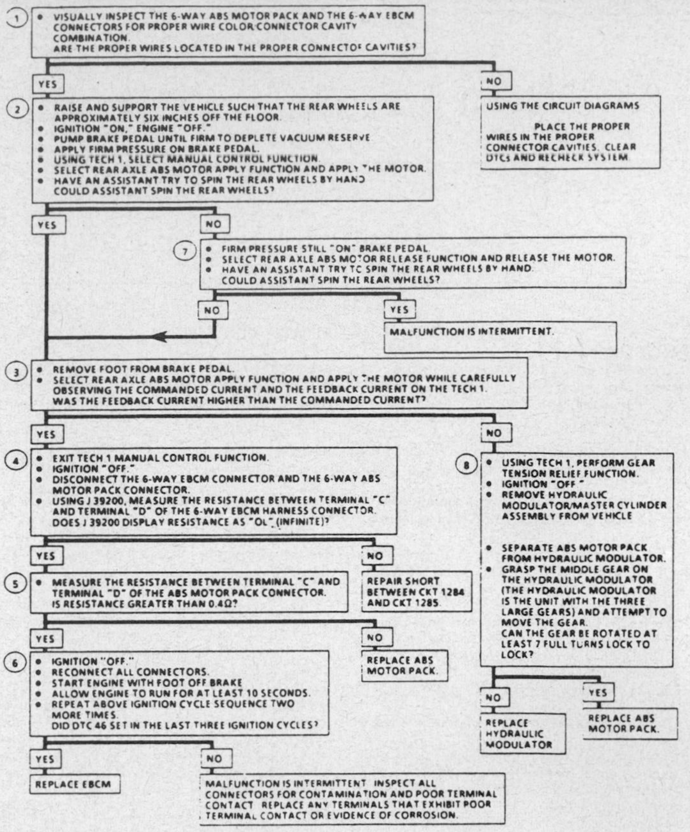
1
• VISUALLY INSPECT THE 6-WAY ABS MOTOR PACK AND THE 6-WAY EBCM CONNECTORS FOR PROPER WIRE COLOR CONNECTOR CAVITY COMBINATION.
ARE THE PROPER WIRES LOCATED IN THE PROPER CONNECTOR CAVITIES?
YES
NO
USING THE CIRCUIT DIAGRAMS
PLACE THE PROPER WIRES IN THE PROPER CONNECTOR CAVITIES. CLEAR DTCs AND RECHECK SYSTEM.
2
• RAISE AND SUPPORT THE VEHICLE SUCH THAT THE REAR WHEELS ARE APPROXIMATELY SIX INCHES OFF THE FLOOR.
• IGNITION "ON," ENGINE "OFF."
• PUMP BRAKE PEDAL UNTIL FIRM TO DEPLETE VACUUM RESERVE.
• APPLY FIRM PRESSURE ON BRAKE PEDAL.
• USING TECH 1, SELECT MANUAL CONTROL FUNCTION.
• SELECT REAR AXLE ABS MOTOR APPLY FUNCTION AND APPLY THE MOTOR.
• HAVE AN ASSISTANT TRY TO SPIN THE REAR WHEELS BY HAND.
COULD ASSISTANT SPIN THE REAR WHEELS?
YES
NO
7
• FIRM PRESSURE STILL "ON" BRAKE PEDAL.
• SELECT REAR AXLE ABS MOTOR RELEASE FUNCTION AND RELEASE THE MOTOR.
• HAVE AN ASSISTANT TRY TO SPIN THE REAR WHEELS BY HAND.
COULD ASSISTANT SPIN THE REAR WHEELS?
NO
YES
MALFUNCTION IS INTERMITTENT.
3
• REMOVE FOOT FROM BRAKE PEDAL.
• SELECT REAR AXLE ABS MOTOR APPLY FUNCTION AND APPLY THE MOTOR WHILE CAREFULLY OBSERVING THE COMMANDED CURRENT AND THE FEEDBACK CURRENT ON THE TECH 1.
WAS THE FEEDBACK CURRENT HIGHER THAN THE COMMANDED CURRENT?
YES
NO
4
• EXIT TECH 1 MANUAL CONTROL FUNCTION.
• IGNITION "OFF."
• DISCONNECT THE 6-WAY EBCM CONNECTOR AND THE 6-WAY ABS MOTOR PACK CONNECTOR.
• USING J 39200, MEASURE THE RESISTANCE BETWEEN TERMINAL "C" AND TERMINAL "D" OF THE 6-WAY EBCM HARNESS CONNECTOR.
DOES J 39200 DISPLAY RESISTANCE AS "OL" (INFINITE)?
8
• USING TECH 1, PERFORM GEAR TENSION RELIEF FUNCTION.
• IGNITION "OFF."
• REMOVE HYDRAULIC MODULATOR/MASTER CYLINDER ASSEMBLY FROM VEHICLE
• SEPARATE ABS MOTOR PACK FROM HYDRAULIC MODULATOR.
• GRASP THE MIDDLE GEAR ON THE HYDRAULIC MODULATOR (THE HYDRAULIC MODULATOR IS THE UNIT WITH THE THREE LARGE GEARS) AND ATTEMPT TO MOVE THE GEAR.
CAN THE GEAR BE ROTATED AT LEAST 7 FULL TURNS LOCK TO LOCK?
YES
NO
REPAIR SHORT BETWEEN CKT 1284 AND CKT 1285.
5
• MEASURE THE RESISTANCE BETWEEN TERMINAL "C" AND TERMINAL "D" OF THE ABS MOTOR PACK CONNECTOR.
IS RESISTANCE GREATER THAN 0.4Ω?
YES
NO
REPLACE ABS MOTOR PACK.
6
• IGNITION "OFF."
• RECONNECT ALL CONNECTORS.
• START ENGINE WITH FOOT OFF BRAKE
• ALLOW ENGINE TO RUN FOR AT LEAST 10 SECONDS.
• REPEAT ABOVE IGNITION CYCLE SEQUENCE TWO MORE TIMES.
DID DTC 46 SET IN THE LAST THREE IGNITION CYCLES?
NO
YES
REPLACE HYDRAULIC MODULATOR
REPLACE ABS MOTOR PACK.
YES
NO
REPLACE EBCM
MALFUNCTION IS INTERMITTENT. INSPECT ALL CONNECTORS FOR CONTAMINATION AND POOR TERMINAL CONTACT. REPLACE ANY TERMINALS THAT EXHIBIT POOR TERMINAL CONTACT OR EVIDENCE OF CORROSION.

GC402940094200BX

Fig. 157 Rear Channel Will Not Move. 1994 Cutlass Supreme, Lumina & Regal

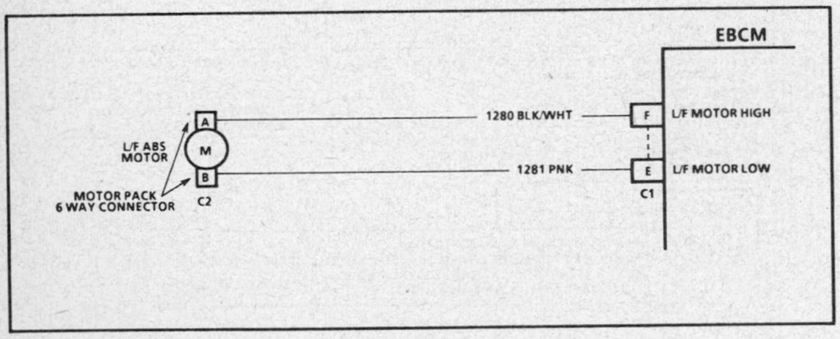
EBCM
1280 BLK/WHT
F
L/F MOTOR HIGH
1281 PNK
E
L/F MOTOR LOW
C1
A
M
B
C2
L/F ABS MOTOR
MOTOR PACK 6 WAY CONNECTOR

DTC A047

LEFT FRONT MOTOR FREE SPINS

Circuit Description:

This DTC is designed to detect a stripped nut or gear assembly during initialization. During the homing sequence, the piston should reach the top of the bore resulting in a stalled motor. If this does not occur, the motor must be spinning with little or no resistance, indicating a nut/screw or gear failure.

Failure Condition:

DTC A047 can only be set during initialization. If the feedback current is less than the command current for a specified period to time, a malfunction exists.

Action Taken:

A malfunction DTC is stored, ABS is disabled, and the ABS indicator lamp is turned "ON."

Test Description: Number(s) below refer to circled number(s) on the diagnostic chart.

1. This step compares feedback current to command current during apply. If either is 0 amps, the EBCM is not functioning properly.
2. This step compares feedback current to command current during release. If either is 0 amps, the EBCM is not functioning properly.
3. Steps 1, 2 and 3 verify malfunction exists. This step also moves the position to the top of the bore.
4. This step checks for a stripped motor pack gear.
5. This step checks for a stripped hydraulic modulator gear.
6. This test checks the ability of the motor to operate properly when commanded.

Diagnostic Aids:

An "Intermittent" malfunction in this DTC may result from a mechanical part of the system that sticks, binds, or slips.

The frequency of the malfunction can be checked by using the enhanced diagnostic function of the Tech 1 as described in "Enhanced Diagnostics," found in this section. If DTC only fails once and DTC A056 also fails see DTC A056. If intermittent and enhanced diagnostics shows this DTC fails during ABS, see DTC A056.

Depending on the frequency of the malfunction, a physical inspection of the mechanical parts suspected may be necessary.

GC402930078800AX

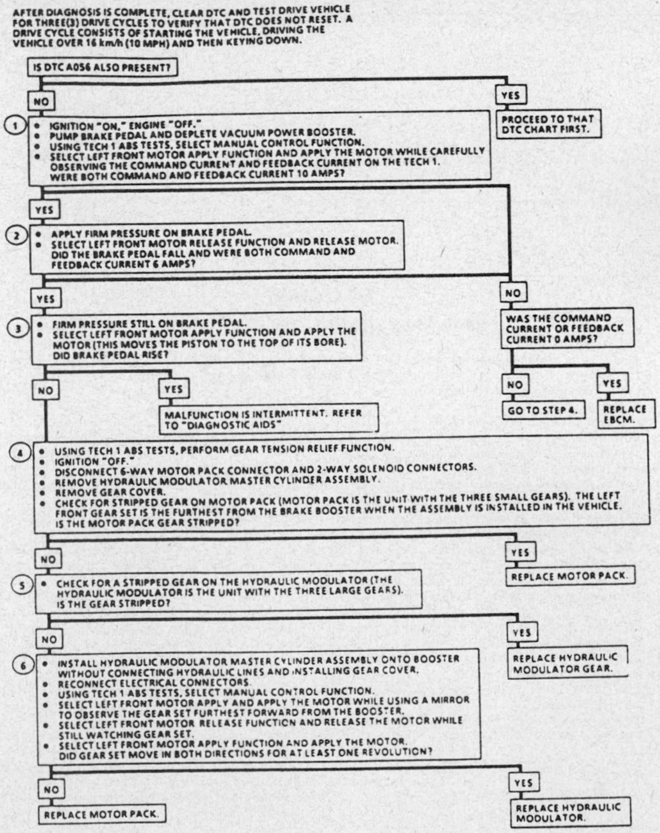
AFTER DIAGNOSIS IS COMPLETE, CLEAR DTC AND TEST DRIVE VEHICLE FOR THREE(3) DRIVE CYCLES TO VERIFY THAT DTC DOES NOT RESET. A DRIVE CYCLE CONSISTS OF STARTING THE VEHICLE, DRIVING THE VEHICLE OVER 16 km/h (10 MPH) AND THEN KEYING DOWN.
IS DTC A056 ALSO PRESENT?
NO
YES
PROCEED TO THAT DTC CHART FIRST.
1
• IGNITION "ON," ENGINE "OFF."
• PUMP BRAKE PEDAL AND DEPLETE VACUUM POWER BOOSTER.
• USING TECH 1 ABS TESTS, SELECT MANUAL CONTROL FUNCTION.
• SELECT LEFT FRONT MOTOR APPLY FUNCTION AND APPLY THE MOTOR WHILE CAREFULLY OBSERVING THE COMMAND CURRENT AND FEEDBACK CURRENT ON THE TECH 1.
WERE BOTH COMMAND AND FEEDBACK CURRENT 10 AMPS?
YES
2
• APPLY FIRM PRESSURE ON BRAKE PEDAL.
• SELECT LEFT FRONT MOTOR RELEASE FUNCTION AND RELEASE MOTOR.
DID THE BRAKE PEDAL FALL AND WERE BOTH COMMAND AND FEEDBACK CURRENT 6 AMPS?
YES
NO
WAS THE COMMAND CURRENT OR FEEDBACK CURRENT 0 AMPS?
3
• FIRM PRESSURE STILL ON BRAKE PEDAL.
• SELECT LEFT FRONT MOTOR APPLY FUNCTION AND APPLY THE MOTOR (THIS MOVES THE PISTON TO THE TOP OF ITS BORE).
DID BRAKE PEDAL RISE?
NO
YES
MALFUNCTION IS INTERMITTENT. REFER TO "DIAGNOSTIC AIDS"
NO
YES
GO TO STEP 4.
REPLACE EBCM.
4
• USING TECH 1 ABS TESTS, PERFORM GEAR TENSION RELIEF FUNCTION.
• IGNITION "OFF."
• DISCONNECT 6-WAY MOTOR PACK CONNECTOR AND 2-WAY SOLENOID CONNECTORS.
• REMOVE HYDRAULIC MODULATOR MASTER CYLINDER ASSEMBLY.
• REMOVE GEAR COVER.
• CHECK FOR STRIPPED GEAR ON MOTOR PACK (MOTOR PACK IS THE UNIT WITH THE THREE SMALL GEARS). THE LEFT FRONT GEAR SET IS THE FURTHEST FROM THE BRAKE BOOSTER WHEN THE ASSEMBLY IS INSTALLED IN THE VEHICLE.
IS THE MOTOR PACK GEAR STRIPPED?
NO
YES
REPLACE MOTOR PACK.
5
• CHECK FOR A STRIPPED GEAR ON THE HYDRAULIC MODULATOR (THE HYDRAULIC MODULATOR IS THE UNIT WITH THE THREE LARGE GEARS).
IS THE GEAR STRIPPED?
NO
YES
REPLACE HYDRAULIC MODULATOR GEAR.
6
• INSTALL HYDRAULIC MODULATOR MASTER CYLINDER ASSEMBLY ONTO BOOSTER WITHOUT CONNECTING HYDRAULIC LINES AND INSTALLING GEAR COVER.
• RECONNECT ELECTRICAL CONNECTORS.
• USING TECH 1 ABS TESTS, SELECT MANUAL CONTROL FUNCTION.
• SELECT LEFT FRONT MOTOR APPLY AND APPLY THE MOTOR WHILE USING A MIRROR TO OBSERVE THE GEAR SET FURTHEST FORWARD FROM THE BOOSTER.
• SELECT LEFT FRONT MOTOR RELEASE FUNCTION AND RELEASE THE MOTOR WHILE STILL WATCHING GEAR SET.
• SELECT LEFT FRONT MOTOR APPLY FUNCTION AND APPLY THE MOTOR.
DID GEAR SET MOVE IN BOTH DIRECTIONS FOR AT LEAST ONE REVOLUTION?
NO
YES
REPLACE MOTOR PACK.
REPLACE HYDRAULIC MODULATOR.

GC402930078800BX

Fig. 158 Code A047: Left Front Motor Free Spins. 1993–94 Cavalier, Sunbird, Beretta, Corsica & Achieva, Grand Am & Skylark Less VES

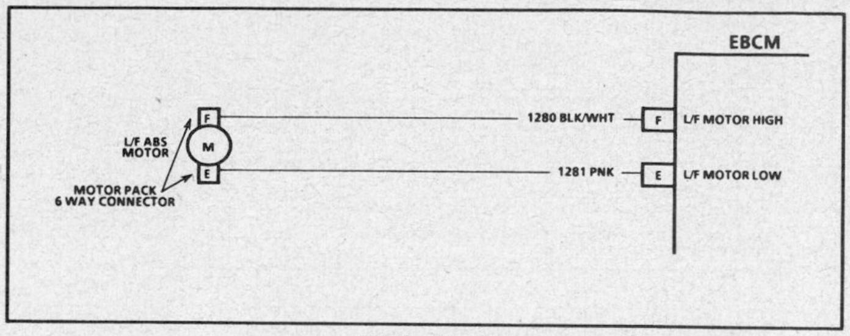
EBCM
L/F ABS MOTOR
M
F
E
MOTOR PACK 6 WAY CONNECTOR
1280 BLK/WHT
1281 PNK
F
E
L/F MOTOR HIGH
L/F MOTOR LOW

DTC A047

LEFT FRONT MOTOR FREE SPINS

Circuit Description:
This DTC is designed to detect a stripped nut or gear assembly during initialization. During the homing sequence, the piston should reach the top of the bore resulting in a stalled motor. If this does not occur, the motor must be spinning with little or no resistance, indicating a nut/screw or gear malfunction.

Failure Condition:
DTC A047 can only be set during initialization. If the feedback current is less than the command current for a specified period of time, a malfunction exists.

Action Taken:
A malfunction DTC is stored, ABS is disabled, and the ABS indicator lamp is turned "ON."

Test Description: Number(s) below refer to circled number(s) on the diagnostic chart.

1. This step checks to see if the corresponding open motor DTC is also set.
2. This step verifies that the motor was actually applied as command by observing feedback current.
3. This step verifies that the motor can release.
4. This step verifies that the motor can be applied by observing pedal movement.
5. This step checks for a stripped gear on the motor pack (unit with three small gears).
6. This step checks for a stripped gear on the hydraulic modulator (unit with three large gears).
7. This step determines whether the hydraulic modulator or the motor pack has an internal malfunction.
8. This step checks for a malfunctioning EBCM.

Diagnostic Aids:

An "Intermittent" malfunction in this DTC may result from a mechanical part of the system that sticks, binds, or slips.

The frequency of the malfunction can be checked by using the enhanced diagnostic function of the Tech 1, as described in "Tech 1 Diagnostics" found in this section. If the DTC only fails once and DTC A056 also fails, refer to DTC A056. If intermittent and enhanced diagnostics shows this DTC fails during ABS, refer to DTC A056.

Depending on the frequency of the malfunction, a physical inspection of the mechanical parts suspected may be necessary.

GC402930078900AX

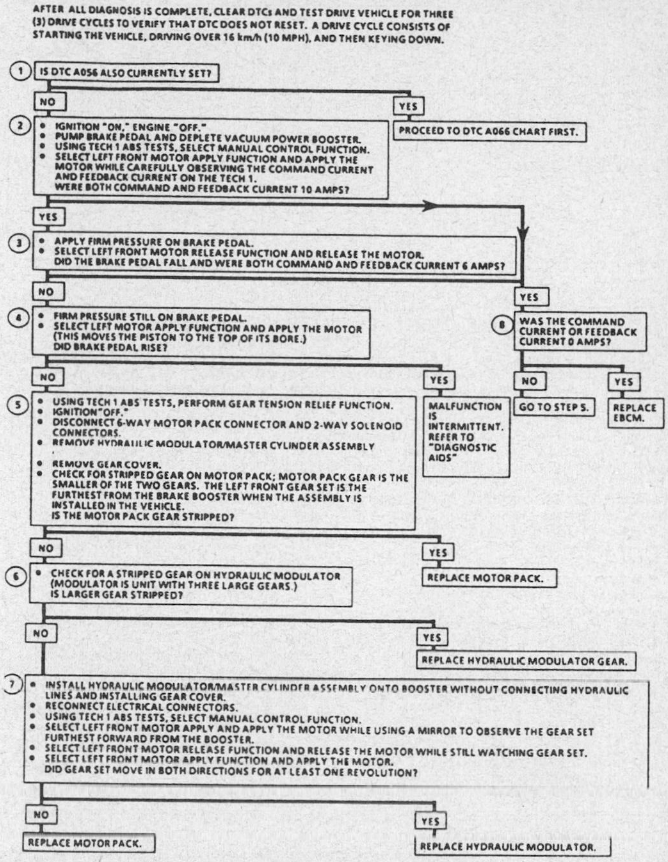
AFTER ALL DIAGNOSIS IS COMPLETE, CLEAR DTCs AND TEST DRIVE VEHICLE FOR THREE (3) DRIVE CYCLES TO VERIFY THAT DTC DOES NOT RESET. A DRIVE CYCLE CONSISTS OF STARTING THE VEHICLE, DRIVING OVER 16 km/h (10 MPH), AND THEN KEYING DOWN.
1
IS DTC A056 ALSO CURRENTLY SET?
NO
YES
PROCEED TO DTC A066 CHART FIRST.
2
• IGNITION "ON," ENGINE "OFF."
• PUMP BRAKE PEDAL AND DEPLETE VACUUM POWER BOOSTER.
• USING TECH 1 ABS TESTS, SELECT MANUAL CONTROL FUNCTION.
• SELECT LEFT FRONT MOTOR APPLY FUNCTION AND APPLY THE MOTOR WHILE CAREFULLY OBSERVING THE COMMAND CURRENT AND FEEDBACK CURRENT ON THE TECH 1.
WERE BOTH COMMAND AND FEEDBACK CURRENT 10 AMPS?
YES
3
• APPLY FIRM PRESSURE ON BRAKE PEDAL.
• SELECT LEFT FRONT MOTOR RELEASE FUNCTION AND RELEASE THE MOTOR.
DID THE BRAKE PEDAL FALL AND WERE BOTH COMMAND AND FEEDBACK CURRENT 6 AMPS?
NO
YES
4
• FIRM PRESSURE STILL ON BRAKE PEDAL.
• SELECT LEFT MOTOR APPLY FUNCTION AND APPLY THE MOTOR (THIS MOVES THE PISTON TO THE TOP OF ITS BORE.)
DID BRAKE PEDAL RISE?
8
WAS THE COMMAND CURRENT OR FEEDBACK CURRENT 0 AMPS?
NO
YES
NO
YES
GO TO STEP 5.
REPLACE EBCM.
MALFUNCTION IS INTERMITTENT. REFER TO "DIAGNOSTIC AIDS"
5
• USING TECH 1 ABS TESTS, PERFORM GEAR TENSION RELIEF FUNCTION.
• IGNITION "OFF."
• DISCONNECT 6-WAY MOTOR PACK CONNECTOR AND 2-WAY SOLENOID CONNECTORS.
• REMOVE HYDRAULIC MODULATOR/MASTER CYLINDER ASSEMBLY
• REMOVE GEAR COVER.
• CHECK FOR STRIPPED GEAR ON MOTOR PACK; MOTOR PACK GEAR IS THE SMALLER OF THE TWO GEARS. THE LEFT FRONT GEAR SET IS THE FURTHEST FROM THE BRAKE BOOSTER WHEN THE ASSEMBLY IS INSTALLED IN THE VEHICLE.
IS THE MOTOR PACK GEAR STRIPPED?
NO
YES
REPLACE MOTOR PACK.
6
• CHECK FOR A STRIPPED GEAR ON HYDRAULIC MODULATOR (MODULATOR IS UNIT WITH THREE LARGE GEARS.)
IS LARGER GEAR STRIPPED?
NO
YES
REPLACE HYDRAULIC MODULATOR GEAR.
7
• INSTALL HYDRAULIC MODULATOR/MASTER CYLINDER ASSEMBLY ONTO BOOSTER WITHOUT CONNECTING HYDRAULIC LINES AND INSTALLING GEAR COVER.
• RECONNECT ELECTRICAL CONNECTORS.
• USING TECH 1 ABS TESTS, SELECT MANUAL CONTROL FUNCTION.
• SELECT LEFT FRONT MOTOR APPLY AND APPLY THE MOTOR WHILE USING A MIRROR TO OBSERVE THE GEAR SET FURTHEST FORWARD FROM THE BOOSTER.
• SELECT LEFT FRONT MOTOR RELEASE FUNCTION AND RELEASE THE MOTOR WHILE STILL WATCHING GEAR SET.
• SELECT LEFT FRONT MOTOR APPLY FUNCTION AND APPLY THE MOTOR.
DID GEAR SET MOVE IN BOTH DIRECTIONS FOR AT LEAST ONE REVOLUTION?
NO
YES
REPLACE MOTOR PACK.
REPLACE HYDRAULIC MODULATOR.

GC402930078900BX

Fig. 159 Code A047: Left Front Motor Free Spins. 1993 Cutlass Supreme, Grand Prix, Lumina & Regal

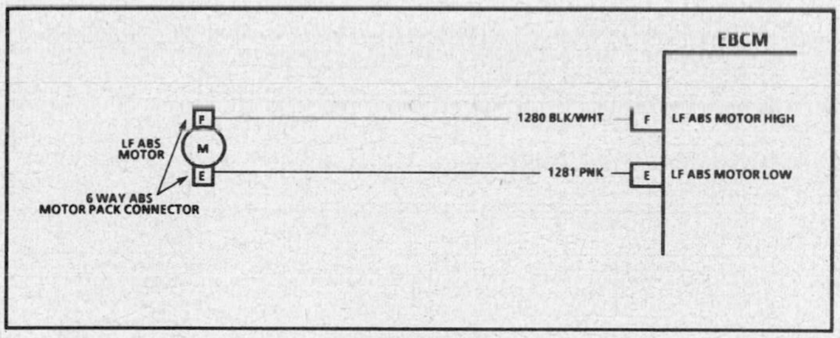
EBCM
LF ABS MOTOR
M
F
E
6 WAY ABS MOTOR PACK CONNECTOR
1280 BLK/WHT
1281 PNK
F
E
LF ABS MOTOR HIGH
LF ABS MOTOR LOW

DTC 47

(Page 1 of 2)

LEFT FRONT ABS MOTOR FREE SPINS

Circuit Description:
This DTC is designed to detect a stripped nut or gear assembly during initialization. During the homing sequence, the piston should reach the top of the bore resulting in a stalled ABS motor. If this does not occur, the ABS motor must be spinning with little or no resistance, indicating a nut/screw or gear malfunction.

DTC Will Set When: DTC 47 can only be set during initialization. If the feedback current is less than the command current for a specified period of time, a malfunction exists.

Action Taken: A malfunction DTC is stored, ABS is disabled, and the ABS warning lamp is turned "ON."

DTC Chart Test Description: Number(s) below refer to circled number(s) on the diagnostic chart.

1. Checks to see if the corresponding open motor DTC 56 is also set.
2. Verifies that the ABS motor was actually applied as command by observing feedback current.
3. Verifies that the ABS motor can release.
4. Verifies that the ABS motor can be applied by observing pedal movement.
5. Checks for an open in the ABS motor "HIGH" circuitry.
6. Checks for an open in the ABS motor "LOW" circuitry.
7. Checks for an ABS motor that is internally shorted.

Diagnostic Aids: An "Intermittent" malfunction in this DTC may result from a mechanical part of the system that sticks, binds, or slips.

The frequency of the malfunction can be checked by using the enhanced diagnostic function of the Tech 1

If the DTC only occurs once and DTC 56 also occurs, refer to DTC 56. If intermittent and enhanced diagnostics shows this DTC occurs during ABS, refer to DTC 56.

Depending on the frequency of the malfunction, a physical inspection of the mechanical parts suspected may be necessary.

GC402940094301AX

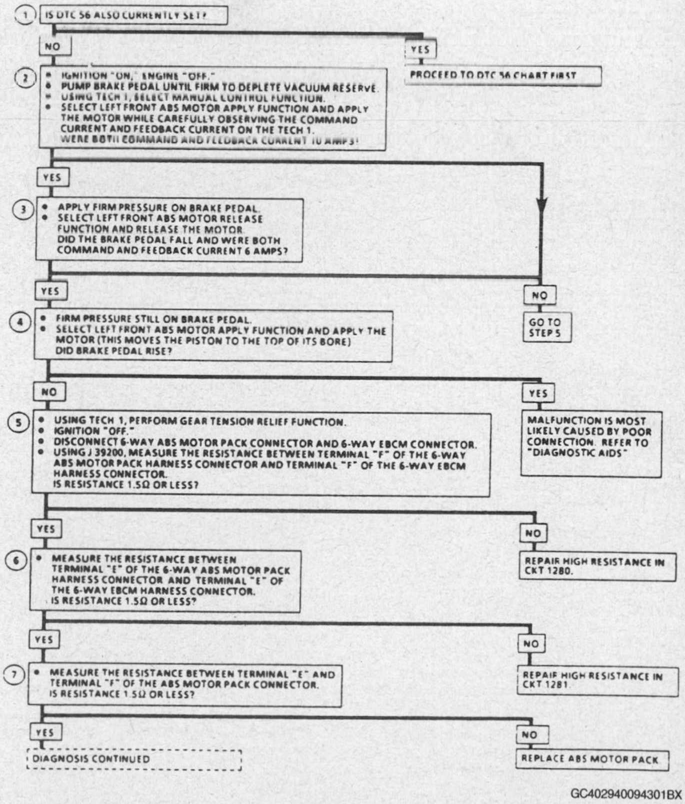
1
IS DTC 56 ALSO CURRENTLY SET?
NO
YES
PROCEED TO DTC 56 CHART FIRST
2
• IGNITION "ON," ENGINE "OFF."
• PUMP BRAKE PEDAL UNTIL FIRM TO DEPLETE VACUUM RESERVE.
• USING TECH 1, SELECT MANUAL CONTROL FUNCTION.
• SELECT LEFT FRONT ABS MOTOR APPLY FUNCTION AND APPLY THE MOTOR WHILE CAREFULLY OBSERVING THE COMMAND CURRENT AND FEEDBACK CURRENT ON THE TECH 1.
WERE BOTH COMMAND AND FEEDBACK CURRENT 10 AMPS?
YES
3
• APPLY FIRM PRESSURE ON BRAKE PEDAL.
• SELECT LEFT FRONT ABS MOTOR RELEASE FUNCTION AND RELEASE THE MOTOR.
DID THE BRAKE PEDAL FALL AND WERE BOTH COMMAND AND FEEDBACK CURRENT 6 AMPS?
YES
NO
GO TO STEP 5
4
• FIRM PRESSURE STILL ON BRAKE PEDAL.
• SELECT LEFT FRONT ABS MOTOR APPLY FUNCTION AND APPLY THE MOTOR (THIS MOVES THE PISTON TO THE TOP OF ITS BORE)
DID BRAKE PEDAL RISE?
NO
YES
MALFUNCTION IS MOST LIKELY CAUSED BY POOR CONNECTION. REFER TO "DIAGNOSTIC AIDS"
5
• USING TECH 1, PERFORM GEAR TENSION RELIEF FUNCTION.
• IGNITION "OFF."
• DISCONNECT 6-WAY ABS MOTOR PACK CONNECTOR AND 6-WAY EBCM CONNECTOR.
• USING J 39200, MEASURE THE RESISTANCE BETWEEN TERMINAL "F" OF THE 6-WAY ABS MOTOR PACK HARNESS CONNECTOR AND TERMINAL "F" OF THE 6-WAY EBCM HARNESS CONNECTOR.
IS RESISTANCE 1.5Ω OR LESS?
YES
NO
REPAIR HIGH RESISTANCE IN CKT 1280.
6
• MEASURE THE RESISTANCE BETWEEN TERMINAL "E" OF THE 6-WAY ABS MOTOR PACK HARNESS CONNECTOR AND TERMINAL "E" OF THE 6-WAY EBCM HARNESS CONNECTOR.
IS RESISTANCE 1.5Ω OR LESS?
YES
NO
REPAIR HIGH RESISTANCE IN CKT 1281
7
• MEASURE THE RESISTANCE BETWEEN TERMINAL "E" AND TERMINAL "F" OF THE ABS MOTOR PACK CONNECTOR.
IS RESISTANCE 1.5Ω OR LESS?
YES
NO
DIAGNOSIS CONTINUED
REPLACE ABS MOTOR PACK.

GC402940094301BX

Fig. 160 Code A047: Left Front Motor Free Spins (1 of 2). 1994 Cutlass Supreme, Lumina & Regal

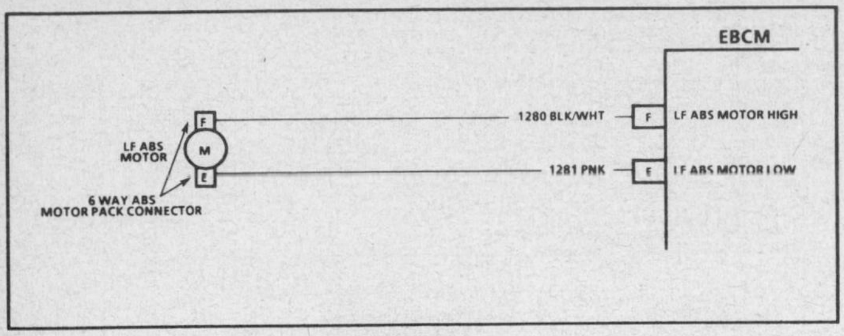
EBCM
1280 BLK/WHT
F
LF ABS MOTOR HIGH
LF ABS MOTOR
M
E
1281 PNK
E
LF ABS MOTOR LOW
6 WAY ABS MOTOR PACK CONNECTOR

DTC 47

(Page 2 of 2)

LEFT FRONT ABS MOTOR FREE SPINS

Circuit Description:

This DTC is designed to detect a stripped nut or gear assembly during initialization. During the homing sequence, the piston should reach the top of the bore resulting in a stalled ABS motor. If this does not occur, the ABS motor must be spinning with little or no resistance, indicating a nut/screw or gear malfunction.

DTC Will Set When: DTC 47 can only be set during initialization. If the feedback current is less than the command current for a specified period of time, a malfunction exists.

Action Taken: A malfunction DTC is stored, ABS is disabled, and the ABS warning lamp is turned "ON."

DTC Chart Test Description: Number(s) below refer to circled number(s) on the diagnostic chart.

8. Checks for a stripped gear on the ABS motor pack (unit with three small gears).
9. Checks for a stripped gear on the hydraulic modulator (unit with three large gears).
10. Checks to see if the ABS motor pack has an internal malfunction.
11. Checks for a malfunctioning hydraulic modulator.
12. Ensures malfunction was not due to poor terminal contact.

Diagnostic Aids: An "Intermittent" malfunction in this DTC may result from a mechanical part of the system that sticks, binds, or slips.

The frequency of the malfunction can be checked by using the enhanced diagnostic function of the Tech 1.

If the DTC only occurs once and DTC 56 also occurs, refer to DTC 56. If intermittent and enhanced diagnostics shows this DTC occurs during ABS, refer to DTC 56.

Depending on the frequency of the malfunction, a physical inspection of the mechanical parts suspected may be necessary.

GC402940094302AX

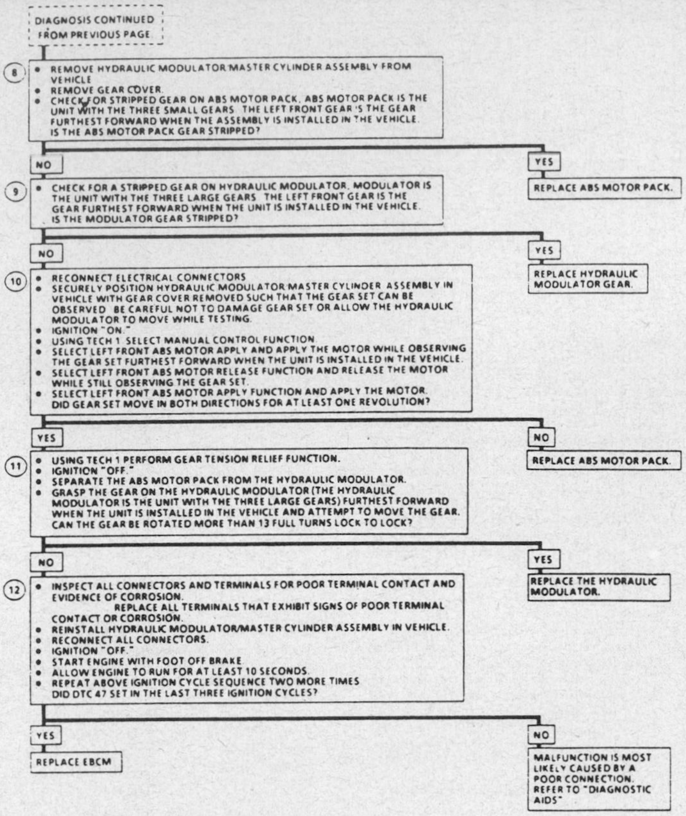
DIAGNOSIS CONTINUED FROM PREVIOUS PAGE
8
• REMOVE HYDRAULIC MODULATOR/MASTER CYLINDER ASSEMBLY FROM VEHICLE
• REMOVE GEAR COVER.
• CHECK FOR STRIPPED GEAR ON ABS MOTOR PACK. ABS MOTOR PACK IS THE UNIT WITH THE THREE SMALL GEARS. THE LEFT FRONT GEAR IS THE GEAR FURTHEST FORWARD WHEN THE ASSEMBLY IS INSTALLED IN THE VEHICLE. IS THE ABS MOTOR PACK GEAR STRIPPED?
NO
YES
REPLACE ABS MOTOR PACK.
9
• CHECK FOR A STRIPPED GEAR ON HYDRAULIC MODULATOR. MODULATOR IS THE UNIT WITH THE THREE LARGE GEARS. THE LEFT FRONT GEAR IS THE GEAR FURTHEST FORWARD WHEN THE UNIT IS INSTALLED IN THE VEHICLE. IS THE MODULATOR GEAR STRIPPED?
NO
YES
REPLACE HYDRAULIC MODULATOR GEAR.
10
• RECONNECT ELECTRICAL CONNECTORS
• SECURELY POSITION HYDRAULIC MODULATOR/MASTER CYLINDER ASSEMBLY IN VEHICLE WITH GEAR COVER REMOVED SUCH THAT THE GEAR SET CAN BE OBSERVED. BE CAREFUL NOT TO DAMAGE GEAR SET OR ALLOW THE HYDRAULIC MODULATOR TO MOVE WHILE TESTING.
• IGNITION "ON."
• USING TECH 1 SELECT MANUAL CONTROL FUNCTION
• SELECT LEFT FRONT ABS MOTOR APPLY AND APPLY THE MOTOR WHILE OBSERVING THE GEAR SET FURTHEST FORWARD WHEN THE UNIT IS INSTALLED IN THE VEHICLE.
• SELECT LEFT FRONT ABS MOTOR RELEASE FUNCTION AND RELEASE THE MOTOR WHILE STILL OBSERVING THE GEAR SET.
• SELECT LEFT FRONT ABS MOTOR APPLY FUNCTION AND APPLY THE MOTOR. DID GEAR SET MOVE IN BOTH DIRECTIONS FOR AT LEAST ONE REVOLUTION?
YES
NO
REPLACE ABS MOTOR PACK.
11
• USING TECH 1 PERFORM GEAR TENSION RELIEF FUNCTION.
• IGNITION "OFF."
• SEPARATE THE ABS MOTOR PACK FROM THE HYDRAULIC MODULATOR.
• GRASP THE GEAR ON THE HYDRAULIC MODULATOR (THE HYDRAULIC MODULATOR IS THE UNIT WITH THE THREE LARGE GEARS) FURTHEST FORWARD WHEN THE UNIT IS INSTALLED IN THE VEHICLE AND ATTEMPT TO MOVE THE GEAR. CAN THE GEAR BE ROTATED MORE THAN 13 FULL TURNS LOCK TO LOCK?
NO
YES
REPLACE THE HYDRAULIC MODULATOR.
12
• INSPECT ALL CONNECTORS AND TERMINALS FOR POOR TERMINAL CONTACT AND EVIDENCE OF CORROSION. REPLACE ALL TERMINALS THAT EXHIBIT SIGNS OF POOR TERMINAL CONTACT OR CORROSION.
• REINSTALL HYDRAULIC MODULATOR/MASTER CYLINDER ASSEMBLY IN VEHICLE.
• RECONNECT ALL CONNECTORS.
• IGNITION "OFF."
• START ENGINE WITH FOOT OFF BRAKE
• ALLOW ENGINE TO RUN FOR AT LEAST 10 SECONDS.
• REPEAT ABOVE IGNITION CYCLE SEQUENCE TWO MORE TIMES. DID DTC 47 SET IN THE LAST THREE IGNITION CYCLES?
YES
NO
REPLACE EBCM
MALFUNCTION IS MOST LIKELY CAUSED BY A POOR CONNECTION. REFER TO "DIAGNOSTIC AIDS"

GC402940094302BX

Fig. 160 Code A047: Left Front Motor Free Spins (2 of 2). 1994 Cutlass Supreme, Lumina & Regal

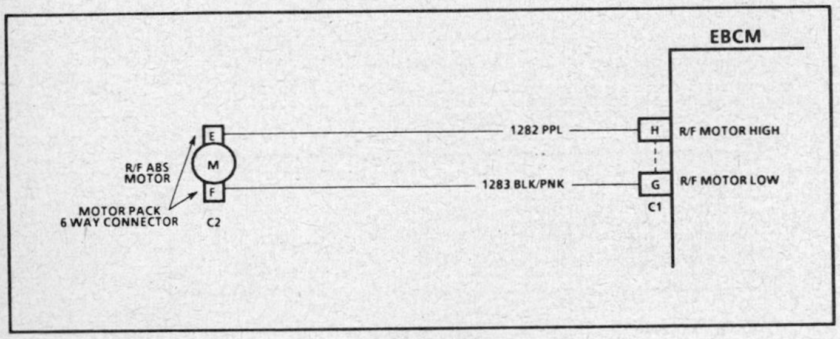
EBCM
R/F ABS MOTOR
M
E
F
1282 PPL
H
R/F MOTOR HIGH
1283 BLK/PNK
G
R/F MOTOR LOW
C1
MOTOR PACK 6 WAY CONNECTOR
C2

DTC A048

RIGHT FRONT MOTOR FREE SPINS

Circuit Description:

This DTC is designed to detect a stripped nut or gear assembly during initialization. During the homing sequence, the piston should reach the top of the bore resulting in a stalled motor. If this does not occur, the motor must be spinning with little or no resistance, indicating a nut/screw or gear failure.

Failure Condition:

DTC A048 can only be set during initialization. If the feedback current is less than the command current for a specified period of time, a malfunction exists.

Action Taken:

A malfunction DTC is stored, ABS is disabled, and the ABS indicator lamp is turned "ON."

Test Description: Number(s) below refer to circled number(s) on the diagnostic chart.

1. This step compares feedback current to command current during apply. If either is 0 amps, the EBCM is not functioning properly.
2. This step compares feedback current to command current during release. If either is 0 amps, the EBCM is not functioning properly.
3. Steps 1, 2 and 3 verify malfunction exists. This step also moves the piston to the top of the bore.
4. This step checks for a stripped motor pack gear.
5. This step checks for a stripped hydraulic modulator gear.
6. This test checks the ability of the motor to operate properly when commanded.

Diagnostic Aids:

An "Intermittent" malfunction in this DTC may result from a mechanical part of the system that sticks, binds, or slips.

The frequency of the malfunction can be checked by using the enhanced diagnostic function of the Tech 1 as described in "Enhanced Diagnostics," found in this section. If DTC only fails once and DTC A061 also fails see DTC A061. If intermittent and enhanced diagnostics shows this DTC fails during ABS, see DTC A061.

Depending on the frequency of the malfunction, a physical inspection of the mechanical parts suspected may be necessary.

GC402930079000AX

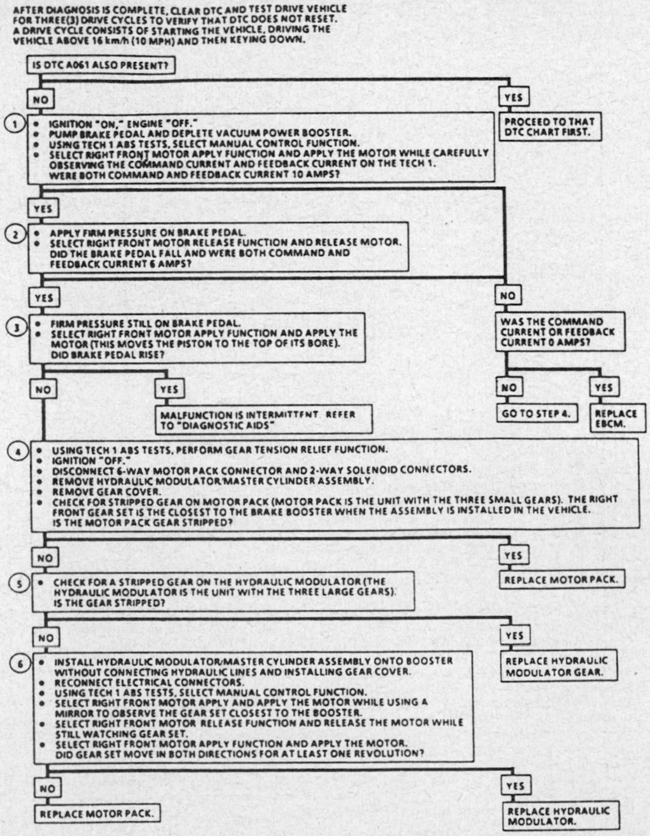
AFTER DIAGNOSIS IS COMPLETE, CLEAR DTC AND TEST DRIVE VEHICLE FOR THREE(3) DRIVE CYCLES TO VERIFY THAT DTC DOES NOT RESET. A DRIVE CYCLE CONSISTS OF STARTING THE VEHICLE, DRIVING THE VEHICLE ABOVE 16 km/h (10 MPH) AND THEN KEYING DOWN.
IS DTC A061 ALSO PRESENT?
NO
YES
PROCEED TO THAT DTC CHART FIRST.
1
• IGNITION "ON," ENGINE "OFF."
• PUMP BRAKE PEDAL AND DEPLETE VACUUM POWER BOOSTER.
• USING TECH 1 ABS TESTS, SELECT MANUAL CONTROL FUNCTION.
• SELECT RIGHT FRONT MOTOR APPLY FUNCTION AND APPLY THE MOTOR WHILE CAREFULLY OBSERVING THE COMMAND CURRENT AND FEEDBACK CURRENT ON THE TECH 1. WERE BOTH COMMAND AND FEEDBACK CURRENT 10 AMPS?
YES
2
• APPLY FIRM PRESSURE ON BRAKE PEDAL.
• SELECT RIGHT FRONT MOTOR RELEASE FUNCTION AND RELEASE MOTOR. DID THE BRAKE PEDAL FALL AND WERE BOTH COMMAND AND FEEDBACK CURRENT 6 AMPS?
YES
NO
WAS THE COMMAND CURRENT OR FEEDBACK CURRENT 0 AMPS?
3
• FIRM PRESSURE STILL ON BRAKE PEDAL.
• SELECT RIGHT FRONT MOTOR APPLY FUNCTION AND APPLY THE MOTOR (THIS MOVES THE PISTON TO THE TOP OF ITS BORE). DID BRAKE PEDAL RISE?
NO
YES
MALFUNCTION IS INTERMITTENT. REFER TO "DIAGNOSTIC AIDS"
NO
YES
GO TO STEP 4.
REPLACE EBCM.
4
• USING TECH 1 ABS TESTS, PERFORM GEAR TENSION RELIEF FUNCTION.
• IGNITION "OFF."
• DISCONNECT 6-WAY MOTOR PACK CONNECTOR AND 2-WAY SOLENOID CONNECTORS.
• REMOVE HYDRAULIC MODULATOR/MASTER CYLINDER ASSEMBLY.
• REMOVE GEAR COVER.
• CHECK FOR STRIPPED GEAR ON MOTOR PACK (MOTOR PACK IS THE UNIT WITH THE THREE SMALL GEARS). THE RIGHT FRONT GEAR SET IS THE CLOSEST TO THE BRAKE BOOSTER WHEN THE ASSEMBLY IS INSTALLED IN THE VEHICLE. IS THE MOTOR PACK GEAR STRIPPED?
NO
YES
REPLACE MOTOR PACK.
5
• CHECK FOR A STRIPPED GEAR ON THE HYDRAULIC MODULATOR (THE HYDRAULIC MODULATOR IS THE UNIT WITH THE THREE LARGE GEARS). IS THE GEAR STRIPPED?
NO
YES
REPLACE HYDRAULIC MODULATOR GEAR.
6
• INSTALL HYDRAULIC MODULATOR/MASTER CYLINDER ASSEMBLY ONTO BOOSTER WITHOUT CONNECTING HYDRAULIC LINES AND INSTALLING GEAR COVER.
• RECONNECT ELECTRICAL CONNECTORS.
• USING TECH 1 ABS TESTS, SELECT MANUAL CONTROL FUNCTION.
• SELECT RIGHT FRONT MOTOR APPLY AND APPLY THE MOTOR WHILE USING A MIRROR TO OBSERVE THE GEAR SET CLOSEST TO THE BOOSTER.
• SELECT RIGHT FRONT MOTOR RELEASE FUNCTION AND RELEASE THE MOTOR WHILE STILL WATCHING GEAR SET.
• SELECT RIGHT FRONT MOTOR APPLY FUNCTION AND APPLY THE MOTOR. DID GEAR SET MOVE IN BOTH DIRECTIONS FOR AT LEAST ONE REVOLUTION?
NO
YES
REPLACE MOTOR PACK.
REPLACE HYDRAULIC MODULATOR.

GC402930079000BX

Fig. 161 Code A048: Right Front Motor Free Spins. 1993–94 Cavalier, Sunbird, Beretta, Corsica & Achieva, Grand Am & Skylark Less VES

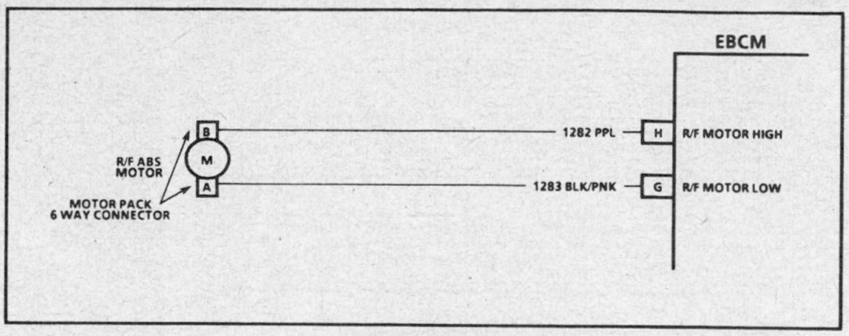
EBCM
B
M
A
R/F ABS MOTOR
MOTOR PACK 6 WAY CONNECTOR
1282 PPL
H
R/F MOTOR HIGH
1283 BLK/PNK
G
R/F MOTOR LOW

DTC A048

RIGHT FRONT MOTOR FREE SPINS

Circuit Description:

This DTC is designed to detect a stripped nut or gear assembly during initialization. During the homing sequence, the piston should reach the top of the bore resulting in a stalled motor. If this does not occur, the motor must be spinning with little or no resistance, indicating a nut/screw or gear malfunction.

Failure Condition:

DTC A048 can only be set during initialization. If the feedback current is less than the command current for a specified period of time, a malfunction exists.

Action Taken:

A malfunction DTC is stored, ABS is disabled, and the ABS indicator lamp is turned "ON."

Test Description: Number(s) below refer to circled number(s) on the diagnostic chart.

1. This step checks to see if the corresponding open motor DTC is also set.
2. This step verifies that the motor was actually applied as command by observing feedback current.
3. This step verifies that the motor can release.
4. This step verifies that the motor can be applied by observing pedal movement.
5. This step checks for a stripped gear on the motor pack (unit with three small gears).
6. This step checks for a stripped gear on the hydraulic modulator (unit with three large gears).
7. This step determines whether the hydraulic modulator or the motor pack has an internal malfunction.
8. This step checks for a malfunctioning EBCM.

Diagnostic Aids:

An "Intermittent" malfunction in this DTC may result from a mechanical part of the system that sticks, binds, or slips.

The frequency of the malfunction can be checked by using the enhanced diagnostic function of the Tech 1, as described in "Tech 1 Diagnostics" found in this section. If the DTC only fails once and DTC A061 also fails, refer to DTC A061. If intermittent and enhanced diagnostics shows this DTC fails during ABS, refer to DTC A061.

Depending on the frequency of the malfunction, a physical inspection of the mechanical parts suspected may be necessary.

GC40293007/9100AX

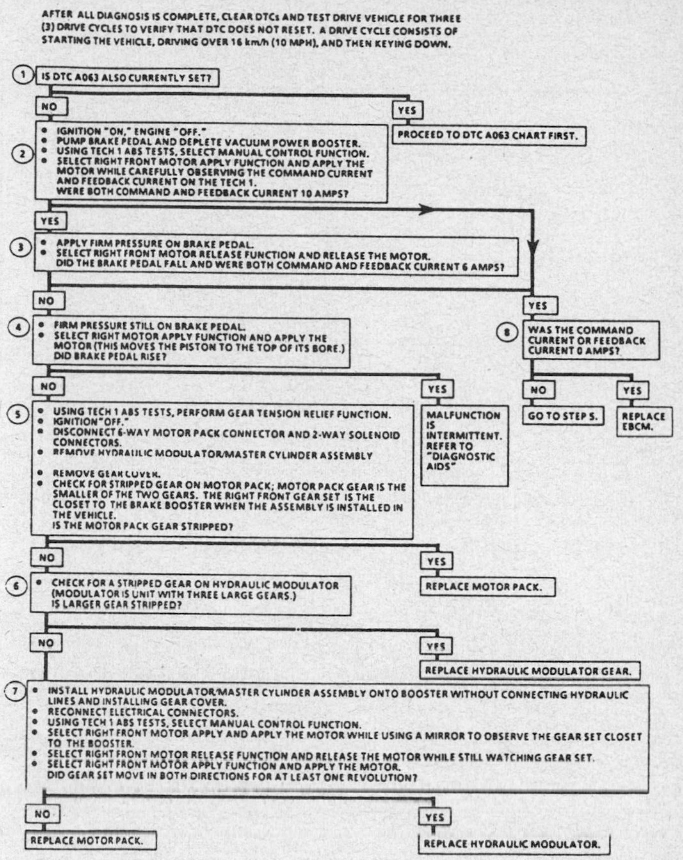
AFTER ALL DIAGNOSIS IS COMPLETE, CLEAR DTCs AND TEST DRIVE VEHICLE FOR THREE (3) DRIVE CYCLES TO VERIFY THAT DTC DOES NOT RESET. A DRIVE CYCLE CONSISTS OF STARTING THE VEHICLE, DRIVING OVER 16 km/h (10 MPH), AND THEN KEYING DOWN.
1
IS DTC A063 ALSO CURRENTLY SET?
NO
YES
PROCEED TO DTC A063 CHART FIRST.
2
• IGNITION "ON," ENGINE "OFF."
• PUMP BRAKE PEDAL AND DEPLETE VACUUM POWER BOOSTER.
• USING TECH 1 ABS TESTS, SELECT MANUAL CONTROL FUNCTION.
• SELECT RIGHT FRONT MOTOR APPLY FUNCTION AND APPLY THE MOTOR WHILE CAREFULLY OBSERVING THE COMMAND CURRENT AND FEEDBACK CURRENT ON THE TECH 1.
WERE BOTH COMMAND AND FEEDBACK CURRENT 10 AMPS?
YES
3
• APPLY FIRM PRESSURE ON BRAKE PEDAL.
• SELECT RIGHT FRONT MOTOR RELEASE FUNCTION AND RELEASE THE MOTOR.
DID THE BRAKE PEDAL FALL AND WERE BOTH COMMAND AND FEEDBACK CURRENT 6 AMPS?
NO
YES
4
• FIRM PRESSURE STILL ON BRAKE PEDAL.
• SELECT RIGHT MOTOR APPLY FUNCTION AND APPLY THE MOTOR (THIS MOVES THE PISTON TO THE TOP OF ITS BORE.)
DID BRAKE PEDAL RISE?
8
WAS THE COMMAND CURRENT OR FEEDBACK CURRENT 0 AMPS?
NO
YES
GO TO STEP 5.
REPLACE EBCM.
NO
YES
MALFUNCTION IS INTERMITTENT. REFER TO "DIAGNOSTIC AIDS"
5
• USING TECH 1 ABS TESTS, PERFORM GEAR TENSION RELIEF FUNCTION.
• IGNITION "OFF."
• DISCONNECT 6-WAY MOTOR PACK CONNECTOR AND 2-WAY SOLENOID CONNECTORS.
• REMOVE HYDRAULIC MODULATOR/MASTER CYLINDER ASSEMBLY
• REMOVE GEAR COVER.
• CHECK FOR STRIPPED GEAR ON MOTOR PACK; MOTOR PACK GEAR IS THE SMALLER OF THE TWO GEARS. THE RIGHT FRONT GEAR SET IS THE CLOSET TO THE BRAKE BOOSTER WHEN THE ASSEMBLY IS INSTALLED IN THE VEHICLE.
IS THE MOTOR PACK GEAR STRIPPED?
NO
YES
REPLACE MOTOR PACK.
6
• CHECK FOR A STRIPPED GEAR ON HYDRAULIC MODULATOR (MODULATOR IS UNIT WITH THREE LARGE GEARS.)
IS LARGER GEAR STRIPPED?
NO
YES
REPLACE HYDRAULIC MODULATOR GEAR.
7
• INSTALL HYDRAULIC MODULATOR/MASTER CYLINDER ASSEMBLY ONTO BOOSTER WITHOUT CONNECTING HYDRAULIC LINES AND INSTALLING GEAR COVER.
• RECONNECT ELECTRICAL CONNECTORS.
• USING TECH 1 ABS TESTS, SELECT MANUAL CONTROL FUNCTION.
• SELECT RIGHT FRONT MOTOR APPLY AND APPLY THE MOTOR WHILE USING A MIRROR TO OBSERVE THE GEAR SET CLOSET TO THE BOOSTER.
• SELECT RIGHT FRONT MOTOR RELEASE FUNCTION AND RELEASE THE MOTOR WHILE STILL WATCHING GEAR SET.
• SELECT RIGHT FRONT MOTOR APPLY FUNCTION AND APPLY THE MOTOR.
DID GEAR SET MOVE IN BOTH DIRECTIONS FOR AT LEAST ONE REVOLUTION?
NO
YES
REPLACE MOTOR PACK.
REPLACE HYDRAULIC MODULATOR.

GC402930079100BX

Fig. 162 Code A048: Right Front Motor Free Spins. 1993 Cutlass Supreme, Grand Prix, Lumina & Regal

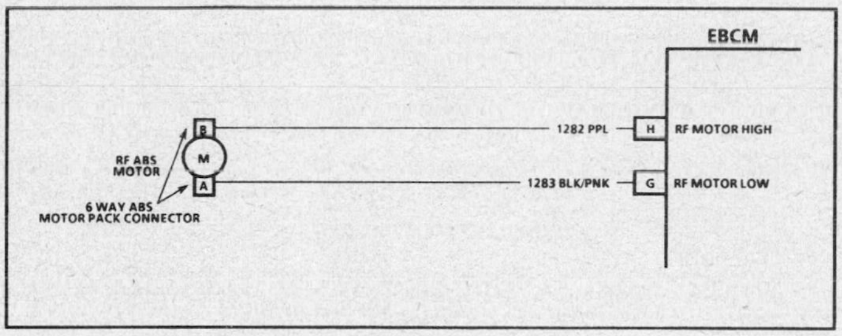
EBCM
B
M
A
RF ABS MOTOR
6 WAY ABS MOTOR PACK CONNECTOR
1282 PPL
H
RF MOTOR HIGH
1283 BLK/PNK
G
RF MOTOR LOW

DTC 48

(Page 1 of 2)

RIGHT FRONT ABS MOTOR FREE SPINS

Circuit Description:

This DTC is designed to detect a stripped nut or gear assembly during initialization. During the homing sequence, the piston should reach the top of the bore resulting in a stalled ABS motor. If this does not occur, the ABS motor must be spinning with little or no resistance, indicating a nut/screw or gear malfunction.

DTC Will Set When: DTC 48 can only be set during initialization. If the feedback current is less than the command current for a specified period of time, a malfunction exists.

Action Taken: A malfunction DTC is stored, ABS is disabled, and the ABS warning lamp is turned "ON."

DTC Chart Test Description: Number(s) below refer to circled number(s) on the diagnostic chart.

1. Checks to see if the corresponding open ABS motor DTC is also set.
2. Verifies that the ABS motor was actually applied as commanded by observing feedback current.
3. Verifies that the ABS motor can release.
4. Verifies that the ABS motor can be applied by observing pedal movement.
5. Checks for high resistance in the ABS motor "HIGH" circuitry.
6. Checks for high resistance in the ABS motor "LOW" circuitry.
7. Checks for proper resistance of the ABS motor windings.

Diagnostic Aids: An "Intermittent" malfunction in this DTC may result from a mechanical part of the system that sticks, binds, or slips.

The frequency of the malfunction can be checked by using the enhanced diagnostic function of the Tech 1.

If the DTC only occurs once and DTC 61 also, refer to DTC 61. If intermittent and enhanced diagnostics shows this DTC during ABS, refer to DTC 61.

Depending on the frequency of the malfunction, a physical inspection of the mechanical parts suspected may be necessary.

GC402940094401AX

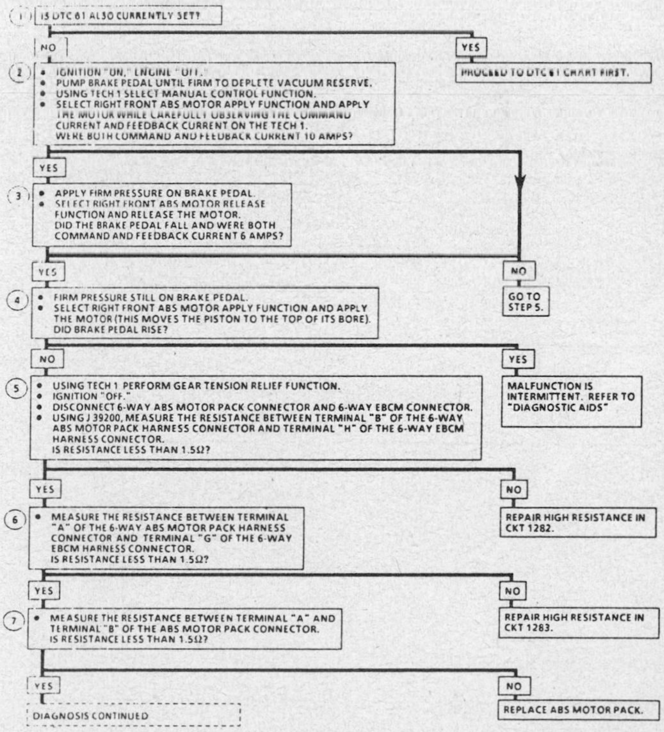
1
IS DTC 61 ALSO CURRENTLY SET?
NO
YES
PROCEED TO DTC 61 CHART FIRST.
2
• IGNITION "ON," ENGINE "OFF."
• PUMP BRAKE PEDAL UNTIL FIRM TO DEPLETE VACUUM RESERVE.
• USING TECH 1 SELECT MANUAL CONTROL FUNCTION.
• SELECT RIGHT FRONT ABS MOTOR APPLY FUNCTION AND APPLY THE MOTOR WHILE CAREFULLY OBSERVING THE COMMAND CURRENT AND FEEDBACK CURRENT ON THE TECH 1.
WERE BOTH COMMAND AND FEEDBACK CURRENT 10 AMPS?
YES
3
• APPLY FIRM PRESSURE ON BRAKE PEDAL.
• SELECT RIGHT FRONT ABS MOTOR RELEASE FUNCTION AND RELEASE THE MOTOR.
DID THE BRAKE PEDAL FALL AND WERE BOTH COMMAND AND FEEDBACK CURRENT 6 AMPS?
YES
NO
GO TO STEP 5.
4
• FIRM PRESSURE STILL ON BRAKE PEDAL.
• SELECT RIGHT FRONT ABS MOTOR APPLY FUNCTION AND APPLY THE MOTOR (THIS MOVES THE PISTON TO THE TOP OF ITS BORE).
DID BRAKE PEDAL RISE?
NO
YES
MALFUNCTION IS INTERMITTENT. REFER TO "DIAGNOSTIC AIDS"
5
• USING TECH 1 PERFORM GEAR TENSION RELIEF FUNCTION.
• IGNITION "OFF."
• DISCONNECT 6-WAY ABS MOTOR PACK CONNECTOR AND 6-WAY EBCM CONNECTOR.
• USING J 39200, MEASURE THE RESISTANCE BETWEEN TERMINAL "B" OF THE 6-WAY ABS MOTOR PACK HARNESS CONNECTOR AND TERMINAL "H" OF THE 6-WAY EBCM HARNESS CONNECTOR.
IS RESISTANCE LESS THAN 1.5Ω?
YES
NO
REPAIR HIGH RESISTANCE IN CKT 1282.
6
• MEASURE THE RESISTANCE BETWEEN TERMINAL "A" OF THE 6-WAY ABS MOTOR PACK HARNESS CONNECTOR AND TERMINAL "G" OF THE 6-WAY EBCM HARNESS CONNECTOR.
IS RESISTANCE LESS THAN 1.5Ω?
YES
NO
REPAIR HIGH RESISTANCE IN CKT 1283.
7
• MEASURE THE RESISTANCE BETWEEN TERMINAL "A" AND TERMINAL "B" OF THE ABS MOTOR PACK CONNECTOR.
IS RESISTANCE LESS THAN 1.5Ω?
YES
NO
DIAGNOSIS CONTINUED
REPLACE ABS MOTOR PACK.

GC402940094401BX

Fig. 163 Code A048: Right Front ABS Motor Free Spins (Part 1 of 2). 1994 Cutlass Supreme, Lumina & Regal

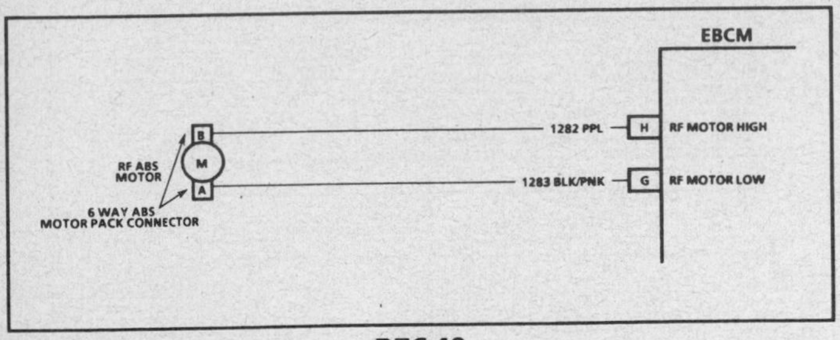
EBCM
1282 PPL
H
RF MOTOR HIGH
B
M
RF ABS MOTOR
A
1283 BLK/PNK
G
RF MOTOR LOW
6 WAY ABS MOTOR PACK CONNECTOR

DTC 48

(Page 2 of 2)

RIGHT FRONT ABS MOTOR FREE SPINS

Circuit Description:

This DTC is designed to detect a stripped nut or gear assembly during initialization. During the homing sequence, the piston should reach the top of the bore resulting in a stalled ABS motor. If this does not occur, the ABS motor must be spinning with little or no resistance, indicating a nut/screw or gear malfunction.

DTC Will Set When: DTC 48 can only be set during initialization. If the feedback current is less than the command current for a specified period of time, a malfunction exists.

Action Taken: A malfunction DTC is stored, ABS is disabled, and the ABS warning lamp is turned "ON."

DTC Chart Test Description: Number(s) below refer to circled number(s) on the diagnostic chart.

8. Checks for a stripped gear on the ABS motor pack (unit with three small gears).
9. Checks for a stripped gear on the hydraulic modulator (unit with three large gears).
10. Verifies that the ABS motor can be applied under a load situation.
11. Verifies that the hydraulic modulator is functioning properly.
12. Ensures malfunction was not due to poor terminal contact.

Diagnostic Aids: An "Intermittent" malfunction in this DTC may result from a mechanical part of the system that sticks, binds, or slips.

The frequency of the malfunction can be checked by using the enhanced diagnostic function of the Tech 1

If the DTC only occurs once and DTC 61 also occurs, refer to DTC 61. If intermittent and enhanced diagnostics shows this DTC occurs during ABS, refer to DTC 61.

Depending on the frequency of the malfunction, a physical inspection of the mechanical parts suspected may be necessary.

GC402940094402AX

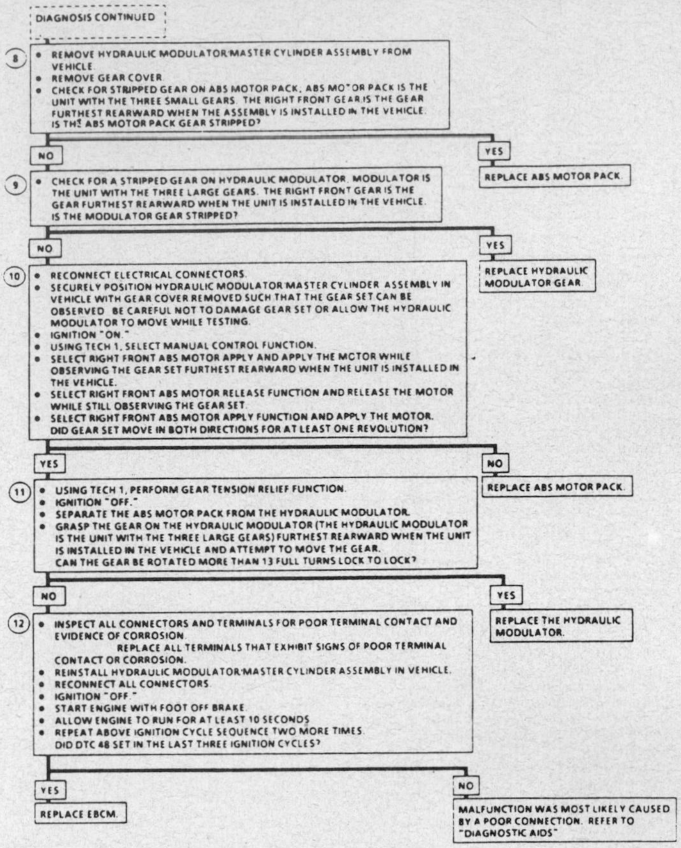
DIAGNOSIS CONTINUED
8
• REMOVE HYDRAULIC MODULATOR/MASTER CYLINDER ASSEMBLY FROM VEHICLE.
• REMOVE GEAR COVER.
• CHECK FOR STRIPPED GEAR ON ABS MOTOR PACK. ABS MOTOR PACK IS THE UNIT WITH THE THREE SMALL GEARS. THE RIGHT FRONT GEAR IS THE GEAR FURTHEST REARWARD WHEN THE ASSEMBLY IS INSTALLED IN THE VEHICLE. IS THE ABS MOTOR PACK GEAR STRIPPED?
NO
YES
REPLACE ABS MOTOR PACK.
9
• CHECK FOR A STRIPPED GEAR ON HYDRAULIC MODULATOR. MODULATOR IS THE UNIT WITH THE THREE LARGE GEARS. THE RIGHT FRONT GEAR IS THE GEAR FURTHEST REARWARD WHEN THE UNIT IS INSTALLED IN THE VEHICLE. IS THE MODULATOR GEAR STRIPPED?
NO
YES
REPLACE HYDRAULIC MODULATOR GEAR.
10
• RECONNECT ELECTRICAL CONNECTORS.
• SECURELY POSITION HYDRAULIC MODULATOR/MASTER CYLINDER ASSEMBLY IN VEHICLE WITH GEAR COVER REMOVED SUCH THAT THE GEAR SET CAN BE OBSERVED. BE CAREFUL NOT TO DAMAGE GEAR SET OR ALLOW THE HYDRAULIC MODULATOR TO MOVE WHILE TESTING.
• IGNITION "ON."
• USING TECH 1, SELECT MANUAL CONTROL FUNCTION.
• SELECT RIGHT FRONT ABS MOTOR APPLY AND APPLY THE MOTOR WHILE OBSERVING THE GEAR SET FURTHEST REARWARD WHEN THE UNIT IS INSTALLED IN THE VEHICLE.
• SELECT RIGHT FRONT ABS MOTOR RELEASE FUNCTION AND RELEASE THE MOTOR WHILE STILL OBSERVING THE GEAR SET.
• SELECT RIGHT FRONT ABS MOTOR APPLY FUNCTION AND APPLY THE MOTOR. DID GEAR SET MOVE IN BOTH DIRECTIONS FOR AT LEAST ONE REVOLUTION?
YES
NO
REPLACE ABS MOTOR PACK.
11
• USING TECH 1, PERFORM GEAR TENSION RELIEF FUNCTION.
• IGNITION "OFF."
• SEPARATE THE ABS MOTOR PACK FROM THE HYDRAULIC MODULATOR.
• GRASP THE GEAR ON THE HYDRAULIC MODULATOR (THE HYDRAULIC MODULATOR IS THE UNIT WITH THE THREE LARGE GEARS) FURTHEST REARWARD WHEN THE UNIT IS INSTALLED IN THE VEHICLE AND ATTEMPT TO MOVE THE GEAR. CAN THE GEAR BE ROTATED MORE THAN 13 FULL TURNS LOCK TO LOCK?
NO
YES
REPLACE THE HYDRAULIC MODULATOR.
12
• INSPECT ALL CONNECTORS AND TERMINALS FOR POOR TERMINAL CONTACT AND EVIDENCE OF CORROSION.
REPLACE ALL TERMINALS THAT EXHIBIT SIGNS OF POOR TERMINAL CONTACT OR CORROSION.
• REINSTALL HYDRAULIC MODULATOR/MASTER CYLINDER ASSEMBLY IN VEHICLE.
• RECONNECT ALL CONNECTORS.
• IGNITION "OFF."
• START ENGINE WITH FOOT OFF BRAKE.
• ALLOW ENGINE TO RUN FOR AT LEAST 10 SECONDS.
• REPEAT ABOVE IGNITION CYCLE SEQUENCE TWO MORE TIMES. DID DTC 48 SET IN THE LAST THREE IGNITION CYCLES?
YES
REPLACE EBCM.
NO
MALFUNCTION WAS MOST LIKELY CAUSED BY A POOR CONNECTION. REFER TO "DIAGNOSTIC AIDS"

GC402940094402BX

Fig. 163 Code A048: Right Front ABS Motor Free Spins (Part 2 of 2). 1994 Cutlass Supreme, Lumina & Regal

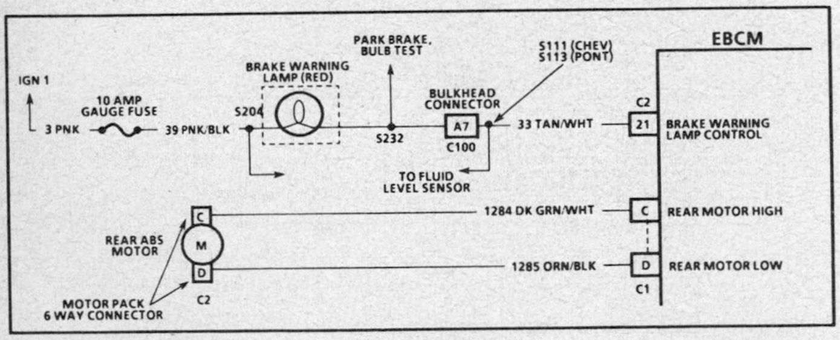
EBCM
PARK BRAKE, BULB TEST
S111 (CHEV)
S113 (PONT)
IGN 1
BRAKE WARNING LAMP (RED)
10 AMP GAUGE FUSE
3 PNK
39 PNK/BLK
S204
S232
BULKHEAD CONNECTOR
A7
C100
33 TAN/WHT
C2
21
BRAKE WARNING LAMP CONTROL
TO FLUID LEVEL SENSOR
1284 DK GRN/WHT
C
REAR MOTOR HIGH
REAR ABS MOTOR
M
D
1285 ORN/BLK
REAR MOTOR LOW
C1
MOTOR PACK 6 WAY CONNECTOR

GC402930079200AX

Cavalier & Sunbird

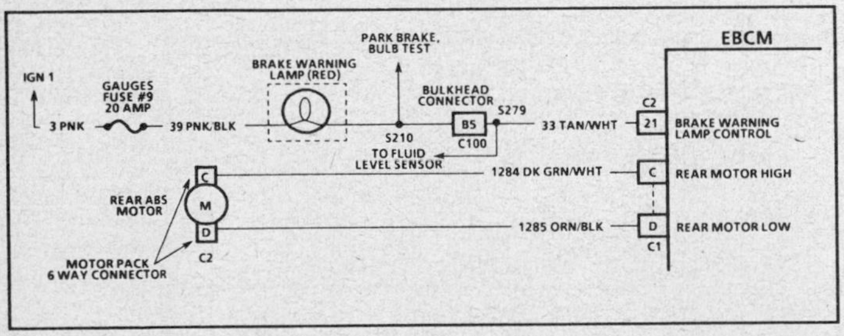
EBCM
PARK BRAKE, BULB TEST
IGN 1
BRAKE WARNING LAMP (RED)
GAUGES FUSE #9 20 AMP
3 PNK
39 PNK/BLK
BULKHEAD CONNECTOR
B5
S279
S210
C100
33 TAN/WHT
C2
21
BRAKE WARNING LAMP CONTROL
TO FLUID LEVEL SENSOR
1284 DK GRN/WHT
C
REAR MOTOR HIGH
REAR ABS MOTOR
M
D
1285 ORN/BLK
REAR MOTOR LOW
C1
MOTOR PACK 6 WAY CONNECTOR

GC402930079200BX

Achieva, Beretta, Corsica, Grand Am & Skylark

DTC A051

REAR AXLE MOTOR FREE SPINS

Circuit Description:

This DTC is designed to detect a stripped nut or gear assembly during initialization. During the homing sequence, the piston should reach the top of the bore resulting in a stalled motor. If this does not occur, the motor must be spinning with little or no resistance, indicating a nut/screw or gear failure.

Failure Condition:

DTC A051 can be set during initialization. If the feedback current is less than the command current for a specified period of time, a malfunction exists.

Action Taken:

A malfunction DTC is stored, ABS is disabled, and the ABS indicator lamp is turned "ON."

Test Description: Number(s) below refer to circled number(s) on the diagnostic chart.

1. This step compares feedback current to command current during apply. If either is 0 amps, the EBCM is not functioning properly.
2. This step compares feedback current to command current during release. If either is 0 amps, the EBCM is not functioning properly.
3. Steps 1, 2 and 3 verify malfunction exists. This step also moves the piston to the top of the bore.
4. This step checks for a stripped motor pack gear.
5. This step checks for a stripped hydraulic modulator gear.
6. This test checks the ability of the motor to operator properly when commanded.

Diagnostic Aids:

An "Intermittent" malfunction in this DTC may result from a mechanical part of the system that sticks, binds, or slips.

The frequency of the malfunction can be checked by using the enhanced diagnostic function of the Tech 1

If DTC only fails once and DTC A064 also fails, see DTC A064. If intermittent and enhanced diagnostics show this DTC fails during ABS, see DTC A064.

Depending on the frequency of the failure, a physical inspection of the mechanical parts suspected may be necessary.

GC402930079200CX

Fig. 164 Code A051: Rear Axle Motor Free Spins (Part 1 of 2). 1993-94 Cavalier, Sunbird, Beretta, Corsica & Achieva, Grand Am & Skylark Less VES

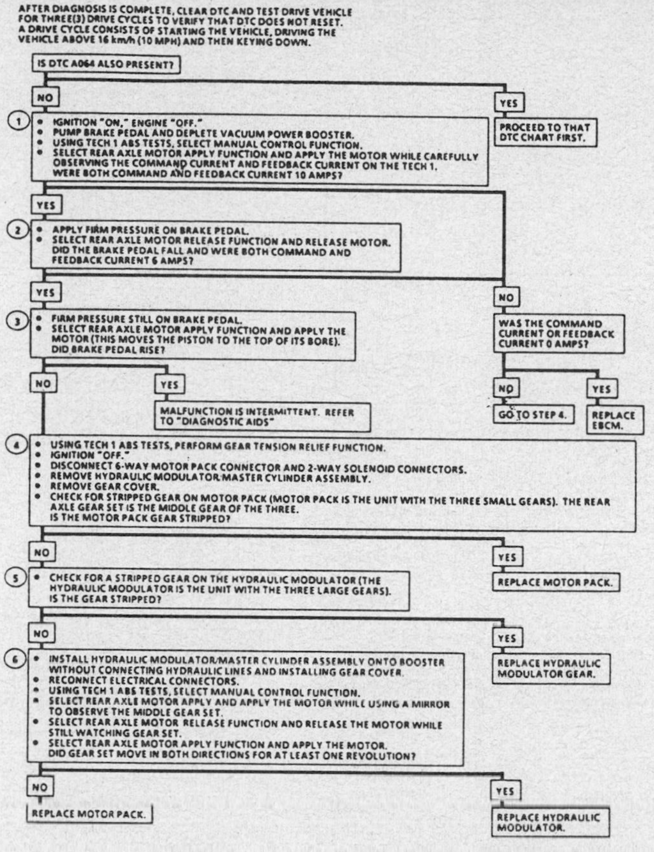

AFTER DIAGNOSIS IS COMPLETE, CLEAR DTC AND TEST DRIVE VEHICLE FOR THREE(3) DRIVE CYCLES TO VERIFY THAT DTC DOES NOT RESET. A DRIVE CYCLE CONSISTS OF STARTING THE VEHICLE, DRIVING THE VEHICLE ABOVE 16 km/h (10 MPH) AND THEN KEYING DOWN.
IS DTC A064 ALSO PRESENT?
NO
YES
PROCEED TO THAT DTC CHART FIRST.
1
• IGNITION "ON," ENGINE "OFF."
• PUMP BRAKE PEDAL AND DEPLETE VACUUM POWER BOOSTER.
• USING TECH 1 ABS TESTS, SELECT MANUAL CONTROL FUNCTION.
• SELECT REAR AXLE MOTOR APPLY FUNCTION AND APPLY THE MOTOR WHILE CAREFULLY OBSERVING THE COMMAND CURRENT AND FEEDBACK CURRENT ON THE TECH 1. WERE BOTH COMMAND AND FEEDBACK CURRENT 10 AMPS?
YES
2
• APPLY FIRM PRESSURE ON BRAKE PEDAL.
• SELECT REAR AXLE MOTOR RELEASE FUNCTION AND RELEASE MOTOR. DID THE BRAKE PEDAL FALL AND WERE BOTH COMMAND AND FEEDBACK CURRENT 6 AMPS?
YES
NO
WAS THE COMMAND CURRENT OR FEEDBACK CURRENT 0 AMPS?
3
• FIRM PRESSURE STILL ON BRAKE PEDAL.
• SELECT REAR AXLE MOTOR APPLY FUNCTION AND APPLY THE MOTOR (THIS MOVES THE PISTON TO THE TOP OF ITS BORE). DID BRAKE PEDAL RISE?
NO
YES
MALFUNCTION IS INTERMITTENT. REFER TO "DIAGNOSTIC AIDS"
NO
YES
GO TO STEP 4.
REPLACE EBCM.
4
• USING TECH 1 ABS TESTS, PERFORM GEAR TENSION RELIEF FUNCTION.
• IGNITION "OFF."
• DISCONNECT 6-WAY MOTOR PACK CONNECTOR AND 2-WAY SOLENOID CONNECTORS.
• REMOVE HYDRAULIC MODULATOR/MASTER CYLINDER ASSEMBLY.
• REMOVE GEAR COVER.
• CHECK FOR STRIPPED GEAR ON MOTOR PACK (MOTOR PACK IS THE UNIT WITH THE THREE SMALL GEARS). THE REAR AXLE GEAR SET IS THE MIDDLE GEAR OF THE THREE. IS THE MOTOR PACK GEAR STRIPPED?
NO
YES
REPLACE MOTOR PACK.
5
• CHECK FOR A STRIPPED GEAR ON THE HYDRAULIC MODULATOR (THE HYDRAULIC MODULATOR IS THE UNIT WITH THE THREE LARGE GEARS). IS THE GEAR STRIPPED?
NO
YES
REPLACE HYDRAULIC MODULATOR GEAR.
6
• INSTALL HYDRAULIC MODULATOR/MASTER CYLINDER ASSEMBLY ONTO BOOSTER WITHOUT CONNECTING HYDRAULIC LINES AND INSTALLING GEAR COVER.
• RECONNECT ELECTRICAL CONNECTORS.
• USING TECH 1 ABS TESTS, SELECT MANUAL CONTROL FUNCTION.
• SELECT REAR AXLE MOTOR APPLY AND APPLY THE MOTOR WHILE USING A MIRROR TO OBSERVE THE MIDDLE GEAR SET.
• SELECT REAR AXLE MOTOR RELEASE FUNCTION AND RELEASE THE MOTOR WHILE STILL WATCHING GEAR SET.
• SELECT REAR AXLE MOTOR APPLY FUNCTION AND APPLY THE MOTOR. DID GEAR SET MOVE IN BOTH DIRECTIONS FOR AT LEAST ONE REVOLUTION?
NO
YES
REPLACE MOTOR PACK.
REPLACE HYDRAULIC MODULATOR.

GC402930079200DX

Fig. 164 Code A051: Rear Axle Motor Free Spins (Part 2 of 2). 1993-94 Cavalier, Sunbird, Beretta, Corsica & Achieva, Grand Am & Skylark Less VES

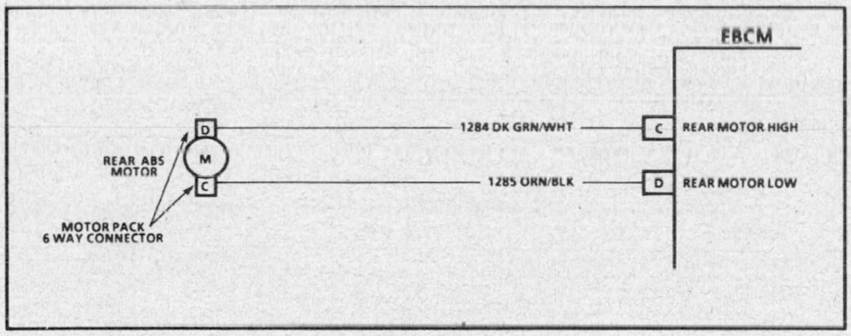

EBCM
REAR ABS MOTOR
M
D
C
MOTOR PACK 6 WAY CONNECTOR
1284 DK GRN/WHT
1285 ORN/BLK
C
D
REAR MOTOR HIGH
REAR MOTOR LOW

DTC A051

REAR AXLE MOTOR FREE SPINS

Circuit Description:

This DTC is designed to detect a stripped nut or gear assembly during initialization. During the homing sequence, the piston should reach the top of the bore resulting in a stalled motor. If this does not occur, the motor must be spinning with little or no resistance, indicating a nut/screw or gear malfunction.

Failure Condition:

DTC A051 can be set during initialization. If the feedback current is less than the command current for a specified period of time, a malfunction exists.

Action Taken:

A malfunction DTC is stored, ABS is disabled, and the ABS indicator lamp is turned "ON."

Test Description: Number(s) below refer to circled number(s) on the diagnostic chart.

1. This step checks to see if the corresponding open motor DTC is also set.
2. This step verifies that the motor was actually applied as command by observing feedback current.
3. This step verifies that the motor can release.
4. This step verifies that the motor can be applied by observing pedal movement.
5. This step checks for a stripped gear on the motor pack (unit with three small gears).
6. This step checks for a stripped gear on the hydraulic modulator (unit with three large gears).
7. This step determines whether the hydraulic modulator or the motor pack has an internal malfunction.
8. This step checks for a malfunctioning EBCM.

Diagnostic Aids:

An "Intermittent" malfunction in this DTC may result from a mechanical part of the system that sticks, binds, or slips.

The frequency of the malfunction can be checked by using the enhanced diagnostic function of the Tech 1, as described in "Tech 1 Diagnostics" found in this section. If the DTC only fails once and DTC A064 also fails, refer to DTC A064. If intermittent and enhanced diagnostics show this DTC fails during ABS, refer to DTC A064.

Depending on the frequency of the malfunction, a physical inspection of the mechanical parts suspected may be necessary.

GC402930079300AX

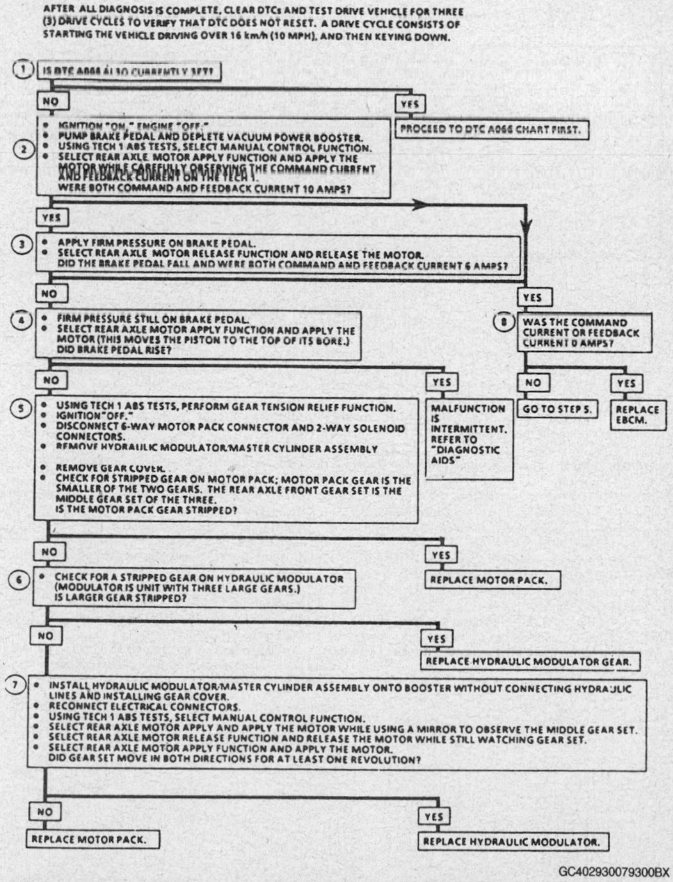

AFTER ALL DIAGNOSIS IS COMPLETE, CLEAR DTCs AND TEST DRIVE VEHICLE FOR THREE (3) DRIVE CYCLES TO VERIFY THAT DTC DOES NOT RESET. A DRIVE CYCLE CONSISTS OF STARTING THE VEHICLE DRIVING OVER 16 km/h (10 MPH), AND THEN KEYING DOWN.
1
NO
YES
PROCEED TO DTC A066 CHART FIRST.
2
• IGNITION "ON," ENGINE "OFF."
• PUMP BRAKE PEDAL AND DEPLETE VACUUM POWER BOOSTER.
• USING TECH 1 ABS TESTS, SELECT MANUAL CONTROL FUNCTION.
WERE BOTH COMMAND AND FEEDBACK CURRENT 10 AMPS?
YES
3
• APPLY FIRM PRESSURE ON BRAKE PEDAL.
• SELECT REAR AXLE MOTOR RELEASE FUNCTION AND RELEASE THE MOTOR. DID THE BRAKE PEDAL FALL AND WERE BOTH COMMAND AND FEEDBACK CURRENT 6 AMPS?
NO
YES
4
• FIRM PRESSURE STILL ON BRAKE PEDAL.
• SELECT REAR AXLE MOTOR APPLY FUNCTION AND APPLY THE MOTOR (THIS MOVES THE PISTON TO THE TOP OF ITS BORE.) DID BRAKE PEDAL RISE?
8
WAS THE COMMAND CURRENT OR FEEDBACK CURRENT 0 AMPS?
NO
YES
NO
YES
5
• USING TECH 1 ABS TESTS, PERFORM GEAR TENSION RELIEF FUNCTION.
• IGNITION "OFF."
• DISCONNECT 6-WAY MOTOR PACK CONNECTOR AND 2-WAY SOLENOID CONNECTORS.
• REMOVE GEAR COVER.
• CHECK FOR STRIPPED GEAR ON MOTOR PACK; MOTOR PACK GEAR IS THE SMALLER OF THE TWO GEARS. THE REAR AXLE FRONT GEAR SET IS THE MIDDLE GEAR SET OF THE THREE. IS THE MOTOR PACK GEAR STRIPPED?
MALFUNCTION IS INTERMITTENT. REFER TO "DIAGNOSTIC AIDS"
GO TO STEP 5.
REPLACE EBCM.
NO
YES
REPLACE MOTOR PACK.
6
• CHECK FOR A STRIPPED GEAR ON HYDRAULIC MODULATOR (MODULATOR IS UNIT WITH THREE LARGE GEARS.) IS LARGER GEAR STRIPPED?
NO
YES
REPLACE HYDRAULIC MODULATOR GEAR.
7
• INSTALL HYDRAULIC MODULATOR/MASTER CYLINDER ASSEMBLY ONTO BOOSTER WITHOUT CONNECTING HYDRAULIC LINES AND INSTALLING GEAR COVER.
• RECONNECT ELECTRICAL CONNECTORS.
• USING TECH 1 ABS TESTS, SELECT MANUAL CONTROL FUNCTION.
• SELECT REAR AXLE MOTOR APPLY AND APPLY THE MOTOR WHILE USING A MIRROR TO OBSERVE THE MIDDLE GEAR SET.
• SELECT REAR AXLE MOTOR RELEASE FUNCTION AND RELEASE THE MOTOR WHILE STILL WATCHING GEAR SET.
• SELECT REAR AXLE MOTOR APPLY FUNCTION AND APPLY THE MOTOR. DID GEAR SET MOVE IN BOTH DIRECTIONS FOR AT LEAST ONE REVOLUTION?
NO
YES
REPLACE MOTOR PACK.
REPLACE HYDRAULIC MODULATOR.

GC402930079300BX

Fig. 165 Code A051: Rear Axle Motor Free Spins. 1993 Cutlass Supreme, Grand Prix, Lumina & Regal

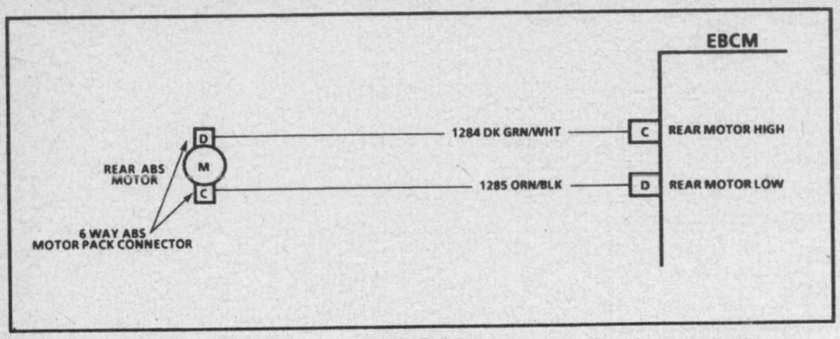
EBCM
REAR ABS MOTOR
M
D
C
1284 DK GRN/WHT
1285 ORN/BLK
C REAR MOTOR HIGH
D REAR MOTOR LOW
6 WAY ABS MOTOR PACK CONNECTOR

DTC 51

(Page 1 of 2)

REAR ABS MOTOR FREE SPINS

Circuit Description:

This DTC is designed to detect a stripped nut or gear assembly during initialization. During the homing sequence, the piston should reach the top of the bore resulting in a stalled ABS motor. If this does not occur, the ABS motor must be spinning with little or no resistance, indicating a nut/screw or gear malfunction.

DTC Will Set When: DTC 51 can be set during initialization. If the feedback current is less than the command current for a specified period of time, a malfunction exists.

Action Taken: A malfunction DTC is stored, ABS is disabled, and the ABS warning lamp is turned "ON."

DTC Chart Test Description: Number(s) below refer to circled number(s) on the diagnostic chart.

1. Checks to see if the corresponding open ABS motor DTC 64 is also set.
2. Verifies that the ABS motor was actually applied as commanded by observing feedback current.
3. Verifies that the ABS motor can release.
4. Verifies that the ABS motor can be applied by observing pedal movement.
5. Checks for high resistance in the ABS motor "HIGH" circuitry.
6. Checks for high resistance in the ABS motor "LOW" circuitry.
7. Checks for proper resistance of the ABS motor windings.

Diagnostic Aids: An "Intermittent" malfunction in this DTC may result from a mechanical part of the system that sticks, binds, or slips.

The frequency of the malfunction can be checked by using the enhanced diagnostic function of the Tech 1

If the DTC only occurs once and DTC 64 also occurs, refer to DTC 64. If intermittent and enhanced diagnostics show this DTC occurs during ABS, refer to DTC 64.

Depending on the frequency of the malfunction, a physical inspection of the mechanical parts suspected may be necessary.

GC402940094501AX

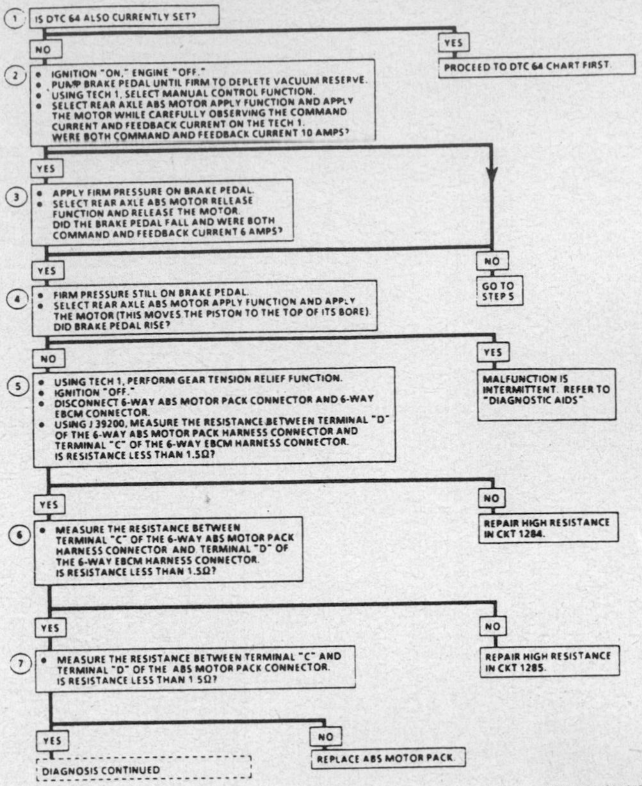
1 IS DTC 64 ALSO CURRENTLY SET?
NO
YES
PROCEED TO DTC 64 CHART FIRST.
2 • IGNITION "ON," ENGINE "OFF."
• PUMP BRAKE PEDAL UNTIL FIRM TO DEPLETE VACUUM RESERVE.
• USING TECH 1, SELECT MANUAL CONTROL FUNCTION.
• SELECT REAR AXLE ABS MOTOR APPLY FUNCTION AND APPLY THE MOTOR WHILE CAREFULLY OBSERVING THE COMMAND CURRENT AND FEEDBACK CURRENT ON THE TECH 1.
WERE BOTH COMMAND AND FEEDBACK CURRENT 10 AMPS?
YES
3 • APPLY FIRM PRESSURE ON BRAKE PEDAL.
• SELECT REAR AXLE ABS MOTOR RELEASE FUNCTION AND RELEASE THE MOTOR.
DID THE BRAKE PEDAL FALL AND WERE BOTH COMMAND AND FEEDBACK CURRENT 6 AMPS?
NO
GO TO STEP 5
YES
4 • FIRM PRESSURE STILL ON BRAKE PEDAL.
• SELECT REAR AXLE ABS MOTOR APPLY FUNCTION AND APPLY THE MOTOR (THIS MOVES THE PISTON TO THE TOP OF ITS BORE).
DID BRAKE PEDAL RISE?
NO
YES
MALFUNCTION IS INTERMITTENT. REFER TO "DIAGNOSTIC AIDS"
5 • USING TECH 1, PERFORM GEAR TENSION RELIEF FUNCTION.
• IGNITION "OFF."
• DISCONNECT 6-WAY ABS MOTOR PACK CONNECTOR AND 6-WAY EBCM CONNECTOR.
• USING J 39200, MEASURE THE RESISTANCE BETWEEN TERMINAL "D" OF THE 6-WAY ABS MOTOR PACK HARNESS CONNECTOR AND TERMINAL "C" OF THE 6-WAY EBCM HARNESS CONNECTOR.
IS RESISTANCE LESS THAN 1.5Ω?
YES
NO
REPAIR HIGH RESISTANCE IN CKT 1284.
6 • MEASURE THE RESISTANCE BETWEEN TERMINAL "C" OF THE 6-WAY ABS MOTOR PACK HARNESS CONNECTOR AND TERMINAL "D" OF THE 6-WAY EBCM HARNESS CONNECTOR.
IS RESISTANCE LESS THAN 1.5Ω?
YES
NO
REPAIR HIGH RESISTANCE IN CKT 1285.
7 • MEASURE THE RESISTANCE BETWEEN TERMINAL "C" AND TERMINAL "D" OF THE ABS MOTOR PACK CONNECTOR.
IS RESISTANCE LESS THAN 1 5Ω?
YES
NO
DIAGNOSIS CONTINUED
REPLACE ABS MOTOR PACK.

GC402940094501BX

Fig. 166 Code A051: Rear Axle Motor Free Spins (1 of 2). 1994 Cutlass Supreme, Lumina & Regal

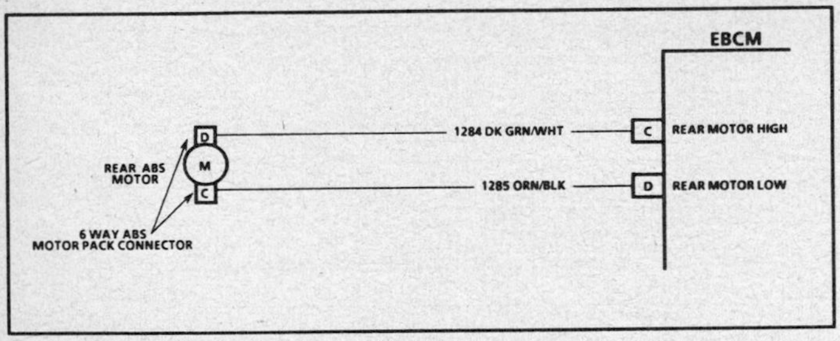
EBCM
REAR ABS MOTOR
M
D
C
1284 DK GRN/WHT
1285 ORN/BLK
C REAR MOTOR HIGH
D REAR MOTOR LOW
6 WAY ABS MOTOR PACK CONNECTOR

DTC 51

(Page 2 of 2)

REAR ABS MOTOR FREE SPINS

Circuit Description:

This DTC is designed to detect a stripped nut or gear assembly during initialization. During the homing sequence, the piston should reach the top of the bore resulting in a stalled motor. If this does not occur, the ABS motor must be spinning with little or no resistance, indicating a nut/screw or gear malfunction.

DTC Will Set When: DTC 51 can be set during initialization. If the feedback current is less than the command current for a specified period of time, a malfunction exists.

Action Taken: A malfunction DTC is stored, ABS is disabled, and the ABS warning lamp is turned "ON."

DTC Chart Test Description: Number(s) below refer to circled number(s) on the diagnostic chart.

8. Checks for a stripped gear on the ABS motor pack (unit with three small gears).
9. Checks for a stripped gear on the hydraulic modulator (unit with three large gears).
10. Verifies that the ABS motor can be applied under a load situation.
11. Verifies that the hydraulic modulator is functioning properly.
12. Ensures malfunction was not due to poor terminal contact.

Diagnostic Aids: An "Intermittent" malfunction in this DTC may result from a mechanical part of the system that sticks, binds, or slips.

The frequency of the malfunction can be checked by using the enhanced diagnostic function of the Tech 1

If the DTC only occurs once and DTC 64 also occurs, refer to DTC 64. If intermittent and enhanced diagnostics show this DTC occurs during ABS, refer to DTC 64.

Depending on the frequency of the malfunction, a physical inspection of the mechanical parts suspected may be necessary.

GC402940094502AX

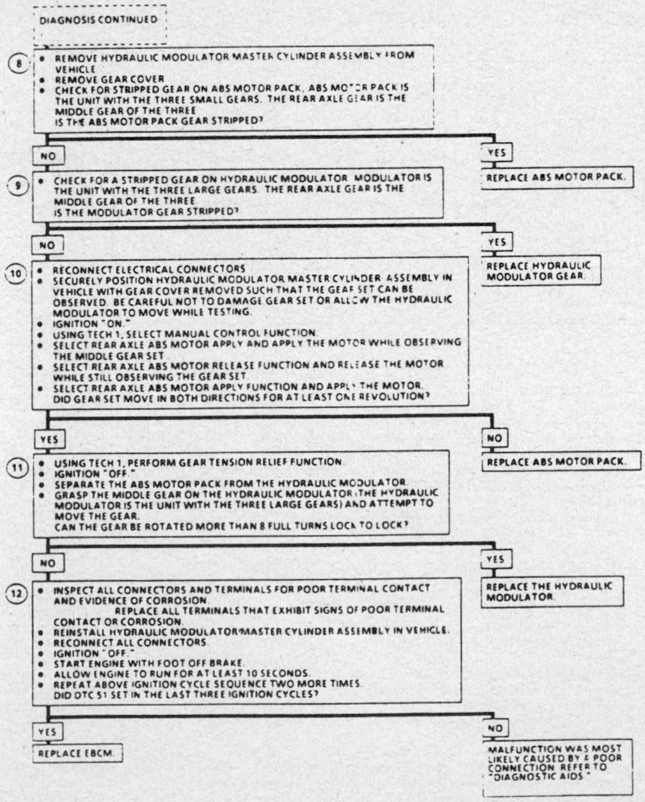
DIAGNOSIS CONTINUED
8 • REMOVE HYDRAULIC MODULATOR MASTER CYLINDER ASSEMBLY FROM VEHICLE
• REMOVE GEAR COVER
• CHECK FOR STRIPPED GEAR ON ABS MOTOR PACK, ABS MOTOR PACK IS THE UNIT WITH THE THREE SMALL GEARS. THE REAR AXLE GEAR IS THE MIDDLE GEAR OF THE THREE
IS THE ABS MOTOR PACK GEAR STRIPPED?
NO
YES
REPLACE ABS MOTOR PACK.
9 • CHECK FOR A STRIPPED GEAR ON HYDRAULIC MODULATOR MODULATOR IS THE UNIT WITH THE THREE LARGE GEARS. THE REAR AXLE GEAR IS THE MIDDLE GEAR OF THE THREE
IS THE MODULATOR GEAR STRIPPED?
NO
YES
REPLACE HYDRAULIC MODULATOR GEAR.
10 • RECONNECT ELECTRICAL CONNECTORS
• SECURELY POSITION HYDRAULIC MODULATOR MASTER CYLINDER ASSEMBLY IN VEHICLE WITH GEAR COVER REMOVED SUCH THAT THE GEAR SET CAN BE OBSERVED. BE CAREFUL NOT TO DAMAGE GEAR SET OR ALLOW THE HYDRAULIC MODULATOR TO MOVE WHILE TESTING.
• IGNITION "ON."
• USING TECH 1, SELECT MANUAL CONTROL FUNCTION.
• SELECT REAR AXLE ABS MOTOR APPLY AND APPLY THE MOTOR WHILE OBSERVING THE MIDDLE GEAR SET.
• SELECT REAR AXLE ABS MOTOR RELEASE FUNCTION AND RELEASE THE MOTOR WHILE STILL OBSERVING THE GEAR SET.
• SELECT REAR AXLE ABS MOTOR APPLY FUNCTION AND APPLY THE MOTOR.
DID GEAR SET MOVE IN BOTH DIRECTIONS FOR AT LEAST ONE REVOLUTION?
YES
NO
REPLACE ABS MOTOR PACK.
11 • USING TECH 1, PERFORM GEAR TENSION RELIEF FUNCTION.
• IGNITION "OFF."
• SEPARATE THE ABS MOTOR PACK FROM THE HYDRAULIC MODULATOR.
• GRASP THE MIDDLE GEAR ON THE HYDRAULIC MODULATOR (THE HYDRAULIC MODULATOR IS THE UNIT WITH THE THREE LARGE GEARS) AND ATTEMPT TO MOVE THE GEAR.
CAN THE GEAR BE ROTATED MORE THAN 8 FULL TURNS LOCK TO LOCK?
NO
YES
REPLACE THE HYDRAULIC MODULATOR.
12 • INSPECT ALL CONNECTORS AND TERMINALS FOR POOR TERMINAL CONTACT AND EVIDENCE OF CORROSION.
REPLACE ALL TERMINALS THAT EXHIBIT SIGNS OF POOR TERMINAL CONTACT OR CORROSION.
• REINSTALL HYDRAULIC MODULATOR/MASTER CYLINDER ASSEMBLY IN VEHICLE.
• RECONNECT ALL CONNECTORS.
• IGNITION "OFF."
• START ENGINE WITH FOOT OFF BRAKE.
• ALLOW ENGINE TO RUN FOR AT LEAST 10 SECONDS.
• REPEAT ABOVE IGNITION CYCLE SEQUENCE TWO MORE TIMES.
DID DTC 51 SET IN THE LAST THREE IGNITION CYCLES?
YES
REPLACE EBCM.
NO
MALFUNCTION WAS MOST LIKELY CAUSED BY A POOR CONNECTION. REFER TO "DIAGNOSTIC AIDS."

GC402940094502BX

Fig. 166 Code A051: Rear Axle Motor Free Spins (2 of 2). 1994 Cutlass Supreme, Lumina & Regal

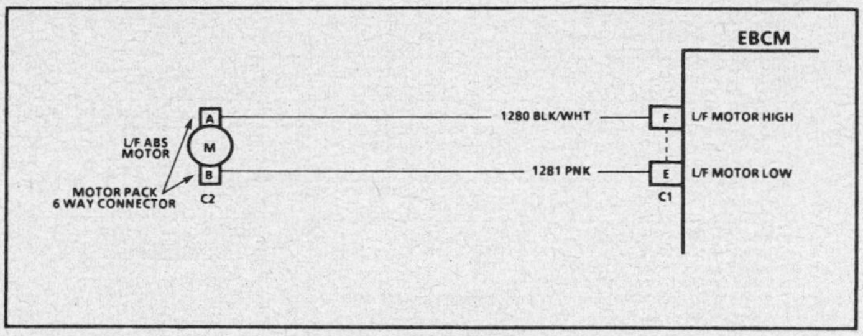
EBCM
1280 BLK/WHT
F
L/F MOTOR HIGH
L/F ABS MOTOR
M
A
B
1281 PNK
E
L/F MOTOR LOW
MOTOR PACK
6 WAY CONNECTOR
C2
C1

DTC A052

LEFT FRONT CHANNEL IN RELEASE TOO LONG

Circuit Description:

This DTC will diagnose a motor that is energized longer than expected. This could occur if a wheel speed sensor is faulty, the motor does not turn, the left front solenoid mechanically fails open, the brakes are dragging, or the motor wires are crossed.

Failure Condition:

DTC A052 can be set only during an ABS stop. If the EBCM commands the left front channel in release for three seconds, a malfunction exists.

Action Taken:

A malfunction DTC is stored, ABS is disabled, and the ABS indicator lamp is turned "ON."

Test Description: Number(s) below refer to circled number(s) on the diagnostic chart.

1. This step identifies a malfunction in a wheel speed sensor that may cause the system to be in release too long.
2. This step identifies a motor fault as being failed or wired incorrectly.
3. This step checks for a solenoid that may have mechanically failed open.
4. If Step 3 has failed, this serves to isolate the cause of the hydraulic problem, to either the solenoid or the ABS hydraulic modulator.
5. This step is used to release the tension of the motor pack.
6. This step checks for proper operation of hydraulic modulator.

Diagnostic Aids:

An "Intermittent" malfunction may be caused by a mechanical part of the system that sticks or binds.

The frequency of the malfunction can be checked by using the enhanced diagnostic function of the "Tech 1, as described in "Enhanced Diagnostics," found in this section. DTC A052 may fail if on ice and steering wheel is turned to lock during braking. Using Tech 1 perform Hydraulic test to ensure total brake system is functional.

Any circuitry, that is suspected as causing the intermittent complaint, should be thoroughly checked for backed out terminals, improper mating, broken locks, improperly formed or damaged terminals, poor terminal to wiring connections or physical damage to the wiring harness.

GC402930079400AX

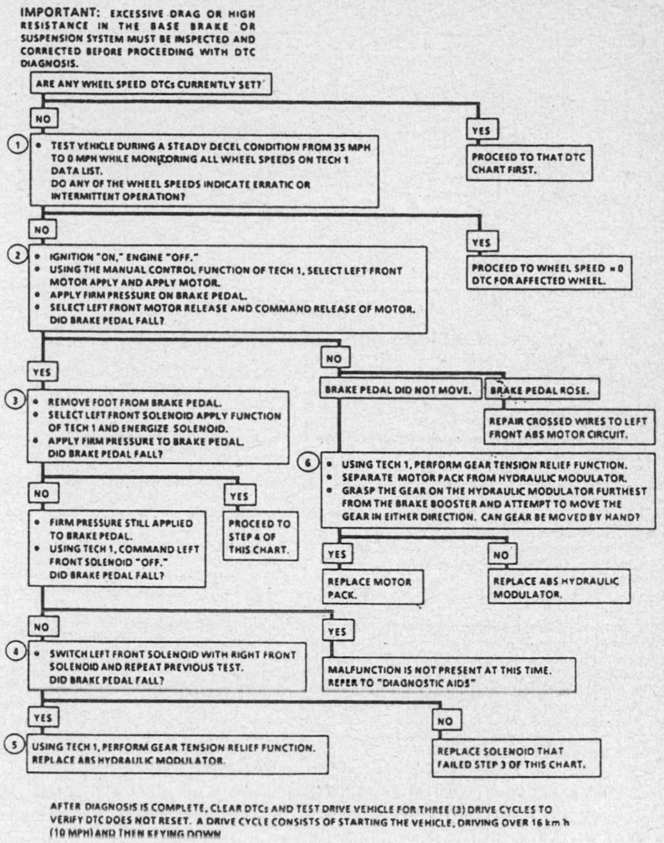
IMPORTANT: EXCESSIVE DRAG OR HIGH RESISTANCE IN THE BASE BRAKE OR SUSPENSION SYSTEM MUST BE INSPECTED AND CORRECTED BEFORE PROCEEDING WITH DTC DIAGNOSIS.
ARE ANY WHEEL SPEED DTCs CURRENTLY SET?
NO
YES
PROCEED TO THAT DTC CHART FIRST.
1
• TEST VEHICLE DURING A STEADY DECEL CONDITION FROM 35 MPH TO 0 MPH WHILE MONITORING ALL WHEEL SPEEDS ON TECH 1 DATA LIST.
DO ANY OF THE WHEEL SPEEDS INDICATE ERRATIC OR INTERMITTENT OPERATION?
NO
YES
PROCEED TO WHEEL SPEED = 0 DTC FOR AFFECTED WHEEL.
2
• IGNITION "ON," ENGINE "OFF."
• USING THE MANUAL CONTROL FUNCTION OF TECH 1, SELECT LEFT FRONT MOTOR APPLY AND APPLY MOTOR.
• APPLY FIRM PRESSURE ON BRAKE PEDAL.
• SELECT LEFT FRONT MOTOR RELEASE AND COMMAND RELEASE OF MOTOR.
DID BRAKE PEDAL FALL?
YES
NO
BRAKE PEDAL DID NOT MOVE.
BRAKE PEDAL ROSE.
REPAIR CROSSED WIRES TO LEFT FRONT ABS MOTOR CIRCUIT.
3
• REMOVE FOOT FROM BRAKE PEDAL.
• SELECT LEFT FRONT SOLENOID APPLY FUNCTION OF TECH 1 AND ENERGIZE SOLENOID.
• APPLY FIRM PRESSURE TO BRAKE PEDAL.
DID BRAKE PEDAL FALL?
6
• USING TECH 1, PERFORM GEAR TENSION RELIEF FUNCTION.
• SEPARATE MOTOR PACK FROM HYDRAULIC MODULATOR.
• GRASP THE GEAR ON THE HYDRAULIC MODULATOR FURTHEST FROM THE BRAKE BOOSTER AND ATTEMPT TO MOVE THE GEAR IN EITHER DIRECTION. CAN GEAR BE MOVED BY HAND?
NO
YES
• FIRM PRESSURE STILL APPLIED TO BRAKE PEDAL.
• USING TECH 1, COMMAND LEFT FRONT SOLENOID "OFF."
DID BRAKE PEDAL FALL?
PROCEED TO STEP 4 OF THIS CHART.
YES
NO
REPLACE MOTOR PACK.
REPLACE ABS HYDRAULIC MODULATOR.
NO
YES
4
• SWITCH LEFT FRONT SOLENOID WITH RIGHT FRONT SOLENOID AND REPEAT PREVIOUS TEST.
DID BRAKE PEDAL FALL?
MALFUNCTION IS NOT PRESENT AT THIS TIME. REFER TO "DIAGNOSTIC AIDS"
YES
NO
5
USING TECH 1, PERFORM GEAR TENSION RELIEF FUNCTION. REPLACE ABS HYDRAULIC MODULATOR.
REPLACE SOLENOID THAT FAILED STEP 3 OF THIS CHART.
AFTER DIAGNOSIS IS COMPLETE, CLEAR DTCs AND TEST DRIVE VEHICLE FOR THREE (3) DRIVE CYCLES TO VERIFY DTC DOES NOT RESET. A DRIVE CYCLE CONSISTS OF STARTING THE VEHICLE, DRIVING OVER 16 km/h (10 MPH) AND THEN KEYING DOWN
GC402930079400BX

Fig. 167 Code A052: Left Front Channel Release Too Long. 1993 Cutlass Supreme, Grand Prix, Lumina, Regal & 1993–94 Cavalier, Sunbird, Beretta, Corsica & Achieva, Grand Am & Skylark Less VES

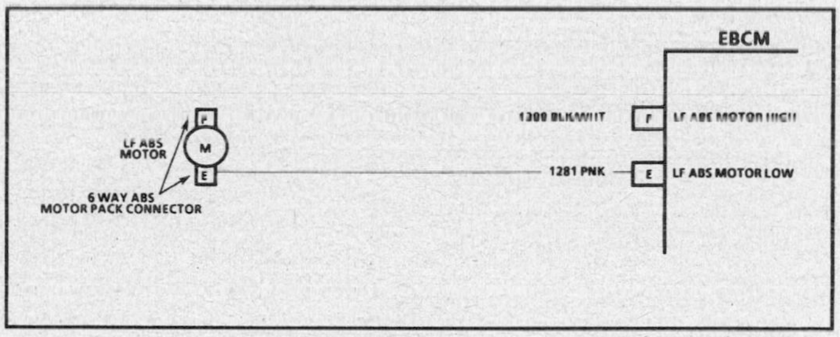
EBCM
LF ABS MOTOR
M
F
E
1281 PNK
LF ABS MOTOR LOW
6 WAY ABS
MOTOR PACK CONNECTOR

DTC 52

LEFT FRONT CHANNEL IN RELEASE TOO LONG

Circuit Description:

This DTC will diagnose an ABS motor that is energized longer than expected. This could occur if a wheel speed sensor is malfunctioning, the ABS motor does not turn, the left front solenoid mechanically fails open, or the ABS motor wires are crossed.

DTC Will Set When: DTC 52 can be set only during an ABS stop. If the EBCM commands the left front ABS channel in release for three seconds, a malfunction exists.

Action Taken: A malfunction DTC is stored, ABS is disabled and the ABS warning lamp is turned "ON."

DTC Chart Test Description: Number(s) below refer to circled number(s) on the diagnostic chart.

1. Identifies a problem in a wheel speed sensor that may cause the system to be in release too long.
2. Identifies an ABS motor as being failed or wired incorrectly.
3. Checks for a solenoid that may have mechanically failed open.
4. Verifies proper solenoid operation.
5. This serves to isolate the cause of the hydraulic problem, to either the solenoid or the ABS hydraulic modulator assembly.
6. Determines whether a malfunctioning ABS motor pack or hydraulic modulator is the reason for DTC 52 being set.

Diagnostic Aids: An "Intermittent" malfunction may be caused by a mechanical part of the system that sticks or binds.

The frequency of the malfunction can be checked by using the enhanced diagnostic function of the Tech 1.

DTC 52 may occur if on ice and steering wheel is turned to lock during braking. Using the Tech 1, perform hydraulic test to ensure total brake system is functional.

Any circuitry, that is suspected as causing the intermittent complaint, should be thoroughly checked for backed out terminals, improper mating, broken locks, improperly formed or damaged terminals, poor terminal to wiring connections or physical damage to the wiring harness.

GC402940094600AX

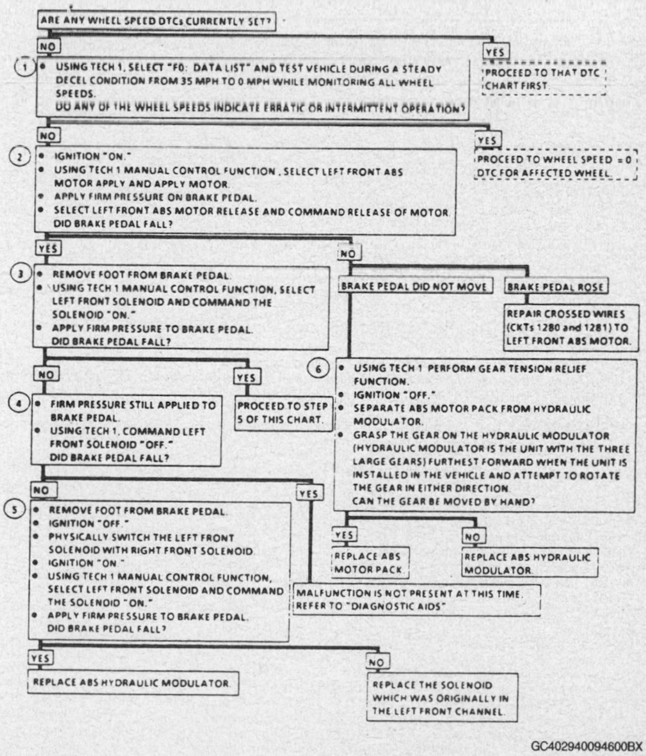
ARE ANY WHEEL SPEED DTCs CURRENTLY SET?
NO
YES
PROCEED TO THAT DTC CHART FIRST.
1
• USING TECH 1, SELECT "F0: DATA LIST" AND TEST VEHICLE DURING A STEADY DECEL CONDITION FROM 35 MPH TO 0 MPH WHILE MONITORING ALL WHEEL SPEEDS.
DO ANY OF THE WHEEL SPEEDS INDICATE ERRATIC OR INTERMITTENT OPERATION?
NO
YES
PROCEED TO WHEEL SPEED = 0 DTC FOR AFFECTED WHEEL.
2
• IGNITION "ON."
• USING TECH 1 MANUAL CONTROL FUNCTION, SELECT LEFT FRONT ABS MOTOR APPLY AND APPLY MOTOR.
• APPLY FIRM PRESSURE ON BRAKE PEDAL.
• SELECT LEFT FRONT ABS MOTOR RELEASE AND COMMAND RELEASE OF MOTOR.
DID BRAKE PEDAL FALL?
YES
NO
BRAKE PEDAL DID NOT MOVE
BRAKE PEDAL ROSE
REPAIR CROSSED WIRES (CKTs 1280 and 1281) TO LEFT FRONT ABS MOTOR.
3
• REMOVE FOOT FROM BRAKE PEDAL.
• USING TECH 1 MANUAL CONTROL FUNCTION, SELECT LEFT FRONT SOLENOID AND COMMAND THE SOLENOID "ON."
• APPLY FIRM PRESSURE TO BRAKE PEDAL.
DID BRAKE PEDAL FALL?
6
• USING TECH 1 PERFORM GEAR TENSION RELIEF FUNCTION.
• IGNITION "OFF."
• SEPARATE ABS MOTOR PACK FROM HYDRAULIC MODULATOR.
• GRASP THE GEAR ON THE HYDRAULIC MODULATOR (HYDRAULIC MODULATOR IS THE UNIT WITH THE THREE LARGE GEARS) FURTHEST FORWARD WHEN THE UNIT IS INSTALLED IN THE VEHICLE AND ATTEMPT TO ROTATE THE GEAR IN EITHER DIRECTION.
CAN THE GEAR BE MOVED BY HAND?
NO
YES
4
• FIRM PRESSURE STILL APPLIED TO BRAKE PEDAL.
• USING TECH 1, COMMAND LEFT FRONT SOLENOID "OFF."
DID BRAKE PEDAL FALL?
PROCEED TO STEP 5 OF THIS CHART.
NO
YES
5
• REMOVE FOOT FROM BRAKE PEDAL.
• IGNITION "OFF."
• PHYSICALLY SWITCH THE LEFT FRONT SOLENOID WITH RIGHT FRONT SOLENOID.
• IGNITION "ON."
• USING TECH 1 MANUAL CONTROL FUNCTION, SELECT LEFT FRONT SOLENOID AND COMMAND THE SOLENOID "ON."
• APPLY FIRM PRESSURE TO BRAKE PEDAL.
DID BRAKE PEDAL FALL?
YES
NO
REPLACE ABS MOTOR PACK.
REPLACE ABS HYDRAULIC MODULATOR.
MALFUNCTION IS NOT PRESENT AT THIS TIME. REFER TO "DIAGNOSTIC AIDS"
YES
NO
REPLACE ABS HYDRAULIC MODULATOR.
REPLACE THE SOLENOID WHICH WAS ORIGINALLY IN THE LEFT FRONT CHANNEL.
GC402940094600BX

Fig. 168 Code A052: Left Front Channel Release Too Long. 1994 Cutlass Supreme, Lumina & Regal

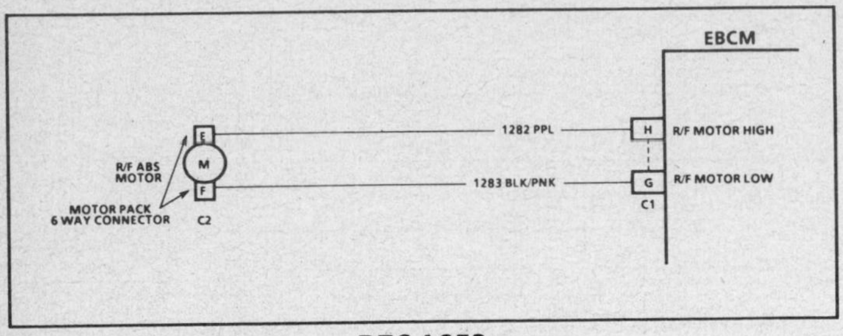
EBCM
R/F ABS MOTOR
M
E
F
MOTOR PACK 6 WAY CONNECTOR
C2
1282 PPL
1283 BLK/PNK
H
G
C1
R/F MOTOR HIGH
R/F MOTOR LOW

DTC A053

RIGHT FRONT CHANNEL IN RELEASE TOO LONG

Circuit Description:
This DTC will diagnose a motor that is energized longer than expected. This could occur if a wheel speed sensor is faulty, the motor does not turn, the right front solenoid mechanically fails open, the brakes are dragging, or the motor wires are crossed.

Failure Condition:
DTC A053 can be set only during an ABS stop. If the EBCM commands the right front channel in release for three seconds, a malfunction exists.

Action Taken:
A malfunction DTC is stored, ABS is disabled, and the ABS indicator lamp is turned "ON."

Test Description: Number(s) below refer to circled number(s) on the diagnostic chart.

1. This step identifies a malfunction in a wheel speed sensor that may cause the system to be in release too long.
2. This step identifies a motor fault as being failed or wired incorrectly.
3. This step checks for a solenoid that may have mechanically failed open.
4. If Step 3 has failed, this serves to isolate the cause of the hydraulic problem, to either the solenoid or the ABS hydraulic modulator.
5. This step is used to release the tension of the motor pack prior to removal.
6. This step checks for proper operation of hydraulic modulator.

Diagnostic Aids:

An "Intermittent" malfunction may be caused by a mechanical part of the system that sticks or binds.

The frequency of the malfunction can be checked by using the enhanced diagnostic function of the Tech 1.

DTC A053 may fail on ice if steering wheel is turned to lock during braking. Using Tech 1 perform Hydraulic test to ensure total brake system is functional.

Any circuitry, that is suspected as causing the intermittent complaint, should be thoroughly checked for backed out terminals, improper mating, broken locks, improperly formed or damaged terminals, poor terminal to wiring connections or physical damage to the wiring harness.

GC402930079500AX

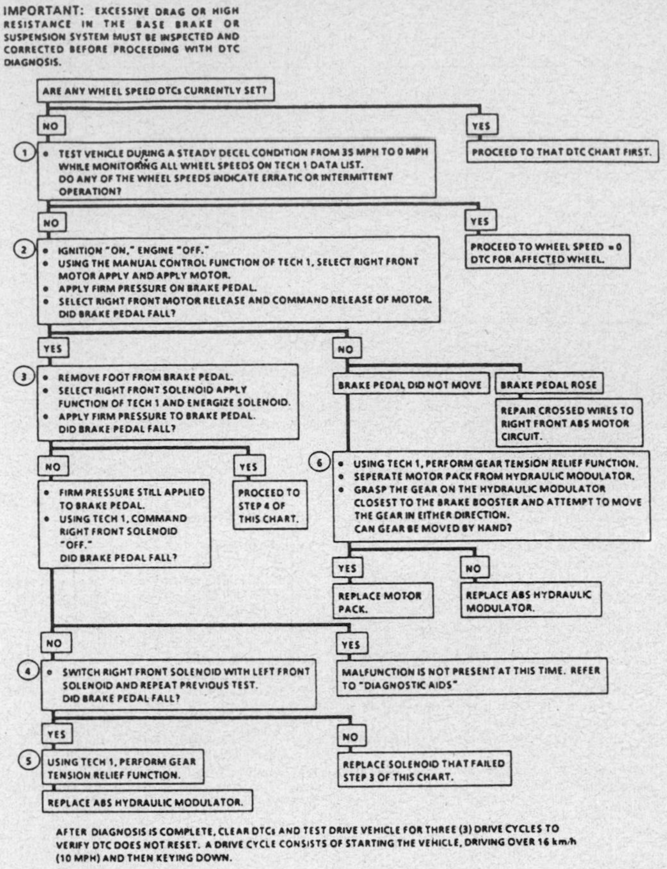
IMPORTANT: EXCESSIVE DRAG OR HIGH RESISTANCE IN THE BASE BRAKE OR SUSPENSION SYSTEM MUST BE INSPECTED AND CORRECTED BEFORE PROCEEDING WITH DTC DIAGNOSIS.
ARE ANY WHEEL SPEED DTCs CURRENTLY SET?
NO
YES
PROCEED TO THAT DTC CHART FIRST.
1
• TEST VEHICLE DURING A STEADY DECEL CONDITION FROM 35 MPH TO 0 MPH WHILE MONITORING ALL WHEEL SPEEDS ON TECH 1 DATA LIST. DO ANY OF THE WHEEL SPEEDS INDICATE ERRATIC OR INTERMITTENT OPERATION?
NO
YES
PROCEED TO WHEEL SPEED = 0 DTC FOR AFFECTED WHEEL.
2
• IGNITION "ON," ENGINE "OFF."
• USING THE MANUAL CONTROL FUNCTION OF TECH 1, SELECT RIGHT FRONT MOTOR APPLY AND APPLY MOTOR.
• APPLY FIRM PRESSURE ON BRAKE PEDAL.
• SELECT RIGHT FRONT MOTOR RELEASE AND COMMAND RELEASE OF MOTOR. DID BRAKE PEDAL FALL?
YES
NO
BRAKE PEDAL DID NOT MOVE
BRAKE PEDAL ROSE
REPAIR CROSSED WIRES TO RIGHT FRONT ABS MOTOR CIRCUIT.
3
• REMOVE FOOT FROM BRAKE PEDAL.
• SELECT RIGHT FRONT SOLENOID APPLY FUNCTION OF TECH 1 AND ENERGIZE SOLENOID.
• APPLY FIRM PRESSURE TO BRAKE PEDAL. DID BRAKE PEDAL FALL?
NO
YES
PROCEED TO STEP 4 OF THIS CHART.
• FIRM PRESSURE STILL APPLIED TO BRAKE PEDAL.
• USING TECH 1, COMMAND RIGHT FRONT SOLENOID "OFF." DID BRAKE PEDAL FALL?
6
• USING TECH 1, PERFORM GEAR TENSION RELIEF FUNCTION.
• SEPERATE MOTOR PACK FROM HYDRAULIC MODULATOR.
• GRASP THE GEAR ON THE HYDRAULIC MODULATOR CLOSEST TO THE BRAKE BOOSTER AND ATTEMPT TO MOVE THE GEAR IN EITHER DIRECTION. CAN GEAR BE MOVED BY HAND?
YES
NO
REPLACE MOTOR PACK.
REPLACE ABS HYDRAULIC MODULATOR.
NO
YES
MALFUNCTION IS NOT PRESENT AT THIS TIME. REFER TO "DIAGNOSTIC AIDS"
4
• SWITCH RIGHT FRONT SOLENOID WITH LEFT FRONT SOLENOID AND REPEAT PREVIOUS TEST. DID BRAKE PEDAL FALL?
YES
NO
5
USING TECH 1, PERFORM GEAR TENSION RELIEF FUNCTION.
REPLACE SOLENOID THAT FAILED STEP 3 OF THIS CHART.
REPLACE ABS HYDRAULIC MODULATOR.
AFTER DIAGNOSIS IS COMPLETE, CLEAR DTCs AND TEST DRIVE VEHICLE FOR THREE (3) DRIVE CYCLES TO VERIFY DTC DOES NOT RESET. A DRIVE CYCLE CONSISTS OF STARTING THE VEHICLE, DRIVING OVER 16 km/h (10 MPH) AND THEN KEYING DOWN.

GC402930079500BX

Fig. 169 Code A053: Right Front Channel Release Too Long. 1993 Cutlass Supreme, Grand Prix, Lumina, Regal & 1993–94 Cavalier, Sunbird, Beretta, Corsica & Achieva, Grand Am & Skylark Less VES

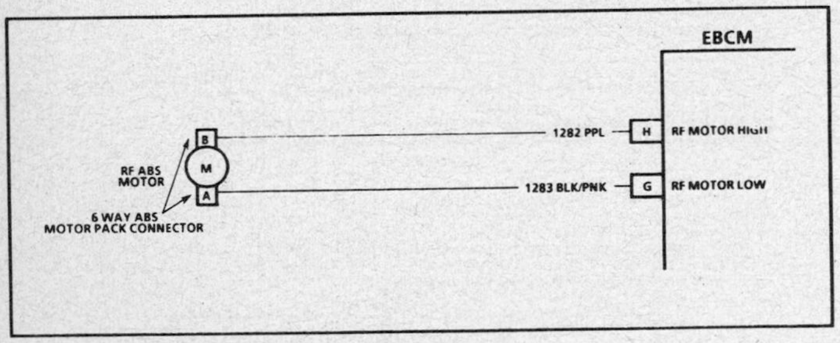
EBCM
RF ABS MOTOR
M
B
A
6 WAY ABS MOTOR PACK CONNECTOR
1282 PPL
1283 BLK/PNK
H
G
RF MOTOR HIGH
RF MOTOR LOW

DTC 53

RIGHT FRONT CHANNEL IN RELEASE TOO LONG

Circuit Description:
This DTC will diagnose an ABS motor that is energized longer than expected. This could occur if a wheel speed sensor is malfunctioning, the ABS motor does not turn, the right front solenoid mechanically fails open, or the ABS motor wires are crossed.

DTC Will Set When: DTC 53 can be set only during an ABS stop. If the EBCM commands the right front channel in release for three seconds, a malfunction exists.

Action Taken: A malfunction DTC is stored, ABS is disabled and the ABS warning lamp is turned "ON."

DTC Chart Test Description: Number(s) below refer to circled number(s) on the diagnostic chart.

1. Identifies a problem in a wheel speed sensor that may cause the system to be in release too long.
2. Identifies an ABS motor as being failed or wired incorrectly.
3. Checks for a solenoid that may have mechanically failed open.
4. Checks for a solenoid that may have mechanically failed closed.
5. This serves to isolate the cause of the hydraulic problem, to either the solenoid or the ABS hydraulic modulator assembly.
6. Determines whether a malfunction ABS motor pack or hydraulic modulator is the reason for DTC 53 being set.

Diagnostic Aids: An "Intermittent" malfunction may be caused by a mechanical part of the system that sticks or binds.

The frequency of the malfunction can be checked by using the enhanced diagnostic function of the Tech 1.

DTC 53 may occur on ice if steering wheel is turned to lock during braking. Using the Tech 1 perform hydraulic test to ensure total brake system is functional.

Any circuitry, that is suspected as causing the intermittent complaint, should be thoroughly checked for backed out terminals, improper mating, broken locks, improperly formed or damaged terminals, poor terminal to wiring connections or physical damage to the wiring harness.

GC402940094700AX

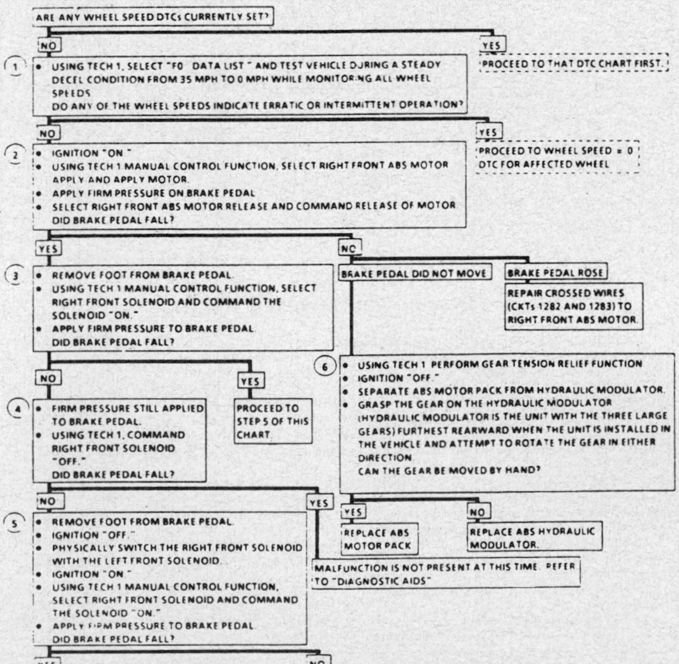
ARE ANY WHEEL SPEED DTCs CURRENTLY SET?
NO
YES
PROCEED TO THAT DTC CHART FIRST.
1
• USING TECH 1, SELECT "F0 DATA LIST" AND TEST VEHICLE DURING A STEADY DECEL CONDITION FROM 35 MPH TO 0 MPH WHILE MONITORING ALL WHEEL SPEEDS DO ANY OF THE WHEEL SPEEDS INDICATE ERRATIC OR INTERMITTENT OPERATION?
NO
YES
PROCEED TO WHEEL SPEED = 0 DTC FOR AFFECTED WHEEL
2
• IGNITION "ON"
• USING TECH 1 MANUAL CONTROL FUNCTION, SELECT RIGHT FRONT ABS MOTOR APPLY AND APPLY MOTOR.
• APPLY FIRM PRESSURE ON BRAKE PEDAL
• SELECT RIGHT FRONT ABS MOTOR RELEASE AND COMMAND RELEASE OF MOTOR DID BRAKE PEDAL FALL?
YES
NO
BRAKE PEDAL DID NOT MOVE
BRAKE PEDAL ROSE
REPAIR CROSSED WIRES (CKTs 1282 AND 1283) TO RIGHT FRONT ABS MOTOR.
3
• REMOVE FOOT FROM BRAKE PEDAL.
• USING TECH 1 MANUAL CONTROL FUNCTION, SELECT RIGHT FRONT SOLENOID AND COMMAND THE SOLENOID "ON."
• APPLY FIRM PRESSURE TO BRAKE PEDAL. DID BRAKE PEDAL FALL?
6
• USING TECH 1 PERFORM GEAR TENSION RELIEF FUNCTION
• IGNITION "OFF."
• SEPARATE ABS MOTOR PACK FROM HYDRAULIC MODULATOR.
• GRASP THE GEAR ON THE HYDRAULIC MODULATOR (HYDRAULIC MODULATOR IS THE UNIT WITH THE THREE LARGE GEARS) FURTHEST REARWARD WHEN THE UNIT IS INSTALLED IN THE VEHICLE AND ATTEMPT TO ROTATE THE GEAR IN EITHER DIRECTION. CAN THE GEAR BE MOVED BY HAND?
NO
YES
PROCEED TO STEP 5 OF THIS CHART.
4
• FIRM PRESSURE STILL APPLIED TO BRAKE PEDAL.
• USING TECH 1, COMMAND RIGHT FRONT SOLENOID "OFF." DID BRAKE PEDAL FALL?
NO
YES
YES
NO
REPLACE ABS MOTOR PACK
REPLACE ABS HYDRAULIC MODULATOR.
MALFUNCTION IS NOT PRESENT AT THIS TIME REFER TO "DIAGNOSTIC AIDS"
5
• REMOVE FOOT FROM BRAKE PEDAL.
• IGNITION "OFF."
• PHYSICALLY SWITCH THE RIGHT FRONT SOLENOID WITH THE LEFT FRONT SOLENOID.
• IGNITION "ON."
• USING TECH 1 MANUAL CONTROL FUNCTION, SELECT RIGHT FRONT SOLENOID AND COMMAND THE SOLENOID "ON."
• APPLY FIRM PRESSURE TO BRAKE PEDAL DID BRAKE PEDAL FALL?
YES
NO
REPLACE ABS HYDRAULIC MODULATOR
REPLACE THE SOLENOID WHICH WAS ORIGINALLY IN THE RIGHT FRONT CHANNEL.

GC402940094700BX

Fig. 170 Code A053: Right Front Channel Release Too Long. 1994 Cutlass Supreme, Lumina & Regal

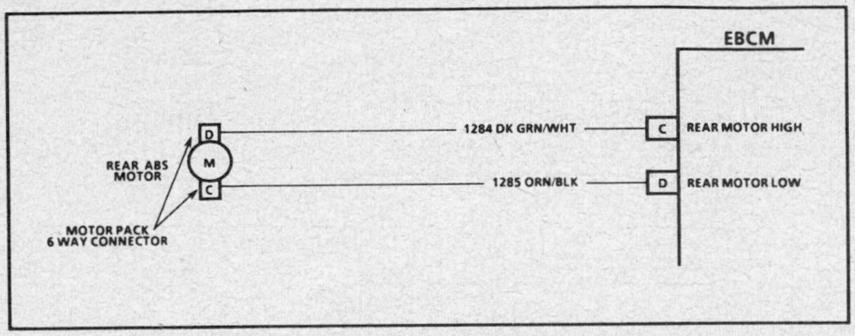

EBCM
REAR ABS MOTOR
M
D
C
1284 DK GRN/WHT
C
REAR MOTOR HIGH
1285 ORN/BLK
D
REAR MOTOR LOW
MOTOR PACK 6 WAY CONNECTOR

DTC A054

REAR AXLE CHANNEL IN RELEASE TOO LONG

Circuit Description:
This DTC will diagnose a motor that is energized longer than expected. This could occur if a wheel speed sensor is malfunctioning, the motor does not turn, or the motor wires are crossed.

Failure Condition:
DTC A054 can be set only during an ABS stop. If the EBCM commands the rear axle channel in release for three seconds, a malfunction exists.

Action Taken:
A malfunction DTC is stored, ABS is disabled and the ABS indicator lamp is turned "ON."

Test Description: Number(s) below refer to circled number(s) on the diagnostic chart.

1. This step identifies a problem in a wheel speed sensor that may cause the system to be in release too long.
2. This checks for a wheel that may stick or bind because of a mechanical fault.
3. This checks to see if the motor is capable of moving and applying the hydraulic piston for the rear wheels.
4. This step insures that the motor wiring is not crossed.
5. This isolates the fault of a "no-apply" situation to either the motor pack or ABS hydraulic modulator assembly.

Diagnostic Aids:

An "Intermittent" malfunction may be caused by a mechanical part of the system that sticks or binds.

The frequency of the malfunction can be checked by using the enhanced diagnostic function of the Tech 1.

Using the Tech 1, perform hydraulic test to ensure total brake system is functional.

Any circuitry, that is suspected as causing the intermittent complaint, should be thoroughly checked for backed out terminals, improper mating, broken locks, improperly formed or damaged terminals, poor terminal to wiring connections or physical damage to the wiring harness.

GC402930079600AX

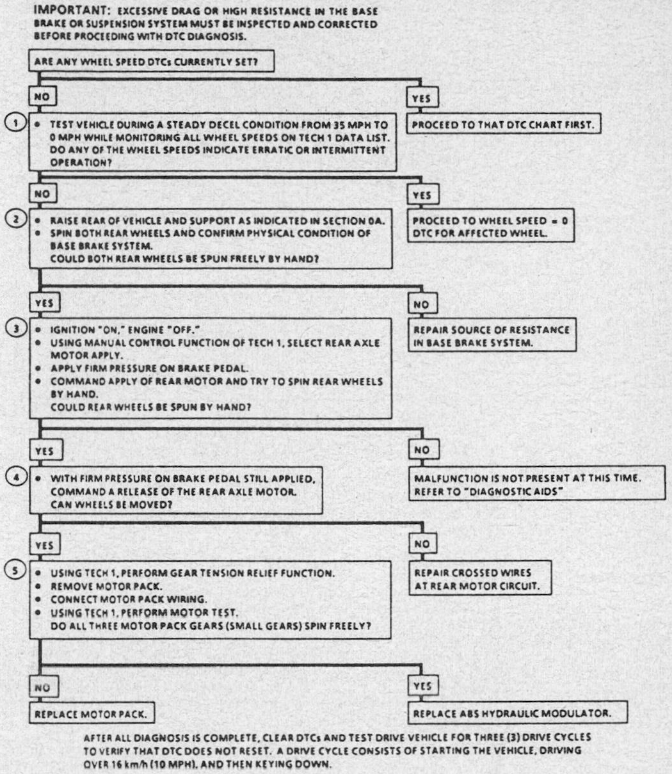

IMPORTANT: EXCESSIVE DRAG OR HIGH RESISTANCE IN THE BASE BRAKE OR SUSPENSION SYSTEM MUST BE INSPECTED AND CORRECTED BEFORE PROCEEDING WITH DTC DIAGNOSIS.
ARE ANY WHEEL SPEED DTCs CURRENTLY SET?
NO
YES
1
• TEST VEHICLE DURING A STEADY DECEL CONDITION FROM 35 MPH TO 0 MPH WHILE MONITORING ALL WHEEL SPEEDS ON TECH 1 DATA LIST. DO ANY OF THE WHEEL SPEEDS INDICATE ERRATIC OR INTERMITTENT OPERATION?
PROCEED TO THAT DTC CHART FIRST.
NO
YES
2
• RAISE REAR OF VEHICLE AND SUPPORT AS INDICATED IN SECTION 0A.
• SPIN BOTH REAR WHEELS AND CONFIRM PHYSICAL CONDITION OF BASE BRAKE SYSTEM.
COULD BOTH REAR WHEELS BE SPUN FREELY BY HAND?
PROCEED TO WHEEL SPEED = 0 DTC FOR AFFECTED WHEEL.
YES
NO
3
• IGNITION "ON," ENGINE "OFF."
• USING MANUAL CONTROL FUNCTION OF TECH 1, SELECT REAR AXLE MOTOR APPLY.
• APPLY FIRM PRESSURE ON BRAKE PEDAL.
• COMMAND APPLY OF REAR MOTOR AND TRY TO SPIN REAR WHEELS BY HAND.
COULD REAR WHEELS BE SPUN BY HAND?
REPAIR SOURCE OF RESISTANCE IN BASE BRAKE SYSTEM.
YES
NO
4
• WITH FIRM PRESSURE ON BRAKE PEDAL STILL APPLIED, COMMAND A RELEASE OF THE REAR AXLE MOTOR. CAN WHEELS BE MOVED?
MALFUNCTION IS NOT PRESENT AT THIS TIME. REFER TO "DIAGNOSTIC AIDS"
YES
NO
5
• USING TECH 1, PERFORM GEAR TENSION RELIEF FUNCTION.
• REMOVE MOTOR PACK.
• CONNECT MOTOR PACK WIRING.
• USING TECH 1, PERFORM MOTOR TEST.
DO ALL THREE MOTOR PACK GEARS (SMALL GEARS) SPIN FREELY?
REPAIR CROSSED WIRES AT REAR MOTOR CIRCUIT.
NO
YES
REPLACE MOTOR PACK.
REPLACE ABS HYDRAULIC MODULATOR.
AFTER ALL DIAGNOSIS IS COMPLETE, CLEAR DTCs AND TEST DRIVE VEHICLE FOR THREE (3) DRIVE CYCLES TO VERIFY THAT DTC DOES NOT RESET. A DRIVE CYCLE CONSISTS OF STARTING THE VEHICLE, DRIVING OVER 16 km/h (10 MPH), AND THEN KEYING DOWN.

GC402930079600BX

Fig. 171 Code A054: Rear Axle Channel In Release Too Long. 1993 Cutlass Supreme, Grand Prix, Lumina, Regal & 1993–94 Cavalier, Sunbird, Beretta, Corsica & Achieva, Grand Am & Skylark Less VES

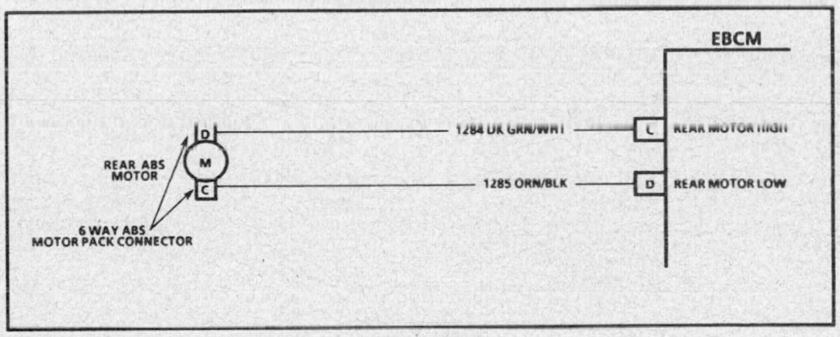

EBCM
REAR ABS MOTOR
M
D
C
1284 DK GRN/WHT
C
REAR MOTOR HIGH
1285 ORN/BLK
D
REAR MOTOR LOW
6 WAY ABS MOTOR PACK CONNECTOR

DTC 54

REAR CHANNEL IN RELEASE TOO LONG

Circuit Description:
This DTC will diagnose an ABS motor that is energized longer than expected. This could occur if a wheel speed sensor is malfunctioning, the ABS motor does not turn, or the ABS motor wires are crossed.

DTC Will Set When: DTC 54 can be set only during an ABS stop. If the EBCM commands the rear ABS channel in release for three seconds, a malfunction exists.

Action Taken: A malfunction DTC is stored, ABS is disabled and the ABS warning lamp is turned "ON."

DTC Chart Test Description: Number(s) below refer to circled number(s) on the diagnostic chart.

1. Identifies a problem in a wheel speed sensor that may cause the system to be in release too long.
2. Checks for a wheel that may stick or bind because of a mechanical fault.
3. Checks to see if the ABS motor is capable of moving and applying the hydraulic piston for the rear wheels.
4. Ensures that the ABS motor wiring is not crossed.
5. Isolates the fault of a "no-apply" situation to either the ABS motor pack or ABS hydraulic modulator assembly.

Diagnostic Aids: An "Intermittent" malfunction may be caused by a mechanical part of the system that sticks or binds.

The frequency of the malfunction can be checked by using the enhanced diagnostic function of the Tech 1.

Using the Tech 1, perform hydraulic test to ensure total brake system is functional.

Any circuitry, that is suspected as causing the intermittent complaint, should be thoroughly checked for backed out terminals, improper mating, broken locks, improperly formed or damaged terminals, poor terminal to wiring connections or physical damage to the wiring harness.

GC402940094800AX

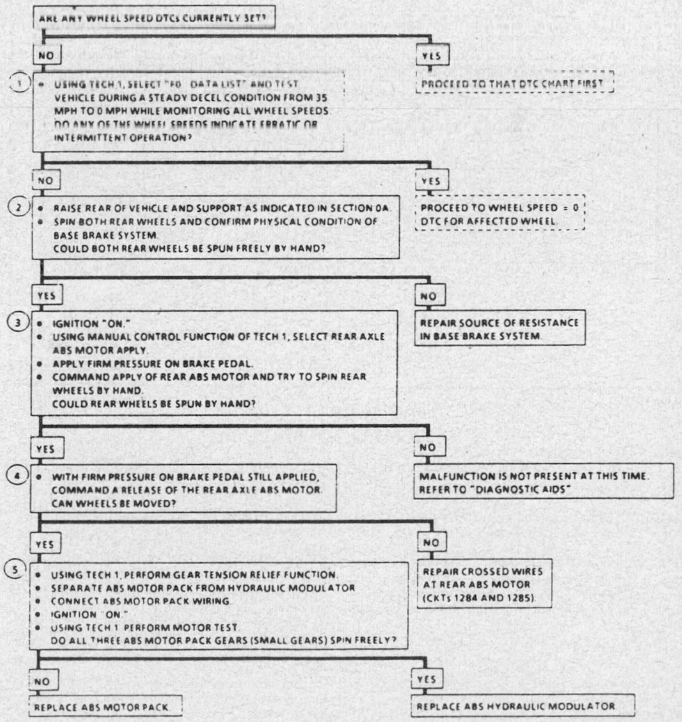

ARE ANY WHEEL SPEED DTCs CURRENTLY SET?
NO
YES
1
• USING TECH 1, SELECT "F0: DATA LIST" AND TEST VEHICLE DURING A STEADY DECEL CONDITION FROM 35 MPH TO 0 MPH WHILE MONITORING ALL WHEEL SPEEDS. DO ANY OF THE WHEEL SPEEDS INDICATE ERRATIC OR INTERMITTENT OPERATION?
PROCEED TO THAT DTC CHART FIRST
NO
YES
2
• RAISE REAR OF VEHICLE AND SUPPORT AS INDICATED IN SECTION 0A.
• SPIN BOTH REAR WHEELS AND CONFIRM PHYSICAL CONDITION OF BASE BRAKE SYSTEM.
COULD BOTH REAR WHEELS BE SPUN FREELY BY HAND?
PROCEED TO WHEEL SPEED = 0 DTC FOR AFFECTED WHEEL.
YES
NO
3
• IGNITION "ON."
• USING MANUAL CONTROL FUNCTION OF TECH 1, SELECT REAR AXLE ABS MOTOR APPLY.
• APPLY FIRM PRESSURE ON BRAKE PEDAL.
• COMMAND APPLY OF REAR ABS MOTOR AND TRY TO SPIN REAR WHEELS BY HAND.
COULD REAR WHEELS BE SPUN BY HAND?
REPAIR SOURCE OF RESISTANCE IN BASE BRAKE SYSTEM.
YES
NO
4
• WITH FIRM PRESSURE ON BRAKE PEDAL STILL APPLIED, COMMAND A RELEASE OF THE REAR AXLE ABS MOTOR. CAN WHEELS BE MOVED?
MALFUNCTION IS NOT PRESENT AT THIS TIME. REFER TO "DIAGNOSTIC AIDS"
YES
NO
5
• USING TECH 1, PERFORM GEAR TENSION RELIEF FUNCTION.
• SEPARATE ABS MOTOR PACK FROM HYDRAULIC MODULATOR.
• CONNECT ABS MOTOR PACK WIRING.
• IGNITION "ON."
• USING TECH 1, PERFORM MOTOR TEST.
DO ALL THREE ABS MOTOR PACK GEARS (SMALL GEARS) SPIN FREELY?
REPAIR CROSSED WIRES AT REAR ABS MOTOR (CKTs 1284 AND 1285).
NO
YES
REPLACE ABS MOTOR PACK.
REPLACE ABS HYDRAULIC MODULATOR.

GC402940094800BX

Fig. 172 Code A054: Rear Channel In Release Too Long. 1994 Cutlass Supreme, Lumina & Regal

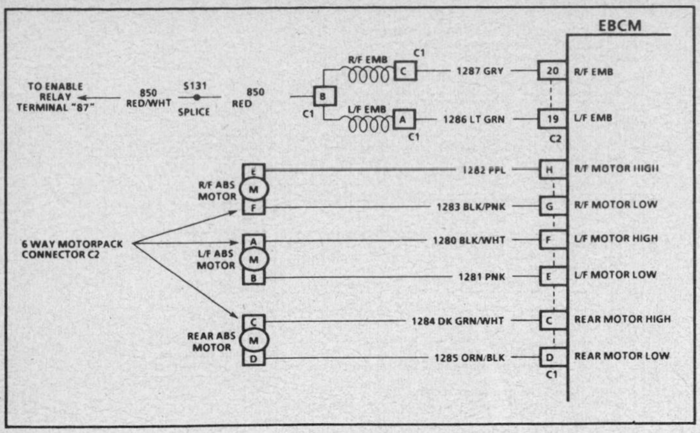
EBCM
TO ENABLE RELAY TERMINAL "87"
850 RED/WHT
S131 SPLICE
850 RED
R/F EMB
L/F EMB
C1
1287 GRY
1286 LT GRN
20 R/F EMB
19 L/F EMB
C2
R/F ABS MOTOR
L/F ABS MOTOR
REAR ABS MOTOR
6 WAY MOTORPACK CONNECTOR C2
1282 PPL
H R/F MOTOR HIGH
1283 BLK/PNK
G R/F MOTOR LOW
1280 BLK/WHT
F L/F MOTOR HIGH
1281 PNK
E L/F MOTOR LOW
1284 DK GRN/WHT
C REAR MOTOR HIGH
1285 ORN/BLK
D REAR MOTOR LOW

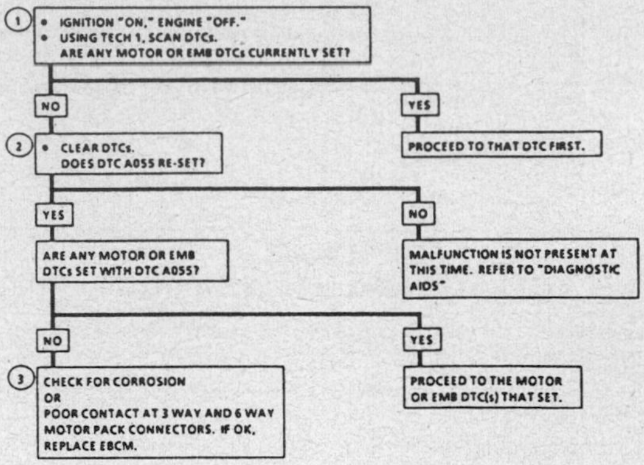
1 • IGNITION "ON," ENGINE "OFF."
• USING TECH 1, SCAN DTCs.
ARE ANY MOTOR OR EMB DTCs CURRENTLY SET?
NO
YES
PROCEED TO THAT DTC FIRST.
2 • CLEAR DTCs.
DOES DTC A055 RE-SET?
YES
NO
ARE ANY MOTOR OR EMB DTCs SET WITH DTC A055?
MALFUNCTION IS NOT PRESENT AT THIS TIME. REFER TO "DIAGNOSTIC AIDS"
NO
YES
3 CHECK FOR CORROSION OR POOR CONTACT AT 3 WAY AND 6 WAY MOTOR PACK CONNECTORS. IF OK, REPLACE EBCM.
PROCEED TO THE MOTOR OR EMB DTC(s) THAT SET.

DTC A055

MOTOR DRIVER FAULT DETECTED

Circuit Description:

This DTC identifies a malfunction detected by the MDI custom IC. It also ensures the cause of the malfunction is not a result of a malfunction with the enable relay under a DTC A055 failure. The MDI malfunction tests will be run to identify which circuit has failed and may also cause additional DTCs to set to pinpoint the malfunctioning circuit.

Failed Condition:

DTC A055 is set simultaneously with one or more of DTCs A056 through A072.

Action Taken:

A malfunction DTC is stored, ABS is disabled and the ABS indicator lamp is turned "ON."

Test Description: Number(s) below refer to circled number(s) on the diagnostic chart.

1. This insures the DTC A055 malfunction was not set due to a motor or EMB malfunction.
2. This checks to see if the malfunction is still present.
3. This step insures that DTC A055 was not due to poor terminal contact at the motor pack connector.

Diagnostic Aids:

An "Intermittent" malfunction may be caused by a poor connection, rubbed through wire insulation, or a wire that is broken inside the insulation.

The frequency of the malfunction can be checked by using the enhanced diagnostic function of the Tech 1.

Any circuitry, that is suspected as causing the intermittent complaint, should be thoroughly checked for backed out terminals, improper mating, broken locks, improperly formed or damaged terminals, poor terminal to wiring connections or physical damage to the wiring harness.

GC402930079700AX

AFTER DIAGNOSIS IS COMPLETE, CLEAR DTCs AND TEST DRIVE VEHICLE FOR THREE (3) DRIVE CYCLES TO VERIFY DTC DOES NOT RESET. A DRIVE CYCLE CONSISTS OF STARTING THE VEHICLE, DRIVING OVER 16 km/h (10 MPH) AND THEN KEYING DOWN.

GC402930079700BX

Fig. 173 Code A055: EBCM Failure. 1993–94 Cavalier, Sunbird, Beretta, Corsica & Achieva, Grand Am & Skylark Less VES

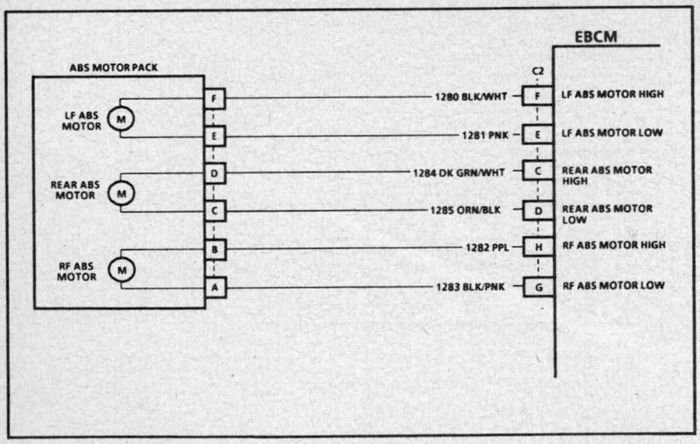
EBCM
ABS MOTOR PACK
C2
LF ABS MOTOR
REAR ABS MOTOR
RF ABS MOTOR
1280 BLK/WHT
F LF ABS MOTOR HIGH
1281 PNK
E LF ABS MOTOR LOW
1284 DK GRN/WHT
C REAR ABS MOTOR HIGH
1285 ORN/BLK
D REAR ABS MOTOR LOW
1282 PPL
H RF ABS MOTOR HIGH
1283 BLK/PNK
G RF ABS MOTOR LOW

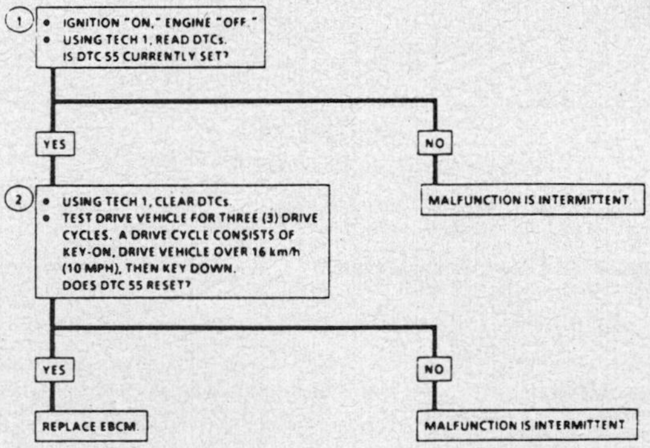
1 • IGNITION "ON," ENGINE "OFF."
• USING TECH 1, READ DTCs.
IS DTC 55 CURRENTLY SET?
YES
NO
MALFUNCTION IS INTERMITTENT
2 • USING TECH 1, CLEAR DTCs.
• TEST DRIVE VEHICLE FOR THREE (3) DRIVE CYCLES. A DRIVE CYCLE CONSISTS OF KEY-ON, DRIVE VEHICLE OVER 16 km/h (10 MPH), THEN KEY DOWN.
DOES DTC 55 RESET?
YES
NO
REPLACE EBCM
MALFUNCTION IS INTERMITTENT

GC402930079800BA

DTC 55

EBCM MALFUNCTION

Circuit Description:

This DTC identifies a malfunction detected by the MDI custom IC. It also ensures the cause of the malfunction is not a result of a problem with the ABS enable relay under a DTC 55 malfunction.

Action Taken: A malfunction DTC is stored, ABS is disabled and the ABS warning lamp is turned "ON."

DTC Chart Test Description: Number(s) below refer to circled number(s) on the diagnostic chart.

1. Checks to see if the malfunction is still present.
2. Checks to see if the malfunction is intermittent.

Diagnostic Aids: An "Intermittent" malfunction may be caused by a poor connection, rubbed through wire insulation, or a wire that is broken inside the insulation.

The frequency of the malfunction can be checked by using the enhanced diagnostic function of the Tech 1.

Any circuitry, that is suspected as causing the intermittent complaint, should be thoroughly checked for backed out terminals, improper mating, broken locks, improperly formed or damaged terminals, poor terminal to wiring connections or physical damage to the wiring harness.

GC402930079800AA

Fig. 174 Code A055: EBCM Failure. 1993 Grand Prix, 1993–94 Cutlass Supreme, Lumina & Regal

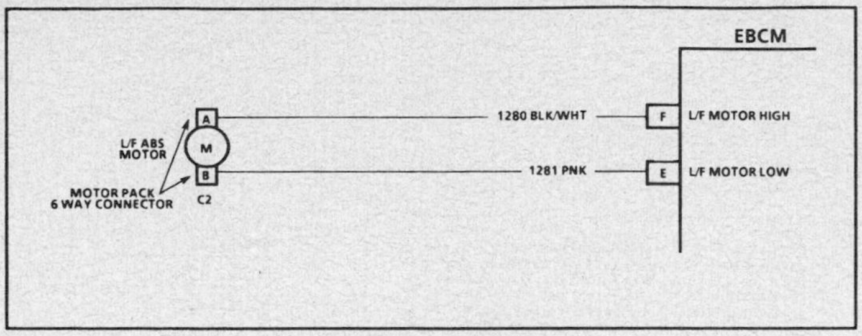

EBCM
L/F ABS MOTOR
M
A
B
MOTOR PACK 6 WAY CONNECTOR
C2
1280 BLK/WHT
1281 PNK
F
E
L/F MOTOR HIGH
L/F MOTOR LOW

DTC A056

LEFT FRONT MOTOR CIRCUIT OPEN

Circuit Description:
This DTC identifies a motor that cannot be energized due to an open in its circuitry. This malfunction will not allow proper front ABS operation.

Failure Condition:
DTC A056 can be set only when the motor is commanded "OFF." If the EBCM detects an out of range voltage in either of the left front motor circuits indicating an open circuit, a malfunction exists.

Action Taken:
An open motor will not activate when requested. A malfunction DTC is stored, ABS is disabled and the ABS indicator lamp is turned "ON."

Test Description: Number(s) below refer to circled number(s) on the diagnostic chart.

1. This step checks for proper resistance of the motor.
2. This step is used to release the tension of the motor pack prior to removal.
3. This step checks for an open in the motor "high" circuitry.
4. This step checks for an open in the motor "low" circuitry.

Diagnostic Aids:

Using Tech 1, select manual control function, and exercise motor movement of affected channel in both directions while applying light pressure on the brake pedal.

If erratic or "jumpy" brake pedal movement is detected while performing an "apply" or "release" function of the motor, an intermittent malfunction may be indicated.

An "Intermittent" malfunction may be caused by a poor connection, rubbed through wire insulation, or a wire that is broken inside the insulation.

If the malfunction is not current, wiggle the wires of the affected channel and check if the DTC resets. This will help to pinpoint an intermittent malfunction in the motor circuitry or connections.

The frequency of the malfunction can be checked by using the enhanced diagnostic function of the Tech 1.

Any circuitry, that is suspected as causing the intermittent complaint, should be thoroughly checked for backed out terminals, improper mating, broken locks, improperly formed or damaged terminals, poor terminal to wiring connections or physical damage to the wiring harness.

GC402930079900AX

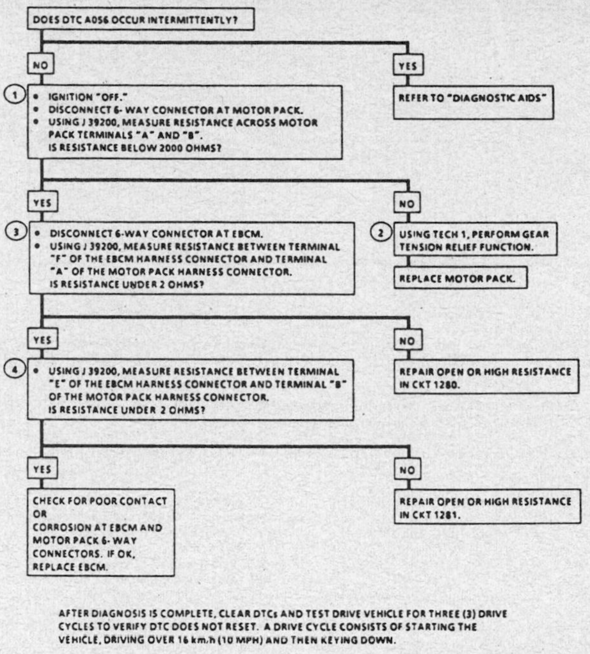

DOES DTC A056 OCCUR INTERMITTENTLY?
NO
YES
REFER TO "DIAGNOSTIC AIDS"
1
• IGNITION "OFF."
• DISCONNECT 6-WAY CONNECTOR AT MOTOR PACK.
• USING J 39200, MEASURE RESISTANCE ACROSS MOTOR PACK TERMINALS "A" AND "B".
IS RESISTANCE BELOW 2000 OHMS?
YES
NO
2
USING TECH 1, PERFORM GEAR TENSION RELIEF FUNCTION.
REPLACE MOTOR PACK.
3
• DISCONNECT 6-WAY CONNECTOR AT EBCM.
• USING J 39200, MEASURE RESISTANCE BETWEEN TERMINAL "F" OF THE EBCM HARNESS CONNECTOR AND TERMINAL "A" OF THE MOTOR PACK HARNESS CONNECTOR.
IS RESISTANCE UNDER 2 OHMS?
YES
NO
REPAIR OPEN OR HIGH RESISTANCE IN CKT 1280.
4
• USING J 39200, MEASURE RESISTANCE BETWEEN TERMINAL "E" OF THE EBCM HARNESS CONNECTOR AND TERMINAL "B" OF THE MOTOR PACK HARNESS CONNECTOR.
IS RESISTANCE UNDER 2 OHMS?
YES
NO
CHECK FOR POOR CONTACT OR CORROSION AT EBCM AND MOTOR PACK 6-WAY CONNECTORS. IF OK, REPLACE EBCM.
REPAIR OPEN OR HIGH RESISTANCE IN CKT 1281.
AFTER DIAGNOSIS IS COMPLETE, CLEAR DTCs AND TEST DRIVE VEHICLE FOR THREE (3) DRIVE CYCLES TO VERIFY DTC DOES NOT RESET. A DRIVE CYCLE CONSISTS OF STARTING THE VEHICLE, DRIVING OVER 16 km/h (10 MPH) AND THEN KEYING DOWN.

GC402930079900BX

Fig. 175 Code A056: Left Front Motor Circuit Open. 1993–94 Cavalier, Sunbird, Beretta, Corsica & Achieva, Grand Am & Skylark Less VES

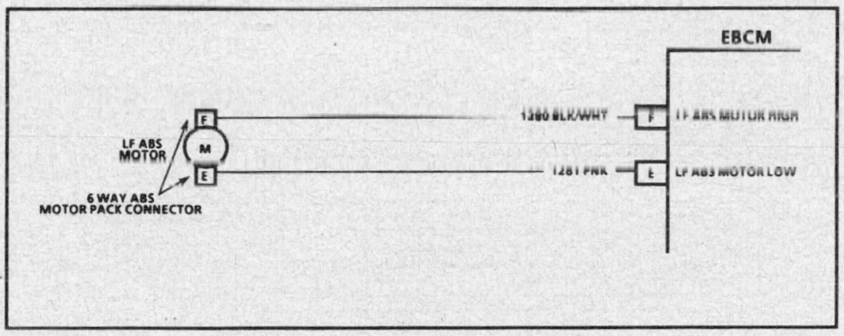

EBCM
LF ABS MOTOR
M
F
E
6 WAY ABS MOTOR PACK CONNECTOR
1281 PNK

DTC 56

LEFT FRONT ABS MOTOR CIRCUIT OPEN

Circuit Description:
This DTC identifies an ABS motor that cannot be energized due to an open in its circuitry.

DTC Will Set When: DTC 56 can be set only when the motor is commanded "OFF." If the EBCM detects an out of range voltage on either of the left front ABS motor circuits indicating an open circuit, a malfunction exists.

Action Taken: An open ABS motor will not activate when requested. A malfunction DTC is stored, ABS is disabled and the ABS warning lamp is turned "ON."

DTC Chart Test Description: Number(s) below refer to circled number(s) on the diagnostic chart.

1. Checks for proper resistance of the ABS motor.
2. Checks for an open in the ABS motor "HIGH" circuitry.
3. Checks for an open in the ABS motor "LOW" circuitry.
4. Ensures malfunction was not due to poor terminal contact.

Diagnostic Aids: Using Tech 1, select manual control function, and exercise ABS motor movement of affected channel in both directions while applying light pressure on the brake pedal.

If erratic or "jumpy" brake pedal movement is detected while performing an "apply" or "release" function of the ABS motor, an intermittent malfunction may be indicated.

An "Intermittent" malfunction may be caused by a poor connection, rubbed through wire insulation, or a wire that is broken inside the insulation.

If the malfunction is not current, wiggle the wires of the affected channel and check if the DTC resets. This will help to pinpoint an intermittent malfunction in the motor circuitry or connections.

The frequency of the malfunction can be checked by using the enhanced diagnostic function of the Tech 1

Any circuitry, that is suspected as causing the intermittent complaint, should be thoroughly checked for backed out terminals, improper mating, broken locks, improperly formed or damaged terminals, poor terminal to wiring connections or physical damage to the wiring harness.

GC402930080000AA

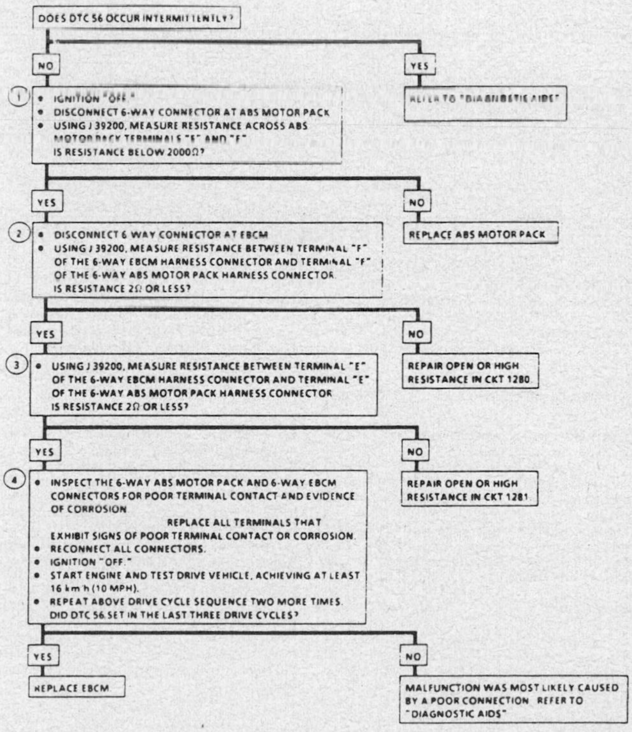

DOES DTC 56 OCCUR INTERMITTENTLY?
NO
YES
1
• IGNITION "OFF."
• DISCONNECT 6-WAY CONNECTOR AT ABS MOTOR PACK
• USING J 39200, MEASURE RESISTANCE ACROSS ABS
IS RESISTANCE BELOW 2000Ω?
YES
NO
2
• DISCONNECT 6 WAY CONNECTOR AT EBCM
• USING J 39200, MEASURE RESISTANCE BETWEEN TERMINAL "F" OF THE 6-WAY EBCM HARNESS CONNECTOR AND TERMINAL "F" OF THE 6-WAY ABS MOTOR PACK HARNESS CONNECTOR.
IS RESISTANCE 2Ω OR LESS?
REPLACE ABS MOTOR PACK
YES
NO
3
• USING J 39200, MEASURE RESISTANCE BETWEEN TERMINAL "E" OF THE 6-WAY EBCM HARNESS CONNECTOR AND TERMINAL "E" OF THE 6-WAY ABS MOTOR PACK HARNESS CONNECTOR
IS RESISTANCE 2Ω OR LESS?
REPAIR OPEN OR HIGH RESISTANCE IN CKT 1280
YES
NO
4
• INSPECT THE 6-WAY ABS MOTOR PACK AND 6-WAY EBCM CONNECTORS FOR POOR TERMINAL CONTACT AND EVIDENCE OF CORROSION
REPLACE ALL TERMINALS THAT EXHIBIT SIGNS OF POOR TERMINAL CONTACT OR CORROSION.
• RECONNECT ALL CONNECTORS.
• IGNITION "OFF."
• START ENGINE AND TEST DRIVE VEHICLE, ACHIEVING AT LEAST 16 km/h (10 MPH).
• REPEAT ABOVE DRIVE CYCLE SEQUENCE TWO MORE TIMES.
DID DTC 56 SET IN THE LAST THREE DRIVE CYCLES?
REPAIR OPEN OR HIGH RESISTANCE IN CKT 1281
YES
NO
REPLACE EBCM
MALFUNCTION WAS MOST LIKELY CAUSED BY A POOR CONNECTION. REFER TO "DIAGNOSTIC AIDS"

GC402930080000BA

Fig. 176 Code A056: Left Front Motor Circuit Open. 1993 Grand Prix, 1993–94 Cutlass Supreme, Lumina & Regal

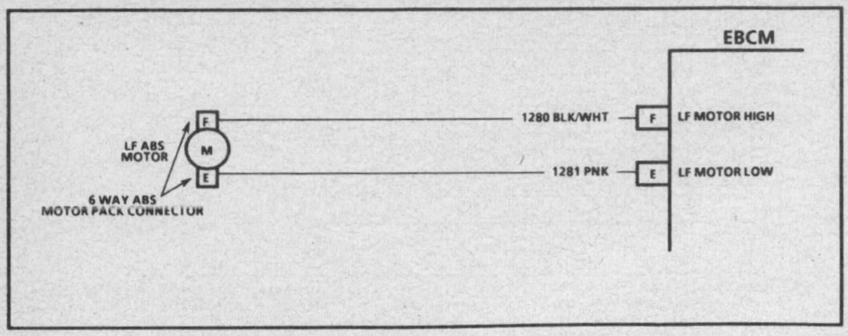
EBCM
1280 BLK/WHT
F
LF MOTOR HIGH
1281 PNK
E
LF MOTOR LOW
LF ABS MOTOR
M
6 WAY ABS MOTOR PACK CONNECTOR

DTC 57

LEFT FRONT ABS MOTOR CIRCUIT SHORTED TO GROUND

Circuit Description:

This DTC identifies an ABS motor circuit that is shorted to ground. This malfunction will not allow the ABS motor to be controlled at the commanded current rate or will cause the driver circuit to allow current directly to ground.

DTC Will Set When: DTC 57 can be set anytime. If the EBCM detects an out of range voltage on either of the left front ABS motor circuits indicating a circuit shorted to ground, a malfunction exists.

Action Taken: A malfunction DTC is stored, ABS is disabled and the ABS warning lamp is turned "ON."

DTC Chart Test Description: Number(s) below refer to circled number(s) on the diagnostic chart.

1. Checks for a short to ground in the ABS motor "HIGH" circuitry.
2. Checks for a short to ground in the ABS motor "LOW" circuitry.
3. Checks for an ABS motor that is internally shorted to ground.
4. Ensures malfunction was not due to physical damage of the circuitry.

Diagnostic Aids: Using Tech 1, select manual control function, and exercise ABS motor movement of affected channel in both directions while applying light pressure on the brake pedal.

If erratic or "jumpy" brake pedal movement is detected while performing an "apply" or "release" function of the ABS motor, an intermittent malfunction may be indicated.

An "Intermittent" malfunction may be caused by a poor connection, rubbed through wire insulation, or a wire that is broken inside the insulation.

If the malfunction is not current, wiggle the wires of the affected channel and check if the DTC resets. This will help to pinpoint an intermittent malfunction in the motor circuitry or connections.

The frequency of the malfunction can be checked by using the enhanced diagnostic function of the Tech 1.

Any circuitry, that is suspected as causing the intermittent complaint, should be thoroughly checked for backed out terminals, improper mating, broken locks, improperly formed or damaged terminals, poor terminal to wiring connections or physical damage to the wiring harness.

GC402930080200AA

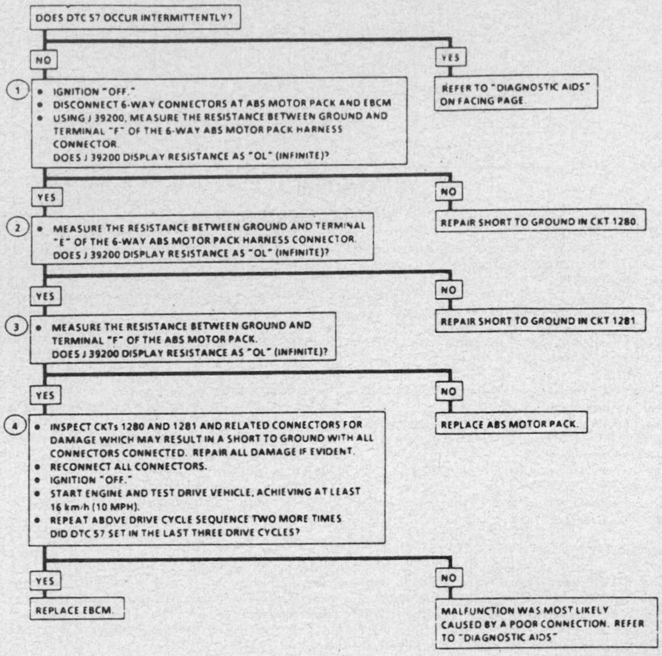
DOES DTC 57 OCCUR INTERMITTENTLY?
NO
YES
REFER TO "DIAGNOSTIC AIDS" ON FACING PAGE.
1
• IGNITION "OFF."
• DISCONNECT 6-WAY CONNECTORS AT ABS MOTOR PACK AND EBCM
• USING J 39200, MEASURE THE RESISTANCE BETWEEN GROUND AND TERMINAL "F" OF THE 6-WAY ABS MOTOR PACK HARNESS CONNECTOR.
DOES J 39200 DISPLAY RESISTANCE AS "OL" (INFINITE)?
YES
NO
REPAIR SHORT TO GROUND IN CKT 1280.
2
• MEASURE THE RESISTANCE BETWEEN GROUND AND TERMINAL "E" OF THE 6-WAY ABS MOTOR PACK HARNESS CONNECTOR.
DOES J 39200 DISPLAY RESISTANCE AS "OL" (INFINITE)?
YES
NO
REPAIR SHORT TO GROUND IN CKT 1281.
3
• MEASURE THE RESISTANCE BETWEEN GROUND AND TERMINAL "F" OF THE ABS MOTOR PACK.
DOES J 39200 DISPLAY RESISTANCE AS "OL" (INFINITE)?
YES
NO
REPLACE ABS MOTOR PACK.
4
• INSPECT CKTs 1280 AND 1281 AND RELATED CONNECTORS FOR DAMAGE WHICH MAY RESULT IN A SHORT TO GROUND WITH ALL CONNECTORS CONNECTED. REPAIR ALL DAMAGE IF EVIDENT.
• RECONNECT ALL CONNECTORS.
• IGNITION "OFF."
• START ENGINE AND TEST DRIVE VEHICLE, ACHIEVING AT LEAST 16 km/h (10 MPH).
• REPEAT ABOVE DRIVE CYCLE SEQUENCE TWO MORE TIMES
DID DTC 57 SET IN THE LAST THREE DRIVE CYCLES?
YES
REPLACE EBCM.
NO
MALFUNCTION WAS MOST LIKELY CAUSED BY A POOR CONNECTION. REFER TO "DIAGNOSTIC AIDS"

GC402930080200BA

Fig. 177 Code A057: Left Front Motor Circuit Shorted To Ground. 1993–94 Cavalier, Sunbird, Beretta, Corsica & Achieva, Grand Am & Skylark Less VES

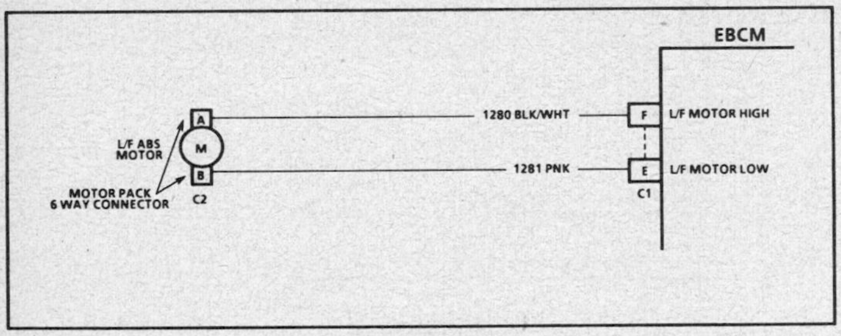
EBCM
1280 BLK/WHT
F
L/F MOTOR HIGH
1281 PNK
E
L/F MOTOR LOW
C1
L/F ABS MOTOR
M
A
B
MOTOR PACK 6 WAY CONNECTOR
C2

DTC A057

LEFT FRONT MOTOR CIRCUIT SHORTED TO GROUND

Circuit Description:

This DTC identifies a motor circuit that is shorted to ground. This malfunction will not allow the motor to be controlled at the commanded current rate or will cause the driver circuit to allow current directly to ground.

Failure Condition:

DTC A057 can be set anytime. If the EBCM detects an out of range voltage in either of the left front motor circuits indicating a circuit shorted to ground, a malfunction exists.

Action Taken:

A malfunction DTC is stored, ABS is disabled and the ABS indicator lamp is turned "ON."

Test Description: Number(s) below refer to circled number(s) on the diagnostic chart.

1. This step checks for a motor that is internally shorted to ground.
2. This step checks for a short to ground in the motor circuitry.
3. This step ensures malfunction was not due to a poor connection.
4. This step is used to release the tension of the motor pack prior to removal.

Diagnostic Aids:

Using Tech 1, select manual control function, and exercise motor movement of affected channel in both directions while applying light pressure on the brake pedal.

If erratic or "jumpy" brake pedal movement is detected while performing an "apply" or "release" function of the motor, an intermittent malfunction may be indicated.

An "Intermittent" malfunction may be caused by a poor connection, rubbed through wire insulation, or a wire that is broken inside the insulation.

If the malfunction is not current, wiggle the wires of the affected channel and check if the DTC resets. This will help to pinpoint an intermittent malfunction in the motor circuitry or connections.

The frequency of the malfunction can be checked by using the enhanced diagnostic function of the Tech 1.

Any circuitry, that is suspected as causing the intermittent complaint, should be thoroughly checked for backed out terminals, improper mating, broken locks, improperly formed or damaged terminals, poor terminal to wiring connections or physical damage to the wiring harness.

GC402930080100AX

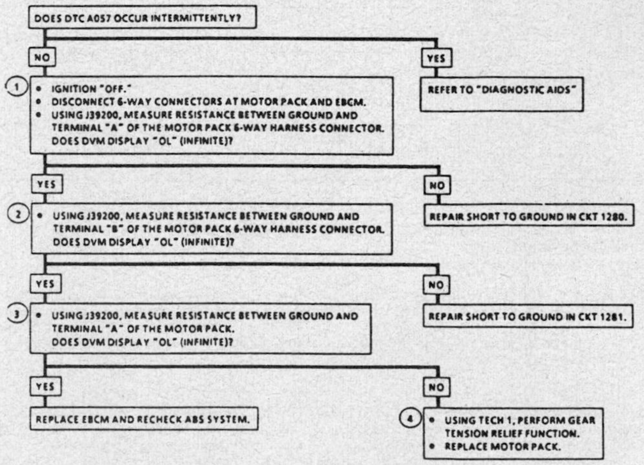
DOES DTC A057 OCCUR INTERMITTENTLY?
NO
YES
REFER TO "DIAGNOSTIC AIDS"
1
• IGNITION "OFF."
• DISCONNECT 6-WAY CONNECTORS AT MOTOR PACK AND EBCM.
• USING J39200, MEASURE RESISTANCE BETWEEN GROUND AND TERMINAL "A" OF THE MOTOR PACK 6-WAY HARNESS CONNECTOR.
DOES DVM DISPLAY "OL" (INFINITE)?
YES
NO
REPAIR SHORT TO GROUND IN CKT 1280.
2
• USING J39200, MEASURE RESISTANCE BETWEEN GROUND AND TERMINAL "B" OF THE MOTOR PACK 6-WAY HARNESS CONNECTOR.
DOES DVM DISPLAY "OL" (INFINITE)?
YES
NO
REPAIR SHORT TO GROUND IN CKT 1281.
3
• USING J39200, MEASURE RESISTANCE BETWEEN GROUND AND TERMINAL "A" OF THE MOTOR PACK.
DOES DVM DISPLAY "OL" (INFINITE)?
YES
REPLACE EBCM AND RECHECK ABS SYSTEM.
NO
4
• USING TECH 1, PERFORM GEAR TENSION RELIEF FUNCTION.
• REPLACE MOTOR PACK.

AFTER DIAGNOSIS IS COMPLETE, CLEAR DTCs AND TEST DRIVE VEHICLE FOR THREE (3) DRIVE CYCLES TO VERIFY DTC DOES NOT RESET. A DRIVE CYCLE CONSISTS OF STARTING THE VEHICLE, DRIVING OVER 16 km/h (10 MPH) AND THEN KEYING DOWN.

GC402930080100BX

Fig. 178 Code A057: Left Front Motor Circuit Shorted To Ground. 1993 Grand Prix, 1993–94 Cutlass Supreme, Lumina & Regal

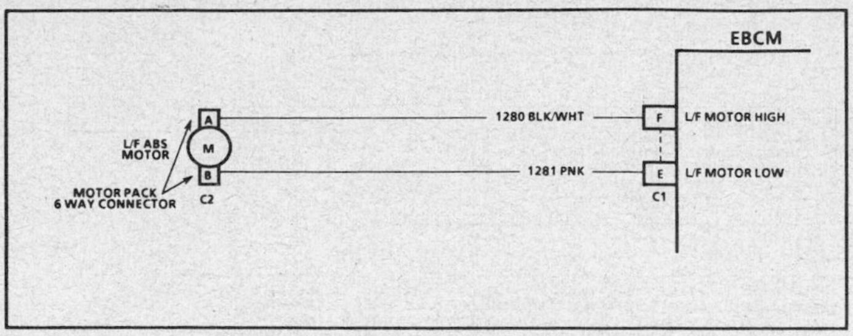
EBCM
L/F ABS MOTOR
M
A
B
MOTOR PACK 6 WAY CONNECTOR
C2
1280 BLK/WHT
1281 PNK
F
E
C1
L/F MOTOR HIGH
L/F MOTOR LOW

DTC A058

LEFT FRONT MOTOR CIRCUIT SHORTED TO BATTERY OR MOTOR SHORTED

Circuit Description:

This DTC identifies a motor circuit that is shorted to battery or a motor that has low or no resistance. This malfunction will not allow the motor to be controlled at the commanded current rate or will cause the motor to turn in the opposite direction, or not at all.

Failure Condition:

DTC A058 can be set anytime. If the EBCM detects an out of range voltage in either of the left front motor circuits indicating a circuit shorted to battery or a motor shorted, a malfunction exists.

Action Taken:

A malfunction DTC is stored, ABS is disabled and the ABS indicator lamp is turned "ON."

Test Description: Number(s) below refer to circled number(s) on the diagnostic chart.

1. This step checks for a short to voltage in the motor "high" circuitry.
2. This step checks for a short to voltage in the motor "low" circuitry.
3. This step checks for a motor that is internally shorted.
4. This step is used to release the tension of the motor pack prior to removal.

Diagnostic Aids:

Using Tech 1, select manual control function, and exercise motor movement of affected channel in both directions while applying light pressure on the brake pedal.

If erratic or "jumpy" brake pedal movement is detected while performing an "apply" or "release" function of the motor, an intermittent malfunction may be indicated.

An "Intermittent" malfunction may be caused by a poor connection, rubbed through wire insulation, or a wire that is broken inside the insulation.

If the malfunction is not current, wiggle the wires of the affected channel and check if the DTC resets. This will help to pinpoint an intermittent malfunction in the motor circuitry or connections.

The frequency of the malfunction can be checked by using the enhanced diagnostic function of the Tech 1.

If DTC A038 sets as a current DTC and A058 is an infrequent history DTC, see DTC A038 diagnostics.

Any circuitry, that is suspected as causing the intermittent complaint, should be thoroughly checked for backed out terminals, improper mating, broken locks, improperly formed or damaged terminals, poor terminal to wiring connections or physical damage to the wiring harness.

GC402930080300AX

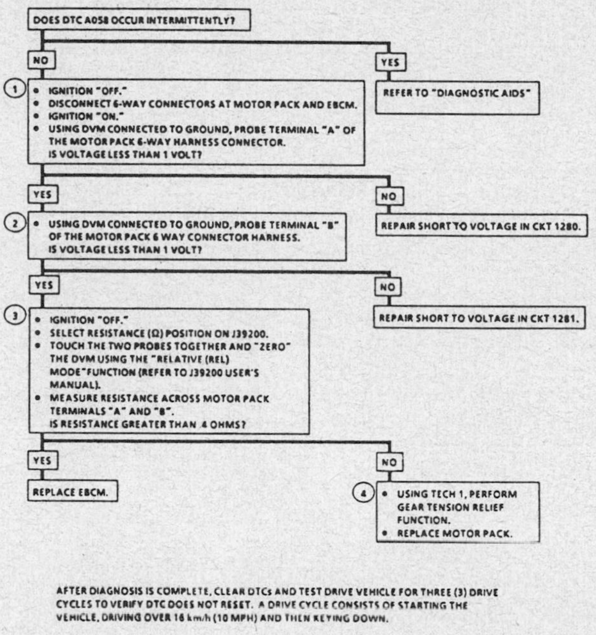
DOES DTC A058 OCCUR INTERMITTENTLY?
NO
YES
REFER TO "DIAGNOSTIC AIDS"
1
• IGNITION "OFF."
• DISCONNECT 6-WAY CONNECTORS AT MOTOR PACK AND EBCM.
• IGNITION "ON."
• USING DVM CONNECTED TO GROUND, PROBE TERMINAL "A" OF THE MOTOR PACK 6-WAY HARNESS CONNECTOR.
IS VOLTAGE LESS THAN 1 VOLT?
YES
NO
REPAIR SHORT TO VOLTAGE IN CKT 1280.
2
• USING DVM CONNECTED TO GROUND, PROBE TERMINAL "B" OF THE MOTOR PACK 6 WAY CONNECTOR HARNESS.
IS VOLTAGE LESS THAN 1 VOLT?
YES
NO
REPAIR SHORT TO VOLTAGE IN CKT 1281.
3
• IGNITION "OFF."
• SELECT RESISTANCE (Ω) POSITION ON J39200.
• TOUCH THE TWO PROBES TOGETHER AND "ZERO" THE DVM USING THE "RELATIVE (REL) MODE" FUNCTION (REFER TO J39200 USER'S MANUAL).
• MEASURE RESISTANCE ACROSS MOTOR PACK TERMINALS "A" AND "B".
IS RESISTANCE GREATER THAN 4 OHMS?
YES
NO
REPLACE EBCM.
4
• USING TECH 1, PERFORM GEAR TENSION RELIEF FUNCTION.
• REPLACE MOTOR PACK.
AFTER DIAGNOSIS IS COMPLETE, CLEAR DTCs AND TEST DRIVE VEHICLE FOR THREE (3) DRIVE CYCLES TO VERIFY DTC DOES NOT RESET. A DRIVE CYCLE CONSISTS OF STARTING THE VEHICLE, DRIVING OVER 16 km/h (10 MPH) AND THEN KEYING DOWN.

GC402930080300BX

Fig. 179 Code A058: Left Front Motor Circuit Shorted To Battery Or Motor Shorted. 1993–94 Cavalier, Sunbird, Beretta, Corsica & Achieva, Grand Am & Skylark Less VES

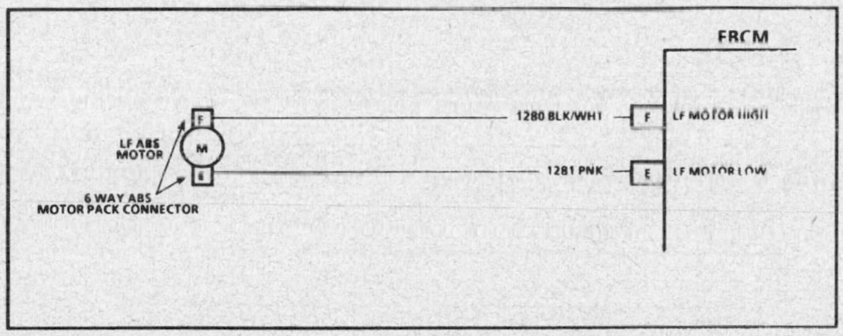
EBCM
LF ABS MOTOR
M
F
E
6 WAY ABS MOTOR PACK CONNECTOR
1280 BLK/WHT
1281 PNK

DTC 58

LEFT FRONT ABS MOTOR CIRCUIT SHORTED TO BATTERY

Circuit Description:

This DTC identifies an ABS motor circuit that is shorted to battery or an ABS motor that has low or no resistance. This malfunction will not allow the ABS motor to be controlled at the commanded current rate or will cause the ABS motor to turn in the opposite direction, or not at all.

DTC Will Set When: DTC 58 can be set only when the ABS motor is commanded "OFF." If the EBCM detects an out of range voltage on either of the left front ABS motor circuits indicating a circuit shorted to battery or an ABS motor shorted, a malfunction exists.

Action Taken: A malfunction DTC is stored, ABS is disabled and the ABS warning lamp is turned "ON."

DTC Chart Test Description: Number(s) below refer to circled number(s) on the diagnostic chart.

1. Checks for a short to voltage in the ABS motor "HIGH" circuitry.
2. Checks for a short to voltage in the ABS motor "LOW" circuitry.
3. Checks for a short between the "HIGH" and "LOW" motor circuits.
4. Checks for an ABS motor that is internally shorted.
5. Ensures malfunction was not due to physical damage of the circuitry.

Diagnostic Aids: Using Tech 1, select manual control function, and exercise ABS motor movement of affected channel in both directions while applying light pressure on the brake pedal.

If erratic or "jumpy" brake pedal movement is detected while performing an "apply" or "release" function of the ABS motor, an intermittent malfunction may be indicated.

An "Intermittent" malfunction may be caused by a poor connection, rubbed through wire insulation, or a wire that is broken inside the insulation.

If the malfunction is not current, wiggle the wires of the affected channel and check if the DTC resets. This will help to pinpoint an intermittent malfunction in the motor circuitry or connections.

The frequency of the malfunction can be checked by using the enhanced diagnostic function of the Tech 1.

Any circuitry, that is suspected as causing the intermittent complaint, should be thoroughly checked for backed out terminals, improper mating, broken locks, improperly formed or damaged terminals, poor terminal to wiring connections or physical damage to the wiring harness.

GC402930080400AA

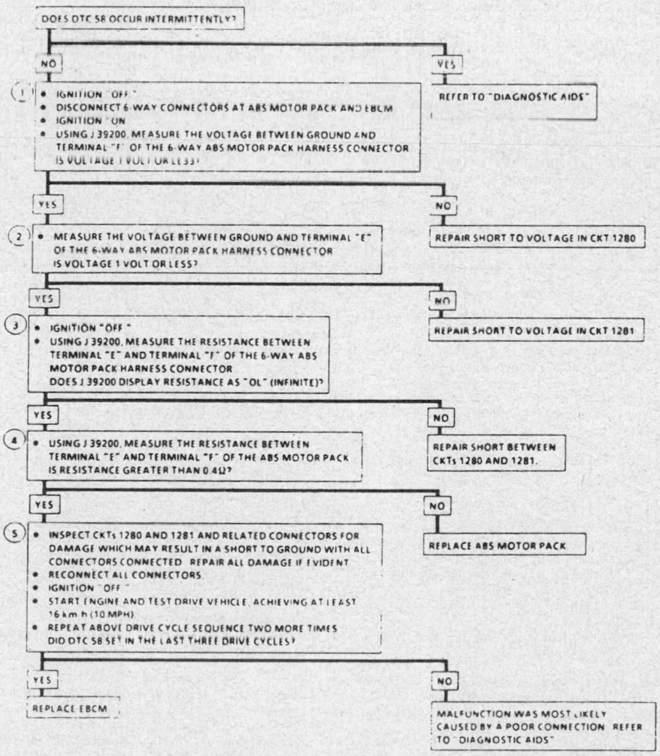
DOES DTC 58 OCCUR INTERMITTENTLY?
NO
YES
REFER TO "DIAGNOSTIC AIDS"
1
• IGNITION "OFF."
• DISCONNECT 6-WAY CONNECTORS AT ABS MOTOR PACK AND EBCM
• IGNITION "ON"
• USING J 39200, MEASURE THE VOLTAGE BETWEEN GROUND AND TERMINAL "F" OF THE 6-WAY ABS MOTOR PACK HARNESS CONNECTOR
IS VOLTAGE 1 VOLT OR LESS?
YES
NO
REPAIR SHORT TO VOLTAGE IN CKT 1280
2
• MEASURE THE VOLTAGE BETWEEN GROUND AND TERMINAL "E" OF THE 6-WAY ABS MOTOR PACK HARNESS CONNECTOR
IS VOLTAGE 1 VOLT OR LESS?
YES
NO
REPAIR SHORT TO VOLTAGE IN CKT 1281
3
• IGNITION "OFF."
• USING J 39200, MEASURE THE RESISTANCE BETWEEN TERMINAL "E" AND TERMINAL "F" OF THE 6-WAY ABS MOTOR PACK HARNESS CONNECTOR
DOES J 39200 DISPLAY RESISTANCE AS "OL" (INFINITE)?
YES
NO
REPAIR SHORT BETWEEN CKTs 1280 AND 1281.
4
• USING J 39200, MEASURE THE RESISTANCE BETWEEN TERMINAL "E" AND TERMINAL "F" OF THE ABS MOTOR PACK
IS RESISTANCE GREATER THAN 0.4Ω?
YES
NO
REPLACE ABS MOTOR PACK
5
• INSPECT CKTs 1280 AND 1281 AND RELATED CONNECTORS FOR DAMAGE WHICH MAY RESULT IN A SHORT TO GROUND WITH ALL CONNECTORS CONNECTED. REPAIR ALL DAMAGE IF EVIDENT
• RECONNECT ALL CONNECTORS.
• IGNITION "OFF."
• START ENGINE AND TEST DRIVE VEHICLE, ACHIEVING AT LEAST 16 km/h (10 MPH)
• REPEAT ABOVE DRIVE CYCLE SEQUENCE TWO MORE TIMES
DID DTC 58 SET IN THE LAST THREE DRIVE CYCLES?
YES
NO
REPLACE EBCM
MALFUNCTION WAS MOST LIKELY CAUSED BY A POOR CONNECTION. REFER TO "DIAGNOSTIC AIDS"

GC402930080400BA

Fig. 180 Code A058: Left Front Motor Circuit Shorted To Battery. 1993 Grand Prix, 1993–94 Cutlass Supreme, Lumina & Regal

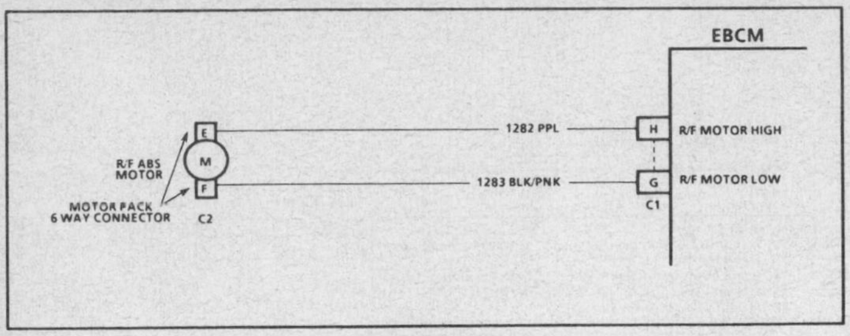
EBCM
R/F ABS MOTOR
M
E
F
MOTOR PACK 6 WAY CONNECTOR
C2
1282 PPL
1283 BLK/PNK
H
G
C1
R/F MOTOR HIGH
R/F MOTOR LOW

DTC A061

RIGHT FRONT MOTOR CIRCUIT OPEN

Circuit Description:
This DTC identifies a motor that cannot be energized due to an open in its circuitry. This malfunction will not allow proper front ABS operation.

Failure Condition:
DTC A061 can be set only when the motor is commanded "OFF." If the EBCM detects an out of range voltage in either of the right front motor circuits indicating an open circuit, a malfunction exists.

Action Taken:
An open motor will not activate when requested. A malfunction DTC is stored, ABS is disabled and the ABS indicator lamp is turned "ON."

Test Description: Number(s) below refer to circled number(s) on the diagnostic chart.
1. This step checks for proper resistance of the motor.
2. This step is used to release the tension of the motor pack prior to removal.
3. This step checks for an open in the motor "high" circuitry.
4. This step checks for an open in the motor "low" circuitry.

Diagnostic Aids:

Using Tech 1, select manual control function, and exercise motor movement of affected channel in both directions while applying light pressure on the brake pedal.

If erratic or "jumpy" brake pedal movement is detected while performing an "apply" or "release" function of the motor, an intermittent malfunction may be indicated.

An "Intermittent" malfunction may be caused by a poor connection, rubbed through wire insulation, or a wire that is broken inside the insulation.

If the malfunction is not current, wiggle the wires of the affected channel and check if the DTC resets. This will help to pinpoint an intermittent malfunction in the motor circuitry or connections.

The frequency of the malfunction can be checked by using the enhanced diagnostic function of the Tech 1.

Any circuitry, that is suspected as causing the intermittent complaint, should be thoroughly checked for backed out terminals, improper mating, broken locks, improperly formed or damaged terminals, poor terminal to wiring connections or physical damage to the wiring harness.

GC402930080500AX

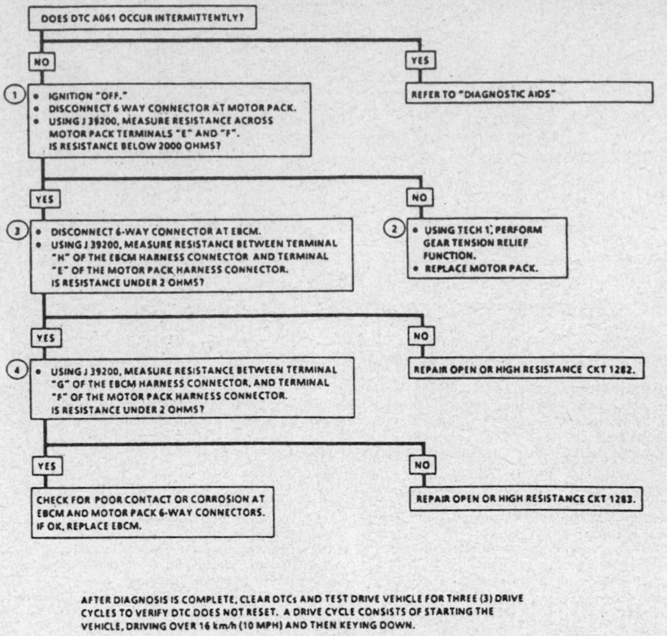
DOES DTC A061 OCCUR INTERMITTENTLY?
NO
YES
REFER TO "DIAGNOSTIC AIDS"
1
• IGNITION "OFF."
• DISCONNECT 6 WAY CONNECTOR AT MOTOR PACK.
• USING J 39200, MEASURE RESISTANCE ACROSS MOTOR PACK TERMINALS "E" AND "F".
IS RESISTANCE BELOW 2000 OHMS?
YES
NO
3
• DISCONNECT 6-WAY CONNECTOR AT EBCM.
• USING J 39200, MEASURE RESISTANCE BETWEEN TERMINAL "H" OF THE EBCM HARNESS CONNECTOR AND TERMINAL "E" OF THE MOTOR PACK HARNESS CONNECTOR.
IS RESISTANCE UNDER 2 OHMS?
2
• USING TECH 1, PERFORM GEAR TENSION RELIEF FUNCTION.
• REPLACE MOTOR PACK.
YES
NO
REPAIR OPEN OR HIGH RESISTANCE CKT 1282.
4
• USING J 39200, MEASURE RESISTANCE BETWEEN TERMINAL "G" OF THE EBCM HARNESS CONNECTOR, AND TERMINAL "F" OF THE MOTOR PACK HARNESS CONNECTOR.
IS RESISTANCE UNDER 2 OHMS?
YES
NO
CHECK FOR POOR CONTACT OR CORROSION AT EBCM AND MOTOR PACK 6-WAY CONNECTORS. IF OK, REPLACE EBCM.
REPAIR OPEN OR HIGH RESISTANCE CKT 1283.
AFTER DIAGNOSIS IS COMPLETE, CLEAR DTCs AND TEST DRIVE VEHICLE FOR THREE (3) DRIVE CYCLES TO VERIFY DTC DOES NOT RESET. A DRIVE CYCLE CONSISTS OF STARTING THE VEHICLE, DRIVING OVER 16 km/h (10 MPH) AND THEN KEYING DOWN.

GC402930080500BX

Fig. 181 Code A061: Right Front Motor Circuit Open. 1993–94 Cavalier, Sunbird, Beretta, Corsica & Achieva, Grand Am & Skylark Less VES

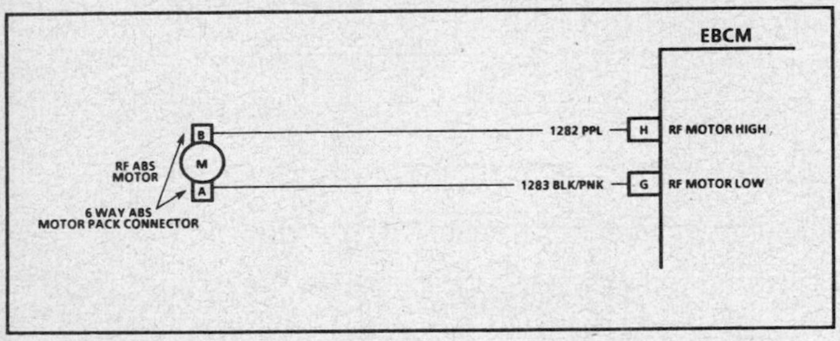
EBCM
RF ABS MOTOR
M
B
A
6 WAY ABS MOTOR PACK CONNECTOR
1282 PPL
1283 BLK/PNK
H
G
RF MOTOR HIGH
RF MOTOR LOW

DTC 61

RIGHT FRONT ABS MOTOR CIRCUIT OPEN

Circuit Description:
This DTC identifies an ABS motor that cannot be energized due to an open in its circuitry. This malfunction will not allow proper front ABS operation.

DTC Will Set When: DTC 61 can be set only when the ABS motor is commanded "OFF." If the EBCM detects an out of range voltage on either of the right front ABS motor circuits indicating an open circuit, a malfunction exists.

Action Taken: An open ABS motor will not activate when requested. A malfunction DTC is stored, ABS is disabled and the ABS warning lamp is turned "ON."

DTC Chart Test Description: Number(s) below refer to circled number(s) on the diagnostic chart.
1. Checks for proper resistance of the ABS motor.
2. Checks for an open in the ABS motor "HIGH" circuitry.
3. Checks for an open in the ABS motor "LOW" circuitry.
4. Ensures malfunction was not due to physical damage of the circuitry.

Diagnostic Aids: Using Tech 1, select manual control function, and exercise ABS motor movement of affected channel in both directions while applying light pressure on the brake pedal.

If erratic or "jumpy" brake pedal movement is detected while performing an "apply" or "release" function of the ABS motor, an intermittent malfunction may be indicated.

An "Intermittent" malfunction may be caused by a poor connection, rubbed through wire insulation, or a wire that is broken inside the insulation.

If the malfunction is not current, wiggle the wires of the affected channel and check if the DTC resets. This will help to pinpoint an intermittent malfunction in the motor circuitry or connections.

The frequency of the malfunction can be checked by using the enhanced diagnostic function of the Tech 1.

Any circuitry, that is suspected as causing the intermittent complaint, should be thoroughly checked for backed out terminals, improper mating, broken locks, improperly formed or damaged terminals, poor terminal to wiring connections or physical damage to the wiring harness.

GC402930080600AA

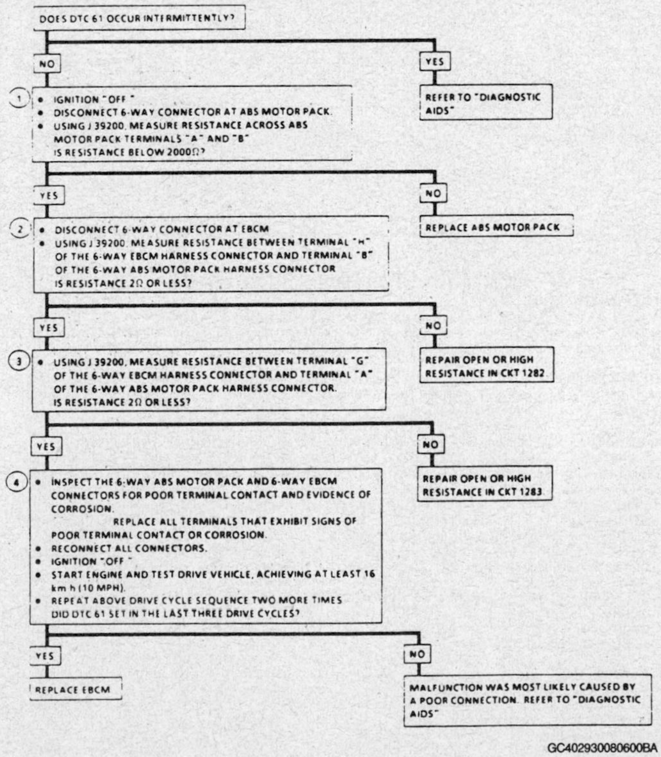
DOES DTC 61 OCCUR INTERMITTENTLY?
NO
YES
REFER TO "DIAGNOSTIC AIDS"
1
• IGNITION "OFF."
• DISCONNECT 6-WAY CONNECTOR AT ABS MOTOR PACK.
• USING J 39200, MEASURE RESISTANCE ACROSS ABS MOTOR PACK TERMINALS "A" AND "B"
IS RESISTANCE BELOW 2000Ω?
YES
NO
REPLACE ABS MOTOR PACK
2
• DISCONNECT 6-WAY CONNECTOR AT EBCM
• USING J 39200, MEASURE RESISTANCE BETWEEN TERMINAL "H" OF THE 6-WAY EBCM HARNESS CONNECTOR AND TERMINAL "B" OF THE 6-WAY ABS MOTOR PACK HARNESS CONNECTOR
IS RESISTANCE 2Ω OR LESS?
YES
NO
REPAIR OPEN OR HIGH RESISTANCE IN CKT 1282
3
• USING J 39200, MEASURE RESISTANCE BETWEEN TERMINAL "G" OF THE 6-WAY EBCM HARNESS CONNECTOR AND TERMINAL "A" OF THE 6-WAY ABS MOTOR PACK HARNESS CONNECTOR.
IS RESISTANCE 2Ω OR LESS?
YES
NO
REPAIR OPEN OR HIGH RESISTANCE IN CKT 1283
4
• INSPECT THE 6-WAY ABS MOTOR PACK AND 6-WAY EBCM CONNECTORS FOR POOR TERMINAL CONTACT AND EVIDENCE OF CORROSION.
REPLACE ALL TERMINALS THAT EXHIBIT SIGNS OF POOR TERMINAL CONTACT OR CORROSION.
• RECONNECT ALL CONNECTORS.
• IGNITION "OFF."
• START ENGINE AND TEST DRIVE VEHICLE, ACHIEVING AT LEAST 16 km/h (10 MPH).
• REPEAT ABOVE DRIVE CYCLE SEQUENCE TWO MORE TIMES
DID DTC 61 SET IN THE LAST THREE DRIVE CYCLES?
YES
NO
REPLACE EBCM
MALFUNCTION WAS MOST LIKELY CAUSED BY A POOR CONNECTION. REFER TO "DIAGNOSTIC AIDS"

GC402930080600BA

Fig. 182 Code A061: Right Front Motor Circuit Open. 1993 Grand Prix, 1993–94 Cutlass Supreme, Lumina & Regal

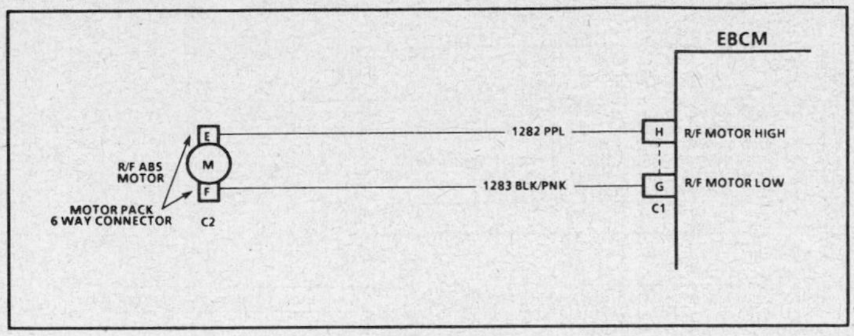
EBCM
R/F ABS MOTOR
M
E
F
MOTOR PACK 6 WAY CONNECTOR
C2
1282 PPL
1283 BLK/PNK
H
G
C1
R/F MOTOR HIGH
R/F MOTOR LOW

DTC A062

RIGHT FRONT MOTOR CIRCUIT SHORTED TO GROUND

Circuit Description:

This DTC identifies a motor circuit that is shorted to ground. This malfunction will not allow the motor to be controlled at the commanded current rate or will cause the motor driver circuit to allow current directly to ground.

Failure Condition:

DTC A062 can be set anytime. If the EBCM detects an out of range voltage in either of the right front motor circuits indicating a circuit shorted to ground, a malfunction exists.

Action Taken:

A malfunction DTC is stored, ABS is disabled and the ABS indicator lamp is turned "ON."

Test Description: Number(s) below refer to circled number(s) on the diagnostic chart.

1. This step checks for a motor that is internally shorted to ground.
2. This step checks for a short to ground in the motor circuitry.
3. This step ensures malfunction was not due to a poor connection.
4. This step is used to release the tension of the motor pack prior to removal.

Diagnostic Aids:

Using Tech 1, select manual control function, and exercise motor movement of affected channel in both directions while applying light pressure on the brake pedal.

If erratic or "jumpy" brake pedal movement is detected while performing an "apply" or "release" function of the motor, an intermittent malfunction may be indicated.

An "Intermittent" malfunction may be caused by a poor connection, rubbed through wire insulation, or a wire that is broken inside the insulation.

If the malfunction is not current, wiggle the wires of the affected channel and check if the DTC resets. This will help to pinpoint an intermittent malfunction in the motor circuitry or connections.

The frequency of the malfunction can be checked by using the enhanced diagnostic function of the Tech 1.

Any circuitry, that is suspected as causing the intermittent complaint, should be thoroughly checked for backed out terminals, improper mating, broken locks, improperly formed or damaged terminals, poor terminal to wiring connections or physical damage to the wiring harness.

GC402930080700AX

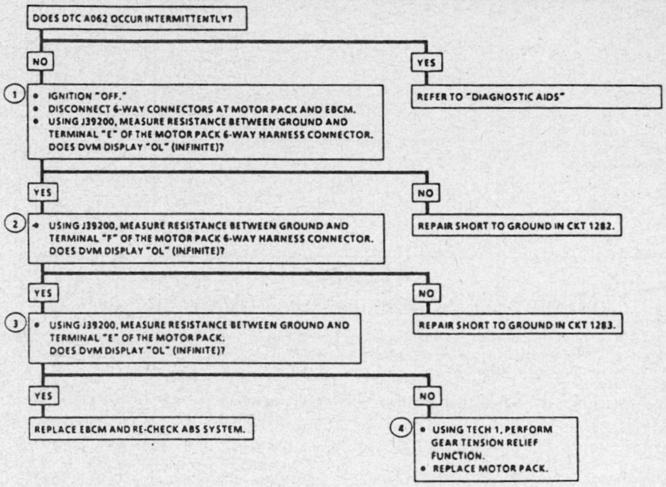
DOES DTC A062 OCCUR INTERMITTENTLY?
NO
YES
REFER TO "DIAGNOSTIC AIDS"
1
• IGNITION "OFF."
• DISCONNECT 6-WAY CONNECTORS AT MOTOR PACK AND EBCM.
• USING J39200, MEASURE RESISTANCE BETWEEN GROUND AND TERMINAL "E" OF THE MOTOR PACK 6-WAY HARNESS CONNECTOR. DOES DVM DISPLAY "OL" (INFINITE)?
YES
NO
REPAIR SHORT TO GROUND IN CKT 1282.
2
• USING J39200, MEASURE RESISTANCE BETWEEN GROUND AND TERMINAL "F" OF THE MOTOR PACK 6-WAY HARNESS CONNECTOR. DOES DVM DISPLAY "OL" (INFINITE)?
YES
NO
REPAIR SHORT TO GROUND IN CKT 1283.
3
• USING J39200, MEASURE RESISTANCE BETWEEN GROUND AND TERMINAL "E" OF THE MOTOR PACK. DOES DVM DISPLAY "OL" (INFINITE)?
YES
NO
REPLACE EBCM AND RE-CHECK ABS SYSTEM.
4
• USING TECH 1, PERFORM GEAR TENSION RELIEF FUNCTION.
• REPLACE MOTOR PACK.

AFTER DIAGNOSIS IS COMPLETE, CLEAR DTCs AND TEST DRIVE VEHICLE FOR THREE (3) DRIVE CYCLES TO VERIFY DTC DOES NOT RESET. A DRIVE CYCLE CONSISTS OF STARTING THE VEHICLE, DRIVING OVER 16 km/h (10 MPH) AND THEN KEYING DOWN.

GC402930080700BX

Fig. 183 Code A062: Right Front Motor Circuit Shorted To Ground. 1993–94 Cavalier, Sunbird, Beretta, Corsica & Achieva, Grand Am & Skylark Less VES

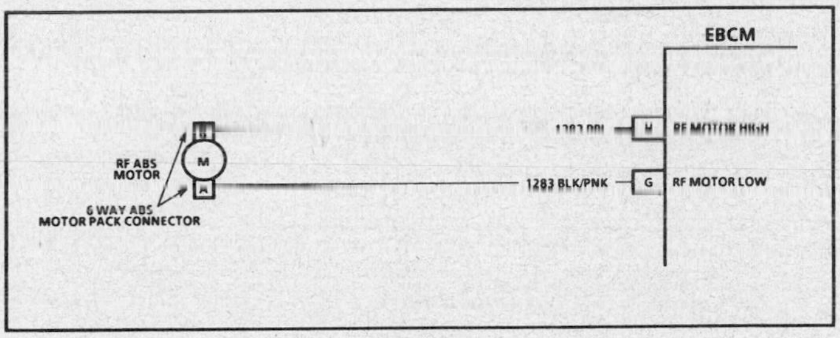
EBCM
RF ABS MOTOR
M
6 WAY ABS MOTOR PACK CONNECTOR
H
RF MOTOR HIGH
1283 BLK/PNK
G
RF MOTOR LOW

DTC 62

RIGHT FRONT ABS MOTOR CIRCUIT SHORTED TO GND

Circuit Description:

This DTC identifies an ABS motor circuit that is shorted to ground. This malfunction will not allow the ABS motor to be controlled at the commanded current rate or will cause the ABS motor driver circuit to allow current directly to ground.

DTC Will Set When: DTC 62 can be set anytime. If the EBCM detects an out of range voltage on either of the right front ABS motor circuits indicating a circuit shorted to ground, a malfunction exists.

Action Taken: A malfunction DTC is stored, ABS is disabled and the ABS warning lamp is turned "ON."

DTC Chart Test Description: Number(s) below refer to circled number(s) on the diagnostic chart.

1. Checks for a short to ground in the ABS motor "HIGH" circuitry.
2. Checks for a short to ground in the ABS motor "LOW" circuitry.
3. Checks for an ABS motor that is internally shorted to ground.
4. Ensures malfunction was not due to physical damage of the circuitry.

Diagnostic Aids: Using Tech 1, select manual control function, and exercise ABS motor movement of affected channel in both directions while applying light pressure on the brake pedal.

If erratic or "jumpy" brake pedal movement is detected while performing an "apply" or "release" function of the ABS motor, an intermittent malfunction may be indicated.

An "Intermittent" malfunction may be caused by a poor connection, rubbed through wire insulation, or a wire that is broken inside the insulation.

If the malfunction is not current, wiggle the wires of the affected channel and check if the DTC resets. This will help to pinpoint an intermittent malfunction in the motor circuitry or connections.

The frequency of the malfunction can be checked by using the enhanced diagnostic function of the Tech 1.

Any circuitry, that is suspected as causing the intermittent complaint, should be thoroughly checked for backed out terminals, improper mating, broken locks, improperly formed or damaged terminals, poor terminal to wiring connections or physical damage to the wiring harness.

GC402930080800AA

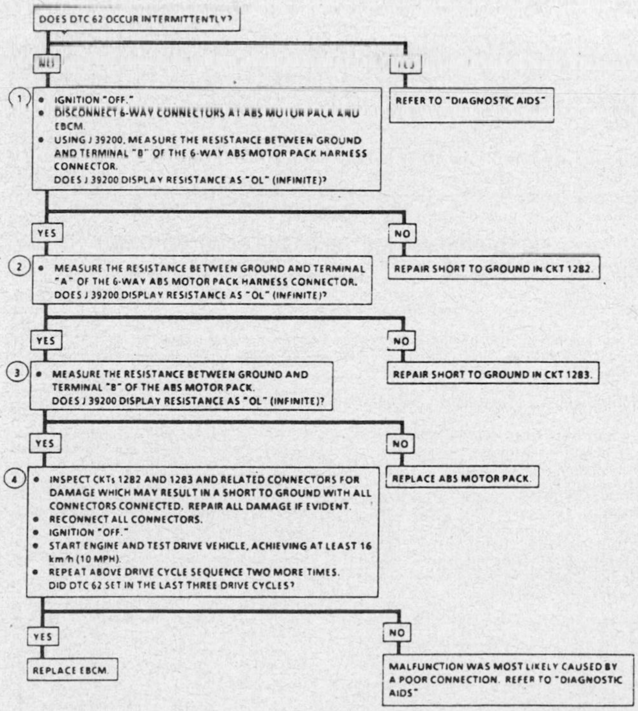
DOES DTC 62 OCCUR INTERMITTENTLY?
REFER TO "DIAGNOSTIC AIDS"
1
• IGNITION "OFF."
• DISCONNECT 6-WAY CONNECTORS AT ABS MOTOR PACK AND EBCM.
• USING J 39200, MEASURE THE RESISTANCE BETWEEN GROUND AND TERMINAL "B" OF THE 6-WAY ABS MOTOR PACK HARNESS CONNECTOR. DOES J 39200 DISPLAY RESISTANCE AS "OL" (INFINITE)?
YES
NO
REPAIR SHORT TO GROUND IN CKT 1282.
2
• MEASURE THE RESISTANCE BETWEEN GROUND AND TERMINAL "A" OF THE 6-WAY ABS MOTOR PACK HARNESS CONNECTOR. DOES J 39200 DISPLAY RESISTANCE AS "OL" (INFINITE)?
YES
NO
REPAIR SHORT TO GROUND IN CKT 1283.
3
• MEASURE THE RESISTANCE BETWEEN GROUND AND TERMINAL "B" OF THE ABS MOTOR PACK. DOES J 39200 DISPLAY RESISTANCE AS "OL" (INFINITE)?
YES
NO
REPLACE ABS MOTOR PACK.
4
• INSPECT CKTs 1282 AND 1283 AND RELATED CONNECTORS FOR DAMAGE WHICH MAY RESULT IN A SHORT TO GROUND WITH ALL CONNECTORS CONNECTED. REPAIR ALL DAMAGE IF EVIDENT.
• RECONNECT ALL CONNECTORS.
• IGNITION "OFF."
• START ENGINE AND TEST DRIVE VEHICLE, ACHIEVING AT LEAST 16 km/h (10 MPH).
• REPEAT ABOVE DRIVE CYCLE SEQUENCE TWO MORE TIMES. DID DTC 62 SET IN THE LAST THREE DRIVE CYCLES?
YES
NO
REPLACE EBCM.
MALFUNCTION WAS MOST LIKELY CAUSED BY A POOR CONNECTION. REFER TO "DIAGNOSTIC AIDS"

GC402930080800BA

Fig. 184 Code A062: Right Front Motor Circuit Shorted To Ground. 1993 Grand Prix, 1993–94 Cutlass Supreme, Lumina & Regal

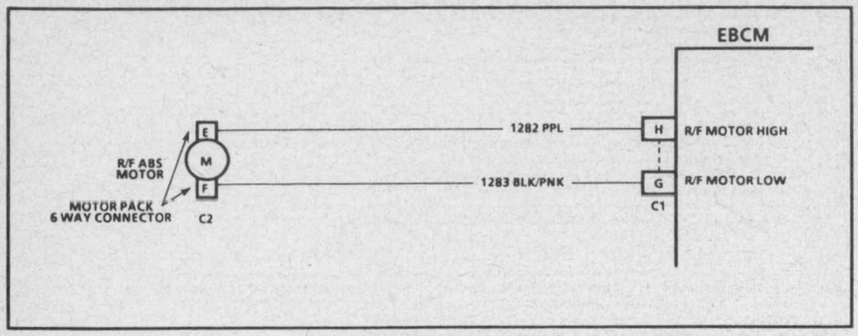

EBCM
1282 PPL
H
R/F MOTOR HIGH
1283 BLK/PNK
G
R/F MOTOR LOW
C1
E
M
F
R/F ABS MOTOR
MOTOR PACK 6 WAY CONNECTOR
C2

DTC A063

RIGHT FRONT MOTOR CIRCUIT SHORTED TO BATTERY OR MOTOR SHORTED

Circuit Description:

This DTC identifies a motor circuit that is shorted to battery or a motor that has low or no resistance. This malfunction will not allow the motor to be controlled at the commanded current rate or will cause the motor to turn in the opposite direction or not at all.

Failure Condition:

DTC A063 can be set anytime. If the EBCM detects an out of range voltage in either of the right front motor circuits indicating a circuit shorted to battery or a motor shorted, a malfunction exists.

Action Taken:

A malfunction DTC is stored, ABS is disabled and the ABS indicator lamp is turned "ON."

Test Description: Number(s) below refer to circled number(s) on the diagnostic chart.

1. This step checks for a short to voltage in the motor "high" circuitry.
2. This step checks for a short to voltage in the motor "low" circuitry.
3. This step checks for a motor that is internally shorted.
4. This test is used to release the tension of the motor pack prior to removal.

Diagnostic Aids:

Using Tech 1, select manual control function, and exercise motor movement of affected channel in both directions while applying light pressure on the brake pedal.

If erratic or "jumpy" brake pedal movement is detected while performing an "apply" or "release" function of the motor, an intermittent malfunction may be indicated.

An "Intermittent" malfunction may be caused by a poor connection, rubbed through wire insulation, or a wire that is broken inside the insulation.

If the malfunction is not current, wiggle the wires of the affected channel and check if the DTC resets. This will help to pinpoint an intermittent malfunction in the motor circuitry or connections.

The frequency of the malfunction can be checked by using the enhanced diagnostic function of the Tech 1.

If DTC A041 sets as a current DTC and A063 is infrequent history DTC, see DTC A041 for diagnosis.

Any circuitry, that is suspected as causing the intermittent complaint, should be thoroughly checked for backed out terminals, improper mating, broken locks, improperly formed or damaged terminals, poor terminal to wiring connections or physical damage to the wiring harness.

GC402930080900AX

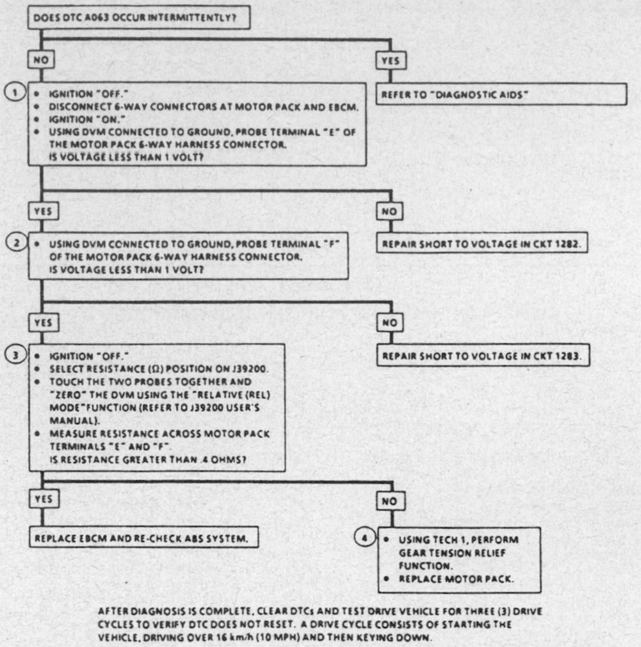

DOES DTC A063 OCCUR INTERMITTENTLY?
NO
YES
REFER TO "DIAGNOSTIC AIDS"
1
IGNITION "OFF."
DISCONNECT 6-WAY CONNECTORS AT MOTOR PACK AND EBCM.
IGNITION "ON."
USING DVM CONNECTED TO GROUND, PROBE TERMINAL "E" OF THE MOTOR PACK 6-WAY HARNESS CONNECTOR.
IS VOLTAGE LESS THAN 1 VOLT?
YES
NO
REPAIR SHORT TO VOLTAGE IN CKT 1282.
2
USING DVM CONNECTED TO GROUND, PROBE TERMINAL "F" OF THE MOTOR PACK 6-WAY HARNESS CONNECTOR.
IS VOLTAGE LESS THAN 1 VOLT?
YES
NO
REPAIR SHORT TO VOLTAGE IN CKT 1283.
3
IGNITION "OFF."
SELECT RESISTANCE (Ω) POSITION ON J39200.
TOUCH THE TWO PROBES TOGETHER AND "ZERO" THE DVM USING THE "RELATIVE (REL) MODE" FUNCTION (REFER TO J39200 USER'S MANUAL).
MEASURE RESISTANCE ACROSS MOTOR PACK TERMINALS "E" AND "F".
IS RESISTANCE GREATER THAN .4 OHMS?
YES
NO
REPLACE EBCM AND RE-CHECK ABS SYSTEM.
4
USING TECH 1, PERFORM GEAR TENSION RELIEF FUNCTION.
REPLACE MOTOR PACK.
AFTER DIAGNOSIS IS COMPLETE, CLEAR DTCs AND TEST DRIVE VEHICLE FOR THREE (3) DRIVE CYCLES TO VERIFY DTC DOES NOT RESET. A DRIVE CYCLE CONSISTS OF STARTING THE VEHICLE, DRIVING OVER 16 km/h (10 MPH) AND THEN KEYING DOWN.

GC402930080900BX

Fig. 185 Code A063: Right Front Motor Circuit Shorted To Battery Or Motor Shorted. 1993–94 Cavalier, Sunbird, Beretta, Corsica & Achieva, Grand Am & Skylark Less VES

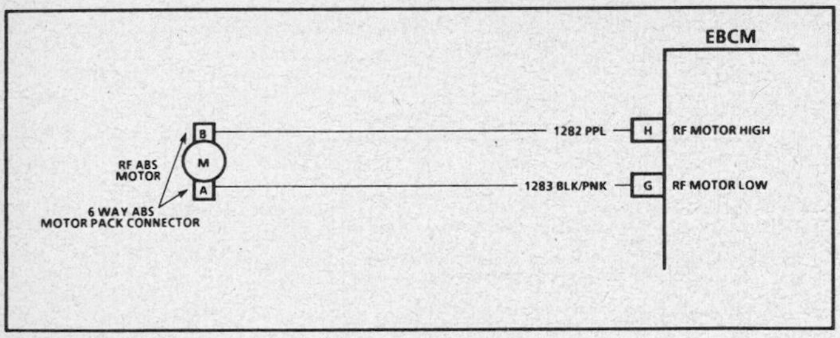

EBCM
1282 PPL
H
RF MOTOR HIGH
1283 BLK/PNK
G
RF MOTOR LOW
B
M
A
RF ABS MOTOR
6 WAY ABS MOTOR PACK CONNECTOR

DTC 63

RIGHT FRONT ABS MOTOR CIRCUIT SHORTED TO BATT

Circuit Description:

This DTC identifies an ABS motor circuit that is shorted to battery or an ABS motor that has low or no resistance. This malfunction will not allow the ABS motor to be controlled at the commanded current rate or will cause the ABS motor to turn in the opposite direction or not at all.

DTC Will Set When: DTC 63 can be set only when the ABS motor is commanded "OFF." If the EBCM detects an out of range voltage on either of the right front ABS motor circuits indicating a circuit shorted to battery or an ABS motor shorted, a malfunction exists.

Action Taken: A malfunction DTC is stored, ABS is disabled and the ABS warning lamp is turned "ON."

DTC Chart Test Description: Number(s) below refer to circled number(s) on the diagnostic chart.

1. Checks for a short to voltage in the ABS motor "HIGH" circuitry.
2. Checks for a short to voltage in the ABS motor "LOW" circuitry.
3. Checks for a short circuit between ABS motor "HIGH" and motor "LOW."
4. Checks for proper resistance of the ABS motor.
5. Ensures malfunction was not due to physical damage of the circuitry.

Diagnostic Aids: Using Tech 1, select manual control function, and exercise ABS motor movement of affected channel in both directions while applying light pressure on the brake pedal.

If erratic or "jumpy" brake pedal movement is detected while performing an "apply" or "release" function of the ABS motor, an intermittent malfunction may be indicated.

An "Intermittent" malfunction may be caused by a poor connection, rubbed through wire insulation, or a wire that is broken inside the insulation.

If the malfunction is not current, wiggle the wires of the affected channel and check if the DTC resets. This will help to pinpoint an intermittent malfunction in the motor circuitry or connections.

The frequency of the malfunction can be checked by using the enhanced diagnostic function of the Tech 1.

Any circuitry, that is suspected as causing the intermittent complaint, should be thoroughly checked for backed out terminals, improper mating, broken locks, improperly formed or damaged terminals, poor terminal to wiring connections or physical damage to the wiring harness.

GC402930081000AA

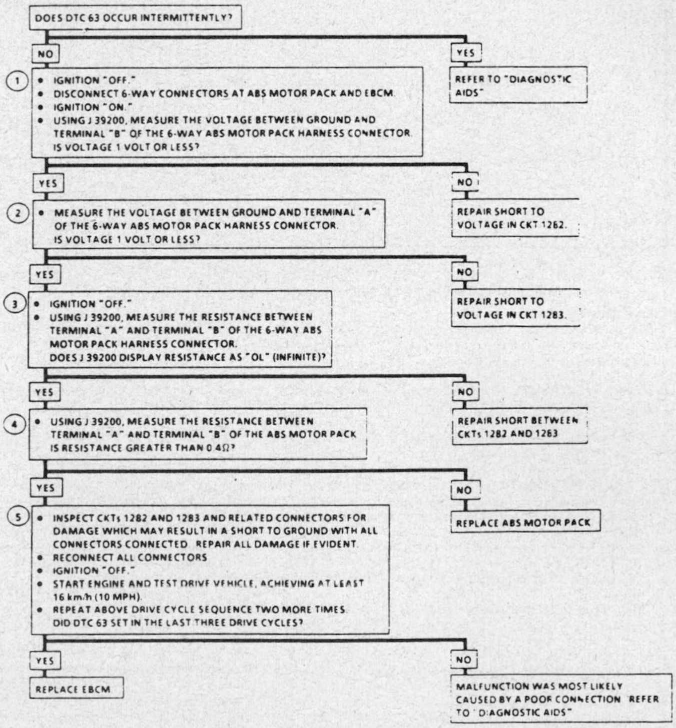

DOES DTC 63 OCCUR INTERMITTENTLY?
NO
YES
REFER TO "DIAGNOSTIC AIDS"
1
IGNITION "OFF."
DISCONNECT 6-WAY CONNECTORS AT ABS MOTOR PACK AND EBCM.
IGNITION "ON."
USING J 39200, MEASURE THE VOLTAGE BETWEEN GROUND AND TERMINAL "B" OF THE 6-WAY ABS MOTOR PACK HARNESS CONNECTOR.
IS VOLTAGE 1 VOLT OR LESS?
YES
NO
REPAIR SHORT TO VOLTAGE IN CKT 1282.
2
MEASURE THE VOLTAGE BETWEEN GROUND AND TERMINAL "A" OF THE 6-WAY ABS MOTOR PACK HARNESS CONNECTOR.
IS VOLTAGE 1 VOLT OR LESS?
YES
NO
REPAIR SHORT TO VOLTAGE IN CKT 1283.
3
IGNITION "OFF."
USING J 39200, MEASURE THE RESISTANCE BETWEEN TERMINAL "A" AND TERMINAL "B" OF THE 6-WAY ABS MOTOR PACK HARNESS CONNECTOR.
DOES J 39200 DISPLAY RESISTANCE AS "OL" (INFINITE)?
YES
NO
REPAIR SHORT BETWEEN CKTs 1282 AND 1283
4
USING J 39200, MEASURE THE RESISTANCE BETWEEN TERMINAL "A" AND TERMINAL "B" OF THE ABS MOTOR PACK
IS RESISTANCE GREATER THAN 0.4Ω?
YES
NO
REPLACE ABS MOTOR PACK
5
INSPECT CKTs 1282 AND 1283 AND RELATED CONNECTORS FOR DAMAGE WHICH MAY RESULT IN A SHORT TO GROUND WITH ALL CONNECTORS CONNECTED. REPAIR ALL DAMAGE IF EVIDENT.
RECONNECT ALL CONNECTORS
IGNITION "OFF."
START ENGINE AND TEST DRIVE VEHICLE, ACHIEVING AT LEAST 16 km/h (10 MPH).
REPEAT ABOVE DRIVE CYCLE SEQUENCE TWO MORE TIMES.
DID DTC 63 SET IN THE LAST THREE DRIVE CYCLES?
YES
REPLACE EBCM
NO
MALFUNCTION WAS MOST LIKELY CAUSED BY A POOR CONNECTION. REFER TO "DIAGNOSTIC AIDS"

GC402930081000BA

Fig. 186 Code A063: Right Front Motor Circuit Shorted To Battery Or Motor shorted. 1993 Grand Prix, 1993–94 Cutlass Supreme, Lumina & Regal

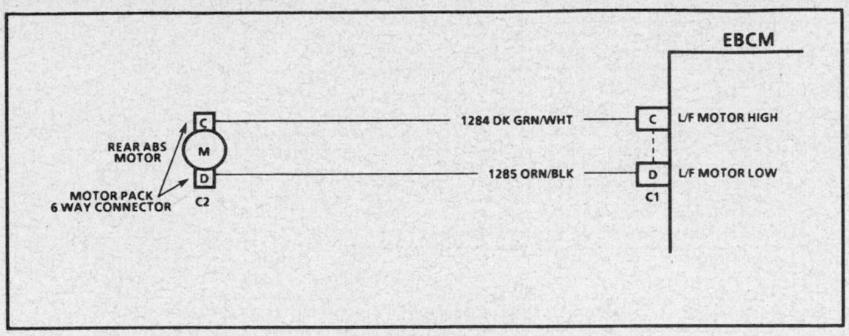
EBCM
REAR ABS MOTOR
M
C
D
MOTOR PACK 6 WAY CONNECTOR
C2
1284 DK GRN/WHT
1285 ORN/BLK
C
D
C1
L/F MOTOR HIGH
L/F MOTOR LOW

DTC A064

REAR AXLE MOTOR CIRCUIT OPEN

Circuit Description:
This DTC identifies a motor that cannot be energized due to an open in its circuitry. This malfunction will not allow proper rear ABS operation.

Failure Condition:
DTC A064 can be set only when the motor is commanded "OFF." If the EBCM detects an out of range voltage in either of the rear axle motor circuits indicating an open circuit, a malfunction exists.

Action Taken:
An open motor will not activate when requested. A malfunction DTC is stored, ABS is disabled and the ABS indicator lamp is turned "ON."

Test Description: Number(s) below refer to circled number(s) on the diagnostic chart.

1. This checks for an open circuit in the motor.
2. This step is used to release the tension of the motor pack prior to removal.
3. This step checks for an open in the motor "high" circuitry.
4. This step checks for an open in the motor "low" circuitry.

Diagnostic Aids:

Using Tech 1, select manual control function, and exercise motor movement of affected channel in both directions while applying light pressure on the brake pedal.

If erratic or "jumpy" brake pedal movement is detected while performing an "apply" or "release" function of the motor, an intermittent malfunction may be indicated.

An "Intermittent" malfunction may be caused by a poor connection, rubbed through wire insulation, or a wire that is broken inside the insulation.

If the malfunction is not current, wiggle the wires of the affected channel and check if the DTC resets. This will help to pinpoint an intermittent malfunction in the motor circuitry or connections.

The frequency of the malfunction can be checked by using the enhanced diagnostic function of the Tech 1.

Any circuitry, that is suspected as causing the intermittent complaint, should be thoroughly checked for backed out terminals, improper mating, broken locks, improperly formed or damaged terminals, poor terminal to wiring connections or physical damage to the wiring harness.

GC402930081100AX

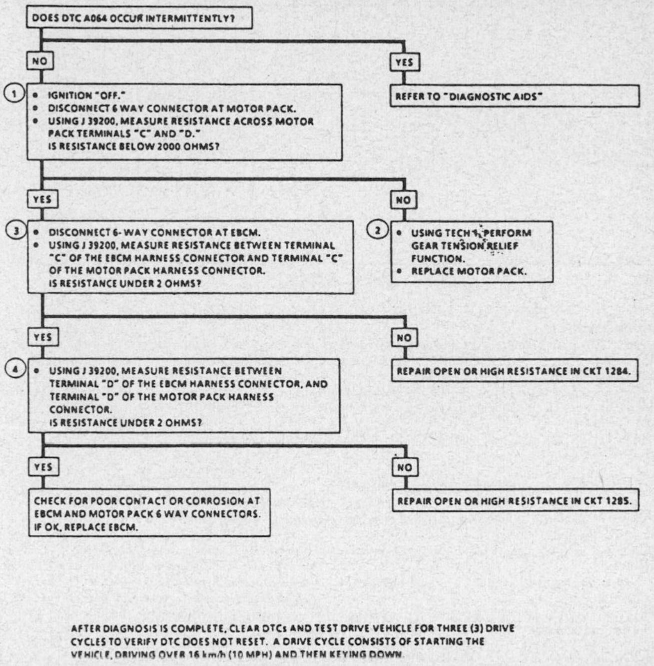
DOES DTC A064 OCCUR INTERMITTENTLY?
NO
YES
1
• IGNITION "OFF."
• DISCONNECT 6 WAY CONNECTOR AT MOTOR PACK.
• USING J 39200, MEASURE RESISTANCE ACROSS MOTOR PACK TERMINALS "C" AND "D."
IS RESISTANCE BELOW 2000 OHMS?
REFER TO "DIAGNOSTIC AIDS"
YES
NO
3
• DISCONNECT 6-WAY CONNECTOR AT EBCM.
• USING J 39200, MEASURE RESISTANCE BETWEEN TERMINAL "C" OF THE EBCM HARNESS CONNECTOR AND TERMINAL "C" OF THE MOTOR PACK HARNESS CONNECTOR.
IS RESISTANCE UNDER 2 OHMS?
2
• USING TECH 1, PERFORM GEAR TENSION RELIEF FUNCTION.
• REPLACE MOTOR PACK.
YES
NO
4
• USING J 39200, MEASURE RESISTANCE BETWEEN TERMINAL "D" OF THE EBCM HARNESS CONNECTOR, AND TERMINAL "D" OF THE MOTOR PACK HARNESS CONNECTOR.
IS RESISTANCE UNDER 2 OHMS?
REPAIR OPEN OR HIGH RESISTANCE IN CKT 1284.
YES
NO
CHECK FOR POOR CONTACT OR CORROSION AT EBCM AND MOTOR PACK 6 WAY CONNECTORS. IF OK, REPLACE EBCM.
REPAIR OPEN OR HIGH RESISTANCE IN CKT 1285.
AFTER DIAGNOSIS IS COMPLETE, CLEAR DTCs AND TEST DRIVE VEHICLE FOR THREE (3) DRIVE CYCLES TO VERIFY DTC DOES NOT RESET. A DRIVE CYCLE CONSISTS OF STARTING THE VEHICLE, DRIVING OVER 16 km/h (10 MPH) AND THEN KEYING DOWN.

GC402930081100BX

Fig. 187 Code A064: Rear Axle Motor Circuit Open. 1993–94 Cavalier, Sunbird, Beretta, Corsica & Achieva, Grand Am & Skylark Less VES

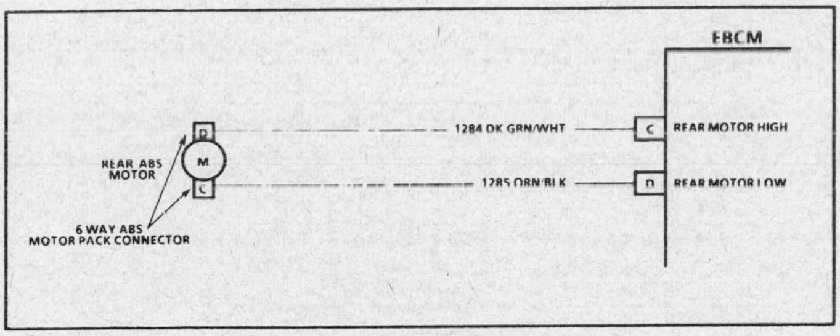
EBCM
REAR ABS MOTOR
M
D
C
6 WAY ABS MOTOR PACK CONNECTOR
1284 DK GRN/WHT
1285 ORN/BLK
C
D
REAR MOTOR HIGH
REAR MOTOR LOW

DTC 64

REAR ABS MOTOR CIRCUIT OPEN

Circuit Description:
This DTC identifies an ABS motor that cannot be energized due to an open in its circuitry. This malfunction will not allow proper rear ABS operation

DTC Will Set When: DTC 64 can be set only when the ABS motor is commanded "OFF." If the EBCM detects an out of range voltage on either of the rear ABS motor circuits indicating an open circuit, a malfunction exists.

Action Taken: An open motor will not activate when requested. A malfunction DTC is stored, ABS is disabled and the ABS warning lamp is turned "ON."

DTC Chart Test Description: Number(s) below refer to circled number(s) on the diagnostic chart.

1. Checks for proper resistance of the ABS motor.
2. Checks for an open in the ABS motor "HIGH" circuitry.
3. Checks for an open in the ABS motor "LOW" circuitry.
4. Ensures malfunction was not due to poor terminal contact.

Diagnostic Aids: Using Tech 1, select manual control function, and exercise ABS motor movement of affected channel in both directions while applying light pressure on the brake pedal.

If erratic or "jumpy" brake pedal movement is detected while performing an "apply" or "release" function of the ABS motor, an intermittent malfunction may be indicated.

An "Intermittent" malfunction may be caused by a poor connection, rubbed through wire insulation, or a wire that is broken inside the insulation.

If the malfunction is not current, wiggle the wires of the affected channel and check if the DTC resets. This will help to pinpoint an intermittent malfunction in the motor circuitry or connections.

The frequency of the malfunction can be checked by using the enhanced diagnostic function of the Tech 1.

Any circuitry, that is suspected as causing the intermittent complaint, should be thoroughly checked for backed out terminals, improper mating, broken locks, improperly formed or damaged terminals, poor terminal to wiring connections or physical damage to the wiring harness.

GC402930081200AA

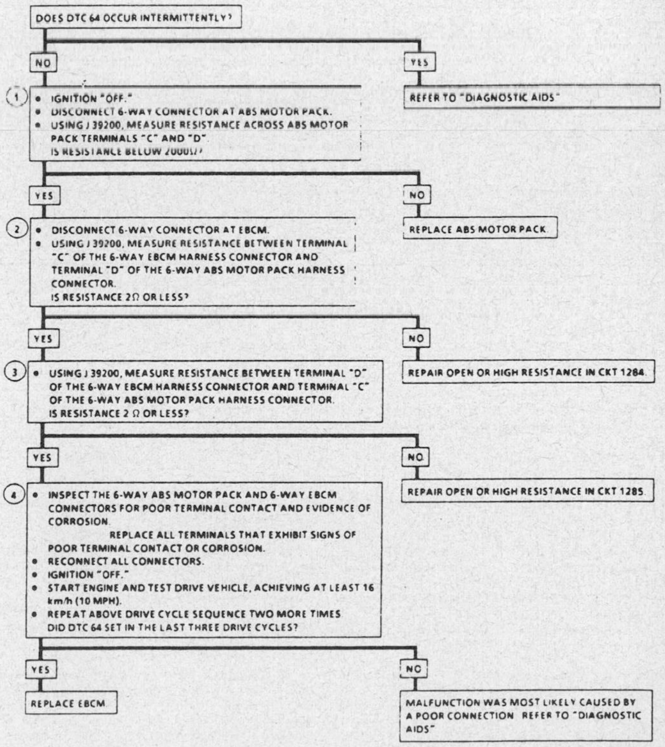
DOES DTC 64 OCCUR INTERMITTENTLY?
NO
YES
1
• IGNITION "OFF."
• DISCONNECT 6-WAY CONNECTOR AT ABS MOTOR PACK.
• USING J 39200, MEASURE RESISTANCE ACROSS ABS MOTOR PACK TERMINALS "C" AND "D".
IS RESISTANCE BELOW 2000Ω?
REFER TO "DIAGNOSTIC AIDS"
YES
NO
2
• DISCONNECT 6-WAY CONNECTOR AT EBCM.
• USING J 39200, MEASURE RESISTANCE BETWEEN TERMINAL "C" OF THE 6-WAY EBCM HARNESS CONNECTOR AND TERMINAL "D" OF THE 6-WAY ABS MOTOR PACK HARNESS CONNECTOR.
IS RESISTANCE 2Ω OR LESS?
REPLACE ABS MOTOR PACK.
YES
NO
3
• USING J 39200, MEASURE RESISTANCE BETWEEN TERMINAL "D" OF THE 6-WAY EBCM HARNESS CONNECTOR AND TERMINAL "C" OF THE 6-WAY ABS MOTOR PACK HARNESS CONNECTOR.
IS RESISTANCE 2 Ω OR LESS?
REPAIR OPEN OR HIGH RESISTANCE IN CKT 1284.
YES
NO
4
• INSPECT THE 6-WAY ABS MOTOR PACK AND 6-WAY EBCM CONNECTORS FOR POOR TERMINAL CONTACT AND EVIDENCE OF CORROSION.
REPLACE ALL TERMINALS THAT EXHIBIT SIGNS OF POOR TERMINAL CONTACT OR CORROSION.
• RECONNECT ALL CONNECTORS.
• IGNITION "OFF."
• START ENGINE AND TEST DRIVE VEHICLE, ACHIEVING AT LEAST 16 km/h (10 MPH).
• REPEAT ABOVE DRIVE CYCLE SEQUENCE TWO MORE TIMES
DID DTC 64 SET IN THE LAST THREE DRIVE CYCLES?
REPAIR OPEN OR HIGH RESISTANCE IN CKT 1285.
YES
NO
REPLACE EBCM
MALFUNCTION WAS MOST LIKELY CAUSED BY A POOR CONNECTION REFER TO "DIAGNOSTIC AIDS"

GC402930081200BA

Fig. 188 Code A064: Rear Axle Motor Circuit Open. 1993 Grand Prix, 1993–94 Cutlass Supreme, Lumina & Regal

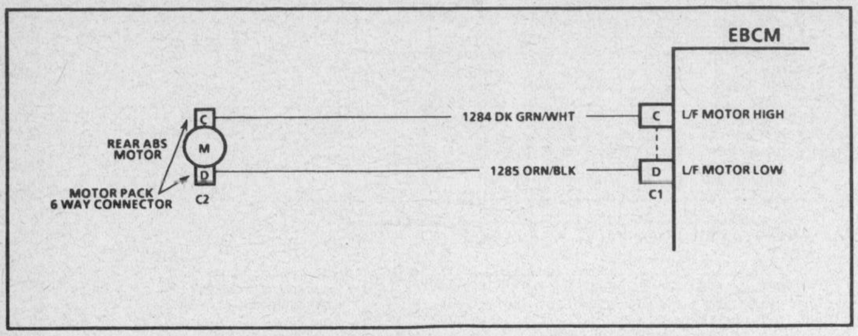
EBCM
1284 DK GRN/WHT
C
L/F MOTOR HIGH
REAR ABS MOTOR
M
C
D
1285 ORN/BLK
D
L/F MOTOR LOW
MOTOR PACK 6 WAY CONNECTOR
C2
C1

DTC A065

REAR AXLE MOTOR CIRCUIT SHORTED TO GROUND

Circuit Description:

This DTC identifies a motor circuit that is shorted to ground. This malfunction will not allow the motor to be controlled at the commanded current rate or will cause the driver circuit to allow current directly to ground.

Failure Condition:

DTC A065 can be set anytime. If the EBCM detects an out of range voltage in either of the rear axle motor circuits indicating a circuit shorted to ground, a malfunction exists.

Action Taken:

A malfunction DTC is stored, ABS is disabled and the ABS indicator lamp is turned "ON."

Test Description: Number(s) below refer to circled number(s) on the diagnostic chart.

1. This step checks for a motor that is internally shorted to ground.
2. This step checks for a short to ground in the motor circuitry.
3. This step ensures malfunction was not due to a poor connection.
4. This step is used to release the tension of the motor pack prior to removal.

Diagnostic Aids:

Using Tech 1, select manual control function, and exercise motor movement of affected channel in both directions while applying light pressure on the brake pedal.

If erratic or "jumpy" brake pedal movement is detected while performing an "apply" or "release" function of the motor, an intermittent malfunction may be indicated.

An "Intermittent" malfunction may be caused by a poor connection, rubbed through wire insulation, or a wire that is broken inside the insulation.

If the malfunction is not current, wiggle the wires of the affected channel and check if the DTC resets. This will help to pinpoint an intermittent malfunction in the motor circuitry or connections.

The frequency of the problem can be checked by using the enhanced diagnostic function of the Tech 1.

Any circuitry, that is suspected as causing the intermittent complaint, should be thoroughly checked for backed out terminals, improper mating, broken locks, improperly formed or damaged terminals, poor terminal to wiring connections or physical damage to the wiring harness.

GC402930081300AX

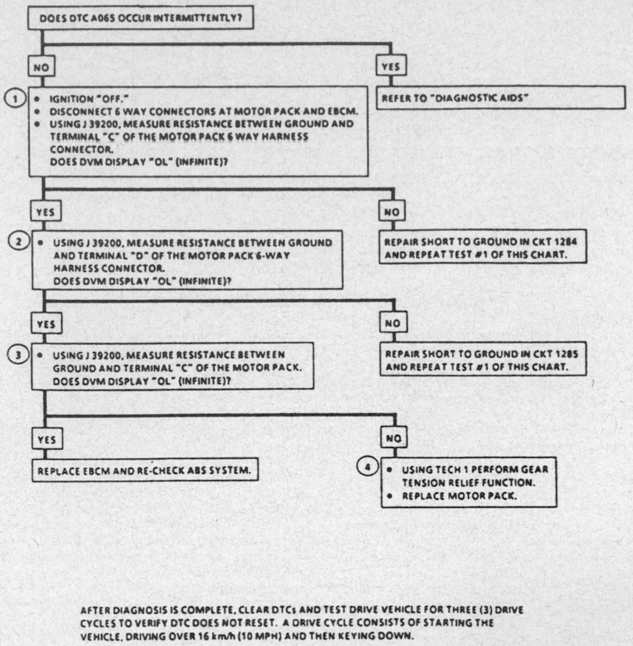
DOES DTC A065 OCCUR INTERMITTENTLY?
NO
YES
REFER TO "DIAGNOSTIC AIDS"
1
• IGNITION "OFF."
• DISCONNECT 6 WAY CONNECTORS AT MOTOR PACK AND EBCM.
• USING J 39200, MEASURE RESISTANCE BETWEEN GROUND AND TERMINAL "C" OF THE MOTOR PACK 6 WAY HARNESS CONNECTOR.
DOES DVM DISPLAY "OL" (INFINITE)?
YES
NO
REPAIR SHORT TO GROUND IN CKT 1284 AND REPEAT TEST #1 OF THIS CHART.
2
• USING J 39200, MEASURE RESISTANCE BETWEEN GROUND AND TERMINAL "D" OF THE MOTOR PACK 6-WAY HARNESS CONNECTOR.
DOES DVM DISPLAY "OL" (INFINITE)?
YES
NO
REPAIR SHORT TO GROUND IN CKT 1285 AND REPEAT TEST #1 OF THIS CHART.
3
• USING J 39200, MEASURE RESISTANCE BETWEEN GROUND AND TERMINAL "C" OF THE MOTOR PACK.
DOES DVM DISPLAY "OL" (INFINITE)?
YES
NO
REPLACE EBCM AND RE-CHECK ABS SYSTEM.
4
• USING TECH 1 PERFORM GEAR TENSION RELIEF FUNCTION.
• REPLACE MOTOR PACK.
AFTER DIAGNOSIS IS COMPLETE, CLEAR DTCs AND TEST DRIVE VEHICLE FOR THREE (3) DRIVE CYCLES TO VERIFY DTC DOES NOT RESET. A DRIVE CYCLE CONSISTS OF STARTING THE VEHICLE, DRIVING OVER 16 km/h (10 MPH) AND THEN KEYING DOWN.

GC402930081300BX

Fig. 189 Code A065: Rear Axle Motor Circuit Shorted To Ground. 1993–94 Cavalier, Sunbird, Beretta, Corsica & Achieva, Grand Am & Skylark Less VES

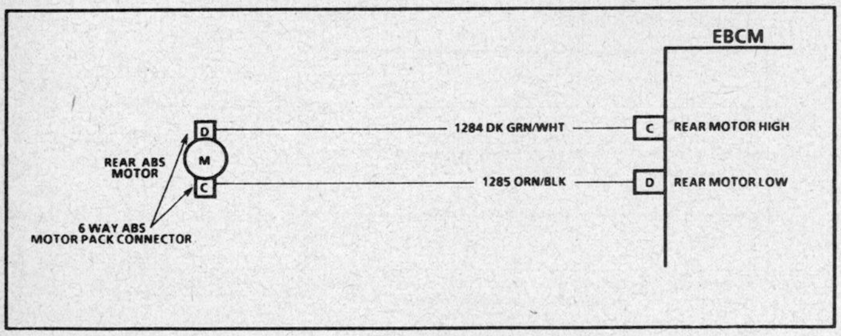
EBCM
1284 DK GRN/WHT
C
REAR MOTOR HIGH
REAR ABS MOTOR
M
D
C
1285 ORN/BLK
D
REAR MOTOR LOW
6 WAY ABS MOTOR PACK CONNECTOR

DTC 65

REAR ABS MOTOR CIRCUIT SHORTED TO GROUND

Circuit Description:

This DTC identifies an ABS motor circuit that is shorted to ground. This malfunction will not allow the ABS motor to be controlled at the commanded current rate or will cause the driver circuit to allow current directly to ground.

DTC Will Set When: DTC 65 can be set anytime. If the EBCM detects an out of range voltage on either of the rear ABS motor circuits indicating a circuit shorted to ground, a malfunction exists.

Action Taken: A malfunction DTC is stored, ABS is disabled and the ABS warning lamp is turned "ON."

DTC Chart Test Description: Number(s) below refer to circled number(s) on the diagnostic chart.

1. Checks for a short to ground in the ABS motor "HIGH" circuitry.
2. Checks for a short to ground in the ABS motor "LOW" circuitry.
3. Checks for an ABS motor that is internally shorted to ground.
4. Ensures malfunction was not due to physical damage of the circuitry

Diagnostic Aids: Using Tech 1, select manual control function, and exercise ABS motor movement of affected channel in both directions while applying light pressure on the brake pedal.

If erratic or "jumpy" brake pedal movement is detected while performing an "apply" or "release" function of the ABS motor, an intermittent malfunction may be indicated

An "Intermittent" malfunction may be caused by a poor connection, rubbed through wire insulation, or a wire that is broken inside the insulation.

If the malfunction is not current, wiggle the wires of the affected channel and check if the DTC resets. This will help to pinpoint an intermittent malfunction in the motor circuitry or connections.

The frequency of the malfunction can be checked by using the enhanced diagnostic function of the Tech 1

Any circuitry, that is suspected as causing the intermittent complaint, should be thoroughly checked for backed out terminals, improper mating, broken locks, improperly formed or damaged terminals, poor terminal to wiring connections or physical damage to the wiring harness.

GC402930081400AA

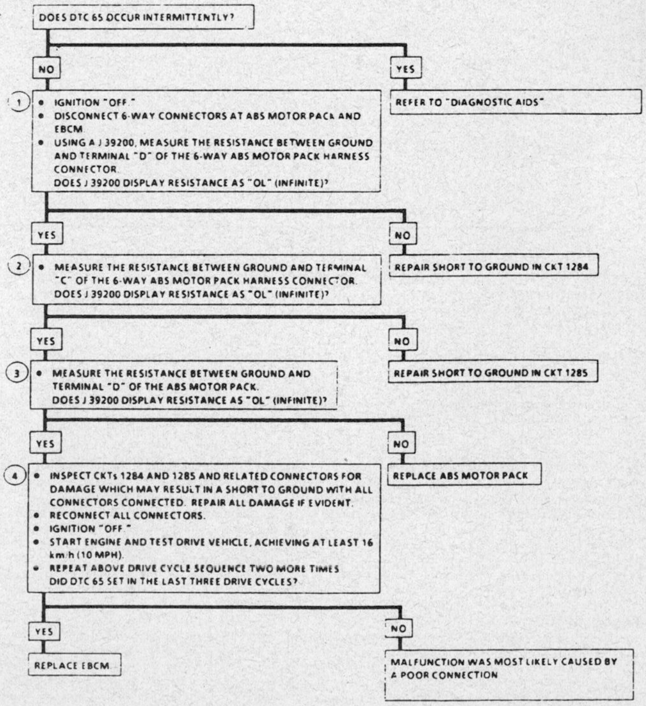
DOES DTC 65 OCCUR INTERMITTENTLY?
NO
YES
REFER TO "DIAGNOSTIC AIDS"
1
• IGNITION "OFF."
• DISCONNECT 6-WAY CONNECTORS AT ABS MOTOR PACK AND EBCM
• USING A J 39200, MEASURE THE RESISTANCE BETWEEN GROUND AND TERMINAL "D" OF THE 6-WAY ABS MOTOR PACK HARNESS CONNECTOR.
DOES J 39200 DISPLAY RESISTANCE AS "OL" (INFINITE)?
YES
NO
REPAIR SHORT TO GROUND IN CKT 1284
2
• MEASURE THE RESISTANCE BETWEEN GROUND AND TERMINAL "C" OF THE 6-WAY ABS MOTOR PACK HARNESS CONNECTOR.
DOES J 39200 DISPLAY RESISTANCE AS "OL" (INFINITE)?
YES
NO
REPAIR SHORT TO GROUND IN CKT 1285
3
• MEASURE THE RESISTANCE BETWEEN GROUND AND TERMINAL "D" OF THE ABS MOTOR PACK.
DOES J 39200 DISPLAY RESISTANCE AS "OL" (INFINITE)?
YES
NO
REPLACE ABS MOTOR PACK
4
• INSPECT CKTs 1284 AND 1285 AND RELATED CONNECTORS FOR DAMAGE WHICH MAY RESULT IN A SHORT TO GROUND WITH ALL CONNECTORS CONNECTED. REPAIR ALL DAMAGE IF EVIDENT.
• RECONNECT ALL CONNECTORS.
• IGNITION "OFF."
• START ENGINE AND TEST DRIVE VEHICLE, ACHIEVING AT LEAST 16 km/h (10 MPH).
• REPEAT ABOVE DRIVE CYCLE SEQUENCE TWO MORE TIMES
DID DTC 65 SET IN THE LAST THREE DRIVE CYCLES?
YES
NO
REPLACE EBCM
MALFUNCTION WAS MOST LIKELY CAUSED BY A POOR CONNECTION

GC402930081400BA

Fig. 190 Code A065: Rear Axle Motor Circuit Shorted To Ground. 1993 Grand Prix, 1993–94 Cutlass Supreme, Lumina & Regal

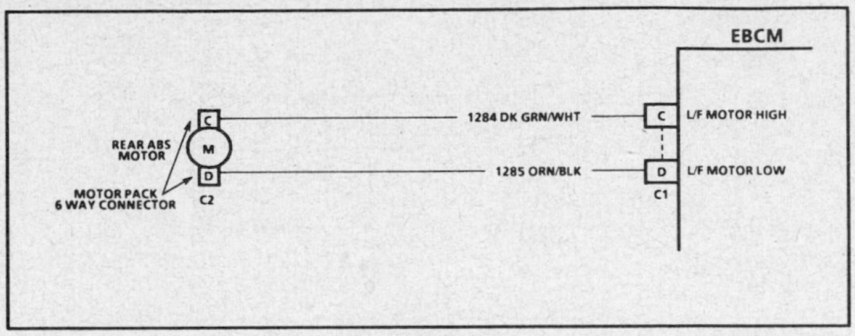
EBCM
REAR ABS MOTOR
M
C
D
1284 DK GRN/WHT
1285 ORN/BLK
C
D
C1
L/F MOTOR HIGH
L/F MOTOR LOW
MOTOR PACK 6 WAY CONNECTOR
C2

DTC A066

REAR AXLE MOTOR CIRCUIT SHORTED TO BATTERY OR MOTOR SHORTED

Circuit Description:

This DTC identifies a motor circuit that is shorted to battery or a motor that has low or zero resistance. This malfunction will not allow the motor to be controlled at the commanded current rate or will cause the motor to turn in the opposite direction or not turn at all.

Failure Condition:

DTC A066 can be set anytime. If the EBCM detects an out of range voltage in either of the rear axle motor circuits indicating a circuit shorted to battery or a motor shorted, a malfunction exists.

Action Taken:

A malfunction DTC is stored, ABS is disabled and the ABS indicator lamp is turned "ON."

Test Description: Number(s) below refer to circled number(s) on the diagnostic chart.

1. This step checks for a short to voltage in the motor "high" circuitry.
2. This step checks for a short to voltage in the motor "low" circuitry.
3. This step checks for a motor that is internally shorted.
4. This step is used to release the tension of the motor pack prior to removal.

Diagnostic Aids:

Using Tech 1, select manual control function, and exercise motor movement of affected channel in both directions while applying light pressure on the brake pedal.

If erratic or "jumpy" brake pedal movement is detected while performing an "apply" or "release" function of the motor, an intermittent malfunction may be indicated.

An "Intermittent" malfunction may be caused by a poor connection, rubbed through wire insulation, or a wire that is broken inside the insulation.

If the malfunction is not current, wiggle the wires of the affected channel and check if the DTC resets. This will help to pinpoint an intermittent malfunction in the motor circuitry or connections.

The frequency of the malfunction can be checked by using the enhanced diagnostic function of the Tech 1.

If DTC A042 sets as current DTC and A066 is infrequent history DTC, see DTC A042 diagnostics.

Any circuitry, that is suspected as causing the intermittent complaint, should be thoroughly checked for backed out terminals, improper mating, broken locks, improperly formed or damaged terminals, poor terminal to wiring connections or physical damage to the wiring harness.

GC402930081500AX

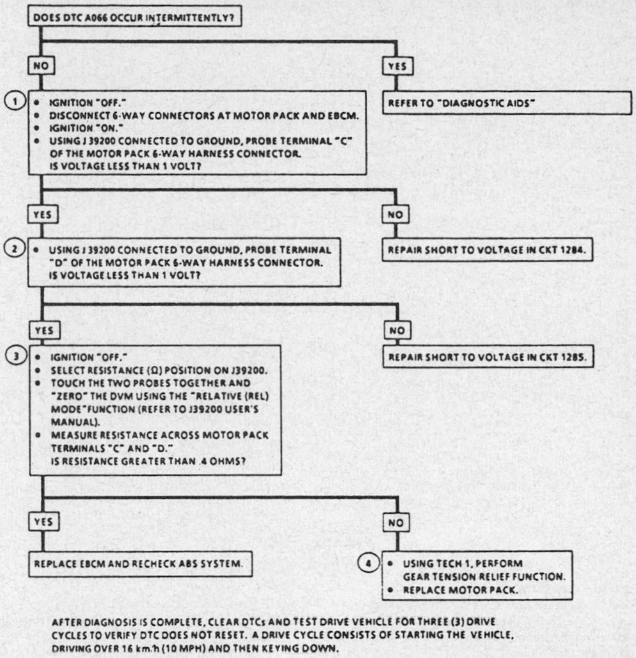
DOES DTC A066 OCCUR INTERMITTENTLY?
NO
YES
REFER TO "DIAGNOSTIC AIDS"
1
• IGNITION "OFF."
• DISCONNECT 6-WAY CONNECTORS AT MOTOR PACK AND EBCM.
• IGNITION "ON."
• USING J 39200 CONNECTED TO GROUND, PROBE TERMINAL "C" OF THE MOTOR PACK 6-WAY HARNESS CONNECTOR.
IS VOLTAGE LESS THAN 1 VOLT?
YES
NO
REPAIR SHORT TO VOLTAGE IN CKT 1284.
2
• USING J 39200 CONNECTED TO GROUND, PROBE TERMINAL "D" OF THE MOTOR PACK 6-WAY HARNESS CONNECTOR.
IS VOLTAGE LESS THAN 1 VOLT?
YES
NO
REPAIR SHORT TO VOLTAGE IN CKT 1285.
3
• IGNITION "OFF."
• SELECT RESISTANCE (Ω) POSITION ON J39200.
• TOUCH THE TWO PROBES TOGETHER AND "ZERO" THE DVM USING THE "RELATIVE (REL) MODE" FUNCTION (REFER TO J39200 USER'S MANUAL).
• MEASURE RESISTANCE ACROSS MOTOR PACK TERMINALS "C" AND "D."
IS RESISTANCE GREATER THAN .4 OHMS?
YES
NO
REPLACE EBCM AND RECHECK ABS SYSTEM.
4
• USING TECH 1, PERFORM GEAR TENSION RELIEF FUNCTION.
• REPLACE MOTOR PACK.
AFTER DIAGNOSIS IS COMPLETE, CLEAR DTCs AND TEST DRIVE VEHICLE FOR THREE (3) DRIVE CYCLES TO VERIFY DTC DOES NOT RESET. A DRIVE CYCLE CONSISTS OF STARTING THE VEHICLE, DRIVING OVER 16 km/h (10 MPH) AND THEN KEYING DOWN.

GC402930081500BX

Fig. 191 Code A066: Rear Axle Motor Circuit Shorted To Battery Or Motor Shorted. 1993–94 Cavalier, Sunbird, Beretta, Corsica & Achieva, Grand Am & Skylark Less VES

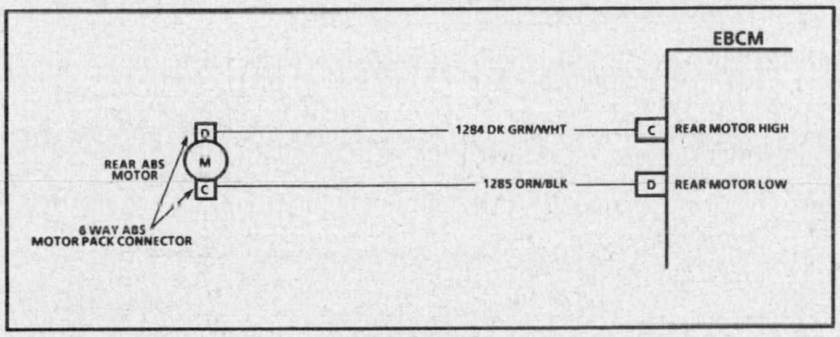
EBCM
REAR ABS MOTOR
M
D
C
1284 DK GRN/WHT
1285 ORN/BLK
C
D
REAR MOTOR HIGH
REAR MOTOR LOW
6 WAY ABS MOTOR PACK CONNECTOR

DTC 66

REAR ABS MOTOR CIRCUIT SHORTED TO BATTERY

Circuit Description:

This DTC identifies an ABS motor circuit that is shorted to battery or an ABS motor that has low or zero resistance. This malfunction will not allow the ABS motor to be controlled at the commanded current rate or will cause the ABS motor to turn in the opposite direction or not turn at all.

DTC Will Set When: DTC 66 can be set only when the ABS motor is commanded "OFF." If the EBCM detects an out of range voltage on either of the rear ABS motor circuits indicating a circuit shorted to battery or an ABS motor shorted, a malfunction exists.

Action Taken: A malfunction DTC is stored, ABS is disabled and the ABS warning lamp is turned "ON."

DTC Chart Test Description: Number(s) below refer to circled number(s) on the diagnostic chart.

1. Checks for a short to voltage in the ABS motor "HIGH" circuitry.
2. Checks for a short to voltage in the ABS motor "LOW" circuitry.
3. Checks for a short circuit between ABS motor "HIGH" and ABS motor "LOW."
4. Checks for proper resistance of the ABS motor.
5. Ensures malfunction was not due to physical damage of the circuitry.

Diagnostic Aids: Using Tech 1, select manual control function, and exercise ABS motor movement of affected channel in both directions while applying light pressure on the brake pedal.

If erratic or "jumpy" brake pedal movement is detected while performing an "apply" or "release" function of the ABS motor, an intermittent malfunction may be indicated.

An "Intermittent" malfunction may be caused by a poor connection, rubbed through wire insulation, or a wire that is broken inside the insulation.

If the malfunction is not current, wiggle the wires of the affected channel and check if the DTC resets. This will help to pinpoint an intermittent malfunction in the motor circuitry or connections.

The frequency of the malfunction can be checked by using the enhanced diagnostic function of the Tech 1

Any circuitry, that is suspected as causing the intermittent complaint, should be thoroughly checked for backed out terminals, improper mating, broken locks, improperly formed or damaged terminals, poor terminal to wiring connections or physical damage to the wiring harness.

GC402930081600AA

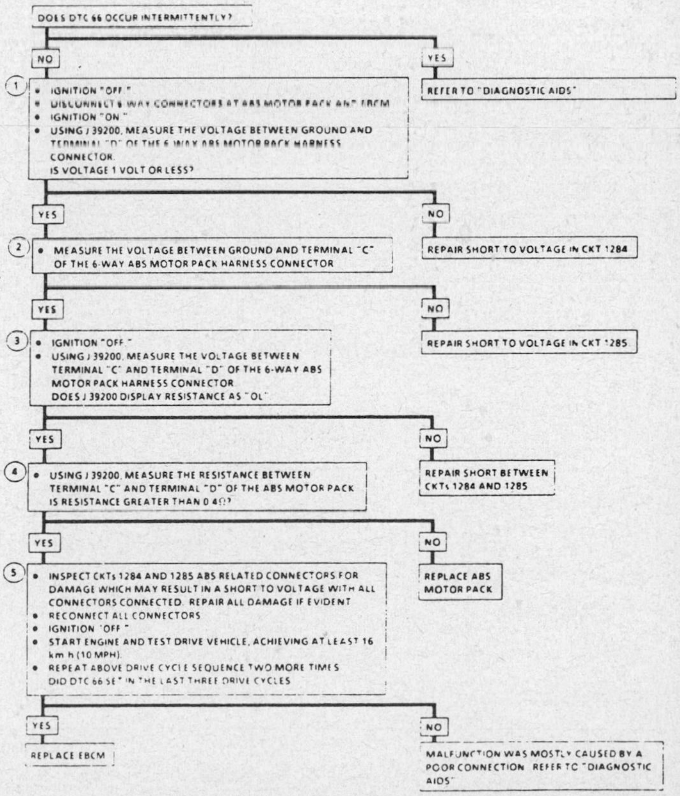
DOES DTC 66 OCCUR INTERMITTENTLY?
NO
YES
REFER TO "DIAGNOSTIC AIDS"
1
• IGNITION "OFF."
• IGNITION "ON."
• USING J 39200, MEASURE THE VOLTAGE BETWEEN GROUND AND
CONNECTOR.
IS VOLTAGE 1 VOLT OR LESS?
YES
NO
REPAIR SHORT TO VOLTAGE IN CKT 1284
2
• MEASURE THE VOLTAGE BETWEEN GROUND AND TERMINAL "C" OF THE 6-WAY ABS MOTOR PACK HARNESS CONNECTOR
YES
NO
REPAIR SHORT TO VOLTAGE IN CKT 1285
3
• IGNITION "OFF."
• USING J 39200, MEASURE THE VOLTAGE BETWEEN TERMINAL "C" AND TERMINAL "D" OF THE 6-WAY ABS MOTOR PACK HARNESS CONNECTOR
DOES J 39200 DISPLAY RESISTANCE AS "OL"
YES
NO
REPAIR SHORT BETWEEN CKTs 1284 AND 1285
4
• USING J 39200, MEASURE THE RESISTANCE BETWEEN TERMINAL "C" AND TERMINAL "D" OF THE ABS MOTOR PACK
IS RESISTANCE GREATER THAN 0.4Ω?
YES
NO
REPLACE ABS MOTOR PACK
5
• INSPECT CKTs 1284 AND 1285 ABS RELATED CONNECTORS FOR DAMAGE WHICH MAY RESULT IN A SHORT TO VOLTAGE WITH ALL CONNECTORS CONNECTED. REPAIR ALL DAMAGE IF EVIDENT
• RECONNECT ALL CONNECTORS
• IGNITION "OFF."
• START ENGINE AND TEST DRIVE VEHICLE, ACHIEVING AT LEAST 16 km/h (10 MPH).
• REPEAT ABOVE DRIVE CYCLE SEQUENCE TWO MORE TIMES
DID DTC 66 SET IN THE LAST THREE DRIVE CYCLES
YES
NO
REPLACE EBCM
MALFUNCTION WAS MOSTLY CAUSED BY A POOR CONNECTION. REFER TO "DIAGNOSTIC AIDS"

GC402930081600BA

Fig. 192 Code A066: Rear Axle Motor Circuit Shorted To Battery. 1993 Grand Prix, 1993–94 Cutlass Supreme, Lumina & Regal

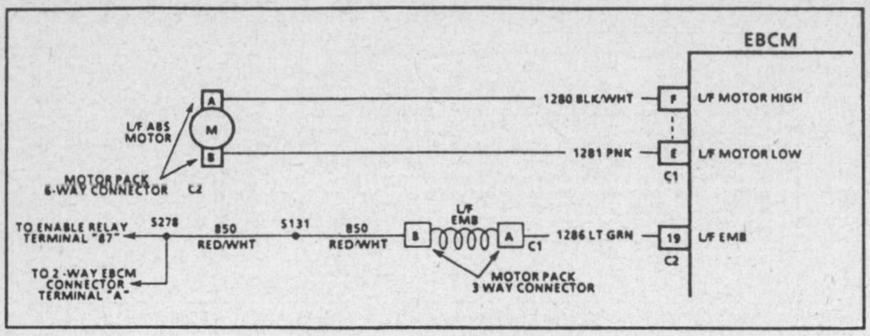
EBCM
1280 BLK/WHT
F
L/F MOTOR HIGH
L/F ABS MOTOR
M
A
B
1281 PNK
E
L/F MOTOR LOW
C1
MOTOR PACK 6-WAY CONNECTOR
C2
TO ENABLE RELAY TERMINAL "87"
S278
850 RED/WHT
S131
850 RED/WHT
L/F EMB
1286 LT GRN
19
L/F EMB
C2
TO 2-WAY EBCM CONNECTOR TERMINAL "A"
MOTOR PACK 3 WAY CONNECTOR

GC402930081700AX

Cavalier & Sunbird

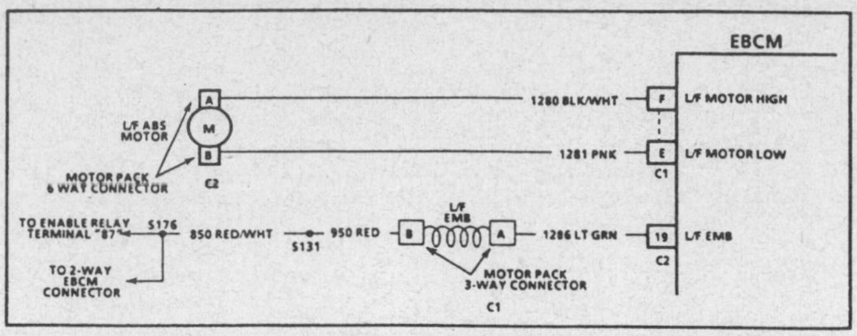
EBCM
1280 BLK/WHT
F
L/F MOTOR HIGH
L/F ABS MOTOR
M
1281 PNK
E
L/F MOTOR LOW
C1
MOTOR PACK 6 WAY CONNECTOR
C2
TO ENABLE RELAY TERMINAL "87"
S176
850 RED/WHT
S131
950 RED
L/F EMB
1286 LT GRN
19
L/F EMB
C2
TO 2-WAY EBCM CONNECTOR
MOTOR PACK 3-WAY CONNECTOR
C1

GC402930081700BX

Achieva, Beretta, Corsica, Grand Am & Skylark

DTC A067

LEFT FRONT EMB CIRCUIT OPEN OR SHORTED TO GROUND

Circuit Description:

This DTC is designed to detect shorts to ground and opens in the EMB release circuit.

A short to ground between the EMB and the ABS EBCM will cause the EMB to be energized indefinitely at an uncontrolled current, causing the EMB to be destroyed.

Failure Condition:

DTC A067 can be set only when the left front EMB is commanded "OFF" (not released). If the EBCM detects the left front EMB control circuit is constantly at ground, a malfunction exists.

Action Taken:

A malfunction DTC is stored, ABS is disabled and the ABS indicator lamp is turned "ON."

Test Description: Number(s) below refer to circled number(s) on the diagnostic chart.

1. This step checks for a short to ground in the EMB control circuitry.
2. This step looks for an open in the EMB control circuitry.
3. This step checks to see if CKT 850 has continuity to the EMB connector.
4. This step ensures the EMB is not internally open.
5. This step is used to release the tension of the motor pack prior to removal.

Diagnostic Aids:

An "Intermittent" malfunction may be caused by a poor connection, rubbed through wire insulation, or a wire that is broken inside the insulation.

The frequency of the malfunction can be checked by using the enhanced diagnostic function of the Tech 1

Any circuitry, that is suspected as causing the intermittent complaint, should be thoroughly checked for backed out terminals, improper mating, broken locks, improperly formed or damaged terminals, poor terminal to wiring connections or physical damage to the wiring harness.

GC402930081700CX

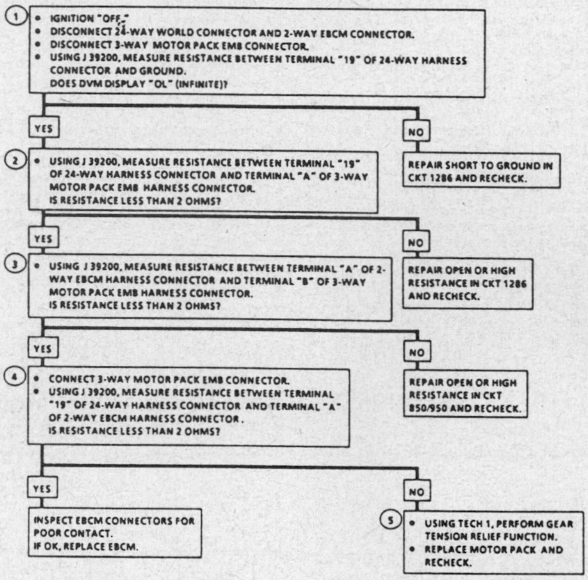
1
• IGNITION "OFF."
• DISCONNECT 24-WAY WORLD CONNECTOR AND 2-WAY EBCM CONNECTOR.
• DISCONNECT 3-WAY MOTOR PACK EMB CONNECTOR.
• USING J 39200, MEASURE RESISTANCE BETWEEN TERMINAL "19" OF 24-WAY HARNESS CONNECTOR AND GROUND.
DOES DVM DISPLAY "OL" (INFINITE)?
YES
NO
2
• USING J 39200, MEASURE RESISTANCE BETWEEN TERMINAL "19" OF 24-WAY HARNESS CONNECTOR AND TERMINAL "A" OF 3-WAY MOTOR PACK EMB HARNESS CONNECTOR.
IS RESISTANCE LESS THAN 2 OHMS?
REPAIR SHORT TO GROUND IN CKT 1286 AND RECHECK.
YES
NO
3
• USING J 39200, MEASURE RESISTANCE BETWEEN TERMINAL "A" OF 2-WAY EBCM HARNESS CONNECTOR AND TERMINAL "B" OF 3-WAY MOTOR PACK EMB HARNESS CONNECTOR.
IS RESISTANCE LESS THAN 2 OHMS?
REPAIR OPEN OR HIGH RESISTANCE IN CKT 1286 AND RECHECK.
YES
NO
4
• CONNECT 3-WAY MOTOR PACK EMB CONNECTOR.
• USING J 39200, MEASURE RESISTANCE BETWEEN TERMINAL "19" OF 24-WAY HARNESS CONNECTOR AND TERMINAL "A" OF 2-WAY EBCM HARNESS CONNECTOR.
IS RESISTANCE LESS THAN 2 OHMS?
REPAIR OPEN OR HIGH RESISTANCE IN CKT 850/950 AND RECHECK.
YES
NO
INSPECT EBCM CONNECTORS FOR POOR CONTACT.
IF OK, REPLACE EBCM.
5
• USING TECH 1, PERFORM GEAR TENSION RELIEF FUNCTION.
• REPLACE MOTOR PACK AND RECHECK.

AFTER DIAGNOSIS IS COMPLETE, CLEAR DTCs AND TEST DRIVE VEHICLE FOR THREE (3) DRIVE CYCLES TO VERIFY DTC DOES NOT RESET. A DRIVE CYCLE CONSISTS OF STARTING THE VEHICLE, DRIVING OVER 16 km/h (10 MPH) AND THEN KEYING DOWN.

GC402930081700DX

Fig. 193 Code A067: Left Front EMB Circuit Open Or Shorted To Ground. 1993–94 Cavalier, Sunbird, Beretta, Corsica & Achieva, Grand Am & Skylark Less VES

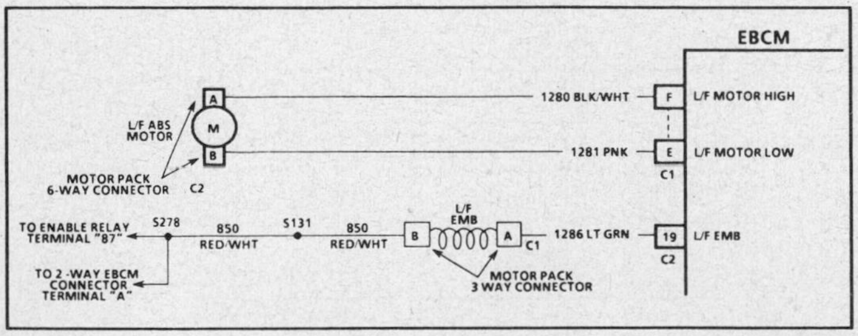
EBCM
1280 BLK/WHT
F
L/F MOTOR HIGH
L/F ABS MOTOR
M
A
B
1281 PNK
E
L/F MOTOR LOW
C1
MOTOR PACK 6-WAY CONNECTOR
C2
TO ENABLE RELAY TERMINAL "87"
S278
850 RED/WHT
S131
850 RED/WHT
L/F EMB
1286 LT GRN
19
L/F EMB
C2
TO 2-WAY EBCM CONNECTOR TERMINAL "A"
MOTOR PACK 3 WAY CONNECTOR

GC402930081800AX

Cavalier & Sunbird

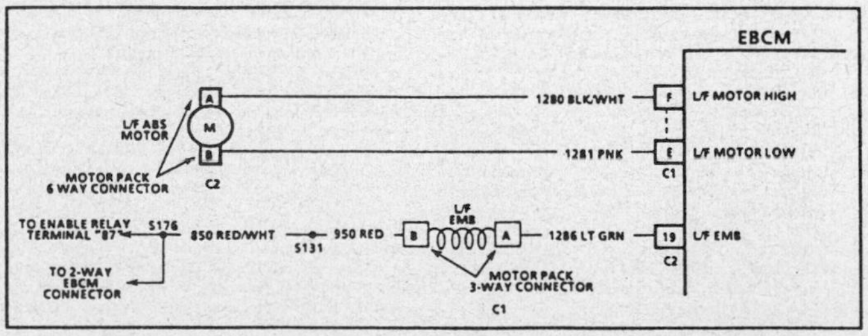
EBCM
1280 BLK/WHT
F
L/F MOTOR HIGH
L/F ABS MOTOR
M
1281 PNK
E
L/F MOTOR LOW
C1
MOTOR PACK 6 WAY CONNECTOR
C2
TO ENABLE RELAY TERMINAL "87"
S176
850 RED/WHT
S131
950 RED
L/F EMB
1286 LT GRN
19
L/F EMB
C2
TO 2-WAY EBCM CONNECTOR
MOTOR PACK 3-WAY CONNECTOR
C1

GC402930081800BX

Achieva, Beretta, Corsica, Grand Am & Skylark

Fig. 194 Code A068: Left Front EMB Circuit Shorted To Battery Or Driver Open (Part 1 of 2). 1993-94 Cavalier, Sunbird, Beretta, Corsica & Achieva, Grand Am & Skylark Less VES

DTC A068

LEFT FRONT EMB CIRCUIT SHORTED TO BATTERY OR DRIVER OPEN

Circuit Description:

This DTC is designed to detect shorts to battery, shorts in the EMB release circuit, or an open EMB driver. These malfunctions will not allow the EMB to be energized (released) when needed.

Failure Condition:

DTC A068 can be set only when the left front EMB is commanded "ON" (released). If an excessive voltage drop is across the motor driver for the left front EMB, a malfunction exists.

Action Taken:

A malfunction DTC is stored, ABS is disabled and the ABS indicator lamp is turned "ON."

Test Description: Number(s) below refer to circled number(s) on the diagnostic chart.

1. This step checks to see if the malfunction is currently present.
2. This step identifies a short to voltage in the EMB control circuitry.
3. This step checks for an EMB that has lower than normal resistance.
4. This step is used to release the tension of the motor pack prior to removal.

Diagnostic Aids:

An "Intermittent" malfunction may be caused by a poor connection, rubbed through wire insulation, or a wire that is broken inside the insulation.

The frequency of the malfunction can be checked by using the enhanced diagnostic function of the Tech 1.

Any circuitry, that is suspected as causing the intermittent complaint, should be thoroughly checked for backed out terminals, improper mating, broken locks, improperly formed or damaged terminals, poor terminal to wiring connections or physical damage to the wiring harness.

GC402930081800CX

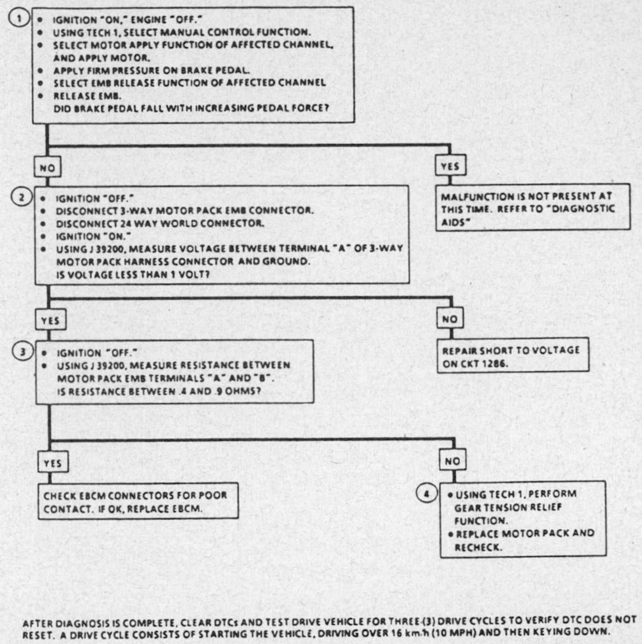
1
• IGNITION "ON," ENGINE "OFF."
• USING TECH 1, SELECT MANUAL CONTROL FUNCTION.
• SELECT MOTOR APPLY FUNCTION OF AFFECTED CHANNEL, AND APPLY MOTOR.
• APPLY FIRM PRESSURE ON BRAKE PEDAL.
• SELECT EMB RELEASE FUNCTION OF AFFECTED CHANNEL
• RELEASE EMB.
DID BRAKE PEDAL FALL WITH INCREASING PEDAL FORCE?
NO
YES
MALFUNCTION IS NOT PRESENT AT THIS TIME. REFER TO "DIAGNOSTIC AIDS"
2
• IGNITION "OFF."
• DISCONNECT 3-WAY MOTOR PACK EMB CONNECTOR.
• DISCONNECT 24 WAY WORLD CONNECTOR.
• IGNITION "ON."
• USING J 39200, MEASURE VOLTAGE BETWEEN TERMINAL "A" OF 3-WAY MOTOR PACK HARNESS CONNECTOR AND GROUND.
IS VOLTAGE LESS THAN 1 VOLT?
YES
NO
REPAIR SHORT TO VOLTAGE ON CKT 1286.
3
• IGNITION "OFF."
• USING J 39200, MEASURE RESISTANCE BETWEEN MOTOR PACK EMB TERMINALS "A" AND "B".
IS RESISTANCE BETWEEN .4 AND .9 OHMS?
YES
NO
CHECK EBCM CONNECTORS FOR POOR CONTACT. IF OK, REPLACE EBCM.
4
• USING TECH 1, PERFORM GEAR TENSION RELIEF FUNCTION.
• REPLACE MOTOR PACK AND RECHECK.
AFTER DIAGNOSIS IS COMPLETE, CLEAR DTCs AND TEST DRIVE VEHICLE FOR THREE (3) DRIVE CYCLES TO VERIFY DTC DOES NOT RESET. A DRIVE CYCLE CONSISTS OF STARTING THE VEHICLE, DRIVING OVER 16 km/h (10 MPH) AND THEN KEYING DOWN.

GC402930081800DX

Fig. 194 Code A068: Left Front EMB Circuit Shorted To Battery Or Driver Open (Part 2 of 2). 1993-94 Cavalier, Sunbird, Beretta, Corsica & Achieva, Grand Am & Skylark Less VES

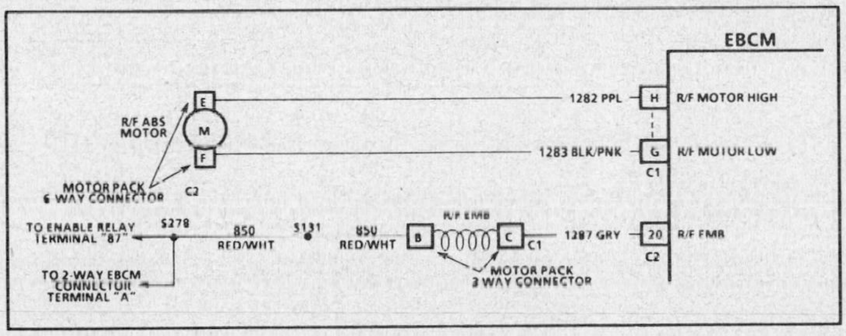
EBCM
R/F ABS MOTOR
M
E
F
1282 PPL
H
R/F MOTOR HIGH
1283 BLK/PNK
G
C1
MOTOR PACK 6 WAY CONNECTOR
C2
TO ENABLE RELAY TERMINAL "87"
S278
850 RED/WHT
S131
850 RED/WHT
R/F EMB
B
C
C1
1287 GRY
20
R/F EMB
C2
MOTOR PACK 3 WAY CONNECTOR
TO 2-WAY EBCM CONNECTOR TERMINAL "A"

GC402930081900AX

Cavalier & Sunbird

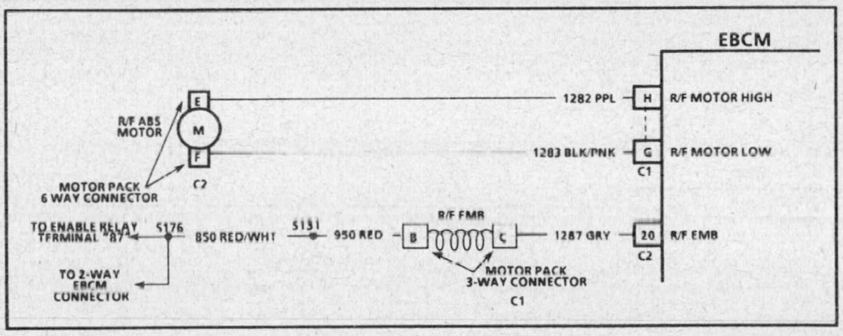
EBCM
R/F ABS MOTOR
M
E
F
1282 PPL
H
R/F MOTOR HIGH
1283 BLK/PNK
G
R/F MOTOR LOW
C1
MOTOR PACK 6 WAY CONNECTOR
C2
TO ENABLE RELAY TERMINAL "87"
S176
850 RED/WHT
S131
950 RED
R/F EMB
B
1287 GRY
20
R/F EMB
C2
MOTOR PACK 3-WAY CONNECTOR
C1
TO 2-WAY EBCM CONNECTOR

GC402930081900BX

Achieva, Beretta, Corsica, Grand Am & Skylark

DTC A071

RIGHT FRONT EMB CIRCUIT OPEN OR SHORTED TO GROUND

Circuit Description:

This DTC is designed to detect shorts to ground and opens in the EMB release circuit.

A short to ground between the EMB and the ABS EBCM will cause the EMB to be energized indefinitely at an uncontrolled current causing the EMB to be destroyed.

Failure Condition:

DTC A071 can be set only when the right front EMB is commanded "OFF" (not released). If the EBCM detects the right front EMB control circuit is constantly at ground, a malfunction exists.

Action Taken:

A malfunction DTC is stored, ABS is disabled and the ABS indicator lamp is turned "ON."

Test Description: Number(s) below refer to circled number(s) on the diagnostic chart.

1. This step checks for a short to ground in the EMB control circuitry.
2. This step looks for an open in the EMB control circuitry.
3. This step checks to see if CKT 850 has continuity to the EMB connector.
4. This step ensures the EMB is not internally open.
5. This step is used to release the tension of the motor pack prior to removal.

Diagnostic Aids:

An "Intermittent" malfunction may be caused by a poor connection, rubbed through wire insulation, or a wire that is broken inside the insulation.

The frequency of the malfunction can be checked by using the enhanced diagnostic function of the Tech 1.

Any circuitry, that is suspected as causing the intermittent complaint, should be thoroughly checked for backed out terminals, improper mating, broken locks, improperly formed or damaged terminals, poor terminal to wiring connections or physical damage to the wiring harness.

GC402930081900CX

Fig. 195 Code A071: Right Front EMB Circuit Shorted To Battery Or Driver Open (Part 1 of 2). 1993-94 Cavalier, Sunbird, Beretta, Corsica & Achieva, Grand Am & Skylark Less VES

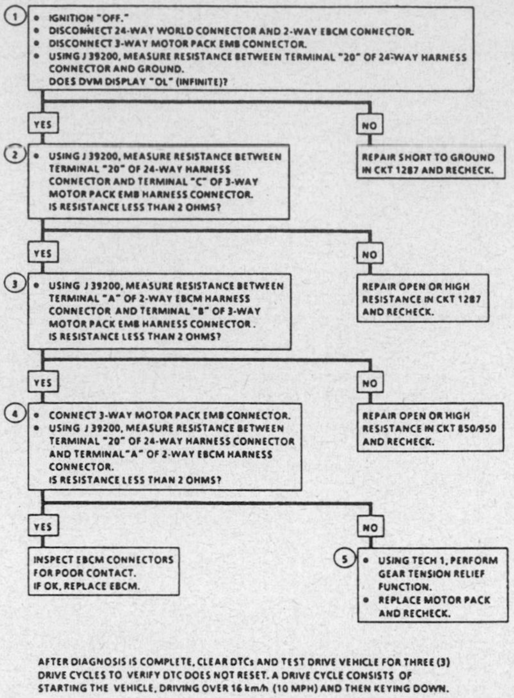
1
• IGNITION "OFF."
• DISCONNECT 24-WAY WORLD CONNECTOR AND 2-WAY EBCM CONNECTOR.
• DISCONNECT 3-WAY MOTOR PACK EMB CONNECTOR.
• USING J 39200, MEASURE RESISTANCE BETWEEN TERMINAL "20" OF 24-WAY HARNESS CONNECTOR AND GROUND.
DOES DVM DISPLAY "OL" (INFINITE)?
YES
NO
REPAIR SHORT TO GROUND IN CKT 1287 AND RECHECK.
2
• USING J 39200, MEASURE RESISTANCE BETWEEN TERMINAL "20" OF 24-WAY HARNESS CONNECTOR AND TERMINAL "C" OF 3-WAY MOTOR PACK EMB HARNESS CONNECTOR.
IS RESISTANCE LESS THAN 2 OHMS?
YES
NO
REPAIR OPEN OR HIGH RESISTANCE IN CKT 1287 AND RECHECK.
3
• USING J 39200, MEASURE RESISTANCE BETWEEN TERMINAL "A" OF 2-WAY EBCM HARNESS CONNECTOR AND TERMINAL "B" OF 3-WAY MOTOR PACK EMB HARNESS CONNECTOR.
IS RESISTANCE LESS THAN 2 OHMS?
YES
NO
REPAIR OPEN OR HIGH RESISTANCE IN CKT 850/950 AND RECHECK.
4
• CONNECT 3-WAY MOTOR PACK EMB CONNECTOR.
• USING J 39200, MEASURE RESISTANCE BETWEEN TERMINAL "20" OF 24-WAY HARNESS CONNECTOR AND TERMINAL "A" OF 2-WAY EBCM HARNESS CONNECTOR.
IS RESISTANCE LESS THAN 2 OHMS?
YES
NO
INSPECT EBCM CONNECTORS FOR POOR CONTACT.
IF OK, REPLACE EBCM.
5
• USING TECH 1, PERFORM GEAR TENSION RELIEF FUNCTION.
• REPLACE MOTOR PACK AND RECHECK.
AFTER DIAGNOSIS IS COMPLETE, CLEAR DTCs AND TEST DRIVE VEHICLE FOR THREE (3) DRIVE CYCLES TO VERIFY DTC DOES NOT RESET. A DRIVE CYCLE CONSISTS OF STARTING THE VEHICLE, DRIVING OVER 16 km/h (10 MPH) AND THEN KEYING DOWN.

GC402930081900DX

Fig. 195 Code A071: Right Front EMB Circuit Shorted To Battery Or Driver Open (Part 2 of 2). 1993-94 Cavalier, Sunbird, Beretta, Corsica & Achieva, Grand Am & Skylark Less VES

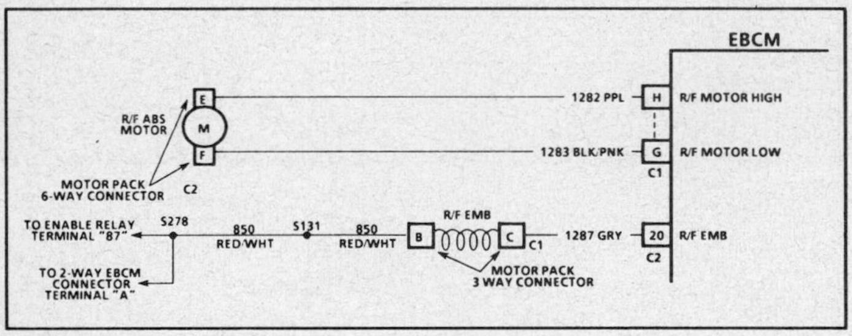
EBCM
R/F ABS MOTOR
M
E
F
1282 PPL
H
R/F MOTOR HIGH
1283 BLK/PNK
G
R/F MOTOR LOW
C1
MOTOR PACK 6-WAY CONNECTOR
C2
TO ENABLE RELAY TERMINAL "87"
S278
850 RED/WHT
S131
850 RED/WHT
R/F EMB
B
C
C1
1287 GRY
20
R/F EMB
C2
TO 2-WAY EBCM CONNECTOR TERMINAL "A"
MOTOR PACK 3 WAY CONNECTOR

GC402930082000AX

Cavalier & Sunbird

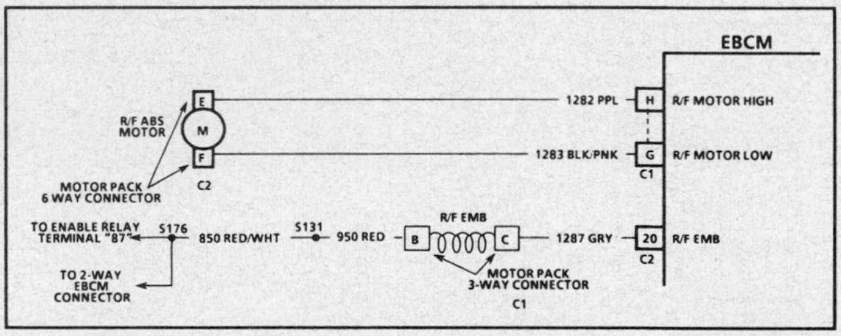
EBCM
R/F ABS MOTOR
M
E
F
1282 PPL
H
R/F MOTOR HIGH
1283 BLK/PNK
G
R/F MOTOR LOW
C1
MOTOR PACK 6 WAY CONNECTOR
C2
TO ENABLE RELAY TERMINAL "87"
S176
850 RED/WHT
S131
950 RED
R/F EMB
B
C
1287 GRY
20
R/F EMB
C2
TO 2-WAY EBCM CONNECTOR
MOTOR PACK 3-WAY CONNECTOR
C1

GC402930082000BX

Achieva, Beretta, Corsica, Grand Am & Skylark

DTC A072

RIGHT FRONT EMB CIRCUIT SHORTED TO BATTERY OR DRIVER OPEN

Circuit Description:

This DTC is designed to detect shorts to battery, shorts in the EMB release circuit, or an open EMB driver. These malfunctions will not allow the EMB to be energized (released) when needed.

Failure Condition:

DTC A072 can be set only when the right front EMB is commanded "ON" (released). If an excessive voltage drop is across the motor driver for the right front EMB, a malfunction exists.

Action Taken:

A malfunction DTC is stored, ABS is disabled and the ABS indicator lamp is turned "ON."

Test Description: Number(s) below refer to circled number(s) on the diagnostic chart.

1. This step checks to see if the malfunction is currently present.
2. This step identifies a short to voltage in the EMB control circuitry.
3. This step checks for an EMB that has lower than normal resistance.
4. This step is used to release the tension of the motor pack prior to removal.

Diagnostic Aids:

An "Intermittent" malfunction may be caused by a poor connection, rubbed through wire insulation, or a wire that is broken inside the insulation.

The frequency of the malfunction can be checked by using the enhanced diagnostic function of the Tech 1.

Any circuitry, that is suspected as causing the intermittent complaint, should be thoroughly checked for backed out terminals, improper mating, broken locks, improperly formed or damaged terminals, poor terminal to wiring connections or physical damage to the wiring harness.

GC402930082000CX

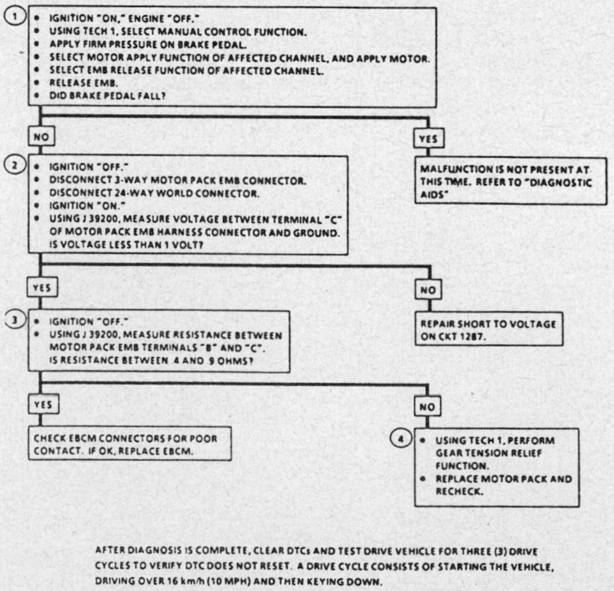
1
• IGNITION "ON," ENGINE "OFF."
• USING TECH 1, SELECT MANUAL CONTROL FUNCTION.
• APPLY FIRM PRESSURE ON BRAKE PEDAL.
• SELECT MOTOR APPLY FUNCTION OF AFFECTED CHANNEL, AND APPLY MOTOR.
• SELECT EMB RELEASE FUNCTION OF AFFECTED CHANNEL.
• RELEASE EMB.
• DID BRAKE PEDAL FALL?
NO
YES
MALFUNCTION IS NOT PRESENT AT THIS TIME. REFER TO "DIAGNOSTIC AIDS"
2
• IGNITION "OFF."
• DISCONNECT 3-WAY MOTOR PACK EMB CONNECTOR.
• DISCONNECT 24-WAY WORLD CONNECTOR.
• IGNITION "ON."
• USING J 39200, MEASURE VOLTAGE BETWEEN TERMINAL "C" OF MOTOR PACK EMB HARNESS CONNECTOR AND GROUND.
IS VOLTAGE LESS THAN 1 VOLT?
YES
NO
REPAIR SHORT TO VOLTAGE ON CKT 1287.
3
• IGNITION "OFF."
• USING J 39200, MEASURE RESISTANCE BETWEEN MOTOR PACK EMB TERMINALS "B" AND "C".
IS RESISTANCE BETWEEN 4 AND 9 OHMS?
YES
NO
CHECK EBCM CONNECTORS FOR POOR CONTACT. IF OK, REPLACE EBCM.
4
• USING TECH 1, PERFORM GEAR TENSION RELIEF FUNCTION.
• REPLACE MOTOR PACK AND RECHECK.
AFTER DIAGNOSIS IS COMPLETE, CLEAR DTCs AND TEST DRIVE VEHICLE FOR THREE (3) DRIVE CYCLES TO VERIFY DTC DOES NOT RESET. A DRIVE CYCLE CONSISTS OF STARTING THE VEHICLE, DRIVING OVER 16 km/h (10 MPH) AND THEN KEYING DOWN.

DUMMY00000000001

Fig. 196 Code A072: Right Front EMB Circuit Shorted To Battery Or Driver Open. 1993–94 Cavalier, Sunbird, Beretta, Corsica & Achieva, Grand Am & Skylark Less VES

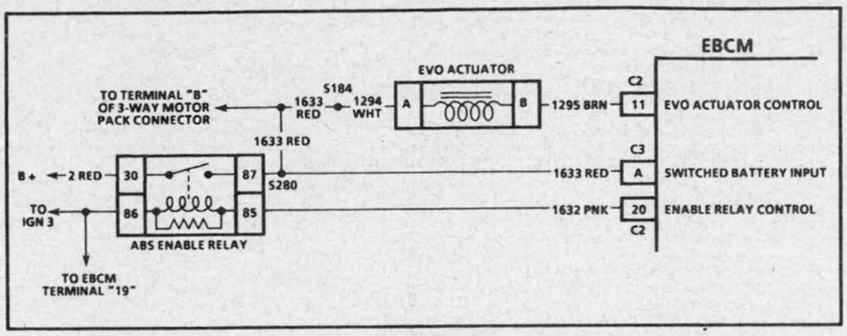
EBCM
EVO ACTUATOR
TO TERMINAL "B" OF 3-WAY MOTOR PACK CONNECTOR
S184
1633 RED
1294 WHT
A
B
1295 BRN
C2
11
EVO ACTUATOR CONTROL
1633 RED
C3
B+
2 RED
30
87
S280
1633 RED
A
SWITCHED BATTERY INPUT
TO IGN 3
86
85
1632 PNK
20
ENABLE RELAY CONTROL
C2
ABS ENABLE RELAY
TO EBCM TERMINAL "19"

DTC 74

EVO ACTUATOR CIRCUIT SHORTED TO BATTERY OR SOLENOID SHORTED (FOR ABS WITH VES ONLY)

Circuit Description:

Battery voltage is supplied to EVO actuator terminal "A" when the EBCM commands the ABS enable relay "ON." Ground for the EVO actuator is provided through EBCM terminal "11" to actuator terminal "B". The EBCM controls the amount of current supplied to the EVO actuator based on input from the wheel speed sensors and the steering wheel speed sensor.

DTC Will Set When: DTC 74 can be set anytime after ABS initialization. A malfunction exists if an excessive voltage drop is across the EVO actuator driver.

Action Taken: A malfunction DTC is stored, VES is disabled and power steering returns to full assist.

DTC Will Clear When: DTC 74 setting conditions no longer exist and the ignition key is turned "OFF."

DTC Chart Test Description: Number(s) below refer to circled number(s) on the diagnostic chart.

1. Checks for a short to voltage in the EVO actuator control circuit.
2. Checks for a shorted actuator solenoid or shorted actuator circuits.
3. Ensures malfunction was not due to physical damage of the EVO actuator circuitry.
4. Isolates the malfunction to either the actuator solenoid or its circuitry.

Diagnostic Aids: An "Intermittent" malfunction is most likely caused by a poor connection, rubbed through wire insulation, or a wire that is broken inside the insulation.

The frequency of the malfunction can be checked by using the enhanced diagnostic function of the Tech 1.

Any circuitry, that is suspected as causing the intermittent malfunction, should be thoroughly checked for backed out terminals, improper mating, broken locks, improperly formed or damaged terminals, poor terminal to wiring connections or physical damage to the wiring harness.

GC402940105300AX

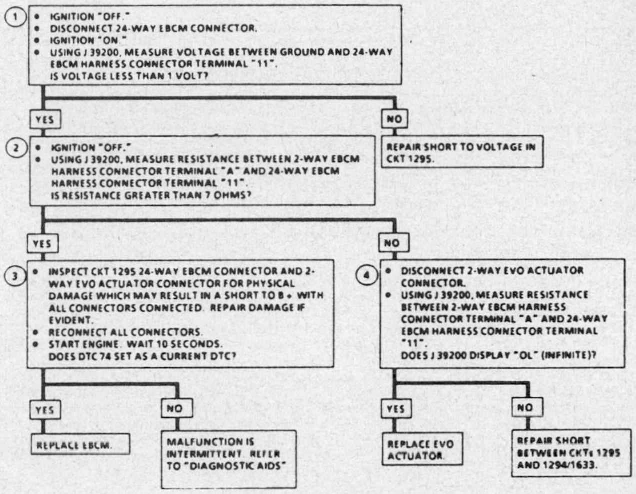
1
IGNITION "OFF."
DISCONNECT 24-WAY EBCM CONNECTOR.
IGNITION "ON."
USING J 39200, MEASURE VOLTAGE BETWEEN GROUND AND 24-WAY EBCM HARNESS CONNECTOR TERMINAL "11".
IS VOLTAGE LESS THAN 1 VOLT?
YES
NO
REPAIR SHORT TO VOLTAGE IN CKT 1295.
2
IGNITION "OFF."
USING J 39200, MEASURE RESISTANCE BETWEEN 2-WAY EBCM HARNESS CONNECTOR TERMINAL "A" AND 24-WAY EBCM HARNESS CONNECTOR TERMINAL "11".
IS RESISTANCE GREATER THAN 7 OHMS?
YES
NO
3
INSPECT CKT 1295 24-WAY EBCM CONNECTOR AND 2-WAY EVO ACTUATOR CONNECTOR FOR PHYSICAL DAMAGE WHICH MAY RESULT IN A SHORT TO B+ WITH ALL CONNECTORS CONNECTED. REPAIR DAMAGE IF EVIDENT.
RECONNECT ALL CONNECTORS.
START ENGINE. WAIT 10 SECONDS.
DOES DTC 74 SET AS A CURRENT DTC?
4
DISCONNECT 2-WAY EVO ACTUATOR CONNECTOR.
USING J 39200, MEASURE RESISTANCE BETWEEN 2-WAY EBCM HARNESS CONNECTOR TERMINAL "A" AND 24-WAY EBCM HARNESS CONNECTOR TERMINAL "11".
DOES J 39200 DISPLAY "OL" (INFINITE)?
YES
NO
REPLACE EBCM.
MALFUNCTION IS INTERMITTENT. REFER TO "DIAGNOSTIC AIDS"
YES
NO
REPLACE EVO ACTUATOR.
REPAIR SHORT BETWEEN CKTs 1295 AND 1294/1633.

GC402940105300BX

Fig. 197 Code A073: EVO Actuator Circuit Shorted To Battery Or Solenoid Shorted. 1994 Achieva, Grand Am & Skylark w/VES

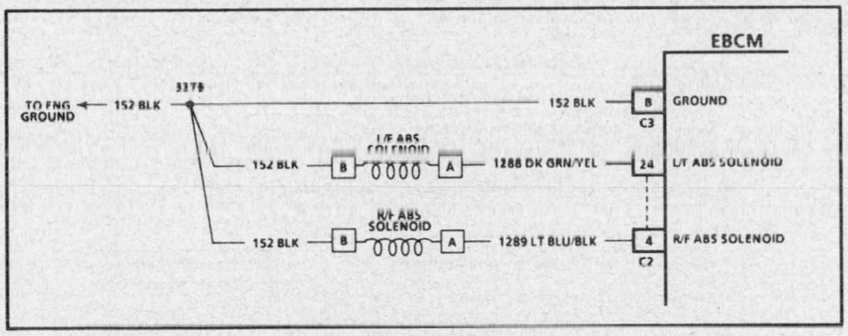
EBCM
TO ENG GROUND
152 BLK
152 BLK
B
GROUND
C3
L/F ABS SOLENOID
152 BLK
B
A
1288 DK GRN/YEL
24
L/T ABS SOLENOID
R/F ABS SOLENOID
152 BLK
B
A
1289 LT BLU/BLK
4
R/F ABS SOLENOID
C2

DTC A076

LEFT FRONT SOLENOID CIRCUIT OPEN OR SHORTED TO BATTERY

Circuit Description:

This DTC identifies a solenoid that cannot be energized due to an open in its circuitry, or a solenoid that is always energized due to a short to battery in its circuitry between the driver and the solenoid. An open will not allow proper ABS operation, but the short to battery simply turns "ON" the solenoid. A path for base brakes is still allowed once the motor re-homes and the check valve is lifted off its seat during key on initialization.

Failure Condition:

DTC A076 can be set only when the solenoid is commanded "OFF." If the EBCM detects an excessive voltage in the left front solenoid control circuit, a malfunction exists.

Action Taken:

A malfunction DTC is stored, ABS is disabled and the ABS indicator lamp is turned "ON."

Test Description: Number(s) below refer to circled number(s) on the diagnostic chart.

1. This checks for a short to voltage in the control circuitry of the solenoid.
2. This checks for an open in the control circuit of the solenoid.
3. This step identifies an open in the solenoid or ground circuit.
4. This step checks for a possible intermittent malfunction in the solenoid circuitry due to poor terminal contact.

Diagnostic Aids:

An "Intermittent" malfunction may be caused by a poor connection, rubbed through wire insulation, or a wire that is broken inside the insulation.

The frequency of the malfunction can be checked by using the enhanced diagnostic function of the Tech 1.

Any circuitry, that is suspected as causing the intermittent complaint, should be thoroughly checked for backed out terminals, improper mating, broken locks, improperly formed or damaged terminals, poor terminal to wiring connections or physical damage to the wiring harness.

GC402930082100AX

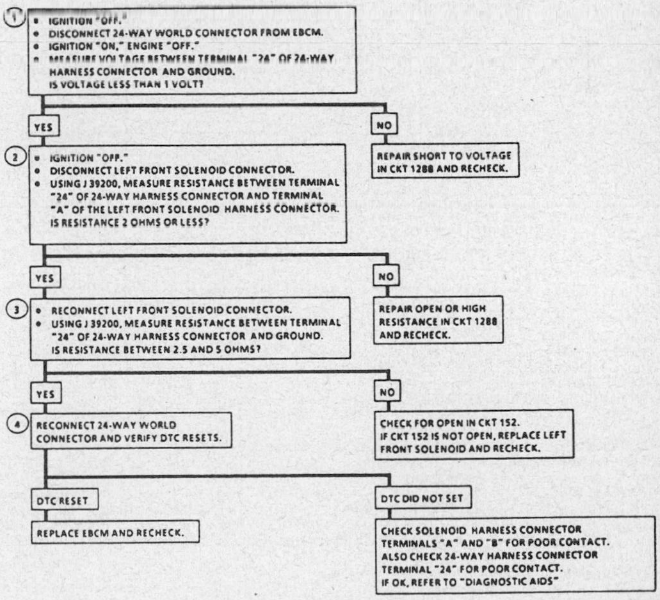
1
IGNITION "OFF."
DISCONNECT 24-WAY WORLD CONNECTOR FROM EBCM.
IGNITION "ON," ENGINE "OFF."
HARNESS CONNECTOR AND GROUND.
IS VOLTAGE LESS THAN 1 VOLT?
YES
NO
REPAIR SHORT TO VOLTAGE IN CKT 1288 AND RECHECK.
2
IGNITION "OFF."
DISCONNECT LEFT FRONT SOLENOID CONNECTOR.
USING J 39200, MEASURE RESISTANCE BETWEEN TERMINAL "24" OF 24-WAY HARNESS CONNECTOR AND TERMINAL "A" OF THE LEFT FRONT SOLENOID HARNESS CONNECTOR.
IS RESISTANCE 2 OHMS OR LESS?
YES
NO
REPAIR OPEN OR HIGH RESISTANCE IN CKT 1288 AND RECHECK.
3
RECONNECT LEFT FRONT SOLENOID CONNECTOR.
USING J 39200, MEASURE RESISTANCE BETWEEN TERMINAL "24" OF 24-WAY HARNESS CONNECTOR AND GROUND.
IS RESISTANCE BETWEEN 2.5 AND 5 OHMS?
YES
NO
CHECK FOR OPEN IN CKT 152.
IF CKT 152 IS NOT OPEN, REPLACE LEFT FRONT SOLENOID AND RECHECK.
4
RECONNECT 24-WAY WORLD CONNECTOR AND VERIFY DTC RESETS.
DTC RESET
REPLACE EBCM AND RECHECK.
DTC DID NOT SET
CHECK SOLENOID HARNESS CONNECTOR TERMINALS "A" AND "B" FOR POOR CONTACT.
ALSO CHECK 24-WAY HARNESS CONNECTOR TERMINAL "24" FOR POOR CONTACT.
IF OK, REFER TO "DIAGNOSTIC AIDS"

GC402930082100BX

Fig. 198 Code A076: Left Front Solenoid Circuit Open Or Shorted To Battery. 1993–94 Cavalier, Sunbird, Beretta, Corsica & Achieva, Grand Am & Skylark Less VES

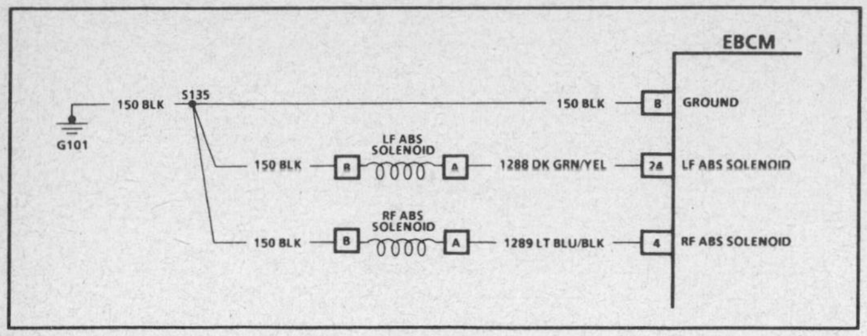
EBCM
150 BLK
S135
G101
150 BLK
8
GROUND
LF ABS
SOLENOID
150 BLK
B
A
1288 DK GRN/YEL
24
LF ABS SOLENOID
RF ABS
SOLENOID
150 BLK
B
A
1289 LT BLU/BLK
4
RF ABS SOLENOID

DTC 76

LEFT FRONT SOL. CIRCUIT SHORTED TO BATT

Circuit Description:

This DTC identifies a solenoid that cannot be energized due to an open in its circuitry, or a solenoid that is always energized due to a short to battery in its circuitry between the driver and the solenoid. An open will not allow proper ABS operation, but the short to battery simply turns "ON" the solenoid. A path for base brakes is still allowed once the motor rehomes and the check ball is lifted off its seat during key "ON" initialization.

DTC Will Set When: DTC 76 can be set only when the solenoid is commanded "OFF." If the EBCM detects an excessive voltage in the left front solenoid control circuit, a malfunction exists.

Action Taken: A malfunction DTC is stored, ABS is disabled and the ABS warning lamp is turned "ON."

DTC Chart Test Description: Number(s) below refer to circled number(s) on the diagnostic chart.

1. Checks for a short to voltage in the control circuitry of the solenoid.
2. Checks for an open in the control circuit of the solenoid.
3. Checks the solenoid coil for proper resistance.
4. Checks for an open in the solenoid ground circuit.
5. Checks for a possible intermittent malfunction in the solenoid circuitry due to poor terminal contact.

Diagnostic Aids: An "Intermittent" malfunction may be caused by a poor connection, rubbed through wire insulation, or a wire that is broken inside the insulation.

The frequency of the malfunction can be checked by using the enhanced diagnostic function of the Tech 1.

Any circuitry, that is suspected as causing the intermittent complaint, should be thoroughly checked for backed out terminals, improper mating, broken locks, improperly formed or damaged terminals, poor terminal to wiring connections or physical damage to the wiring harness.

GC402930082200AA

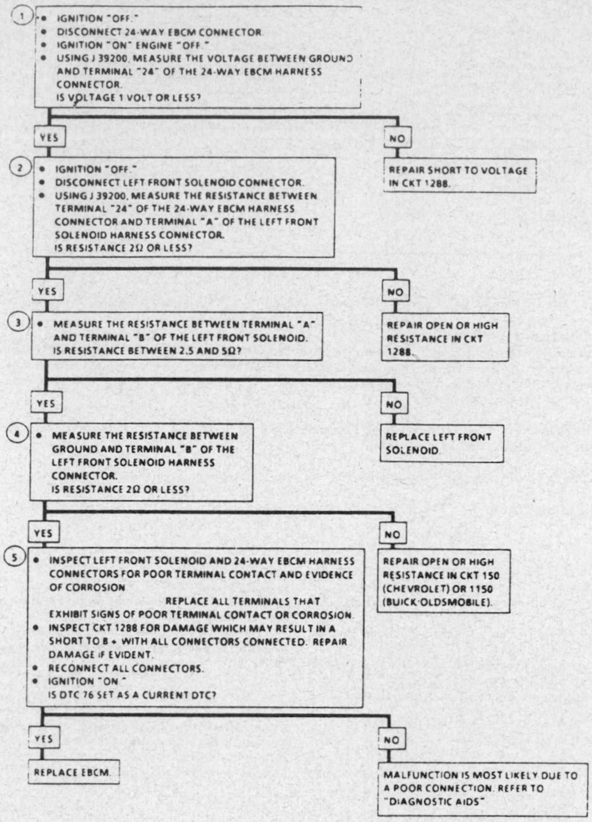
1
• IGNITION "OFF."
• DISCONNECT 24-WAY EBCM CONNECTOR.
• IGNITION "ON" ENGINE "OFF."
• USING J 39200, MEASURE THE VOLTAGE BETWEEN GROUND AND TERMINAL "24" OF THE 24-WAY EBCM HARNESS CONNECTOR.
IS VOLTAGE 1 VOLT OR LESS?
YES
NO
REPAIR SHORT TO VOLTAGE IN CKT 1288.
2
• IGNITION "OFF."
• DISCONNECT LEFT FRONT SOLENOID CONNECTOR.
• USING J 39200, MEASURE THE RESISTANCE BETWEEN TERMINAL "24" OF THE 24-WAY EBCM HARNESS CONNECTOR AND TERMINAL "A" OF THE LEFT FRONT SOLENOID HARNESS CONNECTOR.
IS RESISTANCE 2Ω OR LESS?
YES
NO
REPAIR OPEN OR HIGH RESISTANCE IN CKT 1288.
3
• MEASURE THE RESISTANCE BETWEEN TERMINAL "A" AND TERMINAL "B" OF THE LEFT FRONT SOLENOID.
IS RESISTANCE BETWEEN 2.5 AND 5Ω?
YES
NO
REPLACE LEFT FRONT SOLENOID.
4
• MEASURE THE RESISTANCE BETWEEN GROUND AND TERMINAL "B" OF THE LEFT FRONT SOLENOID HARNESS CONNECTOR.
IS RESISTANCE 2Ω OR LESS?
YES
NO
REPAIR OPEN OR HIGH RESISTANCE IN CKT 150 (CHEVROLET) OR 1150 (BUICK·OLDSMOBILE).
5
• INSPECT LEFT FRONT SOLENOID AND 24-WAY EBCM HARNESS CONNECTORS FOR POOR TERMINAL CONTACT AND EVIDENCE OF CORROSION
REPLACE ALL TERMINALS THAT EXHIBIT SIGNS OF POOR TERMINAL CONTACT OR CORROSION.
• INSPECT CKT 1288 FOR DAMAGE WHICH MAY RESULT IN A SHORT TO B + WITH ALL CONNECTORS CONNECTED. REPAIR DAMAGE IF EVIDENT.
• RECONNECT ALL CONNECTORS.
• IGNITION "ON."
IS DTC 76 SET AS A CURRENT DTC?
YES
NO
REPLACE EBCM.
MALFUNCTION IS MOST LIKELY DUE TO A POOR CONNECTION. REFER TO "DIAGNOSTIC AIDS"

GC402930082200BA

Fig. 199 Code A076: Left Front Solenoid Circuit Open Or Shorted To Battery. 1993 Grand Prix, 1993–94 Cutlass Supreme, Lumina & Regal

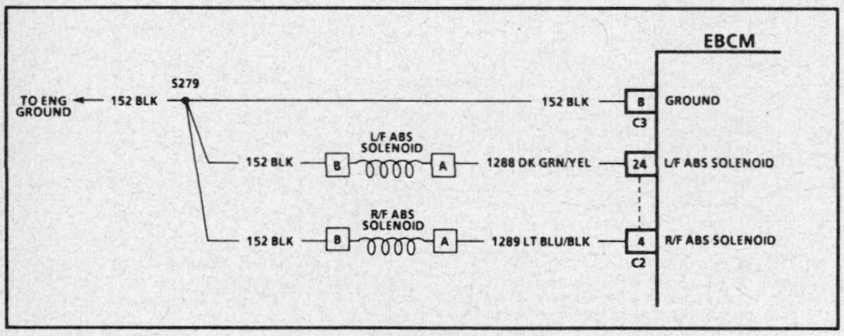
EBCM
S279
TO ENG GROUND
152 BLK
152 BLK
8
C3
GROUND
L/F ABS
SOLENOID
152 BLK
B
A
1288 DK GRN/YEL
24
L/F ABS SOLENOID
R/F ABS
SOLENOID
152 BLK
B
A
1289 LT BLU/BLK
4
C2
R/F ABS SOLENOID

DTC A077

LEFT FRONT SOLENOID CIRCUIT SHORTED TO GROUND OR DRIVER OPEN

Circuit Description:

This DTC identifies a solenoid that cannot be energized due to an open in its driver circuitry, or a short to ground between the solenoid driver and the solenoid. These malfunctions can affect ABS operation since the flow of brake fluid to the wheel cylinder cannot be stopped, making ABS operation for that channel impossible.

Failure Condition:

DTC A077 can be set only when the solenoid is commanded "ON." If the EBCM detects the left front solenoid control circuit voltage is out of specification, a malfunction exists.

Action Taken:

A malfunction DTC is stored, ABS is disabled and the ABS indicator lamp is turned "ON."

Test Description: Number(s) below refer to circled number(s) on the diagnostic chart.

1. This step checks for a solenoid that is internally shorted to ground.
2. This step checks for a solenoid that is not within proper resistance values.
3. This step indicates if a short to ground exists in the solenoid control circuitry.
4. This checks for an open control circuit to the EBCM.

Diagnostic Aids:

An "Intermittent" malfunction may be caused by a poor connection, rubbed through wire insulation, or a wire that is broken inside the insulation.

The frequency of the malfunction can be checked by using the enhanced diagnostic function of the Tech 1.

Any circuitry, that is suspected as causing the intermittent complaint, should be thoroughly checked for backed out terminals, improper mating, broken locks, improperly formed or damaged terminals, poor terminal to wiring connections or physical damage to the wiring harness.

GC402930082300AX

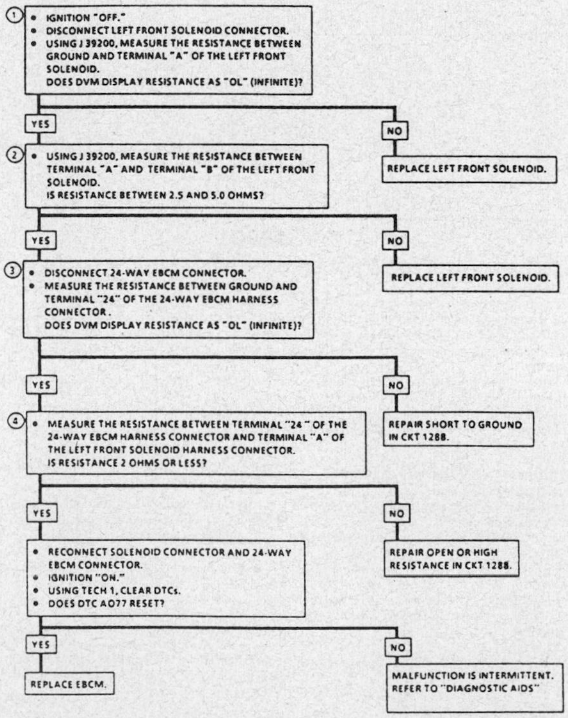
1
• IGNITION "OFF."
• DISCONNECT LEFT FRONT SOLENOID CONNECTOR.
• USING J 39200, MEASURE THE RESISTANCE BETWEEN GROUND AND TERMINAL "A" OF THE LEFT FRONT SOLENOID.
DOES DVM DISPLAY RESISTANCE AS "OL" (INFINITE)?
YES
NO
REPLACE LEFT FRONT SOLENOID.
2
• USING J 39200, MEASURE THE RESISTANCE BETWEEN TERMINAL "A" AND TERMINAL "B" OF THE LEFT FRONT SOLENOID.
IS RESISTANCE BETWEEN 2.5 AND 5.0 OHMS?
YES
NO
REPLACE LEFT FRONT SOLENOID.
3
• DISCONNECT 24-WAY EBCM CONNECTOR.
• MEASURE THE RESISTANCE BETWEEN GROUND AND TERMINAL "24" OF THE 24-WAY EBCM HARNESS CONNECTOR.
DOES DVM DISPLAY RESISTANCE AS "OL" (INFINITE)?
YES
NO
REPAIR SHORT TO GROUND IN CKT 1288.
4
• MEASURE THE RESISTANCE BETWEEN TERMINAL "24" OF THE 24-WAY EBCM HARNESS CONNECTOR AND TERMINAL "A" OF THE LEFT FRONT SOLENOID HARNESS CONNECTOR.
IS RESISTANCE 2 OHMS OR LESS?
YES
NO
REPAIR OPEN OR HIGH RESISTANCE IN CKT 1288.
• RECONNECT SOLENOID CONNECTOR AND 24-WAY EBCM CONNECTOR.
• IGNITION "ON."
• USING TECH 1, CLEAR DTCs.
• DOES DTC A077 RESET?
YES
NO
REPLACE EBCM.
MALFUNCTION IS INTERMITTENT. REFER TO "DIAGNOSTIC AIDS"

GC402930082300BX

Fig. 200 Code A077: Left front Solenoid Circuit Shorted To Ground Or Driver Open. 1993–94 Cavalier, Sunbird, Beretta, Corsica & Achieva, Grand Am & Skylark Less VES

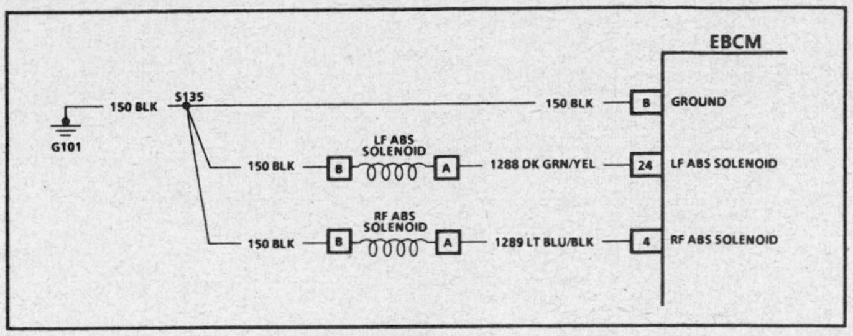
EBCM
150 BLK
S135
G101
150 BLK
B
GROUND
LF ABS SOLENOID
150 BLK
B
A
1288 DK GRN/YEL
24
LF ABS SOLENOID
RF ABS SOLENOID
150 BLK
B
A
1289 LT BLU/BLK
4
RF ABS SOLENOID

DTC 77

LEFT FRONT SOLENOID CIRCUIT SHORTED TO GND

Circuit Description:

This DTC identifies a solenoid that cannot be energized due to an open in its driver circuitry, or a short to ground between the solenoid driver and the solenoid. These malfunctions can affect ABS operation since the flow of brake fluid to the wheel cylinder cannot be stopped, making ABS operation for that channel impossible.

DTC Will Set When: DTC 77 can be set only when the solenoid is commanded "ON." If the EBCM detects the left front solenoid control circuit voltage is out of specification, a malfunction exists.

Action Taken: A malfunction DTC is stored, ABS is disabled and the ABS warning lamp is turned "ON."

DTC Chart Test Description: Number(s) below refer to circled number(s) on the diagnostic chart.

1. Checks for a solenoid that is internally shorted to ground.
2. Checks for solenoid that is not within proper resistance values.
3. Indicates if a short to ground exists in the solenoid circuitry.
4. Checks for a possible intermittent malfunction in the solenoid circuitry due to poor terminal contact.

Diagnostic Aids: An "Intermittent" malfunction may be caused by a poor connection, rubbed through wire insulation, or a wire that is broken inside the insulation.

The frequency of the malfunction can be checked by using the enhanced diagnostic function of the Tech 1

Any circuitry, that is suspected as causing the intermittent complaint, should be thoroughly checked for backed out terminals, improper mating, broken locks, improperly formed or damaged terminals, poor terminal to wiring connections or physical damage to the wiring harness.

GC402930082400AA

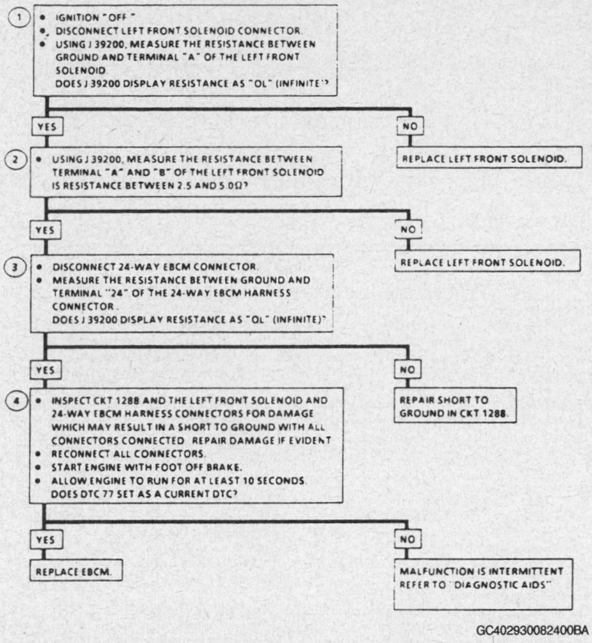
1
• IGNITION "OFF."
• DISCONNECT LEFT FRONT SOLENOID CONNECTOR.
• USING J 39200, MEASURE THE RESISTANCE BETWEEN GROUND AND TERMINAL "A" OF THE LEFT FRONT SOLENOID.
DOES J 39200 DISPLAY RESISTANCE AS "OL" (INFINITE)?
YES
NO
REPLACE LEFT FRONT SOLENOID.
2
• USING J 39200, MEASURE THE RESISTANCE BETWEEN TERMINAL "A" AND "B" OF THE LEFT FRONT SOLENOID
IS RESISTANCE BETWEEN 2.5 AND 5.0Ω?
YES
NO
REPLACE LEFT FRONT SOLENOID.
3
• DISCONNECT 24-WAY EBCM CONNECTOR.
• MEASURE THE RESISTANCE BETWEEN GROUND AND TERMINAL "24" OF THE 24-WAY EBCM HARNESS CONNECTOR.
DOES J 39200 DISPLAY RESISTANCE AS "OL" (INFINITE)?
YES
NO
REPAIR SHORT TO GROUND IN CKT 1288.
4
• INSPECT CKT 1288 AND THE LEFT FRONT SOLENOID AND 24-WAY EBCM HARNESS CONNECTORS FOR DAMAGE WHICH MAY RESULT IN A SHORT TO GROUND WITH ALL CONNECTORS CONNECTED. REPAIR DAMAGE IF EVIDENT.
• RECONNECT ALL CONNECTORS.
• START ENGINE WITH FOOT OFF BRAKE.
• ALLOW ENGINE TO RUN FOR AT LEAST 10 SECONDS.
DOES DTC 77 SET AS A CURRENT DTC?
YES
NO
REPLACE EBCM.
MALFUNCTION IS INTERMITTENT REFER TO "DIAGNOSTIC AIDS"

GC402930082400BA

Fig. 201 Code A077: Left Front Solenoid Circuit Shorted To Ground Or Driver Open. 1993 Grand Prix, 1993–94 Cutlass Supreme, Lumina & Regal

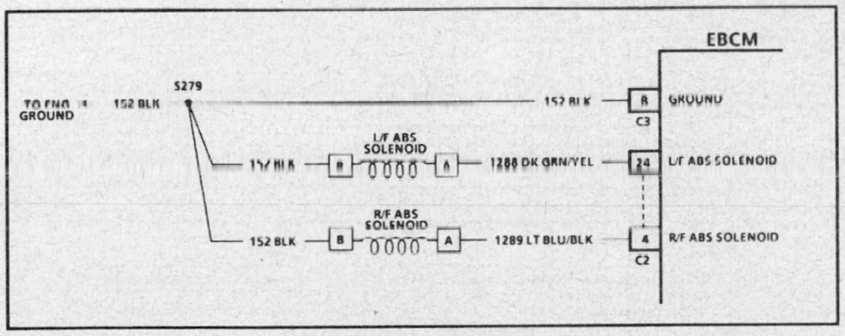
EBCM
S279
152 BLK
GROUND
152 BLK
B
GROUND
C3
L/F ABS SOLENOID
152 BLK
B
A
1288 DK GRN/YEL
24
L/F ABS SOLENOID
R/F ABS SOLENOID
152 BLK
B
A
1289 LT BLU/BLK
4
R/F ABS SOLENOID
C2

DTC A078

RIGHT FRONT SOLENOID CIRCUIT OPEN OR SHORTED TO BATTERY

Circuit Description:

This DTC identifies a solenoid that cannot be energized due to an open in its circuitry, or a solenoid that is always energized due to a short to battery in its circuitry between the driver and the solenoid. An open will not allow proper ABS operation but the short to battery simply turns "ON" the solenoid. A path for base brakes is still allowed once the motor re-homes and the check valve is lifted off its seat during key on initialization.

Failure Condition:

DTC A078 can be set only when the solenoid is commanded "OFF." If the EBCM detects an excessive voltage in the right front solenoid control circuit, a malfunction exists.

Action Taken:

A malfunction DTC is stored, ABS is disabled and the ABS indicator lamp is turned "ON."

Test Description: Number(s) below refer to circled number(s) on the diagnostic chart.

1. This checks for a short to voltage in the control circuitry of the solenoid.
2. This checks for an open in the control circuit of the solenoid.
3. This step identifies an open in the solenoid or ground circuit.
4. This step checks for a possible intermittent malfunction in the solenoid circuitry due to poor terminal contact.

Diagnostic Aids:

An "Intermittent" malfunction may be caused by a poor connection, rubbed through wire insulation, or a wire that is broken inside the insulation.

The frequency of the malfunction can be checked by using the enhanced diagnostic function of the Tech 1.

Any circuitry, that is suspected as causing the intermittent complaint, should be thoroughly checked for backed out terminals, improper mating, broken locks, improperly formed or damaged terminals, poor terminal to wiring connections or physical damage to the wiring harness.

GC402930082500AX

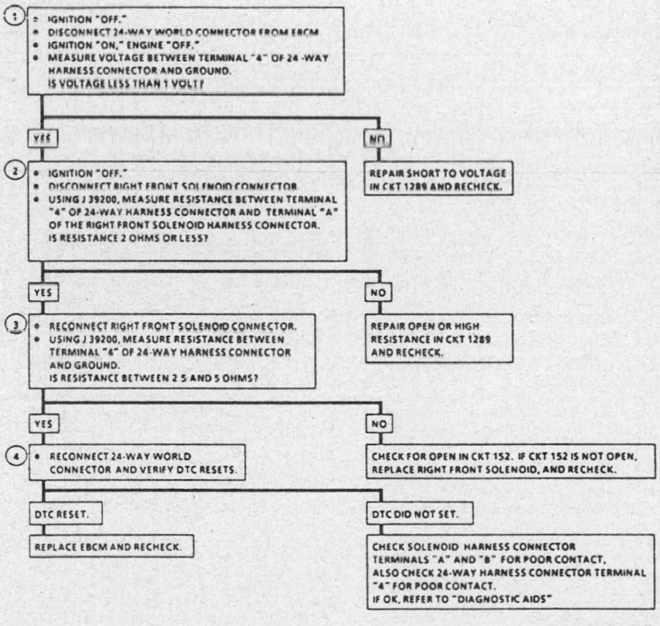
1
• IGNITION "OFF."
• DISCONNECT 24-WAY WORLD CONNECTOR FROM EBCM
• IGNITION "ON," ENGINE "OFF."
• MEASURE VOLTAGE BETWEEN TERMINAL "4" OF 24-WAY HARNESS CONNECTOR AND GROUND.
IS VOLTAGE LESS THAN 1 VOLT?
YES
NO
REPAIR SHORT TO VOLTAGE IN CKT 1289 AND RECHECK.
2
• IGNITION "OFF."
• DISCONNECT RIGHT FRONT SOLENOID CONNECTOR.
• USING J 39200, MEASURE RESISTANCE BETWEEN TERMINAL "4" OF 24-WAY HARNESS CONNECTOR AND TERMINAL "A" OF THE RIGHT FRONT SOLENOID HARNESS CONNECTOR.
IS RESISTANCE 2 OHMS OR LESS?
YES
NO
REPAIR OPEN OR HIGH RESISTANCE IN CKT 1289 AND RECHECK.
3
• RECONNECT RIGHT FRONT SOLENOID CONNECTOR.
• USING J 39200, MEASURE RESISTANCE BETWEEN TERMINAL "4" OF 24-WAY HARNESS CONNECTOR AND GROUND.
IS RESISTANCE BETWEEN 2.5 AND 5 OHMS?
YES
NO
CHECK FOR OPEN IN CKT 152. IF CKT 152 IS NOT OPEN, REPLACE RIGHT FRONT SOLENOID, AND RECHECK.
4
• RECONNECT 24-WAY WORLD CONNECTOR AND VERIFY DTC RESETS.
DTC RESET.
DTC DID NOT SET.
REPLACE EBCM AND RECHECK.
CHECK SOLENOID HARNESS CONNECTOR TERMINALS "A" AND "B" FOR POOR CONTACT, ALSO CHECK 24-WAY HARNESS CONNECTOR TERMINAL "4" FOR POOR CONTACT.
IF OK, REFER TO "DIAGNOSTIC AIDS"

GC402930082500BX

Fig. 202 Code A078: Right Front Solenoid Circuit Open Or Shorted To Battery. 1993–94 Cavalier, Sunbird, Beretta, Corsica & Achieva, Grand Am & Skylark Less VES

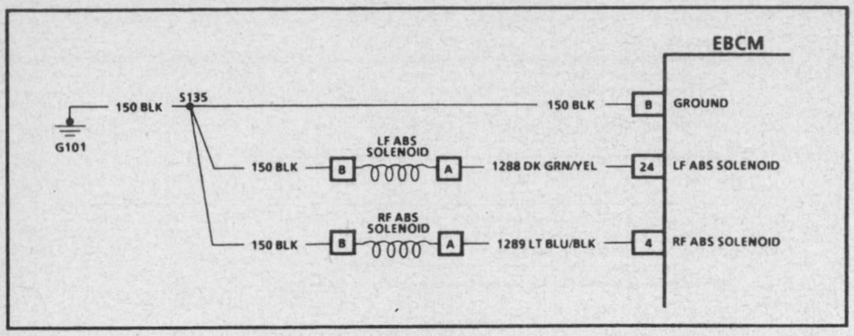
EBCM
150 BLK
S135
G101
150 BLK
B
GROUND
LF ABS
SOLENOID
150 BLK
B
A
1288 DK GRN/YEL
24
LF ABS SOLENOID
RF ABS
SOLENOID
150 BLK
B
A
1289 LT BLU/BLK
4
RF ABS SOLENOID

DTC 78

RIGHT FRONT SOL. CIRCUIT OPEN OR SHORTED TO BATT

Circuit Description:

This DTC identifies a solenoid that cannot be energized due to an open in its circuitry, or a solenoid that is always energized due to a short to battery in its circuitry between the driver and the solenoid. An open will not allow proper ABS operation, but the short to battery simply turns "ON" the solenoid. A path for base brakes is still allowed once the motor rehomes and the check ball is lifted off its seat during key "ON" initialization.

DTC Will Set When: DTC 78 can be set only when the solenoid is commanded "OFF." If the EBCM detects an excessive voltage in the right front solenoid control circuit, a malfunction exists.

Action Taken: A malfunction DTC is stored, ABS is disabled and the ABS warning lamp is turned "ON."

DTC Chart Test Description: Number(s) below refer to circled number(s) on the diagnostic chart.

1. Checks for a short to voltage in the control circuitry of the solenoid.
2. Checks for an open in the control circuit of the solenoid.
3. Checks the solenoid coil for proper resistance.
4. Checks for an open in the solenoid ground circuit.
5. Checks for a possible intermittent malfunction in the solenoid circuitry due to poor terminal contact.

Diagnostic Aids: An "Intermittent" malfunction may be caused by a poor connection, rubbed through wire insulation, or a wire that is broken inside the insulation.

The frequency of the malfunction can be checked by using the enhanced diagnostic function of the Tech 1.

Any circuitry, that is suspected as causing the intermittent complaint, should be thoroughly checked for backed out terminals, improper mating, broken locks, improperly formed or damaged terminals, poor terminal to wiring connections or physical damage to the wiring harness.

GC402930082600AA

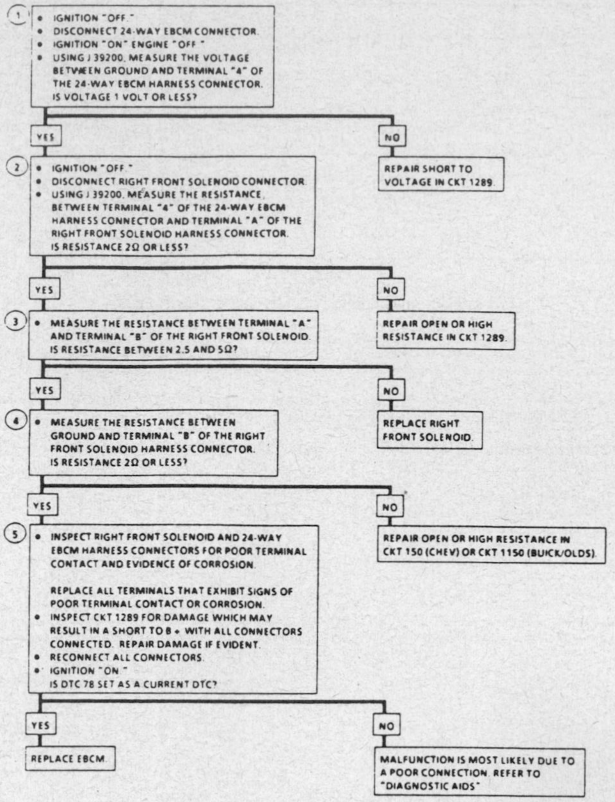
1
• IGNITION "OFF."
• DISCONNECT 24-WAY EBCM CONNECTOR.
• IGNITION "ON" ENGINE "OFF."
• USING J 39200, MEASURE THE VOLTAGE BETWEEN GROUND AND TERMINAL "4" OF THE 24-WAY EBCM HARNESS CONNECTOR.
IS VOLTAGE 1 VOLT OR LESS?
YES
NO
REPAIR SHORT TO VOLTAGE IN CKT 1289.
2
• IGNITION "OFF."
• DISCONNECT RIGHT FRONT SOLENOID CONNECTOR.
• USING J 39200, MEASURE THE RESISTANCE BETWEEN TERMINAL "4" OF THE 24-WAY EBCM HARNESS CONNECTOR AND TERMINAL "A" OF THE RIGHT FRONT SOLENOID HARNESS CONNECTOR.
IS RESISTANCE 2Ω OR LESS?
YES
NO
REPAIR OPEN OR HIGH RESISTANCE IN CKT 1289.
3
• MEASURE THE RESISTANCE BETWEEN TERMINAL "A" AND TERMINAL "B" OF THE RIGHT FRONT SOLENOID.
IS RESISTANCE BETWEEN 2.5 AND 5Ω?
YES
NO
REPLACE RIGHT FRONT SOLENOID.
4
• MEASURE THE RESISTANCE BETWEEN GROUND AND TERMINAL "B" OF THE RIGHT FRONT SOLENOID HARNESS CONNECTOR.
IS RESISTANCE 2Ω OR LESS?
YES
NO
REPAIR OPEN OR HIGH RESISTANCE IN CKT 150 (CHEV) OR CKT 1150 (BUICK/OLDS).
5
• INSPECT RIGHT FRONT SOLENOID AND 24-WAY EBCM HARNESS CONNECTORS FOR POOR TERMINAL CONTACT AND EVIDENCE OF CORROSION.
REPLACE ALL TERMINALS THAT EXHIBIT SIGNS OF POOR TERMINAL CONTACT OR CORROSION.
• INSPECT CKT 1289 FOR DAMAGE WHICH MAY RESULT IN A SHORT TO B+ WITH ALL CONNECTORS CONNECTED. REPAIR DAMAGE IF EVIDENT.
• RECONNECT ALL CONNECTORS.
• IGNITION "ON."
IS DTC 78 SET AS A CURRENT DTC?
YES
NO
REPLACE EBCM.
MALFUNCTION IS MOST LIKELY DUE TO A POOR CONNECTION. REFER TO "DIAGNOSTIC AIDS."

GC402930082600BA

Fig. 203 Code A078: Right Front Solenoid Circuit Open Or Shorted To Battery. 1993 Grand Prix, 1993–94 Cutlass Supreme, Lumina & Regal

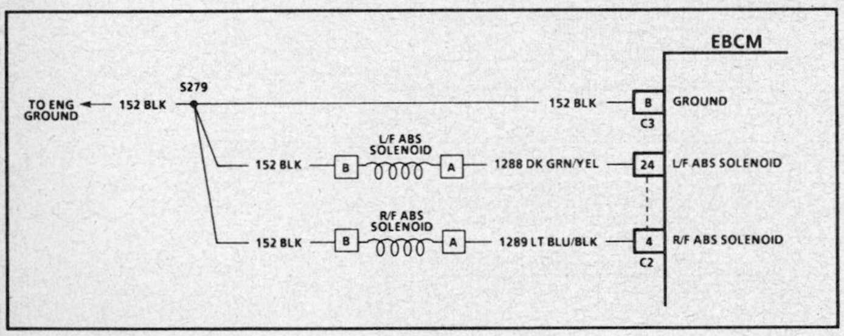
EBCM
S279
TO ENG GROUND
152 BLK
152 BLK
B
C3
GROUND
L/F ABS
SOLENOID
152 BLK
B
A
1288 DK GRN/YEL
24
L/F ABS SOLENOID
R/F ABS
SOLENOID
152 BLK
B
A
1289 LT BLU/BLK
4
C2
R/F ABS SOLENOID

DTC A081

RIGHT FRONT SOLENOID CIRCUIT SHORTED TO GROUND OR DRIVER OPEN

Circuit Description:

This DTC identifies a solenoid that cannot be energized due to an open in its driver circuitry, or a short to ground between the solenoid driver and the solenoid. These malfunctions can affect ABS operation since the flow of brake fluid to the wheel cylinder cannot be stopped, making ABS operation for that channel impossible.

Failure Condition:

DTC A081 can be set only when the solenoid is commanded "ON." If the EBCM detects the right front solenoid control circuit voltage is out of specification, a malfunction exists.

Action Taken:

A malfunction DTC is stored, ABS is disabled and the ABS indicator lamp is turned "ON."

Test Description: Number(s) below refer to circled number(s) on the diagnostic chart.

1. This step checks for a solenoid that is internally shorted to ground.
2. This step checks for a solenoid that is not within proper resistance values.
3. This step indicates if a short to ground exists in the solenoid control circuitry.
4. This checks for an open control circuit to the EBCM.

Diagnostic Aids:

An "Intermittent" malfunction may be caused by a poor connection, rubbed through wire insulation, or a wire that is broken inside the insulation.

The frequency of the malfunction can be checked by using the enhanced diagnostic function of the Tech 1.

Any circuitry, that is suspected as causing the intermittent complaint, should be thoroughly checked for backed out terminals, improper mating, broken locks, improperly formed or damaged terminals, poor terminal to wiring connections or physical damage to the wiring harness.

GC402930082700AX

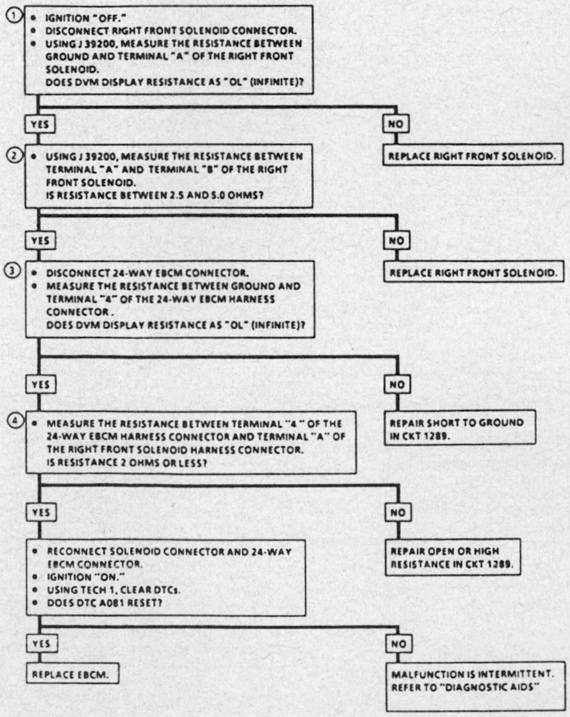
1
• IGNITION "OFF."
• DISCONNECT RIGHT FRONT SOLENOID CONNECTOR.
• USING J 39200, MEASURE THE RESISTANCE BETWEEN GROUND AND TERMINAL "A" OF THE RIGHT FRONT SOLENOID.
DOES DVM DISPLAY RESISTANCE AS "OL" (INFINITE)?
YES
NO
REPLACE RIGHT FRONT SOLENOID.
2
• USING J 39200, MEASURE THE RESISTANCE BETWEEN TERMINAL "A" AND TERMINAL "B" OF THE RIGHT FRONT SOLENOID.
IS RESISTANCE BETWEEN 2.5 AND 5.0 OHMS?
YES
NO
REPLACE RIGHT FRONT SOLENOID.
3
• DISCONNECT 24-WAY EBCM CONNECTOR.
• MEASURE THE RESISTANCE BETWEEN GROUND AND TERMINAL "4" OF THE 24-WAY EBCM HARNESS CONNECTOR.
DOES DVM DISPLAY RESISTANCE AS "OL" (INFINITE)?
YES
NO
REPAIR SHORT TO GROUND IN CKT 1289.
4
• MEASURE THE RESISTANCE BETWEEN TERMINAL "4" OF THE 24-WAY EBCM HARNESS CONNECTOR AND TERMINAL "A" OF THE RIGHT FRONT SOLENOID HARNESS CONNECTOR.
IS RESISTANCE 2 OHMS OR LESS?
YES
NO
REPAIR OPEN OR HIGH RESISTANCE IN CKT 1289.
• RECONNECT SOLENOID CONNECTOR AND 24-WAY EBCM CONNECTOR.
• IGNITION "ON."
• USING TECH 1, CLEAR DTCs.
• DOES DTC A081 RESET?
YES
NO
REPLACE EBCM.
MALFUNCTION IS INTERMITTENT. REFER TO "DIAGNOSTIC AIDS."

GC402930082700BX

Fig. 204 Code A081: Right Front Solenoid Circuit Open Or Shorted To Ground Or Driver Open. 1993–94 Cavalier, Sunbird, Beretta, Corsica & Achieva, Grand Am & Skylark Less VES

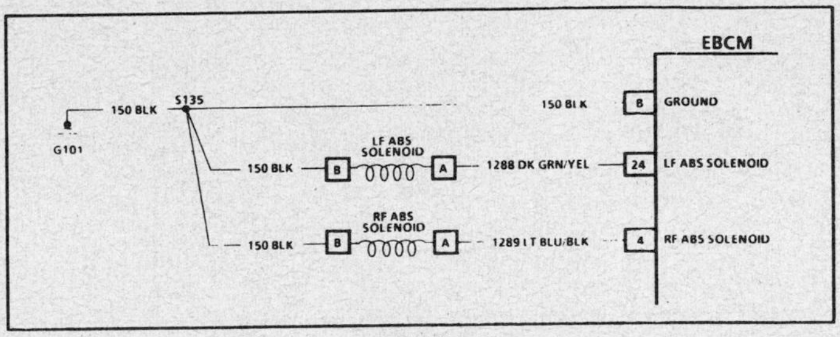
EBCM
150 BLK
S135
G101
150 BLK
8
GROUND
LF ABS SOLENOID
150 BLK
B
A
1288 DK GRN/YEL
24
LF ABS SOLENOID
RF ABS SOLENOID
150 BLK
B
A
1289 LT BLU/BLK
4
RF ABS SOLENOID

DTC 81

RIGHT FRONT SOLENOID CIRCUIT SHORTED TO GND

Circuit Description:

This DTC identifies a solenoid that cannot be energized due to an open in its driver circuitry, or a short to ground between the solenoid driver and the solenoid. These malfunctions can affect ABS operation since the flow of brake fluid to the wheel cylinder cannot be stopped, making ABS operation for that channel impossible.

DTC Will Set When: DTC 81 can be set only when the solenoid is commanded "ON." If the EBCM detects the right front solenoid control circuit voltage is out of specification, a malfunction exists.

Action Taken: A malfunction DTC is stored, ABS is disabled and the ABS warning lamp is turned "ON."

DTC Chart Test Description: Number(s) below refer to circled number(s) on the diagnostic chart.

1. Checks for a solenoid that is internally shorted to ground.
2. Checks for a solenoid that is not within proper resistance values.
3. Indicates if a short to ground exists in the solenoid circuitry.
4. Checks for a possible intermittent malfunction in the solenoid circuitry due to poor terminal contact.

Diagnostic Aids: An "Intermittent" malfunction may be caused by a poor connection, rubbed through wire insulation, or a wire that is broken inside the insulation.

The frequency of the malfunction can be checked by using the enhanced diagnostic function of the Tech 1.

Any circuitry, that is suspected as causing the intermittent complaint, should be thoroughly checked for backed out terminals, improper mating, broken locks, improperly formed or damaged terminals, poor terminal to wiring connections or physical damage to the wiring harness.

GC402930082800AA

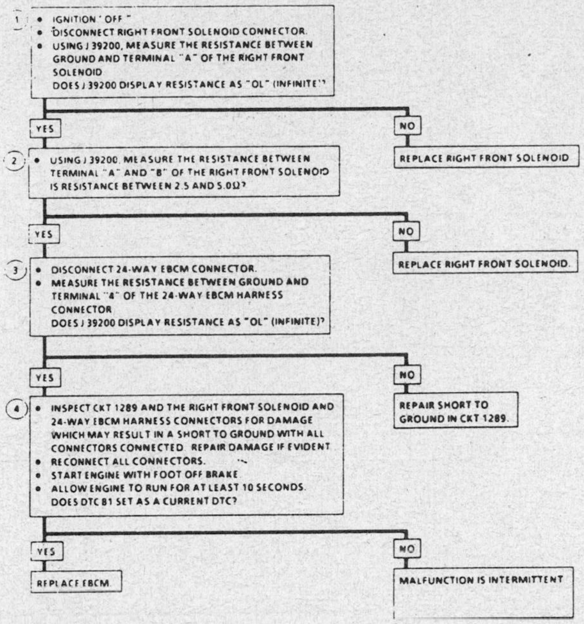
1
• IGNITION "OFF."
• DISCONNECT RIGHT FRONT SOLENOID CONNECTOR.
• USING J 39200, MEASURE THE RESISTANCE BETWEEN GROUND AND TERMINAL "A" OF THE RIGHT FRONT SOLENOID
DOES J 39200 DISPLAY RESISTANCE AS "OL" (INFINITE)?
YES
NO
REPLACE RIGHT FRONT SOLENOID
2
• USING J 39200, MEASURE THE RESISTANCE BETWEEN TERMINAL "A" AND "B" OF THE RIGHT FRONT SOLENOID
IS RESISTANCE BETWEEN 2.5 AND 5.0Ω?
YES
NO
REPLACE RIGHT FRONT SOLENOID.
3
• DISCONNECT 24-WAY EBCM CONNECTOR.
• MEASURE THE RESISTANCE BETWEEN GROUND AND TERMINAL "4" OF THE 24-WAY EBCM HARNESS CONNECTOR
DOES J 39200 DISPLAY RESISTANCE AS "OL" (INFINITE)?
YES
NO
REPAIR SHORT TO GROUND IN CKT 1289.
4
• INSPECT CKT 1289 AND THE RIGHT FRONT SOLENOID AND 24-WAY EBCM HARNESS CONNECTORS FOR DAMAGE WHICH MAY RESULT IN A SHORT TO GROUND WITH ALL CONNECTORS CONNECTED. REPAIR DAMAGE IF EVIDENT
• RECONNECT ALL CONNECTORS.
• START ENGINE WITH FOOT OFF BRAKE.
• ALLOW ENGINE TO RUN FOR AT LEAST 10 SECONDS.
DOES DTC 81 SET AS A CURRENT DTC?
YES
NO
REPLACE EBCM.
MALFUNCTION IS INTERMITTENT

GC402930082800BA

Fig. 205 Code A081: Right Front Solenoid Circuit Open Or Shorted To Ground Or Driver Open. 1993 Grand Prix, 1993–94 Cutlass Supreme, Lumina & Regal

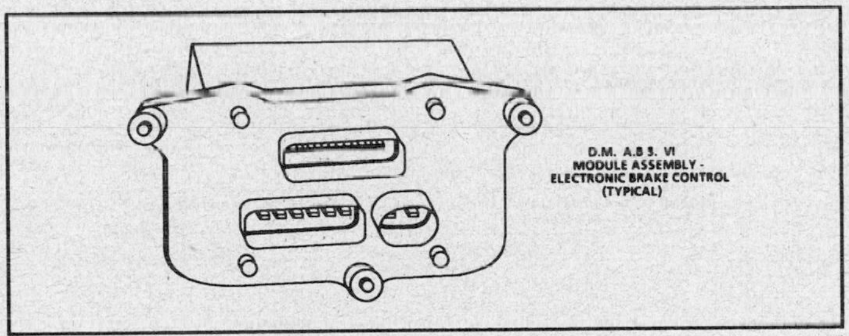
D.M. A.B.S. VI
MODULE ASSEMBLY -
ELECTRONIC BRAKE CONTROL
(TYPICAL)

DTC A082

CALIBRATION MEMORY FAILURE

Circuit Description:

This DTC allows the EBCM to check for a calibration malfunction by comparing the calibration value to a known value stored in the EEPROM.

This DTC is also used as a security measure to prevent improper use of calibrations or changes to these calibrations that may alter the designed function of ABS.

Failure Condition:

DTC A082 can be set at key-up. If the program identifier is incorrect or the memory checksum is incorrect, a malfunction exists.

Action Taken:

A malfunction DTC is stored, ABS is disabled and the ABS indicator lamp is turned "ON."

Test Description: Number(s) below refer to circled number(s) on the diagnostic chart.

1. This step checks to see if the malfunction is present during diagnosis. If present, the EBCM is not functioning correctly and must be replaced.

Important

- At the time of printing, 1993 vehicles with ABS-VI were not being field reprogrammed to correct this failure. A service bulletin will be issued when EEPROM reprogramming is authorized.

Diagnostic Aids:

An intermittent DTC A082 may be caused by a bad cell in the EEPROM that is sensitive to temperature changes. If DTC A082 failed more than once, but is intermittent, replace EBCM.

The frequency of the malfunction can be checked by using the enhanced diagnostic function of the Tech 1.

GC402930082900AX

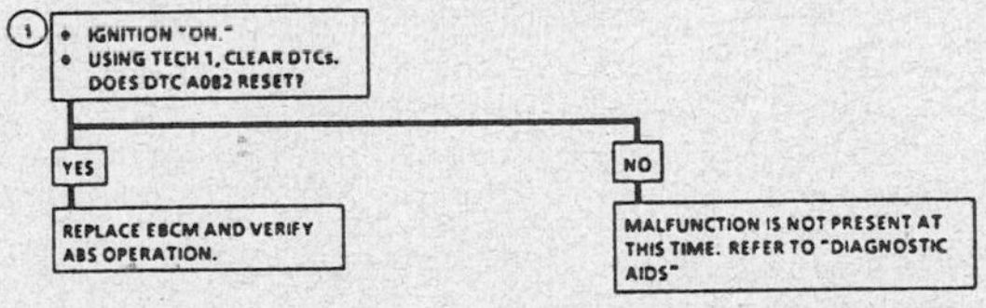
1
• IGNITION "ON."
• USING TECH 1, CLEAR DTCs.
DOES DTC A082 RESET?
YES
NO
REPLACE EBCM AND VERIFY ABS OPERATION.
MALFUNCTION IS NOT PRESENT AT THIS TIME. REFER TO "DIAGNOSTIC AIDS"

GC402930082900BX

Fig. 206 Code A082: Calibration Memory Failure. 1993–94

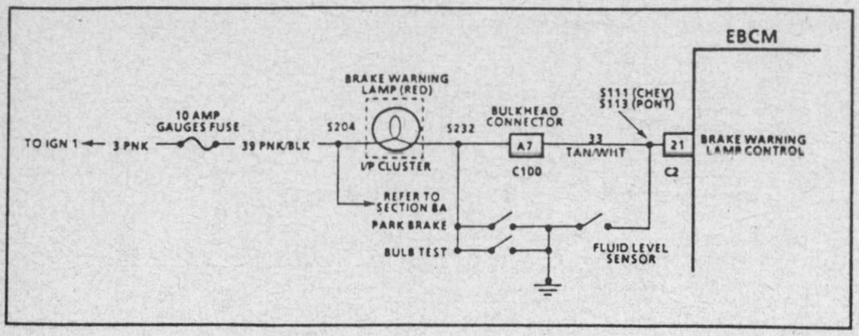
EBCM
BRAKE WARNING LAMP (RED)
10 AMP GAUGES FUSE
S111 (CHEV)
S113 (PONT)
BULKHEAD CONNECTOR
TO IGN 1
3 PNK
39 PNK/BLK
S204
S232
A7
33 TAN/WHT
21
BRAKE WARNING LAMP CONTROL
I/P CLUSTER
C100
C2
REFER TO SECTION 8A
PARK BRAKE
BULB TEST
FLUID LEVEL SENSOR

GC402930083000AX

Cavalier & Sunbird

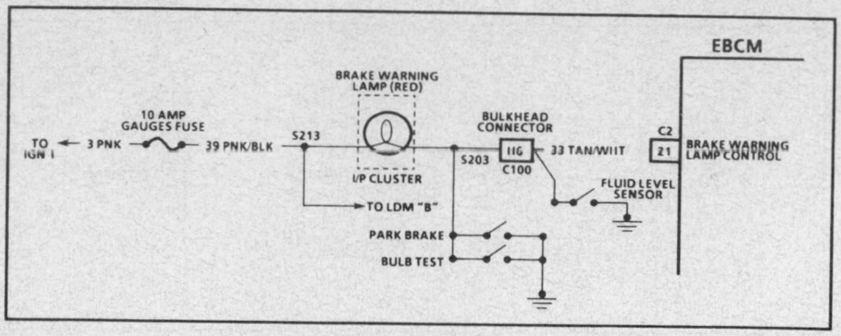
EBCM
BRAKE WARNING LAMP (RED)
10 AMP GAUGES FUSE
BULKHEAD CONNECTOR
TO IGN 1
3 PNK
39 PNK/BLK
S213
S203
I/P CLUSTER
11G
C100
33 TAN/WHT
C2
21
BRAKE WARNING LAMP CONTROL
FLUID LEVEL SENSOR
TO LDM "B"
PARK BRAKE
BULB TEST

GC402930083000BX

Beretta & Corsica

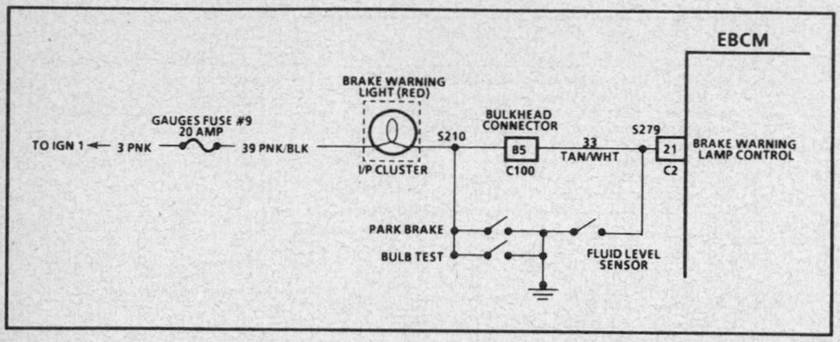
EBCM
BRAKE WARNING LIGHT (RED)
GAUGES FUSE #9 20 AMP
BULKHEAD CONNECTOR
TO IGN 1
3 PNK
39 PNK/BLK
S210
B5
33 TAN/WHT
S279
21
BRAKE WARNING LAMP CONTROL
I/P CLUSTER
C100
C2
PARK BRAKE
BULB TEST
FLUID LEVEL SENSOR

GC402930083000CX

Achieva, Grand Am & Skylark

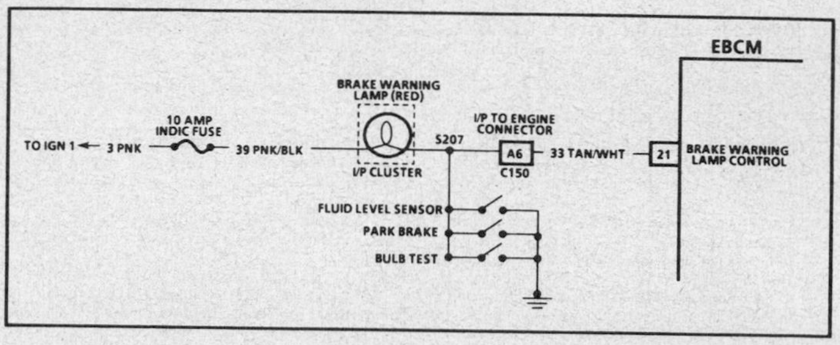
EBCM
BRAKE WARNING LAMP (RED)
10 AMP INDIC FUSE
I/P TO ENGINE CONNECTOR
TO IGN 1
3 PNK
39 PNK/BLK
S207
A6
33 TAN/WHT
21
BRAKE WARNING LAMP CONTROL
I/P CLUSTER
C150
FLUID LEVEL SENSOR
PARK BRAKE
BULB TEST

GC402930083000DX

Cutlass Supreme, Grand Prix, Lumina & Regal

DTC A086

RED BRAKE WARNING LAMP ACTIVATED BY ABS

Circuit Description:

This DTC is provided as an information only test, and reflects the status of the command issued by the ABS EBCM to illuminate the red brake warning lamp. If another diagnostic DTC issues a command to illuminate the red brake warning lamp, DTC A086 will be stored in EEPROM as a history DTC at the conclusion of the ignition cycle.

Test Description: Number(s) below refer to circled number(s) on the diagnostic chart.

1. This step serves to identify if a DTC other than DTC A086 commanded the red brake warning lamp "ON."

Diagnostic Aids:

Any ABS mechanical DTC that issues a command to illuminate the red brake warning lamp will also result in DTC A086 being stored in EEPROM during shut down. These DTCs are: A038, A041, A042, A045, A046, A047, A048 and A051. If the motors are not in their home position, certain electrical DTCs will also command the red brake warning lamp "ON." These DTCs are: A014, A018, A055, A056, A057, A0587, A061, A062, A063, A064, A065, A066, A067, A068, A071 and A072.

If any of these DTCs are indicated along with DTC A086, they must be corrected prior to addressing a DTC A086 malfunction.

GC402930083000EX

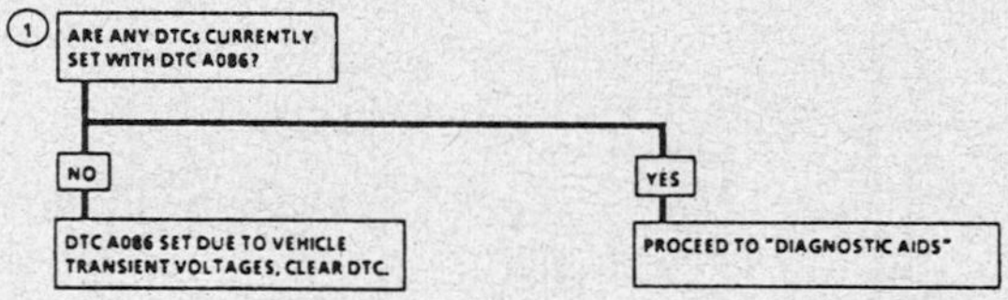
1
ARE ANY DTCs CURRENTLY SET WITH DTC A086?
NO
YES
DTC A086 SET DUE TO VEHICLE TRANSIENT VOLTAGES. CLEAR DTC.
PROCEED TO "DIAGNOSTIC AIDS"

GC402930083000FX

DUMMY00000000001

Fig. 207 Code A086: Red Brake Warning Lamp Activated By ABS. 1993 Cutlass Supreme, Grand Prix, Lumina, Regal & 1993–94 Cavalier, Sunbird, Beretta, Corsica & Achieva, Grand Am & Skylark Less VES

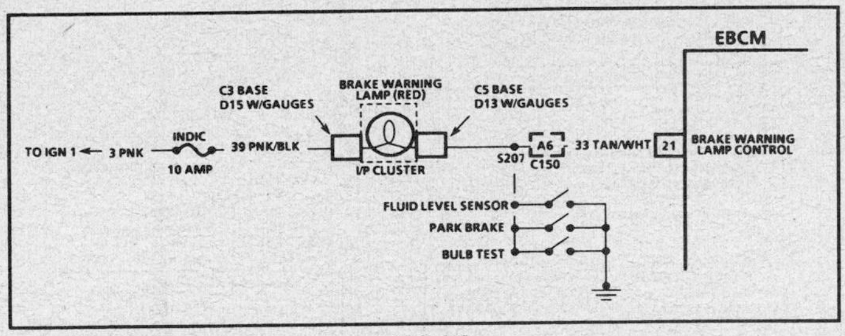
EBCM
C3 BASE
D15 W/GAUGES
BRAKE WARNING LAMP (RED)
C5 BASE
D13 W/GAUGES
TO IGN 1 ← 3 PNK
INDIC
10 AMP
39 PNK/BLK
I/P CLUSTER
S207
A6
C150
33 TAN/WHT
21
BRAKE WARNING LAMP CONTROL
FLUID LEVEL SENSOR
PARK BRAKE
BULB TEST

DTC 86

EBCM TURNED "ON" THE RED "BRAKE" WARNING LAMP

Circuit Description:

This DTC is provided as an information only DTC, and reflects the status of the command issued by the ABS EBCM to illuminate the red "BRAKE" warning lamp. If another DTC issues a command to illuminate the red "BRAKE" warning lamp, DTC 86 will be stored in EEPROM as a history DTC at the conclusion of the ignition cycle.

DTC Chart Test Description: Number(s) below refer to circled number(s) on the diagnostic chart.

1. This step serves to identify if a DTC other than DTC 86 commanded the red "BRAKE" warning lamp "ON."

Diagnostic Aids: Any ABS mechanical DTC that issues a command to illuminate the red "BRAKE" telltale will also result in DTC 86 being stored in EEPROM during shutdown. These DTCs are: 38, 41, 42, 46, and 51. If the motors are not in their home position, certain electrical DTCs will also command the red "BRAKE" telltale "ON." These DTCs are: 14, 16, 18, 55, 56, 57, 58, 61, 62, 63, 64, 65, and 66.

If any of these DTCs are indicated along with DTC 86, they must be corrected prior to addressing a DTC 86 malfunction.

GC402940094900AX

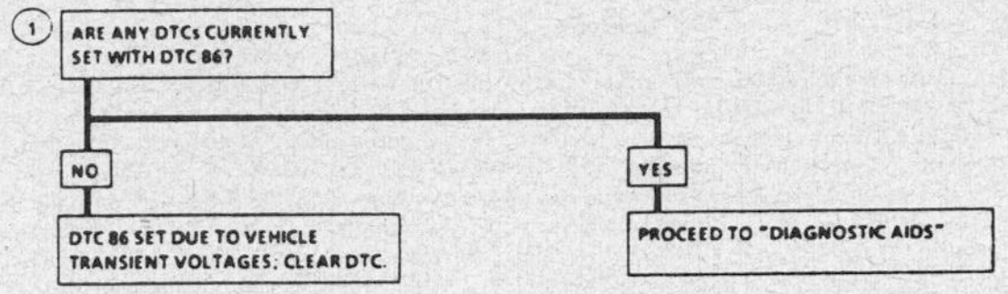
1
ARE ANY DTCs CURRENTLY SET WITH DTC 86?
NO
YES
DTC 86 SET DUE TO VEHICLE TRANSIENT VOLTAGES; CLEAR DTC.
PROCEED TO "DIAGNOSTIC AIDS"

GC402940094900BX

Fig. 208 Code A086: Red Brake Warning Lamp Activated By ABS. 1994 Cutlass Supreme, Lumina & Regal

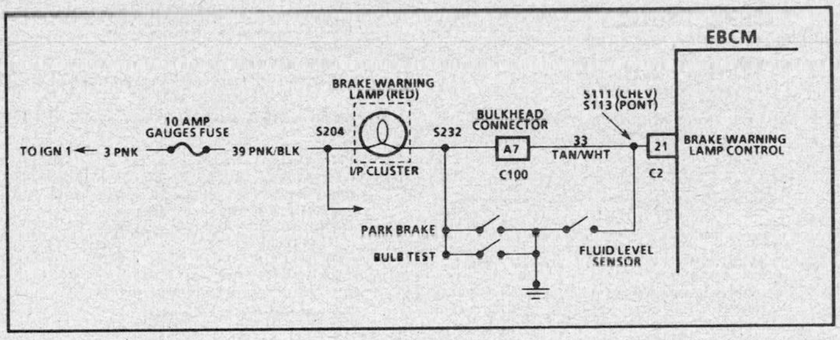
EBCM
BRAKE WARNING LAMP (RED)
10 AMP GAUGES FUSE
S111 (CHEV)
S113 (PONT)
TO IGN 1 ← 3 PNK
39 PNK/BLK
S204
S232
BULKHEAD CONNECTOR
A7
33
TAN/WHT
21
C2
BRAKE WARNING LAMP CONTROL
I/P CLUSTER
C100
PARK BRAKE
BULB TEST
FLUID LEVEL SENSOR

GC402930083100AX

Cavalier & Sunbird

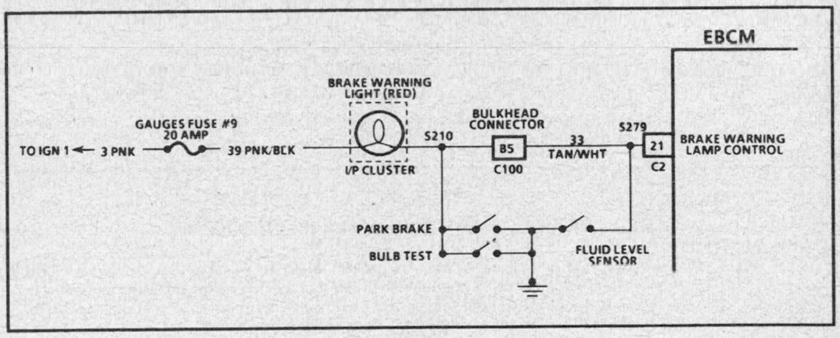
EBCM
BRAKE WARNING LIGHT (RED)
GAUGES FUSE #9 20 AMP
TO IGN 1 ← 3 PNK
39 PNK/BLK
BULKHEAD CONNECTOR
S210
B5
33
TAN/WHT
S279
21
C2
BRAKE WARNING LAMP CONTROL
I/P CLUSTER
C100
PARK BRAKE
BULB TEST
FLUID LEVEL SENSOR

GC402930083100BX

Beretta & Corsica

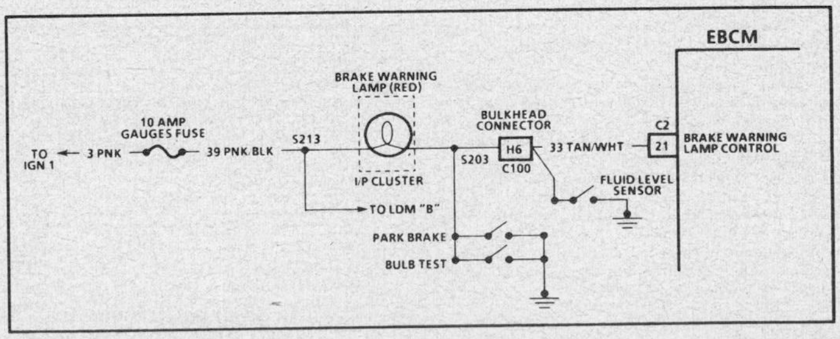
EBCM
BRAKE WARNING LAMP (RED)
10 AMP GAUGES FUSE
TO IGN 1
3 PNK
39 PNK/BLK
S213
BULKHEAD CONNECTOR
S203
H6
C100
33 TAN/WHT
C2
21
BRAKE WARNING LAMP CONTROL
I/P CLUSTER
TO LDM "B"
FLUID LEVEL SENSOR
PARK BRAKE
BULB TEST

GC402930083100CX

Achieva, Grand Am & Skylark

Fig. 209 Code A087: Red Brake Warning Lamp Circuit Open (Part 1 of 2). 1993-94 Cavalier, Sunbird, Beretta, Corsica & Achieva, Grand Am & Skylark Less VES

DTC A087

RED BRAKE WARNING LAMP CIRCUIT OPEN

Circuit Description:

This DTC is used to verify the EBCM has continuity to the brake warning lamp in case the EBCM must turn it "ON." This will only occur if an ABS malfunction is detected that may degrade base brake operation.

Because ABS is not the only device controlling the brake warning lamp (parking brake and low fluid sensor may also turn "ON" the lamp) a short to ground in this circuit can not necessarily be detected. Excessive resistance in the fluid level switch or parking brake circuitry may set this DTC.

Failure Condition:

DTC A087 can be set after initialization is completed. If the red brake warning lamp circuit voltage is out of specification indicating an open circuit, a malfunction exists.

Action Taken:

A malfunction DTC is stored. ABS is not disabled; however, the ABS indicator lamp will flash to indicate a malfunction exists.

Test Description: Number(s) below refer to circled number(s) on the diagnostic chart.

1. This step identifies if the malfunction is currently present.
2. This step indicates if the EBCM and circuitry has the ability to complete the ground to the brake warning lamp and illuminate it.
3. The brake warning lamp has current supplied to it through the 10 amp gauge fuse; therefore, this step would indicate if the ignition circuit is complete to the I/P cluster.
4. This step isolates if the open circuit is due to a EBCM malfunction or open circuitry to the brake warning lamp.
5. This step test for high resistance in park brake circuitry.
6. This step identifies if high resistance is present in the fluid level switch circuitry.

Diagnostic Aids:

An "Intermittent" malfunction may be caused by a poor connection, rubbed through wire insulation, or a wire that is broken inside the insulation.

The frequency of the malfunction can be checked by using the enhanced diagnostic function of the Tech 1, as described in "Enhanced Diagnostics," found in this section. If the Tech 1 is not available, the parking brake handle may be lifted to verify proper lamp operation and continuity of CKTs 3 and 39.

Any circuitry, that is suspected as causing the intermittent complaint, should be thoroughly checked for backed out terminals, improper mating, broken locks, improperly formed or damaged terminals, poor terminal to wiring connections or physical damage to the wiring harness.

GC402930083100DX

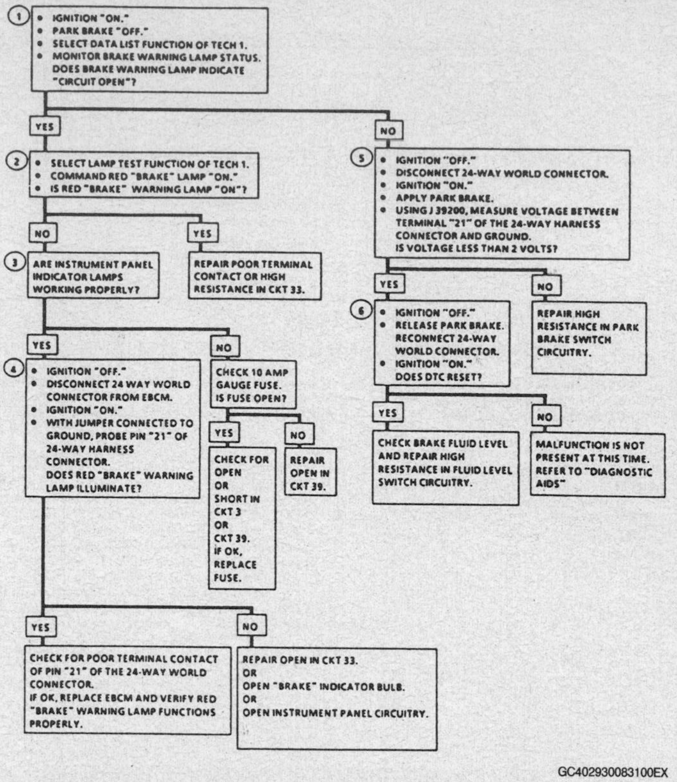
1
IGNITION "ON."
PARK BRAKE "OFF."
SELECT DATA LIST FUNCTION OF TECH 1.
MONITOR BRAKE WARNING LAMP STATUS.
DOES BRAKE WARNING LAMP INDICATE "CIRCUIT OPEN"?
YES
NO
2
SELECT LAMP TEST FUNCTION OF TECH 1.
COMMAND RED "BRAKE" LAMP "ON."
IS RED "BRAKE" WARNING LAMP "ON"?
NO
YES
3
ARE INSTRUMENT PANEL INDICATOR LAMPS WORKING PROPERLY?
REPAIR POOR TERMINAL CONTACT OR HIGH RESISTANCE IN CKT 33.
YES
NO
4
IGNITION "OFF."
DISCONNECT 24 WAY WORLD CONNECTOR FROM EBCM.
IGNITION "ON."
WITH JUMPER CONNECTED TO GROUND, PROBE PIN "21" OF 24-WAY HARNESS CONNECTOR.
DOES RED "BRAKE" WARNING LAMP ILLUMINATE?
CHECK 10 AMP GAUGE FUSE. IS FUSE OPEN?
YES
NO
CHECK FOR OPEN OR SHORT IN CKT 3 OR CKT 39. IF OK, REPLACE FUSE.
REPAIR OPEN IN CKT 39.
YES
NO
CHECK FOR POOR TERMINAL CONTACT OF PIN "21" OF THE 24-WAY WORLD CONNECTOR. IF OK, REPLACE EBCM AND VERIFY RED "BRAKE" WARNING LAMP FUNCTIONS PROPERLY.
REPAIR OPEN IN CKT 33. OR OPEN "BRAKE" INDICATOR BULB. OR OPEN INSTRUMENT PANEL CIRCUITRY.
5
IGNITION "OFF."
DISCONNECT 24-WAY WORLD CONNECTOR.
IGNITION "ON."
APPLY PARK BRAKE.
USING J 39200, MEASURE VOLTAGE BETWEEN TERMINAL "21" OF THE 24-WAY HARNESS CONNECTOR AND GROUND.
IS VOLTAGE LESS THAN 2 VOLTS?
YES
NO
6
IGNITION "OFF."
RELEASE PARK BRAKE. RECONNECT 24-WAY WORLD CONNECTOR.
IGNITION "ON."
DOES DTC RESET?
REPAIR HIGH RESISTANCE IN PARK BRAKE SWITCH CIRCUITRY.
YES
NO
CHECK BRAKE FLUID LEVEL AND REPAIR HIGH RESISTANCE IN FLUID LEVEL SWITCH CIRCUITRY.
MALFUNCTION IS NOT PRESENT AT THIS TIME. REFER TO "DIAGNOSTIC AIDS"
GC402930083100EX

Fig. 209 Code A087: Red Brake Warning Lamp Circuit Open (Part 2 of 2). 1993-94 Cavalier, Sunbird, Beretta, Corsica & Achieva, Grand Am & Skylark Less VES

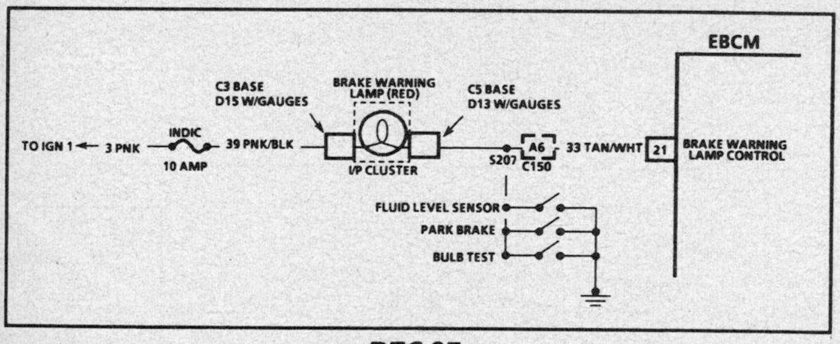
EBCM
C3 BASE D15 W/GAUGES
BRAKE WARNING LAMP (RED)
C5 BASE D13 W/GAUGES
TO IGN 1
3 PNK
INDIC
10 AMP
39 PNK/BLK
I/P CLUSTER
S207
A6
C150
33 TAN/WHT
21
BRAKE WARNING LAMP CONTROL
FLUID LEVEL SENSOR
PARK BRAKE
BULB TEST

DTC 87

RED "BRAKE" WARNING LAMP CIRCUIT OPEN

Circuit Description:

This DTC is used to verify the EBCM has continuity to the red "BRAKE" warning lamp in case the EBCM must turn it "ON." This will only occur if an ABS malfunction is detected that may degrade base brake operation.

Because ABS is not the only device controlling the red "BRAKE" warning lamp (parking brake and low fluid sensor may also turn "ON" the lamp) a short to ground in this circuit cannot be detected.

DTC Will Set When: DTC 87 can be set after initialization is completed. If the red "BRAKE" warning lamp circuit voltage is out of specification indicating an open circuit, a malfunction exists.

Action Taken: A malfunction DTC is stored, ABS is not disabled; however, the ABS warning lamp will flash to indicate a malfunction exists.

DTC Chart Test Description: Number(s) below refer to circled number(s) on the diagnostic chart.

1. Identifies if the ground circuit to the red "BRAKE" warning lamp is completed by a source other than the EBCM.
2. Checks for high resistance in park brake circuitry.
3. Checks for a malfunctioning EBCM.
4. Checks for high resistance in fluid level switch circuitry.
5. Checks for a malfunctioning warning lamp bulb.
6. Checks for open or high resistance in CKT 33.

Diagnostic Aids: An "Intermittent" malfunction may be caused by a poor connection, rubbed through wire insulation, or a wire that is broken inside the insulation.

The frequency of the malfunction can be checked by using the enhanced diagnostic function of the Tech 1

If a Tech 1 or T-100 are not available, the parking brake handle may be lifted to verify proper lamp operation and continuity of CKTs 3 and 39.

Any circuitry, that is suspected as causing the intermittent complaint, should be thoroughly checked for backed out terminals, improper mating, broken locks, improperly formed or damaged terminals, poor terminal to wiring connections or physical damage to the wiring harness.

GC402930083200AA

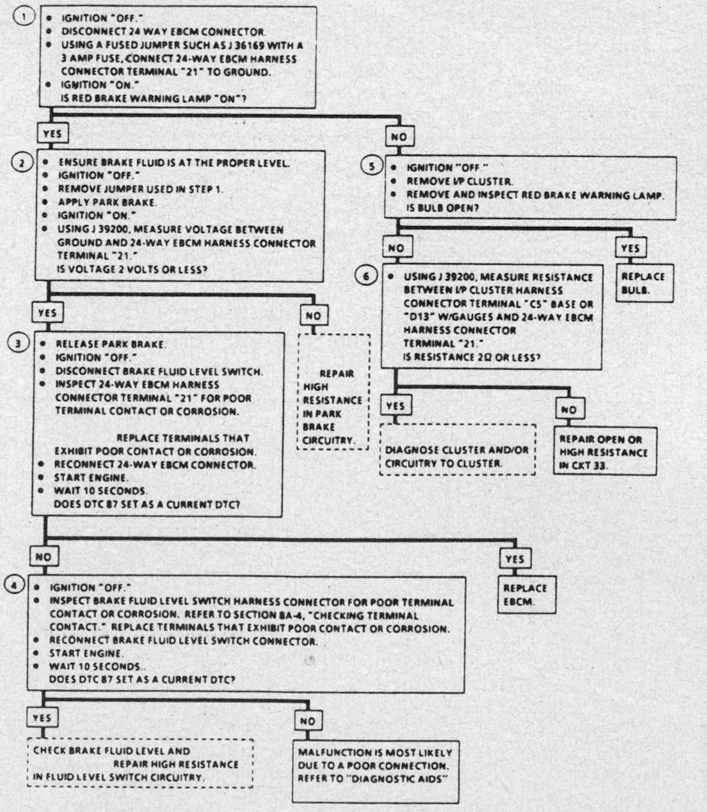
1
IGNITION "OFF."
DISCONNECT 24 WAY EBCM CONNECTOR.
USING A FUSED JUMPER SUCH AS J 36169 WITH A 3 AMP FUSE, CONNECT 24-WAY EBCM HARNESS CONNECTOR TERMINAL "21" TO GROUND.
IGNITION "ON."
IS RED BRAKE WARNING LAMP "ON"?
YES
NO
2
ENSURE BRAKE FLUID IS AT THE PROPER LEVEL.
IGNITION "OFF."
REMOVE JUMPER USED IN STEP 1.
APPLY PARK BRAKE.
IGNITION "ON."
USING J 39200, MEASURE VOLTAGE BETWEEN GROUND AND 24-WAY EBCM HARNESS CONNECTOR TERMINAL "21."
IS VOLTAGE 2 VOLTS OR LESS?
YES
NO
3
RELEASE PARK BRAKE.
IGNITION "OFF."
DISCONNECT BRAKE FLUID LEVEL SWITCH.
INSPECT 24-WAY EBCM HARNESS CONNECTOR TERMINAL "21" FOR POOR TERMINAL CONTACT OR CORROSION.
REPLACE TERMINALS THAT EXHIBIT POOR CONTACT OR CORROSION.
RECONNECT 24-WAY EBCM CONNECTOR.
START ENGINE.
WAIT 10 SECONDS.
DOES DTC 87 SET AS A CURRENT DTC?
REPAIR HIGH RESISTANCE IN PARK BRAKE CIRCUITRY.
NO
YES
4
IGNITION "OFF."
INSPECT BRAKE FLUID LEVEL SWITCH HARNESS CONNECTOR FOR POOR TERMINAL CONTACT OR CORROSION. REFER TO SECTION 8A-4, "CHECKING TERMINAL CONTACT." REPLACE TERMINALS THAT EXHIBIT POOR CONTACT OR CORROSION.
RECONNECT BRAKE FLUID LEVEL SWITCH CONNECTOR.
START ENGINE.
WAIT 10 SECONDS..
DOES DTC 87 SET AS A CURRENT DTC?
REPLACE EBCM.
YES
NO
CHECK BRAKE FLUID LEVEL AND REPAIR HIGH RESISTANCE IN FLUID LEVEL SWITCH CIRCUITRY.
MALFUNCTION IS MOST LIKELY DUE TO A POOR CONNECTION. REFER TO "DIAGNOSTIC AIDS"
5
IGNITION "OFF."
REMOVE I/P CLUSTER.
REMOVE AND INSPECT RED BRAKE WARNING LAMP.
IS BULB OPEN?
NO
YES
6
USING J 39200, MEASURE RESISTANCE BETWEEN I/P CLUSTER HARNESS CONNECTOR TERMINAL "C5" BASE OR "D13" W/GAUGES AND 24-WAY EBCM HARNESS CONNECTOR TERMINAL "21."
IS RESISTANCE 2Ω OR LESS?
REPLACE BULB.
YES
NO
DIAGNOSE CLUSTER AND/OR CIRCUITRY TO CLUSTER.
REPAIR OPEN OR HIGH RESISTANCE IN CKT 33.
GC402930083200BA

Fig. 210 Code A087: Red Brake Warning Lamp Circuit Open. 1993 Grand Prix, 1993–94 Cutlass Supreme, Lumina & Regal

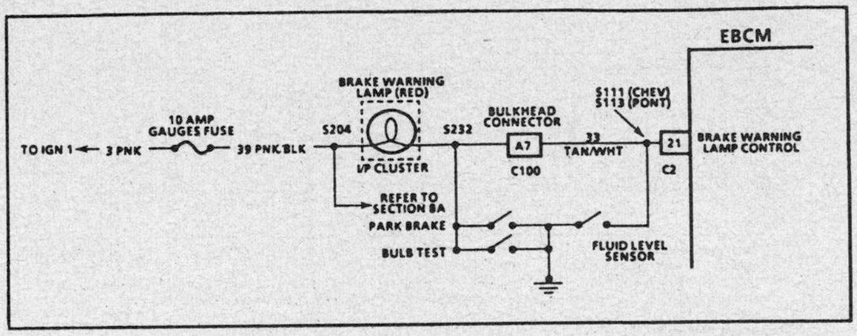
EBCM
BRAKE WARNING LAMP (RED)
10 AMP GAUGES FUSE
S111 (CHEV)
S113 (PONT)
BULKHEAD CONNECTOR
TO IGN 1 3 PNK
39 PNK/BLK
S204
S232
A7
33 TAN/WHT
21
BRAKE WARNING LAMP CONTROL
I/P CLUSTER
C100
C2
REFER TO SECTION 8A
PARK BRAKE
BULB TEST
FLUID LEVEL SENSOR

GC402930083300AX

Cavalier & Sunbird

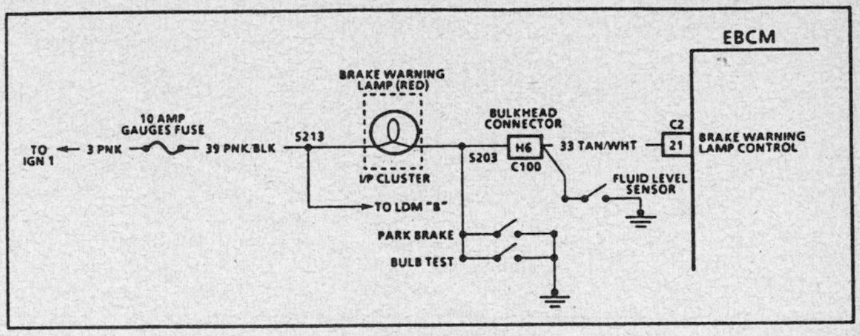
EBCM
BRAKE WARNING LAMP (RED)
10 AMP GAUGES FUSE
BULKHEAD CONNECTOR
TO IGN 1 3 PNK
39 PNK/BLK
S213
H6
33 TAN/WHT
C2
21
BRAKE WARNING LAMP CONTROL
S203
C100
I/P CLUSTER
FLUID LEVEL SENSOR
TO LDM "B"
PARK BRAKE
BULB TEST

GC402930083300BX

Beretta & Corsica

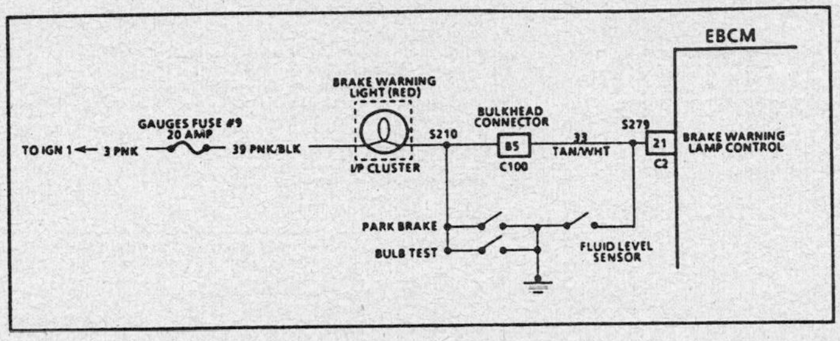
EBCM
BRAKE WARNING LIGHT (RED)
GAUGES FUSE #9 20 AMP
BULKHEAD CONNECTOR
S279
TO IGN 1 3 PNK
39 PNK/BLK
S210
B5
33 TAN/WHT
21
BRAKE WARNING LAMP CONTROL
I/P CLUSTER
C100
C2
PARK BRAKE
BULB TEST
FLUID LEVEL SENSOR

GC402930083300CX

Achieva, Grand Am & Skylark

DTC A088

RED BRAKE WARNING LAMP CIRCUIT SHORTED TO BATTERY

Circuit Description:

This DTC identifies a short to battery between the EBCM and the RED brake warning lamp, or an open driver that does not allow the RED brake warning lamp to be illuminated by the EBCM. This will only occur if an ABS malfunction is detected that may degrade base brake operation.

Failure Condition:

DTC A088 can be set only at the beginning of the three second bulb check. If the EBCM detects battery voltage on the red brake warning lamp control circuit, a malfunction exists.

Action Taken:

A malfunction DTC is stored. ABS is not disabled; however, the ABS indicator lamp will flash to indicate a malfunction exists.

Test Description: Number(s) below refer to circled number(s) on the diagnostic chart.

1. This step identifies if the ground circuit to the red brake warning lamp is being completed by a source other than the EBCM.
2. This step identifies if the malfunction is currently present.
3. By removing the 10 amp gauge fuse, the voltage source is eliminated. This test indicates if voltage is being supplied from a source other than the gauge fuse.

Diagnostic Aids:

An "Intermittent" malfunction may be caused by a poor connection, rubbed through wire insulation, or a wire that is broken inside the insulation.

The frequency of the malfunction can be checked by using the enhanced diagnostic function of the Tech 1

Any circuitry, that is suspected as causing the intermittent complaint, should be thoroughly checked for backed out terminals, improper mating, broken locks, improperly formed or damaged terminals, poor terminal to wiring connections or physical damage to the wiring harness.

GC402930083300DX

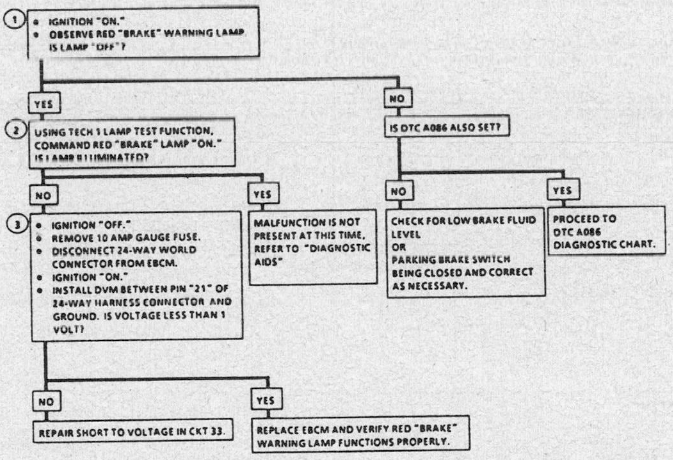
1
IGNITION "ON."
OBSERVE RED "BRAKE" WARNING LAMP
IS LAMP "OFF"?
YES
NO
IS DTC A086 ALSO SET?
2
USING TECH 1 LAMP TEST FUNCTION, COMMAND RED "BRAKE" LAMP "ON." IS LAMP ILLUMINATED?
NO
YES
NO
YES
3
IGNITION "OFF."
REMOVE 10 AMP GAUGE FUSE.
DISCONNECT 24-WAY WORLD CONNECTOR FROM EBCM.
IGNITION "ON."
INSTALL DVM BETWEEN PIN "21" OF 24-WAY HARNESS CONNECTOR AND GROUND. IS VOLTAGE LESS THAN 1 VOLT?
MALFUNCTION IS NOT PRESENT AT THIS TIME. REFER TO "DIAGNOSTIC AIDS"
CHECK FOR LOW BRAKE FLUID LEVEL
OR
PARKING BRAKE SWITCH BEING CLOSED AND CORRECT AS NECESSARY.
PROCEED TO DTC A086 DIAGNOSTIC CHART.
NO
YES
REPAIR SHORT TO VOLTAGE IN CKT 33.
REPLACE EBCM AND VERIFY RED "BRAKE" WARNING LAMP FUNCTIONS PROPERLY.

GC402930083300EX

Fig. 211 Code A088: Red Brake Warning Lamp Circuit Shorted To Battery. 1993–94 Cavalier, Sunbird, Beretta, Corsica & Achieva, Grand Am & Skylark Less VES

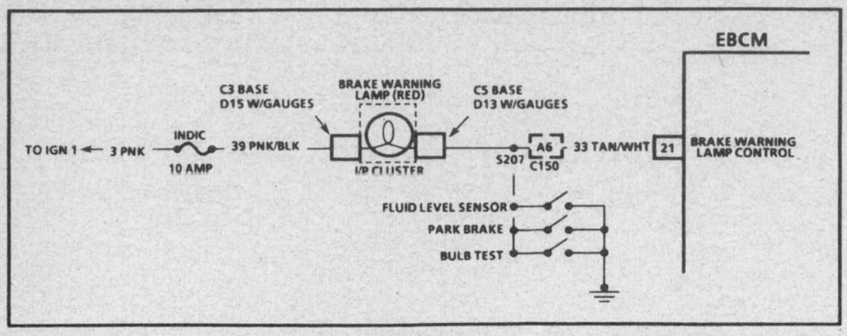
EBCM
C3 BASE
D15 W/GAUGES
BRAKE WARNING
LAMP (RED)
C5 BASE
D13 W/GAUGES
TO IGN 1
3 PNK
INDIC
10 AMP
39 PNK/BLK
I/P CLUSTER
S207
A6
C150
33 TAN/WHT
21
BRAKE WARNING
LAMP CONTROL
FLUID LEVEL SENSOR
PARK BRAKE
BULB TEST

DTC 88

RED "BRAKE" WARNING LAMP CKT SHORTED TO BATT

Circuit Description:

This DTC identifies a short to battery between the EBCM and the red "BRAKE" warning lamp, or an open driver that does not allow the red "BRAKE" warning lamp to be illuminated by the EBCM. This will only occur if an ABS fault is detected that may degrade base brake operation.

DTC Will Set When: DTC 88 can be set only at the beginning of the three second bulb check. If the EBCM detects battery voltage on the red "BRAKE" warning lamp control circuit, a malfunction exists.

Action Taken: A malfunction DTC is stored. ABS is not disabled; however, the ABS warning lamp will flash to indicate a malfunction exists.

DTC Chart Test Description: Number(s) below refer to circled number(s) on the diagnostic chart.

1. Identifies if the ground circuit to the red "BRAKE" warning lamp is being completed by a source other than the EBCM.
2. Identifies if the malfunction is currently present.
3. By removing the 10 amp INDIC fuse, the voltage source is eliminated. This test indicates if voltage is being supplied from a source other than the gauge fuse.
4. Ensures malfunction was not due to physical damage of the circuitry.
5. Checks for DTC 86 also being set.

Diagnostic Aids: An "Intermittent" malfunction may be caused by a poor connection, rubbed through wire insulation, or a wire that is broken inside the insulation.

The frequency of the malfunction can be checked by using the enhanced diagnostic function of the Tech 1.

Any circuitry, that is suspected as causing the intermittent complaint, should be thoroughly checked for backed out terminals, improper mating, broken locks, improperly formed or damaged terminals, poor terminal to wiring connections or physical damage to the wiring harness.

GC402930083400AA

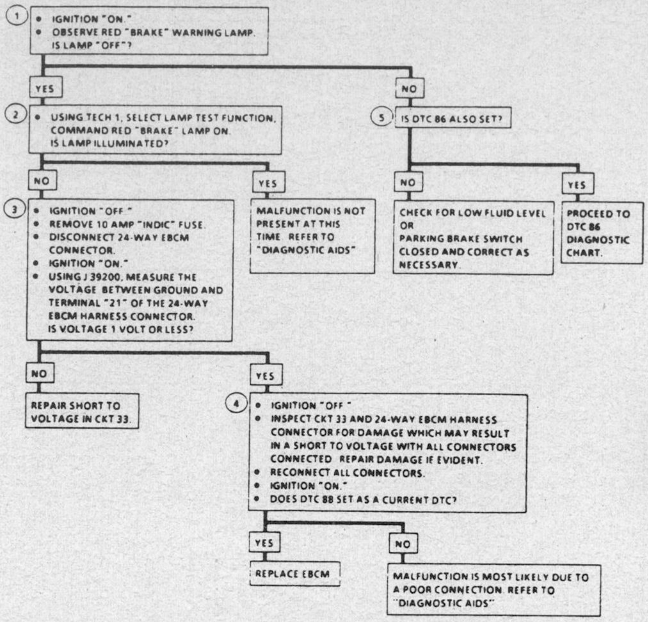
1
IGNITION "ON."
OBSERVE RED "BRAKE" WARNING LAMP. IS LAMP "OFF"?
YES
NO
2
USING TECH 1, SELECT LAMP TEST FUNCTION, COMMAND RED "BRAKE" LAMP ON. IS LAMP ILLUMINATED?
5
IS DTC 86 ALSO SET?
NO
YES
NO
YES
3
IGNITION "OFF."
REMOVE 10 AMP "INDIC" FUSE.
DISCONNECT 24-WAY EBCM CONNECTOR.
IGNITION "ON."
USING J 39200, MEASURE THE VOLTAGE BETWEEN GROUND AND TERMINAL "21" OF THE 24-WAY EBCM HARNESS CONNECTOR. IS VOLTAGE 1 VOLT OR LESS?
MALFUNCTION IS NOT PRESENT AT THIS TIME. REFER TO "DIAGNOSTIC AIDS"
CHECK FOR LOW FLUID LEVEL OR PARKING BRAKE SWITCH CLOSED AND CORRECT AS NECESSARY.
PROCEED TO DTC 86 DIAGNOSTIC CHART.
NO
YES
REPAIR SHORT TO VOLTAGE IN CKT 33.
4
IGNITION "OFF."
INSPECT CKT 33 AND 24-WAY EBCM HARNESS CONNECTOR FOR DAMAGE WHICH MAY RESULT IN A SHORT TO VOLTAGE WITH ALL CONNECTORS CONNECTED. REPAIR DAMAGE IF EVIDENT.
RECONNECT ALL CONNECTORS.
IGNITION "ON."
DOES DTC 88 SET AS A CURRENT DTC?
YES
NO
REPLACE EBCM
MALFUNCTION IS MOST LIKELY DUE TO A POOR CONNECTION. REFER TO "DIAGNOSTIC AIDS"

GC402930083400BA

Fig. 212 Code A088: Red Brake Warning Lamp Circuit Shorted To Battery. 1993 Grand Prix, 1993–94 Cutlass Supreme, Lumina & Regal

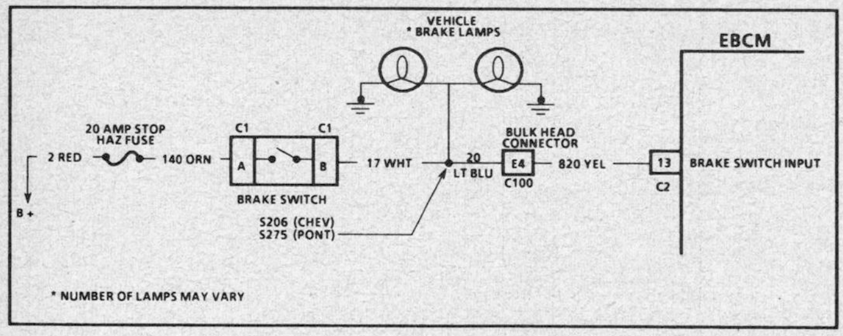
VEHICLE
* BRAKE LAMPS
EBCM
20 AMP STOP
HAZ FUSE
2 RED
140 ORN
C1
A
B
C1
17 WHT
20
LT BLU
BULK HEAD
CONNECTOR
E4
C100
820 YEL
13
C2
BRAKE SWITCH INPUT
B+
BRAKE SWITCH
S206 (CHEV)
S275 (PONT)
* NUMBER OF LAMPS MAY VARY

GC402930083500AX

Cavalier & Sunbird

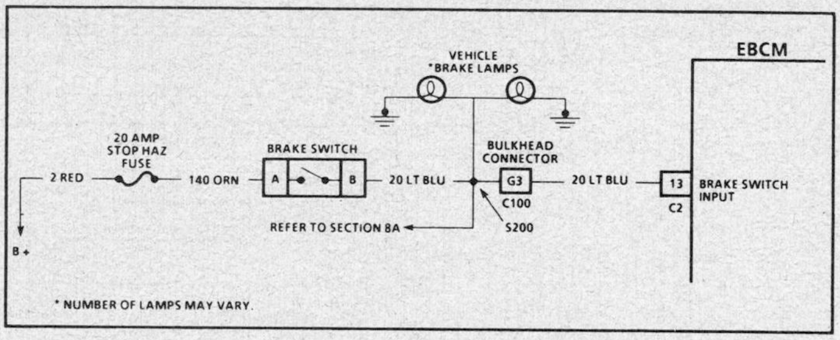
VEHICLE
* BRAKE LAMPS
EBCM
20 AMP
STOP HAZ
FUSE
2 RED
140 ORN
BRAKE SWITCH
A
B
20 LT BLU
BULKHEAD
CONNECTOR
G3
C100
20 LT BLU
13
C2
BRAKE SWITCH
INPUT
B+
REFER TO SECTION 8A
S200
* NUMBER OF LAMPS MAY VARY.

GC402930083500BX

Achieva, Grand Am & Skylark

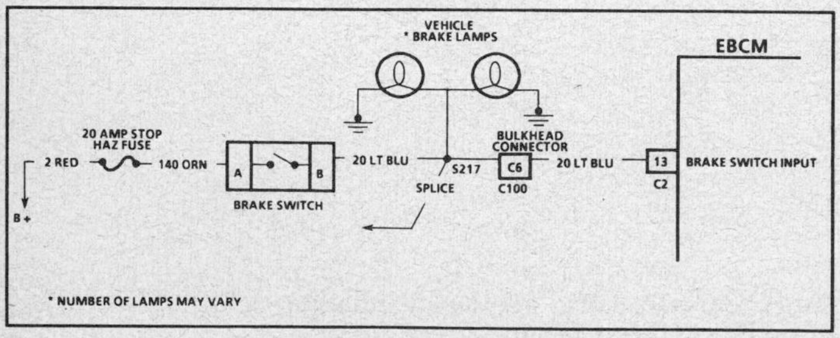
VEHICLE
* BRAKE LAMPS
EBCM
20 AMP STOP
HAZ FUSE
2 RED
140 ORN
A
B
BRAKE SWITCH
20 LT BLU
S217
SPLICE
BULKHEAD
CONNECTOR
C6
C100
20 LT BLU
13
C2
BRAKE SWITCH INPUT
B+
* NUMBER OF LAMPS MAY VARY

GC402930083500CX

Beretta & Corsica

DTC A091

OPEN BRAKE SWITCH CONTACTS DURING DECELERATION

Circuit Description:

This DTC is used to detect an open brake switch in the non-ABS mode. The EBCM looks for decel rates that would indicate braking action and verifies this assumption by requiring several repeats of this detection method. In each case, ABS will not be available since no brake switch is seen.

Failure Condition:

DTC A091 can be set if three deceleration cycles occur with the brake switch "OFF."

Action Taken:

A malfunction DTC is stored, ABS is disabled and the ABS indicator lamp is turned "ON."

Test Description: Number(s) below refer to circled number(s) on the diagnostic chart.

1. This step indicates if the brake switch signal is being received by the EBCM.
2. This step indicates if an open circuit exists in the brake switch or brake lamp circuitry.
3. This step isolates the open circuit to either the brake switch input circuitry, or the EBCM.

Diagnostic Aids:

An "Intermittent" malfunction may be caused by a poor connection, rubbed through wire insulation, or a wire that is broken inside the insulation.

The frequency of the malfunction can be checked by using the enhanced diagnostic function of the Tech 1.

Any circuitry, that is suspected as causing the intermittent complaint, should be thoroughly checked for backed out terminals, improper mating, broken locks, improperly formed or damaged terminals, poor terminal to wiring connections or physical damage to the wiring harness.

GC402930083500DX

Fig. 213 Code A091: Open Brake Switch Contacts During Acceleration (Part 1 of 2. 1993-94 Cavalier, Sunbird, Beretta, Corsica & Achieva, Grand Am & Skylark Less VES

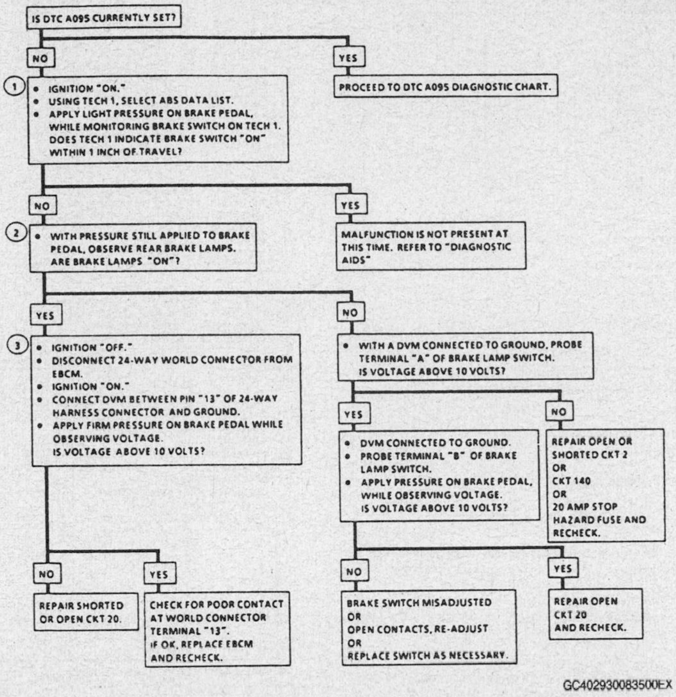
IS DTC A095 CURRENTLY SET?
NO
YES
PROCEED TO DTC A095 DIAGNOSTIC CHART.
1
• IGNITION "ON."
• USING TECH 1, SELECT ABS DATA LIST.
• APPLY LIGHT PRESSURE ON BRAKE PEDAL, WHILE MONITORING BRAKE SWITCH ON TECH 1. DOES TECH 1 INDICATE BRAKE SWITCH "ON" WITHIN 1 INCH OF TRAVEL?
NO
YES
MALFUNCTION IS NOT PRESENT AT THIS TIME. REFER TO "DIAGNOSTIC AIDS"
2
• WITH PRESSURE STILL APPLIED TO BRAKE PEDAL, OBSERVE REAR BRAKE LAMPS. ARE BRAKE LAMPS "ON"?
YES
NO
3
• IGNITION "OFF."
• DISCONNECT 24-WAY WORLD CONNECTOR FROM EBCM.
• IGNITION "ON."
• CONNECT DVM BETWEEN PIN "13" OF 24-WAY HARNESS CONNECTOR AND GROUND.
• APPLY FIRM PRESSURE ON BRAKE PEDAL WHILE OBSERVING VOLTAGE. IS VOLTAGE ABOVE 10 VOLTS?
• WITH A DVM CONNECTED TO GROUND, PROBE TERMINAL "A" OF BRAKE LAMP SWITCH. IS VOLTAGE ABOVE 10 VOLTS?
YES
NO
• DVM CONNECTED TO GROUND.
• PROBE TERMINAL "B" OF BRAKE LAMP SWITCH.
• APPLY PRESSURE ON BRAKE PEDAL, WHILE OBSERVING VOLTAGE. IS VOLTAGE ABOVE 10 VOLTS?
REPAIR OPEN OR SHORTED CKT 2 OR CKT 140 OR 20 AMP STOP HAZARD FUSE AND RECHECK.
NO
YES
REPAIR SHORTED OR OPEN CKT 20.
CHECK FOR POOR CONTACT AT WORLD CONNECTOR TERMINAL "13". IF OK, REPLACE EBCM AND RECHECK.
NO
YES
BRAKE SWITCH MISADJUSTED OR OPEN CONTACTS, RE-ADJUST OR REPLACE SWITCH AS NECESSARY.
REPAIR OPEN CKT 20 AND RECHECK.
GC402930083500EX

Fig. 213 Code A091: Open Brake Switch Contacts During Acceleration (Part 2 of 2. 1993-94 Cavalier, Sunbird, Beretta, Corsica & Achieva, Grand Am & Skylark Less VES

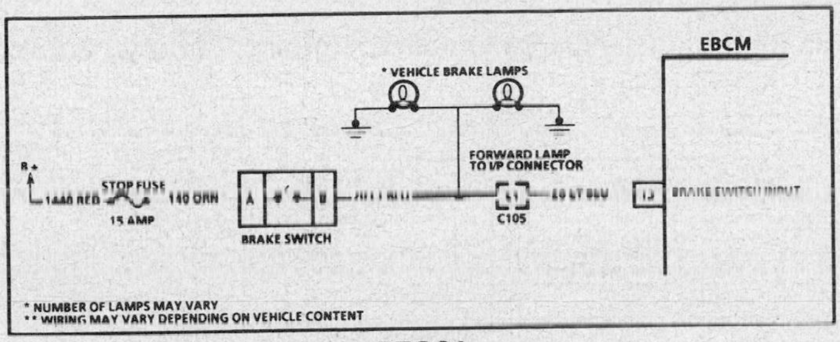
EBCM
* VEHICLE BRAKE LAMPS
B+
STOP FUSE
15 AMP
140 ORN
BRAKE SWITCH
FORWARD LAMP TO I/P CONNECTOR
C105
* NUMBER OF LAMPS MAY VARY
** WIRING MAY VARY DEPENDING ON VEHICLE CONTENT

DTC 91

OPEN BRAKE SWITCH DURING DECELERATION

Circuit Description:

This DTC is used to detect an open brake switch in the non-ABS mode. The EBCM looks for deceleration rates that would indicate braking action and verifies this assumption by requiring several repeats of this detection method. In each case, ABS will not be available since no brake switch is seen.

DTC Will Set When: DTC 91 can be set if three deceleration cycles occur with the brake switch "OFF."

Action Taken: A malfunction DTC is stored, ABS is disabled and the ABS warning lamp is turned "ON."

DTC Chart Test Description: Number(s) below refer to circled number(s) on the diagnostic chart.

1. Indicates if the brake switch signal is being received by the EBCM.
2. Indicates if an open circuit exists in the brake switch or brake lamp circuitry.
3. Isolates the open circuit to either the brake switch input circuitry, or the EBCM.
4. Ensures malfunction was not due to poor terminal contact.
5. Verifies that voltage is available at the brake switch.
6. Verifies that the brake switch is functioning properly.

Diagnostic Aids: An "Intermittent" malfunction may be caused by a poor connection, rubbed through wire insulation, or a wire that is broken inside the insulation.

The frequency of the malfunction can be checked by using the enhanced diagnostic function of the Tech 1

Any circuitry, that is suspected as causing the intermittent complaint, should be thoroughly checked for backed out terminals, improper mating, broken locks, improperly formed or damaged terminals, poor terminal to wiring connections or physical damage to the wiring harness.

GC402930083600AA

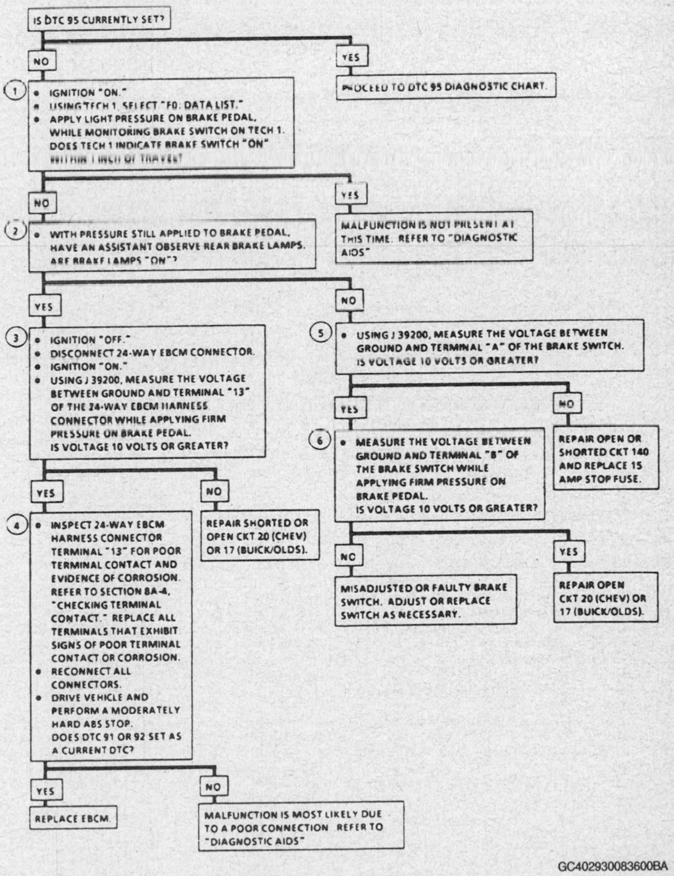
IS DTC 95 CURRENTLY SET?
NO
YES
PROCEED TO DTC 95 DIAGNOSTIC CHART.
1
• IGNITION "ON."
• USING TECH 1, SELECT "F0: DATA LIST."
• APPLY LIGHT PRESSURE ON BRAKE PEDAL, WHILE MONITORING BRAKE SWITCH ON TECH 1. DOES TECH 1 INDICATE BRAKE SWITCH "ON"
NO
YES
MALFUNCTION IS NOT PRESENT AT THIS TIME. REFER TO "DIAGNOSTIC AIDS"
2
• WITH PRESSURE STILL APPLIED TO BRAKE PEDAL, HAVE AN ASSISTANT OBSERVE REAR BRAKE LAMPS. ARE BRAKE LAMPS "ON"?
YES
NO
3
• IGNITION "OFF."
• DISCONNECT 24-WAY EBCM CONNECTOR.
• IGNITION "ON."
• USING J 39200, MEASURE THE VOLTAGE BETWEEN GROUND AND TERMINAL "13" OF THE 24-WAY EBCM HARNESS CONNECTOR WHILE APPLYING FIRM PRESSURE ON BRAKE PEDAL. IS VOLTAGE 10 VOLTS OR GREATER?
5
• USING J 39200, MEASURE THE VOLTAGE BETWEEN GROUND AND TERMINAL "A" OF THE BRAKE SWITCH. IS VOLTAGE 10 VOLTS OR GREATER?
YES
NO
6
• MEASURE THE VOLTAGE BETWEEN GROUND AND TERMINAL "B" OF THE BRAKE SWITCH WHILE APPLYING FIRM PRESSURE ON BRAKE PEDAL. IS VOLTAGE 10 VOLTS OR GREATER?
REPAIR OPEN OR SHORTED CKT 140 AND REPLACE 15 AMP STOP FUSE.
YES
NO
REPAIR SHORTED OR OPEN CKT 20 (CHEV) OR 17 (BUICK/OLDS).
4
• INSPECT 24-WAY EBCM HARNESS CONNECTOR TERMINAL "13" FOR POOR TERMINAL CONTACT AND EVIDENCE OF CORROSION. REFER TO SECTION 8A-4, "CHECKING TERMINAL CONTACT." REPLACE ALL TERMINALS THAT EXHIBIT SIGNS OF POOR TERMINAL CONTACT OR CORROSION.
• RECONNECT ALL CONNECTORS.
• DRIVE VEHICLE AND PERFORM A MODERATELY HARD ABS STOP. DOES DTC 91 OR 92 SET AS A CURRENT DTC?
NO
YES
MISADJUSTED OR FAULTY BRAKE SWITCH. ADJUST OR REPLACE SWITCH AS NECESSARY.
REPAIR OPEN CKT 20 (CHEV) OR 17 (BUICK/OLDS).
YES
NO
REPLACE EBCM.
MALFUNCTION IS MOST LIKELY DUE TO A POOR CONNECTION. REFER TO "DIAGNOSTIC AIDS"
GC402930083600BA

Fig. 214 Code A091: Open Brake Switch Contacts During Acceleration. 1993 Grand Prix, 1993–94 Cutlass Supreme, Lumina & Regal

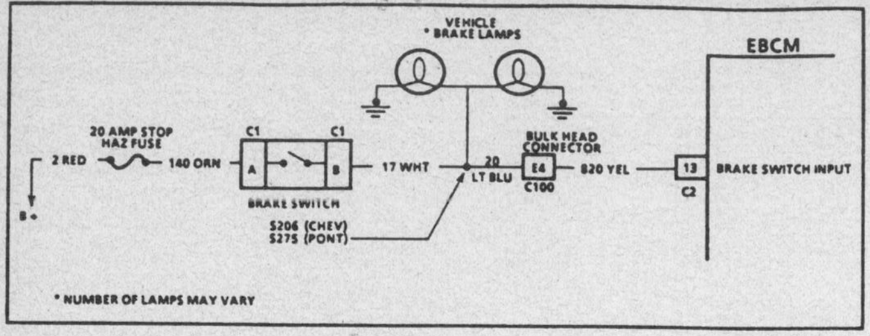
VEHICLE
* BRAKE LAMPS
EBCM
20 AMP STOP HAZ FUSE
2 RED
140 ORN
C1
C1
A
B
BRAKE SWITCH
17 WHT
20 LT BLU
BULK HEAD CONNECTOR
E4
C100
820 YEL
13
C2
BRAKE SWITCH INPUT
B+
S206 (CHEV)
S275 (PONT)
* NUMBER OF LAMPS MAY VARY

GC402930083700AX

DTC A092

OPEN BRAKE SWITCH CONTACTS WHEN ABS WAS REQUIRED

Circuit Description:

This DTC is run to determine the proper operation of the brake switch. This is important because ABS is activated when the brake switch is "ON." If the brake switch is "OFF," ABS will never be activated. Since this malfunction is difficult to detect under normal braking conditions, this malfunction is only detected when ABS is required.

Failure Condition:

DTC A092 can be set if the vehicle's speed is greater than 8 km/h (5 mph). If the brake was not "ON" and a release was required on two channels for .7 seconds, a malfunction exists.

Action Taken:

A malfunction DTC is stored, ABS is disabled and the ABS indicator lamp is turned "ON."

Test Description: Number(s) below refer to circled number(s) on the diagnostic chart.

1. This step indicates if the brake switch signal is being received by the EBCM.
2. This step indicates if an open circuit exists in the brake switch or brake lamp circuitry.
3. This step isolates the open circuit to either the brake switch input circuitry, or the EBCM.

Diagnostic Aids:

An "Intermittent" malfunction may be caused by a poor connection, rubbed through wire insulation, or a wire that is broken inside the insulation.

The frequency of the malfunction can be checked by using the enhanced diagnostic function of the Tech 1

Any circuitry, that is suspected as causing the intermittent complaint, should be thoroughly checked for backed out terminals, improper mating, broken locks, improperly formed or damaged terminals, poor terminal to wiring connections or physical damage to the wiring harness.

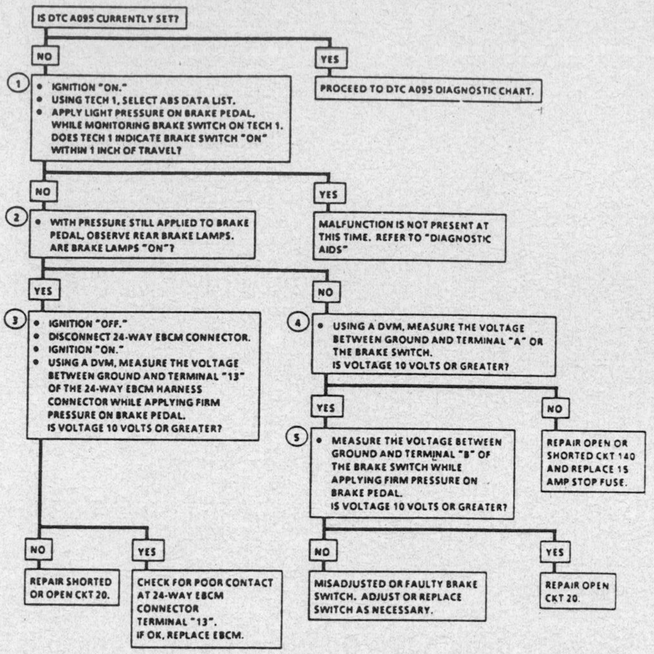
IS DTC A095 CURRENTLY SET?
NO
YES
PROCEED TO DTC A095 DIAGNOSTIC CHART.
1
• IGNITION "ON."
• USING TECH 1, SELECT ABS DATA LIST.
• APPLY LIGHT PRESSURE ON BRAKE PEDAL, WHILE MONITORING BRAKE SWITCH ON TECH 1. DOES TECH 1 INDICATE BRAKE SWITCH "ON" WITHIN 1 INCH OF TRAVEL?
NO
YES
MALFUNCTION IS NOT PRESENT AT THIS TIME. REFER TO "DIAGNOSTIC AIDS"
2
• WITH PRESSURE STILL APPLIED TO BRAKE PEDAL, OBSERVE REAR BRAKE LAMPS. ARE BRAKE LAMPS "ON"?
YES
NO
3
• IGNITION "OFF."
• DISCONNECT 24-WAY EBCM CONNECTOR.
• IGNITION "ON."
• USING A DVM, MEASURE THE VOLTAGE BETWEEN GROUND AND TERMINAL "13" OF THE 24-WAY EBCM HARNESS CONNECTOR WHILE APPLYING FIRM PRESSURE ON BRAKE PEDAL. IS VOLTAGE 10 VOLTS OR GREATER?
4
• USING A DVM, MEASURE THE VOLTAGE BETWEEN GROUND AND TERMINAL "A" OF THE BRAKE SWITCH. IS VOLTAGE 10 VOLTS OR GREATER?
YES
NO
5
• MEASURE THE VOLTAGE BETWEEN GROUND AND TERMINAL "B" OF THE BRAKE SWITCH WHILE APPLYING FIRM PRESSURE ON BRAKE PEDAL. IS VOLTAGE 10 VOLTS OR GREATER?
REPAIR OPEN OR SHORTED CKT 140 AND REPLACE 15 AMP STOP FUSE.
NO
YES
REPAIR SHORTED OR OPEN CKT 20.
CHECK FOR POOR CONTACT AT 24-WAY EBCM CONNECTOR TERMINAL "13". IF OK, REPLACE EBCM.
NO
YES
MISADJUSTED OR FAULTY BRAKE SWITCH. ADJUST OR REPLACE SWITCH AS NECESSARY.
REPAIR OPEN CKT 20.

GC402930083700DX

Fig. 215 Code A092: Open Brake Switch Contacts When ABS Required. 1993–94 Cavalier, Sunbird, Beretta, Corsica & Achieva, Grand Am & Skylark Less VES

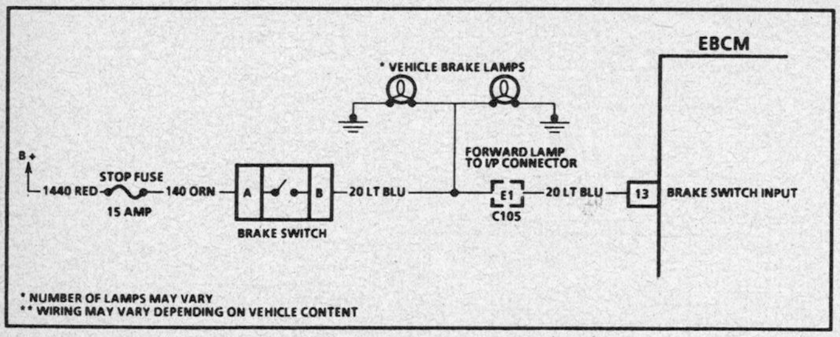
EBCM
* VEHICLE BRAKE LAMPS
B+
STOP FUSE
1440 RED
140 ORN
15 AMP
A
B
BRAKE SWITCH
20 LT BLU
FORWARD LAMP TO I/P CONNECTOR
E1
C105
20 LT BLU
13
BRAKE SWITCH INPUT
* NUMBER OF LAMPS MAY VARY
** WIRING MAY VARY DEPENDING ON VEHICLE CONTENT

DTC 92

OPEN BRAKE SWITCH WHEN ABS WAS REQUIRED

Circuit Description:

This DTC is run to determine the proper operation of the brake switch. This is important because ABS is activated when the brake switch is "ON." If the brake switch is "OFF," ABS will never be activated. Since this malfunction is difficult to detect under normal braking conditions, this malfunction is only detected when ABS is required.

DTC Will Set When: DTC 92 can be set if the vehicle's speed is greater than 8 km/h (5 mph). If the brake was not "ON" and a release was required on two channels for 0.5 second, a malfunction exists.

Action Taken: A malfunction DTC is stored, ABS is disabled and the ABS warning lamp is turned "ON."

DTC Chart Test Description: Number(s) below refer to circled number(s) on the diagnostic chart.

1. Indicates if the brake switch signal is being received by the EBCM.
2. Indicates if an open circuit exists in the brake switch or brake lamp circuitry.
3. Isolates the open circuit to either the brake switch input circuitry, or the EBCM.
4. Ensures malfunction was not due to poor terminal contact.
5. Verifies the voltage is available at the brake switch.
6. Verifies that the brake switch is functioning properly.

Diagnostic Aids: An "Intermittent" malfunction may be caused by a poor connection, rubbed through wire insulation, or a wire that is broken inside the insulation.

The frequency of the malfunction can be checked by using the enhanced diagnostic function of the Tech 1

Any circuitry, that is suspected as causing the intermittent complaint, should be thoroughly checked for backed out terminals, improper mating, broken locks, improperly formed or damaged terminals, poor terminal to wiring connections or physical damage to the wiring harness.

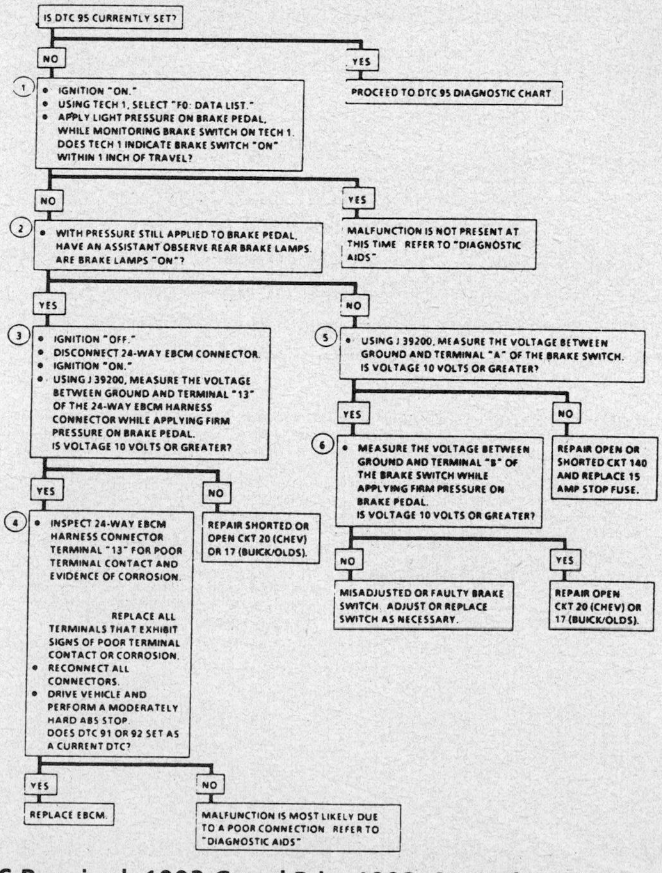
IS DTC 95 CURRENTLY SET?
NO
YES
PROCEED TO DTC 95 DIAGNOSTIC CHART
1
• IGNITION "ON."
• USING TECH 1, SELECT "F0: DATA LIST."
• APPLY LIGHT PRESSURE ON BRAKE PEDAL, WHILE MONITORING BRAKE SWITCH ON TECH 1. DOES TECH 1 INDICATE BRAKE SWITCH "ON" WITHIN 1 INCH OF TRAVEL?
NO
YES
MALFUNCTION IS NOT PRESENT AT THIS TIME. REFER TO "DIAGNOSTIC AIDS"
2
• WITH PRESSURE STILL APPLIED TO BRAKE PEDAL, HAVE AN ASSISTANT OBSERVE REAR BRAKE LAMPS. ARE BRAKE LAMPS "ON"?
YES
NO
3
• IGNITION "OFF."
• DISCONNECT 24-WAY EBCM CONNECTOR.
• IGNITION "ON."
• USING J 39200, MEASURE THE VOLTAGE BETWEEN GROUND AND TERMINAL "13" OF THE 24-WAY EBCM HARNESS CONNECTOR WHILE APPLYING FIRM PRESSURE ON BRAKE PEDAL. IS VOLTAGE 10 VOLTS OR GREATER?
5
• USING J 39200, MEASURE THE VOLTAGE BETWEEN GROUND AND TERMINAL "A" OF THE BRAKE SWITCH. IS VOLTAGE 10 VOLTS OR GREATER?
YES
NO
6
• MEASURE THE VOLTAGE BETWEEN GROUND AND TERMINAL "B" OF THE BRAKE SWITCH WHILE APPLYING FIRM PRESSURE ON BRAKE PEDAL. IS VOLTAGE 10 VOLTS OR GREATER?
REPAIR OPEN OR SHORTED CKT 140 AND REPLACE 15 AMP STOP FUSE.
YES
NO
4
• INSPECT 24-WAY EBCM HARNESS CONNECTOR TERMINAL "13" FOR POOR TERMINAL CONTACT AND EVIDENCE OF CORROSION.
REPLACE ALL TERMINALS THAT EXHIBIT SIGNS OF POOR TERMINAL CONTACT OR CORROSION.
• RECONNECT ALL CONNECTORS.
• DRIVE VEHICLE AND PERFORM A MODERATELY HARD ABS STOP. DOES DTC 91 OR 92 SET AS A CURRENT DTC?
REPAIR SHORTED OR OPEN CKT 20 (CHEV) OR 17 (BUICK/OLDS).
NO
YES
MISADJUSTED OR FAULTY BRAKE SWITCH. ADJUST OR REPLACE SWITCH AS NECESSARY.
REPAIR OPEN CKT 20 (CHEV) OR 17 (BUICK/OLDS).
YES
NO
REPLACE EBCM.
MALFUNCTION IS MOST LIKELY DUE TO A POOR CONNECTION. REFER TO "DIAGNOSTIC AIDS"

GC402930083800AA

Fig. 216 Code A092: Open Brake Switch Contacts When ABS Required. 1993 Grand Prix, 1993–94 Cutlass Supreme, Lumina & Regal

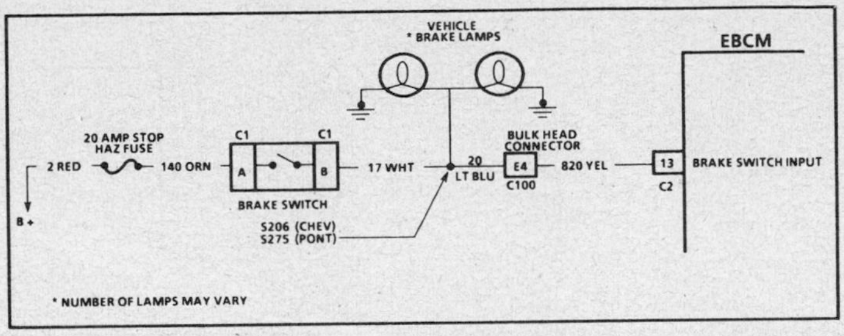

VEHICLE
* BRAKE LAMPS
EBCM
20 AMP STOP
HAZ FUSE
C1
C1
2 RED
140 ORN
A
B
17 WHT
20
LT BLU
BULK HEAD
CONNECTOR
E4
C100
820 YEL
13
C2
BRAKE SWITCH INPUT
B+
BRAKE SWITCH
S206 (CHEV)
S275 (PONT)
* NUMBER OF LAMPS MAY VARY

GC402930083900AX

Cavalier & Sunbird

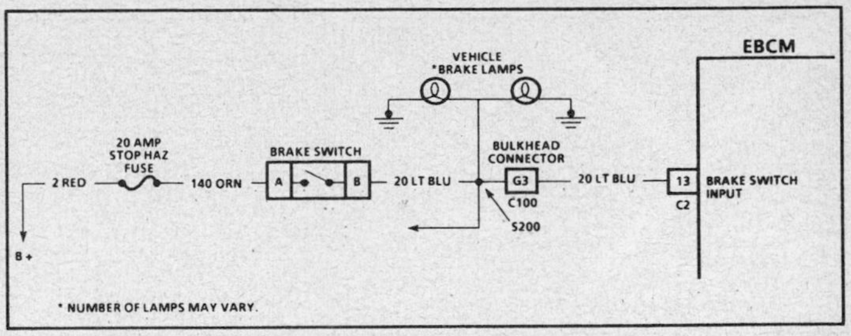

VEHICLE
* BRAKE LAMPS
EBCM
20 AMP
STOP HAZ
FUSE
BRAKE SWITCH
BULKHEAD
CONNECTOR
2 RED
140 ORN
A
B
20 LT BLU
G3
C100
20 LT BLU
13
C2
BRAKE SWITCH
INPUT
S200
B+
* NUMBER OF LAMPS MAY VARY.

GC402930083900BX

Beretta & Corsica

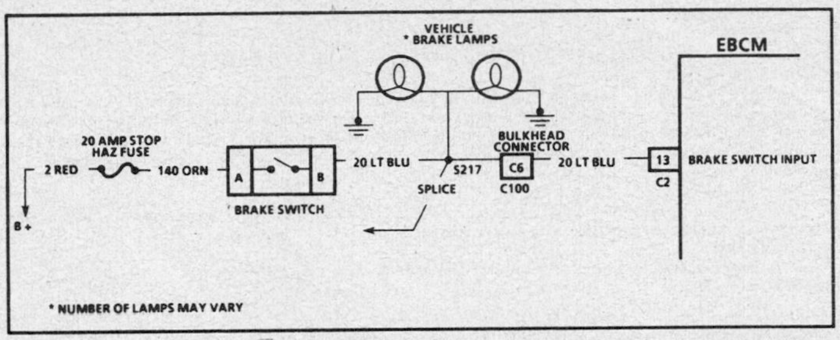

VEHICLE
* BRAKE LAMPS
EBCM
20 AMP STOP
HAZ FUSE
2 RED
140 ORN
A
B
20 LT BLU
S217
SPLICE
BULKHEAD
CONNECTOR
C6
C100
20 LT BLU
13
C2
BRAKE SWITCH INPUT
B+
BRAKE SWITCH
* NUMBER OF LAMPS MAY VARY

GC402930083900CX

Achieva, Grand Am & Skylark

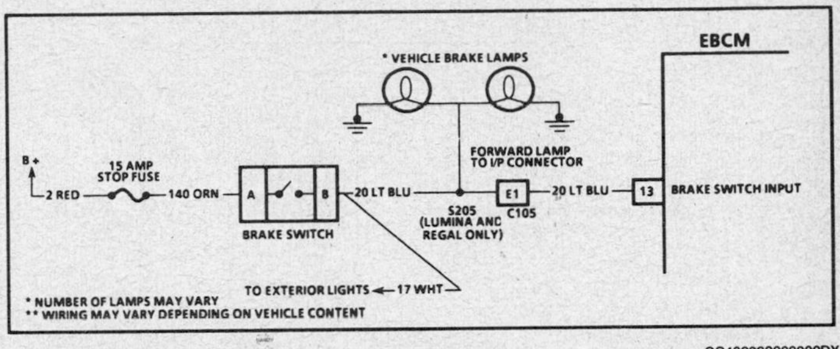

* VEHICLE BRAKE LAMPS
EBCM
B+
15 AMP
STOP FUSE
2 RED
140 ORN
A
B
20 LT BLU
BRAKE SWITCH
FORWARD LAMP
TO I/P CONNECTOR
E1
C105
S205
(LUMINA AND
REGAL ONLY)
20 LT BLU
13
BRAKE SWITCH INPUT
TO EXTERIOR LIGHTS
17 WHT
* NUMBER OF LAMPS MAY VARY
** WIRING MAY VARY DEPENDING ON VEHICLE CONTENT

GC402930083900DX

Cutlass Supreme, Grand Prix, Lumina & Regal

DTC A093

DTCs A091 OR A092 SET IN CURRENT OR PREVIOUS IGNITION CYCLE

Circuit Description:

This DTC is the second portion of DTCs A091 and A092. If DTCs A091 or A092 failed during the last ignition cycle, DTC A093 becomes a current failure during the next ignition cycle, keeping ABS disabled until a brake switch "ON" state is seen. When a change is seen during an ignition cycle in which DTC A093 is a current failure, DTC A091 or A092 will clear itself at the end of the current ignition cycle, and ABS will enable itself at the start of the next ignition cycle. DTC A093 alone indicates DTCs A091 or A092 failed previously, but is intermittent, or has been corrected.

Test Description: Number(s) below refer to circled number(s) on the diagnostic chart.

1. This step indicates which DTC (either A091 or A092) caused DTC A093 to set.
2. This insures that the DTC that set is repaired so that DTC A093 can be cleared.

Diagnostic Aids:

An "Intermittent" malfunction may be caused by a poor connection, rubbed through wire insulation, or a wire that is broken inside the insulation.

The frequency of the malfunction can be checked by using the enhanced diagnostic function of the Tech 1.

Any circuitry, that is suspected as causing the intermittent complaint, should be thoroughly checked for backed out terminals, improper mating, broken locks, improperly formed or damaged terminals, poor terminal to wiring connections or physical damage to the wiring harness.

Also, verify proper brake switch operation using the data list of the Tech 1. As the brake is applied, the data list should display the brake switch "ON" within 1 inch of travel.

GC402930083900EX

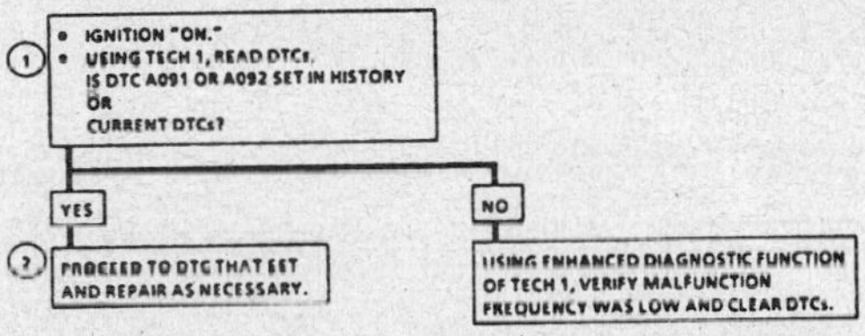

1
• IGNITION "ON."
• USING TECH 1, READ DTCs.
IS DTC A091 OR A092 SET IN HISTORY
OR
CURRENT DTCs?
YES
NO
2
PROCEED TO DTC THAT SET
AND REPAIR AS NECESSARY.
USING ENHANCED DIAGNOSTIC FUNCTION
OF TECH 1, VERIFY MALFUNCTION
FREQUENCY WAS LOW AND CLEAR DTCs.

GC402930083900FX

Fig. 217 Code A093: DTCs A091 Or A092 Set In Current Or Previous Ignition Cycle. 1993 Cutlass Supreme, Grand Prix, Lumina, Regal & 1993–94 Cavalier, Sunbird, Beretta, Corsica & Achieva, Grand Am & Skylark Less VES

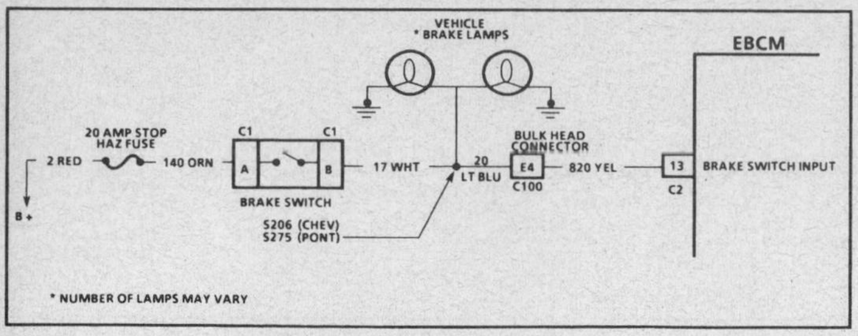
VEHICLE
* BRAKE LAMPS
EBCM
20 AMP STOP HAZ FUSE
2 RED
140 ORN
C1
C1
A
B
BRAKE SWITCH
17 WHT
20 LT BLU
BULK HEAD CONNECTOR
E4
C100
820 YEL
13
C2
BRAKE SWITCH INPUT
S206 (CHEV)
S275 (PONT)
B+
* NUMBER OF LAMPS MAY VARY

GC402930084000AX

Cavalier & Sunbird

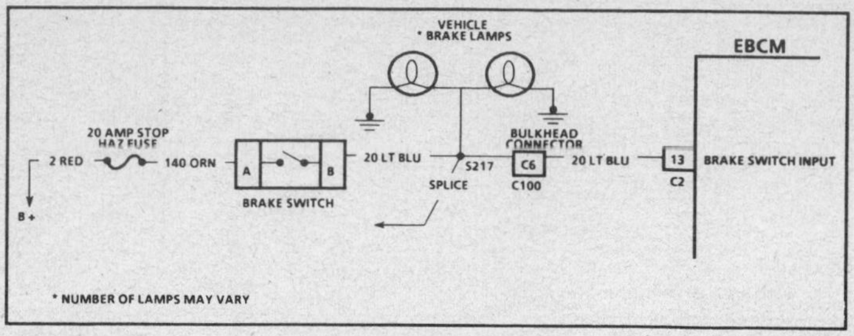
VEHICLE
* BRAKE LAMPS
EBCM
20 AMP STOP HAZ FUSE
2 RED
140 ORN
A
B
BRAKE SWITCH
20 LT BLU
S217
SPLICE
BULKHEAD CONNECTOR
C6
C100
20 LT BLU
13
C2
BRAKE SWITCH INPUT
B+
* NUMBER OF LAMPS MAY VARY

GC402930084000BX

Beretta & Corsica

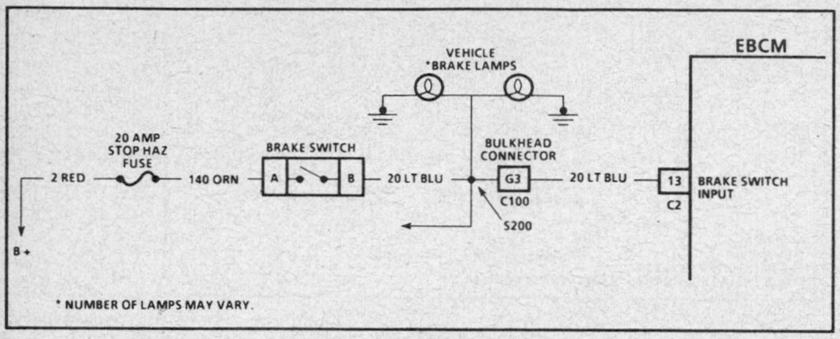
VEHICLE
*BRAKE LAMPS
EBCM
20 AMP STOP HAZ FUSE
BRAKE SWITCH
2 RED
140 ORN
A
B
20 LT BLU
BULKHEAD CONNECTOR
G3
C100
S200
20 LT BLU
13
C2
BRAKE SWITCH INPUT
B+
* NUMBER OF LAMPS MAY VARY.

GC402930084000CX

Achieva, Grand Am & Skylark

DTC A094

BRAKE SWITCH CONTACTS ALWAYS CLOSED

Circuit Description:

This DTC is run to determine the proper operation of the brake switch. This is important because ABS is activated when the brake switch is "ON" and turned "OFF" when the brake is "OFF." If the brake switch is always "ON," ABS operation will always be requested resulting in potential modulator cycling on rough roads. Additionally, this malfunction will most likely result in a dead battery (due to the brake lamps staying "ON") if the driver is not informed of this malfunction.

Failure Condition:

DTC A094 can be set if the vehicle speed reaches at least 40 km/h (25 mph). If the brake was never "OFF" during two consecutive drive cycles, a malfunction exists.

Action Taken:

A malfunction DTC is stored. ABS is not disabled; however, the ABS indicator will flash to indicate a malfunction exists.

Test Description: Number(s) below refer to circled number(s) on the diagnostic chart.

1. This step checks to see if brake lamps are "ON."
2. This step isolates the cause of the malfunction to either a faulty or misadjusted brake switch, or a short to voltage in the brake switch circuitry.
3. This step checks for a resistive short to voltage in the brake switch circuitry.
4. This step ensures malfunction was not due to a poor connection.

Diagnostic Aids:

An "Intermittent" malfunction may be caused by a poor connection, rubbed through wire insulation, or a wire that is broken inside the insulation.

The frequency of the malfunction can be checked by using the enhanced diagnostic function of the Tech 1.

Any circuitry, that is suspected as causing the intermittent complaint, should be thoroughly checked for backed out terminals, improper mating, broken locks, improperly formed or damaged terminals, poor terminal to wiring connections or physical damage to the wiring harness.

GC402930084000DX

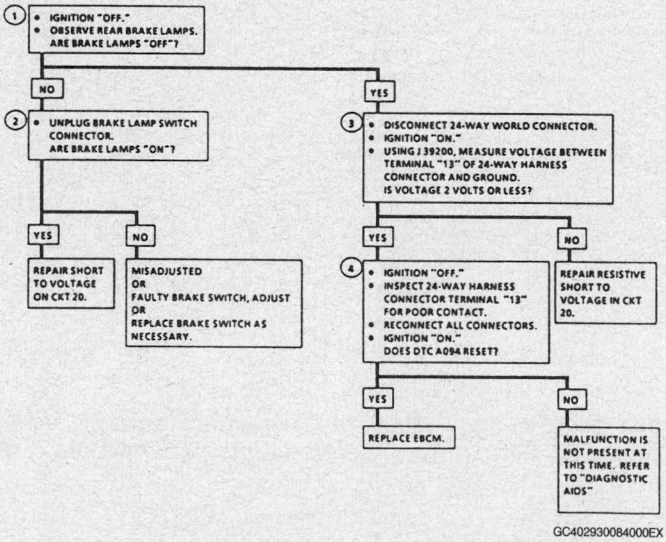
1
• IGNITION "OFF."
• OBSERVE REAR BRAKE LAMPS.
ARE BRAKE LAMPS "OFF"?
NO
YES
2
• UNPLUG BRAKE LAMP SWITCH CONNECTOR.
ARE BRAKE LAMPS "ON"?
3
• DISCONNECT 24-WAY WORLD CONNECTOR.
• IGNITION "ON."
• USING J 39200, MEASURE VOLTAGE BETWEEN TERMINAL "13" OF 24-WAY HARNESS CONNECTOR AND GROUND.
IS VOLTAGE 2 VOLTS OR LESS?
YES
NO
REPAIR SHORT TO VOLTAGE ON CKT 20.
MISADJUSTED OR FAULTY BRAKE SWITCH, ADJUST OR REPLACE BRAKE SWITCH AS NECESSARY.
YES
NO
4
• IGNITION "OFF."
• INSPECT 24-WAY HARNESS CONNECTOR TERMINAL "13" FOR POOR CONTACT.
• RECONNECT ALL CONNECTORS.
• IGNITION "ON."
DOES DTC A094 RESET?
REPAIR RESISTIVE SHORT TO VOLTAGE IN CKT 20.
YES
NO
REPLACE EBCM.
MALFUNCTION IS NOT PRESENT AT THIS TIME. REFER TO "DIAGNOSTIC AIDS"

GC402930084000EX

Fig. 218 Code A094: Brake Switch Contacts Always Closed. 1993–94 Cavalier, Sunbird, Beretta, Corsica & Achieva, Grand Am & Skylark Less VES

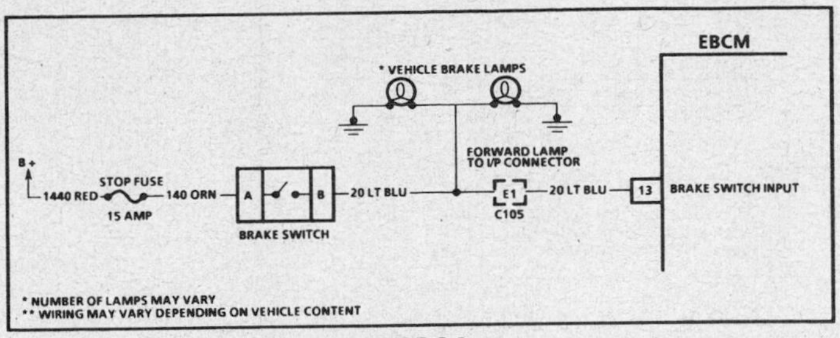
EBCM
* VEHICLE BRAKE LAMPS
FORWARD LAMP TO I/P CONNECTOR
B+
STOP FUSE
1440 RED
140 ORN
15 AMP
BRAKE SWITCH
20 LT BLU
E1
C105
20 LT BLU
13
BRAKE SWITCH INPUT
* NUMBER OF LAMPS MAY VARY
** WIRING MAY VARY DEPENDING ON VEHICLE CONTENT

DTC 94

BRAKE SWITCH CONTACTS ALWAYS CLOSED

Circuit Description:

This DTC is run to determine the proper operation of the brake switch. This is important because ABS is activated when the brake switch is "ON" and turned "OFF" when the brake is "OFF." If the brake switch is always "ON," ABS operation will always be requested resulting in potential modulator cycling on rough roads. Additionally, this malfunction will most likely result in a dead battery (due to the brake lights staying "ON") if the driver is not informed of this malfunction.

DTC Will Set When: DTC 94 can be set when the vehicle reaches at least 40 km/h (25 mph). If the brake was never "OFF" during two consecutive drive cycles, a malfunction exists.

Action Taken: A malfunction DTC is stored. ABS is not disabled; however, the ABS warning will flash to indicate a malfunction exists.

DTC Chart Test Description: Number(s) below refer to circled number(s) on the diagnostic chart.

1. Checks if the malfunction is currently present.
2. Isolates the cause of the malfunction to either a malfunctioning or misadjusted brake switch, or a short to voltage in the brake switch circuitry.
3. Checks for unwanted voltage on the brake switch input circuit.
4. Checks for a possible intermittent malfunction.

Diagnostic Aids: An "Intermittent" malfunction may be caused by a poor connection, rubbed through wire insulation, or a wire that is broken inside the insulation.

The frequency of the malfunction can be checked by using the enhanced diagnostic function of the Tech 1

Any circuitry, that is suspected as causing the intermittent complaint, should be thoroughly checked for backed out terminals, improper mating, broken locks, improperly formed or damaged terminals, poor terminal to wiring connections or physical damage to the wiring harness.

GC402930084100AA

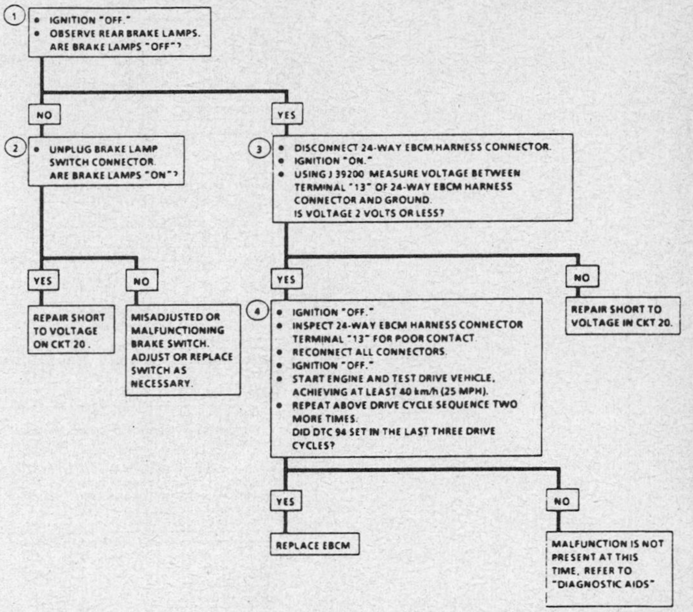
1 • IGNITION "OFF." • OBSERVE REAR BRAKE LAMPS. ARE BRAKE LAMPS "OFF"?
NO
YES
2 • UNPLUG BRAKE LAMP SWITCH CONNECTOR. ARE BRAKE LAMPS "ON"?
3 • DISCONNECT 24-WAY EBCM HARNESS CONNECTOR. • IGNITION "ON." • USING J 39200 MEASURE VOLTAGE BETWEEN TERMINAL "13" OF 24-WAY EBCM HARNESS CONNECTOR AND GROUND. IS VOLTAGE 2 VOLTS OR LESS?
YES
NO
REPAIR SHORT TO VOLTAGE ON CKT 20.
MISADJUSTED OR MALFUNCTIONING BRAKE SWITCH. ADJUST OR REPLACE SWITCH AS NECESSARY.
YES
NO
4 • IGNITION "OFF." • INSPECT 24-WAY EBCM HARNESS CONNECTOR TERMINAL "13" FOR POOR CONTACT. • RECONNECT ALL CONNECTORS. • IGNITION "OFF." • START ENGINE AND TEST DRIVE VEHICLE, ACHIEVING AT LEAST 40 km/h (25 MPH). • REPEAT ABOVE DRIVE CYCLE SEQUENCE TWO MORE TIMES. DID DTC 94 SET IN THE LAST THREE DRIVE CYCLES?
REPAIR SHORT TO VOLTAGE IN CKT 20.
YES
NO
REPLACE EBCM
MALFUNCTION IS NOT PRESENT AT THIS TIME. REFER TO "DIAGNOSTIC AIDS"

GC402930084100BA

DUMMY00000000001

Fig. 219 Code A094: Brake Switch Contacts Always Closed. 1993 Grand Prix, 1993–94 Cutlass Supreme, Lumina & Regal

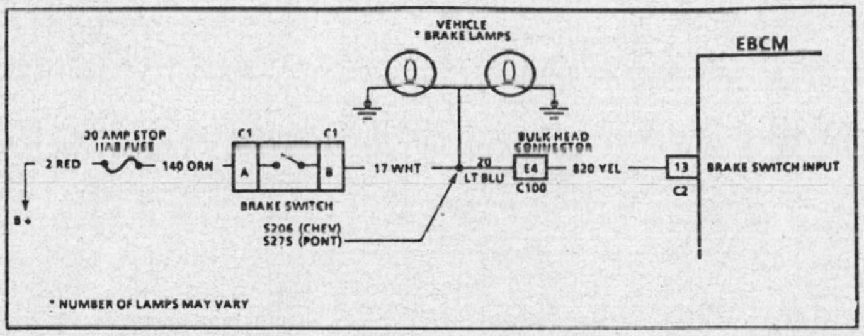
VEHICLE * BRAKE LAMPS
EBCM
20 AMP STOP HAZ FUSE
C1
C1
BULK HEAD CONNECTOR
2 RED
140 ORN
17 WHT
20 LT BLU
E4
820 YEL
13
BRAKE SWITCH INPUT
C100
C2
BRAKE SWITCH
S206 (CHEV)
S275 (PONT)
B+
* NUMBER OF LAMPS MAY VARY

GC402930084200AX

Cavalier & Sunbird

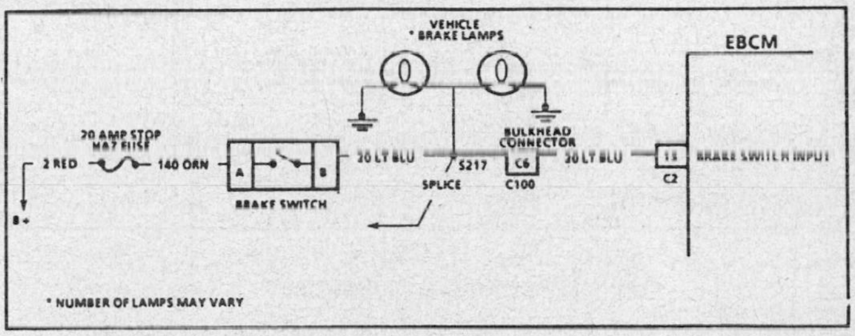
VEHICLE * BRAKE LAMPS
EBCM
20 AMP STOP HAZ FUSE
BULKHEAD CONNECTOR
2 RED
140 ORN
20 LT BLU
S217
C6
20 LT BLU
13
BRAKE SWITCH INPUT
SPLICE
C100
C2
BRAKE SWITCH
B+
* NUMBER OF LAMPS MAY VARY

GC402930084200BX

Beretta & Corsica

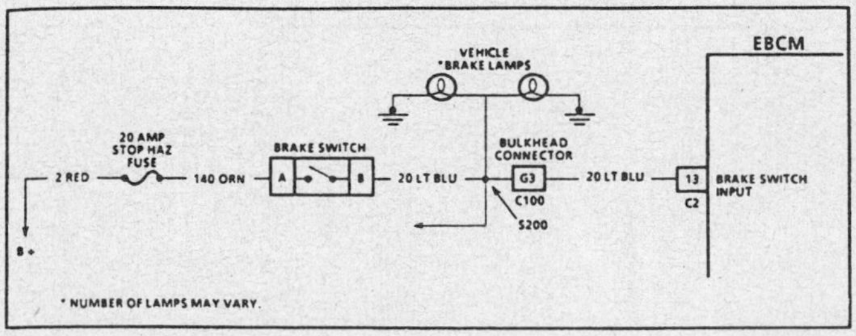
VEHICLE * BRAKE LAMPS
EBCM
20 AMP STOP HAZ FUSE
BRAKE SWITCH
BULKHEAD CONNECTOR
2 RED
140 ORN
20 LT BLU
G3
C100
S200
20 LT BLU
13
C2
BRAKE SWITCH INPUT
B+
* NUMBER OF LAMPS MAY VARY.

GC402930084200CX

Achieva, Grand Am & Skylark

DTC A095

BRAKE SWITCH CIRCUIT OPEN

Circuit Description:

This DTC is used to identify open brake switch circuitry that prevents the brake switch input to the EBCM from changing states when the brake is applied. This DTC is used in conjunction with DTCs A091 and A092 to determine the cause of an open brake switch malfunction.

Failure Condition:

DTC A095 can be set after initialization is completed. If the brake switch input voltage is out of specification for one second indicating an open circuit, a malfunction exists.

Action Taken:

A malfunction DTC is stored, ABS is disabled and the ABS indicator lamp is turned "ON."

Test Description: Number(s) below refer to circled number(s) on the diagnostic chart.

1. This step is used to confirm that an open in the brake switch circuitry currently exists.
2. This step indicates if the brake switch signal is being received by the EBCM.
3. This step indicates if an open circuit exists in the brake switch or brake lamp circuitry.
4. This step isolates the open circuit to either the brake switch input circuitry, or the EBCM.

Diagnostic Aids:

An "Intermittent" malfunction may be caused by a poor connection, rubbed through wire insulation, or a wire that is broken inside the insulation.

The frequency of the malfunction can be checked by using the enhanced diagnostic function of the Tech 1

Any circuitry, that is suspected as causing the intermittent complaint, should be thoroughly checked for backed out terminals, improper mating, broken locks, improperly formed or damaged terminals, poor terminal to wiring connections or physical damage to the wiring harness.

GC402930084200DX

Fig. 220 Code A095: Brake Switch Circuit Open (Part 1 of 2). 1993-94 Cavalier, Sunbird, Beretta, Corsica & Achieva, Grand Am & Skylark Less VES

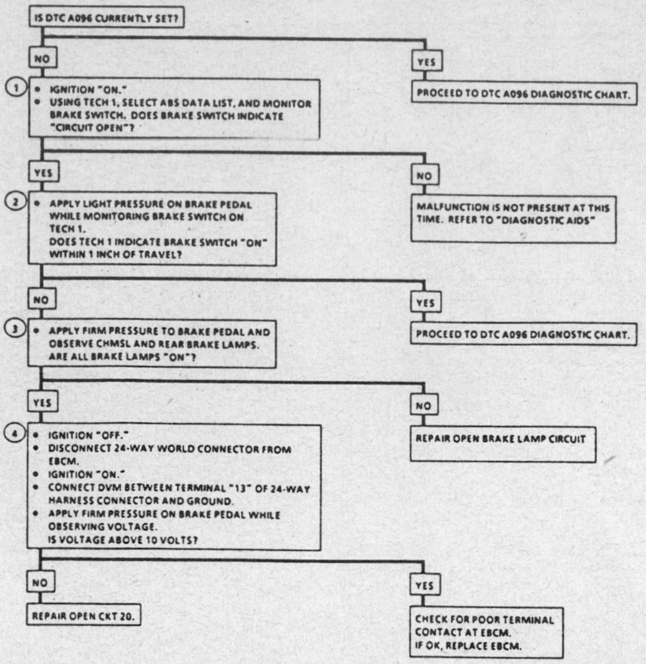
IS DTC A096 CURRENTLY SET?
NO
YES
PROCEED TO DTC A096 DIAGNOSTIC CHART.
1
• IGNITION "ON."
• USING TECH 1, SELECT ABS DATA LIST, AND MONITOR BRAKE SWITCH. DOES BRAKE SWITCH INDICATE "CIRCUIT OPEN"?
YES
NO
MALFUNCTION IS NOT PRESENT AT THIS TIME. REFER TO "DIAGNOSTIC AIDS"
2
• APPLY LIGHT PRESSURE ON BRAKE PEDAL WHILE MONITORING BRAKE SWITCH ON TECH 1.
DOES TECH 1 INDICATE BRAKE SWITCH "ON" WITHIN 1 INCH OF TRAVEL?
NO
YES
PROCEED TO DTC A096 DIAGNOSTIC CHART.
3
• APPLY FIRM PRESSURE TO BRAKE PEDAL AND OBSERVE CHMSL AND REAR BRAKE LAMPS.
ARE ALL BRAKE LAMPS "ON"?
YES
NO
REPAIR OPEN BRAKE LAMP CIRCUIT
4
• IGNITION "OFF."
• DISCONNECT 24-WAY WORLD CONNECTOR FROM EBCM.
• IGNITION "ON."
• CONNECT DVM BETWEEN TERMINAL "13" OF 24-WAY HARNESS CONNECTOR AND GROUND.
• APPLY FIRM PRESSURE ON BRAKE PEDAL WHILE OBSERVING VOLTAGE.
IS VOLTAGE ABOVE 10 VOLTS?
NO
YES
REPAIR OPEN CKT 20.
CHECK FOR POOR TERMINAL CONTACT AT EBCM.
IF OK, REPLACE EBCM.

GC402930084200EX

Fig. 220 Code A095: Brake Switch Circuit Open (Part 2 of 2). 1993-94 Cavalier, Sunbird, Beretta, Corsica & Achieva, Grand Am & Skylark Less VES

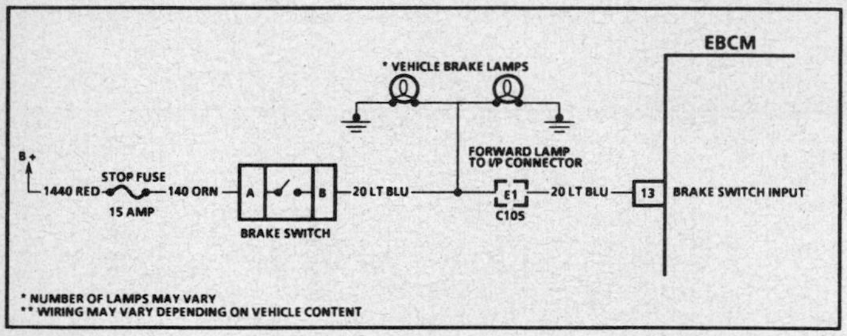
EBCM
* VEHICLE BRAKE LAMPS
B+
STOP FUSE
1440 RED
140 ORN
15 AMP
A
B
BRAKE SWITCH
20 LT BLU
FORWARD LAMP TO I/P CONNECTOR
E1
C105
20 LT BLU
13
BRAKE SWITCH INPUT
* NUMBER OF LAMPS MAY VARY
** WIRING MAY VARY DEPENDING ON VEHICLE CONTENT

DTC 95

BRAKE SWITCH CIRCUIT OPEN

Circuit Description:
This DTC is used to identify open brake switch circuitry that prevents the brake switch input to the EBCM from changing states when the brake is applied. This DTC is used in conjunction with DTCs 91 and 92 to determine the cause of an open brake switch malfunction.

DTC Will Set When: DTC 95 can be set after initialization is completed. If the brake switch input voltage is out of specification for one second indicating an open circuit, a malfunction exists.

Action Taken: A malfunction DTC is stored, ABS is disabled and the ABS warning lamp is turned "ON."

DTC Chart Test Description: Number(s) below refer to circled number(s) on the diagnostic chart.

1. This step is used to confirm that an open in the brake switch circuitry currently exists.
2. Indicates if the brake switch signal is being received by the EBCM.
3. Indicates if an open circuit exists in the brake switch or brake lamp circuitry.
4. Isolates the open circuit to either the brake switch input circuitry, or the EBCM.

Diagnostic Aids: An "Intermittent" malfunction may be caused by a poor connection, rubbed through wire insulation, or a wire that is broken inside the insulation.

The frequency of the malfunction can be checked by using the enhanced diagnostic function of the Tech 1

Any circuitry, that is suspected as causing the intermittent complaint, should be thoroughly checked for backed out terminals, improper mating, broken locks, improperly formed or damaged terminals, poor terminal to wiring connections or physical damage to the wiring harness.

GC402930084300AA

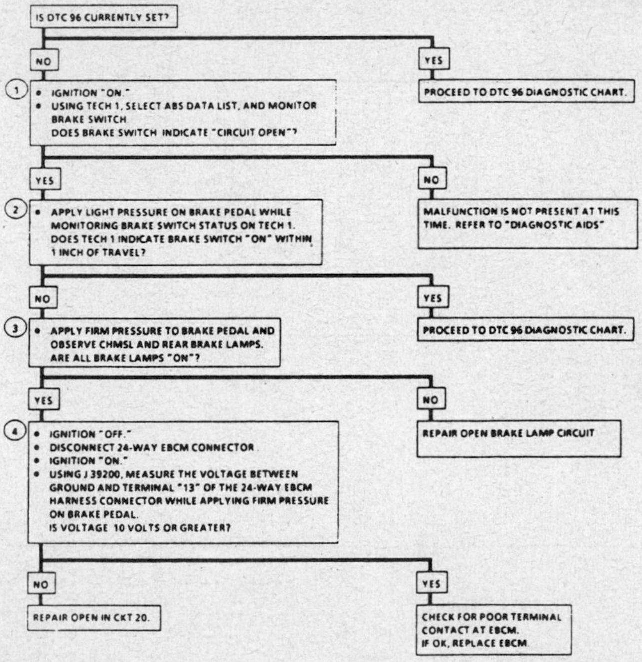
IS DTC 96 CURRENTLY SET?
NO
YES
PROCEED TO DTC 96 DIAGNOSTIC CHART.
1
• IGNITION "ON."
• USING TECH 1, SELECT ABS DATA LIST, AND MONITOR BRAKE SWITCH.
DOES BRAKE SWITCH INDICATE "CIRCUIT OPEN"?
YES
NO
MALFUNCTION IS NOT PRESENT AT THIS TIME. REFER TO "DIAGNOSTIC AIDS"
2
• APPLY LIGHT PRESSURE ON BRAKE PEDAL WHILE MONITORING BRAKE SWITCH STATUS ON TECH 1.
DOES TECH 1 INDICATE BRAKE SWITCH "ON" WITHIN 1 INCH OF TRAVEL?
NO
YES
PROCEED TO DTC 96 DIAGNOSTIC CHART.
3
• APPLY FIRM PRESSURE TO BRAKE PEDAL AND OBSERVE CHMSL AND REAR BRAKE LAMPS.
ARE ALL BRAKE LAMPS "ON"?
YES
NO
REPAIR OPEN BRAKE LAMP CIRCUIT
4
• IGNITION "OFF."
• DISCONNECT 24-WAY EBCM CONNECTOR
• IGNITION "ON."
• USING J 39200, MEASURE THE VOLTAGE BETWEEN GROUND AND TERMINAL "13" OF THE 24-WAY EBCM HARNESS CONNECTOR WHILE APPLYING FIRM PRESSURE ON BRAKE PEDAL.
IS VOLTAGE 10 VOLTS OR GREATER?
NO
YES
REPAIR OPEN IN CKT 20.
CHECK FOR POOR TERMINAL CONTACT AT EBCM.
IF OK, REPLACE EBCM

GC402930084300BA

Fig. 221 Code A095: Brake Switch Circuit Open. 1993 Grand Prix, 1993–94 Cutlass Supreme, Lumina & Regal

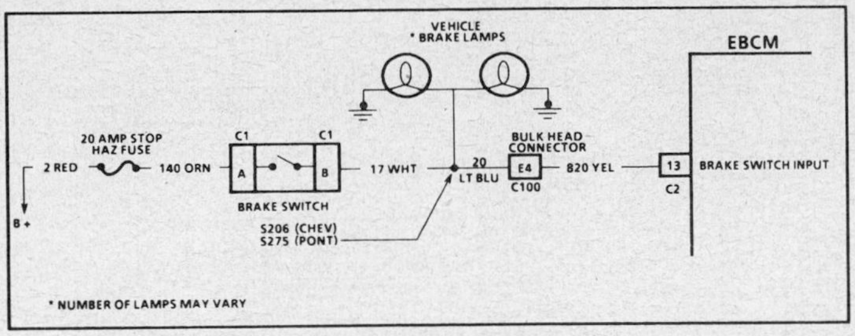
VEHICLE
* BRAKE LAMPS
EBCM
20 AMP STOP
HAZ FUSE
C1
C1
2 RED
140 ORN
A
B
17 WHT
20
LT BLU
BULK HEAD
CONNECTOR
E4
C100
820 YEL
13
C2
BRAKE SWITCH INPUT
BRAKE SWITCH
S206 (CHEV)
S275 (PONT)
B+
* NUMBER OF LAMPS MAY VARY

GC402930084400AX

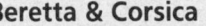

Cavalier & Sunbird

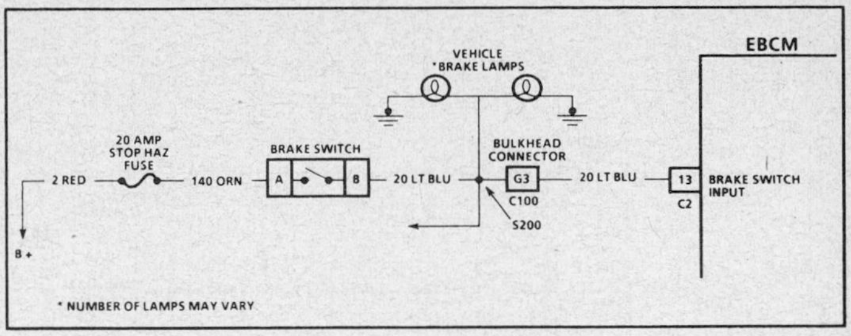
VEHICLE
* BRAKE LAMPS
EBCM
20 AMP
STOP HAZ
FUSE
BRAKE SWITCH
BULKHEAD
CONNECTOR
2 RED
140 ORN
A
B
20 LT BLU
G3
C100
20 LT BLU
13
C2
BRAKE SWITCH
INPUT
S200
B+
* NUMBER OF LAMPS MAY VARY

GC402930084400BX

Beretta & Corsica

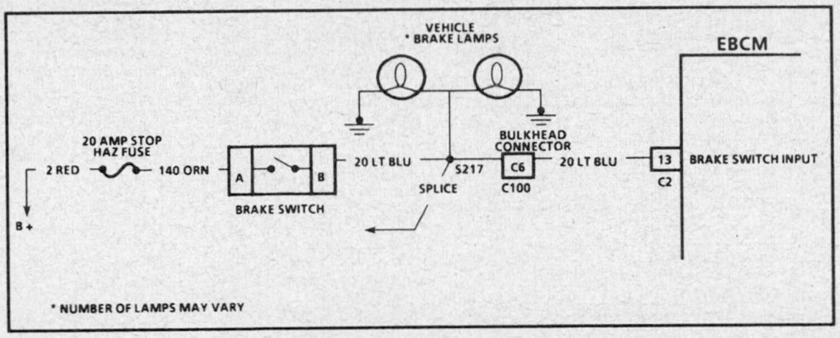
VEHICLE
* BRAKE LAMPS
EBCM
20 AMP STOP
HAZ FUSE
2 RED
140 ORN
A
B
20 LT BLU
S217
SPLICE
BULKHEAD
CONNECTOR
C6
C100
20 LT BLU
13
C2
BRAKE SWITCH INPUT
BRAKE SWITCH
B+
* NUMBER OF LAMPS MAY VARY

GC402930084400CX

Achieva, Grand Am & Skylark

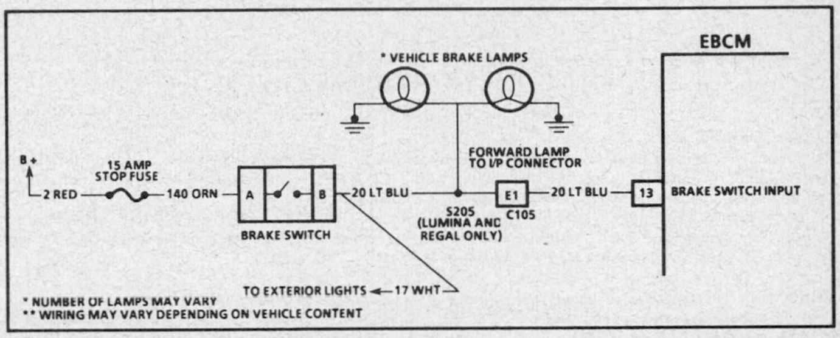
* VEHICLE BRAKE LAMPS
EBCM
B+
15 AMP
STOP FUSE
2 RED
140 ORN
A
B
20 LT BLU
BRAKE SWITCH
FORWARD LAMP
TO I/P CONNECTOR
E1
C105
20 LT BLU
13
BRAKE SWITCH INPUT
S205
(LUMINA AND
REGAL ONLY)
TO EXTERIOR LIGHTS
17 WHT
* NUMBER OF LAMPS MAY VARY
** WIRING MAY VARY DEPENDING ON VEHICLE CONTENT

GC402930084400DX

Cutlass Supreme, Grand Prix, Lumina & Regal

DTC A096

BRAKE LAMPS CIRCUIT OPEN

Circuit Description:

This DTC is designed to isolate the cause of a DTC A095 failure and indicate to the driver ABS is still available. If DTC A095 fails with DTC A096, the brake lamps are open, the brake lamp grounds are open, or the Center High Mounted Stop Lamp (CHMSL) circuit is open during 4 way flasher use. The presence of battery voltage at the brake switch input indicates a valid brake switch input is still available.

Failure Condition:

DTC A096 can be set only after DTC A095 has been set. If the EBCM detects battery voltage on the brake switch input circuit for one second, a malfunction exists.

Action Taken:

A malfunction DTC is stored. ABS is not disabled; however, the ABS indicator lamp will flash indicating a malfunction exists.

Test Description: Number(s) below refer to circled number(s) on the diagnostic chart.

1. As a result of a failure of an additional brake switch circuit DTC, this DTC may be set. To insure proper diagnosis, any additional brake switch DTCs must be repaired first.
2. This step identifies if the malfunction is currently present in the brake circuit.

Diagnostic Aids:

An "Intermittent" malfunction may be caused by a poor connection, rubbed through wire insulation, or a wire that is broken inside the insulation.

The frequency of the malfunction can be checked by using the enhanced diagnostic function of the Tech 1.

Any circuitry, that is suspected as causing the intermittent complaint, should be thoroughly checked for backed out terminals, improper mating, broken locks, improperly formed or damaged terminals, poor terminal to wiring connections or physical damage to the wiring harness.

GC402930084400EX

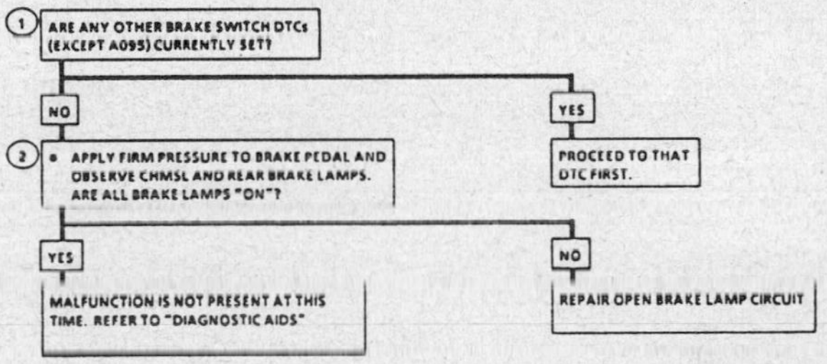
1
ARE ANY OTHER BRAKE SWITCH DTCs (EXCEPT A095) CURRENTLY SET?
NO
YES
2
• APPLY FIRM PRESSURE TO BRAKE PEDAL AND OBSERVE CHMSL AND REAR BRAKE LAMPS. ARE ALL BRAKE LAMPS "ON"?
PROCEED TO THAT DTC FIRST.
YES
NO
MALFUNCTION IS NOT PRESENT AT THIS TIME. REFER TO "DIAGNOSTIC AIDS"
REPAIR OPEN BRAKE LAMP CIRCUIT

GC402930084400FX

Fig. 222 Code A096: Brake Lamps Circuit Open. 1993 Cutlass Supreme, Grand Prix, Lumina, Regal & 1993–94 Cavalier, Sunbird, Beretta, Corsica & Achieva, Grand Am & Skylark Less VES

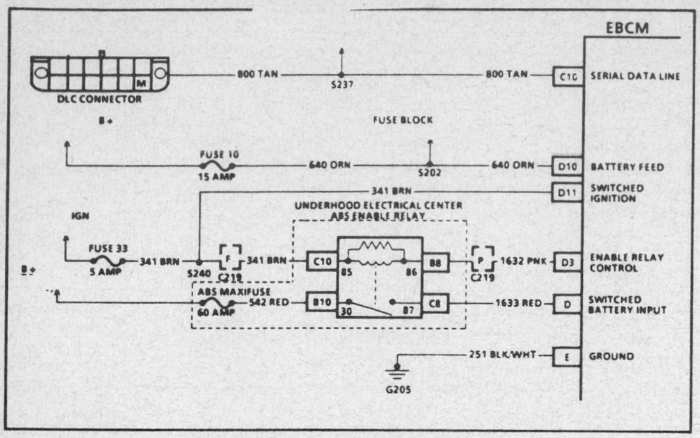
EBCM
DLC CONNECTOR
800 TAN
S237
C10 SERIAL DATA LINE
B+
FUSE BLOCK
FUSE 10
15 AMP
640 ORN
S202
D10 BATTERY FEED
341 BRN
D11 SWITCHED IGNITION
IGN
UNDERHOOD ELECTRICAL CENTER
ABS ENABLE RELAY
FUSE 33
5 AMP
S240
C219
C10
85
86
B8
1632 PNK
D3 ENABLE RELAY CONTROL
ABS MAXIFUSE
60 AMP
542 RED
B10
30
87
C8
1633 RED
D SWITCHED BATTERY INPUT
251 BLK/WHT
E GROUND
G205

DIAGNOSTIC SYSTEM CHECK

(Page 1 of 4)

System Description:

The diagnostic system check is an organized approach to identifying a problem created by an Antilock Brake System (ABS) malfunction. It must be the starting point for any ABS complaint diagnosis because it directs the service technician to the next logical step in diagnosing the complaint.

Serial data is transmitted by the EBCM through terminal "C10". The EBCM is supplied switched ignition voltage through terminal "D11", battery voltage through terminal "D10" and switched battery voltage through terminal "D". The EBCM ground is provided through terminal "E".

Chart Test Description: Number(s) below refer to circled number(s) on the diagnostic chart.

1. Indicates if EBCM is transmitting data.
2. Checks for a serial data line malfunction.
3. Checks for proper Tech 1 connection to DLC.
4. Checks for open 15 amp Fuse 10.
5. Checks for open 5 amp Fuse 33.
6. Checks for high resistance in the EBCM ground circuit.
7. Checks for current DTCs.
8. Checks for proper ABS warning lamp operation.
9. Checks for history DTCs.

Diagnostic Aids: Excessive resistance in the ground or power supply circuits will not allow communication with the EBCM. If communication with the EBCM is not possible, ensure the ABS ground connection is good and that there is no excessive resistance in any of the power supply circuits.

GC402940105401AX

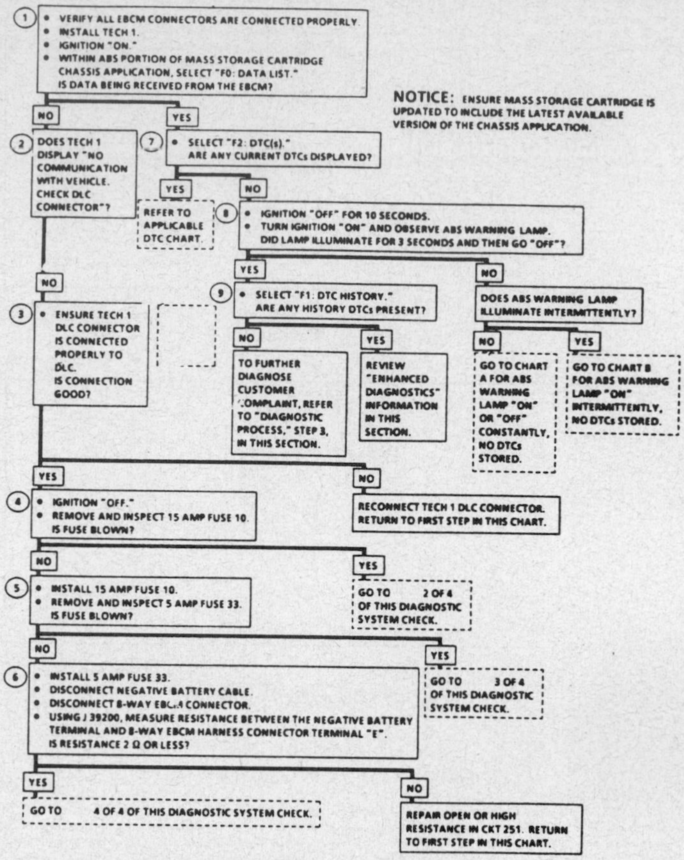
1 • VERIFY ALL EBCM CONNECTORS ARE CONNECTED PROPERLY.
• INSTALL TECH 1.
• IGNITION "ON."
• WITHIN ABS PORTION OF MASS STORAGE CARTRIDGE CHASSIS APPLICATION, SELECT "F0: DATA LIST."
IS DATA BEING RECEIVED FROM THE EBCM?
NOTICE: ENSURE MASS STORAGE CARTRIDGE IS UPDATED TO INCLUDE THE LATEST AVAILABLE VERSION OF THE CHASSIS APPLICATION.
NO
YES
2 DOES TECH 1 DISPLAY "NO COMMUNICATION WITH VEHICLE. CHECK DLC CONNECTOR"?
7 • SELECT "F2: DTC(s)."
ARE ANY CURRENT DTCs DISPLAYED?
YES
NO
REFER TO APPLICABLE DTC CHART.
8 • IGNITION "OFF" FOR 10 SECONDS.
• TURN IGNITION "ON" AND OBSERVE ABS WARNING LAMP.
DID LAMP ILLUMINATE FOR 3 SECONDS AND THEN GO "OFF"?
NO
YES
NO
3 • ENSURE TECH 1 DLC CONNECTOR IS CONNECTED PROPERLY TO DLC.
IS CONNECTION GOOD?
9 • SELECT "F1: DTC HISTORY."
ARE ANY HISTORY DTCs PRESENT?
DOES ABS WARNING LAMP ILLUMINATE INTERMITTENTLY?
NO
YES
NO
YES
TO FURTHER DIAGNOSE CUSTOMER COMPLAINT, REFER TO "DIAGNOSTIC PROCESS," STEP 3, IN THIS SECTION.
REVIEW "ENHANCED DIAGNOSTICS" INFORMATION IN THIS SECTION.
GO TO CHART A FOR ABS WARNING LAMP "ON" OR "OFF" CONSTANTLY, NO DTCs STORED.
GO TO CHART B FOR ABS WARNING LAMP "ON" INTERMITTENTLY, NO DTCs STORED.
YES
NO
4 • IGNITION "OFF."
• REMOVE AND INSPECT 15 AMP FUSE 10.
IS FUSE BLOWN?
RECONNECT TECH 1 DLC CONNECTOR. RETURN TO FIRST STEP IN THIS CHART.
NO
YES
5 • INSTALL 15 AMP FUSE 10.
• REMOVE AND INSPECT 5 AMP FUSE 33.
IS FUSE BLOWN?
GO TO 2 OF 4 OF THIS DIAGNOSTIC SYSTEM CHECK.
NO
YES
6 • INSTALL 5 AMP FUSE 33.
• DISCONNECT NEGATIVE BATTERY CABLE.
• DISCONNECT 8-WAY EBCM CONNECTOR.
• USING J 39200, MEASURE RESISTANCE BETWEEN THE NEGATIVE BATTERY TERMINAL AND 8-WAY EBCM HARNESS CONNECTOR TERMINAL "E".
IS RESISTANCE 2 Ω OR LESS?
GO TO 3 OF 4 OF THIS DIAGNOSTIC SYSTEM CHECK.
YES
NO
GO TO 4 OF 4 OF THIS DIAGNOSTIC SYSTEM CHECK.
REPAIR OPEN OR HIGH RESISTANCE IN CKT 251. RETURN TO FIRST STEP IN THIS CHART.

GC402940105401BX

Fig. 223 Diagnostic circuit check (1 of 4). 1993–94 Camaro & Firebird, 1994 Grand Prix, Century & Cutlass Ciera & Cruiser

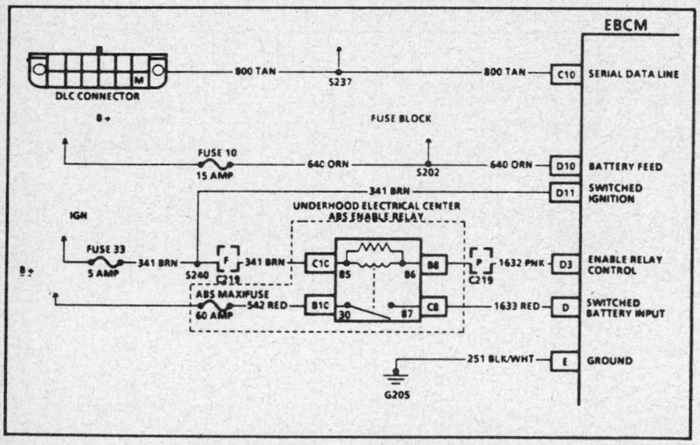
EBCM
DLC CONNECTOR
800 TAN
S237
C10 SERIAL DATA LINE
B+
FUSE BLOCK
FUSE 10
15 AMP
640 ORN
S202
D10 BATTERY FEED
341 BRN
D11 SWITCHED IGNITION
IGN
UNDERHOOD ELECTRICAL CENTER
ABS ENABLE RELAY
FUSE 33
5 AMP
S240
C219
C1C
85
86
B8
1632 PNK
D3 ENABLE RELAY CONTROL
ABS MAXIFUSE
60 AMP
542 RED
B1C
30
87
C8
1633 RED
D SWITCHED BATTERY INPUT
251 BLK/WHT
E GROUND
G205

DIAGNOSTIC SYSTEM CHECK

(Page 2 of 4)

System Description:

The diagnostic system check is an organized approach to identifying a problem created by an Antilock Brake System (ABS) malfunction. It must be the starting point for any ABS complaint diagnosis because it directs the service technician to the next logical step in diagnosing the complaint.

Serial data is transmitted by the EBCM through terminal "C10". The EBCM is supplied switched ignition voltage through terminal "D11", battery voltage through terminal "D10" and switched battery voltage through terminal "D". The EBCM ground is provided through terminal "E".

Chart Test Description: Number(s) below refer to circled number(s) on the diagnostic chart.

10. Checks for possible short to ground in the battery feed circuitry.
11. Checks for possible short to ground in the EBCM.
12. Ensures short to ground is not due to physical damage of the circuitry.

Diagnostic Aids: Excessive resistance in the ground or power supply circuits will not allow communication with the EBCM. If communication with the EBCM is not possible, ensure the ABS ground connection is good and that there is no excessive resistance in any of the power supply circuits.

GC402940105402AX

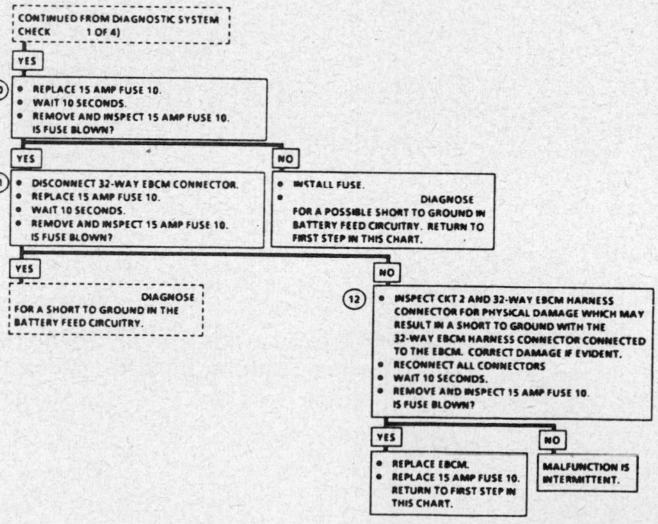
CONTINUED FROM DIAGNOSTIC SYSTEM CHECK 1 OF 4)
YES
10 • REPLACE 15 AMP FUSE 10.
• WAIT 10 SECONDS.
• REMOVE AND INSPECT 15 AMP FUSE 10.
IS FUSE BLOWN?
YES
NO
11 • DISCONNECT 32-WAY EBCM CONNECTOR.
• REPLACE 15 AMP FUSE 10.
• WAIT 10 SECONDS.
• REMOVE AND INSPECT 15 AMP FUSE 10.
IS FUSE BLOWN?
• INSTALL FUSE.
• DIAGNOSE FOR A POSSIBLE SHORT TO GROUND IN BATTERY FEED CIRCUITRY. RETURN TO FIRST STEP IN THIS CHART.
YES
NO
DIAGNOSE FOR A SHORT TO GROUND IN THE BATTERY FEED CIRCUITRY.
12 • INSPECT CKT 2 AND 32-WAY EBCM HARNESS CONNECTOR FOR PHYSICAL DAMAGE WHICH MAY RESULT IN A SHORT TO GROUND WITH THE 32-WAY EBCM HARNESS CONNECTOR CONNECTED TO THE EBCM. CORRECT DAMAGE IF EVIDENT.
• RECONNECT ALL CONNECTORS
• WAIT 10 SECONDS.
• REMOVE AND INSPECT 15 AMP FUSE 10.
IS FUSE BLOWN?
YES
NO
• REPLACE EBCM.
• REPLACE 15 AMP FUSE 10. RETURN TO FIRST STEP IN THIS CHART.
MALFUNCTION IS INTERMITTENT.

GC402940105402BX

Fig. 224 Diagnostic circuit check (2 of 4). 1993–94 Camaro & Firebird, 1994 Grand Prix, Century & Cutlass Ciera & Cruiser

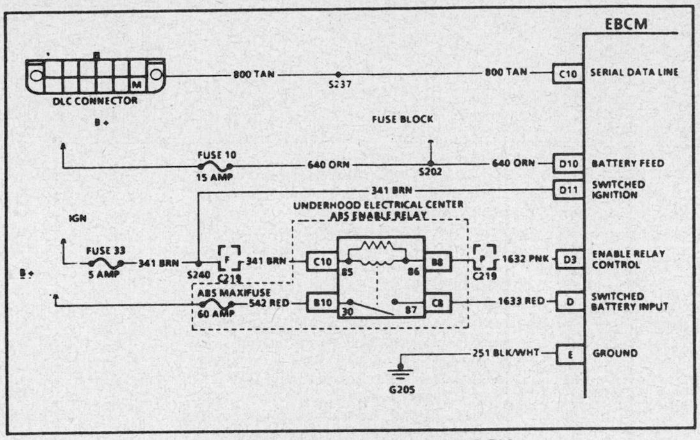
EBCM
DLC CONNECTOR
800 TAN
S237
800 TAN
C10
SERIAL DATA LINE
B+
FUSE BLOCK
FUSE 10
15 AMP
640 ORN
S202
640 ORN
D10
BATTERY FEED
341 BRN
D11
SWITCHED IGNITION
UNDERHOOD ELECTRICAL CENTER
ABS ENABLE RELAY
IGN
FUSE 33
5 AMP
341 BRN
S240
C219
341 BRN
C10
85
86
B8
C219
1632 PNK
D3
ENABLE RELAY CONTROL
B+
ABS MAXIFUSE
60 AMP
542 RED
B10
30
87
C8
1633 RED
D
SWITCHED BATTERY INPUT
251 BLK/WHT
E
GROUND
G205

DIAGNOSTIC SYSTEM CHECK

(Page 3 of 4)

System Description:

The diagnostic system check is an organized approach to identifying a problem created by an Antilock Brake System (ABS) malfunction. It must be the starting point for any ABS complaint diagnosis because it directs the service technician to the next logical step in diagnosing the complaint.

Serial data is transmitted by the EBCM through terminal "C10". The EBCM is supplied switched ignition voltage through terminal "D11", battery voltage through terminal "D10" and switched battery voltage through terminal "D". The EBCM ground is provided through terminal "E".

Chart Test Description: Number(s) below refer to circled number(s) on the diagnostic chart.

13. Checks for possible short to ground in the switched ignition circuitry.
14. Isolates the short to ground to either the circuitry or the EBCM.
15. Ensures short to ground is not due to physical damage of the circuitry.

Diagnostic Aids: Excessive resistance in the ground or power supply circuits will not allow communication with the EBCM. If communication with the EBCM is not possible, ensure the ABS ground connection is good and that there is no excessive resistance in any of the power supply circuits.

GC402940105403AX

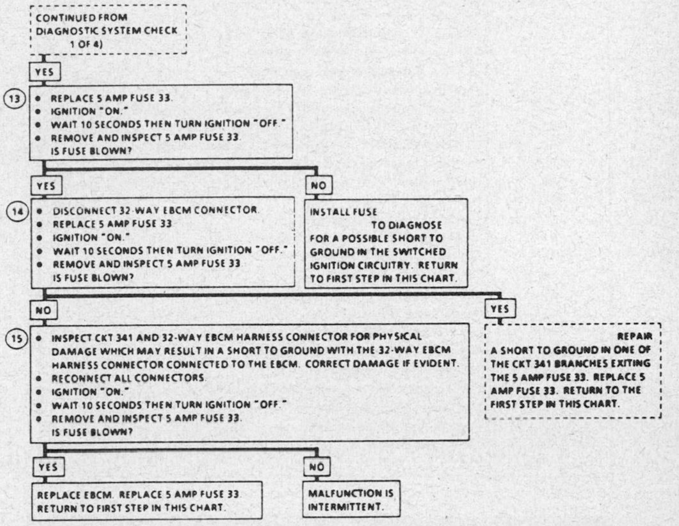
CONTINUED FROM DIAGNOSTIC SYSTEM CHECK (1 OF 4)
YES
13
• REPLACE 5 AMP FUSE 33.
• IGNITION "ON."
• WAIT 10 SECONDS THEN TURN IGNITION "OFF."
• REMOVE AND INSPECT 5 AMP FUSE 33.
IS FUSE BLOWN?
YES
NO
14
• DISCONNECT 32-WAY EBCM CONNECTOR.
• REPLACE 5 AMP FUSE 33.
• IGNITION "ON."
• WAIT 10 SECONDS THEN TURN IGNITION "OFF."
• REMOVE AND INSPECT 5 AMP FUSE 33.
IS FUSE BLOWN?
INSTALL FUSE TO DIAGNOSE FOR A POSSIBLE SHORT TO GROUND IN THE SWITCHED IGNITION CIRCUITRY. RETURN TO FIRST STEP IN THIS CHART.
NO
YES
15
• INSPECT CKT 341 AND 32-WAY EBCM HARNESS CONNECTOR FOR PHYSICAL DAMAGE WHICH MAY RESULT IN A SHORT TO GROUND WITH THE 32-WAY EBCM HARNESS CONNECTOR CONNECTED TO THE EBCM. CORRECT DAMAGE IF EVIDENT.
• RECONNECT ALL CONNECTORS.
• IGNITION "ON."
• WAIT 10 SECONDS THEN TURN IGNITION "OFF."
• REMOVE AND INSPECT 5 AMP FUSE 33.
IS FUSE BLOWN?
REPAIR A SHORT TO GROUND IN ONE OF THE CKT 341 BRANCHES EXITING THE 5 AMP FUSE 33. REPLACE 5 AMP FUSE 33. RETURN TO THE FIRST STEP IN THIS CHART.
YES
NO
REPLACE EBCM. REPLACE 5 AMP FUSE 33. RETURN TO FIRST STEP IN THIS CHART.
MALFUNCTION IS INTERMITTENT.

GC402940105403BX

Fig. 225 Diagnostic circuit check (3 of 4). 1993–94 Camaro & Firebird, 1994 Grand Prix, Century & Cutlass Ciera & Cruiser

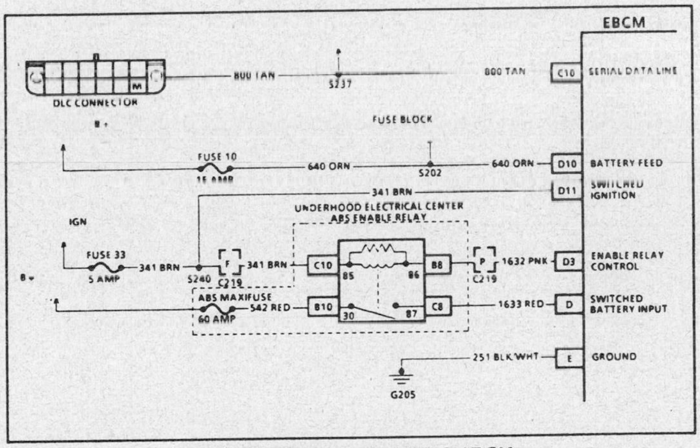
EBCM
DLC CONNECTOR
800 TAN
S237
800 TAN
C10
SERIAL DATA LINE
B+
FUSE BLOCK
FUSE 10
640 ORN
S202
640 ORN
D10
BATTERY FEED
341 BRN
D11
SWITCHED IGNITION
UNDERHOOD ELECTRICAL CENTER
ABS ENABLE RELAY
IGN
FUSE 33
5 AMP
341 BRN
S240
C219
341 BRN
C10
85
86
B8
C219
1632 PNK
D3
ENABLE RELAY CONTROL
B+
ABS MAXIFUSE
60 AMP
542 RED
B10
30
87
C8
1633 RED
D
SWITCHED BATTERY INPUT
251 BLK/WHT
E
GROUND
G205

DIAGNOSTIC SYSTEM CHECK

(Page 4 of 4)

System Description:

The diagnostic system check is an organized approach to identifying a problem created by an Antilock Brake System (ABS) malfunction. It must be the starting point for any ABS complaint diagnosis because it directs the service technician to the next logical step in diagnosing the complaint.

Serial data is transmitted by the EBCM through terminal "C10". The EBCM is supplied switched ignition voltage through terminal "D11", battery voltage through terminal "D10" and switched battery voltage through terminal "D". The EBCM ground is provided through terminal "E".

Chart Test Description: Number(s) below refer to circled number(s) on the diagnostic chart.

16. Checks for an open in CKT 640.
17. Checks for high resistance in battery feed circuitry.
18. Checks for high resistance in the switched ignition circuitry.
19. Ensures malfunction is not due to poor terminal contact.
20. Checks for high resistance in the switched ignition circuit between the fuse block and the EBCM.

Diagnostic Aids: Excessive resistance in the ground or power supply circuits will not allow communication with the EBCM. If communication with the EBCM is not possible, ensure the ABS ground connection is good and that there is no excessive resistance in any of the power supply circuits.

GC402940105404AX

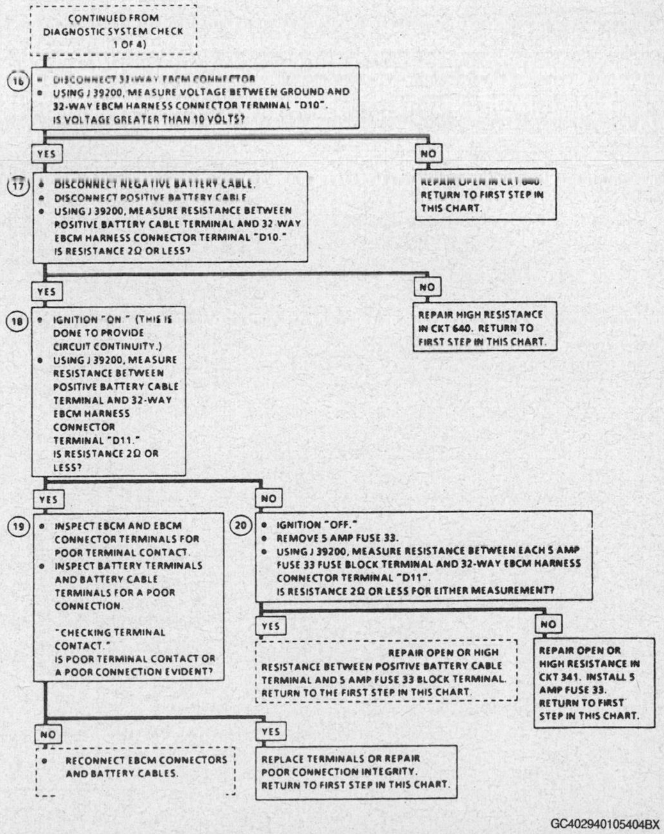
CONTINUED FROM DIAGNOSTIC SYSTEM CHECK (1 OF 4)
16
• DISCONNECT 32-WAY EBCM CONNECTOR.
• USING J 39200, MEASURE VOLTAGE BETWEEN GROUND AND 32-WAY EBCM HARNESS CONNECTOR TERMINAL "D10".
IS VOLTAGE GREATER THAN 10 VOLTS?
YES
NO
17
• DISCONNECT NEGATIVE BATTERY CABLE.
• DISCONNECT POSITIVE BATTERY CABLE.
• USING J 39200, MEASURE RESISTANCE BETWEEN POSITIVE BATTERY CABLE TERMINAL AND 32-WAY EBCM HARNESS CONNECTOR TERMINAL "D10."
IS RESISTANCE 2Ω OR LESS?
REPAIR OPEN IN CKT 640. RETURN TO FIRST STEP IN THIS CHART.
YES
NO
18
• IGNITION "ON." (THIS IS DONE TO PROVIDE CIRCUIT CONTINUITY.)
• USING J 39200, MEASURE RESISTANCE BETWEEN POSITIVE BATTERY CABLE TERMINAL AND 32-WAY EBCM HARNESS CONNECTOR TERMINAL "D11."
IS RESISTANCE 2Ω OR LESS?
REPAIR HIGH RESISTANCE IN CKT 640. RETURN TO FIRST STEP IN THIS CHART.
YES
NO
19
• INSPECT EBCM AND EBCM CONNECTOR TERMINALS FOR POOR TERMINAL CONTACT.
• INSPECT BATTERY TERMINALS AND BATTERY CABLE TERMINALS FOR A POOR CONNECTION.
"CHECKING TERMINAL CONTACT."
IS POOR TERMINAL CONTACT OR A POOR CONNECTION EVIDENT?
20
• IGNITION "OFF."
• REMOVE 5 AMP FUSE 33.
• USING J 39200, MEASURE RESISTANCE BETWEEN EACH 5 AMP FUSE 33 FUSE BLOCK TERMINAL AND 32-WAY EBCM HARNESS CONNECTOR TERMINAL "D11".
IS RESISTANCE 2Ω OR LESS FOR EITHER MEASUREMENT?
YES
NO
REPAIR OPEN OR HIGH RESISTANCE BETWEEN POSITIVE BATTERY CABLE TERMINAL AND 5 AMP FUSE 33 BLOCK TERMINAL. RETURN TO THE FIRST STEP IN THIS CHART.
REPAIR OPEN OR HIGH RESISTANCE IN CKT 341. INSTALL 5 AMP FUSE 33. RETURN TO FIRST STEP IN THIS CHART.
NO
YES
• RECONNECT EBCM CONNECTORS AND BATTERY CABLES.
REPLACE TERMINALS OR REPAIR POOR CONNECTION INTEGRITY. RETURN TO FIRST STEP IN THIS CHART.

GC402940105404BX

Fig. 226 Diagnostic circuit check (4 of 4). 1993–94 Camaro & Firebird, 1994 Grand Prix, Century & Cutlass Ciera & Cruiser

A	ABS (Amber) Warning Lamp "ON" Constantly, No DTCs Stored
B	ABS (Amber) Warning Lamp "ON" Intermittently, No DTCs Stored
C	ABS (Amber) Warning Lamp "OFF" Constantly, No DTCs Stored
11	ABS Warning Lamp Circuit Malfunction
14	ABS Enable Relay Contact Circuit Open (1 of 3)
15	ABS Rly Contact Ckt Short to Batt or Always Closed
16	ABS Enable Relay Coil Circuit Open
17	ABS Enable Relay Coil Circuit Shorted to Gnd
18	ABS Enable Relay Coil Circuit Shorted to Batt
21	Left Front Wheel Speed = 0
22	Right Front Wheel Speed = 0
23	Left Rear Wheel Speed = 0
24	Right Rear Wheel Speed = 0
25	Left Front Excessive Wheel Speed Variation
26	Right Front Excessive Wheel Speed Variation
27	Left Rear Excessive Wheel Speed Variation
28	Right Rear Excessive Wheel Speed Variation
32	LF Wheel Speed Snr Ckt Open or Short to Gnd/Batt (1 of 3)
33	RF Wheel Speed Snr Ckt Open or Short to Gnd/Batt (1 of 3)
34	LR Wheel Speed Snr Ckt Open or Short to Gnd/Batt (1 of 3)
35	RR Wheel Speed Snr Ckt Open or Short to Gnd/Batt (1 of 3)
36	Low System Voltage (1 of 2)
37	High System Voltage
38	Left Front ESB Will Not Hold Motor
41	Right Front ESB Will Not Hold Motor
42	Rear ESB Will Not Hold Motor
44	Left Front Channel Will Not Move
45	Right Front Channel Will Not Move
46	Rear Channel Will Not Move
47	Left Front ABS Motor Free Spins (1 of 2)
48	Right Front ABS Motor Free Spins (1 of 2)
51	Rear ABS Motor Free Spins (1 of 2)
52	Left Front Channel in Release Too Long
53	Right Front Channel In Release Too Long
54	Rear Channel in Release Too Long
55	EBCM Malfunction

GC4029401055010X

Fig. 227 Diagnostic trouble code & symptom table (Part 1 of 2). 1993–94 Camaro & Firebird, 1994 Grand Prix, Century & Cutlass Ciera & Cruiser

56	Left Front ABS Motor Circuit Open
57	Left Front ABS Motor Circuit Shorted to Ground
58	Left Front ABS Motor Circuit Shorted to Battery
61	Right Front ABS Motor Circuit Open
62	Right Front ABS Motor Circuit Shorted to Gnd
63	Right Front ABS Motor Circuit Shorted to Batt
64	Rear ABS Motor Circuit Open
65	Rear ABS Motor Circuit Shorted to Ground
66	Rear ABS Motor Circuit Shorted to Battery
76	Left Front Sol Circuit Open or Shorted to Batt
77	Left Front Solenoid Circuit Shorted to Gnd
78	Right Front Sol Circuit Open or Shorted to Batt
81	Right Front Solenoid Circuit Shorted to Gnd
82	Calibration Malfunction
86	EBCM Turned "ON" the Red "BRAKE" Warning Lamp
87	Red "BRAKE" Warning Lamp Circuit Open
88	Red "BRAKE" Warning Lamp Ckt Shorted to Batt
91	Open Brake Switch During Deceleration
92	Open Brake Switch When ABS Was Required
93	DTC 91 or 92 Set in Current or Prev. Ign Cycle
94	Brake Switch Contacts Always Closed
95	Brake Switch Circuit Open
96	Brake Lamps Circuit Open

GC4029401055020X

Fig. 227 Diagnostic trouble code & symptom table (Part 2 of 2). 1993–94 Camaro & Firebird, 1994 Grand Prix, Century & Cutlass Ciera & Cruiser

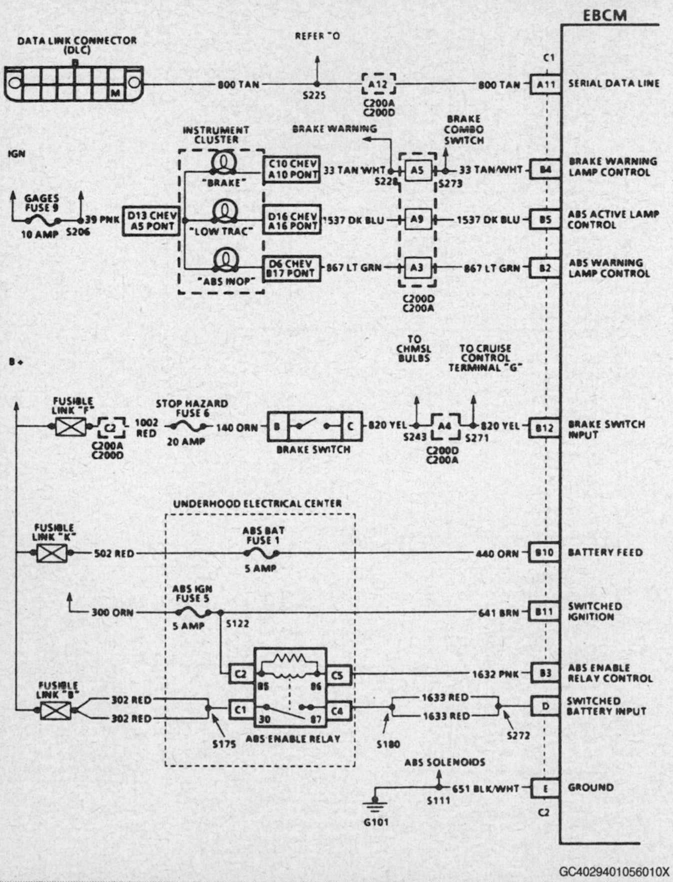
EBCM
DATA LINK CONNECTOR (DLC)
800 TAN
S225
C200A C200D
A11
SERIAL DATA LINE
INSTRUMENT CLUSTER
BRAKE WARNING
BRAKE COMBO SWITCH
IGN
"BRAKE"
"LOW TRAC"
"ABS INOP"
GAGES FUSE 9
10 AMP
S206
39 PNK
33 TAN/WHT
1537 DK BLU
867 LT GRN
BRAKE WARNING LAMP CONTROL
ABS ACTIVE LAMP CONTROL
ABS WARNING LAMP CONTROL
B+
FUSIBLE LINK "F"
STOP HAZARD FUSE 6
20 AMP
140 ORN
820 YEL
BRAKE SWITCH
BRAKE SWITCH INPUT
UNDERHOOD ELECTRICAL CENTER
FUSIBLE LINK "K"
502 RED
ABS BAT FUSE 1
5 AMP
440 ORN
BATTERY FEED
ABS IGN FUSE 5
300 ORN
641 BRN
SWITCHED IGNITION
1632 PNK
ABS ENABLE RELAY CONTROL
FUSIBLE LINK "B"
302 RED
1633 RED
SWITCHED BATTERY INPUT
ABS ENABLE RELAY
ABS SOLENOIDS
651 BLK/WHT
GROUND
G101

GC4029401056010X

Fig. 228 ABS wiring circuit (Part 1 of 2). 1993–94 Camaro & Firebird

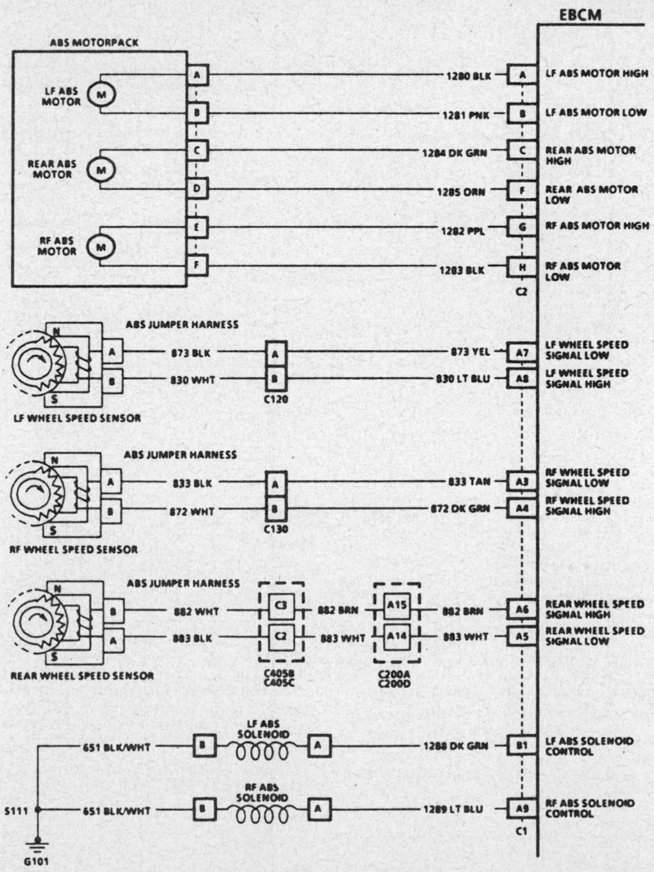
EBCM
ABS MOTORPACK
LF ABS MOTOR
REAR ABS MOTOR
RF ABS MOTOR
1280 BLK
1281 PNK
1284 DK GRN
1285 ORN
1282 PPL
1283 BLK
LF ABS MOTOR HIGH
LF ABS MOTOR LOW
REAR ABS MOTOR HIGH
REAR ABS MOTOR LOW
RF ABS MOTOR HIGH
RF ABS MOTOR LOW
ABS JUMPER HARNESS
873 BLK
830 WHT
873 YEL
830 LT BLU
C120
LF WHEEL SPEED SENSOR
LF WHEEL SPEED SIGNAL LOW
LF WHEEL SPEED SIGNAL HIGH
833 BLK
872 WHT
833 TAN
872 DK GRN
C130
RF WHEEL SPEED SENSOR
RF WHEEL SPEED SIGNAL LOW
RF WHEEL SPEED SIGNAL HIGH
882 WHT
883 BLK
882 BRN
883 WHT
C405B C405C
C200A C200D
REAR WHEEL SPEED SENSOR
REAR WHEEL SPEED SIGNAL HIGH
REAR WHEEL SPEED SIGNAL LOW
651 BLK/WHT
LF ABS SOLENOID
RF ABS SOLENOID
1288 DK GRN
1289 LT BLU
LF ABS SOLENOID CONTROL
RF ABS SOLENOID CONTROL
S111
G101

GC4029401056020X

Fig. 228 ABS wiring circuit. (part 2 of 2). 1993–94 Camaro & Firebird

DTC 11

ABS WARNING LAMP CIRCUIT MALFUNCTION

Circuit Description: This DTC checks the state of both the ABS warning lamp "BRAKE" lamp to identify a situation in which the driver could not be alerted to a system malfunction or of possible slippery driving conditions. Due to an integral lamp driver module within the instrument panel cluster, the EBCM must provide a ground to turn the ABS warning lamp "OFF." The "BRAKE" lamp circuit is such that the EBCM provides a ground to turn "ON" the "BRAKE" lamp.

DTC Will Set When: DTC 11 can only be set during the three second bulb check or when either of the lamps are commanded "ON." If the EBCM cannot control either the ABS warning lamp or the "BRAKE" lamp for two seconds, a malfunction exists.

Action Taken: A malfunction DTC is stored; however, ABS is not disabled.

DTC Chart Test Description: Number(s) below refer to circled number(s) on the diagnostic chart.

1. Determines if the ABS warning lamp can be properly controlled.
2. Determines if the lamp is "ON" constantly.
3. Checks for other DTCs which could turn "ON" the ABS warning lamp.
4. Determines if the ABS warning lamp can be turned "OFF" manually.
5. Checks the integrity of the ABS warning lamp circuitry.
6. Checks for a short to voltage on the ABS warning lamp circuitry.
7. Determines if a malfunctioning EBCM is the cause of DTC 11.
8. Verifies that the other I/P indicator lamps function properly.
9. Determines if the ABS warning lamp can be turned "ON" manually.
10. Checks for a short to ground in the ABS warning lamp circuitry.
11. Verifies condition of the 10 amp Fuse 39.
12. Determines if DTC 11 was set due to an EBCM malfunction.

Diagnostic Aids: An "Intermittent" malfunction may be caused by a poor connection, rubbed through wire insulation, or a wire that is broken inside the insulation.

The lamp test function of the Tech 1 may be used to command the lamp "ON" while looking for an intermittent malfunction in the ABS warning lamp circuitry.

The frequency of the malfunction can be checked by using the enhanced diagnostic function of the Tech 1.

Any circuitry that is suspected as causing the intermittent complaint should be thoroughly checked for backed out terminals, improper mating, broken locks, improperly formed or damaged terminals, poor terminal to wiring connections or physical damage to the wiring harness.

GC402940106500DX

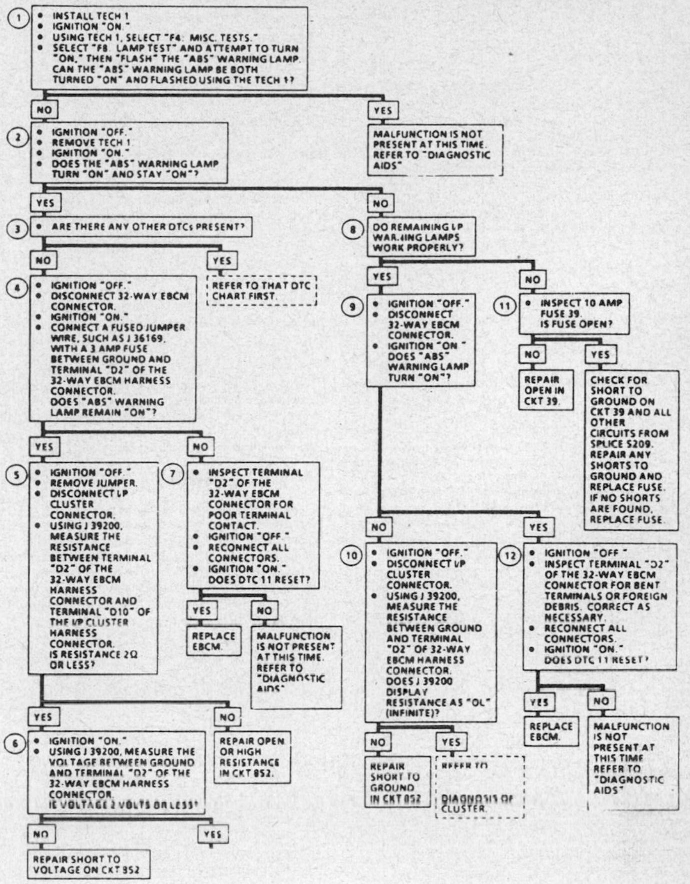
1 • INSTALL TECH 1 • IGNITION "ON." • USING TECH 1, SELECT "F4: MISC. TESTS." • SELECT "F8: LAMP TEST" AND ATTEMPT TO TURN "ON," THEN "FLASH" THE "ABS" WARNING LAMP. CAN THE "ABS" WARNING LAMP BE BOTH TURNED "ON" AND FLASHED USING THE TECH 1?
NO
YES
MALFUNCTION IS NOT PRESENT AT THIS TIME. REFER TO "DIAGNOSTIC AIDS"
2 • IGNITION "OFF." • REMOVE TECH 1. • IGNITION "ON." • DOES THE "ABS" WARNING LAMP TURN "ON" AND STAY "ON"?
YES
NO
3 • ARE THERE ANY OTHER DTCs PRESENT?
8 • DO REMAINING I/P WARNING LAMPS WORK PROPERLY?
NO
YES
REFER TO THAT DTC CHART FIRST.
4 • IGNITION "OFF." • DISCONNECT 32-WAY EBCM CONNECTOR. • IGNITION "ON." • CONNECT A FUSED JUMPER WIRE, SUCH AS J 36169, WITH A 3 AMP FUSE BETWEEN GROUND AND TERMINAL "D2" OF THE 32-WAY EBCM HARNESS CONNECTOR. DOES "ABS" WARNING LAMP REMAIN "ON"?
9 • IGNITION "OFF." • DISCONNECT 32-WAY EBCM CONNECTOR. • IGNITION "ON." DOES "ABS" WARNING LAMP TURN "ON"?
11 • INSPECT 10 AMP FUSE 39. IS FUSE OPEN?
REPAIR OPEN IN CKT 39.
CHECK FOR SHORT TO GROUND ON CKT 39 AND ALL OTHER CIRCUITS FROM SPLICE S209. REPAIR ANY SHORTS TO GROUND AND REPLACE FUSE. IF NO SHORTS ARE FOUND, REPLACE FUSE.
5 • IGNITION "OFF." • REMOVE JUMPER. • DISCONNECT I/P CLUSTER CONNECTOR. • USING J 39200, MEASURE THE RESISTANCE BETWEEN TERMINAL "D2" OF THE 32-WAY EBCM HARNESS CONNECTOR AND TERMINAL "D10" OF THE I/P CLUSTER HARNESS CONNECTOR. IS RESISTANCE 2Ω OR LESS?
7 • INSPECT TERMINAL "D2" OF THE 32-WAY EBCM CONNECTOR FOR POOR TERMINAL CONTACT. • IGNITION "OFF." • RECONNECT ALL CONNECTORS. • IGNITION "ON." DOES DTC 11 RESET?
REPLACE EBCM.
MALFUNCTION IS NOT PRESENT AT THIS TIME. REFER TO "DIAGNOSTIC AIDS"
10 • IGNITION "OFF." • DISCONNECT I/P CLUSTER CONNECTOR. • USING J 39200, MEASURE THE RESISTANCE BETWEEN GROUND AND TERMINAL "D2" OF 32-WAY EBCM HARNESS CONNECTOR. DOES J 39200 DISPLAY RESISTANCE AS "OL" (INFINITE)?
12 • IGNITION "OFF." • INSPECT TERMINAL "D2" OF THE 32-WAY EBCM CONNECTOR FOR BENT TERMINALS OR FOREIGN DEBRIS. CORRECT AS NECESSARY. • RECONNECT ALL CONNECTORS. • IGNITION "ON." DOES DTC 11 RESET?
REPLACE EBCM.
MALFUNCTION IS NOT PRESENT AT THIS TIME. REFER TO "DIAGNOSTIC AIDS"
6 • IGNITION "ON." • USING J 39200, MEASURE THE VOLTAGE BETWEEN GROUND AND TERMINAL "D2" OF THE 32-WAY EBCM HARNESS CONNECTOR. IS VOLTAGE 2 VOLTS OR LESS?
REPAIR OPEN OR HIGH RESISTANCE IN CKT 852.
REPAIR SHORT TO GROUND IN CKT 852
REFER TO DIAGNOSIS OF CLUSTER.
REPAIR SHORT TO VOLTAGE ON CKT 852

GC402940106500EX

Fig. 237 Code A011: ABS warning lamp circuit fault (Part 2 of 2). 1993-94 Camaro & Firebird, 1994 Grand Prix, Century & Cutlass Ciera & Cruiser

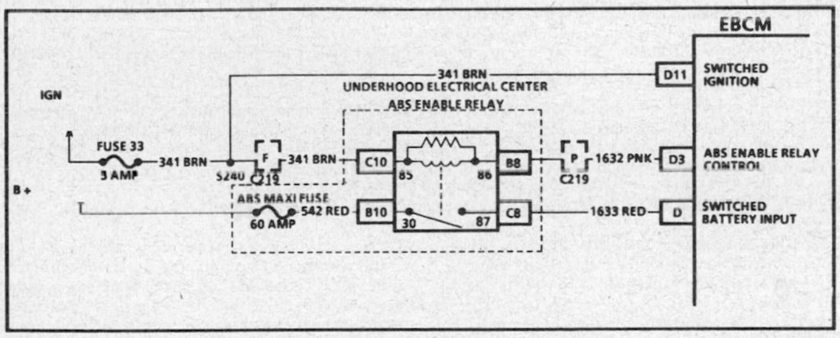
EBCM
IGN
B+
FUSE 33 3 AMP
341 BRN
S240
F
C219
UNDERHOOD ELECTRICAL CENTER
ABS ENABLE RELAY
ABS MAXI FUSE 60 AMP
542 RED
C10
B10
85
86
30
87
B8
C8
P
1632 PNK
1633 RED
D11
D3
D
SWITCHED IGNITION
ABS ENABLE RELAY CONTROL
SWITCHED BATTERY INPUT

GC402940106601AX

Grand Prix

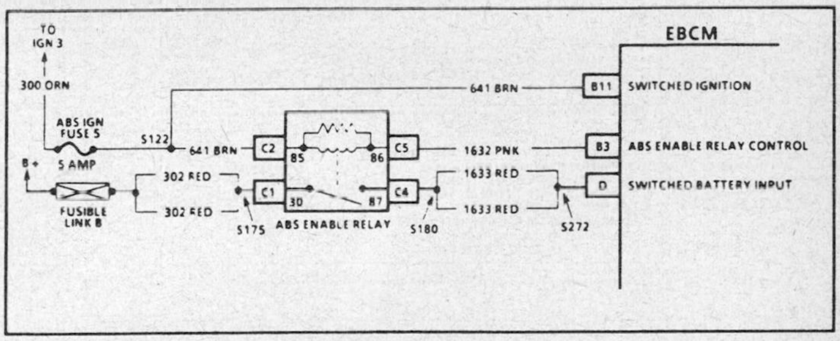
TO IGN 3
300 ORN
ABS IGN FUSE 5 5 AMP
B+
FUSIBLE LINK B
S122
641 BRN
302 RED
C2
C1
85
86
30
87
C5
C4
S175
ABS ENABLE RELAY
S180
1632 PNK
1633 RED
S272
EBCM
B11
B3
D
SWITCHED IGNITION
ABS ENABLE RELAY CONTROL
SWITCHED BATTERY INPUT

GC402940106601BX

Camaro & Firebird

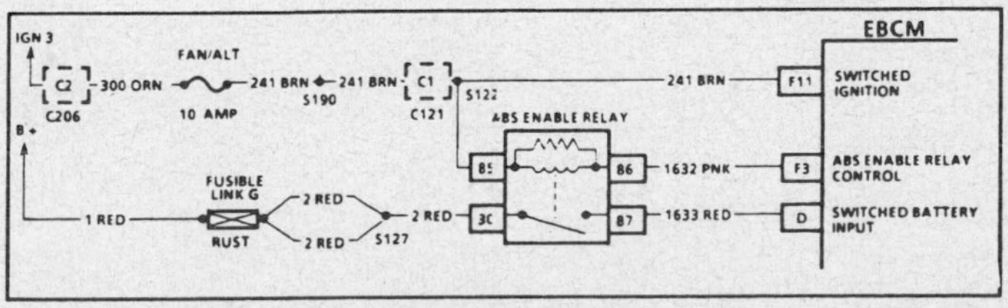
IGN 3
C2
C206
300 ORN
FAN/ALT
10 AMP
241 BRN
S190
C1
C121
S122
B+
ABS ENABLE RELAY
FUSIBLE LINK G
RUST
1 RED
2 RED
S127
85
86
30
87
1632 PNK
1633 RED
EBCM
F11
F3
D
SWITCHED IGNITION
ABS ENABLE RELAY CONTROL
SWITCHED BATTERY INPUT

GC402940106601CX

Century & Cutlass Ciera & Cruiser

Fig. 238 Code A014: ABS Enable Relay Contact Circuit Open (1 of 3). 1993–94 Camaro & Firebird, 1994 Grand Prix, Century & Cutlass Ciera & Cruiser

DTC 14

ABS ENABLE RELAY CONTACT CIRCUIT OPEN

Circuit Description:

Ignition voltage is supplied through terminal "C10" of the ABS enable relay. The EBCM then is able to energize the pull-in coil by completing the ground circuit at terminal "D3" of the EBCM. The magnetic field created closes the ABS enable relay contacts and allows battery voltage and current to be supplied to the EBCM, which supplies power to the motors and solenoids.

DTC Will Set When: DTC 14 can be set anytime after the EBCM commands the ABS enable relay "ON" (the relay is first commanded "ON" during the three second bulb check). This test monitors the availability of current/voltage to the motors and solenoids. This malfunction indicates voltage is not available and would therefore not allow ABS operation if required.

Action Taken: A malfunction DTC is stored, ABS is disabled and the ABS warning lamp is turned "ON."

DTC Chart Test Description: Number(s) below refer to circled number(s) on the diagnostic chart.

1. Checks to see if DTC 16 is also set as current or history. If DTC 16 is also set, proceed to that chart first.
2. Verifies that the malfunction is currently present.
3. Verifies that the relay can be turned "ON" and provide voltage to the EBCM.
4. Checks for high resistance in the switched battery circuit from the relay to the EBCM.
5. Checks for high resistance in the switched battery circuit from the battery to the relay.
6. Verifies the condition of the ABS enable relay.
7. Checks for poor terminal contact or corrosion at the connectors.
8. Determines if the EBCM is the cause of the malfunction.

Diagnostic Aids: An "Intermittent" problem may be caused by a poor connection, rubbed through wire insulation, or a wire that is broken inside the insulation.

The frequency of the problem can be checked by using the enhanced diagnostic function of the Tech 1,

Any circuitry that is suspected as causing the "Intermittent" complaint should be thoroughly checked for backed out terminals, improper mating, broken locks, improperly formed or damaged terminals, poor terminal to wiring connections or physical damage to the wiring harness.

VIBRATION, TEMPERATURE EFFECTS:

Check for vibration effects by performing the relay test function of the Tech 1. With the relay test commanded "ON," lightly tap the top and sides of the relay while monitoring relay voltage. If the relay voltage changes significantly, replace the relay.

If DTC 14 only sets when the vehicle is initially started in cold ambient conditions (temperature less than 32°F-0°C), replace the relay.

GC402940106601DX

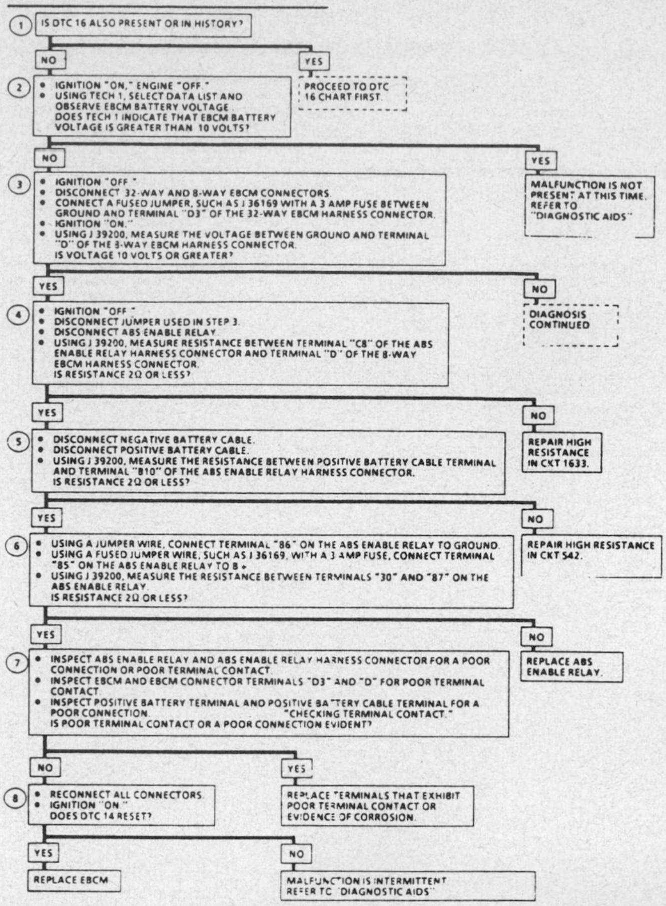
1 IS DTC 16 ALSO PRESENT OR IN HISTORY?
NO
YES
PROCEED TO DTC 16 CHART FIRST.
2 • IGNITION "ON," ENGINE "OFF." • USING TECH 1, SELECT DATA LIST AND OBSERVE EBCM BATTERY VOLTAGE. DOES TECH 1 INDICATE THAT EBCM BATTERY VOLTAGE IS GREATER THAN 10 VOLTS?
NO
YES
MALFUNCTION IS NOT PRESENT AT THIS TIME. REFER TO "DIAGNOSTIC AIDS"
3 • IGNITION "OFF." • DISCONNECT 32-WAY AND 8-WAY EBCM CONNECTORS. • CONNECT A FUSED JUMPER, SUCH AS J 36169 WITH A 3 AMP FUSE BETWEEN GROUND AND TERMINAL "D3" OF THE 32-WAY EBCM HARNESS CONNECTOR. • IGNITION "ON." • USING J 39200, MEASURE THE VOLTAGE BETWEEN GROUND AND TERMINAL "D" OF THE 8-WAY EBCM HARNESS CONNECTOR. IS VOLTAGE 10 VOLTS OR GREATER?
YES
NO
DIAGNOSIS CONTINUED
4 • IGNITION "OFF." • DISCONNECT JUMPER USED IN STEP 3. • DISCONNECT ABS ENABLE RELAY. • USING J 39200, MEASURE RESISTANCE BETWEEN TERMINAL "C8" OF THE ABS ENABLE RELAY HARNESS CONNECTOR AND TERMINAL "D" OF THE 8-WAY EBCM HARNESS CONNECTOR. IS RESISTANCE 2Ω OR LESS?
YES
NO
REPAIR HIGH RESISTANCE IN CKT 1633.
5 • DISCONNECT NEGATIVE BATTERY CABLE. • DISCONNECT POSITIVE BATTERY CABLE. • USING J 39200, MEASURE THE RESISTANCE BETWEEN POSITIVE BATTERY CABLE TERMINAL AND TERMINAL "B10" OF THE ABS ENABLE RELAY HARNESS CONNECTOR. IS RESISTANCE 2Ω OR LESS?
YES
NO
REPAIR HIGH RESISTANCE IN CKT 542.
6 • USING A JUMPER WIRE, CONNECT TERMINAL "86" ON THE ABS ENABLE RELAY TO GROUND. • USING A FUSED JUMPER WIRE, SUCH AS J 36169, WITH A 3 AMP FUSE, CONNECT TERMINAL "85" ON THE ABS ENABLE RELAY TO B+ • USING J 39200, MEASURE THE RESISTANCE BETWEEN TERMINALS "30" AND "87" ON THE ABS ENABLE RELAY. IS RESISTANCE 2Ω OR LESS?
YES
NO
REPLACE ABS ENABLE RELAY.
7 • INSPECT ABS ENABLE RELAY AND ABS ENABLE RELAY HARNESS CONNECTOR FOR A POOR CONNECTION OR POOR TERMINAL CONTACT. • INSPECT EBCM AND EBCM CONNECTOR TERMINALS "D3" AND "D" FOR POOR TERMINAL CONTACT. • INSPECT POSITIVE BATTERY TERMINAL AND POSITIVE BATTERY CABLE TERMINAL FOR A POOR CONNECTION. "CHECKING TERMINAL CONTACT." IS POOR TERMINAL CONTACT OR A POOR CONNECTION EVIDENT?
NO
YES
REPLACE TERMINALS THAT EXHIBIT POOR TERMINAL CONTACT OR EVIDENCE OF CORROSION.
8 • RECONNECT ALL CONNECTORS. • IGNITION "ON." DOES DTC 14 RESET?
YES
REPLACE EBCM
NO
MALFUNCTION IS INTERMITTENT REFER TO "DIAGNOSTIC AIDS"

GC402940106601EX

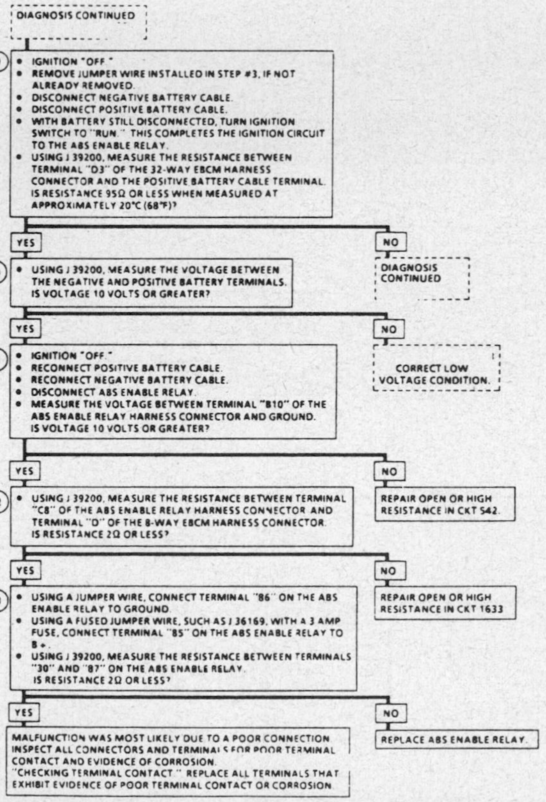
DIAGNOSIS CONTINUED
9 • IGNITION "OFF." • REMOVE JUMPER WIRE INSTALLED IN STEP #3, IF NOT ALREADY REMOVED. • DISCONNECT NEGATIVE BATTERY CABLE. • DISCONNECT POSITIVE BATTERY CABLE. • WITH BATTERY STILL DISCONNECTED, TURN IGNITION SWITCH TO "RUN." THIS COMPLETES THE IGNITION CIRCUIT TO THE ABS ENABLE RELAY. • USING J 39200, MEASURE THE RESISTANCE BETWEEN TERMINAL "D3" OF THE 32-WAY EBCM HARNESS CONNECTOR AND THE POSITIVE BATTERY CABLE TERMINAL. IS RESISTANCE 95Ω OR LESS WHEN MEASURED AT APPROXIMATELY 20°C (68°F)?
YES
NO
DIAGNOSIS CONTINUED
10 • USING J 39200, MEASURE THE VOLTAGE BETWEEN THE NEGATIVE AND POSITIVE BATTERY TERMINALS. IS VOLTAGE 10 VOLTS OR GREATER?
YES
NO
CORRECT LOW VOLTAGE CONDITION.
11 • IGNITION "OFF." • RECONNECT POSITIVE BATTERY CABLE. • RECONNECT NEGATIVE BATTERY CABLE. • DISCONNECT ABS ENABLE RELAY. • MEASURE THE VOLTAGE BETWEEN TERMINAL "B10" OF THE ABS ENABLE RELAY HARNESS CONNECTOR AND GROUND. IS VOLTAGE 10 VOLTS OR GREATER?
YES
NO
REPAIR OPEN OR HIGH RESISTANCE IN CKT 542.
12 • USING J 39200, MEASURE THE RESISTANCE BETWEEN TERMINAL "C8" OF THE ABS ENABLE RELAY HARNESS CONNECTOR AND TERMINAL "D" OF THE 8-WAY EBCM HARNESS CONNECTOR. IS RESISTANCE 2Ω OR LESS?
YES
NO
REPAIR OPEN OR HIGH RESISTANCE IN CKT 1633
13 • USING A JUMPER WIRE, CONNECT TERMINAL "86" ON THE ABS ENABLE RELAY TO GROUND. • USING A FUSED JUMPER WIRE, SUCH AS J 36169, WITH A 3 AMP FUSE, CONNECT TERMINAL "85" ON THE ABS ENABLE RELAY TO B+. • USING J 39200, MEASURE THE RESISTANCE BETWEEN TERMINALS "30" AND "87" ON THE ABS ENABLE RELAY. IS RESISTANCE 2Ω OR LESS?
YES
MALFUNCTION WAS MOST LIKELY DUE TO A POOR CONNECTION. INSPECT ALL CONNECTORS AND TERMINALS FOR POOR TERMINAL CONTACT AND EVIDENCE OF CORROSION. "CHECKING TERMINAL CONTACT." REPLACE ALL TERMINALS THAT EXHIBIT EVIDENCE OF POOR TERMINAL CONTACT OR CORROSION.
NO
REPLACE ABS ENABLE RELAY.

GC402940106602AX

DTC 14

ABS ENABLE RELAY CONTACT CIRCUIT OPEN

Circuit Description:

Ignition voltage is supplied through terminal "C10" of the ABS enable relay. The EBCM then is able to energize the pull-in coil by completing the ground circuit at terminal "D3" of the EBCM. The magnetic field created closes the ABS enable relay contacts and allows battery voltage and current to be supplied to the EBCM, which supplies power to the motors and solenoids.

DTC Will Set When: DTC 14 can be set anytime after the EBCM commands the ABS enable relay "ON" (the relay is first commanded "ON" during the three second bulb check). This test monitors the availability of current/voltage to the motors and solenoids. This malfunction indicates voltage is not available and would therefore not allow ABS operation if required.

Action Taken: A malfunction DTC is stored, ABS is disabled and the ABS warning lamp is turned "ON."

DTC Chart Test Description: Number(s) below refer to circled number(s) on the diagnostic chart.

9. Checks for high resistance in the entire relay coil circuit.
10. Verifies proper battery condition.
11. Verifies proper voltage is available at the ABS enable relay.
12. Checks for an open in the switched battery circuit from the relay to the EBCM.
13. Verifies the condition of the ABS enable relay.

Diagnostic Aids: An "Intermittent" problem may be caused by a poor connection, rubbed through wire insulation, or a wire that is broken inside the insulation.

The frequency of the problem can be checked by using the enhanced diagnostic function of the Tech 1,

Any circuitry that is suspected as causing the "Intermittent" complaint should be thoroughly checked for backed out terminals, improper mating, broken locks, improperly formed or damaged terminals, poor terminal to wiring connections or physical damage to the wiring harness.

VIBRATION, TEMPERATURE EFFECTS:

Check for vibration effects by performing the relay test function of the Tech 1. With the relay test commanded "ON," lightly tap the top and sides of the relay while monitoring relay voltage. If the relay voltage changes significantly, replace the relay.

If DTC 14 only sets when the vehicle is initially started in cold ambient conditions (temperature less than 32°F-0°C), replace the relay.

GC402940106602BX

Fig. 238 Code A014: ABS Enable Relay Contact Circuit Open (2 of 3). 1993–94 Camaro & Firebird, 1994 Grand Prix, Century & Cutlass Ciera & Cruiser

DTC 14

ABS ENABLE RELAY CONTACT CIRCUIT OPEN

Circuit Description:
Ignition voltage is supplied through terminal "C10" of the ABS enable relay. The EBCM then is able to energize the pull-in coil by completing the ground circuit at terminal "D3" of the EBCM. The magnetic field created closes the ABS enable relay contacts and allows battery voltage and current to be supplied to the EBCM, which supplies power to the motors and solenoids.

DTC Will Set When: DTC 14 can be set anytime after the EBCM commands the ABS enable relay "ON" (the relay is first commanded "ON" during the three second bulb check). This test monitors the availability of current/voltage to the motors and solenoids. This malfunction indicates voltage is not available and would therefore not allow ABS operation if required.

Action Taken: A malfunction DTC is stored, ABS is disabled and the ABS warning lamp is turned "ON."

DTC Chart Test Description: Number(s) below refer to circled number(s) on the diagnostic chart.
14. Checks for proper resistance of the relay coil.
15. Checks for high resistance in the ABS enable relay control circuit between the relay and the EBCM.
16. Checks for high resistance in the ABS enable relay control circuit between the battery and the relay.

Diagnostic Aids: An "Intermittent" problem may be caused by a poor connection, rubbed through wire insulation, or a wire that is broken inside the insulation.

The frequency of the problem can be checked by using the enhanced diagnostic function of the Tech 1,

Any circuitry that is suspected as causing the "Intermittent" complaint should be thoroughly checked for backed out terminals, improper mating, broken locks, improperly formed or damaged terminals, poor terminal to wiring connections or physical damage to the wiring harness.

VIBRATION, TEMPERATURE EFFECTS:

Check for vibration effects by performing the relay test function of the Tech 1. With the relay test commanded "ON," lightly tap the top and sides of the relay while monitoring relay voltage. If the relay voltage changes significantly, replace the relay.

If DTC 14 only sets when the vehicle is initially started in cold ambient conditions (temperature less than 32°F-0°C), replace the relay.

GC402940106603AX

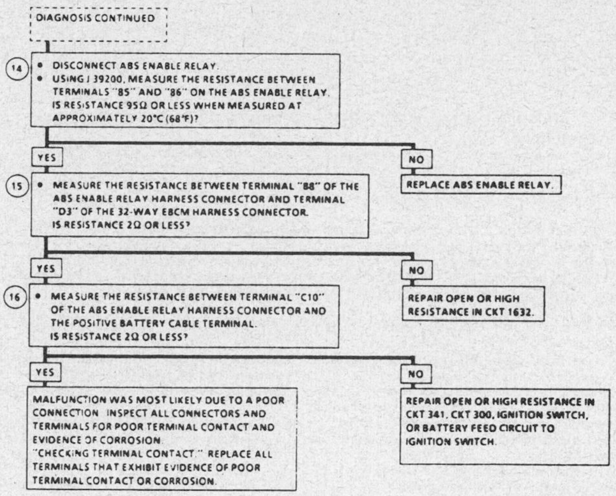
DIAGNOSIS CONTINUED
14
• DISCONNECT ABS ENABLE RELAY.
• USING J 39200, MEASURE THE RESISTANCE BETWEEN TERMINALS "85" AND "86" ON THE ABS ENABLE RELAY. IS RESISTANCE 95Ω OR LESS WHEN MEASURED AT APPROXIMATELY 20°C (68°F)?
YES
NO
REPLACE ABS ENABLE RELAY.
15
• MEASURE THE RESISTANCE BETWEEN TERMINAL "88" OF THE ABS ENABLE RELAY HARNESS CONNECTOR AND TERMINAL "D3" OF THE 32-WAY EBCM HARNESS CONNECTOR. IS RESISTANCE 2Ω OR LESS?
YES
NO
REPAIR OPEN OR HIGH RESISTANCE IN CKT 1632.
16
• MEASURE THE RESISTANCE BETWEEN TERMINAL "C10" OF THE ABS ENABLE RELAY HARNESS CONNECTOR AND THE POSITIVE BATTERY CABLE TERMINAL. IS RESISTANCE 2Ω OR LESS?
YES
NO
MALFUNCTION WAS MOST LIKELY DUE TO A POOR CONNECTION INSPECT ALL CONNECTORS AND TERMINALS FOR POOR TERMINAL CONTACT AND EVIDENCE OF CORROSION. "CHECKING TERMINAL CONTACT." REPLACE ALL TERMINALS THAT EXHIBIT EVIDENCE OF POOR TERMINAL CONTACT OR CORROSION.
REPAIR OPEN OR HIGH RESISTANCE IN CKT 341, CKT 300, IGNITION SWITCH, OR BATTERY FEED CIRCUIT TO IGNITION SWITCH.

GC402940106603BX

Fig. 238 Code A014: ABS Enable Relay Contact Circuit Open (3 of 3). 1993–94 Camaro & Firebird, 1994 Grand Prix, Century & Cutlass Ciera & Cruiser

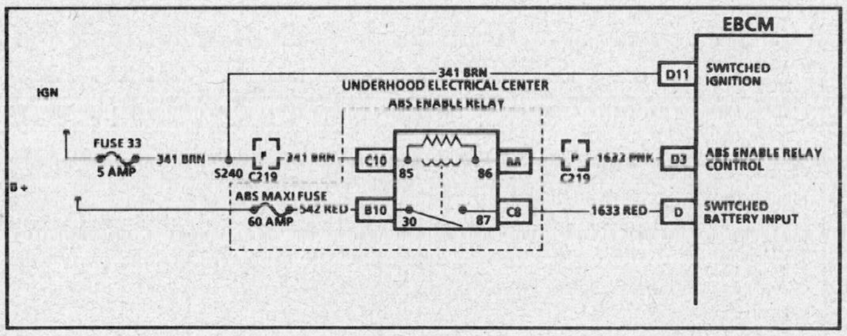
EBCM
IGN
B+
FUSE 33
5 AMP
341 BRN
S240
C219
341 BRN
UNDERHOOD ELECTRICAL CENTER
ABS ENABLE RELAY
ABS MAXI FUSE
60 AMP
542 RED
C10
85
86
B10
30
87
8A
C8
1632 PNK
1633 RED
D11
D3
D
SWITCHED IGNITION
ABS ENABLE RELAY CONTROL
SWITCHED BATTERY INPUT

GC402940106700AX

Grand Prix

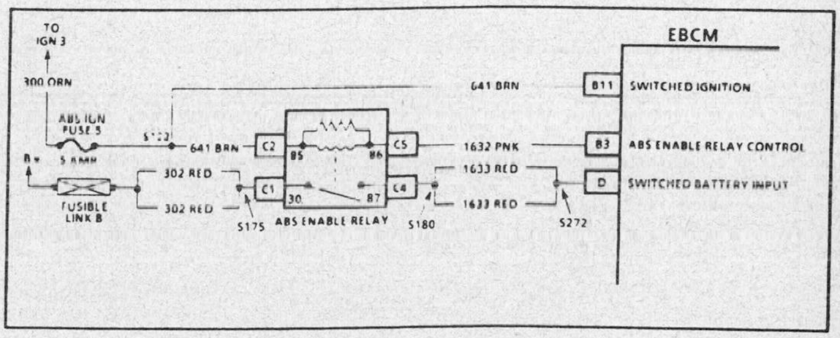
TO IGN 3
300 ORN
EBCM
ABS IGN FUSE 5
5 AMP
B+
FUSIBLE LINK B
641 BRN
302 RED
302 RED
S175
ABS ENABLE RELAY
S180
C2
C1
85
86
30
87
C5
C4
1632 PNK
1633 RED
1633 RED
S272
B11
B3
D
SWITCHED IGNITION
ABS ENABLE RELAY CONTROL
SWITCHED BATTERY INPUT

GC402940106700BX

Camaro & Firebird

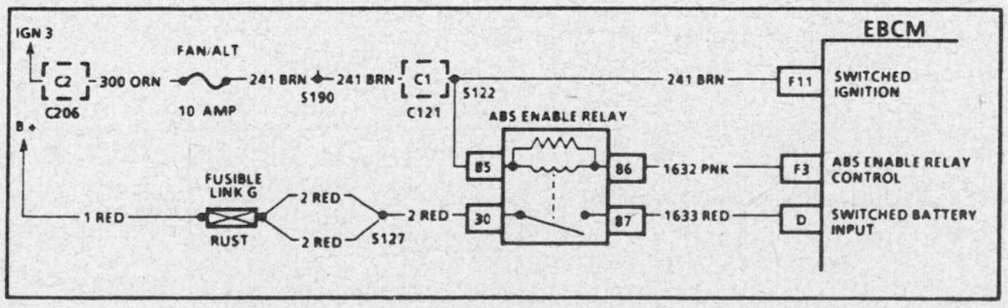
IGN 3
C2
300 ORN
C206
FAN/ALT
10 AMP
241 BRN
241 BRN
S190
C1
C121
S122
241 BRN
EBCM
B+
ABS ENABLE RELAY
85
86
1632 PNK
F11
SWITCHED IGNITION
F3
ABS ENABLE RELAY CONTROL
FUSIBLE LINK G
1 RED
2 RED
2 RED
2 RED
RUST
S127
30
87
1633 RED
D
SWITCHED BATTERY INPUT

GC402940106700CX

Century & Cutlass Ciera & Cruiser

Fig. 239 Code A015: ABS Relay Contact Circuit Short To Battery Or Always Closed (Part 1 of 2). 1993-94 Camaro & Firebird, 1994 Grand Prix, Century & Cutlass Ciera & Cruiser

DTC 15

ABS RLY CONTACT CKT SHORT TO BATT OR ALWAYS CLOSED

Circuit Description:

Ignition voltage is supplied through terminal "C10" of the ABS enable relay. The EBCM then is able to energize the pull-in coil by completing the ground circuit at terminal "D3" of the EBCM. The magnetic field created closes the ABS enable relay contacts and allows battery voltage and current to be supplied to the EBCM, which supplies power to the motors and solenoids.

DTC Will Set When: DTC 15 can be set only before the EBCM commands the relay "ON." This test determines if the ABS enable relay is energized when it should not be. This malfunction would not allow the ABS enable relay to remove power to the ABS system. If a second malfunction were to occur that requires the ABS enable relay to be turned "OFF," that malfunction cannot be removed if the relay cannot be controlled. The malfunction must be present for three consecutive drive cycles before the DTC is set.

Action Taken: A malfunction DTC is stored. ABS is not disabled.

DTC Chart Test Description: Number(s) below refer to circled number(s) on the diagnostic chart.

1. Checks to see if other DTCs are set.
2. Indicates that the EBCM is capable of controlling the ABS enable relay as commanded.
3. Checks for a possible short to battery voltage in CKT 1633.
4. Determines whether the short to voltage is in CKT 1633 or due to a malfunctioning relay.
5. Checks for a possible intermittent in wiring or connectors.

Diagnostic Aids: An "Intermittent" malfunction may be caused by a poor connection, rubbed through wire insulation, or a wire that is broken inside the insulation.

The frequency of the malfunction can be checked by using the enhanced diagnostic function of the Tech 1,

Any circuitry, that is suspected as causing the intermittent complaint, should be thoroughly checked for backed out terminals, improper mating, broken locks, improperly formed or damaged terminals, poor terminal to wiring connections or physical damage to the wiring harness.

GC402940106700DX

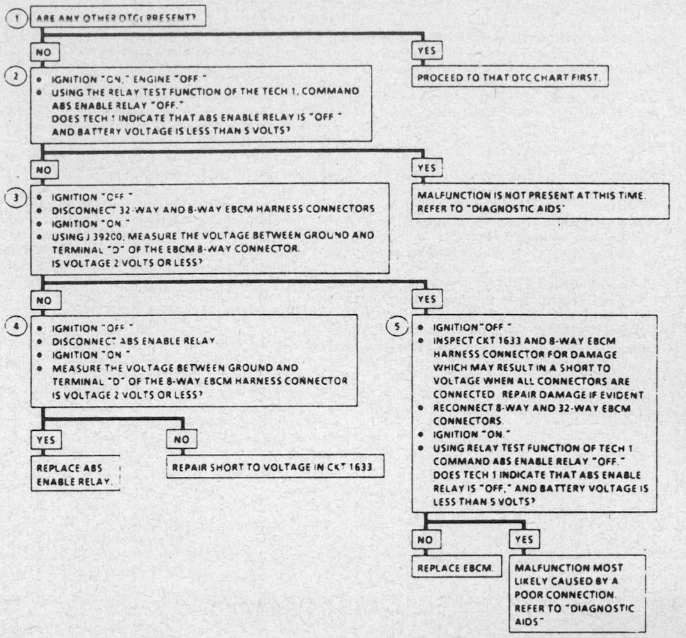
1 ARE ANY OTHER DTCs PRESENT?
NO
YES
PROCEED TO THAT DTC CHART FIRST.
2 • IGNITION "ON," ENGINE "OFF."
• USING THE RELAY TEST FUNCTION OF THE TECH 1, COMMAND ABS ENABLE RELAY "OFF."
DOES TECH 1 INDICATE THAT ABS ENABLE RELAY IS "OFF" AND BATTERY VOLTAGE IS LESS THAN 5 VOLTS?
NO
YES
MALFUNCTION IS NOT PRESENT AT THIS TIME. REFER TO "DIAGNOSTIC AIDS"
3 • IGNITION "OFF."
• DISCONNECT 32-WAY AND 8-WAY EBCM HARNESS CONNECTORS
• IGNITION "ON."
• USING J 39200, MEASURE THE VOLTAGE BETWEEN GROUND AND TERMINAL "D" OF THE EBCM 8-WAY CONNECTOR.
IS VOLTAGE 2 VOLTS OR LESS?
NO
YES
4 • IGNITION "OFF."
• DISCONNECT ABS ENABLE RELAY.
• IGNITION "ON."
• MEASURE THE VOLTAGE BETWEEN GROUND AND TERMINAL "D" OF THE 8-WAY EBCM HARNESS CONNECTOR
IS VOLTAGE 2 VOLTS OR LESS?
YES
REPLACE ABS ENABLE RELAY.
NO
REPAIR SHORT TO VOLTAGE IN CKT 1633.
5 • IGNITION "OFF."
• INSPECT CKT 1633 AND 8-WAY EBCM HARNESS CONNECTOR FOR DAMAGE WHICH MAY RESULT IN A SHORT TO VOLTAGE WHEN ALL CONNECTORS ARE CONNECTED. REPAIR DAMAGE IF EVIDENT
• RECONNECT 8-WAY AND 32-WAY EBCM CONNECTORS.
• IGNITION "ON."
• USING RELAY TEST FUNCTION OF TECH 1 COMMAND ABS ENABLE RELAY "OFF."
DOES TECH 1 INDICATE THAT ABS ENABLE RELAY IS "OFF," AND BATTERY VOLTAGE IS LESS THAN 5 VOLTS?
NO
REPLACE EBCM.
YES
MALFUNCTION MOST LIKELY CAUSED BY A POOR CONNECTION. REFER TO "DIAGNOSTIC AIDS"

GC402940106700EX

Fig. 239 Code A015: ABS Relay Contact Circuit Short To Battery Or Always Closed (Part 2 of 2). 1993-94 Camaro & Firebird, 1994 Grand Prix, Century & Cutlass Ciera & Cruiser

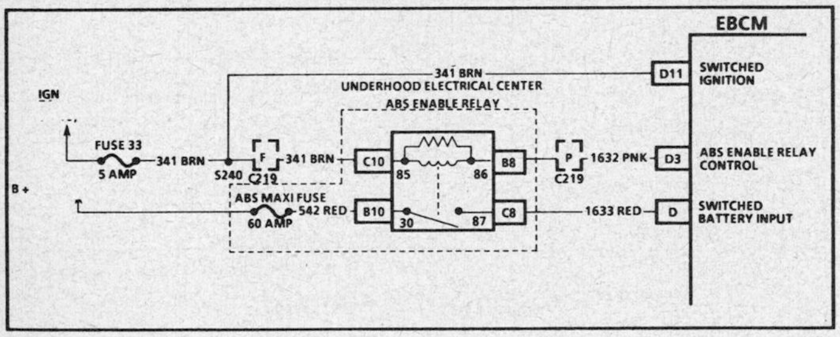
EBCM
IGN
B+
FUSE 33
5 AMP
341 BRN
S240
C219
UNDERHOOD ELECTRICAL CENTER
ABS ENABLE RELAY
ABS MAXI FUSE
60 AMP
542 RED
C10
B10
85
86
30
87
B8
C8
1632 PNK
1633 RED
D11
D3
D
SWITCHED IGNITION
ABS ENABLE RELAY CONTROL
SWITCHED BATTERY INPUT

GC402940106800AX

Grand Prix

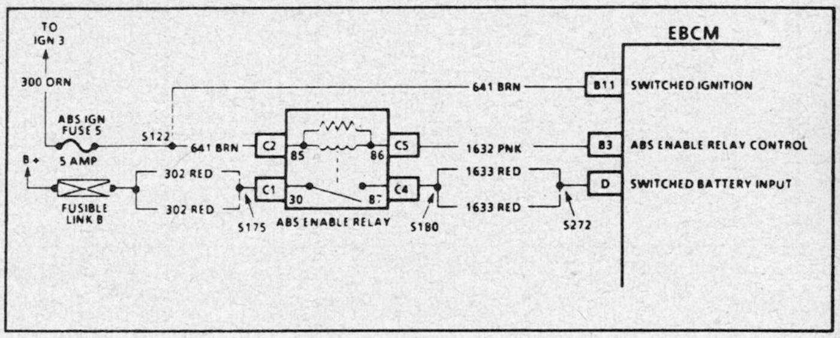
TO IGN 3
300 ORN
ABS IGN FUSE 5
5 AMP
B+
FUSIBLE LINK B
S122
641 BRN
302 RED
C2
C1
C5
C4
85
86
30
87
ABS ENABLE RELAY
S175
S180
1632 PNK
1633 RED
S272
EBCM
B11
B3
D
SWITCHED IGNITION
ABS ENABLE RELAY CONTROL
SWITCHED BATTERY INPUT

GC402940106800BX

Camaro & Firebird

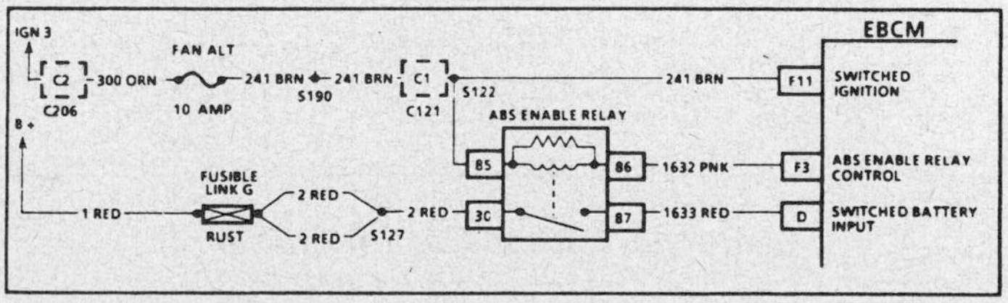
IGN 3
C2
C206
300 ORN
FAN ALT
10 AMP
241 BRN
S190
C1
C121
S122
ABS ENABLE RELAY
B+
FUSIBLE LINK G
RUST
1 RED
2 RED
S127
B5
3C
86
B7
1632 PNK
1633 RED
EBCM
F11
F3
D
SWITCHED IGNITION
ABS ENABLE RELAY CONTROL
SWITCHED BATTERY INPUT

GC402940106800CX

Century & Cutlass Ciera & Cruiser

Fig. 240 Code A016: ABS Enable Relay Coil Circuit Open (Part 1 of 2). 1993-94 Camaro & Firebird, 1994 Grand Prix, Century & Cutlass Ciera & Cruiser

DTC 16

ABS ENABLE RELAY COIL CIRCUIT OPEN

Circuit Description:
Ignition voltage is supplied through terminal "C10" of the ABS enable relay. The EBCM then is able to energize the pull-in coil by completing the ground circuit at terminal "D3" of the EBCM. The magnetic field created closes the ABS enable relay contacts and allows battery voltage and current to be supplied to the EBCM, which supplies power to the motors and solenoids.

DTC Will Set When: DTC 16 can be set only after DTC 14 has been set. This test detects an open in the ABS enable relay coil circuit. An open in this circuit will not allow the ABS enable relay to be energized thus preventing voltage/current to the motors and solenoids. If this malfunction is present and the ignition is turned "OFF" before 5 km/h (3 mph) is reached, DTC 14 is set alone.

Action Taken: A malfunction DTC is stored, ABS is disabled and the ABS warning lamp is turned "ON."

DTC Chart Test Description: Number(s) below refer to circled number(s) on the diagnostic chart.

1. Indicates the EBCM is capable of controlling the ABS enable relay as commanded.
2. Checks to ensure that voltage is available to the pull-in coil of the enable relay.
3. Ensures that there is continuity through the pull-in coil of the enable relay.
4. Verifies the integrity of the relay control circuit.
5. Ensures malfunction was not due to poor terminal contact.

Diagnostic Aids: An "Intermittent" malfunction may be caused by a poor connection, rubbed through wire insulation, or a wire that is broken inside the insulation.

The frequency of the malfunction can be checked by using the enhanced diagnostic function of the Tech 1.

If the frequency of the malfunction is high, but is currently intermittent, check for high coil resistance by measuring between relay terminals "C10" and "B8" using J 39200. If resistance shows greater than 100Ω, replace the relay.

Any circuitry, that is suspected as causing the intermittent complaint, should be thoroughly checked for backed out terminals, improper mating, broken locks, improperly formed or damaged terminals, poor terminal to wiring connections or physical damage to the wiring harness.

GC402940106800DX

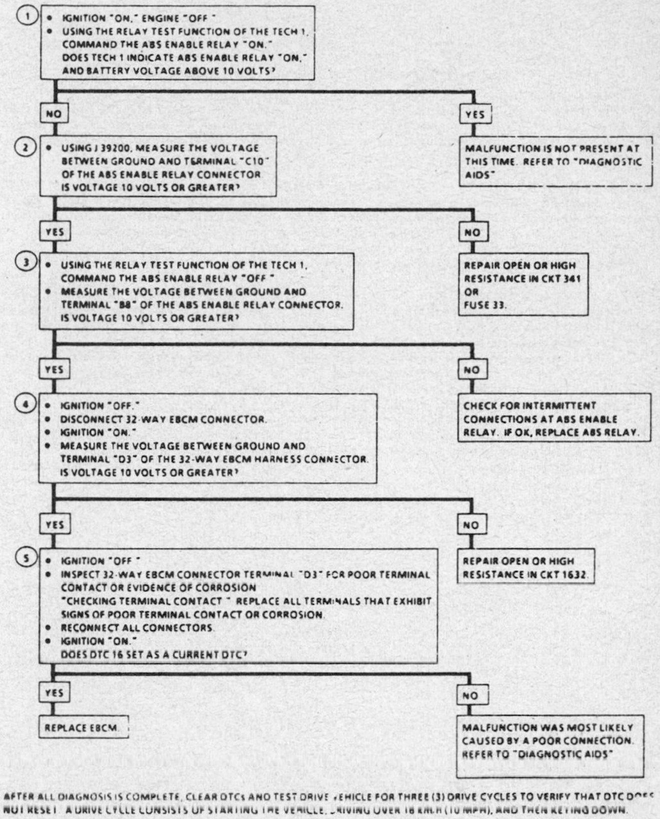

1
• IGNITION "ON," ENGINE "OFF."
• USING THE RELAY TEST FUNCTION OF THE TECH 1, COMMAND THE ABS ENABLE RELAY "ON."
DOES TECH 1 INDICATE ABS ENABLE RELAY "ON," AND BATTERY VOLTAGE ABOVE 10 VOLTS?
NO
YES
MALFUNCTION IS NOT PRESENT AT THIS TIME. REFER TO "DIAGNOSTIC AIDS"
2
• USING J 39200, MEASURE THE VOLTAGE BETWEEN GROUND AND TERMINAL "C10" OF THE ABS ENABLE RELAY CONNECTOR
IS VOLTAGE 10 VOLTS OR GREATER?
YES
NO
REPAIR OPEN OR HIGH RESISTANCE IN CKT 341 OR FUSE 33.
3
• USING THE RELAY TEST FUNCTION OF THE TECH 1, COMMAND THE ABS ENABLE RELAY "OFF."
• MEASURE THE VOLTAGE BETWEEN GROUND AND TERMINAL "B8" OF THE ABS ENABLE RELAY CONNECTOR.
IS VOLTAGE 10 VOLTS OR GREATER?
YES
NO
CHECK FOR INTERMITTENT CONNECTIONS AT ABS ENABLE RELAY. IF OK, REPLACE ABS RELAY.
4
• IGNITION "OFF."
• DISCONNECT 32-WAY EBCM CONNECTOR.
• IGNITION "ON."
• MEASURE THE VOLTAGE BETWEEN GROUND AND TERMINAL "D3" OF THE 32-WAY EBCM HARNESS CONNECTOR.
IS VOLTAGE 10 VOLTS OR GREATER?
YES
NO
REPAIR OPEN OR HIGH RESISTANCE IN CKT 1632.
5
• IGNITION "OFF."
• INSPECT 32-WAY EBCM CONNECTOR TERMINAL "D3" FOR POOR TERMINAL CONTACT OR EVIDENCE OF CORROSION
"CHECKING TERMINAL CONTACT." REPLACE ALL TERMINALS THAT EXHIBIT SIGNS OF POOR TERMINAL CONTACT OR CORROSION.
• RECONNECT ALL CONNECTORS.
• IGNITION "ON."
DOES DTC 16 SET AS A CURRENT DTC?
YES
NO
REPLACE EBCM.
MALFUNCTION WAS MOST LIKELY CAUSED BY A POOR CONNECTION. REFER TO "DIAGNOSTIC AIDS"
AFTER ALL DIAGNOSIS IS COMPLETE, CLEAR DTCs AND TEST DRIVE VEHICLE FOR THREE (3) DRIVE CYCLES TO VERIFY THAT DTC DOES NOT RESET. A DRIVE CYCLE CONSISTS OF STARTING THE VEHICLE, DRIVING OVER 16 KM/H (10 MPH), AND THEN KEYING DOWN.

GC402940106800EX

Fig. 240 Code A016: ABS Enable Relay Coil Circuit Open (Part 2 of 2). 1993-94 Camaro & Firebird, 1994 Grand Prix, Century & Cutlass Ciera & Cruiser

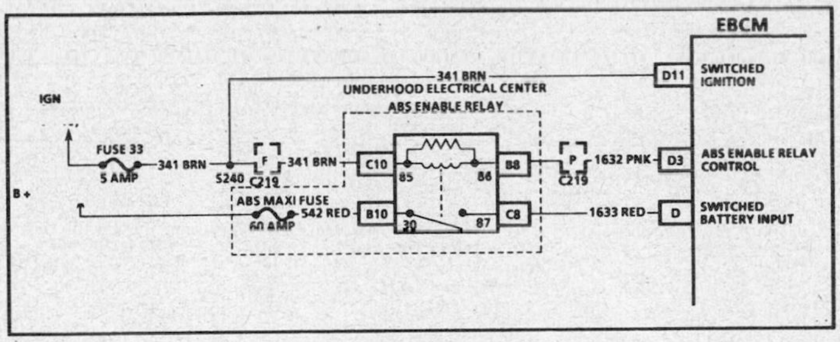

EBCM
IGN
B+
FUSE 33
5 AMP
341 BRN
S240
C219
UNDERHOOD ELECTRICAL CENTER
ABS ENABLE RELAY
ABS MAXI FUSE
60 AMP
542 RED
C10
B10
B8
C8
85
86
30
87
1632 PNK
1633 RED
D11
D3
D
SWITCHED IGNITION
ABS ENABLE RELAY CONTROL
SWITCHED BATTERY INPUT

GC402940106900AX

Grand Prix

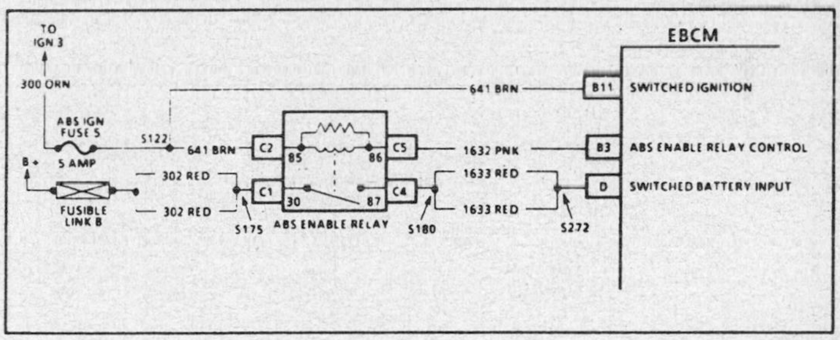

TO IGN 3
300 ORN
ABS IGN FUSE 5
5 AMP
S122
641 BRN
B+
FUSIBLE LINK B
302 RED
S175
ABS ENABLE RELAY
S180
C2
C1
C5
C4
85
86
30
87
1632 PNK
1633 RED
S272
EBCM
B11
B3
D
SWITCHED IGNITION
ABS ENABLE RELAY CONTROL
SWITCHED BATTERY INPUT

GC402940106900BX

Camaro & Firebird

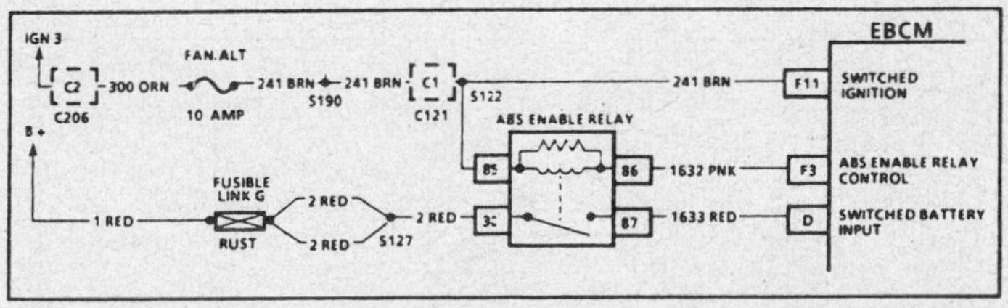

IGN 3
C2
300 ORN
C206
FAN ALT
10 AMP
241 BRN
S190
C1
C121
S122
B+
ABS ENABLE RELAY
FUSIBLE LINK G
1 RED
RUST
2 RED
S127
85
86
30
87
1632 PNK
1633 RED
EBCM
F11
F3
D
SWITCHED IGNITION
ABS ENABLE RELAY CONTROL
SWITCHED BATTERY INPUT

GC402940106900CX

Century & Cutlass Ciera & Cruiser

Fig. 241 Code A017: ABS Enable Relay Coil Circuit Shorted To Ground (Part 1 of 2). 1993-94 Camaro & Firebird, 1994 Grand Prix, Century & Cutlass Ciera & Cruiser

DTC 17

ABS ENABLE RELAY COIL CIRCUIT SHORTED TO GND

Circuit Description:
Ignition voltage is supplied through terminal "C10" of the ABS enable relay. The EBCM then is able to energize the pull-in coil by completing the ground circuit at terminal "D3" of the EBCM. The magnetic field created closes the ABS enable relay contacts and allows battery voltage and current to be supplied to the EBCM, which supplies voltage to the motors and solenoids.

DTC Will Set When: DTC 17 can be set before the EBCM commands the ABS enable relay "ON." This test determines if the ABS enable relay is energized when it should not be. This malfunction would not allow the ABS enable relay to remove power to the ABS system. If a second malfunction were to occur that requires the ABS enable relay to be turned "OFF," that malfunction cannot be removed if the relay cannot be controlled.

Action Taken: A malfunction DTC is stored. ABS is not disabled.

DTC Chart Test Description: Number(s) below refer to circled number(s) on the diagnostic chart.

1. Indicates that the EBCM is capable of controlling the ABS enable relay as commanded.
2. Checks to ensure that the ABS enable relay or control CKT 1632 are not shorted to ground.
3. Checks to see if the EBCM is internally shorted to ground. A grounded terminal "D3" would cause the ABS enable relay to be energized anytime the ignition was in the "ON" position.
4. Checks for a short to ground in control CKT 1632 or a defective relay.

Diagnostic Aids: An "Intermittent" malfunction may be caused by a poor connection, rubbed through wire insulation, or a wire that is broken inside the insulation.

The frequency of the malfunction can be checked by using the enhanced diagnostic function of the Tech 1,

Any circuitry, that is suspected as causing the intermittent complaint, should be thoroughly checked for backed out terminals, improper mating, broken locks, improperly formed or damaged terminals, poor terminal to wiring connections or physical damage to the wiring harness.

GC402940106900DX

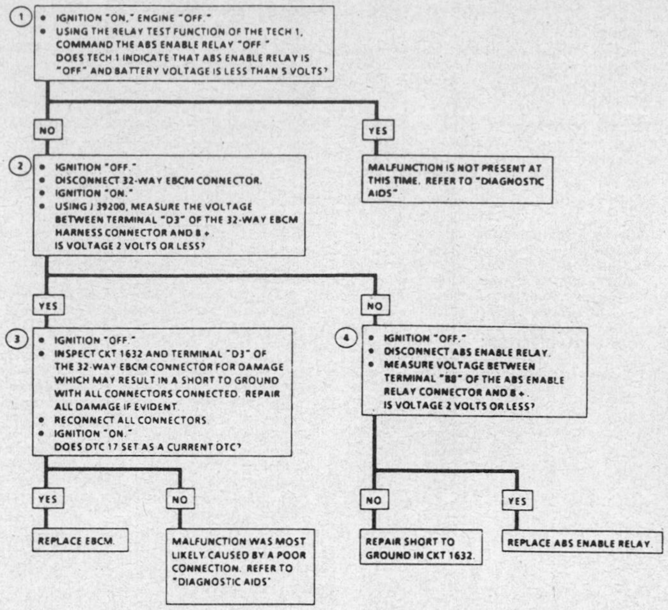
1
• IGNITION "ON," ENGINE "OFF."
• USING THE RELAY TEST FUNCTION OF THE TECH 1, COMMAND THE ABS ENABLE RELAY "OFF."
DOES TECH 1 INDICATE THAT ABS ENABLE RELAY IS "OFF" AND BATTERY VOLTAGE IS LESS THAN 5 VOLTS?
NO
YES
MALFUNCTION IS NOT PRESENT AT THIS TIME. REFER TO "DIAGNOSTIC AIDS".
2
• IGNITION "OFF."
• DISCONNECT 32-WAY EBCM CONNECTOR.
• IGNITION "ON."
• USING J 39200, MEASURE THE VOLTAGE BETWEEN TERMINAL "D3" OF THE 32-WAY EBCM HARNESS CONNECTOR AND B+.
IS VOLTAGE 2 VOLTS OR LESS?
YES
NO
3
• IGNITION "OFF."
• INSPECT CKT 1632 AND TERMINAL "D3" OF THE 32-WAY EBCM CONNECTOR FOR DAMAGE WHICH MAY RESULT IN A SHORT TO GROUND WITH ALL CONNECTORS CONNECTED. REPAIR ALL DAMAGE IF EVIDENT.
• RECONNECT ALL CONNECTORS.
• IGNITION "ON."
DOES DTC 17 SET AS A CURRENT DTC?
4
• IGNITION "OFF."
• DISCONNECT ABS ENABLE RELAY.
• MEASURE VOLTAGE BETWEEN TERMINAL "B8" OF THE ABS ENABLE RELAY CONNECTOR AND B+.
IS VOLTAGE 2 VOLTS OR LESS?
YES
NO
NO
YES
REPLACE EBCM.
MALFUNCTION WAS MOST LIKELY CAUSED BY A POOR CONNECTION. REFER TO "DIAGNOSTIC AIDS"
REPAIR SHORT TO GROUND IN CKT 1632.
REPLACE ABS ENABLE RELAY.

AFTER ALL DIAGNOSIS IS COMPLETE, CLEAR DTCs AND TEST DRIVE VEHICLE FOR THREE (3) DRIVE CYCLES TO VERIFY THAT DTC DOES NOT RESET. A DRIVE CYCLE CONSISTS OF STARTING THE VEHICLE, DRIVING OVER 16 km/h (10 MPH), AND THEN KEYING DOWN.

GC402940106900EX

Fig. 241 Code A017: ABS Enable Relay Coil Circuit Shorted To Ground (Part 2 of 2). 1993-94 Camaro & Firebird, 1994 Grand Prix, Century & Cutlass Ciera & Cruiser

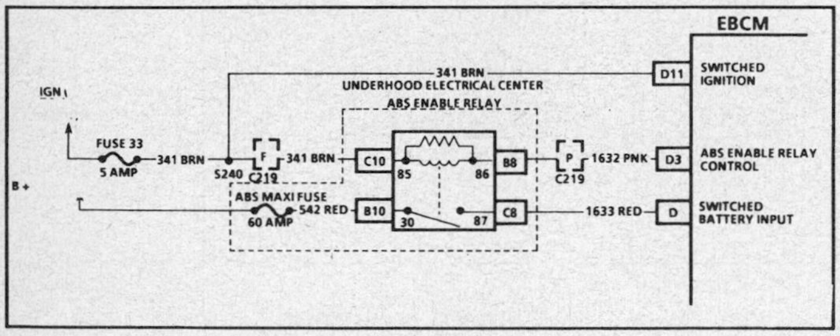
EBCM
341 BRN
UNDERHOOD ELECTRICAL CENTER
ABS ENABLE RELAY
D11
SWITCHED IGNITION
FUSE 33
5 AMP
341 BRN
S240
F
C219
341 BRN
C10
85
86
B8
P
C219
1632 PNK
D3
ABS ENABLE RELAY CONTROL
B+
ABS MAXI FUSE
60 AMP
542 RED
B10
30
87
C8
1633 RED
D
SWITCHED BATTERY INPUT

GC402940107000AX

Grand Prix

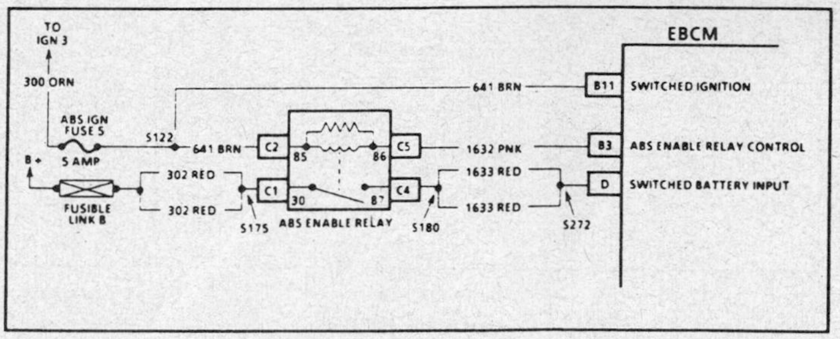
TO IGN 3
300 ORN
EBCM
641 BRN
B11
SWITCHED IGNITION
ABS IGN FUSE 5
5 AMP
S122
641 BRN
C2
85
86
C5
1632 PNK
B3
ABS ENABLE RELAY CONTROL
B+
302 RED
302 RED
FUSIBLE LINK B
C1
30
C4
1633 RED
1633 RED
D
SWITCHED BATTERY INPUT
S175
ABS ENABLE RELAY
S180
S272

GC402940107000BX

Camaro & Firebird

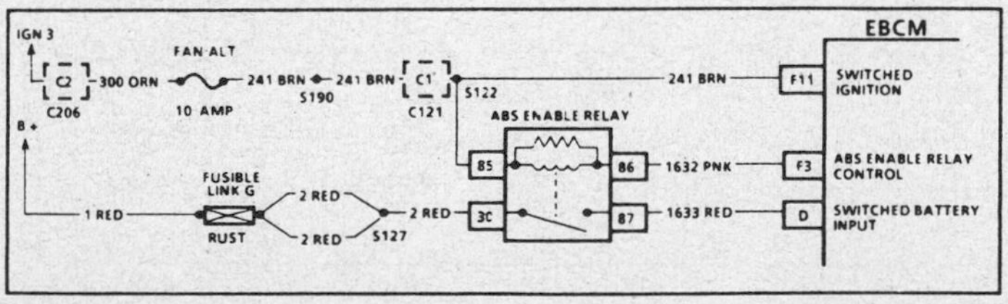
IGN 3
C2
300 ORN
C206
FAN-ALT
10 AMP
241 BRN
S190
241 BRN
C1
C121
S122
241 BRN
EBCM
F11
SWITCHED IGNITION
ABS ENABLE RELAY
B+
85
86
1632 PNK
F3
ABS ENABLE RELAY CONTROL
FUSIBLE LINK G
1 RED
RUST
2 RED
2 RED
S127
2 RED
3C
87
1633 RED
D
SWITCHED BATTERY INPUT

GC402940107000CX

Century & Cutlass Ciera & Cruiser

Fig. 242 Code A018: ABS Enable Relay Coil Circuit Shorted To Battery (Part 1 of 2). 1993-94 Camaro & Firebird, 1994 Grand Prix, Century & Cutlass Ciera & Cruiser

DTC 18

ABS ENABLE RELAY COIL CIRCUIT SHORTED TO BATT

Circuit Description:

Ignition voltage is supplied through terminal "C10" of the ABS enable relay. The EBCM then is able to energize the pull-in coil by completing the ground circuit at terminal "D3" of the EBCM. The magnetic field created closes the ABS enable relay contacts and allows battery voltage and current to be supplied to the EBCM, which supplies voltage to the motors and solenoids.

DTC Will Set When: DTC 18 can be set after the EBCM commands the enable relay "ON." This test monitors the availability of current/voltage to the motors and solenoids. A malfunction of this type will not allow voltage to be available to the motors and solenoids; therefore, ABS operation would not be allowed if required.

Action Taken: A malfunction DTC is stored, ABS is disabled and the ABS warning lamp is turned "ON."

DTC Chart Test Description: Number(s) below refer to circled number(s) on the diagnostic chart.

1. Indicates that the EBCM is capable of controlling the ABS enable relay as commanded.
2. Checks for a short to voltage on the relay control circuit.
3. Verifies that the relay coil has the appropriate resistance.
4. Verifies that the relay contacts are not failed closed.
5. Checks for possible poor terminal contact at the EBCM.

Diagnostic Aids: An "Intermittent" malfunction may be caused by a poor connection, rubbed through wire insulation, or a wire that is broken inside the insulation.

The frequency of the malfunction can be checked by using the enhanced diagnostic function of the Tech 1,

Any circuitry, that is suspected as causing the intermittent complaint, should be thoroughly checked for backed out terminals, improper mating, broken locks, improperly formed or damaged terminals, poor terminal to wiring connections or physical damage to the wiring harness.

GC402940107000DX

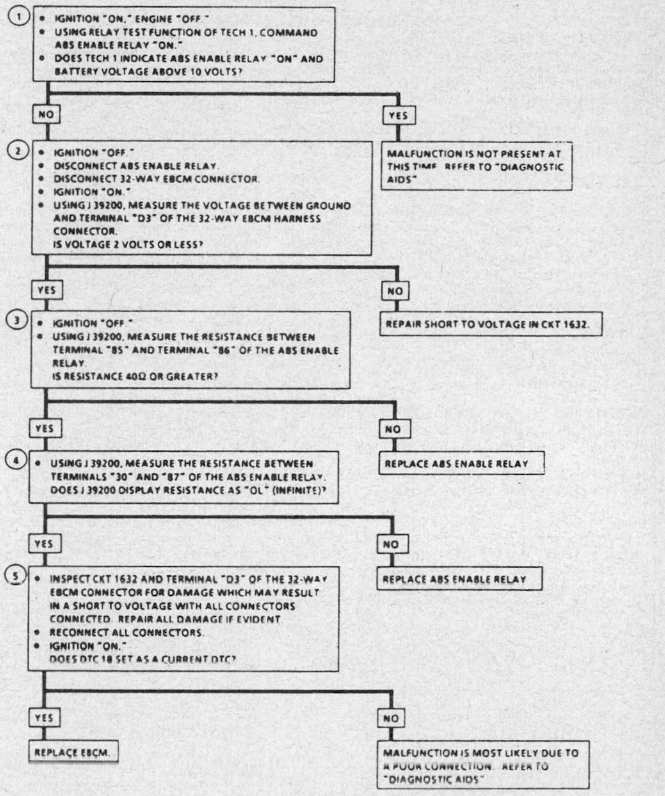
1
• IGNITION "ON," ENGINE "OFF."
• USING RELAY TEST FUNCTION OF TECH 1, COMMAND ABS ENABLE RELAY "ON."
• DOES TECH 1 INDICATE ABS ENABLE RELAY "ON" AND BATTERY VOLTAGE ABOVE 10 VOLTS?
NO
YES
MALFUNCTION IS NOT PRESENT AT THIS TIME REFER TO "DIAGNOSTIC AIDS"
2
• IGNITION "OFF."
• DISCONNECT ABS ENABLE RELAY.
• DISCONNECT 32-WAY EBCM CONNECTOR.
• IGNITION "ON."
• USING J 39200, MEASURE THE VOLTAGE BETWEEN GROUND AND TERMINAL "D3" OF THE 32-WAY EBCM HARNESS CONNECTOR.
IS VOLTAGE 2 VOLTS OR LESS?
YES
NO
REPAIR SHORT TO VOLTAGE IN CKT 1632.
3
• IGNITION "OFF."
• USING J 39200, MEASURE THE RESISTANCE BETWEEN TERMINAL "85" AND TERMINAL "86" OF THE ABS ENABLE RELAY.
IS RESISTANCE 40Ω OR GREATER?
YES
NO
REPLACE ABS ENABLE RELAY
4
• USING J 39200, MEASURE THE RESISTANCE BETWEEN TERMINALS "30" AND "87" OF THE ABS ENABLE RELAY.
DOES J 39200 DISPLAY RESISTANCE AS "OL" (INFINITE)?
YES
NO
REPLACE ABS ENABLE RELAY
5
• INSPECT CKT 1632 AND TERMINAL "D3" OF THE 32-WAY EBCM CONNECTOR FOR DAMAGE WHICH MAY RESULT IN A SHORT TO VOLTAGE WITH ALL CONNECTORS CONNECTED. REPAIR ALL DAMAGE IF EVIDENT.
• RECONNECT ALL CONNECTORS.
• IGNITION "ON."
DOES DTC 18 SET AS A CURRENT DTC?
YES
NO
REPLACE EBCM.
MALFUNCTION IS MOST LIKELY DUE TO A POOR CONNECTION. REFER TO "DIAGNOSTIC AIDS"

AFTER ALL DIAGNOSIS IS COMPLETE, CLEAR DTCs AND TEST DRIVE VEHICLE FOR THREE (3) DRIVE CYCLES TO VERIFY THAT DTC DOES NOT RESET. A DRIVE CYCLE CONSISTS OF STARTING THE VEHICLE, DRIVING OVER 16 km/h (10 MPH), AND THEN KEYING DOWN.

GC402940107000EX

Fig. 242 Code A018: ABS Enable Relay Coil Circuit Shorted To Battery (Part 2 of 2). 1993-94 Camaro & Firebird, 1994 Grand Prix, Century & Cutlass Ciera & Cruiser

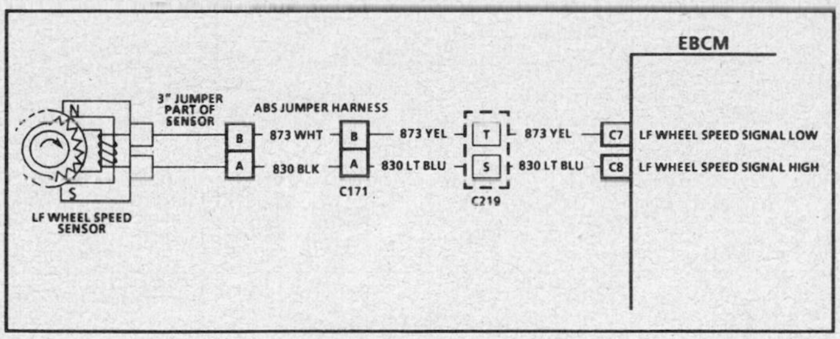
EBCM
3" JUMPER PART OF SENSOR
ABS JUMPER HARNESS
N
S
B
A
873 WHT
830 BLK
B
A
C171
873 YEL
830 LT BLU
T
S
C219
873 YEL
830 LT BLU
C7
C8
LF WHEEL SPEED SIGNAL LOW
LF WHEEL SPEED SIGNAL HIGH
LF WHEEL SPEED SENSOR

GC402940107100AX

Grand Prix

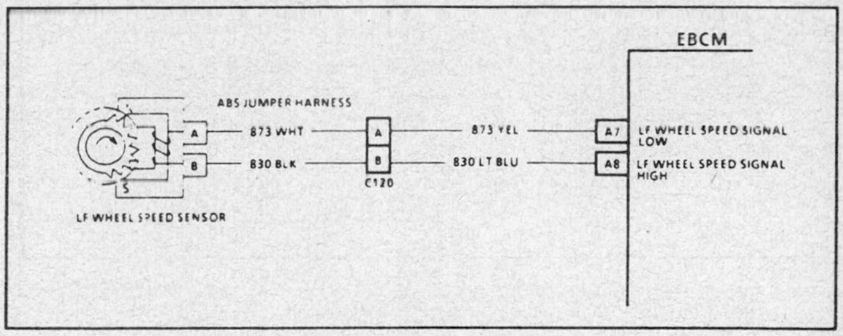
EBCM
ABS JUMPER HARNESS
A
B
873 WHT
830 BLK
A
B
C120
873 YEL
830 LT BLU
A7
A8
LF WHEEL SPEED SIGNAL LOW
LF WHEEL SPEED SIGNAL HIGH
S
LF WHEEL SPEED SENSOR

GC402940107100BX

Camaro & Firebird

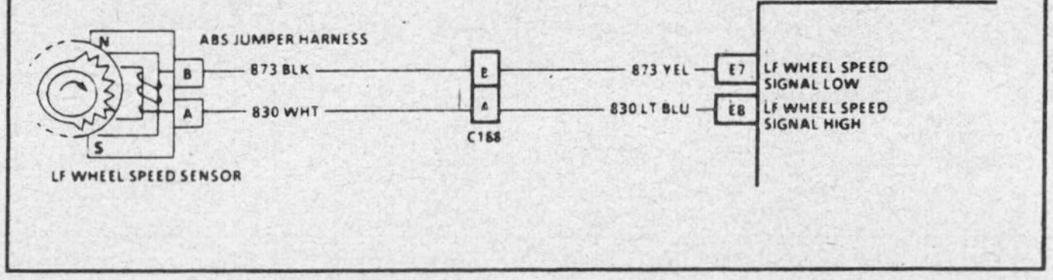
EBCM
ABS JUMPER HARNESS
N
S
B
A
873 BLK
830 WHT
B
A
C188
873 YEL
830 LT BLU
E7
E8
LF WHEEL SPEED SIGNAL LOW
LF WHEEL SPEED SIGNAL HIGH
LF WHEEL SPEED SENSOR

GC402940107100CX

Century & Cutlass Ciera & Cruiser

Fig. 243 Code A021: Left Front Wheel Speed = 0 (Part 1 of 2). 1993-94 Camaro & Firebird, 1994 Grand Prix, Century & Cutlass Ciera & Cruiser

DTC 21

LEFT FRONT WHEEL SPEED = 0

Circuit Description:

As a toothed ring passes by the wheel speed sensor, changes in the electromagnetic field cause the wheel speed sensor to produce a sinusoidal (AC) voltage signal whose frequency is proportional to wheel speed. The magnitude of this signal is directly related to wheel speed and the proximity of the wheel speed sensor to the toothed ring, often referred to as the air gap.

DTC Will Set When: DTC 21 can be set when the vehicle is not in an ABS stop. If the left front wheel speed = 0 and the vehicle's reference speed is greater than 8 km/h (5 mph), a malfunction exists.

Action Taken: A malfunction DTC is stored, ABS is disabled and the ABS warning lamp is turned "ON."

DTC Chart Test Description: Number(s) below refer to circled number(s) on the diagnostic chart.

1. This step identifies a wheel speed sensor or circuitry that is damaged and visibly apparent.
2. Checks to see that the wheel speed sensor coil is within proper resistance values.
3. Verifies that the wheel speed sensor can generate an appropriate output signal.
4. This ensures that the wheel speed circuitry is not shorted together.
5. Ensures that the malfunction was not due to physical damage.

Diagnostic Aids: An "Intermittent" malfunction may be caused by a poor connection, rubbed through wire insulation, or a wire that is broken inside the insulation.

The frequency of the malfunction can be checked by using the enhanced diagnostic function of the Tech 1,

If the customer's comments reflect that the ABS warning lamp is "ON" only during moist environmental changes (rain, snow, vehicle wash), all wheel speed sensor circuitry should be thoroughly inspected for signs of water intrusion. If DTC is not current, clear DTCs and simulate the effects of water intrusion. Use the following procedure. Spray down the suspected area with a 5% salt water solution (two teaspoons of salt to 12 oz. of water). Test drive vehicle over various road surfaces (bumps, turns, etc.) above 24 km/h (15 mph) for at least 30 seconds. If DTC returns, replace suspected harness.

Any circuitry, that is suspected as causing the intermittent complaint, should be thoroughly checked for backed out terminals, improper mating, broken locks, improperly formed or damaged terminals, poor terminal to wiring connections or physical damage to the wiring harness.

Resistance of the wheel speed sensor will increase with an increase in sensor temperature.

When replacing a wheel speed sensor, inspect the sensor terminals and harness connector for corrosion and/or water intrusion. If evidence of corrosion or water intrusion exists, replace wheel speed sensor jumper harness. Likewise, if replacing a wheel speed sensor jumper harness, inspect sensor terminals. If evidence of corrosion or water intrusion exists, replace wheel speed sensor. Refer to "On-Vehicle Service" in this section.

GC402940107100DX

Important

- WHEEL SPEED SENSOR INTERMITTENT MALFUNCTIONS MAY BE DIFFICULT TO LOCATE. CARE SHOULD BE TAKEN NOT TO DISTURB ANY ELECTRICAL CONNECTIONS PRIOR TO AN INDICATED STEP OF THIS CHART. THIS WILL ENSURE THAT AN INTERMITTENT CONNECTION WILL NOT BE CORRECTED BEFORE THE SOURCE OF THE MALFUNCTION IS FOUND.

(1)
- IGNITION "OFF."
- PHYSICALLY INSPECT THE LEFT FRONT WHEEL SPEED SENSOR, LEFT FRONT WHEEL SPEED SENSOR JUMPER HARNESS, AND CONNECTORS FOR DAMAGE. INSPECT THE WHEEL SPEED SENSOR AND TOOTHED RING FOR LOOSENESS OR DAMAGE. PAY PARTICULAR ATTENTION TO THE TOOTHED RING. ANY DEVIATION WILL AFFECT THE WHEEL SPEED SENSOR OUTPUT SIGNAL.

IS PHYSICAL DAMAGE INDICATED?

YES: REPLACE WHEEL SPEED SENSOR AND/OR JUMPER HARNESS IF DAMAGED. REPAIR ANY SENSOR OR TOOTHED RING LOOSENESS. DRIVE VEHICLE ABOVE 24 km/h (15 MPH) TO ENSURE DTC 21 DOES NOT SET.

NO:

(2)
- DISCONNECT LEFT FRONT WHEEL SPEED SENSOR DIRECTLY AT SENSOR.
- USING J 39200, MEASURE THE RESISTANCE BETWEEN SENSOR TERMINALS "A" AND "B."

IS RESISTANCE BETWEEN 1661 AND 1929Ω WHEN SENSOR IS 20°C (68°F)? *(IF TEMPERATURE OF THE SENSOR IS SUSPECTED TO BE OTHER THAN 20°C (68°F), REFER TO THE TABLE BELOW FOR APPLICABLE SENSOR RESISTANCE VALUES; THE VALUES IN THE TABLE ARE FOR TEMPERATURE OF THE SENSOR, NOT AIR TEMPERATURE.)*

NO: REPLACE WHEEL SPEED SENSOR.

YES:

(3)
- WITH J 39200 STILL CONNECTED, SELECT A/C VOLTAGE SCALE.
- SPIN WHEEL BY HAND WHILE OBSERVING VOLTAGE.

IS VOLTAGE AT LEAST 100 mV (VOLTAGE WILL INCREASE AS WHEEL SPEED INCREASES)?

NO: VERIFY THAT TOOTHED RING IS INTACT. IF OK, REPLACE WHEEL SPEED SENSOR

YES:

(4)
- IGNITION "OFF."
- DISCONNECT 32-WAY EBCM CONNECTOR.
- USING J 39200, MEASURE THE RESISTANCE BETWEEN TERMINAL "C7" AND "C8" OF THE 32-WAY EBCM HARNESS CONNECTOR.

DOES J 39200 DISPLAY RESISTANCE AS "OL" (INFINITE)?

NO: REPAIR SHORT BETWEEN CKTs 830 AND 873

YES:

(5)
- INSPECT CKTs 830 AND 873 AND 32-WAY EBCM CONNECTOR FOR DAMAGE WHICH MAY RESULT IN A SHORT BETWEEN CKTs 830 AND 873 WITH ALL CONNECTORS CONNECTED. REPAIR ALL DAMAGE IF EVIDENT.
- RECONNECT ALL CONNECTORS.
- TEST DRIVE VEHICLE ABOVE 24 km/h (15 MPH) FOR AT LEAST 30 SECONDS.

DOES DTC 21 SET AS A CURRENT DTC?

YES: REPLACE EBCM.

NO: MALFUNCTION IS INTERMITTENT. REFER TO "DIAGNOSTIC AIDS"

FRONT WHEEL SPEED SENSOR

TEMPERATURE OF SENSOR VS. SENSOR RESISTANCE (APPROXIMATE

TEMP (°C)	TEMP (°F)	RESISTANCE (OHMS)
-34 TO 4	-30 TO 40	1309 TO 1808
5 TO 43	41 TO 110	1557 TO 2103
44 TO 93	111 TO 200	1811 TO 2482

GC402940107100EX

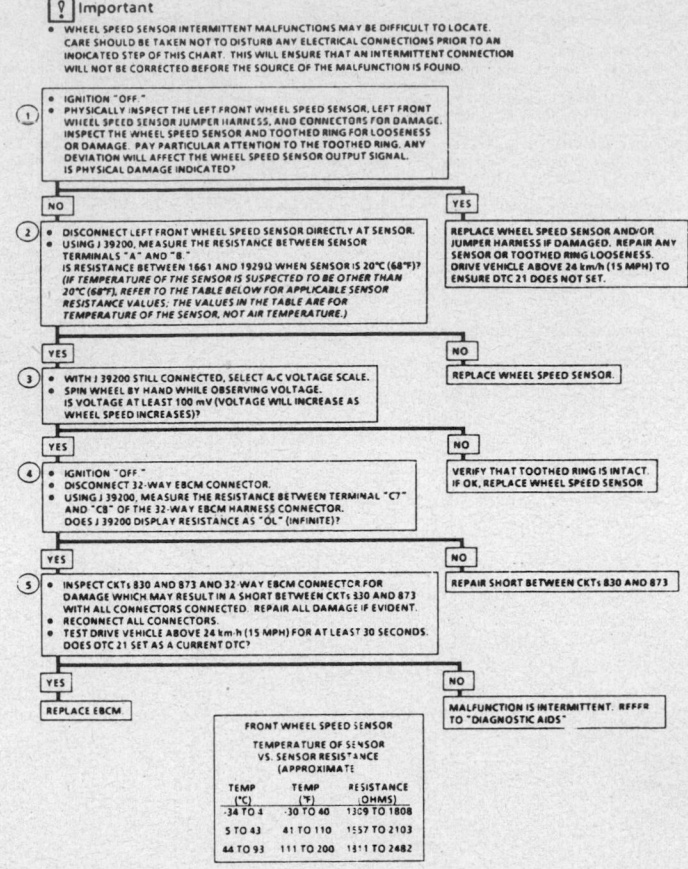

Fig. 243 Code A021: Left Front Wheel Speed = 0 (Part 2 of 2). 1993-94 Camaro & Firebird, 1994 Grand Prix, Century & Cutlass Ciera & Cruiser

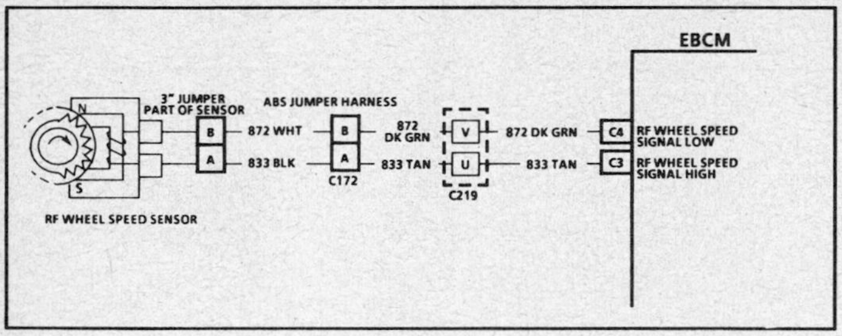
EBCM
3" JUMPER PART OF SENSOR
ABS JUMPER HARNESS
N
S
B
A
872 WHT
833 BLK
C172
872 DK GRN
833 TAN
V
U
C219
872 DK GRN
833 TAN
C6
C3
RF WHEEL SPEED SIGNAL LOW
RF WHEEL SPEED SIGNAL HIGH
RF WHEEL SPEED SENSOR

GC402940107200AX

Grand Prix

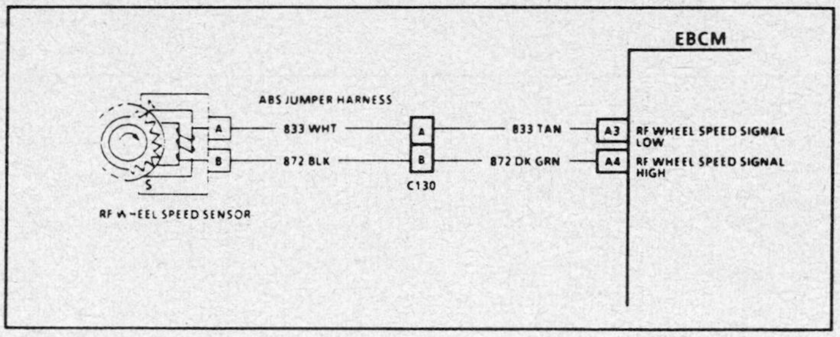
EBCM
ABS JUMPER HARNESS
A
B
833 WHT
872 BLK
C130
833 TAN
872 DK GRN
A3
A4
RF WHEEL SPEED SIGNAL LOW
RF WHEEL SPEED SIGNAL HIGH
S
RF WHEEL SPEED SENSOR

GC402940107200BX

Camaro & Firebird

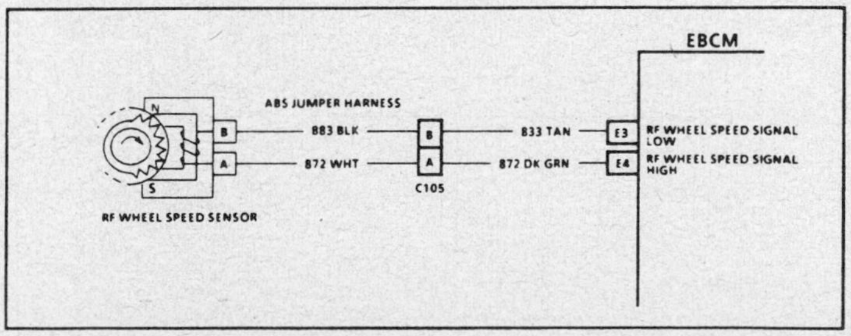
EBCM
ABS JUMPER HARNESS
N
S
B
A
883 BLK
872 WHT
C105
833 TAN
872 DK GRN
E3
E4
RF WHEEL SPEED SIGNAL LOW
RF WHEEL SPEED SIGNAL HIGH
RF WHEEL SPEED SENSOR

GC402940107200CX

Century & Cutlass Ciera & Cruiser

Fig. 244 Code A022: Right Front Wheel Speed = 0 (Part 1 of 2). 1993-94 Camaro & Firebird, 1994 Grand Prix, Century & Cutlass Ciera & Cruiser

DTC 22

RIGHT FRONT WHEEL SPEED = 0

Circuit Description:
As a toothed ring passes by the wheel speed sensor, changes in the electromagnetic field cause the wheel speed sensor to produce a sinusoidal (AC) voltage signal whose frequency is proportional to wheel speed. The magnitude of this signal is directly related to wheel speed and the proximity of the wheel speed sensor to the toothed ring, often referred to as the air gap.

DTC Will Set When: DTC 22 can be set when the vehicle is not in an ABS stop. If the right front wheel speed = 0 and the vehicle's reference speed is greater than 8 km/h (5 mph), a malfunction exists.

Action Taken: A malfunction DTC is stored, ABS is disabled and the ABS warning lamp is turned "ON."

DTC Chart Test Description: Number(s) below refer to circled number(s) on the diagnostic chart.

1. This step identifies a wheel speed sensor or circuitry that is damaged and visibly apparent.
2. Checks to see that the wheel speed sensor coil is within proper resistance values.
3. Verifies that the wheel speed sensor can generate an appropriate output signal.
4. This ensures that the wheel speed circuitry is not shorted together.
5. Ensures that the malfunction was not due to physical damage.

Diagnostic Aids: An "Intermittent" malfunction may be caused by a poor connection, rubbed through wire insulation, or a wire that is broken inside the insulation.

The frequency of the malfunction can be checked by using the enhanced diagnostic function of the Tech 1,

If the customer's comments reflect that the ABS warning lamp is "ON" only during moist environmental changes (rain, snow, vehicle wash), all wheel speed sensor circuitry should be thoroughly inspected for signs of water intrusion. If DTC is not current, clear DTCs and simulate the effects of water intrusion. Use the following procedure. Spray down the suspected area with a 5% salt water solution (two teaspoons of salt to 12 oz. of water). Test drive vehicle over various road surfaces (bumps, turns, etc.) above 24 km/h (15 mph) for at least 30 seconds. If DTC returns, replace suspected harness.

Any circuitry, that is suspected as causing the intermittent complaint, should be thoroughly checked for backed out terminals, improper mating, broken locks, improperly formed or damaged terminals, poor terminal to wiring connections or physical damage to the wiring harness.

Resistance of the wheel speed sensor will increase with an increase in sensor temperature.

When replacing a wheel speed sensor, inspect the sensor terminals and harness connector for corrosion and/or water intrusion. If evidence of corrosion or water intrusion exists, replace wheel speed sensor jumper harness. Likewise, if replacing a wheel speed sensor jumper harness, inspect sensor terminals. If evidence of corrosion or water intrusion exists, replace wheel speed sensor. Refer to "On-Vehicle Service" in this section.

GC402940107200DX

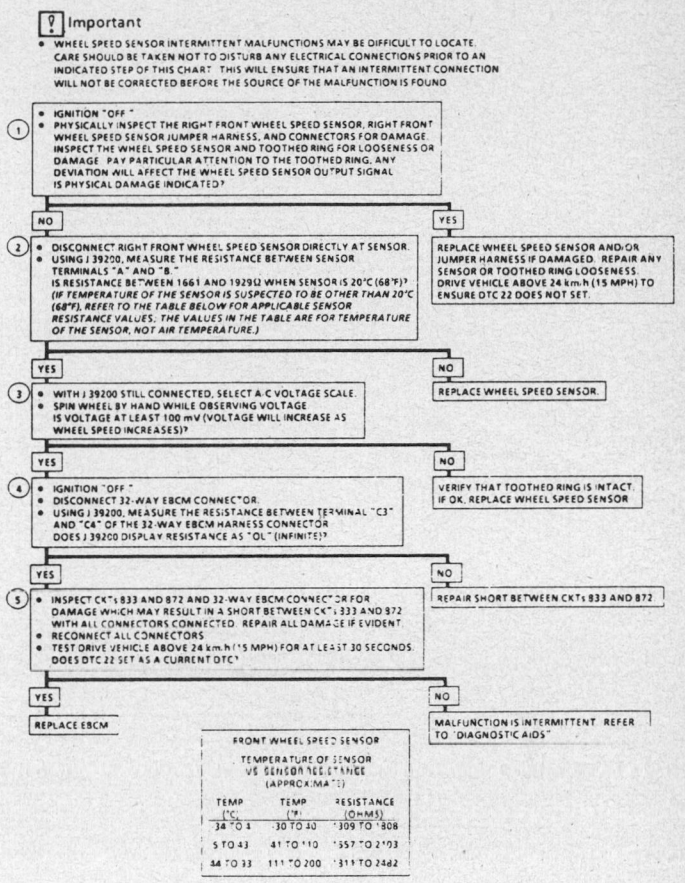

Important

- WHEEL SPEED SENSOR INTERMITTENT MALFUNCTIONS MAY BE DIFFICULT TO LOCATE. CARE SHOULD BE TAKEN NOT TO DISTURB ANY ELECTRICAL CONNECTIONS PRIOR TO AN INDICATED STEP OF THIS CHART. THIS WILL ENSURE THAT AN INTERMITTENT CONNECTION WILL NOT BE CORRECTED BEFORE THE SOURCE OF THE MALFUNCTION IS FOUND

(1)
- IGNITION "OFF."
- PHYSICALLY INSPECT THE RIGHT FRONT WHEEL SPEED SENSOR, RIGHT FRONT WHEEL SPEED SENSOR JUMPER HARNESS, AND CONNECTORS FOR DAMAGE. INSPECT THE WHEEL SPEED SENSOR AND TOOTHED RING FOR LOOSENESS OR DAMAGE. PAY PARTICULAR ATTENTION TO THE TOOTHED RING. ANY DEVIATION WILL AFFECT THE WHEEL SPEED SENSOR OUTPUT SIGNAL

IS PHYSICAL DAMAGE INDICATED?

YES: REPLACE WHEEL SPEED SENSOR AND/OR JUMPER HARNESS IF DAMAGED. REPAIR ANY SENSOR OR TOOTHED RING LOOSENESS. DRIVE VEHICLE ABOVE 24 km/h (15 MPH) TO ENSURE DTC 22 DOES NOT SET.

NO:

(2)
- DISCONNECT RIGHT FRONT WHEEL SPEED SENSOR DIRECTLY AT SENSOR.
- USING J 39200, MEASURE THE RESISTANCE BETWEEN SENSOR TERMINALS "A" AND "B."

IS RESISTANCE BETWEEN 1661 AND 1929Ω WHEN SENSOR IS 20°C (68°F)? *(IF TEMPERATURE OF THE SENSOR IS SUSPECTED TO BE OTHER THAN 20°C (68°F), REFER TO THE TABLE BELOW FOR APPLICABLE SENSOR RESISTANCE VALUES. THE VALUES IN THE TABLE ARE FOR TEMPERATURE OF THE SENSOR, NOT AIR TEMPERATURE.)*

NO: REPLACE WHEEL SPEED SENSOR.

YES:

(3)
- WITH J 39200 STILL CONNECTED, SELECT A/C VOLTAGE SCALE.
- SPIN WHEEL BY HAND WHILE OBSERVING VOLTAGE

IS VOLTAGE AT LEAST 100 mV (VOLTAGE WILL INCREASE AS WHEEL SPEED INCREASES)?

NO: VERIFY THAT TOOTHED RING IS INTACT. IF OK, REPLACE WHEEL SPEED SENSOR

YES:

(4)
- IGNITION "OFF."
- DISCONNECT 32-WAY EBCM CONNECTOR.
- USING J 39200, MEASURE THE RESISTANCE BETWEEN TERMINAL "C3" AND "C4" OF THE 32-WAY EBCM HARNESS CONNECTOR

DOES J 39200 DISPLAY RESISTANCE AS "OL" (INFINITE)?

NO: REPAIR SHORT BETWEEN CKTs 833 AND 872

YES:

(5)
- INSPECT CKTs 833 AND 872 AND 32-WAY EBCM CONNECTOR FOR DAMAGE WHICH MAY RESULT IN A SHORT BETWEEN CKTs 333 AND 872 WITH ALL CONNECTORS CONNECTED. REPAIR ALL DAMAGE IF EVIDENT.
- RECONNECT ALL CONNECTORS
- TEST DRIVE VEHICLE ABOVE 24 km/h (15 MPH) FOR AT LEAST 30 SECONDS.

DOES DTC 22 SET AS A CURRENT DTC?

YES: REPLACE EBCM

NO: MALFUNCTION IS INTERMITTENT. REFER TO "DIAGNOSTIC AIDS"

FRONT WHEEL SPEED SENSOR

TEMPERATURE OF SENSOR VS SENSOR RESISTANCE (APPROXIMATE)

TEMP (°C)	TEMP (°F)	RESISTANCE (OHMS)
-34 TO 4	-30 TO 40	1309 TO 1808
5 TO 43	41 TO 110	1557 TO 2103
44 TO 93	111 TO 200	1811 TO 2482

GC402940107200EX

Fig. 244 Code A022: Right Front Wheel Speed = 0 (Part 2 of 2). 1993-94 Camaro & Firebird, 1994 Grand Prix, Century & Cutlass Ciera & Cruiser

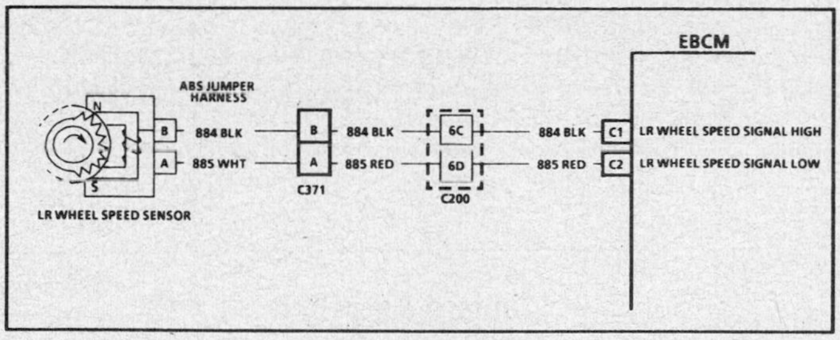

EBCM
ABS JUMPER HARNESS
N
B
A
S
884 BLK
885 WHT
884 BLK
885 RED
6C
6D
C371
C200
C1
C2
LR WHEEL SPEED SIGNAL HIGH
LR WHEEL SPEED SIGNAL LOW
LR WHEEL SPEED SENSOR

GC402940107300AX

Grand Prix

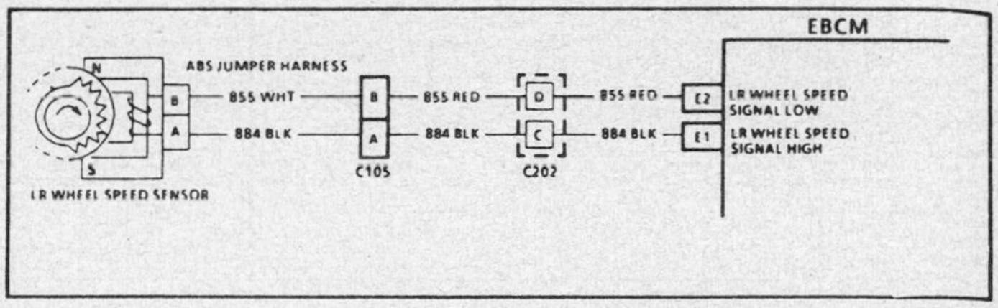

EBCM
ABS JUMPER HARNESS
N
B
A
S
855 WHT
884 BLK
855 RED
884 BLK
D
C
C105
C202
E2
E1
LR WHEEL SPEED SIGNAL LOW
LR WHEEL SPEED SIGNAL HIGH
LR WHEEL SPEED SENSOR

GC402940107300BX

Century & Cutlass Ciera & Cruiser

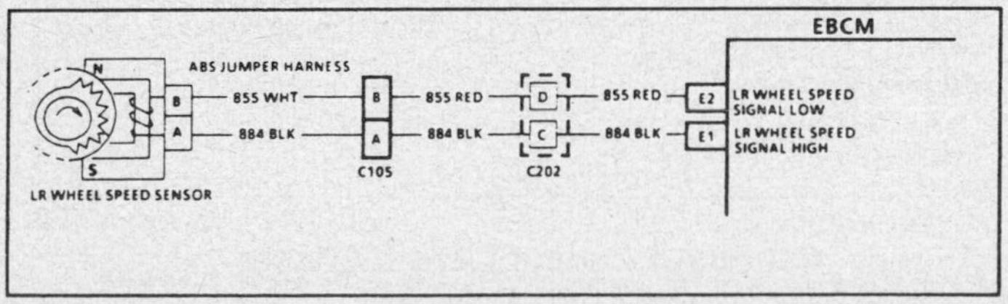

EBCM
ABS JUMPER HARNESS
N
B
A
S
855 WHT
884 BLK
855 RED
884 BLK
D
C
C105
C202
E2
E1
LR WHEEL SPEED SIGNAL LOW
LR WHEEL SPEED SIGNAL HIGH
LR WHEEL SPEED SENSOR

GC402940107300CX

Century & Cutlass Ciera & Cruiser

Fig. 245 Code A023: Left Rear Wheel Speed = 0 (Part 1 of 2). 1994 Grand Prix, Century & Cutlass Ciera & Cruiser

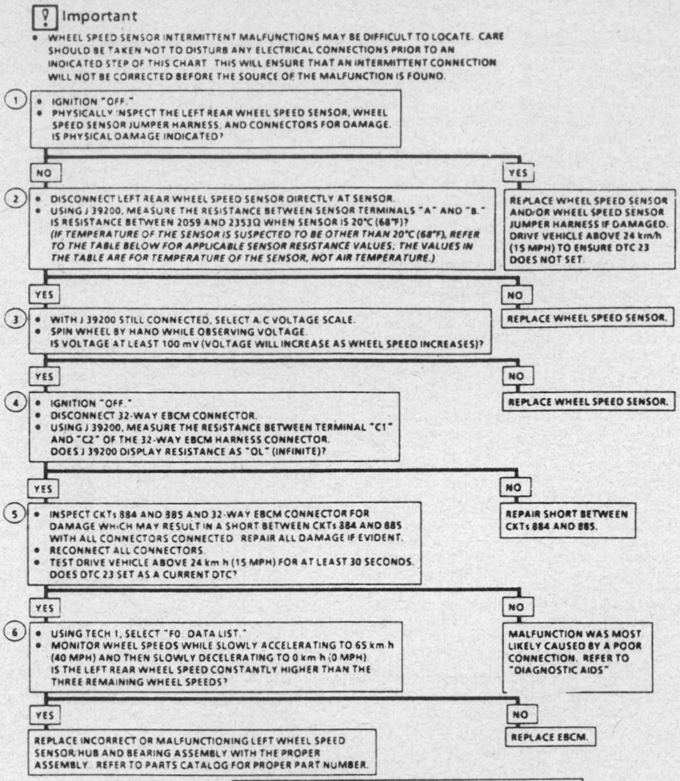
Important
• WHEEL SPEED SENSOR INTERMITTENT MALFUNCTIONS MAY BE DIFFICULT TO LOCATE. CARE SHOULD BE TAKEN NOT TO DISTURB ANY ELECTRICAL CONNECTIONS PRIOR TO AN INDICATED STEP OF THIS CHART. THIS WILL ENSURE THAT AN INTERMITTENT CONNECTION WILL NOT BE CORRECTED BEFORE THE SOURCE OF THE MALFUNCTION IS FOUND.
1
• IGNITION "OFF."
• PHYSICALLY INSPECT THE LEFT REAR WHEEL SPEED SENSOR, WHEEL SPEED SENSOR JUMPER HARNESS, AND CONNECTORS FOR DAMAGE. IS PHYSICAL DAMAGE INDICATED?
NO
YES
2
• DISCONNECT LEFT REAR WHEEL SPEED SENSOR DIRECTLY AT SENSOR.
• USING J 39200, MEASURE THE RESISTANCE BETWEEN SENSOR TERMINALS "A" AND "B." IS RESISTANCE BETWEEN 2059 AND 2353Ω WHEN SENSOR IS 20°C (68°F)? (IF TEMPERATURE OF THE SENSOR IS SUSPECTED TO BE OTHER THAN 20°C (68°F), REFER TO THE TABLE BELOW FOR APPLICABLE SENSOR RESISTANCE VALUES; THE VALUES IN THE TABLE ARE FOR TEMPERATURE OF THE SENSOR, NOT AIR TEMPERATURE.)
REPLACE WHEEL SPEED SENSOR AND/OR WHEEL SPEED SENSOR JUMPER HARNESS IF DAMAGED. DRIVE VEHICLE ABOVE 24 km/h (15 MPH) TO ENSURE DTC 23 DOES NOT SET.
YES
NO
3
• WITH J 39200 STILL CONNECTED, SELECT A/C VOLTAGE SCALE.
• SPIN WHEEL BY HAND WHILE OBSERVING VOLTAGE. IS VOLTAGE AT LEAST 100 mV (VOLTAGE WILL INCREASE AS WHEEL SPEED INCREASES)?
REPLACE WHEEL SPEED SENSOR.
YES
NO
4
• IGNITION "OFF."
• DISCONNECT 32-WAY EBCM CONNECTOR.
• USING J 39200, MEASURE THE RESISTANCE BETWEEN TERMINAL "C1" AND "C2" OF THE 32-WAY EBCM HARNESS CONNECTOR. DOES J 39200 DISPLAY RESISTANCE AS "OL" (INFINITE)?
REPLACE WHEEL SPEED SENSOR.
YES
NO
5
• INSPECT CKTs 884 AND 885 AND 32-WAY EBCM CONNECTOR FOR DAMAGE WHICH MAY RESULT IN A SHORT BETWEEN CKTs 884 AND 885 WITH ALL CONNECTORS CONNECTED. REPAIR ALL DAMAGE IF EVIDENT.
• RECONNECT ALL CONNECTORS.
• TEST DRIVE VEHICLE ABOVE 24 km/h (15 MPH) FOR AT LEAST 30 SECONDS. DOES DTC 23 SET AS A CURRENT DTC?
REPAIR SHORT BETWEEN CKTs 884 AND 885.
YES
NO
6
• USING TECH 1, SELECT "F0: DATA LIST."
• MONITOR WHEEL SPEEDS WHILE SLOWLY ACCELERATING TO 65 km/h (40 MPH) AND THEN SLOWLY DECELERATING TO 0 km/h (0 MPH). IS THE LEFT REAR WHEEL SPEED CONSTANTLY HIGHER THAN THE THREE REMAINING WHEEL SPEEDS?
MALFUNCTION WAS MOST LIKELY CAUSED BY A POOR CONNECTION. REFER TO "DIAGNOSTIC AIDS"
YES
NO
REPLACE INCORRECT OR MALFUNCTIONING LEFT WHEEL SPEED SENSOR/HUB AND BEARING ASSEMBLY WITH THE PROPER ASSEMBLY. REFER TO PARTS CATALOG FOR PROPER PART NUMBER.
REPLACE EBCM.

REAR WHEEL SPEED SENSOR
TEMPERATURE OF SENSOR VS. SENSOR RESISTANCE (APPROXIMATE)

TEMP (°C)	TEMP (°F)	RESISTANCE (OHMS)
-34 TO 4	-30 TO 40	1622 TO 2205
5 TO 43	41 TO 110	1930 TO 2566
44 TO 93	111 TO 200	2245 TO 3028

GC402940107300DX

Fig. 245 Code A023: Left Rear Wheel Speed = 0 (Part 2 of 2). 1994 Grand Prix, Century & Cutlass Ciera & Cruiser

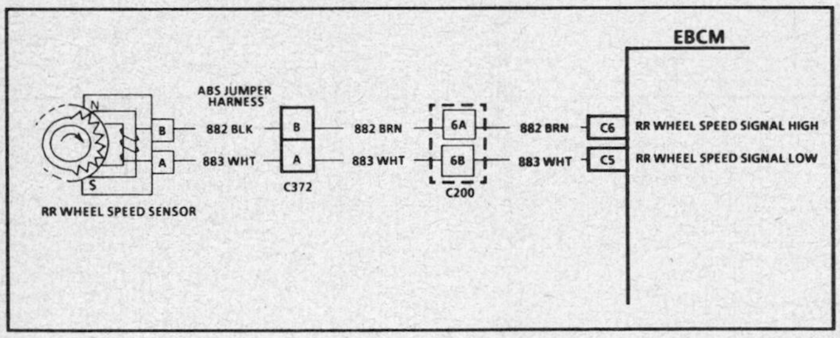
EBCM
ABS JUMPER HARNESS
N
S
B
A
882 BLK
883 WHT
C372
882 BRN
883 WHT
6A
6B
C200
882 BRN
883 WHT
C6
C5
RR WHEEL SPEED SIGNAL HIGH
RR WHEEL SPEED SIGNAL LOW
RR WHEEL SPEED SENSOR

GC402940107400AX

Grand Prix

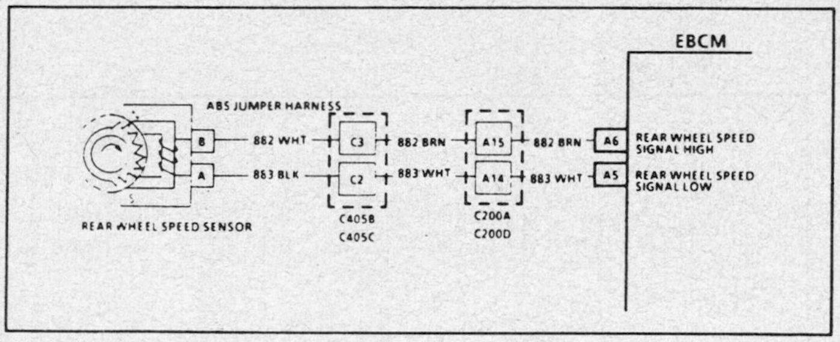
EBCM
ABS JUMPER HARNESS
B
A
882 WHT
883 BLK
C3
C2
C405B
C405C
882 BRN
883 WHT
A15
A14
C200A
C200D
882 BRN
883 WHT
A6
A5
REAR WHEEL SPEED SIGNAL HIGH
REAR WHEEL SPEED SIGNAL LOW
REAR WHEEL SPEED SENSOR

GC402940107400BX

Camaro & Firebird

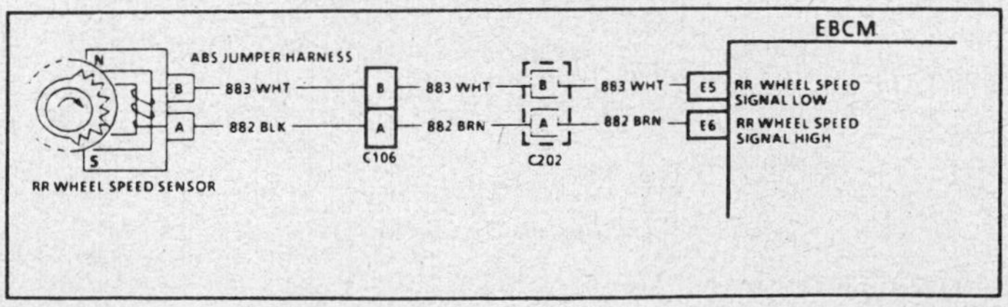
EBCM
ABS JUMPER HARNESS
N
S
B
A
883 WHT
882 BLK
C106
883 WHT
882 BRN
C202
883 WHT
882 BRN
E5
E6
RR WHEEL SPEED SIGNAL LOW
RR WHEEL SPEED SIGNAL HIGH
RR WHEEL SPEED SENSOR

GC402940107400CX

Century & Cutlass Ciera & Cruiser

Fig. 246 Code A024: Right Rear Wheel Speed = 0 (Part 1 of 2). 1993-94 Camaro & Firebird, 1994 Grand Prix, Century & Cutlass Ciera & Cruiser

DTC 24

RIGHT REAR WHEEL SPEED = 0

Circuit Description:
As a toothed ring passes by the wheel speed sensor, changes in the electromagnetic field cause the wheel speed sensor to produce a sinusoidal (AC) voltage signal whose frequency is proportional to wheel speed. The magnitude of this signal is directly related to wheel speed and the proximity of the wheel speed sensor to the toothed ring, often referred to as the air gap.

DTC Will Set When: DTC 24 can be set when the vehicle is not in an ABS stop. If the right rear wheel speed = 0 and the vehicle's reference speed is greater than 8 km/h (5 mph), a malfunction exists.

Action Taken: A malfunction DTC is stored, ABS is disabled and the ABS warning lamp is turned "ON."

DTC Chart Test Description: Number(s) below refer to circled number(s) on the diagnostic chart.

1. This step identifies a wheel speed sensor or circuitry that is damaged and visibly apparent.
2. Checks to see that the wheel speed sensor coil is within proper resistance values.
3. Verifies that the wheel speed sensor can generate an appropriate output signal.
4. Verifies that the wheel speed circuitry is not shorted together.
5. Ensures that the malfunction was not due to physical damage.
6. Checks for an incorrect or malfunctioning hub and bearing assembly.

Diagnostic Aids: An "Intermittent" malfunction may be caused by a poor connection, rubbed through wire insulation, or a wire that is broken inside the insulation.

The frequency of the malfunction can be checked by using the enhanced diagnostic function of the Tech 1.

If the customer's comments reflect that the ABS warning lamp is "ON" only during moist environmental changes (rain, snow, vehicle wash), all wheel speed sensor circuitry should be thoroughly inspected for signs of water intrusion. If DTC is not current, clear DTCs and simulate the effects of water intrusion. Use the following procedure. Spray down the suspected area with a 5% salt water solution (two teaspoons of salt to 12 oz. of water). Test drive vehicle over various road surfaces (bumps, turns, etc.) above 24 km/h (15 mph) for at least 30 seconds. If DTC returns, replace suspected harness.

Any circuitry, that is suspected as causing the intermittent complaint, should be thoroughly checked for backed out terminals, improper mating, broken locks, improperly formed or damaged terminals, poor terminal to wiring connections or physical damage to the wiring harness.

Resistance of the wheel speed sensor will increase with an increase in sensor temperature.

When replacing a wheel speed sensor, inspect the sensor terminals and harness connector for corrosion and/or water intrusion. If evidence of corrosion or water intrusion exists, replace wheel speed sensor jumper harness. Likewise, if replacing a wheel speed sensor jumper harness, inspect sensor terminals. If evidence of corrosion or water intrusion exists, replace wheel speed sensor. Refer to "On-Vehicle Service" in this section.

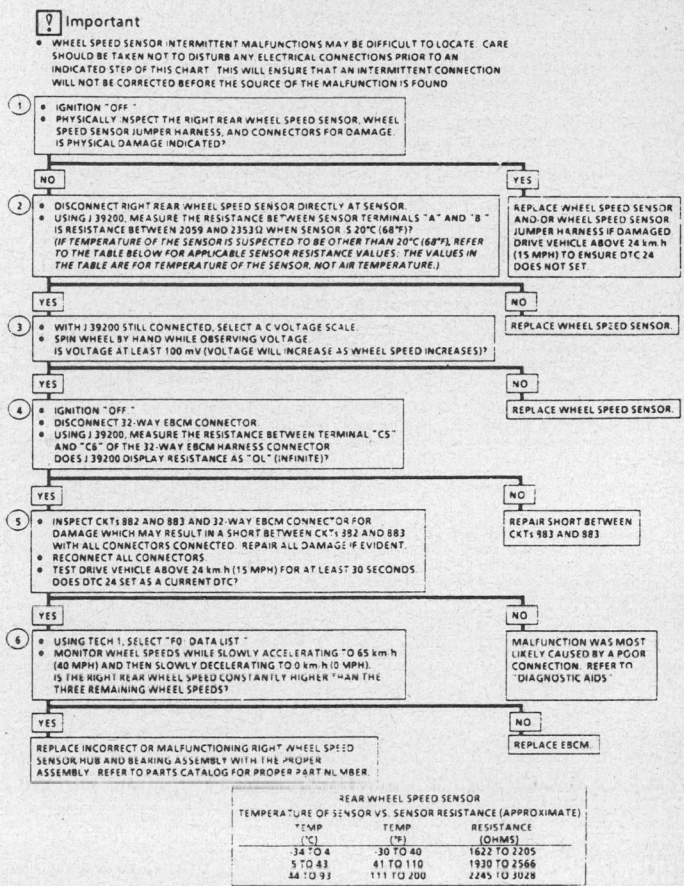

GC402940107400DX

[!] Important

- WHEEL SPEED SENSOR INTERMITTENT MALFUNCTIONS MAY BE DIFFICULT TO LOCATE. CARE SHOULD BE TAKEN NOT TO DISTURB ANY ELECTRICAL CONNECTIONS PRIOR TO AN INDICATED STEP OF THIS CHART. THIS WILL ENSURE THAT AN INTERMITTENT CONNECTION WILL NOT BE CORRECTED BEFORE THE SOURCE OF THE MALFUNCTION IS FOUND.

(1)
- IGNITION "OFF."
- PHYSICALLY INSPECT THE RIGHT REAR WHEEL SPEED SENSOR, WHEEL SPEED SENSOR JUMPER HARNESS, AND CONNECTORS FOR DAMAGE.

IS PHYSICAL DAMAGE INDICATED?

YES: REPLACE WHEEL SPEED SENSOR AND/OR WHEEL SPEED SENSOR JUMPER HARNESS IF DAMAGED. DRIVE VEHICLE ABOVE 24 km/h (15 MPH) TO ENSURE DTC 24 DOES NOT SET.

NO: (2)
- DISCONNECT RIGHT REAR WHEEL SPEED SENSOR DIRECTLY AT SENSOR.
- USING J 39200, MEASURE THE RESISTANCE BETWEEN SENSOR TERMINALS "A" AND "B."

IS RESISTANCE BETWEEN 2059 AND 2353Ω WHEN SENSOR IS 20°C (68°F)?

(IF TEMPERATURE OF THE SENSOR IS SUSPECTED TO BE OTHER THAN 20°C (68°F), REFER TO THE TABLE BELOW FOR APPLICABLE SENSOR RESISTANCE VALUES: THE VALUES IN THE TABLE ARE FOR TEMPERATURE OF THE SENSOR, NOT AIR TEMPERATURE.)

NO: REPLACE WHEEL SPEED SENSOR.

YES: (3)
- WITH J 39200 STILL CONNECTED, SELECT A C VOLTAGE SCALE.
- SPIN WHEEL BY HAND WHILE OBSERVING VOLTAGE.

IS VOLTAGE AT LEAST 100 mV (VOLTAGE WILL INCREASE AS WHEEL SPEED INCREASES)?

NO: REPLACE WHEEL SPEED SENSOR.

YES: (4)
- IGNITION "OFF."
- DISCONNECT 32-WAY EBCM CONNECTOR.
- USING J 39200, MEASURE THE RESISTANCE BETWEEN TERMINAL "C5" AND "C6" OF THE 32-WAY EBCM HARNESS CONNECTOR.

DOES J 39200 DISPLAY RESISTANCE AS "OL" (INFINITE)?

NO: REPAIR SHORT BETWEEN CKTs 983 AND 883.

YES: (5)
- INSPECT CKTs 882 AND 883 AND 32-WAY EBCM CONNECTOR FOR DAMAGE WHICH MAY RESULT IN A SHORT BETWEEN CKTs 382 AND 883 WITH ALL CONNECTORS CONNECTED. REPAIR ALL DAMAGE IF EVIDENT.
- RECONNECT ALL CONNECTORS.
- TEST DRIVE VEHICLE ABOVE 24 km/h (15 MPH) FOR AT LEAST 30 SECONDS.

DOES DTC 24 SET AS A CURRENT DTC?

NO: MALFUNCTION WAS MOST LIKELY CAUSED BY A POOR CONNECTION. REFER TO "DIAGNOSTIC AIDS."

YES: (6)
- USING TECH 1, SELECT "F0: DATA LIST."
- MONITOR WHEEL SPEEDS WHILE SLOWLY ACCELERATING TO 65 km/h (40 MPH) AND THEN SLOWLY DECELERATING TO 0 km/h (0 MPH).

IS THE RIGHT REAR WHEEL SPEED CONSTANTLY HIGHER THAN THE THREE REMAINING WHEEL SPEEDS?

YES: REPLACE INCORRECT OR MALFUNCTIONING RIGHT WHEEL SPEED SENSOR HUB AND BEARING ASSEMBLY WITH THE PROPER ASSEMBLY. REFER TO PARTS CATALOG FOR PROPER PART NUMBER.

NO: REPLACE EBCM.

REAR WHEEL SPEED SENSOR

TEMPERATURE OF SENSOR VS. SENSOR RESISTANCE (APPROXIMATE)

TEMP (°C)	TEMP (°F)	RESISTANCE (OHMS)
-34 TO 4	-30 TO 40	1622 TO 2205
5 TO 43	41 TO 110	1930 TO 2566
44 TO 93	111 TO 200	2245 TO 3028

GC402940107400EX

Fig. 246 Code A024: Right Rear Wheel Speed = 0 (Part 2 of 2). 1993-94 Camaro & Firebird, 1994 Grand Prix, Century & Cutlass Ciera & Cruiser

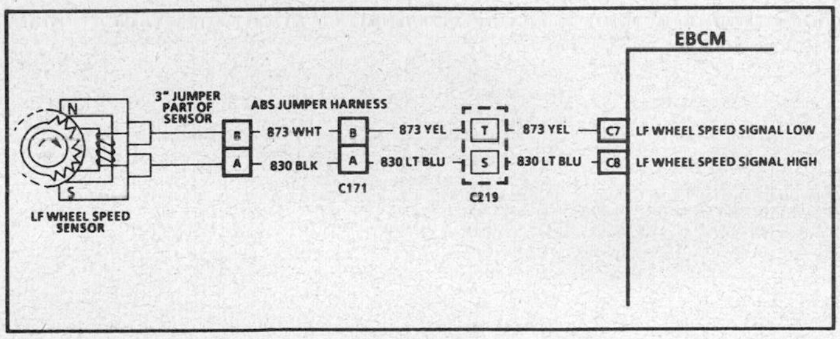
EBCM
3" JUMPER PART OF SENSOR
ABS JUMPER HARNESS
B
873 WHT
B
873 YEL
T
873 YEL
C7
LF WHEEL SPEED SIGNAL LOW
A
830 BLK
A
830 LT BLU
S
830 LT BLU
C8
LF WHEEL SPEED SIGNAL HIGH
N
S
C171
C219
LF WHEEL SPEED SENSOR

GC402940107500AX

Grand Prix

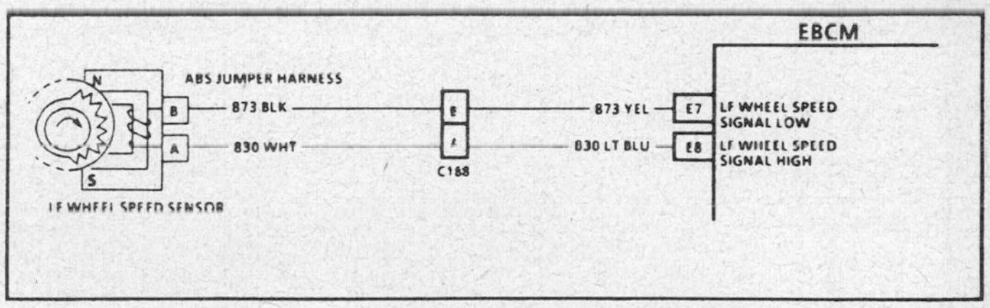
EBCM
ABS JUMPER HARNESS
N
B
873 BLK
873 YEL
E7
LF WHEEL SPEED SIGNAL LOW
A
830 WHT
830 LT BLU
E8
LF WHEEL SPEED SIGNAL HIGH
S
C188

GC402940107500BX

Camaro & Firebird

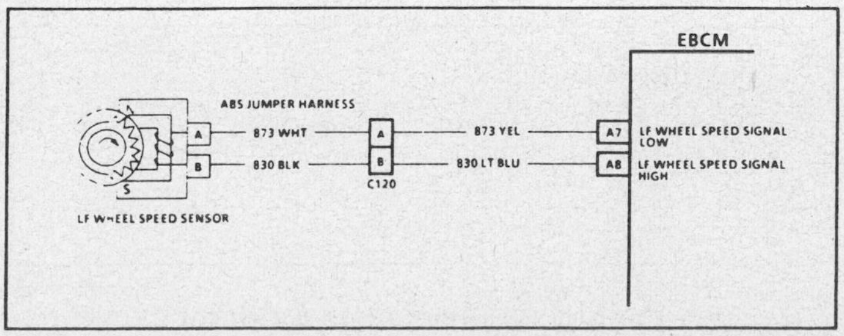
EBCM
ABS JUMPER HARNESS
A
873 WHT
A
873 YEL
A7
LF WHEEL SPEED SIGNAL LOW
B
830 BLK
B
830 LT BLU
A8
LF WHEEL SPEED SIGNAL HIGH
S
C120
LF WHEEL SPEED SENSOR

GC402940107500CX

Century & Cutlass Ciera & Cruiser

Fig. 247 Code A025: Left Front Excessive Wheel Speed Variation (Part 1 of 2). 1993-94 Camaro & Firebird, 1994 Grand Prix, Century & Cutlass Ciera & Cruiser

DTC 25

LEFT FRONT EXCESSIVE WHEEL SPEED VARIATION

Circuit Description:

As a toothed ring passes by the wheel speed sensor, changes in the electromagnetic field cause the wheel speed sensor to produce a sinusoidal (AC) voltage signal whose frequency is proportional to wheel speed. The magnitude of this signal is directly related to wheel speed and the proximity of the wheel speed sensor to the toothed ring, often referred to as the air gap.

DTC Will Set When: DTC 25 can be set when the brake is "OFF." The purpose of this test is to detect a situation in which the left front wheel acceleration or deceleration is beyond specified limits.

Action Taken: A malfunction DTC is stored, ABS is disabled and the ABS warning lamp is turned "ON."

DTC Chart Test Description: Number(s) below refer to circled number(s) on the diagnostic chart.

1. This step identifies a wheel speed sensor or circuitry that is damaged and visibly apparent.
2. Checks to see that the wheel speed sensor coil is within proper resistance values.
3. Verifies that the wheel speed sensor can generate an appropriate output signal.
4. This ensures that the wheel speed circuitry is not shorted together.
5. Ensures that the malfunction was not due to physical damage.

Diagnostic Aids: An "Intermittent" malfunction may be caused by a poor connection, rubbed through wire insulation, or a wire that is broken inside the insulation.

The frequency of the malfunction can be checked by using the enhanced diagnostic function of the Tech 1,

If the customer's comments reflect that the ABS warning lamp is "ON" only during moist environmental changes (rain, snow, vehicle wash), all wheel speed sensor circuitry should be thoroughly inspected for signs of water intrusion. If DTC is not current, clear DTCs and simulate the effects of water intrusion. Use the following procedure. Spray down the suspected area with a 5% salt water solution (two teaspoons of salt to 12 oz. of water). Test drive vehicle over various road surfaces (bumps, turns, etc.) above 24 km/h (15 mph) for at least 30 seconds. If DTC returns, replace suspected harness.

Any circuitry, that is suspected as causing the intermittent complaint, should be thoroughly checked for backed out terminals, improper mating, broken locks, improperly formed or damaged terminals, poor terminal to wiring connections or physical damage to the wiring harness.

Resistance of the wheel speed sensor will increase with an increase in sensor temperature.

When replacing a wheel speed sensor, inspect the sensor terminals and harness connector for corrosion and/or water intrusion. If evidence of corrosion or water intrusion exists, replace wheel speed sensor jumper harness. Likewise, if replacing a wheel speed sensor jumper harness, inspect sensor terminals. If evidence of corrosion or water intrusion exists, replace wheel speed sensor. Refer to "On-Vehicle Service" in this section.

GC402940107500DX

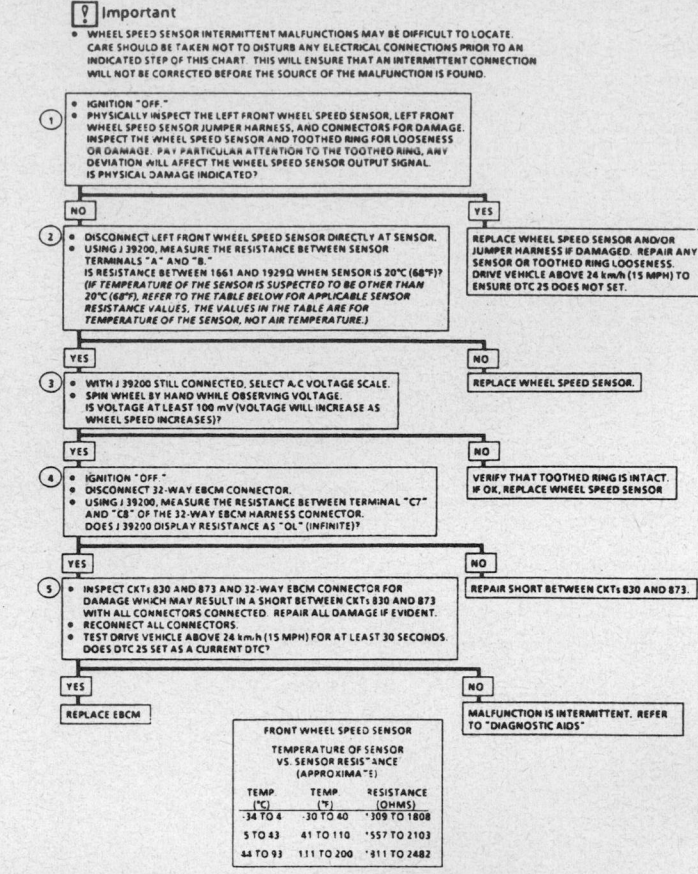

Important

- WHEEL SPEED SENSOR INTERMITTENT MALFUNCTIONS MAY BE DIFFICULT TO LOCATE. CARE SHOULD BE TAKEN NOT TO DISTURB ANY ELECTRICAL CONNECTIONS PRIOR TO AN INDICATED STEP OF THIS CHART. THIS WILL ENSURE THAT AN INTERMITTENT CONNECTION WILL NOT BE CORRECTED BEFORE THE SOURCE OF THE MALFUNCTION IS FOUND.

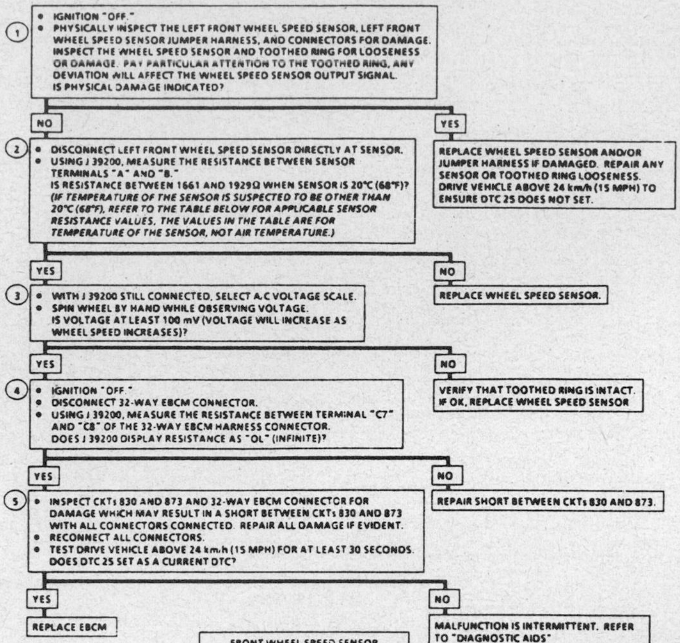
1
• IGNITION "OFF."
• PHYSICALLY INSPECT THE LEFT FRONT WHEEL SPEED SENSOR, LEFT FRONT WHEEL SPEED SENSOR JUMPER HARNESS, AND CONNECTORS FOR DAMAGE. INSPECT THE WHEEL SPEED SENSOR AND TOOTHED RING FOR LOOSENESS OR DAMAGE. PAY PARTICULAR ATTENTION TO THE TOOTHED RING, ANY DEVIATION WILL AFFECT THE WHEEL SPEED SENSOR OUTPUT SIGNAL. IS PHYSICAL DAMAGE INDICATED?
NO
YES
REPLACE WHEEL SPEED SENSOR AND/OR JUMPER HARNESS IF DAMAGED. REPAIR ANY SENSOR OR TOOTHED RING LOOSENESS. DRIVE VEHICLE ABOVE 24 km/h (15 MPH) TO ENSURE DTC 25 DOES NOT SET.
2
• DISCONNECT LEFT FRONT WHEEL SPEED SENSOR DIRECTLY AT SENSOR.
• USING J 39200, MEASURE THE RESISTANCE BETWEEN SENSOR TERMINALS "A" AND "B." IS RESISTANCE BETWEEN 1661 AND 1929Ω WHEN SENSOR IS 20°C (68°F)? (IF TEMPERATURE OF THE SENSOR IS SUSPECTED TO BE OTHER THAN 20°C (68°F), REFER TO THE TABLE BELOW FOR APPLICABLE SENSOR RESISTANCE VALUES. THE VALUES IN THE TABLE ARE FOR TEMPERATURE OF THE SENSOR, NOT AIR TEMPERATURE.)
YES
NO
REPLACE WHEEL SPEED SENSOR.
3
• WITH J 39200 STILL CONNECTED, SELECT A.C VOLTAGE SCALE.
• SPIN WHEEL BY HAND WHILE OBSERVING VOLTAGE. IS VOLTAGE AT LEAST 100 mV (VOLTAGE WILL INCREASE AS WHEEL SPEED INCREASES)?
YES
NO
VERIFY THAT TOOTHED RING IS INTACT. IF OK, REPLACE WHEEL SPEED SENSOR
4
• IGNITION "OFF."
• DISCONNECT 32-WAY EBCM CONNECTOR.
• USING J 39200, MEASURE THE RESISTANCE BETWEEN TERMINAL "C7" AND "C8" OF THE 32-WAY EBCM HARNESS CONNECTOR. DOES J 39200 DISPLAY RESISTANCE AS "OL" (INFINITE)?
YES
NO
REPAIR SHORT BETWEEN CKTs 830 AND 873.
5
• INSPECT CKTs 830 AND 873 AND 32-WAY EBCM CONNECTOR FOR DAMAGE WHICH MAY RESULT IN A SHORT BETWEEN CKTs 830 AND 873 WITH ALL CONNECTORS CONNECTED. REPAIR ALL DAMAGE IF EVIDENT.
• RECONNECT ALL CONNECTORS.
• TEST DRIVE VEHICLE ABOVE 24 km/h (15 MPH) FOR AT LEAST 30 SECONDS. DOES DTC 25 SET AS A CURRENT DTC?
YES
REPLACE EBCM
NO
MALFUNCTION IS INTERMITTENT. REFER TO "DIAGNOSTIC AIDS"

FRONT WHEEL SPEED SENSOR

TEMPERATURE OF SENSOR VS. SENSOR RESISTANCE (APPROXIMATE)

TEMP. (°C)	TEMP. (°F)	RESISTANCE (OHMS)
-34 TO 4	-30 TO 40	1309 TO 1808
5 TO 43	41 TO 110	1557 TO 2103
44 TO 93	111 TO 200	1811 TO 2482

GC402940107500EX

Fig. 247 Code A025: Left Front Excessive Wheel Speed Variation (Part 2 of 2). 1993-94 Camaro & Firebird, 1994 Grand Prix, Century & Cutlass Ciera & Cruiser

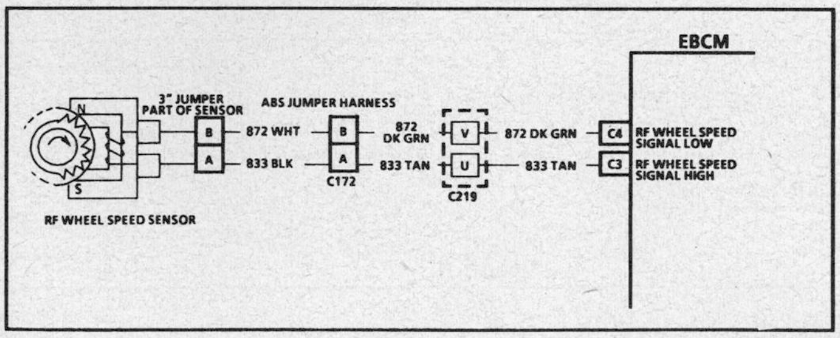
EBCM
3" JUMPER PART OF SENSOR
ABS JUMPER HARNESS
N
S
B
A
872 WHT
833 BLK
B
A
C172
872 DK GRN
833 TAN
V
U
C219
872 DK GRN
833 TAN
C4
C3
RF WHEEL SPEED SIGNAL LOW
RF WHEEL SPEED SIGNAL HIGH
RF WHEEL SPEED SENSOR

GC402940107600AX

Grand Prix

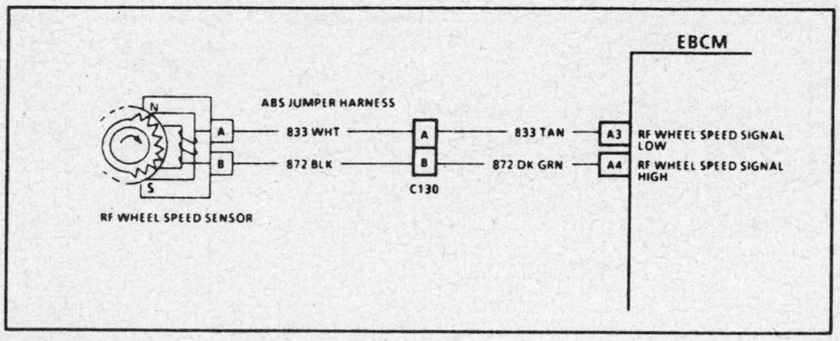
EBCM
ABS JUMPER HARNESS
N
S
A
B
833 WHT
872 BLK
A
B
C130
833 TAN
872 DK GRN
A3
A4
RF WHEEL SPEED SIGNAL LOW
RF WHEEL SPEED SIGNAL HIGH
RF WHEEL SPEED SENSOR

GC402940107600BX

Camaro & Firebird

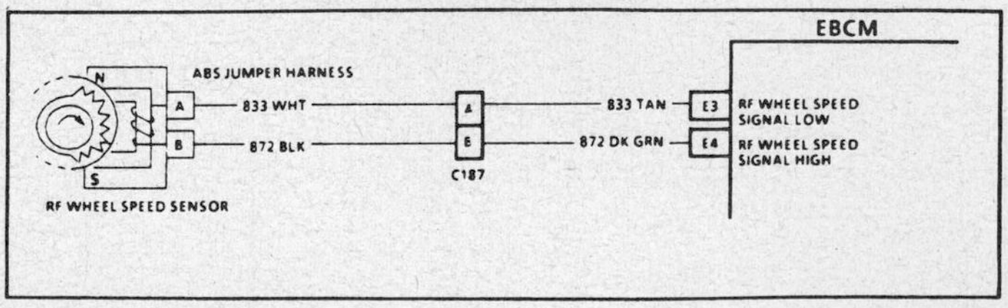
EBCM
ABS JUMPER HARNESS
N
S
A
B
833 WHT
872 BLK
A
B
C187
833 TAN
872 DK GRN
E3
E4
RF WHEEL SPEED SIGNAL LOW
RF WHEEL SPEED SIGNAL HIGH
RF WHEEL SPEED SENSOR

GC402940107600CX

Century & Cutlass Ciera & Cruiser

Fig. 248 Code A026: Right Front Excessive Wheel Speed Variation (Part 1 of 2). 1993-94 Camaro & Firebird, 1994 Grand Prix, Century & Cutlass Ciera & Cruiser

DTC 26

RIGHT FRONT EXCESSIVE WHEEL SPEED VARIATION

Circuit Description:

As a toothed ring passes by the wheel speed sensor, changes in the electromagnetic field cause the wheel speed sensor to produce a sinusoidal (AC) voltage signal whose frequency is proportional to wheel speed. The magnitude of this signal is directly related to wheel speed and the proximity of the wheel speed sensor to the toothed ring, often referred to as the air gap.

DTC Will Set When: DTC 26 can be set when the brake is "OFF." The purpose of this test is to detect a situation in which the right front wheel acceleration or deceleration is beyond specified limits.

Action Taken: A malfunction DTC is stored, ABS is disabled and the ABS warning lamp is turned "ON."

DTC Chart Test Description: Number(s) below refer to circled number(s) on the diagnostic chart.

1. This step identifies a wheel speed sensor or circuitry that is damaged and visibly apparent.
2. Checks to see that the wheel speed sensor coil is within proper resistance values.
3. Verifies that the wheel speed sensor can generate an appropriate output signal.
4. This ensures that the wheel speed circuitry is not shorted together.
5. Ensures that the malfunction was not due to physical damage.

Diagnostic Aids: An "Intermittent" malfunction may be caused by a poor connection, rubbed through wire insulation, or a wire that is broken inside the insulation.

The frequency of the malfunction can be checked by using the enhanced diagnostic function of the Tech 1,

If the customer's comments reflect that the ABS warning lamp is "ON" only during moist environmental changes (rain, snow, vehicle wash), all wheel speed sensor circuitry should be thoroughly inspected for signs of water intrusion. If DTC is not current, clear DTCs and simulate the effects of water intrusion. Use the following procedure. Spray down the suspected area with a 5% salt water solution (two teaspoons of salt to 12 oz. of water). Test drive vehicle over various road surfaces (bumps, turns, etc.) above 24 km/h (15 mph) for at least 30 seconds. If DTC returns, replace suspected harness.

Any circuitry, that is suspected as causing the intermittent complaint, should be thoroughly checked for backed out terminals, improper mating, broken locks, improperly formed or damaged terminals, poor terminal to wiring connections or physical damage to the wiring harness.

Resistance of the wheel speed sensor will increase with an increase in sensor temperature.

When replacing a wheel speed sensor, inspect the sensor terminals and harness connector for corrosion and/or water intrusion. If evidence of corrosion or water intrusion exists, replace wheel speed sensor jumper harness. Likewise, if replacing a wheel speed sensor jumper harness, inspect sensor terminals. If evidence of corrosion or water intrusion exists, replace wheel speed sensor. Refer to "On-Vehicle Service" in this section.

Important

- WHEEL SPEED SENSOR INTERMITTENT MALFUNCTIONS MAY BE DIFFICULT TO LOCATE. CARE SHOULD BE TAKEN NOT TO DISTURB ANY ELECTRICAL CONNECTIONS PRIOR TO AN INDICATED STEP OF THIS CHART. THIS WILL ENSURE THAT AN INTERMITTENT CONNECTION WILL NOT BE CORRECTED BEFORE THE SOURCE OF THE MALFUNCTION IS FOUND.

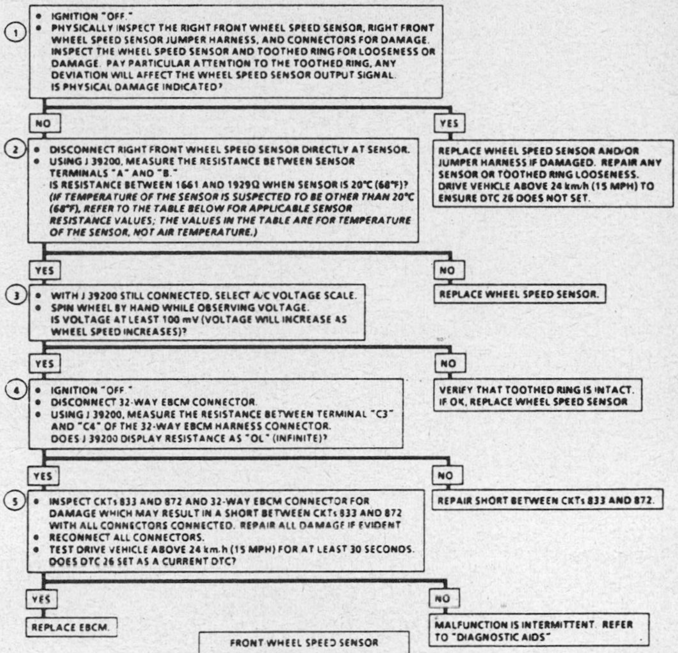
1
• IGNITION "OFF."
• PHYSICALLY INSPECT THE RIGHT FRONT WHEEL SPEED SENSOR, RIGHT FRONT WHEEL SPEED SENSOR JUMPER HARNESS, AND CONNECTORS FOR DAMAGE. INSPECT THE WHEEL SPEED SENSOR AND TOOTHED RING FOR LOOSENESS OR DAMAGE. PAY PARTICULAR ATTENTION TO THE TOOTHED RING, ANY DEVIATION WILL AFFECT THE WHEEL SPEED SENSOR OUTPUT SIGNAL.
IS PHYSICAL DAMAGE INDICATED?
NO
YES
REPLACE WHEEL SPEED SENSOR AND/OR JUMPER HARNESS IF DAMAGED. REPAIR ANY SENSOR OR TOOTHED RING LOOSENESS. DRIVE VEHICLE ABOVE 24 km/h (15 MPH) TO ENSURE DTC 26 DOES NOT SET.
2
• DISCONNECT RIGHT FRONT WHEEL SPEED SENSOR DIRECTLY AT SENSOR.
• USING J 39200, MEASURE THE RESISTANCE BETWEEN SENSOR TERMINALS "A" AND "B."
IS RESISTANCE BETWEEN 1661 AND 1929Ω WHEN SENSOR IS 20°C (68°F)?
(IF TEMPERATURE OF THE SENSOR IS SUSPECTED TO BE OTHER THAN 20°C (68°F), REFER TO THE TABLE BELOW FOR APPLICABLE SENSOR RESISTANCE VALUES; THE VALUES IN THE TABLE ARE FOR TEMPERATURE OF THE SENSOR, NOT AIR TEMPERATURE.)
YES
NO
REPLACE WHEEL SPEED SENSOR.
3
• WITH J 39200 STILL CONNECTED, SELECT A/C VOLTAGE SCALE.
• SPIN WHEEL BY HAND WHILE OBSERVING VOLTAGE.
IS VOLTAGE AT LEAST 100 mV (VOLTAGE WILL INCREASE AS WHEEL SPEED INCREASES)?
YES
NO
VERIFY THAT TOOTHED RING IS INTACT. IF OK, REPLACE WHEEL SPEED SENSOR
4
• IGNITION "OFF."
• DISCONNECT 32-WAY EBCM CONNECTOR.
• USING J 39200, MEASURE THE RESISTANCE BETWEEN TERMINAL "C3" AND "C4" OF THE 32-WAY EBCM HARNESS CONNECTOR.
DOES J 39200 DISPLAY RESISTANCE AS "OL" (INFINITE)?
YES
NO
REPAIR SHORT BETWEEN CKTs 833 AND 872.
5
• INSPECT CKTs 833 AND 872 AND 32-WAY EBCM CONNECTOR FOR DAMAGE WHICH MAY RESULT IN A SHORT BETWEEN CKTs 833 AND 872 WITH ALL CONNECTORS CONNECTED. REPAIR ALL DAMAGE IF EVIDENT
• RECONNECT ALL CONNECTORS.
• TEST DRIVE VEHICLE ABOVE 24 km/h (15 MPH) FOR AT LEAST 30 SECONDS.
DOES DTC 26 SET AS A CURRENT DTC?
YES
REPLACE EBCM.
NO
MALFUNCTION IS INTERMITTENT. REFER TO "DIAGNOSTIC AIDS"

FRONT WHEEL SPEED SENSOR

TEMPERATURE OF SENSOR VS. SENSOR RESISTANCE (APPROXIMATE)

TEMP (°C)	TEMP (°F)	RESISTANCE (OHMS)
-34 TO 4	-30 TO 40	1309 TO 1808
5 TO 43	41 TO 110	1557 TO 2103
44 TO 93	111 TO 200	1811 TO 2482

GC402940107600EX

Fig. 248 Code A026: Right Front Excessive Wheel Speed Variation (Part 2 of 2). 1993-94 Camaro & Firebird, 1994 Grand Prix, Century & Cutlass Ciera & Cruiser

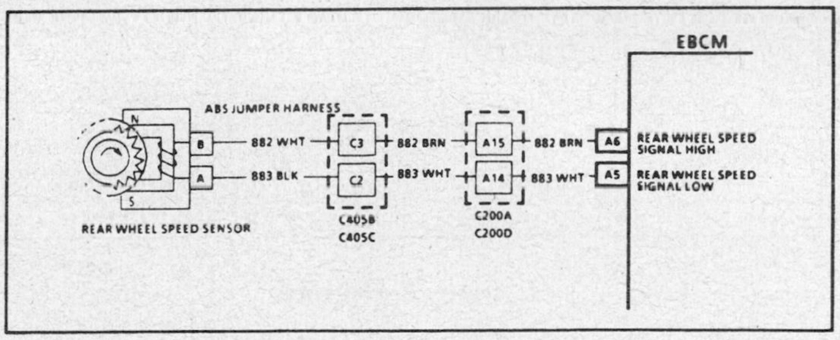
EBCM
ABS JUMPER HARNESS
N
S
B
A
882 WHT
883 BLK
C3
C2
882 BRN
883 WHT
A15
A14
882 BRN
883 WHT
A6
A5
REAR WHEEL SPEED SIGNAL HIGH
REAR WHEEL SPEED SIGNAL LOW
REAR WHEEL SPEED SENSOR
C405B
C405C
C200A
C200D

GC402940107800AX

Grand Prix

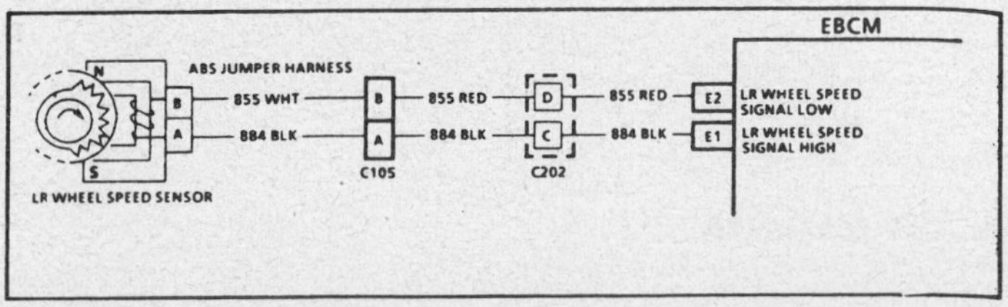
EBCM
ABS JUMPER HARNESS
N
S
B
A
855 WHT
884 BLK
855 RED
884 BLK
D
C
855 RED
884 BLK
E2
E1
LR WHEEL SPEED SIGNAL LOW
LR WHEEL SPEED SIGNAL HIGH
C105
C202
LR WHEEL SPEED SENSOR

GC402940107700BX

Century & Cutlass Ciera & Cruiser

DTC 27

LEFT REAR EXCESSIVE WHEEL SPEED VARIATION

Circuit Description:

As a toothed ring passes by the wheel speed sensor, changes in the electromagnetic field cause the wheel speed sensor to produce a sinusoidal (AC) voltage signal whose frequency is proportional to wheel speed. The magnitude of this signal is directly related to wheel speed and the proximity of the wheel speed sensor to the toothed ring, often referred to as the air gap.

DTC Will Set When: DTC 27 can be set when the brake is "OFF." The purpose of this test is to detect a situation in which the left rear wheel acceleration or deceleration is beyond specified limits.

Action Taken: A malfunction DTC is stored, ABS is disabled and the ABS warning lamp is turned "ON."

DTC Chart Test Description: Number(s) below refer to circled number(s) on the diagnostic chart.

1. This step identifies a wheel speed sensor or circuitry that is damaged and visibly apparent.
2. Checks to see that the wheel speed sensor coil is within proper resistance values.
3. Verifies that the wheel speed sensor can generate an appropriate output signal.
4. This ensures that the wheel speed circuitry is not shorted together.
5. Ensures that the malfunction was not due to physical damage.

Diagnostic Aids: An "Intermittent" malfunction may be caused by a poor connection, rubbed through wire insulation, or a wire that is broken inside the insulation.

The frequency of the malfunction can be checked by using the enhanced diagnostic function of the Tech 1,

If the customer's comments reflect that the ABS warning lamp is "ON" only during moist environmental changes (rain, snow, vehicle wash), all wheel speed sensor circuitry should be thoroughly inspected for signs of water intrusion. If DTC is not current, clear DTCs and simulate the effects of water intrusion. Use the following procedure. Spray down the suspected area with a 5% salt water solution (two teaspoons of salt to 12 oz. of water). Test drive vehicle over various road surfaces (bumps, turns, etc.) above 24 km/h (15 mph) for at least 30 seconds. If DTC returns, replace suspected harness.

Any circuitry, that is suspected as causing the intermittent complaint, should be thoroughly checked for backed out terminals, improper mating, broken locks, improperly formed or damaged terminals, poor terminal to wiring connections or physical damage to the wiring harness.

Resistance of the wheel speed sensor will increase with an increase in sensor temperature.

When replacing a wheel speed sensor, inspect the sensor terminals and harness connector for corrosion and/or water intrusion. If evidence of corrosion or water intrusion exists, replace wheel speed sensor jumper harness. Likewise, if replacing a wheel speed sensor jumper harness, inspect sensor terminals. If evidence of corrosion or water intrusion exists, replace wheel speed sensor. Refer to "On-Vehicle Service" in this section.

GC402940107700CX

Fig. 249 Code A027: Left Rear Excessive Wheel Speed Variation (Part 1 of 2). 1994 Grand Prix, Century & Cutlass Ciera & Cruiser

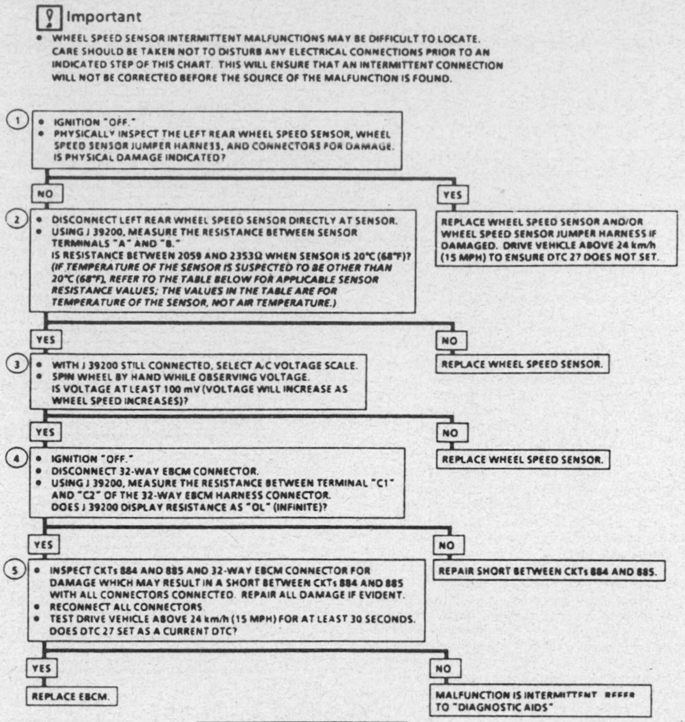
Important
• WHEEL SPEED SENSOR INTERMITTENT MALFUNCTIONS MAY BE DIFFICULT TO LOCATE. CARE SHOULD BE TAKEN NOT TO DISTURB ANY ELECTRICAL CONNECTIONS PRIOR TO AN INDICATED STEP OF THIS CHART. THIS WILL ENSURE THAT AN INTERMITTENT CONNECTION WILL NOT BE CORRECTED BEFORE THE SOURCE OF THE MALFUNCTION IS FOUND.
1
• IGNITION "OFF."
• PHYSICALLY INSPECT THE LEFT REAR WHEEL SPEED SENSOR, WHEEL SPEED SENSOR JUMPER HARNESS, AND CONNECTORS FOR DAMAGE. IS PHYSICAL DAMAGE INDICATED?
NO
YES
REPLACE WHEEL SPEED SENSOR AND/OR WHEEL SPEED SENSOR JUMPER HARNESS IF DAMAGED. DRIVE VEHICLE ABOVE 24 km/h (15 MPH) TO ENSURE DTC 27 DOES NOT SET.
2
• DISCONNECT LEFT REAR WHEEL SPEED SENSOR DIRECTLY AT SENSOR.
• USING J 39200, MEASURE THE RESISTANCE BETWEEN SENSOR TERMINALS "A" AND "B." IS RESISTANCE BETWEEN 2059 AND 2353Ω WHEN SENSOR IS 20°C (68°F)? (IF TEMPERATURE OF THE SENSOR IS SUSPECTED TO BE OTHER THAN 20°C (68°F), REFER TO THE TABLE BELOW FOR APPLICABLE SENSOR RESISTANCE VALUES; THE VALUES IN THE TABLE ARE FOR TEMPERATURE OF THE SENSOR, NOT AIR TEMPERATURE.)
YES
NO
REPLACE WHEEL SPEED SENSOR.
3
• WITH J 39200 STILL CONNECTED, SELECT A/C VOLTAGE SCALE.
• SPIN WHEEL BY HAND WHILE OBSERVING VOLTAGE. IS VOLTAGE AT LEAST 100 mV (VOLTAGE WILL INCREASE AS WHEEL SPEED INCREASES)?
YES
NO
REPLACE WHEEL SPEED SENSOR.
4
• IGNITION "OFF."
• DISCONNECT 32-WAY EBCM CONNECTOR.
• USING J 39200, MEASURE THE RESISTANCE BETWEEN TERMINAL "C1" AND "C2" OF THE 32-WAY EBCM HARNESS CONNECTOR. DOES J 39200 DISPLAY RESISTANCE AS "OL" (INFINITE)?
YES
NO
REPAIR SHORT BETWEEN CKTs 884 AND 885.
5
• INSPECT CKTs 884 AND 885 AND 32-WAY EBCM CONNECTOR FOR DAMAGE WHICH MAY RESULT IN A SHORT BETWEEN CKTs 884 AND 885 WITH ALL CONNECTORS CONNECTED. REPAIR ALL DAMAGE IF EVIDENT.
• RECONNECT ALL CONNECTORS.
• TEST DRIVE VEHICLE ABOVE 24 km/h (15 MPH) FOR AT LEAST 30 SECONDS. DOES DTC 27 SET AS A CURRENT DTC?
YES
NO
REPLACE EBCM.
MALFUNCTION IS INTERMITTENT. REFER TO "DIAGNOSTIC AIDS"

REAR WHEEL SPEED SENSOR

TEMPERATURE OF SENSOR VS. SENSOR RESISTANCE (APPROXIMATE)

TEMP. (°C)	TEMP. (°F)	RESISTANCE (OHMS)
-34 TO 4	-30 TO 40	1622 TO 2205
5 TO 43	41 TO 110	1930 TO 2566
44 TO 93	111 TO 200	2245 TO 3028

GC402940107700DX

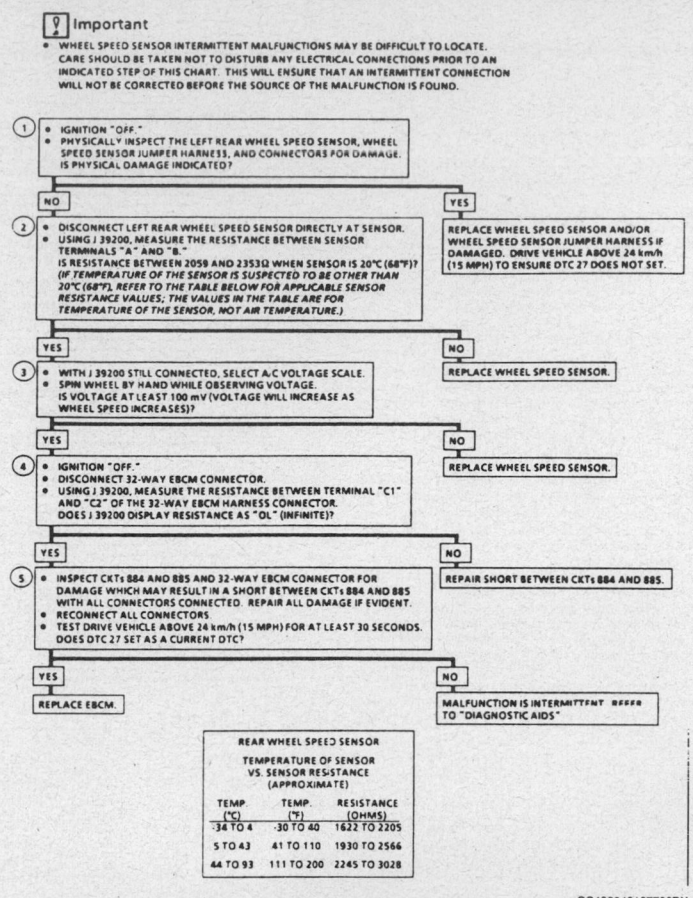

Fig. 249 Code A027: Left Rear Excessive Wheel Speed Variation (Part 2 of 2). 1994 Grand Prix, Century & Cutlass Ciera & Cruiser

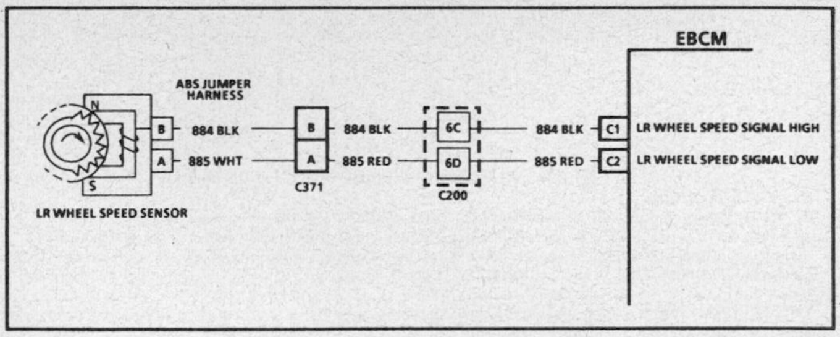
EBCM
ABS JUMPER HARNESS
N
B
A
S
884 BLK
885 WHT
C371
884 BLK
885 RED
6C
6D
C200
884 BLK
885 RED
C1
C2
LR WHEEL SPEED SIGNAL HIGH
LR WHEEL SPEED SIGNAL LOW
LR WHEEL SPEED SENSOR

GC402940107700AX

Grand Prix

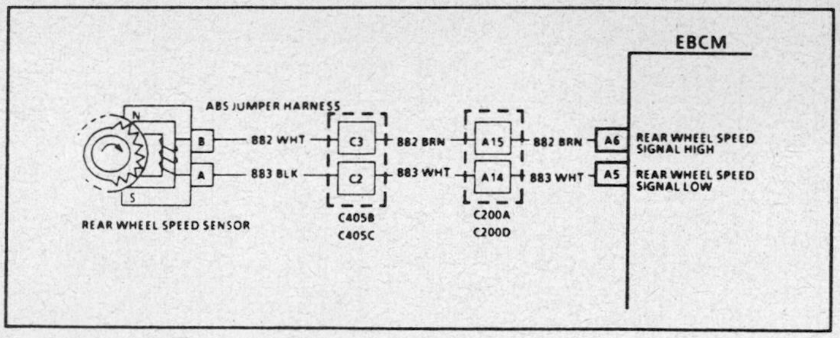
EBCM
ABS JUMPER HARNESS
N
B
A
S
882 WHT
883 BLK
C3
C2
C405B
C405C
882 BRN
883 WHT
A15
A14
C200A
C200D
882 BRN
883 WHT
A6
A5
REAR WHEEL SPEED SIGNAL HIGH
REAR WHEEL SPEED SIGNAL LOW
REAR WHEEL SPEED SENSOR

GC402940107800BX

Camaro & Firebird

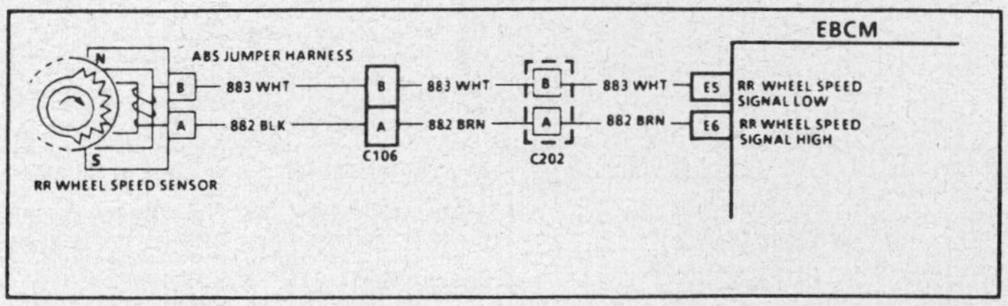
EBCM
ABS JUMPER HARNESS
N
B
A
S
883 WHT
882 BLK
C106
883 WHT
882 BRN
C202
883 WHT
882 BRN
E5
E6
RR WHEEL SPEED SIGNAL LOW
RR WHEEL SPEED SIGNAL HIGH
RR WHEEL SPEED SENSOR

GC402940107800CX

Century & Cutlass Ciera & Cruiser

Fig. 250 Code A028: Right Rear Excessive Wheel Speed Variation (Part 1 of 2). 1993-94 Camaro & Firebird, 1994 Grand Prix, Century & Cutlass Ciera & Cruiser

DTC 28

RIGHT REAR EXCESSIVE WHEEL SPEED VARIATION

Circuit Description:

As a toothed ring passes by the wheel speed sensor, changes in the electromagnetic field cause the wheel speed sensor to produce a sinusoidal (AC) voltage signal whose frequency is proportional to wheel speed. The magnitude of this signal is directly related to wheel speed and the proximity of the wheel speed sensor to the toothed ring, often referred to as the air gap.

DTC Will Set When: DTC 28 can be set when the brake is "OFF." The purpose of this test is to detect a situation in which the right rear wheel acceleration or deceleration is beyond specified limits.

Action Taken: A malfunction DTC is stored, ABS is disabled and the ABS warning lamp is turned "ON."

DTC Chart Test Description: Number(s) below refer to circled number(s) on the diagnostic chart.

1. This step identifies a wheel speed sensor or circuitry that is damaged and visibly apparent.
2. Checks to see that the wheel speed sensor coil is within proper resistance values.
3. Verifies that the wheel speed sensor can generate an appropriate output signal.
4. This ensures that the wheel speed circuitry is not shorted together.
5. Ensures that the malfunction was not due to physical damage.

Diagnostic Aids: An "Intermittent" malfunction may be caused by a poor connection, rubbed through wire insulation, or a wire that is broken inside the insulation.

The frequency of the malfunction can be checked by using the enhanced diagnostic function of the Tech 1,

If the customer's comments reflect that the ABS warning lamp is "ON" only during moist environmental changes (rain, snow, vehicle wash), all wheel speed sensor circuitry should be thoroughly inspected for signs of water intrusion. If DTC is not current, clear DTCs and simulate the effects of water intrusion. Use the following procedure. Spray down the suspected area with a 5% salt water solution (two teaspoons of salt to 12 oz. of water). Test drive vehicle over various road surfaces (bumps, turns, etc.) above 24 km/h (15 mph) for at least 30 seconds. If DTC returns, replace suspected harness.

Any circuitry, that is suspected as causing the intermittent complaint, should be thoroughly checked for backed out terminals, improper mating, broken locks, improperly formed or damaged terminals, poor terminal to wiring connections or physical damage to the wiring harness.

Resistance of the wheel speed sensor will increase with an increase in sensor temperature.

When replacing a wheel speed sensor, inspect the sensor terminals and harness connector for corrosion and/or water intrusion. If evidence of corrosion or water intrusion exists, replace wheel speed sensor jumper harness. Likewise, if replacing a wheel speed sensor jumper harness, inspect sensor terminals. If evidence of corrosion or water intrusion exists, replace wheel speed sensor. Refer to "On-Vehicle Service" in this section.

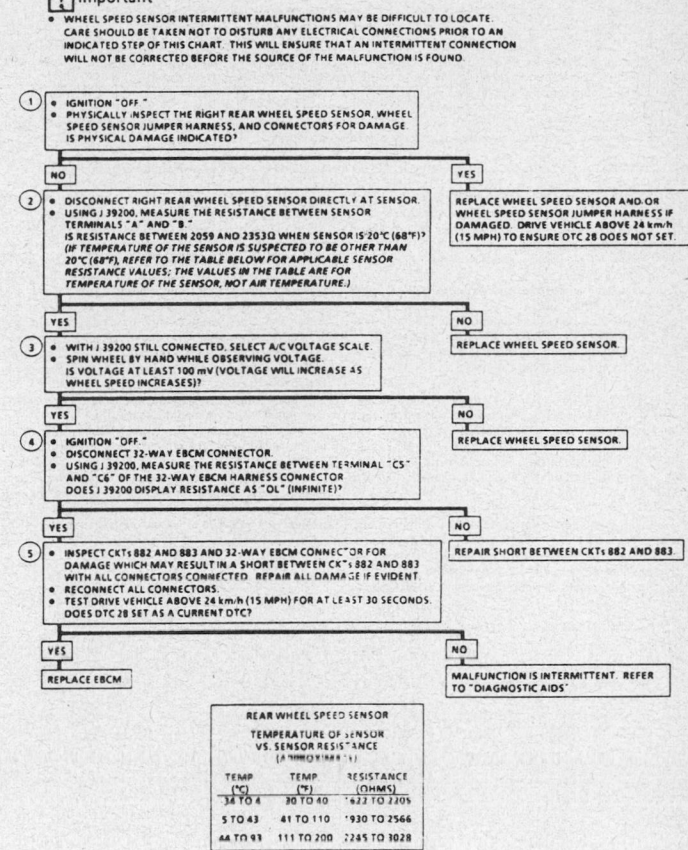

GC402940107800DX

Important

- WHEEL SPEED SENSOR INTERMITTENT MALFUNCTIONS MAY BE DIFFICULT TO LOCATE. CARE SHOULD BE TAKEN NOT TO DISTURB ANY ELECTRICAL CONNECTIONS PRIOR TO AN INDICATED STEP OF THIS CHART. THIS WILL ENSURE THAT AN INTERMITTENT CONNECTION WILL NOT BE CORRECTED BEFORE THE SOURCE OF THE MALFUNCTION IS FOUND.

(1)
- IGNITION "OFF."
- PHYSICALLY INSPECT THE RIGHT REAR WHEEL SPEED SENSOR, WHEEL SPEED SENSOR JUMPER HARNESS, AND CONNECTORS FOR DAMAGE. IS PHYSICAL DAMAGE INDICATED?

YES: REPLACE WHEEL SPEED SENSOR AND/OR WHEEL SPEED SENSOR JUMPER HARNESS IF DAMAGED. DRIVE VEHICLE ABOVE 24 km/h (15 MPH) TO ENSURE DTC 28 DOES NOT SET.

NO:

(2)
- DISCONNECT RIGHT REAR WHEEL SPEED SENSOR DIRECTLY AT SENSOR.
- USING J 39200, MEASURE THE RESISTANCE BETWEEN SENSOR TERMINALS "A" AND "B."
IS RESISTANCE BETWEEN 2059 AND 2353Ω WHEN SENSOR IS 20°C (68°F)? *(IF TEMPERATURE OF THE SENSOR IS SUSPECTED TO BE OTHER THAN 20°C (68°F), REFER TO THE TABLE BELOW FOR APPLICABLE SENSOR RESISTANCE VALUES; THE VALUES IN THE TABLE ARE FOR TEMPERATURE OF THE SENSOR, NOT AIR TEMPERATURE.)*

NO: REPLACE WHEEL SPEED SENSOR.

YES:

(3)
- WITH J 39200 STILL CONNECTED, SELECT A/C VOLTAGE SCALE.
- SPIN WHEEL BY HAND WHILE OBSERVING VOLTAGE.
IS VOLTAGE AT LEAST 100 mV (VOLTAGE WILL INCREASE AS WHEEL SPEED INCREASES)?

NO: REPLACE WHEEL SPEED SENSOR.

YES:

(4)
- IGNITION "OFF."
- DISCONNECT 32-WAY EBCM CONNECTOR.
- USING J 39200, MEASURE THE RESISTANCE BETWEEN TERMINAL "C5" AND "C6" OF THE 32-WAY EBCM HARNESS CONNECTOR
DOES J 39200 DISPLAY RESISTANCE AS "OL" (INFINITE)?

NO: REPAIR SHORT BETWEEN CKTs 882 AND 883.

YES:

(5)
- INSPECT CKTs 882 AND 883 AND 32-WAY EBCM CONNECTOR FOR DAMAGE WHICH MAY RESULT IN A SHORT BETWEEN CKTs 882 AND 883 WITH ALL CONNECTORS CONNECTED. REPAIR ALL DAMAGE IF EVIDENT.
- RECONNECT ALL CONNECTORS.
- TEST DRIVE VEHICLE ABOVE 24 km/h (15 MPH) FOR AT LEAST 30 SECONDS. DOES DTC 28 SET AS A CURRENT DTC?

YES: REPLACE EBCM.

NO: MALFUNCTION IS INTERMITTENT. REFER TO "DIAGNOSTIC AIDS"

REAR WHEEL SPEED SENSOR

TEMPERATURE OF SENSOR VS. SENSOR RESISTANCE (APPROXIMATE)

TEMP (°C)	TEMP (°F)	RESISTANCE (OHMS)
34 TO 4	30 TO 40	1622 TO 2205
5 TO 43	41 TO 110	1930 TO 2566
44 TO 93	111 TO 200	2245 TO 3028

Fig. 250 Code A028: Right Rear Excessive Wheel Speed Variation (Part 2 of 2). 1993-94 Camaro & Firebird, 1994 Grand Prix, Century & Cutlass Ciera & Cruiser

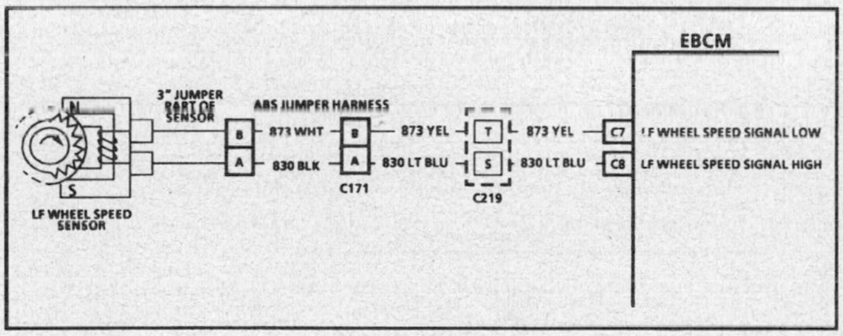
EBCM
3" JUMPER PART OF SENSOR
ABS JUMPER HARNESS
N
S
B
A
873 WHT
830 BLK
C171
873 YEL
830 LT BLU
T
S
C219
C7
C8
LF WHEEL SPEED SIGNAL LOW
LF WHEEL SPEED SIGNAL HIGH
LF WHEEL SPEED SENSOR

GC402940107901AX

Grand Prix

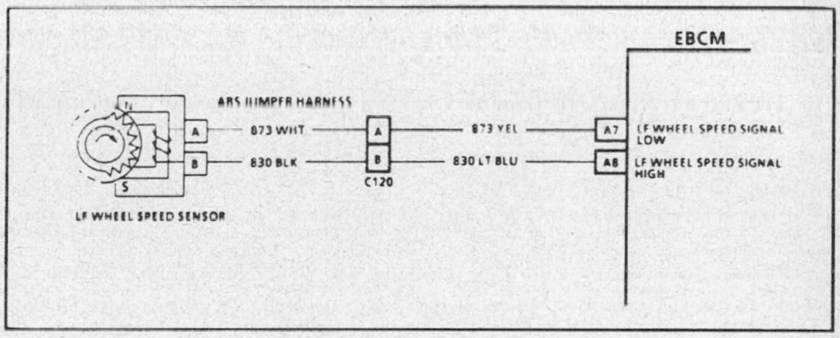
EBCM
ABS JUMPER HARNESS
A
B
873 WHT
830 BLK
C120
873 YEL
830 LT BLU
A7
A8
LF WHEEL SPEED SIGNAL LOW
LF WHEEL SPEED SIGNAL HIGH
S
LF WHEEL SPEED SENSOR

GC402940107901BX

Camaro & Firebird

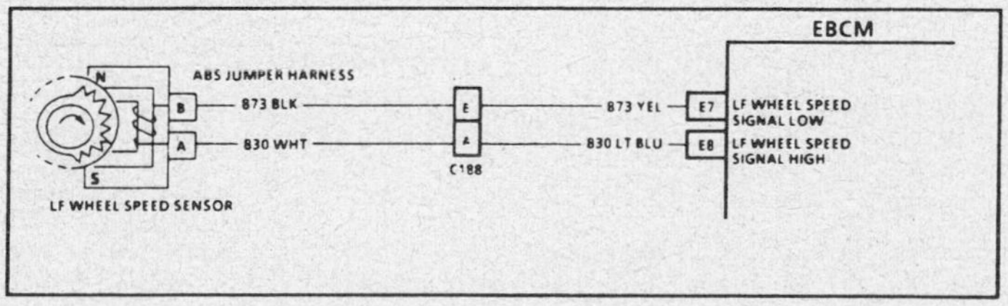
EBCM
ABS JUMPER HARNESS
N
B
A
873 BLK
830 WHT
E
A
C188
873 YEL
830 LT BLU
E7
E8
LF WHEEL SPEED SIGNAL LOW
LF WHEEL SPEED SIGNAL HIGH
S
LF WHEEL SPEED SENSOR

GC402940107901CX

Century & Cutlass Ciera & Cruiser

Fig. 251 Code A032: LF Wheel Speed Sensor Circuit Open Or Shorted To Gnd/Batt (Part 1 of 3). 1993–94 Camaro & Firebird, 1994 Grand Prix, Century & Cutlass Ciera & Cruiser

DTC 32

LF WHEEL SPEED SNR CKT OPEN OR SHORT TO GND/BATT

Circuit Description:

As a toothed ring passes by the wheel speed sensor, changes in the electromagnetic field cause the wheel speed sensor to produce a sinusoidal (AC) voltage signal whose frequency is proportional to wheel speed. The magnitude of this signal is directly related to wheel speed and the proximity of the wheel speed sensor to the toothed ring often referred to as the air gap.

DTC Will Set When: DTC 32 can be set anytime after initialization. If either of the left front wheel speed circuits are open or shorted to voltage or ground, a malfunction exists.

Action Taken: A malfunction DTC is stored, ABS is disabled and the ABS warning lamp is turned "ON."

DTC Chart Test Description: Number(s) below refer to circled number(s) on the diagnostic chart.

1. Checks for proper resistance of the wheel speed sensor coil.
2. Checks for a short to ground in the wheel speed sensor wiring.
3. Checks for a short to voltage in the wheel speed sensor wiring.
4. Checks for a short to voltage in CKT 873.
5. Checks for a short to voltage in CKT 830.
6. Ensures that the malfunction was not due to physical damage of the circuitry.

Diagnostic Aids: An "Intermittent" malfunction may be caused by a poor connection, rubbed through wire insulation, or a wire that is broken inside the insulation.

The frequency of the malfunction can be checked by using the enhanced diagnostic function of the Tech 1,

If the customer's comments reflect that the ABS warning lamp is "ON" only during moist environmental changes (rain, snow, vehicle wash), all wheel speed sensor circuitry should be thoroughly inspected for signs of water intrusion. If DTC is not current, clear DTCs and simulate the effects of water intrusion. Use the following procedure. Spray down the suspected area with a 5% salt water solution (two teaspoons of salt to 12 oz. of water). Test drive vehicle over various road surfaces (bumps, turns, etc.) above 24 km/h (15 mph) for at least 30 seconds. If DTC returns, replace suspected harness.

Any circuitry, that is suspected as causing the intermittent complaint, should be thoroughly checked for backed out terminals, improper mating, broken locks, improperly formed or damaged terminals, poor terminal to wiring connections or physical damage to the wiring harness.

Resistance of the wheel speed sensor will increase with an increase in sensor temperature.

When replacing a wheel speed sensor, inspect the sensor terminals and harness connector for corrosion and/or water intrusion. If evidence of corrosion or water intrusion exists, replace wheel speed sensor jumper harness. Likewise, if replacing a wheel speed sensor jumper harness, inspect sensor terminals. If evidence of corrosion or water intrusion exists, replace wheel speed sensor. Refer to "On-Vehicle Service" in this section.

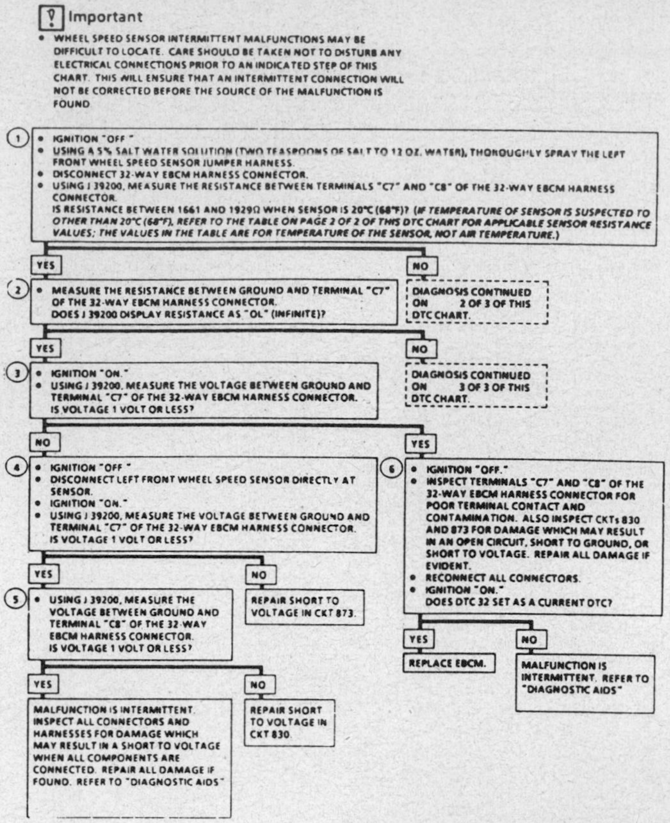
Important
WHEEL SPEED SENSOR INTERMITTENT MALFUNCTIONS MAY BE DIFFICULT TO LOCATE. CARE SHOULD BE TAKEN NOT TO DISTURB ANY ELECTRICAL CONNECTIONS PRIOR TO AN INDICATED STEP OF THIS CHART. THIS WILL ENSURE THAT AN INTERMITTENT CONNECTION WILL NOT BE CORRECTED BEFORE THE SOURCE OF THE MALFUNCTION IS FOUND
1
IGNITION "OFF." USING A 5% SALT WATER SOLUTION (TWO TEASPOONS OF SALT TO 12 OZ. WATER), THOROUGHLY SPRAY THE LEFT FRONT WHEEL SPEED SENSOR JUMPER HARNESS. DISCONNECT 32-WAY EBCM HARNESS CONNECTOR. USING J 39200, MEASURE THE RESISTANCE BETWEEN TERMINALS "C7" AND "C8" OF THE 32-WAY EBCM HARNESS CONNECTOR. IS RESISTANCE BETWEEN 1661 AND 1929Ω WHEN SENSOR IS 20°C (68°F)? (IF TEMPERATURE OF SENSOR IS SUSPECTED TO OTHER THAN 20°C (68°F), REFER TO THE TABLE ON PAGE 2 OF 2 OF THIS DTC CHART FOR APPLICABLE SENSOR RESISTANCE VALUES; THE VALUES IN THE TABLE ARE FOR TEMPERATURE OF THE SENSOR, NOT AIR TEMPERATURE.)
YES
NO
2
MEASURE THE RESISTANCE BETWEEN GROUND AND TERMINAL "C7" OF THE 32-WAY EBCM HARNESS CONNECTOR. DOES J 39200 DISPLAY RESISTANCE AS "OL" (INFINITE)?
DIAGNOSIS CONTINUED ON 2 OF 3 OF THIS DTC CHART.
YES
NO
3
IGNITION "ON." USING J 39200, MEASURE THE VOLTAGE BETWEEN GROUND AND TERMINAL "C7" OF THE 32-WAY EBCM HARNESS CONNECTOR. IS VOLTAGE 1 VOLT OR LESS?
DIAGNOSIS CONTINUED ON 3 OF 3 OF THIS DTC CHART.
NO
YES
4
IGNITION "OFF." DISCONNECT LEFT FRONT WHEEL SPEED SENSOR DIRECTLY AT SENSOR. IGNITION "ON." USING J 39200, MEASURE THE VOLTAGE BETWEEN GROUND AND TERMINAL "C7" OF THE 32-WAY EBCM HARNESS CONNECTOR. IS VOLTAGE 1 VOLT OR LESS?
6
IGNITION "OFF." INSPECT TERMINALS "C7" AND "C8" OF THE 32-WAY EBCM HARNESS CONNECTOR FOR POOR TERMINAL CONTACT AND CONTAMINATION. ALSO INSPECT CKTs 830 AND 873 FOR DAMAGE WHICH MAY RESULT IN AN OPEN CIRCUIT, SHORT TO GROUND, OR SHORT TO VOLTAGE. REPAIR ALL DAMAGE IF EVIDENT. RECONNECT ALL CONNECTORS. IGNITION "ON." DOES DTC 32 SET AS A CURRENT DTC?
YES
NO
5
USING J 39200, MEASURE THE VOLTAGE BETWEEN GROUND AND TERMINAL "C8" OF THE 32-WAY EBCM HARNESS CONNECTOR. IS VOLTAGE 1 VOLT OR LESS?
REPAIR SHORT TO VOLTAGE IN CKT 873.
YES
NO
REPLACE EBCM.
MALFUNCTION IS INTERMITTENT. REFER TO "DIAGNOSTIC AIDS"
YES
NO
MALFUNCTION IS INTERMITTENT. INSPECT ALL CONNECTORS AND HARNESSES FOR DAMAGE WHICH MAY RESULT IN A SHORT TO VOLTAGE WHEN ALL COMPONENTS ARE CONNECTED. REPAIR ALL DAMAGE IF FOUND. REFER TO "DIAGNOSTIC AIDS"
REPAIR SHORT TO VOLTAGE IN CKT 830.

GC402940107902AX

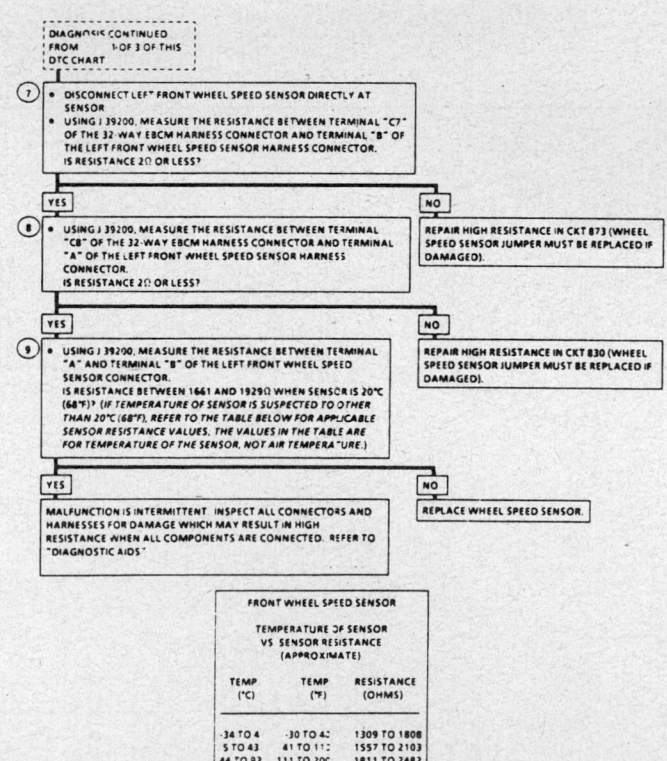

DTC 32

LF WHEEL SPEED SNR CKT OPEN OR SHORT TO GND/BATT

Circuit Description:

As a toothed ring passes by the wheel speed sensor, changes in the electromagnetic field cause the wheel speed sensor to produce a sinusoidal (AC) voltage signal whose frequency is proportional to wheel speed. The magnitude of this signal is directly related to wheel speed and the proximity of the wheel speed sensor to the toothed ring often referred to as the air gap.

DTC Will Set When: DTC 32 can be set anytime after initialization. If either of the left front wheel speed circuits are open or shorted to voltage or ground, a malfunction exists.

Action Taken: A malfunction DTC is stored, ABS is disabled and the ABS warning lamp is turned "ON."

DTC Chart Test Description: Number(s) below refer to circled number(s) on the diagnostic chart.

7. Checks for high resistance in CKT 873.
8. Checks for high resistance in CKT 830.
9. Verifies proper wheel speed sensor resistance.

Diagnostic Aids: An "Intermittent" malfunction may be caused by a poor connection, rubbed through wire insulation, or a wire that is broken inside the insulation.

The frequency of the malfunction can be checked by using the enhanced diagnostic function of the Tech 1,

If the customer's comments reflect that the ABS warning lamp is "ON" only during moist environmental changes (rain, snow, vehicle wash), all wheel speed sensor circuitry should be thoroughly inspected for signs of water intrusion. If DTC is not current, clear DTCs and simulate the effects of water intrusion. Use the following procedure. Spray down the suspected area with a 5% salt water solution (two teaspoons of salt to 12 oz. of water). Test drive vehicle over various road surfaces (bumps, turns, etc.) above 24 km/h (15 mph) for at least 30 seconds. If DTC returns, replace suspected harness.

Any circuitry, that is suspected as causing the intermittent complaint, should be thoroughly checked for backed out terminals, improper mating, broken locks, improperly formed or damaged terminals, poor terminal to wiring connections or physical damage to the wiring harness.

Resistance of the wheel speed sensor will increase with an increase in sensor temperature.

When replacing a wheel speed sensor, inspect the sensor terminals and harness connector for corrosion and/or water intrusion. If evidence of corrosion or water intrusion exists, replace wheel speed sensor jumper harness. Likewise, if replacing a wheel speed sensor jumper harness, inspect sensor terminals. If evidence of corrosion or water intrusion exists, replace wheel speed sensor. Refer to "On-Vehicle Service" in this section.

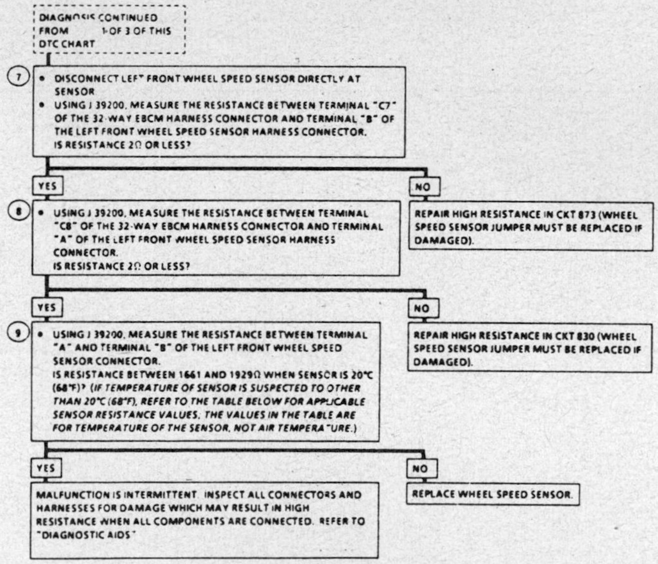
DIAGNOSIS CONTINUED FROM 1 OF 3 OF THIS DTC CHART
7
DISCONNECT LEFT FRONT WHEEL SPEED SENSOR DIRECTLY AT SENSOR. USING J 39200, MEASURE THE RESISTANCE BETWEEN TERMINAL "C7" OF THE 32-WAY EBCM HARNESS CONNECTOR AND TERMINAL "B" OF THE LEFT FRONT WHEEL SPEED SENSOR HARNESS CONNECTOR. IS RESISTANCE 2Ω OR LESS?
YES
NO
8
USING J 39200, MEASURE THE RESISTANCE BETWEEN TERMINAL "C8" OF THE 32-WAY EBCM HARNESS CONNECTOR AND TERMINAL "A" OF THE LEFT FRONT WHEEL SPEED SENSOR HARNESS CONNECTOR. IS RESISTANCE 2Ω OR LESS?
REPAIR HIGH RESISTANCE IN CKT 873 (WHEEL SPEED SENSOR JUMPER MUST BE REPLACED IF DAMAGED).
YES
NO
9
USING J 39200, MEASURE THE RESISTANCE BETWEEN TERMINAL "A" AND TERMINAL "B" OF THE LEFT FRONT WHEEL SPEED SENSOR CONNECTOR. IS RESISTANCE BETWEEN 1661 AND 1929Ω WHEN SENSOR IS 20°C (68°F)? (IF TEMPERATURE OF SENSOR IS SUSPECTED TO OTHER THAN 20°C (68°F), REFER TO THE TABLE BELOW FOR APPLICABLE SENSOR RESISTANCE VALUES. THE VALUES IN THE TABLE ARE FOR TEMPERATURE OF THE SENSOR, NOT AIR TEMPERATURE.)
REPAIR HIGH RESISTANCE IN CKT 830 (WHEEL SPEED SENSOR JUMPER MUST BE REPLACED IF DAMAGED).
YES
NO
MALFUNCTION IS INTERMITTENT. INSPECT ALL CONNECTORS AND HARNESSES FOR DAMAGE WHICH MAY RESULT IN HIGH RESISTANCE WHEN ALL COMPONENTS ARE CONNECTED. REFER TO "DIAGNOSTIC AIDS"
REPLACE WHEEL SPEED SENSOR.

FRONT WHEEL SPEED SENSOR

TEMPERATURE OF SENSOR VS SENSOR RESISTANCE (APPROXIMATE)

TEMP (°C)	TEMP (°F)	RESISTANCE (OHMS)
-34 TO 4	-30 TO 40	1309 TO 1808
5 TO 43	41 TO 110	1557 TO 2103
44 TO 93	111 TO 200	1811 TO 2482

GC402940107902BX

Fig. 251 Code A032: LF Wheel Speed Sensor Circuit Open Or Shorted To Gnd/Batt (Part 2 of 3). 1993–94 Camaro & Firebird, 1994 Grand Prix, Century & Cutlass Ciera & Cruiser

DTC 32

LF WHEEL SPEED SNR CKT OPEN OR SHORT TO GND/BATT

Circuit Description:
As a toothed ring passes by the wheel speed sensor, changes in the electromagnetic field cause the wheel speed sensor to produce a sinusoidal (AC) voltage signal whose frequency is proportional to wheel speed. The magnitude of this signal is directly related to wheel speed and the proximity of the wheel speed sensor to the toothed ring often referred to as the air gap.

DTC Will Set When: DTC 32 can be set anytime after initialization. If either of the left front wheel speed circuits are open or shorted to voltage or ground, a malfunction exists.

Action Taken: A malfunction DTC is stored, ABS is disabled and the ABS warning lamp is turned "ON."

DTC Chart Test Description: Number(s) below refer to circled number(s) on the diagnostic chart.

10. Checks for a short to ground in CKT 873.
11. Checks for a short to ground in CKT 830.
12. Checks for a short to ground in the wheel speed sensor jumper harness.
13. Verifies that wheel speed sensor is not internally shorted to ground.

Diagnostic Aids: An "Intermittent" malfunction may be caused by a poor connection, rubbed through wire insulation, or a wire that is broken inside the insulation.

The frequency of the malfunction can be checked by using the enhanced diagnostic function of the Tech 1,

If the customer's comments reflect that the ABS warning lamp is "ON" only during moist environmental changes (rain, snow, vehicle wash), all wheel speed sensor circuitry should be thoroughly inspected for signs of water intrusion. If DTC is not current, clear DTCs and simulate the effects of water intrusion. Use the following procedure. Spray down the suspected area with a 5% salt water solution (two teaspoons of salt to 12 oz. of water). Test drive vehicle over various road surfaces (bumps, turns, etc.) above 24 km/h (15 mph) for at least 30 seconds. If DTC returns, replace suspected harness.

Any circuitry, that is suspected as causing the intermittent complaint, should be thoroughly checked for backed out terminals, improper mating, broken locks, improperly formed or damaged terminals, poor terminal to wiring connections or physical damage to the wiring harness.

Resistance of the wheel speed sensor will increase with an increase in sensor temperature.

When replacing a wheel speed sensor, inspect the sensor terminals and harness connector for corrosion and/or water intrusion. If evidence of corrosion or water intrusion exists, replace wheel speed sensor jumper harness. Likewise, if replacing a wheel speed sensor jumper harness, inspect sensor terminals. If evidence of corrosion or water intrusion exists, replace wheel speed sensor. Refer to "On-Vehicle Service" in this section.

GC402940107903AX

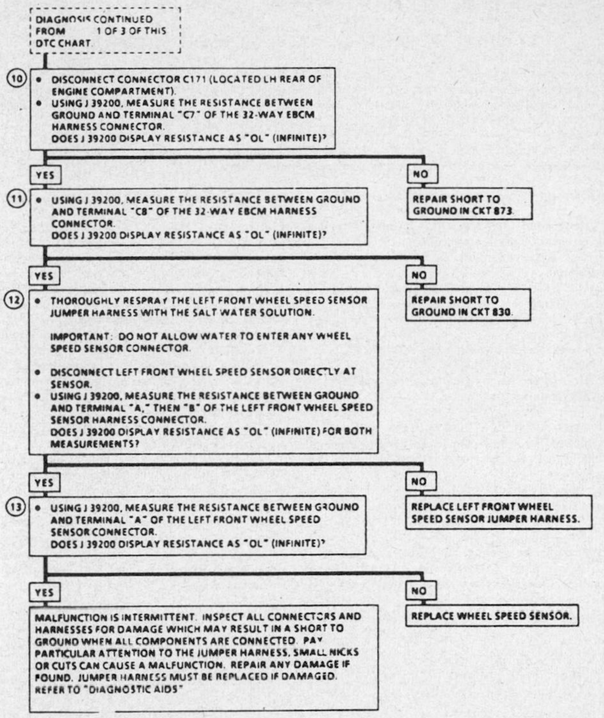

DIAGNOSIS CONTINUED FROM 1 OF 3 OF THIS DTC CHART.
10
• DISCONNECT CONNECTOR C171 (LOCATED LH REAR OF ENGINE COMPARTMENT).
• USING J 39200, MEASURE THE RESISTANCE BETWEEN GROUND AND TERMINAL "C7" OF THE 32-WAY EBCM HARNESS CONNECTOR.
DOES J 39200 DISPLAY RESISTANCE AS "OL" (INFINITE)?
YES
NO
REPAIR SHORT TO GROUND IN CKT 873.
11
• USING J 39200, MEASURE THE RESISTANCE BETWEEN GROUND AND TERMINAL "C8" OF THE 32-WAY EBCM HARNESS CONNECTOR.
DOES J 39200 DISPLAY RESISTANCE AS "OL" (INFINITE)?
YES
NO
REPAIR SHORT TO GROUND IN CKT 830.
12
• THOROUGHLY RESPRAY THE LEFT FRONT WHEEL SPEED SENSOR JUMPER HARNESS WITH THE SALT WATER SOLUTION.
IMPORTANT: DO NOT ALLOW WATER TO ENTER ANY WHEEL SPEED SENSOR CONNECTOR.
• DISCONNECT LEFT FRONT WHEEL SPEED SENSOR DIRECTLY AT SENSOR.
• USING J 39200, MEASURE THE RESISTANCE BETWEEN GROUND AND TERMINAL "A," THEN "B" OF THE LEFT FRONT WHEEL SPEED SENSOR HARNESS CONNECTOR.
DOES J 39200 DISPLAY RESISTANCE AS "OL" (INFINITE) FOR BOTH MEASUREMENTS?
YES
NO
REPLACE LEFT FRONT WHEEL SPEED SENSOR JUMPER HARNESS.
13
• USING J 39200, MEASURE THE RESISTANCE BETWEEN GROUND AND TERMINAL "A" OF THE LEFT FRONT WHEEL SPEED SENSOR CONNECTOR.
DOES J 39200 DISPLAY RESISTANCE AS "OL" (INFINITE)?
YES
NO
REPLACE WHEEL SPEED SENSOR.
MALFUNCTION IS INTERMITTENT. INSPECT ALL CONNECTORS AND HARNESSES FOR DAMAGE WHICH MAY RESULT IN A SHORT TO GROUND WHEN ALL COMPONENTS ARE CONNECTED. PAY PARTICULAR ATTENTION TO THE JUMPER HARNESS. SMALL NICKS OR CUTS CAN CAUSE A MALFUNCTION. REPAIR ANY DAMAGE IF FOUND. JUMPER HARNESS MUST BE REPLACED IF DAMAGED. REFER TO "DIAGNOSTIC AIDS"

GC402940107903BX

Fig. 251 Code A032: LF Wheel Speed Sensor Circuit Open Or Shorted To Gnd/Batt (Part 3 of 3). 1993–94 Camaro & Firebird, 1994 Grand Prix, Century & Cutlass Ciera & Cruiser

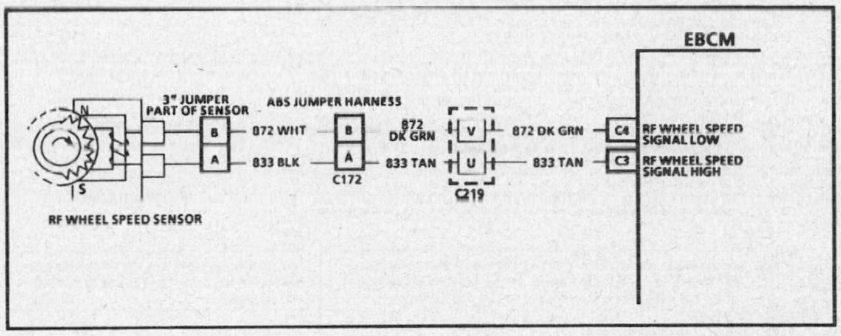

EBCM
3" JUMPER PART OF SENSOR
ABS JUMPER HARNESS
872 WHT
833 BLK
872 DK GRN
833 TAN
C172
872 DK GRN
833 TAN
C219
RF WHEEL SPEED SIGNAL LOW
RF WHEEL SPEED SIGNAL HIGH
RF WHEEL SPEED SENSOR

GC402940108001AX

Grand Prix

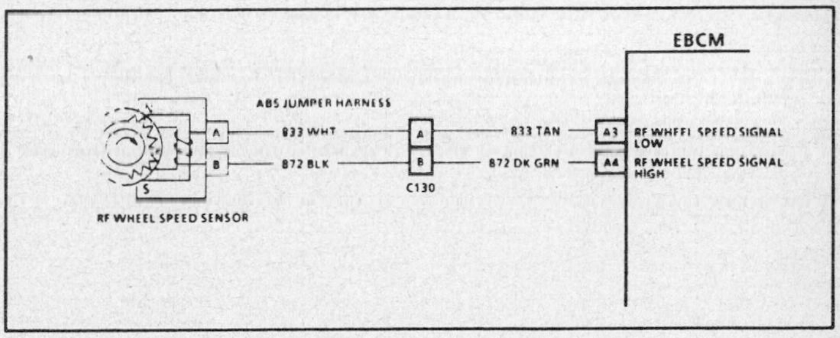

EBCM
ABS JUMPER HARNESS
833 WHT
872 BLK
C130
833 TAN
872 DK GRN
RF WHEEL SPEED SIGNAL LOW
RF WHEEL SPEED SIGNAL HIGH
RF WHEEL SPEED SENSOR

GC402940108001BX

Camaro & Firebird

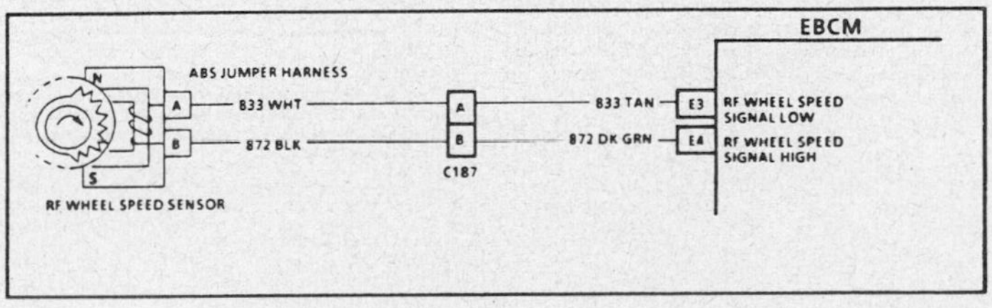

EBCM
ABS JUMPER HARNESS
833 WHT
872 BLK
C187
833 TAN
872 DK GRN
RF WHEEL SPEED SIGNAL LOW
RF WHEEL SPEED SIGNAL HIGH
RF WHEEL SPEED SENSOR

GC402940108001CX

Century & Cutlass Ciera & Cruiser

Fig. 252 Code A033: RF Wheel Speed Sensor Circuit Open Or Shorted To Gnd/Batt (Part 1 of 3). 1993–94 Camaro & Firebird, 1994 Grand Prix, Century & Cutlass Ciera & Cruiser

DTC 33

RF WHEEL SPEED SNR CKT OPEN OR SHORT TO GND/BATT

Circuit Description:

As a toothed ring passes by the wheel speed sensor, changes in the electromagnetic field cause the wheel speed sensor to produce a sinusoidal (AC) voltage signal whose frequency is proportional to wheel speed. The magnitude of this signal is directly related to wheel speed and the proximity of the wheel speed sensor to the toothed ring, often referred to as the air gap.

DTC Will Set When: DTC 33 can be set anytime after initialization. If either of the right front wheel speed circuits are open or shorted to voltage or ground, a malfunction exists.

Action Taken: A malfunction DTC is stored, ABS is disabled and the ABS warning lamp is turned "ON."

DTC Chart Test Description: Number(s) below refer to circled number(s) on the diagnostic chart.

1. Checks for proper resistance of the wheel speed sensor coil.
2. Checks for a short to ground in the wheel speed sensor wiring.
3. Checks for a short to voltage in the wheel speed sensor wiring.
4. Checks for a short to voltage in CKT 833.
5. Checks for short to voltage in CKT 872.
6. Ensures that the malfunction was not due to physical damage of the circuitry.

Diagnostic Aids: An "Intermittent" malfunction may be caused by a poor connection, rubbed through wire insulation, or a wire that is broken inside the insulation.

The frequency of the malfunction can be checked by using the enhanced diagnostic function of the Tech 1,

If the customer's comments reflect that the ABS warning lamp is "ON" only during moist environmental changes (rain, snow, vehicle wash), all wheel speed sensor circuitry should be thoroughly inspected for signs of water intrusion. If DTC is not current, clear DTCs and simulate the effects of water intrusion. Use the following procedure. Spray down the suspected area with a 5% salt water solution (two teaspoons of salt to 12 oz. of water). Test drive vehicle over various road surfaces (bumps, turns, etc.) above 24 km/h (15 mph) for at least 30 seconds. If DTC returns, replace suspected harness.

Any circuitry, that is suspected as causing the intermittent complaint, should be thoroughly checked for backed out terminals, improper mating, broken locks, improperly formed or damaged terminals, poor terminal to wiring connections or physical damage to the wiring harness.

Resistance of the wheel speed sensor will increase with an increase in sensor temperature.

When replacing a wheel speed sensor, inspect the sensor terminals and harness connector for corrosion and/or water intrusion. If evidence of corrosion or water intrusion exists, replace wheel speed sensor jumper harness. Likewise, if replacing a wheel speed sensor jumper harness, inspect sensor terminals. If evidence of corrosion or water intrusion exists, replace wheel speed sensor. Refer to "On-Vehicle Service" in this section.

GC402940108001DX

Important

- WHEEL SPEED SENSOR INTERMITTENT MALFUNCTIONS MAY BE DIFFICULT TO LOCATE. CARE SHOULD BE TAKEN NOT TO DISTURB ANY ELECTRICAL CONNECTIONS PRIOR TO AN INDICATED STEP OF THIS CHART. THIS WILL ENSURE THAT AN INTERMITTENT CONNECTION WILL NOT BE CORRECTED BEFORE THE SOURCE OF THE MALFUNCTION IS FOUND.

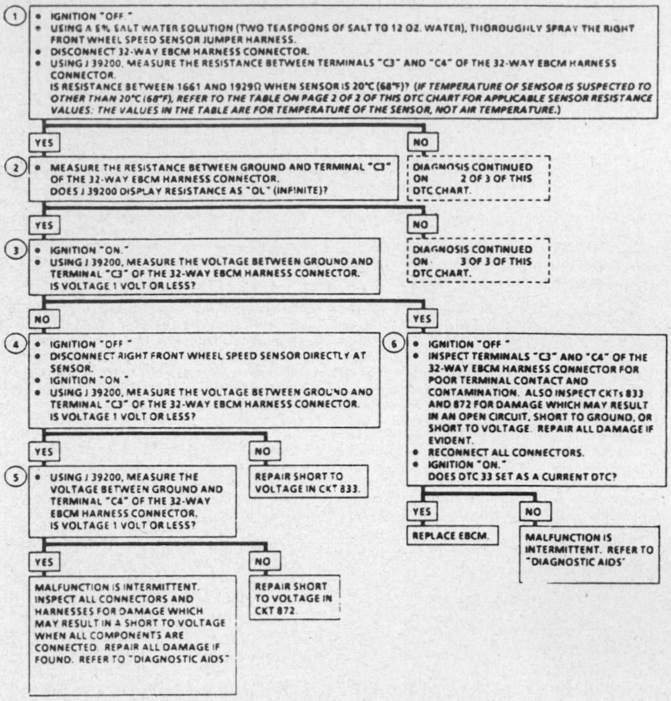
1
• IGNITION "OFF."
• USING A 5% SALT WATER SOLUTION (TWO TEASPOONS OF SALT TO 12 OZ. WATER), THOROUGHLY SPRAY THE RIGHT FRONT WHEEL SPEED SENSOR JUMPER HARNESS.
• DISCONNECT 32-WAY EBCM HARNESS CONNECTOR.
• USING J 39200, MEASURE THE RESISTANCE BETWEEN TERMINALS "C3" AND "C4" OF THE 32-WAY EBCM HARNESS CONNECTOR.
IS RESISTANCE BETWEEN 1661 AND 1929Ω WHEN SENSOR IS 20°C (68°F)? (IF TEMPERATURE OF SENSOR IS SUSPECTED TO OTHER THAN 20°C (68°F), REFER TO THE TABLE ON PAGE 2 OF 2 OF THIS DTC CHART FOR APPLICABLE SENSOR RESISTANCE VALUES: THE VALUES IN THE TABLE ARE FOR TEMPERATURE OF THE SENSOR, NOT AIR TEMPERATURE.)
YES
NO
2
• MEASURE THE RESISTANCE BETWEEN GROUND AND TERMINAL "C3" OF THE 32-WAY EBCM HARNESS CONNECTOR.
DOES J 39200 DISPLAY RESISTANCE AS "OL" (INFINITE)?
DIAGNOSIS CONTINUED ON 2 OF 3 OF THIS DTC CHART.
YES
NO
3
• IGNITION "ON."
• USING J 39200, MEASURE THE VOLTAGE BETWEEN GROUND AND TERMINAL "C3" OF THE 32-WAY EBCM HARNESS CONNECTOR.
IS VOLTAGE 1 VOLT OR LESS?
DIAGNOSIS CONTINUED ON 3 OF 3 OF THIS DTC CHART.
NO
YES
4
• IGNITION "OFF."
• DISCONNECT RIGHT FRONT WHEEL SPEED SENSOR DIRECTLY AT SENSOR.
• IGNITION "ON."
• USING J 39200, MEASURE THE VOLTAGE BETWEEN GROUND AND TERMINAL "C3" OF THE 32-WAY EBCM HARNESS CONNECTOR.
IS VOLTAGE 1 VOLT OR LESS?
6
• IGNITION "OFF."
• INSPECT TERMINALS "C3" AND "C4" OF THE 32-WAY EBCM HARNESS CONNECTOR FOR POOR TERMINAL CONTACT AND CONTAMINATION. ALSO INSPECT CKTs 833 AND 872 FOR DAMAGE WHICH MAY RESULT IN AN OPEN CIRCUIT, SHORT TO GROUND, OR SHORT TO VOLTAGE. REPAIR ALL DAMAGE IF EVIDENT.
• RECONNECT ALL CONNECTORS.
• IGNITION "ON."
DOES DTC 33 SET AS A CURRENT DTC?
YES
NO
5
• USING J 39200, MEASURE THE VOLTAGE BETWEEN GROUND AND TERMINAL "C4" OF THE 32-WAY EBCM HARNESS CONNECTOR.
IS VOLTAGE 1 VOLT OR LESS?
REPAIR SHORT TO VOLTAGE IN CKT 833.
YES
NO
REPLACE EBCM.
MALFUNCTION IS INTERMITTENT. REFER TO "DIAGNOSTIC AIDS"
YES
NO
MALFUNCTION IS INTERMITTENT. INSPECT ALL CONNECTORS AND HARNESSES FOR DAMAGE WHICH MAY RESULT IN A SHORT TO VOLTAGE WHEN ALL COMPONENTS ARE CONNECTED. REPAIR ALL DAMAGE IF FOUND. REFER TO "DIAGNOSTIC AIDS"
REPAIR SHORT TO VOLTAGE IN CKT 872.

GC402940108001EX

DTC 33

RF WHEEL SPEED SNR CKT OPEN OR SHORT TO GND/BATT

Circuit Description:

As a toothed ring passes by the wheel speed sensor, changes in the electromagnetic field cause the wheel speed sensor to produce a sinusoidal (AC) voltage signal whose frequency is proportional to wheel speed. The magnitude of this signal is directly related to wheel speed and the proximity of the wheel speed sensor to the toothed ring, often referred to as the air gap.

DTC Will Set When: DTC 33 can be set anytime after initialization. If either of the right front wheel speed circuits are open or shorted to voltage or ground, a malfunction exists.

Action Taken: A malfunction DTC is stored, ABS is disabled and the ABS warning lamp is turned "ON."

DTC Chart Test Description: Number(s) below refer to circled number(s) on the diagnostic chart.

7. Checks for high resistance in CKT 833.
8. Checks for high resistance in CKT 872.
9. Verifies proper wheel speed sensor resistance.

Diagnostic Aids: An "Intermittent" malfunction may be caused by a poor connection, rubbed through wire insulation, or a wire that is broken inside the insulation.

The frequency of the malfunction can be checked by using the enhanced diagnostic function of the Tech 1,

If the customer's comments reflect that the ABS warning lamp is "ON" only during moist environmental changes (rain, snow, vehicle wash), all wheel speed sensor circuitry should be thoroughly inspected for signs of water intrusion. If DTC is not current, clear DTCs and simulate the effects of water intrusion. Use the following procedure. Spray down the suspected area with a 5% salt water solution (two teaspoons of salt to 12 oz. of water). Test drive vehicle over various road surfaces (bumps, turns, etc.) above 24 km/h (15 mph) for at least 30 seconds. If DTC returns, replace suspected harness.

Any circuitry, that is suspected as causing the intermittent complaint, should be thoroughly checked for backed out terminals, improper mating, broken locks, improperly formed or damaged terminals, poor terminal to wiring connections or physical damage to the wiring harness.

Resistance of the wheel speed sensor will increase with an increase in sensor temperature.

When replacing a wheel speed sensor, inspect the sensor terminals and harness connector for corrosion and/or water intrusion. If evidence of corrosion or water intrusion exists, replace wheel speed sensor jumper harness. Likewise, if replacing a wheel speed sensor jumper harness, inspect sensor terminals. If evidence of corrosion or water intrusion exists, replace wheel speed sensor. Refer to "On-Vehicle Service" in this section.

GC402940108002AX

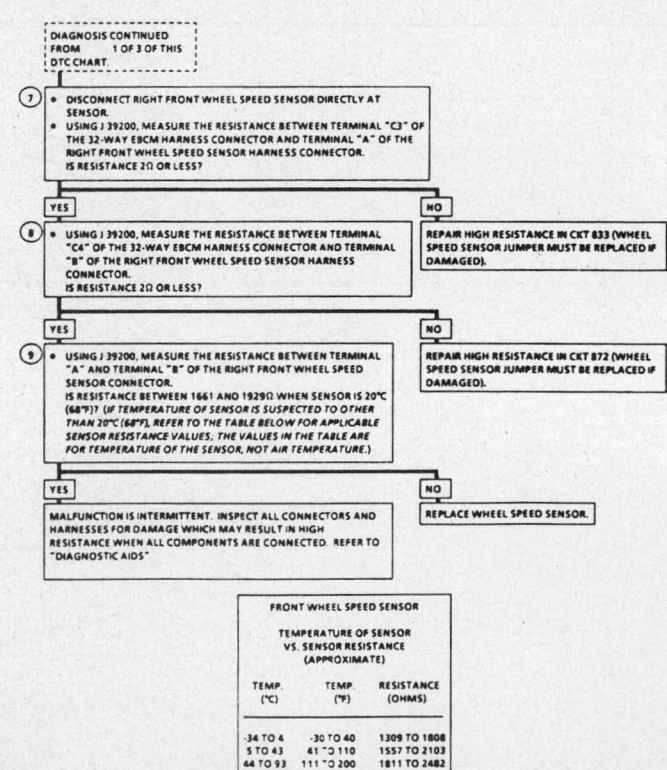

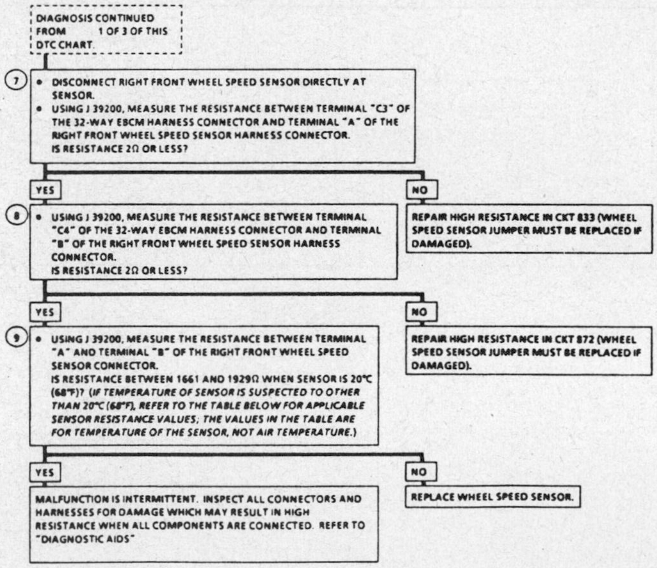
DIAGNOSIS CONTINUED FROM 1 OF 3 OF THIS DTC CHART.
7
• DISCONNECT RIGHT FRONT WHEEL SPEED SENSOR DIRECTLY AT SENSOR.
• USING J 39200, MEASURE THE RESISTANCE BETWEEN TERMINAL "C3" OF THE 32-WAY EBCM HARNESS CONNECTOR AND TERMINAL "A" OF THE RIGHT FRONT WHEEL SPEED SENSOR HARNESS CONNECTOR.
IS RESISTANCE 2Ω OR LESS?
YES
NO
8
• USING J 39200, MEASURE THE RESISTANCE BETWEEN TERMINAL "C4" OF THE 32-WAY EBCM HARNESS CONNECTOR AND TERMINAL "B" OF THE RIGHT FRONT WHEEL SPEED SENSOR HARNESS CONNECTOR.
IS RESISTANCE 2Ω OR LESS?
REPAIR HIGH RESISTANCE IN CKT 833 (WHEEL SPEED SENSOR JUMPER MUST BE REPLACED IF DAMAGED).
YES
NO
9
• USING J 39200, MEASURE THE RESISTANCE BETWEEN TERMINAL "A" AND TERMINAL "B" OF THE RIGHT FRONT WHEEL SPEED SENSOR CONNECTOR.
IS RESISTANCE BETWEEN 1661 AND 1929Ω WHEN SENSOR IS 20°C (68°F)? (IF TEMPERATURE OF SENSOR IS SUSPECTED TO OTHER THAN 20°C (68°F), REFER TO THE TABLE BELOW FOR APPLICABLE SENSOR RESISTANCE VALUES; THE VALUES IN THE TABLE ARE FOR TEMPERATURE OF THE SENSOR, NOT AIR TEMPERATURE.)
REPAIR HIGH RESISTANCE IN CKT 872 (WHEEL SPEED SENSOR JUMPER MUST BE REPLACED IF DAMAGED).
YES
NO
MALFUNCTION IS INTERMITTENT. INSPECT ALL CONNECTORS AND HARNESSES FOR DAMAGE WHICH MAY RESULT IN HIGH RESISTANCE WHEN ALL COMPONENTS ARE CONNECTED. REFER TO "DIAGNOSTIC AIDS"
REPLACE WHEEL SPEED SENSOR.

FRONT WHEEL SPEED SENSOR

TEMPERATURE OF SENSOR VS. SENSOR RESISTANCE (APPROXIMATE)

TEMP. (°C)	TEMP. (°F)	RESISTANCE (OHMS)
-34 TO 4	-30 TO 40	1309 TO 1808
5 TO 43	41 TO 110	1557 TO 2103
44 TO 93	111 TO 200	1811 TO 2482

GC402940108002BX

Fig. 252 Code A033: RF Wheel Speed Sensor Circuit Open Or Shorted To Gnd/Batt (Part 2 of 3). 1993–94 Camaro & Firebird, 1994 Grand Prix, Century & Cutlass Ciera & Cruiser

DTC 33

(Page 3 of 3)

RF WHEEL SPEED SNR CKT OPEN OR SHORT TO GND/BATT

Circuit Description:

As a toothed ring passes by the wheel speed sensor, changes in the electromagnetic field cause the wheel speed sensor to produce a sinusoidal (AC) voltage signal whose frequency is proportional to wheel speed. The magnitude of this signal is directly related to wheel speed and the proximity of the wheel speed sensor to the toothed ring, often referred to as the air gap.

DTC Will Set When: DTC 33 can be set anytime after initialization. If either of the right front wheel speed circuits are open or shorted to voltage or ground, a malfunction exists.

Action Taken: A malfunction DTC is stored, ABS is disabled and the ABS warning lamp is turned "ON."

DTC Chart Test Description: Number(s) below refer to circled number(s) on the diagnostic chart.

10. Checks for a short to ground in CKT 833.
11. Checks for a short to ground in CKT 872.
12. Checks for a short to ground in the wheel speed sensor jumper harness.
13. Verifies that wheel speed sensor is not internally shorted to ground.

Diagnostic Aids: An "Intermittent" malfunction may be caused by a poor connection, rubbed through wire insulation, or a wire that is broken inside the insulation.

The frequency of the malfunction can be checked by using the enhanced diagnostic function of the Tech 1.

If the customer's comments reflect that the ABS warning lamp is "ON" only during moist environmental changes (rain, snow, vehicle wash), all wheel speed sensor circuitry should be thoroughly inspected for signs of water intrusion. If DTC is not current, clear DTCs and simulate the effects of water intrusion. Use the following procedure. Spray down the suspected area with a 5% salt water solution (two teaspoons of salt to 12 oz. of water). Test drive vehicle over various road surfaces (bumps, turns, etc.) above 24 km/h (15 mph) for at least 30 seconds. If DTC returns, replace suspected harness.

Any circuitry, that is suspected as causing the intermittent complaint, should be thoroughly checked for backed out terminals, improper mating, broken locks, improperly formed or damaged terminals, poor terminal to wiring connections or physical damage to the wiring harness.

Resistance of the wheel speed sensor will increase with an increase in sensor temperature.

When replacing a wheel speed sensor, inspect the sensor terminals and harness connector for corrosion and/or water intrusion. If evidence of corrosion or water intrusion exists, replace wheel speed sensor jumper harness. Likewise, if replacing a wheel speed sensor jumper harness, inspect sensor terminals. If evidence of corrosion or water intrusion exists, replace wheel speed sensor. Refer to "On-Vehicle Service" in this section.

GC402940108003AX

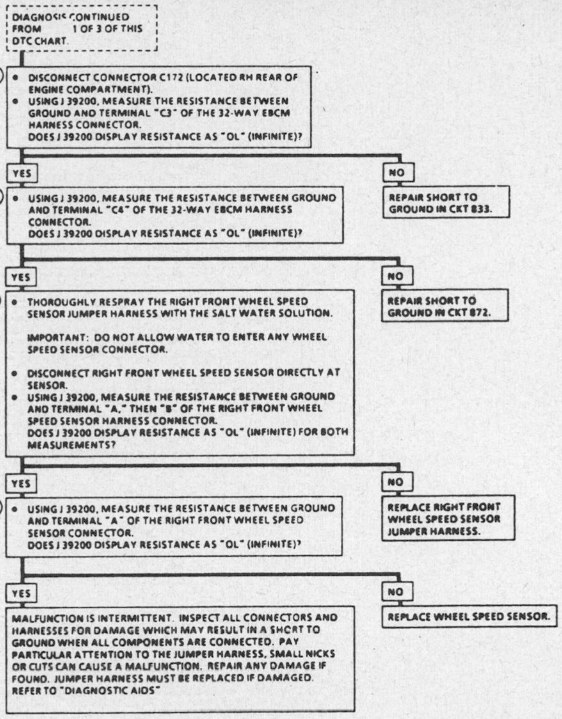
DIAGNOSIS CONTINUED FROM 1 OF 3 OF THIS DTC CHART.
10
• DISCONNECT CONNECTOR C172 (LOCATED RH REAR OF ENGINE COMPARTMENT).
• USING J 39200, MEASURE THE RESISTANCE BETWEEN GROUND AND TERMINAL "C3" OF THE 32-WAY EBCM HARNESS CONNECTOR.
DOES J 39200 DISPLAY RESISTANCE AS "OL" (INFINITE)?
YES
NO
11
• USING J 39200, MEASURE THE RESISTANCE BETWEEN GROUND AND TERMINAL "C4" OF THE 32-WAY EBCM HARNESS CONNECTOR.
DOES J 39200 DISPLAY RESISTANCE AS "OL" (INFINITE)?
REPAIR SHORT TO GROUND IN CKT 833.
YES
NO
12
• THOROUGHLY RESPRAY THE RIGHT FRONT WHEEL SPEED SENSOR JUMPER HARNESS WITH THE SALT WATER SOLUTION.
IMPORTANT: DO NOT ALLOW WATER TO ENTER ANY WHEEL SPEED SENSOR CONNECTOR.
• DISCONNECT RIGHT FRONT WHEEL SPEED SENSOR DIRECTLY AT SENSOR.
• USING J 39200, MEASURE THE RESISTANCE BETWEEN GROUND AND TERMINAL "A," THEN "B" OF THE RIGHT FRONT WHEEL SPEED SENSOR HARNESS CONNECTOR.
DOES J 39200 DISPLAY RESISTANCE AS "OL" (INFINITE) FOR BOTH MEASUREMENTS?
REPAIR SHORT TO GROUND IN CKT 872.
YES
NO
13
• USING J 39200, MEASURE THE RESISTANCE BETWEEN GROUND AND TERMINAL "A" OF THE RIGHT FRONT WHEEL SPEED SENSOR CONNECTOR.
DOES J 39200 DISPLAY RESISTANCE AS "OL" (INFINITE)?
REPLACE RIGHT FRONT WHEEL SPEED SENSOR JUMPER HARNESS.
YES
NO
MALFUNCTION IS INTERMITTENT. INSPECT ALL CONNECTORS AND HARNESSES FOR DAMAGE WHICH MAY RESULT IN A SHORT TO GROUND WHEN ALL COMPONENTS ARE CONNECTED. PAY PARTICULAR ATTENTION TO THE JUMPER HARNESS. SMALL NICKS OR CUTS CAN CAUSE A MALFUNCTION. REPAIR ANY DAMAGE IF FOUND. JUMPER HARNESS MUST BE REPLACED IF DAMAGED. REFER TO "DIAGNOSTIC AIDS"
REPLACE WHEEL SPEED SENSOR.

GC402940108003BX

Fig. 252 Code A033: RF Wheel Speed Sensor Circuit Open Or Shorted To Gnd/Batt (Part 3 of 3). 1993–94 Camaro & Firebird, 1994 Grand Prix, Century & Cutlass Ciera & Cruiser

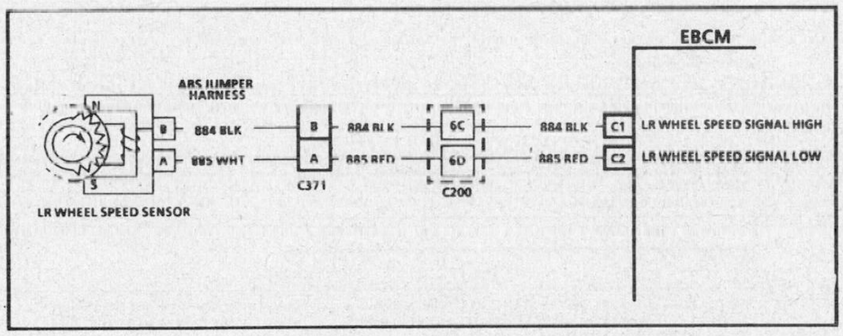
EBCM
ABS JUMPER HARNESS
N
B
A
S
884 BLK
885 WHT
884 BLK
885 RED
C371
6C
6D
C200
884 BLK
885 RED
C1
C2
LR WHEEL SPEED SIGNAL HIGH
LR WHEEL SPEED SIGNAL LOW
LR WHEEL SPEED SENSOR

GC402940108101AX

Grand Prix

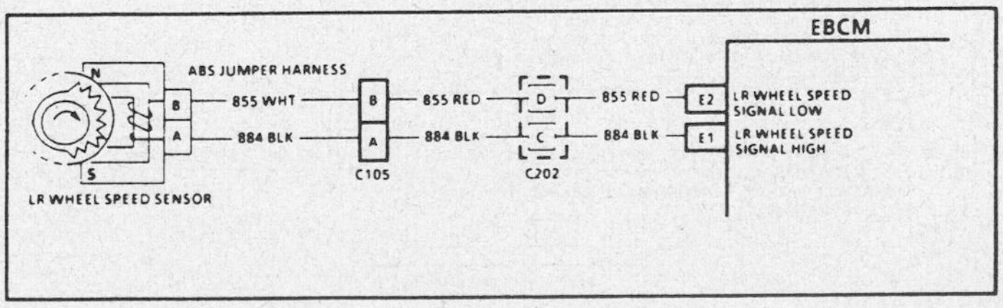
EBCM
ABS JUMPER HARNESS
N
B
A
S
855 WHT
884 BLK
855 RED
884 BLK
C105
D
C
C202
855 RED
884 BLK
E2
E1
LR WHEEL SPEED SIGNAL LOW
LR WHEEL SPEED SIGNAL HIGH
LR WHEEL SPEED SENSOR

GC402940108101BX

Century & Cutlass Ciera & Cruiser

DTC 34

(Page 1 of 3)

LR WHEEL SPEED SNR CKT OPEN OR SHORT TO GND/BATT

Circuit Description:

As a toothed ring passes by the wheel speed sensor, changes in the electromagnetic field cause the wheel speed sensor to produce a sinusoidal (AC) voltage signal whose frequency is proportional to wheel speed. The magnitude of this signal is directly related to wheel speed and the proximity of the wheel speed sensor to the toothed ring, often referred to as the air gap.

DTC Will Set When: DTC 34 can be set anytime after initialization. If either of the left rear wheel speed circuits are open or shorted to voltage or ground, a malfunction exists.

Action Taken: A malfunction DTC is stored, ABS is disabled and the ABS warning lamp is turned "ON."

DTC Chart Test Description: Number(s) below refer to circled number(s) on the diagnostic chart.

1. Checks for proper resistance of the wheel speed sensor coil.
2. Checks for a short to ground in wheel speed sensor wiring.
3. Checks for a short to voltage in the wheel speed sensor wiring.
4. Checks for a short to voltage in CKT 884.
5. Checks for a short to voltage in CKT 885.
6. Ensures that the malfunction was not due to physical damage of the circuitry.

Diagnostic Aids: An "Intermittent" malfunction may be caused by a poor connection, rubbed through wire insulation, or a wire that is broken inside the insulation.

The frequency of the malfunction can be checked by using the enhanced diagnostic function of the Tech 1.

If the customer's comments reflect that the ABS warning lamp is "ON" only during moist environmental changes (rain, snow, vehicle wash), all wheel speed sensor circuitry should be thoroughly inspected for signs of water intrusion. If DTC is not current, clear DTCs and simulate the effects of water intrusion. Use the following procedure. Spray down the suspected area with a 5% salt water solution (two teaspoons of salt to 12 oz. of water). Test drive vehicle over various road surfaces (bumps, turns, etc.) above 24 km/h (15 mph) for at least 30 seconds. If DTC returns, replace suspected harness.

Any circuitry, that is suspected as causing the intermittent complaint, should be thoroughly checked for backed out terminals, improper mating, broken locks, improperly formed or damaged terminals, poor terminal to wiring connections or physical damage to the wiring harness.

Resistance of the wheel speed sensor will increase with an increase in sensor temperature.

When replacing a wheel speed sensor, inspect the sensor terminals and harness connector for corrosion and/or water intrusion. If evidence of corrosion or water intrusion exists, replace wheel speed sensor jumper harness. Likewise, if replacing a wheel speed sensor jumper harness, inspect sensor terminals. If evidence of corrosion or water intrusion exists, replace wheel speed sensor. Refer to "On-Vehicle Service" in this section.

GC402940108101CX

Fig. 253 Code A034: LR Wheel Speed Sensor Circuit Open Or Shorted To Gnd/Batt (Part 1 of 3). 1994 Grand Prix, Century & Cutlass Ciera & Cruiser

Important

- WHEEL SPEED SENSOR INTERMITTENT MALFUNCTIONS MAY BE DIFFICULT TO LOCATE. CARE SHOULD BE TAKEN NOT TO DISTURB ANY ELECTRICAL CONNECTIONS PRIOR TO AN INDICATED STEP OF THIS CHART. THIS WILL ENSURE THAT AN INTERMITTENT CONNECTION WILL NOT BE CORRECTED BEFORE THE SOURCE OF THE MALFUNCTION IS FOUND.

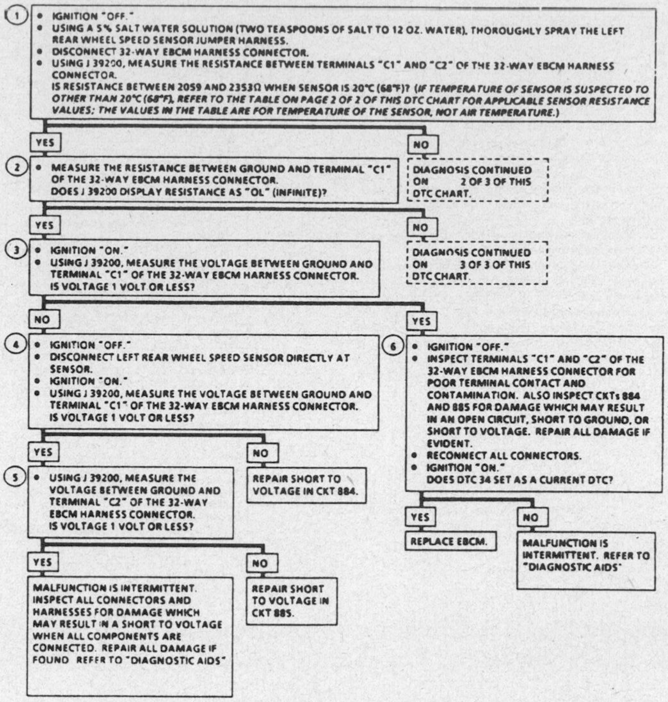

1
• IGNITION "OFF."
• USING A 5% SALT WATER SOLUTION (TWO TEASPOONS OF SALT TO 12 OZ. WATER), THOROUGHLY SPRAY THE LEFT REAR WHEEL SPEED SENSOR JUMPER HARNESS.
• DISCONNECT 32-WAY EBCM HARNESS CONNECTOR.
• USING J 39200, MEASURE THE RESISTANCE BETWEEN TERMINALS "C1" AND "C2" OF THE 32-WAY EBCM HARNESS CONNECTOR.
IS RESISTANCE BETWEEN 2059 AND 2353Ω WHEN SENSOR IS 20°C (68°F)? (IF TEMPERATURE OF SENSOR IS SUSPECTED TO OTHER THAN 20°C (68°F), REFER TO THE TABLE ON PAGE 2 OF 2 OF THIS DTC CHART FOR APPLICABLE SENSOR RESISTANCE VALUES; THE VALUES IN THE TABLE ARE FOR TEMPERATURE OF THE SENSOR, NOT AIR TEMPERATURE.)
YES
NO
2
• MEASURE THE RESISTANCE BETWEEN GROUND AND TERMINAL "C1" OF THE 32-WAY EBCM HARNESS CONNECTOR.
DOES J 39200 DISPLAY RESISTANCE AS "OL" (INFINITE)?
DIAGNOSIS CONTINUED ON 2 OF 3 OF THIS DTC CHART.
YES
NO
3
• IGNITION "ON."
• USING J 39200, MEASURE THE VOLTAGE BETWEEN GROUND AND TERMINAL "C1" OF THE 32-WAY EBCM HARNESS CONNECTOR.
IS VOLTAGE 1 VOLT OR LESS?
DIAGNOSIS CONTINUED ON 3 OF 3 OF THIS DTC CHART.
NO
YES
4
• IGNITION "OFF."
• DISCONNECT LEFT REAR WHEEL SPEED SENSOR DIRECTLY AT SENSOR.
• IGNITION "ON."
• USING J 39200, MEASURE THE VOLTAGE BETWEEN GROUND AND TERMINAL "C1" OF THE 32-WAY EBCM HARNESS CONNECTOR.
IS VOLTAGE 1 VOLT OR LESS?
6
• IGNITION "OFF."
• INSPECT TERMINALS "C1" AND "C2" OF THE 32-WAY EBCM HARNESS CONNECTOR FOR POOR TERMINAL CONTACT AND CONTAMINATION. ALSO INSPECT CKTs 884 AND 885 FOR DAMAGE WHICH MAY RESULT IN AN OPEN CIRCUIT, SHORT TO GROUND, OR SHORT TO VOLTAGE. REPAIR ALL DAMAGE IF EVIDENT.
• RECONNECT ALL CONNECTORS.
• IGNITION "ON."
DOES DTC 34 SET AS A CURRENT DTC?
YES
NO
5
• USING J 39200, MEASURE THE VOLTAGE BETWEEN GROUND AND TERMINAL "C2" OF THE 32-WAY EBCM HARNESS CONNECTOR.
IS VOLTAGE 1 VOLT OR LESS?
REPAIR SHORT TO VOLTAGE IN CKT 884.
YES
NO
REPLACE EBCM.
MALFUNCTION IS INTERMITTENT. REFER TO "DIAGNOSTIC AIDS"
YES
NO
MALFUNCTION IS INTERMITTENT. INSPECT ALL CONNECTORS AND HARNESSES FOR DAMAGE WHICH MAY RESULT IN A SHORT TO VOLTAGE WHEN ALL COMPONENTS ARE CONNECTED. REPAIR ALL DAMAGE IF FOUND REFER TO "DIAGNOSTIC AIDS"
REPAIR SHORT TO VOLTAGE IN CKT 885.

GC402940108101DX

DTC 34

(Page 2 of 3)

LR WHEEL SPEED SNR CKT OPEN OR SHORT TO GND/BATT

Circuit Description:

As a toothed ring passes by the wheel speed sensor, changes in the electromagnetic field cause the wheel speed sensor to produce a sinusoidal (AC) voltage signal whose frequency is proportional to wheel speed. The magnitude of this signal is directly related to wheel speed and the proximity of the wheel speed sensor to the toothed ring, often referred to as the air gap.

DTC Will Set When: DTC 34 can be set anytime after initialization. If either of the left rear wheel speed circuits are open or shorted to voltage or ground, a malfunction exists.

Action Taken: A malfunction DTC is stored, ABS is disabled and the ABS warning lamp is turned "ON."

DTC Chart Test Description: Number(s) below refer to circled number(s) on the diagnostic chart.

7. Checks for high resistance in CKT 884.
8. Checks for high resistance in CKT 885.
9. Verifies proper wheel speed sensor resistance.

Diagnostic Aids: An "Intermittent" malfunction may be caused by a poor connection, rubbed through wire insulation, or a wire that is broken inside the insulation.

The frequency of the malfunction can be checked by using the enhanced diagnostic function of the Tech 1.

If the customer's comments reflect that the ABS warning lamp is "ON" only during moist environmental changes (rain, snow, vehicle wash), all wheel speed sensor circuitry should be thoroughly inspected for signs of water intrusion. If DTC is not current, clear DTCs and simulate the effects of water intrusion. Use the following procedure. Spray down the suspected area with a 5% salt water solution (two teaspoons of salt to 12 oz. of water). Test drive vehicle over various road surfaces (bumps, turns, etc.) above 24 km/h (15 mph) for at least 30 seconds. If DTC returns, replace suspected harness.

Any circuitry, that is suspected as causing the intermittent complaint, should be thoroughly checked for backed out terminals, improper mating, broken locks, improperly formed or damaged terminals, poor terminal to wiring connections or physical damage to the wiring harness.

Resistance of the wheel speed sensor will increase with an increase in sensor temperature.

When replacing a wheel speed sensor, inspect the sensor terminals and harness connector for corrosion and/or water intrusion. If evidence of corrosion or water intrusion exists, replace wheel speed sensor jumper harness. Likewise, if replacing a wheel speed sensor jumper harness, inspect sensor terminals. If evidence of corrosion or water intrusion exists, replace wheel speed sensor. Refer to "On-Vehicle Service" in this section.

GC402940108102AX

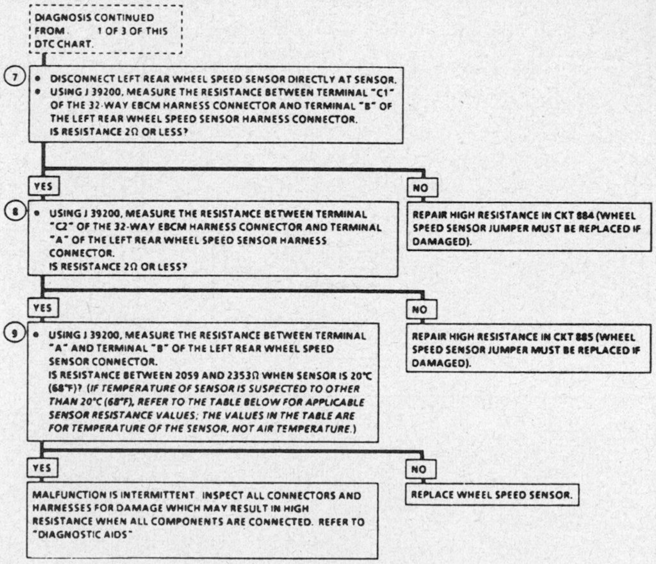

DIAGNOSIS CONTINUED FROM 1 OF 3 OF THIS DTC CHART.
7
• DISCONNECT LEFT REAR WHEEL SPEED SENSOR DIRECTLY AT SENSOR.
• USING J 39200, MEASURE THE RESISTANCE BETWEEN TERMINAL "C1" OF THE 32-WAY EBCM HARNESS CONNECTOR AND TERMINAL "B" OF THE LEFT REAR WHEEL SPEED SENSOR HARNESS CONNECTOR.
IS RESISTANCE 2Ω OR LESS?
YES
NO
8
• USING J 39200, MEASURE THE RESISTANCE BETWEEN TERMINAL "C2" OF THE 32-WAY EBCM HARNESS CONNECTOR AND TERMINAL "A" OF THE LEFT REAR WHEEL SPEED SENSOR HARNESS CONNECTOR.
IS RESISTANCE 2Ω OR LESS?
REPAIR HIGH RESISTANCE IN CKT 884 (WHEEL SPEED SENSOR JUMPER MUST BE REPLACED IF DAMAGED).
YES
NO
9
• USING J 39200, MEASURE THE RESISTANCE BETWEEN TERMINAL "A" AND TERMINAL "B" OF THE LEFT REAR WHEEL SPEED SENSOR CONNECTOR.
IS RESISTANCE BETWEEN 2059 AND 2353Ω WHEN SENSOR IS 20°C (68°F)? (IF TEMPERATURE OF SENSOR IS SUSPECTED TO OTHER THAN 20°C (68°F), REFER TO THE TABLE BELOW FOR APPLICABLE SENSOR RESISTANCE VALUES; THE VALUES IN THE TABLE ARE FOR TEMPERATURE OF THE SENSOR, NOT AIR TEMPERATURE.)
REPAIR HIGH RESISTANCE IN CKT 885 (WHEEL SPEED SENSOR JUMPER MUST BE REPLACED IF DAMAGED).
YES
NO
MALFUNCTION IS INTERMITTENT INSPECT ALL CONNECTORS AND HARNESSES FOR DAMAGE WHICH MAY RESULT IN HIGH RESISTANCE WHEN ALL COMPONENTS ARE CONNECTED. REFER TO "DIAGNOSTIC AIDS"
REPLACE WHEEL SPEED SENSOR.

REAR WHEEL SPEED SENSOR

TEMPERATURE OF SENSOR VS. SENSOR RESISTANCE (APPROXIMATE)

TEMP (°C)	TEMP. (°F)	RESISTANCE (OHMS)
-34 TO 4	-30 TO 40	1622 TO 2205
5 TO 43	41 TO 110	1930 TO 2566
44 TO 93	111 TO 200	2245 TO 3028

GC402940108102BX

Fig. 253 Code A034: LR Wheel Speed Sensor Circuit Open Or Shorted To Gnd/Batt (Part 2 of 3). 1993–94 Camaro & Firebird, 1994 Grand Prix, Century & Cutlass Ciera & Cruiser

DTC 34

(Page 3 of 3)

LR WHEEL SPEED SNR CKT OPEN OR SHORT TO GND/BATT

Circuit Description:

As a toothed ring passes by the wheel speed sensor, changes in the electromagnetic field cause the wheel speed sensor to produce a sinusoidal (AC) voltage signal whose frequency is proportional to wheel speed. The magnitude of this signal is directly related to wheel speed and the proximity of the wheel speed sensor to the toothed ring, often referred to as the air gap.

DTC Will Set When: DTC 34 can be set anytime after initialization. If either of the left rear wheel speed circuits are open or shorted to voltage or ground, a malfunction exists.

Action Taken: A malfunction DTC is stored, ABS is disabled and the ABS warning lamp is turned "ON."

DTC Chart Test Description: Number(s) below refer to circled number(s) on the diagnostic chart.

10. Checks for a short to ground in CKT 884.
11. Checks for a short to ground in CKT 885.
12. Checks for a short to ground in the wheel speed sensor jumper harness.
13. Verifies that wheel speed sensor is not internally shorted to ground.

Diagnostic Aids: An "Intermittent" malfunction may be caused by a poor connection, rubbed through wire insulation, or a wire that is broken inside the insulation.

The frequency of the malfunction can be checked by using the enhanced diagnostic function of the Tech 1.

If the customer's comments reflect that the ABS warning lamp is "ON" only during moist environmental changes (rain, snow, vehicle wash), all wheel speed sensor circuitry should be thoroughly inspected for signs of water intrusion. If DTC is not current, clear DTCs and simulate the effects of water intrusion. Use the following procedure. Spray down the suspected area with a 5% salt water solution (two teaspoons of salt to 12 oz. of water). Test drive vehicle over various road surfaces (bumps, turns, etc.) above 24 km/h (15 mph) for at least 30 seconds. If DTC returns, replace suspected harness.

Any circuitry, that is suspected as causing the intermittent complaint, should be thoroughly checked for backed out terminals, improper mating, broken locks, improperly formed or damaged terminals, poor terminal to wiring connections or physical damage to the wiring harness.

Resistance of the wheel speed sensor will increase with an increase in sensor temperature.

When replacing a wheel speed sensor, inspect the sensor terminals and harness connector for corrosion and/or water intrusion. If evidence of corrosion or water intrusion exists, replace wheel speed sensor jumper harness. Likewise, if replacing a wheel speed sensor jumper harness, inspect sensor terminals. If evidence of corrosion or water intrusion exists, replace wheel speed sensor. Refer to "On-Vehicle Service" in this section.

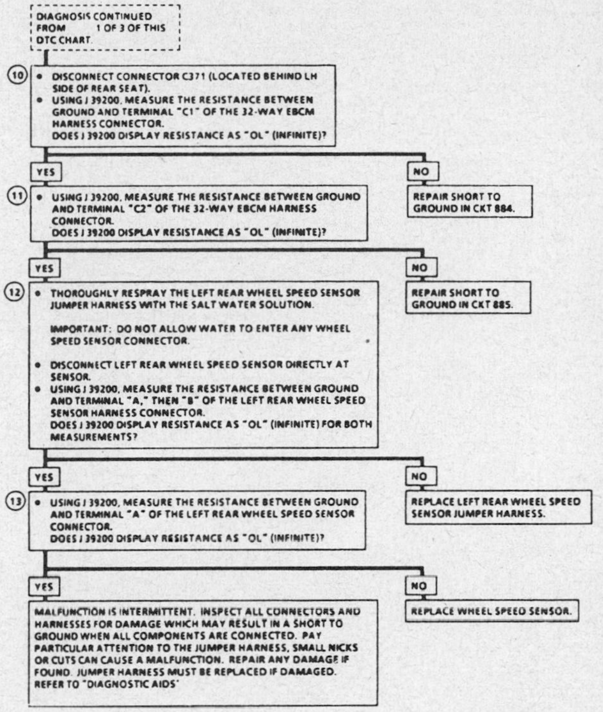
DIAGNOSIS CONTINUED FROM 1 OF 3 OF THIS DTC CHART.
10
• DISCONNECT CONNECTOR C371 (LOCATED BEHIND LH SIDE OF REAR SEAT).
• USING J 39200, MEASURE THE RESISTANCE BETWEEN GROUND AND TERMINAL "C1" OF THE 32-WAY EBCM HARNESS CONNECTOR.
DOES J 39200 DISPLAY RESISTANCE AS "OL" (INFINITE)?
YES
NO
REPAIR SHORT TO GROUND IN CKT 884.
11
• USING J 39200, MEASURE THE RESISTANCE BETWEEN GROUND AND TERMINAL "C2" OF THE 32-WAY EBCM HARNESS CONNECTOR.
DOES J 39200 DISPLAY RESISTANCE AS "OL" (INFINITE)?
YES
NO
REPAIR SHORT TO GROUND IN CKT 885.
12
• THOROUGHLY RESPRAY THE LEFT REAR WHEEL SPEED SENSOR JUMPER HARNESS WITH THE SALT WATER SOLUTION.
IMPORTANT: DO NOT ALLOW WATER TO ENTER ANY WHEEL SPEED SENSOR CONNECTOR.
• DISCONNECT LEFT REAR WHEEL SPEED SENSOR DIRECTLY AT SENSOR.
• USING J 39200, MEASURE THE RESISTANCE BETWEEN GROUND AND TERMINAL "A," THEN "B" OF THE LEFT REAR WHEEL SPEED SENSOR HARNESS CONNECTOR.
DOES J 39200 DISPLAY RESISTANCE AS "OL" (INFINITE) FOR BOTH MEASUREMENTS?
YES
NO
REPLACE LEFT REAR WHEEL SPEED SENSOR JUMPER HARNESS.
13
• USING J 39200, MEASURE THE RESISTANCE BETWEEN GROUND AND TERMINAL "A" OF THE LEFT REAR WHEEL SPEED SENSOR CONNECTOR.
DOES J 39200 DISPLAY RESISTANCE AS "OL" (INFINITE)?
YES
NO
MALFUNCTION IS INTERMITTENT. INSPECT ALL CONNECTORS AND HARNESSES FOR DAMAGE WHICH MAY RESULT IN A SHORT TO GROUND WHEN ALL COMPONENTS ARE CONNECTED. PAY PARTICULAR ATTENTION TO THE JUMPER HARNESS, SMALL NICKS OR CUTS CAN CAUSE A MALFUNCTION. REPAIR ANY DAMAGE IF FOUND. JUMPER HARNESS MUST BE REPLACED IF DAMAGED. REFER TO "DIAGNOSTIC AIDS"
REPLACE WHEEL SPEED SENSOR.

GC402940108103BX

Fig. 253 Code A034: LR Wheel Speed Sensor Circuit Open Or Shorted To Gnd/Batt (Part 3 of 3). 1993–94 Camaro & Firebird, 1994 Grand Prix, Century & Cutlass Ciera & Cruiser

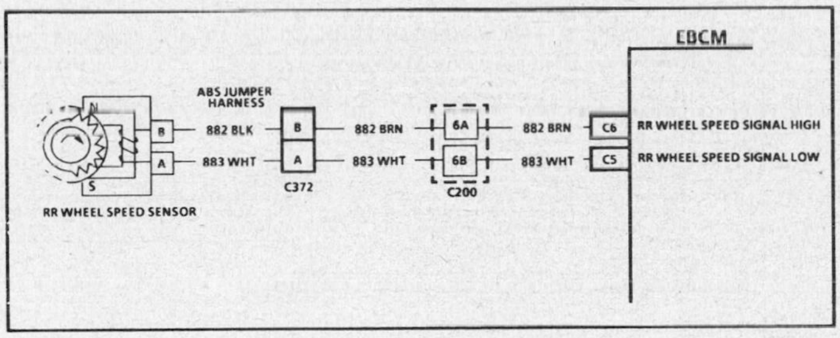
EBCM
ABS JUMPER HARNESS
B
A
N
S
882 BLK
883 WHT
882 BRN
883 WHT
6A
6B
C372
C200
C6
C5
RR WHEEL SPEED SIGNAL HIGH
RR WHEEL SPEED SIGNAL LOW
RR WHEEL SPEED SENSOR

GC402940108201AX

Grand Prix

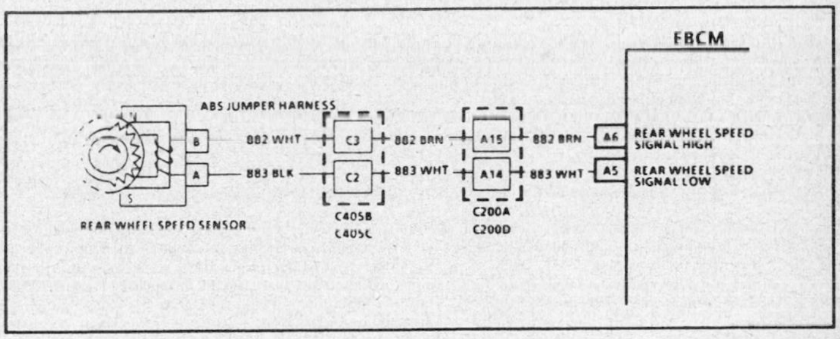
FBCM
ABS JUMPER HARNESS
B
A
S
882 WHT
883 BLK
C3
C2
882 BRN
883 WHT
A15
A14
A6
A5
REAR WHEEL SPEED SIGNAL HIGH
REAR WHEEL SPEED SIGNAL LOW
C405B
C405C
C200A
C200D
REAR WHEEL SPEED SENSOR

GC402940108201BX

Camaro & Firebird

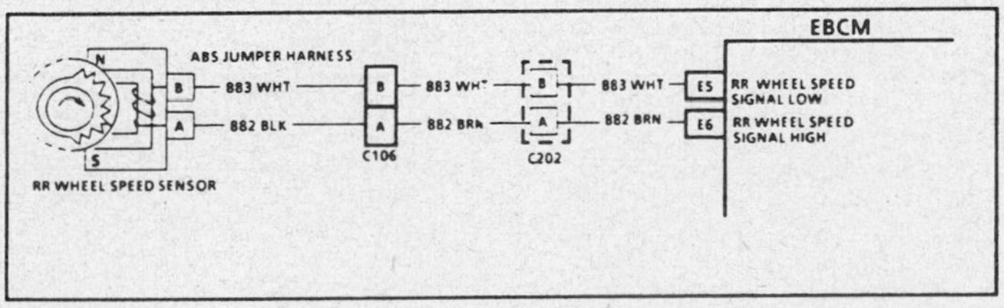
EBCM
ABS JUMPER HARNESS
N
S
B
A
883 WHT
882 BLK
C106
C202
882 BRN
E5
E6
RR WHEEL SPEED SIGNAL LOW
RR WHEEL SPEED SIGNAL HIGH
RR WHEEL SPEED SENSOR

GC402940108201CX

Century & Cutlass Ciera & Cruiser

Fig. 254 Code A035: RR Wheel Speed Sensor Circuit Open Or Shorted To Gnd/Batt (Part 1 of 3). 1993–94 Camaro & Firebird, 1994 Grand Prix, Century & Cutlass Ciera & Cruiser

DTC 35

RR WHEEL SPEED SNR CKT OPEN OR SHORT TO GND/BATT

Circuit Description:

As a toothed ring passes by the wheel speed sensor, changes in the electromagnetic field cause the wheel speed sensor to produce a sinusoidal (AC) voltage signal whose frequency is proportional to wheel speed. The magnitude of this signal is directly related to wheel speed and the proximity of the wheel speed sensor to the toothed ring, often referred to as the air gap.

DTC Will Set When: DTC 35 can be set anytime after initialization. If either of the right rear wheel speed circuits are open or shorted to voltage or ground, a malfunction exists.

Action Taken: A malfunction DTC is stored, ABS is disabled and the ABS warning lamp is turned "ON."

DTC Chart Test Description: Number(s) below refer to circled number(s) on the diagnostic chart.

1. Checks for proper resistance of the wheel speed sensor coil.
2. Checks for a short to ground in the wheel speed sensor wiring.
3. Checks for a short to voltage in the wheel speed sensor wiring.
4. Checks for a short to voltage in CKT 883.
5. Checks for a short to voltage in CKT 882.
6. Ensures that the malfunction was not due to physical damage of the circuitry.

Diagnostic Aids: An "Intermittent" malfunction may be caused by a poor connection, rubbed through wire insulation, or a wire that is broken inside the insulation.

The frequency of the malfunction can be checked by using the enhanced diagnostic function of the Tech 1.

If the customer's comments reflect that the ABS warning lamp is "ON" only during moist environmental changes (rain, snow, vehicle wash), all wheel speed sensor circuitry should be thoroughly inspected for signs of water intrusion. If DTC is not current, clear DTCs and simulate the effects of water intrusion. Use the following procedure. Spray down the suspected area with a 5% salt water solution (two teaspoons of salt to 12 oz. of water). Test drive vehicle over various road surfaces (bumps, turns, etc.) above 24 km/h (15 mph) for at least 30 seconds. If DTC returns, replace suspected harness.

Any circuitry, that is suspected as causing the intermittent complaint, should be thoroughly checked for backed out terminals, improper mating, broken locks, improperly formed or damaged terminals, poor terminal to wiring connections or physical damage to the wiring harness.

Resistance of the wheel speed sensor will increase with an increase in sensor temperature.

When replacing a wheel speed sensor, inspect the sensor terminals and harness connector for corrosion and/or water intrusion. If evidence of corrosion or water intrusion exists, replace wheel speed sensor jumper harness. Likewise, if replacing a wheel speed sensor jumper harness, inspect sensor terminals. If evidence of corrosion or water intrusion exists, replace wheel speed sensor. Refer to "On-Vehicle Service" in this section.

GC402940108201DX

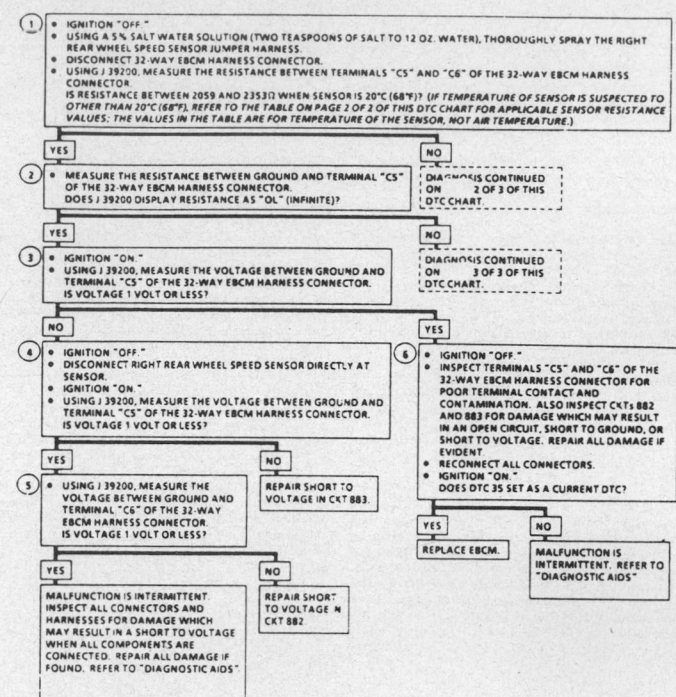

Important

- WHEEL SPEED SENSOR INTERMITTENT MALFUNCTIONS MAY BE DIFFICULT TO LOCATE. CARE SHOULD BE TAKEN NOT TO DISTURB ANY ELECTRICAL CONNECTIONS PRIOR TO AN INDICATED STEP OF THIS CHART. THIS WILL ENSURE THAT AN INTERMITTENT CONNECTION WILL NOT BE CORRECTED BEFORE THE SOURCE OF THE MALFUNCTION IS FOUND.

(1)
- IGNITION "OFF."
- USING A 5% SALT WATER SOLUTION (TWO TEASPOONS OF SALT TO 12 OZ. WATER), THOROUGHLY SPRAY THE RIGHT REAR WHEEL SPEED SENSOR JUMPER HARNESS.
- DISCONNECT 32-WAY EBCM HARNESS CONNECTOR.
- USING J 39200, MEASURE THE RESISTANCE BETWEEN TERMINALS "C5" AND "C6" OF THE 32-WAY EBCM HARNESS CONNECTOR.

IS RESISTANCE BETWEEN 2059 AND 2353Ω WHEN SENSOR IS 20°C (68°F)? *(IF TEMPERATURE OF SENSOR IS SUSPECTED TO OTHER THAN 20°C (68°F), REFER TO THE TABLE ON PAGE 2 OF 2 OF THIS DTC CHART FOR APPLICABLE SENSOR RESISTANCE VALUES; THE VALUES IN THE TABLE ARE FOR TEMPERATURE OF THE SENSOR, NOT AIR TEMPERATURE.)*

YES → (2)
NO → DIAGNOSIS CONTINUED ON 2 OF 3 OF THIS DTC CHART.

(2)
- MEASURE THE RESISTANCE BETWEEN GROUND AND TERMINAL "C5" OF THE 32-WAY EBCM HARNESS CONNECTOR.

DOES J 39200 DISPLAY RESISTANCE AS "OL" (INFINITE)?

YES → (3)
NO → DIAGNOSIS CONTINUED ON 3 OF 3 OF THIS DTC CHART.

(3)
- IGNITION "ON."
- USING J 39200, MEASURE THE VOLTAGE BETWEEN GROUND AND TERMINAL "C5" OF THE 32-WAY EBCM HARNESS CONNECTOR.

IS VOLTAGE 1 VOLT OR LESS?

NO → (4)
YES → (6)

(4)
- IGNITION "OFF."
- DISCONNECT RIGHT REAR WHEEL SPEED SENSOR DIRECTLY AT SENSOR.
- IGNITION "ON."
- USING J 39200, MEASURE THE VOLTAGE BETWEEN GROUND AND TERMINAL "C5" OF THE 32-WAY EBCM HARNESS CONNECTOR.

IS VOLTAGE 1 VOLT OR LESS?

YES → (5)
NO → REPAIR SHORT TO VOLTAGE IN CKT 883.

(5)
- USING J 39200, MEASURE THE VOLTAGE BETWEEN GROUND AND TERMINAL "C6" OF THE 32-WAY EBCM HARNESS CONNECTOR.

IS VOLTAGE 1 VOLT OR LESS?

YES → MALFUNCTION IS INTERMITTENT. INSPECT ALL CONNECTORS AND HARNESSES FOR DAMAGE WHICH MAY RESULT IN A SHORT TO VOLTAGE WHEN ALL COMPONENTS ARE CONNECTED. REPAIR ALL DAMAGE IF FOUND. REFER TO "DIAGNOSTIC AIDS".
NO → REPAIR SHORT TO VOLTAGE IN CKT 882.

(6)
- IGNITION "OFF."
- INSPECT TERMINALS "C5" AND "C6" OF THE 32-WAY EBCM HARNESS CONNECTOR FOR POOR TERMINAL CONTACT AND CONTAMINATION. ALSO INSPECT CKTs 882 AND 883 FOR DAMAGE WHICH MAY RESULT IN AN OPEN CIRCUIT, SHORT TO GROUND, OR SHORT TO VOLTAGE. REPAIR ALL DAMAGE IF EVIDENT.
- RECONNECT ALL CONNECTORS.
- IGNITION "ON."

DOES DTC 35 SET AS A CURRENT DTC?

YES → REPLACE EBCM.
NO → MALFUNCTION IS INTERMITTENT. REFER TO "DIAGNOSTIC AIDS"

GC402940108201EX

DTC 35

RR WHEEL SPEED SNR CKT OPEN OR SHORT TO GND/BATT

Circuit Description:

As a toothed ring passes by the wheel speed sensor, changes in the electromagnetic field cause the wheel speed sensor to produce a sinusoidal (AC) voltage signal whose frequency is proportional to wheel speed. The magnitude of this signal is directly related to wheel speed and the proximity of the wheel speed sensor to the toothed ring, often referred to as the air gap.

DTC Will Set When: DTC 35 can be set anytime after initialization. If either of the right rear wheel speed circuits are open or shorted to voltage or ground, a malfunction exists.

Action Taken: A malfunction DTC is stored, ABS is disabled and the ABS warning lamp is turned "ON."

DTC Chart Test Description: Number(s) below refer to circled number(s) on the diagnostic chart.

7. Checks for high resistance in CKT 883.
8. Checks for high resistance in CKT 882.
9. Verifies proper wheel speed sensor resistance.

Diagnostic Aids: An "Intermittent" malfunction may be caused by a poor connection, rubbed through wire insulation, or a wire that is broken inside the insulation.

The frequency of the malfunction can be checked by using the enhanced diagnostic function of the Tech 1.

If the customer's comments reflect that the ABS warning lamp is "ON" only during moist environmental changes (rain, snow, vehicle wash), all wheel speed sensor circuitry should be thoroughly inspected for signs of water intrusion. If DTC is not current, clear DTCs and simulate the effects of water intrusion. Use the following procedure. Spray down the suspected area with a 5% salt water solution (two teaspoons of salt to 12 oz. of water). Test drive vehicle over various road surfaces (bumps, turns, etc.) above 24 km/h (15 mph) for at least 30 seconds. If DTC returns, replace suspected harness.

Any circuitry, that is suspected as causing the intermittent complaint, should be thoroughly checked for backed out terminals, improper mating, broken locks, improperly formed or damaged terminals, poor terminal to wiring connections or physical damage to the wiring harness.

Resistance of the wheel speed sensor will increase with an increase in sensor temperature.

When replacing a wheel speed sensor, inspect the sensor terminals and harness connector for corrosion and/or water intrusion. If evidence of corrosion or water intrusion exists, replace wheel speed sensor jumper harness. Likewise, if replacing a wheel speed sensor jumper harness, inspect sensor terminals. If evidence of corrosion or water intrusion exists, replace wheel speed sensor. Refer to "On-Vehicle Service" in this section.

GC402940108202AX

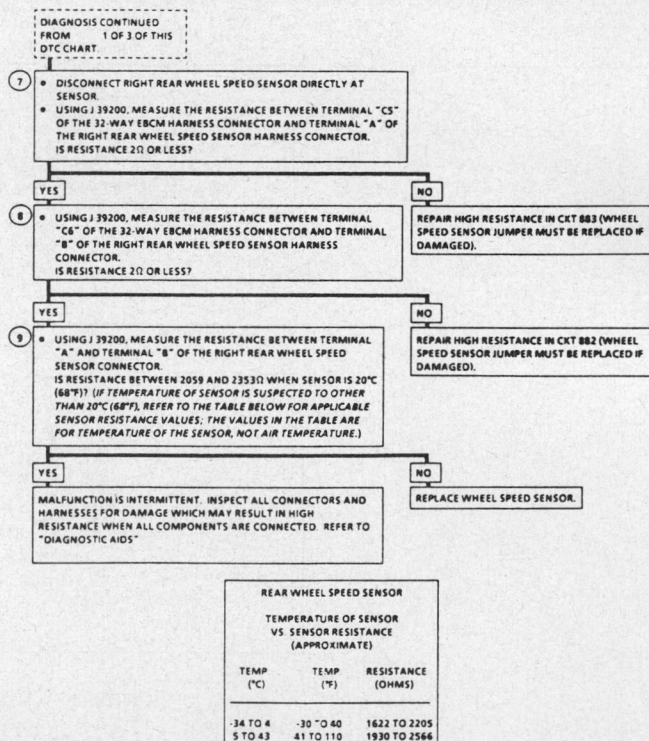

DIAGNOSIS CONTINUED FROM 1 OF 3 OF THIS DTC CHART.

(7)
- DISCONNECT RIGHT REAR WHEEL SPEED SENSOR DIRECTLY AT SENSOR.
- USING J 39200, MEASURE THE RESISTANCE BETWEEN TERMINAL "C5" OF THE 32-WAY EBCM HARNESS CONNECTOR AND TERMINAL "A" OF THE RIGHT REAR WHEEL SPEED SENSOR HARNESS CONNECTOR.

IS RESISTANCE 2Ω OR LESS?

YES → (8)
NO → REPAIR HIGH RESISTANCE IN CKT 883 (WHEEL SPEED SENSOR JUMPER MUST BE REPLACED IF DAMAGED).

(8)
- USING J 39200, MEASURE THE RESISTANCE BETWEEN TERMINAL "C6" OF THE 32-WAY EBCM HARNESS CONNECTOR AND TERMINAL "B" OF THE RIGHT REAR WHEEL SPEED SENSOR HARNESS CONNECTOR.

IS RESISTANCE 2Ω OR LESS?

YES → (9)
NO → REPAIR HIGH RESISTANCE IN CKT 882 (WHEEL SPEED SENSOR JUMPER MUST BE REPLACED IF DAMAGED).

(9)
- USING J 39200, MEASURE THE RESISTANCE BETWEEN TERMINAL "A" AND TERMINAL "B" OF THE RIGHT REAR WHEEL SPEED SENSOR CONNECTOR.

IS RESISTANCE BETWEEN 2059 AND 2353Ω WHEN SENSOR IS 20°C (68°F)? *(IF TEMPERATURE OF SENSOR IS SUSPECTED TO OTHER THAN 20°C (68°F), REFER TO THE TABLE BELOW FOR APPLICABLE SENSOR RESISTANCE VALUES; THE VALUES IN THE TABLE ARE FOR TEMPERATURE OF THE SENSOR, NOT AIR TEMPERATURE.)*

YES → MALFUNCTION IS INTERMITTENT. INSPECT ALL CONNECTORS AND HARNESSES FOR DAMAGE WHICH MAY RESULT IN HIGH RESISTANCE WHEN ALL COMPONENTS ARE CONNECTED. REFER TO "DIAGNOSTIC AIDS"
NO → REPLACE WHEEL SPEED SENSOR.

REAR WHEEL SPEED SENSOR

TEMPERATURE OF SENSOR VS. SENSOR RESISTANCE (APPROXIMATE)

TEMP (°C)	TEMP (°F)	RESISTANCE (OHMS)
-34 TO 4	-30 TO 40	1622 TO 2205
5 TO 43	41 TO 110	1930 TO 2566
44 TO 93	111 TO 200	2245 TO 3028

GC402940108202BX

Fig. 254 Code A035: RR Wheel Speed Sensor Circuit Open Or Shorted To Gnd/Batt (Part 2 of 3). 1993–94 Camaro & Firebird, 1994 Grand Prix, Century & Cutlass Ciera & Cruiser

DTC 35

(Page 2 of 3)

RR WHEEL SPEED SNR CKT OPEN OR SHORT TO GND/BATT

Circuit Description:

As a toothed ring passes by the wheel speed sensor, changes in the electromagnetic field cause the wheel speed sensor to produce a sinusoidal (AC) voltage signal whose frequency is proportional to wheel speed. The magnitude of this signal is directly related to wheel speed and the proximity of the wheel speed sensor to the toothed ring, often referred to as the air gap.

DTC Will Set When: DTC 35 can be set anytime after initialization. If either of the right rear wheel speed circuits are open or shorted to voltage or ground, a malfunction exists.

Action Taken: A malfunction DTC is stored, ABS is disabled and the ABS warning lamp is turned "ON."

DTC Chart Test Description: Number(s) below refer to circled number(s) on the diagnostic chart.

7. Checks for high resistance in CKT 883.
8. Checks for high resistance in CKT 882.
9. Verifies proper wheel speed sensor resistance.

Diagnostic Aids: An "Intermittent" malfunction may be caused by a poor connection, rubbed through wire insulation, or a wire that is broken inside the insulation.

The frequency of the malfunction can be checked by using the enhanced diagnostic function of the Tech 1.

If the customer's comments reflect that the ABS warning lamp is "ON" only during moist environmental changes (rain, snow, vehicle wash), all wheel speed sensor circuitry should be thoroughly inspected for signs of water intrusion. If DTC is not current, clear DTCs and simulate the effects of water intrusion. Use the following procedure. Spray down the suspected area with a 5% salt water solution (two teaspoons of salt to 12 oz. of water). Test drive vehicle over various road surfaces (bumps, turns, etc.) above 24 km/h (15 mph) for at least 30 seconds. If DTC returns, replace suspected harness.

Any circuitry, that is suspected as causing the intermittent complaint, should be thoroughly checked for backed out terminals, improper mating, broken locks, improperly formed or damaged terminals, poor terminal to wiring connections or physical damage to the wiring harness.

Resistance of the wheel speed sensor will increase with an increase in sensor temperature.

When replacing a wheel speed sensor, inspect the sensor terminals and harness connector for corrosion and/or water intrusion. If evidence of corrosion or water intrusion exists, replace wheel speed sensor jumper harness. Likewise, if replacing a wheel speed sensor jumper harness, inspect sensor terminals. If evidence of corrosion or water intrusion exists, replace wheel speed sensor. Refer to "On-Vehicle Service" in this section.

GC402940108202AX

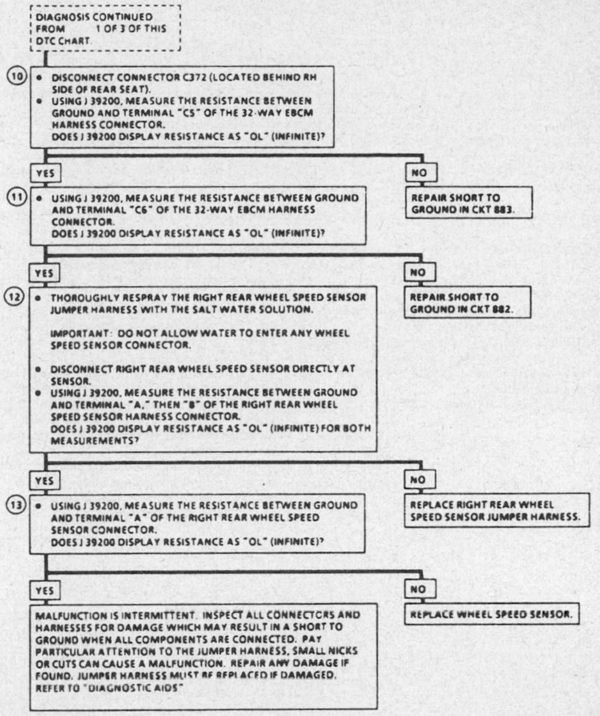
DIAGNOSIS CONTINUED FROM 1 OF 3 OF THIS DTC CHART
10
• DISCONNECT CONNECTOR C372 (LOCATED BEHIND RH SIDE OF REAR SEAT).
• USING J 39200, MEASURE THE RESISTANCE BETWEEN GROUND AND TERMINAL "C5" OF THE 32-WAY EBCM HARNESS CONNECTOR.
DOES J 39200 DISPLAY RESISTANCE AS "OL" (INFINITE)?
YES
NO
REPAIR SHORT TO GROUND IN CKT 883.
11
• USING J 39200, MEASURE THE RESISTANCE BETWEEN GROUND AND TERMINAL "C6" OF THE 32-WAY EBCM HARNESS CONNECTOR.
DOES J 39200 DISPLAY RESISTANCE AS "OL" (INFINITE)?
YES
NO
REPAIR SHORT TO GROUND IN CKT 882.
12
• THOROUGHLY RESPRAY THE RIGHT REAR WHEEL SPEED SENSOR JUMPER HARNESS WITH THE SALT WATER SOLUTION.
IMPORTANT: DO NOT ALLOW WATER TO ENTER ANY WHEEL SPEED SENSOR CONNECTOR.
• DISCONNECT RIGHT REAR WHEEL SPEED SENSOR DIRECTLY AT SENSOR.
• USING J 39200, MEASURE THE RESISTANCE BETWEEN GROUND AND TERMINAL "A," THEN "B" OF THE RIGHT REAR WHEEL SPEED SENSOR HARNESS CONNECTOR.
DOES J 39200 DISPLAY RESISTANCE AS "OL" (INFINITE) FOR BOTH MEASUREMENTS?
YES
NO
REPLACE RIGHT REAR WHEEL SPEED SENSOR JUMPER HARNESS.
13
• USING J 39200, MEASURE THE RESISTANCE BETWEEN GROUND AND TERMINAL "A" OF THE RIGHT REAR WHEEL SPEED SENSOR CONNECTOR.
DOES J 39200 DISPLAY RESISTANCE AS "OL" (INFINITE)?
YES
NO
REPLACE WHEEL SPEED SENSOR.
MALFUNCTION IS INTERMITTENT. INSPECT ALL CONNECTORS AND HARNESSES FOR DAMAGE WHICH MAY RESULT IN A SHORT TO GROUND WHEN ALL COMPONENTS ARE CONNECTED. PAY PARTICULAR ATTENTION TO THE JUMPER HARNESS, SMALL NICKS OR CUTS CAN CAUSE A MALFUNCTION. REPAIR ANY DAMAGE IF FOUND. JUMPER HARNESS MUST BE REPLACED IF DAMAGED. REFER TO "DIAGNOSTIC AIDS"

GC402940108203BX

Fig. 254 Code A035: RR Wheel Speed Sensor Circuit Open Or Shorted To Gnd/Batt (Part 3 of 3). 1993–94 Camaro & Firebird, 1994 Grand Prix, Century & Cutlass Ciera & Cruiser

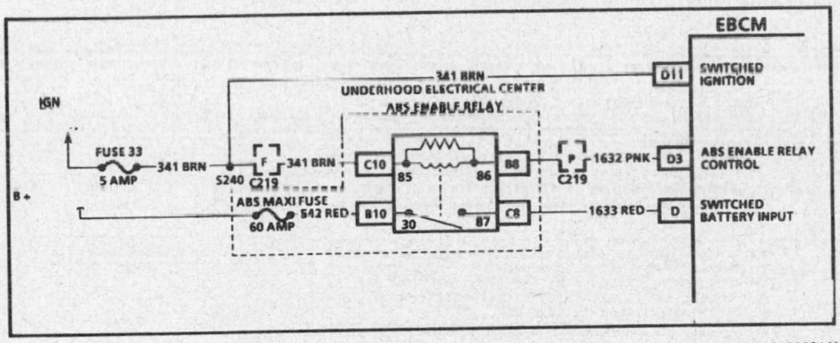
EBCM
IGN
B+
FUSE 33
5 AMP
341 BRN
UNDERHOOD ELECTRICAL CENTER
ABS ENABLE RELAY
ABS MAXI FUSE
60 AMP
542 RED
1632 PNK
1633 RED
SWITCHED IGNITION
ABS ENABLE RELAY CONTROL
SWITCHED BATTERY INPUT

GC402940108301AX

Grand Prix

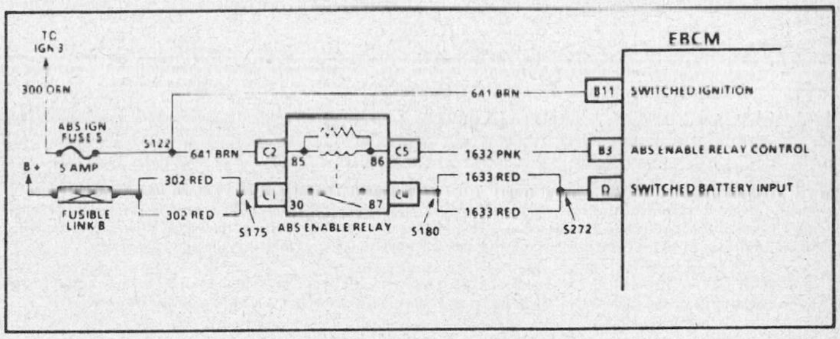
EBCM
641 BRN
SWITCHED IGNITION
1632 PNK
ABS ENABLE RELAY CONTROL
1633 RED
SWITCHED BATTERY INPUT
302 RED
FUSIBLE LINK B
ABS ENABLE RELAY

GC402940108301BX

Camaro & Firebird

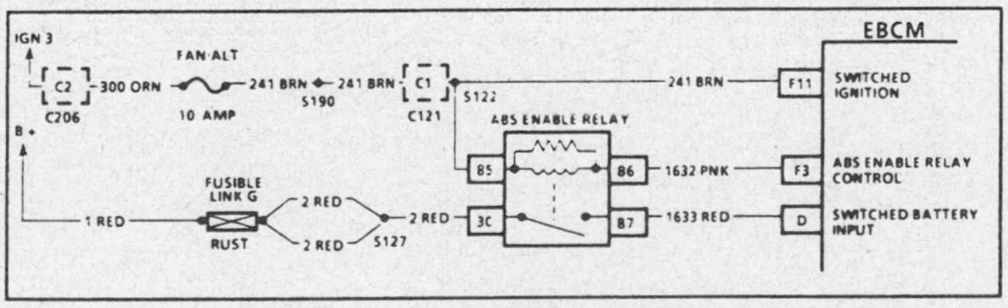
EBCM
IGN 3
300 ORN
FAN-ALT
10 AMP
241 BRN
ABS ENABLE RELAY
SWITCHED IGNITION
1632 PNK
ABS ENABLE RELAY CONTROL
FUSIBLE LINK G
1 RED
2 RED
RUST
1633 RED
SWITCHED BATTERY INPUT

GC402940108301CX

Century & Cutlass Ciera & Cruiser

Fig. 255 Code A036: Low System Voltage (Part 1 of 2). 1993–94 Camaro & Firebird, 1994 Grand Prix, Century & Cutlass Ciera & Cruiser

DTC 36

LOW SYSTEM VOLTAGE

Circuit Description:

This DTC is used to monitor the voltage level available to the EBCM controller. If the voltage drops below 11 volts, full performance of the ABS system cannot be guaranteed. During ABS operation, there are several current requirements that will cause battery voltage to drop. Because of this, voltage is monitored prior to ABS to indicate good charging system condition and also during ABS when voltage may drop significantly.

DTC Will Set When: DTC 36 can only be set if the vehicle's speed is greater than 5 km/h (3 mph). If the switched battery voltage is less than 11.2 volts non-ABS or less than 9.6 volts ABS, a malfunction exists.

Action Taken: A malfunction DTC is stored, ABS is disabled and the ABS warning lamp is turned "ON."

DTC Chart Test Description: Number(s) below refer to circled number(s) on the diagnostic chart.

1. Checks to see what voltage is readily available at terminal "D" of the EBCM. If voltage is representative of good charging system condition, a malfunction is not present.
2. Isolates the condition to high circuit resistance, or improper charging system operation.
3. Isolates which circuit is the source of the high resistance condition.
4. Checks for high resistance in CKTs 542 or 2.

Diagnostic Aids: An "Intermittent" malfunction may be caused by a poor connection, rubbed through wire insulation, or a wire that is broken inside the insulation.

The frequency of the malfunction can be checked by using the enhanced diagnostic function of the Tech 1,

Any circuitry, that is suspected as causing the intermittent complaint, should be thoroughly checked for backed out terminals, improper mating, broken locks, improperly formed or damaged terminals, poor terminal to wiring connections or physical damage to the wiring harness.

While performing a voltage load test, if it is noted that only ignition voltage drops below acceptable voltage levels, CKT 341 should be checked for high resistance or an open condition.

GC402940108301DX

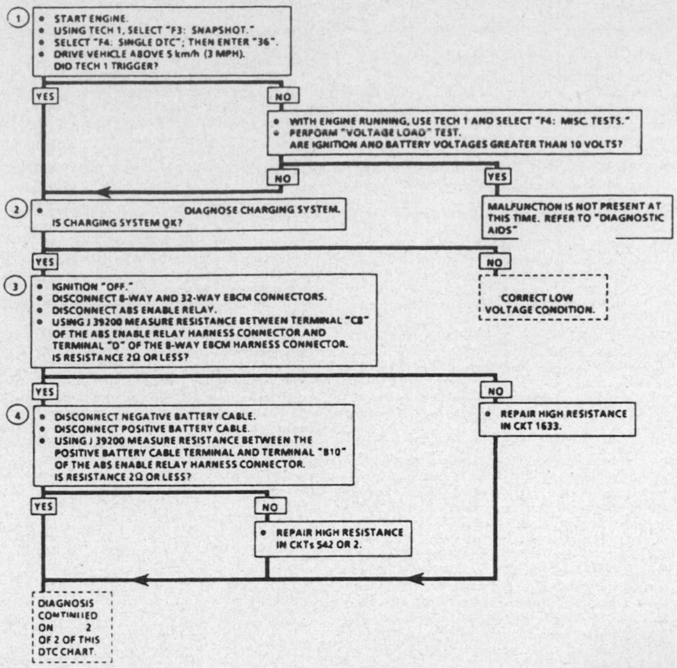
1
START ENGINE.
USING TECH 1, SELECT "F3: SNAPSHOT."
SELECT "F4: SINGLE DTC"; THEN ENTER "36".
DRIVE VEHICLE ABOVE 5 km/h (3 MPH).
DID TECH 1 TRIGGER?
YES
NO
WITH ENGINE RUNNING, USE TECH 1 AND SELECT "F4: MISC. TESTS."
PERFORM "VOLTAGE LOAD" TEST.
ARE IGNITION AND BATTERY VOLTAGES GREATER THAN 10 VOLTS?
NO
YES
MALFUNCTION IS NOT PRESENT AT THIS TIME. REFER TO "DIAGNOSTIC AIDS"
2
DIAGNOSE CHARGING SYSTEM.
IS CHARGING SYSTEM OK?
YES
NO
CORRECT LOW VOLTAGE CONDITION.
3
IGNITION "OFF."
DISCONNECT 8-WAY AND 32-WAY EBCM CONNECTORS.
DISCONNECT ABS ENABLE RELAY.
USING J 39200 MEASURE RESISTANCE BETWEEN TERMINAL "C8" OF THE ABS ENABLE RELAY HARNESS CONNECTOR AND TERMINAL "D" OF THE 8-WAY EBCM HARNESS CONNECTOR.
IS RESISTANCE 2Ω OR LESS?
YES
NO
REPAIR HIGH RESISTANCE IN CKT 1633.
4
DISCONNECT NEGATIVE BATTERY CABLE.
DISCONNECT POSITIVE BATTERY CABLE.
USING J 39200 MEASURE RESISTANCE BETWEEN THE POSITIVE BATTERY CABLE TERMINAL AND TERMINAL "B10" OF THE ABS ENABLE RELAY HARNESS CONNECTOR.
IS RESISTANCE 2Ω OR LESS?
YES
NO
REPAIR HIGH RESISTANCE IN CKTs 542 OR 2.
DIAGNOSIS CONTINUED ON 2 OF 2 OF THIS DTC CHART.

GC402940108301EX

DTC 36

LOW SYSTEM VOLTAGE

Circuit Description:

This DTC is used to monitor the voltage level available to the EBCM controller. If the voltage drops below 11 volts, full performance of the ABS system cannot be guaranteed. During ABS operation, there are several current requirements that will cause battery voltage to drop. Because of this, voltage is monitored prior to ABS to indicate good charging system condition and also during ABS when voltage may drop significantly.

DTC Will Set When: DTC 36 can only be set if the vehicle's speed is greater than 5 km/h (3 mph). If the switched battery voltage is less than 11.2 volts non-ABS or less than 9.6 volts ABS, a malfunction exists.

Action Taken: A malfunction DTC is stored, ABS is disabled and the ABS warning lamp is turned "ON."

DTC Chart Test Description: Number(s) below refer to circled number(s) on the diagnostic chart.

5. Checks for high resistance in CKT 341.
6. Checks for high resistance in the ignition fuse feed circuit.
7. Checks for possible intermittent malfunction or a malfunctioning EBCM.

Diagnostic Aids: An "Intermittent" malfunction may be caused by a poor connection, rubbed through wire insulation, or a wire that is broken inside the insulation.

The frequency of the malfunction can be checked by using the enhanced diagnostic function of the Tech 1,

Any circuitry, that is suspected as causing the intermittent complaint, should be thoroughly checked for backed out terminals, improper mating, broken locks, improperly formed or damaged terminals, poor terminal to wiring connections or physical damage to the wiring harness.

While performing a voltage load test, if it is noted that only ignition voltage drops below acceptable voltage levels, CKT 341 should be checked for high resistance or an open condition.

GC402940108302AX

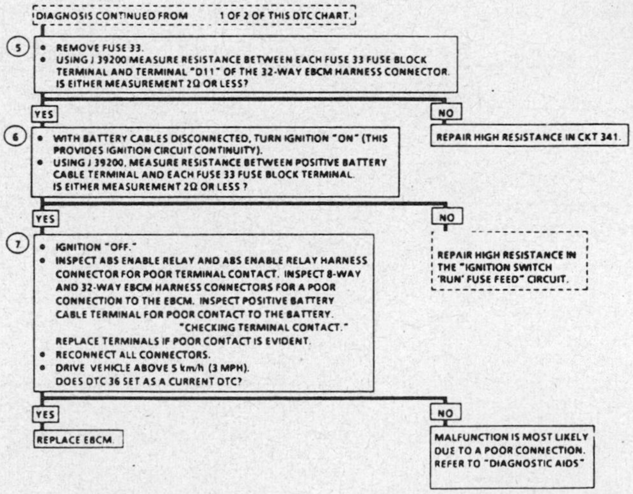
DIAGNOSIS CONTINUED FROM 1 OF 2 OF THIS DTC CHART.
5
REMOVE FUSE 33.
USING J 39200 MEASURE RESISTANCE BETWEEN EACH FUSE 33 FUSE BLOCK TERMINAL AND TERMINAL "D11" OF THE 32-WAY EBCM HARNESS CONNECTOR.
IS EITHER MEASUREMENT 2Ω OR LESS?
YES
NO
REPAIR HIGH RESISTANCE IN CKT 341.
6
WITH BATTERY CABLES DISCONNECTED, TURN IGNITION "ON" (THIS PROVIDES IGNITION CIRCUIT CONTINUITY).
USING J 39200, MEASURE RESISTANCE BETWEEN POSITIVE BATTERY CABLE TERMINAL AND EACH FUSE 33 FUSE BLOCK TERMINAL.
IS EITHER MEASUREMENT 2Ω OR LESS ?
YES
NO
REPAIR HIGH RESISTANCE IN THE "IGNITION SWITCH 'RUN' FUSE FEED" CIRCUIT.
7
IGNITION "OFF."
INSPECT ABS ENABLE RELAY AND ABS ENABLE RELAY HARNESS CONNECTOR FOR POOR TERMINAL CONTACT. INSPECT 8-WAY AND 32-WAY EBCM HARNESS CONNECTORS FOR A POOR CONNECTION TO THE EBCM. INSPECT POSITIVE BATTERY CABLE TERMINAL FOR POOR CONTACT TO THE BATTERY.
"CHECKING TERMINAL CONTACT."
REPLACE TERMINALS IF POOR CONTACT IS EVIDENT.
RECONNECT ALL CONNECTORS.
DRIVE VEHICLE ABOVE 5 km/h (3 MPH).
DOES DTC 36 SET AS A CURRENT DTC?
YES
NO
REPLACE EBCM.
MALFUNCTION IS MOST LIKELY DUE TO A POOR CONNECTION. REFER TO "DIAGNOSTIC AIDS"

GC402940108302BX

Fig. 255 Code A036: Low System Voltage (Part 2 of 2). 1993–94 Camaro & Firebird, 1994 Grand Prix, Century & Cutlass Ciera & Cruiser

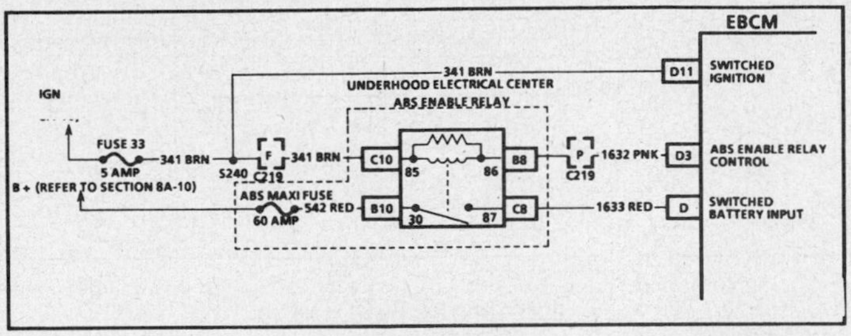
EBCM
IGN
FUSE 33
5 AMP
341 BRN
UNDERHOOD ELECTRICAL CENTER
ABS ENABLE RELAY
S240
C219
B + (REFER TO SECTION 8A-10)
ABS MAXI FUSE
60 AMP
542 RED
C10
B10
85
86
30
87
B8
C8
1632 PNK
1633 RED
D11
D3
D
SWITCHED IGNITION
ABS ENABLE RELAY CONTROL
SWITCHED BATTERY INPUT

GC402940108400AX

Grand Prix

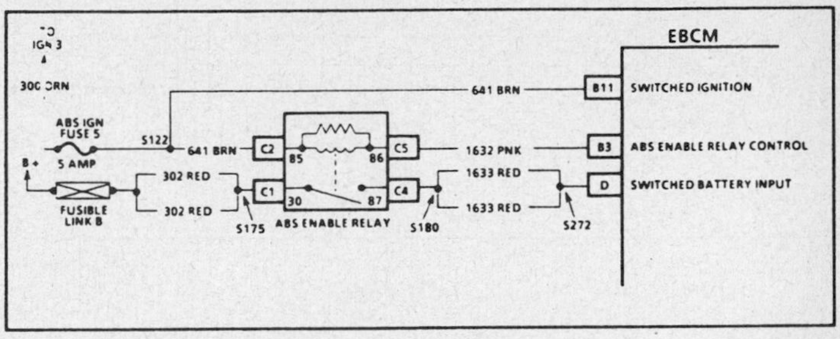
EBCM
300 ORN
ABS IGN FUSE 5
5 AMP
B +
FUSIBLE LINK B
S122
641 BRN
302 RED
C2
C1
C5
C4
85
86
30
87
S175
ABS ENABLE RELAY
S180
1632 PNK
1633 RED
S272
B11
B3
D
SWITCHED IGNITION
ABS ENABLE RELAY CONTROL
SWITCHED BATTERY INPUT

GC402940108400BX

Camaro & Firebird

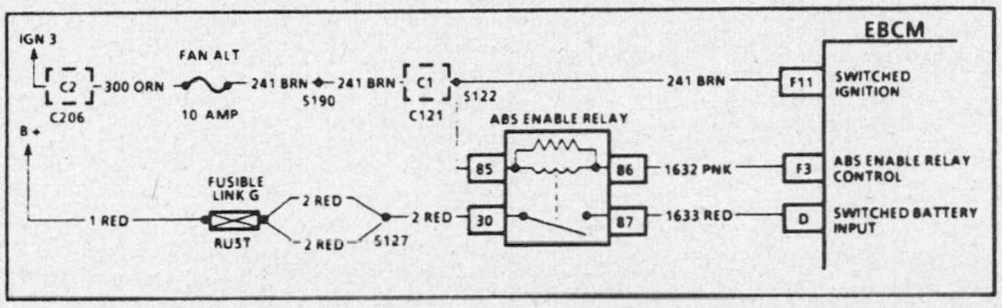
IGN 3
C2
300 ORN
C206
FAN ALT
10 AMP
241 BRN
S190
C1
C121
S122
EBCM
ABS ENABLE RELAY
85
86
30
87
B +
FUSIBLE LINK G
1 RED
2 RED
RUST
S127
1632 PNK
1633 RED
F11
F3
D
SWITCHED IGNITION
ABS ENABLE RELAY CONTROL
SWITCHED BATTERY INPUT

GC402940108400CX

Century & Cutlass Ciera & Cruiser

HIGH SYSTEM VOLTAGE

Circuit Description:
This DTC is designed to detect high vehicle voltage levels prior to any required motor movement (initialization or ABS). If excessive voltage exists, demagnetization of the motor magnets may occur, which would eventually affect or eliminate ABS performance.

DTC Will Set When: DTC 37 can only be set if the vehicle's speed is greater than 5 km/h (3 mph). If the switched battery voltage is greater than 17 volts, a malfunction exists.

Action Taken: A malfunction DTC is stored, ABS is disabled and the ABS warning lamp is turned "ON."

DTC Chart Test Description: Number(s) below refer to circled number(s) on the diagnostic chart.

1. Checks the voltage level being received by the EBCM.
2. Checks to see if high voltage condition is due to charging system malfunction.
3. Checks for poor terminal contact which may cause an intermittent malfunction, or a malfunctioning EBCM.

Diagnostic Aids: An "Intermittent" malfunction may be caused by a poor connection, rubbed through wire insulation, or a wire that is broken inside the insulation.

The frequency of the malfunction can be checked by using the enhanced diagnostic function of the Tech 1.

Any circuitry, that is suspected as causing the intermittent complaint, should be thoroughly checked for backed out terminals, improper mating, broken locks, improperly formed or damaged terminals, poor terminal to wiring connections or physical damage to the wiring harness.

GC402940108400DX

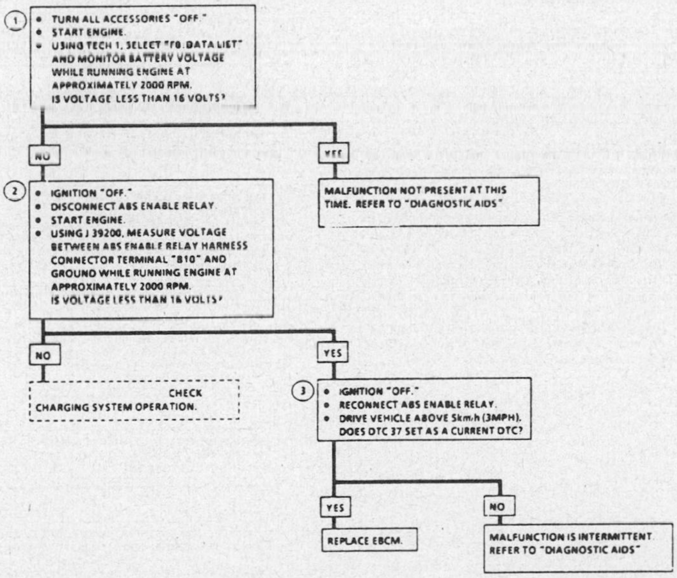
1
TURN ALL ACCESSORIES "OFF."
START ENGINE.
USING TECH 1, SELECT "F0: DATA LIST" AND MONITOR BATTERY VOLTAGE WHILE RUNNING ENGINE AT APPROXIMATELY 2000 RPM.
IS VOLTAGE LESS THAN 16 VOLTS?
NO
YES
MALFUNCTION NOT PRESENT AT THIS TIME. REFER TO "DIAGNOSTIC AIDS"
2
IGNITION "OFF."
DISCONNECT ABS ENABLE RELAY.
START ENGINE.
USING J 39200, MEASURE VOLTAGE BETWEEN ABS ENABLE RELAY HARNESS CONNECTOR TERMINAL "B10" AND GROUND WHILE RUNNING ENGINE AT APPROXIMATELY 2000 RPM.
IS VOLTAGE LESS THAN 16 VOLTS?
NO
YES
CHECK CHARGING SYSTEM OPERATION.
3
IGNITION "OFF."
RECONNECT ABS ENABLE RELAY.
DRIVE VEHICLE ABOVE 5km/h (3MPH).
DOES DTC 37 SET AS A CURRENT DTC?
YES
NO
REPLACE EBCM.
MALFUNCTION IS INTERMITTENT. REFER TO "DIAGNOSTIC AIDS"

GC402940108400EX

Fig. 256 Code A037: High System Voltage. 1993–94 Camaro & Firebird, 1994 Grand Prix, Century & Cutlass Ciera & Cruiser

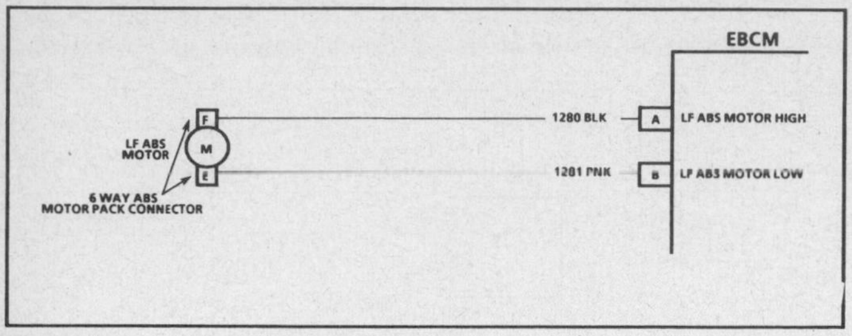
EBCM
LF ABS MOTOR
M
F
E
6 WAY ABS MOTOR PACK CONNECTOR
1280 BLK
1281 PNK
A
B
LF ABS MOTOR HIGH
LF ABS MOTOR LOW

GC402940108500AX

Grand Prix

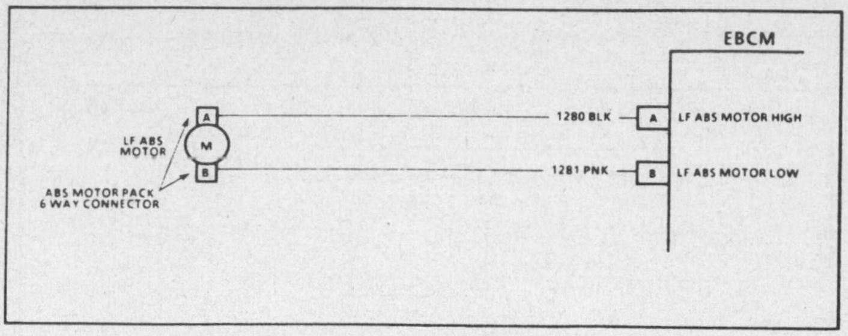
EBCM
LF ABS MOTOR
M
A
B
ABS MOTOR PACK 6 WAY CONNECTOR
1280 BLK
1281 PNK
A
B
LF ABS MOTOR HIGH
LF ABS MOTOR LOW

GC402940108500BX

Camaro & Firebird

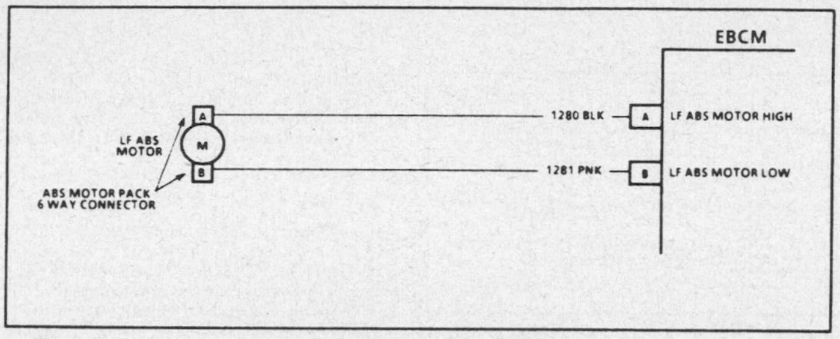
EBCM
LF ABS MOTOR
M
A
B
ABS MOTOR PACK 6 WAY CONNECTOR
1280 BLK
1281 PNK
A
B
LF ABS MOTOR HIGH
LF ABS MOTOR LOW

GC402940108500CX

Century & Cutlass Ciera & Cruiser

DTC 38

LEFT FRONT ESB WILL NOT HOLD MOTOR

Circuit Description:

This DTC is designed to detect a slipping left front ESB. During initialization and braking, the left front motor is rehomed. If the ESB slips, the motor/piston will move. During the next key "ON" initialization, a rehome of the motor verifies the motor/piston remained at the home position. If motor movement is detected, the ESB must be slipping.

DTC Will Set When: DTC 38 can be set during initialization. If the EBCM detects that the ESB could not hold the piston in the home position, a malfunction exists. DTC 86 is always set with DTC 38.

Action Taken: If an ESB cannot hold a piston in the home position, the piston may be backdriven when the brake pedal is applied, causing the brake pedal to drop. A malfunction DTC is stored, ABS is disabled, and the ABS warning lamp and the red "BRAKE" warning lamp are turned "ON."

DTC Chart Test Description: Number(s) below refer to circled number(s) on the diagnostic chart.

1. Checks the left front ESB. A broken or defective ESB would result in the left front piston being backdriven by hydraulic pressure and pedal movement would result.
2. Ensures that the proper motor circuits are located in the proper connector cavities.
3. Checks for high resistance in the motor "HIGH" circuitry.
4. Checks for high resistance in the motor "LOW" circuitry.
5. Checks for proper resistance of the motor windings.
6. Checks for poor terminal contact or corrosion in the connectors.
7. Checks for a malfunctioning EBCM.

Diagnostic Aids: An "Intermittent" malfunction in this DTC may result from a mechanical part of the system that sticks, binds, or slips.

The frequency of the malfunction can be checked by using the enhanced diagnostic function of the Tech 1,

The static modulator test function of the Tech 1 or T-100 may be used to locate an intermittent malfunction associated with the ESB.

GC402940108500DX

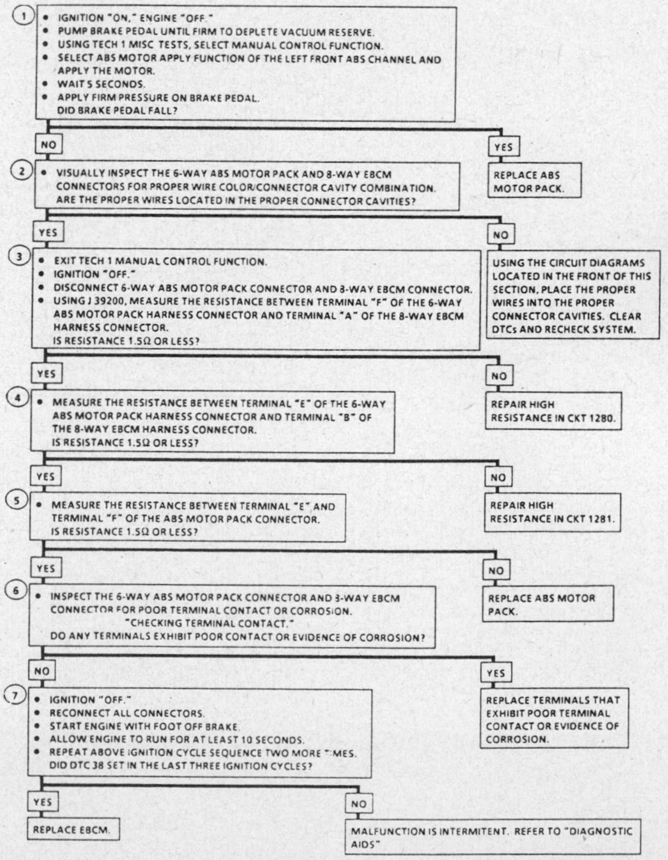
1
• IGNITION "ON," ENGINE "OFF."
• PUMP BRAKE PEDAL UNTIL FIRM TO DEPLETE VACUUM RESERVE.
• USING TECH 1 MISC TESTS, SELECT MANUAL CONTROL FUNCTION.
• SELECT ABS MOTOR APPLY FUNCTION OF THE LEFT FRONT ABS CHANNEL AND APPLY THE MOTOR.
• WAIT 5 SECONDS.
• APPLY FIRM PRESSURE ON BRAKE PEDAL.
DID BRAKE PEDAL FALL?
NO
YES
REPLACE ABS MOTOR PACK.
2
• VISUALLY INSPECT THE 6-WAY ABS MOTOR PACK AND 8-WAY EBCM CONNECTORS FOR PROPER WIRE COLOR/CONNECTOR CAVITY COMBINATION.
ARE THE PROPER WIRES LOCATED IN THE PROPER CONNECTOR CAVITIES?
YES
NO
USING THE CIRCUIT DIAGRAMS LOCATED IN THE FRONT OF THIS SECTION, PLACE THE PROPER WIRES INTO THE PROPER CONNECTOR CAVITIES. CLEAR DTCs AND RECHECK SYSTEM.
3
• EXIT TECH 1 MANUAL CONTROL FUNCTION.
• IGNITION "OFF."
• DISCONNECT 6-WAY ABS MOTOR PACK CONNECTOR AND 8-WAY EBCM CONNECTOR.
• USING J 39200, MEASURE THE RESISTANCE BETWEEN TERMINAL "F" OF THE 6-WAY ABS MOTOR PACK HARNESS CONNECTOR AND TERMINAL "A" OF THE 8-WAY EBCM HARNESS CONNECTOR.
IS RESISTANCE 1.5Ω OR LESS?
YES
NO
REPAIR HIGH RESISTANCE IN CKT 1280.
4
• MEASURE THE RESISTANCE BETWEEN TERMINAL "E" OF THE 6-WAY ABS MOTOR PACK HARNESS CONNECTOR AND TERMINAL "B" OF THE 8-WAY EBCM HARNESS CONNECTOR.
IS RESISTANCE 1.5Ω OR LESS?
YES
NO
REPAIR HIGH RESISTANCE IN CKT 1281.
5
• MEASURE THE RESISTANCE BETWEEN TERMINAL "E" AND TERMINAL "F" OF THE ABS MOTOR PACK CONNECTOR.
IS RESISTANCE 1.5Ω OR LESS?
YES
NO
REPLACE ABS MOTOR PACK.
6
• INSPECT THE 6-WAY ABS MOTOR PACK CONNECTOR AND 3-WAY EBCM CONNECTOR FOR POOR TERMINAL CONTACT OR CORROSION.
"CHECKING TERMINAL CONTACT."
DO ANY TERMINALS EXHIBIT POOR CONTACT OR EVIDENCE OF CORROSION?
NO
YES
REPLACE TERMINALS THAT EXHIBIT POOR TERMINAL CONTACT OR EVIDENCE OF CORROSION.
7
• IGNITION "OFF."
• RECONNECT ALL CONNECTORS.
• START ENGINE WITH FOOT OFF BRAKE.
• ALLOW ENGINE TO RUN FOR AT LEAST 10 SECONDS.
• REPEAT ABOVE IGNITION CYCLE SEQUENCE TWO MORE TIMES.
DID DTC 38 SET IN THE LAST THREE IGNITION CYCLES?
YES
NO
REPLACE EBCM.
MALFUNCTION IS INTERMITENT. REFER TO "DIAGNOSTIC AIDS"

GC402940108500EX

Fig. 257 Code A038: Left Front ESB Will Not Hold Motor. 1993–94 Camaro & Firebird, 1994 Grand Prix, Century & Cutlass Ciera & Cruiser

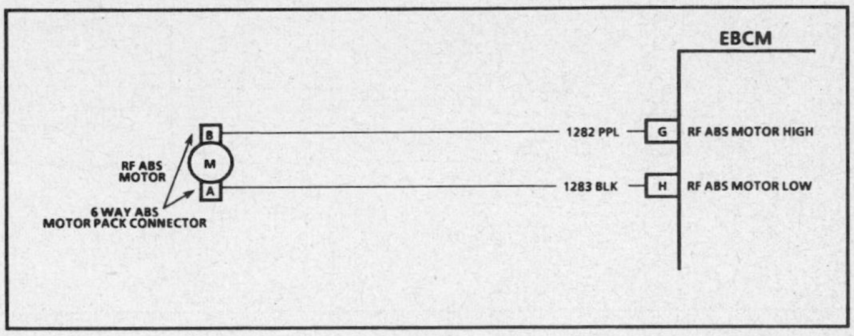
EBCM
1282 PPL
G
RF ABS MOTOR HIGH
B
M
A
RF ABS MOTOR
1283 BLK
H
RF ABS MOTOR LOW
6 WAY ABS MOTOR PACK CONNECTOR

GC402940108600AX

Grand Prix

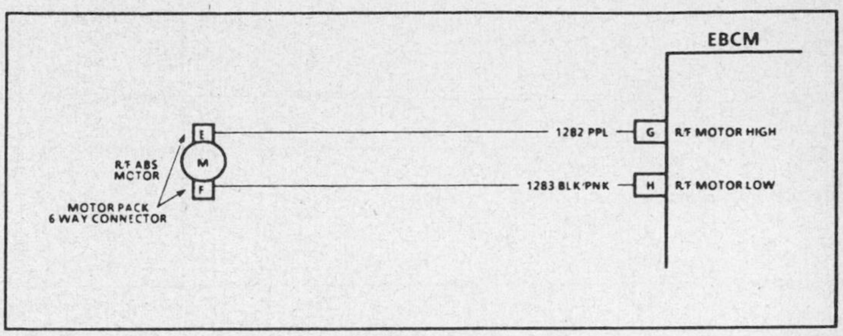
EBCM
1282 PPL
G
RF MOTOR HIGH
E
M
F
RF ABS MOTOR
1283 BLK/PNK
H
RF MOTOR LOW
MOTOR PACK 6 WAY CONNECTOR

GC402940108600BX

Camaro & Firebird

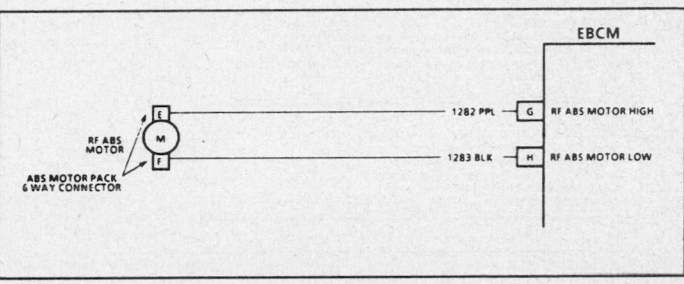
EBCM
1282 PPL
G
RF ABS MOTOR HIGH
E
M
F
RF ABS MOTOR
1283 BLK
H
RF ABS MOTOR LOW
ABS MOTOR PACK 6 WAY CONNECTOR

GC402940108600CX

Century & Cutlass Ciera & Cruiser

DTC 41

RIGHT FRONT ESB WILL NOT HOLD MOTOR

Circuit Description:

This DTC is designed to detect a slipping right front ESB. During initialization and braking, the right front motor is rehomed. If the ESB slips, the motor/piston will move. During the next key "ON" initialization, a rehome of the motor verifies the motor/piston remained at the home position. If motor movement is detected, the ESB must be slipping.

DTC Will Set When: DTC 41 can be set during initialization. If the EBCM detects that the ESB could not hold the piston in the home position, a malfunction exists. DTC 86 is always set with DTC 41.

Action Taken: If an ESB cannot hold a piston in the home position, the piston may be backdriven when the brake pedal is applied, causing the brake pedal to drop. A malfunction DTC is stored, ABS is disabled, and the ABS warning lamp and the red "BRAKE" warning lamp are turned "ON."

DTC Chart Test Description: Number(s) below refer to circled number(s) on the diagnostic chart.

1. Checks the right front ESB. A broken or defective ESB would result in the right front piston being backdriven by hydraulic pressure, and pedal movement would result.
2. Ensures that the proper motor circuits are located in the proper connector cavities.
3. Checks for high resistance in the motor "HIGH" circuitry.
4. Checks for high resistance in the motor "LOW" circuitry.
5. Checks for proper resistance of the motor windings.
6. Checks for poor terminal contact or corrosion in the connectors.
7. Checks for a malfunctioning EBCM.

Diagnostic Aids: An "Intermittent" malfunction in this DTC may result from a mechanical part of the system that sticks, binds, or slips.

The frequency of the malfunction can be checked by using the enhanced diagnostic function of the

The static modulator test function of the Tech 1 or T-100 may be used to locate an intermittent malfunction associated with the ESB.

GC402940108600DX

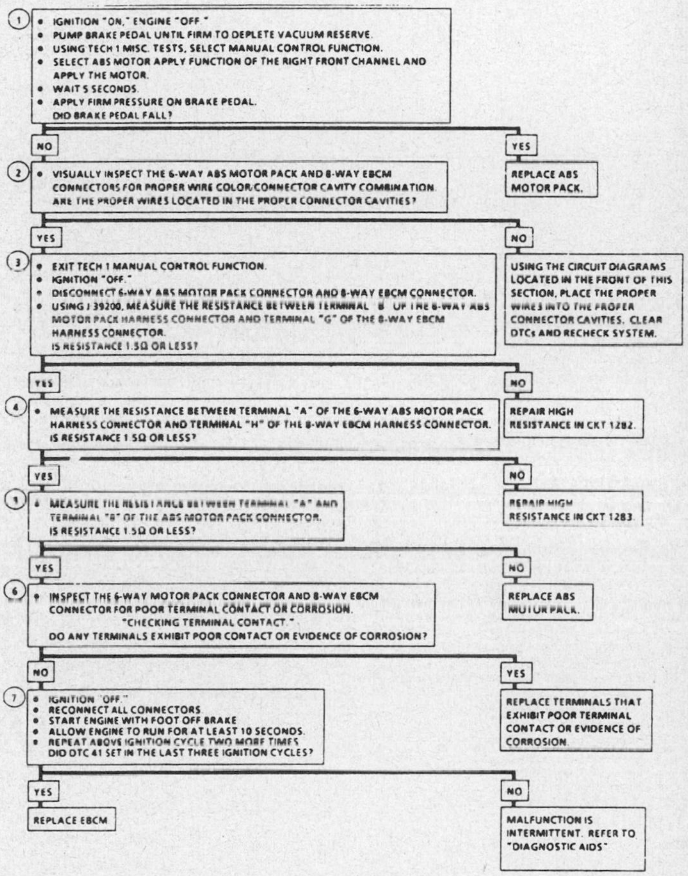
1
• IGNITION "ON," ENGINE "OFF."
• PUMP BRAKE PEDAL UNTIL FIRM TO DEPLETE VACUUM RESERVE.
• USING TECH 1 MISC. TESTS, SELECT MANUAL CONTROL FUNCTION.
• SELECT ABS MOTOR APPLY FUNCTION OF THE RIGHT FRONT CHANNEL AND APPLY THE MOTOR.
• WAIT 5 SECONDS.
• APPLY FIRM PRESSURE ON BRAKE PEDAL.
DID BRAKE PEDAL FALL?
NO
YES
REPLACE ABS MOTOR PACK.
2
• VISUALLY INSPECT THE 6-WAY ABS MOTOR PACK AND 8-WAY EBCM CONNECTORS FOR PROPER WIRE COLOR/CONNECTOR CAVITY COMBINATION.
ARE THE PROPER WIRES LOCATED IN THE PROPER CONNECTOR CAVITIES?
YES
NO
USING THE CIRCUIT DIAGRAMS LOCATED IN THE FRONT OF THIS SECTION, PLACE THE PROPER WIRES INTO THE PROPER CONNECTOR CAVITIES. CLEAR DTCs AND RECHECK SYSTEM.
3
• EXIT TECH 1 MANUAL CONTROL FUNCTION.
• IGNITION "OFF."
• DISCONNECT 6-WAY ABS MOTOR PACK CONNECTOR AND 8-WAY EBCM CONNECTOR.
• USING J 39200, MEASURE THE RESISTANCE BETWEEN TERMINAL "B" OF THE 6-WAY ABS MOTOR PACK HARNESS CONNECTOR AND TERMINAL "G" OF THE 8-WAY EBCM HARNESS CONNECTOR.
IS RESISTANCE 1.5Ω OR LESS?
YES
NO
REPAIR HIGH RESISTANCE IN CKT 1282.
4
• MEASURE THE RESISTANCE BETWEEN TERMINAL "A" OF THE 6-WAY ABS MOTOR PACK HARNESS CONNECTOR AND TERMINAL "H" OF THE 8-WAY EBCM HARNESS CONNECTOR.
IS RESISTANCE 1.5Ω OR LESS?
YES
NO
REPAIR HIGH RESISTANCE IN CKT 1283.
5
• MEASURE THE RESISTANCE BETWEEN TERMINAL "A" AND TERMINAL "B" OF THE ABS MOTOR PACK CONNECTOR.
IS RESISTANCE 1.5Ω OR LESS?
YES
NO
REPLACE ABS MOTOR PACK.
6
• INSPECT THE 6-WAY MOTOR PACK CONNECTOR AND 8-WAY EBCM CONNECTOR FOR POOR TERMINAL CONTACT OR CORROSION.
"CHECKING TERMINAL CONTACT."
DO ANY TERMINALS EXHIBIT POOR CONTACT OR EVIDENCE OF CORROSION?
NO
YES
REPLACE TERMINALS THAT EXHIBIT POOR TERMINAL CONTACT OR EVIDENCE OF CORROSION.
7
• IGNITION "OFF."
• RECONNECT ALL CONNECTORS.
• START ENGINE WITH FOOT OFF BRAKE
• ALLOW ENGINE TO RUN FOR AT LEAST 10 SECONDS.
• REPEAT ABOVE IGNITION CYCLE TWO MORE TIMES
DID DTC 41 SET IN THE LAST THREE IGNITION CYCLES?
YES
REPLACE EBCM
NO
MALFUNCTION IS INTERMITTENT. REFER TO "DIAGNOSTIC AIDS"

GC402940108600EX

Fig. 258 Code A041: Right Front ESB Will Not Hold Motor. 1993–94 Camaro & Firebird, 1994 Grand Prix, Century & Cutlass Ciera & Cruiser

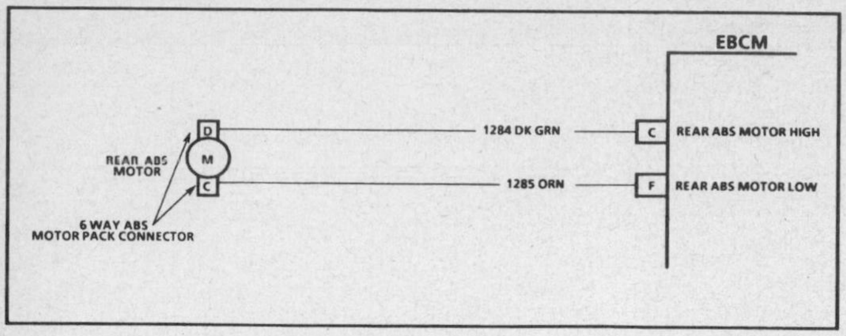
EBCM
REAR ABS MOTOR
M
D
C
6 WAY ABS MOTOR PACK CONNECTOR
1284 DK GRN
1285 ORN
C
F
REAR ABS MOTOR HIGH
REAR ABS MOTOR LOW

GC402940108700AX

Grand Prix

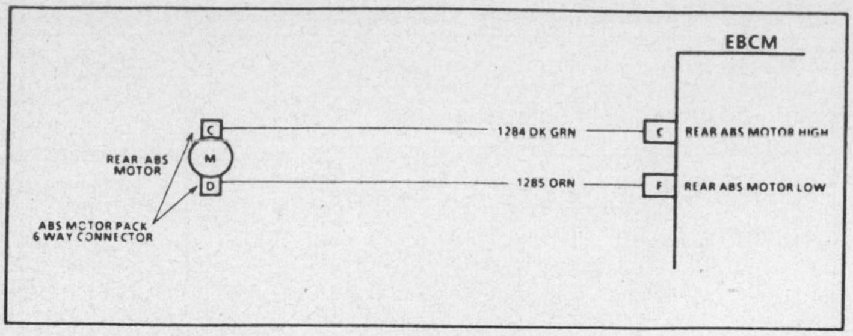
EBCM
REAR ABS MOTOR
M
C
D
ABS MOTOR PACK 6 WAY CONNECTOR
1284 DK GRN
1285 ORN
C
F
REAR ABS MOTOR HIGH
REAR ABS MOTOR LOW

GC402940108700BX

Camaro & Firebird

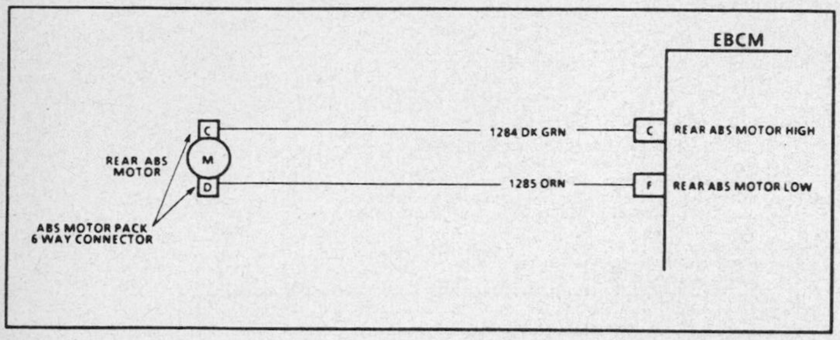
EBCM
REAR ABS MOTOR
M
C
D
ABS MOTOR PACK 6 WAY CONNECTOR
1284 DK GRN
1285 ORN
C
F
REAR ABS MOTOR HIGH
REAR ABS MOTOR LOW

GC402940108700CX

Century & Cutlass Ciera & Cruiser

DTC 42

REAR ESB WILL NOT HOLD MOTOR

Circuit Description:

This DTC is designed to detect a slipping rear axle ESB. During initialization and braking, the rear motor is rehomed. If the ESB slips, the motor/piston will move. During the next key "ON" initialization, a rehome of the motor verifies the motor/piston remained at the home position. If motor movement is detected, the ESB must be slipping.

DTC Will Set When: DTC 42 can be set during initialization. If the EBCM detects that the ESB could not hold the piston in the home position, a malfunction exists. DTC 86 is always set with DTC 42.

Action Taken: If an ESB cannot hold a piston in the home position, the piston may be backdriven when the brake pedal is applied, causing the brake pedal to drop. A malfunction DTC is stored, ABS is disabled, and the ABS warning lamp and the red "BRAKE" warning lamp are turned "ON."

DTC Chart Test Description: Number(s) below refer to circled number(s) on the diagnostic chart.

1. Checks the rear axle ESB. A broken or defective ESB would result in the rear axle pistons being backdriven by hydraulic pressure and wheel movement would result.
2. Ensures that the proper motor circuits are located in the proper connector cavities.
3. Checks for high resistance in the motor "HIGH" circuitry.
4. Checks for high resistance in the motor "LOW" circuitry.
5. Checks for proper resistance of the motor windings.
6. Checks for poor terminal contact or corrosion in the connectors.
7. Checks for a malfunctioning EBCM.

Diagnostic Aids: An "Intermittent" malfunction in this DTC may result from a mechanical part of the system that sticks, binds, or slips.

The frequency of the malfunction can be checked by using the enhanced diagnostic function of the Tech 1.

The static modulator test function of the Tech 1 or T-100 may be used to locate an intermittent malfunction associated with the ESB.

GC402940108700DX

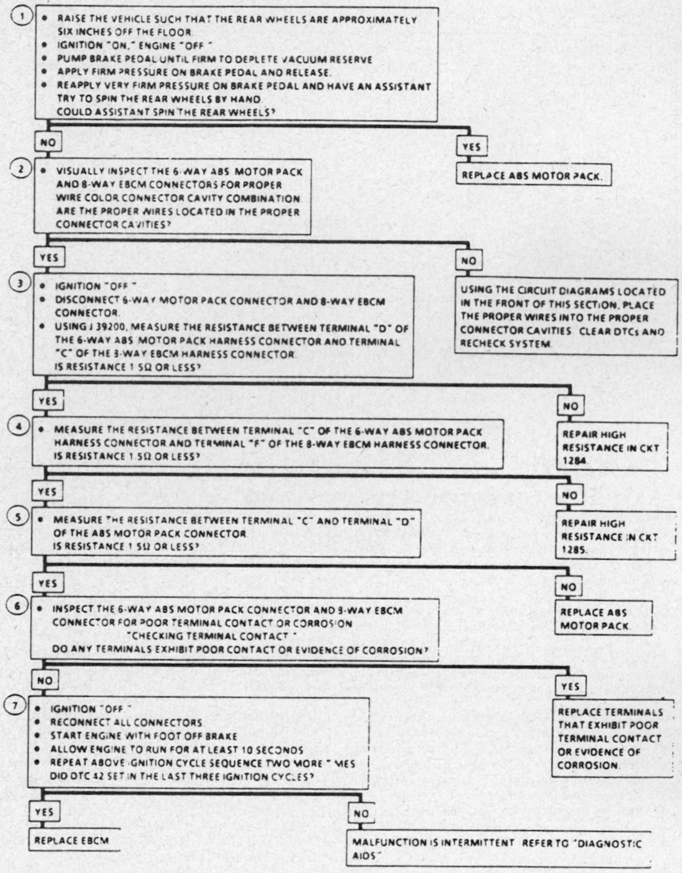
1
• RAISE THE VEHICLE SUCH THAT THE REAR WHEELS ARE APPROXIMATELY SIX INCHES OFF THE FLOOR.
• IGNITION "ON," ENGINE "OFF."
• PUMP BRAKE PEDAL UNTIL FIRM TO DEPLETE VACUUM RESERVE
• APPLY FIRM PRESSURE ON BRAKE PEDAL AND RELEASE.
• REAPPLY VERY FIRM PRESSURE ON BRAKE PEDAL AND HAVE AN ASSISTANT TRY TO SPIN THE REAR WHEELS BY HAND.
COULD ASSISTANT SPIN THE REAR WHEELS?
NO
YES
REPLACE ABS MOTOR PACK.
2
• VISUALLY INSPECT THE 6-WAY ABS MOTOR PACK AND 8-WAY EBCM CONNECTORS FOR PROPER WIRE COLOR CONNECTOR CAVITY COMBINATION
ARE THE PROPER WIRES LOCATED IN THE PROPER CONNECTOR CAVITIES?
YES
NO
USING THE CIRCUIT DIAGRAMS LOCATED IN THE FRONT OF THIS SECTION, PLACE THE PROPER WIRES INTO THE PROPER CONNECTOR CAVITIES. CLEAR DTCs AND RECHECK SYSTEM.
3
• IGNITION "OFF."
• DISCONNECT 6-WAY MOTOR PACK CONNECTOR AND 8-WAY EBCM CONNECTOR.
• USING J 39200, MEASURE THE RESISTANCE BETWEEN TERMINAL "D" OF THE 6-WAY ABS MOTOR PACK HARNESS CONNECTOR AND TERMINAL "C" OF THE 8-WAY EBCM HARNESS CONNECTOR.
IS RESISTANCE 1.5Ω OR LESS?
YES
NO
REPAIR HIGH RESISTANCE IN CKT 1284.
4
• MEASURE THE RESISTANCE BETWEEN TERMINAL "C" OF THE 6-WAY ABS MOTOR PACK HARNESS CONNECTOR AND TERMINAL "F" OF THE 8-WAY EBCM HARNESS CONNECTOR.
IS RESISTANCE 1.5Ω OR LESS?
YES
NO
REPAIR HIGH RESISTANCE IN CKT 1285.
5
• MEASURE THE RESISTANCE BETWEEN TERMINAL "C" AND TERMINAL "D" OF THE ABS MOTOR PACK CONNECTOR.
IS RESISTANCE 1.5Ω OR LESS?
YES
NO
REPLACE ABS MOTOR PACK.
6
• INSPECT THE 6-WAY ABS MOTOR PACK CONNECTOR AND 8-WAY EBCM CONNECTOR FOR POOR TERMINAL CONTACT OR CORROSION
"CHECKING TERMINAL CONTACT."
DO ANY TERMINALS EXHIBIT POOR CONTACT OR EVIDENCE OF CORROSION?
NO
YES
REPLACE TERMINALS THAT EXHIBIT POOR TERMINAL CONTACT OR EVIDENCE OF CORROSION.
7
• IGNITION "OFF."
• RECONNECT ALL CONNECTORS.
• START ENGINE WITH FOOT OFF BRAKE
• ALLOW ENGINE TO RUN FOR AT LEAST 10 SECONDS
• REPEAT ABOVE IGNITION CYCLE SEQUENCE TWO MORE TIMES
DID DTC 42 SET IN THE LAST THREE IGNITION CYCLES?
YES
NO
REPLACE EBCM
MALFUNCTION IS INTERMITTENT. REFER TO "DIAGNOSTIC AIDS."

GC402940108700EX

Fig. 259 Code A042: Rear ESB Will Not hold Motor. 1993–94 Camaro & Firebird, 1994 Grand Prix, Century & Cutlass Ciera & Cruiser

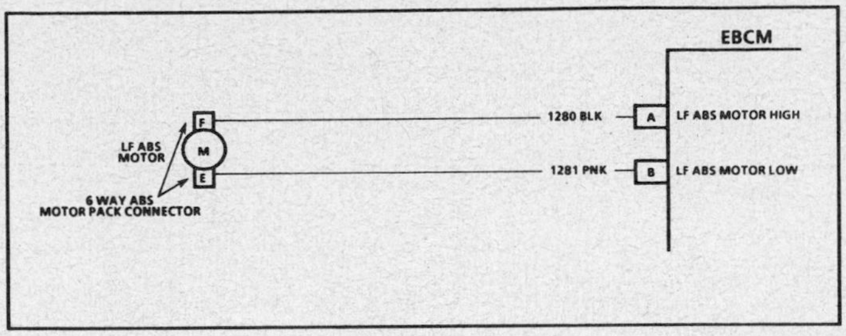
EBCM
LF ABS MOTOR
6 WAY ABS MOTOR PACK CONNECTOR
1280 BLK
1281 PNK
LF ABS MOTOR HIGH
LF ABS MOTOR LOW

GC402940108800AX

Grand Prix

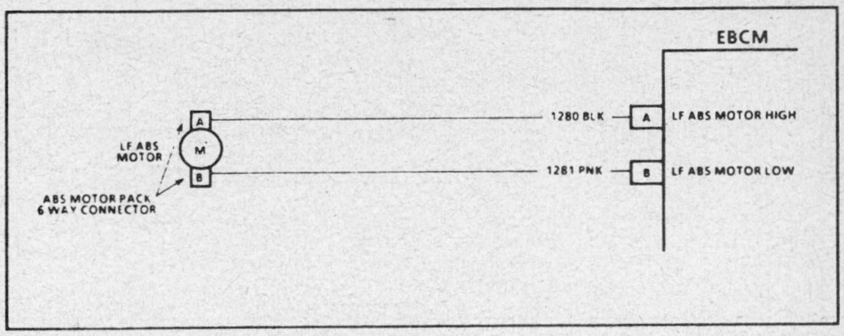
EBCM
LF ABS MOTOR
ABS MOTOR PACK 6 WAY CONNECTOR
1280 BLK
1281 PNK
LF ABS MOTOR HIGH
LF ABS MOTOR LOW

GC402940108800BX

Camaro & Firebird

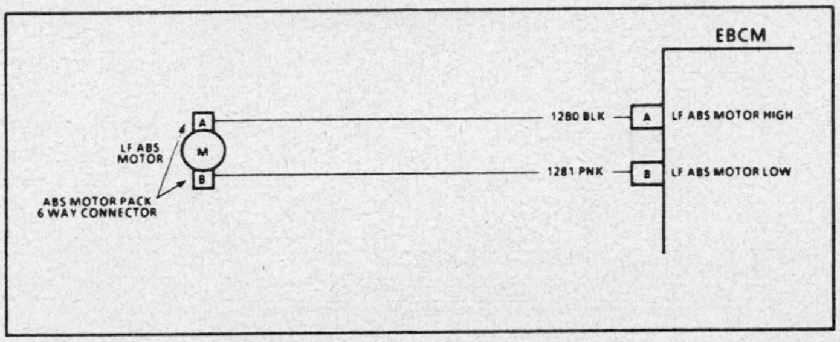
EBCM
LF ABS MOTOR
ABS MOTOR PACK 6 WAY CONNECTOR
1280 BLK
1281 PNK
LF ABS MOTOR HIGH
LF ABS MOTOR LOW

GC402940108800CX

Century & Cutlass Ciera & Cruiser

DTC 44

LEFT FRONT CHANNEL WILL NOT MOVE

Circuit Description:

This DTC is designed to detect bound-up ESB, a stuck ABS motor, or a seized hydraulic modulator. When the release is commanded during initialization, the ESB should release the ABS motor, resulting in sensed current being less than commanded current (motor is spinning freely). If the ABS motor is not moving, sensed current will be equal to stall current.

DTC Will Set When: DTC 44 can be set during normal operation. If the EBCM detects a condition in which it cannot move the ABS motor in either direction, a malfunction exists.

Action Taken: This malfunction indicates the channel cannot be moved properly. A malfunction DTC is stored, ABS is disabled and the ABS warning lamp is turned "ON."

DTC Chart Test Description: Number(s) below refer to circled number(s) on the diagnostic chart.

1. Ensures that proper ABS motor circuits are located in the proper connector cavities.
2. Checks for proper ABS motor movement during apply and release commands from the Tech 1.
3. Compares EBCM command current to ABS motor feedback current.
4. Checks for a short between CKT 1280 and CKT 1281.
5. Checks for an ABS motor that is internally shorted.
6. Checks to see if the malfunction is due to poor terminal contact or a faulty EBCM.
7. Verifies that the ABS motor can actually apply when commanded.
8. Checks for proper hydraulic modulator gear and piston movement.

Diagnostic Aids: An "Intermittent" malfunction in this DTC may result from a mechanical part of the system that sticks, binds, or slips.

The frequency of the malfunction can be checked by using the enhanced diagnostic function of the Tech 1.

DTC 44 may set after modulator disassembly if the modulator pistons are positioned at the bottom of their bore.

Any circuitry, that is suspected as causing the intermittent complaint, should be thoroughly checked for backed out terminals, improper mating, broken locks, improperly formed or damaged terminals, poor terminal to wiring connections or physical damage to the wiring harness.

GC402940108800DX

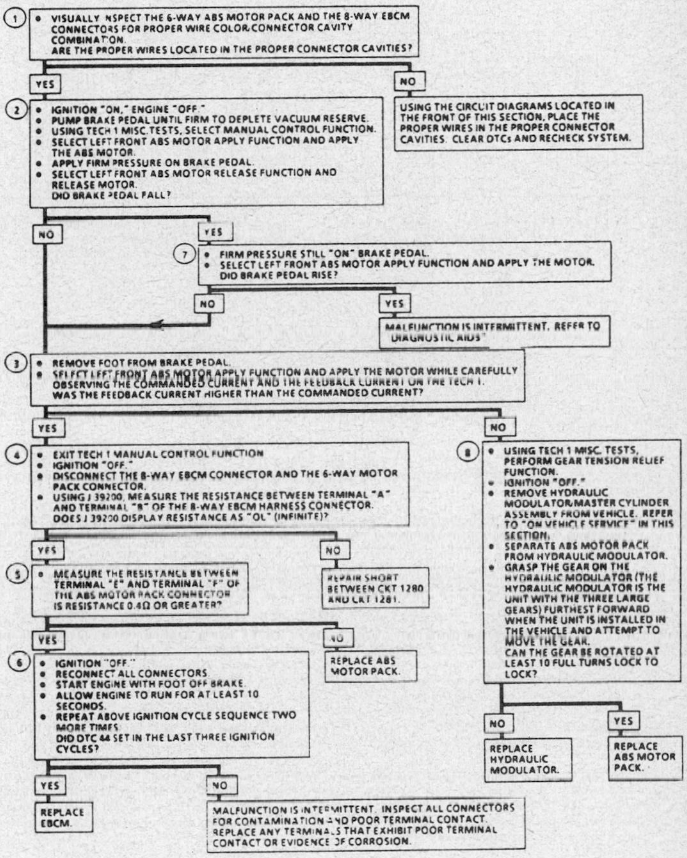
1 • VISUALLY INSPECT THE 6-WAY ABS MOTOR PACK AND THE 8-WAY EBCM CONNECTORS FOR PROPER WIRE COLOR/CONNECTOR CAVITY COMBINATION. ARE THE PROPER WIRES LOCATED IN THE PROPER CONNECTOR CAVITIES?
YES
NO
USING THE CIRCUIT DIAGRAMS LOCATED IN THE FRONT OF THIS SECTION, PLACE THE PROPER WIRES IN THE PROPER CONNECTOR CAVITIES. CLEAR DTCs AND RECHECK SYSTEM.
2 • IGNITION "ON," ENGINE "OFF." • PUMP BRAKE PEDAL UNTIL FIRM TO DEPLETE VACUUM RESERVE. • USING TECH 1 MISC. TESTS, SELECT MANUAL CONTROL FUNCTION. • SELECT LEFT FRONT ABS MOTOR APPLY FUNCTION AND APPLY THE ABS MOTOR. • APPLY FIRM PRESSURE ON BRAKE PEDAL. • SELECT LEFT FRONT ABS MOTOR RELEASE FUNCTION AND RELEASE MOTOR. DID BRAKE PEDAL FALL?
NO
YES
7 • FIRM PRESSURE STILL "ON" BRAKE PEDAL. • SELECT LEFT FRONT ABS MOTOR APPLY FUNCTION AND APPLY THE MOTOR. DID BRAKE PEDAL RISE?
NO
YES
MALFUNCTION IS INTERMITTENT. REFER TO "DIAGNOSTIC AIDS"
3 • REMOVE FOOT FROM BRAKE PEDAL. • SELECT LEFT FRONT ABS MOTOR APPLY FUNCTION AND APPLY THE MOTOR WHILE CAREFULLY OBSERVING THE COMMANDED CURRENT AND THE FEEDBACK CURRENT ON THE TECH 1. WAS THE FEEDBACK CURRENT HIGHER THAN THE COMMANDED CURRENT?
YES
NO
4 • EXIT TECH 1 MANUAL CONTROL FUNCTION • IGNITION "OFF." • DISCONNECT THE 8-WAY EBCM CONNECTOR AND THE 6-WAY MOTOR PACK CONNECTOR. • USING J 39200, MEASURE THE RESISTANCE BETWEEN TERMINAL "A" AND TERMINAL "B" OF THE 8-WAY EBCM HARNESS CONNECTOR. DOES J 39200 DISPLAY RESISTANCE AS "OL" (INFINITE)?
8 • USING TECH 1 MISC. TESTS, PERFORM GEAR TENSION RELIEF FUNCTION. • IGNITION "OFF." • REMOVE HYDRAULIC MODULATOR/MASTER CYLINDER ASSEMBLY FROM VEHICLE. REFER TO "ON VEHICLE SERVICE" IN THIS SECTION. • SEPARATE ABS MOTOR PACK FROM HYDRAULIC MODULATOR. • GRASP THE GEAR ON THE HYDRAULIC MODULATOR (THE HYDRAULIC MODULATOR IS THE UNIT WITH THE THREE LARGE GEARS) FURTHEST FORWARD WHEN THE UNIT IS INSTALLED IN THE VEHICLE AND ATTEMPT TO MOVE THE GEAR. CAN THE GEAR BE ROTATED AT LEAST 10 FULL TURNS LOCK TO LOCK?
YES
NO
5 • MEASURE THE RESISTANCE BETWEEN TERMINAL "E" AND TERMINAL "F" OF THE ABS MOTOR PACK CONNECTOR IS RESISTANCE 0.4Ω OR GREATER?
REPAIR SHORT BETWEEN CKT 1280 AND CKT 1281.
YES
NO
REPLACE ABS MOTOR PACK.
6 • IGNITION "OFF." • RECONNECT ALL CONNECTORS. • START ENGINE WITH FOOT OFF BRAKE. • ALLOW ENGINE TO RUN FOR AT LEAST 10 SECONDS. • REPEAT ABOVE IGNITION CYCLE SEQUENCE TWO MORE TIMES. DID DTC 44 SET IN THE LAST THREE IGNITION CYCLES?
NO
YES
REPLACE HYDRAULIC MODULATOR.
REPLACE ABS MOTOR PACK.
YES
NO
REPLACE EBCM.
MALFUNCTION IS INTERMITTENT. INSPECT ALL CONNECTORS FOR CONTAMINATION AND POOR TERMINAL CONTACT. REPLACE ANY TERMINALS THAT EXHIBIT POOR TERMINAL CONTACT OR EVIDENCE OF CORROSION.

GC402940108800EX

Fig. 260 Code A044: Left Front Channel Will Not Move. 1993–94 Camaro & Firebird, 1994 Grand Prix, Century & Cutlass Ciera & Cruiser

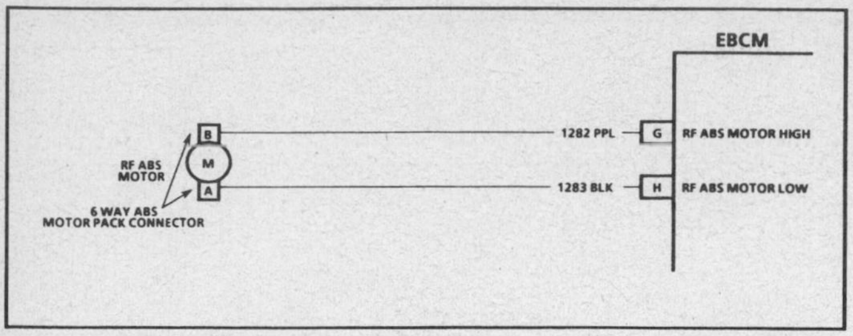
EBCM
1282 PPL
G
RF ABS MOTOR HIGH
1283 BLK
H
RF ABS MOTOR LOW
B
M
A
RF ABS MOTOR
6 WAY ABS MOTOR PACK CONNECTOR

GC402940108900AX

Grand Prix

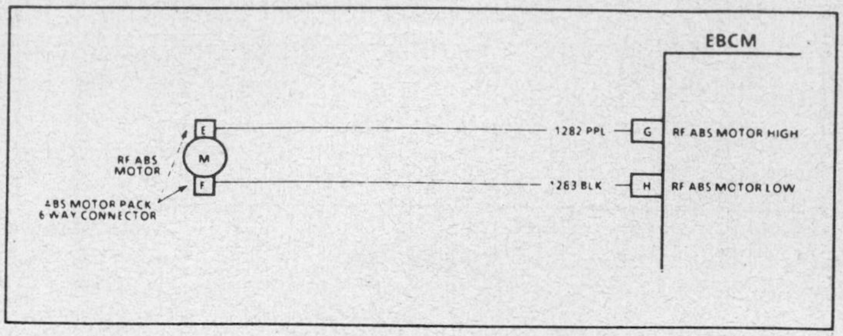
EBCM
1282 PPL
G
RF ABS MOTOR HIGH
1283 BLK
H
RF ABS MOTOR LOW
E
M
F
RF ABS MOTOR
ABS MOTOR PACK 6 WAY CONNECTOR

GC402940108201BX

Camaro & Firebird

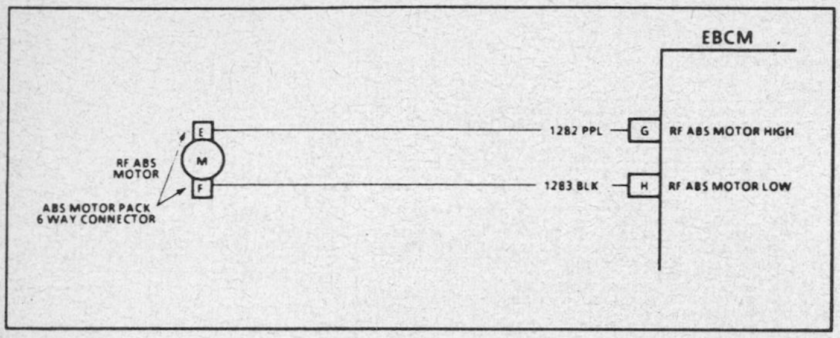
EBCM
1282 PPL
G
RF ABS MOTOR HIGH
1283 BLK
H
RF ABS MOTOR LOW
E
M
F
RF ABS MOTOR
ABS MOTOR PACK 6 WAY CONNECTOR

GC402940108900CX

Century & Cutlass Ciera & Cruiser

DTC 45

RIGHT FRONT CHANNEL WILL NOT MOVE

Circuit Description:

This DTC is designed to detect bound-up ESB, a stuck ABS motor, or a seized hydraulic modulator. When the release is commanded during initialization, the ESB should release the ABS motor, resulting in sensed current being less than commanded current (motor is spinning freely). If the ABS motor is not moving, sensed current will be equal to stall current.

DTC Will Set When: DTC 45 can be set during normal operation. If the EBCM detects a condition in which it cannot move the motor in either direction, a malfunction exists.

Action Taken: This malfunction indicates the channel cannot be moved properly. A malfunction DTC is stored, ABS is disabled and the ABS warning lamp is turned "ON."

DTC Chart Test Description: Number(s) below refer to circled number(s) on the diagnostic chart.

1. Ensures that proper motor circuits are located in the proper connector cavities.
2. Checks for proper ABS motor movement during apply and release commands from the Tech 1.
3. Compares EBCM command current to ABS motor feedback current.
4. Checks for a short between CKT 1282 and CKT 1283.
5. Checks for an ABS motor that is internally shorted.
6. Checks to see if malfunction is due to poor terminal contact or the EBCM.
7. Verifies that the motor can actually apply when commanded.
8. Checks for proper hydraulic modulator gear and piston movement.

Diagnostic Aids: An "Intermittent" malfunction in this DTC may result from a mechanical part of the system that sticks, binds, or slips.

The frequency of the malfunction can be checked by using the enhanced diagnostic function of the Tech 1,

DTC 45 may set after modulator disassembly if the modulator pistons are positioned at the bottom of their bore.

Any circuitry, that is suspected as causing the intermittent complaint, should be thoroughly checked for backed out terminals, improper mating, broken locks, improperly formed or damaged terminals, poor terminal to wiring connections or physical damage to the wiring harness.

GC402940108900DX

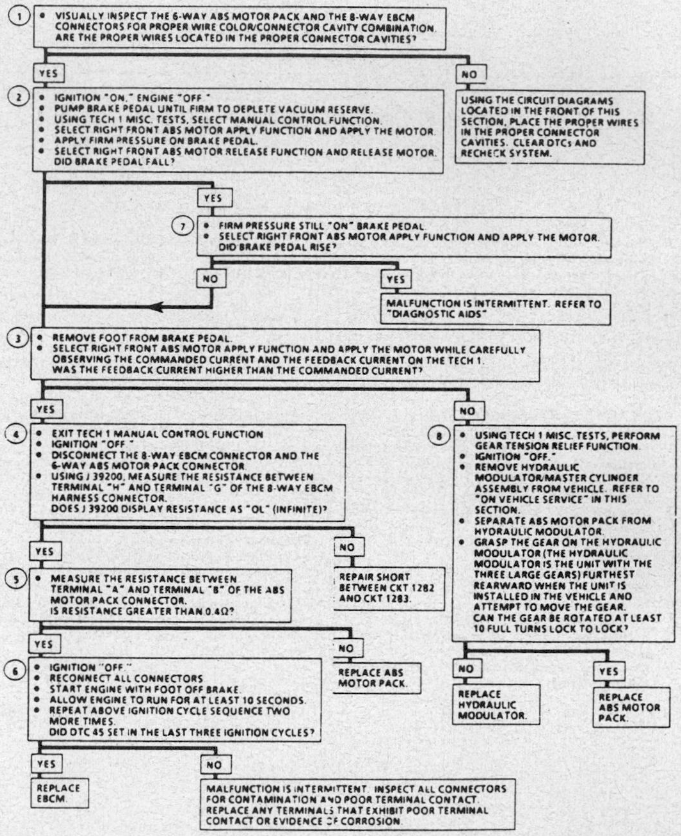
1
• VISUALLY INSPECT THE 6-WAY ABS MOTOR PACK AND THE 8-WAY EBCM CONNECTORS FOR PROPER WIRE COLOR/CONNECTOR CAVITY COMBINATION. ARE THE PROPER WIRES LOCATED IN THE PROPER CONNECTOR CAVITIES?
YES
NO
USING THE CIRCUIT DIAGRAMS LOCATED IN THE FRONT OF THIS SECTION, PLACE THE PROPER WIRES IN THE PROPER CONNECTOR CAVITIES. CLEAR DTCs AND RECHECK SYSTEM.
2
• IGNITION "ON," ENGINE "OFF."
• PUMP BRAKE PEDAL UNTIL FIRM TO DEPLETE VACUUM RESERVE.
• USING TECH 1 MISC. TESTS, SELECT MANUAL CONTROL FUNCTION.
• SELECT RIGHT FRONT ABS MOTOR APPLY FUNCTION AND APPLY THE MOTOR.
• APPLY FIRM PRESSURE ON BRAKE PEDAL.
• SELECT RIGHT FRONT ABS MOTOR RELEASE FUNCTION AND RELEASE MOTOR. DID BRAKE PEDAL FALL?
YES
7
• FIRM PRESSURE STILL "ON" BRAKE PEDAL.
• SELECT RIGHT FRONT ABS MOTOR APPLY FUNCTION AND APPLY THE MOTOR. DID BRAKE PEDAL RISE?
NO
YES
MALFUNCTION IS INTERMITTENT. REFER TO "DIAGNOSTIC AIDS"
3
• REMOVE FOOT FROM BRAKE PEDAL.
• SELECT RIGHT FRONT ABS MOTOR APPLY FUNCTION AND APPLY THE MOTOR WHILE CAREFULLY OBSERVING THE COMMANDED CURRENT AND THE FEEDBACK CURRENT ON THE TECH 1. WAS THE FEEDBACK CURRENT HIGHER THAN THE COMMANDED CURRENT?
YES
NO
4
• EXIT TECH 1 MANUAL CONTROL FUNCTION
• IGNITION "OFF."
• DISCONNECT THE 8-WAY EBCM CONNECTOR AND THE 6-WAY ABS MOTOR PACK CONNECTOR.
• USING J 39200, MEASURE THE RESISTANCE BETWEEN TERMINAL "H" AND TERMINAL "G" OF THE 8-WAY EBCM HARNESS CONNECTOR. DOES J 39200 DISPLAY RESISTANCE AS "OL" (INFINITE)?
8
• USING TECH 1 MISC. TESTS, PERFORM GEAR TENSION RELIEF FUNCTION.
• IGNITION "OFF."
• REMOVE HYDRAULIC MODULATOR/MASTER CYLINDER ASSEMBLY FROM VEHICLE. REFER TO "ON VEHICLE SERVICE" IN THIS SECTION.
• SEPARATE ABS MOTOR PACK FROM HYDRAULIC MODULATOR.
• GRASP THE GEAR ON THE HYDRAULIC MODULATOR (THE HYDRAULIC MODULATOR IS THE UNIT WITH THE THREE LARGE GEARS) FURTHEST REARWARD WHEN THE UNIT IS INSTALLED IN THE VEHICLE AND ATTEMPT TO MOVE THE GEAR. CAN THE GEAR BE ROTATED AT LEAST 10 FULL TURNS LOCK TO LOCK?
YES
NO
REPAIR SHORT BETWEEN CKT 1282 AND CKT 1283.
5
• MEASURE THE RESISTANCE BETWEEN TERMINAL "A" AND TERMINAL "B" OF THE ABS MOTOR PACK CONNECTOR. IS RESISTANCE GREATER THAN 0.4Ω?
YES
NO
REPLACE ABS MOTOR PACK.
NO
REPLACE HYDRAULIC MODULATOR.
YES
REPLACE ABS MOTOR PACK.
6
• IGNITION "OFF."
• RECONNECT ALL CONNECTORS
• START ENGINE WITH FOOT OFF BRAKE.
• ALLOW ENGINE TO RUN FOR AT LEAST 10 SECONDS.
• REPEAT ABOVE IGNITION CYCLE SEQUENCE TWO MORE TIMES. DID DTC 45 SET IN THE LAST THREE IGNITION CYCLES?
YES
REPLACE EBCM.
NO
MALFUNCTION IS INTERMITTENT. INSPECT ALL CONNECTORS FOR CONTAMINATION AND POOR TERMINAL CONTACT. REPLACE ANY TERMINALS THAT EXHIBIT POOR TERMINAL CONTACT OR EVIDENCE OF CORROSION.

GC402940108900EX

Fig. 261 Code A045: Right Front Channel Will Not Move. 1993–94 Camaro & Firebird, 1994 Grand Prix, Century & Cutlass Ciera & Cruiser

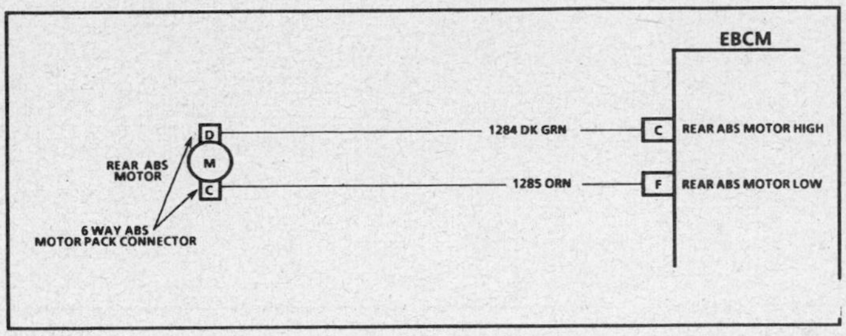
EBCM
REAR ABS MOTOR
M
D
C
6 WAY ABS MOTOR PACK CONNECTOR
1284 DK GRN
1285 ORN
C
F
REAR ABS MOTOR HIGH
REAR ABS MOTOR LOW

GC402940109000AX

Grand Prix

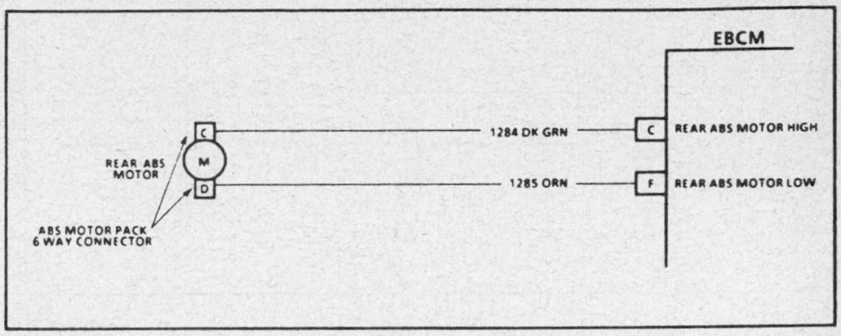
EBCM
REAR ABS MOTOR
M
C
D
ABS MOTOR PACK 6 WAY CONNECTOR
1284 DK GRN
1285 ORN
C
F
REAR ABS MOTOR HIGH
REAR ABS MOTOR LOW

GC402940109000BX

Camaro & Firebird

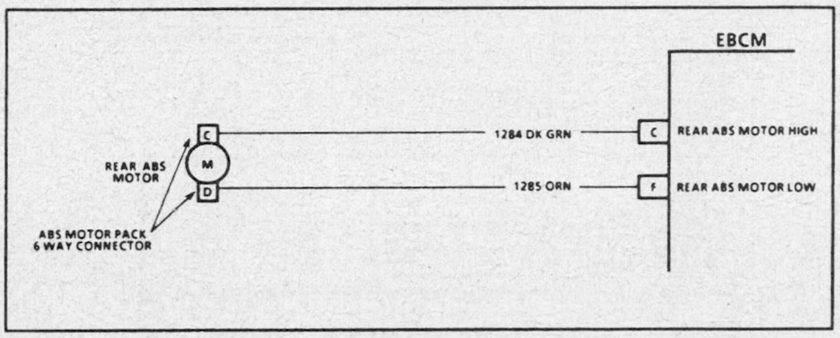
EBCM
REAR ABS MOTOR
M
C
D
ABS MOTOR PACK 6 WAY CONNECTOR
1284 DK GRN
1285 ORN
C
F
REAR ABS MOTOR HIGH
REAR ABS MOTOR LOW

GC402940109000CX

Century & Cutlass Ciera & Cruiser

DTC 46

REAR CHANNEL WILL NOT MOVE

Circuit Description:

This DTC is designed to detect bound-up ESB, a stuck ABS motor, or a seized hydraulic modulator. When the release is commanded during initialization, the ESB should release the ABS motor, resulting in sensed current being less than commanded current (motor is spinning freely). If the ABS motor is not moving, sensed current will be equal to stall current.

DTC Will Set When: DTC 46 can be set during normal operation. If the EBCM detects a condition in which it cannot move the ABS motor in either direction, a malfunction exists.

Action Taken. This malfunction indicates the channel cannot be moved properly. A malfunction DTC is stored, ABS is disabled and the ABS warning lamp is turned "ON."

DTC Chart Test Description: Number(s) below refer to circled number(s) on the diagnostic chart.

1. Ensures that proper motor circuits are located in the proper connector cavities.
2. Checks for proper motor movement during apply and release commands from the Tech 1.
3. Compares EBCM command current to ABS motor feedback current.
4. Checks for a short between CKT 1284 and CKT 1285.
5. Checks for an ABS motor that is internally shorted.
6. Checks to see if malfunction is due to poor terminal contact or the EBCM.
7. Verifies that the motor can actually release when commanded.
8. Checks for proper hydraulic modulator gear and piston movement.

Diagnostic Aids: An "Intermittent" malfunction in this DTC may result from a mechanical part of the system that sticks or binds.

The frequency of the malfunction can be checked by using the enhanced diagnostic function of the Tech 1. ...

DTC 46 may set after modulator disassembly if the modulator pistons are positioned at the bottom of their bore.

Depending on the frequency of the malfunction, a physical inspection of the mechanical parts suspected may be necessary.

Any circuitry, that is suspected as causing the intermittent complaint, should be thoroughly checked for backed out terminals, improper mating, broken locks, improperly formed or damaged terminals, poor terminal to wiring connections or physical damage to the wiring harness.

GC402940109000DX

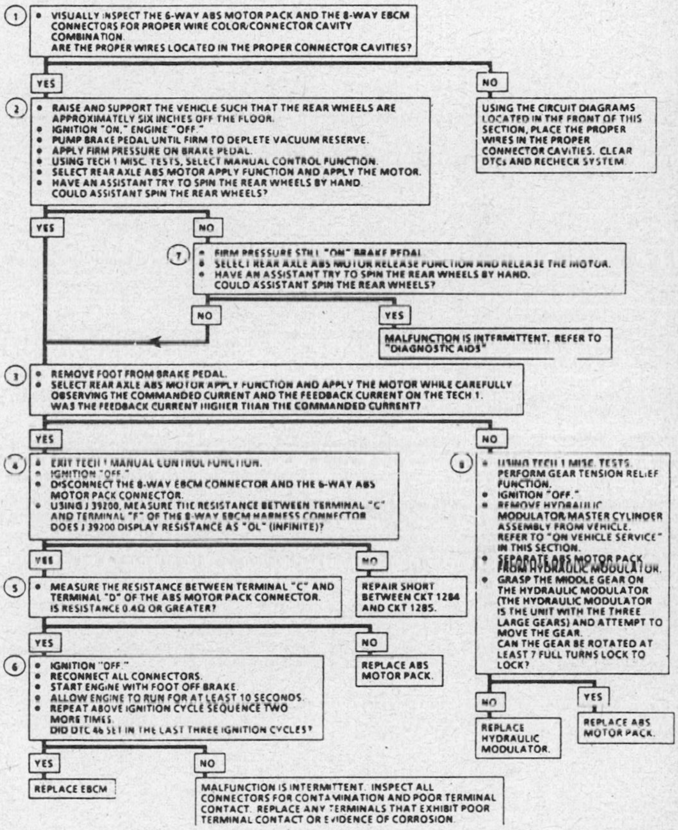
1
VISUALLY INSPECT THE 6-WAY ABS MOTOR PACK AND THE 8-WAY EBCM CONNECTORS FOR PROPER WIRE COLOR/CONNECTOR CAVITY COMBINATION.
ARE THE PROPER WIRES LOCATED IN THE PROPER CONNECTOR CAVITIES?
YES
NO
USING THE CIRCUIT DIAGRAMS LOCATED IN THE FRONT OF THIS SECTION, PLACE THE PROPER WIRES IN THE PROPER CONNECTOR CAVITIES. CLEAR DTCs AND RECHECK SYSTEM.
2
RAISE AND SUPPORT THE VEHICLE SUCH THAT THE REAR WHEELS ARE APPROXIMATELY SIX INCHES OFF THE FLOOR.
IGNITION "ON," ENGINE "OFF."
PUMP BRAKE PEDAL UNTIL FIRM TO DEPLETE VACUUM RESERVE.
APPLY FIRM PRESSURE ON BRAKE PEDAL.
USING TECH 1 MISC. TESTS, SELECT MANUAL CONTROL FUNCTION.
SELECT REAR AXLE ABS MOTOR APPLY FUNCTION AND APPLY THE MOTOR.
HAVE AN ASSISTANT TRY TO SPIN THE REAR WHEELS BY HAND.
COULD ASSISTANT SPIN THE REAR WHEELS?
YES
NO
7
FIRM PRESSURE STILL "ON" BRAKE PEDAL.
SELECT REAR AXLE ABS MOTOR RELEASE FUNCTION AND RELEASE THE MOTOR.
HAVE AN ASSISTANT TRY TO SPIN THE REAR WHEELS BY HAND.
COULD ASSISTANT SPIN THE REAR WHEELS?
NO
YES
MALFUNCTION IS INTERMITTENT. REFER TO "DIAGNOSTIC AIDS"
3
REMOVE FOOT FROM BRAKE PEDAL.
SELECT REAR AXLE ABS MOTOR APPLY FUNCTION AND APPLY THE MOTOR WHILE CAREFULLY OBSERVING THE COMMANDED CURRENT AND THE FEEDBACK CURRENT ON THE TECH 1.
WAS THE FEEDBACK CURRENT HIGHER THAN THE COMMANDED CURRENT?
YES
NO
4
EXIT TECH 1 MANUAL CONTROL FUNCTION.
IGNITION "OFF."
DISCONNECT THE 8-WAY EBCM CONNECTOR AND THE 6-WAY ABS MOTOR PACK CONNECTOR.
USING J 39200, MEASURE THE RESISTANCE BETWEEN TERMINAL "C" AND TERMINAL "F" OF THE 8-WAY EBCM HARNESS CONNECTOR.
DOES J 39200 DISPLAY RESISTANCE AS "OL" (INFINITE)?
8
USING TECH 1 MISC. TESTS, PERFORM GEAR TENSION RELIEF FUNCTION.
IGNITION "OFF."
REMOVE HYDRAULIC MODULATOR/MASTER CYLINDER ASSEMBLY FROM VEHICLE. REFER TO "ON VEHICLE SERVICE" IN THIS SECTION.
SEPARATE ABS MOTOR PACK FROM HYDRAULIC MODULATOR.
GRASP THE MIDDLE GEAR ON THE HYDRAULIC MODULATOR (THE HYDRAULIC MODULATOR IS THE UNIT WITH THE THREE LARGE GEARS) AND ATTEMPT TO MOVE THE GEAR.
CAN THE GEAR BE ROTATED AT LEAST 7 FULL TURNS LOCK TO LOCK?
YES
NO
5
MEASURE THE RESISTANCE BETWEEN TERMINAL "C" AND TERMINAL "D" OF THE ABS MOTOR PACK CONNECTOR.
IS RESISTANCE 0.4Ω OR GREATER?
REPAIR SHORT BETWEEN CKT 1284 AND CKT 1285.
YES
NO
REPLACE ABS MOTOR PACK.
6
IGNITION "OFF."
RECONNECT ALL CONNECTORS.
START ENGINE WITH FOOT OFF BRAKE.
ALLOW ENGINE TO RUN FOR AT LEAST 10 SECONDS.
REPEAT ABOVE IGNITION CYCLE SEQUENCE TWO MORE TIMES.
DID DTC 46 SET IN THE LAST THREE IGNITION CYCLES?
NO
YES
REPLACE HYDRAULIC MODULATOR.
REPLACE ABS MOTOR PACK.
YES
NO
REPLACE EBCM
MALFUNCTION IS INTERMITTENT. INSPECT ALL CONNECTORS FOR CONTAMINATION AND POOR TERMINAL CONTACT. REPLACE ANY TERMINALS THAT EXHIBIT POOR TERMINAL CONTACT OR EVIDENCE OF CORROSION.

GC402940109000EX

Fig. 262 Code A046: Rear Channel Will Not Move. 1993–94 Camaro & Firebird, 1994 Grand Prix, Century & Cutlass Ciera & Cruiser

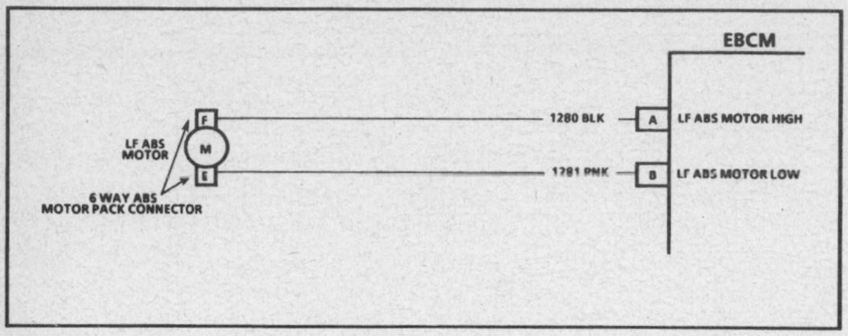
EBCM
LF ABS MOTOR
6 WAY ABS MOTOR PACK CONNECTOR
M
F
E
1280 BLK
1281 PNK
A
B
LF ABS MOTOR HIGH
LF ABS MOTOR LOW

GC402940109101AX

Grand Prix

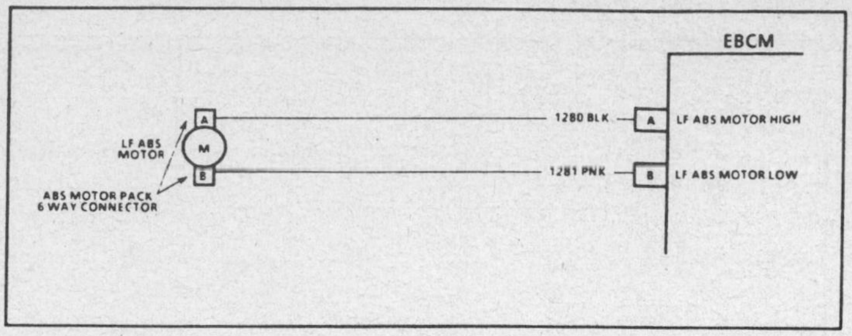
EBCM
LF ABS MOTOR
ABS MOTOR PACK 6 WAY CONNECTOR
M
A
B
1280 BLK
1281 PNK
A
B
LF ABS MOTOR HIGH
LF ABS MOTOR LOW

GC402940109101BX

Camaro & Firebird

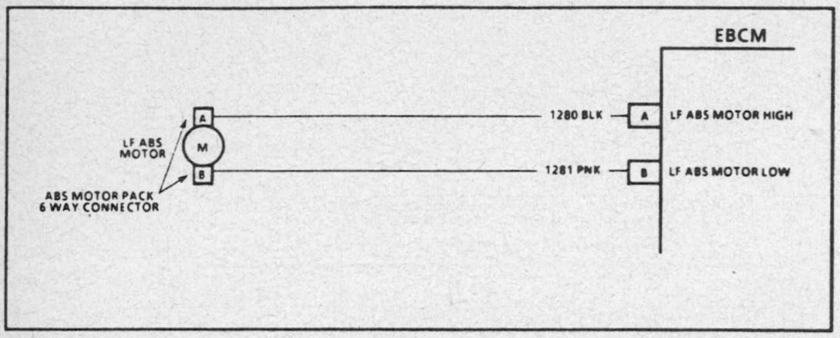
EBCM
LF ABS MOTOR
ABS MOTOR PACK 6 WAY CONNECTOR
M
A
B
1280 BLK
1281 PNK
A
B
LF ABS MOTOR HIGH
LF ABS MOTOR LOW

GC402940109101CX

Century & Cutlass Ciera & Cruiser

DTC 47
(Page 1 of 2)
LEFT FRONT ABS MOTOR FREE SPINS

Circuit Description:

This DTC is designed to detect a stripped nut or gear assembly during initialization. During the homing sequence, the piston should reach the top of the bore resulting in a stalled ABS motor. If this does not occur, the ABS motor must be spinning with little or no resistance, indicating a nut/screw or gear malfunction.

DTC Will Set When: DTC 47 can only be set during initialization. If the feedback current is less than the command current for a specified period of time, a malfunction exists.

Action Taken: A malfunction DTC is stored, ABS is disabled, and the ABS warning lamp is turned "ON."

DTC Chart Test Description: Number(s) below refer to circled number(s) on the diagnostic chart.

1. Checks to see if the corresponding open motor DTC is also set.
2. Verifies that the ABS motor was actually applied as command by observing feedback current.
3. Verifies that the ABS motor can release.
4. Verifies that the ABS motor can be applied by observing pedal movement.
5. Checks for an open in the ABS motor "HIGH" circuitry.
6. Checks for an open in the ABS motor "LOW" circuitry.
7. Checks for an ABS motor that is internally shorted.

Diagnostic Aids: An "Intermittent" malfunction in this DTC may result from a mechanical part of the system that sticks, binds, or slips.

The frequency of the malfunction can be checked by using the enhanced diagnostic function of the Tech 1,

If the DTC only occurs once and DTC 56 also occurs, refer to DTC 56. If intermittent and enhanced diagnostics shows this DTC occurs during ABS, refer to DTC 56.

Depending on the frequency of the malfunction, a physical inspection of the mechanical parts suspected may be necessary.

GC402940109101DX

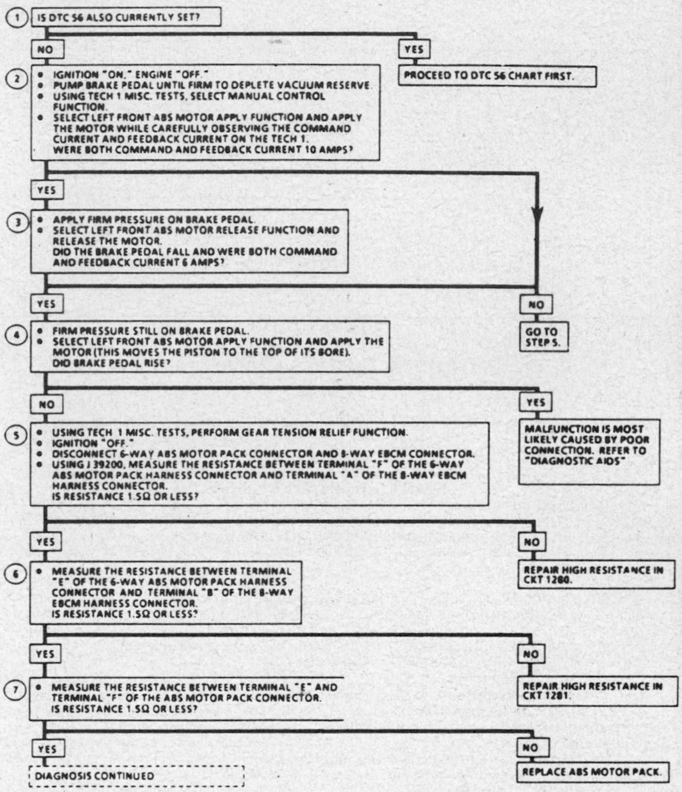
1
IS DTC 56 ALSO CURRENTLY SET?
NO
YES
PROCEED TO DTC 56 CHART FIRST.
2
• IGNITION "ON," ENGINE "OFF."
• PUMP BRAKE PEDAL UNTIL FIRM TO DEPLETE VACUUM RESERVE.
• USING TECH 1 MISC. TESTS, SELECT MANUAL CONTROL FUNCTION.
• SELECT LEFT FRONT ABS MOTOR APPLY FUNCTION AND APPLY THE MOTOR WHILE CAREFULLY OBSERVING THE COMMAND CURRENT AND FEEDBACK CURRENT ON THE TECH 1.
WERE BOTH COMMAND AND FEEDBACK CURRENT 10 AMPS?
YES
3
• APPLY FIRM PRESSURE ON BRAKE PEDAL.
• SELECT LEFT FRONT ABS MOTOR RELEASE FUNCTION AND RELEASE THE MOTOR.
DID THE BRAKE PEDAL FALL AND WERE BOTH COMMAND AND FEEDBACK CURRENT 6 AMPS?
YES
NO
GO TO STEP 5.
4
• FIRM PRESSURE STILL ON BRAKE PEDAL.
• SELECT LEFT FRONT ABS MOTOR APPLY FUNCTION AND APPLY THE MOTOR (THIS MOVES THE PISTON TO THE TOP OF ITS BORE).
DID BRAKE PEDAL RISE?
NO
YES
MALFUNCTION IS MOST LIKELY CAUSED BY POOR CONNECTION. REFER TO "DIAGNOSTIC AIDS"
5
• USING TECH 1 MISC. TESTS, PERFORM GEAR TENSION RELIEF FUNCTION.
• IGNITION "OFF."
• DISCONNECT 6-WAY ABS MOTOR PACK CONNECTOR AND 8-WAY EBCM CONNECTOR.
• USING J 39200, MEASURE THE RESISTANCE BETWEEN TERMINAL "F" OF THE 6-WAY ABS MOTOR PACK HARNESS CONNECTOR AND TERMINAL "A" OF THE 8-WAY EBCM HARNESS CONNECTOR.
IS RESISTANCE 1.5Ω OR LESS?
YES
NO
REPAIR HIGH RESISTANCE IN CKT 1280.
6
• MEASURE THE RESISTANCE BETWEEN TERMINAL "E" OF THE 6-WAY ABS MOTOR PACK HARNESS CONNECTOR AND TERMINAL "B" OF THE 8-WAY EBCM HARNESS CONNECTOR.
IS RESISTANCE 1.5Ω OR LESS?
YES
NO
REPAIR HIGH RESISTANCE IN CKT 1281.
7
• MEASURE THE RESISTANCE BETWEEN TERMINAL "E" AND TERMINAL "F" OF THE ABS MOTOR PACK CONNECTOR.
IS RESISTANCE 1.5Ω OR LESS?
YES
NO
DIAGNOSIS CONTINUED
REPLACE ABS MOTOR PACK.

GC402940109101EX

Fig. 263 Code A047: Left Front ABS Motor Free Spins (Part 1 of 2). 1993–94 Camaro & Firebird, 1994 Grand Prix, Century & Cutlass Ciera & Cruiser

DTC 47

(Page 2 of 2)

LEFT FRONT ABS MOTOR FREE SPINS

Circuit Description:

This DTC is designed to detect a stripped nut or gear assembly during initialization. During the homing sequence, the piston should reach the top of the bore resulting in a stalled ABS motor. If this does not occur, the ABS motor must be spinning with little or no resistance, indicating a nut/screw or gear malfunction.

DTC Will Set When: DTC 47 can only be set during initialization. If the feedback current is less than the command current for a specified period of time, a malfunction exists.

Action Taken: A malfunction DTC is stored, ABS is disabled, and the ABS warning lamp is turned "ON."

DTC Chart Test Description: Number(s) below refer to circled number(s) on the diagnostic chart.

8. Checks for a stripped gear on the ABS motor pack (unit with three small gears).
9. Checks for a stripped gear on the hydraulic modulator (unit with three large gears).
10. Checks to see if the ABS motor pack has an internal malfunction.
11. Checks for a malfunctioning hydraulic modulator.
12. Ensures malfunction was not due to poor terminal contact.

Diagnostic Aids: An "Intermittent" malfunction in this DTC may result from a mechanical part of the system that sticks, binds, or slips.

The frequency of the malfunction can be checked by using the enhanced diagnostic function of the Tech 1,

If the DTC only occurs once and DTC 56 also occurs, refer to DTC 56. If intermittent and enhanced diagnostics shows this DTC occurs during ABS, refer to DTC 56.

Depending on the frequency of the malfunction, a physical inspection of the mechanical parts suspected may be necessary.

GC402940109102AX

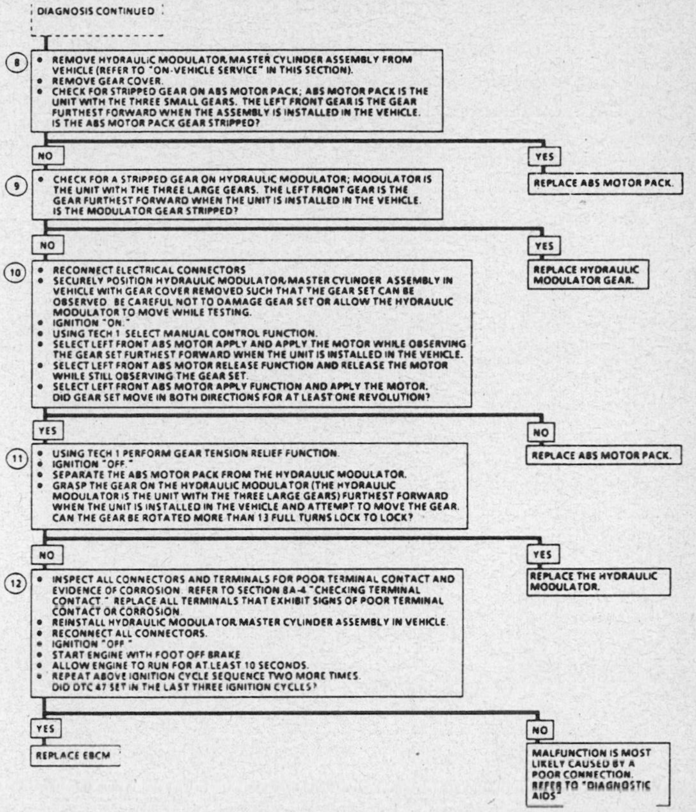
DIAGNOSIS CONTINUED
8
• REMOVE HYDRAULIC MODULATOR/MASTER CYLINDER ASSEMBLY FROM VEHICLE (REFER TO "ON-VEHICLE SERVICE" IN THIS SECTION).
• REMOVE GEAR COVER.
• CHECK FOR STRIPPED GEAR ON ABS MOTOR PACK; ABS MOTOR PACK IS THE UNIT WITH THE THREE SMALL GEARS. THE LEFT FRONT GEAR IS THE GEAR FURTHEST FORWARD WHEN THE ASSEMBLY IS INSTALLED IN THE VEHICLE. IS THE ABS MOTOR PACK GEAR STRIPPED?
NO
YES
REPLACE ABS MOTOR PACK.
9
• CHECK FOR A STRIPPED GEAR ON HYDRAULIC MODULATOR; MODULATOR IS THE UNIT WITH THE THREE LARGE GEARS. THE LEFT FRONT GEAR IS THE GEAR FURTHEST FORWARD WHEN THE UNIT IS INSTALLED IN THE VEHICLE. IS THE MODULATOR GEAR STRIPPED?
NO
YES
REPLACE HYDRAULIC MODULATOR GEAR.
10
• RECONNECT ELECTRICAL CONNECTORS
• SECURELY POSITION HYDRAULIC MODULATOR/MASTER CYLINDER ASSEMBLY IN VEHICLE WITH GEAR COVER REMOVED SUCH THAT THE GEAR SET CAN BE OBSERVED. BE CAREFUL NOT TO DAMAGE GEAR SET OR ALLOW THE HYDRAULIC MODULATOR TO MOVE WHILE TESTING.
• IGNITION "ON."
• USING TECH 1 SELECT MANUAL CONTROL FUNCTION.
• SELECT LEFT FRONT ABS MOTOR APPLY AND APPLY THE MOTOR WHILE OBSERVING THE GEAR SET FURTHEST FORWARD WHEN THE UNIT IS INSTALLED IN THE VEHICLE.
• SELECT LEFT FRONT ABS MOTOR RELEASE FUNCTION AND RELEASE THE MOTOR WHILE STILL OBSERVING THE GEAR SET.
• SELECT LEFT FRONT ABS MOTOR APPLY FUNCTION AND APPLY THE MOTOR. DID GEAR SET MOVE IN BOTH DIRECTIONS FOR AT LEAST ONE REVOLUTION?
YES
NO
REPLACE ABS MOTOR PACK.
11
• USING TECH 1 PERFORM GEAR TENSION RELIEF FUNCTION.
• IGNITION "OFF."
• SEPARATE THE ABS MOTOR PACK FROM THE HYDRAULIC MODULATOR.
• GRASP THE GEAR ON THE HYDRAULIC MODULATOR (THE HYDRAULIC MODULATOR IS THE UNIT WITH THE THREE LARGE GEARS) FURTHEST FORWARD WHEN THE UNIT IS INSTALLED IN THE VEHICLE AND ATTEMPT TO MOVE THE GEAR. CAN THE GEAR BE ROTATED MORE THAN 13 FULL TURNS LOCK TO LOCK?
NO
YES
REPLACE THE HYDRAULIC MODULATOR.
12
• INSPECT ALL CONNECTORS AND TERMINALS FOR POOR TERMINAL CONTACT AND EVIDENCE OF CORROSION. REFER TO SECTION 8A-4 "CHECKING TERMINAL CONTACT." REPLACE ALL TERMINALS THAT EXHIBIT SIGNS OF POOR TERMINAL CONTACT OR CORROSION.
• REINSTALL HYDRAULIC MODULATOR/MASTER CYLINDER ASSEMBLY IN VEHICLE.
• RECONNECT ALL CONNECTORS.
• IGNITION "OFF."
• START ENGINE WITH FOOT OFF BRAKE.
• ALLOW ENGINE TO RUN FOR AT LEAST 10 SECONDS.
• REPEAT ABOVE IGNITION CYCLE SEQUENCE TWO MORE TIMES. DID DTC 47 SET IN THE LAST THREE IGNITION CYCLES?
YES
REPLACE EBCM
NO
MALFUNCTION IS MOST LIKELY CAUSED BY A POOR CONNECTION. REFER TO "DIAGNOSTIC AIDS"

GC402940109102BX

Fig. 263 Code A047: Left Front ABS Motor Free Spins (Part 2 of 2). 1993–94 Camaro & Firebird, 1994 Grand Prix, Century & Cutlass Ciera & Cruiser

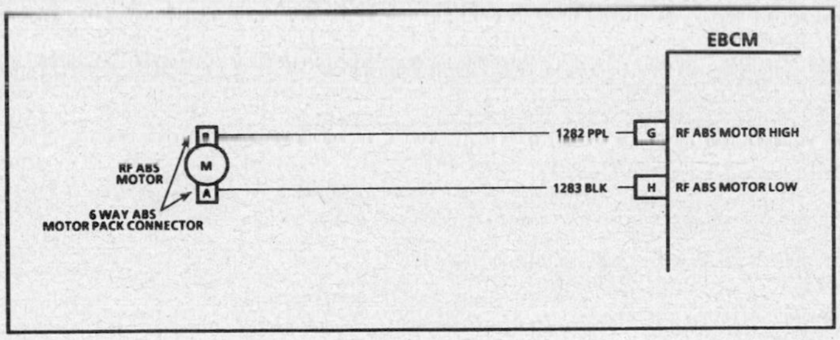
EBCM
B
M
A
RF ABS MOTOR
6 WAY ABS MOTOR PACK CONNECTOR
1282 PPL
G
RF ABS MOTOR HIGH
1283 BLK
H
RF ABS MOTOR LOW

GC402940109201AX

Grand Prix

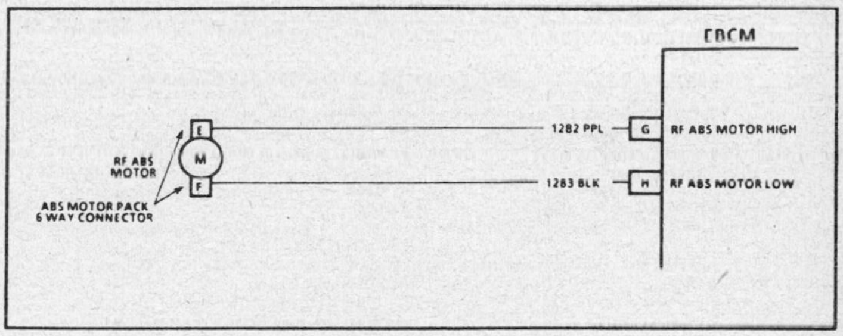
EBCM
E
M
F
RF ABS MOTOR
ABS MOTOR PACK 6 WAY CONNECTOR
1282 PPL
G
RF ABS MOTOR HIGH
1283 BLK
H
RF ABS MOTOR LOW

GC402940109201BX

Camaro & Firebird

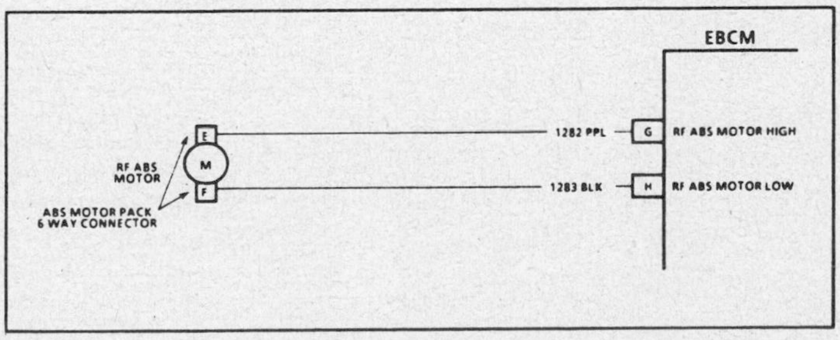
EBCM
E
M
F
RF ABS MOTOR
ABS MOTOR PACK 6 WAY CONNECTOR
1282 PPL
G
RF ABS MOTOR HIGH
1283 BLK
H
RF ABS MOTOR LOW

GC402940109201CX

Century & Cutlass Ciera & Cruiser

Fig. 264 Code A048: Right Front ABS Motor Free Spins (Part 1 of 2). 1993–94 Camaro & Firebird, 1994 Grand Prix, Century & Cutlass Ciera & Cruiser

DTC 48

RIGHT FRONT ABS MOTOR FREE SPINS

Circuit Description:
This DTC is designed to detect a stripped nut or gear assembly during initialization. During the homing sequence, the piston should reach the top of the bore resulting in a stalled ABS motor. If this does not occur, the ABS motor must be spinning with little or no resistance, indicating a nut/screw or gear malfunction.

DTC Will Set When: DTC 48 can only be set during initialization. If the feedback current is less than the command current for a specified period of time, a malfunction exists.

Action Taken: A malfunction DTC is stored, ABS is disabled, and the ABS warning lamp is turned "ON."

DTC Chart Test Description: Number(s) below refer to circled number(s) on the diagnostic chart.

1. Checks to see if the corresponding open ABS motor DTC is also set.
2. Verifies that the ABS motor was actually applied as commanded by observing feedback current.
3. Verifies that the ABS motor can release.
4. Verifies that the ABS motor can be applied by observing pedal movement.
5. Checks for high resistance in the ABS motor "HIGH" circuitry.
6. Checks for high resistance in the ABS motor "LOW" circuitry.
7. Checks for proper resistance of the ABS motor windings.

Diagnostic Aids: An "Intermittent" malfunction in this DTC may result from a mechanical part of the system that sticks, binds, or slips.

The frequency of the malfunction can be checked by using the enhanced diagnostic function of the Tech 1,

n. If the DTC only occurs once and DTC 61 also occurs, refer to DTC 61. If intermittent and enhanced diagnostics shows this DTC occurs during ABS, refer to DTC 61.

Depending on the frequency of the malfunction, a physical inspection of the mechanical parts suspected may be necessary.

GC402940109201DX

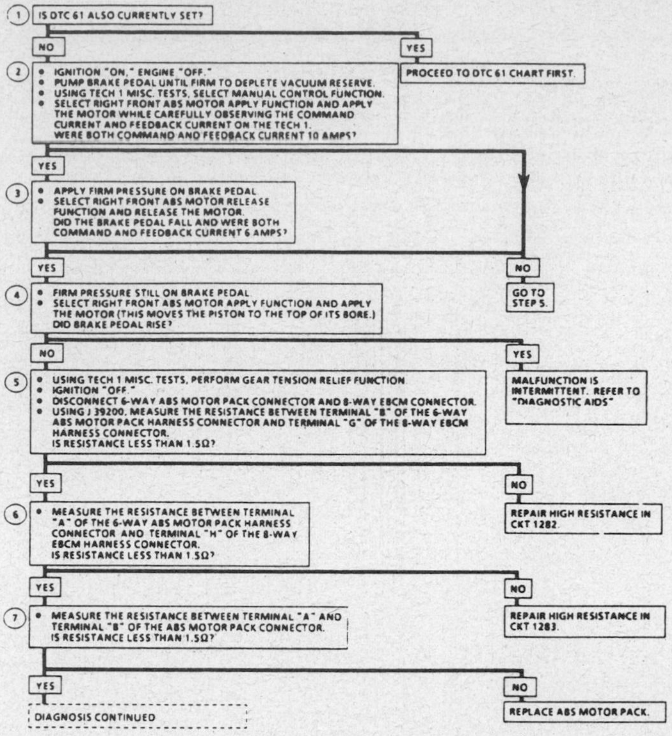
1
IS DTC 61 ALSO CURRENTLY SET?
NO
YES
PROCEED TO DTC 61 CHART FIRST.
2
• IGNITION "ON," ENGINE "OFF."
• PUMP BRAKE PEDAL UNTIL FIRM TO DEPLETE VACUUM RESERVE.
• USING TECH 1 MISC. TESTS, SELECT MANUAL CONTROL FUNCTION.
• SELECT RIGHT FRONT ABS MOTOR APPLY FUNCTION AND APPLY THE MOTOR WHILE CAREFULLY OBSERVING THE COMMAND CURRENT AND FEEDBACK CURRENT ON THE TECH 1.
WERE BOTH COMMAND AND FEEDBACK CURRENT 10 AMPS?
YES
3
• APPLY FIRM PRESSURE ON BRAKE PEDAL.
• SELECT RIGHT FRONT ABS MOTOR RELEASE FUNCTION AND RELEASE THE MOTOR.
DID THE BRAKE PEDAL FALL AND WERE BOTH COMMAND AND FEEDBACK CURRENT 6 AMPS?
YES
NO
GO TO STEP 5.
4
• FIRM PRESSURE STILL ON BRAKE PEDAL.
• SELECT RIGHT FRONT ABS MOTOR APPLY FUNCTION AND APPLY THE MOTOR (THIS MOVES THE PISTON TO THE TOP OF ITS BORE.)
DID BRAKE PEDAL RISE?
NO
YES
MALFUNCTION IS INTERMITTENT. REFER TO "DIAGNOSTIC AIDS"
5
• USING TECH 1 MISC. TESTS, PERFORM GEAR TENSION RELIEF FUNCTION.
• IGNITION "OFF."
• DISCONNECT 6-WAY ABS MOTOR PACK CONNECTOR AND 8-WAY EBCM CONNECTOR.
• USING J 39200, MEASURE THE RESISTANCE BETWEEN TERMINAL "B" OF THE 6-WAY ABS MOTOR PACK HARNESS CONNECTOR AND TERMINAL "G" OF THE 8-WAY EBCM HARNESS CONNECTOR.
IS RESISTANCE LESS THAN 1.5Ω?
YES
NO
REPAIR HIGH RESISTANCE IN CKT 1282.
6
• MEASURE THE RESISTANCE BETWEEN TERMINAL "A" OF THE 6-WAY ABS MOTOR PACK HARNESS CONNECTOR AND TERMINAL "H" OF THE 8-WAY EBCM HARNESS CONNECTOR.
IS RESISTANCE LESS THAN 1.5Ω?
YES
NO
REPAIR HIGH RESISTANCE IN CKT 1283.
7
• MEASURE THE RESISTANCE BETWEEN TERMINAL "A" AND TERMINAL "B" OF THE ABS MOTOR PACK CONNECTOR.
IS RESISTANCE LESS THAN 1.5Ω?
YES
NO
DIAGNOSIS CONTINUED
REPLACE ABS MOTOR PACK.

GC402940109201EX

DTC 48

RIGHT FRONT ABS MOTOR FREE SPINS

Circuit Description:
This DTC is designed to detect a stripped nut or gear assembly during initialization. During the homing sequence, the piston should reach the top of the bore resulting in a stalled ABS motor. If this does not occur, the ABS motor must be spinning with little or no resistance, indicating a nut/screw or gear malfunction.

DTC Will Set When: DTC 48 can only be set during initialization. If the feedback current is less than the command current for a specified period of time, a malfunction exists.

Action Taken: A malfunction DTC is stored, ABS is disabled, and the ABS warning lamp is turned "ON."

DTC Chart Test Description: Number(s) below refer to circled number(s) on the diagnostic chart.

8. Checks for a stripped gear on the ABS motor pack (unit with three small gears).
9. Checks for a stripped gear on the hydraulic modulator (unit with three large gears).
10. Verifies that the ABS motor can be applied under a load situation.
11. Verifies that the hydraulic modulator is functioning properly.
12. Ensures malfunction was not due to poor terminal contact.

Diagnostic Aids: An "Intermittent" malfunction in this DTC may result from a mechanical part of the system that sticks, binds, or slips.

The frequency of the malfunction can be checked by using the enhanced diagnostic function of the Tech 1,

If the DTC only occurs once and DTC 61 also occurs, refer to DTC 61. If intermittent and enhanced diagnostics shows this DTC occurs during ABS, refer to DTC 61.

Depending on the frequency of the malfunction, a physical inspection of the mechanical parts suspected may be necessary.

GC402940109202AX

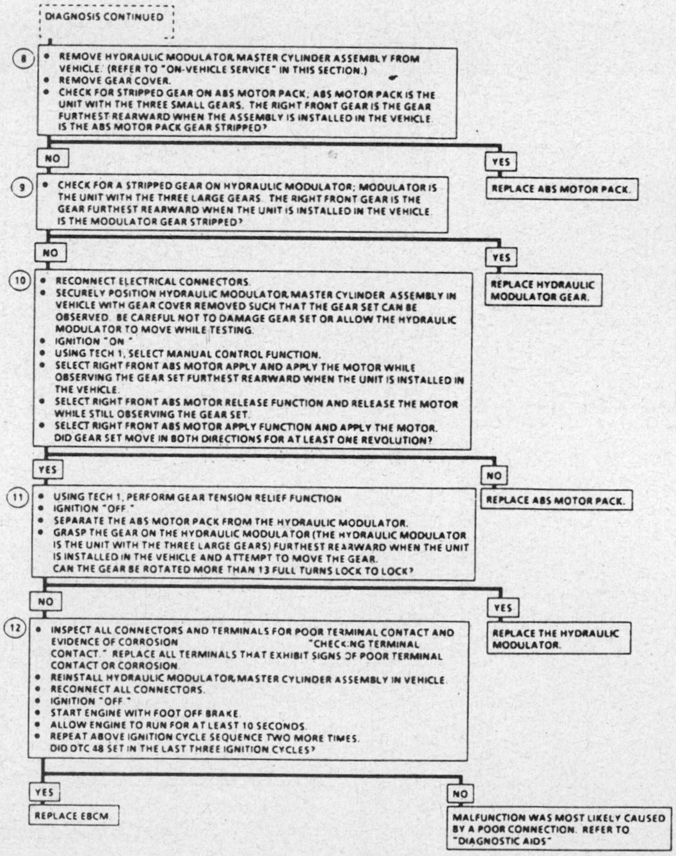
DIAGNOSIS CONTINUED
8
• REMOVE HYDRAULIC MODULATOR/MASTER CYLINDER ASSEMBLY FROM VEHICLE. (REFER TO "ON-VEHICLE SERVICE" IN THIS SECTION.)
• REMOVE GEAR COVER.
• CHECK FOR STRIPPED GEAR ON ABS MOTOR PACK; ABS MOTOR PACK IS THE UNIT WITH THE THREE SMALL GEARS. THE RIGHT FRONT GEAR IS THE GEAR FURTHEST REARWARD WHEN THE ASSEMBLY IS INSTALLED IN THE VEHICLE.
IS THE ABS MOTOR PACK GEAR STRIPPED?
NO
YES
REPLACE ABS MOTOR PACK.
9
• CHECK FOR A STRIPPED GEAR ON HYDRAULIC MODULATOR; MODULATOR IS THE UNIT WITH THE THREE LARGE GEARS. THE RIGHT FRONT GEAR IS THE GEAR FURTHEST REARWARD WHEN THE UNIT IS INSTALLED IN THE VEHICLE.
IS THE MODULATOR GEAR STRIPPED?
NO
YES
REPLACE HYDRAULIC MODULATOR GEAR.
10
• RECONNECT ELECTRICAL CONNECTORS.
• SECURELY POSITION HYDRAULIC MODULATOR/MASTER CYLINDER ASSEMBLY IN VEHICLE WITH GEAR COVER REMOVED SUCH THAT THE GEAR SET CAN BE OBSERVED. BE CAREFUL NOT TO DAMAGE GEAR SET OR ALLOW THE HYDRAULIC MODULATOR TO MOVE WHILE TESTING.
• IGNITION "ON."
• USING TECH 1, SELECT MANUAL CONTROL FUNCTION.
• SELECT RIGHT FRONT ABS MOTOR APPLY AND APPLY THE MOTOR WHILE OBSERVING THE GEAR SET FURTHEST REARWARD WHEN THE UNIT IS INSTALLED IN THE VEHICLE.
• SELECT RIGHT FRONT ABS MOTOR RELEASE FUNCTION AND RELEASE THE MOTOR WHILE STILL OBSERVING THE GEAR SET.
• SELECT RIGHT FRONT ABS MOTOR APPLY FUNCTION AND APPLY THE MOTOR.
DID GEAR SET MOVE IN BOTH DIRECTIONS FOR AT LEAST ONE REVOLUTION?
YES
NO
REPLACE ABS MOTOR PACK.
11
• USING TECH 1, PERFORM GEAR TENSION RELIEF FUNCTION
• IGNITION "OFF."
• SEPARATE THE ABS MOTOR PACK FROM THE HYDRAULIC MODULATOR.
• GRASP THE GEAR ON THE HYDRAULIC MODULATOR (THE HYDRAULIC MODULATOR IS THE UNIT WITH THE THREE LARGE GEARS) FURTHEST REARWARD WHEN THE UNIT IS INSTALLED IN THE VEHICLE AND ATTEMPT TO MOVE THE GEAR.
CAN THE GEAR BE ROTATED MORE THAN 13 FULL TURNS LOCK TO LOCK?
NO
YES
REPLACE THE HYDRAULIC MODULATOR.
12
• INSPECT ALL CONNECTORS AND TERMINALS FOR POOR TERMINAL CONTACT AND EVIDENCE OF CORROSION "CHECKING TERMINAL CONTACT." REPLACE ALL TERMINALS THAT EXHIBIT SIGNS OF POOR TERMINAL CONTACT OR CORROSION.
• REINSTALL HYDRAULIC MODULATOR/MASTER CYLINDER ASSEMBLY IN VEHICLE.
• RECONNECT ALL CONNECTORS.
• IGNITION "OFF."
• START ENGINE WITH FOOT OFF BRAKE.
• ALLOW ENGINE TO RUN FOR AT LEAST 10 SECONDS.
• REPEAT ABOVE IGNITION CYCLE SEQUENCE TWO MORE TIMES.
DID DTC 48 SET IN THE LAST THREE IGNITION CYCLES?
YES
NO
REPLACE EBCM.
MALFUNCTION WAS MOST LIKELY CAUSED BY A POOR CONNECTION. REFER TO "DIAGNOSTIC AIDS"

GC402940109202BX

Fig. 264 Code A047: Right Front ABS Motor Free Spins (Part 2 of 2). 1993–94 Camaro & Firebird, 1994 Grand Prix, Century & Cutlass Ciera & Cruiser

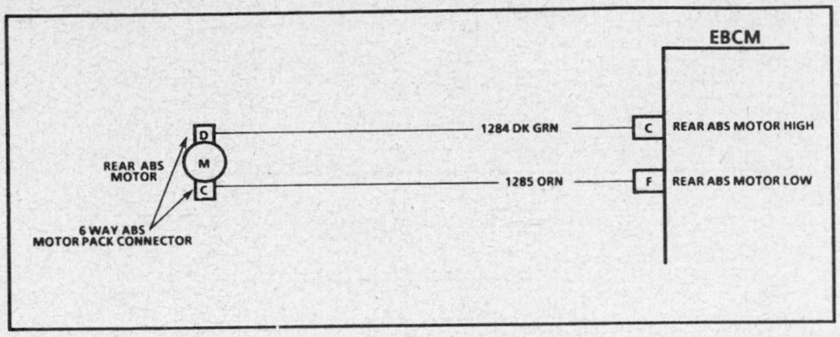
EBCM
REAR ABS MOTOR
1284 DK GRN
1285 ORN
REAR ABS MOTOR HIGH
REAR ABS MOTOR LOW
6 WAY ABS MOTOR PACK CONNECTOR

GC402940109301AX

Grand Prix

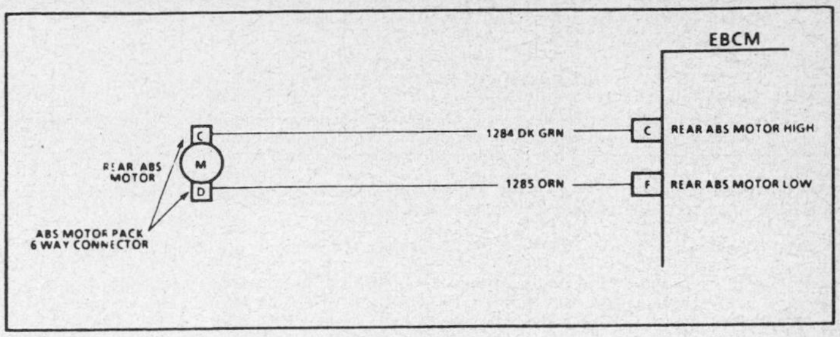
EBCM
REAR ABS MOTOR
1284 DK GRN
1285 ORN
REAR ABS MOTOR HIGH
REAR ABS MOTOR LOW
ABS MOTOR PACK 6 WAY CONNECTOR

GC402940109301BX

Camaro & Firebird

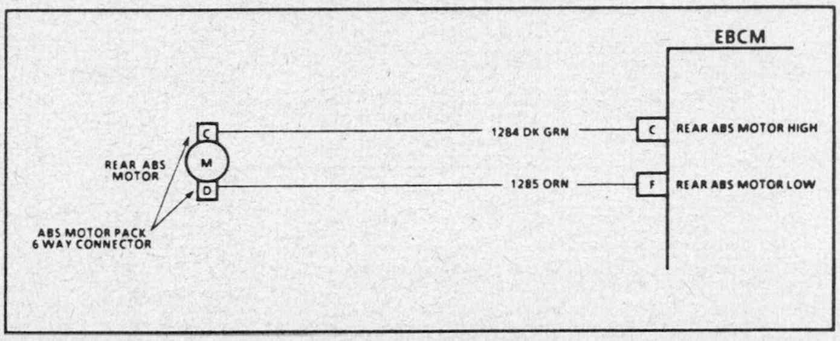
EBCM
REAR ABS MOTOR
1284 DK GRN
1285 ORN
REAR ABS MOTOR HIGH
REAR ABS MOTOR LOW
ABS MOTOR PACK 6 WAY CONNECTOR

GC402940109301CX

Century & Cutlass Ciera & Cruiser

DTC 51

(Page 1 of 2)
REAR ABS MOTOR FREE SPINS

Circuit Description:

This DTC is designed to detect a stripped nut or gear assembly during initialization. During the homing sequence, the piston should reach the top of the bore resulting in a stalled ABS motor. If this does not occur, the ABS motor must be spinning with little or no resistance, indicating a nut/screw or gear malfunction.

DTC Will Set When: DTC 51 can be set during initialization. If the feedback current is less than the command current for a specified period of time, a malfunction exists.

Action Taken: A malfunction DTC is stored, ABS is disabled, and the ABS warning lamp is turned "ON."

DTC Chart Test Description: Number(s) below refer to circled number(s) on the diagnostic chart.

1. Checks to see if the corresponding open ABS motor DTC is also set.
2. Verifies that the ABS motor was actually applied as commanded by observing feedback current.
3. Verifies that the ABS motor can release.
4. Verifies that the ABS motor can be applied by observing pedal movement.
5. Checks for high resistance in the ABS motor "HIGH" circuitry.
6. Checks for high resistance in the ABS motor "LOW" circuitry.
7. Checks for proper resistance of the ABS motor windings,

Diagnostic Aids: An "Intermittent" malfunction in this DTC may result from a mechanical part of the system that sticks, binds, or slips.

The frequency of the malfunction can be checked by using the enhanced diagnostic function of the Tech 1,

If the DTC only occurs once and DTC 64 also occurs, refer to DTC 64. If intermittent and enhanced diagnostics show this DTC occurs during ABS, refer to DTC 64

Depending on the frequency of the malfunction, a physical inspection of the mechanical parts suspected may be necessary

GC402940109301DX

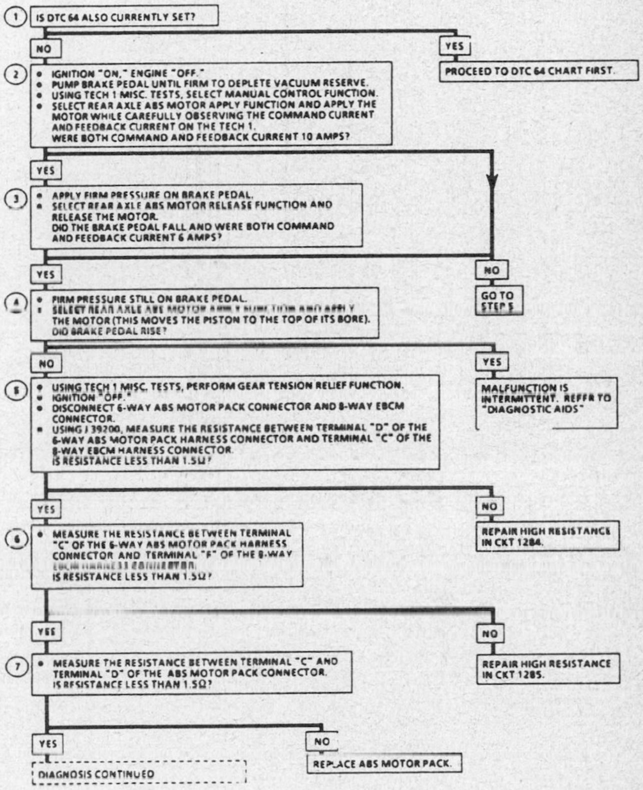
1 IS DTC 64 ALSO CURRENTLY SET?
NO
YES
PROCEED TO DTC 64 CHART FIRST.
2 • IGNITION "ON," ENGINE "OFF."
• PUMP BRAKE PEDAL UNTIL FIRM TO DEPLETE VACUUM RESERVE.
• USING TECH 1 MISC. TESTS, SELECT MANUAL CONTROL FUNCTION.
• SELECT REAR AXLE ABS MOTOR APPLY FUNCTION AND APPLY THE MOTOR WHILE CAREFULLY OBSERVING THE COMMAND CURRENT AND FEEDBACK CURRENT ON THE TECH 1.
WERE BOTH COMMAND AND FEEDBACK CURRENT 10 AMPS?
YES
3 • APPLY FIRM PRESSURE ON BRAKE PEDAL.
• SELECT REAR AXLE ABS MOTOR RELEASE FUNCTION AND RELEASE THE MOTOR.
DID THE BRAKE PEDAL FALL AND WERE BOTH COMMAND AND FEEDBACK CURRENT 6 AMPS?
YES
NO
GO TO STEP 5
4 • FIRM PRESSURE STILL ON BRAKE PEDAL.
THE MOTOR (THIS MOVES THE PISTON TO THE TOP OF ITS BORE).
DID BRAKE PEDAL RISE?
NO
YES
MALFUNCTION IS INTERMITTENT. REFER TO "DIAGNOSTIC AIDS"
5 • USING TECH 1 MISC. TESTS, PERFORM GEAR TENSION RELIEF FUNCTION.
• IGNITION "OFF."
• DISCONNECT 6-WAY ABS MOTOR PACK CONNECTOR AND 8-WAY EBCM CONNECTOR.
• USING J 39200, MEASURE THE RESISTANCE BETWEEN TERMINAL "D" OF THE 6-WAY ABS MOTOR PACK HARNESS CONNECTOR AND TERMINAL "C" OF THE 8-WAY EBCM HARNESS CONNECTOR.
IS RESISTANCE LESS THAN 1.5Ω?
YES
NO
REPAIR HIGH RESISTANCE IN CKT 1284.
6 • MEASURE THE RESISTANCE BETWEEN TERMINAL "C" OF THE 6-WAY ABS MOTOR PACK HARNESS CONNECTOR AND TERMINAL "F" OF THE 8-WAY
IS RESISTANCE LESS THAN 1.5Ω?
YES
NO
REPAIR HIGH RESISTANCE IN CKT 1285.
7 • MEASURE THE RESISTANCE BETWEEN TERMINAL "C" AND TERMINAL "D" OF THE ABS MOTOR PACK CONNECTOR.
IS RESISTANCE LESS THAN 1.5Ω?
YES
NO
DIAGNOSIS CONTINUED
REPLACE ABS MOTOR PACK.

GC402940109301EX

Fig. 265 Code A051: Rear ABS Motor Free Spins (Part 1 of 2). 1993–94 Camaro & Firebird, 1994 Grand Prix, Century & Cutlass Ciera & Cruiser

DTC 51
(Page 2 of 2)
REAR ABS MOTOR FREE SPINS

Circuit Description:

This DTC is designed to detect a stripped nut or gear assembly during initialization. During the homing sequence, the piston should reach the top of the bore resulting in a stalled ABS motor. If this does not occur, the ABS motor must be spinning with little or no resistance, indicating a nut/screw or gear malfunction.

DTC Will Set When: DTC 51 can be set during initialization. If the feedback current is less than the command current for a specified period of time, a malfunction exists.

Action Taken: A malfunction DTC is stored, ABS is disabled, and the ABS warning lamp is turned "ON."

DTC Chart Test Description: Number(s) below refer to circled number(s) on the diagnostic chart.

8. Checks for a stripped gear on the ABS motor pack (unit with three small gears).
9. Checks for a stripped gear on the hydraulic modulator (unit with three large gears).
10. Verifies that the ABS motor can be applied under a load situation.
11. Verifies that the hydraulic modulator is functioning properly.
12. Ensures malfunction was not due to poor terminal contact.

Diagnostic Aids: An "Intermittent" malfunction in this DTC may result from a mechanical part of the system that sticks, binds, or slips.

The frequency of the malfunction can be checked by using the enhanced diagnostic function of the Tech 1.

If the DTC only occurs once and DTC 64 also occurs, refer to DTC 64. If intermittent and enhanced diagnostics show this DTC occurs during ABS, refer to DTC 64.

Depending on the frequency of the malfunction, a physical inspection of the mechanical parts suspected may be necessary.

GC402940109302AX

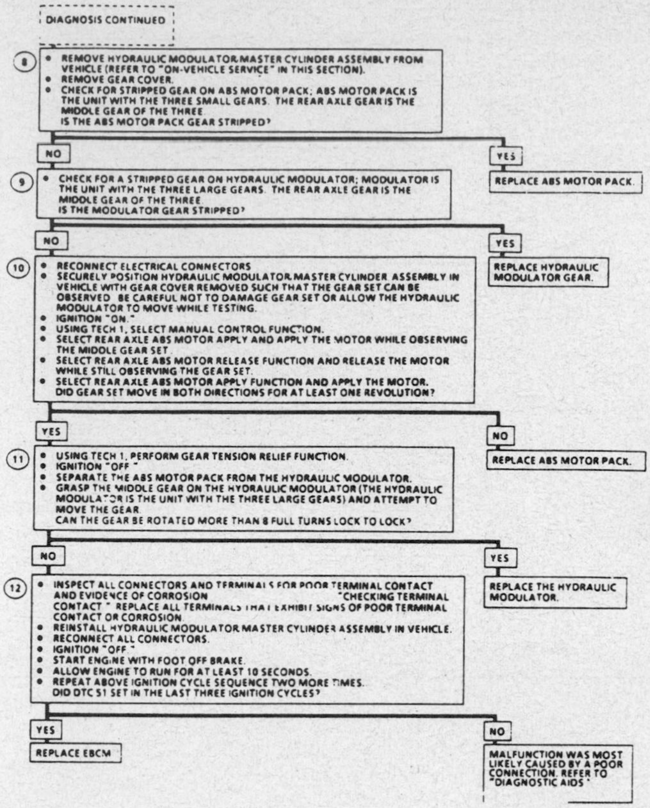
DIAGNOSIS CONTINUED
8
• REMOVE HYDRAULIC MODULATOR/MASTER CYLINDER ASSEMBLY FROM VEHICLE (REFER TO "ON-VEHICLE SERVICE" IN THIS SECTION).
• REMOVE GEAR COVER.
• CHECK FOR STRIPPED GEAR ON ABS MOTOR PACK; ABS MOTOR PACK IS THE UNIT WITH THE THREE SMALL GEARS. THE REAR AXLE GEAR IS THE MIDDLE GEAR OF THE THREE.
IS THE ABS MOTOR PACK GEAR STRIPPED?
NO
YES
REPLACE ABS MOTOR PACK.
9
• CHECK FOR A STRIPPED GEAR ON HYDRAULIC MODULATOR; MODULATOR IS THE UNIT WITH THE THREE LARGE GEARS. THE REAR AXLE GEAR IS THE MIDDLE GEAR OF THE THREE.
IS THE MODULATOR GEAR STRIPPED?
NO
YES
REPLACE HYDRAULIC MODULATOR GEAR.
10
• RECONNECT ELECTRICAL CONNECTORS
• SECURELY POSITION HYDRAULIC MODULATOR/MASTER CYLINDER ASSEMBLY IN VEHICLE WITH GEAR COVER REMOVED SUCH THAT THE GEAR SET CAN BE OBSERVED. BE CAREFUL NOT TO DAMAGE GEAR SET OR ALLOW THE HYDRAULIC MODULATOR TO MOVE WHILE TESTING.
• IGNITION "ON."
• USING TECH 1, SELECT MANUAL CONTROL FUNCTION.
• SELECT REAR AXLE ABS MOTOR APPLY AND APPLY THE MOTOR WHILE OBSERVING THE MIDDLE GEAR SET.
• SELECT REAR AXLE ABS MOTOR RELEASE FUNCTION AND RELEASE THE MOTOR WHILE STILL OBSERVING THE GEAR SET.
• SELECT REAR AXLE ABS MOTOR APPLY FUNCTION AND APPLY THE MOTOR.
DID GEAR SET MOVE IN BOTH DIRECTIONS FOR AT LEAST ONE REVOLUTION?
YES
NO
REPLACE ABS MOTOR PACK.
11
• USING TECH 1, PERFORM GEAR TENSION RELIEF FUNCTION.
• IGNITION "OFF."
• SEPARATE THE ABS MOTOR PACK FROM THE HYDRAULIC MODULATOR.
• GRASP THE MIDDLE GEAR ON THE HYDRAULIC MODULATOR (THE HYDRAULIC MODULATOR IS THE UNIT WITH THE THREE LARGE GEARS) AND ATTEMPT TO MOVE THE GEAR.
CAN THE GEAR BE ROTATED MORE THAN 8 FULL TURNS LOCK TO LOCK?
NO
YES
REPLACE THE HYDRAULIC MODULATOR.
12
• INSPECT ALL CONNECTORS AND TERMINALS FOR POOR TERMINAL CONTACT AND EVIDENCE OF CORROSION "CHECKING TERMINAL CONTACT." REPLACE ALL TERMINALS THAT EXHIBIT SIGNS OF POOR TERMINAL CONTACT OR CORROSION.
• REINSTALL HYDRAULIC MODULATOR/MASTER CYLINDER ASSEMBLY IN VEHICLE.
• RECONNECT ALL CONNECTORS.
• IGNITION "OFF."
• START ENGINE WITH FOOT OFF BRAKE.
• ALLOW ENGINE TO RUN FOR AT LEAST 10 SECONDS.
• REPEAT ABOVE IGNITION CYCLE SEQUENCE TWO MORE TIMES.
DID DTC 51 SET IN THE LAST THREE IGNITION CYCLES?
YES
REPLACE EBCM
NO
MALFUNCTION WAS MOST LIKELY CAUSED BY A POOR CONNECTION. REFER TO "DIAGNOSTIC AIDS."

GC402940109302BX

Fig. 265 Code A051: Rear ABS Motor Free Spins (Part 2 of 2). 1993–94 Camaro & Firebird, 1994 Grand Prix, Century & Cutlass Ciera & Cruiser

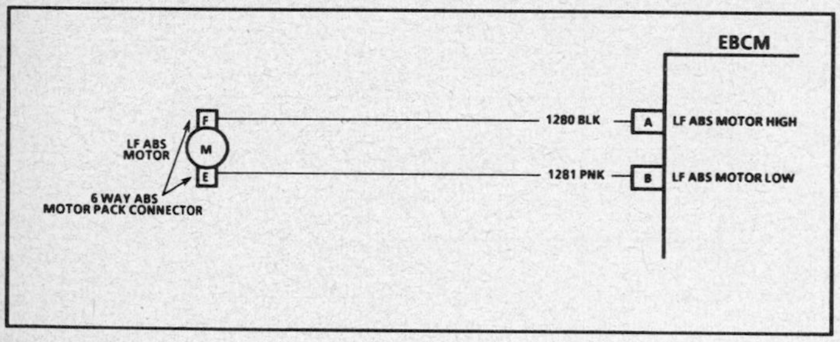
EBCM
F
M
E
LF ABS MOTOR
6 WAY ABS MOTOR PACK CONNECTOR
1280 BLK
A
LF ABS MOTOR HIGH
1281 PNK
B
LF ABS MOTOR LOW

GC402940109400AX

Grand Prix

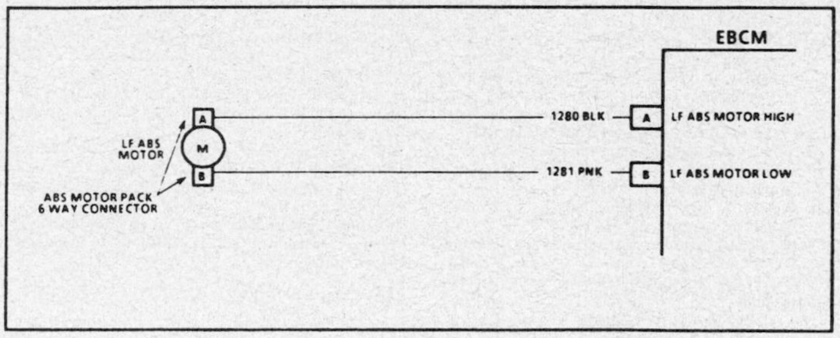
EBCM
A
M
B
LF ABS MOTOR
ABS MOTOR PACK 6 WAY CONNECTOR
1280 BLK
A
LF ABS MOTOR HIGH
1281 PNK
B
LF ABS MOTOR LOW

GC402940109400BX

Camaro & Firebird

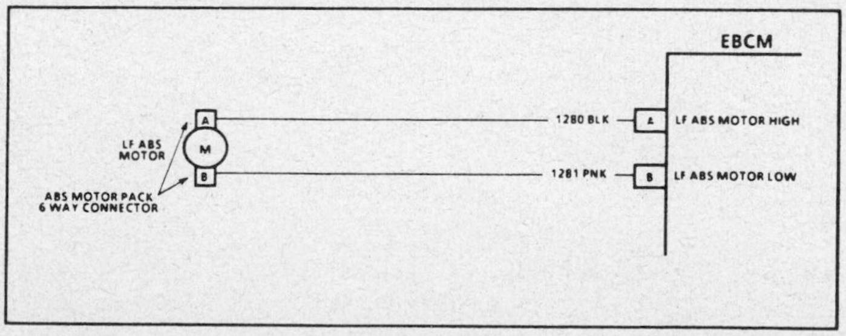
EBCM
A
M
B
LF ABS MOTOR
ABS MOTOR PACK 6 WAY CONNECTOR
1280 BLK
A
LF ABS MOTOR HIGH
1281 PNK
B
LF ABS MOTOR LOW

GC402940109400CX

Century & Cutlass Ciera & Cruiser

Fig. 266 Code A052: Left Front Channel In Release Too Long (Part 1 of 2). 1993-94 Camaro & Firebird, 1994 Grand Prix, Century & Cutlass Ciera & Cruiser

DTC 52

LEFT FRONT CHANNEL IN RELEASE TOO LONG

Circuit Description:
This DTC will diagnose an ABS motor that is energized longer than expected. This could occur if a wheel speed sensor is malfunctioning, the ABS motor does not turn, the left front solenoid mechanically fails open, or the ABS motor wires are crossed.

DTC Will Set When: DTC 52 can be set only during an ABS stop. If the EBCM commands the left front ABS channel in release for three seconds, a malfunction exists.

Action Taken: A malfunction DTC is stored, ABS is disabled and the ABS warning lamp is turned "ON."

DTC Chart Test Description: Number(s) below refer to circled number(s) on the diagnostic chart.

1. Identifies a problem in a wheel speed sensor that may cause the system to be in release too long.
2. Identifies an ABS motor as being failed or wired incorrectly.
3. Checks for a solenoid that may have mechanically failed open.
4. Verifies proper solenoid operation.
5. This serves to isolate the cause of the hydraulic problem, to either the solenoid or the ABS hydraulic modulator assembly.
6. Determines whether a malfunctioning ABS motor pack or hydraulic modulator is the reason for DTC 52 being set.

Diagnostic Aids: An "Intermittent" malfunction may be caused by a mechanical part of the system that sticks or binds.

The frequency of the malfunction can be checked by using the enhanced diagnostic function of the Tech 1,

DTC 52 may occur if on ice and steering wheel is turned to lock during braking. Using the Tech 1, perform hydraulic test to ensure total brake system is functional.

Any circuitry, that is suspected as causing the intermittent complaint, should be thoroughly checked for backed out terminals, improper mating, broken locks, improperly formed or damaged terminals, poor terminal to wiring connections or physical damage to the wiring harness.

GC402940109400DX

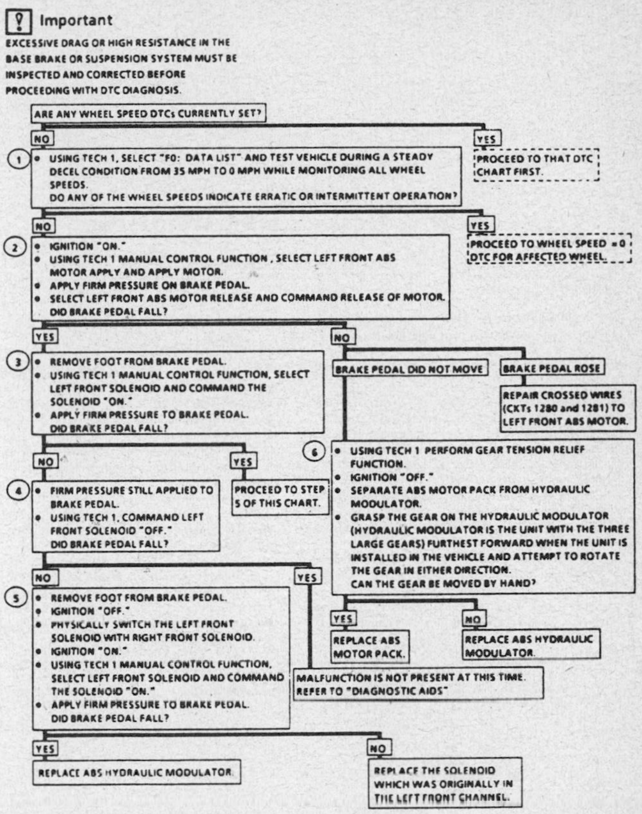
Important
EXCESSIVE DRAG OR HIGH RESISTANCE IN THE BASE BRAKE OR SUSPENSION SYSTEM MUST BE INSPECTED AND CORRECTED BEFORE PROCEEDING WITH DTC DIAGNOSIS.
ARE ANY WHEEL SPEED DTCs CURRENTLY SET?
NO
YES
PROCEED TO THAT DTC CHART FIRST.
1
• USING TECH 1, SELECT "F0: DATA LIST" AND TEST VEHICLE DURING A STEADY DECEL CONDITION FROM 35 MPH TO 0 MPH WHILE MONITORING ALL WHEEL SPEEDS.
DO ANY OF THE WHEEL SPEEDS INDICATE ERRATIC OR INTERMITTENT OPERATION?
NO
YES
PROCEED TO WHEEL SPEED = 0 DTC FOR AFFECTED WHEEL.
2
• IGNITION "ON."
• USING TECH 1 MANUAL CONTROL FUNCTION , SELECT LEFT FRONT ABS MOTOR APPLY AND APPLY MOTOR.
• APPLY FIRM PRESSURE ON BRAKE PEDAL.
• SELECT LEFT FRONT ABS MOTOR RELEASE AND COMMAND RELEASE OF MOTOR.
DID BRAKE PEDAL FALL?
YES
NO
BRAKE PEDAL DID NOT MOVE
BRAKE PEDAL ROSE
REPAIR CROSSED WIRES (CKTs 1280 and 1281) TO LEFT FRONT ABS MOTOR.
3
• REMOVE FOOT FROM BRAKE PEDAL.
• USING TECH 1 MANUAL CONTROL FUNCTION, SELECT LEFT FRONT SOLENOID AND COMMAND THE SOLENOID "ON."
• APPLY FIRM PRESSURE TO BRAKE PEDAL.
DID BRAKE PEDAL FALL?
NO
YES
PROCEED TO STEP 5 OF THIS CHART.
4
• FIRM PRESSURE STILL APPLIED TO BRAKE PEDAL.
• USING TECH 1, COMMAND LEFT FRONT SOLENOID "OFF."
DID BRAKE PEDAL FALL?
NO
YES
MALFUNCTION IS NOT PRESENT AT THIS TIME. REFER TO "DIAGNOSTIC AIDS"
5
• REMOVE FOOT FROM BRAKE PEDAL.
• IGNITION "OFF."
• PHYSICALLY SWITCH THE LEFT FRONT SOLENOID WITH RIGHT FRONT SOLENOID.
• IGNITION "ON."
• USING TECH 1 MANUAL CONTROL FUNCTION, SELECT LEFT FRONT SOLENOID AND COMMAND THE SOLENOID "ON."
• APPLY FIRM PRESSURE TO BRAKE PEDAL.
DID BRAKE PEDAL FALL?
YES
REPLACE ABS HYDRAULIC MODULATOR.
NO
REPLACE THE SOLENOID WHICH WAS ORIGINALLY IN THE LEFT FRONT CHANNEL.
6
• USING TECH 1 PERFORM GEAR TENSION RELIEF FUNCTION.
• IGNITION "OFF."
• SEPARATE ABS MOTOR PACK FROM HYDRAULIC MODULATOR.
• GRASP THE GEAR ON THE HYDRAULIC MODULATOR (HYDRAULIC MODULATOR IS THE UNIT WITH THE THREE LARGE GEARS) FURTHEST FORWARD WHEN THE UNIT IS INSTALLED IN THE VEHICLE AND ATTEMPT TO ROTATE THE GEAR IN EITHER DIRECTION.
CAN THE GEAR BE MOVED BY HAND?
YES
REPLACE ABS MOTOR PACK.
NO
REPLACE ABS HYDRAULIC MODULATOR.

GC402940109400EX

Fig. 266 Code A052: Left Front Channel In Release Too Long (Part 2 of 2). 1993-94 Camaro & Firebird, 1994 Grand Prix, Century & Cutlass Ciera & Cruiser

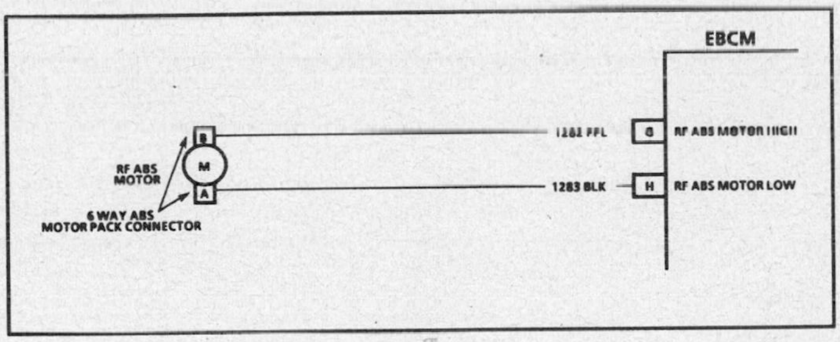
EBCM
RF ABS MOTOR
M
B
A
6 WAY ABS MOTOR PACK CONNECTOR
1282 PPL
G
RF ABS MOTOR HIGH
1283 BLK
H
RF ABS MOTOR LOW

GC402940109500AX

Grand Prix

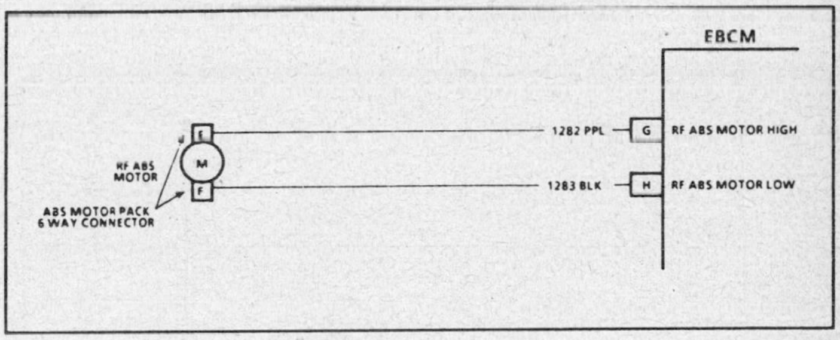
EBCM
RF ABS MOTOR
M
E
F
ABS MOTOR PACK 6 WAY CONNECTOR
1282 PPL
G
RF ABS MOTOR HIGH
1283 BLK
H
RF ABS MOTOR LOW

GC402940109500BX

Camaro & Firebird

EBCM
RF ABS MOTOR
M
E
F
ABS MOTOR PACK 6 WAY CONNECTOR
1282 PPL
G
RF ABS MOTOR HIGH
1283 BLK
H
RF ABS MOTOR LOW

GC402940109500CX

Century & Cutlass Ciera & Cruiser

Fig. 267 Code A053: Right Front Channel In Release Too Long (Part 1 of 2). 1993-94 Camaro & Firebird, 1994 Grand Prix, Century & Cutlass Ciera & Cruiser

DTC 53

RIGHT FRONT CHANNEL IN RELEASE TOO LONG

Circuit Description:

This DTC will diagnose an ABS motor that is energized longer than expected. This could occur if a wheel speed sensor is malfunctioning, the ABS motor does not turn, the right front solenoid mechanically fails open, or the ABS motor wires are crossed.

DTC Will Set When: DTC 53 can be set only during an ABS stop. If the EBCM commands the right front channel in release for three seconds, a malfunction exists.

Action Taken: A malfunction DTC is stored, ABS is disabled and the ABS warning lamp is turned "ON."

DTC Chart Test Description: Number(s) below refer to circled number(s) on the diagnostic chart.

1. Identifies a problem in a wheel speed sensor that may cause the system to be in release too long.
2. Identifies an ABS motor as being failed or wired incorrectly.
3. Checks for a solenoid that may have mechanically failed open.
4. Checks for a solenoid that may have mechanically failed closed.
5. This serves to isolate the cause of the hydraulic problem, to either the solenoid or the ABS hydraulic modulator assembly.
6. Determines whether a malfunction ABS motor pack or hydraulic modulator is the reason for DTC 53 being set.

Diagnostic Aids: An "Intermittent" malfunction may be caused by a mechanical part of the system that sticks or binds.

The frequency of the malfunction can be checked by using the enhanced diagnostic function of the Tech 1,

DTC 53 may occur on ice if steering wheel is turned to lock during braking. Using the Tech 1 perform hydraulic test to ensure total brake system is functional.

Any circuitry, that is suspected as causing the intermittent complaint, should be thoroughly checked for backed out terminals, improper mating, broken locks, improperly formed or damaged terminals, poor terminal to wiring connections or physical damage to the wiring harness.

GC402940109500DX

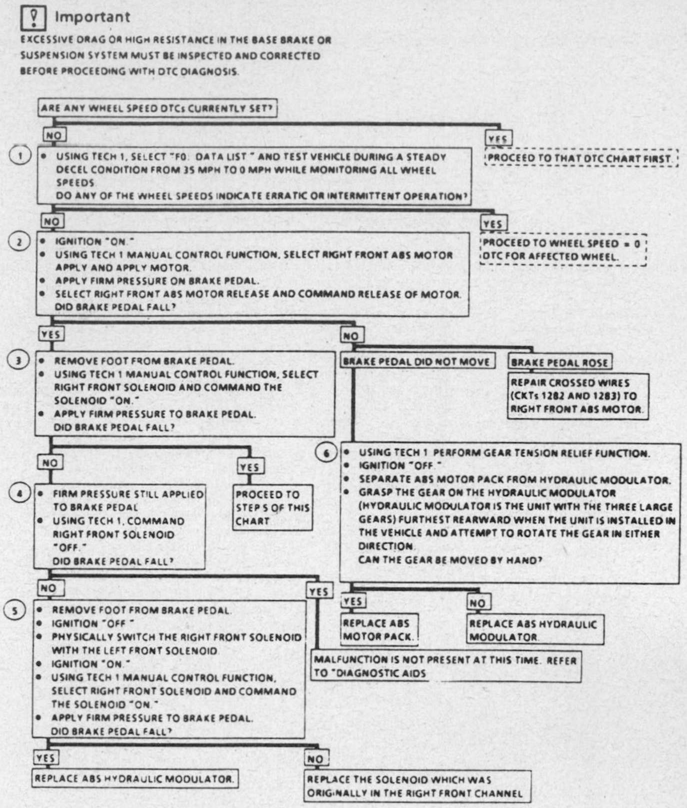
Important
EXCESSIVE DRAG OR HIGH RESISTANCE IN THE BASE BRAKE OR SUSPENSION SYSTEM MUST BE INSPECTED AND CORRECTED BEFORE PROCEEDING WITH DTC DIAGNOSIS.
ARE ANY WHEEL SPEED DTCs CURRENTLY SET?
NO
YES
PROCEED TO THAT DTC CHART FIRST.
1
USING TECH 1, SELECT "F0: DATA LIST" AND TEST VEHICLE DURING A STEADY DECEL CONDITION FROM 35 MPH TO 0 MPH WHILE MONITORING ALL WHEEL SPEEDS.
DO ANY OF THE WHEEL SPEEDS INDICATE ERRATIC OR INTERMITTENT OPERATION?
NO
YES
PROCEED TO WHEEL SPEED = 0 DTC FOR AFFECTED WHEEL.
2
IGNITION "ON."
USING TECH 1 MANUAL CONTROL FUNCTION, SELECT RIGHT FRONT ABS MOTOR APPLY AND APPLY MOTOR.
APPLY FIRM PRESSURE ON BRAKE PEDAL.
SELECT RIGHT FRONT ABS MOTOR RELEASE AND COMMAND RELEASE OF MOTOR.
DID BRAKE PEDAL FALL?
YES
NO
BRAKE PEDAL DID NOT MOVE
BRAKE PEDAL ROSE
REPAIR CROSSED WIRES (CKTs 1282 AND 1283) TO RIGHT FRONT ABS MOTOR.
3
REMOVE FOOT FROM BRAKE PEDAL.
USING TECH 1 MANUAL CONTROL FUNCTION, SELECT RIGHT FRONT SOLENOID AND COMMAND THE SOLENOID "ON."
APPLY FIRM PRESSURE TO BRAKE PEDAL.
DID BRAKE PEDAL FALL?
NO
YES
PROCEED TO STEP 5 OF THIS CHART.
4
FIRM PRESSURE STILL APPLIED TO BRAKE PEDAL
USING TECH 1, COMMAND RIGHT FRONT SOLENOID "OFF."
DID BRAKE PEDAL FALL?
6
USING TECH 1 PERFORM GEAR TENSION RELIEF FUNCTION.
IGNITION "OFF."
SEPARATE ABS MOTOR PACK FROM HYDRAULIC MODULATOR.
GRASP THE GEAR ON THE HYDRAULIC MODULATOR (HYDRAULIC MODULATOR IS THE UNIT WITH THE THREE LARGE GEARS) FURTHEST REARWARD WHEN THE UNIT IS INSTALLED IN THE VEHICLE AND ATTEMPT TO ROTATE THE GEAR IN EITHER DIRECTION.
CAN THE GEAR BE MOVED BY HAND?
NO
YES
YES
NO
REPLACE ABS MOTOR PACK.
REPLACE ABS HYDRAULIC MODULATOR.
5
REMOVE FOOT FROM BRAKE PEDAL.
IGNITION "OFF."
PHYSICALLY SWITCH THE RIGHT FRONT SOLENOID WITH THE LEFT FRONT SOLENOID.
IGNITION "ON."
USING TECH 1 MANUAL CONTROL FUNCTION, SELECT RIGHT FRONT SOLENOID AND COMMAND THE SOLENOID "ON."
APPLY FIRM PRESSURE TO BRAKE PEDAL.
DID BRAKE PEDAL FALL?
MALFUNCTION IS NOT PRESENT AT THIS TIME. REFER TO "DIAGNOSTIC AIDS
YES
NO
REPLACE ABS HYDRAULIC MODULATOR.
REPLACE THE SOLENOID WHICH WAS ORIGINALLY IN THE RIGHT FRONT CHANNEL

GC402940109500EX

Fig. 267 Code A053: Right Front Channel In Release Too Long (Part 2 of 2). 1993-94 Camaro & Firebird, 1994 Grand Prix, Century & Cutlass Ciera & Cruiser

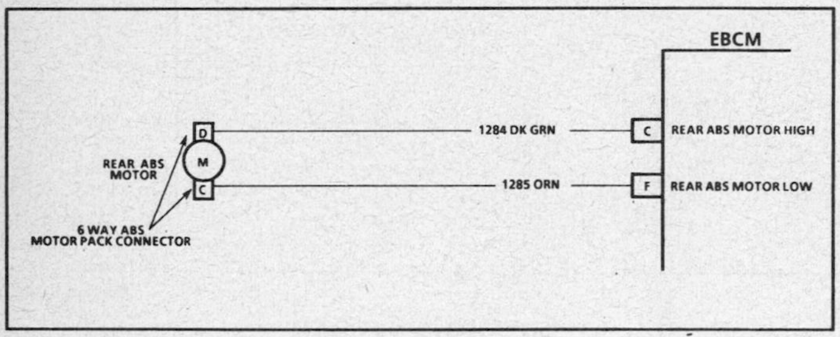
EBCM
D
M
C
REAR ABS MOTOR
6 WAY ABS MOTOR PACK CONNECTOR
1284 DK GRN
1285 ORN
C
F
REAR ABS MOTOR HIGH
REAR ABS MOTOR LOW

GC402940109600AX

Grand Prix

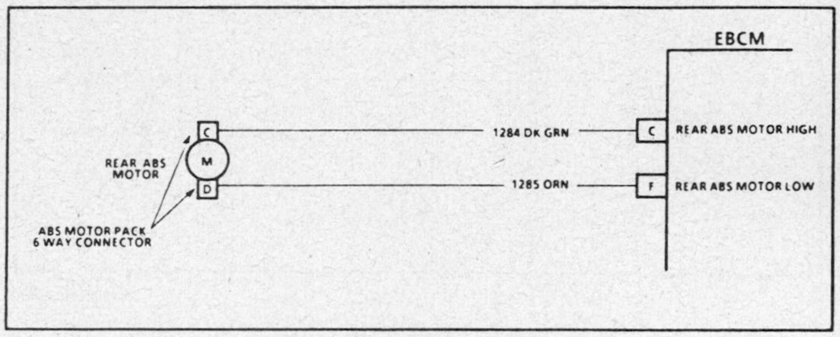
EBCM
C
M
D
REAR ABS MOTOR
ABS MOTOR PACK 6 WAY CONNECTOR
1284 DK GRN
1285 ORN
C
F
REAR ABS MOTOR HIGH
REAR ABS MOTOR LOW

GC402940109600BX

Camaro & Firebird

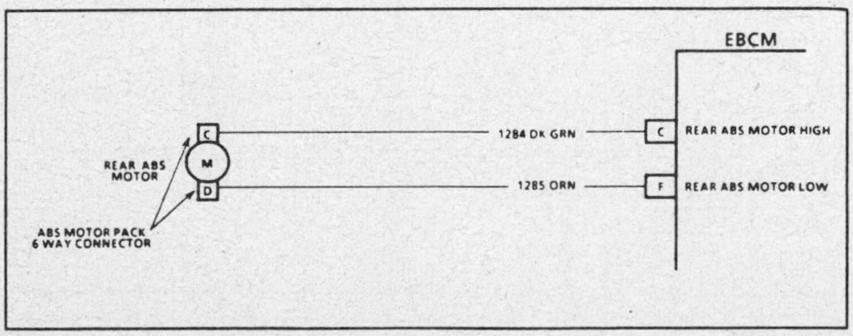
EBCM
C
M
D
REAR ABS MOTOR
ABS MOTOR PACK 6 WAY CONNECTOR
1284 DK GRN
1285 ORN
C
F
REAR ABS MOTOR HIGH
REAR ABS MOTOR LOW

GC402940109600CX

Century & Cutlass Ciera & Cruiser

Fig. 268 Code A054: Rear Channel In Release Too Long (Part 1 of 2). 1993-94 Camaro & Firebird, 1994 Grand Prix, Century & Cutlass Ciera & Cruiser

DTC 54

REAR CHANNEL IN RELEASE TOO LONG

Circuit Description:
This DTC will diagnose an ABS motor that is energized longer than expected. This could occur if a wheel speed sensor is malfunctioning, the ABS motor does not turn, or the ABS motor wires are crossed.

DTC Will Set When: DTC 54 can be set only during an ABS stop. If the EBCM commands the rear channel in release for three seconds, a malfunction exists.

Action Taken: A malfunction DTC is stored, ABS is disabled and the ABS warning lamp is turned "ON."

DTC Chart Test Description: Number(s) below refer to circled number(s) on the diagnostic chart.

1. Identifies a problem in a wheel speed sensor that may cause the system to be in release too long.
2. Checks for a wheel that may stick or bind because of a mechanical fault.
3. Checks to see if the ABS motor is capable of moving and applying the hydraulic piston for the rear wheels.
4. Ensures that the ABS motor wiring is not crossed.
5. Isolates the fault of a "no-apply" situation to either the ABS motor pack or ABS hydraulic modulator assembly.

Diagnostic Aids: An "Intermittent" malfunction may be caused by a mechanical part of the system that sticks or binds.

The frequency of the malfunction can be checked by using the enhanced diagnostic function of the Tech 1,

Using the Tech 1, perform hydraulic test to ensure total brake system is functional.

Any circuitry, that is suspected as causing the intermittent complaint, should be thoroughly checked for backed out terminals, improper mating, broken locks, improperly formed or damaged terminals, poor terminal to wiring connections or physical damage to the wiring harness.

GC402940109600DX

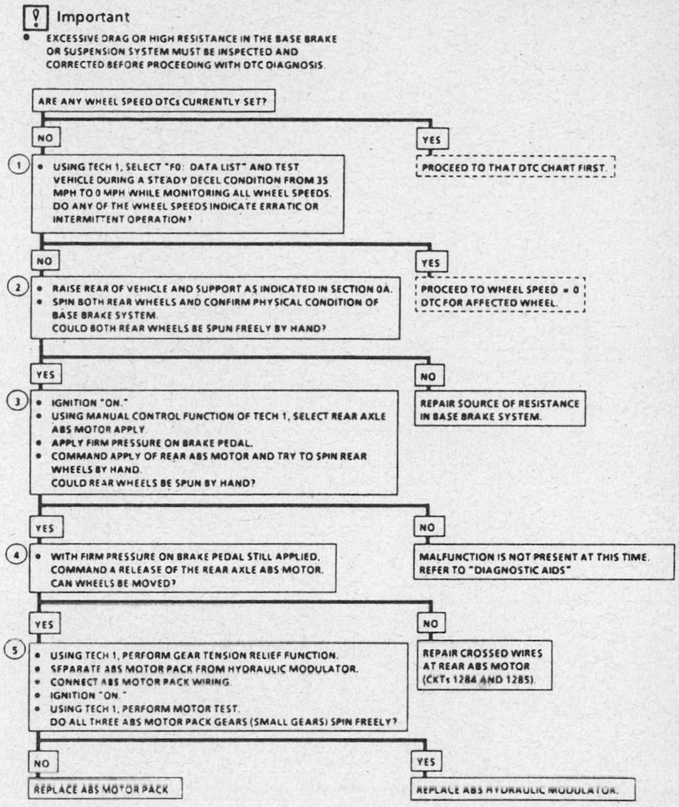
Important
EXCESSIVE DRAG OR HIGH RESISTANCE IN THE BASE BRAKE OR SUSPENSION SYSTEM MUST BE INSPECTED AND CORRECTED BEFORE PROCEEDING WITH DTC DIAGNOSIS.
ARE ANY WHEEL SPEED DTCs CURRENTLY SET?
NO
YES
PROCEED TO THAT DTC CHART FIRST.
1
USING TECH 1, SELECT "F0: DATA LIST" AND TEST VEHICLE DURING A STEADY DECEL CONDITION FROM 35 MPH TO 0 MPH WHILE MONITORING ALL WHEEL SPEEDS. DO ANY OF THE WHEEL SPEEDS INDICATE ERRATIC OR INTERMITTENT OPERATION?
NO
YES
PROCEED TO WHEEL SPEED = 0 DTC FOR AFFECTED WHEEL.
2
RAISE REAR OF VEHICLE AND SUPPORT AS INDICATED IN SECTION 0A.
SPIN BOTH REAR WHEELS AND CONFIRM PHYSICAL CONDITION OF BASE BRAKE SYSTEM.
COULD BOTH REAR WHEELS BE SPUN FREELY BY HAND?
YES
NO
REPAIR SOURCE OF RESISTANCE IN BASE BRAKE SYSTEM.
3
IGNITION "ON."
USING MANUAL CONTROL FUNCTION OF TECH 1, SELECT REAR AXLE ABS MOTOR APPLY.
APPLY FIRM PRESSURE ON BRAKE PEDAL.
COMMAND APPLY OF REAR ABS MOTOR AND TRY TO SPIN REAR WHEELS BY HAND.
COULD REAR WHEELS BE SPUN BY HAND?
YES
NO
MALFUNCTION IS NOT PRESENT AT THIS TIME. REFER TO "DIAGNOSTIC AIDS"
4
WITH FIRM PRESSURE ON BRAKE PEDAL STILL APPLIED, COMMAND A RELEASE OF THE REAR AXLE ABS MOTOR. CAN WHEELS BE MOVED?
YES
NO
REPAIR CROSSED WIRES AT REAR ABS MOTOR (CKTs 1284 AND 1285).
5
USING TECH 1, PERFORM GEAR TENSION RELIEF FUNCTION.
SEPARATE ABS MOTOR PACK FROM HYDRAULIC MODULATOR.
CONNECT ABS MOTOR PACK WIRING.
IGNITION "ON."
USING TECH 1, PERFORM MOTOR TEST.
DO ALL THREE ABS MOTOR PACK GEARS (SMALL GEARS) SPIN FREELY?
NO
YES
REPLACE ABS MOTOR PACK
REPLACE ABS HYDRAULIC MODULATOR.

GC402940109600EX

Fig. 268 Code A054: Rear Channel In Release Too Long (Part 2 of 2). 1993-94 Camaro & Firebird, 1994 Grand Prix, Century & Cutlass Ciera & Cruiser

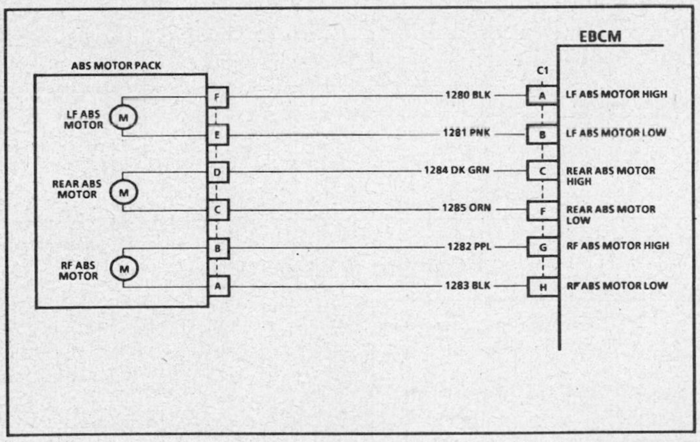
EBCM
ABS MOTOR PACK
C1
LF ABS MOTOR
M
F
E
1280 BLK
A
LF ABS MOTOR HIGH
1281 PNK
B
LF ABS MOTOR LOW
REAR ABS MOTOR
D
C
1284 DK GRN
C
REAR ABS MOTOR HIGH
1285 ORN
F
REAR ABS MOTOR LOW
RF ABS MOTOR
B
A
1282 PPL
G
RF ABS MOTOR HIGH
1283 BLK
H
RF ABS MOTOR LOW

GC402940109700AX

Grand Prix

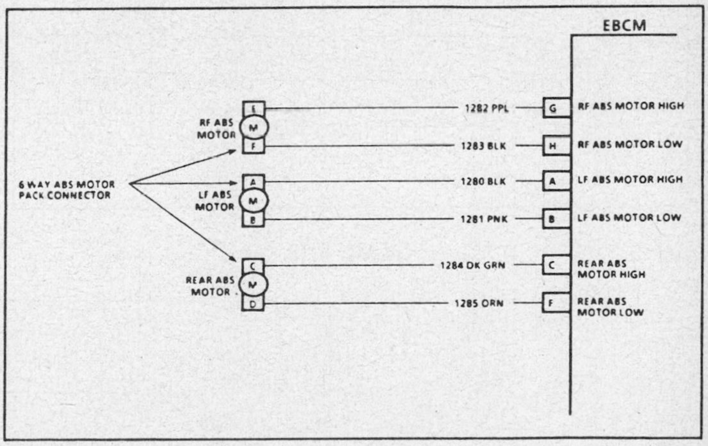
EBCM
RF ABS MOTOR
M
E
F
1282 PPL
G
RF ABS MOTOR HIGH
1283 BLK
H
RF ABS MOTOR LOW
6 WAY ABS MOTOR PACK CONNECTOR
LF ABS MOTOR
A
B
1280 BLK
A
LF ABS MOTOR HIGH
1281 PNK
B
LF ABS MOTOR LOW
REAR ABS MOTOR
C
D
1284 DK GRN
C
REAR ABS MOTOR HIGH
1285 ORN
F
REAR ABS MOTOR LOW

GC402940109700BX

Camaro & Firebird

Fig. 269 Code A055: EBCM Internal Fault (Part 1 of 2). 1993-94 Camaro & Firebird, 1994 Grand Prix, Century & Cutlass Ciera & Cruiser

DTC 55
EBCM MALFUNCTION

Circuit Description:
This DTC identifies a malfunction detected by the MDI custom IC. It also ensures the cause of the malfunction is not a result of a problem with the ABS enable relay under a DTC 55 malfunction.

Action Taken: A malfunction DTC is stored, ABS is disabled and the ABS warning lamp is turned "ON."

DTC Chart Test Description: Number(s) below refer to circled number(s) on the diagnostic chart.
1. Checks to see if the malfunction is still present.
2. Checks to see if the malfunction is intermittent.

Diagnostic Aids: An "Intermittent" malfunction may be caused by a poor connection, rubbed through wire insulation, or a wire that is broken inside the insulation.

The frequency of the malfunction can be checked by using the enhanced diagnostic function of the Tech 1,

Any circuitry, that is suspected as causing the intermittent complaint, should be thoroughly checked for backed out terminals, improper mating, broken locks, improperly formed or damaged terminals, poor terminal to wiring connections or physical damage to the wiring harness.

GC402940109700DX

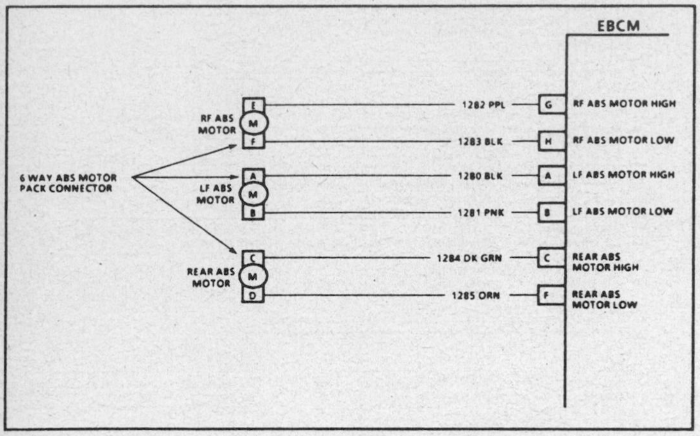
EBCM
RF ABS MOTOR
1282 PPL
G
RF ABS MOTOR HIGH
1283 BLK
H
RF ABS MOTOR LOW
6 WAY ABS MOTOR PACK CONNECTOR
LF ABS MOTOR
1280 BLK
A
LF ABS MOTOR HIGH
1281 PNK
B
LF ABS MOTOR LOW
REAR ABS MOTOR
1284 DK GRN
C
REAR ABS MOTOR HIGH
1285 ORN
F
REAR ABS MOTOR LOW

GC402940109700CX

Century & Cutlass Ciera & Cruiser

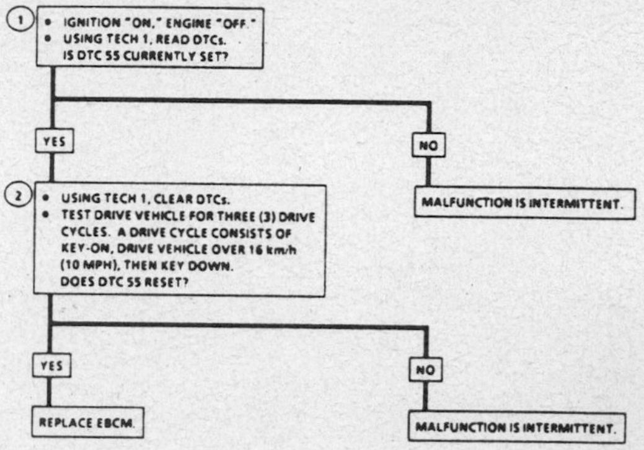
1
IGNITION "ON," ENGINE "OFF."
USING TECH 1, READ DTCs.
IS DTC 55 CURRENTLY SET?
YES
NO
MALFUNCTION IS INTERMITTENT.
2
USING TECH 1, CLEAR DTCs.
TEST DRIVE VEHICLE FOR THREE (3) DRIVE CYCLES. A DRIVE CYCLE CONSISTS OF KEY-ON, DRIVE VEHICLE OVER 16 km/h (10 MPH), THEN KEY DOWN.
DOES DTC 55 RESET?
YES
NO
REPLACE EBCM.
MALFUNCTION IS INTERMITTENT.

GC402940109700EX

Fig. 269 Code A055: EBCM Internal Fault (Part 2 of 2). 1993-94 Camaro & Firebird, 1994 Grand Prix, Century & Cutlass Ciera & Cruiser

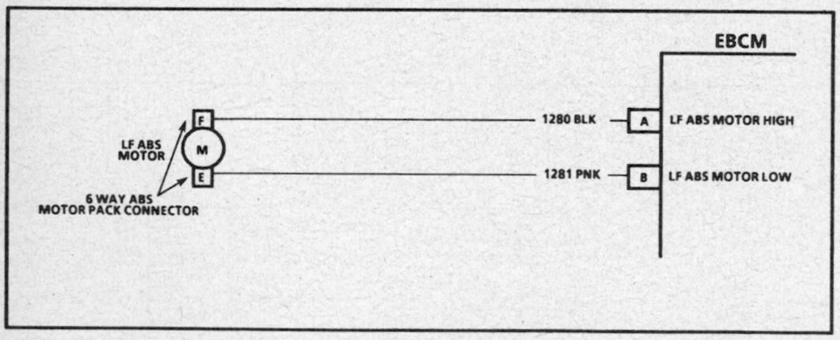
EBCM
LF ABS MOTOR
6 WAY ABS MOTOR PACK CONNECTOR
1280 BLK
A
LF ABS MOTOR HIGH
1281 PNK
B
LF ABS MOTOR LOW

GC402940109800AX

Grand Prix

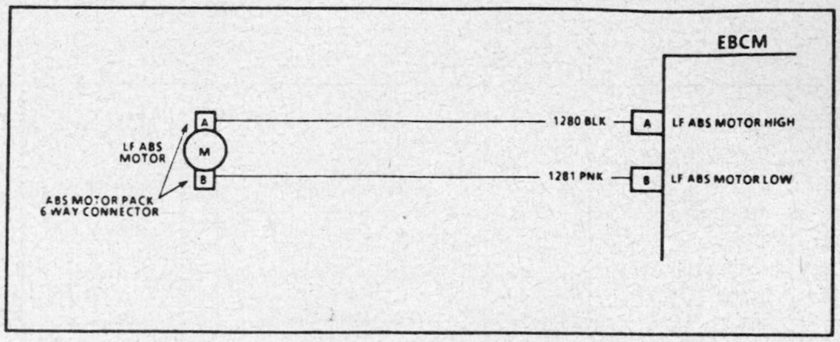
EBCM
LF ABS MOTOR
ABS MOTOR PACK 6 WAY CONNECTOR
1280 BLK
A
LF ABS MOTOR HIGH
1281 PNK
B
LF ABS MOTOR LOW

GC402940109800BX

Camaro & Firebird

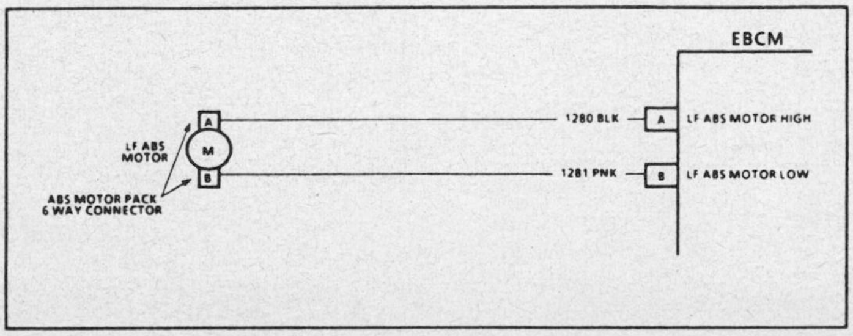
EBCM
LF ABS MOTOR
ABS MOTOR PACK 6 WAY CONNECTOR
1280 BLK
A
LF ABS MOTOR HIGH
1281 PNK
B
LF ABS MOTOR LOW

GC402940109800CX

Century & Cutlass Ciera & Cruiser

Fig. 270 Code A056: Left Front ABS Motor Circuit Open (Part 1 of 2). 1993-94 Camaro & Firebird, 1994 Grand Prix, Century & Cutlass Ciera & Cruiser

DTC 56

LEFT FRONT ABS MOTOR CIRCUIT OPEN

Circuit Description:
This DTC identifies a motor that cannot be energized due to an open in its circuitry.

DTC Will Set When: DTC 56 can be set only when the motor is commanded "OFF." If the EBCM detects an out of range voltage on either of the left front ABS motor circuits indicating an open circuit, a malfunction exists.

Action Taken: An open ABS motor will not activate when requested. A malfunction DTC is stored, ABS is disabled and the ABS warning lamp is turned "ON."

DTC Chart Test Description: Number(s) below refer to circled number(s) on the diagnostic chart.

1. Checks for proper resistance of the ABS motor.
2. Checks for an open in the ABS motor "HIGH" circuitry.
3. Checks for an open in the ABS motor "LOW" circuitry.
4. Ensures malfunction was not due to poor terminal contact.

Diagnostic Aids: Using Tech 1, select manual control function, and exercise ABS motor movement of affected channel in both directions while applying light pressure on the brake pedal.

If erratic or "jumpy" brake pedal movement is detected while performing an "apply" or "release" function of the ABS motor, an intermittent malfunction may be indicated.

An "Intermittent" malfunction may be caused by a poor connection, rubbed through wire insulation, or a wire that is broken inside the insulation.

If the malfunction is not current, wiggle the wires of the affected channel and check if the DTC resets. This will help to pinpoint an intermittent malfunction in the motor circuitry or connections.

The frequency of the malfunction can be checked by using the enhanced diagnostic function of the Tech 1,

Any circuitry, that is suspected as causing the intermittent complaint, should be thoroughly checked for backed out terminals, improper mating, broken locks, improperly formed or damaged terminals, poor terminal to wiring connections or physical damage to the wiring harness.

GC402940109800DX

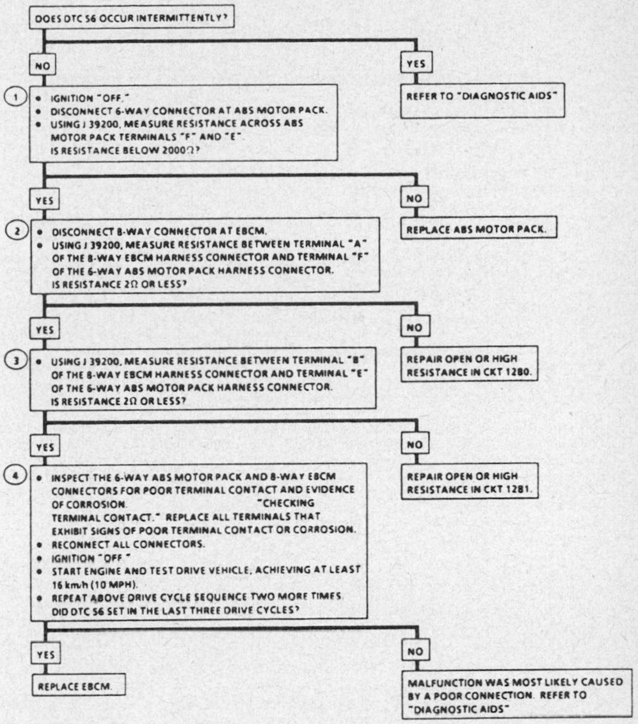
DOES DTC 56 OCCUR INTERMITTENTLY?
NO
YES
REFER TO "DIAGNOSTIC AIDS"
1
• IGNITION "OFF."
• DISCONNECT 6-WAY CONNECTOR AT ABS MOTOR PACK.
• USING J 39200, MEASURE RESISTANCE ACROSS ABS MOTOR PACK TERMINALS "F" AND "E".
IS RESISTANCE BELOW 2000Ω?
YES
NO
REPLACE ABS MOTOR PACK.
2
• DISCONNECT 8-WAY CONNECTOR AT EBCM.
• USING J 39200, MEASURE RESISTANCE BETWEEN TERMINAL "A" OF THE 8-WAY EBCM HARNESS CONNECTOR AND TERMINAL "F" OF THE 6-WAY ABS MOTOR PACK HARNESS CONNECTOR.
IS RESISTANCE 2Ω OR LESS?
YES
NO
REPAIR OPEN OR HIGH RESISTANCE IN CKT 1280.
3
• USING J 39200, MEASURE RESISTANCE BETWEEN TERMINAL "B" OF THE 8-WAY EBCM HARNESS CONNECTOR AND TERMINAL "E" OF THE 6-WAY ABS MOTOR PACK HARNESS CONNECTOR.
IS RESISTANCE 2Ω OR LESS?
YES
NO
REPAIR OPEN OR HIGH RESISTANCE IN CKT 1281.
4
• INSPECT THE 6-WAY ABS MOTOR PACK AND 8-WAY EBCM CONNECTORS FOR POOR TERMINAL CONTACT AND EVIDENCE OF CORROSION. "CHECKING TERMINAL CONTACT." REPLACE ALL TERMINALS THAT EXHIBIT SIGNS OF POOR TERMINAL CONTACT OR CORROSION.
• RECONNECT ALL CONNECTORS.
• IGNITION "OFF."
• START ENGINE AND TEST DRIVE VEHICLE, ACHIEVING AT LEAST 16 km/h (10 MPH).
• REPEAT ABOVE DRIVE CYCLE SEQUENCE TWO MORE TIMES.
DID DTC 56 SET IN THE LAST THREE DRIVE CYCLES?
YES
REPLACE EBCM.
NO
MALFUNCTION WAS MOST LIKELY CAUSED BY A POOR CONNECTION. REFER TO "DIAGNOSTIC AIDS"

GC402940109800EX

Fig. 270 Code A056: Left Front ABS Motor Circuit Open (Part 2 of 2). 1993-94 Camaro & Firebird, 1994 Grand Prix, Century & Cutlass Ciera & Cruiser

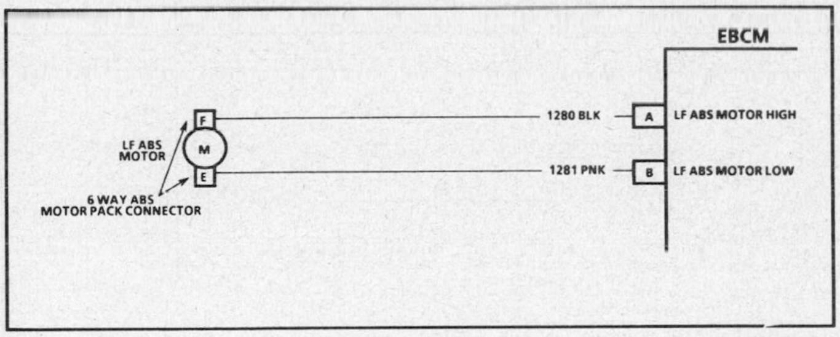
EBCM
1280 BLK
A
LF ABS MOTOR HIGH
F
LF ABS MOTOR
M
1281 PNK
B
LF ABS MOTOR LOW
E
6 WAY ABS MOTOR PACK CONNECTOR

GC402940109900AX

Grand Prix

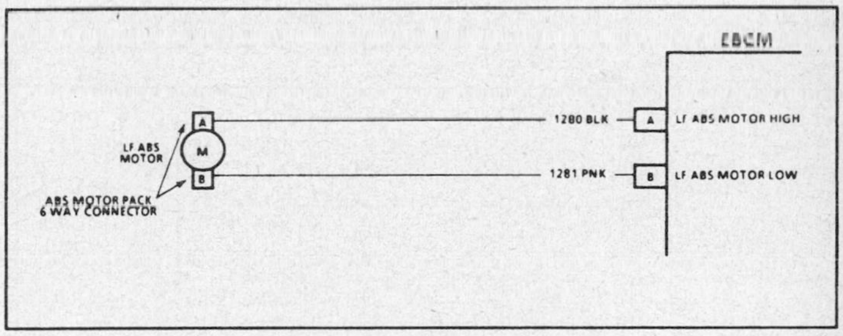
EBCM
A
LF ABS MOTOR
M
1280 BLK
A
LF ABS MOTOR HIGH
1281 PNK
B
LF ABS MOTOR LOW
B
ABS MOTOR PACK 6 WAY CONNECTOR

GC402940109900BX

Camaro & Firebird

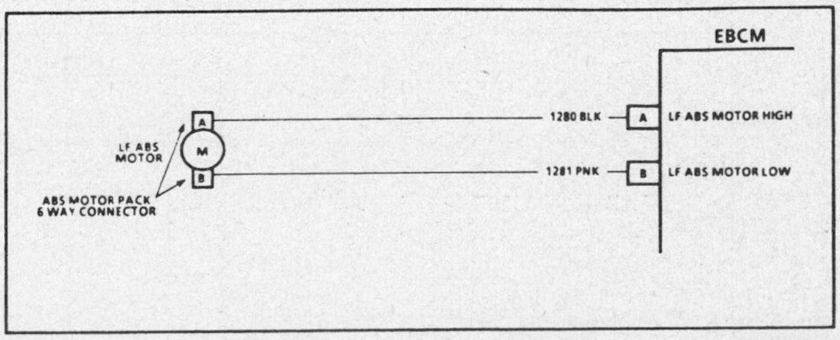
EBCM
A
LF ABS MOTOR
M
1280 BLK
A
LF ABS MOTOR HIGH
1281 PNK
B
LF ABS MOTOR LOW
B
ABS MOTOR PACK 6 WAY CONNECTOR

GC402940109900CX

Century & Cutlass Ciera & Cruiser

Fig. 271 Code A057: Left Front ABS Motor Circuit Shorted To Ground (Part 1 of 2). 1993-94 Camaro & Firebird, 1994 Grand Prix, Century & Cutlass Ciera & Cruiser

DTC 57

LEFT FRONT ABS MOTOR CIRCUIT SHORTED TO GROUND

Circuit Description:

This DTC identifies an ABS motor circuit that is shorted to ground. This malfunction will not allow the ABS motor to be controlled at the commanded current rate or will cause the driver circuit to allow current directly to ground.

DTC Will Set When: DTC 57 can be set anytime. If the EBCM detects an out of range voltage on either of the left front ABS motor circuits indicating a circuit shorted to ground, a malfunction exists.

Action Taken: A malfunction DTC is stored, ABS is disabled and the ABS warning lamp is turned "ON."

DTC Chart Test Description: Number(s) below refer to circled number(s) on the diagnostic chart.

1. Checks for a short to ground in the ABS motor "HIGH" circuitry.
2. Checks for a short to ground in the ABS motor "LOW" circuitry.
3. Checks for an ABS motor that is internally shorted to ground.
4. Ensures malfunction was not due to physical damage of the circuitry.

Diagnostic Aids: Using Tech 1, select manual control function, and exercise ABS motor movement of affected channel in both directions while applying light pressure on the brake pedal.

If erratic or "jumpy" brake pedal movement is detected while performing an "apply" or "release" function of the ABS motor, an intermittent malfunction may be indicated.

An "Intermittent" malfunction may be caused by a poor connection, rubbed through wire insulation, or a wire that is broken inside the insulation.

If the malfunction is not current, wiggle the wires of the affected channel and check if the DTC resets. This will help to pinpoint an intermittent malfunction in the motor circuitry or connections.

The frequency of the malfunction can be checked by using the enhanced diagnostic function of the Tech 1,

Any circuitry, that is suspected as causing the intermittent complaint, should be thoroughly checked for backed out terminals, improper mating, broken locks, improperly formed or damaged terminals, poor terminal to wiring connections or physical damage to the wiring harness.

GC402940109900DX

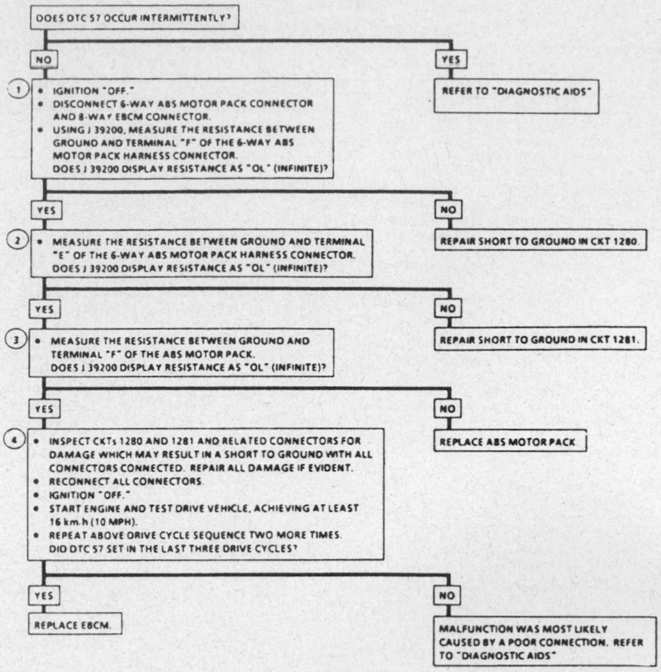
DOES DTC 57 OCCUR INTERMITTENTLY?
NO
YES
REFER TO "DIAGNOSTIC AIDS"
1
• IGNITION "OFF."
• DISCONNECT 6-WAY ABS MOTOR PACK CONNECTOR AND 8-WAY EBCM CONNECTOR.
• USING J 39200, MEASURE THE RESISTANCE BETWEEN GROUND AND TERMINAL "F" OF THE 6-WAY ABS MOTOR PACK HARNESS CONNECTOR.
DOES J 39200 DISPLAY RESISTANCE AS "OL" (INFINITE)?
YES
NO
REPAIR SHORT TO GROUND IN CKT 1280.
2
• MEASURE THE RESISTANCE BETWEEN GROUND AND TERMINAL "E" OF THE 6-WAY ABS MOTOR PACK HARNESS CONNECTOR.
DOES J 39200 DISPLAY RESISTANCE AS "OL" (INFINITE)?
YES
NO
REPAIR SHORT TO GROUND IN CKT 1281.
3
• MEASURE THE RESISTANCE BETWEEN GROUND AND TERMINAL "F" OF THE ABS MOTOR PACK.
DOES J 39200 DISPLAY RESISTANCE AS "OL" (INFINITE)?
YES
NO
REPLACE ABS MOTOR PACK
4
• INSPECT CKTs 1280 AND 1281 AND RELATED CONNECTORS FOR DAMAGE WHICH MAY RESULT IN A SHORT TO GROUND WITH ALL CONNECTORS CONNECTED. REPAIR ALL DAMAGE IF EVIDENT.
• RECONNECT ALL CONNECTORS.
• IGNITION "OFF."
• START ENGINE AND TEST DRIVE VEHICLE, ACHIEVING AT LEAST 16 km/h (10 MPH).
• REPEAT ABOVE DRIVE CYCLE SEQUENCE TWO MORE TIMES.
DID DTC 57 SET IN THE LAST THREE DRIVE CYCLES?
YES
NO
REPLACE EBCM.
MALFUNCTION WAS MOST LIKELY CAUSED BY A POOR CONNECTION. REFER TO "DIAGNOSTIC AIDS"

GC402940109900EX

Fig. 271 Code A057: Left Front ABS Motor Circuit Shorted To Ground (Part 2 of 2). 1993-94 Camaro & Firebird, 1994 Grand Prix, Century & Cutlass Ciera & Cruiser

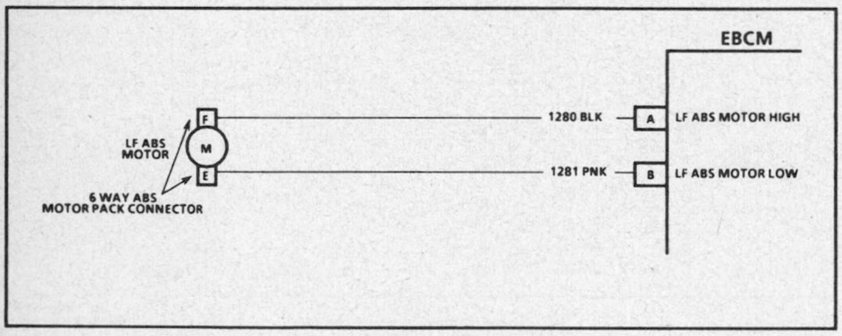
EBCM
F
E
M
LF ABS MOTOR
6 WAY ABS MOTOR PACK CONNECTOR
1280 BLK
1281 PNK
A
B
LF ABS MOTOR HIGH
LF ABS MOTOR LOW

GC402940110000AX

Grand Prix

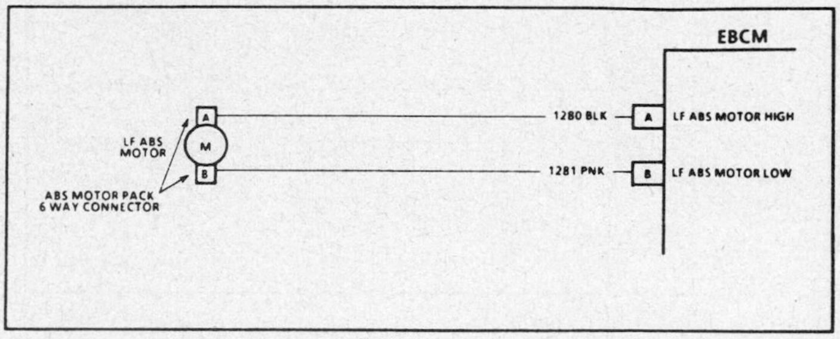
EBCM
A
B
M
LF ABS MOTOR
ABS MOTOR PACK 6 WAY CONNECTOR
1280 BLK
1281 PNK
A
B
LF ABS MOTOR HIGH
LF ABS MOTOR LOW

GC402940110000BX

Camaro & Firebird

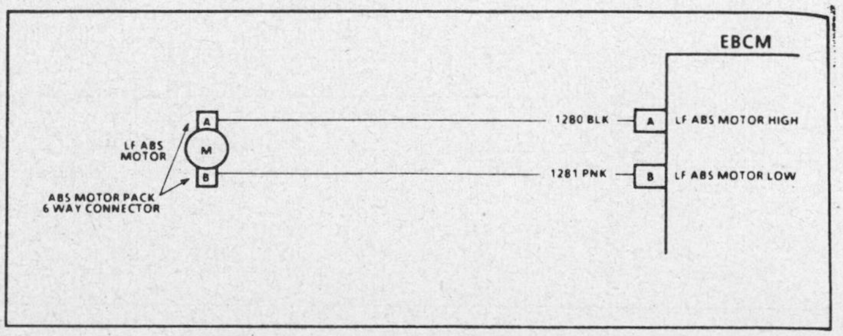
EBCM
A
B
M
LF ABS MOTOR
ABS MOTOR PACK 6 WAY CONNECTOR
1280 BLK
1281 PNK
A
B
LF ABS MOTOR HIGH
LF ABS MOTOR LOW

GC402940110000CX

Century & Cutlass Ciera & Cruiser

Fig. 272 Code A058: Left Front ABS Motor Circuit Shorted To Battery (Part 1 of 2). 1993-94 Camaro & Firebird, 1994 Grand Prix, Century & Cutlass Ciera & Cruiser

LEFT FRONT ABS MOTOR CIRCUIT SHORTED TO BATTERY

Circuit Description:
This DTC identifies an ABS motor circuit that is shorted to battery or an ABS motor that has low or no resistance. This malfunction will not allow the ABS motor to be controlled at the commanded current rate or will cause the ABS motor to turn in the opposite direction, or not at all.

DTC Will Set When: DTC 58 can be set only when the ABS motor is commanded "OFF." If the EBCM detects an out of range voltage on either of the left front ABS motor circuits indicating a circuit shorted to battery or an ABS motor shorted, a malfunction exists.

Action Taken: A malfunction DTC is stored, ABS is disabled and the ABS warning lamp is turned "ON."

DTC Chart Test Description: Number(s) below refer to circled number(s) on the diagnostic chart.

1. Checks for a short to voltage in the ABS motor "HIGH" circuitry.
2. Checks for a short to voltage in the ABS motor "LOW" circuitry.
3. Checks for a short between the "HIGH" and "LOW" ABS motor circuits.
4. Checks for an ABS motor that is internally shorted.
5. Ensures malfunction was not due to physical damage of the circuitry.

Diagnostic Aids: Using Tech 1, select manual control function, and exercise ABS motor movement of affected channel in both directions while applying light pressure on the brake pedal.

If erratic or "jumpy" brake pedal movement is detected while performing an "apply" or "release" function of the ABS motor, an intermittent malfunction may be indicated.

An "Intermittent" malfunction may be caused by a poor connection, rubbed through wire insulation, or a wire that is broken inside the insulation.

If the malfunction is not current, wiggle the wires of the affected channel and check if the DTC resets. This will help to pinpoint an intermittent malfunction in the motor circuitry or connections.

The frequency of the malfunction can be checked by using the enhanced diagnostic function of the Tech 1,

Any circuitry, that is suspected as causing the intermittent complaint, should be thoroughly checked for backed out terminals, improper mating, broken locks, improperly formed or damaged terminals, poor terminal to wiring connections or physical damage to the wiring harness.

GC402940110000DX

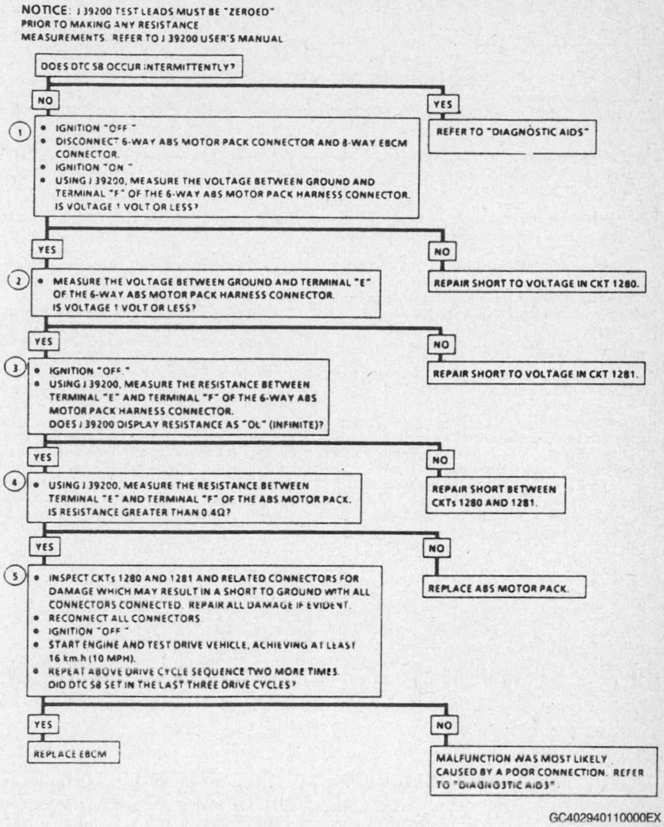

NOTICE: J 39200 TEST LEADS MUST BE "ZEROED" PRIOR TO MAKING ANY RESISTANCE MEASUREMENTS. REFER TO J 39200 USER'S MANUAL.
DOES DTC 58 OCCUR INTERMITTENTLY?
NO
YES
REFER TO "DIAGNOSTIC AIDS"
1
• IGNITION "OFF."
• DISCONNECT 6-WAY ABS MOTOR PACK CONNECTOR AND 8-WAY EBCM CONNECTOR.
• IGNITION "ON."
• USING J 39200, MEASURE THE VOLTAGE BETWEEN GROUND AND TERMINAL "F" OF THE 6-WAY ABS MOTOR PACK HARNESS CONNECTOR. IS VOLTAGE 1 VOLT OR LESS?
YES
NO
REPAIR SHORT TO VOLTAGE IN CKT 1280.
2
• MEASURE THE VOLTAGE BETWEEN GROUND AND TERMINAL "E" OF THE 6-WAY ABS MOTOR PACK HARNESS CONNECTOR. IS VOLTAGE 1 VOLT OR LESS?
YES
NO
REPAIR SHORT TO VOLTAGE IN CKT 1281.
3
• IGNITION "OFF."
• USING J 39200, MEASURE THE RESISTANCE BETWEEN TERMINAL "E" AND TERMINAL "F" OF THE 6-WAY ABS MOTOR PACK HARNESS CONNECTOR. DOES J 39200 DISPLAY RESISTANCE AS "OL" (INFINITE)?
YES
NO
REPAIR SHORT BETWEEN CKTs 1280 AND 1281.
4
• USING J 39200, MEASURE THE RESISTANCE BETWEEN TERMINAL "E" AND TERMINAL "F" OF THE ABS MOTOR PACK. IS RESISTANCE GREATER THAN 0.4Ω?
YES
NO
REPLACE ABS MOTOR PACK.
5
• INSPECT CKTs 1280 AND 1281 AND RELATED CONNECTORS FOR DAMAGE WHICH MAY RESULT IN A SHORT TO GROUND WITH ALL CONNECTORS CONNECTED. REPAIR ALL DAMAGE IF EVIDENT.
• RECONNECT ALL CONNECTORS.
• IGNITION "OFF."
• START ENGINE AND TEST DRIVE VEHICLE, ACHIEVING AT LEAST 16 km.h (10 MPH).
• REPEAT ABOVE DRIVE CYCLE SEQUENCE TWO MORE TIMES. DID DTC 58 SET IN THE LAST THREE DRIVE CYCLES?
YES
NO
REPLACE EBCM
MALFUNCTION WAS MOST LIKELY CAUSED BY A POOR CONNECTION. REFER TO "DIAGNOSTIC AIDS".

GC402940110000EX

Fig. 272 Code A058: Left Front ABS Motor Circuit Shorted To Battery (Part 2 of 2). 1993-94 Camaro & Firebird, 1994 Grand Prix, Century & Cutlass Ciera & Cruiser

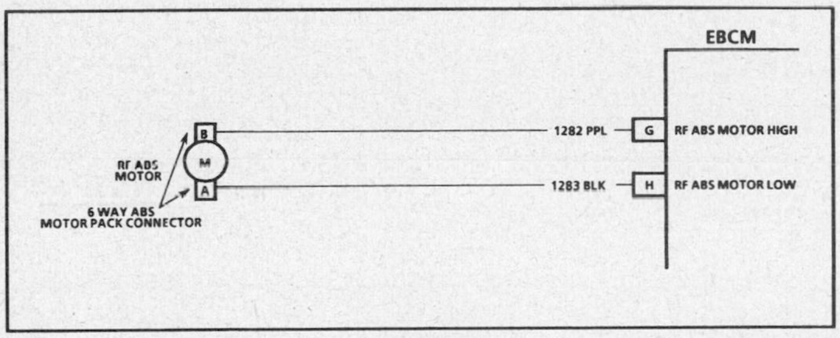

EBCM
RF ABS MOTOR
M
B
A
6 WAY ABS MOTOR PACK CONNECTOR
1282 PPL
1283 BLK
G
H
RF ABS MOTOR HIGH
RF ABS MOTOR LOW

GC402940110100AX

Grand Prix

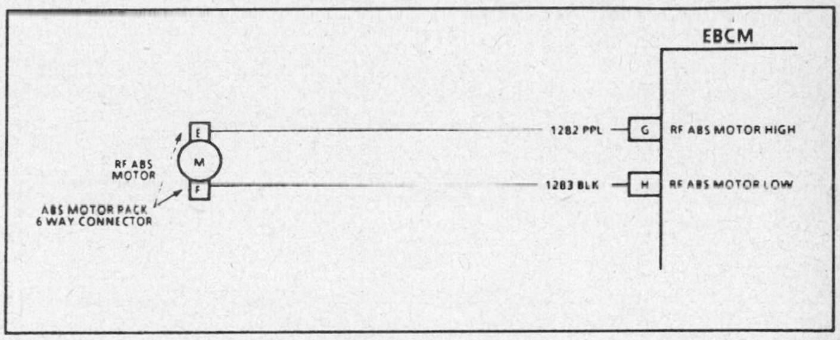

EBCM
RF ABS MOTOR
M
E
F
ABS MOTOR PACK 6 WAY CONNECTOR
1282 PPL
1283 BLK
G
H
RF ABS MOTOR HIGH
RF ABS MOTOR LOW

GC402940110100BX

Camaro & Firebird

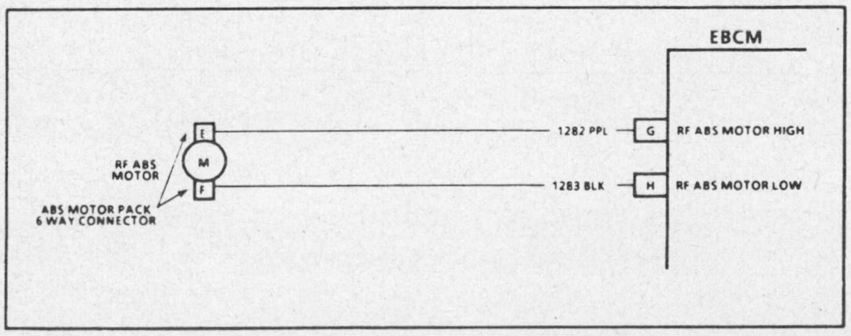

EBCM
RF ABS MOTOR
M
E
F
ABS MOTOR PACK 6 WAY CONNECTOR
1282 PPL
1283 BLK
G
H
RF ABS MOTOR HIGH
RF ABS MOTOR LOW

GC402940110100CX

Century & Cutlass Ciera & Cruiser

Fig. 273 Code A061: Right Front ABS Motor Circuit Open (Part 1 of 2). 1993-94 Camaro & Firebird, 1994 Grand Prix, Century & Cutlass Ciera & Cruiser

DTC 61

RIGHT FRONT ABS MOTOR CIRCUIT OPEN

Circuit Description:

This DTC identifies an ABS motor that cannot be energized due to an open in its circuitry. This malfunction will not allow proper front ABS operation.

DTC Will Set When: DTC 61 can be set only when the ABS motor is commanded "OFF." If the EBCM detects an out of range voltage on either of the right front ABS motor circuits indicating an open circuit, a malfunction exists.

Action Taken: An open ABS motor will not activate when requested. A malfunction DTC is stored, ABS is disabled and the ABS warning lamp is turned "ON."

DTC Chart Test Description: Number(s) below refer to circled number(s) on the diagnostic chart.

1. Checks for proper resistance of the ABS motor.
2. Checks for an open in the ABS motor "HIGH" circuitry.
3. Checks for an open in the ABS motor "LOW" circuitry.
4. Ensures malfunction was not due to physical damage of the circuitry.

Diagnostic Aids: Using Tech 1, select manual control function, and exercise ABS motor movement of affected channel in both directions while applying light pressure on the brake pedal.

If erratic or "jumpy" brake pedal movement is detected while performing an "apply" or "release" function of the ABS motor, an intermittent malfunction may be indicated.

An "Intermittent" malfunction may be caused by a poor connection, rubbed through wire insulation, or a wire that is broken inside the insulation.

If the malfunction is not current, wiggle the wires of the affected channel and check if the DTC resets. This will help to pinpoint an intermittent malfunction in the motor circuitry or connections.

The frequency of the malfunction can be checked by using the enhanced diagnostic function of the Tech 1

Any circuitry, that is suspected as causing the intermittent complaint, should be thoroughly checked for backed out terminals, improper mating, broken locks, improperly formed or damaged terminals, poor terminal to wiring connections or physical damage to the wiring harness.

GC402940110100DX

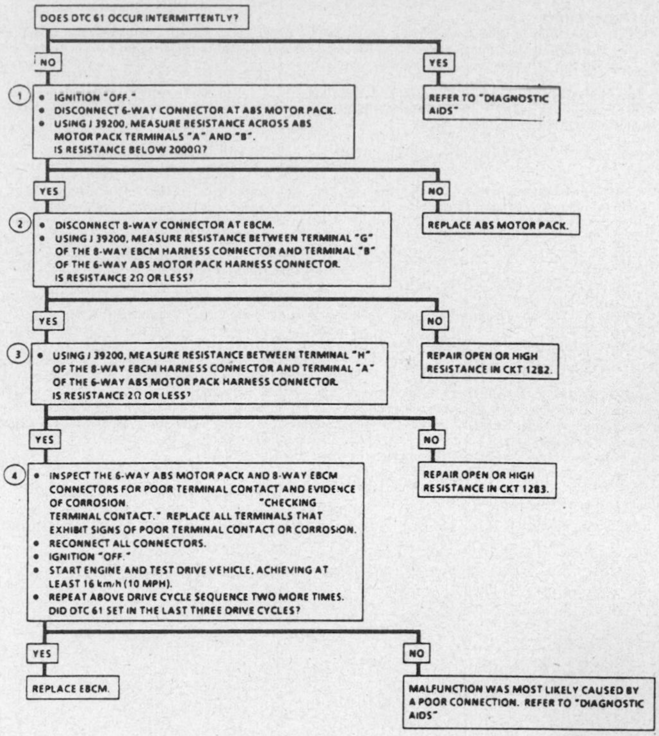
DOES DTC 61 OCCUR INTERMITTENTLY?
NO
YES
REFER TO "DIAGNOSTIC AIDS"
1
• IGNITION "OFF."
• DISCONNECT 6-WAY CONNECTOR AT ABS MOTOR PACK.
• USING J 39200, MEASURE RESISTANCE ACROSS ABS MOTOR PACK TERMINALS "A" AND "B".
IS RESISTANCE BELOW 2000Ω?
YES
NO
REPLACE ABS MOTOR PACK.
2
• DISCONNECT 8-WAY CONNECTOR AT EBCM.
• USING J 39200, MEASURE RESISTANCE BETWEEN TERMINAL "G" OF THE 8-WAY EBCM HARNESS CONNECTOR AND TERMINAL "B" OF THE 6-WAY ABS MOTOR PACK HARNESS CONNECTOR.
IS RESISTANCE 2Ω OR LESS?
YES
NO
REPAIR OPEN OR HIGH RESISTANCE IN CKT 1282.
3
• USING J 39200, MEASURE RESISTANCE BETWEEN TERMINAL "H" OF THE 8-WAY EBCM HARNESS CONNECTOR AND TERMINAL "A" OF THE 6-WAY ABS MOTOR PACK HARNESS CONNECTOR.
IS RESISTANCE 2Ω OR LESS?
YES
NO
REPAIR OPEN OR HIGH RESISTANCE IN CKT 1283.
4
• INSPECT THE 6-WAY ABS MOTOR PACK AND 8-WAY EBCM CONNECTORS FOR POOR TERMINAL CONTACT AND EVIDENCE OF CORROSION. "CHECKING TERMINAL CONTACT." REPLACE ALL TERMINALS THAT EXHIBIT SIGNS OF POOR TERMINAL CONTACT OR CORROSION.
• RECONNECT ALL CONNECTORS.
• IGNITION "OFF."
• START ENGINE AND TEST DRIVE VEHICLE, ACHIEVING AT LEAST 16 km/h (10 MPH).
• REPEAT ABOVE DRIVE CYCLE SEQUENCE TWO MORE TIMES.
DID DTC 61 SET IN THE LAST THREE DRIVE CYCLES?
YES
NO
REPLACE EBCM.
MALFUNCTION WAS MOST LIKELY CAUSED BY A POOR CONNECTION. REFER TO "DIAGNOSTIC AIDS"

GC402940110100EX

Fig. 273 Code A061: Right Front ABS Motor Circuit Open (Part 2 of 2). 1993-94 Camaro & Firebird, 1994 Grand Prix, Century & Cutlass Ciera & Cruiser

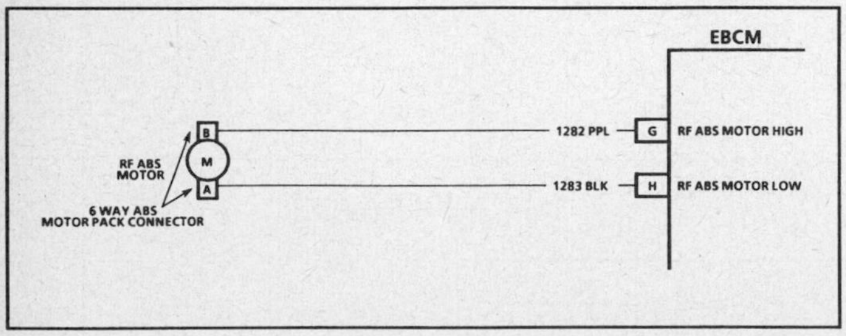
EBCM
B
M
A
RF ABS MOTOR
6 WAY ABS MOTOR PACK CONNECTOR
1282 PPL
G
RF ABS MOTOR HIGH
1283 BLK
H
RF ABS MOTOR LOW

GC402940110200AX

Grand Prix

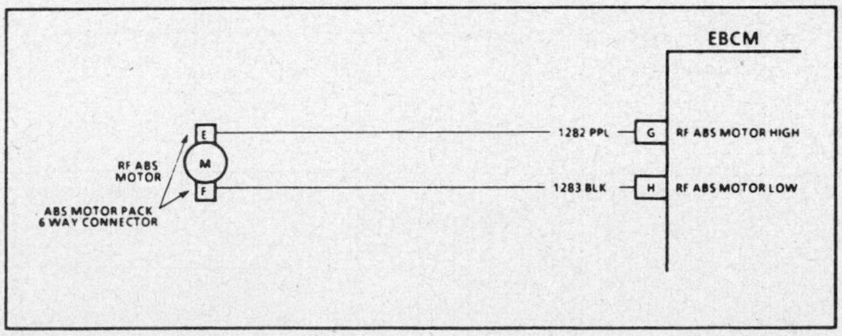
EBCM
E
M
F
RF ABS MOTOR
ABS MOTOR PACK 6 WAY CONNECTOR
1282 PPL
G
RF ABS MOTOR HIGH
1283 BLK
H
RF ABS MOTOR LOW

GC402940110200BX

Century & Cutlass Ciera & Cruiser

Fig. 274 Code A062: Right Front ABS Motor Circuit Shorted To Ground (Part 1 of 2). 1994 Grand Prix, Century & Cutlass Ciera & Cruiser

DTC 62

RIGHT FRONT ABS MOTOR CIRCUIT SHORTED TO GND

Circuit Description:
This DTC identifies an ABS motor circuit that is shorted to ground. This malfunction will not allow the ABS motor to be controlled at the commanded current rate or will cause the ABS motor driver circuit to allow current directly to ground.

DTC Will Set When: DTC 62 can be set anytime. If the EBCM detects an out of range voltage on either of the right front ABS motor circuits indicating a circuit shorted to ground, a malfunction exists.

Action Taken: A malfunction DTC is stored, ABS is disabled and the ABS warning lamp is turned "ON."

DTC Chart Test Description: Number(s) below refer to circled number(s) on the diagnostic chart.

1. Checks for a short to g. und in the ABS motor "HIGH" circuitry.
2. Checks for a short to ground in the ABS motor "LOW" circuitry.
3. Checks for an ABS motor that is internally shorted to ground.
4. Ensures malfunction was not due to physical damage of the circuitry.

Diagnostic Aids: Using Tech 1, select manual control function, and exercise ABS motor movement of affected channel in both directions while applying light pressure on the brake pedal.

If erratic or "jumpy" brake pedal movement is detected while performing an "apply" or "release" function of the ABS motor, an intermittent malfunction may be indicated.

An "Intermittent" malfunction may be caused by a poor connection, rubbed through wire insulation, or a wire that is broken inside the insulation.

If the malfunction is not current, wiggle the wires of the affected channel and check if the DTC resets. This will help to pinpoint an intermittent malfunction in the motor circuitry or connections.

The frequency of the malfunction can be checked by using the enhanced diagnostic function of the Tech 1,

Any circuitry, that is suspected as causing the intermittent complaint, should be thoroughly checked for backed out terminals, improper mating, broken locks, improperly formed or damaged terminals, poor terminal to wiring connections or physical damage to the wiring harness.

GC402940110200CX

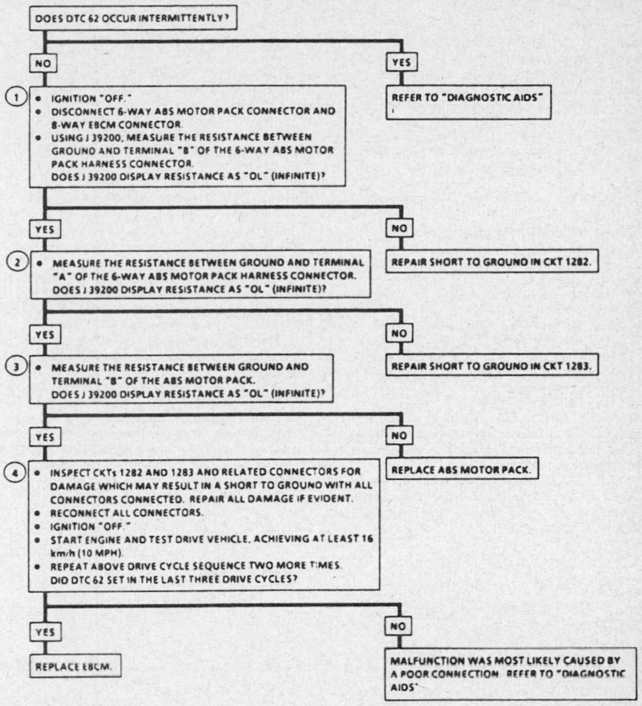
DOES DTC 62 OCCUR INTERMITTENTLY?
NO
YES
REFER TO "DIAGNOSTIC AIDS"
1
• IGNITION "OFF."
• DISCONNECT 6-WAY ABS MOTOR PACK CONNECTOR AND 8-WAY EBCM CONNECTOR.
• USING J 39200, MEASURE THE RESISTANCE BETWEEN GROUND AND TERMINAL "B" OF THE 6-WAY ABS MOTOR PACK HARNESS CONNECTOR.
DOES J 39200 DISPLAY RESISTANCE AS "OL" (INFINITE)?
YES
NO
REPAIR SHORT TO GROUND IN CKT 1282.
2
• MEASURE THE RESISTANCE BETWEEN GROUND AND TERMINAL "A" OF THE 6-WAY ABS MOTOR PACK HARNESS CONNECTOR.
DOES J 39200 DISPLAY RESISTANCE AS "OL" (INFINITE)?
YES
NO
REPAIR SHORT TO GROUND IN CKT 1283.
3
• MEASURE THE RESISTANCE BETWEEN GROUND AND TERMINAL "B" OF THE ABS MOTOR PACK.
DOES J 39200 DISPLAY RESISTANCE AS "OL" (INFINITE)?
YES
NO
REPLACE ABS MOTOR PACK.
4
• INSPECT CKTs 1282 AND 1283 AND RELATED CONNECTORS FOR DAMAGE WHICH MAY RESULT IN A SHORT TO GROUND WITH ALL CONNECTORS CONNECTED. REPAIR ALL DAMAGE IF EVIDENT.
• RECONNECT ALL CONNECTORS.
• IGNITION "OFF."
• START ENGINE AND TEST DRIVE VEHICLE, ACHIEVING AT LEAST 16 km/h (10 MPH).
• REPEAT ABOVE DRIVE CYCLE SEQUENCE TWO MORE TIMES.
DID DTC 62 SET IN THE LAST THREE DRIVE CYCLES?
YES
REPLACE EBCM.
NO
MALFUNCTION WAS MOST LIKELY CAUSED BY A POOR CONNECTION. REFER TO "DIAGNOSTIC AIDS"

GC402940110200DX

Fig. 274 Code A062: Right Front ABS Motor Circuit Shorted To Ground (Part 2 of 2). 1994 Grand Prix, Century & Cutlass Ciera & Cruiser

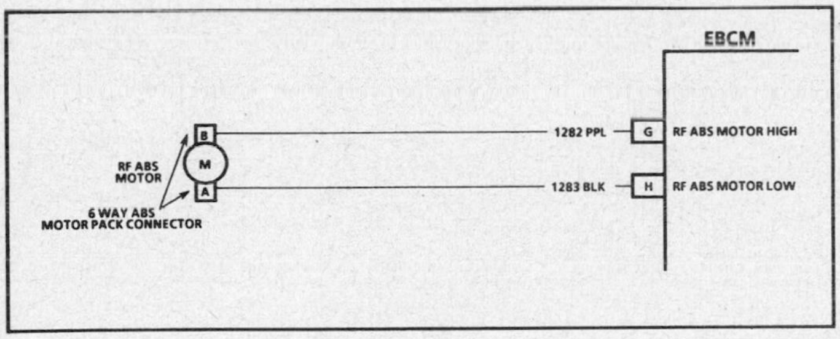
EBCM
RF ABS MOTOR
6 WAY ABS MOTOR PACK CONNECTOR
B
A
M
1282 PPL
G
RF ABS MOTOR HIGH
1283 BLK
H
RF ABS MOTOR LOW

GC402940110300AX

Grand Prix

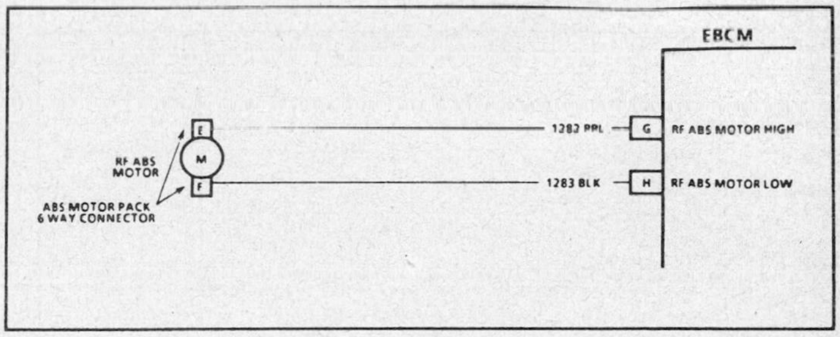
EBCM
RF ABS MOTOR
ABS MOTOR PACK 6 WAY CONNECTOR
E
F
M
1282 PPL
G
RF ABS MOTOR HIGH
1283 BLK
H
RF ABS MOTOR LOW

GC402940110300BX

Camaro & Firebird

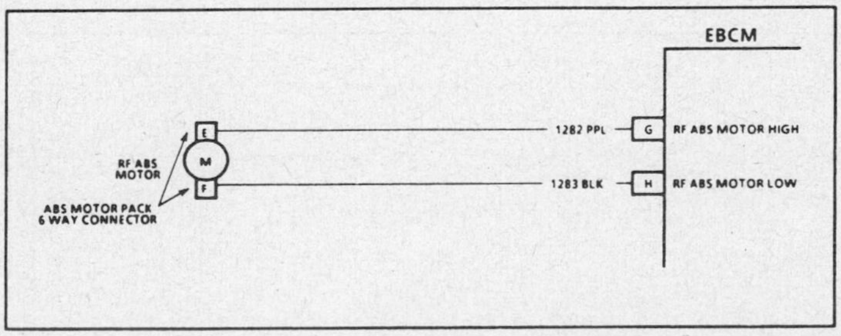
EBCM
RF ABS MOTOR
ABS MOTOR PACK 6 WAY CONNECTOR
E
F
M
1282 PPL
G
RF ABS MOTOR HIGH
1283 BLK
H
RF ABS MOTOR LOW

GC402940110300CX

Century & Cutlass Ciera & Cruiser

Fig. 275 Code A063: Right Front ABS Motor Circuit Shorted To Battery (Part 1 of 2). 1993-94 Camaro & Firebird, 1994 Grand Prix, Century & Cutlass Ciera & Cruiser

DTC 63

RIGHT FRONT ABS MOTOR CIRCUIT SHORTED TO BATT

Circuit Description:
This DTC identifies an ABS motor circuit that is shorted to battery or an ABS motor that has low or no resistance. This malfunction will not allow the ABS motor to be controlled at the commanded current rate or will cause the ABS motor to turn in the opposite direction or not at all.

DTC Will Set When: DTC 63 can be set only when the ABS motor is commanded "OFF." If the EBCM detects an out of range voltage on either of the right front ABS motor circuits indicating a circuit shorted to battery or an ABS motor shorted, a malfunction exists.

Action Taken: A malfunction DTC is stored, ABS is disabled and the ABS warning lamp is turned "ON."

DTC Chart Test Description: Number(s) below refer to circled number(s) on the diagnostic chart.

1. Checks for a short to voltage in the ABS motor "HIGH" circuitry.
2. Checks for a short to voltage in the ABS motor "LOW" circuitry.
3. Checks for a short circuit between ABS motor "HIGH" and ABS motor "LOW."
4. Checks for proper resistance of the ABS motor.
5. Ensures malfunction was not due to physical damage of the circuitry.

Diagnostic Aids: Using Tech 1, select manual control function, and exercise ABS motor movement of affected channel in both directions while applying light pressure on the brake pedal.

If erratic or "jumpy" brake pedal movement is detected while performing an "apply" or "release" function of the ABS motor, an intermittent malfunction may be indicated.

An "Intermittent" malfunction may be caused by a poor connection, rubbed through wire insulation, or a wire that is broken inside the insulation.

If the malfunction is not current, wiggle the wires of the affected channel and check if the DTC resets. This will help to pinpoint an intermittent malfunction in the motor circuitry or connections.

The frequency of the malfunction can be checked by using the enhanced diagnostic function of the Tech 1

Any circuitry, that is suspected as causing the intermittent complaint, should be thoroughly checked for backed out terminals, improper mating, broken locks, improperly formed or damaged terminals, poor terminal to wiring connections or physical damage to the wiring harness.

GC402940110300DX

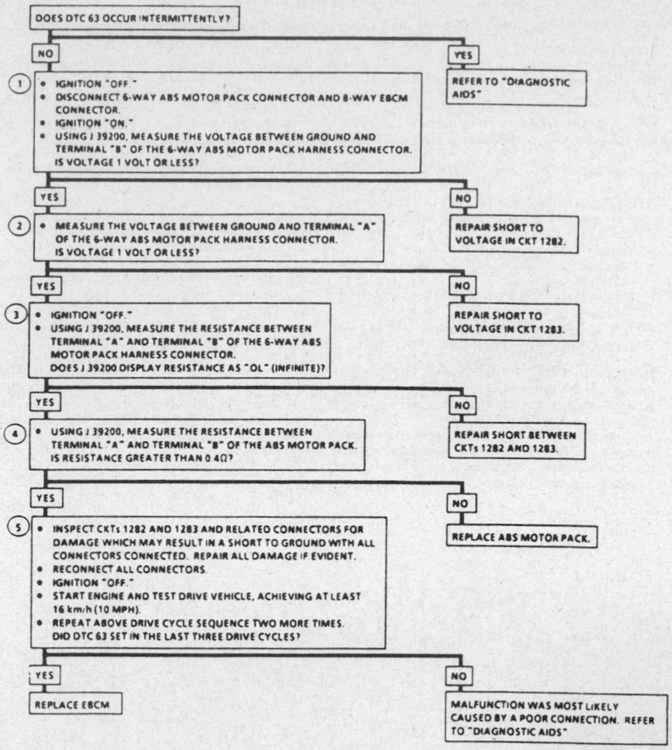
DOES DTC 63 OCCUR INTERMITTENTLY?
NO
YES
REFER TO "DIAGNOSTIC AIDS"
1
• IGNITION "OFF."
• DISCONNECT 6-WAY ABS MOTOR PACK CONNECTOR AND 8-WAY EBCM CONNECTOR.
• IGNITION "ON."
• USING J 39200, MEASURE THE VOLTAGE BETWEEN GROUND AND TERMINAL "B" OF THE 6-WAY ABS MOTOR PACK HARNESS CONNECTOR. IS VOLTAGE 1 VOLT OR LESS?
YES
NO
REPAIR SHORT TO VOLTAGE IN CKT 1282.
2
• MEASURE THE VOLTAGE BETWEEN GROUND AND TERMINAL "A" OF THE 6-WAY ABS MOTOR PACK HARNESS CONNECTOR. IS VOLTAGE 1 VOLT OR LESS?
YES
NO
REPAIR SHORT TO VOLTAGE IN CKT 1283.
3
• IGNITION "OFF."
• USING J 39200, MEASURE THE RESISTANCE BETWEEN TERMINAL "A" AND TERMINAL "B" OF THE 6-WAY ABS MOTOR PACK HARNESS CONNECTOR. DOES J 39200 DISPLAY RESISTANCE AS "OL" (INFINITE)?
YES
NO
REPAIR SHORT BETWEEN CKTs 1282 AND 1283.
4
• USING J 39200, MEASURE THE RESISTANCE BETWEEN TERMINAL "A" AND TERMINAL "B" OF THE ABS MOTOR PACK. IS RESISTANCE GREATER THAN 0.4Ω?
YES
NO
REPLACE ABS MOTOR PACK.
5
• INSPECT CKTs 1282 AND 1283 AND RELATED CONNECTORS FOR DAMAGE WHICH MAY RESULT IN A SHORT TO GROUND WITH ALL CONNECTORS CONNECTED. REPAIR ALL DAMAGE IF EVIDENT.
• RECONNECT ALL CONNECTORS.
• IGNITION "OFF."
• START ENGINE AND TEST DRIVE VEHICLE, ACHIEVING AT LEAST 16 km/h (10 MPH).
• REPEAT ABOVE DRIVE CYCLE SEQUENCE TWO MORE TIMES. DID DTC 63 SET IN THE LAST THREE DRIVE CYCLES?
YES
REPLACE EBCM
NO
MALFUNCTION WAS MOST LIKELY CAUSED BY A POOR CONNECTION. REFER TO "DIAGNOSTIC AIDS"

GC402940110300EX

Fig. 275 Code A063: Right Front ABS Motor Circuit Shorted To Battery (Part 2 of 2). 1993-94 Camaro & Firebird, 1994 Grand Prix, Century & Cutlass Ciera & Cruiser

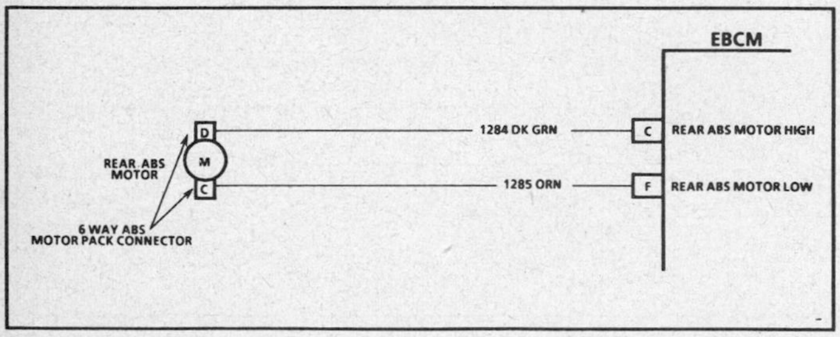
EBCM
D
C
M
REAR ABS MOTOR
6 WAY ABS MOTOR PACK CONNECTOR
1284 DK GRN
1285 ORN
C
F
REAR ABS MOTOR HIGH
REAR ABS MOTOR LOW

GC402940110400AX

Grand Prix

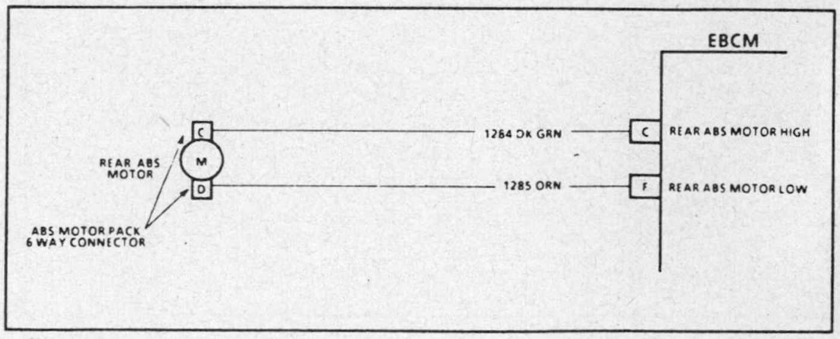
EBCM
C
D
M
REAR ABS MOTOR
ABS MOTOR PACK 6 WAY CONNECTOR
1284 DK GRN
1285 ORN
C
F
REAR ABS MOTOR HIGH
REAR ABS MOTOR LOW

GC402940110400BX

Camaro & Firebird

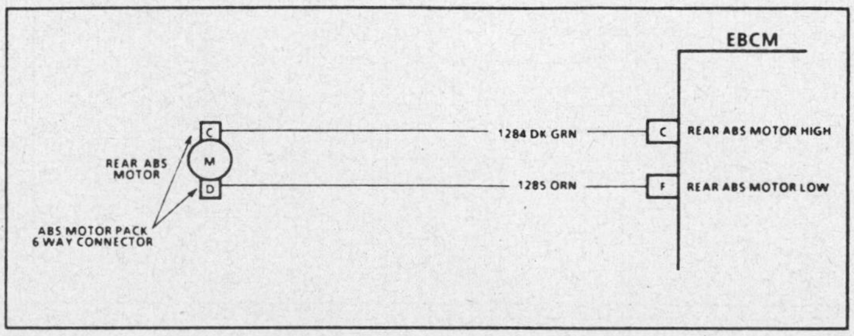
EBCM
C
D
M
REAR ABS MOTOR
ABS MOTOR PACK 6 WAY CONNECTOR
1284 DK GRN
1285 ORN
C
F
REAR ABS MOTOR HIGH
REAR ABS MOTOR LOW

GC402940110400CX

Century & Cutlass Ciera & Cruiser

Fig. 276 Code A064: Rear ABS Motor Circuit Open (Part 1 of 2). 1993-94 Camaro & Firebird, 1994 Grand Prix, Century & Cutlass Ciera & Cruiser

DTC 64

REAR ABS MOTOR CIRCUIT OPEN

Circuit Description:
This DTC identifies an ABS motor that cannot be energized due to an open in its circuitry. This malfunction will not allow proper rear ABS operation.

DTC Will Set When: DTC 64 can be set only when the ABS motor is commanded "OFF." If the EBCM detects an out of range voltage on either of the rear ABS motor circuits indicating an open circuit, a malfunction exists.

Action Taken: An open motor will not activate when requested. A malfunction DTC is stored, ABS is disabled and the ABS warning lamp is turned "ON."

DTC Chart Test Description: Number(s) below refer to circled number(s) on the diagnostic chart.

1. Checks for proper resistance of the ABS motor.
2. Checks for an open in the ABS motor "HIGH" circuitry.
3. Checks for an open in the ABS motor "LOW" circuitry.
4. Ensures malfunction was not due to poor terminal contact.

Diagnostic Aids: Using Tech 1, select manual control function, and exercise ABS motor movement of affected channel in both directions while applying light pressure on the brake pedal.

If erratic or "jumpy" brake pedal movement is detected while performing an "apply" or "release" function of the ABS motor, an intermittent malfunction may be indicated.

An "Intermittent" malfunction may be caused by a poor connection, rubbed through wire insulation, or a wire that is broken inside the insulation.

If the malfunction is not current, wiggle the wires of the affected channel and check if the DTC resets. This will help to pinpoint an intermittent malfunction in the motor circuitry or connections.

The frequency of the malfunction can be checked by using the enhanced diagnostic function of the Tech 1,

Any circuitry, that is suspected as causing the intermittent complaint, should be thoroughly checked for backed out terminals, improper mating, broken locks, improperly formed or damaged terminals, poor terminal to wiring connections or physical damage to the wiring harness.

GC402940110400DX

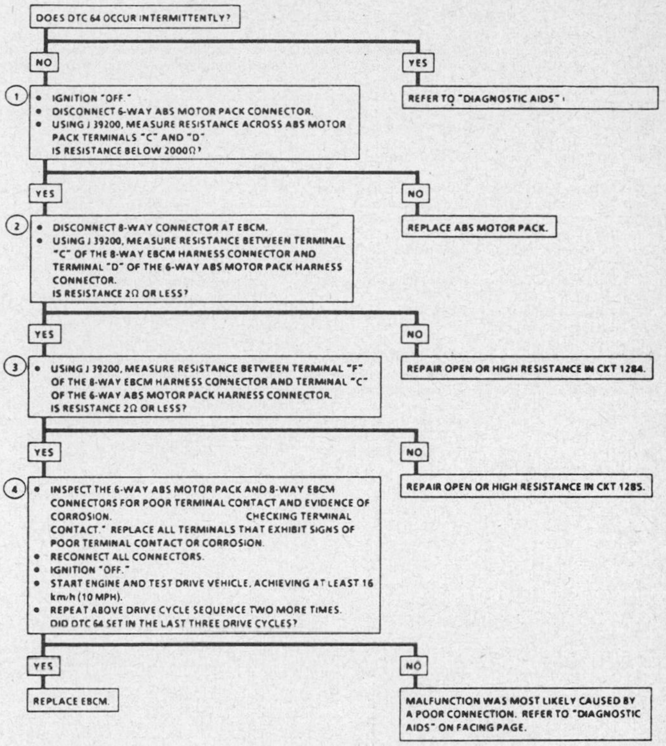

DOES DTC 64 OCCUR INTERMITTENTLY?
NO
YES
REFER TO "DIAGNOSTIC AIDS"
1
IGNITION "OFF."
DISCONNECT 6-WAY ABS MOTOR PACK CONNECTOR.
USING J 39200, MEASURE RESISTANCE ACROSS ABS MOTOR PACK TERMINALS "C" AND "D".
IS RESISTANCE BELOW 2000Ω?
YES
NO
REPLACE ABS MOTOR PACK.
2
DISCONNECT 8-WAY CONNECTOR AT EBCM.
USING J 39200, MEASURE RESISTANCE BETWEEN TERMINAL "C" OF THE 8-WAY EBCM HARNESS CONNECTOR AND TERMINAL "D" OF THE 6-WAY ABS MOTOR PACK HARNESS CONNECTOR.
IS RESISTANCE 2Ω OR LESS?
YES
NO
REPAIR OPEN OR HIGH RESISTANCE IN CKT 1284.
3
USING J 39200, MEASURE RESISTANCE BETWEEN TERMINAL "F" OF THE 8-WAY EBCM HARNESS CONNECTOR AND TERMINAL "C" OF THE 6-WAY ABS MOTOR PACK HARNESS CONNECTOR.
IS RESISTANCE 2Ω OR LESS?
YES
NO
REPAIR OPEN OR HIGH RESISTANCE IN CKT 1285.
4
INSPECT THE 6-WAY ABS MOTOR PACK AND 8-WAY EBCM CONNECTORS FOR POOR TERMINAL CONTACT AND EVIDENCE OF CORROSION. CHECKING TERMINAL CONTACT." REPLACE ALL TERMINALS THAT EXHIBIT SIGNS OF POOR TERMINAL CONTACT OR CORROSION.
RECONNECT ALL CONNECTORS.
IGNITION "OFF."
START ENGINE AND TEST DRIVE VEHICLE, ACHIEVING AT LEAST 16 km/h (10 MPH).
REPEAT ABOVE DRIVE CYCLE SEQUENCE TWO MORE TIMES.
DID DTC 64 SET IN THE LAST THREE DRIVE CYCLES?
YES
NO
REPLACE EBCM.
MALFUNCTION WAS MOST LIKELY CAUSED BY A POOR CONNECTION. REFER TO "DIAGNOSTIC AIDS" ON FACING PAGE.

GC402940110400EX

Fig. 276 Code A064: Rear ABS Motor Circuit Open (Part 2 of 2). 1993-94 Camaro & Firebird, 1994 Grand Prix, Century & Cutlass Ciera & Cruiser

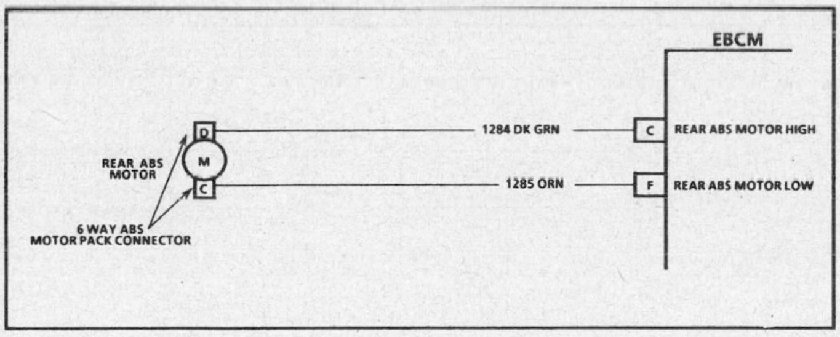

EBCM
1284 DK GRN
C
REAR ABS MOTOR HIGH
REAR ABS MOTOR
D
M
C
1285 ORN
F
REAR ABS MOTOR LOW
6 WAY ABS MOTOR PACK CONNECTOR

GC402940110500DX

Century & Cutlass Ciera & Cruiser

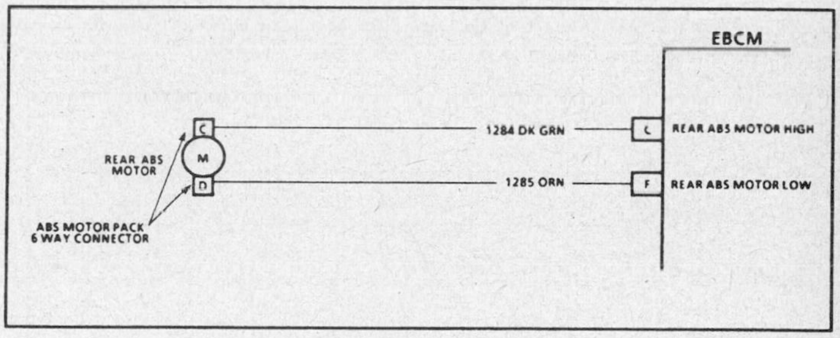

EBCM
1284 DK GRN
C
REAR ABS MOTOR HIGH
REAR ABS MOTOR
M
D
1285 ORN
F
REAR ABS MOTOR LOW
ABS MOTOR PACK 6 WAY CONNECTOR

GC402940110500BX

Camaro & Firebird

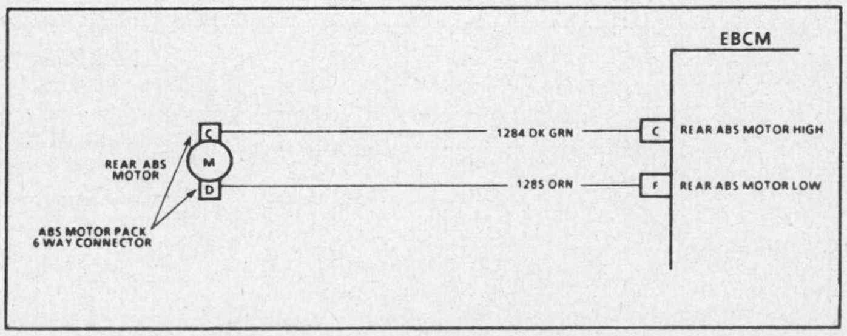

EBCM
1284 DK GRN
C
REAR ABS MOTOR HIGH
REAR ABS MOTOR
M
D
1285 ORN
F
REAR ABS MOTOR LOW
ABS MOTOR PACK 6 WAY CONNECTOR

GC402940110500CX

Century & Cutlass Ciera & Cruiser

Fig. 277 Code A065: Rear ABS Motor Circuit Shorted To Ground (Part 1 of 2). 1993-94 Camaro & Firebird, 1994 Grand Prix, Century Cutlass Ciera & Cruiser

DTC 65

REAR ABS MOTOR CIRCUIT SHORTED TO GROUND

Circuit Description:
This DTC identifies an ABS motor circuit that is shorted to ground. This malfunction will not allow the ABS motor to be controlled at the commanded current rate or will cause the driver circuit to allow current directly to ground.

DTC Will Set When: DTC 65 can be set anytime. If the EBCM detects an out of range voltage on either of the rear ABS motor circuits indicating a circuit shorted to ground, a malfunction exists.

Action Taken: A malfunction DTC is stored, ABS is disabled and the ABS warning lamp is turned "ON."

DTC Chart Test Description: Number(s) below refer to circled number(s) on the diagnostic chart.

1. Checks for a short to ground in the ABS motor "HIGH" circuitry.
2. Checks for a short to ground in the ABS motor "LOW" circuitry.
3. Checks for an ABS motor that is internally shorted to ground.
4. Ensures malfunction was not due to physical damage.

Diagnostic Aids: Using Tech 1, select manual control function, and exercise ABS motor movement of affected channel in both directions while applying light pressure on the brake pedal.

If erratic or "jumpy" brake pedal movement is detected while performing an "apply" or "release" function of the ABS motor, an intermittent malfunction may be indicated.

An "Intermittent" malfunction may be caused by a poor connection, rubbed through wire insulation, or a wire that is broken inside the insulation.

If the malfunction is not current, wiggle the wires of the affected channel and check if the DTC resets. This will help to pinpoint an intermittent malfunction in the motor circuitry or connections.

The frequency of the malfunction can be checked by using the enhanced diagnostic function of the Tech 1,

Any circuitry, that is suspected as causing the intermittent complaint, should be thoroughly checked for backed out terminals, improper mating, broken locks, improperly formed or damaged terminals, poor terminal to wiring connections or physical damage to the wiring harness.

GC402940110500AX

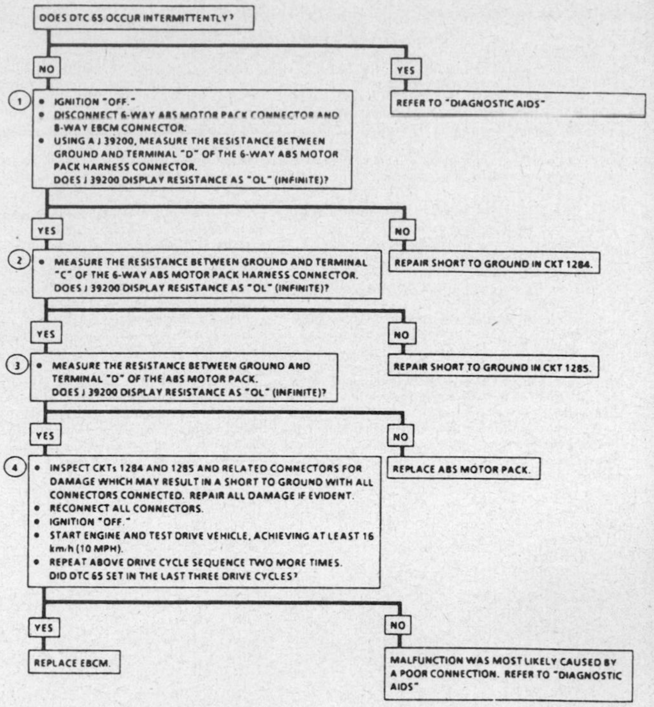
DOES DTC 65 OCCUR INTERMITTENTLY?
NO
YES
REFER TO "DIAGNOSTIC AIDS"
1
• IGNITION "OFF."
• DISCONNECT 6-WAY ABS MOTOR PACK CONNECTOR AND 8-WAY EBCM CONNECTOR.
• USING A J 39200, MEASURE THE RESISTANCE BETWEEN GROUND AND TERMINAL "D" OF THE 6-WAY ABS MOTOR PACK HARNESS CONNECTOR.
DOES J 39200 DISPLAY RESISTANCE AS "OL" (INFINITE)?
YES
NO
REPAIR SHORT TO GROUND IN CKT 1284.
2
• MEASURE THE RESISTANCE BETWEEN GROUND AND TERMINAL "C" OF THE 6-WAY ABS MOTOR PACK HARNESS CONNECTOR.
DOES J 39200 DISPLAY RESISTANCE AS "OL" (INFINITE)?
YES
NO
REPAIR SHORT TO GROUND IN CKT 1285.
3
• MEASURE THE RESISTANCE BETWEEN GROUND AND TERMINAL "D" OF THE ABS MOTOR PACK.
DOES J 39200 DISPLAY RESISTANCE AS "OL" (INFINITE)?
YES
NO
REPLACE ABS MOTOR PACK.
4
• INSPECT CKTs 1284 AND 1285 AND RELATED CONNECTORS FOR DAMAGE WHICH MAY RESULT IN A SHORT TO GROUND WITH ALL CONNECTORS CONNECTED. REPAIR ALL DAMAGE IF EVIDENT.
• RECONNECT ALL CONNECTORS.
• IGNITION "OFF."
• START ENGINE AND TEST DRIVE VEHICLE, ACHIEVING AT LEAST 16 km/h (10 MPH).
• REPEAT ABOVE DRIVE CYCLE SEQUENCE TWO MORE TIMES.
DID DTC 65 SET IN THE LAST THREE DRIVE CYCLES?
YES
NO
REPLACE EBCM.
MALFUNCTION WAS MOST LIKELY CAUSED BY A POOR CONNECTION. REFER TO "DIAGNOSTIC AIDS"

GC402940110500EX

Fig. 277 Code A065: Rear ABS Motor Circuit Shorted To Ground (Part 2 of 2). 1993-94 Camaro & Firebird, 1994 Grand Prix, Century Cutlass Ciera & Cruiser

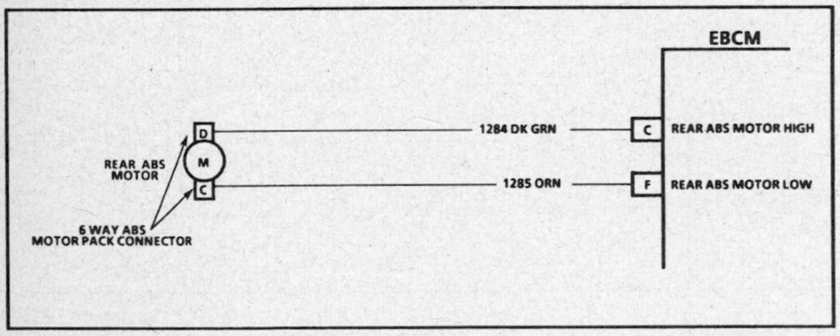
EBCM
D
M
C
REAR ABS MOTOR
6 WAY ABS MOTOR PACK CONNECTOR
1284 DK GRN
1285 ORN
C
F
REAR ABS MOTOR HIGH
REAR ABS MOTOR LOW

GC402940110600AX

Grand Prix

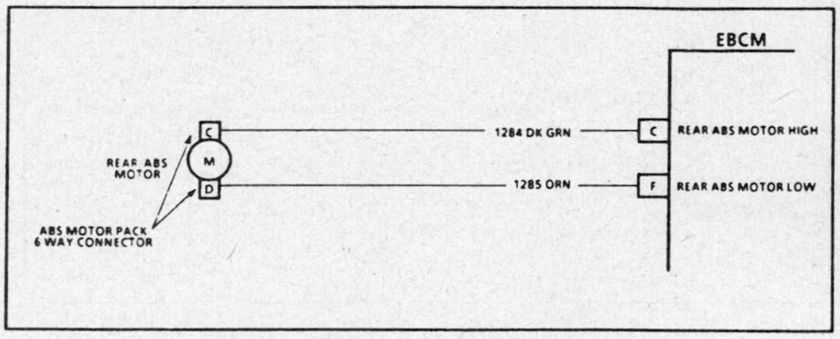
EBCM
C
M
D
REAR ABS MOTOR
ABS MOTOR PACK 6 WAY CONNECTOR
1284 DK GRN
1285 ORN
C
F
REAR ABS MOTOR HIGH
REAR ABS MOTOR LOW

GC402940110600BX

Camaro & Firebird

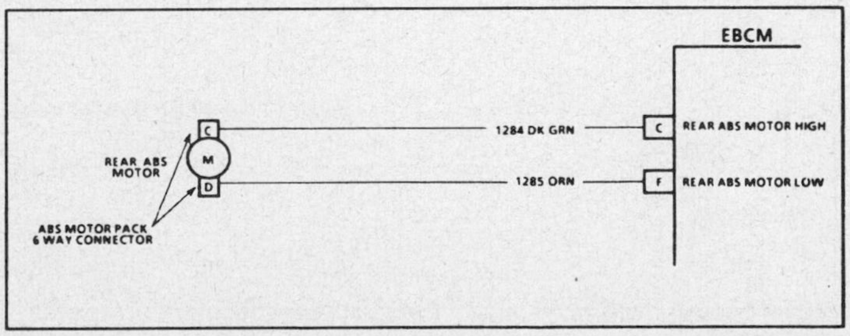
EBCM
C
M
D
REAR ABS MOTOR
ABS MOTOR PACK 6 WAY CONNECTOR
1284 DK GRN
1285 ORN
C
F
REAR ABS MOTOR HIGH
REAR ABS MOTOR LOW

GC402940110600CX

Century & Cutlass Ciera & Cruiser

Fig. 278 Code A066: Rear ABS Motor Circuit Shorted To Battery (Part 1 of 2). 1993-94 Camaro & Firebird, 1994 Grand Prix, Century & Cutlass Ciera & Cruiser

DTC 66

REAR ABS MOTOR CIRCUIT SHORTED TO BATTERY

Circuit Description:

This DTC identifies an ABS motor circuit that is shorted to battery or an ABS motor that has low or zero resistance. This malfunction will not allow the ABS motor to be controlled at the commanded current rate or will cause the ABS motor to turn in the opposite direction or not turn at all.

DTC Will Set When: DTC 66 can be set only when the ABS motor is commanded "OFF." If the EBCM detects an out of range voltage on either of the rear ABS motor circuits indicating a circuit shorted to battery or an ABS motor shorted, a malfunction exists.

Action Taken: A malfunction DTC is stored, ABS is disabled and the ABS warning lamp is turned "ON."

DTC Chart Test Description: Number(s) below refer to circled number(s) on the diagnostic chart.

1. Checks for a short to voltage in the ABS motor "HIGH" circuitry.
2. Checks for a short to voltage in the ABS motor "LOW" circuitry.
3. Checks for a short circuit between ABS motor "HIGH" and ABS motor "LOW."
4. Checks for proper resistance of the ABS motor.
5. Ensures malfunction was not due to physical damage of the circuitry.

Diagnostic Aids: Using Tech 1, select manual control function, and exercise ABS motor movement of affected channel in both directions while applying light pressure on the brake pedal.

If erratic or "jumpy" brake pedal movement is detected while performing an "apply" or "release" function of the ABS motor, an intermittent malfunction may be indicated.

An "Intermittent" malfunction may be caused by a poor connection, rubbed through wire insulation, or a wire that is broken inside the insulation.

If the malfunction is not current, wiggle the wires of the affected channel and check if the DTC resets. This will help to pinpoint an intermittent malfunction in the motor circuitry or connections.

The frequency of the malfunction can be checked by using the enhanced diagnostic function of the Tech 1,

Any circuitry, that is suspected as causing the intermittent complaint, should be thoroughly checked for backed out terminals, improper mating, broken locks, improperly formed or damaged terminals, poor terminal to wiring connections or physical damage to the wiring harness.

GC402940110600DX

NOTICE: J 39200 TEST LEADS MUST BE "ZEROED" PRIOR TO MAKING ANY RESISTANCE MEASUREMENTS. REFER TO J 39200 USER'S MANUAL.

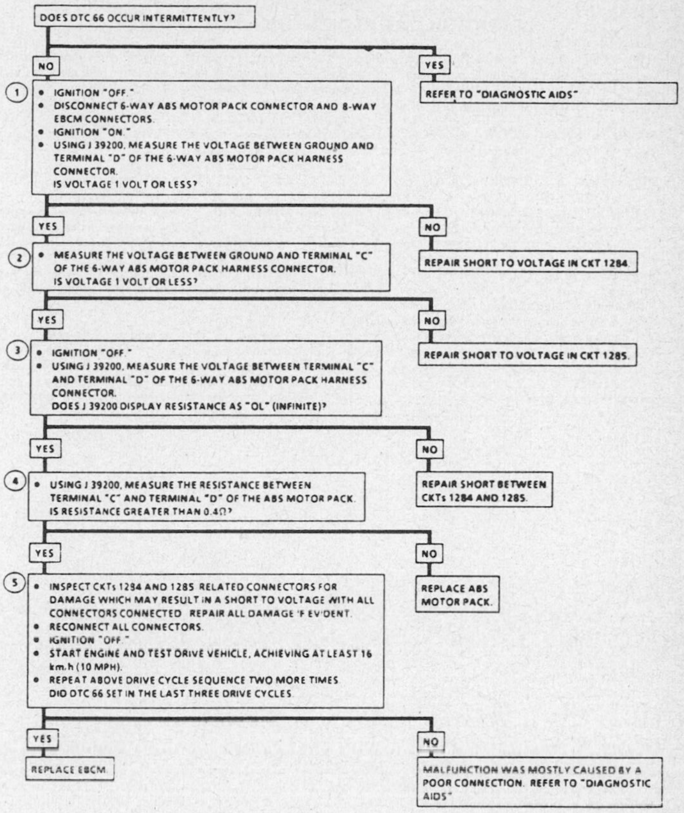
DOES DTC 66 OCCUR INTERMITTENTLY?
NO
YES
REFER TO "DIAGNOSTIC AIDS"
1
• IGNITION "OFF."
• DISCONNECT 6-WAY ABS MOTOR PACK CONNECTOR AND 8-WAY EBCM CONNECTORS.
• IGNITION "ON."
• USING J 39200, MEASURE THE VOLTAGE BETWEEN GROUND AND TERMINAL "D" OF THE 6-WAY ABS MOTOR PACK HARNESS CONNECTOR.
IS VOLTAGE 1 VOLT OR LESS?
YES
NO
REPAIR SHORT TO VOLTAGE IN CKT 1284.
2
• MEASURE THE VOLTAGE BETWEEN GROUND AND TERMINAL "C" OF THE 6-WAY ABS MOTOR PACK HARNESS CONNECTOR.
IS VOLTAGE 1 VOLT OR LESS?
YES
NO
REPAIR SHORT TO VOLTAGE IN CKT 1285.
3
• IGNITION "OFF."
• USING J 39200, MEASURE THE VOLTAGE BETWEEN TERMINAL "C" AND TERMINAL "D" OF THE 6-WAY ABS MOTOR PACK HARNESS CONNECTOR.
DOES J 39200 DISPLAY RESISTANCE AS "OL" (INFINITE)?
YES
NO
REPAIR SHORT BETWEEN CKTs 1284 AND 1285.
4
• USING J 39200, MEASURE THE RESISTANCE BETWEEN TERMINAL "C" AND TERMINAL "D" OF THE ABS MOTOR PACK.
IS RESISTANCE GREATER THAN 0.4Ω?
YES
NO
REPLACE ABS MOTOR PACK.
5
• INSPECT CKTs 1284 AND 1285 RELATED CONNECTORS FOR DAMAGE WHICH MAY RESULT IN A SHORT TO VOLTAGE WITH ALL CONNECTORS CONNECTED. REPAIR ALL DAMAGE IF EVIDENT.
• RECONNECT ALL CONNECTORS.
• IGNITION "OFF."
• START ENGINE AND TEST DRIVE VEHICLE, ACHIEVING AT LEAST 16 km/h (10 MPH).
• REPEAT ABOVE DRIVE CYCLE SEQUENCE TWO MORE TIMES.
DID DTC 66 SET IN THE LAST THREE DRIVE CYCLES.
YES
NO
REPLACE EBCM.
MALFUNCTION WAS MOSTLY CAUSED BY A POOR CONNECTION. REFER TO "DIAGNOSTIC AIDS"

GC402940110600EX

Fig. 278 Code A066: Rear ABS Motor Circuit Shorted To Battery (Part 2 of 2). 1993-94 Camaro & Firebird, 1994 Grand Prix, Century & Cutlass Ciera & Cruiser

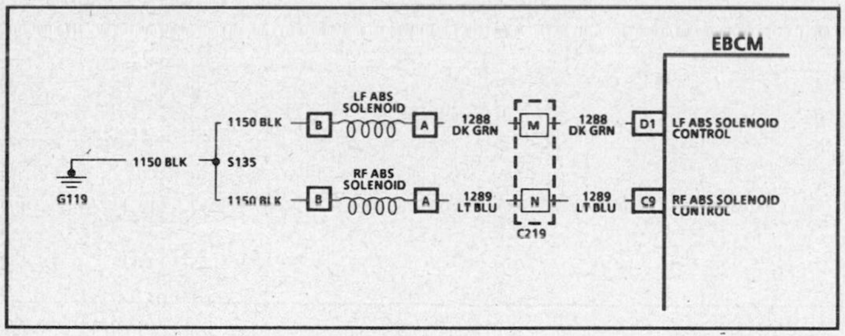
EBCM
LF ABS SOLENOID
1150 BLK
B
A
1288 DK GRN
M
1288 DK GRN
D1
LF ABS SOLENOID CONTROL
1150 BLK
S135
G119
RF ABS SOLENOID
1150 BLK
B
A
1289 LT BLU
N
1289 LT BLU
C9
RF ABS SOLENOID CONTROL
C219

GC402940110700AX

Grand Prix

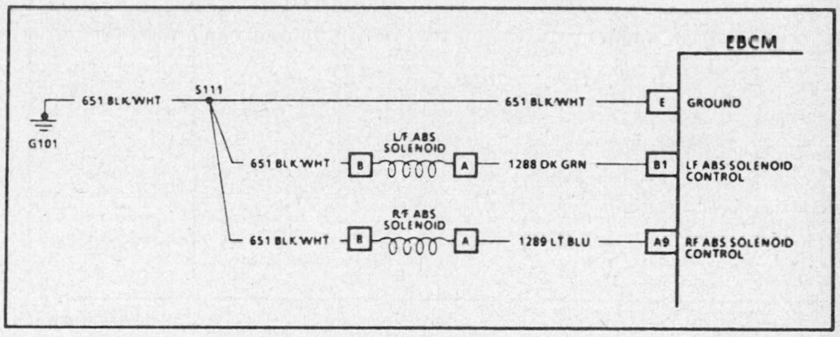
EBCM
S111
651 BLK/WHT
651 BLK/WHT
E
GROUND
G101
LF ABS SOLENOID
651 BLK/WHT
B
A
1288 DK GRN
B1
LF ABS SOLENOID CONTROL
RF ABS SOLENOID
651 BLK/WHT
B
A
1289 LT BLU
A9
RF ABS SOLENOID CONTROL

GC402940110700BX

Camaro & Firebird

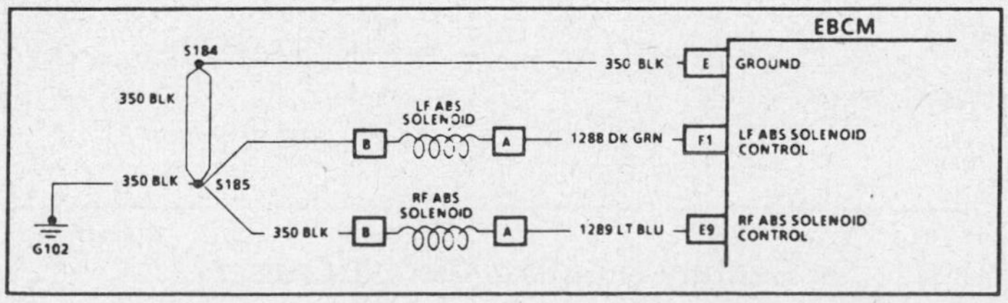
EBCM
S184
350 BLK
E
GROUND
350 BLK
LF ABS SOLENOID
B
A
1288 DK GRN
F1
LF ABS SOLENOID CONTROL
350 BLK
S185
G102
RF ABS SOLENOID
350 BLK
B
A
1289 LT BLU
E9
RF ABS SOLENOID CONTROL

GC402940110700CX

Century & Cutlass Ciera & Cruiser

Fig. 279 Code A076: Left Front Solenoid Circuit Open Or Shorted To Battery (Part 1 of 2). 1993-94 Camaro & Firebird, 1994 Grand Prix, Century & Cutlass Ciera & Cruiser

DTC 76

LEFT FRONT SOL CIRCUIT OPEN OR SHORTED TO BATT

Circuit Description:

This DTC identifies a solenoid that cannot be energized due to an open in its circuitry, or a solenoid that is always energized due to a short to battery in its circuitry between the driver and the solenoid. An open will not allow proper ABS operation, but the short to battery simply turns "ON" the solenoid. A path for base brakes is still allowed once the motor rehomes and the check ball is lifted off its seat during key "ON" initialization.

DTC Will Set When: DTC 76 can be set only when the solenoid is commanded "OFF." If the EBCM detects an excessive voltage in the left front solenoid control circuit, a malfunction exists.

Action Taken: A malfunction DTC is stored, ABS is disabled and the ABS warning lamp is turned "ON."

DTC Chart Test Description: Number(s) below refer to circled number(s) on the diagnostic chart.

1. Checks for a short to voltage in the control circuitry of the solenoid.
2. Checks for an open in the control circuit of the solenoid.
3. Checks the solenoid coil for proper resistance.
4. Checks for an open in the solenoid ground circuit.
5. Checks for a possible intermittent malfunction in the solenoid circuitry due to poor terminal contact.

Diagnostic Aids: An "Intermittent" malfunction may be caused by a poor connection, rubbed through wire insulation, or a wire that is broken inside the insulation.

The frequency of the malfunction can be checked by using the enhanced diagnostic function of the Tech 1

Any circuitry, that is suspected as causing the intermittent complaint, should be thoroughly checked for backed out terminals, improper mating, broken locks, improperly formed or damaged terminals, poor terminal to wiring connections or physical damage to the wiring harness.

GC402940110700DX

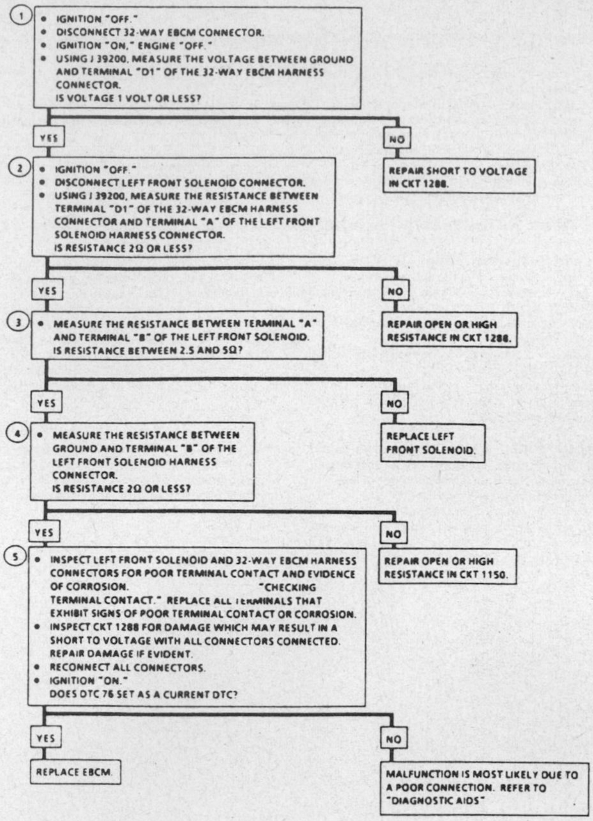
1
• IGNITION "OFF."
• DISCONNECT 32-WAY EBCM CONNECTOR.
• IGNITION "ON," ENGINE "OFF."
• USING J 39200, MEASURE THE VOLTAGE BETWEEN GROUND AND TERMINAL "D1" OF THE 32-WAY EBCM HARNESS CONNECTOR.
IS VOLTAGE 1 VOLT OR LESS?
YES
NO
REPAIR SHORT TO VOLTAGE IN CKT 1288.
2
• IGNITION "OFF."
• DISCONNECT LEFT FRONT SOLENOID CONNECTOR.
• USING J 39200, MEASURE THE RESISTANCE BETWEEN TERMINAL "D1" OF THE 32-WAY EBCM HARNESS CONNECTOR AND TERMINAL "A" OF THE LEFT FRONT SOLENOID HARNESS CONNECTOR.
IS RESISTANCE 2Ω OR LESS?
YES
NO
REPAIR OPEN OR HIGH RESISTANCE IN CKT 1288.
3
• MEASURE THE RESISTANCE BETWEEN TERMINAL "A" AND TERMINAL "B" OF THE LEFT FRONT SOLENOID.
IS RESISTANCE BETWEEN 2.5 AND 5Ω?
YES
NO
REPLACE LEFT FRONT SOLENOID.
4
• MEASURE THE RESISTANCE BETWEEN GROUND AND TERMINAL "B" OF THE LEFT FRONT SOLENOID HARNESS CONNECTOR.
IS RESISTANCE 2Ω OR LESS?
YES
NO
REPAIR OPEN OR HIGH RESISTANCE IN CKT 1150.
5
• INSPECT LEFT FRONT SOLENOID AND 32-WAY EBCM HARNESS CONNECTORS FOR POOR TERMINAL CONTACT AND EVIDENCE OF CORROSION. "CHECKING TERMINAL CONTACT." REPLACE ALL TERMINALS THAT EXHIBIT SIGNS OF POOR TERMINAL CONTACT OR CORROSION.
• INSPECT CKT 1288 FOR DAMAGE WHICH MAY RESULT IN A SHORT TO VOLTAGE WITH ALL CONNECTORS CONNECTED. REPAIR DAMAGE IF EVIDENT.
• RECONNECT ALL CONNECTORS.
• IGNITION "ON."
DOES DTC 76 SET AS A CURRENT DTC?
YES
NO
REPLACE EBCM.
MALFUNCTION IS MOST LIKELY DUE TO A POOR CONNECTION. REFER TO "DIAGNOSTIC AIDS".

GC402940110700EX

Fig. 279 Code A076: Left Front Solenoid Circuit Open Or Shorted To Battery (Part 2 of 2). 1993-94 Camaro & Firebird, 1994 Grand Prix, Century & Cutlass Ciera & Cruiser

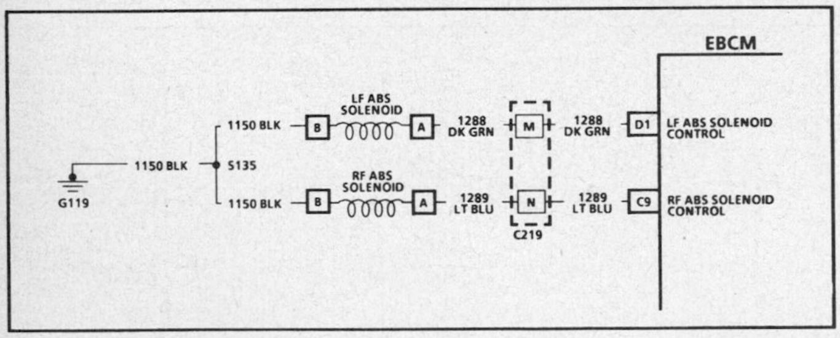
EBCM
LF ABS SOLENOID
RF ABS SOLENOID
1150 BLK
1150 BLK
1150 BLK
S135
G119
B
A
1288 DK GRN
M
1288 DK GRN
D1
LF ABS SOLENOID CONTROL
1289 LT BLU
N
1289 LT BLU
C9
RF ABS SOLENOID CONTROL
C219

GC402940110800AX

Grand Prix

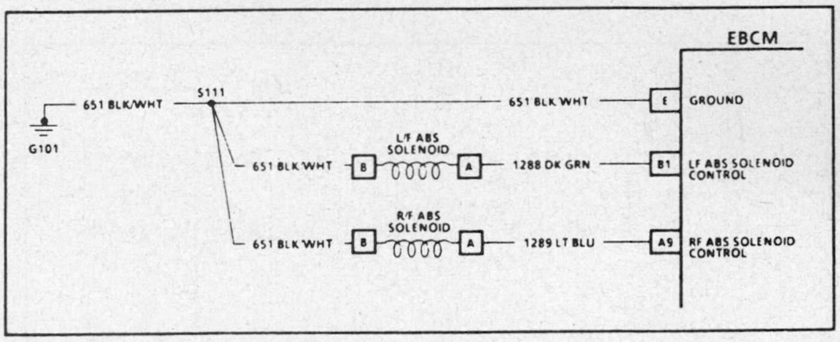
EBCM
651 BLK/WHT
S111
651 BLK WHT
E
GROUND
G101
L/F ABS SOLENOID
651 BLK WHT
B
A
1288 DK GRN
B1
LF ABS SOLENOID CONTROL
R/F ABS SOLENOID
651 BLK WHT
1289 LT BLU
A9
RF ABS SOLENOID CONTROL

GC402940110800BX

Camaro & Firebird

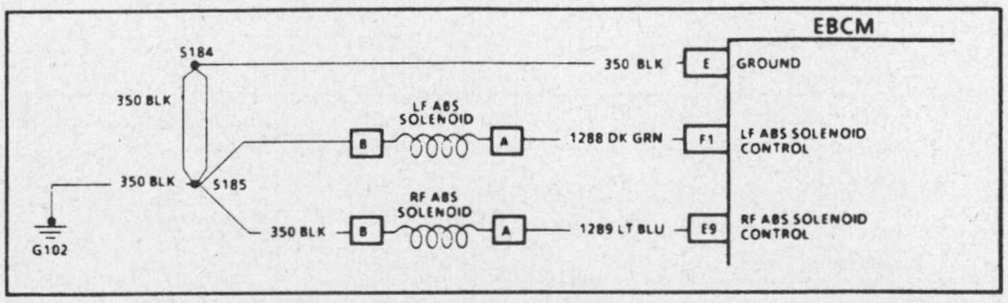
EBCM
S184
350 BLK
E
GROUND
350 BLK
LF ABS SOLENOID
B
A
1288 DK GRN
F1
LF ABS SOLENOID CONTROL
350 BLK
S185
RF ABS SOLENOID
350 BLK
1289 LT BLU
E9
RF ABS SOLENOID CONTROL
G102

GC402940110800CX

Century & Cutlass Ciera & Cruiser

Fig. 280 Code A077: Left Front Solenoid Circuit Shorted To Ground (Part 1 of 2).1993-94 Camaro & Firebird, 1994 Grand Prix, Century & Cutlass Ciera & Cruiser

DTC 77

LEFT FRONT SOLENOID CIRCUIT SHORTED TO GND

Circuit Description:

This DTC identifies a solenoid that cannot be energized due to an open in its driver circuitry, or a short to ground between the solenoid driver and the solenoid. These malfunctions can affect ABS operation since the flow of brake fluid to the wheel cylinder cannot be stopped, making ABS operation for that channel impossible.

DTC Will Set When: DTC 77 can be set only when the solenoid is commanded "ON." If the EBCM detects the left front solenoid control circuit voltage is out of specification, a malfunction exists.

Action Taken: A malfunction DTC is stored, ABS is disabled and the ABS warning lamp is turned "ON."

DTC Chart Test Description: Number(s) below refer to circled number(s) on the diagnostic chart.

1. Checks for a solenoid that is internally shorted to ground.
2. Checks for a solenoid that is not within proper resistance values.
3. Indicates if a short to ground exists in the solenoid circuitry.
4. Checks for a possible intermittent malfunction in the solenoid circuitry.

Diagnostic Aids: An "Intermittent" malfunction may be caused by a poor connection, rubbed through wire insulation, or a wire that is broken inside the insulation.

The frequency of the malfunction can be checked by using the enhanced diagnostic function of the Tech 1

Any circuitry, that is suspected as causing the intermittent complaint, should be thoroughly checked for backed out terminals, improper mating, broken locks, improperly formed or damaged terminals, poor terminal to wiring connections or physical damage to the wiring harness.

GC402940110800DX

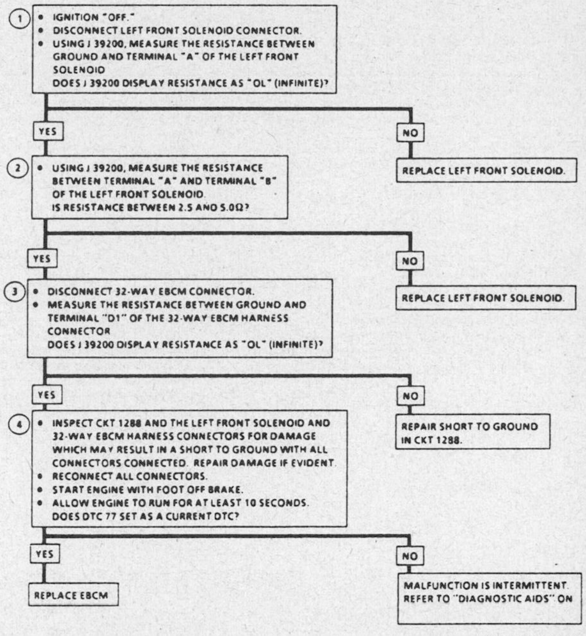
1
• IGNITION "OFF."
• DISCONNECT LEFT FRONT SOLENOID CONNECTOR.
• USING J 39200, MEASURE THE RESISTANCE BETWEEN GROUND AND TERMINAL "A" OF THE LEFT FRONT SOLENOID
DOES J 39200 DISPLAY RESISTANCE AS "OL" (INFINITE)?
YES
NO
REPLACE LEFT FRONT SOLENOID.
2
• USING J 39200, MEASURE THE RESISTANCE BETWEEN TERMINAL "A" AND TERMINAL "B" OF THE LEFT FRONT SOLENOID.
IS RESISTANCE BETWEEN 2.5 AND 5.0Ω?
YES
NO
REPLACE LEFT FRONT SOLENOID.
3
• DISCONNECT 32-WAY EBCM CONNECTOR.
• MEASURE THE RESISTANCE BETWEEN GROUND AND TERMINAL "D1" OF THE 32-WAY EBCM HARNESS CONNECTOR
DOES J 39200 DISPLAY RESISTANCE AS "OL" (INFINITE)?
YES
NO
REPAIR SHORT TO GROUND IN CKT 1288.
4
• INSPECT CKT 1288 AND THE LEFT FRONT SOLENOID AND 32-WAY EBCM HARNESS CONNECTORS FOR DAMAGE WHICH MAY RESULT IN A SHORT TO GROUND WITH ALL CONNECTORS CONNECTED. REPAIR DAMAGE IF EVIDENT.
• RECONNECT ALL CONNECTORS.
• START ENGINE WITH FOOT OFF BRAKE.
• ALLOW ENGINE TO RUN FOR AT LEAST 10 SECONDS.
DOES DTC 77 SET AS A CURRENT DTC?
YES
NO
REPLACE EBCM
MALFUNCTION IS INTERMITTENT. REFER TO "DIAGNOSTIC AIDS" ON

GC402940110800EX

Fig. 280 Code A077: Left Front Solenoid Circuit Shorted To Ground (Part 2 of 2).1993-94 Camaro & Firebird, 1994 Grand Prix, Century & Cutlass Ciera & Cruiser

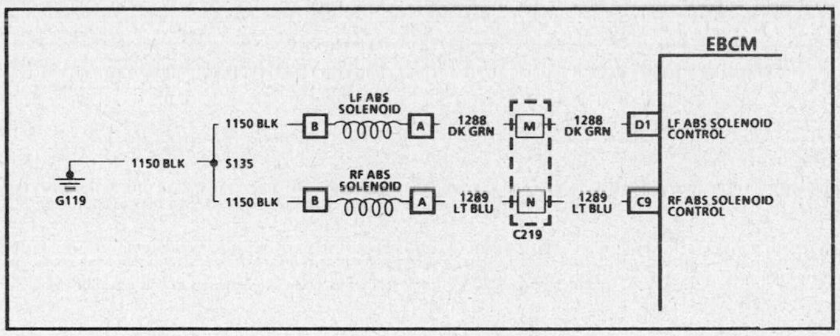
EBCM
LF ABS SOLENOID
1150 BLK
B
A
1288 DK GRN
M
1288 DK GRN
D1
LF ABS SOLENOID CONTROL
1150 BLK
S135
G119
RF ABS SOLENOID
1150 BLK
B
A
1289 LT BLU
N
1289 LT BLU
C9
RF ABS SOLENOID CONTROL
C219

GC402940110900AX

Grand Prix

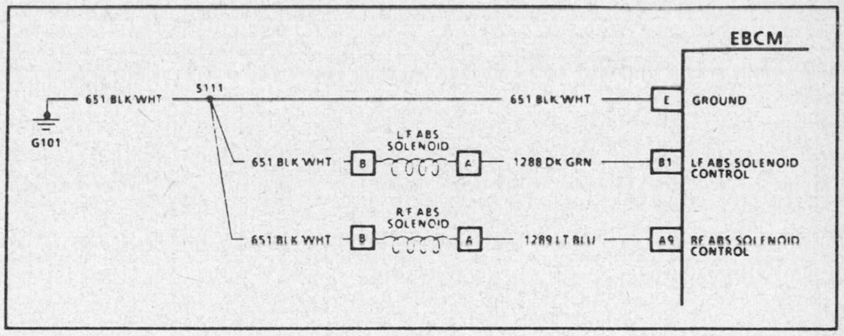
EBCM
651 BLK WHT
S111
651 BLK WHT
E
GROUND
G101
LF ABS SOLENOID
651 BLK WHT
B
A
1288 DK GRN
B1
LF ABS SOLENOID CONTROL
RF ABS SOLENOID
651 BLK WHT
B
A
1289 LT BLU
A9
RF ABS SOLENOID CONTROL

GC402940110900BX

Camaro & Firebird

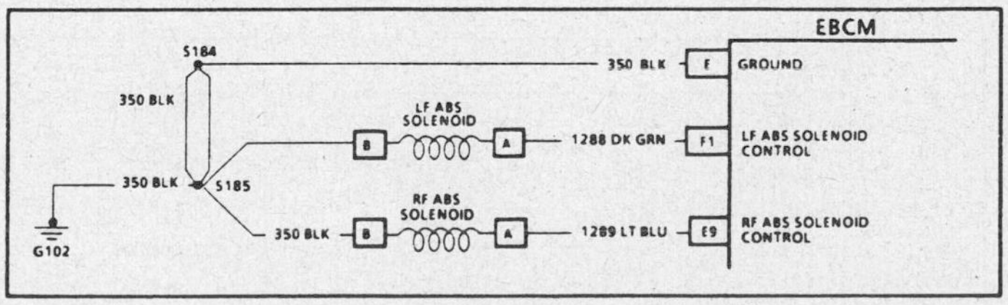
EBCM
S184
350 BLK
E
GROUND
350 BLK
LF ABS SOLENOID
B
A
1288 DK GRN
F1
LF ABS SOLENOID CONTROL
350 BLK
S185
G102
RF ABS SOLENOID
350 BLK
B
A
1289 LT BLU
E9
RF ABS SOLENOID CONTROL

GC402940110900CX

Century & Cutlass Ciera & Cruiser

Fig. 281 Code A078: Right Front Solenoid Circuit Open Or Shorted To Battery (Part 1 of 2). 1993-94 Camaro & Firebird, 1994 Grand Prix, Century & Cutlass Ciera & Cruiser

DTC 78

RIGHT FRONT SOL CIRCUIT OPEN OR SHORTED TO BATT

Circuit Description:

This DTC identifies a solenoid that cannot be energized due to an open in its circuitry, or a solenoid that is always energized due to a short to battery in its circuitry between the driver and the solenoid. An open will not allow proper ABS operation, but the short to battery simply turns "ON" the solenoid. A path for base brakes is still allowed once the motor rehomes and the check ball is lifted off its seat during key "ON" initialization.

DTC Will Set When: DTC 78 can be set only when the solenoid is commanded "OFF." If the EBCM detects an excessive voltage in the right front solenoid control circuit, a malfunction exists.

Action Taken: A malfunction DTC is stored, ABS is disabled and the ABS warning lamp is turned "ON."

DTC Chart Test Description: Number(s) below refer to circled number(s) on the diagnostic chart.

1. Checks for a short to voltage in the control circuitry of the solenoid.
2. Checks for an open in the control circuit of the solenoid.
3. Checks the solenoid coil for proper resistance.
4. Checks for an open in the solenoid ground circuit.
5. Checks for a possible intermittent malfunction in the solenoid circuitry due to poor terminal contact.

Diagnostic Aids: An "Intermittent" malfunction may be caused by a poor connection, rubbed through wire insulation, or a wire that is broken inside the insulation.

The frequency of the malfunction can be checked by using the enhanced diagnostic function of the Tech 1

Any circuitry, that is suspected as causing the intermittent complaint, should be thoroughly checked for backed out terminals, improper mating, broken locks, improperly formed or damaged terminals, poor terminal to wiring connections or physical damage to the wiring harness.

GC402940110900DX

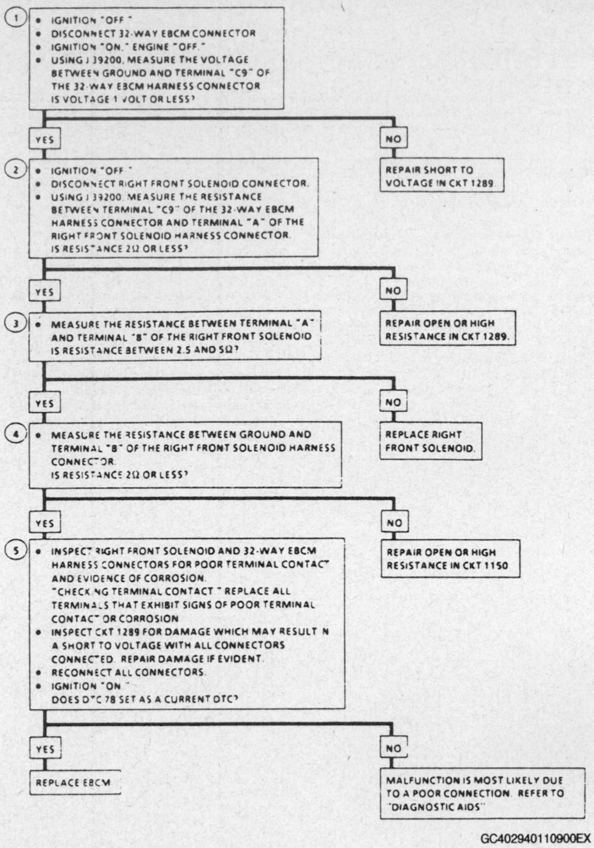
1
IGNITION "OFF."
DISCONNECT 32-WAY EBCM CONNECTOR
IGNITION "ON," ENGINE "OFF."
USING J 39200, MEASURE THE VOLTAGE BETWEEN GROUND AND TERMINAL "C9" OF THE 32-WAY EBCM HARNESS CONNECTOR
IS VOLTAGE 1 VOLT OR LESS?
YES
NO
REPAIR SHORT TO VOLTAGE IN CKT 1289.
2
IGNITION "OFF."
DISCONNECT RIGHT FRONT SOLENOID CONNECTOR.
USING J 39200, MEASURE THE RESISTANCE BETWEEN TERMINAL "C9" OF THE 32-WAY EBCM HARNESS CONNECTOR AND TERMINAL "A" OF THE RIGHT FRONT SOLENOID HARNESS CONNECTOR.
IS RESISTANCE 2Ω OR LESS?
YES
NO
REPAIR OPEN OR HIGH RESISTANCE IN CKT 1289.
3
MEASURE THE RESISTANCE BETWEEN TERMINAL "A" AND TERMINAL "B" OF THE RIGHT FRONT SOLENOID
IS RESISTANCE BETWEEN 2.5 AND 5Ω?
YES
NO
REPLACE RIGHT FRONT SOLENOID.
4
MEASURE THE RESISTANCE BETWEEN GROUND AND TERMINAL "B" OF THE RIGHT FRONT SOLENOID HARNESS CONNECTOR.
IS RESISTANCE 2Ω OR LESS?
YES
NO
REPAIR OPEN OR HIGH RESISTANCE IN CKT 1150
5
INSPECT RIGHT FRONT SOLENOID AND 32-WAY EBCM HARNESS CONNECTORS FOR POOR TERMINAL CONTACT AND EVIDENCE OF CORROSION.
"CHECKING TERMINAL CONTACT." REPLACE ALL TERMINALS THAT EXHIBIT SIGNS OF POOR TERMINAL CONTACT OR CORROSION
INSPECT CKT 1289 FOR DAMAGE WHICH MAY RESULT IN A SHORT TO VOLTAGE WITH ALL CONNECTORS CONNECTED. REPAIR DAMAGE IF EVIDENT.
RECONNECT ALL CONNECTORS.
IGNITION "ON."
DOES DTC 78 SET AS A CURRENT DTC?
YES
NO
REPLACE EBCM
MALFUNCTION IS MOST LIKELY DUE TO A POOR CONNECTION. REFER TO "DIAGNOSTIC AIDS"

GC402940110900EX

Fig. 281 Code A078: Right Front Solenoid Circuit Open Or Shorted To Battery (Part 2 of 2). 1993-94 Camaro & Firebird, 1994 Grand Prix, Century & Cutlass Ciera & Cruiser

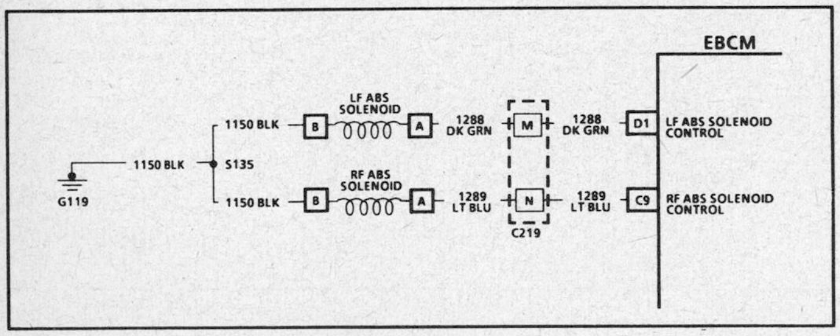
EBCM
LF ABS SOLENOID
1150 BLK
B
A
1288 DK GRN
M
1288 DK GRN
D1
LF ABS SOLENOID CONTROL
1150 BLK
S135
G119
RF ABS SOLENOID
1150 BLK
1289 LT BLU
N
1289 LT BLU
C9
RF ABS SOLENOID CONTROL
C219

GC402940111000AX

Grand Prix

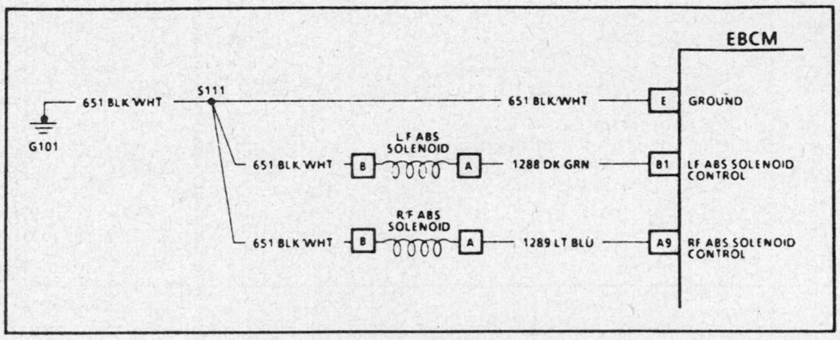
EBCM
651 BLK/WHT
S111
651 BLK/WHT
E
GROUND
G101
LF ABS SOLENOID
651 BLK/WHT
B
A
1288 DK GRN
B1
LF ABS SOLENOID CONTROL
RF ABS SOLENOID
651 BLK/WHT
1289 LT BLU
A9
RF ABS SOLENOID CONTROL

GC402940111000BX

Camaro & Firebird

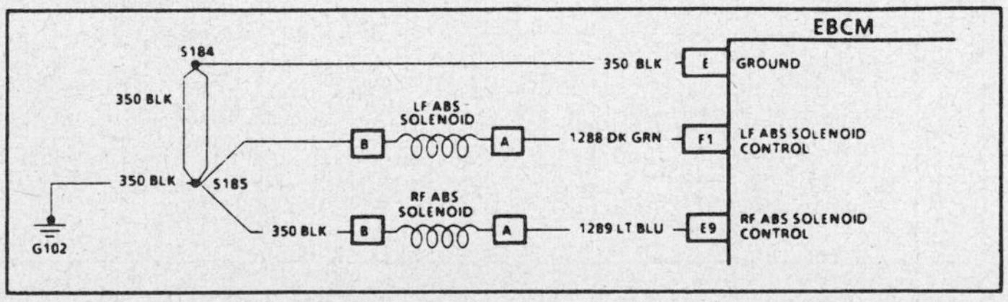
EBCM
S184
350 BLK
E
GROUND
350 BLK
LF ABS SOLENOID
B
A
1288 DK GRN
F1
LF ABS SOLENOID CONTROL
350 BLK
S185
G102
RF ABS SOLENOID
350 BLK
1289 LT BLU
E9
RF ABS SOLENOID CONTROL

GC402940111000CX

Century & Cutlass Ciera & Cruiser

Fig. 282 Code A081: Left Front Solenoid Circuit Shorted To Ground (Part 1 of 2). 1993-94 Camaro & Firebird, 1994 Grand Prix, Century & Cutlass Ciera & Cruiser

DTC 81

RIGHT FRONT SOLENOID CIRCUIT SHORTED TO GND

Circuit Description:

This DTC identifies a solenoid that cannot be energized due to an open in its driver circuitry, or a short to ground between the solenoid driver and the solenoid. These malfunctions can affect ABS operation since the flow of brake fluid to the wheel cylinder cannot be stopped, making ABS operation for that channel impossible.

DTC Will Set When: DTC 81 can be set only when the solenoid is commanded "ON." If the EBCM detects the right front solenoid control circuit voltage is out of specification, a malfunction exists.

Action Taken: A malfunction DTC is stored, ABS is disabled and the ABS warning lamp is turned "ON."

DTC Chart Test Description: Number(s) below refer to circled number(s) on the diagnostic chart.

1. Checks for a solenoid that is internally shorted to ground.
2. Checks for a solenoid that is not within proper resistance values.
3. Indicates if a short to ground exists in the solenoid circuitry.
4. Checks for a possible intermittent malfunction in the solenoid circuitry.

Diagnostic Aids: An "Intermittent" malfunction may be caused by a poor connection, rubbed through wire insulation, or a wire that is broken inside the insulation.

The frequency of the malfunction can be checked by using the enhanced diagnostic function of the Tech 1

Any circuitry, that is suspected as causing the intermittent complaint, should be thoroughly checked for backed out terminals, improper mating, broken locks, improperly formed or damaged terminals, poor terminal to wiring connections or physical damage to the wiring harness.

GC402940111000DX

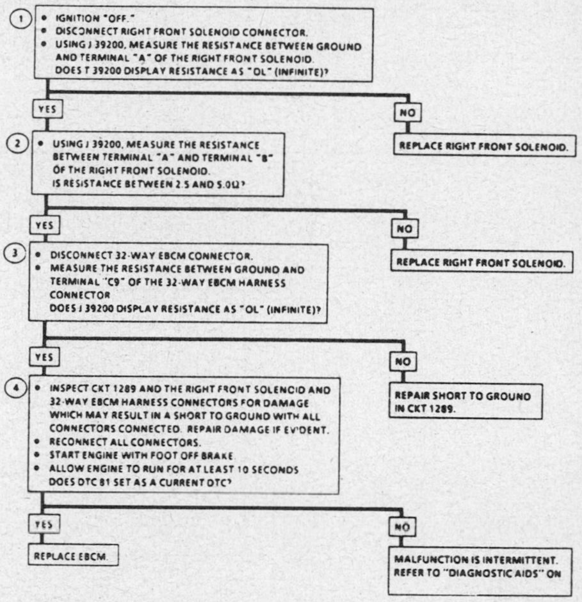
1
• IGNITION "OFF."
• DISCONNECT RIGHT FRONT SOLENOID CONNECTOR.
• USING J 39200, MEASURE THE RESISTANCE BETWEEN GROUND AND TERMINAL "A" OF THE RIGHT FRONT SOLENOID.
DOES T 39200 DISPLAY RESISTANCE AS "OL" (INFINITE)?
YES
NO
REPLACE RIGHT FRONT SOLENOID.
2
• USING J 39200, MEASURE THE RESISTANCE BETWEEN TERMINAL "A" AND TERMINAL "B" OF THE RIGHT FRONT SOLENOID.
IS RESISTANCE BETWEEN 2.5 AND 5.0Ω?
YES
NO
REPLACE RIGHT FRONT SOLENOID.
3
• DISCONNECT 32-WAY EBCM CONNECTOR.
• MEASURE THE RESISTANCE BETWEEN GROUND AND TERMINAL "C9" OF THE 32-WAY EBCM HARNESS CONNECTOR
DOES J 39200 DISPLAY RESISTANCE AS "OL" (INFINITE)?
YES
NO
REPAIR SHORT TO GROUND IN CKT 1289.
4
• INSPECT CKT 1289 AND THE RIGHT FRONT SOLENCID AND 32-WAY EBCM HARNESS CONNECTORS FOR DAMAGE WHICH MAY RESULT IN A SHORT TO GROUND WITH ALL CONNECTORS CONNECTED. REPAIR DAMAGE IF EVIDENT.
• RECONNECT ALL CONNECTORS.
• START ENGINE WITH FOOT OFF BRAKE.
• ALLOW ENGINE TO RUN FOR AT LEAST 10 SECONDS
DOES DTC 81 SET AS A CURRENT DTC?
YES
NO
REPLACE EBCM.
MALFUNCTION IS INTERMITTENT. REFER TO "DIAGNOSTIC AIDS" ON

GC402940111000EX

Fig. 282 Code A081: Left Front Solenoid Circuit Shorted To Ground (Part 2 of 2). 1993-94 Camaro & Firebird, 1994 Grand Prix, Century & Cutlass Ciera & Cruiser

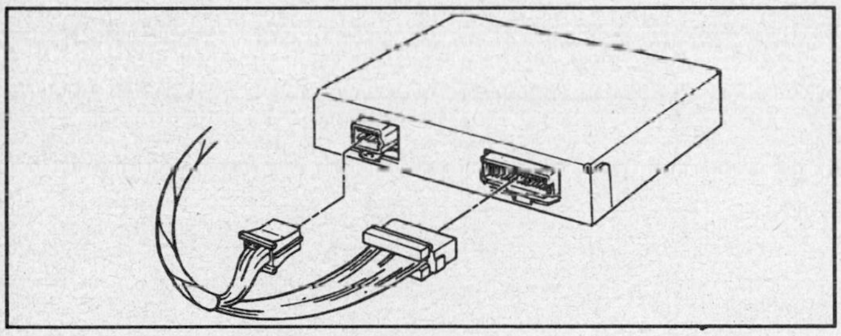

GC402940111100AX

DTC 82

CALIBRATION MALFUNCTION

Circuit Description:

This DTC allows the EBCM to check for a calibration malfunction by comparing the calibration value to a known value stored in the EEPROM.

This DTC is also used as a security measure to prevent improper use of calibrations or changes to these calibrations that may alter the designed function of ABS.

DTC Will Set When: DTC 82 can be set at key-up. If the program identifier is incorrect or the memory checksum is incorrect, a malfunction exists.

Action Taken: A malfunction DTC is stored, ABS is disabled and the ABS warning lamp is turned "ON."

DTC Chart Test Description: Number(s) below refer to circled number(s) on the diagnostic chart.

1. Checks to see if the malfunction is present during diagnosis. If present, the EBCM is not functioning correctly and must be replaced.

Important

- At the time of printing, 1994 vehicles with ABS VI were not being field reprogrammed to correct this failure. A service bulletin will be issued when EEPROM reprogramming is authorized.

Diagnostic Aids: An intermittent DTC 82 may be caused by a bad cell in the EEPROM that is sensitive to temperature changes. If DTC 82 failed more than once, but is intermittent, replace EBCM.

The frequency of the malfunction can be checked by using the enhanced diagnostic function of the Tech 1

GC402940111100BX

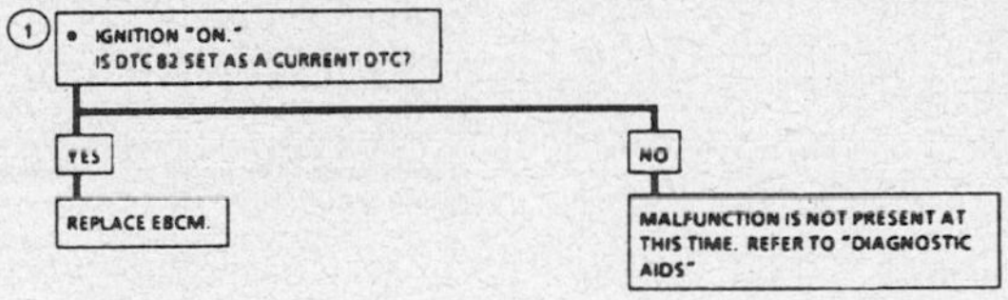
1
• IGNITION "ON."
IS DTC 82 SET AS A CURRENT DTC?
YES
NO
REPLACE EBCM.
MALFUNCTION IS NOT PRESENT AT THIS TIME. REFER TO "DIAGNOSTIC AIDS"

GC402940111100CX

Fig. 283 Code A082: Calibration Fault. 1993–94 Camaro & Firebird, 1994 Grand Prix, Century & Cutlass Ciera & Cruiser

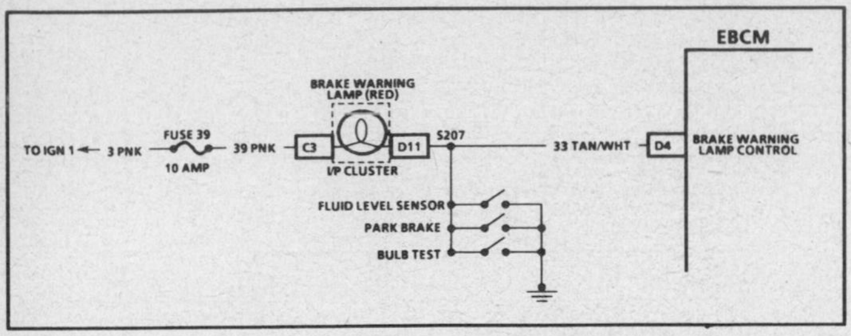
EBCM
BRAKE WARNING LAMP (RED)
TO IGN 1
3 PNK
FUSE 39
10 AMP
39 PNK
C3
D11
I/P CLUSTER
S207
33 TAN/WHT
D4
BRAKE WARNING LAMP CONTROL
FLUID LEVEL SENSOR
PARK BRAKE
BULB TEST

GC402940111200AX

Grand Prix

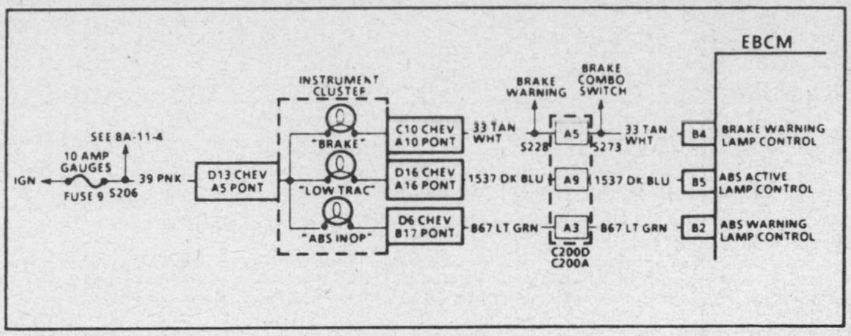
EBCM
INSTRUMENT CLUSTER
BRAKE WARNING
BRAKE COMBO SWITCH
SEE 8A-11-4
10 AMP GAUGES
IGN
FUSE 9
S206
39 PNK
D13 CHEV A5 PONT
"BRAKE"
"LOW TRAC"
"ABS INOP"
C10 CHEV A10 PONT
D16 CHEV A16 PONT
D6 CHEV B17 PONT
33 TAN WHT
S228
S273
A5
A9
A3
1537 DK BLU
867 LT GRN
C200D
C200A
B4
B5
B2
BRAKE WARNING LAMP CONTROL
ABS ACTIVE LAMP CONTROL
ABS WARNING LAMP CONTROL

GC402940111200BX

Camaro & Firebird

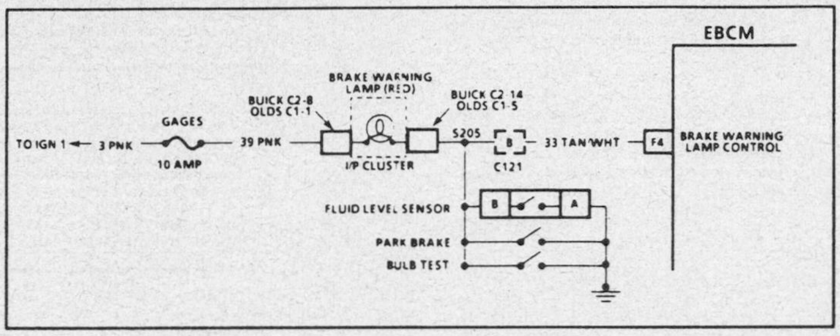
EBCM
BRAKE WARNING LAMP (RED)
BUICK C2-8 OLDS C1-1
BUICK C2-14 OLDS C1-5
GAGES
TO IGN 1
3 PNK
10 AMP
39 PNK
I/P CLUSTER
S205
B
C121
33 TAN/WHT
F4
BRAKE WARNING LAMP CONTROL
FLUID LEVEL SENSOR
B
A
PARK BRAKE
BULB TEST

GC402940111200CX

Century & Cutlass Ciera & Cruiser

DTC 86

EBCM TURNED "ON" THE RED "BRAKE" WARNING LAMP

Circuit Description:

This DTC is provided as an information only DTC, and reflects the status of the command issued by the ABS EBCM to illuminate the red "BRAKE" warning lamp. If another DTC issues a command to illuminate the red "BRAKE" warning lamp, DTC 86 will be stored in EEPROM as a history DTC at the conclusion of the ignition cycle.

DTC Chart Test Description: Number(s) below refer to circled number(s) on the diagnostic chart.

1. This step serves to identify if a DTC other than DTC 86 commanded the red "BRAKE" warning lamp "ON."

Diagnostic Aids: Any ABS mechanical DTC that issues a command to illuminate the red "BRAKE" telltale will also result in DTC 86 being stored in EEPROM during shutdown. These DTCs are: 38, 41, 42, 46, and 51. If the motors are not in their home position, certain electrical DTCs will also command the red "BRAKE" telltale "ON." These DTCs are: 14, 16, 18, 55, 56, 57, 58, 61, 62, 63, 64, 65, and 66.

If any of these DTCs are indicated along with DTC 86, they must be corrected prior to addressing a DTC 86 malfunction.

GC402940111200DX

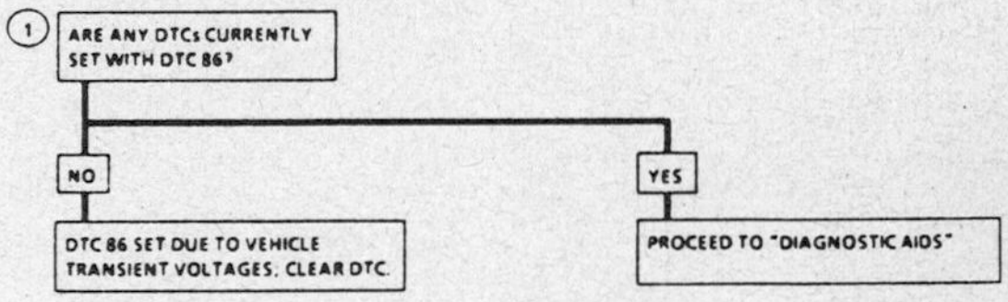
1
ARE ANY DTCs CURRENTLY SET WITH DTC 86?
NO
YES
DTC 86 SET DUE TO VEHICLE TRANSIENT VOLTAGES; CLEAR DTC.
PROCEED TO "DIAGNOSTIC AIDS"

GC402940111200EX

Fig. 284 Code A086: EBCM Turned On The Brake Warning Lamp. 1993–94 Camaro & Firebird, 1994 Grand Prix, Century & Cutlass Ciera & Cruiser

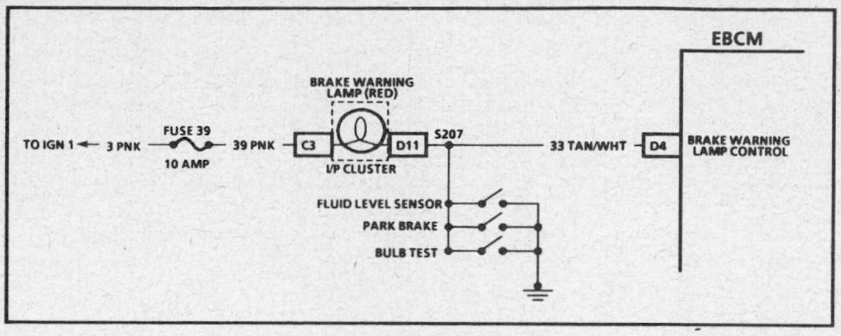
EBCM
BRAKE WARNING LAMP (RED)
TO IGN 1
3 PNK
FUSE 39
10 AMP
39 PNK
C3
D11
I/P CLUSTER
S207
33 TAN/WHT
D4
BRAKE WARNING LAMP CONTROL
FLUID LEVEL SENSOR
PARK BRAKE
BULB TEST

GC402940111300AX

Grand Prix

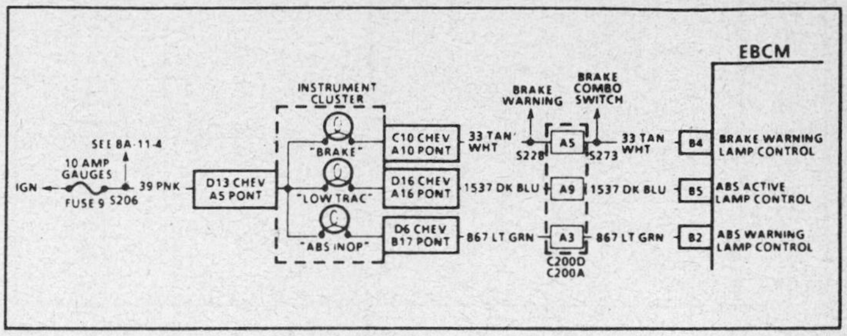
EBCM
INSTRUMENT CLUSTER
BRAKE WARNING
BRAKE COMBO SWITCH
SEE 8A-11-4
10 AMP GAUGES
IGN
FUSE 9
S206
39 PNK
D13 CHEV A5 PONT
"BRAKE"
"LOW TRAC"
"ABS INOP"
C10 CHEV A10 PONT
D16 CHEV A16 PONT
D6 CHEV B17 PONT
33 TAN/WHT
S228
A5
S273
33 TAN WHT
B4
BRAKE WARNING LAMP CONTROL
1537 DK BLU
A9
1537 DK BLU
B5
ABS ACTIVE LAMP CONTROL
867 LT GRN
A3
867 LT GRN
B2
ABS WARNING LAMP CONTROL
C200D
C200A

GC402940111300BX

Camaro & Firebird

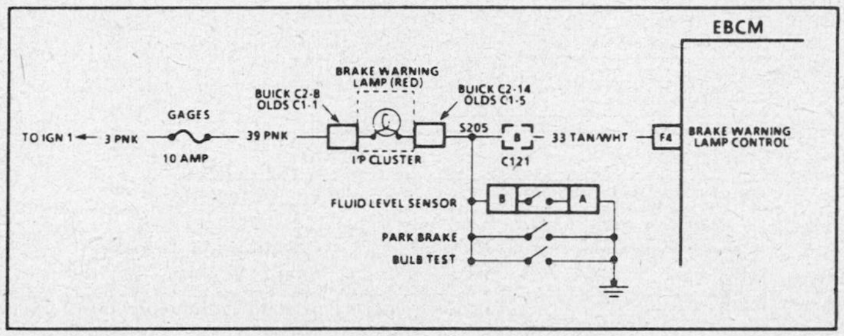
EBCM
BRAKE WARNING LAMP (RED)
BUICK C2-8 OLDS C1-1
BUICK C2-14 OLDS C1-5
GAGES
TO IGN 1
3 PNK
10 AMP
39 PNK
I/P CLUSTER
S205
C121
33 TAN/WHT
F4
BRAKE WARNING LAMP CONTROL
FLUID LEVEL SENSOR
PARK BRAKE
BULB TEST

GC402940111300CX

Century & Cutlass Ciera & Cruiser

DTC 87

RED "BRAKE" WARNING LAMP CIRCUIT OPEN

Circuit Description:

This DTC is used to verify the EBCM has continuity to the red "BRAKE" warning lamp in case the EBCM must turn it "ON." This will only occur if an ABS malfunction is detected that may degrade base brake operation.

Because ABS is not the only device controlling the red "BRAKE" warning lamp (parking brake and low fluid sensor may also turn "ON" the lamp) a short to ground in this circuit cannot be detected.

DTC Will Set When: DTC 87 can be set after initialization is completed. If the red "BRAKE" warning lamp circuit voltage is out of specification indicating an open circuit, a malfunction exists.

Action Taken: A malfunction DTC is stored, ABS is not disabled.

DTC Chart Test Description: Number(s) below refer to circled number(s) on the diagnostic chart.

1. Identifies if the ground circuit to the red "BRAKE" warning lamp is completed by a source other than the EBCM.
2. Checks for high resistance in park brake circuitry.
3. Checks for a malfunctioning EBCM.
4. Checks for high resistance in fluid level switch circuitry.
5. Checks for a malfunctioning warning lamp bulb.
6. Checks for open or high resistance in CKT 33.

Diagnostic Aids: An "Intermittent" malfunction may be caused by a poor connection, rubbed through wire insulation, or a wire that is broken inside the insulation.

The frequency of the malfunction can be checked by using the enhanced diagnostic function of the Tech 1.

If a Tech 1 or T-100 are not available, the parking brake handle may be lifted to verify proper lamp operation and continuity of CKTs 3 and 39.

Any circuitry, that is suspected as causing the intermittent complaint, should be thoroughly checked for backed out terminals, improper mating, broken locks, improperly formed or damaged terminals, poor terminal to wiring connections or physical damage to the wiring harness.

GC402940111300DX

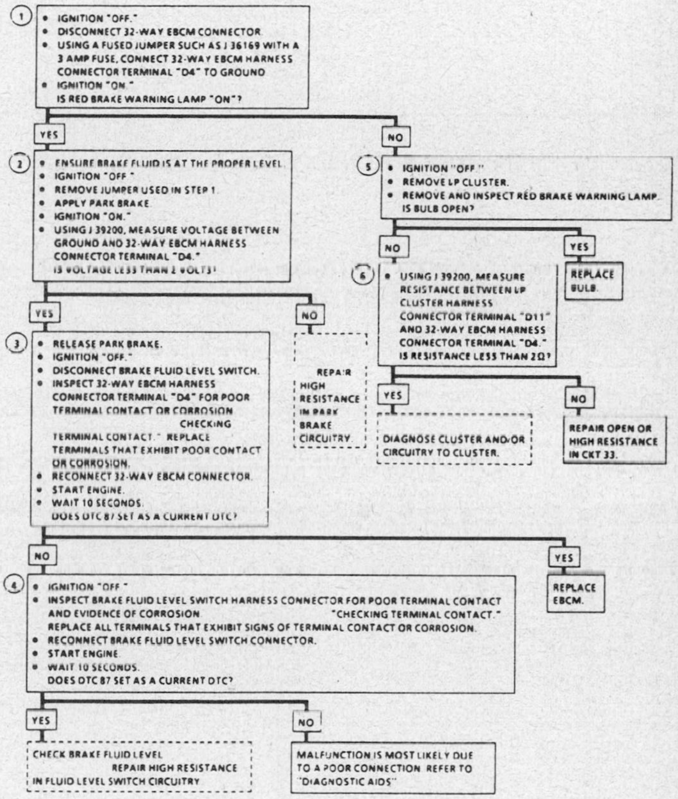
1
• IGNITION "OFF."
• DISCONNECT 32-WAY EBCM CONNECTOR.
• USING A FUSED JUMPER SUCH AS J 36169 WITH A 3 AMP FUSE, CONNECT 32-WAY EBCM HARNESS CONNECTOR TERMINAL "D4" TO GROUND.
• IGNITION "ON."
IS RED BRAKE WARNING LAMP "ON"?
YES
NO
2
• ENSURE BRAKE FLUID IS AT THE PROPER LEVEL.
• IGNITION "OFF."
• REMOVE JUMPER USED IN STEP 1.
• APPLY PARK BRAKE.
• IGNITION "ON."
• USING J 39200, MEASURE VOLTAGE BETWEEN GROUND AND 32-WAY EBCM HARNESS CONNECTOR TERMINAL "D4."
IS VOLTAGE LESS THAN 2 VOLTS?
5
• IGNITION "OFF."
• REMOVE I/P CLUSTER.
• REMOVE AND INSPECT RED BRAKE WARNING LAMP.
IS BULB OPEN?
YES
NO
REPLACE BULB.
6
• USING J 39200, MEASURE RESISTANCE BETWEEN I/P CLUSTER HARNESS CONNECTOR TERMINAL "D11" AND 32-WAY EBCM HARNESS CONNECTOR TERMINAL "D4."
IS RESISTANCE LESS THAN 2Ω?
YES
NO
REPAIR HIGH RESISTANCE IN PARK BRAKE CIRCUITRY.
3
• RELEASE PARK BRAKE.
• IGNITION "OFF."
• DISCONNECT BRAKE FLUID LEVEL SWITCH.
• INSPECT 32-WAY EBCM HARNESS CONNECTOR TERMINAL "D4" FOR POOR TERMINAL CONTACT OR CORROSION. CHECKING TERMINAL CONTACT." REPLACE TERMINALS THAT EXHIBIT POOR CONTACT OR CORROSION.
• RECONNECT 32-WAY EBCM CONNECTOR.
• START ENGINE.
• WAIT 10 SECONDS.
DOES DTC 87 SET AS A CURRENT DTC?
DIAGNOSE CLUSTER AND/OR CIRCUITRY TO CLUSTER.
REPAIR OPEN OR HIGH RESISTANCE IN CKT 33.
REPLACE EBCM.
4
• IGNITION "OFF."
• INSPECT BRAKE FLUID LEVEL SWITCH HARNESS CONNECTOR FOR POOR TERMINAL CONTACT AND EVIDENCE OF CORROSION. "CHECKING TERMINAL CONTACT." REPLACE ALL TERMINALS THAT EXHIBIT SIGNS OF TERMINAL CONTACT OR CORROSION.
• RECONNECT BRAKE FLUID LEVEL SWITCH CONNECTOR.
• START ENGINE.
• WAIT 10 SECONDS.
DOES DTC 87 SET AS A CURRENT DTC?
CHECK BRAKE FLUID LEVEL. REPAIR HIGH RESISTANCE IN FLUID LEVEL SWITCH CIRCUITRY.
MALFUNCTION IS MOST LIKELY DUE TO A POOR CONNECTION. REFER TO "DIAGNOSTIC AIDS"

GC402940111300EX

Fig. 285 Code A087: Red Brake Warning Lamp Circuit Open. 1993–94 Camaro & Firebird, 1994 Grand Prix, Century & Cutlass Ciera & Cruiser

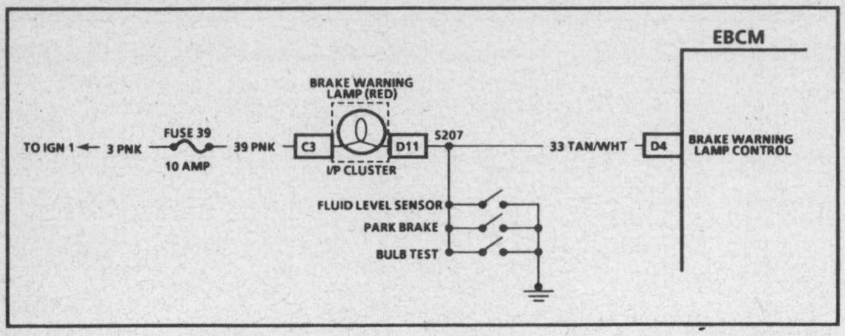
EBCM
BRAKE WARNING LAMP (RED)
TO IGN 1 ← 3 PNK
FUSE 39
10 AMP
39 PNK
C3
D11
I/P CLUSTER
S207
33 TAN/WHT
D4
BRAKE WARNING LAMP CONTROL
FLUID LEVEL SENSOR
PARK BRAKE
BULB TEST

GC402940111400AX

Grand Prix

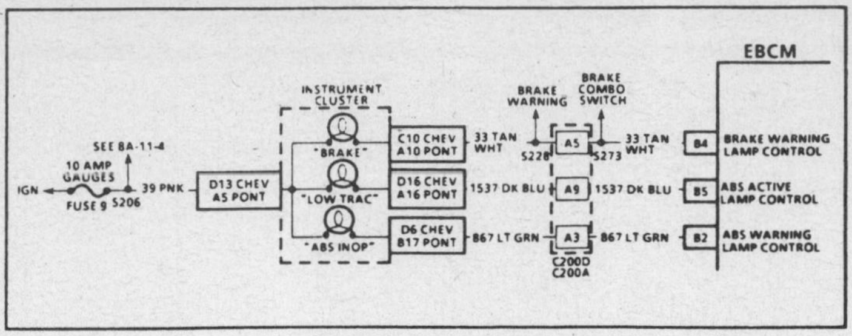
EBCM
INSTRUMENT CLUSTER
BRAKE WARNING
BRAKE COMBO SWITCH
SEE 8A-11-4
10 AMP GAUGES
IGN
FUSE 9
S206
39 PNK
D13 CHEV
A5 PONT
"BRAKE"
"LOW TRAC"
"ABS INOP"
C10 CHEV A10 PONT
D16 CHEV A16 PONT
D6 CHEV B17 PONT
33 TAN WHT
1537 DK BLU
867 LT GRN
S228
S273
A5
A9
A3
C200D
C200A
B4
B5
B2
BRAKE WARNING LAMP CONTROL
ABS ACTIVE LAMP CONTROL
ABS WARNING LAMP CONTROL

GC402940111400BX

Camaro & Firebird

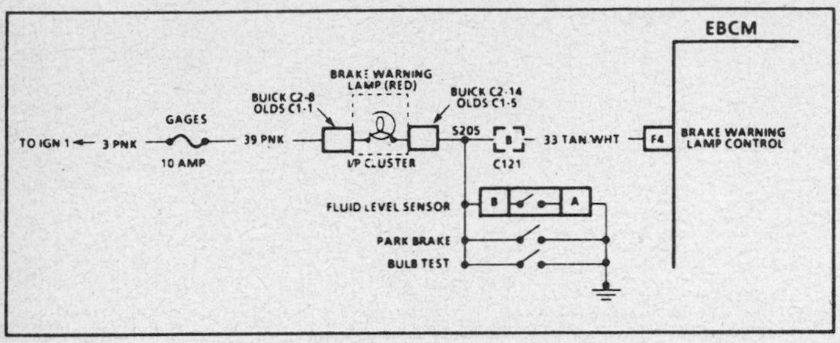
EBCM
BRAKE WARNING LAMP (RED)
BUICK C2-8 OLDS C1-1
BUICK C2-14 OLDS C1-5
GAGES
TO IGN 1 ← 3 PNK
10 AMP
39 PNK
I/P CLUSTER
S205
B
C121
33 TAN WHT
F4
BRAKE WARNING LAMP CONTROL
FLUID LEVEL SENSOR
PARK BRAKE
BULB TEST

GC402940111400CX

Century & Cutlass Ciera & Cruiser

DTC 88

RED "BRAKE" WARNING LAMP CKT SHORTED TO BATT

Circuit Description:
This DTC identifies a short to battery between the EBCM and the red "BRAKE" warning lamp, or an open driver that does not allow the red "BRAKE" warning lamp to be illuminated by the EBCM. This will only occur if an ABS fault is detected that may degrade base brake operation.

DTC Will Set When: DTC 88 can be set only at the beginning of the three second bulb check. If the EBCM detects battery voltage on the red "BRAKE" warning lamp control circuit, a malfunction exists.

Action Taken: A malfunction DTC is stored. ABS is not disabled.

DTC Chart Test Description: Number(s) below refer to circled number(s) on the diagnostic chart.

1. Identifies if the ground circuit to the red "BRAKE" warning lamp is being completed by a source other than the EBCM.
2. Identifies if the malfunction is currently present.
3. By removing Fuse 39, the voltage source is eliminated. This test indicates if voltage is being supplied from a source other than the gauge fuse.
4. Ensures malfunction was not due to physical damage of the circuitry.
5. Checks for DTC 86 also being set.

Diagnostic Aids: An "Intermittent" malfunction may be caused by a poor connection, rubbed through wire insulation, or a wire that is broken inside the insulation.

The frequency of the malfunction can be checked by using the enhanced diagnostic function of the Tech

Any circuitry, that is suspected as causing the intermittent complaint, should be thoroughly checked for backed out terminals, improper mating, broken locks, improperly formed or damaged terminals, poor terminal to wiring connections or physical damage to the wiring harness.

GC402940111400DX

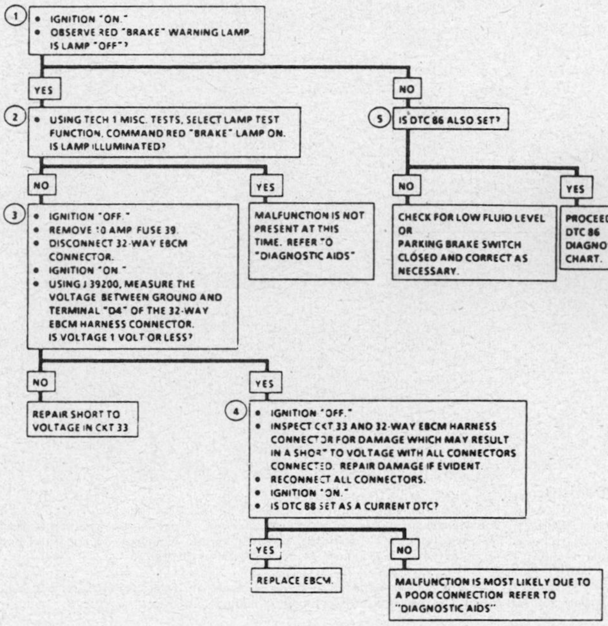
1
• IGNITION "ON."
• OBSERVE RED "BRAKE" WARNING LAMP. IS LAMP "OFF"?
YES
NO
2
• USING TECH 1 MISC. TESTS, SELECT LAMP TEST FUNCTION. COMMAND RED "BRAKE" LAMP ON. IS LAMP ILLUMINATED?
5
IS DTC 86 ALSO SET?
NO
YES
NO
YES
3
• IGNITION "OFF."
• REMOVE 10 AMP FUSE 39.
• DISCONNECT 32-WAY EBCM CONNECTOR.
• IGNITION "ON."
• USING J 39200, MEASURE THE VOLTAGE BETWEEN GROUND AND TERMINAL "D4" OF THE 32-WAY EBCM HARNESS CONNECTOR. IS VOLTAGE 1 VOLT OR LESS?
MALFUNCTION IS NOT PRESENT AT THIS TIME. REFER TO "DIAGNOSTIC AIDS"
CHECK FOR LOW FLUID LEVEL OR PARKING BRAKE SWITCH CLOSED AND CORRECT AS NECESSARY.
PROCEED TO DTC 86 DIAGNOSTIC CHART.
NO
YES
REPAIR SHORT TO VOLTAGE IN CKT 33
4
• IGNITION "OFF."
• INSPECT CKT 33 AND 32-WAY EBCM HARNESS CONNECTOR FOR DAMAGE WHICH MAY RESULT IN A SHORT TO VOLTAGE WITH ALL CONNECTORS CONNECTED. REPAIR DAMAGE IF EVIDENT.
• RECONNECT ALL CONNECTORS.
• IGNITION "ON."
• IS DTC 88 SET AS A CURRENT DTC?
YES
NO
REPLACE EBCM.
MALFUNCTION IS MOST LIKELY DUE TO A POOR CONNECTION. REFER TO "DIAGNOSTIC AIDS"

GC402940111400EX

Fig. 286 Code A088: Red Brake Warning Lamp Circuit Shorted To Battery. 1993–94 Camaro & Firebird, 1994 Grand Prix, Century & Cutlass Ciera & Cruiser

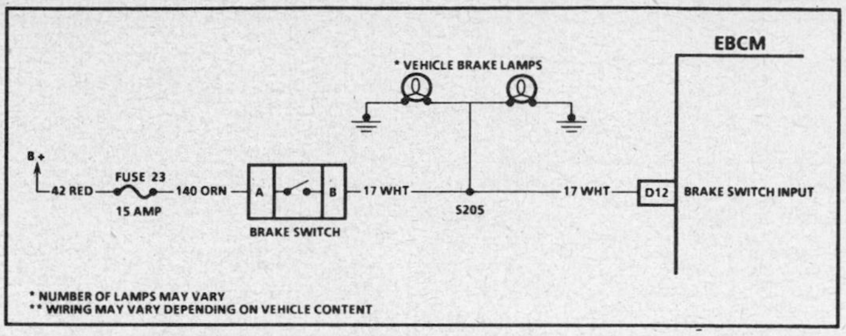
EBCM
* VEHICLE BRAKE LAMPS
B+
FUSE 23
42 RED
15 AMP
140 ORN
A
B
BRAKE SWITCH
17 WHT
S205
17 WHT
D12
BRAKE SWITCH INPUT
* NUMBER OF LAMPS MAY VARY
** WIRING MAY VARY DEPENDING ON VEHICLE CONTENT

GC402940111500AX

Grand Prix

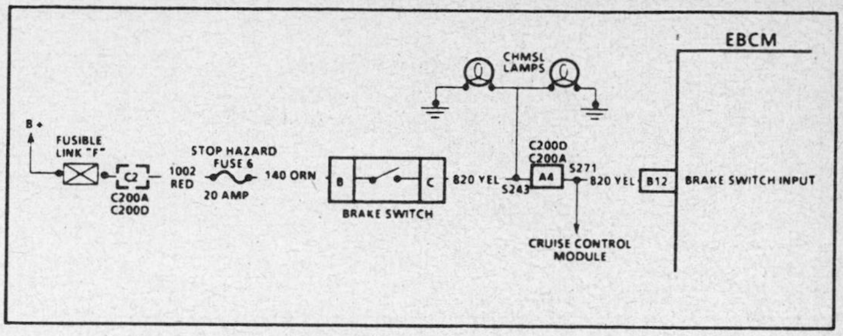
EBCM
CHMSL LAMPS
B+
FUSIBLE LINK "F"
C2
C200A
C200D
1002 RED
STOP HAZARD FUSE 6
20 AMP
140 ORN
B
C
BRAKE SWITCH
820 YEL
C200D
C200A
A4
S243
S271
820 YEL
B12
BRAKE SWITCH INPUT
CRUISE CONTROL MODULE

GC402940111500BX

Camaro & Firebird

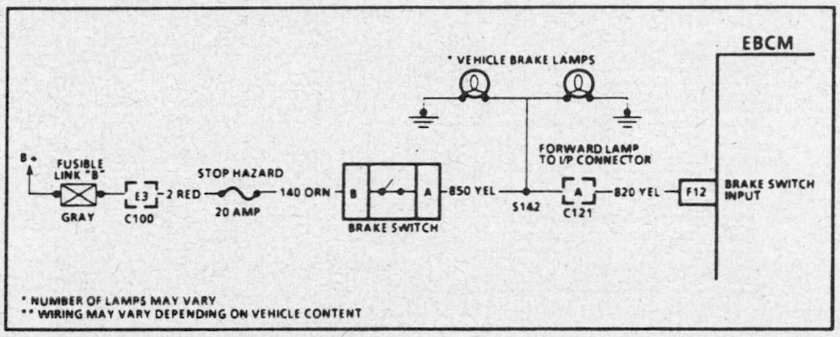
EBCM
* VEHICLE BRAKE LAMPS
B+
FUSIBLE LINK "B"
GRAY
E3
C100
2 RED
STOP HAZARD
20 AMP
140 ORN
B
A
BRAKE SWITCH
850 YEL
FORWARD LAMP TO I/P CONNECTOR
S142
A
C121
820 YEL
F12
BRAKE SWITCH INPUT
* NUMBER OF LAMPS MAY VARY
** WIRING MAY VARY DEPENDING ON VEHICLE CONTENT

GC402940111500CX

Century & Cutlass Ciera & Cruiser

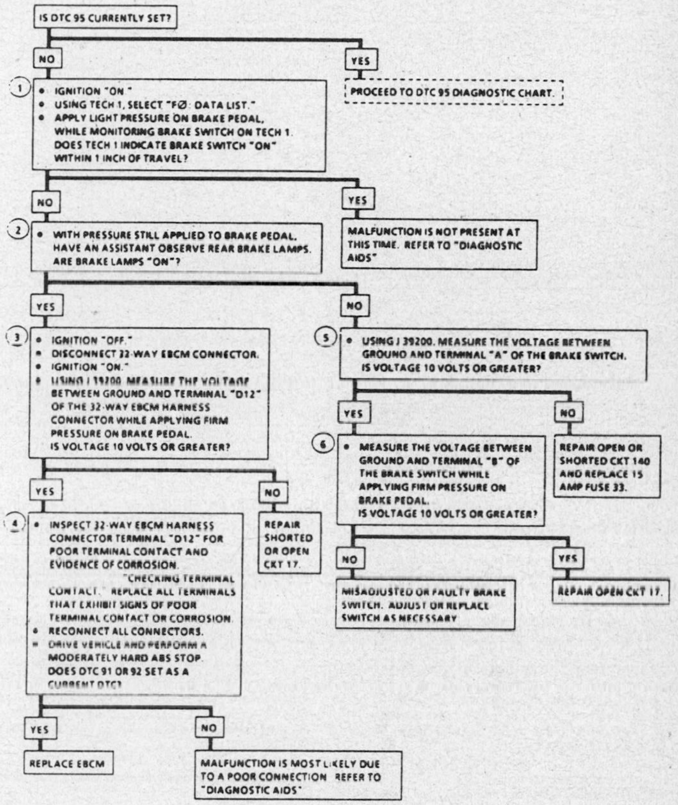
IS DTC 95 CURRENTLY SET?
NO
YES
PROCEED TO DTC 95 DIAGNOSTIC CHART.
1
• IGNITION "ON."
• USING TECH 1, SELECT "FØ: DATA LIST."
• APPLY LIGHT PRESSURE ON BRAKE PEDAL, WHILE MONITORING BRAKE SWITCH ON TECH 1. DOES TECH 1 INDICATE BRAKE SWITCH "ON" WITHIN 1 INCH OF TRAVEL?
NO
YES
MALFUNCTION IS NOT PRESENT AT THIS TIME. REFER TO "DIAGNOSTIC AIDS"
2
• WITH PRESSURE STILL APPLIED TO BRAKE PEDAL, HAVE AN ASSISTANT OBSERVE REAR BRAKE LAMPS. ARE BRAKE LAMPS "ON"?
YES
NO
3
• IGNITION "OFF."
• DISCONNECT 32-WAY EBCM CONNECTOR.
• IGNITION "ON."
• USING J 39200, MEASURE THE VOLTAGE BETWEEN GROUND AND TERMINAL "D12" OF THE 32-WAY EBCM HARNESS CONNECTOR WHILE APPLYING FIRM PRESSURE ON BRAKE PEDAL. IS VOLTAGE 10 VOLTS OR GREATER?
5
• USING J 39200, MEASURE THE VOLTAGE BETWEEN GROUND AND TERMINAL "A" OF THE BRAKE SWITCH. IS VOLTAGE 10 VOLTS OR GREATER?
YES
NO
6
• MEASURE THE VOLTAGE BETWEEN GROUND AND TERMINAL "B" OF THE BRAKE SWITCH WHILE APPLYING FIRM PRESSURE ON BRAKE PEDAL. IS VOLTAGE 10 VOLTS OR GREATER?
REPAIR OPEN OR SHORTED CKT 140 AND REPLACE 15 AMP FUSE 33.
YES
NO
REPAIR SHORTED OR OPEN CKT 17.
4
• INSPECT 32-WAY EBCM HARNESS CONNECTOR TERMINAL "D12" FOR POOR TERMINAL CONTACT AND EVIDENCE OF CORROSION. "CHECKING TERMINAL CONTACT." REPLACE ALL TERMINALS THAT EXHIBIT SIGNS OF POOR TERMINAL CONTACT OR CORROSION.
• RECONNECT ALL CONNECTORS.
• DRIVE VEHICLE AND PERFORM A MODERATELY HARD ABS STOP. DOES DTC 91 OR 92 SET AS A CURRENT DTC?
NO
YES
MISADJUSTED OR FAULTY BRAKE SWITCH. ADJUST OR REPLACE SWITCH AS NECESSARY
REPAIR OPEN CKT 17.
YES
NO
REPLACE EBCM
MALFUNCTION IS MOST LIKELY DUE TO A POOR CONNECTION. REFER TO "DIAGNOSTIC AIDS"

GC402940111500EX

DTC 91

OPEN BRAKE SWITCH DURING DECELERATION

Circuit Description:
This DTC is used to detect an open brake switch in the non-ABS mode. The EBCM looks for deceleration rates that would indicate braking action and verifies this assumption by requiring several repeats of this detection method. In each case, ABS will not be available since no brake switch is seen.

DTC Will Set When: DTC 91 can be set if three deceleration cycles occur with the brake switch "OFF."

Action Taken: A malfunction DTC is stored, ABS is disabled and the ABS warning lamp is turned "ON."

DTC Chart Test Description: Number(s) below refer to circled number(s) on the diagnostic chart.

1. Indicates if the brake switch signal is being received by the EBCM.
2. Indicates if an open circuit exists in the brake switch or brake lamp circuitry.
3. Isolates the open circuit to either the brake switch input circuitry, or the EBCM.
4. Ensures malfunction was not due to poor terminal contact.
5. Verifies that voltage is available at the brake switch.
6. Verifies that the brake switch is functioning properly.

Diagnostic Aids: An "Intermittent" malfunction may be caused by a poor connection, rubbed through wire insulation, or a wire that is broken inside the insulation.

The frequency of the malfunction can be checked by using the enhanced diagnostic function of the Tech 1

Any circuitry, that is suspected as causing the intermittent complaint, should be thoroughly checked for backed out terminals, improper mating, broken locks, improperly formed or damaged terminals, poor terminal to wiring connections or physical damage to the wiring harness.

GC402940111500DX

Fig. 287 Code A091: Open Brake Switch During Deceleration. 1993–94 Camaro & Firebird, 1994 Grand Prix, Century & Cutlass Ciera & Cruiser

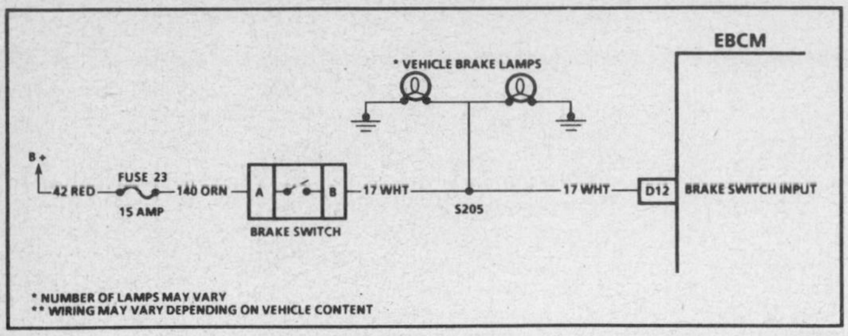
EBCM
* VEHICLE BRAKE LAMPS
B+
FUSE 23
42 RED
140 ORN
15 AMP
BRAKE SWITCH
17 WHT
S205
17 WHT
D12
BRAKE SWITCH INPUT
* NUMBER OF LAMPS MAY VARY
** WIRING MAY VARY DEPENDING ON VEHICLE CONTENT

GC402940111600AX

Grand Prix

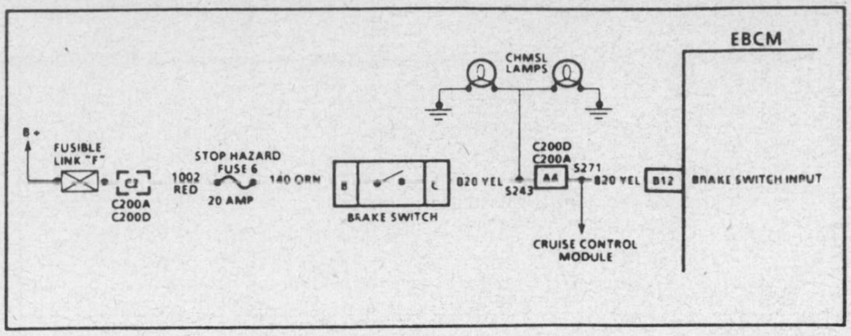
EBCM
CHMSL LAMPS
B+
FUSIBLE LINK "F"
C200A
C200D
STOP HAZARD FUSE 6
1002 RED
20 AMP
140 ORN
BRAKE SWITCH
820 YEL
S243
C200D
C200A
S271
820 YEL
B12
BRAKE SWITCH INPUT
CRUISE CONTROL MODULE

GC402940111600BX

Camaro & Firebird

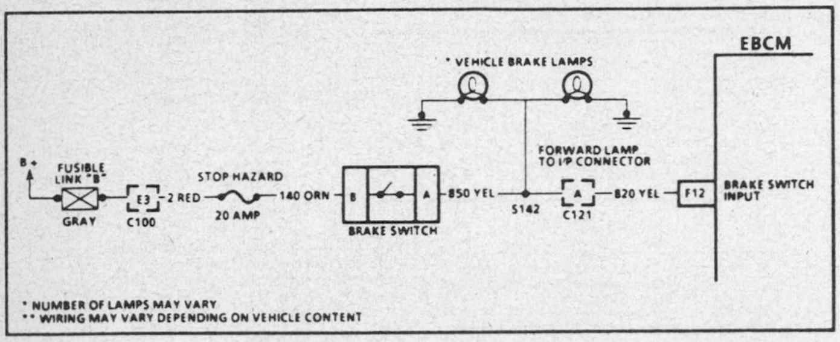
EBCM
* VEHICLE BRAKE LAMPS
FORWARD LAMP TO I/P CONNECTOR
B+
FUSIBLE LINK "B"
GRAY
E3
C100
2 RED
STOP HAZARD
20 AMP
140 ORN
BRAKE SWITCH
850 YEL
S142
C121
820 YEL
F12
BRAKE SWITCH INPUT
* NUMBER OF LAMPS MAY VARY
** WIRING MAY VARY DEPENDING ON VEHICLE CONTENT

GC402940111600CX

Century & Cutlass Ciera & Cruiser

DTC 92

OPEN BRAKE SWITCH WHEN ABS WAS REQUIRED

Circuit Description:

This DTC is run to determine the proper operation of the brake switch. This is important because ABS is activated when the brake switch is "ON." If the brake switch is "OFF," ABS will never be activated. Since this malfunction is difficult to detect under normal braking conditions, this malfunction is only detected when ABS is required.

DTC Will Set When: DTC 92 can be set if the vehicle's speed is greater than 8 km/h (5 mph). If the brake was not "ON" and a release was required on two channels for 0.5 second, a malfunction exists.

Action Taken: A malfunction DTC is stored, ABS is disabled and the ABS warning lamp is turned "ON."

DTC Chart Test Description: Number(s) below refer to circled number(s) on the diagnostic chart.

1. Indicates if the brake switch signal is being received by the EBCM.
2. Indicates if an open circuit exists in the brake switch or brake lamp circuitry.
3. Isolates the open circuit to either the brake switch input circuitry, or the EBCM.
4. Ensures malfunction was not due to poor terminal contact.
5. Verifies the voltage is available at the brake switch.
6. Verifies that the brake switch is functioning properly.

Diagnostic Aids: An "Intermittent" malfunction may be caused by a poor connection, rubbed through wire insulation, or a wire that is broken inside the insulation.

The frequency of the malfunction can be checked by using the enhanced diagnostic function of the Tech 1

Any circuitry, that is suspected as causing the intermittent complaint, should be thoroughly checked for backed out terminals, improper mating, broken locks, improperly formed or damaged terminals, poor terminal to wiring connections or physical damage to the wiring harness.

GC402940111600DX

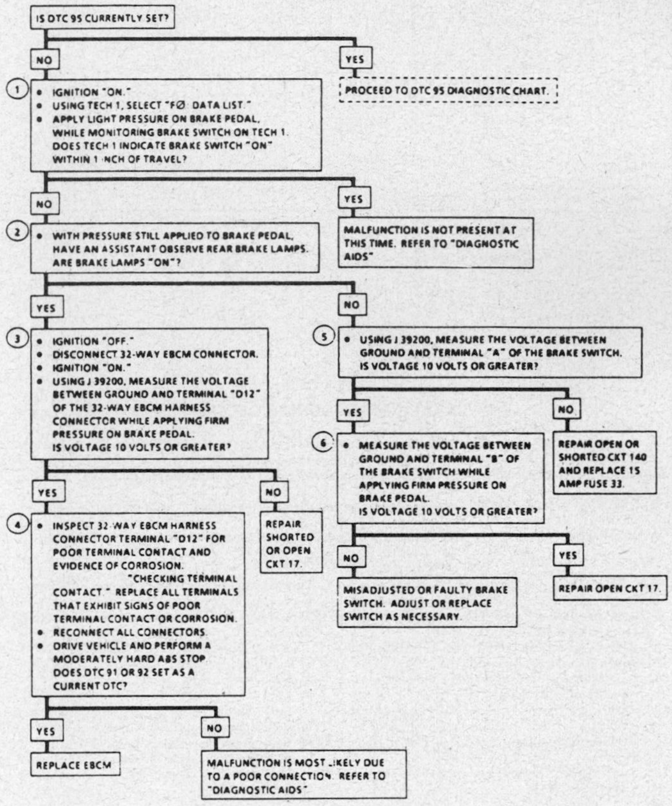
IS DTC 95 CURRENTLY SET?
NO
YES
PROCEED TO DTC 95 DIAGNOSTIC CHART.
1
• IGNITION "ON."
• USING TECH 1, SELECT "FØ: DATA LIST."
• APPLY LIGHT PRESSURE ON BRAKE PEDAL, WHILE MONITORING BRAKE SWITCH ON TECH 1. DOES TECH 1 INDICATE BRAKE SWITCH "ON" WITHIN 1 INCH OF TRAVEL?
NO
YES
MALFUNCTION IS NOT PRESENT AT THIS TIME. REFER TO "DIAGNOSTIC AIDS"
2
• WITH PRESSURE STILL APPLIED TO BRAKE PEDAL, HAVE AN ASSISTANT OBSERVE REAR BRAKE LAMPS. ARE BRAKE LAMPS "ON"?
YES
NO
3
• IGNITION "OFF."
• DISCONNECT 32-WAY EBCM CONNECTOR.
• IGNITION "ON."
• USING J 39200, MEASURE THE VOLTAGE BETWEEN GROUND AND TERMINAL "D12" OF THE 32-WAY EBCM HARNESS CONNECTOR WHILE APPLYING FIRM PRESSURE ON BRAKE PEDAL. IS VOLTAGE 10 VOLTS OR GREATER?
5
• USING J 39200, MEASURE THE VOLTAGE BETWEEN GROUND AND TERMINAL "A" OF THE BRAKE SWITCH. IS VOLTAGE 10 VOLTS OR GREATER?
YES
NO
6
• MEASURE THE VOLTAGE BETWEEN GROUND AND TERMINAL "B" OF THE BRAKE SWITCH WHILE APPLYING FIRM PRESSURE ON BRAKE PEDAL. IS VOLTAGE 10 VOLTS OR GREATER?
REPAIR OPEN OR SHORTED CKT 140 AND REPLACE 15 AMP FUSE 33.
YES
NO
REPAIR SHORTED OR OPEN CKT 17.
4
• INSPECT 32-WAY EBCM HARNESS CONNECTOR TERMINAL "D12" FOR POOR TERMINAL CONTACT AND EVIDENCE OF CORROSION. "CHECKING TERMINAL CONTACT." REPLACE ALL TERMINALS THAT EXHIBIT SIGNS OF POOR TERMINAL CONTACT OR CORROSION.
• RECONNECT ALL CONNECTORS.
• DRIVE VEHICLE AND PERFORM A MODERATELY HARD ABS STOP. DOES DTC 91 OR 92 SET AS A CURRENT DTC?
NO
YES
MISADJUSTED OR FAULTY BRAKE SWITCH. ADJUST OR REPLACE SWITCH AS NECESSARY.
REPAIR OPEN CKT 17.
YES
NO
REPLACE EBCM
MALFUNCTION IS MOST LIKELY DUE TO A POOR CONNECTION. REFER TO "DIAGNOSTIC AIDS"

GC402940111600EX

Fig. 288 Code A092: Open Brake Switch When ABS Was Required. 1993–94 Camaro & Firebird, 1994 Grand Prix, Century & Cutlass Ciera & Cruiser

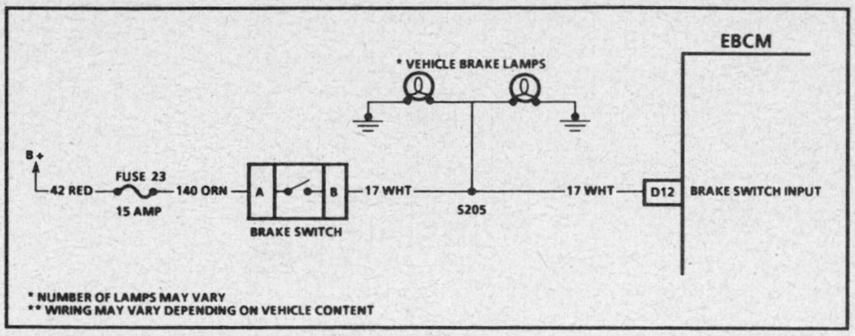
EBCM
* VEHICLE BRAKE LAMPS
B+
42 RED
FUSE 23
15 AMP
140 ORN
A
B
BRAKE SWITCH
17 WHT
S205
17 WHT
D12
BRAKE SWITCH INPUT
* NUMBER OF LAMPS MAY VARY
** WIRING MAY VARY DEPENDING ON VEHICLE CONTENT

GC402940111700AX

Grand Prix

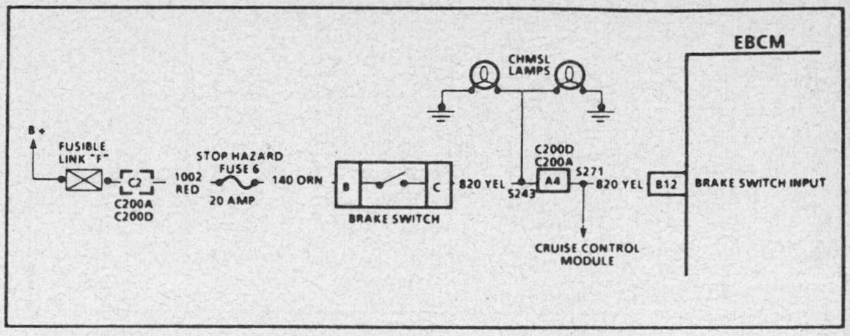
EBCM
CHMSL LAMPS
B+
FUSIBLE LINK "F"
C2
C200A
C200D
1002 RED
STOP HAZARD FUSE 6
20 AMP
140 ORN
B
C
BRAKE SWITCH
820 YEL
S243
C200D
C200A
A4
S271
820 YEL
B12
BRAKE SWITCH INPUT
CRUISE CONTROL MODULE

GC402940111700BX

Camaro & Firebird

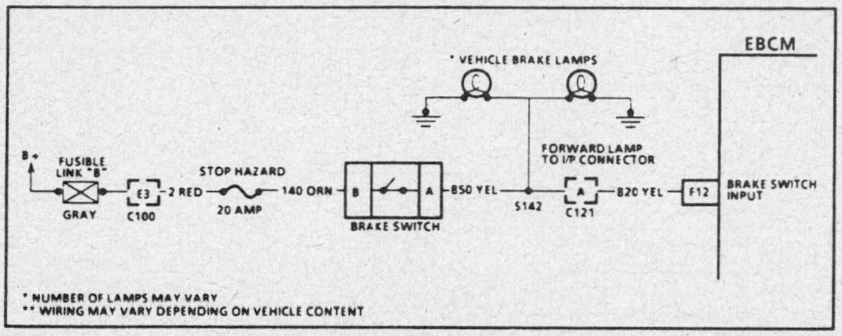
EBCM
* VEHICLE BRAKE LAMPS
B+
FUSIBLE LINK "B"
GRAY
E3
C100
2 RED
STOP HAZARD
20 AMP
140 ORN
B
A
BRAKE SWITCH
850 YEL
FORWARD LAMP TO I/P CONNECTOR
S142
A
C121
820 YEL
F12
BRAKE SWITCH INPUT
* NUMBER OF LAMPS MAY VARY
** WIRING MAY VARY DEPENDING ON VEHICLE CONTENT

GC402940111700CX

Century & Cutlass Ciera & Cruiser

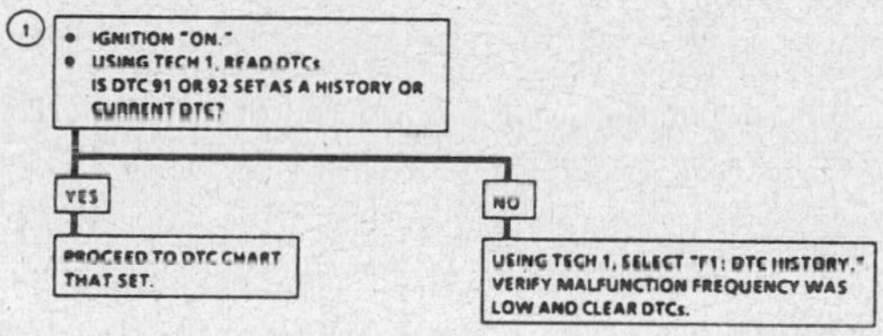
1
• IGNITION "ON."
• USING TECH 1, READ DTCs
IS DTC 91 OR 92 SET AS A HISTORY OR CURRENT DTC?
YES
NO
PROCEED TO DTC CHART THAT SET.
USING TECH 1, SELECT "F1: DTC HISTORY." VERIFY MALFUNCTION FREQUENCY WAS LOW AND CLEAR DTCs.

GC402940111700EX

DTC 93

DTC 91 OR 92 SET IN CURRENT OR PREV. IGN CYCLE

Circuit Description:

This DTC is the second portion of DTCs 91 and 92. If DTCs 91 or 92 failed during the last ignition cycle, DTC 93 becomes a current failure during the next ignition cycle, keeping ABS disabled until a brake switch "ON" state is seen. When a change is seen during an ignition cycle in which DTC 93 is a current malfunction, DTC 91 or 92 will clear itself at the end of the current ignition cycle, and ABS will enable itself at the start of the next ignition cycle. DTC 93 alone indicates 91 or 92 failed previously, but is intermittent, or has been corrected.

DTC Chart Test Description: Number(s) below refer to circled number(s) on the diagnostic chart.

1. Indicates which DTC (either 91 or 92) caused DTC 93 to set.

Diagnostic Aids: An "Intermittent" malfunction may be caused by a poor connection, rubbed through wire insulation, or a wire that is broken inside the insulation.

The frequency of the malfunction can be checked by using the enhanced diagnostic function of the Tech 1

Any circuitry, that is suspected as causing the intermittent complaint, should be thoroughly checked for backed out terminals, improper mating, broken locks, improperly formed or damaged terminals, poor terminal to wiring connections or physical damage to the wiring harness.

Also, verify proper brake switch operation using the data list of the Tech 1. As the brake is applied, the data list should display the brake switch "ON" within 1 inch of travel.

GC402940111700DX

Fig. 289 Code A093: DTC 91 or 92 Set In Current Or Previous Ignition Cycle. 1993–94 Camaro & Firebird, 1994 Grand Prix, Century & Cutlass Ciera & Cruiser

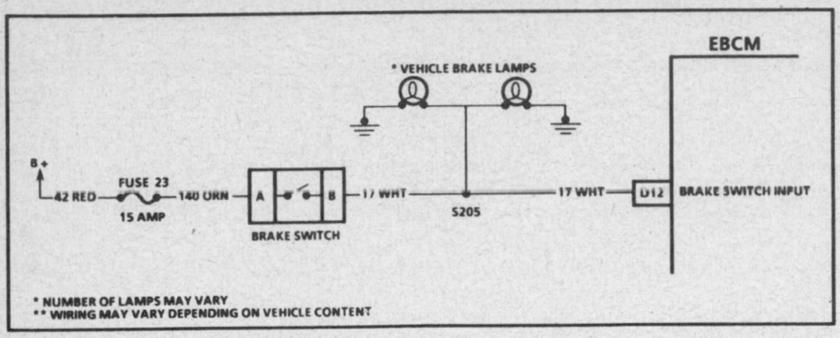
EBCM
* VEHICLE BRAKE LAMPS
B+
FUSE 23
42 RED
15 AMP
140 ORN
BRAKE SWITCH
17 WHT
S205
17 WHT
D12
BRAKE SWITCH INPUT
* NUMBER OF LAMPS MAY VARY
** WIRING MAY VARY DEPENDING ON VEHICLE CONTENT

GC402940111800AX

Grand Prix

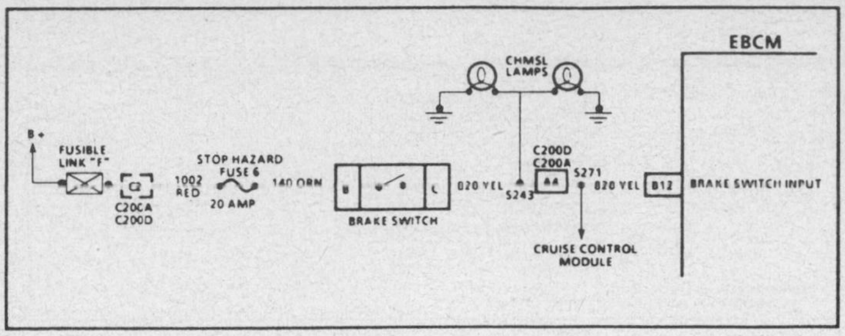
EBCM
CHMSL LAMPS
B+
FUSIBLE LINK "F"
C20CA
C200D
STOP HAZARD FUSE 6
1002 RED
20 AMP
140 ORN
BRAKE SWITCH
820 YEL
S243
C200D
C200A
S271
820 YEL
B12
BRAKE SWITCH INPUT
CRUISE CONTROL MODULE

GC402940111800BX

Camaro & Firebird

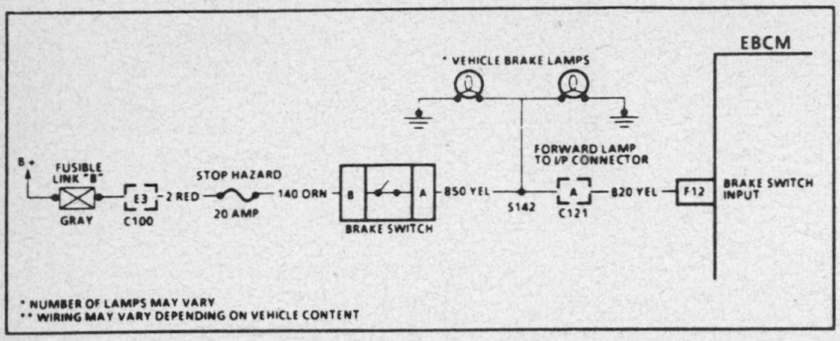
EBCM
* VEHICLE BRAKE LAMPS
B+
FUSIBLE LINK "B"
GRAY
E3
C100
STOP HAZARD
2 RED
20 AMP
140 ORN
BRAKE SWITCH
850 YEL
S142
FORWARD LAMP TO I/P CONNECTOR
C121
820 YEL
F12
BRAKE SWITCH INPUT
* NUMBER OF LAMPS MAY VARY
** WIRING MAY VARY DEPENDING ON VEHICLE CONTENT

GC402940111800CX

Century & Cutlass Ciera & Cruiser

DTC 94

BRAKE SWITCH CONTACTS ALWAYS CLOSED

Circuit Description:

This DTC is run to determine the proper operation of the brake switch. This is important because ABS is activated when the brake switch is "ON" and turned "OFF" when the brake is "OFF." If the brake switch is always "ON," ABS operation will always be requested resulting in potential modulator cycling on rough roads. Additionally, this malfunction will most likely result in a dead battery (due to the brake lights staying "ON") if the driver is not informed of this malfunction.

DTC Will Set When: DTC 94 can be set when the vehicle reaches at least 40 km/h (25 mph). If the brake was never "OFF" during two consecutive drive cycles, a malfunction exists.

Action Taken: A malfunction DTC is stored. ABS is not disabled.

DTC Chart Test Description: Number(s) below refer to circled number(s) on the diagnostic chart.

1. Checks if the malfunction is currently present.
2. Isolates the cause of the malfunction to either a malfunctioning or misadjusted brake switch, or a short to voltage in the brake switch circuitry.
3. Checks for unwanted voltage on the brake switch input circuit.
4. Checks for a possible intermittent malfunction.

Diagnostic Aids: An "Intermittent" malfunction may be caused by a poor connection, rubbed through wire insulation, or a wire that is broken inside the insulation.

The frequency of the malfunction can be checked by using the enhanced diagnostic function of the Tech 1

Any circuitry, that is suspected as causing the intermittent complaint, should be thoroughly checked for backed out terminals, improper mating, broken locks, improperly formed or damaged terminals, poor terminal to wiring connections or physical damage to the wiring harness.

GC402940111800DX

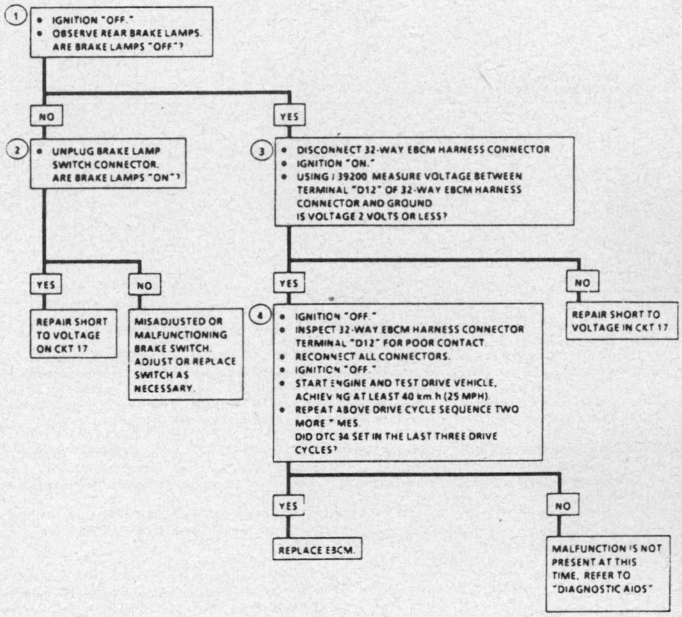
1
• IGNITION "OFF."
• OBSERVE REAR BRAKE LAMPS. ARE BRAKE LAMPS "OFF"?
NO
YES
2
• UNPLUG BRAKE LAMP SWITCH CONNECTOR. ARE BRAKE LAMPS "ON"?
3
• DISCONNECT 32-WAY EBCM HARNESS CONNECTOR
• IGNITION "ON."
• USING J 39200 MEASURE VOLTAGE BETWEEN TERMINAL "D12" OF 32-WAY EBCM HARNESS CONNECTOR AND GROUND IS VOLTAGE 2 VOLTS OR LESS?
YES
NO
REPAIR SHORT TO VOLTAGE ON CKT 17
MISADJUSTED OR MALFUNCTIONING BRAKE SWITCH. ADJUST OR REPLACE SWITCH AS NECESSARY.
YES
NO
REPAIR SHORT TO VOLTAGE IN CKT 17
4
• IGNITION "OFF."
• INSPECT 32-WAY EBCM HARNESS CONNECTOR TERMINAL "D12" FOR POOR CONTACT.
• RECONNECT ALL CONNECTORS.
• IGNITION "OFF."
• START ENGINE AND TEST DRIVE VEHICLE, ACHIEVING AT LEAST 40 km/h (25 MPH).
• REPEAT ABOVE DRIVE CYCLE SEQUENCE TWO MORE TIMES.
DID DTC 94 SET IN THE LAST THREE DRIVE CYCLES?
YES
NO
REPLACE EBCM.
MALFUNCTION IS NOT PRESENT AT THIS TIME. REFER TO "DIAGNOSTIC AIDS"

GC402940111800EX

Fig. 290 Code A094: Brake Switch Contacts Always Closed. 1993–94 Camaro & Firebird, 1994 Grand Prix, Century & Cutlass Ciera & Cruiser

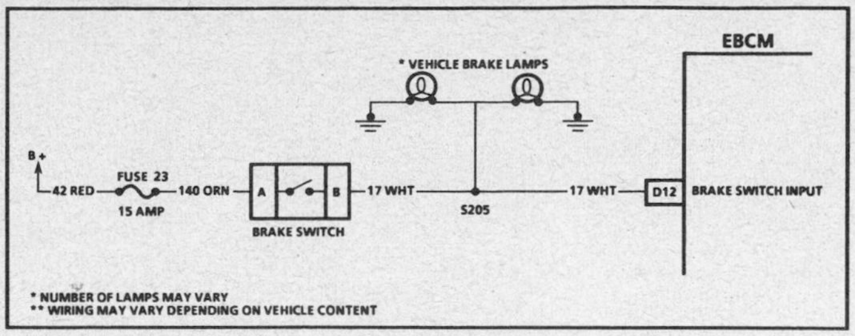
EBCM
* VEHICLE BRAKE LAMPS
B+
FUSE 23
42 RED
140 ORN
15 AMP
A
B
BRAKE SWITCH
17 WHT
S205
17 WHT
D12
BRAKE SWITCH INPUT
* NUMBER OF LAMPS MAY VARY
** WIRING MAY VARY DEPENDING ON VEHICLE CONTENT

GC402940111900AX

Grand Prix

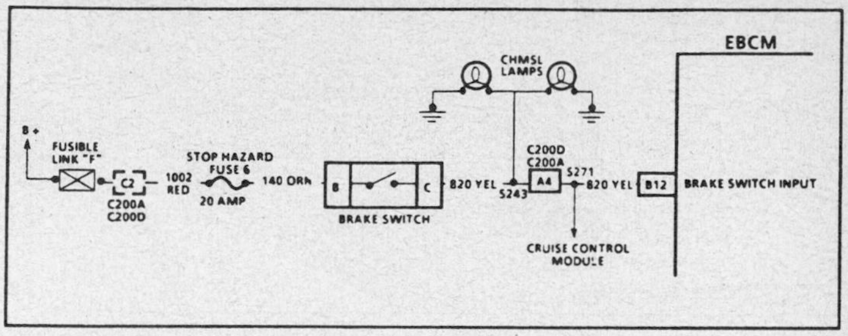
EBCM
CHMSL LAMPS
B+
FUSIBLE LINK "F"
C2
C200A
C200D
1002 RED
STOP HAZARD FUSE 6
20 AMP
140 ORN
B
C
BRAKE SWITCH
820 YEL
C200D
C200A
S271
A4
S243
820 YEL
B12
BRAKE SWITCH INPUT
CRUISE CONTROL MODULE

GC402940111900BX

Camaro & Firebird

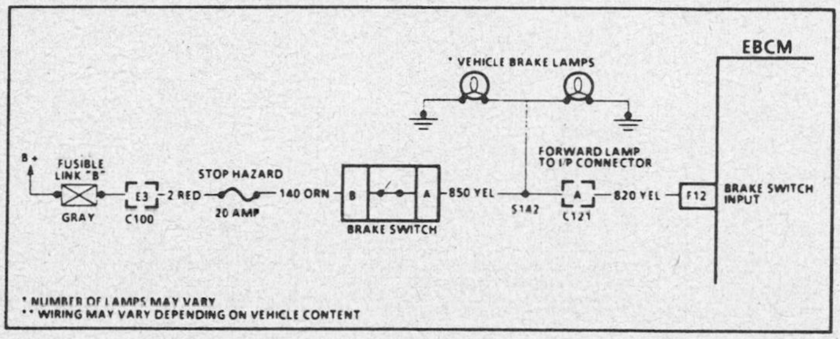
EBCM
* VEHICLE BRAKE LAMPS
B+
FUSIBLE LINK "B"
GRAY
E3
C100
2 RED
STOP HAZARD
20 AMP
140 ORN
B
A
BRAKE SWITCH
850 YEL
S142
FORWARD LAMP TO I/P CONNECTOR
A
C121
820 YEL
F12
BRAKE SWITCH INPUT
* NUMBER OF LAMPS MAY VARY
** WIRING MAY VARY DEPENDING ON VEHICLE CONTENT

GC402940111900CX

Century & Cutlass Ciera & Cruiser

DTC 95

BRAKE SWITCH CIRCUIT OPEN

Circuit Description:

This DTC is used to identify open brake switch circuitry that prevents the brake switch input to the EBCM from changing states when the brake is applied. This DTC is used in conjunction with DTCs 91 and 92 to determine the cause of an open brake switch malfunction.

DTC Will Set When: DTC 95 can be set after initialization is completed. If the brake switch input voltage is out of specification for one second indicating an open circuit, a malfunction exists.

Action Taken: A malfunction DTC is stored, ABS is disabled and the ABS warning lamp is turned "ON."

DTC Chart Test Description: Number(s) below refer to circled number(s) on the diagnostic chart.

1. This step is used to confirm that an open in the brake switch circuitry currently exists.
2. Indicates if the brake switch signal is being received by the EBCM.
3. Indicates if an open circuit exists in the brake switch or brake lamp circuitry.
4. Isolates the open circuit to either the brake switch input circuitry, or the EBCM.

Diagnostic Aids: An "Intermittent" malfunction may be caused by a poor connection, rubbed through wire insulation, or a wire that is broken inside the insulation.

The frequency of the malfunction can be checked by using the enhanced diagnostic function of the Tech 1.

Any circuitry, that is suspected as causing the intermittent complaint, should be thoroughly checked for backed out terminals, improper mating, broken locks, improperly formed or damaged terminals, poor terminal to wiring connections or physical damage to the wiring harness.

GC402940111900DX

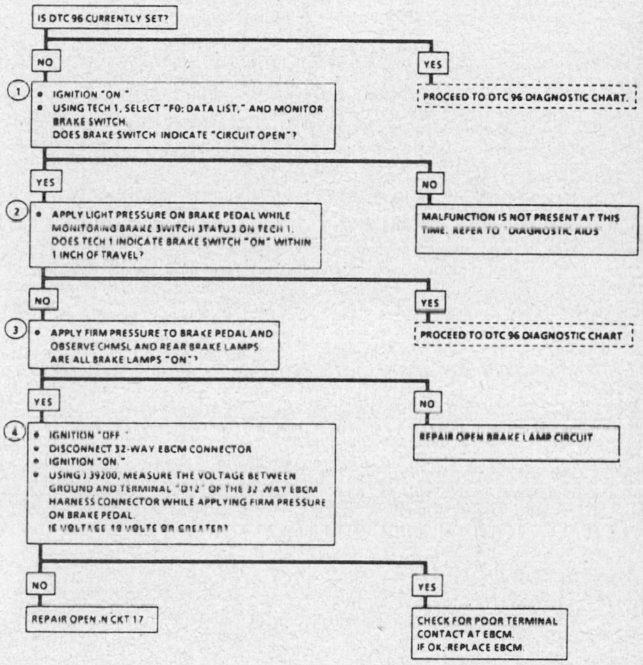
IS DTC 96 CURRENTLY SET?
NO
YES
PROCEED TO DTC 96 DIAGNOSTIC CHART.
1
• IGNITION "ON."
• USING TECH 1, SELECT "F0: DATA LIST," AND MONITOR BRAKE SWITCH.
DOES BRAKE SWITCH INDICATE "CIRCUIT OPEN"?
YES
NO
MALFUNCTION IS NOT PRESENT AT THIS TIME. REFER TO "DIAGNOSTIC AIDS"
2
• APPLY LIGHT PRESSURE ON BRAKE PEDAL WHILE MONITORING BRAKE SWITCH STATUS ON TECH 1.
DOES TECH 1 INDICATE BRAKE SWITCH "ON" WITHIN 1 INCH OF TRAVEL?
NO
YES
PROCEED TO DTC 96 DIAGNOSTIC CHART
3
• APPLY FIRM PRESSURE TO BRAKE PEDAL AND OBSERVE CHMSL AND REAR BRAKE LAMPS
ARE ALL BRAKE LAMPS "ON"?
YES
NO
REPAIR OPEN BRAKE LAMP CIRCUIT
4
• IGNITION "OFF."
• DISCONNECT 32-WAY EBCM CONNECTOR
• IGNITION "ON."
• USING J 39200, MEASURE THE VOLTAGE BETWEEN GROUND AND TERMINAL "D12" OF THE 32-WAY EBCM HARNESS CONNECTOR WHILE APPLYING FIRM PRESSURE ON BRAKE PEDAL.
IS VOLTAGE 10 VOLTS OR GREATER?
NO
YES
REPAIR OPEN IN CKT 17
CHECK FOR POOR TERMINAL CONTACT AT EBCM.
IF OK, REPLACE EBCM.

GC402940111900EX

Fig. 291 Code A095: Brake Switch Circuit Open. 1993–94 Camaro & Firebird, 1994 Grand Prix, Century & Cutlass Ciera & Cruiser

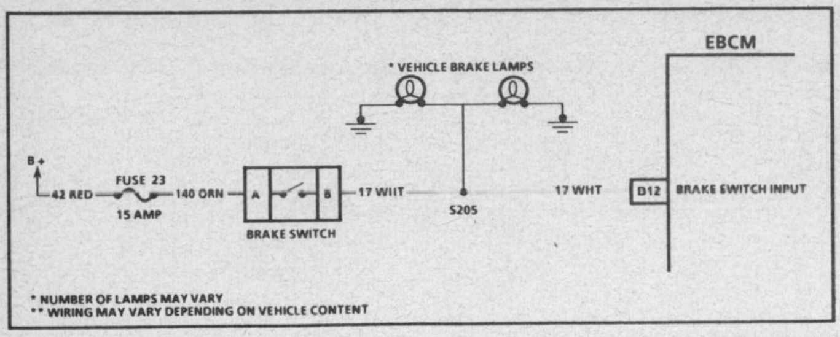
EBCM
* VEHICLE BRAKE LAMPS
B+
42 RED
FUSE 23
15 AMP
140 ORN
A
B
BRAKE SWITCH
17 WHT
S205
17 WHT
D12
BRAKE SWITCH INPUT
* NUMBER OF LAMPS MAY VARY
** WIRING MAY VARY DEPENDING ON VEHICLE CONTENT

GC402940112000AX

Grand Prix

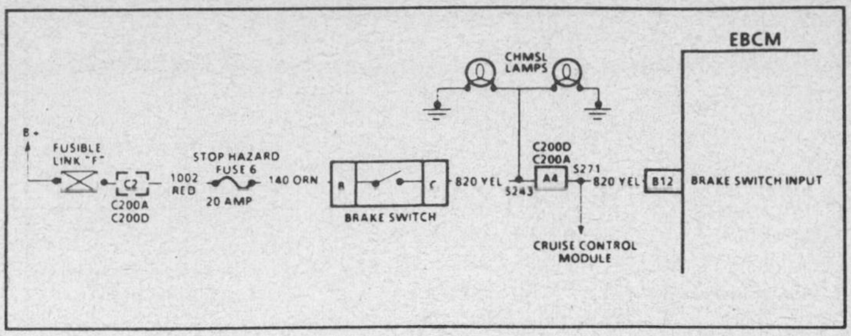
EBCM
CHMSL
LAMPS
B+
FUSIBLE
LINK "F"
C2
C200A
C200D
1002
RED
STOP HAZARD
FUSE 6
20 AMP
140 ORN
B
C
BRAKE SWITCH
820 YEL
S243
C200D
C200A
S271
A4
820 YEL
B12
BRAKE SWITCH INPUT
CRUISE CONTROL
MODULE

GC402940112000BX

Camaro & Firebird

DTC 96

BRAKE LAMPS CIRCUIT OPEN

Circuit Description:
This DTC is designed to isolate the cause of a DTC 95 malfunction and indicate to the driver ABS is still available. If DTC 95 occurs with DTC 96, the brake lamps are open, the brake lamp grounds are open, or the Center High Mounted Stop Lamp (CHMSL) circuit is open during 4-way flasher use. The presence of battery voltage at the brake switch input indicates a valid brake switch input is still available.

DTC Will Set When: DTC 96 can be set only after DTC 95 has been set. If the EBCM detects battery voltage on the brake switch input circuit for 0.5 second, a malfunction exists.

Action Taken: A malfunction DTC is stored. ABS is not disabled.

DTC Chart Test Description: Number(s) below refer to circled number(s) on the diagnostic chart.

1. As a result of a malfunction of an additional brake switch circuit DTC, this DTC may be set. To ensure proper diagnosis, any additional brake switch DTCs must be repaired first.
2. Identifies if the malfunction is currently present in the brake circuit.

Diagnostic Aids: An "Intermittent" malfunction may be caused by a poor connection, rubbed through wire insulation, or a wire that is broken inside the insulation.

The frequency of the malfunction can be checked by using the enhanced diagnostic function of the Tech 1

Any circuitry, that is suspected as causing the intermittent complaint, should be thoroughly checked for backed out terminals, improper mating, broken locks, improperly formed or damaged terminals, poor terminal to wiring connections or physical damage to the wiring harness.

GC402940112000CX

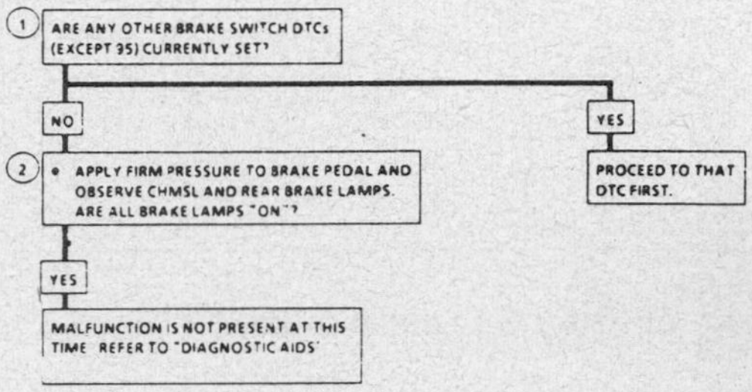
1
ARE ANY OTHER BRAKE SWITCH DTCs (EXCEPT 95) CURRENTLY SET?
NO
YES
PROCEED TO THAT DTC FIRST.
2
• APPLY FIRM PRESSURE TO BRAKE PEDAL AND OBSERVE CHMSL AND REAR BRAKE LAMPS. ARE ALL BRAKE LAMPS "ON"?
YES
MALFUNCTION IS NOT PRESENT AT THIS TIME. REFER TO "DIAGNOSTIC AIDS"

GC402940112000DX

Fig. 292 Code A096: Brake Lamps Circuit Open. 1994 Grand Prix, Century & Cutlass Ciera & Cruiser

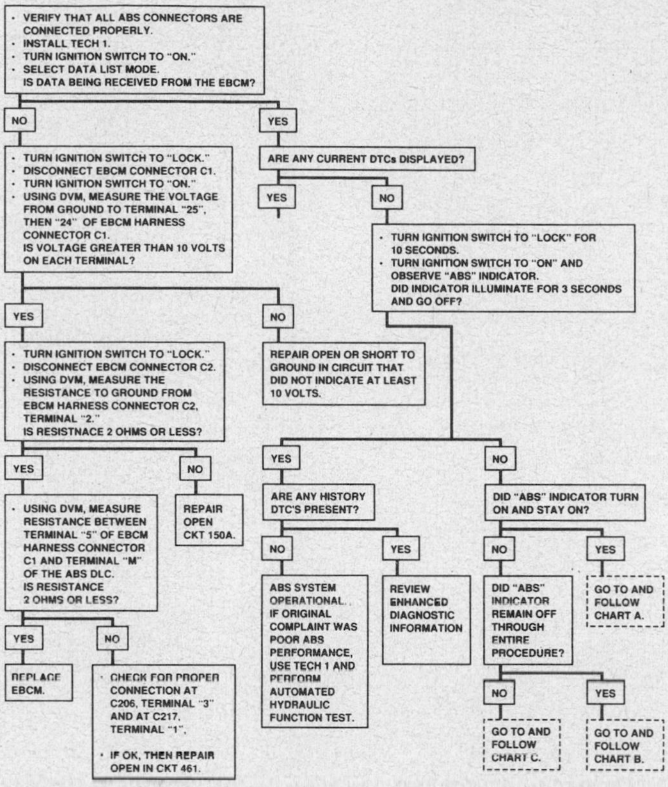

• VERIFY THAT ALL ABS CONNECTORS ARE CONNECTED PROPERLY. • INSTALL TECH 1. • TURN IGNITION SWITCH TO "ON." • SELECT DATA LIST MODE. IS DATA BEING RECEIVED FROM THE EBCM?
NO
YES
• TURN IGNITION SWITCH TO "LOCK." • DISCONNECT EBCM CONNECTOR C1. • TURN IGNITION SWITCH TO "ON." • USING DVM, MEASURE THE VOLTAGE FROM GROUND TO TERMINAL "25", THEN "24" OF EBCM HARNESS CONNECTOR C1. IS VOLTAGE GREATER THAN 10 VOLTS ON EACH TERMINAL?
ARE ANY CURRENT DTCs DISPLAYED?
YES
NO
• TURN IGNITION SWITCH TO "LOCK" FOR 10 SECONDS. • TURN IGNITION SWITCH TO "ON" AND OBSERVE "ABS" INDICATOR. DID INDICATOR ILLUMINATE FOR 3 SECONDS AND GO OFF?
YES
NO
• TURN IGNITION SWITCH TO "LOCK." • DISCONNECT EBCM CONNECTOR C2. • USING DVM, MEASURE THE RESISTANCE TO GROUND FROM EBCM HARNESS CONNECTOR C2, TERMINAL "2." IS RESISTNACE 2 OHMS OR LESS?
REPAIR OPEN OR SHORT TO GROUND IN CIRCUIT THAT DID NOT INDICATE AT LEAST 10 VOLTS.
YES
NO
YES
NO
• USING DVM, MEASURE RESISTANCE BETWEEN TERMINAL "5" OF EBCM HARNESS CONNECTOR C1 AND TERMINAL "M" OF THE ABS DLC. IS RESISTANCE 2 OHMS OR LESS?
REPAIR OPEN CKT 150A.
ARE ANY HISTORY DTC'S PRESENT?
DID "ABS" INDICATOR TURN ON AND STAY ON?
NO
YES
NO
YES
ABS SYSTEM OPERATIONAL. IF ORIGINAL COMPLAINT WAS POOR ABS PERFORMANCE, USE TECH 1 AND PERFORM AUTOMATED HYDRAULIC FUNCTION TEST.
REVIEW ENHANCED DIAGNOSTIC INFORMATION
DID "ABS" INDICATOR REMAIN OFF THROUGH ENTIRE PROCEDURE?
GO TO AND FOLLOW CHART A.
YES
NO
REPLACE EBCM.
• CHECK FOR PROPER CONNECTION AT C206, TERMINAL "3" AND AT C217, TERMINAL "1". • IF OK, THEN REPAIR OPEN IN CKT 461.
NO
YES
GO TO AND FOLLOW CHART C.
GO TO AND FOLLOW CHART B.
GC4029401010000X

Fig. 293 Diagnostic circuit check. 1993–94 Prizm

CHART	SYMPTOM
A	ABS (AMBER) INDICATOR ON CONSTANTLY. NO DTCs STORED
B	ABS (AMBER) INDICATOR ON INTERMITTENTLY. NO DTCs STORED
C	ABS (AMBER) INDICATOR OFF CONSTANTLY. NO DTCs STORED
D	TECH 1 DISPLAYS UNDEFINED DTCs
E	ABS ACTIVE INDICATOR MALFUNCTIONING
DIAGNOSTIC TROUBLE CODE	**DESCRIPTION**
A014	ABS ENABLE RELAY CONTACT CIRCUIT OPEN
A015	ABS ENABLE RELAY CIRCUIT SHORTED TO BATTERY OR ALWAYS CLOSED
A016	ABS ENABLE RELAY COIL CIRCUIT OPEN
A017	ABS ENABLE RELAY COIL CIRCUIT SHORTED TO GROUND
A018	ABS ENABLE RELAY COIL CIRCUIT SHORTED TO BATTERY
A021	LEFT FRONT WHEEL SPEED = 0 OR UNREASONABLE
A022	RIGHT FRONT WHEEL SPEED = 0 OR UNREASONABLE
A023	LEFT REAR WHEEL SPEED = 0 OR UNREASONABLE
A024	RIGHT REAR WHEEL SPEED = 0 OR UNREASONABLE
A025	LEFT FRONT EXCESSIVE WHEEL SPEED VARIATION
A026	RIGHT FRONT EXCESSIVE WHEEL SPEED VARIATION
A027	LEFT REAR EXCESSIVE WHEEL SPEED VARIATION
A028	RIGHT REAR EXCESSIVE WHEEL SPEED VARIATION
A036	LOW SYSTEM VOLTAGE
A037	HIGH SYSTEM VOLTAGE
A038	LEFT FRONT ESB WILL NOT HOLD MOTOR
A041	RIGHT FRONT ESB WILL NOT HOLD MOTOR
A042	REAR ESB WILL NOT HOLD MOTOR
A044	LEFT FRONT CHANNEL WILL NOT MOVE
A045	RIGHT FRONT CHANNEL WILL NOT MOVE
A046	REAR CHANNEL WILL NOT MOVE
A047	LEFT FRONT MOTOR FREE SPINS
A048	RIGHT FRONT MOTOR FREE SPINS
A051	REAR MOTOR FREE SPINS
A052	LEFT FRONT CHANNEL IN RELEASE TOO LONG
A053	RIGHT FRONT CHANNEL IN RELEASE TOO LONG
A054	REAR CHANNEL IN RELEASE TOO LONG
A055	EBCM MALFUNCTION
A056	LEFT FRONT MOTOR CIRCUIT OPEN
A057	LEFT FRONT MOTOR CIRCUIT SHORTED TO GROUND
A058	LEFT FRONT MOTOR CIRCUIT SHORTED TO BATTERY
A061	RIGHT FRONT MOTOR CIRCUIT OPEN
A062	RIGHT FRONT MOTOR CIRCUIT SHORTED TO GROUND
A063	RIGHT FRONT MOTOR CIRCUIT SHORTED TO BATTERY
A064	REAR MOTOR CIRCUIT OPEN
A065	REAR MOTOR CIRCUIT SHORTED TO GROUND

GC4029401003010X

Fig. 294 Diagnostic trouble code & symptom table (Part 1 of 2). 1993–94 Prizm

DIAGNOSTIC TROUBLE CODE	DESCRIPTION
A066	REAR MOTOR CIRCUIT SHORTED TO BATTERY
A076	LEFT FRONT SOLENOID CIRCUIT OPEN OR SHORTED TO BATTERY
A077	LEFT FRONT SOLENOID CIRCUIT SHORTED TO GROUND
A078	RIGHT FRONT SOLENOID CIRCUIT OPEN OR SHORTED TO BATTERY
A081	RIGHT FRONT SOLENOID CIRCUIT SHORTED TO GROUND
A082	CALIBRATION MALFUNCTION
A086	EBCM TURNED ON THE RED BRAKE WARNING LAMP
A087	RED BRAKE WARNING LAMP CIRCUIT SHORTED OPEN
A088	RED BRAKE WARNING LAMP CIRCUIT SHORTED TO BATTERY
A091	OPEN BRAKE SWITCH DURING DECELERATION
A092	OPEN BRAKE SWITCH WHEN ABS WAS REQUIRED
A093	CODE 91 OR 92 SET IN CURRENT OR PREVIOUS IGNITION CYCLE
A094	BRAKE SWITCH CONTACTS ALWAYS CLOSED
A095	BRAKE SWITCH CIRCUIT OPEN
A096	REAR BRAKE LAMP CIRCUIT OPEN

GC4029401003020X

Fig. 294 Diagnostic trouble code & symptom table (Part 2 of 2). 1993–94 Prizm

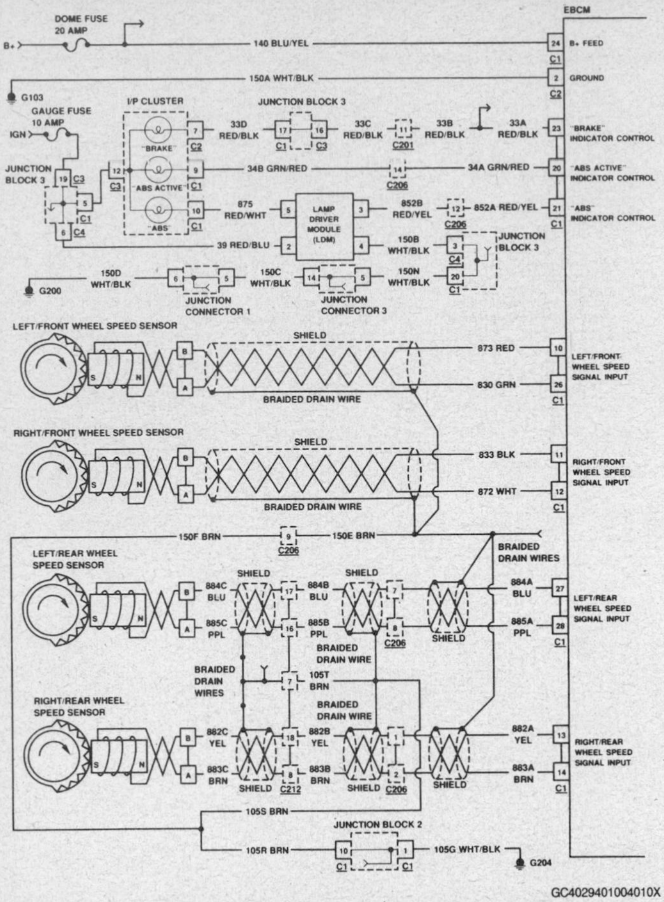
DOME FUSE 20 AMP
B+
140 BLU/YEL
EBCM
24 B+ FEED C1
150A WHT/BLK
2 GROUND C2
G103
GAUGE FUSE 10 AMP
IGN
I/P CLUSTER
JUNCTION BLOCK 3
33D RED/BLK
33C RED/BLK
33B RED/BLK
33A RED/BLK
C201
23 "BRAKE" INDICATOR CONTROL
"BRAKE"
ABS ACTIVE
"ABS"
JUNCTION BLOCK 3
34B GRN/RED
34A GRN/RED
C206
20 "ABS ACTIVE" INDICATOR CONTROL
875 RED/WHT
LAMP DRIVER MODULE (LDM)
852B RED/YEL
852A RED/YEL
21 "ABS" INDICATOR CONTROL
39 RED/BLU
150B WHT/BLK
JUNCTION BLOCK 3
150D WHT/BLK
150C WHT/BLK
150N WHT/BLK
G200
JUNCTION CONNECTOR 1
JUNCTION CONNECTOR 3
LEFT/FRONT WHEEL SPEED SENSOR
SHIELD
873 RED
830 GRN
BRAIDED DRAIN WIRE
10 26 LEFT/FRONT WHEEL SPEED SIGNAL INPUT
RIGHT/FRONT WHEEL SPEED SENSOR
833 BLK
872 WHT
11 12 RIGHT/FRONT WHEEL SPEED SIGNAL INPUT
150F BRN
150E BRN
BRAIDED DRAIN WIRES
LEFT/REAR WHEEL SPEED SENSOR
884C BLU
884B BLU
884A BLU
885C PPL
885B PPL
885A PPL
27 28 LEFT/REAR WHEEL SPEED SIGNAL INPUT
BRAIDED DRAIN WIRES
105T BRN
RIGHT/REAR WHEEL SPEED SENSOR
882C YEL
882B YEL
882A YEL
883C BRN
883B BRN
883A BRN
13 14 RIGHT/REAR WHEEL SPEED SIGNAL INPUT
C212
105S BRN
JUNCTION BLOCK 2
105R BRN
105G WHT/BLK
G204
GC4029401004010X

Fig. 295 ABS wiring circuit (Part 1 of 2). 1993–94 Prizm

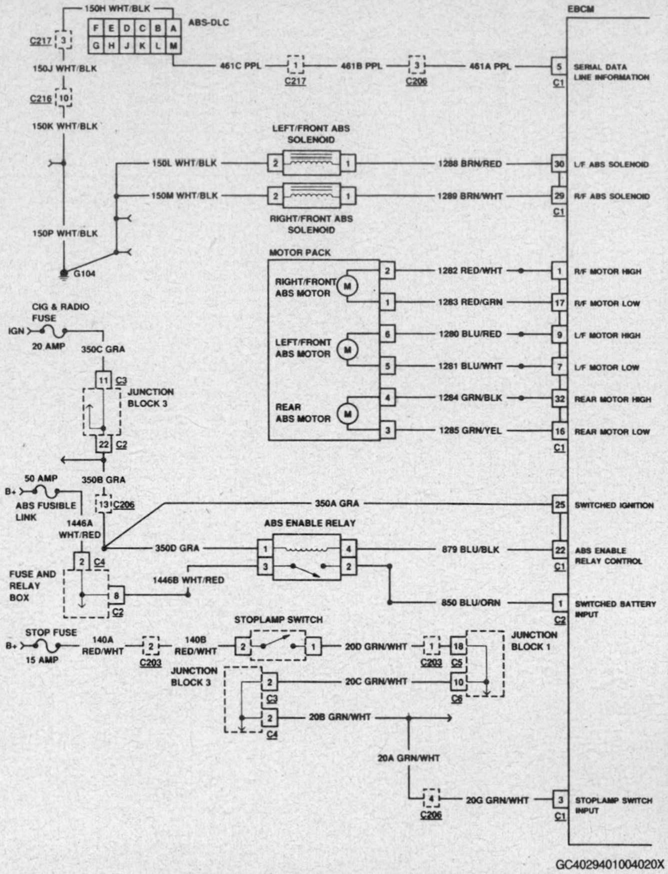
150H WHT/BLK
ABS-DLC
C217
150J WHT/BLK
461C PPL
461B PPL
461A PPL
EBCM
5 SERIAL DATA LINE INFORMATION
C216
150K WHT/BLK
LEFT/FRONT ABS SOLENOID
150L WHT/BLK
1288 BRN/RED
30 L/F ABS SOLENOID
150M WHT/BLK
1289 BRN/WHT
29 R/F ABS SOLENOID
RIGHT/FRONT ABS SOLENOID
150P WHT/BLK
G104
MOTOR PACK
RIGHT/FRONT ABS MOTOR
1282 RED/WHT
1 R/F MOTOR HIGH
1283 RED/GRN
17 R/F MOTOR LOW
LEFT/FRONT ABS MOTOR
1280 BLU/RED
9 L/F MOTOR HIGH
1281 BLU/WHT
7 L/F MOTOR LOW
REAR ABS MOTOR
1284 GRN/BLK
32 REAR MOTOR HIGH
1285 GRN/YEL
16 REAR MOTOR LOW
CIG & RADIO FUSE 20 AMP
IGN
350C GRA
JUNCTION BLOCK 3
50 AMP
ABS FUSIBLE LINK
350B GRA
1446A WHT/RED
350A GRA
25 SWITCHED IGNITION
ABS ENABLE RELAY
350D GRA
879 BLU/BLK
22 ABS ENABLE RELAY CONTROL
FUSE AND RELAY BOX
1446B WHT/RED
850 BLU/ORN
1 SWITCHED BATTERY INPUT
STOPLAMP SWITCH
STOP FUSE 15 AMP
140A RED/WHT
140B RED/WHT
C203
20D GRN/WHT
JUNCTION BLOCK 1
JUNCTION BLOCK 3
20C GRN/WHT
20B GRN/WHT
20A GRN/WHT
20G GRN/WHT
3 STOPLAMP SWITCH INPUT
GC4029401004020X

Fig. 295 ABS wiring circuit. (part 2 of 2). 1993–94 Prizm

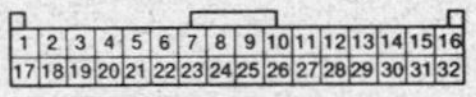
1 2 3 4 5 6 7 8 9 10 11 12 13 14 15 16
17 18 19 20 21 22 23 24 25 26 27 28 29 30 31 32

EBCM CONNECTOR C1

PIN	CIRCUIT NO.	COLOR	CIRCUIT
1	850	RED/WHT	RIGHT FRONT MOTOR HIGH
2	—	—	NOT USED
3	20	GRN/WHT	STOPLAMP SWITCH INPUT
4	—	—	NOT USED
5	461	PPL	SERIAL DATA LINE INFORMATION
6	—	—	NOT USED
7	1281	BLU/WHT	LEFT FRONT MOTOR LOW
8	—	—	NOT USED
9	1280	BLU/RED	LEFT FRONT MOTOR HIGH
10	873	RED	LEFT FRONT WHEEL SPEED SIGNAL INPUT
11	833	BLK	RIGHT FRONT WHEEL SPEED SIGNAL INPUT
12	872	WHT	RIGHT FRONT WHEEL SPEED SIGNAL INPUT
13	882	YEL	RIGHT REAR WHEEL SPEED SIGNAL INPUT
14	883	BRN	RIGHT REAR WHEEL SPEED SIGNAL INPUT
15	—	—	NOT USED
16	1285	GRN/YEL	REAR MOTOR LOW
17	1283	RED/GRN	RIGHT FRONT MOTOR LOW
18	—	—	NOT USED
19	—	—	NOT USED
20	34	GRN/RED	"ABS ACTIVE" INDICATOR CONTROL
21	852	RED/YEL	"ABS" INDICATOR CONTROL
22	879	BLU/BLK	ABS ENABLE RELAY CONTROL
23	33	RED/BLK	"BRAKE" INDICATOR CONTROL
24	140	BLU/YEL	B+ FEED
25	350	GRA	SWITCHED IGNITION
26	830	GRN	LEFT FRONT WHEEL SPEED SIGNAL INPUT
27	884	BLU	LEFT REAR WHEEL SPEED SIGNAL INPUT
28	885	PPL	LEFT REAR WHEEL SPEED SIGNAL INPUT
29	1289	BRN/WHT	RIGHT FRONT ABS SOLENOID
30	1288	BRN/RED	LEFT FRONT ABS SOLENOID
31	—	—	NOT USED
32	1284	GRN/BLK	REAR MOTOR HIGH

GC4029401005010X

Fig. 296 EBCM connector face view. (Part 1 of 2). 1993–94 Prizm

PIN	CIRCUIT NO.	COLOR	CIRCUIT
1	850	BLU/ORN	SWITCHED BATTERY INPUT
2	150A	WHT/BLK	GROUND – G103

GC4029401005020X

Fig. 296 EBCM connector face view. (Part 2 of 2). 1993–94 Prizm

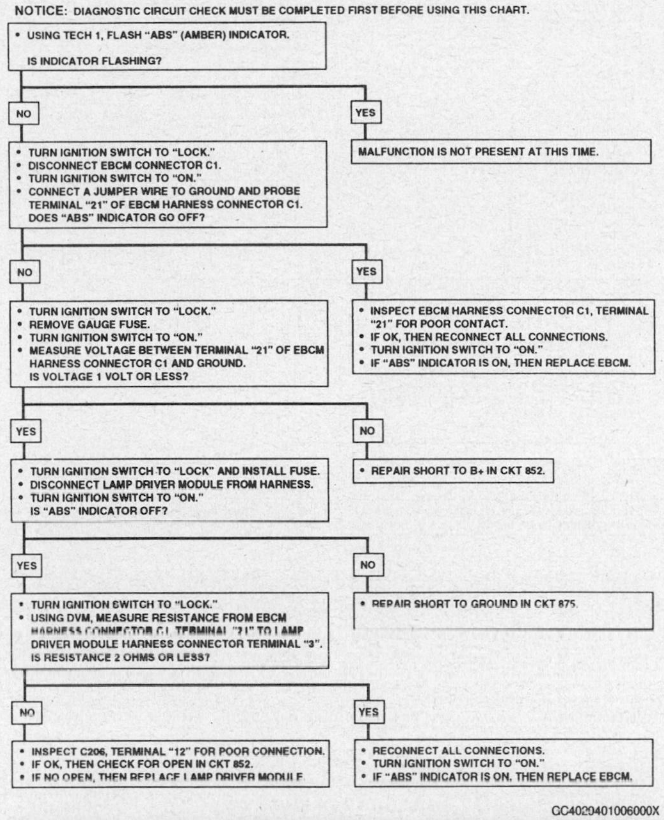
NOTICE: DIAGNOSTIC CIRCUIT CHECK MUST BE COMPLETED FIRST BEFORE USING THIS CHART.
• USING TECH 1, FLASH "ABS" (AMBER) INDICATOR. IS INDICATOR FLASHING?
NO
YES
• TURN IGNITION SWITCH TO "LOCK." • DISCONNECT EBCM CONNECTOR C1. • TURN IGNITION SWITCH TO "ON." • CONNECT A JUMPER WIRE TO GROUND AND PROBE TERMINAL "21" OF EBCM HARNESS CONNECTOR C1. DOES "ABS" INDICATOR GO OFF?
MALFUNCTION IS NOT PRESENT AT THIS TIME.
NO
YES
• TURN IGNITION SWITCH TO "LOCK." • REMOVE GAUGE FUSE. • TURN IGNITION SWITCH TO "ON." • MEASURE VOLTAGE BETWEEN TERMINAL "21" OF EBCM HARNESS CONNECTOR C1 AND GROUND. IS VOLTAGE 1 VOLT OR LESS?
• INSPECT EBCM HARNESS CONNECTOR C1, TERMINAL "21" FOR POOR CONTACT. • IF OK, THEN RECONNECT ALL CONNECTIONS. • TURN IGNITION SWITCH TO "ON." • IF "ABS" INDICATOR IS ON, THEN REPLACE EBCM.
YES
NO
• TURN IGNITION SWITCH TO "LOCK" AND INSTALL FUSE. • DISCONNECT LAMP DRIVER MODULE FROM HARNESS. • TURN IGNITION SWITCH TO "ON." IS "ABS" INDICATOR OFF?
• REPAIR SHORT TO B+ IN CKT 852.
YES
NO
• TURN IGNITION SWITCH TO "LOCK." • USING DVM, MEASURE RESISTANCE FROM EBCM HARNESS CONNECTOR C1, TERMINAL "21" TO LAMP DRIVER MODULE HARNESS CONNECTOR TERMINAL "3". IS RESISTANCE 2 OHMS OR LESS?
• REPAIR SHORT TO GROUND IN CKT 875.
NO
YES
• INSPECT C206, TERMINAL "12" FOR POOR CONNECTION. • IF OK, THEN CHECK FOR OPEN IN CKT 852. • IF NO OPEN, THEN REPLACE LAMP DRIVER MODULE.
• RECONNECT ALL CONNECTIONS. • TURN IGNITION SWITCH TO "ON." • IF "ABS" INDICATOR IS ON, THEN REPLACE EBCM.
GC4029401006000X

Fig. 297 Chart A, ABS indicator on constantly. No DTC's stored . 1993–94 Prizm

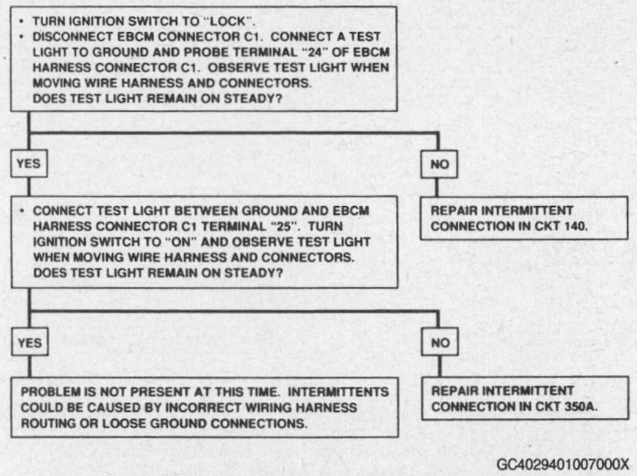
• TURN IGNITION SWITCH TO "LOCK". • DISCONNECT EBCM CONNECTOR C1. CONNECT A TEST LIGHT TO GROUND AND PROBE TERMINAL "24" OF EBCM HARNESS CONNECTOR C1. OBSERVE TEST LIGHT WHEN MOVING WIRE HARNESS AND CONNECTORS. DOES TEST LIGHT REMAIN ON STEADY?
YES
NO
• CONNECT TEST LIGHT BETWEEN GROUND AND EBCM HARNESS CONNECTOR C1 TERMINAL "25". TURN IGNITION SWITCH TO "ON" AND OBSERVE TEST LIGHT WHEN MOVING WIRE HARNESS AND CONNECTORS. DOES TEST LIGHT REMAIN ON STEADY?
REPAIR INTERMITTENT CONNECTION IN CKT 140.
YES
NO
PROBLEM IS NOT PRESENT AT THIS TIME. INTERMITTENTS COULD BE CAUSED BY INCORRECT WIRING HARNESS ROUTING OR LOOSE GROUND CONNECTIONS.
REPAIR INTERMITTENT CONNECTION IN CKT 350A.
GC4029401007000X

Fig. 298 Chart B, ABS indicator on intermittently. No DTC's stored . 1993–94 Prizm

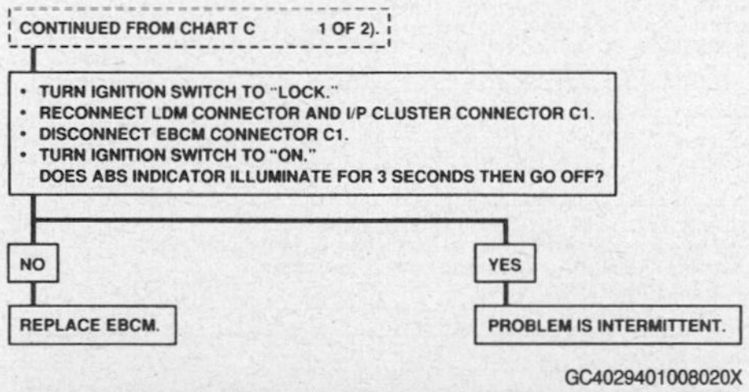
CONTINUED FROM CHART C 1 OF 2).
• TURN IGNITION SWITCH TO "LOCK." • RECONNECT LDM CONNECTOR AND I/P CLUSTER CONNECTOR C1. • DISCONNECT EBCM CONNECTOR C1. • TURN IGNITION SWITCH TO "ON." DOES ABS INDICATOR ILLUMINATE FOR 3 SECONDS THEN GO OFF?
NO
YES
REPLACE EBCM.
PROBLEM IS INTERMITTENT.
GC4029401008020X

Fig. 299 Chart C, ABS indicator off constantly. No DTC's stored (Part 2 of 2). 1993–94 Prizm

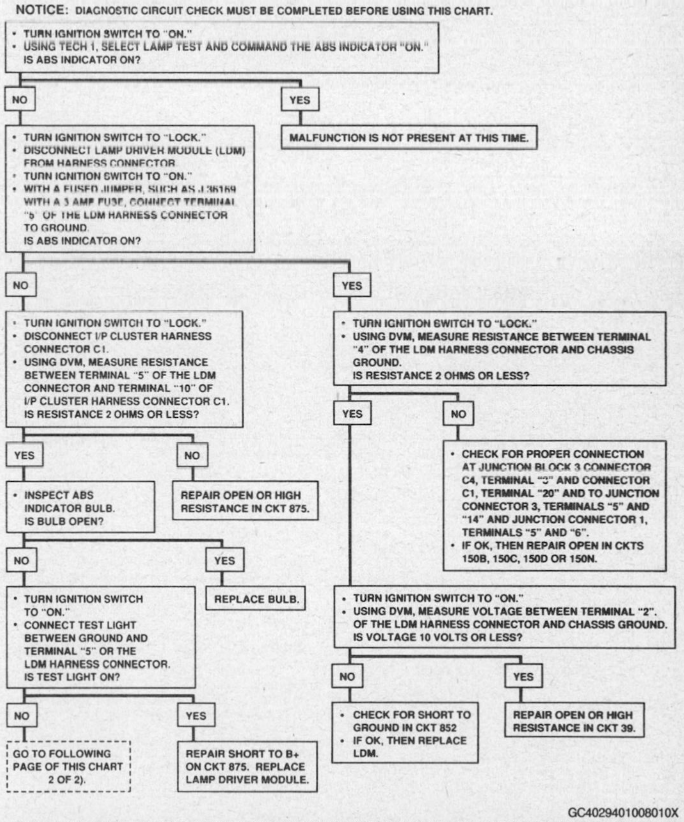
NOTICE: DIAGNOSTIC CIRCUIT CHECK MUST BE COMPLETED BEFORE USING THIS CHART.
• TURN IGNITION SWITCH TO "ON." • USING TECH 1, SELECT LAMP TEST AND COMMAND THE ABS INDICATOR "ON." IS ABS INDICATOR ON?
NO
YES
• TURN IGNITION SWITCH TO "LOCK." • DISCONNECT LAMP DRIVER MODULE (LDM) FROM HARNESS CONNECTOR. • TURN IGNITION SWITCH TO "ON." • WITH A FUSED JUMPER, SUCH AS J36169 WITH A 3 AMP FUSE, CONNECT TERMINAL "5" OF THE LDM HARNESS CONNECTOR TO GROUND. IS ABS INDICATOR ON?
MALFUNCTION IS NOT PRESENT AT THIS TIME.
NO
YES
• TURN IGNITION SWITCH TO "LOCK." • DISCONNECT I/P CLUSTER HARNESS CONNECTOR C1. • USING DVM, MEASURE RESISTANCE BETWEEN TERMINAL "5" OF THE LDM CONNECTOR AND TERMINAL "10" OF I/P CLUSTER HARNESS CONNECTOR C1. IS RESISTANCE 2 OHMS OR LESS?
• TURN IGNITION SWITCH TO "LOCK." • USING DVM, MEASURE RESISTANCE BETWEEN TERMINAL "4" OF THE LDM HARNESS CONNECTOR AND CHASSIS GROUND. IS RESISTANCE 2 OHMS OR LESS?
YES
NO
YES
NO
• INSPECT ABS INDICATOR BULB. IS BULB OPEN?
REPAIR OPEN OR HIGH RESISTANCE IN CKT 875.
• CHECK FOR PROPER CONNECTION AT JUNCTION BLOCK 3 CONNECTOR C4, TERMINAL "3" AND CONNECTOR C1, TERMINAL "20" AND TO JUNCTION CONNECTOR 3, TERMINALS "5" AND "14" AND JUNCTION CONNECTOR 1, TERMINALS "5" AND "6". • IF OK, THEN REPAIR OPEN IN CKTS 150B, 150C, 150D OR 150N.
NO
YES
• TURN IGNITION SWITCH TO "ON." • CONNECT TEST LIGHT BETWEEN GROUND AND TERMINAL "5" OR THE LDM HARNESS CONNECTOR. IS TEST LIGHT ON?
REPLACE BULB.
• TURN IGNITION SWITCH TO "ON." • USING DVM, MEASURE VOLTAGE BETWEEN TERMINAL "2". OF THE LDM HARNESS CONNECTOR AND CHASSIS GROUND. IS VOLTAGE 10 VOLTS OR LESS?
NO
YES
NO
YES
GO TO FOLLOWING PAGE OF THIS CHART 2 OF 2).
REPAIR SHORT TO B+ ON CKT 875. REPLACE LAMP DRIVER MODULE.
• CHECK FOR SHORT TO GROUND IN CKT 852 • IF OK, THEN REPLACE LDM.
REPAIR OPEN OR HIGH RESISTANCE IN CKT 39.
GC4029401008010X

Fig. 299 Chart C, ABS indicator off constantly. No DTC's stored (Part 1 of 2). 1993–94 Prizm

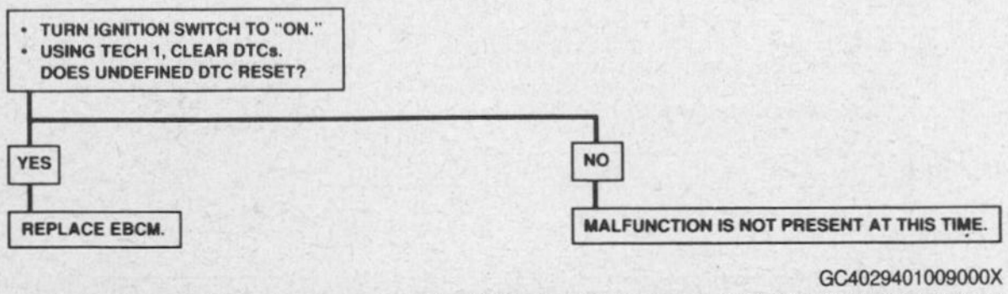
TURN IGNITION SWITCH TO "ON."
USING TECH 1, CLEAR DTCs.
DOES UNDEFINED DTC RESET?
YES
NO
REPLACE EBCM.
MALFUNCTION IS NOT PRESENT AT THIS TIME.
GC4029401009000X

Fig. 300 Chart D, TECH 1 displays undefined DTC's. 1993–94 Prizm

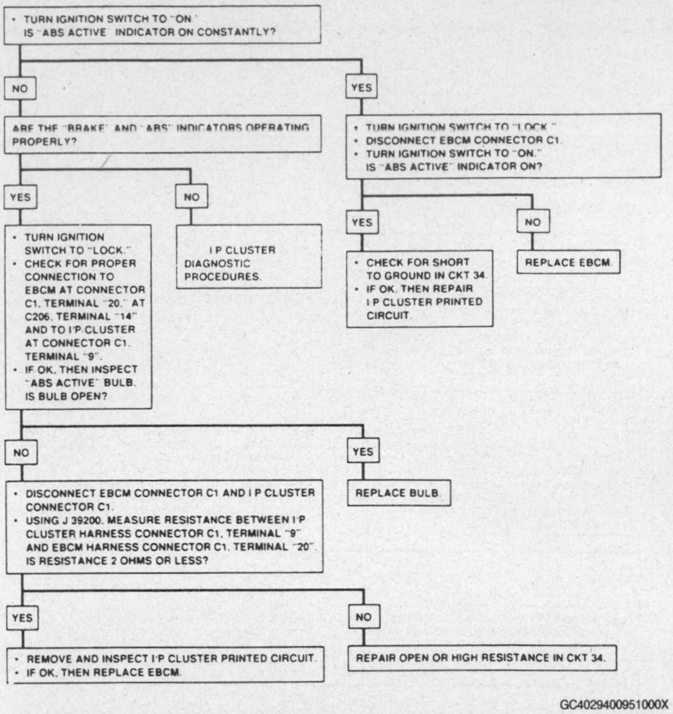
TURN IGNITION SWITCH TO "ON."
IS "ABS ACTIVE" INDICATOR ON CONSTANTLY?
NO
YES
ARE THE "BRAKE" AND "ABS" INDICATORS OPERATING PROPERLY?
TURN IGNITION SWITCH TO "LOCK."
DISCONNECT EBCM CONNECTOR C1.
TURN IGNITION SWITCH TO "ON."
IS "ABS ACTIVE" INDICATOR ON?
YES
NO
YES
NO
TURN IGNITION SWITCH TO "LOCK."
CHECK FOR PROPER CONNECTION TO EBCM AT CONNECTOR C1, TERMINAL "20," AT C206, TERMINAL "14" AND TO I/P CLUSTER AT CONNECTOR C1, TERMINAL "9".
IF OK, THEN INSPECT "ABS ACTIVE" BULB.
IS BULB OPEN?
I P CLUSTER DIAGNOSTIC PROCEDURES.
CHECK FOR SHORT TO GROUND IN CKT 34.
IF OK, THEN REPAIR I P CLUSTER PRINTED CIRCUIT.
REPLACE EBCM.
NO
YES
DISCONNECT EBCM CONNECTOR C1 AND I P CLUSTER CONNECTOR C1.
USING J 39200, MEASURE RESISTANCE BETWEEN I/P CLUSTER HARNESS CONNECTOR C1, TERMINAL "9" AND EBCM HARNESS CONNECTOR C1, TERMINAL "20".
IS RESISTANCE 2 OHMS OR LESS?
REPLACE BULB.
YES
NO
REMOVE AND INSPECT I/P CLUSTER PRINTED CIRCUIT.
IF OK, THEN REPLACE EBCM.
REPAIR OPEN OR HIGH RESISTANCE IN CKT 34.
GC4029400951000X

Fig. 301 Chart E, ABS active indicator malfunction. 1993–94 Prizm

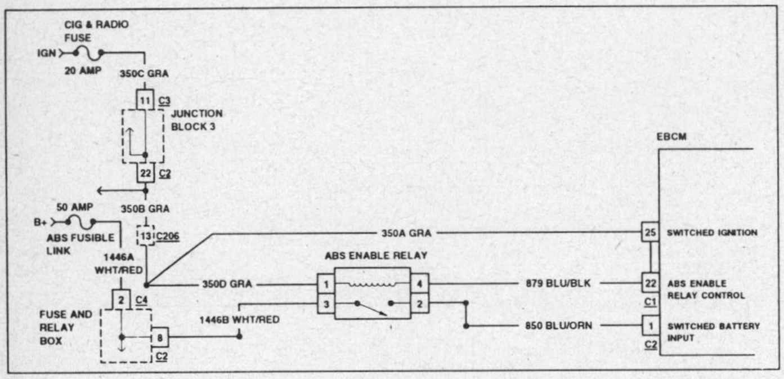
CIG & RADIO FUSE
IGN
20 AMP
350C GRA
11 C3
JUNCTION BLOCK 3
22 C2
50 AMP
B+
ABS FUSIBLE LINK
350B GRA
13 C206
1446A WHT/RED
350A GRA
ABS ENABLE RELAY
350D GRA
1
4
3
2
2 C4
FUSE AND RELAY BOX
8 C2
1446B WHT/RED
879 BLU/BLK
850 BLU/ORN
EBCM
25 SWITCHED IGNITION
22 C1 ABS ENABLE RELAY CONTROL
1 C2 SWITCHED BATTERY INPUT

DTC A014

ABS ENABLE RELAY CONTACT CIRCUIT OPEN

Circuit Description:

Ignition voltage is supplied through terminal "1" of the ABS enable relay. The EBCM then is able to energize the pull-in coil by completing the ground circuit at pin "22" of the EBCM. The magnetic field created closes the ABS enable relay contacts and allows battery voltage and current to be supplied to the EBCM, which supplies power to the motors and solenoids.

Failure Condition:

DTC A014 can be set anytime after the EBCM commands the ABS enable relay on (the relay is first commanded on during initialization). This test monitors the availability of current/voltage to the motors and solenoids. This malfunction indicates voltage is not available and would therefore not allow ABS operation if required.

Action Taken:

A DTC A014 is stored, ABS is disabled and the "ABS" indicator is turned on or will flash. If the rear piston is not in the home position, the red "BRAKE" indicator will also be illuminated.

Test Description: Number(s) below refer to circled number(s) on the diagnostic chart.

1. This step checks to see if the EBCM is sensing battery voltage at C2, terminal "1".
2. This step checks for proper operation of the ABS enable relay and related circuitry.
3. This step checks for excessive resistance in the switched battery input circuitry.
4. This step checks for excessive resistance in the B+ feed circuit.

Diagnostic Aids:

An "intermittent" malfunction may be caused by a poor connection, rubbed through wire insulation or a wire that is broken inside the insulation.

The frequency of the malfunction can be checked by using the enhanced diagnostic function of the TECH 1

Any circuitry that is suspected of causing the intermittent complaint should be thoroughly checked for backed out terminals, improper mating, broken locks, improperly formed or damaged terminals, poor terminal-to-wiring connections or physical damage to the wiring harness.

VIBRATION, TEMPERATURE EFFECTS:

Check for vibration effects by performing the relay test function of the TECH 1. With the relay commanded on, lightly tap the top and sides of the relay while monitoring relay voltage. If the relay voltage changes significantly, replace the relay.

If DTC A014 only occurs when the vehicle is initially started in cold ambient conditions (temperature less than 0°C – 32°F), replace the relay.

GC402940095201AX

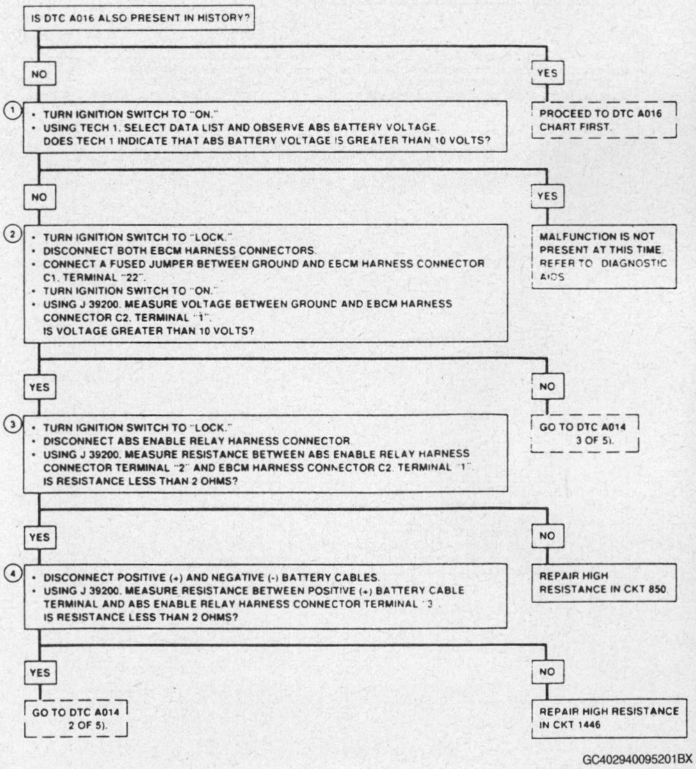
IS DTC A016 ALSO PRESENT IN HISTORY?
NO
YES
1
TURN IGNITION SWITCH TO "ON."
USING TECH 1, SELECT DATA LIST AND OBSERVE ABS BATTERY VOLTAGE.
DOES TECH 1 INDICATE THAT ABS BATTERY VOLTAGE IS GREATER THAN 10 VOLTS?
PROCEED TO DTC A016 CHART FIRST.
NO
YES
2
TURN IGNITION SWITCH TO "LOCK."
DISCONNECT BOTH EBCM HARNESS CONNECTORS.
CONNECT A FUSED JUMPER BETWEEN GROUND AND EBCM HARNESS CONNECTOR C1, TERMINAL "22".
TURN IGNITION SWITCH TO "ON."
USING J 39200, MEASURE VOLTAGE BETWEEN GROUND AND EBCM HARNESS CONNECTOR C2, TERMINAL "1".
IS VOLTAGE GREATER THAN 10 VOLTS?
MALFUNCTION IS NOT PRESENT AT THIS TIME. REFER TO DIAGNOSTIC AIDS
YES
NO
3
TURN IGNITION SWITCH TO "LOCK."
DISCONNECT ABS ENABLE RELAY HARNESS CONNECTOR.
USING J 39200, MEASURE RESISTANCE BETWEEN ABS ENABLE RELAY HARNESS CONNECTOR TERMINAL "2" AND EBCM HARNESS CONNECTOR C2, TERMINAL "1".
IS RESISTANCE LESS THAN 2 OHMS?
GO TO DTC A014 (3 OF 5).
YES
NO
4
DISCONNECT POSITIVE (+) AND NEGATIVE (-) BATTERY CABLES.
USING J 39200, MEASURE RESISTANCE BETWEEN POSITIVE (+) BATTERY CABLE TERMINAL AND ABS ENABLE RELAY HARNESS CONNECTOR TERMINAL "3".
IS RESISTANCE LESS THAN 2 OHMS?
REPAIR HIGH RESISTANCE IN CKT 850.
YES
NO
GO TO DTC A014 (2 OF 5).
REPAIR HIGH RESISTANCE IN CKT 1446.
GC402940095201BX

Fig. 302 Code A014: ABS Enable Contact Circuit Open (Part 1 of 5). 1993–94 Prizm

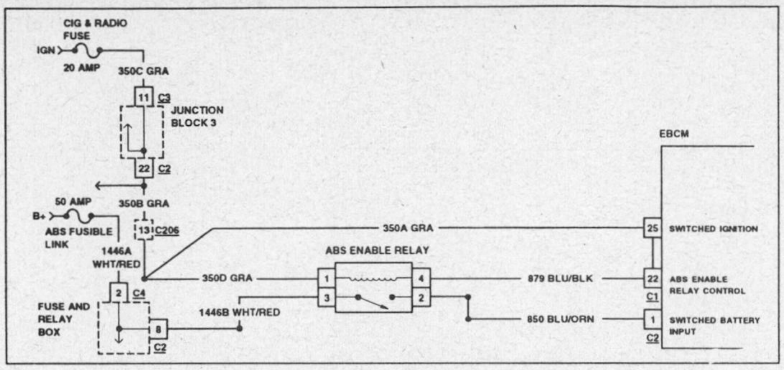
CIG & RADIO FUSE
IGN
20 AMP
350C GRA
11 C3
JUNCTION BLOCK 3
22 C2
50 AMP
350B GRA
B+
ABS FUSIBLE LINK
13 C206
1446A WHT/RED
350A GRA
ABS ENABLE RELAY
350D GRA
FUSE AND RELAY BOX
2 C4
8 C2
1446B WHT/RED
879 BLU/BLK
850 BLU/ORN
EBCM
25 SWITCHED IGNITION
22 ABS ENABLE RELAY CONTROL C1
1 SWITCHED BATTERY INPUT C2

DTC A014
ABS ENABLE RELAY CONTACT CIRCUIT OPEN

Circuit Description:

Ignition voltage is supplied through terminal "1" of the ABS enable relay. The EBCM then is able to energize the pull-in coil by completing the ground circuit at pin "22" of the EBCM. The magnetic field created closes the ABS enable relay contacts and allows battery voltage and current to be supplied to the EBCM, which supplies power to the motors and solenoids.

Failure Condition:

DTC A014 can be set anytime after the EBCM commands the ABS enable relay on (the relay is first commanded on during initialization). This test monitors the availability of current/voltage to the motors and solenoids. This malfunction indicates voltage is not available and would therefore not allow ABS operation if required.

Action Taken:

A DTC A014 is stored, ABS is disabled and the "ABS" indicator is turned on or will flash. If the rear piston is not in the home position, the red "BRAKE" indicator will also be illuminated.

Test Description: Number(s) below refer to circled number(s) on the diagnostic chart.

5. This step determines if the malfunction is due to a poor connection.
6. This step determines if the malfunction is due to the EBCM.

Diagnostic Aids:

An "intermittent" malfunction may be caused by a poor connection, rubbed through wire insulation or a wire that is broken inside the insulation.

The frequency of the malfunction can be checked by using the enhanced diagnostic function of the TECH 1

Any circuitry that is suspected of causing the intermittent complaint should be thoroughly checked for backed out terminals, improper mating, broken locks, improperly formed or damaged terminals, poor terminal-to-wiring connections or physical damage to the wiring harness.

VIBRATION, TEMPERATURE EFFECTS:

Check for vibration effects by performing the relay test function of the TECH 1. With the relay commanded on, lightly tap the top and sides of the relay while monitoring relay voltage. If the relay voltage changes significantly, replace the relay.

If DTC A014 only occurs when the vehicle is initially started in cold ambient conditions (temperature less than 0°C – 32°F), replace the relay.

GC402940095202AX

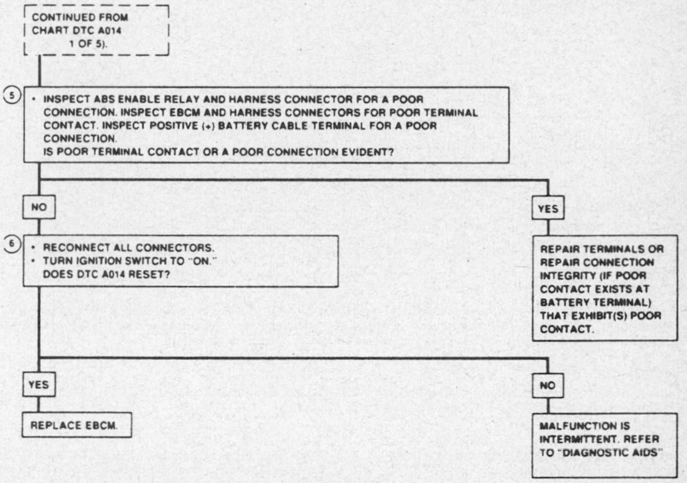
CONTINUED FROM CHART DTC A014 1 OF 5).
5 • INSPECT ABS ENABLE RELAY AND HARNESS CONNECTOR FOR A POOR CONNECTION. INSPECT EBCM AND HARNESS CONNECTORS FOR POOR TERMINAL CONTACT. INSPECT POSITIVE (+) BATTERY CABLE TERMINAL FOR A POOR CONNECTION.
IS POOR TERMINAL CONTACT OR A POOR CONNECTION EVIDENT?
NO
YES
6 • RECONNECT ALL CONNECTORS.
• TURN IGNITION SWITCH TO "ON."
DOES DTC A014 RESET?
REPAIR TERMINALS OR REPAIR CONNECTION INTEGRITY (IF POOR CONTACT EXISTS AT BATTERY TERMINAL) THAT EXHIBIT(S) POOR CONTACT.
YES
NO
REPLACE EBCM.
MALFUNCTION IS INTERMITTENT. REFER TO "DIAGNOSTIC AIDS"

GC402940095202BX

Fig. 302 Code A014: ABS Enable Contact Circuit Open (Part 2 of 5). 1993–94 Prizm

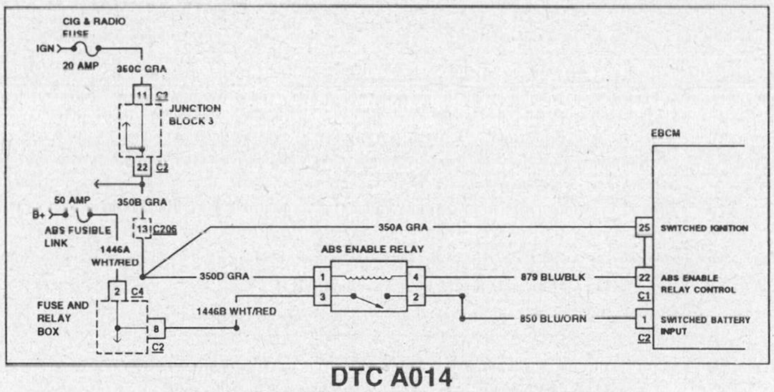
CIG & RADIO FUSE
IGN
20 AMP
350C GRA
11 C3
JUNCTION BLOCK 3
22 C2
50 AMP
350B GRA
B+
ABS FUSIBLE LINK
13 C206
1446A WHT/RED
350A GRA
ABS ENABLE RELAY
350D GRA
FUSE AND RELAY BOX
2 C4
8 C2
1446B WHT/RED
879 BLU/BLK
850 BLU/ORN
EBCM
25 SWITCHED IGNITION
22 ABS ENABLE RELAY CONTROL C1
1 SWITCHED BATTERY INPUT C2

DTC A014
ABS ENABLE RELAY CONTACT CIRCUIT OPEN

Circuit Description:

Ignition voltage is supplied through terminal "1" of the ABS enable relay. The EBCM then is able to energize the pull-in coil by completing the ground circuit at pin "22" of the EBCM. The magnetic field created closes the ABS enable relay contacts and allows battery voltage and current to be supplied to the EBCM, which supplies power to the motors and solenoids.

Failure Condition:

DTC A014 can be set anytime after the EBCM commands the ABS enable relay on (the relay is first commanded on during initialization). This test monitors the availability of current/voltage to the motors and solenoids. This malfunction indicates voltage is not available and would therefore not allow ABS operation if required.

Action Taken:

A DTC A014 is stored, ABS is disabled and the "ABS" indicator is turned on or will flash. If the rear piston is not in the home position, the red "BRAKE" indicator will also be illuminated.

Test Description: Number(s) below refer to circled number(s) on the diagnostic chart.

7. This step checks for excessive resistance in the ABS enable relay control circuitry.
8. This step checks for proper battery voltage.
9. This step checks for an open in the B+ feed circuit.
10. This step checks for an open in the switched battery input circuit.
11. This step checks for proper operation of the ABS enable relay.

Diagnostic Aids:

An "intermittent" malfunction may be caused by a poor connection, rubbed through wire insulation or a wire that is broken inside the insulation.

The frequency of the malfunction can be checked by using the enhanced diagnostic function of the TECH 1

Any circuitry that is suspected of causing the intermittent complaint should be thoroughly checked for backed out terminals, improper mating, broken locks, improperly formed or damaged terminals, poor terminal-to-wiring connections or physical damage to the wiring harness.

VIBRATION, TEMPERATURE EFFECTS:

Check for vibration effects by performing the relay test function of the TECH 1. With the relay commanded on, lightly tap the top and sides of the relay while monitoring relay voltage. If the relay voltage changes significantly, replace the relay.

If DTC A014 only occurs when the vehicle is initially started in cold ambient conditions (temperature less than 0°C – 32°F), replace the relay.

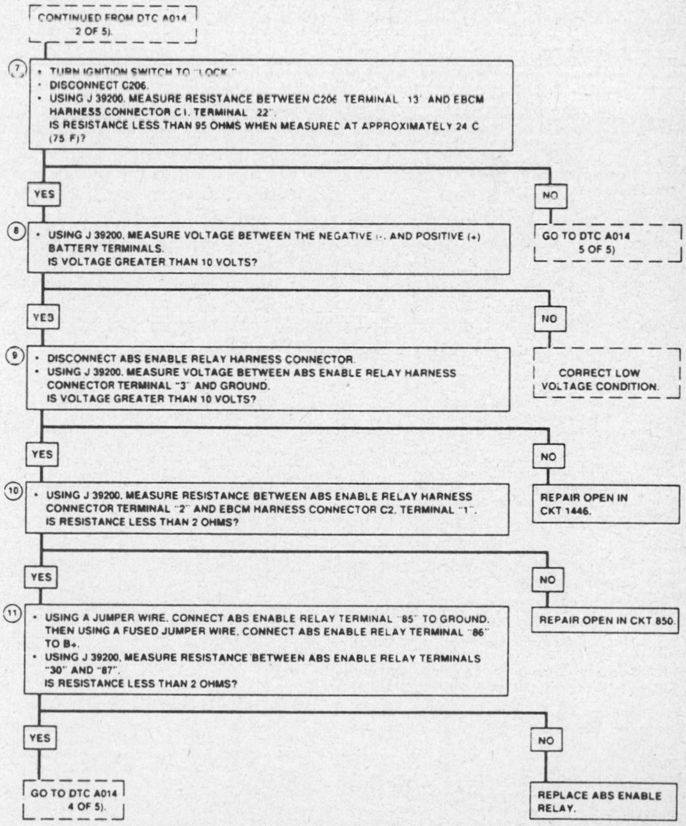
CONTINUED FROM DTC A014 2 OF 5).
7 • TURN IGNITION SWITCH TO "LOCK."
• DISCONNECT C206.
• USING J 39200, MEASURE RESISTANCE BETWEEN C206 TERMINAL "13" AND EBCM HARNESS CONNECTOR C1, TERMINAL "22".
IS RESISTANCE LESS THAN 95 OHMS WHEN MEASURED AT APPROXIMATELY 24 C (75 F)?
YES
NO
GO TO DTC A014 5 OF 5)
8 • USING J 39200, MEASURE VOLTAGE BETWEEN THE NEGATIVE (-) AND POSITIVE (+) BATTERY TERMINALS.
IS VOLTAGE GREATER THAN 10 VOLTS?
YES
NO
CORRECT LOW VOLTAGE CONDITION.
9 • DISCONNECT ABS ENABLE RELAY HARNESS CONNECTOR.
• USING J 39200, MEASURE VOLTAGE BETWEEN ABS ENABLE RELAY HARNESS CONNECTOR TERMINAL "3" AND GROUND.
IS VOLTAGE GREATER THAN 10 VOLTS?
YES
NO
REPAIR OPEN IN CKT 1446.
10 • USING J 39200, MEASURE RESISTANCE BETWEEN ABS ENABLE RELAY HARNESS CONNECTOR TERMINAL "2" AND EBCM HARNESS CONNECTOR C2, TERMINAL "1".
IS RESISTANCE LESS THAN 2 OHMS?
YES
NO
REPAIR OPEN IN CKT 850.
11 • USING A JUMPER WIRE, CONNECT ABS ENABLE RELAY TERMINAL "85" TO GROUND. THEN USING A FUSED JUMPER WIRE, CONNECT ABS ENABLE RELAY TERMINAL "86" TO B+.
• USING J 39200, MEASURE RESISTANCE BETWEEN ABS ENABLE RELAY TERMINALS "30" AND "87".
IS RESISTANCE LESS THAN 2 OHMS?
YES
NO
GO TO DTC A014 4 OF 5).
REPLACE ABS ENABLE RELAY.

GC402940095203BX

GC402940095203AX

Fig. 302 Code A014: ABS Enable Contact Circuit Open (Part 3 of 5). 1993–94 Prizm

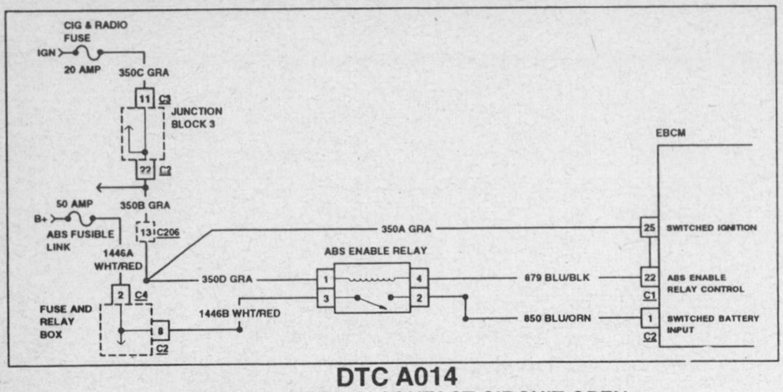
CIG & RADIO FUSE
IGN
20 AMP
350C GRA
JUNCTION BLOCK 3
EBCM
50 AMP
350B GRA
B+
ABS FUSIBLE LINK
C206
350A GRA
SWITCHED IGNITION
1446A WHT/RED
ABS ENABLE RELAY
350D GRA
879 BLU/BLK
ABS ENABLE RELAY CONTROL
FUSE AND RELAY BOX
1446B WHT/RED
850 BLU/ORN
SWITCHED BATTERY INPUT

DTC A014
ABS ENABLE RELAY CONTACT CIRCUIT OPEN

Circuit Description:

Ignition voltage is supplied through terminal "1" of the ABS enable relay. The EBCM then is able to energize the pull-in coil by completing the ground circuit at pin "22" of the EBCM. The magnetic field created closes the ABS enable relay contacts and allows battery voltage and current to be supplied to the EBCM, which supplies power to the motors and solenoids.

Failure Condition:

DTC A014 can be set anytime after the EBCM commands the ABS enable relay on (the relay is first commanded on during initialization). This test monitors the availability of current/voltage to the motors and solenoids. This malfunction indicates voltage is not available and would therefore not allow ABS operation if required.

Action Taken:

A DTC A014 is stored, ABS is disabled and the "ABS" indicator is turned on or will flash. If the rear piston is not in the home position, the red "BRAKE" indicator will also be illuminated.

Test Description: Number(s) below refer to circled number(s) on the diagnostic chart.

12. This step checks for excessive resistance in the ignition switch "ON" feed (CIG & RADIO fuse) circuit.

Diagnostic Aids:

An "intermittent" malfunction may be caused by a poor connection, rubbed through wire insulation or a wire that is broken inside the insulation.

The frequency of the malfunction can be checked by using the enhanced diagnostic function of the TECH 1

Any circuitry that is suspected of causing the intermittent complaint should be thoroughly checked for backed out terminals, improper mating, broken locks, improperly formed or damaged terminals, poor terminal-to-wiring connections or physical damage to the wiring harness.

VIBRATION, TEMPERATURE EFFECTS:

Check for vibration effects by performing the relay test function of the TECH 1. With the relay commanded on, lightly tap the top and sides of the relay while monitoring relay voltage. If the relay voltage changes significantly, replace the relay.

If DTC A014 only occurs when the vehicle is initially started in cold ambient conditions (temperature less than 0°C – 32°F), replace the relay.

GC402940095204AX

CONTINUED FROM DTC A014 (3 OF 5).

(12) • DISCONNECT IGNITION SWITCH HARNESS CONNECTOR
• USING J 39200, MEASURE RESISTANCE BETWEEN IGNITION SWITCH HARNESS CONNECTOR TERMINAL "5" AND C206, TERMINAL "13".
IS RESISTANCE LESS THAN 2 OHMS?

YES: MALFUNCTION WAS DUE TO POOR CONNECTION. REFER TO SECTION 8A TO TEST FOR POOR TERMINAL CONTACT BETWEEN ABS ENABLE RELAY AND HARNESS CONNECTOR AND OR AT C206, TERMINAL "13" AND OR IGNITION SWITCH HARNESS CONNECTOR TO IGNITION SWITCH. REPLACE TERMINALS THAT EXHIBIT POOR TERMINAL CONTACT.

NO: REPAIR HIGH RESISTANCE IN IGNITION SWITCH "ON" FEED (CIG & RADIO FUSE).

GC402940095204BX

Fig. 302 Code A014: ABS Enable Contact Circuit Open (Part 4 of 5). 1993–94 Prizm

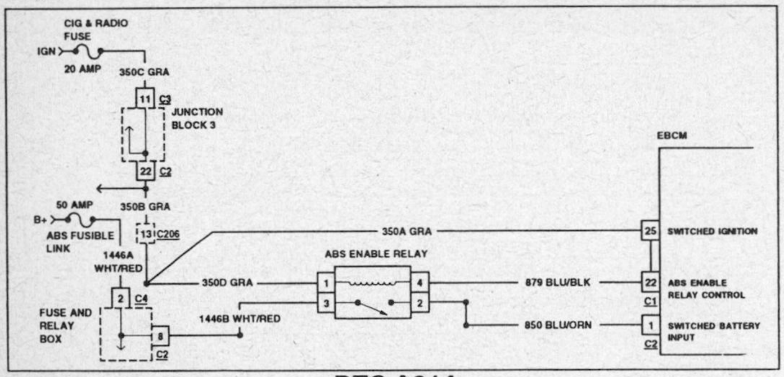
CIG & RADIO FUSE
IGN
20 AMP
350C GRA
JUNCTION BLOCK 3
EBCM
50 AMP
350B GRA
B+
ABS FUSIBLE LINK
C206
350A GRA
SWITCHED IGNITION
1446A WHT/RED
ABS ENABLE RELAY
350D GRA
879 BLU/BLK
ABS ENABLE RELAY CONTROL
FUSE AND RELAY BOX
1446B WHT/RED
850 BLU/ORN
SWITCHED BATTERY INPUT

DTC A014
ABS ENABLE RELAY CONTACT CIRCUIT OPEN

Circuit Description:

Ignition voltage is supplied through terminal "1" of the ABS enable relay. The EBCM then is able to energize the pull-in coil by completing the ground circuit at pin "22" of the EBCM. The magnetic field created closes the ABS enable relay contacts and allows battery voltage and current to be supplied to the EBCM, which supplies power to the motors and solenoids.

Failure Condition:

DTC A014 can be set anytime after the EBCM commands the ABS enable relay on (the relay is first commanded on during initialization). This test monitors the availability of current/voltage to the motors and solenoids. This malfunction indicates voltage is not available and would therefore not allow ABS operation if required.

Action Taken:

A DTC A014 is stored, ABS is disabled and the "ABS" indicator is turned on or will flash. If the rear piston is not in the home position, the red "BRAKE" indicator will also be illuminated.

Test Description: Number(s) below refer to circled number(s) on the diagnostic chart.

13. This step checks for excessive resistance in the ABS enable relay coil.
14. This step checks for excessive resistance in the ABS enable relay control circuit between the relay and the EBCM.
15. This step checks for excessive resistance in the ABS enable relay control circuit between the relay and C206.

Diagnostic Aids:

An "intermittent" malfunction may be caused by a poor connection, rubbed through wire insulation or a wire that is broken inside the insulation.

The frequency of the malfunction can be checked by using the enhanced diagnostic function of the TECH 1

Any circuitry that is suspected of causing the intermittent complaint should be thoroughly checked for backed out terminals, improper mating, broken locks, improperly formed or damaged terminals, poor terminal-to-wiring connections or physical damage to the wiring harness.

VIBRATION, TEMPERATURE EFFECTS:

Check for vibration effects by performing the relay test function of the TECH 1. With the relay commanded on, lightly tap the top and sides of the relay while monitoring relay voltage. If the relay voltage changes significantly, replace the relay.

If DTC A014 only occurs when the vehicle is initially started in cold ambient conditions (temperature less than 0°C – 32°F), replace the relay.

GC402940095205AX

CONTINUED FROM DTC A014 4 OF 5)

(13) • DISCONNECT ABS ENABLE RELAY HARNESS CONNECTOR.
• USING J 39200, MEASURE RESISTANCE BETWEEN ABS ENABLE RELAY TERMINAL "85" AND TERMINAL "86".
IS RESISTANCE LESS THAN 95 OHMS WHEN MEASURED AT APPROXIMATELY 24 C (75 F)?

NO: REPLACE ABS ENABLE RELAY.

YES:

(14) • USING J 39200, MEASURE RESISTANCE BETWEEN ABS ENABLE RELAY HARNESS CONNECTOR TERMINAL "4" AND ECBM HARNESS CONNECTOR C1, TERMINAL "22".
IS RESISTANCE LESS THAN 2 OHMS?

NO: REPAIR HIGH RESISTANCE IN CKT 879.

YES:

(15) • USING J 39200, MEASURE RESISTANCE BETWEEN ABS ENABLE RELAY HARNESS CONNECTOR TERMINAL "1" AND C206, TERMINAL "13".
IS RESISTANCE LESS THAN 2 OHMS?

YES: MALFUNCTION WAS DUE TO A POOR CONNECTION. REFER TO SECTION 8A TO TEST FOR POOR TERMINAL CONTACT BETWEEN ABS ENABLE RELAY AND HARNESS CONNECTOR. REPLACE TERMINALS THAT EXHIBIT POOR TERMINAL CONTACT.

NO: REPAIR HIGH RESISTANCE IN CKT 350D.

GC402940095205BX

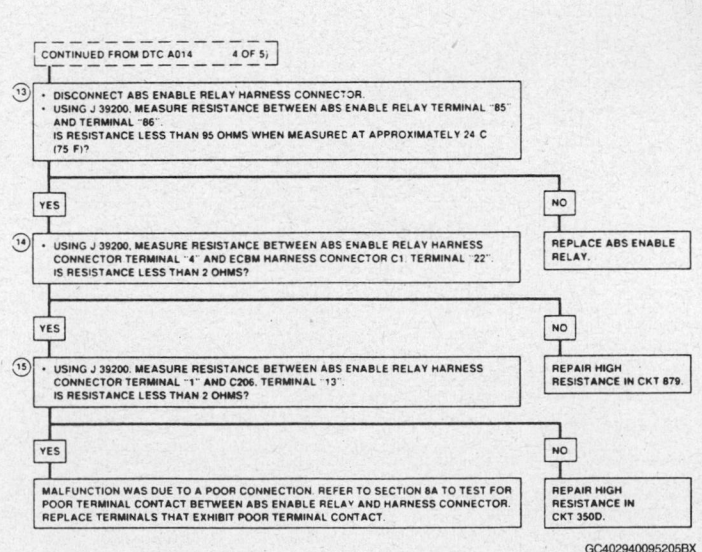

Fig. 302 Code A014: ABS Enable Contact Circuit Open (Part 5 of 5). 1993–94 Prizm

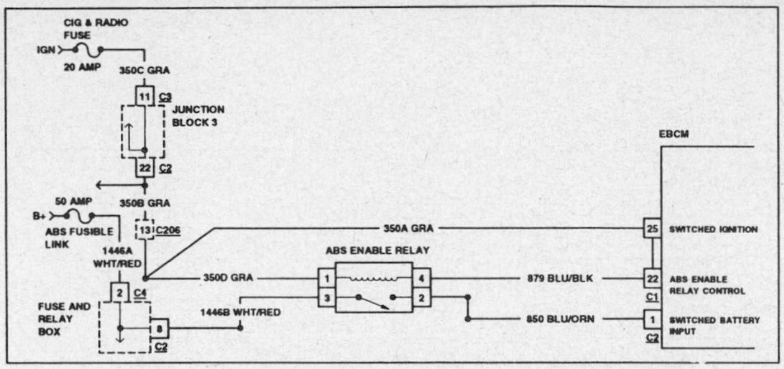
CIG & RADIO FUSE
IGN
20 AMP
350C GRA
11 C3
JUNCTION BLOCK 3
22 C2
50 AMP
350B GRA
B+
ABS FUSIBLE LINK
13 C206
1446A WHT/RED
350A GRA
ABS ENABLE RELAY
350D GRA
879 BLU/BLK
FUSE AND RELAY BOX
2 C4
1446B WHT/RED
8 C2
850 BLU/ORN
EBCM
25 SWITCHED IGNITION
22 ABS ENABLE RELAY CONTROL C1
1 SWITCHED BATTERY INPUT C2

DTC A015

ABS ENABLE RELAY CIRCUIT SHORTED TO BATTERY OR ALWAYS CLOSED

Circuit Description:

Ignition voltage is supplied through terminal "1" of the ABS enable relay. The EBCM then is able to energize the pull-in coil by completing the ground circuit at pin "22" of the EBCM. The magnetic field created closes the ABS enable relay contacts and allows battery voltage and current to be supplied to the EBCM, which supplies power to the motors and solenoids.

Failure Condition:

DTC A015 can be set only before the EBCM commands the relay on. This test determines if the ABS enable relay is energized when it should not be. This malfunction would not allow the ABS enable relay to remove power to the ABS system. If a second malfunction were to occur that requires the ABS enable relay to be turned off, that malfunction can not be removed if the relay can not be controlled. The malfunction must be present for three consecutive drive cycles before the DTC is set.

Action Taken:

A DTC A015 is stored. ABS is not disabled and the "ABS" indicator will not be illuminated.

Test Description: Number(s) below refer to circled number(s) on the diagnostic chart.

1. This step indicates that the EBCM is capable of controlling the ABS enable relay as commanded.
2. This step checks for voltage at terminal "1" of the EBCM harness connector C2. If voltage is present, the malfunction exists in the ABS enable relay and/or its circuitry.
3. This test checks for a short to ground in the ABS enable relay control circuit.
4. This step checks for a short to voltage in CKT 830.
5. This step identifies if the EBCM is malfunctioning.

Diagnostic Aids:

An "intermittent" malfunction may be caused by a poor connection, rubbed through wire insulation or a wire that is broken inside the insulation.

The frequency of the malfunction can be checked by using the enhanced diagnostic function of the TECH 1

Any circuitry that is suspected of causing the intermittent complaint should be thoroughly checked for backed out terminals, improper mating, broken locks, improperly formed or damaged terminals, poor terminal to-wiring connections or physical damage to the wiring harness.

GC402940095300AX

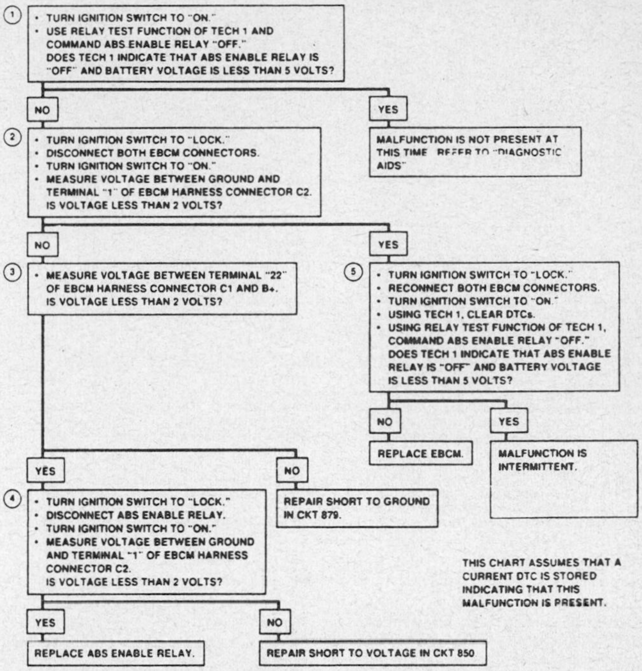
1
• TURN IGNITION SWITCH TO "ON."
• USE RELAY TEST FUNCTION OF TECH 1 AND COMMAND ABS ENABLE RELAY "OFF."
DOES TECH 1 INDICATE THAT ABS ENABLE RELAY IS "OFF" AND BATTERY VOLTAGE IS LESS THAN 5 VOLTS?
NO
YES
MALFUNCTION IS NOT PRESENT AT THIS TIME. REFER TO "DIAGNOSTIC AIDS"
2
• TURN IGNITION SWITCH TO "LOCK."
• DISCONNECT BOTH EBCM CONNECTORS.
• TURN IGNITION SWITCH TO "ON."
• MEASURE VOLTAGE BETWEEN GROUND AND TERMINAL "1" OF EBCM HARNESS CONNECTOR C2.
IS VOLTAGE LESS THAN 2 VOLTS?
NO
YES
3
• MEASURE VOLTAGE BETWEEN TERMINAL "22" OF EBCM HARNESS CONNECTOR C1 AND B+.
IS VOLTAGE LESS THAN 2 VOLTS?
5
• TURN IGNITION SWITCH TO "LOCK."
• RECONNECT BOTH EBCM CONNECTORS.
• TURN IGNITION SWITCH TO "ON."
• USING TECH 1, CLEAR DTCs.
• USING RELAY TEST FUNCTION OF TECH 1, COMMAND ABS ENABLE RELAY "OFF."
DOES TECH 1 INDICATE THAT ABS ENABLE RELAY IS "OFF" AND BATTERY VOLTAGE IS LESS THAN 5 VOLTS?
NO
YES
REPLACE EBCM.
MALFUNCTION IS INTERMITTENT.
YES
NO
4
• TURN IGNITION SWITCH TO "LOCK."
• DISCONNECT ABS ENABLE RELAY.
• TURN IGNITION SWITCH TO "ON."
• MEASURE VOLTAGE BETWEEN GROUND AND TERMINAL "1" OF EBCM HARNESS CONNECTOR C2.
IS VOLTAGE LESS THAN 2 VOLTS?
REPAIR SHORT TO GROUND IN CKT 879.
THIS CHART ASSUMES THAT A CURRENT DTC IS STORED INDICATING THAT THIS MALFUNCTION IS PRESENT.
YES
NO
REPLACE ABS ENABLE RELAY.
REPAIR SHORT TO VOLTAGE IN CKT 850

AFTER DIAGNOSIS IS COMPLETE, CLEAR DTCs AND TEST DRIVE VEHICLE FOR THREE (3) DRIVE CYCLES TO VERIFY DTC DOES NOT RESET. A DRIVE CYCLE CONSISTS OF STARTING THE VEHICLE, DRIVING ABOVE 16 km/h (10 MPH) AND THEN KEYING DOWN.

GC402940095300BX

Fig. 303 Code A015: ABS Enable Circuit Shorted To Battery Or Always Closed. 1993–94 Prizm

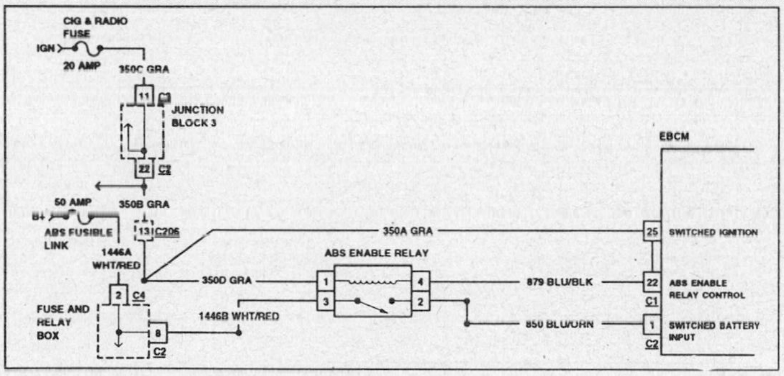
CIG & RADIO FUSE
IGN
20 AMP
350C GRA
11 C3
JUNCTION BLOCK 3
22 C2
50 AMP
350B GRA
B+
ABS FUSIBLE LINK
13 C206
1446A WHT/RED
350A GRA
ABS ENABLE RELAY
350D GRA
879 BLU/BLK
FUSE AND RELAY BOX
2 C4
1446B WHT/RED
8 C2
850 BLU/ORN
EBCM
25 SWITCHED IGNITION
22 ABS ENABLE RELAY CONTROL C1
1 SWITCHED BATTERY INPUT C2

DTC A016

ABS ENABLE RELAY COIL CIRCUIT OPEN

Circuit Description:

Ignition voltage is supplied through terminal "1" of the ABS enable relay. The EBCM then is able to energize the pull-in coil by completing the ground circuit at pin "22" of the EBCM. The magnetic field created closes the ABS enable relay contacts and allows battery voltage and current to be supplied to the EBCM, which supplies power to the motors and solenoids.

Failure Condition:

DTC A016 can be set only after DTC A014 has been set. This test detects an open in the ABS enable relay coil circuit. An open in this circuit will not allow the relay to be energized thus preventing voltage/current to the motors and solenoids. If this malfunction is present and the ignition switch is turned to "LOCK" before 5 km/h (3 mph) is reached, DTC A014 is set alone.

Action Taken:

DTCs A014 and A016 are stored, ABS is disabled and the "ABS" indicator is turned on or will flash. If the rear piston is not in the home position, the red "BRAKE" indicator will also be illuminated.

Test Description: Number(s) below refer to circled number(s) on the diagnostic chart.

1. This step indicates if the EBCM is capable of controlling the ABS enable relay as commanded.
2. This step ensures that there is continuity through the pull-in coil of the relay.
3. This step checks to ensure that voltage is available to the pull-in coil of the relay.
4. This step checks continuity in CKT 879.
5. This step ensures DTC was not set due to a poor connection.

Diagnostic Aids:

An "intermittent" malfunction may be caused by a poor connection, rubbed through wire insulation or a wire that is broken inside the insulation.

The frequency of the malfunction can be checked by using the enhanced diagnostic function of the TECH 1

Any circuitry that is suspected of causing the intermittent complaint should be thoroughly checked for backed out terminals, improper mating, broken locks, improperly formed or damaged terminals, poor terminal-to-wiring connections or physical damage to the wiring harness.

GC402940095400AX

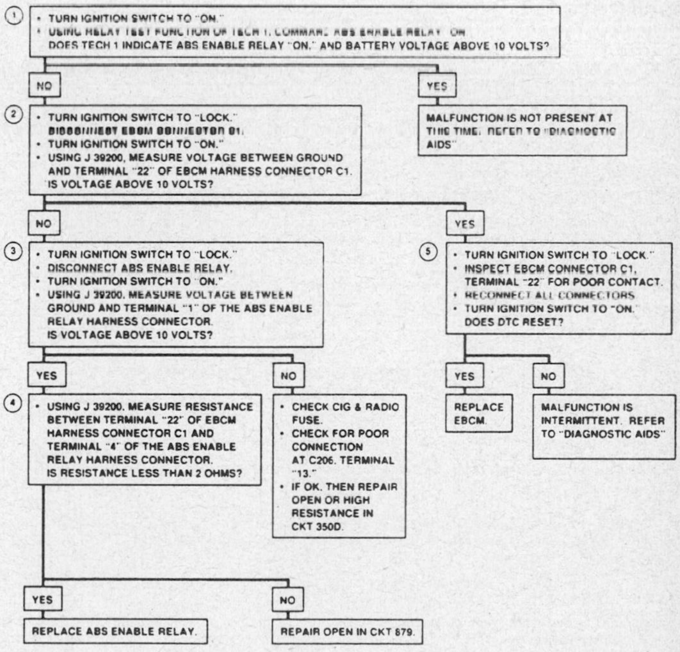
1
• TURN IGNITION SWITCH TO "ON."
DOES TECH 1 INDICATE ABS ENABLE RELAY "ON," AND BATTERY VOLTAGE ABOVE 10 VOLTS?
NO
YES
MALFUNCTION IS NOT PRESENT AT THIS TIME. REFER TO "DIAGNOSTIC AIDS"
2
• TURN IGNITION SWITCH TO "LOCK."
• TURN IGNITION SWITCH TO "ON."
• USING J 39200, MEASURE VOLTAGE BETWEEN GROUND AND TERMINAL "22" OF EBCM HARNESS CONNECTOR C1.
IS VOLTAGE ABOVE 10 VOLTS?
NO
YES
3
• TURN IGNITION SWITCH TO "LOCK."
• DISCONNECT ABS ENABLE RELAY.
• TURN IGNITION SWITCH TO "ON."
• USING J 39200, MEASURE VOLTAGE BETWEEN GROUND AND TERMINAL "1" OF THE ABS ENABLE RELAY HARNESS CONNECTOR.
IS VOLTAGE ABOVE 10 VOLTS?
5
• TURN IGNITION SWITCH TO "LOCK."
• INSPECT EBCM CONNECTOR C1, TERMINAL "22" FOR POOR CONTACT.
• RECONNECT ALL CONNECTORS
• TURN IGNITION SWITCH TO "ON."
DOES DTC RESET?
YES
NO
YES
NO
4
• USING J 39200, MEASURE RESISTANCE BETWEEN TERMINAL "22" OF EBCM HARNESS CONNECTOR C1 AND TERMINAL "4" OF THE ABS ENABLE RELAY HARNESS CONNECTOR.
IS RESISTANCE LESS THAN 2 OHMS?
• CHECK CIG & RADIO FUSE.
• CHECK FOR POOR CONNECTION AT C206, TERMINAL "13."
• IF OK, THEN REPAIR OPEN OR HIGH RESISTANCE IN CKT 350D.
REPLACE EBCM.
MALFUNCTION IS INTERMITTENT. REFER TO "DIAGNOSTIC AIDS"
YES
NO
REPLACE ABS ENABLE RELAY.
REPAIR OPEN IN CKT 879.

AFTER DIAGNOSIS IS COMPLETE, CLEAR DTCs AND TEST DRIVE VEHICLE FOR THREE (3) DRIVE CYCLES TO VERIFY DTC DOES NOT RESET. A DRIVE CYCLE CONSISTS OF STARTING THE VEHICLE, DRIVING OVER 16 km/h (10 MPH) AND THEN KEYING DOWN.

GC402940095400BX

Fig. 304 Code A016: ABS Enable Relay Coil Circuit Open. 1993–94 Prizm

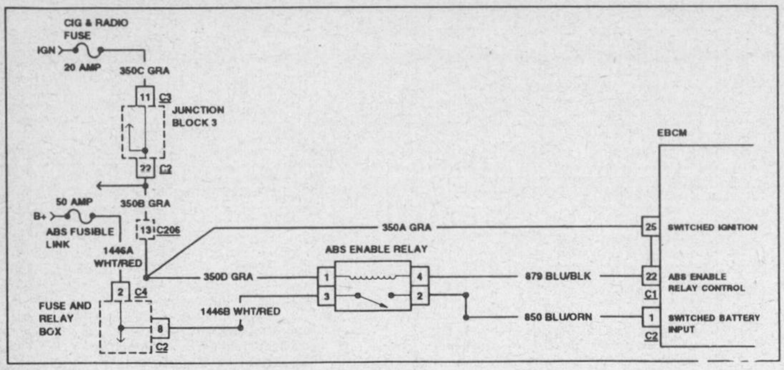
CIG & RADIO FUSE
IGN
20 AMP
350C GRA
11 C3
JUNCTION BLOCK 3
22 C2
50 AMP
B+
ABS FUSIBLE LINK
350B GRA
13 C206
1446A WHT/RED
350A GRA
ABS ENABLE RELAY
350D GRA
2 C4
FUSE AND RELAY BOX
1446B WHT/RED
8 C2
879 BLU/BLK
850 BLU/ORN
EBCM
25 SWITCHED IGNITION
22 C1 ABS ENABLE RELAY CONTROL
1 C2 SWITCHED BATTERY INPUT

DTC A017

ABS ENABLE RELAY COIL CIRCUIT SHORTED TO GROUND

Circuit Description:

Ignition voltage is supplied through terminal "1" of the ABS enable relay. The EBCM then is able to energize the pull-in coil by completing the ground circuit at pin "22" of the EBCM. The magnetic field created closes the ABS enable relay contacts and allows battery voltage and current to be supplied to the EBCM, which supplies power to the motors and solenoids.

Failure Condition:

DTC A017 can be set before the EBCM commands the ABS enable relay on. This test determines if the relay is energized when it should not be. This malfunction would not allow the ABS enable relay to remove power to the ABS. If a second malfunction were to occur that requires the relay to be turned off, that malfunction can not be removed if the relay can not be controlled.

Action Taken:

A DTC A017 is stored. ABS is not disabled and the "ABS" indicator will not be illuminated.

Test Description: Number(s) below refer to circled number(s) on the diagnostic chart.

1. This step indicates if the EBCM is capable of controlling the ABS enable relay as commanded.
2. This checks to ensure the ABS enable relay or control CKT 879 are not shorted to ground.
3. This step ensures DTC was not set due to a poor connection.

Diagnostic Aids:

An "intermittent" malfunction may be caused by a poor connection, rubbed through wire insulation or a wire that is broken inside the insulation.

The frequency of the malfunction can be checked by using the enhanced diagnostic function of the TECH 1

Any circuitry that is suspected of causing the intermittent complaint should be thoroughly checked for backed out terminals, improper mating, broken locks, improperly formed or damaged terminals, poor terminal-to-wiring connections or physical damage to the wiring harness.

GC402940095500AX

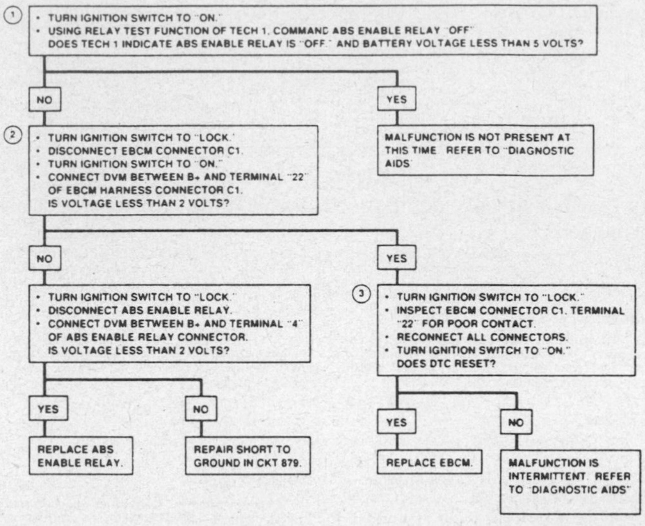
1
TURN IGNITION SWITCH TO "ON."
USING RELAY TEST FUNCTION OF TECH 1, COMMAND ABS ENABLE RELAY "OFF"
DOES TECH 1 INDICATE ABS ENABLE RELAY IS "OFF" AND BATTERY VOLTAGE LESS THAN 5 VOLTS?
NO
YES
2
TURN IGNITION SWITCH TO "LOCK."
DISCONNECT EBCM CONNECTOR C1.
TURN IGNITION SWITCH TO "ON."
CONNECT DVM BETWEEN B+ AND TERMINAL "22" OF EBCM HARNESS CONNECTOR C1.
IS VOLTAGE LESS THAN 2 VOLTS?
MALFUNCTION IS NOT PRESENT AT THIS TIME. REFER TO "DIAGNOSTIC AIDS"
NO
YES
TURN IGNITION SWITCH TO "LOCK."
DISCONNECT ABS ENABLE RELAY.
CONNECT DVM BETWEEN B+ AND TERMINAL "4" OF ABS ENABLE RELAY CONNECTOR.
IS VOLTAGE LESS THAN 2 VOLTS?
3
TURN IGNITION SWITCH TO "LOCK."
INSPECT EBCM CONNECTOR C1. TERMINAL "22" FOR POOR CONTACT.
RECONNECT ALL CONNECTORS.
TURN IGNITION SWITCH TO "ON."
DOES DTC RESET?
YES
NO
YES
NO
REPLACE ABS ENABLE RELAY.
REPAIR SHORT TO GROUND IN CKT 879.
REPLACE EBCM.
MALFUNCTION IS INTERMITTENT. REFER TO "DIAGNOSTIC AIDS"

GC402940095500BX

Fig. 305 Code A017: ABS Enable Relay Coil Shorted To Ground. 1993–94 Prizm

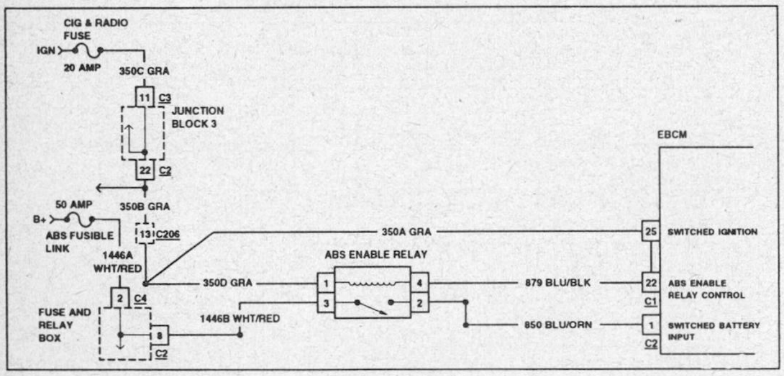
CIG & RADIO FUSE
IGN
20 AMP
350C GRA
11 C3
JUNCTION BLOCK 3
22 C2
50 AMP
B+
ABS FUSIBLE LINK
350B GRA
13 C206
1446A WHT/RED
350A GRA
ABS ENABLE RELAY
350D GRA
2 C4
FUSE AND RELAY BOX
1446B WHT/RED
8 C2
879 BLU/BLK
850 BLU/ORN
EBCM
25 SWITCHED IGNITION
22 C1 ABS ENABLE RELAY CONTROL
1 C2 SWITCHED BATTERY INPUT

DTC A018

ABS ENABLE RELAY COIL CIRCUIT SHORTED TO BATTERY

Circuit Description:

Ignition voltage is supplied through terminal "1" of the ABS enable relay. The EBCM then is able to energize the pull-in coil by completing the ground circuit at pin "22" of the EBCM. The magnetic field created closes the ABS enable relay contacts and allows battery voltage and current to be supplied to the EBCM, which supplies power to the motors and solenoids.

Failure Condition:

DTC A018 can be set after the EBCM commands the ABS enable relay on. This test monitors the availability of current/voltage to the motors and solenoids; therefore, ABS operation would not be allowed if required.

Action Taken:

A DTC A018 is stored, ABS is disabled and the "ABS" indicator is turned on or flashes. If the rear piston is not in the home position, the red "BRAKE" indicator will also be illuminated.

Test Description: Number(s) below refer to circled number(s) on the diagnostic chart.

1. This step indicates if the EBCM is capable of controlling the ABS enable relay as commanded.
2. With the ABS enable relay removed, voltage should not be available at terminal "4". Any voltage at this point would indicate that CKT 879 was shorted to a voltage source.
3. This step checks for a shorted coil.
4. This ensures malfunction was not due to a poor connection.

GC402940095600AX

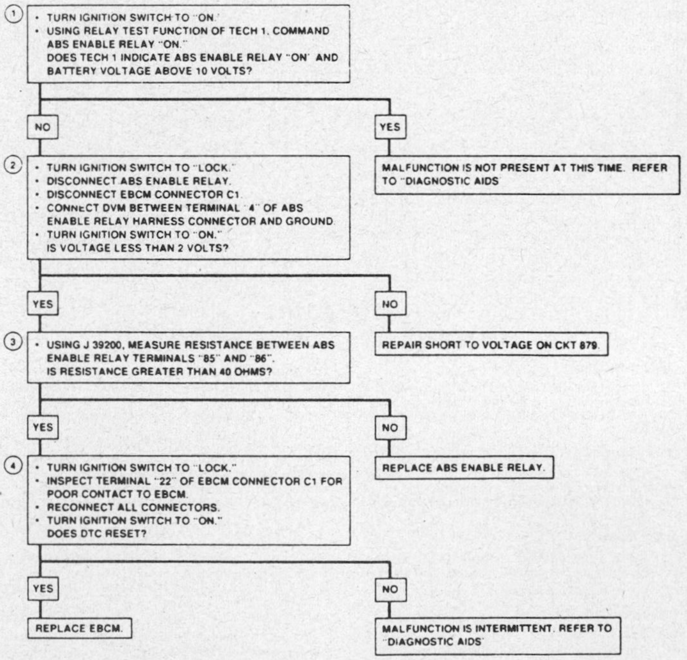
1
TURN IGNITION SWITCH TO "ON."
USING RELAY TEST FUNCTION OF TECH 1, COMMAND ABS ENABLE RELAY "ON."
DOES TECH 1 INDICATE ABS ENABLE RELAY "ON" AND BATTERY VOLTAGE ABOVE 10 VOLTS?
NO
YES
2
TURN IGNITION SWITCH TO "LOCK."
DISCONNECT ABS ENABLE RELAY.
DISCONNECT EBCM CONNECTOR C1.
CONNECT DVM BETWEEN TERMINAL "4" OF ABS ENABLE RELAY HARNESS CONNECTOR AND GROUND.
TURN IGNITION SWITCH TO "ON."
IS VOLTAGE LESS THAN 2 VOLTS?
MALFUNCTION IS NOT PRESENT AT THIS TIME. REFER TO "DIAGNOSTIC AIDS"
YES
NO
3
USING J 39200, MEASURE RESISTANCE BETWEEN ABS ENABLE RELAY TERMINALS "85" AND "86".
IS RESISTANCE GREATER THAN 40 OHMS?
REPAIR SHORT TO VOLTAGE ON CKT 879.
YES
NO
4
TURN IGNITION SWITCH TO "LOCK."
INSPECT TERMINAL "22" OF EBCM CONNECTOR C1 FOR POOR CONTACT TO EBCM.
RECONNECT ALL CONNECTORS.
TURN IGNITION SWITCH TO "ON."
DOES DTC RESET?
REPLACE ABS ENABLE RELAY.
YES
NO
REPLACE EBCM.
MALFUNCTION IS INTERMITTENT. REFER TO "DIAGNOSTIC AIDS"

THIS CHART ASSUMES THAT A CURRENT DTC IS STORED INDICATING THAT THIS MALFUNCTION IS PRESENT.

GC402940095600BX

Fig. 306 Code A018: ABS Enable Relay Coil Circuit Shorted To Battery . 1993–94 Prizm

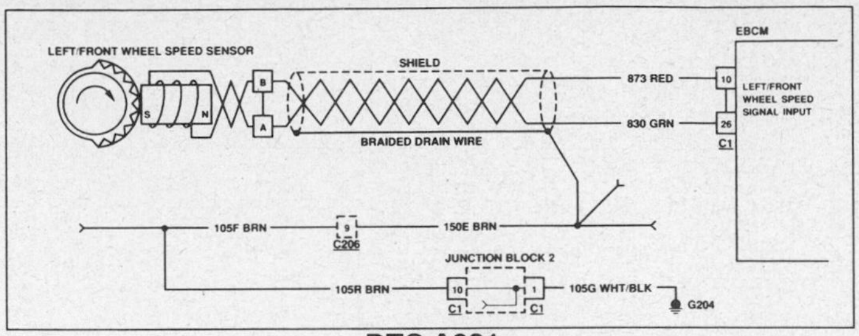
LEFT/FRONT WHEEL SPEED SENSOR
SHIELD
EBCM
873 RED
830 GRN
LEFT/FRONT WHEEL SPEED SIGNAL INPUT
BRAIDED DRAIN WIRE
105F BRN
C206
150E BRN
JUNCTION BLOCK 2
105R BRN
105G WHT/BLK
G204

DTC A021
(Page 1 of 3)
LEFT FRONT WHEEL SPEED = 0 OR UNREASONABLE

Circuit Description:

As a toothed ring passes by the wheel speed sensor, changes in the electromagnetic field cause the wheel speed sensor to produce a sinusoidal (AC) voltage signal whose frequency is proportional to wheel speed. The magnitude of this signal is directly related to wheel speed and the proximity of the wheel speed sensor to the toothed ring (often referred to as the air gap).

Failure Condition:

DTC A021 can be set when the vehicle is not in an ABS stop. If the left front wheel speed is less than 1/2 of the vehicle's reference speed and the vehicle's reference speed is greater than 8 km/h (5 mph), a malfunction exists.

Action Taken:

A DTC A021 is stored, ABS is disabled and the "ABS" indicator is turned on.

Test Description: Number(s) below refer to circled number(s) on the diagnostic chart.

1. This test verifies whether the malfunction is currently present.
2. This step will identify a wheel speed sensor or circuitry that is damaged and visibly apparent.
3. This test checks wheel speed sensor for proper resistance values.
4. This test ensures the wheel speed sensor and sensor ring generate the proper voltage.
5. This step ensures the wheel speed sensor is not shorted to ground.

Diagnostic Aids:

An "intermittent" malfunction may be caused by a poor connection, rubbed through wire insulation or a wire that is broken inside the insulation.

The frequency of the malfunction can be checked by using the enhanced diagnostic function of the TECH 1.

If the customer's comments reflect that the "ABS" indicator is on only during moist environmental changes (rain, snow, vehicle wash, etc.), all wheel speed sensor circuitry should be thoroughly inspected for signs of water intrusion. Use the following procedure:

1. Spray down the suspected area with 5% salt water solution (10 ml [2 teaspoons] of salt to 355 ml [12 fl.oz.] of water).
2. Start vehicle and allow it to run for ten seconds.
3. If the DTC returns immediately, replace the suspected harness.

Any circuitry that is suspected of causing the intermittent complaint should be thoroughly checked for backed out terminals, improper mating, broken locks, improperly formed or damaged terminals, poor terminal-to-wiring connections or physical damage to the wiring harness.

When measuring wheel speed sensor resistance, ensure vehicle is at room temperature (approximately 20°C [68°F]). Wheel speed sensor resistance will vary with temperature.

When replacing a wheel speed sensor, inspect the sensor terminals and harness connector for corrosion and/or water intrusion. If evidence of corrosion or water intrusion exists, replace the wheel speed sensor.

GC402940095701AX

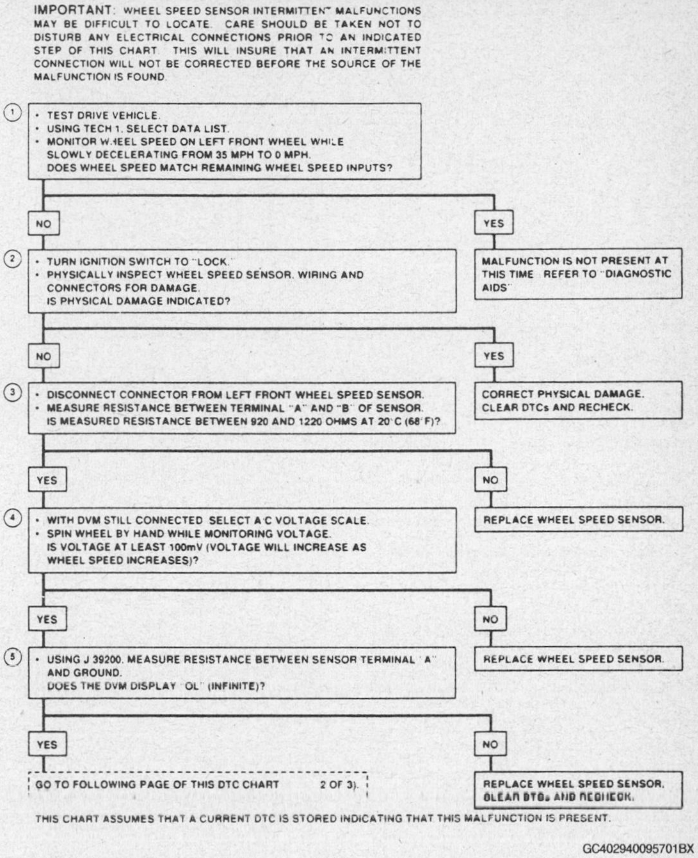
IMPORTANT: WHEEL SPEED SENSOR INTERMITTENT MALFUNCTIONS MAY BE DIFFICULT TO LOCATE. CARE SHOULD BE TAKEN NOT TO DISTURB ANY ELECTRICAL CONNECTIONS PRIOR TO AN INDICATED STEP OF THIS CHART. THIS WILL INSURE THAT AN INTERMITTENT CONNECTION WILL NOT BE CORRECTED BEFORE THE SOURCE OF THE MALFUNCTION IS FOUND.
1
• TEST DRIVE VEHICLE.
• USING TECH 1, SELECT DATA LIST.
• MONITOR WHEEL SPEED ON LEFT FRONT WHEEL WHILE SLOWLY DECELERATING FROM 35 MPH TO 0 MPH.
DOES WHEEL SPEED MATCH REMAINING WHEEL SPEED INPUTS?
NO
YES
MALFUNCTION IS NOT PRESENT AT THIS TIME. REFER TO "DIAGNOSTIC AIDS"
2
• TURN IGNITION SWITCH TO "LOCK."
• PHYSICALLY INSPECT WHEEL SPEED SENSOR, WIRING AND CONNECTORS FOR DAMAGE.
IS PHYSICAL DAMAGE INDICATED?
NO
YES
CORRECT PHYSICAL DAMAGE. CLEAR DTCs AND RECHECK.
3
• DISCONNECT CONNECTOR FROM LEFT FRONT WHEEL SPEED SENSOR.
• MEASURE RESISTANCE BETWEEN TERMINAL "A" AND "B" OF SENSOR.
IS MEASURED RESISTANCE BETWEEN 920 AND 1220 OHMS AT 20°C (68°F)?
YES
NO
REPLACE WHEEL SPEED SENSOR.
4
• WITH DVM STILL CONNECTED SELECT A/C VOLTAGE SCALE.
• SPIN WHEEL BY HAND WHILE MONITORING VOLTAGE.
IS VOLTAGE AT LEAST 100mV (VOLTAGE WILL INCREASE AS WHEEL SPEED INCREASES)?
YES
NO
REPLACE WHEEL SPEED SENSOR.
5
• USING J 39200, MEASURE RESISTANCE BETWEEN SENSOR TERMINAL "A" AND GROUND.
DOES THE DVM DISPLAY "OL" (INFINITE)?
YES
NO
GO TO FOLLOWING PAGE OF THIS DTC CHART 2 OF 3).
REPLACE WHEEL SPEED SENSOR. CLEAR DTCs AND RECHECK.
THIS CHART ASSUMES THAT A CURRENT DTC IS STORED INDICATING THAT THIS MALFUNCTION IS PRESENT.
GC402940095701BX

Fig. 307 Code A021: Left Front Wheel Speed 0 or Unreasonable (Part 1 of 3). 1993–94 Prizm

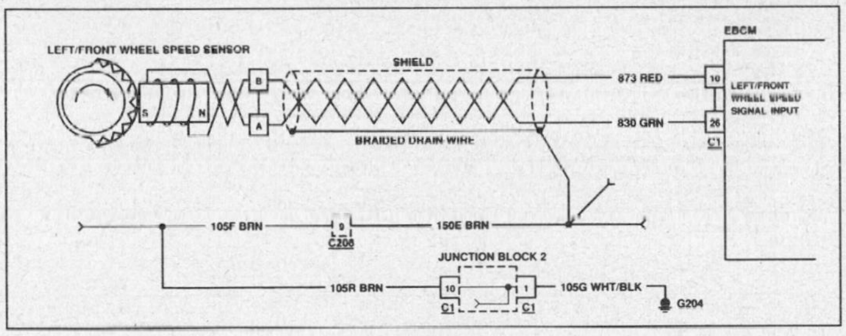
LEFT/FRONT WHEEL SPEED SENSOR
SHIELD
EBCM
873 RED
830 GRN
LEFT/FRONT WHEEL SPEED SIGNAL INPUT
BRAIDED DRAIN WIRE
105F BRN
C206
150E BRN
JUNCTION BLOCK 2
105R BRN
105G WHT/BLK
G204

DTC A021
(Page 2 of 3)
LEFT FRONT WHEEL SPEED = 0 OR UNREASONABLE

Circuit Description:

As a toothed ring passes by the wheel speed sensor, changes in the electromagnetic field cause the wheel speed sensor to produce a sinusoidal (AC) voltage signal whose frequency is proportional to wheel speed. The magnitude of this signal is directly related to wheel speed and the proximity of the wheel speed sensor to the toothed ring (often referred to as the air gap).

Failure Condition:

DTC A021 can be set when the vehicle is not in an ABS stop. If the left front wheel speed is less than 1/2 of the vehicle's reference speed and the vehicle's reference speed is greater than 8 km/h (5 mph), a malfunction exists.

Action Taken:

A DTC A021 is stored, ABS is disabled and the "ABS" indicator is turned on.

Test Description: Number(s) below refer to circled number(s) on the diagnostic chart.

6. This step checks for proper voltages at speed sensor harness connector.
7. This test ensures that the wheel speed sensor circuitry is not internally shorted.
8. This checks for an open in CKT 873.
9. This checks for an open in CKT 830.

Diagnostic Aids:

An "intermittent" malfunction may be caused by a poor connection, rubbed through wire insulation or a wire that is broken inside the insulation.

The frequency of the malfunction can be checked by using the enhanced diagnostic function of the TECH 1.

If the customer's comments reflect that the "ABS" indicator is on only during moist environmental changes (rain, snow, vehicle wash, etc.), all wheel speed sensor circuitry should be thoroughly inspected for signs of water intrusion. Use the following procedure:

1. Spray down the suspected area with 5% salt water solution (10 ml [2 teaspoons] of salt to 355 ml [12 fl.oz.] of water).
2. Start vehicle and allow it to run for ten seconds.
3. If the DTC returns immediately, replace the suspected harness.

Any circuitry that is suspected of causing the intermittent complaint should be thoroughly checked for backed out terminals, improper mating, broken locks, improperly formed or damaged terminals, poor terminal-to-wiring connections or physical damage to the wiring harness.

When measuring wheel speed sensor resistance, ensure vehicle is at room temperature (approximately 20°C [68°F]). Wheel speed sensor resistance will vary with temperature.

When replacing a wheel speed sensor, inspect the sensor terminals and harness connector for corrosion and/or water intrusion. If evidence of corrosion or water intrusion exists, replace the wheel speed sensor.

GC402940095702AX

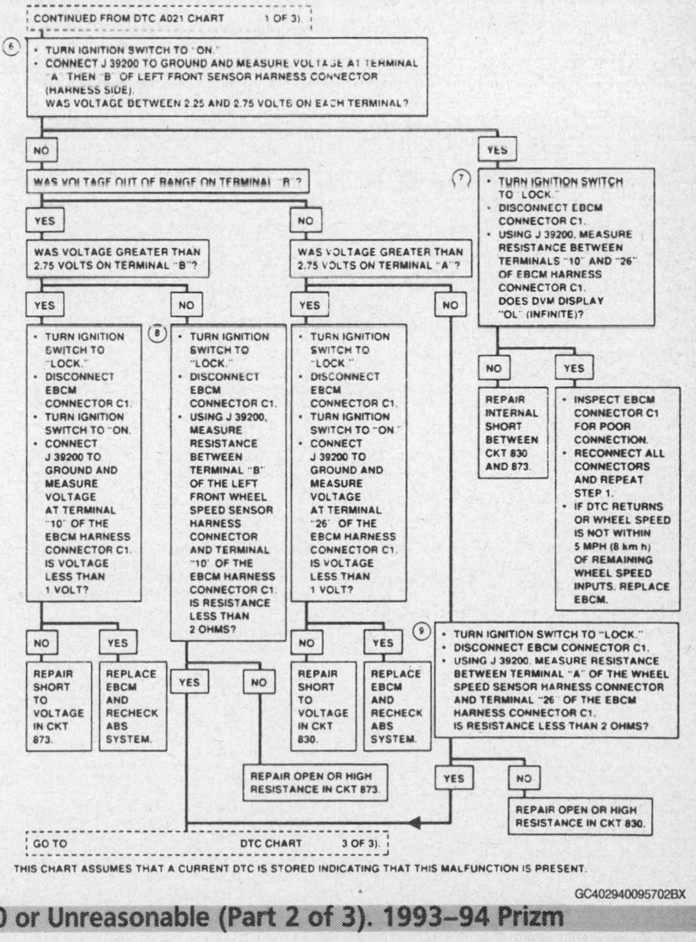
CONTINUED FROM DTC A021 CHART 1 OF 3).
6
• TURN IGNITION SWITCH TO "ON."
• CONNECT J 39200 TO GROUND AND MEASURE VOLTAGE AT TERMINAL "A" THEN "B" OF LEFT FRONT SENSOR HARNESS CONNECTOR (HARNESS SIDE).
WAS VOLTAGE BETWEEN 2.25 AND 2.75 VOLTS ON EACH TERMINAL?
NO
YES
WAS VOLTAGE OUT OF RANGE ON TERMINAL "B"?
7
• TURN IGNITION SWITCH TO "LOCK."
• DISCONNECT EBCM CONNECTOR C1.
• USING J 39200, MEASURE RESISTANCE BETWEEN TERMINALS "10" AND "26" OF EBCM HARNESS CONNECTOR C1.
DOES DVM DISPLAY "OL" (INFINITE)?
YES
NO
WAS VOLTAGE GREATER THAN 2.75 VOLTS ON TERMINAL "B"?
WAS VOLTAGE GREATER THAN 2.75 VOLTS ON TERMINAL "A"?
YES
NO
YES
NO
• TURN IGNITION SWITCH TO "LOCK."
• DISCONNECT EBCM CONNECTOR C1.
• TURN IGNITION SWITCH TO "ON."
• CONNECT J 39200 TO GROUND AND MEASURE VOLTAGE AT TERMINAL "10" OF THE EBCM HARNESS CONNECTOR C1.
IS VOLTAGE LESS THAN 1 VOLT?
8
• TURN IGNITION SWITCH TO "LOCK."
• DISCONNECT EBCM CONNECTOR C1.
• USING J 39200, MEASURE RESISTANCE BETWEEN TERMINAL "B" OF THE LEFT FRONT WHEEL SPEED SENSOR HARNESS CONNECTOR AND TERMINAL "10" OF THE EBCM HARNESS CONNECTOR C1.
IS RESISTANCE LESS THAN 2 OHMS?
• TURN IGNITION SWITCH TO "LOCK."
• DISCONNECT EBCM CONNECTOR C1.
• TURN IGNITION SWITCH TO "ON."
• CONNECT J 39200 TO GROUND AND MEASURE VOLTAGE AT TERMINAL "26" OF THE EBCM HARNESS CONNECTOR C1.
IS VOLTAGE LESS THAN 1 VOLT?
NO
YES
REPAIR INTERNAL SHORT BETWEEN CKT 830 AND 873.
• INSPECT EBCM CONNECTOR C1 FOR POOR CONNECTION.
• RECONNECT ALL CONNECTORS AND REPEAT STEP 1.
• IF DTC RETURNS OR WHEEL SPEED IS NOT WITHIN 5 MPH (8 km h) OF REMAINING WHEEL SPEED INPUTS, REPLACE EBCM.
NO
YES
NO
YES
9
• TURN IGNITION SWITCH TO "LOCK."
• DISCONNECT EBCM CONNECTOR C1.
• USING J 39200, MEASURE RESISTANCE BETWEEN TERMINAL "A" OF THE WHEEL SPEED SENSOR HARNESS CONNECTOR AND TERMINAL "26" OF THE EBCM HARNESS CONNECTOR C1.
IS RESISTANCE LESS THAN 2 OHMS?
REPAIR SHORT TO VOLTAGE IN CKT 873.
REPLACE EBCM AND RECHECK ABS SYSTEM.
YES
NO
REPAIR SHORT TO VOLTAGE IN CKT 830.
REPLACE EBCM AND RECHECK ABS SYSTEM.
REPAIR OPEN OR HIGH RESISTANCE IN CKT 873.
YES
NO
REPAIR OPEN OR HIGH RESISTANCE IN CKT 830.
GO TO DTC CHART 3 OF 3).
THIS CHART ASSUMES THAT A CURRENT DTC IS STORED INDICATING THAT THIS MALFUNCTION IS PRESENT.
GC402940095702BX

Fig. 307 Code A021: Left Front Wheel Speed 0 or Unreasonable (Part 2 of 3). 1993–94 Prizm

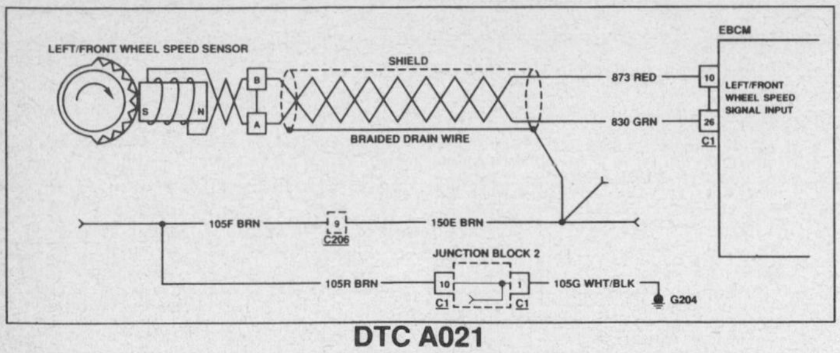
EBCM
LEFT/FRONT WHEEL SPEED SENSOR
SHIELD
873 RED
830 GRN
LEFT/FRONT WHEEL SPEED SIGNAL INPUT
BRAIDED DRAIN WIRE
105F BRN
C206
150E BRN
JUNCTION BLOCK 2
105R BRN
105G WHT/BLK
G204

DTC A021

(Page 3 of 3)

LEFT FRONT WHEEL SPEED = 0 OR UNREASONABLE

Circuit Description:

As a toothed ring passes by the wheel speed sensor, changes in the electromagnetic field cause the wheel speed sensor to produce a sinusoidal (AC) voltage signal whose frequency is proportional to wheel speed. The magnitude of this signal is directly related to wheel speed and the proximity of the wheel speed sensor to the toothed ring (often referred to as the air gap).

Failure Condition:

DTC A021 can be set when the vehicle is not in an ABS stop. If the left front wheel speed is less than 1/2 of the vehicle's reference speed and the vehicle's reference speed is greater than 8 km/h (5 mph), a malfunction exists.

Action Taken:

A DTC A021 is stored, ABS is disabled and the "ABS" indicator is turned on.

Test Description: Number(s) below refer to circled number(s) on the diagnostic chart.

10. This checks for a short to ground in both wheel speed signal circuits.
11. This step ensures that DTC A021 was not set due to a poor connection between the EBCM and connector C1.

DiagnosticAids:

An "intermittent" malfunction may be caused by a poor connection, rubbed through wire insulation or a wire that is broken inside the insulation.

The frequency of the malfunction can be checked by using the enhanced diagnostic function of the TECH 1.

If the customer's comments reflect that the "ABS" indicator is on only during moist environmental changes (rain, snow, vehicle wash, etc.), all wheel speed sensor circuitry should be thoroughly inspected for signs of water intrusion. use the following procedure:

1. Spray down the suspected area with 5% salt water solution (10 ml [2 teaspoons] of salt to 355 ml [12 fl.oz.] of water).
2. Start vehicle and allow it to run for ten seconds.
3. If the DTC returns immediately, replace the suspected harness.

Any circuitry that is suspected of causing the intermittent complaint should be thoroughly checked for backed out terminals, improper mating, broken locks, improperly formed or damaged terminals, poor terminal-to-wiring connections or physical damage to the wiring harness.

When measuring wheel speed sensor resistance, ensure vehicle is at room temperature (approximately 20°C [68°F]). Wheel speed sensor resistance will vary with temperature.

When replacing a wheel speed sensor, inspect the sensor terminals and harness connector for corrosion and/or water intrusion. If evidence of corrosion or water intrusion exists, replace the wheel speed sensor.

GC402940095703AX

CONTINUED FROM DTC A021 CHART 2 OF 3).

(10)
- USING J 39200, MEASURE RESISTANCE BETWEEN GROUND AND TERMINAL "10" THEN "26" OF THE EBCM HARNESS CONNECTOR C1. DOES DVM DISPLAY "OL" (INFINITE)?

YES → (11)
- INSPECT EBCM CONNECTOR C1 FOR POOR CONNECTION.
- RECONNECT ALL CONNECTORS AND REPEAT STEP 1.
- IF DTC RETURNS OR WHEEL SPEED IS NOT WITHIN 5 MPH (8 km/h) OF REMAINING WHEEL SPEED INPUTS, REPLACE EBCM.

NO → REPAIR SHORT TO GROUND IN CKTs 873 AND 830.

GC402940095703BX

Fig. 307 Code A021: Left Front Wheel Speed 0 or Unreasonable (Part 3 of 3). 1993–94 Prizm

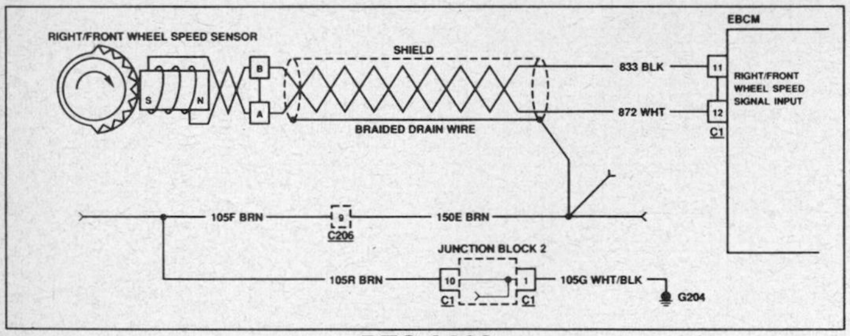
EBCM
RIGHT/FRONT WHEEL SPEED SENSOR
SHIELD
833 BLK
872 WHT
RIGHT/FRONT WHEEL SPEED SIGNAL INPUT
BRAIDED DRAIN WIRE
105F BRN
C206
150E BRN
JUNCTION BLOCK 2
105R BRN
105G WHT/BLK
G204

DTC A022

(Page 1 of 3)

RIGHT FRONT WHEEL SPEED = 0 OR UNREASONABLE

Circuit Description:

As a toothed ring passes by the wheel speed sensor, changes in the electromagnetic field cause the wheel speed sensor to produce a sinusoidal (AC) voltage signal whose frequency is proportional to wheel speed. The magnitude of this signal is directly related to wheel speed and the proximity of the wheel speed sensor to the toothed ring (often referred to as the air gap).

Failure Condition:

DTC A022 can be set when the vehicle is not in an ABS stop. If the right front wheel speed is less than 1/2 of the vehicle's reference speed and the vehicle's reference speed is greater than 8 km/h (5 mph), a malfunction exists.

Action Taken:

A DTC A022 is stored, ABS is disabled and the "ABS" indicator is turned on.

Test Description: Number(s) below refer to circled number(s) on the diagnostic chart.

1. This test verifies whether the malfunction is currently present.
2. This step will identify a wheel speed sensor or circuitry that is damaged and visibly apparent.
3. This test checks wheel speed sensor for proper resistance values.
4. This test ensures the wheel speed sensor and sensor ring generate the proper voltage.
5. This step ensures the wheel speed sensor is not shorted to ground.

Diagnostic Aids:

An "intermittent" malfunction may be caused by a poor connection, rubbed through wire insulation or a wire that is broken inside the insulation.

The frequency of the malfunction can be checked by using the enhanced diagnostic function of the TECH 1.

If the customer's comments reflect that the "ABS" indicator is on only during moist environmental changes (rain, snow, vehicle wash, etc.), all wheel speed sensor circuitry should be thoroughly inspected for signs of water intrusion. Use the following procedure:

1. Spray down the suspected area with 5% salt water solution (10 ml [2 teaspoons] of salt to 355 ml [12 fl.oz.] of water).
2. Start vehicle and allow it to run for ten seconds.
3. If the DTC returns immediately, replace the suspected harness.

Any circuitry that is suspected of causing the intermittent complaint should be thoroughly checked for backed out terminals, improper mating, broken locks, improperly formed or damaged terminals, poor terminal-to-wiring connections or physical damage to the wiring harness.

When measuring wheel speed sensor resistance, ensure vehicle is at room temperature (approximately 20°C [68°F]). Wheel speed sensor resistance will vary with temperature.

When replacing a wheel speed sensor, inspect the sensor terminals and harness connector for corrosion and/or water intrusion. If evidence of corrosion or water intrusion exists, replace the wheel speed sensor.

GC402940095801AX

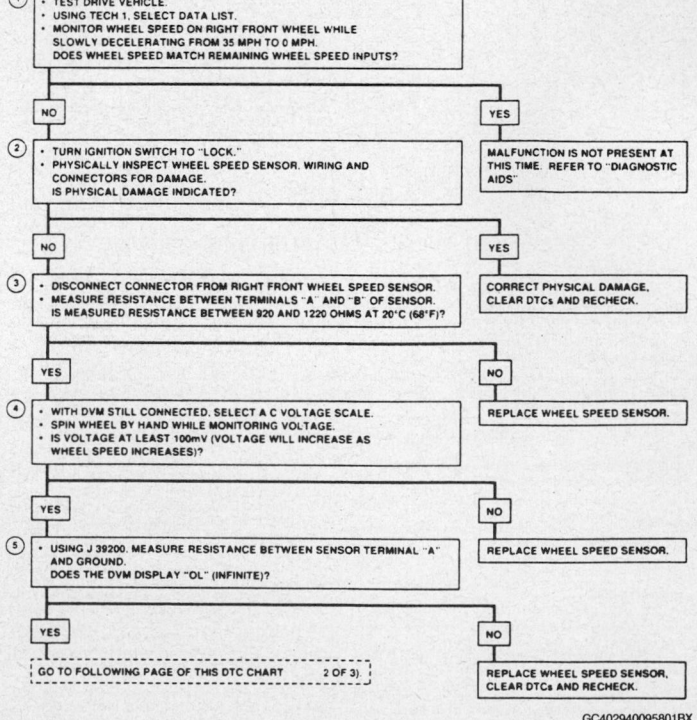

IMPORTANT: WHEEL SPEED SENSOR INTERMITTENT MALFUNCTIONS MAY BE DIFFICULT TO LOCATE. CARE SHOULD BE TAKEN NOT TO DISTURB ANY ELECTRICAL CONNECTIONS PRIOR TO AN INDICATED STEP OF THIS CHART. THIS WILL INSURE THAT AN INTERMITTENT CONNECTION WILL NOT BE CORRECTED BEFORE THE SOURCE OF THE MALFUNCTION IS FOUND.

(1)
- TEST DRIVE VEHICLE.
- USING TECH 1, SELECT DATA LIST.
- MONITOR WHEEL SPEED ON RIGHT FRONT WHEEL WHILE SLOWLY DECELERATING FROM 35 MPH TO 0 MPH. DOES WHEEL SPEED MATCH REMAINING WHEEL SPEED INPUTS?

YES → MALFUNCTION IS NOT PRESENT AT THIS TIME. REFER TO "DIAGNOSTIC AIDS"

NO → (2)
- TURN IGNITION SWITCH TO "LOCK."
- PHYSICALLY INSPECT WHEEL SPEED SENSOR, WIRING AND CONNECTORS FOR DAMAGE. IS PHYSICAL DAMAGE INDICATED?

YES → CORRECT PHYSICAL DAMAGE, CLEAR DTCs AND RECHECK.

NO → (3)
- DISCONNECT CONNECTOR FROM RIGHT FRONT WHEEL SPEED SENSOR.
- MEASURE RESISTANCE BETWEEN TERMINALS "A" AND "B" OF SENSOR. IS MEASURED RESISTANCE BETWEEN 920 AND 1220 OHMS AT 20°C (68°F)?

NO → REPLACE WHEEL SPEED SENSOR.

YES → (4)
- WITH DVM STILL CONNECTED, SELECT A C VOLTAGE SCALE.
- SPIN WHEEL BY HAND WHILE MONITORING VOLTAGE.
- IS VOLTAGE AT LEAST 100mV (VOLTAGE WILL INCREASE AS WHEEL SPEED INCREASES)?

NO → REPLACE WHEEL SPEED SENSOR.

YES → (5)
- USING J 39200, MEASURE RESISTANCE BETWEEN SENSOR TERMINAL "A" AND GROUND. DOES THE DVM DISPLAY "OL" (INFINITE)?

NO → REPLACE WHEEL SPEED SENSOR, CLEAR DTCs AND RECHECK.

YES → GO TO FOLLOWING PAGE OF THIS DTC CHART 2 OF 3).

GC402940095801BX

Fig. 308 Code A022: Right Front Wheel Speed 0 or Unreasonable (Part 1 of 3). 1993–94 Prizm

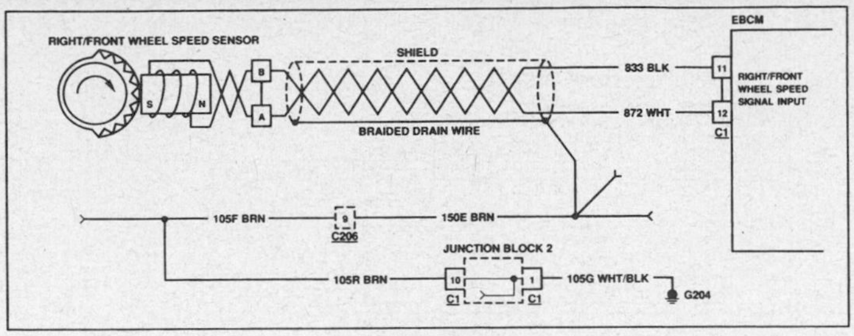
RIGHT/FRONT WHEEL SPEED SENSOR
SHIELD
EBCM
833 BLK
872 WHT
RIGHT/FRONT WHEEL SPEED SIGNAL INPUT
BRAIDED DRAIN WIRE
105F BRN
150E BRN
C206
JUNCTION BLOCK 2
105R BRN
105G WHT/BLK
G204

DTC A022

(Page 2 of 3)

RIGHT FRONT WHEEL SPEED = 0 OR UNREASONABLE

Circuit Description:

As a toothed ring passes by the wheel speed sensor, changes in the electromagnetic field cause the wheel speed sensor to produce a sinusoidal (AC) voltage signal whose frequency is proportional to wheel speed. The magnitude of this signal is directly related to wheel speed and the proximity of the wheel speed sensor to the toothed ring (often referred to as the air gap).

Failure Condition:

DTC A022 can be set when the vehicle is not in an ABS stop. If the right front wheel speed is less than 1/2 of the vehicle's reference speed and the vehicle's reference speed is greater than 8 km/h (5 mph), a malfunction exists.

Action Taken:

A DTC A022 is stored, ABS is disabled and the "ABS" indicator is turned on.

Test Description: Number(s) below refer to circled number(s) on the diagnostic chart.

6. This step checks for proper voltages at speed sensor harness connector.
7. This test ensures that the wheel speed sensor circuitry is not internally shorted.
8. This checks for an open in CKT 833.
9. This checks for an open in CKT 872.

Diagnostic Aids:

An "intermittent" malfunction may be caused by a poor connection, rubbed through wire insulation or a wire that is broken inside the insulation.

The frequency of the malfunction can be checked by using the enhanced diagnostic function of the TECH 1.

If the customer's comments reflect that the "ABS" indicator is on only during moist environmental changes (rain, snow, vehicle wash, etc.), all wheel speed sensor circuitry should be thoroughly inspected for signs of water intrusion. Use the following procedure:

1. Spray down the suspected area with 5% salt water solution (10 ml [2 teaspoons] of salt to 355 ml [12 fl.oz.] of water).
2. Start vehicle and allow it to run for ten seconds.
3. If the DTC returns immediately, replace the suspected harness.

Any circuitry that is suspected of causing the intermittent complaint should be thoroughly checked for backed out terminals, improper mating, broken locks, improperly formed or damaged terminals, poor terminal-to-wiring connections or physical damage to the wiring harness.

When measuring wheel speed sensor resistance, ensure vehicle is at room temperature (approximately 20°C [68°F]). Wheel speed sensor resistance will vary with temperature.

When replacing a wheel speed sensor, inspect the sensor terminals and harness connector for corrosion and/or water intrusion. If evidence of corrosion or water intrusion exists, replace the wheel speed sensor.

GC402940095802AX

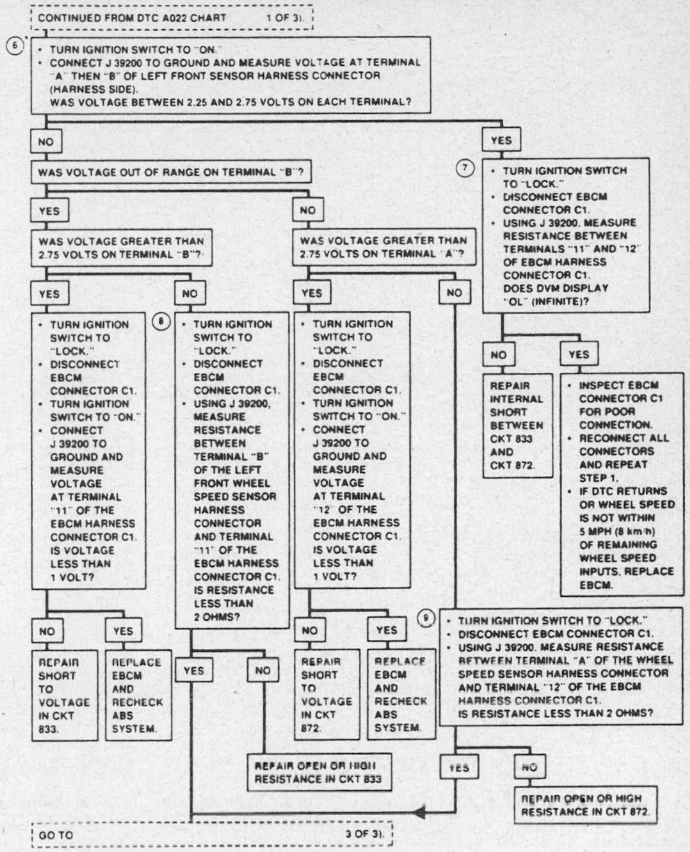
CONTINUED FROM DTC A022 CHART 1 OF 3).
6
• TURN IGNITION SWITCH TO "ON."
• CONNECT J 39200 TO GROUND AND MEASURE VOLTAGE AT TERMINAL "A" THEN "B" OF LEFT FRONT SENSOR HARNESS CONNECTOR (HARNESS SIDE).
WAS VOLTAGE BETWEEN 2.25 AND 2.75 VOLTS ON EACH TERMINAL?
NO
YES
WAS VOLTAGE OUT OF RANGE ON TERMINAL "B"?
7
• TURN IGNITION SWITCH TO "LOCK."
• DISCONNECT EBCM CONNECTOR C1.
• USING J 39200, MEASURE RESISTANCE BETWEEN TERMINALS "11" AND "12" OF EBCM HARNESS CONNECTOR C1. DOES DVM DISPLAY "OL" (INFINITE)?
YES
NO
WAS VOLTAGE GREATER THAN 2.75 VOLTS ON TERMINAL "B"?
WAS VOLTAGE GREATER THAN 2.75 VOLTS ON TERMINAL "A"?
YES
NO
YES
NO
• TURN IGNITION SWITCH TO "LOCK."
• DISCONNECT EBCM CONNECTOR C1.
• TURN IGNITION SWITCH TO "ON."
• CONNECT J 39200 TO GROUND AND MEASURE VOLTAGE AT TERMINAL "11" OF THE EBCM HARNESS CONNECTOR C1. IS VOLTAGE LESS THAN 1 VOLT?
8
• TURN IGNITION SWITCH TO "LOCK."
• DISCONNECT EBCM CONNECTOR C1.
• USING J 39200, MEASURE RESISTANCE BETWEEN TERMINAL "B" OF THE LEFT FRONT WHEEL SPEED SENSOR HARNESS CONNECTOR AND TERMINAL "11" OF THE EBCM HARNESS CONNECTOR C1. IS RESISTANCE LESS THAN 2 OHMS?
• TURN IGNITION SWITCH TO "LOCK."
• DISCONNECT EBCM CONNECTOR C1.
• TURN IGNITION SWITCH TO "ON."
• CONNECT J 39200 TO GROUND AND MEASURE VOLTAGE AT TERMINAL "12" OF THE EBCM HARNESS CONNECTOR C1. IS VOLTAGE LESS THAN 1 VOLT?
NO
YES
REPAIR INTERNAL SHORT BETWEEN CKT 833 AND CKT 872.
• INSPECT EBCM CONNECTOR C1 FOR POOR CONNECTION.
• RECONNECT ALL CONNECTORS AND REPEAT STEP 1.
• IF DTC RETURNS OR WHEEL SPEED IS NOT WITHIN 5 MPH (8 km/h) OF REMAINING WHEEL SPEED INPUTS, REPLACE EBCM.
NO
YES
NO
YES
9
• TURN IGNITION SWITCH TO "LOCK."
• DISCONNECT EBCM CONNECTOR C1.
• USING J 39200, MEASURE RESISTANCE BETWEEN TERMINAL "A" OF THE WHEEL SPEED SENSOR HARNESS CONNECTOR AND TERMINAL "12" OF THE EBCM HARNESS CONNECTOR C1. IS RESISTANCE LESS THAN 2 OHMS?
REPAIR SHORT TO VOLTAGE IN CKT 833.
REPLACE EBCM AND RECHECK ABS SYSTEM.
YES
NO
REPAIR SHORT TO VOLTAGE IN CKT 872.
REPLACE EBCM AND RECHECK ABS SYSTEM.
REPAIR OPEN OR HIGH RESISTANCE IN CKT 833
YES
NO
REPAIR OPEN OR HIGH RESISTANCE IN CKT 872.
GO TO 3 OF 3).

GC402940095802BX

Fig. 308 Code A022: Right Front Wheel Speed 0 or Unreasonable (Part 2 of 3). 1993–94 Prizm

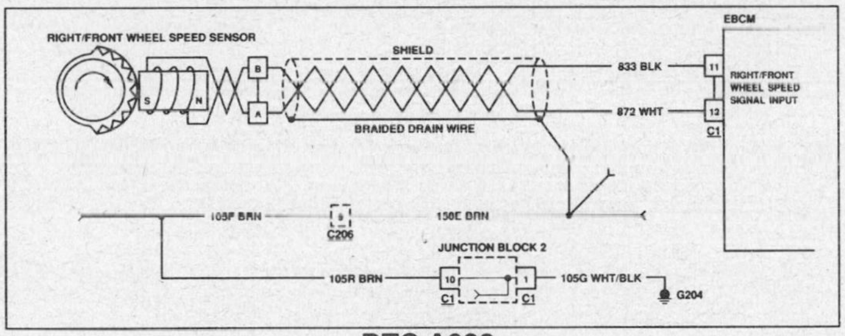
RIGHT/FRONT WHEEL SPEED SENSOR
SHIELD
EBCM
833 BLK
872 WHT
RIGHT/FRONT WHEEL SPEED SIGNAL INPUT
BRAIDED DRAIN WIRE
105F BRN
150E BRN
C206
JUNCTION BLOCK 2
105R BRN
105G WHT/BLK
G204

DTC A022

(Page 3 of 3)

RIGHT FRONT WHEEL SPEED = 0 OR UNREASONABLE

Circuit Description:

As a toothed ring passes by the wheel speed sensor, changes in the electromagnetic field cause the wheel speed sensor to produce a sinusoidal (AC) voltage signal whose frequency is proportional to wheel speed. The magnitude of this signal is directly related to wheel speed and the proximity of the wheel speed sensor to the toothed ring (often referred to as the air gap).

Failure Condition:

DTC A022 can be set when the vehicle is not in an ABS stop. If the right front wheel speed is less than 1/2 of the vehicle's reference speed and the vehicle's reference speed is greater than 8 km/h (5 mph), a malfunction exists.

Action Taken:

A DTC A022 is stored, ABS is disabled and the "ABS" indicator is turned on.

Test Description: Number(s) below refer to circled number(s) on the diagnostic chart.

10. This checks for a short to ground in both wheel speed signal circuits.
11. This step ensures that DTC A022 was not set due to a poor connection between the EBCM and connector C1.

Diagnostic Aids:

An "intermittent" malfunction may be caused by a poor connection, rubbed through wire insulation or a wire that is broken inside the insulation.

The frequency of the malfunction can be checked by using the enhanced diagnostic function of the TECH 1.

If the customer's comments reflect that the "ABS" indicator is on only during moist environmental changes (rain, snow, vehicle wash, etc.), all wheel speed sensor circuitry should be thoroughly inspected for signs of water intrusion. Use the following procedure:

1. Spray down the suspected area with 5% salt water solution (10 ml [2 teaspoons] of salt to 355 ml [12 fl.oz.] of water).
2. Start vehicle and allow it to run for ten seconds.
3. If the DTC returns immediately, replace the suspected harness.

Any circuitry that is suspected of causing the intermittent complaint should be thoroughly checked for backed out terminals, improper mating, broken locks, improperly formed or damaged terminals, poor terminal-to-wiring connections or physical damage to the wiring harness.

When measuring wheel speed sensor resistance, ensure vehicle is at room temperature (approximately 20°C [68°F]). Wheel speed sensor resistance will vary with temperature.

When replacing a wheel speed sensor, inspect the sensor terminals and harness connector for corrosion and/or water intrusion. If evidence of corrosion or water intrusion exists, replace the wheel speed sensor.

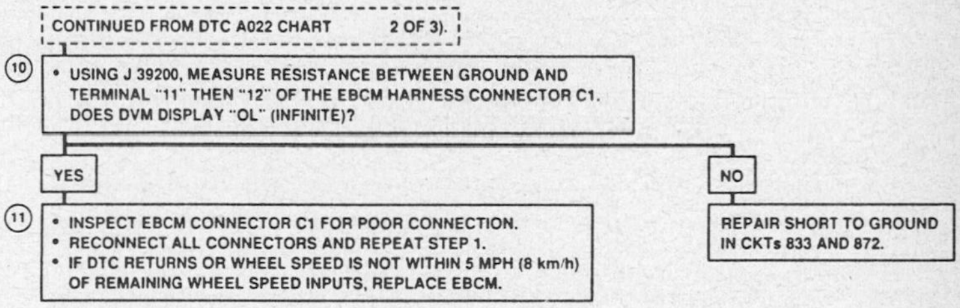
CONTINUED FROM DTC A022 CHART 2 OF 3).
10
• USING J 39200, MEASURE RESISTANCE BETWEEN GROUND AND TERMINAL "11" THEN "12" OF THE EBCM HARNESS CONNECTOR C1. DOES DVM DISPLAY "OL" (INFINITE)?
YES
NO
11
• INSPECT EBCM CONNECTOR C1 FOR POOR CONNECTION.
• RECONNECT ALL CONNECTORS AND REPEAT STEP 1.
• IF DTC RETURNS OR WHEEL SPEED IS NOT WITHIN 5 MPH (8 km/h) OF REMAINING WHEEL SPEED INPUTS, REPLACE EBCM.
REPAIR SHORT TO GROUND IN CKTs 833 AND 872.

GC402940095803AX

Fig. 308 Code A022: Right Front Wheel Speed 0 or Unreasonable (Part 3 of 3).1993-94 Prizm

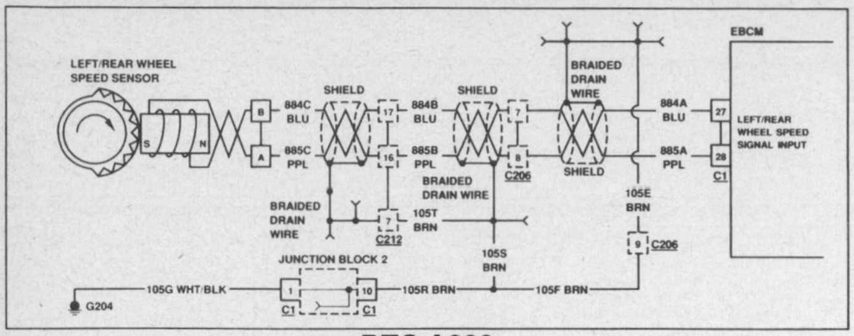
EBCM
LEFT/REAR WHEEL SPEED SENSOR
SHIELD
884C BLU
885C PPL
884B BLU
885B PPL
BRAIDED DRAIN WIRE
884A BLU
885A PPL
LEFT/REAR WHEEL SPEED SIGNAL INPUT
C206
C1
105E BRN
105T BRN
C212
JUNCTION BLOCK 2
105S BRN
105G WHT/BLK
105R BRN
105F BRN
G204

DTC A023
(Page 1 of 3)
LEFT REAR WHEEL SPEED = 0 OR UNREASONABLE

Circuit Description:

As a toothed ring passes by the wheel speed sensor, changes in the electromagnetic field cause the wheel speed sensor to produce a sinusoidal (AC) voltage signal whose frequency is proportional to wheel speed. The magnitude of this signal is directly related to wheel speed and the proximity of the wheel speed sensor to the toothed ring (often referred to as the air gap).

Failure Condition:

DTC A023 can be set when the vehicle is not in an ABS stop. If the left rear wheel speed is less than 1/2 of the vehicle's reference speed and the vehicle's reference speed is greater than 8 km/h (5 mph), a malfunction exists.

Action Taken:

A DTC A023 is stored, ABS is disabled and the "ABS" indicator is turned on.

Test Description: Number(s) below refer to circled number(s) on the diagnostic chart.

1. This test verifies whether the malfunction is currently present.
2. This step will identify a wheel speed sensor or circuitry that is damaged and visibly apparent.
3. This test checks wheel speed sensor for proper resistance values.
4. This test ensures the wheel speed sensor and sensor ring generate the proper voltage.
5. This step ensures the wheel speed sensor is not shorted to ground.

Diagnostic Aids:

An "intermittent" malfunction may be caused by a poor connection, rubbed through wire insulation or a wire that is broken inside the insulation.

The frequency of the malfunction can be checked by using the enhanced diagnostic function of the TECH 1.

If the customer's comments reflect that the "ABS" indicator is on only during moist environmental changes (rain, snow, vehicle wash, etc.), all wheel speed sensor circuitry should be thoroughly inspected for signs of water intrusion. Use the following procedure:

1. Spray down the suspected area with 5% salt water solution (10 ml [2 teaspoons] of salt to 355 ml [12 fl.oz.] of water).
2. Start vehicle and allow it to run for ten seconds.
3. If the DTC returns immediately, replace the suspected harness.

Any circuitry that is suspected of causing the intermittent complaint should be thoroughly checked for backed out terminals, improper mating, broken locks, improperly formed or damaged terminals, poor terminal-to-wiring connections or physical damage to the wiring harness.

When measuring wheel speed sensor resistance, ensure vehicle is at room temperature (approximately 20°C [68°F]). Wheel speed sensor resistance will vary with temperature.

When replacing a wheel speed sensor, inspect the sensor terminals and harness connector for corrosion and/or water intrusion. If evidence of corrosion or water intrusion exists, replace the wheel speed sensor.

GC402940095901AX

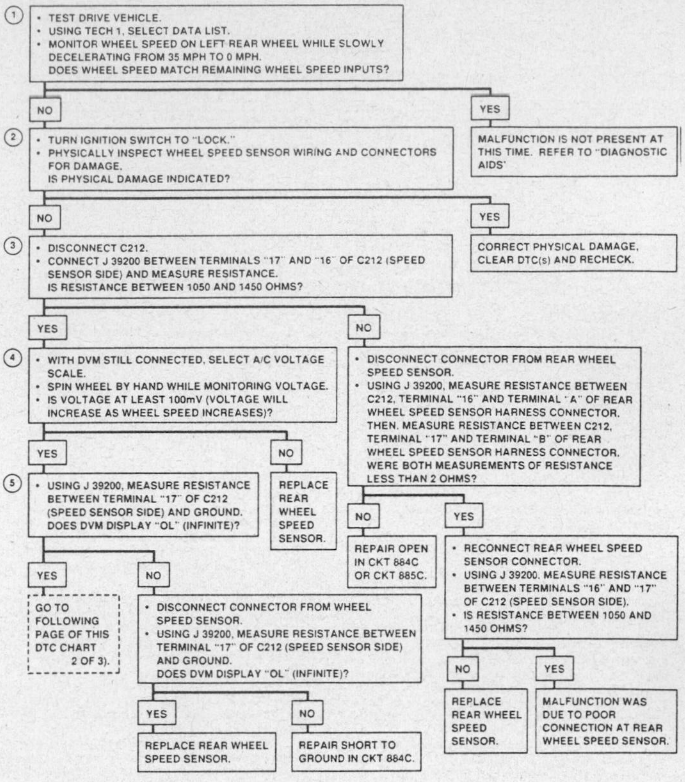
1
• TEST DRIVE VEHICLE.
• USING TECH 1, SELECT DATA LIST.
• MONITOR WHEEL SPEED ON LEFT REAR WHEEL WHILE SLOWLY DECELERATING FROM 35 MPH TO 0 MPH.
DOES WHEEL SPEED MATCH REMAINING WHEEL SPEED INPUTS?
NO
YES
MALFUNCTION IS NOT PRESENT AT THIS TIME. REFER TO "DIAGNOSTIC AIDS"
2
• TURN IGNITION SWITCH TO "LOCK."
• PHYSICALLY INSPECT WHEEL SPEED SENSOR WIRING AND CONNECTORS FOR DAMAGE.
IS PHYSICAL DAMAGE INDICATED?
NO
YES
CORRECT PHYSICAL DAMAGE, CLEAR DTC(s) AND RECHECK.
3
• DISCONNECT C212.
• CONNECT J 39200 BETWEEN TERMINALS "17" AND "16" OF C212 (SPEED SENSOR SIDE) AND MEASURE RESISTANCE.
IS RESISTANCE BETWEEN 1050 AND 1450 OHMS?
YES
NO
4
• WITH DVM STILL CONNECTED, SELECT A/C VOLTAGE SCALE.
• SPIN WHEEL BY HAND WHILE MONITORING VOLTAGE.
• IS VOLTAGE AT LEAST 100mV (VOLTAGE WILL INCREASE AS WHEEL SPEED INCREASES)?
• DISCONNECT CONNECTOR FROM REAR WHEEL SPEED SENSOR.
• USING J 39200, MEASURE RESISTANCE BETWEEN C212, TERMINAL "16" AND TERMINAL "A" OF REAR WHEEL SPEED SENSOR HARNESS CONNECTOR. THEN, MEASURE RESISTANCE BETWEEN C212, TERMINAL "17" AND TERMINAL "B" OF REAR WHEEL SPEED SENSOR HARNESS CONNECTOR. WERE BOTH MEASUREMENTS OF RESISTANCE LESS THAN 2 OHMS?
YES
NO
REPLACE REAR WHEEL SPEED SENSOR.
5
• USING J 39200, MEASURE RESISTANCE BETWEEN TERMINAL "17" OF C212 (SPEED SENSOR SIDE) AND GROUND. DOES DVM DISPLAY "OL" (INFINITE)?
NO
YES
REPAIR OPEN IN CKT 884C OR CKT 885C.
• RECONNECT REAR WHEEL SPEED SENSOR CONNECTOR.
• USING J 39200, MEASURE RESISTANCE BETWEEN TERMINALS "16" AND "17" OF C212 (SPEED SENSOR SIDE).
• IS RESISTANCE BETWEEN 1050 AND 1450 OHMS?
YES
NO
GO TO FOLLOWING PAGE OF THIS DTC CHART 2 OF 3).
• DISCONNECT CONNECTOR FROM WHEEL SPEED SENSOR.
• USING J 39200, MEASURE RESISTANCE BETWEEN TERMINAL "17" OF C212 (SPEED SENSOR SIDE) AND GROUND.
DOES DVM DISPLAY "OL" (INFINITE)?
NO
YES
REPLACE REAR WHEEL SPEED SENSOR.
MALFUNCTION WAS DUE TO POOR CONNECTION AT REAR WHEEL SPEED SENSOR.
YES
NO
REPLACE REAR WHEEL SPEED SENSOR.
REPAIR SHORT TO GROUND IN CKT 884C.

GC402940095901BX

Fig. 309 Code A023: Left Rear Wheel Speed 0 Or Unreasonable (Part 1 of 3). 1993–94 Prizm

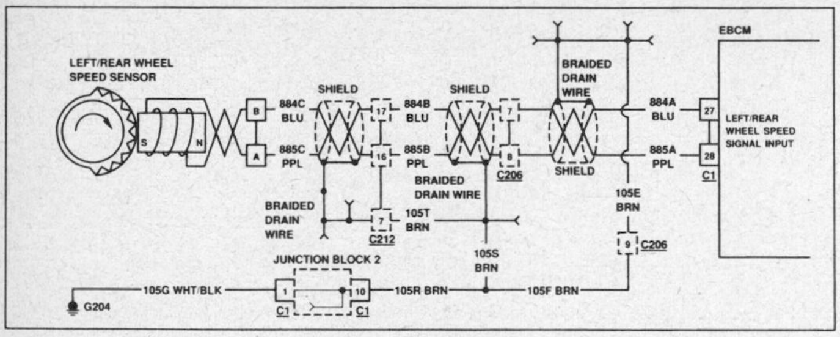
EBCM
LEFT/REAR WHEEL SPEED SENSOR
SHIELD
884C BLU
885C PPL
884B BLU
885B PPL
BRAIDED DRAIN WIRE
884A BLU
885A PPL
LEFT/REAR WHEEL SPEED SIGNAL INPUT
C206
C1
105E BRN
105T BRN
C212
JUNCTION BLOCK 2
105S BRN
105G WHT/BLK
105R BRN
105F BRN
G204

DTC A023
(Page 2 of 3)
LEFT REAR WHEEL SPEED = 0 OR UNREASONABLE

Circuit Description:

As a toothed ring passes by the wheel speed sensor, changes in the electromagnetic field cause the wheel speed sensor to produce a sinusoidal (AC) voltage signal whose frequency is proportional to wheel speed. The magnitude of this signal is directly related to wheel speed and the proximity of the wheel speed sensor to the toothed ring (often referred to as the air gap).

Failure Condition:

DTC A023 can be set when the vehicle is not in an ABS stop. If the left rear wheel speed is less than 1/2 of the vehicle's reference speed and the vehicle's reference speed is greater than 8 km/h (5 mph), a malfunction exists.

Action Taken:

A DTC A023 is stored, ABS is disabled and the "ABS" indicator is turned on.

Test Description: Number(s) below refer to circled number(s) on the diagnostic chart.

6. This step checks for proper voltages at speed sensor harness connector.
7. This test ensures that the wheel speed sensor circuitry is not internally shorted.
8. This checks for an open in CKT 884.
9. This checks for an open in CKT 885.

Diagnostic Aids:

An "intermittent" malfunction may be caused by a poor connection, rubbed through wire insulation or a wire that is broken inside the insulation.

The frequency of the malfunction can be checked by using the enhanced diagnostic function of the TECH 1.

If the customer's comments reflect that the "ABS" indicator is on only during moist environmental changes (rain, snow, vehicle wash, etc.), all wheel speed sensor circuitry should be thoroughly inspected for signs of water intrusion. Use the following procedure:

1. Spray down the suspected area with 5% salt water solution (10 ml [2 teaspoons] of salt to 355 ml [12 fl.oz.] of water).
2. Start vehicle and allow it to run for ten seconds.
3. If the DTC returns immediately, replace the suspected harness.

Any circuitry that is suspected of causing the intermittent complaint should be thoroughly checked for backed out terminals, improper mating, broken locks, improperly formed or damaged terminals, poor terminal-to-wiring connections or physical damage to the wiring harness.

When measuring wheel speed sensor resistance, ensure vehicle is at room temperature (approximately 20°C [68°F]). Wheel speed sensor resistance will vary with temperature.

When replacing a wheel speed sensor, inspect the sensor terminals and harness connector for corrosion and/or water intrusion. If evidence of corrosion or water intrusion exists, replace the wheel speed sensor.

GC402940095902AX

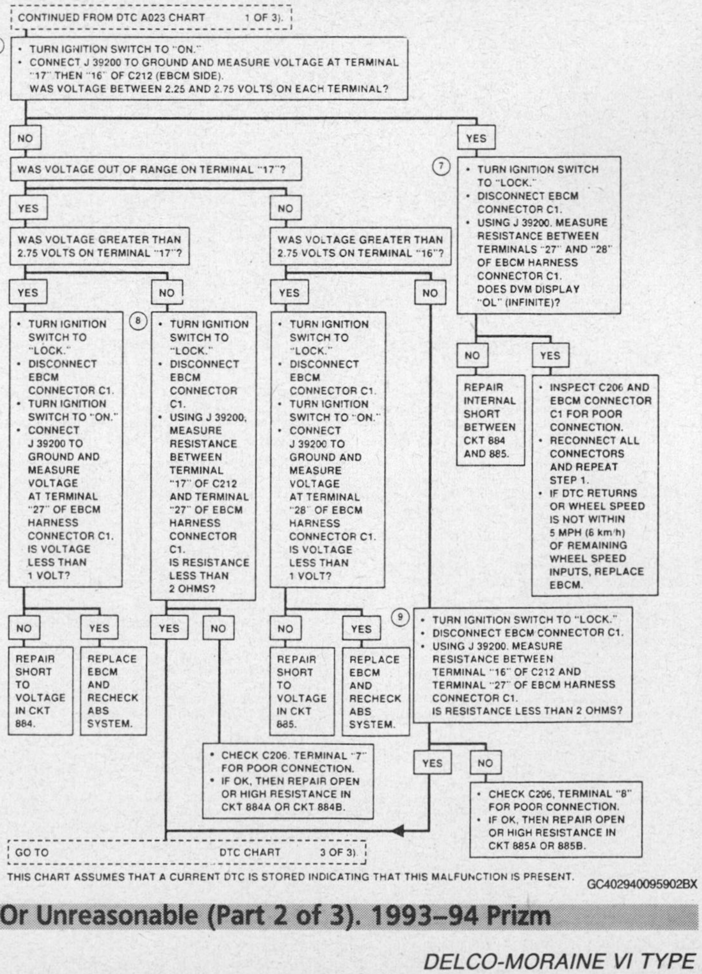
CONTINUED FROM DTC A023 CHART 1 OF 3).
6
• TURN IGNITION SWITCH TO "ON."
• CONNECT J 39200 TO GROUND AND MEASURE VOLTAGE AT TERMINAL "17" THEN "16" OF C212 (EBCM SIDE).
WAS VOLTAGE BETWEEN 2.25 AND 2.75 VOLTS ON EACH TERMINAL?
NO
YES
WAS VOLTAGE OUT OF RANGE ON TERMINAL "17"?
7
• TURN IGNITION SWITCH TO "LOCK."
• DISCONNECT EBCM CONNECTOR C1.
• USING J 39200, MEASURE RESISTANCE BETWEEN TERMINALS "27" AND "28" OF EBCM HARNESS CONNECTOR C1.
DOES DVM DISPLAY "OL" (INFINITE)?
YES
NO
WAS VOLTAGE GREATER THAN 2.75 VOLTS ON TERMINAL "17"?
WAS VOLTAGE GREATER THAN 2.75 VOLTS ON TERMINAL "16"?
YES
NO
YES
NO
• TURN IGNITION SWITCH TO "LOCK."
• DISCONNECT EBCM CONNECTOR C1.
• TURN IGNITION SWITCH TO "ON."
• CONNECT J 39200 TO GROUND AND MEASURE VOLTAGE AT TERMINAL "27" OF EBCM HARNESS CONNECTOR C1. IS VOLTAGE LESS THAN 1 VOLT?
8
• TURN IGNITION SWITCH TO "LOCK."
• DISCONNECT EBCM CONNECTOR C1.
• USING J 39200, MEASURE RESISTANCE BETWEEN TERMINAL "17" OF C212 AND TERMINAL "27" OF EBCM HARNESS CONNECTOR C1.
IS RESISTANCE LESS THAN 2 OHMS?
• TURN IGNITION SWITCH TO "LOCK."
• DISCONNECT EBCM CONNECTOR C1.
• TURN IGNITION SWITCH TO "ON."
• CONNECT J 39200 TO GROUND AND MEASURE VOLTAGE AT TERMINAL "28" OF EBCM HARNESS CONNECTOR C1. IS VOLTAGE LESS THAN 1 VOLT?
NO
YES
REPAIR INTERNAL SHORT BETWEEN CKT 884 AND 885.
• INSPECT C206 AND EBCM CONNECTOR C1 FOR POOR CONNECTION.
• RECONNECT ALL CONNECTORS AND REPEAT STEP 1.
• IF DTC RETURNS OR WHEEL SPEED IS NOT WITHIN 5 MPH (8 km/h) OF REMAINING WHEEL SPEED INPUTS, REPLACE EBCM.
NO
YES
YES
NO
NO
YES
REPAIR SHORT TO VOLTAGE IN CKT 884.
REPLACE EBCM AND RECHECK ABS SYSTEM.
REPAIR SHORT TO VOLTAGE IN CKT 885.
REPLACE EBCM AND RECHECK ABS SYSTEM.
9
• TURN IGNITION SWITCH TO "LOCK."
• DISCONNECT EBCM CONNECTOR C1.
• USING J 39200, MEASURE RESISTANCE BETWEEN TERMINAL "16" OF C212 AND TERMINAL "27" OF EBCM HARNESS CONNECTOR C1.
IS RESISTANCE LESS THAN 2 OHMS?
• CHECK C206, TERMINAL "7" FOR POOR CONNECTION.
• IF OK, THEN REPAIR OPEN OR HIGH RESISTANCE IN CKT 884A OR CKT 884B.
YES
NO
• CHECK C206, TERMINAL "8" FOR POOR CONNECTION.
• IF OK, THEN REPAIR OPEN OR HIGH RESISTANCE IN CKT 885A OR 885B.
GO TO DTC CHART 3 OF 3).

THIS CHART ASSUMES THAT A CURRENT DTC IS STORED INDICATING THAT THIS MALFUNCTION IS PRESENT.

GC402940095902BX

Fig. 309 Code A023: Left Rear Wheel Speed 0 Or Unreasonable (Part 2 of 3). 1993–94 Prizm

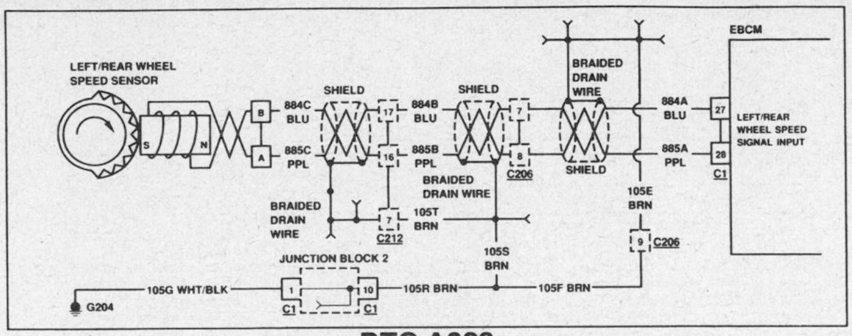

EBCM
LEFT/REAR WHEEL SPEED SENSOR
SHIELD
884C BLU
885C PPL
884B BLU
885B PPL
BRAIDED DRAIN WIRE
884A BLU
885A PPL
LEFT/REAR WHEEL SPEED SIGNAL INPUT
C206
C1
105E BRN
105T BRN
C212
JUNCTION BLOCK 2
105S BRN
105G WHT/BLK
105R BRN
105F BRN
G204

DTC A023

(Page 3 of 3)
LEFT REAR WHEEL SPEED = 0 OR UNREASONABLE

Circuit Description:

As a toothed ring passes by the wheel speed sensor, changes in the electromagnetic field cause the wheel speed sensor to produce a sinusoidal (AC) voltage signal whose frequency is proportional to wheel speed. The magnitude of this signal is directly related to wheel speed and the proximity of the wheel speed sensor to the toothed ring (often referred to as the air gap).

Failure Condition:

DTC A023 can be set when the vehicle is not in an ABS stop. If the left rear wheel speed is less than 1/2 of the vehicle's reference speed and the vehicle's reference speed is greater than 8 km/h (5 mph), a malfunction exists.

Action Taken:

A DTC A023 is stored, ABS is disabled and the "ABS" indicator is turned on.

Test Description: Number(s) below refer to circled number(s) on the diagnostic chart.

10. This checks for a short to ground in both wheel speed signal circuits.
11. This step ensures that DTC A023 was not set due to a poor connection between the EBCM and connector C1.

Diagnostic Aids:

An "intermittent" malfunction may be caused by a poor connection, rubbed through wire insulation or a wire that is broken inside the insulation.

The frequency of the malfunction can be checked by using the enhanced diagnostic function of the TECH 1.

If the customer's comments reflect that the "ABS" indicator is on only during moist environmental changes (rain, snow, vehicle wash, etc.), all wheel speed sensor circuitry should be thoroughly inspected for signs of water intrusion. Use the following procedure:

1. Spray down the suspected area with 5% salt water solution (10 ml [2 teaspoons] of salt to 355 ml [12 fl.oz.] of water).
2. Start vehicle and allow it to run for ten seconds.
3. If the DTC returns immediately, replace the suspected harness.

Any circuitry that is suspected of causing the intermittent complaint should be thoroughly checked for backed out terminals, improper mating, broken locks, improperly formed or damaged terminals, poor terminal-to wiring connections or physical damage to the wiring harness.

When measuring wheel speed sensor resistance, ensure vehicle is at room temperature (approximately 20°C [68°F]). Wheel speed sensor resistance will vary with temperature.

When replacing a wheel speed sensor, inspect the sensor terminals and harness connector for corrosion and/or water intrusion. If evidence of corrosion or water intrusion exists, replace the wheel speed sensor.

GC402940095903AY

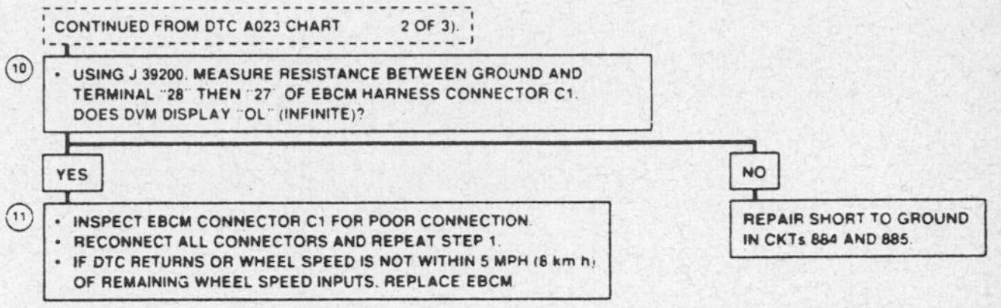

CONTINUED FROM DTC A023 CHART 2 OF 3).
10
• USING J 39200, MEASURE RESISTANCE BETWEEN GROUND AND TERMINAL "28" THEN "27" OF EBCM HARNESS CONNECTOR C1.
DOES DVM DISPLAY "OL" (INFINITE)?
YES
NO
11
• INSPECT EBCM CONNECTOR C1 FOR POOR CONNECTION.
• RECONNECT ALL CONNECTORS AND REPEAT STEP 1.
• IF DTC RETURNS OR WHEEL SPEED IS NOT WITHIN 5 MPH (8 km/h) OF REMAINING WHEEL SPEED INPUTS, REPLACE EBCM.
REPAIR SHORT TO GROUND IN CKTs 884 AND 885.

GC402940095903BX

Fig. 309 Code A023: Left Rear Wheel Speed 0 Or Unreasonable (Part 3 of 3). 1993–94 Prizm

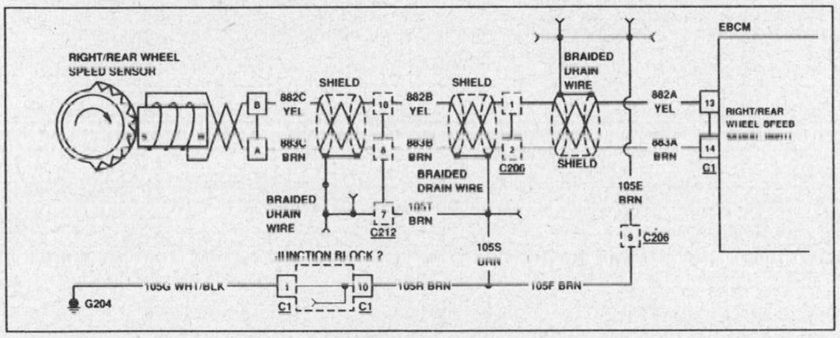

EBCM
RIGHT/REAR WHEEL SPEED SENSOR
SHIELD
882C YEL
883C BRN
882B YEL
883B BRN
BRAIDED DRAIN WIRE
882A YEL
883A BRN
C206
C1
105E BRN
105T BRN
C212
JUNCTION BLOCK 2
105S BRN
105G WHT/BLK
105R BRN
105F BRN
G204

DTC A024

(Page 1 of 3)
RIGHT REAR WHEEL SPEED = 0 OR UNREASONABLE

Circuit Description:

As a toothed ring passes by the wheel speed sensor, changes in the electromagnetic field cause the wheel speed sensor to produce a sinusoidal (AC) voltage signal whose frequency is proportional to wheel speed. The magnitude of this signal is directly related to wheel speed and the proximity of the wheel speed sensor to the toothed ring (often referred to as the air gap).

Failure Condition:

DTC A024 can be set when the vehicle is not in an ABS stop. If the right rear wheel speed is less than 1/2 of the vehicle's reference speed and the vehicle's reference speed is greater than 8 km/h (5 mph), a malfunction exists.

Action Taken:

A DTC A024 is stored, ABS is disabled and the "ABS" indicator is turned on.

Test Description: Number(s) below refer to circled number(s) on the diagnostic chart.

1. This test verifies whether the malfunction is currently present.
2. This step will identify a wheel speed sensor or circuitry that is damaged and visibly apparent.
3. This test checks wheel speed sensor for proper resistance values.
4. This test ensures the wheel speed sensor and sensor ring generate the proper voltage.
5. This step ensures the wheel speed sensor is not shorted to ground.

Diagnostic Aids:

An "intermittent" malfunction may be caused by a poor connection, rubbed through wire insulation or a wire that is broken inside the insulation.

The frequency of the malfunction can be checked by using the enhanced diagnostic function of the TECH 1.

If the customer's comments reflect that the "ABS" indicator is on only during moist environmental changes (rain, snow, vehicle wash, etc.), all wheel speed sensor circuitry should be thoroughly inspected for signs of water intrusion. Use the following procedure:

1. Spray down the suspected area with 5% salt water solution (10 ml [2 teaspoons] of salt to 355 ml [12 fl.oz.] of water).
2. Start vehicle and allow it to run for ten seconds.
3. If the DTC returns immediately, replace the suspected harness.

Any circuitry that is suspected of causing the intermittent complaint should be thoroughly checked for backed out terminals, improper mating, broken locks, improperly formed or damaged terminals, poor terminal-to-wiring connections or physical damage to the wiring harness.

When measuring wheel speed sensor resistance, ensure vehicle is at room temperature (approximately 20°C [68°F]). Wheel speed sensor resistance will vary with temperature.

When replacing a wheel speed sensor, inspect the sensor terminals and harness connector for corrosion and/or water intrusion. If evidence of corrosion or water intrusion exists, replace the wheel speed sensor.

GC402940096001AX

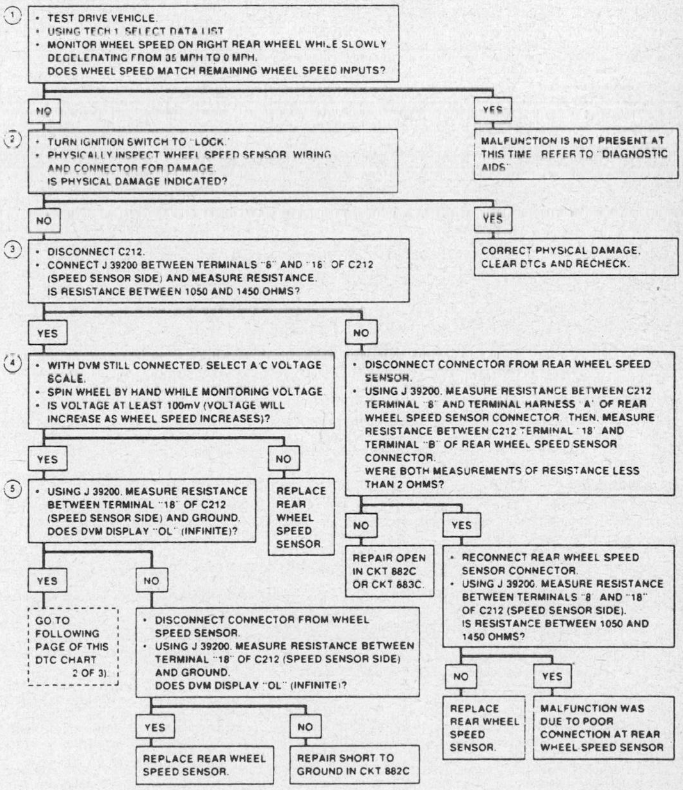

1
• TEST DRIVE VEHICLE.
• USING TECH 1, SELECT DATA LIST.
• MONITOR WHEEL SPEED ON RIGHT REAR WHEEL WHILE SLOWLY DECELERATING FROM 35 MPH TO 0 MPH.
DOES WHEEL SPEED MATCH REMAINING WHEEL SPEED INPUTS?
NO
YES
MALFUNCTION IS NOT PRESENT AT THIS TIME. REFER TO "DIAGNOSTIC AIDS"
2
• TURN IGNITION SWITCH TO "LOCK."
• PHYSICALLY INSPECT WHEEL SPEED SENSOR, WIRING AND CONNECTOR FOR DAMAGE.
IS PHYSICAL DAMAGE INDICATED?
NO
YES
CORRECT PHYSICAL DAMAGE. CLEAR DTCs AND RECHECK.
3
• DISCONNECT C212.
• CONNECT J 39200 BETWEEN TERMINALS "8" AND "18" OF C212 (SPEED SENSOR SIDE) AND MEASURE RESISTANCE.
IS RESISTANCE BETWEEN 1050 AND 1450 OHMS?
YES
NO
4
• WITH DVM STILL CONNECTED, SELECT A/C VOLTAGE SCALE.
• SPIN WHEEL BY HAND WHILE MONITORING VOLTAGE.
• IS VOLTAGE AT LEAST 100mV (VOLTAGE WILL INCREASE AS WHEEL SPEED INCREASES)?
• DISCONNECT CONNECTOR FROM REAR WHEEL SPEED SENSOR.
• USING J 39200, MEASURE RESISTANCE BETWEEN C212 TERMINAL "8" AND TERMINAL HARNESS "A" OF REAR WHEEL SPEED SENSOR CONNECTOR. THEN, MEASURE RESISTANCE BETWEEN C212 TERMINAL "18" AND TERMINAL "B" OF REAR WHEEL SPEED SENSOR CONNECTOR.
WERE BOTH MEASUREMENTS OF RESISTANCE LESS THAN 2 OHMS?
YES
NO
5
• USING J 39200, MEASURE RESISTANCE BETWEEN TERMINAL "18" OF C212 (SPEED SENSOR SIDE) AND GROUND.
DOES DVM DISPLAY "OL" (INFINITE)?
REPLACE REAR WHEEL SPEED SENSOR
NO
YES
REPAIR OPEN IN CKT 882C OR CKT 883C.
• RECONNECT REAR WHEEL SPEED SENSOR CONNECTOR.
• USING J 39200, MEASURE RESISTANCE BETWEEN TERMINALS "8" AND "18" OF C212 (SPEED SENSOR SIDE).
IS RESISTANCE BETWEEN 1050 AND 1450 OHMS?
YES
NO
GO TO FOLLOWING PAGE OF THIS DTC CHART 2 OF 3).
• DISCONNECT CONNECTOR FROM WHEEL SPEED SENSOR.
• USING J 39200, MEASURE RESISTANCE BETWEEN TERMINAL "18" OF C212 (SPEED SENSOR SIDE) AND GROUND.
DOES DVM DISPLAY "OL" (INFINITE)?
NO
YES
REPLACE REAR WHEEL SPEED SENSOR.
MALFUNCTION WAS DUE TO POOR CONNECTION AT REAR WHEEL SPEED SENSOR
YES
NO
REPLACE REAR WHEEL SPEED SENSOR.
REPAIR SHORT TO GROUND IN CKT 882C

GC402940096001BX

Fig. 310 Code A024: Right Rear Wheel Speed 0 Or Unreasonable (Part 1 of 3). 1993–94 Prizm

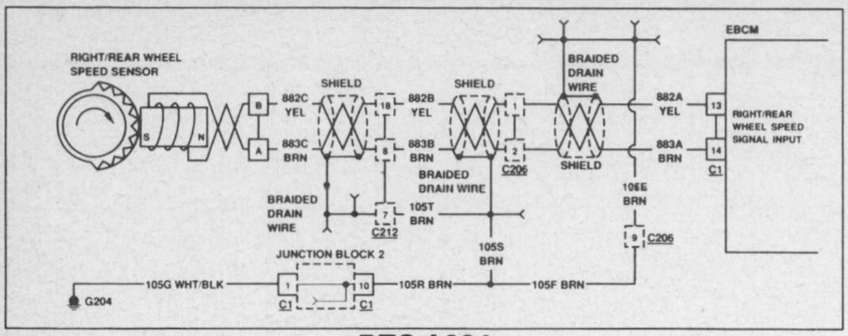

EBCM
RIGHT/REAR WHEEL SPEED SENSOR
SHIELD
SHIELD
BRAIDED DRAIN WIRE
882C YEL
883C BRN
882B YEL
883B BRN
882A YEL
883A BRN
RIGHT/REAR WHEEL SPEED SIGNAL INPUT
BRAIDED DRAIN WIRE
BRAIDED DRAIN WIRE
SHIELD
C206
C212
105T BRN
105E BRN
105S BRN
C206
JUNCTION BLOCK 2
105G WHT/BLK
105R BRN
105F BRN
C1
G204

DTC A024

(Page 2 of 3)

RIGHT REAR WHEEL SPEED = 0 OR UNREASONABLE

Circuit Description:

As a toothed ring passes by the wheel speed sensor, changes in the electromagnetic field cause the wheel speed sensor to produce a sinusoidal (AC) voltage signal whose frequency is proportional to wheel speed. The magnitude of this signal is directly related to wheel speed and the proximity of the wheel speed sensor to the toothed ring (often referred to as the air gap).

Failure Condition:

DTC A024 can be set when the vehicle is not in an ABS stop. If the right rear wheel speed is less than 1/2 of the vehicle's reference speed and the vehicle's reference speed is greater than 8 km/h (5 mph), a malfunction exists.

Action Taken:

A DTC A024 is stored. ABS is disabled and the "ABS" indicator is turned on.

Test Description: Number(s) below refer to circled number(s) on the diagnostic chart.

6. This step checks for proper voltages at speed sensor harness connector.
7. This test ensures that the wheel speed sensor circuitry is not internally shorted.
8. This checks for an open in CKT 882.
9. This checks for an open in CKT 883.

Diagnostic Aids:

An "intermittent" malfunction may be caused by a poor connection, rubbed through wire insulation or a wire that is broken inside the insulation.

The frequency of the malfunction can be checked by using the enhanced diagnostic function of the TECH 1.

If the customer's comments reflect that the "ABS" indicator is on only during moist environmental changes (rain, snow, vehicle wash, etc.), all wheel speed sensor circuitry should be thoroughly inspected for signs of water intrusion. Use the following procedure:

1. Spray down the suspected area with 5% salt water solution (10 ml [2 teaspoons] of salt to 355 ml [12 fl.oz.] of water).
2. Start vehicle and allow it to run for ten seconds.
3. If the DTC returns immediately, replace the suspected harness.

Any circuitry that is suspected of causing the intermittent complaint should be thoroughly checked for backed out terminals, improper mating, broken locks, improperly formed or damaged terminals, poor terminal-to-wiring connections or physical damage to the wiring harness.

When measuring wheel speed sensor resistance, ensure vehicle is at room temperature (approximately 20°C [68°F]). Wheel speed sensor resistance will vary with temperature.

When replacing a wheel speed sensor, inspect the sensor terminals and harness connector for corrosion and/or water intrusion. If evidence of corrosion or water intrusion exists, replace the wheel speed sensor.

GC402940096002AX

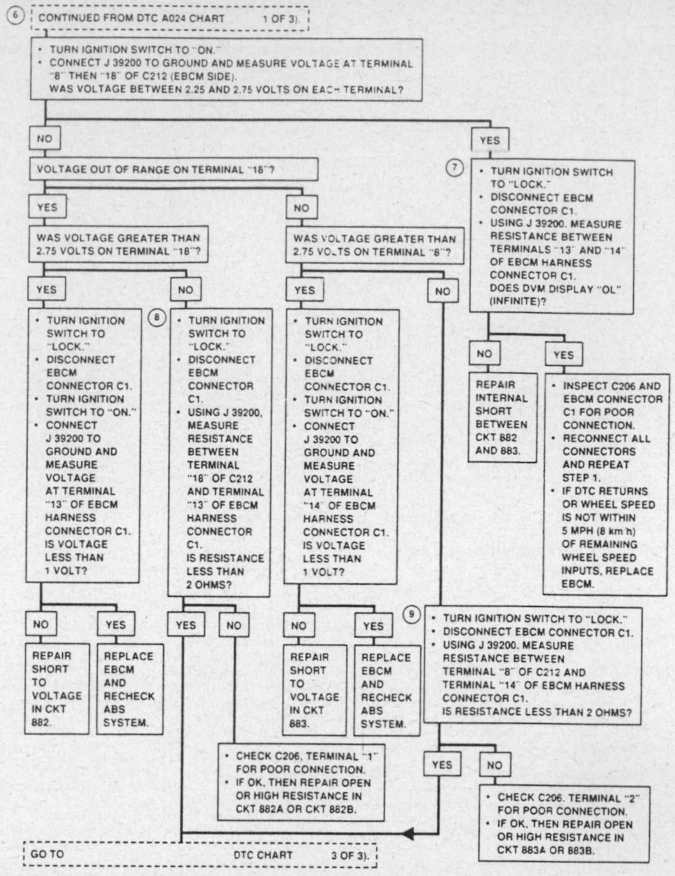

6 CONTINUED FROM DTC A024 CHART (1 OF 3).
• TURN IGNITION SWITCH TO "ON."
• CONNECT J 39200 TO GROUND AND MEASURE VOLTAGE AT TERMINAL "8" THEN "18" OF C212 (EBCM SIDE).
WAS VOLTAGE BETWEEN 2.25 AND 2.75 VOLTS ON EACH TERMINAL?
NO
YES
VOLTAGE OUT OF RANGE ON TERMINAL "18"?
7 • TURN IGNITION SWITCH TO "LOCK." • DISCONNECT EBCM CONNECTOR C1. • USING J 39200, MEASURE RESISTANCE BETWEEN TERMINALS "13" AND "14" OF EBCM HARNESS CONNECTOR C1. DOES DVM DISPLAY "OL" (INFINITE)?
YES
NO
WAS VOLTAGE GREATER THAN 2.75 VOLTS ON TERMINAL "18"?
WAS VOLTAGE GREATER THAN 2.75 VOLTS ON TERMINAL "8"?
YES
NO
YES
NO
• TURN IGNITION SWITCH TO "LOCK." • DISCONNECT EBCM CONNECTOR C1. • TURN IGNITION SWITCH TO "ON." • CONNECT J 39200 TO GROUND AND MEASURE VOLTAGE AT TERMINAL "13" OF EBCM HARNESS CONNECTOR C1. IS VOLTAGE LESS THAN 1 VOLT?
8 • TURN IGNITION SWITCH TO "LOCK." • DISCONNECT EBCM CONNECTOR C1. • USING J 39200, MEASURE RESISTANCE BETWEEN TERMINAL "16" OF C212 AND TERMINAL "13" OF EBCM HARNESS CONNECTOR C1. IS RESISTANCE LESS THAN 2 OHMS?
• TURN IGNITION SWITCH TO "LOCK." • DISCONNECT EBCM CONNECTOR C1. • TURN IGNITION SWITCH TO "ON." • CONNECT J 39200 TO GROUND AND MEASURE VOLTAGE AT TERMINAL "14" OF EBCM HARNESS CONNECTOR C1. IS VOLTAGE LESS THAN 1 VOLT?
NO
YES
REPAIR INTERNAL SHORT BETWEEN CKT 882 AND 883.
• INSPECT C206 AND EBCM CONNECTOR C1 FOR POOR CONNECTION. • RECONNECT ALL CONNECTORS AND REPEAT STEP 1. • IF DTC RETURNS OR WHEEL SPEED IS NOT WITHIN 5 MPH (8 km/h) OF REMAINING WHEEL SPEED INPUTS, REPLACE EBCM.
NO
YES
YES
NO
NO
YES
9
REPAIR SHORT TO VOLTAGE IN CKT 882.
REPLACE EBCM AND RECHECK ABS SYSTEM.
REPAIR SHORT TO VOLTAGE IN CKT 883.
REPLACE EBCM AND RECHECK ABS SYSTEM.
• TURN IGNITION SWITCH TO "LOCK." • DISCONNECT EBCM CONNECTOR C1. • USING J 39200, MEASURE RESISTANCE BETWEEN TERMINAL "8" OF C212 AND TERMINAL "14" OF EBCM HARNESS CONNECTOR C1. IS RESISTANCE LESS THAN 2 OHMS?
• CHECK C206, TERMINAL "1" FOR POOR CONNECTION. • IF OK, THEN REPAIR OPEN OR HIGH RESISTANCE IN CKT 882A OR CKT 882B.
YES
NO
• CHECK C206, TERMINAL "2" FOR POOR CONNECTION. • IF OK, THEN REPAIR OPEN OR HIGH RESISTANCE IN CKT 883A OR 883B.
GO TO DTC CHART (3 OF 3).

GC402940096002BX

Fig. 310 Code A024: Right Rear Wheel Speed 0 Or Unreasonable (Part 2 of 3). 1993–94 Prizm

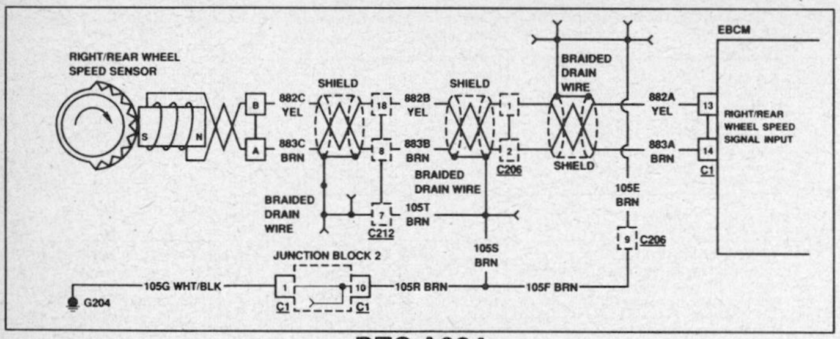

EBCM
RIGHT/REAR WHEEL SPEED SENSOR
SHIELD
SHIELD
BRAIDED DRAIN WIRE
882C YEL
883C BRN
882B YEL
883B BRN
882A YEL
883A BRN
RIGHT/REAR WHEEL SPEED SIGNAL INPUT
BRAIDED DRAIN WIRE
BRAIDED DRAIN WIRE
SHIELD
C206
C212
105T BRN
105E BRN
105S BRN
C206
JUNCTION BLOCK 2
105G WHT/BLK
105R BRN
105F BRN
C1
G204

DTC A024

(Page 3 of 3)

RIGHT REAR WHEEL SPEED = 0 OR UNREASONALBE

Circuit Description:

As a toothed ring passes by the wheel speed sensor, changes in the electromagnetic field cause the wheel speed sensor to produce a sinusoidal (AC) voltage signal whose frequency is proportional to wheel speed. The magnitude of this signal is directly related to wheel speed and the proximity of the wheel speed sensor to the toothed ring (often referred to as the air gap).

Failure Condition:

DTC A024 can be set when the vehicle is not in an ABS stop. If the right rear wheel speed is less than 1/2 of the vehicle's reference speed and the vehicle's reference speed is greater than 8 km/h (5 mph), a malfunction exists.

Action Taken:

A DTC A024 is stored. ABS is disabled and the "ABS" indicator is turned on.

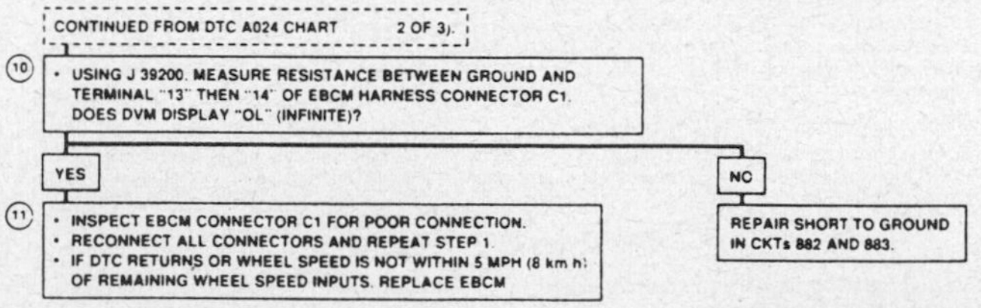

CONTINUED FROM DTC A024 CHART (2 OF 3).
10 • USING J 39200, MEASURE RESISTANCE BETWEEN GROUND AND TERMINAL "13" THEN "14" OF EBCM HARNESS CONNECTOR C1. DOES DVM DISPLAY "OL" (INFINITE)?
YES
NO
11 • INSPECT EBCM CONNECTOR C1 FOR POOR CONNECTION. • RECONNECT ALL CONNECTORS AND REPEAT STEP 1. • IF DTC RETURNS OR WHEEL SPEED IS NOT WITHIN 5 MPH (8 km/h) OF REMAINING WHEEL SPEED INPUTS, REPLACE EBCM
REPAIR SHORT TO GROUND IN CKTs 882 AND 883.

GC402940096003BX

Test Description: Number(s) below refer to circled number(s) on the diagnostic chart.

10. This checks for a short to ground in both wheel speed signal circuits.
11. This step ensures that DTC A024 was not set due to a poor connection between the EBCM and connector C1.

Diagnostic Aids:

An "intermittent" malfunction may be caused by a poor connection, rubbed through wire insulation or a wire that is broken inside the insulation.

The frequency of the malfunction can be checked by using the enhanced diagnostic function of the TECH 1.

If the customer's comments reflect that the "ABS" indicator is on only during moist environmental changes (rain, snow, vehicle wash, etc.), all wheel speed sensor circuitry should be thoroughly inspected for signs of water intrusion. Use the following procedure:

1. Spray down the suspected area with 5% salt water solution (10 ml [2 teaspoons] of salt to 355 ml [12 fl.oz.] of water).
2. Start vehicle and allow it to run for ten seconds.
3. If the DTC returns immediately, replace the suspected harness.

Any circuitry that is suspected of causing the intermittent complaint should be thoroughly checked for backed out terminals, improper mating, broken locks, improperly formed or damaged terminals, poor terminal-to-wiring connections or physical damage to the wiring harness.

When measuring wheel speed sensor resistance, ensure vehicle is at room temperature (approximately 20°C [68°F]). Wheel speed sensor resistance will vary with temperature.

When replacing a wheel speed sensor, inspect the sensor terminals and harness connector for corrosion and/or water intrusion. If evidence of corrosion or water intrusion exists, replace the wheel speed sensor.

GC402940096003AX

Fig. 310 Code A024: Right Rear Wheel Speed 0 Or Unreasonable (Part 3 of 3). 1993–94 Prizm

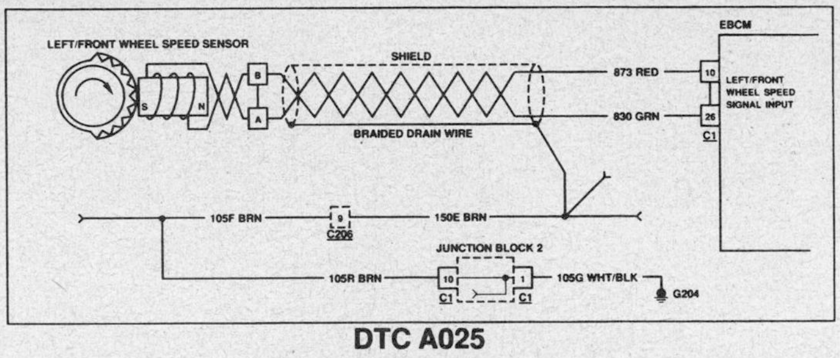

EBCM
LEFT/FRONT WHEEL SPEED SENSOR
SHIELD
873 RED
830 GRN
LEFT/FRONT WHEEL SPEED SIGNAL INPUT
BRAIDED DRAIN WIRE
105F BRN
C206
150E BRN
JUNCTION BLOCK 2
105R BRN
105G WHT/BLK
G204

DTC A025

(Page 1 of 3)

LEFT FRONT EXCESSIVE WHEEL SPEED VARIATION

Circuit Description:

As a toothed ring passes by the wheel speed sensor, changes in the electromagnetic field cause the wheel speed sensor to produce a sinusoidal (AC) voltage signal whose frequency is proportional to wheel speed. The magnitude of this signal is directly related to wheel speed and the proximity of the wheel speed sensor to the toothed ring (often referred to as the air gap).

Failure Condition:

DTC A025 can be set when the brake is off. The purpose of this test is to detect a situation in which the left front wheel acceleration or deceleration is beyond specified limits.

Action Taken:

A DTC A025 is stored, ABS is disabled and the "ABS" indicator is turned on.

Test Description: Number(s) below refer to circled number(s) on the diagnostic chart.

1. This test verifies whether the malfunction is currently present.
2. This test checks to see if excessive wheel bearing end play caused the DTC.
3. This step will identify a wheel speed sensor or circuitry that is damaged and visibly apparent.
4. This test checks wheel speed sensor for proper resistance values.
5. This test ensures the wheel speed sensor and sensor ring generate the proper voltage.
6. This step ensures the wheel speed sensor is not shorted to ground.

Diagnostic Aids:

An "intermittent" malfunction may be caused by a poor connection, rubbed through wire insulation or a wire that is broken inside the insulation.

The frequency of the malfunction can be checked by using the enhanced diagnostic function of the TECH 1.

If the customer's comments reflect that the "ABS" indicator is on only during moist environmental changes (rain, snow, vehicle wash, etc.), all wheel speed sensor circuitry should be thoroughly inspected for signs of water intrusion. Use the following procedure:

1. Spray down the suspected area with 5% salt water solution (10 ml [2 teaspoons] of salt to 355 ml [12 fl.oz.] of water).
2. Start vehicle and allow it to run for ten seconds.
3. If the DTC returns immediately, replace the suspected harness.

Any circuitry that is suspected of causing the intermittent complaint should be thoroughly checked for backed out terminals, improper mating, broken locks, improperly formed or damaged terminals, poor terminal-to-wiring connections or physical damage to the wiring harness.

When measuring wheel speed sensor resistance, ensure vehicle is at room temperature (approximately 20°C [68°F]). Wheel speed sensor resistance will vary with temperature.

When replacing a wheel speed sensor, inspect the sensor terminals and harness connector for corrosion and/or water intrusion. If evidence of corrosion or water intrusion exists, replace the wheel speed sensor.

GC402940096101AX

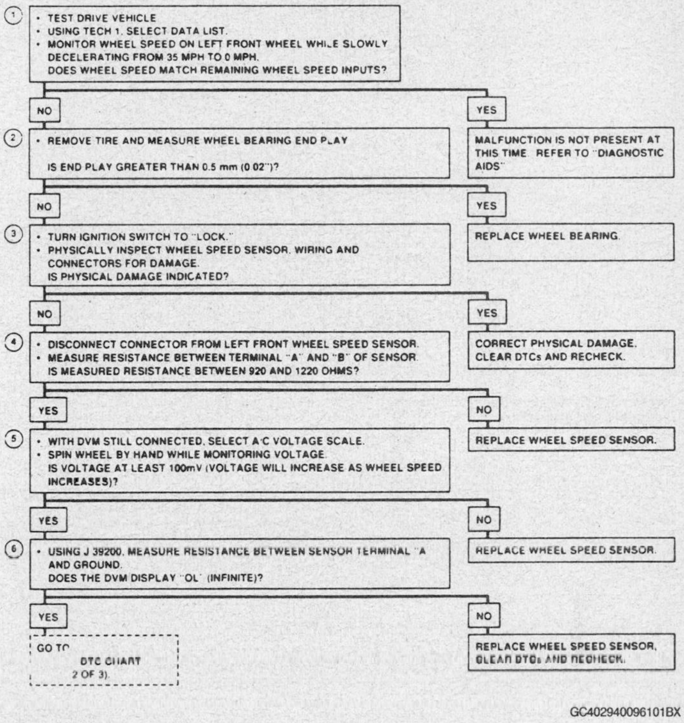

1 • TEST DRIVE VEHICLE
• USING TECH 1, SELECT DATA LIST.
• MONITOR WHEEL SPEED ON LEFT FRONT WHEEL WHILE SLOWLY DECELERATING FROM 35 MPH TO 0 MPH.
DOES WHEEL SPEED MATCH REMAINING WHEEL SPEED INPUTS?
NO
YES
MALFUNCTION IS NOT PRESENT AT THIS TIME. REFER TO "DIAGNOSTIC AIDS"
2 • REMOVE TIRE AND MEASURE WHEEL BEARING END PLAY
IS END PLAY GREATER THAN 0.5 mm (0.02")?
NO
YES
REPLACE WHEEL BEARING.
3 • TURN IGNITION SWITCH TO "LOCK."
• PHYSICALLY INSPECT WHEEL SPEED SENSOR, WIRING AND CONNECTORS FOR DAMAGE.
IS PHYSICAL DAMAGE INDICATED?
NO
YES
CORRECT PHYSICAL DAMAGE. CLEAR DTCs AND RECHECK.
4 • DISCONNECT CONNECTOR FROM LEFT FRONT WHEEL SPEED SENSOR.
• MEASURE RESISTANCE BETWEEN TERMINAL "A" AND "B" OF SENSOR.
IS MEASURED RESISTANCE BETWEEN 920 AND 1220 OHMS?
YES
NO
REPLACE WHEEL SPEED SENSOR.
5 • WITH DVM STILL CONNECTED, SELECT A/C VOLTAGE SCALE.
• SPIN WHEEL BY HAND WHILE MONITORING VOLTAGE.
IS VOLTAGE AT LEAST 100mV (VOLTAGE WILL INCREASE AS WHEEL SPEED INCREASES)?
YES
NO
REPLACE WHEEL SPEED SENSOR.
6 • USING J 39200, MEASURE RESISTANCE BETWEEN SENSOR TERMINAL "A" AND GROUND.
DOES THE DVM DISPLAY "OL" (INFINITE)?
YES
NO
GO TO DTC CHART 2 OF 3).
REPLACE WHEEL SPEED SENSOR, CLEAR DTCs AND RECHECK.
GC402940096101BX

Fig. 311 Code A025: Left Front Wheel Excessive Wheel Speed Variation (Part 1 of 3). 1993–94 Prizm

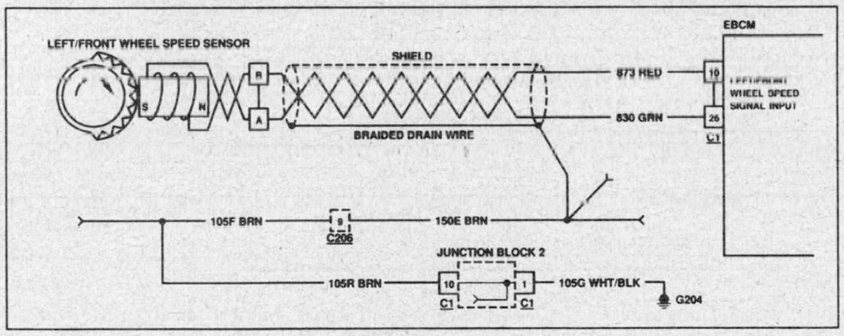

EBCM
LEFT/FRONT WHEEL SPEED SENSOR
SHIELD
873 RED
830 GRN
WHEEL SPEED SIGNAL INPUT
BRAIDED DRAIN WIRE
105F BRN
C206
150E BRN
JUNCTION BLOCK 2
105R BRN
105G WHT/BLK
G204

DTC A025

(Page 2 of 3)

LEFT FRONT EXCESSIVE WHEEL SPEED VARIATION

Circuit Description:

As a toothed ring passes by the wheel speed sensor, changes in the electromagnetic field cause the wheel speed sensor to produce a sinusoidal (AC) voltage signal whose frequency is proportional to wheel speed. The magnitude of this signal is directly related to wheel speed and the proximity of the wheel speed sensor to the toothed ring (often referred to as the air gap).

Failure Condition:

DTC A025 can be set when the brake is off. The purpose of this test is to detect a situation in which the left front wheel acceleration or deceleration is beyond specified limits.

Action Taken:

A DTC A025 is stored, ABS is disabled and the "ABS" indicator is turned on.

Test Description: Number(s) below refer to circled number(s) on the diagnostic chart.

7. This step checks for proper voltages at speed sensor harness connector.
8. This test ensures that the wheel speed sensor circuitry is not internally shorted.
9. This checks for an open in CKT 873.
10. This checks for an open in CKT 830.

Diagnostic Aids:

An "intermittent" malfunction may be caused by a poor connection, rubbed through wire insulation or a wire that is broken inside the insulation.

The frequency of the malfunction can be checked by using the enhanced diagnostic function of the TECH 1.

If the customer's comments reflect that the "ABS" indicator is on only during moist environmental changes (rain, snow, vehicle wash, etc.), all wheel speed sensor circuitry should be thoroughly inspected for signs of water intrusion. Use the following procedure:

1. Spray down the suspected area with 5% salt water solution (10 ml [2 teaspoons] of salt to 355 ml [12 fl.oz.] of water).
2. Start vehicle and allow it to run for ten seconds.
3. If the DTC returns immediately, replace the suspected harness.

Any circuitry that is suspected of causing the intermittent complaint should be thoroughly checked for backed out terminals, improper mating, broken locks, improperly formed or damaged terminals, poor terminal-to-wiring connections or physical damage to the wiring harness.

When measuring wheel speed sensor resistance, ensure vehicle is at room temperature (approximately 20°C [68°F]). Wheel speed sensor resistance will vary with temperature.

When replacing a wheel speed sensor, inspect the sensor terminals and harness connector for corrosion and/or water intrusion. If evidence of corrosion or water intrusion exists, replace the wheel speed sensor.

GC402940096102AX

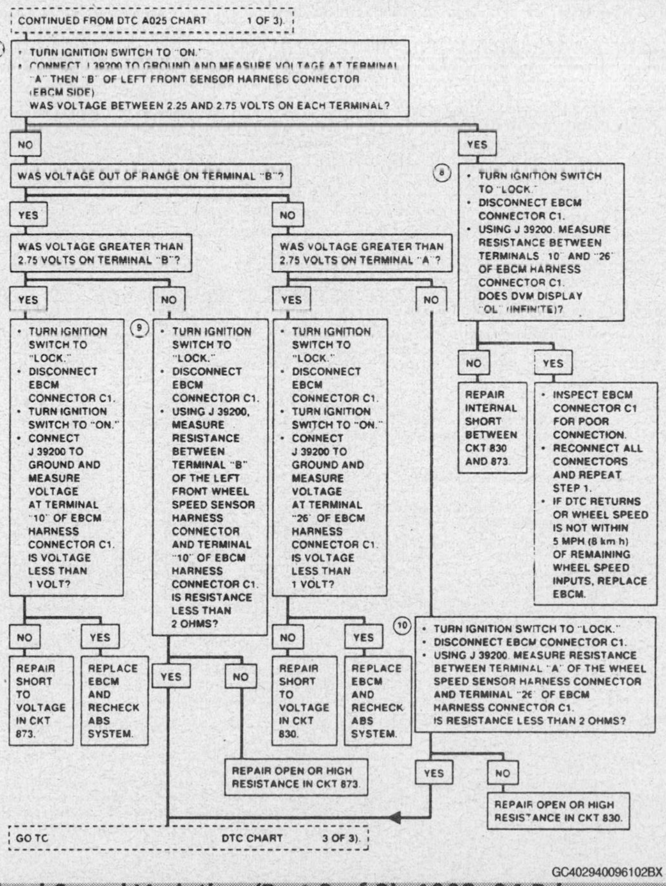

CONTINUED FROM DTC A025 CHART 1 OF 3).
7 • TURN IGNITION SWITCH TO "ON."
• CONNECT J 39200 TO GROUND AND MEASURE VOLTAGE AT TERMINAL "A" THEN "B" OF LEFT FRONT SENSOR HARNESS CONNECTOR (EBCM SIDE).
WAS VOLTAGE BETWEEN 2.25 AND 2.75 VOLTS ON EACH TERMINAL?
NO
YES
WAS VOLTAGE OUT OF RANGE ON TERMINAL "B"?
8 • TURN IGNITION SWITCH TO "LOCK."
• DISCONNECT EBCM CONNECTOR C1.
• USING J 39200, MEASURE RESISTANCE BETWEEN TERMINALS "10" AND "26" OF EBCM HARNESS CONNECTOR C1.
DOES DVM DISPLAY "OL" (INFINITE)?
YES
NO
WAS VOLTAGE GREATER THAN 2.75 VOLTS ON TERMINAL "B"?
WAS VOLTAGE GREATER THAN 2.75 VOLTS ON TERMINAL "A"?
YES
NO
YES
NO
• TURN IGNITION SWITCH TO "LOCK."
• DISCONNECT EBCM CONNECTOR C1.
• TURN IGNITION SWITCH TO "ON."
• CONNECT J 39200 TO GROUND AND MEASURE VOLTAGE AT TERMINAL "10" OF EBCM HARNESS CONNECTOR C1.
IS VOLTAGE LESS THAN 1 VOLT?
9 • TURN IGNITION SWITCH TO "LOCK."
• DISCONNECT EBCM CONNECTOR C1.
• USING J 39200, MEASURE RESISTANCE BETWEEN TERMINAL "B" OF THE LEFT FRONT WHEEL SPEED SENSOR HARNESS CONNECTOR AND TERMINAL "10" OF EBCM HARNESS CONNECTOR C1.
IS RESISTANCE LESS THAN 2 OHMS?
• TURN IGNITION SWITCH TO "LOCK."
• DISCONNECT EBCM CONNECTOR C1.
• TURN IGNITION SWITCH TO "ON."
• CONNECT J 39200 TO GROUND AND MEASURE VOLTAGE AT TERMINAL "26" OF EBCM HARNESS CONNECTOR C1.
IS VOLTAGE LESS THAN 1 VOLT?
NO
YES
REPAIR INTERNAL SHORT BETWEEN CKT 830 AND 873.
• INSPECT EBCM CONNECTOR C1 FOR POOR CONNECTION.
• RECONNECT ALL CONNECTORS AND REPEAT STEP 1.
• IF DTC RETURNS OR WHEEL SPEED IS NOT WITHIN 5 MPH (8 km h) OF REMAINING WHEEL SPEED INPUTS, REPLACE EBCM.
NO
YES
NO
YES
REPAIR SHORT TO VOLTAGE IN CKT 873.
REPLACE EBCM AND RECHECK ABS SYSTEM.
YES
NO
REPAIR SHORT TO VOLTAGE IN CKT 830.
REPLACE EBCM AND RECHECK ABS SYSTEM.
10 • TURN IGNITION SWITCH TO "LOCK."
• DISCONNECT EBCM CONNECTOR C1.
• USING J 39200, MEASURE RESISTANCE BETWEEN TERMINAL "A" OF THE WHEEL SPEED SENSOR HARNESS CONNECTOR AND TERMINAL "26" OF EBCM HARNESS CONNECTOR C1.
IS RESISTANCE LESS THAN 2 OHMS?
REPAIR OPEN OR HIGH RESISTANCE IN CKT 873.
YES
NO
REPAIR OPEN OR HIGH RESISTANCE IN CKT 830.
GO TO DTC CHART 3 OF 3).
GC402940096102BX

Fig. 311 Code A025: Left Front Wheel Excessive Wheel Speed Variation (Part 2 of 3). 1993–94 Prizm

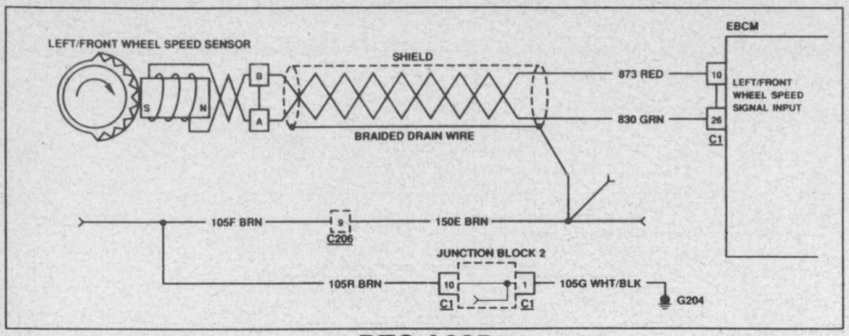
EBCM
LEFT/FRONT WHEEL SPEED SENSOR
SHIELD
873 RED
830 GRN
LEFT/FRONT WHEEL SPEED SIGNAL INPUT
BRAIDED DRAIN WIRE
C1
105F BRN
150E BRN
C206
JUNCTION BLOCK 2
105R BRN
105G WHT/BLK
G204

DTC A025
(Page 3 of 3)
LEFT FRONT EXCESSIVE WHEEL SPEED VARIATION

Circuit Description:

As a toothed ring passes by the wheel speed sensor, changes in the electromagnetic field cause the wheel speed sensor to produce a sinusoidal (AC) voltage signal whose frequency is proportional to wheel speed. The magnitude of this signal is directly related to wheel speed and the proximity of the wheel speed sensor to the toothed ring (often referred to as the air gap).

Failure Condition:

DTC A025 can be set when the brake is off. The purpose of this test is to detect a situation in which the left front wheel acceleration or deceleration is beyond specified limits.

Action Taken:

A DTC A025 is stored, ABS is disabled and the "ABS" indicator is turned on.

Test Description: Number(s) below refer to circled number(s) on the diagnostic chart.

11. This test checks for a short to ground in both wheel speed signal circuits.
12. This step ensures that DTC A025 was not set due to a poor connection between the EBCM connector C1 and the EBCM.

Diagnostic Aids:

An "intermittent" malfunction may be caused by a poor connection, rubbed through wire insulation or a wire that is broken inside the insulation.

The frequency of the malfunction can be checked by using the enhanced diagnostic function of the TECH 1.

If the customer's comments reflect that the "ABS" indicator is on only during moist environmental changes (rain, snow, vehicle wash, etc.), all wheel speed sensor circuitry should be thoroughly inspected for signs of water intrusion. Use the following procedure:

1. Spray down the suspected area with 5% salt water solution (10 ml [2 teaspoons] of salt to 355 ml [12 fl.oz.] of water).
2. Start vehicle and allow it to run for ten seconds.
3. If the DTC returns immediately, replace the suspected harness.

Any circuitry that is suspected of causing the intermittent complaint should be thoroughly checked for backed out terminals, improper mating, broken locks, improperly formed or damaged terminals, poor terminal-to-wiring connections or physical damage to the wiring harness.

When measuring wheel speed sensor resistance, ensure vehicle is at room temperature (approximately 20°C [68°F]). Wheel speed sensor resistance will vary with temperature.

When replacing a wheel speed sensor, inspect the sensor terminals and harness connector for corrosion and/or water intrusion. If evidence of corrosion or water intrusion exists, replace the wheel speed sensor.

GC402940096103AX

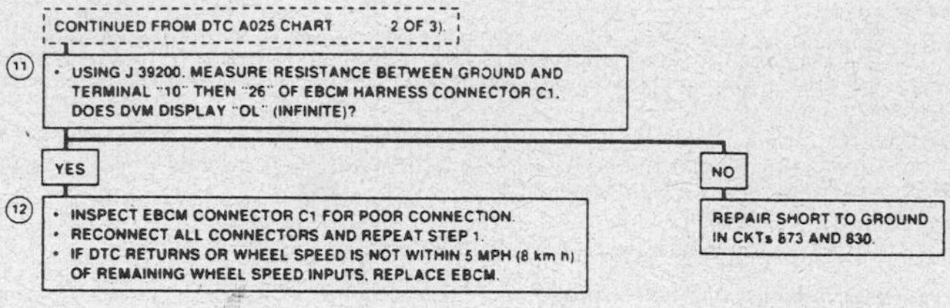
CONTINUED FROM DTC A025 CHART (2 OF 3).
11
• USING J 39200, MEASURE RESISTANCE BETWEEN GROUND AND TERMINAL "10" THEN "26" OF EBCM HARNESS CONNECTOR C1. DOES DVM DISPLAY "OL" (INFINITE)?
YES
NO
12
• INSPECT EBCM CONNECTOR C1 FOR POOR CONNECTION.
• RECONNECT ALL CONNECTORS AND REPEAT STEP 1.
• IF DTC RETURNS OR WHEEL SPEED IS NOT WITHIN 5 MPH (8 km/h) OF REMAINING WHEEL SPEED INPUTS, REPLACE EBCM.
REPAIR SHORT TO GROUND IN CKTs 873 AND 830.

GC402940096103BX

Fig. 311 Code A025: Left Front Wheel Excessive Wheel Speed Variation (Part 3 of 3). 1993–94 Prizm

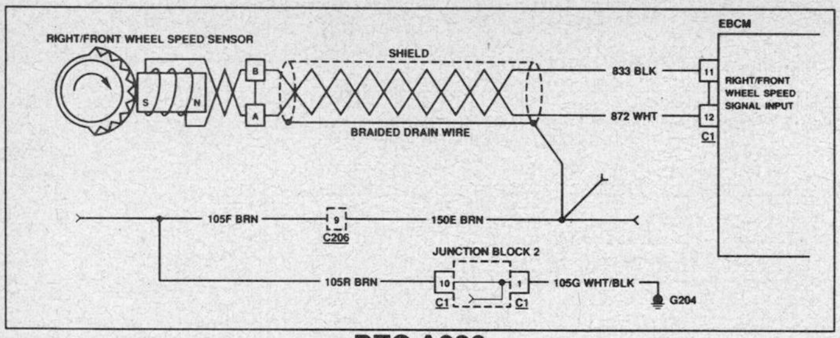
EBCM
RIGHT/FRONT WHEEL SPEED SENSOR
SHIELD
833 BLK
872 WHT
RIGHT/FRONT WHEEL SPEED SIGNAL INPUT
BRAIDED DRAIN WIRE
C1
105F BRN
150E BRN
C206
JUNCTION BLOCK 2
105R BRN
105G WHT/BLK
G204

DTC A026
(Page 1 of 3)
RIGHT FRONT EXCESSIVE WHEEL SPEED VARIATION

Circuit Description:

As a toothed ring passes by the wheel speed sensor, changes in the electromagnetic field cause the wheel speed sensor to produce a sinusoidal (AC) voltage signal whose frequency is proportional to wheel speed. The magnitude of this signal is directly related to wheel speed and the proximity of the wheel speed sensor to the toothed ring (often referred to as the air gap).

Failure Condition:

DTC A026 can be set when the brake is off. The purpose of this test is to detect a situation in which the right front wheel acceleration or deceleration is beyond specified limits.

Action Taken:

A DTC A026 is stored, ABS is disabled and the "ABS" indicator is turned on.

Test Description: Number(s) below refer to circled number(s) on the diagnostic chart.

1. This test verifies whether the malfunction is currently present.
2. This test checks to see if excessive wheel bearing end play caused the DTC.
3. This step will identify a wheel speed sensor or circuitry that is damaged and visibly apparent.
4. This test checks wheel speed sensor for proper resistance values.
5. This test ensures the wheel speed sensor and sensor ring generate the proper voltage.
6. This step ensures the wheel speed sensor is not shorted to ground.

Diagnostic Aids:

An "intermittent" malfunction may be caused by a poor connection, rubbed through wire insulation or a wire that is broken inside the insulation.

The frequency of the malfunction can be checked by using the enhanced diagnostic function of the TECH 1.

If the customer's comments reflect that the "ABS" indicator is on only during moist environmental changes (rain, snow, vehicle wash, etc.), all wheel speed sensor circuitry should be thoroughly inspected for signs of water intrusion. Use the following procedure:

1. Spray down the suspected area with 5% salt water solution (10 ml [2 teaspoons] of salt to 355 ml [12 fl.oz.] of water).
2. Start vehicle and allow it to run for ten seconds.
3. If the DTC returns immediately, replace the suspected harness.

Any circuitry that is suspected of causing the intermittent complaint should be thoroughly checked for backed out terminals, improper mating, broken locks, improperly formed or damaged terminals, poor terminal-to-wiring connections or physical damage to the wiring harness.

When measuring wheel speed sensor resistance, ensure vehicle is at room temperature (approximately 20°C [68°F]). Wheel speed sensor resistance will vary with temperature.

When replacing a wheel speed sensor, inspect the sensor terminals and harness connector for corrosion and/or water intrusion. If evidence of corrosion or water intrusion exists, replace the wheel speed sensor.

GC402940096201AX

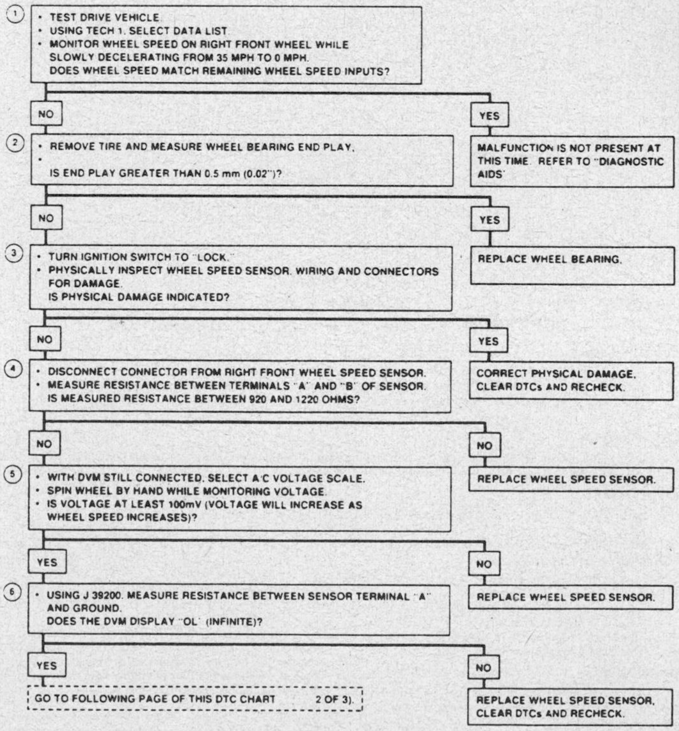
1
• TEST DRIVE VEHICLE.
• USING TECH 1, SELECT DATA LIST.
• MONITOR WHEEL SPEED ON RIGHT FRONT WHEEL WHILE SLOWLY DECELERATING FROM 35 MPH TO 0 MPH. DOES WHEEL SPEED MATCH REMAINING WHEEL SPEED INPUTS?
NO
YES
2
• REMOVE TIRE AND MEASURE WHEEL BEARING END PLAY.
IS END PLAY GREATER THAN 0.5 mm (0.02")?
MALFUNCTION IS NOT PRESENT AT THIS TIME. REFER TO "DIAGNOSTIC AIDS"
NO
YES
3
• TURN IGNITION SWITCH TO "LOCK."
• PHYSICALLY INSPECT WHEEL SPEED SENSOR, WIRING AND CONNECTORS FOR DAMAGE. IS PHYSICAL DAMAGE INDICATED?
REPLACE WHEEL BEARING.
NO
YES
4
• DISCONNECT CONNECTOR FROM RIGHT FRONT WHEEL SPEED SENSOR.
• MEASURE RESISTANCE BETWEEN TERMINALS "A" AND "B" OF SENSOR. IS MEASURED RESISTANCE BETWEEN 920 AND 1220 OHMS?
CORRECT PHYSICAL DAMAGE. CLEAR DTCs AND RECHECK.
NO
NO
5
• WITH DVM STILL CONNECTED, SELECT A/C VOLTAGE SCALE.
• SPIN WHEEL BY HAND WHILE MONITORING VOLTAGE.
• IS VOLTAGE AT LEAST 100mV (VOLTAGE WILL INCREASE AS WHEEL SPEED INCREASES)?
REPLACE WHEEL SPEED SENSOR.
YES
NO
6
• USING J 39200, MEASURE RESISTANCE BETWEEN SENSOR TERMINAL "A" AND GROUND. DOES THE DVM DISPLAY "OL" (INFINITE)?
REPLACE WHEEL SPEED SENSOR.
YES
NO
GO TO FOLLOWING PAGE OF THIS DTC CHART (2 OF 3).
REPLACE WHEEL SPEED SENSOR. CLEAR DTCs AND RECHECK.

GC402940096201BX

Fig. 312 Code A026: Right Front Wheel Excessive Wheel Speed Variation (Part 1 of 3). 1993–94 Prizm

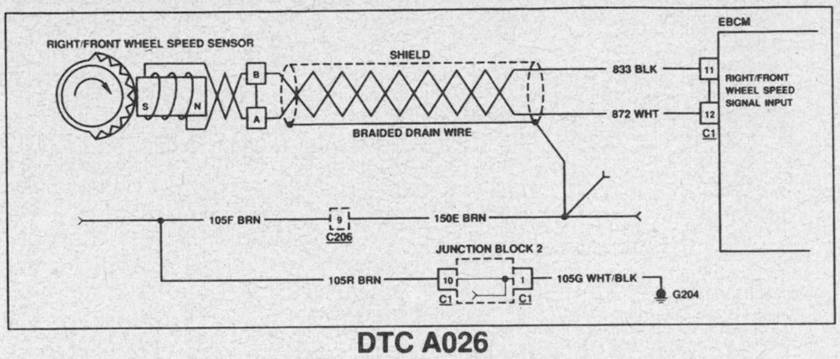
RIGHT/FRONT WHEEL SPEED SENSOR
SHIELD
EBCM
833 BLK
872 WHT
11
12
C1
RIGHT/FRONT WHEEL SPEED SIGNAL INPUT
BRAIDED DRAIN WIRE
105F BRN
9
C206
150E BRN
JUNCTION BLOCK 2
105R BRN
10
1
105G WHT/BLK
G204

DTC A026

(Page 2 of 3)

RIGHT FRONT EXCESSIVE WHEEL SPEED VARIATION

Circuit Description:

As a toothed ring passes by the wheel speed sensor, changes in the electromagnetic field cause the wheel speed sensor to produce a sinusoidal (AC) voltage signal whose frequency is proportional to wheel speed. The magnitude of this signal is directly related to wheel speed and the proximity of the wheel speed sensor to the toothed ring (often referred to as the air gap).

Failure Condition:

DTC A026 can be set when the brake is off. The purpose of this test is to detect a situation in which the right front wheel acceleration or deceleration is beyond specified limits.

Action Taken:

A DTC A026 is stored, ABS is disabled and the "ABS" indicator is turned on.

Test Description: Number(s) below refer to circled number(s) on the diagnostic chart.

7. This step checks for proper voltages at speed sensor harness connector.
8. This test ensures that the wheel speed sensor circuitry is not internally shorted.
9. This checks for an open in CKT 833.
10. This checks for an open in CKT 873.

Diagnostic Aids:

An "intermittent" malfunction may be caused by a poor connection, rubbed through wire insulation or a wire that is broken inside the insulation.

The frequency of the malfunction can be checked by using the enhanced diagnostic function of the TECH 1.

If the customer's comments reflect that the "ABS" indicator is on only during moist environmental changes (rain, snow, vehicle wash, etc.), all wheel speed sensor circuitry should be thoroughly inspected for signs of water intrusion. Use the following procedure:

1. Spray down the suspected area with 5% salt water solution (10 ml [2 teaspoons] of salt to 355 ml [12 fl.oz.] of water).
2. Start vehicle and allow it to run for ten seconds.
3. If the DTC returns immediately, replace the suspected harness.

Any circuitry that is suspected of causing the intermittent complaint should be thoroughly checked for backed out terminals, improper mating, broken locks, improperly formed or damaged terminals, poor terminal-to-wiring connections or physical damage to the wiring harness.

When measuring wheel speed sensor resistance, ensure vehicle is at room temperature (approximately 20°C [68°F]). Wheel speed sensor resistance will vary with temperature.

When replacing a wheel speed sensor, inspect the sensor terminals and harness connector for corrosion and/or water intrusion. If evidence of corrosion or water intrusion exists, replace the wheel speed sensor.

GC402940096202AX

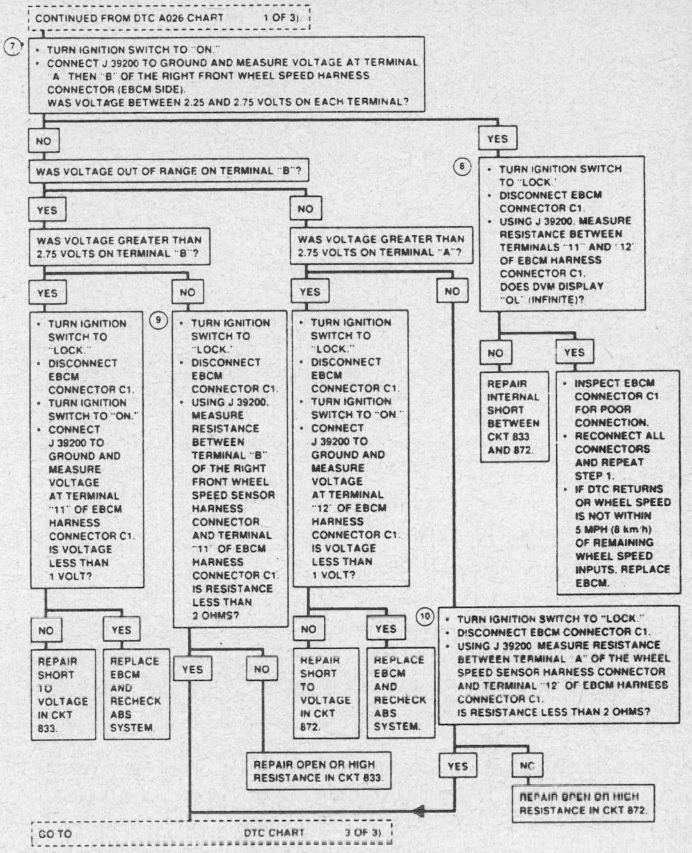
CONTINUED FROM DTC A026 CHART 1 OF 3).
7
• TURN IGNITION SWITCH TO "ON."
• CONNECT J 39200 TO GROUND AND MEASURE VOLTAGE AT TERMINAL "A" THEN "B" OF THE RIGHT FRONT WHEEL SPEED HARNESS CONNECTOR (EBCM SIDE).
WAS VOLTAGE BETWEEN 2.25 AND 2.75 VOLTS ON EACH TERMINAL?
NO
YES
WAS VOLTAGE OUT OF RANGE ON TERMINAL "B"?
YES
NO
WAS VOLTAGE GREATER THAN 2.75 VOLTS ON TERMINAL "B"?
WAS VOLTAGE GREATER THAN 2.75 VOLTS ON TERMINAL "A"?
8
• TURN IGNITION SWITCH TO "LOCK."
• DISCONNECT EBCM CONNECTOR C1.
• USING J 39200, MEASURE RESISTANCE BETWEEN TERMINALS "11" AND "12" OF EBCM HARNESS CONNECTOR C1.
DOES DVM DISPLAY "OL" (INFINITE)?
YES
NO
YES
NO
• TURN IGNITION SWITCH TO "LOCK."
• DISCONNECT EBCM CONNECTOR C1.
• TURN IGNITION SWITCH TO "ON."
• CONNECT J 39200 TO GROUND AND MEASURE VOLTAGE AT TERMINAL "11" OF EBCM HARNESS CONNECTOR C1.
IS VOLTAGE LESS THAN 1 VOLT?
9
• TURN IGNITION SWITCH TO "LOCK."
• DISCONNECT EBCM CONNECTOR C1.
• USING J 39200, MEASURE RESISTANCE BETWEEN TERMINAL "B" OF THE RIGHT FRONT WHEEL SPEED SENSOR HARNESS CONNECTOR AND TERMINAL "11" OF EBCM HARNESS CONNECTOR C1.
IS RESISTANCE LESS THAN 2 OHMS?
• TURN IGNITION SWITCH TO "LOCK."
• DISCONNECT EBCM CONNECTOR C1.
• TURN IGNITION SWITCH TO "ON."
• CONNECT J 39200 TO GROUND AND MEASURE VOLTAGE AT TERMINAL "12" OF EBCM HARNESS CONNECTOR C1.
IS VOLTAGE LESS THAN 1 VOLT?
NO
YES
REPAIR INTERNAL SHORT BETWEEN CKT 833 AND 872.
• INSPECT EBCM CONNECTOR C1 FOR POOR CONNECTION.
• RECONNECT ALL CONNECTORS AND REPEAT STEP 1.
• IF DTC RETURNS OR WHEEL SPEED IS NOT WITHIN 5 MPH (8 km/h) OF REMAINING WHEEL SPEED INPUTS, REPLACE EBCM.
NO
YES
REPAIR SHORT TO VOLTAGE IN CKT 833.
REPLACE EBCM AND RECHECK ABS SYSTEM.
YES
NO
NO
YES
REPAIR SHORT TO VOLTAGE IN CKT 872.
REPLACE EBCM AND RECHECK ABS SYSTEM.
10
• TURN IGNITION SWITCH TO "LOCK."
• DISCONNECT EBCM CONNECTOR C1.
• USING J 39200, MEASURE RESISTANCE BETWEEN TERMINAL "A" OF THE WHEEL SPEED SENSOR HARNESS CONNECTOR AND TERMINAL "12" OF EBCM HARNESS CONNECTOR C1.
IS RESISTANCE LESS THAN 2 OHMS?
REPAIR OPEN OR HIGH RESISTANCE IN CKT 833.
YES
NO
REPAIR OPEN OR HIGH RESISTANCE IN CKT 872.
GO TO DTC CHART 3 OF 3).

GC402940096202BX

Fig. 312 Code A026: Right Front Wheel Excessive Wheel Speed Variation (Part 2 of 3). 1993–94 Prizm

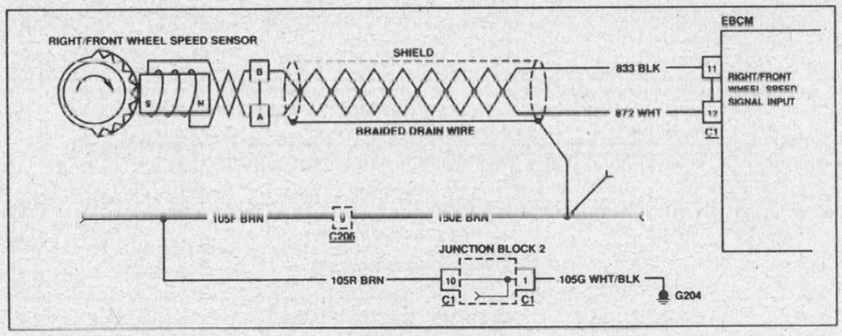
RIGHT/FRONT WHEEL SPEED SENSOR
SHIELD
EBCM
833 BLK
872 WHT
11
12
C1
RIGHT/FRONT WHEEL SPEED SIGNAL INPUT
BRAIDED DRAIN WIRE
105F BRN
9
C206
150E BRN
JUNCTION BLOCK 2
105R BRN
10
1
105G WHT/BLK
G204

DTC A026

(Page 3 of 3)

RIGHT FRONT EXCESSIVE WHEEL SPEED VARIATION

Circuit Description:

As a toothed ring passes by the wheel speed sensor, changes in the electromagnetic field cause the wheel speed sensor to produce a sinusoidal (AC) voltage signal whose frequency is proportional to wheel speed. The magnitude of this signal is directly related to wheel speed and the proximity of the wheel speed sensor to the toothed ring (often referred to as the air gap).

Failure Condition:

DTC A026 can be set when the brake is off. The purpose of this test is to detect a situation in which the right front wheel acceleration or deceleration is beyond specified limits.

Action Taken:

A DTC A026 is stored, ABS is disabled and the "ABS" indicator is turned on.

Test Description: Number(s) below refer to circled number(s) on the diagnostic chart.

11. This test checks for a short to ground in both wheel speed signal circuits.
12. This step ensures that DTC A026 was not set due to a poor connection between the EBCM connector C1 and the EBCM.

Diagnostic Aids:

An "intermittent" malfunction may be caused by a poor connection, rubbed through wire insulation or a wire that is broken inside the insulation.

The frequency of the malfunction can be checked by using the enhanced diagnostic function of the TECH 1.

If the customer's comments reflect that the "ABS" indicator is on only during moist environmental changes (rain, snow, vehicle wash, etc.), all wheel speed sensor circuitry should be thoroughly inspected for signs of water intrusion. Use the following procedure:

1. Spray down the suspected area with 5% salt water solution (10 ml [2 teaspoons] of salt to 355 ml [12 fl.oz.] of water).
2. Start vehicle and allow it to run for ten seconds.
3. If the DTC returns immediately, replace the suspected harness.

Any circuitry that is suspected of causing the intermittent complaint should be thoroughly checked for backed out terminals, improper mating, broken locks, improperly formed or damaged terminals, poor terminal-to-wiring connections or physical damage to the wiring harness.

When measuring wheel speed sensor resistance, ensure vehicle is at room temperature (approximately 20°C [68°F]). Wheel speed sensor resistance will vary with temperature.

When replacing a wheel speed sensor, inspect the sensor terminals and harness connector for corrosion and/or water intrusion. If evidence of corrosion or water intrusion exists, replace the wheel speed sensor.

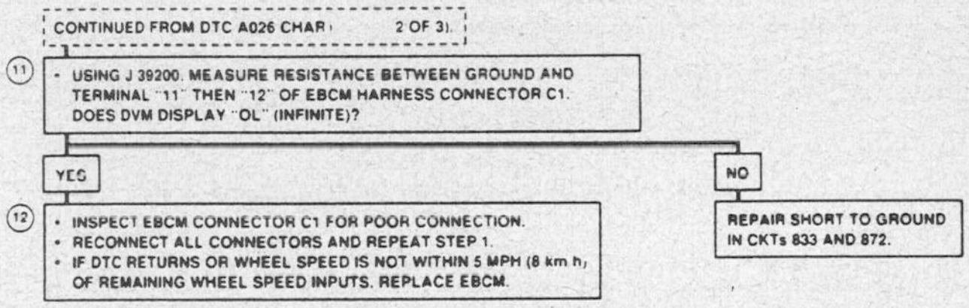
CONTINUED FROM DTC A026 CHART 2 OF 3).
11
• USING J 39200, MEASURE RESISTANCE BETWEEN GROUND AND TERMINAL "11" THEN "12" OF EBCM HARNESS CONNECTOR C1.
DOES DVM DISPLAY "OL" (INFINITE)?
YES
NO
12
• INSPECT EBCM CONNECTOR C1 FOR POOR CONNECTION.
• RECONNECT ALL CONNECTORS AND REPEAT STEP 1.
• IF DTC RETURNS OR WHEEL SPEED IS NOT WITHIN 5 MPH (8 km/h) OF REMAINING WHEEL SPEED INPUTS, REPLACE EBCM.
REPAIR SHORT TO GROUND IN CKTs 833 AND 872.

GC402940096203BX

Fig. 312 Code A026: Right Front Wheel Excessive Wheel Speed Variation (Part 3 of 3). 1993–94 Prizm

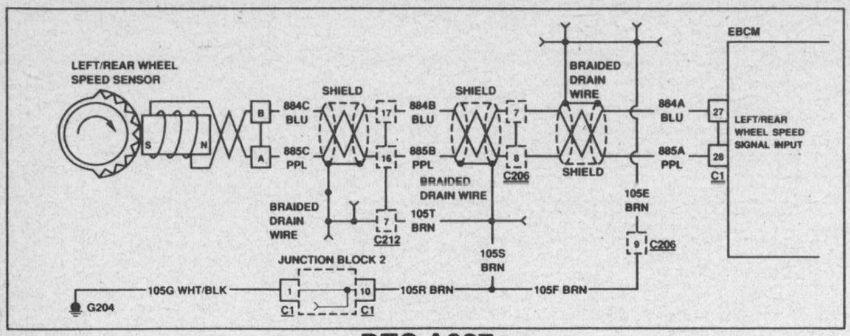
LEFT/REAR WHEEL SPEED SENSOR
SHIELD
884C BLU
885C PPL
884B BLU
885B PPL
BRAIDED DRAIN WIRE
SHIELD
C206
BRAIDED DRAIN WIRE
884A BLU
885A PPL
EBCM
LEFT/REAR WHEEL SPEED SIGNAL INPUT
C1
105E BRN
105T BRN
C212
JUNCTION BLOCK 2
105S BRN
C206
105G WHT/BLK
105R BRN
105F BRN
G204

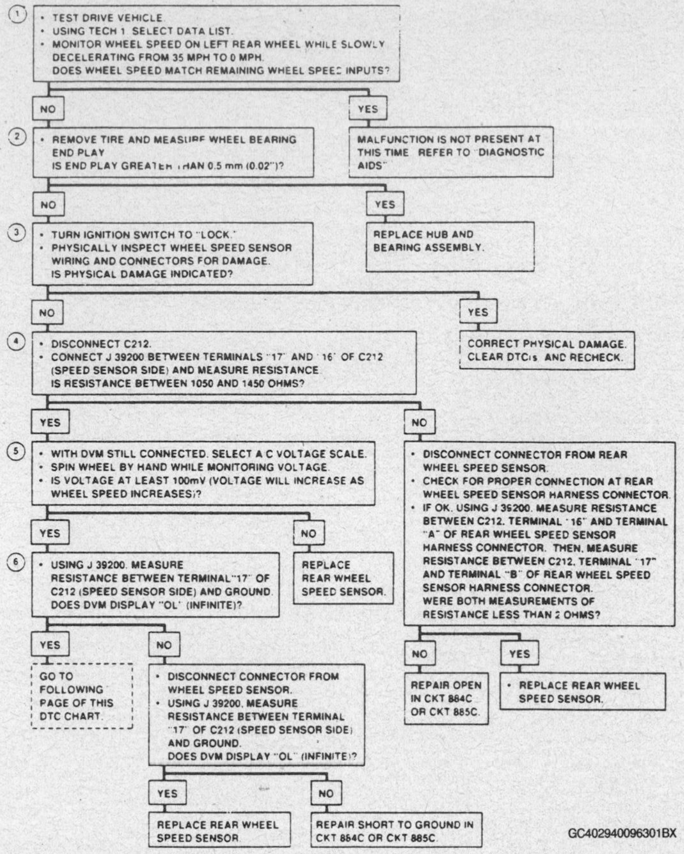
1 • TEST DRIVE VEHICLE.
• USING TECH 1 SELECT DATA LIST.
• MONITOR WHEEL SPEED ON LEFT REAR WHEEL WHILE SLOWLY DECELERATING FROM 35 MPH TO 0 MPH.
DOES WHEEL SPEED MATCH REMAINING WHEEL SPEED INPUTS?
NO
YES
MALFUNCTION IS NOT PRESENT AT THIS TIME. REFER TO "DIAGNOSTIC AIDS".
2 • REMOVE TIRE AND MEASURE WHEEL BEARING END PLAY.
IS END PLAY GREATER THAN 0.5 mm (0.02")?
NO
YES
REPLACE HUB AND BEARING ASSEMBLY.
3 • TURN IGNITION SWITCH TO "LOCK."
• PHYSICALLY INSPECT WHEEL SPEED SENSOR WIRING AND CONNECTORS FOR DAMAGE.
IS PHYSICAL DAMAGE INDICATED?
NO
YES
CORRECT PHYSICAL DAMAGE. CLEAR DTCs AND RECHECK.
4 • DISCONNECT C212.
• CONNECT J 39200 BETWEEN TERMINALS "17" AND "16" OF C212 (SPEED SENSOR SIDE) AND MEASURE RESISTANCE.
IS RESISTANCE BETWEEN 1050 AND 1450 OHMS?
YES
NO
5 • WITH DVM STILL CONNECTED, SELECT A C VOLTAGE SCALE.
• SPIN WHEEL BY HAND WHILE MONITORING VOLTAGE.
• IS VOLTAGE AT LEAST 100mV (VOLTAGE WILL INCREASE AS WHEEL SPEED INCREASES)?
• DISCONNECT CONNECTOR FROM REAR WHEEL SPEED SENSOR.
• CHECK FOR PROPER CONNECTION AT REAR WHEEL SPEED SENSOR HARNESS CONNECTOR.
• IF OK, USING J 39200, MEASURE RESISTANCE BETWEEN C212, TERMINAL "16" AND TERMINAL "A" OF REAR WHEEL SPEED SENSOR HARNESS CONNECTOR. THEN, MEASURE RESISTANCE BETWEEN C212, TERMINAL "17" AND TERMINAL "B" OF REAR WHEEL SPEED SENSOR HARNESS CONNECTOR.
WERE BOTH MEASUREMENTS OF RESISTANCE LESS THAN 2 OHMS?
YES
NO
REPLACE REAR WHEEL SPEED SENSOR.
6 • USING J 39200, MEASURE RESISTANCE BETWEEN TERMINAL "17" OF C212 (SPEED SENSOR SIDE) AND GROUND.
DOES DVM DISPLAY "OL" (INFINITE)?
YES
NO
NO
YES
GO TO FOLLOWING PAGE OF THIS DTC CHART.
• DISCONNECT CONNECTOR FROM WHEEL SPEED SENSOR.
• USING J 39200, MEASURE RESISTANCE BETWEEN TERMINAL "17" OF C212 (SPEED SENSOR SIDE) AND GROUND.
DOES DVM DISPLAY "OL" (INFINITE)?
REPAIR OPEN IN CKT 884C OR CKT 885C.
• REPLACE REAR WHEEL SPEED SENSOR.
YES
NO
REPLACE REAR WHEEL SPEED SENSOR.
REPAIR SHORT TO GROUND IN CKT 884C OR CKT 885C.
GC402940096301BX

DTC A027
(Page 1 of 3)
LEFT REAR EXCESSIVE WHEEL SPEED VARIATION

Circuit Description:

As a toothed ring passes by the wheel speed sensor, changes in the electromagnetic field cause the wheel speed sensor to produce a sinusoidal (AC) voltage signal whose frequency is proportional to wheel speed. The magnitude of this signal is directly related to wheel speed and the proximity of the wheel speed sensor to the toothed ring (often referred to as the air gap).

Failure Condition:

DTC A027 can be set when the brake is off. The purpose of this test is to detect a situation in which the left rear wheel acceleration or deceleration is beyond specified limits.

Action Taken:

A DTC A027 is stored, ABS is disabled and the "ABS" indicator is turned on.

Test Description: Number(s) below refer to circled number(s) on the diagnostic chart.

1. This test verifies whether the malfunction is currently present.
2. This test checks to see if excessive wheel beaing end play caused the DTC.
3. This step will identify a wheel speed sensor or circuitry that is damaged and visibly apparent.
4. This test checks wheel speed sensor for proper resistance values.
5. This test ensures the wheel speed sensor and sensor ring generate the proper voltage.
6. This step ensures the wheel speed sensor is not shorted to ground.

Diagnostic Aids:

An "intermittent" malfunction may be caused by a poor connection, rubbed through wire insulation or a wire that is broken inside the insulation.

The frequency of the malfunction can be checked by using the enhanced diagnostic function of the TECH 1.

If the customer's comments reflect that the "ABS" indicator is on only during moist environmental changes (rain, snow, vehicle wash, etc.), all wheel speed sensor circuitry should be thoroughly inspected for signs of water intrusion. Use the following procedure:

1. Spray down the suspected area with 5% salt water solution (10 ml [2 teaspoons] of salt to 355 ml [12 fl.oz.] of water).
2. Start vehicle and allow it to run for ten seconds.
3. If the DTC returns immediately, replace the suspected harness.

Any circuitry that is suspected of causing the intermittent complaint should be thoroughly checked for backed out terminals, improper mating, broken locks, improperly formed or damaged terminals, poor terminal-to-wiring connections or physical damage to the wiring harness.

When measuring wheel speed sensor resistance, ensure vehicle is at room temperature (approximately 20°C [68°F]). Wheel speed sensor resistance will vary with temperature.

When replacing a wheel speed sensor, inspect the sensor terminals and harness connector for corrosion and/or water intrusion. If evidence of corrosion or water intrusion exists, replace the wheel speed sensor harness.

GC402940096301AX

Fig. 313 Code A027: Left Rear Excessive Wheel Speed Variation (Part 1 of 3). 1993–94 Prizm

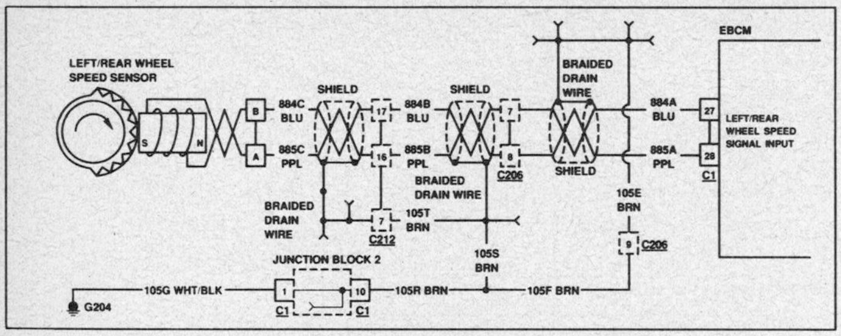
LEFT/REAR WHEEL SPEED SENSOR
SHIELD
884C BLU
885C PPL
884B BLU
885B PPL
BRAIDED DRAIN WIRE
SHIELD
C206
BRAIDED DRAIN WIRE
884A BLU
885A PPL
EBCM
LEFT/REAR WHEEL SPEED SIGNAL INPUT
C1
105E BRN
105T BRN
C212
JUNCTION BLOCK 2
105S BRN
C206
105G WHT/BLK
105R BRN
105F BRN
G204

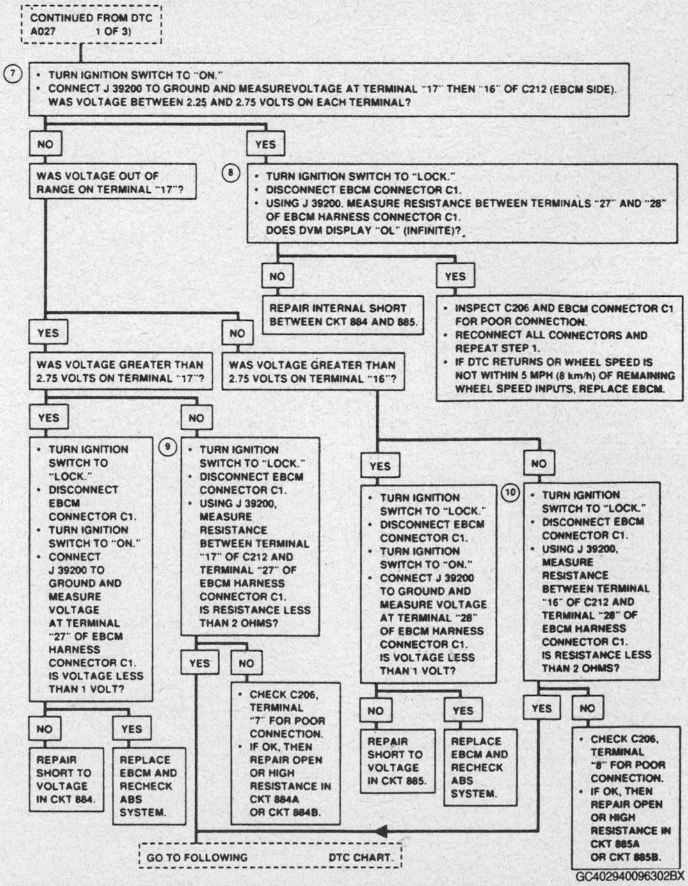
CONTINUED FROM DTC A027 (PAGE 1 OF 3)
7 • TURN IGNITION SWITCH TO "ON."
• CONNECT J 39200 TO GROUND AND MEASURE VOLTAGE AT TERMINAL "17" THEN "16" OF C212 (EBCM SIDE).
WAS VOLTAGE BETWEEN 2.25 AND 2.75 VOLTS ON EACH TERMINAL?
NO
YES
WAS VOLTAGE OUT OF RANGE ON TERMINAL "17"?
8 • TURN IGNITION SWITCH TO "LOCK."
• DISCONNECT EBCM CONNECTOR C1.
• USING J 39200, MEASURE RESISTANCE BETWEEN TERMINALS "27" AND "28" OF EBCM HARNESS CONNECTOR C1.
DOES DVM DISPLAY "OL" (INFINITE)?
NO
YES
REPAIR INTERNAL SHORT BETWEEN CKT 884 AND 885.
• INSPECT C206 AND EBCM CONNECTOR C1 FOR POOR CONNECTION.
• RECONNECT ALL CONNECTORS AND REPEAT STEP 1.
• IF DTC RETURNS OR WHEEL SPEED IS NOT WITHIN 5 MPH (8 km/h) OF REMAINING WHEEL SPEED INPUTS, REPLACE EBCM.
YES
NO
WAS VOLTAGE GREATER THAN 2.75 VOLTS ON TERMINAL "17"?
WAS VOLTAGE GREATER THAN 2.75 VOLTS ON TERMINAL "16"?
YES
NO
• TURN IGNITION SWITCH TO "LOCK."
• DISCONNECT EBCM CONNECTOR C1.
• TURN IGNITION SWITCH TO "ON."
• CONNECT J 39200 TO GROUND AND MEASURE VOLTAGE AT TERMINAL "27" OF EBCM HARNESS CONNECTOR C1.
IS VOLTAGE LESS THAN 1 VOLT?
9 • TURN IGNITION SWITCH TO "LOCK."
• DISCONNECT EBCM CONNECTOR C1.
• USING J 39200, MEASURE RESISTANCE BETWEEN TERMINAL "17" OF C212 AND TERMINAL "27" OF EBCM HARNESS CONNECTOR C1.
IS RESISTANCE LESS THAN 2 OHMS?
YES
NO
• TURN IGNITION SWITCH TO "LOCK."
• DISCONNECT EBCM CONNECTOR C1.
• TURN IGNITION SWITCH TO "ON."
• CONNECT J 39200 TO GROUND AND MEASURE VOLTAGE AT TERMINAL "28" OF EBCM HARNESS CONNECTOR C1.
IS VOLTAGE LESS THAN 1 VOLT?
10 • TURN IGNITION SWITCH TO "LOCK."
• DISCONNECT EBCM CONNECTOR C1.
• USING J 39200, MEASURE RESISTANCE BETWEEN TERMINAL "16" OF C212 AND TERMINAL "28" OF EBCM HARNESS CONNECTOR C1.
IS RESISTANCE LESS THAN 2 OHMS?
YES
NO
• CHECK C206, TERMINAL "7" FOR POOR CONNECTION.
• IF OK, THEN REPAIR OPEN OR HIGH RESISTANCE IN CKT 884A OR CKT 884B.
NO
YES
REPAIR SHORT TO VOLTAGE IN CKT 884.
REPLACE EBCM AND RECHECK ABS SYSTEM.
NO
YES
REPAIR SHORT TO VOLTAGE IN CKT 885.
REPLACE EBCM AND RECHECK ABS SYSTEM.
YES
NO
• CHECK C206, TERMINAL "8" FOR POOR CONNECTION.
• IF OK, THEN REPAIR OPEN OR HIGH RESISTANCE IN CKT 885A OR CKT 885B.
GO TO FOLLOWING DTC CHART.
GC402940096302BX

DTC A027
(Page 2 of 3)
LEFT REAR EXCESSIVE WHEEL SPEED VARIATION

Circuit Description:

As a toothed ring passes by the wheel speed sensor, changes in the electromagnetic field cause the wheel speed sensor to produce a sinusoidal (AC) voltage signal whose frequency is proportional to wheel speed. The magnitude of this signal is directly related to wheel speed and the proximity of the wheel speed sensor to the toothed ring (often referred to as the air gap).

Failure Condition:

DTC A027 can be set when the brake is off. The purpose of this test is to detect a situation in which the left rear wheel acceleration or deceleration is beyond specified limits.

Action Taken:

A DTC A027 is stored, ABS is disabled and the "ABS" indicator is turned on.

Test Description: Number(s) below refer to circled number(s) on the diagnostic chart.

7. This step checks for proper voltages at speed sensor harness connector.
8. This test ensures that the wheel speed sensor circuitry is not internally shorted.
9. This checks for an open in CKT 884A or CKT 884B.
10. This checks for an open in CKT 885A or CKT 885B.

Diagnostic Aids:

An "intermittent" malfunction may be caused by a poor connection, rubbed through wire insulation or a wire that is broken inside the insulation.

The frequency of the malfunction can be checked by using the enhanced diagnostic function of the TECH 1.

If the customer's comments reflect that the "ABS" indicator is on only during moist environmental changes (rain, snow, vehicle wash, etc.), all wheel speed sensor circuitry should be thoroughly inspected for signs of water intrusion. Use the following procedure:

1. Spray down the suspected area with 5% salt water solution (10 ml [2 teaspoons] of salt to 355 ml [12 fl.oz.] of water).
2. Start vehicle and allow it to run for ten seconds.
3. If the DTC returns immediately, replace the suspected harness.

Any circuitry that is suspected of causing the intermittent complaint should be thoroughly checked for backed out terminals, improper mating, broken locks, improperly formed or damaged terminals, poor terminal-to-wiring connections or physical damage to the wiring harness.

When measuring wheel speed sensor resistance, ensure vehicle is at room temperature (approximately 20°C [68°F]). Wheel speed sensor resistance will vary with temperature.

When replacing a wheel speed sensor, inspect the sensor terminals and harness connector for corrosion and/or water intrusion. If evidence of corrosion or water intrusion exists, replace the wheel speed sensor.

GC402940096302AX

Fig. 313 Code A027: Left Rear Excessive Wheel Speed Variation (Part 2 of 3). 1993–94 Prizm

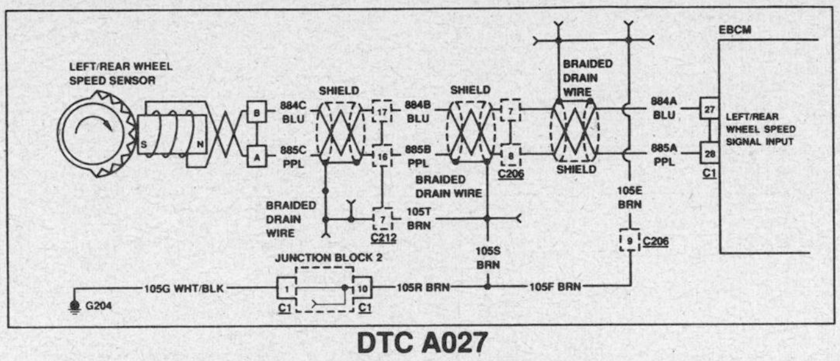

EBCM
LEFT/REAR WHEEL SPEED SENSOR
SHIELD
884C BLU
885C PPL
884B BLU
885B PPL
BRAIDED DRAIN WIRE
884A BLU
885A PPL
LEFT/REAR WHEEL SPEED SIGNAL INPUT
C1
C206
SHIELD
105E BRN
105T BRN
C212
JUNCTION BLOCK 2
105S BRN
105G WHT/BLK
105R BRN
105F BRN
G204

DTC A027

(Page 3 of 3)

LEFT REAR EXCESSIVE WHEEL SPEED VARIATION

Circuit Description:

As a toothed ring passes by the wheel speed sensor, changes in the electromagnetic field cause the wheel speed sensor to produce a sinusoidal (AC) voltage signal whose frequency is proportional to wheel speed. The magnitude of this signal is directly related to wheel speed and the proximity of the wheel speed sensor to the toothed ring (often referred to as the air gap).

Failure Condition:

DTC A027 can be set when the brake is off. The purpose of this test is to detect a situation in which the left rear wheel acceleration or deceleration is beyond specified limits.

Action Taken:

A DTC A027 is stored, ABS is disabled and the "ABS" indicator is turned on.

Test Description: Number(s) below refer to circled number(s) on the diagnostic chart.

11. This test checks for a short to ground in both wheel speed signal circuits.
12. This step ensures that DTC A027 was not set due to a poor connection between the EBCM connector C1 and the EBCM.

Diagnostic Aids:

An "intermittent" malfunction may be caused by a poor connection, rubbed through wire insulation or a wire that is broken inside the insulation.

The frequency of the malfunction can be checked by using the enhanced diagnostic function of the TECH 1.

If the customer's comments reflect that the "ABS" indicator is on only during moist environmental changes (rain, snow, vehicle wash, etc.), all wheel speed sensor circuitry should be thoroughly inspected for signs of water intrusion. Use the following procedure:

1. Spray down the suspected area with 5% salt water solution (10 ml [2 teaspoons] of salt to 355 ml [12 fl.oz.] of water).
2. Start vehicle and allow it to run for ten seconds.
3. If the DTC returns immediately, replace the suspected harness.

Any circuitry that is suspected of causing the intermittent complaint should be thoroughly checked for backed out terminals, improper mating, broken locks, improperly formed or damaged terminals, poor terminal-to-wiring connections or physical damage to the wiring harness.

When measuring wheel speed sensor resistance, ensure vehicle is at room temperature (approximately 20°C [68°F]). Wheel speed sensor resistance will vary with temperature.

When replacing a wheel speed sensor, inspect the sensor terminals and harness connector for corrosion and/or water intrusion. If evidence of corrosion or water intrusion exists, replace the wheel speed sensor.

GC402940096303AX

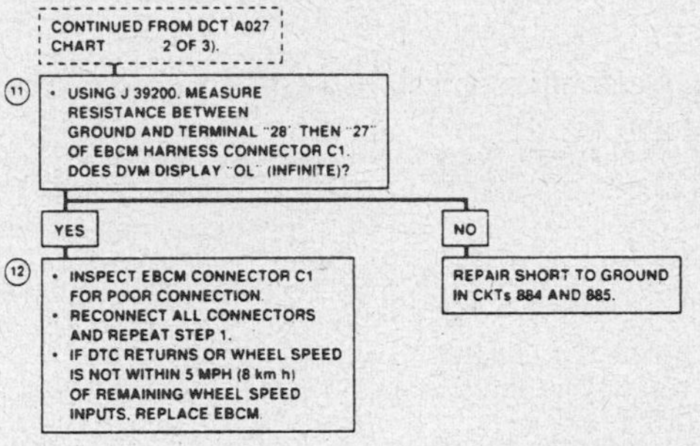

CONTINUED FROM DCT A027 CHART 2 OF 3).
11
• USING J 39200, MEASURE RESISTANCE BETWEEN GROUND AND TERMINAL "28" THEN "27" OF EBCM HARNESS CONNECTOR C1. DOES DVM DISPLAY "OL" (INFINITE)?
YES
NO
12
• INSPECT EBCM CONNECTOR C1 FOR POOR CONNECTION.
• RECONNECT ALL CONNECTORS AND REPEAT STEP 1.
• IF DTC RETURNS OR WHEEL SPEED IS NOT WITHIN 5 MPH (8 km/h) OF REMAINING WHEEL SPEED INPUTS, REPLACE EBCM.
REPAIR SHORT TO GROUND IN CKTs 884 AND 885.

GC402940096303BX

Fig. 313 Code A027: Left Rear Excessive Wheel Speed Variation (Part 3 of 3). 1993–94 Prizm

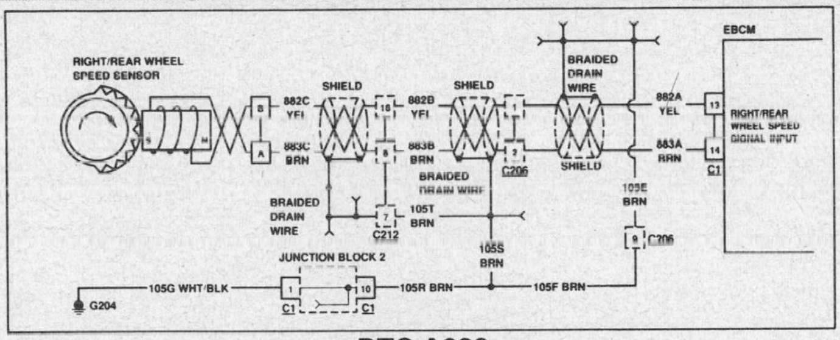

EBCM
RIGHT/REAR WHEEL SPEED SENSOR
SHIELD
882C YEL
883C BRN
882B YEL
883B BRN
BRAIDED DRAIN WIRE
882A YEL
883A BRN
RIGHT/REAR WHEEL SPEED SIGNAL INPUT
C1
C206
SHIELD
105E BRN
105T BRN
C212
JUNCTION BLOCK 2
105S BRN
105G WHT/BLK
105R BRN
105F BRN
G204

DTC A028

(Page 1 of 3)

RIGHT REAR EXCESSIVE WHEEL SPEED VARIATION

Circuit Description:

As a toothed ring passes by the wheel speed sensor, changes in the electromagnetic field cause the wheel speed sensor to produce a sinusoidal (AC) voltage signal whose frequency is proportional to wheel speed. The magnitude of this signal is directly related to wheel speed and the proximity of the wheel speed sensor to the toothed ring (often referred to as the air gap).

Failure Condition:

DTC A028 can be set when the brake is off. The purpose of this test is to detect a situation in which the right rear wheel acceleration or deceleration is beyond specified limits.

Action Taken:

A DTC A028 is stored, ABS is disabled and the "ABS" indicator is turned on.

Test Description: Number(s) below refer to circled number(s) on the diagnostic chart.

1. This test verifies whether the malfunction is currently present.
2. This test checks to see if exvessive wheel bearing end play caused the DTC.
3. This step will identify a wheel speed sensor or circuitry that is damaged and visibly apparent.
4. This test checks wheel speed sensor for proper resistance values.
5. This test ensures the wheel speed sensor and sensor ring generate the proper voltage.
6. This step ensures the wheel speed sensor is not shorted to ground.

Diagnostic Aids:

An "intermittent" malfunction may be caused by a poor connection, rubbed through wire insulation or a wire that is broken inside the insulation.

The frequency of the malfunction can be checked by using the enhanced diagnostic function of the TECH 1.

If the customer's comments reflect that the "ABS" indicator is on only during moist environmental changes (rain, snow, vehicle wash, etc.), all wheel speed sensor circuitry should be thoroughly inspected for signs of water intrusion. Use the following procedure:

1. Spray down the suspected area with 5% salt water solution (10 ml [2 teaspoons] of salt to 355 ml [12 fl.oz.] of water).
2. Start vehicle and allow it to run for ten seconds.
3. If the DTC returns immediately, replace the suspected harness.

Any circuitry that is suspected of causing the intermittent complaint should be thoroughly checked for backed out terminals, improper mating, broken locks, improperly formed or damaged terminals, poor terminal-to-wiring connections or physical damage to the wiring harness.

When measuring wheel speed sensor resistance, ensure vehicle is at room temperature (approximately 20°C [68°F]). Wheel speed sensor resistance will vary with temperature.

When replacing a wheel speed sensor, inspect the sensor terminals and harness connector for corrosion and/or water intrusion. If evidence of corrosion or water intrusion exists, replace the wheel speed sensor.

GC402940096401AX

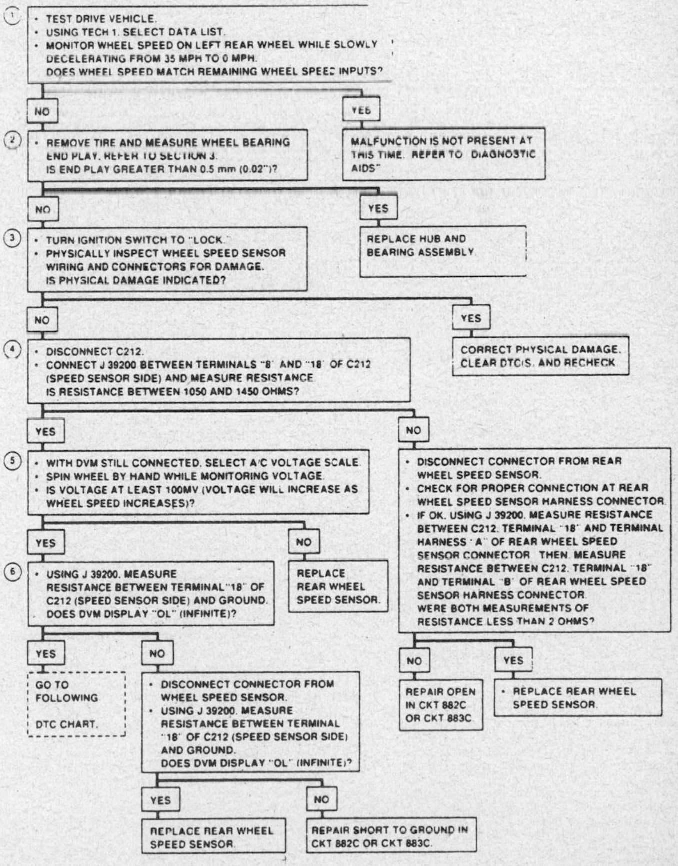

1
• TEST DRIVE VEHICLE.
• USING TECH 1, SELECT DATA LIST.
• MONITOR WHEEL SPEED ON LEFT REAR WHEEL WHILE SLOWLY DECELERATING FROM 35 MPH TO 0 MPH. DOES WHEEL SPEED MATCH REMAINING WHEEL SPEED INPUTS?
NO
YES
MALFUNCTION IS NOT PRESENT AT THIS TIME. REFER TO "DIAGNOSTIC AIDS"
2
• REMOVE TIRE AND MEASURE WHEEL BEARING END PLAY, REFER TO SECTION 3. IS END PLAY GREATER THAN 0.5 mm (0.02")?
NO
YES
REPLACE HUB AND BEARING ASSEMBLY.
3
• TURN IGNITION SWITCH TO "LOCK."
• PHYSICALLY INSPECT WHEEL SPEED SENSOR WIRING AND CONNECTORS FOR DAMAGE. IS PHYSICAL DAMAGE INDICATED?
NO
YES
CORRECT PHYSICAL DAMAGE, CLEAR DTC(S), AND RECHECK
4
• DISCONNECT C212.
• CONNECT J 39200 BETWEEN TERMINALS "8" AND "18" OF C212 (SPEED SENSOR SIDE) AND MEASURE RESISTANCE. IS RESISTANCE BETWEEN 1050 AND 1450 OHMS?
YES
NO
5
• WITH DVM STILL CONNECTED, SELECT A/C VOLTAGE SCALE.
• SPIN WHEEL BY HAND WHILE MONITORING VOLTAGE.
• IS VOLTAGE AT LEAST 100MV (VOLTAGE WILL INCREASE AS WHEEL SPEED INCREASES)?
• DISCONNECT CONNECTOR FROM REAR WHEEL SPEED SENSOR.
• CHECK FOR PROPER CONNECTION AT REAR WHEEL SPEED SENSOR HARNESS CONNECTOR.
• IF OK, USING J 39200, MEASURE RESISTANCE BETWEEN C212, TERMINAL "18" AND TERMINAL HARNESS "A" OF REAR WHEEL SPEED SENSOR CONNECTOR. THEN, MEASURE RESISTANCE BETWEEN C212, TERMINAL "18" AND TERMINAL "B" OF REAR WHEEL SPEED SENSOR HARNESS CONNECTOR. WERE BOTH MEASUREMENTS OF RESISTANCE LESS THAN 2 OHMS?
YES
NO
REPLACE REAR WHEEL SPEED SENSOR.
6
• USING J 39200, MEASURE RESISTANCE BETWEEN TERMINAL "18" OF C212 (SPEED SENSOR SIDE) AND GROUND. DOES DVM DISPLAY "OL" (INFINITE)?
YES
NO
GO TO FOLLOWING DTC CHART.
• DISCONNECT CONNECTOR FROM WHEEL SPEED SENSOR.
• USING J 39200, MEASURE RESISTANCE BETWEEN TERMINAL "18" OF C212 (SPEED SENSOR SIDE) AND GROUND. DOES DVM DISPLAY "OL" (INFINITE)?
YES
NO
REPLACE REAR WHEEL SPEED SENSOR.
REPAIR SHORT TO GROUND IN CKT 882C OR CKT 883C.
NO
YES
REPAIR OPEN IN CKT 882C OR CKT 883C.
• REPLACE REAR WHEEL SPEED SENSOR.

GC402940096401BX

Fig. 314 Code A028: Right Rear Excessive Wheel Speed Variation (Part 1 of 3). 1993–94 Prizm

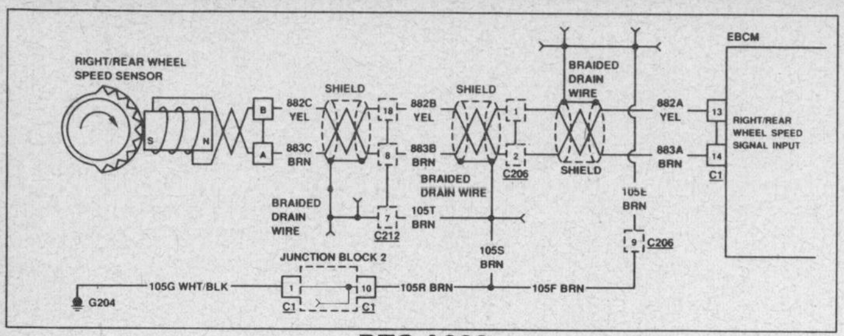
RIGHT/REAR WHEEL SPEED SENSOR
SHIELD
882C YEL
883C BRN
SHIELD
882B YEL
883B BRN
BRAIDED DRAIN WIRE
SHIELD
882A YEL
883A BRN
EBCM
RIGHT/REAR WHEEL SPEED SIGNAL INPUT
C1
C206
BRAIDED DRAIN WIRE
105T BRN
C212
105E BRN
105S BRN
C206
JUNCTION BLOCK 2
105G WHT/BLK
105R BRN
105F BRN
G204

DTC A028

(Page 2 of 3)
RIGHT REAR EXCESSIVE WHEEL SPEED VARIATION

Circuit Description:

As a toothed ring passes by the wheel speed sensor, changes in the electromagnetic field cause the wheel speed sensor to produce a sinusoidal (AC) voltage signal whose frequency is proportional to wheel speed. The magnitude of this signal is directly related to wheel speed and the proximity of the wheel speed sensor to the toothed ring (often referred to as the air gap).

Failure Condition:

DTC A028 can be set when the brake is off. The purpose of this test is to detect a situation in which the right rear wheel acceleration or deceleration is beyond specified limits.

Action Taken:

A DTC A028 is stored. ABS is disabled and the "ABS" indicator is turned on.

Test Description: Number(s) below refer to circled number(s) on the diagnostic chart.

7. This step checks for proper voltages at speed sensor harness connector.
8. This test ensures that the wheel speed sensor circuitry is not internally shorted.
9. This checks for an open in CKT 882A and CKT 882B.
10. This checks for an open in CKT 883A and CKT 883B.

Diagnostic Aids:

An "intermittent" malfunction may be caused by a poor connection, rubbed through wire insulation or a wire that is broken inside the insulation.

The frequency of the malfunction can be checked by using the enhanced diagnostic function of the TECH 1.

If the customer's comments reflect that the "ABS" indicator is on only during moist environmental changes (rain, snow, vehicle wash, etc.), all wheel speed sensor circuitry should be thoroughly inspected for signs of water intrusion. Use the following procedure:

1. Spray down the suspected area with 5% salt water solution (10 ml [2 teaspoons] of salt to 355 ml [12 fl.oz.] of water).
2. Start vehicle and allow it to run for ten seconds.
3. If the DTC returns immediately, replace the suspected harness.

Any circuitry that is suspected of causing the intermittent complaint should be thoroughly checked for backed out terminals, improper mating, broken locks, improperly formed or damaged terminals, poor terminal-to-wiring connections or physical damage to the wiring harness.

When measuring wheel speed sensor resistance, ensure vehicle is at room temperature (approximately 20°C [68°F]). Wheel speed sensor resistance will vary with temperature.

When replacing a wheel speed sensor, inspect the sensor terminals and harness connector for corrosion and/or water intrusion. If evidence of corrosion or water intrusion exists, replace the wheel speed sensor.

GC402940096402AX

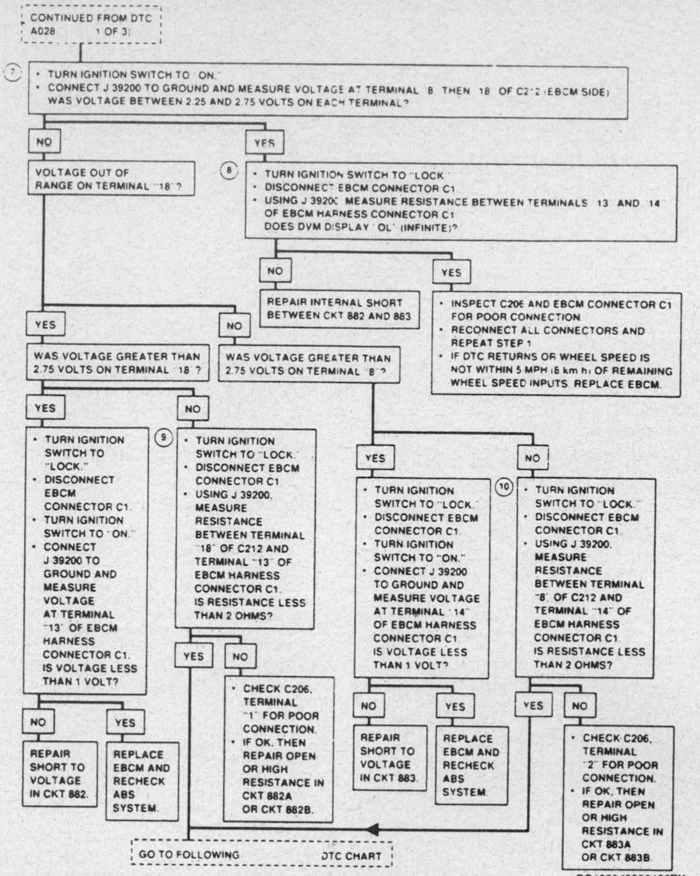
CONTINUED FROM DTC A028 (1 OF 3)
7
• TURN IGNITION SWITCH TO "ON."
• CONNECT J 39200 TO GROUND AND MEASURE VOLTAGE AT TERMINAL "8" THEN "18" OF C212 (EBCM SIDE).
WAS VOLTAGE BETWEEN 2.25 AND 2.75 VOLTS ON EACH TERMINAL?
NO
YES
VOLTAGE OUT OF RANGE ON TERMINAL "18"?
8
• TURN IGNITION SWITCH TO "LOCK."
• DISCONNECT EBCM CONNECTOR C1.
• USING J 39200 MEASURE RESISTANCE BETWEEN TERMINALS "13" AND "14" OF EBCM HARNESS CONNECTOR C1.
DOES DVM DISPLAY "OL" (INFINITE)?
NO
YES
REPAIR INTERNAL SHORT BETWEEN CKT 882 AND 883.
• INSPECT C206 AND EBCM CONNECTOR C1 FOR POOR CONNECTION.
• RECONNECT ALL CONNECTORS AND REPEAT STEP 1.
• IF DTC RETURNS OR WHEEL SPEED IS NOT WITHIN 5 MPH (8 km/h) OF REMAINING WHEEL SPEED INPUTS, REPLACE EBCM.
YES
NO
WAS VOLTAGE GREATER THAN 2.75 VOLTS ON TERMINAL "18"?
WAS VOLTAGE GREATER THAN 2.75 VOLTS ON TERMINAL "8"?
YES
NO
• TURN IGNITION SWITCH TO "LOCK."
• DISCONNECT EBCM CONNECTOR C1.
• TURN IGNITION SWITCH TO "ON."
• CONNECT J 39200 TO GROUND AND MEASURE VOLTAGE AT TERMINAL "13" OF EBCM HARNESS CONNECTOR C1.
IS VOLTAGE LESS THAN 1 VOLT?
9
• TURN IGNITION SWITCH TO "LOCK."
• DISCONNECT EBCM CONNECTOR C1.
• USING J 39200, MEASURE RESISTANCE BETWEEN TERMINAL "18" OF C212 AND TERMINAL "13" OF EBCM HARNESS CONNECTOR C1.
IS RESISTANCE LESS THAN 2 OHMS?
YES
NO
• TURN IGNITION SWITCH TO "LOCK."
• DISCONNECT EBCM CONNECTOR C1.
• TURN IGNITION SWITCH TO "ON."
• CONNECT J 39200 TO GROUND AND MEASURE VOLTAGE AT TERMINAL "14" OF EBCM HARNESS CONNECTOR C1.
IS VOLTAGE LESS THAN 1 VOLT?
10
• TURN IGNITION SWITCH TO "LOCK."
• DISCONNECT EBCM CONNECTOR C1.
• USING J 39200, MEASURE RESISTANCE BETWEEN TERMINAL "8" OF C212 AND TERMINAL "14" OF EBCM HARNESS CONNECTOR C1.
IS RESISTANCE LESS THAN 2 OHMS?
YES
NO
NO
YES
• CHECK C206, TERMINAL "1" FOR POOR CONNECTION.
• IF OK, THEN REPAIR OPEN OR HIGH RESISTANCE IN CKT 882A OR CKT 882B.
NO
YES
YES
NO
REPAIR SHORT TO VOLTAGE IN CKT 882.
REPLACE EBCM AND RECHECK ABS SYSTEM.
REPAIR SHORT TO VOLTAGE IN CKT 883.
REPLACE EBCM AND RECHECK ABS SYSTEM.
• CHECK C206, TERMINAL "2" FOR POOR CONNECTION.
• IF OK, THEN REPAIR OPEN OR HIGH RESISTANCE IN CKT 883A OR CKT 883B.
GO TO FOLLOWING DTC CHART

GC402940096402BX

Fig. 314 Code A028: Right Rear Excessive Wheel Speed Variation (Part 2 of 3). 1993–94 Prizm

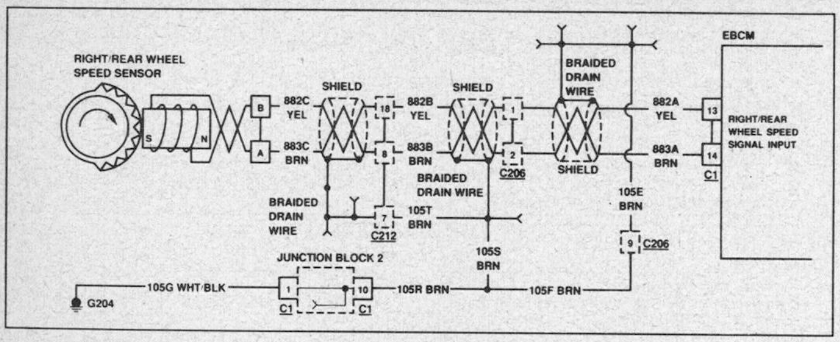
RIGHT/REAR WHEEL SPEED SENSOR
SHIELD
882C YEL
883C BRN
SHIELD
882B YEL
883B BRN
BRAIDED DRAIN WIRE
SHIELD
882A YEL
883A BRN
EBCM
RIGHT/REAR WHEEL SPEED SIGNAL INPUT
C1
C206
BRAIDED DRAIN WIRE
105T BRN
C212
105E BRN
105S BRN
C206
JUNCTION BLOCK 2
105G WHT/BLK
105R BRN
105F BRN
G204

DTC A028

(Page 3 of 3)
RIGHT REAR EXCESSIVE WHEEL SPEED VARIATION

Circuit Description:

As a toothed ring passes by the wheel speed sensor, changes in the electromagnetic field cause the wheel speed sensor to produce a sinusoidal (AC) voltage signal whose frequency is proportional to wheel speed. The magnitude of this signal is directly related to wheel speed and the proximity of the wheel speed sensor to the toothed ring (often referred to as the air gap).

Failure Condition:

DTC A028 can be set when the brake is off. The purpose of this test is to detect a situation in which the right rear wheel acceleration or deceleration is beyond specified limits.

Action Taken:

A DTC A028 is stored. ABS is disabled and the "ABS" indicator is turned on.

Test Description: Number(s) below refer to circled number(s) on the diagnostic chart.

11. This test checks for a short to ground in both wheel speed signal circuits.
12. This step ensures that DTC A028 was not set due to a poor connection between the EBCM connector C1 and the EBCM.

Diagnostic Aids:

An "intermittent" malfunction may be caused by a poor connection, rubbed through wire insulation or a wire that is broken inside the insulation.

The frequency of the malfunction can be checked by using the enhanced diagnostic function of the TECH 1.

If the customer's comments reflect that the "ABS" indicator is on only during moist environmental changes (rain, snow, vehicle wash, etc.), all wheel speed sensor circuitry should be thoroughly inspected for signs of water intrusion. Use the following procedure:

1. Spray down the suspected area with 5% salt water solution (10 ml [2 teaspoons] of salt to 355 ml [12 fl.oz.] of water).
2. Start vehicle and allow it to run for ten seconds.
3. If the DTC returns immediately, replace the suspected harness.

Any circuitry that is suspected of causing the intermittent complaint should be thoroughly checked for backed out terminals, improper mating, broken locks, improperly formed or damaged terminals, poor terminal-to-wiring connections or physical damage to the wiring harness.

When measuring wheel speed sensor resistance, ensure vehicle is at room temperature (approximately 20°C [68°F]). Wheel speed sensor resistance will vary with temperature.

When replacing a wheel speed sensor, inspect the sensor terminals and harness connector for corrosion and/or water intrusion. If evidence of corrosion or water intrusion exists, replace the wheel speed sensor.

GC402940096403AX

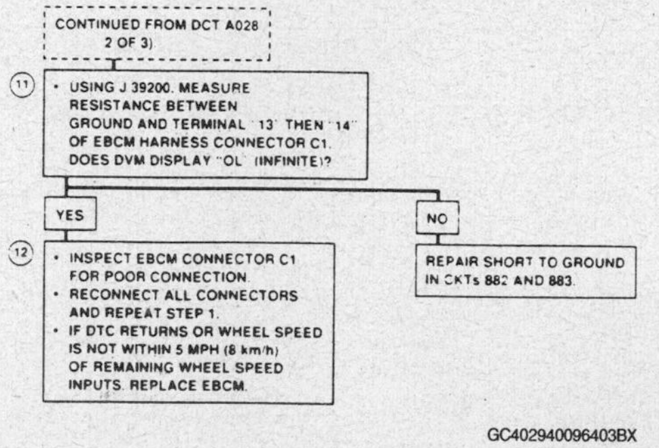
CONTINUED FROM DCT A028 (2 OF 3)
11
• USING J 39200, MEASURE RESISTANCE BETWEEN GROUND AND TERMINAL "13" THEN "14" OF EBCM HARNESS CONNECTOR C1.
DOES DVM DISPLAY "OL" (INFINITE)?
YES
NO
12
• INSPECT EBCM CONNECTOR C1 FOR POOR CONNECTION.
• RECONNECT ALL CONNECTORS AND REPEAT STEP 1.
• IF DTC RETURNS OR WHEEL SPEED IS NOT WITHIN 5 MPH (8 km/h) OF REMAINING WHEEL SPEED INPUTS, REPLACE EBCM.
REPAIR SHORT TO GROUND IN CKTs 882 AND 883.

GC402940096403BX

DUMMY00000000001

Fig. 314 Code A028: Right Rear Excessive Wheel Speed Variation (Part 3 of 3). 1993–94 Prizm

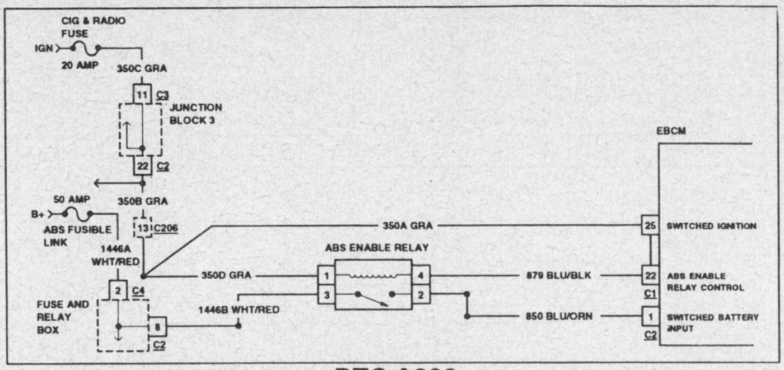

CIG & RADIO FUSE
IGN
20 AMP
350C GRA
C3
JUNCTION BLOCK 3
C2
50 AMP
350B GRA
B+
ABS FUSIBLE LINK
C206
1446A WHT/RED
350A GRA
ABS ENABLE RELAY
350D GRA
879 BLU/BLK
1446B WHT/RED
850 BLU/ORN
C4
FUSE AND RELAY BOX
EBCM
SWITCHED IGNITION
ABS ENABLE RELAY CONTROL
SWITCHED BATTERY INPUT
C1
C2

DTC A036
LOW SYSTEM VOLTAGE

Circuit Description:

This DTC is used to monitor the voltage level available to the EBCM. If the voltage drops below 11 volts, full performance of the ABS cannot be guaranteed. During ABS operation, there are several current requirements that will cause battery voltage to drop. Because of this, voltage is monitored prior to ABS operation to indicate good charging system condition and also during ABS operation when voltage may drop significantly.

Failure Condition:

DTC A036 can only be set if the vehicle's speed is greater than 8 km/h (5 mph). If the switched battery voltage is less than 11.8 volts before ABS operation or 9.3 volts during ABS operation, a malfunction exists.

Action Taken:

A DTC A036 is stored, ABS is disabled and the "ABS" indicator is turned on or will flash. If the rear motor is not in the home position, the "BRAKE" indicator is also turned on.

Test Description: Number(s) below refer to circled number(s) on the diagnostic chart.

1. This test checks to see what voltage is readily available at terminal "1" of the EBCM connector C2. If voltage is representative of good charging system condition, a malfunction is not present.
2. This step isolates the EBCM to check the condition of the circuitry and charging system.
3. This step isolates the low voltage condition to high circuit resistance or improper charging system operation.
4. This step checks for a possible intermittent malfunction.
5. This step checks for adequate voltage at the EBCM when a load is applied to the system.
6. This step isolates which circuit is the source of the low voltage condition.

Diagnostic Aids:

An "intermittent" malfunction may be caused by a poor connection, rubbed through wire insulation or a wire that is broken inside the insulation.

The frequency of the malfunction can be checked by using the enhanced diagnostic function of the TECH 1

Any circuitry that is suspected of causing the intermittent complaint should be thoroughly checked for backed out terminals, improper mating, broken locks, improperly formed or damaged terminals, poor terminal-to-wiring connections or physical damage to the wiring harness.

While performing a voltage load test, if it is noted that only ignition voltage drops below acceptable voltage levels, CKT 350D should be checked for high resistance or an open condition.

GC402940096500AX

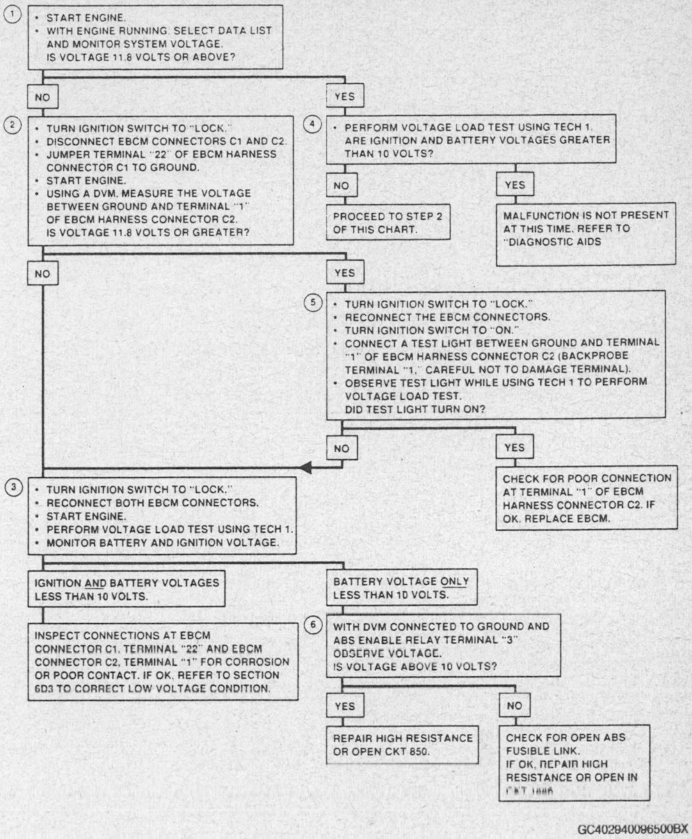

1
• START ENGINE.
• WITH ENGINE RUNNING, SELECT DATA LIST AND MONITOR SYSTEM VOLTAGE.
IS VOLTAGE 11.8 VOLTS OR ABOVE?
NO
YES
2
• TURN IGNITION SWITCH TO "LOCK."
• DISCONNECT EBCM CONNECTORS C1 AND C2.
• JUMPER TERMINAL "22" OF EBCM HARNESS CONNECTOR C1 TO GROUND.
• START ENGINE.
• USING A DVM, MEASURE THE VOLTAGE BETWEEN GROUND AND TERMINAL "1" OF EBCM HARNESS CONNECTOR C2.
IS VOLTAGE 11.8 VOLTS OR GREATER?
4
• PERFORM VOLTAGE LOAD TEST USING TECH 1.
ARE IGNITION AND BATTERY VOLTAGES GREATER THAN 10 VOLTS?
NO
YES
PROCEED TO STEP 2 OF THIS CHART.
MALFUNCTION IS NOT PRESENT AT THIS TIME. REFER TO "DIAGNOSTIC AIDS
NO
YES
5
• TURN IGNITION SWITCH TO "LOCK."
• RECONNECT THE EBCM CONNECTORS.
• TURN IGNITION SWITCH TO "ON."
• CONNECT A TEST LIGHT BETWEEN GROUND AND TERMINAL "1" OF EBCM HARNESS CONNECTOR C2 (BACKPROBE TERMINAL "1," CAREFUL NOT TO DAMAGE TERMINAL).
• OBSERVE TEST LIGHT WHILE USING TECH 1 TO PERFORM VOLTAGE LOAD TEST.
DID TEST LIGHT TURN ON?
NO
YES
CHECK FOR POOR CONNECTION AT TERMINAL "1" OF EBCM HARNESS CONNECTOR C2. IF OK, REPLACE EBCM.
3
• TURN IGNITION SWITCH TO "LOCK."
• RECONNECT BOTH EBCM CONNECTORS.
• START ENGINE.
• PERFORM VOLTAGE LOAD TEST USING TECH 1.
• MONITOR BATTERY AND IGNITION VOLTAGE.
IGNITION AND BATTERY VOLTAGES LESS THAN 10 VOLTS.
BATTERY VOLTAGE ONLY LESS THAN 10 VOLTS.
INSPECT CONNECTIONS AT EBCM CONNECTOR C1, TERMINAL "22" AND EBCM CONNECTOR C2, TERMINAL "1" FOR CORROSION OR POOR CONTACT. IF OK, REFER TO SECTION 6D3 TO CORRECT LOW VOLTAGE CONDITION.
6
WITH DVM CONNECTED TO GROUND AND ABS ENABLE RELAY TERMINAL "3" OBSERVE VOLTAGE.
IS VOLTAGE ABOVE 10 VOLTS?
YES
NO
REPAIR HIGH RESISTANCE OR OPEN CKT 850.
CHECK FOR OPEN ABS FUSIBLE LINK.
IF OK, REPAIR HIGH RESISTANCE OR OPEN IN
GC402940096500BX

Fig. 315 Code 036: Low System Voltage. 1993–94 Prizm

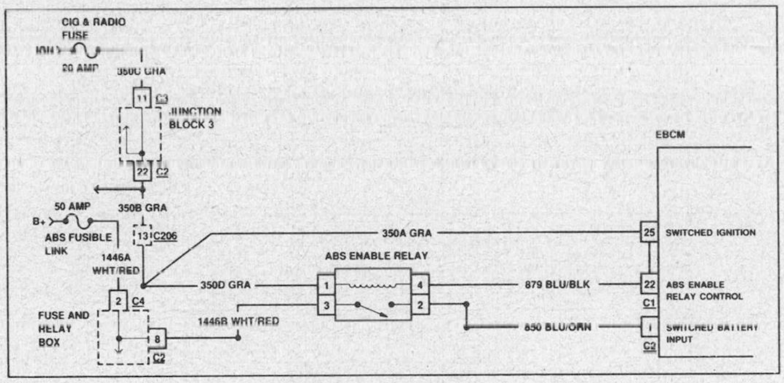

CIG & RADIO FUSE
IGN
20 AMP
350C GRA
C3
JUNCTION BLOCK 3
C2
50 AMP
350B GRA
B+
ABS FUSIBLE LINK
C206
1446A WHT/RED
350A GRA
ABS ENABLE RELAY
350D GRA
879 BLU/BLK
1446B WHT/RED
850 BLU/ORN
C4
FUSE AND RELAY BOX
EBCM
SWITCHED IGNITION
ABS ENABLE RELAY CONTROL
SWITCHED BATTERY INPUT
C1
C2

DTC A037
HIGH SYSTEM VOLTAGE

Circuit Description:

This DTC is designed to detect high vehicle voltage levels prior to any required motor movement (initialization or ABS operation). If excessive voltage exists, demagnetization of the motor magnets may occur, which would eventually affect or eliminate ABS performance.

Failure Condition:

DTC A037 can only be set if the vehicle's speed is greater then 8 km/h (5 mph). If the switched battery voltage is greater than 17 volts, a malfunction exists.

Action Taken:

A DTC A037 is stored, ABS is disabled and the "ABS" indicator lamps is turned on.

Test Description: Number(s) below refer to circled number(s) on the diagnostic chart.

1. This step checks the voltage level being received by the EBCM.
2. This step indicates whether the high voltage condition is caused by a malfunctioning charging system or EBCM.

Diagnostic Aids:

An "intermittent" malfunction may be caused by a poor connection, rubbed through wire insulation or a wire that is broken inside the insulation.

The frequency of the malfunction can be checked by using the enhanced diagnostic function of the TECH 1.

Any circuitry that is suspected of causing the intermittent complaint should be thoroughly checked for backed out terminals, improper mating, broken locks, improperly formed or damaged terminals, poor terminal-to-wiring connections or physical damage to the wiring harness.

GC402940096600AX

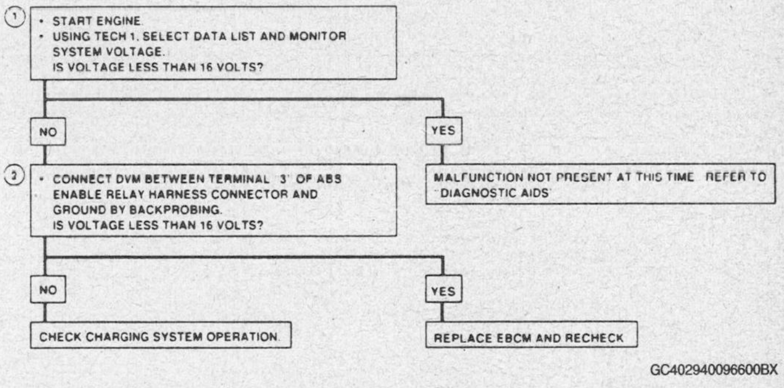

1
• START ENGINE.
• USING TECH 1, SELECT DATA LIST AND MONITOR SYSTEM VOLTAGE.
IS VOLTAGE LESS THAN 16 VOLTS?
NO
YES
2
• CONNECT DVM BETWEEN TERMINAL "3" OF ABS ENABLE RELAY HARNESS CONNECTOR AND GROUND BY BACKPROBING.
IS VOLTAGE LESS THAN 16 VOLTS?
MALFUNCTION NOT PRESENT AT THIS TIME. REFER TO "DIAGNOSTIC AIDS"
NO
YES
CHECK CHARGING SYSTEM OPERATION.
REPLACE EBCM AND RECHECK.
GC402940096600BX

Fig. 316 Code A037: High System Voltage. 1993–94 Prizm

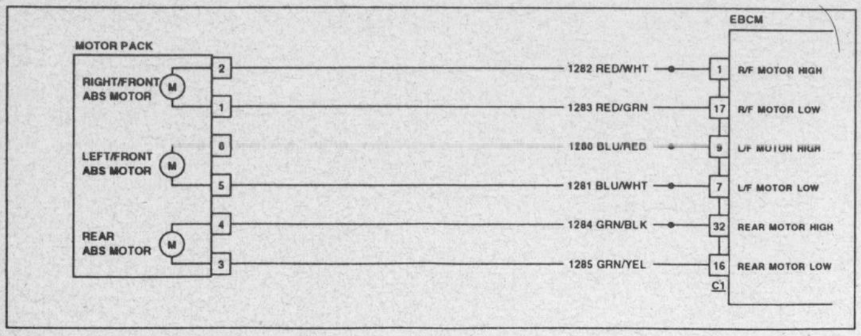
EBCM
MOTOR PACK
RIGHT/FRONT ABS MOTOR
LEFT/FRONT ABS MOTOR
REAR ABS MOTOR
1282 RED/WHT
1283 RED/GRN
1280 BLU/RED
1281 BLU/WHT
1284 GRN/BLK
1285 GRN/YEL
R/F MOTOR HIGH
R/F MOTOR LOW
L/F MOTOR HIGH
L/F MOTOR LOW
REAR MOTOR HIGH
REAR MOTOR LOW
C1

DTC A038

LEFT FRONT ESB WILL NOT HOLD MOTOR

Circuit Description:

This DTC is designed to detect a slipping left front ESB. During initialization and braking, the left front motor is re-homed. If the ESB slips, the motor/piston will move. During the next ignition "ON" initialization, a rehome of the motor verifies that the motor/piston remained at the home position. If motor movement is detected, the ESB must be slipping.

Failure Condition:

DTC A038 can be set during initialization. If the EBCM detects that the ESB could not hold the piston in the home position, a malfunction exists.

Action Taken:

If an ESB cannot hold a piston in the home position, the piston may be backdriven when the brake pedal is applied, causing the brake pedal to drop. DTCs A038 and A086 are stored, ABS is disabled and the "ABS" indicator is turned on.

Test Description: Number(s) below refer to circled number(s) on the diagnostic chart.

1. This step checks the left front ESB. A broken or defective ESB would result in the left front piston being backdriven by hydraulic pressure and pedal movement would result.
2. This test checks for high resistance in the left front motor high circuit.
3. This test checks for high resistance in the left front motor low circuit.
4. This test checks for high resistance in the left front motor.
5. This test determines if the fault is due to poor terminal contact or corrosion.
6. This test determines if the fault is due to a faulty EBCM.

Diagnostic Aids:

An "intermittent" malfunction in this DTC may result from a mechanical part of the system that sticks, binds or slips.

The frequency of the malfunction can be checked by using the enhanced diagnostic feature of the TECH 1

The static modulator test function of the TECH 1 may be used to locate an intermittent malfunction associated with the ESB.

GC402940096700AX

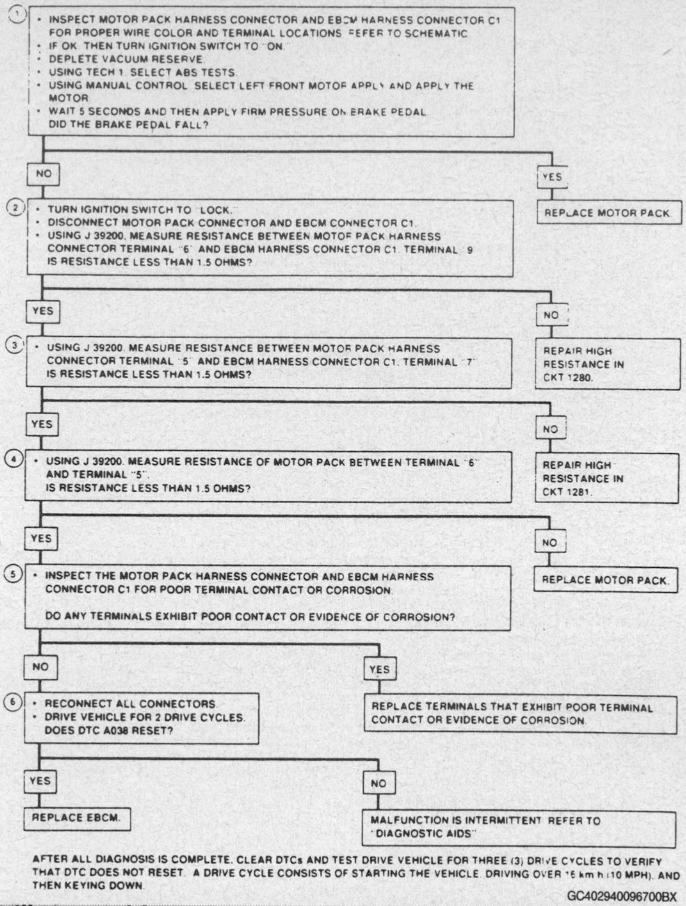
1
• INSPECT MOTOR PACK HARNESS CONNECTOR AND EBCM HARNESS CONNECTOR C1 FOR PROPER WIRE COLOR AND TERMINAL LOCATIONS REFER TO SCHEMATIC
• IF OK THEN TURN IGNITION SWITCH TO "ON."
• DEPLETE VACUUM RESERVE.
• USING TECH 1 SELECT ABS TESTS.
• USING MANUAL CONTROL SELECT LEFT FRONT MOTOR APPLY AND APPLY THE MOTOR
• WAIT 5 SECONDS AND THEN APPLY FIRM PRESSURE ON BRAKE PEDAL.
DID THE BRAKE PEDAL FALL?
NO
YES
REPLACE MOTOR PACK
2
• TURN IGNITION SWITCH TO "LOCK."
• DISCONNECT MOTOR PACK CONNECTOR AND EBCM CONNECTOR C1.
• USING J 39200. MEASURE RESISTANCE BETWEEN MOTOR PACK HARNESS CONNECTOR TERMINAL "6" AND EBCM HARNESS CONNECTOR C1. TERMINAL "9
IS RESISTANCE LESS THAN 1.5 OHMS?
YES
NO
3
• USING J 39200. MEASURE RESISTANCE BETWEEN MOTOR PACK HARNESS CONNECTOR TERMINAL "5" AND EBCM HARNESS CONNECTOR C1. TERMINAL "7"
IS RESISTANCE LESS THAN 1.5 OHMS?
REPAIR HIGH RESISTANCE IN CKT 1280.
YES
NO
4
• USING J 39200. MEASURE RESISTANCE OF MOTOR PACK BETWEEN TERMINAL "6" AND TERMINAL "5".
IS RESISTANCE LESS THAN 1.5 OHMS?
REPAIR HIGH RESISTANCE IN CKT 1281.
YES
NO
5
• INSPECT THE MOTOR PACK HARNESS CONNECTOR AND EBCM HARNESS CONNECTOR C1 FOR POOR TERMINAL CONTACT OR CORROSION.
DO ANY TERMINALS EXHIBIT POOR CONTACT OR EVIDENCE OF CORROSION?
REPLACE MOTOR PACK.
NO
YES
6
• RECONNECT ALL CONNECTORS.
• DRIVE VEHICLE FOR 2 DRIVE CYCLES.
DOES DTC A038 RESET?
REPLACE TERMINALS THAT EXHIBIT POOR TERMINAL CONTACT OR EVIDENCE OF CORROSION.
YES
NO
REPLACE EBCM.
MALFUNCTION IS INTERMITTENT REFER TO "DIAGNOSTIC AIDS"
AFTER ALL DIAGNOSIS IS COMPLETE. CLEAR DTCs AND TEST DRIVE VEHICLE FOR THREE (3) DRIVE CYCLES TO VERIFY THAT DTC DOES NOT RESET. A DRIVE CYCLE CONSISTS OF STARTING THE VEHICLE DRIVING OVER 16 km h (10 MPH). AND THEN KEYING DOWN.

GC402940096700BX

Fig. 317 Code A038: Left Front EBS Will Not Hold Motor. 1993–94 Prizm

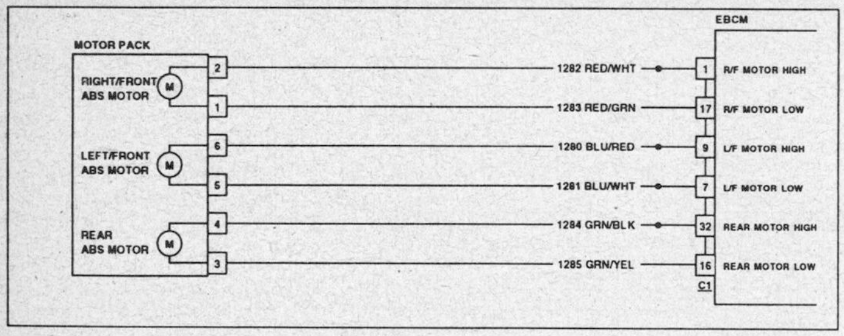
EBCM
MOTOR PACK
RIGHT/FRONT ABS MOTOR
LEFT/FRONT ABS MOTOR
REAR ABS MOTOR
1282 RED/WHT
1283 RED/GRN
1280 BLU/RED
1281 BLU/WHT
1284 GRN/BLK
1285 GRN/YEL
R/F MOTOR HIGH
R/F MOTOR LOW
L/F MOTOR HIGH
L/F MOTOR LOW
REAR MOTOR HIGH
REAR MOTOR LOW
C1

DTC A041

RIGHT FRONT ESB WILL NOT HOLD MOTOR

Circuit Description:

This DTC is designed to detect a slipping right front ESB. During initialization and braking, the right front motor is rehomed. If the ESB slips, the motor/piston will move. During the next ignition "ON" initialization, a rehome of the motor verifies that the motor/piston remained at the home position. If motor movement is detected, the ESB must be slipping.

Failure Condition:

DTC A041 can be set during initialization. If the EBCM detects that the ESB could not hold the piston in the home position, a malfunction exists.

Action Taken:

If an ESB cannot hold a piston in the home position, the piston may be backdriven when the brake pedal is applied, causing the brake pedal to drop. DTCs A041 and A086 are stored, ABS is disabled and the "ABS" indicator is turned on.

Test Description: Number(s) below refer to circled number(s) on the diagnostic chart.

1. This step checks the right front ESB. A broken or defective ESB would result in the right front piston being backdriven by hydraulic pressure and pedal movement would result.
2. This test checks for high resistance in the right front motor high circuit.
3. This test checks for high resistance in the right front motor low circuit.
4. This test checks for high resistance in the right front motor.
5. This test determines if the fault is due to poor terminal contact or corrosion.
6. This test determines if the fault is due to a faulty EBCM.

Diagnostic Aids:

An "intermittent" malfunction in this DTC may result from a mechanical part of the system that sticks, binds or slips.

The frequency of the malfunction can be checked by using the enhanced diagnostic feature of the TECH 1

The static modulator test function of the TECH 1 may be used to locate an intermittent malfunction associated with the ESB.

GC402940096800AX

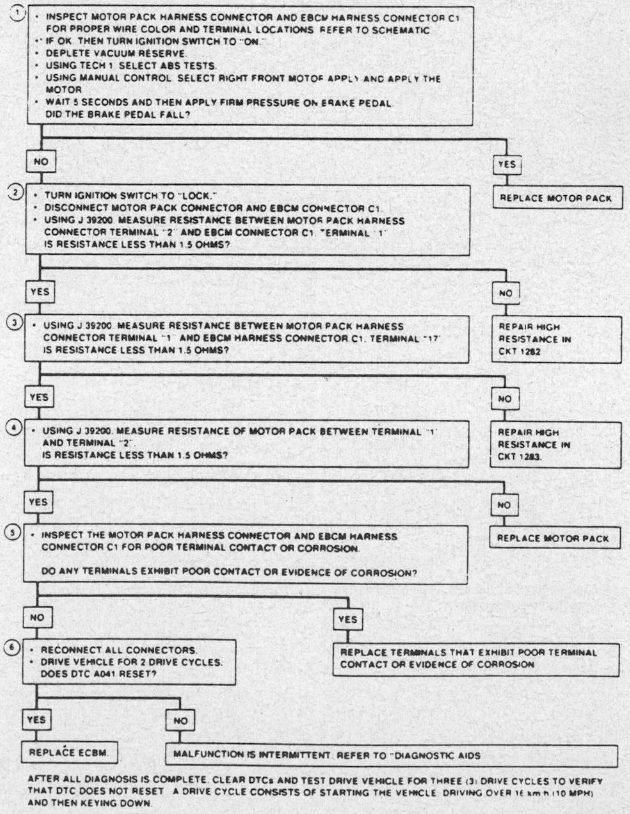
1
• INSPECT MOTOR PACK HARNESS CONNECTOR AND EBCM HARNESS CONNECTOR C1 FOR PROPER WIRE COLOR AND TERMINAL LOCATIONS REFER TO SCHEMATIC
• IF OK. THEN TURN IGNITION SWITCH TO "ON."
• DEPLETE VACUUM RESERVE.
• USING TECH 1 SELECT ABS TESTS.
• USING MANUAL CONTROL SELECT RIGHT FRONT MOTOR APPLY AND APPLY THE MOTOR
• WAIT 5 SECONDS AND THEN APPLY FIRM PRESSURE ON BRAKE PEDAL.
DID THE BRAKE PEDAL FALL?
NO
YES
REPLACE MOTOR PACK
2
• TURN IGNITION SWITCH TO "LOCK."
• DISCONNECT MOTOR PACK CONNECTOR AND EBCM CONNECTOR C1.
• USING J 39200. MEASURE RESISTANCE BETWEEN MOTOR PACK HARNESS CONNECTOR TERMINAL "2" AND EBCM CONNECTOR C1. TERMINAL "1"
IS RESISTANCE LESS THAN 1.5 OHMS?
YES
NO
3
• USING J 39200. MEASURE RESISTANCE BETWEEN MOTOR PACK HARNESS CONNECTOR TERMINAL "1" AND EBCM HARNESS CONNECTOR C1. TERMINAL "17"
IS RESISTANCE LESS THAN 1.5 OHMS?
REPAIR HIGH RESISTANCE IN CKT 1282
YES
NO
4
• USING J 39200. MEASURE RESISTANCE OF MOTOR PACK BETWEEN TERMINAL "1" AND TERMINAL "2".
IS RESISTANCE LESS THAN 1.5 OHMS?
REPAIR HIGH RESISTANCE IN CKT 1283.
YES
NO
5
• INSPECT THE MOTOR PACK HARNESS CONNECTOR AND EBCM HARNESS CONNECTOR C1 FOR POOR TERMINAL CONTACT OR CORROSION.
DO ANY TERMINALS EXHIBIT POOR CONTACT OR EVIDENCE OF CORROSION?
REPLACE MOTOR PACK
NO
YES
6
• RECONNECT ALL CONNECTORS.
• DRIVE VEHICLE FOR 2 DRIVE CYCLES.
DOES DTC A041 RESET?
REPLACE TERMINALS THAT EXHIBIT POOR TERMINAL CONTACT OR EVIDENCE OF CORROSION
YES
NO
REPLACE ECBM.
MALFUNCTION IS INTERMITTENT REFER TO "DIAGNOSTIC AIDS
AFTER ALL DIAGNOSIS IS COMPLETE. CLEAR DTCs AND TEST DRIVE VEHICLE FOR THREE (3) DRIVE CYCLES TO VERIFY THAT DTC DOES NOT RESET A DRIVE CYCLE CONSISTS OF STARTING THE VEHICLE DRIVING OVER 16 km h (10 MPH) AND THEN KEYING DOWN.

GC402940096800BX

Fig. 318 Code A041: Right Front EBS Will Not Hold Motor. 1993–94 Prizm

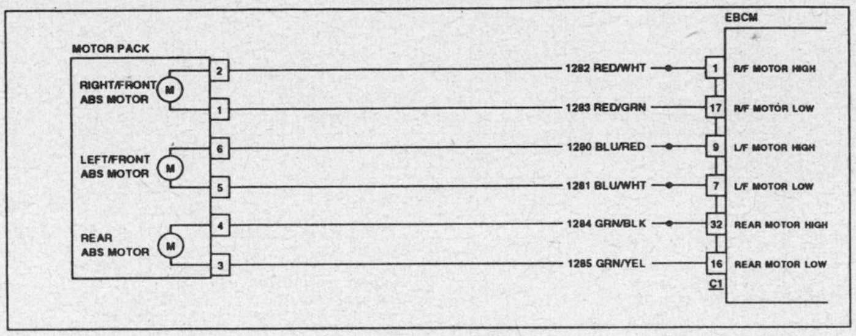
EBCM
MOTOR PACK
RIGHT/FRONT ABS MOTOR
LEFT/FRONT ABS MOTOR
REAR ABS MOTOR
M
2
1
6
5
4
3
1282 RED/WHT
1283 RED/GRN
1280 BLU/RED
1281 BLU/WHT
1284 GRN/BLK
1285 GRN/YEL
1 R/F MOTOR HIGH
17 R/F MOTOR LOW
9 L/F MOTOR HIGH
7 L/F MOTOR LOW
32 REAR MOTOR HIGH
16 REAR MOTOR LOW
C1

DTC A042

REAR ESB WILL NOT HOLD MOTOR

Circuit Description:

This DTC is designed to detect a slipping rear ESB. During initialization and braking, the rear motor is rehomed. If the ESB slips, the motor/piston will move. During the next ignition "ON" initialization, a rehome of the motor verifies that the motor/piston remained at the home position. If motor movement is detected, the ESB must be slipping.

Failure Condition:

DTC A042 can be set during initialization. If the EBCM detects that the ESB could not hold the piston in the home position, a malfunction exists. DTC A086 is always set with DTC A042.

Action Taken:

If an ESB cannot hold a piston in the home position, the piston may be backdriven when the brake pedal is applied, causing the brake pedal to drop. DTCs A042 and A086 are stored, ABS is disabled and the "ABS" and "BRAKE" indicators are turned on. The "ABS" indicator will flash if the EBCM cannot illuminate the "BRAKE" indicator.

Test Description: Number(s) below refer to circled number(s) on the diagnostic chart.

1. This step checks the rear ESB. A broken or defective ESB would result in the rear piston being backdriven by hydraulic pressure and pedal movement would result.
2. This test checks for high resistance in the rear motor high circuit.
3. This test checks for high resistance in the rear motor low circuit.
4. This test checks for high resistance in the rear motor.
5. This test determines if the fault is due to poor terminal contact or corrosion.
6. This test determines if the fault is due to a faulty ECBM.

Diagnostic Aids:

An "intermittent" malfunction in this DTC may result from a mechanical part of the system that sticks, binds or slips.

The frequency of the malfunction can be checked by using the enhanced diagnostic feature of the TECH 1.

The static modulator test function of the TECH 1 may be used to locate an intermittent malfunction associated with the ESB.

GC402940096900AX

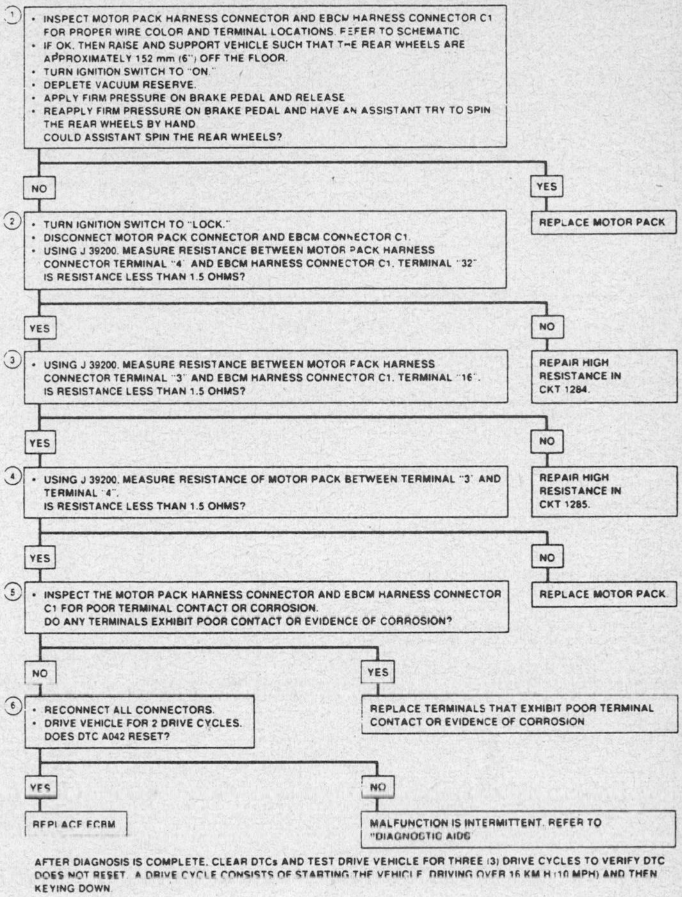
1
• INSPECT MOTOR PACK HARNESS CONNECTOR AND EBCM HARNESS CONNECTOR C1 FOR PROPER WIRE COLOR AND TERMINAL LOCATIONS. REFER TO SCHEMATIC.
• IF OK, THEN RAISE AND SUPPORT VEHICLE SUCH THAT THE REAR WHEELS ARE APPROXIMATELY 152 mm (6") OFF THE FLOOR.
• TURN IGNITION SWITCH TO "ON."
• DEPLETE VACUUM RESERVE.
• APPLY FIRM PRESSURE ON BRAKE PEDAL AND RELEASE.
• REAPPLY FIRM PRESSURE ON BRAKE PEDAL AND HAVE AN ASSISTANT TRY TO SPIN THE REAR WHEELS BY HAND.
COULD ASSISTANT SPIN THE REAR WHEELS?
NO
YES
REPLACE MOTOR PACK
2
• TURN IGNITION SWITCH TO "LOCK."
• DISCONNECT MOTOR PACK CONNECTOR AND EBCM CONNECTOR C1.
• USING J 39200, MEASURE RESISTANCE BETWEEN MOTOR PACK HARNESS CONNECTOR TERMINAL "4" AND EBCM HARNESS CONNECTOR C1, TERMINAL "32".
IS RESISTANCE LESS THAN 1.5 OHMS?
YES
NO
3
• USING J 39200, MEASURE RESISTANCE BETWEEN MOTOR PACK HARNESS CONNECTOR TERMINAL "3" AND EBCM HARNESS CONNECTOR C1, TERMINAL "16".
IS RESISTANCE LESS THAN 1.5 OHMS?
REPAIR HIGH RESISTANCE IN CKT 1284.
YES
NO
4
• USING J 39200, MEASURE RESISTANCE OF MOTOR PACK BETWEEN TERMINAL "3" AND TERMINAL "4".
IS RESISTANCE LESS THAN 1.5 OHMS?
REPAIR HIGH RESISTANCE IN CKT 1285.
YES
NO
5
• INSPECT THE MOTOR PACK HARNESS CONNECTOR AND EBCM HARNESS CONNECTOR C1 FOR POOR TERMINAL CONTACT OR CORROSION.
DO ANY TERMINALS EXHIBIT POOR CONTACT OR EVIDENCE OF CORROSION?
REPLACE MOTOR PACK
NO
YES
6
• RECONNECT ALL CONNECTORS.
• DRIVE VEHICLE FOR 2 DRIVE CYCLES.
DOES DTC A042 RESET?
REPLACE TERMINALS THAT EXHIBIT POOR TERMINAL CONTACT OR EVIDENCE OF CORROSION
YES
NO
REPLACE ECBM
MALFUNCTION IS INTERMITTENT. REFER TO "DIAGNOSTIC AIDS"
AFTER DIAGNOSIS IS COMPLETE, CLEAR DTCs AND TEST DRIVE VEHICLE FOR THREE (3) DRIVE CYCLES TO VERIFY DTC DOES NOT RESET. A DRIVE CYCLE CONSISTS OF STARTING THE VEHICLE, DRIVING OVER 16 KM/H (10 MPH) AND THEN KEYING DOWN.

GC402940096900BX

Fig. 319 Code A042: Rear EBS Will Not Hold Motor. 1993–94 Prizm

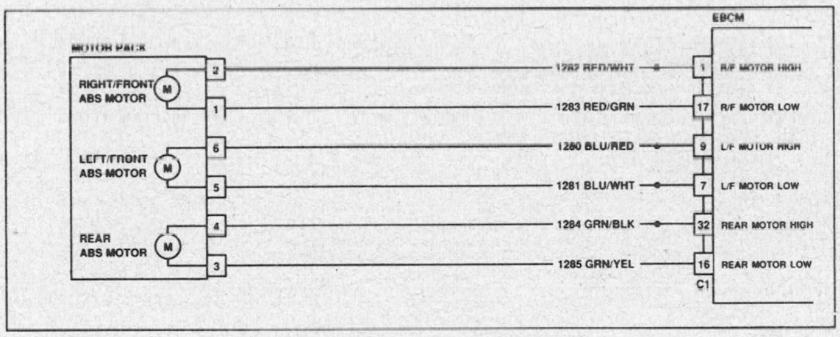
EBCM
MOTOR PACK
RIGHT/FRONT ABS MOTOR
LEFT/FRONT ABS MOTOR
REAR ABS MOTOR
M
2
1
6
5
4
3
1282 RED/WHT
1283 RED/GRN
1280 BLU/RED
1281 BLU/WHT
1284 GRN/BLK
1285 GRN/YEL
1 R/F MOTOR HIGH
17 R/F MOTOR LOW
9 L/F MOTOR HIGH
7 L/F MOTOR LOW
32 REAR MOTOR HIGH
16 REAR MOTOR LOW
C1

DTC A044

LEFT FRONT CHANNEL WILL NOT MOVE

Circuit Description:

This DTC is designed to detect a bound-up ESB, a stuck motor or a seized hydraulic modulator. When the release is commanded during initialization, the ESB should release the motor, resulting in sensed current being less than commanded current (motor is spinning freely). If the motor is not moving, sensed current will be equal to stall current.

Failure Condition:

DTC A044 can be set during normal operation. If the EBCM detects a condition in which it cannot move the motor in either direction, a malfunction exists.

Action Taken:

This malfunction indicates the channel cannot be moved properly. A DTC A044 is stored, ABS is disabled and the "ABS" indicator is turned on.

Test Description: Number(s) below refer to circled number(s) on the diagnostic chart.

1. This step checks for proper motor movement during apply and release commands from the TECH 1.
2. This step compares EBCM command current to motor feedback current.
3. This step checks for proper hydraulic modulator gear and piston movement.
4. This step verifies that the motor can actually apply when commanded.
5. This test determines if the malfunction is caused by a defective EBCM or by a short circuit.

Diagnostic Aids:

An "intermittent" malfunction may be caused by a poor connection, rubbed through wire insulation or a wire that is broken inside the insulation.

The frequency of the malfunction can be checked by using the enhanced diagnostic function of the TECH 1.

DTC A044 may set after modulator disassembly if the modulator pistons are positioned at the bottom of their bore.

Any circuitry that is suspected of causing the intermittent complaint should be thoroughly checked for backed out terminals, improper mating, broken locks, improperly formed or damaged terminals, poor terminal-to-wiring connections or physical damage to the wiring harness.

GC402940097000AX

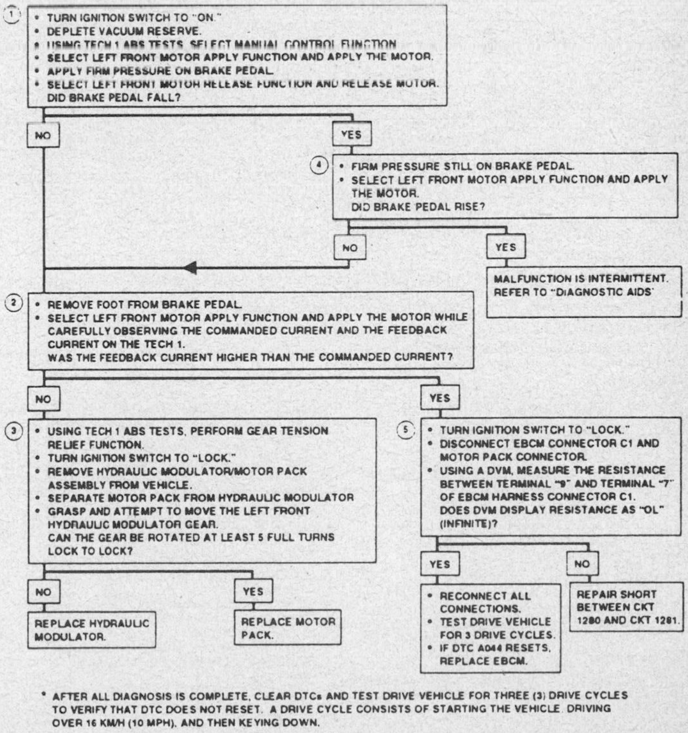
1
• TURN IGNITION SWITCH TO "ON."
• DEPLETE VACUUM RESERVE.
• USING TECH 1 ABS TESTS, SELECT MANUAL CONTROL FUNCTION.
• SELECT LEFT FRONT MOTOR APPLY FUNCTION AND APPLY THE MOTOR.
• APPLY FIRM PRESSURE ON BRAKE PEDAL.
• SELECT LEFT FRONT MOTOR RELEASE FUNCTION AND RELEASE MOTOR.
DID BRAKE PEDAL FALL?
NO
YES
4
• FIRM PRESSURE STILL ON BRAKE PEDAL.
• SELECT LEFT FRONT MOTOR APPLY FUNCTION AND APPLY THE MOTOR.
DID BRAKE PEDAL RISE?
NO
YES
MALFUNCTION IS INTERMITTENT. REFER TO "DIAGNOSTIC AIDS"
2
• REMOVE FOOT FROM BRAKE PEDAL.
• SELECT LEFT FRONT MOTOR APPLY FUNCTION AND APPLY THE MOTOR WHILE CAREFULLY OBSERVING THE COMMANDED CURRENT AND THE FEEDBACK CURRENT ON THE TECH 1.
WAS THE FEEDBACK CURRENT HIGHER THAN THE COMMANDED CURRENT?
NO
YES
3
• USING TECH 1 ABS TESTS, PERFORM GEAR TENSION RELIEF FUNCTION.
• TURN IGNITION SWITCH TO "LOCK."
• REMOVE HYDRAULIC MODULATOR/MOTOR PACK ASSEMBLY FROM VEHICLE.
• SEPARATE MOTOR PACK FROM HYDRAULIC MODULATOR.
• GRASP AND ATTEMPT TO MOVE THE LEFT FRONT HYDRAULIC MODULATOR GEAR.
CAN THE GEAR BE ROTATED AT LEAST 5 FULL TURNS LOCK TO LOCK?
5
• TURN IGNITION SWITCH TO "LOCK."
• DISCONNECT EBCM CONNECTOR C1 AND MOTOR PACK CONNECTOR.
• USING A DVM, MEASURE THE RESISTANCE BETWEEN TERMINAL "9" AND TERMINAL "7" OF EBCM HARNESS CONNECTOR C1.
DOES DVM DISPLAY RESISTANCE AS "OL" (INFINITE)?
NO
YES
YES
NO
REPLACE HYDRAULIC MODULATOR.
REPLACE MOTOR PACK.
• RECONNECT ALL CONNECTIONS.
• TEST DRIVE VEHICLE FOR 3 DRIVE CYCLES.
• IF DTC A044 RESETS, REPLACE EBCM.
REPAIR SHORT BETWEEN CKT 1280 AND CKT 1281.
* AFTER ALL DIAGNOSIS IS COMPLETE, CLEAR DTCs AND TEST DRIVE VEHICLE FOR THREE (3) DRIVE CYCLES TO VERIFY THAT DTC DOES NOT RESET. A DRIVE CYCLE CONSISTS OF STARTING THE VEHICLE, DRIVING OVER 16 KM/H (10 MPH), AND THEN KEYING DOWN.

GC402940097000BX

Fig. 320 Code A044: Left Front Channel Will Not Move. 1993–94 Prizm

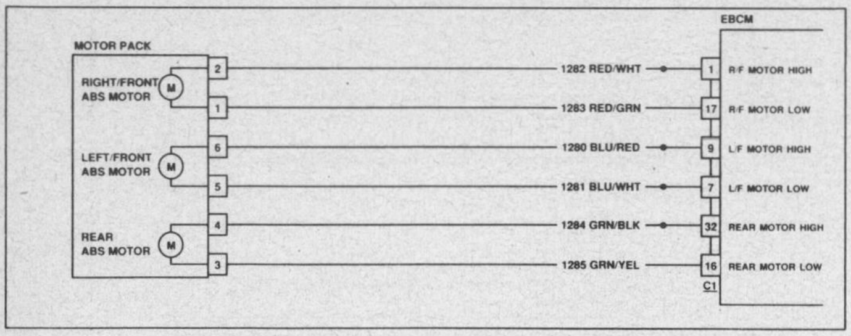
EBCM
MOTOR PACK
RIGHT/FRONT ABS MOTOR
LEFT/FRONT ABS MOTOR
REAR ABS MOTOR
1282 RED/WHT
1283 RED/GRN
1280 BLU/RED
1281 BLU/WHT
1284 GRN/BLK
1285 GRN/YEL
R/F MOTOR HIGH
R/F MOTOR LOW
L/F MOTOR HIGH
L/F MOTOR LOW
REAR MOTOR HIGH
REAR MOTOR LOW
C1

DTC A045

RIGHT FRONT CHANNEL WILL NOT MOVE

Circuit Description:

This DTC is designed to detect a bound-up ESB, a stuck motor or a seized hydraulic modulator. When the release is commanded during initialization, the ESB should release the motor, resulting in sensed current being less than commanded current (motor is spinning freely). If the motor is not moving, sensed current will be equal to stall current.

Failure Condition:

DTC A045 can be set during normal operation. If the EBCM detects a condition in which it cannot move the motor in either direction, a malfunction exists.

Action Taken:

This malfunction indicates the channel cannot be moved properly. A DTC A045 is stored, ABS is disabled and the "ABS" indicator is turned on.

Test Description: Number(s) below refer to circled number(s) on the diagnostic chart.

1. This step checks for proper motor movement during apply and release commands from the TECH 1.
2. This step compares EBCM command current to motor feedback current.
3. This step checks for proper hydraulic modulator gear and piston movement.
4. This step verifies that the motor can actually apply when commanded.
5. This test determines if the malfunction is caused by a defective EBCM or by a short circuit.

Diagnostic Aids:

An "intermittent" malfunction may be caused by a poor connection, rubbed through wire insulation or a wire that is broken inside the insulation.

The frequency of the malfunction can be checked by using the enhanced diagnostic function of the TECH 1.

DTC A045 may set after modulator disassembly if the modulator pistons are positioned at the bottom of their bore.

Any circuitry that is suspected of causing the intermittent complaint should be thoroughly checked for backed out terminals, improper mating, broken locks, improperly formed or damaged terminals, poor terminal-to-wiring connections or physical damage to the wiring harness.

GC402940097100AX

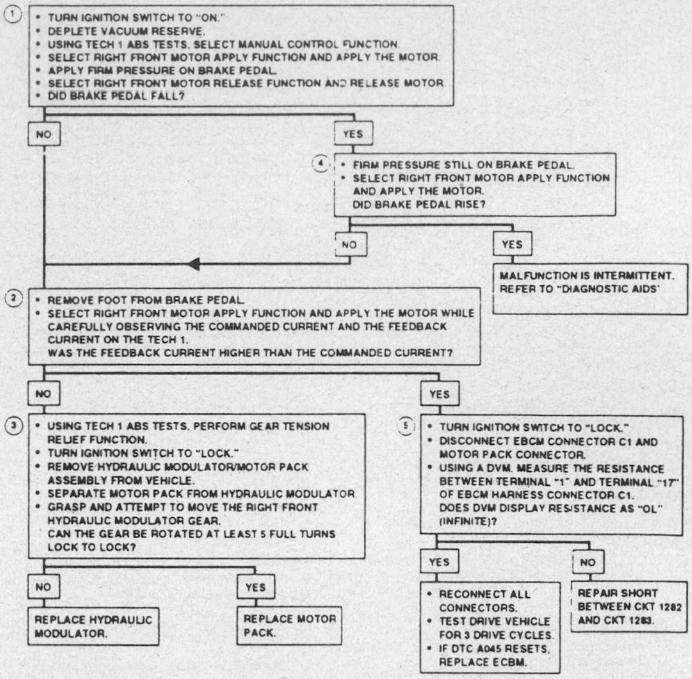
1
• TURN IGNITION SWITCH TO "ON."
• DEPLETE VACUUM RESERVE.
• USING TECH 1 ABS TESTS, SELECT MANUAL CONTROL FUNCTION.
• SELECT RIGHT FRONT MOTOR APPLY FUNCTION AND APPLY THE MOTOR.
• APPLY FIRM PRESSURE ON BRAKE PEDAL.
• SELECT RIGHT FRONT MOTOR RELEASE FUNCTION AND RELEASE MOTOR.
• DID BRAKE PEDAL FALL?
NO
YES
4
• FIRM PRESSURE STILL ON BRAKE PEDAL.
• SELECT RIGHT FRONT MOTOR APPLY FUNCTION AND APPLY THE MOTOR.
DID BRAKE PEDAL RISE?
NO
YES
MALFUNCTION IS INTERMITTENT. REFER TO "DIAGNOSTIC AIDS"
2
• REMOVE FOOT FROM BRAKE PEDAL.
• SELECT RIGHT FRONT MOTOR APPLY FUNCTION AND APPLY THE MOTOR WHILE CAREFULLY OBSERVING THE COMMANDED CURRENT AND THE FEEDBACK CURRENT ON THE TECH 1.
WAS THE FEEDBACK CURRENT HIGHER THAN THE COMMANDED CURRENT?
NO
YES
3
• USING TECH 1 ABS TESTS, PERFORM GEAR TENSION RELIEF FUNCTION.
• TURN IGNITION SWITCH TO "LOCK."
• REMOVE HYDRAULIC MODULATOR/MOTOR PACK ASSEMBLY FROM VEHICLE.
• SEPARATE MOTOR PACK FROM HYDRAULIC MODULATOR.
• GRASP AND ATTEMPT TO MOVE THE RIGHT FRONT HYDRAULIC MODULATOR GEAR.
CAN THE GEAR BE ROTATED AT LEAST 5 FULL TURNS LOCK TO LOCK?
NO
YES
REPLACE HYDRAULIC MODULATOR.
REPLACE MOTOR PACK.
5
• TURN IGNITION SWITCH TO "LOCK."
• DISCONNECT EBCM CONNECTOR C1 AND MOTOR PACK CONNECTOR.
• USING A DVM, MEASURE THE RESISTANCE BETWEEN TERMINAL "1" AND TERMINAL "17" OF EBCM HARNESS CONNECTOR C1.
DOES DVM DISPLAY RESISTANCE AS "OL" (INFINITE)?
YES
NO
• RECONNECT ALL CONNECTORS.
• TEST DRIVE VEHICLE FOR 3 DRIVE CYCLES.
• IF DTC A045 RESETS, REPLACE ECBM.
REPAIR SHORT BETWEEN CKT 1282 AND CKT 1283.

* AFTER ALL DIAGNOSIS IS COMPLETE, CLEAR DTCs AND TEST DRIVE VEHICLE FOR THREE (3) DRIVE CYCLES TO VERIFY THAT DTC DOES NOT RESET. A DRIVE CYCLE CONSISTS OF STARTING THE VEHICLE, DRIVING OVER 16 KM/H (10 MPH), AND THEN KEYING DOWN.

GC402940097100BX

Fig. 321 Code A045: Right Front Channel Will Not Move. 1993–94 Prizm

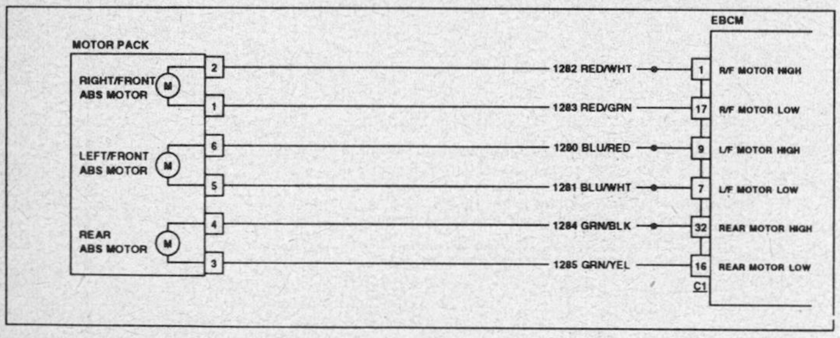
EBCM
MOTOR PACK
RIGHT/FRONT ABS MOTOR
LEFT/FRONT ABS MOTOR
REAR ABS MOTOR
1282 RED/WHT
1283 RED/GRN
1280 BLU/RED
1281 BLU/WHT
1284 GRN/BLK
1285 GRN/YEL
R/F MOTOR HIGH
R/F MOTOR LOW
L/F MOTOR HIGH
L/F MOTOR LOW
REAR MOTOR HIGH
REAR MOTOR LOW
C1

DTC A046

REAR CHANNEL WILL NOT MOVE

Circuit Description:

This DTC is designed to detect a bound-up ESB, a stuck motor or a seized hydraulic modulator. When the release is commanded during initialization, the ESB should release the motor, resulting in sensed current being less than commanded current (motor is spinning freely). If the motor is not moving, sensed current will be equal to stall current.

Failure Condition:

DTC A046 can be set during normal operation. If the EBCM detects a condition in which it cannot move the motor in either direction, a malfunction exists.

Action Taken:

This malfunction indicates the channel cannot be moved properly. A DTC A046 and a DTC A086 are stored, ABS is disabled and the "ABS" and "BRAKE" indicators are turned on. The "ABS" indicator will flash if the EBCM cannot illuminate the "BRAKE" indicator.

Test Description: Number(s) below refer to circled number(s) on the diagnostic chart.

1. This step checks for proper motor movement during apply and release commands from the TECH 1.
2. This step compares EBCM command current to motor feedback current.
3. This step checks for proper hydraulic modulator gear and piston movement.
4. This step verifies that the motor can actually apply when commanded.
5. This test determines if the malfunction is caused by a defective EBCM or by a short circuit.

Diagnostic Aids:

An "intermittent" malfunction may be caused by a poor connection, rubbed through wire insulation or a wire that is broken inside the insulation.

The frequency of the malfunction can be checked by using the enhanced diagnostic function of the TECH 1.

DTC A046 may set after modulator disassembly if the modulator pistons are positioned at the bottom of their bore.

Depending on the frequency of the malfunction, a physical inspection of the mechanical parts suspected may be necessary.

Any circuitry that is suspected of causing the intermittent complaint should be thoroughly checked for backed out terminals, improper mating, broken locks, improperly formed or damaged terminals, poor terminal-to-wiring connections or physical damage to the wiring harness.

GC402940097200AX

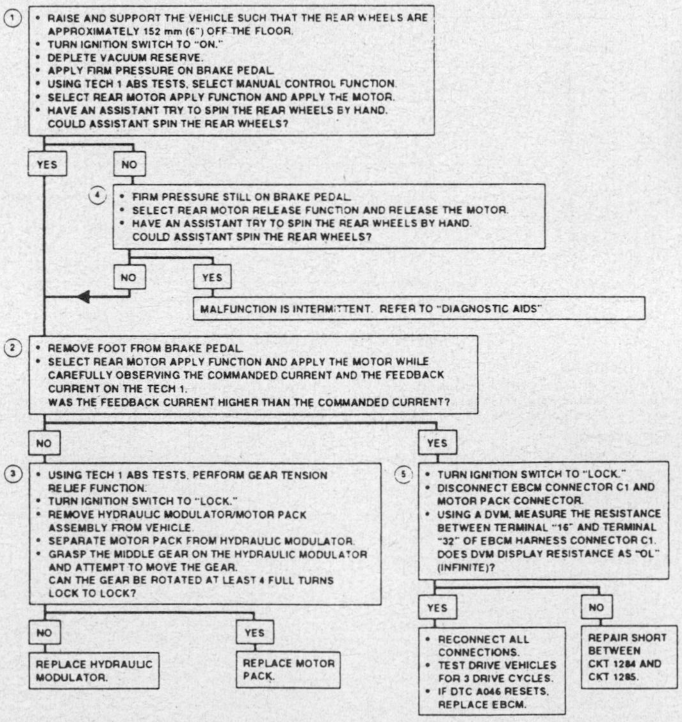
1
• RAISE AND SUPPORT THE VEHICLE SUCH THAT THE REAR WHEELS ARE APPROXIMATELY 152 mm (6") OFF THE FLOOR.
• TURN IGNITION SWITCH TO "ON."
• DEPLETE VACUUM RESERVE.
• APPLY FIRM PRESSURE ON BRAKE PEDAL.
• USING TECH 1 ABS TESTS, SELECT MANUAL CONTROL FUNCTION.
• SELECT REAR MOTOR APPLY FUNCTION AND APPLY THE MOTOR.
• HAVE AN ASSISTANT TRY TO SPIN THE REAR WHEELS BY HAND.
COULD ASSISTANT SPIN THE REAR WHEELS?
YES
NO
4
• FIRM PRESSURE STILL ON BRAKE PEDAL.
• SELECT REAR MOTOR RELEASE FUNCTION AND RELEASE THE MOTOR.
• HAVE AN ASSISTANT TRY TO SPIN THE REAR WHEELS BY HAND.
COULD ASSISTANT SPIN THE REAR WHEELS?
NO
YES
MALFUNCTION IS INTERMITTENT. REFER TO "DIAGNOSTIC AIDS"
2
• REMOVE FOOT FROM BRAKE PEDAL.
• SELECT REAR MOTOR APPLY FUNCTION AND APPLY THE MOTOR WHILE CAREFULLY OBSERVING THE COMMANDED CURRENT AND THE FEEDBACK CURRENT ON THE TECH 1.
WAS THE FEEDBACK CURRENT HIGHER THAN THE COMMANDED CURRENT?
NO
YES
3
• USING TECH 1 ABS TESTS, PERFORM GEAR TENSION RELIEF FUNCTION.
• TURN IGNITION SWITCH TO "LOCK."
• REMOVE HYDRAULIC MODULATOR/MOTOR PACK ASSEMBLY FROM VEHICLE.
• SEPARATE MOTOR PACK FROM HYDRAULIC MODULATOR.
• GRASP THE MIDDLE GEAR ON THE HYDRAULIC MODULATOR AND ATTEMPT TO MOVE THE GEAR.
CAN THE GEAR BE ROTATED AT LEAST 4 FULL TURNS LOCK TO LOCK?
NO
YES
REPLACE HYDRAULIC MODULATOR.
REPLACE MOTOR PACK.
5
• TURN IGNITION SWITCH TO "LOCK."
• DISCONNECT EBCM CONNECTOR C1 AND MOTOR PACK CONNECTOR.
• USING A DVM, MEASURE THE RESISTANCE BETWEEN TERMINAL "16" AND TERMINAL "32" OF EBCM HARNESS CONNECTOR C1.
DOES DVM DISPLAY RESISTANCE AS "OL" (INFINITE)?
YES
NO
• RECONNECT ALL CONNECTIONS.
• TEST DRIVE VEHICLES FOR 3 DRIVE CYCLES.
• IF DTC A046 RESETS, REPLACE EBCM.
REPAIR SHORT BETWEEN CKT 1284 AND CKT 1285.

* AFTER ALL DIAGNOSIS IS COMPLETE, CLEAR DTCs AND TEST DRIVE VEHICLE FOR THREE (3) DRIVE CYCLES TO VERIFY THAT DTC DOES NOT RESET. A DRIVE CYCLE CONSISTS OF STARTING THE VEHICLE, DRIVING OVER 16 km/h (10 MPH), AND THEN KEYING DOWN.

GC402940097200BX

Fig. 322 Code A046: Rear Channel Will Not Move. 1993–94 Prizm

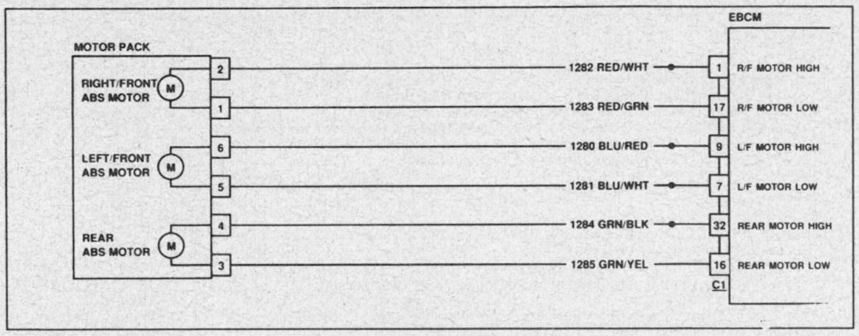

EBCM
MOTOR PACK
RIGHT/FRONT ABS MOTOR
LEFT/FRONT ABS MOTOR
REAR ABS MOTOR
M
2
1
6
5
4
3
1282 RED/WHT
1283 RED/GRN
1280 BLU/RED
1281 BLU/WHT
1284 GRN/BLK
1285 GRN/YEL
1 R/F MOTOR HIGH
17 R/F MOTOR LOW
9 L/F MOTOR HIGH
7 L/F MOTOR LOW
32 REAR MOTOR HIGH
16 REAR MOTOR LOW
C1

DTC A047
(Page 1 of 2)
LEFT FRONT MOTOR FREE SPINS

Circuit Description:

This DTC is designed to detect a stripped nut or gear assembly during initialization. During the homing sequence, the piston should reach the top of the bore resulting in a stalled motor. If this does not occur, the motor must be spinning with little or no resistance. This indicates a nut/screw or gear malfunction.

Failure Condition:

DTC A047 can only be set during initialization. If the feedback current is less than the command current for a specified period of time, a malfunction exists.

Action Taken:

A DTC A047 is stored, ABS is disabled and the "ABS" indicator is turned on.

Test Description: Number(s) below refer to circled number(s) on the diagnostic chart.

1. This step checks to see if the corresponding open motor DTC is also set.
2. This step verifies that the motor was actually applied as commanded by observing feedback current.
3. This step verifies that the motor can release.
4. This step verifies that the motor can be applied by observing pedal movement.
5. This step checks for a stripped gear on the motor pack.
6. This step checks for a stripped gear on the hydraulic modulator.
7. This step checks for a malfunctioning EBCM.

Diagnostic Aids:

An "intermittent" malfunction in this DTC may result from a mechanical part of the system that sticks, binds or slips.

The frequency of the malfunction can be checked by using the enhanced diagnostic function of the TECH 1

If the DTC only fails once and DTC A056 also fails, refer to DTC A056. If intermittent and enhanced diagnostics show this DTC fails during ABS operation, refer to DTC A056.

Depending on the frequency of the malfunction, a physical inspection of the mechanical parts suspected may be necessary.

GC402940097301AX

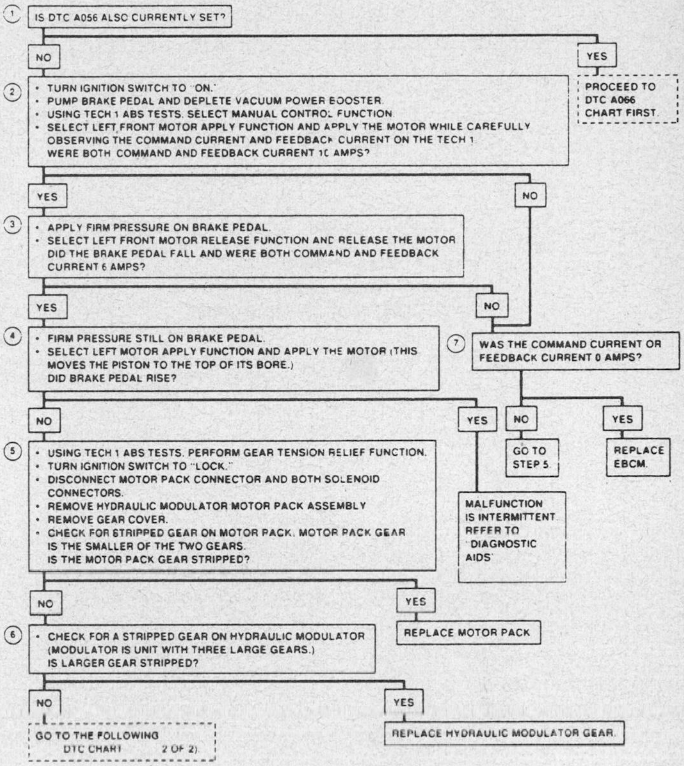

1
IS DTC A056 ALSO CURRENTLY SET?
NO
YES
PROCEED TO DTC A066 CHART FIRST.
2
• TURN IGNITION SWITCH TO "ON."
• PUMP BRAKE PEDAL AND DEPLETE VACUUM POWER BOOSTER.
• USING TECH 1 ABS TESTS, SELECT MANUAL CONTROL FUNCTION.
• SELECT LEFT FRONT MOTOR APPLY FUNCTION AND APPLY THE MOTOR WHILE CAREFULLY OBSERVING THE COMMAND CURRENT AND FEEDBACK CURRENT ON THE TECH 1.
WERE BOTH COMMAND AND FEEDBACK CURRENT 10 AMPS?
YES
NO
3
• APPLY FIRM PRESSURE ON BRAKE PEDAL.
• SELECT LEFT FRONT MOTOR RELEASE FUNCTION AND RELEASE THE MOTOR.
DID THE BRAKE PEDAL FALL AND WERE BOTH COMMAND AND FEEDBACK CURRENT 6 AMPS?
YES
NO
4
• FIRM PRESSURE STILL ON BRAKE PEDAL.
• SELECT LEFT MOTOR APPLY FUNCTION AND APPLY THE MOTOR (THIS MOVES THE PISTON TO THE TOP OF ITS BORE.)
DID BRAKE PEDAL RISE?
7
WAS THE COMMAND CURRENT OR FEEDBACK CURRENT 0 AMPS?
NO
YES
NO
GO TO STEP 5.
YES
REPLACE EBCM.
5
• USING TECH 1 ABS TESTS, PERFORM GEAR TENSION RELIEF FUNCTION.
• TURN IGNITION SWITCH TO "LOCK."
• DISCONNECT MOTOR PACK CONNECTOR AND BOTH SOLENOID CONNECTORS.
• REMOVE HYDRAULIC MODULATOR MOTOR PACK ASSEMBLY.
• REMOVE GEAR COVER.
• CHECK FOR STRIPPED GEAR ON MOTOR PACK. MOTOR PACK GEAR IS THE SMALLER OF THE TWO GEARS.
IS THE MOTOR PACK GEAR STRIPPED?
MALFUNCTION IS INTERMITTENT. REFER TO "DIAGNOSTIC AIDS"
NO
YES
REPLACE MOTOR PACK
6
• CHECK FOR A STRIPPED GEAR ON HYDRAULIC MODULATOR (MODULATOR IS UNIT WITH THREE LARGE GEARS.)
IS LARGER GEAR STRIPPED?
NO
YES
GO TO THE FOLLOWING DTC CHART (2 OF 2).
REPLACE HYDRAULIC MODULATOR GEAR.

GC402940097301BX

Fig. 323 Code A047: Left Front Motor Spins Free (Part 1 of 2). 1993–94 Prizm

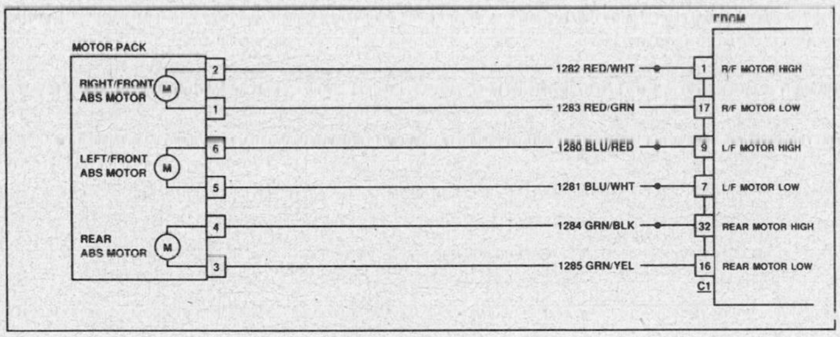

FROM
MOTOR PACK
RIGHT/FRONT ABS MOTOR
LEFT/FRONT ABS MOTOR
REAR ABS MOTOR
M
2
1
6
5
4
3
1282 RED/WHT
1283 RED/GRN
1280 BLU/RED
1281 BLU/WHT
1284 GRN/BLK
1285 GRN/YEL
1 R/F MOTOR HIGH
17 R/F MOTOR LOW
9 L/F MOTOR HIGH
7 L/F MOTOR LOW
32 REAR MOTOR HIGH
16 REAR MOTOR LOW
C1

DTC A047
(Page 2 of 2)
LEFT FRONT MOTOR FREE SPINS

Circuit Description:

This DTC is designed to detect a stripped nut or gear assembly during initialization. During the homing sequence, the piston should reach the top of the bore resulting in a stalled motor. If this does not occur, the motor must be spinning with little or no resistance. This indicates a nut/screw or gear malfunction.

Failure Condition:

DTC A047 can only be set during initialization. If the feedback current is less than the command current for a specified period of time, a malfunction exists.

Action Taken:

A DTC A047 is stored, ABS is disabled and the "ABS" indicator is turned on.

Test Description: Number(s) below refer to circled number(s) on the diagnostic chart.

8. This step determines whether the motor pack has an internal malfunction.
9. This test checks for high resistance in the left front motor high circuit.
10. This test checks for high resistance in the left front motor low circuit.
11. This test determines whether the fault is due to a faulty hydraulic modulator or a faulty motor pack.

Diagnostic Aids:

An "intermittent" malfunction in this DTC may result from a mechanical part of the system that sticks, binds or slips.

The frequency of the malfunction can be checked by using the enhanced diagnostic function of the TECH 1

If the DTC only fails once and DTC A056 also fails, refer to DTC A056. If intermittent and enhanced diagnostics show this DTC fails during ABS operation, refer to DTC A056.

Depending on the frequency of the malfunction, a physical inspection of the mechanical parts suspected may be necessary.

GC402940097302AX

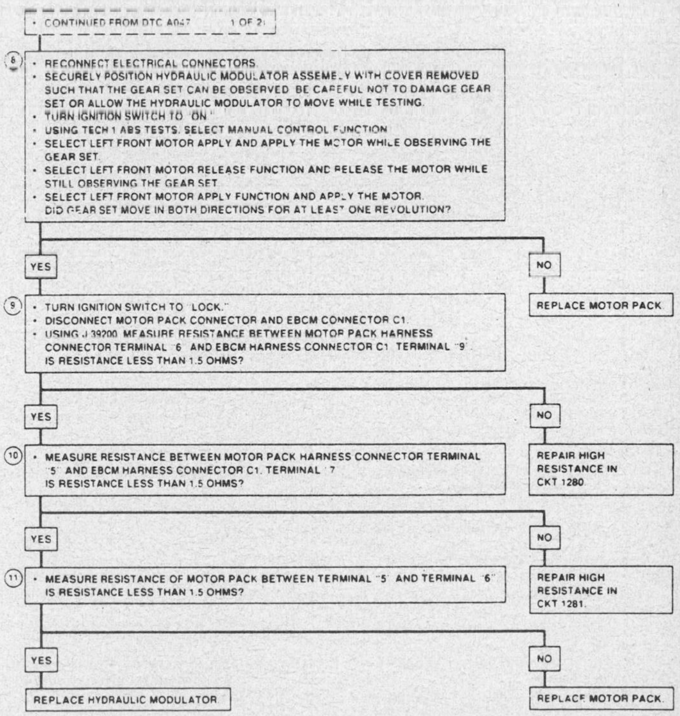

• CONTINUED FROM DTC A047 (1 OF 2)
8
• RECONNECT ELECTRICAL CONNECTORS.
• SECURELY POSITION HYDRAULIC MODULATOR ASSEMBLY WITH COVER REMOVED SUCH THAT THE GEAR SET CAN BE OBSERVED. BE CAREFUL NOT TO DAMAGE GEAR SET OR ALLOW THE HYDRAULIC MODULATOR TO MOVE WHILE TESTING.
• TURN IGNITION SWITCH TO "ON."
• USING TECH 1 ABS TESTS, SELECT MANUAL CONTROL FUNCTION.
• SELECT LEFT FRONT MOTOR APPLY AND APPLY THE MOTOR WHILE OBSERVING THE GEAR SET.
• SELECT LEFT FRONT MOTOR RELEASE FUNCTION AND RELEASE THE MOTOR WHILE STILL OBSERVING THE GEAR SET.
• SELECT LEFT FRONT MOTOR APPLY FUNCTION AND APPLY THE MOTOR.
DID GEAR SET MOVE IN BOTH DIRECTIONS FOR AT LEAST ONE REVOLUTION?
YES
NO
REPLACE MOTOR PACK.
9
• TURN IGNITION SWITCH TO "LOCK."
• DISCONNECT MOTOR PACK CONNECTOR AND EBCM CONNECTOR C1.
• USING J 39200, MEASURE RESISTANCE BETWEEN MOTOR PACK HARNESS CONNECTOR TERMINAL "6" AND EBCM HARNESS CONNECTOR C1, TERMINAL "9".
IS RESISTANCE LESS THAN 1.5 OHMS?
YES
NO
10
• MEASURE RESISTANCE BETWEEN MOTOR PACK HARNESS CONNECTOR TERMINAL "5" AND EBCM HARNESS CONNECTOR C1, TERMINAL "7".
IS RESISTANCE LESS THAN 1.5 OHMS?
REPAIR HIGH RESISTANCE IN CKT 1280.
YES
NO
11
• MEASURE RESISTANCE OF MOTOR PACK BETWEEN TERMINAL "5" AND TERMINAL "6".
IS RESISTANCE LESS THAN 1.5 OHMS?
REPAIR HIGH RESISTANCE IN CKT 1281.
YES
NO
REPLACE HYDRAULIC MODULATOR
REPLACE MOTOR PACK.

GC402940097302BX

Fig. 323 Code A047: Left Front Motor Spins Free (Part 2 of 2) . 1993–94 Prizm

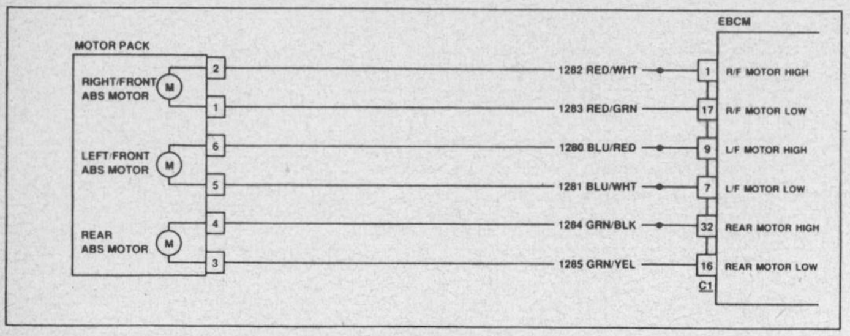
EBCM
MOTOR PACK
RIGHT/FRONT ABS MOTOR
LEFT/FRONT ABS MOTOR
REAR ABS MOTOR
M
2
1
6
5
4
3
1282 RED/WHT
1283 RED/GRN
1280 BLU/RED
1281 BLU/WHT
1284 GRN/BLK
1285 GRN/YEL
1
17
9
7
32
16
C1
R/F MOTOR HIGH
R/F MOTOR LOW
L/F MOTOR HIGH
L/F MOTOR LOW
REAR MOTOR HIGH
REAR MOTOR LOW

DTC A048

(Page 1 of 2)

RIGHT FRONT MOTOR FREE SPINS

Circuit Description:

This DTC is designed to detect a stripped nut or gear assembly during initialization. During the homing sequence, the piston should reach the top of the bore resulting in a stalled motor. If this does not occur, the motor must be spinning with little or no resistance. This indicates a nut/screw or gear malfunction.

Failure Condition:

DTC A048 can only be set during initialization. If the feedback current is less than the command current for a specified period of time, a malfunction exists.

Action Taken:

A DTC A048 is stored, ABS is disabled and the "ABS" indicator is turned on.

Test Description: Number(s) below refer to circled number(s) on the diagnostic chart.

1. This step checks to see if the corresponding open motor DTC is also set.
2. This step verifies that the motor was actually applied as commanded by observing feedback current.
3. This step verifies that the motor can release.
4. This step verifies that the motor can be applied by observing pedal movement.
5. This step checks for a stripped gear on the motor pack.
6. This step checks for a stripped gear on the hydraulic modulator.
7. This step checks for a malfunctioning EBCM.

Diagnostic Aids:

An "intermittent" malfunction in this DTC may result from a mechanical part of the system that sticks, binds or slips.

The frequency of the malfunction can be checked by using the enhanced diagnostic function of the TECH 1

If the DTC only fails once and DTC A061 also fails, refer to DTC A061. If intermittent and enhanced diagnostics show this DTC fails during ABS operation, refer to DTC A061.

Depending on the frequency of the malfunction, a physical inspection of the mechanical parts suspected may be necessary.

GC402940097401AX

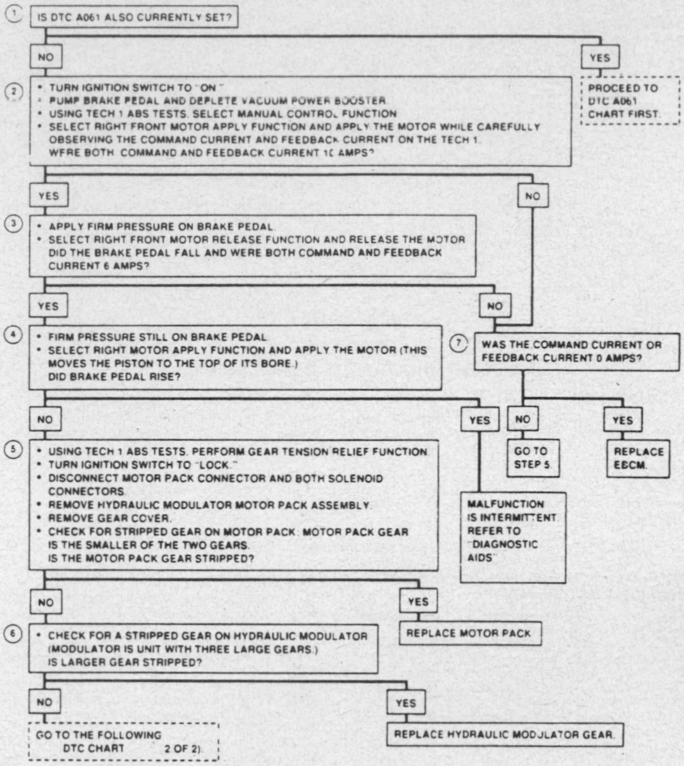
1 IS DTC A061 ALSO CURRENTLY SET?
NO
YES
PROCEED TO DTC A061 CHART FIRST.
2 • TURN IGNITION SWITCH TO "ON."
• PUMP BRAKE PEDAL AND DEPLETE VACUUM POWER BOOSTER.
• USING TECH 1 ABS TESTS. SELECT MANUAL CONTROL FUNCTION.
• SELECT RIGHT FRONT MOTOR APPLY FUNCTION AND APPLY THE MOTOR WHILE CAREFULLY OBSERVING THE COMMAND CURRENT AND FEEDBACK CURRENT ON THE TECH 1.
WERE BOTH COMMAND AND FEEDBACK CURRENT 10 AMPS?
YES
NO
3 • APPLY FIRM PRESSURE ON BRAKE PEDAL.
• SELECT RIGHT FRONT MOTOR RELEASE FUNCTION AND RELEASE THE MOTOR.
DID THE BRAKE PEDAL FALL AND WERE BOTH COMMAND AND FEEDBACK CURRENT 6 AMPS?
YES
NO
4 • FIRM PRESSURE STILL ON BRAKE PEDAL.
• SELECT RIGHT MOTOR APPLY FUNCTION AND APPLY THE MOTOR (THIS MOVES THE PISTON TO THE TOP OF ITS BORE.)
DID BRAKE PEDAL RISE?
7 WAS THE COMMAND CURRENT OR FEEDBACK CURRENT 0 AMPS?
NO
YES
NO
YES
GO TO STEP 5.
REPLACE EBCM.
5 • USING TECH 1 ABS TESTS. PERFORM GEAR TENSION RELIEF FUNCTION.
• TURN IGNITION SWITCH TO "LOCK."
• DISCONNECT MOTOR PACK CONNECTOR AND BOTH SOLENOID CONNECTORS.
• REMOVE HYDRAULIC MODULATOR MOTOR PACK ASSEMBLY.
• REMOVE GEAR COVER.
• CHECK FOR STRIPPED GEAR ON MOTOR PACK. MOTOR PACK GEAR IS THE SMALLER OF THE TWO GEARS.
IS THE MOTOR PACK GEAR STRIPPED?
MALFUNCTION IS INTERMITTENT. REFER TO "DIAGNOSTIC AIDS"
NO
YES
REPLACE MOTOR PACK.
6 • CHECK FOR A STRIPPED GEAR ON HYDRAULIC MODULATOR (MODULATOR IS UNIT WITH THREE LARGE GEARS.)
IS LARGER GEAR STRIPPED?
NO
YES
GO TO THE FOLLOWING DTC CHART (2 OF 2).
REPLACE HYDRAULIC MODULATOR GEAR.

GC402940097401BX

Fig. 324 Code A048: Right Front Motor Spins Free (Part 1 of 2). 1993–94 Prizm

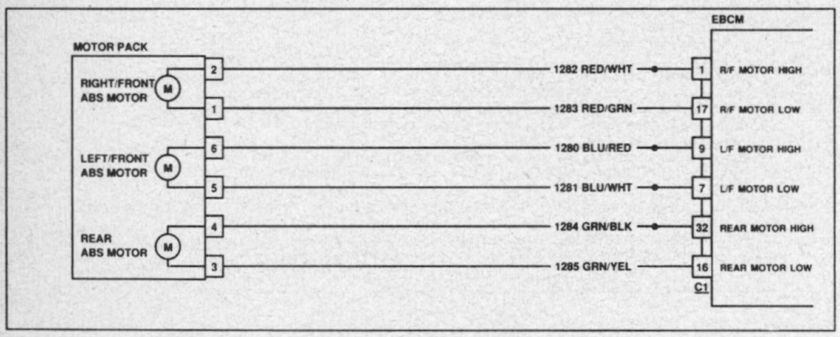
EBCM
MOTOR PACK
RIGHT/FRONT ABS MOTOR
LEFT/FRONT ABS MOTOR
REAR ABS MOTOR
M
2
1
6
5
4
3
1282 RED/WHT
1283 RED/GRN
1280 BLU/RED
1281 BLU/WHT
1284 GRN/BLK
1285 GRN/YEL
1
17
9
7
32
16
C1
R/F MOTOR HIGH
R/F MOTOR LOW
L/F MOTOR HIGH
L/F MOTOR LOW
REAR MOTOR HIGH
REAR MOTOR LOW

DTC A048

(Page 2 of 2)

RIGHT FRONT MOTOR FREE SPINS

Circuit Description:

This DTC is designed to detect a stripped nut or gear assembly during initialization. During the homing sequence, the piston should reach the top of the bore resulting in a stalled motor. If this does not occur, the motor must be spinning with little or no resistance. This indicates a nut/screw or gear malfunction.

Failure Condition:

DTC A048 can only be set during initialization. If the feedback current is less than the command current for a specified period of time, a malfunction exists.

Action Taken:

A DTC A048 is stored, ABS is disabled and the "ABS" indicator is turned on.

Test Description: Number(s) below refer to circled number(s) on the diagnostic chart.

8. This step determines whether the motor pack has an internal malfunction.
9. This test checks for high resistance in the right front motor high circuit.
10. This test checks for high resistance in the right front motor low circuit.
11. This test determines whether the fault is due to a faulty hydraulic modulator or a faulty motor pack.

Diagnostic Aids:

An "intermittent" malfunction in this DTC may result from a mechanical part of the system that sticks, binds or slips.

The frequency of the malfunction can be checked by using the enhanced diagnostic function of the TECH 1

If the DTC only fails once and DTC A061 also fails, refer to DTC A061. If intermittent and enhanced diagnostics show this DTC fails during ABS operation, refer to DTC A061.

Depending on the frequency of the malfunction, a physical inspection of the mechanical parts suspected may be necessary.

GC402940097402AX

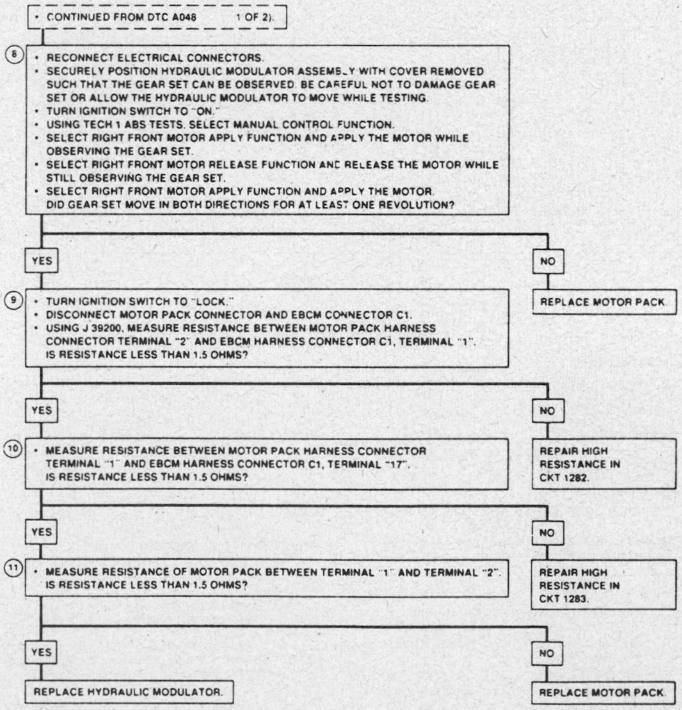
• CONTINUED FROM DTC A048 (1 OF 2).
8 • RECONNECT ELECTRICAL CONNECTORS.
• SECURELY POSITION HYDRAULIC MODULATOR ASSEMBLY WITH COVER REMOVED SUCH THAT THE GEAR SET CAN BE OBSERVED. BE CAREFUL NOT TO DAMAGE GEAR SET OR ALLOW THE HYDRAULIC MODULATOR TO MOVE WHILE TESTING.
• TURN IGNITION SWITCH TO "ON."
• USING TECH 1 ABS TESTS. SELECT MANUAL CONTROL FUNCTION.
• SELECT RIGHT FRONT MOTOR APPLY FUNCTION AND APPLY THE MOTOR WHILE OBSERVING THE GEAR SET.
• SELECT RIGHT FRONT MOTOR RELEASE FUNCTION AND RELEASE THE MOTOR WHILE STILL OBSERVING THE GEAR SET.
• SELECT RIGHT FRONT MOTOR APPLY FUNCTION AND APPLY THE MOTOR.
DID GEAR SET MOVE IN BOTH DIRECTIONS FOR AT LEAST ONE REVOLUTION?
YES
NO
REPLACE MOTOR PACK.
9 • TURN IGNITION SWITCH TO "LOCK."
• DISCONNECT MOTOR PACK CONNECTOR AND EBCM CONNECTOR C1.
• USING J 39200, MEASURE RESISTANCE BETWEEN MOTOR PACK HARNESS CONNECTOR TERMINAL "2" AND EBCM HARNESS CONNECTOR C1, TERMINAL "1".
IS RESISTANCE LESS THAN 1.5 OHMS?
YES
NO
10 • MEASURE RESISTANCE BETWEEN MOTOR PACK HARNESS CONNECTOR TERMINAL "1" AND EBCM HARNESS CONNECTOR C1, TERMINAL "17".
IS RESISTANCE LESS THAN 1.5 OHMS?
REPAIR HIGH RESISTANCE IN CKT 1282.
YES
NO
11 • MEASURE RESISTANCE OF MOTOR PACK BETWEEN TERMINAL "1" AND TERMINAL "2".
IS RESISTANCE LESS THAN 1.5 OHMS?
REPAIR HIGH RESISTANCE IN CKT 1283.
YES
NO
REPLACE HYDRAULIC MODULATOR.
REPLACE MOTOR PACK.

GC402940097402BX

Fig. 324 Code A048: Right Front Motor Spins Free (Part 2 of 2). 1993–94 Prizm

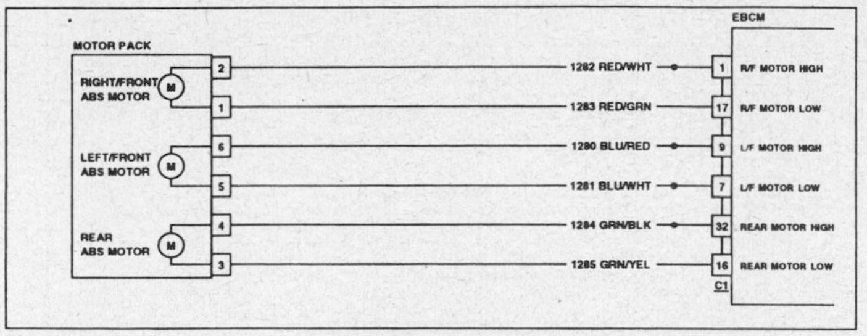
EBCM
MOTOR PACK
RIGHT/FRONT ABS MOTOR
LEFT/FRONT ABS MOTOR
REAR ABS MOTOR
M
2
1
6
5
4
3
1282 RED/WHT
1283 RED/GRN
1280 BLU/RED
1281 BLU/WHT
1284 GRN/BLK
1285 GRN/YEL
1 R/F MOTOR HIGH
17 R/F MOTOR LOW
9 L/F MOTOR HIGH
7 L/F MOTOR LOW
32 REAR MOTOR HIGH
16 REAR MOTOR LOW
C1

DTC A051
(Page 1 of 2)
REAR MOTOR FREE SPINS

Circuit Description:

This DTC is designed to detect a stripped nut or gear assembly during initialization. During the homing sequence, the piston should reach the top of the bore resulting in a stalled motor. If this does not occur, the motor must be spinning with little or no resistance. This indicates a nut/screw or gear malfunction.

Failure Condition:

DTC A051 can only be set during initialization. If the feedback current is less than the command current for a specified period of time, a malfunction exists.

Action Taken:

A DTC A051 and a DTC A086 are stored, ABS is disabled and the "ABS" and "BRAKE" indicators are turned on. The "ABS" indicator will flash if the EBCM cannot illuminate the "BRAKE" indicator.

Test Description: Number(s) below refer to circled number(s) on the diagnostic chart.

1. This step checks to see if the corresponding open motor DTC is also set.
2. This step verifies that the motor was actually applied as commanded by observing feedback current.
3. This step verifies that the motor can release.
4. This step verifies that the motor can be applied by observing pedal movement.
5. This step checks for a stripped gear on the motor pack.
6. This step checks for a stripped gear on the hydraulic modulator.
7. This step checks for a malfunctioning EBCM.

Diagnostic Aids:

An "intermittent" malfunction in this DTC may result from a mechanical part of the system that sticks, binds or slips.

The frequency of the malfunction can be checked by using the enhanced diagnostic function of the TECH 1

If the DTC only fails once and DTC A064 also fails, refer to DTC A064. If intermittent and enhanced diagnostics show this DTC fails during ABS operation, refer to DTC A064.

Depending on the frequency of the malfunction, a physical inspection of the mechanical parts suspected may be necessary.

GC402940097501AX

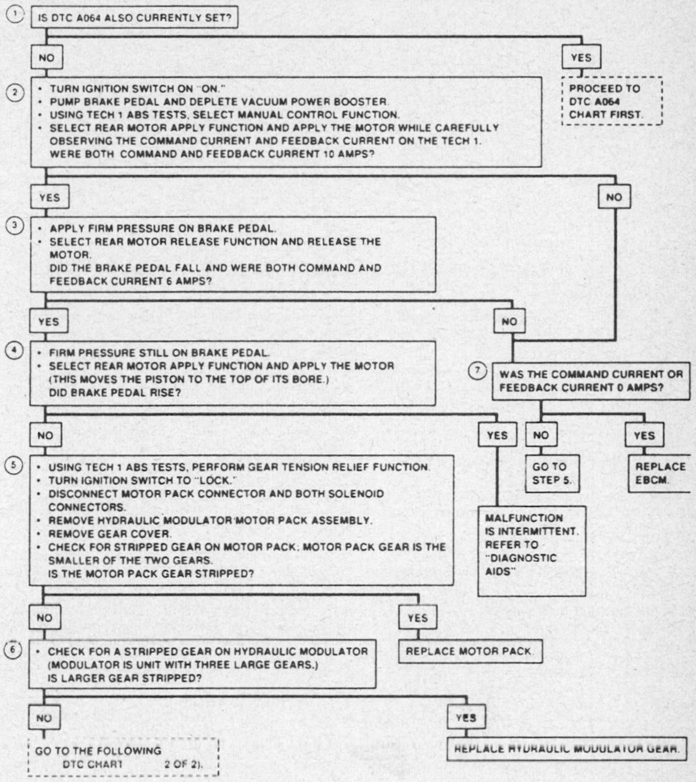
1 IS DTC A064 ALSO CURRENTLY SET?
NO
YES
PROCEED TO DTC A064 CHART FIRST.
2 • TURN IGNITION SWITCH ON "ON."
• PUMP BRAKE PEDAL AND DEPLETE VACUUM POWER BOOSTER.
• USING TECH 1 ABS TESTS, SELECT MANUAL CONTROL FUNCTION.
• SELECT REAR MOTOR APPLY FUNCTION AND APPLY THE MOTOR WHILE CAREFULLY OBSERVING THE COMMAND CURRENT AND FEEDBACK CURRENT ON THE TECH 1.
WERE BOTH COMMAND AND FEEDBACK CURRENT 10 AMPS?
YES
NO
3 • APPLY FIRM PRESSURE ON BRAKE PEDAL.
• SELECT REAR MOTOR RELEASE FUNCTION AND RELEASE THE MOTOR.
DID THE BRAKE PEDAL FALL AND WERE BOTH COMMAND AND FEEDBACK CURRENT 6 AMPS?
YES
NO
4 • FIRM PRESSURE STILL ON BRAKE PEDAL.
• SELECT REAR MOTOR APPLY FUNCTION AND APPLY THE MOTOR (THIS MOVES THE PISTON TO THE TOP OF ITS BORE.)
DID BRAKE PEDAL RISE?
7 WAS THE COMMAND CURRENT OR FEEDBACK CURRENT 0 AMPS?
NO
YES
NO
YES
GO TO STEP 5.
REPLACE EBCM.
5 • USING TECH 1 ABS TESTS, PERFORM GEAR TENSION RELIEF FUNCTION.
• TURN IGNITION SWITCH TO "LOCK."
• DISCONNECT MOTOR PACK CONNECTOR AND BOTH SOLENOID CONNECTORS.
• REMOVE HYDRAULIC MODULATOR/MOTOR PACK ASSEMBLY.
• REMOVE GEAR COVER.
• CHECK FOR STRIPPED GEAR ON MOTOR PACK; MOTOR PACK GEAR IS THE SMALLER OF THE TWO GEARS.
IS THE MOTOR PACK GEAR STRIPPED?
MALFUNCTION IS INTERMITTENT. REFER TO "DIAGNOSTIC AIDS"
NO
YES
6 • CHECK FOR A STRIPPED GEAR ON HYDRAULIC MODULATOR (MODULATOR IS UNIT WITH THREE LARGE GEARS.)
IS LARGER GEAR STRIPPED?
REPLACE MOTOR PACK.
NO
YES
GO TO THE FOLLOWING DTC CHART 2 OF 2).
REPLACE HYDRAULIC MODULATOR GEAR.

GC402940097501BX

DUMMY00000000001

Fig. 325 Code A051: Rear Motor Spins Free (Part 1 of 2). 1993–94 Prizm

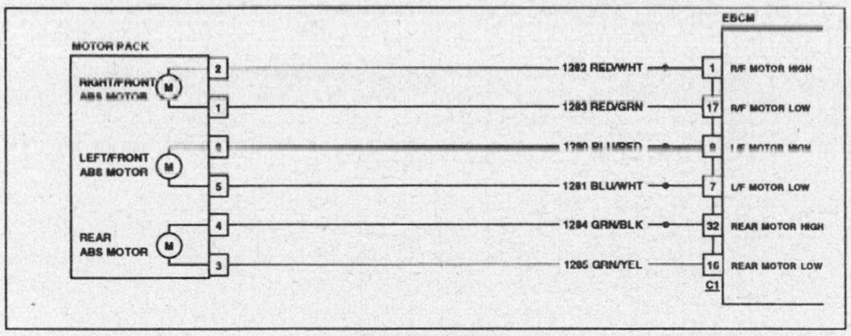
EBCM
MOTOR PACK
RIGHT/FRONT ABS MOTOR
LEFT/FRONT ABS MOTOR
REAR ABS MOTOR
M
2
1
6
5
4
3
1282 RED/WHT
1283 RED/GRN
1281 BLU/WHT
1284 GRN/BLK
1285 GRN/YEL
1 R/F MOTOR HIGH
17 R/F MOTOR LOW
7 L/F MOTOR LOW
32 REAR MOTOR HIGH
16 REAR MOTOR LOW
C1

DTC A051
(Page 2 of 2)
REAR MOTOR FREE SPINS

Circuit Description:

This DTC is designed to detect a stripped nut or gear assembly during initialization. During the homing sequence, the piston should reach the top of the bore resulting in a stalled motor. If this does not occur, the motor must be spinning with little or no resistance. This indicates a nut/screw or gear malfunction.

Failure Condition:

DTC A051 can only be set during initialization. If the feedback current is less than the command current for a specified period of time, a malfunction exists.

Action Taken:

A DTC A051 and a DTC A086 are stored, ABS is disabled and the "ABS" and "BRAKE" indicators are turned on. The "ABS" indicator will flash if the EBCM cannot illuminate the "BRAKE" indicator.

Test Description: Number(s) below refer to circled number(s) on the diagnostic chart.

8. This step determines whether the motor pack has an internal malfunction.
9. This test checks for high resistance in the rear motor high circuit.
10. This test checks for high resistance in the rear motor low circuit.
11. This test determines whether the fault is due to a faulty hydraulic modulator or a faulty motor park.

Diagnostic Aids:

An "intermittent" malfunction in this DTC may result from a mechanical part of the system that sticks, binds or slips.

The frequency of the malfunction can be checked by using the enhanced diagnostic function of the TECH 1

If the DTC only fails once and DTC A064 also fails, refer to DTC A064. If intermittent and enhanced diagnostics show this DTC fails during ABS operation, refer to DTC A064.

Depending on the frequency of the malfunction, a physical inspection of the mechanical parts suspected may be necessary.

GC402940097502AX

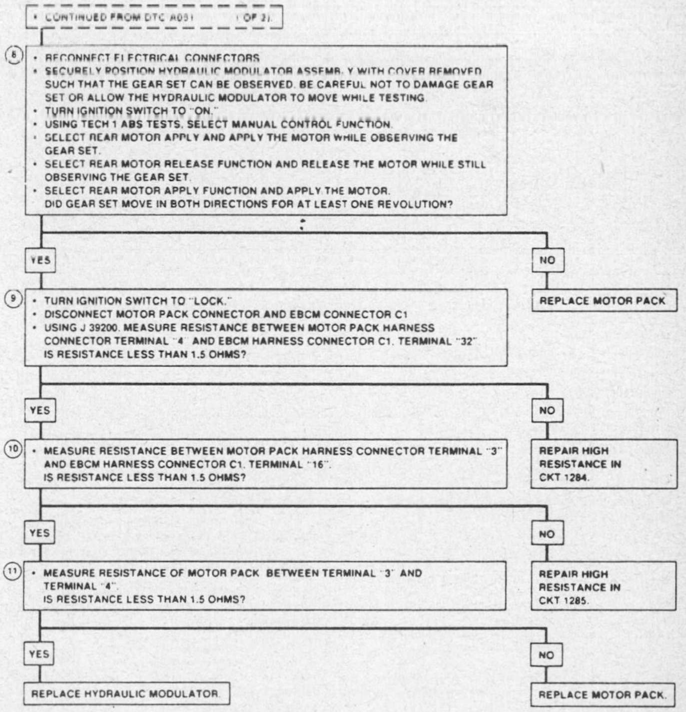
• CONTINUED FROM DTC A051 (OF 2).
8 • RECONNECT ELECTRICAL CONNECTORS
• SECURELY POSITION HYDRAULIC MODULATOR ASSEMBLY WITH COVER REMOVED SUCH THAT THE GEAR SET CAN BE OBSERVED. BE CAREFUL NOT TO DAMAGE GEAR SET OR ALLOW THE HYDRAULIC MODULATOR TO MOVE WHILE TESTING.
• TURN IGNITION SWITCH TO "ON."
• USING TECH 1 ABS TESTS, SELECT MANUAL CONTROL FUNCTION.
• SELECT REAR MOTOR APPLY AND APPLY THE MOTOR WHILE OBSERVING THE GEAR SET.
• SELECT REAR MOTOR RELEASE FUNCTION AND RELEASE THE MOTOR WHILE STILL OBSERVING THE GEAR SET.
• SELECT REAR MOTOR APPLY FUNCTION AND APPLY THE MOTOR.
DID GEAR SET MOVE IN BOTH DIRECTIONS FOR AT LEAST ONE REVOLUTION?
YES
NO
REPLACE MOTOR PACK
9 • TURN IGNITION SWITCH TO "LOCK."
• DISCONNECT MOTOR PACK CONNECTOR AND EBCM CONNECTOR C1
• USING J 39200, MEASURE RESISTANCE BETWEEN MOTOR PACK HARNESS CONNECTOR TERMINAL "4" AND EBCM HARNESS CONNECTOR C1, TERMINAL "32"
IS RESISTANCE LESS THAN 1.5 OHMS?
YES
NO
10 • MEASURE RESISTANCE BETWEEN MOTOR PACK HARNESS CONNECTOR TERMINAL "3" AND EBCM HARNESS CONNECTOR C1, TERMINAL "16".
IS RESISTANCE LESS THAN 1.5 OHMS?
REPAIR HIGH RESISTANCE IN CKT 1284.
YES
NO
11 • MEASURE RESISTANCE OF MOTOR PACK BETWEEN TERMINAL "3" AND TERMINAL "4".
IS RESISTANCE LESS THAN 1.5 OHMS?
REPAIR HIGH RESISTANCE IN CKT 1285.
YES
NO
REPLACE HYDRAULIC MODULATOR
REPLACE MOTOR PACK.

GC402940097502BX

Fig. 325 Code A051: Rear Motor Spins Free (Part 2 of 2). 1993–94 Prizm

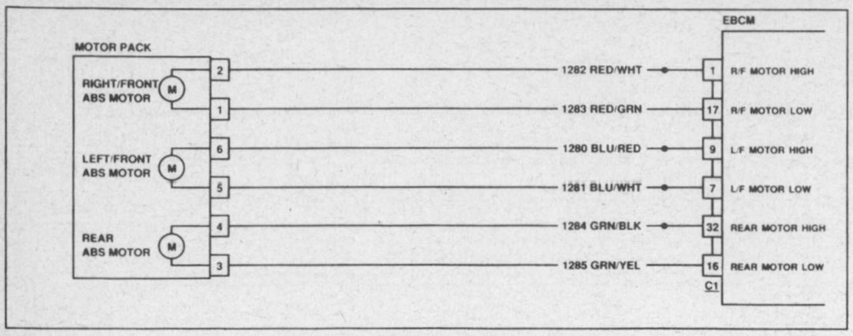
EBCM
MOTOR PACK
RIGHT/FRONT ABS MOTOR
LEFT/FRONT ABS MOTOR
REAR ABS MOTOR
2
1
6
5
4
3
1282 RED/WHT
1283 RED/GRN
1280 BLU/RED
1281 BLU/WHT
1284 GRN/BLK
1285 GRN/YEL
1 R/F MOTOR HIGH
17 R/F MOTOR LOW
9 L/F MOTOR HIGH
7 L/F MOTOR LOW
32 REAR MOTOR HIGH
16 REAR MOTOR LOW
C1

DTC A052

LEFT FRONT CHANNEL IN RELEASE TOO LONG

Circuit Description:

This DTC will diagnose a motor that is energized longer than expected. This could occur if a wheel speed sensor is malfunctioning, the motor does not turn, the left front solenoid mechanically fails open or the motor wires are crossed.

Failure Condition:

DTC A052 can be set only during an ABS stop. If the EBCM commands the left front channel in release for three seconds, a malfunction exists.

Action Taken:

A DTC A052 is stored, ABS is disabled and the "ABS" indicator is turned on.

Test Description: Number(s) below refer to circled number(s) on the diagnostic chart.

1. This step identifies a problem in a wheel speed sensor that may cause the system to be in release too long.
2. This step identifies a motor as being failed or wired incorrectly.
3. This step checks for a solenoid that may have mechanically failed open.
4. If Step 3 has failed, this serves to isolate the cause of the hydraulic problem to either the solenoid or the hydraulic modulator.
5. This step determines whether a malfunctioning motor pack or hydraulic modulator is the reason for DTC A052 being set.

Diagnostic Aids:

An "intermittent" malfunction may be caused by a mechanical part of the system that sticks or binds.

The frequency of the malfunction can be checked by using the enhanced diagnostic function of the TECH 1.

DTC A052 may fail if on ice and the steering wheel is turned to lock during braking. Using the TECH 1, perform the hydraulic test to ensure that the total brake system is functional.

Any circuitry that is suspected of causing the intermittent complaint should be thoroughly checked for backed out terminals, improper mating, broken locks, improperly formed or damaged terminals, poor terminal-to-wiring connections or physical damage to the wiring harness.

GC402940097600AX

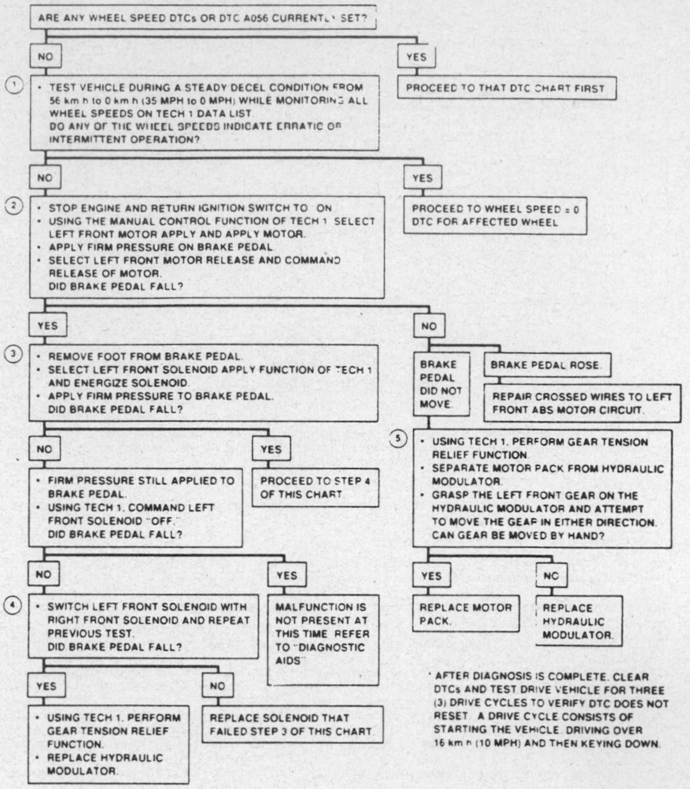
ARE ANY WHEEL SPEED DTCs OR DTC A056 CURRENTLY SET?
NO
YES
PROCEED TO THAT DTC CHART FIRST
1
• TEST VEHICLE DURING A STEADY DECEL CONDITION FROM 56 km/h to 0 km/h (35 MPH to 0 MPH) WHILE MONITORING ALL WHEEL SPEEDS ON TECH 1 DATA LIST.
DO ANY OF THE WHEEL SPEEDS INDICATE ERRATIC OR INTERMITTENT OPERATION?
NO
YES
PROCEED TO WHEEL SPEED = 0 DTC FOR AFFECTED WHEEL
2
• STOP ENGINE AND RETURN IGNITION SWITCH TO ON.
• USING THE MANUAL CONTROL FUNCTION OF TECH 1, SELECT LEFT FRONT MOTOR APPLY AND APPLY MOTOR.
• APPLY FIRM PRESSURE ON BRAKE PEDAL.
• SELECT LEFT FRONT MOTOR RELEASE AND COMMAND RELEASE OF MOTOR.
DID BRAKE PEDAL FALL?
YES
NO
3
• REMOVE FOOT FROM BRAKE PEDAL.
• SELECT LEFT FRONT SOLENOID APPLY FUNCTION OF TECH 1 AND ENERGIZE SOLENOID.
• APPLY FIRM PRESSURE TO BRAKE PEDAL.
DID BRAKE PEDAL FALL?
BRAKE PEDAL DID NOT MOVE.
BRAKE PEDAL ROSE.
REPAIR CROSSED WIRES TO LEFT FRONT ABS MOTOR CIRCUIT.
NO
YES
• FIRM PRESSURE STILL APPLIED TO BRAKE PEDAL.
• USING TECH 1, COMMAND LEFT FRONT SOLENOID "OFF."
DID BRAKE PEDAL FALL?
PROCEED TO STEP 4 OF THIS CHART.
5
• USING TECH 1, PERFORM GEAR TENSION RELIEF FUNCTION.
• SEPARATE MOTOR PACK FROM HYDRAULIC MODULATOR.
• GRASP THE LEFT FRONT GEAR ON THE HYDRAULIC MODULATOR AND ATTEMPT TO MOVE THE GEAR IN EITHER DIRECTION.
CAN GEAR BE MOVED BY HAND?
NO
YES
YES
NO
4
• SWITCH LEFT FRONT SOLENOID WITH RIGHT FRONT SOLENOID AND REPEAT PREVIOUS TEST.
DID BRAKE PEDAL FALL?
MALFUNCTION IS NOT PRESENT AT THIS TIME. REFER TO "DIAGNOSTIC AIDS"
REPLACE MOTOR PACK.
REPLACE HYDRAULIC MODULATOR.
YES
NO
• USING TECH 1, PERFORM GEAR TENSION RELIEF FUNCTION.
• REPLACE HYDRAULIC MODULATOR.
REPLACE SOLENOID THAT FAILED STEP 3 OF THIS CHART.
* AFTER DIAGNOSIS IS COMPLETE, CLEAR DTCs AND TEST DRIVE VEHICLE FOR THREE (3) DRIVE CYCLES TO VERIFY DTC DOES NOT RESET. A DRIVE CYCLE CONSISTS OF STARTING THE VEHICLE, DRIVING OVER 16 km/h (10 MPH) AND THEN KEYING DOWN.

GC402940097600BX

Fig. 326 Code A052: Left Front Channel In Release Too Long. 1993–94 Prizm

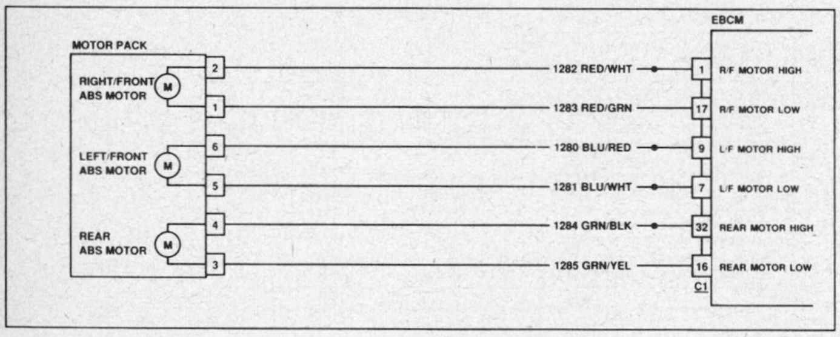
EBCM
MOTOR PACK
RIGHT/FRONT ABS MOTOR
LEFT/FRONT ABS MOTOR
REAR ABS MOTOR
2
1
6
5
4
3
1282 RED/WHT
1283 RED/GRN
1280 BLU/RED
1281 BLU/WHT
1284 GRN/BLK
1285 GRN/YEL
1 R/F MOTOR HIGH
17 R/F MOTOR LOW
9 L/F MOTOR HIGH
7 L/F MOTOR LOW
32 REAR MOTOR HIGH
16 REAR MOTOR LOW
C1

DTC A053

RIGHT FRONT CHANNEL IN RELEASE TOO LONG

Circuit Description:

This DTC will diagnose a motor that is energized longer than expected. This could occur if a wheel speed sensor is malfunctioning, the motor does not turn, the right front solenoid mechanically fails open or the motor wires are crossed.

Failure Condition:

DTC A053 can be set only during an ABS stop. If the EBCM commands the left front channel in release for three seconds, a malfunction exists.

Action Taken:

A DTC A053 is stored, ABS is disabled and the "ABS" indicator is turned on.

Test Description: Number(s) below refer to circled number(s) on the diagnostic chart.

1. This step identifies a problem in a wheel speed sensor that may cause the system to be in release too long.
2. This step identifies a motor as being failed or wired incorrectly.
3. This step checks for a solenoid that may have mechanically failed open.
4. If Step 3 has failed, this serves to isolate the cause of the hydraulic problem to either the solenoid or the hydraulic modulator.
5. This step determines whether a malfunctioning motor pack or hydraulic modulator is the reason for DTC A053 being set.

Diagnostic Aids:

An "intermittent" malfunction may be caused by a mechanical part of the system that sticks or binds.

The frequency of the malfunction can be checked by using the enhanced diagnostic function of the TECH 1.

DTC A053 may fail if on ice and the steering wheel is turned to lock during braking. Using the TECH 1, perform the hydraulic test to ensure that the total brake system is functional.

Any circuitry that is suspected of causing the intermittent complaint should be thoroughly checked for backed out terminals, improper mating, broken locks, improperly formed or damaged terminals, poor terminal-to-wiring connections or physical damage to the wiring harness.

GC402940097700AX

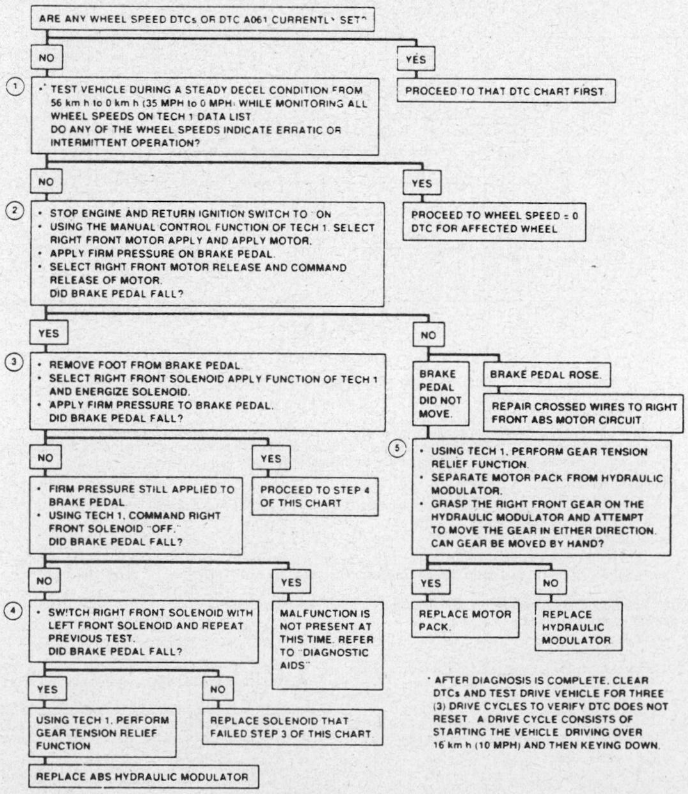
ARE ANY WHEEL SPEED DTCs OR DTC A061 CURRENTLY SET?
NO
YES
PROCEED TO THAT DTC CHART FIRST.
1
• TEST VEHICLE DURING A STEADY DECEL CONDITION FROM 56 km/h to 0 km/h (35 MPH to 0 MPH) WHILE MONITORING ALL WHEEL SPEEDS ON TECH 1 DATA LIST.
DO ANY OF THE WHEEL SPEEDS INDICATE ERRATIC OR INTERMITTENT OPERATION?
NO
YES
PROCEED TO WHEEL SPEED = 0 DTC FOR AFFECTED WHEEL
2
• STOP ENGINE AND RETURN IGNITION SWITCH TO ON.
• USING THE MANUAL CONTROL FUNCTION OF TECH 1, SELECT RIGHT FRONT MOTOR APPLY AND APPLY MOTOR.
• APPLY FIRM PRESSURE ON BRAKE PEDAL.
• SELECT RIGHT FRONT MOTOR RELEASE AND COMMAND RELEASE OF MOTOR.
DID BRAKE PEDAL FALL?
YES
NO
3
• REMOVE FOOT FROM BRAKE PEDAL.
• SELECT RIGHT FRONT SOLENOID APPLY FUNCTION OF TECH 1 AND ENERGIZE SOLENOID.
• APPLY FIRM PRESSURE TO BRAKE PEDAL.
DID BRAKE PEDAL FALL?
BRAKE PEDAL DID NOT MOVE.
BRAKE PEDAL ROSE.
REPAIR CROSSED WIRES TO RIGHT FRONT ABS MOTOR CIRCUIT.
NO
YES
• FIRM PRESSURE STILL APPLIED TO BRAKE PEDAL.
• USING TECH 1, COMMAND RIGHT FRONT SOLENOID "OFF."
DID BRAKE PEDAL FALL?
PROCEED TO STEP 4 OF THIS CHART
5
• USING TECH 1, PERFORM GEAR TENSION RELIEF FUNCTION.
• SEPARATE MOTOR PACK FROM HYDRAULIC MODULATOR.
• GRASP THE RIGHT FRONT GEAR ON THE HYDRAULIC MODULATOR AND ATTEMPT TO MOVE THE GEAR IN EITHER DIRECTION.
CAN GEAR BE MOVED BY HAND?
NO
YES
YES
NO
4
• SWITCH RIGHT FRONT SOLENOID WITH LEFT FRONT SOLENOID AND REPEAT PREVIOUS TEST.
DID BRAKE PEDAL FALL?
MALFUNCTION IS NOT PRESENT AT THIS TIME. REFER TO "DIAGNOSTIC AIDS"
REPLACE MOTOR PACK.
REPLACE HYDRAULIC MODULATOR
YES
NO
USING TECH 1, PERFORM GEAR TENSION RELIEF FUNCTION
REPLACE SOLENOID THAT FAILED STEP 3 OF THIS CHART.
REPLACE ABS HYDRAULIC MODULATOR
* AFTER DIAGNOSIS IS COMPLETE, CLEAR DTCs AND TEST DRIVE VEHICLE FOR THREE (3) DRIVE CYCLES TO VERIFY DTC DOES NOT RESET. A DRIVE CYCLE CONSISTS OF STARTING THE VEHICLE, DRIVING OVER 16 km/h (10 MPH) AND THEN KEYING DOWN.

GC402940097700BX

Fig. 327 Code A053: Right Front Channel In Release Too Long. 1993–94 Prizm

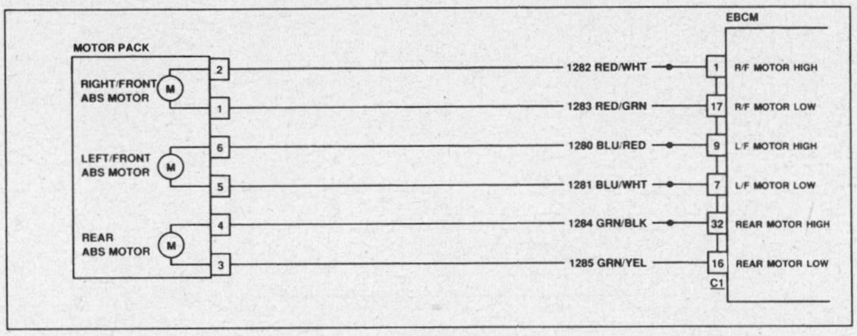
EBCM
MOTOR PACK
RIGHT/FRONT ABS MOTOR
LEFT/FRONT ABS MOTOR
REAR ABS MOTOR
1282 RED/WHT
1283 RED/GRN
1280 BLU/RED
1281 BLU/WHT
1284 GRN/BLK
1285 GRN/YEL
R/F MOTOR HIGH
R/F MOTOR LOW
L/F MOTOR HIGH
L/F MOTOR LOW
REAR MOTOR HIGH
REAR MOTOR LOW
C1

DTC A054

(Page 1 of 2)
REAR CHANNEL IN RELEASE TOO LONG

Circuit Description:

This DTC will diagnose a motor that is energized longer than expected. This could occur if a wheel speed sensor is malfunctioning, the motor does not turn or the motor wires are crossed.

Failure Condition:

DTC A054 can be set only during an ABS stop. If the EBCM commands the rear channel in release for three seconds, a malfunction exists.

Action Taken:

A DTC A054 is stored, ABS is disabled and the "ABS" indicator is turned on.

Test Description: Number(s) below refer to circled number(s) on the diagnostic chart.

1. This step identifies a problem in a wheel speed sensor that may cause the system to be in release too long.
2. This checks for a wheel that may stick or bind because of a mechanical fault.
3. This checks to see if the motor is capable of moving and applying the hydraulic piston for the rear wheels.

Diagnostic Aids:

An "intermittent" malfunction may be caused by a mechanical part of the system that sticks or binds.

The frequency of the malfunction can be checked by using the enhanced diagnostic function of the TECH 1

Using the TECH 1, perform the hydraulic test to ensure that the total brake system is functional.

Any circuitry that is suspected of causing the intermittent complaint should be thoroughly checked for backed out terminals, improper mating, broken locks, improperly formed or damaged terminals, poor terminal-to-wiring connections or physical damage to the wiring harness.

GC402940097801AX

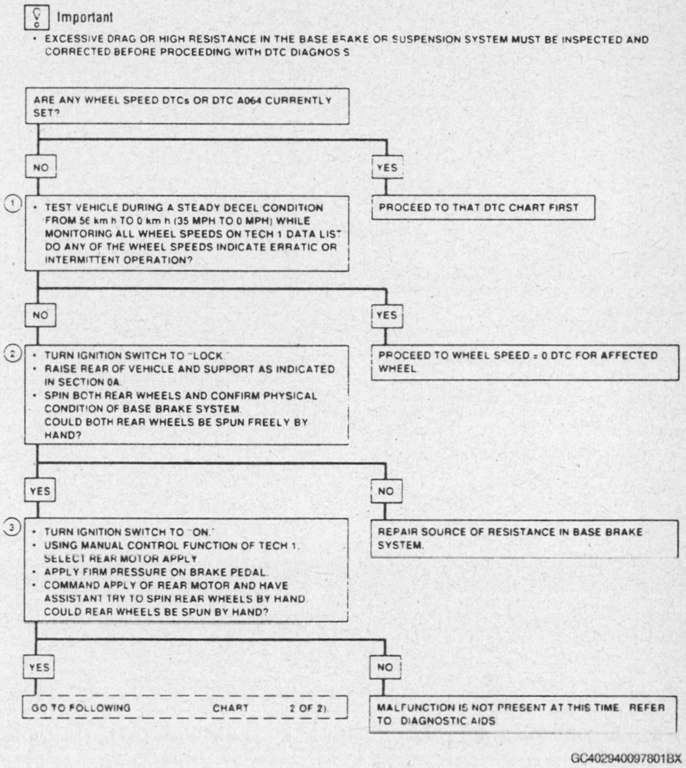
Important
• EXCESSIVE DRAG OR HIGH RESISTANCE IN THE BASE BRAKE OR SUSPENSION SYSTEM MUST BE INSPECTED AND CORRECTED BEFORE PROCEEDING WITH DTC DIAGNOSIS.
ARE ANY WHEEL SPEED DTCs OR DTC A064 CURRENTLY SET?
NO
YES
PROCEED TO THAT DTC CHART FIRST
1
• TEST VEHICLE DURING A STEADY DECEL CONDITION FROM 56 km/h TO 0 km/h (35 MPH TO 0 MPH) WHILE MONITORING ALL WHEEL SPEEDS ON TECH 1 DATA LIST. DO ANY OF THE WHEEL SPEEDS INDICATE ERRATIC OR INTERMITTENT OPERATION?
NO
YES
PROCEED TO WHEEL SPEED = 0 DTC FOR AFFECTED WHEEL
2
• TURN IGNITION SWITCH TO "LOCK."
• RAISE REAR OF VEHICLE AND SUPPORT AS INDICATED IN SECTION 0A.
• SPIN BOTH REAR WHEELS AND CONFIRM PHYSICAL CONDITION OF BASE BRAKE SYSTEM. COULD BOTH REAR WHEELS BE SPUN FREELY BY HAND?
YES
NO
REPAIR SOURCE OF RESISTANCE IN BASE BRAKE SYSTEM.
3
• TURN IGNITION SWITCH TO "ON."
• USING MANUAL CONTROL FUNCTION OF TECH 1, SELECT REAR MOTOR APPLY.
• APPLY FIRM PRESSURE ON BRAKE PEDAL.
• COMMAND APPLY OF REAR MOTOR AND HAVE ASSISTANT TRY TO SPIN REAR WHEELS BY HAND. COULD REAR WHEELS BE SPUN BY HAND?
YES
NO
GO TO FOLLOWING CHART (2 OF 2).
MALFUNCTION IS NOT PRESENT AT THIS TIME. REFER TO DIAGNOSTIC AIDS
GC402940097801BX

Fig. 328 Code A054: Rear Channel In Release Too Long (Part 1 of 2). 1993–94 Prizm

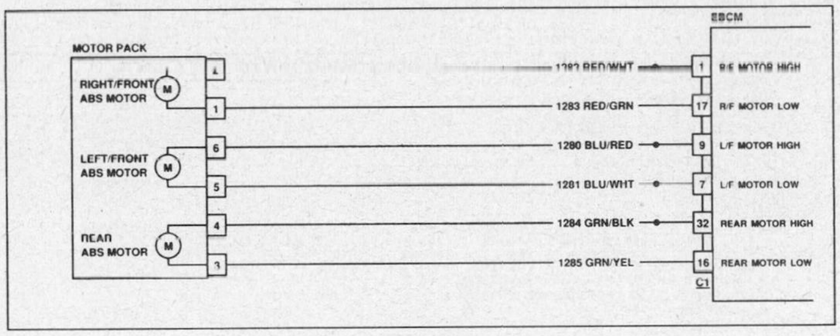
EBCM
MOTOR PACK
RIGHT/FRONT ABS MOTOR
LEFT/FRONT ABS MOTOR
REAR ABS MOTOR
1282 RED/WHT
1283 RED/GRN
1280 BLU/RED
1281 BLU/WHT
1284 GRN/BLK
1285 GRN/YEL
R/F MOTOR HIGH
R/F MOTOR LOW
L/F MOTOR HIGH
L/F MOTOR LOW
REAR MOTOR HIGH
REAR MOTOR LOW
C1

DTC A054

(Page 2 of 2)
REAR CHANNEL IN RELEASE TOO LONG

Circuit Description:

This DTC will diagnose a motor that is energized longer than expected. This could occur if a wheel speed sensor is malfunctioning, the motor does not turn or the motor wires are crossed.

Failure Condition:

DTC A054 can be set only during an ABS stop. If the EBCM commands the rear channel in release for three seconds, a malfunction exists.

Action Taken:

A DTC A054 is stored, ABS is disabled and the "ABS" indicator is turned on.

Test Description: Number(s) below refer to circled number(s) on the diagnostic chart.

4. This step ensures that the motor wiring is not crossed.
5. This isolates the fault of a "no-apply" situation to either the motor pack or the hydraulic modulator.

Diagnostic Aids:

An "intermittent" malfunction may be caused by a mechanical part of the system that sticks or binds.

The frequency of the malfunction can be checked by using the enhanced diagnostic function of the TECH 1

Using the TECH 1, perform the hydraulic test to ensure that the total brake system is functional.

Any circuitry that is suspected of causing the intermittent complaint should be thoroughly checked for backed out terminals, improper mating, broken locks, improperly formed or damaged terminals, poor terminal-to-wiring connections or physical damage to the wiring harness.

GC402940097802AX

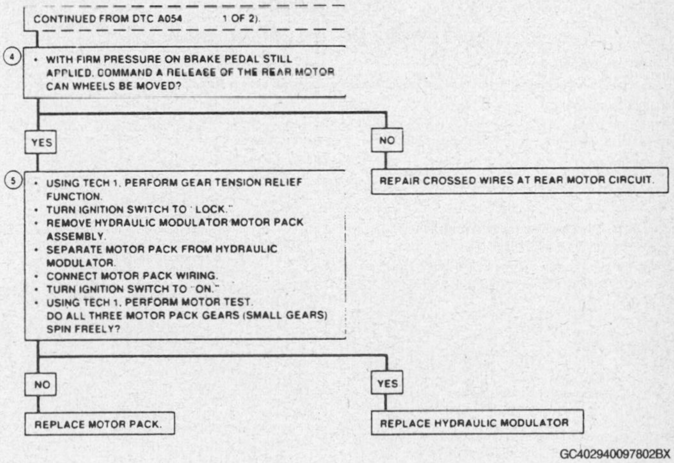
CONTINUED FROM DTC A054 (1 OF 2).
4
• WITH FIRM PRESSURE ON BRAKE PEDAL STILL APPLIED, COMMAND A RELEASE OF THE REAR MOTOR. CAN WHEELS BE MOVED?
YES
NO
REPAIR CROSSED WIRES AT REAR MOTOR CIRCUIT.
5
• USING TECH 1, PERFORM GEAR TENSION RELIEF FUNCTION.
• TURN IGNITION SWITCH TO "LOCK."
• REMOVE HYDRAULIC MODULATOR/MOTOR PACK ASSEMBLY.
• SEPARATE MOTOR PACK FROM HYDRAULIC MODULATOR.
• CONNECT MOTOR PACK WIRING.
• TURN IGNITION SWITCH TO "ON."
• USING TECH 1, PERFORM MOTOR TEST. DO ALL THREE MOTOR PACK GEARS (SMALL GEARS) SPIN FREELY?
NO
YES
REPLACE MOTOR PACK.
REPLACE HYDRAULIC MODULATOR
GC402940097802BX

Fig. 328 Code A054: Rear Channel In Release Too Long (Part 2 of 2). 1993–94 Prizm

DTC A055
EBCM MALFUNCTION

Circuit Description:

This DTC identifies a malfunction detected by the MDI custom IC. It also insures the cause of the malfunction is not a result of a problem with the enable relay under a DTC A055 malfunction.

Action Taken:

A DTC A055 is stored, ABS is disabled and the "ABS" indicator is turned on or will flash.

Test Description: Number(s) below refer to circled number(s) on the diagnostic chart.

1. This checks to see if the malfunction is still present.
2. This step checks to see if the malfunction is intermittent.

Diagnostic Aids:

The frequency of the malfunction can be checked by using the enhanced diagnostic function of the TECH 1

GC402940097900AX

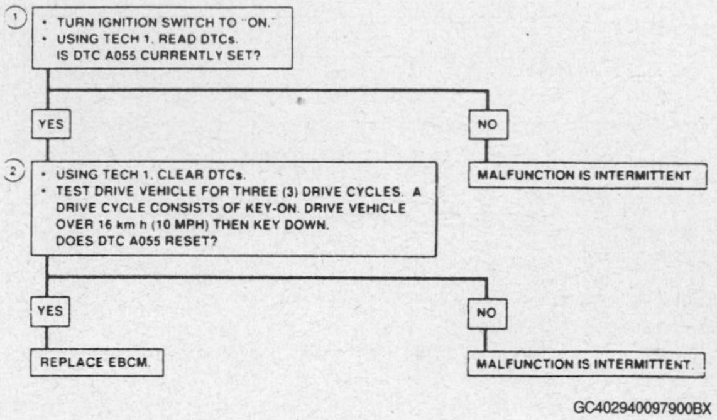
1
• TURN IGNITION SWITCH TO "ON."
• USING TECH 1, READ DTCs.
IS DTC A055 CURRENTLY SET?
YES
NO
MALFUNCTION IS INTERMITTENT
2
• USING TECH 1, CLEAR DTCs.
• TEST DRIVE VEHICLE FOR THREE (3) DRIVE CYCLES. A DRIVE CYCLE CONSISTS OF KEY-ON, DRIVE VEHICLE OVER 16 km h (10 MPH) THEN KEY DOWN.
DOES DTC A055 RESET?
YES
NO
REPLACE EBCM.
MALFUNCTION IS INTERMITTENT.

GC402940097900BX

Fig. 329 Code A055: EBCM Malfunction. 1993–94 Prizm

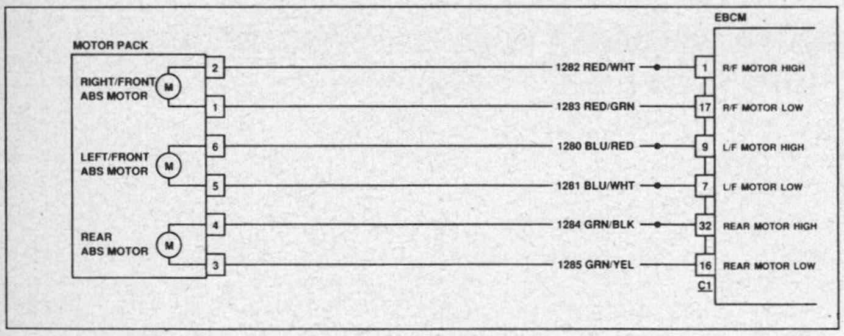
EBCM
MOTOR PACK
RIGHT/FRONT ABS MOTOR
LEFT/FRONT ABS MOTOR
REAR ABS MOTOR
M
2
1
6
5
4
3
1282 RED/WHT
1283 RED/GRN
1280 BLU/RED
1281 BLU/WHT
1284 GRN/BLK
1285 GRN/YEL
1
17
9
7
32
16
C1
R/F MOTOR HIGH
R/F MOTOR LOW
L/F MOTOR HIGH
L/F MOTOR LOW
REAR MOTOR HIGH
REAR MOTOR LOW

DTC A056
LEFT FRONT MOTOR CIRCUIT OPEN

Circuit Description:

This DTC identifies a motor that cannot be energized due to an open in its circuitry.

Failure Condition:

DTC A056 can be set only when the motor is commanded off. If the EBCM detects an out of range voltage on either of the left front motor circuits (indicating an open circuit), a malfunction exists.

Action Taken:

An open motor will not activate when requested. A DTC A056 is stored, ABS is disabled and the "ABS" indicator is turned on.

Test Description: Number(s) below refer to circled number(s) on the diagnostic chart.

1. This step checks for proper resistance of the motor.
2. This step checks for an open in the motor high circuitry.
3. This step checks for an open in the motor low circuitry.

Diagnostic Aids:

Using TECH 1, select manual control function and exercise motor movement of affected channel in both directions while applying light pressure on the brake pedal.

If erratic or "jumpy" brake pedal movement is detected while performing an "apply" or "release" function of the motor, an intermittent malfunction may be indicated.

An "intermittent" malfunction may be caused by a poor connection, rubbed through wire insulation or a wire that is broken inside the insulation.

If the malfunction is not current, wiggle the wires of the affected channel and check if the DTC resets. This will help to pinpoint an intermittent malfunction in the motor circuitry or connections.

The frequency of the malfunction can be checked by using the enhanced diagnostic function of the TECH 1

Any circuitry that is suspected of causing the intermittent complaint should be thoroughly checked for backed out terminals, improper mating, broken locks, improperly formed or damaged terminals, poor terminal-to-wiring connections or physical damage to the wiring harness.

GC402940098000AX

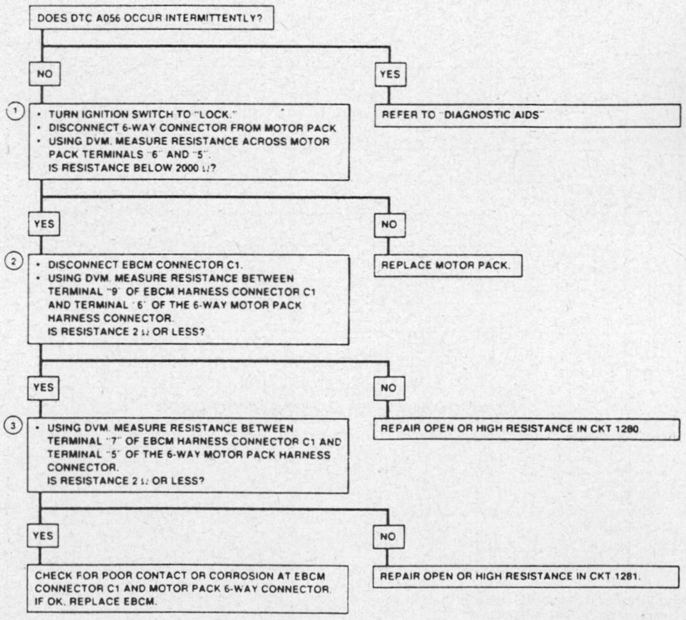
DOES DTC A056 OCCUR INTERMITTENTLY?
NO
YES
REFER TO "DIAGNOSTIC AIDS"
1
• TURN IGNITION SWITCH TO "LOCK."
• DISCONNECT 6-WAY CONNECTOR FROM MOTOR PACK
• USING DVM, MEASURE RESISTANCE ACROSS MOTOR PACK TERMINALS "6" AND "5".
IS RESISTANCE BELOW 2000 Ω?
YES
NO
REPLACE MOTOR PACK.
2
• DISCONNECT EBCM CONNECTOR C1.
• USING DVM, MEASURE RESISTANCE BETWEEN TERMINAL "9" OF EBCM HARNESS CONNECTOR C1 AND TERMINAL "6" OF THE 6-WAY MOTOR PACK HARNESS CONNECTOR.
IS RESISTANCE 2 Ω OR LESS?
YES
NO
REPAIR OPEN OR HIGH RESISTANCE IN CKT 1280.
3
• USING DVM, MEASURE RESISTANCE BETWEEN TERMINAL "7" OF EBCM HARNESS CONNECTOR C1 AND TERMINAL "5" OF THE 6-WAY MOTOR PACK HARNESS CONNECTOR.
IS RESISTANCE 2 Ω OR LESS?
YES
NO
CHECK FOR POOR CONTACT OR CORROSION AT EBCM CONNECTOR C1 AND MOTOR PACK 6-WAY CONNECTOR. IF OK, REPLACE EBCM.
REPAIR OPEN OR HIGH RESISTANCE IN CKT 1281.

GC402940098000BX

Fig. 330 Code A056: Left Front Motor Circuit Open. 1993–94 Prizm

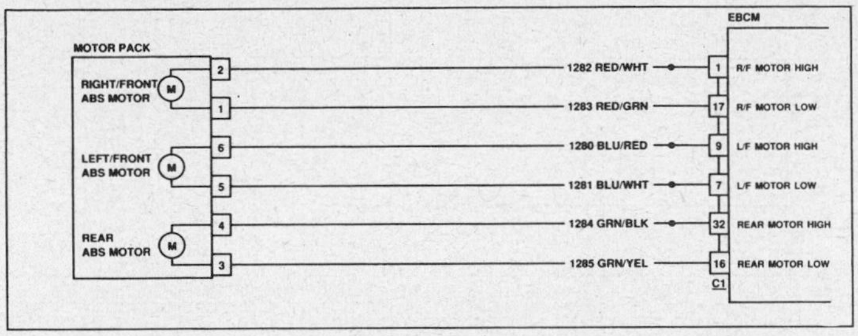
EBCM
MOTOR PACK
RIGHT/FRONT ABS MOTOR
LEFT/FRONT ABS MOTOR
REAR ABS MOTOR
1282 RED/WHT
1283 RED/GRN
1280 BLU/RED
1281 BLU/WHT
1284 GRN/BLK
1285 GRN/YEL
R/F MOTOR HIGH
R/F MOTOR LOW
L/F MOTOR HIGH
L/F MOTOR LOW
REAR MOTOR HIGH
REAR MOTOR LOW
C1

DTC A057

LEFT FRONT MOTOR CIRCUIT SHORTED TO GROUND

Circuit Description:

This DTC identifies a motor circuit that is shorted to ground. This malfunction will not allow the motor to be controlled at the commanded current rate or will cause the driver circuit to allow current directly to ground.

Failure Condition:

DTC A057 can be set anytime. If the EBCM detects an out of range voltage on either of the left front motor circuits (indicating a circuit shorted to ground), a malfunction exists.

Action Taken:

A DTC A057 is stored. ABS is disabled and the "ABS" indicator is turned on.

Test Description: Number(s) below refer to circled number(s) on the diagnostic chart.

1. This step checks for a short to ground in the motor high circuit.
2. This step checks for a short to ground in the motor low circuit.
3. This step checks for a motor that is internally shorted to ground.

Diagnostic Aids:

Using TECH 1, select manual control function and exercise motor movement of affected channel in both directions while applying light pressure on the brake pedal.

If erratic or "jumpy" brake pedal movement is detected while performing an "apply" or "release" function of the motor, an intermittent malfunction may be indicated.

An "intermittent" malfunction may be caused by a poor connection, rubbed through wire insulation or a wire that is broken inside the insulation.

If the malfunction is not current, wiggle the wires of the affected channel and check if the DTC resets. This will help to pinpoint an intermittent malfunction in the motor circuitry or connections.

The frequency of the malfunction can be checked by using the enhanced diagnostic function of the TECH 1.

Any circuitry that is suspected of causing the intermittent complaint should be thoroughly checked for backed out terminals, improper mating, broken locks, improperly formed or damaged terminals, poor terminal-to-wiring connections or physical damage to the wiring harness.

GC402940098100AX

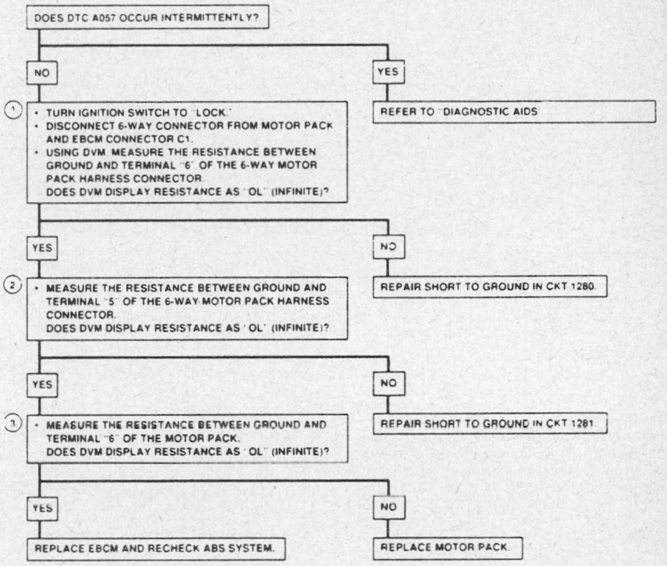
DOES DTC A057 OCCUR INTERMITTENTLY?
NO
YES
1
• TURN IGNITION SWITCH TO "LOCK."
• DISCONNECT 6-WAY CONNECTOR FROM MOTOR PACK AND EBCM CONNECTOR C1.
• USING DVM MEASURE THE RESISTANCE BETWEEN GROUND AND TERMINAL "6" OF THE 6-WAY MOTOR PACK HARNESS CONNECTOR.
DOES DVM DISPLAY RESISTANCE AS "OL" (INFINITE)?
REFER TO "DIAGNOSTIC AIDS"
YES
NO
2
• MEASURE THE RESISTANCE BETWEEN GROUND AND TERMINAL "5" OF THE 6-WAY MOTOR PACK HARNESS CONNECTOR.
DOES DVM DISPLAY RESISTANCE AS "OL" (INFINITE)?
REPAIR SHORT TO GROUND IN CKT 1280.
YES
NO
3
• MEASURE THE RESISTANCE BETWEEN GROUND AND TERMINAL "6" OF THE MOTOR PACK.
DOES DVM DISPLAY RESISTANCE AS "OL" (INFINITE)?
REPAIR SHORT TO GROUND IN CKT 1281
YES
NO
REPLACE EBCM AND RECHECK ABS SYSTEM.
REPLACE MOTOR PACK.

GC402940098100BX

Fig. 331 Code A057: Left Front Motor Circuit Shorted To Ground. 1993-94 Prizm

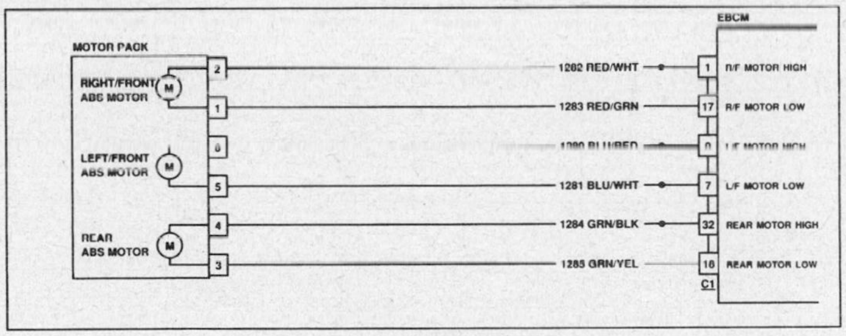
EBCM
MOTOR PACK
RIGHT/FRONT ABS MOTOR
LEFT/FRONT ABS MOTOR
REAR ABS MOTOR
1282 RED/WHT
1283 RED/GRN
1281 BLU/WHT
1284 GRN/BLK
1285 GRN/YEL
R/F MOTOR HIGH
R/F MOTOR LOW
L/F MOTOR LOW
REAR MOTOR HIGH
REAR MOTOR LOW
C1

DTC A058

LEFT FRONT MOTOR CIRCUIT SHORTED TO BATTERY

Circuit Description:

This DTC identifies a motor circuit that is shorted to battery or a motor that has low or no resistance. This malfunction will not allow the motor to be controlled at the commanded current rate or will cause the motor to turn in the opposite direction or not at all.

Failure Condition:

DTC A058 can be set only when the motor is commanded off. If the EBCM detects an out of range voltage on either of the left front motor circuits (indicating a circuit shorted to battery or a motor shorted), a malfunction exists.

Action Taken:

A DTC A058 is stored. ABS is disabled and the "ABS" indicator is turned on.

Test Description: Number(s) below refer to circled number(s) on the diagnostic chart.

1. This step checks for a short to voltage in the motor high circuitry.
2. This step checks for a short to voltage in the motor low circuitry.
3. This step checks for a motor that is internally shorted.

Diagnostic Aids:

Using TECH 1, select manual control function and exercise motor movement of affected channel in both directions while applying light pressure on the brake pedal.

If erratic or "jumpy" brake pedal movement is detected while performing an "apply" or "release" function of the motor, an intermittent malfunction may be indicated.

An "intermittent" malfunction may be caused by a poor connection, rubbed through wire insulation or a wire that is broken inside the insulation.

If the malfunction is not current, wiggle the wires of the affected channel and check if the DTC resets. This will help to pinpoint an intermittent malfunction in the motor circuitry or connections.

The frequency of the malfunction can be checked by using the enhanced diagnostic function of the TECH 1.

Any circuitry that is suspected of causing the intermittent complaint should be thoroughly checked for backed out terminals, improper mating, broken locks, improperly formed or damaged terminals, poor terminal-to-wiring connections or physical damage to the wiring harness.

GC402940098200AX

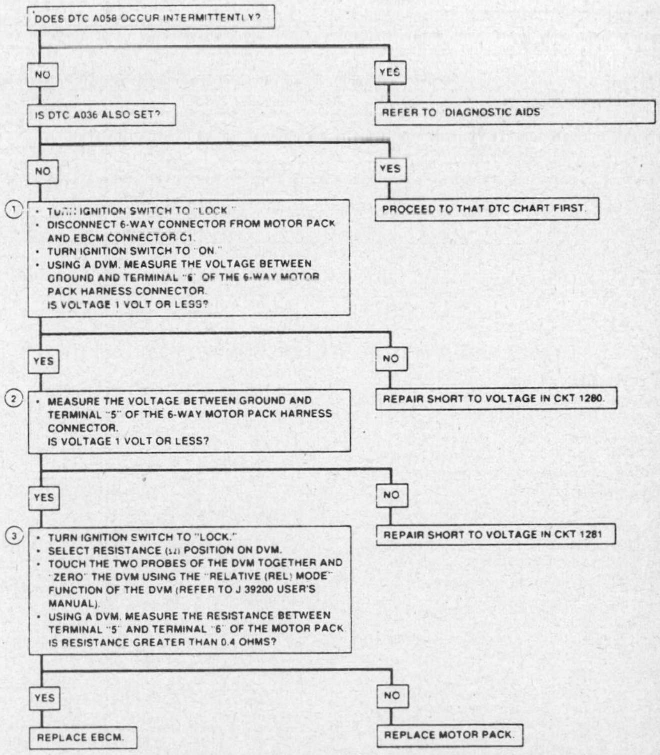
DOES DTC A058 OCCUR INTERMITTENTLY?
NO
YES
IS DTC A036 ALSO SET?
REFER TO "DIAGNOSTIC AIDS"
NO
YES
1
• DISCONNECT 6-WAY CONNECTOR FROM MOTOR PACK AND EBCM CONNECTOR C1.
• TURN IGNITION SWITCH TO "ON."
• USING A DVM, MEASURE THE VOLTAGE BETWEEN GROUND AND TERMINAL "6" OF THE 6-WAY MOTOR PACK HARNESS CONNECTOR.
IS VOLTAGE 1 VOLT OR LESS?
PROCEED TO THAT DTC CHART FIRST.
YES
NO
2
• MEASURE THE VOLTAGE BETWEEN GROUND AND TERMINAL "5" OF THE 6-WAY MOTOR PACK HARNESS CONNECTOR.
IS VOLTAGE 1 VOLT OR LESS?
REPAIR SHORT TO VOLTAGE IN CKT 1280.
YES
NO
3
• TURN IGNITION SWITCH TO "LOCK."
• SELECT RESISTANCE POSITION ON DVM.
• TOUCH THE TWO PROBES OF THE DVM TOGETHER AND "ZERO" THE DVM USING THE "RELATIVE (REL) MODE" FUNCTION OF THE DVM (REFER TO J 39200 USER'S MANUAL).
• USING A DVM, MEASURE THE RESISTANCE BETWEEN TERMINAL "5" AND TERMINAL "6" OF THE MOTOR PACK.
IS RESISTANCE GREATER THAN 0.4 OHMS?
REPAIR SHORT TO VOLTAGE IN CKT 1281
YES
NO
REPLACE EBCM.
REPLACE MOTOR PACK.

* AFTER ALL DIAGNOSIS IS COMPLETE, CLEAR DTCs AND TEST DRIVE VEHICLE FOR THREE (3) DRIVE CYCLES TO VERIFY THAT DTC DOES NOT RESET. A DRIVE CYCLE CONSISTS OF STARTING THE VEHICLE, DRIVING OVER 16 km/h (10 MPH), AND THEN KEYING DOWN.

GC402940098200BX

Fig. 332 Code A058: Left Front Motor Circuit Shorted To Battery. 1993-94 Prizm

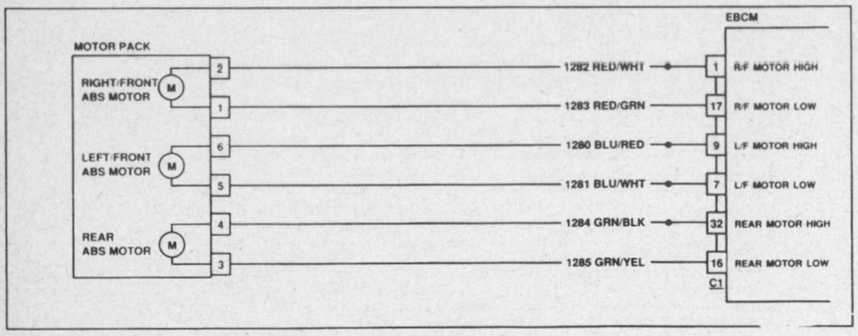
EBCM
MOTOR PACK
RIGHT/FRONT ABS MOTOR
LEFT/FRONT ABS MOTOR
REAR ABS MOTOR
1282 RED/WHT
1283 RED/GRN
1280 BLU/RED
1281 BLU/WHT
1284 GRN/BLK
1285 GRN/YEL
R/F MOTOR HIGH
R/F MOTOR LOW
L/F MOTOR HIGH
L/F MOTOR LOW
REAR MOTOR HIGH
REAR MOTOR LOW
C1

DTC A061

RIGHT FRONT MOTOR CIRCUIT OPEN

Circuit Description:

This DTC identifies a motor that cannot be energized due to an open in its circuitry.

Failure Condition:

DTC A061 can be set only when the motor is commanded off. If the EBCM detects an out of range voltage on either of the right front motor circuits (indicating an open circuit), a malfunction exists.

Action Taken:

An open motor will not activate when requested. A DTC A061 is stored, ABS is disabled and the "ABS" indicator is turned on.

Test Description: Number(s) below refer to circled number(s) on the diagnostic chart.

1. This step checks for proper resistance of the motor.
2. This step checks for an open in the motor high circuitry.
3. This step checks for an open in the motor low circuitry.

Diagnostic Aids:

Using TECH 1, select manual control function and exercise motor movement of affected channel in both directions while applying light pressure on the brake pedal.

If erratic or "jumpy" brake pedal movement is detected while performing an "apply" or "release" function of the motor, an intermittent malfunction may be indicated.

An "intermittent" malfunction may be caused by a poor connection, rubbed through wire insulation or a wire that is broken inside the insulation.

If the malfunction is not current, wiggle the wires of the affected channel and check if the DTC resets. This will help to pinpoint an intermittent malfunction in the motor circuitry or connections.

The frequency of the malfunction can be checked by using the enhanced diagnostic function of the TECH 1

Any circuitry that is suspected of causing the intermittent complaint should be thoroughly checked for backed out terminals, improper mating, broken locks, improperly formed or damaged terminals, poor terminal-to-wiring connections or physical damage to the wiring harness.

GC402940098300AX

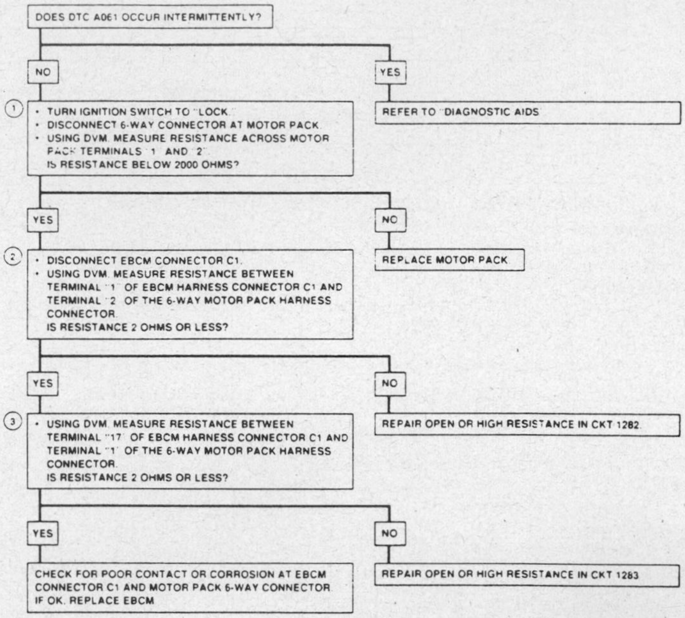
DOES DTC A061 OCCUR INTERMITTENTLY?
NO
YES
REFER TO "DIAGNOSTIC AIDS
1
• TURN IGNITION SWITCH TO "LOCK.
• DISCONNECT 6-WAY CONNECTOR AT MOTOR PACK.
• USING DVM, MEASURE RESISTANCE ACROSS MOTOR PACK TERMINALS "1" AND "2".
IS RESISTANCE BELOW 2000 OHMS?
YES
NO
REPLACE MOTOR PACK.
2
• DISCONNECT EBCM CONNECTOR C1.
• USING DVM, MEASURE RESISTANCE BETWEEN TERMINAL "1" OF EBCM HARNESS CONNECTOR C1 AND TERMINAL "2" OF THE 6-WAY MOTOR PACK HARNESS CONNECTOR.
IS RESISTANCE 2 OHMS OR LESS?
YES
NO
REPAIR OPEN OR HIGH RESISTANCE IN CKT 1282.
3
• USING DVM, MEASURE RESISTANCE BETWEEN TERMINAL "17" OF EBCM HARNESS CONNECTOR C1 AND TERMINAL "1" OF THE 6-WAY MOTOR PACK HARNESS CONNECTOR.
IS RESISTANCE 2 OHMS OR LESS?
YES
NO
CHECK FOR POOR CONTACT OR CORROSION AT EBCM CONNECTOR C1 AND MOTOR PACK 6-WAY CONNECTOR. IF OK, REPLACE EBCM.
REPAIR OPEN OR HIGH RESISTANCE IN CKT 1283.

GC402940098300BX

Fig. 333 Code A061: Right Front Motor Circuit Open. 1993–94 Prizm

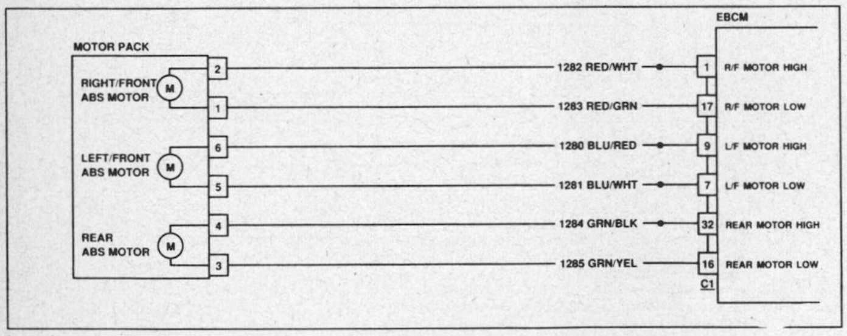
EBCM
MOTOR PACK
RIGHT/FRONT ABS MOTOR
LEFT/FRONT ABS MOTOR
REAR ABS MOTOR
1282 RED/WHT
1283 RED/GRN
1280 BLU/RED
1281 BLU/WHT
1284 GRN/BLK
1285 GRN/YEL
R/F MOTOR HIGH
R/F MOTOR LOW
L/F MOTOR HIGH
L/F MOTOR LOW
REAR MOTOR HIGH
REAR MOTOR LOW
C1

DTC A062

RIGHT FRONT MOTOR CIRCUIT SHORTED TO GROUND

Circuit Description:

This DTC identifies a motor circuit that is shorted to ground. This malfunction will not allow the motor to be controlled at the commanded current rate or will cause the driver circuit to allow current directly to ground.

Failure Condition:

DTC A062 can be set anytime. If the EBCM detects an out of range voltage on either of the right front motor circuits (indicating a circuit shorted to ground), a malfunction exists.

Action Taken:

A DTC A062 is stored, ABS is disabled and the "ABS" indicator is turned on.

Test Description: Number(s) below refer to circled number(s) on the diagnostic chart.

1. This step checks for a short to ground in the motor high circuit.
2. This step checks for a short to ground in the motor low circuit.
3. This step checks for a motor that is internally shorted to ground.

Diagnostic Aids:

Using TECH 1, select manual control function and exercise motor movement of affected channel in both directions while applying light pressure on the brake pedal.

If erratic or "jumpy" brake pedal movement is detected while performing an "apply" or "release" function of the motor, an intermittent malfunction may be indicated.

An "intermittent" malfunction may be caused by a poor connection, rubbed through wire insulation or a wire that is broken inside the insulation.

If the malfunction is not current, wiggle the wires of the affected channel and check if the DTC resets. This will help to pinpoint an intermittent malfunction in the motor circuitry or connections.

The frequency of the malfunction can be checked by using the enhanced diagnostic function of the TECH 1

Any circuitry that is suspected of causing the intermittent complaint should be thoroughly checked for backed out terminals, improper mating, broken locks, improperly formed or damaged terminals, poor terminal-to-wiring connections or physical damage to the wiring harness.

GC402940098400AX

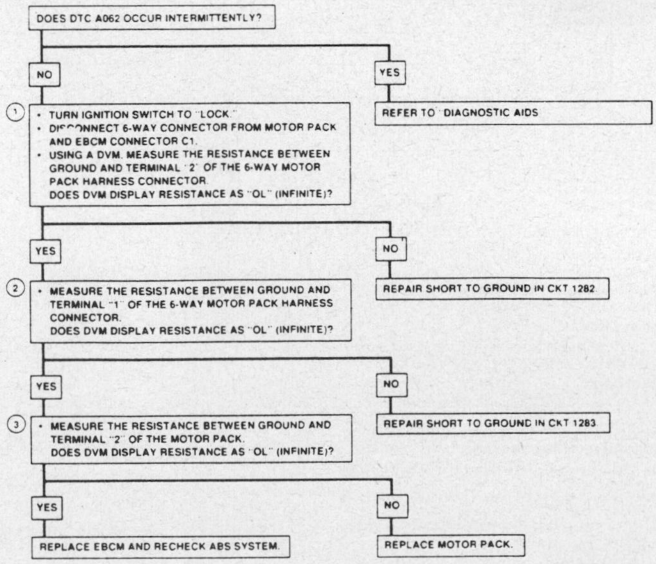
DOES DTC A062 OCCUR INTERMITTENTLY?
NO
YES
REFER TO "DIAGNOSTIC AIDS
1
• TURN IGNITION SWITCH TO "LOCK."
• DISCONNECT 6-WAY CONNECTOR FROM MOTOR PACK AND EBCM CONNECTOR C1.
• USING A DVM, MEASURE THE RESISTANCE BETWEEN GROUND AND TERMINAL "2" OF THE 6-WAY MOTOR PACK HARNESS CONNECTOR.
DOES DVM DISPLAY RESISTANCE AS "OL" (INFINITE)?
YES
NO
REPAIR SHORT TO GROUND IN CKT 1282.
2
• MEASURE THE RESISTANCE BETWEEN GROUND AND TERMINAL "1" OF THE 6-WAY MOTOR PACK HARNESS CONNECTOR.
DOES DVM DISPLAY RESISTANCE AS "OL" (INFINITE)?
YES
NO
REPAIR SHORT TO GROUND IN CKT 1283.
3
• MEASURE THE RESISTANCE BETWEEN GROUND AND TERMINAL "2" OF THE MOTOR PACK.
DOES DVM DISPLAY RESISTANCE AS "OL" (INFINITE)?
YES
NO
REPLACE EBCM AND RECHECK ABS SYSTEM.
REPLACE MOTOR PACK.

GC402940098400BX

Fig. 334 Code A062: Right Front Motor Circuit Shorted To Ground. 1993–94 Prizm

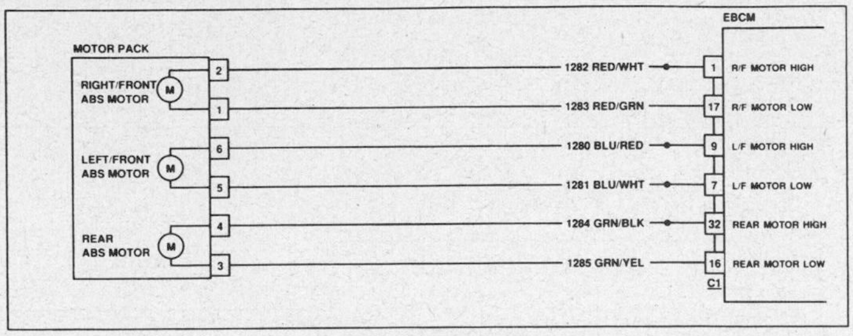
EBCM
MOTOR PACK
RIGHT/FRONT ABS MOTOR
LEFT/FRONT ABS MOTOR
REAR ABS MOTOR
M
2
1
6
5
4
3
1282 RED/WHT
1283 RED/GRN
1280 BLU/RED
1281 BLU/WHT
1284 GRN/BLK
1285 GRN/YEL
1
17
9
7
32
16
C1
R/F MOTOR HIGH
R/F MOTOR LOW
L/F MOTOR HIGH
L/F MOTOR LOW
REAR MOTOR HIGH
REAR MOTOR LOW

DTC A063

RIGHT FRONT MOTOR CIRCUIT SHORTED TO BATTERY

Circuit Description:

This DTC identifies a motor circuit that is shorted to battery or a motor that has low or no resistance. This malfunction will not allow the motor to be controlled at the commanded current rate or will cause the motor to turn in the opposite direction or not at all.

Failure Condition:

DTC A063 can be set only when the motor is commanded off. If the EBCM detects an out of range voltage on either of the right front motor circuits (indicating a circuit shorted to battery or a motor shorted), a malfunction exists.

Action Taken:

A DTC A063 is stored. ABS is disabled and the "ABS" indicator is turned on.

Test Description: Number(s) below refer to circled number(s) on the diagnostic chart.

1. This step checks for a short to voltage in the motor high circuitry.
2. This step checks for a short to voltage in the motor low circuitry.
3. This step checks for a motor that is internally shorted.

Diagnostic Aids:

Using TECH 1, select manual control function and exercise motor movement of affected channel in both directions while applying light pressure on the brake pedal.

If erratic or "jumpy" brake pedal movement is detected while performing an "apply" or "release" function of the motor, an intermittent malfunction may be indicated.

An "intermittent" malfunction may be caused by a poor connection, rubbed through wire insulation or a wire that is broken inside the insulation.

If the malfunction is not current, wiggle the wires of the affected channel and check if the DTC resets. This will help to pinpoint an intermittent malfunction in the motor circuitry or connections.

The frequency of the malfunction can be checked by using the enhanced diagnostic function of the TECH 1

Any circuitry that is suspected of causing the intermittent complaint should be thoroughly checked for backed out terminals, improper mating, broken locks, improperly formed or damaged terminals, poor terminal-to-wiring connections or physical damage to the wiring harness.

GC402940098500AX

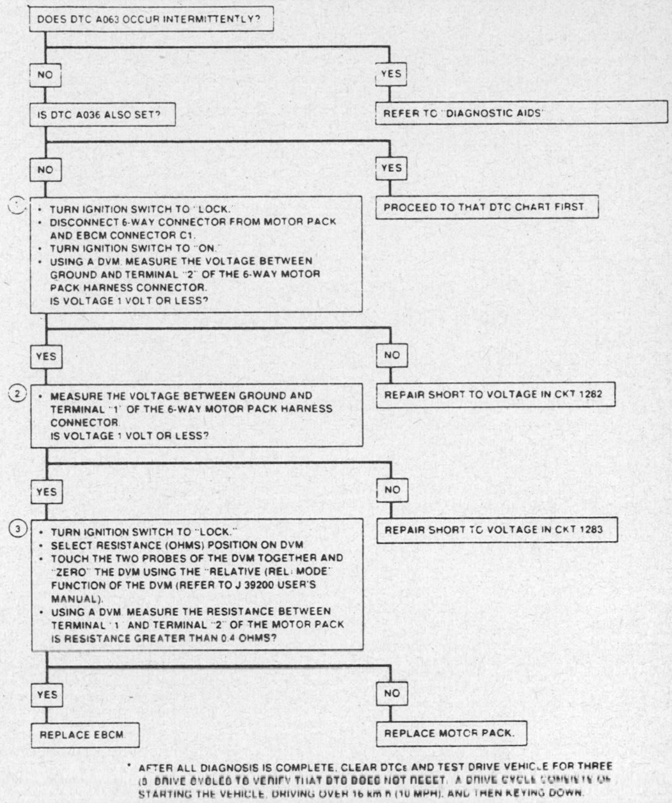
DOES DTC A063 OCCUR INTERMITTENTLY?
NO
YES
IS DTC A036 ALSO SET?
REFER TO "DIAGNOSTIC AIDS"
NO
YES
PROCEED TO THAT DTC CHART FIRST
• TURN IGNITION SWITCH TO "LOCK."
• DISCONNECT 6-WAY CONNECTOR FROM MOTOR PACK AND EBCM CONNECTOR C1.
• TURN IGNITION SWITCH TO "ON."
• USING A DVM, MEASURE THE VOLTAGE BETWEEN GROUND AND TERMINAL "2" OF THE 6-WAY MOTOR PACK HARNESS CONNECTOR.
IS VOLTAGE 1 VOLT OR LESS?
YES
NO
REPAIR SHORT TO VOLTAGE IN CKT 1282
2
• MEASURE THE VOLTAGE BETWEEN GROUND AND TERMINAL "1" OF THE 6-WAY MOTOR PACK HARNESS CONNECTOR.
IS VOLTAGE 1 VOLT OR LESS?
YES
NO
REPAIR SHORT TO VOLTAGE IN CKT 1283
3
• TURN IGNITION SWITCH TO "LOCK."
• SELECT RESISTANCE (OHMS) POSITION ON DVM
• TOUCH THE TWO PROBES OF THE DVM TOGETHER AND "ZERO" THE DVM USING THE "RELATIVE (REL) MODE" FUNCTION OF THE DVM (REFER TO J 39200 USER'S MANUAL).
• USING A DVM, MEASURE THE RESISTANCE BETWEEN TERMINAL "1" AND TERMINAL "2" OF THE MOTOR PACK
IS RESISTANCE GREATER THAN 0.4 OHMS?
YES
NO
REPLACE EBCM.
REPLACE MOTOR PACK.
* AFTER ALL DIAGNOSIS IS COMPLETE, CLEAR DTCs AND TEST DRIVE VEHICLE FOR THREE (3) DRIVE CYCLES TO VERIFY THAT DTC DOES NOT RESET. A DRIVE CYCLE CONSISTS OF STARTING THE VEHICLE, DRIVING OVER 16 km/h (10 MPH), AND THEN KEYING DOWN.

GC402940098500BX

Fig. 335 Code A063: Right Front Motor Circuit Shorted To Battery. 1993–94 Prizm

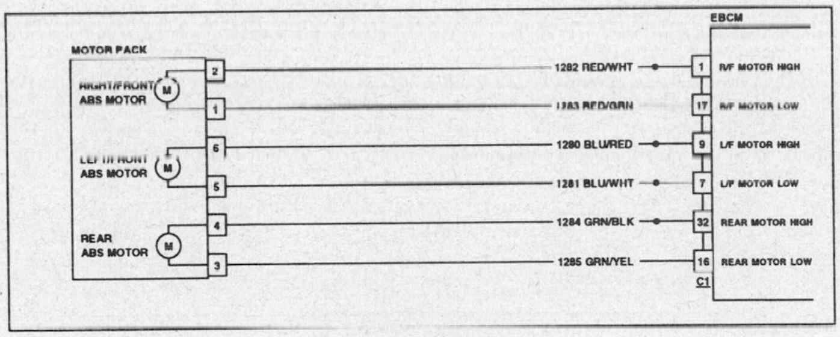
EBCM
MOTOR PACK
RIGHT/FRONT ABS MOTOR
LEFT/FRONT ABS MOTOR
REAR ABS MOTOR
M
2
1
6
5
4
3
1282 RED/WHT
1283 RED/GRN
1280 BLU/RED
1281 BLU/WHT
1284 GRN/BLK
1285 GRN/YEL
1
17
9
7
32
16
C1
R/F MOTOR HIGH
R/F MOTOR LOW
L/F MOTOR HIGH
L/F MOTOR LOW
REAR MOTOR HIGH
REAR MOTOR LOW

DTC A064

REAR MOTOR CIRCUIT OPEN

Circuit Description:

This DTC identifies a motor that cannot be energized due to an open in its circuitry.

Failure Condition:

DTC A064 can be set only when the motor is commanded off. If the EBCM detects an out of range voltage on either of the rear motor circuits (indicating an open circuit), a malfunction exists.

Action Taken:

An open motor will not activate when requested. A DTC A064 is stored, ABS is disabled and the "ABS" indicator is turned on or will flash.

Test Description: Number(s) below refer to circled number(s) on the diagnostic chart.

1. This step checks for proper resistance of the motor.
2. This step checks for an open in the motor high circuitry.
3. This step checks for an open in the motor low circuitry.

Diagnostic Aids:

Using TECH 1, select manual control function and exercise motor movement of affected channel in both directions while applying light pressure on the brake pedal.

If erratic or "jumpy" brake pedal movement is detected while performing an "apply" or "release" function of the motor, an intermittent malfunction may be indicated.

An "intermittent" malfunction may be caused by a poor connection, rubbed through wire insulation or a wire that is broken inside the insulation.

If the malfunction is not current, wiggle the wires of the affected channel and check if the DTC resets. This will help to pinpoint an intermittent malfunction in the motor circuitry or connections.

The frequency of the malfunction can be checked by using the enhanced diagnostic function of the TECH 1

Any circuitry that is suspected of causing the intermittent complaint should be thoroughly checked for backed out terminals, improper mating, broken locks, improperly formed or damaged terminals, poor terminal-to-wiring connections or physical damage to the wiring harness.

GC402940098600AX

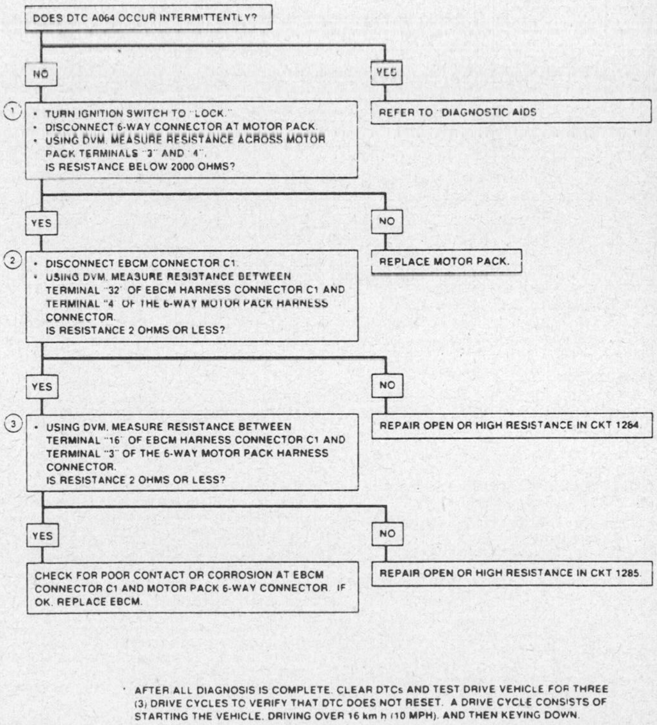
DOES DTC A064 OCCUR INTERMITTENTLY?
NO
YES
1
• TURN IGNITION SWITCH TO "LOCK."
• DISCONNECT 6-WAY CONNECTOR AT MOTOR PACK.
• USING DVM, MEASURE RESISTANCE ACROSS MOTOR PACK TERMINALS "3" AND "4".
IS RESISTANCE BELOW 2000 OHMS?
REFER TO "DIAGNOSTIC AIDS"
YES
NO
REPLACE MOTOR PACK.
2
• DISCONNECT EBCM CONNECTOR C1.
• USING DVM, MEASURE RESISTANCE BETWEEN TERMINAL "32" OF EBCM HARNESS CONNECTOR C1 AND TERMINAL "4" OF THE 6-WAY MOTOR PACK HARNESS CONNECTOR.
IS RESISTANCE 2 OHMS OR LESS?
YES
NO
REPAIR OPEN OR HIGH RESISTANCE IN CKT 1284.
3
• USING DVM, MEASURE RESISTANCE BETWEEN TERMINAL "16" OF EBCM HARNESS CONNECTOR C1 AND TERMINAL "3" OF THE 6-WAY MOTOR PACK HARNESS CONNECTOR.
IS RESISTANCE 2 OHMS OR LESS?
YES
NO
CHECK FOR POOR CONTACT OR CORROSION AT EBCM CONNECTOR C1 AND MOTOR PACK 6-WAY CONNECTOR. IF OK, REPLACE EBCM.
REPAIR OPEN OR HIGH RESISTANCE IN CKT 1285.
* AFTER ALL DIAGNOSIS IS COMPLETE, CLEAR DTCs AND TEST DRIVE VEHICLE FOR THREE (3) DRIVE CYCLES TO VERIFY THAT DTC DOES NOT RESET. A DRIVE CYCLE CONSISTS OF STARTING THE VEHICLE, DRIVING OVER 16 km/h (10 MPH), AND THEN KEYING DOWN.

GC402940098600BX

Fig. 336 Code A064: Rear Motor Circuit Open. 1993–94 Prizm

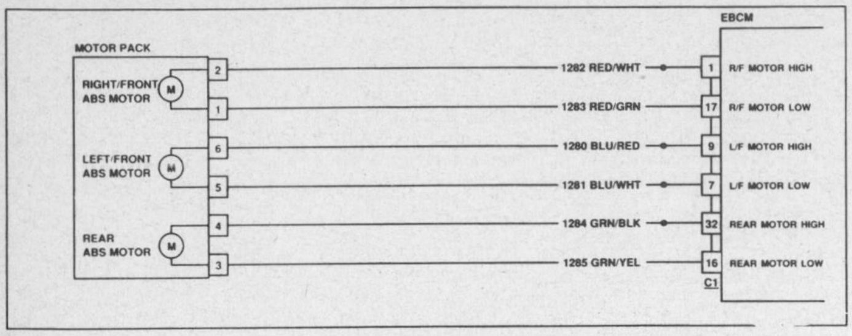
EBCM
MOTOR PACK
RIGHT/FRONT ABS MOTOR
LEFT/FRONT ABS MOTOR
REAR ABS MOTOR
1282 RED/WHT
1283 RED/GRN
1280 BLU/RED
1281 BLU/WHT
1284 GRN/BLK
1285 GRN/YEL
R/F MOTOR HIGH
R/F MOTOR LOW
L/F MOTOR HIGH
L/F MOTOR LOW
REAR MOTOR HIGH
REAR MOTOR LOW
C1

DTC A061

RIGHT FRONT MOTOR CIRCUIT OPEN

Circuit Description:

This DTC identifies a motor that cannot be energized due to an open in its circuitry.

Failure Condition:

DTC A061 can be set only when the motor is commanded off. If the EBCM detects an out of range voltage on either of the right front motor circuits (indicating an open circuit), a malfunction exists.

Action Taken:

An open motor will not activate when requested. A DTC A061 is stored, ABS is disabled and the "ABS" indicator is turned on.

Test Description: Number(s) below refer to circled number(s) on the diagnostic chart.

1. This step checks for proper resistance of the motor.
2. This step checks for an open in the motor high circuitry.
3. This step checks for an open in the motor low circuitry.

Diagnostic Aids:

Using TECH 1, select manual control function and exercise motor movement of affected channel in both directions while applying light pressure on the brake pedal.

If erratic or "jumpy" brake pedal movement is detected while performing an "apply" or "release" function of the motor, an intermittent malfunction may be indicated.

An "intermittent" malfunction may be caused by a poor connection, rubbed through wire insulation or a wire that is broken inside the insulation.

If the malfunction is not current, wiggle the wires of the affected channel and check if the DTC resets. This will help to pinpoint an intermittent malfunction in the motor circuitry or connections.

The frequency of the malfunction can be checked by using the enhanced diagnostic function of the TECH 1

Any circuitry that is suspected of causing the intermittent complaint should be thoroughly checked for backed out terminals, improper mating, broken locks, improperly formed or damaged terminals, poor terminal-to-wiring connections or physical damage to the wiring harness.

GC402940098700AX

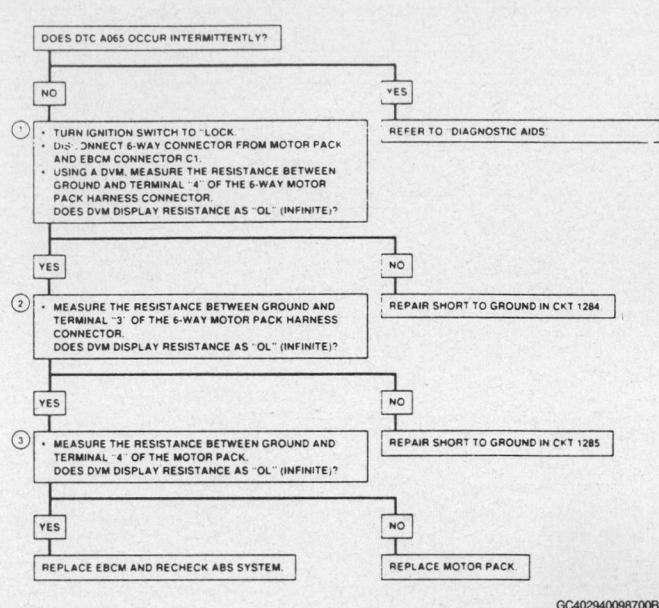

DOES DTC A065 OCCUR INTERMITTENTLY?

- YES → REFER TO "DIAGNOSTIC AIDS"
- NO →

(1)
- TURN IGNITION SWITCH TO "LOCK."
- DISCONNECT 6-WAY CONNECTOR FROM MOTOR PACK AND EBCM CONNECTOR C1.
- USING A DVM, MEASURE THE RESISTANCE BETWEEN GROUND AND TERMINAL "4" OF THE 6-WAY MOTOR PACK HARNESS CONNECTOR.

DOES DVM DISPLAY RESISTANCE AS "OL" (INFINITE)?

- NO → REPAIR SHORT TO GROUND IN CKT 1284
- YES →

(2)
- MEASURE THE RESISTANCE BETWEEN GROUND AND TERMINAL "3" OF THE 6-WAY MOTOR PACK HARNESS CONNECTOR.

DOES DVM DISPLAY RESISTANCE AS "OL" (INFINITE)?

- NO → REPAIR SHORT TO GROUND IN CKT 1285
- YES →

(3)
- MEASURE THE RESISTANCE BETWEEN GROUND AND TERMINAL "4" OF THE MOTOR PACK.

DOES DVM DISPLAY RESISTANCE AS "OL" (INFINITE)?

- YES → REPLACE EBCM AND RECHECK ABS SYSTEM.
- NO → REPLACE MOTOR PACK.

GC402940098700BX

Fig. 337 Code A065: Rear Motor Shorted To Ground. 1993–94 Prizm

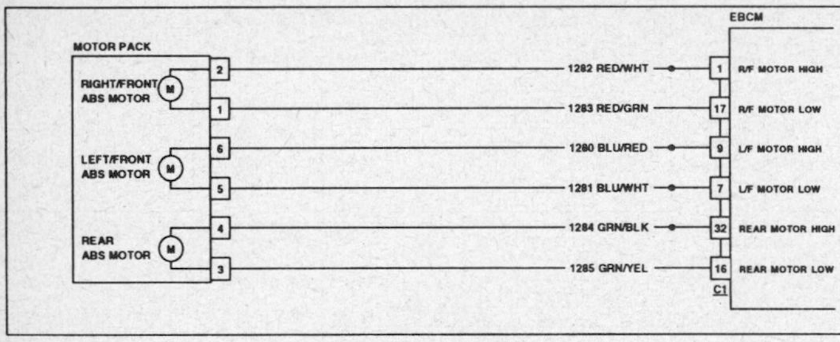
EBCM
MOTOR PACK
RIGHT/FRONT ABS MOTOR
LEFT/FRONT ABS MOTOR
REAR ABS MOTOR
1282 RED/WHT
1283 RED/GRN
1280 BLU/RED
1281 BLU/WHT
1284 GRN/BLK
1285 GRN/YEL
R/F MOTOR HIGH
R/F MOTOR LOW
L/F MOTOR HIGH
L/F MOTOR LOW
REAR MOTOR HIGH
REAR MOTOR LOW
C1

DTC A066

REAR MOTOR CIRCUIT SHORTED TO BATTERY

Circuit Description:

This DTC identifies a motor circuit that is shorted to battery or a motor that has low or no resistance. This malfunction will not allow the motor to be controlled at the commanded current rate or will cause the motor to turn in the opposite direction or not at all.

Failure Condition:

DTC A066 can be set only when the motor is commanded off. If the EBCM detects an out of range voltage on either of the rear motor circuits (indicating a circuit shorted to battery or a motor shorted), a malfunction exists.

Action Taken:

A DTC A066 is stored, ABS is disabled and the "ABS" indicator is turned on or will flash.

Test Description: Number(s) below refer to circled number(s) on the diagnostic chart.

1. This step checks for a short to voltage in the motor high circuitry.
2. This step checks for a short to voltage in the motor low circuitry.
3. This step checks for a motor that is internally shorted.

Diagnostic Aids:

Using TECH 1, select manual control function and exercise motor movement of affected channel in both directions while applying light pressure on the brake pedal.

If erratic or "jumpy" brake pedal movement is detected while performing an "apply" or "release" function of the motor, an intermittent malfunction may be indicated.

An "intermittent" malfunction may be caused by a poor connection, rubbed through wire insulation or a wire that is broken inside the insulation.

If the malfunction is not current, wiggle the wires of the affected channel and check if the DTC resets. This will help to pinpoint an intermittent malfunction in the motor circuitry or connections.

The frequency of the malfunction can be checked by using the enhanced diagnostic function of the TECH 1

Any circuitry that is suspected of causing the intermittent complaint should be thoroughly checked for backed out terminals, improper mating, broken locks, improperly formed or damaged terminals, poor terminal-to-wiring connections or physical damage to the wiring harness.

GC402940098800AX

DOES DTC A066 OCCUR INTERMITTENTLY?

- YES → REFER TO "DIAGNOSTIC AIDS"
- NO → IS DTC A036 ALSO SET?
  - YES → PROCEED TO THAT DTC CHART FIRST.
  - NO →

(1)
- TURN IGNITION SWITCH TO "LOCK."
- DISCONNECT 6-WAY CONNECTOR FROM MOTOR PACK AND EBCM CONNECTOR C1.
- TURN IGNITION SWITCH TO "ON."
- USING A DVM, MEASURE THE VOLTAGE BETWEEN GROUND AND TERMINAL "4" OF THE 6-WAY MOTOR PACK HARNESS CONNECTOR.

IS VOLTAGE 1 VOLT OR LESS?

- NO → REPAIR SHORT TO VOLTAGE IN CKT 1284.
- YES →

(2)
- MEASURE THE VOLTAGE BETWEEN GROUND AND TERMINAL "3" OF THE 6-WAY MOTOR PACK HARNESS CONNECTOR.

IS VOLTAGE 1 VOLT OR LESS?

- NO → REPAIR SHORT TO VOLTAGE IN CKT 1285.
- YES →

(3)
- TURN IGNITION SWITCH TO "LOCK."
- SELECT RESISTANCE (OHMS) POSITION ON DVM.
- TOUCH THE TWO PROBES OF THE DVM TOGETHER AND "ZERO" THE DVM USING THE "RELATIVE (REL) MODE" FUNCTION OF THE DVM (REFER TO J 39200 USER'S MANUAL).
- USING A DVM, MEASURE THE RESISTANCE BETWEEN TERMINAL "3" AND TERMINAL "4" OF THE MOTOR PACK.

IS RESISTANCE GREATER THAN 0.4 OHMS?

- YES → REPLACE EBCM.
- NO → REPLACE MOTOR PACK.

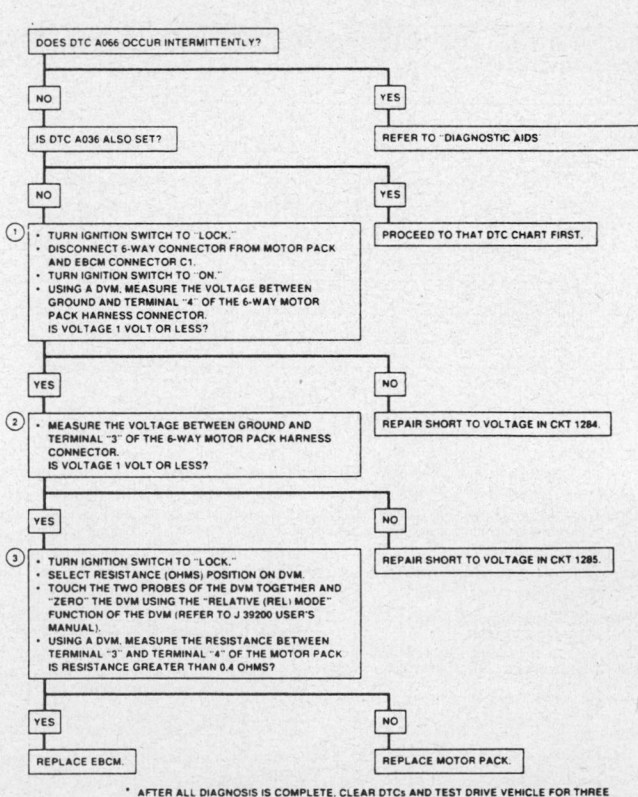

* AFTER ALL DIAGNOSIS IS COMPLETE, CLEAR DTCs AND TEST DRIVE VEHICLE FOR THREE (3) DRIVE CYCLES TO VERIFY THAT DTC DOES NOT RESET. A DRIVE CYCLE CONSISTS OF STARTING THE VEHICLE, DRIVING OVER 16 km/h (10 MPH), AND THEN KEYING DOWN.

GC402940098800BX

Fig. 338 Code A066: Rear Motor Circuit Shorted To Battery. 1993–94 Prizm

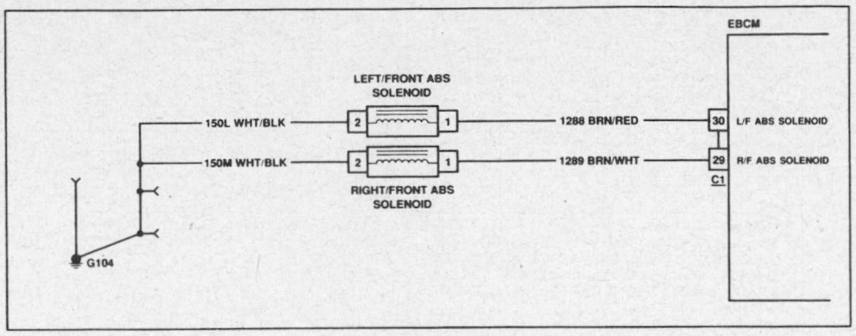
EBCM
LEFT/FRONT ABS SOLENOID
150L WHT/BLK
1288 BRN/RED
30
L/F ABS SOLENOID
150M WHT/BLK
1289 BRN/WHT
29
R/F ABS SOLENOID
C1
RIGHT/FRONT ABS SOLENOID
G104

DTC A076

LEFT FRONT SOLENOID CIRCUIT OPEN OR SHORTED TO BATTERY

Circuit Description:

This DTC identifies a solenoid that cannot be energized due to an open in its circuitry, or a solenoid that is always energized due to a short to battery in its circuitry between the driver and the solenoid. An open will not allow proper ABS operation, but the short to battery simply turns the solenoid on. A path for base brakes is still allowed once the motor re-homes and the check ball is lifted off its seat during initialization.

Failure Condition:

DTC A076 can be set only when the solenoid is commanded off. If the EBCM detects an excessive voltage in the left front solenoid control circuit, a malfunction exists.

Action Taken:

A DTC A076 is stored, ABS is disabled and the "ABS" indicator is turned on.

Test Description: Number(s) below refer to circled number(s) on the diagnostic chart.

1. This checks for a short to voltage in the control circuitry of the solenoid.
2. This checks for an open in the control circuit of the solenoid.
3. This step checks the solenoid coil for proper resistance.
4. This step checks for an open in the solenoid ground circuit.
5. This step checks for a possible intermittent malfunction in the solenoid circuitry due to poor terminal contact.

Diagnostic Aids:

An "intermittent" malfunction may be caused by a poor connection, rubbed through wire insulation or a wire that is broken inside the insulation.

The frequency of the malfunction can be checked by using the enhanced diagnostic function of the TECH 1.

Any circuitry that is suspected of causing the intermittent complaint should be thoroughly checked for backed out terminals, improper mating, broken locks, improperly formed or damaged terminals, poor terminal-to-wiring connections or physical damage to the wiring harness.

GC402940098900AX

1. • TURN IGNITION SWITCH TO "LOCK."
   • DISCONNECT EBCM CONNECTOR C1.
   • TURN IGNITION SWITCH TO "ON."
   • USING A DVM, MEASURE THE VOLTAGE BETWEEN GROUND AND TERMINAL "30" OF EBCM HARNESS CONNECTOR C1.
   IS VOLTAGE 1 VOLT OR LESS?
   - YES: go to step 2
   - NO: REPAIR SHORT TO VOLTAGE IN CKT 1288.
2. • TURN IGNITION SWITCH TO "LOCK."
   • DISCONNECT LEFT FRONT SOLENOID CONNECTOR.
   • USING A DVM, MEASURE THE RESISTANCE BETWEEN TERMINAL "30" OF EBCM HARNESS CONNECTOR C1 AND TERMINAL "1" OF THE LEFT FRONT SOLENOID HARNESS CONNECTOR.
   IS RESISTANCE 2 OHMS OR LESS?
   - YES: go to step 3
   - NO: REPAIR OPEN OR HIGH RESISTANCE IN CKT 1288.
3. • MEASURE THE RESISTANCE BETWEEN TERMINAL "1" AND TERMINAL "2" OF THE LEFT FRONT SOLENOID.
   IS RESISTANCE BETWEEN 2.5 AND 5 OHMS?
   - YES: go to step 4
   - NO: REPLACE LEFT FRONT SOLENOID.
4. • MEASURE THE RESISTANCE BETWEEN GROUND AND TERMINAL "2" OF THE LEFT FRONT SOLENOID HARNESS CONNECTOR.
   IS RESISTANCE 2 OHMS OR LESS?
   - YES: go to step 5
   - NO: REPAIR OPEN OR HIGH RESISTANCE IN CKT 150L.
5. • RECONNECT SOLENOID CONNECTOR AND EBCM CONNECTOR C1.
   • TURN IGNITION SWITCH TO "ON."
   • USING TECH 1, CLEAR DTCs.
   DOES DTC A076 RESET?
   - YES: REPLACE EBCM.
   - NO: MALFUNCTION IS INTERMITTENT. REFER TO "DIAGNOSTIC AIDS"

GC402940098900BX

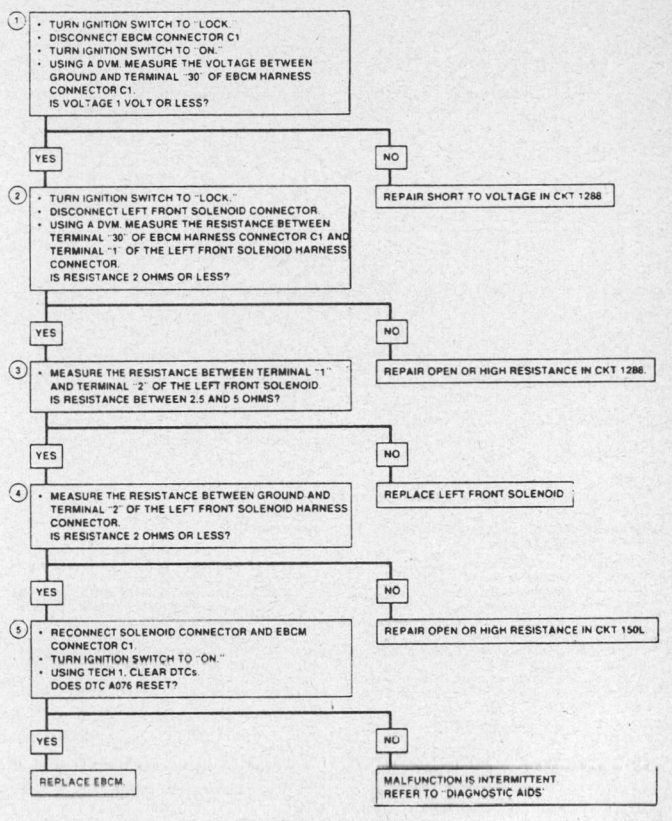

Fig. 339 Code A076: Left Front Solenoid Circuit Open Or Shorted To Battery. 1993–94 Prizm

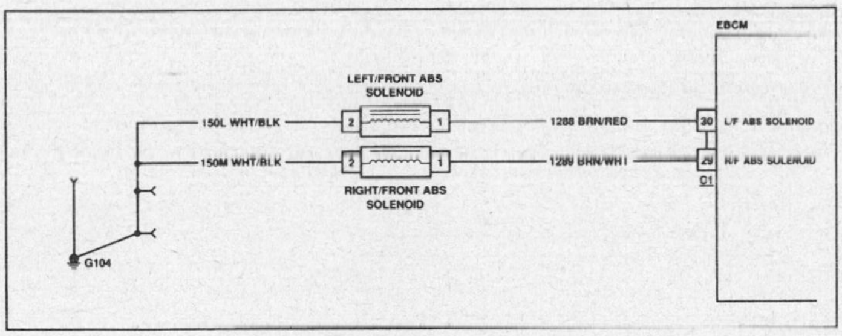
EBCM
LEFT/FRONT ABS SOLENOID
150L WHT/BLK
1288 BRN/RED
30
L/F ABS SOLENOID
150M WHT/BLK
29
C1
RIGHT/FRONT ABS SOLENOID
G104

DTC A077

LEFT FRONT SOLENOID CIRCUIT SHORTED TO GROUND

Circuit Description:

This DTC identifies a solenoid that cannot be energized due to an open in its driver circuitry or a short to ground between the solenoid driver and the solenoid. These malfunctions can affect ABS operation since the flow of brake fluid to the caliper cannot be stopped, making ABS operation for that channel impossible.

Failure Condition:

DTC A077 can be set only when the solenoid is commanded on. If the EBCM detects the left front solenoid control circuit voltage is out of specification, a malfunction exists.

Action Taken:

A DTC A077 is stored, ABS is disabled and the "ABS" indicator is turned on.

Test Description: Number(s) below refer to circled number(s) on the diagnostic chart.

1. This step checks for a solenoid that is internally shorted to ground.
2. This step checks for a solenoid that is not within proper resistance values.
3. This step indicates if a short to ground exists in the solenoid circuitry.
4. This checks for an open control circuit to the EBCM.
5. This step checks for a possible intermittent malfunction in the solenoid control circuitry due to poor terminal contact.

Diagnostic Aids:

An "intermittent" malfunction may be caused by a poor connection, rubbed through wire insulation or a wire that is broken inside the insulation.

The frequency of the malfunction can be checked by using the enhanced diagnostic function of the TECH 1.

Any circuitry that is suspected of causing the intermittent complaint should be thoroughly checked for backed out terminals, improper mating, broken locks, improperly formed or damaged terminals, poor terminal-to-wiring connections or physical damage to the wiring harness.

GC402940099000AX

1. • TURN IGNITION SWITCH TO "LOCK."
   • DISCONNECT LEFT FRONT SOLENOID CONNECTOR.
   • USING J 39200, MEASURE THE RESISTANCE BETWEEN GROUND AND TERMINAL "1" OF THE LEFT FRONT SOLENOID.
   DOES DVM DISPLAY RESISTANCE AS "OL" (INFINITE)?
   - YES: go to step 2
   - NO: REPLACE LEFT FRONT SOLENOID.
2. • USING DVM, MEASURE THE RESISTANCE BETWEEN TERMINAL "1" AND TERMINAL "2" OF THE LEFT FRONT SOLENOID.
   IS RESISTANCE BETWEEN 2.5 AND 5.0 OHMS?
   - YES: go to step 3
   - NO: REPLACE LEFT FRONT SOLENOID.
3. • DISCONNECT EBCM CONNECTOR C1.
   • MEASURE THE RESISTANCE BETWEEN GROUND AND TERMINAL "30" OF EBCM HARNESS CONNECTOR C1.
   DOES DVM DISPLAY RESISTANCE AS "OL" (INFINITE)?
   - YES: go to step 4
   - NO: REPAIR SHORT TO GROUND IN CKT 1288.
4. • MEASURE THE RESISTANCE BETWEEN TERMINAL "30" OF EBCM HARNESS CONNECTOR C1 AND TERMINAL "1" OF THE LEFT FRONT SOLENOID HARNESS CONNECTOR.
   IS RESISTANCE 2 OHMS OR LESS?
   - YES: go to step 5
   - NO: REPAIR OPEN OR HIGH RESISTANCE IN CKT 1288.
5. • RECONNECT SOLENOID CONNECTOR AND EBCM CONNECTOR C1.
   • TURN IGNITION SWITCH TO "ON."
   • USING TECH 1, CLEAR DTCs.
   DOES DTC A077 RESET?
   - YES: REPLACE EBCM.
   - NO: MALFUNCTION IS INTERMITTENT. REFER TO "DIAGNOSTIC AIDS"

GC402940099000BX

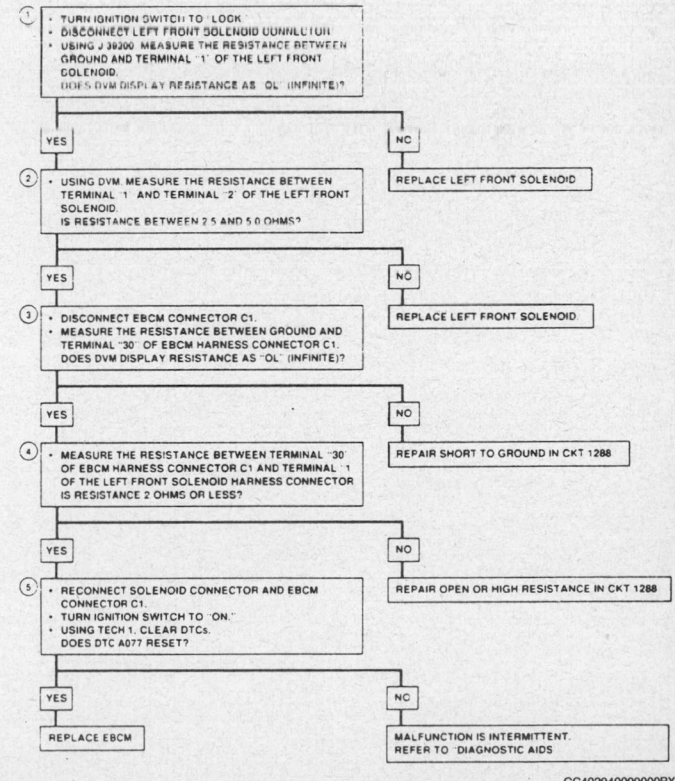

Fig. 340 Code A077: Left Front Solenoid Circuit Shorted To Ground. 1993–94 Prizm

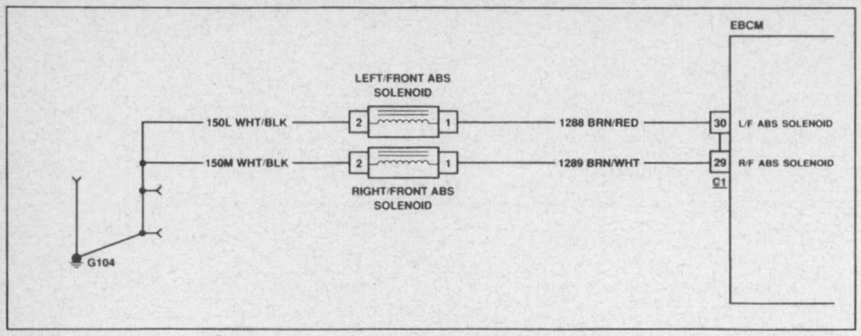
EBCM
LEFT/FRONT ABS SOLENOID
150L WHT/BLK
1288 BRN/RED
30 L/F ABS SOLENOID
150M WHT/BLK
1289 BRN/WHT
29 R/F ABS SOLENOID
C1
RIGHT/FRONT ABS SOLENOID
G104

DTC A078

RIGHT FRONT SOLENOID CIRCUIT OPEN OR SHORTED TO BATTERY

Circuit Description:

This DTC identifies a solenoid that cannot be energized due to an open in its circuitry, or a solenoid that is always energized due to a short to battery in its circuitry between the driver and the solenoid. An open will not allow proper ABS operation, but the short to battery simply turns the solenoid on. A path for base brakes is still allowed once the motor re-homes and the check ball is lifted off its seat during initialization.

Failure Condition:

DTC A078 can be set only when the solenoid is commanded off. If the EBCM detects an excessive voltage in the right front solenoid control circuit, a malfunction exists.

Action Taken:

A DTC A078 is stored, ABS is disabled and the "ABS" indicator is turned on.

Test Description: Number(s) below refer to circled number(s) on the diagnostic chart.

1. This checks for a short to voltage in the control circuitry of the solenoid.
2. This checks for an open in the control circuit of the solenoid.
3. This step checks the solenoid coil for proper resistance.
4. This step checks for an open in the solenoid ground circuit.
5. This step checks for a possible intermittent malfunction in the solenoid circuitry due to poor terminal contact.

Diagnostic Aids:

An "intermittent" malfunction may be caused by a poor connection, rubbed through wire insulation or a wire that is broken inside the insulation.

The frequency of the malfunction can be checked by using the enhanced diagnostic function of the TECH 1.

Any circuitry that is suspected of causing the intermittent complaint should be thoroughly checked for backed out terminals, improper mating, broken locks, improperly formed or damaged terminals, poor terminal-to-wiring connections or physical damage to the wiring harness.

GC402940099100AX

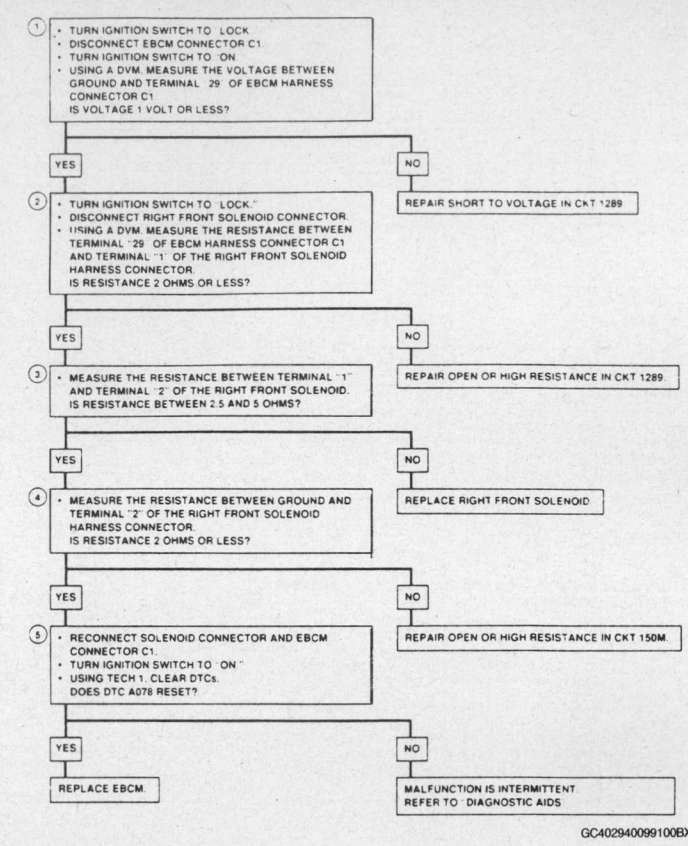

(1)
- TURN IGNITION SWITCH TO "LOCK."
- DISCONNECT EBCM CONNECTOR C1.
- TURN IGNITION SWITCH TO "ON."
- USING A DVM, MEASURE THE VOLTAGE BETWEEN GROUND AND TERMINAL "29" OF EBCM HARNESS CONNECTOR C1.

IS VOLTAGE 1 VOLT OR LESS?

- YES: go to (2)
- NO: REPAIR SHORT TO VOLTAGE IN CKT 1289.

(2)
- TURN IGNITION SWITCH TO "LOCK."
- DISCONNECT RIGHT FRONT SOLENOID CONNECTOR.
- USING A DVM, MEASURE THE RESISTANCE BETWEEN TERMINAL "29" OF EBCM HARNESS CONNECTOR C1 AND TERMINAL "1" OF THE RIGHT FRONT SOLENOID HARNESS CONNECTOR.

IS RESISTANCE 2 OHMS OR LESS?

- YES: go to (3)
- NO: REPAIR OPEN OR HIGH RESISTANCE IN CKT 1289.

(3)
- MEASURE THE RESISTANCE BETWEEN TERMINAL "1" AND TERMINAL "2" OF THE RIGHT FRONT SOLENOID.

IS RESISTANCE BETWEEN 2.5 AND 5 OHMS?

- YES: go to (4)
- NO: REPLACE RIGHT FRONT SOLENOID.

(4)
- MEASURE THE RESISTANCE BETWEEN GROUND AND TERMINAL "2" OF THE RIGHT FRONT SOLENOID HARNESS CONNECTOR.

IS RESISTANCE 2 OHMS OR LESS?

- YES: go to (5)
- NO: REPAIR OPEN OR HIGH RESISTANCE IN CKT 150M.

(5)
- RECONNECT SOLENOID CONNECTOR AND EBCM CONNECTOR C1.
- TURN IGNITION SWITCH TO "ON."
- USING TECH 1, CLEAR DTCs.

DOES DTC A078 RESET?

- YES: REPLACE EBCM.
- NO: MALFUNCTION IS INTERMITTENT. REFER TO "DIAGNOSTIC AIDS."

GC402940099100BX

Fig. 341 Code A078: Right Front Solenoid Circuit Shorted To Ground. 1993–94 Prizm

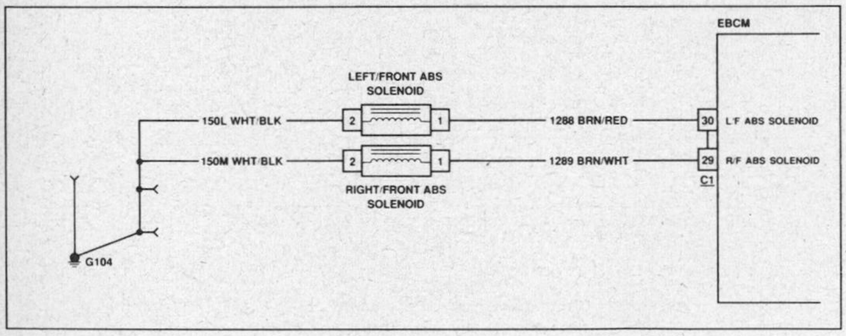
EBCM
LEFT/FRONT ABS SOLENOID
150L WHT/BLK
1288 BRN/RED
30 L/F ABS SOLENOID
150M WHT/BLK
1289 BRN/WHT
29 R/F ABS SOLENOID
C1
RIGHT/FRONT ABS SOLENOID
G104

DTC A081

RIGHT FRONT SOLENOID CIRCUIT SHORTED TO GROUND

Circuit Description:

This DTC identifies a solenoid that cannot be energized due to an open in its driver circuitry or a short to ground between the solenoid driver and the solenoid. These malfunctions can affect ABS operation since the flow of brake fluid to the caliper cannot be stopped, making ABS operation for that channel impossible.

Failure Condition:

DTC A081 can be set only when the solenoid is commanded on. If the EBCM detects the right front solenoid control circuit voltage is out of specification, a malfunction exists.

Action Taken:

A DTC A081 is stored, ABS is disabled and the "ABS" indicator is turned on.

Test Description: Number(s) below refer to circled number(s) on the diagnostic chart.

1. This step checks for a solenoid that is internally shorted to ground.
2. This step checks for a solenoid that is not within proper resistance values.
3. This step indicates if a short to ground exists in the solenoid circuitry.
4. This checks for an open control circuit to the EBCM.
5. This step checks for a possible intermittent malfunction in the solenoid control circuitry due to poor terminal contact.

Diagnostic Aids:

An "intermittent" malfunction may be caused by a poor connection, rubbed through wire insulation or a wire that is broken inside the insulation.

The frequency of the malfunction can be checked by using the enhanced diagnostic function of the TECH 1.

Any circuitry that is suspected of causing the intermittent complaint should be thoroughly checked for backed out terminals, improper mating, broken locks, improperly formed or damaged terminals, poor terminal-to-wiring connections or physical damage to the wiring harness.

GC402940099200AX

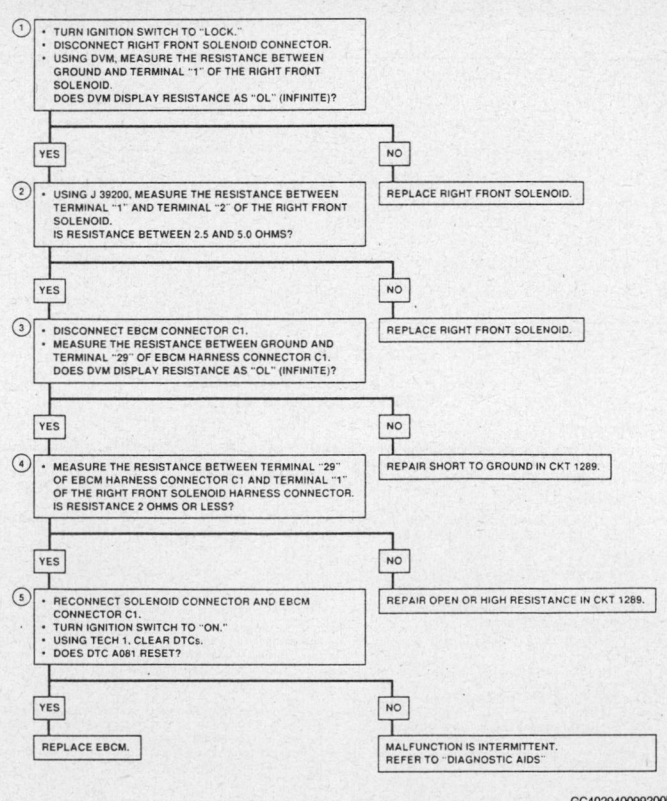

(1)
- TURN IGNITION SWITCH TO "LOCK."
- DISCONNECT RIGHT FRONT SOLENOID CONNECTOR.
- USING DVM, MEASURE THE RESISTANCE BETWEEN GROUND AND TERMINAL "1" OF THE RIGHT FRONT SOLENOID.

DOES DVM DISPLAY RESISTANCE AS "OL" (INFINITE)?

- YES: go to (2)
- NO: REPLACE RIGHT FRONT SOLENOID.

(2)
- USING J 39200, MEASURE THE RESISTANCE BETWEEN TERMINAL "1" AND TERMINAL "2" OF THE RIGHT FRONT SOLENOID.

IS RESISTANCE BETWEEN 2.5 AND 5.0 OHMS?

- YES: go to (3)
- NO: REPLACE RIGHT FRONT SOLENOID.

(3)
- DISCONNECT EBCM CONNECTOR C1.
- MEASURE THE RESISTANCE BETWEEN GROUND AND TERMINAL "29" OF EBCM HARNESS CONNECTOR C1.

DOES DVM DISPLAY RESISTANCE AS "OL" (INFINITE)?

- YES: go to (4)
- NO: REPAIR SHORT TO GROUND IN CKT 1289.

(4)
- MEASURE THE RESISTANCE BETWEEN TERMINAL "29" OF EBCM HARNESS CONNECTOR C1 AND TERMINAL "1" OF THE RIGHT FRONT SOLENOID HARNESS CONNECTOR.

IS RESISTANCE 2 OHMS OR LESS?

- YES: go to (5)
- NO: REPAIR OPEN OR HIGH RESISTANCE IN CKT 1289.

(5)
- RECONNECT SOLENOID CONNECTOR AND EBCM CONNECTOR C1.
- TURN IGNITION SWITCH TO "ON."
- USING TECH 1, CLEAR DTCs.
- DOES DTC A081 RESET?

- YES: REPLACE EBCM.
- NO: MALFUNCTION IS INTERMITTENT. REFER TO "DIAGNOSTIC AIDS."

GC402940099200BX

Fig. 342 Code A081: Right Front Solenoid Circuit Shorted To Ground. 1993–94 Prizm

DTC A082
CALIBRATION MALFUNCTION

Circuit Description:

This DTC allows the EBCM to check for a calibration malfunction by comparing the calibration value to a known value stored in the EEPROM. This DTC is also used a security measure to prevent improper use of calibrations or changes to these calibrations that may alter the designed function of ABS.

Failure Condition:

DTC A082 can be set at key-up. If the program identifier is incorrect or the memory checksum is incorrect, a malfunction exists.

Action Taken:

A DTC A082 is stored, ABS is disabled and the "ABS" indicator is turned on.

Test Description: Number(s) below refer to circled number(s) on the diagnostic chart.

1. This step checks to see if the malfunction is present during diagnosis. If present, the EBCM is not functioning correctly and must be replaced.

Important

- At the time of printing, 1993 vehicles with ABS-VI were not being field reprogrammed to correct this failure. A service bulletin will be issued when EEPROM reprogramming is authorized.

Diagnostic Aids:

An intermittent DTC A082 may be caused by a bad cell in the EEPROM that is sensitive to temperature changes. If DTC A082 failed more than once, but is intermittent, replace the EBCM.

The frequency of the malfunction can be checked by using the enhanced diagnostic function of the TECH 1

GC402940099300AX

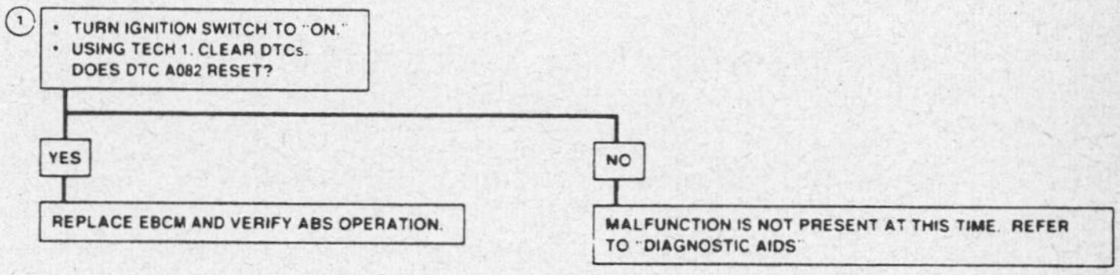
1
• TURN IGNITION SWITCH TO "ON."
• USING TECH 1, CLEAR DTCs.
DOES DTC A082 RESET?
YES
NO
REPLACE EBCM AND VERIFY ABS OPERATION.
MALFUNCTION IS NOT PRESENT AT THIS TIME. REFER TO "DIAGNOSTIC AIDS"

GC402940099300BX

Fig. 343 Code A082: Calibration Malfunction. 1993–94 Prizm

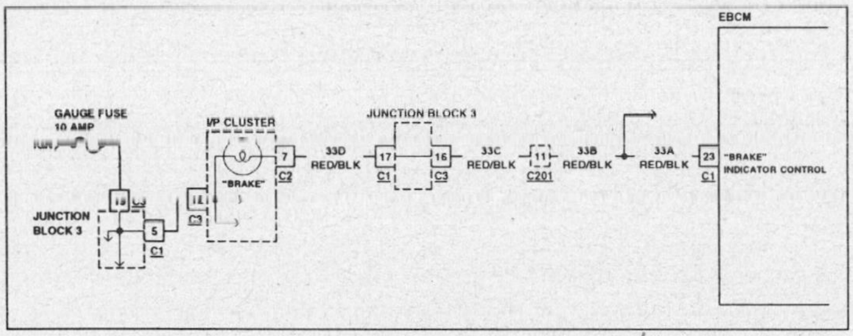
EBCM
GAUGE FUSE
10 AMP
I/P CLUSTER
"BRAKE"
JUNCTION BLOCK 3
33D
RED/BLK
33C
RED/BLK
33B
RED/BLK
33A
RED/BLK
C201
"BRAKE"
INDICATOR CONTROL
JUNCTION
BLOCK 3

DTC A086
EBCM TURNED ON THE RED BRAKE WARNING LAMP

Circuit Description:

This DTC is provided as an informational only DTC, and reflects the status of the command issued by the EBCM to illuminate the "BRAKE" indicator. If another DTC issues a command to illuminate the "BRAKE" indicator, DTC A086 will be stored in EEPROM as a history DTC at the conclusion of the ignition cycle.

Test Description: Number(s) below refer to circled number(s) on the diagnostic chart.

1. This step serves to identify if a DTC other than DTC A086 commanded the "BRAKE" indicator on.

Diagnostic Aids:

Any ABS mechanical DTC that issues a command to illuminate the "BRAKE" indicator will also result in DTC A086 being stored in EEPROM during shut down. These DTCs are: A042, A046 and A051. If the motors are not in their home position, certain electrical DTCs will also command the "BRAKE" indicator on. These DTCs are: A014, A016, A018, A055, A064, A065 and A066.

If any of these DTCs are indicated along with DTC A086, they must be corrected prior to addressing a DTC A086 malfunction.

GC402940099400AX

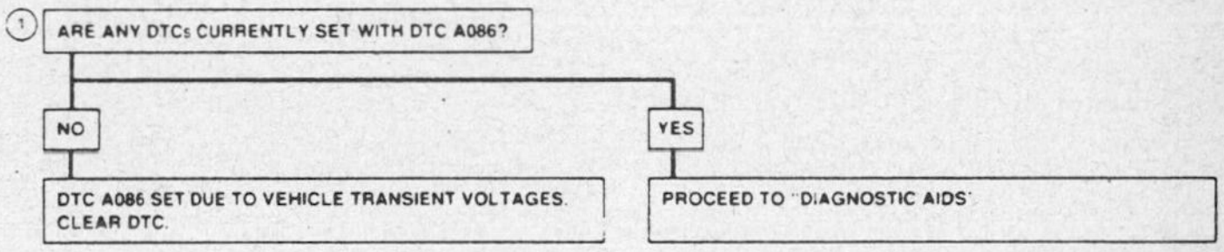
1
ARE ANY DTCs CURRENTLY SET WITH DTC A086?
NO
YES
DTC A086 SET DUE TO VEHICLE TRANSIENT VOLTAGES. CLEAR DTC.
PROCEED TO "DIAGNOSTIC AIDS"

GC402940099400BX

Fig. 344 Code A086: EBCM Turned On The Red Brake Warning Lamp. 1993–94 Prizm

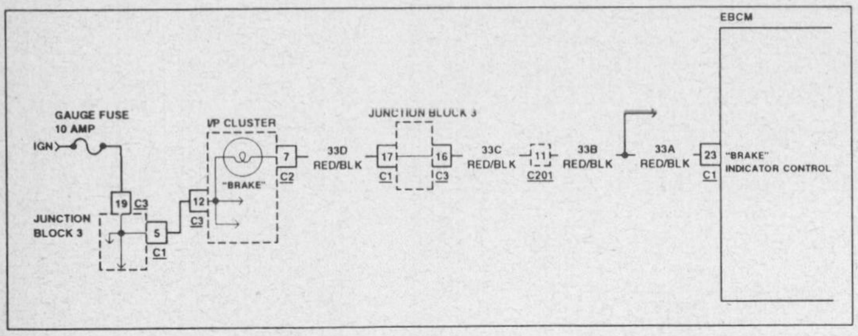
EBCM
GAUGE FUSE
10 AMP
IGN
I/P CLUSTER
"BRAKE"
JUNCTION BLOCK 3
33D
RED/BLK
33C
RED/BLK
33B
RED/BLK
33A
RED/BLK
C201
"BRAKE" INDICATOR CONTROL
JUNCTION BLOCK 3

DTC A087

(Page 1 of 2)

RED BRAKE WARNING LAMP CIRCUIT SHORTED OPEN

Circuit Description:

This DTC is used to verify the EBCM has continuity to the "BRAKE" indicator in case the EBCM must turn it on. This will only occur if an ABS malfunction is detected that may degrade base brake operation. Because ABS is not the only device controlling the "BRAKE" indicator (parking brake switch and brake fluid level switch may also turn it on), a short to ground in this circuit cannot be detected.

Failure Condition:

DTC A087 can be set after vehicle speed exceeds 8 km/h (5 mph). If the "BRAKE" indicator circuit voltage is out of specification (indicating an open circuit), a malfunction exists.

Action Taken:

A DTC A087 is stored. ABS is not disabled and the "ABS" indicator will not be illuminated.

Test Description: Number(s) below refer to circled number(s) on the diagnostic chart.

1. This step identifies if the malfunction is currently present.
2. This step indicates if the EBCM and circuitry has the ability to complete the ground to the "BRAKE" indicator and illuminate it.
3. This step checks for an open in the parking brake circuitry.
4. This step determines whether or not the condition is intermittent.

Diagnostic Aids:

An "intermittent" malfunction may be caused by a poor connection, rubbed through wire insulation or a wire that is broken inside the insulation.

The frequency of the malfunction can be checked by using the enhanced diagnostic function of the TECH 1.

Any circuitry that is suspected of causing the intermittent complaint should be thoroughly checked for backed out terminals, improper mating, broken locks, improperly formed or damaged terminals, poor terminal-to-wiring connections or physical damage to the wiring harness.

GC402940099501AX

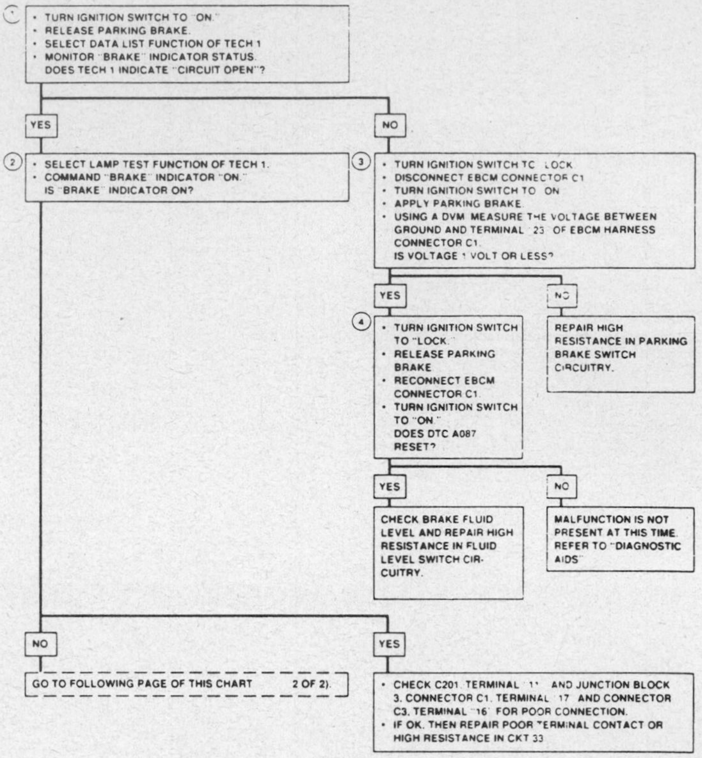
1
• TURN IGNITION SWITCH TO "ON."
• RELEASE PARKING BRAKE.
• SELECT DATA LIST FUNCTION OF TECH 1.
• MONITOR "BRAKE" INDICATOR STATUS.
DOES TECH 1 INDICATE "CIRCUIT OPEN"?
YES
NO
2
• SELECT LAMP TEST FUNCTION OF TECH 1.
• COMMAND "BRAKE" INDICATOR "ON."
IS "BRAKE" INDICATOR ON?
3
• TURN IGNITION SWITCH TO "LOCK."
• DISCONNECT EBCM CONNECTOR C1.
• TURN IGNITION SWITCH TO "ON."
• APPLY PARKING BRAKE.
• USING A DVM, MEASURE THE VOLTAGE BETWEEN GROUND AND TERMINAL "23" OF EBCM HARNESS CONNECTOR C1.
IS VOLTAGE 1 VOLT OR LESS?
YES
NO
4
• TURN IGNITION SWITCH TO "LOCK."
• RELEASE PARKING BRAKE.
• RECONNECT EBCM CONNECTOR C1.
• TURN IGNITION SWITCH TO "ON."
DOES DTC A087 RESET?
REPAIR HIGH RESISTANCE IN PARKING BRAKE SWITCH CIRCUITRY.
YES
NO
CHECK BRAKE FLUID LEVEL AND REPAIR HIGH RESISTANCE IN FLUID LEVEL SWITCH CIRCUITRY.
MALFUNCTION IS NOT PRESENT AT THIS TIME. REFER TO "DIAGNOSTIC AIDS."
NO
YES
GO TO FOLLOWING PAGE OF THIS CHART (2 OF 2).
• CHECK C201, TERMINAL "11" AND JUNCTION BLOCK 3, CONNECTOR C1, TERMINAL "17" AND CONNECTOR C3, TERMINAL "16" FOR POOR CONNECTION.
• IF OK, THEN REPAIR POOR TERMINAL CONTACT OR HIGH RESISTANCE IN CKT 33.

GC402940099501BX

Fig. 345 Code A087: Red Brake Warning Lamp Circuit Shorted Open (Part 1 of 2). 1993–94 Prizm

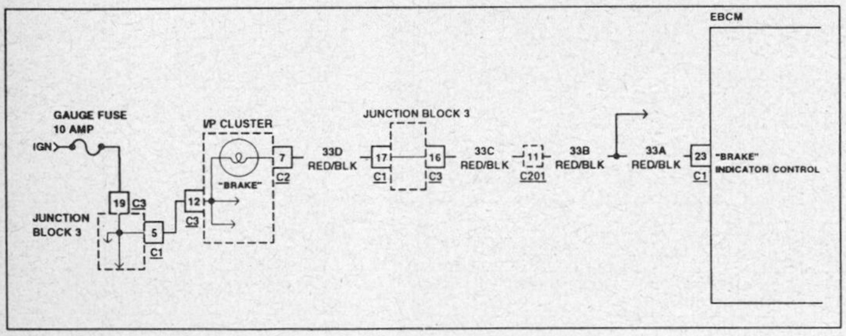
EBCM
GAUGE FUSE
10 AMP
IGN
I/P CLUSTER
"BRAKE"
JUNCTION BLOCK 3
33D
RED/BLK
33C
RED/BLK
33B
RED/BLK
33A
RED/BLK
C201
"BRAKE" INDICATOR CONTROL
JUNCTION BLOCK 3

DTC A087

(Page 2 of 2)

RED BRAKE WARNING LAMP CIRCUIT SHORTED OPEN

Circuit Description:

This DTC is used to verify the EBCM has continuity to the "BRAKE" indicator in case the EBCM must turn it on. This will only occur if an ABS malfunction is detected that may degrade base brake operation. Because ABS is not the only device controlling the "BRAKE" indicator (parking brake switch and brake fluid level switch may also turn it on), a short to ground in this circuit cannot be detected.

Failure Condition:

DTC A087 can be set after vehicle speed exceeds 8 km/h (5 mph). If the "BRAKE" indicator circuit voltage is out of specification (indicating an open circuit), a malfunction exists.

Action Taken:

A DTC A087 is stored. ABS is not disabled and the "ABS" indicator will not be illuminated.

Test Description: Number(s) below refer to circled number(s) on the diagnostic chart.

5. Because the "BRAKE" indicator has current supplied to it through the GAUGE fuse, this step would indicate if the ignition circuit is complete to the I/P cluster.
6. This step determines whether the open circuit is due to an EBCM failure or an open wire to the "BRAKE" indicator.

Diagnostic Aids:

An "intermittent" malfunction may be caused by a poor connection, rubbed through wire insulation or a wire that is broken inside the insulation.

The frequency of the malfunction can be checked by using the enhanced diagnostic function of the TECH 1.

Any circuitry that is suspected as causing the intermittent complaint, should be thoroughly checked for backed out terminals, improper mating, broken locks, improperly formed or damaged terminals, poor terminal-to-wiring connections or physical damage to the wiring harness.

GC402940099502AX

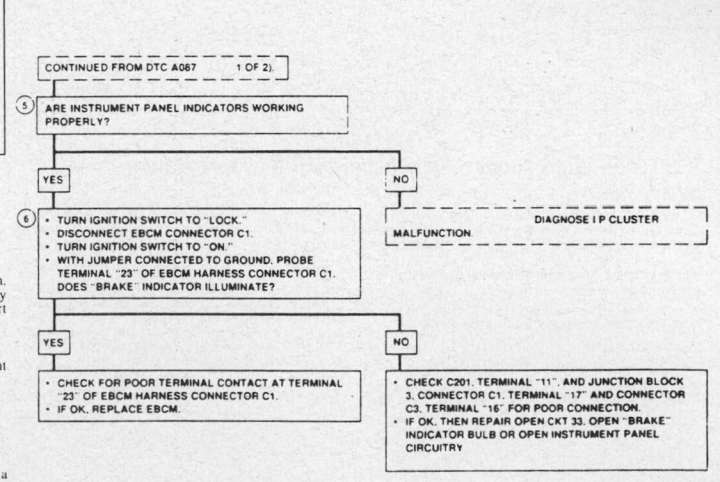

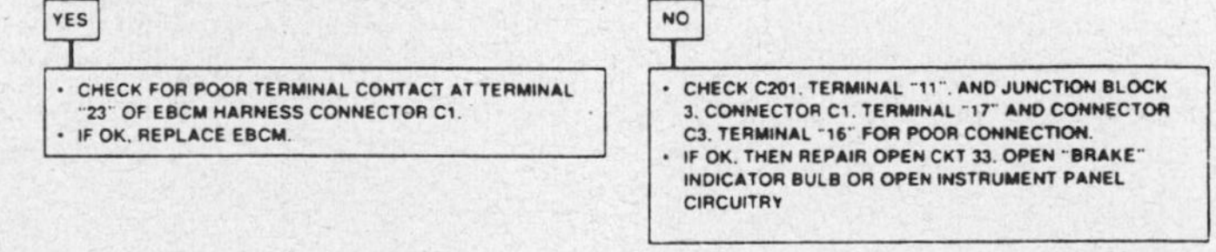
CONTINUED FROM DTC A087 (1 OF 2).
5
ARE INSTRUMENT PANEL INDICATORS WORKING PROPERLY?
YES
NO
6
• TURN IGNITION SWITCH TO "LOCK."
• DISCONNECT EBCM CONNECTOR C1.
• TURN IGNITION SWITCH TO "ON."
• WITH JUMPER CONNECTED TO GROUND, PROBE TERMINAL "23" OF EBCM HARNESS CONNECTOR C1.
DOES "BRAKE" INDICATOR ILLUMINATE?
DIAGNOSE I/P CLUSTER MALFUNCTION.
YES
NO
• CHECK FOR POOR TERMINAL CONTACT AT TERMINAL "23" OF EBCM HARNESS CONNECTOR C1.
• IF OK, REPLACE EBCM.
• CHECK C201, TERMINAL "11", AND JUNCTION BLOCK 3, CONNECTOR C1, TERMINAL "17" AND CONNECTOR C3, TERMINAL "16" FOR POOR CONNECTION.
• IF OK, THEN REPAIR OPEN CKT 33, OPEN "BRAKE" INDICATOR BULB OR OPEN INSTRUMENT PANEL CIRCUITRY.

GC402940099502BX

Fig. 345 Code A087: Red Brake Warning Lamp Circuit Shorted Open (Part 2 of 2). 1993–94 Prizm

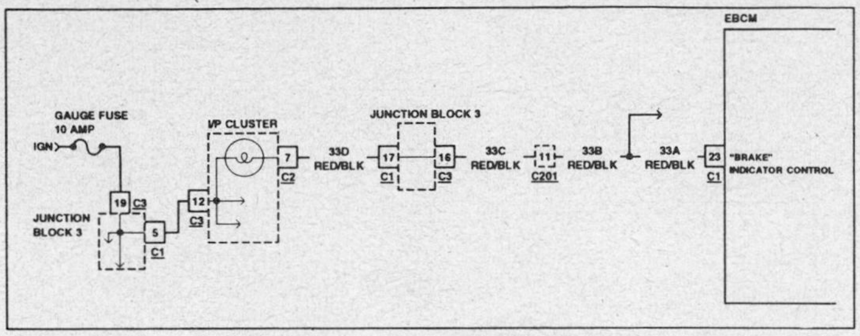
EBCM
GAUGE FUSE
10 AMP
IGN
I/P CLUSTER
JUNCTION BLOCK 3
33D
RED/BLK
33C
RED/BLK
33B
RED/BLK
33A
RED/BLK
C201
"BRAKE" INDICATOR CONTROL
JUNCTION BLOCK 3

DTC A088

RED BRAKE WARNING LAMP CIRCUIT SHORTED TO BATTERY

Circuit Description:

This DTC identifies a short to battery between the EBCM and the "BRAKE" indicator or an open driver that does not allow the "BRAKE" indicator to be illuminated by the EBCM. This will only occur if an ABS fault is detected that may degrade base brake performance.

Failure Condition:

DTC A088 can be set only at the beginning of the three second bulb check or when the EBCM turns on the "BRAKE" indicator because of another DTC. If the EBCM detects battery voltage on the "BRAKE" indicator lamp control circuit, a malfunction exists.

Action Taken:

A DTC A088 is stored. ABS is not disabled and the "ABS" indicator will not be illuminated.

Test Description: Number(s) below refer to circled number(s) on the diagnostic chart.

1. This step identifies if the ground circuit to the "BRAKE" indicator is being completed by a source other than the EBCM.
2. This step identifies if the malfunction is currently present.
3. By removing the GAUGE fuse, the voltage source is eliminated. This test indicates if voltage is being supplied from a source other than the GAUGE fuse.
4. This step checks for DTC A086 also being set.

Diagnostic Aids:

An "intermittent" malfunction may be caused by a poor connection, rubbed through wire insulation or a wire that is broken inside the insulation.

The frequency of the malfunction can be checked by using the enhanced diagnostic function of the TECH 1

Any circuitry that is suspected as causing the intermittent complaint, should be thoroughly checked for backed out terminals, improper mating, broken locks, improperly formed or damaged terminals, poor terminal-to-wiring connections or physical damage to the wiring harness.

GC402940099600AX

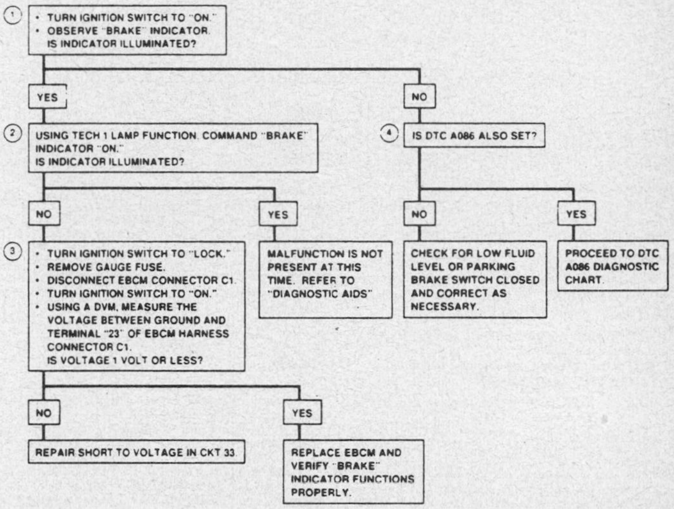
1
• TURN IGNITION SWITCH TO "ON."
• OBSERVE "BRAKE" INDICATOR.
IS INDICATOR ILLUMINATED?
YES
NO
2
USING TECH 1 LAMP FUNCTION, COMMAND "BRAKE" INDICATOR "ON."
IS INDICATOR ILLUMINATED?
4
IS DTC A086 ALSO SET?
NO
YES
NO
YES
3
• TURN IGNITION SWITCH TO "LOCK."
• REMOVE GAUGE FUSE.
• DISCONNECT EBCM CONNECTOR C1.
• TURN IGNITION SWITCH TO "ON."
• USING A DVM, MEASURE THE VOLTAGE BETWEEN GROUND AND TERMINAL "23" OF EBCM HARNESS CONNECTOR C1.
IS VOLTAGE 1 VOLT OR LESS?
MALFUNCTION IS NOT PRESENT AT THIS TIME. REFER TO "DIAGNOSTIC AIDS"
CHECK FOR LOW FLUID LEVEL OR PARKING BRAKE SWITCH CLOSED AND CORRECT AS NECESSARY.
PROCEED TO DTC A086 DIAGNOSTIC CHART.
NO
YES
REPAIR SHORT TO VOLTAGE IN CKT 33.
REPLACE EBCM AND VERIFY "BRAKE" INDICATOR FUNCTIONS PROPERLY.

GC402940099600BX

Fig. 346 Code A088: Red Brake Warning Lamp Circuit Shorted To Battery. 1993–94 Prizm

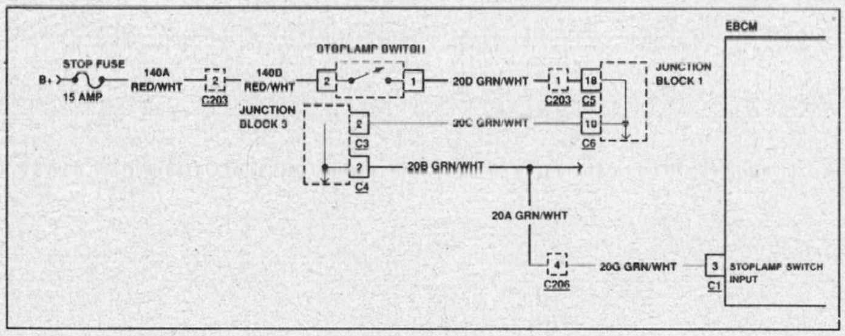
EBCM
STOPLAMP SWITCH
STOP FUSE
15 AMP
B+
140A
RED/WHT
C203
140D
RED/WHT
JUNCTION BLOCK 3
20D GRN/WHT
20C GRN/WHT
20B GRN/WHT
20A GRN/WHT
20G GRN/WHT
C203
JUNCTION BLOCK 1
C206
STOPLAMP SWITCH INPUT

DTC A091

OPEN BRAKE SWITCH DURING DECELERATION

Circuit Description:

This DTC is used to detect an open stoplamp switch in the non-ABS mode. The EBCM looks for deceleration rates that would indicate braking action and verifies this assumption by requiring several repeats of this detection method. In each case, ABS will not be available since no stoplamp switch input is seen.

Failure Condition:

DTC A091 can be set if three deceleration cycles occur without a stoplamp switch input to the EBCM.

Action Taken:

A DTC A091 is stored. ABS is disabled and the "ABS" indicator is turned on.

Test Description: Number(s) below refer to circled number(s) on the diagnostic chart.

1. This step indicates if the stoplamp switch signal is being received by the EBCM.
2. This step indicates if an open circuit exists in the stoplamp switch or the rear combination lamp circuitry.
3. This step isolates the open circuit to either the stoplamp switch input circuitry or the EBCM.
4. This step verifies that voltage is available at the stoplamp switch.
5. This step verifies that the stoplamp switch is functioning properly.

Diagnostic Aids:

An "intermittent" malfunction may be caused by a poor connection, rubbed through wire insulation or a wire that is broken inside the insulation.

The frequency of the malfunction can be checked by using the enhanced diagnostic function of the TECH 1

Any circuitry that is suspected as causing the intermittent complaint, should be thoroughly checked for backed out terminals, improper mating, broken locks, improperly formed or damaged terminals, poor terminal-to-wiring connections or physical damage to the wiring harness.

GC402940099700AX

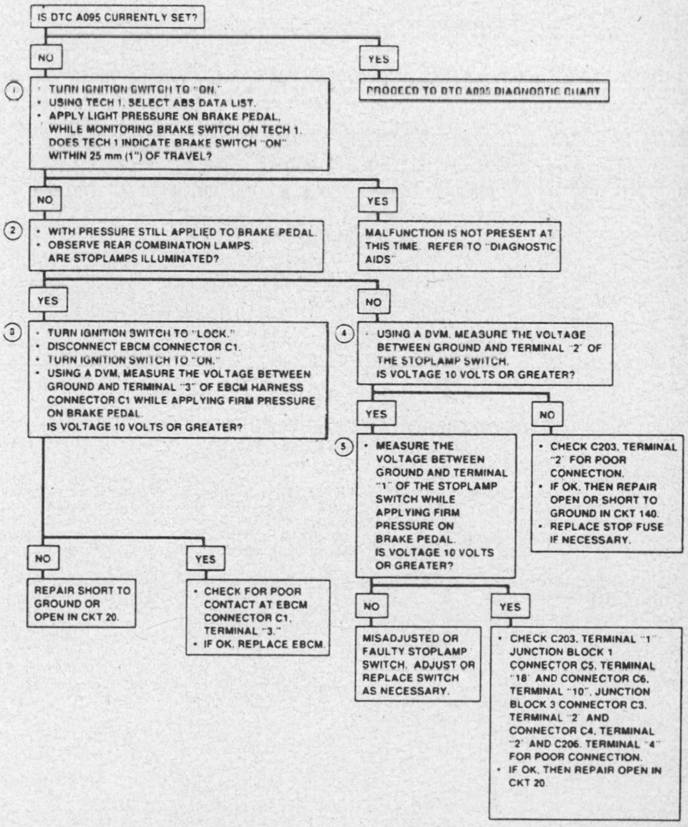
IS DTC A095 CURRENTLY SET?
NO
YES
1
• TURN IGNITION SWITCH TO "ON."
• USING TECH 1, SELECT ABS DATA LIST.
• APPLY LIGHT PRESSURE ON BRAKE PEDAL, WHILE MONITORING BRAKE SWITCH ON TECH 1.
DOES TECH 1 INDICATE BRAKE SWITCH "ON" WITHIN 25 mm (1") OF TRAVEL?
PROCEED TO DTC A095 DIAGNOSTIC CHART
NO
YES
2
• WITH PRESSURE STILL APPLIED TO BRAKE PEDAL.
• OBSERVE REAR COMBINATION LAMPS.
ARE STOPLAMPS ILLUMINATED?
MALFUNCTION IS NOT PRESENT AT THIS TIME. REFER TO "DIAGNOSTIC AIDS"
YES
NO
3
• TURN IGNITION SWITCH TO "LOCK."
• DISCONNECT EBCM CONNECTOR C1.
• TURN IGNITION SWITCH TO "ON."
• USING A DVM, MEASURE THE VOLTAGE BETWEEN GROUND AND TERMINAL "3" OF EBCM HARNESS CONNECTOR C1 WHILE APPLYING FIRM PRESSURE ON BRAKE PEDAL.
IS VOLTAGE 10 VOLTS OR GREATER?
4
• USING A DVM, MEASURE THE VOLTAGE BETWEEN GROUND AND TERMINAL "2" OF THE STOPLAMP SWITCH.
IS VOLTAGE 10 VOLTS OR GREATER?
YES
NO
5
• MEASURE THE VOLTAGE BETWEEN GROUND AND TERMINAL "1" OF THE STOPLAMP SWITCH WHILE APPLYING FIRM PRESSURE ON BRAKE PEDAL.
IS VOLTAGE 10 VOLTS OR GREATER?
• CHECK C203, TERMINAL "2" FOR POOR CONNECTION.
• IF OK, THEN REPAIR OPEN OR SHORT TO GROUND IN CKT 140.
• REPLACE STOP FUSE IF NECESSARY.
NO
YES
REPAIR SHORT TO GROUND OR OPEN IN CKT 20.
• CHECK FOR POOR CONTACT AT EBCM CONNECTOR C1, TERMINAL "3."
• IF OK, REPLACE EBCM.
NO
YES
MISADJUSTED OR FAULTY STOPLAMP SWITCH. ADJUST OR REPLACE SWITCH AS NECESSARY.
• CHECK C203, TERMINAL "1" JUNCTION BLOCK 1 CONNECTOR C5, TERMINAL "18" AND CONNECTOR C6, TERMINAL "10", JUNCTION BLOCK 3 CONNECTOR C3, TERMINAL "2" AND CONNECTOR C4, TERMINAL "2" AND C206, TERMINAL "4" FOR POOR CONNECTION.
• IF OK, THEN REPAIR OPEN IN CKT 20.

GC402940099700BX

Fig. 347 Code A091: Open Brake Switch During Deceleration. 1993–94 Prizm

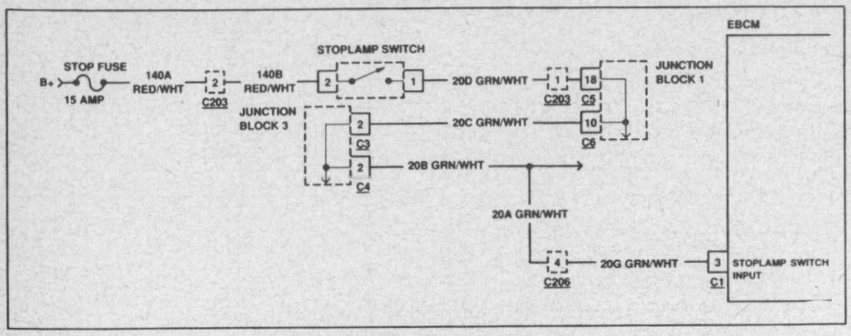
EBCM
STOPLAMP SWITCH
STOP FUSE
B+
15 AMP
140A RED/WHT
2
C203
140B RED/WHT
2
1
20D GRN/WHT
1
18
C203
C5
JUNCTION BLOCK 1
JUNCTION BLOCK 3
2
20C GRN/WHT
10
C6
C3
2
20B GRN/WHT
C4
20A GRN/WHT
4
C206
20G GRN/WHT
3
C1
STOPLAMP SWITCH INPUT

DTC A092

OPEN BRAKE SWITCH WHEN ABS WAS REQUIRED

Circuit Description:

This DTC is run to determine the proper operation of the stoplamp switch. This is important because ABS is activated when the stoplamp switch is closed. If the stoplamp switch is open, ABS will never be activated. Since this malfunction is difficult to detect under normal braking conditions, this malfunction is only detected when ABS is required.

Failure Condition:

DTC A092 can be set if the vehicle's speed is greater than 8 km/h (5 mph). If the stoplamp switch was not closed and a release was required on two channels for 0.5 seconds, a malfunction exists.

Action Taken:

A DTC A092 is stored, ABS is disabled and the "ABS" indicator is turned on.

Test Description: Number(s) below refer to circled number(s) on the diagnostic chart.

1. This step indicates if the stoplamp switch signal is being received by the EBCM.
2. This step indicates if an open circuit exists in the stoplamp switch or the rear combination lamp circuitry.
3. This step isolates the open circuit to either the stoplamp switch input circuitry or the EBCM.
4. This step verifies that voltage is available at the stoplamp switch.
5. This step verifies that the stoplamp switch is functioning properly.

Diagnostic Aids:

An "intermittent" malfunction may be caused by a poor connection, rubbed through wire insulation or a wire that is broken inside the insulation.

The frequency of the malfunction can be checked by using the enhanced diagnostic function of the TECH 1

Any circuitry that is suspected as causing the intermittent complaint, should be thoroughly checked for backed out terminals, improper mating, broken locks, improperly formed or damaged terminals, poor terminal-to-wiring connections or physical damage to the wiring harness.

GC402940099800AX

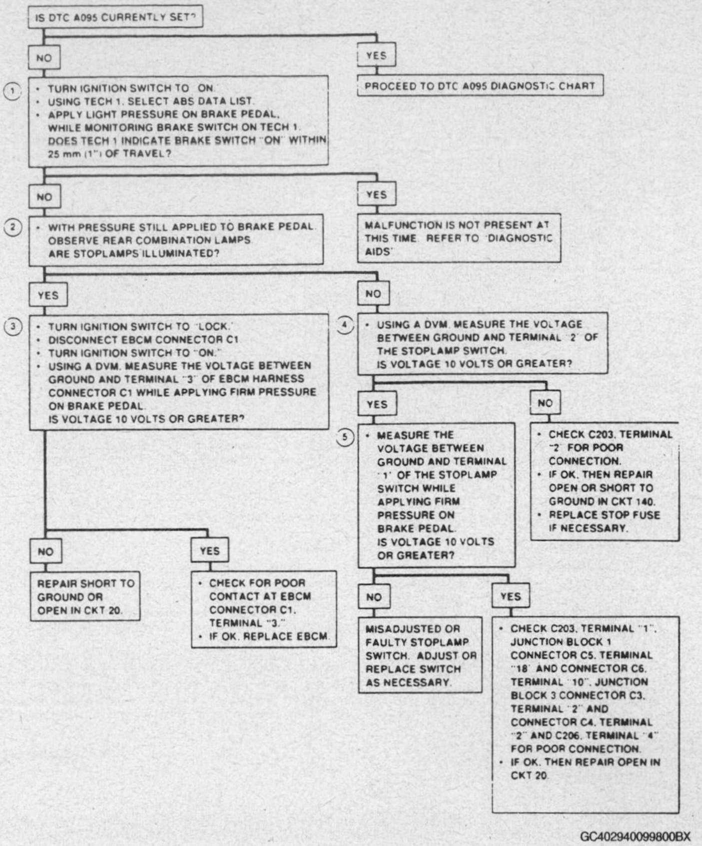
IS DTC A095 CURRENTLY SET?
NO
YES
PROCEED TO DTC A095 DIAGNOSTIC CHART
1
• TURN IGNITION SWITCH TO "ON."
• USING TECH 1, SELECT ABS DATA LIST.
• APPLY LIGHT PRESSURE ON BRAKE PEDAL, WHILE MONITORING BRAKE SWITCH ON TECH 1. DOES TECH 1 INDICATE BRAKE SWITCH "ON" WITHIN 25 mm (1") OF TRAVEL?
NO
YES
MALFUNCTION IS NOT PRESENT AT THIS TIME. REFER TO "DIAGNOSTIC AIDS"
2
• WITH PRESSURE STILL APPLIED TO BRAKE PEDAL, OBSERVE REAR COMBINATION LAMPS. ARE STOPLAMPS ILLUMINATED?
YES
NO
3
• TURN IGNITION SWITCH TO "LOCK."
• DISCONNECT EBCM CONNECTOR C1.
• TURN IGNITION SWITCH TO "ON."
• USING A DVM, MEASURE THE VOLTAGE BETWEEN GROUND AND TERMINAL "3" OF EBCM HARNESS CONNECTOR C1 WHILE APPLYING FIRM PRESSURE ON BRAKE PEDAL. IS VOLTAGE 10 VOLTS OR GREATER?
4
• USING A DVM, MEASURE THE VOLTAGE BETWEEN GROUND AND TERMINAL "2" OF THE STOPLAMP SWITCH. IS VOLTAGE 10 VOLTS OR GREATER?
YES
NO
5
• MEASURE THE VOLTAGE BETWEEN GROUND AND TERMINAL "1" OF THE STOPLAMP SWITCH WHILE APPLYING FIRM PRESSURE ON BRAKE PEDAL. IS VOLTAGE 10 VOLTS OR GREATER?
• CHECK C203, TERMINAL "2" FOR POOR CONNECTION.
• IF OK, THEN REPAIR OPEN OR SHORT TO GROUND IN CKT 140.
• REPLACE STOP FUSE IF NECESSARY.
NO
YES
REPAIR SHORT TO GROUND OR OPEN IN CKT 20.
• CHECK FOR POOR CONTACT AT EBCM CONNECTOR C1, TERMINAL "3."
• IF OK, REPLACE EBCM.
NO
YES
MISADJUSTED OR FAULTY STOPLAMP SWITCH. ADJUST OR REPLACE SWITCH AS NECESSARY.
• CHECK C203, TERMINAL "1", JUNCTION BLOCK 1 CONNECTOR C5, TERMINAL "18" AND CONNECTOR C6, TERMINAL "10", JUNCTION BLOCK 3 CONNECTOR C3, TERMINAL "2" AND CONNECTOR C4, TERMINAL "2" AND C206, TERMINAL "4" FOR POOR CONNECTION.
• IF OK, THEN REPAIR OPEN IN CKT 20.

GC402940099800BX

Fig. 348 Code A092: Open Brake Switch When ABS Required. 1993–94 Prizm

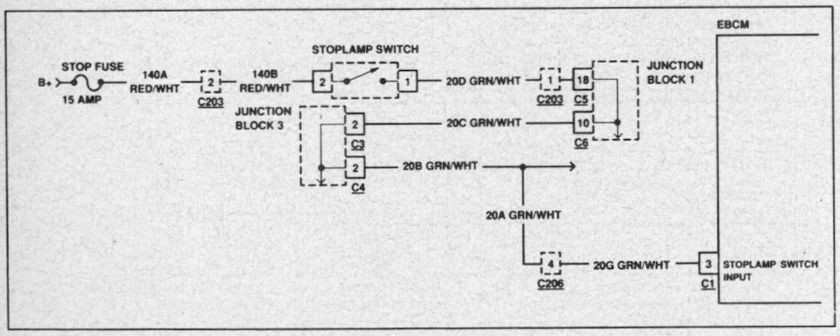
EBCM
STOPLAMP SWITCH
STOP FUSE
B+
15 AMP
140A RED/WHT
2
C203
140B RED/WHT
2
1
20D GRN/WHT
1
18
C203
C5
JUNCTION BLOCK 1
JUNCTION BLOCK 3
2
20C GRN/WHT
10
C6
C3
2
20B GRN/WHT
C4
20A GRN/WHT
4
C206
20G GRN/WHT
3
C1
STOPLAMP SWITCH INPUT

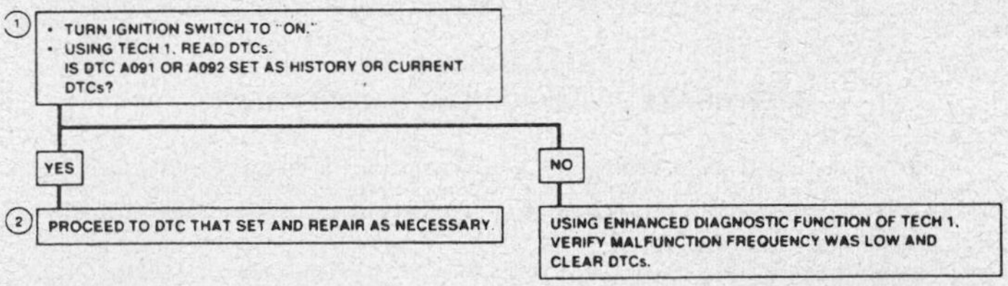
1
• TURN IGNITION SWITCH TO "ON."
• USING TECH 1, READ DTCs. IS DTC A091 OR A092 SET AS HISTORY OR CURRENT DTCs?
YES
NO
2
PROCEED TO DTC THAT SET AND REPAIR AS NECESSARY.
USING ENHANCED DIAGNOSTIC FUNCTION OF TECH 1, VERIFY MALFUNCTION FREQUENCY WAS LOW AND CLEAR DTCs.

GC402940099900BX

DTC A093

CODE A091 OR A092 SET IN CURRENT OR PREVIOUS IGNITION CYCLE

Circuit Description:

This DTC is the second portion of DTCs A091 and A092. If DTCs A091 or A092 failed during the last ignition cycle, DTC A093 becomes a current failure during the next ignition cycle, keeping ABS disabled until a stoplamp switch input is seen. When a change is seen during an ignition cycle in which DTC A093 is a current malfunction, DTC A091 or A092 will clear itself and the end of the current ignition cycle and ABS will enable itself at the start of the next ignition cycle. DTC A093 alone indicates DTCs A091 or A092 failed previously, but is intermittent or has been corrected.

Test Description: Number(s) below refer to circled number(s) on the diagnostic chart.

1. This step indicates which DTC (either A091 or A092) caused DTC A093 to set.
2. This insures that the DTC that set is repaired so that DTC A093 can be cleared.

Diagnostic Aids:

An "intermittent" malfunction may be caused by a poor connection, rubbed through wire insulation or a wire that is broken inside the insulation.

The frequency of the malfunction can be checked by using the enhanced diagnostic function of the TECH 1

Any circuitry that is suspected as causing the intermittent complaint, should be thoroughly checked for backed out terminals, improper mating, broken locks, improperly formed or damaged terminals, poor terminal-to-wiring connections or physical damage to the wiring harness.

Also, verify proper stoplamp switch operation using the data list of the TECH 1. As the brake is applied, the data list should display the brake switch "ON" within 25 mm (1-inch) of travel.

GC402940099900AX

Fig. 349 Code A093: Code A091 Or A092 Set In Current Or Previous Ignition Cycle. 1993–94 Prizm

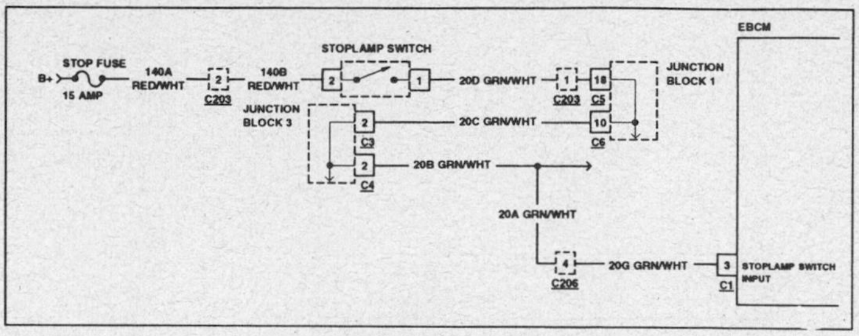
EBCM
STOPLAMP SWITCH
STOP FUSE
B+
15 AMP
140A RED/WHT
2
C203
140B RED/WHT
2
1
20D GRN/WHT
1
18
C203
C5
JUNCTION BLOCK 1
JUNCTION BLOCK 3
2
C3
20C GRN/WHT
10
C6
2
C4
20B GRN/WHT
20A GRN/WHT
4
C206
20G GRN/WHT
3
C1
STOPLAMP SWITCH INPUT

DTC A094

BRAKE SWITCH CONTACTS ALWAYS CLOSED

Circuit Description:

This DTC is run to determine the proper operation of the stoplamp switch. This is important because ABS is activated when the stoplamp switch is closed and deactivated when the switch is open. If the stoplamp switch is always closed, ABS operation will always be requested, resulting in potential hydraulic modulator cycling on rough roads. Additionally, this malfunction will most likely result in a discharged battery (due to the stoplamps remaining illuminated) if the driver is not informed of this malfunction.

Failure Condition:

DTC A094 can be set when the vehicle reaches at least 40 km/h (25 mph). If the stoplamp switch was never open during two consecutive drive cycles, a malfunction exists.

Action Taken:

A DTC A094 is stored. ABS is not disabled and the "ABS" indicator will not be illuminated.

Test Description: Number(s) below refer to circled number(s) on the diagnostic chart.

1. This checks if the malfunction is currently present.
2. This step isolates the cause of the malfunction to either a malfunctioning or misadjusted stoplamp switch or a short to voltage in the stoplamp switch circuitry.
3. This step checks for unwanted voltage on the stoplamp switch input circuit.
4. This step checks for a possible intermittent malfunction.

Diagnostic Aids:

An "intermittent" malfunction may be caused by a poor connection, rubbed through wire insulation or a wire that is broken inside the insulation.

The frequency of the malfunction can be checked by using the enhanced diagnostic function of the TECH 1

Any circuitry that is suspected as causing the intermittent complaint, should be thoroughly checked for backed out terminals, improper mating, broken locks, improperly formed or damaged terminals, poor terminal-to-wiring connections or physical damage to the wiring harness.

GC402940100000AX

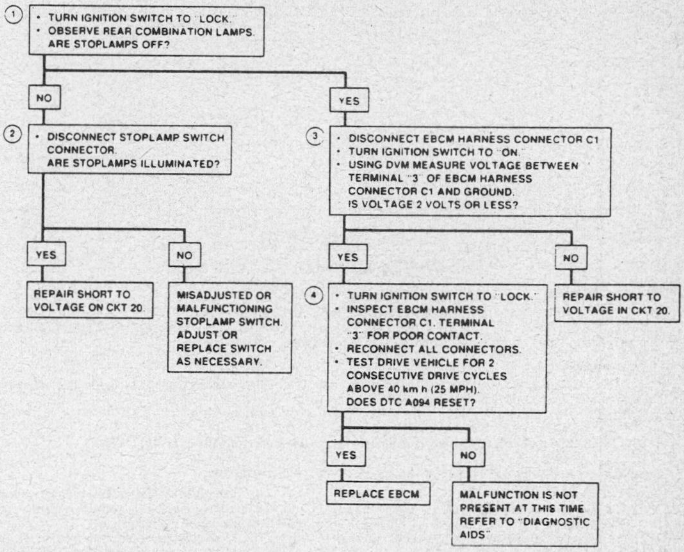
1
• TURN IGNITION SWITCH TO "LOCK."
• OBSERVE REAR COMBINATION LAMPS. ARE STOPLAMPS OFF?
NO
YES
2
• DISCONNECT STOPLAMP SWITCH CONNECTOR. ARE STOPLAMPS ILLUMINATED?
3
• DISCONNECT EBCM HARNESS CONNECTOR C1.
• TURN IGNITION SWITCH TO "ON."
• USING DVM MEASURE VOLTAGE BETWEEN TERMINAL "3" OF EBCM HARNESS CONNECTOR C1 AND GROUND. IS VOLTAGE 2 VOLTS OR LESS?
YES
NO
YES
NO
REPAIR SHORT TO VOLTAGE ON CKT 20.
MISADJUSTED OR MALFUNCTIONING STOPLAMP SWITCH. ADJUST OR REPLACE SWITCH AS NECESSARY.
4
• TURN IGNITION SWITCH TO "LOCK."
• INSPECT EBCM HARNESS CONNECTOR C1, TERMINAL "3" FOR POOR CONTACT.
• RECONNECT ALL CONNECTORS.
• TEST DRIVE VEHICLE FOR 2 CONSECUTIVE DRIVE CYCLES ABOVE 40 km h (25 MPH). DOES DTC A094 RESET?
REPAIR SHORT TO VOLTAGE IN CKT 20.
YES
NO
REPLACE EBCM
MALFUNCTION IS NOT PRESENT AT THIS TIME REFER TO "DIAGNOSTIC AIDS"

GC402940100000BX

Fig. 350 Code A094: Brake Switch Contacts Always Closed. 1993–94 Prizm

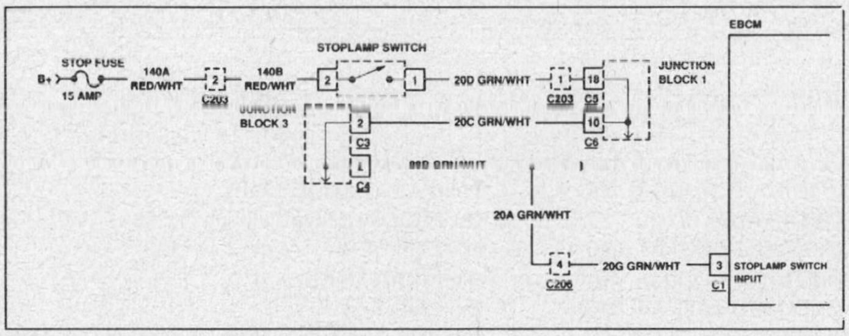
EBCM
STOPLAMP SWITCH
STOP FUSE
B+
15 AMP
140A RED/WHT
2
C203
140B RED/WHT
2
1
20D GRN/WHT
1
18
C203
C5
JUNCTION BLOCK 1
JUNCTION BLOCK 3
2
C3
20C GRN/WHT
10
C6
C4
20A GRN/WHT
4
C206
20G GRN/WHT
3
C1
STOPLAMP SWITCH INPUT

DTC A095

BRAKE SWITCH CIRCUIT OPEN

Circuit Description:

This DTC is used to identify open stoplamp switch circuitry that prevent the stoplamp switch input to the EBCM from changing states when the brake is applied. This DTC is used in conjunction with DTCs A091 and A092 to determine the cause of an open stoplamp switch malfunction.

Failure Condition:

DTC A095 can be set after initialization is completed. If the stoplamp switch input voltage is out of specification for one second (indicating an open circuit), a malfunction exists.

Action Taken:

A DTC A095 is stored, ABS is disabled and the "ABS" indicator is turned on.

Test Description: Number(s) below refer to circled number(s) on the diagnostic chart.

1. This step is used to confirm that an open in the stoplamp switch circuitry currently exists.
2. This step indicates if the stoplamp switch signal is being received by the EBCM.
3. This step indicates if an open circuit exists in the stoplamp switch or stoplamp circuitry.
4. This step isolates the open circuit to either the stoplamp switch input circuitry or the EBCM.

Diagnostic Aids:

An "intermittent" malfunction may be caused by a poor connection, rubbed through wire insulation or a wire that is broken inside the insulation.

The frequency of the malfunction can be checked by using the enhanced diagnostic function of the TECH 1

Any circuitry that is suspected as causing the intermittent complaint, should be thoroughly checked for backed out terminals, improper mating, broken locks, improperly formed or damaged terminals, poor terminal-to-wiring connections or physical damage to the wiring harness.

GC402940100100AX

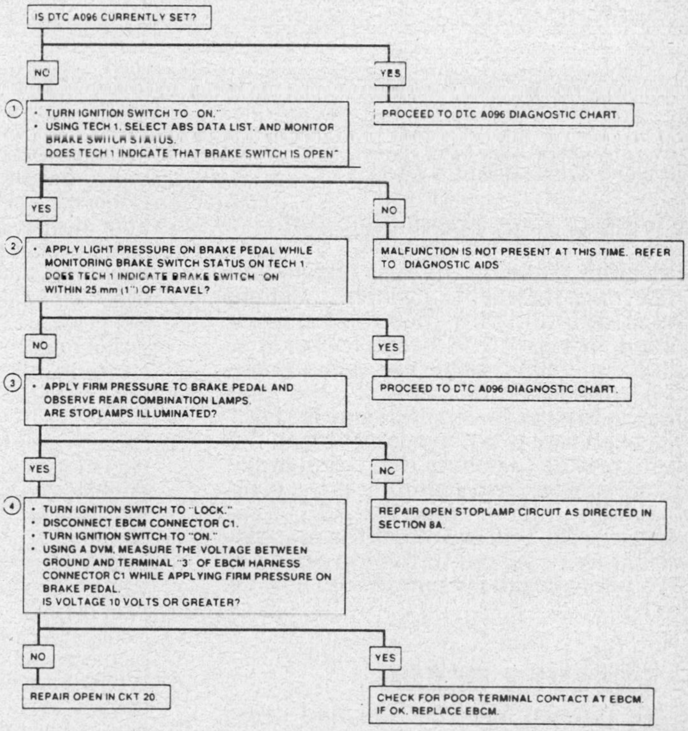
IS DTC A096 CURRENTLY SET?
NO
YES
1
• TURN IGNITION SWITCH TO "ON."
• USING TECH 1, SELECT ABS DATA LIST, AND MONITOR BRAKE SWITCH STATUS. DOES TECH 1 INDICATE THAT BRAKE SWITCH IS OPEN?
PROCEED TO DTC A096 DIAGNOSTIC CHART.
YES
NO
2
• APPLY LIGHT PRESSURE ON BRAKE PEDAL WHILE MONITORING BRAKE SWITCH STATUS ON TECH 1. DOES TECH 1 INDICATE BRAKE SWITCH "ON" WITHIN 25 mm (1") OF TRAVEL?
MALFUNCTION IS NOT PRESENT AT THIS TIME. REFER TO DIAGNOSTIC AIDS
NO
YES
3
• APPLY FIRM PRESSURE TO BRAKE PEDAL AND OBSERVE REAR COMBINATION LAMPS. ARE STOPLAMPS ILLUMINATED?
PROCEED TO DTC A096 DIAGNOSTIC CHART.
YES
NO
4
• TURN IGNITION SWITCH TO "LOCK."
• DISCONNECT EBCM CONNECTOR C1.
• TURN IGNITION SWITCH TO "ON."
• USING A DVM, MEASURE THE VOLTAGE BETWEEN GROUND AND TERMINAL "3" OF EBCM HARNESS CONNECTOR C1 WHILE APPLYING FIRM PRESSURE ON BRAKE PEDAL. IS VOLTAGE 10 VOLTS OR GREATER?
REPAIR OPEN STOPLAMP CIRCUIT AS DIRECTED IN SECTION 8A.
NO
YES
REPAIR OPEN IN CKT 20.
CHECK FOR POOR TERMINAL CONTACT AT EBCM. IF OK, REPLACE EBCM.

GC402940100100BX

Fig. 351 Code A095: Brake Circuit Open. 1993–94 Prizm

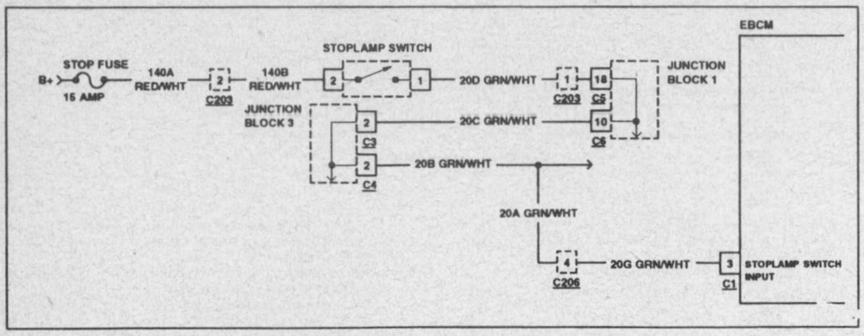

EBCM
STOPLAMP SWITCH
STOP FUSE
B+
15 AMP
140A RED/WHT
C203
140B RED/WHT
JUNCTION BLOCK 3
C3
C4
20D GRN/WHT
20C GRN/WHT
20B GRN/WHT
20A GRN/WHT
20G GRN/WHT
JUNCTION BLOCK 1
C5
C6
C206
STOPLAMP SWITCH INPUT
C1

DTC A096

REAR BRAKE LAMP CIRCUIT OPEN

Circuit Description:

This DTC is designed to isolate the cause of a DTC A095 malfunction and indicate to the driver that ABS is available. If DTC A095 fails with DTC A096, the stoplamps circuit are open. The presence of battery voltage at the stoplamp switch input indicates that a valid stoplamp switch input is still available.

Failure Condition:

DTC A096 can be set only after DTC A095 has been set. If the EBCM detects battery voltage on the stoplamp switch input circuit for 0.5 second, a malfunction exists.

Action Taken:

A DTC A096 is stored. ABS is not disabled and the "ABS" indicator will not be illuminated.

Test Description: Number(s) below refer to circled number(s) on the diagnostic chart.

1. As a result of a malfunction of an additional stoplamp switch circuit DTC, DTC A096 may be set. To insure proper diagnosis, any additional stoplamp switch DTC must be repaired first.
2. This step identifies if the malfunction is currently present in the stoplamp circuit.

Diagnostic Aids:

An "intermittent" malfunction may be caused by a poor connection, rubbed through wire insulation or a wire that is broken inside the insulation.

The frequency of the malfunction can be checked by using the enhanced diagnostic function of the TECH 1

Any circuitry that is suspected as causing the intermittent complaint, should be thoroughly checked for backed out terminals, improper mating, broken locks, improperly formed or damaged terminals, poor terminal-to-wiring connections or physical damage to the wiring harness.

GC402940100200AX

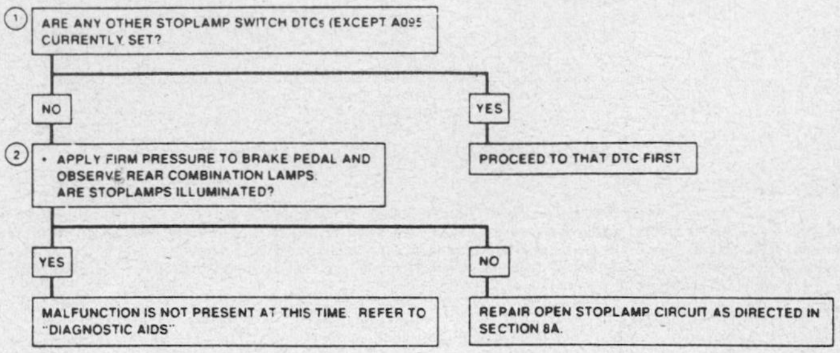

1
ARE ANY OTHER STOPLAMP SWITCH DTCs (EXCEPT A095) CURRENTLY SET?
NO
YES
PROCEED TO THAT DTC FIRST
2
• APPLY FIRM PRESSURE TO BRAKE PEDAL AND OBSERVE REAR COMBINATION LAMPS. ARE STOPLAMPS ILLUMINATED?
YES
NO
MALFUNCTION IS NOT PRESENT AT THIS TIME. REFER TO "DIAGNOSTIC AIDS"
REPAIR OPEN STOPLAMP CIRCUIT AS DIRECTED IN SECTION 8A.

GC402940100200BX

Fig. 352 Code A096: Rear Brake Lamp Circuit Open. 1993–94 Prizm

SYSTEM SERVICE

Brake System Bleed

Before bleeding the rear brakes, the rear displacement cylinder pistons must be returned to their top most position. Using a TECH 1 scan tool or suitable equivalent, enter the manual control function and "APPLY" the rear motor. Ensure the enable relay is "ON." If a scan tool is not available, bleed the front brakes to ensure that a firm brake pedal exists, then carefully drive vehicle over 4 mph to cause the ABS to initialize itself. This will return the rear displacement cylinder to the top position. The entire brake system should now be rebled.

PRESSURE BLEED

To prevent air, moisture and other contaminants from entering system, only diaphragm type pressure bleeding equipment should be used.

1. **On all models,** attach bleeder adapter tool J35589 or equivalent to master cylinder reservoir, then the adapter tool to the pressure bleeder.
2. Connect a clear plastic hose to the front bleeder valve on the control assembly, then put opposite end of the hose into a clean container partially filled with brake fluid.
3. Set pressure bleeder to 5-10 psi and wait for approximately 30 seconds to insure there is no leakage.
4. Set pressure bleed equipment to 30-35 psi.
5. Slowly open bleeder valve and allow fluid to flow into container until no air bubbles are seen in fluid, then close the bleeder valve and **torque** to 65 inch. lbs.
6. Attach bleeder hose to rear bleeder valve of the control assembly and repeat step 5.
7. Position a cloth under hydraulic brake pipe connections.
8. Working from front of the control assembly to the rear, slowly turn each pipe nut and check for air in escaping fluid.
9. When air flow ceases, **torque** pipe nut to 13 ft. lbs.
10. Raise and support vehicle, then bleed wheel cylinders and calipers using the following sequence:
    a. Right rear.
    b. Left rear.
    c. Right front.
    d. Left front.
11. Lower vehicle and remove bleeder adapter tool from master cylinder.
12. Check fluid level in reservoir, fill as necessary.
13. Turn on ignition and note pedal travel and feel as follows:
    a. If pedal feels firm and constant, start the engine and recheck pedal travel, if pedal still feels firm and constant, proceed to step 14.
    b. If pedal feels soft or has excessive travel either initially or after engine is started, repeat bleeding procedure.
14. Road test vehicle, make several normal stops from a moderate speed, then make one or two ABS stops at approximately 50 mph.
15. Ensure pedal is still firm and constant.

MANUAL BLEED

1. **On all models,** remove master cylinder reservoir cover, then fill reservoir as necessary.

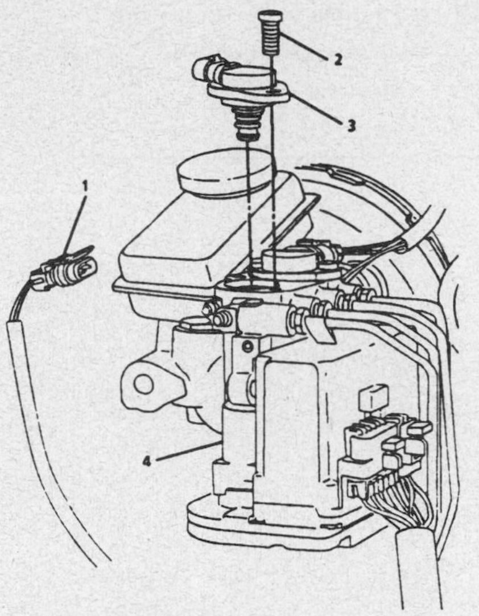
1
2
3
4

1 SOLENOID ELECTRICAL CONNECTOR
2 TORX® HEAD BOLTS
3 SOLENOID ASSEMBLY
4 ABS HYDRAULIC MODULATOR

GC4029100845000X

Fig. 353 Brake control solenoid removal

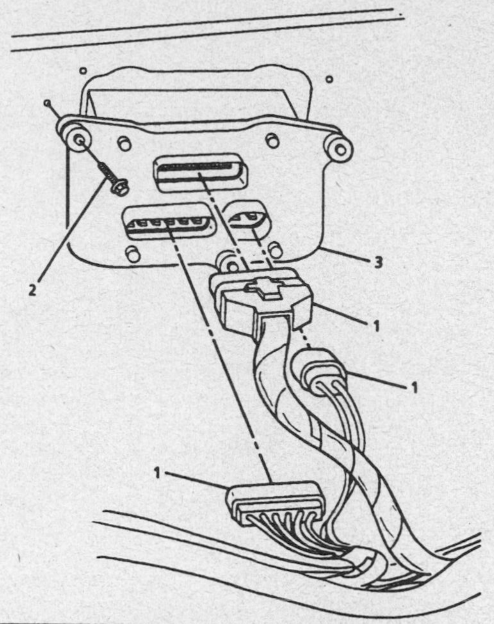
1
1
1
2
3

1 EBCM ELECTRICAL CONNECTORS
2 HEX HEAD SCREWS
3 EBCM

GC4029100846000X

Fig. 354 EBCM assembly removal. Except Cutlass Supreme, Grand Prix, Lumina & Regal

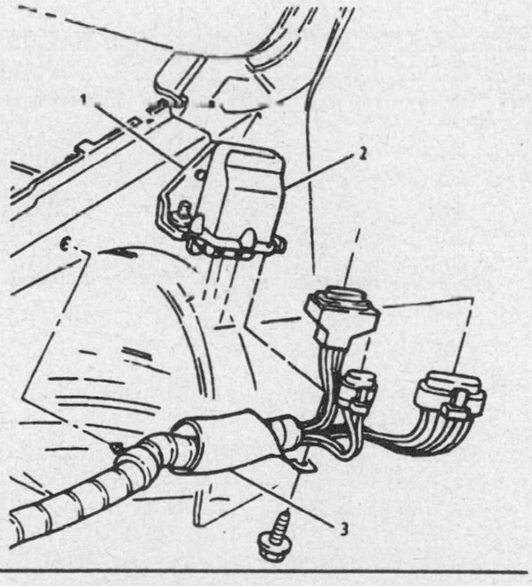
1
2
3

1 EBCM MOUNTING BRACKET
2 EBCM
3 ELECTROMAGNETIC COMPATIBILITY (EMC) SHEILD

GC4029100847000X

Fig. 355 EBCM assembly removal. Cutlass Supreme, Grand Prix, Lumina & Regal

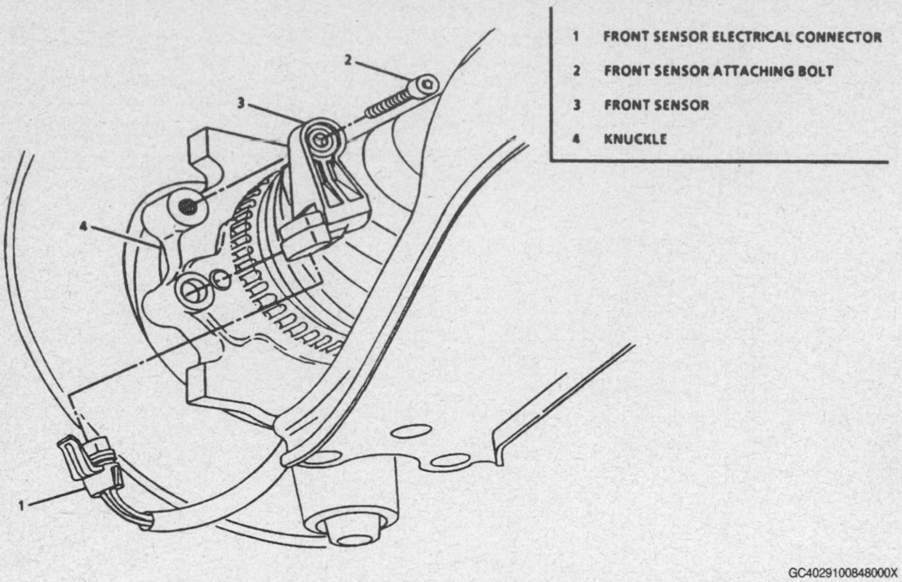
1 FRONT SENSOR ELECTRICAL CONNECTOR
2 FRONT SENSOR ATTACHING BOLT
3 FRONT SENSOR
4 KNUCKLE
1
2
3
4
GC4029100848000X

Fig. 356 Front wheel speed sensor removal

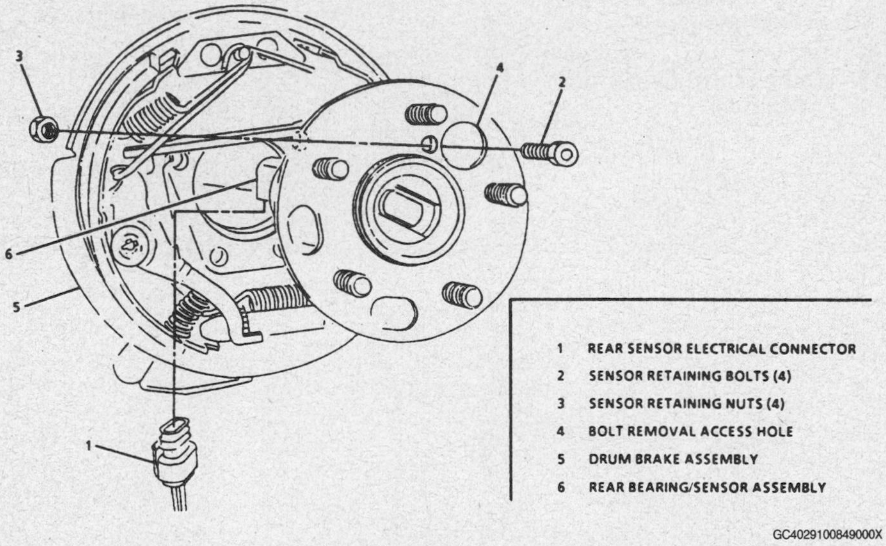
1 REAR SENSOR ELECTRICAL CONNECTOR
2 SENSOR RETAINING BOLTS (4)
3 SENSOR RETAINING NUTS (4)
4 BOLT REMOVAL ACCESS HOLE
5 DRUM BRAKE ASSEMBLY
6 REAR BEARING/SENSOR ASSEMBLY
1
2
3
4
5
6
GC4029100849000X

Fig. 357 Rear wheel bearing & speed sensor removal

2. Attach one end of a clear plastic hose to rear bleeder valve of the brake control assembly, then put opposite end of the hose into a clean container.
3. While depressing brake pedal, slowly open bleeder valve, until fluid begins to flow.
4. Close valve and release brake pedal, then repeat procedure for front bleeder valve.
5. Ensure master cylinder is full, then raise and support vehicle.
6. Bleed wheel cylinders and calipers using the following sequence:
   a. Right rear.
   b. Left rear.
   c. Right front.
   d. Left front.
7. Lower vehicle and check fluid level in reservoir, fill as necessary.
8. Turn on ignition and note pedal travel and feel as follows:
   a. If pedal feels firm and constant, start the engine and recheck pedal travel, if pedal still feels firm and constant, proceed to step 14.
   b. If pedal feels soft or has excessive travel either initially or after engine is started, repeat bleeding procedure.
9. Road test vehicle, make several normal stops from a moderate speed, then make one or two ABS stops at approximately 50 mph.
10. Ensure pedal is still firm and constant.

Component Replace

BRAKE CONTROL SOLENOID ASSEMBLY

1. Disconnect solenoid electrical connector, **Fig. 353.**
2. Remove solenoid assembly retaining bolt, then the solenoid from the modulator.
3. Reverse procedure to install, **torque** retaining bolt to 39 inch lbs. and bleed ABS brake control assembly as described under "Brake System Bleeding." Rearm air bag system as outlined under "Precautions."

ELECTRONIC BRAKE CONTROL MODULE (EBCM)

Except Cutlass Supreme, Grand Prix, Lumina & Regal

1. Disconnect EBCM electrical connectors, **Fig. 354.**
2. Remove ECU to dash panel attaching

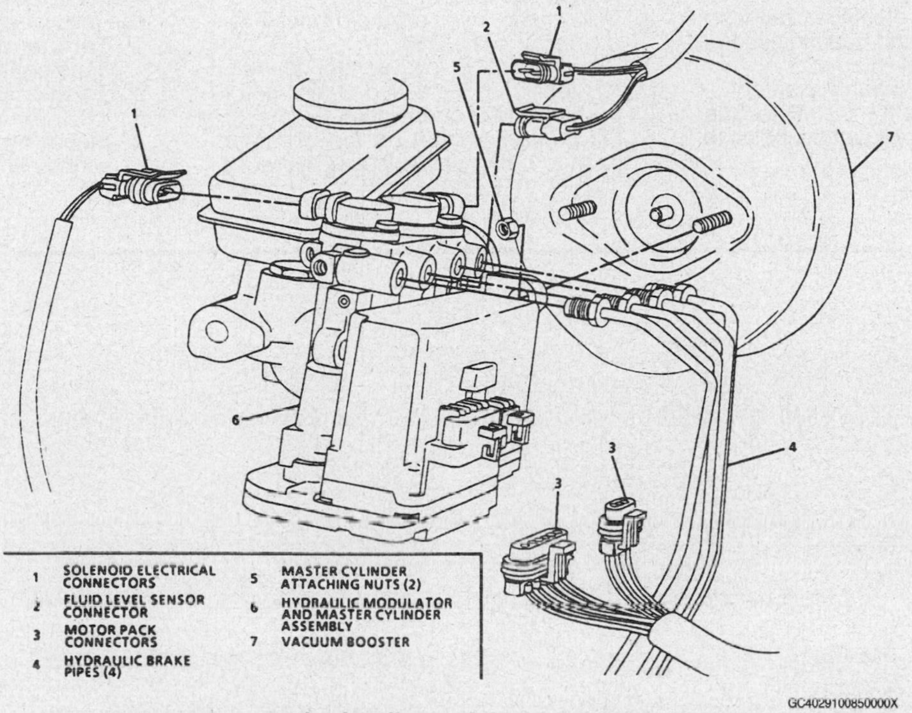
1 SOLENOID ELECTRICAL CONNECTORS
2 FLUID LEVEL SENSOR CONNECTOR
3 MOTOR PACK CONNECTORS
4 HYDRAULIC BRAKE PIPES (4)
5 MASTER CYLINDER ATTACHING NUTS (2)
6 HYDRAULIC MODULATOR AND MASTER CYLINDER ASSEMBLY
7 VACUUM BOOSTER
GC4029100850000X

Fig. 358 ABS hydraulic modulator assembly removal

screws, then the ECU from dash panel.

3. Reverse procedure to install, ensure all four plastic grommets are located properly and **torque** screws to 14 inch lbs. Rearm air bag system as outlined under "Precautions."

Cutlass Supreme, Grand Prix, Lumina & Regal

1. Raise and support vehicle, then remove left front tire and wheel assembly.
2. Remove inner fender retaining screws.
3. Remove screw retaining Electromagnetic Compatibility (EMC) shield, **Fig. 355.**
4. Slide shield back on harness, then remove EBCM retaining screws.
5. Disconnect EBCM electrical connectors and remove EBCM.
6. Reverse procedure to install.

FRONT WHEEL SPEED SENSOR

1. Raise and support vehicle.
2. Disconnect wheel sensor electrical connector, **Fig. 356.**
3. Remove sensor attaching bolt, then the sensor from the mounting bracket.
4. Reverse procedure to install, ensure sensor is properly aligned and lays flat against bracket bosses, **torque** attaching bolt to 9 ft. lbs.

REAR WHEEL BEARING & SPEED SENSOR

Except Cutlass Supreme, Grand Prix, Lumina & Regal

1. Raise and support vehicle, then remove rear wheel and tire assembly.
2. Remove rear brake drum, then disconnect sensor electrical connector, **Fig. 357.**
3. Remove wheel bearing and sensor attaching nuts and bolts, then then bearing and sensor assembly. **After bolts are removed, the rear brake assembly will be held in place by the hydraulic pipe. Use care not to bump or exert any force on the brake assembly to prevent any damage to the hydraulic pipe.**
4. Reverse procedure to install, noting the following:
   a. Align bolt holes in wheel bearing and speed sensor assembly, drum brake assembly and rear suspension bracket.
   b. When installing bolts, rotate axle flange to align large hole with each

bolt location, then install bolt while holding nut.

The rear speed sensors and rings on these models are an integral part of the hub and bearing assembly. If speed sensors or rings are defective, the entire assembly must be replaced as a unit.

1. Raise and support vehicle, then remove tire and wheel assembly.
2. Remove brake hose bracket, caliper and rotor.
3. Disconnect ABS electrical harness, then remove hub and bearing assembly mounting bolts.
4. Remove hub and bearing assembly.
5. Reverse procedure top install, **torque** bearing assembly mounting bolts to 52 ft. lbs.

ABS HYDRAULIC MODULATOR ASSEMBLY

To avoid personal injury, due to a retained load on the modulator assembly, the "Gear Tension Relief" function of the TECH 1 scan tool must be performed prior to removal of the brake control and motor assembly. Refer to "Component Testing" for procedure.

1. **On all models,** disconnect battery ground cable.
2. Disconnect two solenoid electrical connectors, **Fig. 358.**
3. Disconnect fluid level sensor connector, then the 6-pin and 3-pin motor pack electrical connectors.
4. Place a shop cloth on top of motor pack to catch any dripping hydraulic fluid, then disconnect four hydraulic pipes from modulator assembly. **Plug open lines to prevent any fluid loss.**
5. Remove two modulator assembly to brake booster attaching nuts. It may be necessary to remove vacuum check valve from the booster to gain access to nut closest to check valve.
6. Remove modulator assembly from vehicle.
7. Reverse procedure to install, noting the following:
   a. **Torque** modulator assembly to booster attaching nuts to 20 ft. lbs.
   b. **Torque** hydraulic pipe nuts to 13 ft. lbs.
   c. Bleed hydraulic system as described in "Hydraulic Brakes."

AUTOMATIC TRANSMISSIONS/TRANSAXLES

TABLE OF CONTENTS

Application Chart

	1992		1993		1994	
Model	Type	Page No.	Type	Page No.	Type	Page No.
Achieva, Grand Am & Skylark	3T40	33-12	3T40	33-12	3T40	33-12
Beretta & Corsica	3T40	33-12	3T40	33-12	3T40/4T60-E	33-12/21
Bonneville, Fleetwood (FWD), LeSabre, Park Avenue/Ultra 88 & 98 & 1992-93 DeVille	4T60-E	33-21	4T60-E	33-21	4T60-E	33-21
Brougham	4L60	33-34	—	—	—	—
Camaro & Firebird	4L60	33-34	4L60	33-34	4L60-E	33-34
Caprice, Custom Cruise, Fleetwood (RWD) & Roadmaster	4L60	33-34	4L60	33-34	4L60-E	33-34
Cavalier & Sunbird	3T40	33-12	3T40	33-12	3T40	33-12
Century, Cutlass Ciera & Cutlass Cruiser	3T40/4T60	33-12/21	3T40/4T60	33-12/21	3T40/4T60-E	33-12/21
Eldorado, Seville & 1994 DeVille	4T60-E/4T80E	33-21/46	4T60-E	33-21/46	4T60-E	33-21/46
Corvette	4L60	33-34	4L60	33-34	4L60-E	33-34
Cutlass Supreme, Grand Prix, Lumina & Regal	3T40/4T60/4T60-E	33-12/21	3T40/4T60-E	33-12/21	4T60-E	33-21
LeMans	3T40	33-12	3T40	33-12	—	—
Metro	Aisin-Seiki	33-61	Aisin-Seiki	33-61	Aisin-Seiki	33-61
Prizm	A131L & A240E	33-2/5	A131L & A245E	33-2/8	A131L/A245E	33-2/8
Riviera	4T60-E	33-21	4T60-E	33-21	—	—
Storm	KF 400/JF403E	33-72	KF 400/JF403E	33-72	KF400/JF403E	33-72
Toronado & Trofeo	4T60–E	33-21	—	—	—	—

Aisin Warner A131L Automatic Transaxle

INDEX

IDENTIFICATION

The transaxle identification number is stamped at top of transaxle rear cover at rear of transaxle, **Fig. 1**.

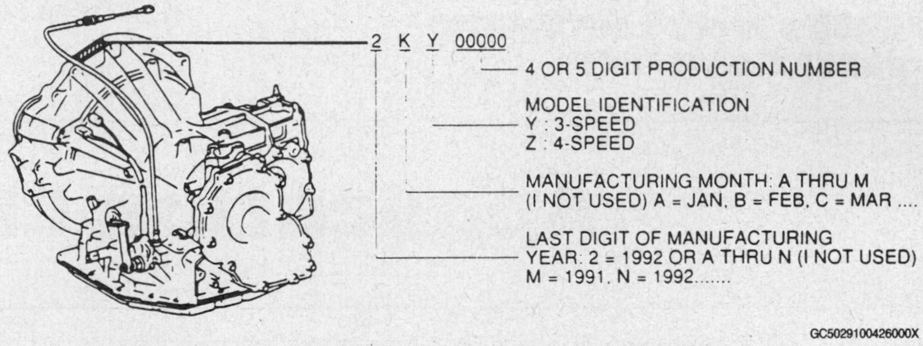
2 K Y 00000
4 OR 5 DIGIT PRODUCTION NUMBER
MODEL IDENTIFICATION
Y : 3-SPEED
Z : 4-SPEED
MANUFACTURING MONTH: A THRU M
(I NOT USED) A = JAN, B = FEB, C = MAR ....
LAST DIGIT OF MANUFACTURING
YEAR: 2 = 1992 OR A THRU N (I NOT USED)
M = 1991, N = 1992.......
GC5029100426000X

Fig. 1 Transaxle identification number plate location

DESCRIPTION

The A131L 3 speed automatic transaxle is used on Geo Prizm. The torque converter is equipped with an integral lock-up clutch. For higher performance, greater fuel economy and quietness, a high efficiency torque converter, wider gear ratio, compact high-precision valve body, high efficiency oil pump and a light weight durable integral transaxle case are used.

TROUBLESHOOTING

FLUID DISCOLORED OR SMELLS BURNED

1. Contaminated fluid.
2. Faulty torque converter.
3. Faulty transaxle.

VEHICLE DOES NOT MOVE IN ANY DRIVE GEAR

1. Improperly adjusted transaxle control cable.
2. Faulty valve body or primary regulator.
3. Faulty transaxle.

VEHICLE DOES NOT MOVE IN ANY RANGE

1. Faulty park lock pawl.
2. Faulty valve body or primary regulator.
3. Faulty torque converter.
4. Broken converter driveplate.
5. Blocked oil pump intake strainer.
6. Faulty transaxle.

INCORRECT SHIFT LEVER POSITION

1. Improperly adjusted transaxle control cable.
2. Faulty manual valve and lever.
3. Faulty transaxle.

HARSH ENGAGEMENT INTO ANY DRIVE RANGE

1. Improperly adjusted transaxle control cable.
2. Faulty valve body or primary regulator.
3. Faulty accumulator pistons.
4. Faulty transaxle.

DELAYED UPSHIFTS & DOWNSHIFTS

1. Improperly adjusted throttle cable.
2. Faulty governors.
3. Faulty valve body.

SLIPS ON UPSHIFTS OR SHUDDERS ON TAKE-OFF

1. Improperly adjusted transaxle control cable.
2. Improperly adjusted throttle cable.
3. Faulty valve body.
4. Faulty transaxle.

DRAG OR BINDING ON UPSHIFT

1. Improperly adjusted transaxle control cable.
2. Faulty valve body.
3. Faulty transaxle.

HARSH DOWNSHIFT

1. Improperly adjusted throttle cable.
2. Faulty accumulator pistons.
3. Faulty valve body.
4. Faulty transaxle.

NO DOWNSHIFT WHEN COASTING

1. Faulty governor.
2. Faulty valve body.

INCORRECT DOWNSHIFT

1. Improperly adjusted throttle cable.
2. Faulty governor.
3. Faulty valve body.
4. Faulty transaxle.

NO KICKDOWN

1. Improperly adjusted throttle cable.
2. Faulty governor.
3. Faulty valve body.

NO ENGINE BRAKING

1. Faulty valve body.
2. Faulty transaxle.

NO HOLD IN PARK

1. Improperly adjusted transaxle control cable.
2. Faulty parking lock pawl and rod.

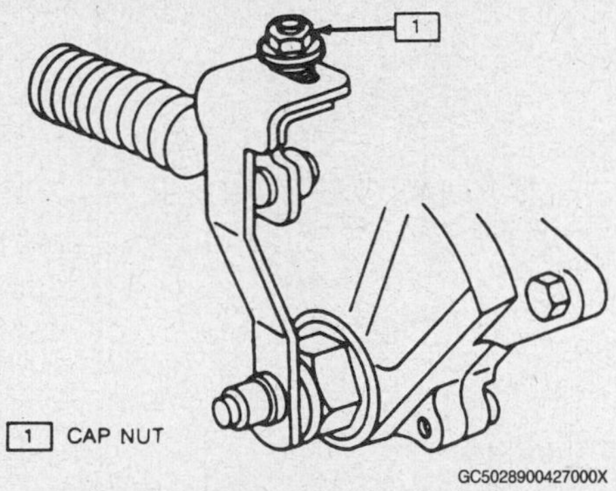
1
1 CAP NUT
GC5028900427000X

Fig. 2 Manual shift linkage adjustment

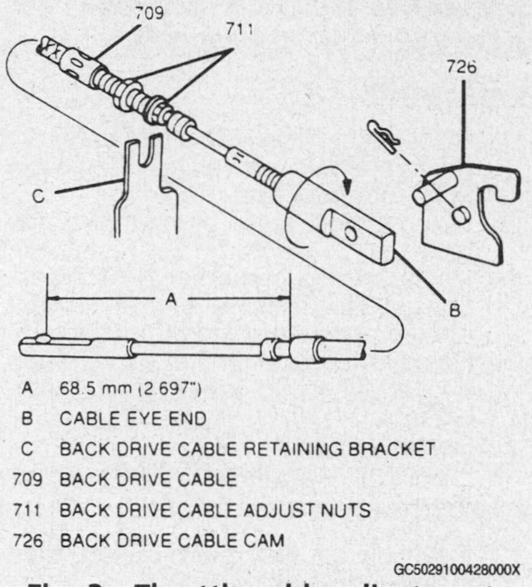
709
711
726
C
A
B
A 68.5 mm (2.697")
B CABLE EYE END
C BACK DRIVE CABLE RETAINING BRACKET
709 BACK DRIVE CABLE
711 BACK DRIVE CABLE ADJUST NUTS
726 BACK DRIVE CABLE CAM
GC5029100428000X

Fig. 3 Throttle cable adjustment

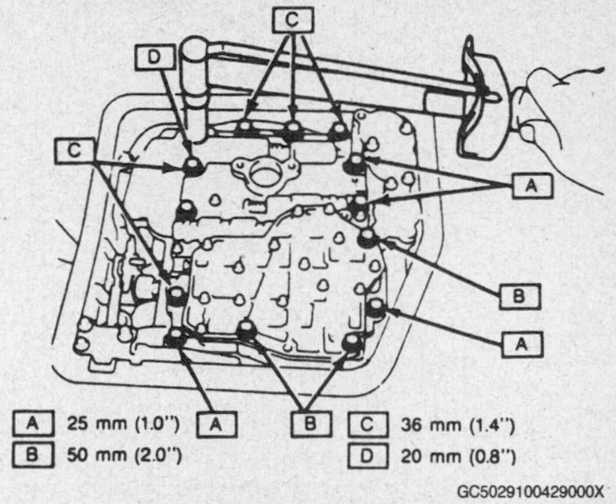
C
D
C
A
B
A
A 25 mm (1.0")
B 50 mm (2.0")
C 36 mm (1.4")
D 20 mm (0.8")
GC5029100429000X

Fig. 4 Valve body bolt identification

MAINTENANCE

FLUID CHANGE

Refer to "Lubricant Data Chart" in the appropriate chassis chapter of this manual for transmission fluid specifications.

1. Raise and support vehicle, then place a suitable container under transaxle drain plug.
2. Remove drain plug and drain fluid, then reinstall and **torque** drain plug to 29 ft. lbs.
3. With engine off.
4. Start engine, then move selector lever through all ranges and end in "Park."
5. With engine idling, check fluid level, then if necessary, add fluid as necessary to bring fluid to "Cool" level on dipstick.

ADJUSTMENTS

MANUAL SHIFT LINKAGE

1. Loosen swivel nut on lever, then push manual lever fully toward right side of vehicle, **Fig. 2.**
2. Return lever two notches to Neutral position, then place selector lever in Neutral position.
3. Shift manual shift lever to N range, then tighten swivel nut.

THROTTLE CABLE

1. Hold accelerator pedal in fully depressed position, then loosen cable adjusting nuts. **Fig. 3.**
2. Adjust cable to obtain .04 inch between end of boot and stopper on cable, then tighten adjusting nut.
3. Fully depress accelerator pedal and recheck adjustment, then road test vehicle.

NEUTRAL SAFETY SWITCH

1. Loosen neutral start switch attaching bolts, then place selector lever in Neutral position.
2. Disconnect electrical connector, then connect a suitable ohmmeter between terminals.
3. Rotate switch until meter indicates continuity, then **torque** switch retaining bolts to 69 inch lbs. to secure adjustment.

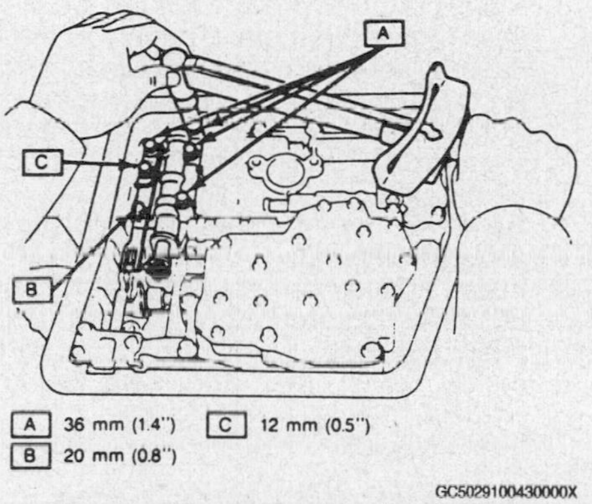
A
C
B
A 36 mm (1.4")
C 12 mm (0.5")
B 20 mm (0.8")
GC5029100430000X

Fig. 5 Manual valve body bolt identification

4. Reconnect electrical connector to switch then ensure engine starts with selector lever in Neutral and Park only.

IN-VEHICLE REPAIRS

VALVE BODY, REPLACE

Removal

1. Disconnect negative battery cable.
2. Raise and support vehicle.
3. Clean area around pan, then drain transmission fluid.
4. Remove oil pan and gasket, then the oil strainer.
5. Remove oil apply tube bracket attaching bolts, then the apply tube.
6. Remove oil tubes using a suitable screwdriver, then the manual detent spring.
7. Remove manual valve attaching bolts, then the manual valve assembly.
8. Remove valve body to cable bracket attaching bolt, then disconnect throttle cable.
9. Remove valve body attaching bolts, then valve body, governor, apply gasket and governor oil gasket.

Installation

1. Install governor oil gasket, then the governor and governor apply gasket.
2. Hold valve body in place, then manually retain cam in downward position and slip cable end into slot.
3. Position valve body into place, then insert and finger tighten 14 attaching bolts. **Torque** bolts to 89 inch lbs. **Attaching bolt lengths (mm) are indicated in Fig. 4.**
4. Align manual valve with pin on manual valve lever, then install manual valve body.
5. Insert and finger tighten attaching bolts, then **torque** to 89 inch lbs. **Attaching bolt lengths (mm) are indicated in Fig. 5.**
6. Install detent spring, then insert and finger tighten attaching bolts. **Torque** attaching bolts to 89 inch lbs.
7. Ensure manual lever is in contact with center of roller at tip of detent spring, then install oil tubes.
8. Install apply tube bracket, then the oil strainer.
9. Insert magnet into pan, then install oil pan with new gasket.
10. Insert oil pan attaching bolts, then **torque** to 44 inch lbs.
11. Install drain plug with new gasket, then **torque** to 29 ft. lbs.
12. Fill transaxle to specifications, then ensure proper fluid level.

THROTTLE CABLE, REPLACE

Removal

1. Disconnect negative battery cable.
2. Loosen throttle valve cable jamb nuts.
3. Disconnect throttle cable from bracket and throttle plate.
4. Remove neutral start and back-up switch.
5. Remove valve body as previously described, then throttle cable end from throttle pressure valve cam.
6. Pull cable from transaxle case.

Installation

1. Insert cable into transaxle case, then install retaining plate and bolt.
2. Install valve body as previously de-

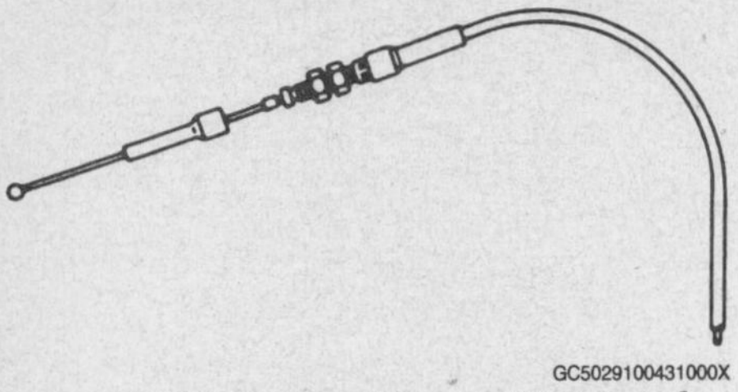

GC5029100431000X

Fig. 6 Throttle cable positioning for stopper installation

scribed, then position cable stop for adjustment reference as follows. **Cable stop is not staked in place on replacement cable.**

a. Bend cable to a radius of approximately 7.87 inches as shown, **Fig. 6.**
b. Lightly pull inner cable from housing until a slight resistance is felt, then hold in position.
c. Stake stopper onto inner cable so that .031-.059 inch clearance exists between stop and cable housing.

3. Connect throttle cable to throttle linkage, then adjust cable as previously described.
4. Install neutral safety switch, then the manual shift lever. Adjust switch as previously described.
5. Ensure transaxle fluid level is to specifications, then road test vehicle.

GOVERNOR VALVE, REPLACE

Removal

1. Raise and support vehicle.
2. Remove transaxle cover, then the lefthand driveshaft.
3. Remove governor cover, then the O-ring.
4. Remove governor body with thrust washer.
5. Remove washer, then the governor body adapter.

Installation

1. Install governor body adapter, then the governor body with thrust washer.
2. Install governor cover with O-ring, then the lefthand driveshaft.
3. Install transaxle dust cover, then ensure transaxle fluid level is to specifications.
4. Road test vehicle.

SECOND BRAKE SERVO ASSEMBLY, REPLACE

Removal

1. Disconnect negative battery cable.
2. Raise and support vehicle, then drain fluid from transaxle.
3. Remove shift cable bracket at transaxle.
4. Install second brake servo compressor tool No. J-35549-A or equivalent and compress second brake servo.
5. Remove second brake servo snap ring and second brake servo compressor.
6. Remove cover.
7. Remove piston, then the outer spring.

Installation

1. Insert piston, less outer spring, then install snap ring.
2. Install brake apply rod tool No. J-35679, then observe groove on plunger of tool.
3. Push button on tool, **Fig. 7**. This allows tool to push brake apply rod into case. If groove is visible, piston stroke is correct (.059-.118 inch). If stroke is greater than specified, replace piston rod with 2.870 inch or 2.811 inch rod as needed.
4. Remove snap ring, then install piston and outer spring.
5. Install spring compressor tool No. J-35549 to compress spring, then insert snap ring.
6. Install cover, then the shift cable bracket.
7. Lower vehicle.

TRANSAXLE REPLACE

1. Install engine support fixture No. J-28467-A or equivalent.
2. Remove battery hold-down, battery and battery tray.
3. Remove air cleaner assembly and neutral start switch connector.
4. Disconnect ground cable at transaxle and throttle cable from throttle body.
5. Disconnect transmission cooling lines and plug them to prevent excess leakage.
6. Remove shift cable retainer and end clip, then disconnect shift cable from brackets and lay aside.
7. Disconnect upper shift cable bracket from transaxle.
8. Remove left transaxle mount brace and through bolt.

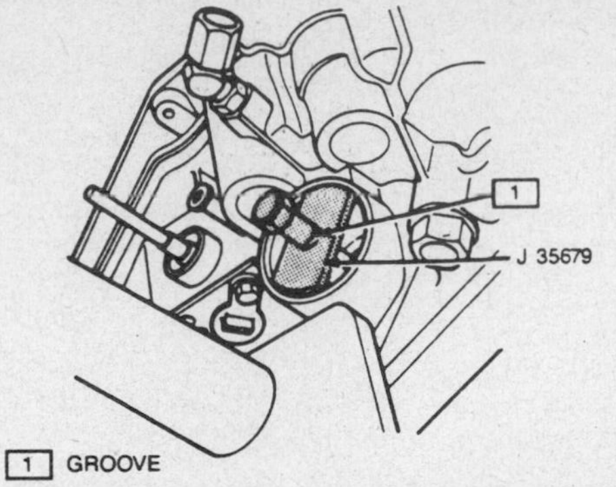
1
J 35679
1 GROOVE

GC5028900432000X

Fig. 7 Second brake servo plunger installation

9. Remove two upper transaxle to engine bolts, upper starter bolts and speedometer cable.
10. Raise and support vehicle.
11. Remove right and left lower stone shields and drain transaxle oil.
12. Disconnect starter electrical connectors and remove bottom starter bolt and starter.
13. Remove front drive axles as described in "Front Drive Axles section."
14. Remove three center crossmember to radiator support bolts and front and center mount bolt shields.
15. Remove two front mount bolts, two center mount bolts, two rear mount nuts and two center crossmember to main crossmember bolts.
16. Remove three exhaust hanger bracket nuts and exhaust hanger, eight main crossmember to underbody bolts and two lower A-frame bracket to underbody bolts, then remove main crossmember.
17. Remove front mount through bolt and mount, front mount bracket and center mount from transaxle.
18. Remove torque converter bolt shield and torque converter to flywheel bolts.
19. Remove two lower transaxle bracket to mount bolts, then lower vehicle.
20. Remove remaining transaxle mount to bracket bolt, then lower transaxle with engine support fixture to gain necessary clearance to remove transaxle.
21. Raise and support vehicle.
22. Support transaxle with a suitable transmission jack, then remove front and rear lower transaxle to engine bolts.
23. Remove transaxle from vehicle.
24. Reverse procedure to install, referring to "Tightening Specifications" chart for proper bolt and nut torques.

TIGHTENING SPECIFICATIONS

Component	Torque/Ft. Lbs.
Cable End Bolt	15
Center Crossmember To Main Crossmember Bolts	45
Center Crossmember To Radiator Support Bolts	45
Center Mount Mounting Nuts	45
Center Mount To Transaxle Bolts	45
Differential Check Fill Plug	29
Differential Fill And Drain Plug	29
Exhaust Hanger Bracket Nuts	115①
Fill Tube To Case Bolt	97①
Front, Center And Rear Mount Bolts	45
Front Mount Bracket Bolts	13
Front Mount Bolts	45
Front Mount Through Bolt	64
Governor Cover Bolts	97①
Left Mount Brace Bolts	13
Left Mount Through Bolt	66
Lower A-Frame To Underbody Bolts	94
Lower Mount To Bracket Bolts	45
Lower Starter Motor Bolt	29
Lower Transaxle Mount Bolts	45
Main Crossmember To Underbody Bolts	152
Manual Lever Cap Nut	89①

Component	Torque/Ft. Lbs.
Manual Valve and Manual Detent Spring Bolts	89①
Mount Cover And Brace Bolts	13
Neutral Start Switch Bolts	69①
Oil Apply Tube Retainer Bolts	44①
Oil Cooler Line Nuts	20
Oil Cooler Pipe Fittings	15
Oil Filter Bolts	89①
Oil Pan Drain Plug Bolt	29
Oil Pan Bolts	44①
Oil Pump Bolts	16
Rear Mount Through Bolt	64
Shift Control Assembly Bolts	15
Shift Control Bolts	15
Side Case Cover Bolts	44①
Throttle Valve Cable Housing Locknuts	89①
Torque Converter Bolts	31
Transaxle Fluid Drain Plug	29
Transaxle To Engine Bolts	34
Upper Mount To Bracket Bolts	45
Upper Starter Bolt	29
Upper Transaxle Mount Bracket Bolt	45
Valve Body Bolts	89①
Wheel Lug Nuts	76

①—Inch lbs.

Aisin Warner A240E Automatic Transaxle

INDEX

IDENTIFICATION

The transaxle identification number is stamped on top of the transaxle rear cover at the rear of the transaxle, **Fig. 1.**

DESCRIPTION

The A240E 4 speed automatic transaxle is used on the 1992 Geo Prizm. The torque converter is equipped with an Electronic lock-up clutch and is computer controlled.

TROUBLESHOOTING

FLUID DISCOLORED OR SMELLS BURNED

1. Contaminated fluid.
2. Faulty torque converter.
3. Faulty transaxle.

VEHICLE DOES NOT MOVE IN ANY RANGE

1. Faulty control cable.
2. Faulty valve body or primary regulator.
3. Faulty parking pawl.
4. Faulty torque converter.
5. Blocked oil pump strainer.
6. Faulty transaxle.

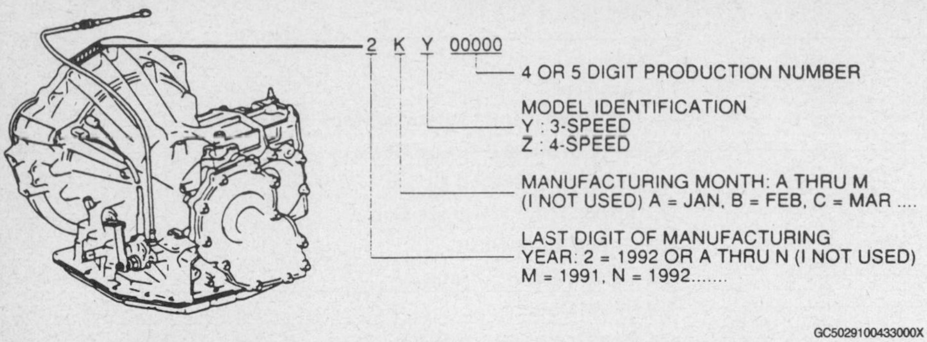
2 K Y 00000
4 OR 5 DIGIT PRODUCTION NUMBER
MODEL IDENTIFICATION
Y : 3-SPEED
Z : 4-SPEED
MANUFACTURING MONTH: A THRU M
(I NOT USED) A = JAN, B = FEB, C = MAR ....
LAST DIGIT OF MANUFACTURING
YEAR: 2 = 1992 OR A THRU N (I NOT USED)
M = 1991, N = 1992.......
GC5029100433000X

Fig. 1 Transaxle identification number plate location

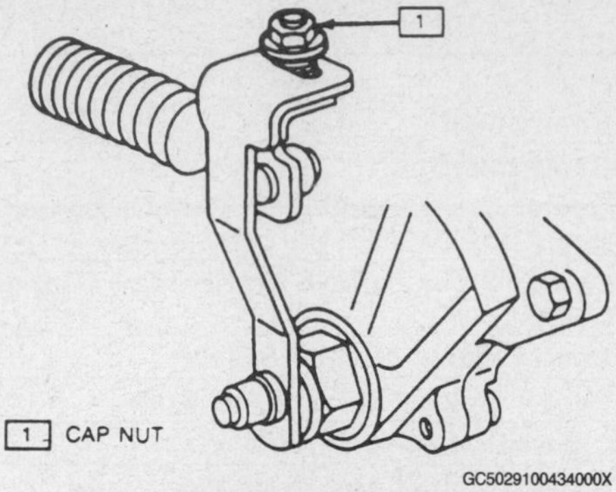
1
1 CAP NUT
GC5029100434000X

Fig. 2 Manual shift linkage adjustment

INCORRECT SHIFT LEVER POSITION

1. Improperly adjusted transaxle linkage.
2. Faulty manual valve or lever.
3. Faulty transaxle.

HARSH ENGAGEMENT INTO ANY DRIVE RANGE

1. Improperly adjusted throttle cable.
2. Faulty valve body or primary regulator.
3. Faulty transaxle.

DELAYED UPSHIFTS & DOWNSHIFTS

1. Improperly adjusted throttle cable.
2. Faulty valve body.
3. Faulty solenoid valve.
4. Faulty governor.

SLIPS ON UPSHIFTS OR SHUDDERS ON TAKE-OFF

1. Improperly adjusted transaxle control cable.
2. Improperly adjusted throttle cable.
3. Faulty valve body.
4. Faulty solenoid valve.
5. Faulty transaxle.

NO HOLD IN PARK

1. Improperly adjusted transaxle control linkage.
2. Faulty parking pawl.

DRAG OR BINDING ON UPSHIFTS

1. Improperly adjusted transaxle control cable.
2. Faulty valve body.
3. Faulty transaxle.

NO LOCK-UP IN 2ND, 3RD OR OVERDRIVE

1. Faulty electronic control.
2. Faulty valve body.
3. Faulty solenoid valve.
4. Faulty transaxle.

HARSH DOWNSHIFT

1. Improperly adjusted throttle cable.
2. Faulty valve body.
3. Faulty transaxle.

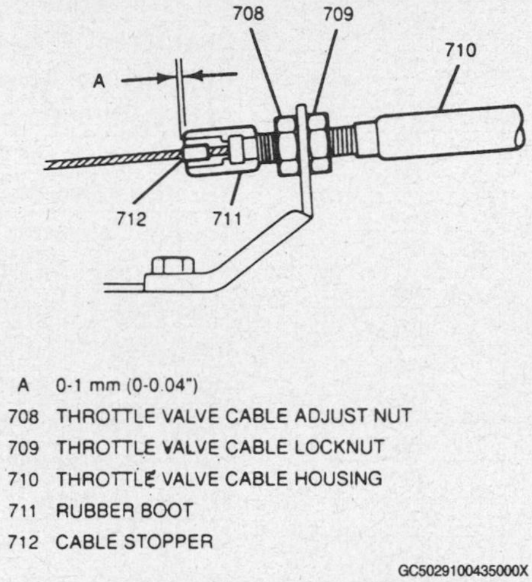
708
709
710
A
712
711
A 0-1 mm (0-0.04")
708 THROTTLE VALVE CABLE ADJUST NUT
709 THROTTLE VALVE CABLE LOCKNUT
710 THROTTLE VALVE CABLE HOUSING
711 RUBBER BOOT
712 CABLE STOPPER
GC5029100435000X

Fig. 3 Throttle cable adjustment

NO DOWNSHIFT WHEN COASTING

1. Faulty governor.
2. Faulty valve body.
3. Faulty solenoid valve.
4. Faulty electronic control.

INCORRECT DOWNSHIFT

1. Improperly adjusted throttle cable.
2. Faulty governor.
3. Faulty valve body.
4. Faulty transaxle.
5. Faulty solenoid valve.
6. Faulty electronic control.

NO KICKDOWN

1. Improperly adjusted throttle cable.
2. Faulty governor.
3. Faulty solenoid valve.
4. Faulty electronic control.
5. Faulty valve body.

NO ENGINE BRAKING IN 2 OR L RANGE

1. Faulty solenoid valve.
2. Faulty electronic control.
3. Faulty valve body.
4. Faulty transaxle.

MAINTENANCE

FLUID CHANGE

Refer to "Lubricant Data Chart" in the appropriate chassis chapter of this manual for transmission fluid specifications.

1. Raise and support vehicle, then position suitable drain pan under transaxle oil pan.
2. Remove transaxle drain plug and allow fluid to drain, then reinstall drain plug and **torque** to 13 ft. lbs.
3. Add fluid to transaxle.
4. Start engine and move selector lever through all selector lever positions, then return to Park.
5. With engine idling, check fluid level and add fluid as necessary.

ADJUSTMENTS

MANUAL LINKAGE

1. Loosen swivel nut on lever, then push manual lever fully forward toward the right side of the vehicle, **Fig. 2.**
2. Return lever two notches to the Neutral position, then place selector lever in Neutral position.
3. Shift manual shift lever to N range, then tighten swivel nut.

THROTTLE CABLE

1. Hold accelerator pedal in the fully depressed position, the loosen cable adjusting nuts, **Fig. 3.**
2. Adjust cable to obtain .04 inch clearance between end of boot and stopper on cable, then tighten adjusting nut.
3. Fully depress accelerator pedal and recheck adjustment, then road test vehicle.

NEUTRAL SAFETY SWITCH

1. Loosen neutral safety switch attaching bolts.
2. Place selector lever in the Neutral position.
3. Disconnect electrical connector.
4. Align groove with neutral basic line, **Fig. 4.**
5. **Torque** switch attaching bolts to 44 inch lbs.
6. Connect electrical connector and check to ensure engine starts on when selector lever is Neutral or Park.

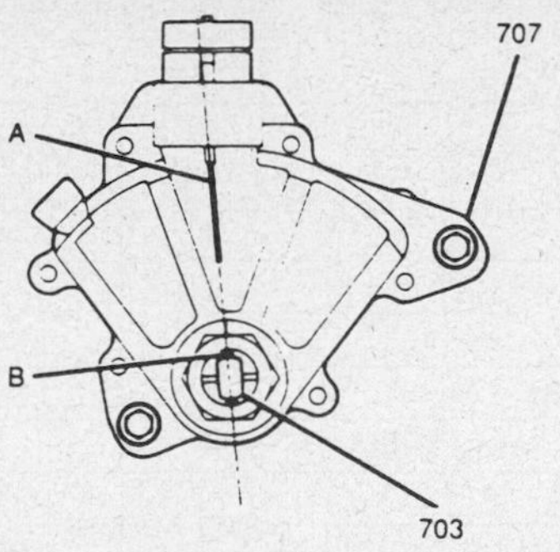
707
A
B
703
A NEUTRAL BASIC LINE
B GROOVE
703 MANUAL SHIFT SHAFT
707 NEUTRAL SAFETY SWITCH
GC5029100436000X

Fig. 4 Neutral safety switch adjustment

IN-VEHICLE REPAIRS

VALVE BODY, REPLACE

Removal

1. Raise and support vehicle.
2. Drain fluid from transaxle and remove oil pan.
3. Remove oil strainer, oil tube bracket and five oil tubes.
4. Remove manual valve detent spring and three solenoid electrical connectors.
5. Remove 12 valve body bolts and lower valve body slightly to unhook throttle valve cable end from throttle valve cam.
6. Disconnect manual valve connecting rod, then remove valve body, valve body gasket and intermediate clutch apply passage O-ring seal.

Installation

1. Install a new intermediate clutch apply passage O-ring seal.
2. Install a new valve body gasket on valve body.
3. Install valve body to transaxle attaching manual valve and throttle cable valve.
4. Install 12 valve body bolts and **torque** to 84 inch lbs.
5. Connect three solenoid electrical connectors and install manual valve detent spring. **Torque** manual valve detent spring retaining bolts to 84 inch lbs.
6. Install five oil tubes and oil tube clamp bolt and bracket. **Torque** oil tube clamp bolt to 84 inch lbs.
7. Install oil strainer and new gasket.
8. Install oil pan and fill transaxle to proper level.

THROTTLE VALVE CABLE, REPLACE

Removal

1. Disconnect throttle valve cable from engine throttle body and retaining clamps.
2. Raise and support vehicle.
3. Drain fluid from transaxle, then remove oil pan and neutral safety switch.
4. Disconnect throttle cable retaining plate from transaxle.
5. Pull throttle cable out of transaxle case and remove from vehicle.

Installation

1. Install throttle cable into transaxle.
2. Connect throttle cable retaining plate to transaxle and **torque** bolts to 53 inch lbs.
3. Stake stopper to inner cable as follows:
   a. Bend cable until there is a 7.87 inch radius, **Fig. 5.**
   b. Pull lightly on inner cable until a slight resistance is felt.
   c. Stake the stopper .031-.059 inch from end of outer cable while holding inner cable.
4. Install transaxle oil pan and neutral safety switch.
5. Lower vehicle, then Install throttle valve cable to engine throttle body and retaining clamps and adjust as described under "Throttle Cable Adjust."
6. Fill transaxle to proper level.

SHIFT LOCK MODULE, SOLENOID & SWITCH, REPLACE

Removal

1. Disconnect battery ground cable.
2. Remove five retaining screws from rear center console and rear center console.
3. Remove two retaining screws from shift selector cover and shift selector cover.
4. Disconnect shift lock control module electrical connectors.
5. Remove shift lock control module retaining screw and shift lock control module.
6. Disconnect shift lock solenoid and shift lock switch electrical connectors.
7. Remove two shift lock solenoid retaining screws and shift lock solenoid.
8. Remove two shift lock control switch retaining screws and shift lock control switch.

Installation

1. Install shift lock control switch and two retaining screws.
2. Install shift lock solenoid and two retaining screws.
3. Connect shift lock solenoid and shift lock switch electrical connectors.

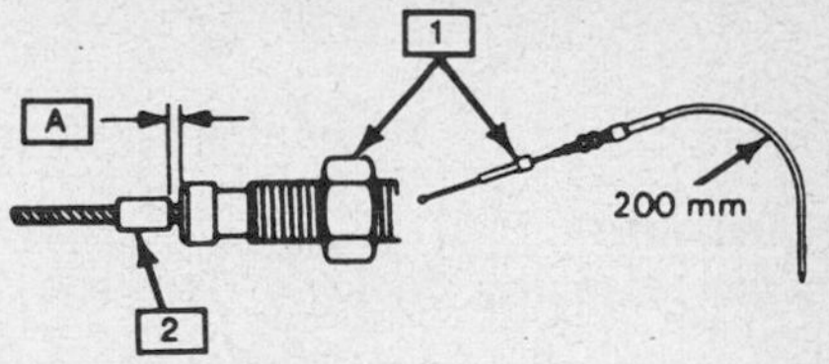
1
A
200 mm
2
A 0.8-1.5 mm (0.031-0.059")
1 THROTTLE CABLE
2 CABLE STOPPER
GC5029100437000X

Fig. 5 Throttle cable positioning for stopper installation

4. Install shift lock control module and retaining screw.
5. Connect shift lock control electrical connectors.
6. Install shift selector cover and two retaining screws.
7. Install rear center console and five retaining screws.
8. Connect battery ground cable.

TRANSAXLE REPLACE

1. Disconnect battery ground cable.
2. Remove air cleaner assembly.
3. Disconnect transaxle solenoids, neutral safety switch and speed sensor electrical connectors.
4. Disconnect speedometer cable.
5. Disconnect throttle cable from engine throttle body and retaining clamps.
6. Remove thermostat housing to transaxle case retaining bolt and nut.
7. Remove two top transaxle to engine bolts.
8. Disconnect battery ground cable from transaxle case.
9. Install engine support fixture tool No. J-28467-A or equivalent.
10. Raise and support vehicle, then drain fluid from transaxle.
11. Remove dust covers from crossmember.
12. Remove front wheel and tire assemblies.
13. Remove front drive axles as described in "Front Drive Axles section."
14. Remove front and rear mount retaining bolts, control cable clamp bolts and center crossmember.
15. Disconnect and cap oil cooler lines.
16. Disconnect front exhaust pipe from exhaust manifold.
17. Remove shifter control cable to shift lever clip.
18. Remove shifter control cable bracket retaining bolts and set cable aside.
19. Remove starter and engine to trans axle support bracket.
20. Remove flywheel inspection cover and six torque converter bolts.
21. Remove left engine mount.
22. Place suitable transmission jack under transaxle and remove front and rear engine block to transaxle bolts, then remove transaxle.
23. Reverse procedure to install, referring to "Tightening specifications" chart for proper bolt and nut torques.

TIGHTENING SPECIFICATIONS

Component	Torque/Ft. Lbs.
Battery Negative Cable To Transaxle Case Bolt	20
Center Crossmember Bolts	29
Control Cable Bracket Bolts	20
Engine to Transaxle Bolts	47
Engine to Transaxle Support Bracket Nut And Bolt	38
Flywheel Inspection Cover Bolts	20
Front and Rear Engine Mount Bolts	29
Left Engine Mount Bolts	38
Manual Shift Lever Nut	22①
Manual Shift Shaft Nut	62①
Manual Valve Detent Spring Bolts	84①
Neutral Safety Switch Bolts	44①

Component	Torque/Ft. Lbs.
Oil Pan Bolts	44①
Oil Pan Drain Plug	13
Oil Tube Clamp Bolts	84①
Pressure Detection Plug	80①
Shifter Control Cable Clamp Bolts	10
Shifter Control Bolts	20
Strainer Screen Bolts	84①
Thermostat Housing To Transaxle Case Nut	20
Throttle Cable Retaining Plate Bolt	53①
Torque Converter Bolts	20
Valve Body Bolts	84①
Wheel Lug Nuts	76

①—Inch lbs.

Aisin Warner A245E Automatic Transaxle

INDEX

IDENTIFICATION

The A245E 4-speed automatic transaxle identification number is located on top of the transaxle case in front of the vent tube, **Fig. 1.**

DESCRIPTION

The A245E is used on the 1993-94 Geo Prizm. The A245E transaxle is an improved version of the A240E transaxle. It is equipped with an integral lock-up mechanism and fuel consumption has been reduced and power output increased by more precise shift control and monitoring of the throttle opening angle.

TROUBLESHOOTING

FLUID DISCOLORED OR BURNED

1. Contaminated fluid.
2. Faulty torque converter.
3. Faulty transaxle.

VEHICLE DOES NOT MOVE IN ANY DRIVE GEAR

1. Incorrectly adjusted transaxle control cable.
2. Faulty valve body or primary regulator.
3. Faulty transaxle.

VEHICLE DOES NOT MOVE IN ANY RANGE

1. Faulty park lock pawl.
2. Faulty valve body or Primary regulator.
3. Faulty torque converter.
4. Broken converter driveplate.
5. Blocked oil pump intake strainer.
6. Faulty transaxle.

INCORRECT SHIFT LEVER POSITION

1. Incorrectly adjusted transaxle control cable.
2. Faulty manual valve and lever.
3. Faulty transaxle.

HARSH ENGAGEMENT INTO ANY DRIVE RANGE

1. Incorrectly adjusted throttle cable.
2. Incorrectly adjusted transaxle control cable.
3. Faulty valve body or primary regulator.
4. Faulty accumulator pistons.
5. Faulty transaxle.

DELAYED UPSHIFTS & DOWNSHIFTS

1. Incorrectly adjusted throttle cable.
2. Faulty governors.
3. Faulty valve body.
4. Faulty solenoid valve.

SLIPS ON UPSHIFTS OR SHUDDERS ON TAKEOFFS

1. Incorrectly adjusted transaxle control cable.

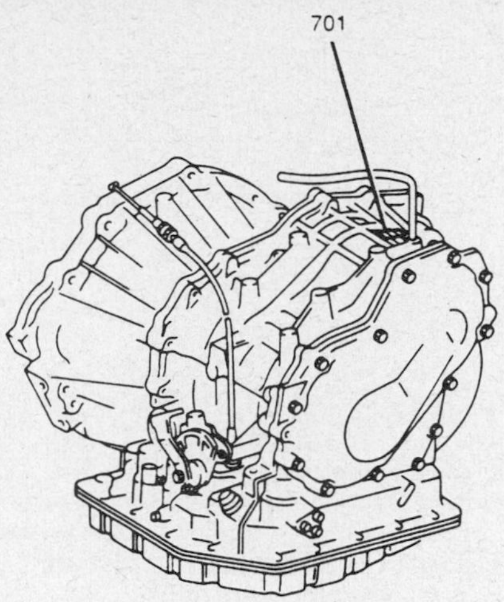
701

701 TRANSAXLE IDENTIFICATION NUMBER LOCATION

GC5029300438000X

Fig. 1 Transaxle identification number location.

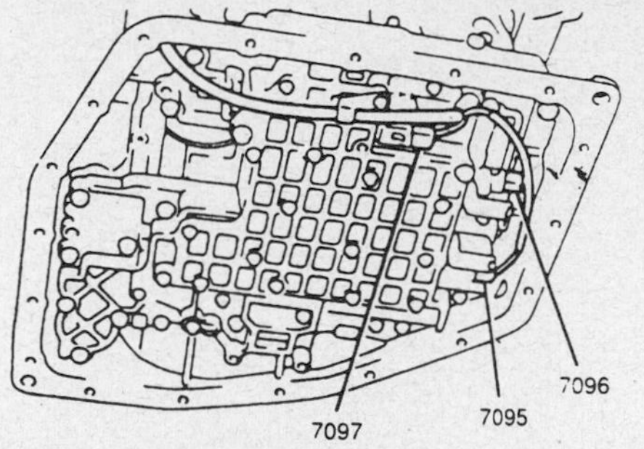
7096
7097
7095

7095 SHIFT SOLENOID NO. 1 ELECTRICAL CONNECTOR

7096 SHIFT SOLENOID NO. 2 ELECTRICAL CONNECTOR

7097 TORQUE CONVERTER CLUTCH (TCC) SOLENOID ELECTRICAL CONNECTOR

GC5029300439000X

Fig. 2 Solenoid electrical connectors.

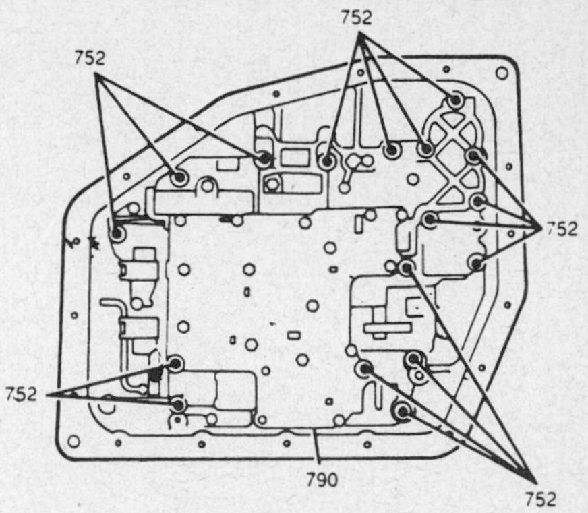
752
752
752
752
790
752

752 VALVE BODY ASSEMBLY BOLTS

790 VALVE BODY ASSEMBLY

GC5029300440000X

Fig. 3 Valve body bolt location.

2. Incorrectly adjusted throttle cable.
3. Faulty valve body.
4. Faulty transaxle.
5. Faulty solenoid valve.

DRAG OR BINDING ON UPSHIFTS

1. Incorrectly adjusted transaxle control cable.
2. Faulty valve body.
3. Faulty transaxle.

HARSH DOWNSHIFT

1. Incorrectly adjusted throttle cable.
2. Faulty accumulator pistons.
3. Faulty valve body.
4. Faulty transaxle.

NO DOWNSHIFT WHEN COASTING

1. Faulty governor.
2. Faulty valve body.
3. Faulty solenoid valve.
4. Faulty electronic controls.

INCORRECT DOWNSHIFT

1. Incorrectly adjusted throttle cable.
2. Faulty governor.
3. Faulty valve body.
4. Faulty transaxle.
5. Faulty solenoid valve.
6. Faulty electronic control.

NO LOCK-UP IN 2, 3 OR O/D

1. Faulty valve body.
2. Faulty transaxle.
3. Faulty solenoid valve.
4. Faulty electronic control.
5. Faulty torque converter.

NO KICKDOWN

1. Incorrectly adjusted throttle cable.
2. Faulty governor.
3. Faulty valve body.
4. Faulty solenoid valve.
5. Faulty electronic control.

NO ENGINE BRAKING IN 2

1. Faulty valve body.
2. Faulty transaxle.
3. Faulty solenoid valve.
4. Faulty electronic control.

NO HOLD IN P

1. Incorrectly adjusted transaxle control cable.
2. Faulty parking lock pawl and rod.

NO CENTER DIFFERENTIAL CONTROL

1. Faulty electronic controls.
2. Faulty valve body.
3. Faulty transfer.
4. Faulty C/D clutch.

MAINTENANCE

FLUID CHECK

1. Start engine, allow transaxle fluid to reach 158-176°F.
2. Position vehicle on level surface, then set parking brake.
3. With engine idling, brake pedal depressed, move shift lever through all positions.
4. Remove transaxle dipstick, wipe clean, then replace.
5. Remove dipstick again, check fluid at HOT level.
6. Refer to "Lubricant Data" for capacities.

FLUID CHANGE

Refer to "Lubricant Data Chart" in the appropriate chassis chapter of this manual for transmission fluid specifications.

1. Drain transaxle fluid.
2. Install drain plug and new gasket.
3. Add fluid through filler tube. Do not overfill.
4. Start engine, ensure smooth shift operation in all positions.
5. With engine at idle, check fluid COOL level, fill as required.
6. Allow vehicle to reach normal operating temperatures, then recheck level.

IN-VEHICLE REPAIRS

VALVE BODY & ACCUMULATOR, REPLACE

1. Disconnect battery ground cable, then raise and support vehicle.
2. Remove six bolts and left splash shield from vehicle.
3. Place a drain pan or suitable container under transaxle fluid pan, then remove drain plug, drain transaxle fluid and remove transaxle fluid pan. **When removing transaxle fluid pan, use caution to not damage mating surfaces. Use a rubber mallet and wooden block if pan is frozen to transaxle; do not use metal objects (crow bar, screwdriver, etc.) to free pan.**
4. Remove filter and screen from valve body, then disconnect solenoid electrical connectors from shift solenoid Nos. 1 and 2 and TCC solenoid, **Fig. 2.**
5. Remove bolt and solenoid wire harness clip from valve body, then detent spring.
6. Remove TV cable from throttle valve cam. **The B2 accumulator, check ball and spring may drop from transaxle during valve body removal. The B2 accumulator is under intense spring pressure and may push valve body down after valve body bolts are loosened.**
7. Remove seventeen bolts **Fig. 3** and valve body from transaxle while simultaneously disconnecting manual valve link from manual lever.
8. Remove check ball body and spring from transaxle, then B2 accumulator piston and spring. When using compressed air to remove components from transaxle case, air pressure should never exceed 14 psi.
9. Remove C2, C1 and C3 accumulator pistons and springs from transaxle

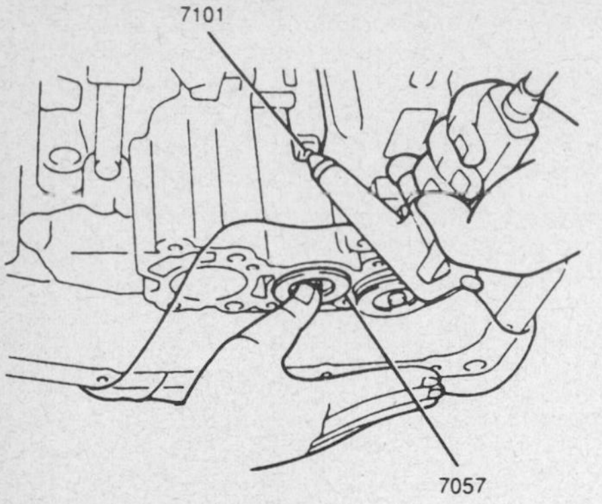
7101
7057

7057 C2 ACCUMULATOR PISTON
7101 C2 ACCUMULATOR APPLY PASSAGE

GC5029300441000X

Fig. 4 C2 accumulator piston & spring removal.

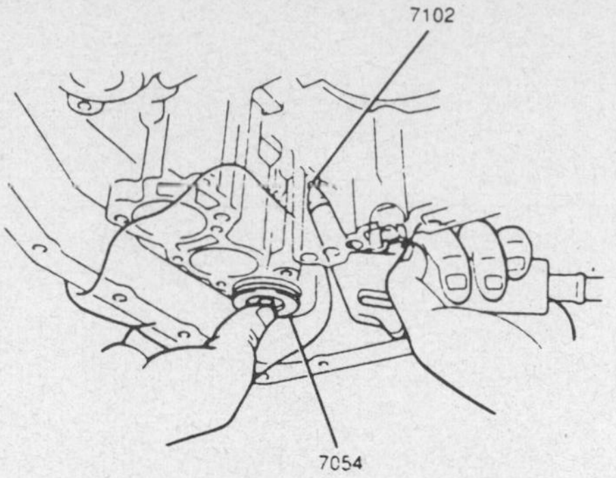
7102
7054

7054 C1 ACCUMULATOR PISTON
7102 C1 ACCUMULATOR APPLY PASSAGE

GC5029300442000X

Fig. 5 C1 accumulator piston & spring removal.

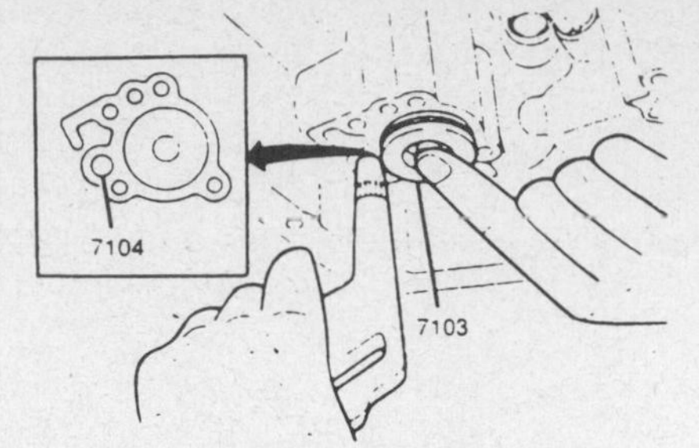
7104
7103

7103 C3 ACCUMULATOR PISTON
7104 C3 ACCUMULATOR APPLY PASSAGE

GC5029300443000X

Fig. 6 C3 accumulator piston & spring removal.

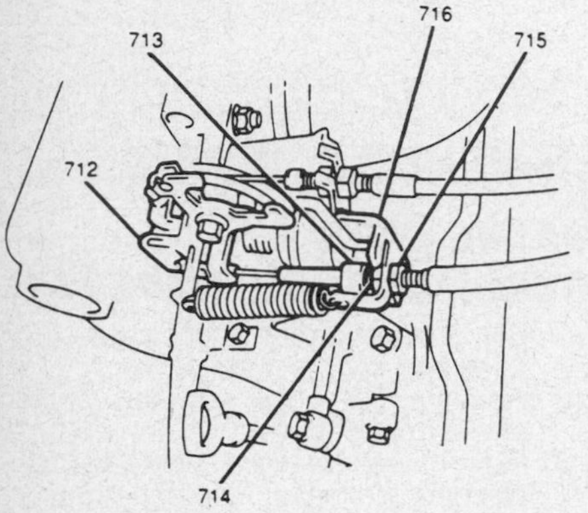
716
713
715
712
714

712 THROTTLE VALVE LINKAGE
713 OUTER CABLE BOOT
714 TV CABLE ADJUST NUT
715 TV CABLE LOCKNUT
716 TV CABLE BRACKET

GC5029300444000X

Fig. 7 TV cable locknut & adjust nut location.

case by slowly applying low pressure compressed air into accumulator apply passages, **Figs. 4 through 6.**

10. Reverse procedure to install. Prior to installation, inspect transaxle case for nicks or scars, accumulator seals for cuts or damage and accumulator pistons for cracks or porosity.

TV CABLE, REPLACE

1. Disconnect battery ground cable, then loosen TV cable locknut and adjust nut, **Fig. 7.**
2. Disconnect TV cable from throttle valve linkage and TV cable bracket, then from cable guide bracket at top of transaxle.
3. Raise and support vehicle and remove left splash shield.
4. Disconnect Park/Neutral Switch from transaxle, then place a drain pan or suitable container under transaxle fluid pan.
5. Drain transaxle fluid, then remove transaxle pan.
6. Disconnect TV cable from throttle valve cam at valve body, then remove cable retaining bolt and cable.
7. Inspect TV cable for fraying, kinks, excessive wear or damage.
8. **New TV cables do not have a staked TV cable stopper. A new stopper must be staked if using a new cable.** To stake cable stopper, bend cable to a radius of approximately 7.87 inches as shown, **Fig. 8.** Lightly pull inner cable from housing until a slight resistance is felt, then hold in position. Stake stopper onto inner cable so that .031-.059 inch clearance exists between stop and cable housing.
9. Reverse procedure to install.

TRANSAXLE

REPLACE

1. Remove battery, hold down bracket and tray.
2. Disconnect intake air temperature (IAT) connector from IAT sensor.
3. Remove air cleaner cover and air cleaner, then disconnect Park/Neutral Position switch connector.
4. Disconnect solenoid wire harness electrical connector from solenoid wire harness.
5. Remove ground strap from transaxle case and loosen TV cable locknut and adjust nut. Disconnect TV cable from throttle linkage and TV cable bracket.
6. Disconnect vehicle speed sensor (VSS) electrical connector.
7. Remove shift select cable from manual lever and shift select cable bracket.
8. Remove cable guise bracket from transaxle case, then remove two upper transaxle-to-engine bolts.
9. Remove upper starter motor retaining bolt from starter motor, then left transaxle mounting bracket reinforcement bolts and bracket from transaxle.
10. Remove one bolt from left transaxle mounting bracket, then raise and support vehicle and place a drain pan or suitable container under transaxle fluid pan. Drain transaxle fluid.

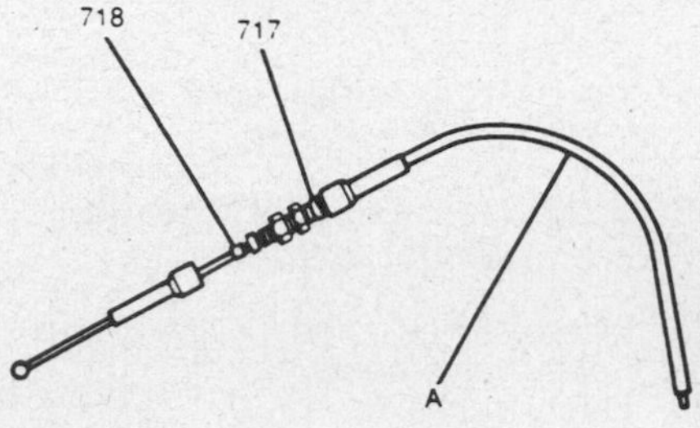
718
717
A

A 200 mm (7.87") RADIUS
717 TV CABLE
718 TV CABLE STOPPER

GC5029300445000X

Fig. 8 Bending TV cable for stopper staking.

11. Remove starter positive terminal nut, positive battery cable and electrical connector from starter, then lower starter retaining bolt and starter.
12. Remove both splash shields, then plug fluid cooler pipes to prevent transaxle fluid cooler leakage.
13. Remove inner and outer cooler hoses and pipes at transaxle.
14. Remove two bolts from left transaxle mounting bracket, then both front wheel assemblies.
15. Remove both drive axles as outlined under -Front Wheel Drive Axles.-
16. Remove exhaust pipe support bolts and center crossmember.
17. **On Federal models,** remove front exhaust pipe-to-three way catalytic converter mating flange bolts.
18. **On California models,** remove front exhaust pipe-to-warm up three way catalytic converter mating flange nuts and front exhaust pipe.
19. **On all models,** remove front exhaust pipe-to-exhaust manifold mating flange nuts and front exhaust pipe.
20. Remove enter crossmember plastic access cover from center crossmember, then bolts and nuts from front transaxle mount.
21. Remove front suspension crossmember and center crossmember, then

support transaxle with a suitable jack.

22. Remove flywheel access cover from engine rear end plate, then six flywheel-to-torque converter bolts from flywheel. Remove drain pan from underneath transaxle.
23. Remove two lower transaxle-to-engine bolts from transaxle. Disconnect transaxle from engine by carefully moving transaxle away from engine toward left side of engine compartment and very slowly lowering hydraulic jack ensuring no obstructions exist.
24. Reverse procedure to install.

TIGHTENING SPECIFICATIONS

Component	Torque/Ft. Lbs.
Air Cleaner Bolts	44①
Battery Ground Cable	11
Battery Hold-Down Bracket Bolt	44①
Battery Hold-Down Bracket Nut	71①
Center Crossmember Rear Bolt And Nuts	45
Detent Spring Bolts	89①
Fluid Filter Screen Bolts	89①
Flywheel To Torque Converter Bolts	14
Front Exhaust Pipe Support Nuts And Bolts	14
Front Exhaust Pipe To Exhaust Manifold Nuts	46
Front Exhaust Pipe To Three Way Catalytic Converter Mating Flange Bolts	32
Front Exhaust Pipe To Warm Up Three Way Catalytic Converter Mating Flange Nuts	46
Front Exhaust Pipe Support Bolts	14
Front Suspension Crossmember Bolts	152
Front Transaxle Mount Bolts	35
Front Transaxle Mount Through Bolt And Nut	64
Ground Strap Bolt	115①

Component	Torque/Ft. Lbs.
Left Transaxle Mount Through Bolt	64
Left Transaxle Mounting Bracket Bolts	35
Left Transaxle Mounting Bracket Reinforcement Bolts	15
Lower Engine Reinforcement Brace Bolts	47
Rear Transaxle Mount Nuts	42
Rear Transaxle Mount Through Bolt	64
Solenoid Wire Harness Clip Bolt	53①
Solenoid Wire Harness Retaining Bolt	53①
Splash Shield Bolts	44①
Starter Motor Positive Terminal Nut	44①
Starter Motor Retaining Bolts	29
Transaxle Fluid Drain Plug	13
Transaxle Fluid Pan Bolts	43①
Transaxle To Engine Bolts	47
TV Cable Guide Bracket Bolt	71①
TV Cable Locknut	71①
TV Cable Retaining Bolt	71①

①—Inch lbs.

Turbo Hydra-Matic 3T40 Automatic Transaxle

INDEX

IDENTIFICATION

This transaxle may be identified by a model tag attached to the case exterior, **Fig. 1.**

DESCRIPTION

This automatic transaxle consists primarily of a 3 element torque converter, compound planetary gear set and dual sprockets, drive link assembly and a pressure plate and damper assembly. A differential and final drive gear set is also incorporated in the transaxle case. Three multiple disc clutches, a roller clutch and a band provide the friction elements required to obtain the desired functions of the planetary gear set. Hydraulic pressure required to operate the friction elements and automatic control is provided by a vane type pump.

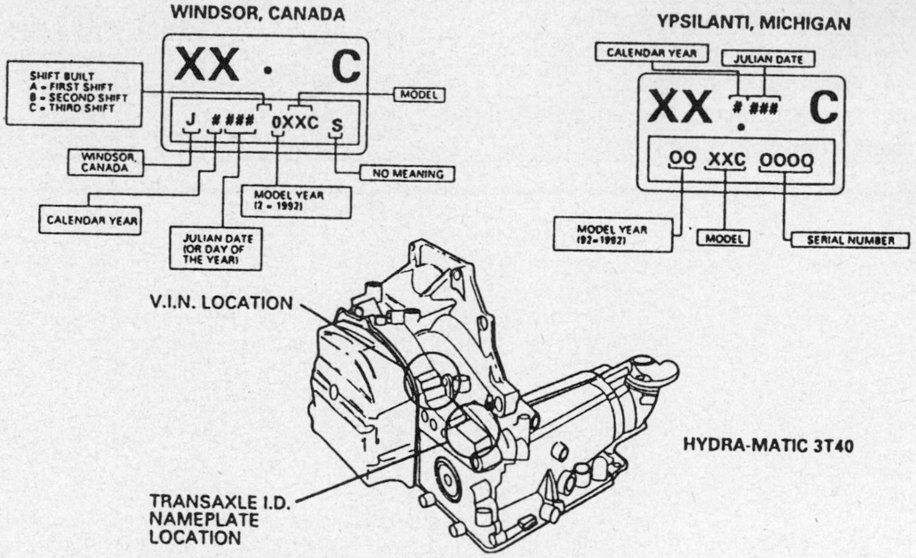

WINDSOR, CANADA
XX · C
SHIFT BUILT
A = FIRST SHIFT
B = SECOND SHIFT
C = THIRD SHIFT
J #### 0XXC S
MODEL
WINDSOR, CANADA
NO MEANING
MODEL YEAR (2 = 1992)
CALENDAR YEAR
JULIAN DATE (OR DAY OF THE YEAR)
YPSILANTI, MICHIGAN
CALENDAR YEAR
JULIAN DATE
XX #### C
OO XXC OOOO
MODEL YEAR (92=1992)
MODEL
SERIAL NUMBER
V.I.N. LOCATION
HYDRA-MATIC 3T40
TRANSAXLE I.D. NAMEPLATE LOCATION

TH5028800099000X

Fig. 1 Transaxle identification

TROUBLESHOOTING

Always check for the following conditions when troubleshooting any type of transaxle malfunction:

1. Incorrect oil level.
2. Improperly adjusted, disconnected, bound or broken TV cable.
3. Manual linkage improperly adjusted.
4. Incorrect oil pressure.

CHATTERS OR SLIPS IN FIRST GEAR

1. Low oil level
2. Restricted feed to forward clutch.
3. Burned clutch plates.
4. Drive sprocket support.
5. Incorrect case cover gasket.

NO REVERSE OR SLIPS IN REVERSE

1. Forward clutch:
   a. Burned clutch plates.
   b. Seal ring off piston.
   c. Exhaust check ball sticking.
2. Lo and reverse clutch:
   a. Housing cup plug assembly restricted or not fully seated.
   b. Leaking seals.
3. Low and reverse pipe O-ring seal damaged or missing.
4. Incorrect, damaged or leaking case to cover gasket.
5. Burned direct clutch plates.
6. Burned low and reverse clutch plates.
7. Low line pressure.

NO UPSHIFTS, DELAYED UPSHIFTS OR FULL THROTTLE SHIFTS

1. Governor or speed sensor:
   a. Cover worn.
   b. Thrust washer missing.
   c. Governor seal worn or cut.
   d. Governor spring not seated.
   e. Governor weights binding on pin.
   f. Ball missing.
   g. Governor driven gear stripped.

2. Intermediate servo:
   a. Wrong or sticking apply pin.
   b. Seals cut, damaged or missing.
   c. Porosity in case servo bore.
3. Control valve assembly:
   a. Valves sticking.
   b. Spacer plate gaskets leaking or incorrectly installed.
4. Valve body spacer:
   a. Governor feed orifice to 1-2 and 2-3 shift valve plugged.
   b. Drive to governor orifice plugged.
5. Burned or worn intermediate band.
6. Case cover:
   a. Porosity.
   b. Undrilled holes.
   c. Missing cup plugs.
   d. Second oil passage leaking.
7. Leaks in governor passage and/or pipe.

SLIPPING OR ROUGH 1-2 SHIFT

1. Intermediate servo:
   a. Seals cut, damaged or leaking.
   b. Piston damaged.
   c. Servo bore in case damaged.
   d. Apply pin too long or too short.
   e. Servo orifice bleed cup plug missing.
   f. Leak between servo apply pin and case.
2. Binding intermediate servo band apply pin.
3. Incorrect TV link or bent TV link.
4. Control valve assembly:
   a. TV plunger binding.
   b. Shift TV linkage binding.
   c. 1-2 accumulator valve binding.
5. 1-2 accumulator:
   a. Binding piston.
   b. Broken spring.
   c. Piston seal or groove damaged.
   d. Bore damaged.
6. Incorrect spacer plate or gasket, or gasket incorrectly installed.
7. Second oil passage leaking.

2-3 SHIFT ROUGH OR DELAYED

1. Plugged accumulator exhaust port.
2. Direct clutch exhaust No. 1 check ball mispositioned or missing.
3. Control valve assembly:
   a. Binding plunger and throttle valve.
   b. Binding shift TV valve.

2-3 SHIFT SOFT, SLIPS OR EARLY

1. Intermediate servo:
   a. Piston to case oil seal damaged.
   b. Servo piston damaged.
   c. Servo bore in case damaged.
2. Accumulator exhaust check valve not seating in case.
3. Spacer plate:
   a. Plugged or restricted direct clutch feed orifice.
   b. Incorrect case cover gaskets.
   c. Drive sprocket support passages interconnected, leaking or restricted.
   d. Sleeve loose or out of position.
4. Direct clutch:
   a. Check ball leaking.
   b. Check ball capsule damaged.
   c. Damaged or missing seals.
   d. Cracked or damaged housing or piston.
   e. Missing or incorrect apply ring.
   f. Wrong number of clutch plates.

NO 2-3 SHIFT OR 2-3 SHIFT DELAYED

1. Governor or speed sensor:
   a. Cover worn.
   b. Thrust washer missing.
   c. Governor seal worn or cut.
   d. Governor weights binding on pin.
   e. Governor spring not seated.
   f. Ball missing.
   g. Governor driven gear stripped.
2. Intermediate servo:
   a. Piston to case oil seal damaged.
   b. Servo piston damaged.
   c. Servo bore damaged.
   d. Servo orifice bleed cup plug missing in case.
3. Accumulator exhaust check valve is not seating in case.
4. Case:
   a. Direct clutch accumulator cup plug (third oil) leaking or missing.
   b. Case to governor shaft sleeve missing or damaged.
   c. Center gasket leaking.
5. Case cover:
   a. Case cover bolts loose.
   b. Drive sprocket support passages interconnected, leaking or restricted.
   c. Drive sprocket support oil seal rings damaged or missing.
   d. Sleeve loose or out of position.
6. Throttle lever and bracket assembly binding.
7. TV link incorrect, disconnected or binding.
8. Control valve assembly:
   a. 2-3 shift valve, 2-3 TV valve sticking.
   b. Shift TV valve sticking.
   c. Governor feed to 2-3 shift valve restricted.
   d. Direct clutch feed orifice restricted.
   e. No. 5 check ball missing or mislocated.
9. Spacer place or gaskets leaking, damaged or incorrectly installed.
10. Case to governor shaft sleeve damaged or missing.
11. Direct clutch:
    a. Check ball leaking.
    b. Check ball capsule damaged.
    c. Seals damaged or missing.
    d. Cracked or damaged housing or piston.
    e. Backing plate snap ring out of groove.
    f. Clutch plates damaged or missing.

DELAY IN DRIVE & REVERSE

1. Converter, drive sprocket and support bushings.
2. Turbine shaft:
   a. Scarf seals damaged or leaking.

NO DRIVE IN DRIVE OR INTERMEDIATE RANGE

1. Lo roller clutch springs missing, rollers galled or missing.

NO DRIVE IN ANY FORWARD RANGE

1. Manual linkage not moving manual valve.
2. Drive sprocket support:
   a. Drive oil passage blocked in driven sprocket support.
   b. Sleeve loose or mislocated.
3. Case cover drive oil passage leak.
4. Forward clutch plates burned or damaged.
5. Control valve assembly body pipe leaking or missing.

NO DRIVE IN ALL RANGES

1. Oil pressure:
   a. Pressure regulator valve sticking in bushing.
   b. Worn pump seals.
   c. Oil pump shaft broken.
2. Differential damaged or broken.
3. Drive link broken or interference between drive link and sprocket.
4. Manual valve retainer clip missing.
5. Input shaft loose or broken away from forward clutch drum.
6. Reaction carrier broken at Lo roller clutch cam.

NO DRIVE IN DRIVE RANGE

1. Forward clutch feed in input shaft restricted with cold engine at fast Idle.
2. Case cover:
   a. Leak between case cover and driven sprocket passages.
   b. Incorrect gaskets between case cover and driven sprocket support passages.

SECOND SPEED START

1. Governor springs distorted or out of position.
2. Governor weights binding on pin.
3. Control valve:
   a. 1-2 sift valve sticking in upshifted position.
   b. 1-2 throttle valve sticking in upshifted position.

SHIFTS 1-3, MISSES SECOND

1. Intermediate servo:
   a. Wrong or sticking apply pin.
   b. Seals cut, damaged or missing.
2. Accumulator exhaust valve sticking or not seating.
3. Control valve assembly 1-2 shift valve sticking.
4. Spacer plate:
   a. Gaskets incorrectly installed.
   b. Governor feed to 1-2 shift valve blocked.
   c. Intermediate band apply feed orifice blocked.
   d. Wrong spacer plate.
5. Intermediate servo apply passage blocked.

CONDITION	INSPECT COMPONENT	FOR CAUSE
NOISE IN ALL RANGES OR (A Whine Which May Be RPM Or Load Sensitive Or Ceases When The TCC Engages)	• Torque Converter (1)	– Verify noise internal to torque converter by placing left foot on brake with the gear selector in Drive and momentarily stall engine. Torque converter noise increases under load.
A High Pitch Whine Which Will Intensify With Engine RPM Or Is Oil Pressure Sensitive	• Oil Pump System	– Verify noise internal to oil pump during preliminary oil pressure check. An increase in line pressure will vary an oil pump noise.
A "Popping" Noise Similar To Popcorn Popping		– Pump cavitation–indicated by bubbles on fluid level indicator. – Transmission fluid strainer for filter seam leak. – Transmission fluid strainer seal for proper positioning or cut seal.
A Buzz Or High Frequency Rattle Sound	• Trace Cooler Pipes And Check For Binding Or Contact At The Radiator Other Than The Cooler Pipe Connectors	– Verify pressure buzz by watching for a needle vibration on the pressure gage. (Road test may be necessary.)
A Whine Or Growl That Increases And Fades With Vehicle Speed And Is Most Noticeable Under Light Throttle	• Drive Link Assembly System Verify noise from sprockets and/or drive link assembly (chain) by placing left foot on brake and moving gear selector from Park or Neutral to Drive or Reverse. If noise stops, check items below:	
	• Drive Link (Chain) Assembly	– Stretched.
	• Drive Sprocket And Driven Sprocket	– Teeth broken or sheared. – Bearing surfaces nicked or scored.
	• Drive And Driven Sprocket Support Bearing Assemblies	– Bearing race or roller bearing surfaces rough or pitted.
	• Drive Sprocket Support And Driven Sprocket Support	– Bearing outer race support rough or nicked.

TH5028800101010X

Fig. 2 Noise troubleshooting (Part 1 Of 2)

CONDITION	INSPECT COMPONENT	FOR CAUSE
NOISE IN 1ST OR REVERSE A Gear Noise, Or Whine Is Most Noticeable In First Or Reverse And Is Related To Vehicle Speed. Whine May Diminish Or Go Away After An Upshift To Second Gear.	• Input Gear Set • Input Internal Gear • Input Carrier Assembly • Input Sun Gear	– Gears worn or pitted. – Thrust washer mating surfaces rough or pitted.
NOISE IN SECOND	• Reaction Gear Set • Reaction Internal Gear • Reaction Carrier Assembly • Reaction Sun Gear	– Gears worn or pitted. – Thrust washer or thrust bearing mating surfaces rough or pitted.
	• Reaction Sun Gear To Reaction Internal Gear Thrust Bearing	– Thrust bearing races or roller bearing surfaces rough or pitted.
A Final Drive Noise, Or Hum, Is Most Noticeable Under Light Throttle Acceleration And/Or Turns Noise In First, Second, Or Third	• Final Drive Gear Set • Final Drive Internal Gear • Differential Carrier • Final Drive Sun Gear • Differential Pinions • Differential Side Gears	– Gears worn or pitted. – Thrust washer or thrust bearing mating surfaces rough or pitted.
	• Final Drive Sun Gear To Final Drive Internal Gear Thrust Bearing • Final Drive Sun Gear To Differential Carrier Thrust Bearing • Differential Carrier To Case Thrust Bearing	– Thrust bearing races or roller bearing surfaces rough or pitted.
A Light Metallic Rattle Noise Most Noticeable In Second Or Third Between 25 MPH And 40 MPH Under Coast Or Drive Operation	• Lo And Reverse Clutch Pack	– Steel plates not flat. – Clutch pack clearance. – Parallel grooved fiber plates.
	• Case	– Excess plate-to-case clearance due to case machining.

TH5029200101020X

Fig. 2 Noise troubleshooting (Part 2 Of 2)

6. Intermediate band improperly installed, burned or broken.

SHIFTS 3-1 AT HIGH SPEEDS FOR PASSING GEAR

1. Governor or speed sensor:
   a. Cover worn.
   b. Thrust washer missing.
   c. Governor seal worn or cut.
   d. Governor spring not seated.
   e. Governor weights binding on pin.
   f. Ball missing.
   g. Governor driven gear stripped.
2. Intermediate servo sticking.
3. Restriction in direct clutch orifice controlled by No. 2 check ball.
4. 1-2 accumulator piston missing or seal leaking.

NO FULL THROTTLE DOWNSHIFT

1. Throttle cable assembly not opening sufficiently.
2. Control valve assembly shift TV valve binding.
3. Spacer plate holes plugged, gasket not positioned correctly or damaged.

NO OVERRUN BRAKING IN LO

1. Manual linkage improperly adjusted.
2. LO and Reverse clutch pipe leaking.
3. Control valve assembly LO blow off valve damaged.

NO INTERMEDIATE RANGE

1. Intermediate servo oil seal ring missing or damaged.
2. Intermediate band mispositioned, broken or burned.
3. 1-2 accumulator piston or pin missing or damaged.

BINDS IN THIRD GEAR

1. Direct clutch center seal missing.

NOISE IN ALL RANGES

Refer to **Fig. 2**, for noise troubleshooting procedures.

MAINTENANCE

To check fluid, drive vehicle for at least 15 minutes to bring fluid to operating temperature (200°F). With vehicle on a level surface and engine idling in Park and parking brake applied, the level on the dipstick should be at the "Full" mark. To bring the fluid level from the ADD mark to the FULL mark requires one pint of fluid. If vehicle cannot be driven sufficiently to bring fluid to operating temperature, the level on the dipstick should be between the two dimples on the dipstick with fluid temperature at 70°F. Note that the two dimples are located above the FULL mark.

If additional fluid is required, use only Dexron II automatic transmission fluid.

An early change to a darker color from the usual red color and or a strong odor that is usually associated with overheated fluid is normal and should not be considered as a positive sign of required maintenance or unit failure.

When adding fluid, do not overfill, as foaming and loss of fluid through the vent may occur as the fluid heats up. Also, if fluid level is too low, complete loss of drive may occur especially when cold, which can cause transaxle failure.

Every 100,000 miles, the oil should be drained, the oil pan removed, the screen cleaned and fresh fluid added. For vehicles subjected to more severe use such as heavy city traffic especially in hot weather, prolonged periods of idling or towing, this maintenance should be performed every 15,000 miles.

FLUID CHANGE

Refer to "Lubricant Data Chart" in the appropriate chassis chapter of this manual for transmission fluid specifications.

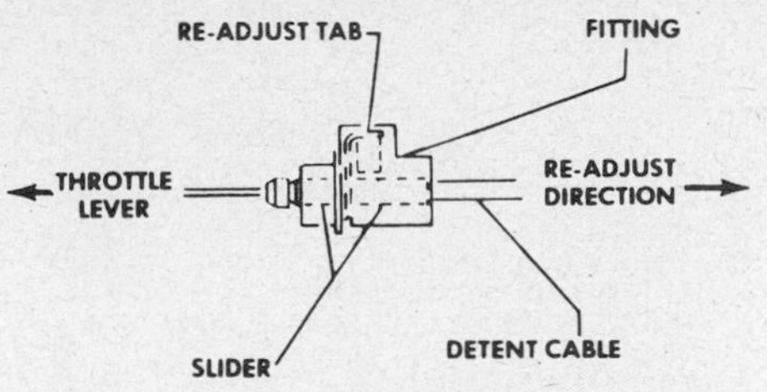
RE-ADJUST TAB
FITTING
THROTTLE LEVER
RE-ADJUST DIRECTION
SLIDER
DETENT CABLE

Copyrighted Material Reprinted with Permission from Hydra-Matic Div., GM Corp.

TH5028800107000X

Fig. 3 Detent/TV cable adjuster. Models w/lock tab adjusting cable

1. Raise and support vehicle, then position drain pan under oil pan.
2. Remove front and side oil pan attaching bolts, then loosen rear pan attaching bolts.
3. Carefully pry oil pan loose from transaxle case and allow fluid to drain.
4. Remove remaining attaching bolt, oil pan and gasket. Thoroughly clean pan before reinstalling.
5. Remove and discard screen and O-ring seal.
6. Install replacement screen and O-ring seal, locating screen against dipstick stop.
7. Install gasket on oil pan, then install pan and **torque** attaching bolts to 8 ft. lbs.
8. Lower vehicle and add fluid.
9. With selector in park, parking brake applied and engine at idle speed and operating temperature, check fluid level and add fluid as necessary. **Do not race engine. Move shift lever through ranges, then back to "Park position.**

ADJUSTMENTS

MANUAL LINKAGE

Beretta, Cavalier, Corsica, & Sunbird

1. Position shift lever to Neutral.
2. Install cable to bracket and to column or floorshift lever.
3. Snap cable onto transaxle shift lever, then tighten nut with lever held out of Park.

Except Beretta, Cavalier, Corsica & Sunbird

1. Lift shift cable locking button up.
2. Position transaxle shift lever to Neutral by rotating selector shaft clockwise from Park through Reverse to Neutral.
3. Position shift control assembly to Neutral.
4. Lock shift cable by pressing locking button down.

DETENT/T.V. CABLE

MODELS w/LOCK TAB ADJUSTING CABLE

1. Depress and hold readjust tab, **Fig. 3.**
2. Move slider back through fitting in direction away from throttle idler lever until slider stops against fitting, then release readjust tab.
3. **On all models except Grand Am and Skylark with 2.5L/4-151 engine,** rotate throttle idler lever to full travel stop position, then release throttle lever.
4. **On Grand Am and Skylark models with 2.5L/4-151 engine,** press accelerator pedal to full travel, then release accelerator pedal.

MODELS LESS LOCK TAB ADJUSTING CABLE

Except 3.3L/V6-204 Engine

1. Ensure cable is in "Non-Adjusted" position as shown, **Fig. 4.**
2. Using a suitable torque wrench, rotate idler pulley counterclockwise to 65 inch lbs. on all except Grand Am and Skylark models, or 75 inch lbs. on Grand Am and Skylark models.
3. Ensure cable moves freely, then test drive vehicle.

3.3L/V6-204 Engine

1. Ensure TV cable and throttle cable are properly installed in throttle lever and TV cable slider is in full non-adjusted position. **Fig. 5.**

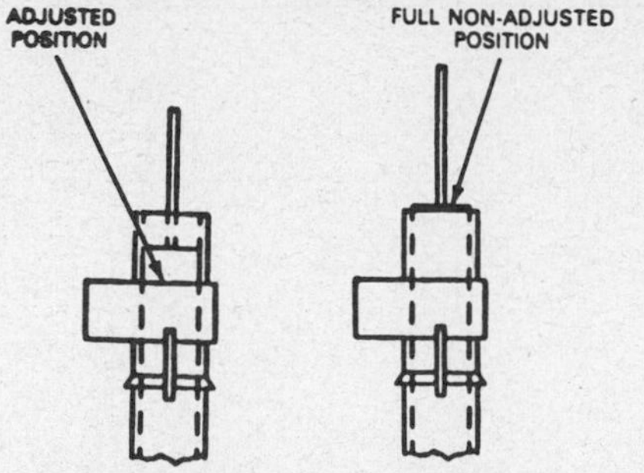
ADJUSTED POSITION
FULL NON-ADJUSTED POSITION

Copyrighted Material Reprinted with Permission from Hydra-Matic Div., GM Corp.

TH5028800108000X

Fig. 4 Detent/TV cable adjustment. Except 3.3L/V6-204

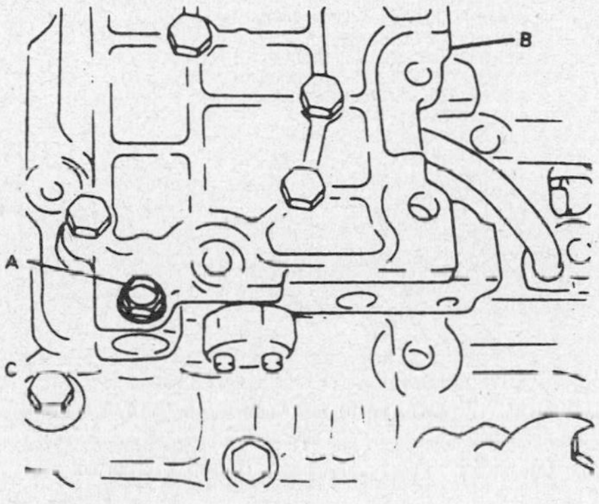
A
B
C

A BOLT
B AUXILIARY VALVE BODY
C VALVE BODY

Copyrighted Material Reprinted with Permission from Hydra-Matic Div., GM Corp.

TH5028800110000X

Fig. 6 Valve body bolt location

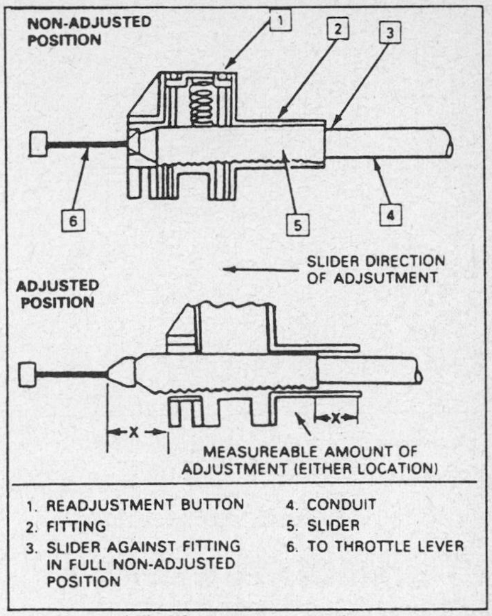
NON-ADJUSTED POSITION
1
2
3
6
5
4
SLIDER DIRECTION OF ADJSUTMENT
ADJUSTED POSITION
X
X
MEASUREABLE AMOUNT OF ADJUSTMENT (EITHER LOCATION)
1. READJUSTMENT BUTTON
2. FITTING
3. SLIDER AGAINST FITTING IN FULL NON-ADJUSTED POSITION
4. CONDUIT
5. SLIDER
6. TO THROTTLE LEVER

Copyrighted Material Reprinted with Permission from Hydra Matic Div., GM Corp.

TH5028800109000X

Fig. 5 Detent/TV cable adjustment. 3.3L/V6-204

2. Rotate throttle lever to full travel position, applying no more torque than necessary to reach throttle body stop.
3. Depress and hold adjustment button.
4. Pull cable conduit out until slider contacts against adjustment.
5. Release button. Repeat procedure to ensure proper adjustment.

IN-VEHICLE REPAIRS

AUXILIARY VALVE BODY, VALVE BODY & OIL PUMP ASSEMBLY, REPLACE

1. Disconnect battery ground cable, then the TV cable.
2. Raise and support vehicle.
3. Remove left front wheel and tire assembly.
4. Remove valve body cover retaining bolts and the cover.
5. Remove TCC solenoid retaining bolt and the solenoid. Disconnect TCC solenoid and 3rd gear pressure switch electrical connectors.
6. Remove bolt securing linkage/bracket to valve body, then remove TV linkage.
7. Remove remaining valve body retaining bolts, then the valve body and six check balls. Do not remove the bolts marked "A" **Fig. 6,** at this time.
8. Remove bolt "A" and separate auxiliary valve body from the valve body.
9. Remove oil pump drive rod, auxiliary valve body and cover.
10. Remove oil pump assembly.
11. Reverse procedure to install noting the following:
    a. Tighten bolts in a clockwise pattern, starting from center.
    b. Refer to **Fig. 7** for check ball location.
    c. Adjust TV cable and fluid level.

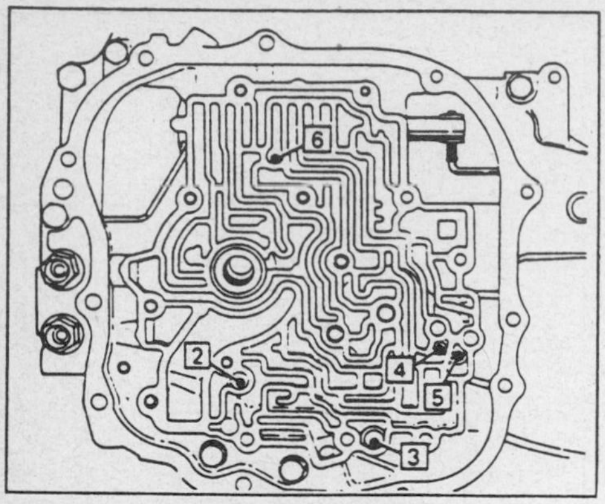

Copyrighted Material Reprinted with Permission from Hydra-Matic Div., GM Corp.

TH5020000111000X

Fig. 7 Check ball locations

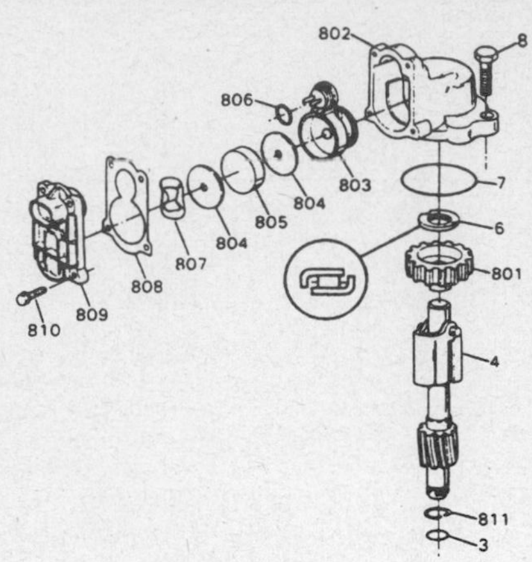

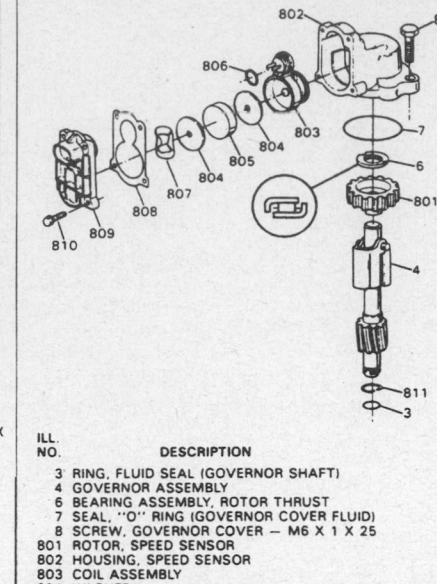

ILL. NO.	DESCRIPTION
3	RING, FLUID SEAL (GOVERNOR SHAFT)
4	GOVERNOR ASSEMBLY
6	BEARING ASSEMBLY, ROTOR THRUST
7	SEAL, "O" RING (GOVERNOR COVER FLUID)
8	SCREW, GOVERNOR COVER — M6 X 1 X 25
801	ROTOR, SPEED SENSOR
802	HOUSING, SPEED SENSOR
803	COIL ASSEMBLY
804	WASHER
805	MAGNET
806	SEAL, "O" RING
807	WASHER, WAVE SPRING
808	GASKET, COVER
809	COVER, SPEED SENSOR HOUSING
810	SCREW, SPEED SENSOR COVER — M4 X 0.7 X 13
811	RING, GOVERNOR COMPRESSION

Copyrighted Material Reprinted with Permission from Hydra-Matic Div., GM Corp.

TH5028800112000X

Fig. 8 Governor replacement

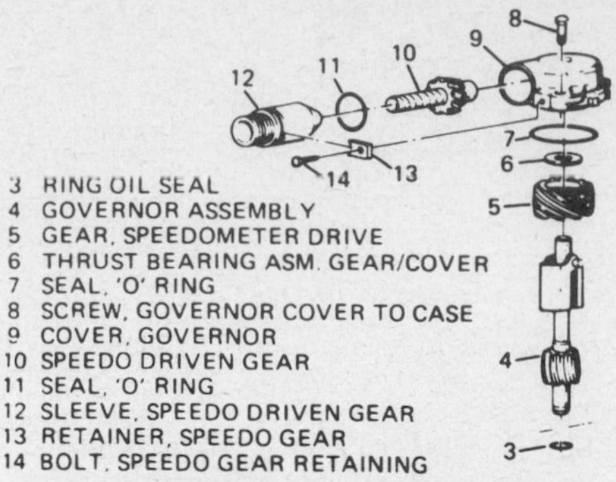
3 RING OIL SEAL
4 GOVERNOR ASSEMBLY
5 GEAR, SPEEDOMETER DRIVE
6 THRUST BEARING ASM. GEAR/COVER
7 SEAL, 'O' RING
8 SCREW, GOVERNOR COVER TO CASE
9 COVER, GOVERNOR
10 SPEEDO DRIVEN GEAR
11 SEAL, 'O' RING
12 SLEEVE, SPEEDO DRIVEN GEAR
13 RETAINER, SPEEDO GEAR
14 BOLT, SPEEDO GEAR RETAINING

Copyrighted Material Reprinted with Permission from Hydra-Matic Div., GM Corp.

TH5028800113000X

Fig. 9 Governor assembly

INTERMEDIATE SERVO & ACCUMULATOR CHECK VALVE, REPLACE

1. Raise and support vehicle.
2. Remove transaxle oil pan and gasket, then remove screen and O-ring.
3. Remove reverse oil pipe retaining brackets, intermediate servo cover and gasket.
4. Remove accumulator valve and spring.
5. Remove intermediate servo assembly.
6. Reverse procedure to install

GOVERNOR, REPLACE

Century, Cutlass Ciera, Cutlass Cruiser, Cutlass Supreme, Grand Prix & Lumina

Refer to **Fig. 8** when performing the following procedure.

1. Remove screws, speed sensor housing and oil seal.
2. Remove bearing and rotor.
3. Remove governor assembly.
4. Remove fluid seal ring.
5. Reverse procedure to install.

Achieva, Beretta, Cavalier, Corsica, Grand Am, Skylark & Sunbird

1. Raise and support vehicle.
2. Remove engine to transaxle brace attaching bolts, then the heat shield if equipped.
3. Remove speedometer cable or wire connector from transaxle.
4. Remove speedometer driven gear and sleeve assembly or speed sensor if equipped.
5. Remove governor cover and O-ring.
6. Remove speedometer drive gear thrust washer and gear, then the governor assembly, **Fig. 9.**
7. Reverse procedure to install.

PARKING PAWL SHAFT, REPLACE

1. Raise and support vehicle.
2. Remove transaxle oil pan.
3. Remove oil strainer and filter seal.
4. Remove fluid level indicator stop.
5. Remove rod retainer and parking lock bracket.
6. Remove clip, pin, rod and spring.
7. Reverse procedure to install.

TRANSAXLE SIDE CASE COVER, REPLACE

1. Remove valve body cover and gasket as described under "Valve Body, Replace."
2. Loosen lefthand side drive axle nut one turn.
3. Remove left side brake caliper and rotor.
4. Remove drive axle shaft nut and washer.
5. Loosen hub/bearing to knuckle attaching bolts
6. Using front hub spindle remover tool No. J 28733-A or equivalent, push axle splines back out of hub bearing.
7. Remove hub/bearing to knuckle attaching bolts. **Protect axle seals from damage during handling.**
8. Remove ABS sensor mounting bolt and position aside to prevent damage.
9. Remove hub/bearing assembly.
10. Using axle shaft remover tool No. J 33008 and slide hammer tool No. J 2619-01 or equivalents, remove left side axle shaft from transaxle.
11. Disconnect TCC wires from case connector.
12. Remove auxiliary valve body and control valve assembly. **Do not lose check balls.**
13. Remove oil pump drive shaft.
14. Remove shifter bracket bolts and position bracket aside.
15. Remove manual valve linkage, spacer plate and gaskets.
16. Remove side case cover attaching bolts and manual valve.
17. Check drive link as follows:
    a. Midway between sprockets, and at right angles to drive link, push bottom strand of the drive link until all slack is removed and mark case with a pencil on bottom side of drive link.
    b. Push bottom strand up in the same manner and put a second mark on the case, ensure both marks are made at the same point on the chain.
    c. Measure distance between two marks.
    d. If distance exceeds 7/8 inch, replace drive link.
18. Reverse procedure to install, using a new drive axle nut and **torque** to 184 ft. lbs.

TRANSAXLE REPLACE

LEMANS

1. Disconnect battery ground cable, then remove air cleaner assembly.
2. Disconnect throttle valve cable from throttle and transaxle.
3. Disconnect selector cable from transaxle lever.
4. Remove selector cable bracket, leaving cable attached to bracket.
5. Disconnect electrical connectors from speed sensor, torque converter clutch and neutral safety switch.
6. Disconnect vent hose at top of transaxle.
7. Remove starter support bolts and starter from transaxle.
8. Disconnect speedometer drive cable from transaxle.
9. Remove top three engine to transaxle attaching bolts.
10. Install engine support fixture No. J28467-A with adapter No. J228467-70 or equivalent.

11. Raise and support vehicle.
12. Remove both front wheel and tire assemblies.
13. Remove lower ball joint retaining clips and stud nuts, then separate ball joints from steering knuckles using ball joint tool No. J36226 or equivalent. **Disregard "This Side Towards Wheel" marking on tool. Tool must be turned to opposite position when used on these vehicles.**
14. Remove both axle shafts from transaxle.
15. Disconnect oil cooler lines from transaxle.
16. Remove converter cover attaching bolts and the cover.
17. Mark relationship between flywheel and torque converter for installation reference, then remove torque converter-to-flywheel attaching bolts.
18. Remove left transaxle mount attaching bolts and the mount.
19. Support transaxle with a suitable jack, then remove rear transaxle mount attaching bolts and the mount.
20. Remove right transaxle mount attaching bolts and the mount.
21. Remove remaining transaxle to engine attaching bolts, then carefully lower transaxle from vehicle.
22. Reverse procedure to install referring to "Tightening Specifications" chart.

CENTURY & CUTLASS CIERA

Except 3.1L/V6-191 Engine

1. Disconnect battery ground cable from transaxle, then remove air cleaner and air duct assembly.
2. Remove bolt securing TV cable to transaxle, then remove shift cable.
3. Disconnect neutral switch electrical connector, then remove torque convertor clutch and speedometer speed sensor.
4. Disconnect and plug transaxle oil cooler lines from transaxle and bracket.
5. Remove transaxle to engine bolts. Leave one bolt near starter loosely installed.
6. Install engine support fixture tool No. J-28467-A or equivalent, and engine support adapter leg tool No. J-36462 or equivalent.
7. Raise and support vehicle, then remove left front wheel and splash shield.
8. Disconnect left lower ball joint from control arm.
9. Remove intermediate shaft to steering gear stub shaft retaining bolt. **Failure to disconnect intermediate shaft from rack and pinion tube shaft will result in damage to steering gear and/or intermediate shaft. This damage could result in loss of steering control.**
10. Disconnect stabilizer bar from left control arm. Remove left and right stabilizer mount bolts from frame.
11. Center punch two spot welds at frame crossmember near left stabilizer bar to frame mount. Drill out spot welds enough to separate frame and crossmember.
12. Remove left steering gear to frame bolt, then remove left to right frame section retaining bolts.
13. Support frame with suitable jack stand and remove left frame to body bolts.
14. Remove transaxle mounting nuts from frame, then carefully remove jack stand and the frame assembly.
15. Remove starter and converter shields.
16. Remove three flywheel to converter bolts, the remove two transaxle extension bolts from engine to transaxle bracket.
17. Remove rear transaxle mount bracket assembly. It may be necessary to raise transaxle.
18. Position transaxle jack to transaxle case, then remove two bolts from braces to right end of transaxle.
19. Remove left drive axle, then the remaining engine to transaxle bolt, located near starter.
20. Carefully remove transaxle along with right drive axle, as an assembly.
21. Reverse procedure to install, noting the following:
    a. Align and insert right axle shaft while transaxle is being lifted into position.
    b. Ensure intermediate shaft is seated prior to pinch bolt installation. **If pinch bolt is inserted into coupling before shaft installation, two mating shafts may disengage.**
    c. Refer to "Tightening Specifications chart.
    d. Adjust shift linkage, TV cable and fluid level.

3.1L/V6-191 Engine

1. Disconnect battery ground cable.
2. Remove air cleaner, mounting bracket, MAF sensor and air tube as an assembly.
3. Remove exhaust crossover bolts at RH manifold, then LH manifold bolts at cylinder head. **If necessary, raise and support manifold/crossover assembly.**
4. Disconnect TV cable from throttle lever and transaxle, then transaxle to vent pipe rubber hose.
5. Disconnect shift cable from transaxle.
6. Disconnect neutral start switch and TCC electrical connectors.
7. Remove fluid level indicator and fill tube.
8. Install engine support fixture tool No. J-28467 and adapter No. J-35953 or equivalent.
9. Remove nut attaching wiring harness from transaxle.
10. Remove transaxle mount through bolt, then mount bracket and mount from transaxle.
11. Remove upper transaxle to engine attaching bolts, then raise and support vehicle.
12. Remove both front wheels, then LH splash shield.
13. Remove transaxle converter cover, then scribe alignment marks on flexplate and torque converter for reassembly.
14. Remove torque converter to flexplate attaching bolts.
15. Remove torsional strut and lateral strut from transaxle, then transaxle bracket bolts.
16. Disconnect speedometer connector from transaxle, then shift cable bracket.
17. Install drive axle boot seal protectors No. J-34754 or equivalent on inner seals. **Failure to install seal protectors can result in seal damage and possible joint failure.**
18. Remove both drive axles.
19. Remove left stabilizer bar link pin bolt, left stabilizer bar frame bushing attaching nuts, then the left frame support assembly.
20. Remove transaxle cooler lines. **Plug lines to prevent leakage or dirt from entering system.**
21. Position a suitable jack under transaxle, then remove remaining transaxle to engine attaching bolts.
22. Remove transaxle assembly from vehicle.
23. Reverse procedure to install, noting the following:
    a. Refer to "Tightening Specifications chart.
    b. Adjust shift linkage, TV cable and fluid level.
    c. Check front suspension alignment after transaxle installation.

BERETTA & CORSICA

1. Disconnect battery ground cable and remove TV cable from throttle lever and transaxle.
2. **On models with 3.1L/V6-191 engines**, remove battery
3. **On all models,** remove fluid level indicator and filler tube.
4. Remove bolt securing wiring harness to transaxle, then disconnect electrical connectors from TCC and park/neutral switch.
5. Remove upper shift control cable bracket and disconnect cable form shift lever at transaxle.
6. Remove rubber hose from vent pipe to transaxle.
7. **On models with 3.1L/V6-191 engines,** remove exhaust crossover pipe.
8. **On all models,** install engine support tools No. J28467 and J35943 or equivalents.
9. Remove top two transaxle to engine mounting bolts and transaxle mounting bracket bolts, then the mounting bracket.
10. Remove remaining upper transaxle to engine bolts. Raise and support vehicle.
11. Remove front wheels and left front engine splash shield.
12. Install axle boot protector tool No. J34754 to protect boot from damage. **Failure to protect boot may result in boot damage and joint failure.**

13. Remove left and right drive axles as follows:
    a. Place a screwdriver through caliper, into rotor, to prevent from turning.
    b. Remove drive axle nut and washer.
    c. Remove ball joint cotter pin and nut. Separate ball joint from control arm with removal tool No. J29330 or equivalent.
    d. Disengage axle from hub and bearing using removal tool No. J28733-A or equivalent.
    e. Separate hub and bearing assembly from drive axle and move strut and knuckle assembly rearward.
    f. Remove inner joints from transaxle using inner joint removal tools No. J28468 and J29794 or equivalents.
14. Remove both stabilizer links and left stabilizer bar clamp nuts.
15. Remove left suspension supports and bolts.
16. Remove transaxle strut bolts from transaxle, then disconnect vehicle speed sensor electrical connector from transaxle.
17. Remove converter cover, then the flywheel to converter bolts. Mark relationship of flywheel to converter to ease installation.
18. Disconnect and plug transaxle cooler lines. Remove shift cable from lower cable bracket.
19. Remove transaxle to engine brace bolts.
20. Position suitable transaxle jack below assembly. Remove remaining engine to transaxle mounting bolts.
21. Carefully lower transaxle from vehicle.
22. Reverse procedure to install, noting the following:
    a. Refer to "Tightening Specifications chart.
    b. Adjust TV cable, shift linkage and fluid level. Check for leaks.

ACHIEVA, CAVALIER, GRAND AM, SKYLARK & SUNBIRD

2.0L/4-121, 2.2L/4-134 & 3.1L/V6-191 Engines

1. Disconnect battery ground cable, then remove air cleaner assembly.
2. Drain cooling system, then disconnect heater core hoses using clamp tool No. J-37097 or equivalent.
3. Disconnect TV cable from throttle lever and transaxle.
4. Remove fluid level indicator and fill tube.
5. Install engine support fixture tool No. J-28467-A, or equivalent.
6. Remove wire harness to transaxle attaching nut, then disconnect electrical connectors from speed sensor, TCC connector, park/neutral and back-up lamp switch.
7. Disconnect shift linkage from transaxle. Remove two top transaxle to engine attaching bolts, then the left upper transaxle mount and bracket assembly.
8. Remove transaxle to vent pipe rubber hose, then the remaining upper engine to transaxle attaching bolts.
9. Raise and support vehicle, then remove both front wheels.
10. Drain transaxle fluid, then remove shift linkage and bracket assembly.
11. Install drive axle boot seal protectors No. J-34754 or equivalent on inner seals, then disconnect both ball joints from control arms. Failure to install seal protectors can result in seal damage and possible joint failure.
12. Remove both drive axles.
13. Remove transaxle mounting strut, then left stabilizer bar link pin bolt.
14. Remove left stabilizer bar frame bushing clamp attaching nuts, then the left frame support assembly.
15. **On models equipped with 4 cylinder engines,** disconnect exhaust pipe from manifold.
16. **On models equipped with V6 cylinder engines,** remove front exhaust manifold and pipe.
17. **On all models,** disconnect speedometer connector from transaxle, then remove starter motor, if necessary.
18. Remove transaxle converter cover, then disconnect and plug transaxle cooler lines.
19. Mark relationship of flywheel and torque converter to ease installation, then remove converter to flywheel bolts.
20. Remove transaxle to engine support bracket, then position a suitable jack below transaxle.
21. Remove remaining transaxle to engine attaching bolts, then lower transaxle from vehicle.
22. Reverse procedure to install, noting the following:
    a. Refer to "Tightening Specifications chart.
    b. Check and adjust fluid level, shift linkage and TV cable.
    c. Check front suspension alignment following transaxle installation.

2.3L/4-138 Engine

1. Disconnect battery ground cable and remove intake air duct.
2. Drain cooling system and disconnect heater hoses at heater core.
3. Remove cable control cover and disconnect throttle and TV cables.
4. Remove shift cable and bracket from transaxle.
5. Remove throttle cable from throttle body, then disconnect vacuum lines and electrical connectors.
6. Remove power steering pump and fluid filler tube.
7. Install engine support tool No. J28467-A or equivalent.
8. Remove top engine to transaxle bolts, then raise and support vehicle.
9. Remove front wheels and left inner engine splash shield. Disconnect lower ball joints from control arms.
10. Remove stabilizer shaft links.
11. Remove front air deflector and left suspension support assembly.
12. Install drive axle seal protector tools No. J34754 or equivalent.
13. Remove both drive axles.
14. Remove flywheel cover, then the flywheel to converter bolts. Mark relationship of flywheel and converter to ease in installation.
15. Disconnect and plug transaxle cooler lines.
16. Remove bolt securing ground wires from engine and transaxle.
17. Remove cooler pipe brace and exhaust brace.
18. Remove bolts from engine to transaxle mount.
19. Support transaxle with suitable jack, remove remaining engine to transaxle bolts.
20. Carefully remove transaxle from vehicle.
21. Reverse procedure to install, noting the following:
    a. Ensure torque converter is properly seated in oil pump.
    b. Install transaxle assembly into position with jack, while installing right drive axle.
    c. Refer to "Tightening Specifications chart.
    d. Adjust TV cable, shift linkage and fluid level.

CUTLASS SUPREME, GRAND PRIX & LUMINA

1. Disconnect battery ground cable.
2. **On Cutlass Supreme and Grand Prix models,** remove coolant recovery reservoir.
3. **On all models,** disconnect shift control and TV cable from transaxle.
4. Remove throttle cable bracket, then disconnect brake booster hose if equipped.
5. Remove both torque struts from engine.
6. Remove left torque strut bracket, then disconnect and plug oil cooler lines from transaxle.
7. Install engine support fixture No. J28467-A with adapter tools No. J28467-90 and J36462 or equivalents.
8. Raise and support vehicle, then remove front wheels.
9. Remove calipers, rotors and lower engine splash shields.
10. Remove nuts and washers from driveshafts, then separate hub/bearing assemblies from axle splines using hub spindle removal tool No. J28733 or equivalent.
11. Remove hub/bearing assembly to knuckle attaching bolts. If equipped, remove ABS sensor attaching bolts and position sensors aside.
12. Remove hub/bearing assemblies from vehicle.
13. Using axle shaft removal tool No. J33008, extension tool No. J29794 and slide hammer tool No. J2619-01 or equivalents, separate right and left axles from transaxle.
14. Remove axle assemblies from knuckles, then disconnect tie rod ends and ball joints from steering knuckle.
15. **On Lumina models,** drain oil and re-

move oil filter, then remove and support A/C compressor. **Do not disconnect refrigerant lines.**

16. **On all models,** remove heat shield from rack and pinion, then disconnect electrical connector.
17. Remove main engine wiring harness to transaxle case retaining bolts.
18. Secure rack and pinion unit to exhaust system, then remove rack and pinion to frame attaching bolts.
19. Remove power steering line to frame retaining bolts.
20. Remove engine and transaxle mounts from frame.
21. Support frame with jackstands, then remove frame bolts. Remove frame and jackstands from vehicle.
22. Remove flywheel access cover, then the torque converter bolts.
23. Remove starter retaining bolts, then support starter with wire. **Do not allow starter to hang from electrical wires.**
24. Disconnect battery ground cable from transaxle and remove transaxle fill tube bolt.
25. Remove transaxle mount bracket, then lower vehicle.
26. Disconnect transaxle electrical connector and remove fill tube.
27. Using engine support, lower left side of engine approximately four inches.
28. Raise and support vehicle.
29. **On Cutlass Supreme and Grand Prix models,** remove fuel line bracket from transaxle.
30. **On all models,** position a jack under transaxle, remove transaxle to engine retaining bolts and lower transaxle from vehicle.
31. Reverse procedure to install noting the following:
    a. Refer to "Tightening Specifications chart.
    b. Adjust shift linkage, TV cable and fluid level.
    c. Check front suspension alignment.

TIGHTENING SPECIFICATIONS

Component	Torque/Ft. Lbs.
ACHIEVA, GRAND AM & SKYLARK	
Cooler Lines At Radiator	20
Cooler Lines At Transaxle	16
Flywheel Cover	115①
Governor Cover	133①
Neutral Start Switch	22
Oil Pan Bolts	133①
Shift Cable To Shift Lever	90①
Starter Bolts	32
Throttle Cable To Case	90①
Torque Converter Bolts	46
Transaxle Mount Bolts	22
Transaxle To Engine Bolts	55
Wheel Lug Nuts	100
BERETTA & CORSICA	
Case Cover Bolts	10
Clutch Switches	97①
Cooler Lines At Radiator	20
Cooler Lines At Transaxle	16
Filler Tube Mounting Bolt②	20
Filler Tube Mounting Bolt③	32
Floor Shift Control	17
Flywheel Cover	115①
Governor Cover	97①
Neutral Start Switch	20
Oil Pan Bolts	97①
Shift Control Cable Grommet	17①
Shift Lever	15
TCC Solenoid	97①
Throttle Cable Bolt	89①
Torque Converter Bolts	46
Transaxle Brace	37
Transaxle Mount Bracket To Transaxle	40
Transaxle To Engine Bolts	55
Transaxle Strut Bolts	40
Upper Shift Cable Bracket Nut & Bolt	18
Valve Body Cover Bolts	97①
Wheel Lug Nuts	100

Component	Torque/Ft. Lbs.
CAVALIER & SUNBIRD	
Cooler Lines At Radiator	20
Cooler Lines At Transaxle	16
Flywheel Cover	115①
Governor Cover	133①
Neutral Start Switch	22
Oil Pan Bolts	133①
Starter Bolts	32
Shift Cable To Shift Lever Nut	90①
Throttle Cable To Transaxle	90①
Torque Converter Bolts	46
Transaxle Mount Bolts	22
Transaxle To Engine Bolts	55
Wheel Lug Nuts	100
CENTURY, CUTLASS CIERA & CUTLASS CRUISER	
Bracket To Transaxle Bolt	41
Channel Plate Attaching Bolts	41
Console Shift Control Assembly Nut	18
Fill Tube Bolt	18
Flywheel Cover Bolts	89①
Governor Housing Bolts	98①
Mount To Bracket Nut	35
Oil Pan Bolts	98①
Park/Neutral Switch Bolts	21
Shift Control Bracket	18
Shift Control Lever	15
TCC Solenoid Screws	125①
Torque Converter Bolts	46
Transaxle Case Side Cover	125①
Transaxle Cooler Pipe Clip Bolt	35
Transaxle Cooler Pipe To Radiator	13
Valve Body Bolts	125①
Wheel Lug Nuts	100

TIGHTENING SPECIFICATIONS —Continued

Component	Torque/Ft. Lbs.
CUTLASS SUPREME, GRAND PRIX & LUMINA	
Auxiliary Oil Cooler Bolt	18
Auxiliary Oil Cooler Nut	89 ①
Bracket To Transaxle Front Bolts	35
Bracket To Transaxle Top Stud	40
Bracket To Transaxle Rear Bolt	61
Console Shift Control Nut	18
Engine To Transaxle Brace Bolt	35
Fill Tube Bolt	18
Flywheel Cover Bolt	89 ①
Governor Housing Bolts	98 ①
Mount To Bracket Nut	22
Neutral Start Switch	18
Oil Cooler Line Clip Bolt	35
Oil Cooler Line To Radiator	13
Oil Pan Bolts	98 ①
Shift Control Bracket	18
Shift Control Lever	15
TCC Solenoid Screws	125 ①
Throttle Cable Bolt	89 ①
Torque Converter Bolt	44
Transaxle Case Side Cover	125 ①
Transaxle To Engine Bolts	55
Valve Body Bolts	125 ①
Wheel Lug Nuts	100

Component	Torque/Ft. Lbs.
LEMANS	
Brake Band Booster Cover	8
Cooler Lines At Radiator	16
Cooler Lines At Transaxle	28
Cooler Line Bracket At Transaxle	18
Drive Chain Sprocket Carrier	18
Governor Cover To Case	8
Intermediate Servo Cover	8
Left Transaxle Mount At Transaxle	16
Oil Pan Bolts w/Coated Cork Gasket	10
Oil Pan Bolts Without Less Cork Gasket	7.5
Oil Pressure Tap Port	8
Parking Pawl Bracket	18
Right Transaxle Mount At Engine	30
Selector Lever Shaft Nut	20
Torque Converter Bolts	44
Transaxle To Engine Bolts	55
Throttle Cable At Transaxle	7.5
Transaxle Housing Cover Retaining Spring	28
Wheel Lug Nuts	66

Turbo Hydra-Matic 4T60 & 4T60–E Automatic Transaxle

INDEX

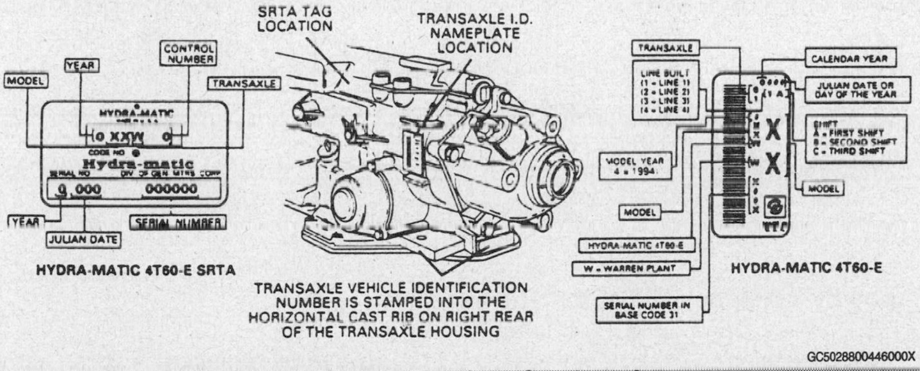

SRTA TAG LOCATION
TRANSAXLE I.D. NAMEPLATE LOCATION
MODEL
YEAR
CONTROL NUMBER
TRANSAXLE
SERIAL NUMBER
JULIAN DATE
HYDRA-MATIC 4T60-E SRTA
TRANSAXLE VEHICLE IDENTIFICATION NUMBER IS STAMPED INTO THE HORIZONTAL CAST RIB ON RIGHT REAR OF THE TRANSAXLE HOUSING
CALENDAR YEAR
JULIAN DATE OR DAY OF THE YEAR
MODEL YEAR
MODEL
W = WARREN PLANT
SERIAL NUMBER IN BASE CODE 31
HYDRA-MATIC 4T60-E
GC5028800446000X

Fig. 1 Transaxle identification plate

IDENTIFICATION

This transaxle may be identified by codes stamped into the horizontal cast rib on the right rear side of the transaxle housing, **Fig. 1.**

DESCRIPTION

The 4T60 and 4T60-E transaxles **Figs. 2 and 3** are fully automatic units which provide four forward speeds including an overdrive top gear. The transmission unit includes a three element hydraulic torque converter and lock-up clutching element, four multiple disc clutch, two bands and a compound reaction planetary gear set, Power transmitted to the drive wheels from the planetary gear through a final drive gear set and differential assembly.

The converter is designed to provide torque multiplication during acceleration and at slow vehicle speed, and lock-up during normal operation for increase operating economy. Operation of the converter lock-up is controlled automatically by the engine fuel system electronic control module. In addition, the converter drives the vane type oil pump by means of a shaft splined to the converter cover.

The torque converter hydraulically couples the engine to the planetary gears through a turbine and shaft assembly which drives the transmission output shaft by means of a drive link chain and sprockets.

TROUBLESHOOTING

OIL LEAK

1. Side cover distorted.
2. Oil pan attaching bolts loose.
3. Oil pan gaskets damaged.
4. T.V. cable, fill tube and/or electrical connector seal damaged.
5. Manual shaft seal assembly damaged.
6. Governor cover and/or servo covers O-rings damaged.
7. Cooler fittings and/or pressure taps insufficiently tightened, or threads stripped.
8. Converter seal damaged, or garter spring missing.
9. Axle seals damaged, or garter spring missing.
10. Modulator O-ring damaged.
11. Parking plunger guide O-ring damaged.
12. Speedometer O-ring damaged.

OIL FORCED OUT VENT OR FOAMING OIL

1. High fluid level.
2. Overheated or contaminated oil.
3. Damaged filter or filter seal.
4. Leaking accumulator cover pipe or drive socket support lubrication pipes.
5. Thermo element not closing properly.
6. Thermo element improperly installed or incorrect pin height.
7. Defective or improperly installed modulator port gasket.
8. Plugged drive sprocket support drain back holes.

OIL PRESSURE HIGH OR LOW

1. Incorrect fluid level.
2. Contaminated fluid or engine overheating.
3. Vacuum line leaking.

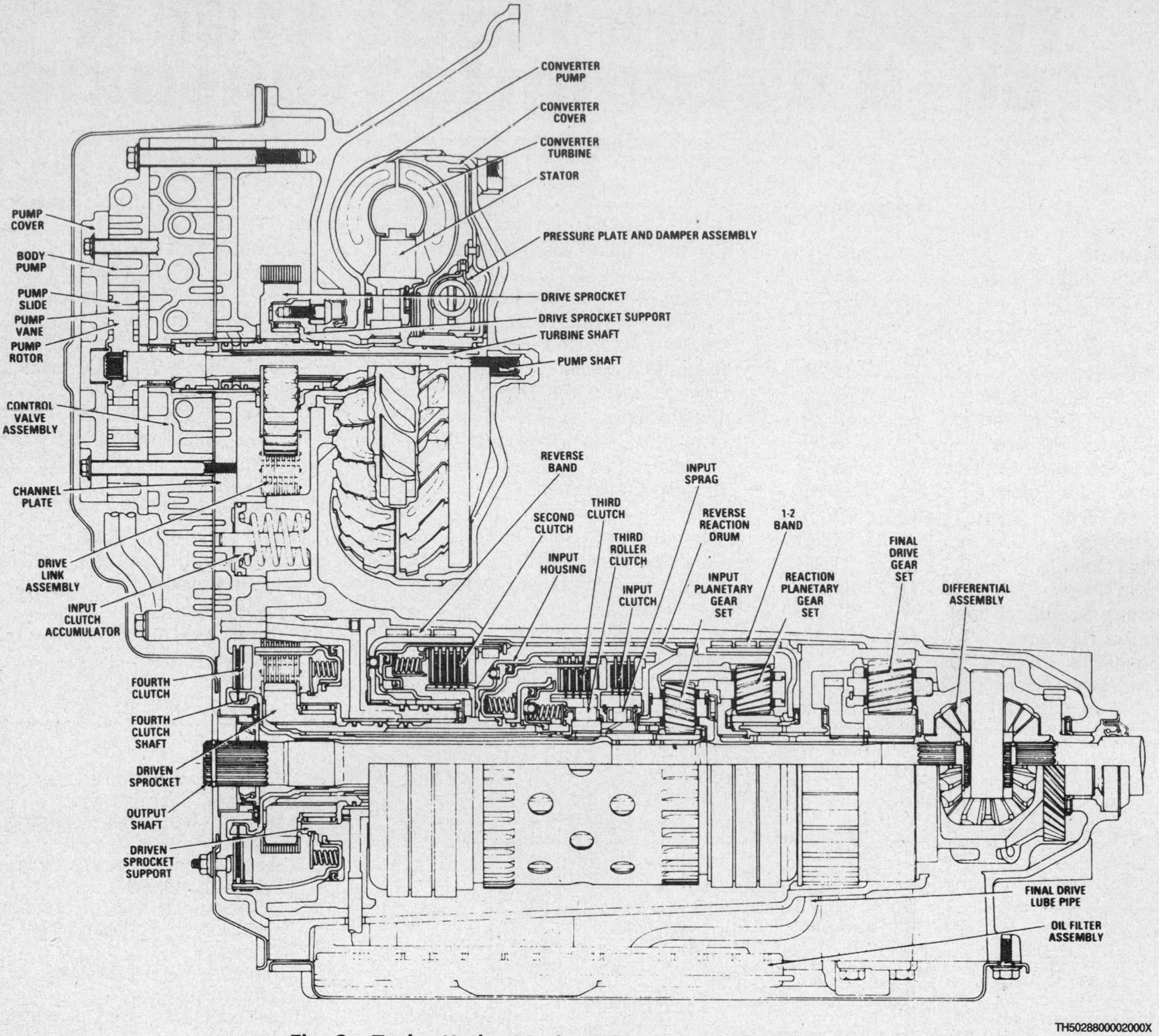

CONVERTER PUMP
CONVERTER COVER
CONVERTER TURBINE
STATOR
PRESSURE PLATE AND DAMPER ASSEMBLY
DRIVE SPROCKET
DRIVE SPROCKET SUPPORT
TURBINE SHAFT
PUMP SHAFT
PUMP COVER
BODY PUMP
PUMP SLIDE
PUMP VANE
PUMP ROTOR
CONTROL VALVE ASSEMBLY
CHANNEL PLATE
DRIVE LINK ASSEMBLY
INPUT CLUTCH ACCUMULATOR
REVERSE BAND
INPUT SPRAG
SECOND CLUTCH
THIRD CLUTCH
REVERSE REACTION DRUM
1-2 BAND
THIRD ROLLER CLUTCH
INPUT HOUSING
INPUT CLUTCH
INPUT PLANETARY GEAR SET
REACTION PLANETARY GEAR SET
FINAL DRIVE GEAR SET
DIFFERENTIAL ASSEMBLY
FOURTH CLUTCH
FOURTH CLUTCH SHAFT
DRIVEN SPROCKET
OUTPUT SHAFT
DRIVEN SPROCKET SUPPORT
FINAL DRIVE LUBE PIPE
OIL FILTER ASSEMBLY
TH5028800002000X

Fig. 2 Turbo Hydra-Matic 4T60 automatic transaxle

4. Modulator leaking or modulator diaphragm damaged.
5. Nicked, scored or stuck modulator valve.
6. Pressure regulator valve or spring damaged.
7. Pressure relief valve spring damaged or ball missing.
8. Oil pump damaged or restricted.
9. Aspirator "T" blocked or incorrectly installed.

DELAYED ENGAGEMENT

1. Low oil level.
2. Cooler check ball not seating.
3. Damaged or defective reverse servo seal.
4. Damaged or defective 1-2 servo seal.
5. Leaking 1-2 servo oil pipes.

NO DRIVE IN D RANGE

1. Low fluid level.
2. Low oil pressure.
3. Manual linkage improperly adjusted or disconnected.
4. Torque converter stator roller clutch sluggish or converter not properly attached to flex plate.
5. Drive axles disengaged.
6. Damaged or broken drive link chain, sprockets or bearings.
7. Damaged 1-2 servo or incorrect apply pin.
8. 1-2 servo oil pipes or pipe seals leaking.
9. Damaged oil pump or pump driveshaft.
10. Input clutch reverse check ball out of position.
11. Burned input clutch plates, damaged clutch seals or damaged piston.
12. Leaking input housing check ball.
13. Damaged input shaft seals or blocked input shaft passages.
14. Defective input sprag or improper sprag and input sun gear assembly. **When servicing transaxle for intermittent or complete loss of drive, the input sprag assembly should always be replaced. A sprag causing intermittent loss of drive may appear in satisfactory condition while still being susceptible to "pop-out" during operation.**
15. Third roller clutch burned due to lack of lubrication.
16. Damaged input carrier and/or reaction carrier.
17. Damaged or improperly installed output shaft.
18. Burned or improperly installed 1-2 band.
19. Damaged final drive assembly and/or final drive sun gear shaft.
20. Broken parking pawl spring.

SLIPS IN DRIVE

1. Incorrect oil level.
2. Cut or damaged vacuum line to modulator or defective modulator.
3. Low oil pressure.
4. Damaged 1-2 servo or servo piston seal.
5. Plugged filter screen.
6. Leaking servo oil pipes or pipe seals.

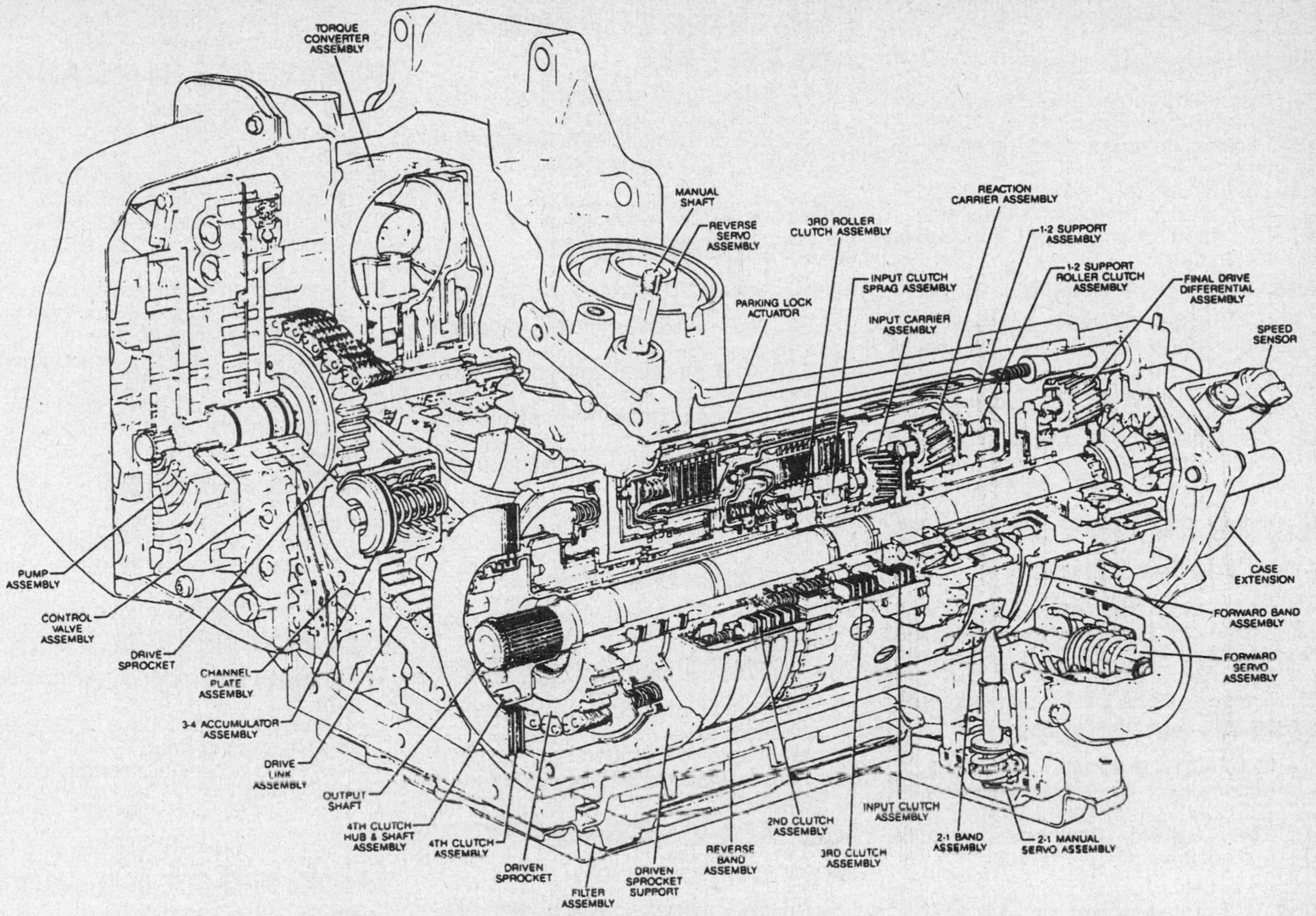
TORQUE CONVERTER ASSEMBLY
MANUAL SHAFT
REVERSE SERVO ASSEMBLY
3RD ROLLER CLUTCH ASSEMBLY
REACTION CARRIER ASSEMBLY
1-2 SUPPORT ASSEMBLY
1-2 SUPPORT ROLLER CLUTCH ASSEMBLY
FINAL DRIVE DIFFERENTIAL ASSEMBLY
INPUT CLUTCH SPRAG ASSEMBLY
PARKING LOCK ACTUATOR
INPUT CARRIER ASSEMBLY
SPEED SENSOR
PUMP ASSEMBLY
CONTROL VALVE ASSEMBLY
DRIVE SPROCKET
CHANNEL PLATE ASSEMBLY
3-4 ACCUMULATOR ASSEMBLY
DRIVE LINK ASSEMBLY
OUTPUT SHAFT
4TH CLUTCH HUB & SHAFT ASSEMBLY
4TH CLUTCH ASSEMBLY
DRIVEN SPROCKET
FILTER ASSEMBLY
DRIVEN SPROCKET SUPPORT
REVERSE BAND ASSEMBLY
2ND CLUTCH ASSEMBLY
3RD CLUTCH ASSEMBLY
INPUT CLUTCH ASSEMBLY
2-1 BAND ASSEMBLY
2-1 MANUAL SERVO ASSEMBLY
CASE EXTENSION
FORWARD BAND ASSEMBLY
FORWARD SERVO ASSEMBLY

TH5029200003000X

Fig. 3 Turbo Hydra-Matic 4T60–E automatic transaxle

7. Defective converter stator clutch.
8. Defective input clutch accumulator or damaged input shaft seals.
9. Damaged or defective input clutch or leaks at ball capsule.

NO 1-2 UPSHIFT, 1ST SPEED ONLY

1. Governor weights binding.
2. Governor springs or gear damaged.
3. Leaking governor oil pipes.
4. Leaking governor retainer or blocked governor screen.
5. Leaking accumulator cover, retainer or oil pipes.
6. 1-2 shift valve sticking or binding.
7. Valve body spacer plate or gaskets damaged or improperly positioned.
8. Damaged driven sprocket support oil rings.
9. Damaged or improperly assembled second clutch.
10. Clutch housing check ball damaged.
11. Damaged reverse reaction drum splines or missing drum plate.

HARSH OR SOFT 1-2 SHIFT

1. Incorrect oil pressure.
2. Accumulator cover bolts improperly tightened.
3. Accumulator pistons, seals or springs damaged.
4. Control valve assembly accumulator valve binding.
5. Check ball No. 8 missing or improperly installed.

INCORRECT SHIFT SPEED

4T60 Transmission

1. T.V. cable disconnected or improperly adjusted.
2. T.V. link, lever or bracket damaged.
3. T.V. valve and plunger binding.
4. Governor pressure incorrect.

NO 2-3 UPSHIFT, 1ST & 2ND SPEEDS ONLY

1. Governor damaged.
2. Accumulator cover oil hole blocked.
3. Leaking drive sprocket support oil pipe.
4. 2-3 shift valve binding or sticking.
5. Control valve assembly bolts improperly torqued.
6. Leaking or improperly positioned check balls.
7. Sticking 2-3 accumulator valve.
8. Leaking 1-2 servo release oil pipe.
9. Improperly installed channel plate gasket.
10. Blocked oil passage to driven sprocket support.
11. Damaged input housing and shaft seals or blocked oil passages.
12. Damaged third clutch assembly.
13. Damaged third clutch piston check ball.
14. Damaged third roller clutch assembly.
15. Third roller clutch improperly assembled on input sun gear shaft.

HARSH OR SOFT 2-3 SHIFT

4T60 Transmission

1. Incorrect oil pressure.
2. Leaking 1-2 servo check ball and capsule assembly.
3. Leaking 1-2 servo release oil pipe or pipe seals.
4. Improperly located 1-2 servo feed passage check ball.

4T60-E Transmission

1. Incorrect oil pressure.
2. Number 4 checkball mislocated causing a soft shift.
3. Number 9 checkball mislocated causing a harsh shift.
4. Missing or damaged seals or springs on 2-3 accumulator piston.

NO 3-4 UPSHIFT

4T60 Transmission

1. Incorrect throttle valve adjustment.
2. Defective governor.
3. Leaking governor feed or return oil pipes.
4. 3-4 shift valve binding or stuck.
5. Damaged fourth clutch shift spline.
6. Damaged or improperly assembled fourth clutch.

4T60-E Transmission

1. 3-4 shift valve binding or stuck.
2. 4-3 manual shift valve binding or stuck.
3. Spline damage on fourth clutch shaft.
4. Damaged fourth clutch shift spline.
5. Damaged or improperly assembled fourth clutch.

HARSH OR SOFT 3-4 SHIFT

4T60 Transmission

1. Incorrect oil pressure.
2. Accumulator cover and pistons seal damaged or cover bolts improperly tightened.
3. Check ball No. 1 improperly located.

4T60-E Transmission

1. Incorrect oil pressure.
2. Accumulator cover and pistons seal damaged or springs missing.
3. Check ball No. 10 improperly located.
4. 3-4 accumulator valve stuck.

NO CONVERTER CLUTCH OPERATION

4T60 Transmission

1. ECM malfunction.
2. Damaged, loose or corroded connectors.
3. Pinched wires.
4. Third clutch switch inoperative.
5. Inoperative solenoid.
6. Solenoid screen blocked.
7. Solenoid seal leaking.
8. Converter clutch shift valve and/or apply valve sticking.
9. Damaged or defective torque converter.
10. Damaged turbine shaft seals.
11. Damaged pump shaft seals.
12. Converter clutch blow-off check ball not properly seated in channel plate.

4T60-E Transmission

1. Verify proper PCM operation or wiring.
2. Pinched wires or damaged connectors.
3. Stuck converter clutch valve.
4. Stuck converter clutch regulator valve.
5. TCC solenoid O-ring leaking.
6. Solenoid screen blocked.
7. Damaged torque converter.
8. Damaged turbine shaft seals.
9. Damaged oil pump driveshaft seal.
10. Improperly seated or damaged converter clutch blow-off check ball.
11. Number 1 check ball missing.

CONVERTER CLUTCH DOES NOT RELEASE

1. No ECM signal to solenoid or defective solenoid, if equipped.
2. Sticking converter clutch apply piston.
3. Missing TCC orifice screen.

ROUGH CONVERTER CLUTCH OPERATION

4T60 Transmission

1. Sticking converter clutch regulator valve.
2. Turbine shaft seals damaged or missing.
3. Converter clutch blow-off valve check ball damaged.
4. Damaged converter clutch accumulator piston or seal.
5. Damaged or incorrect TCC blow-off spring.

4T60-E Transmission

1. Sticking converter clutch regulator valve.
2. Turbine shaft seals damaged or missing.
3. Converter clutch blow-off valve check ball damaged.
4. Drive sprocket support bushing worn.
5. Worn or glazed fiber material in torque converter.

HARSH 4-3 DOWNSHIFT

4T60 Transmission

1. Control valve assembly check ball No. 1 missing.

4T60-E Transmission

1. Control valve assembly check ball No. 10 missing.
2. 3-4 accumulator seal cut or damaged.
3. 3-4 accumulator valve stuck.

HARSH 3-2 DOWNSHIFT

4T60 Transmission

1. Improper vacuum signal or defective modulator.
2. Sticking 1-2 servo control valve.
3. No. 12 check ball missing.
4. Sticking 3-2 control valve.
5. No. 4 check ball missing.
6. Sticking 3-2 coast valve.
7. No. 2 check ball missing or improperly positioned.

4T60-E Transmission

1. Control valve assembly No. 9 check ball missing.
2. 2-3 accumulator seal cut or damaged.
3. 2-3 accumulator valve stuck.

HARSH 2-1 DOWNSHIFT

4T60 Transmission

1. Control valve assembly check ball No. 8 missing.
2. No. 2 check ball missing or improperly positioned.

4T60-E Transmission

1. Wrong spacer plate installed.
2. 1-2 accumulator seal cut or damaged.
3. 1-2 accumulator valve stuck.

NO REVERSE IN R RANGE

1. Incorrect oil pressure.
2. Damaged reverse servo piston or seal.
3. Reverse servo improperly assembled or improper apply pin installed.
4. Damaged or defective oil pump.
5. Damaged input clutch accumulator piston seal.
6. Damaged drive link assembly.
7. Burned, damaged or improperly installed reverse band.
8. Damaged or defective input clutch.
9. Defective input sprag.
10. Reverse reaction drum splines, input carrier and/or reaction carrier damaged.

SLIPS IN REVERSE

1. Incorrect oil pressure.
2. Damaged reverse servo seal.
3. Damaged reverse reaction carrier splines.
4. Refer to "Slips In Drive" comments.

WILL NOT HOLD IN PARK

1. Damaged or disconnect manual linkage.
2. Damaged parking pawl spring, pawl and/or parking gear.
3. Damaged actuator assembly or actuator spring.

HARSH N-D OR D-N SHIFT

4T60 Transmission

1. Improper vacuum signal to modulator or defective modulator.
2. Aspirator T-fitting improperly installed or plugged.
3. No. 9 check ball missing from control valve (harsh into reverse).
4. No. 12 check ball missing from control valve (harsh into drive).
5. Thermal element does not close when hot.

4T60-E Transmission

1. Improper vacuum signal to modulator or defective modulator.
2. Broken reverse servo cushion spring.
3. No. 5 check ball missing from control valve (harsh into reverse).
4. No. 6 check ball missing from control valve (harsh into drive).
5. Broken forward servo cushion spring.
6. Thermal element does not close when hot.

2ND GEAR STARTS

4T60 Transmission

1. Incorrect oil pressure.
2. 1-2 shift valve stuck.
3. Governor weights stuck.
4. 1-2 throttle valve bushing retainer installed too deep.

4T60-E Transmission

1. 1-2 shift valve stuck.

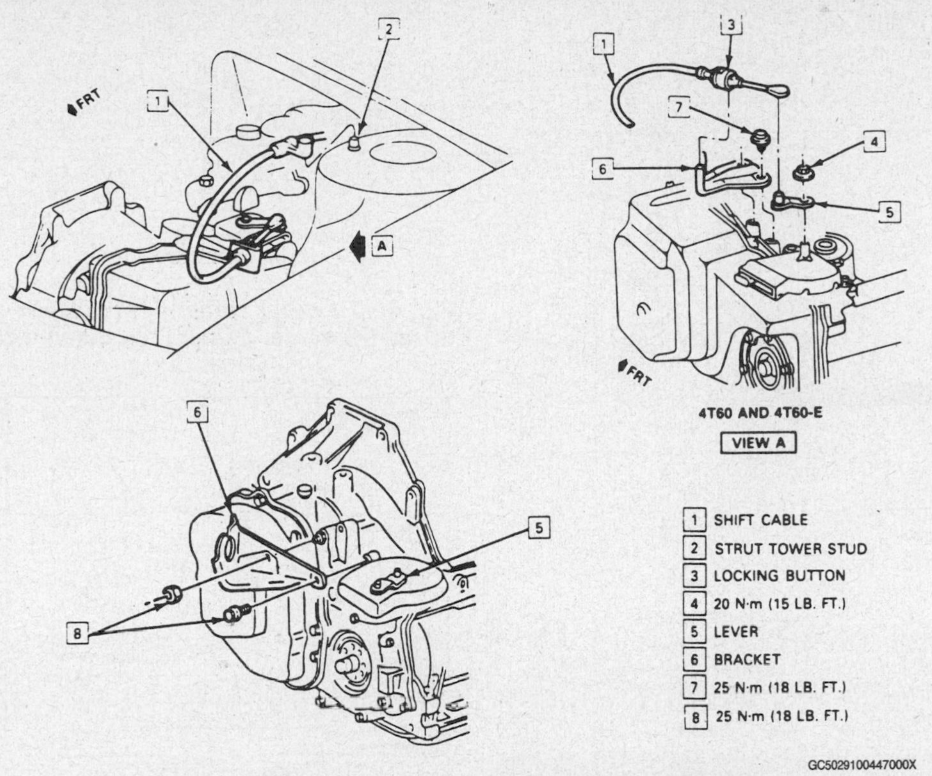
FRT
A
4T60 AND 4T60-E
VIEW A
1 SHIFT CABLE
2 STRUT TOWER STUD
3 LOCKING BUTTON
4 20 N·m (15 LB. FT.)
5 LEVER
6 BRACKET
7 25 N·m (18 LB. FT.)
8 25 N·m (18 LB. FT.)
GC5029100447000X

Fig. 4 Shift control cable adjustment. 1992–93

HARSH ENGAGEMENT OR SHUDDER IN REVERSE

4T60 Transmission

1. 2ND clutch housing drum assembly surface scored or hot spots caused by band slippage.
2. Burned fiber material on reverse band assembly.
3. Reverse servo apply pin too short.

4T60-E Transmission

1. 2ND clutch housing drum assembly surface scored or hot spots caused by band slippage.
2. Burned fiber material on reverse band assembly.
3. Number 5 checkball missing or mislocated.
4. Damaged servo cushion spring.

MAINTENANCE

Refer to "Lubricant Data Chart" in the appropriate chassis chapter of this manual for transmission fluid specifications.

FLUID CHECK

To check fluid, drive vehicle for at least 15 minutes to bring fluid to operating temperature (200°F). With vehicle on a level surface and engine idling in Park and parking brake applied, the level on the dipstick should be at the FULL mark. To bring the fluid level from the ADD mark to the FULL mark requires one pint of fluid. If vehicle cannot be driven sufficiently to bring fluid to operating temperature, the level on the dipstick should be between the two dimples on the dipstick with fluid temperature at 70°F. Note that the two dimples are located above the FULL mark.

An early change to a darker color from the usual red color and/or a strong odor that is usually associated with overheated fluid is normal and should not be considered as a positive sign of required maintenance or unit failure.

When adding fluid, do not overfill, as foaming and loss of fluid through the vent may occur as the fluid heats up. Also, if fluid level is too low, complete loss of drive may occur especially when cold, which can cause transmission failure.

Every 100,000 miles, the oil should be drained, the oil pan removed, the screen cleaned and fresh fluid added. For vehicles subjected to more severe use such as heavy city traffic especially in hot weather, prolonged periods of idling or towing, this maintenance should be performed every 15,000 miles.

FLUID CHANGE

This procedure has been modified by a Technical Service Bulletin.

1. Raise and support vehicle, then position drain pan under oil pan.
2. Remove front and side oil pan attaching bolts, then loosen rear pan attaching bolts.
3. Carefully pry oil pan loose from transaxle case and allow fluid to drain.
4. Remove remaining attaching bolt, oil pan and gasket. Thoroughly clean pan before reinstalling.
5. Remove and discard screen and O-ring seal.
6. Install replacement screen and O-ring seal, locating screen against dipstick stop.
7. Install gasket on oil pan, then apply Loctite 242 or equivalent to oil pan bolts to prevent leakage.
8. **Torque** oil pan bolts to 12-13 ft. lbs.
9. Lower vehicle and add fluid.
10. With selector in park, parking brake applied and engine at idle speed and operating temperature, check fluid level and add fluid as necessary. **Do not race engine or move shift lever through ranges.**

ADJUSTMENTS

SHIFT CONTROL CABLE

1992–93

1. Lift up on cable lock button, located near transaxle cable bracket.
2. Place transaxle manual control lever in Neutral position. Neutral position can be obtained by rotating the manual lever counterclockwise to Park position, then rotate lever clockwise from Park, through Reverse to Neutral.
3. Place transaxle selector lever in the Neutral position.
4. Push down on cable lock button **Fig. 4.**

1994

1. Apply parking brake and block wheels.
2. Position range selector into the NEUTRAL position.
3. Lift up range selector cable locking button.
4. Remove range selector cable end from transaxle range selector level, **Fig. 5.**
5. Position range selector lever into LOW position.
6. Position transaxle range selector lever into LOW position. Obtain LOW position by rotating transaxle range selector lever toward front of vehicle until it stops.
7. Snap range selector cable end onto transaxle range selector lever.
8. Press range selector cable locking button down into the locked position.
9. Position range selector lever into PARK position.
10. Remove wheel blocks and release parking brake.

THROTTLE CABLE

Except Cutlass Supreme, Grand Prix, Lumina & Regal

1. Ensure ignition is in the Off position.
2. Depress and hold metal adjustment tab at engine end of T.V. cable, **Fig. 6.**
3. Move slider until it contacts fitting, then release tab.
4. Check cable for sticking or binding and road test vehicle. **Recheck cable after engine has reached normal**

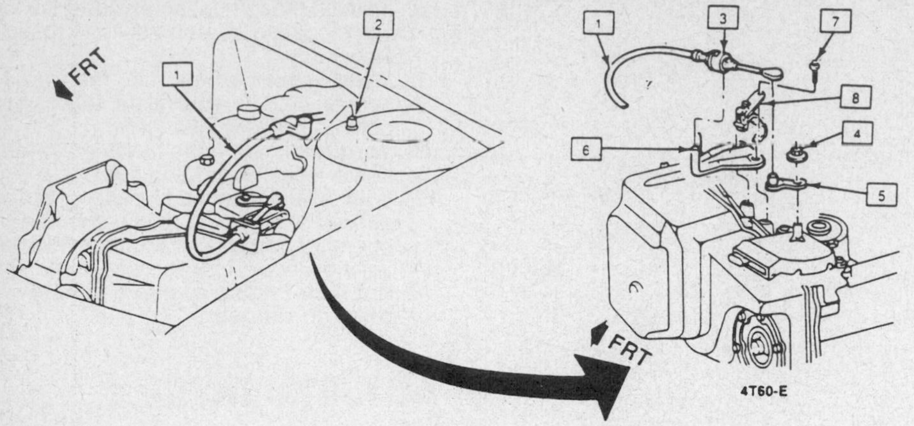
FRT
2
1
3
7
8
4
6
5
FRT
4T60-E

1	CABLE, SHIFT
2	STUD, STRUT TOWER
3	LOCK, CABLE
4	NUT, RANGE SELECTOR LEVER
5	LEVER, RANGE SELECTOR
6	BRACKET, RANGE SELECTOR LEVER
7	BOLT/SCREW, RANGE SELECTOR LEVER CABLE BRACKET
8	CLIP, NEUTRAL START

GC5029400448000X

Fig. 5 Shift control cable adjustment. 1994

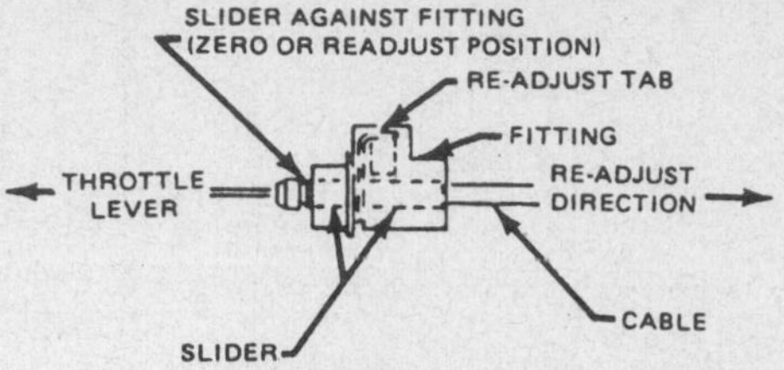
SLIDER AGAINST FITTING
(ZERO OR READJUST POSITION)
RE-ADJUST TAB
FITTING
THROTTLE LEVER
RE-ADJUST DIRECTION
CABLE
SLIDER

Copyrighted Material Reprinted with Permission from Hydra-Matic Div., GM Corp.

TH5028800015000X

Fig. 6 TV cable adjustment. Except Cutlass Supreme, Grand Prix, Lumina & Regal

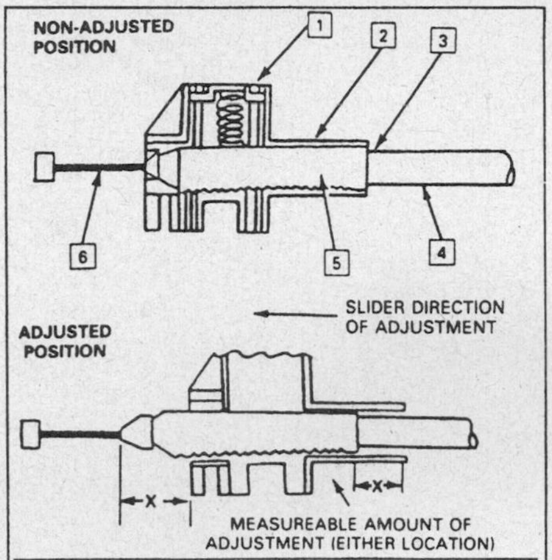
NON-ADJUSTED POSITION
1
2
3
6
5
4
SLIDER DIRECTION OF ADJUSTMENT
ADJUSTED POSITION
X
X
MEASUREABLE AMOUNT OF ADJUSTMENT (EITHER LOCATION)

1. READJUSTMENT BUTTON
2. FITTING
3. SLIDER AGAINST FITTING IN FULL NON-ADJUSTED POSITION
4. CONDUIT
5. SLIDER
6. TO THROTTLE LEVER

Copyrighted Material Reprinted with Permission from Hydra-Matic Div., GM Corp.

TH5028800016000X

Fig. 7 TV cable adjustment. Cutlass Supreme, Grand Prix, Lumina & Regal

operating temperature, as cable may appear to operate properly with engine cold.

Cutlass Supreme, Grand Prix, Lumina & Regal

1. Depress and hold adjustment button, **Fig. 7.**
2. Pull cable conduit out until slider hits against adjustment.
3. Release button.
4. Repeat adjustment.

IN-VEHICLE REPAIRS

VALVE BODY, REPLACE

Lumina, Cutlass Supreme, Grand Prix & Regal Except 3.4L/V6-204 Engine

1. Disconnect negative battery cable and remove air cleaner assembly.
2. Install engine support fixture tool No. J-28467-A, engine support fixture adapter tool No. J-28467-90 and engine support adapter leg tool No. J-36462 or equivalents.
3. Disconnect torque struts at engine mounts.
4. Remove exhaust crossover pipe and two bolts at top of transaxle mount bracket.
5. Raise and support vehicle, then remove left front tire and wheel assembly.
6. Remove left front brake caliper and bracket.
7. Remove four bolts at hub and bearing assembly, then remove front drive axle.
8. Disconnect left lower ball joint, then remove left inner splash shield.
9. Remove pinch bolt at intermediate steering shaft.
10. Support left and right sides of frame with jack stands.
11. Remove frame to body bolts, then adjust left jackstand to lower left side of frame.
12. Remove transaxle mount and mount support.
13. Lower left side of engine/transaxle using engine support fixture.
14. Remove two clamps holding wiring harness to transaxle mount bracket.
15. Remove transaxle mount bracket & case side cover pan.
16. Disconnect electrical connectors from pressure switches.
17. Remove pump to valve body bolts. **Do not remove the three Torx screws that hold the pump assembly together.**
18. Remove 1-2 servo pipe clip and bolt from valve body.
19. Remove valve body to channel plate bolts.
20. Remove valve body, keeping spacer plate with transaxle.
21. Reverse procedure to install.

Lumina, Cutlass Supreme & Grand Prix W/3.4L/V6-204 Engine

1. Disconnect negative battery cable and remove air cleaner assembly.
2. Remove exhaust crossover pipe and bolt at top of transaxle mount bracket.
3. Install engine support fixture tool No. J-28467-A, engine support fixture adapter tool No. J-28467-90 and engine support adapter leg tool No. J-36462 or equivalents.
4. Raise and support vehicle, then remove left front tire and wheel assembly.
5. Remove left inner splash shield.
6. Remove transaxle mount and loosen engine mount nuts at frame.
7. Remove pinch bolt at intermediate steering shaft.
8. Disconnect ball joints at steering knuckle.
9. Support left and right sides of frame with jack stands.
10. Remove left side frame to body bolts, then loosen right side frame to body bolts.
11. Remove left side steering rack bolt and left side drive axle.
12. Remove transaxle mount bracket and case side cover pan.
13. Disconnect electrical connectors from pressure switches.
14. Remove pump to valve body bolts. **Do not remove the three screws that hold the pump assembly together.**

15. Remove valve body to channel plate bolts.
16. Remove valve body, keeping spacer plate with transaxle.
17. Reverse procedure to install.

Century, Cutlass Ciera & Cutlass Cruiser

1. Disconnect battery ground cable and remove air cleaner assembly.
2. **Remove air cleaner housing and intake tube.**
3. **Remove torque struts at engine mounts.**
4. **Disconnect crossover pipe-to-left manifold clamp.**
5. **Loosen crossover pipe-to-right manifold clamp.**
6. **Remove two (2) bolts at top of transaxle mount bracket. Pry crossover pipe to allow removal of front bolt. DO NOT pry on crossover pipe heat shield. If shield is bent, heat damage to other components may occur.**
7. Install engine support assembly J-28467 or equivalent.
8. Rotate steering wheel until bolt securing intermediate shaft to steering gear is facing up, remove bolt, then disconnect intermediate shaft from steering gear stub shaft.
9. Remove upper case side cover retaining bolts.
10. Raise and support vehicle, position jack and block of wood under engine to act as support during cradle removal, then remove left front wheel.
11. Disconnect brake line support clip from underbody.
12. Remove power steering line brackets, steering gear brackets and driveline vibration damper as needed.
13. Remove pinch bolt from left steering knuckle and disconnect lower ball joint.
14. Disconnect stabilizer bar from left control arm, then remove both front stabilizer bar reinforcements and bushings from left and right side members.
15. Disconnect engine and transaxle mounts from cradle.
16. Remove side member to crossmember bolts.
17. Remove bolts securing left side body mounts.
18. Remove left side member and front crossmember assembly. **It may be necessary to pull or gently pry crossmember loose.**
19. Disconnect and remove AIR pipe, if equipped.
20. Remove jack and lower vehicle, then lower transaxle by adjusting engine support fixture.
21. Remove remaining bolts securing transaxle side cover pan.
22. Disconnect drive axle and remove nuts surrounding flange at channel plate. **Do not pry against case side cover to remove axle. Insert pry bar behind axle and use suitable block of wood as fulcrum when removing axle.**
23. Remove case side cover pan and gaskets.
24. Remove valve body retaining bolts, valve body and oil pump as an assembly, **Fig. 8. Do not remove three pump cover to valve body retaining bolts.**
25. Reverse procedure to install.

Bonneville, LeSabre, Park Avenue, Riviera, Toronado, Trofeo, 88 & 98

1. Disconnect battery ground cable.
2. Disconnect vacuum hoses from cruise control servo unit, if equipped.
3. Disconnect electrical connector from neutral/back-up lamp switch.
4. Raise and support vehicle, then remove left front wheel.
5. Remove inner splash shield.
6. Disconnect left tie rod from steering knuckle using suitable puller.
7. Disconnect stabilizer link from left control arm.
8. Install drive axle boot seal protectors, as needed. **Models using silicone (gray) boots on drive axle joints require the use of seal protectors J-33162 or equivalent. Models using thermoplastic boots (black) do not require use of seal protectors.**
9. Disconnect ball joint from left steering knuckle.
10. Disconnect left drive axle from transaxle, using suitable puller, and secure drive axle aside, taking care not to extend drive axle joints.
11. Remove pinch bolt securing intermediate shaft to steering gear and disconnect intermediate shaft from gear.
12. Position suitable jack under transaxle oil pan and raise jack until weight of transaxle is supported.
13. Remove 3 bolts securing frame to body on left side.
14. Lower transaxle just enough to gain access to side cover pan bolts.
15. Disconnect cooler lines from transaxle and plug lines and open fittings.
16. Remove side cover bolts, side cover and gaskets.
17. Remove valve body retaining bolts, valve body, oil pump and gaskets as an assembly, **Fig. 8. Do not remove three No. 40 Torx bolts securing oil pump together.**
18. Reverse procedure to install.

DeVille & Fleetwood (FWD)

1. Disconnect battery ground cable and remove air cleaner.
2. Install engine support fixture J-28467 or equivalent.
3. Remove upper side cover retaining bolts and the fuel pipe bracket.
4. Raise and support vehicle, and remove left front wheel.
5. Disconnect stabilizer shaft from left control arm, noting position of bushings and spacers.
6. Support control arm using suitable jack, then disconnect ball joint from left steering knuckle using suitable puller.
7. Remove left engine splash shield.
8. Remove vacuum pump mounting bolts and secure pump aside, leaving hoses connected.
9. Install drive boot seal protectors J-34754 or equivalent.
10. Disconnect left drive axle from transaxle and secure aside, taking care not to extend drive axle joints.
11. Support transaxle using suitable jack and remove left front transaxle mount.
12. Remove right front engine mount as follows: **Vehicle should be supported at each front frame horn to prevent vehicle from tipping on hoist.**
    a. Disconnect brace between engine bracket and engine.
    b. Remove two nuts securing mount to frame.
    c. Remove two nuts securing transaxle bracket to mount.
    d. Remove two nuts securing transaxle mount to frame bracket.
    e. Raise engine using support fixture, then remove stud and two bolts securing mount bracket to block.
    f. Remove mount and bracket by pulling forward.
13. Loosen left and right rear transaxle mounts.
14. Remove left cradle mounts, separate left cradle and remove from vehicle, **Fig. 9 and 10.**
15. Loosen but do not remove right cradle mounts 2 and 3.
16. Remove jacks ensuring vehicle remains stable, then lower vehicle.
17. Note position of engine support fixture support rods and lower engine/transaxle assembly as follows. **In order to obtain maximum clearance for side cover removal it is necessary to tilt front of engine downwards.**
    a. Move left (driver's side) rear support rod until it extends approximately six inches above "T" nut.
    b. Lower left front support rod until top is flush with top of "T" nut.
18. Raise and support vehicle.
19. Disconnect transaxle cooler lines from bracket and secure aside.
20. Remove remaining side cover retaining bolts and nuts securing axle opening cover.
21. Remove side cover pan and gaskets.
22. Remove wiring harness and VCC solenoid, disconnecting harness from pressure switches and case connector.
23. Remove TV lever, bracket and link assembly.
24. Remove oil pump retaining bolts and the pump assembly. **Do not remove three bolts (A), Fig. 8, securing pump cover to valve body.**
25. Remove valve body retaining bolts and the valve body, noting position of four control valve to spacer plate check balls.
26. Remove oil pump driveshaft.
27. Remove spacer plate and gaskets, noting position of eight spacer to channel plate check balls.
28. Reverse procedure to install.

30 GASKET, SPACER PLATE/CHANNEL PLATE
31 PLATE, VALVE BODY SPACER
32 GASKET, SPACER PLATE/VALVE BODY
34 BALL, CHECK VALVE (8)
35 VALVE ASSEMBLY, CONTROL
44 PUMP ASSEMBLY
45 BOLT, PUMP BODY TO CASE (2)
46 BOLT, PUMP COVER TO CHANNEL PLATE (10)
47 BOLT, PUMP COVER TO VALVE BODY (1)
48 HARNESS, WIRING
49 LINK, THROTTLE LEVER TO CABLE
50 LEVER & BRACKET ASSEMBLY, THROTTLE
51 PAN, CASE SIDE COVER
52 SCREW, SPECIAL M8X1.25X16.0
53 NUT, FLANGED HEX (M6X1.0)
61 CLIP, TWO WIRE
62 CLIP, TWO WIRE
64 GASKET, SIDE COVER PAN
65 GASKET, SIDE COVER TO CHANNEL PLATE

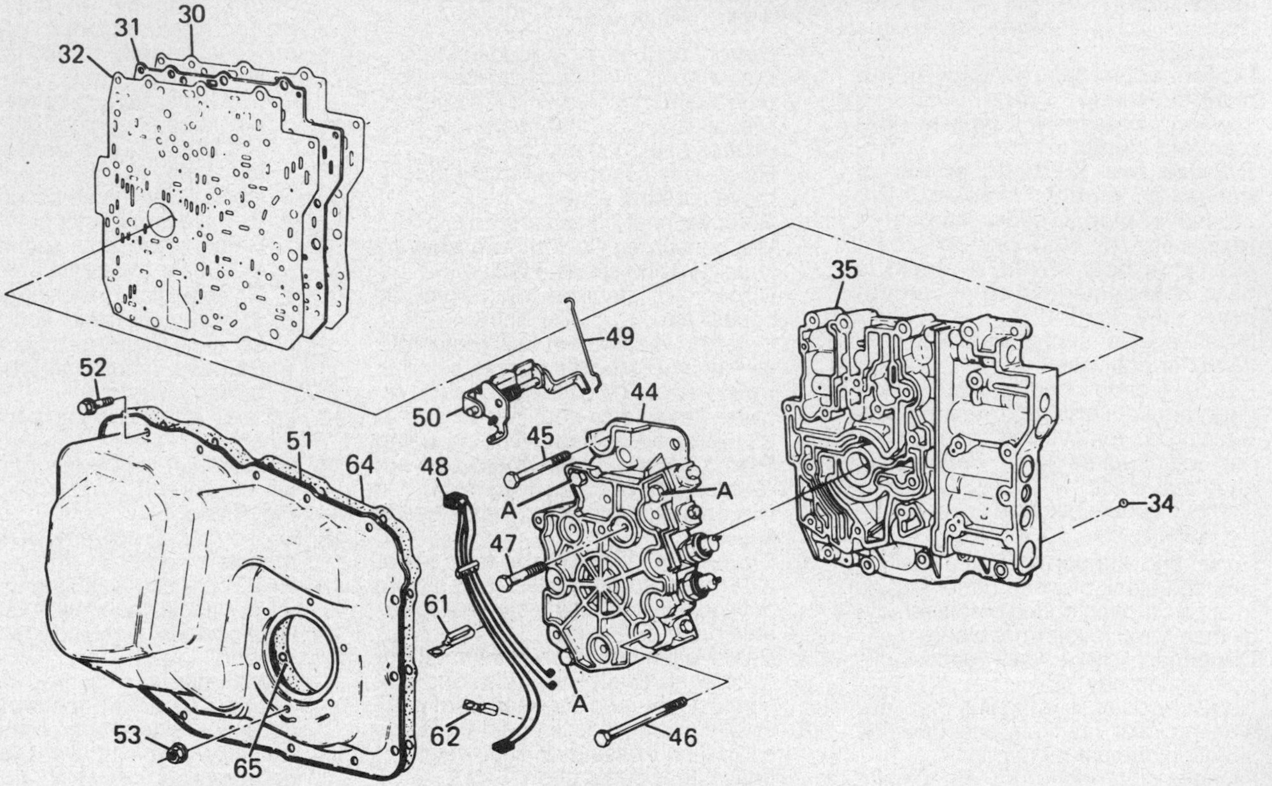
30
31
32
35
49
52
50
44
51
64
48
45
A
A
47
34
61
A
62
46
53
65
TH5028800018000X

Fig. 8 Valve body assembly

Eldorado & Seville

1. Disconnect battery ground cable and remove air cleaner assembly.
2. Remove inner engine cooling fan assembly.
3. Disconnect vacuum hoses from cruise control servo and vacuum modulator (if equipped).
4. Disconnect electrical connectors from cruise control servo, distributor, oil pressure sending unit and transaxle.
5. Disconnect TV cable from throttle lever and bracket, and from transaxle.
6. Remove vacuum modulator (if equipped).
7. Install engine support fixture J-28467 or equivalent and note position of left side support hooks.
8. Raise and support vehicle, then remove left wheel assembly.
9. Remove right and left wheel housing lower splash shields.
10. Remove left stabilizer bar link and support left control arm with suitable jack.
11. Remove left ball joint cotter pin and nut, then disconnect ball joint using suitable puller.
12. Remove four nuts securing transaxle to cradle and bracket.
13. Remove A/C compressor splash shield, No. 1 cradle mount insulator cover, **Fig. 9,** and the left side engine mount and damper fasteners.
14. Remove six right front cradle joining bolts, **Fig. 10.**
15. Remove left stabilizer mount retaining bolts.
16. Remove two left rear cradle joining bolts, **Fig. 10.**
17. Disconnect wire loom and vacuum hoses from retainers on cradle and transaxle.
18. Disconnect hoses from AIR pipe and disconnect pipe retainer from rear of cradle.
19. Lower vehicle.
20. Raise engine/transaxle assembly two inches using support fixture hooks at flywheel end of engine.
21. Raise and support vehicle.
22. Remove No. 1 insulator bolt and separate right front corner of cradle assembly, **Fig. 10,** then remove left cradle section.
23. Disconnect AIR valve from transaxle and position aside.
24. Remove stud bolts securing transaxle bracket to bellhousing, noting position of bolts for installation.
25. Lower vehicle, the lower engine/transaxle assembly to position noted in step 7.
26. Remove transaxle mount bracket upper stud bolts and the bracket, rotating bracket clockwise to air removal.
27. Lower left side of transaxle to limit allowed by support hooks.
28. Raise vehicle and install suitable drive axle boot seal protectors.
29. Disconnect drive axle and secure toward rear of vehicle, taking care not to overextend drive axle joints.
30. Remove case side cover pan bolts, pan and gaskets.
31. Remove wiring harness and VCC solenoid from pressure switches and case connector.
32. Remove TV lever, bracket and link as-

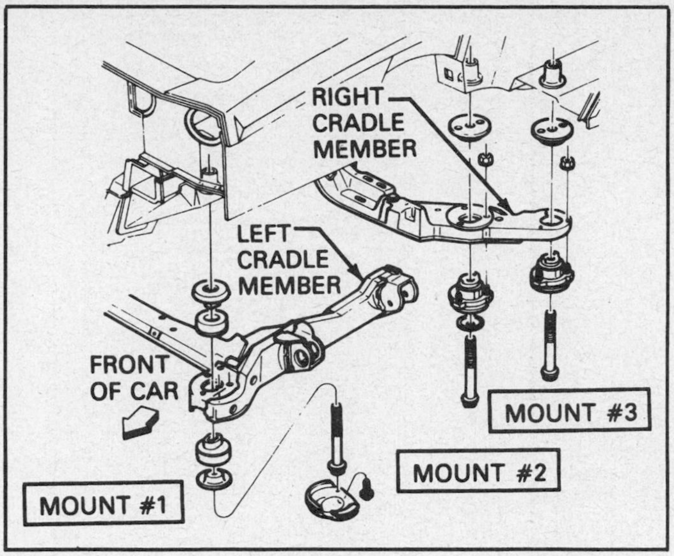
RIGHT
CRADLE
MEMBER
LEFT
CRADLE
MEMBER
FRONT
OF CAR
MOUNT #3
MOUNT #2
MOUNT #1
TH5028800019000X

Fig. 9 Support cradle mounting. Cadillac

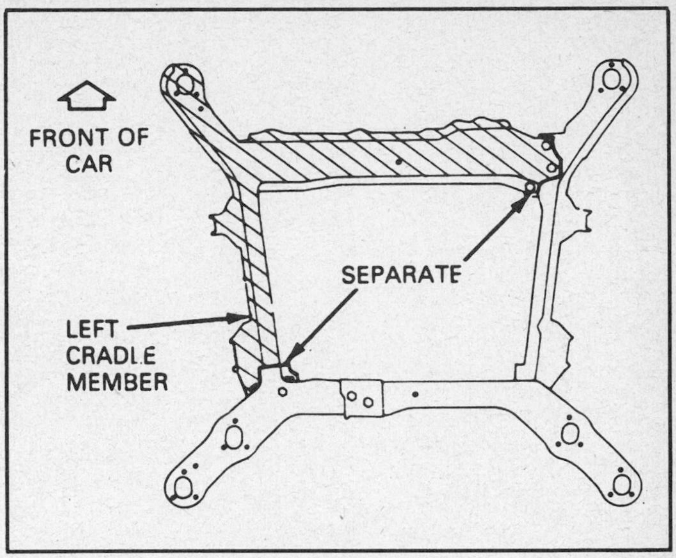
FRONT OF
CAR
SEPARATE
LEFT
CRADLE
MEMBER
TH5028800020000X

Fig. 10 Support cradle separating. Cadillac

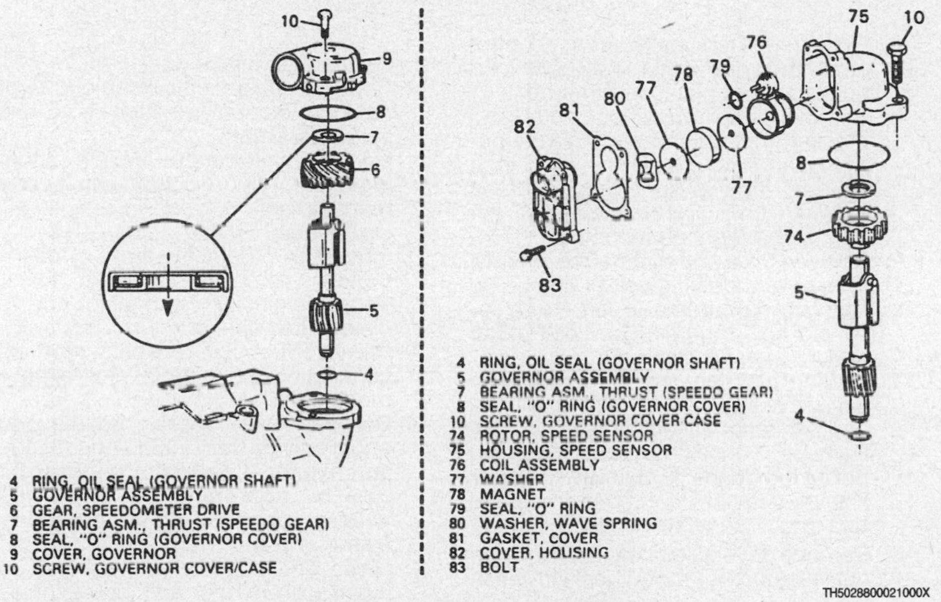
4 RING, OIL SEAL (GOVERNOR SHAFT)
5 GOVERNOR ASSEMBLY
6 GEAR, SPEEDOMETER DRIVE
7 BEARING ASM., THRUST (SPEEDO GEAR)
8 SEAL, "O" RING (GOVERNOR COVER)
9 COVER, GOVERNOR
10 SCREW, GOVERNOR COVER/CASE
4 RING, OIL SEAL (GOVERNOR SHAFT)
5 GOVERNOR ASSEMBLY
7 BEARING ASM., THRUST (SPEEDO GEAR)
8 SEAL, "O" RING (GOVERNOR COVER)
10 SCREW, GOVERNOR COVER CASE
74 ROTOR, SPEED SENSOR
75 HOUSING, SPEED SENSOR
76 COIL ASSEMBLY
77 WASHER
78 MAGNET
79 SEAL, "O" RING
80 WASHER, WAVE SPRING
81 GASKET, COVER
82 COVER, HOUSING
83 BOLT
TH5028800021000X

Fig. 11 Governor assembly

sembly.
33. Remove oil pump retaining bolts and the pump assembly. **Do not remove three bolts (A), Fig. 8, securing pump cover to valve body.**
34. Remove valve body retaining bolts and the valve body, noting position of four control valve to spacer plate check balls.
35. Remove oil pump driveshaft.
36. Remove spacer plate and gaskets, noting position of eight spacer to channel plate check balls.
37. Reverse procedure to install.

GOVERNOR, REPLACE

4T60 Transmission

1. Raise and support vehicle.
2. Remove speed sensor assembly.
3. Remove governor cover attaching bolts, then the cover and seal.
4. Remove governor complete with sleeve and speedometer drive gear, **Fig. 11.**
5. Reverse procedure to install.

ACCUMULATOR, REPLACE

1. Raise and support vehicle.
2. Drain transaxle fluid into a suitable container, then remove oil pan.
3. Remove oil filter and seal, then the accumulator cover attaching bolts and cover.
4. Remove accumulator piston, oil seal and spring.
5. Reverse procedure to install.

1-2 & REVERSE SERVO, REPLACE

4T60 Transmission

1. Disconnect exhaust crossover pipe.
2. Depress servo cover, then remove snap ring and servo cover.
3. Remove servo piston, sealing ring, apply pin and servo spring, **Fig. 12.**
4. Reverse procedure to install.

REVERSE SERVO, REPLACE

4T60-E Transmission

1. Remove air cleaner assembly and exhaust crossover pipe.
2. Raise drivers side of car so it is higher than differential side. This will ensure that the reverse band will be in the proper location.
3. Depress servo cover, then remove snap ring, servo cover, servo piston, sealing ring, apply pin and servo spring, **Fig. 6.**
4. Reverse procedure to install.

FORWARD SERVO, REPLACE

4T60-E Transmission

1. Install engine support fixture tool No. J-28467-A, engine support fixture adapter tool No. J-28467-90 and engine support adapter leg tool No. J-36462 or equivalents.
2. Raise and support vehicle.
3. Remove power steering rack and pinion heat shield.
4. Remove power steering rack and pinion mounting bolts and hang steering rack from exhaust pipe flange.
5. Disconnect transaxle and engine mounts.
6. Support rear of frame with jackstand, then loosen front frame bolts and remove rear frame bolts.
7. Lower frame from jackstand, then disconnect power steering lines from right side of frame.
8. Remove servo cover bolts, servo cover, servo piston, sealing ring, apply pin, servo spring retainer and servo spring, **Fig. 2.**
9. Reverse procedure to install.

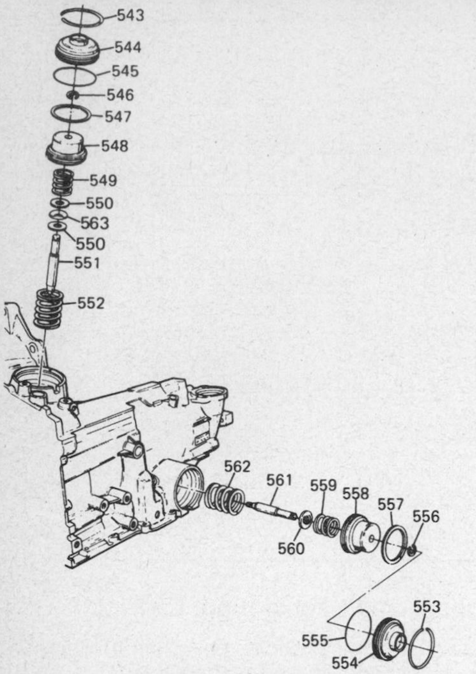
543
544
545
546
547
548
549
550
563
550
551
552
562
561
559
558
557
556
560
553
555
554

543 RING, SERVO COVER RETAINING
544 COVER, SERVO (REVERSE)
545 SEAL, "O" RING (COVER TO CASE)
546 RING, SNAP (BAND APPLY PIN)
547 RING, OIL SEAL PISTON
548 PISTON, REVERSE SERVO
549 SPRING, REVERSE SERVO CUSHION
550 RETAINER, SERVO CUSHION SPRING
551 PIN, REVERSE APPLY
552 SPRING, SERVO RETURN
553 RING, SERVO COVER RETAINING
554 COVER, SERVO (1-2)
555 SEAL, "O" RING (COVER TO CASE)
556 RING, SNAP (BAND APPLY PIN)
557 RING, OIL SEAL PISTON
558 PISTON, 1-2 SERVO
559 SPRING, 1-2 SERVO CUSHION
560 RETAINER, SERVO CUSHION SPRING
561 PIN, 1-2 BAND APPLY
562 SPRING, SERVO RETURN
563 SPRING, WAVE

TH5028800022000X

Fig. 12 1-2 & reverse servo assembly

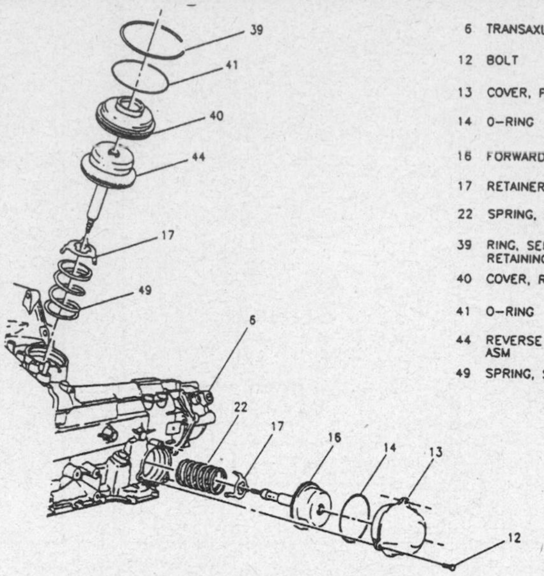
39
41
40
44
17
49
6
22
17
16
14
13
12

6 TRANSAXLE EXTENSION CASE
12 BOLT
13 COVER, FORWARD SERVO
14 O-RING
16 FORWARD SERVO PISTON ASM
17 RETAINER
22 SPRING, SERVO RETURN
39 RING, SERVO COVER RETAINING
40 COVER, REVERSE SERVO
41 O-RING
44 REVERSE SERVO PISTON ASM
49 SPRING, SERVO RETURN

TH5029200023000X

Fig. 13 Reverse & forward servo. 4T60–E

TRANSAXLE

REPLACE

CENTURY, CUTLASS CIERA & CUTLASS CRUISER

1. Disconnect battery ground cable, then remove air cleaner and duct assembly.
2. Disconnect the following electrical connectors: TCC switch, A/C low pressure switch and Park/Neutral Position switch.
3. Disconnect TV cable from throttle body and transaxle, then shift control cable from transaxle mounting bracket and lever.
4. Disconnect vacuum modulator line from modulator, then remove three upper transaxle bolts from engine and ground wires.
5. Remove steering shaft pinch bolt, then install engine support fixture.
6. Raise and support vehicle, then remove front wheel assemblies and splash shields.
7. Remove pinch bolts from control arms, then stabilizer shaft bolts and reinforcement plates from frame.
8. Remove stabilizer shaft nuts and bracket from control arm, then separate shaft from arm. Using a $^{7}/_{16}$ inch drill bit, drill two spot welds located between front and rear holes of left front stabilizer shaft mounting.
9. Remove front and rear transaxle nuts, then power steering cooler line bolts.
10. Remove right frame to left frame retaining bolt, then position jack stand under frame for support.
11. Loosen two right frame mounts and discard bolts, then two left frame bolts and left frame assembly.
12. Remove transaxle mount retaining bolts from transaxle case, then mount.
13. Remove transaxle converter covers and torque converter bolts.
14. Remove drive axles from transaxle as outlined under "Front Wheel Drive Axles."
15. Remove transaxle support bracket bolts from transaxle, then disconnect vehicle speed sensor electrical connector from transaxle.
16. Disconnect transaxle cooler lines, then install transaxle jack.
17. Remove rear transaxle bolts from engine, remaining transaxle bolts, then transaxle.
18. Reverse procedure to install.

BONNEVILLE, LESABRE, PARK AVENUE, RIVIERA, TORONADO, TROFEO, 88 & 98

1. Disconnect battery ground cable.
2. Disconnect cross brace from struts towers as follows:
   a. Loosen bar assembly through-bolts.
   b. Remove inboard strut nuts.
   c. Remove brace assembly.
   d. Install inboard strut nuts.
3. Remove air intake duct.
4. Remove cruise control cable at throttle body, vacuum hoses at servo, then servo assembly.
5. Remove shift control linkage mounting bracket at transaxle, then lever at manual shaft.
6. Disconnect wiring connectors at: transaxle Park/Neutral Position switch and back up lamp switch, transaxle electrical connector and vehicle speed sensor.
7. Remove fuel pipe retainers, then disconnect vacuum modulator hose at modulator.
8. Remove top three transaxle-to-engine bolts, then install engine support fixture. **-Load- the support fixture by tightening the wing nuts several turns to relieve tension on frame and mounts.**
9. Raise and support vehicle, then remove front wheel and ball joint assemblies.
10. Separate control arms from steering knuckles. **Drive axle seal protector J 34754 should be modified and installed on any drive axle prior to service. Failure to observe this can result in damage and possible joint failure.**
11. Remove right drive axle from transaxle **only; do not remove from hub/knuckle assembly.**
12. Remove left drive axle from transaxle **and** hub/knuckle assembly.
13. Support transaxle with jackstand, then remove left front transaxle mount.
14. Remove torque strut bracket from transaxle, then left rear transaxle mount-to-transaxle bolts.
15. Remove transaxle brace from engine bracket, then stabilizer shaft link-to-control arm bolt.
16. Remove flywheel cover bolts, flywheel cover and flywheel-to-converter bolts. Mark flywheel to converter relationship to ensure proper

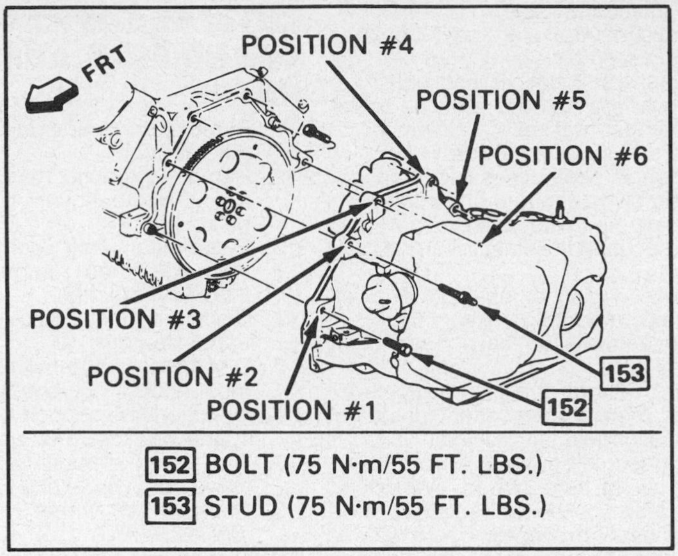
FRT
POSITION #4
POSITION #5
POSITION #6
POSITION #3
POSITION #2
POSITION #1
153
152
152 BOLT (75 N·m/55 FT. LBS.)
153 STUD (75 N·m/55 FT. LBS.)

TH5028800024000X

Fig. 14 Bellhousing bolt removal. Cadillac

installation.

17. Remove bolts attaching rear frame member to front frame dog leg.
18. Remove front left frame-to-body bolts, then front left frame dog leg-to-right frame member bolts.
19. Remove frame assembly by swinging aside and supporting with suitable stand, then disconnect cooler pipes at transaxle.
20. Remove remaining transaxle-to-engine bolts. **One bolt is located between transaxle case and engine block and is installed in opposite direction.**
21. Lower transaxle away from vehicle.
22. Reverse procedure to install.

DEVILLE & FLEETWOOD (FWD)

1. Disconnect battery ground cable and remove air cleaner assembly.
2. Remove T.V. cable (if equipped) and cable-to-cooler line bracket.
3. Remove exhaust crossover pipe.
4. Disconnect shift cable bracket and manual lever from transaxle, then secure cable, bracket and lever aside.
5. Disconnect electrical connectors from transaxle, cruise control servo and neutral/back-up lamp switch.
6. Remove upper bolts and studs securing bellhousing to engine block (positions 2, 3, 4 and 5), **Fig. 14.**
7. Disconnect vacuum line from modulator (if equipped).
8. Install engine support fixture J-28467 or equivalent, noting the following:
   a. Ensure fixture is installed in extreme forward position across both strut towers.
   b. The two-piece, link-type hook should be used at passenger side rear engine hook, and both drivers side hooks should be positioned vertically.
   c. Hooks should be tightened to remove all looseness and slack, but it is not necessary to actually raise engine.
9. Raise and support vehicle, then remove front wheels.
10. Support lower control arms using suitable jacks, then disconnect both ball joints from steering knuckles using suitable puller.
11. Install suitable drive axle boot seal protectors, separate drive axles from transaxle, then secure drive axles aside. **Care must be taken not to overextend driveshaft pot joints, as joint will be damaged.**
12. Remove left stabilizer link and mounting clamp bolts, then clamp, bushings and spacers, noting position for installation.
13. Remove A/C compressor and left engine splash shields, left No. 1 mount cover and wiring harness cover.
14. Remove vacuum pump from left cradle and secure aside, then disconnect electrical connector from vehicle speed sensor.
15. Remove fasteners securing right and left front engine/transaxle mounts to cradle.
16. Remove left No. 1 mount bolts, then separate and remove left cradle assembly.
17. Disconnect and plug cooler lines, then unfasten cooler line bracket.
18. Remove transaxle-to-engine support bracket.
19. Remove right rear mount-to-transaxle bracket and fasteners securing left rear mount to transaxle.
20. Remove flexplate dust cover and colts securing flexplate to torque converter.
21. Support transaxle with suitable jack, then remove bellhousing-to-engine bolts at positions No. 1 and 6, **Fig. 14. To remove bolt No. 6, it is necessary to use a suitable extension and access bolt through right wheel house opening.**
22. Separate and remove transaxle assembly.
23. Reverse procedure to install.

ELDORADO & SEVILLE

1. Disconnect battery ground cable and remove air cleaner assembly.
2. Disconnect and remove T.V. cable (if equipped).
3. Remove cruise control servo.
4. Disconnect electrical connectors from distributor, oil pressure sending unit and transaxle.
5. Remove engine oil cooler line bracket.
6. Disconnect shift cable bracket and manual lever from transaxle, then secure cable, bracket and lever aside.
7. Remove fuel line bracket and disconnect neutral safety switch electrical connector.
8. Remove vacuum modulator (if equipped).
9. Remove T.V. cable support bracket (if equipped) and remaining engine oil cooler line bracket.
10. Remove bellhousing bolts No. 2, 3, 4 and 6, **Fig. 14.**
11. Disconnect AIR crossover pipe fitting and reposition pipe.
12. Remove radiator hose bracket and fasteners securing transaxle mount to bracket.
13. Install engine support bracket J-28467 or equivalent, and note position of support hooks.
14. Raise and support vehicle and remove front wheels.
15. Remove left and right stabilizer link bolts, ball joint cotter pins and ball joint retaining nuts.
16. Support control arms using suitable jacks, then disconnect left and right ball joints using suitable puller.
17. Remove A/C compressor splash shield and No. 1 cradle mount cover.
18. Disconnect AIR pipe end hose connections and rear mounting clip.
19. Disconnect vacuum hoses and wire loom from front of cradle.
20. Remove fasteners securing engine mount, damper and transaxle mount to cradle and wire loom to transaxle bracket.
21. Lower vehicle, then raise transaxle 2 inches from position noted in step 13 using left support hooks of engine support fixture.
22. Raise and support vehicle.

23. Remove left side stabilizer mounting bolts and bolts joining cradle at right front and left rear corners.
24. Remove No. 1 cradle mount bolts. Separate cradle at right front corner, then remove left cradle section.
25. Disconnect AIR management valve bracket from transaxle mounting bracket and secure valve and bracket assembly to transaxle stud bolt.
26. Lower vehicle, then lower engine/transaxle assembly to position noted in step 13.
27. Remove transaxle mounting bracket.
28. Raise and support vehicle.
29. Remove bracket from right transaxle mount to transaxle and bolts securing engine/transaxle brace to transaxle.
30. Disconnect electrical connector from vehicle speed sensor.
31. Remove flexplate dust covers and bolts securing flexplate to torque converter.
32. Support transaxle with suitable jack, then remove bellhousing bolts No. 1 and 6, **Fig. 14.To remove bolt No. 6, use suitable extension to gain access through right front wheel house opening.**
33. Disconnect cooler lines from transaxle, then plug lines and open fittings.
34. Install suitable drive axle boot seal protectors, separate drive axles from transaxle and secure axles aside. **Care must be taken not to overextend drive axle pot joints, as joint will be damaged.**
35. Separate and remove transaxle assembly.
36. Reverse procedure to install.

RIVIERA, TORONADO & TROFEO

1. Disconnect battery ground cable and install engine support fixture J-28467 or equivalent.
2. Disconnect vacuum hose from modulator (if equipped) and electrical connectors from transaxle.
3. Disconnect T.V. cable (if equipped) from throttle body and transaxle.
4. Remove cruise control servo, if equipped.
5. Disconnect selector cable bracket and manual selector lever from transaxle, then secure cable, bracket and lever assembly aside.
6. Remove neutral start/back-up lamp switch assembly.
7. Remove top 3 bellhousing bolts, securing wiring harness and the driveline damper bracket.
8. Raise and support vehicle.
9. Disconnect cooler lines from transaxle, then plug lines and open fittings.
10. Remove flexplate dust cover and bolts securing flexplate to torque converter.
11. Remove engine mount nuts and left transaxle mounting bolts.
12. Remove sway bar links from lower control arms.
13. Ensure control arm is properly supported, then remove cotter pin and nut and disconnect left ball joint.
14. Disconnect left drive axle from transaxle, taking care not to overextend drive axle pot joints. **Use drive axle boot seal protector J-33162 or equivalent on models with silicone (gray) drive axle boots. Models with thermoplastic (black) boots do not require the use of protectors.**
15. Remove left side frame (cradle) as follows:
    a. Remove bolt securing lower control arm assembly to frame and the strut rod nut, then rotate control arm aside.
    b. Remove engine splash shield.
    c. Disconnect wiring harness from front crossmember.
    d. Remove lower nut securing driveline vibration damper and 2 nuts securing front engine mount to frame.
    e. Disconnect left transaxle mount from frame.
    f. Remove 3 bolts from rear left side of rail and 4 bolts from right end of front crossmember.
    g. Remove left front frame mount cover and mounting bolt.
    h. Separate and remove left frame section.
16. Support transaxle with suitable jack, then remove 2 remaining bellhousing bolts.
17. Remove engine-to-transaxle brace.
18. Disconnect right drive axle and secure aside, taking care not to overextend drive axle pot joints.
19. Separate and remove transaxle.
20. Reverse procedure to install.

CUTLASS SUPREME, GRAND PRIX, LUMINA & REGAL

1. Remove air cleaner assembly and intake air tube.
2. Remove exhaust crossover pipe to lefthand exhaust manifold attaching bolts.
3. Disconnect shift control cable at transaxle, then remove cable from mounting bracket.
4. Disconnect electrical connection at transaxle.
5. Disconnect vacuum line from vacuum modulator (if equipped).
6. Install engine support fixture J28477-1, adapter 28467-90 and leg J36462.
7. Raise and support vehicle, then remove both wheel and tire assemblies.
8. Remove left wheel housing splash shield.
9. Disconnect power steering rack and pinion and support it to body.
10. Disconnect right and left ball joints at steering knuckle. Use ball joint remover tool No. J35917 or equivalent to separate ball joints at steering knuckle.
11. Disconnect power steering cooler lines from frame.
12. Remove engine mount nuts, then loosen splash shield. Support frame with jackstand, then disconnect frame from vehicle.
13. Remove support.
14. **On models equipped with 3.4L/V6-204 engine,** remove generator splash shield.
15. **On all models,** remove torque converter cover and converter-to-flywheel bolts/screws.
16. Disconnect wiring harness at transaxle.
17. Disconnect drive axles from transaxle.
18. Install jackstand to transaxle, then disconnect ground wires at transaxle.
19. Remove lower transaxle oil cooler lines at transaxle, then disconnect engine wiring harness.
20. Lower transaxle side using engine support fixture.
21. Transaxle oil cooler lines should be flushed whenever transaxle has been removed for overhaul or replacement of torque converter, pump or case.
22. Reverse procedure to install

TIGHTENING SPECIFICATIONS

Component	Torque/Ft. Lbs.
BONNEVILLE, LESABRE, PARK AVENUE, 88 & 98	
Flywheel Cover	136①
Governor Cover	132①
Left Front And Right Rear Mount To Transaxle	40
Left Rear Mount To Transaxle	30
Neutral Start & Back-Up Switch	20
Oil Cooler Lines At Radiator	20
Oil Cooler Lines At Transaxle	16
Starter Bolts	32
Throttle Cable To Transaxle	75①
Transaxle Mount To Frame Nuts	30
Transaxle To Engine Bolts	55
Torque Converter Bolts	46
Wheel Lug Nuts	100
CENTURY, CUTLASS CIERA & CUTLASS CRUISER	
Bracket To Transaxle Bolt	41
Channel Plate Attaching Bolts	41
Console Shift Control Assembly Nut	18
Fill Tube Bolt	18
Flywheel Cover Bolts	89①
Governor Housing Bolts	98①
Modulator retaining bolt	20
Mount To Bracket Nut	35
Oil Pan Bolts	12
Park/Neutral Switch Bolts	21
Shift Control Bracket	18
Shift Control Lever	15
TCC Solenoid Screws	125①
Torque Converter Bolts	46
Transaxle Case Side Cover	125①
Transaxle Cooler Pipe Clip Bolt	35
Transaxle Cooler Pipe To Radiator	13
Valve Body Bolts	125①
Wheel Lug Nuts	100
CUTLASS SUPREME, GRAND PRIX, LUMINA & REGAL	
Auxiliary Oil Cooler Bolt	18
Auxiliary Oil Cooler Nut	89①
Bracket To Transaxle Front Bolts	35
Bracket To Transaxle Top Bolt	61
Console Shift Control Nut	18
Engine To Transaxle Brace Bolt	35
Fill Tube Bolt	18
Flywheel Cover Bolt	89①
Governor Housing Bolts	98①
Modulator Retaining Bolt	18
Mount To Support Nut	35
Neutral Start Switch	18
Oil Cooler Line Clip Bolt	35
Oil Cooler Line To Radiator	13
Oil Pan Bolts②	12

Component	Torque/Ft. Lbs.
CUTLASS SUPREME, GRAND PRIX, LUMINA & REGAL-Continued	
Oil Pan Bolts③	13
Oil Scoop Retaining Bolt②	116①
Oil Scoop Retaining Bolt③	71①
Shift Control Bracket	18
Shift Control Lever	15
Support Frame Bolt	38
Support Frame Nut	32
TCC Solenoid Screws	125①
Throttle Cable Bolt	89①
Torque Converter Bolt	44
Transaxle Case Side Cover	125①
Transaxle To Engine Bolts	55
Valve Body Bolts	125①
Wheel Lug Nuts	100
DEVILLE, ELDORADO, FLEETWOOD & SEVILLE	
Accumulator Assembly Bolt	20
Case Side Cover Bolts	7–10
Extension Cover Bolts	22–30
Filler Tube Bracket Bolt	15
Flywheel Cover Bolts	10
Frame To Body Bolts	83
Modular Retainer Bolt	15–20
Oil Cooler Line And Tube Nut	24–33
Oil Cooler Line Ballcheck Fitting At Transaxle	34–43
Oil Pan Bolt	12–13
Oil Scoop Retaining Bolt	4–8
Shift Control Cable Bracket To Transaxle	18
Speed Sensor To Transaxle Extension Bolt	8
Torque Converter Bolts	46
Wheel Lug Nuts	100
RIVIERA, TORONADO & TROFEO	
Accumulator Assembly Attaching Bolt	20
Auxiliary Oil Cooler Mounting Bolt	15
Auxiliary Oil Cooler Pipe Fitting	20
Brace To Engine Bracket Bolt	37
Brace To Transaxle Bolt	33
Bracket To Case Extension Bolt	50
Bracket To Transaxle Mount Nut	30
Case Extension Bolt	27
Case Side Cover Bolt	7–10
Engine Bracket To Engine Bolt	70
Extension Cover Bolt	22–30
Filler Tube Bracket Bolt	15
Flywheel Cover Bolt	115①
Frame Nut	30
Frame To Body Bolt	83
Front Side Of Bracket To Transaxle Bolt/Stud	47
Front Top Of Bracket To Transaxle/Engine Bolt	55

TIGHTENING SPECIFICATIONS-Continued

Component	Torque/Ft. Lbs.
Modulator Bolt	15–20
Neutral Start Switch Shift Lever Nut	15
Neutral Start Switch Bolt	20
Oil Cooler Line Ballcheck Fitting At Transaxle	34–43
Oil Cooler Line To Radiator	20
Oil Cooler Line To Transaxle	24–33
Oil Pan Bolt	12–13
Oil Scoop Bolt	44–97①
Rear Top Of Bracket To Transaxle Bolt	43
Shift Control Cable Bracket To Transaxle	18
Shift Lever To Neutral Start Switch	15
Speed Sensor To Case Extension Bolt	97①
Starter Bolts	32
Torque Converter Bolts	46
Wheel Lug Nuts	100

①—Inch lbs.
②—4T60.
③—4T60-E.

Turbo Hydra-Matic 4L60 & 4L60—E Automatic Transmissions

INDEX

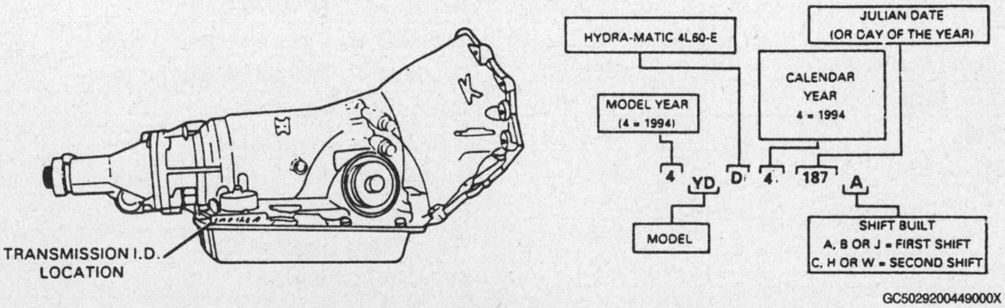

TRANSMISSION I.D. LOCATION
HYDRA-MATIC 4L60-E
JULIAN DATE (OR DAY OF THE YEAR)
CALENDAR YEAR 4 = 1994
MODEL YEAR (4 = 1994)
4
YD
D
4
187
A
MODEL
SHIFT BUILT
A, B OR J = FIRST SHIFT
C, H OR W = SECOND SHIFT
GC5029200449000X

Fig. 1 Transmission identification number location

IDENTIFICATION

The 4L60 and 4L60-E transmissions have a metal identification nameplate attached to the case exterior or a stamped identification number on the pan rail, **Fig. 1.**

DESCRIPTION

4L60 TRANSMISSION

The 4L60, **Fig. 2,** is a fully automatic transmission consisting of a 3-element hydraulic torque converter with the addition of a converter clutch.

Also two planetary gear sets, five multiple-disc type clutches, two roller or one-way clutches and a band are used which provide the friction elements to produce four forward speeds, the last of which is overdrive.

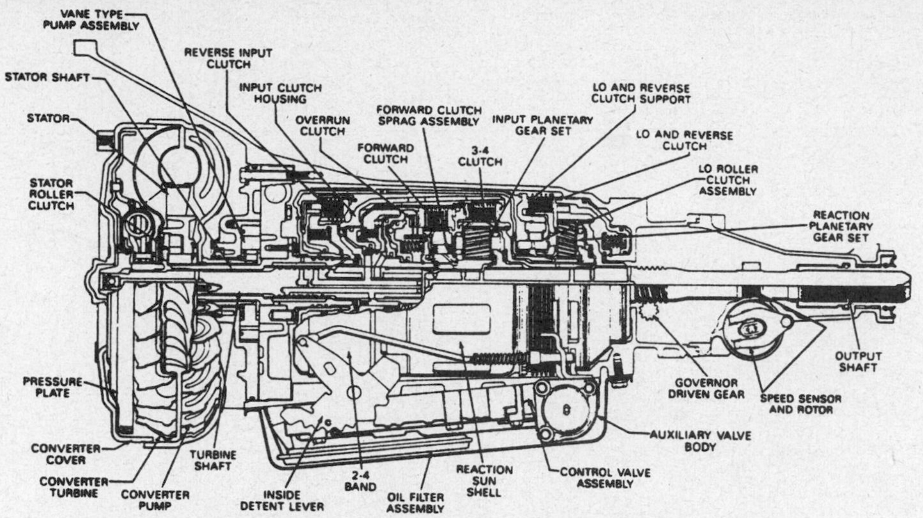
VANE TYPE PUMP ASSEMBLY
REVERSE INPUT CLUTCH
STATOR SHAFT
INPUT CLUTCH HOUSING
LO AND REVERSE CLUTCH SUPPORT
FORWARD CLUTCH SPRAG ASSEMBLY
STATOR
OVERRUN CLUTCH
INPUT PLANETARY GEAR SET
LO AND REVERSE CLUTCH
FORWARD CLUTCH
3-4 CLUTCH
LO ROLLER CLUTCH ASSEMBLY
STATOR ROLLER CLUTCH
REACTION PLANETARY GEAR SET
OUTPUT SHAFT
GOVERNOR DRIVEN GEAR
SPEED SENSOR AND ROTOR
PRESSURE PLATE
AUXILIARY VALVE BODY
CONVERTER COVER
TURBINE SHAFT
REACTION SUN SHELL
CONTROL VALVE ASSEMBLY
2-4 BAND
CONVERTER TURBINE
CONVERTER PUMP
INSIDE DETENT LEVER
OIL FILTER ASSEMBLY

Copyrighted Material Reprinted with Permission from Hydra-Matic Div., GM Corp.

TH5028800360000X

Fig. 2 4L60 automatic transmission

The torque converter, through oil, couples the engine power to the gear sets and hydraulically provides additional torque multiplication when required. Also, through the converter clutch, the converter drive and driven members operate as one unit when applied, providing mechanical drive from the engine through the transmission.

The gear ratio changes are fully automatic in relation to the vehicle speed and engine torque. Vehicle speed and engine torque are directed to the transmission providing the proper gear ratio for maximum efficiency and performance at all throttle openings.

A hydraulic system pressurized by a variable capacity vane-type pump, provides the operating pressure required for the operation of the friction elements and automatic controls.

4L60–E TRANSMISSION

The 4L60-E **Fig. 3** is an electronically controlled version of the 4L60 transmission. A Power Control Module (PCM) manages engine and transmission functions as a single system. The PCM retards engine spark for an instant during each gear shift which reduces engine torque as the gear is engaged. After the shift is completed, spark is advanced and torque is brought to normal operating levels. Shifting is accomplished by sensor-driven servos located within the transmission valve body.

TROUBLESHOOTING

OIL PRESSURE HIGH OR LOW

1. Oil pump assembly pressure regulator valve stuck.
2. Oil pump assembly pressure regulator valve spring damaged.
3. Oil pump rotor guide missing or incorrectly installed.
4. Oil pump rotor cracked or damaged.
5. T.V. valve and reverse boost valve or bushing stuck, damaged or incorrectly installed.
6. Orifice hole in pressure regulator valve plugged.
7. Oil pump assembly slide sticking or excessive rotor clearance.
8. Oil pump pressure relief ball not sealed or damaged.
9. Oil pump cover or body porous.
10. Incorrect pump cover or defective pump faces.
11. Oil filter intake pipe and filter body restricted or cracked.
12. Oil filter O-ring seal missing, cut or damaged.
13. T.V. exhaust ball stuck or damaged.
14. Throttle lever and bracket assembly or throttle link binding, damaged or incorrectly installed.
15. Valve body manual valve scored or damaged.
16. Valve body spacer plate or gaskets incorrect, damaged or incorrectly installed.
17. Valve body throttle valve sticking, sleeve rotated in bore or retaining pin not seated.
18. T.V. limit valve, line bias valve, modulated downshift valve or 2-3 shift valve stuck.
19. Valve body check balls missing or incorrectly installed.

HIGH OR LOW SHIFT POINTS

1. T.V. cable binding or incorrectly adjusted.
2. T.V. exhaust ball stuck or damaged.
3. Throttle lever and bracket assembly binding, damaged or incorrectly installed.
4. Sticking oil pump slide, pressure regulator valve or T.V. boost valve.
5. Valve body modulated T.V. up or down valves sticking.
6. T.V. limit valve, throttle valve or plunger sticking.
7. Valve body spacer plate or gaskets damaged or incorrect.

FIRST SPEED ONLY—NO UPSHIFT

1. Governor valve sticking.
2. Governor driven gear loose or damaged.
3. Governor driven gear retaining pin missing.
4. Nicks or burrs on output shaft, governor sleeve or case bore.
5. Governor support pin in case too long or short.
6. Governor weights or springs missing, binding or damaged.
7. 1-2 shift valve sticking.
8. Valve body spacer plate or gaskets damaged or incorrectly installed.
9. Case to valve body face not flat or damaged.
10. Governor screen restricted or damaged.
11. Restricted or blocked 2-4 servo assembly apply passages.
12. Nicks or burrs on 2-4 servo assembly pin or pin bore in case.
13. Missing or damaged 2-4 servo assembly piston or pin seals.
14. Fourth servo piston installed backwards.
15. 2-4 band assembly worn or damaged.
16. 2-4 band assembly anchor pin not engaged.

SLIPS IN FIRST GEAR

1. Forward clutch assembly plates worn.
2. Porosity or damage in forward clutch piston.
3. Forward clutch piston inner and outer seals missing, cut or damaged.
4. Input housing to forward clutch housing O-ring seal missing, cut or damaged.
5. Forward clutch housing damaged.
6. Forward clutch housing retainer and ball assembly not sealing or damaged.
7. Turbine shaft seals missing, cut or damaged.
8. Valve body accumulator valve stuck.
9. Valve body face not flat, damaged lands or interconnected passages.
10. Valve body spacer plate or gaskets incorrect, damaged or incorrectly installed.
11. T.V. cable binding or broken.
12. Damaged ring grooves on 1-2 accumulator piston.
13. 1-2 accumulator piston seal missing, cut or damaged.
14. 1-2 accumulator cover gasket missing or damaged.
15. Leak between 1-2 accumulator piston and pin.
16. Broken 1-2 accumulator spring.
17. Fourth servo piston installed backwards.
18. Incorrect oil pressure. Refer to "High Or Low Oil Pressure."

1-2 SHIFT SPEED HIGH OR LOW

1. T.V. cable binding, broken or incorrectly adjusted.

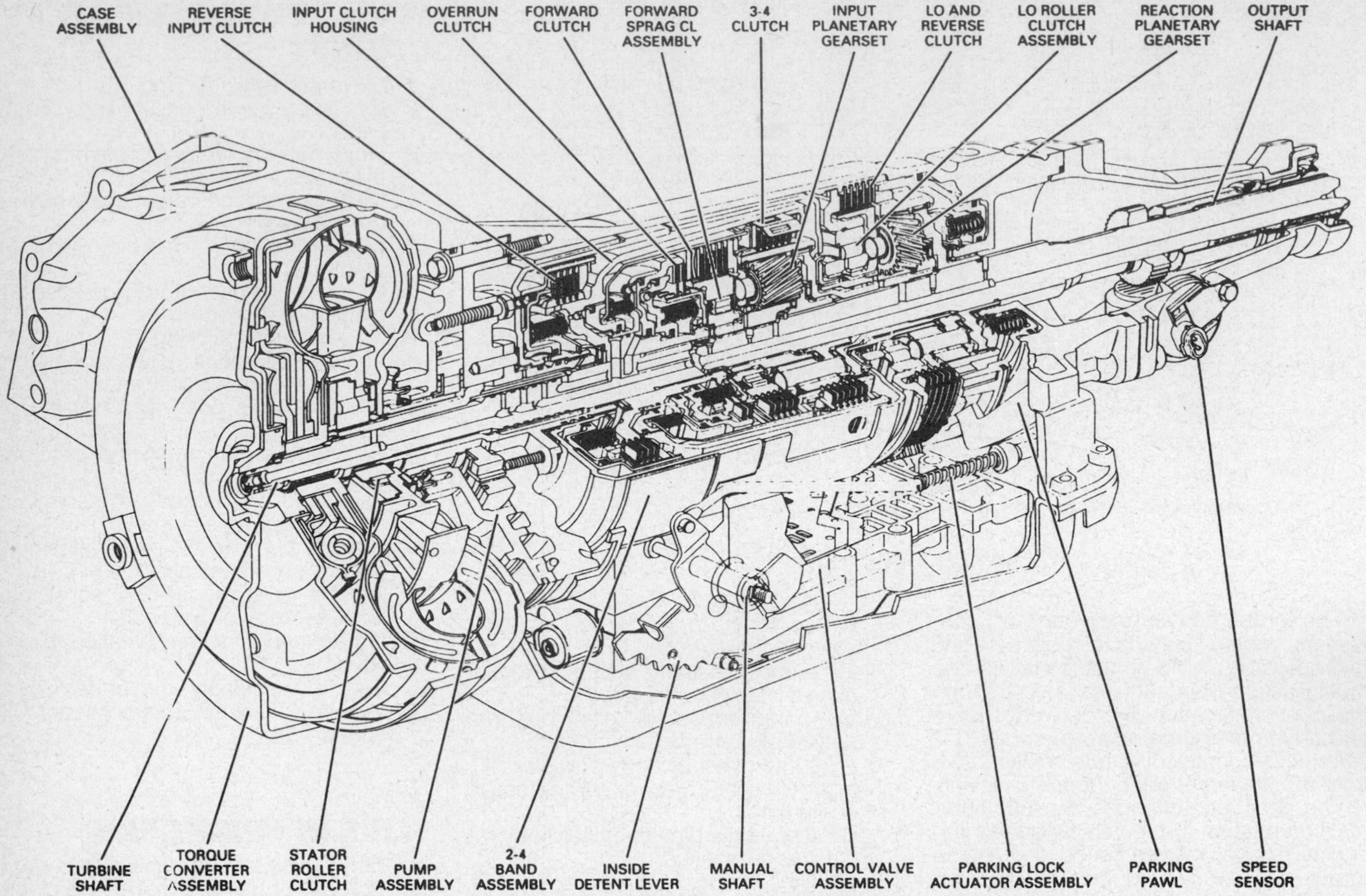
CASE ASSEMBLY
REVERSE INPUT CLUTCH
INPUT CLUTCH HOUSING
OVERRUN CLUTCH
FORWARD CLUTCH
FORWARD SPRAG CL ASSEMBLY
3-4 CLUTCH
INPUT PLANETARY GEARSET
LO AND REVERSE CLUTCH
LO ROLLER CLUTCH ASSEMBLY
REACTION PLANETARY GEARSET
OUTPUT SHAFT
TURBINE SHAFT
TORQUE CONVERTER ASSEMBLY
STATOR ROLLER CLUTCH
PUMP ASSEMBLY
2-4 BAND ASSEMBLY
INSIDE DETENT LEVER
MANUAL SHAFT
CONTROL VALVE ASSEMBLY
PARKING LOCK ACTUATOR ASSEMBLY
PARKING PAWL
SPEED SENSOR

TH5029400481000X

Fig. 3 Cross-sectional view of 4L60-E transmission

2. Faulty governor assembly. Refer to "First Speed Only – No Upshift."
3. Throttle lever and bracket assembly damaged, binding or incorrectly installed.
4. T.V. link missing, binding or damaged.
5. T.V. exhaust check ball and T.V. plunger sticking.
6. Valve body or oil pump assembly face not flat.

1-2 SHIFT SLIPPING OR ROUGH

1. Throttle lever and bracket assembly incorrectly installed or damaged.
2. T.V. cable damaged.
3. Throttle valve sticking.
4. T.V. bushing turned in its bore.
5. 1-2 shift valve train stuck.
6. Valve body assembly gaskets or spacer plate incorrect, damaged or incorrectly installed.
7. T.V. limit valve, line bias valve or accumulator valve stuck.
8. Valve body face not flat.
9. 2-4 servo assembly apply pin too long or short.
10. 2-4 servo seals or O-ring seals missing, cut or damaged.
11. 2-4 servo assembly bore damaged.
12. Restricted or missing 2-4 servo assembly oil passages.
13. Porosity in 1-2 accumulator housing or piston.
14. Second accumulator piston seal or groove damaged.
15. Nicks or burrs in 1-2 accumulator housing.
16. 2-4 band worn or incorrectly installed.
17. Oil pump assembly faces not flat.

NO 2-3 SHIFT OR 2-3 SHIFT SLIPPING, ROUGH OR HUNTING

1. Internal converter damage.
2. Governor valve stuck.
3. Governor assembly drive gear retaining pin missing or loose.
4. Governor weights binding.
5. Governor drive gear damaged.
6. Governor support pin in case too long or short.
7. Oil pump stator shaft sleeve scored or improperly installed.
8. Accumulator valve, throttle valve, T.V. limit valve or 2-3 valve train stuck.
9. Valve body spacer plate or gaskets incorrect, damaged or incorrectly installed.
10. Forward or 3-4 clutch plates worn.
11. Excessive clutch plate travel.
12. Cut or damaged piston seals in input housing assembly.
13. Porosity in 3-4 clutch housing or piston.
14. 3-4 piston check ball stuck, damaged or incorrectly sealing.
15. Restricted input housing assembly apply passages.
16. Forward clutch piston retainer and ball assembly not seating.
17. Input housing assembly sealing balls loose or missing.
18. Third accumulator retainer and ball assembly not seating.
19. Second apply piston seals missing, cut or damaged.
20. 2-4 servo pin seals missing, cut or damaged.

NO 3-4 SHIFT OR ROUGH 3-4 SHIFT

1. Governor weights bonding.
2. Governor valve stuck.
3. Governor drive gear retaining pin missing or loose.
4. Governor drive gear damaged.
5. Governor support pin in case too long or short.
6. Oil pump assembly faces not flat.
7. Pump cover retainer and ball assembly missing or damaged.
8. Accumulator valve, throttle valve, T.V. limit valve, 3-2 control valve, 1-2 shift valve train or 2-3 shift valve train stuck.

9. Manual valve link bent or damaged.
10. Valve body assembly spacer plates or gaskets incorrect, damaged or incorrectly installed.
11. Incorrect 2-4 servo assembly band apply pin.
12. Missing or damaged 2-4 servo seals.
13. Porosity in 2-4 servo pistons, cover and case.
14. Damaged 2-4 servo piston seal grooves.
15. Plugged or missing orifice cup plug in 2-4 servo assembly.
16. Third accumulator retainer and ball assembly leaking.
17. Porosity in 3-4 accumulator piston or bore.
18. 3-4 accumulator piston seal or seal grooves damaged.
19. Plugged or missing orifice cup plug.
20. Restricted case oil passage.
21. Faulty input housing assembly. Refer to"No 2-3 Shift Or 2-3 Shift Slipping, Rough Or Hunting."
22. 2-4 band assembly worn or incorrectly installed.

NO REVERSE OR SLIPS IN REVERSE

1. 3-4 apply ring stuck in applied position.
2. Forward clutch not releasing.
3. Turbine shaft seals missing, cut or damaged.
4. Manual linkage incorrectly adjusted.
5. Oil pump retainer and ball assembly missing or damaged.
6. Oil pump stator shaft sleeve scored or damaged.
7. Reverse boost valve stuck, damaged or incorrectly installed.
8. Oil pump cup plug missing.
9. Oil pump converter clutch apply valve stuck.
10. Oil pump face not flat or restricted oil passage.
11. 2-3 shift valve stuck.
12. Valve body spacer plate and gaskets incorrect, damaged or incorrectly installed.
13. Reverse input clutch plate worn.
14. Reverse input housing and drum assembly cracked at weld.
15. Reverse input clutch plate retaining ring out of groove.
16. Reverse input clutch return spring assembly retaining ring out of groove.
17. Reverse input clutch seals cut or damaged.
18. Reverse input clutch retainer and ball assembly not sealing.
19. Restricted oil apply passage in reverse input clutch.
20. Lo and reverse clutch plates worn.
21. Lo and reverse clutch plate retaining ring incorrectly installed.
22. Porosity in low and reverse clutch piston.
23. Low and reverse clutch seals damaged or oil apply passage restricted.
24. Case cover plate gasket missing, damaged or incorrectly torqued.

NO PART THROTTLE OR DELAYED DOWNSHIFTS

1. Throttle linkage incorrectly adjusted.
2. 2-4 servo assembly apply pin cut or damaged.
3. 2-4 servo cover retaining ring missing or incorrectly installed.
4. Fourth apply piston damaged or incorrectly installed.
5. 2-4 servo inner housing damaged or incorrectly installed.
6. Governor weights binding.
7. Governor valve stuck.
8. Throttle valve, 3-2 control valve or T.V. modulated downshift valve stuck.
9. T.V. sleeve turned in bore.
10. 4-3 sequence valve body channel blocked.
11. Number 5 check ball missing from valve body.

NO OVERRUN BRAKING — MANUAL 3-2-1

1. Throttle linkage incorrectly adjusted.
2. Throttle valve or 4-3 sequence valve stuck.
3. Number 3 check ball incorrectly installed.
4. Valve body spacer plate and gaskets incorrect, damaged or incorrectly installed.
5. Turbine shaft oil passages plugged or not drilled.
6. Turbine shaft seal rings damaged.
7. Turbine shaft sealing balls loose or missing.
8. Porosity in forward or overrun clutch piston.
9. Overrun piston seals cut or damaged.
10. Overrun piston check ball not seating.

NO CONVERTER CLUTCH APPLY

1. 12 volts not being applied to the transmission.
2. Defective outside electrical connector.
3. Defective inside electrical connector, wiring harness or solenoid.
4. Solenoid shorted or incorrectly grounded.
5. Incorrect or damaged pressure switches.
6. Internal converter damage.
7. Oil pump converter clutch apply valve stuck or incorrectly installed.
8. Oil pump converter clutch apply valve retaining ring incorrectly installed.
9. Oil pump to case gasket incorrectly installed.
10. Oil pump orifice cup plug clogged.
11. Oil pump solenoid O-ring seal cut or damaged.
12. Oil pump orifice cup plug missing from cooler in passage.
13. High or uneven oil pump body to cover bolt torque.
14. Converter clutch shift valve or throttle valve stuck.
15. Turbine shaft O-ring seal cut or damaged.
16. Turbine shaft retainer and ball assembly plugged.

CONVERTER SHUDDER

1. Internal torque converter damage.
2. Converter clutch shift valve stuck.
3. Oil pump converter clutch apply valve stuck.
4. Restricted oil pump oil passage.
5. Crack in oil filter body or restriction in filter neck.
6. Oil filter O-ring seal cut or damaged.
7. Low oil pressure or engine not properly tuned.
8. Turbine shaft O-ring cut or damaged.
9. Turbine shaft retainer and ball assembly damaged.

NO CONVERTER CLUTCH RELEASE

1. Oil pump converter clutch apply valve stuck.
2. Internal torque converter damage.
3. Solenoid grounded.

DRIVES IN NEUTRAL

1. Forward clutch burned or not releasing.
2. Manual linkage disconnected or incorrectly adjusted.
3. Internal leakage in case or case face not flat.

SECOND GEAR START IN DRIVE RANGE

1. Governor valve stuck.
2. Governor support pin too long or missing.
3. Forward sprag clutch assembly installed backwards.

NO PARK

1. Parking linkage actuator rod assembly bent or damaged.
2. Parking linkage actuator rod spring binding or improperly crimped.
3. Parking linkage actuator rod not attached to inside detent lever.
4. Parking linkage bracket damaged or not torqued properly.
5. Inside detent lever not torqued properly.
6. Detent roller improperly installed.
7. Parking pawl binding or damaged.

RATCHETING NOISE

1. Parking pawl return spring weak, damaged or incorrectly installed.

OIL OUT OF THE VENT

1. Chamfer in oil pump body rotor pocket too large.
2. T.V. limit valve stuck.

VIBRATION IN REVERSE & WHINING NOISE IN PARK

1. Broken vane rings in oil pump.

NO DRIVE IN ALL RANGES

1. Torque converter to flex plate bolts missing.

NO DRIVE IN DRIVE RANGE

1. Stator roller clutch not holding.
2. Torque converter not bolted to flex plate.

DELAY IN DRIVE & REVERSE

1. Torque converter drain back.

MAINTENANCE

Refer to "Lubricant Data Chart" in the appropriate chassis chapter of this manual for transmission fluid specifications.

FLUID CHECK

Fluid level should be checked at every engine oil change. Frequency of change for transmission fluid is dependent on the type of driving conditions in which the vehicle is used. If the transmission is subjected to severe service such as: use in heavy city traffic when the outside temperature regularly reaches 90°F, use in very hilly or mountainous areas, commercial use such as taxi or delivery service, the fluid should be changed every 15,000 miles. Otherwise, change the fluid every 100,000 miles. To check fluid at operating temperature (190°-200°F), which is obtained only after 15 miles of highway-type driving:

1. Apply parking brake and block wheels.
2. Place selector lever in park then start, but do not race, engine. Move selector lever through each range pausing three seconds in each.
3. Check fluid immediately with selector lever in park, engine running at slow idle, and vehicle on level surface. Fluid level should be at full hot mark.

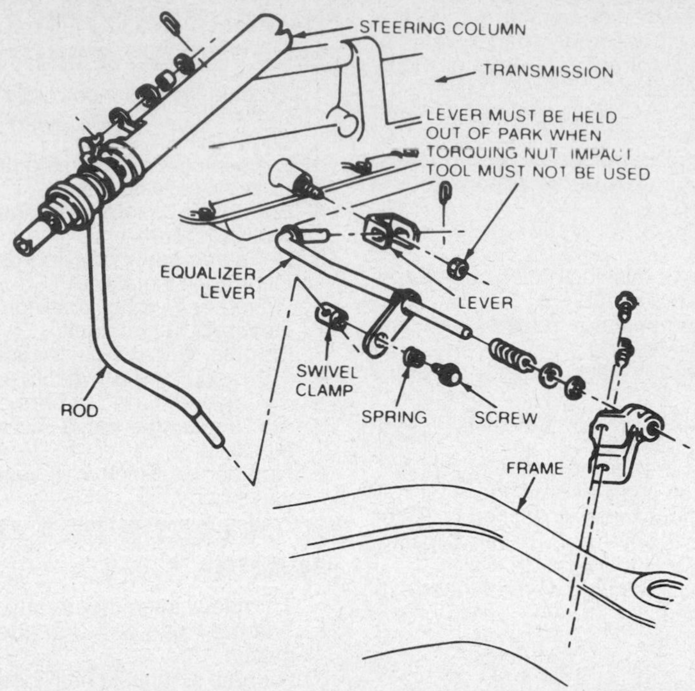
STEERING COLUMN
TRANSMISSION
LEVER MUST BE HELD OUT OF PARK WHEN TORQUING NUT IMPACT TOOL MUST NOT BE USED
EQUALIZER LEVER
LEVER
SWIVEL CLAMP
ROD
SPRING
SCREW
FRAME

Copyrighted Material Reprinted with Permission from Hydra-Matic Div., GM Corp.

TH5028800371000X

Fig. 4 Shift linkage adjustment. Brougham, Caprice, Custom Cruiser, Fleetwood (RWD), Impala SS & Roadmaster

FLUID CHANGE

1. Raise and support vehicle.
2. **On Caprice, Custom Cruiser, Impala SS and Roadmaster,** proceed as follows:
   a. Loosen transmission mount to support attaching nut.
   b. Loosen two bolts attaching right side of transmission support to frame rail.
   c. Remove two bolts attaching left side transmission support to frame rail.
   d. Using suitable transmission jack, support and slightly raise transmission.
   e. Slide transmission support rearward enough to access rear oil pan attaching bolts.
3. **On all models,** place drain pan under transmission oil pan, loosen pan bolts on front of pan, pry carefully with screwdriver to loosen oil pan, and allow fluid to drain.
4. Remove remaining oil pan bolts, oil pan, and gasket.
5. Drain fluid from pan, then clean pan and dry thoroughly with compressed air.
6. Remove oil filter to valve body bolt, then remove filter and gasket, replace with new filter and gasket and install filter attaching bolt.
7. Install new gasket on oil pan, then install oil pan and **torque** bolts to 12 ft. lbs.
8. Lower vehicle and add five quarts of automatic transmission fluid through filler tube.
9. With selector lever in park and parking brake applied, start engine and let idle. Do not race engine.
10. Move selector lever through each range, return to park position, check fluid, and add additional fluid to bring level between dimples on dipstick.

ADDING FLUID TO FILL DRY TRANSMISSION & CONVERTER

1. Add fluid through filler tube until oil level is between add and hot marks on dipstick.
2. Place selector lever in park, depress accelerator to place carburetor on fast idle cam, and move selector lever through each range. Do not race engine.
3. With selector lever in park, engine running at idle (1-3 minutes), and vehicle on level surface, check fluid level and add additional fluid to bring level between dimples on dipstick.

ADJUSTMENTS

MANUAL LINKAGE OR SHIFT CONTROL CABLE

Camaro & Firebird

1. Place transmission control lever in neutral position.
2. Loosen cable attachment nut(s) or bolt(s) at shift lever.
3. Rotate shift lever "clockwise" to park detent and then back to neutral position.
4. **Torque** cable attaching nuts or bolts to 11 ft. lbs. **Control lever must be held out of "Park" position when tightening nut.**
5. Check cable adjustment by rotating transmission control lever through each detent position.

Brougham, Caprice, Custom Cruiser, Fleetwood (RWD), Impala SS & Roadmaster

1. Loosen swivel clamp screw.
2. Position shift lever in neutral gate.
3. Position transmission lever in neutral detent.
4. While holding swivel clamp flush against equalizer lever, tighten swivel clamp screw, **Fig. 4. Do not exert force in either direction on rod or equalizer lever while tightening swivel clamp screw.**

Corvette

1. Disconnect battery ground cable.
2. Place transmission control lever in neutral position.
3. Loosen cable attachment at shift lever.
4. Rotate shift lever "clockwise" to park detent and then back to neutral position.
5. **Torque** cable attachment to 15 ft. lbs. **Lever must be held out of park when tightening the nut.**
6. Check cable adjustment by rotating control lever through the detents, reconnect battery ground cable.

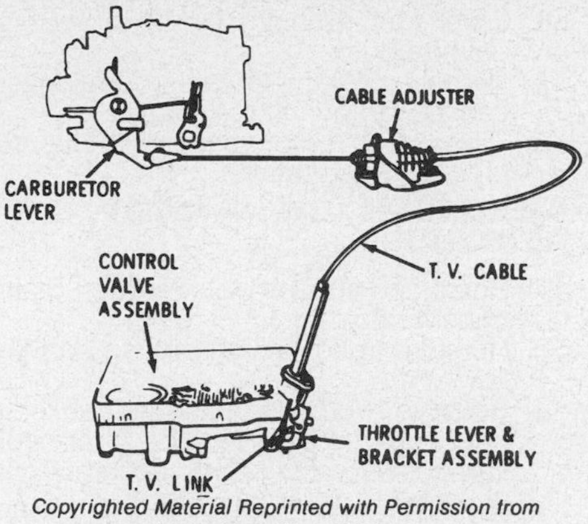
CABLE ADJUSTER
CARBURETOR LEVER
CONTROL VALVE ASSEMBLY
T. V. CABLE
THROTTLE LEVER & BRACKET ASSEMBLY
T. V. LINK

Copyrighted Material Reprinted with Permission from Hydra-Matic Div., GM Corp.

TH5028800368000X

Fig. 5 T.V. cable & linkage

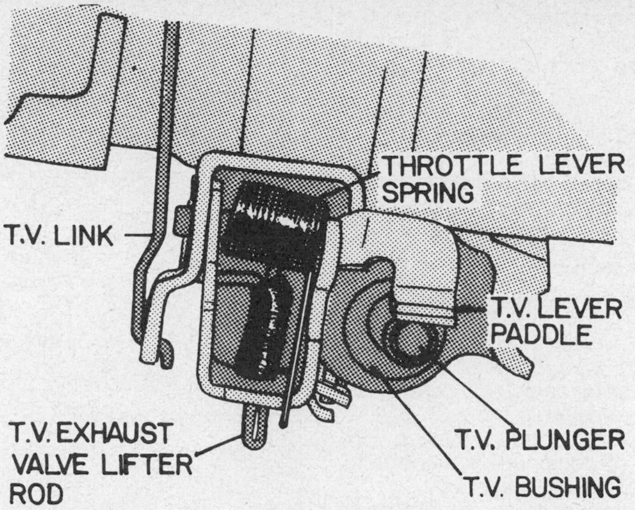
THROTTLE LEVER SPRING
T.V. LINK
T.V. LEVER PADDLE
T.V. EXHAUST VALVE LIFTER ROD
T.V. PLUNGER
T.V. BUSHING

Copyrighted Material Reprinted with Permission from Hydra-Matic Div., GM Corp.

TH5028800369000X

Fig. 6 Throttle lever & bracket assembly

THROTTLE VALVE CABLE

The TV cable should not be thought of as an automatic downshift cable. It controls line pressures, shift points, shift feel, part throttle downshifts, and detent downshifts. The function of the cable is similar to the combined functions of a vacuum modulator and detent downshift cable. The TV cable operates throttle lever and bracket assembly, **Fig. 5 and 6.**

1. Stop engine.
2. Depress and hold down readjust tab, **Fig. 7,** move slider through fitting, away from lever assembly, until slider stops against fitting.
3. Release readjust tab, then open throttle lever to its full throttle position to automatically adjust cable.
4. Release throttle lever and check cable for sticking or binding. **The cable may appear to function properly with engine stopped and cold. Recheck cable with engine at normal operating temperature.**
5. Road test vehicle.

IN-VEHICLE REPAIRS

4L60 TRANSMISSION

SERVO ASSEMBLY, REPLACE

Brougham, Caprice, Custom Cruiser, Fleetwood (RWD) & Roadmaster

1. Raise and support vehicle.
2. Remove floor pan reinforcement, then the catalytic converter heat shield.
3. Remove transmission mount to transmission support attaching nut.
4. Remove transmission support to frame attaching bolts.
5. Using a transmission jack, support, then raise transmission slightly.
6. Remove transmission support, then lower transmission to gain access to servo cover.
7. Remove two oil pan bolts from below servo cover.
8. Install servo cover compressor tool No. J-29714 or equivalent on oil pan flange and depress servo cover.
9. Remove servo cover retaining ring.

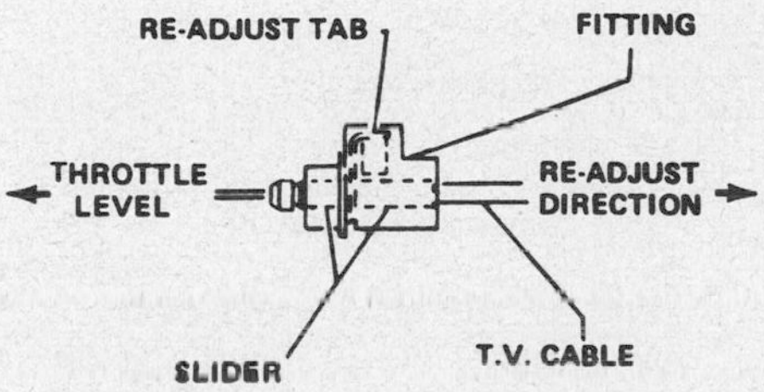
RE-ADJUST TAB
FITTING
THROTTLE LEVEL
RE-ADJUST DIRECTION
SLIDER
T.V. CABLE

Copyrighted Material Reprinted with Permission from Hydra-Matic Div., GM Corp.

TH5028800370000X

Fig. 7 T.V. cable adjustment

10. Remove servo cover and seal ring.
11. Remove servo piston and bore-apply pin assembly.
12. Reverse procedure to install. **Whenever any servo parts are replaced, apply-pin length must be checked.**

1992 Camaro & Firebird

1. Raise and support vehicle.
2. Remove rear suspension torque arm to transmission attaching bolts.
3. Remove propeller shaft as follows:
   a. Using a center punch or suitable equivalent, mark propeller shaft and rear axle yoke for installation reference.
   b. Remove propeller shaft strap bolts and retaining straps.
   c. Slide propeller shaft slip yoke out of the transmission.
4. Remove exhaust hanger and support transmission with suitable lifting device.
5. Remove transmission upper support and mount.
6. Lower transmission, then remove two oil pan bolts from below servo cover.
7. Install servo cover compressor tool No. J-29714 or equivalent on oil pan flange and depress servo cover.
8. Remove servo cover retaining ring.
9. Remove servo cover and seal ring.
10. Remove servo piston and bore-apply pin assembly.
11. Reverse procedure to install. **Whenever any servo parts are replaced, apply-pin length must be checked.**

1993 Camaro & Firebird

1. Raise and support vehicle.
2. Remove crossover pipe assembly and catalytic converter hanger assembly.
3. Remove propeller shaft as follows:
   a. Using a center punch or suitable equivalent, mark propeller shaft and pinion gear yoke for installation reference.
   b. If removing a two-piece shaft, remove bolts/screws from center support bearing, then center support bearing and washers from torque arm.
   c. Remove four bolts and two retainers.
   d. Slide propeller shaft slip yoke out of the transmission.
4. Remove rear axle torque arm, then support transmission with suitable stand.
5. Remove transmission upper support and mount.
6. Remove catalytic converter heat shield.
7. Lower transmission, then remove two oil pan bolts from below servo cover.
8. Install servo cover compressor tool No. J-29714 or equivalent on oil pan flange and depress servo cover.
9. Remove servo cover retaining ring.
10. Remove servo cover and seal ring.
11. Remove servo piston and bore-apply pin assembly.
12. Reverse procedure to install. **Whenever any servo parts are replaced, apply-pin length must be checked.**

Corvette

1. Disconnect battery ground cable.
2. Raise and support vehicle.
3. Remove upper and lower body braces, if equipped.
4. Remove exhaust system.
5. Remove oil pan retaining bolt directly below servo cover.

6. Install servo cover compressor tool No. J29714-A or equivalent, then depress servo cover and remove retaining ring.
7. Remove cover, seal ring, servo piston and bore apply pin assembly.
8. Reverse procedure to install. **Whenever any servo parts are replaced, apply-pin length must be checked.**

SPEEDOMETER DRIVEN GEAR, REPLACE

Except 1993 Camaro & Firebird

1. Disconnect speedometer cable or P.M. generator electrical connector from transmission.
2. Remove retainer bolt, retainer, P.M. generator (if equipped), speedometer driven gear and O-ring seal.
3. Reverse procedure to install, using new O-ring and adjusting fluid level.

1993 Camaro & Firebird

1. Raise and support vehicle.
2. Remove propeller shaft assembly as follows:
   a. Using a center punch or suitable equivalent, mark propeller shaft and pinion gear yoke for installation reference.
   b. If removing a two-piece shaft, remove bolts/screws from center support bearing, then center support bearing and washers from torque arm.
   c. Remove four bolts and two retainers.
   d. Slide propeller shaft slip yoke out of the transmission.
3. Remove rear axle torque arm assembly.
4. Remove catalytic converter hanger assembly.
5. Remove vehicle speed sensor and speedometer driven gear.
6. Remove extension with seal. Discard and replace seal.
7. Remove sleeve, seal (if necessary), drive gear and clip.
8. Reverse procedure to install.

REAR OIL SEAL, REPLACE

1. Remove driveshaft, and tunnel strap, if equipped.
2. Using suitable tool, pry out lip oil seal.
3. Coat outer casting of new oil seal with suitable sealer and drive into place with seal installer tool No. J-21426.
4. Install tunnel strap if used, then install driveshaft.

GOVERNOR, REPLACE

Except 1993 Camaro & Firebird

1. Raise and support vehicle
2. **On Corvette models,** remove upper and lower body braces, then the complete exhaust system.
3. **On Caprice, Custom Cruiser, Fleetwood (RWD) and Roadmaster models,** proceed as follows:

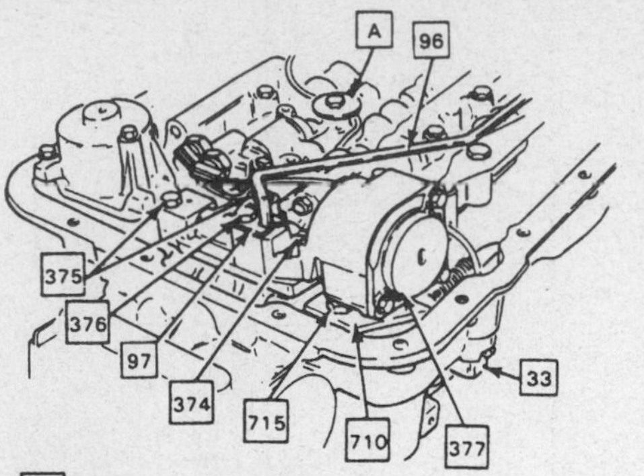
A
96
375
376
97
374
715
710
377
33

A	WASHER, WIRE RETAINING
33	CONNECTOR, ELECTRICAL
96	TUBE, AUXILIARY ACCUMULATOR VALVE
97	CLAMP
374	BOLT, SPECIAL HEX HEAD (M6 X 1 X 16)
375	BOLT, HEX HEAD (M6 X 1 X 35)
376	BOLT, HEX HEAD (M6 X 1 X 45)
377	AUXILIARY ACCUM. VALVE BODY ASM.
710	BRACKET, PARKING LOCK
715	BOLT, PARKING LOCK BRACKET

TH5028800376000X

Fig. 8 Auxiliary valve body replacement. 4L60 transmission

   a. Remove transmission mount to support nut.
   b. Remove support to frame attaching bolts.
   c. Using a transmission jack, support and raise transmission slightly.
   d. Remove transmission support, then lower transmission to gain access to governor cover.
4. **On all models,** remove governor cover from case using extreme care not to damage cover. If cover is damaged, it should be replaced.
5. Remove governor.
6. Reverse procedure to install and check fluid level.

1993 Camaro & Firebird

1. Raise and support vehicle.
2. Remove propeller shaft assembly as follows:
   a. Using a center punch or suitable equivalent, mark propeller shaft and pinion gear yoke for installation reference.
   b. If removing a two-piece shaft, remove bolts/screws from center support bearing, then center support bearing and washers from torque arm.
   c. Remove four bolts and two retainers.
   d. Slide propeller shaft slip yoke out of the transmission.
3. Remove rear axle torque arm assembly.
4. Remove catalytic converter hanger assembly.
5. Support transmission with a suitable stand, then remove transmission support member assembly.
6. lower transmission slightly to access governor.
7. Remove cover, then tap around cover flange with punch to remove.
8. Remove governor assembly. Reverse procedure to install.

AUXILIARY VALVE BODY, REPLACE

1. Raise and support vehicle, then drain transmission fluid.
2. Remove transmission oil pan and filter.
3. Remove two bolts that attach auxiliary accumulator valve tube to control valve assembly and accumulator valve body assembly, **Fig. 8.**
4. Remove two tube clamps, gently pry tube loose from oil pump assembly and auxiliary accumulator valve body assembly.
5. Remove three auxiliary accumulator valve body to transmission case attaching bolts.
6. Remove auxiliary valve body and check ball.
7. Reverse procedure to install.

CONTROL VALVE ASSEMBLY, REPLACE

Except 1993 Camaro & Firebird

1. Disconnect battery ground cable.
2. Disconnect TV cable at throttle lever, then raise and support vehicle.
3. Drain transmission fluid, then remove transmission oil pan, filter and gasket.
4. Remove two bolts that attach auxiliary accumulator valve tube to control valve assembly and accumulator valve body assembly, **Fig. 8.**
5. Remove two tube clamps, gently pry tube loose from oil pump assembly, then the auxiliary accumulator valve body assembly.
6. Disconnect electrical connectors at valve body.
7. Remove detent spring and roller assembly from valve body and remove valve body-to-case bolts.
8. Remove valve body assembly while disconnecting manual control valve link from range selector inner lever and removing throttle lever bracket from TV link.
9. Reverse procedure to install.

1993 Camaro & Firebird

1. Disconnect battery ground cable.
2. Disconnect TV cable at throttle lever, then raise and support vehicle.
3. Drain transmission fluid, then remove transmission oil pan, filter and gasket.
4. Remove two bolts that attach auxiliary accumulator valve tube to control valve assembly and auxiliary valve body assembly.
5. Remove two retainers, then accumulator tube.
6. Remove attaching clip and solenoid wire from harness connectors from pressure switch and temperature switch.

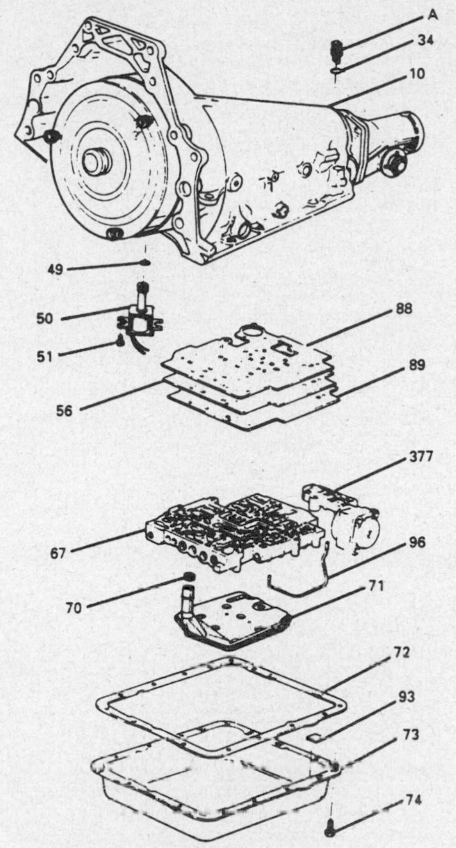
A
34
10
49
50
51
88
89
56
377
67
96
71
70
72
93
73
74

A CONNECTOR, ELECTRICAL
10 CASE, AUTOMATIC TRANSMISSION
34 SEAL, AUTOMATIC TRANSMISSION WIRING CONNECTOR (O-RING)
49 SEAL, CONVERTER CLUTCH SOLENOID VALVE (O-RING)
50 VALVE ASSEMBLY, CONVERTER CLUTCH SOLENOID
51 BOLT/SCREW, CONVERTER CLUTCH SOLENOID VALVE, 11 N•m (97 LB. IN.)
56 PLATE, VALVE BODY SPACER
67 VALVE ASSEMBLY, CONTROL
70 SEAL, AUTOMATIC TRANSMISSION OIL FILTER (O-RING)
71 FILTER ASSEMBLY, AUTOMATIC TRANSMISSION OIL
72 GASKET, AUTOMATIC TRANSMISSION OIL PAN
73 PAN, AUTOMATIC TRANSMISSION OIL
74 BOLT/SCREW, AUTOMATIC TRANSMISSION OIL PAN, 16 N•m (12 LB. FT.)
88 GASKET, SPACER PLATE-TO-CASE
89 GASKET, SPACER PLATE-TO-VALVE BODY
93 MAGNET, AUTOMATIC TRANSMISSION OIL PAN
96 TUBE, AUTOMATIC TRANSMISSION REAR CLUTCH ACCUMULATOR
377 BODY, AUXILIARY VALVE

GC5029300459000X

Fig. 9 Control valve body replacement. 1993 Camaro & Firebird w/4L60 transmission

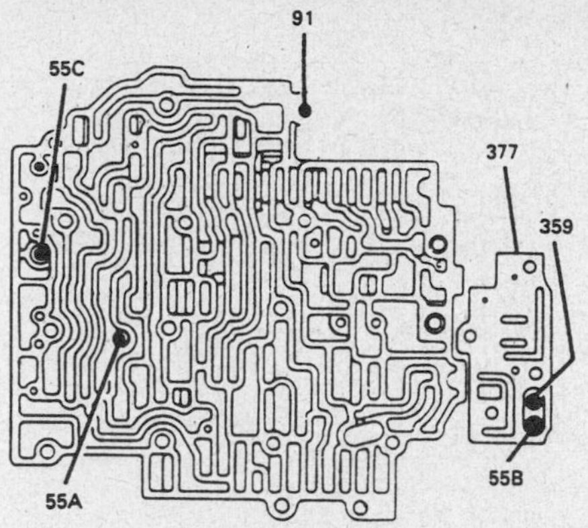
91
55C
377
359
55A
55B

55A BALL, #2 CHECK (3RD CLUTCH ACCUMULATOR)
55B BALL, #12 CHECK (FORWARD CLUTCH)
55C BALL, #6 CHECK (DRIVE 3)
91 BALL, #10 CHECK (TV EXHAUST) (COPPER FLASH)
359 CUP PLUG, ORIFICE
377 BODY, AUXILIARY VALVE

GC5029300460000X

Fig. 10 Control valve body check ball locations. 4L60 transmission

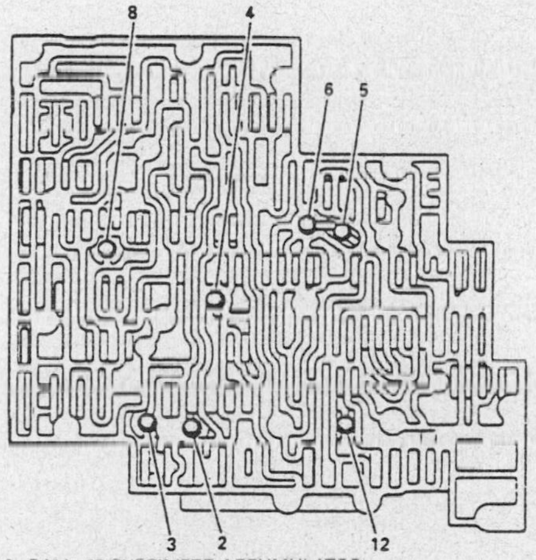
8
4
6
5
3
2
12

2 BALL, #2 CHECK (3RD ACCUMULATOR)
3 BALL, #3 CHECK (REVERSE INPUT)
4 BALL, #4 CHECK (3-4 CLUTCH EXHAUST)
5 BALL, #5 CHECK (OVERRUN CLUTCH FEED)
6 BALL, #6 CHECK (OVERRUN CLUTCH CONTROL)
8 BALL, #8 CHECK (1-2 UPSHIFT)
12 BALL, #2 CHECK (FORWARD CLUTCH ACCUM.)

GC5029400457000X

Fig. 12 Control valve body check ball locations. 4L60-E transmission

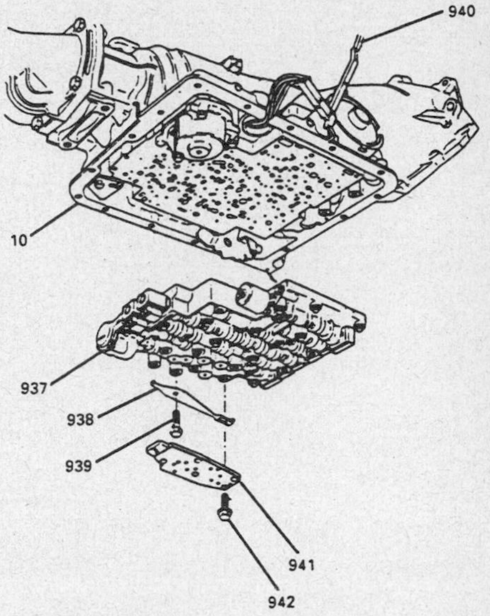
940
10
937
938
939
941
942

10 CASE, TRANSMISSION
937 VALVE ASSEMBLY, CONTROL BODY
938 SPRING ASSEMBLY, MANUAL DETENT
939 BOLT/SCREW, MANUAL DETENT SPRING
940 SOLENOID ASSEMBLY, WIRING HARNESS AND
941 SWITCH ASSEMBLY, TRANSMISSION PRESSURE
942 BOLT/SCREW, PRESSURE SWITCH ASSEMBLY

GC5029400450000X

Fig. 11 Control valve & pressure switch assembly. 4L60-E transmission

7. Remove temperature switch to control valve assembly bolt/screw, then temperature switch.
8. Loosen bolt/screw attaching wire retainer washer to control valve assembly.
9. Disconnect solenoid wire harness connector from transmission wiring electrical connector assembly by prying back lock tabs. Allow harness to be suspended from solenoid valve assembly.
10. Remove bolt/screw and manual shift detent assembly, then TV lever to control valve attaching bolt/screws.
11. Loosen remaining bolt/screws completely. Bolt/screws should remain in control valve assembly to aid in reassembly.
12. Remove manual valve link assembly. Pick up control valve assembly while holding manual valve link assembly and rotate control valve assembly to disconnect manual link assembly from manual valve.
13. Remove control valve assembly and check balls 2, 6, and 10, **Fig. 9.**
14. Reverse procedure to install, ensure control valve body check balls are in their correct location. Refer to **Fig. 10** for check ball locations.

4L60–E TRANSMISSION

CONTROL VALVE BODY & PRESSURE SWITCH, REPLACE

1. Raise and support vehicle.
2. Remove oil pan and gasket
3. Remove oil filter and filter seal.
4. Disconnect electrical connectors from control valve body components.
5. Remove TCC solenoid bolts and solenoid assembly with O-ring seal.
6. Remove wiring harness retaining bolts, then set harness aside, **Fig. 11.**
7. Remove manual detent spring assembly attaching bolt.
8. Remove remaining control valve body attaching bolts.
9. Remove manual valve link, then the control valve body.
10. Reverse procedure to install, noting the following:
    a. Before installing valve body, ensure valve body and transmission case check balls are in their correct location. Refer to **Figs. 12 and 13** for check ball locations.
    b. Install all control valve body bolts.
    c. Using spiral sequence shown in **Fig. 14, torque** bolts to 97 inch lbs. **If bolts are tightened in a random sequence, valve bores may be distorted and will inhibit valve operation.**

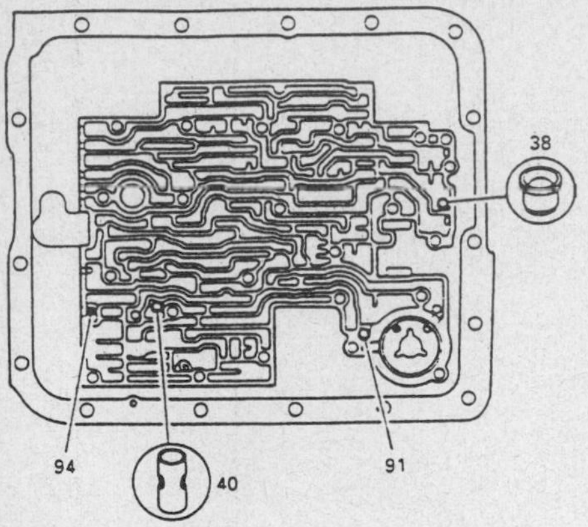
38
94
40
91

38 PLUG, TRANSMISSION CASE (ACCUM. BLEED)
40 RETAINER AND BALL ASSEMBLY, 3RD ACCUM.
91 NO. 1 CHECKBALL
94 SCREEN, TCC

GC5029400458000X

Fig. 13 Transmission case check ball locations. 4L60-E transmission

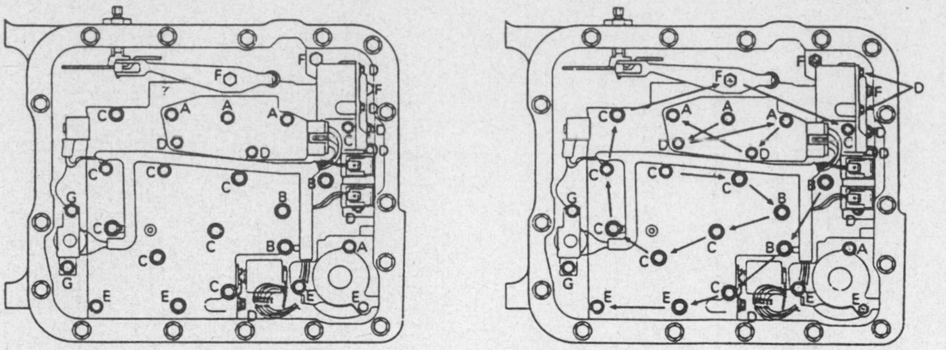

A M6 X 1.0 X 65.0
B M6 X 1.0 X 54.4
C M6 X 1.0 X 47.5
D M6 X 1.0 X 18.0
E M6 X 1.0 X 35.0
F M8 X 1.25 X 20.0
G M6 X 1.0 X 12.0

GC5029400451000X

Fig. 14 Control valve body bolts & tightening pattern. 4L60-E transmission

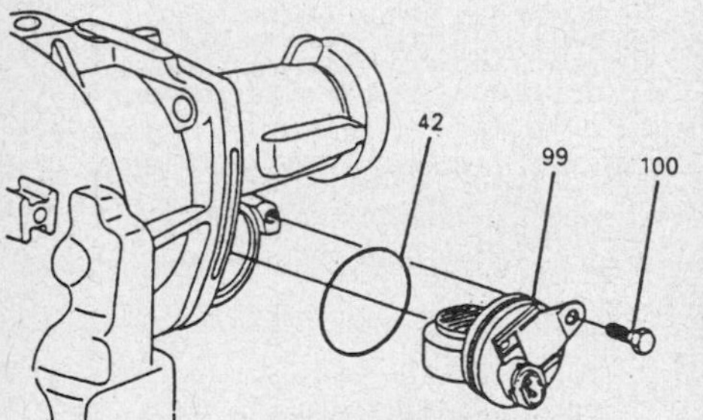
42
99
100

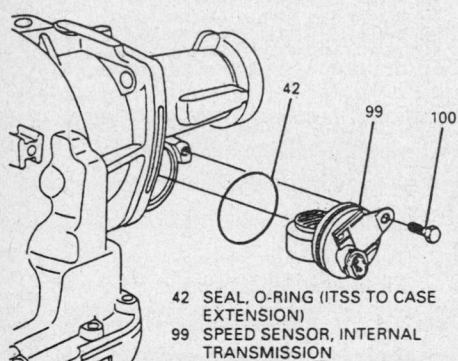

42 SEAL, O-RING (ITSS TO CASE EXTENSION)
99 SPEED SENSOR, INTERNAL TRANSMISSION
100 BOLT/SCREW, SPEED SENSOR RETAINING

GC5029400452000X

Fig. 15 Vehicle speed sensor. 4L60-E transmission

VEHICLE SPEED SENSOR, REPLACE

1. Raise and support vehicle.
2. Disconnect speed sensor electrical connector.
3. Remove speed sensor retaining bolt, **Fig. 15.**
4. Remove speed sensor and O-ring seal.
5. Reverse procedure to install, **torque** speed sensor retaining bolt to 97 inch lbs.

ACCUMULATOR, REPLACE

1. Raise and support vehicle.
2. Remove oil pan and gasket.
3. Remove oil filter and filter seal.
4. Remove control valve body as described under "Control Valve Body & Pressure Switch, Replace."
5. Remove accumulator cover bolts, **Fig. 16.**
6. Remove 1-2 accumulator cover, piston and spring.
7. Remove spacer plate support bolts.
8. Remove spacer plate and spacer plate gaskets.
9. Remove 3-4 accumulator spring, piston and pin.
10. Remove accumulator assembly.
11. Reverse procedure to install, noting the following:
    a. When installing 3-4 accumulator piston onto the pin, the piston legs must face the valve body.
    b. When installing case and valve body gaskets. The case gasket will be marked with a "C" and the valve body gasket will be marked with a "V."
    c. **Torque** spacer plate support bolts to 97 inch lbs.

CONTROL & SHIFT SOLENOIDS, REPLACE

1. Raise and support vehicle.
2. Remove oil pan, oil filter and filter seal.
3. Remove accumulator cover bolts.
4. Remove 1-2 accumulator cover, piston and spring.
5. Disconnect control and shift solenoid electrical connectors.
6. Remove pressure control solenoid retainer bolt, then the retainer and solenoid, **Fig. 17.**
7. Remove shift solenoid retainers and shift solenoids.
8. Remove 3-2 control solenoid retainer and control solenoid.
9. Reverse procedure to install.

TCC SOLENOID & WIRING HARNESS, REPLACE

Corvette

1. Disconnect battery ground cable.

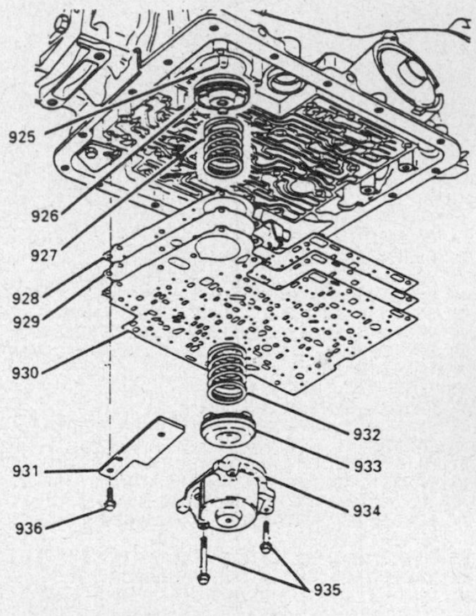
925
926
927
928
929
930
931
932
933
934
935
936

925 PIN, ACCUMULATOR PISTON
926 PISTON, 3-4 ACCUMULATOR
927 SPRING, 3-4 ACCUMULATOR
928 GASKET, SPACER PLATE TO CASE
929 PLATE, VALVE BODY SPACER
930 GASKET, SPACER PLATE TO VALVE BODY
931 PLATE, SPACER PLATE SUPPORT
932 1-2 ACCUMULATOR
933 1-2 ACCUMULATOR
934 COVER AND PIN ASSEMBLY, 1-2 ACCUMULATOR
935 BOLT/SCREW, ACCUMULATOR COVER
936 BOLT/SCREW, SPACER PLATE SUPPORT

GC5029400453000X

Fig. 16 Accumulator assembly. 4L60-E transmission

2. Raise and support vehicle.
3. Remove underbody braces.
4. Disconnect oxygen sensor electrical connector.
5. Remove righthand side catalytic converter to exhaust manifold attaching bolts.
6. Remove lefthand side catalytic converter to exhaust pipe attaching bolts.

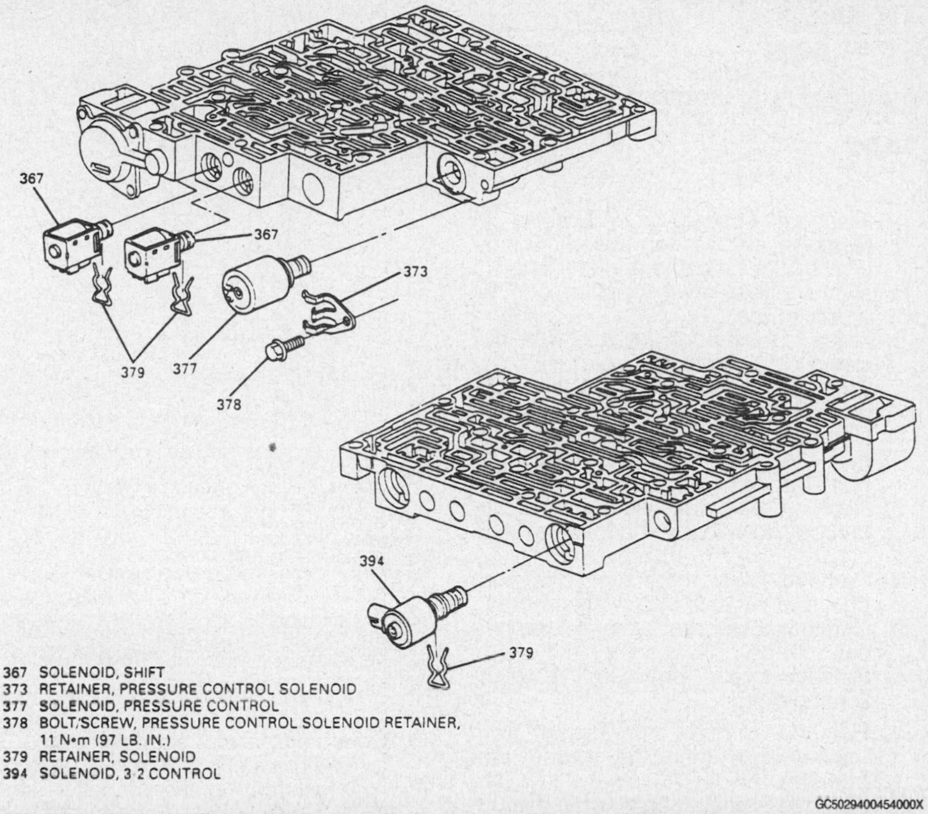
367
367
373
379
377
378
394
379
367 SOLENOID, SHIFT
373 RETAINER, PRESSURE CONTROL SOLENOID
377 SOLENOID, PRESSURE CONTROL
378 BOLT/SCREW, PRESSURE CONTROL SOLENOID RETAINER, 11 N•m (97 LB. IN.)
379 RETAINER, SOLENOID
394 SOLENOID, 3-2 CONTROL
GC5029400454000X

Fig. 17 Electrical component locations. 4L60-E transmission

7. Remove front exhaust hanger to exhaust pipe attaching bolts.
8. Remove rear exhaust hanger to exhaust pipe attaching bolts.
9. Remove muffler to muffler hanger retaining nuts.
10. Remove exhaust system from vehicle.
11. Remove transmission oil pan, oil filter and seal.
12. Disconnect external wiring harness connector from transmission pass-through connector.
13. Remove accumulator cover bolts, 1-2 accumulator cover, piston and spring.
14. Disconnect component electrical connectors.
15. Remove pressure control solenoid retainer bolt, then the retainer and solenoid.
16. Remove TCC solenoid attaching bolts.
17. Remove pass-through electrical connector from transmission case by positioning the small end of power piston seal protector and diaphragm retainer installer tool No. J 28458 or equivalent over the top of the connector, then twist tool to release the four tabs while at the same time pulling the harness through the case.
18. Remove TCC solenoid with wiring harness from transmission case.
19. Reverse procedure to install, noting the following:
    a. **Torque** TCC solenoid retaining bolt to 97 inch lbs.
    b. **Torque** pressure control solenoid retaining bolt to 97 inch lbs.
    c. When installing 1-2 accumulator piston to accumulator cover, the piston legs must face towards the case.
    d. **Torque** accumulator attaching bolts to 97 inch lbs.

Camaro & Firebird

1. Disconnect battery ground cable.
2. Raise and support vehicle.
3. Remove exhaust crossover pipe to exhaust manifold retaining nuts.
4. Remove exhaust pipe to catalytic converter attaching bolts and nuts.
5. Remove catalytic converter and crossover pipe assembly.
6. Remove transmission oil pan, oil filter and seal.
7. Disconnect external wiring harness connector from transmission pass-through connector.
8. Remove accumulator cover bolts, 1-2 accumulator cover, piston and spring.
9. Disconnect component electrical connectors.
10. Remove pressure control solenoid retainer bolt, then the retainer and solenoid.
11. Remove TCC solenoid attaching bolts.
12. Remove pass-through electrical connector from transmission case by positioning the small end of power piston seal protector and diaphragm retainer installer tool No. J 28458 or equivalent over the top of the connector, then twist tool to release the four tabs while at the same time pulling the harness through the case.
13. Remove TCC solenoid with wiring harness from transmission case.
14. Reverse procedure to install, noting the following:
    a. **Torque** TCC solenoid retaining bolt to 97 inch lbs.
    b. **Torque** pressure control solenoid retaining bolt to 97 inch lbs.
    c. When installing 1-2 accumulator piston to accumulator cover, the piston legs must face towards the case.
    d. **Torque** accumulator attaching bolts to 97 inch lbs.

Caprice, Custom Cruiser, Fleetwood (RWD), Impala SS & Roadmaster

1. Raise and support vehicle.
2. Disconnect heated oxygen sensor.
3. Remove catalytic converter to muffler attaching bolts and nuts.
4. Remove catalytic converter hanger to catalytic converter bolts.
5. Remove righthand side dampner assembly.
6. Remove nuts holding exhaust pipe to exhaust manifold.
7. Remove converter and pipe assembly from vehicle.
8. Remove oil pan and oil filter assembly.
9. Disconnect external wiring harness from transmission pass through connector.
10. Remove accumulator cover attaching bolts.
11. Remove 1-2 accumulator cover, piston and spring.
12. Disconnect electrical connectors.
13. Remove pressure control solenoid retainer bolt, then the retainer and solenoid.
14. Remove TCC solenoid retaining bolts.
15. Remove pass-through electrical connector from transmission case by positioning the small end of power piston seal protector and diaphragm retainer installer tool No. J 28458 or equivalent, over the top of the connector, then twist tool to release the four tabs while at the same time pulling the harness through the case.
16. Remove TCC solenoid with wiring harness from transmission case.
17. Reverse procedure to install, noting the following:
    a. **Torque** TCC solenoid retaining bolt to 97 inch lbs.
    b. **Torque** pressure control solenoid retaining bolt to 97 inch lbs.
    c. When installing 1-2 accumulator piston to accumulator cover, the piston legs must face towards the case.
    d. **Torque** accumulator attaching bolts to 97 inch lbs.

SERVO ASSEMBLY, REPLACE

1. Disconnect battery ground cable.
2. Remove exhaust system as described under "TCC Solenoid & Wiring Harness, Replace."
3. Remove transmission oil pan bolt be-

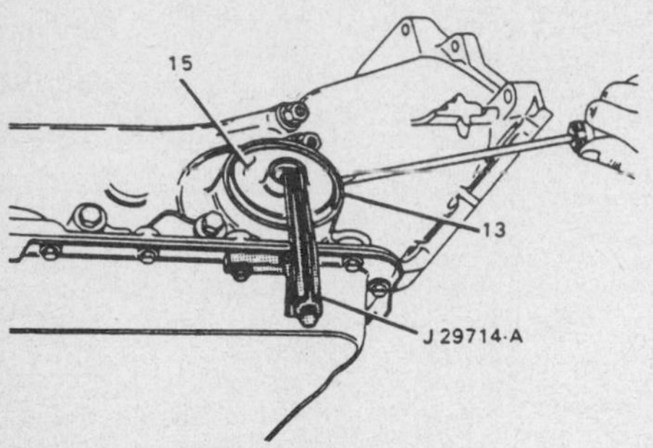
15
13
J 29714-A

13 RING, 2-4 BAND SERVO COVER RETAINING
15 COVER, 2-4 BAND SERVO

GC5029400455000X

Fig. 18 Servo cover removal. 4L60-E transmission

low servo cover, **Fig. 18.**

4. Install servo cover depressor tool No. J 29714-A or equivalent on oil pan and install bolt included with tool, **Fig. 18.**
5. Depress servo cover and remove retaining ring.
6. Remove tool from oil pan.
7. Remove cover and seal ring.
8. Remove servo piston and bore apply pin assembly.
9. Reverse procedure to install.

PUMP PRESSURE REGULATOR VALVE, REPLACE

1. Raise and support vehicle.
2. Remove transmission oil pan and gasket.
3. Compress pressure regulator valve with a small screwdriver, **Fig. 19.**
4. Remove retaining ring and slowly release spring tension.
5. Remove pressure regulator bore plug, valve, spring and guide.
6. Reverse procedure to install.

REAR OIL SEAL, REPLACE

1. Disconnect battery ground cable.
2. Remove exhaust system as described under "TCC Solenoid & Wiring Harness, Replace."
3. Remove propeller shaft as follows:
   a. Support transmission with suitable jack.
   b. Remove driveline support bolts, washers and nuts.
   c. Position driveline support aside to gain clearance.
   d. Mark relationship of propeller shaft to pinion yoke and disconnect rear universal joint by removing propeller shaft retainers. **Tape bearing cups to trunnion to prevent dropping and loss of roller bearings.**
   e. Slide slip yoke from transmission and remove propeller shaft from vehicle.
4. Remove rear oil seal from transmission rear case extension.
5. Reverse procedure to install.

TRANSMISSION REPLACE

CAMARO & FIREBIRD

1992

1. Disconnect battery ground cable.
2. Remove air cleaner assembly and disconnect TV cable at upper end.
3. Remove fluid level indicator and oil dipstick tube.
4. Raise and support vehicle. **Do not use a twin post type hoist.**
5. Support rear axle with an adjustable jackstand.
6. Remove track bar mounting bolt at axle assembly, then loosen track bar bolt at body brace.
7. Remove rear brake hose clip at underbody to allow for additional axle drop.
8. Remove lower mounting bolts from right and left side shock absorbers.
9. Carefully lower rear axle and remove coil springs.
10. Remove torque arm to rear axle attaching bolts.
11. Remove torque arm clamp from transmission, then the torque arm from the vehicle.
12. Remove propeller shaft, then disconnect shift linkage at the transmission.
13. Disconnect any electrical leads at transmission, then remove any clips that hold leads to transmission case.
14. Remove flywheel cover, then mark relationship between flywheel and converter for installation reference.
15. Remove torque converter attaching bolts.
16. Remove catalytic converter support bracket, then the transmission mount to support attaching nut.
17. Remove transmission support to frame bolts, then any insulators, if used.
18. Using a transmission jack, support and raise transmission slightly.
19. Slide transmission support rearward, then lower transmission to gain access to oil cooler pipes and TV cable attachments.
20. Disconnect oil cooler pipes from transmission, cap all openings.
21. Disconnect speedometer cable or P.M. generator, then the TV cable from transmission.
22. Support engine assembly, then remove transmission to engine attaching bolts.
23. Install torque converter holding fixture tool, No. J-21366 or equivalent, then carefully lower transmission from vehicle.
24. Reverse procedure to install.

1993–94

1. Disconnect battery ground cable.
2. **On 4L60 transmissions,** disconnect TV cable at throttle lever.
3. **On all transmissions,** raise and support vehicle, then mark position of propeller shaft to pinion yoke.

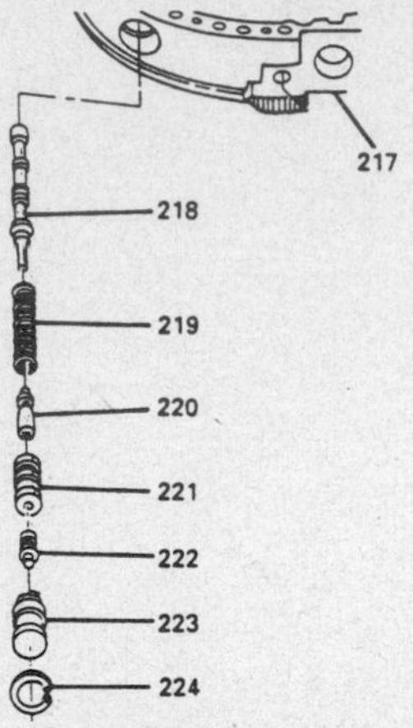
217
218
219
220
221
222
223
224

217 PUMP ASSEMBLY, AUTOMATIC TRANSMISSION OI
218 VALVE, PRESSURE REGULATOR
219 SPRING, PRESSURE REGULATOR VALVE
220 VALVE, REVERSE BOOST
221 BUSHING, REVERSE BOOST VALVE
222 VALVE, TV BOOST
223 BUSHING, TV BOOST VALVE
224 RING, TV BOOST VALVE BUSHING RETAINER

GC5029400456000X

Fig. 19 Pressure regulator valve assembly. 4L60-E transmission

4. Remove propeller shaft as follows:
   a. Using a center punch or suitable equivalent, mark propeller shaft and pinion gear yoke for installation reference.
   b. If removing a two-piece shaft, remove bolts/screws from center support bearing, then center support bearing and washers from torque arm.
   c. Remove four bolts and two retainers.
   d. Slide propeller shaft slip yoke out of the transmission.
5. Support transmission, then remove washer and nut from support and transmission.
6. Remove bolt/screws from support and rail, then remove support from transmission and rail.
7. Remove rear axle torque arm and catalytic converter hanger assembly.
8. Remove bolt/screws from torque converter cover, then cover from transmission.
9. Remove bolt/screws from converter, then flywheel from converter.
10. Move catalytic converter heat shield if necessary.
11. Remove range selector lever cable and transmission cooler pipes from pipe clips.
12. Disconnect electrical connectors at transmission, then remove transmission fluid level indicator bolts/screws and indicator.
13. Separate transmission from engine.
14. **On 4L60 transmissions,** disconnect TV cable at transmission.
15. **On 4L60-E transmissions,** disconnect all electrical connectors.
16. **On all transmissions,** disconnect transmission oil cooler lines, then lower transmission from vehicle.
17. Reverse procedure to install.

CAPRICE, CUSTOM CRUISER, IMPALA SS & ROADMASTER

1. Disconnect battery ground cable.
2. Remove air cleaner assembly, if necessary.
3. **On 4L60 transmission,** disconnect TV cable at its upper end.
4. **On all transmissions,** remove transmission oil dipstick.
5. Raise and support vehicle, then remove the propeller shaft.
6. Disconnect speedometer cable, shift linkage, then all the electrical leads at transmission and any clips that retain the leads to the transmission case.
7. Remove flywheel cover, mark flywheel and torque converter for installation reference.
8. Remove torque converter to flywheel bolts.
9. Remove catalytic converter support bracket.
10. Remove floor pan reinforcement if it interferes with removal or installation of propeller shaft.
11. Remove transmission support to transmission mount bolt and transmission support to frame bolts and insulators, if used.
12. Using a suitable jack transmission, support and raise transmission slightly, then slide transmission support rearward.
13. Lower transmission to gain access to oil cooler lines, then disconnect oil cooler lines and cap all openings.
14. **On 4L60 transmissions,** disconnect TV cable.
15. **On 4L60-E transmissions,** disconnect all electrical connectors.
16. **On all transmissions,** support engine with suitable tool, remove transmission to engine attaching bolts.
17. Install torque converter holding fixture tool, No. J-21366 or equivalent, then carefully lower transmission assembly from vehicle.
18. Reverse procedure to install.

CORVETTE

1. Disconnect battery ground cable.
2. **On 4L60 transmissions,** disconnect TV cable at upper end.
3. **On all transmissions,** remove dipstick.
4. Raise and support vehicle.
5. Remove upper and lower underbody braces, if equipped.
6. Remove complete exhaust system, then support transmission with a suitable transmission jack.
7. Remove driveline support beam.
8. Mark propeller shaft trunnion and axle yoke for installation reference, then remove propeller shaft.
9. Disconnect speedometer cable or P.M. generator electrical connector, shift linkage, and all electrical leads at transmission as well as any clips that retain the leads to transmission case.
10. Remove flywheel cover, then mark flywheel and torque converter to maintain original balance. Remove torque converter to flywheel bolts.
11. Lower transmission to gain access to oil cooler lines, then disconnect oil cooler lines and cap all openings.
12. **On 4L60 transmissions,** disconnect TV cable.
13. **On 4L60-E transmissions,** disconnect all electrical connectors.
14. **On all transmissions,** support engine with suitable tool, remove transmission to engine attaching bolts.
15. Support engine using suitable jack, then remove transmission to engine attaching bolts.
16. Separate transmission assembly from engine, install torque converter holding fixture tool, No. J-21366, then lower transmission from vehicle.
17. Reverse procedure to install.

BROUGHAM & FLEETWOOD (RWD)

1. Disconnect battery ground cable.
2. Remove air cleaner assembly
3. **On 4L60 transmission,** disconnect TV cable at upper end.
4. **On all transmissions,** remove transmission oil dipstick, dipstick tube retaining bolt and dipstick tube.
5. Raise and support vehicle.
6. Remove propeller shaft. If necessary remove floor pan reinforcement.
7. Disconnect speedometer cable, shift linkage and all electrical connectors.
8. Remove flexplate cover, then mark flexplate and torque converter to maintain original balance. Remove torque converter-to-flexplate attaching nuts and/or bolts.
9. Remove catalytic converter support bracket.
10. Remove transmission support to transmission mount bolt, then transmission support to frame bolts and insulator if used.
11. Position a suitable jack under transmission, then raise transmission slightly and slide transmission support rearward.
12. Lower transmission slightly, then disconnect oil cooler lines.
13. **On 4L60 transmission,** disconnect TV cable.
14. **On 4L60-E transmissions,** disconnect all electrical connectors.
15. **On all transmissions,** support engine, then remove transmission to engine bolts and disconnect transmission assembly. **Use caution not to damage cables, lines or linkage.**
16. Using torque converter holding fixture tool No. J-21366 or equivalent remove transmission assembly from vehicle.
17. Reverse procedure to install.

TIGHTENING SPECIFICATIONS

Component	Torque/Ft. Lbs.
CAMARO & FIREBIRD	
Accumulator Cover	97①
Auxiliary Valve Body Bolt	97①
Case Extension Bolt	26
Filler Tube To Transmission Case②	35
Filler Tube To Transmission Case③	55
Floorshift Control Bolt	44①
Flywheel Cover	89①
Manual Shift Detent Assembly	16
Neutral Safety/Back-up Lamp Switch	18①
Oil Cooler Connector At Transmission	28
Oil Cooler Connector At Radiator	20
Oil Pan Bolts	12
Pressure Control Solenoid Retainer	97①
Shift Cable Nut	11

Component	Torque/Ft. Lbs.
CAMARO & FIREBIRD -Continued	
Spacer Plate Support	97①
TCC Solenoid Valve	97①
Torque Converter Bolts	46
Transmission Case Extension To Transmission	26
Transmission To Engine Bolt	35
Transmission To Engine Bolts	70②
Transmission Support To Frame Bolt	40
Transmission Mount To Transmission Bolt	40
Transmission Mount To Transmission Support Nut	35
T.V. Cable To Transmission Bolt	89①
Valve Body Bolts	97①
Vehicle Speed Sensor	97①
Vehicle Speed Sensor Retainer	89①
Wheel Lug Nuts	81

TIGHTENING SPECIFICATIONS-Continued

Component	Torque/Ft. Lbs.
CAPRICE, CUSTOM CRUISER, IMPALA SS & ROADMSTER -Continued	
Accumulator Cover	97①
Backup Lamp Switch	18①
Case Extension To Case	26
Converter Clutch Solenoid	97①
Equalizer Lever To Control Rod	21
Flywheel	46
Flywheel Cover Bolts	89①
Forward Accumulator Cover	97①
Manual Detent Spring	18
Mount To Transmission Bolts④	30
Oil Cooler Lines To Radiator	20
Oil Pan Bolts	12
Torque Converter Bolts	46
Transmission Support To Frame Bolt	25
Transmission To Engine Bolts	35
Transmission To Mount Bolt	35
Valve Body Bolts	11
Wheel Lug Nuts	100
Corvette	
Accumulator Cover	97①
Converter Cover	89①
Filler Tube To Transmission Bolt	35

Component	Torque/Ft. Lbs.
CAPRICE, CUSTOM CRUISER, IMPALA SS & ROADMSTER -Continued	
Floorshift Control Bolt	89①
Flywheel Cover Bolt	89①
Neutral Safety/Back-Up Lamp Switch	27①
Oil Cooler Line Fitting At Radiator	20
Oil Cooler Line Fitting At Transmission	11
Oil Cooler Line Retaining Clip Bolt	107①
Oil Pan Bolt	12
Park/Neutral Position Switch	27①
Pressure Control Solenoid	97①
Shift Control Cable Attachment	15
TCC Solenoid	97①
Throttle Valve Link To Transmission Case	89①
Torque Converter Bolts	46
Transmission To Engine Bolts	35
Underbody Brace Stud Nut	20
Underbody Brace To Frame Bolt	47
Valve Body Bolts	97①
Vehicle Speed Sensor	97①
Wheel Lug Nuts	100

①—Inch lbs.
②—V-8 engine.
③—V-6 engine.
④—1992 models.

Turbo Hydra-Matic 4T80–E Automatic Transaxle

INDEX

IDENTIFICATION

Refer to **Fig. 1** for transaxle identification location.

DESCRIPTION

The 4T80-E transaxle **Fig. 2**, is a fully automatic electronically controlled transaxle. It has four forward ranges, including overdrive. Two shift solenoids, operated by the PCM, control shift points. Oil pressure is supplied by three gear type oil pumps and regulated by a transaxle pressure control solenoid (force motor) which is controlled by the PCM. Shift schedule and TCC apply rates, which are influenced by many sensor inputs, are controlled by the PCM.

TROUBLESHOOTING

Refer to **Fig. 3** for troubleshooting diagnosis.

MAINTENANCE

Refer to "Lubricant Data Chart" in the appropriate chassis chapter of this manual for transmission fluid specifications.

FLUID CHECK

COLD TRANSAXLE FLUID

This procedure is valid when vehicle is cold, has not been driven and transmission

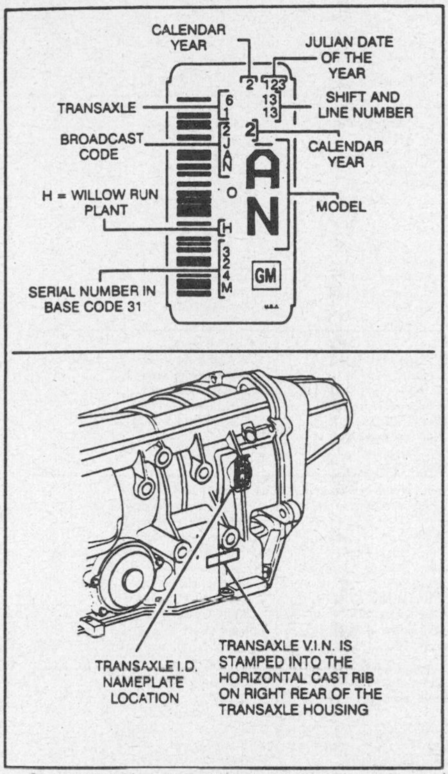
CALENDAR YEAR
JULIAN DATE OF THE YEAR
TRANSAXLE
SHIFT AND LINE NUMBER
BROADCAST CODE
CALENDAR YEAR
H = WILLOW RUN PLANT
MODEL
SERIAL NUMBER IN BASE CODE 31
GM
TRANSAXLE I.D. NAMEPLATE LOCATION
TRANSAXLE V.I.N. IS STAMPED INTO THE HORIZONTAL CAST RIB ON RIGHT REAR OF THE TRANSAXLE HOUSING

Copyrighted Material Reprinted with Permission from Hydra-Matic Div., GM Corp.

THA059000035000X

Fig. 1 Transaxle identification location

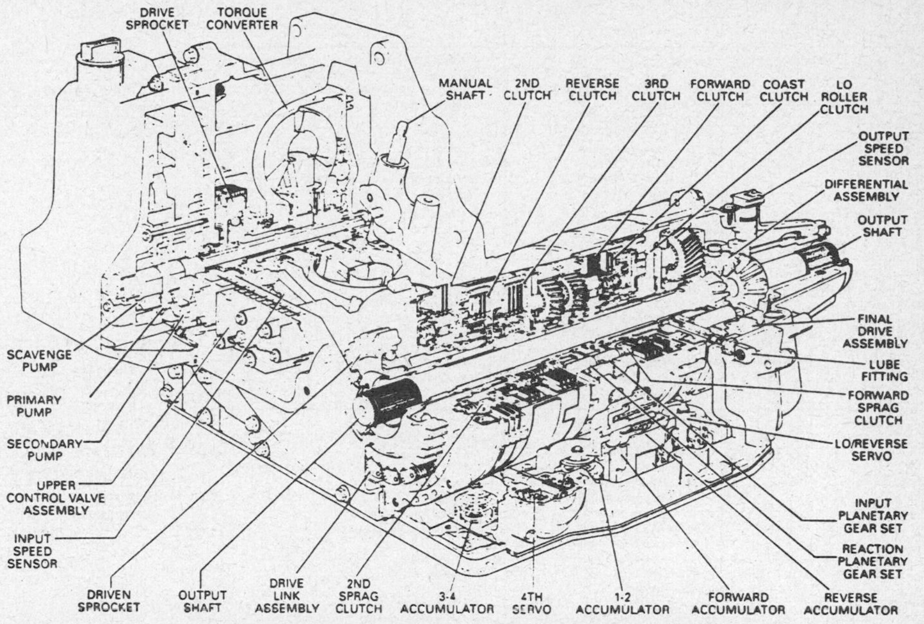
DRIVE SPROCKET
TORQUE CONVERTER
MANUAL SHAFT
2ND CLUTCH
REVERSE CLUTCH
3RD CLUTCH
FORWARD CLUTCH
COAST CLUTCH
LO ROLLER CLUTCH
OUTPUT SPEED SENSOR
DIFFERENTIAL ASSEMBLY
OUTPUT SHAFT
FINAL DRIVE ASSEMBLY
LUBE FITTING
FORWARD SPRAG CLUTCH
LO/REVERSE SERVO
INPUT PLANETARY GEAR SET
REACTION PLANETARY GEAR SET
SCAVENGE PUMP
PRIMARY PUMP
SECONDARY PUMP
UPPER CONTROL VALVE ASSEMBLY
INPUT SPEED SENSOR
DRIVEN SPROCKET
OUTPUT SHAFT
DRIVE LINK ASSEMBLY
2ND SPRAG CLUTCH
3-4 ACCUMULATOR
4TH SERVO
1-2 ACCUMULATOR
FORWARD ACCUMULATOR
REVERSE ACCUMULATOR

Copyrighted Material Reprinted with Permission from Hydra-Matic Div., GM Corp.

THA059300036000X

Fig. 2 Cross sectional view of 4T80-E transaxle

fluid temperature is between 70° and 90°F. The vehicle should be parked on a level surface. Approximately five minutes are available to finish this procedure before cold temperature is exceeded and the test becomes invalid.

1. Apply brake and start engine.
2. Hold brake and move shifter through each gear range, pausing three seconds in each. Return shifter to Park.
3. Apply parking brake and allow engine to idle for two to three minutes.
4. For remainder of test, shifter should be in Park, parking brake should be applied and foot brake NOT applied (foot brake will affect oil level).
5. Remove dipstick and wipe clean, then insert dipstick for three seconds and pull out.
6. Check both sides of dipstick. Fluid level on lower side must be in cold range of indicator.
7. If level is in cold range, no level adjustment is necessary.
8. If level is not in cold range, add fluid until level reaches middle of cold range. Transaxle will need to be warmed and fluid level checked again. Refer to "Hot Transaxle Fluid" checking procedure.

HOT TRANSAXLE FLUID

Wait at least 30 minutes before checking transaxle fluid if the vehicle has been driven when the outside temperature is above 90°F, at high speed for an extended period of time and/or in heavy traffic (especially in hot weather). To obtain an accurate reading, the fluid must be at normal operating temperature (180°-200°F). Bring the vehicle up to operating temperature by driving about 15 miles when outside temperature is above 15°F.

1. Park vehicle on level surface, then place shifter in Park.
2. Apply brake, move shifter through each gear range, pausing for three seconds in each range, then place shifter in Park.
3. Apply parking brake, then allow engine to idle for three to five minutes.
4. For remainder of test, shifter should be in Park, parking brake should be applied and foot brake should NOT be on applied (foot brake will affect oil level).
5. Remove dipstick and wipe clean, then insert dipstick for three seconds and pull out.
6. Check both sides of dipstick. Fluid level on lower side must be in hot range of indicator.
7. If level is in hot range, no level adjustment is necessary.
8. If level is not in hot range, add fluid until level reaches middle of hot range.

FLUID CHANGE

1. Raise and support vehicle, then place drain pan under transaxle fluid pan to catch fluid.
2. Loosen bottom pan bolts in proper sequence, **Fig. 4**, and drain fluid into drain pan.
3. Removing fluid pan will only partially drain transaxle fluid. Remaining fluid is held in side cover and torque converter; removing drain plug in case after fluid pan removal will drain fluid from side cover. It is not necessary to drain torque converter during most service procedures.
4. Remove fluid pan and transaxle case bolts, pan and gasket.
5. Remove left and right scavenger screens, **Fig. 5**.
6. Inspect fluid pan for and transaxle case for dents or nicks in sealing surface, replacing if damaged.
7. Inspect bolts for thread damage, replacing if damaged.
8. Reverse procedure to install noting the following:
   a. Install new fluid pan gasket.
   b. Add Dexron IIE transaxle fluid. Refer to "Transaxle Fluid Checking Procedure" as outlined.
   c. Reset transaxle oil life indicator if complete fluid change was necessary. Refer to "Resetting Transaxle Oil Life Indicator" as outlined.

RESETTING TRANSAXLE OIL LIFE INDICATOR

The PCM maintains a value for transaxle oil life which indicates the percentage of oil life remaining and is calculated based on transaxle temperature and speed. When the vehicle is new, the transaxle oil life is 100%; as mileage accumulates, oil life will eventually decrease to 0%. When the value reaches 1%, the CCDIC displays the message CHANGE TRANSAXLE OIL.

The oil life indicator should be reset to 100% when transaxle oil is changed or when the transaxle is replaced. Transaxle oil life value should be recorded prior to PCM replacement and programmed into the new PCM. To reset the transaxle oil life indicator, proceed as follows:

1. Turn ignition key On, with engine Off.
2. Enter diagnostics, then select PCM override PS15 (TRANS OIL).

CONDITION	INSPECT	FOR CAUSE
High Line Pressure (Harsh Shifts)	• Press. Reg. Valve (211) • Pressure Control Solenoid (339) - Possible Codes; 56, 75, 76, 86, 89 • T.P.C.S. Feed Valve • P.R. Boost Valve (213) • PSM (936) • Transmission Harness (12) • Checkballs (65)	– Stuck at high torque signal due to under sized bore, sediment or T.P.C.S. – Failed "off", intermittent short – Loose connector – Stuck – Stuck open – Loose connector – Loose connection at vehicle harness – Missing
(Harsh Engagement)	• Final Drive Internal Gear Snap Ring (135) • Actuator Feed Limit Valve (309)	– Missing – Stuck open
Inadequate Lube or Low Line Pressure	• Scavenge Pump Body (225) • Scavenge Pipe (54) • Scavenge Pipe Seal (53) • Primary Pump Body (200) • Scavenge Screens (51 and 52) • P.R. Valve (211) • Secondary Pump Body (203) • Transaxle Fluid • Cooler Lines	– Leakage at gasket or pump body – Restriction – Damaged, cut or leaking – Leakage at gasket or pump body – Clogged – Stuck due to sediment – Leakage at gasket or pump body – Low level – Clogged or restricted
Second Gear Starts	• "A" Shift Solenoid (909) - Possible Codes; 29, 16, 94 • Transaxle Pressure Control Solenoid (339) • Starts At HI Line Only, Driven Sprocket Support (418)	– Stuck off – Pinched wire to ground – Inoperative – Leakage – Pinched wire to ground – Staked checkball missing
Transaxle Slips in Reverse	• Fluid Level • Line Pressure • Scavenge Pump (223, 224, 225) • Primary Pump (200, 201, 202) • Scavenge Pipe (54) • Scavenge Pipe Seal (53) • Rev. Clutch Seals (506, 507) • Plates (511, 512, 513) • Reverse Band (13) • Rev. Servo Piston (928) • Rev. Servo Seals (929 and 930) • Rev. Servo Pin (931) • Rev. Band Anchor Pins (9)	– Too high or low – Too low – Gears worn or broken – Gears worn or broken – Debris in pipe – Cut or damaged – Cut, damaged or leaking – Damaged or burned – Damaged, burned, slipping – Damaged or cracked – Cut, damaged or leaking – Binding, too short – Loose, missing
Soft Shifts	• Line Pressure • Transaxle Pressure Control Solenoid (339) • Transaxle Pressure Switch (PSM) (Clip) Clamp (340) - Possible Code; 28 • Calibration Prom	– Too low – Stuck "on" – Broken clip causing leakage – Pinched wire to ground – Incorrect

TH5029300512010X

Fig. 3 Troubleshooting, harsh or soft shift condition (Part 1 of 8)

CONDITION	INSPECT	FOR CAUSE
D2, D3, D4 No First Gear	• Checkballs • Lo/Rev Servo Apply Pin (931) • 1-2 Shift Valve (919) • FWD/CC Support Seals (829) • FWD/CC Studs (5) • Lo Roller Clutch (830) • "A" Shift Solenoid (909) - Possible Code 94 • Forward C. Piston (807) • Forward C. Piston Seals (808 and 809) • Support Housing Seal Rings (829) • Forward Sprag (716) • Checkball No. 8	– Missing from FWD/coast clutch – Apply pin damage – Stuck in up shifted position – Damaged – Damaged, broken – Worn or damaged – Debris, or fialed off – Pinched or damaged wires, inoperative – Damaged or cracked – Rolled, cut or damaged – Leaking, damaged or cut – Damaged, not holding – Missing
D2, D3 No Second Gear	• Clutch Plates (431-435) • Piston (430) • Springs (428) • Piston Seals on Piston (430) • 2nd Sprag (517) • "A" Shift Solenoid (909) • 1-2 Shift Valve (919 and 920)	– Burned or damaged – Cracked or damaged – Broken, out of position – Rolled, damaged or leaking – Damaged, not holding – Stuck on – Stuck in 1st gear
D3 No Third Gear	• 3/4 Shift Valve Bore Plug (914) • Driven Sprocket Support (418) • 3rd Clutch Plates (610-613) • 3rd Clutch Piston (606) • 3rd Clutch Seals on Piston (606) • Checkballs (437) • "B" Shift Solenoid (909) - Possible Codes: 29, 117 • "A" Shift Solenoid (909) - Code 94, 117	– Misassembled – Exhaust valve cup plug or valve improperly installed – Burned, splines damaged – Cracked, damaged, checkball damage – Cut or rolled – Missing, stuck – Debris – Wires pinched or damaged – Inoperative
No Fourth Gear	• "A" Shift Solenoid (909) - possible code: 94 • 4th Band (523) • 4th Servo Pin (527) • 4th Servo Piston (529) • 4th Servo Seals (525 and 532) • 4th Servo Cover (524) • 3/4 Shift Valve Bore Plug (914)	– Inoperative – Debris – Pinched wires – Burned, slipping, missing – Broken, seized – Damaged – Rolled, cut or damaged – Cracked – Misassembled

TH5029300512020X

Fig. 3 Troubleshooting, poor performance (Part 2 of 8)

3. Press WARMER button to increase value or COOLER button to decrease value.

An alternate way to reset oil life indicator is as follows:

1. Turn ignition key On, with engine Off.
2. Press and hold OFF and REAR DEFOG buttons on CCDIC until message TRANSAXLE OIL LIFE RESET appears on CCDIC.

TRANSAXLE OIL COOLER FLUSHING

Use J 35944 cooler flusher, **Fig. 6,** and J 35944-20 flushing solution funnel. Do not substitute the recommended flushing solution. The use of other solutions can result in damage to the tool, components or other improper flushing of the cooler. **Air supply must be equipped with a water/oil filter and must not exceed 120 psi. Excess air pressure may rupture the flushing tool or cooler, causing personal injury.**

1. Fill flushing tool J 35944 with 20-21 ounces of flushing solution J 35944-20. **Do not overfill.**
2. Secure cap, then pressurize can to 80-120 psi.
3. Connect discharge hose to transaxle fitting end of oil cooler pipe that goes to top fitting at radiator, then clip discharge hose into drain container.
4. Mount flushing tool to undercarriage using hook provided.
5. Connect hose from flushing tool to remaining oil cooler pipe, then with water valve (on flushing tool) in Off position, connect water hose from water supply to flushing tool.
6. Open water supply at faucet, then switch water valve (on flushing tool) to On position and allow water to flow through oil cooler for 10 seconds. **If water does not flow through cooler, do not continue with flushing procedure; cooling system may be plugged. Excess pressure may cause personal injury. Replacement of cooler pipe and/or cooler may be necessary.**
7. Switch water valve (on flushing tool) to Off position and clip discharge hose into a five gallon pail with a lid, or place a shop towel over end of discharge hose to prevent splash. **Discharge will foam when solution and water mix.**
8. Switch water valve (on flushing tool) to On position and depress trigger on handle. **Use bale clip provided on handle to hold trigger.**
9. Flush cooler for two minutes while applying air to air valve for 3-5 seconds. **Apply air at 15-20 seconds intervals to create surging action.**
10. Release trigger and switch water valve (on flushing tool) to Off position, then disconnect hoses from cooler pipes. Reverse positions and reconnect and reconnect to cooler pipes to back flush system.
11. Repeat Steps 8 and 9, then release trigger and allow water to flow to rinse oil cooler for one minute.
12. Switch water valve (on flushing tool) to Off position, then turn off water supply at faucet.
13. Dry system with compressed air for two minutes (minimum) or until there is no moisture coming from discharge hose. Use an air chuck clip, if available.
14. **Excess residual moisture may corrode cooler, pipes and damage transaxle. If Steps 14 through 18 cannot be completed at this time, use a squirt type oil can filled with transmission fluid to rinse cooler and pipes.** Connect cooler feed pipe to transaxle (top connector is feed, bottom connector is cooler return).
15. Attach discharge hose to cooler return pipe, then place into oil drain container.
16. Fill transaxle to appropriate level with transmission fluid (Dexron IIE). Start engine and allow to run for 30 seconds. A minimum of two quarts must flow through discharge hose.

CONDITION	INSPECT	FOR CAUSE
No First Gear	• Lo Roller Clutch (830) • Forward Sprag (716) • Oil Transfer Sleeve • Forward Clutch Plate (815-817) • Seals (808 and 809) • Detent Lever (17) • FWD/Coast Housing (801) • Piston (807) • "A" and/or "B" Shift Solenoid (909) - Possible Codes: 16, 29, 94 - Refer to Section 6E • Manual Valve (916) • Checkball (437) in Housing	– Worn or damaged – Damaged, not holding – Misaligned, damaged, leaking – Burned, damaged – Leaking, cut or rolled – Misaligned – Broken or spline damage – Cracked or damaged – Debris – Pinched or damaged wires – "A" and "B" Shift Solenoids Disabled – Misaligned – Leaking
Inconsistent Shifts	• "A" and "B" Shift Solenoids (909)	– O-ring seal damage – No compression
Third and Fourth Gear Only	• "B" Shift Solenoid (909) - Possible Codes: 117	– Stuck "on" – Pinched wire to ground
No Engine Braking	• Oil Transfer Sleeve (824) • Drive Chain (414) • Sprockets (407 and 415) • Drive Axle	– Misaligned – Broken, slipping – Damaged – Splines damaged
No Overrun Braking in D3	• Coast C. Plates (812-814) • Coast C. Seal/Checkball (810) • Forward Clutch Housing (801) • Oil Level • 3-4 Shift Valve (912) • "A" Shift Solenoid (909) - Possible Code: 94	– Burned or damaged – Cut, worn or nicked – Splines damaged – Housing cracked – Low – Stuck in upshift position – Debris, stuck
No Overrun Braking in D2	• 4th Band (523) • 4th Band Servo Pin (527) • 4th Servo Piston (529) • 4th Servo Seals (525 and 532) • Coast Clutch Plates(812-814) • Coast Clutch Seal/Checkball (810) • Transaxle Pressure Switch - Code 28 • Coast Clutch Support Seals (829)	– Slipping, burned – Stuck, broken – Damaged, cracked – Cut, rolled or damaged – Burned, damaged – Cut, worn or nicked – Inoperative – Damaged, missing
No Engine Braking in D1	• Transaxle Pressure Switch (936) Possible Code: 28 • Coast Clutch Plates (812-814) • Coast Clutch Seal/Checkball (810) • Checkball No. 6 • Lo/Rev Band (13) • Lo/Rev Servo Piston (928) Seals (929 and 930)	– Inoperative – Burned, damaged – Cut, worn or nicked – Missing – Slipping, burned, damaged – Damaged, seized – Leaking, rolled

TH5029300512030X

Fig. 3 Troubleshooting, poor performance (Part 3 of 8)

CONDITION	INSPECT	FOR CAUSE
Forward Motion in N	• Manual Valve (916) • Forward Clutch Springs (820) • Forward Clutch Piston (807) • Forward Clutch Plates (815-817) • Forward Clutch Housing (801) • Sprocket Support Hub (822) • Shift Linkage	– Mispositioned or stuck – Jammed – Jammed – Seized or jammed – Feed hole plugged, inspect tower – Holes plugged – Mispositioned – Disconnected
Engine Stall	• TCC • Converter Feed Valve (312) • TCC Solenoid (336) - Possible Code: 39 • Converter Feed Valve (312) • Turbine Shaft (410)	– Stuck on or dragging – Stuck open – Stuck on – Pinched wire to ground – Inoperative – Stuck open – Spline damaged
Loss of Power	• Transaxle • "A" and "B" Shift Solenoids (909) - Possible Codes: 16, 29, 94 • TCC System • Torque Converter (1) • Turbine Shaft (410)	– Low fluid – 2nd gear starts – TCC stuck on or dragging – Debris – Bushing damage
Loss of Drive	• Torque Converter (1) • Scavenger, Primary Pumps (225 and 200) • Pump Shaft (2) • Channel Plates (33, 900) • Gaskets (228, 326, 328, 935) • Scavenge Pipe Seal (53) • Drive Sprockets (407 and 415) • Drive Chain (414) • Driven Sprocket Support (418) • Final Drive • F.D. Pinions (103) • Roller, Forward Sprag • Forward/Coast Support (822) • Manual Valve and Link (915 and 916) • Turbine Shaft (410)	– Broken lug, failed lug weld – Sheared lug bolts – Worn turbine shaft splines – Low fluid – Pump hub cracked or broken – Internal failure – Closure weld failure – Cover cracked at weld – Seized, broken pump gears – Broken – Damaged – Damaged – Damaged or missing – Broken – Broken – Damaged, porosity, leaking – Damaged, splines worn – Spalled pins or pinions – Lack of lube – Worn, broken or locked – No lube – Not attached to detent lever – Dislodged, stripped splines

TH5029300512040X

Fig. 3 Troubleshooting, poor performance (Part 4 of 8)

17. If fluid flow is not sufficient, disconnect oil feed line at radiator, then restart engine and check flow rate. If flow rate is not sufficient, inspect oil cooler feed and transaxle for cause. If flow rate is sufficient, repeat oil cooler flushing and fluid flow check procedures. If flow is not sufficient, replace oil cooler.
18. Remove discharge hose, then connect cooler return pipe to transaxle and fill transaxle to proper fluid level as outlined.
19. Thoroughly clean flushing tool with water. **Do not store tool with flushing solution in tank.**

RESETTING TRANSAXLE ADAPTS

The PCM maintains three types of transaxle adapt parameters which are used to modify transaxle line pressure under specific conditions. By modifying line pressure, the PCM maintains transaxle shift tolerance at a constant level, regardless of wear or variation of tolerance inside the transaxle. The three types of transaxle adapts are: garage shift adapt (controls Park to Drive or Reverse feel), upshift adapt (controls feel of 1/2, 2/3 and 3/4 upshifts) and steady state adapt (reduces slippage of clutches in all drive ranges).

1. Turn key On, enter diagnostics, then select PCM override PS13 (TP SENSOR LEARN).
2. Press Warmer button. CCDIC should display 09, indicating that garage shift adapt has been reset.
3. Select PCM override PS14 (TRAN ADAPT). Press cooler button. CCDIC should display 90, indicating upshift adapt value has been reset.
4. Press Warmer button. CCDIC should display 09, indicating steady state adapt value has been reset.

ADJUSTMENTS

TRANSAXLE RANGE CONTROL (SHIFTER) CABLE

1. Remove air cleaner duct and housing.
2. Use a flat head screwdriver to pry lock button on shifter cable to unlocked position, **Fig. 7.**
3. Place transaxle shifter in Neutral, then select Neutral position at lever on transaxle manual shaft.
4. Depress lock button on shifter cable into LOCKED position, **Fig. 7.**
5. Install air cleaner duct and housing.

IN-VEHICLE REPAIRS

TRANSAXLE RANGE CONTROL (SHIFTER) CABLE

Removal

Refer to **Figs. 8 and 7** when servicing shifter cable.

1. Remove air cleaner duct and housing, then disconnect shifter cable at lever on transaxle manual shaft.
2. Disconnect shifter cable at bracket on transaxle, then remove attaching bolts and bracket at transaxle (if bracket replacement is necessary), **Fig. 8.**
3. Remove shifter knob and console trim plate in passenger compartment, **Fig. 9.**
4. Disconnect shifter cable at shifter assembly.
5. Loosen carpet attachments on front left side of passenger compartment to allow access to cable routing.
6. Remove cable grommet through cowl, then cable from vehicle.

Installation

1. Install cable through cowl and grommet into cowl, then rout cable under carpet and attach carpet in front left side of passenger compartment.

CONDITION	INSPECT	FOR CAUSE
Engine Starts in Gear	• Manual Valve (916) • Transaxle Range Switch	– Not engaged to detent lever – Stuck in wrong position – Not working, mispositioned
No Gear Selections	• Detent Lever (17) • Manual Valve (916) • Spacer Plate Gasket (935) • Valve Bodies/Case	– Nut loose or missing – Stuck – Blocked holes – Blocked channels
Shift Lever Indicates Wrong Gear	• Manual Valve (916) • Detent Roller Pin (26) • Detent Roller (26) • Spring (27) • Manual Detent Pivot (26) • Manual Shaft (16) • Indicator Linkage	– Not engaged to detent lever – Missing, damaged – Broken or disconnected – Loose or missing – Flats not parallel – Misadjusted
No TCC	• TCC Solenoid (336) • PCM • Brake Switch • TCC Control Valve (317) • TCC Regulating Valve (318) • TCC Feed Valve (312) • Oil Pressure Screen (342) • O-Ring (412) • Torque Converter (1) • O-Ring (412) • Possible Codes; - 16, 29, 88, 117 - 39, 90	– Stuck off – O-ring failed – No voltage to solenoid – Poor connection – No signal to solenoid – Contact corroded – Poor connection – Pinched wire – Misadjusted – No supply voltage – Stuck off due to sediment or undersized bore – Stuck off due to sediment or undersized bore – Stuck off due to sediment or undersized bore – Clogged – Damaged or leaking – Ballooning – Worn – TCC not engaging fully or slipping
Soft TCC Apply	• Turbine Shaft Seal (412) • TCC Solenoid (336) • Transmission Fluid • Conv. Clutch Feed Valve (312)	– Worn or damaged – Malfunction – Low – Sticking
Early TCC Engagement	• Trans Temp Sensor (350) - Possible Codes; - 59 Open Circuit	– Shorted
TCC Not Disengaging	• TCC Solenoid (336) • Converter Feed Valve (312)	– Stuck on due to debris – Stuck on due to debris
Converter Ballooning	• Converter Feed Valve (312)	– Stuck open due to sediment or undersized bore

TH5029300512050X

Fig. 3 Troubleshooting, poor performance/TCC condition (Part 5 of 8)

CONDITION	INSPECT	FOR CAUSE
Engine Starts in Gear	• Manual Valve (916) • Transaxle Range Switch	– Not engaged to detent lever – Stuck in wrong position – Not working, mispositioned
No Gear Selections	• Detent Lever (17) • Manual Valve (916) • Spacer Plate Gasket (935) • Valve Bodies/Case	– Nut loose or missing – Stuck – Blocked holes – Blocked channels
Shift Lever Indicates Wrong Gear	• Manual Valve (916) • Detent Roller Pin (26) • Detent Roller (26) • Spring (27) • Manual Detent Pivot (26) • Manual Shaft (16) • Indicator Linkage	– Not engaged to detent lever – Missing, damaged – Broken or disconnected – Loose or missing – Flats not parallel – Misadjusted
No TCC	• TCC Solenoid (336) • PCM • Brake Switch • TCC Control Valve (317) • TCC Regulating Valve (318) • TCC Feed Valve (312) • Oil Pressure Screen (342) • O-Ring (412) • Torque Converter (1) • O-Ring (412) • Possible Codes; - 16, 29, 88, 117 - 39, 90	– Stuck off – O-ring failed – No voltage to solenoid – Poor connection – No signal to solenoid – Contact corroded – Poor connection – Pinched wire – Misadjusted – No supply voltage – Stuck off due to sediment or undersized bore – Stuck off due to sediment or undersized bore – Stuck off due to sediment or undersized bore – Clogged – Damaged or leaking – Ballooning – Worn – TCC not engaging fully or slipping
Soft TCC Apply	• Turbine Shaft Seal (412) • TCC Solenoid (336) • Transmission Fluid • Conv. Clutch Feed Valve (312)	– Worn or damaged – Malfunction – Low – Sticking
Early TCC Engagement	• Trans Temp Sensor (350) - Possible Codes; - 59 Open Circuit	– Shorted
TCC Not Disengaging	• TCC Solenoid (336) • Converter Feed Valve (312)	– Stuck on due to debris – Stuck on due to debris
Converter Ballooning	• Converter Feed Valve (312)	– Stuck open due to sediment or undersized bore

TH5029300512060X

Fig. 3 Troubleshooting, delayed or no engagement into D or R (Part 6 of 8)

2. Connect shifter cable at shifter assembly, then install trim plate and shifter knob in passenger compartment.
3. Install cable bracket and attaching bolts at transaxle (if bracket replacement was necessary), then **torque** bolts to 35 ft. lbs.
4. Connect shifter cable at bracket on transaxle and at lever on transaxle manual shaft.
5. Adjust cable as follows:
   a. Use a flat head screwdriver to pry lock button on shifter cable to unlocked position, **Fig. 7.**
   b. Place transaxle shifter in Neutral, then select Neutral position at lever on transaxle manual shaft.
   c. Depress lock button on shifter cable into LOCKED position, **Fig. 7.**
6. Install air cleaner duct and housing.

PARK LOCK CABLE (CONSOLE SHIFT)

Removal

Refer to **Figs. 7** and 9 when servicing park lock (console shift) cable.

1. Place shifter in Park, then remove left instrument panel sound insulator and loosen left front carpet to allow access to park lock cable routing.
2. Remove steering column reinforcement plate, then steering column bolts and lower steering column.
3. Turn ignition key to Run position. **Do not attempt to perform Step 4 with ignition key in any other position than Run.**
4. Slip a flat head screwdriver blade into ignition switch inhibitor slot, then depress cable latch and pull Park lock cable from inhibitor.
5. Remove radio and console trim plates.
6. Disconnect park lock cable at shifter assembly.
7. Remove park lock cable from vehicle.

Installation

1. Using a flat head screwdriver, pry lock button of park lock cable into UNLOCKED position, then connect park lock cable at shifter assembly. **Do not attempt Step 3 with ignition key in any other position than RUN.**
2. With shifter in Park and ignition key in Run, snap park lock cable into inhibitor housing.
3. Turn key to Lock position, then snap cable end onto pin of shifter lever.
4. Push park lock cable toward shifter lever assembly to remove slack.
5. Push lock button on park lock cable down into locked position.
6. With shifter in Park and ignition key in Lock position, ensure shifter cannot move to another position. Ignition key should not be removable from its cylinder.
7. Turn ignition key to Run position and move shifter to Neutral. Ensure ignition key cannot be turned to Lock position.
8. If checks in Steps 7 and 8 are OK, proceed with procedure. If checks are not OK, readjust park lock cable beginning with Step 1.
9. Raise steering column, then install bolts and reinforcement plate
10. Install console and radio trim plates, then secure left front carpet and left instrument panel sound insulator.

BRAKE-TRANSAXLE SHIFT INTERLOCK (BTSI), REPLACE

1. Remove shifter knob and console trim plate, **Fig. 9.**
2. Disconnect electrical connector, then BTSI solenoid at shifter assembly.
3. Reverse procedure to install.

CONDITION	INSPECT	FOR CAUSE
No Torque Multiplication	• Drive Sprocket Support (400)	– Broken or detached from case – Spline damage
No Reverse	• Reaction Carrier Shell (633) • Lo/Reverse Anchor Pin (9) • Driven Sprocket Support (418) Support Seals (422 and 423) Support Bolts • Reverse Band (13) • Reverse Band Apply Pin (931) • Reverse Piston (505) • Seal (506 and 507) • Checkball in Piston • Gasket (43 and 44) • Case Cover (33) • Fluid Pressure • Steel Plates (511) • Friction Plates (513) • Spring Assembly (508) • Housing (500) • Snap Ring (515)	– Missing, teeth damaged – Anchor pin broken or not positioned – Porosity or broken – Feed holes blocked – Leaking – Loose, not in grooves, mislocated – Broken, worn not anchored – Too short or binding in case. – Broken – Binding in case. – Leaking, damaged or worn – Missing – Damaged or displaced – Damaged – Too low – Splines worn – Splines or friction worn – Jammed – Cracked – Out
Will not stay in park	• Detent Spring (27) • Detent Lever (17) • Actuator Rod (21) • Park Pawl Pivot Pin (23) • Parking Lock Gear (833) • Park Pawl (22) • Manual Linkage	– Weak or broken – Mislocated or broken – Bent – Guide damaged – Missing – Damaged teeth – Damaged (tooth) – Misadjusted or disconnected
Extended or Delayed Upshifts	• Possible Codes: - 21, 22, 24 - Transaxle Pressure Switch Code 28 • Pressure Regulator Boost Valve (213)	 – Inoperative – Stuck in bushing
Transaxle Seized	• Cooler Circuit Lines • Cooler Fittings (3, 38) • Spacer Plate Gasket (328) • Scavenger Pipe (54) • Valve Bodies (300 and 903) • Filter (236) • Filter Seal (209) • Screen Assemblies (51 and 52)	– Blocked or leaking – Blocked or leaking – Holes missing, off location – Damaged, clogged – Poor seal at pipe – Loose, broken or missing bolts – Sitting in side cover – Cut damaged neck seal – Clogged or not seated in case
Noise	• Torque Converter (1) • Transaxle/Engine • Case Extension (134)	– Loose lug bolts – Out of balance – Internal failure – Misaligned – Axle support bushing worn

TH5029300512070X

Fig. 3 Troubleshooting, noise (Part 7 of 8)

CONDITION	INSPECT	FOR CAUSE
NOISE IN ALL RANGES or (A whine which may RPM load sensitive or ceases when the TCC engages.)	• Torque Converter (1)	– Verify noise internal to torque converter by placing left foot on brake with gear or selector in Drive and momentarily stall engine. Torque converter noise increases under load.
A High Pitch WHINE which will intensify with engine RPM or is Oil Pressure sensitive.	• Oil Pump System	– Verify noise internal to oil pump during preliminary oil pressure check. An increase in line pressure will vary an oil pump noise.
A Popping noise similar to Popcorn popping.		– Pump cavitation-indicated by bubbles on fluid level indicator. – Transaxle fluid strainer for filter seam leak. – Transaxle fluid strainer seal for proper positioning or cut seal.
A BUZZ or High Frequency Rattle sound.	• Trace cooler pipes and check for binding or contact at the at the Radiator other than the Cooler pipe connectors	– Verify pressure buzz by watching for a needle vibration on the pressure gage. (Road test may be necessary.)
A Whine or Growl that increases and fades with Vehicle speed and is most Noticeable under Light Acceleration	• Drive Link Assembly System • Verify noise from sprockets and/or drive link assembly (chain) by placing left foot on brake and moving gear selector from Park or Reverse. If noise stops check items below: • Drive Chain (414) • Drive Sprocket and Driven Sprocket (407 and 415) • Drive Sprocket Support and Driven Sprocket Support (400 and 418)	 – Stretched – Teeth broken or sheared – Bearing surfaces nicked or scored – Bearing race or roller bearing surfaces on gear Support Inner Bearings rough or pitted. – Bearing damage – Bearing outer race support rough or nicked.
A Final Drive Noise or Hum, is most noticeable Under light throttle Acceleration and/or turns	• Final Drive Gear Set (100) Final Drive Internal Gear (120) • Differential Carrier (110) Differential Side Gears (116)	– Worn, planet pinions or washers – Worn, tooth damage – Gears worn or pitted – Thrust washer damage
Noise in 1st, 2nd, 3rd or 4th	• Final Drive Sun Gear (121) Final Drive Pinions (103)	– Gear worn or damage – Gears worn or damaged

TH5029300512080X

Fig. 3 Troubleshooting, vibration/fluid leaks/foaming (Part 8 of 8)

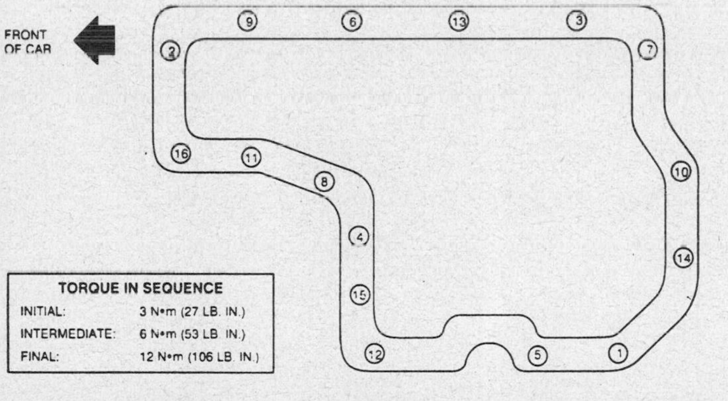
FRONT OF CAR
TORQUE IN SEQUENCE
INITIAL: 3 N•m (27 LB. IN.)
INTERMEDIATE: 6 N•m (53 LB. IN.)
FINAL: 12 N•m (106 LB. IN.)

THA059000037000X

Fig. 4 Transaxle bottom pan bolt loosening & tightening sequence

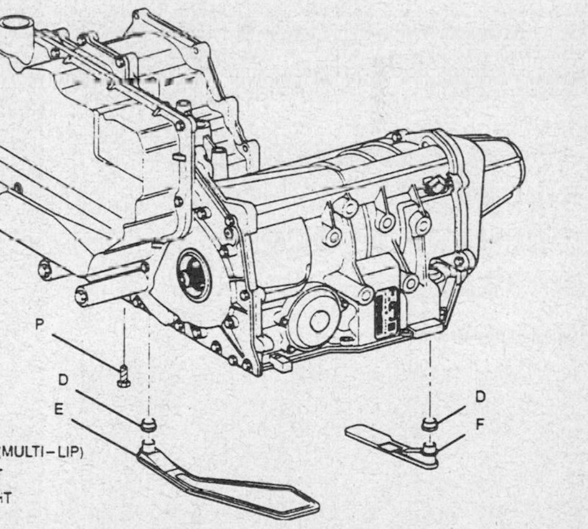
P
D
E
D
F

D SEAL, SCAVENGER FILTER (MULTI-LIP)
E SCAVENGER SCREEN, LEFT
F SCAVENGER SCREEN, RIGHT
P PLUG, DRAIN

TH5029300511000X

Fig. 5 Transaxle scavenger screens & drain plug

VALVE BODY, REPLACE

Refer to **Fig. 10** when servicing lower control valve.

1. Raise and support vehicle, then remove bottom pan, scavenger screens and seals as outlined.
2. Using a small screwdriver, bend back small tabs to disconnect shift solenoids A, B and transaxle pressure switch connectors, **Fig. 11.**
3. Disconnect manual valve linkage clip with a small screwdriver.
4. Disconnect wiring harness from retaining clips on lower controls assembly.
5. Remove oil transfer plate.
6. Remove bolts, then two nuts using 10 mm socket. **Do not remove five bolts in lower channel plate, Fig. 12.**
7. Lower channel plate, valve and accumulator assemblies from case.
8. Position the low reverse band using a .02-.03 inch shim, **Fig. 13.**
9. Place lower controls against forward support studs.
10. Hand start bolts into channel plate, then remove shim stock.

11. Place oil transfer plate over open gasket area. Hand start bolts to hold plate in place noting installation order.
12. Install two nuts on forward support studs, then **torque** bolts and nuts to 71-116 inch lbs.
13. Connect manual valve to detent lever. Route harness over spacer plate rib and detent lever and snap into retaining clips on lower controls assembly.
14. Connect wiring harness to shift solenoids A and B and transaxle pressure sensor.
15. Install scavenger screens, lip seals, bottom pan and gasket as outlined.
16. Add transaxle fluid as outlined.
17. Reset transaxle oil life indicator, if a complete fluid change was necessary, as outlined.

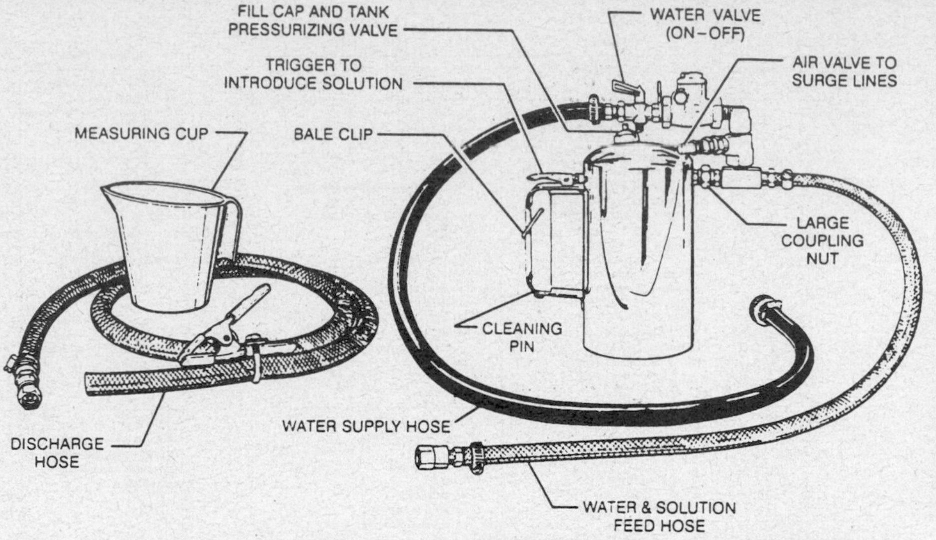
FILL CAP AND TANK
PRESSURIZING VALVE
WATER VALVE
(ON–OFF)
TRIGGER TO
INTRODUCE SOLUTION
AIR VALVE TO
SURGE LINES
MEASURING CUP
BALE CLIP
LARGE
COUPLING
NUT
CLEANING
PIN
WATER SUPPLY HOSE
DISCHARGE
HOSE
WATER & SOLUTION
FEED HOSE

Copyrighted Material Reprinted with Permission from Hydra-Matic Div., GM Corp.

TH5029300524000X

Fig. 6 Transaxle oil cooler flushing tool

SOLENOIDS A & B (1/2 & 2/3 SHIFT SOLENOIDS), REPLACE

Refer to **Fig. 10** when servicing shift solenoid assemblies.

1. Raise and support vehicle, then remove bottom pan and gasket, scavenger screens and seals as outlined.
2. Remove lower controls assembly as outlined.
3. Remove transaxle pressure switch manifold bolts, then transaxle pressure switch manifold.
4. Remove lower control valve assembly and gasket from lower channel plate.
5. Remove solenoids A and B retaining clips, then solenoids.
6. Reverse procedure to install, noting the following:
   a. Add transaxle fluid as outlined.
   b. Reset transaxle oil life indicator, if a complete fluid change was necessary, as outlined.

1/2, 3/4, FORWARD & REVERSE ACCUMULATORS, REPLACE

Removal

1. Raise and support vehicle, then remove bottom pan and gasket, scavenger screens and lip seals as outlined.
2. Remove lower controls assembly as outlined.
3. Remove nine bolts (three from channel side).
4. Remove accumulator housing from channel plate, then remove check balls. **Do not lose check balls.**
5. Remove spring.
6. Remove accumulator piston top snap rings from housing side, then remove 1/2 and 3/4 accumulator assemblies.
7. Remove five accumulator housing cover bolts, then accumulator housing cover and gasket.
8. Remove forward accumulator assembly, then reverse accumulator assembly.

Inspection

1. Inspect accumulator pins for straightness by rolling on a flat surface.
2. Inspect accumulator seals for tearing or roll over and snap rings for overexpansion
3. Inspect accumulator bores for scratches or nicks.
4. Replace gasket and inspect springs for cracking or damage.

Installation

Use a light coat of transmission fluid to lubricate all seals before installing accumulator assemblies.

1. Install forward accumulator assembly, then reverse accumulator assembly.
2. Install new gasket, then accumulator housing cover.
3. Install accumulator housing cover bolts, then **torque** bolts to 71-98 inch lbs.
4. Install 1/2 accumulator pin. Retain with two snap rings.
5. Install 1/2 accumulator spring, piston and seal.
6. Install snap ring and spring.
7. Install 3/4 accumulator pin. Retain with two snap rings.
8. Install 3/4 accumulator spring, piston and seal.
9. Install snap ring.
10. Install check balls.
11. Install guide pins J 39630-2 or equivalent for accumulator housing, then install accumulator housing to lower channel plate.
12. Remove guide pins and install remaining bolts. **Torque** bolts to 98-115 inch lbs.
13. Install lower controls assembly as outlined.
14. Install bottom pan and gasket, scavenger screens and lip seals as outlined.
15. Add transaxle fluid as outlined.
16. Reset transaxle oil life indicator, if a complete fluid change was necessary, as outlined.

LOWER VALVE ASSEMBLY, SPACER PLATE & CHANNEL PLATE, REPLACE

1. Raise and support vehicle, then remove bottom pan and gasket, scavenger screens and seals as outlined.
2. Remove lower controls assembly as outlined.
3. Remove nine accumulator housing bolts (three from channel plate side).
4. Remove accumulator housing from channel plate, then four check balls.
5. Remove transaxle pressure switch manifold bolts, then manifold.
6. Remove eleven bolts (two on channel plate side), then lower control valve assembly and gasket from lower channel plate.
7. Remove four check balls.
8. Remove manual valve link and clip, then manual valve.
9. Remove lo/reverse servo piston retaining ring. Push lo/reverse apply pin to remove servo assembly.
10. Remove return spring and clip, then push out servo pin.
11. Remove servo cushion spring and spring washer. **Inspect check valves for movement.**
12. Remove clips and shift solenoids A and B, then solenoid screen.
13. Remove 1/2 shift valves A and B, then 1/2 shift valve spring.
14. Remove 2/3 shift valves C and D, then 2/3 shift valve spring.
15. Remove coiled spring pin.
16. Remove forward bypass valve spring, then forward bypass valve.
17. Remove retaining clip, then bore plug.
18. Remove 3/4 shift valve, 3/4 shift valve spring, then coiled spring pin.
19. Remove reverse orifice bypass valve spring, then reverse orifice bypass valve.
20. Remove retaining sleeve.

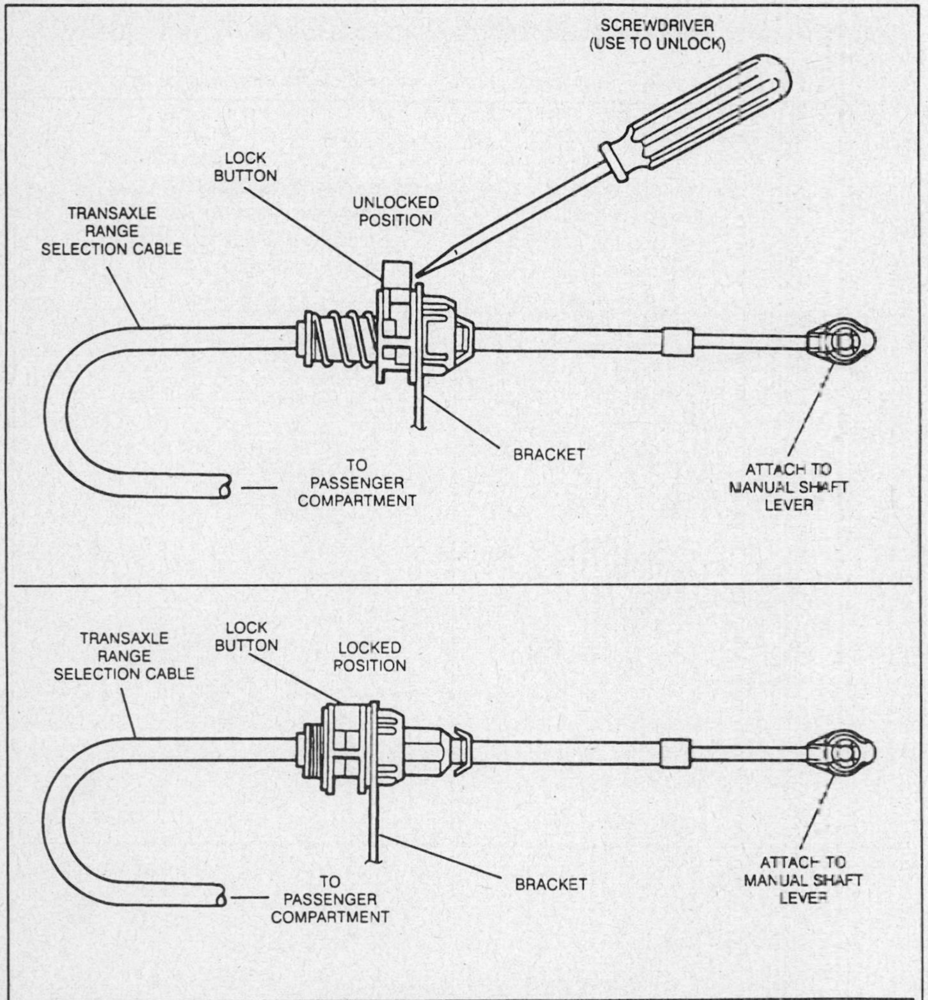
SCREWDRIVER
(USE TO UNLOCK)
LOCK
BUTTON
UNLOCKED
POSITION
TRANSAXLE
RANGE
SELECTION CABLE
BRACKET
TO
PASSENGER
COMPARTMENT
ATTACH TO
MANUAL SHAFT
LEVER
TRANSAXLE
RANGE
SELECTION CABLE
LOCK
BUTTON
LOCKED
POSITION
BRACKET
TO
PASSENGER
COMPARTMENT
ATTACH TO
MANUAL SHAFT
LEVER

CABLE PROCEDURE: ADJUSTMENT

1 INSTALL CABLE
2 USING SCREWDRIVER, PRY UP LOCK BUTTON TO "UNLOCKED" POSITION
3 MOVE TRANSAXLE MANUAL SHAFT TO "NEUTRAL" RANGE
4 MOVE PASSENGER COMPARTMENT RANGE SELECTION LEVER TO "NEUTRAL" RANGE
5 DEPRESS LOCK BUTTON TO "LOCK"

Copyrighted Material Reprinted with Permission from Hydra-Matic Div., GM Corp.

TH5029300522000X

Fig. 7 Transaxle range control cable adjustment

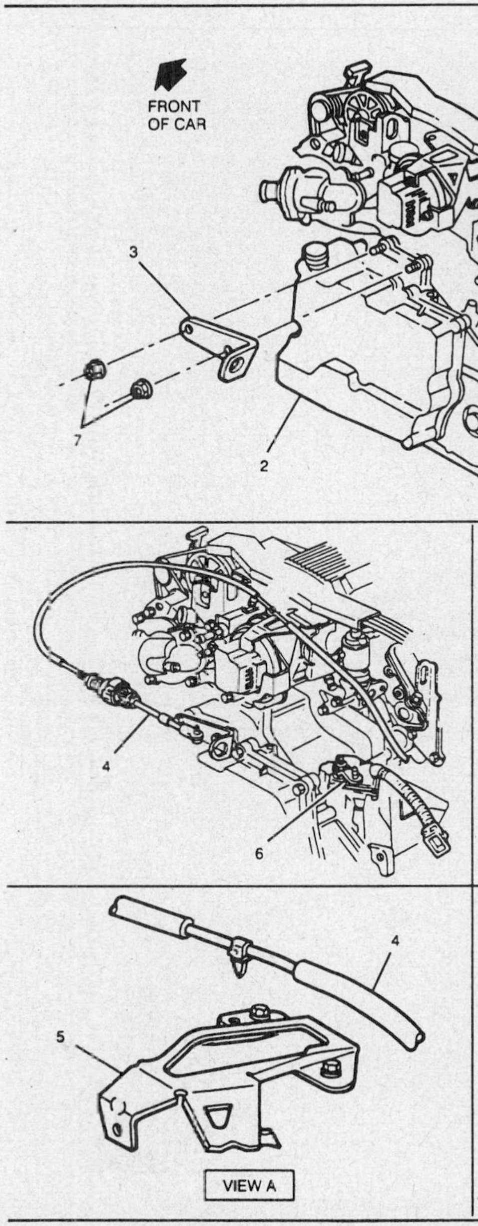
FRONT
OF CAR
1
2
3
7
4
6
4
6
4
5
VIEW A

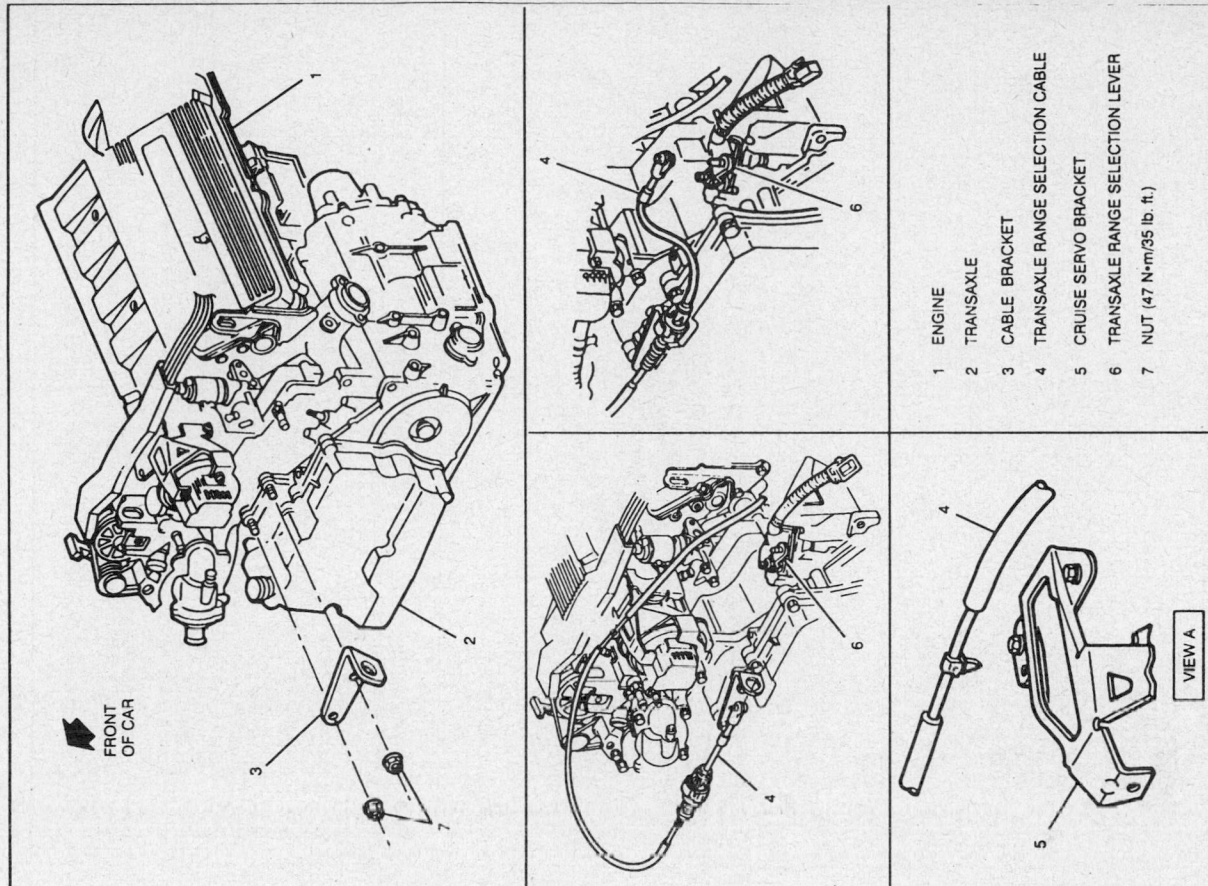

1 ENGINE
2 TRANSAXLE
3 CABLE BRACKET
4 TRANSAXLE RANGE SELECTION CABLE
5 CRUISE SERVO BRACKET
6 TRANSAXLE RANGE SELECTION LEVER
7 NUT (47 N•m/35 lb. ft.)

Copyrighted Material Reprinted with Permission from Hydra-Matic Div., GM Corp.

TH5029300520000

Fig. 8 Transaxle range control system, engine compartment

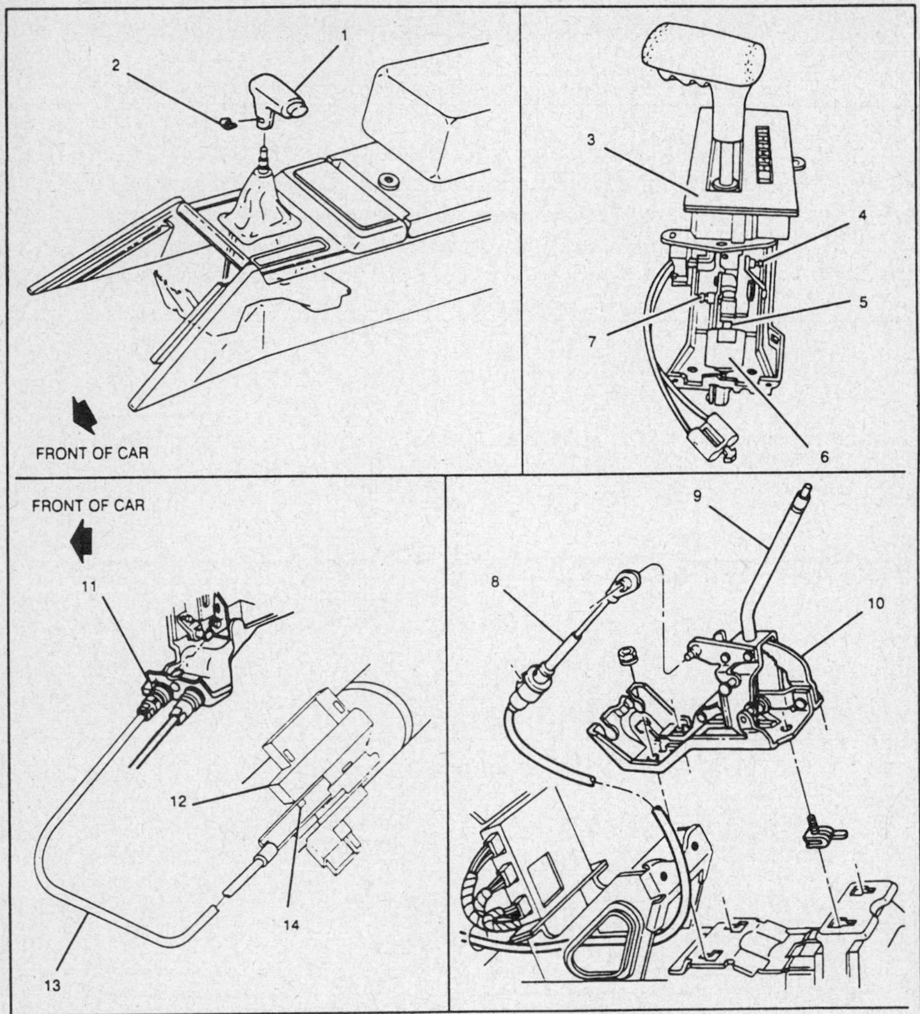
FRONT OF CAR
FRONT OF CAR

1	SHIFT HANDLE	8	SHIFT CONTROL CABLE
2	SHIFT HANDLE RETAINING CLIP	9	SHIFT CONTROL LEVER
3	PRNDL ASM (SHIFT INDICATOR)	10	SHIFT CONTROL ASM
4	TRANSMISSION SHIFT CABLE STUD	11	PARK LOCK ADJUSTER
5	BTSI SOLENOID CONNECTOR (2–PIN)	12	STEERING COLUMN UNIT
6	BTSI SOLENOID	13	PARK LOCK CABLE
7	PARK LOCK CABLE STUD	14	PARK LOCK CABLE RELEASE SLOT

Copyrighted Material Reprinted with Permission from Hydra-Matic Div., GM Corp.

TH5029300521000X

Fig. 9 Transaxle range control system

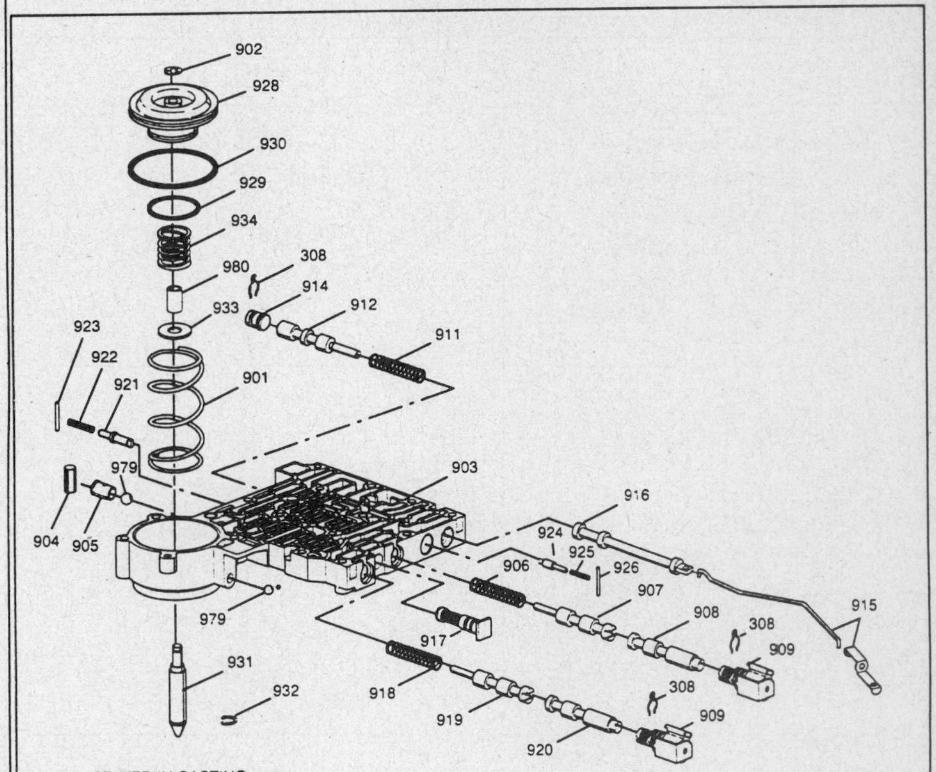
* STAKED IN CASTING

308	CLIP,RETAINER (3)	919	VALVE, SHIFT 1–2 A
901	SPRING, RETURN	920	VALVE, SHIFT 1–2 B
902	RING, RETAINING	921	VALVE, REVERSE ORIFICE BYPASS
903	VALVE BODY, LOWER CONTROL	922	SPRING, REVERSE ORIFICE BYPASS VALVE
904	RETAINER, SPRING	923	PIN, COILED SPRING FLAG
905	CAPSULE, BALL CHECK	924	VALVE, FORWARD ORIFICE BYPASS
906	SPRING, 2–3 SHIFT VALVE	925	SPRING, FORWARD ORIFICE BYPASS VALVE
907	VALVE, SHIFT 2–3 C	926	PIN, COILED SPRING FLAG
908	VALVE, SHIFT 2–3 D	928	PISTON, LOW/REVERSE SERVC
909	SOLENOID, SHIFT (1–2 AND 2–3)	929	SEAL, LOW/REVERSE SERVO (SMALL)
911	SPRING, 3–4 SHIFT VALVE	930	SEAL, LOW/REVERSE SERVO (LARGE)
912	VALVE, 3–4 SHIFT	931	PIN, LOW/REVERSE SERVO APPLY
914	PLUG, BORE	932	RING, RETAINING
915	MANUAL LINK AND CLIP ASSEMBLY	933	WASHER, SERVO CUSHION SPRING
916	VALVE, MANUAL	934	SPRING, SERVO CUSHION
917	SCREEN ASSEMBLY, SOLENOID	979	BALL (.375 DIA.)
918	SPRING, 1–2 SHIFT VALVE	980	SLEEVE, LO REVERSE CUSHION

Copyrighted Material Reprinted with Permission from Hydra-Matic Div., GM Corp.

TH5029300530000X

Fig. 10 Exploded view of lower controls assembly

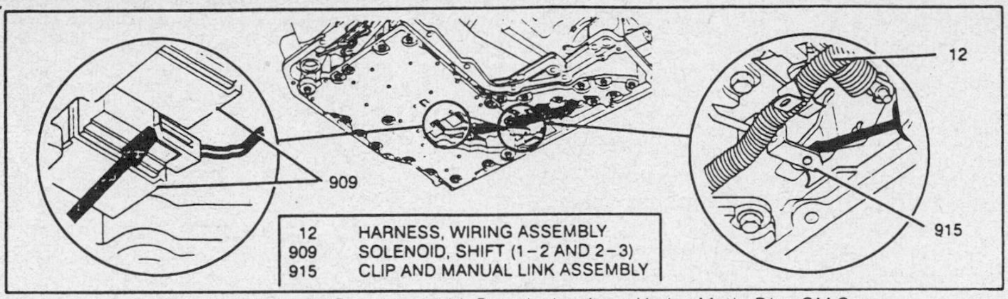
12
909
915
12 HARNESS, WIRING ASSEMBLY
909 SOLENOID, SHIFT (1–2 AND 2–3)
915 CLIP AND MANUAL LINK ASSEMBLY

Copyrighted Material Reprinted with Permission from Hydra-Matic Div., GM Corp.

TH5029300527000X

Fig. 11 Disengaging connector tabs

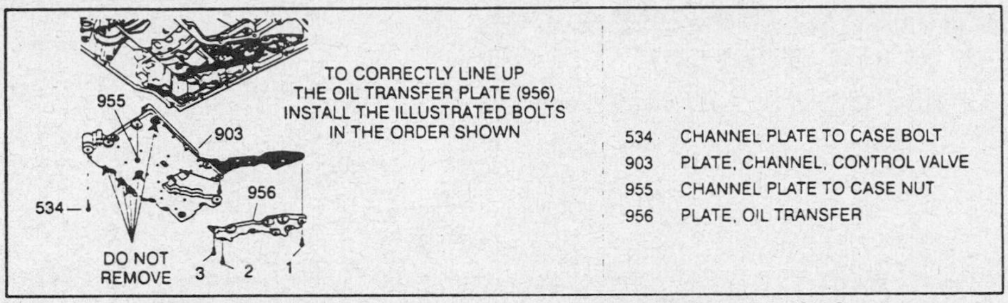
TO CORRECTLY LINE UP THE OIL TRANSFER PLATE (956) INSTALL THE ILLUSTRATED BOLTS IN THE ORDER SHOWN
955
903
956
534
DO NOT REMOVE
3
2
1
534 CHANNEL PLATE TO CASE BOLT
903 PLATE, CHANNEL, CONTROL VALVE
955 CHANNEL PLATE TO CASE NUT
956 PLATE, OIL TRANSFER

Copyrighted Material Reprinted with Permission from Hydra-Matic Div., GM Corp.

TH5029300528000X

Fig. 12 Oil transfer, channel & control valve plates

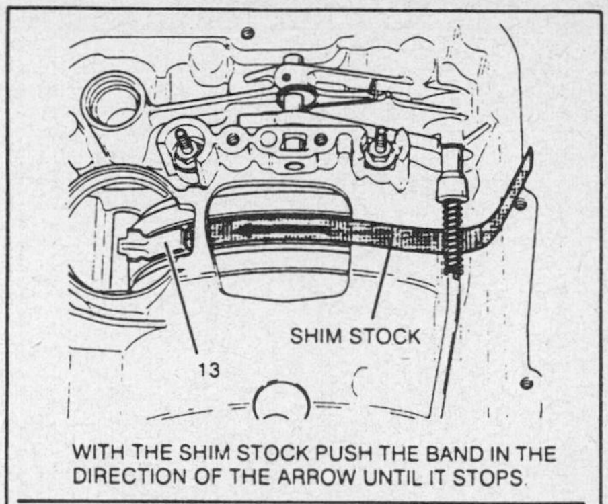
SHIM STOCK
13
WITH THE SHIM STOCK PUSH THE BAND IN THE DIRECTION OF THE ARROW UNTIL IT STOPS.

13 BAND, LO/REVERSE

Copyrighted Material Reprinted with Permission from Hydra-Matic Div., GM Corp.

TH5029300529000X

Fig. 13 Positioning low/reverse band

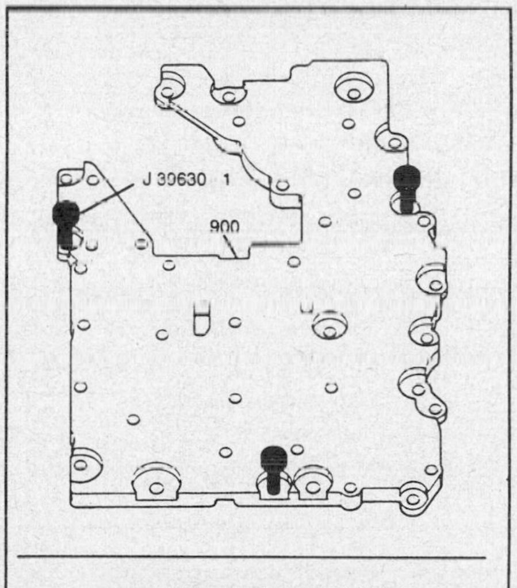
J 39630 1
900

900 CHANNEL PLATE, LOWER

Copyrighted Material Reprinted with Permission from Hydra-Matic Div., GM Corp.

TH5029300531000X

Fig. 14 Guide pins to lower channel plate installation

21. Remove ball check capsule and checkball.
22. Remove bolts and plate from channel plate.
23. Remove spacer plate and gasket.
24. Inspect servo seals for roll over, tearing or cuts.
25. Inspect springs for damage and retaining clips for overexpansion
26. Inspect all valve and piston bores for nicks and wear.
27. Inspect lo/reverse servo apply pin for straightness by rolling on flat surface.

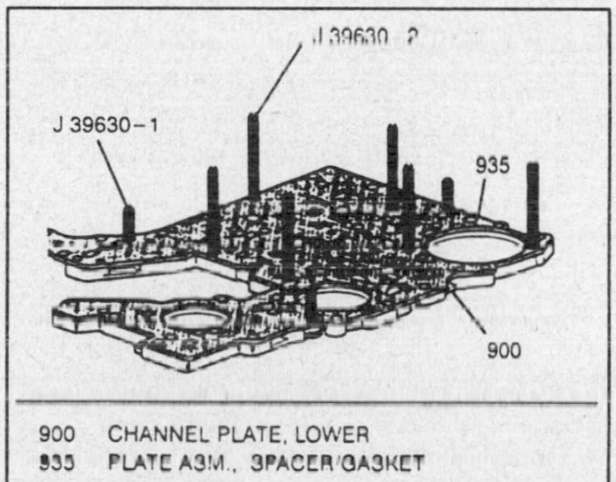
J 39630 2
J 39630–1
935
900
900 CHANNEL PLATE, LOWER
935 PLATE ASM., SPACER/GASKET

Copyrighted Material Reprinted with Permission from Hydra-Matic Div., GM Corp.

TH5029300532000X

Fig. 15 Spacer plate/gasket installation

28. Inspect solenoid screen for particles or damage.
29. Inspect checkball in valve body for freedom of movement.
30. Inspect valve body channel plate passages for debris.
31. Reverse procedure to install noting the following:
    a. Install guide pins as shown in **Figs. 14 through 17.**
    b. Remove guide pins and install retaining bolts as needed.

ROAD SPEED SENSOR, REPLACE

1. Raise and support vehicle, then remove right front wheel.
2. Disconnect electrical connector at sensor, then remove retaining bolt and sensor, **Fig. 18.**
3. Reverse procedure to install.

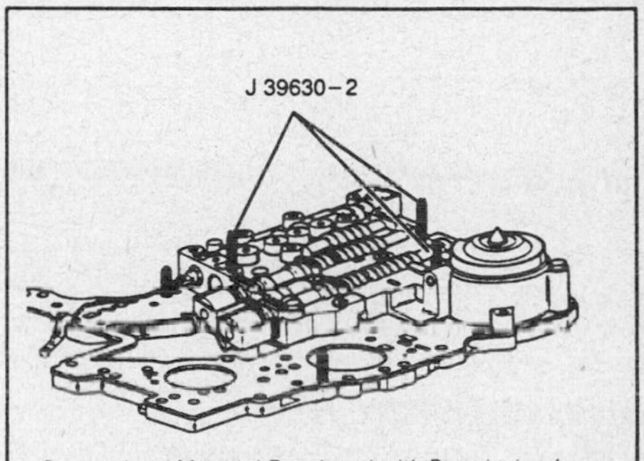
J 39630–2

Copyrighted Material Reprinted with Permission from Hydra-Matic Div., GM Corp.

TH5029300533000X

Fig. 16 Lower valve body installation

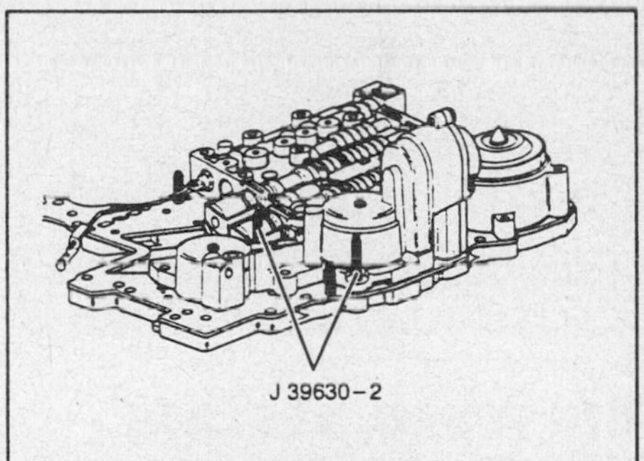
J 39630–2

Copyrighted Material Reprinted with Permission from Hydra-Matic Div., GM Corp.

TH5029300534000X

Fig. 17 Accumulator assembly installation

SELECTOR SWITCH, REPLACE

Removal

1. Remove air cleaner duct and housing, then disconnect shifter cable at lever on transaxle manual shaft.
2. Disconnect shifter cable from transaxle, then remove shifter cable bracket, **Fig. 8.**

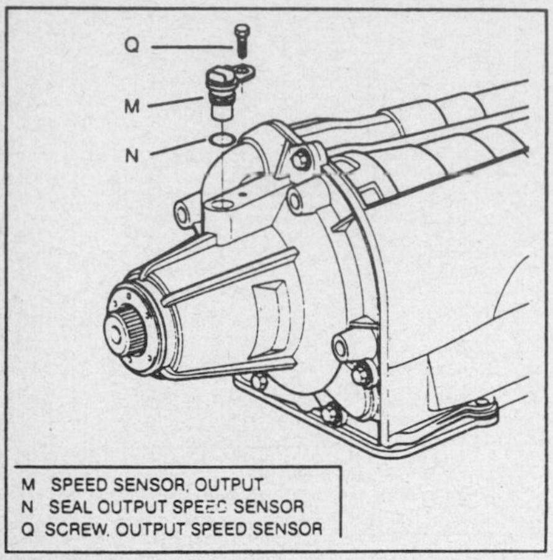
Q
M
N
M SPEED SENSOR, OUTPUT
N SEAL OUTPUT SPEED SENSOR
Q SCREW, OUTPUT SPEED SENSOR

TH5029300525000X

Fig. 18 Output speed sensor replacement

3. Remove retaining nut and transaxle manual shaft lever.
4. Disconnect electrical connector and hose, then remove retaining bolts and transaxle range switch, **Fig. 19.**

Installation

1. Install transaxle range switch and retaining bolts finger tight, then rotate transaxle manual shaft to Neutral position.
2. Rotate range switch so service gage pin can be installed, **Fig. 19. Torque** transaxle range switch bolts to 106 inch lbs.
3. Remove service gage pin, then connect electrical connector and hose.
4. Install transaxle manual shaft lever and **torque** retaining nut to 15 ft. lbs.
5. Install shift cable bracket onto transaxle, then connect cable.
6. Install shift cable at lever on transaxle manual shaft.
7. Install air cleaner duct and housing.

4th SERVO, REPLACE

Removal

1. Raise and support vehicle, then remove three bolts, **Fig. 20.** Hold servo cover in place until all bolts are removed. If cover is not held in place, apply pin will damage bore in case.
2. Remove cover and servo assembly, **Fig. 20.**
3. Inspect piston for cracking, then check apply pin and springs for damage.
4. Remove seal and servo cover seal.
5. Remove snap ring, pin and springs.

Installation

1. Install new seal onto piston, then pin, small spring, retainer, snap ring and seal to cover.
2. Install 4th servo and large spring into cover. **Ensure tab on piston is aligned with notch in case bore (early models).**
3. Ensure flat spring is centered between bosses on cover (early models). A light mark may be scribed on top of piston for a reference. **Do not mark side of piston or a fluid leak or binding condition may result.**
4. Install cover attaching screws. Hand start screws, then **torque** in a star pattern to 98-125 inch lbs.
5. Lower vehicle, then add transmission fluid as outlined.

SCAVENGER SCREENS & LIP SEALS, REPLACE

1. Raise and support vehicle, then remove bottom pan as outlined.
2. Remove left and/or right scavenger screens and seals with small screwdriver. **Do not score or damage case.**
3. Inspect screen lip seals for nicks or cuts.
4. Clean or replace scavenger screen, then install.
5. Install pan as outlined.

DRIVE AXLE SEAL, REPLACE

Refer to **Fig. 21** when removing drive axle.

1. Remove drive axle as follows:
   a. Raise and support vehicle, then remove wheel and tire.
   b. Install suitable seal protector on outer joint.
   c. Remove hub nut. Insert drift or screwdriver into caliper and rotor to prevent rotor from turning.
   d. Remove ball joint cotter pin and nut, then loosen joint using suitable ball joint separator. If removing right axle, turn wheel to left; if removing left axle, turn wheel to right.
   e. Remove drive axle from hub using suitable front hub spindle remover, then move strut and knuckle rearward. Remove drive axle from transaxle with suitable prybar.
2. Use screwdriver to pry outer seal from transaxle, then use pliers to remove remaining housing of drive axle seal from transaxle.
3. Inspect transaxle case for damage after removing seal.
4. Clean drive axle seal mating surface on housing with crocus cloth.
5. Install drive axle seal using J-39051 axle seal installer or equivalent and hammer.
6. Install drive axle as follows:
   a. If installing right drive axle, install suitable axle seal protector so it can be pulled out after drive axle is installed.
   b. Drive axle into transaxle. Ensure drive axle snap ring is properly seated by grasping inner joint housing and pulling outboard. **Do not pull on drive axle.** Driveshaft will remain in place when snap ring is properly seated.
   c. Drive axle into hub and bearing assembly.
   d. Connect ball joint to knuckle. **Torque** ball joint nut to 84 inch lbs, then tighten an additional 120° (two flats). When tightening nut, a minimum **torque** of 37 ft. lbs. must be obtained. If 37 ft. lbs. cannot be obtained, inspect for stripped threads. If threads are OK, replace ball joint and knuckle. If required, turn nut up to an additional 60° (one flat) to allow for installation of cotter pin.
   e. Install hub nut and **torque** to 110

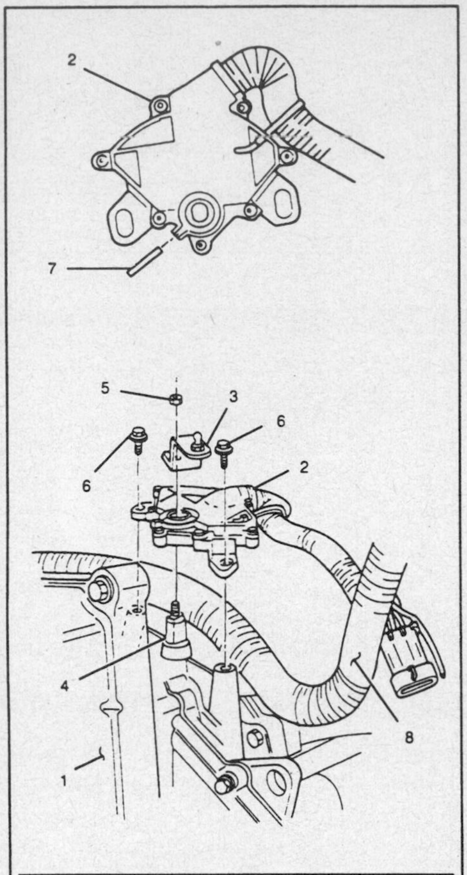
2
7
5
3
6
6
2
4
8
1

1 TRANSAXLE
2 TRANSAXLE RANGE SWITCH
3 RANGE SELECTION LEVER
4 TRANSAXLE MANUAL SHAFT
5 NUT (20 N•m/15 LB. FT.)
6 BOLT (28 N•m/21 LB.FT.)
7 SERVICE GAUGE PIN (2.34MM/3/32 IN.)
8 ENGINE WIRING HARNESS

TH5029300523000X

Fig. 19 Transaxle range switch replacement

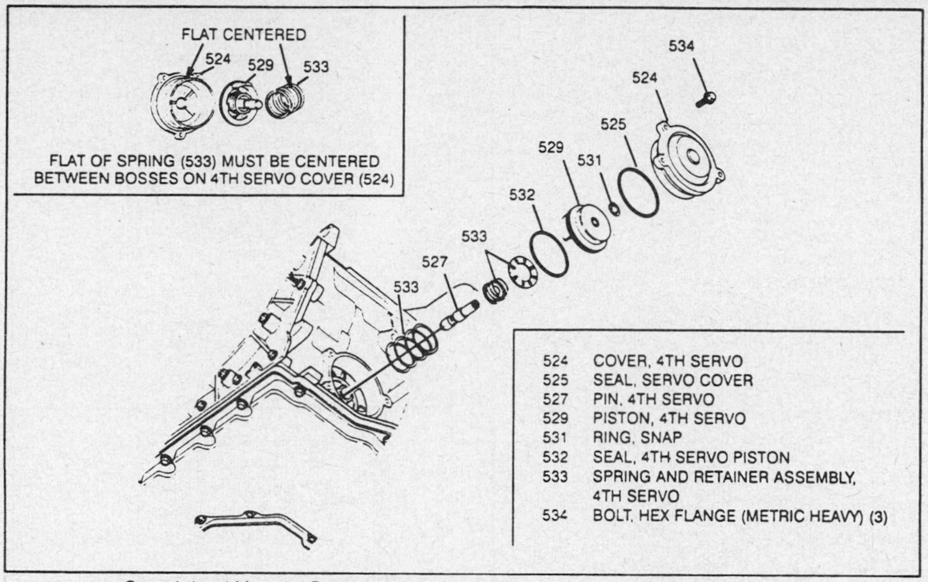
FLAT CENTERED
524
529
533
FLAT OF SPRING (533) MUST BE CENTERED BETWEEN BOSSES ON 4TH SERVO COVER (524)
534
524
525
529
531
532
533
527
533
524 COVER, 4TH SERVO
525 SEAL, SERVO COVER
527 PIN, 4TH SERVO
529 PISTON, 4TH SERVO
531 RING, SNAP
532 SEAL, 4TH SERVO PISTON
533 SPRING AND RETAINER ASSEMBLY, 4TH SERVO
534 BOLT, HEX FLANGE (METRIC HEAVY) (3)

Copyrighted Material Reprinted with Permission from Hydra-Matic Div., GM Corp.

TH5029300526000X

Fig. 20 Exploded view of 4th servo assembly

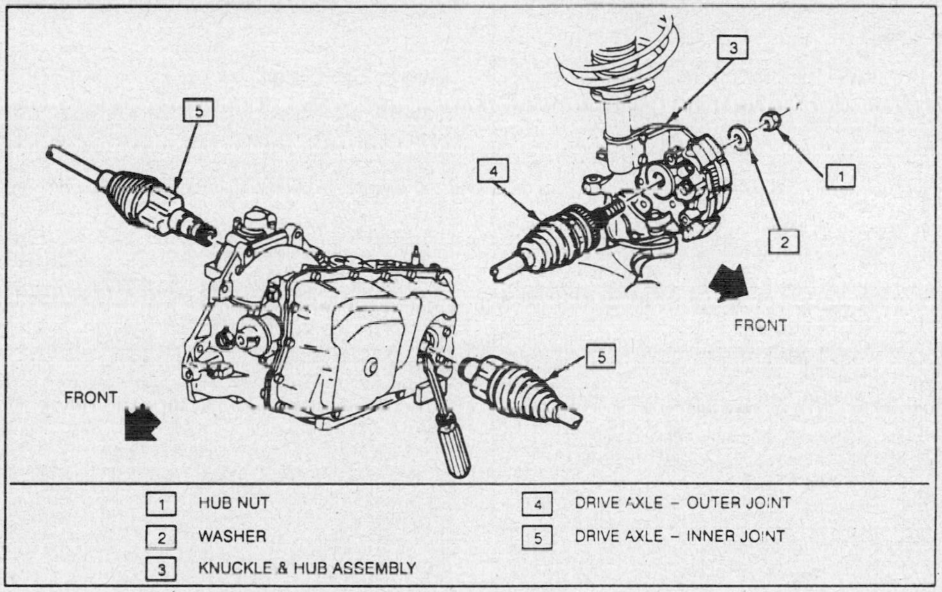
3
5
4
1
2
FRONT
5
FRONT
1 HUB NUT
2 WASHER
3 KNUCKLE & HUB ASSEMBLY
4 DRIVE AXLE – OUTER JOINT
5 DRIVE AXLE – INNER JOINT

Copyrighted Material Reprinted with Permission from Hydra-Matic Div., GM Corp.

TH5029300536000X

Fig. 21 Drive axle removal

ft. lbs. Prevent drive axle from turning by inserting a screwdriver into rotor fins.

f. Remove seal protector. If a axle seal protector was installed, remove it by pulling inline with handle. Ensure it is completely removed and no pieces are left inside of transaxle.

g. Install wheel and tire, then lower vehicle.

CASE EXTENSION & SCAVENGER PIPE, REPLACE

Removal

1. Raise and support vehicle, then remove right front wheel assembly and splash shields.
2. Remove Real Time Damping (RTD) sensor from lower control arm.
3. Disconnect right stabilizer link, right tie rod, then right ball joint from steering knuckle.
4. Remove right drive axle as outlined.
5. Support transaxle using suitable support fixture.
6. Disconnect power steering pressure switch connector and wiring harness.
7. Disconnect right transaxle mount and bracket connector and wiring harness, then remove right transaxle to engine bracket and heat shield.
8. Disconnect VSS connector and ground from case.

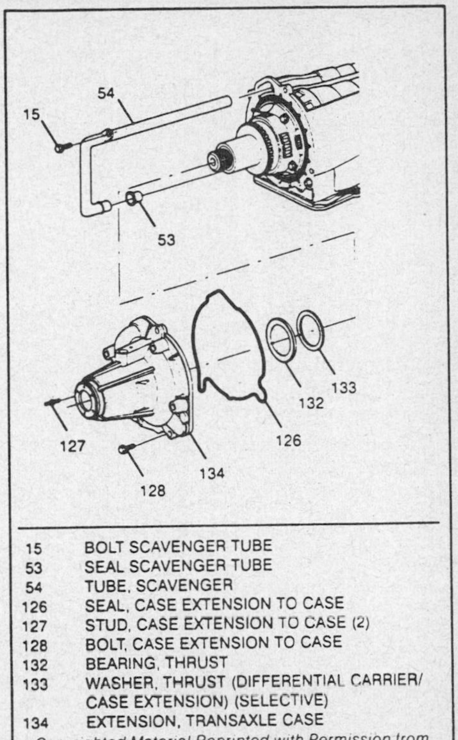
54
15
53
133
132
126
127
134
128
15 BOLT SCAVENGER TUBE
53 SEAL SCAVENGER TUBE
54 TUBE, SCAVENGER
126 SEAL, CASE EXTENSION TO CASE
127 STUD, CASE EXTENSION TO CASE (2)
128 BOLT, CASE EXTENSION TO CASE
132 BEARING, THRUST
133 WASHER, THRUST (DIFFERENTIAL CARRIER/ CASE EXTENSION) (SELECTIVE)
134 EXTENSION, TRANSAXLE CASE

Copyrighted Material Reprinted with Permission from Hydra-Matic Div., GM Corp.

TH5029300537000X

Fig. 22 Exploded view of case extension & scavenger pipe

9. Remove case extension bolts and stud using a torque wrench, then case extension and seal, **Fig. 22**. Seal may remain in extension.
10. Remove roller thrust bearing and selective washer, then bolt.
11. Remove scavenger pipe by prying on differential, then remove seal.
12. Inspect scavenger tube for damage and clogging.
13. Inspect case extension and case mating surfaces for scoring and damage.

Installation

1. Install scavenger tube seal into case, **Fig. 22**, then tap scavenger tube into case using a plastic hammer to ensure fit. Pipe rib will remain exposed; this is normal.
2. Install scavenger bolt and **torque** to 71-116 inch lbs.
3. Install selective washer and thrust roller bearing onto differential output shaft.
4. Insert case extension seal into case extension, then install case extension onto case.
5. Using star pattern, install bolts and stud with stud in 11 o'clock position. **Torque** bolts to 36-40 ft. lbs.
6. Connect VSS connector and ground to case.
7. Install right transaxle to engine bracket and heat shield, then right transaxle mount and bolts.
8. Install power steering pressure switch connector and wiring harness.
9. Remove transaxle support.
10. Install drive axle as outlined.

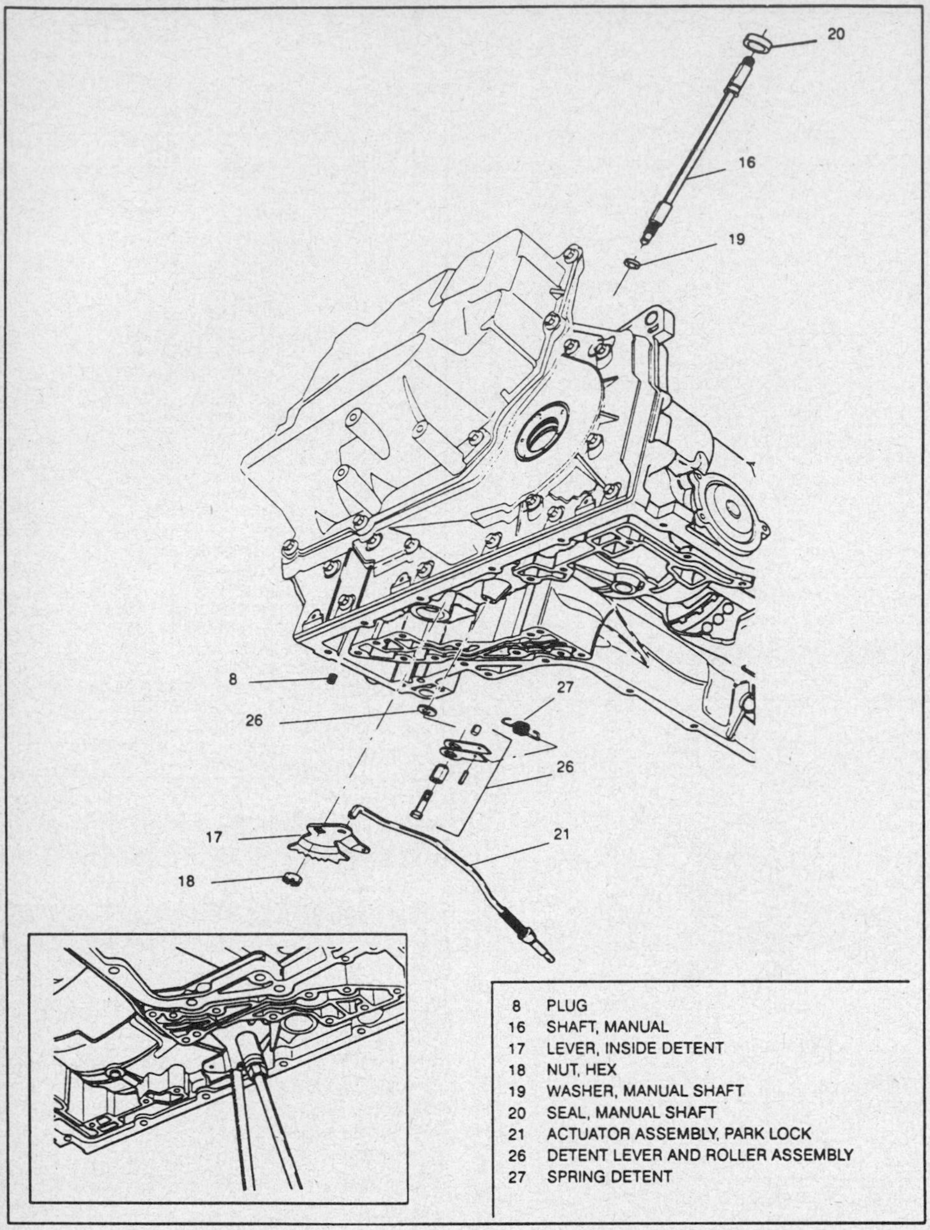
20
16
19
8
27
26
26
17
21
18
8 PLUG
16 SHAFT, MANUAL
17 LEVER, INSIDE DETENT
18 NUT, HEX
19 WASHER, MANUAL SHAFT
20 SEAL, MANUAL SHAFT
21 ACTUATOR ASSEMBLY, PARK LOCK
26 DETENT LEVER AND ROLLER ASSEMBLY
27 SPRING DETENT

TH5029300535000X

Fig. 23 Exploded view of manual shift & detent lever assembly

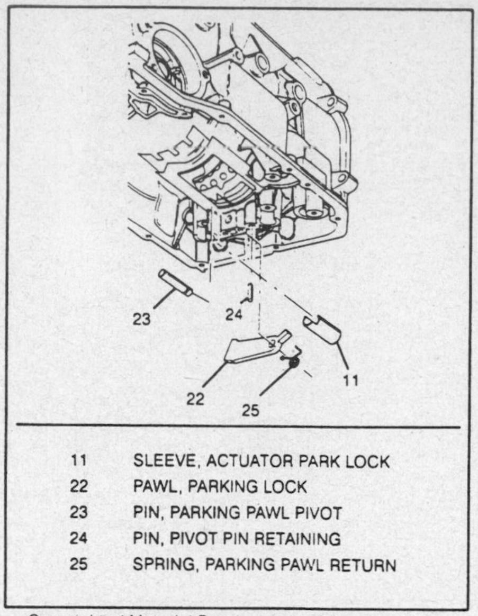
23
24
11
22
25
11 SLEEVE, ACTUATOR PARK LOCK
22 PAWL, PARKING LOCK
23 PIN, PARKING PAWL PIVOT
24 PIN, PIVOT PIN RETAINING
25 SPRING, PARKING PAWL RETURN

TH5029300540000X

Fig. 24 Parking pawl & actuator sleeve components

11. Connect right ball joint, right tie rod and right stabilizer link to steering knuckle.
12. Install RTD sensor to lower control arm.
13. Install splash shields, then wheel assembly.
14. Add transmission fluid as outlined.

MANUAL SHAFT/PARK ACTUATOR, REPLACE

Removal

Refer to Fig. 23 when servicing he manual shaft/park lock actuator assemblies.

1. Remove transaxle range switch as outlined, then raise and support vehicle.
2. Remove bottom pan and gasket, scavenger screens and seals as outlined.
3. Remove lower controls assembly as outlined.
4. Remove detent spring. Grasp detent roller end of spring with pliers to remove.
5. Remove detent roller bolt, pivot arm, sleeve and washer.
6. Remove manual shaft nut. **Detent lever must be held in place when removing nut to prevent damage to actuator rod.**
7. Remove detent lever and actuator rod. Discard detent lever as it is not reusable.
8. Remove manual shaft, then lower vehicle.
9. Remove seal and washer.
10. Inspect actuator guide for excessive wear and actuator rod for cracked end, bent rod or broken spring.

Installation

1. Install new manual shaft seal into case, then raise and support vehicle.
2. Install manual shaft, then seat manual shaft (flush with case) seal with appropriate socket.
3. Attach new detent lever and actuator rod to manual shaft and hold detent lever in place with a screwdriver to prevent bending of actuator rod. Install manual shaft nut and **torque** to 20-25 ft. lbs.
4. Install detent roller washer, pivot arm and sleeves.
5. Install detent roller assembly bolt and **torque** to 98-125 inch lbs.
6. Install detent return spring to detent roller assembly and manual shaft.
7. Install lower controls assembly as outlined.
8. Install bottom pan and gasket, scavenger screens and lip seals as outlined. Lower vehicle.
9. Add transaxle fluid as outlined.
10. If complete fluid change was necessary, reset transaxle oil life indicator as outlined.

PARKING PAWL, SPRING & SLEEVE, REPLACE

Removal

Refer to Fig. 24 when servicing parking pawl assembly.

1. Raise and support vehicle.
2. Remove bottom pan and gasket, scavenger screen and seals as outlined.
3. Remove lower controls assembly as outlined.
4. Remove final drive assembly as outlined.
5. Move manual shaft from Park position.

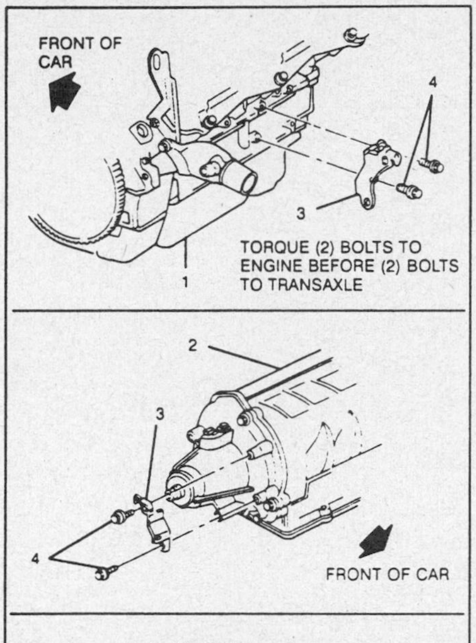
FRONT OF CAR
TORQUE (2) BOLTS TO ENGINE BEFORE (2) BOLTS TO TRANSAXLE
FRONT OF CAR
1 ENGINE
2 TRANSAXLE
3 ENGINE-TO-TRANSAXLE BRACE
4 BOLT (47 N•m/35 LB. FT.)

Copyrighted Material Reprinted with Permission from Hydra-Matic Div., GM Corp.

TH5029300543000X

Fig. 25 Engine to transaxle brace removal

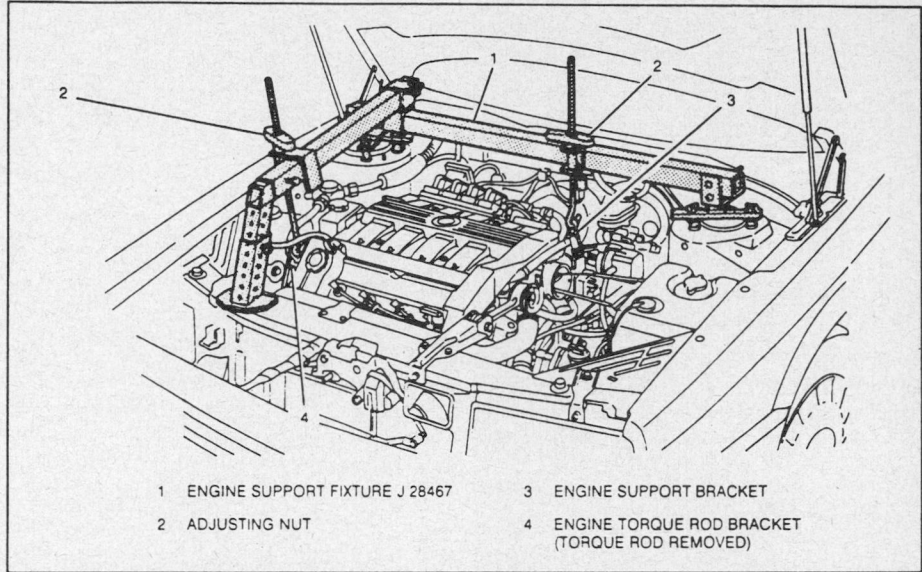

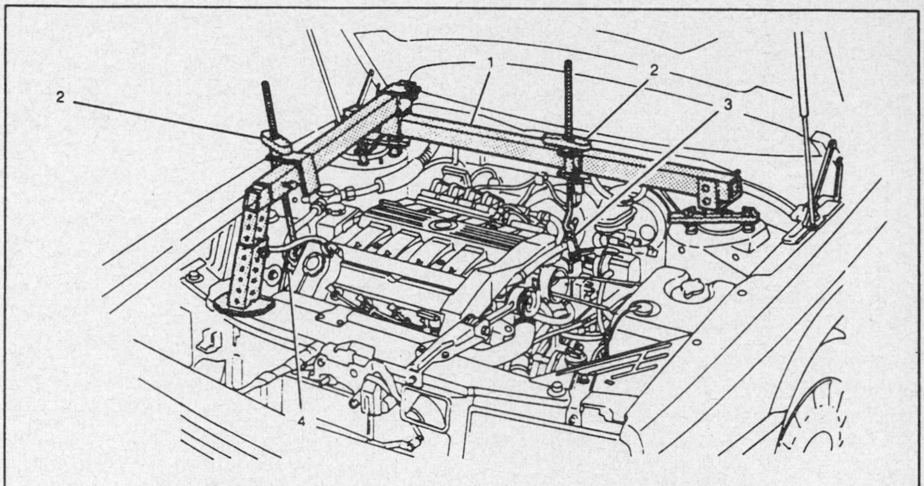
1 ENGINE SUPPORT FIXTURE J 28467
2 ADJUSTING NUT
3 ENGINE SUPPORT BRACKET
4 ENGINE TORQUE ROD BRACKET (TORQUE ROD REMOVED)

Copyrighted Material Reprinted with Permission from Hydra-Matic Div., GM Corp.

TH5029300544000X

Fig. 26 Engine support fixture installation

6. Drive out pivot pin retaining pin.
7. Drive parking pawl pivot pin towards extension housing with pin punch. Push down on spring while driving shaft out.
8. Remove parking pawl and spring.
9. Remove park lock sleeve using a rubber mallet. Drive out towards case extension portion of case.

Inspection

1. Inspect parking pawl tooth for damage.
2. Inspect parking pawl spring for overexpansion
3. Inspect pivot pin for scorning and excessive wear.

Installation

1. Place pawl in case slot, then attach spring to pawl.
2. Insert pivot pin through spring and pawl. The hook end of spring locates on case and square end of top of parking pawl.
3. Install retaining pin using a hammer and pin punch, then install actuator sleeve.
4. Install final drive assembly as outlined.
5. Install lower controls assembly as outlined.
6. Install bottom pan and gasket, scavenger screens and lip seals as outlined.
7. Lower vehicle.
8. Add transmission fluid, then reset transaxle oil life indicator as outlined.

CONVERTER COVER, REPLACE

1. Raise and support vehicle.
2. Remove engine to transaxle brace bolts, then torque converter cover bolt and cover.
3. Reverse procedure to install. **Torque** converter cover bolt to 106 inch lbs. and engine to transaxle brace bolt to 35 ft. lbs.

TRANSAXLE REPLACE

Refer to **Figs. 25 through 27** when removing and installing transaxle.

1. Disconnect battery ground cable, then remove headlamp housing upper filler panel and diagonal brace.
2. Remove air cleaner assembly, then disconnect shifter cable and bracket at transaxle.
3. Remove torque struts.
4. Disconnect oil cooler lines and oil sending line at transaxle.
5. Remove two upper bellhousing bolts.
6. Disconnect power steering hose at auxiliary cooler. Plug cooler holes and return hose to prevent fluid leakage and contamination.
7. Install engine support fixture J-28467 or equivalent, then raise powertrain until weight is off mounts.
8. Raise and support vehicle, then remove both front wheel and splash shield assemblies.
9. Disconnect both front suspension position sensors from lower control arms and position aside.
10. Separate both tie rods from steering knuckles, then both ball joints from struts.
11. Remove both drive axles from hubs and transaxle.
12. Disconnect power steering filter at cradle.
13. Remove A/C splash shield from frame.
14. Remove ABS modulator from bracket and support.
15. Remove engine oil pan to transaxle bracket.
16. Remove torque converter cover, then flywheel to converter bolts. Mark flywheel to converter position for assembly purposes.
17. Remove powertrain mount nuts from cradle.
18. Rotate steering intermediate shaft until steering gear stub shaft clamp bolt is accessible through left wheel opening. Remove clamp bolt through left wheel opening.
19. Remove steering intermediate shaft from steering gear. **Failure to disconnect intermediate shaft from rack and pinion stub shaft can result in damage to steering gear and/or intermediate shaft. This damage could result in loss of steering control which could cause personal injury. Do not rotate steering wheel or move position of steering gear when intermediate shaft is disconnected; SIR coil in steering column will become uncentered. If coil becomes uncentered, it may be damaged during vehicle operation.**
20. Disconnect electrical harness from front of cradle, then support rear of cradle with a jackstand.
21. Remove four rear cradle bolts, then lower jack stand enough to gain access to power steering gear heat shield and return line fitting.
22. Remove power steering gear heat shield and return line at gear. Plug steering gear and pressure line to avoid leakage and contamination.

23. Disconnect power steering electrical connector.
24. Raise jack stand and install one rear cradle bolt on each side to finger tightness to support cradle. Remove jack stand.
25. Support frame, then remove six frame mount bolts.
26. Lower frame and/or raise vehicle with steering gear attached.
27. Disconnect the following connectors:
    a. Three transaxle connectors.
    b. VSS connector.
    c. Ground strap.
    d. Transaxle harness from transaxle clip.
28. Disconnect fuel line bundle from transaxle.
29. Remove left and right transaxle mount and bracket assemblies from transaxle.
30. Install transaxle support fixture tool No. J-28664, or equivalent.
31. Remove engine to transaxle heat shield and bracket, then two engine to transaxle bolts.
32. Lower transaxle.
33. Disconnect manual shaft linkage and neutral start switch.
34. Disconnect speed sensor and oil return pipe.
35. Reverse procedure to install, noting the following:
    a. Install six frame mount bolts in following order: left side No. 2 mount bolt into body, left side No. 1 mount bolt into body, then remaining bolts in no specific order. Tighten six frame mount bolts to specifications.
    b. Flush transaxle oil cooler as outlined.
    c. Adjust transaxle range switch as outlined.
    d. Adjust range control cable as outlined.
    e. Bleed power steering system.
    f. Add transmission fluid as outlined.
    g. Check front suspension alignment, set toe as necessary.
    h. Reset transaxle adapts as outlined.
    i. Reset transaxle oil life indicator as outlined.

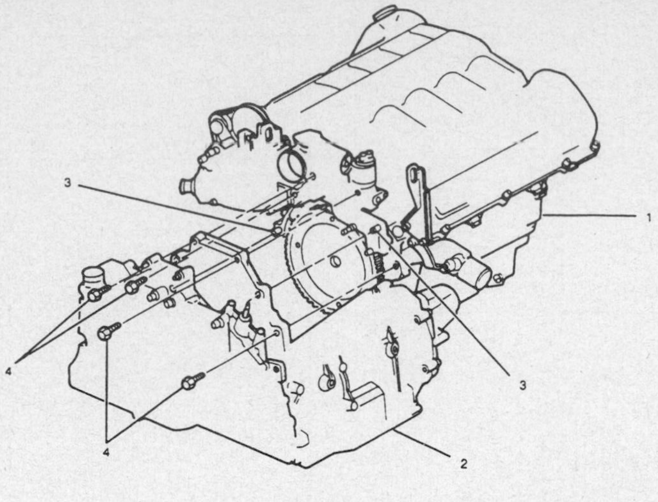
3
1
4
3
4
2

1 ENGINE
2 TRANSAXLE
3 LOCATING PIN
4 BOLT (47 N•m/35 LB. FT.)

Copyrighted Material Reprinted with Permission from Hydra-Matic Div., GM Corp.

TH5029300545000X

Fig. 27 Transaxle to engine attachment locations

TIGHTENING SPECIFICATIONS

Component	Torque/Ft. Lbs.
Accumulator Cover Bolts (8 mm)	6-10
Actuator Rod Nut	20-25
Bottom Pan Bolts	②
Case Cover Bolts & Studs	20
Case Extension Bolts (Except 10 mm Bolt) & Stud	37-40
Case Extension Bolt (10 mm)	15-20
Case To Forward Clutch Support Studs	14-20
Channel Plate To Accumulator Housing Bolts (10 mm)	6-10
Channel Plate To Lower Control Valve Body Bolt (10 mm)	6-10
Cooler Fitting	19-21
Detent Roller Assembly Bolt	6-10
Differential Housing Bolts	52-56
Drive Axle Hub Nuts	110
Drive Sprocket Support Bolts	8-9.5
Engine Oil Pan To Transaxle Bracket	35
Engine To Transaxle Bracket & Heat Shield	35
Engine To Transaxle Lower Bolts	35
Frame Mount Bolts	74
Flywheel To Converter Bolt	35
Lower Control Valve Body To Channel Plate Bolts (10 mm)	6-10
Manual Shaft Nut	15
Oil Transfer Plate Bolts & Nuts	6-10

Component	Torque/Ft. Lbs.
Power Steering Pressure Hose Fitting	20
Pressure Control (PC) Solenoid (Bolt)	8-9.5
Pump Assembly Bolts	8-9.5
Range Control Cable Bracket Bolts	106①
Scavenge Bolt	6-10
Scavenge Pump Body Cover Bolts (10 mm)	8-9.5
Side Cover Bolt (13 mm)	15-20
Side Cover Bolts (15 mm)	37-40
Spacer Plate Support To Channel Plate Bolts (8mm)	6-10
Speed Sensor Bolt	6-10
Stabilizer Link To Strut Nuts	49
Steering Intermediate Shaft To Steering Gear Bolt	35
Temperature Sensor	30①
Torque Converter Cover Bolts	106①
Transaxle Mount Bolts	35
Transaxle Mount Bracket Bolts	35
Transaxle Range Switch	106①
Upper Control Valve Assembly Bolts	8-9.5
Wiring Harness Bolts	8-9.5
4th Servo Cover Bolts	6-10

①—Inch Lbs.
②—Torque bolt in three steps; first 27 inch lbs., second, 53 inch lbs., then 106 inch lbs.

Aisin Seiki (Metro) Automatic Transaxle

INDEX

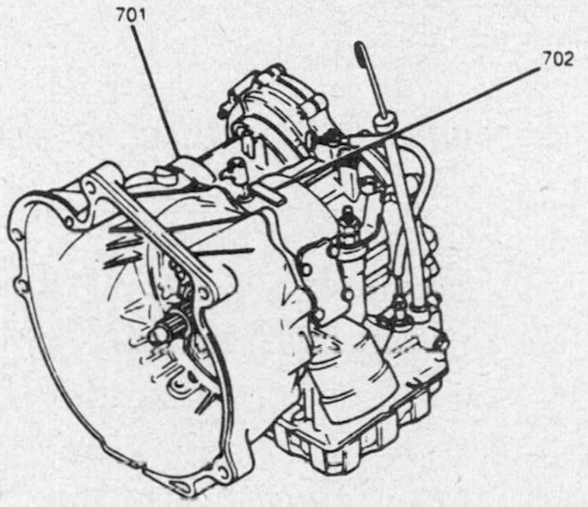
701
702

701 TRANSAXLE CASE
702 TRANSAXLE IDENTIFICATION NUMBER LOCATION

GC5029200461000X

Fig. 1 Transaxle identification number location

IDENTIFICATION

The transaxle identification number is located on the top center of the transaxle assembly, **Fig. 1.**

TROUBLESHOOTING

In conjunction with the prerequisites noted below, refer to charts, **Figs. 2 through 5,** when troubleshooting the transaxle:

1. Engine coolant is at normal operating temperature.
2. Engine idle speed is 800-900 RPM.
3. Transaxle fluid level is correct and at normal operating temperature.
4. Accelerator cable, oil pressure control cable and selector cable are properly adjusted.
5. Gear shift control system wiring is in good condition.
6. Vacuum switch hose is properly connected.

MAINTENANCE

Refer to "Lubricant Data Chart" in the appropriate chassis chapter of this manual for transmission fluid specifications.

FLUID CHECK

1. Drive vehicle for approximately 15 minutes to bring fluid up to normal operating temperature.
2. With vehicle on level surface, apply parking brake and block drive wheels.
3. With selector lever in Park, start engine, then move selector lever through each range and return to Park.
4. Remove dipstick and check fluid level.
5. Fluid level should be between the two "HOT" marks on dipstick.
6. Add fluid as required to bring fluid to specified level.

FLUID CHANGE

Under normal driving conditions, fluid should be changed and oil strainer cleaned every 100,000 miles. Under harsh driving conditions fluid should be changed every 15,000 miles. To service, proceed as follows:

1. Raise and support front of vehicle.
2. Remove drain plug and drain fluid from oil pan.
3. Remove oil pan attaching bolts and the oil pan.
4. Remove oil strainer to valve body attaching bolts, then the oil strainer.
5. Clean strainer and oil pan in solvent. Engine magnet in oil pan is positioned directly below oil strainer.
6. Install oil strainer and attaching bolts. **Torque** bolts to 53 inch lbs.
7. Install oil pan using new gasket. **Torque** attaching bolts to 53 inch lbs.

   Two of the oil pan attaching bolts have crossed grooves on the bolt head. When installing these two bolts, coat threads with sealant and install in positions shown in Fig. 6.
8. Lower vehicle and refill oil pan.
9. Check fluid level as previously described and adjust as necessary.

ADJUSTMENTS

1992

Interlock Drive Solenoid

1. Shift selector lever to Park.
2. Adjust solenoid position so that solenoid operates as follows:
   a. When ignition switch is turned Off (solenoid is not operated) and On (solenoid is operated), lock plate should be positioned as shown in **Fig. 7.**
   b. There should be no clearance between lock plate and guide plate as shown in **Fig. 8.**
3. After adjusting solenoid position, tighten solenoid screws.
4. After tightening solenoid screws, check the following:
   a. When ignition switch is turned Off, selector lever is locked in Park range and cannot be shifted into any other range.
   b. When ignition switch is turned On, selector lever can be shifted into any other range.
   c. If manual release knob is pulled with ignition switch Off, selector lever can be shifted into any other range.

Interlock Cable

1. Shift selector lever to Park.
2. Loosen nuts (A) and (B) as shown in **Fig. 9**
3. With outer wire pulled forward so that there is no deflection on inner wire, tighten nut (A), then nut (B) hand-tight.
4. Tighten nuts (A) and (B) again, then check the following:
   a. With selector lever in Park, ensure ignition key can be turned from ACC to LOCK position and removed from ignition switch.
   b. With selector lever shifted in any

drive range other than Park, ignition key cannot be turned from ACC to LOCKposition.

Oil Pressure Control Cable

1. Check and, if necessary, adjust accelerator cable.
2. Start engine and allow to reach normal operating temperature.
3. Remove control cable cover and check that boot to inner cable stopper clearance is 0-.020 inch as shown, **Fig. 10.**
4. If clearance is not as specified, loosen, then tighten adjusting nuts (A) until specified clearance is obtained. If clearance is still not within specifications, turn adjusting nuts (B) and repeat procedure outlined above.

1993–94

TV Cable

Refer to **Fig. 11** when performing the following adjustment procedure.

1. Check accelerator cable for play, adjust as necessary.
2. Start engine and allow it to run at idle speed until operating temperature is reached.
3. Remove TV cable adjustment cover.
4. Using a feeler gauge, measure TV cable boot to inner stopper clearance. If clearance is more than .02 inch, adjust TV cable.
5. Turn TV cable adjustment nuts "A" until correct clearance is obtained. If correct clearance cannot be obtained using adjustment nuts "A," use adjustment nuts "B."

Park/Neutral Position Switch

1. Remove Park/Neutral position switch from transaxle as described under "Park/Neutral Position Switch, Replace."
2. Move transaxle lever to neutral position.
3. Using a flat-bladed screwdriver, turn Park/Neutral switch joint clockwise or counterclockwise until a distinct "click noise is heard in the position shown in **Fig. 12.**
4. Install switch back on transaxle.

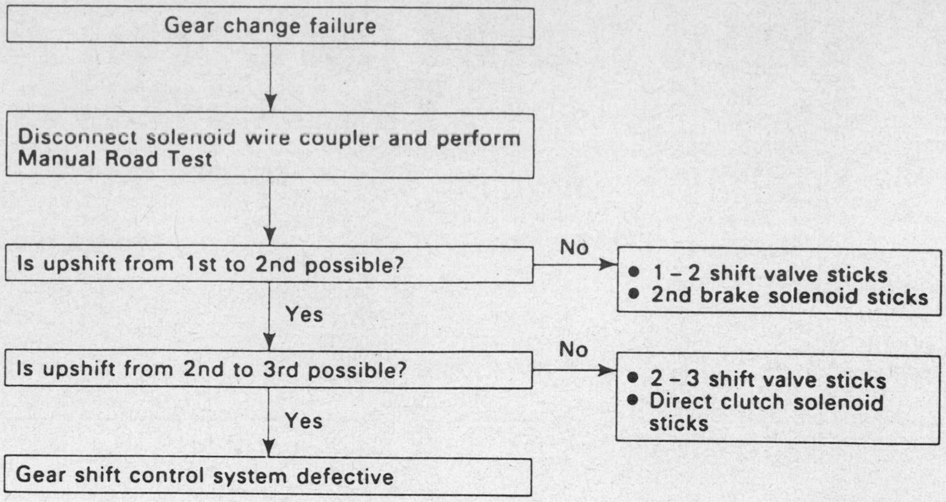
Gear change failure
Disconnect solenoid wire coupler and perform Manual Road Test
Is upshift from 1st to 2nd possible?
No
• 1 – 2 shift valve sticks
• 2nd brake solenoid sticks
Yes
Is upshift from 2nd to 3rd possible?
No
• 2 – 3 shift valve sticks
• Direct clutch solenoid sticks
Yes
Gear shift control system defective
GC5029100462000X

Fig. 2 Transaxle troubleshooting chart. Gear change failure. 1992

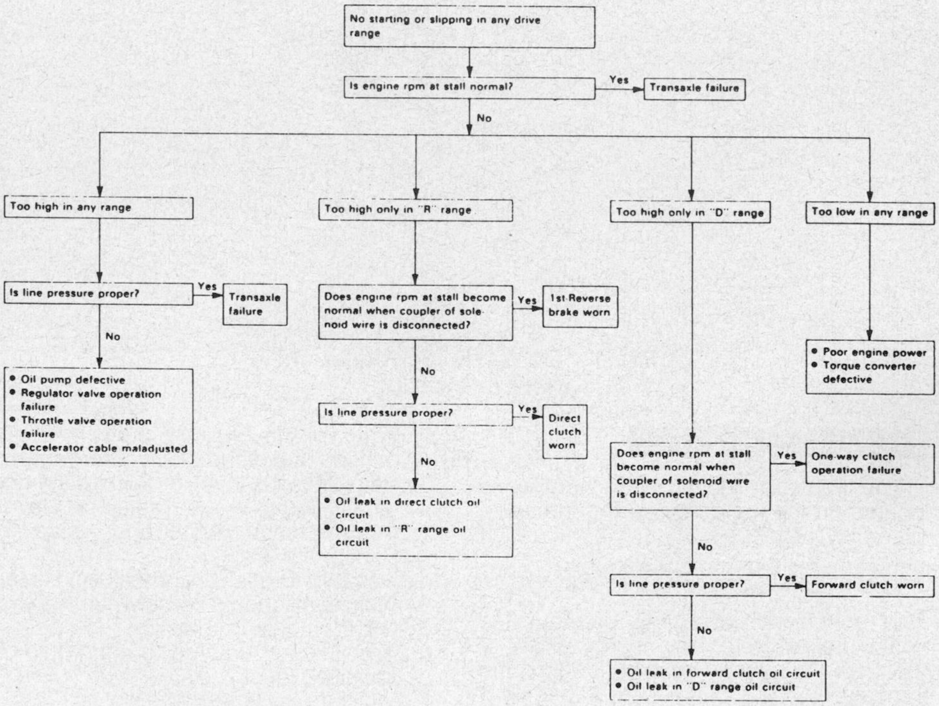
No starting or slipping in any drive range
Is engine rpm at stall normal?
Yes
Transaxle failure
No
Too high in any range
Too high only in "R" range
Too high only in "D" range
Too low in any range
Is line pressure proper?
Yes
Transaxle failure
No
• Oil pump defective
• Regulator valve operation failure
• Throttle valve operation failure
• Accelerator cable maladjusted
Does engine rpm at stall become normal when coupler of solenoid wire is disconnected?
Yes
1st-Reverse brake worn
No
Is line pressure proper?
Yes
Direct clutch worn
No
• Oil leak in direct clutch oil circuit
• Oil leak in "R" range oil circuit
Does engine rpm at stall become normal when coupler of solenoid wire is disconnected?
Yes
One-way clutch operation failure
No
Is line pressure proper?
Yes
Forward clutch worn
No
• Oil leak in forward clutch oil circuit
• Oil leak in "D" range oil circuit
• Poor engine power
• Torque converter defective
GC5029100463000X

Fig. 3 Transaxle troubleshooting chart. No starting or slipping in any drive range. 1992

IN-VEHICLE REPAIRS

1992

DIRECT CLUTCH & SECOND BRAKE SOLENOIDS, REPLACE

1. Disconnect battery ground cable.
2. Drain transaxle fluid and remove oil pan.
3. Disconnect electrical connectors from direct clutch and second brake solenoids, then remove the solenoids, **Fig. 13.**
4. Remove solenoid wire harness with grommet from upper side.
5. Reverse procedure to install.

OIL PRESSURE CONTROL CABLE, REPLACE

1. Remove cable cover, then disconnect oil pressure control cable from accelerator cable, **Fig. 14.**
2. Drain transaxle fluid and remove oil pan.
3. Disconnect oil pressure control cable from throttle valve cam, then remove the cable from transaxle case.
4. Reverse procedure to install, then adjust cable as previously described.

TRANSAXLE SELECTOR LEVER, REPLACE

1. Disconnect battery ground cable.
2. Remove selector lever knob, then the console assembly.
3. Remove selector indicator assembly, then disconnect cable from selector lever.
4. Disconnect back drive cable and the back drive solenoid electrical connector.
5. Raise and support vehicle.
6. Remove four housing attaching nuts, then the housing seat and housing with selector lever.
7. Reverse procedure to install.

TRANSAXLE SELECTOR CABLE, REPLACE

Removal

1. Remove console assembly, then the selector indicator assembly.

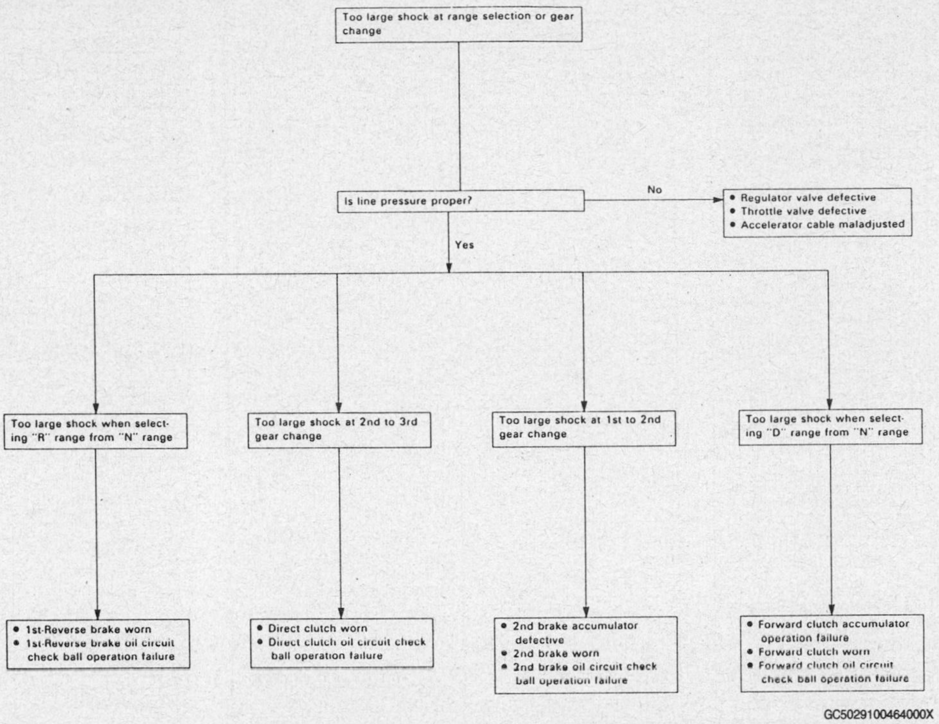
Too large shock at range selection or gear change
Is line pressure proper?
No
• Regulator valve defective
• Throttle valve defective
• Accelerator cable maladjusted
Yes
Too large shock when selecting "R" range from "N" range
Too large shock at 2nd to 3rd gear change
Too large shock at 1st to 2nd gear change
Too large shock when selecting "D" range from "N" range
• 1st-Reverse brake worn
• 1st-Reverse brake oil circuit check ball operation failure
• Direct clutch worn
• Direct clutch oil circuit check ball operation failure
• 2nd brake accumulator defective
• 2nd brake worn
• 2nd brake oil circuit check ball operation failure
• Forward clutch accumulator operation failure
• Forward clutch worn
• Forward clutch oil circuit check ball operation failure
GC5029100464000X

Fig. 4 Transaxle troubleshooting chart. Too large shock at range selection of gear change. 1992

CONDITION	INSPECT COMPONENT	FOR CAUSE
HARSH ENGAGEMENT INTO ANY FORWARD RANGE	FLUID LEVEL INDICATOR	LOW FLUID LEVEL
	TV CABLE	– MISADJUSTED, BINDING OR DAMAGED
	SHIFT SELECT CABLE	– MISADJUSTED, BINDING OR DAMAGED
	VALVE BODY	– MANUAL VALVE BINDING OR STICKING – THROTTLE VALVE BINDING OR STICKING – B2 CONTROL VALVE BINDING OR STICKING
	ACCUMULATORS	– PISTONS DAMAGED OR LEAKING – SEALS CUT OR DAMAGED – BROKEN OR DISTORTED SPRINGS
	FLUID PRESSURE	– (SEE CAUSES OF HIGH OR LOW FLUID PRESSURE)
SLIPS IN 1ST GEAR	FLUID LEVEL INDICATOR	– LOW FLUID LEVEL
	TV CABLE	– MISADJUSTED, BINDING OR DAMAGED
	SHIFT SELECT CABLE	– MISADJUSTED, BINDING OR DAMAGED
	VALVE BODY	– THROTTLE VALVE BINDING OR STICKING – PRIMARY REGULATOR VALVE BINDING OR STICKING
	ACCUMULATORS	– PISTONS DAMAGED OR LEAKING – SEALS CUT OR DAMAGED – BROKEN OR DISTORTED SPRINGS
	FORWARD CLUTCH	– CLUTCH DISCS WORN – FORWARD CLUTCH PISTON OR SEAL LEAKING OR DAMAGED – INPUT SHAFT O-RINGS CUT OR DAMAGED
	ONE-WAY CLUTCH	– NOT HOLDING OR DAMAGED
	FLUID PRESSURE	– (SEE CAUSES OF HIGH OR LOW FLUID PRESSURE)

GC5029300495010X

Fig. 5 Troubleshooting chart (Part 1 of 6). 1993-94

2. Disconnect selector cable from selector lever, floor and transaxle.
3. Raise and support vehicle.
4. Remove selector cable from front panel.

Installation

1. Raise and support vehicle.
2. Position selector cable in front panel, then lower vehicle.
3. Apply grease to selector cable pin, then connect cable to lever.
4. Install selector indicator, then the console assembly.
5. Connect cable to bracket on transaxle, then slide cable into manual select joint hole and position manual shift lever in Neutral range.
6. Turn nut (A), **Fig. 15,** by hand until it contacts manual select cable joint, then tighten nut (B) with wrench.
7. After tightening cable nuts, check the following:
   a. With selector lever in Park, vehicle can not move when pushed.
   b. With selector lever in Neutral, vehicle cannot be driven.
   c. With selector in Drive, Second or Low ranges, vehicle can be driven.
   d. With selector lever in Reverse, vehicle can be backed up.

SHIFT LEVER SWITCH, REPLACE

Removal

1. Disconnect battery ground cable.
2. Disconnect electrical connectors from shift lever switch.
3. Remove shift lever switch from manual shift shaft.

Installation

1. Shift manual shift lever to Manual range.
2. Using a screwdriver, turn shift lever switch to the position shown in **Fig. 16** and ensure a click is heard from joint at this position.
3. Install switch to manual shift shaft, then move the shaft in direction of arrow, **Fig. 17,** until a click is heard. Stop at this position and **torque** attaching bolts to 9.5-16.5 ft. lbs.
4. Connect electrical connectors to switch, then install clamp.
5. Apply parking brake and block wheels, then check the following:
   a. With selector lever in Park and ignition switch On, starter motor operates.
   b. With selector lever in Neutral and ignition switch On, starter motor operates.
   c. After moving selector lever from Neutral to Low, then back to Neutral, starter motor operates with ignition switch On.
   d. With selector lever in Park and ignition switch On, starter motor operates.
   e. In any range other than Park or Neutral, starter motor cannot be operated.
   f. With selector lever in Reverse and ignition switch On (engine not running), back-up lamps light.

1993–94

BRAKE TRANSAXLE SHIFT INTERLOCK, REPLACE

1. Remove two selector knob to selector lever attaching screws, **Fig. 18.**
2. Remove six center console attaching screws, then the center console.

CONDITION	INSPECT COMPONENT	FOR CAUSE
1ST GEAR ONLY — NO UPSHIFT	TV CABLE	– MISADJUSTED, BINDING OR DAMAGED
	VALVE BODY	– THROTTLE VALVE BINDING OR STICKING – 1–2 SHIFT VALVE BINDING OR STICKING – PRIMARY REGULATOR VALVE BINDING OR STICKING
	INTERMEDIATE SERVO	– SEALS CUT OR DAMAGED – PISTON BINDING OR STICKING – PISTON ROD NOT ENGAGED
	2ND BRAKE BAND	– WORN OR MISALIGNED
	FLUID PRESSURE	– (SEE CAUSES OF HIGH OR LOW FLUID PRESSURE)
SLIPPING OR ROUGH 1–2 UPSHIFT	FLUID LEVEL INDICATOR	– LOW FLUID LEVEL
	TV CABLE	– MISADJUSTED, BINDING OR DAMAGED
	VALVE BODY	– THROTTLE VALVE BINDING OR STICKING – 1–2 SHIFT VALVE BINDING OR STICKING – PRIMARY REGULATOR VALVE BINDING OR STICKING
	INTERMEDIATE SERVO	– SEALS CUT OR DAMAGED – PISTON BINDING OR STICKING – PISTON ROD NOT ENGAGED
	2ND BRAKE BAND	– WORN OR MISALIGNED
	TORQUE CONVERTER	– INTERNAL DAMAGE
	FORWARD CLUTCH	– CLUTCH DISCS WORN – FORWARD CLUTCH PISTON OR SEAL LEAKING OR DAMAGED – INPUT SHAFT O-RINGS CUT OR DAMAGED
	FLUID PRESSURE	– (SEE CAUSES OF HIGH OR LOW FLUID PRESSURE)

GC5029300495020X

Fig. 5 Troubleshooting chart (Part 2 of 6). 1993-94

CONDITION	INSPECT COMPONENT	FOR CAUSE
NO 2–3 SHIFT OR 2–3 SHIFT SLIPPING	FLUID LEVEL INDICATOR	– LOW FLUID LEVEL
	TV CABLE	– MISADJUSTED, BINDING OR DAMAGED
	VALVE BODY	– THROTTLE VALVE BINDING OR STICKING – 2–3 SHIFT VALVE BINDING OR STICKING – PRIMARY REGULATOR VALVE BINDING OR STICKING
	INTERMEDIATE SERVO	– PISTON BINDING OR STICKING – PISTON ROD BINDING
	2ND BRAKE BAND	– NOT RELEASING
	TORQUE CONVERTER	– INTERNAL DAMAGE
	DIRECT CLUTCH	– CLUTCH DISCS WORN – DIRECT CLUTCH PISTON OR SEAL LEAKING OR DAMAGED
	FLUID PRESSURE	– (SEE CAUSES OF HIGH OR LOW FLUID PRESSURE)
HIGH OR LOW SHIFT POINTS	FLUID LEVEL INDICATOR	– LOW FLUID LEVEL
	TV CABLE	– MISADJUSTED, BINDING OR DAMAGED
	VALVE BODY	– SPACER PLATE OR GASKETS MISPOSITIONED OR DAMAGED – THROTTLE VALVE BINDING OR STICKING – CHECK BALLS OMITTED OR MISPOSITIONED
	TORQUE CONVERTER	– INTERNAL DAMAGE
	FORWARD CLUTCH	– FORWARD CLUTCH PISTON OR SEAL LEAKING OR DAMAGED – INPUT SHAFT O-RINGS CUT OR DAMAGED
	DIRECT CLUTCH	– DIRECT CLUTCH PISTON OR SEAL LEAKING OR DAMAGED
	FLUID PRESSURE	– (SEE CAUSES OF HIGH OR LOW FLUID PRESSURE)

GC5029300495030X

Fig. 5 Troubleshooting chart (Part 3 of 6). 1993-94

CONDITION	INSPECT COMPONENT	FOR CAUSE
NO PART THROTTLE OR DELAYED DOWNSHIFT	TV CABLE	– MISADJUSTED, BINDING OR DAMAGED
	VALVE BODY	– THROTTLE VALVE BINDING OR STICKING – 2–3 SHIFT VALVE BINDING OR STICKING – 1–2 SHIFT VALVE BINDING OR STICKING – PRIMARY REGULATOR VALVE BINDING OR STICKING – BROKEN OR DISTORTED VALVE SPRINGS – DAMAGED OR POROUS VALVE BODY CASTING
	INTERMEDIATE SERVO	– PISTON BINDING OR STICKING – PISTON SEALS CUT OR DAMAGED – PISTON ROD BINDING
	2ND BRAKE BAND	– WORN OR MISPOSITIONED
	1ST-REVERSE BRAKE	– CLUTCH DISCS WORN – 1ST-REVERSE BRAKE PISTON OR SEAL LEAKING OR DAMAGED
	ONE-WAY CLUTCH	– NOT HOLDING OR DAMAGED
NO ENGINE BRAKING OR 3–2–1 MANUAL DOWNSHIFT	SHIFT SELECT CABLE	– MISADJUSTED, BINDING OR DAMAGED
	VALVE BODY	– MANUAL VALVE BINDING OR STICKING – 2–3 SHIFT VALVE BINDING OR STICKING – 1–2 SHIFT VALVE BINDING OR STICKING – PRIMARY REGULATOR VALVE BINDING OR STICKING – BROKEN OR DISTORTED VALVE SPRINGS – DAMAGED OR POROUS VALVE BODY CASTING
	INTERMEDIATE SERVO	– PISTON BINDING OR STICKING – PISTON SEALS CUT OR DAMAGED – PISTON ROD BINDING
	2ND BRAKE BAND	– WORN OR MISPOSITIONED
	1ST-REVERSE BRAKE	– CLUTCH DISCS WORN – 1ST-REVERSE BRAKE PISTON OR SEAL LEAKING OR DAMAGED
	ONE-WAY CLUTCH	– NOT HOLDING OR DAMAGED

GC5029300495040X

Fig. 5 Troubleshooting chart (Part 4 of 6). 1993-94

CONDITION	INSPECT COMPONENT	FOR CAUSE
HARSH ENGAGEMENT INTO ANY FORWARD RANGE	FLUID LEVEL INDICATOR	– LOW FLUID LEVEL
	TV CABLE	– MISADJUSTED, BINDING OR DAMAGED
	SHIFT SELECT CABLE	– MISADJUSTED, BINDING OR DAMAGED
	VALVE BODY	– MANUAL VALVE BINDING OR STICKING – THROTTLE VALVE BINDING OR STICKING – B2 CONTROL VALVE BINDING OR STICKING
	ACCUMULATORS	– PISTONS DAMAGED OR LEAKING – SEALS CUT OR DAMAGED – BROKEN OR DISTORTED SPRINGS
	FLUID PRESSURE	– (SEE CAUSES OF HIGH OR LOW FLUID PRESSURE)
SLIPS IN 1ST GEAR	FLUID LEVEL INDICATOR	– LOW FLUID LEVEL
	TV CABLE	– MISADJUSTED, BINDING OR DAMAGED
	SHIFT SELECT CABLE	– MISADJUSTED, BINDING OR DAMAGED
	VALVE BODY	– THROTTLE VALVE BINDING OR STICKING – PRIMARY REGULATOR VALVE BINDING OR STICKING
	ACCUMULATORS	– PISTONS DAMAGED OR LEAKING – SEALS CUT OR DAMAGED – BROKEN OR DISTORTED SPRINGS
	FORWARD CLUTCH	– CLUTCH DISCS WORN – FORWARD CLUTCH PISTON OR SEAL LEAKING OR DAMAGED – INPUT SHAFT O-RINGS CUT OR DAMAGED
	ONE-WAY CLUTCH	– NOT HOLDING OR DAMAGED
	FLUID PRESSURE	– (SEE CAUSES OF HIGH OR LOW FLUID PRESSURE)

GC5029300495010X

Fig. 5 Troubleshooting chart (Part 5 of 6). 1993-94

CONDITION	INSPECT COMPONENT	FOR CAUSE
NO PARK OR RATCHETING NOISE IN PARK	SHIFT SELECT CABLE	- MISADJUSTED BINDING OR DAMAGED
	LOCK PAWL SPRING	- DISCONNECTED OR BROKEN
	PARKING LOCK ROD	- DISCONNECTED OR BROKEN
	PARKING LOCK PAWL	- LOOSE OR DISCONNECTED
	LOCK PAWL SPRING	- WEAK OR DAMAGED
VEHICLE DOES NOT MOVE IN ANY RANGE — FORWARD OR REVERSE	FLUID LEVEL INDICATOR	- LITTLE OR NO FLUID
	SHIFT SELECT CABLE	- MISADJUSTED BINDING OR DAMAGED
	PARKING LOCK PAWL	- MECHANISM LOCKED OR FROZEN
	TORQUE CONVERTER	- BROKEN TORQUE CONVERTER-TO-FLYWHEEL BOLTS - STATOR ONE WAY CLUTCH NOT HOLDING - INTERNAL DAMAGE
	VALVE BODY	- SPACER PLATE OR GASKETS MISPOSITIONED OR DAMAGED - CHECK BALLS OMITTED OR MISPOSITIONED - MANUAL VALVE BINDING OR STICKING - MANUAL VALVE LINK DISCONNECTED
	FLUID PRESSURE	- (SEE CAUSES OF HIGH OR LOW FLUID PRESSURE)

GC5029300495060X

Fig. 5 Troubleshooting chart (Part 6 of 6). 1993-94

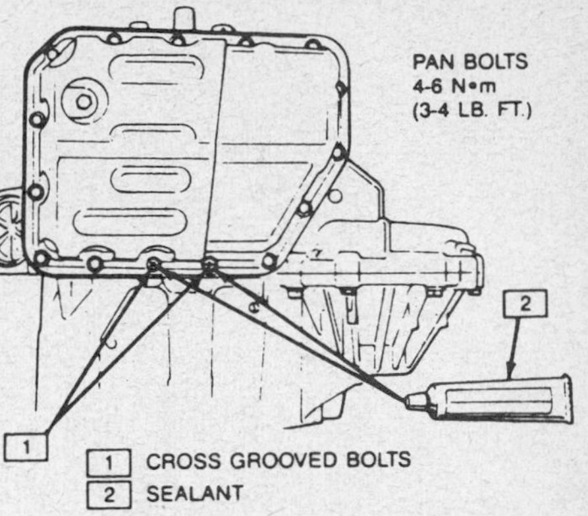
PAN BOLTS
4-6 N•m
(3-4 LB. FT.)
1
2
1 CROSS GROOVED BOLTS
2 SEALANT
GC5029100465000X

Fig. 6 Oil pan installation

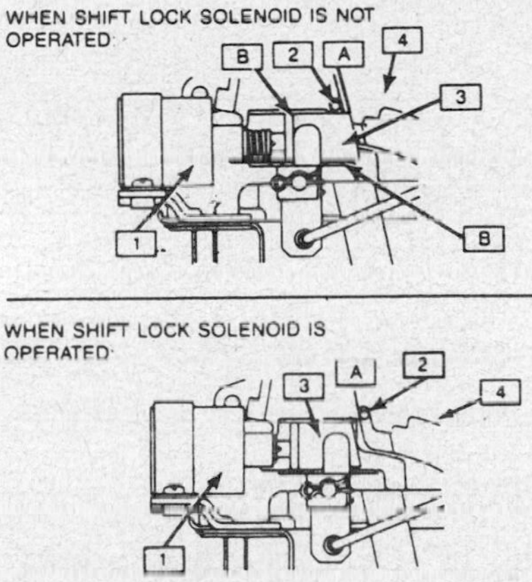
WHEN SHIFT LOCK SOLENOID IS NOT OPERATED
B
2
A
4
3
1
B
WHEN SHIFT LOCK SOLENOID IS OPERATED
3
A
2
4
1

1 SHIFT LOCK SOLENOID
2 DETENT PIN
3 LOCK PLATE
4 DETENT PLATE
A MORE THAN 1.0 MM (0.040 IN)
B APPLY GREASE HERE

GC5029100466000X

Fig. 7 Interlock solenoid adjustment

3. Remove manual selector bulb socket from manual selector cover.
4. Remove four manual selector cover to selector lever attaching screws.
5. Remove retainer clip, clevis pin, then disconnect shift select cable from selector lever.
6. Disconnect interlock cable end from key release plate on manual selector.
7. Remove interlock cable to selector assembly attaching bolt, then disconnect cable from assembly.
8. Disconnect shift lock solenoid electrical connector located under the carpet.
9. Raise and support vehicle.
10. Remove four selector lever assembly housing seat retaining nuts.
11. Lower vehicle and remove selector lever housing and selector lever from floor.
12. Reverse procedure to install, noting the following:
   a. **Torque** four selector lever housing seat nuts to 25 ft. lbs.
   b. Refer to "Interlock Cable, Replace" to adjust interlock cable.
   c. Refer to "Shift Select Cable, Replace" to adjust shift select cable.
   d. Apply lithium grease under solenoid lock plate as shown **Fig. 19.**

SHIFT SELECT CABLE, REPLACE

Refer to **Fig. 20** when replacing the shift select cable.

1. Remove two selector lever knob to selector lever attaching screws.
2. Remove six center console attaching screws, then the center console.
3. Remove manual selector cover lamp bulb socket from selector cover.
4. Remove four selector cover to selector lever attaching screws.
5. Remove retainer clip, clevis pin and shift select cable from selector lever.
6. Remove front carpet retainers, then pull back carpet.
7. Remove retaining clip and shift select cable from transaxle retaining bracket.
8. Remove nut, then disconnect shift select cable from manual shift lever.
9. Remove two bolts from bulkhead grommet, then pull shift select cable out of bulkhead from engine compartment side of bulkhead.
10. Reverse procedure to install, noting the following:
   a. **Torque** bulkhead grommet bolts to 15 ft. lbs.
   b. After connecting shift select cable to transaxle retaining bracket, tighten adjustment nut "A" by hand until it contacts shift select cable joint, **Fig. 21.**

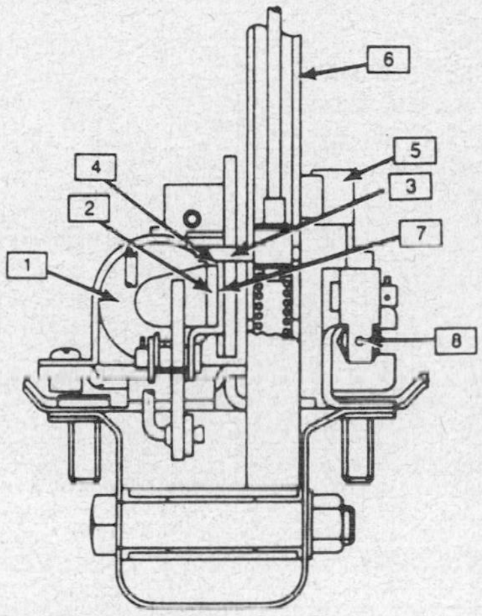
6
5
4
3
2
7
1
8

1 SHIFT LOCK SOLENOID
2 LOCK PLATE
3 GUIDE PLATE
4 "NO CLEARANCE"
5 DETENT PIN
6 SELECTOR LEVER
7 KEY RELEASE PLATE
8 INTERLOCK CABLE

GC5029100467000X

Fig. 8 Interlock solenoid lock plate clearance

   c. Using an open end wrench, tighten adjustment nut "B" until it is jammed against manual shift select cable joint.
   d. Apply lithium grease to shift select cable clevis pin.

PARK/NEUTRAL POSITION SWITCH, REPLACE

1. Disconnect battery ground cable.
2. Disconnect Park/Neutral position switch electrical connector.
3. Remove position switch wiring harness from retaining clips.
4. Remove switch to transaxle retaining bolt.
5. Reverse procedure to install, noting the following:
   a. Adjust position switch as described in "Park/Neutral Position Switch" under "Adjustments."
   b. **Torque** position switch attaching bolt to 17 ft. lbs.

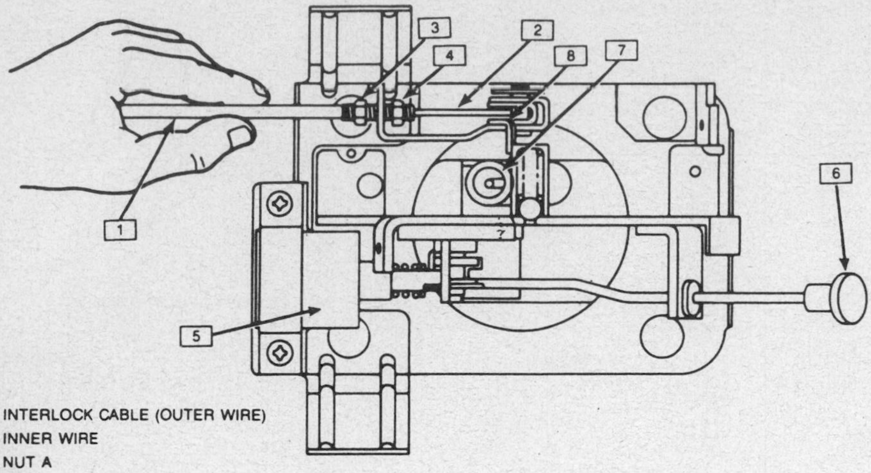
3
4
2
8
7
6
1
5

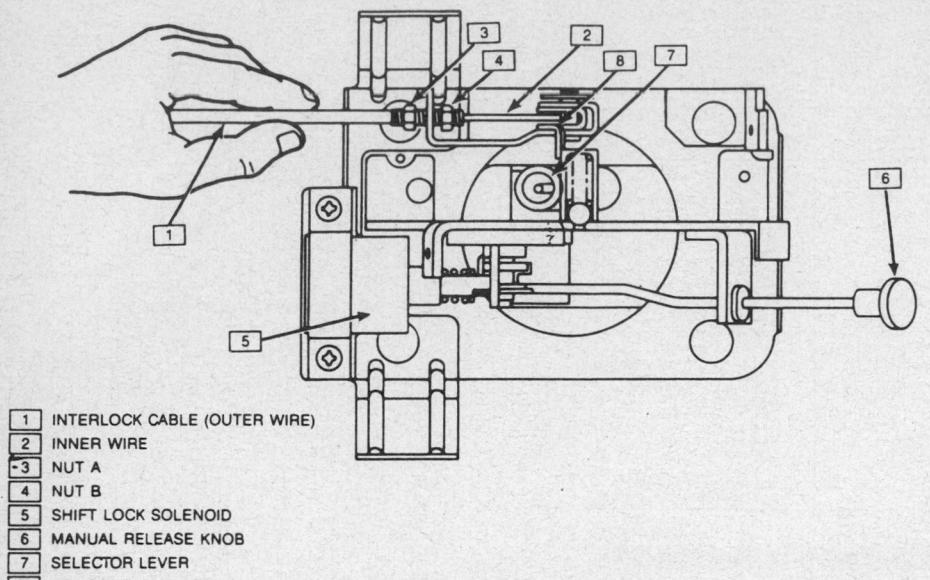

1 INTERLOCK CABLE (OUTER WIRE)
2 INNER WIRE
3 NUT A
4 NUT B
5 SHIFT LOCK SOLENOID
6 MANUAL RELEASE KNOB
7 SELECTOR LEVER
8 KEY RELEASE PLATE

GC5029100468000X

Fig. 9 Interlock cable adjustment

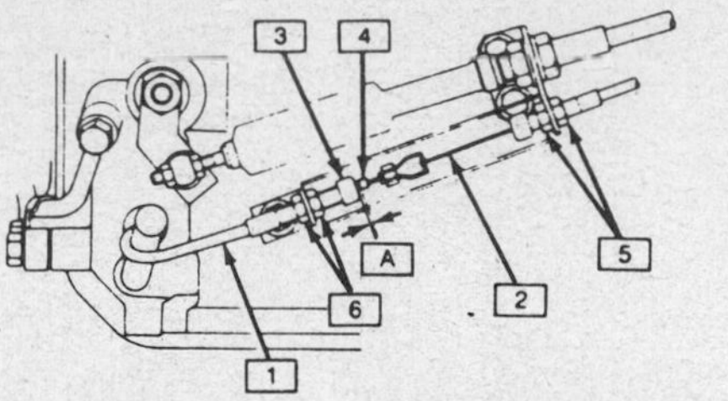
3
4
A
5
6
2
1

1 OIL PRESSURE CONTROL CABLE
2 ACCELERATOR CABLE
3 BOOT
4 INNER CABLE STOPPER
5 ADJUSTING NUTS A
6 ADJUSTING NUTS B
A 0-0.5MM (0-0.02 IN.)

GC5029100469000X

Fig. 10 Oil pressure control cable adjustment

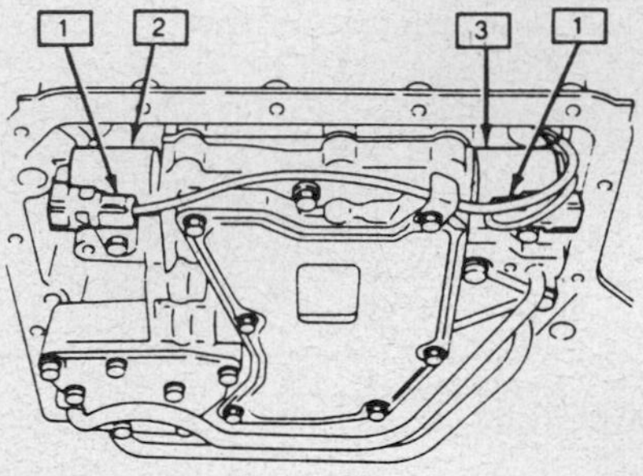
1
2
3
1

1 COUPLERS
2 2ND BRAKE SOLENOID
3 DIRECT CLUTCH SOLENOID

GC5029100471000X

Fig. 13 Direct clutch & second brake solenoid replacement

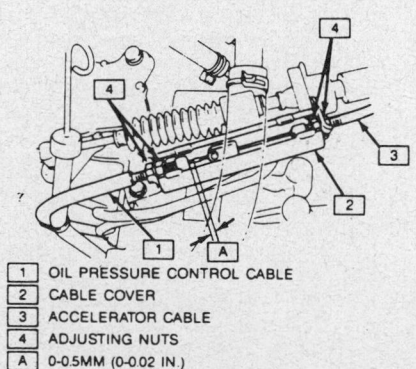

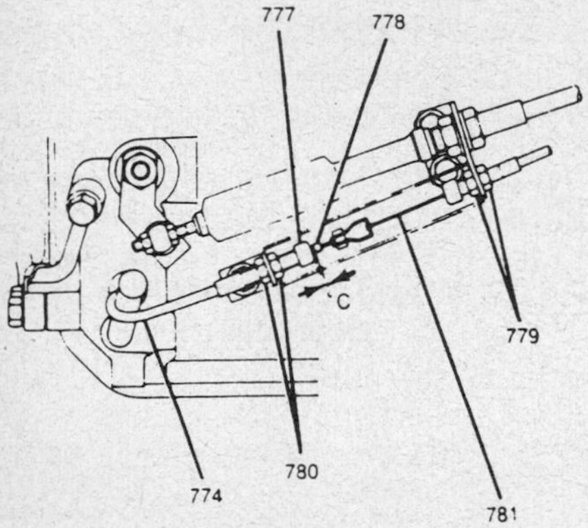
777
778
C
779
780
774
781

C 0.0–0.5 mm (0.0–0.02")
774 TV CABLE ASSEMBLY
777 TV CABLE BOOT
778 INNER CABLE STOPPER
779 ACCELERATOR CABLE ADJUSTMENT NUTS "B"
780 TV CABLE ADJUSTMENT NUTS "A"
781 ACCELERATOR CABLE

GC5029300477000X

Fig. 11 Adjusting TV cable. 1993-94

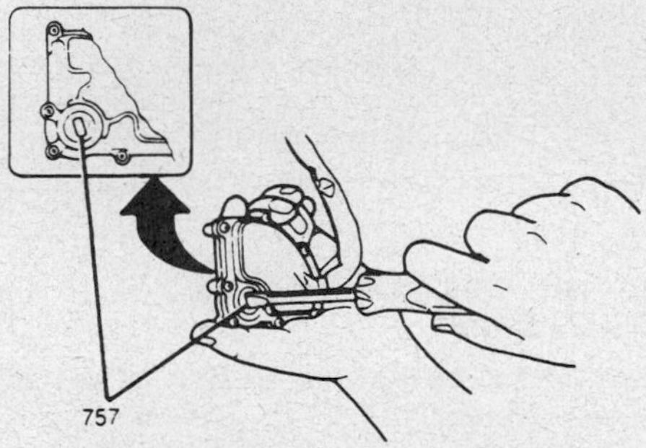
757

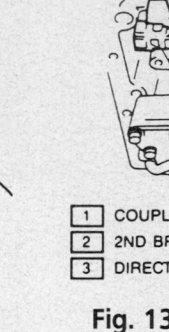

757 PNP SWITCH JOINT

GC5029300482000X

Fig. 12 Adjusting Park/Neutral position switch. 1993-94

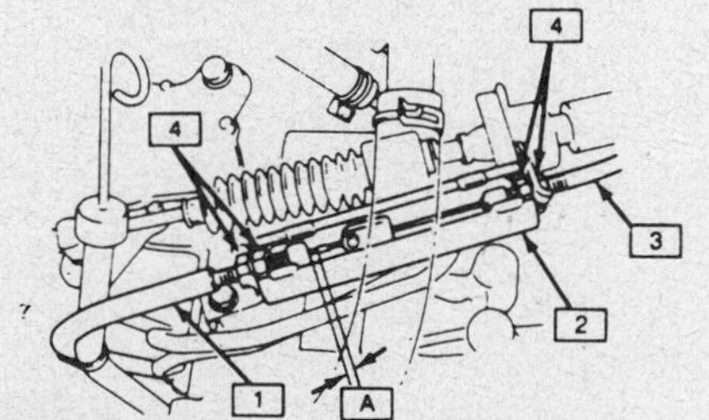
4
4
3
2
1
A

1 OIL PRESSURE CONTROL CABLE
2 CABLE COVER
3 ACCELERATOR CABLE
4 ADJUSTING NUTS
A 0-0.5MM (0-0.02 IN.)

GC5029100470000X

Fig. 14 Oil pressure control cable replacement

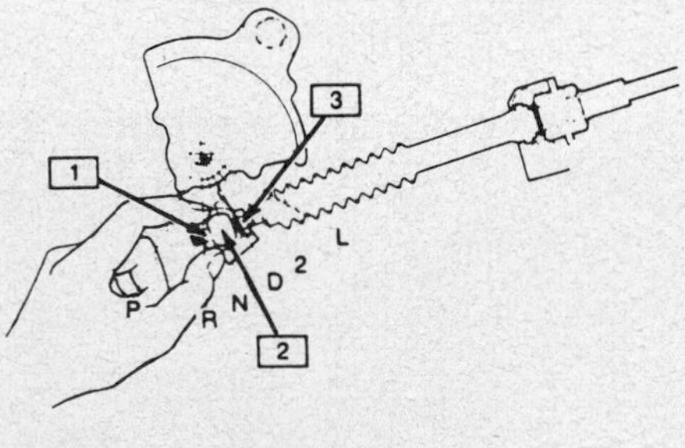
3
1
L
2
D
P
R
N
2

1 NUT A
2 MANUAL SELECT CABLE JOINT
3 NUT B

GC5029100472000X

Fig. 15 Transaxle selector cable installation

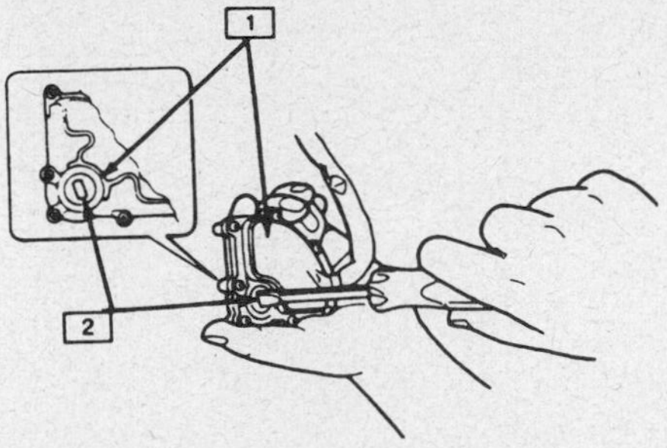
1
2

1 NEUTRAL SAFETY SWITCH
2 NEUTRAL SAFETY SWITCH JOINT

GC5029100473000X

Fig. 16 Shift lever switch installation

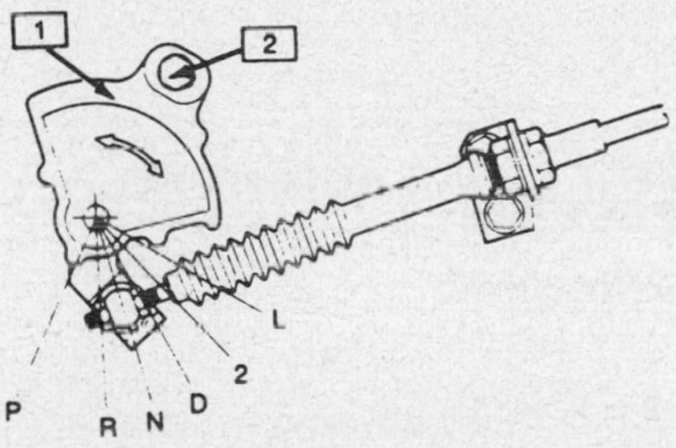
1
2
L
2
P
R
N
D

1 NEUTRAL SAFETY SWITCH
2 BOLT

GC5029100474000X

Fig. 17 Shift lever switch adjustment

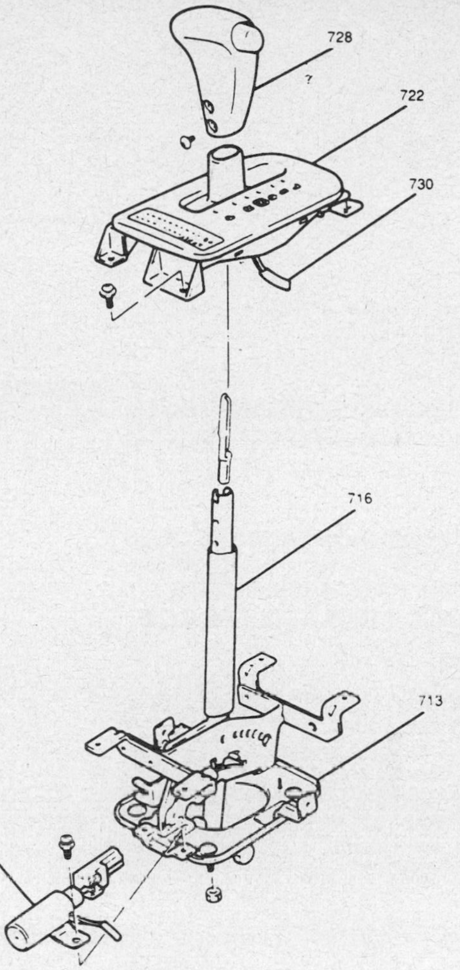
728
722
730
716
713
732

713 SELECTOR LEVER HOUSING
716 SELECTOR LEVER
722 SELECTOR COVER
728 SELECTOR LEVER KNOB
730 INDICATOR LAMP
732 SHIFT LOCK SOLENOID

GC5029300478000X

Fig. 18 Manual selector assembly. 1994-94

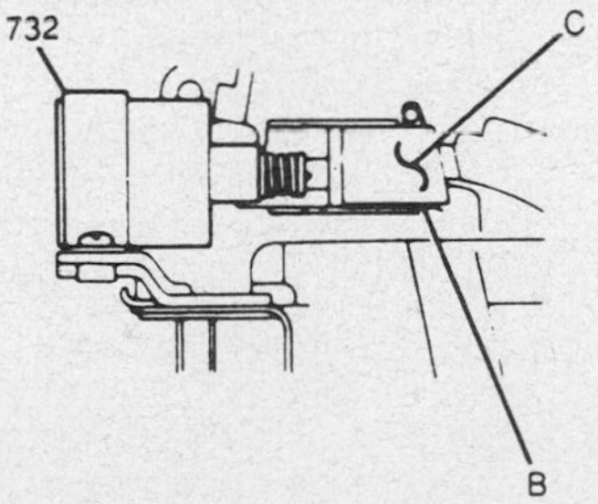
732
C
B

B LITHIUM GREASE
C MANUAL OVERRIDE SOLENOID LOCK PLATE
732 SHIFT LOCK SOLENOID

GC5029300479000X

Fig. 19 Solenoid lock plate. 1993-94

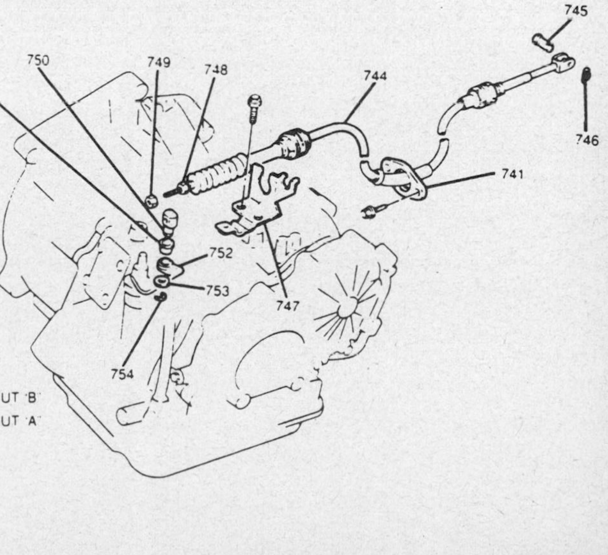
745
751
750
749
748
744
746
741
752
753
747
754

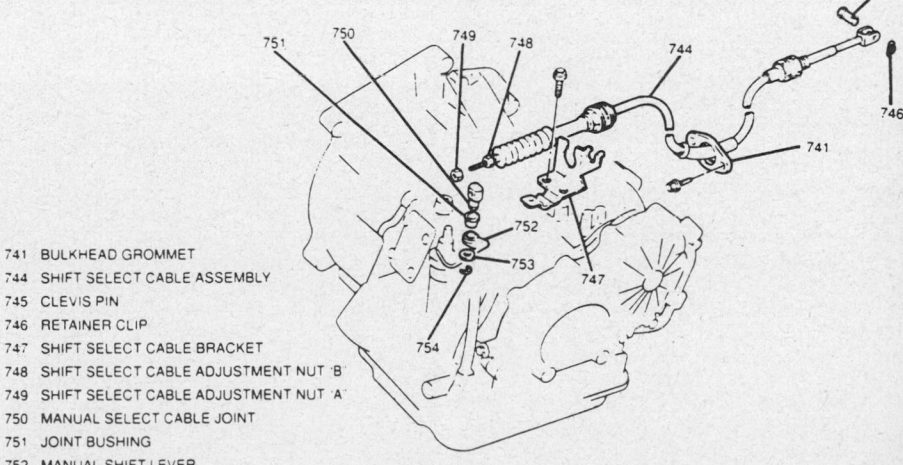

741 BULKHEAD GROMMET
744 SHIFT SELECT CABLE ASSEMBLY
745 CLEVIS PIN
746 RETAINER CLIP
747 SHIFT SELECT CABLE BRACKET
748 SHIFT SELECT CABLE ADJUSTMENT NUT 'B'
749 SHIFT SELECT CABLE ADJUSTMENT NUT 'A'
750 MANUAL SELECT CABLE JOINT
751 JOINT BUSHING
752 MANUAL SHIFT LEVER
753 WASHER
754 E-RING RETAINER

GC5029300480000X

Fig. 20 Shift select cable assembly. 1993-94

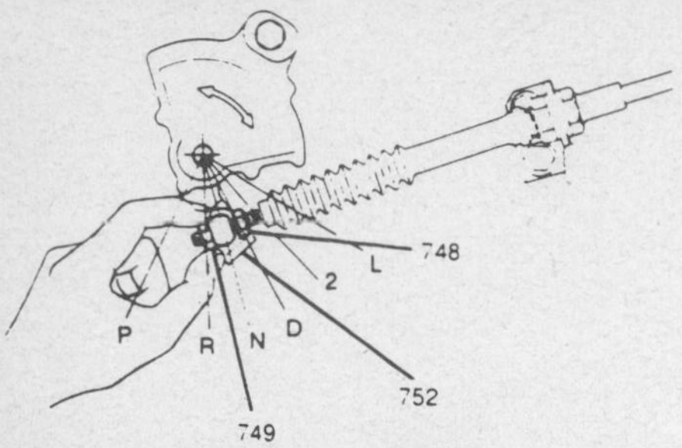
748
2
L
P
R
N
D
752
749

748 SHIFT SELECT CABLE ADJUSTMENT NUT "B"
749 SHIFT SELECT CABLE ADJUSTMENT NUT "A"
752 MANUAL SHIFT LEVER

GC5029300481000X

Fig. 21 Installing shift select cable. 1993-94

c. Verify that engine starts in PARK and NEUTRAL, and does not start in reverse or any drive position.

INTERLOCK CABLE, REPLACE

Removal

1. Remove two selector lever knob to selector lever attaching screws.
2. Remove six center console attaching screws, then the center console.
3. Remove manual selector cover lamp bulb socket from selector cover.
4. Remove four selector cover to selector lever attaching screws.
5. Disconnect interlock cable end from key release plate on manual selector, **Fig. 22.**
6. Remove interlock cable attaching bolt.
7. Disconnect interlock cable from selector lever housing bracket.
8. Remove front carpet retainers and pull back front carpet.
9. Remove upper and lower steering column covers.
10. Remove upper and lower steering column mounting nuts and lower steering column.
11. Remove screw and interlock cable retaining clamp from ignition switch.
12. Push release shaft in at ignition switch lock mechanism.
13. Remove cable end from ignition switch, then the interlock cable from vehicle.

Installation

1. Install cable into vehicle and route it to ignition switch.
2. Push release shaft in at ignition switch and insert cable end.
3. Attach interlock cable retaining clamp to ignition switch and secure with screw.
4. Reposition steering column and install mounting nuts.
5. Install steering column covers.
6. Refit front carpet and install carpet retainers.
7. Attach interlock cable to selector lever housing bracket.
8. Attach cable end to key release plate.
9. Move selector lever to PARK and hold selector button in.

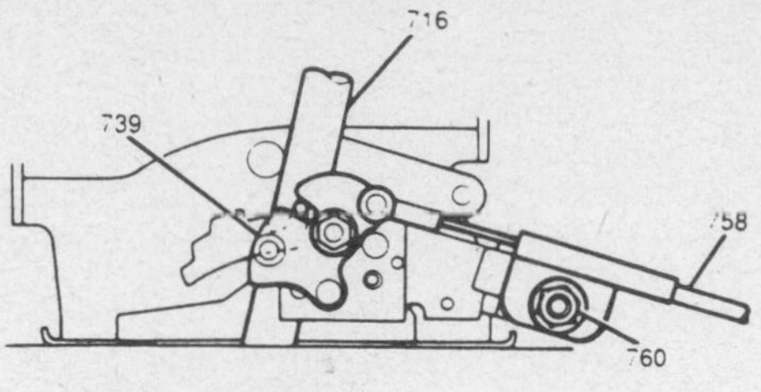
716
739
758
760

716 SELECTOR LEVER
739 KEY RELEASE PLATE
758 INTERLOCK CABLE ASSEMBLY
760 INTERLOCK CABLE BOLT

GC5029300483000X

Fig. 22 Interlock cable & manual selector assembly. 1993-94

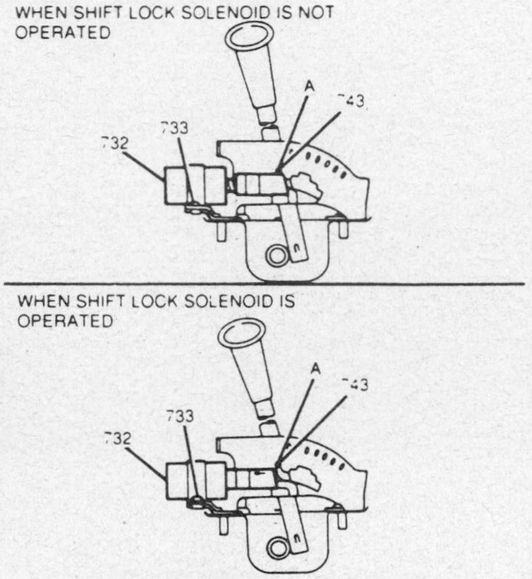
WHEN SHIFT LOCK SOLENOID IS NOT OPERATED
A
743
733
732
WHEN SHIFT LOCK SOLENOID IS OPERATED
A
743
733
732

A APPLY LITHIUM GREASE
732 SHIFT LOCK SOLENOID
733 SHIFT LOCK SOLENOID RETAINING SCREW
743 DETENT PIN

GC5029300485000X

Fig. 24 Shift lock solenoid operation. 1993-94

10. Rotate key release plate and insert a small screwdriver through key release plate to hold it in position, **Fig. 23.**
11. Allow retaining spring to position interlock control bracket.
12. **Torque** interlock cable bolt to 115 inch lbs.
13. Ensure that when selector lever is in the PARK position that the ignition key can be moved from "ACC" to "LOCK" and the ignition key can be removed from the ignition switch.
14. Ensure that when selector lever is in any position other than PARK that the ignition switch cannot be turned to "ACC" or "PARK."
15. Install manual selector cover onto selector lever.
16. Install manual selector cover lamp bulb socket into cover.
17. Install console, then the selector knob.

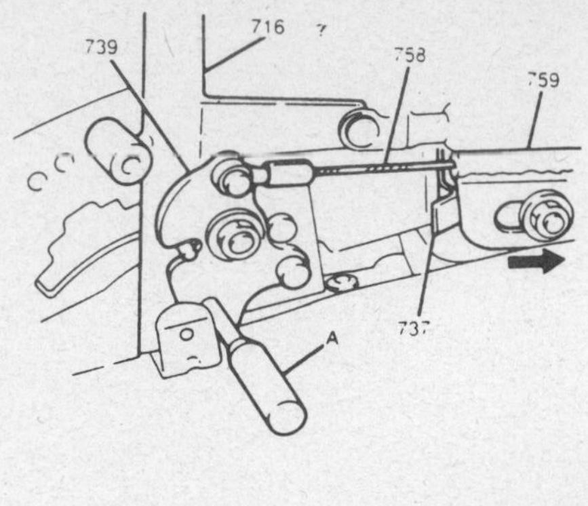
739
716
758
759
A
737

A SMALL SCREWDRIVER
716 SELECTOR LEVER
737 RETAINING SPRING
739 KEY RELEASE PLATE
758 INTERLOCK CABLE
759 INTERLOCK CABLE BRACKET

GC5029300484000X

Fig. 23 Adjusting interlock cable. 1993-94

SHIFT LOCK SOLENOID, REPLACE

Removal

1. Disconnect battery ground cable.
2. Remove two selector lever knob to selector lever attaching screws.
3. Remove six center console attaching screws, then the center console.
4. Remove selector lever upper cover, then the lower cover.
5. Disconnect shift solenoid electrical connector located under the carpet.
6. Remove two shift lock solenoid attaching screws, then the shift lock solenoid from selector lever housing, **Fig. 24.**

Installation

1. Move selector lever to PARK position.
2. Apply lithium grease to upper and lower edges of solenoid lock plate.
3. Attach shift lock solenoid to selector lever housing and hand tighten two retaining screws.
4. Connect shift lock solenoid electrical connector.
5. Adjust shift lock solenoid so that it operates as follows:
   a. When ignition switch is turned off, solenoid is not actuated.
   b. When ignition switch is turned on and the brake pedal is depressed, solenoid is actuated and solenoid lock plate should be positioned as shown in **Fig. 24.**
   c. There should be no clearance between solenoid lock plate and selector lever.
   d. If manual override is enabled with ignition switch in the OFF position, the selector lever can be moved to any range or position.
6. Tighten shift lock solenoid retaining

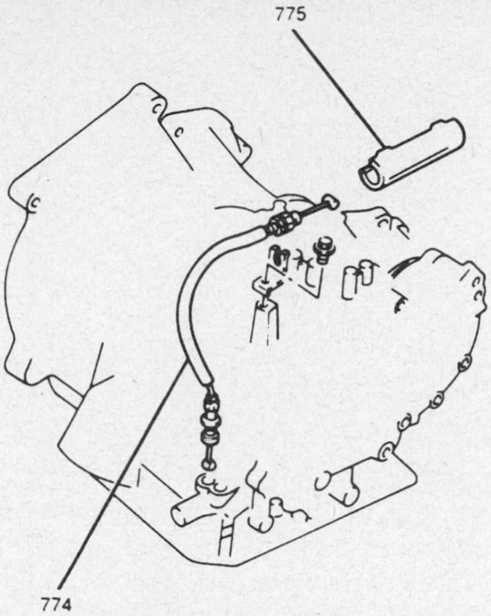
775
774

774 TV CABLE ASSEMBLY
775 TV CABLE ADJUSTMENT COVER

GC5029300486000X

Fig. 25 TV cable & adjustment cover. 1993-94

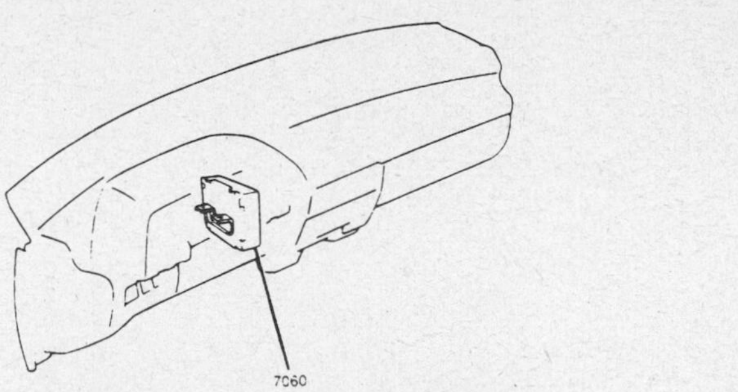
7060

GC5029300487000X

Fig. 26 Transaxle control module location. 1993-94

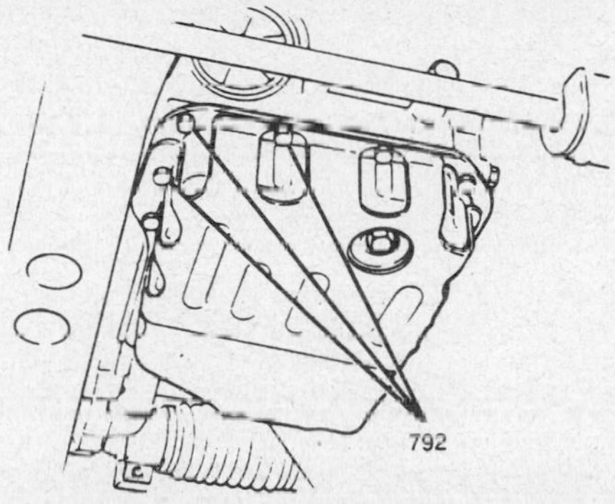
792

792 TRANSAXLE FLUID PAN BOLTS

GC5029300488000X

Fig. 27 Transaxle fluid pan bolts. 1993-94

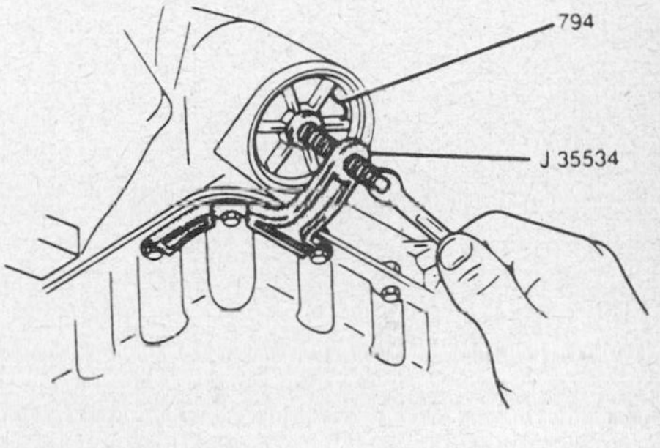
794
J 35534

794 SERVO COVER

GC5029300489000X

Fig. 28 Compressing servo cover. 1993-94

screws. **Ensure selector lever locks in PARK position and cannot be shifted to any other position.**
7. Install lower cover onto selector lever.
8. Install upper cover onto selector lever.
9. Install console, then the selector lever knob.
10. Connect battery ground cable.

TV CABLE, REPLACE

1. Remove TV cable adjustment cover, **Fig. 25.**
2. Disconnect TV cable from accelerator cable and bracket assembly.
3. Raise and support vehicle.
4. Remove transaxle drain plug and drain fluid from transaxle.
5. Remove transaxle fluid pan guard, fluid pan and fluid pan gasket.
6. Disconnect TV cable from throttle valve cam.
7. Reverse procedure to install, adjust TV cable as described in "TV Cable" under "Adjustments." **Torque** fluid pan bolts to 53 inch lbs. and drain plug to 17 ft. lbs.

TRANSAXLE CONTROL MODULE (TCM), REPLACE

1. Disconnect battery ground cable.
2. Disconnect TCM electrical connectors.
3. Remove two TCM attaching bolts, then the TCM from under lefthand side of the instrument panel, **Fig. 28.**
4. Reverse procedure to install, **Torque** TCM retaining bolts to 11 ft. lbs.

INTERMEDIATE SERVO, REPLACE

1. Raise and support vehicle.
2. Remove three transaxle fluid pan bolts shown in **Fig. 27.**
3. Install piston cover depressor too No. J 35534 or equivalent onto transaxle oil pan, **Fig. 28.**
4. Tighten adjustment bolt on tool until servo cover snap ring can be removed.
5. Remove servo cover snap ring, then slowly loosen adjustment bolt.
6. Remove servo cover, servo piston, springs and piston rod, **Fig. 29.**
7. Reverse procedure to install, liberally apply transmission fluid to all servo components prior to installation.

VEHICLE SPEED SENSOR, REPLACE

1. Disconnect battery ground cable.
2. Disconnect vehicle speed electrical connector.
3. Remove vehicle speed sensor retaining bolt, then the speed sensor.
4. Reverse procedure to install, **torque** retaining bolt to 17 ft. lbs.

SPEEDOMETER DRIVEN GEAR, REPLACE

1. Slide speedometer driven gear case boot up speedometer cable and off speedometer driven gear case, **Fig. 30.**
2. Remove speedometer cable retaining clip and speedometer cable from speedometer driven gear case.
3. Remove retaining bolt and speedometer driven gear from transaxle case.
4. Using a drift punch and hammer, remove driven gear case roll pin from speedometer driven gear case.
5. Remove speedometer driven gear from driven gear case.
6. Remove driven gear case O-ring, then the driven gear case lip seal.
7. Reverse procedure to install, lubricate speedometer driven gear, lip seal and O-ring with Transjel transmission assembly lubricant No. J 36850 or equivalent, **torque** driven gear retaining bolt to 11 ft. lbs.

DRIVE AXLE SHAFT FLUID SEAL, REPLACE

1. Raise and support vehicle.
2. Remove wheel cover or center cap.
3. Unstake drive axle nut.
4. Remove drive axle nut and washer.
5. Remove tire and wheel assembly.
6. Drain transaxle fluid and install two boot protectors tool No. J 28712 or equivalent onto inner and outer drive axle boots.
7. Using a large screwdriver, pry differential side joint away from transaxle.
8. Remove differential side gear snap ring.

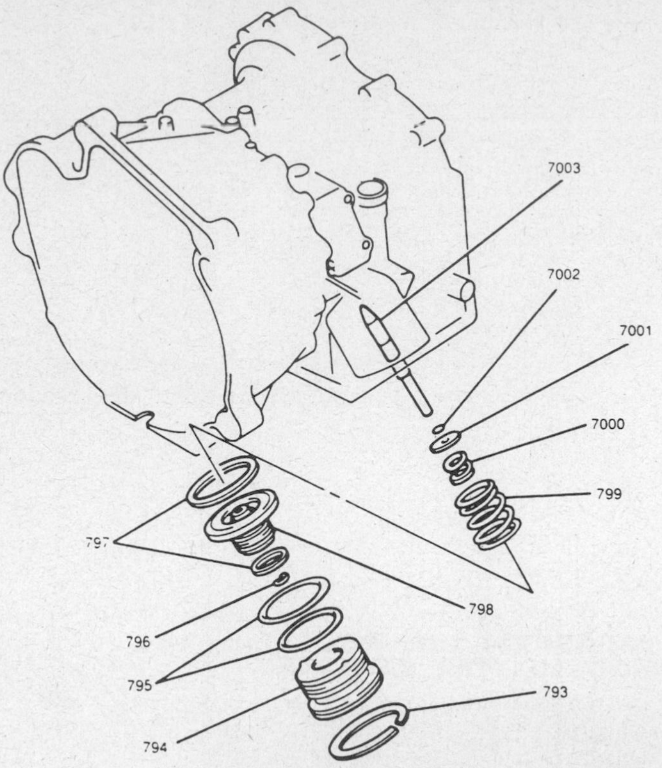
7003
7002
7001
7000
799
797
798
796
795
793
794

793 SERVO COVER SNAP RING
794 SERVO COVER
795 SERVO COVER SEAL(S)
796 PISTON ROD SNAP RING
797 PISTON SEAL
798 SERVO PISTON
799 PISTON SPRING
7000 PISTON ROD SPRING
7001 PISTON ROD WASHER
7002 PISTON ROD SEAL
7003 PISTON ROD

GC5029300490000X

Fig. 29 Intermediate servo components. 1993-94

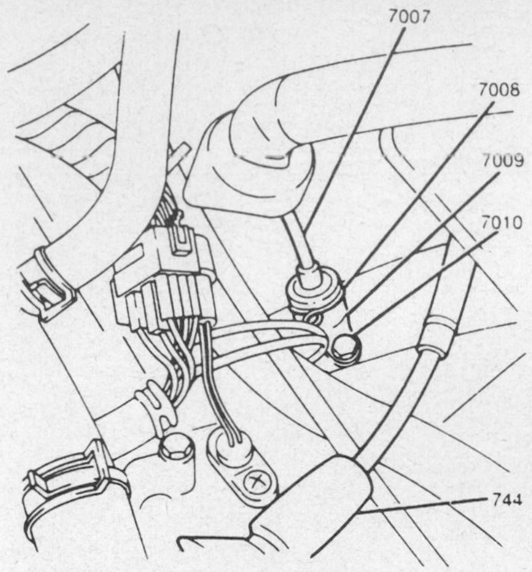
7007
7008
7009
7010
744

744 SHIFT SELECT CABLE ASSEMBLY
7007 SPEEDOMETER CABLE
7008 SPEEDOMETER CABLE RETAINING CLIP
7009 SPEEDOMETER DRIVEN GEAR CASE
7010 SPEEDOMETER DRIVEN GEAR CASE RETAINING BOLT

GC5029300491000X

Fig. 30 Speedometer driven gear case. 1993-94

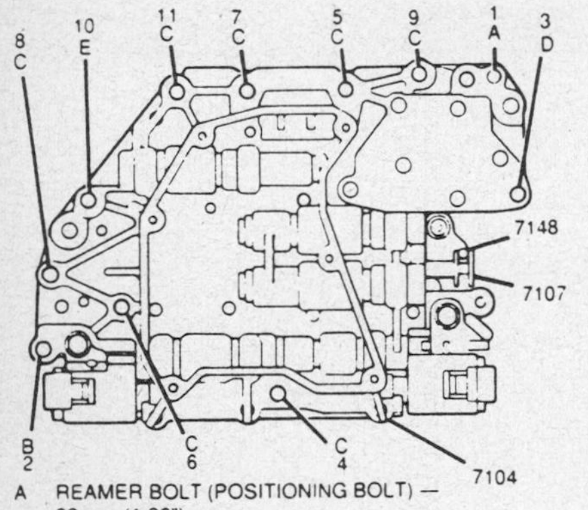
8 C
10 E
11 C
7 C
5 C
9 C
1 A
3 D
7148
7107
B 2
6 C
C 4
7104

A REAMER BOLT (POSITIONING BOLT) — 32 mm (1.26")
B REAMER BOLT (POSITIONING BOLT) — 25 mm (0.98")
C BOLT — 35 mm (1.38")
D BOLT — 47 mm (1.85")
E BOLT — 25 mm (0.98")
7104 LOWER VALVE BODY
7107 MANUAL VALVE
7148 SHIFT LEVER PIN

GC5029300492000X

Fig. 31 Valve body bolt locations. 1993-94

9. Remove ball stud and nut, then separate steering knuckle from control arm.
10. Remove drive axle assembly by removing differential side joint from differential side gear.
11. Remove drive axle oil seal from transaxle.
12. Reverse procedure to install, noting the following:
    a. Coat transaxle oil pan drain plug with Loctite pipe sealant part No. 1052080 or equivalent, **torque** drain plug to 17 ft. lbs.
    b. **Torque** ball stud nut to 44 ft. lbs.
    c. **Torque** drive axle nut to 129 ft. lbs.
    d. Refill transaxle with fluid and check level.

VALVE BODY & ACCUMULATOR, REPLACE

Removal

1. Disconnect battery ground cable.
2. Raise and support vehicle.
3. Drain transaxle fluid, then remove oil pan and gasket.
4. Disconnect direct clutch and 2nd brake solenoid electrical connectors.
5. Using a screwdriver, pry forward clutch accumulator and 2nd brake fluid pipes from lower valve body.
6. Disconnect TV cable from throttle valve cam.
7. Remove six fluid filter screen to lower valve body attaching bolts.
8. Remove valve body attaching bolts, **Fig. 31.**
9. Remove forward clutch and 2nd brake accumulators from transaxle case by covering accumulator bores with a cloth and slowly applying low pressure compressed air into fluid pressure passage, **Fig. 32.**

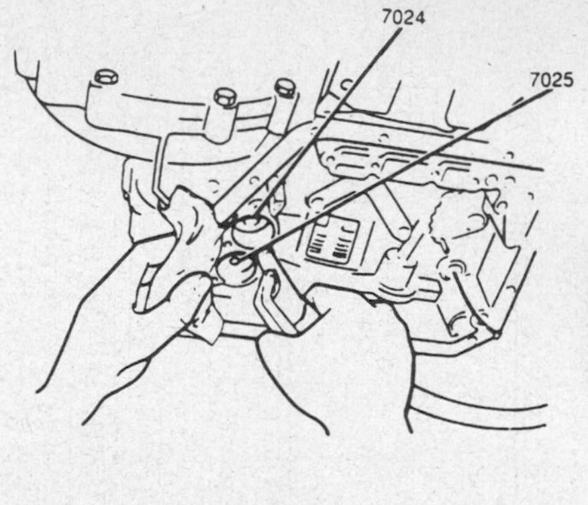
7024
7025

7024 FORWARD CLUTCH ACCUMULATOR
7025 2ND BRAKE ACCUMULATOR

GC5029300493000X

Fig. 32 Accumulator removal. 1993-94

Installation

Torque sequence and specification is very important to valve body operation. If bolts are tightened at random, valve bores may become distorted and inhibit valve operation. Make sure all parts are clean and free of damage prior to their installation. When installing valve body to case, make sure accumulators and springs are in their correct positions and all valve body bolts are installed according to length and position. Do not use air powered tools when installing valve body.

1. Apply Transjel transmission assembly lubricant No. J 36850 or equivalent to forward clutch and 2nd brake accumulator seals.

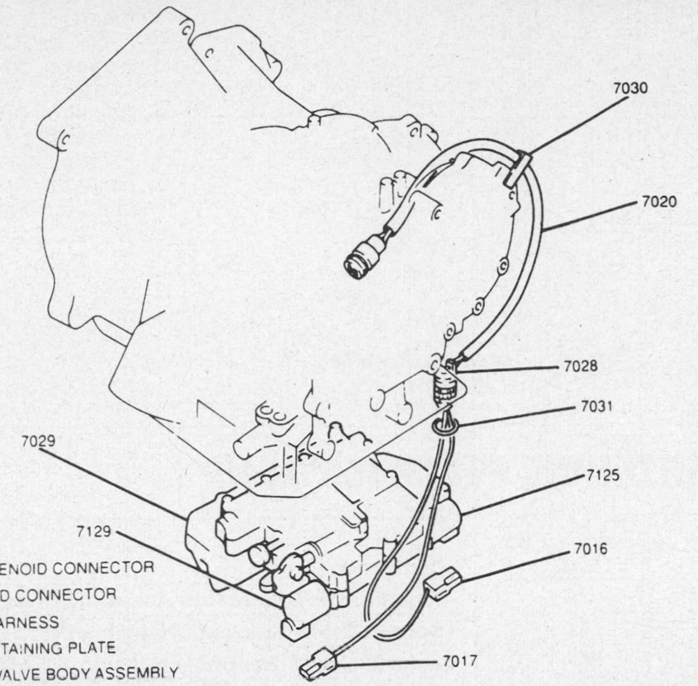
7030
7020
7028
7031
7029
7125
7129
7016
7017

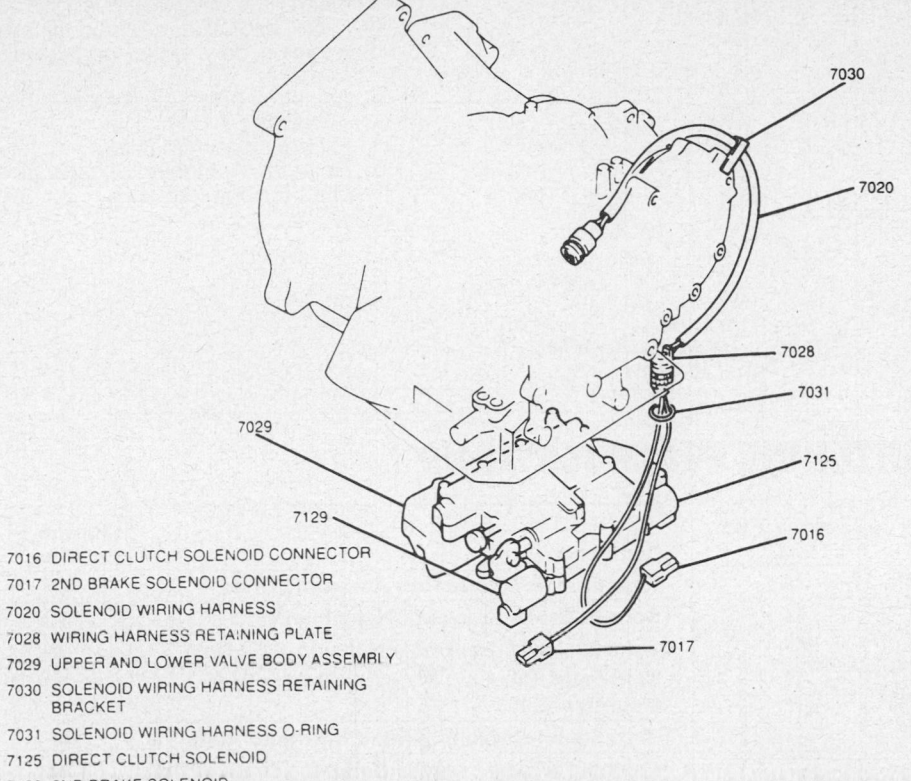

7016 DIRECT CLUTCH SOLENOID CONNECTOR
7017 2ND BRAKE SOLENOID CONNECTOR
7020 SOLENOID WIRING HARNESS
7028 WIRING HARNESS RETAINING PLATE
7029 UPPER AND LOWER VALVE BODY ASSEMBLY
7030 SOLENOID WIRING HARNESS RETAINING BRACKET
7031 SOLENOID WIRING HARNESS O-RING
7125 DIRECT CLUTCH SOLENOID
7129 2ND BRAKE SOLENOID

GC5029300494000X

Fig. 33 Shift solenoids & wiring harness. 1993-94

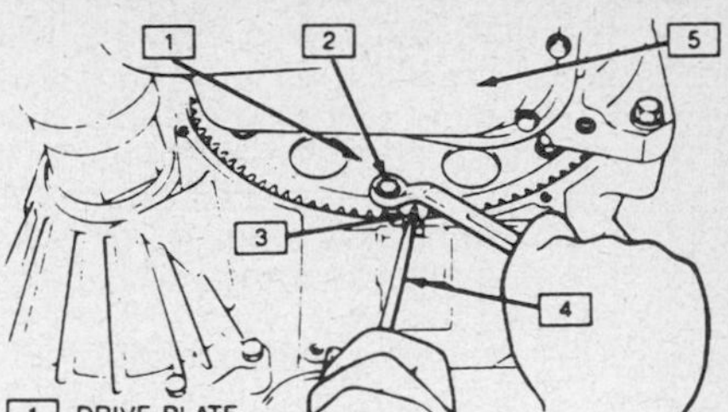
1
2
3
4
5

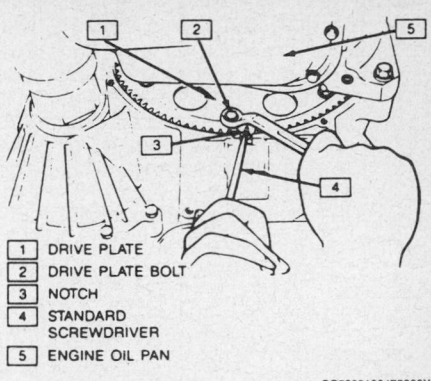

1 DRIVE PLATE
2 DRIVE PLATE BOLT
3 NOTCH
4 STANDARD SCREWDRIVER
5 ENGINE OIL PAN

GC5029100475000X

Fig. 34 Driveplate bolt removal

2. Install forward clutch and 2nd brake accumulators in their case bores.
3. Install valve body into transaxle case aligning manual valve with shift lever pin, install and hand tighten valve body bolts in their correct position, **Fig. 31.**
4. **Torque** valve body reamer (positioning) bolts to 8 ft. lbs.
5. **Torque** remaining valve body bolts in a diagonal pattern to 8 ft. lbs.
6. Install fluid filter screen onto lower valve body and **torque** bolts to 53 inch lbs.
7. Attach TV cable to throttle valve cam.
8. Install forward clutch accumulator and 2nd brake fluid pipes to lower valve body.
9. Connect direct clutch and 2nd brake solenoid connectors.
10. Install oil pan with new fluid pan gasket, **torque** pan bolts to 53 inch lbs.
11. Coat transaxle oil pan drain plug with Loctite pipe sealant part No. 1052080 or equivalent, **torque** drain plug to 17 ft. lbs.
12. Refill transaxle with fluid and check level.

SHIFT SOLENOIDS & WIRING HARNESS, REPLACE

Refer to **Fig. 33** when performing the following replacement procedure.

1. Disconnect battery ground cable.
2. Raise and support vehicle.
3. Drain transaxle fluid, then remove transaxle oil pan.
4. Disconnect electrical connectors from direct clutch and 2nd brake solenoids.
5. Remove direct clutch solenoid and 2nd brake solenoid to lower valve body attaching bolts.
6. Remove solenoid wiring harness retaining nut and plate.
7. Pull wiring harness out of transaxle case.
8. Reverse procedure to install, noting the following:
   a. **Torque** solenoid wiring harness retaining plate nut to 15 ft. lbs.
   b. **Torque** solenoid wiring harness retaining bracket bolt to 15 ft. lbs.
   c. **Torque** direct clutch and 2nd brake solenoid to lower valve body attaching bolts to 35 inch lbs.
   d. **Torque** transaxle oil pan bolts to 53 inch lbs.
   e. Coat transaxle oil pan drain plug with Loctite pipe sealant part No. 1052080 or equivalent, **torque** drain plug to 17 ft. lbs.
   f. Refill transaxle with fluid and check level.

TRANSAXLE

REPLACE

1. Disconnect battery ground cable.
2. Remove air suction guide from air cleaner.
3. Disconnect battery cables and remove battery and tray.
4. Remove ground cable from transaxle.
5. Disconnect solenoid and shift lever connectors.
6. Remove wire harness and speedometer cable from transaxle.
7. Remove oil pressure control cable from accelerator cable, then the accelerator cable from transaxle.
8. Disconnect select cable from transaxle, then remove starter.
9. Drain transaxle fluid.
10. Disconnect oil outlet and inlet hoses from oil pipes. Plug all openings.
11. Raise and support vehicle.
12. Remove exhaust system components as necessary, then the clutch housing lower plate.
13. Remove driveplate attaching bolts using a screwdriver in notch provided to hold driveplate, **Fig. 34.**
14. Remove LH front drive axle as follows:
    a. Remove wheel center cap, then the cotter pin and driveshaft nut.
    b. Remove wheel nuts, then the wheel and tire assembly.
    c. Remove snap ring from spline of differential side joint using a screwdriver.
    d. Remove stabilizer bar bracket bolts and ball stud bolt.
    e. Disconnect ball stud from steering knuckle by pulling down on stabilizer bar.
    f. Disconnect inboard joint from differential side gear and wheel side joint from steering knuckle, then remove the drive axle assembly.
15. Disconnect inboard joint of RH drive axle from differential.
16. Remove RH side transaxle mounting member bolts, then secure transaxle using a jack.
17. Remove LH side transaxle mounting bolts.
18. Remove engine-to-transaxle attaching bolts.
19. Remove transaxle from engine by sliding toward left side and carefully lowering jack.
20. Reverse procedure to install, noting the following:
    a. Apply suitable grease around the cup at center of torque converter.

b. Measure distance A, **Fig. 35.** Distance should measure more than .85 inch. If distance is less than specified, converter installation is improper and must be corrected.
c. Guide right drive axle into differential side gear as transaxle is being raised.
d. After installing inboard joints into differential side gear, push inboard joints into side gears until snap rings on drive axles engage side gears.
e. Adjust oil pressure control cable if necessary.
f. Fill transaxle with fluid.
g. Refer to "Tightening Specifications chart for bolt torques.

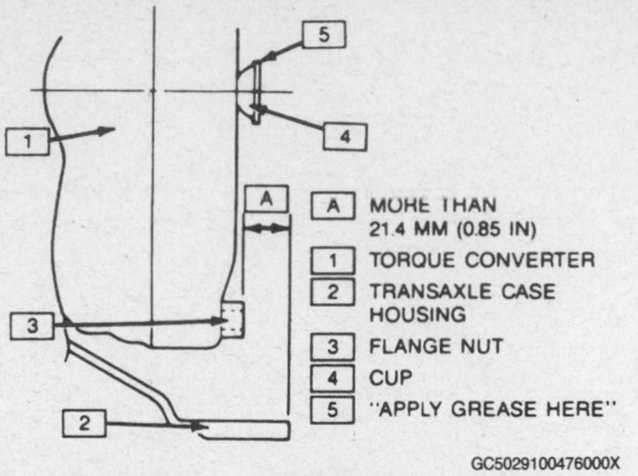
5
1
4
A
A MORE THAN 21.4 MM (0.85 IN)
1 TORQUE CONVERTER
2 TRANSAXLE CASE HOUSING
3 FLANGE NUT
4 CUP
5 "APPLY GREASE HERE"
3
2
GC5029100476000X

Fig. 35 Torque converter installation

TIGHTENING SPECIFICATIONS

Component	Torque/Ft. Lbs.
Automatic Transaxle Controller Retaining Bolts	11
Ball Stud Nuts & Bolts	44
Direct Clutch Solenoid Retaining Bolt	35①
Engine Wiring Harness Bracket Bolts	12
Filler Tube Bracket Bolt	53①
Fluid Filter Screen Bolts	53①
Flywheel Cover Bolts	89①
Flywheel To Torque Converter Bolts	14
Inlet & Outlet Union Bolts	20
Left Transaxle Mount Bracket Bolts	40
Left Transaxle Mount Retaining Nuts	40
Lower Valve Body Cover Bolts	②
Lower Engine To Transaxle Retaining Bolt	40
Lower Rear Engine Mount To Bulkhead Bolt	40
Lower Valve Body Bolts	106①
Negative Battery Cable To Negative Battery Terminal Retainer	11
Negative Battery Cable To Transaxle Case Bolt	11
Rear Engine Mount Bracket Bolts & Nuts	40

Component	Torque/Ft. Lbs.
Rear Engine Torque Rod Assembly Bolts	40
Second Brake Solenoid Retaining Bolt	35①
Selector Lever Assembly Housing Seat Nuts	25
Shift Lever Back-up & Neutral Safety Switch Mounting Bolt	17
Shift Select Cable Bulkhead Grommet Bolts	15
Solenoid Wiring Harness Retaining Bracket Bolt	15
Solenoid Wiring Harness Retaining Plate Nut	15
Speedometer Driven Gear Case Bolt	11
Starter Motor Bolts	17
Stoplamp Switch Adjustment Locknut	11
Transaxle Cooler Pipe Retaining Bracket Bolt	20
Transaxle Drain Plug	17
Transaxle Fluid Pan Bolts	53①
Upper Rear Transaxle Mount To Bulkhead Bolt	40
Upper Transaxle To Engine Retaining Bolts	40
Upper Valve Body Bolts	53①
Vehicle Speed Sensor Retaining Bolt	17

①—Inch lbs.
②—Refer to text.

KF 400 & JF403E Automatic Transaxles (Storm)

INDEX

IDENTIFICATION

The transaxle identification number for the JF403E is located on top of the transaxle near the transaxle VIN plate and on the KF 400, the identification number is located at the front left side of the transaxle near the engine, **Fig. 1.**

DESCRIPTION

KF 400

The KF 400 is a 3-speed automatic

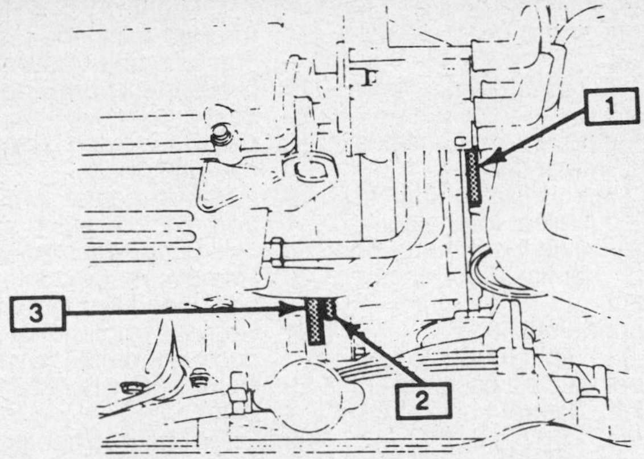
1
2
3

1 TRANSAXLE NUMBER (4 SPEED AUTOMATIC)
2 TRANSAXLE NUMBER (3 SPEED AUTOMATIC AND MANUAL)
3 ENGINE IDENTIFICATION NUMBER

GC5028900496000X

Fig. 1 Transaxle identification number location

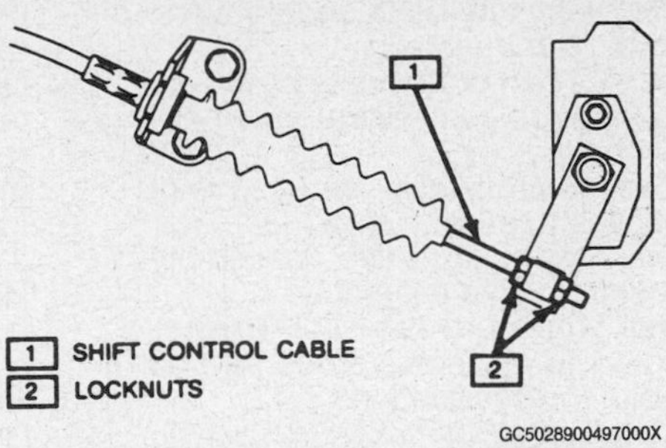
1
2
1 SHIFT CONTROL CABLE
2 LOCKNUTS
GC5028900497000X

Fig. 2 Shift cable adjustment

transaxle. Power is transferred from the output gear through the ring gear to the idler gear.

The output gear, idler gear and differential gear case are supported by tapered roller bearings. The preload on the roller bearings can be adjusted by using shims.

The final drive gear is a helical type design.

JF403E

The JF403E is a 4-speed automatic transaxle. This transaxle utilizes a microcomputer as a control unit to evaluate driving conditions including throttle opening and vehicle speed.

This transaxle also incorporates a shift mode change control. The economy mode (ECON switch ON) is suitable for economical driving. The normal mode (ECON switch OFF) is suitable for hill climbing and/or acceleration.

MAINTENANCE

Refer to "Lubricant Data Chart" in the appropriate chassis chapter of this manual for transmission fluid specifications.

Check transaxle fluid level every 7,500 miles, adding fluid as necessary.

Change transaxle fluid and filter every 30,000 miles under normal driving conditions, or every 15,000 miles if vehicle is operated under severe conditions such as city driving during hot weather or driving over hilly or mountainous terrain.

FLUID CHECK

1. Park vehicle on level ground.
2. Start engine and operate for 15 minutes to allow fluid to reach operating temperature.
3. Move gear selector through all gear positions, then to park.
4. Remove and check fluid level on dipstick, add as necessary. **Do not over fill.**

FLUID CHANGE

1. Raise and support vehicle.
2. Remove drain plug at bottom of differential and drain fluid.
3. Remove oil pan and discard pan gasket.
4. Clean drain pan, then using a new gasket, install gasket and pan to transaxle. Torque pan bolts to specifications.
5. Install drain plug and **torque** to 20 ft. lbs., then fill transaxle through oil filler tube with automatic transmission fluid.

ADJUSTMENTS

MANUAL LINKAGE

Shift Control Cable

1. Place the ignition key in the LOCK position.
2. Set the gear selector lever in the Park position.
3. Loosen the adjuster nuts at the transaxle **Fig. 2.**
4. Ensure shift lever at the transaxle is in the "PARK" position.
5. Pull the cable forward and tighten forward adjuster nut until it contacts shift lever.
6. Tighten rear adjuster nut until it contacts shift lever, then tighten both adjuster nuts.

Back Drive Cable

1. Place shift lever in Park position.
2. Place ignition switch to the LOCK position.
3. Pull cable forward at shift lever bracket, then tighten forward adjuster nut until contact is made against the bracket.
4. Tighten rear nut until it makes contact with shift lever bracket, then tighten both adjuster nuts.

IN-VEHICLE REPAIRS

SHIFTER CONTROL, REPLACE

1. Disconnect battery ground cable.
2. Remove ashtray, shift trim bezel, heater control knobs, then radio bezel.
3. Remove lower console, then shift knob from lever.
4. Disconnect back drive cable for shift control.
5. Disconnect shift lock out module from shift control, then electrical connections.
6. Disconnect shift control cable from shift control.
7. Remove shift control retaining bolts, then shift control.
8. Remove solenoid and switch assembly from shift control.
9. Reverse procedure to install.

SPEEDOMETER DRIVEN GEAR, REPLACE

1. Disconnect battery ground cable.
2. Remove air breather tube, then air intake duct from air cleaner assembly.
3. Disconnect speedometer cable at transaxle.
4. Remove speedometer driven gear retaining bolt, then gear and O-ring seal.
5. Reverse procedure to install, noting the following:
   a. Replace speedometer O-ring seal.
   b. Torque speedometer driven gear retaining bolt to specifications.

CONTROL VALVE ASSEMBLY, REPLACE

KF 400

1. Disconnect negative battery cable.
2. Raise and support vehicle.
3. Remove left and right undercovers.
4. Drain transaxle fluid.
5. Remove oil pan attaching bolts, then oil pan.
6. Remove control valve assembly bolts, then control valve assembly.
7. Reverse procedure to install, noting the following:
   a. Torque control valve assembly bolts specifications.
   b. Torque oil pan bolts to specifications.
   c. Refill transaxle fluid as described under "Changing Fluid."

JF403E

1. Disconnect negative battery cable, then the terminal assembly connector.
2. Remove the terminal assembly clip.
3. Raise and support vehicle.

4. Remove left and right undercovers, then drain the transaxle.
5. Remove oil pan protector and oil pan.
6. Remove the fifteen control valve assembly bolts.
7. Remove control valve and terminal assemblies from transaxle.
8. Remove terminal valve assembly from control valve assembly.
9. Reverse procedure to install. **Torque** Control valve assembly bolts and oil pan bolts to specifications.

TRANSAXLE

REPLACE

1. Disconnect negative battery cable.
2. Remove battery and battery tray.
3. Remove air duct, then air breather tube from air cleaner assembly.
4. **On KF 400 models,** disconnect vacuum diaphragm at vacuum hose.
5. **On all models,** disconnect electrical connectors from transaxle, then shift cable from lever.
6. Disconnect shift cable bracket from transaxle case.
7. remove breather hose from transaxle, then the speedometer cable.
8. Install engine support fixture tool No. J 28467-A or equivalent to engine.
9. Remove left transaxle mount through bolt, then four transaxle to engine mounting bolts.
10. Raise and support vehicle.
11. Remove left and right undercovers, then front wheel and tire assemblies
12. Disconnect left control arm from steering knuckle.
13. Drain transaxle fluid.
14. Disconnect drive axles from transaxle.
15. Remove front transaxle mount through bolt, then dampener from rear mount through bolt.
16. Remove rear transaxle mount through bolt, then two front center crossmember mounting bolts.
17. Disconnect front pipe to exhaust manifold.
18. Remove two rear crossmember mounting bolts.
19. Remove center crossmember bolts from vehicle, place suitable transaxle jack under transaxle.
20. Remove rear mount to transaxle case bolt, then front mount retaining bolt.
21. Remove front mount bracket from the engine, then the flywheel cover.
22. Remove flywheel to torque converter bolts.
23. Disconnect oil cooler lines from transaxle.
24. Remove two rear mount transaxle bolts, then carefully lower transaxle from vehicle.
25. Reverse procedure to install. Refer to "Tightening Specifications" chart for bolt torques.

TIGHTENING SPECIFICATIONS

Component	Torque/Ft. Lbs.
Automatic Transaxle Control Module Bolts	11
Back-up/Neutral Switch	15
Center Crossmember Bolts	45
Center Crossmember Strut Nut & Bolt	37
Dampner Nut	18
Drive Axle Nuts	137
Fluid Temperature Sensor Bolt③	71①
Fluid Filler Tube Bracket Bolts③	44①
Fluid Filler Tube Retaining Bolt	44①
Fluid Filter Screen Bolts②	53①
Fluid Filter Screen Bolts③	71①
Flywheel Cover Bolts②	89①
Flywheel To Torque Converter Bolts	31
Front Engine Mounting Strut Bracket Bolts	45
Front Engine Mounting Strut Stud Nut	45
Front Engine Mounting Strut Through Bolt & Nut	64
Front Exhaust Pipe Bracket Bolts	32
Front Exhaust Pipe To Catalytic Converter Bolts	32
Front Exhaust Pipe To Exhaust Manifold Nuts	46
Governor Bolts②	71①
Inhibitor Switch Mounting Bolts	26①
Inlet Fluid Cooler Pipe Bracket Bolt②	15
Inlet Fluid Cooler Union Bolt	11
Interlock Cable Adjustment Nuts	35①
Kickdown Switch Locknuts②	44①
Left Transaxle Mount Bolts	29
Left Transaxle Mount Through Bolt	64
Lower Valve Body Bolts	71①
Lower Valve Body To Upper Valve Body Bolts②	26①
Manual Selector Mounting Bolts	20

Component	Torque/Ft. Lbs.
Manual Shift Shaft Nut	20
Negative Battery Cable To Negative Battery Terminal Retainer	11
Oil Pan Bolts②	62①
Oil Pan Bolts③	71①
Outlet Fluid Cooler Union Bolt	11
Positive Battery Cable To Positive Battery Terminal Retainer	11
Rear Engine Mounting Bracket Nut & Bolts	45
Rear Transaxle Mount Bolts	29
Rear Transaxle Mount Through Bolt	64
Shift Select Cable Adjustment Nut	42
Shift Select Cable Cover Bolts	89①
Shift Select Cable Retaining Nuts	20
Speedometer Driven Gear Case Bolt	44①
Stoplamp Switch Locknut②	11
Sub Body Bolts & Nut②	26①
Suction Bolts③	71①
Support Plate Bolts③	71①
Transaxle Solenoid Bolts③	71
Upper Transaxle To Engine Bolts	31
Upper Valve Body Side Plate Bolts②	26①
Valve Body Locating Bolts②	53①
Valve Body Locating Bolts③	71①
Valve Body Mounting Bolts②	89①
Valve Body Mounting Bolts③	71①
Vehicle Speed Sensor Bolt③	53①

①—Inch lbs.
②—KF400
③—JF403E

FRONT WHEEL DRIVE AXLES

INDEX

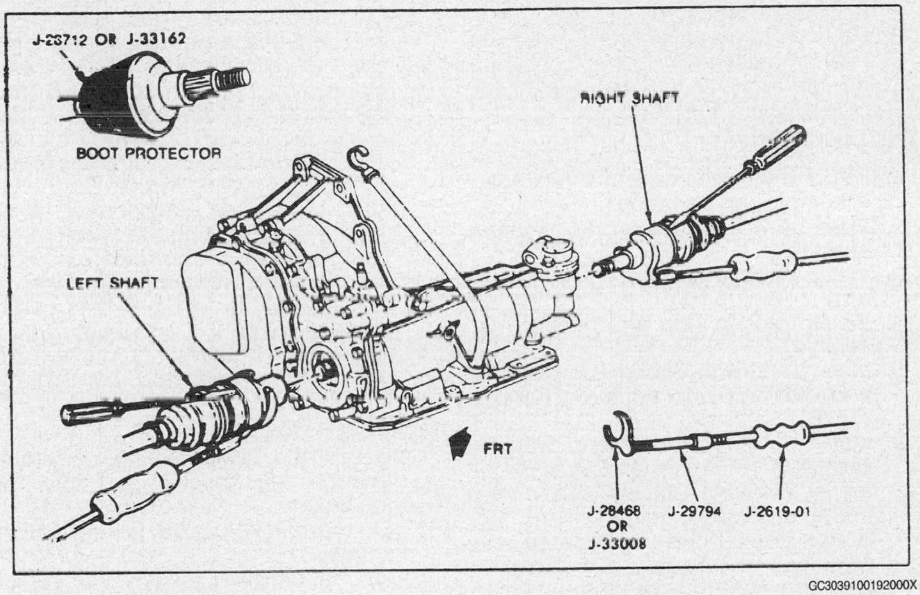
J-28712 OR J-33162
BOOT PROTECTOR
RIGHT SHAFT
LEFT SHAFT
FRT
J-28468
OR
J-33008
J-29794
J-2619-01
GC3039100192000X

Fig. 1 FWD components & axle shaft removal. Except Geo & LeMans

DESCRIPTION

The front wheel drive system, **Figs. 1 and 2,** consists of left and righthand output shafts and drive axles. Each drive axle consists of an axle shaft, with a ball type constant velocity joint at the outboard end and a tri-pot joint at the inboard end.

On all models except Geo and LeMans, a ball type constant velocity joint is used at the outboard end, while a tri-pot type joint is used at the inboard end, **Fig. 3.** Snap rings are used to lock the male splines of the axle shafts into the transaxle gears, except for the left side inboard joint used with the automatic transaxles. The left side inboard joint used on automatic transaxle models utilizes a female spline which installs over a transaxle stub shaft.

On some manual transaxles, a constant velocity joint is used on the inboard end of the drive axle, **Fig. 4.**

On Storm models, a ball type constant velocity joint is used at the outboard end, while a tri-pot type joint is used at the inboard end.

On Metro models, a constant velocity ball joint is used on the outboard side of the drive axle and a constant velocity tripod joint on the inboard side, **Fig. 5.**

TROUBLESHOOTING

CLICKING NOISE IN TURNS

Worn or damaged outboard joint.

CLUNK WHEN ACCELERATING FROM COAST TO DRIVE

Worn or damaged constant velocity joint.

SHUDDER OR VIBRATION DURING ACCELERATION

1. Excessive CV joint angle.
2. Incorrect toe in or out.
3. Incorrect trim height.
4. Worn or damaged inboard or outboard CV joints.
5. Sticking tri-pot joint spider assembly.

VIBRATION AT HIGHWAY SPEEDS

1. Out-of-balance front tires or wheels.
2. Out-of-round front tires.
3. Worn CV joint.
4. Binding or tight CV joint.

DRIVESHAFT

REPLACE

On models equipped with tri-pot joints on inboard axles, care must be taken not to overextend joints. When either or both ends are disconnected, overextending the tri-pot joint could result in internal joint separation.

On vehicles equipped with ball type constant velocity inboard joints, install inner drive joint seal protector tool No. J-34754, or equivalent, on inboard seal and install axle boot protector tool No. J-28712, or equivalent, on outboard seal if necessary. On vehicles equipped with tri-pot inboard joints, install axle boot seal protector tool No. J-28712, or equivalent, on outboard seal and tool No. J-33162, or equivalent, on inboard seal, if necessary.

ELDORADO, RIVIERA, SEVILLE, TORONADO & TROFEO

Removal

1. Remove hub nut, then raise and support vehicle and remove wheel and tire assembly.
2. Remove brake caliper and rotor assembly.
3. Remove stabilizer link or stabilizer bar from control arm.
4. Remove tie rod end at steering knuckle, then remove lower ball joint stud at steering knuckle.
5. Remove axle from transaxle using a prybar or screwdriver and a wood block as a fulcrum to protect case cover.
6. Drive axle from hub and bearing assembly using drive axle spindle remover tool No. J-28733, or equivalent.
7. Remove axle from vehicle.

Installation

1. Install drive axle at steering knuckle.
2. Install lower ball joint stud at steering knuckle.
3. Install stabilizer link or stabilizer bar to lower control arm.
4. Install tie rod end at steering knuckle.
5. Install brake caliper, rotor and new caliper mounting bolts.
6. Install new torque prevailing nut and washer.
7. Insert a screwdriver or drift into caliper and rotor to prevent rotor from turning, then install hub nut and **torque** to 183 ft. lbs., **Fig. 6.**
8. Seat the drive axle into the transaxle by placing a screwdriver into the groove on the joint housing and tapping until seated, then grasp the inner housing and pull outward. If the snap ring is properly seated, the axle will remain in place, **Fig. 2.**
9. Install the front wheel and tire assembly and lower vehicle.

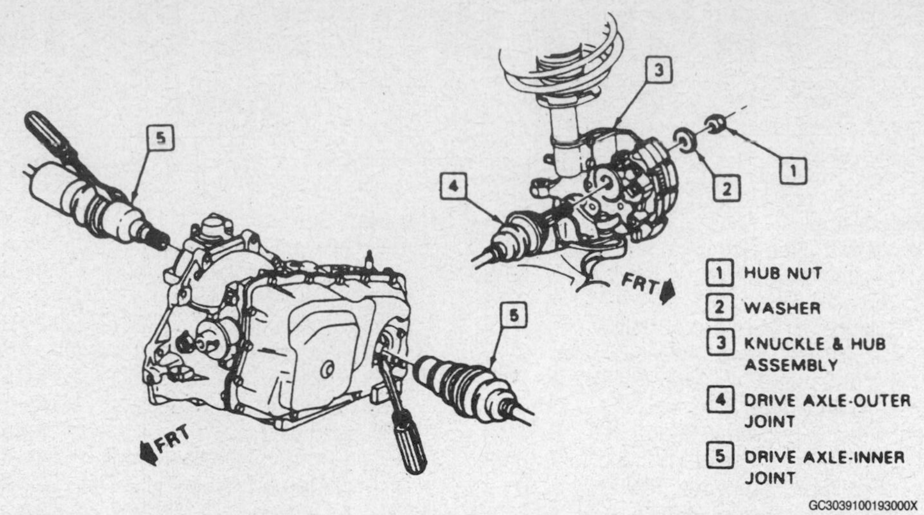
5
3
4
2
1
FRT
5
FRT
1 HUB NUT
2 WASHER
3 KNUCKLE & HUB ASSEMBLY
4 DRIVE AXLE-OUTER JOINT
5 DRIVE AXLE-INNER JOINT
GC3039100193000X

Fig. 2 FWD components & axle shaft installation. Except Metro & Storm (Typical)

BONNEVILLE, CAVALIER, CENTURY, CUTLASS CIERA, CUTLASS CRUISER, LESABRE, PARK AVENUE, SKYLARK, SUNBIRD, 88 & 98

Removal

1. Raise and support vehicle, then remove tire and wheel assembly.
2. Install a brass drift or a screwdriver to prevent the rotor from turning, **Fig. 6.**
3. Remove shaft nut and washer using shaft nut socket tool No. J-34826, or equivalent.
4. Remove brake caliper from steering knuckle and suspend caliper assembly.
5. Remove rotor from hub and bearing assembly, then stabilizer shaft or link from control arm.
6. Remove ball joint from steering knuckle.
7. Remove drive axle from transaxle using axle shaft remover tool Nos. J-33008, J-29794 and slide hammer tool No. J-2619-01, or equivalents, if necessary, **Fig. 1.**
8. Remove drive axle from hub and bearing assembly using front hub spindle remover tool No. J-28733-A, or equivalent, **Fig. 7.**

Installation

1. Install drive axle into hub and bearing assembly and transaxle.
2. Install lower ball joint to steering knuckle.
3. Install stabilizer shaft or link to control arm.
4. Install rotor to hub and bearing assembly.
5. Insert a screwdriver or drift into caliper and rotor to prevent rotor from turning, **Fig. 6.**
6. Install a new hub nut and washer, **torque** to 185 ft. lbs. On Cavalier, Celebrity, Century, Cutlass, Grand Am, LeSabre, Skylark and Sunbird. On Bonneville, 88 and 98, LeSabre and Park Avenue **torque** to 192 ft. lbs.
7. Seat the drive axle into the transaxle by placing a screwdriver into the groove on the joint housing and tapping until seated.
8. Ensure drive axle is seated by pulling outward on the housing. **Do not pull on drive axle.**
9. Install tire and wheel assembly and lower vehicle.

CUTLASS SUPREME, GRAND PRIX, LUMINA & REGAL

Removal

1. Raise and support vehicle, then remove tire and wheel assembly.
2. Remove brake caliper and bracket assembly, then the rotor.
3. Remove the four bolts holding the hub/bearing assembly to the knuckle.
4. **On models equipped with Anti-Lock Brake System (ABS),** remove the ABS sensor mounting bolt, then position the sensor aside to avoid damage.
5. **On models equipped with 125C and HM-282 transaxles and right shaft of vehicles with 440-T4 transaxles,** separate the drive axle from the transaxle using axle shaft remover tool No. J-3308, extension tool No. J-29794 and puller tool No. J-2619-01, or equivalents, **Fig. 1.** On the left shaft of vehicles equipped with 440-T4 transaxles, using the frame for leverage, separate the drive axle from the transaxle with a screwdriver or prybar in the groove provided on the inner joint, **Fig. 2.**
6. **On all models,** remove the axle/bearing assembly through the knuckle.

Installation

1. Install the axle/bearing assembly through the knuckle and into the transaxle.
2. **On models with ABS,** install ABS assembly.
3. **On all models,** loosely secure the bearing to knuckle bolts.
4. Seat the drive axle into the transaxle by placing a screwdriver into the groove on the joint housing and tapping until seated, then grasp the inner housing and pull outward. If the snap ring is properly seated, the axle will remain in place, **Fig. 2.**
5. Using a new nut and washer, install the hub and bearing assembly to axle, **torque** hub and bearing assembly to knuckle attaching bolts to 52 ft. lbs.
6. Install rotor and brake assembly.
7. Install tire and wheel assembly.
8. **Torque** drive axle nut to 184 ft. lbs, then lower vehicle.

DEVILLE & FLEETWOOD (FWD)

Removal

1. Raise and support vehicle, then remove tire and wheel assembly.

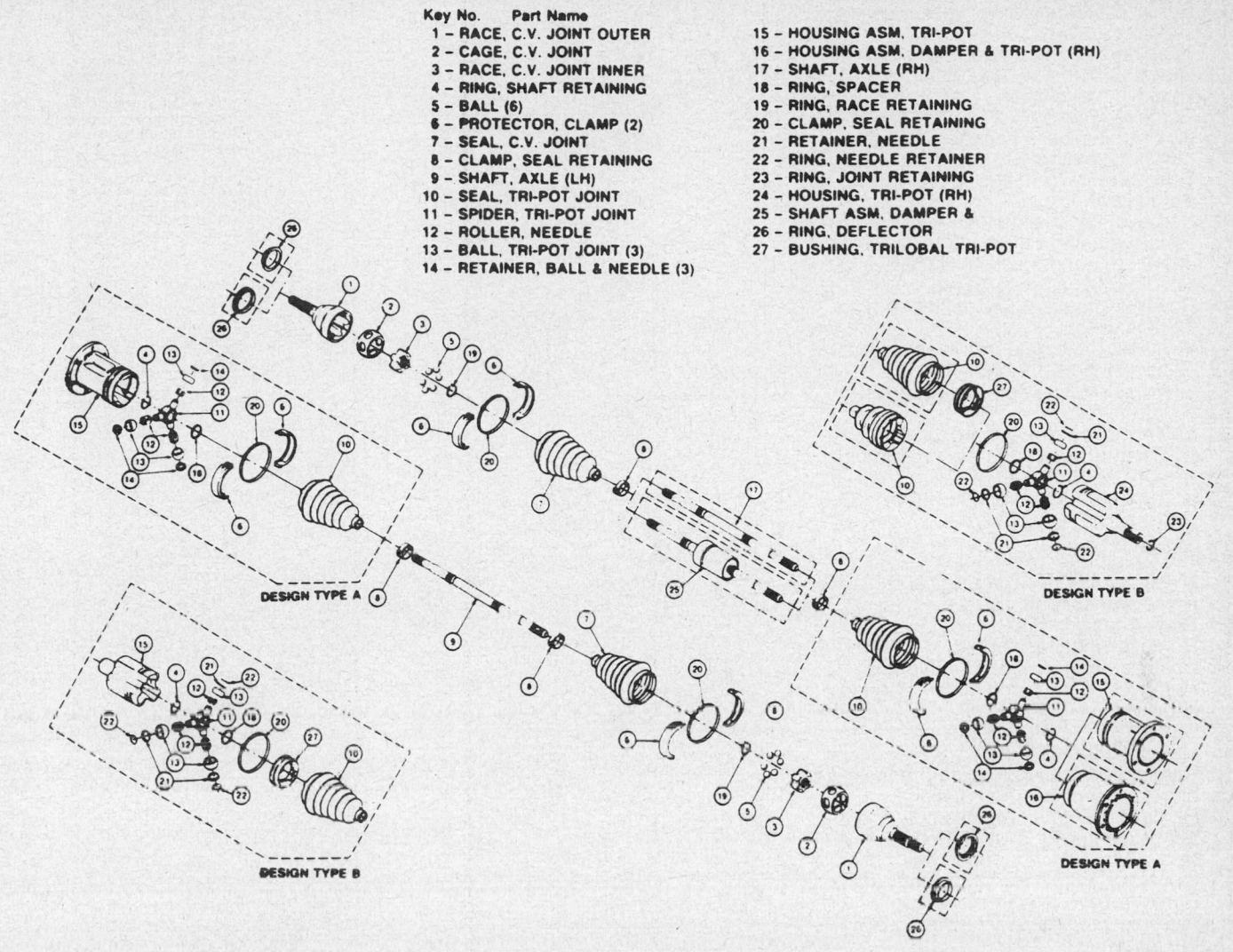

Key No.	Part Name	Key No.	Part Name
1	RACE, C.V. JOINT OUTER	15	HOUSING ASM, TRI-POT
2	CAGE, C.V. JOINT	16	HOUSING ASM, DAMPER & TRI-POT (RH)
3	RACE, C.V. JOINT INNER	17	SHAFT, AXLE (RH)
4	RING, SHAFT RETAINING	18	RING, SPACER
5	BALL (6)	19	RING, RACE RETAINING
6	PROTECTOR, CLAMP (2)	20	CLAMP, SEAL RETAINING
7	SEAL, C.V. JOINT	21	RETAINER, NEEDLE
8	CLAMP, SEAL RETAINING	22	RING, NEEDLE RETAINER
9	SHAFT, AXLE (LH)	23	RING, JOINT RETAINING
10	SEAL, TRI-POT JOINT	24	HOUSING, TRI-POT (RH)
11	SPIDER, TRI-POT JOINT	25	SHAFT ASM, DAMPER &
12	ROLLER, NEEDLE	26	RING, DEFLECTOR
13	BALL, TRI-POT JOINT (3)	27	BUSHING, TRILOBAL TRI-POT
14	RETAINER, BALL & NEEDLE (3)		

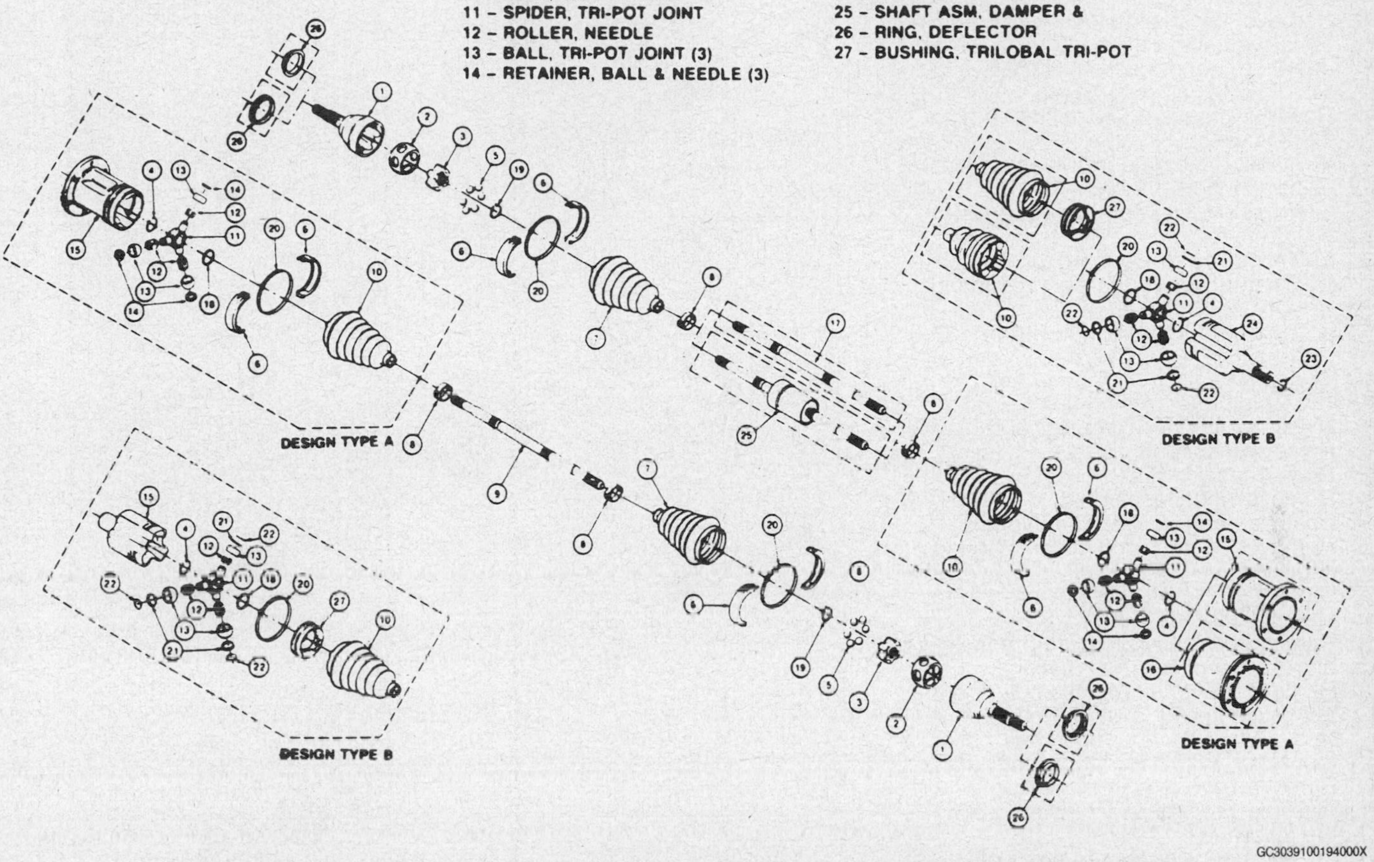
DESIGN TYPE A
DESIGN TYPE B
DESIGN TYPE B
DESIGN TYPE A
GC3039100194000X

Fig. 3 Exploded view of drive axle w/tri-pot inboard joint. Except Geo & LeMans

2. Install a brass drift or a screwdriver to prevent the rotor from turning, **Fig. 6.**
3. Remove shaft nut and washer.
4. Remove lower ball joint cotter and nut, then loosen ball joint using ball joint separator tool No. J-29330, or equivalent. If removing right axle, turn wheel to left, if removing left axle, turn wheel to the right.
5. Separate the joint by using a pry bar between the suspension support and lower control arm.
6. Pull out on lower knuckle area and with a plastic or rubber mallet strike the end of the axle shaft to disengage axle from hub and bearing.
7. Separate hub and bearing assembly from drive axle and move strut and knuckle assembly rearward.
8. **On models equipped with intermediate shaft,** remove inner joint from transaxle using axle shaft remover tool Nos. J-28468 or J-33008, or equivalents, **Fig. 1.**

Installation

1. Seat the drive axle into the transaxle by placing a screwdriver into the groove on the joint housing and tapping until seated, then grasp the inner housing and pull outward. If the snap ring is properly seated, the axle will remain in place, **Fig. 2.**
2. Drive axle into hub and bearing assembly.
3. Install lower ball joint to knuckle, **torque** to 41-50 ft. lbs., then install cotter pin.
4. Install washer and new shaft nut.
5. Insert a screwdriver or drift into caliper and rotor to prevent rotor from turning, **Fig. 6.**
6. Install hub nut, **torque** to 192 ft. lbs.
7. Install tire and wheel assembly and lower vehicle.

METRO

1. Remove wheel center cap.
2. Remove caulking, driveshaft nut and washer.
3. Raise and support vehicle.
4. Remove wheel and tire assembly.
5. Drain transaxle fluid.
6. Pry inboard driveshaft from transaxle using a large screwdriver or equivalent.
7. Remove lower ball joint retaining nut, then separate suspension arm from steering knuckle.
8. Remove drive axle assembly from transaxle, then from steering knuckle.
9. Reverse procedure to install, noting the following:
   a. Clean front wheel bearing seal, then apply grease to seal.
   b. Check seal for breakage or deterioration, replace if necessary.
   c. Apply sealant to drain plug for manual transaxle.
   d. Install the wheel side joint to the steering knuckle, then the differential-side joint to the transaxle. Push drive axle into transaxle by hand until snap ring is seated in spline. **Torque** hub nut to 129 ft. lbs. and ball joint stud bolt to 44 ft. lbs.

PRIZM

1. Disconnect battery ground cable.
2. Raise and support vehicle.
3. Drain transaxle fluid.
4. Remove hub nut cap, then cotter pin, hub nut and washer.
5. Remove tie rod end from steering knuckle.

6. Remove brake caliper from steering knuckle.
7. Disconnect control arm from steering knuckle.
8. Remove brake rotor.
9. Remove drive axle from hub assembly using a plastic hammer. **If shaft is difficult to remove, use crankshaft gear puller tool No. J 25287, or equivalent.**
10. Remove drive axle assembly from transaxle using slide hammer tool No. J 6125-1B and axle shaft puller tool No. J 35762, or equivalents.
11. Reverse procedure to install, noting the following:
    a. Install drive axle in transaxle first, then hub assembly.
    b. **Torque** lower control arm bolts to 105 ft. lbs.
    c. **Torque** tie rod end nut to 36 ft. lbs.
    d. **Torque** brake caliper mounting bolts to 65 ft. lbs.
    e. **Torque** drive axle hub nut to 137 ft.lbs.

STORM

1. Disconnect battery ground cable.
2. Raise and support vehicle.
3. Drain transaxle fluid.
4. Remove wheel assembly.
5. Unstake hub nut, then remove nut.
6. Remove tie rod end from steering knuckle.
7. Disconnect lower control arm from steering knuckle.
8. Remove drive axle from hub assembly, using a plastic hammer.
9. Remove drive axle assembly from transaxle, using slide hammer tool Nos. J 2619-01 and axle shaft puller tool No. J 35762, or equivalents.
10. Remove drive axle from vehicle.
11. Reverse procedure to install, noting the following:
    a. **Torque** lower control arm bolts to 115 ft. lbs.
    b. **Torque** tie rod end to 40 ft. lbs.
    c. **Torque** hub nut to 137 ft. lbs., then stake nut.

LEMANS

Removal

1. Loosen both upper strut mount attaching bolts.
2. Remove wheel cover, then loosen wheel lug nuts and remove cotter pin and drive axle shaft-to-hub nut and washer.
3. Raise and support vehicle.
4. Remove wheel and tire assembly.
5. Remove ball joint retaining clip and stud nut, then separate ball joint from steering knuckle using ball joint separator tool No. J-36226, or equivalent. **Disregard "This Side Towards Wheel" marking on tool. Tool must be turned to opposite position when used on these vehicles.**
6. Remove tie rod nut, then separate tie rod from steering knuckle using tie rod separator tool No. J-24319-01, or equivalent.
7. Separate drive axle shaft from wheel hub using axle shaft to hub separator tool No. J-37105, or equivalent.

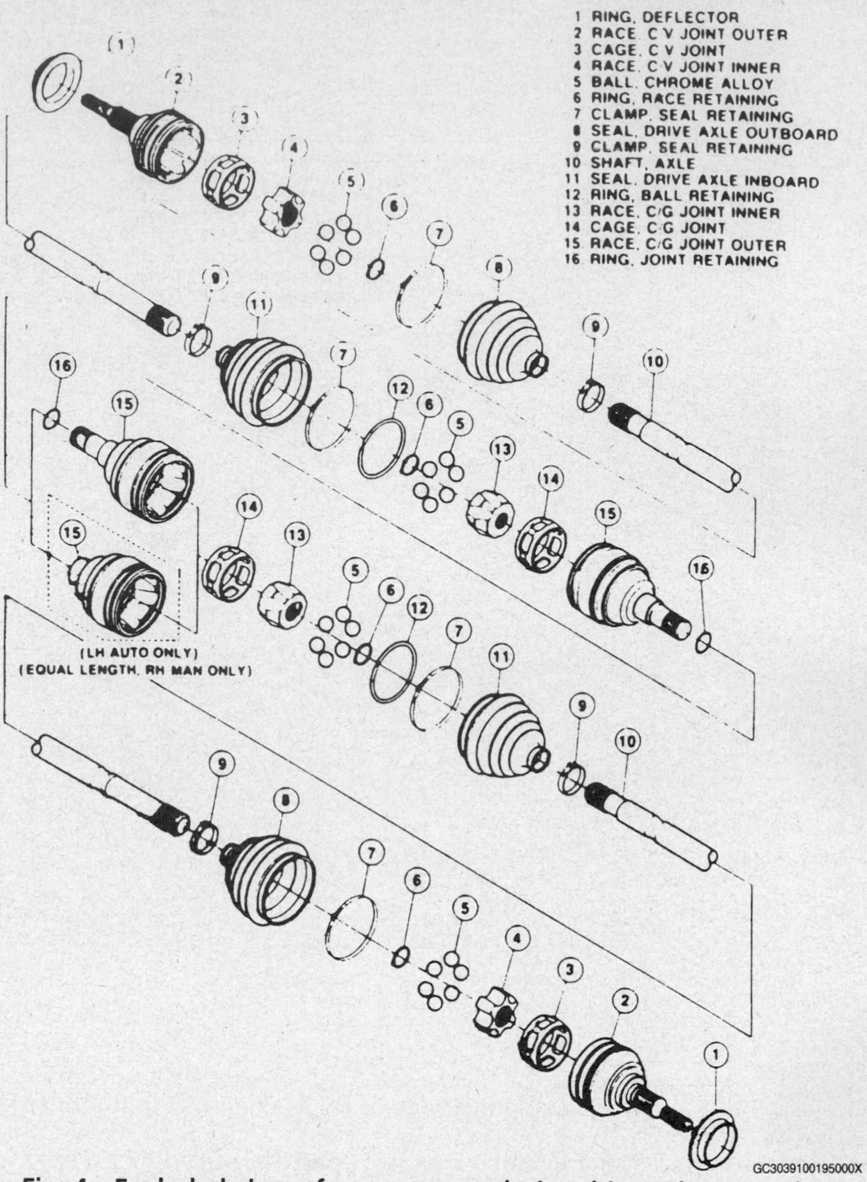
1 RING, DEFLECTOR
2 RACE, C V JOINT OUTER
3 CAGE, C V JOINT
4 RACE, C V JOINT INNER
5 BALL, CHROME ALLOY
6 RING, RACE RETAINING
7 CLAMP, SEAL RETAINING
8 SEAL, DRIVE AXLE OUTBOARD
9 CLAMP, SEAL RETAINING
10 SHAFT, AXLE
11 SEAL, DRIVE AXLE INBOARD
12 RING, BALL RETAINING
13 RACE, C/G JOINT INNER
14 CAGE, C/G JOINT
15 RACE, C/G JOINT OUTER
16 RING, JOINT RETAINING
(LH AUTO ONLY)
(EQUAL LENGTH, RH MAN ONLY)
GC3039100195000X

Fig. 4 Exploded view of cross-groove design drive axle. Manual transaxle except Geo & LeMans

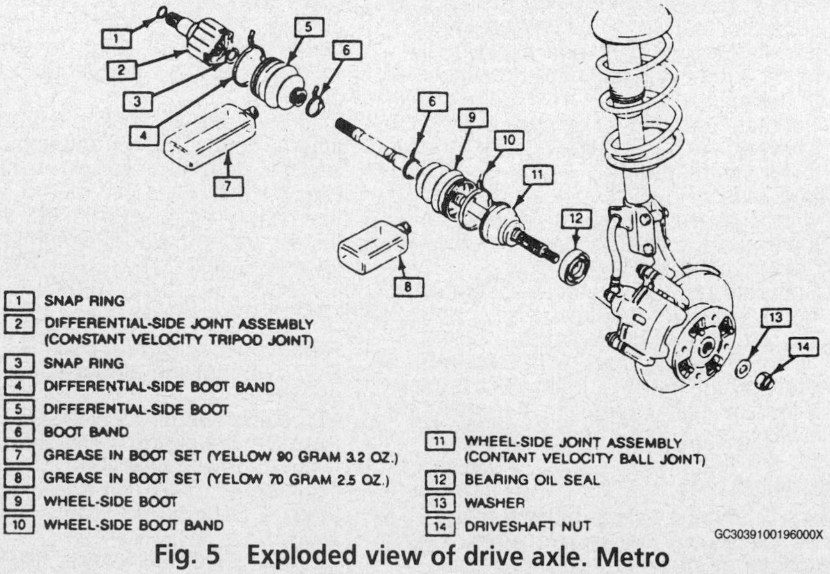
1 SNAP RING
2 DIFFERENTIAL-SIDE JOINT ASSEMBLY (CONSTANT VELOCITY TRIPOD JOINT)
3 SNAP RING
4 DIFFERENTIAL-SIDE BOOT BAND
5 DIFFERENTIAL-SIDE BOOT
6 BOOT BAND
7 GREASE IN BOOT SET (YELLOW 90 GRAM 3.2 OZ.)
8 GREASE IN BOOT SET (YELOW 70 GRAM 2.5 OZ.)
9 WHEEL-SIDE BOOT
10 WHEEL-SIDE BOOT BAND
11 WHEEL-SIDE JOINT ASSEMBLY (CONTANT VELOCITY BALL JOINT)
12 BEARING OIL SEAL
13 WASHER
14 DRIVESHAFT NUT
GC3039100196000X

Fig. 5 Exploded view of drive axle. Metro

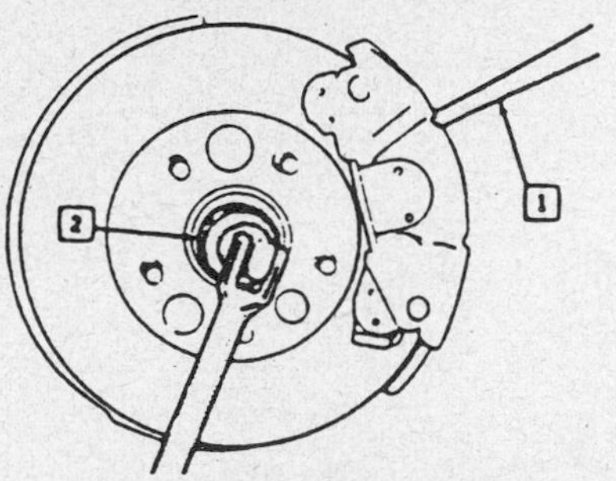
1. DRIFT PUNCH
2. 6 POINT DEEP WELL SOCKET
1
2
GC3039100197000X

Fig. 6 Axle shaft nut replacement

8. Position a drain pan under transaxle, then remove drive axle from transaxle using axle shaft to transaxle separator tool No. J-36639 and slide hammer tool No. J-23907, or equivalents.

Installation

1. Install drive axle into transaxle, using care to avoid damaging seal. Pull on outer joint race to ensure it will not come out of transaxle.
2. Install drive axle into knuckle hub bearing.
3. Install steering knuckle onto lower ball joint, then connect tie rod to the knuckle. **Torque** tie rod nut to 45 ft. lbs. and ball joint stud nut to 50 ft. lbs., then tie rod nut cotter pin and stud nut retaining clip.
4. Install drive axle shaft-to-wheel hub washer and nut.
5. Install wheel and tire assembly, then lower vehicle.
6. With weight of vehicle on wheels, **torque** new drive axle-to-hub nut to 74 ft. lbs., then back off nut and **retorque** to 15 ft. lbs. Tighten nut an additional 1/4 turn, then install cotter pin. If necessary, loosen nut slightly to align cotter pin holes.
7. **Torque** upper strut mount attaching nuts to 22 ft. lbs.
8. Check transaxle fluid and replenish as needed.

BERETTA & CORSICA

Removal

1. Disconnect battery ground cable.
2. Raise and support vehicle, then remove wheel and tire assembly.
3. Install drive axle seal protector tool No. J-34754, or equivalent, on outer joint.
4. Insert a screwdriver or drift into caliper and rotor to prevent rotor from turning and remove hub nut and washer, **Fig. 6.**
5. Remove lower ball joint cotter pin and nut, then loosen joint using tool No. J-29330, or equivalent. If right axle is being removed, turn wheel to left, if left axle is being removed, turn wheel to right.
6. Insert a prybar between suspension support and lower control arm and separate joint.
7. Disengage axle from hub and bearing using tool No. J-28733-A, or equivalent.
8. Separate hub and bearing assembly from drive axle and move strut and knuckle assembly rearward.
9. Remove inner joint from transaxle or intermediate shaft (if equipped) using tool No. J-28468 or J-33008 attached to tool Nos. J-29794 and J-2619-01, or equivalents.
10. Remove drive axle from vehicle.

Installation

1. Install seal protector tool No. J-37292-B, or equivalents, into transaxle.
2. Install drive axle into the transaxle by placing a screwdriver into the groove on the joint housing and tapping until seated, then grasp the inner housing and pull outward. If the snap ring is properly seated, the axle will remain in place, **Fig. 2.**
3. Lubricate inside diameter of seal lips and completely fill cavity between hub and bearing assembly and seal with chassis grease.
4. Install drive axle into hub and bearing assembly and lower ball joint to knuckle.
5. **Torque** ball joint to steering knuckle nut to 26 ft. lbs. plus 60° rotation, then install cotter pin.
6. Insert a screwdriver or drift into caliper and rotor to prevent rotor from turning and install hub nut and washer, **Fig. 6.**
7. **Torque** hub nut to 192 ft. lbs.
8. Remove both seal protectors and install wheel and tire assembly.
9. Lower vehicle and connect battery ground cable.

ACHIEVA, GRAND AM & SKYLARK

Removal

1. Disconnect battery ground cable.
2. Raise and support vehicle, then remove wheel and tire assembly.
3. Install drive axle seal protector tool No. J-34754, or equivalent, on outer joint.
4. Insert a screwdriver or drift into caliper and rotor to prevent rotor from turning and remove hub nut and washer, **Fig. 6.**
5. Remove lower ball joint cotter pin and nut, then loosen joint using tool No. J-29330, or equivalent. If right axle is being removed, turn wheel to left, if left axle is being removed, turn wheel to right.
6. Insert a prybar between suspension support and lower control arm and separate joint.
7. Disengage axle from hub and bearing using tool No. J-28733-A, or equivalent.
8. Separate hub and bearing assembly from drive axle and move strut and knuckle assembly rearward.
9. Remove inner joint from transaxle or intermediate shaft (if equipped) using tool No. J-28468 or J-33008 attached

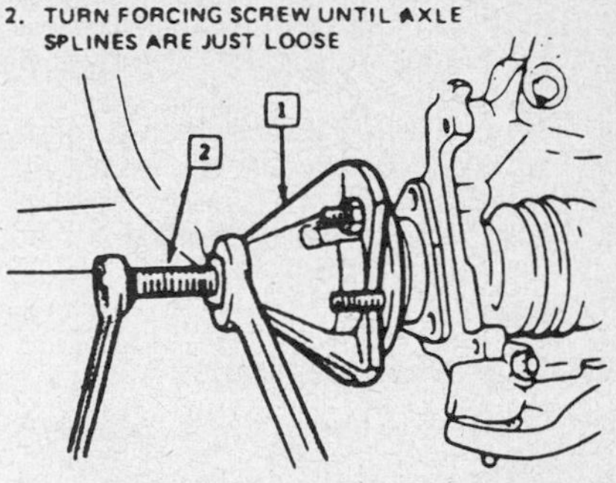
1. J-28733
2. TURN FORCING SCREW UNTIL AXLE SPLINES ARE JUST LOOSE
1
2
GC3039100198000X

Fig. 7 Drive axle from hub & bearing assembly removal

to tool Nos. J-29794 and J-2619-01, or equivalents.
10. Remove drive axle from vehicle.

Installation

1. Install seal protector tool No. J-37292-B, or equivalent, into transaxle.
2. Install drive axle into the transaxle by placing a screwdriver into the groove on the joint housing and tapping until seated, then grasp the inner housing and pull outward. If the snap ring is properly seated, the axle will remain in place, **Fig. 2.**
3. Lubricate inside diameter of seal lips and completely fill cavity between hub and bearing assembly and seal with chassis grease.
4. Install drive axle into hub and bearing assembly and lower ball joint to knuckle.
5. **Torque** ball joint to steering knuckle nut to 41-50 ft. lbs.
6. Insert a screwdriver or drift into caliper and rotor to prevent rotor from turning and install hub nut and washer, **Fig. 6.**
7. **Torque** hub nut to 185 ft. lbs.
8. Remove both seal protectors and install wheel and tire assembly.
9. Lower vehicle and connect battery ground cable.

DRIVESHAFT SERVICE

Inner Constant Velocity Joint & Seal Replacement

DISASSEMBLE

LEMANS

1. Secure axle shaft in a soft-jawed vise.
2. Cut off seal clamps and remove seals, then spread bearing retaining rings, **Fig. 8.**
3. Mark relationship between shaft and joints for assembly reference, then tap joints off shaft using a plastic mallet.
4. Inspect all components for excessive wear or damage and replace as necessary.

METRO

Do not disassemble outboard joint or differential side ball joint. If any malfunction is detected in these components, replace as an assembly.

1. Remove tripod joint boot band, **Fig. 5.**
2. Remove tripod joint housing.
3. Using snap ring pliers, remove snap ring from shaft.
4. Remove tripod joint spider from shaft.
5. Remove boot band from inner driveshaft joint, then boot.
6. Release boot bands from outer boot, then remove boot.

STORM

Double Offset Joint

1. Secure axle assembly in a soft-jawed vise.
2. Remove boot band from differential side joint.
3. Move boot slightly and remove circular clip.
4. Separate case from shaft and remove 6 balls using a suitable screwdriver
5. Turn ball guide on an angle and move it to center shaft side.
6. Remove snap ring from shaft, **Fig. 9,** then slide out ball guide and retainer.
7. Remove boot from shaft, and if necessary, tap damper off shaft with a brass hammer

Tripod Joint

1. Secure axle assembly in a soft-jawed vise.
2. Using a screwdriver, remove boot band from differential side joint.
3. Place alignment marks on both housing and shaft, then remove housing from shaft.
4. Remove snap ring from shaft, then make alignment marks on both shaft and tripod.
5. Using a hammer and brass drift, remove tripod from shaft. **Ensure care is taken not to hit roller.**
6. Remove boot from shaft, and if necessary, tap damper off shaft with brass hammer.

PRIZM

1. Secure axle assembly in a soft-jawed vise.
2. Remove boot retaining clamps, **Fig. 10.**
3. Remove race retaining ring using snap ring pliers.
4. Disconnect inner race from drive axle shaft.
5. Remove boot from axle shaft.
6. Tilt cage, then remove ball bearings.
7. Tilt cage and inner race 90°, then pull from outer race.

ASSEMBLE

Metro

Thoroughly inspect parts for wear prior to assembling. Replace any excessively worn parts. Ensure wheel-side joint assembly and tripod joint housing are washed and air dried, and that the boots are cleaned with a cloth.

1. Apply joint grease liberally to wheel-side joint, **Fig. 11.**
2. Install wheel-side boot on shaft, then fill inside of boot with joint grease, approximately 80 grams.
3. Install boot bands.

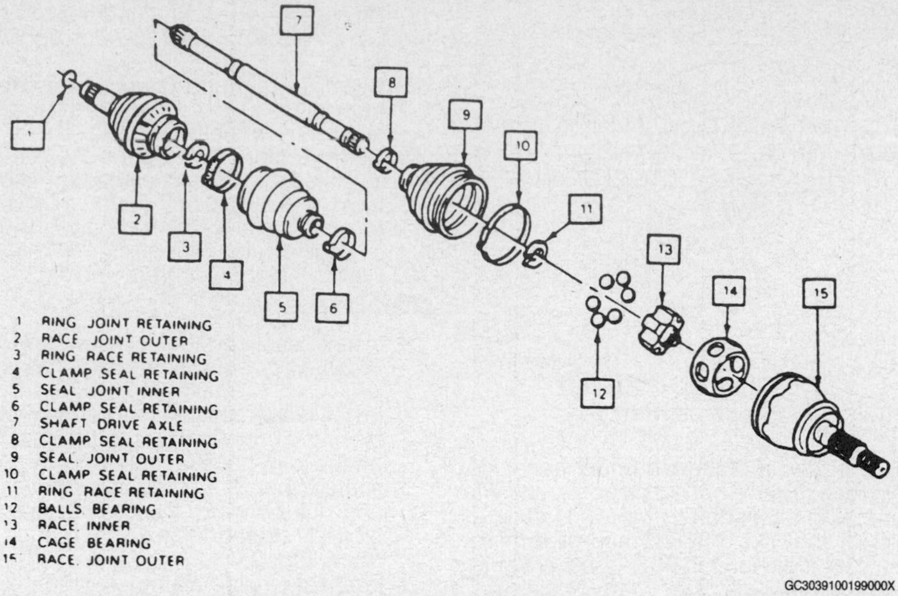
1
2
3
4
5
6
7
8
9
10
11
12
13
14
15
1 RING JOINT RETAINING
2 RACE JOINT OUTER
3 RING RACE RETAINING
4 CLAMP SEAL RETAINING
5 SEAL JOINT INNER
6 CLAMP SEAL RETAINING
7 SHAFT DRIVE AXLE
8 CLAMP SEAL RETAINING
9 SEAL JOINT OUTER
10 CLAMP SEAL RETAINING
11 RING RACE RETAINING
12 BALLS BEARING
13 RACE INNER
14 CAGE BEARING
15 RACE JOINT OUTER
GC3039100199000X

Fig. 8 Exploded view of front drive axle assembly. LeMans

4. Install transaxle-side boot clamp, then boot onto shaft.
5. Apply yellow grease liberally to transaxle-side joint.
6. Install spider joint on shaft with beveled side facing wheel-side joint.
7. Install spider joint snap ring.
8. Fill inside of transaxle-side boot with joint grease, approximately 130 grams.
9. Install spider joint housing, then boot band.
10. Check boots for distortion or dents, correct as necessary.

Storm

1. Install boot clamp on shaft, then boot.
2. Install ball guide and ball retainer on shaft, then snap ring.
3. Move ball guide into place, then install six balls into ball guide.
4. Install circular clip in outer race.
5. Pack one half of joint with GM grease part No.7845393, or equivalent.
6. Remove drive axle from vise.

Prizm

1. Apply GM grease part No. 7845393, or equivalent to tri-pot housing and spider joint.
2. Install boot clamp on drive axle shaft, then boot.
3. Install spider joint assembly on drive axle using a brass drift and hammer.
4. Install outboard snap ring.
5. Install spider assembly in tri-pot housing.
6. Connect boot and boot clamp to tri-pot housing.
7. Remove driveshaft assembly from vise.

LeMans

1. Pack joints with suitable grease, then tap joint assemblies into shaft splines until retaining rings are properly seated.
2. Install inner joint on long side of shaft and outer joint on short side of shaft.
3. Install joint seals and with new clamps. Secure clamps using seal clamp installer tool No. J-22610, or equivalent.

Cross Groove Design Front Axle

For removal and installation procedures refer to **Fig. 12.**

Outer Constant Velocity Joint & Seal Replacement

EXCEPT GEO & LEMANS

For removal and installation procedures refer to **Figs. 13 and 14.**

GEO & LEMANS

For replacement procedure, refer to "Axle Shaft Service, Disassemble."

Inner Tri-Pot Seal Replacement

EXCEPT GEO & LEMANS

For removal and installation procedures, refer to **Figs. 15 and 16.**

GEO & LEMANS

For replacement procedure, refer to "Axle Shaft Service, Disassemble."

Deflector Ring Replacement

EXCEPT GEO & LEMANS

For removal and installation procedures, refer to **Fig. 17.**

GEO & LEMANS

1. Disconnect battery ground cable.
2. Raise and support vehicle.

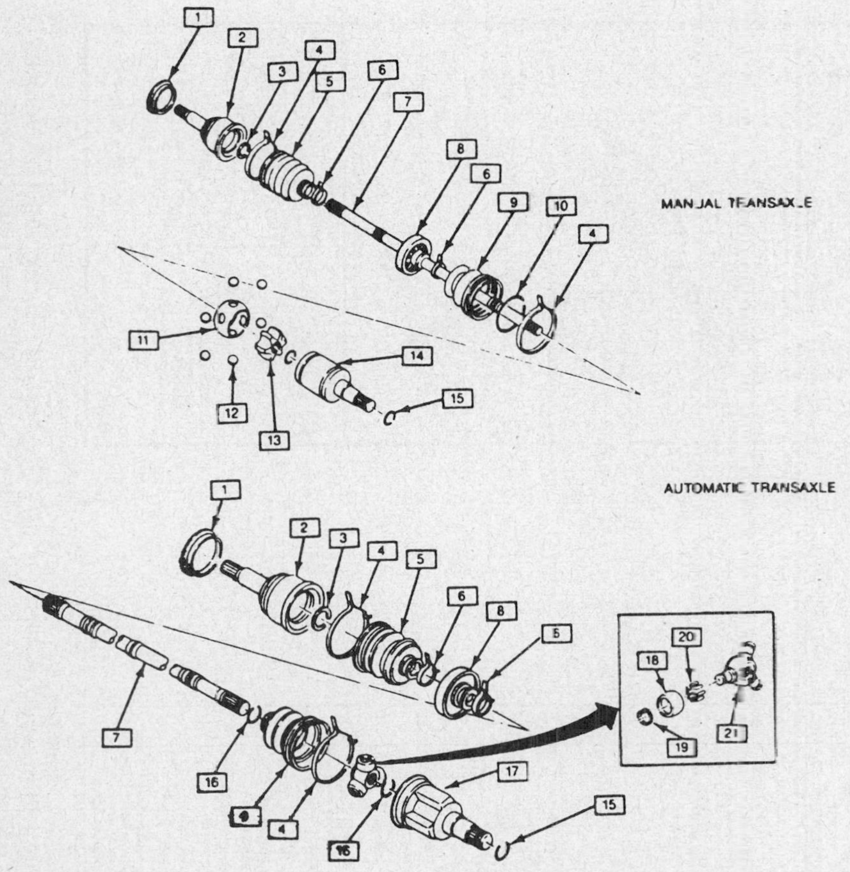
MANUAL TRANSAXLE
AUTOMATIC TRANSAXLE

- 1 DEFLECTOR RING
- 2 CONSTANT VELOCITY JOINT HOUSING
- 3 AXLE SHAFT SNAP RING
- 4 LARGE BOOT CLAMP
- 5 OUTER BOOT
- 6 SMALL BOOT CLAMP
- 7 LEFT-HAND DRIVE AXLE SHAFT
- 8 DRIVE AXLE DAMPENER
- 9 INNER BOOT
- 10 CIRCULAR CLIP
- 11 BALL GUIDE
- 12 BALLS
- 13 BALL RETAINER
- 14 DOUBLE OFFSET JOINT-OUTER RACE
- 15 AXLE SHAFT RETAINING CLIP
- 16 AXLE SHAFT SNAP RING
- 17 TRI-POT JOINT HOUSING
- 18 TRI-POT JOINT BALL
- 19 TRI-POT JOINT BALL AND BEARING RETAINER
- 20 TRI-POT JOINT NEEDLE BEARINGS
- 21 TRI-POT JOINT SPIDER

GC3039 0020000X

Fig. 9 Exploded view of front drive axle assembly. Storm

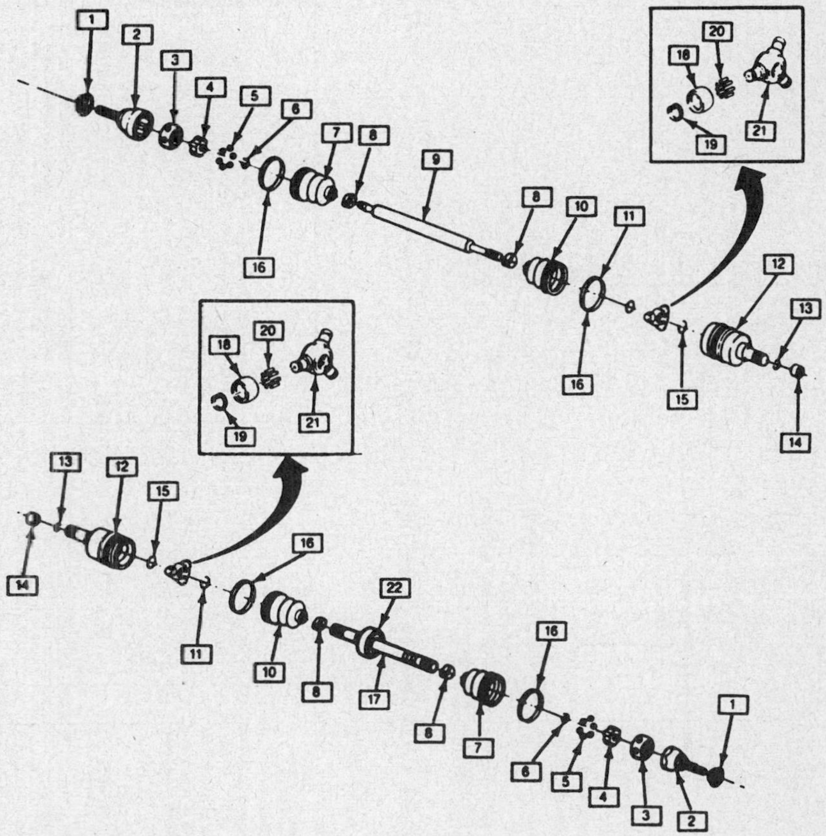

- 1 DEFLECTOR RING
- 2 CONSTANT VELOCITY JOINT OUTER RACE
- 3 CASE
- 4 CONSTANT VELOCITY JOINT INNER RACE
- 5 BALLS
- 6 AXLE SNAFT SHAP RING
- 7 OUTBOARD BOOT
- 8 SMALL BOOT CLAMP
- 9 RIGHT HAND DRIVE AXLE SHAFT
- 10 TRI-POT BOOT
- 11 AXLE SHAFT RETAINING RING
- 12 TRI-POT JOINT HOUSING
- 13 AXLE SHAFT RETAINING PINS
- 14 DRIVE AXLE DUST COVER
- 15 AXLE SHAFT SNAP RING
- 16 LARGE BOOT CLAMPS
- 17 LEFT HAND DRIVE AXLE SHAFT
- 18 TRI-POT JOINT BALL
- 19 TRI-POT JOINT BALL AND BEARING RETAINER
- 20 TRI-POT JOINT NEEDLE BEARINGS
- 21 TRI-POT JOINT SPIDER
- 22 DRIVE AXLE DAMPENER

GC3039100201000X

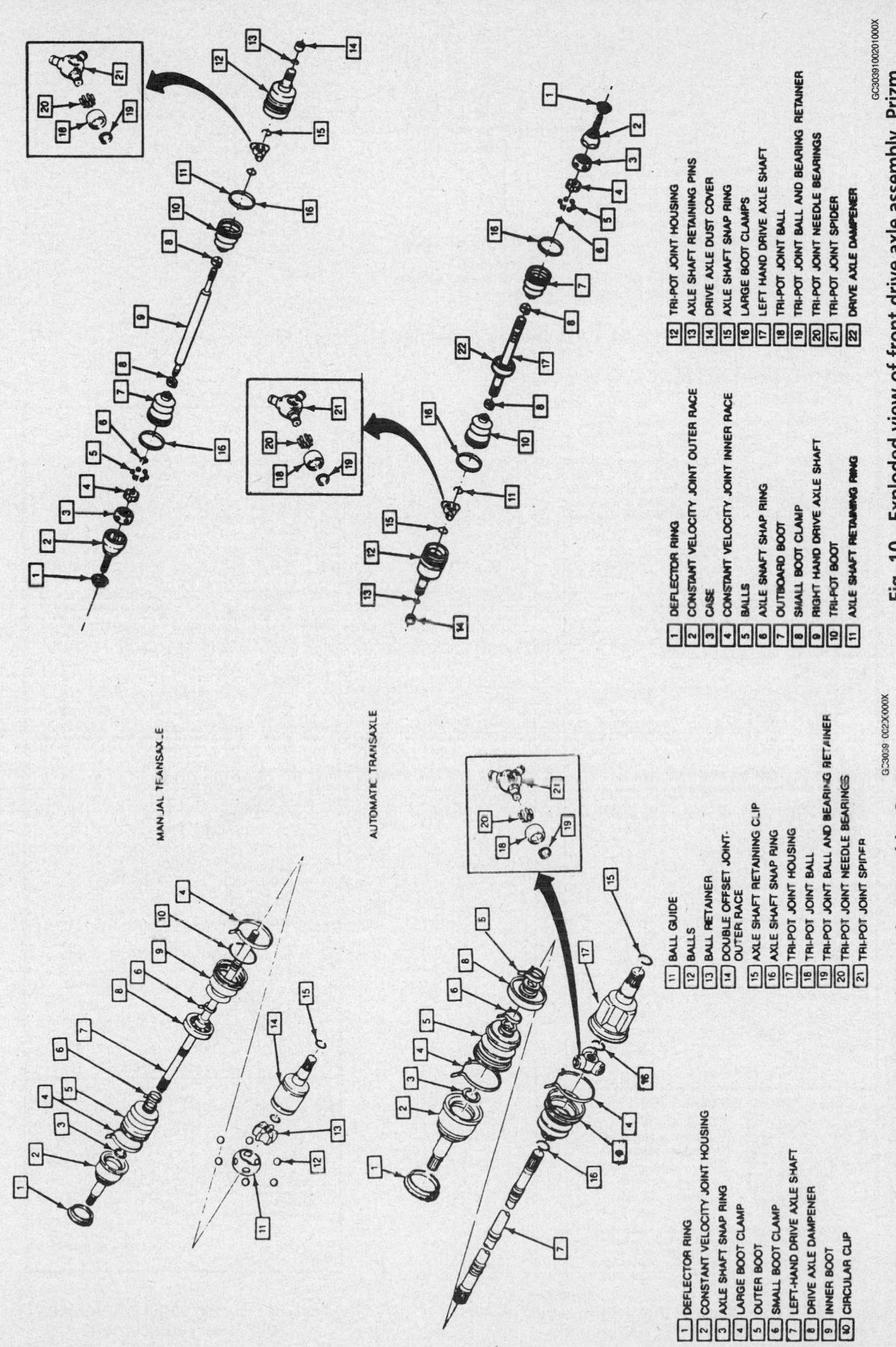

Fig. 10 Exploded view of front drive axle assembly. Prizm

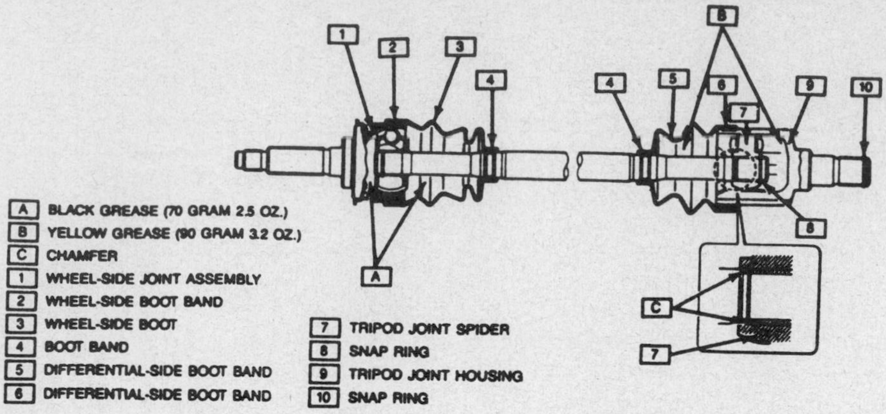
A BLACK GREASE (70 GRAM 2.5 OZ.)
B YELLOW GREASE (90 GRAM 3.2 OZ.)
C CHAMFER
1 WHEEL-SIDE JOINT ASSEMBLY
2 WHEEL-SIDE BOOT BAND
3 WHEEL-SIDE BOOT
4 BOOT BAND
5 DIFFERENTIAL-SIDE BOOT BAND
6 DIFFERENTIAL-SIDE BOOT BAND
7 TRIPOD JOINT SPIDER
8 SNAP RING
9 TRIPOD JOINT HOUSING
10 SNAP RING
GC3039100202000X

Fig. 11 Assembling drive axle assembly. Metro

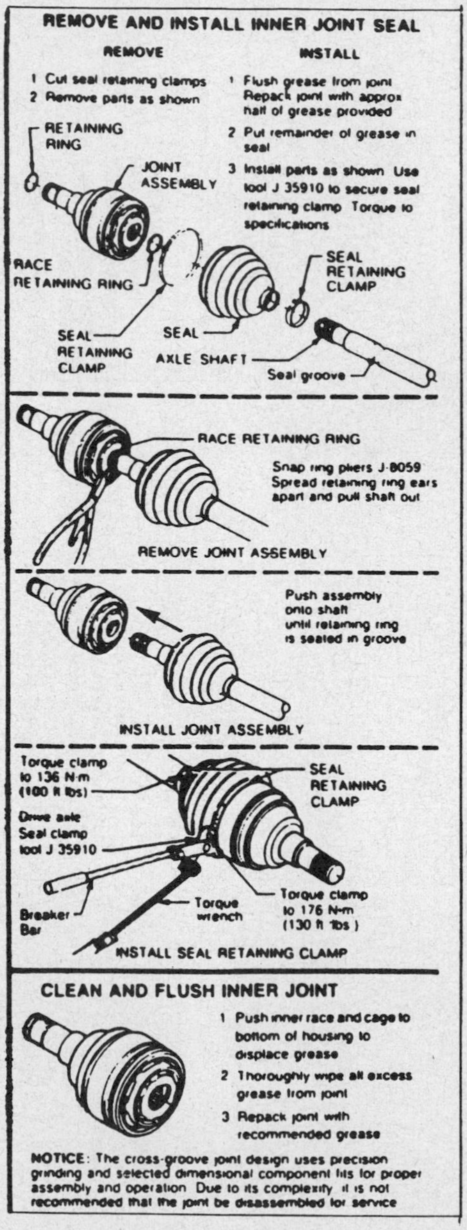
REMOVE AND INSTALL INNER JOINT SEAL
REMOVE
1 Cut seal retaining clamps
2 Remove parts as shown
INSTALL
1 Flush grease from joint Repack joint with approx half of grease provided
2 Put remainder of grease in seal
3 Install parts as shown Use tool J 35910 to secure seal retaining clamp Torque to specifications
RETAINING RING
JOINT ASSEMBLY
RACE RETAINING RING
SEAL RETAINING CLAMP
SEAL
SEAL RETAINING CLAMP
AXLE SHAFT
Seal groove
RACE RETAINING RING
Snap ring pliers J-8059 Spread retaining ring ears apart and pull shaft out
REMOVE JOINT ASSEMBLY
Push assembly onto shaft until retaining ring is seated in groove
INSTALL JOINT ASSEMBLY
Torque clamp to 136 N·m (100 ft lbs)
SEAL RETAINING CLAMP
Drive axle Seal clamp tool J 35910
Breaker Bar
Torque wrench
Torque clamp to 176 N·m (130 ft lbs)
INSTALL SEAL RETAINING CLAMP
CLEAN AND FLUSH INNER JOINT
1 Push inner race and cage to bottom of housing to displace grease
2 Thoroughly wipe all excess grease from joint
3 Repack joint with recommended grease
NOTICE: The cross-groove joint design uses precision grinding and selected dimensional component fits for proper assembly and operation Due to its complexity it is not recommended that the joint be disassembled for service
GC3039100209000X

Fig. 12 Cross groove inner joint seal replacement. With cross groove inner joint

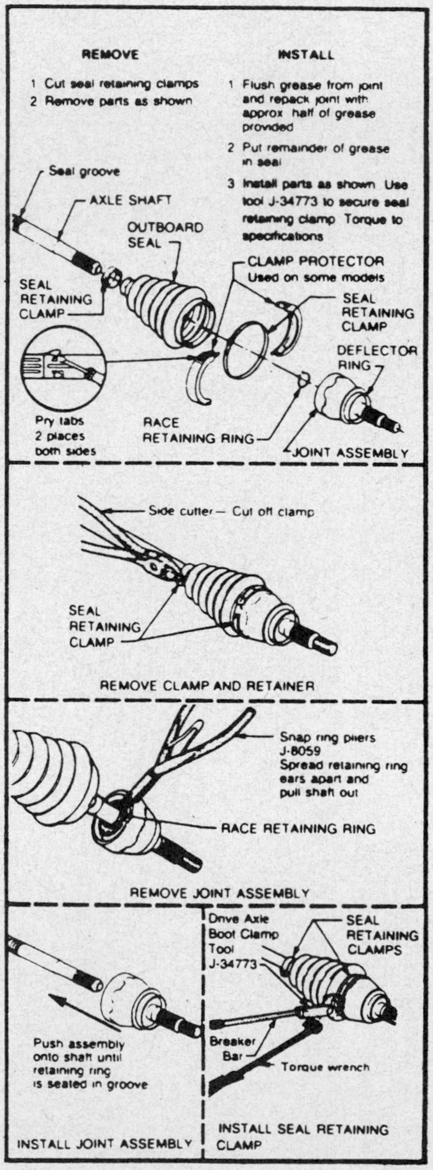
REMOVE
1 Cut seal retaining clamps
2 Remove parts as shown
INSTALL
1 Flush grease from joint and repack joint with approx half of grease provided
2 Put remainder of grease in seal
3 Install parts as shown Use tool J-34773 to secure seal retaining clamp Torque to specifications
Seal groove
AXLE SHAFT
OUTBOARD SEAL
CLAMP PROTECTOR Used on some models
SEAL RETAINING CLAMP
SEAL RETAINING CLAMP
DEFLECTOR RING
Pry tabs 2 places both sides
RACE RETAINING RING
JOINT ASSEMBLY
Side cutter — Cut off clamp
SEAL RETAINING CLAMP
REMOVE CLAMP AND RETAINER
Snap ring pliers J-8059 Spread retaining ring ears apart and pull shaft out
RACE RETAINING RING
REMOVE JOINT ASSEMBLY
Drive Axle Boot Clamp Tool J-34773
SEAL RETAINING CLAMPS
Breaker Bar
Torque wrench
Push assembly onto shaft until retaining ring is seated in groove
INSTALL JOINT ASSEMBLY
INSTALL SEAL RETAINING CLAMP
GC3039100205000X

Fig. 13 Outer constant velocity joint seal replacement

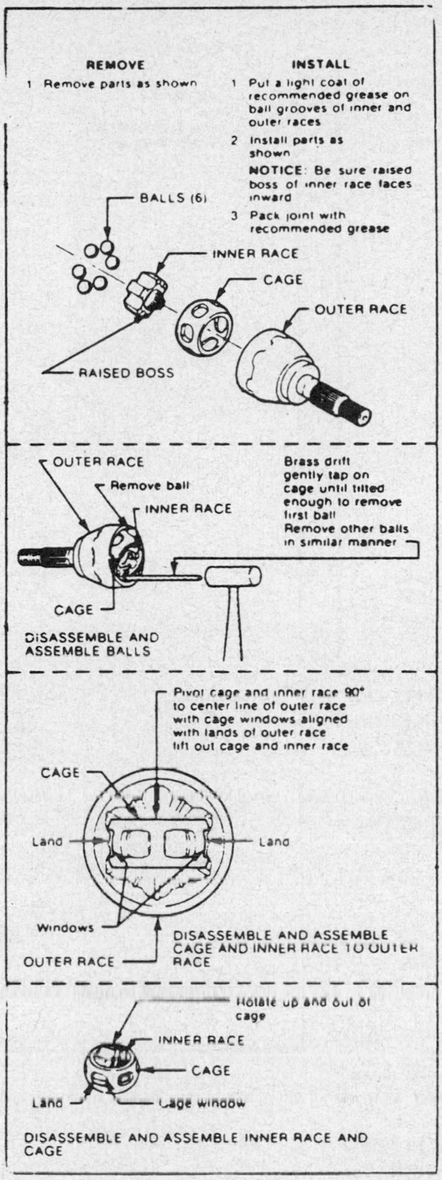
REMOVE
1 Remove parts as shown
INSTALL
1 Put a light coat of recommended grease on ball grooves of inner and outer races
2 Install parts as shown
NOTICE: Be sure raised boss of inner race faces inward
3 Pack joint with recommended grease
BALLS (6)
INNER RACE
CAGE
OUTER RACE
RAISED BOSS
OUTER RACE
Remove ball
INNER RACE
Brass drift gently tap on cage until tilted enough to remove first ball Remove other balls in similar manner
CAGE
DISASSEMBLE AND ASSEMBLE BALLS
Pivot cage and inner race 90° to center line of outer race with cage windows aligned with lands of outer race lift out cage and inner race
CAGE
Land
Land
Windows
OUTER RACE
DISASSEMBLE AND ASSEMBLE CAGE AND INNER RACE TO OUTER RACE
Rotate up and out of cage
INNER RACE
CAGE
Land
Cage window
DISASSEMBLE AND ASSEMBLE INNER RACE AND CAGE

GC3039100206000X

Fig. 14 Outer constant velocity joint

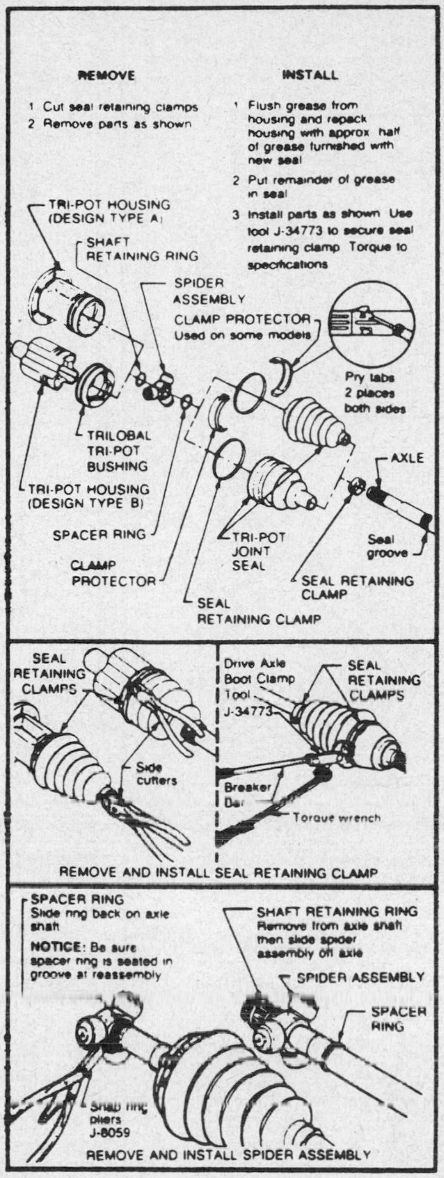
REMOVE
1 Cut seal retaining clamps
2 Remove parts as shown
INSTALL
1 Flush grease from housing and repack housing with approx half of grease furnished with new seal
2 Put remainder of grease in seal
3 Install parts as shown Use tool J-34773 to secure seal retaining clamp Torque to specifications
TRI-POT HOUSING (DESIGN TYPE A)
SHAFT RETAINING RING
SPIDER ASSEMBLY
CLAMP PROTECTOR
Used on some models
Pry tabs 2 places both sides
TRILOBAL TRI-POT BUSHING
AXLE
TRI-POT HOUSING (DESIGN TYPE B)
SPACER RING
TRI-POT JOINT SEAL
Seal groove
CLAMP PROTECTOR
SEAL RETAINING CLAMP
SEAL RETAINING CLAMP
SEAL RETAINING CLAMPS
Side cutters
Drive Axle Boot Clamp Tool J-34773
SEAL RETAINING CLAMPS
Breaker Bar
Torque wrench
REMOVE AND INSTALL SEAL RETAINING CLAMP
SPACER RING
Slide ring back on axle shaft
NOTICE: Be sure spacer ring is seated in groove at reassembly
SHAFT RETAINING RING
Remove from axle shaft then slide spider assembly off axle
SPIDER ASSEMBLY
SPACER RING
Snap ring pliers J-8059
REMOVE AND INSTALL SPIDER ASSEMBLY

GC3039100207000X

Fig. 15 Inner tri-pot seal replacement. Less bearing blocks

3. Remove drive axle assembly.
4. Remove deflector ring using shaft removal fork (Part No. J-37780).
5. Reverse procedure to install.

INTERMEDIATE SHAFT REPLACE

EXCEPT CUTLASS SUPREME, GRAND PRIX & LUMINA

1. Install engine support fixture tool No. J-28467-A, or equivalent, then raise and support vehicle.
2. Remove right tire assembly. Using shop towels, protect outer joint front any sharp edges.
3. Remove stabilizer shaft from right control arm, then disconnect right ball joint from knuckle.
4. Remove rear engine mount through bolt, then separate drive axle from intermediate shaft.
5. Remove intermediate shaft support bracket to engine bolts.
6. Disengage intermediate shaft from transaxle, then remove intermediate shaft from vehicle.
7. Reverse procedure to install, noting the following:
   a. **Torque** intermediate shaft support bracket bolts to 37 ft. lbs.
   b. **Torque** rear engine mount through bolt to 55 ft. lbs.

CUTLASS SUPREME, GRAND PRIX & LUMINA 1992

1. Raise and support vehicle, then remove right wheel assembly.
2. Drain transaxle fluid, then remove right drive axle.
3. Remove intermediate shaft housing to bracket bolts, then the bracket.
4. Remove housing to transaxle bolts.
5. Disengage intermediate axle shaft from transaxle, then remove intermediate shaft assembly from vehicle.
6. Reverse procedure to install, noting the following:
   a. **Torque** housing to transaxle bolts to 18 ft. lbs.
   b. **Torque** bracket to engine case to 37 ft. lbs.

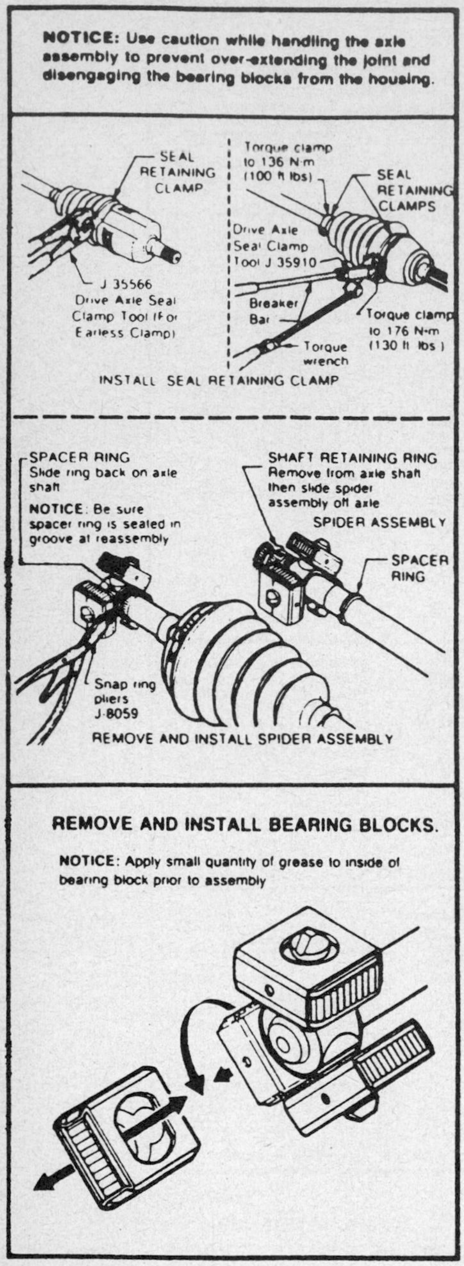
NOTICE: Use caution while handling the axle assembly to prevent over-extending the joint and disengaging the bearing blocks from the housing.
SEAL RETAINING CLAMP
Torque clamp to 136 N·m (100 ft lbs)
SEAL RETAINING CLAMPS
Drive Axle Seal Clamp Tool J 35910
J 35566 Drive Axle Seal Clamp Tool (For Earless Clamp)
Breaker Bar
Torque wrench
Torque clamp to 176 N·m (130 ft lbs)
INSTALL SEAL RETAINING CLAMP
SPACER RING Slide ring back on axle shaft
NOTICE: Be sure spacer ring is sealed in groove at reassembly
SHAFT RETAINING RING Remove from axle shaft then slide spider assembly off axle
SPIDER ASSEMBLY
SPACER RING
Snap ring pliers J-8059
REMOVE AND INSTALL SPIDER ASSEMBLY
REMOVE AND INSTALL BEARING BLOCKS.
NOTICE: Apply small quantity of grease to inside of bearing block prior to assembly

GC3039100208010X

Fig. 16 Inner tri-pot seal replacement (Part 1 of 2). w/bearing blocks

c. **Torque** housing to bracket bolts to 27 ft. lbs.
d. Coat splines of intermediate axle shaft with chassis grease.

1993–94

1. Remove transaxle from vehicle.
2. Remove intermediate shaft to transaxle bolts, then the intermediate shaft from transaxle.
3. Reverse procedure to install, noting the following:
   a. **Torque** intermediate shaft to transaxle bolts to 18 ft. lbs.
   b. Lubricate splines of intermediate shaft with chassis grease.

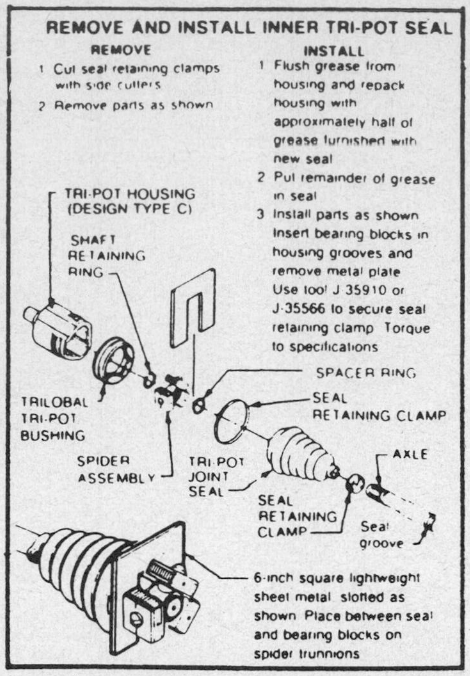
REMOVE AND INSTALL INNER TRI-POT SEAL
REMOVE
1 Cut seal retaining clamps with side cutters
2 Remove parts as shown
INSTALL
1 Flush grease from housing and repack housing with approximately half of grease furnished with new seal
2 Put remainder of grease in seal
3 Install parts as shown Insert bearing blocks in housing grooves and remove metal plate Use tool J 35910 or J-35566 to secure seal retaining clamp Torque to specifications
TRI-POT HOUSING (DESIGN TYPE C)
SHAFT RETAINING RING
SPACER RING
SEAL RETAINING CLAMP
TRILOBAL TRI-POT BUSHING
SPIDER ASSEMBLY
TRI-POT JOINT SEAL
AXLE
SEAL RETAINING CLAMP
Seal groove
6-inch square lightweight sheet metal slotted as shown Place between seal and bearing blocks on spider trunnions

GC3039100208020X

Fig. 16 Inner tri-pot seal replacement (Part 2 of 2). w/bearing blocks

INTERMEDIATE SHAFT SERVICE

DISASSEMBLE

Except Cutlass Supreme, Grand Prix & Lumina

1. Remove retaining ring and lip seal, **Fig. 18.**
2. Using split plate No. J-22912-1, or equivalent, behind inner slinger, press shaft from bearing.
3. Remove retainer from support screws.
4. Using replacer No. J-23694, or equivalent, press bearing from support.

Cutlass Supreme, Grand Prix & Lumina

1. Remove intermediate shaft from vehicle.
2. Remove lip seal, snap ring and washer from housing, **Fig. 19.**
3. Using handle tool No. J-8592 and bearing remover tool No. J-8810, or equivalents, press spacer and bearing from housing.

ASSEMBLE

Except Cutlass Supreme, Grand Prix & Lumina

1. Press bearing into support using press arbor plate across bearing.
2. Using split plate tool No. J-22912-1, or equivalent, press inner slinger on shaft.
3. Install retainer over shaft.

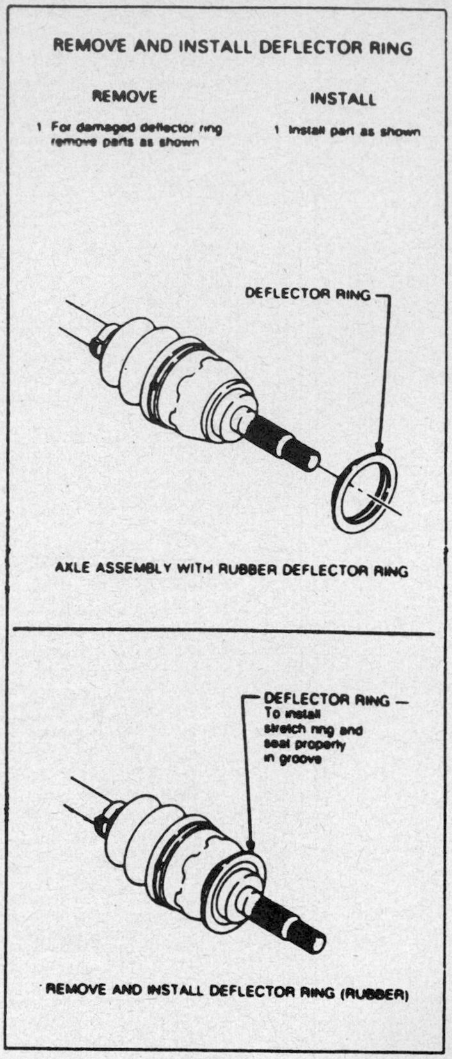
REMOVE AND INSTALL DEFLECTOR RING
REMOVE
1 For damaged deflector ring remove parts as shown
INSTALL
1 Install part as shown
DEFLECTOR RING
AXLE ASSEMBLY WITH RUBBER DEFLECTOR RING
DEFLECTOR RING — To install stretch ring and seal properly in groove
REMOVE AND INSTALL DEFLECTOR RING (RUBBER)

GC3039100210000X

Fig. 17 Deflector ring replacement. Except Geo & LeMans

4. Place support with bearing on press arbor plate and press shaft into bearing until bearing inner race contacts chamfer on shaft. **Do not press bearing beyond where chamfer begins on shaft.**
5. Using split plate, press outer slinger on shaft.
6. Apply sealer to outer slinger and shaft joint, then install lip seal using seal installer tool No. J-34115, or equivalent.
7. Install retaining ring.
8. Install retainer to support. **Torque** screws to 89 inch lbs.

Cutlass Supreme, Grand Prix & Lumina

1. Using bearing installer tool No. J-36379, or equivalent, press bearing into housing support.
2. Install spacer, washer and snap ring into housing, **Fig. 19.**
3. Using seal installer tool No. J-23771, or equivalent, install lip seal.
4. Install intermediate shaft assembly in vehicle.

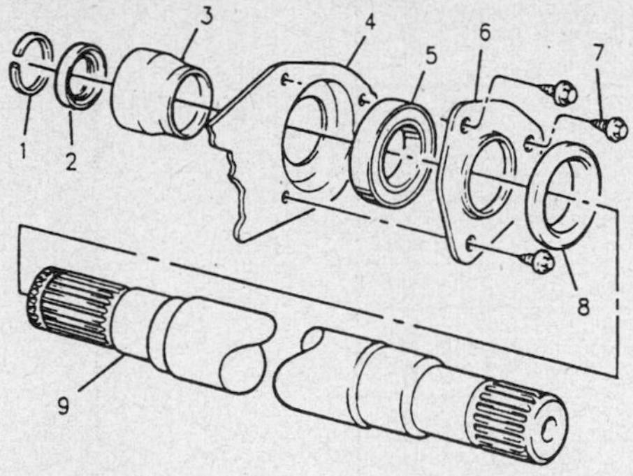

1 RETAINING RING
2 LIP SEAL
3 OUTER SLINGER
4 SUPPORT
5 BEARING
6 RETAINER
7 SCREW
8 INNER SLINGER
9 SHAFT

GC3039100203000X

Fig. 18 Exploded view of intermediate shaft. Except Cutlass Supreme, Grand Prix & Lumina

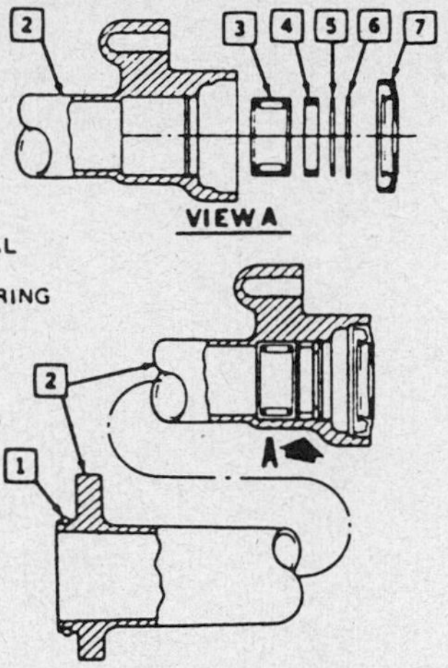
VIEW A

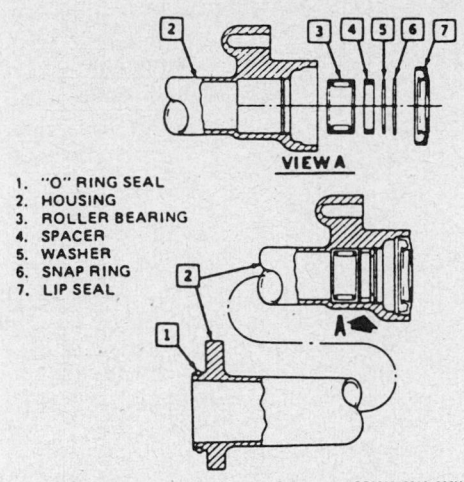

1. "O" RING SEAL
2. HOUSING
3. ROLLER BEARING
4. SPACER
5. WASHER
6. SNAP RING
7. LIP SEAL

GC3039100204000X

Fig. 19 Exploded view of intermediate shaft. Cutlass Supreme, Grand Prix & Lumina

TIGHTENING SPECIFICATIONS

Component	Model	Torque/Ft. Lbs.
Caliper Bolts	Prizm & Storm	65
Hub Nut	Metro	129
	Prizm & Storm	137
	LeMans	③
	④	185
	⑤	192
	⑥	184
	Cutlass Supreme, Grand Prix, Lumina & Regal	183
Lower Ball Joint	Metro	44
	LeMans	50
	Beretta & Corsica	③
	Achieva, Deville, Fleetwood; 1992-94 Grand Am & Skylark	41–50
Lower Control Arm Bolts	Prizm & Storm	105①
Tie Rod Nut	Prizm & Storm	36②
	LeMans	45
Upper Strut Mount Nut	LeMans	22
Wheel Hub To Knuckle Bolts	Cutlass Supreme, Grand Prix, Lumina & Regal	52
Wheel Lug Nuts	Prizm	76
	Storm	87
	Metro	44
	LeMans	66
	⑦	100

①—Storm, 115 ft. lbs.
②—Storm, 40 ft. lbs.
③—See text.
④—Achieva, Cavalier, Century, Cutlass, Grand Am, Skylark, Sunbird.
⑤—88 & 98, LeSabre, Park Avenue; Beretta, Corsica, DeVille & Fleetwood (FWD).
⑥—Eldorado, Riviera, Seville, Toronado & Trofeo.
⑦—Except Prizm, Storm, Metro & LeMans.

DRIVE AXLES

TABLE OF CONTENTS

Identification

Axle identification numbers can be found on either the code tag or sticker attached to the axle housing cover or stamped on the right front section of the axle shaft housing and on Corvette, the axle I.D. is underneath the differential.

Model	Axle Code		Gear Ratio	Ring Gear Diameter
	Standard	Limited Slip		
1992				
Brougham	4MF	—	3.08	8.50
	4ML	—	3.73	9.50
	—	4MM	3.73	9.50
Camaro	6HP	—	2.73	7.62
	—	6HT	2.73	7.62
	6HK	—	3.08	7.62
	—	6HF	3.08	7.62
	—	6HB	3.08	7.62
	6HJ	—	3.23	7.62
	—	6PM	3.23	7.62
	—	6HL	3.42	7.62
	—	6PN	3.42	7.62
Caprice	6GD	—	2.56	7.50
	6GE	—	2.56	7.50
	6GK	—	2.56	8.50
	6GM	—	2.56	8.50
	—	6ZA	2.56	8.50
	6ZC	—	2.56	8.50
	6YL	—	2.73	8.50
	4LM	—	3.08	8.50
	6LA	—	3.08	8.50
	8LM	—	3.08	8.50
	—	4NQ	3.08	8.50
	—	6NC	3.08	8.50
	—	8NQ	3.08	8.50
	6YE	—	3.23	8.50
	—	6YF	3.23	8.50
	—	6YM	3.23	8.50
	—	6LN	3.23	8.50
	—	6GJ	3.23	8.50
	—	6YK	3.23	8.50
	6ZD	—	3.42	8.50
	6GN	—	3.42	8.50
	6GS	—	3.42	8.50

Model	Axle Code		Gear Ratio	Ring Gear Diameter
	Standard	Limited Slip		
1992 -Continued				
Caprice	—	6ZB	3.42	8.50
	—	6GL	3.42	8.50
	—	6GP	3.42	8.50
Corvette	—	CQT ①	2.59	7.87
	—	CQU ①	2.73	7.87
	—	CQW ①	3.07	7.87
	—	CQR ②	3.45	8.50
	—	CQX ②	3.54	8.50
Custom Cruiser	6YL	—	2.73	8.50
	—	6YM	3.23	8.50
Firebird	6HP	—	2.73	7.62
	—	6HT	2.73	7.62
	6HK	—	3.08	7.62
	—	6HF	3.08	7.62
	—	6HB	3.08	7.62
	6HJ	—	3.23	7.62
	—	6PM	3.23	7.62
	—	6HL	3.42	7.62
	—	6PN	3.42	7.62
Roadmaster	4LL	—	2.56	8.50
	6YL	—	2.73	8.50
	4LM	—	3.08	8.50
	4NQ	—	3.08	8.50
	6YF	—	3.23	8.50
	—	6YM	3.23	8.00
1993				
Camaro	—	2PH	2.73	7.62
	9HM	—	3.23	7.62
Caprice	8GD	—	2.56	7.50
	8GE	—	2.56	7.50
	6GM	—	2.56	8.50

Continued

Model	Axle Code Standard	Axle Code Limited Slip	Gear Ratio	Ring Gear Diameter
1993 -Continued				
Caprice	—	6GK	2.56	8.50
	6YL	—	2.73	8.50
	8LA	—	3.08	8.50
	8LM	—	3.08	8.50
	—	8LN	3.08	8.50
	—	8NC	3.08	8.50
	—	8NG	3.08	8.50
	—	8NQ	3.08	8.50
	6YE	—	3.23	8.50
	—	6YM	3.23	8.50
	6GS	—	3.42	8.50
	—	6GD	3.42	8.50
Corvette	—	CQT①	2.59	7.87
	—	CQU①	2.73	7.87
	—	CQW①	3.07	7.87
	—	CQR②	3.45	8.50
Fleetwood	6MA	—	2.56	8.50
	6MD	—	3.08	8.50
	4MM	—	3.73	9.50
	6MF	—	3.73	8.50
	—	4ML	3.73	9.50
Firebird	—	2PH	2.73	7.62
	9HM	—	3.23	7.62
Roadmaster	6YE	—	3.23	8.50
	—	6YM	3.23	8.50
1994				
Camaro	—	2PH	2.73	7.62
	9HM	—	3.23	7.62
Caprice & Impala SS	2YN	—	2.56	8.50

Model	Axle Code Standard	Axle Code Limited Slip	Gear Ratio	Ring Gear Diameter
1994 -Continued				
	2GA	—	2.73	7.60
	2GB	—	2.73	7.60
	2GH	—	2.73	8.50
	2YF	—	2.93	8.50
	—	2LQ	2.93	8.50
	—	2YG	2.93	8.50
	2LW	—	3.08	8.50
	—	2LX	3.08	8.50
	2LR	—	3.23	8.50
	2LY	—	3.23	8.50
	2LT	—	3.23	8.50
	6YF	—	3.23	8.50
	—	2ND	3.23	8.50
	—	2LZ	3.23	8.50
	—	2LS	3.23	8.50
Corvette	—	CQT①	2.59	7.87
	—	CQU①	2.73	7.87
	—	CQW①	3.07	7.87
	—	CQR②	3.45	8.50
Fleetwood	2MA	—	2.56	8.50
	2MC	—	2.93	8.50
	2MK	—	2.93	9.50
	2MG	—	3.42	8.62
	2MP	—	3.42	9.50
Firebird	—	2PH	2.73	7.62
	9HM	—	3.23	7.62
Roadmaster	2YF	—	2.93	8.50
	—	2NS	2.93	8.50

①—Automatic Transmission
②—Manual Transmission

Troubleshooting

INDEX

PRELIMINARY CHECKS

Before the rear axle is to be serviced, ensure the source of the problem is the rear axle itself and not from other sources such as noise from the tires, road surface, engine, transmission, wheel bearings, muffler or body parts. Perform the following procedures to check for other sources that could be mistaken for axle noise:

1. Ensure rear axle lubricant is at the correct level and type, then select a level asphalt road to reduce tire and body noise.
2. After vehicle has been driven far enough to warm lubricant, note at which speed the noise occurs then stop vehicle. With vehicle in neutral run engine slowly through the RPM range that the noise occurred to check if noise was caused by the exhaust or power train.
3. Check for tire noise by temporarily inflating all tires to approximately 50 psi for test purposes only. Drive vehicle on a level asphalt road and note if a change in noise occurs compared to noise while tires are inflated at normal pressure. After test is completed ensure tires are inflated to manufacturer's specification.
4. Check the front and rear wheel bearings by lightly applying the brakes while keeping vehicle speed steady. If the noise diminishes, inspect front and rear wheel bearings by jacking up

the front wheels, then spinning or shaking them to determine if bearings are loose. Replace if necessary.
5. With vehicle jacked up, check for metal to metal contact between the spring and the spring opening in the frame, upper and lower control arm bushings and frame and axle housing brackets. Ensure there is no metal to metal contact between the floor of the body and the frame. Replace bushings or rubber insulators if necessary.

REAR AXLE NOISES

After noise has been determined to be in the axle and not from other sources, check for the specific type of axle noise as follows:

ROUGH GROWL OR GRATING

1. Faulty pinion or rear axle case side bearing.

CHATTER ON TURNS

1. Wrong lubricant in axle.
2. Clutch cones worn.

KNOCK AT LOW SPEEDS

1. Worn universal joint.
2. Side gear hub counterbore in the differential case worn oversize.

CLUNK WHILE ACCELERATING OR DECELERATING

1. Worn differential case.
2. Excessive clearance between the axle shaft and side gear splines.
3. Excessive clearance between side gear hub and counterbore in case.
4. Excessive drive pinion and ring gear backlash.
5. Worn pinion and side gear teeth.
6. Worn thrust washers.

CONSTANT SCRAPING NOISE AT LOW SPEEDS

1. Defective or worn pinion bearing.

CONSTANT WHINE WHILE DRIVING

1. Defective or worn ring and pinion gear.

GROAN IN FORWARD OR REVERSE

1. Wrong lubricant in axle.

WHINE LOUDER WHILE TURNING

1. Defective or worn axle side gear and/or pinion.

LIMITED SLIP AXLE OPERATION

On all models, improper operation is often indicated by clutch slipping or grabbing which produces a whirring or chattering noise. These noises do not always indicate an axle failure but could be from lack of propor lubrication or normal noise when axle clutches are engaged during certain road conditions. Since the operational life of the limited slip unit is dependent on equal rotation of the wheels while driving straight ahead, it is important that there is no major difference in rear wheel tire size, air pressure or wear pattern, otherwise the vehicle may swerve during acceleration. If improper limited slip differential problems are not caused by the above, check for proper operation as follows:

AUBURN CONE TYPE DIFFERENTIAL

1. With parking brake released and automatic transmission in park or manual transmission in gear, raise both tires off the floor.
2. Remove hubcap or wheel disc and apply torque wrench and axle shaft puller tool No. J-21579 to either wheel. Measure torque required to rotate one wheel. **Torque** should be between 125 and 225 ft. lbs.
3. Place transmission in neutral position, then lower one rear tire to the ground.
4. Measure torque required to rotate the raised wheel. **On full size wagons and sedans, torque** should be between 45 and 110 ft. lbs. **On Camaro and Firebird models, torque** should be between 44 and 66 ft. lbs.
5. The differential case must be replaced as a unit if proper specifications are not obtained.

BORG WARNER 4 PINION DIFFERENTIAL

1. With automatic transmission in park and manual transmission in gear, raise rear of vehicle until one rear tire is off the ground.
2. Remove the rear tire and wheel assembly, then attach side hammer assembly tool No. J-2619-01 and axle shaft remover tool No. J-21579 to axle shaft flange and then a 1/2 inch X 13 bolt into adapter.
3. Raise the other tire off the ground and attach torque wrench to side hammer assembly tool No. J-2619-01, then measure torque required to rotate axle shaft. If **torque** reading is less than 48 ft. lbs., remove and repair the differential unit.

Except Borg Warner Four Pinion Differential

INDEX

REMOVAL

DIFFERENTIAL ASSEMBLY

Except Corvette & 1993–94 Camaro & Firebird

1. Raise and support rear of vehicle, then loosen axle housing cover bolts and allow lubricant to drain into suitable container, **Fig. 1.**
2. Remove axle housing cover, then proceed as follows:
   a. Wipe excess lubricant from inside axle housing, then visually inspect parts for wear and/or damage.
   b. Rotate gears and check for roughness, indicating damaged bearings or gears.
   c. Install dial indicator on axle housing cover flange, then check and record ring gear to drive pinion backlash.
3. Remove rear axles and propeller shaft
4. If not previously marked, scribe reference marks on differential bearing caps to be used during reassembly, then loosen bearing cap bolts.

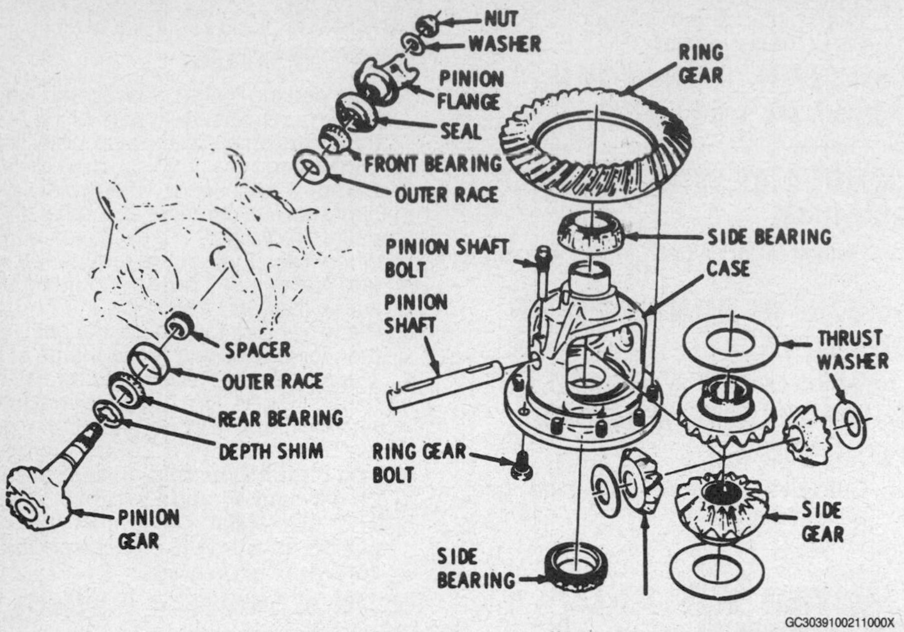
NUT
WASHER
PINION FLANGE
SEAL
FRONT BEARING
OUTER RACE
RING GEAR
PINION SHAFT BOLT
PINION SHAFT
SIDE BEARING
CASE
THRUST WASHER
SPACER
OUTER RACE
REAR BEARING
DEPTH SHIM
RING GEAR BOLT
PINION GEAR
SIDE GEAR
SIDE BEARING
GC3039100211000X

Fig. 1 Exploded view of rear axle assembly. Except Corvette

5. Using suitable tool, pry differential case, bearing races and shims out of housing until loose in the bearing caps. Remove bearing races, then the differential assembly. Mark side cups and shims for reference during reassembly.

Corvette

1. Remove rear axle assembly.
2. Remove axle housing cover and allow lubricant to drain.
3. Mount carrier assembly in a holding fixture, then remove snap rings retaining yoke shafts and the yoke shafts. Tag snap rings indicating which side they were removed from.
4. Remove bearing cap bolts, then the bearing caps. **When removing bearing caps, note matched letters stamped on caps and carrier. During reassembly, the caps must be installed in the exact position they were removed from.**
5. Install spreader tool, J-24385-01, adapter, J-24385 and a dial indicator set, **Fig. 2.** Zero indicator and ensure indicator stylus contacts one side of housing opening.
6. While observing micrometer, spread housing with tool. Do not spread housing more than 0.010 inch or distortion could result.
7. Using two pry bars, pry differential assembly upwards to remove. **Tag bearing cups and shims to indicate which side removed from.**
8. Remove spreader tool to prevent housing from taking a set.

1993–94 Camaro & Firebird w/Drum Brakes

1. Remove rear axle assembly.
2. Remove rear brake pipe assemblies from rear brake cylinders, then disconnect center hose assembly from junction block.
3. Remove rear brake assemblies from housing, then rear axle shaft bearings and seals.
4. Remove rear backing plates, then differential case and differential drive pinion gear.

1993–94 Camaro & Firebird w/Disc Brakes

A shim may be installed between the rear brake caliper mounting plate and axle shaft tube flange on housing. This shim centers the rear brake caliper and pads over the brake rotor, ensuring even brake pad assembly pressure during braking. This shim may have to be changes when the housing is replaced.

1. Remove rear axle assembly.
2. Remove rear brake pipe assemblies from rear brake hose junction block, then junction block from housing.
3. Remove rear brake pipe and hose assemblies from housing.
4. Remove brake shaft bearing assemblies and seals, then caliper anchor brackets and mounting plates.
5. Remove shim, if installed.
6. Remove differential case, then differential drive pinion gear.

DRIVE PINION

1. Scribe reference mark between drive pinion and driveshaft yoke, then hold yoke with suitable tool and remove pinion nut and yoke. **If yoke shows wear in the seal-to-flange contacting surface, the yoke should be replaced.**

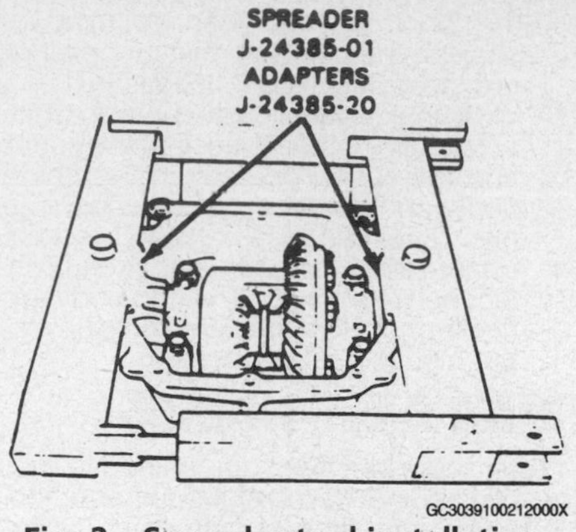
SPREADER
J-24385-01
ADAPTERS
J-24385-20
GC3039100212000X

Fig. 2 Spreader tool installation. Corvette

2. Install original pinion nut a few turns on pinion shaft, then using hammer and drift, tap pinion shaft out of pinion housing. **Hold gear end of pinion shaft when removing to prevent it from falling from axle housing. On Corvette models, the pinion preload shims may stick to the pinion housing or the rear bearing during removal. These shims must be collected and kept together for use during reassembly.**
3. Remove and discard pinion nut and collapsible spacer.
4. If being replaced, remove front and rear bearing races from pinion housing using drift positioned in race slots and hammer.
5. If rear pinion bearing is being replaced, remove using arbor press and adapters. Measure and record thickness of shim which is found under rear bearing.

DIFFERENTIAL CASE OVERHAUL

STANDARD DIFFERENTIAL

1. If side carrier bearings are to be replaced, remove bearings using a bearing puller.
2. Remove differential pinion shaft lock bolt and the pinion shaft, **Fig. 1.**
3. Remove differential pinions and thrust washers, side gears and side gear thrust washers, noting installation position for assembly. Keep thrust washers with respective gears.
4. Remove ring gear bolts, then the ring gear, driving ring gear from case using drift and hammer. **Ring gear bolts have left hand threads. Do not pry between ring gear and case, as mating surfaces will be damaged.**
5. Inspect components as outlined in "Cleaning and Inspection" and replace as needed.
6. Install thrust washers on side gears and mount side gears in case. **Lubricate all components with specified gear lubricant prior to assembly.**

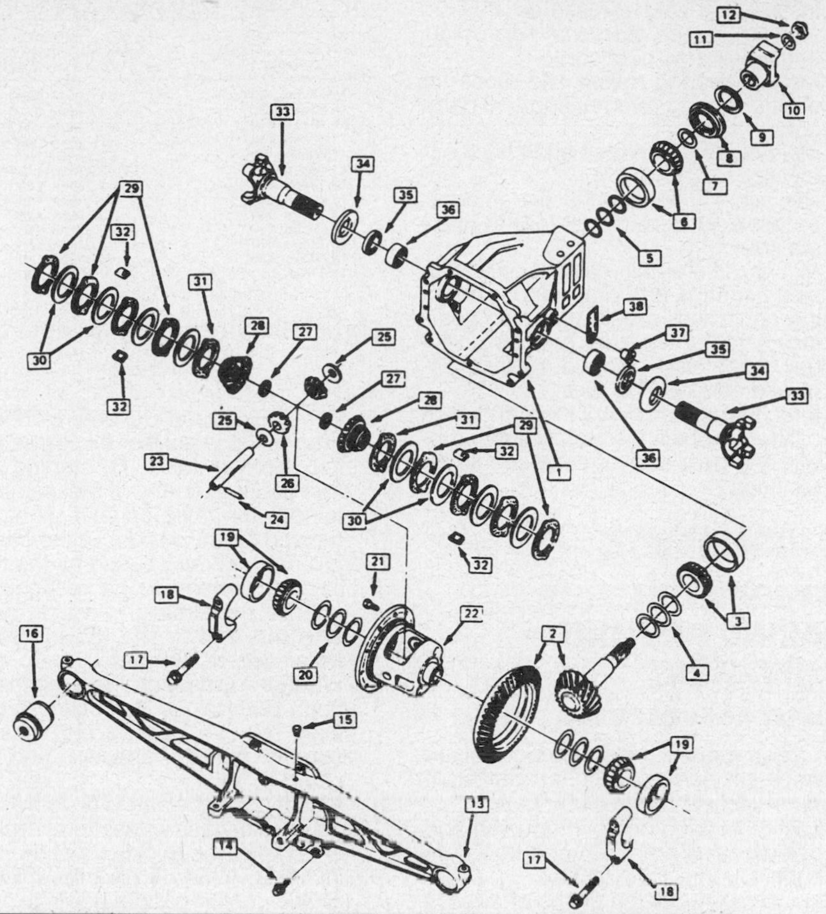

1. CARRIER
2. RING AND PINION GEARS
3. INNER PINION BEARING AND CUP
4. PINION DEPTH SHIMS
5. PINION BEARING PRELOAD SHIMS
6. OUTER PINION BEARING AND CUP
7. OIL SLINGER
8. PINION YOKE SEAL
9. PINION YOKE SEAL DUST SHIELD
10. PINION YOKE
11. WASHER
12. PINION NUT
13. CARRIER COVER BEAM
14. COVER BEAM BOLT
15. VENT
16. BUSHING
17. SIDE BEARING BOLT
18. SIDE BEARING CAP
19. SIDE BEARING AND CUP
20. SIDE BEARING SHIMS
21. RING GEAR BOLT
22. CASE
23. PINION SHAFT
24. PINION SHAFT RETAINER
25. THRUST WASHER
26. PINION GEAR
27. YOKE (AXLE)SHAFT SNAP RING RETAINER
28. SIDE GEAR
29. CLUTCH PACK PLATES
30. CLUTCH PACK DISCS
31. BELLEVILLE SPRING SPACER
32. CLUTCH PACK RETAINER CLIP
33. YOKE (AXLE) SHAFT
34. YOKE (AXLE) SEAL DUST SHIELD
35. YOKE (AXLE) SEAL
36. YOKE (AXLE) BEARING
37. LUBRICANT FILLER PLUG
38. LUBRICANT IDENTIFICATION TAG

GC3039100213000X

Fig. 3 Exploded view of Dana Trac-Lok limited slip differential. Corvette

7. Position one differential pinion (less thrust washer) between side gears and rotate gears until pinion is directly opposite case loading opening.
8. Install other pinion with pinion shaft holes aligned, then rotate side gears and ensure pinions align with shaft openings in case.
9. When pinions are properly aligned, rotate pinions toward loading opening just enough to allow thrust washer installation and install washers.
10. Align pinions with shaft opening in case, insert pinion shaft through case, install new lock bolt. It is not necessary to torque lock bolt at this time.
11. Ensure ring gear and case mating surfaces are clean and free from burrs, mount gear on case, install 2 new retaining bolts at opposite sides of gear and alternately tighten bolts to draw gear on case.
12. Install remaining ring gear bolts hand tight and ensure gear is squarely seated on case. **Always use new bolts of proper type when installing ring gear. Do not reuse old bolts.**
13. Alternately **torque** ring gear bolts to 89 ft. lbs.
14. Press side bearings onto case. If old bearings are reused, ensure bearings are installed in their original position.

2 PINION CONE TYPE (AUBURN) DIFFERENTIAL

Except Corvette

1. Remove case side bearings using tool J-22888.
2. Remove all but two opposite ring gear attaching bolts, then loosen the two remaining bolts.
3. Loosen ring gear by tapping on bolts, then remove ring gear from differential.

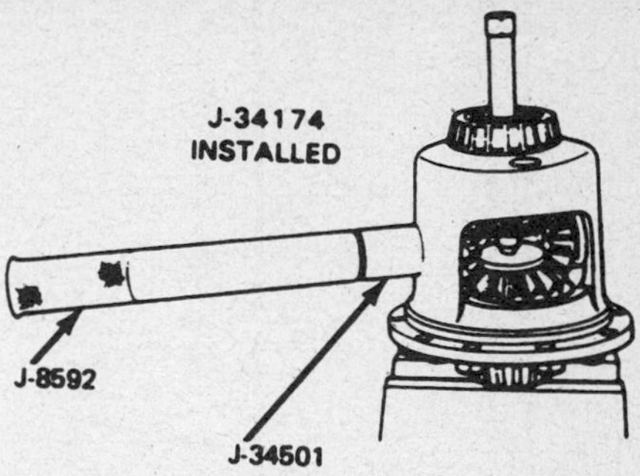
J-34174
INSTALLED
J-8592
J-34501

GC3039100214000X

Fig. 4 Installing special tools

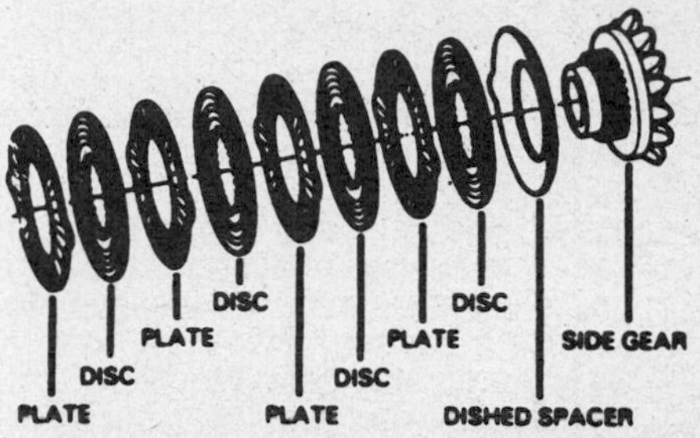
DISC
PLATE
DISC
PLATE
DISC
PLATE
SIDE GEAR
DISC
DISC
PLATE
PLATE
DISHED SPACER

GC3039100215000X

Fig. 5 Clutch plate arrangement. Dana Trac-Lok

4. This limited slip rear axle case is not serviceable. If differential case is not satisfactory, replace complete assembly.

DANA TRAC-LOK LIMITED SLIP DIFFERENTIAL

Corvette

For side gear removal, refer to "Standard Differential."

1. Remove ring gear bolts, then using a brass drift tap gear from case, **Fig. 3.**
2. Remove cross pin retainers, then using punch and hammer, tap cross pin from case.
3. Assemble adapter plate from tool J-34174 into bottom side gear, then install threaded adapter plate into top side gear. Thread forcing screw into threaded adapter, and tighten until snug. This will force dished spacers to collapse and allow a loose condition in the case, **Fig. 4.**
4. Using a .020 inch feeler gauge, push out both pinion gear spherical washers, then back off forcing screw.
5. Using suitable tools, rotate case assembly until pinion gears can be removed. Remove pinion and differential gears, then the top side gear and clutch pack. **Keep stack of plates and discs in order they were removed from case.**
6. Remove retaining clips from plate tangs then separate plates and discs. **Note position of plates and discs before disassembling.**
7. Lubricate, then install dished spacer, discs and plates on side gear splines, **Fig. 5. When lubricating parts during assembly always use special limited slip differential lubricant.**

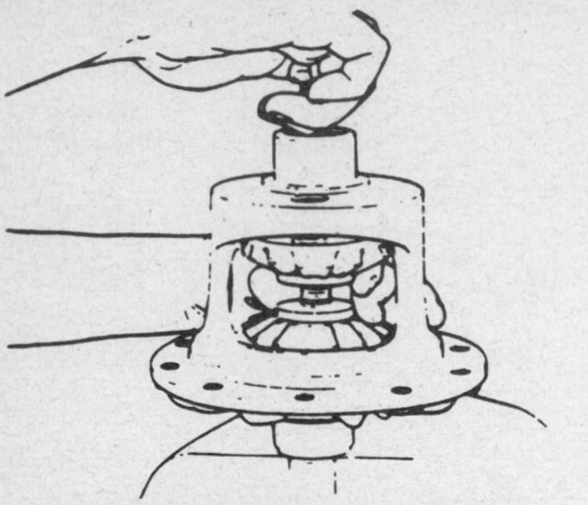

GC3039100216000X

Fig. 6 Tool & pinion installation

8. Install retaining clips on plate tangs, ensuring clips are completely seated on tangs.
9. Install side gear and clutch packs in case, ensuring retaining clips are properly seated in case recesses. Assemble adapter plate from tool J-34174 onto side gear, **Fig. 6.**
10. Install plates and discs on other differential gear and install in same manner.
11. Install threaded adapter plate into side gear. Thread forcing screw into threaded adapter, and tighten until snug. This will hold clutch packs in position.
12. Position pinion gears in case. Rotate differential case with suitable tool until pinion gear holes align with case bores.
13. Lubricate and install spherical washers, using a screwdriver. **Ensure pinion gear and spherical washer holes are aligned with case bores.**
14. Remove tools, then lubricate and install cross pin shaft and install retainers.
15. Do not install ring gear at this time. The ring gear will be installed during Final Assembly & Backlash Adjustment.

CLEANING & INSPECTION

1. Clean components in solvent and blow dry with compressed air, noting the following:
   a. Do not use brush when cleaning bearings.
   b. Do not spin dry bearings, as bearings will be damaged.
   c. Lightly lubricate components after cleaning to retard corrosion.
   d. Keep all components in order to ensure proper assembly.
2. Inspect gears for cracks, chipped teeth, wear and scoring, and damaged bearing or mounting surfaces. Replace gears that are damaged or excessively worn. **Ring gear and pinion must be replaced as an assembly.**
3. Inspect differential case for cracks, damage, worn side gear bores and scored bearing surfaces and replace as needed.
4. Inspect housing for scored bearing mount surfaces, cracks and distortion, and replace as needed.
5. Inspect bearing rollers and races for pitting, scoring, overheating and damage.
6. Mate bearing with race and check operation.
7. Replace any bearing that is damaged, excessively worn or that fails to operate smoothly.
8. Mount differential case along with side bearings and ring gear in housing, and check runout with side bearings adjusted for zero preload and a dial indicator positioned against machined edge of ring gear.
9. If runout exceeds .003 inch, and gear cannot be positioned to eliminate runout, ring gear and/or case should be replaced.

ADJUSTMENTS

DIFFERENTIAL SIDE BEARING PRELOAD ADJUSTMENT

Except Corvette

On these models, side bearing preload should be set before pinion is installed. If pinion is installed, remove ring gear.

1. Ensure bearing bores in housing and bearing caps are clean and free from burrs.
2. Measure production shims or service spacer and shim packs removed during disassembly to determine approximate thickness of shims needed for installation. **Do not reuse cast iron production shims as they may break during installation. If service spacers and shims were previously installed, they can be reused.**
3. In addition to .170 inch service spacers for each side, refer to chart, **Fig. 7,** and select service shim thickness required based on measurements made in step 2.
4. Place outer races over side bearings, mount differential assembly in housing and insert service spacer between each bearing race and housing with chamfered edge against housing.
5. Install left bearing cap to retain case assembly and tighten bolts hand tight so that case can be moved while checking adjustments. **A bearing cap bolt can be installed in lower right bearing cap hole to prevent case from dropping while performing shim adjustments.**
6. Select one or two shims totaling thickness calculated in step 3 and insert shims between right bearing cap and service spacer.
7. Insert progressively larger feeler gauges between shim and service spacer until noticeable increase in drag can be felt, pushing gauge down until it contacts housing bore to obtain proper reading. **Rotate case while inserting gauges to ensure even readings.**

4.32mm (.170") SERVICE SPACER

TOTAL THICKNESS OF BOTH PROD. SHIMS REMOVED	TOTAL THICKNESS OF SERVICE SHIMS TO BE USED AS A STARTING POINT
10.57mm .420"	1.52mm .060"
10.92mm .430"	1.78mm .070"
11.18mm .440"	2.03mm .080"
11.43mm .450"	2.29mm .090"
11.68mm .460"	2.54mm .100"
11.94mm .470"	2.79mm .110"
12.19mm .480"	3.05mm .120"
12.45mm .490"	3.30mm .130"
12.70mm .500"	3.56mm .140"
12.95mm .510"	3.81mm .150"
13.21mm .520"	4.06mm .160"
13.46mm .530"	4.32mm .170"
13.97mm .550"	4.83mm .190"

GC3039100217000X

Fig. 7 Service shim thickness chart

8. The gauge used just before additional drag is felt is correct thickness to obtain "zero preload." By starting with a thin gauge a sense of feel can be obtained for the original light drag caused by the weight of the case, allowing the drag caused by the beginning of preload to be recognized. **It will be necessary to work case in and out and to the left in order to insert feeler gauges.**
9. When the proper gauge thickness has been determined to obtain zero preload, remove bearing cap, case assembly service spacers and shim pack.
10. Select 2 service shims of approximate equal thickness whose total thickness is equal to the thickness of the shims installed in step 6 plus the thickness of the feeler gauge used to obtain zero preload.
11. Shims selected during this procedure allow differential assembly to be installed at zero preload, the equivalent of a "slip-fit" in case, during backlash adjustment. Final preload is not added until backlash has been adjusted.

Corvette

This procedure is performed before the drive pinion or ring gear is installed. If yoke seals and bearings were removed, install then at this time.

1. Ensure bearing bores and caps are clean and free of burrs.
2. Install master differential bearings J-34170 on 7.874 inch axles or J-35505 on 8.5 inch axles.
3. Assemble case assembly into carrier. Mount dial indicator with plunger travel of at least .200 inch to supporting fixture with plunger on the flange face.
4. Force case assembly as far as possible in dial indicator direction. With force still applied to case, zero dial indicator.
5. While observing dial indicator movement, force differential case in opposite direction. Repeat this step until the same reading is obtained.
6. Record dial indicator reading. The reading will be used during "Final Assembly And Backlash Adjustment."
7. Remove differential case assembly from carrier.

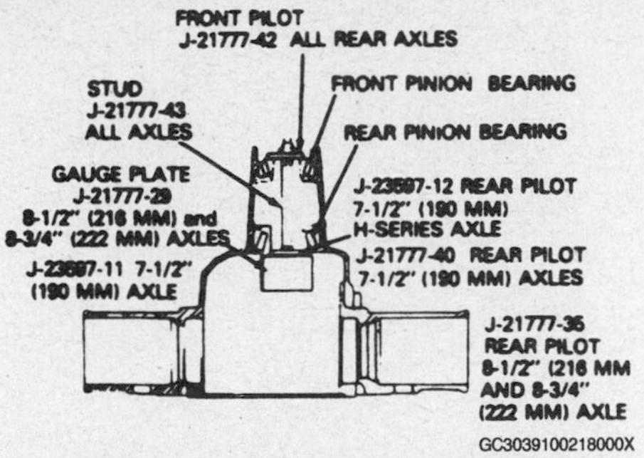
FRONT PILOT
J-21777-42 ALL REAR AXLES
STUD
J-21777-43
ALL AXLES
FRONT PINION BEARING
REAR PINION BEARING
GAUGE PLATE
J-21777-29
8-1/2" (216 MM) and
8-3/4" (222 MM) AXLES
J-23597-11 7-1/2"
(190 MM) AXLE
J-23597-12 REAR PILOT
7-1/2" (190 MM)
H-SERIES AXLE
J-21777-40 REAR PILOT
7-1/2" (190 MM) AXLES
J-21777-36
REAR PILOT
8-1/2" (216 MM
AND 8-3/4"
(222 MM) AXLE
GC3039100218000X

Fig. 8 Pinion gauge plate installation

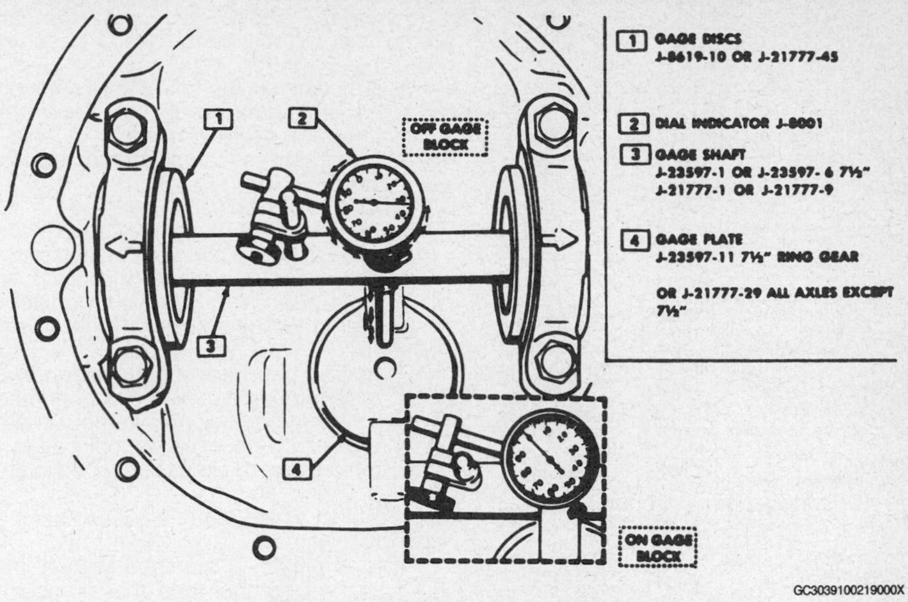
1
2
3
4
OFF GAGE BLOCK
ON GAGE BLOCK
1 GAGE DISCS
J-8619-10 OR J-21777-45
2 DIAL INDICATOR J-8001
3 GAGE SHAFT
J-23597-1 OR J-23597- 6 7½"
J-21777-1 OR J-21777-9
4 GAGE PLATE
J-23597-11 7½" RING GEAR
OR J-21777-29 ALL AXLES EXCEPT 7½"
GC3039100219000X

Fig. 9 Checking pinion depth

DRIVE PINION INSTALLATION & ADJUSTMENT

EXCEPT CORVETTE

Pinion Depth Adjustment

1. Install pinion bearing races in housing using a suitable driver.
2. Lubricate pinion bearings and install bearings in races.
3. Mount depth gauging jig in housing, **Fig. 8**, noting the following:
   a. Assemble gauge plate onto preload stud.
   b. Hold pinion bearings in position, insert stud through rear bearing and pilot and front bearing and pilot, then install retaining nut and tighten nut until snug.
   c. Rotate tool to ensure bearings are properly seated.
   d. Hold preload stud and tighten nut until 20 inch lbs. of torque which is required to rotate stud. To prevent damage to bearing, **tighten nut in small increments, checking rotating torque after each adjustment.**
   e. Mount side bearing discs on arbor, using step for disc that corresponds to base of housing.
   f. Mount arbor and plunger assembly in housing, ensuring side bearing discs are properly seated, install bearing caps and tighten cap bolts to prevent bearing discs from moving, **Fig. 9.**
4. Mount dial indicator on arbor stud with indicator contact button bearing against top of arbor plunger.
5. Preload indicator 3/4 revolution and secure to arbor mounting stud in this position.
6. Place arbor plunger on gauge plate, rotating plate as needed so that plunger rests directly on button corresponding to ring gear size.
7. Slowly rock plunger rod back and forth across button while observing dial indicator.
8. At point on button where indicator registers greatest deflection, zero dial indicator. **Perform steps 7 and 8 several times to ensure correct setting.**
9. Once verified zero reading is obtained, swing plunger aside until it is clear of gauge plate button and record dial indicator reading. **Indicator will now read required pinion depth shim thickness for a "nominal" pinion.**
10. Inspect rear face of drive pinion to be installed for a pinion code number. This number indicates in thousandths of an inch necessary modification of pinion shim thickness obtained in step 9.
11. Select pinion depth adjusting shim as follows:
    a. If pinion is stamped with a plus (+) number, add that number of thousandths to dimension obtained in step 9.
    b. If pinion is stamped with a minus (-) number, subtract that many thousandths from dimension obtained in step 9.
    c. If pinion is not stamped with plus or minus number, dimension obtained in step 9 is correct shim thickness.
12. Remove gauging tools and pinion bearings from housing, noting installation position of bearings.

Pinion Installation

1. Install selected shim onto pinion shaft, lubricate rear pinion bearing with specified axle lubricant, then press rear bearing onto pinion using suitable spacers.
2. Install new collapsible spacer onto pinion shaft, then insert pinion assembly into housing.
3. Lubricate front pinion bearing, install bearing into housing and tap bearing over pinion shaft with a drift while assistant holds pinion in place. **Old pinion nut and a large washer can be used to seat front bearing on pinion, but care must be taken not to collapse spacer if this method is used.**
4. Install new pinion seal in housing, coat seal lips with grease, then mount driveshaft yoke on pinion shaft, lightly tapping yoke until several pinion shaft threads protrude from yoke.
5. Coat rear of pinion washer with suitable sealer, then install washer and new pinion nut.
6. Hold driveshaft yoke with suitable tool, then alternately tighten pinion nut and rotate pinion until endplay is reduced to zero.
7. When endplay is reduced to zero, check pinion bearing preload using a torque wrench.
8. **On models except 1993-94 Camaro and Firebird,** continue tightening pinion nut in small increments until 35-40 inch lbs. of bearing preload is obtained with new bearings or 20-25 inch lbs. of bearing preload is obtained with used bearings, rotating pinion and checking preload after each adjustment. **Exceeding preload specification will compress collapsible spacer too far, requiring replacement of spacer. If preload specification is exceeded, spacer must be replaced and adjustment procedure must be repeated. Do not loosen pinion nut to reduce preload.**
9. **On 1993-94 Camaro and Firebird models,** nut should be further tightened only slightly and preload should be checked after each tightening. Exceeding preload specifications will compress the collapsible spacer too far and require installation of a new spacer. Set preload at 15-30 inch lbs. on new inner and outer bearing assemblies or 10-15 inch lbs. on used inner and outer bearing assemblies. Rotate drive pinion several times to ensure that inner and outer baring assemblies have been seated, then check preload again. If preload has been reduced by rotating drive pinion gear, reset preload to specifications.

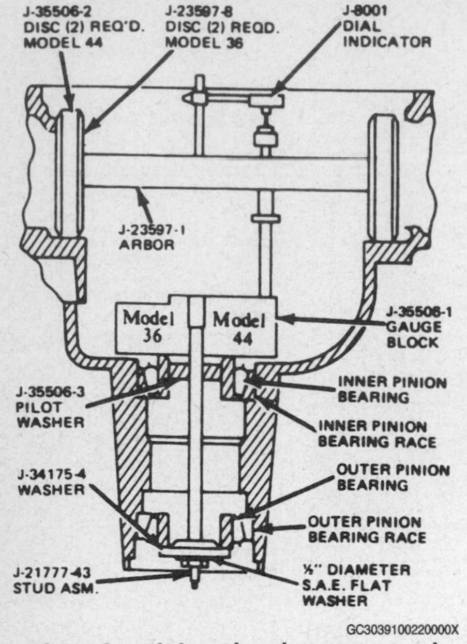
J-35506-2
DISC (2) REQ'D.
MODEL 44
J-23597-8
DISC (2) REQD.
MODEL 36
J-8001
DIAL
INDICATOR
J-23597-1
ARBOR
Model 36
Model 44
J-35506-1
GAUGE
BLOCK
J-35506-3
PILOT
WASHER
INNER PINION
BEARING
INNER PINION
BEARING RACE
J-34175-4
WASHER
OUTER PINION
BEARING
OUTER PINION
BEARING RACE
J-21777-43
STUD ASM.
½" DIAMETER
S.A.E. FLAT
WASHER
GC3039100220000X

Fig. 10 Pinion depth gauge tool installation. Corvette

CORVETTE

Pinion Depth Adjustment

The standard setting for the drive pinion is 2.565 inches on 7.874 ring gear axles or 2.625 inches on 8.5 inch ring gear axles.

1. Install pinion bearing races in housing using suitable driver.
2. Lubricate pinion bearings and install bearings in races.
3. Mount depth gauging jig in housing, **Fig. 10,** noting the following:
   a. Assemble gauge plate onto preload stud.
   b. Hold pinion bearings in position, insert stud through rear bearing and pilot and front bearing and pilot, then install retaining nut and tighten nut until snug.
   c. Rotate tool to ensure bearings are properly seated.
   d. Hold preload stud and tighten nut until 10 inch lbs. of **torque** which is required to rotate stud. To prevent damage to bearing, **tighten nut in small increments, checking rotating torque after each adjustment.**
   e. Mount proper side bearing discs on arbor.
   f. Mount arbor and plunger assembly in housing, ensuring side bearing discs are properly seated, install bearing caps and tighten cap bolts until a slight resistance is felt while rotating arbor.
4. Mount a dial indicator on arbor stud with indicator contact button bearing against top of arbor plunger.
5. Preload indicator 3/4 revolution and secure to arbor mounting stud in this position.
6. Place arbor plunger on gauge plate, rotating plate as needed so that plunger rests directly on button corresponding to ring gear size.
7. Slowly rock plunger rod back and forth across button while observing dial indicator.
8. At point on button where indicator registers greatest deflection, zero dial indicator. **Perform steps 7 and 8 several times to ensure correct setting.**
9. Once verified zero reading is obtained, swing plunger aside until it is clear of gauge plate button and record dial indicator reading. **Indicator will now read required pinion depth shim thickness for a "nominal" pinion.**
10. Inspect rear face of drive pinion to be installed for a pinion code number. This number indicates in thousandths of an inch necessary modification of pinion shim thickness obtained in step 9.
11. Select pinion depth adjusting shim as follows:
    a. If pinion is stamped with a plus (+) number, add that number of thousandths to dimension obtained in step 9.
    b. If pinion is stamped with a minus (-) number, subtract that many thousandths from dimension obtained in step 9.
    c. If pinion is not stamped with plus or minus number, dimension obtained in step 9 is correct shim thickness.
12. Remove gauging tools and pinion bearings from housing, noting installation position of bearings.

Pinion Installation

1. Install correct pinion depth shim in axle housing bearing cup bore, then install inner bearing cup using a bearing installer.
2. Apply appropriate axle lubricant to inner and outer pinion bearings. Apply oil to pinion seal, then install with seal installer.
3. Assemble new pinion preload shim stack with thickness being the same as was removed, then place preload stack on pinion and install pinion, oil slinger and end yoke in axle housing. Use a wooden hammer to tap end yoke onto pinion splines.
4. Install pinion nut and washer. While holding end yoke, **torque** pinion nut to 200 ft. lbs.
5. Using an inch lbs. torque wrench, check rotating torque of pinion shaft. Pinion rotating **torque** should be 25 inch lbs on 7.875 axles or 30 inch lbs. on 8.5 axles with new bearings. To increase preload, remove shims. To decrease preload, add shims.

FINAL ASSEMBLY & BACKLASH ADJUSTMENT

Except Corvette

1. Ensure pinion depth and bearing preload are properly adjusted.
2. Install differential case assembly and selected side bearing shims as outlined in "Differential Side Bearing Preload, Adjust."

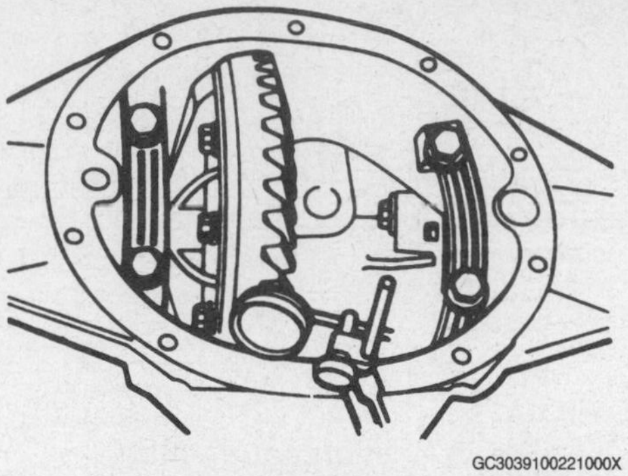
GC3039100221000X

Fig. 11 Checking ring gear & pinion backlash

3. Install bearing caps in proper position and **torque** cap bolts to 55 ft. lbs.
4. Rotate assembly to ensure bearings are properly seated.
5. Mount dial indicator on housing with plunger bearing against tooth on ring gear, **Fig. 11.** Use small contact button on indicator plunger so that contact can be made at heel end of tooth and position dial indicator with plunger inline with gear rotation and perpendicular to gear tooth.
6. Hold pinion stationary and rock ring gear back and forth while reading backlash on indicator.
7. Check backlash at 3 evenly spaced positions around ring gear and record readings. **If backlash varies by more than .002 inch at any position, check ring gear installation and runout, and correct as needed.**
8. If backlash is not within specifications, remove differential case assembly and bearing shims keeping shims in order.
9. Backlash is adjusted by increasing thickness of one shim while decreasing thickness of opposite side shim by the same amount in order to maintain proper side bearing preload. Select shims to adjust backlash as follows:
   a. If backlash is excessive, increase thickness of shim on gear tooth side and decrease thickness of shim on opposite side by the same amount.
   b. If backlash is less than specified, decrease thickness of shim on gear tooth side while increasing thickness of opposite shim by the same amount. **Each .002 inch change in shim thickness alters backlash by .001 inch.**
10. Reinstall differential assembly, shims and bearing caps, **torque** bearing cap bolts to 55 ft. lbs., then recheck backlash and adjust as needed.
11. If side bearing preload was set to zero during side bearing preload adjustment, proceed as follows:
    a. Remove both bearing caps and shim packs, keeping shim packs in respective left or right positions.
    b. Select left side differential preload shim from specifications chart and insert shim between left bearing race and spacer, then install left bearing cap with bolts hand tight.

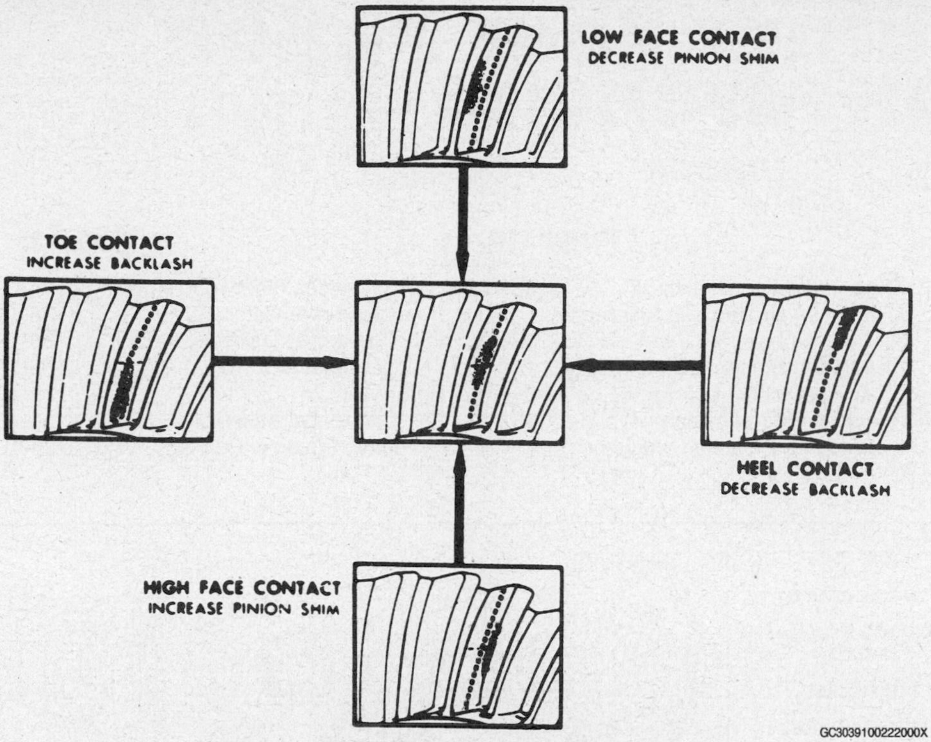
LOW FACE CONTACT
DECREASE PINION SHIM
TOE CONTACT
INCREASE BACKLASH
HEEL CONTACT
DECREASE BACKLASH
HIGH FACE CONTACT
INCREASE PINION SHIM
GC3039100222000X

Fig. 12 Gear tooth contact pattern check

c. Select right side differential preload shim from specifications chart and insert shim between right bearing race and spacer using a soft faced hammer.
d. Install right bearing cap and **torque** all cap bolts to 55 ft. lbs.

12. Ensure ring gear teeth are clean and free from oil, then coat both drive and coast side of each tooth with marking compound.
13. Apply braking force to "load" ring gear, then rotate driveshaft yoke with wrench so that ring gear rotates one full revolution in each direction. **Test made without "loading" gears will not yield satisfactory pattern, and excessive rotating of gears is not recommended.**
14. Compare gear tooth pattern with **Fig. 12,** and correct assembly adjustments as needed.
15. When proper gear tooth contact pattern has been obtained, clean marking compound from gears.
16. Install axles and driveshaft. Refer to "Rear Axle, Propeller Shaft & Brakes" for procedure.
17. Install rear cover using RTV or new gasket and **torque** cover bolts to 20 ft. lbs., then fill rear axle with appropriate lubricant. On models equipped with limited slip differential, add additive No. 1050428 or equivalent to rear axle lubricant.

CORVETTE

1. Ensure differential case flange is free of nicks and burrs, then install ring gear on case using new bolts. **Torque** attaching bolts to 80 ft. lbs. **Tighten bolts evenly so that ring gear will be properly seated on case.**
2. Install master differential bearings J-34170 on 7.874 inch axles or J-35505 on 8.5 inch axles.
3. Assemble case assembly into carrier and install bearing caps with retaining bolts finger tight, then mount dial indicator to supporting fixture.
4. Force differential case away from pinion gear until completely seated against carrier cross bore face. With force still applied to case, place dial indicator plunger on a flat machined surface of differential case, if available, or on the head of a ring gear screw. Zero dial indicator.
5. Force ring gear to mesh with drive pinion. Rock gear slightly to ensure gear teeth are meshed and note dial indicator reading. Repeat procedure several times to ensure the reading is accurate. Ensure dial indicator reads zero each time the case is seated against cross bore face. The reading, .006 inch for preload and backlash adjustment will be the size of the shim pack between differential case and differential bearing on ring gear side.
6. Remove dial indicator, differential case and master bearings.
7. Assemble shim pack as determined in step 5 to ring gear side hub, then install bearing cone.
8. Take measurement obtained during differential side bearing preload adjustment and subtract shim pack dimension determined in step 5. The resulting dimension should be .015-.020 inch on models with 7.874 inch axle or .008-.012 inch on models with 8.5 inch rear axle.
9. Assemble shim pack as determined in step 8 to hub opposite ring gear, then install bearing cone.
10. Install spreader tool, J-24385-01, adapter, J-24385 and dial indicator set, **Fig. 2.** Zero indicator and ensure indicator stylus contacts one side of housing opening.
11. While observing micrometer, spread housing with tool. Do not spread housing more than 0.010 inch or distortion could result.
12. Assemble differential bearing cups on case, then install case in rear housing. If necessary, use a soft faced hammer to seat case in carrier cross bore.
13. Install bearing caps and bolts. Ensure letters stamped on caps correspond in position and direction with letters stamped in carrier. **Torque** bolts to 45 ft. lbs. on models with 7.874 inch rear axle or 63 ft. lbs. on models with 8.5 inch rear axle.
14. Check ring gear and pinion backlash at three equally spaced points with dial indicator. Backlash tolerance is .006-.009. Backlash cannot vary between points checked more than .001-.0015.
15. If backlash is excessive, move shims from side opposite ring gear to ring gear side, but do not change the combined total thickness of both shim packs.
16. If backlash is too small, move shims from ring gear side to side opposite ring gear, but do not change the combined total thickness of both shim packs.
17. Install inner yoke shafts into carrier, then the shaft snap rings. Check axle shaft endplay. If endplay is not within .0005-.0085 inch, install thicker or narrower axle shaft snap ring as necessary.
18. Install axle housing cover with RTV or gasket to rear housing and install bolts.
19. Install rear axle assembly. Refer to "Rear Axle, Propeller Shaft & Brakes" for procedure.
20. Add four ounces of limited slip additive No. 1052358 or equivalent to rear axle, then top off with rear axle lubricant No. 1052271 or equivalent.

Borg Warner Four Pinion Differential

INDEX

REMOVAL

DIFFERENTIAL ASSEMBLY

1. Raise and support rear of vehicle, then loosen axle housing cover bolts and allow lubricant to drain into a container.
2. Remove axle housing cover, then proceed as follows:
   a. Wipe excess lubricant from inside axle housing, then visually inspect parts for wear and/or damage.
   b. Rotate gears and check for roughness, indicating damaged bearings or gears.
   c. Install dial indicator on axle housing cover flange, then check and record ring gear to drive pinion backlash.
3. Remove rear axles and propeller shaft.
4. If not previously marked, scribe reference marks on differential bearing caps to be used during reassembly, then remove bearing cap attaching bolts and caps.
5. Remove differential assembly from carrier by putting a box wrench on ring gear bolt and rotating companion flange with suitable tool. When differential assembly is removed from carrier, shims will also come out. Mark shims for reference during reassembly.

DRIVE PINION & BEARINGS

1. Remove pinion nut and companion flange using tool J-8614-01 or equivalent.
2. Remove drive pinion gear through rear of carrier using a hammer.
3. Pry front seal out of carrier assembly, then remove bearing cone.
4. Remove rear pinion bearing using tool J-33868 or equivalent and press.
5. Remove rear bearing cone from carrier using a punch.
6. Remove selective spacer washer.

1–DIFF. CASE
2–SIDE GEAR (2)
3–THRUST WASHER (S. G.) (2)
4–DIFF. CASE
5–PINION CROSS SHAFT (1)
6–RETAINER PINS (3)
7–PINION SHAFT (SHORT) (2)
8–THRUST WASHERS (DIFF PINION) (4)
9–DIFF. PINIONS (4)
10–THRUST BLOCK (1)
11–SIDE CASE BEARINGS

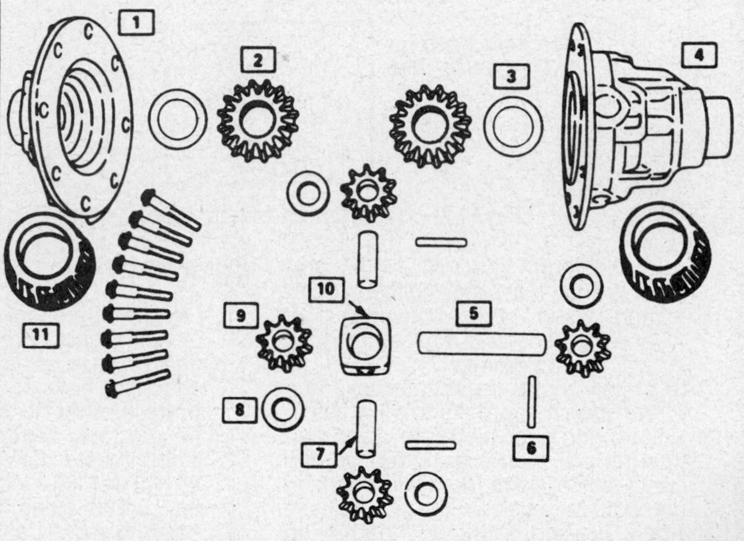

1
2
3
4
5
6
7
8
9
10
11

GC3039100223000X

Fig. 1 Exploded view of Borg Warner 4 pinion standard differential

DIFFERENTIAL CASE OVERHAUL

4 PINION STANDARD DIFFERENTIAL ASSEMBLY

1. Remove ring gear attaching bolts, then the ring gear from differential housing.
2. Drive out three differential pinion cross shaft retaining pins, **Fig. 1**, using a punch.
3. Drive three differential pinion shafts from housing using a punch. Remove long pinion shaft first.
4. Scribe alignment marks on differential case halves, then separate differential case halves by holding one side and tapping against other side with a soft hammer.
5. Remove four differential pinions, side gears and thrust washers from housing.
6. Remove differential case bearings using puller tool J-22888-20 or equivalent.
7. Inspect components as outlined in "Cleaning & Inspection" and replace as required.
8. Lubricate all gears and thrust washers with appropriate lubricant.
9. Install side gear thrust washers in differential case. Hold washers in position with grease.
10. Install side gear in large half of differential case.
11. Install thrust block in case, then drive long pinion cross shaft through case, pinion and thrust block bores. Align retainer pin hole with hole in case. **Use caution not to damage differential pinion thrust washers.**
12. Install two remaining pinions and thrust washers in large half of differential case. Drive two short pinion cross shafts through case, pinions and into thrust block bores. Align retainer pin hole with hole in case.
13. Install three cross shaft retaining pins through case and shafts. Ensure long cross shaft retaining pin extends 6 mm from case.
14. Install remaining side gear and thrust washer in small case half.

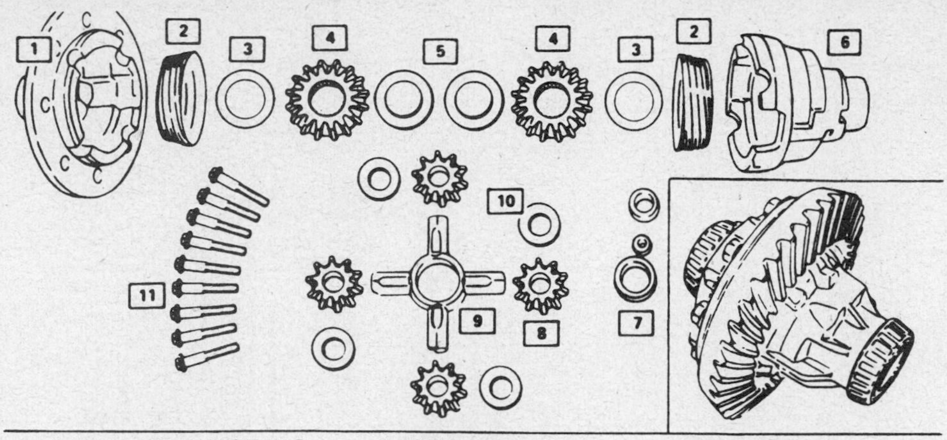

1—DIFF. CASE—FLANGE HALF
2—BRAKE CONES (2)
3—SPRING PLATES (2)
4—SIDE GEARS (2)
5—SHIMS (SIDE GEAR) (IF REQUIRED)
6—DIFF. CASE—CAP HALF
7—COMPRESSION SPRINGS
8—DIFF. PINIONS (4)
9—PINION SHAFT
10—THRUST WASHERS (DIFF. PINION) (4)
11—MOUNTING SCREWS (8)

GC3039100224000X

Fig. 2 Exploded view of Borg Warner 4 pinion limited slip differential

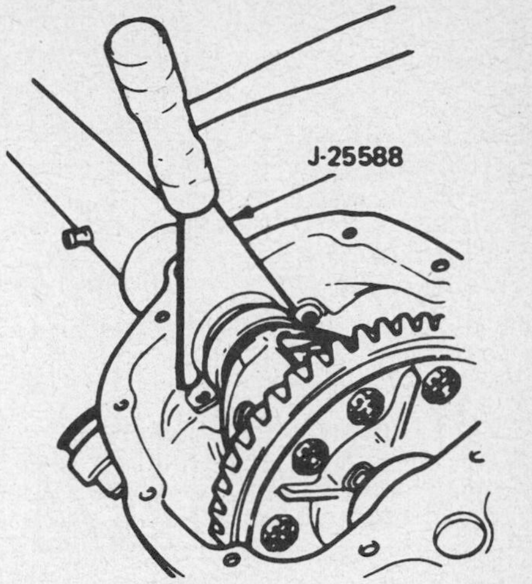
J-25588

GC3039100225000X

Fig. 3 Installing shims

15. Install side gear through case bore, then align case halves on retaining pin. Rotate side gear to ensure gears are meshing.
16. Install ring gear and ring gear attaching bolts onto housing. **Torque** ring gear attaching bolts to 101 ft. lbs.
17. Press differential bearings on housing journals using tool J-21784 or equivalent.

4 PINION LIMITED SLIP DIFFERENTIAL ASSEMBLY

1. Remove ring gear attaching bolts, then the ring gear from differential housing.
2. Scribe alignment marks on differential case halves, then remove differential housing half attaching bolts and separate halves.
3. Scribe alignment marks on brake cones and shims, then remove pinion shaft, four differential pinions, thrust washer side gears, side gear shims if required, spring plates, compression springs and brake cones from housing, **Fig. 2.** Discard used compression springs.
4. Remove differential bearing using puller tool J-22888-20 or equivalent.
5. Inspect components as outlined in "Cleaning & Inspection" and replace as required.
6. Install brake cones in case, then select correct side gear positioning shim as follows:
   a. With brake cones fully seated, measure distance from case mating surface to flat surface on brake cone.
   b. If distance is 1.155-1.162 inches, no shims are required. If distance is 1.163-1.167 inches, .005 inch shim is required. If distance is 1.168-1.172 inches, .010 inch shim is required.
   c. Remove brake cones.
7. Apply suitable lubricant to both sides of pinion thrust washers, pinion bores and differential pinion shafts.
8. Install four pinions and spherical thrust washers.
9. Install brake cones, shims (if required) and side gear in cap half of differential case, then apply suitable lubricant to face of side gear. If cone or case is defective, they should be replaced as an assembly.
10. Install spring plate on side gear with convex side towards flange half.
11. Install differential pinion shaft, pinions and spherical thrust washers into cap half of differential case with pinions meshing with side gear.
12. Install three new concentric thrust washer springs through center of pinion shaft spider, then assemble second spring plate and spring with convex side toward springs.
13. Apply suitable lubricant to other side gear face, then install side gear shim, if required.
14. Install brake cone on spring plate.
15. Install flange half of case on top of assembly. Ensure oil channels are aligned.
16. Install two case attaching bolts 180° apart and tighten finger tight.
17. Align side gear and brake cone splines with axle shafts. Install clamp on one axle shaft so 3 inches extends beyond clamp.
18. Install differential housing on axle shaft splines, flanged half first.
19. Install remaining axle shaft through cap side of differential case, aligning side gear and cone splines.
20. Install remaining case attaching bolts. **Torque** bolts to 29 ft. lbs.
21. Install ring gear and ring gear attaching bolts. **Torque** attaching bolts to 101 ft. lbs.
22. Install differential bearings using tool J-21784 or equivalent.

CLEANING & INSPECTION

1. Clean components in solvent and blow dry with compressed air, noting the following:
   a. Do not use brush when cleaning bearings.
   b. Do not "spin dry" bearings, as bearings will be damaged.
   c. Lightly lubricate components after cleaning to retard corrosion.
   d. Keep all components in order to ensure proper assembly.
2. Inspect gears for cracks, chipped teeth, wear and scoring, and damaged bearing or mounting surfaces. Replace gears that are damaged or excessively worn.
3. Inspect differential case for cracks, damage, worn side gear bores and scored bearing surfaces and replace as needed.
4. Inspect housing for scored bearing mount surfaces, cracks and distortion, and replace as needed.
5. Inspect bearing rollers and races for pitting, scoring, overheating and damage.
6. Mate bearing with race and check operation.
7. Replace any bearing that is damaged, excessively worn or that fails to operate smoothly.

ASSEMBLE

DIFFERENTIAL BEARING PRELOAD ADJUSTMENT

To adjust differential side bearing preload, change thickness of right and left shims equally so original backlash is not disturbed.

1. Ensure side bearing surfaces are clean and free of burrs.
2. Apply suitable lubricant to side bearings. **If original bearings are to be reused, original outer races should also be used.**
3. Install differential case in carrier, with bearing outer races in position.

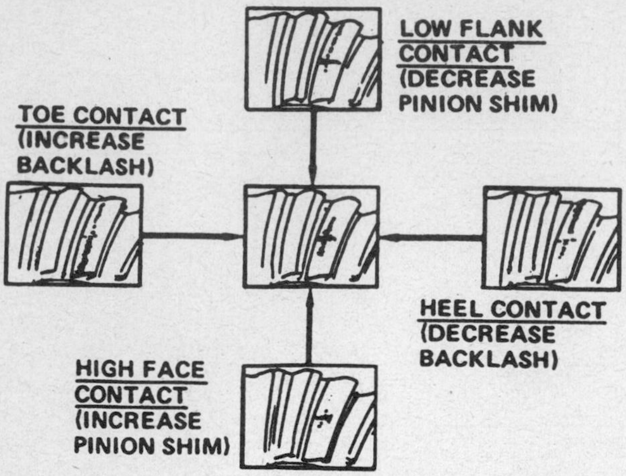
LOW FLANK CONTACT (DECREASE PINION SHIM)
TOE CONTACT (INCREASE BACKLASH)
HEEL CONTACT (DECREASE BACKLASH)
HIGH FACE CONTACT (INCREASE PINION SHIM)
GC3039100226000X

Fig. 4 Gear tooth contact pattern check

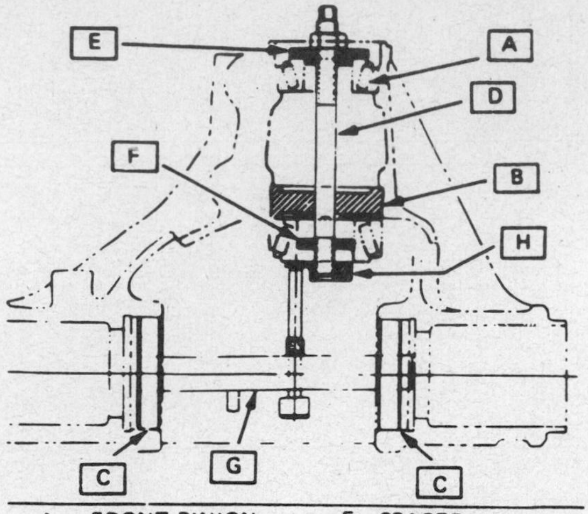
E
A
D
F
B
H
C
G
C

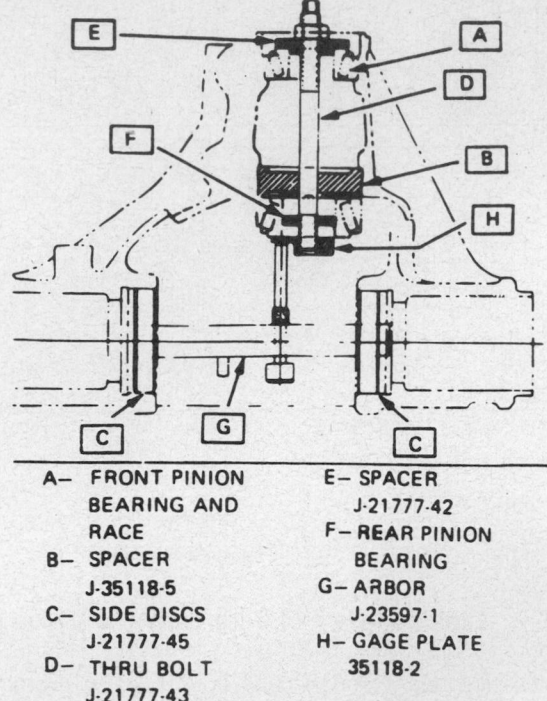

A– FRONT PINION BEARING AND RACE
B– SPACER J-35118-5
C– SIDE DISCS J-21777-45
D– THRU BOLT J-21777-43
E– SPACER J-21777-42
F– REAR PINION BEARING
G– ARBOR J-23597-1
H– GAGE PLATE 35118-2

GC3039100227000X

Fig. 5 Drive pinion & bearing shim adjustment

4. Install left bearing cap and cap attaching bolts loosely so case may be moved during adjustment.
5. Measure original spacers and subtract .004 inch from each reading. Use caution not to interchange right and left spacers.
6. Select a service spacer for each side equal to thickness of original shim minus .004 inch, then install shim as shown in **Fig. 3.** Ensure flat edge of spacer faces against housing.
7. At this point, bearings should have no play and no drag (zero preload). If zero preload is not present, shims should be added or removed equally from both sides as necessary.
8. Check case for zero endplay using a dial indicator. **If shim installation causes excessive pinion to ring gear clearance, select thinner left shim and add difference to right side. Keep total shim thickness at a value equal to that obtained in step 6.**
9. Install both bearing caps and cap attaching bolts. **Torque** bolts 40 ft. lbs.
10. If pinion was not removed, check backlash and tooth pattern as follows:
    a. Apply marking compound on ring gear teeth.
    b. Rotate drive pinion one revolution and check gear tooth contact pattern as shown on **Fig. 4.** Add or remove shims as required.
    c. After backlash and tooth pattern operation has been completed, remove shim packs using caution not to mix them.
    d. Select new shims for each side .004 inch thicker than those removed, then install each shim on its proper side. This additional thickness will ensure proper bearing preload.
    e. Check total rotational torque. Total **torque** with differential case preloaded and pinion installed should be 16-29 inch lbs. if new bearings are installed or 10-16 inch lbs. if original bearings are installed.
    f. If total rotational torque is not as specified, repeat steps 4 through 10.
11. If drive pinion was removed, remove differential case and shims, then proceed to "Drive Pinion & Bearing Shim Adjustment" procedure.

DRIVE PINION & BEARING SHIM ADJUSTMENT

1. Install front pinion bearing cup in carrier using tool J-7817 or equivalent.
2. Install spacer (E) into carrier bore, **Fig. 5.**
3. Slide rear pinion bearing and cap (F) onto thru bolt (D) and rear bearing into axle housing.
4. Install thru bolt (D), rear bearing and cap (F) into axle housing.
5. Assemble front bearing cone (A) and spacer (B) onto thru bolt.
6. Rotate nut and shaft while increasing torque on nut until a rotational **torque** of 15-22 inch lbs. is obtained. Rotate thru bolt back and forth when tightening nut to properly seat bearing.
7. Install discs on thru bolt assembly as shown in **Fig. 5.** Position carrier so dial indicator contact rod is directly over gauging area of gauge plate J-35118-2. **Discs must be fully seated in side bearing bores.**
8. Install bearing caps over gauge shaft discs, then the cap attaching bolts. **torque** attaching bolts to 40 ft. lbs.
9. With dial indicator rod contacting gauging area of J-35118-2, rock gauge shaft back and forth until dial indicator measures the greatest deflection, then zero dial indicator.
10. Rotate gauge shaft until shaft does not contact gauge plate, then note measurement.
11. Select correct pinion shim as follows:
    a. If reusing production pinion, and pinion is marked with a "+," correct shim will have a thickness equal to gauge reading minus amount specified on pinion.
    b. If reusing production pinion, and pinion is marked with a "-," correct shim will have a thickness equal to gauge reading plus amount specified on pinion.
    c. If using a production or service pinion which has no marking, correct shim will have a thickness equal to gauge reading.
12. Install selected pinion shim into carrier, then press rear pinion bearing cup into carrier using tool J-5590 or equivalent.
13. Press rear pinion bearing onto pinion using a bearing installation tool, then install pinion in carrier.
14. Install collapsible spacer and front bearing onto pinion while supporting pinion under head.
15. Install oil seal, companion flange and new nut on pinion, then tighten pinion nut until a rotating **torque** of 10-25 inch lbs. with new bearings or 5-12 inch lbs. with original bearings is obtained while rotating pinion forwards to seat bearings.
16. If preload is excessive after tightening pinion nut, replace collapsible spacer and repeat steps 14 and 15.

FINAL ASSEMBLY & BACKLASH ADJUSTMENT

1. Ensure pinion depth and bearing preload are properly adjusted.
2. Install differential case assembly and selected side bearing shims as outlined in "Differential Bearing Preload Adjustment" procedure.
3. Rotate assembly to ensure bearings are properly seated.
4. Mount dial indicator on housing with indicator stem against tooth on ring gear. Use small contact button on indicator stem so that contact can be made at heel end of tooth and position dial indicator with stem inline with gear rotation and perpendicular to gear tooth.
5. Hold pinion stationary and rock ring gear back and forth while reading backlash on indicator.
6. Check backlash at 3 evenly spaced positions around ring gear and record readings. **If backlash varies by more than .002 inch at any position, check ring gear installation and runout, and correct as needed.**
7. If backlash is not within .004-.007 inch, remove differential case assembly and bearing shims keeping shims in order.
8. Backlash is adjusted by increasing thickness of one shim while decreasing thickness of opposite side shim by the same amount in order to maintain proper side bearing preload. Select shims to adjust backlash as follows:
   a. If backlash is excessive, increase thickness of shim on gear tooth side and decrease thickness of shim on opposite side by the same amount.
   b. If backlash is less than specified, decrease thickness of shim on gear tooth side while increasing thickness of opposite shim by the same amount. **Each .002 inch change in shim thickness alters backlash by .001 inch.**
9. Reinstall differential assembly, shims and bearing caps, **torque** bearing cap bolts to 40 ft. lbs., then recheck backlash and adjust as needed.
10. Ensure ring gear teeth are clean and free from oil, then coat both drive and coast side of each tooth with marking compound.
11. Apply braking force to "load" ring gear, then rotate driveshaft yoke with wrench so that ring gear rotates one full revolution in each direction. **Test made without "loading" gears will not yield satisfactory pattern, and excessive rotating of gears is not recommended.**
12. Compare gear tooth pattern with **Fig. 4**, and correct assembly adjustments as needed.
13. When proper gear tooth contact pattern has been obtained, clean marking compound from gears.
14. Install axles and driveshaft.
15. Install rear cover using new gasket, then fill rear axle with appropriate lubricant.

DRIVE AXLE SPECIFICATIONS

CAMARO & FIREBIRD

Year	Axle Model	Ring Gear Diameter, Inch	Ring Gear Backlash, Inch	Pinion Bearing Preload, Inch Lbs.		Total Assembly Preload, Inch Lbs.		Side Bearing Preload, Inch Lbs.		Differential Bearings, Inch Lbs.	
				New	Used	New	Used	New	Used	Used	New
1992	GM	7.62	.005-.009	15-30	9-12	32-55	16-28	—	—	—	—
1993-94	GM	7.62	.005-.009	15-30	10-15	32-55	16-28	—	—	—	—

BROUGHAM, CAPRICE & IMPALA SS, CUSTOM CRUISER, FLEETWOOD & ROADMASTER

Year	Model	Ring Gear Back Lash, Inch	Pinion Bearing Preload, Inch Lbs.①		Differential Assembly Preload, Inch Lbs.①	
			New Bearings	Used Bearings	New Bearings	Used Bearings
1992-94	All	.005-.009	②	10-15	35-40	20-25

①—Rotating torque with new seal.
②—7½ ring gear, 15-30 inch lbs., 8½ ring gear, 18-36 inch lbs.

CORVETTE

Year	Axle Model	Carrier Type	Ring Gear Backlash		Pinion Bearing Preload		Side Gear Preload	
			Method	Adjustment, Inch	Method	New Bearings Inch Lbs.	Method	Adjustment, Inch
1992–94	Dana Model 36①	Integral	Shims	.006–.009	Shims	15–35	Shims	.015–.020
	Dana Model 44②	Integral	Shims	.006–.009	Shims	20–40	Shims	.008–.012

①—Models with automatic transmission.
②—Models with manual transmission.

ACTIVE SUSPENSION SYSTEMS

TABLE OF CONTENTS

Application Chart

Model	Year	Type	Page No.
Bonneville	1992-94	Electronic Level Control	36-2
Brougham	1992	Electronic Level Control	36-2
Caprice	1992-94	Electronic Level Control	36-2
Impala SS	1994	Electronic Level Control	36-2
Corvette	1992-94	Selective Ride Control	36-30
Custom Cruiser	1992	Electronic Level Control	36-2
DeVille	1992-94	Computer Command Ride Control	36-36
	1992-94	Electronic Level Control	36-2
Eldorado	1992-94	Computer Command Ride Control	36-36
	1993–94	Electronic Level Control	36-2
	1993–94	Road Sensing Suspension	36-48
	1993–94	Speed Sensitive Suspension	36-44
Fleetwood (FWD)	1992	Computer Command Ride Control	36-36
	1992	Electronic Level Control	36-2
Fleetwood (RWD)	1993–94	Electronic Level Control	36-2
LeSabre	1992-94	Electronic Level Control	36-2
	1993–94	Computer Command Ride Control	36-36
Park Avenue	1992-94	Electronic Level Control	36-2
	1993–94	Computer Command Ride Control	36-36
Riviera	1992-93	Electronic Level Control	36-2
Roadmaster	1992-94	Electronic Level Control	36-2
Seville	1992	Computer Command Ride Control	36-36
	1992-94	Electronic Level Control	36-2
	1993–94	Road Sensing Suspension	36-48
	1993–94	Speed Sensitive Suspension	36-44
Toronado/Trofeo	1992	Electronic Level Control	36-2
88	1992-94	Electronic Level Control	36-2
	1993–94	Computer Command Ride Control	36-36
98	1992-94	Electronic Level Control	36-2
	1993–94	Computer Command Ride Control	36-36

Electronic Level Controls (ELC)

NOTE: On Air Bag Equipped Models, Refer To Air Bag System Precautions Located In The Front Of This Manual For System Disarming & Arming Procedures.

INDEX

PRECAUTIONS

AIR BAG SYSTEMS

Refer to "Air Bag System Precautions" in front of this manual for system arming and disarming procedures.

DESCRIPTION

The Electronic Level Control (ELC) system adjusts rear trim height in response to changes in vehicle loading. This system consists of an air compressor assembly, air dryer, exhaust solenoid, compressor relay, height sensor, air adjustable shocks and air tubing. The compressor is activated when the ignition is On and weight is added to the vehicle. The exhaust solenoid is connected directly to the positive side of the battery, allowing the system to exhaust when the ignition is Off and excess weight is removed.

SYSTEM COMPONENTS

Compressor

This assembly is a single-piston air pump powered by a 12 volt DC permanent magnet motor. The compressor head casting contains intake and exhaust valves plus a solenoid-operated exhaust valve which releases air from the system when energized. On Bonneville, Brougham, Delta 88 & 98, Deville, Fleetwood and Park Avenue the compressor is located on the left side of the engine compartment. On Eldorado, Riviera, Seville, Toronado and 1992 full size station wagons the compressor is located at the top of the rear suspension support.

Air Dryer

The air dryer, attached to the compressor outlet, performs two system functions. The dryer contains a dry chemical that absorbs moisture from the air before it is delivered to the shocks. Moisture is removed from the chemical and returned to the air when system is being exhausted. The air dryer also contains a valving arrangement that maintains a minimum air pressure of 7-14 psi in the shocks.

Exhaust Solenoid

The exhaust solenoid is located in the compressor head assembly and provides two functions. The solenoid exhausts air from the system when energized by the height sensor. It also acts as a pressure relief valve to limit maximum pressure output of the compressor.

Compressor Relay

The compressor relay is controlled by the height sensor and completes the 12 volt circuit to the compressor.

Height Sensor

The height sensor controls two circuits, compressor relay coil ground circuit and exhaust solenoid coil ground circuit. To prevent energizing the compressor relay and exhaust solenoid circuits during normal ride motions, the sensor circuit provides a predetermined delay before the ground circuit is completed.

The sensor electronically limits compressor run time and exhaust solenoid energized time. This limit function is necessary to prevent continuous compressor operation in case of a system leak or continuous exhaust solenoid operation. This timer is reset whenever the ignition is turned Off and On, or height sensor exhaust or compressor signal changes.

The height sensor is mounted to the body frame in the rear of the vehicle. The sensor actuator arm is attached to the control arm by a short link.

Air Adjustable Shocks

The shocks are constructed with a plastic sleeve attached to the dust tube and reservoir. This sleeve forms a flexible chamber which will extend the shock when air pressure is increased. In order to maintain proper operation and reliability, a minimum pressure of 7-14 psi must be maintained in the system at all times.

SYSTEM OPERATION

When a load is added to the vehicle, the body is moved down causing the height sensor arm to rotate upward. This movement activates the internal timing circuit which, after a predetermined delay of 8--15 seconds, grounds pin No. 3, thus completing the compressor relay circuit to ground. When the relay circuit is energized, the circuit to the compressor is complete, allowing the compressor to send pressurized air to the shocks.

As the shocks inflate, the vehicle body moves upward, causing the sensor arm to rotate downward. Once the body reaches its original height, the sensor opens the compressor relay circuit and shuts the compressor Off.

When excess load is removed from the rear of the vehicle, the body rises upward, which causes the sensor arm to rotate downward. This movement activates the internal timing circuit which, after a predetermined delay of 8-15 seconds, allows the sensor to complete the exhaust solenoid circuit to ground. With the solenoid energized, air exhausts from the shocks back through the air dryer and exhaust solenoid valve.

As the vehicle body lowers, the height sensor arm is rotated upward until the vehicle reaches its original height. When this height is reached, the sensor opens the exhaust solenoid circuit which prevents air from escaping.

The height sensor position is checked when the ignition is turned On. If the height sensor indicates that it is not necessary to raise or lower the vehicle, the internal timer circuit is activated. After 40 seconds, the compressor will run for four seconds. This ensures the shocks are filled with the proper residual pressure (7-14 psi). If weight is added or removed from the vehicle during this 40 second delay, the air replenishment cycle will be overridden and the vehicle will raise or lower after normal delay.

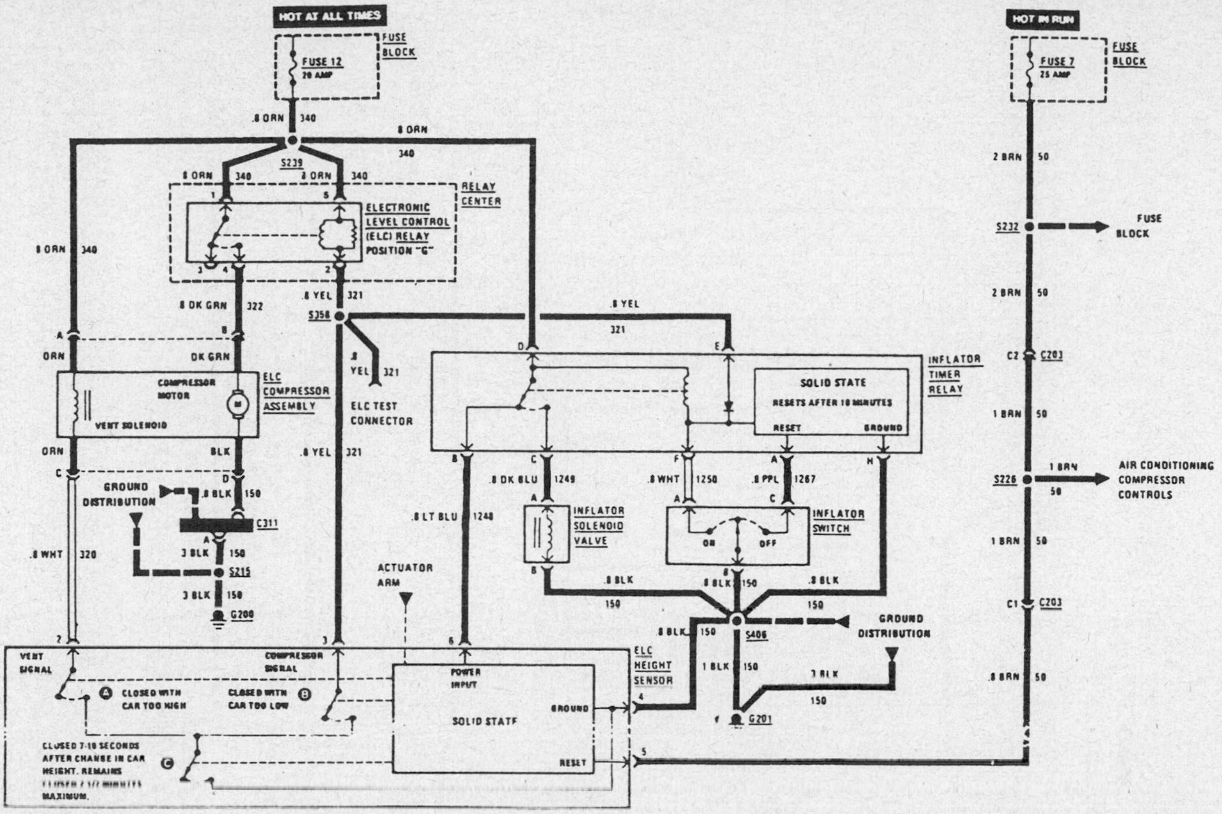
HOT AT ALL TIMES
FUSE 12
20 AMP
FUSE BLOCK
HOT IN RUN
FUSE 7
25 AMP
FUSE BLOCK
RELAY CENTER
ELECTRONIC LEVEL CONTROL (ELC) RELAY POSITION "G"
S239
S232
S358
FUSE BLOCK
COMPRESSOR MOTOR
VENT SOLENOID
ELC COMPRESSOR ASSEMBLY
ELC TEST CONNECTOR
SOLID STATE
RESETS AFTER 10 MINUTES
RESET
GROUND
INFLATOR TIMER RELAY
C203
S226
AIR CONDITIONING COMPRESSOR CONTROLS
GROUND DISTRIBUTION
C311
S215
G200
INFLATOR SOLENOID VALVE
INFLATOR SWITCH
ON
OFF
ACTUATOR ARM
S406
G201
ELC HEIGHT SENSOR
VENT SIGNAL
COMPRESSOR SIGNAL
CLOSED WITH CAR TOO HIGH
CLOSED WITH CAR TOO LOW
POWER INPUT
SOLID STATE
RESET

GC2019100033000X

Fig. 1 ELC wiring diagram. Bonneville

ADJUSTMENTS

When repair or adjustment procedures require that vehicle be raised on a hoist, it is important that the rear axle assembly remains in the normal trim height position at all times. When a frame contact hoist is used, two additional jack stands should be used to support the rear axle or control arms in the normal trim height position.

HEIGHT SENSOR

The link should be properly attached to the sensor arm and track bar, when making this adjustment.

1. Loosen lock bolt that secures metal arm to height sensor plastic arm.
2. To raise vehicle trim height, move plastic arm upward and tighten lock bolt.
3. To lower vehicle trim height, follow step 1 and move plastic arm down.
4. If adjustment cannot be made, check for correct sensor.

DIAGNOSIS & TESTING

When diagnostic procedures require that vehicle be raised on a hoist, it is important that the rear axle assembly remains in the normal trim height position at all times. When a frame contact hoist is used, two additional jack stands should be used to support the rear axle or control arms in the normal trim height position.

ELECTRICAL DIAGNOSIS

Except Eldorado & Seville W/4.6L/V8-279 Engine

If ELC system is inoperative, check fuse in the fuse block.

Refer to ELC wiring circuits, **Figs. 1 through 10** and diagnostic charts, **Figs. 11 through 29**, when performing electrical diagnosis on the ELC system.

Eldorado & Seville W/4.6L/V8-279 Engine

On these models the ELC system is controlled by the Road Sensing Suspension (RSS) control module. For diagnostic procedures on this system, refer to "Road Sensing Suspension."

RESIDUAL AIR CHECK

1. Remove air line from dryer fitting and attach air line from pressure gauge tool No. J 22124-A or equivalent, to dryer fitting as shown in **Fig. 30.**
2. Disconnect electrical connection to pump and jumper 12 volt dark green wire terminal to run compressor. Pump should run until a pressure of 100 psi is reached.
3. Disconnect wiring from compressor exhaust solenoid and jumper 12 volt to one terminal and ground the other terminal to the exhaust system.
4. Air should be exhausted from the system until gauge indicates 7-14 psi.

COMPRESSOR/DRYER PERFORMANCE TEST

1. Disconnect wiring from compressor motor and exhaust solenoid terminals.
2. Disconnect existing pressure line from dryer and attach pressure gauge tool No. J 22124-A or equivalent, to dryer fitting.
3. Connect an ammeter to 12 volt source and to compressor.
4. Operate compressor and note the following:
   a. Current draw should not exceed 14 amps.
   b. When gauge reads at least 100 psi, turn compressor Off by disconnecting power supply and observe if pressure leaks down. Compressor should not leak below 90 psi. If compressor is permitted to run until it reaches maximum output pressure of 180 psi, the solenoid exhaust valve will act as a relief valve. The resulting leak down when compressor is shutoff will indicate a false leak.
   c. Refer to chart shown in **Fig. 31** if compressor fails to meet specification.
   d. If performance is satisfactory, install compressor and connect wiring and air lines.

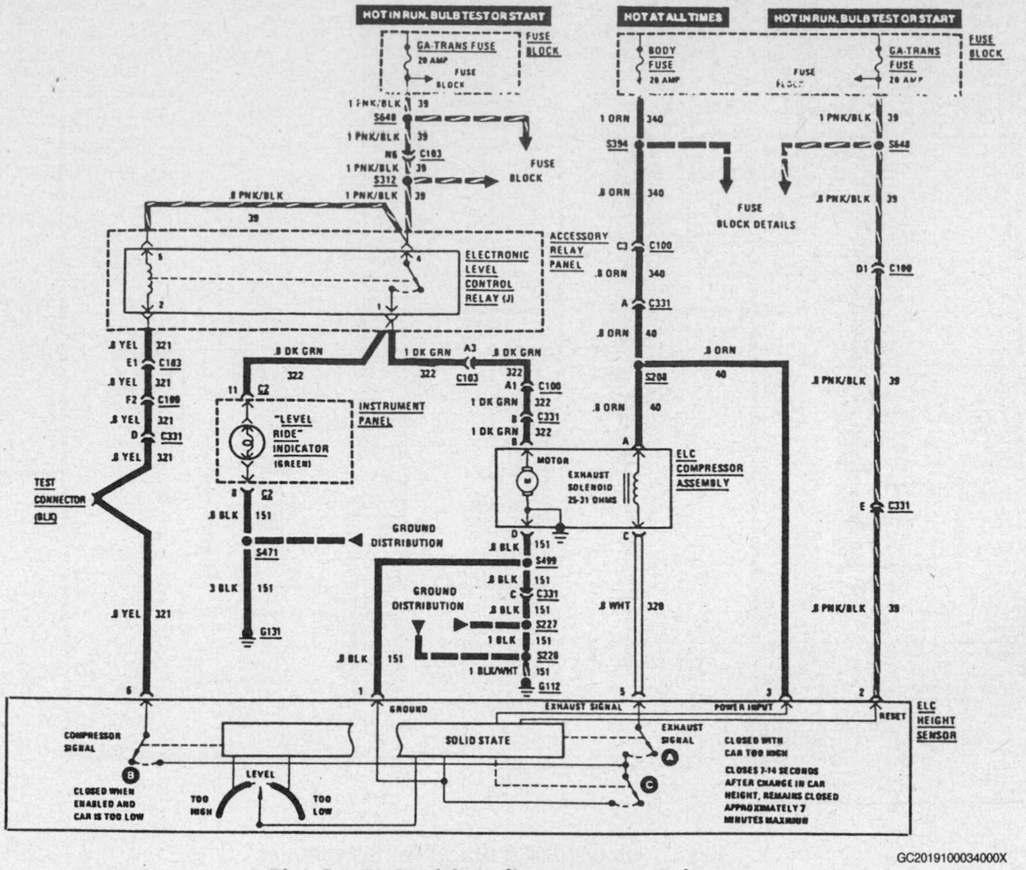
HOT IN RUN, BULB TEST OR START
HOT AT ALL TIMES
HOT IN RUN, BULB TEST OR START
FUSE BLOCK
FUSE BLOCK DETAILS
ACCESSORY RELAY PANEL
ELECTRONIC LEVEL CONTROL RELAY (J)
INSTRUMENT PANEL
"LEVEL RIDE" INDICATOR (GREEN)
TEST CONNECTOR (BLK)
GROUND DISTRIBUTION
ELC COMPRESSOR ASSEMBLY
EXHAUST SOLENOID 25-31 OHMS
ELC HEIGHT SENSOR
SOLID STATE
LEVEL
TOO HIGH
TOO LOW
GC2019100034000X

Fig. 2 ELC wiring diagram. Brougham

ELC SYSTEM LEAK TEST

1. Tee pressure gauge tool No. J 22124-A or equivalent, into ELC system between dryer assembly and pressure regulator valve. Install so that shut-off valve is on the compressor side of gauge.
2. With shutoff valve open, apply service air pressure through service valve on gauge until gauge reads 100 psi.
3. If leak is indicated, close shutoff valve and continue to observe for pressure drop. Closing valve isolates the compressor from the rest of the system.
4. If gauge pressure continues to drop, leak is external to the compressor. Leak test all connections with soap and water or suitable leak test solution.
5. If gauge pressure does not continue to drop, leak is in the compressor. Refer to **Fig. 32** to check compressor for leaks.
6. If pressure builds up rapidly but vehicle does not raise, check for pinched air lines and stuck or binding shocks.

HEIGHT SENSOR OPERATIONAL CHECK

1. Turn ignition Off, then On. This will reset height sensor timer circuits.
2. Raise vehicle on hoist. Ensure rear wheels or axle housing are supported and that vehicle is at proper trim height.
3. Disconnect link from height sensor arm, then ensure sensor wiring and harness ground are connected properly.
4. Move sensor arm upward. There should be a delay of 8-15 seconds before compressor turns on and shocks start to inflate. As soon as shocks start to fill, stop compressor by moving sensor arm down.
5. Move sensor arm down below position where compressor stopped. There should be a delay of 8-15 seconds before shocks start to deflate and vehicle lowers.

SYSTEM SERVICE

When repair or adjustment procedures require that vehicle be raised on a hoist, it is important that the rear axle assembly remains in the normal trim height position at all times. When a frame contact hoist is used, two additional jack stands should be used to support the rear axle or control arms in the normal trim height position.

AIR COMPRESSOR SERVICE

Disassemble

1. Remove the seven compressor cover screws, then the compressor cover and gasket, **Fig. 33.**
2. Remove head and solenoid assembly.
3. Remove two filters, exhaust valve, spring and air dryer O-ring from head assembly.
4. Remove solenoid from head by lifting slightly and sliding to the dryer outlet side.
5. Remove O-ring from solenoid assembly.
6. Remove head gasket from cylinder assembly.
7. Remove four mounting bracket screws, then the bracket and gasket. Note position of ground wire for installation.

Assemble

1. Install gasket and mounting bracket, then the ground wire and screws.
2. Install head gasket on cylinder assembly.
3. Install O-ring on solenoid assembly, then the solenoid in the head with valve opposite air dryer outlet.
4. Install two filters, exhaust valve and spring on head assembly.
5. Install gasket and cover on head assembly, then four short cover screws.
6. Install head and cover assembly to cylinder assembly using three long screws. **Torque** all seven screws in sequence, **Fig. 34,** to 36 inch lbs.
7. Install air dryer O-ring on compressor.

Continued on page 36-21

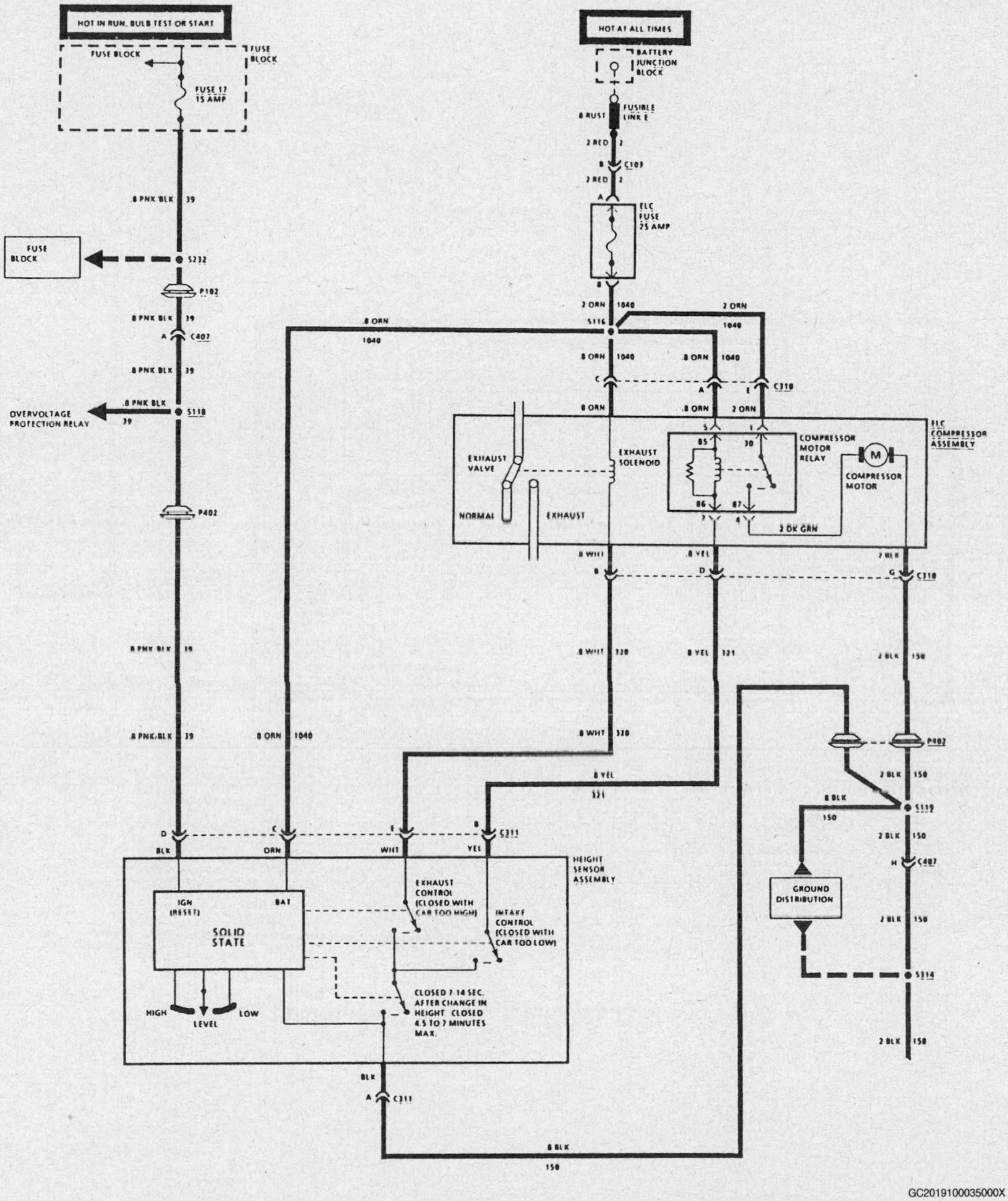
HOT IN RUN, BULB TEST OR START
FUSE BLOCK
FUSE BLOCK
FUSE 17
15 AMP
.8 PNK BLK 39
FUSE BLOCK
S232
P102
.8 PNK BLK 39
A C407
.8 PNK BLK 39
.8 PNK BLK
OVERVOLTAGE PROTECTION RELAY
39
S118
P402
HOT AT ALL TIMES
BATTERY JUNCTION BLOCK
.8 RUST
FUSIBLE LINK E
2 RED 2
B C103
2 RED 2
A
ELC FUSE 25 AMP
B
2 ORN 1040
S116
2 ORN
1040
.8 ORN 1040
.8 ORN 1040
C
A
E
C310
.8 ORN
.8 ORN
2 ORN
ELC COMPRESSOR ASSEMBLY
EXHAUST VALVE
EXHAUST SOLENOID
COMPRESSOR MOTOR RELAY
85
30
86
87
COMPRESSOR MOTOR
NORMAL
EXHAUST
2 DK GRN
.8 WHT
.8 YEL
2 BLK
B
D
G
C310
.8 ORN
1040
.8 WHT 320
.8 YEL 321
2 BLK 150
.8 PNK/BLK 39
.8 ORN 1040
.8 WHT 320
.8 YEL
321
P402
2 BLK 150
.8 BLK
150
S119
2 BLK 150
H C407
D
C
E
B
C311
BLK
ORN
WHT
YEL
HEIGHT SENSOR ASSEMBLY
IGN (RESET)
BAT
SOLID STATE
EXHAUST CONTROL (CLOSED WITH CAR TOO HIGH)
INTAKE CONTROL (CLOSED WITH CAR TOO LOW)
CLOSED 7-14 SEC. AFTER CHANGE IN HEIGHT CLOSED 4.5 TO 7 MINUTES MAX.
HIGH
LEVEL
LOW
GROUND DISTRIBUTION
2 BLK 150
S314
2 BLK 150
BLK
A C311
.8 BLK
150
GC2019100035000X

Fig. 3 ELC wiring diagram. 1992 Caprice, Custom Cruiser & Roadmaster

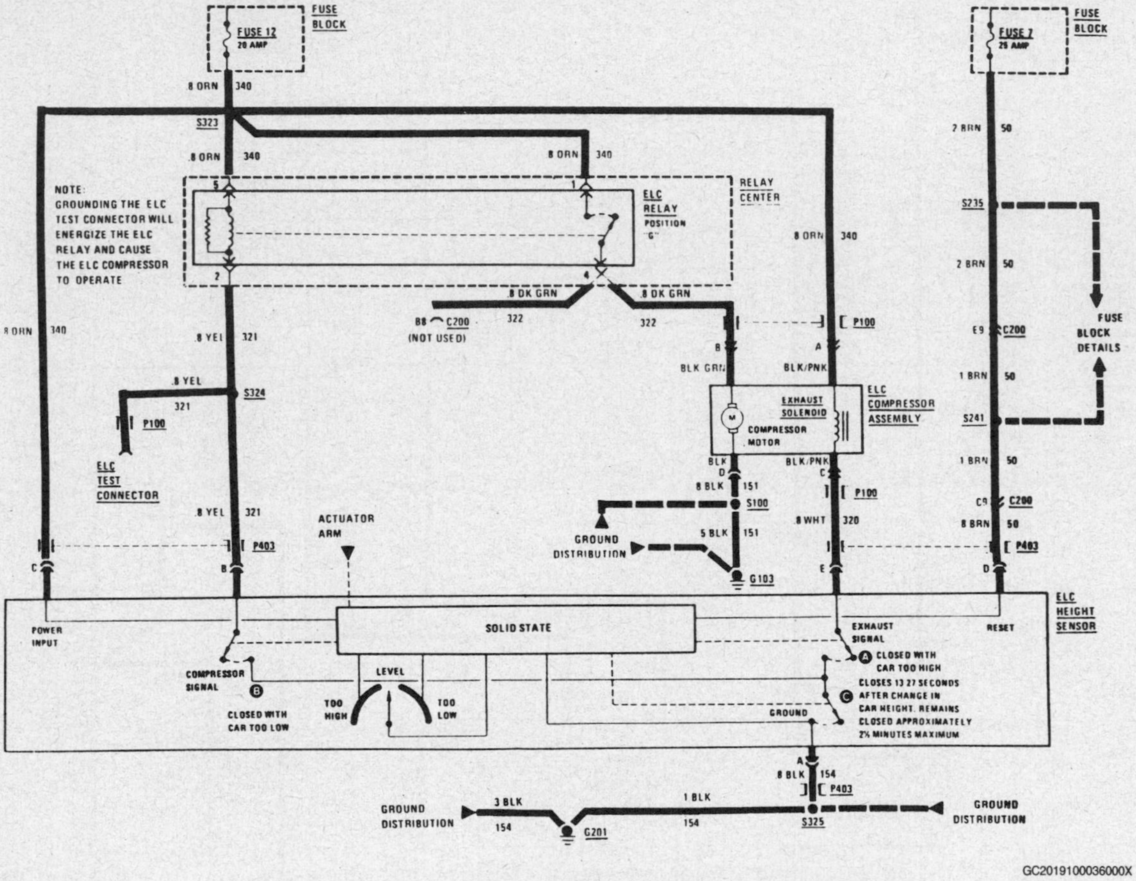
FUSE BLOCK
FUSE 12
20 AMP
8 ORN 340
S323
.8 ORN 340
8 ORN 340
NOTE:
GROUNDING THE ELC TEST CONNECTOR WILL ENERGIZE THE ELC RELAY AND CAUSE THE ELC COMPRESSOR TO OPERATE
ELC RELAY
POSITION "G"
RELAY CENTER
.8 DK GRN
322
B8 C200
(NOT USED)
8 ORN 340
.8 YEL 321
.8 YEL
321
S324
P100
ELC TEST CONNECTOR
.8 YEL 321
P403
ACTUATOR ARM
P100
B
A
BLK GRN
BLK/PNK
EXHAUST SOLENOID
COMPRESSOR MOTOR
ELC COMPRESSOR ASSEMBLY
BLK
D
8 BLK 151
S100
GROUND DISTRIBUTION
5 BLK 151
G103
BLK/PNK
C
P100
.8 WHT 320
E
FUSE BLOCK
FUSE 7
25 AMP
2 BRN 50
S235
2 BRN 50
E9 C200
FUSE BLOCK DETAILS
1 BRN 50
S241
1 BRN 50
C9 C200
8 BRN 50
P403
D
ELC HEIGHT SENSOR
POWER INPUT
SOLID STATE
COMPRESSOR SIGNAL
B
CLOSED WITH CAR TOO LOW
LEVEL
TOO HIGH
TOO LOW
EXHAUST SIGNAL
RESET
A CLOSED WITH CAR TOO HIGH
CLOSES 13 27 SECONDS
C AFTER CHANGE IN CAR HEIGHT. REMAINS CLOSED APPROXIMATELY 2¼ MINUTES MAXIMUM
GROUND
A
8 BLK 154
P403
GROUND DISTRIBUTION
3 BLK
154
G201
1 BLK
154
S325
GROUND DISTRIBUTION
GC2019100036000X

Fig. 4 ELC wiring diagram. DeVille & Fleetwood (FWD)

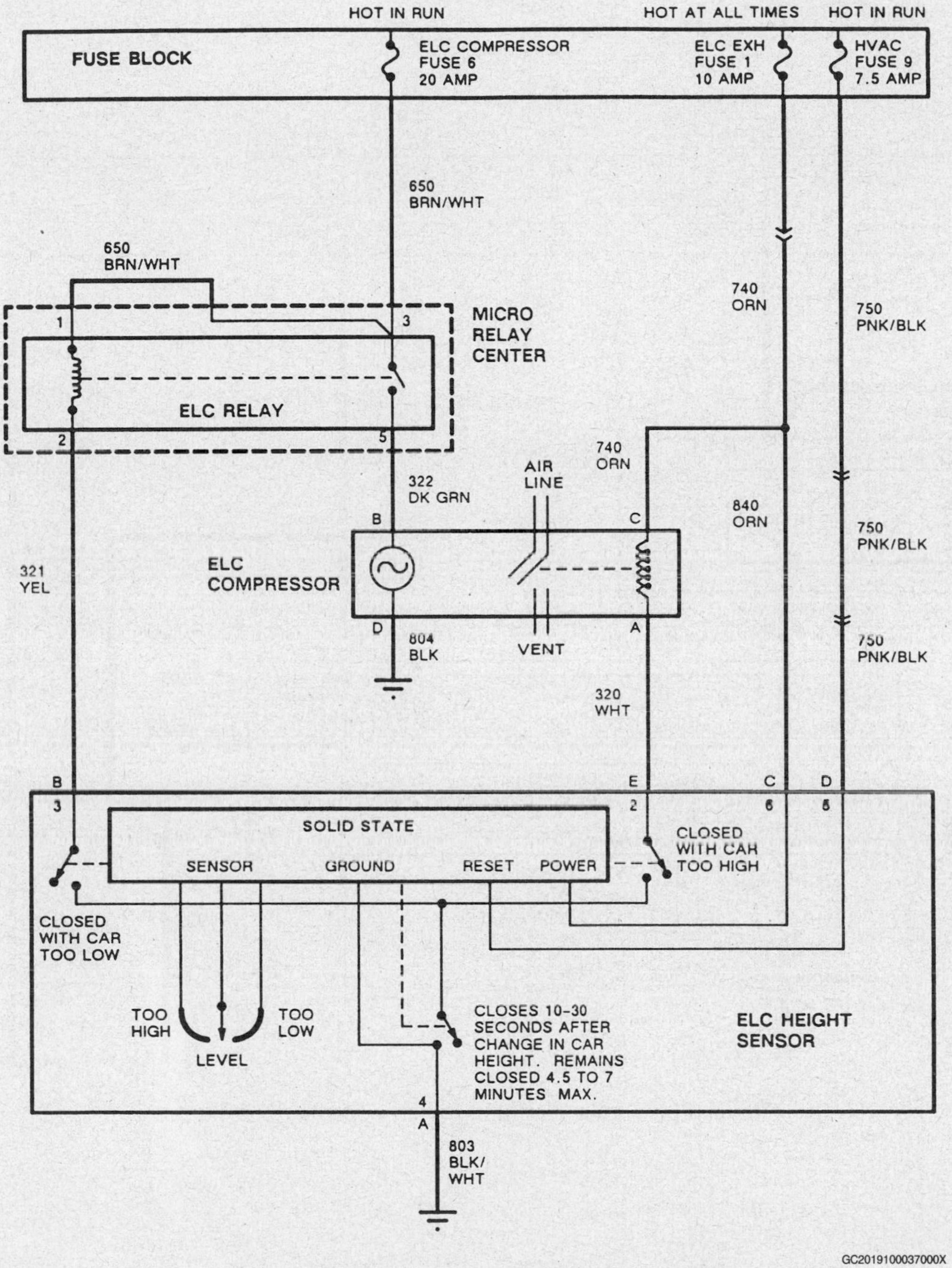
HOT IN RUN
HOT AT ALL TIMES
HOT IN RUN
FUSE BLOCK
ELC COMPRESSOR FUSE 6 20 AMP
ELC EXH FUSE 1 10 AMP
HVAC FUSE 9 7.5 AMP
650 BRN/WHT
650 BRN/WHT
740 ORN
750 PNK/BLK
MICRO RELAY CENTER
ELC RELAY
740 ORN
AIR LINE
322 DK GRN
840 ORN
750 PNK/BLK
321 YEL
ELC COMPRESSOR
804 BLK
VENT
750 PNK/BLK
320 WHT
SOLID STATE
SENSOR
GROUND
RESET
POWER
CLOSED WITH CAR TOO HIGH
CLOSED WITH CAR TOO LOW
TOO HIGH
TOO LOW
LEVEL
CLOSES 10-30 SECONDS AFTER CHANGE IN CAR HEIGHT. REMAINS CLOSED 4.5 TO 7 MINUTES MAX.
ELC HEIGHT SENSOR
803 BLK/ WHT
GC2019100037000X

Fig. 5 ELC wiring diagram. Eldorado & Seville

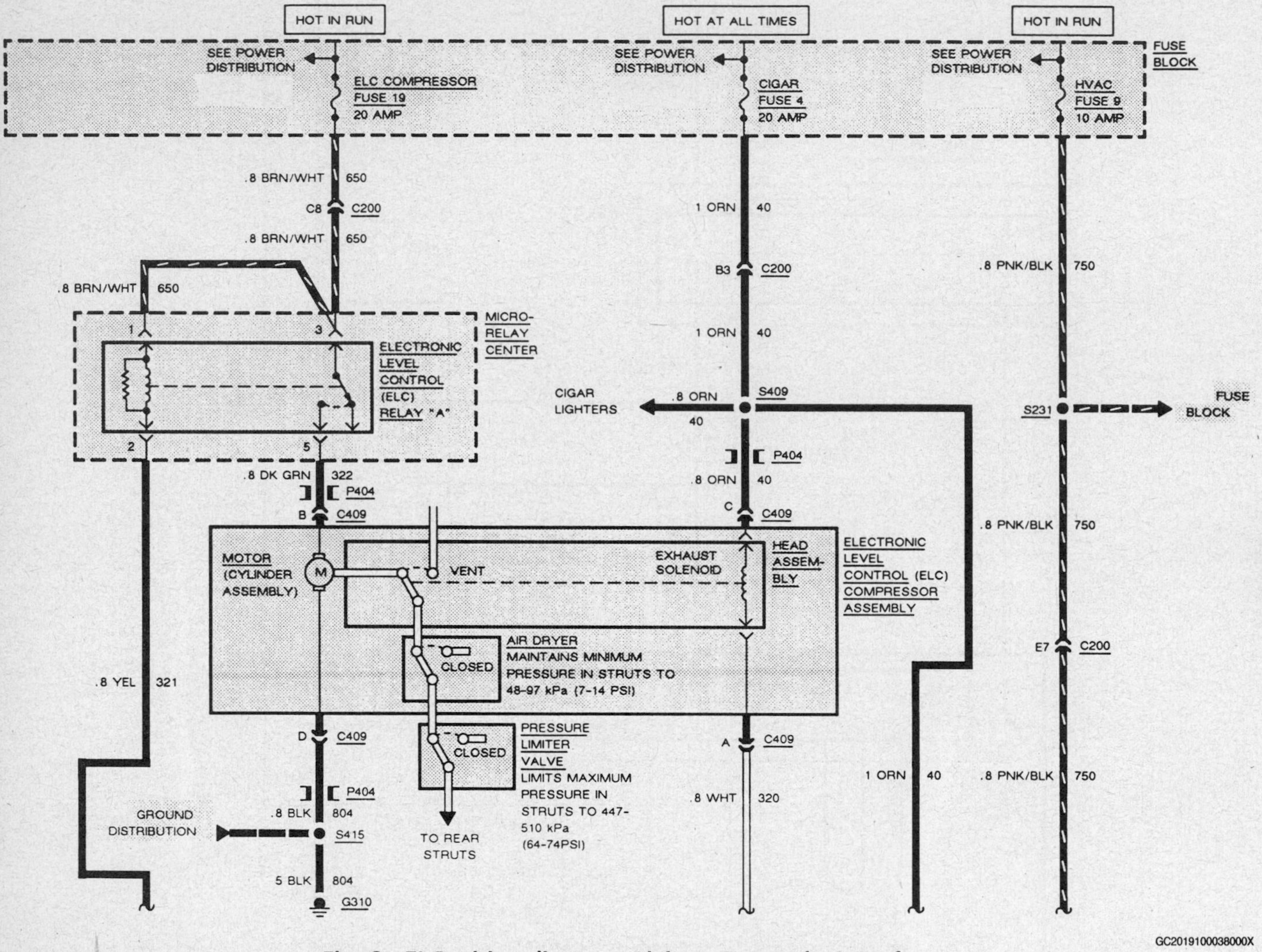
HOT IN RUN
HOT AT ALL TIMES
HOT IN RUN
SEE POWER DISTRIBUTION
ELC COMPRESSOR FUSE 19 20 AMP
SEE POWER DISTRIBUTION
CIGAR FUSE 4 20 AMP
SEE POWER DISTRIBUTION
HVAC FUSE 9 10 AMP
FUSE BLOCK
.8 BRN/WHT 650
C8 C200
.8 BRN/WHT 650
.8 BRN/WHT 650
1 ORN 40
B3 C200
1 ORN 40
.8 PNK/BLK 750
MICRO-RELAY CENTER
ELECTRONIC LEVEL CONTROL (ELC) RELAY "A"
CIGAR LIGHTERS
.8 ORN 40
S409
S231
FUSE BLOCK
P404
.8 ORN 40
C C409
.8 DK GRN 322
P404
B C409
.8 PNK/BLK 750
MOTOR (CYLINDER ASSEMBLY)
VENT
EXHAUST SOLENOID
HEAD ASSEMBLY
ELECTRONIC LEVEL CONTROL (ELC) COMPRESSOR ASSEMBLY
AIR DRYER MAINTAINS MINIMUM PRESSURE IN STRUTS TO 48-97 kPa (7-14 PSI)
CLOSED
E7 C200
.8 YEL 321
D C409
PRESSURE LIMITER VALVE LIMITS MAXIMUM PRESSURE IN STRUTS TO 447-510 kPa (64-74PSI)
CLOSED
A C409
P404
.8 WHT 320
1 ORN 40
.8 PNK/BLK 750
GROUND DISTRIBUTION
.8 BLK 804
S415
TO REAR STRUTS
5 BLK 804
G310
GC2019100038000X

Fig. 6 ELC wiring diagram. Riviera, Toronado & Trofeo

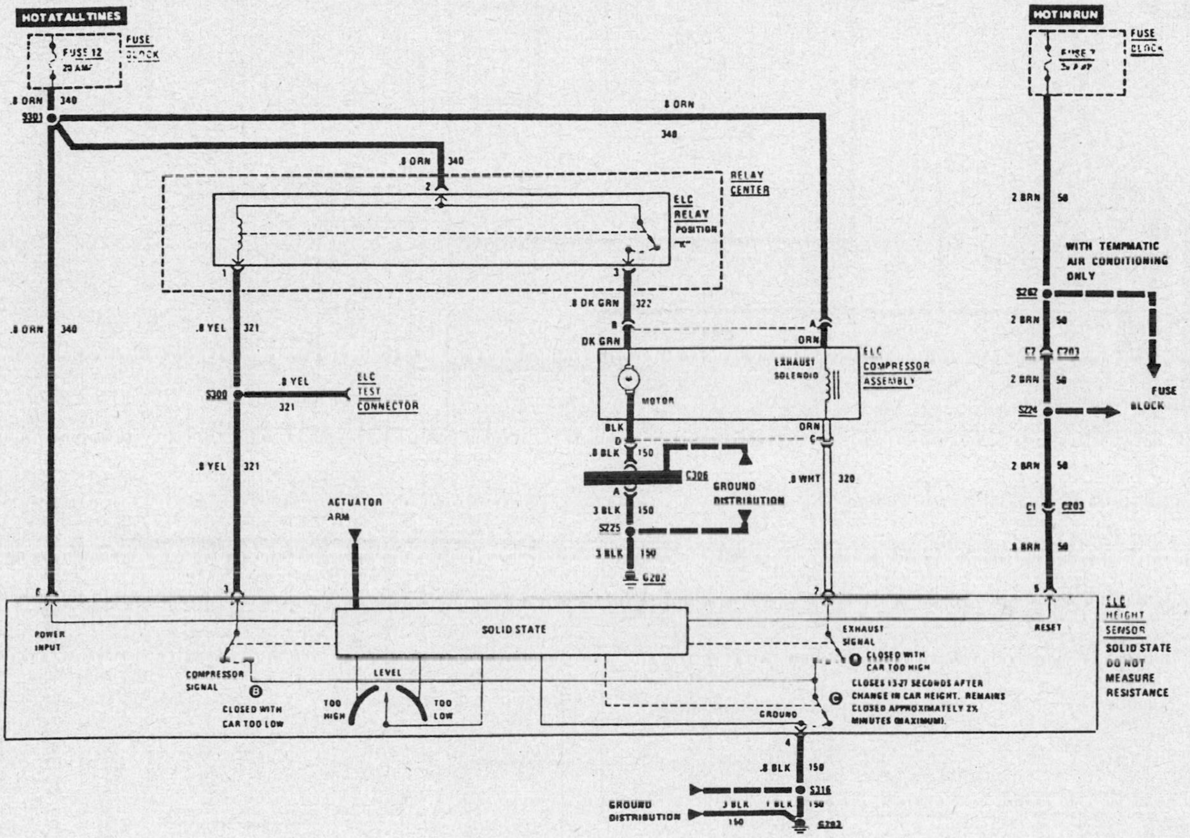
HOT AT ALL TIMES
FUSE 12
FUSE
.8 ORN 340
S301
.8 ORN
340
.8 ORN 340
RELAY CENTER
ELC RELAY POSITION "K"
.8 ORN 340
.8 YEL 321
.8 DK GRN 322
DK GRN
ORN
EXHAUST SOLENOID
MOTOR
ELC COMPRESSOR ASSEMBLY
S300
.8 YEL
321
ELC TEST CONNECTOR
BLK
ORN
.8 BLK 150
C306
GROUND DISTRIBUTION
.8 YEL 321
.8 WHT 320
ACTUATOR ARM
3 BLK 150
S225
3 BLK 150
G202
HOT IN RUN
FUSE BLOCK
2 BRN 50
WITH TEMPMATIC AIR CONDITIONING ONLY
S262
2 BRN 50
C7 C203
2 BRN 50
S224
FUSE BLOCK
2 BRN 50
C1 C203
.8 BRN 50
POWER INPUT
SOLID STATE
COMPRESSOR SIGNAL
CLOSED WITH CAR TOO LOW
LEVEL
TOO HIGH
TOO LOW
EXHAUST SIGNAL
CLOSED WITH CAR TOO HIGH
CLOSES 13-27 SECONDS AFTER CHANGE IN CAR HEIGHT. REMAINS CLOSED APPROXIMATELY 2½ MINUTES (MAXIMUM).
GROUND
RESET
ELC HEIGHT SENSOR
SOLID STATE DO NOT MEASURE RESISTANCE
.8 BLK 150
S316
GROUND DISTRIBUTION
3 BLK
1 BLK 150
150
G203

GC2019100039000X

Fig. 7 ELC wiring diagram. 88 & 98

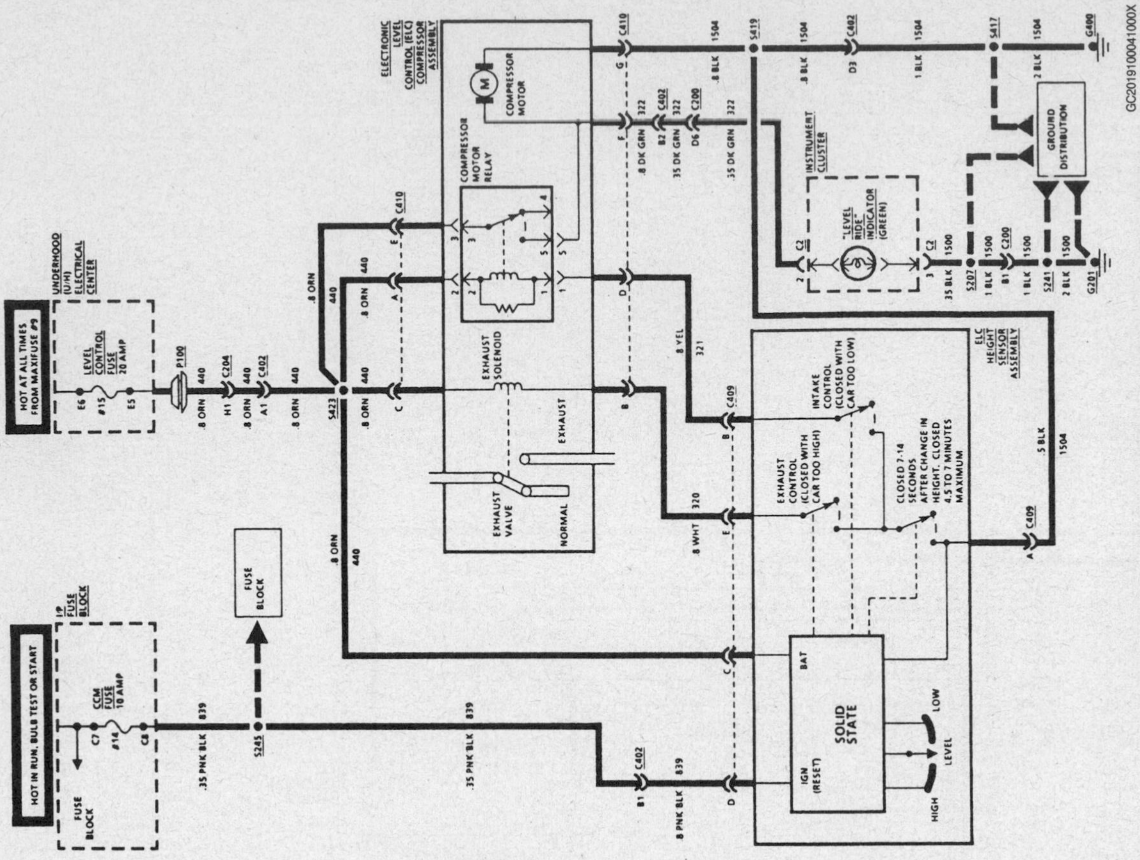
HOT AT ALL TIMES FROM MAXIFUSE #9
UNDERHOOD (UH) ELECTRICAL CENTER
LEVEL CONTROL FUSE 20 AMP
HOT IN RUN, BULB TEST OR START
I/P FUSE BLOCK
CCM FUSE 10 AMP
FUSE BLOCK
ELECTRONIC LEVEL CONTROL (ELC) COMPRESSOR ASSEMBLY
COMPRESSOR MOTOR
COMPRESSOR MOTOR RELAY
EXHAUST SOLENOID
EXHAUST
EXHAUST VALVE
NORMAL
INSTRUMENT CLUSTER
"LEVEL RIDE" INDICATOR (GREEN)
GROUND DISTRIBUTION
ELC HEIGHT SENSOR ASSEMBLY
INTAKE CONTROL (CLOSED WITH CAR TOO LOW)
EXHAUST CONTROL (CLOSED WITH CAR TOO HIGH)
CLOSED 7-14 SECONDS AFTER CHANGE IN HEIGHT, CLOSED 4.5 TO 7 MINUTES MAXIMUM
SOLID STATE
BAT
IGN (RESET)
HIGH
LEVEL
LOW
GC2019100041000X

Fig. 9 ELC wiring diagram. Fleetwood (RWD)

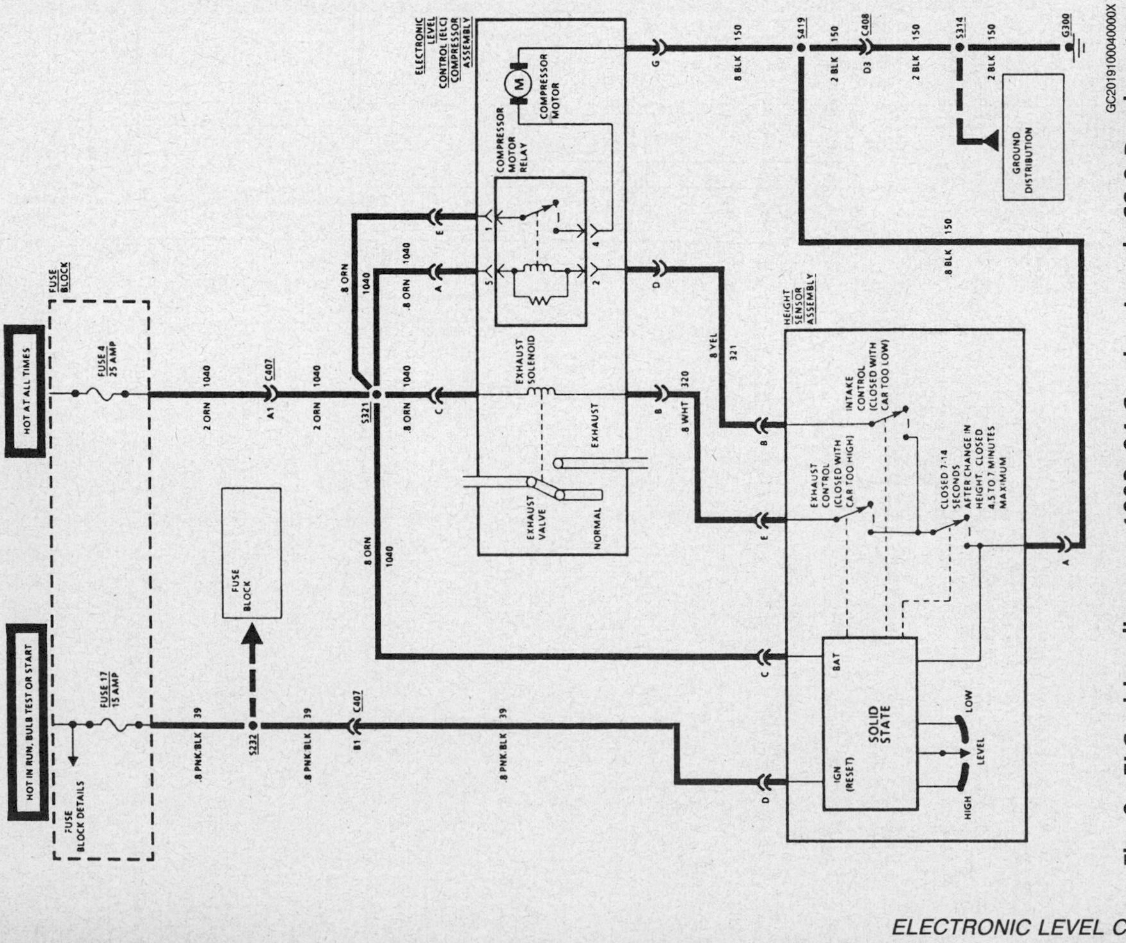
HOT AT ALL TIMES
FUSE BLOCK
FUSE 4 25 AMP
HOT IN RUN, BULB TEST OR START
FUSE 17 15 AMP
FUSE BLOCK DETAILS
ELECTRONIC LEVEL CONTROL (ELC) COMPRESSOR ASSEMBLY
COMPRESSOR MOTOR
COMPRESSOR MOTOR RELAY
EXHAUST SOLENOID
EXHAUST
EXHAUST VALVE
NORMAL
GROUND DISTRIBUTION
HEIGHT SENSOR ASSEMBLY
INTAKE CONTROL (CLOSED WITH CAR TOO LOW)
EXHAUST CONTROL (CLOSED WITH CAR TOO HIGH)
CLOSED 7-14 SECONDS AFTER CHANGE IN HEIGHT, CLOSED 4.5 TO 7 MINUTES MAXIMUM
SOLID STATE
BAT
IGN (RESET)
HIGH
LEVEL
LOW
GC2019100040000X

Fig. 8 ELC wiring diagram. 1993–94 Caprice, Impala SS & Roadmaster

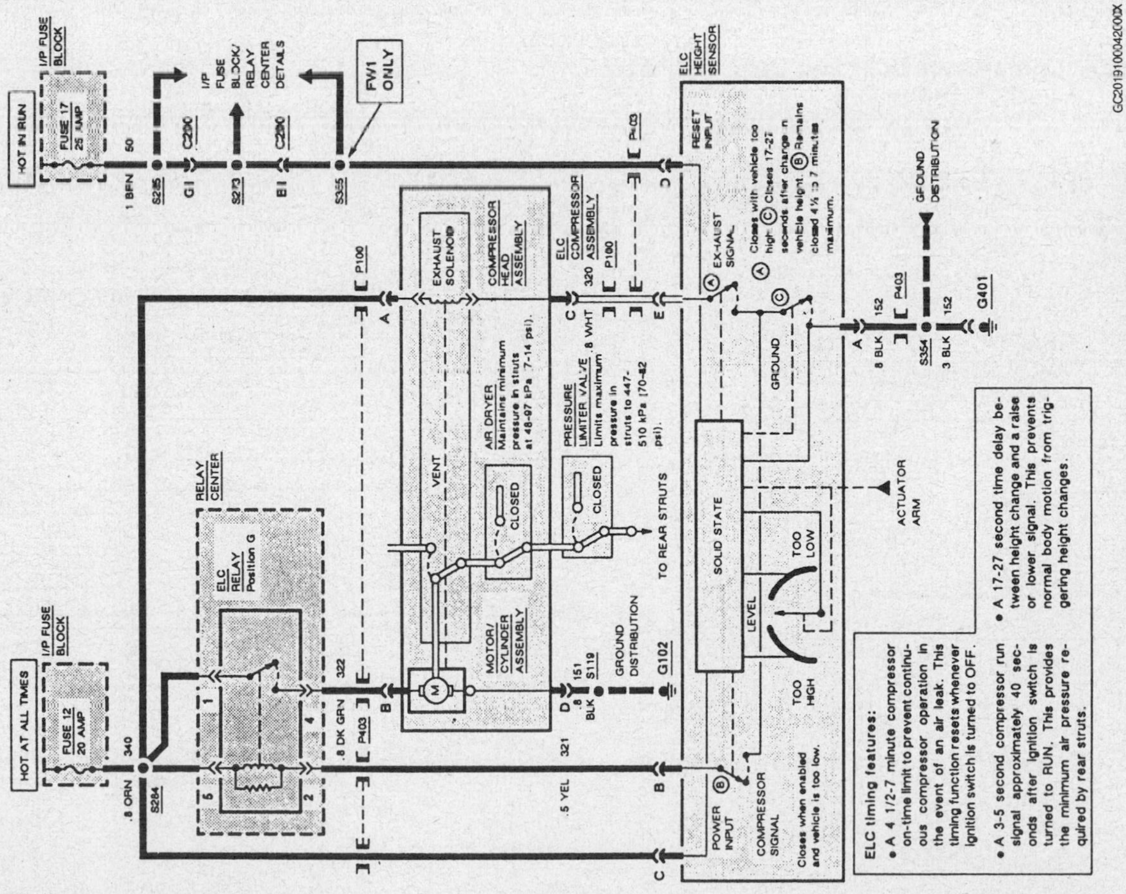
HOT AT ALL TIMES
I/P FUSE BLOCK
FUSE 12 20 AMP
HOT IN RUN
I/P FUSE BLOCK
FUSE 17 25 AMP
RELAY CENTER
ELC RELAY Position G
I/P FUSE BLOCK/ RELAY CENTER DETAILS
FW1 ONLY
.8 ORN
S284
340
.8 DK GRN
P403
322
.5 YEL
321
1 BRN
50
S235
C200
S273
S355
P403
EXHAUST SOLENOID
COMPRESSOR HEAD ASSEMBLY
VENT
AIR DRYER
Maintains minimum pressure in struts at 48-97 kPa (7-14 psi).
CLOSED
PRESSURE LIMITER VALVE
Limits maximum pressure in struts to 447-510 kPa (70-42 psi).
CLOSED
MOTOR/ CYLINDER ASSEMBLY
TO REAR STRUTS
ELC COMPRESSOR ASSEMBLY
P100
320
.8 WHT
151
.8 BLK
S119
GROUND DISTRIBUTION
G102
POWER INPUT
COMPRESSOR SIGNAL
Closes when enabled and vehicle is too low.
TOO HIGH
LEVEL
TOO LOW
SOLID STATE
ACTUATOR ARM
GROUND
EXHAUST SIGNAL
Closes with vehicle too high. Closes 17-27 seconds after change in vehicle height. Remains closed 4½ to 7 minutes maximum.
RESET INPUT
ELC HEIGHT SENSOR
8 BLK
152
S354
3 BLK
G401
GROUND DISTRIBUTION
ELC timing features:
• A 4 1/2-7 minute compressor on-time limit to prevent continuous compressor operation in the event of an air leak. This timing function resets whenever ignition switch is turned to OFF.
• A 3-5 second compressor run signal approximately 40 seconds after ignition switch is turned to RUN. This provides the minimum air pressure required by rear struts.
• A 17-27 second time delay between height change and a raise or lower signal. This prevents normal body motion from triggering height changes.
GC2019100042000X

Fig. 10 ELC wiring diagram. LeSabre & Park Avenue

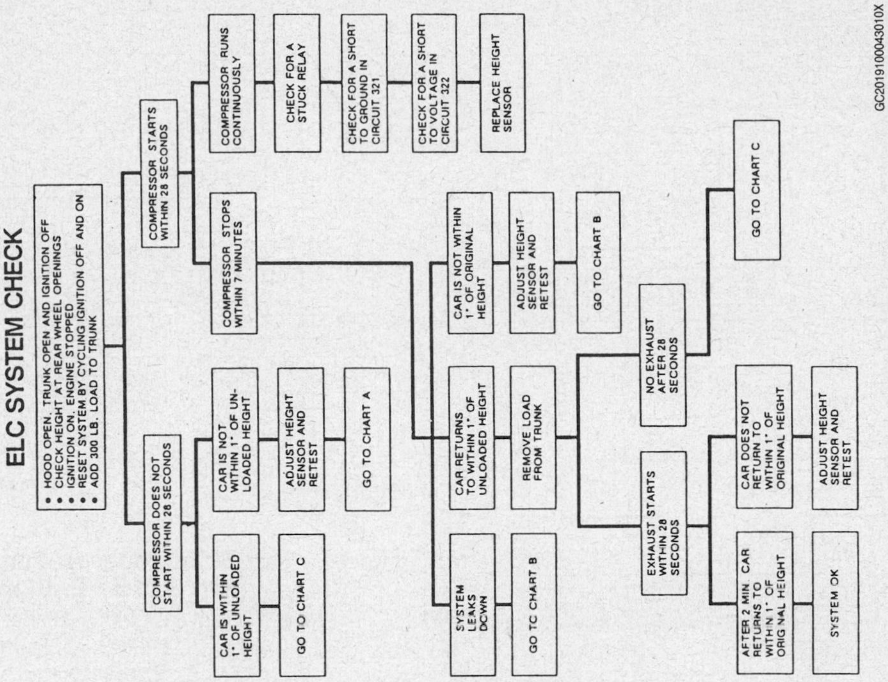
ELC SYSTEM CHECK
• HOOD OPEN, TRUNK OPEN AND IGNITION OFF
• CHECK HEIGHT AT REAR WHEEL OPENINGS
• IGNITION ON, ENGINE STOPPED
• RESET SYSTEM BY CYCLING IGNITION OFF AND ON
• ADD 300 LB. LOAD TO TRUNK
COMPRESSOR DOES NOT START WITHIN 28 SECONDS
COMPRESSOR STARTS WITHIN 28 SECONDS
CAR IS WITHIN 1" OF UNLOADED HEIGHT
GO TO CHART C
CAR IS NOT WITHIN 1" OF UNLOADED HEIGHT
ADJUST HEIGHT SENSOR AND RETEST
GO TO CHART A
COMPRESSOR STOPS WITHIN 7 MINUTES
COMPRESSOR RUNS CONTINUOUSLY
CHECK FOR A STUCK RELAY
CHECK FOR A SHORT TO GROUND IN CIRCUIT 321
CHECK FOR A SHORT TO VOLTAGE IN CIRCUIT 322
REPLACE HEIGHT SENSOR
SYSTEM LEAKS DOWN
GO TO CHART B
CAR RETURNS TO WITHIN 1" OF UNLOADED HEIGHT
REMOVE LOAD FROM TRUNK
CAR IS NOT WITHIN 1" OF ORIGINAL HEIGHT
ADJUST HEIGHT SENSOR AND RETEST
GO TO CHART B
EXHAUST STARTS WITHIN 28 SECONDS
NO EXHAUST AFTER 28 SECONDS
GO TO CHART C
AFTER 2 MIN. CAR RETURNS TO WITHIN 1" OF ORIGINAL HEIGHT
SYSTEM OK
CAR DOES NOT RETURN TO WITHIN 1" OF ORIGINAL HEIGHT
ADJUST HEIGHT SENSOR AND RETEST
GC2019100043010X

Fig. 11 ELC System Check (Part 1 of 5). Brougham

CHART A – COMPRESSOR DOES NOT OPERATE

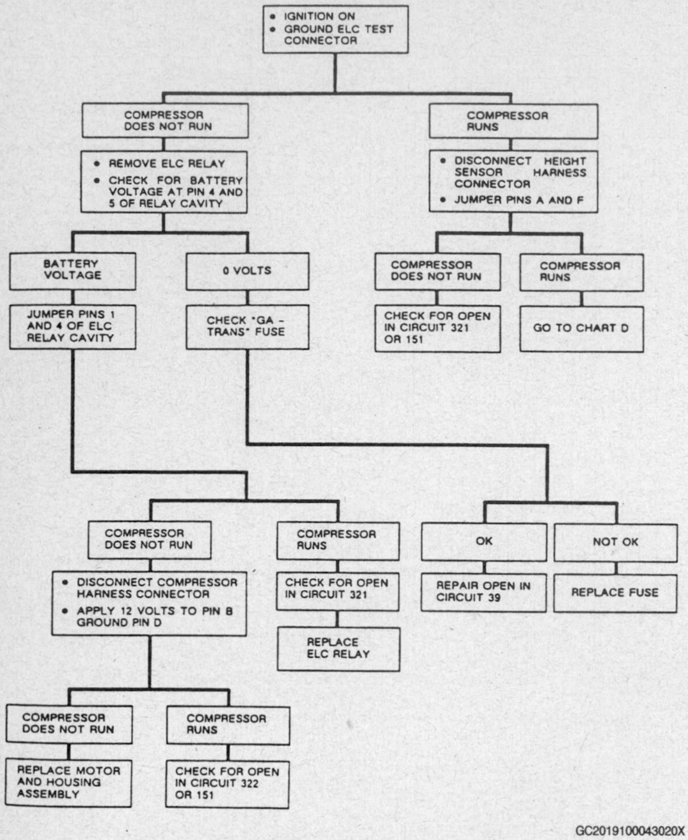
• IGNITION ON
• GROUND ELC TEST CONNECTOR
COMPRESSOR DOES NOT RUN
COMPRESSOR RUNS
• REMOVE ELC RELAY
• CHECK FOR BATTERY VOLTAGE AT PIN 4 AND 5 OF RELAY CAVITY
• DISCONNECT HEIGHT SENSOR HARNESS CONNECTOR
• JUMPER PINS A AND F
BATTERY VOLTAGE
0 VOLTS
COMPRESSOR DOES NOT RUN
COMPRESSOR RUNS
JUMPER PINS 1 AND 4 OF ELC RELAY CAVITY
CHECK "GA - TRANS" FUSE
CHECK FOR OPEN IN CIRCUIT 321 OR 151
GO TO CHART D
COMPRESSOR DOES NOT RUN
COMPRESSOR RUNS
OK
NOT OK
• DISCONNECT COMPRESSOR HARNESS CONNECTOR
• APPLY 12 VOLTS TO PIN B GROUND PIN D
CHECK FOR OPEN IN CIRCUIT 321
REPAIR OPEN IN CIRCUIT 39
REPLACE FUSE
REPLACE ELC RELAY
COMPRESSOR DOES NOT RUN
COMPRESSOR RUNS
REPLACE MOTOR AND HOUSING ASSEMBLY
CHECK FOR OPEN IN CIRCUIT 322 OR 151
GC2019100043020X

Fig. 11 Test A: Compressor Does Not Operate (Part 2 of 5). Brougham

CHART B – IMPROPER OR CONTINUOUS EXHAUST

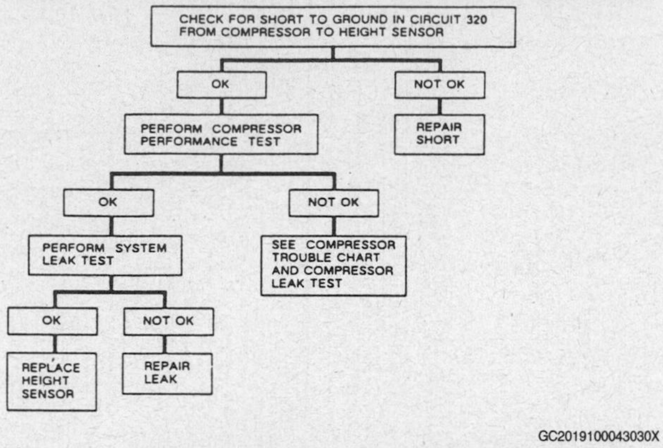
CHECK FOR SHORT TO GROUND IN CIRCUIT 320 FROM COMPRESSOR TO HEIGHT SENSOR
OK
NOT OK
PERFORM COMPRESSOR PERFORMANCE TEST
REPAIR SHORT
OK
NOT OK
PERFORM SYSTEM LEAK TEST
SEE COMPRESSOR TROUBLE CHART AND COMPRESSOR LEAK TEST
OK
NOT OK
REPLACE HEIGHT SENSOR
REPAIR LEAK
GC2019100043030X

Fig. 11 Test B: Improper Or Continuous Exhaust (Part 3 of 5). Brougham

CHART C – NO EXHAUST

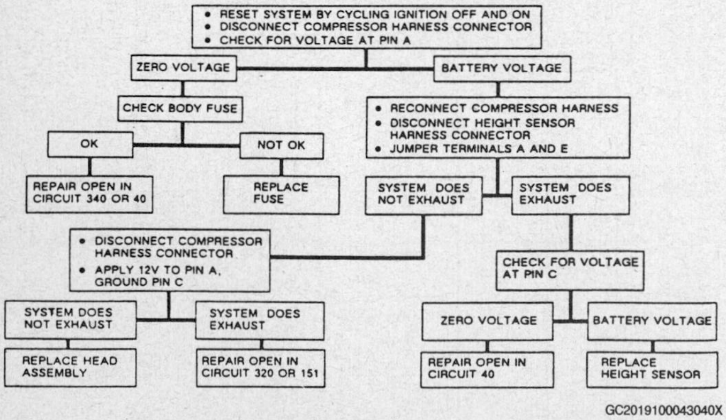
• RESET SYSTEM BY CYCLING IGNITION OFF AND ON
• DISCONNECT COMPRESSOR HARNESS CONNECTOR
• CHECK FOR VOLTAGE AT PIN A
ZERO VOLTAGE
BATTERY VOLTAGE
CHECK BODY FUSE
• RECONNECT COMPRESSOR HARNESS
• DISCONNECT HEIGHT SENSOR HARNESS CONNECTOR
• JUMPER TERMINALS A AND E
OK
NOT OK
REPAIR OPEN IN CIRCUIT 340 OR 40
REPLACE FUSE
SYSTEM DOES NOT EXHAUST
SYSTEM DOES EXHAUST
• DISCONNECT COMPRESSOR HARNESS CONNECTOR
• APPLY 12V TO PIN A, GROUND PIN C
CHECK FOR VOLTAGE AT PIN C
SYSTEM DOES NOT EXHAUST
SYSTEM DOES EXHAUST
ZERO VOLTAGE
BATTERY VOLTAGE
REPLACE HEAD ASSEMBLY
REPAIR OPEN IN CIRCUIT 320 OR 151
REPAIR OPEN IN CIRCUIT 40
REPLACE HEIGHT SENSOR
GC2019100043040X

Fig. 11 Test C: No Exhaust (Part 4 of 5). Brougham

CHART D – RESET CIRCUIT OPERATIONAL CHECK

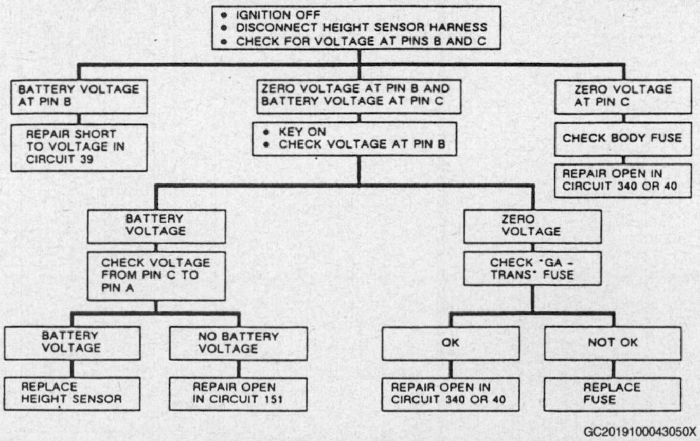
• IGNITION OFF
• DISCONNECT HEIGHT SENSOR HARNESS
• CHECK FOR VOLTAGE AT PINS B AND C
BATTERY VOLTAGE AT PIN B
ZERO VOLTAGE AT PIN B AND BATTERY VOLTAGE AT PIN C
ZERO VOLTAGE AT PIN C
REPAIR SHORT TO VOLTAGE IN CIRCUIT 39
• KEY ON
• CHECK VOLTAGE AT PIN B
CHECK BODY FUSE
REPAIR OPEN IN CIRCUIT 340 OR 40
BATTERY VOLTAGE
ZERO VOLTAGE
CHECK VOLTAGE FROM PIN C TO PIN A
CHECK "GA - TRANS" FUSE
BATTERY VOLTAGE
NO BATTERY VOLTAGE
OK
NOT OK
REPLACE HEIGHT SENSOR
REPAIR OPEN IN CIRCUIT 151
REPAIR OPEN IN CIRCUIT 340 OR 40
REPLACE FUSE
GC2019100043050X

Fig. 11 Test D: Reset Circuit Operational Check (Part 5 of 5). Brougham

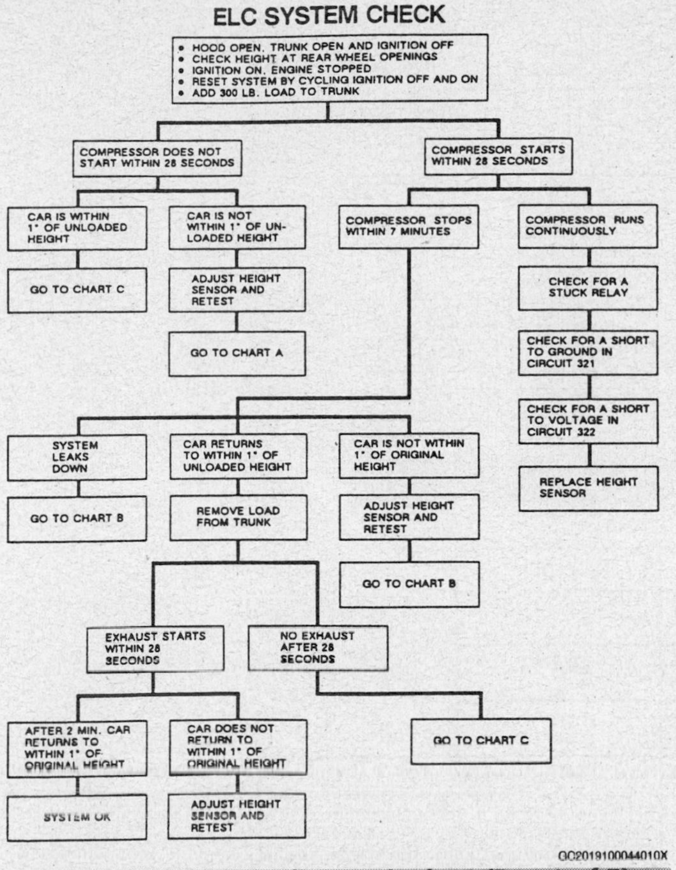
ELC SYSTEM CHECK
• HOOD OPEN, TRUNK OPEN AND IGNITION OFF
• CHECK HEIGHT AT REAR WHEEL OPENINGS
• IGNITION ON, ENGINE STOPPED
• RESET SYSTEM BY CYCLING IGNITION OFF AND ON
• ADD 300 LB. LOAD TO TRUNK
COMPRESSOR DOES NOT START WITHIN 28 SECONDS
COMPRESSOR STARTS WITHIN 28 SECONDS
CAR IS WITHIN 1" OF UNLOADED HEIGHT
CAR IS NOT WITHIN 1" OF UNLOADED HEIGHT
COMPRESSOR STOPS WITHIN 7 MINUTES
COMPRESSOR RUNS CONTINUOUSLY
GO TO CHART C
ADJUST HEIGHT SENSOR AND RETEST
CHECK FOR A STUCK RELAY
GO TO CHART A
CHECK FOR A SHORT TO GROUND IN CIRCUIT 321
CHECK FOR A SHORT TO VOLTAGE IN CIRCUIT 322
SYSTEM LEAKS DOWN
CAR RETURNS TO WITHIN 1" OF UNLOADED HEIGHT
CAR IS NOT WITHIN 1" OF ORIGINAL HEIGHT
REPLACE HEIGHT SENSOR
GO TO CHART B
REMOVE LOAD FROM TRUNK
ADJUST HEIGHT SENSOR AND RETEST
GO TO CHART B
EXHAUST STARTS WITHIN 28 SECONDS
NO EXHAUST AFTER 28 SECONDS
AFTER 2 MIN. CAR RETURNS TO WITHIN 1" OF ORIGINAL HEIGHT
CAR DOES NOT RETURN TO WITHIN 1" OF ORIGINAL HEIGHT
GO TO CHART C
SYSTEM OK
ADJUST HEIGHT SENSOR AND RETEST
GC2019100044010X

Fig. 12 ELC system diagnostic chart (Part 1 of 5). Eldorado, Riviera, Seville, Toronado & Trofeo

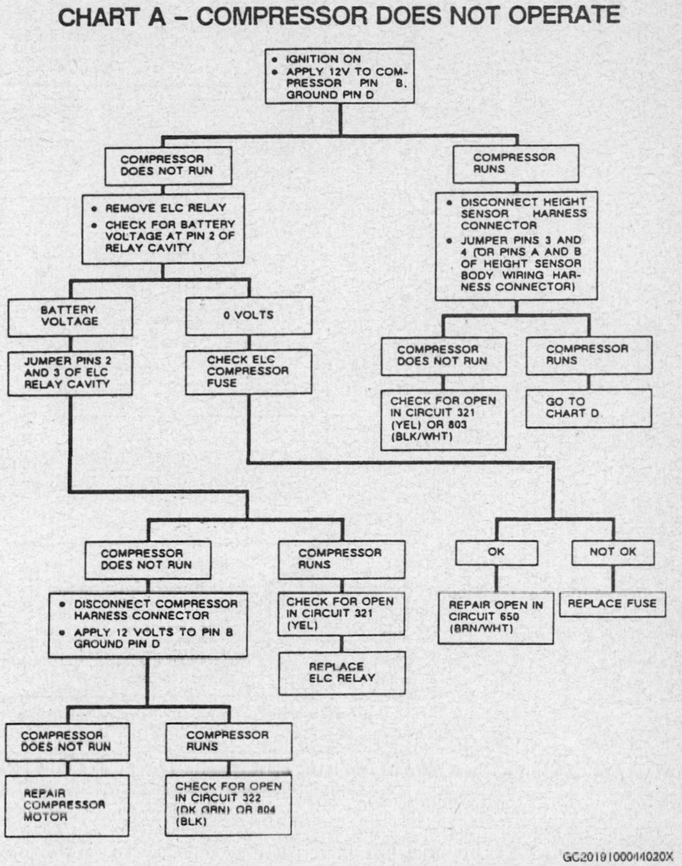
CHART A – COMPRESSOR DOES NOT OPERATE
• IGNITION ON
• APPLY 12V TO COMPRESSOR PIN B, GROUND PIN D
COMPRESSOR DOES NOT RUN
COMPRESSOR RUNS
• REMOVE ELC RELAY
• CHECK FOR BATTERY VOLTAGE AT PIN 2 OF RELAY CAVITY
• DISCONNECT HEIGHT SENSOR HARNESS CONNECTOR
• JUMPER PINS 3 AND 4 (OR PINS A AND B OF HEIGHT SENSOR BODY WIRING HARNESS CONNECTOR)
BATTERY VOLTAGE
0 VOLTS
JUMPER PINS 2 AND 3 OF ELC RELAY CAVITY
CHECK ELC COMPRESSOR FUSE
COMPRESSOR DOES NOT RUN
COMPRESSOR RUNS
CHECK FOR OPEN IN CIRCUIT 321 (YEL) OR 803 (BLK/WHT)
GO TO CHART D
COMPRESSOR DOES NOT RUN
COMPRESSOR RUNS
OK
NOT OK
• DISCONNECT COMPRESSOR HARNESS CONNECTOR
• APPLY 12 VOLTS TO PIN B GROUND PIN D
CHECK FOR OPEN IN CIRCUIT 321 (YEL)
REPAIR OPEN IN CIRCUIT 650 (BRN/WHT)
REPLACE FUSE
REPLACE ELC RELAY
COMPRESSOR DOES NOT RUN
COMPRESSOR RUNS
REPAIR COMPRESSOR MOTOR
CHECK FOR OPEN IN CIRCUIT 322 (DK GRN) OR 804 (BLK)
GC2019100044020X

Fig. 12 Test A: Compressor Does Not Operate (Part 2 of 5). Eldorado, Riviera, Seville, Toronado & Trofeo

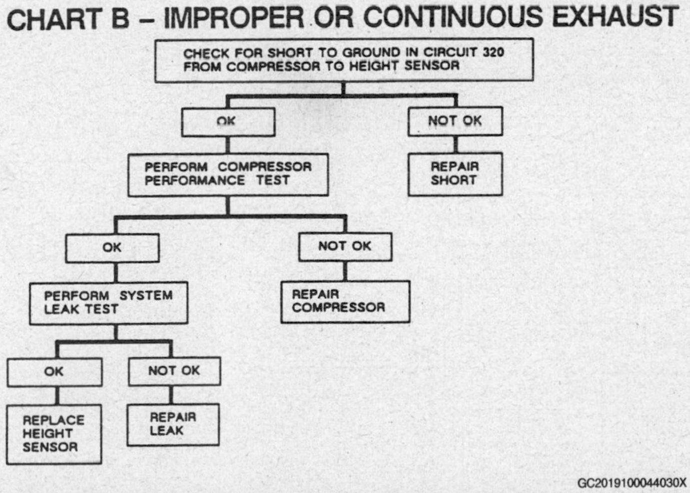
CHART B – IMPROPER OR CONTINUOUS EXHAUST
CHECK FOR SHORT TO GROUND IN CIRCUIT 320 FROM COMPRESSOR TO HEIGHT SENSOR
OK
NOT OK
PERFORM COMPRESSOR PERFORMANCE TEST
REPAIR SHORT
OK
NOT OK
PERFORM SYSTEM LEAK TEST
REPAIR COMPRESSOR
OK
NOT OK
REPLACE HEIGHT SENSOR
REPAIR LEAK
GC2019100044030X

Fig. 12 Test B: Improper Or Continuous Exhaust (Part 3 of 5). Eldorado, Riviera, Seville, Toronado & Trofeo

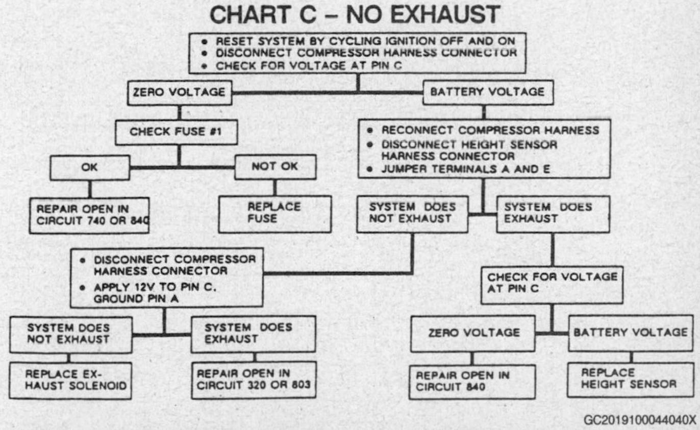
CHART C – NO EXHAUST
• RESET SYSTEM BY CYCLING IGNITION OFF AND ON
• DISCONNECT COMPRESSOR HARNESS CONNECTOR
• CHECK FOR VOLTAGE AT PIN C
ZERO VOLTAGE
BATTERY VOLTAGE
CHECK FUSE #1
• RECONNECT COMPRESSOR HARNESS
• DISCONNECT HEIGHT SENSOR HARNESS CONNECTOR
• JUMPER TERMINALS A AND E
OK
NOT OK
REPAIR OPEN IN CIRCUIT 740 OR 840
REPLACE FUSE
SYSTEM DOES NOT EXHAUST
SYSTEM DOES EXHAUST
• DISCONNECT COMPRESSOR HARNESS CONNECTOR
• APPLY 12V TO PIN C, GROUND PIN A
CHECK FOR VOLTAGE AT PIN C
SYSTEM DOES NOT EXHAUST
SYSTEM DOES EXHAUST
ZERO VOLTAGE
BATTERY VOLTAGE
REPLACE EXHAUST SOLENOID
REPAIR OPEN IN CIRCUIT 320 OR 803
REPAIR OPEN IN CIRCUIT 840
REPLACE HEIGHT SENSOR
GC2019100044040X

Fig. 12 Test C: No Exhaust (Part 4 of 5). Eldorado, Riviera, Seville, Toronado & Trofeo

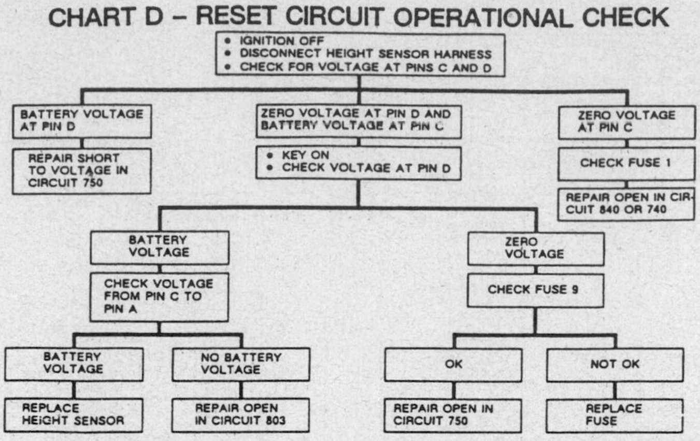
CHART D – RESET CIRCUIT OPERATIONAL CHECK
• IGNITION OFF
• DISCONNECT HEIGHT SENSOR HARNESS
• CHECK FOR VOLTAGE AT PINS C AND D
BATTERY VOLTAGE AT PIN D
REPAIR SHORT TO VOLTAGE IN CIRCUIT 750
ZERO VOLTAGE AT PIN D AND BATTERY VOLTAGE AT PIN C
• KEY ON
• CHECK VOLTAGE AT PIN D
ZERO VOLTAGE AT PIN C
CHECK FUSE 1
REPAIR OPEN IN CIRCUIT 840 OR 740
BATTERY VOLTAGE
CHECK VOLTAGE FROM PIN C TO PIN A
ZERO VOLTAGE
CHECK FUSE 9
BATTERY VOLTAGE
NO BATTERY VOLTAGE
OK
NOT OK
REPLACE HEIGHT SENSOR
REPAIR OPEN IN CIRCUIT 803
REPAIR OPEN IN CIRCUIT 750
REPLACE FUSE
GC2019100044050X

Fig. 12 Test D: Reset Circuit Operational Check (Part 5 of 5). Eldorado, Riviera, Seville, Toronado & Trofeo

SYMPTOM	PROCEDURE
Compressor Motor does not turn "ON" to raise rear of vehicle.	Chart #1
ELC System does not vent to lower rear of vehicle (checks Exhaust Solenoid).	Chart #2
Compressor Motor runs continuously (longer than 7 minutes).	Chart #3
Compressor Motor runs for maximum run time (approximately 4.5 to 7 minutes) then stops.	Check for air leaks in the ELC System and for proper adjustment of the Height Sensor Assembly. If no air leaks are found and sensor is adjusted properly, check for a short to ground in CKT 320 between Height Sensor Assembly and Exhaust Solenoid. If OK, replace Height Sensor Assembly.
ELC System continuously relevels vehicle with no change in load.	Check for air leaks in the ELC System.

GC2019100045000X

Fig. 13 ELC system symptom chart. 1992 Caprice, Custom Cruiser & Roadmaster

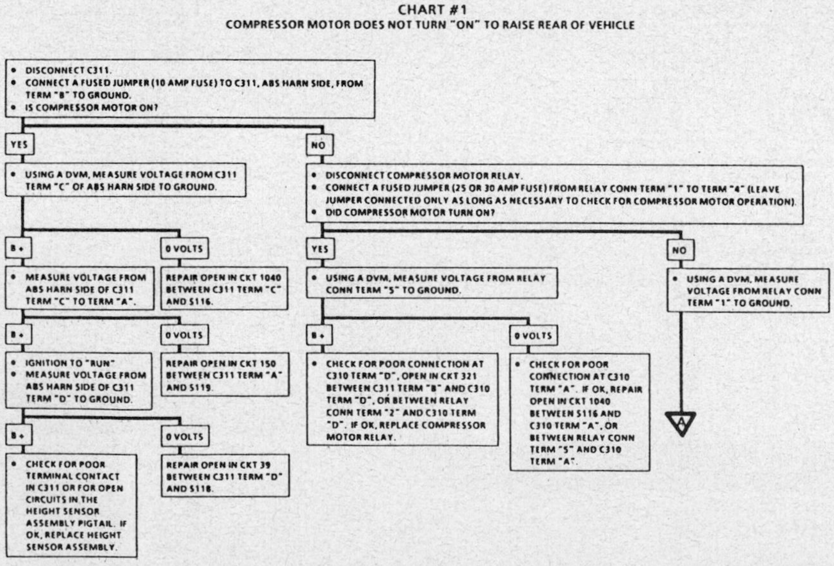
CHART #1
COMPRESSOR MOTOR DOES NOT TURN "ON" TO RAISE REAR OF VEHICLE
• DISCONNECT C311.
• CONNECT A FUSED JUMPER (10 AMP FUSE) TO C311, ABS HARN SIDE, FROM TERM "B" TO GROUND.
• IS COMPRESSOR MOTOR ON?
YES
NO
• USING A DVM, MEASURE VOLTAGE FROM C311 TERM "C" OF ABS HARN SIDE TO GROUND.
• DISCONNECT COMPRESSOR MOTOR RELAY.
• CONNECT A FUSED JUMPER (25 OR 30 AMP FUSE) FROM RELAY CONN TERM "1" TO TERM "4" (LEAVE JUMPER CONNECTED ONLY AS LONG AS NECESSARY TO CHECK FOR COMPRESSOR MOTOR OPERATION).
• DID COMPRESSOR MOTOR TURN ON?
B+
0 VOLTS
YES
NO
• MEASURE VOLTAGE FROM ABS HARN SIDE OF C311 TERM "C" TO TERM "A".
REPAIR OPEN IN CKT 1040 BETWEEN C311 TERM "C" AND S116.
• USING A DVM, MEASURE VOLTAGE FROM RELAY CONN TERM "5" TO GROUND.
• USING A DVM, MEASURE VOLTAGE FROM RELAY CONN TERM "1" TO GROUND.
B+
0 VOLTS
B+
0 VOLTS
• IGNITION TO "RUN"
• MEASURE VOLTAGE FROM ABS HARN SIDE OF C311 TERM "D" TO GROUND.
REPAIR OPEN IN CKT 150 BETWEEN C311 TERM "A" AND S119.
• CHECK FOR POOR CONNECTION AT C310 TERM "D", OPEN IN CKT 321 BETWEEN C311 TERM "B" AND C310 TERM "D", OR BETWEEN RELAY CONN TERM "2" AND C310 TERM "D". IF OK, REPLACE COMPRESSOR MOTOR RELAY.
• CHECK FOR POOR CONNECTION AT C310 TERM "A". IF OK, REPAIR OPEN IN CKT 1040 BETWEEN S116 AND C310 TERM "A", OR BETWEEN RELAY CONN TERM "5" AND C310 TERM "A".
A
B+
0 VOLTS
• CHECK FOR POOR TERMINAL CONTACT IN C311 OR FOR OPEN CIRCUITS IN THE HEIGHT SENSOR ASSEMBLY PIGTAIL. IF OK, REPLACE HEIGHT SENSOR ASSEMBLY.
REPAIR OPEN IN CKT 39 BETWEEN C311 TERM "D" AND S118.
GC2019100046010X

Fig. 14 ELC system diagnostic chart (Part 1 of 4). 1992 Caprice, Custom Cruiser & Roadmaster

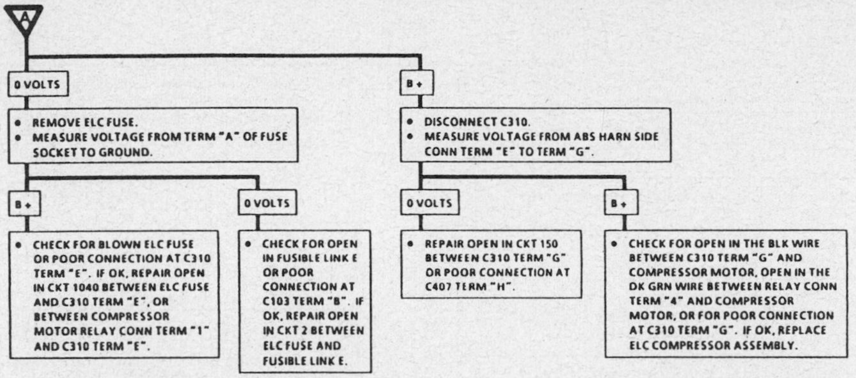

A
0 VOLTS
B+
• REMOVE ELC FUSE.
• MEASURE VOLTAGE FROM TERM "A" OF FUSE SOCKET TO GROUND.
• DISCONNECT C310.
• MEASURE VOLTAGE FROM ABS HARN SIDE CONN TERM "E" TO TERM "G".
B+
0 VOLTS
0 VOLTS
B+
• CHECK FOR BLOWN ELC FUSE OR POOR CONNECTION AT C310 TERM "E". IF OK, REPAIR OPEN IN CKT 1040 BETWEEN ELC FUSE AND C310 TERM "E", OR BETWEEN COMPRESSOR MOTOR RELAY CONN TERM "1" AND C310 TERM "E".
• CHECK FOR OPEN IN FUSIBLE LINK E OR POOR CONNECTION AT C103 TERM "B". IF OK, REPAIR OPEN IN CKT 2 BETWEEN ELC FUSE AND FUSIBLE LINK E.
• REPAIR OPEN IN CKT 150 BETWEEN C310 TERM "G" OR POOR CONNECTION AT C407 TERM "H".
• CHECK FOR OPEN IN THE BLK WIRE BETWEEN C310 TERM "G" AND COMPRESSOR MOTOR, OPEN IN THE DK GRN WIRE BETWEEN RELAY CONN TERM "4" AND COMPRESSOR MOTOR, OR FOR POOR CONNECTION AT C310 TERM "G". IF OK, REPLACE ELC COMPRESSOR ASSEMBLY.

GC2019100046020X

Fig. 14 ELC system diagnostic chart (Part 2 of 4). 1992 Caprice, Custom Cruiser & Roadmaster

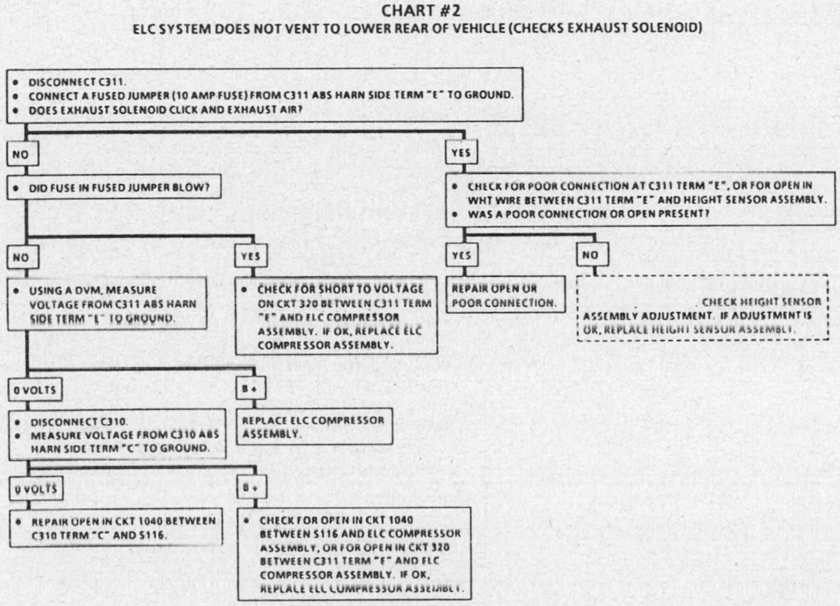

CHART #2
ELC SYSTEM DOES NOT VENT TO LOWER REAR OF VEHICLE (CHECKS EXHAUST SOLENOID)
• DISCONNECT C311.
• CONNECT A FUSED JUMPER (10 AMP FUSE) FROM C311 ABS HARN SIDE TERM "E" TO GROUND.
• DOES EXHAUST SOLENOID CLICK AND EXHAUST AIR?
NO
YES
• DID FUSE IN FUSED JUMPER BLOW?
• CHECK FOR POOR CONNECTION AT C311 TERM "E", OR FOR OPEN IN WHT WIRE BETWEEN C311 TERM "E" AND HEIGHT SENSOR ASSEMBLY.
• WAS A POOR CONNECTION OR OPEN PRESENT?
NO
YES
YES
NO
• USING A DVM, MEASURE VOLTAGE FROM C311 ABS HARN SIDE TERM "E" TO GROUND.
• CHECK FOR SHORT TO VOLTAGE ON CKT 320 BETWEEN C311 TERM "E" AND ELC COMPRESSOR ASSEMBLY. IF OK, REPLACE ELC COMPRESSOR ASSEMBLY.
REPAIR OPEN OR POOR CONNECTION.
CHECK HEIGHT SENSOR ASSEMBLY ADJUSTMENT. IF ADJUSTMENT IS OK, REPLACE HEIGHT SENSOR ASSEMBLY.
0 VOLTS
B+
• DISCONNECT C310.
• MEASURE VOLTAGE FROM C310 ABS HARN SIDE TERM "C" TO GROUND.
REPLACE ELC COMPRESSOR ASSEMBLY.
0 VOLTS
B+
• REPAIR OPEN IN CKT 1040 BETWEEN C310 TERM "C" AND S116.
• CHECK FOR OPEN IN CKT 1040 BETWEEN S116 AND ELC COMPRESSOR ASSEMBLY, OR FOR OPEN IN CKT 320 BETWEEN C311 TERM "E" AND ELC COMPRESSOR ASSEMBLY. IF OK, REPLACE ELC COMPRESSOR ASSEMBLY.

GC2019100046030X

Fig. 14 ELC system diagnostic chart (Part 3 of 4). 1992 Caprice, Custom Cruiser & Roadmaster

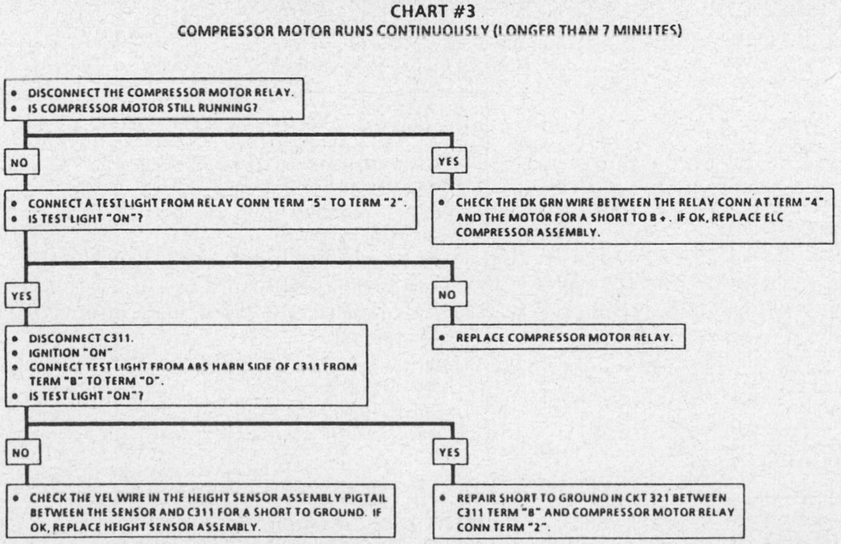

CHART #3
COMPRESSOR MOTOR RUNS CONTINUOUSLY (LONGER THAN 7 MINUTES)
• DISCONNECT THE COMPRESSOR MOTOR RELAY.
• IS COMPRESSOR MOTOR STILL RUNNING?
NO
YES
• CONNECT A TEST LIGHT FROM RELAY CONN TERM "5" TO TERM "2".
• IS TEST LIGHT "ON"?
• CHECK THE DK GRN WIRE BETWEEN THE RELAY CONN AT TERM "4" AND THE MOTOR FOR A SHORT TO B+. IF OK, REPLACE ELC COMPRESSOR ASSEMBLY.
YES
NO
• DISCONNECT C311.
• IGNITION "ON"
• CONNECT TEST LIGHT FROM ABS HARN SIDE OF C311 FROM TERM "B" TO TERM "D".
• IS TEST LIGHT "ON"?
• REPLACE COMPRESSOR MOTOR RELAY.
NO
YES
• CHECK THE YEL WIRE IN THE HEIGHT SENSOR ASSEMBLY PIGTAIL BETWEEN THE SENSOR AND C311 FOR A SHORT TO GROUND. IF OK, REPLACE HEIGHT SENSOR ASSEMBLY.
• REPAIR SHORT TO GROUND IN CKT 321 BETWEEN C311 TERM "B" AND COMPRESSOR MOTOR RELAY CONN TERM "2".

GC2019100046040X

Fig. 14 ELC system diagnostic chart (Part 4 of 4). 1992 Caprice, Custom Cruiser & Roadmaster

SYMPTOM	FOR DIAGNOSIS
Compressor does not run	Do Test A
System does not exhaust	Do Test B
Compressor runs for more than 7 minutes; vehicle stays at maximum height	Disconnect the ELC Height Sensor connector • If the Compressor does not run, replace the ELC Height Sensor. • If the Compressor runs, check YEL (321) wire for a short to ground; check for sticking relay
Compressor runs for maximum time (7 minutes) then turns off; vehicle does not reach proper height	Do Test C
ELC Compressor Assembly cycles on and off frequently	Do Test C

GC2019100047000X

Fig. 15 ELC system symptom chart. Bonneville, DeVille, Fleetwood (FWD), 88 & 98

A: ELC RELAY AND COMPRESSOR MOTOR TEST

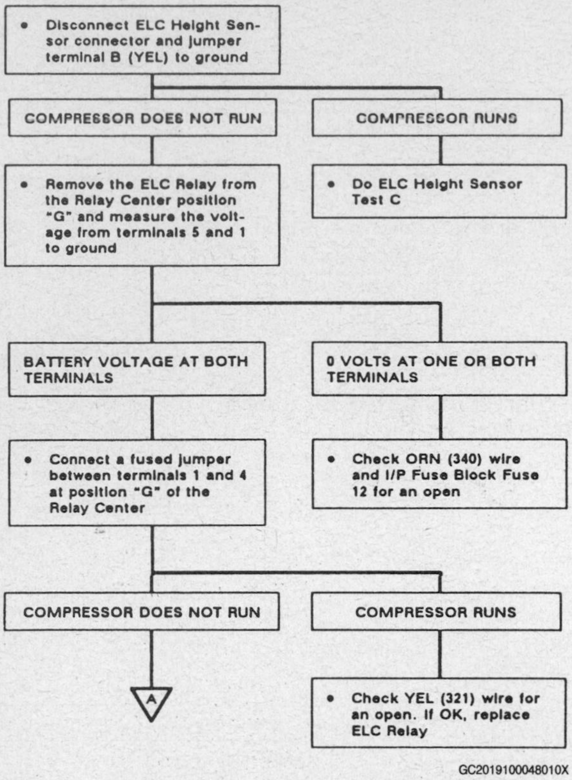
• Disconnect ELC Height Sensor connector and jumper terminal B (YEL) to ground
COMPRESSOR DOES NOT RUN
COMPRESSOR RUNS
• Remove the ELC Relay from the Relay Center position "G" and measure the voltage from terminals 5 and 1 to ground
• Do ELC Height Sensor Test C
BATTERY VOLTAGE AT BOTH TERMINALS
0 VOLTS AT ONE OR BOTH TERMINALS
• Connect a fused jumper between terminals 1 and 4 at position "G" of the Relay Center
• Check ORN (340) wire and I/P Fuse Block Fuse 12 for an open
COMPRESSOR DOES NOT RUN
COMPRESSOR RUNS
A
• Check YEL (321) wire for an open. If OK, replace ELC Relay
GC2019100048010X

Fig. 16 ELC system diagnostic chart (Part 1 of 6). Bonneville, DeVille, Fleetwood (FWD), 88 & 98

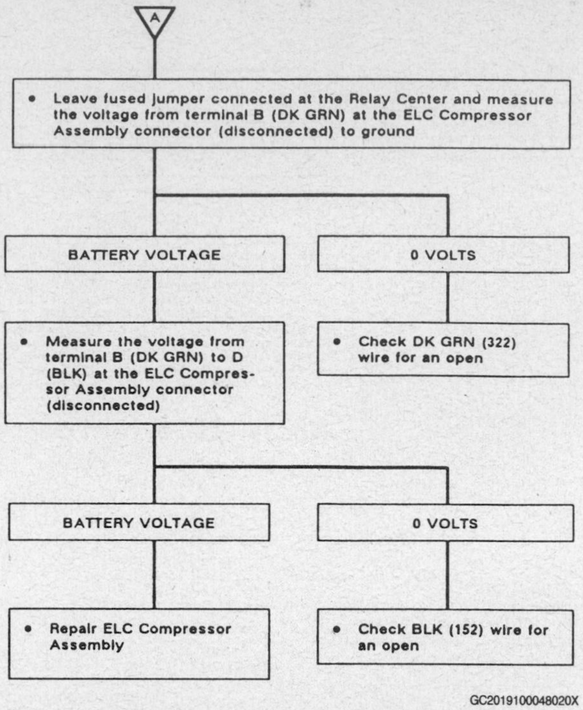
A
• Leave fused jumper connected at the Relay Center and measure the voltage from terminal B (DK GRN) at the ELC Compressor Assembly connector (disconnected) to ground
BATTERY VOLTAGE
0 VOLTS
• Measure the voltage from terminal B (DK GRN) to D (BLK) at the ELC Compressor Assembly connector (disconnected)
• Check DK GRN (322) wire for an open
BATTERY VOLTAGE
0 VOLTS
• Repair ELC Compressor Assembly
• Check BLK (152) wire for an open
GC2019100048020X

Fig. 16 ELC system diagnostic chart (Part 2 of 6). Bonneville, DeVille, Fleetwood (FWD), 88 & 98

B: EXHAUST SOLENOID TEST

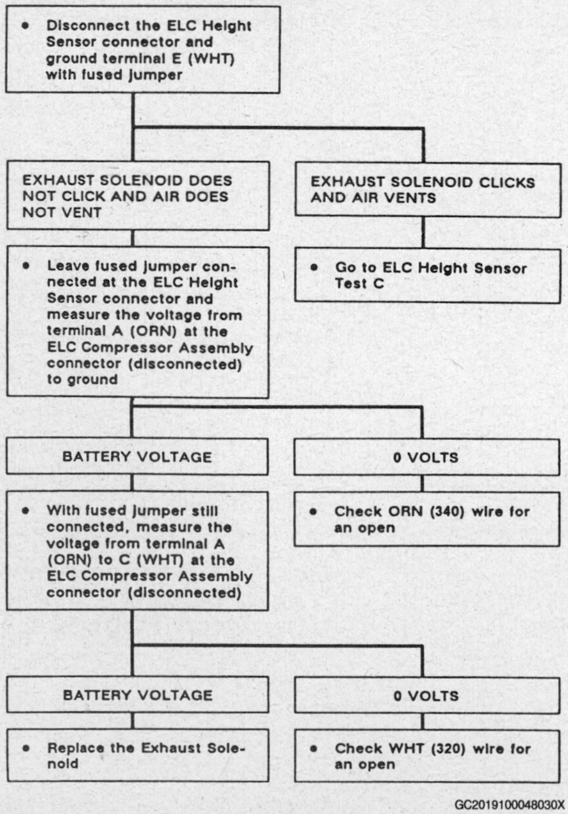
• Disconnect the ELC Height Sensor connector and ground terminal E (WHT) with fused jumper
EXHAUST SOLENOID DOES NOT CLICK AND AIR DOES NOT VENT
EXHAUST SOLENOID CLICKS AND AIR VENTS
• Leave fused jumper connected at the ELC Height Sensor connector and measure the voltage from terminal A (ORN) at the ELC Compressor Assembly connector (disconnected) to ground
• Go to ELC Height Sensor Test C
BATTERY VOLTAGE
0 VOLTS
• With fused jumper still connected, measure the voltage from terminal A (ORN) to C (WHT) at the ELC Compressor Assembly connector (disconnected)
• Check ORN (340) wire for an open
BATTERY VOLTAGE
0 VOLTS
• Replace the Exhaust Solenoid
• Check WHT (320) wire for an open
GC2019100048030X

Fig. 16 ELC system diagnostic chart (Part 3 of 6). Bonneville, DeVille, Fleetwood (FWD), 88 & 98

C: ELC HEIGHT SENSOR TEST (TABLE 1)

Measure: VOLTAGE
At: ELC HEIGHT SENSOR CONNECTOR (Disconnected)
Condition:
• Ignition Switch: RUN

Between	Voltage	Diagnosis
C (ORN) & Ground	Battery	See 1
C (ORN) & A (BLK)	Battery	See 2
D (BRN) & A (BLK)	Battery	See 3
B (YEL) & A (BLK)	Battery	See 4
E (WHT) & A (BLK)	Battery	See 5

- If all voltages are correct, reconnect the connector and go to Table 2.

1. Check/repair ORN (340) wire for an open (see schematic).
2. Check/repair BLK (154) wire for an open (see schematic).
3. Check/repair BRN (50) wire for an open (see schematic).
4. Check/repair YEL (321) wire for an open (see schematic).
5. Check/repair WHT (320) wire for an open or short to ground (see schematic).

GC2019100048040X

Fig. 16 ELC system diagnostic chart (Part 4 of 6). Bonneville, DeVille, Fleetwood (FWD), 88 & 98

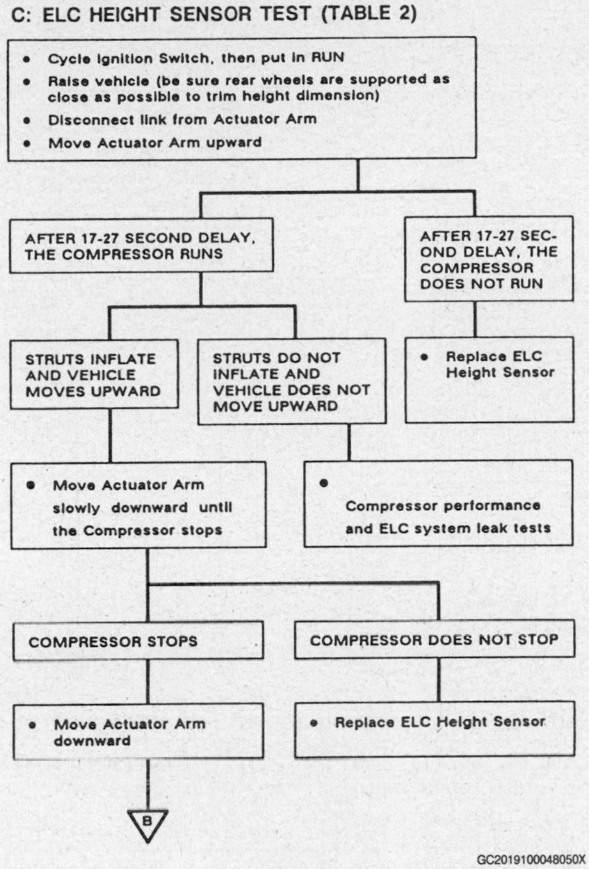
C: ELC HEIGHT SENSOR TEST (TABLE 2)
• Cycle Ignition Switch, then put in RUN
• Raise vehicle (be sure rear wheels are supported as close as possible to trim height dimension)
• Disconnect link from Actuator Arm
• Move Actuator Arm upward
AFTER 17-27 SECOND DELAY, THE COMPRESSOR RUNS
AFTER 17-27 SECOND DELAY, THE COMPRESSOR DOES NOT RUN
STRUTS INFLATE AND VEHICLE MOVES UPWARD
STRUTS DO NOT INFLATE AND VEHICLE DOES NOT MOVE UPWARD
• Replace ELC Height Sensor
• Move Actuator Arm slowly downward until the Compressor stops
• Compressor performance and ELC system leak tests
COMPRESSOR STOPS
COMPRESSOR DOES NOT STOP
• Move Actuator Arm downward
• Replace ELC Height Sensor
B
GC2019100048050X

Fig. 16 ELC system diagnostic chart (Part 5 of 6). Bonneville, DeVille, Fleetwood (FWD), 88 & 98

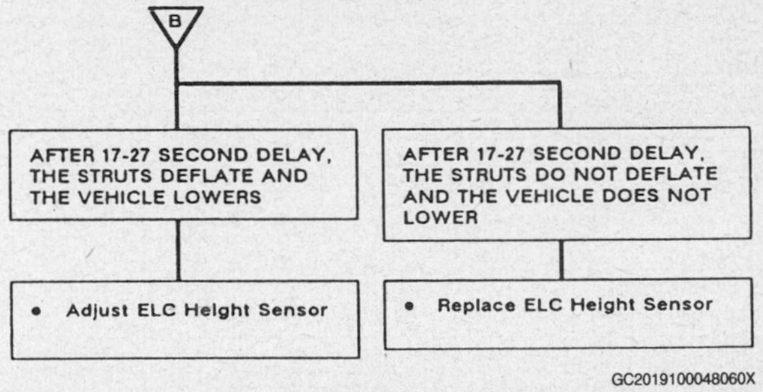
B
AFTER 17-27 SECOND DELAY, THE STRUTS DEFLATE AND THE VEHICLE LOWERS
AFTER 17-27 SECOND DELAY, THE STRUTS DO NOT DEFLATE AND THE VEHICLE DOES NOT LOWER
• Adjust ELC Height Sensor
• Replace ELC Height Sensor
GC2019100048060X

Fig. 16 ELC system diagnostic chart (Part 6 of 6). Bonneville, DeVille, Fleetwood (FWD), 88 & 98

SYMPTOM	PROCEDURE
Compressor Motor does not turn "ON" to raise rear of vehicle.	Chart #1
ELC System does not vent to lower rear of vehicle (checks Exhaust Solenoid).	Chart #2
Compressor Motor runs continuously (longer than 7 minutes).	Chart #3
Compressor Motor runs for maximum run time (approximately 4.5 to 7 minutes) then stops	Check for air leaks in the ELC System and for proper adjustment of the Height Sensor Assembly. If OK, replace Height Sensor Assembly.
ELC System continuously re-levels vehicle with no change in load.	Check for air leaks in the ELC System

GC2019300049000X

Fig. 17 ELC system symptom chart. 1993–94 Caprice, Imapla SS & Roadmaster

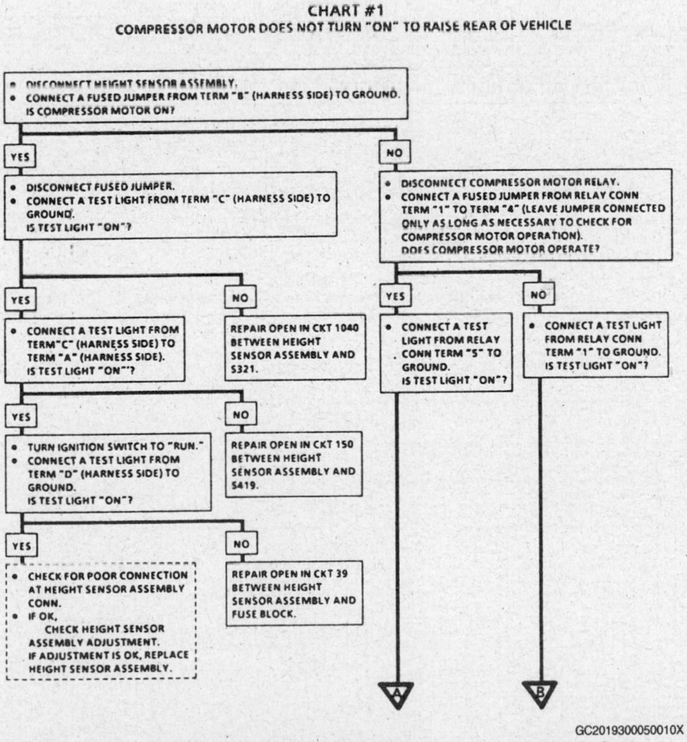
CHART #1
COMPRESSOR MOTOR DOES NOT TURN "ON" TO RAISE REAR OF VEHICLE
• DISCONNECT HEIGHT SENSOR ASSEMBLY.
• CONNECT A FUSED JUMPER FROM TERM "B" (HARNESS SIDE) TO GROUND.
IS COMPRESSOR MOTOR ON?
YES
NO
• DISCONNECT FUSED JUMPER.
• CONNECT A TEST LIGHT FROM TERM "C" (HARNESS SIDE) TO GROUND.
IS TEST LIGHT "ON"?
• DISCONNECT COMPRESSOR MOTOR RELAY.
• CONNECT A FUSED JUMPER FROM RELAY CONN TERM "1" TO TERM "4" (LEAVE JUMPER CONNECTED ONLY AS LONG AS NECESSARY TO CHECK FOR COMPRESSOR MOTOR OPERATION).
DOES COMPRESSOR MOTOR OPERATE?
• CONNECT A TEST LIGHT FROM TERM "C" (HARNESS SIDE) TO TERM "A" (HARNESS SIDE).
IS TEST LIGHT "ON"?
REPAIR OPEN IN CKT 1040 BETWEEN HEIGHT SENSOR ASSEMBLY AND S321.
• CONNECT A TEST LIGHT FROM RELAY CONN TERM "5" TO GROUND.
IS TEST LIGHT "ON"?
• CONNECT A TEST LIGHT FROM RELAY CONN TERM "1" TO GROUND.
IS TEST LIGHT "ON"?
• TURN IGNITION SWITCH TO "RUN."
• CONNECT A TEST LIGHT FROM TERM "D" (HARNESS SIDE) TO GROUND.
IS TEST LIGHT "ON"?
REPAIR OPEN IN CKT 150 BETWEEN HEIGHT SENSOR ASSEMBLY AND S419.
• CHECK FOR POOR CONNECTION AT HEIGHT SENSOR ASSEMBLY CONN.
• IF OK, CHECK HEIGHT SENSOR ASSEMBLY ADJUSTMENT.
IF ADJUSTMENT IS OK, REPLACE HEIGHT SENSOR ASSEMBLY.
REPAIR OPEN IN CKT 39 BETWEEN HEIGHT SENSOR ASSEMBLY AND FUSE BLOCK.
A
B
GC2019300050010X

Fig. 18 ELC system diagnostic chart (Part 1 of 4). 1993–94 Caprice, Impala SS & Roadmaster

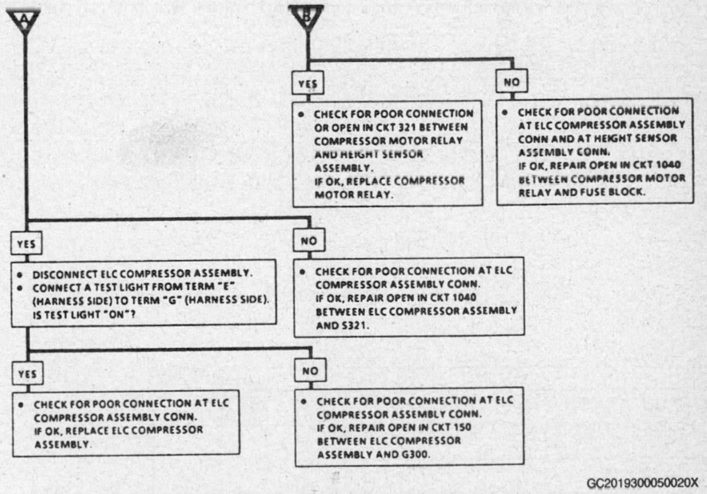
A
B
YES
NO
• CHECK FOR POOR CONNECTION OR OPEN IN CKT 321 BETWEEN COMPRESSOR MOTOR RELAY AND HEIGHT SENSOR ASSEMBLY.
IF OK, REPLACE COMPRESSOR MOTOR RELAY.
• CHECK FOR POOR CONNECTION AT ELC COMPRESSOR ASSEMBLY CONN AND AT HEIGHT SENSOR ASSEMBLY CONN.
IF OK, REPAIR OPEN IN CKT 1040 BETWEEN COMPRESSOR MOTOR RELAY AND FUSE BLOCK.
• DISCONNECT ELC COMPRESSOR ASSEMBLY.
• CONNECT A TEST LIGHT FROM TERM "E" (HARNESS SIDE) TO TERM "G" (HARNESS SIDE).
IS TEST LIGHT "ON"?
• CHECK FOR POOR CONNECTION AT ELC COMPRESSOR ASSEMBLY CONN.
IF OK, REPAIR OPEN IN CKT 1040 BETWEEN ELC COMPRESSOR ASSEMBLY AND S321.
• CHECK FOR POOR CONNECTION AT ELC COMPRESSOR ASSEMBLY CONN.
IF OK, REPLACE ELC COMPRESSOR ASSEMBLY.
• CHECK FOR POOR CONNECTION AT ELC COMPRESSOR ASSEMBLY CONN.
IF OK, REPAIR OPEN IN CKT 150 BETWEEN ELC COMPRESSOR ASSEMBLY AND G300.
GC2019300050020X

Fig. 18 ELC system diagnostic chart (Part 2 of 4). 1993–94 Caprice, Impala SS & Roadmaster

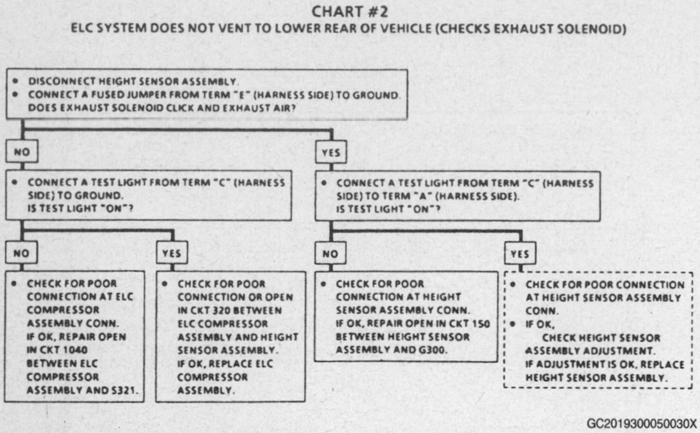
CHART #2
ELC SYSTEM DOES NOT VENT TO LOWER REAR OF VEHICLE (CHECKS EXHAUST SOLENOID)
• DISCONNECT HEIGHT SENSOR ASSEMBLY.
• CONNECT A FUSED JUMPER FROM TERM "E" (HARNESS SIDE) TO GROUND.
DOES EXHAUST SOLENOID CLICK AND EXHAUST AIR?
NO
YES
• CONNECT A TEST LIGHT FROM TERM "C" (HARNESS SIDE) TO GROUND. IS TEST LIGHT "ON"?
• CONNECT A TEST LIGHT FROM TERM "C" (HARNESS SIDE) TO TERM "A" (HARNESS SIDE). IS TEST LIGHT "ON"?
NO
YES
NO
YES
• CHECK FOR POOR CONNECTION AT ELC COMPRESSOR ASSEMBLY CONN. IF OK, REPAIR OPEN IN CKT 1040 BETWEEN ELC COMPRESSOR ASSEMBLY AND S321.
• CHECK FOR POOR CONNECTION OR OPEN IN CKT 320 BETWEEN ELC COMPRESSOR ASSEMBLY AND HEIGHT SENSOR ASSEMBLY. IF OK, REPLACE ELC COMPRESSOR ASSEMBLY.
• CHECK FOR POOR CONNECTION AT HEIGHT SENSOR ASSEMBLY CONN. IF OK, REPAIR OPEN IN CKT 150 BETWEEN HEIGHT SENSOR ASSEMBLY AND G300.
• CHECK FOR POOR CONNECTION AT HEIGHT SENSOR ASSEMBLY CONN.
• IF OK, CHECK HEIGHT SENSOR ASSEMBLY ADJUSTMENT. IF ADJUSTMENT IS OK, REPLACE HEIGHT SENSOR ASSEMBLY.
GC2019300050030X

Fig. 18 ELC system diagnostic chart (Part 3 of 4). 1993–94 Caprice, Impala SS & Roadmaster

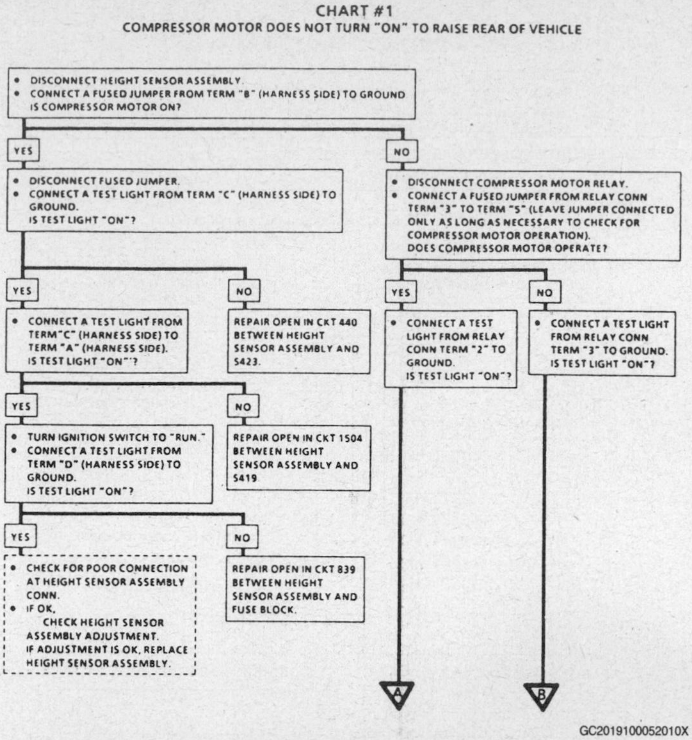
CHART #1
COMPRESSOR MOTOR DOES NOT TURN "ON" TO RAISE REAR OF VEHICLE
• DISCONNECT HEIGHT SENSOR ASSEMBLY.
• CONNECT A FUSED JUMPER FROM TERM "B" (HARNESS SIDE) TO GROUND
IS COMPRESSOR MOTOR ON?
YES
NO
• DISCONNECT FUSED JUMPER.
• CONNECT A TEST LIGHT FROM TERM "C" (HARNESS SIDE) TO GROUND. IS TEST LIGHT "ON"?
• DISCONNECT COMPRESSOR MOTOR RELAY.
• CONNECT A FUSED JUMPER FROM RELAY CONN TERM "3" TO TERM "5" (LEAVE JUMPER CONNECTED ONLY AS LONG AS NECESSARY TO CHECK FOR COMPRESSOR MOTOR OPERATION). DOES COMPRESSOR MOTOR OPERATE?
YES
NO
YES
NO
• CONNECT A TEST LIGHT FROM TERM "C" (HARNESS SIDE) TO TERM "A" (HARNESS SIDE). IS TEST LIGHT "ON"?
REPAIR OPEN IN CKT 440 BETWEEN HEIGHT SENSOR ASSEMBLY AND S423.
• CONNECT A TEST LIGHT FROM RELAY CONN TERM "2" TO GROUND. IS TEST LIGHT "ON"?
• CONNECT A TEST LIGHT FROM RELAY CONN TERM "3" TO GROUND. IS TEST LIGHT "ON"?
YES
NO
• TURN IGNITION SWITCH TO "RUN."
• CONNECT A TEST LIGHT FROM TERM "D" (HARNESS SIDE) TO GROUND. IS TEST LIGHT "ON"?
REPAIR OPEN IN CKT 1504 BETWEEN HEIGHT SENSOR ASSEMBLY AND S419
YES
NO
• CHECK FOR POOR CONNECTION AT HEIGHT SENSOR ASSEMBLY CONN.
• IF OK, CHECK HEIGHT SENSOR ASSEMBLY ADJUSTMENT. IF ADJUSTMENT IS OK, REPLACE HEIGHT SENSOR ASSEMBLY.
REPAIR OPEN IN CKT 839 BETWEEN HEIGHT SENSOR ASSEMBLY AND FUSE BLOCK.
A
B
GC2019100052010X

Fig. 20 ELC system diagnostic chart (Part 1 of 4). Fleetwood (RWD)

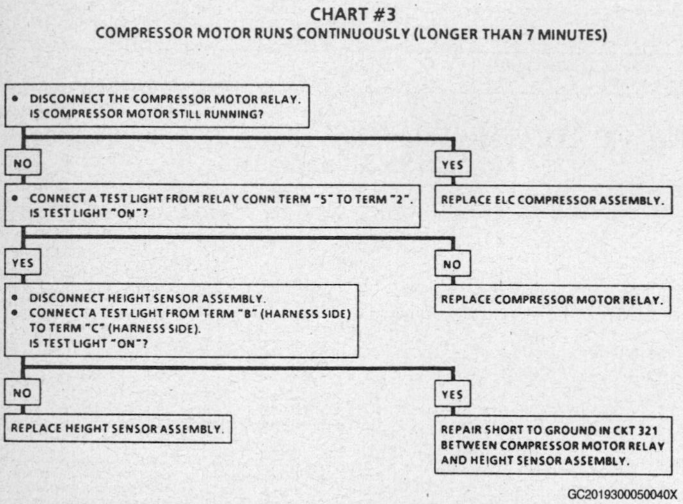
CHART #3
COMPRESSOR MOTOR RUNS CONTINUOUSLY (LONGER THAN 7 MINUTES)
• DISCONNECT THE COMPRESSOR MOTOR RELAY. IS COMPRESSOR MOTOR STILL RUNNING?
NO
YES
• CONNECT A TEST LIGHT FROM RELAY CONN TERM "5" TO TERM "2". IS TEST LIGHT "ON"?
REPLACE ELC COMPRESSOR ASSEMBLY.
YES
NO
• DISCONNECT HEIGHT SENSOR ASSEMBLY.
• CONNECT A TEST LIGHT FROM TERM "B" (HARNESS SIDE) TO TERM "C" (HARNESS SIDE). IS TEST LIGHT "ON"?
REPLACE COMPRESSOR MOTOR RELAY.
NO
YES
REPLACE HEIGHT SENSOR ASSEMBLY.
REPAIR SHORT TO GROUND IN CKT 321 BETWEEN COMPRESSOR MOTOR RELAY AND HEIGHT SENSOR ASSEMBLY.
GC2019300050040X

Fig. 18 ELC system diagnostic chart (Part 4 of 4). 1993–94 Caprice, Impala SS & Roadmaster

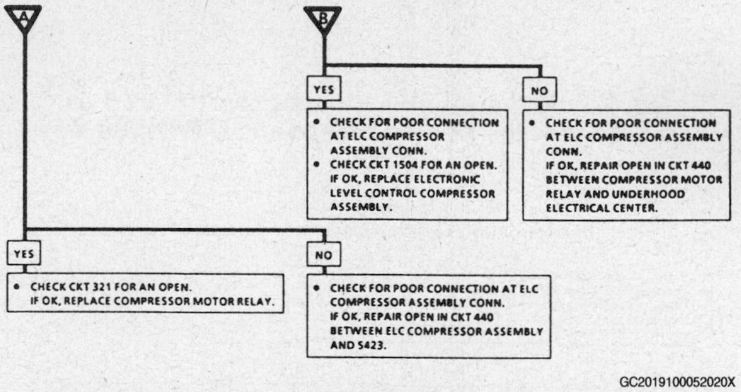
A
B
YES
NO
• CHECK FOR POOR CONNECTION AT ELC COMPRESSOR ASSEMBLY CONN.
• CHECK CKT 1504 FOR AN OPEN. IF OK, REPLACE ELECTRONIC LEVEL CONTROL COMPRESSOR ASSEMBLY.
• CHECK FOR POOR CONNECTION AT ELC COMPRESSOR ASSEMBLY CONN. IF OK, REPAIR OPEN IN CKT 440 BETWEEN COMPRESSOR MOTOR RELAY AND UNDERHOOD ELECTRICAL CENTER.
YES
NO
• CHECK CKT 321 FOR AN OPEN. IF OK, REPLACE COMPRESSOR MOTOR RELAY.
• CHECK FOR POOR CONNECTION AT ELC COMPRESSOR ASSEMBLY CONN. IF OK, REPAIR OPEN IN CKT 440 BETWEEN ELC COMPRESSOR ASSEMBLY AND S423.
GC2019100052020X

Fig. 20 ELC system diagnostic chart (Part 2 of 4). Fleetwood (RWD)

SYMPTOM	PROCEDURE
Compressor Motor does not turn "ON" to raise rear of vehicle.	Chart #1
ELC System does not vent to lower rear of vehicle (checks Exhaust Solenoid).	Chart #2
Compressor Motor runs continuously (longer than 7 minutes).	Chart #3
Compressor Motor runs for maximum run time (approximately 4.5 to 7 minutes) then stops	Check for air leaks in the ELC System and for proper adjustment of the Height Sensor Assembly. If OK, replace Height Sensor Assembly.
ELC System continuously re-levels vehicle with no change in load.	Check for air leaks in the ELC System.
"LEVEL RIDE" Indicator inoperative, ELC System operates normally.	Check for an open in CKT 322 or CKT 1500. If OK, check bulb. If bulb is OK, remove cluster for service.

GC2019100051000X

Fig. 19 ELC system symptom chart. Fleetwood (RWD)

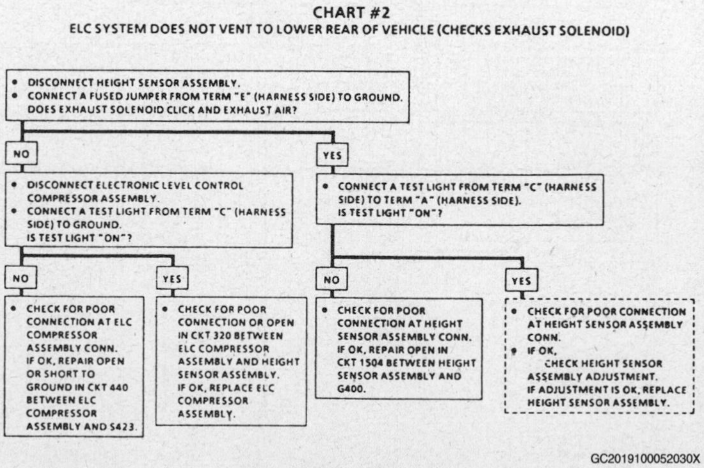
CHART #2
ELC SYSTEM DOES NOT VENT TO LOWER REAR OF VEHICLE (CHECKS EXHAUST SOLENOID)
• DISCONNECT HEIGHT SENSOR ASSEMBLY.
• CONNECT A FUSED JUMPER FROM TERM "E" (HARNESS SIDE) TO GROUND.
DOES EXHAUST SOLENOID CLICK AND EXHAUST AIR?
NO
YES
• DISCONNECT ELECTRONIC LEVEL CONTROL COMPRESSOR ASSEMBLY.
• CONNECT A TEST LIGHT FROM TERM "C" (HARNESS SIDE) TO GROUND. IS TEST LIGHT "ON"?
• CONNECT A TEST LIGHT FROM TERM "C" (HARNESS SIDE) TO TERM "A" (HARNESS SIDE). IS TEST LIGHT "ON"?
NO
YES
NO
YES
• CHECK FOR POOR CONNECTION AT ELC COMPRESSOR ASSEMBLY CONN. IF OK, REPAIR OPEN OR SHORT TO GROUND IN CKT 440 BETWEEN ELC COMPRESSOR ASSEMBLY AND S423.
• CHECK FOR POOR CONNECTION OR OPEN IN CKT 320 BETWEEN ELC COMPRESSOR ASSEMBLY AND HEIGHT SENSOR ASSEMBLY. IF OK, REPLACE ELC COMPRESSOR ASSEMBLY.
• CHECK FOR POOR CONNECTION AT HEIGHT SENSOR ASSEMBLY CONN. IF OK, REPAIR OPEN IN CKT 1504 BETWEEN HEIGHT SENSOR ASSEMBLY AND G400.
• CHECK FOR POOR CONNECTION AT HEIGHT SENSOR ASSEMBLY CONN.
• IF OK, CHECK HEIGHT SENSOR ASSEMBLY ADJUSTMENT. IF ADJUSTMENT IS OK, REPLACE HEIGHT SENSOR ASSEMBLY.
GC2019100052030X

Fig. 20 ELC system diagnostic chart (Part 3 of 4). Fleetwood (RWD)

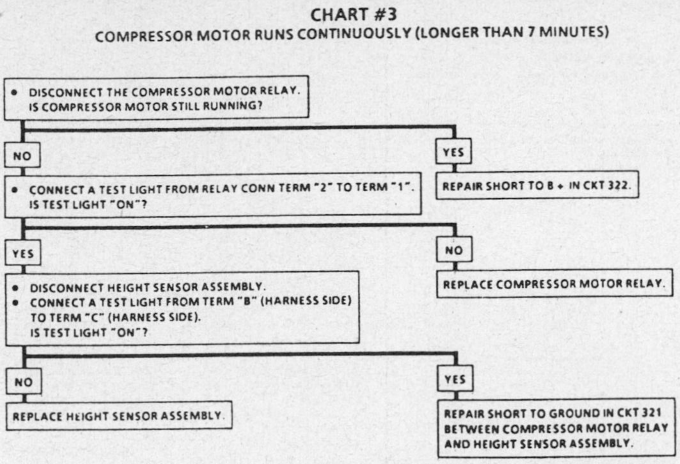
CHART #3
COMPRESSOR MOTOR RUNS CONTINUOUSLY (LONGER THAN 7 MINUTES)
• DISCONNECT THE COMPRESSOR MOTOR RELAY. IS COMPRESSOR MOTOR STILL RUNNING?
NO
YES
REPAIR SHORT TO B + IN CKT 322.
• CONNECT A TEST LIGHT FROM RELAY CONN TERM "2" TO TERM "1". IS TEST LIGHT "ON"?
YES
NO
REPLACE COMPRESSOR MOTOR RELAY.
• DISCONNECT HEIGHT SENSOR ASSEMBLY.
• CONNECT A TEST LIGHT FROM TERM "B" (HARNESS SIDE) TO TERM "C" (HARNESS SIDE). IS TEST LIGHT "ON"?
NO
YES
REPLACE HEIGHT SENSOR ASSEMBLY.
REPAIR SHORT TO GROUND IN CKT 321 BETWEEN COMPRESSOR MOTOR RELAY AND HEIGHT SENSOR ASSEMBLY.

GC2019100052040X

Fig. 20 ELC system diagnostic chart (Part 4 of 4). Fleetwood (RWD)

SYMPTOM	DIAGNOSIS				
	Raise vehicle Check that link is attached between sensor actuator arm and lower control arm.	Do ELC Relay And Compressor Motor Test A.	Do Exhaust Solenoid Test D.	Do ELC Height Sensor Actuator Arm Test C.	Disconnect ELC height sensor. If ELC compressor motor stops: replace sensor. If not: check wiring (CKT 321) for a short to gound; If OK, replace ELC relay.
ELC compressor motor does not run.	• Do 1st	• Do 2nd			
System does not exhaust. Vehicle does not lower when weight is removed.	• Do 1st		• Do 2nd		
ELC compressor motor runs for more than 7 minutes. Vehicle stays at maximum height.	• Do 1st				• Do 2nd
ELC compressor motor runs for 4 1/2 to 7 minutes and turns off. Vehicle does not reach proper height	• Do 1st			• Do 2nd	
ELC compressor motor cycles on and off frequently.	• Do 1st			• Do 2nd	

GC2019100053000X

Fig. 21 ELC system symptom chart. LeSabre & Park Avenue

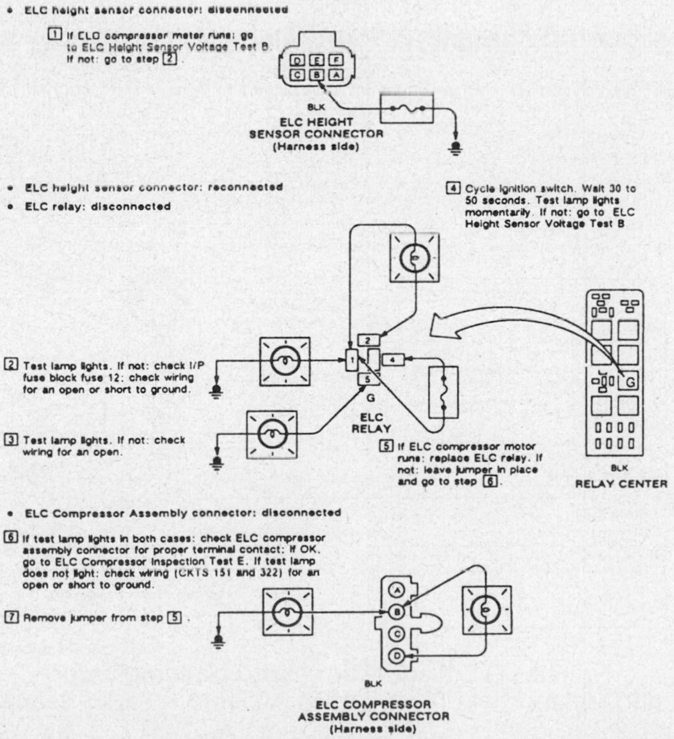
• ELC height sensor connector: disconnected
1 If ELC compressor motor runs: go to ELC Height Sensor Voltage Test B. If not: go to step 2.
BLK
ELC HEIGHT SENSOR CONNECTOR (Harness side)
• ELC height sensor connector: reconnected
• ELC relay: disconnected
4 Cycle ignition switch. Wait 30 to 50 seconds. Test lamp lights momentarily. If not: go to ELC Height Sensor Voltage Test B
2 Test lamp lights. If not: check I/P fuse block fuse 12; check wiring for an open or short to ground.
3 Test lamp lights. If not: check wiring for an open.
G
ELC RELAY
5 If ELC compressor motor runs: replace ELC relay. If not: leave jumper in place and go to step 6.
BLK
RELAY CENTER
• ELC Compressor Assembly connector: disconnected
6 If test lamp lights in both cases: check ELC compressor assembly connector for proper terminal contact; If OK, go to ELC Compressor Inspection Test E. If test lamp does not light: check wiring (CKTS 151 and 322) for an open or short to ground.
7 Remove jumper from step 5.
BLK
ELC COMPRESSOR ASSEMBLY CONNECTOR (Harness side)

GC2019100054000X

Fig. 22 ELC diagnostic chart, ELC relay & compressor motor test. LeSabre & Park Avenue

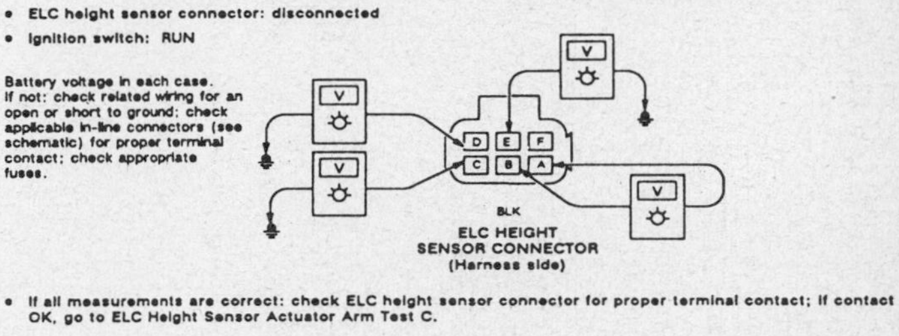
• ELC height sensor connector: disconnected
• Ignition switch: RUN
Battery voltage in each case. If not: check related wiring for an open or short to ground; check applicable in-line connectors (see schematic) for proper terminal contact; check appropriate fuses.
BLK
ELC HEIGHT SENSOR CONNECTOR (Harness side)
• If all measurements are correct: check ELC height sensor connector for proper terminal contact; If contact OK, go to ELC Height Sensor Actuator Arm Test C.

GC2019100055000X

Fig. 23 ELC diagnostic chart, ELC height sensor voltage test. LeSabre & Park Avenue

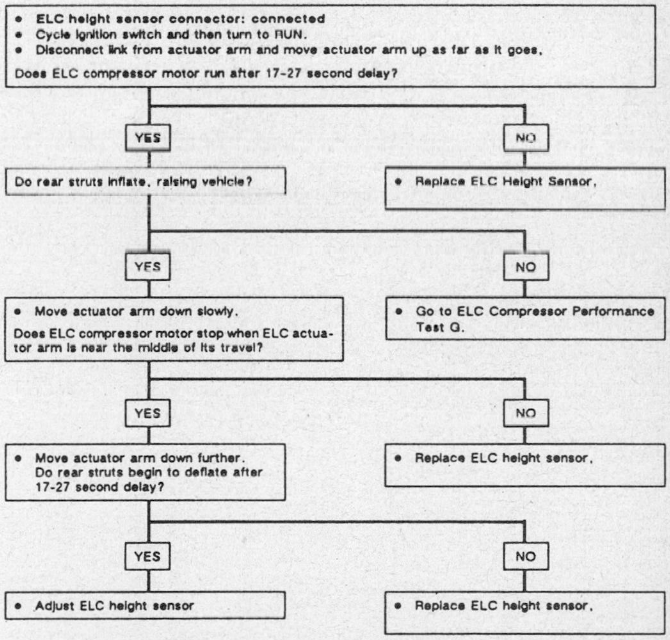
• ELC height sensor connector: connected
• Cycle ignition switch and then turn to RUN.
• Disconnect link from actuator arm and move actuator arm up as far as it goes.
Does ELC compressor motor run after 17-27 second delay?
YES
NO
Do rear struts inflate, raising vehicle?
• Replace ELC Height Sensor.
YES
NO
• Move actuator arm down slowly.
Does ELC compressor motor stop when ELC actuator arm is near the middle of its travel?
• Go to ELC Compressor Performance Test G.
YES
NO
• Move actuator arm down further. Do rear struts begin to deflate after 17-27 second delay?
• Replace ELC height sensor.
YES
NO
• Adjust ELC height sensor
• Replace ELC height sensor.

GC2019100056000X

Fig. 24 ELC diagnostic chart, ELC height sensor actuator arm test. LeSabre & Park Avenue

- ELC height sensor connector: disconnected

[1] Jumper ELC height sensor connector as shown to pressurize system.

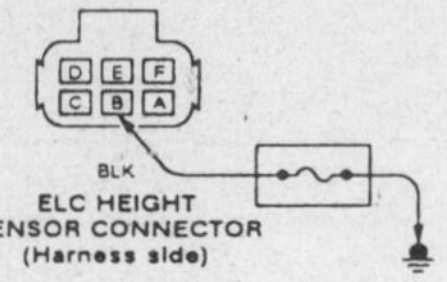
D E F
C B A
BLK
ELC HEIGHT
SENSOR CONNECTOR
(Harness side)

[2] If exhaust solenoid vents system: go to ELC Height Sensor Actuator Arm Test C; otherwise leave jumper in place and go to [3].

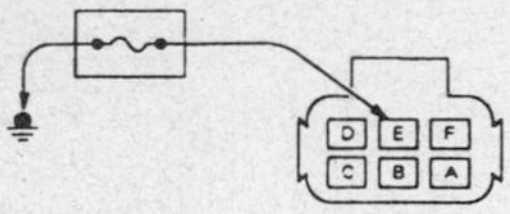
D E F
C B A
BLK
ELC HEIGHT
SENSOR CONNECTOR
(Harness side)

- ELC compressor assembly connector: disconnected

[3] If test lamp lights in both cases: check ELC compressor assembly (terminals A and C) and ELC height sensor (terminal E) pigtail connectors for proper terminal contact; check pigtail wiring for an open or short to ground; if wiring and contacts are OK, go to Air Dryer Test F. If test lamp does not light: check wiring (CKTS 320 and 340) for an open or short to ground.

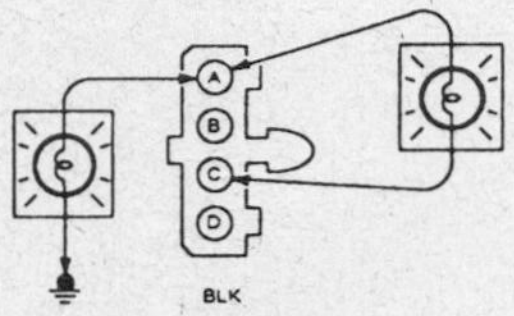
A
B
C
D
BLK
ELC COMPRESSOR
ASSEMBLY CONNECTOR
(Harness side)

GC2019100057000X

Fig. 25 ELC diagnostic chart, Exhaust solenoid test. LeSabre & Park Avenue

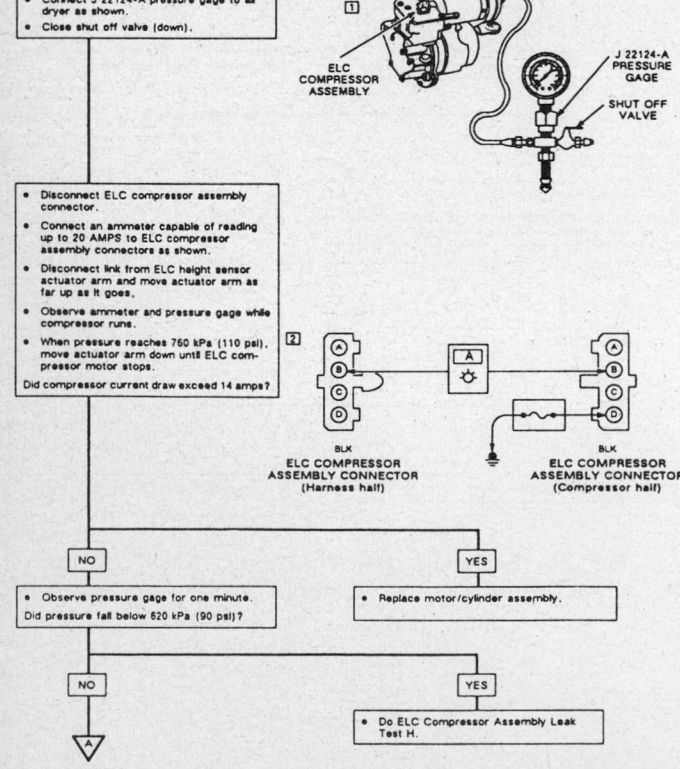

- Remove ELC compressor assembly.
- Remove two motor case attaching screws.
- Pull case and magnet assembly off armature.

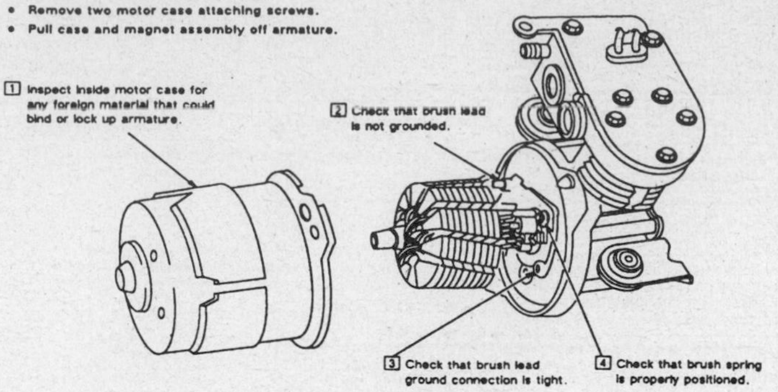
[1] Inspect inside motor case for any foreign material that could bind or lock up armature.
[2] Check that brush lead is not grounded.
[3] Check that brush lead ground connection is tight.
[4] Check that brush spring is properly positioned.

- If no defects can be found: replace motor/cylinder assembly.

GC2019100058000X

Fig. 26 ELC diagnostic chart, ELC compressor inspection test. LeSabre & Park Avenue

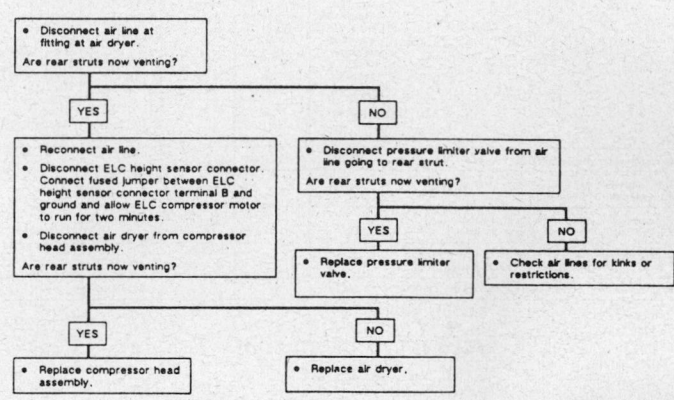

- Disconnect air line at fitting at air dryer.

Are rear struts now venting?

YES:
- Reconnect air line.
- Disconnect ELC height sensor connector. Connect fused jumper between ELC height sensor connector terminal B and ground and allow ELC compressor motor to run for two minutes.
- Disconnect air dryer from compressor head assembly.

Are rear struts now venting?

YES:
- Replace compressor head assembly.

NO:
- Replace air dryer.

NO:
- Disconnect pressure limiter valve from air line going to rear strut.

Are rear struts now venting?

YES:
- Replace pressure limiter valve.

NO:
- Check air lines for kinks or restrictions.

GC2019100059000X

Fig. 27 ELC diagnostic chart, Air dryer test. LeSabre & Park Avenue

- Connect J 22124-A pressure gage to air dryer as shown.
- Close shut off valve (down).

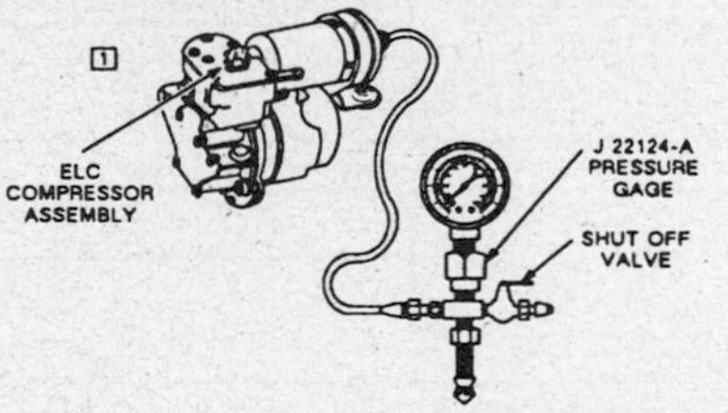
[1]
ELC
COMPRESSOR
ASSEMBLY
J 22124-A
PRESSURE
GAGE
SHUT OFF
VALVE

- Disconnect ELC compressor assembly connector.
- Connect an ammeter capable of reading up to 20 AMPS to ELC compressor assembly connectors as shown.
- Disconnect link from ELC height sensor actuator arm and move actuator arm as far up as it goes.
- Observe ammeter and pressure gage while compressor runs.
- When pressure reaches 760 kPa (110 psi), move actuator arm down until ELC compressor motor stops.

Did compressor current draw exceed 14 amps?

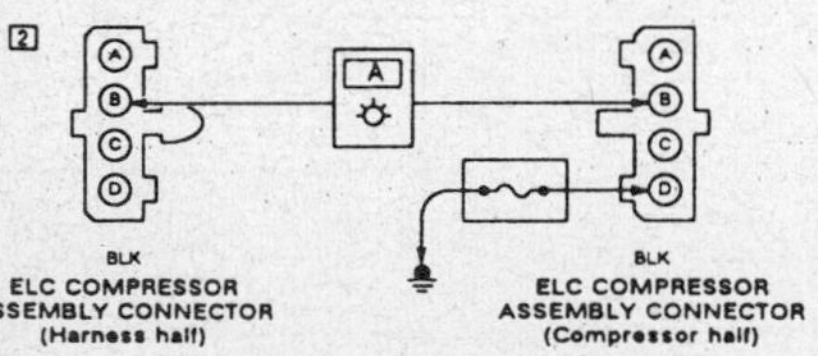
[2]
A
B
C
D
A
BLK
ELC COMPRESSOR
ASSEMBLY CONNECTOR
(Harness half)
BLK
ELC COMPRESSOR
ASSEMBLY CONNECTOR
(Compressor half)

YES:
- Replace motor/cylinder assembly.

NO:
- Observe pressure gage for one minute.

Did pressure fall below 620 kPa (90 psi)?

YES:
- Do ELC Compressor Assembly Leak Test H.

NO: → A Continued

GC2019100060010X

Fig. 28 ELC diagnostic chart, ELC compressor performance test (Part 1 of 2). LeSabre & Park Avenue

Continued A

- ELC height sensor connector: disconnected.
- Open shut off valve (up).
- Connect J 22124-A pressure gage in place of pressure limiter valve. Install so that the shut off valve is on compressor side of gage.
- Connect fused jumper between ELC height sensor connector (terminal B) and ground.
- Disconnect ELC height sensor fused jumper when pressure reaches 760 to 830 kPa (110 to 120 psi).
- Close shut off valve (down) and observe pressure gage for one minute.

Is pressure dropping?

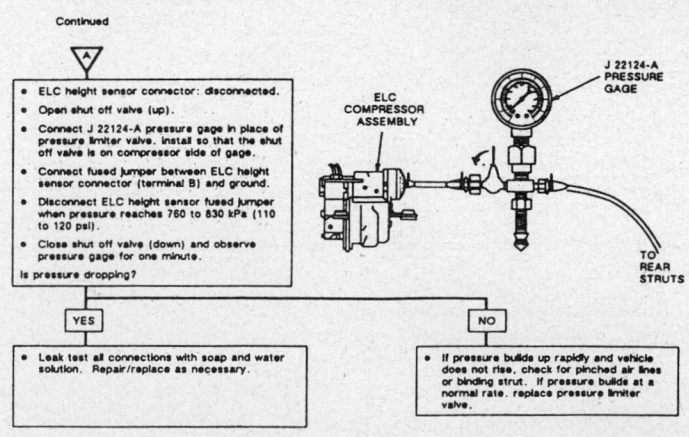

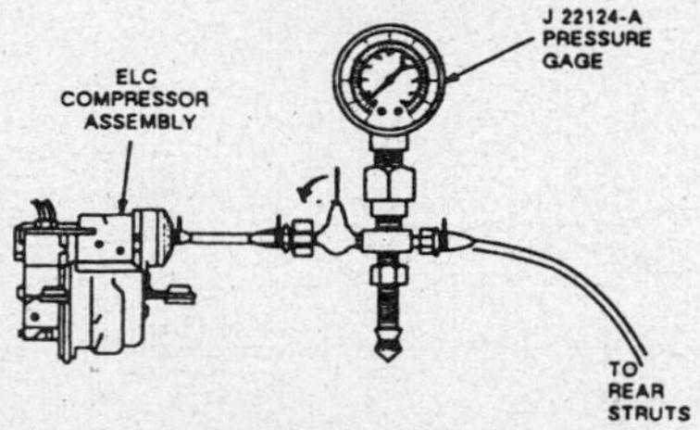
ELC
COMPRESSOR
ASSEMBLY
J 22124-A
PRESSURE
GAGE
TO
REAR
STRUTS

YES:
- Leak test all connections with soap and water solution. Repair/replace as necessary.

NO:
- If pressure builds up rapidly and vehicle does not rise, check for pinched air lines or binding strut. If pressure builds at a normal rate, replace pressure limiter valve.

GC2019100060020X

Fig. 28 ELC diagnostic chart, ELC compressor performance test (Part 2 of 2). LeSabre & Park Avenue

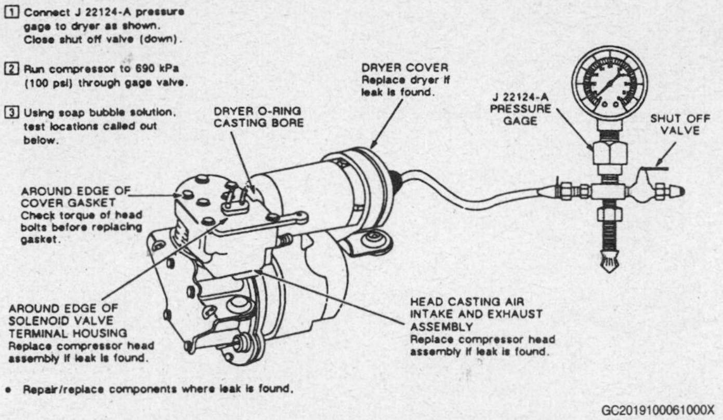
1 Connect J 22124-A pressure gage to dryer as shown. Close shut off valve (down).
2 Run compressor to 690 kPa (100 psi) through gage valve.
3 Using soap bubble solution, test locations called out below.
DRYER O-RING CASTING BORE
DRYER COVER Replace dryer if leak is found.
J 22124-A PRESSURE GAGE
SHUT OFF VALVE
AROUND EDGE OF COVER GASKET Check torque of head bolts before replacing gasket.
AROUND EDGE OF SOLENOID VALVE TERMINAL HOUSING Replace compressor head assembly if leak is found.
HEAD CASTING AIR INTAKE AND EXHAUST ASSEMBLY Replace compressor head assembly if leak is found.
• Repair/replace components where leak is found.
GC2019100061000X

Fig. 29 ELC diagnostic chart, ELC compressor assembly leak test. LeSabre & Park Avenue

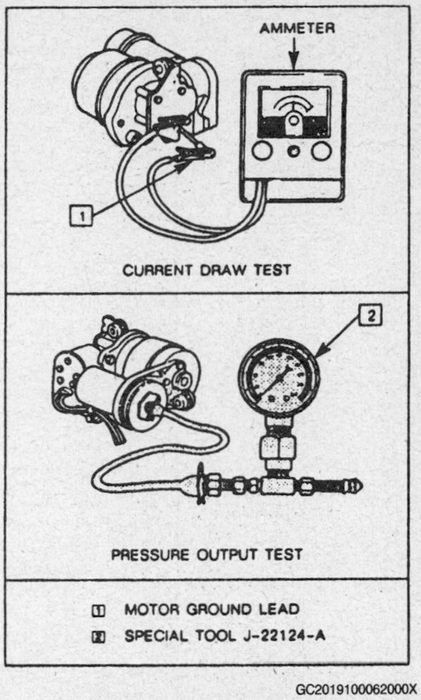
AMMETER
1
CURRENT DRAW TEST
2
PRESSURE OUTPUT TEST
1 MOTOR GROUND LEAD
2 SPECIAL TOOL J-22124-A
GC2019100062000X

Fig. 30 Compressor performance test

MALFUNCTION	CORRECTION
1. Compressor runs but current draw exceeds 14 amps.	1. Replace compressor.
2. Compressor inoperative	2. Replace compressor.
3. Compressor output less than 758 kPa (110 psi)	3. Perform compressor/dryer leak test, if no leak is found, replace compressor.
4. Pressure leaks down to 0 kPa (0 psi)	4. Perform compressor/dryer leak test, and make corrections as required.
5. Pressure build up ok, but leaks down below 60 kPa (90 psi) before holding steady. (Does not go to 0 psi.)	5. Replace head assembly

GC2019100126000X

Fig. 31 Compressor/Dryer trouble chart

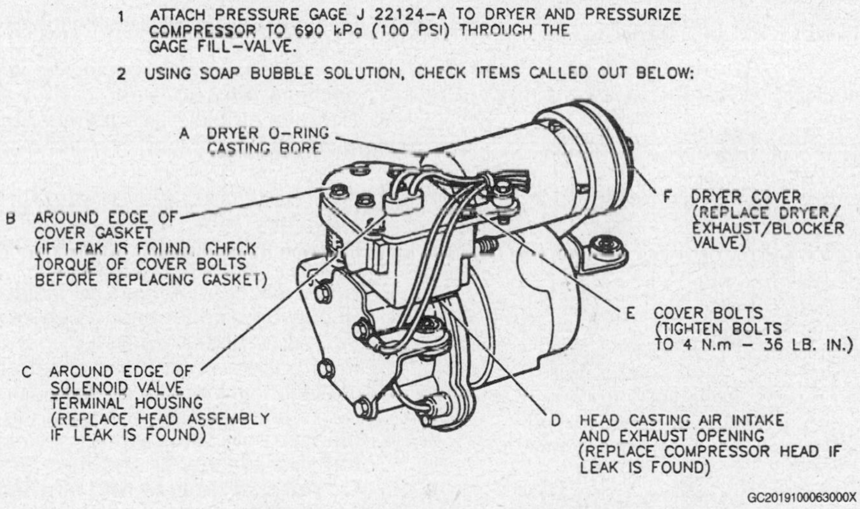
1 ATTACH PRESSURE GAGE J 22124-A TO DRYER AND PRESSURIZE COMPRESSOR TO 690 kPa (100 PSI) THROUGH THE GAGE FILL-VALVE.
2 USING SOAP BUBBLE SOLUTION, CHECK ITEMS CALLED OUT BELOW:
A DRYER O-RING CASTING BORE
B AROUND EDGE OF COVER GASKET (IF LEAK IS FOUND, CHECK TORQUE OF COVER BOLTS BEFORE REPLACING GASKET)
C AROUND EDGE OF SOLENOID VALVE TERMINAL HOUSING (REPLACE HEAD ASSEMBLY IF LEAK IS FOUND)
D HEAD CASTING AIR INTAKE AND EXHAUST OPENING (REPLACE COMPRESSOR HEAD IF LEAK IS FOUND)
E COVER BOLTS (TIGHTEN BOLTS TO 4 N.m - 36 LB. IN.)
F DRYER COVER (REPLACE DRYER/EXHAUST/BLOCKER VALVE)
GC2019100063000X

Fig. 32 Compressor leak test

VEHICLE TRIM HEIGHT CHECK

Trim heights are checked with tires at recommended pressure, fuel tank at capacity, front seat in rear position, no passengers and trunk empty, except for spare tire and jack.

Refer to **Figs. 35 through 43** for trim height measurements.

VEHICLE TRIM HEIGHT ADJUSTMENT

1. Loosen locknut securing metal arm to height sensor plastic arm, **Fig. 44.**
2. To increase trim height, move plastic actuator arm upward and tighten locknut.
3. To decrease trim height, move plastic actuator arm downward and tighten locknut.
4. If proper adjustment cannot be made, ensure correct height sensor is installed.

COMPONENT REPLACEMENT

When repair or adjustment procedures require that vehicle be raised on a hoist, it is important that the rear axle assembly remains in the normal trim height position at all times. When a frame contact hoist is used, two additional jack stands should be used to support the rear axle or control arms in the normal trim height position.

SHIELD, COMPRESSOR & BRACKET

1. Disconnect battery ground cable.
2. Raise and support vehicle.
3. Remove compressor shield, if equipped, then deflate system.
4. Disconnect high pressure line at air dryer by revolving spring clip 90° while holding connector end and removing tube assembly.
5. Disconnect electrical connector from compressor pigtail harness.
6. Remove three compressor mounting screws, then the compressor.
7. Remove three compressor mounting bracket screws, then the bracket.
8. If replacing compressor assembly, remove dryer and dryer bracket.
9. Reverse procedure to install. After connecting battery ground cable, cycle ignition switch, then test system operation, looking for air leaks at dryer.

AIR DRYER

1. Remove compressor as described in "Shield, Compressor & Bracket."
2. Rotate dryer retainer spring 90° and pull dryer and O-ring out of compressor head assembly, **Fig. 45.**
3. Reverse procedure to install.

COMPRESSOR HEAD ASSEMBLY

1. Remove air dryer assembly as described in "Air Dryer."
2. Remove three compressor head

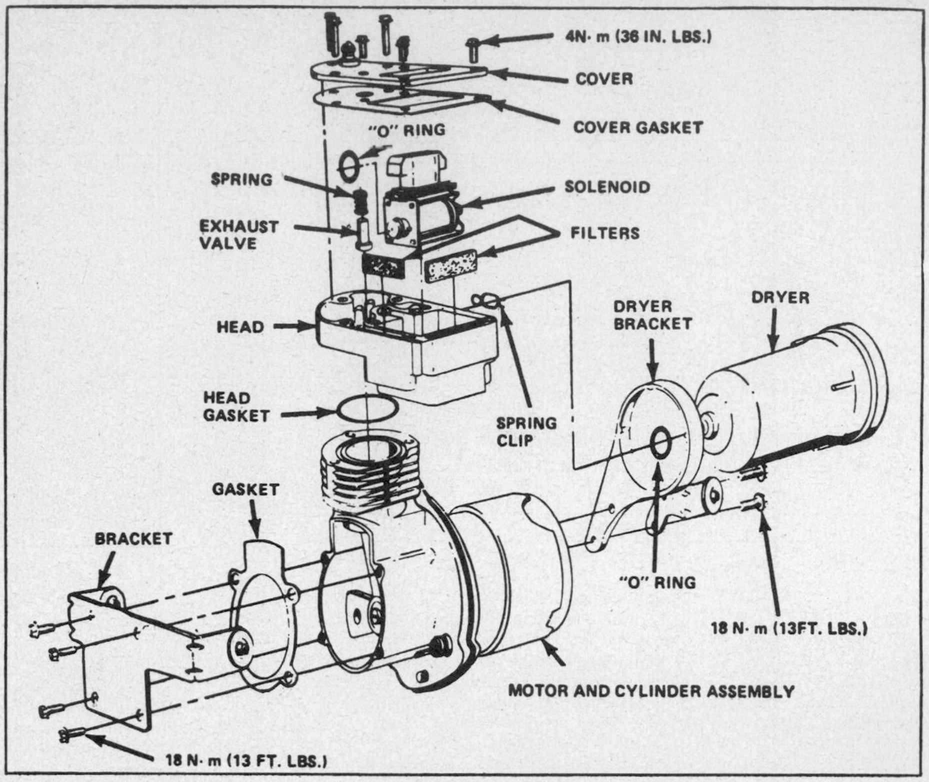
4N· m (36 IN. LBS.)
COVER
COVER GASKET
"O" RING
SPRING
SOLENOID
EXHAUST VALVE
FILTERS
DRYER BRACKET
DRYER
HEAD
HEAD GASKET
SPRING CLIP
GASKET
BRACKET
"O" RING
18 N· m (13FT. LBS.)
MOTOR AND CYLINDER ASSEMBLY
18 N· m (13 FT. LBS.)

GC2019100066000X

Fig. 33 Air compressor disassembled

mounting bolts and head assembly, **Fig. 46.**

3. Reverse procedure to install, using a new O-ring and **torquing** head mounting bolts to 36 inch lbs.

SOLENOID VALVE ASSEMBLY

If solenoid valve assembly requires replacement, it should be replaced with compressor head assembly. Refer to "Compressor Head Assembly"

HEIGHT SENSOR & BRACKET

1. Disconnect battery ground cable.
2. Raise and support vehicle.
3. Disconnect harness from sensor electrical connector by squeezing oval sides of the connector lock to release locking tabs.
4. Remove link from height sensor arm, then remove sensor mounting screws or nuts and the sensor.
5. Remove sensor mounting bracket to underbody attaching screws and remove bracket.
6. Reverse procedure to install, noting the following:
   a. When connecting harness to sensor electrical connector, push connector into sensor plug until sloped shoulder on rear edge of boss is visible in plug slot. Push oval connector lock onto plug until its two locking tabs snap over shoulder of sensor plug.
   b. Perform height sensor operational check and adjustment procedure as described in "System Service" and "Adjustments"

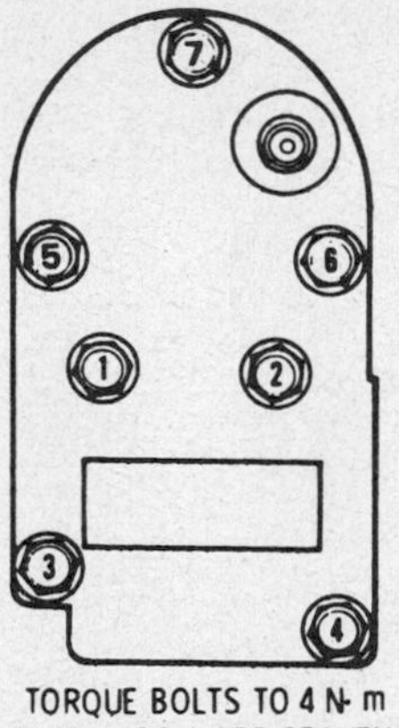
7
5
6
1
2
3
4
TORQUE BOLTS TO 4 N· m
(36 IN. LBS.) PER SEQUENCE

GC2019100067000X

Fig. 34 Air compressor head tightening sequence

STRUT AIR BLADDER

Removal

1. Remove strut from vehicle.
2. Scribe alignment marks between upper mount and outer tube.
3. Clamp strut in a suitable vise using wooden blocks.
4. Remove upper mount from strut, **Fig. 47.**
5. Cut and remove outer clamp with a hacksaw, **Fig. 48.**
6. Cut air bladder from outer tube and slide the inner tube upward.
7. Remove O-ring from inside top of outer tube, **Fig. 49.**
8. Cut and remove inner clamp with a hacksaw, **Fig. 50.**
9. Remove air bladder from inner tube.

Installation

1. Lubricate new O-ring and O-ring groove with silicone lubricant. Install O-ring in groove, **Fig. 49.**
2. Apply silicone lubricant to inside top of new air bladder and the entire outside of air bladder, **Fig. 51.**
3. Fold bottom of air bladder before installation on inner tube. Place air bladder over inner tube, continuing to fold bladder from the bottom up. Position top of air bladder as shown in **Fig. 52. Do not use tools to fold air bladder as damage may occur, causing air leakage.**
4. Place inner clamp in position as shown in **Fig. 52.** Tighten clamp with sealing ring compressor tool No. J-34649 or equivalent.
5. Fold bottom of air bladder upward and fold top of 4 inch section downward.
6. Apply silicone lubricant to polished diameter of inner shaft tube.
7. Place outer tube over air bladder and push downward against folded portion of bladder. **The outer tube must be completely seated over shaft.**
8. Install upper mount onto strut, aligning marks made during disassembly, and **torque** nut to 74 ft.lbs. **The upper mount and tube air fitting must be properly positioned with the bottom strut mount, Fig. 53.**

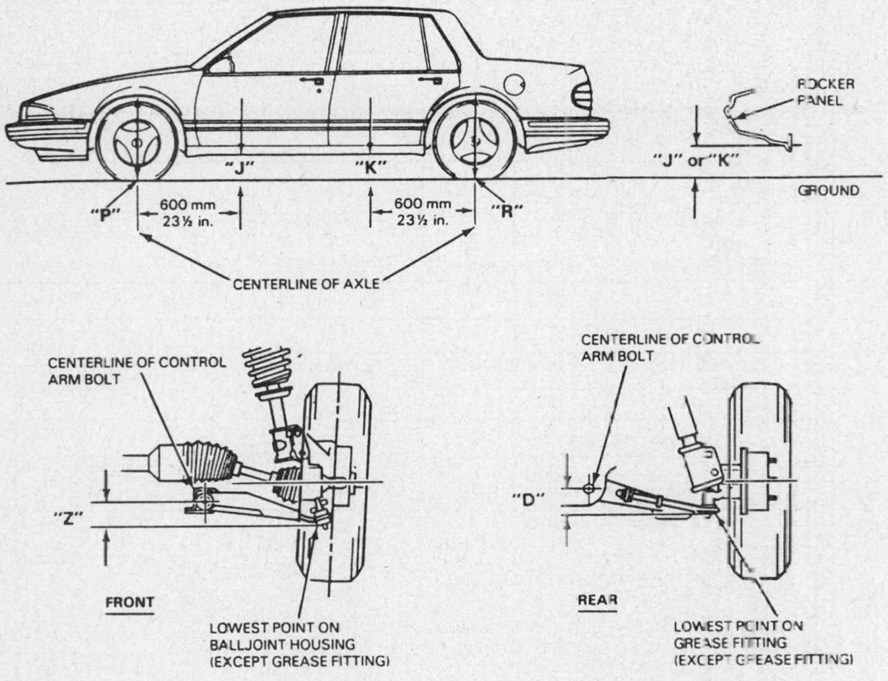

ROCKER PANEL
"J" or "K"
GROUND
"J"
"K"
"P"
600 mm
23½ in.
600 mm
23½ in.
"R"
CENTERLINE OF AXLE
CENTERLINE OF CONTROL ARM BOLT
"Z"
FRONT
LOWEST POINT ON BALLJOINT HOUSING (EXCEPT GREASE FITTING)
CENTERLINE OF CONTROL ARM BOLT
"D"
REAR
LOWEST POINT ON GREASE FITTING (EXCEPT GREASE FITTING)

TRIM HEIGHT CHECK PROCEDURE

1. VEHICLE MUST BE ON LEVEL GROUND.
2. TIRES MUST BE INFLATED TO PROPER PRESSURE.
3. FUEL TANK SHOULD BE FULL.
4. NO PASSENGERS OR ADDED WEIGHT SHOULD BE IN THE VEHICLE. THE TRUNK MUST BE EMPTY EXCEPT FOR THE SPARE TIRE AND JACK.
5. PLACE THE FRONT SEAT IN THE REAR POSITION.
6. IGNITION SWITCH ON TO ACTIVATE ELECTRONIC LEVEL CONTROL (ELC). (IF EQUIPPED)
7. "BOUNCE" THE CAR THREE TIMES AT THE FRONT AND REAR TO NORMALIZE THE SUSPENSION.
8. MEASURE FROM THE LOWEST POINT ON THE BALLJOINT HOUSING TO CONTROL ARM BOLT CENTERLINE AT "D" AND "Z" POSITIONS. (SEE ILLUSTRATIONS ABOVE)
9. MEASURE FROM KNOWN LEVEL FLOOR TO ROCKER PANEL AT "J" AND "K" POSITIONS. EXCEPT SSE MODELS.
10. MEASURE FROM KNOWN LEVEL FLOOR TO THE WHEEL OPENING AT "P" AND "R" POSITIONS.

MAXIMUM VARIATION SIDE TO SIDE & FRONT TO REAR IS 19MM (¾ IN)

LOAD CONDITIONS – COOLANT TO CAPACITY AND FULL TANK OF FUEL

"Z"	"D"	"P"	"R"	"J"	"K"
55-75 mm 2 5/32-2 61/64 in.	70-90 mm 2 3/4-3 35/64 in.	708-728 mm 27 57/64-28 21/32 in.	710-730 mm 27 61/64-28 3/4 in.	231-25 mm 9 3/32-9 7/8 in.	231-251 mm 9 3/32-9 7/8 in.

GC2019100075000X

Fig. 35 Vehicle trim height measurements. Bonneville

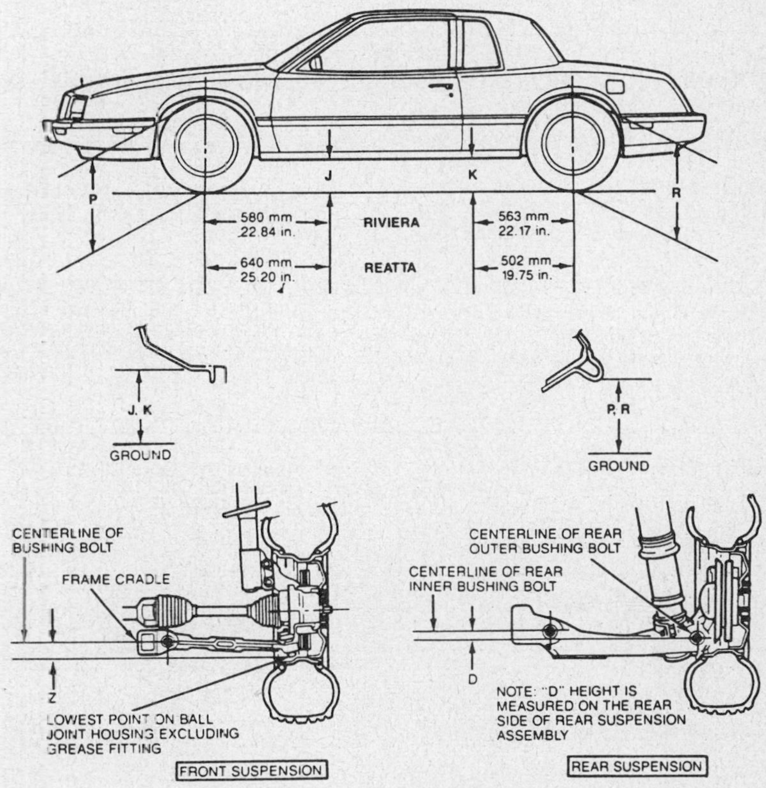

P
J
K
R
580 mm
22.84 in.
RIVIERA
563 mm
22.17 in.
640 mm
25.20 in.
REATTA
502 mm
19.75 in.
J, K
GROUND
P, R
GROUND
CENTERLINE OF BUSHING BOLT
FRAME CRADLE
Z
LOWEST POINT ON BALL JOINT HOUSING EXCLUDING GREASE FITTING
FRONT SUSPENSION
CENTERLINE OF REAR OUTER BUSHING BOLT
CENTERLINE OF REAR INNER BUSHING BOLT
D
NOTE: "D" HEIGHT IS MEASURED ON THE REAR SIDE OF REAR SUSPENSION ASSEMBLY
REAR SUSPENSION

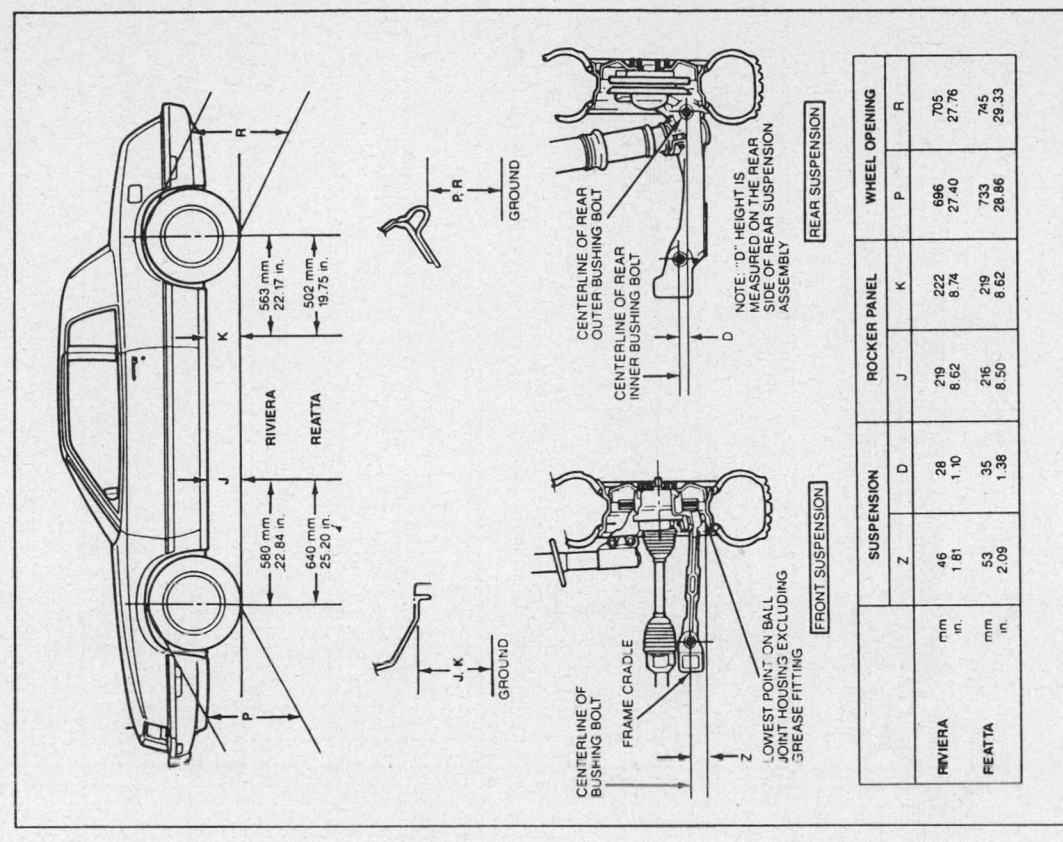

		SUSPENSION		ROCKER PANEL		WHEEL OPENING	
		Z	D	J	K	P	R
RIVIERA	mm	46	28	219	222	696	705
	in.	1.81	1.10	8.62	8.74	27.40	27.76
REATTA	mm	53	35	216	219	733	745
	in.	2.09	1.38	8.50	8.62	28.86	29.33

GC2019100076000X

Fig. 36 Vehicle trim height measurements. Riviera

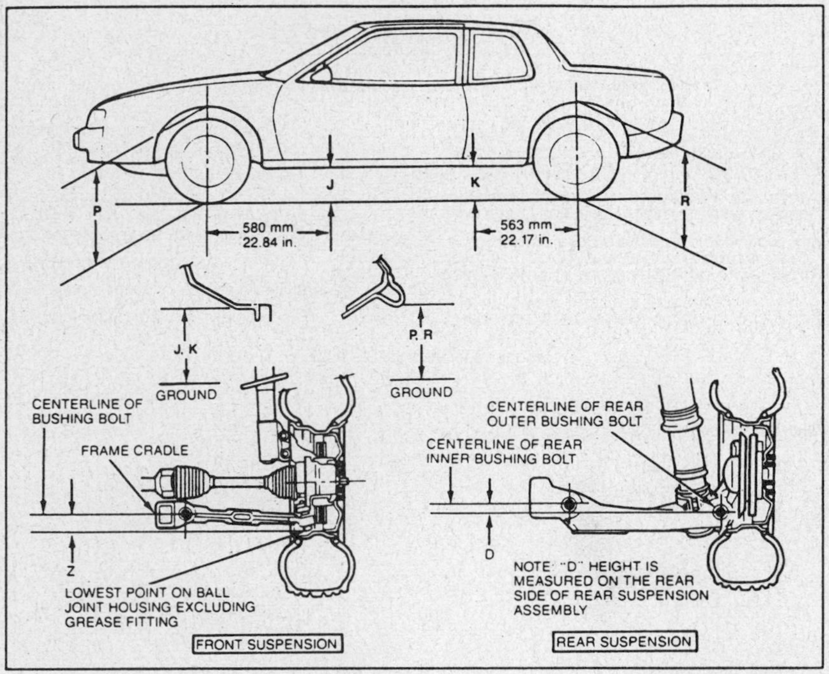
CENTERLINE OF BUSHING BOLT
FRAME CRADLE
LOWEST POINT ON BALL JOINT HOUSING EXCLUDING GREASE FITTING
FRONT SUSPENSION
CENTERLINE OF REAR OUTER BUSHING BOLT
CENTERLINE OF REAR INNER BUSHING BOLT
NOTE: "D" HEIGHT IS MEASURED ON THE REAR SIDE OF REAR SUSPENSION ASSEMBLY
REAR SUSPENSION
GROUND
J, K
P, R
580 mm
22.84 in.
563 mm
22.17 in.
P
J
K
R
Z
D

		SUSPENSION		ROCKER PANEL		WHEEL OPENING	
		Z	D	J	K	P	R
TORONADO	mm	57	34	231	231	706	718
	in.	2.24	1.34	9.09	9.09	27.80	28.27

GC2019200077000X

Fig. 37 Vehicle trim height measurements. Toronado & Trofeo

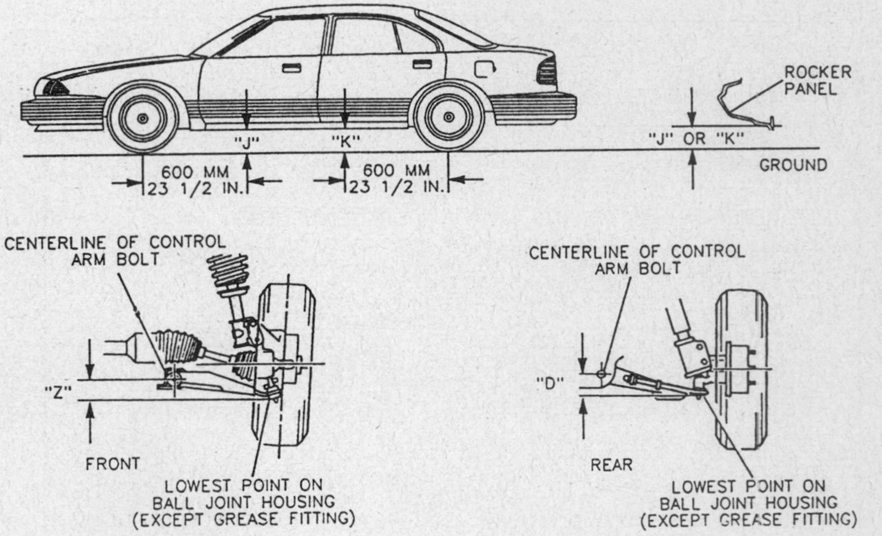
ROCKER PANEL
"J" OR "K"
GROUND
"J"
"K"
600 MM
23 1/2 IN.
600 MM
23 1/2 IN.
CENTERLINE OF CONTROL ARM BOLT
"Z"
FRONT
LOWEST POINT ON BALL JOINT HOUSING (EXCEPT GREASE FITTING)
CENTERLINE OF CONTROL ARM BOLT
"D"
REAR
LOWEST POINT ON BALL JOINT HOUSING (EXCEPT GREASE FITTING)

Eighty-Eight:
- D = 68-88 mm (2 11/16 - 3 7/16 in.)
- Z = 50-70 mm (1 15/16 - 2 3/4 in.)
- J = 229-249 mm (9 - 9 13/16 in.)
- K = 236-256 mm (9 9/32 - 10 1/16 in.)

LeSabre:
- D = 68-88 mm (2 11/16 - 3 7/16 in.)
- Z = 50-70 mm (1 15/16 - 2 3/4 in.)
- J = 229-249 mm (9 - 9 13/16 in.)
- K = 236-256 mm (9 9/32 - 10 1/16 in.)

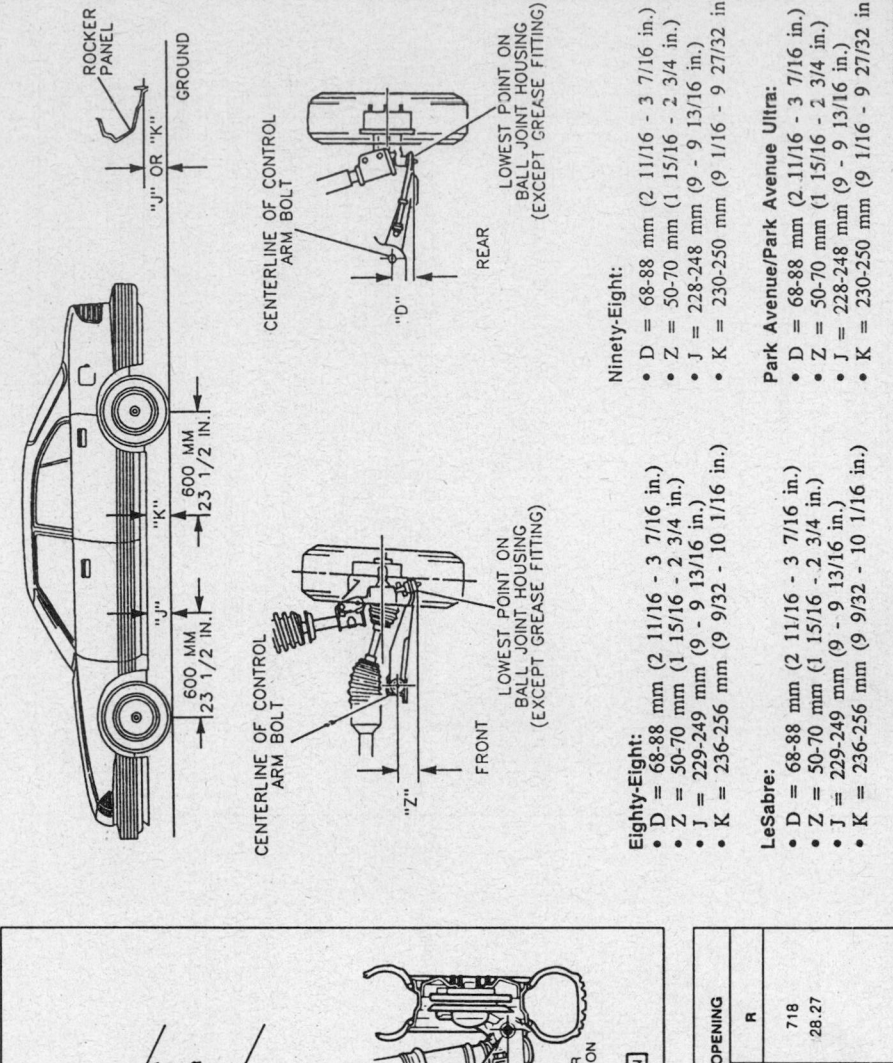

Ninety-Eight:
- D = 68-88 mm (2 11/16 - 3 7/16 in.)
- Z = 50-70 mm (1 15/16 - 2 3/4 in.)
- J = 228-248 mm (9 - 9 13/16 in.)
- K = 230-250 mm (9 1/16 - 9 27/32 in.)

Park Avenue/Park Avenue Ultra:
- D = 68-88 mm (2 11/16 - 3 7/16 in.)
- Z = 50-70 mm (1 15/16 - 2 3/4 in.)
- J = 228-248 mm (9 - 9 13/16 in.)
- K = 230-250 mm (9 1/16 - 9 27/32 in.)

GC2019100078000X

Fig. 38 Vehicle trim height measurements. LeSabre, Park Avenue, 88 & 98

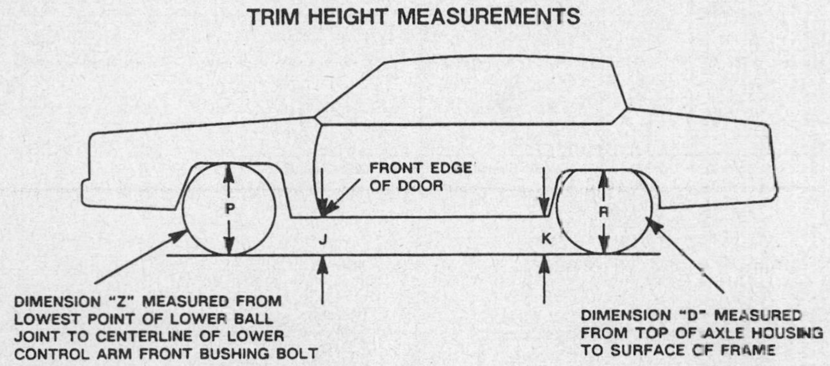
TRIM HEIGHT MEASUREMENTS
FRONT EDGE OF DOOR
P
J
K
R
DIMENSION "Z" MEASURED FROM LOWEST POINT OF LOWER BALL JOINT TO CENTERLINE OF LOWER CONTROL ARM FRONT BUSHING BOLT
DIMENSION "D" MEASURED FROM TOP OF AXLE HOUSING TO SURFACE OF FRAME

		SUSPENSION		ROCKER PANEL		WHEEL OPENING	
		Z	D	J	K	P	R
BROUGHAM	mm	55	160	268	277	736	613
	in.	2.17	6.30	10.55	10.91	28.98	24.13

THE SPECIFICATIONS SHOWN ARE FOR THE VEHICLE ON A LEVEL SURFACE WITH A FULL TANK OF FUEL, PROPER TIRE INFLATION PRESSURE, A PROPERLY OPERATING ELC SYSTEM AND NO PASSENGERS OR ADDITIONAL WEIGHT IN CAR. BOUNCE VEHICLE THREE TIMES AT FRONT AND REAR TO NORMALIZE SUSPENSION. ALL MEASUREMENTS ARE ±10 MM. MAXIMUM VARIATION SIDE TO SIDE IS 9 MM (3/8 INCH).

GC2019100079000X

Fig. 39 Vehicle trim height measurements. Brougham

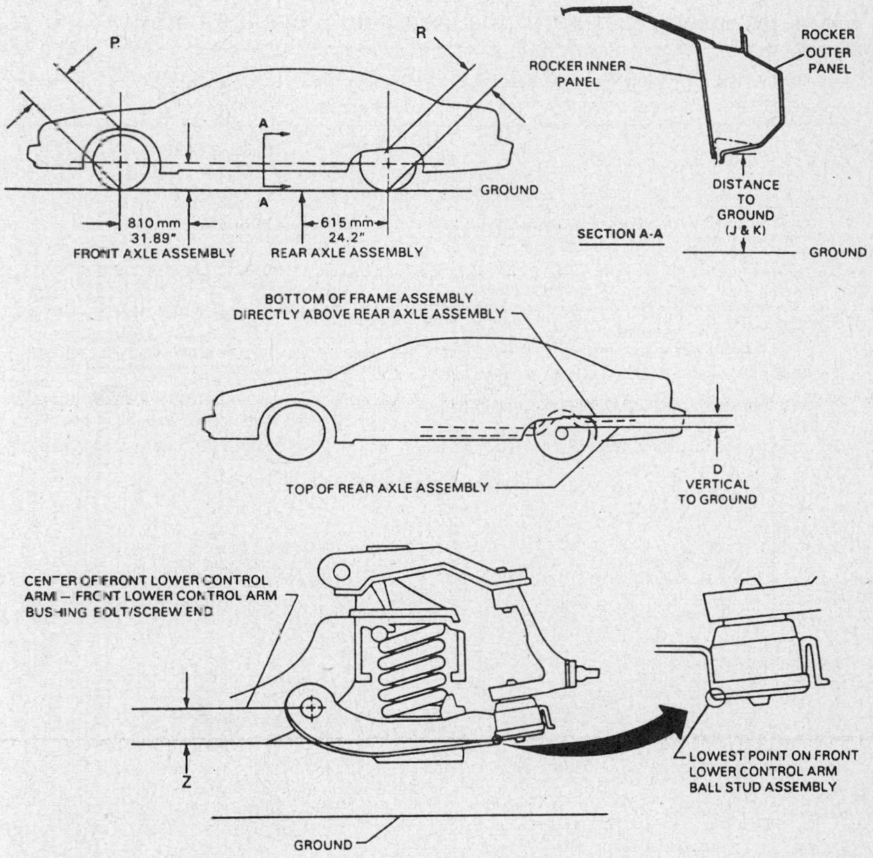
P
R
A
A
GROUND
810 mm
31.89"
FRONT AXLE ASSEMBLY
615 mm
24.2"
REAR AXLE ASSEMBLY
ROCKER INNER PANEL
ROCKER OUTER PANEL
DISTANCE TO GROUND (J & K)
SECTION A-A
GROUND
BOTTOM OF FRAME ASSEMBLY DIRECTLY ABOVE REAR AXLE ASSEMBLY
TOP OF REAR AXLE ASSEMBLY
D VERTICAL TO GROUND
CENTER OF FRONT LOWER CONTROL ARM – FRONT LOWER CONTROL ARM BUSHING BOLT/SCREW END
Z
LOWEST POINT ON FRONT LOWER CONTROL ARM BALL STUD ASSEMBLY
GROUND

MODEL	SUSPENSION	TIRE	J		K		P		R		D		Z	
			mm	INCH	mm	INCH	mm	INCH	mm	INCH	mm	INCH	mm	INCH
SEDAN	FE1	235-70	252	9.9	264	10.4	737	29.0	546	21.5	147	5.8	56	2.2
	FE2/F41	225-70	252	9.9	264	10.4	737	29.0	546	21.5	152	6.0	61	2.4

NOTE: Trim heights should be within ± 10 mm (0.4 inch).

GC2019300080000X

Fig. 40 Vehicle trim height measurements. 1993–94 Fleetwood (RWD)

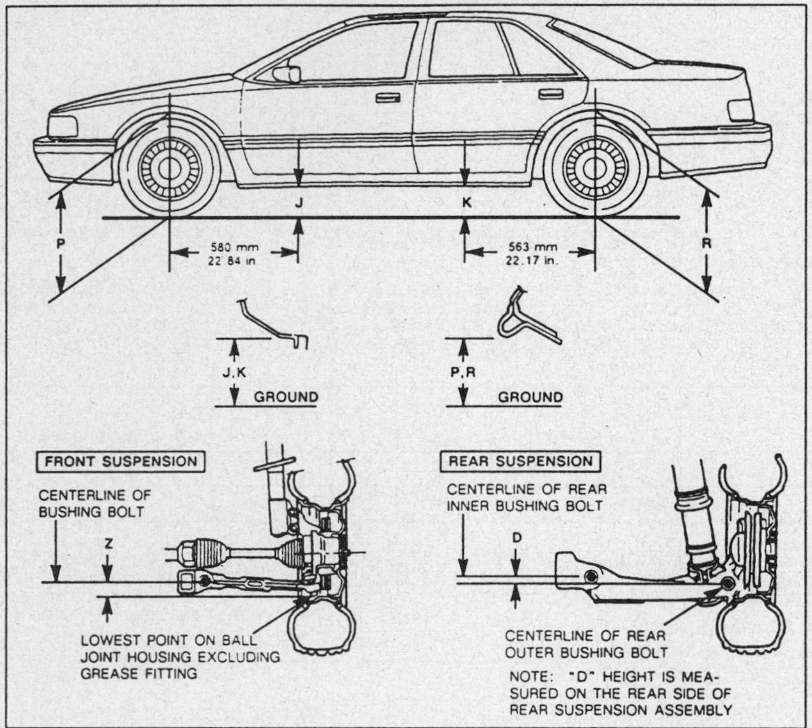
J
K
P
R
580 mm
22.84 in
563 mm
22.17 in.
J,K
GROUND
P,R
GROUND
FRONT SUSPENSION
CENTERLINE OF
BUSHING BOLT
Z
LOWEST POINT ON BALL
JOINT HOUSING EXCLUDING
GREASE FITTING
REAR SUSPENSION
CENTERLINE OF REAR
INNER BUSHING BOLT
D
CENTERLINE OF REAR
OUTER BUSHING BOLT
NOTE: "D" HEIGHT IS MEA-
SURED ON THE REAR SIDE OF
REAR SUSPENSION ASSEMBLY

		SUSPENSION		ROCKER PANEL		WHEEL OPENING	
		Z	D	J	K	P	R
ELDORADO	mm	52	30	223	221	717	716
	in.	2.05	1.18	8.78	8.70	28.23	28.19
SEVILLE	mm	56	34	245	245	726	726
	in.	2.21	1.34	9.65	9.65	28.68	28.68
SEVILLE STS	mm	52	31	241	241	722	722
	in.	2.05	1.22	9.49	9.49	28.43	28.43

THE SPECIFICATIONS SHOWN ARE FOR THE VEHICLE ON A LEVEL SURFACE WITH A FULL TANK OF FUEL, PROPER TIRE INFLATION PRESSURE, NO PASSENGERS OR ADDITIONAL WEIGHT IN CAR, AND A PROPERLY OPERATING ELECTRONIC LEVEL CONTROL SYSTEM. BOUNCE VEHICLE THREE TIMES AT FRONT AND REAR TO NORMALIZE SUSPENSION. ALL MEASUREMENTS ARE ± 10MM. MAXIMUM VARIATION SIDE TO SIDE IS 12 MM (0.5 INCH).

GC2019100081000X

Fig. 41 Vehicle trim height measurements. Eldorado & Seville

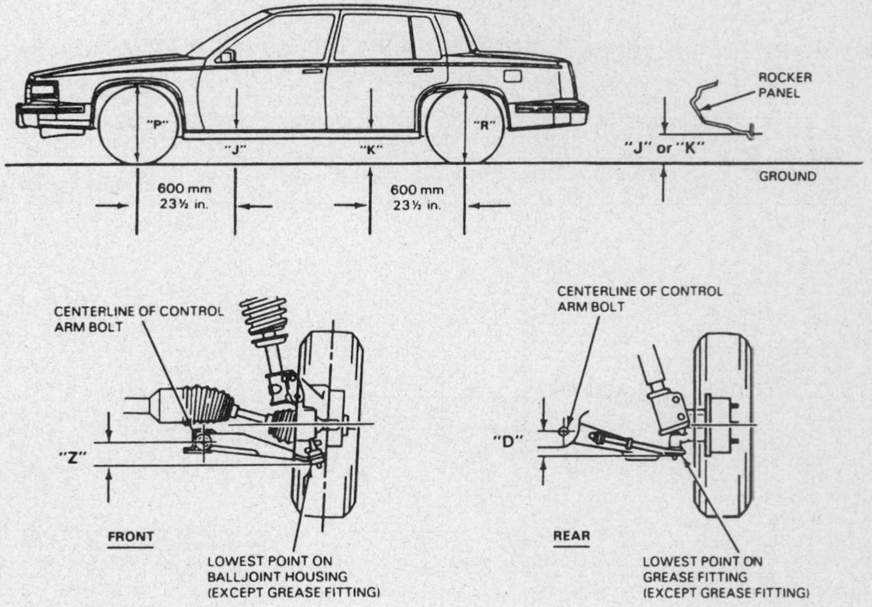
"P"
"J"
"K"
"R"
"J" or "K"
ROCKER
PANEL
GROUND
600 mm
23½ in.
600 mm
23½ in.
CENTERLINE OF CONTROL
ARM BOLT
"Z"
FRONT
LOWEST POINT ON
BALLJOINT HOUSING
(EXCEPT GREASE FITTING)
CENTERLINE OF CONTROL
ARM BOLT
"D"
REAR
LOWEST POINT ON
GREASE FITTING
(EXCEPT GREASE FITTING)

TRIM HEIGHT CHECK PROCEDURE

1. VEHICLE MUST BE ON LEVEL GROUND.
2. TIRES MUST BE INFLATED TO PROPER PRESSURE.
3. FUEL TANK SHOULD BE FULL.
4. NO PASSENGERS OR ADDED WEIGHT SHOULD BE IN THE VEHICLE. THE TRUNK MUST BE EMPTY EXCEPT FOR THE SPARE TIRE AND JACK.
5. PLACE THE FRONT SEAT IN THE REAR POSITION.
6. IGNITION SWITCH ON TO ACTIVATE ELECTRONIC LEVEL CONTROL (ELC). (IF EQUIPPED)
7. "BOUNCE" THE CAR THREE TIMES AT THE FRONT AND REAR TO NORMALIZE THE SUSPENSION.
8. MEASURE FROM THE LOWEST POINT ON THE BALLJOINT HOUSING TO CONTROL ARM BOLT CENTERLINE AT "D" AND "Z" POSITIONS. (SEE ILLUSTRATIONS ABOVE)
9. MEASURE FROM KNOWN LEVEL FLOOR TO ROCKER PANEL AT "J" AND "K" POSITIONS. EXCEPT SSE MODELS.
10. MEASURE FROM KNOWN LEVEL FLOOR TO THE WHEEL OPENING AT "P" AND "R" POSITIONS.

MAXIMUM VARIATION SIDE TO SIDE & FRONT TO REAR IS 19MM (¾ IN)

LOAD CONDITIONS – COOLANT TO CAPACITY AND FULL TANK OF FUEL

"Z"	"D"	"P"	"R"	"J"	"K"
64-84 mm	71-91 mm	706-726 mm	656-676 mm	230-250 mm	230-250 mm
$2\frac{33}{64}$-$3\frac{5}{16}$ in.	$2\frac{51}{64}$-$3\frac{19}{32}$ in.	$27\frac{51}{64}$-$28\frac{37}{64}$ in.	$25\frac{53}{64}$-$26\frac{39}{64}$ in.	$9\frac{1}{64}$-$9\frac{27}{32}$ in.	$9\frac{1}{64}$-$9\frac{27}{32}$ in.

GC2019100082000X

Fig. 42 Vehicle trim height measurements. DeVille & Fleetwood (FWD)

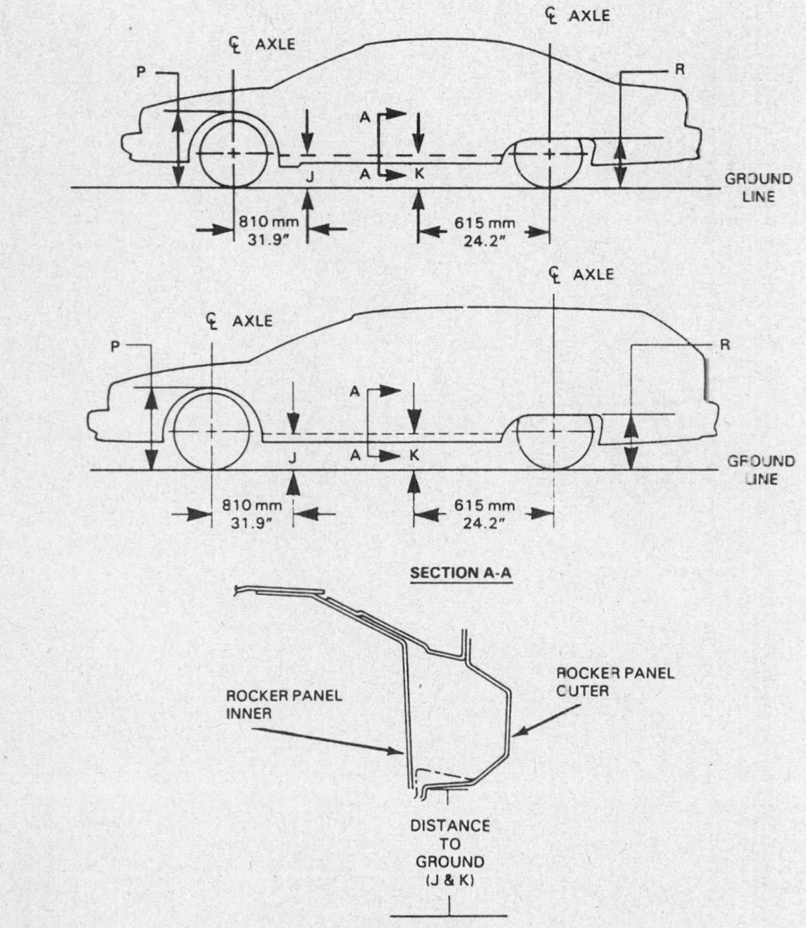
℄ AXLE
℄ AXLE
P
R
A
A
J
K
GROUND LINE
810 mm
31.9"
615 mm
24.2"
SECTION A-A
ROCKER PANEL INNER
ROCKER PANEL OUTER
DISTANCE TO GROUND (J & K)

TRIM HEIGHTS CHART

VEHICLE	SUSPENSION	TIRE	J		K		P		R	
			mm	INCH	mm	INCH	mm	INCH	mm	INCH
SEDAN	FEI	205-75	252.00	9.92	264.00	10.39	742.00	29.52	539.00	21.22
		225-70	252.00	9.92	264.00	10.39	742.00	29.52	539.00	21.22
	FE2	225-70	252.00	9.92	264.00	10.39	742.00	29.52	539.00	21.22
	Police	205-75	252.00	9.92	264.00	10.39	742.00	29.52	539.00	21.22
		225-75*	252.00	9.92	264.00	10.39	742.00	29.52	539.00	21.22
		235-70*	252.00	9.92	264.00	10.39	742.00	29.21	539.00	21.22
WAGON	ALL	225-75	252.00	9.92	264.00	10.39	742.00	29.21	550.00	21.65
		225-70	252.00	9.92	264.00	10.39	742.00	29.21	550.00	21.65

*Speed Rated Tires
NOTE: All dimensions shown are vertical to the ground. Trim heights should be within ± 10 mm (0.4 inch) to be considered correct.

GC2019100083000X

Fig. 43 Vehicle trim height measurements. Caprice, Custom Cruiser, Impala SS & Roadmaster

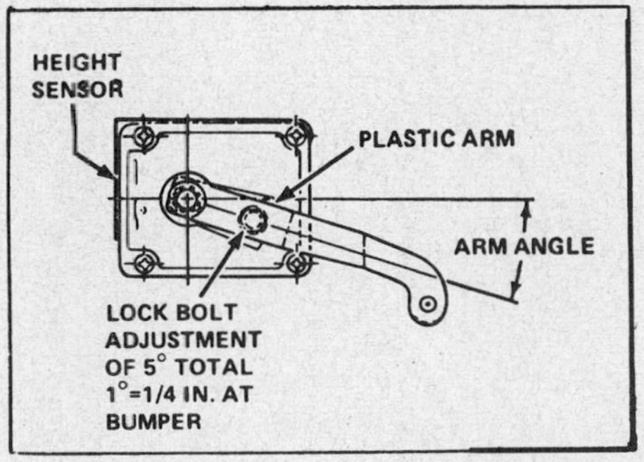
HEIGHT SENSOR
PLASTIC ARM
ARM ANGLE
LOCK BOLT
ADJUSTMENT
OF 5° TOTAL
1°=1/4 IN. AT
BUMPER

GC2019100084000X

Fig. 44 Vehicle trim height adjustment

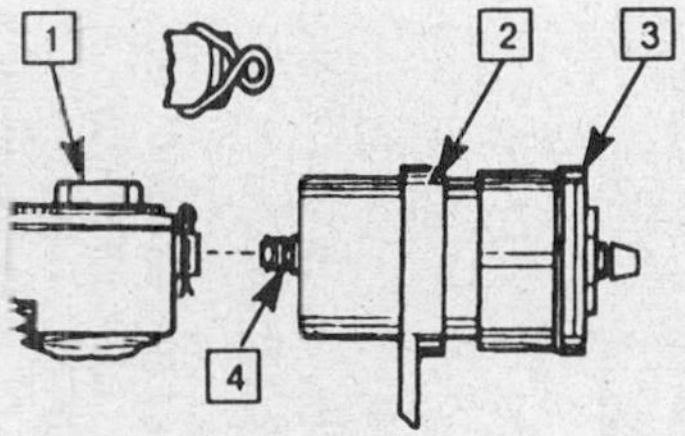
1
2
3
4

[1] COMPRESSOR HEAD ASSEMBLY
[2] DRIER BRACKET
[3] AIR DRIER
[4] O'RING

GC2019100064000X

Fig. 45 Air dryer assembly

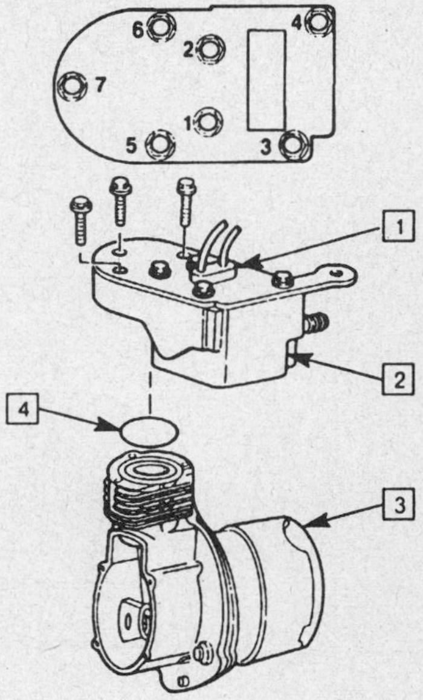
1
2
3
4
5
6
7

[1] EXHAUST SOLENOID CONNECTOR
[2] HEAD ASSEMBLY
[3] CYLINDER AND MOTOR ASSEMBLY
[4] CYLINDER HEAD O'RING

GC2019100065000X

Fig. 46 Compressor head assembly

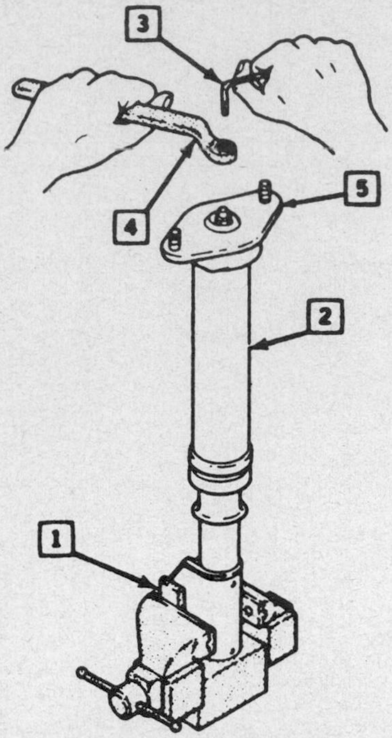
3
4
5
2
1

1. VISE WITH 3/16" SHIMS
2. STRUT
3. HOLD NUMBER 50 TORX
4. TURN 12 PT. BOX WRENCH
5. UPPER MOUNT

GC2019100068000X

Fig. 47 Upper strut mount removal

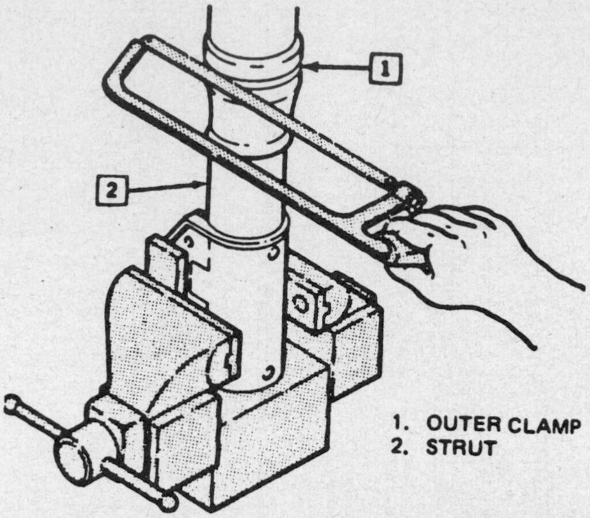
1
2

1. OUTER CLAMP
2. STRUT

GC2019100069000X

Fig. 48 Outer clamp removal

1. OUTER TUBE
2. "O" RING – LUBRICATE WITH SILICONF
3. "O" RING GROVE

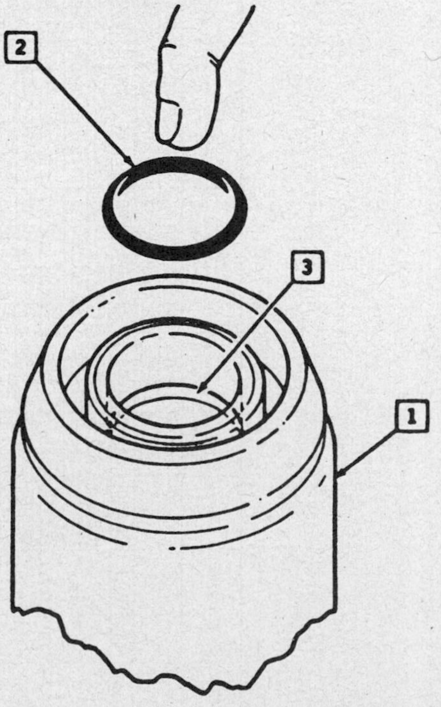
2
3
1

GC2019100070000X

Fig. 49 O-ring replacement

1. INNER CLAMP
2. AIR BLADDER
3. STRUT

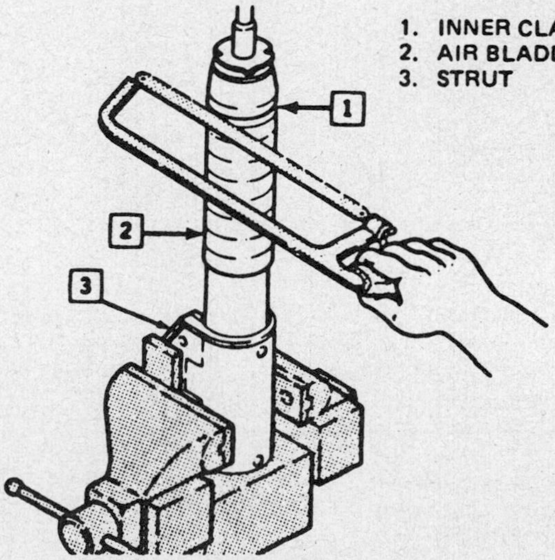
1
2
3

GC2019100071000X

Fig. 50 Inner clamp removal

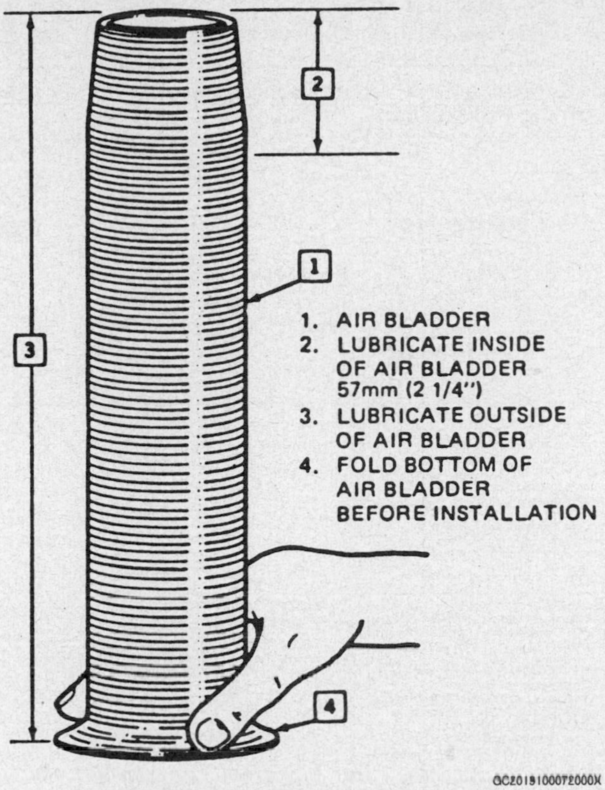
1. AIR BLADDER
2. LUBRICATE INSIDE OF AIR BLADDER 57mm (2 1/4")
3. LUBRICATE OUTSIDE OF AIR BLADDER
4. FOLD BOTTOM OF AIR BLADDER BEFORE INSTALLATION
GC2019100072000X

Fig. 51 Air bladder replacement

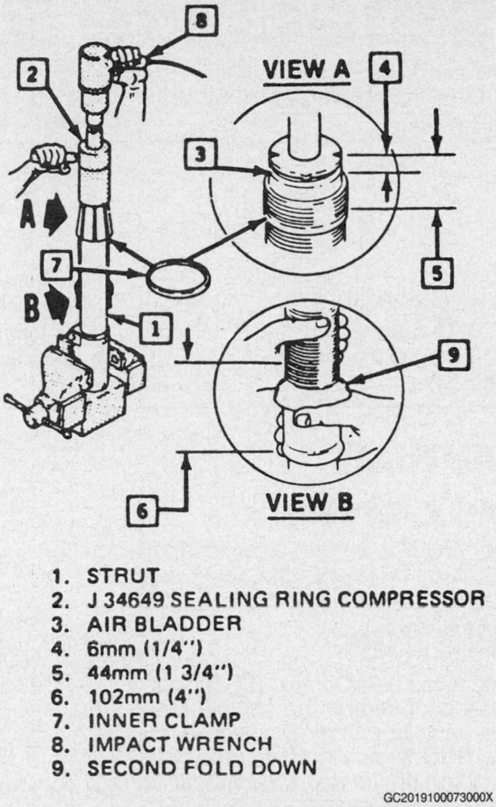
VIEW A
VIEW B
A
B
1. STRUT
2. J 34649 SEALING RING COMPRESSOR
3. AIR BLADDER
4. 6mm (1/4")
5. 44mm (1 3/4")
6. 102mm (4")
7. INNER CLAMP
8. IMPACT WRENCH
9. SECOND FOLD DOWN
GC2019100073000X

Fig. 52 Inner clamp & air bladder position

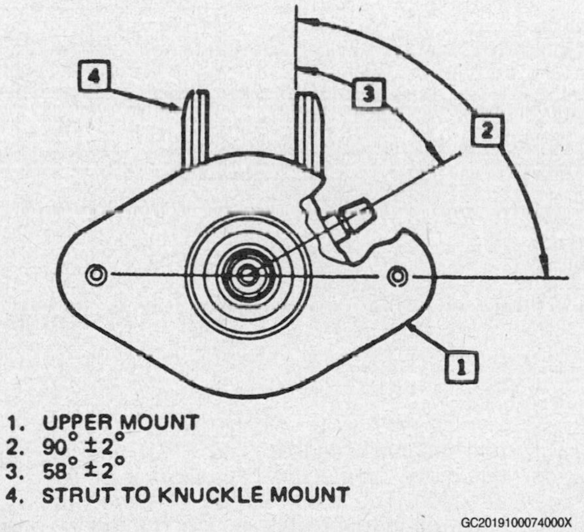
1. UPPER MOUNT
2. 90° ±2°
3. 58° ±2°
4. STRUT TO KNUCKLE MOUNT
GC2019100074000X

Fig. 53 Air fitting position

9. Apply silicone lubricant to outer tube.
10. Install air bladder over outer tube by folding upward over tube and push over tube.
11. Install and tighten hose clamp over grooved area of air bladder.
12. Support strut and partially inflate air bladder. Check for leaks with soap solution.
13. Install strut into vehicle.

Selective Ride Control (SRC)

NOTE: On Air Bag Equipped Models, Refer To "Air Bag System Precautions" Located In The Front Of This Manual For System Disarming & Arming Procedures.

INDEX

PRECAUTIONS

AIR BAG SYSTEMS

Refer to "Air Bag System Precautions" in the front of this manual for system disarming and arming procedures.

DESCRIPTION

The Selective Ride Control (SRC) system is capable of setting the vehicle suspension to various damping positions by use of the SRC switch and/or automatically depending on vehicle speed input to SRC module. This system consists of front and rear adjustable shock absorbers, electrical actuators, a selective ride control switch and control module.

The selective ride control shock absorber operates in the same manner as the standard gas shock absorber. The shock absorbers are gas charged to reduce aeration (foaming) of shock fluid which results in unlimited damping control. They also reduce impact harshness and improve road isolation. An electrical actuator is positioned on top of each adjustable shock absorber. The control module is located in the left rear storage compartment behind the driver's seat and the control switch is located on the floor console.

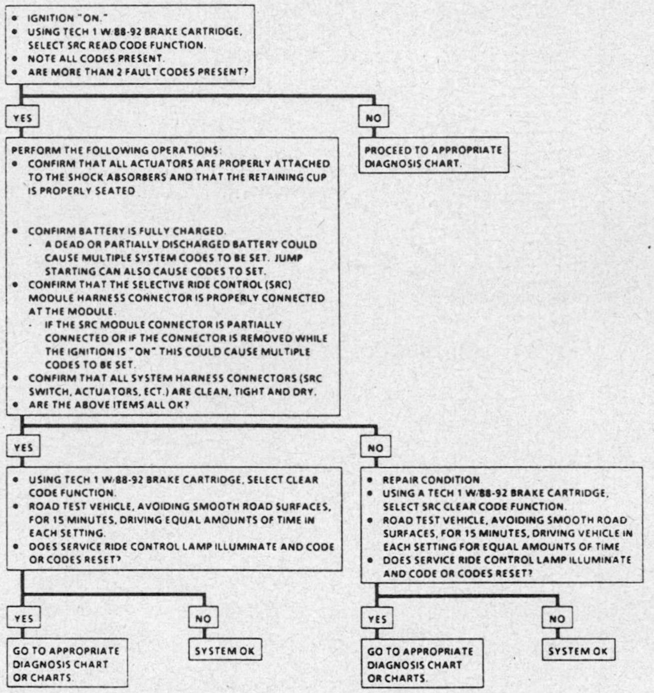

• IGNITION "ON."
• USING TECH 1 W/88-92 BRAKE CARTRIDGE, SELECT SRC READ CODE FUNCTION.
• NOTE ALL CODES PRESENT.
• ARE MORE THAN 2 FAULT CODES PRESENT?
YES
NO
PROCEED TO APPROPRIATE DIAGNOSIS CHART.
PERFORM THE FOLLOWING OPERATIONS:
• CONFIRM THAT ALL ACTUATORS ARE PROPERLY ATTACHED TO THE SHOCK ABSORBERS AND THAT THE RETAINING CUP IS PROPERLY SEATED
• CONFIRM BATTERY IS FULLY CHARGED.
- A DEAD OR PARTIALLY DISCHARGED BATTERY COULD CAUSE MULTIPLE SYSTEM CODES TO BE SET. JUMP STARTING CAN ALSO CAUSE CODES TO SET.
• CONFIRM THAT THE SELECTIVE RIDE CONTROL (SRC) MODULE HARNESS CONNECTOR IS PROPERLY CONNECTED AT THE MODULE.
- IF THE SRC MODULE CONNECTOR IS PARTIALLY CONNECTED OR IF THE CONNECTOR IS REMOVED WHILE THE IGNITION IS "ON" THIS COULD CAUSE MULTIPLE CODES TO BE SET.
• CONFIRM THAT ALL SYSTEM HARNESS CONNECTORS (SRC SWITCH, ACTUATORS, ECT.) ARE CLEAN, TIGHT AND DRY.
• ARE THE ABOVE ITEMS ALL OK?
YES
NO
• USING TECH 1 W/88-92 BRAKE CARTRIDGE, SELECT CLEAR CODE FUNCTION.
• ROAD TEST VEHICLE, AVOIDING SMOOTH ROAD SURFACES, FOR 15 MINUTES, DRIVING EQUAL AMOUNTS OF TIME IN EACH SETTING.
• DOES SERVICE RIDE CONTROL LAMP ILLUMINATE AND CODE OR CODES RESET?
• REPAIR CONDITION.
• USING A TECH 1 W/88-92 BRAKE CARTRIDGE, SELECT SRC CLEAR CODE FUNCTION.
• ROAD TEST VEHICLE, AVOIDING SMOOTH ROAD SURFACES, FOR 15 MINUTES, DRIVING VEHICLE IN EACH SETTING FOR EQUAL AMOUNTS OF TIME
• DOES SERVICE RIDE CONTROL LAMP ILLUMINATE AND CODE OR CODES RESET?
YES
NO
GO TO APPROPRIATE DIAGNOSIS CHART OR CHARTS.
SYSTEM OK
YES
NO
GO TO APPROPRIATE DIAGNOSIS CHART OR CHARTS.
SYSTEM OK
GC2019200085000X

Fig. 1 System diagnosis chart

SYSTEM COMPONENTS

Module

The SRC module provides electronic control logic and electrical output drive for the system, based on driver preference and vehicle speed input data. The SRC module receives its speed signal from the transmission VSS sensor assembly. Once a speed signal has been detected, the SRC module adjusts the damper valving to one of six specific settings according to vehicle speed and Select Ride Switch setting (PERF, SPORT or TOUR.) The damping rate increases with vehicle speed and only within the selected setting. The SRC module has ability to store system trouble codes.

Electrical Actuators

This system utilizes external electrical actuators to adjust the valve position of each shock absorber as dictated by SRC module. The actuators consist of a bi-directional DC motor with an integral position feedback sensor. The SRC module can move the electrical actuators in either direction. The motor range of travel for valve adjustment while attached to shock absorber is from 0° to 90°. The SRC module determines position of the valve by counting ground pulses on position sensor input from the actuator position feedback sensors.

Shock Absorbers

The shocks are pressurized gas type and provide damping by forcing oil through internal orifices to resist suspension movement. The variable damping feature is provided by changing orifice size. The orifice size is controlled by adjusting a shaft which extends through top of shock absorber. The shaft is turned by the electrical actuator, mounted on top of shock absorber.

DIAGNOSIS & TESTING

Accessing Diagnostic Trouble Codes

Selective ride trouble codes may be read with the vehicle stopped using a Tech 1 with and 88-92 brake cartridge or by grounding terminal "C" of the Assembly Line Diagnostic Link (ALDL). Observe the "Service Ride Control" indicator with the ignition switch in "Run." The trouble codes are comprised of two digits. A digit is read by counting the number of flashes that occur within a half second of each other. The second digit will appear about one second after the first digit has gone.

Each code will repeat three times before the next code begins with a three second pause between codes. The entire trouble

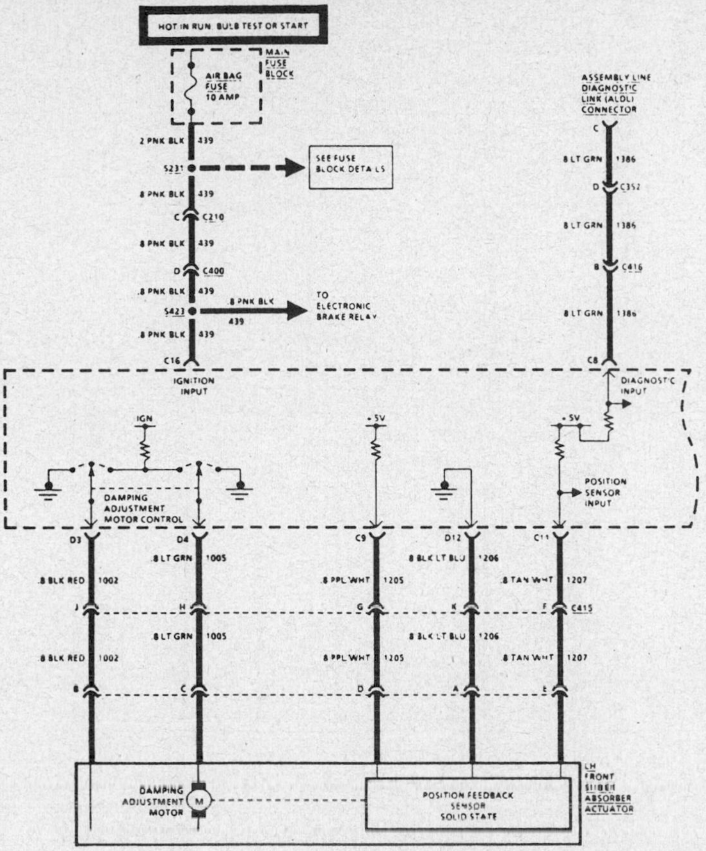
HOT IN RUN, BULB TEST OR START
IGNITION INPUT
DIAGNOSTIC INPUT
POSITION SENSOR INPUT
DAMPING ADJUSTMENT MOTOR CONTROL
DAMPING ADJUSTMENT MOTOR
POSITION FEEDBACK SENSOR SOLID STATE
GC201920008601AX

Fig. 2 Selective ride wiring diagram (Part 1 of 4). 1992

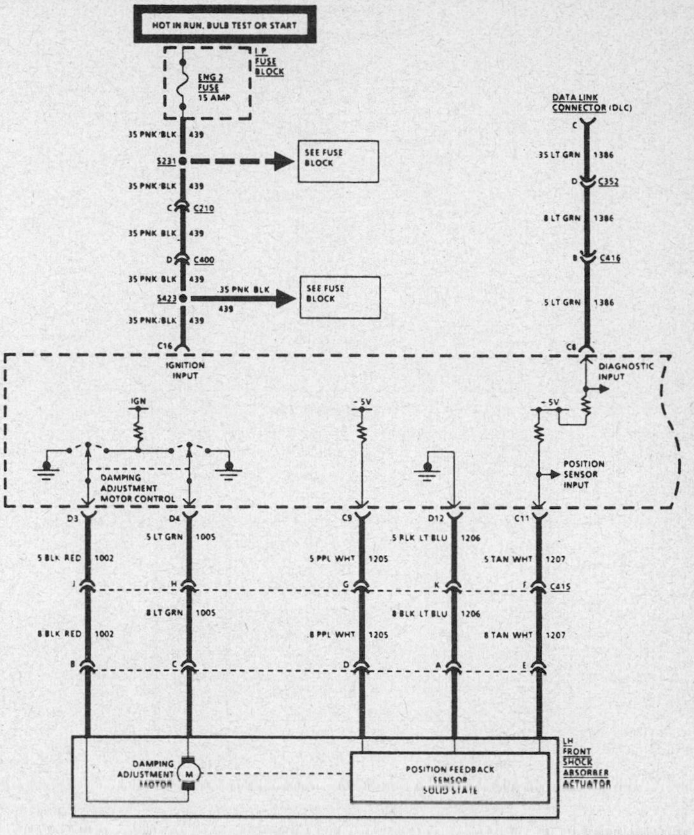
HOT IN RUN, BULB TEST OR START
DATA LINK CONNECTOR (DLC)
IGNITION INPUT
DIAGNOSTIC INPUT
POSITION SENSOR INPUT
DAMPING ADJUSTMENT MOTOR CONTROL
DAMPING ADJUSTMENT MOTOR
POSITION FEEDBACK SENSOR SOLID STATE
LH FRONT SHOCK ABSORBER ACTUATOR
GC201930008601BX

Fig. 2 Selective ride wiring diagram (Part 1 of 4). 1993–94

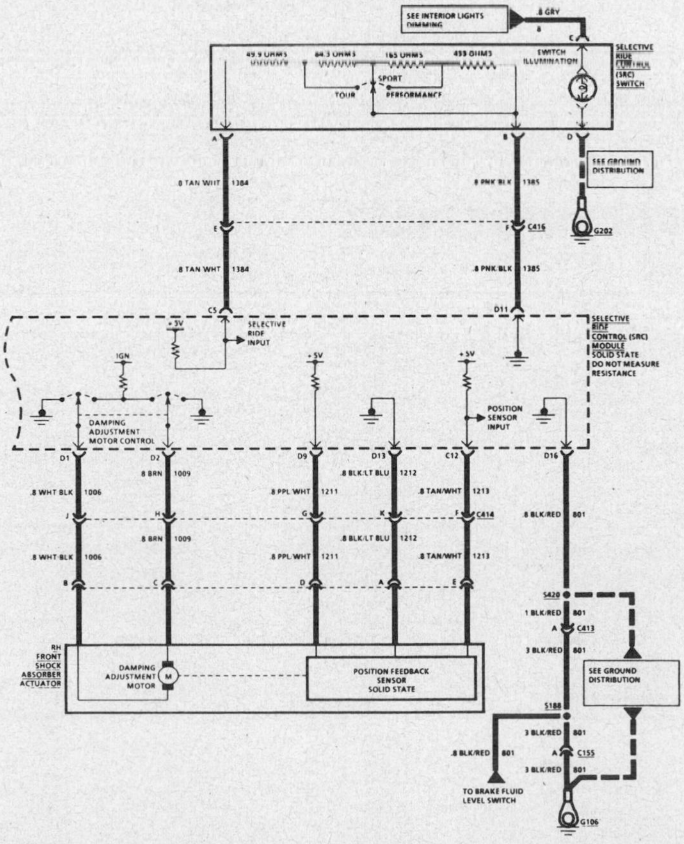
SELECTIVE RIDE CONTROL (SRC) SWITCH
SELECTIVE RIDE CONTROL (SRC) MODULE
DAMPING ADJUSTMENT MOTOR
POSITION FEEDBACK SENSOR SOLID STATE
SEE GROUND DISTRIBUTION
GC2019200086020X

Fig. 2 Selective ride wiring diagram (Part 2 of 4)

code sequence will reappear as long as terminal "C" is grounded. The trouble code display begins by showing code 12 three times, marking the beginning of the sequence.

Diagnostic Trouble Code Interpretation

Diagnose selective ride control system by reading the diagnostic trouble codes stored in the selective ride control module. Refer to **Fig. 1**, for system diagnosis chart, **Fig. 2**, for wiring diagram and **Figs. 3 through 8**, for diagnostic trouble code diagnosis charts.

Clearing Diagnostic Trouble Codes

When the diagnosis is complete and any necessary repairs have been made, the trouble codes must be cleared to prevent further misdiagnosis. To clear the system, select clear code function using Tech 1 with an 88-92 brake cartridge or ground pin "C" of the ALDL connector for two seconds and repeat the procedure twice for a total of three groundings.

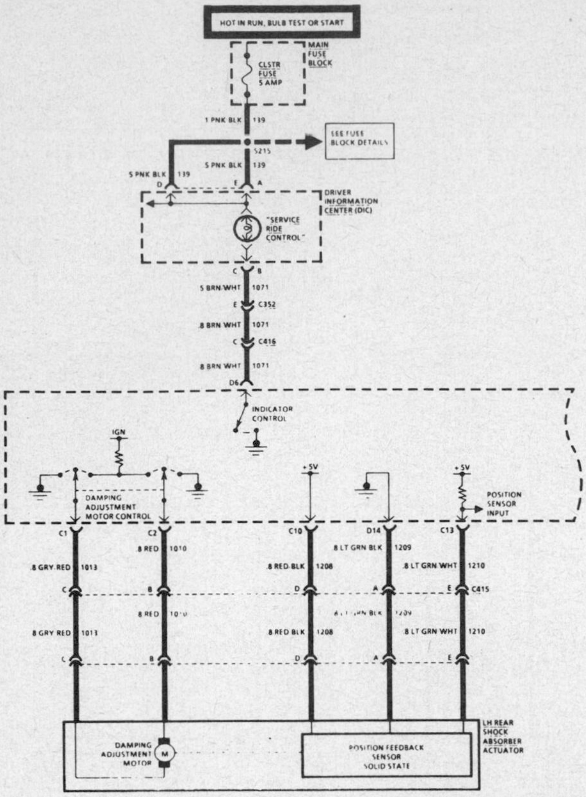

GC2019200086030X

Fig. 2 Selective ride wiring diagram (Part 3 of 4)

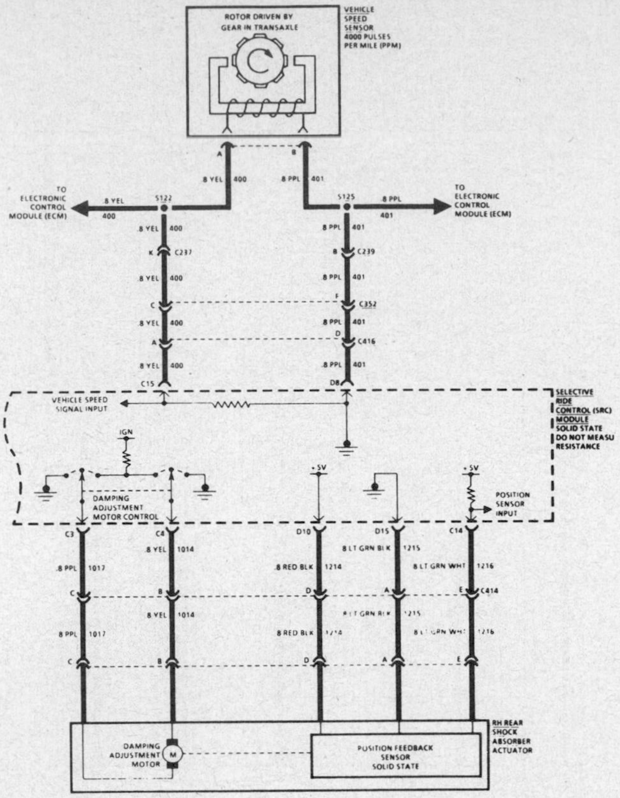

GC2019200086040X

Fig. 2 Selective ride wiring diagram (Part 4 of 4)

DIAGNOSTIC CHART INDEX

Code	Description	Year	Page No.	Fig. No.
13	Left Rear Or Right Rear Time Out	1992–94	36-33	4
14	Right Front Or Left Front SRC Actuator Time Out	1992–94	36-34	5
21	Right Front Or Left Front SRC Actuator Time Out	1992–94	36-34	5
22	Left Rear Or Right Rear Time Out	1992–94	36-33	4
23	Loss Of Vehicle Speed Signal	1992–94	36-33	3
31	SRC Actuator Out Of Position	1992–94	36-35	8
32	SRC Actuator Out Of Position	1992–94	36-35	8
33	SRC Actuator Out Of Position	1992–94	36-35	8
34	SRC Actuator Out Of Position	1992–94	36-35	8
41	Selective Ride Control Switch Circuit Fault	1992–94	36-34	6
42	Selective Ride Control Switch Circuit Fault	1992–94	36-34	6
43	Selective Ride Control Switch Circuit Fault	1992–94	36-34	6

Important

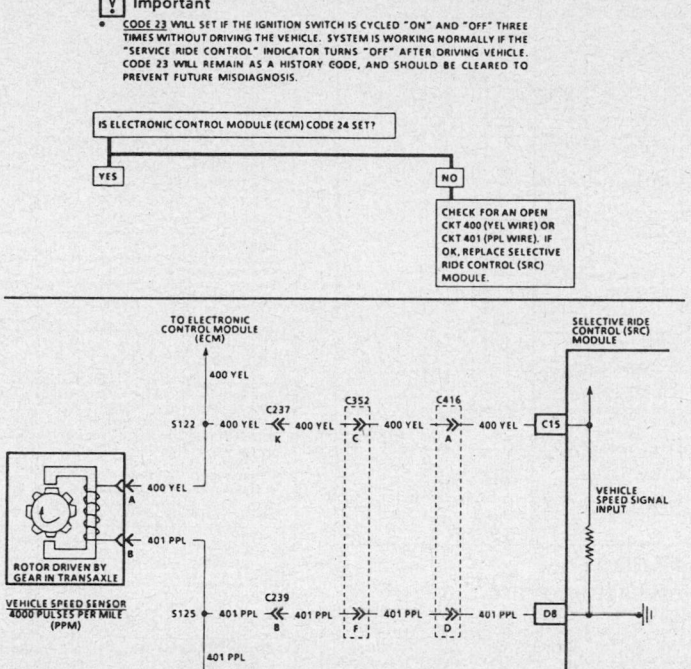

- CODE 23 WILL SET IF THE IGNITION SWITCH IS CYCLED "ON" AND "OFF" THREE TIMES WITHOUT DRIVING THE VEHICLE. SYSTEM IS WORKING NORMALLY IF THE "SERVICE RIDE CONTROL" INDICATOR TURNS "OFF" AFTER DRIVING VEHICLE. CODE 23 WILL REMAIN AS A HISTORY CODE, AND SHOULD BE CLEARED TO PREVENT FUTURE MISDIAGNOSIS.

IS ELECTRONIC CONTROL MODULE (ECM) CODE 24 SET?

YES

NO → CHECK FOR AN OPEN CKT 400 (YEL WIRE) OR CKT 401 (PPL WIRE). IF OK, REPLACE SELECTIVE RIDE CONTROL (SRC) MODULE.

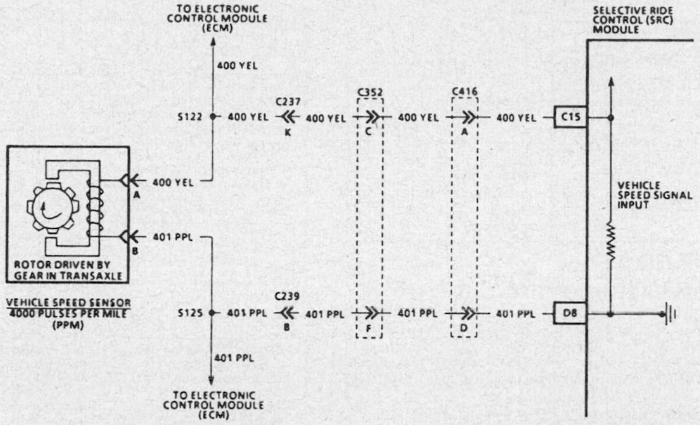

TO ELECTRONIC CONTROL MODULE (ECM)
400 YEL
SELECTIVE RIDE CONTROL (SRC) MODULE
C237
C352
C416
S122
400 YEL
K
C
A
C15
VEHICLE SPEED SIGNAL INPUT
400 YEL
401 PPL
ROTOR DRIVEN BY GEAR IN TRANSAXLE
VEHICLE SPEED SENSOR 4000 PULSES PER MILE (PPM)
C239
S125
401 PPL
B
F
D
D8
TO ELECTRONIC CONTROL MODULE (ECM)

GC2019200087000X

Fig. 3 Code 23: Loss Of Vehicle Speed Signal. 1992–94

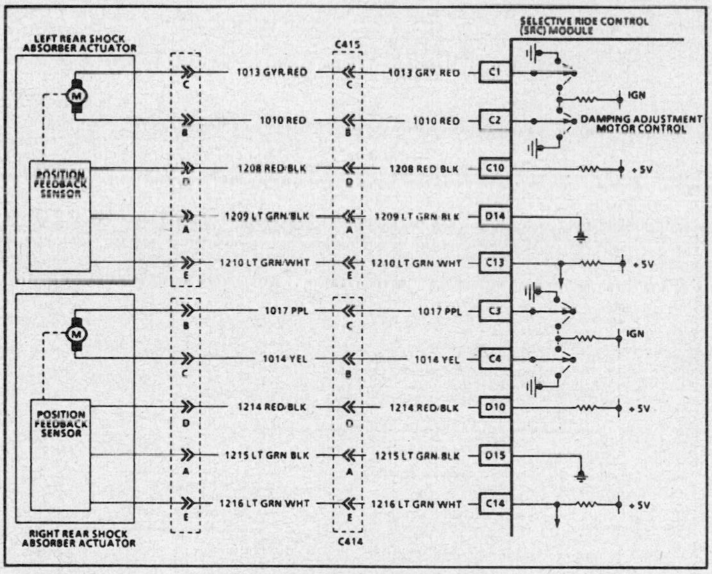

SELECTIVE RIDE CONTROL (SRC) MODULE
LEFT REAR SHOCK ABSORBER ACTUATOR
C415
1013 GRY RED
1010 RED
1208 RED BLK
1209 LT GRN BLK
1210 LT GRN WHT
POSITION FEEDBACK SENSOR
C1
C2
C10
D14
C13
IGN
DAMPING ADJUSTMENT MOTOR CONTROL
+5V
1017 PPL
1014 YEL
1214 RED BLK
1215 LT GRN BLK
1216 LT GRN WHT
C3
C4
D10
D15
C14
RIGHT REAR SHOCK ABSORBER ACTUATOR
C414

CODES 13 AND 22

LEFT REAR OR RIGHT REAR TIME-OUT

Circuit Description:

The Selective Ride Control (SRC) module supplies power and ground to the electrical actuators and can drive them in either direction, depending on the requested damper position. At each ignition cycle, the SRC module drives the actuators to a fail-safe position until a vehicle speed signal is received. This is referred to as system initialization. The electrical actuator has an integral Hall-effect sensor which reports the actuator's position to the SRC module by way of a position feedback circuit.

Codes 13 and 22 are stored in the SRC module's diagnostic memory if the module senses that the corresponding SRC modules electrical actuator is not moving or moving too slowly or not receiving the correct feedback signal.

Test Description: Number(s) below refer to circled number(s) on the diagnostic chart.

1. This test will determine if the actuator motor moves to the fail-safe position under system initialization.
2. If the actuator motor moved under system initialization the position feedback circuit is suspect. This test will determine if there is approximately 5 volts present on the position feedback circuits.
3. If the actuator motor did not move under system initialization, this test will determine if the actuator is receiving voltage from the SRC module. If no voltage is present, the circuit between the actuator and the SRC module or the SRC module is suspect. If voltage is present, the actuator is faulty.
4. This test will determine if there is physical damage to the shock absorber that is not allowing the adjustment shaft to turn or turn freely.

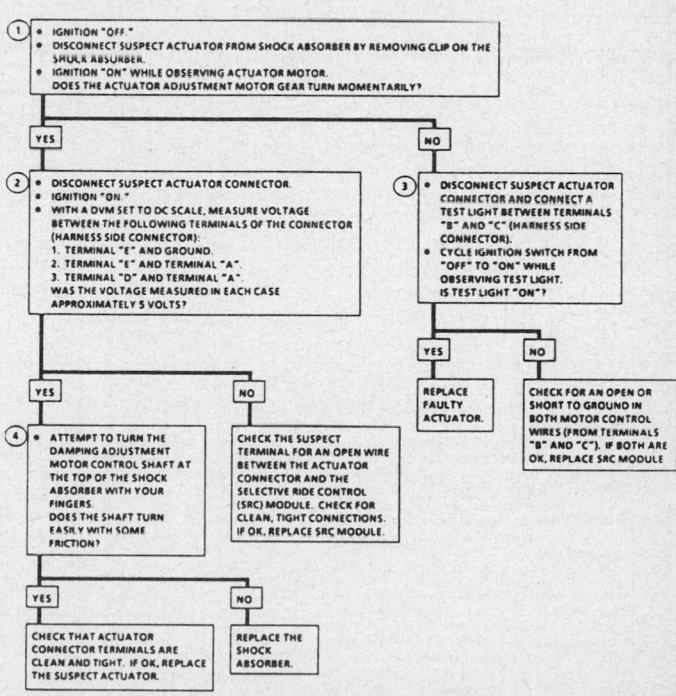

CODES 13, 22 ARE STORED IN THE SELECTIVE RIDE CONTROL (SRC) MODULE SENSES THAT THE CORRESPONDING ELECTRICAL ACTUATOR IS MOVING TOO SLOWLY OR NOT RECEIVING THE CORRECT FEEDBACK SIGNAL.

(1)
- IGNITION "OFF."
- DISCONNECT SUSPECT ACTUATOR FROM SHOCK ABSORBER BY REMOVING CLIP ON THE SHOCK ABSORBER.
- IGNITION "ON" WHILE OBSERVING ACTUATOR MOTOR.

DOES THE ACTUATOR ADJUSTMENT MOTOR GEAR TURN MOMENTARILY?

YES → (2)
- DISCONNECT SUSPECT ACTUATOR CONNECTOR.
- IGNITION "ON."
- WITH A DVM SET TO DC SCALE, MEASURE VOLTAGE BETWEEN THE FOLLOWING TERMINALS OF THE CONNECTOR (HARNESS SIDE CONNECTOR):
  1. TERMINAL "E" AND GROUND.
  2. TERMINAL "E" AND TERMINAL "A".
  3. TERMINAL "D" AND TERMINAL "A".

WAS THE VOLTAGE MEASURED IN EACH CASE APPROXIMATELY 5 VOLTS?

- YES → (4)
  - ATTEMPT TO TURN THE DAMPING ADJUSTMENT MOTOR CONTROL SHAFT AT THE TOP OF THE SHOCK ABSORBER WITH YOUR FINGERS.

  DOES THE SHAFT TURN EASILY WITH SOME FRICTION?
  - YES → CHECK THAT ACTUATOR CONNECTOR TERMINALS ARE CLEAN AND TIGHT. IF OK, REPLACE THE SUSPECT ACTUATOR.
  - NO → REPLACE THE SHOCK ABSORBER.
- NO → CHECK THE SUSPECT TERMINAL FOR AN OPEN WIRE BETWEEN THE ACTUATOR CONNECTOR AND THE SELECTIVE RIDE CONTROL (SRC) MODULE. CHECK FOR CLEAN, TIGHT CONNECTIONS. IF OK, REPLACE SRC MODULE.

NO → (3)
- DISCONNECT SUSPECT ACTUATOR CONNECTOR AND CONNECT A TEST LIGHT BETWEEN TERMINALS "B" AND "C" (HARNESS SIDE CONNECTOR).
- CYCLE IGNITION SWITCH FROM "OFF" TO "ON" WHILE OBSERVING TEST LIGHT.

IS TEST LIGHT "ON"?

- YES → REPLACE FAULTY ACTUATOR.
- NO → CHECK FOR AN OPEN OR SHORT TO GROUND IN BOTH MOTOR CONTROL WIRES (FROM TERMINALS "B" AND "C"). IF BOTH ARE OK, REPLACE SRC MODULE

GC2019200088000X

Fig. 4 Code 13 & 22: Left Rear Or Right Rear Time Out. 1992–94

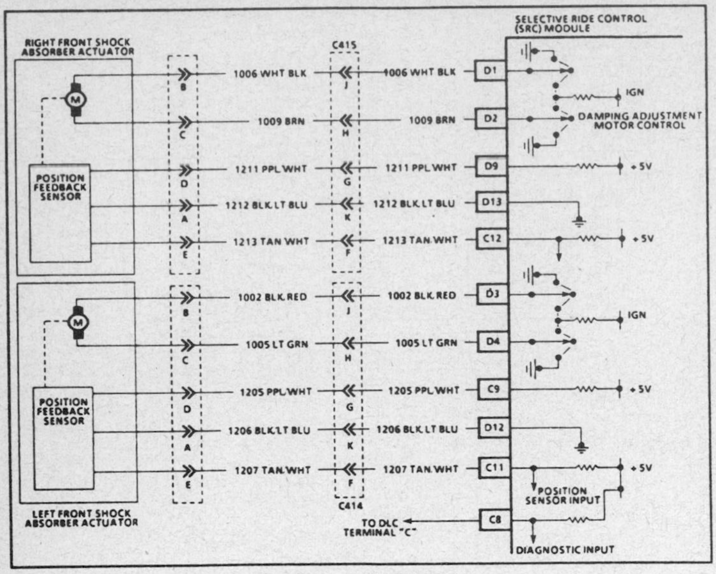
SELECTIVE RIDE CONTROL (SRC) MODULE
RIGHT FRONT SHOCK ABSORBER ACTUATOR
C415
1006 WHT BLK
1009 BRN
1211 PPL WHT
1212 BLK LT BLU
1213 TAN WHT
POSITION FEEDBACK SENSOR
D1
D2
D9
D13
C12
IGN
DAMPING ADJUSTMENT MOTOR CONTROL
+5V
1002 BLK RED
1005 LT GRN
1205 PPL WHT
1206 BLK LT BLU
1207 TAN WHT
D3
D4
C9
D12
C11
C8
C414
LEFT FRONT SHOCK ABSORBER ACTUATOR
TO DLC TERMINAL "C"
POSITION SENSOR INPUT
DIAGNOSTIC INPUT

CODES 14 AND 21

RIGHT FRONT OR LEFT FRONT SRC ACTUATOR TIME-OUT

Circuit Description:

The Selective Ride Control (SRC) module supplies power and ground to the electrical actuators and can drive them in either direction, depending on the requested damper position. At each ignition cycle, the SRC module drives the actuators to a fail-safe position until a vehicle speed signal is received. This is referred to as system initialization. The electrical actuator has an integral Hall-effect sensor which reports the actuator's position to the SRC module by way of a position feedback circuit.

Codes 14 and 21 are stored in the SRC modules diagnostic memory if the module senses that the corresponding SRC module's electrical actuator is not moving or moving too slowly or not receiving the correct feedback signal.

Test Description: Number(s) below refer to circled number(s) on the diagnostic chart.

1. This test will determine if the actuator motor moves to the fail-safe position under system initialization.
2. If the actuator motor moved under system initialization, the position feedback circuit is suspect. This test will determine if there is approximately 5 volts present on the position feedback circuits.
3. If the actuator motor did not move under system initialization, this test will determine if the actuator is receiving voltage from the SRC module. If no voltage is present, the circuit between the actuator and the SRC module or the SRC module is suspect. If voltage is present, the actuator is faulty.
4. This test will determine if there is physical damage to the shock absorber that is not allowing the adjustment shaft to turn or turn freely.

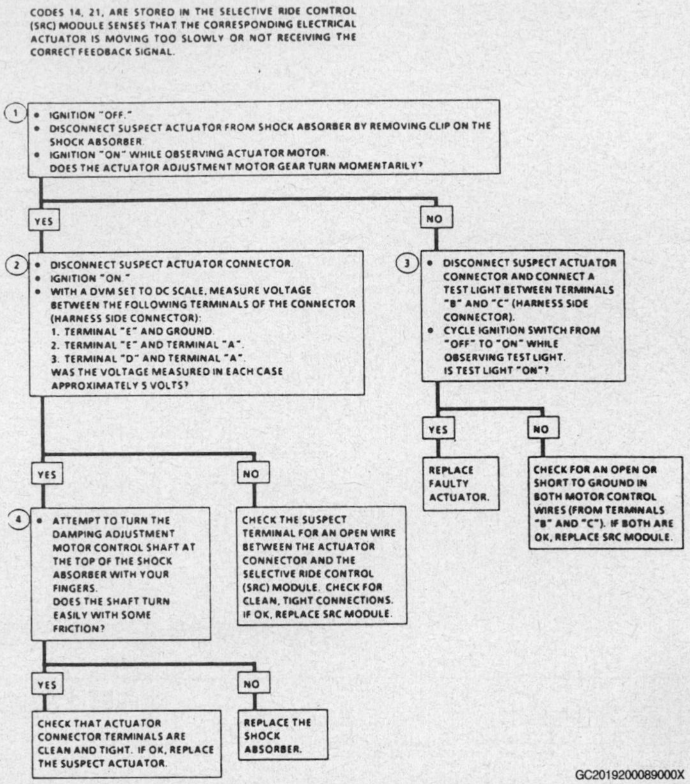
CODES 14, 21, ARE STORED IN THE SELECTIVE RIDE CONTROL (SRC) MODULE SENSES THAT THE CORRESPONDING ELECTRICAL ACTUATOR IS MOVING TOO SLOWLY OR NOT RECEIVING THE CORRECT FEEDBACK SIGNAL.
1
• IGNITION "OFF."
• DISCONNECT SUSPECT ACTUATOR FROM SHOCK ABSORBER BY REMOVING CLIP ON THE SHOCK ABSORBER.
• IGNITION "ON" WHILE OBSERVING ACTUATOR MOTOR.
DOES THE ACTUATOR ADJUSTMENT MOTOR GEAR TURN MOMENTARILY?
YES
NO
2
• DISCONNECT SUSPECT ACTUATOR CONNECTOR.
• IGNITION "ON."
• WITH A DVM SET TO DC SCALE, MEASURE VOLTAGE BETWEEN THE FOLLOWING TERMINALS OF THE CONNECTOR (HARNESS SIDE CONNECTOR):
1. TERMINAL "E" AND GROUND.
2. TERMINAL "E" AND TERMINAL "A".
3. TERMINAL "D" AND TERMINAL "A".
WAS THE VOLTAGE MEASURED IN EACH CASE APPROXIMATELY 5 VOLTS?
3
• DISCONNECT SUSPECT ACTUATOR CONNECTOR AND CONNECT A TEST LIGHT BETWEEN TERMINALS "B" AND "C" (HARNESS SIDE CONNECTOR).
• CYCLE IGNITION SWITCH FROM "OFF" TO "ON" WHILE OBSERVING TEST LIGHT.
IS TEST LIGHT "ON"?
YES
NO
REPLACE FAULTY ACTUATOR.
CHECK FOR AN OPEN OR SHORT TO GROUND IN BOTH MOTOR CONTROL WIRES (FROM TERMINALS "B" AND "C"). IF BOTH ARE OK, REPLACE SRC MODULE.
YES
NO
4
• ATTEMPT TO TURN THE DAMPING ADJUSTMENT MOTOR CONTROL SHAFT AT THE TOP OF THE SHOCK ABSORBER WITH YOUR FINGERS.
DOES THE SHAFT TURN EASILY WITH SOME FRICTION?
CHECK THE SUSPECT TERMINAL FOR AN OPEN WIRE BETWEEN THE ACTUATOR CONNECTOR AND THE SELECTIVE RIDE CONTROL (SRC) MODULE. CHECK FOR CLEAN, TIGHT CONNECTIONS. IF OK, REPLACE SRC MODULE.
YES
NO
CHECK THAT ACTUATOR CONNECTOR TERMINALS ARE CLEAN AND TIGHT. IF OK, REPLACE THE SUSPECT ACTUATOR.
REPLACE THE SHOCK ABSORBER.

GC2019200089000X

Fig. 5 Code 14 & 21: Right Front Or Left Front SRC Actuator Time Out. 1992–94

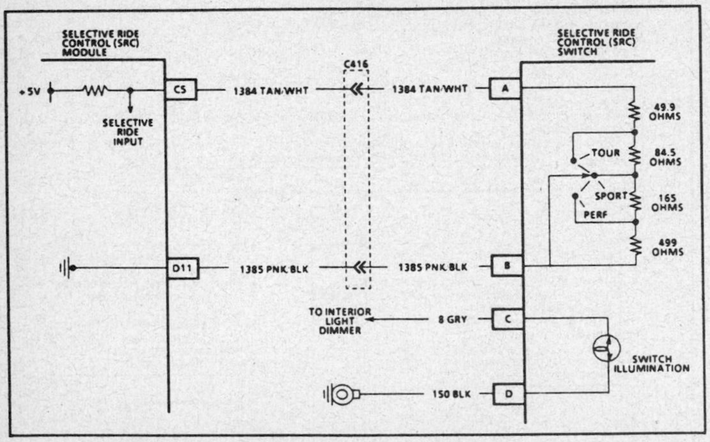
SELECTIVE RIDE CONTROL (SRC) MODULE
SELECTIVE RIDE CONTROL (SRC) SWITCH
C416
+5V
SELECTIVE RIDE INPUT
C5
1384 TAN/WHT
A
49.9 OHMS
TOUR
84.5 OHMS
SPORT
165 OHMS
PERF
499 OHMS
D11
1385 PNK/BLK
B
TO INTERIOR LIGHT DIMMER
8 GRY
C
SWITCH ILLUMINATION
150 BLK
D

CODES 41, 42 AND 43

SELECTIVE RIDE CONTROL (SRC) SWITCH CIRCUIT FAULT

Circuit Description:

The selective ride control module inputs a 5 volt reference signal to the SRC switch which modifies that voltage to identify the selected position (tour, sport, perf.). A Code 41 will set if the SRC module senses a short to ground at module terminal "D11". A Code 42 will set if the SRC module senses an open contact in the SRC switch. A Code 43 will set if the SRC module senses an open at terminal "D11".

Test Description: Number(s) below refer to circled number(s) on the diagnostic chart.

Important

- A Code 42 may set if the selective ride control switch connector terminals are making poor contact to switch or if there is a small amount of corrosion on the terminals. Please check for those conditions before attempting to use the diagnosis chart. As this may correct the problem.

1. This test will determine if the switch is in the correct resistance range while in the "Perf" position. Always make sure the switch is all the way to the "Perf" position before performing this test.
2. This test will determine if the SRC switch is receiving the correct reference voltage from the SRC module.
3. This test will determine if the SRC module is faulty. If the switch is determined to be OK and is receiving the proper inputs from the SRC module but Codes 41, 42 or 43 are still present, the SRC module should be replaced.

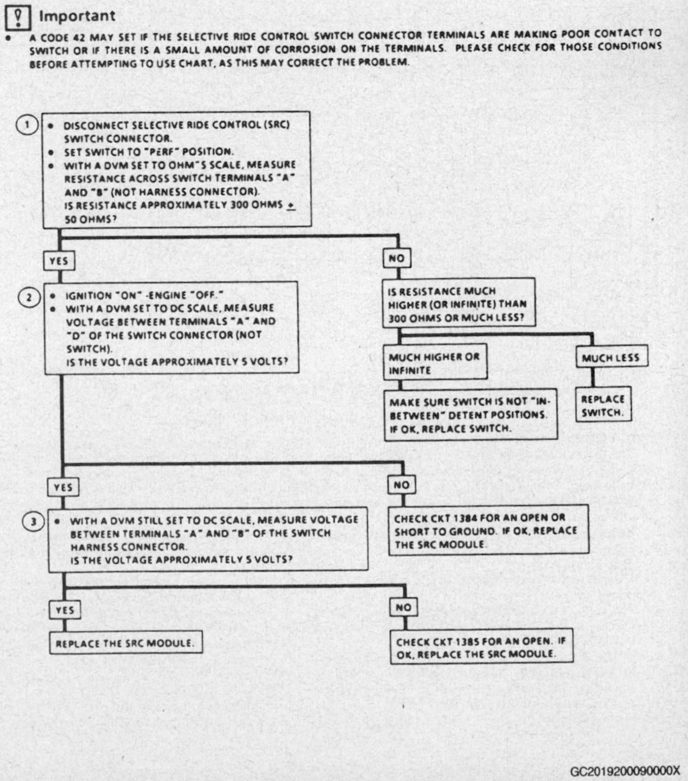
Important
• A CODE 42 MAY SET IF THE SELECTIVE RIDE CONTROL SWITCH CONNECTOR TERMINALS ARE MAKING POOR CONTACT TO SWITCH OR IF THERE IS A SMALL AMOUNT OF CORROSION ON THE TERMINALS. PLEASE CHECK FOR THOSE CONDITIONS BEFORE ATTEMPTING TO USE CHART, AS THIS MAY CORRECT THE PROBLEM.
1
• DISCONNECT SELECTIVE RIDE CONTROL (SRC) SWITCH CONNECTOR.
• SET SWITCH TO "PERF" POSITION.
• WITH A DVM SET TO OHM'S SCALE, MEASURE RESISTANCE ACROSS SWITCH TERMINALS "A" AND "B" (NOT HARNESS CONNECTOR).
IS RESISTANCE APPROXIMATELY 300 OHMS ± 50 OHMS?
YES
NO
2
• IGNITION "ON" -ENGINE "OFF."
• WITH A DVM SET TO DC SCALE, MEASURE VOLTAGE BETWEEN TERMINALS "A" AND "D" OF THE SWITCH CONNECTOR (NOT SWITCH).
IS THE VOLTAGE APPROXIMATELY 5 VOLTS?
IS RESISTANCE MUCH HIGHER (OR INFINITE) THAN 300 OHMS OR MUCH LESS?
MUCH HIGHER OR INFINITE
MUCH LESS
MAKE SURE SWITCH IS NOT "IN-BETWEEN" DETENT POSITIONS. IF OK, REPLACE SWITCH.
REPLACE SWITCH.
YES
NO
3
• WITH A DVM STILL SET TO DC SCALE, MEASURE VOLTAGE BETWEEN TERMINALS "A" AND "B" OF THE SWITCH HARNESS CONNECTOR.
IS THE VOLTAGE APPROXIMATELY 5 VOLTS?
CHECK CKT 1384 FOR AN OPEN OR SHORT TO GROUND. IF OK, REPLACE THE SRC MODULE.
YES
NO
REPLACE THE SRC MODULE.
CHECK CKT 1385 FOR AN OPEN. IF OK, REPLACE THE SRC MODULE.

GC2019200090000X

Fig. 6 Code 41, 42 & 43: Selective Ride Control Switch Circuit Fault. 1992–94

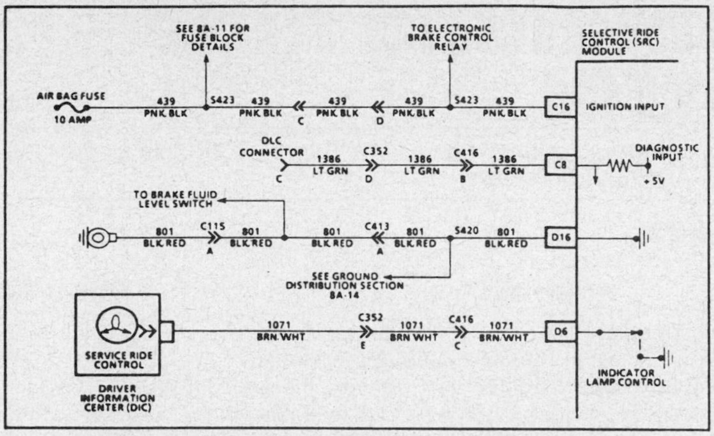
SEE 8A-11 FOR FUSE BLOCK DETAILS
TO ELECTRONIC BRAKE CONTROL RELAY
SELECTIVE RIDE CONTROL (SRC) MODULE
AIR BAG FUSE 10 AMP
439 PNK BLK
S423
C16
IGNITION INPUT
DLC CONNECTOR
1386 LT GRN
C352
C416
C8
DIAGNOSTIC INPUT
+5V
TO BRAKE FLUID LEVEL SWITCH
801 BLK RED
C115
C413
S420
D16
SEE GROUND DISTRIBUTION SECTION 8A-14
1071 BRN WHT
D6
INDICATOR LAMP CONTROL
SERVICE RIDE CONTROL
DRIVER INFORMATION CENTER (DIC)

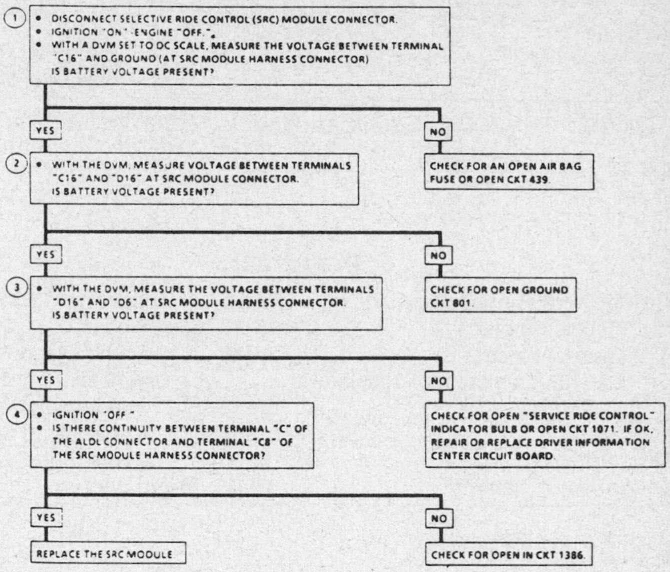
1 • DISCONNECT SELECTIVE RIDE CONTROL (SRC) MODULE CONNECTOR.
• IGNITION "ON", ENGINE "OFF."
• WITH A DVM SET TO DC SCALE, MEASURE THE VOLTAGE BETWEEN TERMINAL "C16" AND GROUND (AT SRC MODULE HARNESS CONNECTOR) IS BATTERY VOLTAGE PRESENT?
YES
NO
2 • WITH THE DVM, MEASURE VOLTAGE BETWEEN TERMINALS "C16" AND "D16" AT SRC MODULE CONNECTOR. IS BATTERY VOLTAGE PRESENT?
CHECK FOR AN OPEN AIR BAG FUSE OR OPEN CKT 439.
YES
NO
3 • WITH THE DVM, MEASURE THE VOLTAGE BETWEEN TERMINALS "D16" AND "D6" AT SRC MODULE HARNESS CONNECTOR. IS BATTERY VOLTAGE PRESENT?
CHECK FOR OPEN GROUND CKT 801.
YES
NO
4 • IGNITION "OFF."
• IS THERE CONTINUITY BETWEEN TERMINAL "C" OF THE ALDL CONNECTOR AND TERMINAL "C8" OF THE SRC MODULE HARNESS CONNECTOR?
CHECK FOR OPEN "SERVICE RIDE CONTROL" INDICATOR BULB OR OPEN CKT 1071. IF OK, REPAIR OR REPLACE DRIVER INFORMATION CENTER CIRCUIT BOARD.
YES
NO
REPLACE THE SRC MODULE
CHECK FOR OPEN IN CKT 1386.

SELECTIVE RIDE CONTROL (SRC) FAULT CODES CANNOT BE READ

Circuit Description:

When the ignition switch is first turned "ON" (Run) system voltage is applied from the AIR BAG Fuse to the SRC module at the "Ignition 1" input terminal "C16". The SRC module responds by turning "ON" the "Service Ride Control" warning lamp for a few seconds while performing tests on the SRC system.

Grounding terminal "C" of the ALDL connector pulls the "Diagnostic Request" input terminal "C8" of the SRC module low and signals the module to enter the "Flash Code" diagnostic display mode.

Test Description: Number(s) below refer to circled number(s) on the diagnostic chart.

1. This test will determine if there is battery voltage at terminal "C16" (ignition input) of the Selective Ride Control (SRC) Module.
2. This test will determine if the SRC module has ground at terminal "D16".
3. This test will determine if battery voltage is present on CKT 1071 to turn the "Service Ride Control" lamp "ON."
4. This test will determine if there is an open in CKT 1386. If continuity is established on CKT 1386, then the SRC module has an internal fault and should be replaced.

GC2019200091000X

Fig. 7 Selective ride control fault codes cannot be read. 1992–94

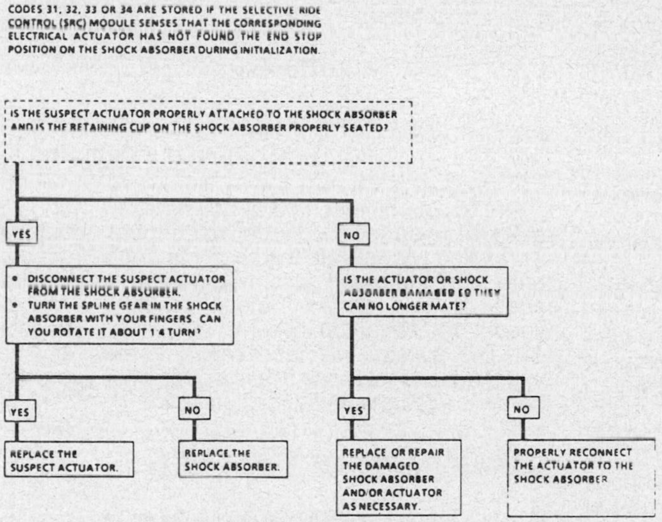
CODES 31, 32, 33 OR 34 ARE STORED IF THE SELECTIVE RIDE CONTROL (SRC) MODULE SENSES THAT THE CORRESPONDING ELECTRICAL ACTUATOR HAS NOT FOUND THE END STOP POSITION ON THE SHOCK ABSORBER DURING INITIALIZATION.
IS THE SUSPECT ACTUATOR PROPERLY ATTACHED TO THE SHOCK ABSORBER AND IS THE RETAINING CUP ON THE SHOCK ABSORBER PROPERLY SEATED?
YES
NO
• DISCONNECT THE SUSPECT ACTUATOR FROM THE SHOCK ABSORBER.
• TURN THE SPLINE GEAR IN THE SHOCK ABSORBER WITH YOUR FINGERS. CAN YOU ROTATE IT ABOUT 1/4 TURN?
IS THE ACTUATOR OR SHOCK ABSORBER DAMAGED SO THEY CAN NO LONGER MATE?
YES
NO
YES
NO
REPLACE THE SUSPECT ACTUATOR.
REPLACE THE SHOCK ABSORBER.
REPLACE OR REPAIR THE DAMAGED SHOCK ABSORBER AND/OR ACTUATOR AS NECESSARY.
PROPERLY RECONNECT THE ACTUATOR TO THE SHOCK ABSORBER

GC2019200092000X

Fig. 8 Code 31, 32, 33 & 34: SRC Actuator Out Of Position. 1992–94

Computer Command Ride Control

NOTE: On Air Bag Equipped Models, Refer To "Air Bag System Precautions" Located In The Front Of This Manual For System Disarming & Arming Procedures.

INDEX

PRECAUTIONS

AIR BAG SYSTEMS

Refer to "Air Bag System Precautions" in the front of this manual for system disarming and arming procedures.

DESCRIPTION

The Computer Command Ride Control (CCR) system **Fig. 1,** controls the vehicle's ride firmness by controlling an actuator in each of the four struts to increase ride firmness as speed increases. On three damping mode systems the three modes are comfort, normal and sport. On two damping mode systems the modes are firm and comfort. Damping mode selection is controlled by the CCR controller according to vehicle speed conditions, vehicle accelerometer input and any error conditions which may exist.

On three-mode systems, the CCR controller located on a bracket under the driver's seat, controls and monitors the system. Using speed and accelerometer input signals the CCR determines the optimum mode strut valving. The controller monitors feedback signals from the struts to determine proper system operation. If the controller receives an incorrect feedback signal, a diagnostic trouble code is set in the controller and the fault indicator on the controller will light. The fault indicator will flash diagnostic trouble codes when the controller's diagnostic enable circuit is grounded.

On two-mode systems, the driver select switch determines the operating mode of the system. In the "Normal" switch position, the damping level depends on vehicle speed and accelerometer inputs. In the "Firm" switch position, the system will place the damping level in the firm mode regardless of vehicle speed and accelerometer inputs.

Each strut contains an electrical actuator that rotates a selector valve to a specific location commanded by the CCR controller. The selector valve contains different sized orifices which increase or decrease the strut's damping rate to control ride firmness.

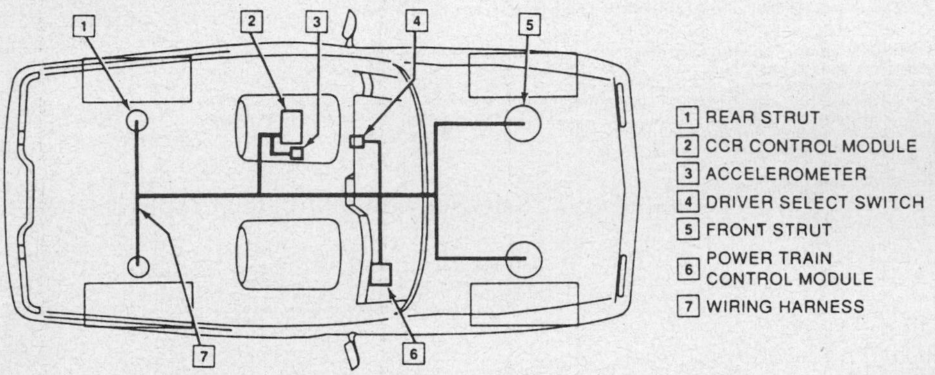

1 REAR STRUT
2 CCR CONTROL MODULE
3 ACCELEROMETER
4 DRIVER SELECT SWITCH
5 FRONT STRUT
6 POWER TRAIN CONTROL MODULE
7 WIRING HARNESS

GC2019100093000X

Fig. 1 Computer Command Ride (CCR) system

The accelerometer/lateral acceleration switch is used for lift, dive or roll control. The switch will activate the sport mode on three damping mode systems or the firm mode on two damping mode systems when it detects any excessive lift, dive or roll. The system will then return to its speed dependent mode two seconds after the switch returns to its inactive state.

DIAGNOSIS & TESTING

Accessing Diagnostic Trouble Codes

The CCR diagnostic systems may be actuated by either of two methods. Grounding the diagnostic enable circuit at pin "C" of the ALDL connector or by using the control module wiring harness connector, **Figs. 2 through 5.** To read codes using the control module connector on models except LeSabre and Park Avenue, ground pin "D2" to pin "D16." To read codes using the control module connector on LeSabre and Park Avenue models, ground terminal "F2" of the connector.

Both driver select switch L.E.D.'s will blink in unison to transmit blink code diagnostics. Error codes can be read by counting the number of flashes of the L.E.D.'s. The error code display will start after pin D2 or F2 has been grounded for three seconds before beginning the blink code sequence. The sequence starts with a three second L.E.D. off period. Then code 12 is displayed three times to mark the beginning of the sequence. Next, each stored code is blinked out in ascending order. Each code is displayed three times before proceeding to the next code. If pins D2 and D16 remain connected or terminal F2 remains grounded, the entire error code sequence will repeat beginning with code 12 flashing three times. Refer to **Fig. 6** for an example of an error code format.

Refer to **Figs. 7 through 9** for trouble code identification and description. Refer to **Figs. 10 through 13** for system wiring diagrams to help in the repair and diagnosis of the trouble codes.

Diagnostic Trouble Code Interpretation

TWO-MODE SYSTEMS

Any system error will cause both the driver select switch L.E.D.'s to be illuminated. The error display will exist as long as the error code is active. If the fault corrects itself, the error display will no longer be illuminated, but the error code will be stored in the controller memory.

If the displays are not indicating an error condition, one or the other will be on to follow the driver select switch position, with

DESCRIPTION	CKT.	CAV.	CAV.	CKT.	DESCRIPTION
GROUND	804	D16	C16	1176	IGNITION 3
		D15	C15	1020	MESSAGE OUTPUT
LR DRIVE	1010	D14	C14	1014	RR DRIVE
LF DRIVE	1002	D13	C13	1006	RF DRIVE
		D12	C12		
LF GROUND	1005	D11	C11		
RF GROUND	1009	D10	C10		
LR GROUND	1013	D9	C9		
RR GROUND	1017	D8	C8		
LATERAL ACCEL.	1308	D7	C7	817	SPEED SIGNAL
LF FEEDBACK	1004	D6	C6		
RF FEEDBACK	1008	D5	C5		
LR FEEDBACK	1012	D4	C4		
RR FEEDBACK	1016	D3	C3	1490	LIFT / DIVE SIGNAL
DIAGNOSTIC ENABLE	1050	D2	C2	1309	LATERAL ACCEL.
		D1	C1		

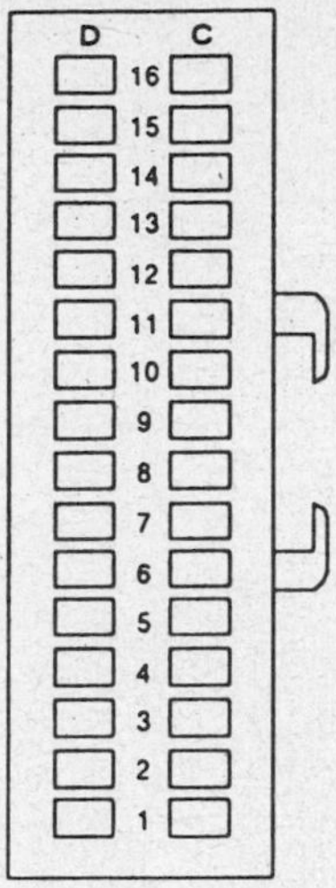
D
C
16
15
14
13
12
11
10
9
8
7
6
5
4
3
2
1

GC2019100094000X

Fig. 2 Control module connector. Eldorado & Seville

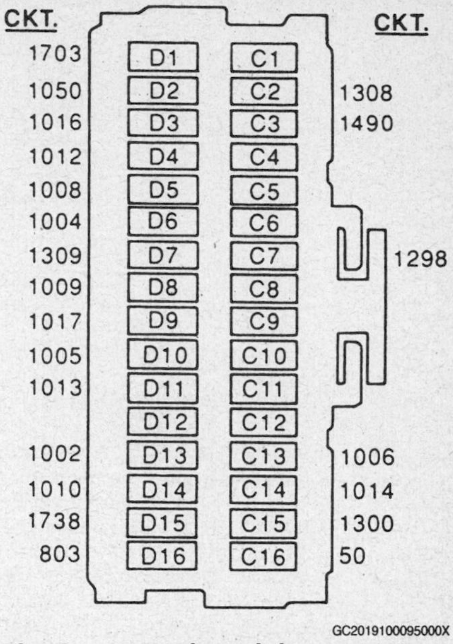
CKT.
CKT.
1703 D1 C1
1050 D2 C2 1308
1016 D3 C3 1490
1012 D4 C4
1008 D5 C5
1004 D6 C6
1309 D7 C7 1298
1009 D8 C8
1017 D9 C9
1005 D10 C10
1013 D11 C11
D12 C12
1002 D13 C13 1006
1010 D14 C14 1014
1738 D15 C15 1300
803 D16 C16 50
GC2019100095000X

Fig. 3 Control module connector. DeVille, Fleetwood (FWD) & Sixty Special

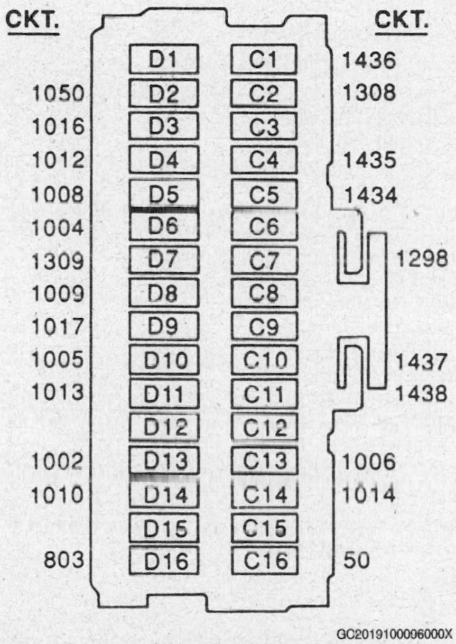
CKT.
CKT.
D1 C1 1436
1050 D2 C2 1308
1016 D3 C3
1012 D4 C4 1435
1008 D5 C5 1434
1004 D6 C6
1309 D7 C7 1298
1009 D8 C8
1017 D9 C9
1005 D10 C10 1437
1013 D11 C11 1438
D12 C12
1002 D13 C13 1006
1010 D14 C14 1014
D15 C15
803 D16 C16 50
GC2019100096000X

Fig. 4 Control module connector. 88 & 98

the following exception. When the driver select switch is in the "Normal" position and the system is in the firm mode due to accelerometer input, the "Firm" L.E.D. will illuminate to show a shift to the firm mode. The "Normal" L.E.D. then will turn back on when the system returns to the comfort mode.

If a code is set, a one second self diagnostic test is performed at three minute intervals and whenever the driver select switch position is changed. Both L.E.D.'s will be on during this test and will go out if the fault code is corrected. If the fault still exists, the L.E.D.'s will remain on.

THREE-MODE SYSTEMS

LeSabre & Park Avenue

Any system error will cause the fault indicator to illuminate. The fault indicator remains lit as long as the diagnostic trouble code is active. If the fault corrects itself, the fault indicator will turn off, but the diagnostic trouble code will remain in the CCR controller's non-volatile memory.

If a diagnostic trouble code is set, a one second self-diagnostic test is performed at three minute intervals. The fault indicator comes on during this test and goes out if the fault is corrected. If the fault still exists, the indicator will remain on.

Eldorado & Seville

When the ignition switch is turned on the system performs a self-test that lasts for 7.5 seconds. The error lamp will remain on during the self-test. After the self-test, the control module will be in either the normal operating mode, error mode or reset mode. When the control module is in the "Normal Mode," the error lamp is on below 10 mph and goes off above 10 mph to indicate proper operation of the CCR system and to verify that the control module is receiving speed information. When the control module is in the "Error Mode," the error lamp is off below 10 mph and on above 10 mph. When the control module is in the "Reset Mode," the error lamp is turned off to indicate a CCR control module problem.

Any system error will cause a "SERVICE CCR SYSTEM" message to be displayed on the Driver Information Center (DIC). The message will be displayed as long as the error code is active. If the fault corrects itself, the "SERVICE CCR SYSTEM" message will turn off, but the error code will remain in the control module non-volatile memory.

If a code is set, a one second self-diagnostic test is performed at three minute intervals. The error lamp will remain on during this test and will go out if the fault is corrected. If the fault still exists, the lamp will be off below 10 mph and on above 10 mph.

DeVille, Fleetwood (FWD) & Sixty Special

Any system error will cause the "SERVICE CCR/SERVICE SSS" telltale lamp to

E
F
1 2 3 4 5 6 7 8 9 10 11 12 13 14 15 16
1 2 3 4 5 6 7 8 9 10 11 12 13 14 15 16
GC2019100097000X

Fig. 5 Control module connector. LeSabre & Park Avenue

illuminate. The error display will exist as long as the error code is active. If the fault corrects itself, the "SERVICE CCR/SERVICE SSS" telltale lamp will turn off, but the error code will be retained in the control module non-volatile memory.

If the code is set, a one second self-diagnostic test is performed at three minute intervals. The error lamp will be on during this test and will go out if the fault is corrected. If the fault still exists, the lamp will remain on.

Clearing Diagnostic Trouble Codes

To clear error codes, connect one end of a jumper wire to pin "A" of the ALDL connector. Alternately plug into and remove the opposite end of the jumper from pin "C three times. Hold each connection one second and pause one second between connections.

On models with driver switch L.E.D.'s, once the ALDL has been cleared, it will turn both the L.E.D.'s off for one second, and then turn them on for two seconds. If the L.E.D.'s do not go out, then the error codes have not been cleared successfully. Repeat clearing sequence.

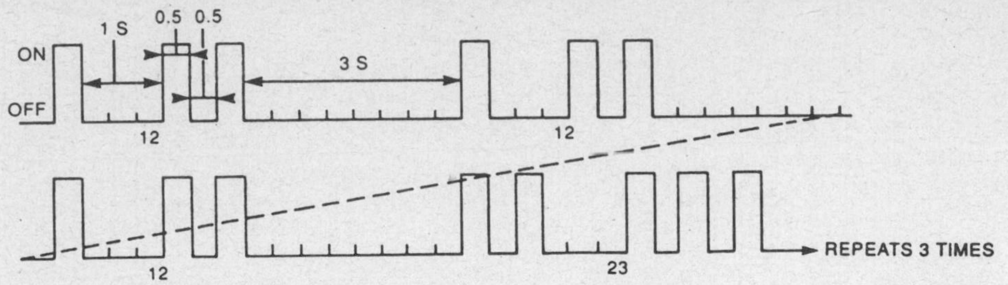
1 S
0.5 0.5
ON
OFF
3 S
12
12
12
23
REPEATS 3 TIMES
GC2019100098000X

Fig. 6 Error code format

Code 12	Initialization (System Normal – No Error)
Code 23	Left Front Actuator Position Error
Code 24	Right Front Actuator Position Error
Code 25	Left Rear Actuator Position Error
Code 26	Right Rear Actuator Position Error
Code 31	Lift/Dive Signal Error
Code 32	Lateral Accelerator Switch Error
Code 34	Vehicle Speed Signal Error
Code 35	Speed Sensitive Steering Error

GC2019100099000X

Fig. 7 Trouble code identification. DeVille, Fleetwood (FWD), LeSabre, Park Avenue & Sixty Special

Code 12	Initiation Code
Code 13	Left Front Actuator Over Current
Code 14	Right Front Actuator Over Current
Code 15	Left Rear Actuator Over Current
Code 16	Right Rear Actuator Over Current
Code 23	Left Front Actuator Position Error
Code 24	Right Front Actuator Position Error
Code 25	Left Rear Actuator Position Error
Code 26	Right Rear Actuator Position Error
Code 31	Lift / Dive Input Error
Code 32	Lateral Acceleration Switch Error

GC2019100100000X

Fig. 8 Trouble code identification. Eldorado & Seville

Code 12	Initialization
Code 13	Left Front Actuator Over Current
Code 14	Right Front Actuator Over Current
Code 15	Left Rear Actuator Over Current
Code 16	Right Rear Actuator Over Current
Code 23	Left Front Actuator Position Error
Code 24	Right Front Actuator Position Error
Code 25	Left Rear Actuator Position Error
Code 26	Right Rear Actuator Position Error
Code 32	Mercury Switch Accelerometer Error
Code 33	Driver Select Switch Input Error
Code 34	Vehicle Speed Signal Error

GC2019100101000X

Fig. 9 Trouble code identification. 88 & 98

COMPONENT REPLACEMENT

CONTROL MODULE

Except Eldorado & Seville

1. Move driver seat forward.
2. **On LeSabre and Park Avenue models,** remove driver's seat.
3. **On models except LeSabre and Park Avenue,** cut carpet back under driver seat to expose the control module, **Figs. 14 and 15.**
4. **On all models,** disconnect control module electrical connector.
5. Remove control module retaining screws, then the control module.
6. Reverse procedure to install.

Eldorado & Seville

1. Open luggage compartment and remove front of trunk trim panel.
2. Disconnect control module electrical connector.
3. Remove control module to bracket retaining screws, then the control module.
4. Reverse procedure to install.

LATERAL ACCELERATION/ ACCELERATOR SWITCH

Except Eldorado & Seville

1. Move driver seat forward.
2. **On LeSabre and Park Avenue models,** remove driver's seat.
3. **On models except LeSabre and Park Avenue,** cut carpet back under driver seat to expose the switch, **Fig. 14.**
4. **On all models,** disconnect switch electrical connector.
5. Remove switch retaining screws, then the switch.
6. Reverse procedure to install.

Eldorado & Seville

1. Remove gear selector retaining clip and handle.
2. Remove two center console storage compartment assembly retaining screws, then the storage compartment from the center console.
3. Remove ashtray, then disconnect cigarette lighter electrical connector.
4. Remove ashtray housing assembly retaining screw, then the ashtray housing from the center console.
5. Remove five upper console retaining screws.
6. Remove upper console illumination bulbs and sockets, then the upper console assembly from lower console.
7. Remove lower console to bracket retaining screw and nuts.
8. Remove two console to instrument panel screws.
9. Remove support rod, then the lower console.
10. Cut carpet back approximately two inches to gain access to switch, **Fig. 16.**
11. Disconnect switch electrical connector.
12. Remove switch retaining screws, then the switch from frame rail.
13. Reverse procedure to install.

ACCELEROMETER

1. Move driver seat forward.
2. Cut carpet back under driver's seat to expose accelerometer, **Fig. 15.**
3. Disconnect accelerometer electrical connector.
4. Remove accelerometer retaining screws, then the accelerometer.
5. Reverse procedure to install.

STRUT

Refer to "Front Suspension & Steering" or "Rear Axle & Suspension" in appropriate chassis section.

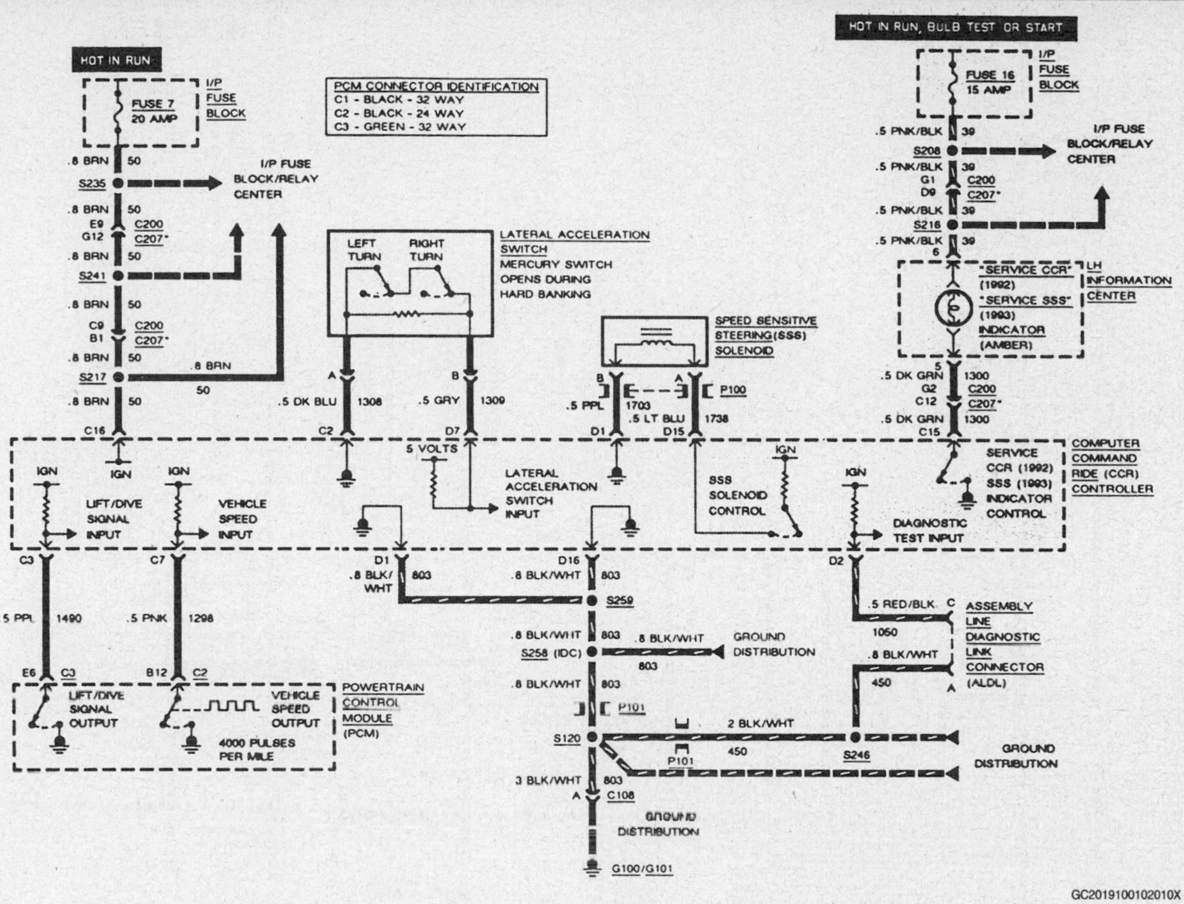

Fig. 10 CCR wiring diagram (Part 1 of 2). DeVille, Fleetwood (FWD) & Sixty Special

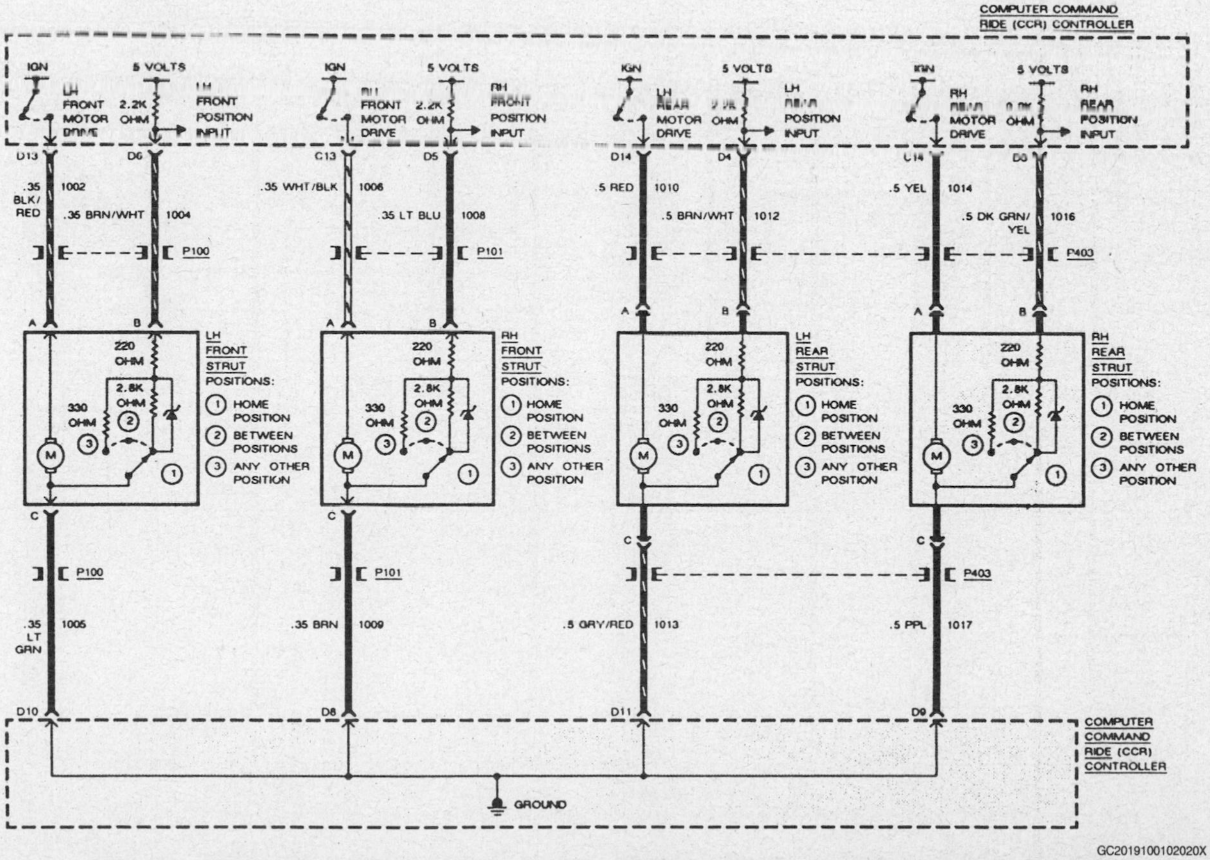

Fig. 10 CCR wiring diagram (Part 2 of 2). DeVille, Fleetwood (FWD) & Sixty Special

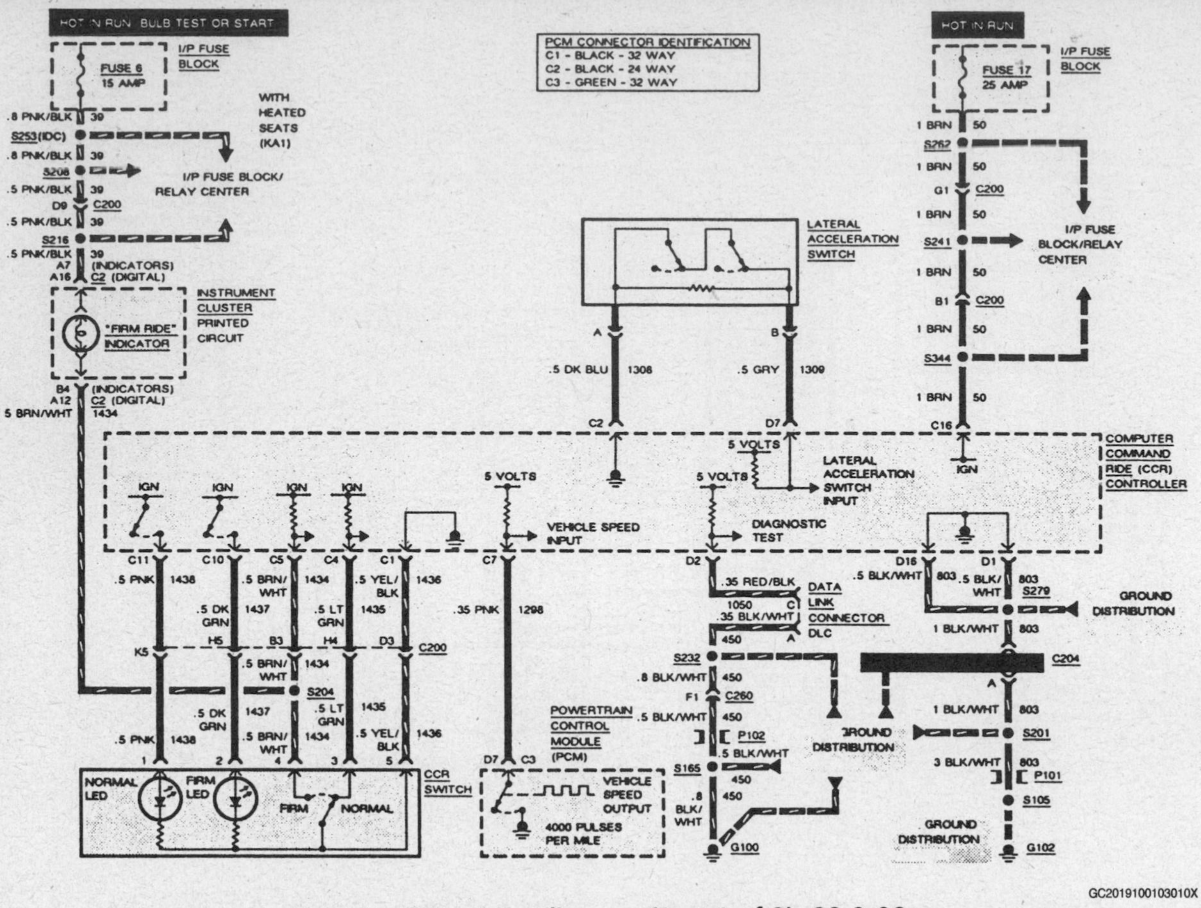
HOT IN RUN, BULB TEST OR START
FUSE 6 15 AMP
I/P FUSE BLOCK
WITH HEATED SEATS (KA1)
I/P FUSE BLOCK/ RELAY CENTER
.8 PNK/BLK 39
S253(IDC)
S208
.5 PNK/BLK 39
D9 C200
S216
A7 (INDICATORS)
A16 C2 (DIGITAL)
INSTRUMENT CLUSTER PRINTED CIRCUIT
"FIRM RIDE" INDICATOR
B4 (INDICATORS)
A12 C2 (DIGITAL)
5 BRN/WHT 1434
PCM CONNECTOR IDENTIFICATION
C1 - BLACK - 32 WAY
C2 - BLACK - 24 WAY
C3 - GREEN - 32 WAY
LATERAL ACCELERATION SWITCH
.5 DK BLU 1308
.5 GRY 1309
HOT IN RUN
FUSE 17 25 AMP
I/P FUSE BLOCK
1 BRN 50
S262
G1 C200
S241
I/P FUSE BLOCK/RELAY CENTER
B1 C200
S344
C16
COMPUTER COMMAND RIDE (CCR) CONTROLLER
5 VOLTS
LATERAL ACCELERATION SWITCH INPUT
IGN
VEHICLE SPEED INPUT
DIAGNOSTIC TEST
C11 C10 C5 C4 C1 C7 D2 D16 D1
.5 PNK 1438
.5 DK GRN 1437
.5 BRN/WHT 1434
.5 LT GRN 1435
.5 YEL/BLK 1436
.35 PNK 1298
.35 RED/BLK 1050
DATA LINK CONNECTOR DLC
.35 BLK/WHT 450
.5 BLK/WHT 803
S279
GROUND DISTRIBUTION
1 BLK/WHT 803
K5 H5 B3 H4 D3 C200
S204
S232
.8 BLK/WHT 450
F1 C260
C204
POWERTRAIN CONTROL MODULE (PCM)
P102
S201
S165
3 BLK/WHT 803
P101
S105
G100
G102
NORMAL LED
FIRM LED
FIRM
NORMAL
CCR SWITCH
VEHICLE SPEED OUTPUT
4000 PULSES PER MILE
GC2019100103010X

Fig. 11 CCR wiring diagram (Part 1 of 2). 88 & 98

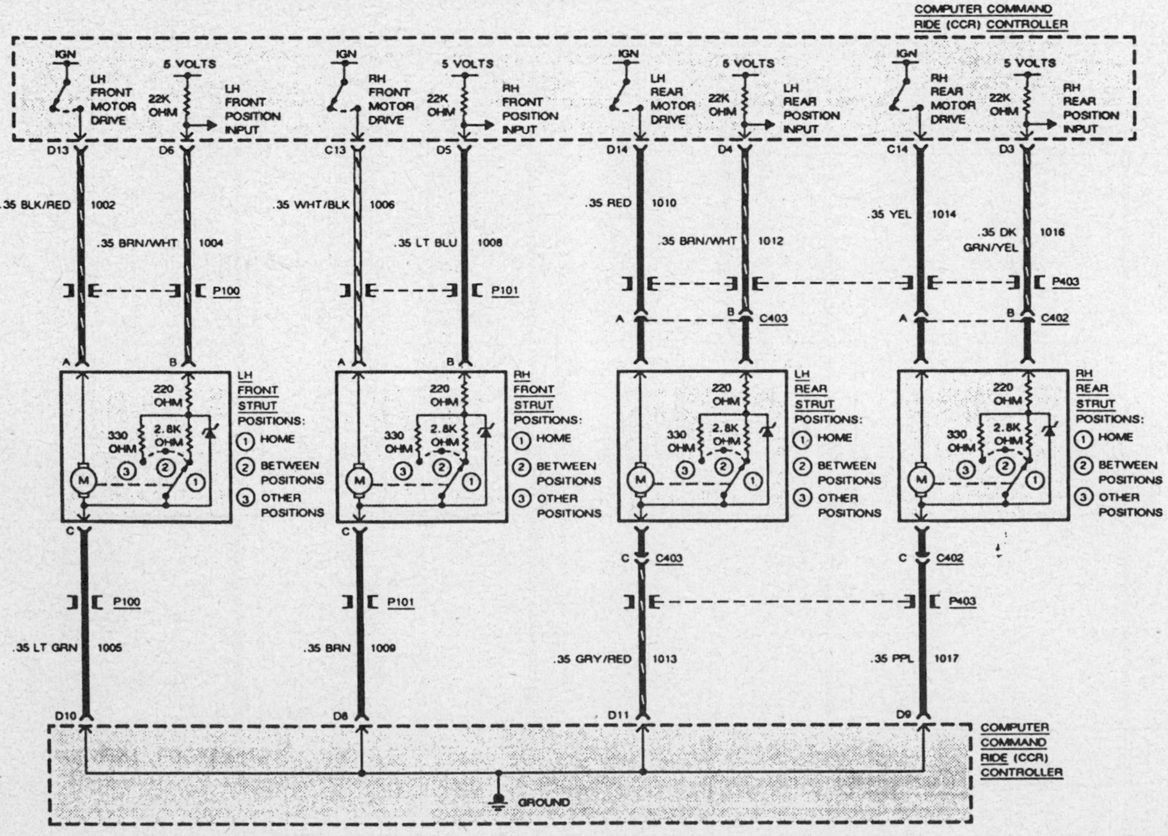
COMPUTER COMMAND RIDE (CCR) CONTROLLER
IGN
5 VOLTS
22K OHM
LH FRONT MOTOR DRIVE
LH FRONT POSITION INPUT
RH FRONT MOTOR DRIVE
RH FRONT POSITION INPUT
LH REAR MOTOR DRIVE
LH REAR POSITION INPUT
RH REAR MOTOR DRIVE
RH REAR POSITION INPUT
D13 D6 C13 D5 D14 D4 C14 D3
.35 BLK/RED 1002
.35 BRN/WHT 1004
.35 WHT/BLK 1006
.35 LT BLU 1008
.35 RED 1010
.35 BRN/WHT 1012
.35 YEL 1014
.35 DK GRN/YEL 1016
P100
P101
P403
C403
C402
220 OHM
330 OHM
2.8K OHM
LH FRONT STRUT POSITIONS:
RH FRONT STRUT POSITIONS:
LH REAR STRUT POSITIONS:
RH REAR STRUT POSITIONS:
1 HOME
2 BETWEEN POSITIONS
3 OTHER POSITIONS
.35 LT GRN 1005
.35 BRN 1009
.35 GRY/RED 1013
.35 PPL 1017
D10 D8 D11 D9
GROUND
COMPUTER COMMAND RIDE (CCR) CONTROLLER
GC2019100103020X

Fig. 11 CCR wiring diagram (Part 2 of 2). 88 & 98

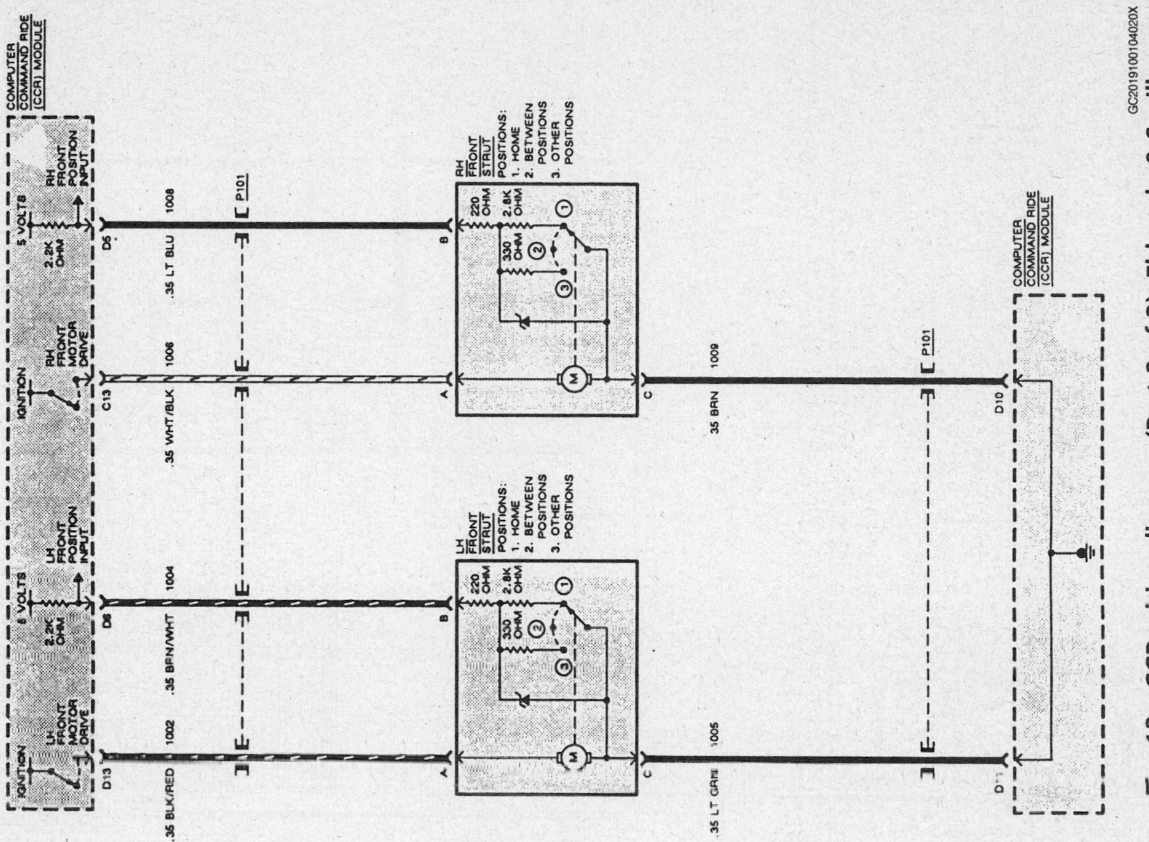
COMPUTER COMMAND RIDE (CCR) MODULE
IGNITION
5 VOLTS
2.2K OHM
LH FRONT MOTOR DRIVE
LH FRONT POSITION INPUT
RH FRONT MOTOR DRIVE
RH FRONT POSITION INPUT
.35 BLK/RED
.35 BRN/WHT
.35 WHT/BLK
.35 LT BLU
.35 LT GRN
.35 BRN
P101
LH FRONT STRUT
RH FRONT STRUT
POSITIONS:
1. HOME
2. BETWEEN POSITIONS
3. OTHER POSITIONS
220 OHM
2.8K OHM
330 OHM
GC2019100104020X

Fig. 12 CCR wiring diagram (Part 2 of 3). Eldorado & Seville

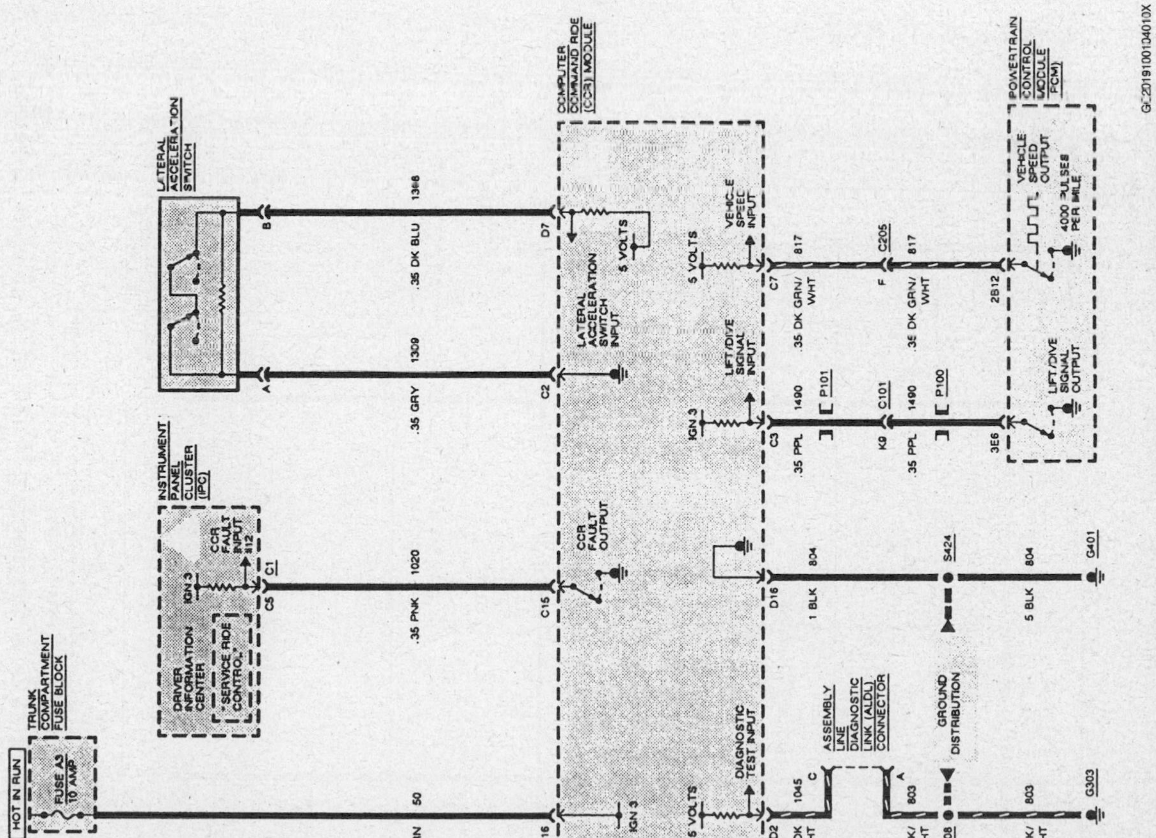
HOT IN RUN
TRUNK COMPARTMENT FUSE BLOCK
FUSE A3 10 AMP
DRIVER INFORMATION CENTER
SERVICE RIDE CONTROL
INSTRUMENT PANEL CLUSTER (IPC)
CCR FAULT INPUT
LATERAL ACCELERATION SWITCH
COMPUTER COMMAND RIDE (CCR) MODULE
CCR FAULT OUTPUT
LATERAL ACCELERATION SWITCH INPUT
DIAGNOSTIC TEST INPUT
LIFT/DIVE SIGNAL INPUT
VEHICLE SPEED INPUT
ASSEMBLY LINE DIAGNOSTIC LINK (ALDL) CONNECTOR
GROUND DISTRIBUTION
POWERTRAIN CONTROL MODULE (PCM)
LIFT/DIVE SIGNAL OUTPUT
VEHICLE SPEED OUTPUT
4000 PULSES PER MILE
.35 BRN
.35 PNK
.35 GRY
.35 DK BLU
.35 DK GRN/WHT
.35 PPL
.35 BLK/WHT
1 BLK
5 BLK
3 BLK/WHT
S208
S424
G303
G401
C205
C101
P100
P101
GC2019100104010X

Fig. 12 CCR wiring diagram (Part 1 of 3). Eldorado & Seville

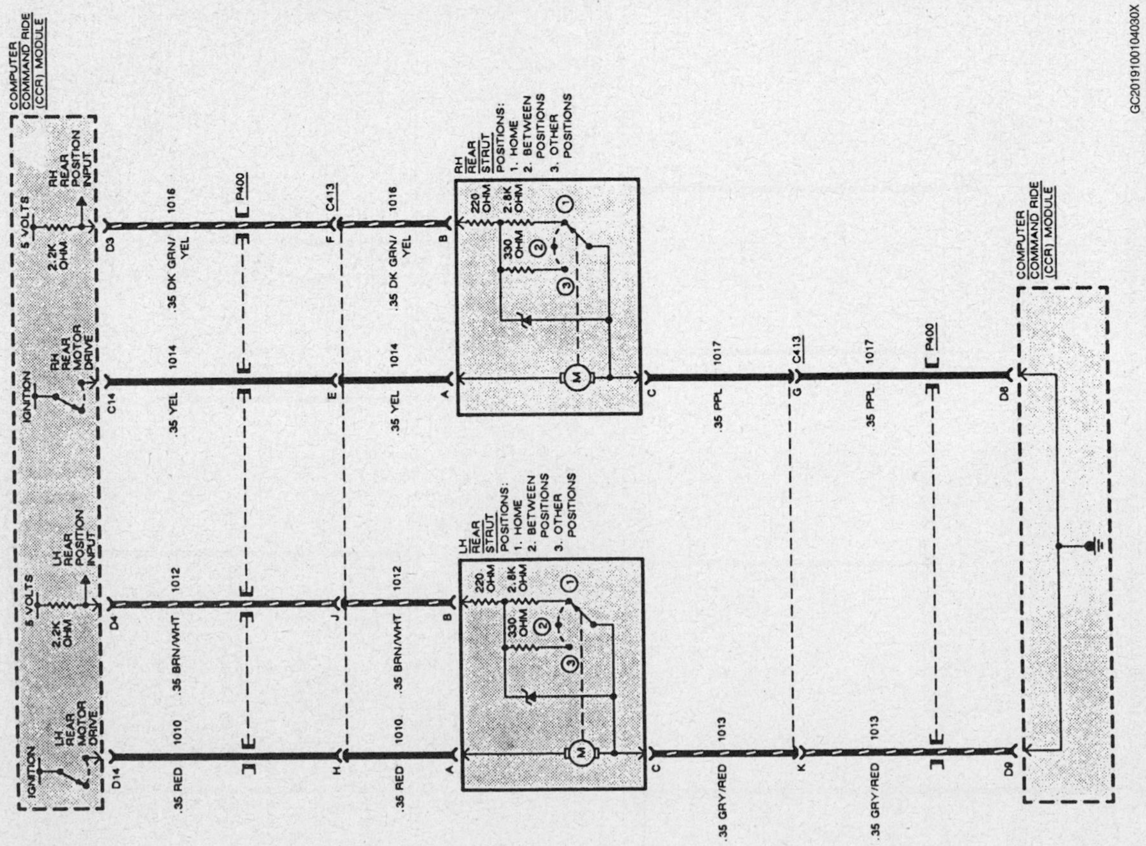
COMPUTER COMMAND RIDE (CCR) MODULE
IGNITION
LH REAR MOTOR DRIVE
5 VOLTS
2.2K OHM
LH REAR POSITION INPUT
RH REAR MOTOR DRIVE
RH REAR POSITION INPUT
D14
D4
C14
D3
.35 RED
1010
.35 BRN/WHT
1012
.35 YEL
1014
.35 DK GRN/YEL
1016
P400
C413
LH REAR STRUT POSITIONS:
1. HOME
2. BETWEEN POSITIONS
3. OTHER POSITIONS
RH REAR STRUT POSITIONS:
1. HOME
2. BETWEEN POSITIONS
3. OTHER POSITIONS
220 OHM
2.8K OHM
330 OHM
.35 GRY/RED
1013
.35 PPL
1017
D9
D8
GC2019100104030X

Fig. 12 CCR wiring diagram (Part 3 of 3). Eldorado & Seville

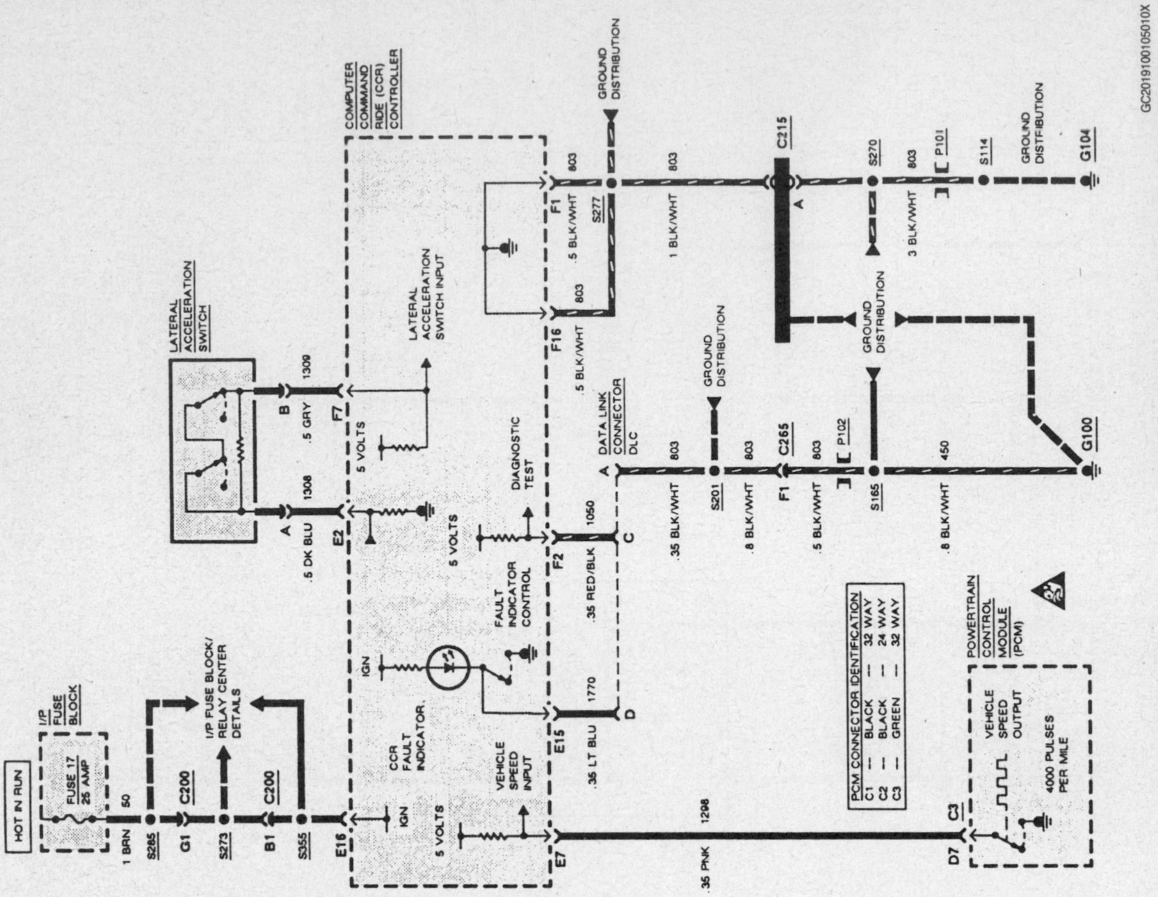
HOT IN RUN
I/P FUSE BLOCK
FUSE 17 25 AMP
1 BRN
50
S285
C200
G1
S273
B1
S355
I/P FUSE BLOCK/ RELAY CENTER DETAILS
E16
IGN
5 VOLTS
CCR FAULT INDICATOR
VEHICLE SPEED INPUT
E7
E15
.35 LT BLU
1770
.35 PNK
1298
COMPUTER COMMAND RIDE (CCR) CONTROLLER
LATERAL ACCELERATION SWITCH
.5 DK BLU
1308
.5 GRY
1309
E2
F7
LATERAL ACCELERATION SWITCH INPUT
DIAGNOSTIC TEST
FAULT INDICATOR CONTROL
F2
.35 RED/BLK
1050
F16
.5 BLK/WHT
803
F1
S277
GROUND DISTRIBUTION
DATA LINK CONNECTOR DLC
.35 BLK/WHT
S201
.8 BLK/WHT
C265
P102
S165
450
G100
1 BLK/WHT
C215
S270
3 BLK/WHT
P101
S114
G104
PCM CONNECTOR IDENTIFICATION
C1 — BLACK — 32 WAY
C2 — BLACK — 24 WAY
C3 — GREEN — 32 WAY
POWERTRAIN CONTROL MODULE (PCM)
VEHICLE SPEED OUTPUT
4000 PULSES PER MILE
C3
D7
GC2019100105010X

Fig. 13 CCR wiring diagram (Part 1 of 3). LeSabre & Park Avenue

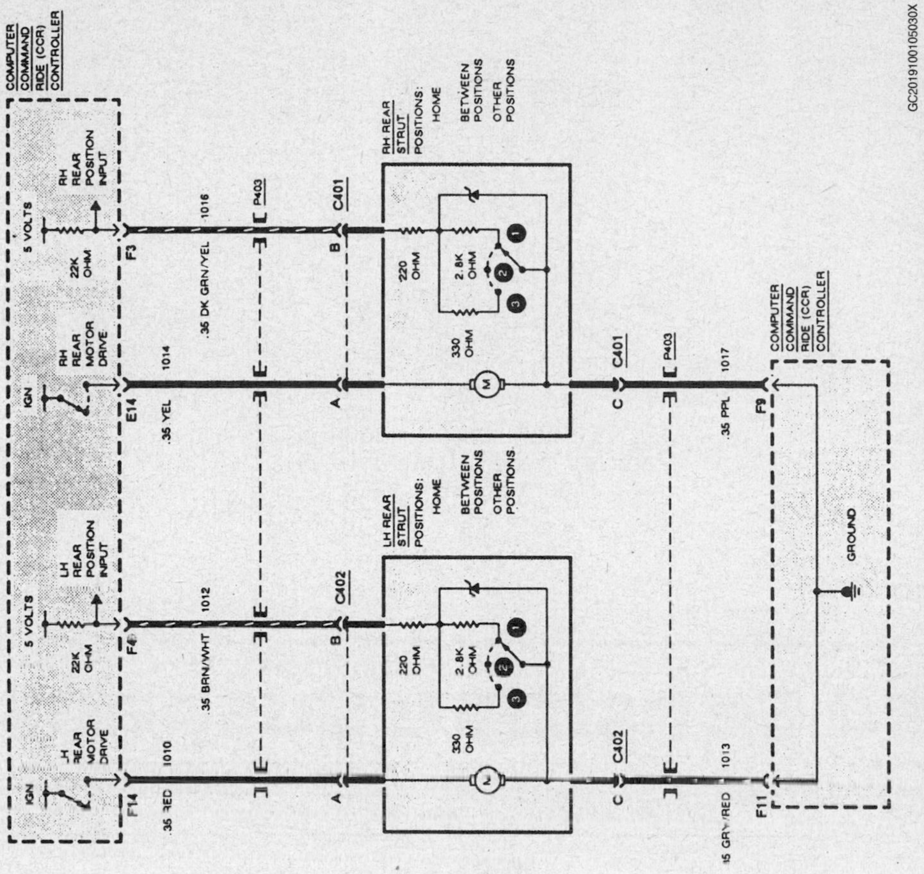

Fig. 13 CCR wiring diagram (Part 3 of 3). LeSabre & Park Avenue

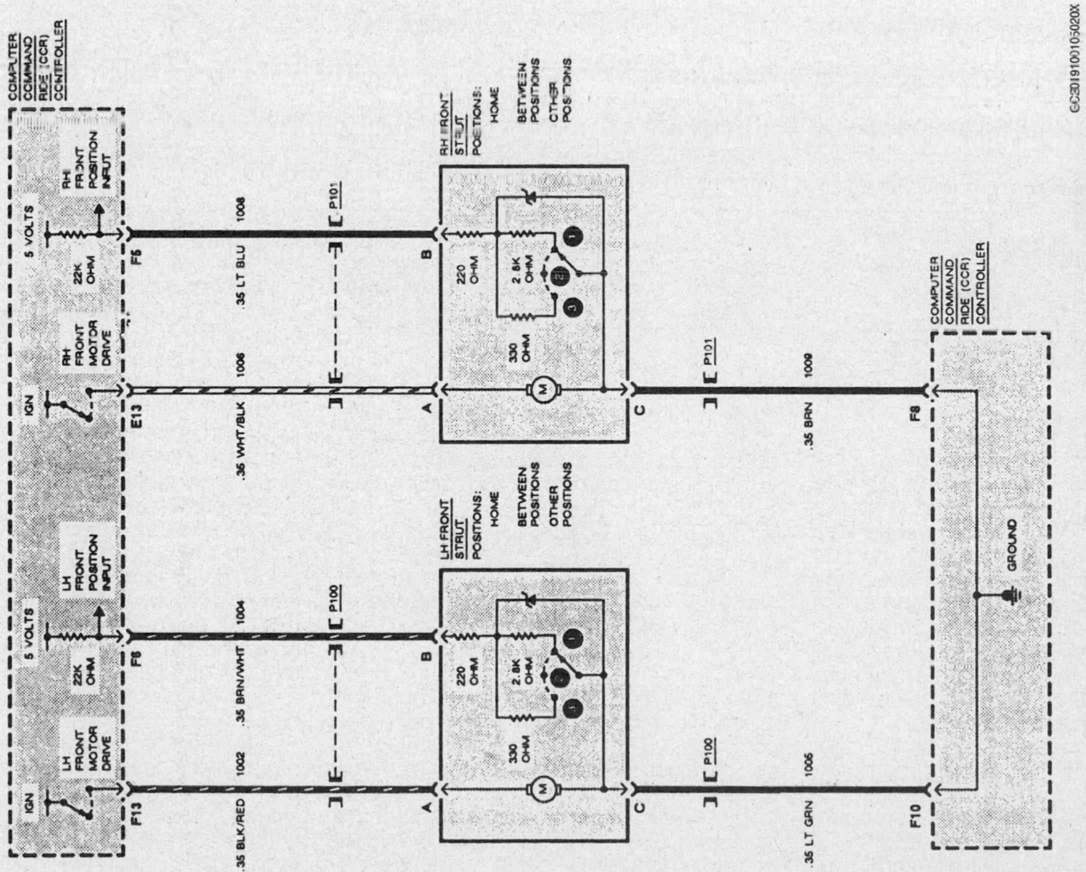

Fig. 13 CCR wiring diagram (Part 2 of 3). LeSabre & Park Avenue

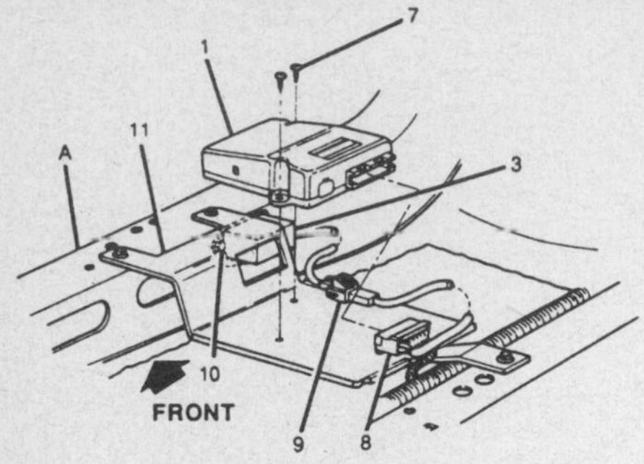
7
1
11
A
3
10
FRONT
9
8

A BAR, SEAT
1 CONTROL MODULE, CCR
3 SWITCH, LATERAL ACCELERATOR
7 SCREW (2)
8 CONNECTOR, ELECTRICAL
9 CONNECTOR, ELECTRICAL
10 SCREW (2)
11 BRACKET

GC2019100106000X

Fig. 14 CCR control module & lateral accelerator switch mounting. DeVille & Fleetwood (FWD)

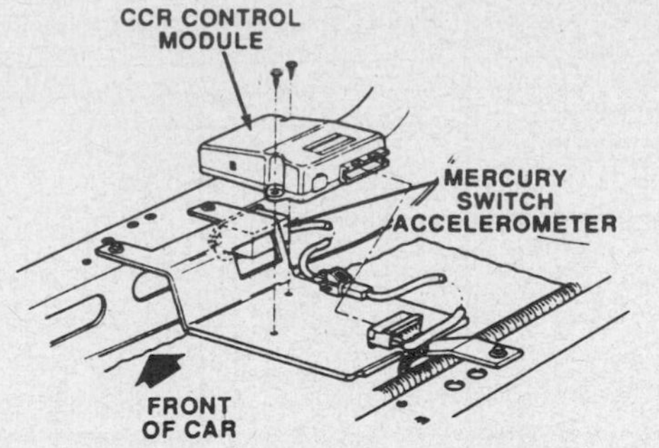
CCR CONTROL MODULE
MERCURY SWITCH ACCELEROMETER
FRONT OF CAR

GC2019100107000X

Fig. 15 CCR control module & mercury switch accelerometer mounting. 88 & 98

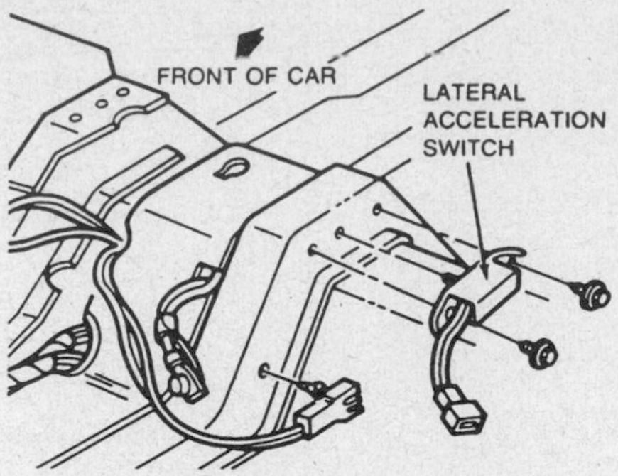
FRONT OF CAR
LATERAL ACCELERATION SWITCH

GC2019100108000X

Fig. 16 Lateral accelerator switch mounting. Eldorado & Seville

Speed Sensitive Suspension

NOTE: On Air Bag Equipped Models, Refer To "Air Bag System Precautions" Located In The Front Of This Manual For System Disarming & Arming Procedures.

INDEX

PRECAUTIONS

AIR BAG SYSTEMS

Refer to "Air Bag System Precautions" in the front of this manual for system disarming and arming procedures.

DESCRIPTION

The Speed-Sensitive Suspension system controls the firmness of the car's ride by automatically controlling an actuator in each of the four struts. The system has three damping modes; comfort, normal and firm. The control module determines damping mode selection according to vehicle speed conditions, lift/dive input, lateral acceleration switch input and any error conditions which may exist. When two demanded positions conflict, the system will go to the firmest damping position.

The control module located on the right electronics bay in the luggage compartment controls and monitors the speed-sensitive suspension system. The control module also controls the Speed-Sensitive Steering system. The control module receives speed, lift/dive and lateral acceleration input and determines the optimum mode strut valving for current operating conditions. The control module also receives feedback from the struts to determine proper system operation. If the control module receives an incorrect feedback signal for two successive ignition cycles, an error code will be set in memory and a "SERVICE RIDE CONTROL" message will be displayed on the driver information center.

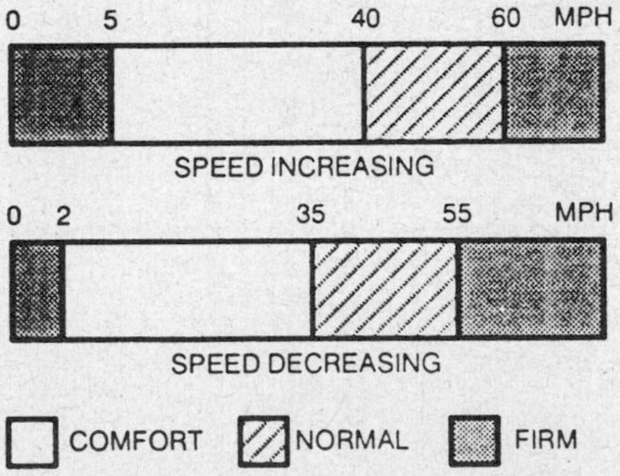
0 5 40 60 MPH
SPEED INCREASING
0 2 35 55 MPH
SPEED DECREASING
COMFORT
NORMAL
FIRM

GC2019100109000X

Fig. 1 Damping mode to speed input comparison

Each strut contains an electrical actuator which rotates a selector valve to a specific location commanded by the control module. The selector valve contains different size orifices which will increase or decrease the damping rate of the strut to control ride firmness. The actuators are an integral part of the strut and cannot be serviced separately.

To determine which damping mode the system should be in based on speed input, refer to **Fig. 1.**

Lift/dive input is received from the Powertrain Control Module (PCM). The system will go to the firm mode during wide open throttle to provide anti-lift. The system will go to the firm mode when there is a high deceleration rate to provide anti-dive.

The lateral acceleration switch (accelerometer) provides the control module with body roll information. The control module will command the struts to the firm mode when the switch senses lateral acceleration.

Each actuator provides a feedback volt-

DESCRIPTION	CKT.	CAV.	CAV.	CKT.	DESCRIPTION
GROUND	804	D16	C16	50	IGNITION 3
STEERING SOLENOID	1294	D15	C15	1020	MESSAGE OUTPUT
LR DRIVE	1010	D14	C14	1014	RR DRIVE
LF DRIVE	1002	D13	C13	1006	RF DRIVE
		D12	C12		
LF GROUND	1005	D11	C11		
RF GROUND	1009	D10	C10		
LR GROUND	1013	D9	C9		
RR GROUND	1017	D8	C8		
LATERAL ACCEL.	1308	D7	C7	817	SPEED SIGNAL
LF FEEDBACK	1004	D6	C6		
RF FEEDBACK	1008	D5	C5		
LR FEEDBACK	1012	D4	C4		
RR FEEDBACK	1016	D3	C3	1490	LIFT / DIVE SIGNAL
DIAGNOSTIC ENABLE	1045	D2	C2	1309	LATERAL ACCEL.
STEERING SOLENOID	1295	D1	C1		

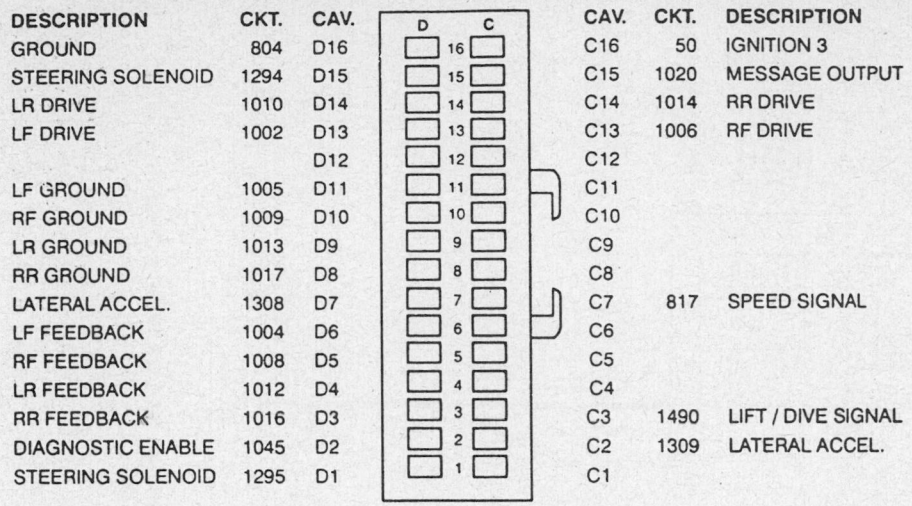

GC2019100110000X

Fig. 2 Control module connector

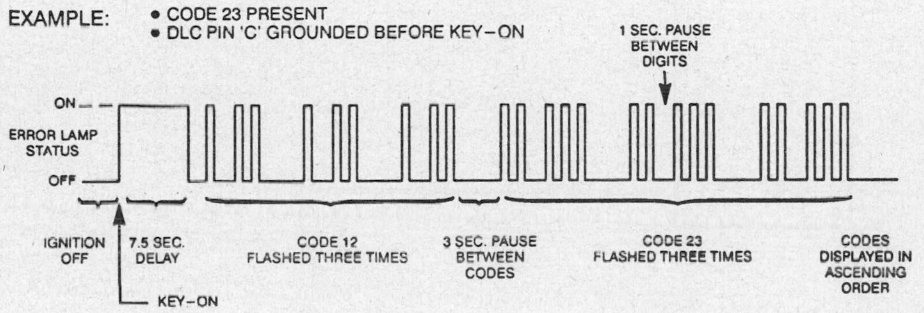
EXAMPLE:
• CODE 23 PRESENT
• DLC PIN 'C' GROUNDED BEFORE KEY–ON
1 SEC. PAUSE BETWEEN DIGITS
ON
ERROR LAMP STATUS
OFF
IGNITION OFF
7.5 SEC. DELAY
KEY–ON
CODE 12 FLASHED THREE TIMES
3 SEC. PAUSE BETWEEN CODES
CODE 23 FLASHED THREE TIMES
CODES DISPLAYED IN ASCENDING ORDER

GC2019100111000X

Fig. 3 Trouble code sequence example

age signifying the actuator position relative to a "Home" position. A single three volt pad signifies the home position which correlates to the first comfort damping position of the actuator, while subsequent zero to one volt pads signify the remaining damping positions. Each damping position is separated by a five volt pad.

DIAGNOSIS & TESTING

Accessing Diagnostic Trouble Codes

The diagnostic system can be accessed by grounding the Diagnostic Enable circuit at pin "C" of the Diagnostic Link Connector (DLC) or by grounding pin "D2" to pin "D16 of the control module connector, **Fig. 2.** After pin "C" is grounded, the lamp will come on for 7.5 seconds before beginning the blink code diagnostic sequence. This is followed by displaying code 12, three times to indicate the beginning of the sequence. Then each stored code is blinked out, in ascending order. Each code will be displayed three times before proceeding to the next code. When all codes have been read, the entire code sequence will repeat, beginning with code 12. The sequence will repeat until the Diagnostic Enable circuit is disconnected.

Codes are read by counting the number of flashes of the L.E.D. on the control module. A code 12 would be indicated by the lamp flashing once, followed by a one second pause, followed by two flashes with a half second pause between flashes. There is a three second pause between codes. Refer to **Fig. 3** for an example of a code sequence.

Diagnostic Trouble Code Interpretation

When the ignition switch is turned on the system performs a self-test which lasts 7.5 seconds. The error lamp will be on for this period. After the self-test, the control module may be in "Normal Operating Mode," "Error Mode" or "Reset Mode." When the control module is in the "Normal Operating Mode" the error lamp is on below 10 mph to indicate proper system operation and to verify that the control module is receiving speed information. When the control module is in "Error Mode" the error lamp is off below 10 mph and turns on above 10 mph. When the control module is in "Reset Mode" the error lamp is turned off to indicate a control module problem.

Any system error that is active for two successive ignition cycles will cause the "SERVICE RIDE CONTROL" message to be displayed on the driver information center (except for the accelerometer code 32 which is displayed immediately). The message will be displayed as long as the error code is active. If the fault code corrects itself, the "SERVICE RIDE CONTROL" message will turn off, but the error code will be stored in the control module's non-volatile memory.

If a diagnostic trouble code is set, a one second self-diagnosis test is performed at three minute intervals. The error lamp will be on during this test and will go out if the code is corrected. If the fault still exists, the lamp will be off below 10 mph and on above 10 mph.

If diagnostic mode is entered and no codes are stored in memory, the control module will continually display code 12. System trouble codes are as follows:

Code 12: Initiation code.
Code 23: Left front actuator error.
Code 24: Right front actuator error.
Code 25: Left rear actuator error.
Code 26: Right rear actuator error.
Code 31: Lift/dive input error.
Code 32: Lateral acceleration switch error.
Code 35: Speed-sensitive steering error.

Refer to **Fig. 4,** for the system wiring diagram to help in the repair and diagnosis of the trouble codes.

Clearing Diagnostic Trouble Codes

The diagnostic trouble codes can be cleared by grounding the diagnostic enable circuit (pin "C" to pin "A" of the DLC or pin "D2" to pin "D16" of the control module connector) three times for approximately one second within 30 seconds. The control module will indicate that the codes are cleared by turning off the error lamp for one second. The codes cannot be cleared by disconnecting battery or control module connectors. When error codes are cleared, the ignition cycle counter is disabled until the control module completes a successful self-test. A code 31 (lift/dive error) requires a cycle of the ignition switch to retest.

COMPONENT REPLACEMENT

CONTROL MODULE

1. Remove front of luggage compartment trim panel.
2. Disconnect control module electrical connector, **Fig. 5.**
3. Remove control module retaining screws, then the control module.
4. Reverse procedure to install.

LATERAL ACCELERATION SWITCH

1. Remove center console storage compartment by pulling up and out.
2. Remove shift handle retaining clip and shift handle.
3. Remove console upper trim panel.
4. Disconnect cigarette lighter electrical connector.

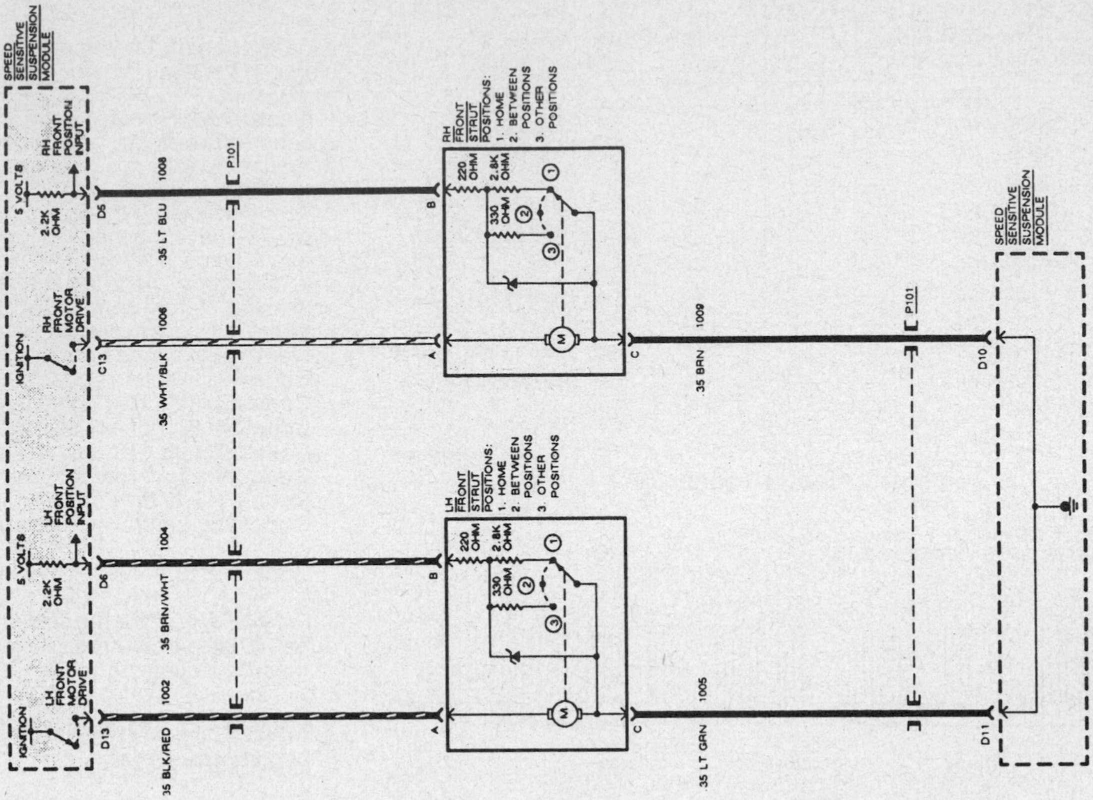

GC2019100112020X

Fig. 4 Speed-sensitive suspension system wiring diagram (Part 2 of 3)

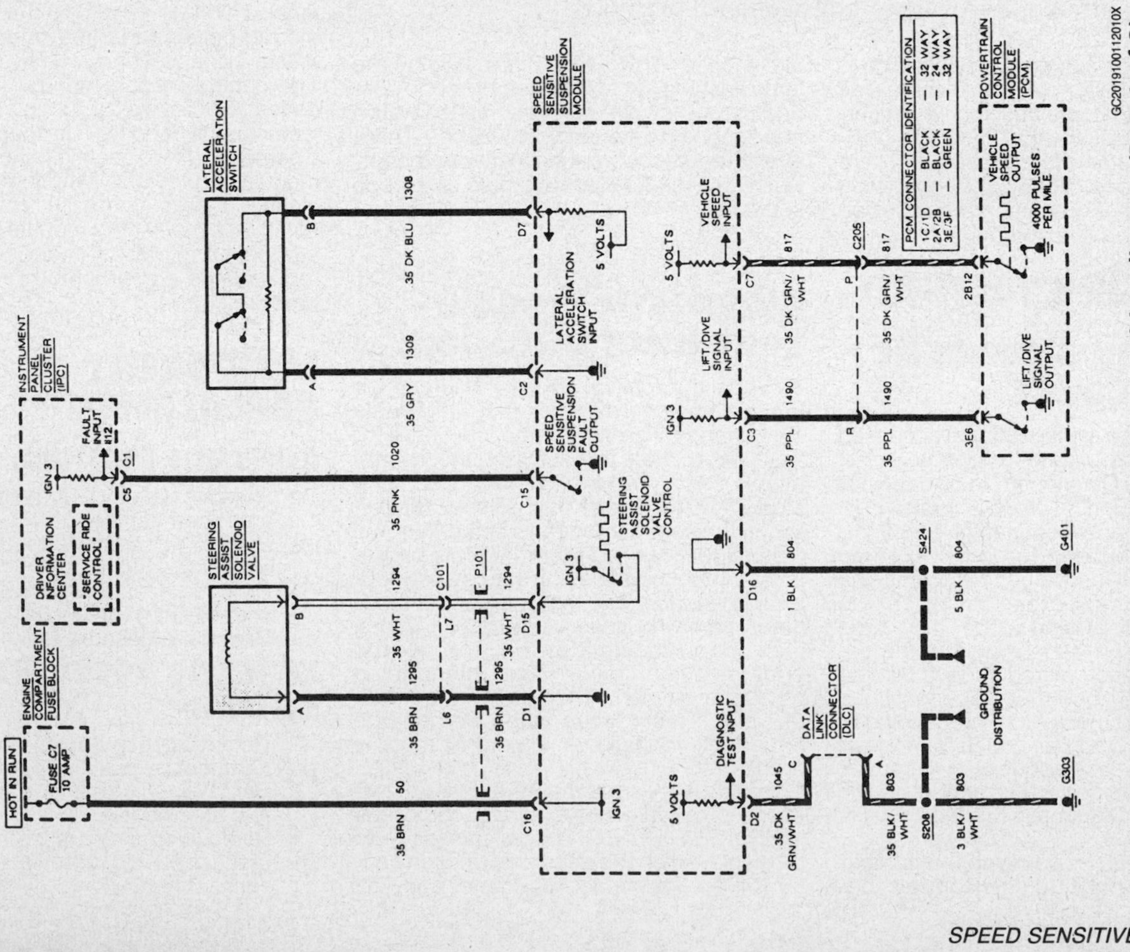

GC2019100112010X

Fig. 4 Speed-sensitive suspension system wiring diagram (Part 1 of 3)

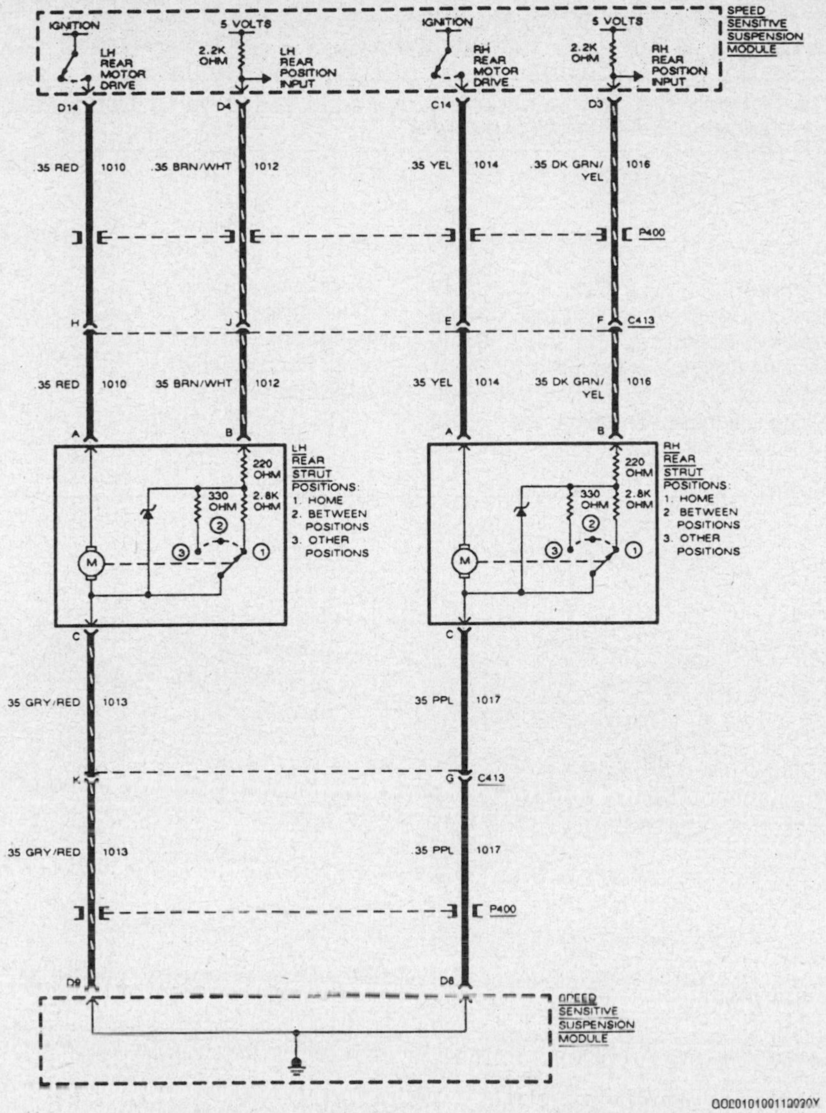
SPEED SENSITIVE SUSPENSION MODULE
IGNITION
5 VOLTS
LH REAR MOTOR DRIVE
2.2K OHM
LH REAR POSITION INPUT
RH REAR MOTOR DRIVE
RH REAR POSITION INPUT
D14
D4
C14
D3
.35 RED 1010
.35 BRN/WHT 1012
.35 YEL 1014
.35 DK GRN/YEL 1016
P400
C413
LH REAR STRUT POSITIONS: 1. HOME 2. BETWEEN POSITIONS 3. OTHER POSITIONS
RH REAR STRUT POSITIONS: 1. HOME 2. BETWEEN POSITIONS 3. OTHER POSITIONS
220 OHM
330 OHM
2.8K OHM
.35 GRY/RED 1013
.35 PPL 1017
D9
D8
GC2010100113030X

Fig. 4 Speed-sensitive suspension system wiring diagram (Part 3 of 3)

5. Remove radio trim plate.
6. Remove two retaining nuts from bottom of radio control head.
7. Twist radio control head so that the right side is removed first in order to clear connectors on the left side.
8. Disconnect electrical connectors, then remove the radio.
9. Remove four console to instrument panel retaining screws.
10. Remove gear selector trim plate and PRNDL illumination lamp socket.
11. Remove two shifter plate upper mounting bolts, then the two shifter assembly to floor retaining nuts.
12. Working through the storage compartment opening, remove two console to floor retaining nuts.
13. Remove console blower air supply duct.

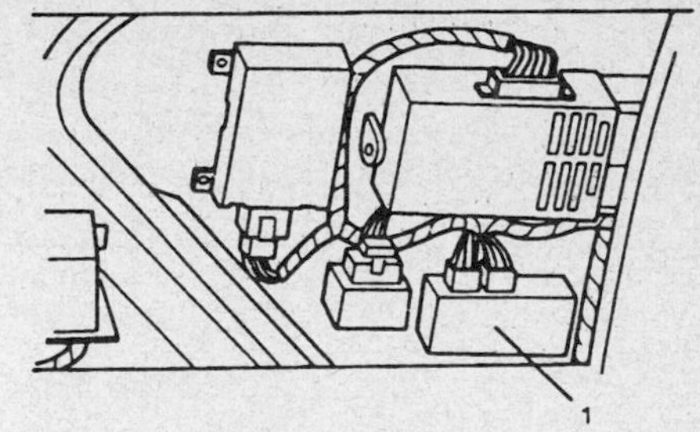
1
1 CONTROL MODULE
GC2019100113000X

Fig. 5 Control module mounting

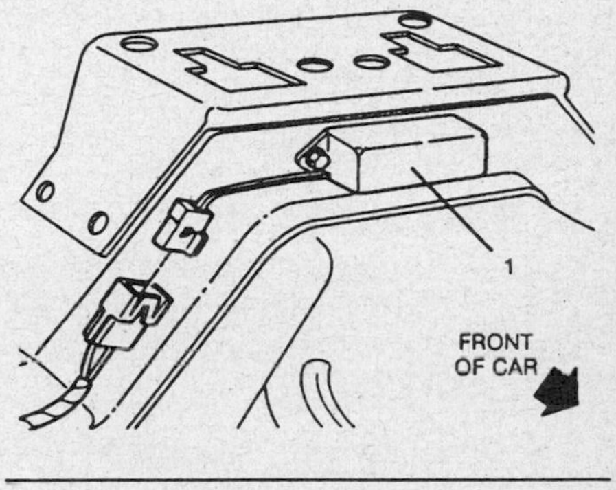
1
FRONT OF CAR
1 LATERAL ACCELERATION SWITCH
GC2019100114000X

Fig. 6 Lateral acceleration switch mounting

14. Slide console forward and disconnect electrical connectors.
15. Slide console rearward to clear shifter assembly, then remove center console.
16. Pull carpet rearward to gain access to lateral acceleration switch.
17. Disconnect lateral acceleration switch electrical connector, then remove switch from body rail, **Fig. 6.**
18. Reverse procedure to install.

STRUT

Refer to "Front Suspension & Steering" and "Rear Axle & Suspension" sections of "Buick Riviera, Cadillac Eldorado & Seville, Oldsmobile Toronado & Trofeo" for strut replacement procedures.

Road Sensing Suspension

NOTE: On Air Bag Equipped Models, Refer To "Air Bag System Precautions" Located In The Front Of This Manual For System Disarming & Arming Procedures.

INDEX

PRECAUTIONS

AIR BAG SYSTEMS

Refer to "Air Bag System Precautions" in the front of this manual for system disarming and arming procedures.

DESCRIPTION

The Road Sensing Suspension/Real Time Damping (RSS/RTD) system **Fig. 1**, controls damping forces in the shock absorbers and struts in response to various road and driving conditions. The system is capable of making these changes within 10-15 milliseconds.

The RSS module receives the following inputs; vertical acceleration, wheel-to-body position, vehicle speed and lift/dive. The RSS module evaluates the input data and uses it to control the solenoid valves in each of the dampers independently to provide varied levels of suspension control.

The system also controls the Speed-Sensitive Steering (SSS) system and Electronic Level Control (ELC) system. The SSS system changes driver steering effort based on vehicle speed. The ELC system maintains proper vehicle trim height under various vehicle loading conditions.

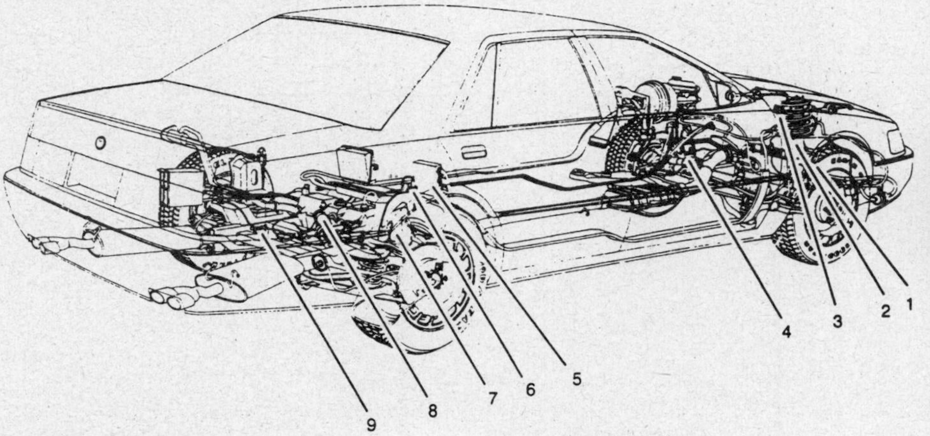
1
2
3
4
5
6
7
8
9

1 FRONT POSITION SENSOR
2 FRONT STRUT
3 FRONT ACCELEROMETER
4 SPEED SENSITIVE STEERING SOLENOID
5 RSS MODULE
6 REAR POSITION SENSOR
7 REAR SHOCK
8 ELC COMPRESSOR
9 REAR ACCELEROMETER
10 RESISTOR MODULE (NOT VISIBLE)

GC2019100115000X

Fig. 1 Road Sensing Suspension (RSS) system

SYSTEM COMPONENTS

RSS Module

The RSS module located on the right electronics bay in the luggage compartment controls the Road Sensing Suspension, Speed Sensitive Steering and Electronic Level Control Systems.

Position Sensors

Position sensors are mounted at each corner of the vehicle between a control arm and the body. The position sensors provide the system with relative wheel to body position and velocity. The rear position sensors input is also used by the Electronic Level Control (ELC) system for trim height information.

Accelerometer

An accelerometer is mounted on each corner of the vehicle. The accelerometer supplies the controller with the vertical acceleration of the body.

Speed Sensor

Vehicle speed input is received from the Powertrain Control Module (PCM) and is used to determine the amount of damper control and steering assist required.

Lift/Dive

Lift/dive input is received from the Powertrain Control Module (PCM). When the system receives a lift or dive signal it will adjust the suspension system to the firm position on all corners. The lift signal is calculated in the PCM based of throttle position, transmission gear and vehicle speed. The dive signal, calculated by the PCM, checks the rate of change in vehicle speed.

Damper

The damper contains a solenoid valve that is controlled by the RSS module. The solenoid provides two levels of damping, firm and soft. The soft mode is accomplished by switching the solenoid to the "ON" state, causing the damper oil to bypass the main damper valving. The firm mode is accomplished by switching the solenoid to the "OFF" state causing the damper oil to flow through the main damper valving. Each mode is much softer/firmer than a passive damper would be. The solenoid is an integral part of the damper and cannot be serviced separately.

RSS Resistor Module

The RSS resistor module is located in the luggage compartment in the right quarter panel, external to the RSS module and consists of four resistors inside a ceramic material. When a solenoid is switched to the "ON" state, full system voltage is applied for a short period of time to quickly activate the solenoid. It is undesirable to maintain this high current to the solenoid any longer than required, therefore a resistor is put into the circuit. This "Hold" mode provides enough current to hold the solenoid in the "ON" position.

Steering Solenoid

The steering solenoid valve is a device that is controlled to vary power assist le-

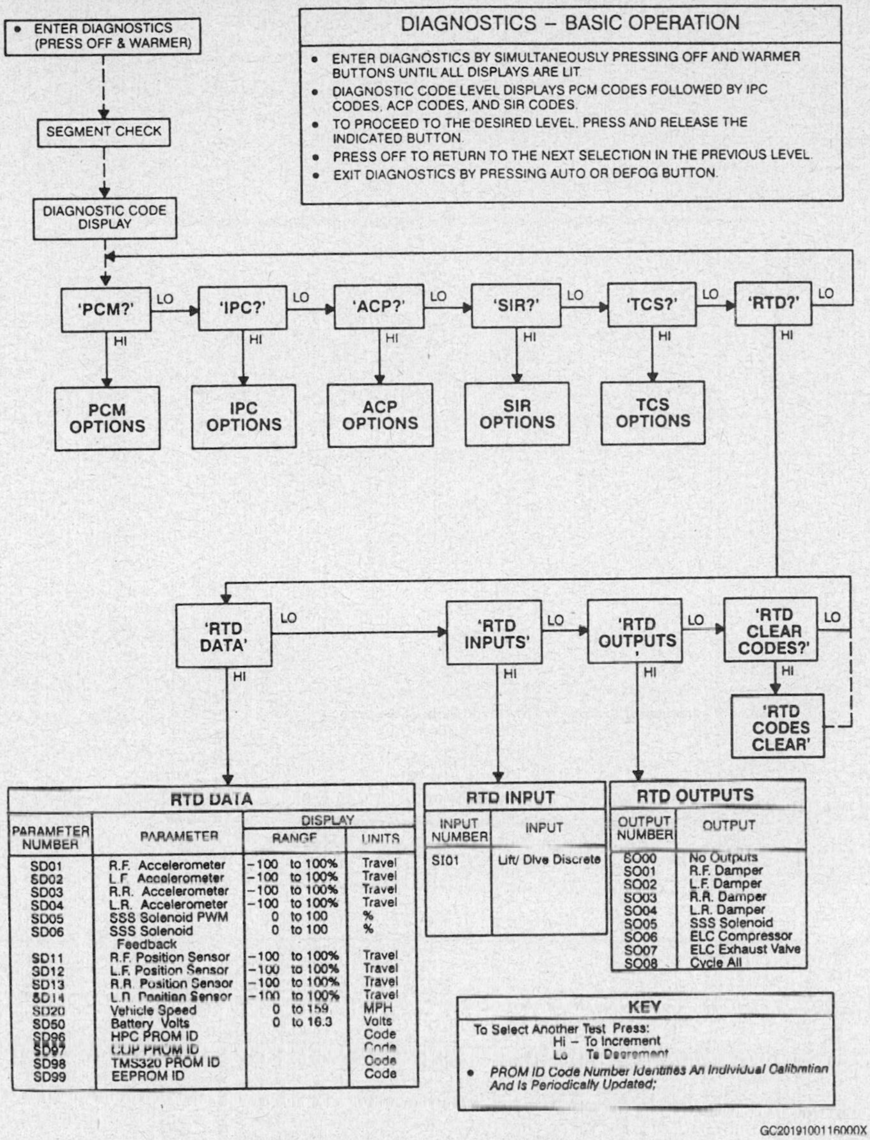
ENTER DIAGNOSTICS (PRESS OFF & WARMER)
SEGMENT CHECK
DIAGNOSTIC CODE DISPLAY
DIAGNOSTICS – BASIC OPERATION
• ENTER DIAGNOSTICS BY SIMULTANEOUSLY PRESSING OFF AND WARMER BUTTONS UNTIL ALL DISPLAYS ARE LIT.
• DIAGNOSTIC CODE LEVEL DISPLAYS PCM CODES FOLLOWED BY IPC CODES, ACP CODES, AND SIR CODES.
• TO PROCEED TO THE DESIRED LEVEL, PRESS AND RELEASE THE INDICATED BUTTON.
• PRESS OFF TO RETURN TO THE NEXT SELECTION IN THE PREVIOUS LEVEL.
• EXIT DIAGNOSTICS BY PRESSING AUTO OR DEFOG BUTTON.
'PCM?'
'IPC?'
'ACP?'
'SIR?'
'TCS?'
'RTD?'
LO
HI
PCM OPTIONS
IPC OPTIONS
ACP OPTIONS
SIR OPTIONS
TCS OPTIONS
'RTD DATA'
'RTD INPUTS'
'RTD OUTPUTS'
'RTD CLEAR CODES?'
'RTD CODES CLEAR'
KEY
To Select Another Test Press:
Hi – To Increment
Lo To Decrement
• PROM ID Code Number Identifies An Individual Calibration And Is Periodically Updated;
GC2019100116000X

RTD DATA

PARAMETER NUMBER	PARAMETER	DISPLAY RANGE	DISPLAY UNITS
SD01	R.F. Accelerometer	−100 to 100%	Travel
SD02	L.F. Accelerometer	−100 to 100%	Travel
SD03	R.R. Accelerometer	−100 to 100%	Travel
SD04	L.R. Accelerometer	−100 to 100%	Travel
SD05	SSS Solenoid PWM	0 to 100	%
SD06	SSS Solenoid Feedback	0 to 100	%
SD11	R.F. Position Sensor	−100 to 100%	Travel
SD12	L.F. Position Sensor	−100 to 100%	Travel
SD13	R.R. Position Sensor	−100 to 100%	Travel
SD14	L.R. Position Sensor	−100 to 100%	Travel
SD20	Vehicle Speed	0 to 159	MPH
SD50	Battery Volts	0 to 16.3	Volts
SD96	HPC PROM ID		Code
SD97	CUP PROM ID		Code
SD98	TMS320 PROM ID		Code
SD99	EEPROM ID		Code

RTD INPUT

INPUT NUMBER	INPUT
SI01	Lift/ Dive Discrete

RTD OUTPUTS

OUTPUT NUMBER	OUTPUT
SO00	No Outputs
SO01	R.F. Damper
SO02	L.F. Damper
SO03	R.R. Damper
SO04	L.R. Damper
SO05	SSS Solenoid
SO06	ELC Compressor
SO07	ELC Exhaust Valve
SO08	Cycle All

Fig. 2 Vehicle self-diagnostic system operation

vels. The solenoid is driven by the controller using pulse width modulation (varying the amount of time the solenoid is on) as a function of the vehicle speed. When the solenoid is in the "OFF" position, the vehicle will have full power steering assist.

Electronic Level Control (ELC) System

The ELC system automatically adjusts the rear trim height in response to vehicle loading. On vehicles with the 4.6L/V8-279 engine, the height sensing function is performed by the RSS rear position sensors. Rear trim height information is input from the rear position sensors to the RSS control module which controls the ELC compressor and exhaust solenoid information. Refer to "Electronic Level Controls" for system operation and on-vehicle service.

DIAGNOSIS & TESTING

Accessing Diagnostic Trouble Codes

To access trouble codes and perform system tests, refer to **Fig. 2.** When performing system diagnosis and repair, refer to **Fig. 3** for diagnostic information and **Figs. 4 and 5** for system wiring diagram and electrical connectors.

Diagnostic Trouble Code Interpretation

The RSS control module continually monitors operating conditions for possible system malfunctions. By comparing system conditions against standard operating limits, certain circuit and component malfunctions can be detected. A four digit alpha-numeric diagnostic trouble code is stored in the computer memory when a problem is detected by this self-diagnostic system.

Clearing Diagnostic Trouble Codes

To clear system trouble codes, refer to **Fig. 2.**

SYSTEM SERVICE

TRIM HEIGHT ADJUSTMENT

A TECH 1 scan tool or equivalent, is necessary to adjust vehicle trim height.

1. Place vehicle on a level surface, with doors closed and no passengers or extra weight in the car.
2. If any RTD rear position or rear damper codes are set, they must be repaired prior to adjusting trim height.
3. Check rear position sensor values in diagnostics (RTD parameters SD13 and SD14) to ensure they are in normal range as shown in **Fig. 3.** If parameters are not within normal range, check for bent position sensor brackets or disconnected sensors.
4. Check fuel level reading In IPC (data parameter ID40) and round up to nearest gallon.
5. Connect TECH 1 scan tool or equivalent, to DLC connector, then run ignition key to the "ON" position.
6. Adjust trim height per TECH 1 instructions, then remove TECH 1 from the vehicle.

COMPONENT REPLACEMENT

RSS MODULE

After replacing the RSS module it will be necessary to calibrate the new RSS module. A TECH 1 scan tool or equivalent, is required to calibrate the new RSS module.

1. Remove luggage compartment front trim panel.
2. Disconnect control module electrical connectors, **Fig. 6.**
3. Remove module from right electronics bay.
4. Reverse procedure to install, calibrate new module as follows:
   a. Ensure TECH 1 scan tool or equivalent, has latest version of chassis application program.
   b. Connect scan tool to Data Line Connector (DLC).
   c. Turn ignition key on, but do not start engine.
   d. Calibrate module per instructions on TECH 1 readout.
   e. After calibrating the RSS module, adjust vehicle trim height as described in "Trim Height, Adjustment."

Continued on page 36-55

ERROR CODES

S010 LF Damper Solenoid Short To B+
S011 LF Damper Solenoid Short To Ground / Open
S015 RF Damper Solenoid Short To B+
S016 RF Damper Solenoid Short To Ground / Open
S020 LR Damper Solenoid Short To B+
S021 LR Damper Solenoid Short To Ground / Open
S025 RR Damper Solenoid Short To B+
S026 RR Damper Solenoid Short To Ground / Open
S030 Speed Sensitive Steering Solenoid Fault
S035 ELC Compressor Short To B+
S036 ELC Compressor Short To Ground / Open
S037 ELC Exhaust Valve Short To B+
S038 ELC Exhaust Valve Short To Ground / Open
S043 Speed Signal Fault
S044 Lift / Dive Signal Fault [1]
S050 RSS Module Fault
S055 RSS Resistor Module Short To Ground / Open
S060 LF Position Sensor Fault
S061 RF Position Sensor Fault
S062 LR Position Sensor Fault
S063 RR Position Sensor Fault
S064 LF Position Sensor Overcurrent [1]
S065 RF Position Sensor Overcurrent [1]
S066 LR Position Sensor Overcurrent [1]
S067 RR Position Sensor Overcurrent [1]
S070 LF Accelerometer Fault
S071 RF Accelerometer Fault
S072 LR Accelerometer Fault
S073 RR Accelerometer Fault
S074 LF Accelerometer Overcurrent [1]
S075 RF Accelerometer Overcurrent [1]
S076 LR Accelerometer Overcurrent [1]
S077 RR Accelerometer Overcurrent [1]

RTD DATA PARAMETER DISPLAY

CODE	COMPONENT	RANGE	UNITS	NORMAL VALUE [2]
SD01	RF Accelerometer	−100 to 100	% Travel	−5 to +5
SD02	LF Accelerometer	−100 to 100	% Travel	−5 to +5
SD03	RR Accelerometer	−100 to 100	% Travel	−5 to +5
SD04	LR Accelerometer	−100 to 100	% Travel	−5 to +5
SD05	SSS Solenoid PWM	0 to 100	Percent	0
SD06	SSS Solenoid Feedback	0 to 100	Percent	8 to 15
SD11	RF Position Sensor	−100 to 100	% Travel	−20 to −10
SD12	LF Position Sensor	−100 to 100	% Travel	−20 to −10
SD13	RR Position Sensor	−100 to 100	% Travel	−20 to +20
SD14	LR Position Sensor	−100 to 100	% Travel	−20 to +20
SD20	Vehicle Speed	0 to 159	MPH	0
SD50	Battery Volts	0 to 16.3	Batt Volts	11 to 15
SD96	HPC PROM ID		Code	2401
SD97	COP PROM ID		Code	2014
SD98	TMS320 ID		Code	1012
SD99	EEPROM ID [3]		Code	32 (E VIN Y), 35 (ETC), 52 (STS)

RTD INPUTS

SI01	Lift / Dive Discrete	HI / LO

RTD OUTPUTS

SO00	No Discrete Outputs	
SO01	RF Damper	HI / LO
SO02	LF Damper	HI / LO
SO03	RR Damper	HI / LO
SO04	LR Damper	HI / LO
SO05	SSS Solenoid	HI / LO
SO06	ELC Compressor	HI / LO
SO07	ELC Exhaust Valve	HI / LO
SO08	Cycle All	HI / LO

[1] This code will not turn on the "SERVICE RIDE CONTROL" message, but will be retained in memory.

[2] Normal Values are based on car sitting on a level surface at curb weight. Individual vehicles may vary. Components should not be replaced if they do not fall within the range specified, however, the vehicle should be inspected for bent brackets or disconnected sensors.

[3] EEPROM ID may change if the RSS control module has been recalibrated.

GC2019100117000X

Fig. 3 Diagnostic information

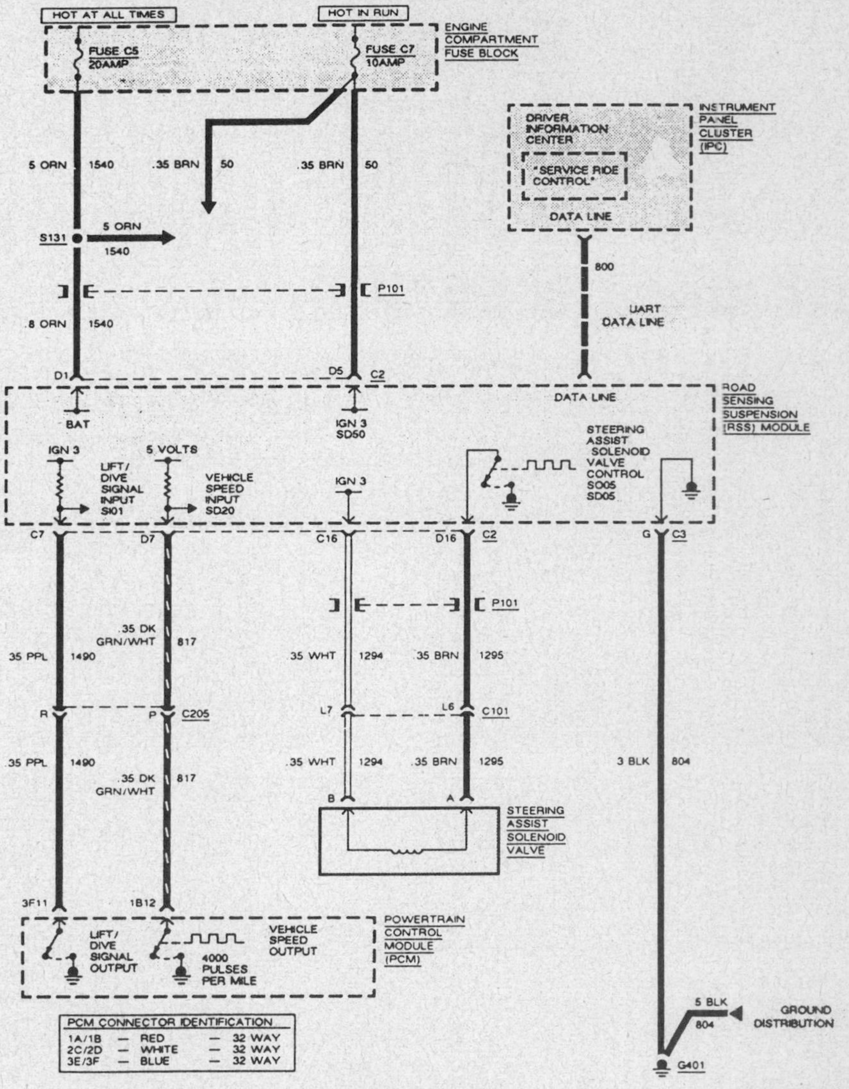
HOT AT ALL TIMES
HOT IN RUN
FUSE C5 20AMP
FUSE C7 10AMP
ENGINE COMPARTMENT FUSE BLOCK
5 ORN 1540
.35 BRN 50
.35 BRN 50
S131
5 ORN 1540
P101
.8 ORN 1540
INSTRUMENT PANEL CLUSTER (IPC)
DRIVER INFORMATION CENTER
"SERVICE RIDE CONTROL"
DATA LINE
800
UART DATA LINE
D1
D5
C2
DATA LINE
ROAD SENSING SUSPENSION (RSS) MODULE
BAT
IGN 3 SD50
IGN 3
5 VOLTS
LIFT/ DIVE SIGNAL INPUT SI01
VEHICLE SPEED INPUT SD20
IGN 3
STEERING ASSIST SOLENOID VALVE CONTROL SO05 SD05
C7
D7
C16
D16
C2
G
C3
P101
.35 DK GRN/WHT 817
.35 PPL 1490
.35 WHT 1294
.35 BRN 1295
R
P
C205
L7
L6
C101
3 BLK 804
B
A
STEERING ASSIST SOLENOID VALVE
3F11
1B12
LIFT/ DIVE SIGNAL OUTPUT
4000 PULSES PER MILE
VEHICLE SPEED OUTPUT
POWERTRAIN CONTROL MODULE (PCM)
PCM CONNECTOR IDENTIFICATION
1A/1B — RED — 32 WAY
2C/2D — WHITE — 32 WAY
3E/3F — BLUE — 32 WAY
5 BLK 804
GROUND DISTRIBUTION
G401
GC2019100118010X

Fig. 4 RSS system wiring diagram (Part 1 of 6)

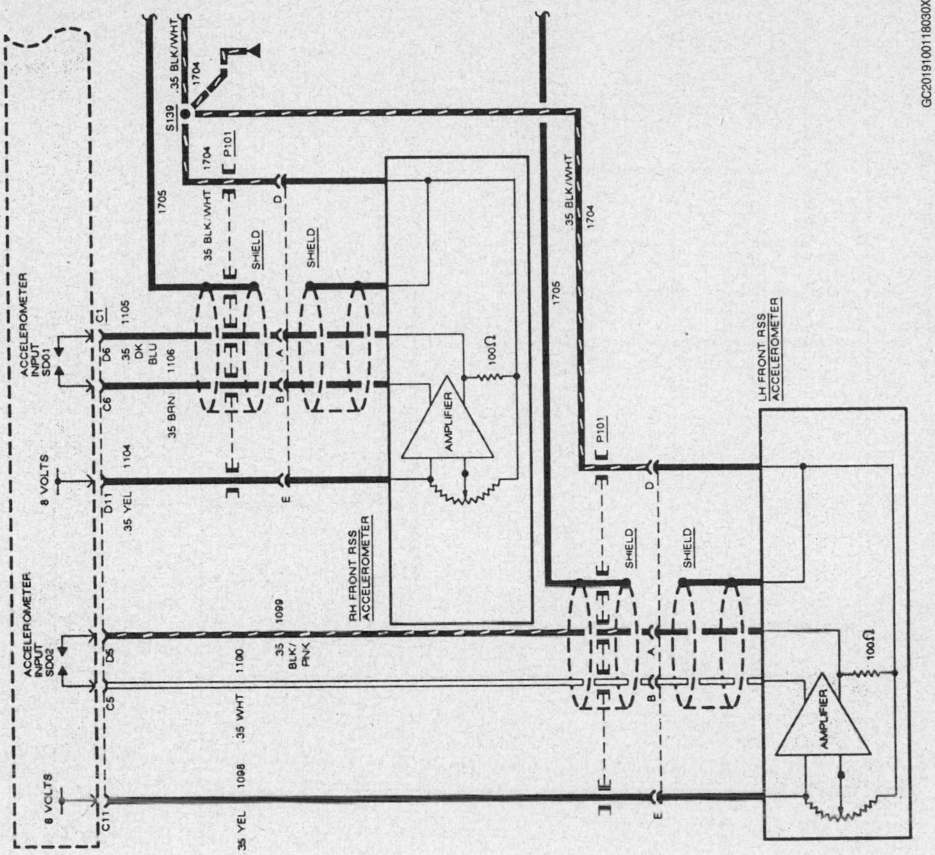
RH FRONT RSS ACCELEROMETER
LH FRONT RSS ACCELEROMETER
AMPLIFIER
SHIELD
GC2019100118030X

Fig. 4 RSS system wiring diagram (Part 3 of 6)

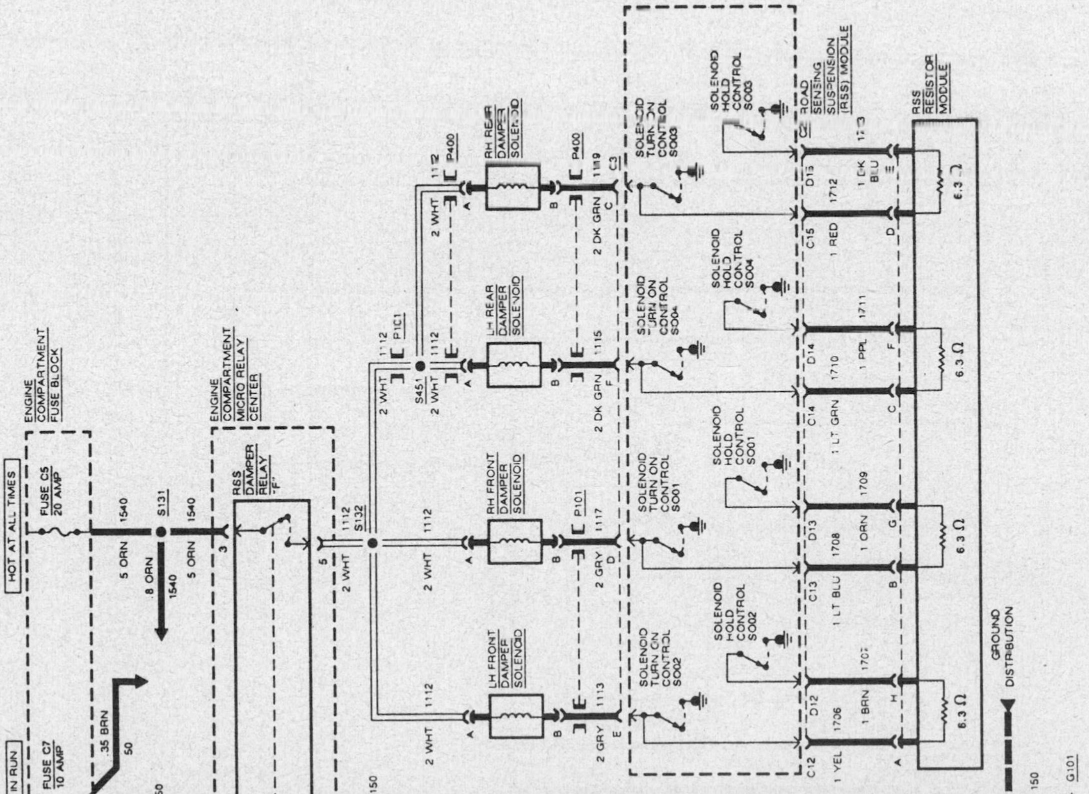
HOT IN RUN
HOT AT ALL TIMES
FUSE C7 10 AMP
FUSE C5 20 AMP
ENGINE COMPARTMENT FUSE BLOCK
ENGINE COMPARTMENT MICRO RELAY CENTER
RSS DAMPER RELAY "F"
LH FRONT DAMPER SOLENOID
RH FRONT DAMPER SOLENOID
LH REAR DAMPER SOLENOID
RH REAR DAMPER SOLENOID
ROAD SENSING SUSPENSION (RSS) MODULE
RSS RESISTOR MODULE
GROUND DISTRIBUTION
GC2019100118020X

Fig. 4 RSS system wiring diagram (Part 2 of 6)

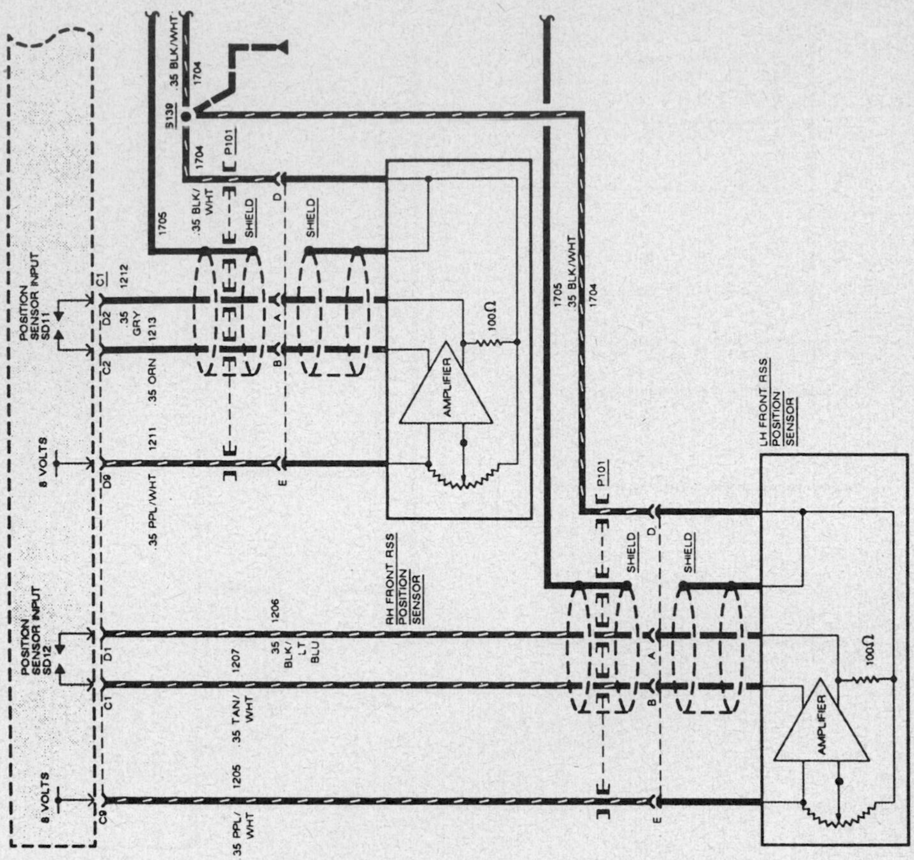

GC2019100118050X
POSITION SENSOR INPUT SD11
POSITION SENSOR INPUT SD12
8 VOLTS
RH FRONT RSS POSITION SENSOR
LH FRONT RSS POSITION SENSOR
AMPLIFIER
100Ω
SHIELD
S130
P101
.35 BLK/WHT
.35 PPL/WHT
.35 ORN
.35 GRY
.35 TAN/WHT
.35 BLK/LT BLU
1704
1705
1205
1206
1207
1211
1212
1213

Fig. 4 RSS system wiring diagram (Part 5 of 6)

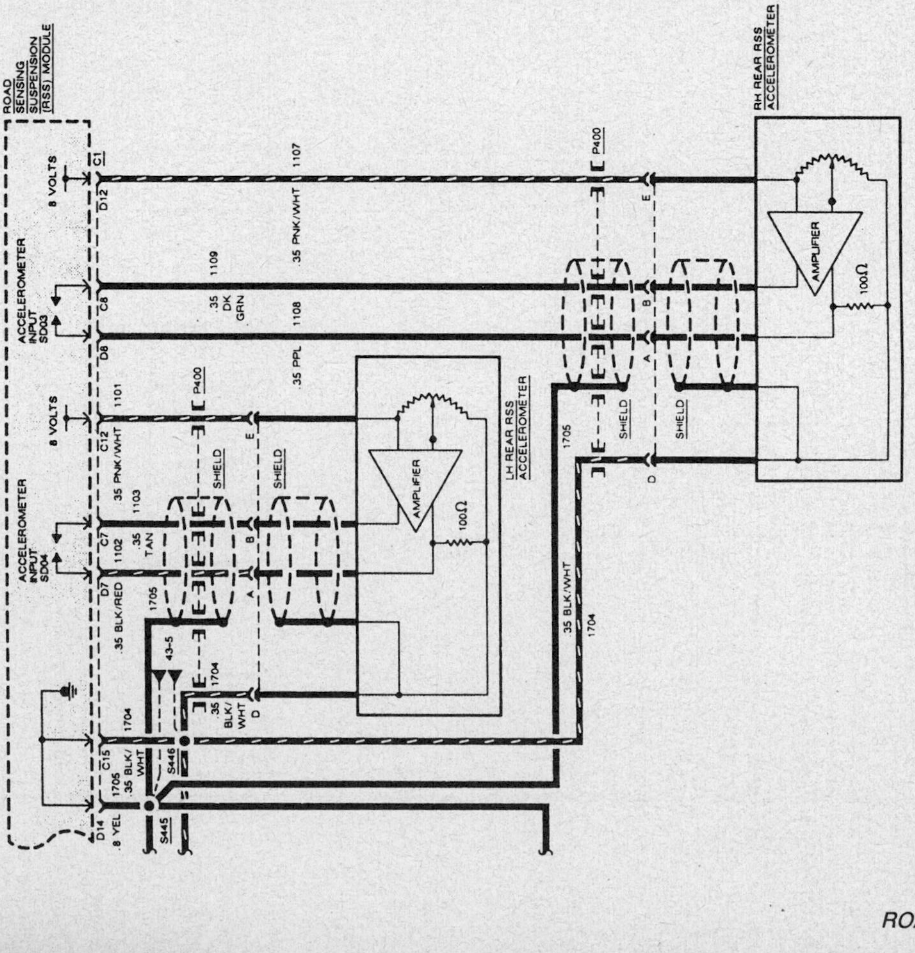

GC2019100118040X
ROAD SENSING SUSPENSION (RSS) MODULE
ACCELEROMETER INPUT SD04
ACCELEROMETER INPUT SD03
8 VOLTS
LH REAR RSS ACCELEROMETER
RH REAR RSS ACCELEROMETER
AMPLIFIER
100Ω
SHIELD
S445
S446
P400
43-5
.8 YEL
.35 BLK/WHT
.35 BLK/RED
.35 TAN
.35 PNK/WHT
.35 PPL
.35 DK GRN
1101
1102
1103
1107
1108
1109
1704
1705

Fig. 4 RSS system wiring diagram (Part 4 of 6)

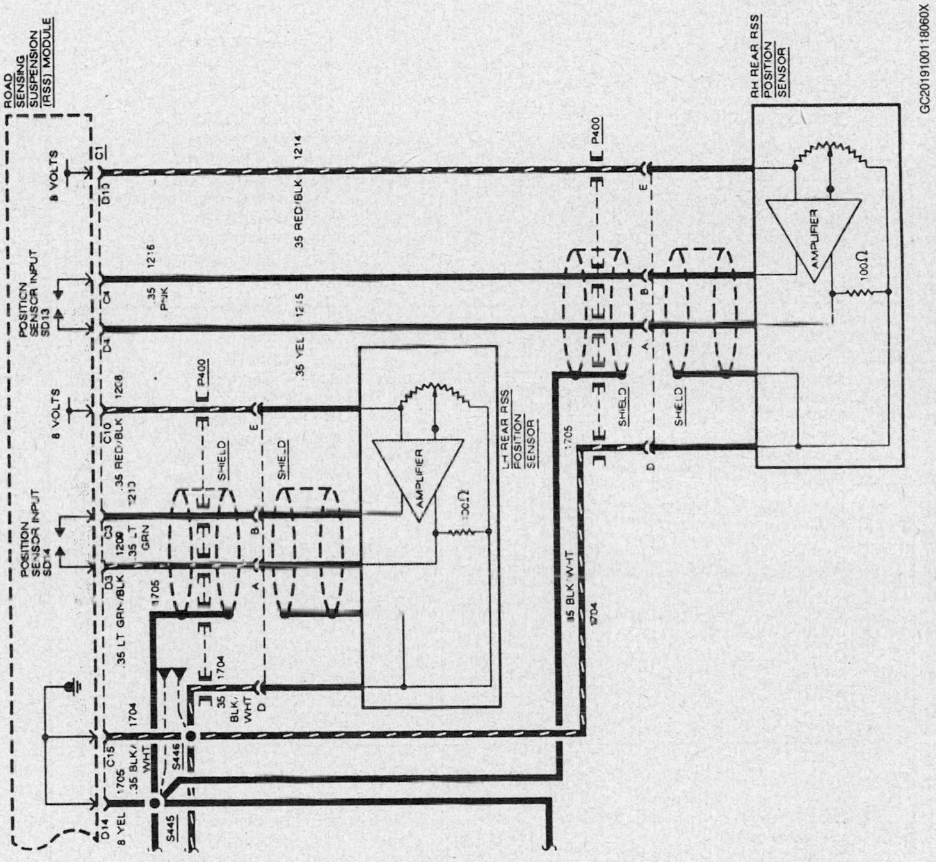
ROAD SENSING SUSPENSION (RSS) MODULE
POSITION SENSOR INPUT SD13
POSITION SENSOR INPUT SD14
8 VOLTS
LH REAR RSS POSITION SENSOR
RH REAR RSS POSITION SENSOR
AMPLIFIER
SHIELD
P400
S445
S446
GC2019100118060X

Fig. 4 RSS system wiring diagram (Part 6 of 6)

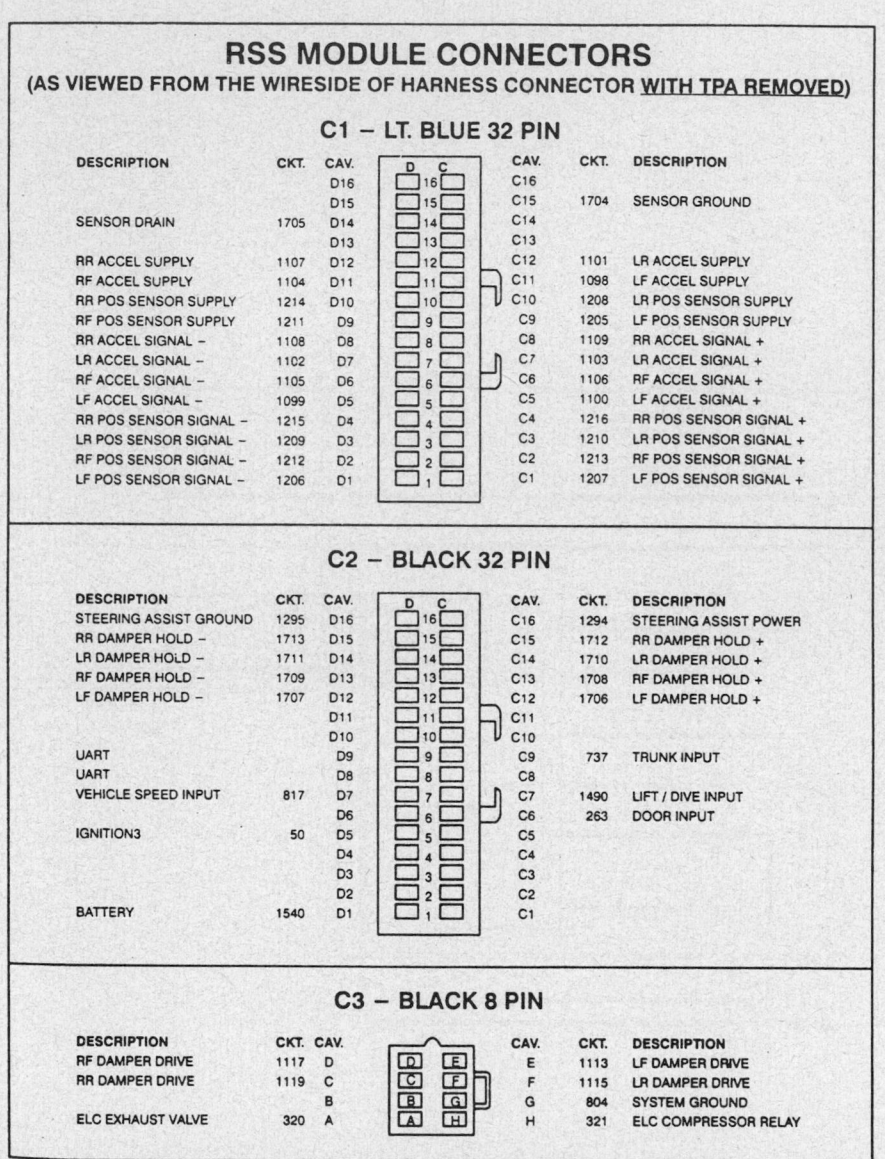

RSS MODULE CONNECTORS

(AS VIEWED FROM THE WIRESIDE OF HARNESS CONNECTOR WITH TPA REMOVED)

C1 – LT. BLUE 32 PIN

DESCRIPTION	CKT.	CAV.	CAV.	CKT.	DESCRIPTION
		D16	C16		
		D15	C15	1704	SENSOR GROUND
SENSOR DRAIN	1705	D14	C14		
		D13	C13		
RR ACCEL SUPPLY	1107	D12	C12	1101	LR ACCEL SUPPLY
RF ACCEL SUPPLY	1104	D11	C11	1098	LF ACCEL SUPPLY
RR POS SENSOR SUPPLY	1214	D10	C10	1208	LR POS SENSOR SUPPLY
RF POS SENSOR SUPPLY	1211	D9	C9	1205	LF POS SENSOR SUPPLY
RR ACCEL SIGNAL –	1108	D8	C8	1109	RR ACCEL SIGNAL +
LR ACCEL SIGNAL –	1102	D7	C7	1103	LR ACCEL SIGNAL +
RF ACCEL SIGNAL –	1105	D6	C6	1106	RF ACCEL SIGNAL +
LF ACCEL SIGNAL –	1099	D5	C5	1100	LF ACCEL SIGNAL +
RR POS SENSOR SIGNAL –	1215	D4	C4	1216	RR POS SENSOR SIGNAL +
LR POS SENSOR SIGNAL –	1209	D3	C3	1210	LR POS SENSOR SIGNAL +
RF POS SENSOR SIGNAL –	1212	D2	C2	1213	RF POS SENSOR SIGNAL +
LF POS SENSOR SIGNAL –	1206	D1	C1	1207	LF POS SENSOR SIGNAL +

C2 – BLACK 32 PIN

DESCRIPTION	CKT.	CAV.	CAV.	CKT.	DESCRIPTION
STEERING ASSIST GROUND	1295	D16	C16	1294	STEERING ASSIST POWER
RR DAMPER HOLD –	1713	D15	C15	1712	RR DAMPER HOLD +
LR DAMPER HOLD –	1711	D14	C14	1710	LR DAMPER HOLD +
RF DAMPER HOLD –	1709	D13	C13	1708	RF DAMPER HOLD +
LF DAMPER HOLD –	1707	D12	C12	1706	LF DAMPER HOLD +
		D11	C11		
		D10	C10		
UART		D9	C9	737	TRUNK INPUT
UART		D8	C8		
VEHICLE SPEED INPUT	817	D7	C7	1490	LIFT / DIVE INPUT
		D6	C6	263	DOOR INPUT
IGNITION3	50	D5	C5		
		D4	C4		
		D3	C3		
		D2	C2		
BATTERY	1540	D1	C1		

C3 – BLACK 8 PIN

DESCRIPTION	CKT.	CAV.	CAV.	CKT.	DESCRIPTION
RF DAMPER DRIVE	1117	D	E	1113	LF DAMPER DRIVE
RR DAMPER DRIVE	1119	C	F	1115	LR DAMPER DRIVE
		B	G	804	SYSTEM GROUND
ELC EXHAUST VALVE	320	A	H	321	ELC COMPRESSOR RELAY

GC2019100119000X

Fig. 5 RSS system connectors

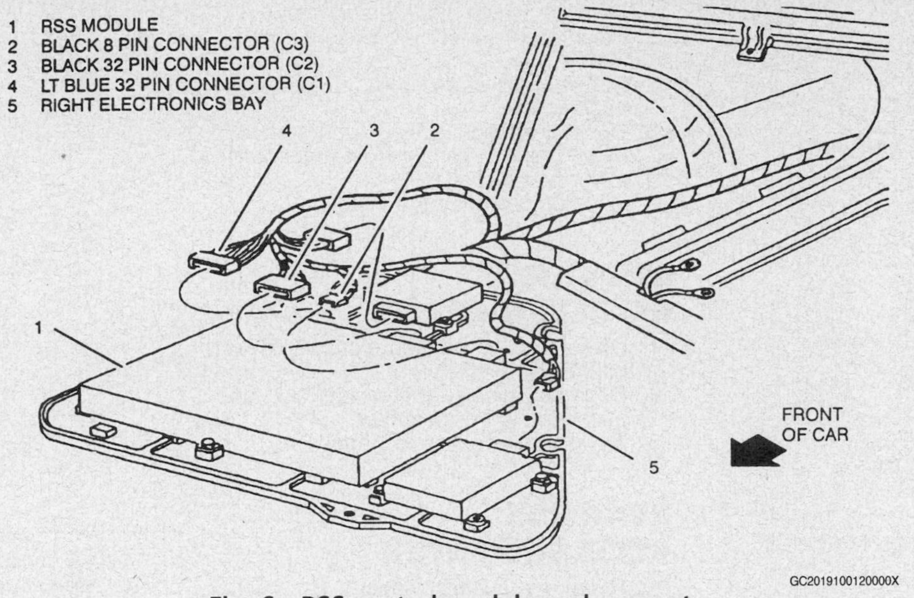
1 RSS MODULE
2 BLACK 8 PIN CONNECTOR (C3)
3 BLACK 32 PIN CONNECTOR (C2)
4 LT BLUE 32 PIN CONNECTOR (C1)
5 RIGHT ELECTRONICS BAY
FRONT OF CAR
GC2019100120000X

Fig. 6 RSS control module replacement

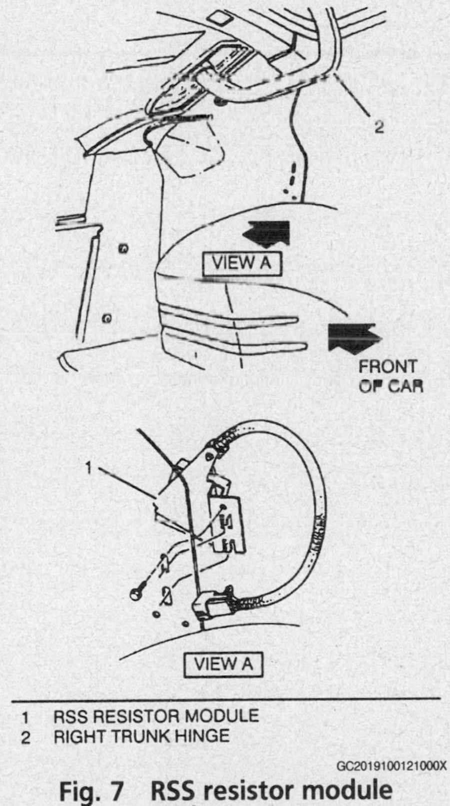
VIEW A
FRONT OF CAR
VIEW A
1 RSS RESISTOR MODULE
2 RIGHT TRUNK HINGE
GC2019100121000X

Fig. 7 RSS resistor module replacement

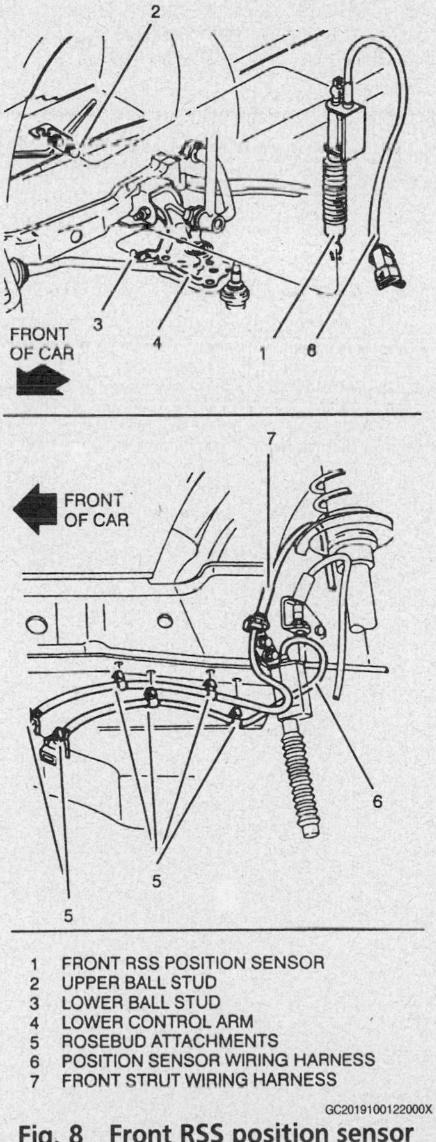
FRONT OF CAR
FRONT OF CAR
1 FRONT RSS POSITION SENSOR
2 UPPER BALL STUD
3 LOWER BALL STUD
4 LOWER CONTROL ARM
5 ROSEBUD ATTACHMENTS
6 POSITION SENSOR WIRING HARNESS
7 FRONT STRUT WIRING HARNESS
GC2019100122000X

Fig. 8 Front RSS position sensor replacement

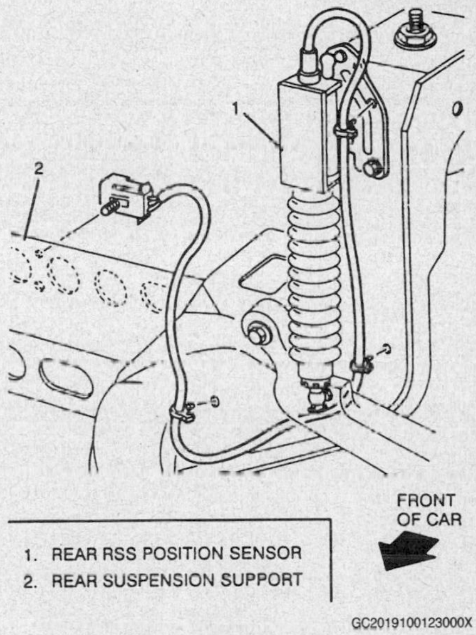
FRONT OF CAR
1. REAR RSS POSITION SENSOR
2. REAR SUSPENSION SUPPORT
GC2019100123000X

Fig. 9 Rear RSS position sensor replacement

RSS RESISTOR MODULE

The resistor module is receiving a high amount of current and can get very hot 480°F (250°C). Extreme care should be taken when replacing or working around the resistor module.

1. Remove luggage compartment trim panel.
2. Disconnect resistor module electrical connector, **Fig. 7.**
3. Remove resistor module from vehicle.
4. Reverse procedure to install.

FRONT RSS POSITION SENSOR

1. Raise and support vehicle.
2. Remove wheel and tire assembly.
3. Disconnect position sensor electrical connector, **Fig. 8.**
4. Disconnect wires from frame rail.
5. Unlatch sensor locking tabs and remove position sensor from upper and lower ball studs.
6. Reverse procedure to install.

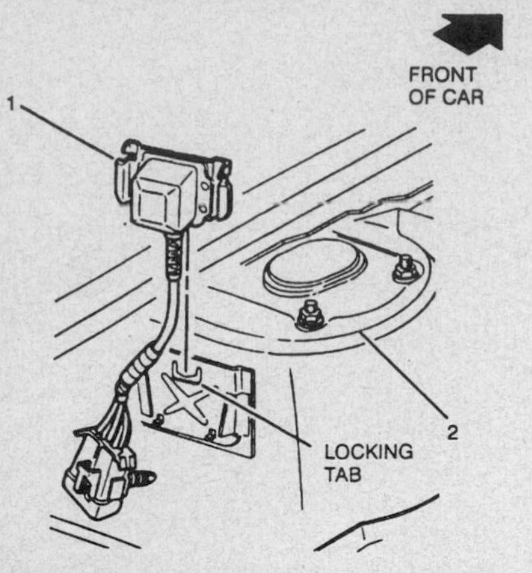

FRONT OF CAR
1
2
LOCKING TAB

1. FRONT RSS ACCELEROMETER
2. FRONT STRUT TOWER

GC2019100124000X

Fig. 10 Front accelerometer replacement

REAR RSS POSITION SENSOR

1. Raise and support vehicle.
2. Remove wheel and tire assembly.
3. Disconnect sensor electrical connector, **Fig. 9.**
4. Disconnect wires from suspension support.
5. Unlatch sensor locking tabs and remove position sensor from upper and lower ball studs.
6. Reverse procedure to install.

FRONT RSS ACCELEROMETER

1. Disconnect accelerometer electrical connector, **Fig. 10.**
2. Depress accelerometer locking tab and remove from bracket.
3. Reverse procedure to install.

REAR RSS ACCELEROMETER

1. Raise and support vehicle.
2. Disconnect accelerometer electrical connector, **Fig. 11.**
3. Depress accelerometer locking tab and remove from bracket.
4. Reverse procedure to install.

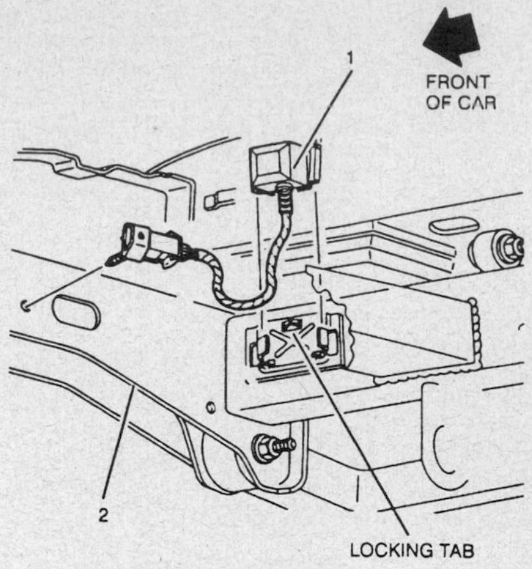

FRONT OF CAR
1
2
LOCKING TAB

1. REAR RSS ACCELEROMETER
2. REAR SUSPENSION SUPPORT

GC2019100125000X

Fig. 11 Rear accelerometer replacement

TROUBLESHOOTING

INDEX

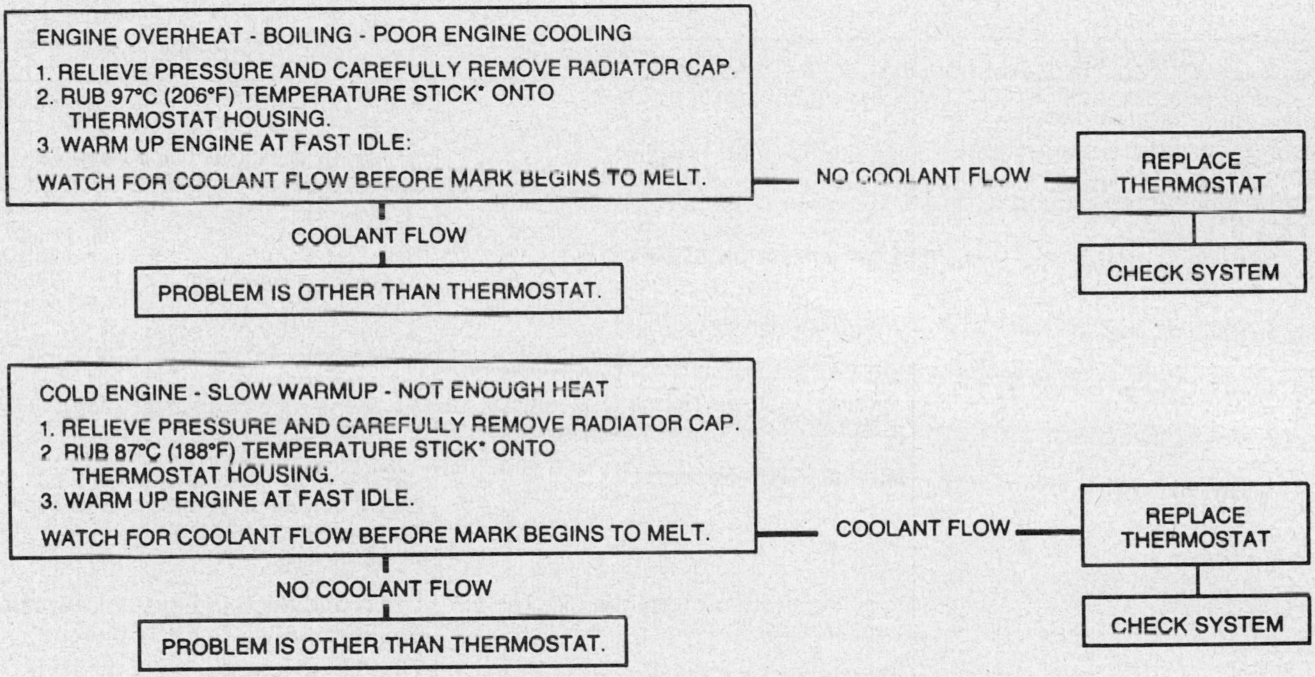

ENGINE OVERHEAT - BOILING - POOR ENGINE COOLING
1. RELIEVE PRESSURE AND CAREFULLY REMOVE RADIATOR CAP.
2. RUB 97°C (206°F) TEMPERATURE STICK* ONTO THERMOSTAT HOUSING.
3. WARM UP ENGINE AT FAST IDLE:
WATCH FOR COOLANT FLOW BEFORE MARK BEGINS TO MELT.
NO COOLANT FLOW
REPLACE THERMOSTAT
CHECK SYSTEM
COOLANT FLOW
PROBLEM IS OTHER THAN THERMOSTAT.
COLD ENGINE - SLOW WARMUP - NOT ENOUGH HEAT
1. RELIEVE PRESSURE AND CAREFULLY REMOVE RADIATOR CAP.
2. RUB 87°C (188°F) TEMPERATURE STICK* ONTO THERMOSTAT HOUSING.
3. WARM UP ENGINE AT FAST IDLE.
WATCH FOR COOLANT FLOW BEFORE MARK BEGINS TO MELT.
COOLANT FLOW
REPLACE THERMOSTAT
CHECK SYSTEM
NO COOLANT FLOW
PROBLEM IS OTHER THAN THERMOSTAT.

* NOTE: THE TEMPERATURE STICK IS A PENCIL LIKE DEVICE WHICH HAS A WAX MATERIAL CONTAINING CERTAIN CHEMICALS WHICH MELT AT A GIVEN TEMPERATURE. TEMPERATURE STICKS CAN BE USED TO DETERMINE A THERMOSTAT'S OPERATING TEMPERATURE BY RUBBING 87°C (188°F) AND 97°C (206°F) STICKS ON THE THERMOSTAT HOUSING. THE MARKS MADE BY THE STICKS SHOULD MELT WHEN COOLANT TEMPERATURES OF 87°C (188°F) AND 97°C (206°F) ARE REACHED, RESPECTIVELY. THESE TEMPERATURES ARE THE NORMAL OPERATING RANGE OF THE THERMOSTAT.

GC1139100104000X

Fig. 1 Thermostat

COOLING SYSTEM DIAGNOSIS

1. Does overheating occur while pulling a trailer?

   Yes — how heavy trailer? If trailer weight is greater than 454 kg (1,000 lbs.) and vehicle is equipped with normal duty cooling system, a heavy duty cooling package is required (per trailer hauling specs.). Further diagnostic checks should not be required.

2. Is vehicle equipped with add-on or after market air conditioning system?

   Yes — was heavy duty radiator installed with the system? If not, install heavy duty radiator for the vehicle model involved. Further diagnostic checks should not be required.

3. Is overheating occurring after prolonged idle in gear, A/C system operating?

   Yes — instruct owner on driving techniques that would avoid overheating, such as:
   a. Idle in Neutral as much as possible — increase engine RPM to get coolant flow through radiator.
   b. Turn A/C system off during extended idles if overheating is indicated by hot lamp or temperature gage. Further diagnostic checks should not be required.

4. Is overheating occurring after prolonged driving in slow city traffic, traffic jams, etc?

   Yes — instruct owner on driving techniques that would avoid overheating — same as for prolonged idles. Further diagnostic checks should not be required.

CONDITION	POSSIBLE CAUSE	CORRECTION
Engine overheats (engine temperature lamp comes on and stays on, or temperature gauge shows hot, or coolant overflows from reservoir onto ground while engine is running.	Loss of coolant.	Refer to "Loss of Coolant" condition.
	Loss of system pressure.	Pressure check with BT-7518 or J-24460-01 with J-23699. Correct as necessary.
	Low coolant protection.	Solution should be −37°C (−34°F). Correct as necessary.
	Incorrect belt tension.	Check tensioner, replace if necessary.
	Timing retarded by malfunctioning Electronic Control Module (ECM).	
	Radiator fins obstructed.	Remove or relocate add-on parts that block air to radiator. Remove bugs, leaves, debris, etc. from radiator fins.
	Cooling system passages blocked by rust or scale.	Drain and flush the system. Repair as necessary.
	Reservoir hose pinched or kinked.	Reroute or replace hose as necessary.
	Cooling fan inoperative.	

GC1139100105010X

Fig. 2 Cooling system (Part 1 of 3)

COOLING SYSTEM DIAGNOSIS (CONTINUED)		
CONDITION	**POSSIBLE CAUSE**	**CORRECTION**
Engine overheats (engine temperature lamp comes on and stays on, or temperature gauge shows hot, or coolant overflows from reservoir onto ground while engine is running. (cont'd.)	Loose, damaged and/or missing deflector.	Repair or replace as necessary.
	Thermostat stuck in closed position.	Replace thermostat.
	Faulty coolant pump.	Replace coolant pump.
	Incorrect radiator.	Install correct radiator.
Loss of coolant.	Leaking radiator.	Repair or replace as necessary.
	Faulty cooling system pressure cap.	Replace cap.
	Leaking coolant reservoir or hose.	Replace reservoir or hose as necessary.
	Loose or damaged hoses or connections.	Repair or replace hoses or clamps as necessary.
	Coolant pump seal leaking.	Replace coolant pump.
	Coolant pump gasket leaking.	Replace gasket.
	Improper cylinder head bolt torque.	Tighten bolts to specifications, replace cylinder head gasket(s) if required.
	Leaking intake manifold or cylinder head or gaskets, cylinder head or block core plug, heater core.	Repair or replace as necessary.
Engine fails to reach normal operating temperature. (Cool air from heater.)	Thermostat stuck open. Incorrect thermostat.	Replace thermostat. Install correct thermostat.
	Coolant below add mark.	Add coolant as necessary. Use correct solution.
Hot lamp on or high temperature gage reading, no loss of coolant.	Faulty engine temperature switch or circuit.	

GC1139100105020X

Fig. 2 Cooling system (Part 2 of 3)

A. Problems not requiring disassembly of cooling system —
   1. Large obstructions blocking radiator or condenser
      a. Auxiliary oil coolers — relocate
      b. Ice, mud or snow — remove
   2. Engine oil overfill — check engine oil dipstick
   3. Incorrect radiator for application — install correct radiator
   4. Missing or damaged lower air baffle — repair or replace as necessary

B. Problems requiring disassembly of cooling system —
   1. Incorrect or damaged fan — repair or replace as necessary
   2. Faulty emission system components (could cause overheating at idle) — replace faulty component
      a. PCV valve
      b. TVS or TCS
   3. Pressure check cooling system with pressure cap installed
   4. Faulty coolant pump — replace coolant pump
   5. Plugged radiator tubes
   6. Internal system leaks
      a. Head gasket
      b. Cracked block
      c. Timing chain/belt cover
      d. Intake manifold gasket
   7. Plugged coolant passages in cylinder head(s) — remove head(s) and check visually

GC1139100105030X

Fig. 2 Cooling system (Part 3 of 3)

SYMPTOM	POSSIBLE CAUSES/CORRECTIONS
BODY/CHASSIS — GENERAL	
Abnormal noise	• Control arm bushings or tie rod ends worn: Inspect and replace as needed. • Spring improperly positioned: Reposition spring. • Stabilizer shaft loose: Inspect mounting bolts and links; torque to specifications. • Strut or strut mounting worn: Inspect and service as needed. • Suspension bolts loose: Torque to specifications. • Suspension components damaged: Inspect and repair/replace components as needed. • Wheel nuts loose: Inspect wheel for out of round lug holes; torque nuts to specifications. • Wheel covers: Repair/replace. • Steering gear loose. Torque mounting bolts to specifications.
Body leans or sways in corners	• Springs broken or sagging: Inspect and service as needed. • Stabilizer shaft loose: Inspect mounting bolts and links: torque to specifications. • Strut worn: Inspect and service as needed. • Vehicle overloaded: Reduce load. • Tire pressure(s) incorrect: Inflate to specifications.
"Dog" tracking	• Frame to underbody alignment incorrect: Inspect and service as needed. • Rear control arm damaged or bushings worn: Repair/replace components, as needed. • Rear toe incorrect: Check and perform alignment. • Faulty or bent rear suspension component: Repair/replace components as needed.
Low or uneven trim height	• Springs incorrect, broken, sagging or weak: Inspect and service as needed. • Vehicle overloaded: Reduce load. • Tire pressure(s) incorrect: Inflate to specifications.
Suspension bottoms	• Springs incorrect, broken, sagging or weak: Inspect and service as needed. • Strut worn: Inspect and service as needed. • Vehicle overloaded: Reduce load.

GC1139100106010X

Fig. 3 Front suspension, steering & wheel alignment (Part 1 of 5)

SYMPTOM	POSSIBLE CAUSES/CORRECTIONS
RIDE	
Too harsh	• Incorrect springs: Determine correct component(s) and install. • Incorrect strut: Determine correct component(s) and install. • Tire pressure(s) incorrect: Inflate to specifications.
Too soft	• Springs sagging or incorrect: Inspect and service as needed. • Strut worn: Inspect and service as needed. • Tire pressure(s) incorrect: Inflate to specifications.
SHIMMY, SHAKE OR VIBRATION	• Brake rotor imbalance: Refinish and/or replace as needed. • Brake rotor(s) warped (vibration occurs during braking): Refinish and/or replace as needed. • Ball joints worn: Inspect and replace as needed. • Excessive loaded radial runout of tire and wheel: Balance wheel/tire, correct tire non-uniformity, and recheck for vibration. If still present and runout exceeds specifications, replace wheel. • Tie rod ends worn: Replace as needed. • Tire pressure(s) incorrect: Inflate to specifications. • Tire(s)/wheel(s) out of balance: Balance as needed. • Tire(s)/wheel(s) out of round: Service and/or replace as needed. • Excessive wheel or wheel stud runout: Service and/or replace as needed. • Wheel trim imbalance: Adjust trim and balance as needed. • Wheel bearings worn: Replace hub and bearing.
STEERING	
Erratic when braking	• Caster uneven or incorrect: Inspect components for wear and perform alignment. • Control arm loose: Inspect control arm, bushings, ball joint and mounting hardware; replace and/or torque to specifications. • Rotors warped: Refinish and/or replace as needed. • Springs broken or sagging: Inspect and service as needed. • Wheel bearings worn: Replace hub and bearing.

GC1139100106020X

Fig. 3 Front suspension, steering & wheel alignment (Part 2 of 5)

SYMPTOM	POSSIBLE CAUSES/CORRECTIONS
STEERING (Continued)	
Erratic when braking (Continued)	• Wheel caliper leaking: Inspect and service as needed.
Hard steering	• Bind or catch in steering gear: Check for correct rack bearing preload and for steering gear damage; adjust and/or replace, as needed. • Low fluid; excessive internal leakage of steering components: Add fluid, as needed. • Steering gear loose: Torque mounting bolts to specifications. • Intermediate shaft bolt torque too high: Torque to specifications.
Poor returnability	• Ball joints binding: Inspect and replace as needed. • Front wheel alignment: Check and perform alignment. • Steering gear valve sticking: Flush and bleed system; if symptom persists, service partial steering gear. • Steering gear loose: Torque mounting bolts to specifications. • Intermediate shaft bolt torque too high: Torque to specifications. • Lower coupling binding on steering gear: Inspect and repair/replace components as needed. • Rack preload misadjusted (too tight): Torque to specifications. • Steering column binding: Check column alignment, mounting, and bearings; adjust, repair and/or replace, as needed. • Tire pressures incorrect: Inflate to specifications.
Steering wheel kick-back	• Air in power steering system: Inspect and bleed system. • Joints from column to steering gear loose or worn: Check for correct torque; replace components as needed. • Steering gear loose: Torque mounting bolts to specifications. • Tie rod ends loose: Inspect and replace as needed.

GC1139100106030X

Fig. 3 Front suspension, steering & wheel alignment (Part 3 of 5)

SYMPTOM	POSSIBLE CAUSES/CORRECTIONS
STEERING (Continued)	
Steering wheel kick-back (Continued)	• Wheel bearings worn: Replace hub and bearings. • See "Too Much Play In Steering."
Steering wheel surges or jerks	• Hydraulic system: Diagnose and service as needed. • Low fluid level: Add fluid, as needed. • Pump drive belt loose: Adjust or replace as needed. See specific engine section. • Steering gear valve sluggish: Flush and bleed system; if symptom persists, service partial steering gear.
Too much play in steering	• Joints from column to steering gear loose or worn: Check for correct torque; replace components as needed. • Steering gear loose: Torque mounting bolts to specifications. • Wheel bearings worn: Replace hub and bearing.
Wander or poor steering stability	• Front or rear wheel alignment: Check and perform alignment. • Rack preload misadjusted (too loose): Torque to specifications. • Springs broken or sagging: Inspect and service as needed. • Stabilizer shaft loose: Inspect mounting bolts and links; torque to specifications. • Strut worn: Inspect and service as needed. • Tires uneven/misaligned: Service and/or replace as needed. Check and perform alignment.
TIRES/WHEELS	
Abnormal/excessive wear	• Front or rear wheel alignment; excessive toe: Inspect components for wear and perform alignment. • Hard driving. • Tire pressure low: Inflate to specifications. • Springs broken or sagging: Inspect and service as needed.

GC1139100106040X

Fig. 3 Front suspension, steering & wheel alignment (Part 4 of 5)

SYMPTOM	POSSIBLE CAUSES/CORRECTIONS
TIRES/WHEELS (Continued)	
Abnormal/excessive wear (Continued)	• Strut(s) worn: Inspect and service as needed. • Tires not rotated properly: Inspect tire(s); service and/or replace as needed. • Tire(s) out of balance: Balance as needed. • Vehicle overloaded: Reduce load.
Scuffed	• Excessive speed on turns. • Control arm bent or twisted: Inspect and replace as needed. • Toe incorrect: Check and perform alignment.
Cupped	• Ball joint worn: Replace ball joint. • Front or rear wheel alignment: Check and perform alignment. • Strut worn: Inspect and service as needed. • Tire/wheel runout excessive: Service and/or replace as needed. • Wheel bearing worn: Replace hub and bearing. • Steering gear loose: Torque mounting bolts to specifications.
Wheel tramp	• Improper strut action: Service and/or replace as needed. • Tire/wheel out of balance: Balance as needed. • Blister or bump on tire.
VEHICLE LEADS/PULLS	• Front brakes dragging: • Front wheel alignment: Check and perform alignment. • Radial tire lateral force: Inspect tire(s); service and/or replace as needed. • Steering gear valve off center (unbalanced). Inspect and adjust. • Springs broken or sagging: Inspect and service as needed. • Tire pressure incorrect: Inflate to specifications. • Tires mismatched/uneven: Service and/or replace as needed.

GC 1391001060 50X

Fig. 3 Front suspension, steering & wheel alignment (Part 5 of 5)

ENGINE REBUILDING SPECIFICATIONS

NOTE: For Engine Tightening Specifications, Refer To The Engine Section In The Appropriate Chassis Chapter Of This Manual.

INDEX

CYLINDER HEAD, VALVE GUIDE & VALVE SEATS

All Measurements Given In Inches, Unless Otherwise Specified.

Engine Liter/ CID/VIN	Year	Cylinder Head Warpage Limit	Cylinder Head Overall Thickness	Valve Guides			Valve Seats			
				Standard Inside Diameter	Stem To Guide Clearance		Seat Angle	Seat Width		Runout
					Intake	Exhaust		Intake	Exhaust	
1.0L/3-61/6	1992-94	.002	—	.2165-.2170	.0008-.0027	.0018-.0035	45°	.0512-.0590	.0512-.0590	—
1.6L/4-97/5③	1992	.002	—	.2366-.2374	.0010-.0024	.0012-.0026	45°	.0390-.0551	.0390-.0551	—
1.6L/4-97/6①	1992-93	—	3.77	.2780⑦	.0008-.0020	.0016-.0028	46°	.0500-.0701	.0500-.0701	.002
1.6L/4-97/6②	1992-93	.002	—	.2366-.2374	.0010-.0031	.0012-.0039	45°	.0390-.0551	.0390-.0551	—
1.6L/4-97/6④	1992-93	.0158	—	—	.0009	.0012	—	.0870	.0790	—
1.6L/4-97/6⑩	1994	.002	—	.2366-.2374	.0010-.0031	.0012-.0039	45°	.0470-.0630	.0470-.0630	—
1.8L/4-110/8⑤	1992-93	.008	—	—	.0009	.0012	—	.0870	.0790	—
1.8L/4-108/8⑧	1993-94	.002	—	.2366-.2374	.0010-.0031	.0012-.0039	45°	.0470-.0630	.0470-.0630	—
2.0L/4-121/H	1992-94	⑥	—	.2766-.2772	.0006-.0017	.0012-.0024	45°	.0500-.0701	.0500-.0701	.002
2.2L/4-133/4	1992-94	⑥	—	—	.0010-.0027	.0014-.0031	46°	.0490-.0590	.0630-.0750	.002
2.3L/4-138/A,D,3	1992-94	.008	—	.2762-.2772	.0010-.0027	.0010-.0027	45°	.0370-.0748	.0370-.0748	.0015
2.5L/4-151/R	1992	.007	—	—	.0011-.0027	.0013-.0040	46°	.0350-.0750	.0580-.1050	.002
3.1L/V6-192/T,V	1992-94	⑥	—	—	.0008-.0021	.0014-.0030	46°	.0610-.0730	.0670-.0790	.001
3.1L/V6-192/M	1994	⑥	—	—	.0010-.0027	.001-.0027	45°	.0610-.0730	.0670-.0790	.001
3.3L/V6-204/N	1992-93	.002	—	—	.0015-.0035	.0015-.0035	45°	.0600-.0800	.0900-.1100	.002
3.4L/V6-204/X	1992-94	⑥	—	—	.0011-.0026	.0018-.0033	46°	.0492-.0591	.0630-.0748	.003
3.4L/V6-204/S	1993-94	⑥	—	—	.0014-.0027	.0015-.0029	46°	.061-.073	.067-.079	.001
3.8L/V6-231/L,1	1992-94	⑥	—	—	.0015-.0035	.0015-.0032	45°	.060-.080	.090-.110	.002
4.3L/V6-262/Z	1992-93	—	—	—	.0011-.0027	.0011-.0027	46°	.0350-.0600	.0620-.0930	.002
4.3L/V8-265/W	1994	⑥	—	—	.0009-.0037	.0009-.0047	46°	.045-.070	.065-.098	.002
4.6L/V8-279/Y,9	1993-94	.002	—	.235	.0010-.0030	.0020-.0040	46°	.003	.0035	.002
4.9L/V8-300/B	1992-94	—	—	.343	.0010-.0030	.0020-.0040	45°	.0620	.0930	.004
5.0L/V8-305/E,F	1992-93	—	—	—	.0011-.0027	.0011-.0027	46°	.0350-.0600	.0600-.0940	.002
5.7L/V8-350/7,8	1992-93	—	—	—	.0011-.0027	.0011-.0027	46°	.0350-.0600	.0600-.0940	.002
5.7L/V8-350/P	1992-94	—	—	—	.0009-.0037	.0009-.0047	46°	.030-.065	.060-.098	.002
5.7L/V8-350/J	1992-94	—	—	—	.0012-.0394	.0014-.0030	44°	.0569-.0734	.0569-.0734	.004

①—LeMans.
②—Prizm w/4A-FE 16 valve engine.
③—Prizm w/GSI 4A-GE 16 valve engine.
④—Storm w/12 valve engine.
⑤—Storm w/16 valve engine.
⑥—Maximum surface refinish, .010 inch.
⑦—Intake, 45°; exhaust, 31°.
⑧—Intake, .002 inch; exhaust, .004 inch.
⑨—Minimum.
⑩—Prizm w/16-valve engine.

VALVE SPRINGS

All Measurements Given In Inches, Unless Otherwise Specified.

Engine Liter/CID/ VIN	Year	Free Length	Installed Height	Seated Pressure Pounds @ Inches	Comp. Pressure Pounds @ Inches	Out Of Square Limit
1.0L/3-61/6	1992-93	1.6035	1.28	41-47.2 @ 1.28	—	.079
1.0L/3-61/6	1994	1.6142-1.6649	1.28	46.1-51.8 @ 1.28	—	.079
1.6L/4-97/6 ①	1992-93	—	1.24	62 @ 1.24	140 @ .85	—
1.6L/4-97/5 ②	1992	1.6177	—	—	—	.098
1.6L/4-97/6 ③	1992-93	1.724	—	—	—	.098
1.6L/4-97/6 ③	1994	1.5185	1.248	37.3 @ 1.248	—	.079
1.6L/4-97/6 ④	1992-93	⑤	—	—	—	—
1.8L/4-110 ⑥	1992-93	—	—	—	—	—
1.8L/4-108 ⑦	1993-94	1.5185	1.248	37.3 @ 1.248	—	.079
2.0L/4-121/H	1992-94	—	1.476	⑧	165-179 @ 1.043	.062
2.2L/4-133/4	1992-94	1.95	1.71	75-81 @ 1.71	220-236 @ 1.278	—
2.3L/4-138/A,D,3	1992-94	—	1.437	71-79 @ 1.437	193-207 @ 1.0433	—
2.5L/4-151/R	1992	2.01	1.68	75 @ 1.68	173 @ 1.24	—
3.1L/V6-192/T	1992-94	1.91	1.693	90 @ 1.701	215 @ 1.291	—
3.1L/V6-192/M	1994	1.89	1.71	80 @ 1.71	250 @ 1.239	—
3.3L/V6-204/N	1992-93	1.981	1.69-1.75	76-84 @ 1.75	200-220 @ 1.315	—
3.4L/V6-204/X	1992-93	1.66	1.40	75 @ 1.40	180 @ 1.03	—
3.4L/V6-204/S	1993-94	1.91	1.61	80 @ 1.61	190 @ 1.20	—
3.8L/V6-231/L,1	1992-94	1.981	1.69-1.75	76-84 @ 1.75	200-220 @ 1.315	—
4.3L/V6-262/Z	1992-93	2.03	1.69-.171	76-84 @ 1.70	194-206 @ 1.25	—
4.3L/V8-265/W	1994	2.02	1.70	76-84 @ 1.70	187-203 @ 1.27	—
4.6L/V8-279/Y,9	1993-94	1.575	1.19	53 @ 1.19	109 @ .823	—
4.9L/V8-300/B	1992-94	1.95	1.73	68-76 @ 1.73	214-232 @ 1.35	—
5.0L/V8-305/E,F	1992-93	2.03 ⑨	1.7	76-84 @ 1.7	194-206 @ 1.25	—
5.7L/V8-350/7,8	1992-93	2.03 ⑨	1.7	76-84 @ 1.7	194-206 @ 1.25	—
5.7L/V8-350/P	1992-93	2.01	1.78	81-89 @ 1.78	252-272 @ 1.31	—
5.7L/V8-350/P	1994	2.02	1.70	76-84 @ 1.70	187-203 @ 1.27	—
5.7L/V8-350/J	1992-94	⑩	⑪	⑫	⑬	—

① —LeMans.
② —Prizm w/GSI 4A-GE 16 valve engine.
③ —Prizm w/4A-FE 16 valve engine.
④ —Storm w/12 valve engine.
⑤ —Intake, 1.73 inch; exhaust, 1.67 inch.
⑥ —Storm w/16 valve engine.
⑦ —Prizm w/16 valve engine.
⑧ —VIN H & K, 63-71 lbs. @ 1.476 inch; VIN M, 74-82 lbs. @ 1.476 inch.
⑨ —Damper spring, 1.86 inch.
⑩ —Inner spring, 1.54 inch; outer spring, 1.71 inch.
⑪ —Inner spring, 1.18 inch; outer spring, 1.34 inch.
⑫ —Inner spring, 34.2-37.8 lbs. @ 1.18 inch; outer spring, 64.1-76.4 lbs. @ 1.34 inch.
⑬ —Inner spring, 75.5-81.8 lbs. @ .79 inch; outer spring, 146.8-166.4 lbs. @ .95 inch.

VALVES

All Measurements Given In Inches, Unless Otherwise Specified.

Engine Liter/CID/ VIN	Year	Stem Diameter		Clearance		Face Angle	Margin ①
		Intake	Exhaust	Intake	Exhaust		
1.0L/3-61/6	1992-94	.2148-.2157	.2142-.2148	.0008-.0027	.0018-.0035	45°	②
1.6L/4-97/5 ⑥	1992	.2350-.2356	.2348-.2354	.006-.010 ③	.008-.012 ③	45.5°	.0315
1.6L/4-97/6 ④	1992-93	.276 ①	.275 ①	—	—	46°	—
1.6L/4-97/6 ⑦	1992-93	.2335	.2335	.006 ③	.010 ③	—	.0315
1.6L/4-97/6 ⑤	1992-94	.2350-.2356	.2348-.2354	.0010-.0031 ③	.0012-.0039 ③	45°	.020
1.8L/4-110/8 ⑧	1992-93	.232	.232	—	—	—	.0315
1.8L/4-108/8 ⑪	1993-94	.2350-.2356	.2348-.2354	.0010-.0031	.0012-.0039	45°	.020-.047
2.0L/4-121/H	1992-94	.2755-.2760	.2747-.2753	.0006.0017	.0012-.0024	46°	.031
2.2L/4-133/4	1992-94	—	—	.0010-.0027	.0014-.0031	45°	.031
2.3L/4-138/A,D,3	1992-94	.27445-.27512	.2740-.2747	.0010-.0027	.0015-.0032	⑨	.0098
2.5L/4-151/R	1992	—	—	—	—	45°	—
3.1L/V6-192/T,M	1992-94	—	—	.001-.0027	.001-.0027	45°	—
3.3L/V6-204/N	1992-93	—	—	—	—	45°	.025
3.4L/V6-204/X	1992-94	—	—	.0011-.0026	.0018-.0033	45°	.029

Continued

VALVE—Continued

Engine Liter/CID/VIN	Year	Stem Diameter		Clearance		Face Angle	Margin①
		Intake	Exhaust	Intake	Exhaust		
3.4L/V6-204/S	1993-94	—	—	.0014-.0027	.0015-.0029	45°	—
3.8L/V6-231/L,1	1992-94	—	—	—	—	45°	.025
4.3L/V6-262/Z	1992-93	—	—	—	—	45°	—
4.3L/V8-265/W	1994	—	—	.0009-.0037	.0009-.0047	45°	—
4.6L/V8-279/Y,9	1993-94	.2331-.2339	.2331-.2339	.001-.003	.001-.003	45°	—
4.9L/V8-300/B	1992-94	.3413-.3420	.3401-.3408	—	—	45°	⑩
5.0L/V8-305/E,F	1992-93	—	—	—	—	45°	.031
5.7L/V8-350/7,8	1992-93	—	—	—	—	45°	—
5.7L/V8-350/P	1992-94	—	—	.0009-.0037	.0009-.0047	45°	—
5.7L/V8-350/J	1992-94	—	—	.0012-.0026	.0014-.0030	45°	—

①—Minimum.
②—Intake, .039 inch; exhaust, .047 inch.
③—Cold.
④—LeMans.
⑤—Prizm w/4A-FE 16 valve engine.
⑥—Prizm w/GSI 4A-GE 16 valve engine.
⑦—Storm w/12 valve engine.
⑧—Storm w/16 valve engine.
⑨—Intake, 44°; exhaust, 44.5°.
⑩—Intake, .005 inch; exhaust, .030 inch.
⑪—Prizm w/16 valve engine.

CAMSHAFT

All Measurements Given In Inches Unless Otherwise Specified.

Engine Liter/CID/VIN	Year	Camshaft Journal Diameter	Maximum Journal Runout	Camshaft Bearing Clearance	Camshaft Endplay	Rocker Arm Oil Clearance	Lifter Bore Diameter	Lifter Diameter	Lifter To Bore Clearance
1.0L/3-60/5,6	1992-94	①	.0039	.0008-.0024	—	—	1.2205-1.2214	1.2188-1.2194	.0010-.0059
1.6L/4-97/5⑥	1992	1.0610-1.0616	.0016	.0014-.0028	.0031-.0075	—	—	1.1014-1.1018	.0006-.0008
1.6L/4-97/6②	1992-93	③	—	.0018-.0035	.0035-.0083	—	—	—	—
1.6L/4-97/6⑦	1992-93	1.0157	.0040	.0059	.008	.0002-.0008	—	—	—
1.6L/4-97/6④	1992-93	⑤	.0016	.0014-.0028	.0043	—	—	—	.0006-.0018
1.6L/4-97/6④	1994	.9035-.9041	.0016	.0014-.0028	.0043	—	1.2205-1.2215	1.2191-1.2195	.0009-.0028
1.8L/4-108/8⑪	1993-94	.9035-.9041	.0016	—	—	—	1.2205-1.2215	1.2191-1.2195	.0009-.0028
1.8L/4-110/8⑥	1992-93	1.0157	.0039	.0059	.008	—	—	1.219	—
2.0L/4-121/H	1992-94	⑨	—	.0011-.0035	.0016-.0063	—	—	—	—
2.2L/4-133/4	1992-94	1.867-1.869	—	.0010-.0039	—	—	—	—	—
2.3L/4-138/A,D,3	1992-94	⑩	—	.0019-.0043	.0009-.0088	—	1.3775-1.3787	1.3763-1.3770	.0006-.0024
2.5L/4-151/R	1992	1.869	—	.0007-.0027	.0015-.0050	—	.8405-.8411	.8412-.8427	.0006-.0023
3.1L/V6-192/T	1992-94	⑬	—	.001-.004	—	—	—	—	—
3.1L/V6-192/M	1994	1.868-1.869	—	—	—	—	—	—	—
3.3L/V6-204/N	1992-93	1.785-1.786	—	⑫	—	—	—	—	—
3.4L/V6-204/X	1992-94	2.1643-2.1647	—	.0019-.0040	—	—	—	—	—
3.4L/V6-204/S	1993-94	1.868-1.871	—	.001-.004	—	—	—	—	—
3.8L/V6-231/L,1	1992-94	1.785-1.786	—	.0005-.0035	—	—	—	—	—
4.3L/V6-262/Z	1992-93	1.8682-1.8692	—	—	.001-.009	—	—	—	—
4.3L/V8-265/W	1994	1.8677-1.8697	—	—	.004-.012	—	—	—	—
4.6L/V8-279/Y,9	1993-94	1.061-1.062	—	.002-.003	—	—	1.2992	1.297-1.298	.001-.003
4.9L/V8-300/B	1992-94	—	.0009	.0018-.0037	—	—	—	—	.0007-.0027
5.0L/V8-305/E,F	1992-93	1.8682-1.8692	—	—	.004-.012	—	—	—	—
5.7L/V8-350/7,8,P	1992-93	1.8682-1.8692	—	—	.004-.012	—	—	—	—
5.7L/V8-350/P	1994	1.8677-1.8697	—	—	.004-.012	—	—	—	—
5.7L/V8-350/J	1992-94	1.140-1.141	—	—	.0055-.0138	—	—	—	—

①—Journal No. 1, 1.0220-1.0228; journal No. 2 & 3, 1.1795-1.1803.
②—LeMans.
③—Journal No. 1, 1.5520-1.5530 inch; journal No. 2, 1.5624-1.5630 inch; journal No. 3, 1.5722-1.5730 inch; journal No. 4, 1.5820-1.5828 inch; journal No. 5, 1.5919-1.5927 inch.
④—Prizm w/4A-FE 16 valve engine.
⑤—Journal No. 1, .9822 inch; journal No. 2, 3, 4 & 5, .9035 inch.
⑥—Prizm w/GSI 4A-GE 16 valve engine.
⑦—Storm w/12 valve engine.
⑧—Storm w/16 valve engine.
⑨—Journal No. 1, 1.6706-1.6712; No. 2, 1.6812-1.6818; No. 3, 1.6911-1.6917; No. 4, 1.7009-1.7015; No. 5, 1.7100-1.7106.
⑩—Journal No. 1, 1.5720-1.5728 inch; journals. 2, 3, 4 & 5, 1.3751-1.3759 inch.
⑪—Prizm w/16-valve engine.
⑫—Journals 1 & 4, .0016-.0044 inch; journals 2 & 3, .0019-.0047 inch.
⑬—Journals 1 & 4, 2.009-2.011 inch; journals 2 & 3, 1.999-2.001 inch.

Continued

CRANKSHAFT, BEARINGS & RODS

All Measurements Given In Inches Unless Otherwise Specified.

Engine Liter/CID/VIN	Year	Crankshaft				Bearing Clearance			Connecting Rod Side Clearance
		Standard Journal Diameter		Out of Round All①	Taper All①				
		Main Bearing	Crank Pin			Main Bearings	Connecting Rod Bearings	Thrust Bearing Clearance	
1.0L/3-61/5,6	1992-94	②	1.6529-1.6535	.0004	.0004	.0008-.0023	.0012-.0031	.0044-.0122	.0039-.0078
1.6L/4-97/5⑤	1992	1.8891-1.8898	1.6529-1.6535	.0004	.0004	.0006-.0013	.0008-.0020	.0008-.0087	.0059-.0098
1.6L/4-97/6⑥	1992-93	2.0440-2.0448	1.5722-1.5728	.0020	.0020	.0008-.0020	.0008-.0018	.0024-.0095	.0079-.0138
1.6L/4-97/6③	1992-93	2.17	1.6918-1.6920	.0002	.0002	.0006-.0020	.00177-.00354	.0047-.0138	.0028-.0095
1.6L/4-97/6④	1992-94	1.8891-1.8898	1.5742-1.5748	.0008	.0008	.0006-.0039	.0008-.0031	.0008-.0118	.0059-.0098
1.8L/4-108/8⑪	1993-94	⑫	—	.0008	.0008	.0006-.0039	.0008-.0031	.0008-.0118	.0008-.0031
1.8L/4-110/8⑦	1992-93	2.0440-2.0448	1.8083-1.8089	.0002	.0002	.00079-.00199	—	.0024-.0095	—
2.0L/4-121/H	1992-94	2.2828-2.2833	1.9279-1.9287	.0002	.0002	.0006-.0016	.0007-.0025	.0028-.0118	.0028-.0095
2.2L/4-133/4	1992-94	2.4945-2.4954	1.9983-1.9994	.0019	.0019	.0006-.0019	.0010-.0031	.002-.007	.0039-.0149
2.3L/4-138/A,D,3	1992-94	2.0470-2.0480	1.8887-1.8897	.0005	.0005	.0005-.0023	.0005-.0020	.0034-.0095	.0059-.0177
2.5L/4-151/R	1992	2.300	2.00	.0005	.0005	.0005-.0022	.0005-.0027	.0005-.016	.0059-.0236
3.1L/V6-192/T,M	1992-94	2.6473-2.6483	1.9983-1.9994	.0002	.0002	.0012-.0030	.0011-.0037	.0012-.0030	.0071-.0173
3.3L/V6-204/N	1992-93	2.4988-2.4998	2.2487-2.2499	.0003	.0003	.0008-.0022	.0008-.0022	.003-.011	.003-.015
3.4L/V6-204/X,S	1992-94	2.6472-2.6479	1.9987-1.9994	.0002	.0002	.0013-.0030	.0011-.0032	.0013-.0030	.0071-.0173
3.8L/V6-231/L,1	1992-94	2.4988-2.4998	2.2487-2.2499	.0003	.0003	.0008-.0022	.0008-.0022	.003-.011	.003-.015
4.3L/V6-262/Z	1992-93	⑧	2.2487-2.2498	.0002	.0002	⑨	.0013-.0035	.001-.007	.006-.014
4.3L/V8-265/W	1994	2.4485-2.4491	2.0978-2.0998	.0010	.0010	⑬	.0013-.0030	.001-.007	.006-.014
4.6L/V8-279/Y,9	1993-94	2.52	—	.0005	.0005	.0005-.003	.001-.003	—	.008-.020
4.9L/V8-300/B	1992-94	2.6354-2.6364	1.927-1.928	.0003	—	⑩	—	.0010-.007	.008-.020
5.0L/V8-305/E,F	1992-93	⑭	2.0893-2.0998	.0002	.0002	⑨	.0013-.0035	.001-.007	.006-.014
5.7L/V8-350/7,8,P	1992-94	⑭	2.0978-2.0998	.001	.001	⑬	.0013-.0035	.001-.007	.006-.014
5.7L/V8-350/J	1992-94	2.755-2.756	2.0993-2.1000	.0003	.0002	.0007-.0023	.0007-.0027	.010-.040	.008-.028

①—Maximum.
②—The counter weights of No. 1 cylinder have four stamped numbers, they indicate the journal diameters at bearing caps respectively. No. 1, 1.7714-1.7716 inch; No. 2, 1.7712-1.7714 inch & No. 3, 1.7710-1.7712 inch.
③—LeMans.
④—Prizm w/4A-FE engine.
⑤—Prizm w/4A-GE 16 valve engine.
⑥—Storm w/12 valve engine.
⑦—Storm w/16 valve engine.
⑧—Journal No. 1, .0008-.0020 inch; journal No. 2, 3, 4, .0011-.0023 inch; journal No. 5, .0017-.0032 inch.
⑨—Journal No. 1, .0008-.0020 inch; journal No. 2, 3 & 4, .0011-.0020 inch; journal No. 5, .0017-.0032 inch.
⑩—Journal No. 1, .0008-.0031 inch; journal No. 2, 3, 4 & 5, .0016-.0039 inch.
⑪—Prizm w/16-valve engine.
⑫—Stamping No. 1, 2.0482–2.0485; stamping No. 2, 2.0485–2.0487; stamping No. 3, 2.0487–2.0489.
⑬—Journal No. 1, .0010-.0015 inch; journal No. 2, 3 & 4, .0011-.0025 inch; journal No. 5, .0017-.0035 inch.
⑭—Diameter No. 1, 2.4484-2.4493 inch; diameter No. 2, 3 & 4, 2.4481-2.4490 inch; journal No. 5, 2.4479-2.4488 inch.

PISTONS, PINS & RINGS

All Measurements Given In Inches Unless Otherwise Specified.

Engine Liter/CID/VIN	Year	Piston Diameter (Std.)	Piston Clearance	Piston Pin Diameter①	Piston Pin To Piston Clearance	Piston Ring End Gap ②		Piston Ring Side Clearance	
						Comp.	Oil	Comp.	Oil
1.0L/3-60/5,6	1992-94	2.9122-2.9130	.0008-.0015	—	—	.0079-.0276	.0079-.0708	③	—
1.6L/4-97/5⑩	1992	⑪	.0039-.0047	.7876-.7880	.0002-.0003	⑫	.0059	.0012-.0028	.0039-.0236
1.6L/4-97/6⑬	1992-93	㉛	.0011-.0019	.7094-.7095	—	⑯	.0039	㉜	.0039-.0236
1.6L/4-97/6⑥	1992-93	3.110	.0008	.7200	.0003-.0004	.01-.02	—	⑦	—
1.6L/4-97/6⑧	1992-93	⑨	.0024-.0031	—	—	④	.0039	⑤	—
1.6L/4-97/6⑧	1994	㊱	.0008-.0015	—	—	.0413	.0413	⑤	—
1.8L/4-108/8㉕	1993-94	㊱	.0008-.0015	—	—	㉟	.0413	—	.0033-.0051
1.8L/4-110/8⑭	1992-93	⑮	.0019-.0027	.7871-.7872	—	㉝	.0039	㉞	—
2.0L/4-121/H	1992-94	⑱	⑲	.8264-.8267	.0004-.0005	⑳	—	㉑	—
2.2L/4-133/4	1992-94	—	.0007-.0017	.8000-.8002	.0004-.0009	.010-.020	.010-.050	.0019-.0027	.0019-.0082
2.3L/4-138/A,D,3	1992-94	3.6203-3.6210	.0007-.0020	.8659-.8661	㉒	㉓	.0157-.0551	㉔	.01957-.02060
2.5L/4-151/R	1992	—	.0014-.0022	.9270-.9280	.0003-.0005	.0118	.0196	㉖	.0149-.0551

Continued

PISTONS, PINS & RINGS -Continued

All Measurements Given In Inches Unless Otherwise Specified.

Engine Liter/CID/ VIN	Year	Piston Diameter (Std.)	Piston Clearance	Piston Pin Diameter (1)	Piston Pin To Piston Clearance	Piston Ring End Gap (2)		Piston Ring Side Clearance	
						Comp.	Oil	Comp.	Oil
3.1L/V6-192/T,M	1992-94	3.5026-3.5037	.0009-.0027	.9052-.9054	.0004-.0010	(27)	.008	.0016-.0035	.002-.008
3.3L/V6-204/N	1992-93	—	.0004-.0022	.9053-.9055	.0004-.0008	.010	.015	.0013-.0031	.0011-.0081
3.4L/V6-204/X,S	1992-94	3.6208-3.6217	.0013-.0027	.9052-.9054	.0005-.0009	(30)	.008	.0016-.0035	.008
3.8L/V6-231/L,1	1992-94	—	.0004-.0022	.9053-.9055	.0004-.0008	.025	.025	.0013-.0031	.0011-.0081
4.3L/V6-262/Z	1992-93	—	.0007-.0017	.9270-.9273	.0004-.0008	.010-.017	.015	.0014-.0032	.0014-.0032
4.3L/V8-265/W	1994	—	.0010-.0027	.9270-.9271	.0004-.0010	.010-.035	.010-.065	.0012-.0042	.002-.008
4.6L/V8-279/Y,9	1993-94	—	.0004-.0020	.865-.866	—	.010-016	.010-.030	.002-.004	(28)
4.9L/V8-300/B	1992-94	—	.0004-.0020	.8659-.8661	.0003-.0007	.012	.0004	.016-.0037	(28)
5.0L/V8-305/E,F	1992-93	—	.0007-.0021	.9270-.9273	.0002-.0003	(17)	.015	.0012-.0032	.002-.007
5.7L/V8-350/7,8	1992-93	—	.0005-.0022	.9270-.9273	.0002-.0003	(17)	.015	.0012-.0032	.002-.007
5.7L/V8-350/P	1992-94	—	.0007-.0027	.9270-.9271	.0004-.0010	.035	.065	.0012-.0042	.002-.008
5.7L/V8-350/J	1992-94	—	—	.9841-.9843	.0002-.0007	(29)	.024	.002-.003	.001-.002

(1)—Pistons & pins are matched set & should be replaced as an assembly.
(2)—Maximum.
(3)—Top ring, .0012-.0027 inch; 2nd ring, .0008-.0023 inch.
(4)—Top ring, .0098 inch; 2nd ring, .0059 inch.
(5)—Top ring, .0016-.0031 inch; 2nd ring, .0012-.0028 inch.
(6)—LeMans.
(7)—Top ring, .0024-.0036 inch; 2nd ring, .0019-.0032 inch.
(8)—Prizm w/4A-FE 16 valve engine.
(9)—There are three standard sizes of pistons marked with a No. on top. No. 1, 3.1862-3.1866 inch; No. 2, 3.1866-3.1870 inch; No. 3, 3.1870-3.1874 inch.
(10)—Prizm w/GSI 4A-GE 16 valve engine
(11)—There are three standard sizes of pistons marked w/a No. on top. No. 1, 3.1846-3.1850 inch; No. 2, 3.1850-3.1854 inch; No. 3, 3.1854-3.1858 inch.
(12)—Top ring, .0098 inch; 2nd ring, .0079 inch.
(13)—Storm w/12 valve engine.
(14)—Storm w/16 valve engine.
(15)—There are three standard sizes of pistons marked with a No. on top. No. 1, 3.1473-3.1477 inch; No. 2, 3.1477-3.1481 inch; No. 3, 3.1481-3.1485 inch.
(16)—Top ring, .0011 inch; 2nd ring, .0018 inch.
(17)—Top ring, .010 inch; 2nd ring, .018 inch.
(18)—VIN K & H, 3.3844-3.3860 inch; VIN M, 3.3837-3.3852 inch.
(19)—VIN K & H, .0004-.0012 inch; VIN M, .0012-.0020 inch.
(20)—Top ring, .0177 inch; 2nd ring, .0197 inch.
(21)—Top ring, .0024-.0036 inch; 2nd ring, .0019-.0032 inch.
(22)—VIN A, .0003-.0006 inch. 1992-93 VIN D & 3, .00007-.00043 inch.
(23)—Top ring, .0138-.0236 inch; 2nd ring, .0157-.0256 inch.
(24)—VIN A: top ring, .0027-.0047 inch.; 2nd ring, .0157-.0031 inch. VIN D: top ring, .0019-.0039 inch.; 2nd ring, .0157-.0031 inch.
(25)—Prizm w/16-valve engine.
(26)—Top ring, .0020-.0031 inch; 2nd ring, .0011-.0031 inch.
(27)—Top ring, .010 inch; 2nd ring, .028 inch.
(28)—Zero clearance; side sealing ring.
(29)—Top ring, .026 inch; 2nd ring, .039 inch.
(30)—Top ring, .016 inch; 2nd ring, .029 inch.
(31)—There are three standard sizes of pistons marked with a letter on top. A, 3.1480-3.1484 inch; B, 3.1484-3.1488-8 inch; C, 3.1488-3.1492 inch.
(32)—Top ring, .00117-.00315 inch; 2nd ring, .00078-.00236 inch.
(33)—Top ring, .00110-.0157 inch; 2nd ring, .0177-.0236 inch.
(34)—Top ring, .00177-.00315 inch; 2nd ring, .00078-.00236 inch.
(35)—Top ring, .0413 inch; lower ring, .0472 inch.
(36)—There are three standard sizes of pistons marked with a No. on top. No. 1, 3.1852-3.1856 inch; No. 2, 3.1856-3.1860 inch; No. 3, 3.1860-3.1864 inch.

CYLINDER BLOCK

All Measurements Given In Inches, Unless Otherwise Specified.

Engine Liter/CID/VIN	Year	Cylinder Bore Diameter (Std.)	Cylinder Bore Taper Max.	Cylinder Bore Out of Round Max.
1.0L/3-61/5,6	1992-94	(1)	.0039	.0039
1.6L/4-97/6 (2)	1992-93	3.110	.0005	.0005
1.6L/4-97/6 (5)	1992-93	3.1496-3.1512	.005	.005
1.6L/4-97/5,6 (3) (4)	1992-94	3.1980-3.2177	.0005	.005
1.8L/4-108/8 (9)	1993-94	3.1890-3.2177	.005	.005
1.8L/4-110/8 (6)	1992-93	3.1496-3.1508	.005	.005
2.0L/4-121/H	1992-94	3.3852-3.3868	.0005	.0005
2.2L/4-133/4	1992-94	3.5036-3.5043	.0005	.0005
2.3L/4-138/A,D,3	1992-94	3.6217-3.6223	.0003	.0004
2.5L/4-151/R	1992	4.0000	.005	.001
3.1L/V6-192/T,M	1992-94	3.5046-3.5053	.0005	.0005
3.3L/V6-204/N	1992-93	3.700	.0005	.0004
3.4L/V6-204/X	1992-93	3.6213-3.6224	—	.0003
3.4L/V6-204/S	1993-94	3.6228-3.6235	.0005	.0004
3.4L/V6-204/X	1994	3.6228-3.6235	.0005	.0004
3.8L/V6-231/L,1	1992-94	3.800	.0005	.0004
4.3L/V6-262/Z	1992-93	4.0007-4.0017	(7)	.001

Continued

CYLINDER BLOCK —Continued

Engine Liter/CID/VIN	Year	Cylinder Bore Diameter (Std.)	Cylinder Bore Taper Max.	Cylinder Bore Out of Round Max.
4.3L/V8-265/W	1994	3.7355-3.7385	.001	.001
4.6L/V8-279/Y,9	1993-94	3.6807-3.6815	.0004	.0008
4.9L/V8-300/B	1992-94	⑧	.0248	.0008
5.0L/V8-305/E,F	1992-93	3.7350-3.7385	⑦	.001
5.7L/V8-350/7,8,P	1992-94	4.0007-4.0017	⑦	.002
5.7L/V8-350/J	1992-94	3.8971-3.8981	—	—

①—Cylinder bore diameter Nos. are stamped on the top of the block in sequence. No. 1, 2.9138-2.9142 inch & No. 2, 2.9134-2.9138 inch.
②—LeMans.
③—Prizm w/4A-FE 16 valve engine, VIN 6.
④—Prizm w/GSI 4A-GE 16 valve engine, VIN 5.
⑤—Storm w/12 valve engine.
⑥—Storm w/16 valve engine.
⑦—Thrust side, .0005 inch; relief side, .0010 inch.
⑧—Nominal cylinder bore diameter, 3.622 inches. Liner protrusion, flush to .0032 inch above block deck. Maximum variation between liners, .0039 inch. Piston & liner are matched set & must be replaced as an assembly if liner protrusion, taper, out of round or piston to liner clearance are not within specifications.
⑨—Prizm w/16-valve engine.

OIL PUMP

All Measurements Given In Inches Unless Otherwise Specified.

Engine Liter/CID/VIN	Year	Gear Backlash	Gear To Body Clearance	Gear Endplay ①	Gear Pocket Depth	Gear Pocket Diameter	Pump Gear Thickness	Pump Gear Diameter	Relief Valve To Body Clearance
1.0L/3-60/5,6	1992-94	—	.0122	.0059	—	—	—	—	—
1.6L/4-97/5⑥	1992	.0138	.0039	.0079	—	—	—	—	—
1.6L/4-97/6②	1992-93	.004-.008	.0043-.0074	.001-.004	.3948-.3968	③	—	④	—
1.6L/4-97/6⑦	1992-93	.0012	.004	.0078	—	—	—	—	—
1.6L/4-97/6⑤	1992-94	.0138	.0039	.0079	—	—	—	—	—
1.8L/4-108/8⑧	1993-94	—	.0031-.0079	.0010-.0039	—	—	—	—	—
1.8L/4-110/8⑧	1992-93	.0012	.004	.008	—	—	—	—	—
2.0L/4-121/H	1992-94	.004-.008	.0043-.0074	.001-.004	.395-.397	③	—	④	—
2.2L/4-133/4	1992-94	.004-.008	.0015-.0035	.002-.007	1.195-1.198	1.503-1.506	1.199-1.200	1.498-1.500	.0015-.0035
2.3L/4-138/A,D,3	1992-94	.0091-.0201	—	.0059	.6736-.6756	2.1273-2.1292	.6727-.6731	2.124-2.126	—
2.5L/4-151/R	1992	—	—	—	.514-.516	—	.511-.512	—	—
3.1L/V6-192/T⑨	1992-94	.0037-.0077	.003-.004	.002-.006	1.202-1.205	1.504-1.506	1.199-1.200	1.498-1.500	.0015-.0035
3.1L/V6-192/T,M ⑩	1992-94	.0037-.0077	.003-.004	.002-.006	1.202-1.205	1.504-1.506	1.199-1.200	1.498-1.500	.0015-.0035
3.3L/V6-204/N	1992-93	—	.008-.015	.001-.0035	.4610-.4625	3.508-3.512	—	—	.0015-.0030
3.4L/V6-204/X	1992	⑪	⑪	⑪	⑪	⑪	⑪	⑪	⑪
3.4L/V6-204/X,S	1993-94	.0037-.0077	.003-.004	.002-.006	1.202-1.205	1.504-1.506	1.199-1.200	1.498-1.500	.0015-.0035
3.8L/V6-231/L,1	1992-94	.006	.008-.015	.001-.0035	.4610-.4625	3.508-3.512	—	—	.0015-.0030
4.3L/V6-262/Z	1992-93	⑪	⑪	⑪	⑪	⑪	⑪	⑪	⑪
4.3L/V8-265/W	1994	⑪	⑪	⑪	⑪	⑪	⑪	⑪	⑪
4.6L/V8-279/Y,9	1993-94	⑪	⑪	⑪	⑪	⑪	⑪	⑪	⑪
4.9L/V8-300/B	1992-94	⑪	⑪	⑪	⑪	⑪	⑪	⑪	⑪
5.0L/V8-305/E,F	1992-93	⑪	⑪	⑪	⑪	⑪	⑪	⑪	⑪
5.7L/V8-350/7,8,P	1992-94	⑪	⑪	⑪	⑪	⑪	⑪	⑪	⑪
5.7L/V8-350/J	1992-94	⑪	⑪	⑪	⑪	⑪	⑪	⑪	⑪

①—Measured between pump cover & end of gears using straightedge & feeler gauge.
②—LeMans.
③—Inner gear, 1.614-1.615 inch; outer gear, 3.231-3.234 inch.
④—Inner gear, 1.612-1.613 inch; outer gear, 3.2248-3.2269 inch.
⑤—Prizm w/4A-FE 16 valve engine.
⑥—Prizm w/GSI 4A-GE 16 valve engine.
⑦—Storm w/12 valve engine.
⑧—Storm w/16 valve engine.
⑨—Aluminum body pump.
⑩—Cast iron body pump.
⑪—Pump components are not serviced separately. If any component is damaged or worn, pump should be replaced.

SATURN

INDEX OF SERVICE OPERATIONS

NOTE: For Service Operations Not Listed Below, Refer To The Table Of Contents In The Front Of This Manual.

Specifications

GENERAL ENGINE SPECIFICATIONS

Year	Engine, Liter/ CID	Fuel Injection System	Bore & Stoke	Compression Ratio	Net H.P. @ RPM	Maximum Torque, Ft. Lbs. @ RPM	Normal Oil Pressure ①
1992	1.9L/4-116②	TBI④	3.23 X 3.55	9.3	85@5000	107@2400	36
	1.9L/4-116③	MPFI⑤	3.23 X 3.55	9.5	124@5600	119@4800	36
1993	1.9L/4-116②	TBI④	3.23 X 3.55	9.3	85@5000	107@2400	36
	1.9L/4-116③	MPFI⑤	3.23 X 3.55	9.5	124@5600	119@4800	36
1994	1.9L/4-116②	TBI④	3.23 X 3.55	9.3	85@5000	107@2400	36
	1.9L/4-116③	MPFI⑤	3.23 X 3.55	9.5	124@5600	119@4800	36
1995	1.9L/4-116②	MPFI⑤	3.23 X 3.55	9.3	100@5000	114@2400	36
	1.9L/4-116③	MPFI⑤	3.23 X 3.55	9.5	124@5600	122@4800	36

①—At 2000 RPM.
②—SOHC-Single overhead cam.
③—DOHC-Dual overhead cam.
④—Throttle body injection.
⑤—Multi-point fuel injection.

TUNE UP SPECIFICATIONS

Year	Spark Plug Gap	Ignition Timing, BTDC				Curb Idle Speed		Fast Idle Speed		Fuel Pump Pressure
		Firing Order	Man. Trans.	Auto Trans.	Mark Fig.	Man. Trans.	Auto Trans.	Man. Trans.	Auto Trans.	
1992-95	.040	1-3-4-2	—	—	—	①	②	③	③	46-94

BTDC—Before top dead center.
①—On SOHC, 700-800 RPM, on DOHC, 800-900 RPM in Neutral.
②—On SOHC, 600-700 RPM, on DOHC, 700-800 RPM in Drive.
③—Controlled by idle air control (IAC) valve.

FRONT WHEEL ALIGNMENT SPECIFICATIONS

Year	Caster Angle, Degrees		Camber Angle, Degrees				Toe, Degrees①
			Limits		Desired		
	Limits	Desired	Left	Right	Left	Right	
1992-94	+1.1 to +2.7	+1.7	-1.2 to +.65	-1 to +1	0	0	.10 to +.30
1995	+1.1 to +2.3	+1.7	-1.2 to +.20	-1.2 to +.20	-.50	-.50	.10 to +.30

①—Toe degrees equals total toe for both wheels.

REAR WHEEL ALIGNMENT SPECIFICATIONS

Year	Camber Angle, Degrees		Toe, Degrees①
	Limits	Desired	
1992-94	-1.55 to 0.0	-.6	.10 to +.30
1995	-1.40 to 0.0	-.7	.10 to +.30

①—Toe degrees equals total toe for both wheels.

COOLING SYSTEM & CAPACITY DATA

Year	Engine, Liter/ CID	Coolant Capacity, Qts.		Radiator Cap Relief Pressure, Lbs.	Thermo. Opening Temp.°F	Fuel Tank, Gals.	Engine Oil, Qts.	Transaxle Oil	
		Less A/C	With A/C					Man. Trans., Qts.	Auto Trans., Qts.
1992-94	1.9L/4-116	7	7	13-20	182-190	13.2	4①	2.6	3.75②
1995	1.9L/4-116	7	7	13-20	182-190	12.8	4①	2.6	4.2②

①—Change w/filter.
②—Includes fluid change w/pressure filter.

LUBRICANT DATA

Year	Lubricant Type				
	Transaxle		Power Steering	Brake System	Hydraulic Clutch
	Manual	Automatic			
1992-94	Dexron IIE	Dexron IIE	①	②	②
1995	Dexron IIE or Dexron III	Dexron IIE or Dexron III	①	②	②

①—Must meet GM specification 9985010.
②—Delco Supreme II or DOT 3.

Electrical

NOTE: On Air Bag Equipped Models, Refer To "Air Bag System Precautions" Located In The Front Of This Manual For System Disarming & Arming Procedures.

INDEX

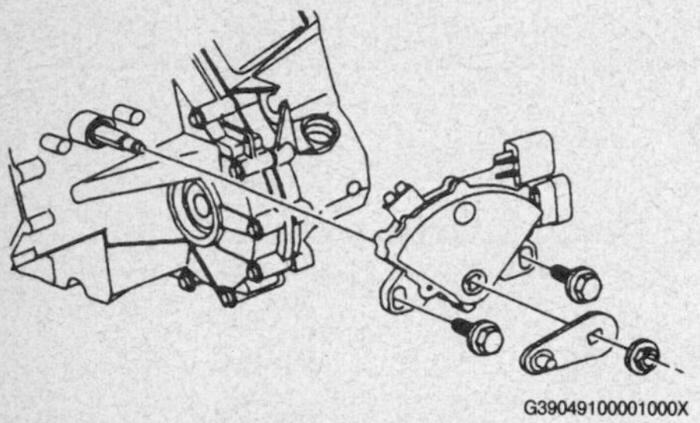
G39049100001000X

Fig. 1 Neutral start switch removal

PRECAUTIONS

AIR BAG SYSTEMS

Refer to "Air Bag System Precautions" in the front of this manual for system disarming and arming procedures.

FUSE PANEL & FLASHER LOCATION

The underhood junction block is located at the lefthand front of the engine compartment at the fender apron. The instrument panel junction block is located behind the center instrument panel in front of the console.

RELAY CENTER LOCATION

The primary relays are in the underhood junction block, which is located in the front left corner of the engine compartment near the wheel well. Secondary relays are located at the instrument fuse panel.

STARTER

REPLACE

1. Remove air inlet tube and fresh air hose, on DOHC models, lift resonator upward to disengage from engine support bracket.
2. Remove upper starter attaching bolt through access hole near intake manifold support bracket.
3. Raise and support vehicle.
4. **On 1992-93 models,** remove starter shield pin using pliers, then lift shield upward to release from solenoid.
5. **On 1994-95 models,** remove starter shield by pulling outward to release bottom of shield, then lift shield upward to right to remove.
6. **On all models,** disconnect starter electrical connectors and position aside.
7. Remove lower starter attaching bolt.
8. **On 1992–93 models,** remove rear starter support bracket attaching bolt.
9. **On 1992-93 models,** rotate starter until bracket clears axle shaft support bracket, pull rearward toward lefthand side of vehicle to remove.
10. **On 1994-95 models,** pull starter rearward, toward lefthand side of vehicle to remove.
11. **On all models,** reverse procedure to install. **Torque** starter attaching bolts to 26 ft. lbs., starter bracket bolts to 22 ft. lbs. on 1992-93 models or 27 ft. lbs. on 1994-95 models, starter solenoid terminal to 44 inch lbs. and starter positive terminal to 89 inch lbs. on 1992-93 models or 71 inch lbs. on 1994-95 models.

IGNITION LOCK

REPLACE

1. Remove ignition lock bezel.
2. Remove upper steering column shroud panel.
3. Insert ignition key to switch, then rotate to ACC position.
4. Depress square locking button at top of ignition lock assembly, then remove lock cylinder.
5. Reverse procedure to install.

CLUTCH START SWITCH

REPLACE

1. Disconnect clutch switch electrical connector.

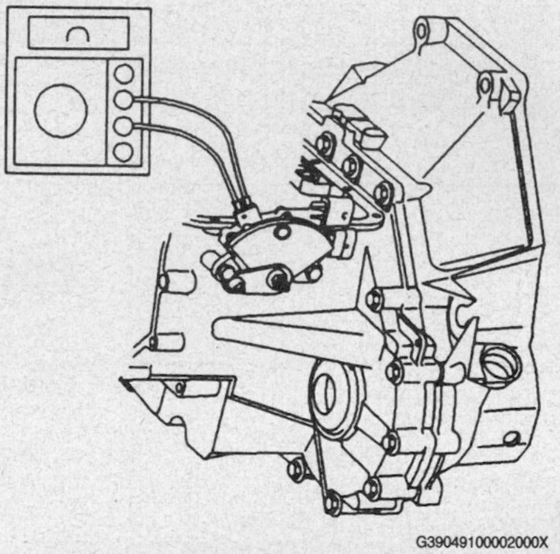
G39049100002000X

Fig. 2 Neutral start switch adjustment

2. Remove clutch switch attaching bolt, then remove switch.
3. Reverse procedure to install **Torque** clutch switch attaching bolt to 89 inch lbs.

NEUTRAL SAFETY SWITCH

REPLACE

1. **On DOHC models,** remove air filter box, then lift resonator upward to disengage from support bracket.
2. **On all models,** remove air induction tube.
3. Disconnect gear selector switch electrical connector.
4. Disconnect control lever shift cable.
5. Remove control lever shaft attaching nut, then remove manual lever, noting lever position, **Fig. 1.**
6. Remove two selector switch to transaxle case attaching bolts, then remove switch.
7. Reverse procedure to install, noting the following:
   a. **Torque** manual lever to control shaft attaching nut to 8 ft. lbs.

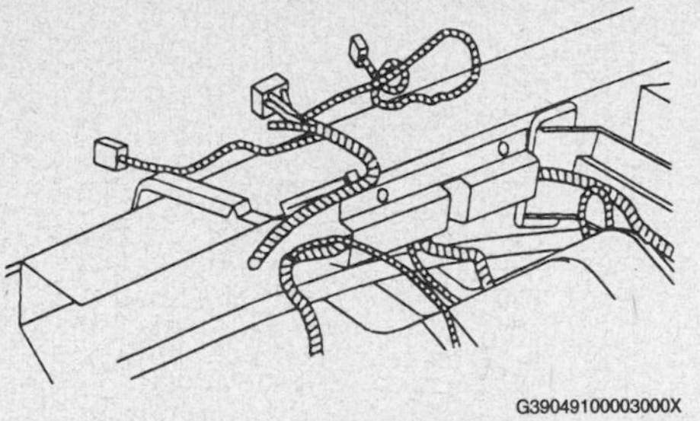
G39049100003000X

Fig. 3 Connector position assurance removal. 1992–94

b. Adjust switch, place transaxle in D4 position, then using a suitable ohmmeter, check for continuity across terminals, **Fig. 2**, if continuity is not indicated, rotate switch until continuity is present.
c. **Torque** switch to case bolts to 142 inch lbs.
d. **Torque** air induction tube to 15 inch lbs.

BACK-UP LAMP SWITCH
REPLACE

1. **On models equipped with ABS**, remove air induction tube.
2. **On all models**, disconnect back-up light electrical connectors.
3. Unscrew switch, then remove.
4. Reverse procedure to install. **Torque** switch to 23 ft. lbs.

STEERING WHEEL
REPLACE

1992

1. Pull edge of horn pad to unclip.
2. Disconnect horn pad electrical connectors, then remove pad.
3. Remove steering column shaft clip, then remove wheel attaching nut.
4. Using steering wheel puller tool No. J-1859-03 or equivalent, remove steering wheel.
5. Reverse procedure to install noting to **torque** steering wheel attaching nut to 30 ft. lbs.

1993–1995

1. Remove screw caps on steering wheel with flat head screwdriver.
2. Remove inflator module screws.
3. Remove inflator module from steering wheel.
4. Remove integral connector lock device.
5. Disconnect electrical connector and remove inflator module.
6. Disconnect horn switch electrical connector and cruise control electrical connector, if equipped.
7. Remove steering wheel attaching nut.
8. Remove steering wheel with suitable steering wheel puller.
9. Feed electrical wiring through steering wheel and remove steering wheel.
10. Insert yellow tab into SIR coil assembly or use tape to prevent rotating SIR coil.

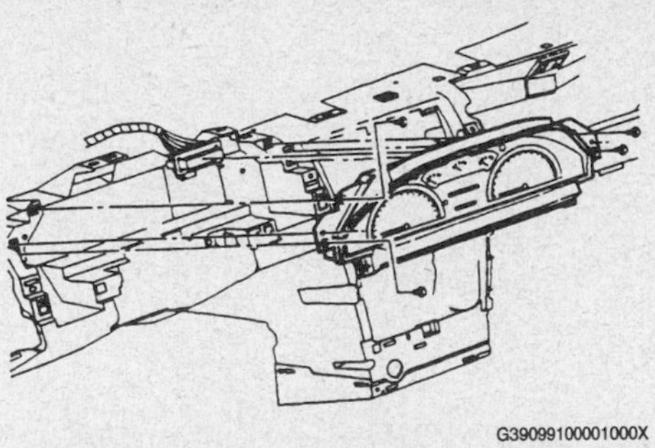
G39099100001000X

Fig. 4 Instrument cluster removal. 1992–94

11. Reverse procedure to install, noting the following:
    a. Install new steering wheel attaching nut and **torque** to 30 ft. lbs.
    b. **Torque** inflator module attaching bolts to 89 inch lbs.

INSTRUMENT CLUSTER
REPLACE

1992–94

1. Remove instrument panel left and right end cap attaching screws, then pull rearward to unclip.
2. Remove left and right lower trim panel extensions by disconnecting from Velcro fasteners, then pull rearward at upper clips to remove.
3. **On 1993-94 models,** disconnect traction control/fog lamp electrical connector.
4. **On all models,** remove center air outlet trim panel by pulling outward, starting at bottom of panel and working upward.
5. Remove trim panel extension strip by pulling rearward to unclip.
6. Remove cluster trim panel attaching screws, then pull rearward to unclip.
7. Remove connect position assurance devices, **Fig. 3**, and disconnect electrical connectors from instrument panel lighting rheostat and rear window defogger switches.
8. Remove instrument cluster trim panel.
9. Remove instrument cluster attaching screws, **Fig. 4**, then pull rearward to gain access.
10. Disconnect cluster electrical connectors by depressing retainer legs, then remove instrument cluster.
11. Reverse procedure to install.

1995

1. Remove DLC connector and steering filler panel.
2. Remove hood release cable from lever.
3. Remove steering column filler panel.
4. Disconnect ignition switch electrical connector at right steering column bolt.
5. Remove steering column bolts, then lower column onto front seat.
6. Remove two push pin fasteners in top portion of instrument cluster trim bezel and pull trim bezel rearward at side clip locations.

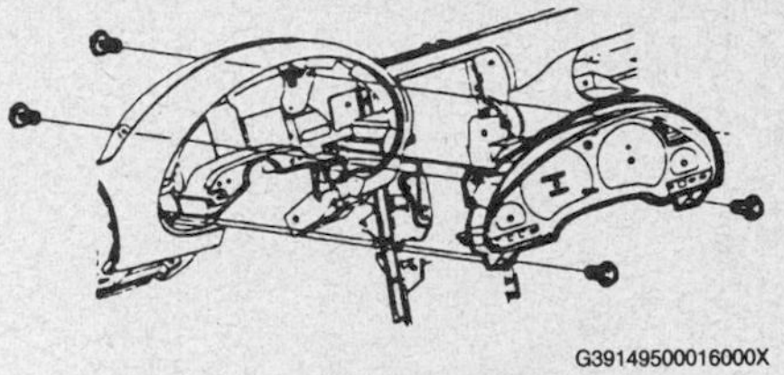
G39149500016000X

Fig. 5 Instrument cluster replacement. 1995

7. Remove connector locking pins and disconnect electrical connectors from instrument cluster by depressing tabs on each side of connector.
8. Remove front and rear instrument cluster screws, **Fig. 5**.
9. Remove instrument cluster.
10. Reverse procedure to install. **Torque** steering column bolts to 26 ft. lbs.

RADIO
REPLACE

1992–94

1. Remove instrument panel center air outlet trim panel, by pulling rearward to unclip, start at bottom and work upward.
2. **On 1993-94 models,** disconnect traction control/fog lamp electrical connector.
3. **On all models,** remove radio attaching screws, then slide radio rearward.
4. Disconnect radio electrical connectors and antenna.
5. Reverse procedure to install.

1995

1. Remove two control cover push pin fasteners and pull radio/HVAC control cover rearward.
2. Disconnect single traction control, fog lamp and rear defog electrical connector.
3. Remove radio screws.
4. Depress both side spring clips on radio and pull out slightly.
5. Disconnect antenna and electrical connector.
6. **On models equipped with base radio,** remove storage tray by pulling out towards front of radio.
7. **On all models,** remove radio.
8. Reverse procedure to install.

WIPER MOTOR
REPLACE

1. Remove wiper arm finish cap and attaching screw.
2. Lift wiper blade assembly from windshield, then remove wiper arm from pivot.
3. Remove cowl trim panel, **Fig. 6.**
4. Using a 13 mm wrench, move wiper

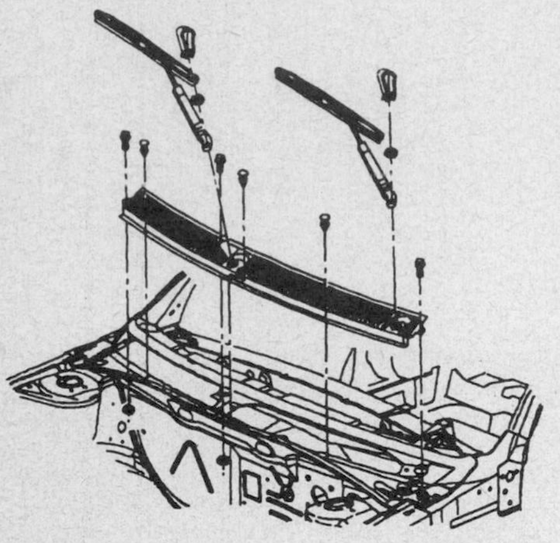

G39149100001000X

Fig. 6 Windshield cowl trim panel removal

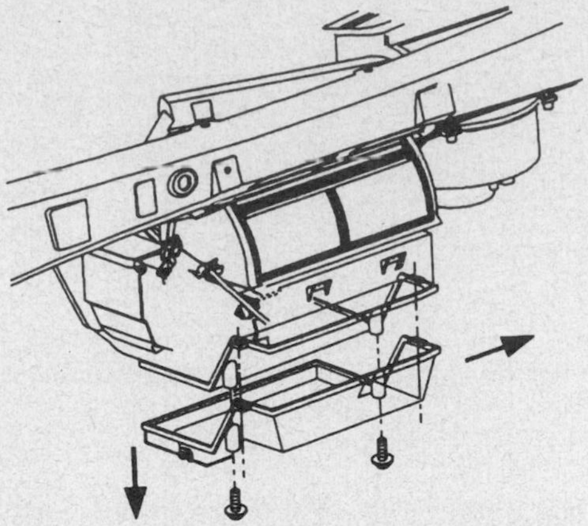

G37029100001000X

Fig. 7 Lower heater duct removal

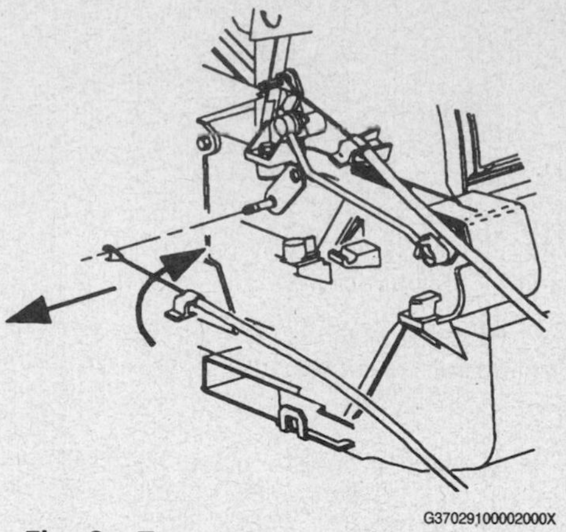

G37029100002000X

Fig. 8 Temperature cable release

motor crank arm to 12 o'clock position to access rear wiper module fasteners.

5. Remove wiper module attaching screws, then lift module to disconnect motor and module electrical connectors.
6. Remove wiper module, then move wiper motor crank arm to 9 o'clock or park position.
7. Remove crank arm nut, then disconnect crank arm from motor shaft.
8. Remove wiper motor attaching nut and bolts, then remove motor from transmission.
9. Reverse procedure to install. **Torque** wiper motor crank arm on wiper motor shaft to 21 ft. lbs., wiper module to 89 inch lbs. and wiper arms to 19 ft. lbs.

WIPER TRANSMISSION

REPLACE

Refer to "Wiper Motor, Replace" for wiper motor transmission replacement procedure.

BLOWER MOTOR

REPLACE

1. Remove right instrument panel lower sound insulator, if equipped.
2. Disconnect blower motor electrical connector.
3. Remove blower motor attaching screws, then remove motor.
4. Reverse procedure to install.

HEATER CORE

REPLACE

1. Drain coolant.
2. Raise and support vehicle.
3. Move heater hose clamps upward.
4. Lower vehicle.
5. **On DOHC models,** remove air cleaner housing cover and air induction at intake manifold.
6. **On SOHC models,** remove air cleaner housing.
7. **On all models,** remove heater hoses

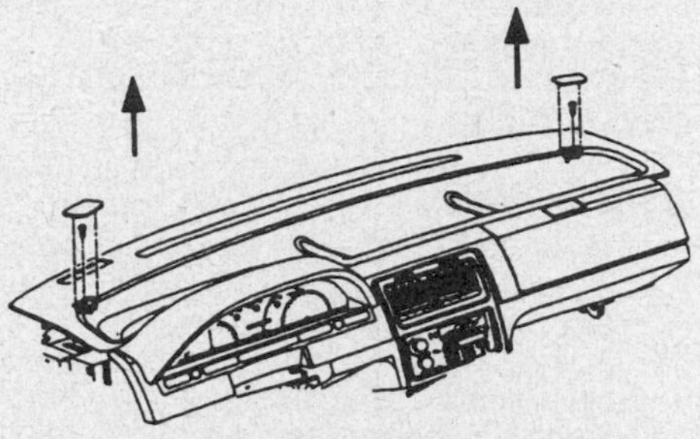

G39149100002000X

Fig. 9 Upper instrument panel removal. 1992–94

at core, then blow coolant from heater core with an air hose.

8. Disconnect left and right center instrument panel trim panel Velcro tabs, then pull outward to unclip.
9. Remove lower heater duct attaching screws, then drop straight down and slide out sideways, **Fig. 7. Use caution to not damage the rear floor heater duct seal.**
10. Release temperature cable holddown clip from lower heater core cover by lifting upward on plastic tab while down on top of cable, **Fig. 8.**
11. Depress temperature valve pin, then pull temperature cable straight out.
12. Remove heater core side cover attaching screws, then remove.
13. Remove lower heater core cover.
14. Remove heater core pipe clamp attaching screw.
15. Remove lower heater core retainer attaching screws.
16. Remove heater core.
17. Reverse procedure to install.

EVAPORATOR CORE

REPLACE

1. Discharge A/C system, then drain cooling system.
2. **On DOHC models,** remove air cleaner cover and air induction hose at intake manifold.
3. **On SOHC models,** remove air cleaner housing.
4. **On all models,** remove suction hose and liquid line from thermal expansion valve.
5. Place protective cover over A/C hoses, lines and expansion module to prevent A/C contamination.
6. Remove thermal expansion valve from evaporator.
7. Raise and support vehicle.
8. Move heater core inlet and outlet clamps up.
9. Lower vehicle.
10. Remove heater core hoses, then using an air hose, blow excess coolant from heater core.
11. Remove left and right instrument panel end caps.
12. Remove left and right center instrument panel extensions by disconnecting Velcro fasteners, then pulling rearward to unclip.
13. Remove center air outlet trim panel by pulling outward, start at bottom then work upward.
14. **On 1993-95 models,** disconnect traction control/fog lamp electrical connector.
15. **On all models,** unclip trim panel extension strip.
16. Remove upper trim panel, noting the following:
    a. **On 1992-94 models,** remove upper trim panel screw caps and screws. Then remove upper trim panel, **Fig. 9.**
    b. **On 1995 models,** remove upper trim panel screw caps and screws. Then remove upper trim panel and upper trim panel insulator **Figs. 10 and 11**
    c. **On all models,** lift upper trim panel to disengage clips at rear edge.
    d. Pull panel rearward out of clips at bottom of windshield, then remove upper trim panel.
17. Open glove compartment.
18. Remove cluster trim panel attaching screws, then pull upward to unclip.
19. Remove lockpins, then disconnect electrical connectors from instrument panel lighting rheostat and rear window defogger switches and Connector Position Assurance (CPA) devices, **Fig. 3.**

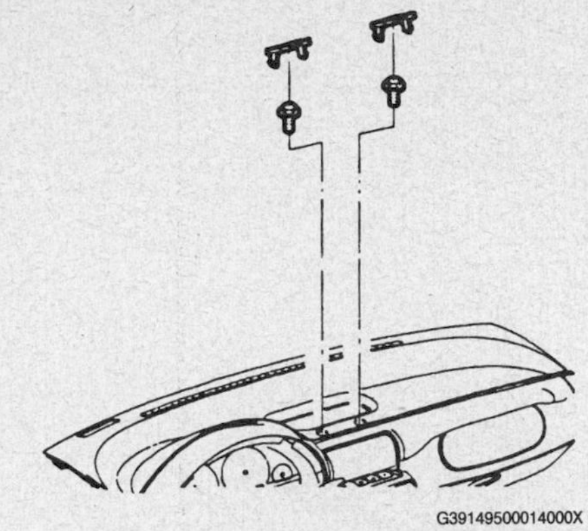
G39149500014000X

Fig. 10 Upper instrument panel removal. 1995

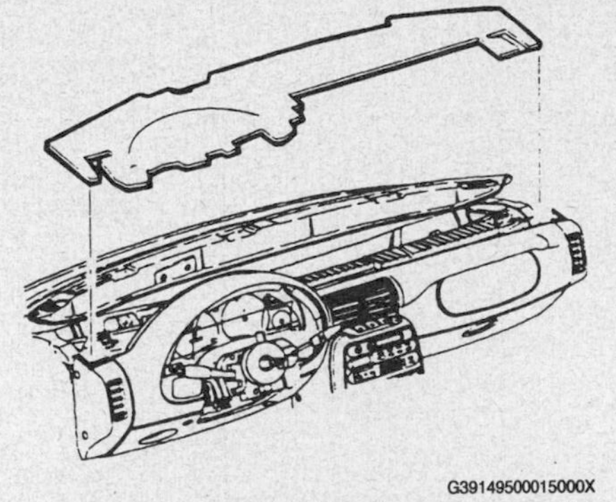
G39149500015000X

Fig. 11 Upper instrument panel insulator removal. 1995

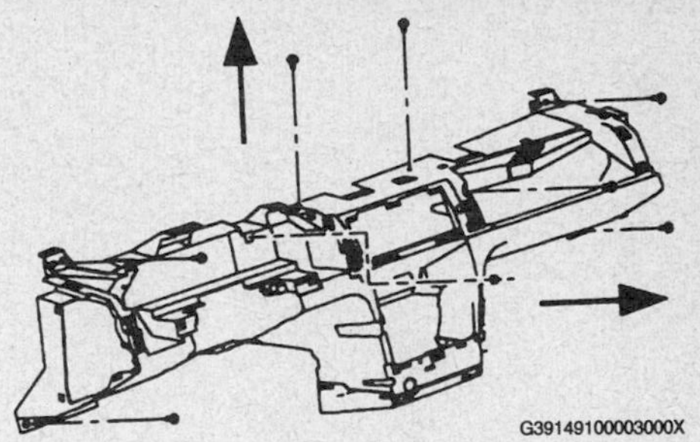
G39149100003000X

Fig. 12 Instrument panel removal

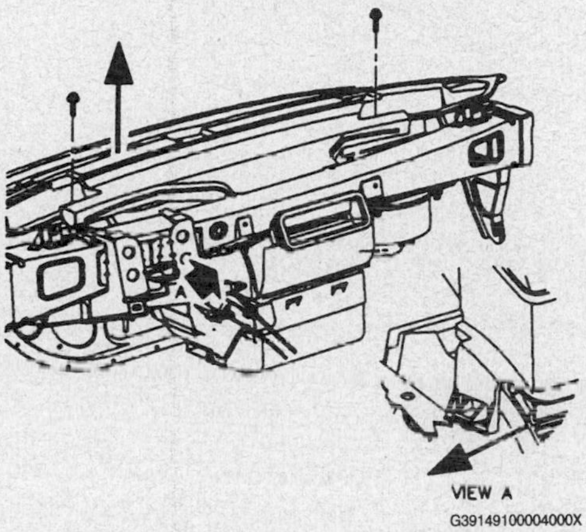
VIEW A
G39149100004000X

Fig. 13 Windshield defroster nozzle removal

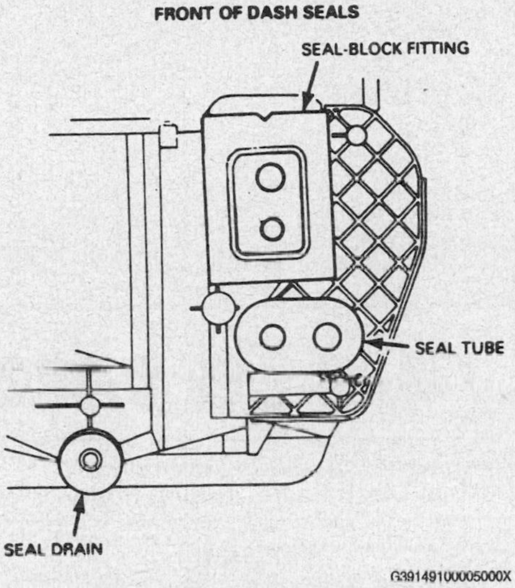
FRONT OF DASH SEALS
SEAL-BLOCK FITTING
SEAL TUBE
SEAL DRAIN
G39149100005000X

Fig. 14 Front dash seal removal

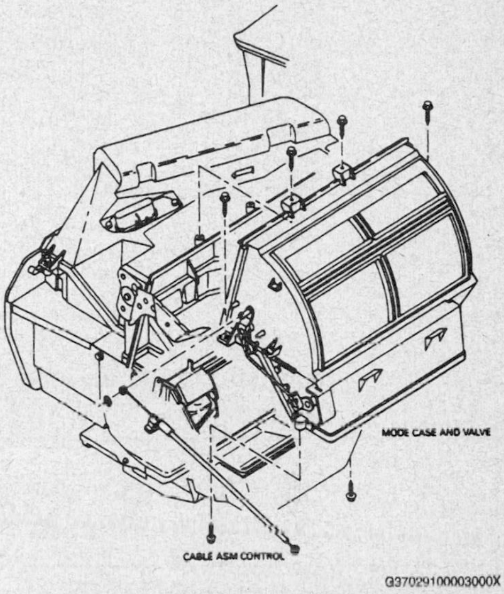
MODE CASE AND VALVE
CABLE ASM CONTROL
G37029100003000X

Fig. 15 Mode valve removal

20. Remove instrument cluster, then remove glove box attaching screws, then remove glove compartment.
21. Remove passenger side air bag harness from cross car beam and energy absorber.
22. Remove ALDL attaching screws, then ALDL connector.
23. Remove steering column filler panel attaching screws. Do not scratch console with mounting tabs.
24. Remove hood release lever.
25. Remove instrument cluster attaching screws, then pull rearward.
26. Disconnect cluster electrical connectors, then remove cluster.
27. Remove radio and HVAC control panels.
28. Disconnect lighter connector, then remove lighter bulb holder by rotating counterclockwise and pull straight rearward.
29. Apply parking brake, then lift and remove parking brake filler panel at rear edge.
30. **On models equipped with manual transaxle,** remove gear shift knob by pulling straight upward.
31. **On all models,** remove ashtray, then unclip ashtray bulb holder.
32. Remove window/mirror switch by lifting at back edge and pulling rearward.
33. Remove lockpins and disconnect window/mirror electrical connectors.
34. Remove console rear storage compartment liner.
35. Remove console side screws, then remove console rear compartment attaching screws.
36. Lift rear of console, push seat belt bezels from console.
37. Remove instrument fuse block attaching screws, then remove dash reinforcement ground wire.
38. Remove instrument panel junction block electrical connector and attaching screw.
39. **On models equipped with automatic transaxle,** disconnect two way instrument panel to body electrical connector and CPA devices.
40. **On all models,** remove antenna hold-down clips and electrical connectors.
41. Loosen floor shifter assembly.
42. Remove attaching nuts and bolts, then lift lower reinforcement bracket from stud, then slide bracket rearward.
43. Remove instrument panel retainer and reinforcement bracket attaching screws and nuts, **Fig. 12.**
44. Remove steering column attaching screws, then lower steering column to seat, then cover steering column.
45. Remove instrument panel assembly.
46. Lift rear heater duct from mounting bolt, then remove. Do not remove rear foam seal.
47. Remove center air outlet duct attaching screws, then remove.
48. Remove windshield defroster nozzle from mode valve assembly, **Fig. 13.**
49. Rotate front of defroster nozzle up and away from windshield, then remove.
50. Remove CPA devices and disconnect blower motor resistor connector.
51. Remove HVAC module hold-down clips and disconnect electrical connector.
52. Disconnect blower motor and recirc motor electrical connectors.
53. Remove HVAC module attaching screws and nuts, then remove module.
54. Remove and discard drain, heater core pipes, evaporator block and evaporator pipe O-ring front of dash seals, **Fig. 14.**
55. Remove mode valve assembly attaching screws, **Fig. 15,** then lift mode valve assembly upward to remove.
56. Remove upper air inlet case attaching screws, then lift upward to remove, **Fig. 16.**
57. Remove evaporator pipe clamp attaching screws, then lift evaporator upward to remove, **Fig. 17.**
58. Reverse procedure to install, noting the following:
    a. **Torque** steering column attaching screws to 33 ft. lbs.
    b. **Torque** thermal expansion valve to evaporator to 89 ft. lbs.
    c. **Torque** thermal expansion valve liquid and suction lines to 19 ft. lbs.

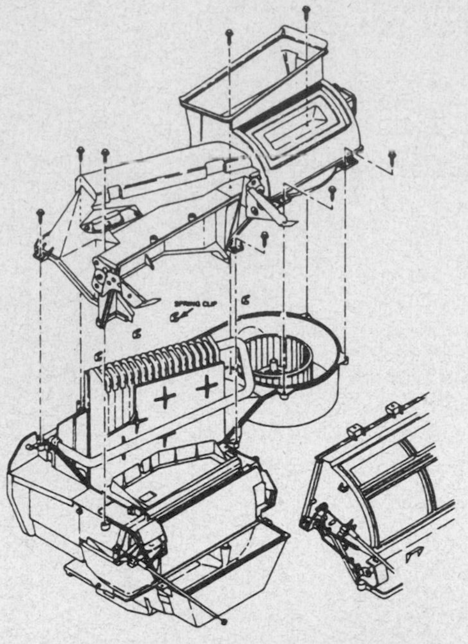
SPRING CLIP

G37029100004000X

Fig. 16 Upper air inlet case removal

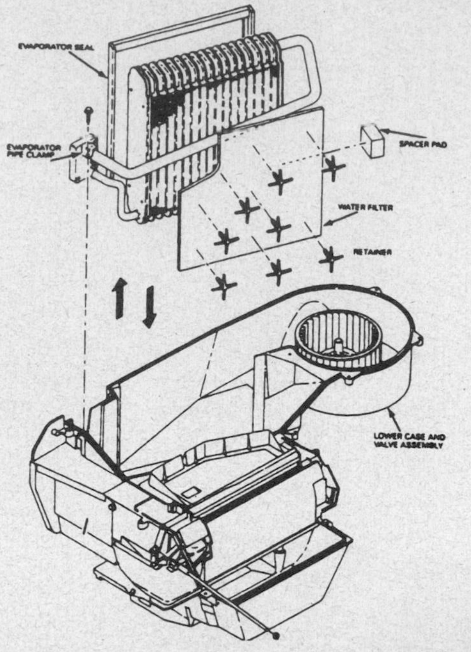
EVAPORATOR SEAL
EVAPORATOR PIPE CLAMP
SPACER PAD
WATER FILTER
RETAINER
LOWER CASE AND VALVE ASSEMBLY

G37029100005000X

Fig. 17 Evaporator removal

1.9L/4-116 ENGINE

NOTE: On Air Bag Equipped Models, Refer To "Air Bag System Precautions" Located In The Front Of This Manual For System Disarming & Arming Procedures.

INDEX

PRECAUTIONS

AIR BAG SYSTEMS

Refer to "Air Bag System Precautions" in the front of this manual for system disarming and arming procedures.

FUEL PRESSURE RELIEF

To relief fuel pressure, connect fuel gauge bar kit tool No. SA9127E, or equivalent, to fuel pressure test port using adapter tool No. SA9403E, or equivalent. Then place end of bleed hose into a suitable approved container and open valve to bleed system pressure. Once pressure is bled, remove gauge from fuel pressure test port and replace the cap.

ENGINE MOUNT

REPLACE

1. Remove two engine mount to midrail bracket attaching nuts, **Fig. 1.**
2. Position a floor jack under oil pan. Using a block of wood between pan and floor jack, raise engine enough to unload mount.
3. Remove three engine to front cover attaching nuts **Fig. 2,** then remove engine mount.
4. Reverse procedure to install. Tighten mount to midrail bracket and engine mount to front cover attaching nuts to specifications.

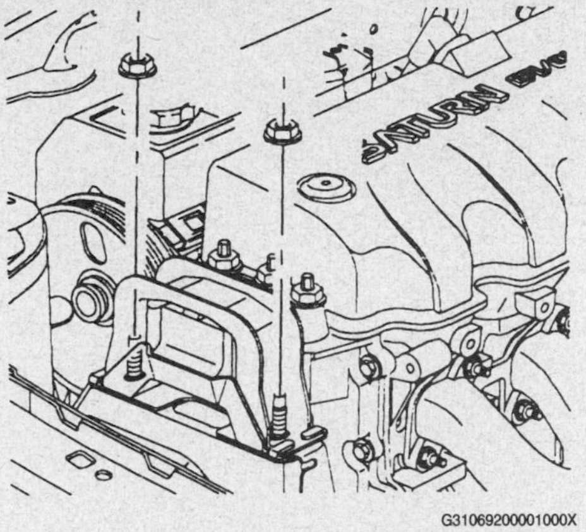
G31069200001000X

Fig. 1 Engine mount to midrail bracket removal

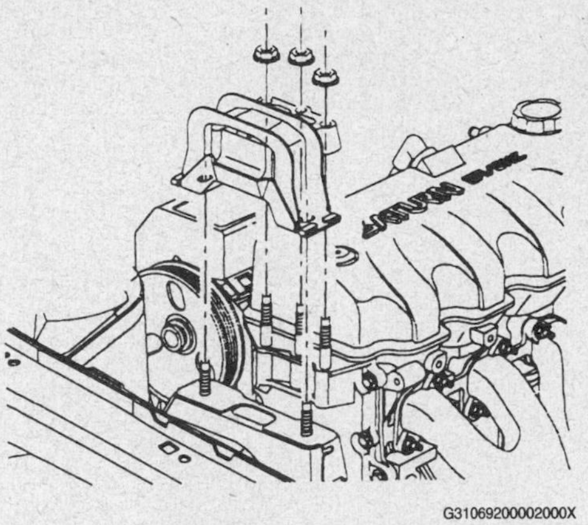
G31069200002000X

Fig. 2 Engine mount to front cover removal

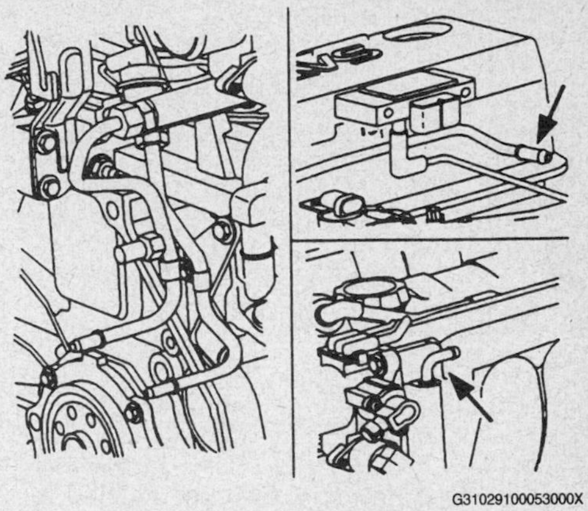
G31029100053000X

Fig. 3 Fuel line removal

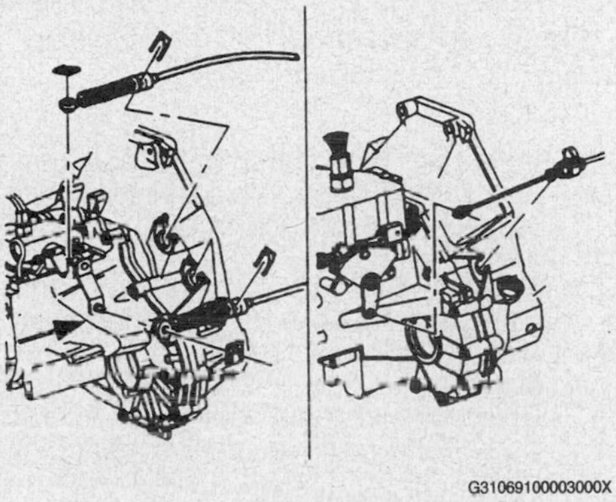
G31069100003000X

Fig. 4 Transaxle shifter cable removal

ENGINE REPLACE

1. Remove coolant bottle cap, then drain coolant.
2. **On DOHC models,** lift resonator upward to disengage from engine service support bracket.
3. **On all models,** remove air cleaner assembly.
4. Disconnect the following electrical connectors:
   a. Two coolant temperature sensors.
   b. Oxygen sensor and clip, at front transaxle mount bracket.
   c. Idles air control valve.
   d. Two ignition coil connectors.
   e. Manifold absolute pressure sensor.
   f. EGR solenoid.
   g. Brake booster hose at booster or intake manifold.
   h. Two grounds located rear of cylinder head at transaxle.
   i. Injector connectors.
5. Disconnect transaxle connectors as follows:
   a. Three neutral safety/selector switch.
   b. Valve body actuator.
   c. Turbine speed sensor.
   d. Temperature sensor.
   e. Back-up light switch.
6. Disconnect accelerator cables.
7. Bleed fuel pressure using tool No. SST 9127E or equivalent into a suitable container, then disconnect fuel lines using tool No. SA9157E or equivalent, **Fig. 3. Place a cloth around fitting before disconnecting.**
8. Using wire, tie fuel lines to brake master cylinder, to prevent fuel leakage.
9. Disconnect upper radiator hose and de-aeration hose at engine.
10. Disconnect A/C compressor and position aside.
11. Pinch tabs to disconnect and plug cooler lines at transaxle, then wrap transaxle cooler line fittings with a cloth.
12. **On models equipped with automatic transaxle,** disconnect shifter cable, **Fig. 4.**
13. **On models equipped with manual transaxle,** proceed as follows:
    a. Remove hydraulic damper to clutch housing stud nuts, then slide damper and bracket from studs.
    b. Rotate clutch actuator 1/4 turn counterclockwise while pushing toward housing to disengage connector and remove.
    c. Position clutch hydraulic system aside.
14. **On all models,** secure radiator, condenser and fan module to front crossbar using wire.
15. Raise and support vehicle.
16. Remove front wheel assemblies, then front and side shields from cradle.
17. Remove brake caliper bracket attaching bolts, then position caliper aside.
18. Disconnect lower radiator and heater inlet and return hoses at engine.
19. Disconnect steering shaft and power steering pressure switch electrical connector, if equipped.
20. Remove front exhaust pipe, catalytic converter, then powertrain stiffener bracket. **Do not remove torque restrictor bracket to transaxle.**
21. Remove automatic transaxle flywheel cover and torque converter to flexplate attaching bolts.
22. Remove alternator and starter shields.
23. Disconnect the following electrical connectors:

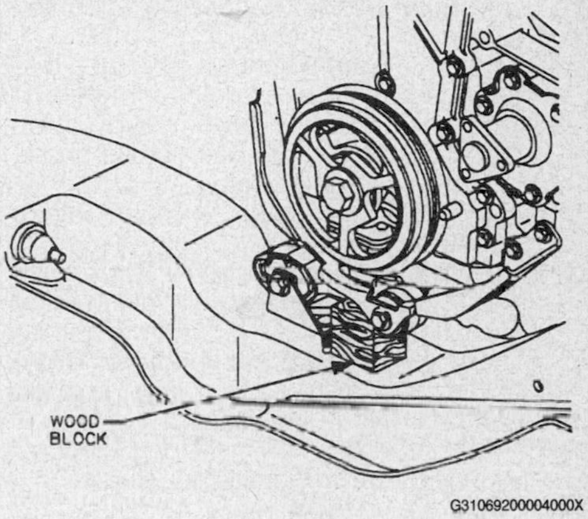
WOOD
BLOCK
G31069200004000X

Fig. 5 Support between torque strut & cradle

    a. Starter feed.
    b. Alternator feed.
    c. Oil pressure sensor.
    d. Knock sensor.
    e. Crankshaft position sensor.
    f. EVO solenoid, if equipped.
    g. Vehicle speed sensor.
    h. Canister purge solenoid.
    i. PCM/EC and oxygen sensor.
    j. ABS wheel sensor ground connectors, if equipped.
24. Unclip brake lines from rear of cradle, then remove electrical harness from engine, then low vehicle, to lay electrical harness on underhood junction block and battery cover.
25. Place a one inch by one inch by 2 inch long block of wood between torque strut and cradle, **Fig. 5.**
26. Position suitable powertrain support dolly and two four inch by four inch by 36 inch wood pieces to support cradle.
27. Remove cradle to body attaching bolts, then lower cradle, ensuring two large rear cradle spacers are attached.
28. Install suitable engine lifting equipment.
29. Remove spark plug wire ends at ignition module.
30. Remove power steering pump with bracket, then using wire, attach in upright position to steering gear or cradle.

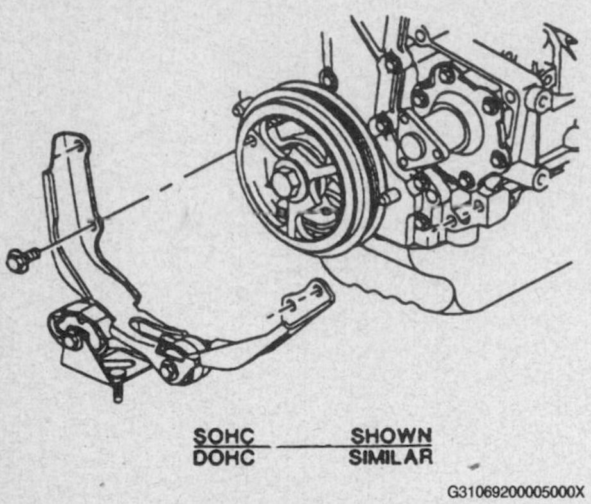
SOHC SHOWN
DOHC SIMILAR
G31069200005000X

Fig. 6 Engine strut bracket & torque strut removal

31. Remove transaxle housing attaching bolts.
32. Remove front engine mount, then disconnect motion restrictor, if required.
33. Place 1/2 inch by one inch by three inch block of wood below axle shaft.
34. Remove starter bracket.
35. **On DOHC models,** remove intake manifold bracket.
36. **On all models,** remove three axle shaft bracket bolts, then allow bracket to rotate rearward. It may be necessary to lift engine slightly to allow clearance between starter bracket and driveshaft bracket.
37. Place a 4 X 4 X 6 inch long block of wood under transaxle housing.
38. Remove engine strut bracket and torque strut assembly. The engine may have to lifted just enough for the engine strut removal, **Fig. 6.**
39. Remove four transaxle housing attaching bolts.
40. Carefully lift engine, then install to engine stand.
41. Remove the following:
    a. Starter and alternator.
    b. Water pump.
    c. Oil Pressure sending unit.
    d. Knock sensor.
    e. Crankshaft position sensor.
    f. Clutch assembly (flexplate) and flywheel.
    g. Using tool No. SST SA9123 E or equivalent, cut oil pan seal from front cover oil seal rear seal carrier, then remove oil pan and filter.
    h. Oil pick up tube.
    i. **On DOHC models,** remove baffle plate.
42. Reverse procedure to install.

INTAKE MANIFOLD

REPLACE

SOHC

1. Drain engine coolant.
2. Remove air cleaner assembly, then disconnect fresh air hose at cam cover.
3. Remove PCV hose.
4. Connect tool No. SA9127E or equivalent to fuel pressure, **Fig. 7,** when fuel line is disconnected wrap with a cloth before disconnecting.

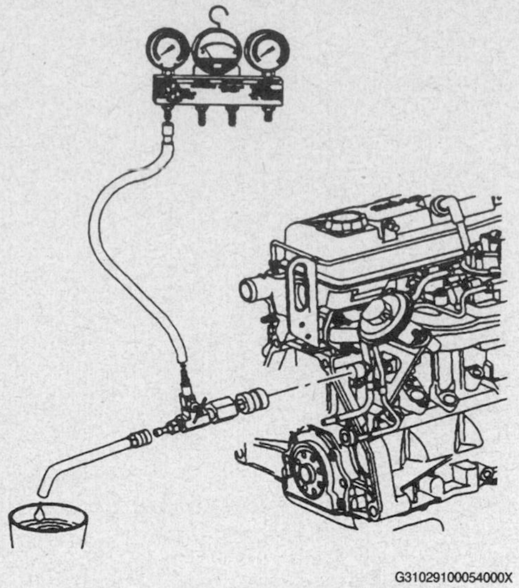
G31029100054000X

Fig. 7 Fuel pressure bleed

5. Install fuel bleed hose to suitable container, then open valve to bleed system, once pressure is bled, remove tool.
6. Remove fuel line bracket bolt, then using tool No. SA9157E or equivalent, disconnect fuel supply and return lines.
7. Disconnect throttle cable from throttle body, then remove bracket attaching nuts.
8. Disconnect the following electrical connectors:
    a. Fuel injectors.
    b. Idle air control (IAC).
    c. Throttle position sensor (TPS).
    d. EGR valve.
    e. Manifold absolute pressure sensor.
9. Remove wires with tubes, the position harness onto fuel relay.
10. Disconnect and label TBI tube module assembly vacuum hoses.
11. Disconnect heater hose, then remove cylinder head coolant outlet deaeration line fitting and clamps, then position aside.
12. Remove intake manifold support bracket to block attaching bolt, then remove accessory drive belt.
13. Remove power steering pump attaching bolts, then position aside.
14. Remove intake manifold attaching nuts, then remove manifold and gasket.
15. Reverse procedure to install. Tighten intake manifold attaching nuts to specifications in sequence as shown in, **Fig. 8.**

DOHC

1. Drain engine coolant.
2. Remove air inlet tube/resonator assembly, then disconnect fresh air hose at cam cover, lift resonator upward to disengage from engine.
3. Remove PCV hose.
4. Connect tool No. SA9127E or equivalent to fuel pressure, **Fig. 7,** when fuel line is disconnected wrap with a cloth before disconnecting.

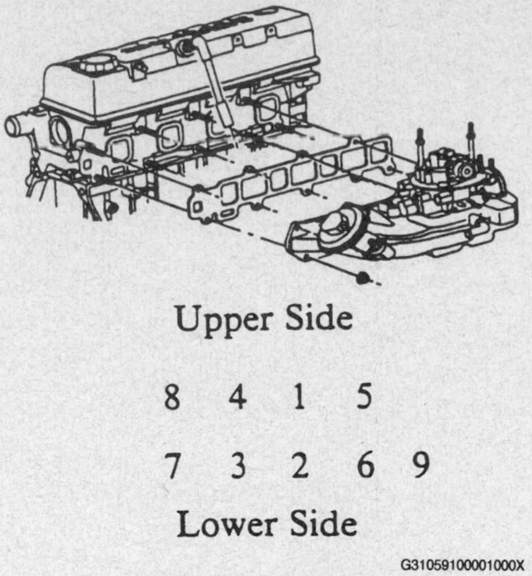
Upper Side
8 4 1 5
7 3 2 6 9
Lower Side
G31059100001000X

Fig. 8 Intake manifold tightening sequence. SOHC

5. Install fuel bleed hose to suitable container, then open valve to bleed system, once pressure is bled, remove tool.
6. Remove fuel line bracket bolt, then using tool No. SA9157E or equivalent, disconnect fuel supply and return lines.
7. Disconnect throttle cable from throttle body, then remove bracket attaching nuts.
8. Disconnect the following electrical connectors:
    a. Fuel injectors.
    b. Idle air control (IAC).
    c. Throttle position sensor (TPS).
    d. Manifold absolute pressure sensor.
9. Disconnect heater and de-aeration hoses at intake manifold outlet.
10. Disconnect EGR solenoid vacuum hose.
11. Position electrical harness over brake master cylinder.
12. Remove intake manifold support bracket to block attaching bolt, then remove accessory drive belt.
13. Remove power steering pump attaching bolts, then position aside.
14. Remove upper intake manifold attaching nuts.
15. Raise and support vehicle, then remove lower power steering unit bracket.
16. Remove intake manifold bracket attaching bolt.
17. Disconnect canister purge relay and brake booster vacuum hose.
18. Remove lower intake manifold attaching stud, then lower vehicle, remove manifold.
19. Reverse procedure to install. Tighten intake manifold attaching nuts to specifications in sequence as shown in, **Fig. 9.**

EXHAUST MANIFOLD

REPLACE

1. Raise and support vehicle.
2. **On 1992 models,** remove exhaust

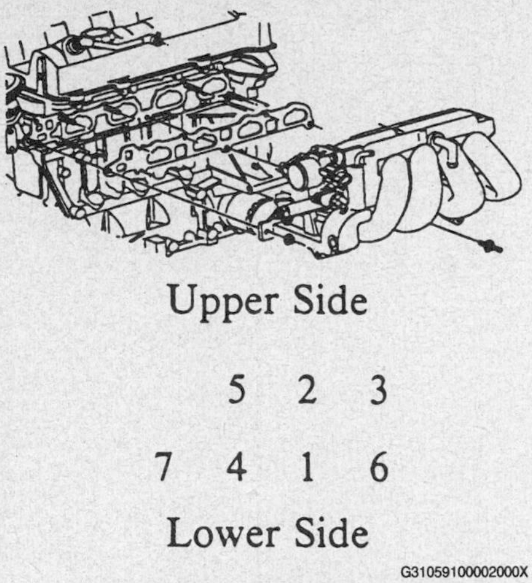
Upper Side
5 2 3
7 4 1 6
Lower Side
G31059100002000X

Fig. 9 Intake manifold tightening sequence. DOHC

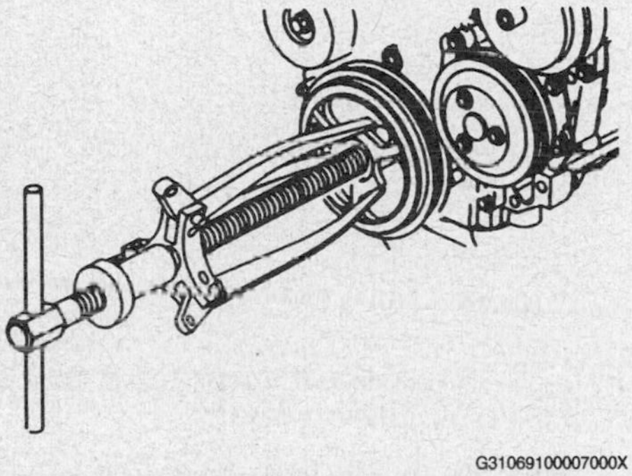
G31069100007000X

Fig. 12 Crankshaft damper removal

pipe to manifold attaching nuts, then lower pipe and discard gasket.
3. **On all models,** lower vehicle.
4. Remove A/C compressor and rear compressor bracket.
5. **On 1993-95 models,** remove two front exhaust pipe to engine stiffening bracket attaching bolts.
6. **On all models,** disconnect oxygen sensor electrical connector, then remove sensor.
7. Remove exhaust manifold attaching nuts, then remove manifold and discard gasket.
8. Reverse procedure to install. Tighten exhaust manifold attaching nuts to specification in sequence, **Fig. 10.**

CYLINDER HEAD
REPLACE
SOHC

1. Remove coolant bottle cap.
2. Drain coolant from engine and radiator.
3. Remove air cleaner and air inlet duct, then disconnect PCV and fresh air hose.
4. Disconnect accelerator cable from TBI throttle lever and bracket from intake manifold.
5. Disconnect the following electrical connectors:
   a. Coolant temperature and PCM connectors.

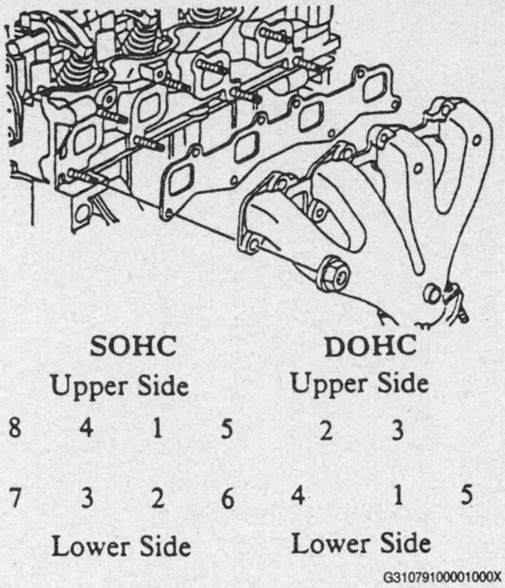
SOHC
Upper Side
8 4 1 5
7 3 2 6
Lower Side
DOHC
Upper Side
2 3
4 1 5
Lower Side
G31079100001000X

Fig. 10 Exhaust manifold tightening sequence

   b. Injectors.
   c. Idle air control valve.
   d. Manifold air pressure sensor.
   e. Throttle position switch.
   f. Spark plug wires.
   g. Oxygen sensor.
   h. A/C Compressor.
6. Position electrical harness on underhood junction block.
7. Disconnect and label the following vacuum hoses:
   a. Canister purge valve.
   b. EGR valve.
   c. MAP sensor.
   d. Brake booster at intake manifold or brake booster.
   e. TBI assembly.
8. Disconnect upper radiator hose at cylinder head, heater hose at intake manifold and de-aeration hose at TBI assembly.
9. Using tool No. SA9127E or equivalent, bleed fuel pressure into suitable container.
10. Remove fuel line clamp to intake manifold base attaching bolt.
11. Disconnect fuel supply and return lines at TBI assembly, then remove lower intake manifold support bracket stud.
12. Unclip lower splash shield and place a one by one by 2 inch long block of wood between torque strut and cradle.
13. Remove three righthand upper engine torque axis mount to front cover attaching nuts, allowing engine to rest on block of wood.
14. Remove accessory drive belt.
15. Disconnect de-aeration line at cylinder head water outlet and support bracket then remove rocker cover, **Fig. 11.**
16. Remove three A/C compressor front bracket to cylinder head attaching bolts, then rear bracket attaching bolts, then position compressor aside.
17. Remove power steering pump bracket attaching bolts, then position pump aside.

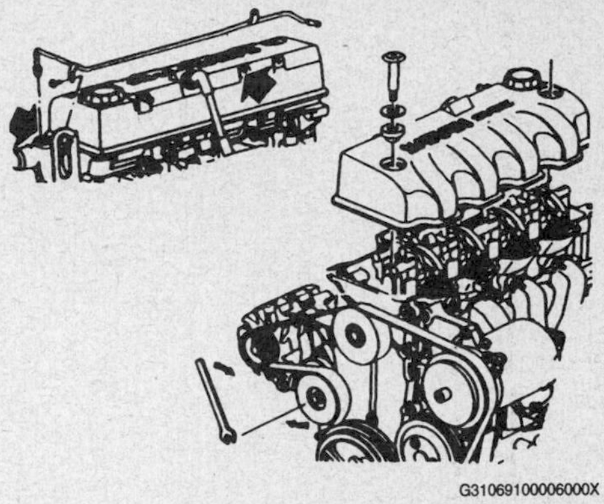
G31069100006000X

Fig. 11 Valve cover removal. SOHC engine

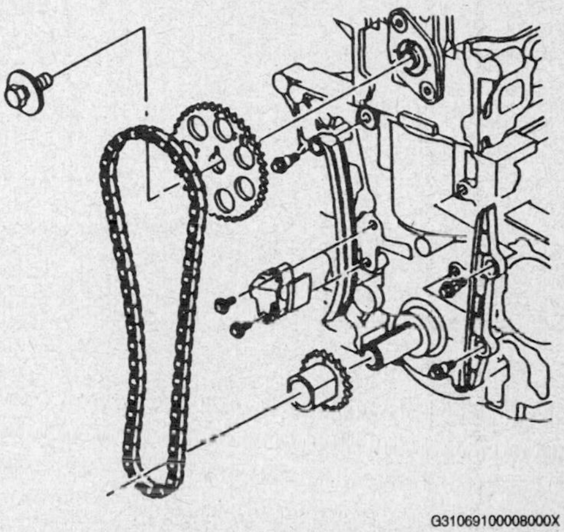
G31069100008000X

Fig. 13 Timing chain removal. SOHC engine

18. Raise and support vehicle, then drain engine oil.
19. Remove lefthand wheel assembly and splash shield.
20. Remove drive belt tensioner.
21. Using a universal three jaw puller, **Fig. 12,** while holding damper, remove front crankshaft damper assembly. **Do not pry against cover.**
22. Using tool No. SA9104 E or equivalent with flat side toward crankshaft sprocket, to hold front crankshaft timing sprocket.
23. Remove four front oil pan attaching bolts and 14 front cover attaching bolts.
24. Using tool No. SA9123E or equivalent, cut RTV seal from front cover.
25. Using front cover pry tangs, remove cover, then remove and discard two oil gallery transfer seals.
26. **Positioning crankshaft 90° off top dead center (TDC) ensures pistons will not contact valves during assembly.**
27. Rotate crankshaft clockwise, viewed from crankshaft accessory belt end, ensuring timing mark on crankshaft sprocket and keyway align with main bearing cap split line.
28. Remove timing chain, tensioner, guides, camshaft sprocket and chained, using a 7/8 inch wrench to hold camshaft when removing sprocket, **Fig. 13.**

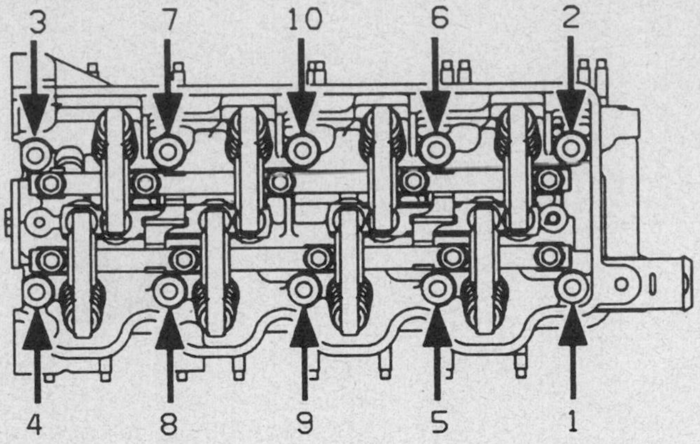
3 7 10 6 2
4 8 9 5 1
G31069100009000X

Fig. 14 Cylinder head bolt loosening sequence

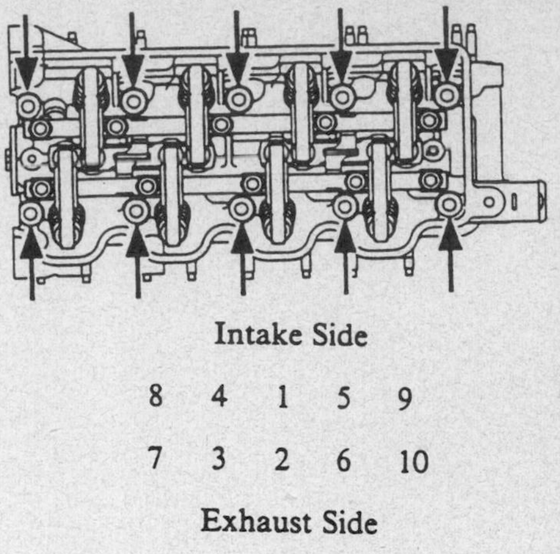
Intake Side
8 4 1 5 9
7 3 2 6 10
Exhaust Side
G31069100010000X

Fig. 15 Cylinder head bolt tightening sequence

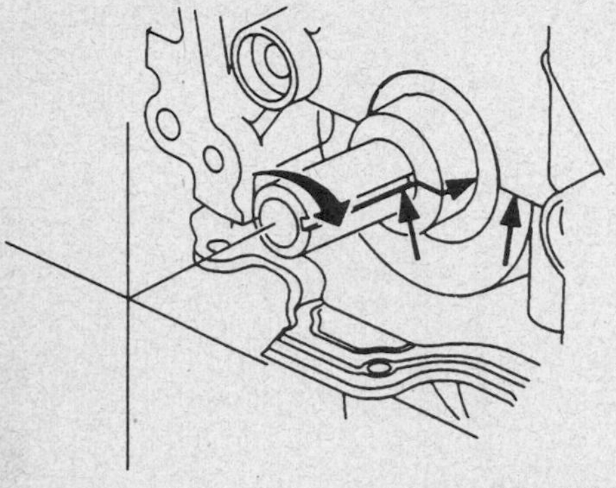
G31069100011000X

Fig. 16 Crankshaft at 90° past TDC

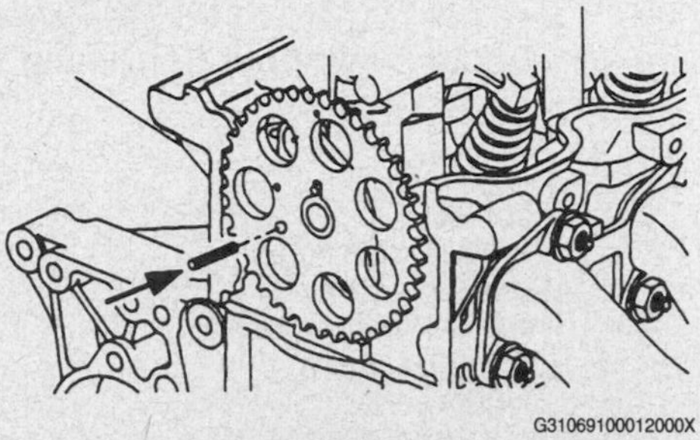
G31069100012000X

Fig. 17 Camshaft at No. 1 TDC. SOHC engine

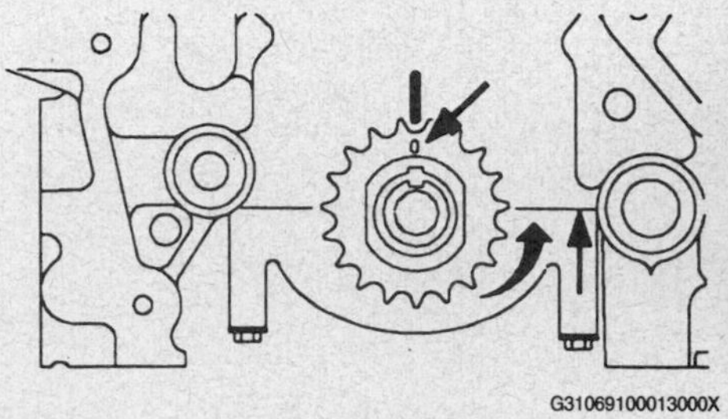
G31069100013000X

Fig. 18 Crankshaft sprocket & block timing mark

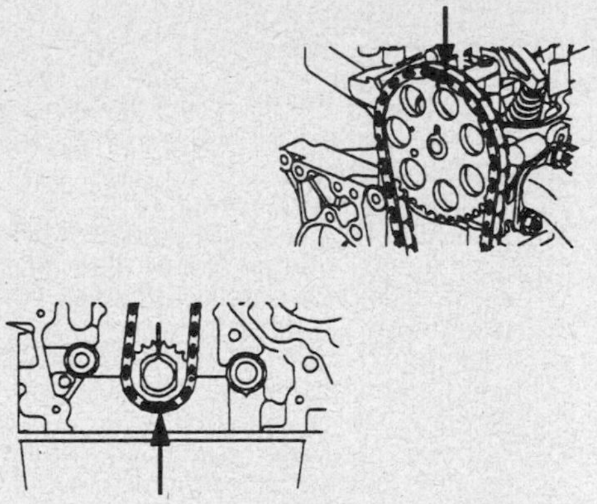
G31069100014000X

Fig. 19 Timing chain installation. SOHC

29. Remove TBI assembly, discard gasket, then cover intake manifold opening.
30. Using a six point socket, uniformly loosen and remove ten head bolts in sequence shown, **Fig. 14.**
31. Lift cylinder head from cylinder block dowels.
32. Reverse procedure to install, noting the following:
    a. Install cylinder head bolts in sequence shown, **Fig. 15.** Tighten to specifications.
    b. Ensure crankshaft is 90° past TDC, **Fig. 16,** as required, position camshaft to No. 1 TDC by loosely installing sprocket and rotating clockwise until timing pin may be installed, **Fig. 17.**
    c. Rotate crankshaft counterclockwise until No. 1 cylinder is TDC, crankshaft sprocket timing mark will align with cylinder block timing mark, **Fig. 18.**
    d. One silver link plate aligns to camshaft sprocket pip marks and another paired link plates align with crankshaft sprocket tooth that is located at the 6 o'clock position. Crankshaft sprocket pip mark must be aligned with block timing mark.
    e. Place timing chain over camshaft sprocket and under crankshaft sprocket, camshaft sprocket FRT letters must face forward, **Fig. 19.**
    f. **Keep excess chain slack to chain tensioner side of cylinder block when installing timing chain.**
    g. Install camshaft sprocket timing pin, using a 3/16 inch drill, **Fig. 17.**
    h. Install camshaft washer and bolt, tighten to specifications, while holding cam.
    i. Install chain guides.

DOHC

1. Remove coolant bottle cap.
2. Drain coolant from radiator and engine.
3. Remove air cleaner cover and air inlet duct, lift resonator upward to disengage button from engine support bracket.
4. Disconnect cam cover air hose at cam cover.
5. Disconnect accelerator cable from throttle body and intake manifold bracket.
6. Remove the following electrical connectors:
    a. Coolant temperature gauge and PCM connectors.
    b. Injector connectors.
    c. Idle air control valve.
    d. Throttle position switch.
    e. Manifold air pressure sensor.
    f. Remove oxygen sensor.
    g. Remove spark plug wires.
    h. A/C compressor.
7. Lay electrical harness onto underhood junction block and battery cover.
8. Disconnect and label the following vacuum hoses:
    a. Canister purge valve.
    b. PCV valve at cam cover.
    c. EGR valve.
    d. Fuel regulator.
    e. Throttle body connector.
9. Disconnect the following hose clamps using tool No. SA911E or equivalent:
    a. Upper radiator head at cylinder head outlet.
    b. De-aeration hose at intake manifold.
    c. Heater hose at intake manifold or front of dash.
    d. Vacuum brake booster hose.
10. Using tool No. SA9127E or equivalent, bleed fuel pressure into suitable container.
11. Remove fuel line clamp to intake manifold base attaching bolt.
12. Using tool No. SA9157E or equivalent, disconnect fuel supply and return line to fuel rail.

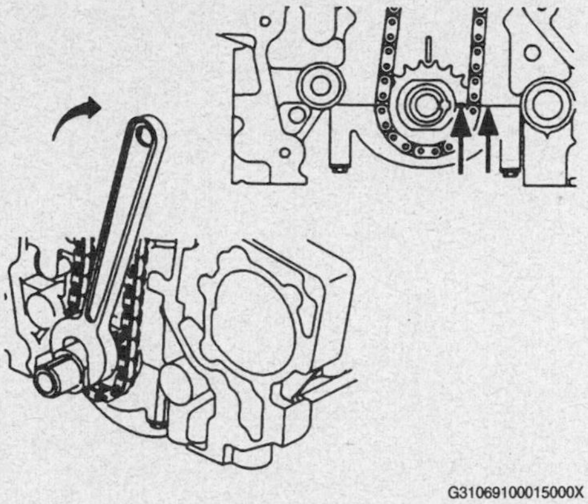

G31069100015000X

Fig. 20 Crankshaft sprocket & keyway alignment. DOHC engine

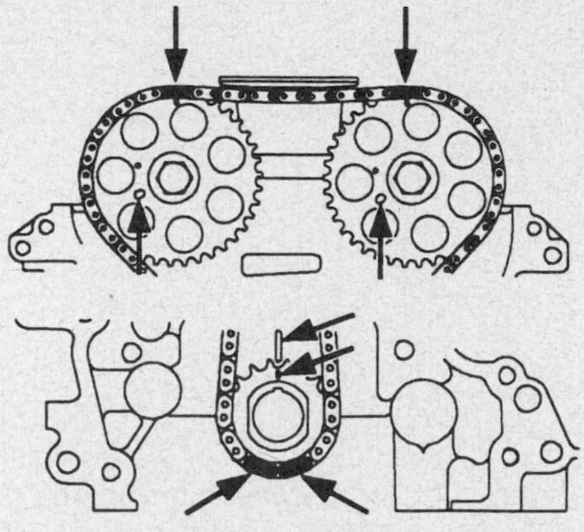

G31069100016000X

Fig. 21 Crankshaft alignment. DOHC

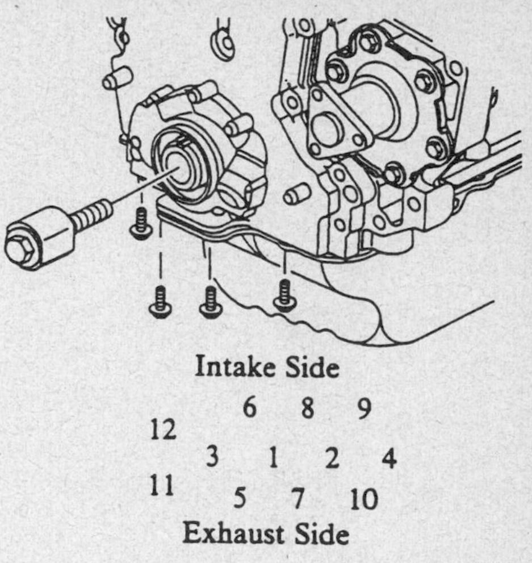
Intake Side
12
6 8 9
3 1 2 4
11
5 7 10
Exhaust Side

G31069100017000X

Fig. 22 Cam cover tightening sequence. DOHC

13. Disconnect fuel line at regulator.
14. Remove upper intake manifold support bracket attaching bolt.
15. Unclip lower splash shield and place a one by one by 2 inch long block of wood between torque strut and cradle.
16. Remove three righthand upper engine torque axis mount to front cover attaching nuts, allowing engine to rest on block of wood.
17. Remove accessory drive belt and tensioner. Do not remove water pump pulley.
18. Remove accessory drive belt idler pulley.
19. Remove camshaft front cover assembly.
20. Remove power steering pump bracket attaching bolts, then position pump aside.
21. Remove A/C compressor front and rear bracket attaching bolts, then position compressor aside.
22. Raise and support vehicle, then drain engine oil.
23. Remove left wheel assembly and splash shield.
24. Remove intake manifold bracket to intake manifold attaching bolts.
25. Remove front damper assembly, hold damper with a strap wrench or 3/4 inch square by 12 inch long piece of wood wedged between damper spoke and rear, lower side of front cover.
26. Using a universal three jaw puller, **Fig. 12**, while holding damper, remove front crankshaft damper assembly. **Do not pry against cover.**
27. Disconnect exhaust pipe from exhaust manifold.
28. Install tool No. SA9104E or equivalent with flat side toward sprocket to hold sprocket.
29. Remove four front oil pan bolts, the using tool No. SA9123E or equivalent, cut seal from front cover.
30. Remove front cover attaching bolts, then use a screwdriver to pry front cover from cylinder block.
31. **Position crankshaft 90° off top dead center ensures pistons will not contact valves upon assembly.**
32. Rotate crankshaft clockwise, viewed from crankshaft accessory belt end, ensuring timing mark on sprocket and keyway align with main bearing cap split line, **Fig. 20.**
33. Remove timing chain tensioner, guides, camshaft sprockets and chain, then using a 7/8 inch wrench to hold camshaft while removing sprocket bolts. **Do place fingers or tools between camshaft sprocket and chain during removal or assembly.**
34. Loosen and remove cylinder head bolts in sequence, **Fig. 14.**
35. Lift cylinder head from dowels on engine block, then remove head.
36. Reverse to install, noting the following:
    a. Install cylinder head bolts in sequence shown, **Fig. 15.** Tighten to specifications.
    b. Ensure crankshaft is 90° past TDC, **Fig. 16,** install camshaft timing gears attaching bolts and washer, the letters FRT on sprocket must face forward away from cylinder head, then hold camshafts while tightening bolts to specifications. **Do not torque camshaft attaching bolts against 3/16 inch timing pins as cylinder head damage may result.**
    c. Turn camshaft up to No. 1 TDC by rotating camshaft and sprocket until timing pins can be installed.
    d. Rotate crankshaft counterclockwise until No. 1 cylinder is TDC, crankshaft sprocket timing mark will align with cylinder block timing mark, **Fig. 18.**
    e. Two separated silver link plates align to camshaft sprocket pip marks and another two paired link plates align crankshaft sprocket tooth that is located at the 6 o'clock position. Crankshaft sprocket pip mark must be aligned with block timing mark.
    f. Place timing chain over camshaft sprockets and under crankshaft sprocket.
    g. **Keep excess chain slack to chain tensioner side (movable guide) of cylinder block when installing timing chain or camshaft sprockets will not be correctly timed.**
    h. Position silver colored link plates over pip mark on cam sprocket, then position crankshaft sprocket tooth that is pointed downward at 6 o'clock position between two silver colored links. Crankshaft sprocket pip mark should be aligned with block timing mark.
    i. Align timing pin holes, crankshaft sprocket pip mark with block mark, colored links with camshaft and crankshaft, **Fig. 21.**
    j. Install cam covers, tighten to sequence, **Fig. 22,** to specifications.

CAMSHAFT LOBE LIFT SPECIFICATIONS

Engine	Intake	Exhaust
SOHC	.2531-.2556	.2531-.2556
DOHC	.3528-.3559	.3409-.3441

VALVE CLEARANCE SPECIFICATIONS

Engine	Intake	Exhaust
SOHC	.0010-.0025	.0015-.0020
DOHC (1992-94)	.0010-.0025	.0010-.0020
DOHC (1995)	.0010-.0025	.0015-.0032

VALVE ADJUSTMENT

This engine is equipped with hydraulic lifters and no adjustment is required.

VALVE GUIDES

Valve guides are an integral part of the cylinder head and are pressed in. If valve stem clearance becomes excessive, the valve guides must be reamed to the oversize and the oversize valves installed. Valves are available in .010 inch oversize.

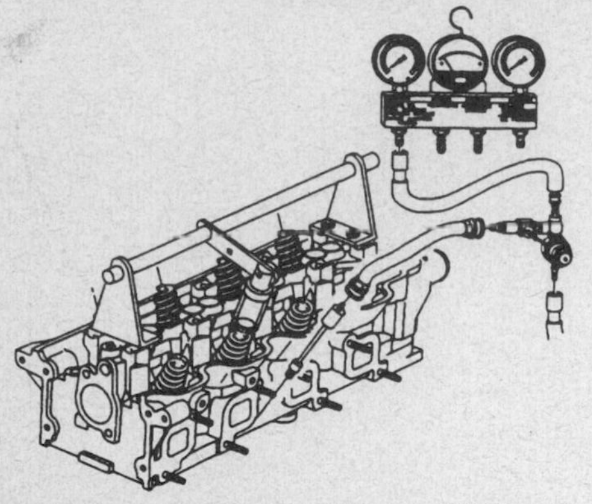
G31069100018000X
Fig. 23 Pressurizing cylinder

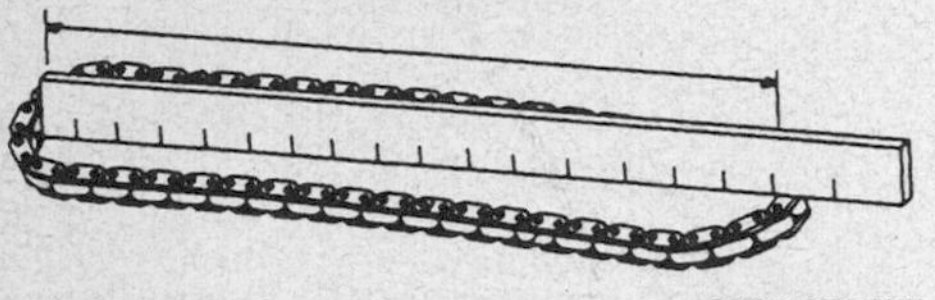
G31069100021000X
Fig. 26 Timing chain length inspection

VALVE SPRING & SEALS
REPLACE

1. **On SOHC models,** remove spark plugs, rocker cover and rocker arm assemblies.
2. **On DOHC models,** remove spark plugs, cam cover and camshaft.
3. **On all models,** install angle supports tool No. SA9127E or equivalent, then on SOHC engines, use four M8 X 25 mm bolts, and DOHC engines use four M6 X 25 mm bolts to mount supports to end rocker arm shaft threaded holes with support flange toward center of cylinder head, then **torque** to 124 inch lbs. on SOHC models, or 89 inch lbs. on DOHC models.
4. While sliding rods through support, install compressor lever arm assembly.
5. Install spark plug adapter tool SA9127E or equivalent, to each cylinder.
6. With piston at TDC, pressurize cylinder to 100 psi, **Fig. 23.**
7. Tap compressor lever with plastic mallet while applying slight amount of pressure to breaker bar.
8. Position lever over valve spring, then use a 1/2 inch breaker bar to compress spring.
9. Remove valve spring cap retainers, then release spring tension.
10. Remove cap and spring.
11. Using tool No. SA9102E or equivalent, remove valve stem seal.
12. Reverse procedure to install.

FRONT COVER
REPLACE

1. Unclip lower splash shield and place a one by one by 2 inch long block of wood between torque strut and cradle.

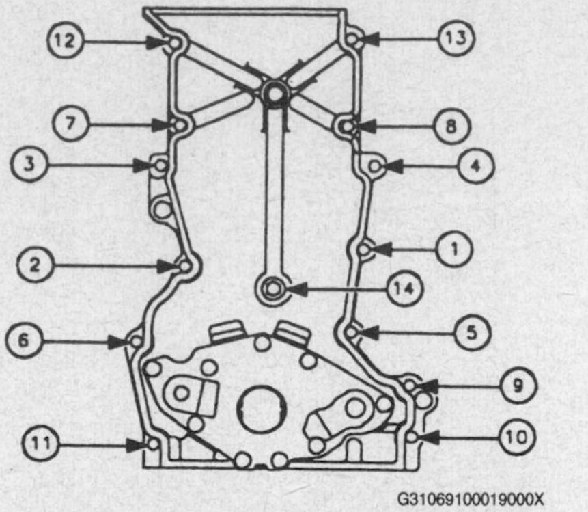
12
13
7
8
3
4
2
1
14
6
5
9
11
10
G31069100019000X
Fig. 24 Front cover tightening sequence. SOHC

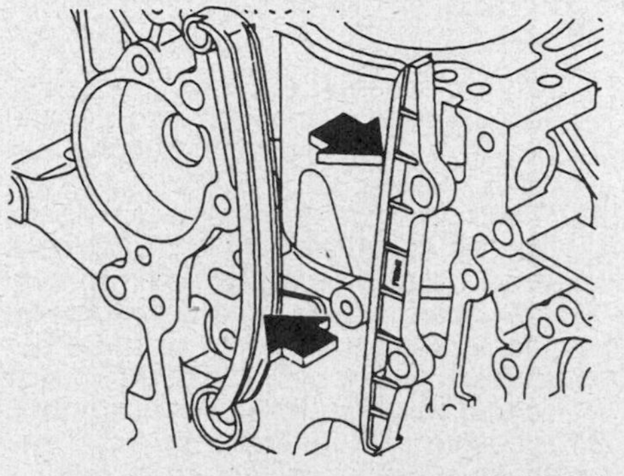
G31069100022000X
Fig. 27 Timing chain guide track wear

2. Remove three righthand upper engine torque axis mount to front cover attaching nuts, allowing engine to rest on block of wood.
3. Remove accessory drive belt, idler pulley, tensioner, crankshaft damper and power steering pump.
4. Remove front cover attaching bolts.
5. Using a screwdriver, pry front cover at upper and lower corners to remove.
6. Reverse procedure to install. Tighten attaching bolts to specifications, in sequence, **Fig. 24 and 25.**

TIMING CHAIN
REPLACE
SOHC

Refer to "Cylinder Head, Replace" for timing chain replacement procedure.

1. Inspect timing chain as follows:
   a. Inspect chain for wear and damaged links.
   b. Using ruler, measure chain inner diameter, standard I.D. is 16.50-16.61 inch and service limit is 16.77 inch, **Fig. 26.**
   c. Inspect chain guides for wear and cracks, measure chain track wear, standard is 0.0 inch, service limit is .0984 inch, **Fig. 27.**
   d. Inspect timing sprocket teeth on crankshaft, camshaft and key for wear. Inspect camshaft thrust plate and sprocket thrust surface for

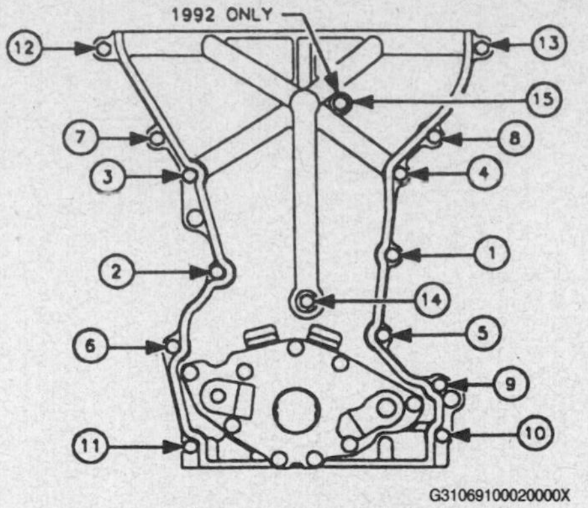
1992 ONLY
12
13
15
7
8
3
4
1
2
14
6
5
9
11
10
G31069100020000X
Fig. 25 Front cover tightening sequence. DOHC

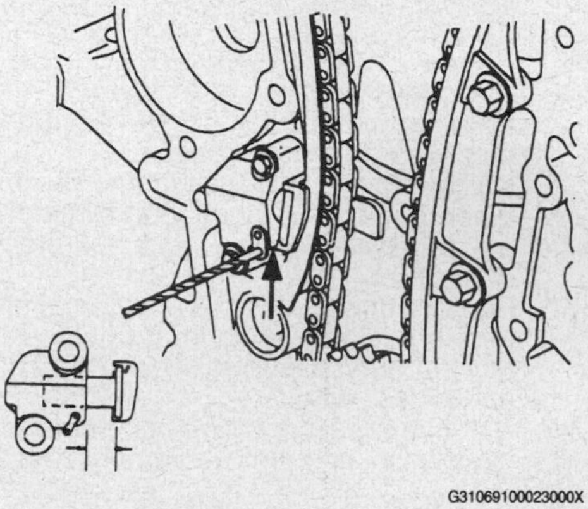
G31069100023000X
Fig. 28 Timing chain tensioner check

   cracks and wear.
   e. Inspect tensioner operation, release plunger lock, ensuring piston moves freely.
   f. Ensure oil feed hole is open, submerge tensioner in oil or solvent, depress plunger and check flow from tensioner body, check cylinder block port for blockage.
   g. With timing chain and guides installed, measure plunger travel, **Fig. 28,** standard is .0696-.438 inch, service limit is .8626 inch.

DOHC

Refer to "Cylinder Head, Replace" for timing chain replacement procedure.

1. Inspect timing chain as follows:
   a. Inspect chain for wear and damaged links.
   b. Using a ruler, measure chain inner diameter, standard I.D. is 22.83-22.95 inch and service limit is 23.15 inch, **Fig. 26.**
   c. Inspect chain guides for wear and cracks, measure chain track wear, standard is 0.0 inch, service limit is .0984 inch, **Fig. 27.**
   d. Inspect timing sprocket teeth on crankshaft, camshaft and key for wear. Inspect camshaft thrust plate and sprocket thrust surface for cracks and wear.
   e. Inspect tensioner operation, release plunger lock, ensuring piston moves freely.
   f. Ensure oil feed hole is open, submerge tensioner in oil or solvent,

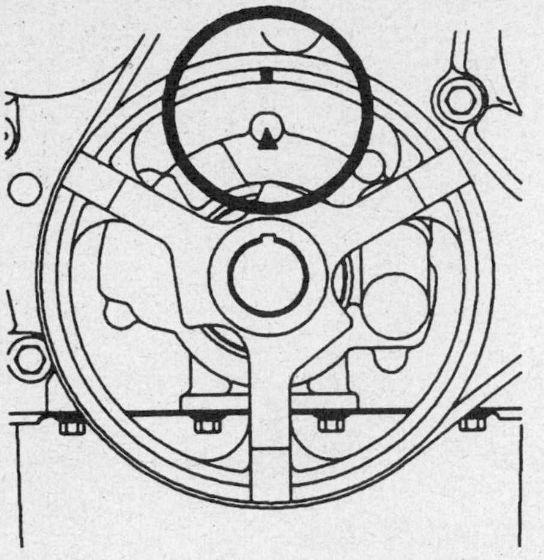
G31069100024000X

Fig. 29 No. 1 cylinder at TDC. DOHC

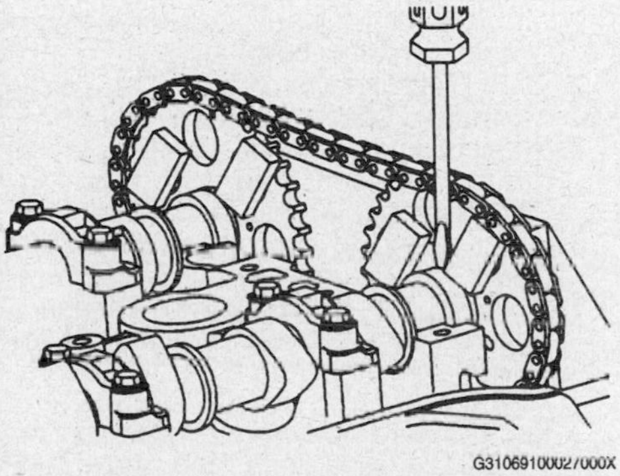
G31069100027000X

Fig. 32 Camshaft removal. DOHC

depress plunger and check flow from tensioner body, check cylinder block port for blockage.
g. With timing chain and guides installed, measure plunger travel, **Fig. 28,** standard is .045-.388 inch, service limit is .8626 inch.

CAMSHAFT
REPLACE
SOHC

1. Remove cylinder head as outlined under "Cylinder Head, Replace."
2. Remove spark plugs.
3. Remove intake and exhaust manifold attaching nuts, then remove.
4. Remove rocker arm assembly attaching bolts, then remove two rocker arm shafts and rocker arm guide plates and lifters.
5. Remove battery cover and battery, then using suitable punch and hammer, remove rear camshaft plug.
6. Measure camshaft thrust clearance while moving camshaft back and forth, using a dial indicator. Standard thrust is .028-.0079 inches and service limit is .0098 inch. If clearance is not as indicated, replace camshaft and/or thrust plate.
7. Remove camshaft from either end of cylinder head.

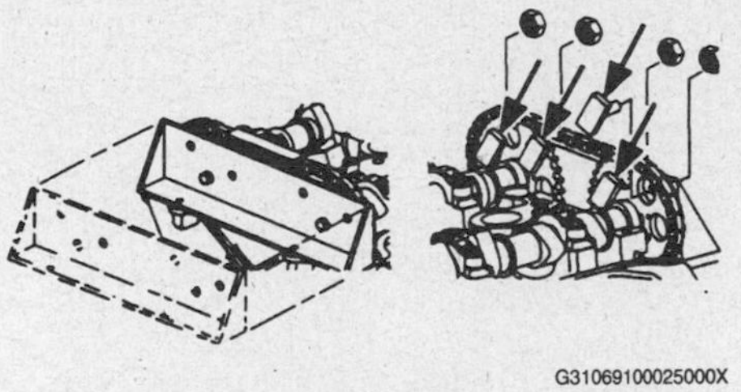
G31069100025000X

Fig. 30 Camshaft front support fixture. DOHC

8. Reverse procedure to install, noting the following:
   a. If camshaft is removed through rear of cylinder head, install new plug.
   b. If camshaft is removed through front, install new Torx screws.

DOHC

1. Remove spark plug wires, accessory drive belt, EGR valve solenoid attaching screw, PCV fresh air hose and cam cover assembly.
2. Position No. 1 cylinder to TDC, **Fig. 29,** align damper mark with front cover arrow mark.
3. Hold camshaft using a 7/8 inch open end wrench, then remove camshaft timing sprocket attaching bolts and washer.
4. Install front support fixture, align two holes in each camshaft sprocket, sprocket adapter and front support fixture, install but do not tighten four attaching nut, **Fig. 30.**
5. Install suitable camshaft sprocket adapter to each camshaft, but do not tighten pilot bolts, **Fig. 31.**
6. Remove upper timing chain guide and front camshaft bearing caps.
7. While holding camshaft, **torque** sprocket pilot bolts to 18 ft. lbs. using a 7/8 inch wrench.
8. Move camshaft sprocket off end of each camshaft onto sprocket adapter,**Fig. 32.**
9. Install four 3/8 inch nuts and bolts with blocks through camshaft sprocket, sprocket adapter and front support fixture, install steel blocks against rearward side of camshaft sprocket. **Torque** nuts and bolts to 18 ft. lbs.
10. Install two 6 mm front support fixture hex bolts to front cover, **torque** bolts to 7 ft. lbs.
11. While holding camshaft with a 7/8 inch wrench, remove camshaft sprocket pilot bolt.
12. Move cam rearward enough to ensure camshaft end is no longer inside sprocket pilot.
13. Loosen and remove camshaft bearing cap attaching bolts in several passes. **If lifters are removed, keep in order for installation, store lifters with camshaft contact facing downward.**
14. Reverse procedure to install.

G31069100026000X

Fig. 31 Camshaft support fixture installation. DOHC

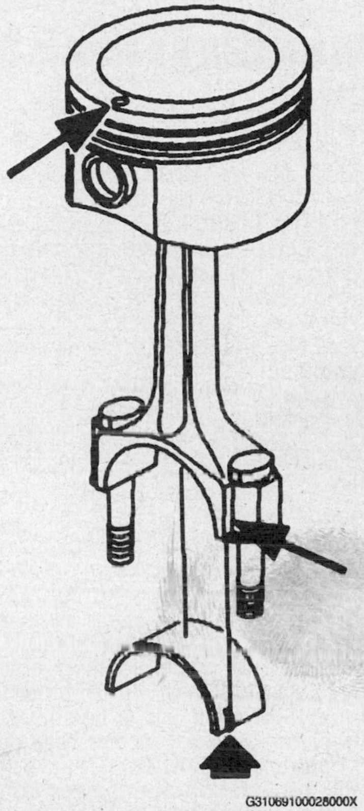
G31069100028000X

Fig. 33 Piston assembly

PISTON & ROD ASSEMBLY

Assemble the piston and connecting rod by aligning the mark on top of the piston with the front of the engine. Assemble connecting rod to the piston with the bearing tang slots directed toward the exhaust manifold, **Fig. 33.**

PISTONS, PINS & RINGS

Pistons are available in .005 inch (.125 mm) and .0157 inch (.400 mm) oversizes.

To check piston fit in bore, using a micrometer, measure piston diameter at right angle to piston pin hole center line, .20 inch (5 mm) from bottom of piston. Piston diameter plus piston clearance minus .002 inch allowance for finish honing will give piston size to be bored to.

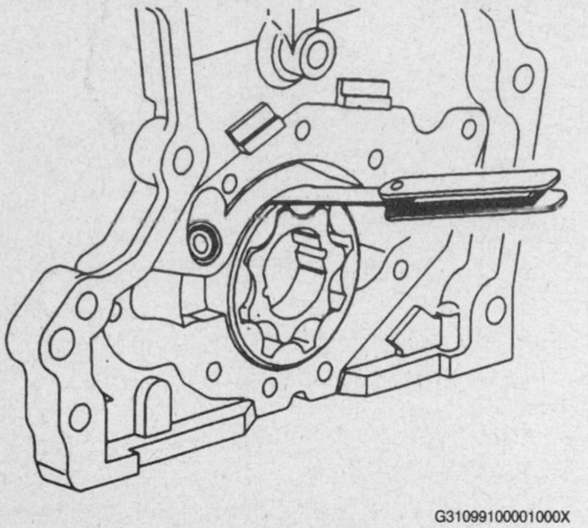
G31099100001000X

Fig. 34 Oil pump body clearance

CRANKSHAFT REAR OIL SEAL

REPLACE

1. Remove transaxle, flywheel, cover and two lower oil pan bolts.
2. Using a suitable rolling head pry bar or pinch bar, separate rear seal carrier from cylinder block.
3. Remove oil seal with a screwdriver.
4. Reverse procedure to install. Using tool No. SA 9121E or equivalent, install seal.

OIL PAN

REPLACE

1. Drain engine oil, then remove front exhaust pipe.
2. Remove right side tire, splash shield and vibration damper.
3. Loosen, but do not remove, four front engine mount attaching bolts about 1/2 inch.
4. Remove oil pan attaching bolts, on models equipped with manual transaxle, a suitable 8mm flexible socket may be used to access rear oil pan bolts next to flywheel.
5. Pry front engine mount away from cylinder block to allow oil pan removal.
6. Using RTV removal tool No. SAE9123E or equivalent, drive sharp edge between pan and block.
7. Drive tool around pan to shear seal, then using a suitable rubber mallet, tap pan sideways to remove.
8. Reverse procedure to install, apply .160 inch bead RTV to inside edge of oil panel groove.

OIL PUMP

REPLACE

1. Raise and support vehicle.
2. Drain engine oil.
3. Remove righthand front wheel assembly and splash shield.
4. Using a universal three jaw puller, **Fig. 12,** while holding damper, remove front crankshaft damper assembly. **Do not pry against cover.**
5. Remove accessory drive belt idler pulley, to allow front cover to be removed and replaced in vehicle.

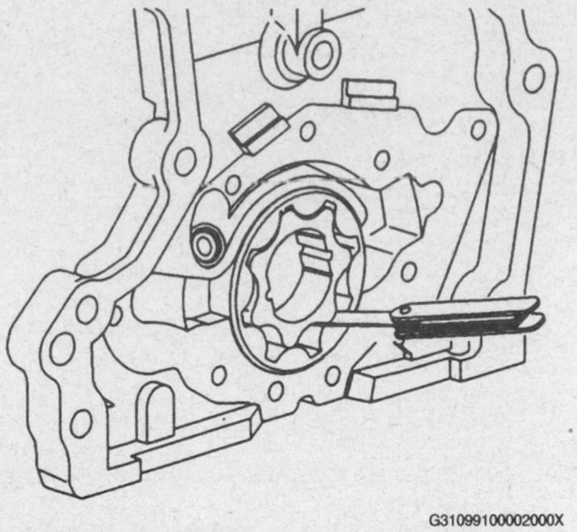
G31099100002000X

Fig. 35 Oil pump tip clearance

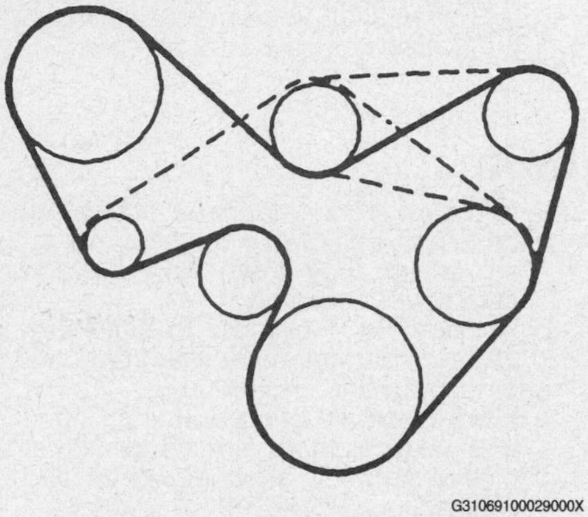
G31069100029000X

Fig. 37 Serpentine belt routing

6. Remove engine accessory drive belt.
7. Remove power steering pump and position aside.
8. Remove belt tensioner.
9. **On SOHC models,** remove rocker cover.
10. **On DOHC models,** remove cam cover.
11. **On all models,** remove three righthand upper engine torque axis mount to front cover attaching nuts, allowing engine to rest on block of wood.
12. Hold front crankshaft timing sprocket using tool No. SA9104E or equivalent with flat side toward crankshaft sprocket.
13. Remove four front oil pan attaching bolts and 14 front cover attaching bolts.
14. Using tool No. SA9123E or equivalent, cut RTV seal from front cover.
15. Using front cover pry tangs, remove cover, then remove and discard two oil gallery transfer seals.
16. Reverse procedure to install.

OIL PUMP SERVICE

DISASSEMBLE

1. Remove cover plate attaching bolts, then remove drive and riven rotor.
2. Remove and discard relief valve using tool No. SA9103E or equivalent.

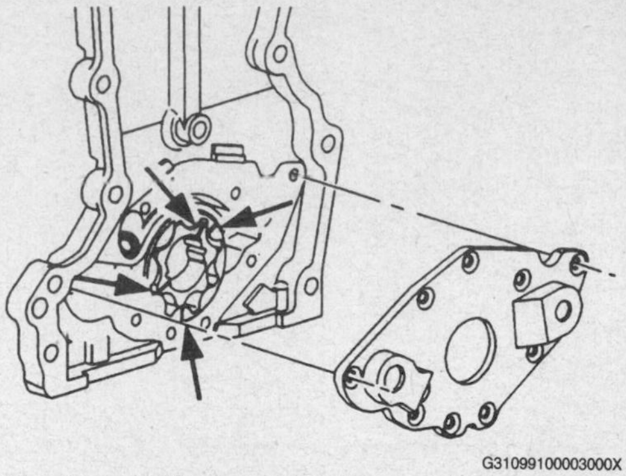
G31099100003000X

Fig. 36 Oil pump end to end clearance

INSPECTION

1. Inspect body clearance as follows:
   a. Using a feeler gauge, measure clearance between driven rotor and pump body, **Fig. 34.**
   b. Standard clearance should be .006-.011 inch and maximum clearance is .0042 inch.
   c. If clearance is greater than maximum, replace oil pump rotor set.
2. Inspect tip clearance using a feeler gauge between both rotor tips, **Fig. 35,** clearance should be .006 inch.
3. Inspect end to end clearance as follows:
   a. Using a feeler gauge, measure clearance between side of gear rotor assembly and cover plate, **Fig. 36.**
   b. Standard clearance should be .0016-.0049 inch and maximum clearance is .005 inch.

ASSEMBLE

1. Using a screwdriver or punch, remove front cover oil seal.
2. Install new oil seal using tool No. SA9140E or equivalent and a press or hammer.
3. Coat relief valve with engine oil, then using tool No. SA9103E or equivalent and a hammer, install relief valve.
4. Pack oil pump assembly with petroleum jelly.
5. Install drive and driven rotors to pump body with chamfer toward front oil seal.
6. Install pump body cover and tighten bolts to specifications.

BELT TENSION DATA

Belt	New Lbs.	Used Lbs.
Accessory	50—65	45

SERPENTINE DRIVE BELT

BELT ROUTING

Refer to **Fig. 37,** for serpentine belt routing.

BELT TENSIONER, REPLACE

Tensioner internal components are nor serviceable, do not disassemble tensioner.

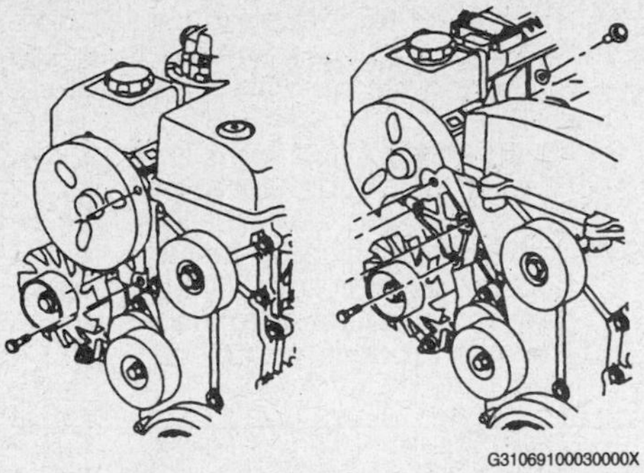
G31069100030000X

Fig. 38 Belt tensioner removal

1. Unclip lower splash shield and place a one by one by 2 inch long block of wood between torque strut and cradle.
2. Remove three righthand upper engine torque axis mount to front cover attaching nuts, allowing engine to rest on block of wood.
3. Remove belt as outlined under "Belt, Replace."
4. Remove power steering pump with bracket.
5. Remove tensioner upper and lower attaching bolts, **Fig. 38.**
6. Install a pry bar between steel engine mount and steel frame rail, then move engine slightly toward drivers fender, as required, then remove tensioner.
7. Reverse procedure to Install.

BELT, REPLACE

Removal

1. Using suitable 14 mm or 9/16 inch wrench, depress tensioner arm, **Fig. 39.**
2. Remove belt from A/C compressor and idler pulley, then remove belt.

Installation

1. Route belt over all pulleys, except front cover idler or A/C compressor.
2. Using 14 mm or 9/16 inch wrench, depress tensioner arm, **Fig. 39.**
3. Install belt to idler pulley and A/C compressor.
4. Tighten idler pulley to specifications.

COOLING SYSTEM BLEED

These engines do not require a special bleed procedure. After filling cooling system, run engine and allow to reach normal operating temperature with pressure cap off. Air will then automatically bleed through cap opening.

THERMOSTAT

REPLACE

REMOVAL

Do not remove pressure cap while engine is running or when engine is still warm.

1. Remove engine drain plug at right front of engine, to drain coolant from radiator, then open draincock at lower part of radiator. Ensure coolant level is below thermostat housing.
2. Disconnect lower radiator hose at thermostat housing using Snap On Tool HCP10 or equivalent, then remove two water inlet housing retaining bolts.
3. Remove water inlet and thermostat as an assembly, then remove and discard O-ring.
4. Remove thermostat element with service tool provided with replacement part. The new part will not function correctly if oil comes in contact with part. If oil is found in coolant, flush entire system before replacing thermostat.
5. Ensure no damage or seat deterioration is found within water inlet housing. Use care not to damage machined aluminum surfaces.

INSTALLATION

1. Install new thermostat with service tool provided, ensuring tangs are properly seated in the legs and the piston is correctly positioned in water inlet housing.
2. Install new O-ring on the water inlet housing, then the water inlet housing, thermostat into cylinder block.
3. Install retaining bolts and tighten to specifications.
4. Close radiator and engine drain plugs and tighten to specification.
5. Install lower radiator hose. Ensure vehicle is on level surface.
6. Fill coolant system using only recommended mixture of 50/50 mixture of water and non phosphate ethylene glycol-base coolant.
7. Start engine and run for several minutes, then fill cooling system surge tank to full cold line.
8. Install pressure cap and check for leaks.

WATER PUMP

REPLACE

1. Drain coolant.
2. Raise and support vehicle.
3. Remove right wheel assembly, then inner wheelwell splash shield.
4. Remove A/C compressor attaching bolts, then position aside.
5. Place one inch wood block between crankshaft and water pump pulley, then remove water pump bolts and allow pulley to hang on pump hub.
6. Remove water pump attaching bolts, then remove water pump and discard gasket.
7. Reverse procedure to install. Tighten water pump bolts to specification in crossing pattern.

RADIATOR

REPLACE

1. Drain cooling system and disconnect battery ground cable.
2. Remove air intake duct.
3. Remove upper radiator clamp and hose.

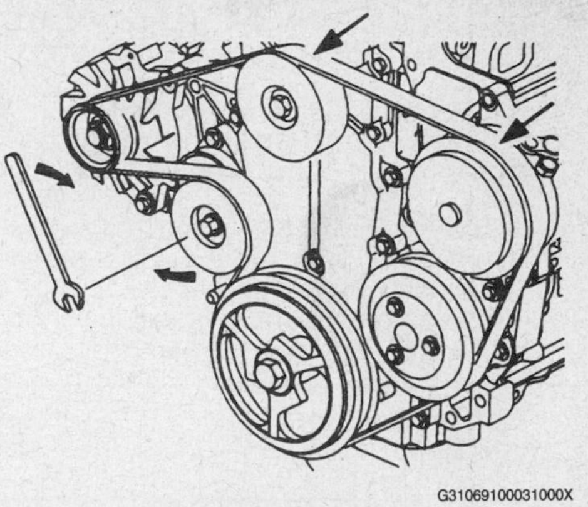
G31069100031000X

Fig. 39 Belt tensioner arm

4. **On models with automatic transaxles,** remove upper transaxle oil cooler line.
5. **On all models,** remove electric cooling fan assembly.
6. Disconnect lower radiator hose.
7. Raise and support vehicle.
8. Remove lower splash shield.
9. **On models with automatic transaxles,** remove lower transaxle oil cooler line.
10. **On all models,** remove two lower condenser bracket to radiator bolts. Then support condenser to vehicle with wire.
11. Lower vehicle, then remove upper radiator attaching nuts and brackets.
12. **On models with A/C,** remove upper radiator seal.
13. **On all models,** remove radiator from vehicle.
14. Reverse procedure to install.

FUEL PUMP

REPLACE

1. Remove fuel tank as follows:
   a. Remove fuel filler cap.
   b. Disconnect battery ground cable.
   c. When fuel line is disconnected or removed wrap fuel fitting in cloth before disconnecting.
   d. Remove fuel delivery line Schraeder valve cap, in engine compartment.
   e. Using tool No. SA9127E or equivalent, on Schraeder valve, released fuel system pressure.
   f. Raise and support rear of vehicle 28 inches higher than front.
   g. Place container below fuel tank fill neck hose, then loosen connecting tube and vent hose clamps.
   h. Wrap a cloth around filler neck connecting tube, then remove tube from tank.
   i. Using a socket extension, push filler neck check ball into fuel tank.
   j. Install siphon hose in fuel tank through fuel filler, then siphon fuel from tank into a container.
   k. Remove fill neck bracket, then disconnect fuel supply and return lines.

l. Remove fuel tank support straps, then disconnect electrical connector.
m. Remove fuel tank assembly.
2. Using tool No. SA9156E or equivalent, remove fuel pump module cam lock ring.
3. Lift assembly at 45° angle to remove.
4. Remove and discard large fuel pump module to tank O-ring.
5. Reverse procedure to install.

FUEL FILTER
REPLACE

1. Disconnect fresh air inlet hose from rocker cam cover, then remove air inlet tube.
2. Place a shop towel around fuel line, using tool No. SA9157E or equivalent, disconnect large fuel line quick connect, located near intake manifold support brace on lefthand side of vehicle.
3. Raise and support vehicle, then disconnect quick connect at fuel filter inlet by pinching two plastic tangs together and pulling on fuel line.
4. Loosen fuel filter band clamp fastener, then remove filter from bracket.
5. Reverse procedure to install.

TIGHTENING SPECIFICATIONS

Component	Torque/Ft. Lbs.
A/C Compressor Front Bracket To Block	35
A/C Compressor Front/Rear Bracket To Head	22
A/C Compressor To Front Bracket	35
A/C Compressor To Rear Bracket	22
Accelerator Bracket To Front Dash	106①
Accelerator Cable Bracket To Intake Manifold	19
Accelerator Control Cable Stud②	62①
Air Cleaner Duct Clamp	15①
Air Cleaner/Resonator Bolts	89①
Air Cleaner/Resonator Clamps	18①
Alternator Positive Terminal	89①
Alternator To Block	27
Axle Shaft Intermediate Bracket To Block	41
Battery Cable	151①
Battery Cable To Alternator	7
Belt Idler Pulley To Front Cover	33
Belt Tensioner Pulley	22
Belt Tensioner To Block	22
Block Oil Gallery Plug	22
Camshaft Bearing Cap To Head③	124①
Camshaft Cover To Head③	89①
Camshaft Sprocket To Camshaft	75
Camshaft Thrust Bearing To Head②	18
Canister Band Clamp	31①
Canister Purge Solenoid To Block	22
Catalytic Converter To Isolator	19
Clutch Pressure Plate To Flywheel	19
Connecting Rod Cap To Rod	33
Coolant/Cylinder Block Heater	19
Coolant Drain Plug	26
Coolant Temperature Sensor	71①
Cradle To Body	151
Crankshaft Bearing Cap To Block	37
Crankshaft Damper To Crankshaft	159
Crankshaft Position Sensor	80①
Crankshaft Rear Oil Seal Carrier To Block	97①
Cylinder Head Bolts②	④
Cylinder Head Bolts③	⑦
Cylinder Head Core Hole Plug	53①
Cylinder Head Water Jacket③	55
De-Aeration Line Clamp②	80①
De-Aeration Line Fitting To Head	97①

Component	Torque/Ft. Lbs.
De-Aeration Line Nut To Head②	151①
De-Aeration Line To Cam Cover	53①
EGR Solenoid Bracket③	89①
EGR Solenoid Bracket②	19
EGR Valve Nut To Head	21
EGR Valve Stud To Head	62①
Engine Block Heater To Block	18
Engine Lift Bracket To Block⑥	36
Engine Lift Bracket To Block⑥	22
Engine Mount To Front Cover	7
Engine Support Bracket	28
ESC Knock Sensor	133①
Exhaust Manifold Studs To Front Pipe	115①
Exhaust Manifold Studs To Head	106①
Exhaust Manifold To Head②	16
Exhaust Manifold To Head③	23
Exhaust Pipe To Converter	33
Flexplate To Converter	41
Flexplate To Crankshaft	44
Flywheel/Flexplate Cover	89①
Flywheel To Crankshaft	59
Front Cover To Block (Center)	89①
Front Cover To Block (Perimeter)	22
Front Engine Mount To Block	52
Fuel Canister Bracket To Frame Rail	22
Fuel Line Support Bracket	22
Fuel Line Support Clip	106①
Fuel Rail To Intake Manifold	22
Fuel Return Pipe Nut To Pressure Regulator③	133①
Fuel Supply Pipe③	18
Fuel Tank Fill Hose	27①
Fuel Tank Fill Pipe	18①
Fuel Tank Fill Pipe Bracket	53①
Fuel Tank Straps	25
Fuel/Vapor Line To Body	27①
Heater Outlet To Intake Manifold	19
Heater Return Nipple	37
Idle Air Control Sensor	28
Idle Air Control Valve	18①
Ignition Module To Transaxle Case	71①
Induction Air Sensor	44①
Intake Manifold Bracket To Block (LH)	22

Continued

TIGHTENING SPECIFICATIONS-Continued

Component	Torque/Ft. Lbs.
Intake Manifold Bracket To Block (RH)③	41
Intake Manifold Bracket To Manifold②	21
Intake Manifold Bracket To Manifold③	22
Intake Manifold Stud To Fuel Line Clamp②	62①
Intake Manifold Stud To Head	106①
Intake Manifold Stud To Head (P/S Bracket)②	188①
Intake Manifold Stud To Head (P/S Bracket)③	22
Intake Manifold To Head	22
MAP Sensor②	53①
MAP Sensor③	27
Motion Restrictor Bracket	40
Motion Restrictor To Side Of Block	22
Mount To Midrail Bracket	⑧
Oil Baffle Plate To Block	41
Oil Drain Plug	26
Oil Filter	⑤
Oil Pan To Block	80①
Oil Pickup Tube③	133①
Oil Pipe Bracket To Block③	133①
Oil Pipe Bracket To Block②	41
Oil Pressure Sensor	26
Oil Pump Cover	97①
Oxygen Sensor	19
Power Steering Hoses	20
Power Steering Pump Bracket	22
Power Steering Pump To Bracket	28
Power Steering Return Hose Clamp	18①
Radiator Upper Bracket	89①
Rear Engine Mount To Block	35
Rocker Arm Cover To Head②	22
Rocker Arm Shaft To Head	19
Spark Plug	20
Starter Bracket To Starter	89①
Starter Motor	27
Starter Motor Bracket To Axle Shaft	22
Starter Positive Terminal	89①

Component	Torque/Ft. Lbs.
Starter Solenoid Terminal	35①
Steering Joint To Gear	35
Stiffening Bracket	40
Strut To Knuckle	148
TBI Assembly Fuel Line	19
TBI Assembly To Air Intake Manifold	24
TBI Injector	18①
Thermostat Housing To Block	22
Throttle Body To Air Intake Manifold③	23
Throttle Position Sensor	18①
Timing Chain Guides	19
Timing Chain Tensioner	168①
Transaxle Case To Block (Lower)	96
Transaxle Case To Block (Upper)	66
Transaxle Lower Mount To Cradle	41
Transaxle Lower Mount To Transaxle	23
Transaxle Rear Mount	36
Vapor Canister To Body	22
Vehicle Speed Sensor	19①
Water Pump	22
Water Pump Pulley	18

①—Inch lbs.
②—SOHC.
③—DOHC.
④—Tighten in sequence to 22 ft. lbs., then to 33 ft. lbs., then install cylinder head bolt tool No. SA9140E or equivalent, calibrate to zero, then in sequence turn each bolt an additional 90°.
⑤—Tighten to gasket, then turn and additional ¾ to 1 turn.
⑥—Less A/C.
⑦—Tighten in sequence to 22 ft. lbs., then to 37 ft. lbs., then install cylinder head bolt tool No. SA9140E or equivalent, calibrate to zero, then in sequence turn each bolt an additional 90°.
⑧—1992–93 models, 52 ft. lbs., 1994–95 models, 37 ft. lbs.

Clutch & Manual Transaxle

NOTE: On Air Bag Equipped Models, Refer To "Air Bag System Precautions" Located In The Front Of This Manual For System Disarming & Arming Procedures.

INDEX

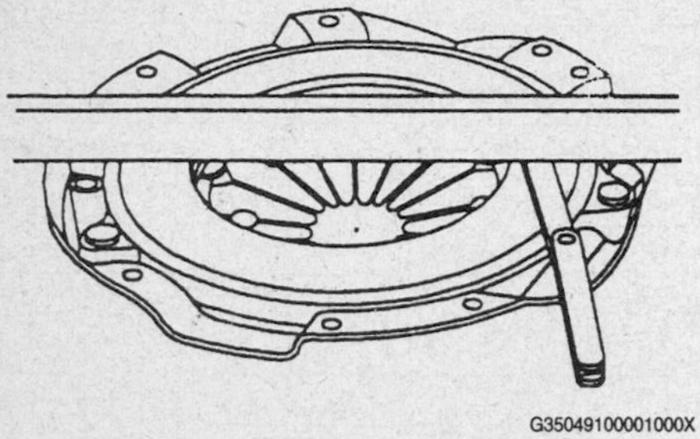

G35049100001000X

Fig. 1 Clutch pedal height

PRECAUTIONS

AIR BAG SYSTEMS

Refer to "Air Bag System Precautions" in the front of this manual for system disarming and arming procedures.

ADJUSTMENTS

CLUTCH PEDAL HEIGHT

The hydraulic clutch system provides automatic clutch adjustment, therefore, there is no adjustment provision. The clutch pedal height can be measured, **Fig. 1,** 5.3-6.2 inch should be indicated. If not, check carpet or floor mat under pedal, a faulty bushing or damaged pedal may be indicated.

HYDRAULIC SYSTEM SERVICE

HYDRAULIC CLUTCH SYSTEM BLEED

The hydraulic system is serviced as a unit, it has been filled with fluid and bled of air. If the system requires any fluid, check the hydraulic components for leakage. Remove the slave cylinder from the clutch housing and check for leakage at the piston, a slightly wet surface is normal, if excessive, replace system.

Use only DOT 3 brake fluid. **Do not use mineral oil or a paraffin base oil in the hydraulic system as damage to rubber parts will occur.** Clean the cap and sides of reservoir before removing cap, then remove diaphragm. Carefully replace diaphragm and cover after filling.

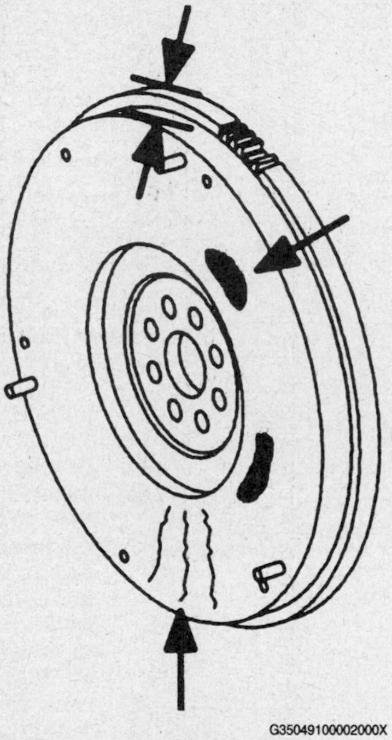

G35049100002000X

Fig. 2 Measuring pressure plate

SLAVE CYLINDER, REPLACE

1. Block clutch pedal.
2. **On DOHC models,** lift resonator upward, to disengage from engine bracket.
3. **On all models,** remove air induction tube.
4. Rotate actuator 1/4 turn counterclockwise while pushing toward housing to disengage, then remove actuator from clutch housing. **Removal of hydraulic damper prior to actuator removal will result in a broken hydraulic line.**
5. Remove hydraulic damper to clutch housing attaching nuts, then slide damper and bracket assembly from studs.
6. Remove clutch pedal pin to slave cylinder pushrod attaching clip, then disconnect pushrod from pedal.
7. Turn slave cylinder about 1/8 turn clockwise, then remove.

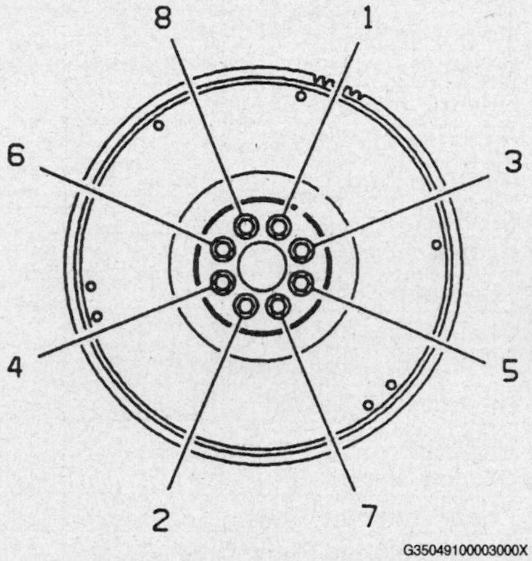

8
1
6
3
4
5
2
7
G35049100003000X

Fig. 3 Measuring flywheel

8. Reverse procedure to install.

CLUTCH

REPLACE

REMOVAL & INSPECTION

1. Remove transaxle as outlined under "Transaxle, Replace."
2. Remove unsnap release fork and bearing from ball stud to remove.
3. Slide release bearing from release fork, then check release bearing for excessive play or minimal drag, replace as required. **Do not wash bearing in solvent.**
4. Using a feeler gauge, measure between pressure plate and flywheel, .205-.287 inch should be indicated, if not, replace clutch disc.
5. Remove pressure plate to flywheel attaching bolts in progressive crisscross pattern.
6. Remove pressure plate and clutch disc.
7. Inspect pressure plate for excessive wear, chatter marks, cracks or overheating, replace as required. **Random black spotting on friction surface is normal.**
8. Using a straightedge and feeler gauge, measure pressure plate warpage, **Fig. 2,** maximum warpage is .006 inch.

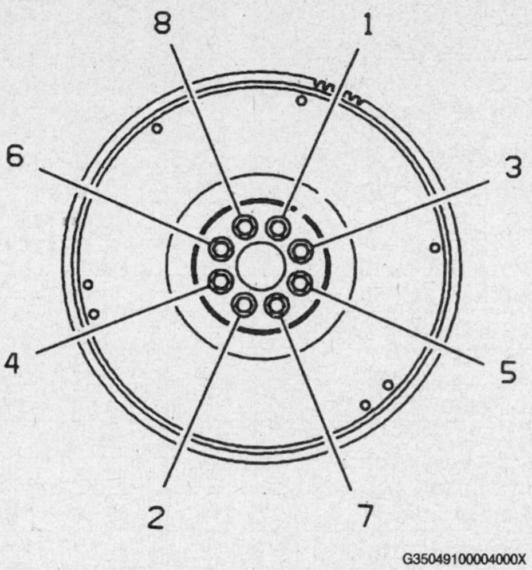
8
1
6
3
4
5
2
7
G35049100004000X

Fig. 4 Flywheel tightening sequence

9. Inspect clutch disc for oil, burnt spots, loose damper springs, hub and rivets, replace as required.
10. Inspect flywheel ring gear for wear or damage, replace as required.
11. Measure flywheel thickness, **Fig. 3**, minimum thickness is 1.102 inch, replace is required.
12. Using a dial indicator, measure flywheel runout, push crankshaft forward to take up thrust bearing clearance, maximum runout is .006 inch, replace as required.
13. Remove flywheel to crankshaft attaching bolts, then remove flywheel.

INSTALLATION

1. Install flywheel to crankshaft attaching bolts, then tighten in order, **Fig. 4**, to specifications.
2. Install clutch disc and pressure plate, with pressure plate yellow dot aligned with flywheel mark, then start pressure plate to flywheel bolts.
3. Install clutch disc alignment tool No. SA9145T or equivalent, until bottoms out in crankshaft.
4. Tighten bolts in crisscross pattern to specifications.
5. Remove clutch alignment tool, then install fork clip.
6. Lube fork pivot using high temperature grease part No. 21005995 or equivalent, then install release bearing to fork. **Do not lube release bearing or quill.**
7. Install release fork and bearing to ball stud.
8. Lube input shaft splines, then install transaxle assembly.

TRANSAXLE

REPLACE

1. **On models equipped with SOHC engine,** remove two air inlet duct attaching screws, disconnect air temperature sensor electrical connector, then remove air inlet duct.
2. **On models equipped with DOHC engine,** remove two cross car duct attaching screws, disconnect air temperature sensor electrical connector, then remove cross car duct.
3. Loosen flex tube to air box clamp, remove three air body attaching screws, then remove air box.
4. **On all models,** remove transaxle strut to cradle bracket attaching bolt, the loosen transaxle strut to transaxle bracket attaching bolt and position strut aside.
5. Disconnect the following electrical connectors:
   a. Back-up light switch.
   b. Vehicle speed sensor.
   c. Remove and discard vent tube clip.
   d. Two upper clutch housing ground terminals.
   e. Oxygen sensor from clutch housing.
6. Remove upper clutch housing the engine bolts, then install four inch guide bolts in upper rear clutch housing bolt hole.
7. Remove DIS coil attaching screws, then remove.
8. Loosen two front transaxle mount bolts.
9. Remove shift cables from shift arms and clutch housing, **Fig. 5.**
10. Turn clutch slave cylinder 1/4 counterclockwise while pushing into clutch housing, then remove cylinder.
11. Secure radiator to upper support with mechanics wire.
12. Install engine lifting equipment.
13. Raise and support vehicle, then drain transaxle fluid.
14. Remove front wheels, then right, left and front splash shields.
15. Remove engine mount to cradle attaching nuts.
16. Remove engine strut cradle bracket to cradle fasteners.

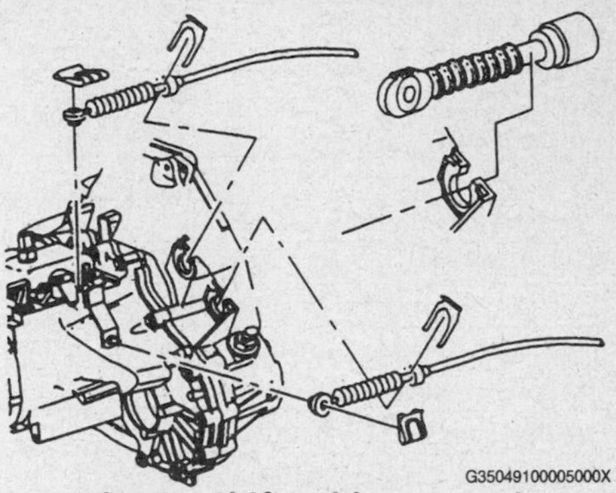
G35049100005000X

Fig. 5 Shift cable removal

17. Remove transaxle to cradle mount.
18. Remove front exhaust pipe.
19. Remove steering gear to cradle attaching bolts and support steering gear with suitable wire.
20. Remove brake line bracket push pin at rear of cradle.
21. Remove engine to transaxle stiffening bracket.
22. Remove clutch housing dust cover.
23. Remove and discard lower ball joint cotter pins, then loosen nut to top of bolt thread.
24. Using tool No. SA9132S or equivalent, separate ball joint from lower control arm. **On models with ABS, outer CV joint has a speed sensor ring, failure to use the proper tool will result in loss of ABS or system damage.**
25. Using suitable large screwdriver or pry bar, separate left side axle from transaxle, pull axle slightly rearward and install axle seal protector tool No. SA91112T or equivalent.
26. Position a suitable powertrain support dolly and two four inch by four inch by 36 inch wood pieces to support cradle.
27. Remove cradle to body attaching bolts, then lower cradle, ensuring two large rear cradle spacers are attached.
28. Support transaxle with a jack stand.
29. Using a screwdriver or pry bar, separate left axle from transaxle. **Do not allow tool to contact or damage axle seal.**
30. Separate transaxle from engine enough to clear intermediate shaft, then lower transaxle to remove.
31. Reverse procedure to install.

TIGHTENING SPECIFICATIONS

Component	Torque/Ft. Lbs.
Air Box	89①
Clutch Fork Stabilizer	18
Clutch Housing Dust Cover	89①
Clutch Housing To Engine Stud	74
Clutch Hydraulic Damper Nuts	18
Converter Housing Ground Terminal	18
Cradle Bracket To Cradle	52
Down Pipe To Convertor	33
Down Pipe To Exhaust Manifold	23
Down Pipe To Stiffening Bracket	23
Engine Mount To Cradle	66
Flex Tube	18①
Flywheel	59
Ignition Module	61①
Lower Ball Joint	55
Lower Converter Housing	96
Lower Transaxle Mount	52
Pressure Plate	18
Rear Transaxle Mount	52
Steering Gear To Cradle	40
Strut Cradle Bracket To Cradle	52
Tie Rod End	33
Transaxle Bracket To Transaxle	40
Transaxle Drain Plug	40②
Transaxle Stiffening Bracket	35
Transaxle Strut To Cradle	52
Transaxle Strut To Transaxle Bracket	52
Wheel Lug Nuts	100

①—Inch lbs.
②—1993–95 models do not require drain plug seal replacement.

Rear Axle & Suspension

INDEX

HUB & BEARING

REPLACE

DISC BRAKES

1. Raise and support vehicle, then remove wheel assembly.
2. **On models equipped with ABS,** disconnect wheel speed sensor electrical connector.
3. **On all models,** remove caliper to knuckle attaching bolts, then hang caliper with wire.
4. Remove brake rotor, then four hub to knuckle attaching bolts, remove hub.
5. Reverse procedure to install.

DRUM BRAKES

1. Raise and support vehicle, then remove wheel assembly.
2. Remove brake drum, then four hub to knuckle attaching bolts, then remove.
3. Reverse procedure to install.

STRUT

REPLACE

1. **On Coupe models,** remove rear seat bottom cushion, then right and left interior rocker panel molding.
2. **On Coupe models,** remove left and right interior rear sail panel.
3. **On Sedan models,** remove left or right interior C-pillar molding.
4. **On all models,** fold down rear seats, then remove rear set bolsters.
5. **On Coupe models,** remove cargo area package shelf attaching screws and carpet.
6. **On all models,** remove speaker grilles and seat belt bezel, then separate belts from shelf.
7. Raise and support vehicle, then remove wheel assembly.
8. Loosen but do not remove steering knuckle to strut attaching nuts.
9. Using a floor jack, support knuckle, then remove upper strut attaching nuts.
10. **On models equipped with ABS,** disconnect ABS electrical harness from strut.
11. **On all models,** remove strut to

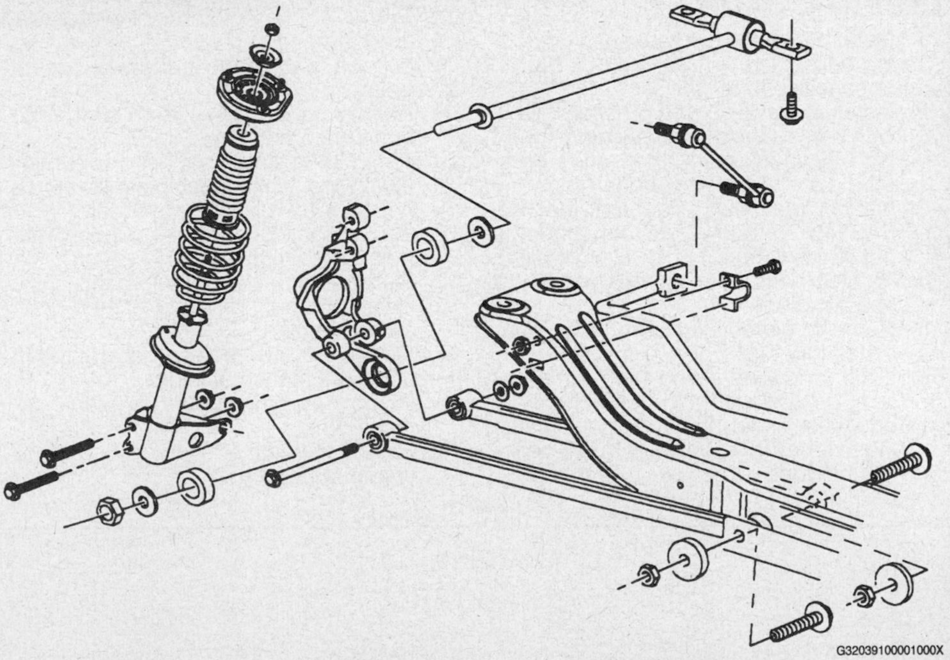
G32039100001000X

Fig. 1 Exploded view of rear suspension

knuckle nuts, then remove strut.
12. Reverse procedure to install, tighten attaching nuts to specification.

KNUCKLE
REPLACE
DISC BRAKES

1. Raise and support vehicle, then remove wheel assembly.
2. Disconnect ABS wheel speed sensor electrical connector.
3. Remove caliper to knuckle attaching bolts. Suspend caliper with mechanics wire, then remove rotor.
4. Remove hub to knuckle attaching bolts, then remove hub and backing plate.
5. Loosen but do not remove lateral link to knuckle attaching bolts.
6. Loosen but do not remove strut to knuckle attaching bolts.
7. Remove trailing arm to knuckle attaching nut, then arm to body bolts.
8. Remove lateral link to knuckle attaching nuts, then remove knuckle to strut bolts, remove knuckle.
9. Reverse procedure to install.

DRUM BRAKES

1. Raise and support vehicle.
2. Remove wheel assembly and brake drum.
3. Remove hub to knuckle attaching bolts, then remove hub.
4. Using wire, position brake assembly aside.
5. Loosen but do not remove lateral link and strut to knuckle attaching bolts.
6. Remove trailing arm to knuckle attaching nut, then arm to body bolts, then slide arm from knuckle.
7. Remove link and strut to knuckle attaching bolts, then remove link.
8. Reverse procedure to install.

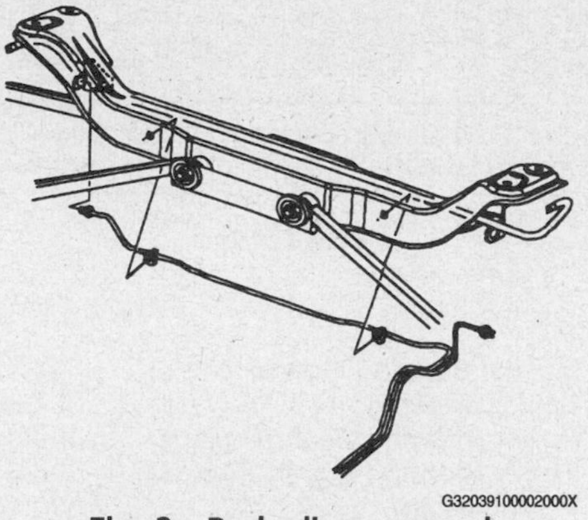
G32039100002000X

Fig. 2 Brake line removal

TRAILING ARM
REPLACE

1. Raise and support vehicle.
2. Remove wheel assemblies.
3. Remove trailing arm to knuckle attaching nut, **Fig. 1.**
4. Remove trailing arm to body attaching bolts, then slide arm from knuckle.
5. Reverse procedure to install.

STABILIZER BAR
REPLACE

1. Raise and support vehicle, then remove wheel assembly.
2. Position drain container at left rear brake line, then disconnect and plug left brake line.
3. Remove right and left stabilizer bar link to knuckle attaching nuts, then bar to crossmember nuts.
4. Loosen but do not remove lateral link to knuckle attaching bolts, the remove trailing arm to knuckle and arm to body attaching nuts.
5. Slide trailing arm from knuckle, then remove lateral link bolt, swing link downward.
6. Disconnect brake lines from crossmember, **Fig. 2.**
7. Remove stabilizer bar.
8. Reverse procedure to install.

LATERAL LINK
REPLACE

1. To remove front lateral link, remove fuel tank as follows:
   a. Remove fuel filler cap.
   b. When fuel line is disconnected or removed, wrap fuel fitting in cloth before disconnecting.
   c. Remove fuel delivery line Schraeder valve cap, in engine compartment.
   d. Using tool No. SA9127E or equivalent, on Schraeder valve, released fuel system pressure.
   e. Raise and support rear of vehicle 28 inches higher than front.
   f. Place a container below fuel tank fill neck hose, then loosen connecting tube and vent hose clamps.
   g. Wrap cloth around filler neck connecting tube, then remove tube from tank.
   h. Using a socket extension, push filler neck check ball into fuel tank.
   i. Install siphon hose in fuel tank through fuel filler, then siphon fuel from tank into container.
   j. Remove fill neck bracket, then disconnect fuel supply and return lines.
   k. Remove fuel tank support straps, then disconnect electrical connector.
   l. Remove fuel tank assembly.
2. Raise and support vehicle, then remove wheel assembly.
3. Remove lateral link to knuckle attaching bolt, then lateral link to crossmember bolts, **Fig. 1.**
4. Remove lateral link.
5. Reverse procedure to install.

TIGHTENING SPECIFICATIONS

Component	Torque/Ft. Lbs.
ABS Electrical Harness	53①
Brake Line	14
Crossmember To Body	89
Front Lateral Link To Crossmember (Bolt)	126
Front Lateral Link To Crossmember (Nut)	89
Fuel Fill Neck Bracket	53①
Fuel Tank Straps	30
Fuel Vent & Fill Line Clamps	25①
Hub To Knuckle	63
Lateral Link To Knuckle	122
Rear Caliper To Knuckle	63

Component	Torque/Ft. Lbs.
Rear Lateral Link To Crossmember	89
Stabilizer Bar Link To Bracket	30
Stabilizer Bar To Crossmember	41
Stabilizer Bar To Link	30
Strut Shaft Nut	37
Strut To Knuckle	148
Trailing Arm To Body	89
Trailing Arm To Knuckle	74
Upper Strut Nuts	21
Wheel Lug Nut	100

①—Inch lbs.

Front Suspension & Steering

NOTE: On Air Bag Equipped Models, Refer To "Air Bag System Precautions" Located In The Front Of This Manual For System Disarming & Arming Procedures.

INDEX

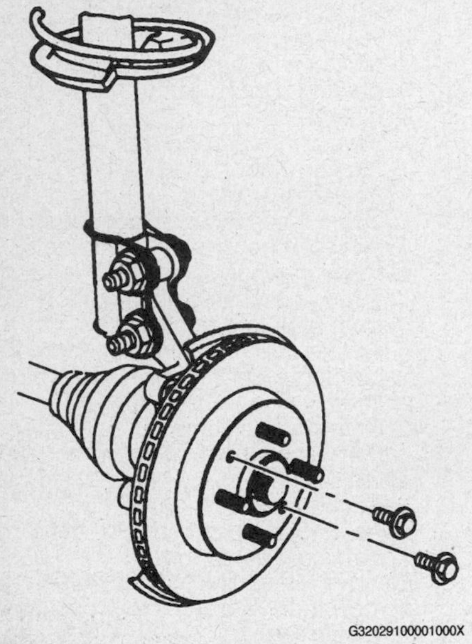
G32029100001000X

Fig. 1 Brake rotor removal

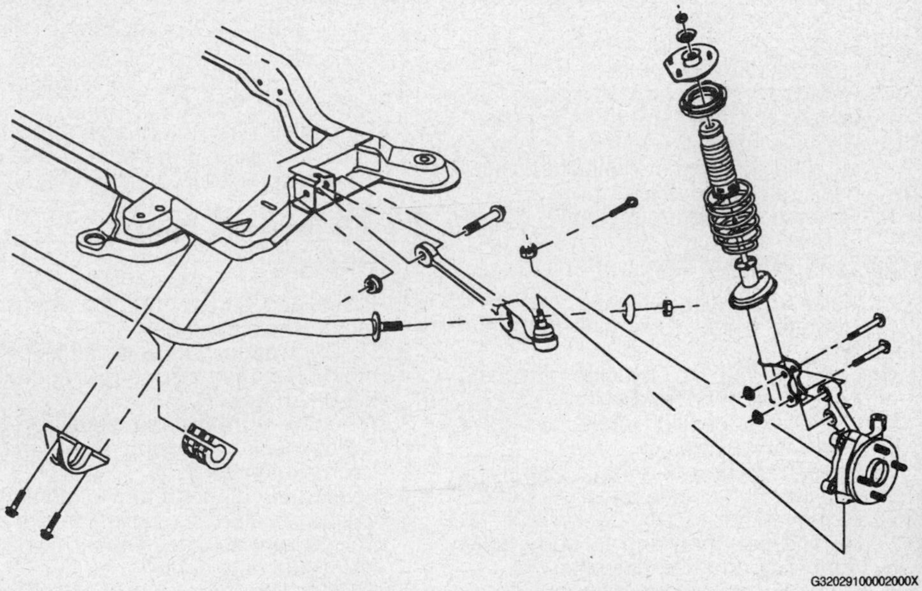
G32029100002000X

Fig. 2 Exploded view of front suspension

PRECAUTIONS

AIR BAG SYSTEMS

Refer to "Air Bag System Precautions" in the front of this manual for system disarming and arming procedures.

HUB & BEARING REPLACE

1. Depress brake pedal, then loosen axle to hub nut.
2. Raise and support vehicle, then remove wheel assembly.
3. Remove caliper to knuckle attaching bolts. Suspend caliper with mechanics wire.
4. Loosen but do not remove knuckle to strut attaching bolts.
5. If rotor is difficult to remove, use two M8 X 1.25 self tapping bolts, to remove, **Fig. 1.**
6. Remove axle nut and washer, then remove and discard lower control arm ball stud cotter pin.
7. Loosen castle nut until level with top of ball stud.
8. Remove and discard tie rod cotter pin.
9. Remove tie rod and castle nut.
10. Using tool No. SA9132A or equivalent, separate lower control arm from knuckle. **Do not use wedge type tool to separate or ABS speed sensor ring or seal damage may occur.**
11. Remove lower ball joint castle nut, **Fig. 2.**
12. Using tool No. SA91100C or equivalent, separate tie rod end from steering knuckle.
13. **On models equipped with ABS brakes,** disconnect wheel speed sensor electrical connector.
14. **On all models,** support or suspend drive axle assembly.
15. Remove strut to knuckle attaching bolts, then remove knuckle and hub assembly. If difficult to separate axle from hub, tap end of drive axle shaft using a block of wood and hammer. **Do not hammer end of axle.**
16. Reverse procedure to install.

HUB & BEARING SERVICE

1. Remove splash shields, then ABS wheel speed sensor, is equipped.
2. Install wheel bearing/hub removal tool No. SA9159S or equivalent, **Fig. 3,** then place assembly in a soft jawed vise, **Fig. 4.**
3. Hold hub drive with a wrench. Tighten driver screw to remove hub.
4. Install inner race puller, **Fig. 5,** then remove inner bearing race.
5. Remove steering knuckle from vise, then remove bridge retainer and bridge.
6. Remove bridge snap ring using snap ring pliers.
7. Using knuckle support tube and small driver, **Fig. 6,** press out bearing.
8. Reverse to assemble.

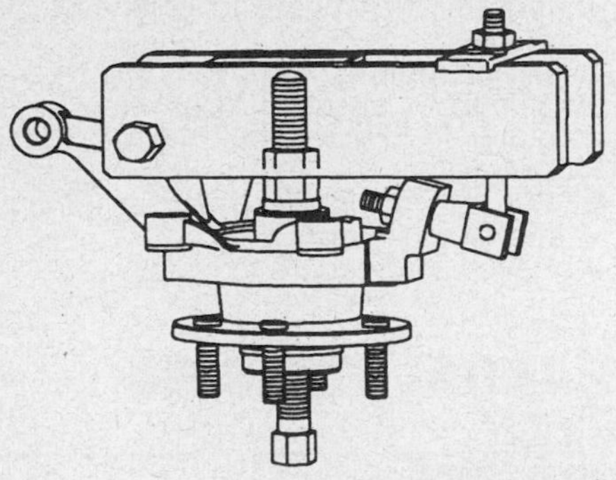

Fig. 3 Wheel bearing/hub removal

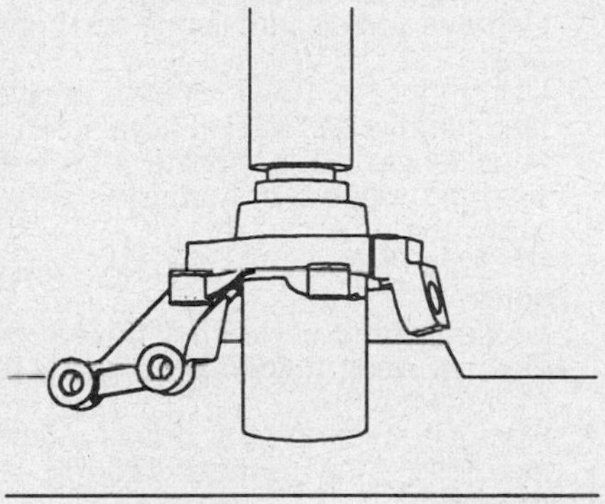

Fig. 6 Bearing removal

BALL JOINT
REPLACE
LOWER

The ball joint and the lower control arm are a unit and serviced as an assembly, refer to "Control Arm, Replace" for replacement procedure.

COIL SPRING
REPLACE

Refer to "Strut, Replace" for coil spring removal procedure.

STRUT
REPLACE
REMOVAL

1. Raise and support vehicle, then remove wheel assembly.
2. **On models equipped with ABS,** disconnect wheel speed sensor electrical connector bracket.
3. **On all models,** loosen but do not remove steering knuckle to strut housing attaching bolts.
4. Place a floor jack below lower control arm and support.
5. Remove upper strut attaching nuts.
6. Slowly raise vehicle, then lower strut assembly.
7. Remove knuckle to housing attaching bolts, **Fig. 2,** then place cloth over CV joint seal.
8. Remove strut assembly.

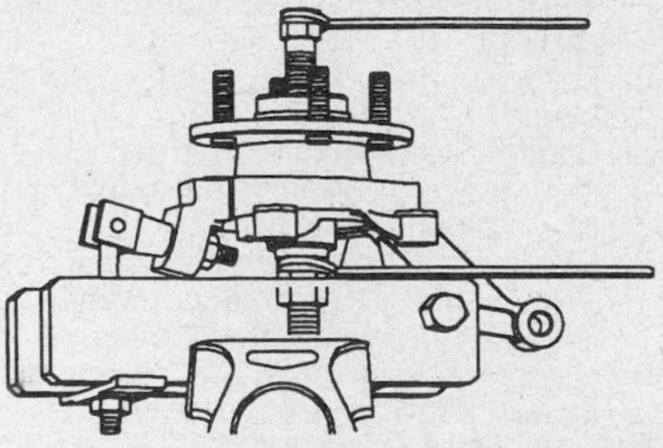

Fig. 4 Hub vise installation

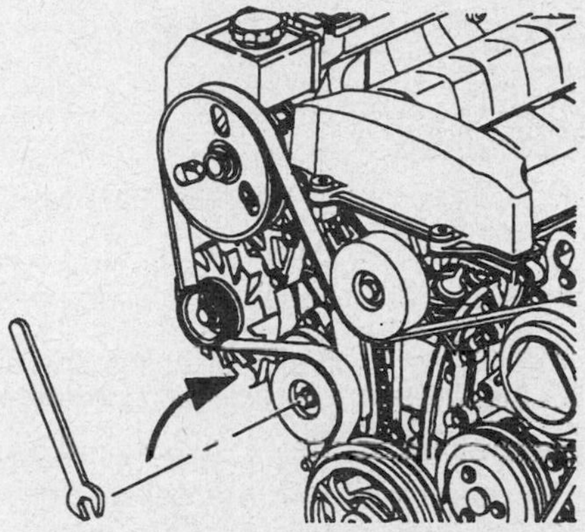

Fig. 7 Belt spring tension release

DISASSEMBLE

1. Using spring compressor tool No. SA9155C or equivalent and holding fixture, compress spring to unload upper strut mount.
2. While holding strut shaft, remove strut shaft nut.
3. Release spring compressor, then tilt strut assembly outward.
4. Remove upper strut assembly, check for damage. replace as required.
5. Remove strut spring and dust shield, inspect for damage, replace as required.
6. Remove strut.

ASSEMBLE

1. Place strut in compressor tool, then attach with strut to knuckle bolt, through lower mounting hole.
2. Extend strut shaft to travel limit.
3. Install dust shield, spring, spring isolator and mount, ensuring spring is properly seated in seat and isolator.
4. Compress spring, then install strut shaft attaching nut and tighten to specifications.

INSTALLATION

1. Install upper strut attaching nuts, tighten to specification.
2. Install strut to steering knuckle attaching bolts, tighten to specification.
3. **On models equipped with ABS brakes,** install sensor electrical connector bracket, tighten to specifications.
4. **On all models,** install wheel and tighten nuts to specifications.
5. Lower vehicle.

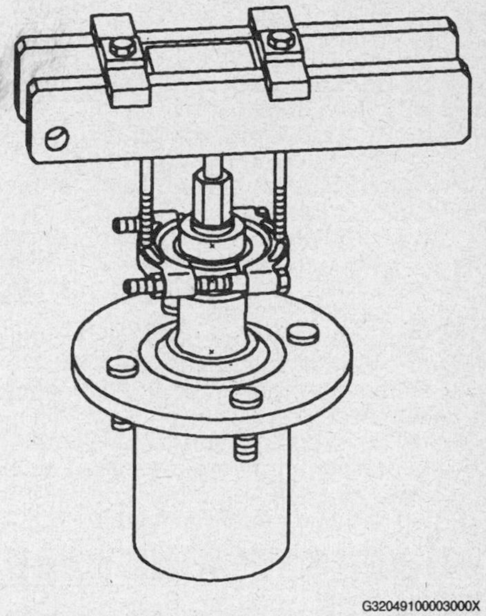

Fig. 5 Inner bearing race removal

CONTROL ARM
REPLACE
LOWER

1. Raise and support vehicle, then remove wheel assembly.
2. Remove and discard lower control arm ball stud cotter pin.
3. Loosen lower control ball stud castle nut until level with top of ball stud.
4. Using tool No. SA9132S or equivalent, separate lower control arm from knuckle. **Do not use wedge type tool or ABS speed sensor ring or seal may be damaged.**
5. Remove lower control arm ball stud castle nut.
6. Remove inner front fender splash shield.
7. Remove lower control arm to cradle attaching nut and bolt, **Fig. 2.**
8. Remove lower control arm to tension strut attaching nut, then remove arm.
9. Reverse procedure to install.

STEERING KNUCKLE
REPLACE

Refer to "Hub & Bearing, Replace" for procedure.

TENSION STRUT
REPLACE

1. Raise and support vehicle, then remove wheel assembly.
2. Remove and discard lower control arm ball stud cotter pin.
3. Loosen but do not remove left lower control arm ball stud castle nut.
4. **For lefthand side of vehicle,** proceed as follows:
    a. Using tool No. SA9132S or equivalent, separate lower control arm from steering knuckle. **Do not use wedge type tool or ABS speed**

sensor ring or seal damage may occur.
b. Remove lower control arm ball joint castle nut.
c. Remove left front inner fender splash shield.
d. Remove lower control arm to cradle attaching nut and bolt.
5. **For righthand side of vehicle,** proceed as follows:
a. Turn wheel left to gain access, then remove tension strut to lower control arm attaching nut and washer.
6. **For both sides,** remove tension strut to cradle bracket attaching bolts.
7. Remove tension strut and left control arm assembly.
8. Remove control arm to tension strut attaching nut and washer, then separate.
9. Reverse procedure to install.

POWER STEERING GEAR

REPLACE

1. Raise and support vehicle.
2. Remove and discard tie rod end cotter pins.
3. Remove tie rod end to knuckle castle nuts.
4. Using tool No. SA91100C or equivalent, remove tie rod end from steering knuckle. **Do not separate joint using wedge-type tool or damage may result.**
5. Remove left inner fender splash shield.
6. Loosen intermediate shaft cover from steering gear, then raise slightly, remove pinch bolt.
7. Disconnect power steering pressure switch, then place drain container below pressure and return hoses.
8. Disconnect pressure and return hoses and allow system to drain.
9. Remove steering gear attaching bolts, then remove through left fenderwell.
10. Reverse procedure to install.

POWER STEERING PUMP

REPLACE

1. Remove power steering pump reservoir fill cap.
2. Raise and support vehicle.
3. Place a drain pan below steering gear hoses.
4. Remove steering gear hoses and allow system to drain. **Do not rotate steering wheel.**
5. Using a box end wrench, relieve spring tension from accessory drive belt, then remove belt, **Fig. 7.**
6. **On models equipped with DOHC,** remove pump to intake manifold bracket, then pump to engine block bracket.
7. **On all models,** remove pump to engine block attaching bolts, then raise pump to disconnect EVO electrical connector.
8. Remove pump and hose assembly, then remove hoses.
9. Reverse procedure to install.

MANUAL STEERING GEAR

REPLACE

1. Raise and support vehicle.
2. Remove front wheel assemblies.
3. Remove and discard tie rod end cotter pins.
4. Using tool No. SA91100C or equivalent, remove tie rod end from steering knuckle. **Do not separate joint with wedge type tool or damage may result.**
5. Remove left inner fender splash shield.
6. Loosen intermediate shaft cover from steering gear, then raise slightly, remove pinch bolt.
7. Remove steering gear cradle attaching bolts, then remove through left fenderwell.
8. Reverse procedure to install.

TIGHTENING SPECIFICATIONS

Component	Torque/Ft. Lbs.
ABS Electrical Connector Bracket	6
Axle To Hub Nut	148
Ball Joint Stud Castle Nut	55
Brake Dust Shield	18
Caliper Bracket To Knuckle	81
Control Arm To Cradle (Bolt)	92
Control Arm To Cradle (Nut)	74
Control Arm To Tension Strut	106
Intermediate Shaft To Steering Gear Pinch Bolt	35
Power Steering Pump Bracket	28
Power Steering Pressure & Return Line Fittings	20
Pump To Engine Block Bolts	28
Pump To Engine Block Bracket ①	22
Pump To Intake Manifold Bracket ①	22
Steering Gear Cradle Bolts	40
Strut Shaft Nut	37
Strut To Steering Knuckle	148
Tension Strut Bracket To Cradle	103
Tie Rod End To Steering Knuckle	33
Upper Strut Mount	21
Wheel Lug Nuts	100

①—DOHC.

Wheel Alignment

INDEX

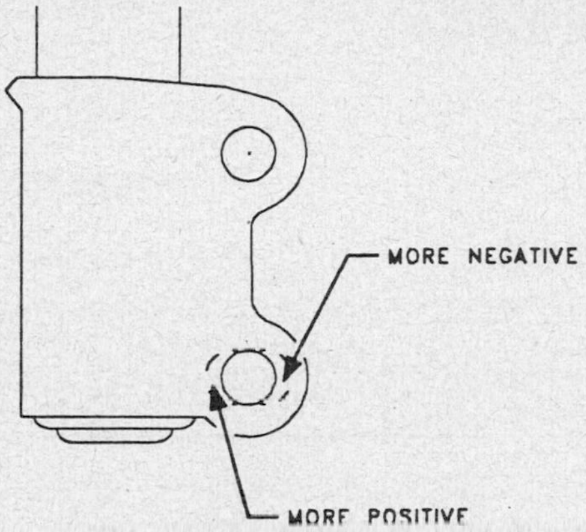

MORE NEGATIVE
MORE POSITIVE

Fig. 1 Front & rear camber adjustment

PRELIMINARY INSPECTION

1. Road test vehicle.
2. Inspect tires for proper inflation, wear pattern or out of round condition.
3. Inspect suspension and steering components for wear and damage.
4. Inspect strut bushings for wear or damage.
5. Inspect vehicle ride height.

FRONT WHEEL ALIGNMENT

Rear wheel alignment must be set to specifications before front alignment adjustment.

CASTER

1. Lock steering wheel in straight ahead position.
2. Remove upper strut mount attaching nuts.
3. Slide strut forward or rearward, to adjust, 1.57 inch will change caster by about 1/2°. **Body attachment holes may need to be filed or ground into oval slots, to allow enough front to rear strut movement to adjust caster to specifications, do not exceed .354 inch in slot width.**
4. Install upper strut mount attaching nuts, then **torque** to 74 ft. lbs.
5. Recheck caster angle.

CAMBER

1. Lock steering wheel in straight ahead position.

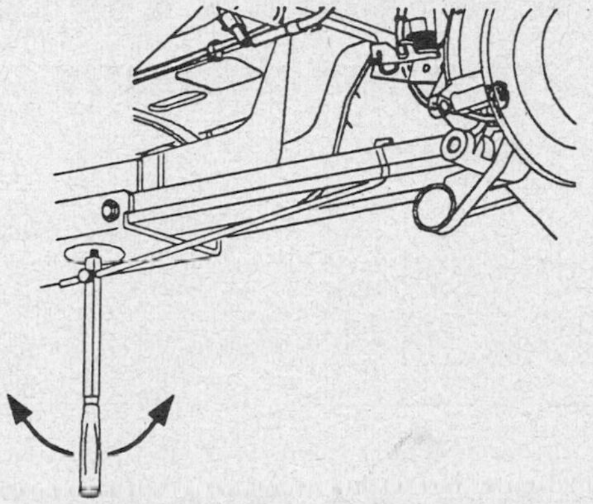

Fig. 2 Rear toe adjustment

2. Loosen two strut to knuckle fasteners, then pull or push to adjust.
3. If more then three degrees or camber is desired, check for bent suspension components.
4. If suspension is good, proceed as follows:
   a. Raise and support vehicle.
   b. Remove wheel assembly.
   c. Remove strut to knuckle attaching bolts, then separate knuckle from strut bracket.
   d. Using a file or grinder, remove material from strut bracket lower hole, **Fig. 3.**
   e. To increase negative camber, remove from outside hole, to increase positive camber, remove from inside hole.
   f. **Torque** strut to knuckle attaching bolts to 148 ft. lbs.
   g. Install wheel assembly, **torque** wheel lug nuts to 100 ft. lbs., then recheck camber setting, lower vehicle.

TOE IN

1. Lock steering wheel in straight ahead position.
2. Loosen left and right outer tie rod jam nuts.
3. Turn inner tie rod, by flats, to change toe.
4. After adjustment, **torque** outer tie rod end jam nuts 74 ft. lbs.
5. **Ensure seals do not become twisted.**
6. Recheck toe angle.

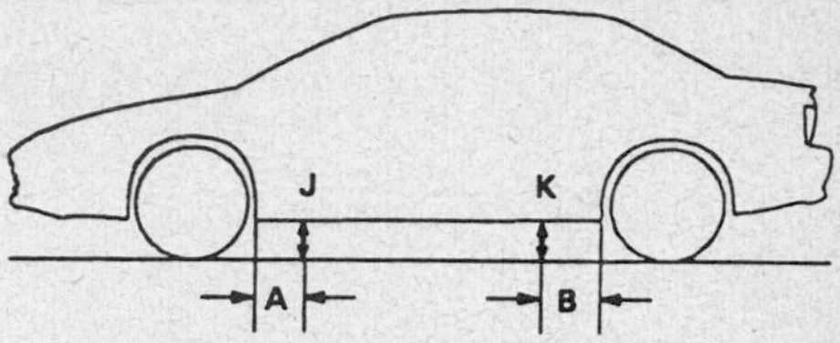

J
K
A
B

Fig. 3 Measuring vehicle trim height

REAR WHEEL ALIGNMENT

CASTER

Rear wheel caster is not adjustable.

CAMBER

1. Loosen two strut to knuckle fasteners, then pull or push to adjust.
2. If more then 1.5° of camber is desired, check for bent suspension components.
3. If suspension is good, proceed as follows:
   a. Raise and support vehicle.
   b. Remove wheel assembly.
   c. Remove strut to knuckle attaching bolts, then separate knuckle from strut bracket.
   d. Using a file or grinder, remove material from strut bracket lower hole, **Fig. 3.**
   e. To increase negative camber, remove from outside hole, to increase positive camber, remove from inside hole.
   f. **Torque** strut to knuckle attaching bolts to 148 ft. lbs.
   g. Install wheel assembly, **torque** wheel lug nuts to 100 ft. lbs., then recheck camber setting, lower vehicle.

TOE IN

1. Loosen rearmost lateral link to crossmember attaching bolts.
2. Using tool No. SA9158C or equivalent, move lateral link to adjust, **Fig. 4.**
3. **Torque** lateral link to 89 ft. lbs.
4. Recheck toe, then repeat for other wheel.

VEHICLE RIDE HEIGHT

1. Place vehicle on level surface.
2. If fuel tank is not full, the following weight must be added to the trunk, to simulate a full tank:
   a. 1/8 tank, add 70 lbs.
   b. 1/4 tank, add 60 lbs.

c. 3/8 tank, add 50 lbs.
d. 1/2 tank, add 40 lbs.
e. 5/8 tank, add 30 lbs.
f. 3/4 tank, add 20 lbs.
g. 7/8 tank, add 10 lbs.

3. Bounce front and rear suspension to allow suspension to settle.
4. With front tire pressure of 30 psi and rear of 26 psi, measure vehicle ride height, **Fig. 5.**
5. Measure from front (A) or rear (B) of rocker flange, to locate vehicle height measuring points J (front rocker height) and K (rear rocker height).
6. **On Sedan models,** A is 4.6 inch and B is 4.1 inch.
7. **On Coupe models,** A is 5.9 inch and B is 5.4 inch.
8. **On all models**, measure vehicle height from level surface, to bottom horizontal surface of rocker panel. **Do not measure from rocker/jacking flange**
9. **On Coupe models,** J should be 7.8-9.1 inch and K should be 7.9-9.4 inch.
10. **On Sedan models,** J should be 7.8-9.0 inch and K should be 8.0-9.3 inch.
11. **On Coupe SC 1 models with aluminum wheels,** J should be 8.2-9.1 inch and K should be 8.3–9.5 inch.
12. **On Wagon models,** J should be 7.8-9.1 inch and K should be 8.1–9.5 inch.
13. **On all models,** when measuring alignment angles, vehicle trim height must be accurate, if not, add or remove weight until height is correct.

AIR CONDITIONING

TABLE OF CONTENTS

System Testing

INDEX

PRECAUTIONS

R12 SYSTEM

The Freon refrigerant used is also known as R12. It is colorless and odorless both as a gas and a liquid. Since it boils (vaporizes) at -21.7°F, it will usually be in a vapor state when being handled. If a portion of the liquid coolant should come in contact with the hands or face, note that its temperature momentarily will be at least -22°F.

Protective goggles should be worn when opening any refrigerant lines. If liquid coolant does touch the eyes, bathe eyes quickly in cold water, then apply a bland disinfectant oil. See an eye doctor.

When checking a system for leaks with a torch type leak detector, do not breathe the vapors coming from the flame. Do not discharge refrigerant near a live flame. A poisonous phosgene gas is produced when R12 is burned.

Never allow the temperature of refrigerant drums to exceed 125°F. The excessive increase in temperature will cause a corresponding increase in pressure which may cause the safety plug to release or the drum to burst.

When connecting and disconnecting service gauges on an A/C system, ensure gauge hand valves are fully closed and compressor service valves, if equipped, are in the back-seated (fully counterclockwise) position. Do not disconnect hoses from service port adapters, if used, while gauges are connected to the A/C system.

To disconnect hoses, always remove adapter from service port. Do not disconnect hoses from gauge manifold while connected to the A/C system, as refrigerant will be rapidly discharged.

After disconnecting gauge lines, check the valve areas to be sure service valves are correctly seated and Schraeder valves, if used, are not leaking.

R134a SYSTEM

Always wear goggles and wrap clean cloth around fittings, valves and connections when performing work that involves opening the refrigerant system. Keep work area well ventilated and do not steam clean or weld on or near any of the air conditioning lines or components. If liquid coolant does touch the eyes, bathe eyes quickly in cold water, then apply a bland disinfectant oil. See an eye doctor.

Before removing and replacing any of the air conditioning refrigeration lines or components, the refrigerant must be completely removed. The refrigerant system may be evacuated and charged using an air conditioning service charging station or a manifold and gauge set with a 30 lb. drum of R134a. **Never charge the air conditioning system through the high pressure side of the system.**

For efficient operation of the air conditioning system, be careful not to contaminate the system with foreign materials, such as dirt, air, or moisture. Contamination of the air conditioning system will change the chemical stability of the R134a refrigerant, in turn changing the viscosity of the refrigerant oil. They will also effect pressure, temperature and create corrosion and abnormal wear of moving parts.

If the ambient air temperature is . . .	The pressure gauge should read–(P.S.I.)	The pressure gauge should read–(P.S.I.)	The right center air should read–(°F)
DEGREES °F	SUCTION	DISCHARGE	OUTLET °F
70	25~30	140~190	40~45
80	25~32	200~250	45~50
90	25~34	260~310	50~55
100	27~35	320~370	55~60

G37029100006000X

Fig. 1 Service stall test specifications. R12 system

If the ambient air temperature is . . .	The pressure gauge should read–(psi)	The pressure gauge should read–(psi)	The right center air should read–(°F)
DEGREES °F	SUCTION	DISCHARGE	OUTLET °F
70	26~30	115~170	40~48
80	24~28	180~215	42~49
90	22~26	225~270	43~50
100	23~27	275~320	50~56

G37029500025000X

Fig. 2 Service stall test specifications. R134a system

If the ambient air temperature is . . .	The pressure gauge should read–(P.S.I.)	The pressure gauge should read–(P.S.I.)	The right center air should read–(°F)
DEGREES °F	SUCTION	DISCHARGE	OUTLET °F
70	30~36	100~120	41~51
80	28~34	130~160	42~52
90	25~31	170~200	44~54
100	24~30	220~260	47~57

G37029100007000X

Fig. 3 45 MPH test specifications. R12 system

TROUBLESHOOTING

PRELIMINARY CHECKS

Most A/C system malfunctions can be detected by a thorough inspection of the system and components.

1. Check the air intake duct, lower air deflector, condenser to radiator seal and the rear hood seal for missing or damaged parts.
2. Check outer surfaces of radiator and condenser cores to ensure air flow is not blocked by dirt, leaves or other matter.
3. Check for kinks in hoses and lines and refrigerant leaks using an electronic leak detector.
4. Check for a worn or loose compressor belt or malfunctioning belt tensioner.
5. Check blower motor operation at all speeds.
6. With blower on High, check for equal distribution of air out of all outlets.
7. Check operation of control mode lever and the distribution of air from the designated outlets.
8. Press "Recirc" button with blower on high. A noticeable increase in air flow and sound should occur. Indicator should illuminate.
9. Start engine and run until normal operating temperature is reached.
10. Check operation of temperature control lever and air outlet temperature from hot to cold.
11. Press "A/C" button. Indicator should illuminate.
12. Check compressor for clutch engagement, slippage or noise.
13. Check electric cooling fan operation with A/C on.
14. Turn A/C off. Compressor clutch should disengage.

PERFORMANCE TEST

SERVICE STALL TEST

Record the manifold gauge pressures and outlet temperature with the following preset vehicle conditions:

1. Install thermometer in right center outlet.
2. Open doors and windows to stabilize interior temperature with outside ambient air temperature.
3. Press "Recirc" button.
4. Set temperature lever to full cold.
5. Select 3rd blower speed.
6. Press "A/C" button.
7. With engine warm, run at 2000 RPM.
8. Continue running until system pressures and outlet temperature stabilize (three to five minutes).
9. Record pressure and temperature.
10. Compare readings to normal system performance chart, **Fig. 1 for R12 system and Fig. 2 for R134a system.**

45 MPH TEST

Recorded manifold gauge pressures and outlet temperature with the vehicle conditions listed under "Service Stall Test, except for the following conditions:

1. "Recirc" off (outside air).
2. Vehicle running at 45 MPH with engine fully warm.
3. Compare readings to normal system performance chart, **Fig. 3** for R12 system and **Fig. 4 for R134a system.**

LEAK TEST

Whenever a refrigerant leak is suspected in the system or a service operation performed which results in disturbing lines or connections, it is recommended to test for leaks.

LIQUID LEAK DETECTORS

There are a number of locations on the air conditioning system where a liquid leak detector solution may be used to pinpoint refrigerant leaks. Apply soap solution to the area in question. Any indication of bubbles will indicate a system leak.

ELECTRONIC LEAK DETECTORS

For restricted access areas, an electronic leak detector J-23400 or equivalent should be used.

The H-10 leak detector No. J-26934 or equivalent, is a 110 volt AC powered tester, while the refrigerant leak detector No. J-29547 or equivalent, is a portable, battery operated model. Both models provide visual and/or audible signals to indicate leak detection.

The successful use of electronic leak detectors depends upon carefully following the manufacturer's instructions regarding calibration, operation and maintenance.

Battery condition is especially important to the accuracy of the portable battery powered model and is monitored by a low battery indicator.

NORMAL SYSTEM PERFORMANCE 45 MPH

If the ambient air temperature is . . . DEGREES °F	The pressure gauge should read–(psi) SUCTION	The pressure gauge should read–(psi) DISCHARGE	The right center air should read–(°F) OUTLET °F
70	29~33	90 ~125	44~48
80	28~32	120~170	44~49
90	26~30	150~200	44~50
100	24~32	180~240	47~53

G37029500026000X

Fig. 4 45 MPH test specifications. R134a system

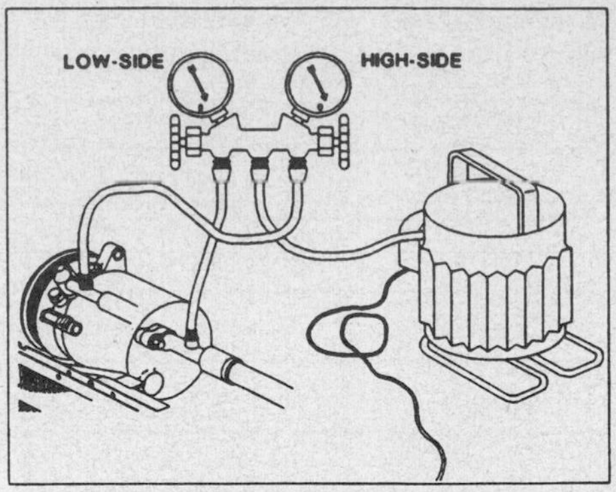
LOW-SIDE
HIGH-SIDE

G37029100010000X

Fig. 5 High & low side Schraeder valve locations. R12 system

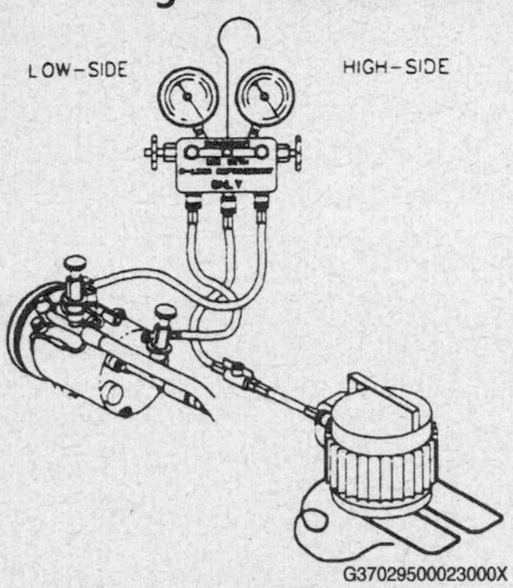
LOW-SIDE
HIGH-SIDE

G37029500023000X

Fig. 6 High & low side Schraeder valve locations. R134a system

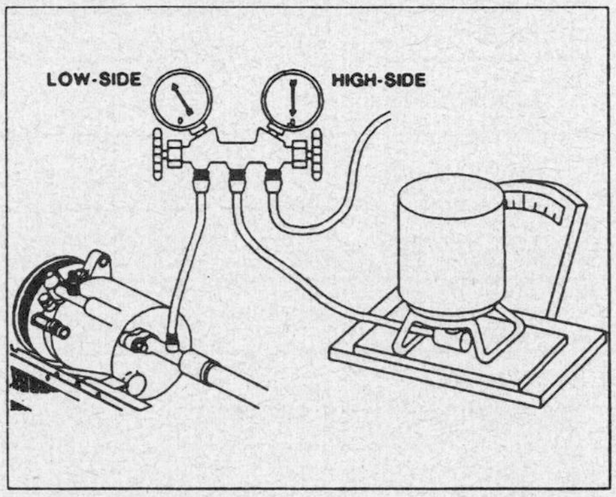
LOW-SIDE
HIGH-SIDE

G37029100011000X

Fig. 7 System charging valve connections. R12 system

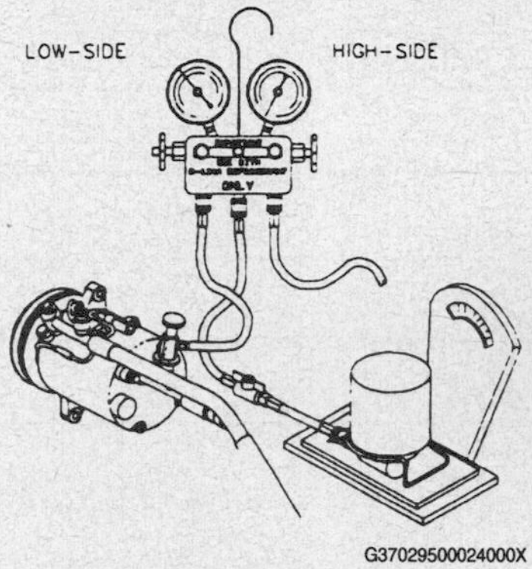
LOW-SIDE
HIGH-SIDE

G37029500024000X

Fig. 8 System charging valve connections. R134a system

DISCHARGING SYSTEM

Before removing or replacing any of the A/C refrigerant lines or components, the refrigerant must be completely recovered using and A/C refrigerant recovery and recycling system. Always check the A/C system for pressure with a manifold gauge set to determine if refrigerant is present in the system. Performing recovery on an A/C system that is exposed to the atmosphere as a result of a leak, would allow the recovery station to pull only air into the tank.

SYSTEM EVACUATION

1. Connect manifold gauge set and vacuum pump to high and low side Schraeder valves, **Fig. 5** for R12 system and **Fig. 6** for R134a system.
2. Turn vacuum pump on and slowly open high and low side valves to pump. Allow system to evacuate for 20-30 minutes. Note vacuum gauge reading.
3. Close high and low side valves. Shut-off vacuum pump.
4. Watch low side gauge for vacuum loss (1-3 minutes).
5. If loss is less than 1 inch Hg., from level recorded in previous step, proceed to "System Charging."
6. If vacuum loss is greater than 1 inch Hg., from level recorded in previous step, charge with ½ lb. of R12 or R134a refrigerant, depending on system type.
7. Leak test, repair leaks and retest. Disconnect high side adapter from service port and check for vacuum loss before leak testing.

CHARGING SYSTEM

Never remove a gauge line from its adapter when line is connected to the A/C system. Always remove the line adapter from the service fitting to disconnect a line. Do not remove charging hose at the gauge set while attached to the service low-side fitting. This will result in a complete discharge of the system due to the depressed Schraeder valve in service low-side fitting and may cause personal injury due to escaping R12.

1. Open R12 or R134a source valve and allow 1 lb. of liquid R12 or R134a to flow into system through low-side service fitting, **Fig. 7** for R12 system and **Fig. 8** for R134a system.
2. As soon as 1 lb. has been added to system, start engine, set A/C control to upper outlets, temperature lever to Max cold, blower speed on high and push A/C compressor button to the On position (button should illuminate).
3. Slowly draw in remainder of refrigerant charge.
4. Turn off R12 or R134a source valve and run engine for 30 seconds to clear lines and gauges.
5. With engine running, remove the charging low-side hose adapter from the suction pipe service fitting. Remove quickly to avoid excess refrigerant escaping from the system.
6. Ensure an O-ring seal is inside of caps before installation, because cap is primary seal for A/C service fittings. Failure to tighten cap will result in refrigerant leakage.
7. Install protective caps on service fittings and hand tighten.
8. Turn engine off, then check system for leaks with electronic leak detector.

DRUM METHOD

Place R12 or R134a drum on scale and note total weight before charging. Watch scale during charging to determine amount of R12 or R134a used.

1. Connect manifold gauge set as follows:
   a. Connect low pressure gauge hose to low pressure service fitting on suction pipe at rear of compressor, **Fig. 7**for R12 system and **Fig. 8** for R134a system. Do not connect high pressure line to A/C system.
   b. Connect center hose to R12 or R134a source.
2. Open valve on drum to start flow of refrigerant.

CHARGING STATION METHOD

Follow charging station manufacturer's instructions with the following exceptions:

1. Do not connect high pressure line to

air conditioning system.
2. Keep high pressure valve on the charging station closed at all times.
3. Perform the entire evacuation and charge procedure through the low-side pressure service fitting on the suction pipe, **Fig. 7**for R12 system and **Fig. 8** for R134a system.
4. Following these procedures will prevent accidental high-side vehicle system pressure being subjected to the charging station in the event an error is made in valve sequence during compressor operation to pull in the R12 or R134a charge.

System Service

INDEX

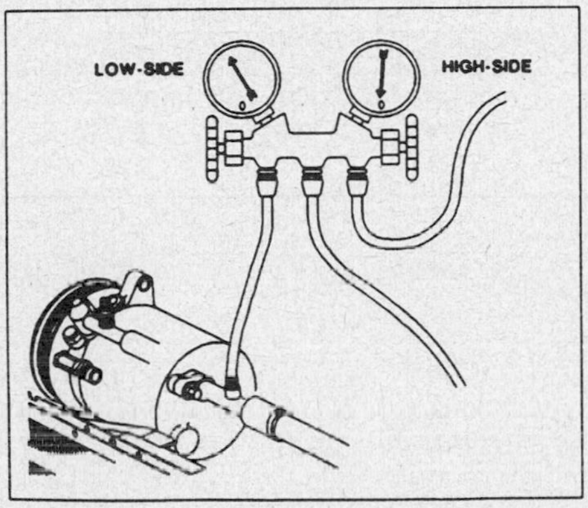

LOW-SIDE
HIGH-SIDE
G37029100008000X

Fig. 1 Low pressure gauge hose connection

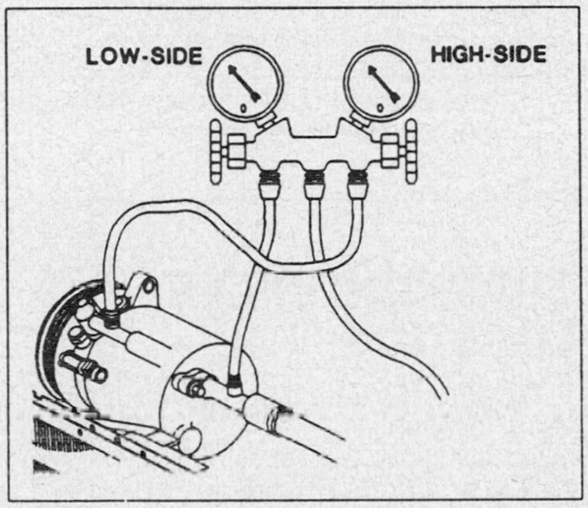

LOW-SIDE
HIGH-SIDE
G37029100009000X

Fig. 2 High pressure gauge hose connection

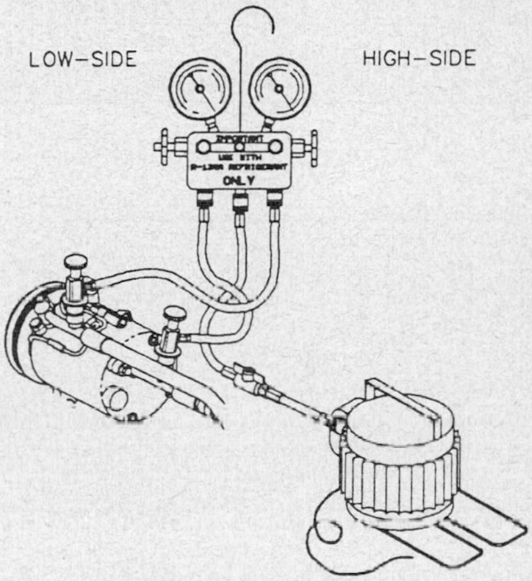

LOW-SIDE
HIGH-SIDE

Fig. 3 High & low pressure hose connection. R134a

MANIFOLD GAUGE SET INSTALLATION

Always wear goggles and wrap a clean cloth around fittings, valves and connections when performing work that involves opening the refrigerant system.

Ensure gauges read zero before installing manifold gauge set.

1. Close both hand valves of manifold gauge set.
2. Connect low pressure (blue) gauge hose to suction service port, located on the suction pipe **Fig. 1** for R12 system and **Fig. 3** for R134a system.
3. Hand tighten gauge hose nut, then connect adapter to high pressure gauge hose, **Fig. 2** for R12 system and **Fig. 3** for R134a system.
4. Connect high pressure (red) gauge hose to discharge service port, located on the discharge pipe.
5. Hand tighten adapter hose nut to discharge service port.

OIL CHARGE

ADDING OIL

Adding oil to the A/C system should take place after recovery and before evacuation procedure.

1. Remove refrigeration discharge hose at the compressor pipe connection.
2. Pour the correct quantity of new Saturn compressor oil, or equivalent, into the discharge hose pipe.
3. Always lubricate new O-rings with clean compressor oil prior to assembly.
4. Properly connect hose to compressor with new O-ring. Add new oil to components before installation.

OIL CHARGE REQUIREMENTS

The A/C system requires 200 cc of Saturn Compressor Oil or equivalent.

New oil quantities must be added to the system during component replacement, as follows:

1. **Compressor:** Remove, drain and measure oil. Drain replacement compressor. Add same amount of new compressor oil as was drained from removed compressor.
2. **Evaporator:** Add three ounces of new compressor oil.
3. **Condenser:** Add one ounce of new compressor oil.
4. **Receiver-Dehydrator:** Add one ounce of new compressor oil.

CHARGING VALVE LOCATION

Refer to **Figs. 1 through 8** for service valve locations.

OIL LEVEL CHECK

1. To measure compressor oil, compressor must be removed from engine.
2. Install high and low side compressor oil drain adapters tool Nos. SA9149AC-6 and SA9149AC-5 on low and high side ports.
3. Drain oil into suitable clean container from high side port first and move compressor to a different position to remove all the oil possible. Turn compressor over to drain oil from low side port and rotate compressor drive plate in both directions to remove oil from compressor chambers.
4. Move compressor to different positions to remove all oil possible. turn compressor back to high side port to re-drain and back to low side port to remove maximum amount of oil. Stop oil draining when oil coming from low and high side ports becomes only drops. Measure oil removed and record.
5. Inspect extracted oil for color change from clear to dark brown or black. Also inspect oil for presence of foreign substances, such as metal filings. If oil extracted is found as mentioned, the receiver drier must be replaced.
6. Discard extracted oil properly and replace with 200 cc of new Saturn PAG compressor oil.

Air Conditioning Specifications

INDEX

A/C SPECIFICATIONS

Year	Refrigerant Type	Refrigerant Capacity, Lbs.	Refrigeration Oil: Total System Capacity, Qts.	Refrigeration Oil: Compressor Oil Level	Compressor Clutch Air Gap, Inch
1992-93	R-12	2.25	.212①	②	.012-.024
1994-95	R-134a	1.5	.212①	②	.01-.02

①—200 cc.
②—Oil level may not be checked. If replacement is necessary, measure amount removed from old compressor, then add same amount to new compressor.

CHARGING VALVE LOCATION

Refer to "System Service" for charging valve locations.

BELT TENSION

Belt	New Lbs.	Used Lbs.
Accessory	50—65	45

COOLING FANS

NOTE: Electrical Symbol & Wire Color Code Identification Located In The Front Of This Manual Can Be Used As An Aid When Using Wiring Circuits Found In This Section.

INDEX

DESCRIPTION

On vehicles with A/C, the cooling fan has five unequally spaced blades to provide air flow through the radiator and condenser. the fan is driven by an electric motor which is attached to the radiator support. The fan motor is activated by a coolant temperature switch.

On models less A/C, the cooling fan has four unequally spaced blades that have curled tips to provide minimum noise. A fan shroud is used to prevent recirculation of air around the fan.

SYSTEM DIAGNOSIS & TESTING

Refer to **Fig. 1** for electric cooling fan wiring circuit.

COOLING FAN INOPERATIVE

Refer to **Fig. 2** for electric cooling fan inoperative diagnosis.

COOLING FAN OPERATES CONSTANTLY

Refer to **Fig. 3** for electric cooling fan operates constantly diagnosis.

COMPONENT REPLACEMENT

COOLING FAN ASSEMBLY

1. Disconnect battery ground cable.
2. **On DOHC models,** remove intake air ducts and temperature sensor connector.
3. **On all models,** remove wiring harness from cooling fan motor.
4. Loosen and remove top hold-down bolts from cooling fan assembly.
5. **On models with automatic transaxles and A/C,** it may be necessary to

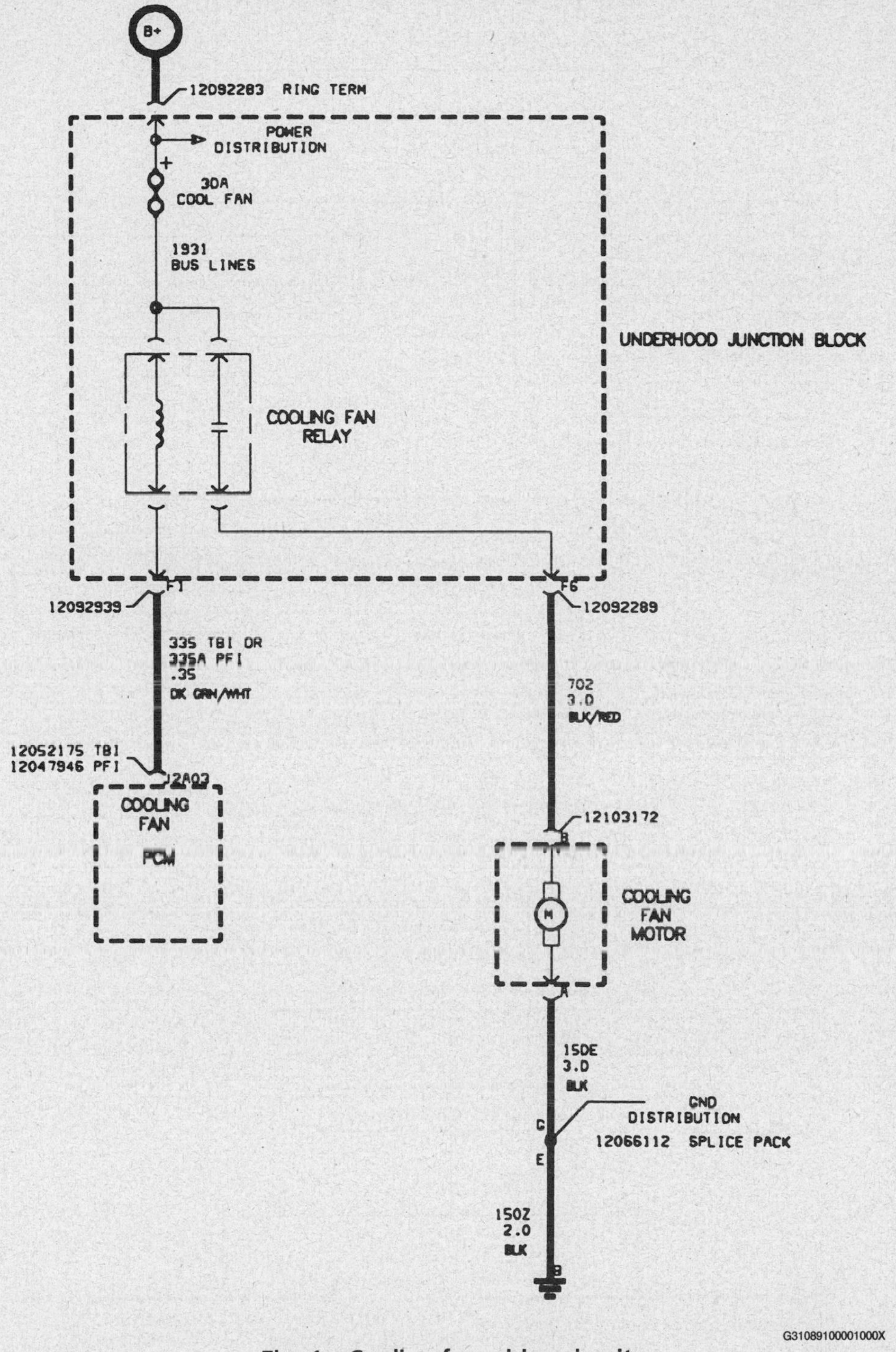
B+
12092283 RING TERM
POWER DISTRIBUTION
30A
COOL FAN
1931
BUS LINES
UNDERHOOD JUNCTION BLOCK
COOLING FAN
RELAY
12092939
12092289
335 TBI OR
335A PFI
.35
DK GRN/WHT
702
3.0
BLK/RED
12052175 TBI
12047946 PFI
COOLING
FAN
PCM
12103172
COOLING
FAN
MOTOR
150E
3.0
BLK
GND
DISTRIBUTION
12066112 SPLICE PACK
150Z
2.0
BLK
G31089100001000X

Fig. 1 Cooling fan wiring circuit

loosen the top transaxle oil cooler line for clearance.

6. **On all models,** lift cooling fan off of lower mounting brackets. Move assembly to left and rotate counterclockwise while lifting upward past upper radiator hose.
7. Remove cooling fan assembly from vehicle.
8. Reverse procedure to install.

COOLING FAN MOTOR

1. Remove cooling fan assembly as described under "Cooling Fan Assembly
2. While holding fan, remove fan to motor nut (lefthand thread). Pull fan off of motor shaft.
3. Remove screws securing fan motor to shroud.
4. Remove motor from fan shroud.
5. Reverse procedure to install. **Torque** motor nut to 27-44 inch lbs.

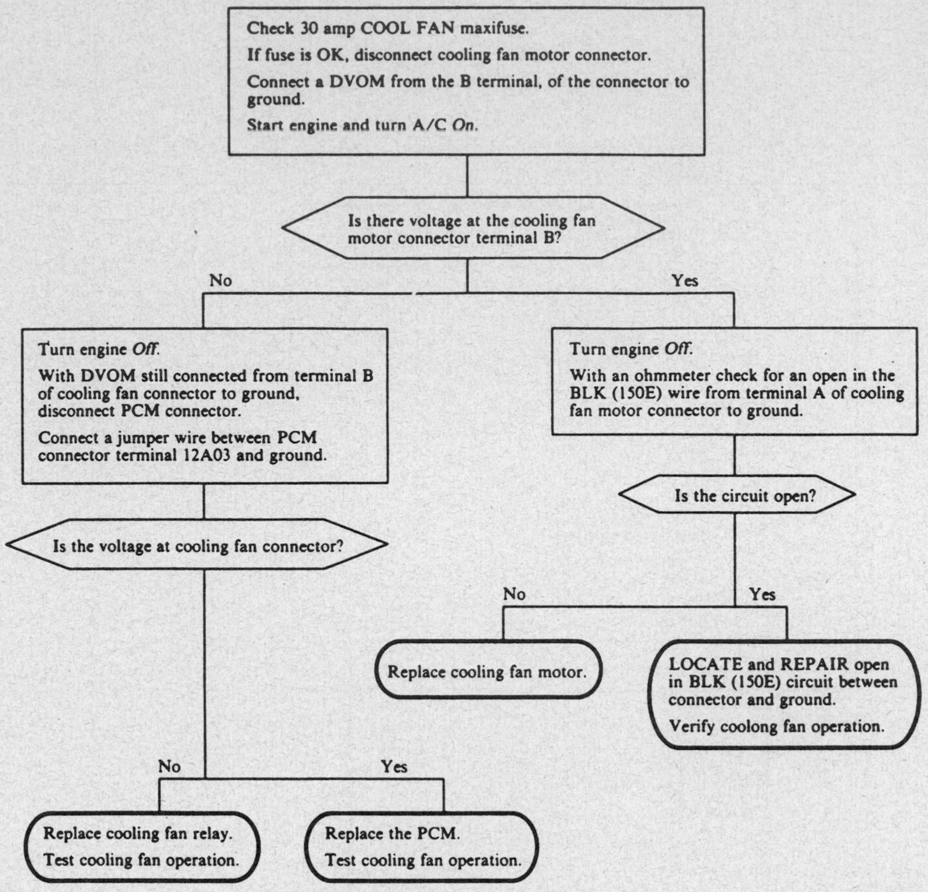
Check 30 amp COOL FAN maxifuse.
If fuse is OK, disconnect cooling fan motor connector.
Connect a DVOM from the B terminal, of the connector to ground.
Start engine and turn A/C *On*.
Is there voltage at the cooling fan motor connector terminal B?
No
Yes
Turn engine *Off*.
With DVOM still connected from terminal B of cooling fan connector to ground, disconnect PCM connector.
Connect a jumper wire between PCM connector terminal 12A03 and ground.
Turn engine *Off*.
With an ohmmeter check for an open in the BLK (150E) wire from terminal A of cooling fan motor connector to ground.
Is the circuit open?
Is the voltage at cooling fan connector?
No
Yes
Replace cooling fan motor.
LOCATE and REPAIR open in BLK (150E) circuit between connector and ground.
Verify coolong fan operation.
No
Yes
Replace cooling fan relay.
Test cooling fan operation.
Replace the PCM.
Test cooling fan operation.

G31089100002000X

Fig. 2 Cooling fan inoperative diagnosis

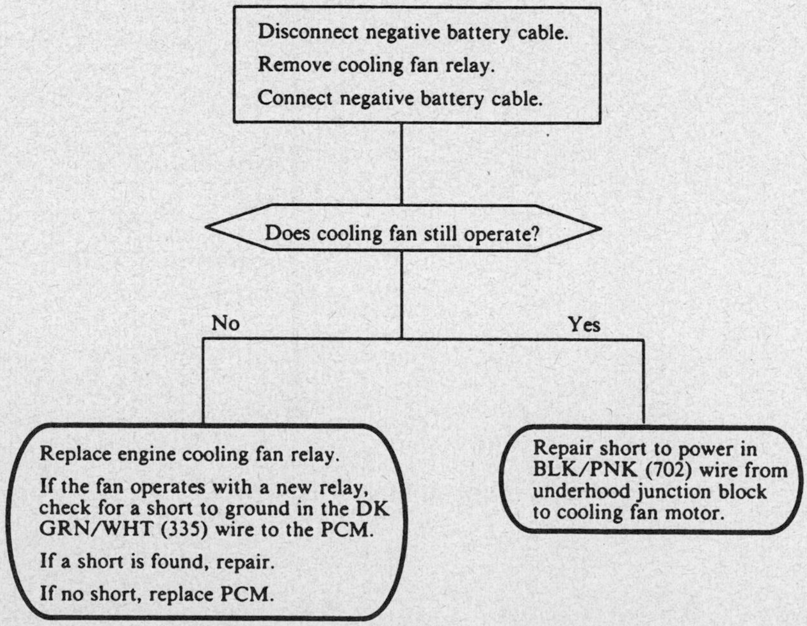
Disconnect negative battery cable.
Remove cooling fan relay.
Connect negative battery cable.
Does cooling fan still operate?
No
Yes
Replace engine cooling fan relay.
If the fan operates with a new relay, check for a short to ground in the DK GRN/WHT (335) wire to the PCM.
If a short is found, repair.
If no short, replace PCM.
Repair short to power in BLK/PNK (702) wire from underhood junction block to cooling fan motor.

G31089100003000X

Fig. 3 Cooling fan operates constantly diagnosis

DASH GAUGES

INDEX

IMPORTANT: To diagnose the cluster correctly, all diagnostic steps must be completed and followed in order.

IMPORTANT: Allow a short time for the gage to stabilize.

DIAGNOSTIC STEP	INPUT RESISTANCE	FUEL GAGE READING
1.	31Ω	At FULL or slightly above
2.	44.5Ω	At FULL or slightly below
3.	92Ω	At MID or slightly above
4.	106Ω	At MID or slightly below
5.	204Ω	At EMPTY or slightly above
6.	301Ω	At EMPTY or slightly below

G39099100002000X

Fig. 1 Fuel level gauge diagnosis

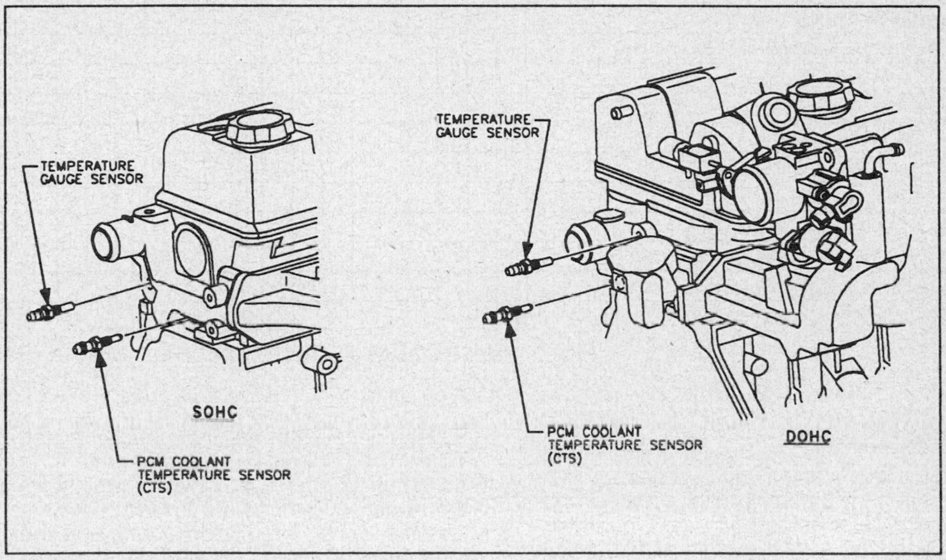
TEMPERATURE GAUGE SENSOR
SOHC
PCM COOLANT TEMPERATURE SENSOR (CTS)
TEMPERATURE GAUGE SENSOR
PCM COOLANT TEMPERATURE SENSOR (CTS)
DOHC

G39099100003000X

Fig. 2 Temperature gauge sensor connector locations

IMPORTANT: To diagnose the cluster correctly, all diagnostic steps must be completed and followed in order.

IMPORTANT: Allow a short time for the gage to stabilize.

DIAGNOSTIC STEP	INPUT RESISTANCE	READING
1.	5000Ω	At COLD mark or slightly below
2.	560Ω	At COLD mark or slightly above
3.	183Ω	At MID mark or slightly below
4.	151Ω	At MID mark or slightly above
5.	65Ω	At HOT mark or slightly below
6.	54Ω	At HOT mark or slightly above

G39099100004000X

Fig. 3 Temperature gauge diagnosis

IMPORTANT: To diagnose the cluster correctly, all diagnostic steps must be completed and followed in order.

IMPORTANT: Allow a short time for the gage to stabilize.

DIAGNOSTIC STEP	INPUT RESISTANCE	READING
1.	5Ω	At LOW mark or slightly below
2.	15Ω	At LOW mark or slightly above
3.	68Ω	At MID mark or slightly below
4.	89Ω	At MID mark or slightly above
5.	145Ω	At 3/4 mark or slightly below
6.	222Ω	At 3/4 mark or slightly above

G39099100005000X

Fig. 4 Oil pressure gauge diagnosis

GAUGES

FUEL LEVEL GAUGE

The fuel gauge receives a variable resistance signal from the fuel sender, located in the fuel tank. This signal is a function of the amount of fuel remaining in the tank. This variable resistance regulates the current through the coil windings of the fuel gauge, which in turn deflects the gauge pointer.

Diagnosis

1. Disconnect in-line fuel connector, located in the rear compartment on the driver side behind the carpet.
2. Using cluster tester tool No. SA9205Z or equivalent, and a digital multimeter (set to OHMS scale), connect the leads to terminals B and C of the connector going to the front of the vehicle.
3. Turn ignition switch to Run position (do not start engine).
4. Set resistances as shown in **Fig. 1.**
5. If fuel gauge reading is not accurate, replace cluster.

TEMPERATURE GAUGE

The temperature gauge receives a variable resistance signal from the coolant temperature gauge sender. This variable resistance regulates the current through the coil windings of the temperature gauge, which in turn deflects the gauge pointer.

Diagnosis

1. Disconnect coolant temperature sensor connector, located on the upper front left side of engine, **Fig. 2.**
2. Using cluster tester tool No. SA9205Z or equivalent, and a digital multimeter (set to OHMS scale), connect one lead to coolant temperature sensor connector and the other lead to engine ground.
3. Turn ignition to Run position (do not start engine).
4. Set input resistances as shown in **Fig. 3.**
5. If temperature gauge is not accurate, replace cluster.

OIL PRESSURE GAUGE

The oil pressure gauge receives a variable resistance signal from the oil pressure sender/switch. This variable resistance regulates the current through the coil windings of the oil pressure gauge, which in turn deflects the gauge pointer.

X — Most Probable Cause(s)
● — Possible Causes

COMPLAINT–CONDITION / CAUSE	IGN4 Fuse	IGN1 Fuse	IP Batt Fuse	HB TT Fuse	INJ Fuse	Circuit 153T	Circuit 153K	Circuit 30A/30/30B	Circuit 803B/803/803A	Circuit 135/135A	Circuit 31/31A	Circuit 11E	Circuit 990A/990	Circuit 419/419A or 419AA	Circuit 33B	Circuit 33B/33C/153P	Circuit 33B/33E	Circuit 33B/33/155E	Circuit 35/35A or 35AA	Circuit 231/231A	Circuit 231/231A	Circuit 231/231B	Circuit 25/25A	Circuit 237A/237	Circuit 237A/237/981/155RR	Circuit 237A/237/238/155LL	Circuit 996/996A	Circuit 456/456A	Circuit 1290	Circuit 153S	Circuit 68/68A	
Only the Highbeam Telltale Operable	X																															
High Beam Telltale Inoperable			X	X								●																				
Only Highbeam Telltale and Low Coolant Level Telltale Operable		X																														
Low Coolant level Telltale Inoperable						X																									X	
Fuel Level Gage always on E									X	X																						
Fuel Level Gage always on F									X																							
Engine Temp Gage always on C										X																						
Engine Temp Gage always on H										X																						
Oil Pressure Gage always on L											X																					
Oil Pressure Gage always on H											X																					

G39099100006010X

Fig. 5 Dash gauge & cluster troubleshooting (Part 1 of 4)

Diagnosis

1. Disconnect oil pressure sender/switch connector, located on right side of engine.
2. Using cluster tester tool No. SA9205Z or equivalent, and a digital multimeter (set to OHMS scale), connect one lead to oil pressure sender/switch connector and one lead to engine ground.
3. Turn ignition switch to Run position (do not start engine).
4. Set input resistances as shown in **Fig. 4.**
5. If oil pressure gauge reading is not correct, replace cluster.

WARNING LAMPS

OIL PRESSURE INDICATOR LAMP

The oil pressure indicator lamp is switched to ground by the oil pressure switch. When the lamp is switched to ground, ignition voltage flows through the lamp, allowing it to illuminate. This indicates that oil pressure has dropped below a specified limit.

WARNING SYSTEM

LOW COOLANT LEVEL INDICATOR

The low coolant indicator lamp is connected to ground by an 820 ohm, 1/2 watt resistor, located in the instrument cluster. When the coolant level is adequate, it is pulled up to IGNITION 1 by the coolant level switch. If the coolant level is below a specified level, this switch opens and the input level drops to GROUND. This signal activates a counter integrated circuit (IC) which, after a 8-12 second delay, drives an NPN transistor and turns on the indicator lamp. This indicates that the coolant level is low.

During engine start-up, the LOW COOLANT indicator lamp is illuminated, for 2-3 seconds, by the integrated circuit built into the instrument cluster for a bulb check.

SPEEDOMETERS

The speedometer receives vehicle speed information from the powertrain control module (PCM). The vehicle speed signal is passed through an RC filter to the input of the speedometer/odometer drive integrated circuit (IC), located in the instrument cluster. The high-to-low edge of the square wave input triggers the IC to produce a well defined pulse of current to the moving coil inside the speedometer gauge. The IC also counts the input transitions and uses this information to drive the stepper motor for both odometers. The vehicle completes one mile for every 4983 pulses received from the PCM.

DIAGNOSIS

If the speedometer or odometer is inoperative, a voltmeter can be used to see if there is an active signal present. Since the duty cycle of the signal is always 50 percent, the voltage will be averaged.

If a correct signal is received, half ignition voltage will be present. If the signal is stuck high, full ignition voltage will be present. If signal is shorted to ground, zero volts will be present.

TACHOMETER

The tachometer receives engine RPM information from the distributorless ignition system (DIS) module. The engine RPM signal is buffered by an RC filter/limiting diode and sent to the tachometer drive integrated circuit (IC), both located within the instrument cluster. The IC receives a low-to-high square wave signal, and produces a well defined pulse of current to the moving coil inside the tachometer. The engine completes one revolution for every two pulses received from the DIS module.

UPSHIFT INDICATOR LAMP

The upshift indicator lamp is pulled to ground by the powertrain control module (PCM). When the lamp is pulled to ground, ignition voltage flows through the lamp, allowing it to illuminate. This indicates when to shift to the next highest gear for maximum fuel mileage.

TROUBLESHOOTING

Refer to **Fig. 5,** for dash gauges and cluster troubleshooting.

X — Most Probable Cause(s)
● — Possible Causes

COMPLAINT–CONDITION / CAUSE	Circuit 1932	Circuit 1936/2A	Circuit 940	Circuit 39C	Circuit 39E	Circuit 817B/817A/817E or 817EE	Circuit 3B	Circuit 121A/121	Circuit 8J	Circuit 139F/68/68A	Circuit 663	Circuit 664	Ignition Switch	I/P cluster	DIS Module	Fuel Level Gage Sensor	Coolant Temp Gage Sensor	Oil Pressure Switch/Sensor	Coolant Level Switch	Passive Restraint control Module	PCM	Low Brake Fluid Switch	ABS Control Module	Parking Brake Switch	Headlamp Switch	Oil Pressure Switch	Generator	Passive Restraint Latch Switch	Driver's Lap Belt Switch	Highbeam Telltale Bulb	Circuit 153Y / 153Z / 153G	Circuit 3A
Only the Highbeam Telltale Operable	X												●																			
High Beam Telltale Inoperable		X	X																						●					X	●	
Highbeam Telltale and Low Coolant Level Telltale Operable				X	X								●																			X
Low Coolant level Telltale Inoperable							X			X				●					●													
Speedometer, Odometer Inoperable				X		X								X							●											
Tachometer Inoperable								X						●	●																	
Fuel Level Gage always on E														●		●																
Fuel Level Gage always on F														●		●																
Engine Temp Gage always on C														●			●															
Engine Temp Gage always on H														●			●															
Oil Pressure Gage always on L														●				●														
Oil Pressure Gage always on H														●				●														
Fuel Level, Engine Temp, Oil Pressure Gages always on E. C. L. respectively					X																											

G39099100006020X

Fig. 5 Dash gauge & cluster troubleshooting (Part 2 of 4)

X — Most Probable Cause(s)
● — Possible Causes

COMPLAINT–CONDITION / CAUSE	IGN4 Fuse	IGN1 Fuse	IP Batt Fuse	HB TT Fuse	INJ Fuse	Circuit 153T	Circuit 153K	Circuit 30A/30/30B	Circuit 303B/803/803A	Circuit 135/135A	Circuit 31/31A	Circuit 11E	Circuit 1625A/1625	Circuit 419/419A or 419A[illegible]	Circuit 33B	Circuit 33B/33C/153P	Circuit 33B/33E	Circuit 33B/33/155E	Circuit 35/35A or 35AA	Circuit 231/231A	Circuit 231/231A	Circuit 231/231B	Circuit 25/25A	Circuit 237A/237	Circuit 237A/237/98[illegible]/155[illegible]R	Circuit 237A/237/23[illegible]/155[illegible]L	Circuit 996/996A	Circuit 456/456A	Circuit 1290	Circuit 153S
Lapbelt Telltale Inoperable													X																	
Service Engine Soon Telltale Inoperable														X																
Brake Telltale Never On															X															
Brake Telltale Always On																X	X	X												
Engine Temp Telltale Inoperable																			X											
Highbeam Telltale Always On												X																		
Oil Pressure Telltale Inoperable																					X	X								
Charge Telltale Inoperable																							X							
Left Turn Signal Indicator does not Flash																														
Right Turn Signal Indicator does not Flash																														
Seatbelt Telltale Never On																								X						
Seatbelt Telltale Always On																									X	X				
Shift to D2 Telltale Telltale Inoperable																											X			
Upshift Telltale Inoperable																												X		

G39099100006030X

Fig. 5 Dash gauge & cluster troubleshooting (Part 3 of 4)

X — Most Probable Cause(s)
● — Possible Causes

COMPLAINT–CONDITION / CAUSE	Circuit 1932/3A	Circuit 1936	Circuit 940	Circuit 39C	Circuit 39E	Circuit 817B/817A/817E or 817EE	Circuit 3B	Circuit 121A/121	Circuit 8J	Circuit 139F/68/68A	Circuit 663	Circuit 664	Battery Cable 2C/2B	Ignition Switch	I/P Cluster	Dis Module	Fuel Level Gage Sensor	Coolant Temp Gage Sensor	Oil Pressure Switch/Sensor	Coolant Level Switch	Passive restraint Control Module	PCM	Low Brake Fluid Switch	ABS Control Module	Parking Brake Switch	Headlamp Switch	Oil Pressure Switch	Generator	Passive Restraint Latch Switch	Driver's Lap Belt Switch	I/P Cluster Telltale Bulb
Lapbelt Telltale Inoperable															●						●									●	X
Service Engine Soon Telltale Inoperable															●							●									X
Brake Telltale Never On															●																X
Brake Telltale Always On															●								●	●	●						
Engine Temp Telltale Inoperable															●							●									X
Highbeam Telltale Always On															●																
Oil Pressure Telltale Inoperable															●				●								●				X
Charge Telltale Inoperable															●													●			X
Left Turn Signal Indicator does not Flash											X				●																X
Right Turn Signal Indicator does not Flash												X			●																X
Seatbelt Telltale Never On															●														●		X
Seatbelt Telltale Always On															●														●		
Shift to D2 Telltale Telltale Inoperable															●							●									X
Upshift Telltale Inoperable															●							●									X

G39099100006040X

Fig. 5 Dash gauge & cluster troubleshooting (Part 4 of 4)

STARTER MOTORS

INDEX

APPLICATION CHART

Year	Type	Model
1992-95	AC-Delco	—

DESCRIPTION

Automatic transmission models use a 1.876 hp (1.4 kW) planetary gear reduction starter. While manual transmission models use a 1.072 hp (0.8 kW) planetary gear reduction starter.

These planetary gear reduction starters consist of an armature, a frame with permanent magnet poles, a planetary drive mechanism, a solenoid and a housing.

The starters use a planetary gear drive between the armature and motor pinion. The gear drive allows the use of permanent magnets eliminating heat that normally would be produced by coil fields, and also simplifies motor construction since there are no internal field coils and connections.

TROUBLESHOOTING

Refer to **Fig. 1**, for starter motor troubleshooting.

DIAGNOSIS & TESTING

ON-VEHICLE STARTER TEST

Ensure battery is in satisfactory condition before performing test. If battery power is insufficient, the start motor will not function properly.

Electronic System Tester tool No. SA9154Z or equivalent, is required for the following starter system test.

X — Most Probable Cause(s)
● — Possible Causes

COMPLAINT–CONDITION / CAUSE		IGN3 Fuse	Circuit 151A	Circuit 1930A	Circuit 5/6/6B (Manual Trans only)	Circuit 5A/6A/6X (Auto Trans only)	Circuit 2B	Ignition Switch	Clutch Starter Switch	Neutral Starter Switch	Starter Moror/Solenoid	Battery	Engine Mechanical	Flywheel-Pinion gap	Extreme Cold	Mating Surfaces	Theft Deterrent
Starter Dead, No Click From Solenoid		X		X	X	X		●	●	●	X	X					●
Starter Dead, Solenoid Does Click							X				X	X	●		●		
Starter Cranks Slowly	X										●	X	●		●	●	
Starter Does Not Engage											X			●			

G31129100001010X

Fig. 1 Troubleshooting (Part 1 of 3)

Complaint/Condition	Possible Causes	Correction
High pitched whine during cranking (before the engine fires over), but engine cranks and starts.	The distance between the flywheel and starter pinion is too great. Check the flywheel for damage such as a bent flywheel or excessive or unusual wear patterns.	Start the engine and carefully touch the outside diameter of the flywheel with chalk or crayon to show high point of tooth runout when the engine is turned off. Turn the engine off and rotate the engine by hand so that the marked teeth are in the area of inspection. If the runout is present, the flywheel may have to be replaced. If no runout exists, check the starter drive gear and starter housing for any unusual conditions that would cause it not to mesh properly. If a problem exists, replace the starter motor. **IMPORTANT:** starter motors are not shimmed.
High pitched whine after engine fires over as key is being released (starter hang in, or solenoid weak).	The distance between the flywheel and starter pinion is too small.	Check flywheel runout if it is acceptable, replace the starter motor. **IMPORTANT:** The starter motor is not shimmed for service.
A loud whoop after the engine fires over; but while the starter is still engaged. May sound like a siren if engine is revved while the starter is engaged.	The most probable cause is a damaged or over-running clutch.	Replace the starter motor.
A rumble or growl, or in several cases a knock as the starter motor is coasting down to a stop after starting the engine.	The most probable cause is a bent or unbalanced starter armature.	Replace the starter motor.
High pitched whine during starting.	Check the flywheel for damage such as a bent flywheel or unusual wear patterns.	Start the engine and, using chalk, mark the high point of the tooth runout when the engine is turned off. If the runout is present, the flywheel may have to be replaced. If no runout exists, the starter gear or housing may be preventing the gears from meshing properly. If a condition exists, replace the starter motor.
High pitched whine after the engine fires over.	Check flywheel runout.	If flywheel runout is acceptable, replace the starter motor.
Loud whoop after the engine fires over.	Starter motor.	Replace the starter motor.
Rumble or knock as starter motor coasts down after starting.	Starter motor.	Replace the starter motor.

G31129100001020X

Fig. 1 Troubleshooting (Part 2 of 3)

1. Connect red and black tester cables to battery. Place gray inductive current pick-up around positive battery cable.
2. Ensure arrow on gray inductive current pick-up is pointing toward starter motor solenoid.
3. Disable ignition system by disconnecting electrical connection at ignition module.
4. Press "Starter Test" button on system tester.
5. Position tester so the display can be seen from driver's seat. When display reads "Crank Engine," turn ignition to Start position.
6. Tester will continue to display "Crank Engine" for 15 seconds.
7. The System Tester will display the following information:
   a. Cranking Amps: This displays the average amperage drawn by the starter motor during cranking. Refer to **Fig. 2**, for normal operation amperage specifications.
   b. Cranking Voltage: This displays the average battery voltage during cranking. If the voltage is below 9.5 volts, ensure battery is in satisfactory condition and properly charged. Correct cranking voltage and a slow stator indicates loose or corroded cables.
   c. Good Starter/Bad Starter: If display reads "Bad Starter," replace starter motor only after determining there is no engine mechanical malfunctions or flywheel binding problems.

CLUTCH START SWITCH

1. Check resistance through switch.
2. Circuit should be open with clutch is engaged.
3. Less than two ohms should exist when clutch is fully depressed.

NEUTRAL START SWITCH

1. Check resistance through switch from Pin A to Pin B.
2. Circuit should be open when transaxle shifter is in R, 3 or 2.
3. Resistance should be less than 2 ohms when transaxle shifter is in P or N.

COMPLAINT	POSSIBLE CAUSE	CORRECTION
No click, no crank during starting.	If voltage at the starter switch terminal is less than 9 volts, then the control circuit is the probable cause.	Check starter ground: a. paint on mounting surface b. battery negative ground. c. other loose connections
	If voltage at the starter switch terminal is greater than 9 volts, then the motor is the probable root cause.	Replace the starter motor.
Click, no crank during startup.	If voltage at the starter switch terminal is greater than 6 volts, possible causes could be damaged internal starter ground, excess solenoid temperature, excess voltage drop between the brushes and commutator, or defect at internal solenoid connection.	Replace the starter motor.
	If voltage at the starter switch terminal is greater than 6 volts a possible cause could be the radial and axial fit between the pinion and flywheel.	Replace starter or flywheel, whichever is found to be damaged.
	Check distance between the flywheel and pinion, check flywheel runout.	NOTE: Saturn starter motors are not to be shimmed.
Starter motor continues to run with pinion extended after starting.	Starter motor internal short (at contact assembly or solenoid coil) or external short between battery and switch terminal.	Check external ring terminals and wires for possible touching between battery and switch terminal lead. If no external short exists, replace starter motor.
Starter motor continues to run with pinion retracted after startup.	Internal starter motor damage; either electrical (welded contact, short between motor and battery terminal) or mechanical (contact rod).	Replace starter motor.
Whine on disengagement after starting.	Internal starter motor mechanical problem (spline to drive interference, shift mechanism hang–up, plunger hang–up) or pinion to ring rear interference.	Replace starter motor. Check flywheel to pinion distance and runout.
Noisy during starting.	Internal starter motor problem: gear noise or pole rub with armature.	Replace starter motor.

G31129100001030X

Fig. 1 Troubleshooting (Part 3 of 3)

Room Temperature: 5°–27°C (40°–80°F)	80–120 amps
Hot Engine: Coolant above 50°C (120°F)	70 – 110 amps
Cold Engine: 5°C (40°F)	90 – 130 amps

G31129100004000X

Fig. 2 Cranking amperage specifications

STARTER SPECIFICATIONS

Year	Type	No Load Test		
		Volts	Amps ①	RPM
1992-95	AC-Delco	9.5	80-120	—

①—At room temperature. Subtract 10 amps for hot engine.

ALTERNATORS

NOTE: Electrical Symbol & Wire Color Code Identification Located In The Front Of This Manual Can Be Used As An Aid When Using Wiring Circuits Found In This Section.

INDEX

APPLICATION CHART

Year	Type	Model
1992-95	Saturn	CS130

X — Most Probable Cause(s)
• — Possible Causes

COMPLAINT–CONDITION / CAUSE	IGN4 Fuse	IGN3 Fuse	IGN1 Fuse	Circuit 15A (Battery Ground)	Circuit 2C/2B	Circuit 1932	Circuit 1930A	Circuit 3A	Circuit 300/250A/250	Circuit 39C	Circuit 25/25A	I/P Cluster	Generator	Ignition Switch	Excessive Electrical Load	Constant Running at Low RPM	Loose Belt	Broken Belt	Loose Mounting Bolts	Parasitic Load
Charge Warning Telltale Lamp Does Not Light	X		X		X			X		X	X	•	•	•						
Charge Warning Telltale Lamp stays on with Engine on											X	•	•		•	•	•	•		
Battery is Undercharged				X	X								•		•	•	•	•		X
Battery is Overcharged													X							
Lights Dim at Idle															X	•	•	X		
Lights Dim at Over 1000 RPM																	X	•	•	
Mechanical Noise													•				X		•	
Radio Noise/Hum or Whistle													•							
Output Exceeds 16V													X							

G31129100002000X

Fig. 1 Alternator system troubleshooting chart

DESCRIPTION

The alternator is constructed of a rotor mounted on bearings in two end frames, a stator assembly, six silicon diodes, an internally mounted voltage regulator and an integral mounted shield. the alternator develops AC voltages which are converted to DC current by a rectifier circuit.

The Powertrain Control Module (PCM) monitors battery voltage and will increase idle speed if battery voltage drops below a calibrated amount.

TROUBLESHOOTING

Refer to **Fig. 1** for alternator system troubleshooting procedures and **Fig. 2**, for alternator system wiring circuit.

DIAGNOSIS & TESTING

PRECAUTIONS

Before connecting any test equipment to alternator, ensure engine and ignition are off and drive belt is at correct tension.

CHARGING SYSTEM FUNCTION TEST

1. Turn ignition key to Off position. Charge indicator lamp should be off.
2. Turn ignition key to On position. Charge indicator lamp should be on.
3. Crank engine. Charge indicator lamp should turn off and stay off once the engine is running.

ALTERNATOR TEST

Electronic System Tester tool No. SA9154Z or equivalent, is required for the following starter system test.

1. Clean battery terminals and attach Electronic System Tester clamps to appropriate terminals.
2. Clamp current probe to wire leading to battery ground terminal. Arrow on probe should point toward battery.
3. Press "Charging System Test." The display should show the correct number of cylinders.
4. Run engine at 2000 RPM until display flashes "Maintain 2000 RPM."
5. Hold at 2000 RPM until counter counts down from ten seconds.
6. When ten seconds are over, run engine at idle until display reads "Maintain Idle." Hold this momentarily until the display reads "Test Complete."
7. Press "Continue" to see results. The Electronic System Tester will display voltage and current output of the alternator as follows:
   a. Voltage output should be above 13 volts.
   b. Current output should be a minimum of 60 amps.
8. If alternator does not meet the above specifications:
   a. Verify battery is charged correctly.
   b. Ensure vehicle does not have any excessive electrical loads.
   c. Replace alternator.
   d. Repeat test to verify repairs.

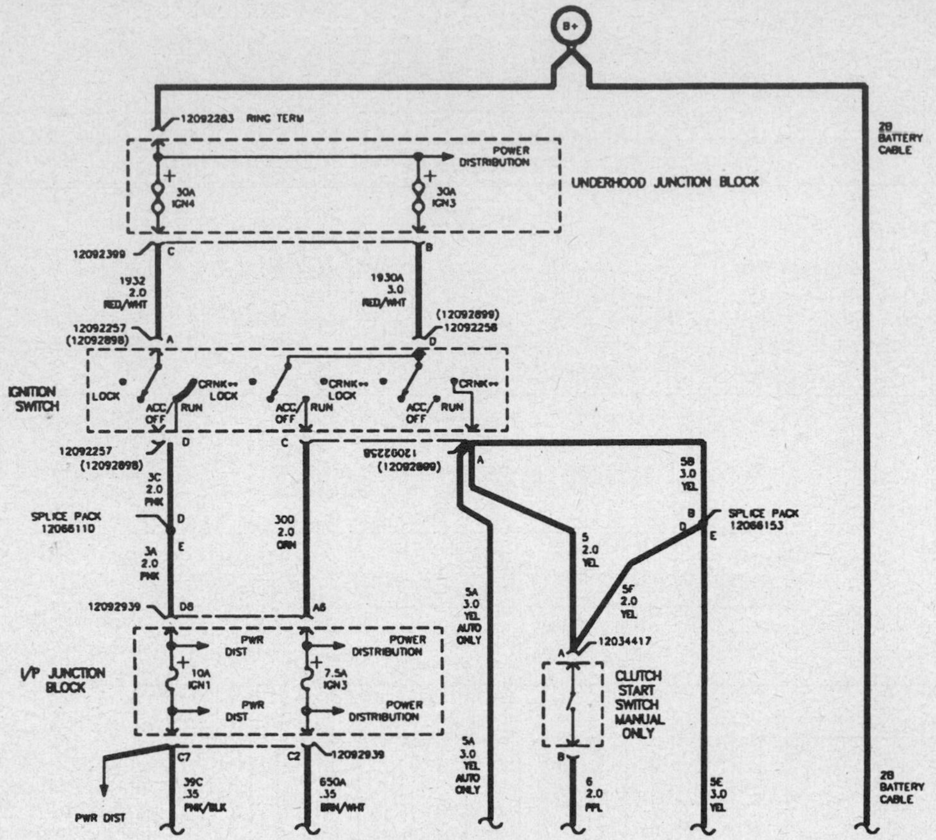
B+
12092283 RING TERM
POWER DISTRIBUTION
30A IGN4
30A IGN3
UNDERHOOD JUNCTION BLOCK
2B BATTERY CABLE
12092399
1932 2.0 RED/WHT
1930A 3.0 RED/WHT
12092257 (12092898)
(12092899) 12092258
IGNITION SWITCH
LOCK
CRNK
ACC/OFF
RUN
SPLICE PACK 12066110
3C 2.0 PNK
3A 2.0 PNK
300 2.0 ORN
5B 3.0 YEL
SPLICE PACK 12068153
5 2.0 YEL
5F 2.0 YEL
5A 3.0 YEL AUTO ONLY
12034417
12092939
I/P JUNCTION BLOCK
PWR DIST
10A IGN1
7.5A IGN3
POWER DISTRIBUTION
CLUTCH START SWITCH MANUAL ONLY
PWR DIST
39C .35 PNK/BLK
650A .35 BRN/WHT
6 2.0 PPL
5E 3.0 YEL

G31129100003010X

Fig. 2 Charging system wiring circuit (Part 1 of 2)

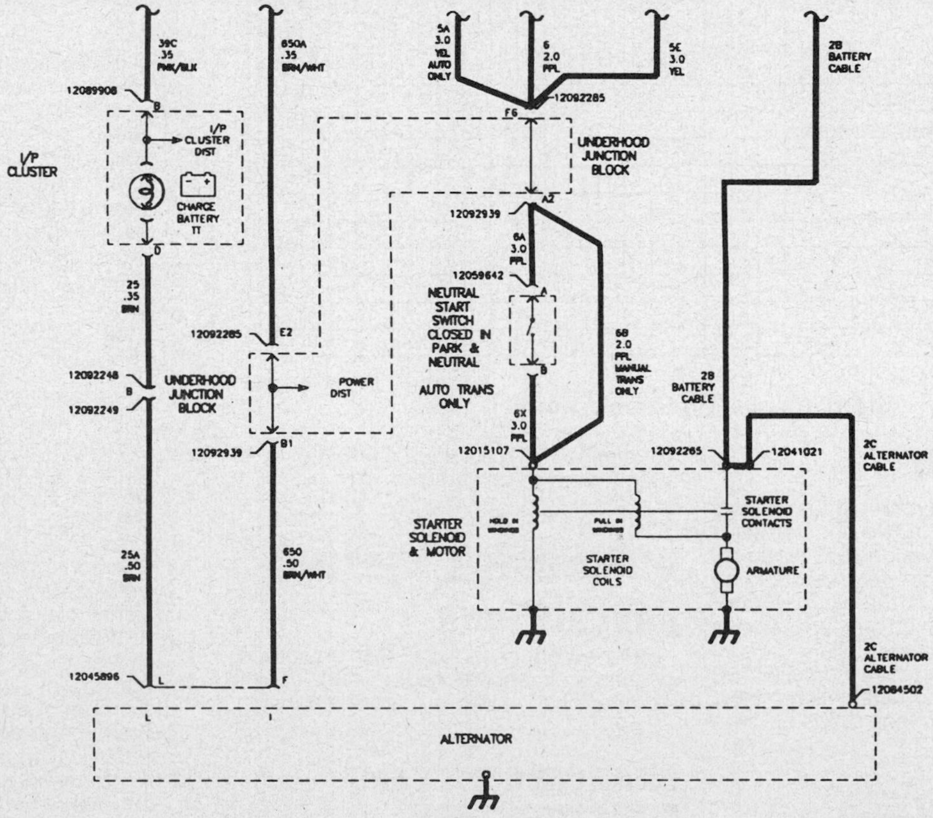
39C .35 PNK/BLK
650A .35 BRN/WHT
5A 3.0 YEL AUTO ONLY
6 2.0 PPL
5E 3.0 YEL
2B BATTERY CABLE
12092285
12089908
I/P CLUSTER
I/P CLUSTER DIST
CHARGE BATTERY TT
UNDERHOOD JUNCTION BLOCK
12092939
6A 3.0 PPL
12059642
NEUTRAL START SWITCH CLOSED IN PARK & NEUTRAL
AUTO TRANS ONLY
6B 2.0 PPL MANUAL TRANS ONLY
25 .35 BRN
12092248
12092249
POWER DIST
6X 3.0 PPL
12015107
12041021
2C ALTERNATOR CABLE
STARTER SOLENOID & MOTOR
HOLD IN WINDINGS
PULL IN WINDINGS
STARTER SOLENOID CONTACTS
STARTER SOLENOID COILS
ARMATURE
25A .50 BRN
650 .50 BRN/WHT
12045896
12084502
ALTERNATOR

G31129100003020X

Fig. 2 Charging system wiring circuit (Part 2 of 2)

ALTERNATOR SPECIFICATIONS

Year	Type	Model	Max. Ratted Output Amps	Approx. Output Amps @ RPM
1992-95	Saturn	CS130	96	①

①—At 81°F, 91 @ 2000; at 221°F, 71 @ 2000.

SPEED CONTROL SYSTEMS

NOTE: Electrical Symbol & Wire Color Code Identification Located In The Front Of This Manual Can Be Used As An Aid When Using Wiring Circuits Found In This Section.

INDEX

DESCRIPTION

The system consists of a cruise control module, located in the passenger compartment on the driver's side above the accelerator pedal between the steering column and HVAC control head, control switches, cruise brake switch and on models equipped with manual transmission, a cruise clutch switch.

The completely electronic system does not require vacuum or a vacuum servo motor to control throttle movement. A cable from the cruise control module pulls the accelerator linkage at the accelerator pedal.

The on/off switch enables and disables the speed control system. In the on position the cruise control will activate and in the off position the cruise control will immediately be disabled.

When the cruise in enabled, depressing the set/coast switch will engage the cruise. When cruise is engaged the cruise control module will maintain the desired speed within one mph. When the set/coast switch is held down the vehicle speed will coast down until the switch is released.

If the vehicle has been in the cruise control engage mode, and cruise has been disabled by pressing the brake or clutch switch, then vehicle can return to the previous cruise set by momentarily depressing the resume/accel switch one time.

The vehicle speed in miles per hour is used for tap up and tap down cruise speed adjustments. Once tap up or tap down button is depressed, vehicle speed will increase or decrease by one mph for each time the switch is depressed.

The cruise control system has five circuits linking it to various input signals and a ground circuit. The IGN3 circuit sends ignition on signal to the module when the switch is in the on position. The cruise control switch supplies battery power to the power-up module, through the enable circuit. The vehicle speed information comes from the powertrain control module (PCM) at 4987 pulses per minutes, on all models except Coupe, or 4995 pulses per minute on Coupe models. The cruise control module receives input from the set/coast/resume/accel switch, located on the steering wheel. The cruise control module determines the command by the amount of voltage received. Brake and clutch switch inputs are received when the pedal is depressed to disengage the system.

ADJUSTMENTS

CONTROL CABLE

With Scan Tool

1. Install scan tool according to manufacturers instructions.
2. Check throttle position sensor voltage, tighten or loosen cable. If cable is too tight then loosen by turning cable until scan tool reads 0 or quits moving, then loosen two more turns. If cable is too loose, then tighten cable until TPS has a reading, then loosen two adjuster two turns.
3. If slug at end of cruise control to throttle cable comes off and cable comes out of cruise control module, replace speed control module. The cable and adjuster assembly may be replaced separately only if slug has not been separated from cable at module end of assembly.
4. Adjust cable by pulling forward and turning ring on adjuster until TPS voltage reads 0 volts, then loosen two more turns.

Less Scan Tool

1. Remove air intake tube at throttle body.
2. Check throttle blade position.
3. Adjust cable by pulling forward and turning ring on adjuster until throttle blade if fully closed, then loosen two more turns.
4. Install air intake tube.
5. Cable and adjuster assembly are not repairable, replace as an assembly. Do not remove cable and adjuster from cruise control module.

BRAKE & CLUTCH SWITCH

Loosen switch attaching bolts, then slide forward or rearward. Switch plunger should be fully depressed with brake pedal released.

SYSTEM DIAGNOSIS & TESTING

SYSTEM PERFORMANCE TEST

Perform the following procedure to confirm speed control system is operating correctly.

1. Test drive vehicle at 25 mph or more, ensuring speed controls operate with switch in On position.
2. Depress set/coast switch for a minimum of 1 second to engage speed controls.
3. Release accelerator pedal, ensuring car maintains speed.

4. Depress brake or clutch to disengage system, ensuring vehicle decelerates.
5. Depress resume/accelerate switch for at least 1 second, vehicle should resume original speed.
6. Depress resume/accelerate switch for 1.5-4.5 seconds, vehicle speed should increase by one mph.
7. Repeat step 6.
8. Turn speed control on/off switch to off position, vehicle should decelerate.

ELECTRICAL TEST

Refer to **Fig. 1,** for electrical wiring circuit.

1. Remove CPA from cruise control module electrical connector.
2. Disconnect module electrical connector, then install cruise/cluster tester connector.
3. Install module electrical connector to tester.
4. Plug cruise/cluster tester power cord to lighter.
5. Select road or shop tester mode.
6. Perform the following diagnostic tests:
   a. For inoperative cruise control system, refer to **Fig. 2.**
   b. For intermittent cruise operation, refer to **Fig. 3.**
   c. For vehicle road test, refer to **Fig. 4.**

COMPONENT DIAGNOSIS & TESTING

BRAKE & CLUTCH SWITCH

With switch depressed, switch contacts should be closed, continuity exists. With switch depressed, switch contacts should be open, no continuity should exist.

COMPONENT REPLACEMENT

CRUISE CONTROL MODULE

1. Disconnect battery ground cable.
2. Remove connector position assurance (CPA), then disconnect cruise control electrical connector.
3. Disconnect speed control cable from accelerator pedal.
4. Remove module attaching nuts, then remove.
5. Reverse procedure to install. **Torque** module attaching nuts to 44 inch lbs.

SPEED CONTROL SWITCH

1992

1. Disconnect battery ground cable.
2. Carefully pry switch button from horn pad.
3. Disconnect switch electrical connector, then remove switch.
4. Reverse procedure to install.

1993–94

1. Disable SIR system, then remove air bag by prying off screw caps on steering wheel and removing attaching screws with a flat head screw driver. Lift inflator module out of steering wheel.
2. Remove integral connector lock device then disconnect electrical connector and remove inflator module.
3. Disconnect speed control switch and remove two speed control switch attaching screws then remove switch.
4. Reverse procedure to install.

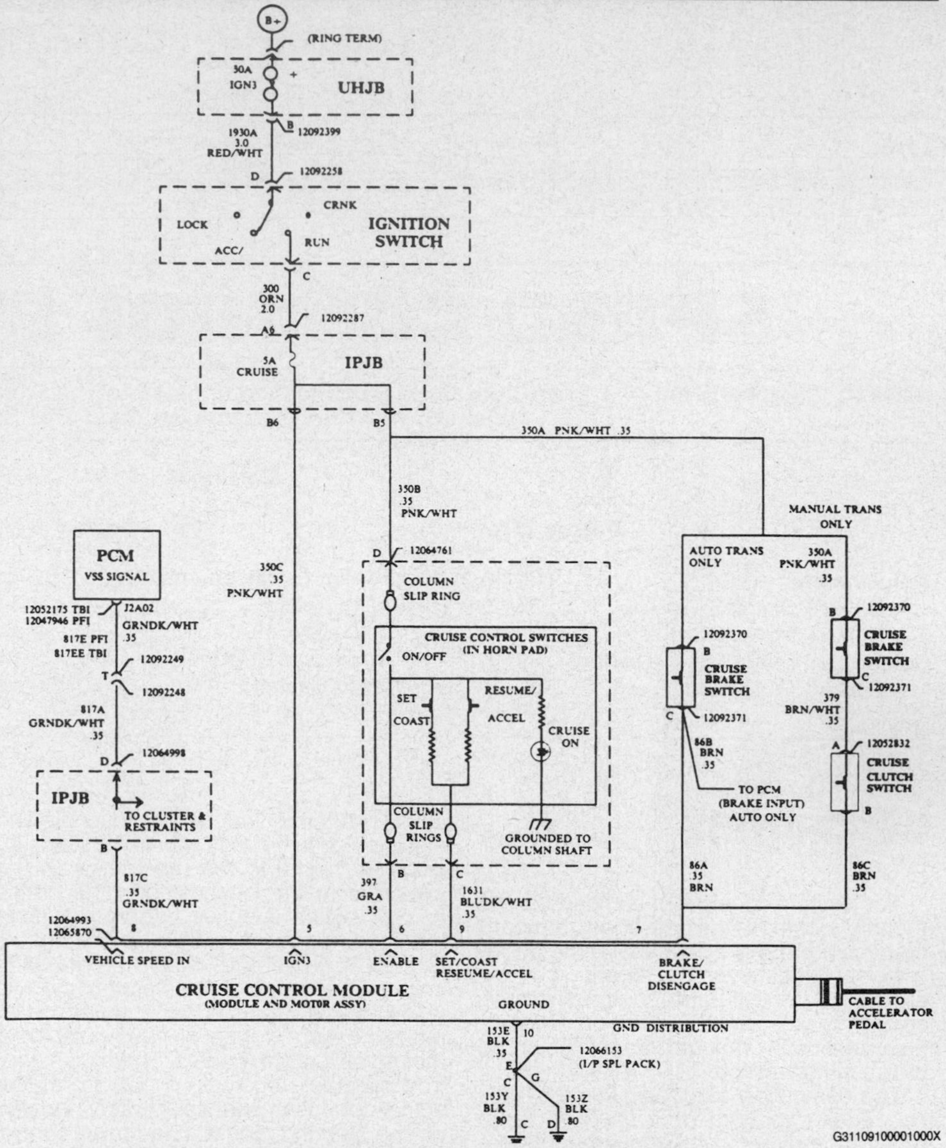
B+
(RING TERM)
UHJB
IGNITION SWITCH
LOCK
ACC/
CRNK
RUN
IPJB
CRUISE
PCM
VSS SIGNAL
IPJB
TO CLUSTER & RESTRAINTS
COLUMN SLIP RING
CRUISE CONTROL SWITCHES (IN HORN PAD)
ON/OFF
SET/COAST
RESUME/ACCEL
CRUISE ON
COLUMN SLIP RINGS
GROUNDED TO COLUMN SHAFT
MANUAL TRANS ONLY
AUTO TRANS ONLY
CRUISE BRAKE SWITCH
CRUISE CLUTCH SWITCH
TO PCM (BRAKE INPUT) AUTO ONLY
VEHICLE SPEED IN
IGN3
ENABLE
SET/COAST RESEUME/ACCEL
BRAKE/ CLUTCH DISENGAGE
CRUISE CONTROL MODULE (MODULE AND MOTOR ASSY)
GROUND
CABLE TO ACCELERATOR PEDAL
GND DISTRIBUTION
(I/P SPL PACK)
G31109100001000X

Fig. 1 Speed control wiring circuit

BRAKE SWITCH

1. Disconnect battery ground cable.
2. Disconnect clutch switch electrical connector.
3. Remove switch attaching bolt, then remove switch.
4. Reverse procedure to install. **Torque** switch bolt to 89 inch lbs.

CLUTCH SWITCH

1. Disconnect battery ground cable.
2. Disconnect clutch switch electrical connector.
3. Remove switch attaching bolt, then remove switch.
4. Reverse procedure to install. **Torque** switch bolt to 89 inch lbs.

STEERING COLUMN SLIP RING

1. Disconnect battery ground cable.
2. **On 1992 models,** remove steering wheel horn pad, then disconnect electrical connector.
3. **On 1993-94 models, Disable SIR system then remove air bag by prying off screw caps on steering wheel and removing attaching screws with a flat head screw driver. Lift inflator module out of steering wheel.**
4. Remove integral connector lock device then disconnect electrical connector and remove inflator module.
5. **On all models,** remove steering wheel attaching nut.
6. Remove steering wheel with a standard steering wheel puller tool.
7. Remove upper and lower steering column covers.
8. Remove three electrical harness attaching screws, then disconnect electrical connectors.
9. Remove steering column slip ring.
10. Reverse procedure to install.

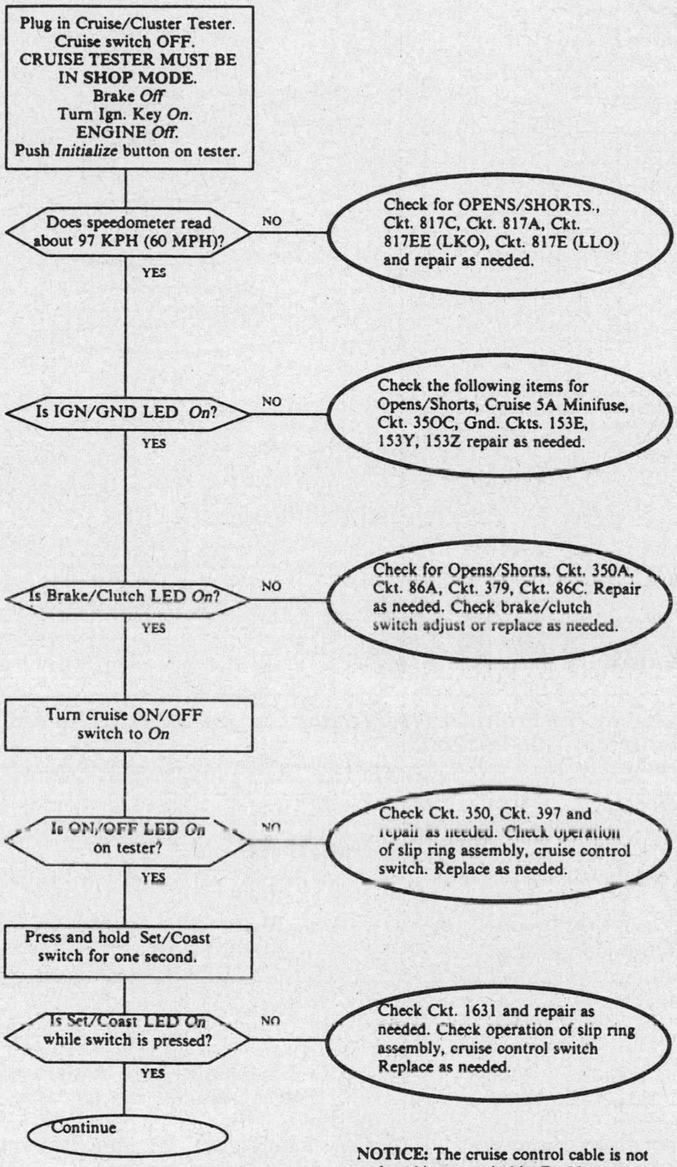
Plug in Cruise/Cluster Tester.
Cruise switch OFF.
CRUISE TESTER MUST BE IN SHOP MODE.
Brake Off
Turn Ign. Key On.
ENGINE Off.
Push Initialize button on tester.
Does speedometer read about 97 KPH (60 MPH)?
NO
Check for OPENS/SHORTS., Ckt. 817C, Ckt. 817A, Ckt. 817EE (LKO), Ckt. 817E (LLO) and repair as needed.
YES
Is IGN/GND LED On?
NO
Check the following items for Opens/Shorts, Cruise 5A Minifuse, Ckt. 350C, Gnd. Ckts. 153E, 153Y, 153Z repair as needed.
YES
Is Brake/Clutch LED On?
NO
Check for Opens/Shorts, Ckt. 350A, Ckt. 86A, Ckt. 379, Ckt. 86C. Repair as needed. Check brake/clutch switch adjust or replace as needed.
YES
Turn cruise ON/OFF switch to On
Is ON/OFF LED On on tester?
NO
Check Ckt. 350, Ckt. 397 and repair as needed. Check operation of slip ring assembly, cruise control switch. Replace as needed.
YES
Press and hold Set/Coast switch for one second.
Is Set/Coast LED On while switch is pressed?
NO
Check Ckt. 1631 and repair as needed. Check operation of slip ring assembly, cruise control switch Replace as needed.
YES
Continue

NOTICE: The cruise control cable is not replaceable or repairable. Do Not attempt to remove the cable from the Cruise Control Module. Damage to the module could result. Refer to cable adjustment procedures.

G31109100002010X

Fig. 2 Cruise control inoperative diagnostic chart (Part 1 of 3)

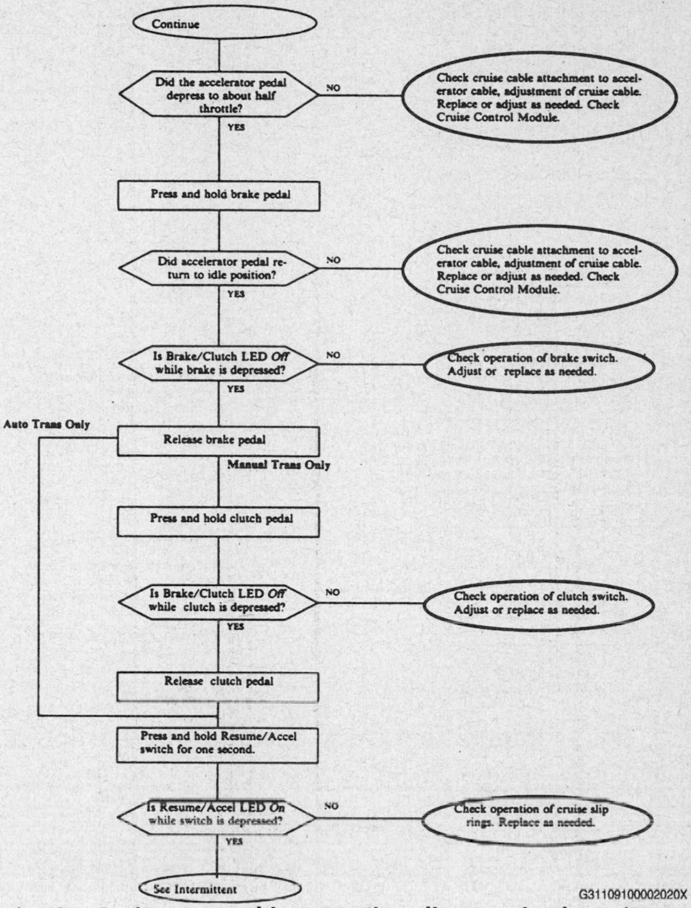
Continue
Did the accelerator pedal depress to about half throttle?
NO
Check cruise cable attachment to accelerator cable, adjustment of cruise cable. Replace or adjust as needed. Check Cruise Control Module.
YES
Press and hold brake pedal
Did accelerator pedal return to idle position?
NO
Check cruise cable attachment to accelerator cable, adjustment of cruise cable. Replace or adjust as needed. Check Cruise Control Module.
YES
Is Brake/Clutch LED Off while brake is depressed?
NO
Check operation of brake switch. Adjust or replace as needed.
YES
Auto Trans Only
Release brake pedal
Manual Trans Only
Press and hold clutch pedal
Is Brake/Clutch LED Off while clutch is depressed?
NO
Check operation of clutch switch. Adjust or replace as needed.
YES
Release clutch pedal
Press and hold Resume/Accel switch for one second.
Is Resume/Accel LED On while switch is depressed?
NO
Check operation of cruise slip rings. Replace as needed.
YES
See Intermittent

G31109100002020X

Fig. 2 Cruise control inoperative diagnostic chart (Part 2 of 3)

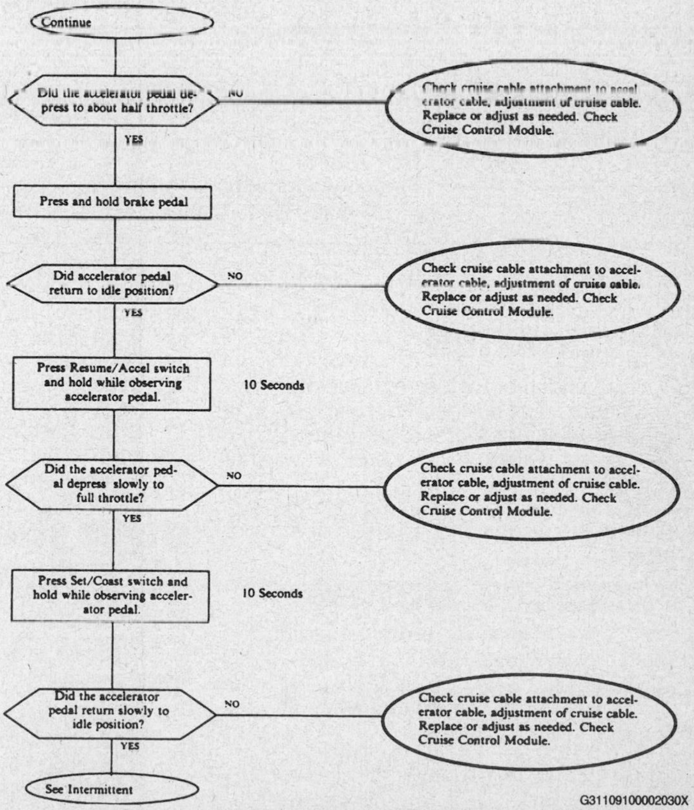
Continue
Did the accelerator pedal depress to about half throttle?
NO
Check cruise cable attachment to accelerator cable, adjustment of cruise cable. Replace or adjust as needed. Check Cruise Control Module.
YES
Press and hold brake pedal
Did accelerator pedal return to idle position?
NO
Check cruise cable attachment to accelerator cable, adjustment of cruise cable. Replace or adjust as needed. Check Cruise Control Module.
YES
Press Resume/Accel switch and hold while observing accelerator pedal.
10 Seconds
Did the accelerator pedal depress slowly to full throttle?
NO
Check cruise cable attachment to accelerator cable, adjustment of cruise cable. Replace or adjust as needed. Check Cruise Control Module.
YES
Press Set/Coast switch and hold while observing accelerator pedal.
10 Seconds
Did the accelerator pedal return slowly to idle position?
NO
Check cruise cable attachment to accelerator cable, adjustment of cruise cable. Replace or adjust as needed. Check Cruise Control Module.
YES
See Intermittent

G31109100002030X

Fig. 2 Cruise control inoperative diagnostic chart (Part 3 of 3)

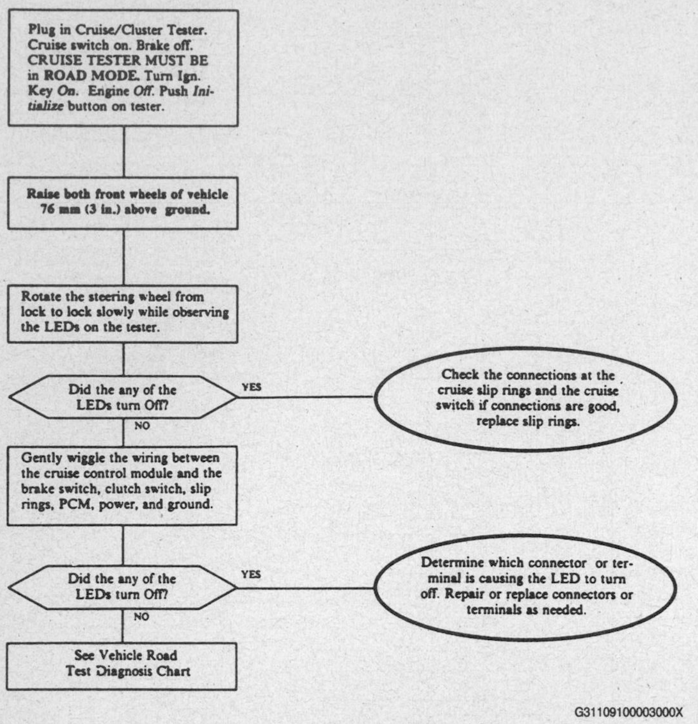
Plug in Cruise/Cluster Tester. Cruise switch on. Brake off. CRUISE TESTER MUST BE in ROAD MODE. Turn Ign. Key On. Engine Off. Push Initialize button on tester.
Raise both front wheels of vehicle 76 mm (3 in.) above ground.
Rotate the steering wheel from lock to lock slowly while observing the LEDs on the tester.
Did the any of the LEDs turn Off?
YES
NO
Check the connections at the cruise slip rings and the cruise switch if connections are good, replace slip rings.
Gently wiggle the wiring between the cruise control module and the brake switch, clutch switch, slip rings, PCM, power, and ground.
Did the any of the LEDs turn Off?
YES
NO
Determine which connector or terminal is causing the LED to turn off. Repair or replace connectors or terminals as needed.
See Vehicle Road Test Diagnosis Chart
G31109100003000X

Fig. 3 Intermittent cruise operation diagnostic chart

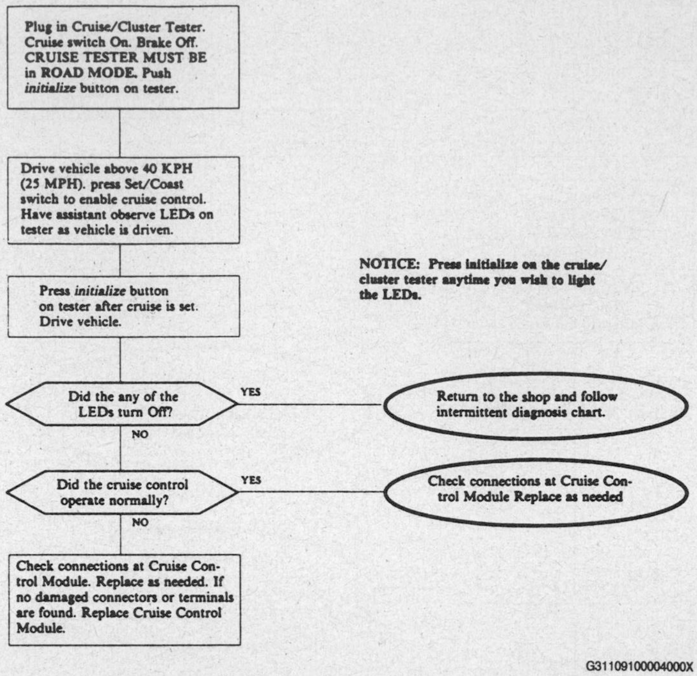
Plug in Cruise/Cluster Tester. Cruise switch On. Brake Off. CRUISE TESTER MUST BE in ROAD MODE. Push initialize button on tester.
Drive vehicle above 40 KPH (25 MPH). press Set/Coast switch to enable cruise control. Have assistant observe LEDs on tester as vehicle is driven.
NOTICE: Press initialize on the cruise/cluster tester anytime you wish to light the LEDs.
Press initialize button on tester after cruise is set. Drive vehicle.
Did the any of the LEDs turn Off?
YES
NO
Return to the shop and follow intermittent diagnosis chart.
Did the cruise control operate normally?
YES
NO
Check connections at Cruise Control Module Replace as needed
Check connections at Cruise Control Module. Replace as needed. If no damaged connectors or terminals are found. Replace Cruise Control Module.
G31109100004000X

Fig. 4 Vehicle road test diagnostic chart

WIPER SYSTEMS

NOTE: Electrical Symbol & Wire Color Code Identification Located In The Front Of This Manual Can Be Used As An Aid When Using Wiring Circuits Found In This Section.

INDEX

DESCRIPTION

The windshield wiper and washer system consists of a stalk mounted switch, a windshield wiper motor/control module, a two-speed wiper motor and a washer pump motor.

The windshield wipers and washers operate with the ignition in the Run or Acc positions.

TROUBLESHOOTING

Refer to **Fig. 1,** for troubleshooting the wiper/washer system.

SYSTEM DIAGNOSIS & TESTING

WIPER MODULE

1. Check the circuits, connectors and terminals that are attached to the wiper terminal, **Fig. 2.**
2. Test wiper module in vehicle. It must be connected to the windshield wiper switch to work properly.
3. Wiper module and motor are serviced as an assembly. Repair is by replacement only.
4. Check terminals and connections for damage and corrosion.

WIPER SWITCH

Test resistance between pin A and C. Refer to **Fig. 3** for correct resistance specifications.

SYSTEM PERFORMANCE TEST

1. Turn ignition switch to ACC position and turn wiper switch to "Intermittent 1" position.
   a. Wipers should immediately activate.
   b. On "Intermittent 1," the time interval between cycles (one cycle being one back-and-forth motion of the blades) should be two seconds.
   c. On "Intermittent 2," the interval should be seven seconds.
   d. On "Intermittent 3,"the interval should be 12 seconds.
2. Start engine and put wiper switch on "Low" speed position. Wipers should immediately activate and speed should be 42-53 cycles per minute.
3. Put wiper switch on "High" speed position. Wipers should activate within one second and have a speed of 61-73 cycles per minute on a wet windshield.
4. Push down on wiper switch to the "Mist" position. Wipers should cycle once as long as the switch is being held.
5. Pull wiper switch to "Wash" position. Washer pump and wipers should both activate within one second. Wipers

X — Most Probable Cause(s)
• — Possible Causes

COMPLAINT–CONDITION	WIPER/WASHER SYSTEM	IGN4 Fuse	Wiper Fuse	Circuit 153R	Circuit 153F	Circuit 150J	Circuit 92	Circuit 96	Circuit 1932/4/93	Circuit 94A/94	Ignition Switch	Column Switch	Battery	Wiper Motor/Module	Washer Pump	Washer Fluid Hose	Friction	Over Torque of Mounting Bolts
Wipers do not work at all		X	X	X	X				X		•	•	•	•			•	
Works on HI speed only								X			•			•				
HI speed does not work					X		X					X		•				
Works on INTERMITTENT only												X		•				
INTERMITTENT does not work												•		•				
Slow wipers				•					•				X				X	
Jerky wipers				X					X					•			X	
Wipers stop, then restart after several minutes														•			X	
Wipers on with switch on OFF							X	X				•						
Wipers work when engine being cranked																		
Excessive motor noise														X			•	X
No washer fluid on windshield																X		
Washer pump does not work						X				X					•			
Washer fluid pressure low										•					X	X		

G39029100001000X

Fig. 1 Wiper system troubleshooting chart

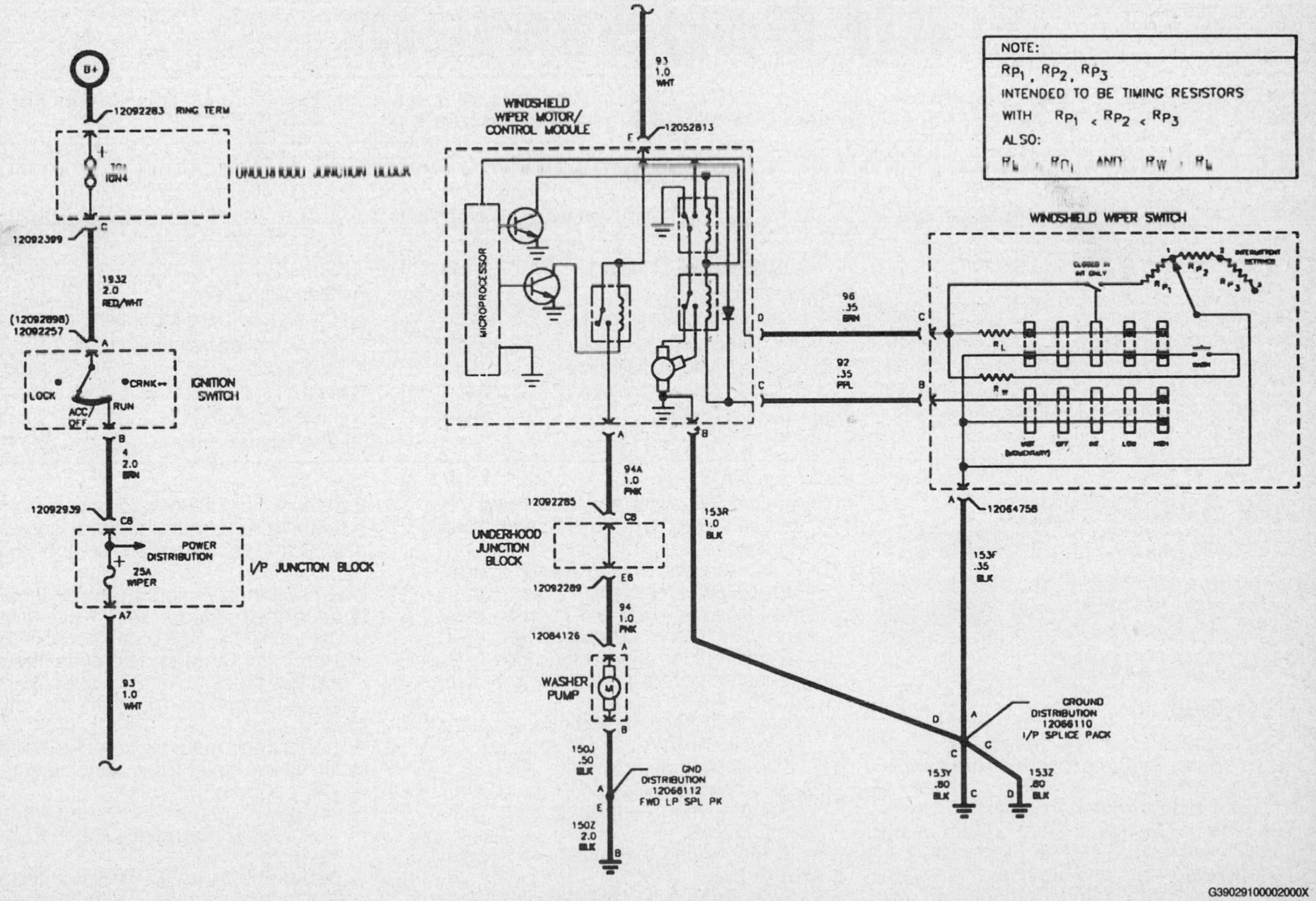
B+
12092283 RING TERM
IGN4
C
12092399
1932
2.0
RED/WHT
(12092898)
12092257
A
LOCK
CRNK
ACC/OFF
RUN
IGNITION SWITCH
B
4
2.0
BRN
12092939
C8
POWER DISTRIBUTION
25A WIPER
I/P JUNCTION BLOCK
A7
93
1.0
WHT
93
1.0
WHT
WINDSHIELD WIPER MOTOR/ CONTROL MODULE
F
12052813
MICROPROCESSOR
D
C
96
.35
BRN
92
.35
PPL
A
B
94A
1.0
PNK
12092285
C8
UNDERHOOD JUNCTION BLOCK
E6
12092289
94
1.0
PNK
12084126
A
WASHER PUMP
B
150J
.50
BLK
GND DISTRIBUTION 12066112 FWD LP SPL PK
E
150Z
2.0
BLK
153R
1.0
BLK
NOTE:
RP1, RP2, RP3
INTENDED TO BE TIMING RESISTORS
WITH RP1 < RP2 < RP3
ALSO:
WINDSHIELD WIPER SWITCH
RL
RW
12064758
153F
.35
BLK
GROUND DISTRIBUTION 12066110 I/P SPLICE PACK
153Y
.80
BLK
153Z
.80
BLK
G39029100002000X

Fig. 2 Wiper system wiring circuit

should cycle twice and washer pump should remain on as long as the switch lever is being pulled into the position. The wipers will complete two cycles before parking after the wash is complete.

6. With wipers on "Low" speed, crank engine. Wipers should stop moving and start again once the ignition is back in the RUN position.

Measure Resistance from Pin C to Pin A.	
Switch Position	Resistance in OHMS *
OFF	OPEN
LOW	300 ohms (.300 k ohms)
HIGH	300 ohms (.300 k ohms)
MIST	300 ohms (.300 k ohms)
INT. 1	2090 ohms (2.09 k ohms)
INT. 2	990 ohms (.990 k ohms)
INT. 3	560 ohms (.560 k ohms)
WASH	130 ohms (.13 k ohms)

* Resistance measurements should be ± 10 %

Check for continuity from Pin A to Pin B of the Column Switch. There should be less than ONE (1) OHM when the switch is in HIGH; and OPEN when switch is in any other position.

G39029100003000X

Fig. 3 Wiper switch resistance specifications

PASSIVE RESTRAINT SYSTEMS

Air Bag System

NOTE: On Air Bag Equipped Models, Refer To "Air Bag System Precautions" Located In The Front Of This Manual For System Disarming & Arming Procedures.

INDEX

AIR BAG SYSTEM DISARMING & ARMING

Refer to "Air Bag System Precautions" in the front of this manual for system disarming and arming procedures.

PRECAUTIONS

SYSTEM

Safe handling of live and deployed air bag modules requires following the following procedures:

1. Perform SIR diagnostic system check under "Reading and Diagnosing Codes" as the first and last task during diagnosis and service.
2. Before attempting service on or around SIR components or wiring, disarm the SIR system as described under "Air Bag System Disarming & Arming."
3. The Diagnostic Energy Reserve Module (DERM) maintains voltage after the ignition switch is turned to OFF and the battery is disconnected. Wait 10 minutes for this back-up power to discharge before performing any service on the SIR system.
4. Inspect SIR system components after an accident that may or may not involve air bag deployment.
5. Use special electrical connector adapters when performing diagnostic tests.
6. Replace wiring terminals with special repair kits.
7. Never strike or jar a sensor in a way that could cause deployment.
8. If a sensor or DERM is dropped from a height greater than 2 feet or shows any signs of damage, replace the component.
9. Use caution in ensuring proper location of the sensors to the vehicle structure. The keying of the sensors to the structure through differently sized mounting holes and the wiring harness must not be modified for any reason.
10. All sensor and mounting bracket bolts must be carefully torqued to assure proper operation.
11. Never power up the SIR system when any sensor is not rigidly attached to the vehicle.
12. Avoid touching the DERM terminals to prevent damage due to electrostatic discharge.

HANDLING LIVE (UNDEPLOYED) AIR BAG MODULES

Special care is necessary when handling and storing a live (undeployed) inflator module. The rapid gas generation produced during deployment of the air bag could cause the inflator module or an object in front of the inflator module to be thrown through the air.

When carrying a live inflator module, be sure the air bag and trim cover are pointed away from you. Never carry the inflator module by the wires or by the connector on module. In case of accidental deployment, the air bag will deploy with minimal chance of injury.

When placing air bag modules on a bench or other surface, always face the air bag and trim cover away from the surface. Never rest a steering wheel with the inflator face down and the column vertical. A free space must be provided to allow for air bag expansion in case of accidental deployment.

HANDLING DEPLOYED MODULES

After the air bag has been deployed, the surface of the air bag may contain a powdery residue. This powder consists primarily of corn starch (used to lubricate the air bag as it inflates) and by-products of the chemical reaction. Sodium hydroxide dust (similar to lye dust) is produced as a by-product of the deployment reaction. The sodium hydroxide then quickly reacts with atmospheric moisture and is converted to sodium carbonate and sodium bicarbonate (baking soda). Therefore, it is unlikely that sodium hydroxide will be present after deployment. Always wear safety glasses and gloves when handling a deployed module, and wash hands with mild soap and water afterward.

VEHICLE SCRAPPING

Some SIR equipped vehicles that have live (undeployed) inflator modules may have to be scrapped because they have completed their useful life or have been severely damaged in a non-deployment type accident. The following procedure should be followed when scrapping a vehicle with an undeployed module.

1. Place ignition switch in Off position.
2. Ensure inflator module is secured to steering wheel.
3. Remove all loose objects from front seat and module cover.
4. Disconnect air bag yellow electrical connector at base of steering column.
5. Disconnect yellow two-way connector at base of steering wheel.
6. Cut yellow 2-way connector away from vehicle harness leaving at least 6 inches of wire at the connector.
7. Splice two 18 gauge wires, 15 feet long, into steering wheel module circuit wiring at base of steering column.
8. Connect air bag yellow electrical connector at base of steering wheel.
9. Ensure vehicle interior is free of all people and loose or flammable objects.
10. Stretch wires away from vehicle to their full length.
11. Apply 12 volts across wires to deploy module. **Do not touch metal areas of inflator module for 10 minutes due to heat generated by deployment.**

AIR BAG DISPOSAL

When a deployed module has been removed from a vehicle, it may be disposed of with any other scrap material. Handle with gloves and safety glasses and wash hands after handling. **The inflator module must be deactivated prior to disposal. Failure to deactivate before disposing may result in personal injury since the module contains explosive material.**

COLLISION INSPECTION

In all types of accidents, regardless of air bag deployment, visually inspect the following components and their mounting points and replace as required:

1. Inflator modules
2. Steering wheel
3. SIR coil assembly
4. Steering column
5. Knee bolster and instrument panel mounting attachments
6. Driver seat and belts
7. Discriminating sensors
8. Arming sensors
9. DERM
10. Resistor module

Sensors in the damaged area should be replaced, even if the sensors do not appear to be damaged. Do not attempt to determine whether a sensor is OK, always replace the sensor if it is located in a damaged area.

Also inspect the SIR coil assembly wiring, steering wheel and passenger side dash panel for signs of scorching, melting, or other damage due to excessive heat. If the coil assembly wiring or steering wheel is damaged, replace them. Check the steering column and wheel dimensions to determine if they are damaged.

Do not attempt to repair the forward discriminating sensors, the arming sensor, the DERM, the resistor module, the SIR coil assembly, the inflator modules, the steering wheel or the steering column. Service of these items is replacement only. Verify the replacement part numbers.

Never use SIR parts from another vehicle.

Proper operation of the sensors and the SIR system requires that any repairs to the vehicle structure return it to its original production configuration.

DIAGNOSIS & TESTING

Refer to MOTOR's "Air Bag Manual" for complete diagnosis and testing procedures.

COMPONENT SERVICE

INFLATOR MODULE, REPLACE

1. Remove four inflator module screws, then lift module out of steering wheel. Discard screws.
2. Remove connector positive assurance (CPA), then disconnect connector and remove inflator module.
3. Reverse procedure to install. **Torque** new inflator module screws to 89 in. lbs.

STEERING WHEEL, REPLACE

1. Remove inflator module as described under "Inflator Module, Replace."
2. Disconnect cruise control switch, if equipped, then the horn switch connector.
3. Remove steering wheel attaching nut, then discard nut.
4. Install steering wheel puller onto steering wheel and remove steering wheel, feeding wiring through wheel.
5. Insert yellow tab into SIR coil assembly to prevent SIR coil from rotating. If tab is not available, tape coil.
6. Reverse procedure to install. **Torque** new steering wheel attaching nut to 30 ft. lbs.

SIR COIL ASSEMBLY, REPLACE

1. Remove steering wheel as described under "Steering Wheel, Replace."
2. Remove upper and lower steering column shrouds.
3. Align front wheels to straight ahead position and remove SIR coil assembly from lever control switch. **If coil is removed without wheels facing straight ahead and steering wheel has not been moved, original coil can be reinstalled if the coil hub also has not been rotated.**
4. Route pigtail of SIR coil down steering column and install SIR coil to lever control switch.
5. Route wiring through steering wheel.
6. Reverse steps 1 through 3 to install.

STEERING COLUMN, REPLACE

1. Remove steering wheel as described under "Steering Wheel, Replace."
2. Remove upper steering column shroud screws and shroud.
3. Remove ignition lock bezel, then the lower steering column cover screws and cover.
4. Remove lefthand and righthand lower trim panel extensions.
5. Remove center plate and trim panel extension strip.
6. Remove upper dash trim panel screw caps, screws and panel.
7. Remove four cluster trim panel screws, then disengage retainers.
8. Disconnect harness from rear window defog and instrument panel dimmer switches.

9. Remove cluster trim panel.
10. Remove six knee bolster screws and knee bolster.
11. Remove connector position assurance (CPA) device and disconnect connectors from lever control switch.
12. Remove lever control switch.
13. Remove two ignition switch screws and disconnect switch from ignition module.
14. Remove steering column bolts and lower column onto front seat.
15. Remove upper bolt from intermediate shaft and disconnect shaft from column.
16. Remove steering column from vehicle.
17. Position steering column in vise at upper bracket, then use center punch to mark center of shear bolts on ignition module assembly.
18. Drill small hole at center mark of shear bolts, then remove bolts with shear extractor.
19. Remove ignition module assembly and clamp from steering column.
20. Reverse procedure to install, noting the following:
    a. Install new shear bolts on ignition module assembly, tightening until heads break off.
    b. **Torque** intermediate shaft bolt to 33 ft. lbs.
    c. **Torque** steering column upper bolts to 26 ft. lbs.

DISCRIMINATING SENSORS, REPLACE

1. Remove bolts and sensor from upper radiator support.
2. Remove connector position assurance (CPA) device and disconnect connector. Note position and routing of wiring for installation reference.
3. Reverse procedure to install. **Torque** sensor bolts to 89 in. lbs.

ARMING SENSOR, REPLACE

1. Remove upper dash trim panel screw caps, screws and panel.
2. Remove arming sensor bolts, then the arming sensor from cross-car beam.
3. Remove connector position assurance (CPA) device and disconnect connector.
4. Reverse procedure to install. **Torque** arming sensor bolts to 71 in. lbs.

DERM, REPLACE

1. Remove upper trim panel screw caps, screws and panel.
2. Pulling DERM straight up, remove from bracket.
3. Pull lock tab up and push connector lock down to disconnect connector.
4. Reverse procedure to install.

RESISTOR MODULE, REPLACE

1. Remove DERM as described under "DERM, Removal."
2. Remove DERM bracket nuts, then pull bracket off studs.
3. Remove connector position assurance (CPA) device and disconnect connector.
4. Squeezing back of clips, remove resistor module.
5. Reverse procedure to install. Tighten DERM bracket nuts to 71 in. lbs.

KNEE BOLSTER, REPLACE

If knee bolster shows any visible damage, it should be replaced, not repaired.

1. Remove lefthand and righthand lower trim panel extensions.
2. Remove center air outlet/trim panel.
3. Remove upper trim panel screw caps, screws and panel.
4. Open glove box.
5. Tilt steering wheel down.
6. Remove four cluster trim panel screws, then disengage panel from retainers.
7. Remove connector position assurance (CPA) devices and disconnect electrical connectors from instrument panel lighting rheostat and rear window defogger switches.
8. Remove cluster trim panel.
9. Remove screws and data link connector (DLC).
10. Remove knee bolster screws and knee bolster.
11. Reverse procedure to install.

TIGHTENING SPECIFICATIONS

Component	Torque/Ft. Lbs.
Arming Sensor Bolts	71①
DERM Bracket Bolts	71①
Discriminating Sensor Bolt	89①
Inflator Module Screws	89①
Intermediate shaft Bolt	33
Steering Column Upper Bolts	26
Steering Wheel Nut	30

①—Inch Lbs.

Automatic Seat Belts

NOTE: Electrical Symbol & Wire Color Code Identification Located In The Front Of This Manual Can Be Used As An Aid When Using Wiring Circuits Found In This Section.

INDEX

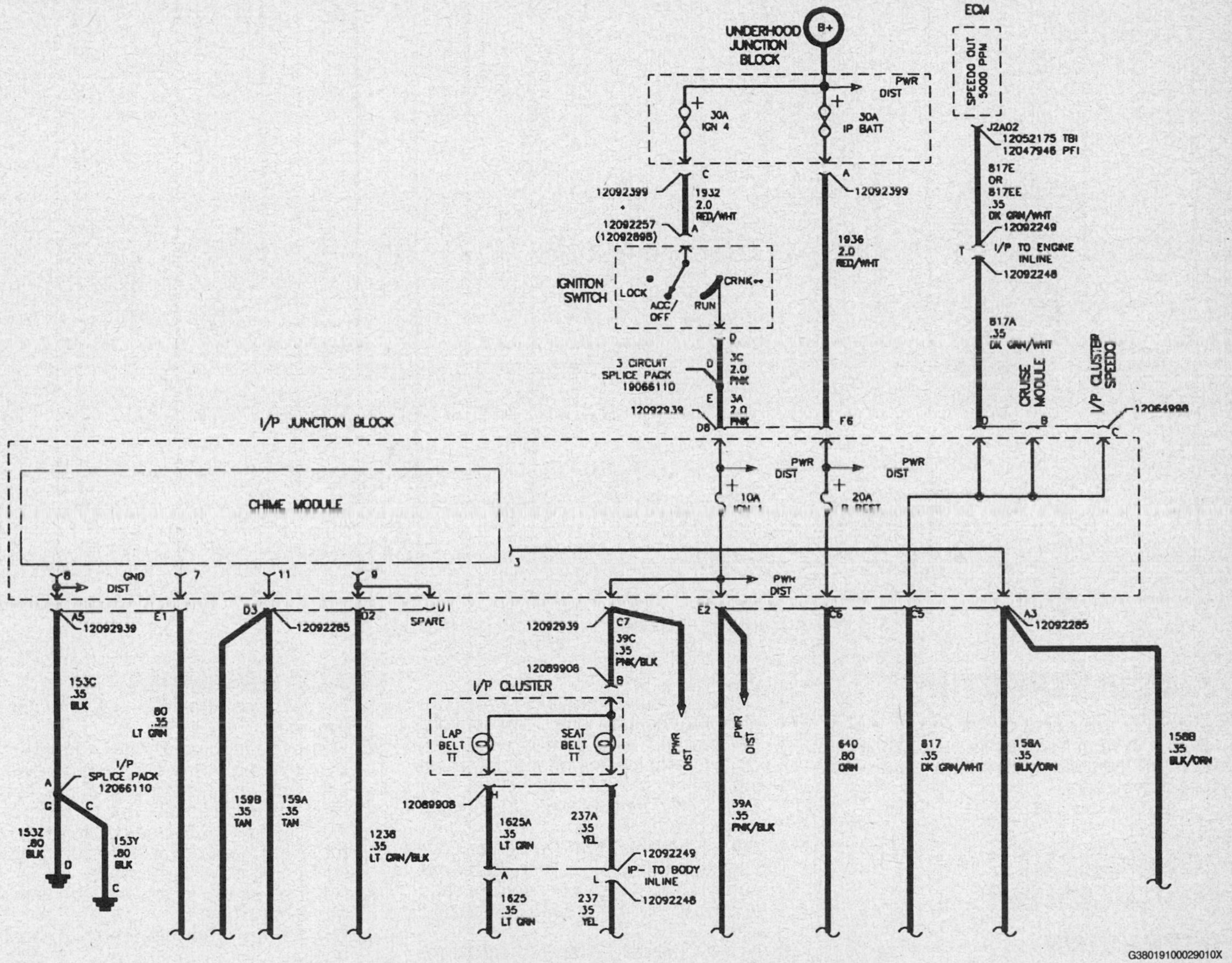

UNDERHOOD JUNCTION BLOCK
B+
PWR DIST
30A IGN 4
30A IP BATT
ECM
SPEEDO OUT 5000 PPM
J2A02
12052175 TBI
12047946 PFI
817E OR 817EE .35 DK GRN/WHT
12092249
I/P TO ENGINE INLINE
12092248
12092399
1932 2.0 RED/WHT
12092257 (12092898)
1936 2.0 RED/WHT
IGNITION SWITCH
LOCK
ACC/OFF
RUN
CRNK
817A .35 DK GRN/WHT
CRUISE MODULE
I/P CLUSTER SPEEDO
12064998
3 CIRCUIT SPLICE PACK 19066110
3C 2.0 PNK
3A 2.0 PNK
12092939
I/P JUNCTION BLOCK
CHIME MODULE
10A IGN 1
20A R REST
GND DIST
SPARE
12092285
153C .35 BLK
80 .35 LT GRN
I/P SPLICE PACK 12066110
153Z .80 BLK
153Y .80 BLK
159B .35 TAN
159A .35 TAN
1236 .35 LT GRN/BLK
39C .35 PNK/BLK
12089908
I/P CLUSTER
LAP BELT TT
SEAT BELT TT
1625A .35 LT GRN
237A .35 YEL
IP- TO BODY INLINE
1625 .35 LT GRN
237 .35 YEL
PWR DIST
39A .35 PNK/BLK
640 .80 ORN
817 .35 DK GRN/WHT
158A .35 BLK/ORN
158B .35 BLK/ORN
G38019100029010X

Fig. 1 Automatic seat belt wiring circuit (Part 1 of 2)

DESCRIPTION

The passive restraint control module (PRCM), located in the console, controls the power for the passive restraint belt system and the lap and shoulder belt reminder system. The system allows independent operation of both front shoulder belts.

OPERATION

The PRCM controls shoulder belt operation according to conditions detected by the PRCM through inputs received from various switches. The PRCM receives these signals and operates the shoulder belts according to its internal program.

Under normal operation, the shoulder belt will move to the B-pillar when the ignition switch is ON and the door is closed, or the vehicle speed is greater than 13 mph.

The shoulder belt moves to the A-pillar when the door opens and vehicle speed is less than 13 mph.

On the driver's side, the shoulder belt will move to the A-pillar if the ignition is OFF and the key is removed from the ignition.

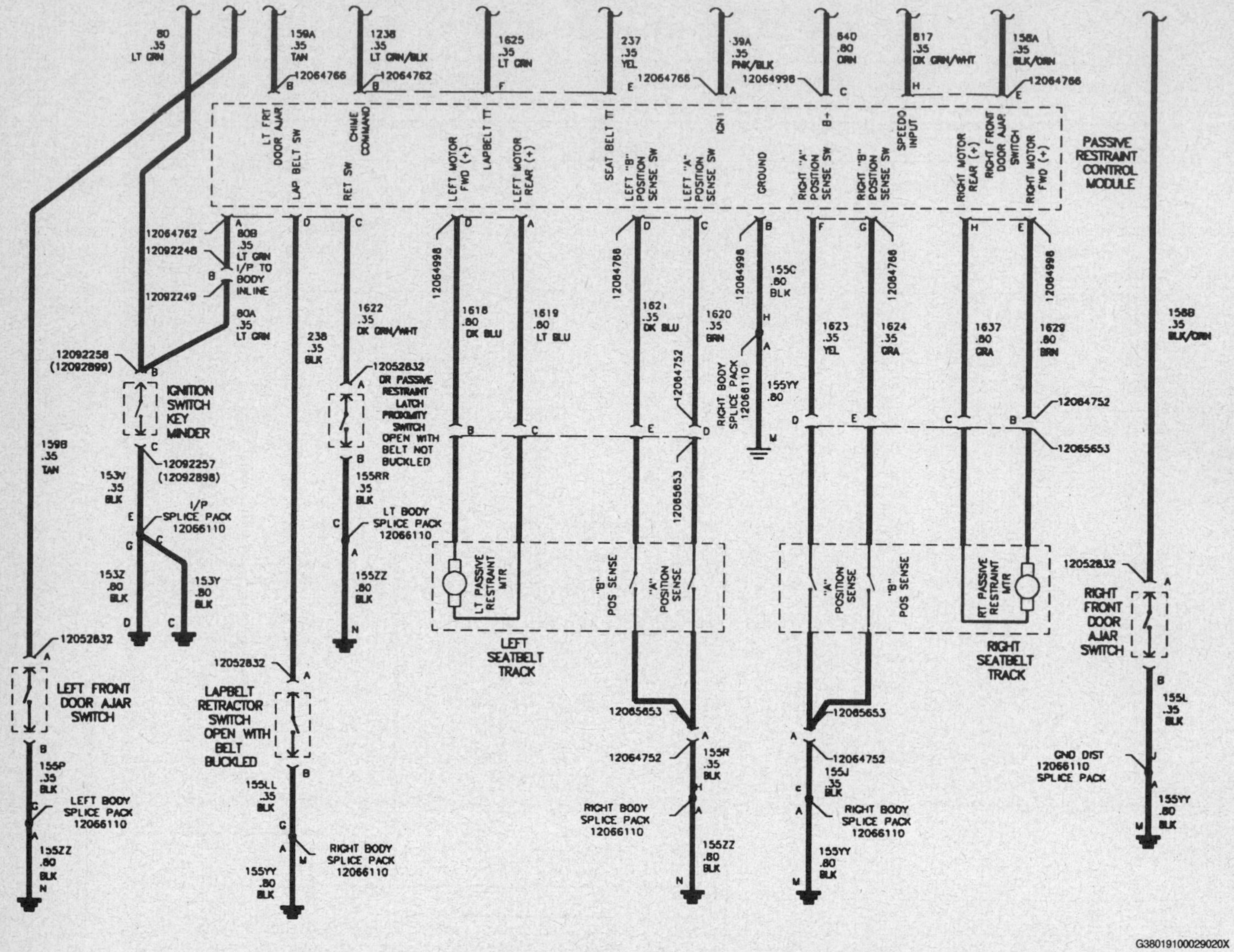
PASSIVE RESTRAINT CONTROL MODULE
IGNITION SWITCH KEY MINDER
I/P SPLICE PACK 12066110
LEFT FRONT DOOR AJAR SWITCH
LEFT BODY SPLICE PACK 12066110
LAPBELT RETRACTOR SWITCH OPEN WITH BELT BUCKLED
RIGHT BODY SPLICE PACK 12066110
LT BODY SPLICE PACK 12066110
LEFT SEATBELT TRACK
RIGHT SEATBELT TRACK
RIGHT FRONT DOOR AJAR SWITCH
GND DIST 12066110 SPLICE PACK
G38019100029020X

Fig. 1 Automatic seat belt wiring circuit (Part 2 of 2)

TROUBLESHOOTING

Refer to the wiring circuit, **Fig. 1**, along with the system troubleshooting chart, **Fig. 2**, when troubleshooting the automatic seat belt system.

COMPONENT REPLACEMENT

RETRACTOR

1. **On models with manual transaxle,** remove transaxle shift knob.
2. **On models with automatic transaxle,** tape release button in depressed position on shift lever handle.
3. **On all models,** remove liner in rear storage tray and remove two screws below the liner.
4. Remove two screws on front sides of console.
5. Apply parking brake and remove trim plate below park brake lever by lifting at rear edge and working the plate up evenly.
6. Remove both ashtrays, then disconnect front ashtray lamp from console.
7. **On models with power windows,** remove window/mirror switch by sliding switch forward then lifting rear edge. Disconnect switch electrical connectors.
8. **On all models,** remove center console side trim panels, then lift rear of console. From below console, release and push out both seat belt bezels, **Fig. 3.**
9. Remove center fastener, then the retractor anchor bolts.
10. Remove retractors. Disconnect electrical connector on driver's side.
11. Reverse procedure to install, noting the following:
    a. Apply Loctite 242 Threadlocker or equivalent, to all restraint bolts/nuts prior to installation.
    b. **Torque** retractor anchor bolts to 35 ft. lbs.
    c. To ease installation, fully recline both front seats and set front of console over shifter.

TRACK ASSEMBLY

1. Remove instrument panel end cap, **Fig. 4.**
2. Remove instrument panel top cover by removing screw caps and screws. Lift panel at rear edge to disengage clips and slide panel out of clips at windshield, **Fig. 5.** Use caution when removing top cover to keep from scratching garnish moldings.
3. Remove screw in top of front lower garnish molding.
4. **On Coupe models,** remove coat hook.
5. **On all models,** starting at front of molding, pull firmly on molding at clip locations to remove. Partially remove front garnish/sill molding at center pillar garnish molding, **Fig. 6.**
6. Partially remove rear garnish/sill molding and remove center pillar lower molding fasteners. Release center pillar lower molding from center pillar, **Fig. 7.**
7. Slide lap belt through center pillar lower molding and remove molding, **Fig. 7.**

X — Most Probable Cause(s)
● — Possible Causes

COMPLAINT–CONDITION / CAUSE	IP Batt Fuse	IGN4 Fuse	IGN1 fuse	Prest Fuse (Passive Restraint)	GND. CKT. 155C/155Y	GND. CKT. 159A, 159B, 155P	GND. CKT. 158A, 158B, 155L	GND. CKT. 238, 155L	GND. CKT. 1622, 155RR	GND. CKT. 1620, 1621, 155R	GND. CKT. 1623, 1624, 155J	CKT. 3A, 39A	CKT. 640, 1936	CKT. 817, 817A, 817E	CKT. 1618, 1619	CKT. 1637, 1629	CKT. 39C, 1625A, 237A	CKT. 80A/80B	Passive Restraint Control Module	Battery	Chime Module	Intermittent Connection	Friction/Binding Extreme Cold
Mouse Stuck:																							
Both at *B* Pillar	●			X		X							X						●	●			
Both at *A* Pillar	●	●	X	X		X						X	X						●	●			
One at *B* the Other at *A*	●			X		X							X						●	●			
One at *B* the Other Okay							X	X							X	X			●				
One at *A* the Other Okay							X	X							X	X			●				
One or Both in Middle	●	●		X		X													●	●			X
Slow Mouse																				X			X
Jerky Mouse																						X	X
No Lap Telltale								X									X						
No Shoulder Telltale									X								X						
Chime Inappropriate								X	X												X		
No Driver Side Release with Key Out																		X					
Shoulder TT Always On									X	X	X											X	

G38019100030000X

Fig. 2 Automatic seat belt system troubleshooting

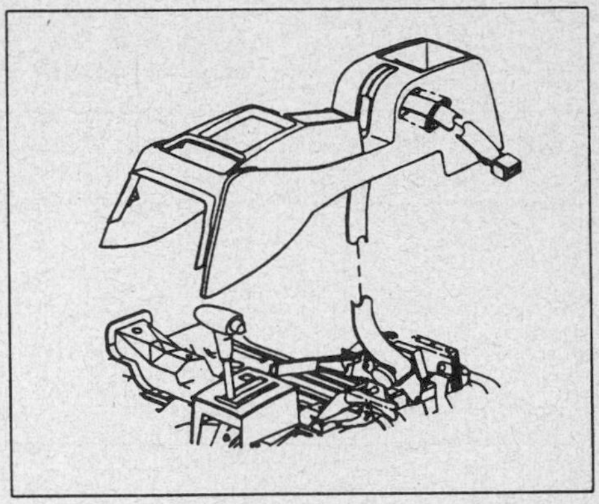

G38019100031000X

Fig. 3 Seat belt bezel removal

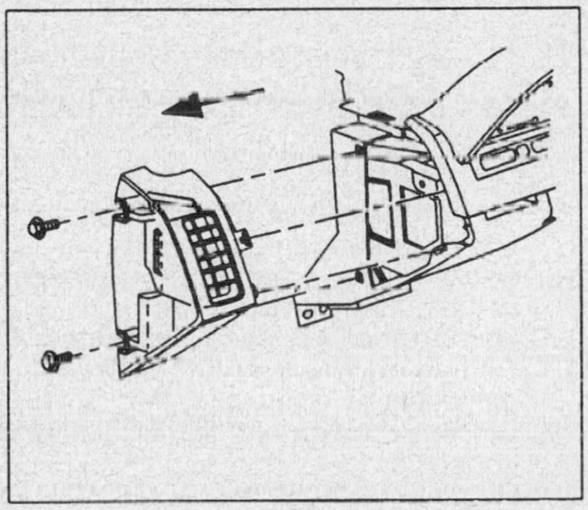

G38019100032000X

Fig. 4 Instrument panel end cap removal

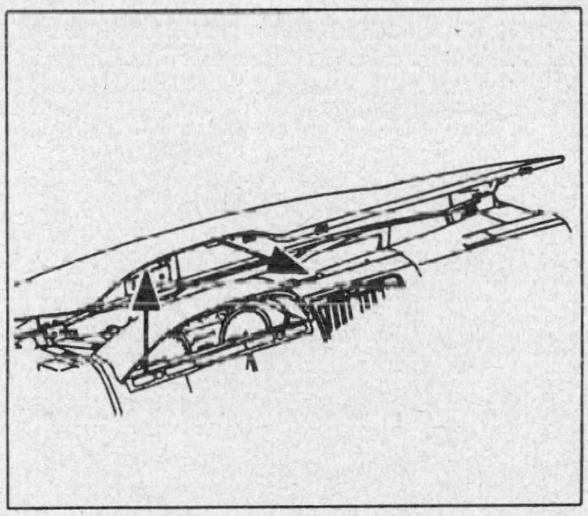

G38019100033000X

Fig. 5 Instrument panel top cover removal

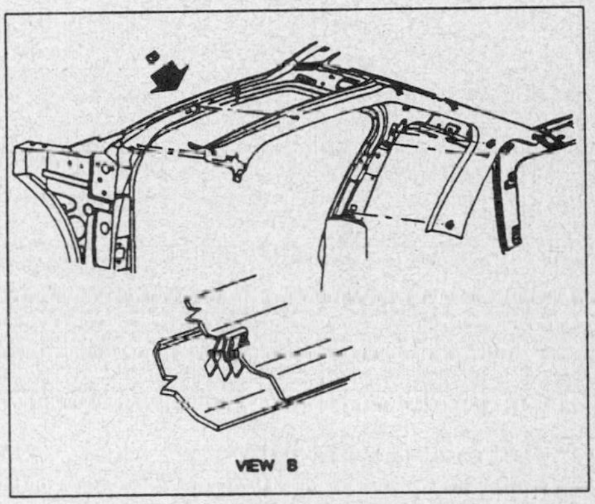
VIEW B

G38019100034000X

Fig. 6 Front garnish/sill molding removal

8. Disconnect wiring harness leading to shoulder belt track assembly.
9. Remove shoulder belt track assembly, **Fig. 8.**
10. Reverse procedure to install, noting the following:
    a. Apply Loctite No. 242 Threadlocker or equivalent, to all restraint bolts/nuts before installation.
    b. **Torque** two bottom guide tube clip bolts to 27 inch lbs.
    c. **Torque** all other guide track bolts to 53 inch lbs.
    d. **Torque** shoulder belt upper anchor Torx head bolt to 30 ft. lbs.

PASSIVE RESTRAINT CONTROL MODULE (PRCM)

1. Remove access panel above PRCM in center console.
2. Remove four screws securing center console.
3. Raise parking brake handle as far as possible.
4. Raise center console from rear until access to PRCM is possible from rear of console.
5. Gently press plastic tab at rear of PRCM and lift up at same time.
6. Disconnect electrical connectors and remove from rear.
7. Reverse procedure to install.

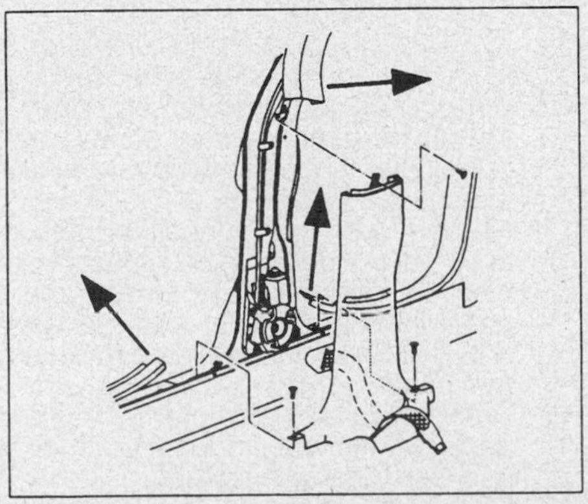

G38019100035000X

Fig. 7 Center pillar lower molding removal

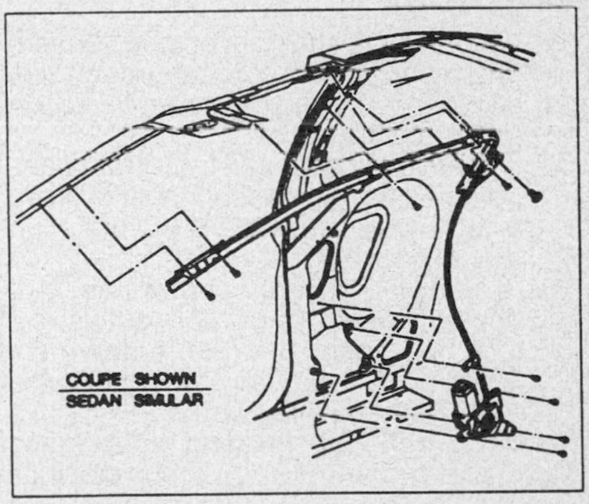
COUPE SHOWN
SEDAN SIMILAR

G38019100036000X

Fig. 8 Track assembly replacement

DASH PANEL SERVICE

NOTE: On Air Bag Equipped Models, Refer To "Air Bag System Precautions" Located In The Front Of This Manual For System Disarming & Arming Procedures.

INDEX

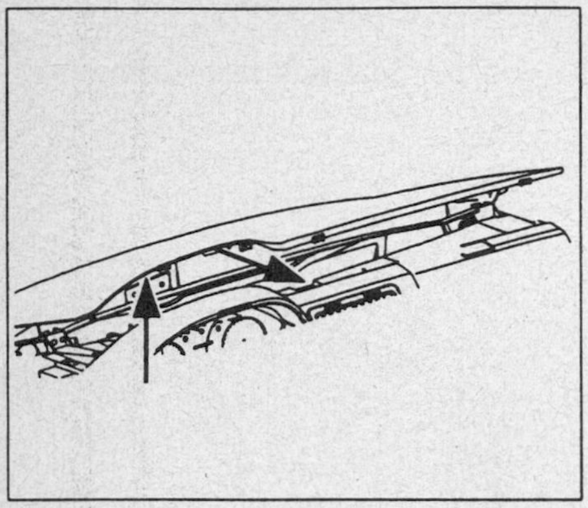

G39149100006000X

Fig. 1 Upper trim panel removal

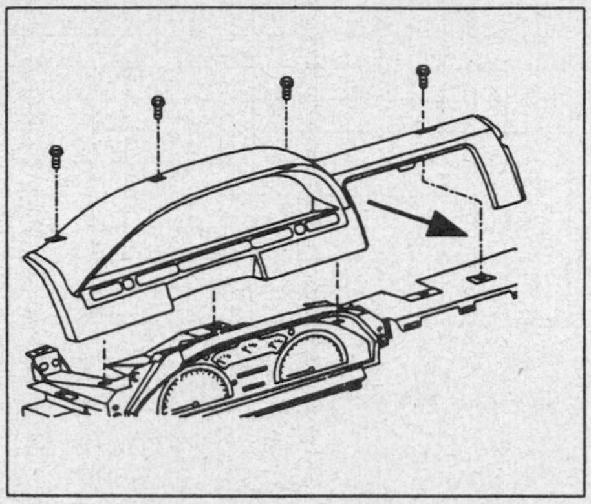

G39149100007000X

Fig. 2 Cluster trim panel removal

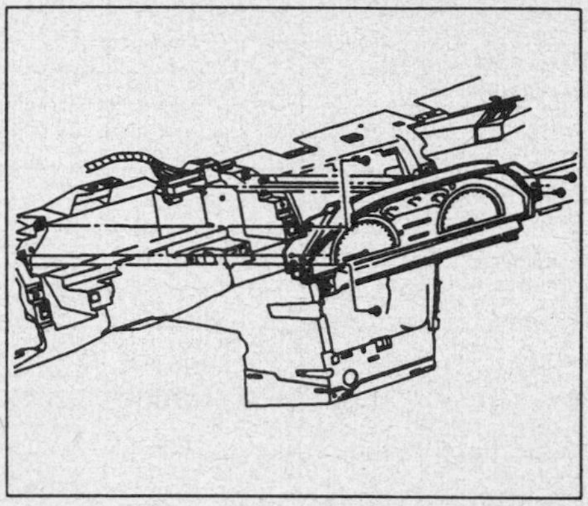

G39149100008000X

Fig. 3 Instrument cluster removal

PRECAUTIONS

AIR BAG SYSTEMS

Refer to "Air Bag System Precautions" in the front of this manual for system disarming and arming procedures.

DASH PANEL

REPLACE

1. Remove left and right end cap assembly by removing end cap attachment screw and pulling out board to disconnect retainer clips.
2. Remove left and right lower trim panel extensions by disconnecting lower Velcro fasteners and pulling out at upper clip locations.
3. Carefully remove center air outlet/trim panel by pulling outward at clip locations. Start at bottom and work up. Do not use instruments that may damage trim panel.
4. **On 1993-95 models,** disconnect traction control/fog lamp electrical connector.
5. **On all models,** remove trim panel extension strip by pulling outward at clip locations.
6. Remove upper trim panel screw caps by carefully prying with a small screwdriver, then remove upper trim panel screws.
7. Lift upper trim panel to disengage clips at rear edge, **Fig. 1.**
8. Remove upper trim panel by pulling rearward out of clips at bottom of windshield.

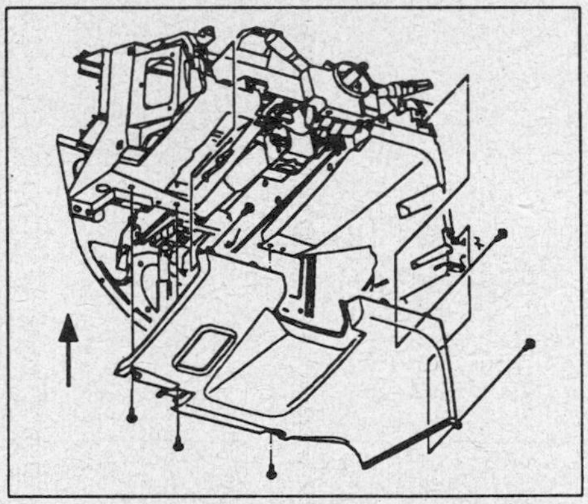

G39149100013000X

Fig. 4 Steering column filler panel removal

9. **On 1995 models,** remove glove compartment, air bag module attaching screws, pull module rearward, then disconnect yellow eelctrical connector and remove air bag module.
10. **On all models,** remove screws and pull cluster trim panel rearward to disengage retainers, **Fig. 2.**
11. Remove connector position assurance (CPA) devices and disconnect electrical connectors from instrument panel lighting rheostat and rear window defrost switches. Remove cluster trim panel.
12. Remove screws and pull instrument panel cluster out enough to disconnect electrical connectors.
13. Disconnect electrical connector by depressing retainer legs. **Fig. 3.** Remove instrument cluster.
14. Remove wiring harness clips from dash reinforcement.
15. Loosen screws and remove assembly line diagnostic link connector.
16. Loosen screws and remove steering column filler panel, **Fig. 4.**
17. Remove hood release lever screw.
18. Remove radio and HVAC dash control assembly.
19. Disconnect cigarette lighter electrical connector.
20. Remove cigarette lighter bulb holder by rotating counterclockwise and pulling straight out.
21. Apply parking brake, then remove parking brake filler panel by carefully lifting at rear edge.
22. **On models with manual transaxles,** remove gear selector knob by pulling straight up.
23. **On models with automatic transaxles,** move gear selector to No. 2 position.
24. **On models with power windows,** remove ashtray and disconnect ashtray bulb holder.
25. Remove window/mirror switch by sliding switch forward, then lifting rear edge.
26. **On models with standard windows,** remove connector position assurance (CPA) devices and disconnect window/mirror electrical connectors, then remove console.
27. **On all models,** loosen screws and remove instrument panel junction block from dash reinforcement, **Fig. 5.**
28. Remove ground wire from dash reinforcement, then loosen screw and remove rear electrical connector from instrument panel fuse block.
29. Remove CPA device and disconnect

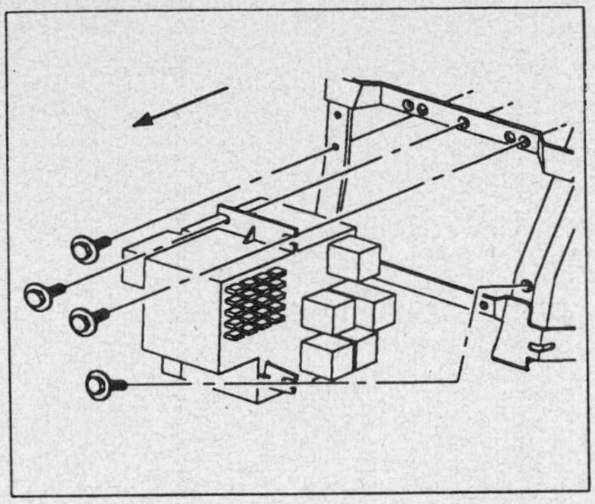

G39149100009000X

Fig. 5 Instrument panel junction block

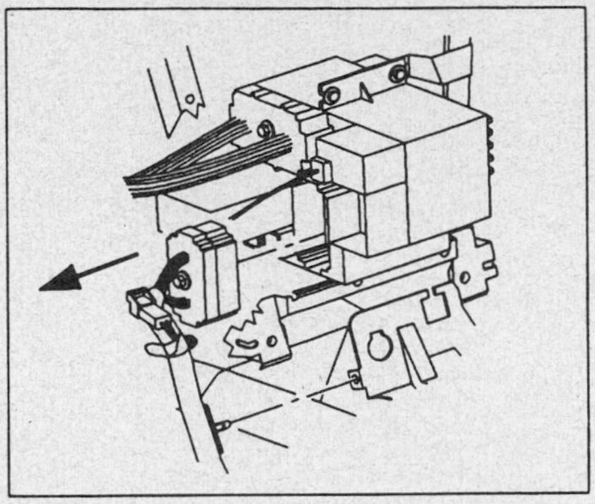

G39149100010000X

Fig. 6 Two-way instrument panel connector

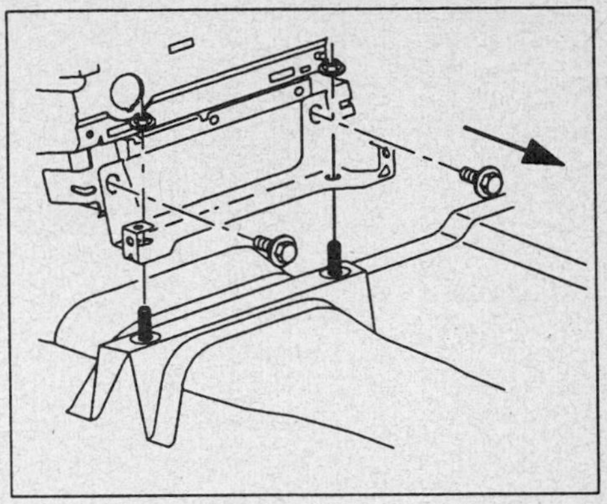

G39149100011000X

Fig. 7 Lower bracket removal

two-way instrument panel to body harness connector, **Fig. 6.**

30. Remove wire harness and antenna hold-down clips from instrument panel reinforcement.
31. Loosen floor shifter assembly. Remove two nuts, lift lower reinforcement bracket off of studs and slide bracket rearward, **Fig. 7.**
32. Loosen mounting nuts and lower cruise control module, if equipped.
33. Remove screws and nuts from instrument panel retainer and reinforcement bracket, **Fig. 8.**

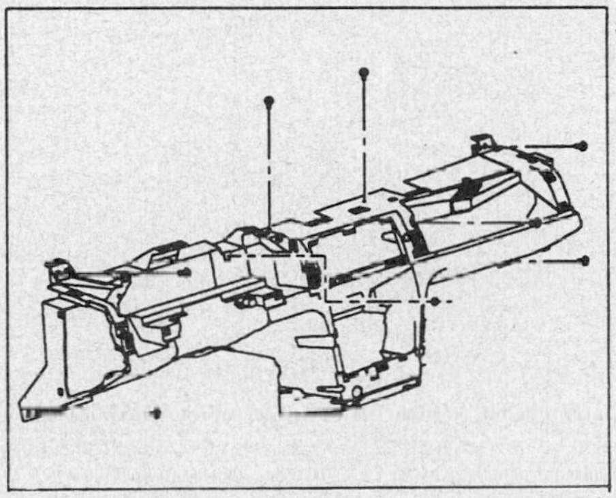

G39149100012000X

Fig. 8 Instrument panel & reinforcement bracket screw locations

34. Remove bolts and lower steering column assembly onto front seat.
35. Carefully remove instrument panel/retainer assembly.
36. Reverse procedure to install, noting the following:
    a. Feed fuse block and wire harness through lower reinforcement and into position.
    b. **Torque** steering column retaining bolts to 26 ft. lbs.

STEERING COLUMNS

NOTE: On Air Bag Equipped Models, Refer To "Air Bag System Precautions" Located In The Front Of This Manual For System Disarming & Arming Procedures.

INDEX

PRECAUTIONS

AIR BAG SYSTEMS

Refer to "Air Bag System Precautions" in the front of this manual for system disarming and arming procedures.

STEERING COLUMN

REPLACE

REMOVAL

1. Disconnect battery ground cable.
2. Remove steering wheel as outlined under "Steering Wheel, Replace" in the "Electrical" section.
3. Remove two screws and upper steering column cover.
4. Remove ignition lock bezel. Remove two screws and the lower steering column cover.
5. Remove left and right lower trim panel extensions by disconnecting lower Velcro fasteners and pulling panels out of two upper fasteners, **Fig. 1.**
6. Remove center trim plate by pulling on bottom to disengage lower fasteners, then pull top of trim plate to disengage upper fasteners, **Fig. 2.**
7. Remove trim panel extension strip by pulling out at fastener locations.
8. Remove both upper trim panel screw caps, **Fig. 3,** then remove two screws and lift panel to disengage six clips at rear edge.
9. Slide panel out of three clips at windshield and remove upper panel. Remove trim panel extension strip by pulling out at fastener locations, **Fig. 3.**
10. Remove four screws and lift cluster trim panel to disengage rear retainers, **Fig. 4.** Disconnect harness from rear window defroster and thermostat switches, then remove trim panel.
11. Remove six screws to remove steering column opening filler assembly, **Fig. 5.**
12. Remove connector position assurance (CPA) device and disconnect wires from lower control switch.
13. Disconnect lever control switch connector, then disconnect ignition

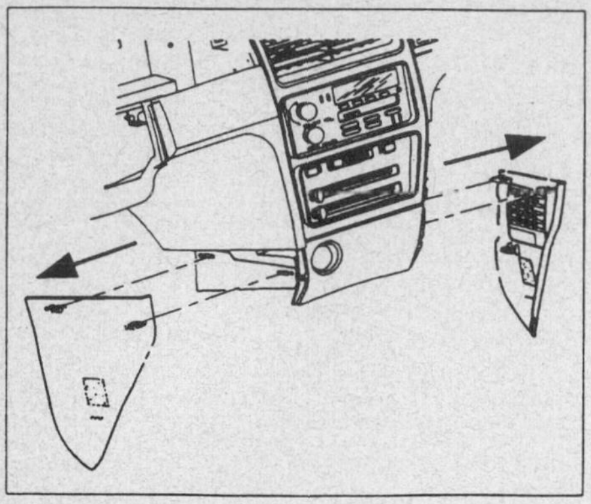

G36049100001000X

Fig. 1 Lower trim panel removal

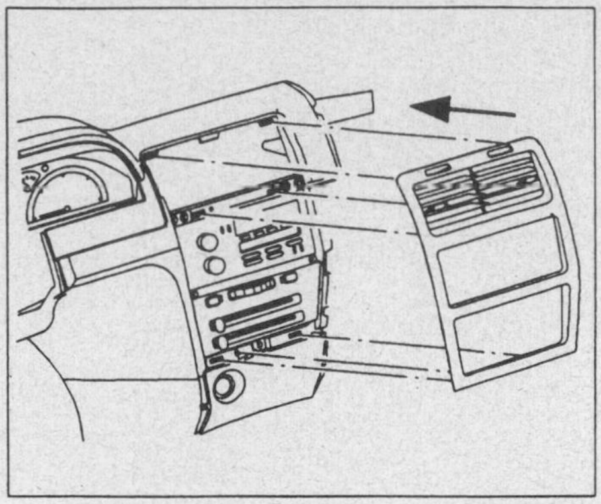

G36049100002000X

Fig. 2 Center trim plate removal

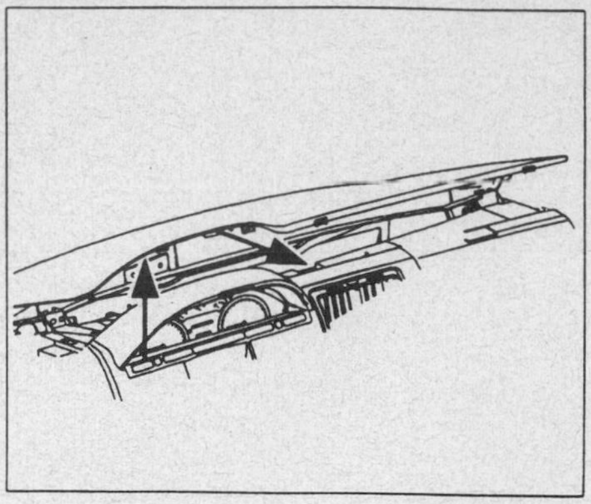

G36049100003000X

Fig. 3 Upper trim panel removal

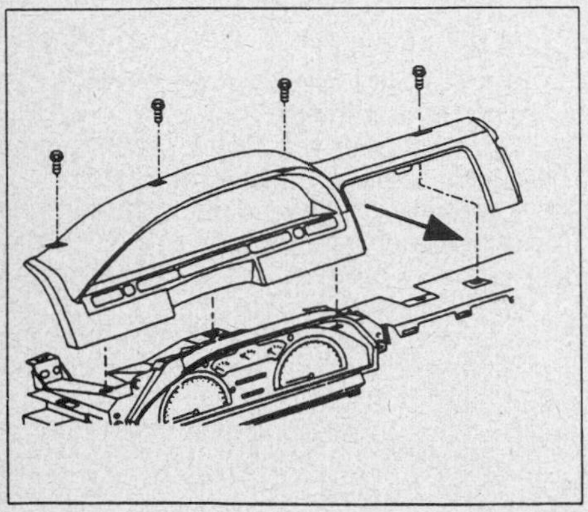

G36049100004000X

Fig. 4 Cluster trim panel removal

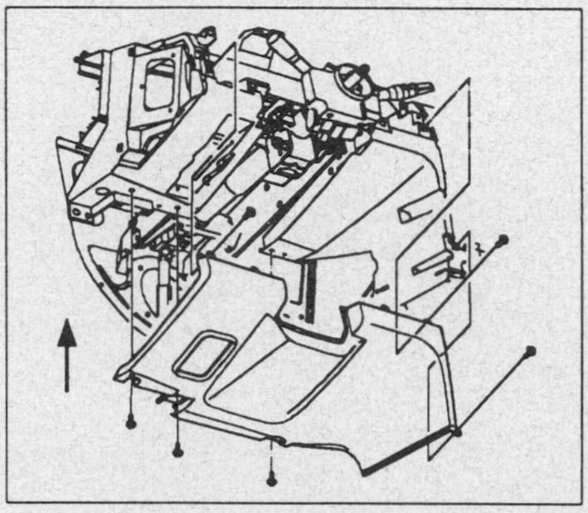

G36049100005000X

Fig. 5 Steering column opening filler removal

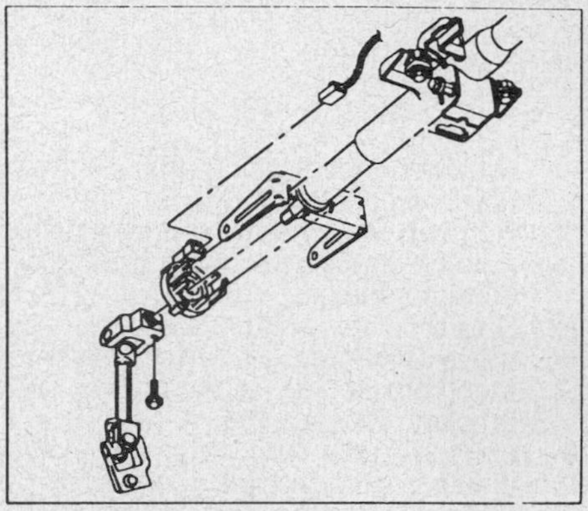

G36049100006000X

Fig. 6 Handwheel sensor replacement

switch from ignition module.

14. Remove two upper steering column bolts. Carefully lower steering column onto front seat.
15. Remove upper bolt from intermediate shaft and disconnect shaft from column.
16. **On Coupe models,** disconnect handwheel sensor electrical sensor.
17. **On all models,** remove two bolts to disconnect steering column at hinge point.
18. Remove steering column from vehicle.
19. **On Coupe models,** remove handwheel sensor from lower steering column support bracket by releasing both sensor locking tabs and remove sensor from column.
20. **On all models,** position steering column in a vise at the upper bracket. Using a center punch, mark center of shear bolts on ignition module assembly.
21. Drill a small hole (1/8 inch) in shear bolts at the center mark. Remove shear bolts with a screw extractor. Remove ignition module assembly and clamp from column.

INSTALLATION

1. Using new shear bolts, install ignition module onto steering column. Tighten shear bolts until heads break off.
2. **On Coupe models,** install handwheel sensor onto steering column. Position electrical connector to top of column and attach to lower support bracket by snapping sensor locking tabs into bracket.
3. **On all models,** install steering column at hinge point.
4. Connect intermediate shaft. **Torque** bolt to 33 ft. lbs.
5. **On Coupe models,** connect handwheel sensor electrical sensor.
6. **On all models,** raise steering column up to instrument panel and install two bolts. **Torque** to 26 ft. lbs.
7. Install lever control switch by fitting into bottom locating holes on ignition module. Tighten lower screw first to ensure correct location.
8. Install ignition switch to ignition module.
9. Install steering column opening filler.
10. Install cluster trim panel.
11. Install instrument panel top cover. Use six new clips.
12. Install trim panel extension strip, center trim plate and lower trim panel extensions.
13. Install steering column covers.
14. Install steering wheel.
15. Connect battery ground cable.

HANDWHEEL SENSOR

REPLACE

COUPE

1. Rotate steering wheel until clamp bolt at lower steering column intermediate shaft joint is accessible.
2. Remove clamp bolt at lower steering column intermediate shaft joint, **Fig. 6**
3. Slide intermediate shaft off lower steering column.
4. Remove handwheel sensor from lower steering column support bracket by releasing both sensor locking tabs.
5. Rotate handwheel sensor 180° until electrical connector is easily accessible, then disconnect electrical connector from sensor.
6. Remove handwheel sensor.
7. Reverse procedure to install, noting the following:
   a. Ensure electrical connector is facing up.
   b. **Torque** intermediate shaft pinch bolt to 35 ft. lbs.

STEERING COLUMN SERVICE

The steering column is only serviced as an assembly. If a steering column malfunction or defect is found, replacement is required.

MANUAL STEERING GEARS

INDEX

Complaint/Condition	Possible Cause(s)	Correction(s)
Hard Steering	Front tire(s) improperly inflated.	Inflate tire(s) correctly.
	Improperly adjusted, improperly lubricated or damaged steering gear.	Adjust, lubricate (check for damaged seals) or replace steering gear.
	Worn or binding lower control arm ball stud(s).	Replace lower control arm(s).
	Worn or binding inner or outer tie rod end(s).	Replace inner or outer tie rod end(s).
	Worn or binding upper strut mount(s).	Replace mount(s).
	Worn or binding intermediate shaft joint(s).	Replace intermediate shaft.
	Binding within steering column or intermediate shaft boot.	Correct condition.
Poor return of steering wheel to center	Front tire(s) improperly inflated.	Inflate tire(s) correctly
	Improperly adjusted, improperly lubricated or damaged steering gear.	Adjust, lubricate (check for damaged seals) or replace steering gear.
	Worn or binding lower control arm ball stud(s).	Replace lower control arm(s).
	Worn or binding inner or outer tie rod end(s).	Replace inner or outer tie rod end(s).
	Worn or binding upper strut mount(s).	Replace mount(s).
	Worn or binding intermediate shaft joint(s).	Replace intermediate shaft
	Binding within steering column or intermediate shaft boot.	Correct condition
	Incorrect front wheel caster.	Adjust front wheel caster.
Excessive free play in steering	Wheel bearing(s) worn.	Replace wheel bearing(s)
	Steering gear mounting bolt(s) loose.	Tighten bolt(s).
	Steering gear out of adjustment or worn.	Adjust or replace steering gear.
	Inner or outer steering tie rod(s) worn.	Replace tie rod(s).
	Lower control arm ball stud(s) worn.	Replace lower control arm(s).
	Tension strut bushings worn.	Replace bushings.
Rattle clunking noise in steering	Inner or outer tie rod end(s) worn.	Replace tie rod end(s).
	Steering gear out of adjustment or worn.	Adjust or replace steering gear.
	Intermediate shaft joint(s) worn.	Replace intermediate shaft.
	Steering gear mounting bolt(s) loose.	Tighten bolt(s).
	Worn wheel bearing(s).	Replace wheel bearing(s).

G34020100070000X

Fig. 1 Steering system troubleshooting

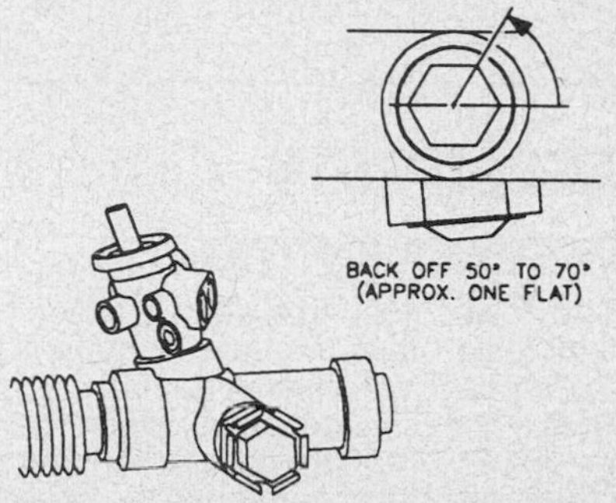
BACK OFF 50° TO 70°
(APPROX. ONE FLAT)

G34029100080000X

Fig. 2 Bearing preload adjustment

DESCRIPTION

The manual steering system is a rack and pinion design. The major components of the steering system are the steering wheel, steering column and shaft, intermediate shaft, manual steering gear, tie rods and steering knuckles.

When the steering wheel is turned, the steering shaft turns the intermediate shaft which turns the pinion of the steering gear. The gear teeth on the pinion mesh with the mating teeth on the straight rack inside the steering gear. Rotation of the pinion converts to a straight-line motion of the rack across the vehicle that moves the tie rods either left or right. This motion causes the steering knuckle to pivot either clockwise or counterclockwise, steering the front wheels.

TROUBLESHOOTING

Refer to **Fig. 1** for manual steering system troubleshooting.

ADJUSTMENTS

BEARING PRELOAD

The following adjustment should be made with the front wheels raised and the steering wheel centered.

1. Loosen adjuster plug locknut on steering gear housing.
2. Turn adjuster plug clockwise until it bottoms in steering gear housing, **Fig. 2.**
3. **Torque** adjuster plug to 106 inch lbs.
4. Back-off adjuster plug 50-70° (approximately one flat of nut).
5. **Torque** locknut, while holding adjuster plug, to 52 ft. lbs.
6. Check steering wheel returnability following adjustment.

POWER STEERING

INDEX

DESCRIPTION

STEERING SYSTEM

The power steering system is a rack and pinion design, featuring an Electronic Variable Orifice (EVO) design pump.

Unlike conventional power steering systems, the EVO feature adjusts the amount of steering assist according to the speed of the vehicle, which is monitored by a vehicle speed sensor (VSS). This information is read electronically by the Powertrain Control Module (PCM), which commands the EVO actuator to control the power steering pump output flow.

At low speeds, where high levels of assist are desired, the EVO actuator is open further, providing more flow to the steering gear and greater assist. At higher speeds, the actuator is closed further, providing less pump flow and less steering assist and improved road feeling. All of the additional flow of the pump that is not needed by the gear is allowed to return to the reservoir through a bypass.

POWER STEERING PRESSURE SWITCH

The power steering pressure switch is an input to the powertrain control module (PCM). If the pressure exceeds 450-650 psi, the switch opens, signalling to the PCM to increase engine idle RPM and turn the A/C compressor off to compensate for the additional load of the power steering pump.

EVO ACTUATOR

The EVO actuator is a 10 ohm linear solenoid. The PCM controls the current to the high and low side of the actuator so current control is retained in the presence of any output fault condition.

The control of the actuator is accomplished by pulse width modulating (PWM) voltage to the actuator ad monitoring the actual current flow. The PCM varies the PWM signal in order to make the actual current equal to the desired current.

TROUBLESHOOTING

Refer to **Fig. 1** for power steering system troubleshooting.

DIAGNOSIS & TESTING

HYDRAULIC SYSTEM TEST

1. Disconnect high pressure line at steering gear and install power steering system tester tool No. SA9134C or equivalent.
2. Open gate valve on power steering system tester.
3. Run engine until it has reached normal operating temperature. Replace any power steering fluid lost during tester installation, then bleed system if necessary.
4. With engine idling, record pressure and flow rate. If the pressure reading is greater than 150 psi, stop engine and check power steering lines for restrictions. **Do not turn steering wheel while performing this test.**
5. Slowly close gate valve until 700 psi is indicated on the power steering tester. Record pressure and flow rate.
6. Flow rate should not drop more than 1 gallon per minute from flow rate recorded in step 4.
7. If flow rate drops more than 1 gallon per minute, replace ring, rotor and the vanes in the pump. Also inspect pressure plate and thrust plates for wear.
8. Completely close and open gate valve three times. **Do not close gate valve for more than five seconds at a time.** Record fluid pressure each time the valve is closed.
9. If all three readings are not within 50 psi, replace flow control valve.
10. With gate valve open, increase engine speed to 1600 RPM and record fluid pressure and flow rate. **Do not turn steering wheel.**
11. Flow rate should not vary more than 1 gallon per minute from the flow rate recorded in step 4.
12. Ensure flow control valve moves freely in pump housing. Inspect valve for burrs.
13. Turn steering wheel completely to left, then completely to right. Record fluid pressure and flow rate at each stop.
14. If flow rate is greater then 1 gallon per minute, steering gear is leaking internally and must be replaced.

EVO SUBSYSTEM TEST

1. Disconnect high pressure line at power steering pump and install Power Steering System Tester tool No. SA9134C or equivalent.
2. Connect a Powertrain Diagnostic Tool (PDT) to ALDL diagnostic port. Follow tool manufacturer's instructions.
3. Open gate valve on steering system tester.
4. Run engine until normal operating temperature is reached. Replace any power steering fluid lost during tester installation, then bleed system if necessary.
5. Select "EVO Subsystem Test" using the PDT tool, in the special test menu.
6. Using the PDT, command the EVO actuator to provide "full assist." Record power steering fluid flow rate, as indicated on the power steering system tester. If flow rate is not between 2.35-2.85 gallons per minute, replace EVO actuator.
7. Using the PDT, command the EVO actuator to provide "no assist." Record fluid flow rate, as indicated on steering tester. If flow rate is not between 0.4-0.9 gallons per minute, replace EVO actuator.

POWER STEERING SYSTEM SERVICE

Steering Pump Overhaul

DISASSEMBLE

1. Remove power steering pump from vehicle.
2. Remove reservoir retaining clips from reservoir assembly.
3. Remove reservoir from housing.
4. Remove O-ring seal from pump housing, then remove pulley using puller tool No. SA9162C or equivalent.
5. Remove three power steering pump to bracket fasteners and remove bracket from pump.
6. Remove EVO actuator assembly using removal tool No. SA9116C or equivalent.
7. Remove flow control valve and spring.
8. Remove retaining ring, **Fig. 2**, as follows:
   a. Use a C-clamp (one side on end cover, the other on pump driveshaft) to depress end cover, easing removal of retaining ring.
   b. Insert a piece of wood between C-

Complaint/Condition	Possible Cause(s)	Correction(s)
Hard Steering	Front tire(s) improperly inflated.	Inflate tire(s) correctly.
	Improperly adjusted, improperly lubricated or damaged steering gear.	Adjust, lubricate (check for damaged seals) or replace steering gear.
	Worn or binding lower control arm ball stud(s).	Replace lower control arm(s).
	Worn or binding inner or outer tie rod(s).	Replace inner or outer tie rod end(s).
	Worn or binding upper strut mount(s).	Replace mount(s).
	Worn or binding intermediate shaft joint(s).	Replace intermediate shaft.
	Accessory drive belt loose.	Check accessory drive belt tension.
	Power steering fluid level low.	Add power steering fluid.
	Insufficient power steering pump pressure.	Repair or replace power steering pump.
	Faulty EVO actuator.	Replace EVO actuator.
	Restricted or leaking power steering hoses.	Replace hoses or tighten hose connections.
	High internal leakage in steering gear.	Replace steering gear.
	Excessive front wheel caster.	Adjust front wheel caster.
	Binding within steering column or intermediate shaft boot.	Correct condition.
Poor return of steering wheel to center	Front tire(s) improperly inflated.	Inflate tire(s) correctly.
	Improperly adjusted, improperly lubricated or binding steering gear.	Adjust, lubricate (check for damaged seals) or replace steering gear.
	Incorrect front wheel caster.	Adjust front wheel caster.
	Worn or binding inner or outer tie rod end(s).	Replace inner or outer tie rod end(s).
	Worn or binding upper strut mount(s).	Replace mount(s).
	Worn or binding intermediate shaft joint(s).	Replace intermediate shaft.
	Binding within steering column or intermediate shaft boot.	Correct condition.
Excessive free play in steering	Wheel bearing(s) worn.	Replace wheel bearing(s).
	Steering gear mounting bolt(s) loose.	Tighten bolt(s).
	Steering gear out of adjustment or worn.	Adjust or replace steering gear.
	Inner or outer steering tie rod(s).	Replace tie rod(s).
	Lower control arm ball stud(s) worn.	Replace lower control arm(s).
	Tension strut bushings worn.	Replace bushings.

G36029100001010X

Fig. 1 Power steering system troubleshooting (Part 1 of 3)

Complaint/Condition	Possible Cause(s)	Correction(s)
Rattl[illegible]unking noise in steering	Inner or outer tie rod end(s) worn.	Replace inner or outer tie rod end(s).
	Steering gear out of adjustment or worn.	Adjust or replace steering gear.
	Intermediate shaft joint(s) worn.	Replace intermediate shaft.
	Steering gear mounting bolt(s) loose.	Tighten bolt(s).
	Worn wheel bearing(s).	Replace wheel bearing(s).
Momentary increase in steering effort when steering wheel is turned quickly	High internal leakage in steering gear.	Replace steering gear.
	Low power steering fluid level.	Correct power steering fluid level.
	Insufficient pump pressure.	Repair or replace power steering pump.
	Damaged EVO actuator.	Replace actuator.
	Damaged handwheel sensor (Coupe only).	Replace handwheel sensor.
	EVO electrical circuit malfunction.	Correct condition.
Steering wheel surges or jerks when turning at low speeds	Insufficient power steering pump pressure.	Repair or replace power steering pump.
	High internal leakage in steering gear.	Replace steering gear.
	Loose accessory drive belt.	Check accessory drive belt tension.
Insufficient system pressure – caused by pump	Flow control valve stuck or inoperative.	Free or replace flow control valve.
	EVO system malfunction.	EVO system
	Pressure plate not flat against pump ring.	Correct condition.
	Worn pump ring.	Replace pump ring.
	Scored pressure, thrust plate or rotor.	Replace components.
	Vane(s) sticking in rotor slot(s).	Clean rotor/vanes or replace component(s).
	Cracked or broken thrust, or pressure plate.	Replace components.
Insufficient system pressure – caused by steering gear	Scored steering gear housing bore.	Replace steering gear.
	Leaking steering gear piston seals or inner rack seal.	Replace steering gear.
Growling noise in power steering pump	Excessive back pressure in hoses or steering gear caused by restriction.	Eliminate restriction.
	Scored pressure plate, thrust plate or rotor.	Replace component(s)
	Worn pump ring.	Replace pump ring.
	Air in power steering fluid.	Add power steering and bleed system.
	Pump mounting loose.	Tighten pump mounting.
	Restricted fluid lines.	Eliminate restriction.

G36029100001020X

Fig. 1 Power steering system troubleshooting (Part 2 of 3)

Complaint/Condition	Possible Cause(s)	Correction(s)
Rattling noise in power steering pump	Vane(s) sticking in rotor slot(s).	Clean rotor/vanes or replace component(s).
	Worn pump shaft bearing.	Replace bearing, pump or housing.
Swishing noise in power steering pump	Damaged flow control valve.	Replace flow control valve.
Whining noise in power steering pump	Pump shaft being scored.	Correct condition.

G36029100001030X

Fig. 1 Power steering system troubleshooting (Part 3 of 3)

clamp and pump driveshaft.

c. Place a punch into pump housing access hole and remove retaining ring.

9. Gently push on driveshaft to assist in removing end cover.
10. Remove internal pump components in two groups, **Fig. 3**, as follows:
    a. Remove end cover, O-ring, pressure plate spring and pressure plate.
    b. Remove driveshaft with pump rotor, pump vanes, pump ring, thrust plate and shaft retaining ring.
11. Remove O-ring seal (A), two dowel pins (B) and driveshaft seal (C) from pump housing, **Fig. 4.**
12. Remove pressure plate, pressure plate spring and O-ring from end cover.
13. Remove shaft retaining ring from driveshaft.
14. Remove pump rotor, pump vanes, pump ring and thrust plate from driveshaft, **Fig. 5.**
15. Separate pump rotor, pump vanes and pump ring.
16. Clean all parts with new power steering fluid.
17. Inspect pump ring, pump vanes, thrust plate and driveshaft for scoring, pitting or chatter marks.
18. Replace any damaged components. Do not attempt to remove damage with abrasive cleaners.
19. A wavy pattern on pump ring face will be present with low mileage and should not be mistaken for premature wear or damage.

ASSEMBLE

1. Lubricate driveshaft with new power steering fluid.
2. Install new driveshaft seal into pump housing using a suitably sized socket as a driver.
3. Install thrust plate and pump rotor onto driveshaft.
4. Install driveshaft/rotor/thrust plate assembly into housing, **Fig. 6.**
5. Install pump ring dowel pins into pump housing through thrust plate. Install pump ring (with holes correctly positioned onto dowel pins) into housing, **Fig. 7.**
6. Pump ring face has a indentation on one side near the dowel hole. The ring must be installed with the indentation facing up. **If ring is installed upside down, the pump will not function.**
7. Install vanes into pump rotor. Vanes may be installed in either direction.
8. Lubricate new pump housing O-ring with power steering fluid and install into groove in housing.
9. Align pressure plate dowel holes with dowel pins and install plate into housing.
10. Position pressure plate spring against pressure plate. Lubricate new end cover O-ring with power steering fluid and install onto end cover, **Fig. 8.**
11. Lubricate outer edit of end cover with power steering fluid, then press end cover into pump housing.
12. Install retaining ring into groove in pump housing, with ring opening near

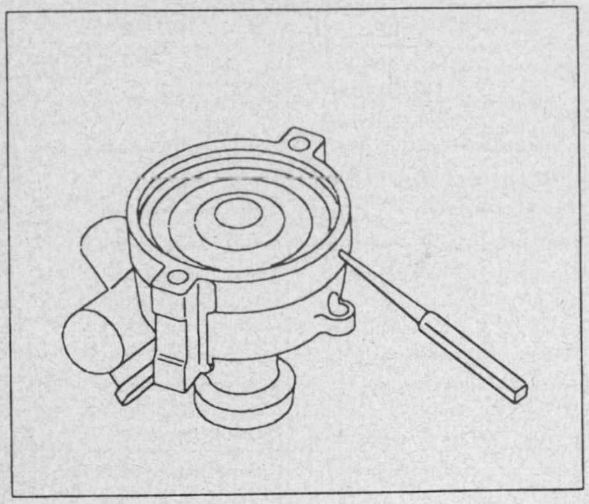

G36029100005000X

Fig. 2 Pump retaining ring removal

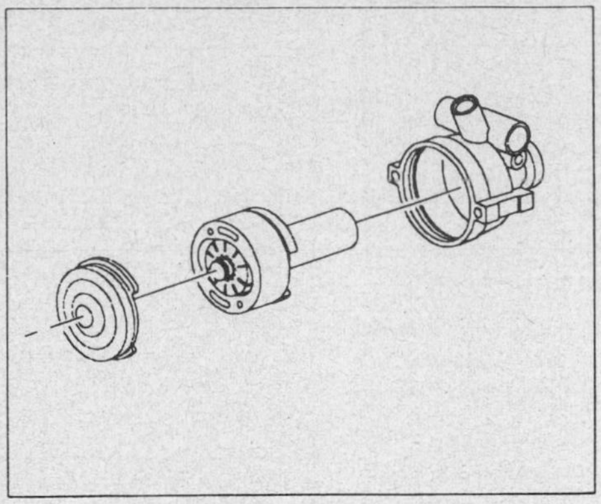

G36029100006000X

Fig. 3 Pump internal component removal

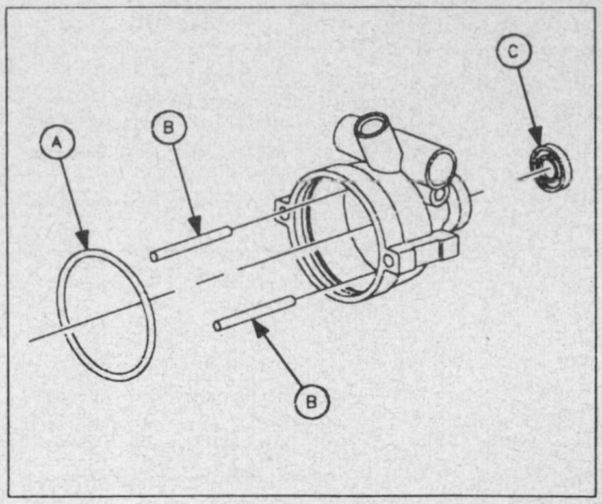
A
B
C
B

G36029100007000X

Fig. 4 Pump housing O-ring seal, dowel pins and driveshaft seal removal

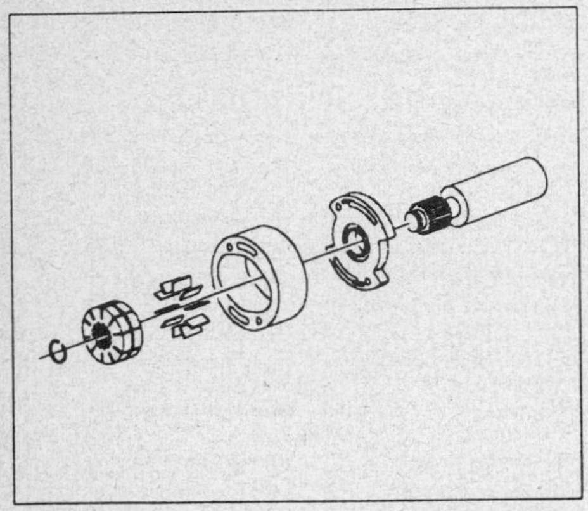

G36029100008000X

Fig. 5 Removing rotor, vanes, ring and thrust plate from driveshaft

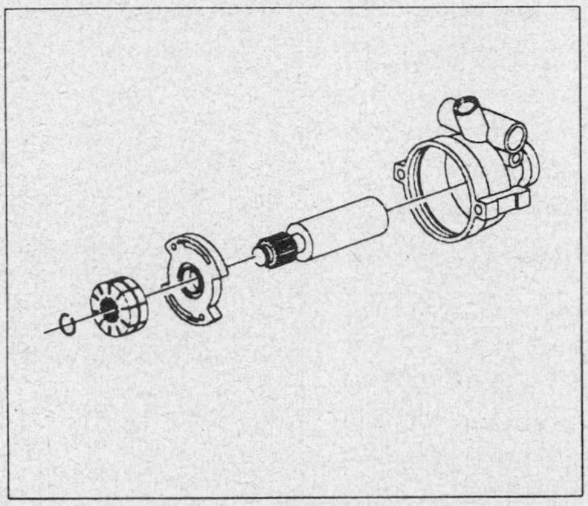

G36029100009000X

Fig. 6 Driveshaft/rotor/thrust plate assembly

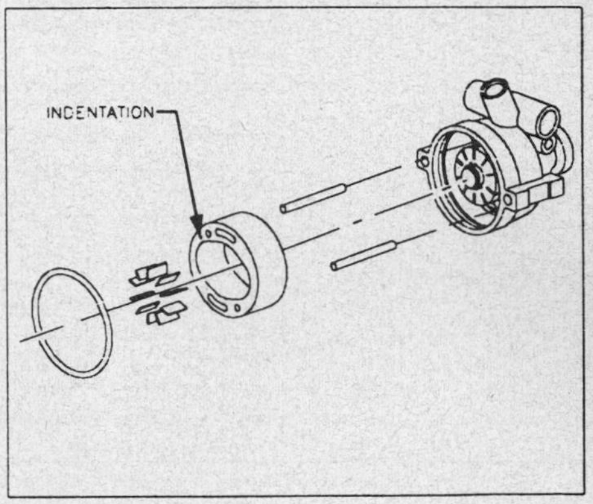
INDENTATION

G36029100010000X

Fig. 7 Pump ring dowel pins & pump ring assembly

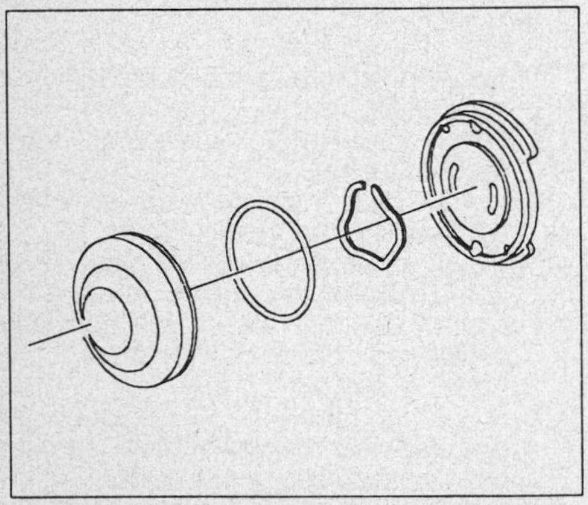

G36029100011000X

Fig. 8 Pressure plate assembly

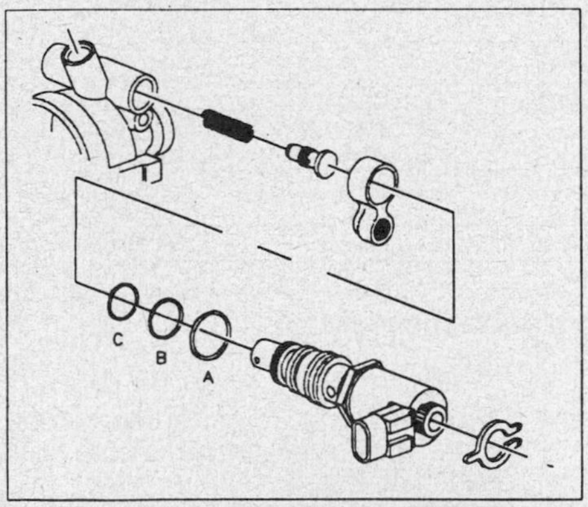
C
B
A

G36029100004000X

Fig. 9 EVO actuator O-ring locations

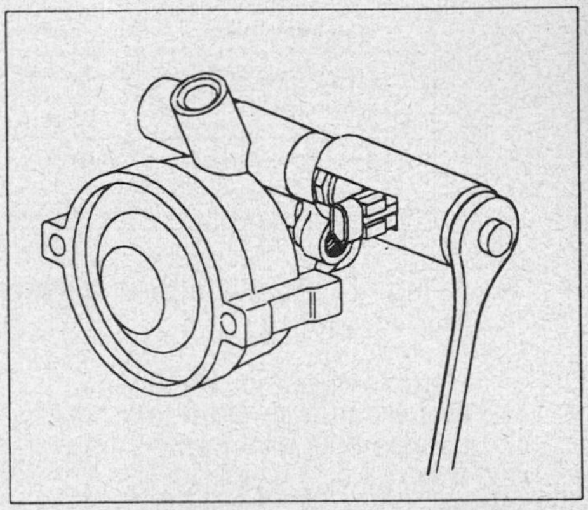

G36029100003000X

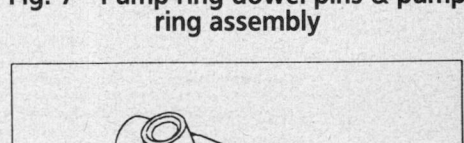

Fig. 10 EVO actuator replacement

access hole in housing. Ensure ring is fully seated in housing groove.

13. Install three O-ring seals onto EVO actuator, if removed during disassembly procedure. **Install three seals (A, B and C) in correct position as shown in Fig. 9.**
14. Correctly position EVO actuator and discharge fitting to pump assembly, **Fig. 10.**
15. **Torque** EVO actuator with installation tool NO. SA9116C or equivalent, to 46 ft. lbs., **Fig. 10.**
16. Install power steering pump bracket onto power steering pump with three fasteners. **Torque** to 28 ft. lbs.
17. Install pump pulley using installation tool No. SA9162C or equivalent.
18. Lubricate new reservoir O-ring with power steering fluid and install onto reservoir.
19. Install reservoir into pump housing. Push reservoir straight into housing, then install retaining clips.
20. Install pump into vehicle and bleed power steering system.

POWER STEERING SYSTEM BLEED

1. With engine off, front wheels raised and turned completely left, check reservoir fluid level. Add fluid if necessary.
2. Bleed system by turning wheels from side to side several times, without contacting stops.
3. Start engine and check fluid level. Add fluid if necessary.
4. Return steering wheel to straight ahead position, lower front wheels and allow engine to idle for two to three minutes.
5. Road test vehicle to ensure steering functions normally and is free from noise.

Adjustments

STEERING GEAR BEARING PRELOAD

The following adjustment should be made with the front wheel raised and the steering wheel centered.

1. Loosen adjuster plug locknut on steering gear housing.
2. Turn adjuster plug clockwise until it bottoms in steering gear housing, **Fig. 11.**
3. **Torque** adjuster plug to 106 inch lbs.
4. Back-off adjuster plug 50-70° (approximately one flat of nut).
5. **Torque** locknut, while holding adjuster plug, to 52 ft. lbs.
6. Check steering wheel returnability following adjustment.

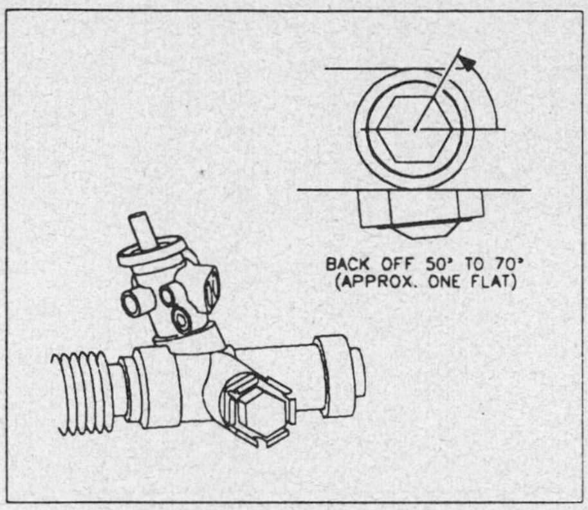
BACK OFF 50° TO 70°
(APPROX. ONE FLAT)
G36029100002000X

Fig. 11 Steering gear bearing preload adjustment

PRESSURE SWITCH

REPLACE

1. Disconnect battery ground cable, then raise and support vehicle.
2. Disconnect electrical connection at power steering pressure switch.
3. Remove switch.
4. Reverse procedure to install, noting the following:
   a. Inspect O-ring and replace if necessary.
   b. **Torque** switch to 97 inch lbs.

ELECTRONIC VARIABLE ORIFICE (EVO) ACTUATOR

REPLACE

1. Disconnect battery ground cable.
2. Remove pump from vehicle, then disconnect EVO electrical connector locating clip.
3. Remove EVO actuator assembly using socket removal tool No. SA91116C or equivalent, **Fig. 10.** Do not pivot socket tool during removal.
4. Remove discharge fitting from actuator.
5. Remove three O-ring seals from actuator. Note size and location of O-ring seals.
6. Reverse procedure to install, noting the following:
   a. Refer to **Fig. 9** for three O-ring seals locations.
   b. **Torque** EVO actuator to 46 ft. lbs.
   c. Install pump and bleed power steering system.

DISC BRAKES

INDEX

BRAKE SYSTEM BLEED

Use only DOT 3 brake fluid from a clean sealed container. **Do not use DOT 5 silicone fluid.** Do not allow fluid to come in contact with painted surfaces.

MANUAL PROCEDURE

1. Fill master cylinder reservoir, ensure reservoir is at least half full during bleed procedure.
2. If master cylinder is suspected to have air in its bore, proceed as follows:
   a. Loosen front master cylinder brake line.
   b. Using a container, allow brake fluid to flow from front master cylinder port.
   c. Install and tighten brake line to master cylinder.
   d. Slowly depress brake pedal one time and hold.
   e. Loosen front master cylinder brake line to purge air, then tighten brake line, then release pedal.
   f. Repeat until all air is bleed from cylinder.
3. If caliper or wheel cylinder is suspected, proceed as follows:
   a. Install a wrench over bleeder valve, then install a piece of transparent hose over bleeder nipple, submerge other end in transparent container of clean new brake fluid.
   b. Loosen bleeder screw.
   c. Apply brake pedal slowly and hold.
   d. Tighten bleeder screw.
   e. Release brake pedal.
   f. Repeat procedure until all air is removed from brake lines.
4. If more than one brake line is to be bled, bleed in sequence:
   a. Right rear.
   b. Left front.
   c. Left rear.
   d. Right front.
5. Check brake pedal for sponginess, if indicated, repeat procedure.
6. When bleeding is complete, check and fill reservoir.

PRESSURE PROCEDURE

1. Clean brake fluid reservoir cap, then remove cap.
2. Fill master cylinder.
3. Install bleeder adapter tool No. SA9150BR or equivalent, to brake fluid reservoir.
4. Connect a suitable pressure bleeder to adapter.
5. Charge pressure bleeder to 20-25 psi.
6. Perform steps 2 through 6 under "Manual Procedure" for to complete bleeding process.

BRAKE PAD SERVICE

FRONT DISC BRAKE

Brake Pad Replacement

1. Raise and support vehicle.
2. Remove front wheel assemblies.
3. Remove caliper lockpin.
4. Pivot caliper upward around guide pin.
5. Remove brake pads.
6. Remove two pad clips from caliper support.
7. Reverse procedure to install.

Caliper Replacement

1. Raise and support vehicle.
2. Remove wheel assemblies.
3. Disconnect caliper brake fluid lines and plug opening.
4. Remove caliper lockpin, guide pin and pin boots.

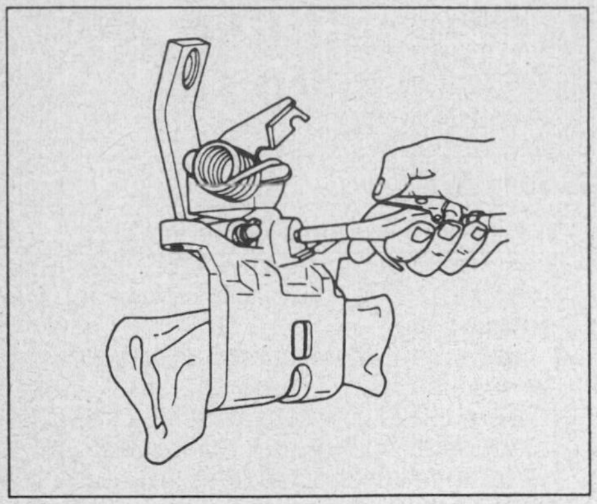

G34079100003000X

Fig. 1 Rear caliper piston removal

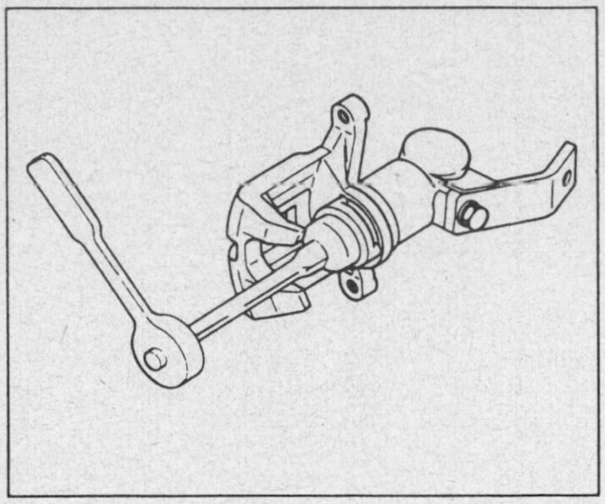

G34079100004000X

Fig. 2 Rear caliper piston installation

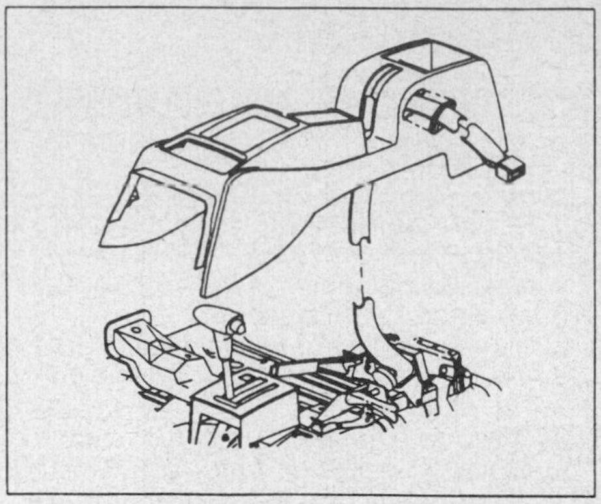

G34079100001000X

Fig. 3 Center console removal

5. Remove caliper from caliper support, ensuring not to damage pin boots.
6. Remove brake pads.
7. Remove two pad clips from caliper support.
8. Reverse procedure to install.

REAR DISC BRAKE

Brake Pads Replacement

1. Raise and support vehicle.
2. Remove wheel assemblies.
3. Remove caliper lockpin and guide pin.
4. Remove caliper from support and suspend with mechanics wire.
5. Remove brake pads from caliper support.
6. Remove two pad clips from caliper support.
7. Reverse procedure to install.

Caliper Replacement

1. Raise and support vehicle.
2. Remove wheel assemblies.
3. Disconnect caliper brake fluid lines and plug opening.
4. Slip parking brake cable end from brake lever, then using cable release tool No. SA9151BR or equivalent, remove cable outer housing.
5. Remove caliper lockpin and guide pin.
6. Remove caliper from caliper support, ensuring not to damage pin boots.
7. Remove lockpin and guide pins from caliper support.
8. Reverse procedure to install.

CALIPER SERVICE

FRONT

Disassemble

1. Inspect lockpin and guide pin boots for damage. replace as required.
2. Inspect piston boot and lockpin for damage, replace as required.
3. Using a small screwdriver, remove piston boot ring and boot.
4. Pad caliper interior with a suitable cushion, then apply non-lubricated compressed air to caliper inlet hole to remove piston.
5. Remove piston seal, then bleeder valve and cap.
6. Clean all parts in clean denatured alcohol, then dry with non-lubricated compressed air, then blow out all caliper body and bleeder valve passages.
7. Inspect piston for damage, replace as required.
8. Inspect caliper bore for damage, slight corrosion may be removed using suitable crocus cloth, is excessive damage, replace caliper. **Do not hone caliper bore.**
9. Inspect seal groove for damage, replace as required.

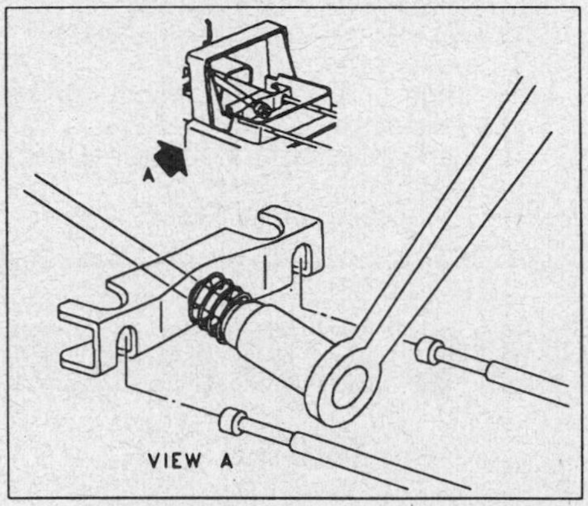
A
VIEW A

G34079100002000X

Fig. 4 Parking brake adjustment

Assemble

1. Install bleeder valve.
2. Lubricate piston seal using clean brake fluid, then install, ensuring seal is not twisted.
3. Install lubricated piston boot to piston.
4. Install lubricated piston to body, push piston to bottom of bore.
5. Install boot ring, ensure piston boot outer edge is smoothly seated in counterbore, work boot ring into groove near open end of caliper bore. **Do not pinch piston ring between boot ring and body.**
6. Lift piston boot inner edge to release trapped air, then install caliper and bleed brake system.

REAR

Disassemble

1. Inspect lockpin and guide pin boots for damage. replace as required.
2. Inspect piston boot and lockpin for damage, replace as required.
3. Using a small screwdriver, remove piston boot ring and boot.
4. Pad caliper interior with suitable cushion, then apply non-lubricated compressed air to caliper inlet hole to remove piston **Fig. 1.**
5. Remove piston seal, then bleeder valve and cap.
6. Clean all parts in clean denatured alcohol, then dry with non-lubricated compressed air, then blow out all caliper body and bleeder valve passages.
7. Inspect piston for damage, replace as required.
8. Inspect caliper bore for damage, slight corrosion may be removed using suitable crocus cloth, is excessive damage, replace caliper. **Do not hone caliper bore.**
9. Inspect seal groove for damage, replace as required.

Assemble

1. Install bleeder valve and cap.
2. Lubricate piston seal using clean brake fluid, then install, ensuring seal is not twisted.
3. Install lubricated piston boot to piston.
4. Install lubricated piston to body, push piston by hand, then install tool No. SA91110NE or equivalent to piston slots, rotate piston clockwise to install, **Fig. 2.**
5. Install boot ring, ensure piston boot outer edge is smoothly seated in counterbore, work boot ring into groove near open end of caliper bore. **Do not pinch piston ring between boot ring and body.**
6. Lift piston boot inner edge to release trapped air, then install caliper and bleed brake system.

ROTOR

REPLACE

1. Raise and support vehicle.
2. Remove road wheel.
3. Remove caliper support to steering knuckle bolts, then remove and suspend caliper from strut spring with wire.
4. Remove rotor.
5. Reverse procedure to install. Tighten to specifications.

PARKING BRAKE SERVICE

PARKING CABLE, REPLACE

1. Remove console as described under "Adjustments."
2. Remove adjuster nut, equalizer and cable from threaded rod.
3. Using tool No. SA9151BR or equivalent, remove parking brake cables from console bracket.
4. Raise and support vehicle.
5. Remove park brake grommet and cable assembly from floor pan.
6. Remove trailing arm/park brake cable to body attaching fasteners.
7. Remove cable attaching nut at floor pan.
8. Disconnect cable from caliper lever, then using tool No. SA9151BR or equivalent, remove cable from brake, then remove from vehicle.
9. Reverse procedure to install.

ADJUSTMENTS

PARKING BRAKE

1. Disconnect battery ground cable.
2. Remove center console assembly as follows:
   a. **On models with automatic transaxles,** tape release button in on the shift lever.
   b. **On models with manual transaxles,** remove shifter knob.
   c. **On all models,** remove liner in rear storage tray and remove two screws under liner.
   d. Remove two screws on front side of console, then apply parking brake and remove trim plate below park brake lever by lifting at rear edge and working plate up evenly.
   e. Remove both ash trays, then disconnect front ash tray light from console.
   f. **On models with power windows and mirrors,** remove window/mirror switch by pushing switch forward and lifting rear edge. Disconnect electrical connectors.
   g. **On all models,** remove side trim panels from center console.
   h. Lift rear of console, **Fig. 3.** Release and push out both seat belt bezels from below console.
   i. Lift console out while feeding seat belts through console.
3. Raise and support vehicle.
4. Pull parking brake lever to third click from released position.
5. Tighten adjuster nut, **Fig. 4,** until slight brake drag is felt at rear wheel.
6. Apply and release parking brake several times.
7. Pull lever up to second click. There should be no brake drag at rear wheels.
8. Pull brake lever to third click. There should be slight drag at rear wheels. Adjust if necessary.
9. Pull lever to fourth click. Rear wheels should not turn by hand.
10. Reverse procedure to install center console assembly.

DISC BRAKE SPECIFICATIONS

Year	New Thickness	Minimum Refinish Thickness①	Discard Thickness	Thickness Variation (Parallelism)	Lateral Runout (T.I.R.)
1992-95②	.710	.633	6.25	—	—
1992-95③	.430-.440	.370	.350	—	—

①—All brake rotors have a discard dimension cast into them. This is a wear dimension, not a refinish dimension. Any rotor that does not meet specifications should be discarded.
②—Front.
③—Rear.

TIGHTENING SPECIFICATIONS

Component	Torque/Ft. Lbs.
Brake Lever To Floor Bolt	35
Brake Lever To Floor Nut	23
Brake Line To Master Cylinder	18
Brake Pedal Pivot	16
Brake Pipe To Body	20
Master Cylinder To Brake Booster	20
Backing Plate To Knuckle③	63
Bleed Valve②	97①
Bleed Valve③	66①
Brake Dust Shield②	18
Brake Hose To Caliper②	32
Brake Hose To Caliper③	32

Component	Torque/Ft. Lbs.
Brake Line To Brake Hose (RL)③	14
Brake Line To Wheel Cylinder②	32
Brake Pipe To Brake Hose②	18
Brake Pipe To Brake Hose③	168①
Caliper Lock & Guide Pins	27
Caliper Mount Bracket②	81
Caliper To Caliper Support②	27
Caliper To Knuckle③	63
Wheel Lug Nuts	103
Wheel Speed Sensor To Knuckle②	89①

①—Inch lbs.
②—Front.
③—Rear.

DRUM BRAKES

INDEX

INSPECTION

1. Release parking brake.
2. Raise and support vehicle.
3. Remove rear wheels.
4. Remove brake drum. **Do not pry against brake backing plate.**
5. Inspect adjuster assembly, ensuring screw threads turn smoothly into nut over full threaded length.
6. Inspect wheel cylinder for damage, leakage or seizure, replace as required.

BRAKE SERVICE

Removal

1. Release parking brake.
2. Raise and support vehicle.
3. Remove rear wheels.
4. Remove brake drum. **Do not pry against brake backing plate.**
5. Remove lower return spring, **Fig. 1.**
6. Remove adjuster spring.
7. Remove leading brake shoe hold-down, spring and pin.
8. Remove adjuster assembly and lever. If difficult, pull leading shoe toward front of vehicle, then remove or turn star wheel on adjuster to shorten length.
9. Twist shoe from upper return spring engagement to remove.
10. Remove parking brake shoe upper return spring.
11. Remove park brake shoe hold-down cup, spring and pin.
12. Push park brake lever into cable spring to remove park brake cable from lever.
13. Remove park brake lever retainer and wave washer and separate from park brake shoe.
14. Reverse procedure to install.

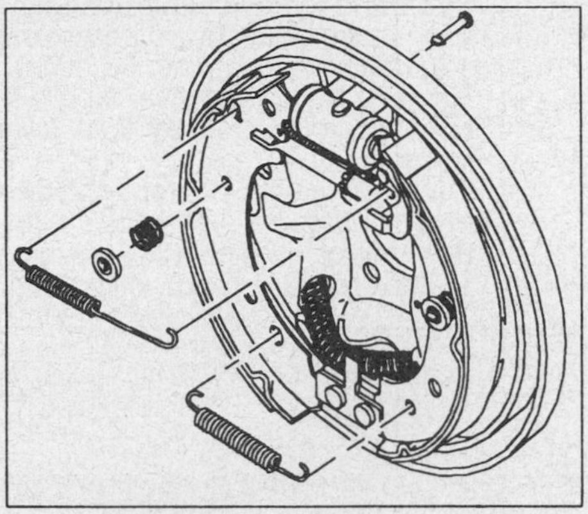

G34089100001000X

Fig. 1 Rear brake assembly

Installation

1. Lubricate adjuster assembly, adjuster lever surface, backing plate at shoe contact pads and park brake lever pin and brake shoe web contact surface.
2. Install park brake lever assembly.
3. Install park brake cable, through cable spring onto brake lever.
4. Install park brake shoe, hold-down pin, spring and cup.
5. Install long, straight end of upper return spring to park brake shoe.
6. Install other end of return spring to back of leading shoe.
7. While pulling leading shoe toward front of vehicle, install adjuster assembly.
8. Install adjuster lever.
9. Install leading brake shoe by installing hold-down pin, spring and cup.
10. Install adjuster spring.
11. Install lower return spring.
12. Using brake drum clearance tool No. SA91109NE or equivalent, drum inner diameter, then measure brake shoe assembly outer diameter, adjust brake adjuster to obtain .050 inch measurement less than drum inner diameter.

ADJUSTMENTS

Parking Brake

Refer to "Adjustments" under "Disc Brakes" for parking brake adjustment.

DRUM BRAKE SPECIFICATIONS

Model	Brake Drum I.D., Inch	Minimum Refinish Diameter, Inch	Discard Diameter, Inch
All	.787	.790	7.93

TIGHTENING SPECIFICATIONS

Component	Torque/Ft. Lbs.
Backing Plate To Knuckle	63
Bleed Valve	66①
Brake Line To Brake Hose (RL)	14
Brake Pipe To Brake Hose	168①
Wheel Cylinder To Backing Plate	89①
Wheel Lug Nuts	103

①—Inch lbs.

HYDRAULIC BRAKE SYSTEMS

INDEX

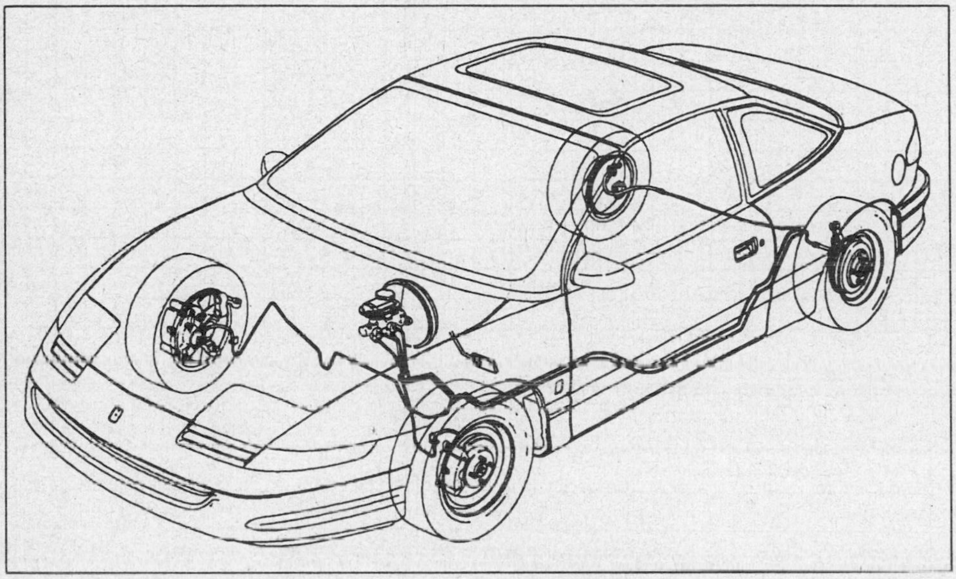
G34099100001000X

Fig. 1 Diagonally split brake system

DESCRIPTION

These vehicles use a diagonally split hydraulic system, **Fig. 1.** This system combines the left front and right rear brake on one hydraulic circuit, while the right front and left rear are on the other.

Installed in master cylinder are integral brake proportioning valves, which limit the fluid pressure to the rear brakes after a predetermined rear brake pressure has been reached. These valves are used to minimize the occurrence of rear wheel lock-up when the brakes are applied and the vehicle is lightly loaded in the rear.

A brake fluid level sensor, located in the brake fluid reservoir, will activate the brake warning lamp if the brake fluid becomes low. After the brake fluid level is corrected and a moderately high brake pedal force is applied, the brake warning lamp should go off.

TROUBLESHOOTING

When troubleshooting the hydraulic brake system, perform the following checks and inspections. If a malfunction still exists within the system, refer to the brake system diagnosis chart, **Fig. 2,** and the troubleshooting chart, **Fig. 3.**

ROAD TESTING

When testing brakes, ensure the road is level and dry. Test brakes at both light and heavy pedal pressure. Do not lock up brakes or slide tires during a brake test.

Check the tires on the vehicle before performing a brake test. Tires should be equally inflated, identical in size and of equal tread pattern. Excessive camber and caster will cause the brakes to pull. An overloaded vehicle will also brake erratically.

FLUID LEAKS

Start engine and depress the brake pedal. If the pedal gradually falls under constant pressure, the hydraulic system may be leaking. Raise and support vehicle and check all tubing lines and backing plates for signs of leakage. It may be necessary to lift or remove the carpeting or floor mats to check for booster or master cylinder leakage.

COMPONENT REPLACEMENT

MASTER CYLINDER

1. Disconnect battery ground cable.
2. Remove brake fluid level sensor electrical connector from master cylinder reservoir.
3. Remove brake line fitting nuts from master cylinder. **Plug open lines and fittings to prevent brake fluid loss and contamination.**
4. Remove two master cylinder to brake booster attaching nuts and master cylinder.
5. Reverse procedure to install.

FLUID RESERVOIR

1. Remove master cylinder from vehicle as described under "Master Cylinder."
2. Wipe reservoir cap clean, remove cap and inspect reservoir cap and diaphragm for cuts, nicks or deformation. Replace damaged parts as necessary.
3. Drain brake fluid from reservoir.
4. **On models equipped with anti-lock brakes,** remove modulator and motor pack from master cylinder.
5. **On all models,** remove brake fluid level sensor.
6. Place master cylinder in vice. **Do not clamp on master cylinder body.**
7. Drive out spring pins using a 1/8 inch punch, **Fig. 4.**
8. Pull reservoir out of cylinder body, then remove O-rings from grooves in reservoir bayonets, **Fig. 5.**
9. Clean reservoir with clean denatured alcohol and inspect reservoir for cracks or deformation. Replace reservoir if damaged.
10. Reverse procedure to install using new O-rings.

COMPONENT SERVICE

MASTER CYLINDER OVERHAUL

Disassemble

1. Remove master cylinder from vehicle as described under "Master Cylinder."
2. Wipe reservoir cap clean, remove cap and inspect reservoir cap and diaphragm for cuts, nicks or deformation. Replace damaged parts as necessary.
3. Drain brake fluid from reservoir.
4. **On models equipped with anti-lock brakes,** remove modulator and motor pack from master cylinder.

X — Most Probable Cause(s)
● — Possible Causes

COMPLAINT–CONDITION / CAUSE	Low Brake Fluid Level	Leaking Brake Line or Connection	Leaking Wheel Cylinder or Piston Seal	Leaking Master Cylinder	Air in Brake System	Contaminated or Improper Brake Fluid	Leaking Vacuum System	Restricted Air Passage in Vacuum Booster	Damaged Vacuum Booster	Worn Out Brake Lining	Glazed Brake Lining	Uneven Brake Lining Wear	Incorrect Lining Material	Contaminated Brake Lining	Linings Damaged by Abusive Use	Excessive Brake Lining Dust	Heat Spotted/Scored Drums/Rotors	Out-of-Round Brake Drums	Improper Rotor Thickness Variation	Excessive Lateral Runout	Faulty Automatic Adjusters	Incorrect Wheel Cylinder Sizes	Weak or Incorrect Brake Shoe Springs	Brake Asm. Bolts Missing or Loose	Insufficient Brake Shoe Guide Lubricant	Restricted Fluid Passage	Sticking Wheel Cylinder Piston	Incorrect Stoplamp Switch Adjustment	Brake Pedal Linkage Interference/Binding	Improperly Adjusted Park Brake
Excessive Brake Pedal Travel	●	●	●	●	X							●								●	●			●						
Brake Pedal Travel Gradually Increases		X	X	X																						●	●			
Excessive Brake Pedal Effort	●						X	●	●	●	X		●		●	●						●				●	●		●	
Excessive Braking Action			●						●	●		●	●	X	X	X	●					●	●							
Brakes Slow to Respond						●	●	X	●		●															●	●		●	
Brakes Slow to Release						●		●	●														●		●	●	●		X	
Brakes Drag						●			●												●		X	●	●	●	●	●	X	●
Uneven Braking Action (Side–to–Side)		●	●							●	●	●	●	X	●	X	●				●	●	●	●	●	●	●			
Uneven Braking Action (Front–to–Rear)		●			●					●	●	●	●	X	●	X	●				●	●	●	●	●	●	●			
Scraping Noise from Brakes										●		●		●	●	●							X	●	X					
Brakes Squeak During Application										●	●	●		●	●	●	●			●			●		X					
Brakes Squeak During Stop										●	●	●	●	●	●	X	●	●					X	●						
Brakes Pulsate (Roughness)																	X	X	X	●				●						
Brakes Groan at End of Stop										●			●	●	●	●	●							●						
Brake Warning Lamp Glows	X	●	●	●																										

G34099100002000X

Fig. 2 Brake diagnosis chart

5. **On all models,** remove brake fluid level sensor.
6. Remove reservoir as described under "Fluid Reservoir."
7. While depressing master cylinder piston, remove retainer clip, **Fig. 6.**
8. Apply low pressure non-lubricated compressed air into upper brake fluid output port, **Fig. 7.** This will facilitate removal of primary and secondary piston assemblies as well as spring and spring retainer.
9. Clean all parts with clean denatured alcohol. Dry with unlubricated, low pressure compressed air. Blow out all passages in cylinder body.
10. Inspect pistons and seals for nicks, cuts, cracks, wear or corrosion. Replace all worn or damaged parts.
11. Inspect master cylinder bore for scoring or corrosion. If cylinder bore is damaged, replace master cylinder. Do not hone master cylinder bore.

Assemble

1. Lubricate secondary seal and master cylinder bore with clean brake fluid.
2. Install spring and secondary piston assembly into master cylinder bore, **Fig. 8.**
3. Lubricate primary seal and master cylinder bore with clean brake fluid.
4. Install primary piston assembly into master cylinder bore.
5. While depressing master cylinder piston, install retainer clip.
6. Remove reservoir as described under "Fluid Reservoir."
7. Install brake fluid level sensor.

Complaint/Condition	Possible Cause(s)	Correction(s)
Pedal Feel		
Excessive Pedal Travel	Air in brake system.	Bleed brake system.
	Front or rear brakes not adjusting to lining wear.	Check adjuster mechanism and replace or repair as needed.
	Leaking wheel cylinder or caliper piston seal.	Replace wheel cylinder or overhaul caliper
	Leaking at brake line or hose connections.	Tighten connection. Replace line or hose.
	Internal master cylinder seal leak.	Overhaul or replace master cylinder.
	Uneven lining wear or damaged lining.	Replace lining.
	Rotor or drum out of specifications (i.e. rotor too thin, parallelism, out of round, bell shaped etc.).	Replace rotor, or drum.
	Improper vacuum booster to master cylinder length.	Replace booster and pushrod.
Pedal Creeps Down	Internal master cylinder seal leak or defective master cylinder bore.	Repair or replace master cylinder.
	Leaking wheel cylinder or caliper piston seal.	Replace wheel cylinder or overhaul caliper
	Leaking at brake line or hose connections.	Tighten connection. Replace lines or hose.
	Damaged vacuum booster check valve or grommet.	Replace check valve and grommet.
Pedal Pulses	Rotor or drum out of specifications (i.e. lateral runout, parallelism, out of round, bell shaped etc.).	Replace or turn rotor or drum.
	Worn out linings or linings wearing unevenly.	Replace linings.
	Wheel bearings worn.	Replace wheel bearing.
	Damaged suspension, knuckle or axle.	Replace defective parts.

G34099100003010X

Fig. 3 Brake pedal feel diagnosis chart (Part 1 of 6)

Complaint/Condition	Possible Cause(s)	Correction(s)
Excessive Pedal Effort	Leaking or damaged vacuum booster (i.e. cut diaphragm, restricted vacuum hose, damaged vacuum check valve, cracked power piston, restricted air passages)	Replace booster.
	Worn out brake linings (glazed)	Replace linings.
	Damage to braking surface of rotor or drum.	Replace rotor or drum.
	Crimped brake line or collapsed brake hose.	Replace line or hose.
	Engine out of specifications.	Check engine to specification.
Pedal Goes to the Floor	Low fluid level, large amount of air in system.	Bleed brake system.
	Broken brake line or brake hose.	Replace line or hose.
	Cut, torn or nicked master cylinder secondary seals.	Repair or replace master cylinder.
	Brake pedal not connected to push rod.	Check connection and repair.
	Wheel cylinder or caliper piston falls out.	Check assembly and repair.

G34099100003020X

Fig. 3 Brake pedal feel diagnosis chart (Part 2 of 6)

Complaint/Condition	Possible Cause(s)	Correction(s)
Noise		
Squeal/Scrape While Not Braking	Worn linings, sensor scraping on rotor (normal).	Replace linings.
	Loose drum brake component (spring, lever, adjuster, etc.).	Check drum brake and repair.
	Loose front suspension attachments.	Tighten attachments or replace.
	Caliper interference with rotor.	Check clearance and repair.
	Bent or cracked suspension parts.	Replace components.
	Drum or rotor contacting backing plate or dust shield.	Check clearance and repair.
Squeal/Scrape While Braking	Linings worn out, shoe contacting drum or rotor.	Replace linings.
	Lack of lubrication on backing plate or on adjuster screw.	Lubricate backing plate or adjuster screw.
	Lack of lubrication on caliper sliding surfaces.	Lubricate.
	Lack of lubrication on brake pedal attachments.	Lubricate.
	Damage to insulator between disc brake shoe and caliper piston.	Replace insulator and pads as needed.
	Hot spots or worn surface on drum or rotor.	Replace rotor or drum.
	Weak hold down springs or worn drum brake components.	Replace drum brake springs.
Chatters/Rattles	Hot spots or worn surface on drum or rotor.	Replace drum or rotor.
	Rotor or drum out of specifications (i.e. lateral runout, parallelism, out of round, bell shaped, etc.).	Replace or turn rotor or drum.
	Lining contaminated with foreign substances.	Replace linings.
	Linings wearing unevenly.	Replace linings.
	Bent or loose brake shoes.	Replace show and linings.
	Weak or broken retractor springs.	Replace drum brake springs.
	Loose brake cable, brake line, or ABS wiring.	Check cable or line connection and tighten or replace as needed.
Groans (at/near stop)	Linings worn out.	Replace linings.
	Incorrect or damaged lining material.	Replace linings.
	Hot spots or worn surface on drum or rotor.	Replace drum or rotor.
	Cracked or bent knuckle or suspension parts.	Replace suspension component.
	Loose suspension.	Tighten suspension or replace.

G34099100003030X

Fig. 3 Brake pedal feel diagnosis chart (Part 3 of 6)

8. **On models equipped with anti-lock brakes,** install modulator and motor pack from master cylinder.
9. **On all models,** install master cylinder as outlined under "Master Cylinder."

WHEEL CYLINDER OVERHAUL

Wheel cylinders on these models are non-serviceable and must be replaced as an assembly.

BRAKE SYSTEM BLEED

Brake fluid is corrosive to painted surfaces. Care must be taken not to allow brake fluid to come in contact with painted surfaces on vehicle.

MANUAL PROCEDURE

1. Fill master cylinder reservoir with Dot 3 type brake fluid. Keep reservoir at least half full during bleeding procedure.
2. If master cylinder is suspected to have air trapped inside, it must be bled before bleeding brake lines. Bleed master cylinder as follows:
   a. Depress brake pedal slowly one time and hold.
   b. Loosen front brake line at master cylinder and allow brake fluid to flow from front master cylinder port, then tighten front brake line to master cylinder.
   c. Repeat sequence until all air is removed from master cylinder bore.
3. Loosen, then slightly retighten bleeder valves at all four wheels. Repair any broken, stripped or frozen valves at this time.
4. Proceed to appropriate wheel first and follow set sequence according to "Bleed Sequence."
5. Place transparent tube over bleeder valve, then allow tube to hang down into transparent container. Ensure end of tube is submerged in clean brake fluid.
6. Instruct an assistant to slowly depress brake pedal one time and hold.
7. Crack open bleeder valve, purging air from cylinder. Retighten bleeder screw and slowly release pedal.
8. Repeat steps 6 and 7 until all air is bled from system.
9. Check fluid level after bleeding each wheel and fill as necessary.

PRESSURE PROCEDURE

Pressure bleeding equipment must be the diaphragm type. It must have a rubber diaphragm between the air supply and the brake fluid to prevent air, moisture and other contaminants from entering brake system.

1. Clean brake fluid reservoir cap and area around cap, then remove cap.
2. Fill master cylinder reservoir with Dot 3 type brake fluid.
3. Install bleeder adapter tool No. SA9150BR or equivalent to brake fluid reservoir, **Fig. 9.**
4. Connect pressure bleeder to adapter and set pressure to 20-25 psi.

Complaint/Condition	Possible Cause(s)	Correction(s)
Performance		
Brake Pull Left/Right	Caliper pistons sticking.	Overhaul caliper and replace piston.
	Loose wheel bearings or suspension attachments.	Replace wheel bearings or tighten suspension attachments.
	Worn suspension components.	Replace suspension components.
	Loose steering or steering gear.	Repair or replace steering components.
	Uneven wear on tires, tires not properly inflated or incorrect tires for vehicle.	Check tire and replace if necessary.
	Uneven worn linings.	Replace linings.
	Front suspension out of line.	Align suspension.
	Restricted brake line or hose.	Replace line or hose.
Brakes Grab	Contaminated brake linings.	Replace linings.
	Damage to braking surface of rotors or drums.	Replace rotors or drums.
	Rotor or drum out of specifications (i.e. lateral runout, parallelism, out of round, bell shaped, etc.).	Replace or turn rotor or drum.
	Damaged vacuum booster.	Replace booster.
Brakes Drag	Caliper pistons stuck.	Overhaul caliper and replace piston.
	Corroded caliper bolts. Caliper will not retract.	Replace bolts and bolt boots.
	Compensating port or bypass hole in master cylinder clogged.	Clean master cylinder and rebuild.
	Worn or damaged drum brake return springs.	Replace drum brake springs.
	Contaminated or improper brake fluid, rubber seals are swollen.	Flush brake system and replace all rubber parts including hoses.
	Parking brake not releasing.	Check cable and cable attachments.
	Self-adjusters over adjusting for lining wear.	Overhaul or replace adjusters.
	Improper vacuum booster push rod length.	Gage booster push rod and replace if needed.
Brake Action Uneven (Front - Rear)	Uneven wear on tires, tires improperly inflated or incorrect tires installed.	Check tires and replace if needed.
	Proportioning valve not functioning properly.	Replace master cylinder.
	Linings wearing unevenly front to rear.	Replace linings.
	Fluid leak in system.	Check system for leaks and repair or replace components.
	Hot spots or worn surface on drum or rotor.	Replace drum or rotor.

G34099100003040X

Fig. 3 Brake pedal feel diagnosis chart (Part 4 of 6)

5. Loosen front brake line at master cylinder and allow brake fluid to flow from front master cylinder port until all air is bled, then tighten front brake line to master cylinder.
6. Open each bleeder valve until all air is bled, then tighten bleeder screw.
7. Remove pressure bleeder and ensure fluid level is full.

BLEED SEQUENCE

All models: RR-LF-LR-RF.

HYDRAULIC BRAKE SYSTEM FLUSH

If brake fluid is old, rusty or contaminated, or whenever new parts are installed in hydraulic system, the system must be flushed. Bleed brakes, allowing at least one quart of clean brake fluid to pass through system. Any rubber parts in hydraulic system which were exposed to contaminated fluid must be replaced.

Complaint/Condition	Possible Cause(s)	Correction(s)
Brakes Slow to Release	Caliper piston sticking.	Overhaul caliper and replace piston.
	Corroded caliper bolts. Caliper will not retract.	Replace bolts and bolt boots.
	Contaminated or improper brake fluid, rubber seals are swollen.	Flush brake system and replace all rubber parts including hoses.
	Worn caliper piston seals.	Overhaul calipers.
	Worn or damaged drum brake return springs.	Replace drum brake springs.
	Worn or damaged master cylinder seals.	Overhaul master cylinder.
	Damage to mechanical action of brake pedal.	Check pedal and repair or replace.
Slow Response/Excessive Stopping Distance	Rotor not turned to proper surface finish.	Check rotor surface finish and turn rotor or replace.
	Linings not adjusting properly, damaged self-adjusters or worn piston seal.	Overhaul drum brake or caliper.
	Caliper pistons sticking.	Overhaul caliper and replace piston.
	Worn or glazed linings.	Replace linings.
	Proportioning valve not functioning properly.	Replace master cylinder.
Odor	Linings over heated.	
	Lining contaminated with foreign substances.	Replace lining.
Poor Fuel Economy	Linings over heated.	
	Egg shaped drum or bent rotor/knuckle.	Replace drum, rotor or knuckle.

G34099100003050X

Fig. 3 Brake pedal feel diagnosis chart (Part 5 of 6)

Complaint/Condition	Possible Cause(s)	Correction(s)
Telltale		
Red (Brake) Telltale On	Park brake on.	Release park brake.
	Low brake fluid level in master cylinder (check for leaks).	Fill reservoir. Check for leaks.
	Improperly adjusted park brake switch.	Check park brake switch connection and adjustment.
	Damaged park brake switch or switch circuit.	Replace switch or repair circuit.
	Antilock brake system (ABS) problem	Refer to ABS
Amber (ABS) Telltale On (Solid/Flashing)	Refer to ABS	
Parking Brake		
Does Not Hold	Park brake not adjusted properly.	Adjust park brake.
	Brakes not adjusting properly.	Check brake adjusters and repair or replace as needed.
	Linings worn out.	Replace linings.
	Linings contaminated with foreign material.	Replace linings.
	Cable disconnected from lever.	Connect cable.
	Lever bent or loose.	Replace lever.
	Cable slipping.	Replace cable.
Does Not Release	Park brake cables binding.	Check cable and cable attachments.
	Release lever broken or binding.	Replace park brake lever.
Parking Brake Lever Hard to Apply	Lack of lubrication on apply mechanism.	Lubricate apply mechanism.
	Park brake cables binding.	Check cables and cable attachments.

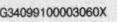

G34099100003060X

Fig. 3 Brake pedal feel diagnosis chart (Part 6 of 6)

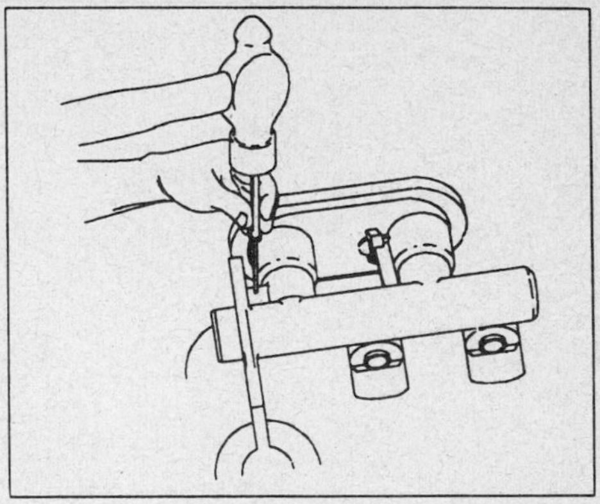

G34099100005000X

Fig. 4 Master cylinder reservoir spring pin removal

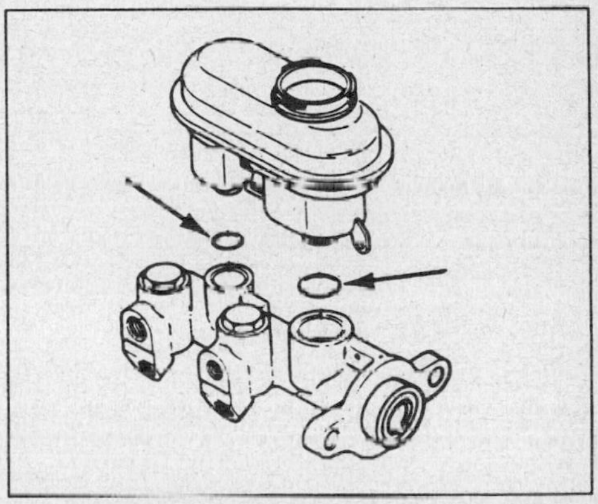

G34099100006000X

Fig. 5 Removing reservoir & O-rings from cylinder body

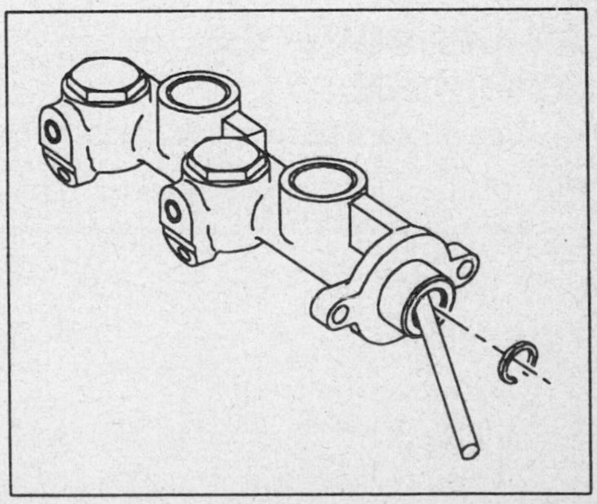

G34099100007000X

Fig. 6 Master cylinder retainer clip removal

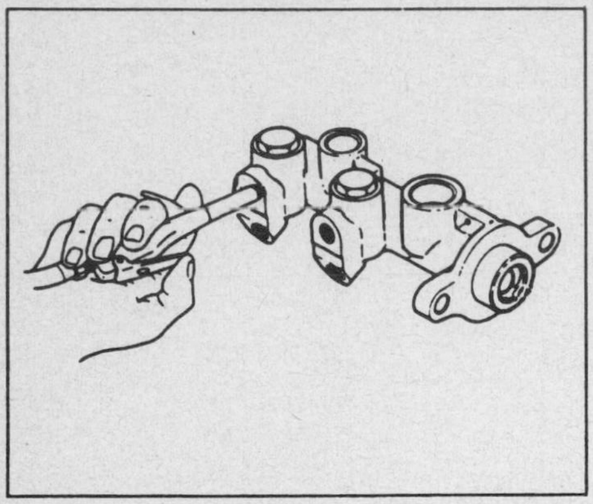

Fig. 7 Removing master cylinder pistons w/air pressure

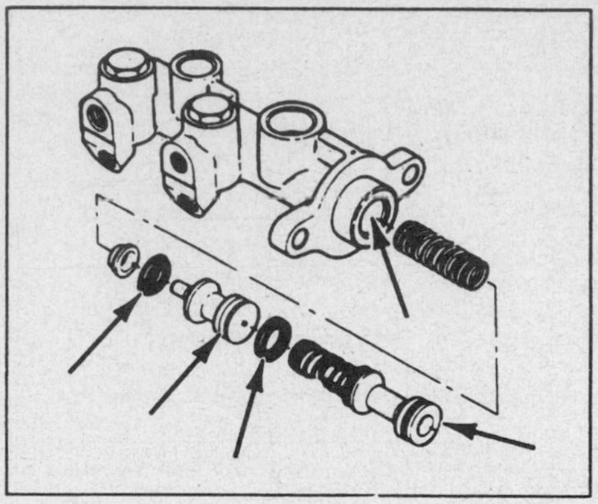

Fig. 8 Master cylinder piston & seal installation

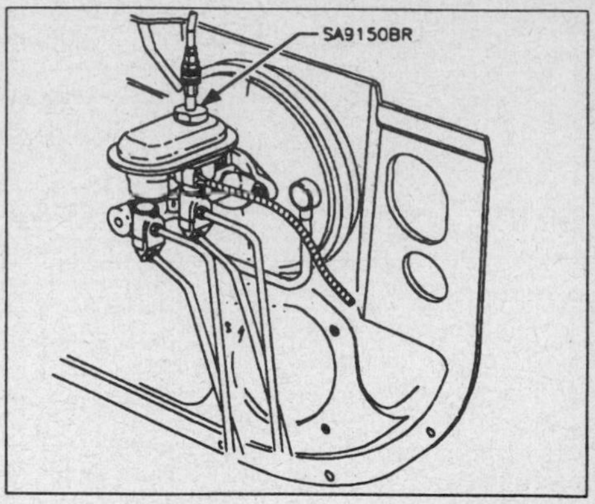
SA9150BR

Fig. 9 Brake pressure bleeder adapter installation

POWER BRAKE UNITS

INDEX

DESCRIPTION

The vacuum brake booster is a single diaphragm vacuum suspended unit. Engine vacuum is provided to the booster through a hose and a vacuum check valve. When the brakes are not applied, internal valves within the booster provide vacuum to both sides of the diaphragm. When the brakes are applied, air at atmospheric pressure is applied to one side of the diaphragm. Since a higher pressure now exists on one side of the diaphragm than the other, a force is created, assisting the brake application.

POWER BRAKE UNIT SERVICE

BRAKE BOOSTER OVERHAUL

Vacuum brake boosters on these vehicles are non-serviceable and must be replaced as an assembly.

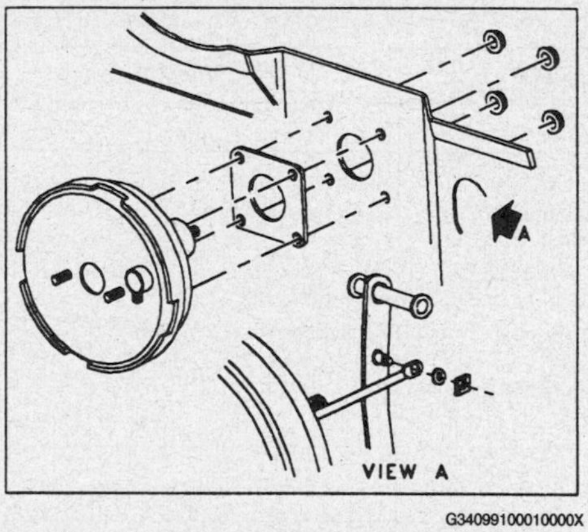
A
VIEW A

Fig. 1 Brake booster mounting

BRAKE BOOSTER, REPLACE

1. Disconnect battery ground cable and remove air cleaner.
2. **On models with anti-lock brakes,** remove battery, battery box and tray.
3. **On all models,** remove two master cylinder to brake booster nuts and move master cylinder away from booster without bending brake lines.
4. Disconnect vacuum hose from vacuum check valve.
5. Remove booster pushrod retainer and washer, then remove pushrod from brake pedal pin, **Fig. 1.**
6. Remove four nuts attaching brake booster, then remove booster from vehicle.
7. Reverse procedure to install. **Torque** booster to body nuts and master cylinder to booster nuts to 20 ft. lbs.

ANTI-LOCK BRAKES

NOTE: On Air Bag Equipped Models, Refer To "Air Bag System Precautions" Located In The Front Of This Manual For System Disarming & Arming Procedures.

INDEX

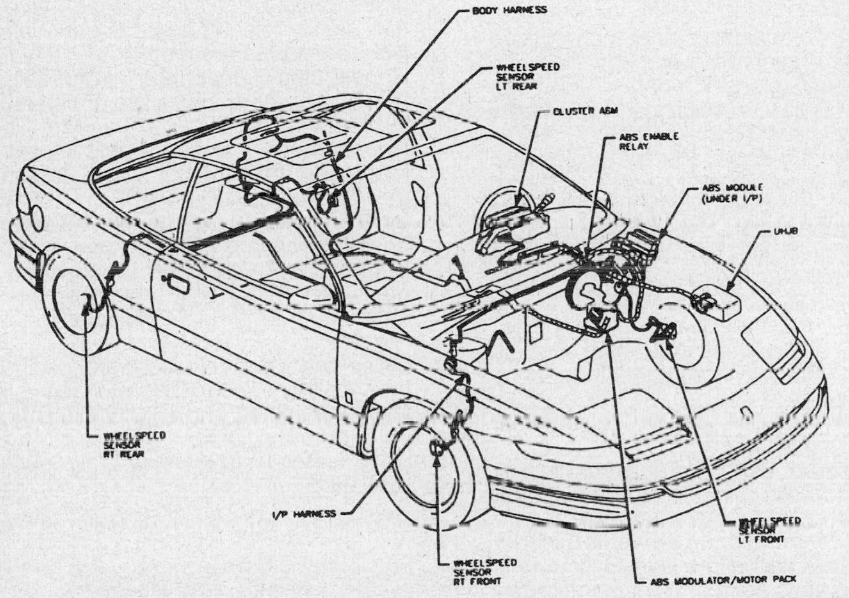

BODY HARNESS
WHEELSPEED SENSOR LT REAR
CLUSTER ABM
ABS ENABLE RELAY
ABS MODULE (UNDER I/P)
WHEELSPEED SENSOR RT REAR
I/P HARNESS
WHEELSPEED SENSOR LT FRONT
WHEELSPEED SENSOR RT FRONT
ABS MODULATOR/MOTOR PACK
G34029100001000X

Fig. 1 Anti-lock brake system

GENERAL INFORMATION		KEY ON	EXPLANATION
T–Codes	xxx	No	Indicates if trouble codes are present
LF Wheel SPD MPH	xx	0 MPH	Speed of left front wheel
RF Wheel SPD MPH	xx	0 MPH	Speed of right front wheel
LR Wheel SPD MPH	xx	0 MPH	Speed of left rear wheel
RR Wheel SPD MPH	xx	0 MPH	Speed of right rear wheel
Vehicle REF MPH	xx	0 MPH	Filtered average of all 4 wheel speeds
LF Solenoid	xxx	Off	Solenoid status (on during ABS stop)
RF Solenoid	xxx	Off	Solenoid status (on during ABS stop)
LF Command AMP	xx.x	0.0	Desired motor current during ABS stop
LF Sensed AMP	xx.x	0.0	Actual motor current during ABS stop
RF Command AMP	xx.x	0.0	Desired motor current during ABS stop
RF Sensed AMP	xx.x	0.0	Actual motor current during ABS stop
R Command AMP	xx.x	0.0	Desired motor current during ABS stop
R Sensed AMP	xx.x	0.0	Actual motor current during ABS stop
BAT Enable V	xx.x	12.6	Ignition voltage to ABS control module
LF Brake	xxxxxxx	Release	Motor direction during ABS stop
RF Brake	xxxxxxx	Release	Motor direction during ABS stop
Brake Switch	xxx	Off	Current status of brake switch
Brake Switch Cycled	xxx	No	Has brake switch been on this IGN cycle?
Brake Switch Open	xxx	No	Indicate an open brake switch circuit
ABS TT	xxx	On	Status of ABS telltale
ABS TT Flash	xxx	Off	Indicated telltale is flashing
Enable Relay	xxx	On	Indicated status of ABS Enable Relay
ABS Stop	xxx	No	Indicated if vehicle is in an ABS stop
Brake TT	xxx	Off	Indicates status of ABS telltale
Brake TT Open	xxx	No	Indicates an open brake telltale circuit
25 MPH Reached	xxx	No	Has 25 MPH been reached this IGN cycle?

G34029100002000X

Fig. 2 ABS scan tool information

PRECAUTIONS

AIR BAG SYSTEMS

Refer to "Air Bag System Precautions" in the front of this manual for system disarming and arming procedures.

DESCRIPTION

The Anti-Lock Brake System (ABS) **Fig. 1**, minimizes wheel lockup during heavy braking on most road surfaces. The system performs this function by monitoring wheel speed and controlling the brake fluid pressure during braking. This allows the driver to retain directional stability and better steering capability.

TROUBLESHOOTING

When troubleshooting the ABS braking system refer to "Diagnosis & Testing".

DIAGNOSIS & TESTING

This system contains a sophisticated on-board diagnostic system that can by accessed with a bidirectional "SCAN" tool. **To properly diagnose the ABS system, a SATURN bidirectional scan tool or equivalent is necessary.** The scan tool can be used to identify system faults as specifically as possible including whether or not the fault is intermittent. The scan tool can also be used to monitor the input and output signals of the Anti-Lock Brake Control Module (ABCM), manually control system components and perform automated functional tests. Using the scan tool allows for accurate fault confirmation and repair verification. Refer to **Fig. 2** for ABS scan tool information.

VISUAL/PHYSICAL UNDERHOOD INSPECTION

Before beginning any system diagnosis, it is important that a careful visual and physical inspection be performed. Inspect all vacuum hoses for correct routing, pinches, cuts or disconnects. Inspect all wires in the engine compartment and to wheel speed sensors for proper routing and connections.

ANTI-LOCK TELLTALE LAMP & RED BRAKE WARNING LAMP

The Anti-Lock Telltale lamp, located in the instrument cluster, has several functions. If the lamp comes on solid, a malfunction has occurred and the ABS system has been disabled and should be serviced as soon as possible. If the telltale lamp is flashing, a malfunction has occurred, but the ABS system is still operational. The vehicle should still be serviced as soon as possible. Because the telltale lamp is also used to perform a bulb and system check, it will come on with the key on and the engine not running. When the engine is started, the lamp will turn off after approximately three seconds. If the lamp remains on or begins to flash, the self-diagnostic system has detected a malfunction.

The red brake telltale lamp will light if any of the following conditions are met: low brake fluid in the master cylinder, parking brake switch is closed, activated by the ABCM.

READING DIAGNOSTIC TROUBLE CODES

When performing ABS system diagnosis refer to wiring circuits, **Figs. 3 through 5**, system electrical connectors, **Fig. 6**, and ABCM pin identification **Fig. 7.**

To access diagnostic trouble codes, connect the SATURN scan tool or suitable equivalent to the ALDL connector located under the instrument panel. The scan tool can now communicate directly to the ABCM. Any code(s) stored in the ABCM memory can now be displayed. When an ABS fault is detected, the ABS telltale lamp is lit and code(s) are placed in the General Information Table (Current Codes). When the ignition is switched off, the current codes are moved to the MALF History Table (Past Codes) and cleared from the General Information Table (Current Codes).

Refer to the "Diagnostic Chart Index" for code description and chart location.

CLEARING DIAGNOSTIC TROUBLE CODES

Current codes are cleared every time the ignition is turned off. To clear MALF History (Past Codes) select "Clear Codes" function on the scan tool. Past codes will clear themselves after 100 ignition cycles with no fault occurring. **Disconnecting power to the ABCM has no effect on stored codes.**

INTERMITTENTS

Most intermittent malfunctions are caused by loose or damaged electrical wiring and connectors. The scan tool can be used in several ways to aid in intermittent diagnosis. Connect scan tool to the ALDL connector with the engine not running, then manipulate wiring harnesses or components under the hood while observing the scan tool. Leaving scan tool connected to the ALDL connector, drive vehicle under conditions similar to those present when the ABS fault first occurred. If the problem seems to be related to certain parameters that can be checked with the scan tool, they should be checked at this time. If there does not seem to be any correlation between the problem and any specific circuit, the scan tool can be checked on each position, watching for a period of time to see if there is any change in the readings that would indicate an intermittent malfunction.

The ABCM has the ability to take a snapshot of data with the last code stored. This can be done using the Malf History function of the scan tool and can be very useful when trying to diagnose an intermittent code.

SYSTEM SERVICE

Brake System Bleed

Before bleeding the rear brakes, the rear displacement cylinder pistons must be returned to the topmost position. Using a SATURN scan tool or suitable equivalent, perform "RUN ABS MOTORS, PISTON UP-HOME." This will run the pistons to the top of their travel.

Use only Dot 3 brake fluid from a clean and sealed container. Do not use Dot 5 brake fluid.

ABS SYSTEM BLEEDING

Pressure Bleeding

1. Remove master cylinder cover and ensure reservoir is properly filled.
2. Connect bleeder adapter tool No. SA9150BR or equivalent to master cylinder reservoir.
3. Connect bleeder adapter to pressure bleeding equipment.
4. Connect a clear plastic bleeder hose to modulator assembly rearward bleeder valve and submerge other end of hose into clean container partially filled with brake fluid.
5. Adjust pressure bleeding equipment to 5-10 psi, then wait approximately 30 seconds to ensure that there is no leakage.
6. Adjust pressure bleed equipment to 30-35 psi.
7. To bleed ABS hydraulic modulator and master cylinder, proceed as follows:
   a. Slowly open rearward bleeder valve and allow fluid to flow until no air is seen in fluid, then **torque** valve to 65 inch lbs.
   b. Attach bleeder hose to modulator assembly forward bleeder hose.
   c. Slowly open forward bleeder valve and allow fluid to flow until no air is seen in fluid, then **torque** valve to 65 inch lbs.
8. To bleed wheel brakes, proceed as follows:
   a. Raise and support vehicle.
   b. Attach bleeder hose to bleeder valve of right rear wheel and submerge other end of hose into clean container partially filled with brake fluid.
   c. Loosen bleeder valve and allow fluid to flow until air bubbles are no longer present, then close valve.
   d. Repeat steps b and c, first for left rear wheel, then the right front caliper, then the left front caliper.
9. Road test vehicle, to verify brake performance.

Manual Bleeding

1. Ensure that brake fluid reservoir is properly filled.
2. Attach bleeder hose to modulator assembly rearward bleed valve and submerge other end of hose in clean container partially filled with brake fluid.
3. Pump brake pedal several times, then slowly open bleeder valve 1/2 to 3/4 turns.
4. Depress brake pedal and hold until fluid begins to flow.
5. Close valve and repeat steps 3 and 4 on forward valve. Once fluid is seen to flow from both the forward and rearward valves, modulator valve and master cylinder are filled sufficiently with fluid. However, these components may not be purged of air. At this point, bleed the wheel brakes.
6. Raise and support vehicle.
7. Attach bleeder hose to bleeder valve of right rear wheel and submerge other end of hose in clean container partially filled with brake fluid.
8. Open bleeder valve and slowly depress brake pedal, then close valve and slowly release brake pedal. Wait five seconds to proceed.
9. Repeat step 8 until brake pedal feels firm and no air bubbles are observed in bleeder hose.
10. Repeat steps 7, 8 and 9, first for left rear wheel, then the right front caliper, then the left front caliper.
11. Lower vehicle and attach bleeder hose to rearward bleeder valve.
12. Depress brake pedal using moderate pressure, then slowly open bleeder valve 1/2 to 3/4 turns and allow fluid to flow.
13. Close valve and release brake pedal, then wait five seconds to proceed.
14. Repeat steps 12 and 13 until all air is purged from system.
15. Road test vehicle to verify brake performance.

Component Replace

ANTI-LOCK BRAKE CONTROL MODULE (ABCM)

The ABCM is located under the instrument panel, to the left of the steering column. The ABCM and Powertrain Control Module (PCM) are located in the same carrier. The ABCM is outboard of the PCM, closest to the lefthand side kick panel.

1. Disconnect battery ground cable.
2. Remove connector position assurance locking pin from 2-way ABCM connector, then disconnect connector, **Fig. 8.**
3. Disconnect 32-way ABCM connector, then turn ABCM retaining screw 1/4 turn.
4. Remove module by pulling downward. **Avoid snagging wiring.**
5. Reverse procedure to install. **The ABCM contains a Electronically Erasable Programmable Read Only Memory (EE PROM) that must be reprogrammed when a service replacement module is installed or a Code 82 will result.**

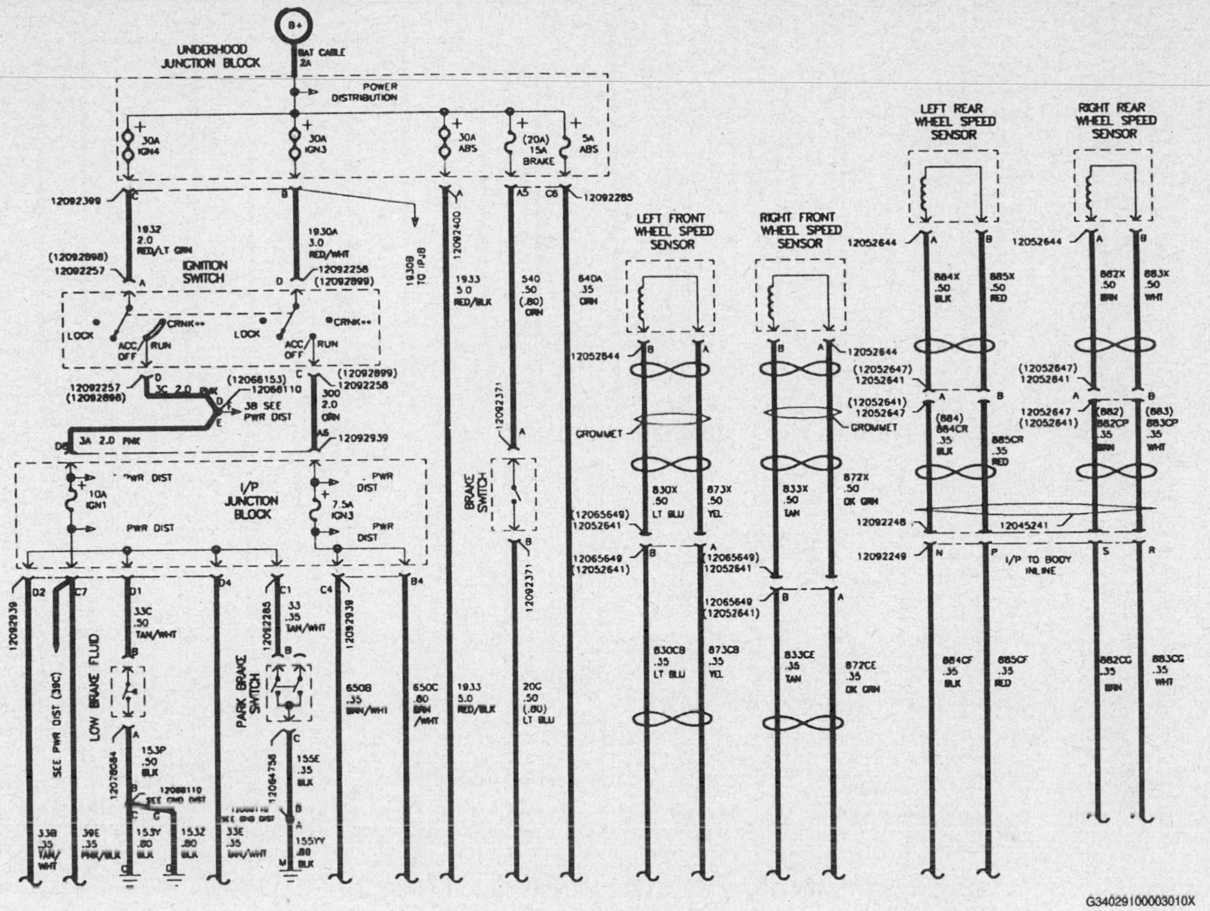
B+
UNDERHOOD
JUNCTION BLOCK
BAT CABLE
2A
POWER
DISTRIBUTION
30A
IGN4
30A
IGN3
30A
ABS
(20A)
15A
BRAKE
5A
ABS
IGNITION
SWITCH
LOCK
ACC
OFF
RUN
CRNK
I/P
JUNCTION
BLOCK
PWR DIST
10A
IGN1
7.5A
IGN3
BRAKE
SWITCH
LOW BRAKE FLUID
PARK BRAKE
SWITCH
SEE PWR DIST (39C)
LEFT FRONT
WHEEL SPEED
SENSOR
RIGHT FRONT
WHEEL SPEED
SENSOR
LEFT REAR
WHEEL SPEED
SENSOR
RIGHT REAR
WHEEL SPEED
SENSOR
GROMMET
I/P TO BODY
INLINE
G34029100003010X

Fig. 3 Anti-lock brake system wiring circuit (Part 1 of 2). 1992

ANTI-LOCK BRAKE SOLENOID VALVE

1. Disconnect battery ground cable.
2. Clean dirt from solenoid valve and area around solenoid.
3. Disconnect electrical connector from solenoid valve, **Fig. 9.**
4. Remove two solenoid to modulator Torx head retaining screws, then the solenoid from the modulator.
5. Reverse procedure to install, and **torque** Torx retaining screws to 45 inch lbs. **There are two different designs of solenoids used on this ABS system. The solenoids are not interchangeable. Each is identified by an eight digit number on the top of the solenoid. Ensure correct solenoid is installed.**

ANTI-LOCK BRAKE CONTROL & MASTER CYLINDER ASSEMBLY

The control assembly drive gears are under spring tension and will turn during disassembly if not unloaded. To remove tension, use the SATURN scan tool or equivalent to perform the "RUN ABS MOTORS, PISTONS DOWN-REL" before removing the brake control assembly. Do not drive vehicle with anti-lock brake control assembly in the tension released position. Excessive brake pedal travel and reduced brake effectiveness could occur. Always perform "RUN ABS MOTORS, PISTONS UP-HOME" before driving vehicle.

1. Disconnect battery cables, then remove battery from vehicle.
2. Disconnect two electrical connectors from solenoid valves, then the brake fluid level sensor connector at the master cylinder.
3. Remove CPA locking pin from 6-way motor pack connector, **Fig. 10,** then detach connector from motor pack.
4. Place a shop cloth on top of motor pack assembly, then remove brake line fitting nuts from modulator. **Plug open lines to prevent brake fluid loss and contamination.**
5. Remove two brake control assembly to brake booster attaching nuts.
6. Remove brake control and master cylinder assembly from vehicle.
7. Reverse procedure to install. **Torque** assembly to brake booster attaching nuts to 20 ft. lbs. and brake line fitting nuts to 18 ft. lbs.

WHEEL SPEED SENSORS

Front

1. Disconnect battery ground cable, then raise and support vehicle.
2. Disconnect wheel speed sensor electrical connector, **Fig. 11.**
3. Remove wheel speed sensor to steering knuckle Torx head bolt, then the wheel speed sensor. **When removing speed sensor, be careful not to damage speed sensor ring. Even a minor scratch on the sensor ring can cause a loss of ABS operation. The front speed sensor has a locating pin which may become stuck in the steering knuckle. This pin may separate from sensor during removal and remain in the knuckle. If this pin cannot be pulled out of the knuckle it must be drilled out using an 8mm drill bit. Be careful not to enlarge the pin hole when drilling pin out of knuckle.**
4. Reverse procedure to install. **Torque** Torx head bolt to 89 inch lbs.

Rear

1. Disconnect battery ground cable, then raise and support vehicle.
2. Remove tire and wheel assembly, then disconnect electrical connector from speed sensor.
3. Remove two caliper to knuckle mounting bolts, then suspend caliper from strut spring with wire.
4. Remove rotor from hub, then the four hub to knuckle attaching bolts, **Fig. 12.**
5. Remove hub and bearing assembly.
6. Reverse procedure to install, **torque** hub to knuckle bolts and caliper to knuckle bolts to 63 ft. lbs.

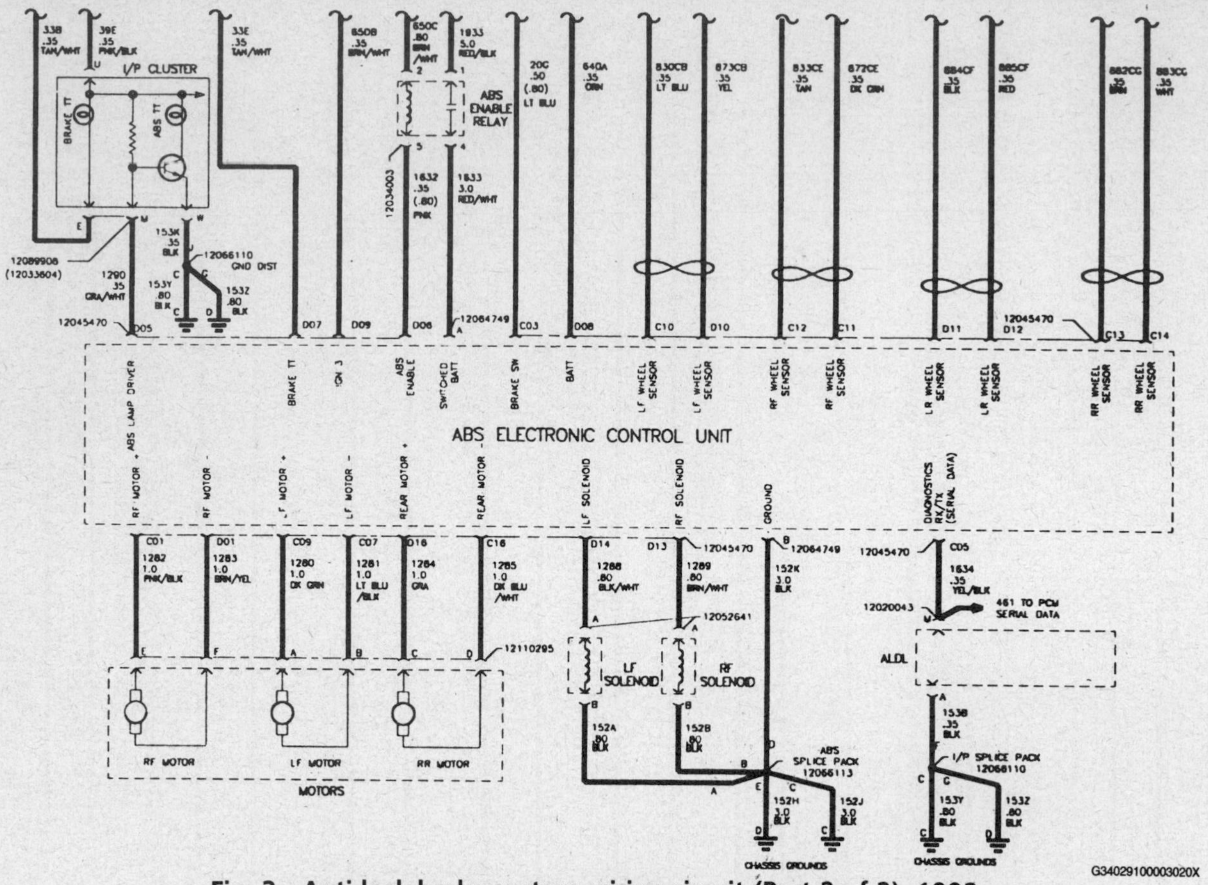
I/P CLUSTER
ABS ENABLE RELAY
ABS ELECTRONIC CONTROL UNIT
LF SOLENOID
RF SOLENOID
ALDL
RF MOTOR
LF MOTOR
RR MOTOR
MOTORS
CHASSIS GROUNDS
G34029100003020X

Fig. 3 Anti-lock brake system wiring circuit (Part 2 of 2). 1992

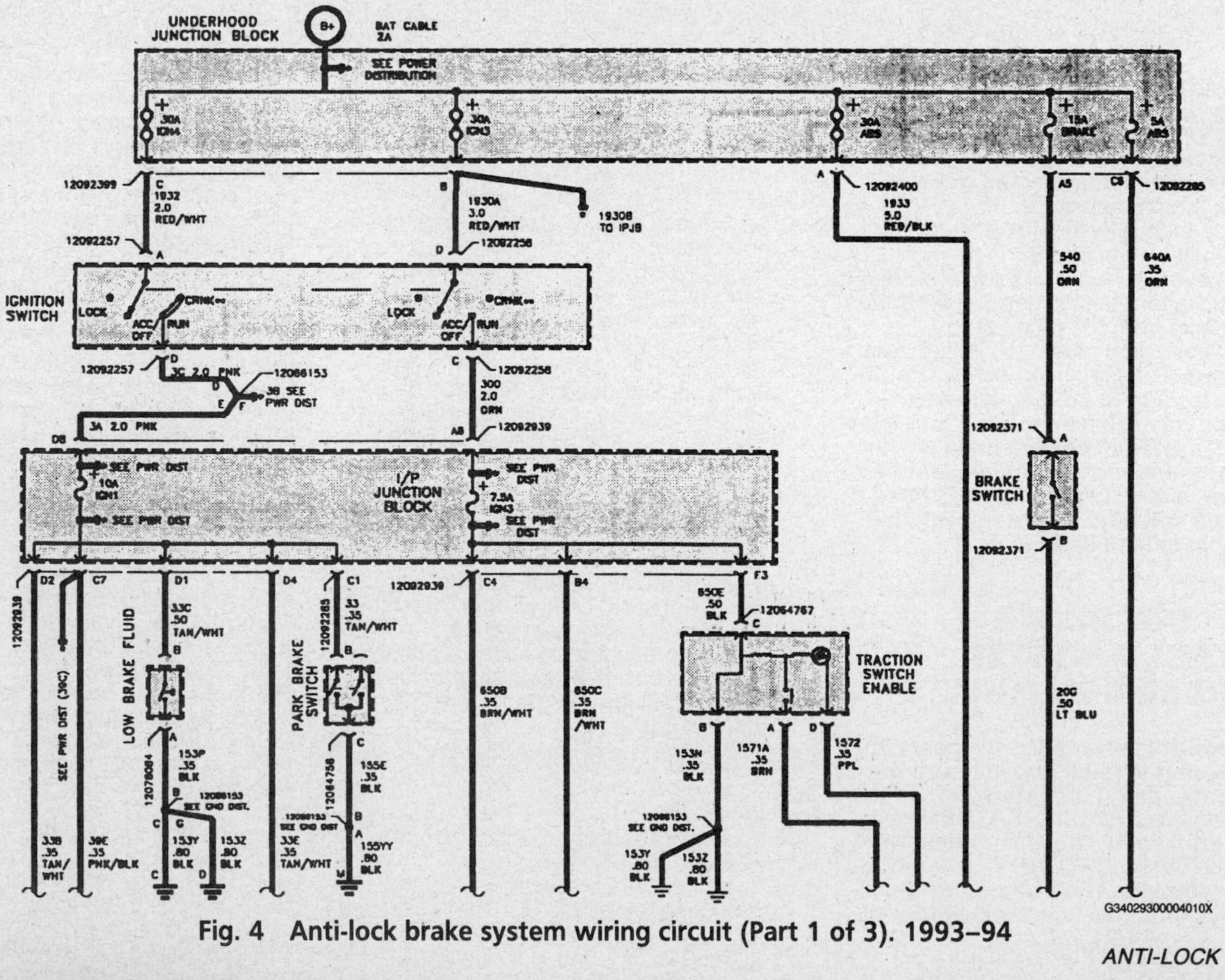
UNDERHOOD JUNCTION BLOCK
IGNITION SWITCH
I/P JUNCTION BLOCK
BRAKE SWITCH
TRACTION SWITCH ENABLE
LOW BRAKE FLUID
PARK BRAKE SWITCH
G34029300004010X

Fig. 4 Anti-lock brake system wiring circuit (Part 1 of 3). 1993–94

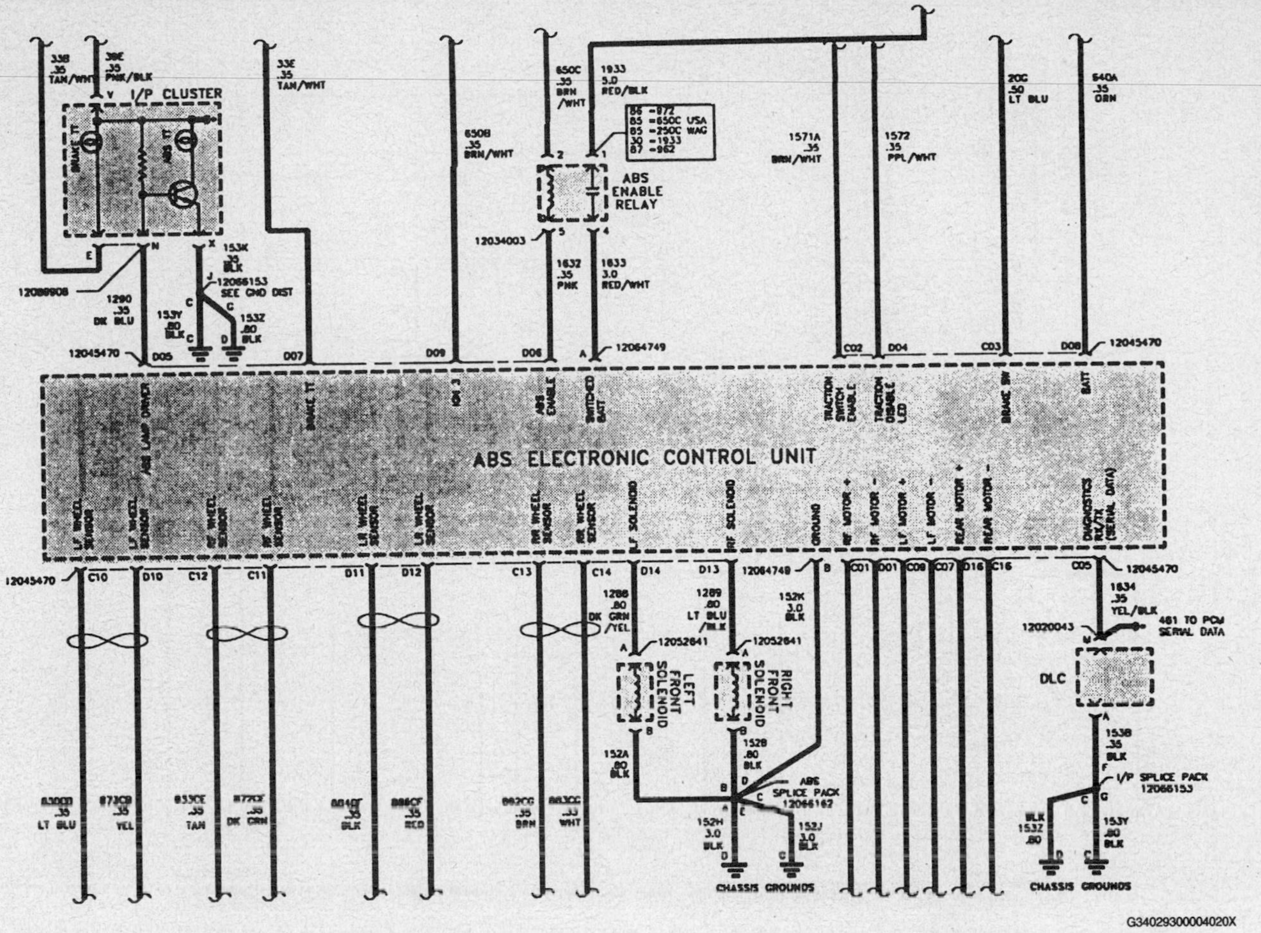
I/P CLUSTER
ABS ENABLE RELAY
ABS ELECTRONIC CONTROL UNIT
LEFT FRONT SOLENOID
RIGHT FRONT SOLENOID
DLC
CHASSIS GROUNDS
CHASSIS GROUNDS
G34029300004020X

Fig. 4 Anti-lock brake system wiring circuit (Part 2 of 3). 1993–94

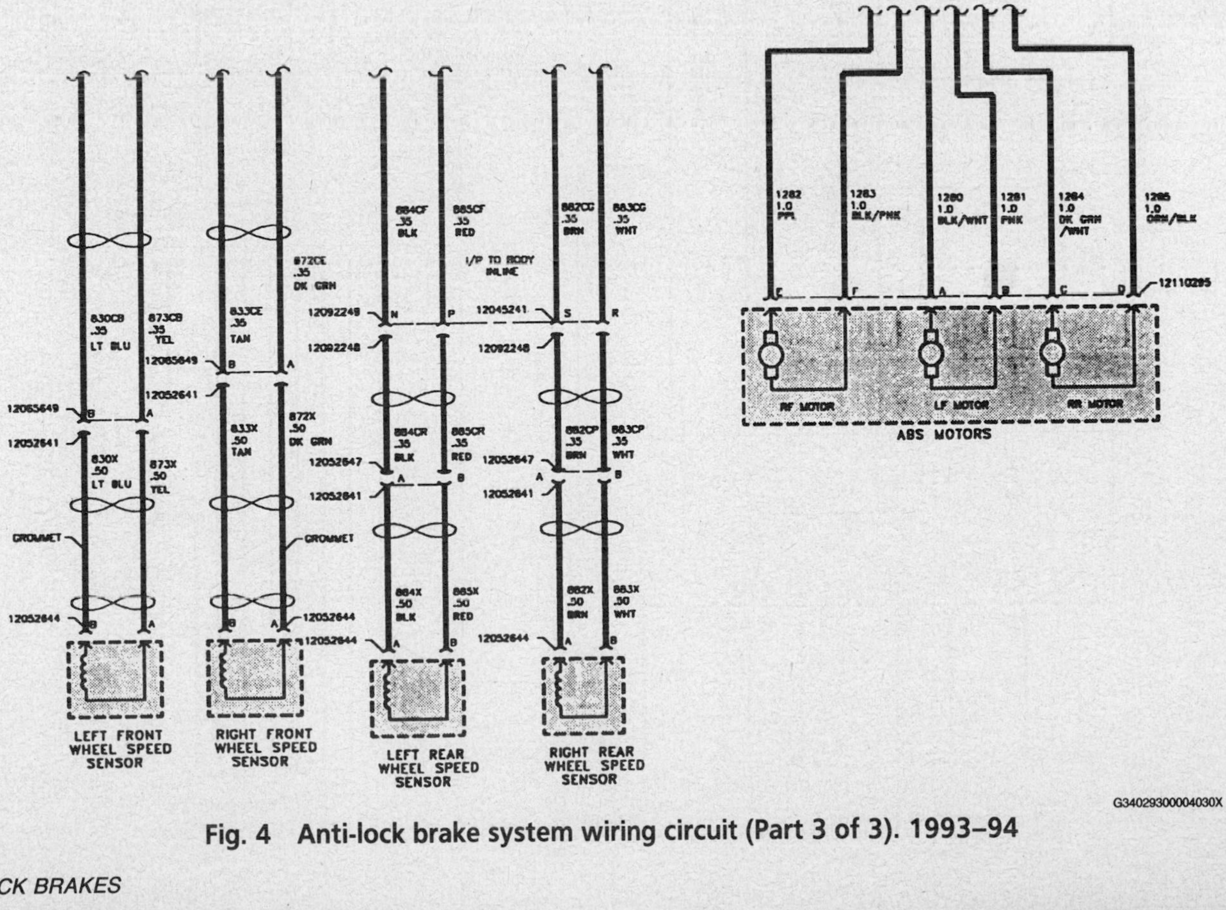
LEFT FRONT WHEEL SPEED SENSOR
RIGHT FRONT WHEEL SPEED SENSOR
LEFT REAR WHEEL SPEED SENSOR
RIGHT REAR WHEEL SPEED SENSOR
ABS MOTORS
G34029300004030X

Fig. 4 Anti-lock brake system wiring circuit (Part 3 of 3). 1993–94

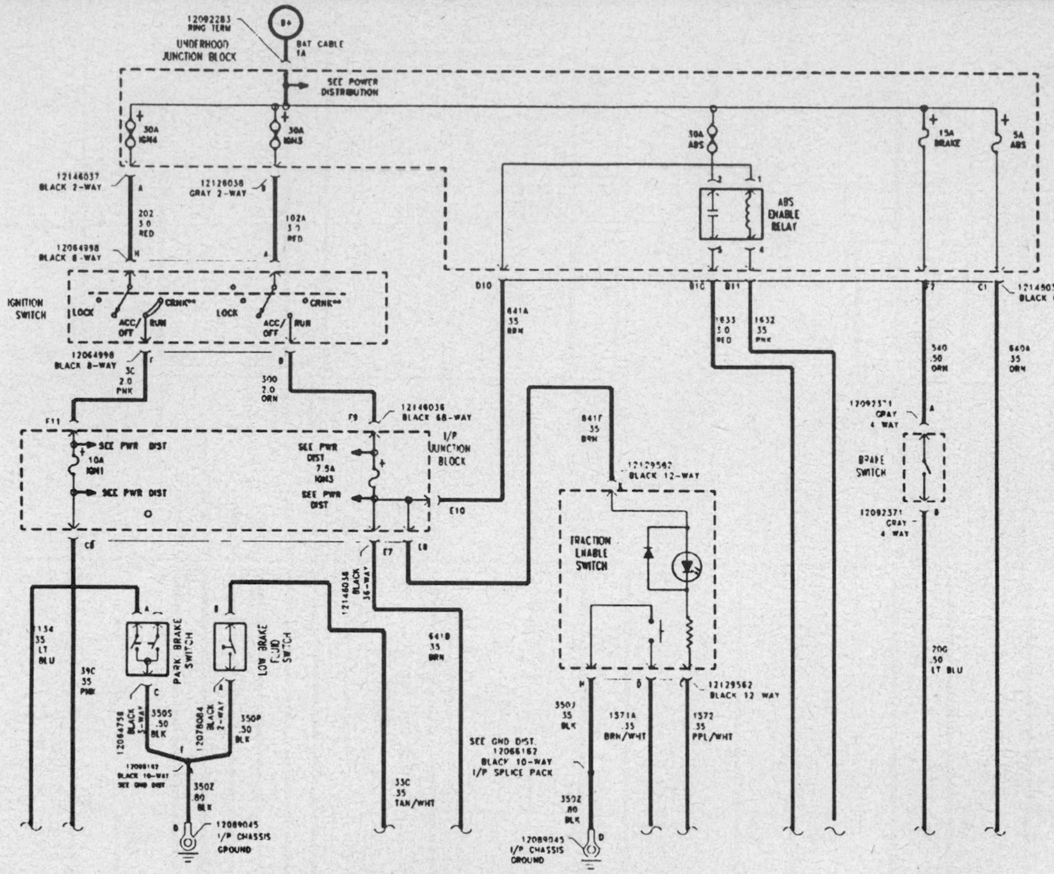
UNDERHOOD JUNCTION BLOCK
SEE POWER DISTRIBUTION
ABS ENABLE RELAY
IGNITION SWITCH
I/P JUNCTION BLOCK
TRACTION ENABLE SWITCH
BRAKE SWITCH
PARK BRAKE SWITCH
LOW BRAKE FLUID SWITCH

G34029500081010X

Fig. 5 Anti-lock brake system wiring circuit (Part 1 of 3). 1995

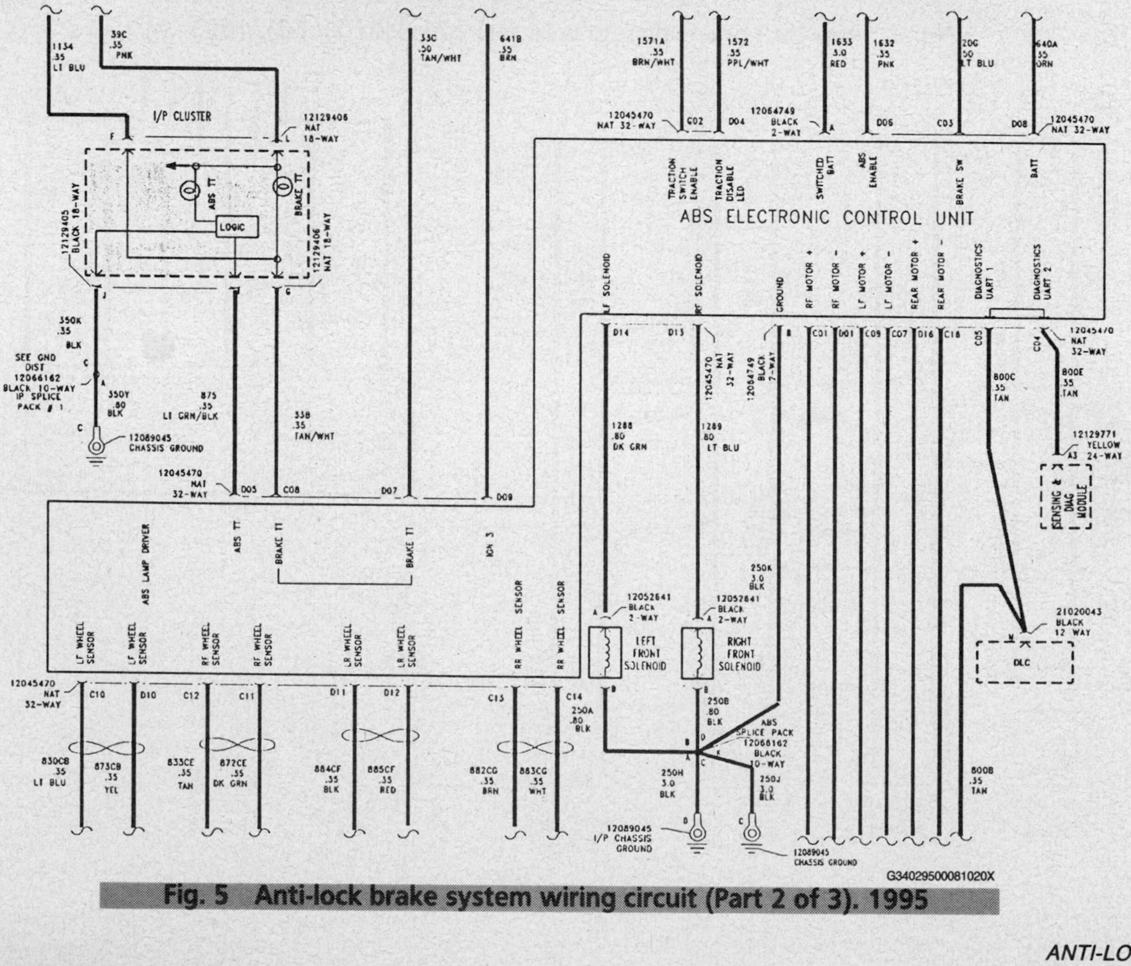
I/P CLUSTER
LOGIC
ABS ELECTRONIC CONTROL UNIT
LEFT FRONT SOLENOID
RIGHT FRONT SOLENOID
DLC
SENSING & DIAG MODULE

G34029500081020X

Fig. 5 Anti-lock brake system wiring circuit (Part 2 of 3). 1995

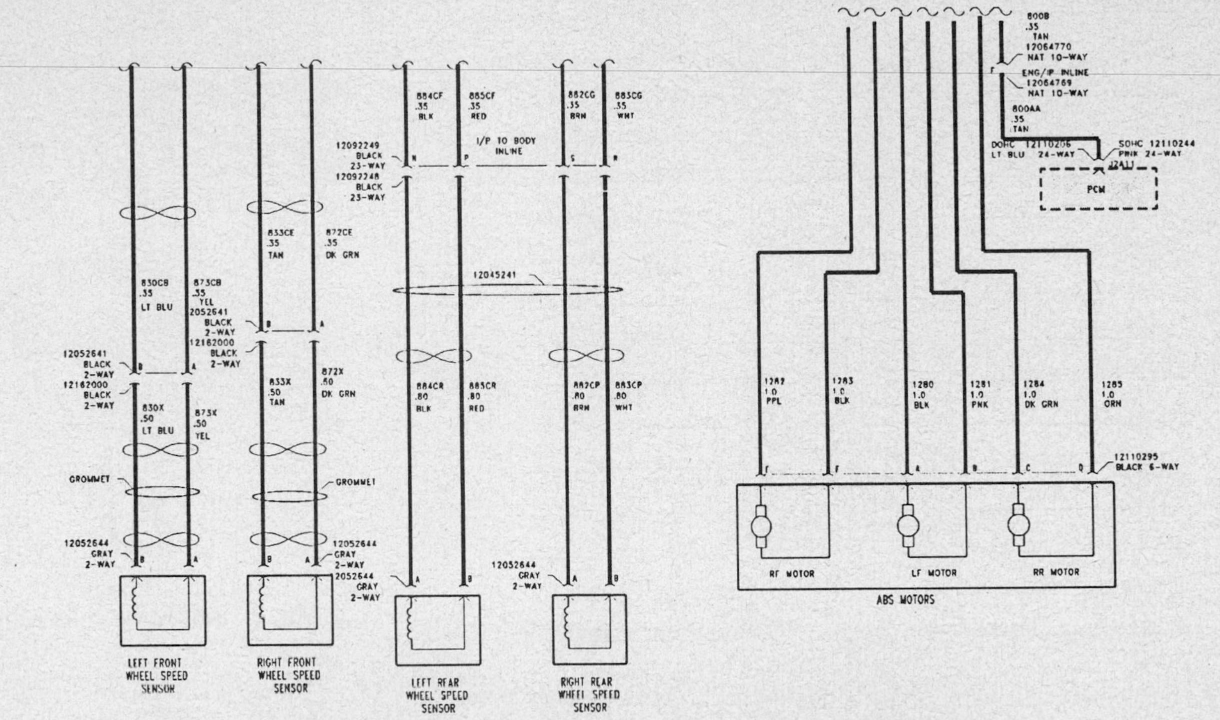
800B
.35
TAN
12064770
NAT 10-WAY
ENG/IP INLINE
12064769
NAT 10-WAY
800AA
.35
TAN
DOHC 12110206
LT BLU 24-WAY
SOHC 12110244
PINK 24-WAY
PCM
884CF
.35
BLK
885CF
.35
RED
882CG
.35
BRN
883CG
.35
WHT
12092249
BLACK
23-WAY
12092248
BLACK
23-WAY
I/P TO BODY
INLINE
833CE
.35
TAN
872CE
.35
DK GRN
12045241
830CB
.35
LT BLU
873CB
.35
YEL
12052641
BLACK
2-WAY
12162000
BLACK
2-WAY
833X
.50
TAN
872X
.50
DK GRN
884CR
.80
BLK
885CR
.80
RED
882CP
.80
BRN
883CP
.80
WHT
830X
.50
LT BLU
873X
.50
YEL
GROMMET
12052644
GRAY
2-WAY
1282
1.0
PPL
1283
1.0
BLK
1280
1.0
BLK
1281
1.0
PNK
1284
1.0
DK GRN
1285
1.0
ORN
12110295
BLACK 6-WAY
RF MOTOR
LF MOTOR
RR MOTOR
ABS MOTORS
LEFT FRONT
WHEEL SPEED
SENSOR
RIGHT FRONT
WHEEL SPEED
SENSOR
LEFT REAR
WHEEL SPEED
SENSOR
RIGHT REAR
WHEEL SPEED
SENSOR
G34029500081030X

Fig. 5 Anti-lock brake system wiring circuit (Part 3 of 3). 1995

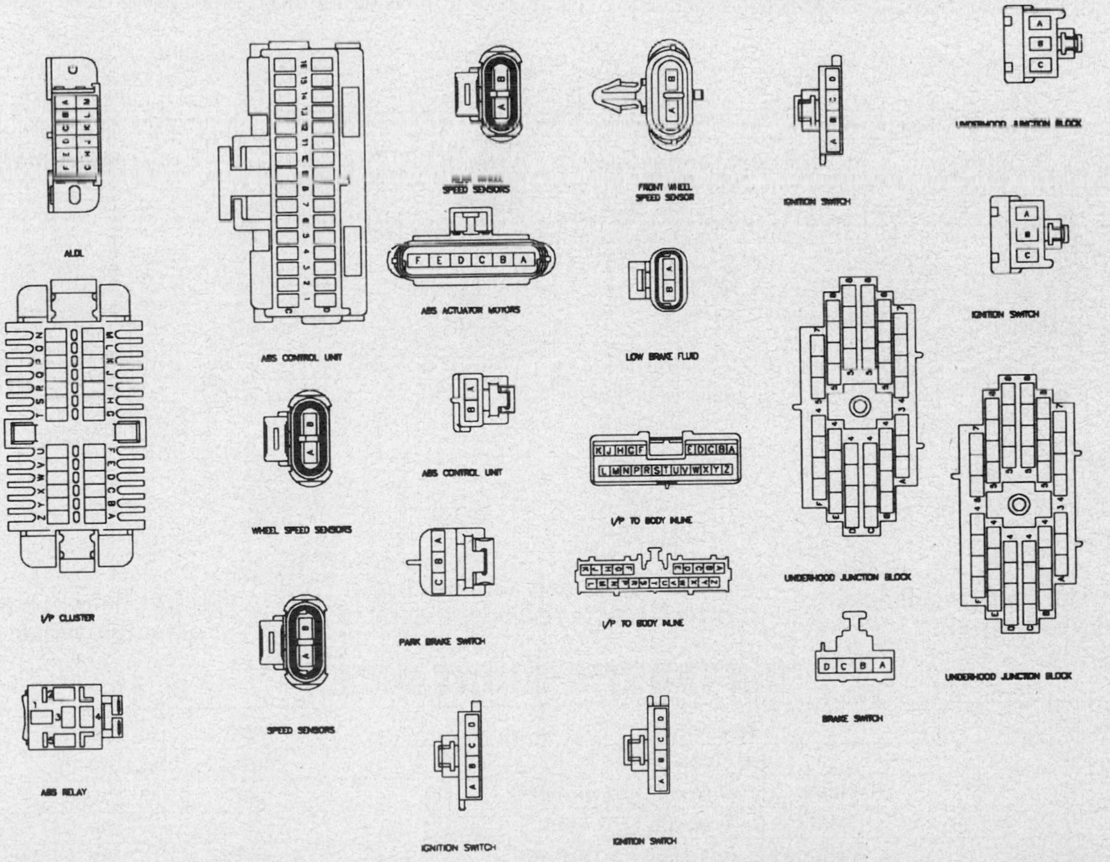
ALDL
ABS CONTROL UNIT
REAR WHEEL SPEED SENSORS
FRONT WHEEL SPEED SENSOR
IGNITION SWITCH
UNDERHOOD JUNCTION BLOCK
ABS ACTUATOR MOTORS
LOW BRAKE FLUID
IGNITION SWITCH
I/P CLUSTER
WHEEL SPEED SENSORS
ABS CONTROL UNIT
I/P TO BODY INLINE
UNDERHOOD JUNCTION BLOCK
PARK BRAKE SWITCH
I/P TO BODY INLINE
UNDERHOOD JUNCTION BLOCK
SPEED SENSORS
BRAKE SWITCH
ABS RELAY
IGNITION SWITCH
IGNITION SWITCH
G34029100005000X

Fig. 6 Anti-lock brake system electrical connectors

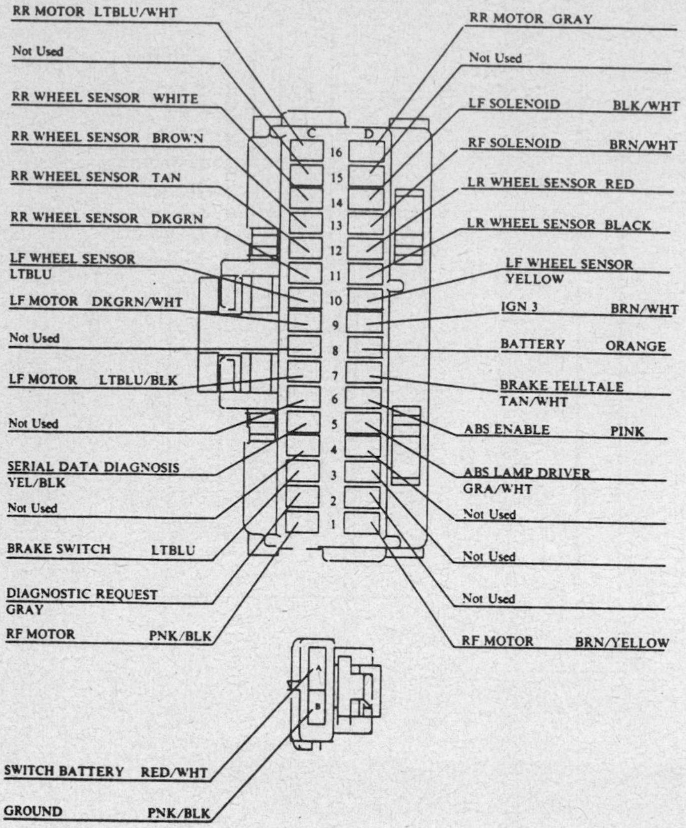
RR MOTOR LTBLU/WHT
Not Used
RR WHEEL SENSOR WHITE
RR WHEEL SENSOR BROWN
RR WHEEL SENSOR TAN
RR WHEEL SENSOR DKGRN
LF WHEEL SENSOR LTBLU
LF MOTOR DKGRN/WHT
Not Used
LF MOTOR LTBLU/BLK
Not Used
SERIAL DATA DIAGNOSIS YEL/BLK
Not Used
BRAKE SWITCH LTBLU
DIAGNOSTIC REQUEST GRAY
RF MOTOR PNK/BLK
RR MOTOR GRAY
Not Used
LF SOLENOID BLK/WHT
RF SOLENOID BRN/WHT
LR WHEEL SENSOR RED
LR WHEEL SENSOR BLACK
LF WHEEL SENSOR YELLOW
IGN 3 BRN/WHT
BATTERY ORANGE
BRAKE TELLTALE TAN/WHT
ABS ENABLE PINK
ABS LAMP DRIVER GRA/WHT
Not Used
Not Used
Not Used
RF MOTOR BRN/YELLOW
C
D
16
15
14
13
12
11
10
9
8
7
6
5
4
3
2
1
A
B
SWITCH BATTERY RED/WHT
GROUND PNK/BLK
G34029100006000X

Fig. 7 ABCM pin identification

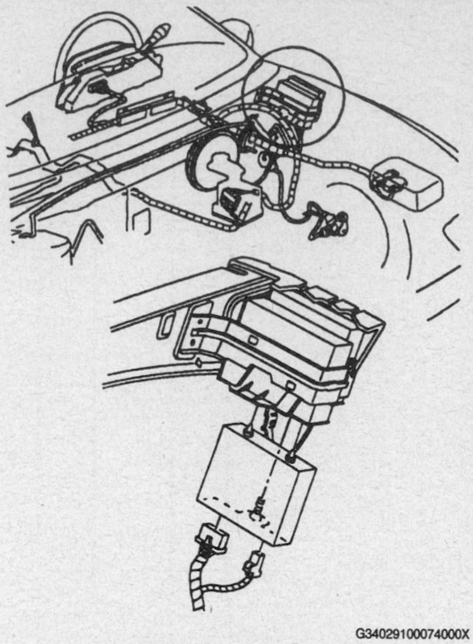
G34029100074000X

Fig. 8 ABCM module removal

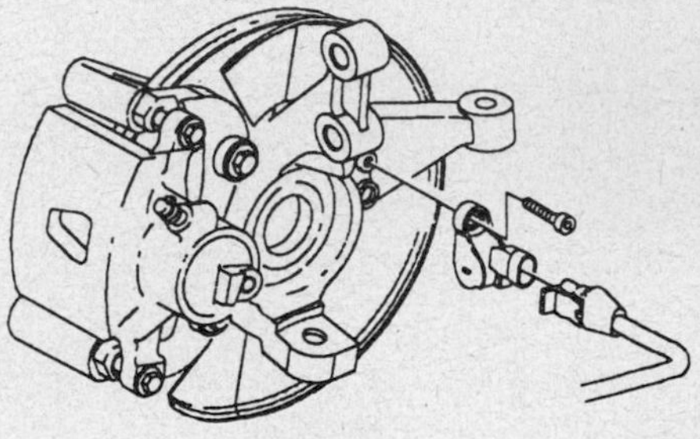
G34029100077000X

Fig. 11 Front speed sensor replacement

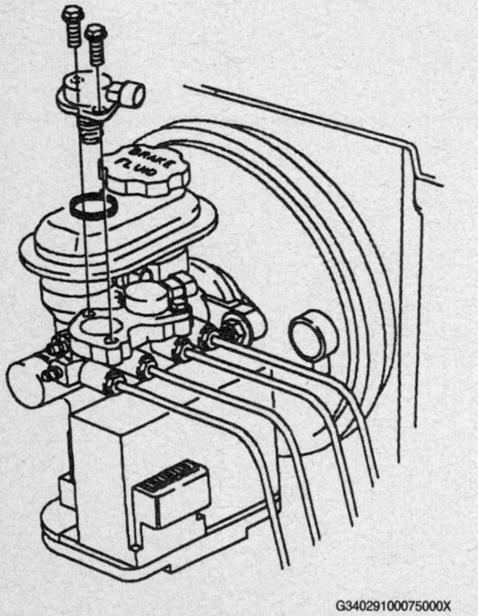
G34029100075000X

Fig. 9 Anti-lock brake solenoid valve removal

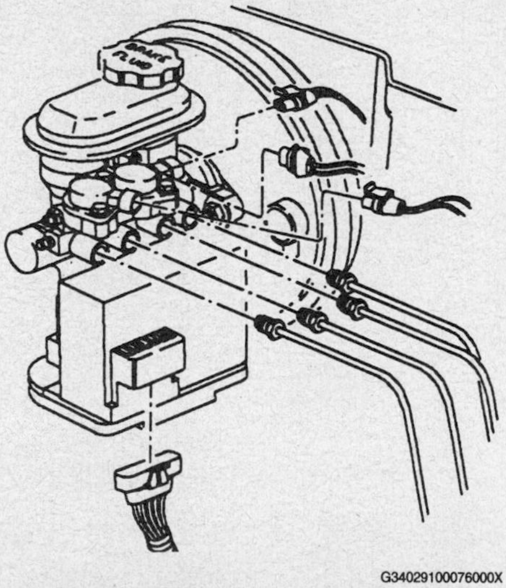
G34029100076000X

Fig. 10 Removing anti-lock brake control & master cylinder assembly

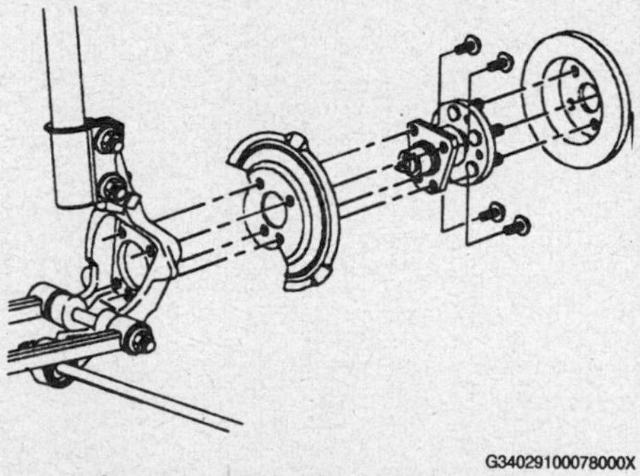
G34029100078000X

Fig. 12 Rear hub & bearing assembly replacement

DIAGNOSTIC CHART INDEX

Trouble Code	Description	Year	Page No.	Fig. No.
-	No Scan Data	1992-95	39-80	13
Code 11	Telltale Circuit Open Or Grounded	1992	39-80	14
Code 12	Telltale Or Traction LED Fault	1993-95	39-80	15
Code 13	Telltale Circuit Shorted To B +	1992	39-81	16
Code 14	Switched Battery Circuit Open	1992-93	39-81	17
Code 14	Switched Battery Circuit Open	1994-95	39-82	18

Continued

DIAGNOSTIC CHART INDEX —Continued

Trouble Code	Description	Year	Page No.	Fig. No.
Code 15	Switched Battery Circuit Shorted B +	1992-93	39-82	19
Code 15	Switched Battery Circuit Shorted B +	1994-95	39-82	20
Code 16	Enable Relay Coil Circuit Open	1992-93	39-82	21
Code 16	Enable Relay Coil Circuit Open	1994-95	39-83	22
Code 17	Enable Relay Coil Circuit Grounded	1992-93	39-83	23
Code 17	Enable Relay Coil Circuit Grounded	1994-95	39-83	24
Code 18	Enable Relay Coil Circuit Shorted To B +	1992-93	39-84	25
Code 18	Enable Relay Coil Circuit Shorted To B +	1994-95	39-84	26
Code 21	LF Wheel Speed—0 MPH	1992-95	39-84	27
Code 22	RF Wheel Speed—0 MPH	1992—95	39-85	28
Code 23	LR Wheel Speed—0 MPH	1992-95	39-85	29
Code 24	RR Wheel Speed—0 MPH	1992-95	39-86	30
Code 25	LF Wheel Speed Acceleration Fault	1992-95	39-86	31
Code 26	RF Wheel Speed Acceleration Fault	1992-95	39-87	32
Code 27	LR Wheel Speed Acceleration Fault	1992-95	39-87	33
Code 28	RR Wheel Speed Acceleration Fault	1992-95	39-88	34
Code 31	Any Two Wheel Speeds—0	1992-95	39-88	35
Code 36	System Voltage Low	1992-95	39-89	36
Code 37	ABS System Voltage High	1992-95	39-89	37
Code 38	Left Front ESB Does Not Hold Motor	1992-95	39-89	38
Code 41	Right Front ESB Does Not Hold Motor	1992-95	39-90	39
Code 42	Rear ESB Does Not Hold Motor	1992-95	39-90	40
Code 44	LF Motor Frozen	1992-95	39-90	41
Code 45	RF Motor Frozen	1992-95	39-90	42
Code 46	Rear Motor Frozen	1992-95	39-90	43
Code 47	LF Motor Circuit Current Low	1992-95	39-90	44
Code 48	RF Motor Circuit Current Low	1992-95	39-91	45
Code 51	Rear Motor Circuit Current Low	1992-95	39-91	46
Code 52	LF In Release Too Long	1992-95	39-91	47
Code 53	RF In Release Too Long	1992-95	39-91	48
Code 54	Rear In Release Too Long	1992-95	39-92	49
Code 55	Motor Circuit Fault Detected	1992-95	39-92	50
Code 56	LF Motor Circuit Open	1992-95	39-92	51
Code 57	LF Motor Circuit Grounded	1992-95	39-92	52
Code 58	LF Motor Circuit Shorted To B +	1992	39-92	53
Code 58	LF Motor Circuit Shorted To B +	1993-95	39-93	54
Code 61	RF Motor Circuit Open	1992	39-93	55
Code 61	RF Motor Circuit Open	1993-95	39-93	56
Code 62	RF Motor Circuit Grounded	1992-95	39-93	57
Code 63	RF Motor Circuit Shorted To B +	1992-95	39-94	58
Code 64	Rear Motor Circuit Open	1992	39-94	59
Code 64	Rear Motor Circuit Open	1993-95	39-94	60
Code 65	Rear Motor Circuit Grounded	1992-95	39-94	61
Code 66	Rear Motor Circuit Shorted To B +	1992-95	39-95	62
Code 76	Solenoid Circuit 1288 Open Or Shorted To B +	1992-93	39-95	63
Code 76	Solenoid Circuit 1288 Open Or Shorted To B +	1994-95	39-95	64
Code 77	Solenoid Circuit 1288 Grounded	1992-95	39-95	65
Code 78	Solenoid Circuit 1289 Open Or Shorted To B +	1992-95	39-96	66
Code 81	Solenoid Circuit 1289 Grounded	1992-95	39-96	67
Code 82	ABS Calibration Fault	1992-92	39-96	68
Code 82	ABS Calibration Fault	1993-95	39-96	69
Code 86	ABS Turned On Red Brake Telltale	1992-95	39-97	70
Code 87	Red Brake Telltale Circuit Open	1992-95	39-97	71
Code 88	Red Brake Telltale Circuit Shorted To B +	1992	39-97	72

Continued

DIAGNOSTIC CHART INDEX —Continued

Trouble Code	Description	Year	Page No.	Fig. No.
-	No Scan Data	1992-95	39-80	13
Code 88	Red Brake Telltale Circuit Shorted To B +	1993-95	39-97	73
Code 91	Brake Switch Circuit Open During Normal Stop	1992-95	39-97	74
Code 92	Brake Switch Circuit Open During ABS Stop	1992-95	39-98	75
Code 93	Brake Switch Circuit Open On Initialization	1992-95	39-98	76
Code 94	Brake Switch Circuit Always Closed	1992-95	39-98	77
Code 95	Stop Lamp Circuit Open NO TAG	1992-95	39-99	78
Code 96	Stop Lamp Circuit Open Or Grounds Open	1992-95	39-99	79

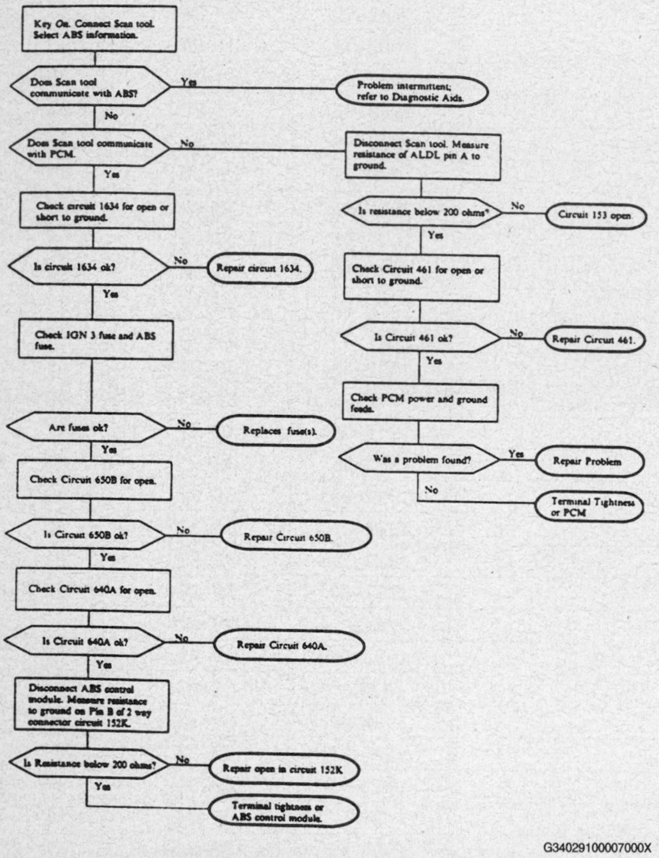

Fig. 13 No scan data

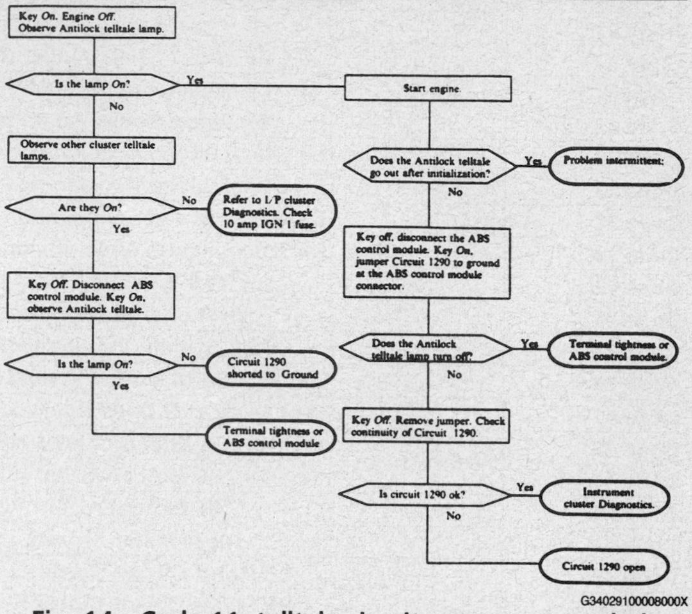

Fig. 14 Code 11, telltale circuit open or grounded. 1992

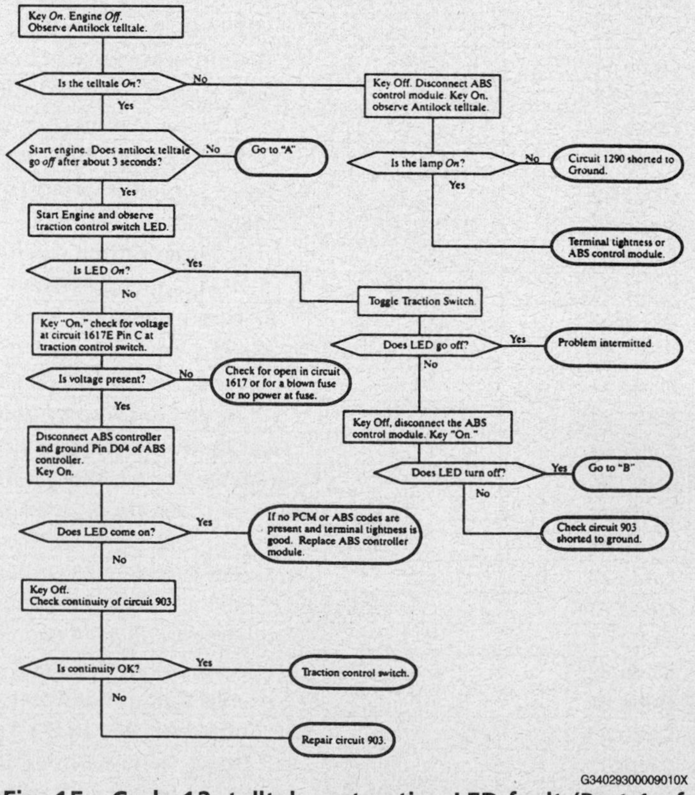

Fig. 15 Code 12, telltale or traction LED fault (Part 1 of 2). 1993-95

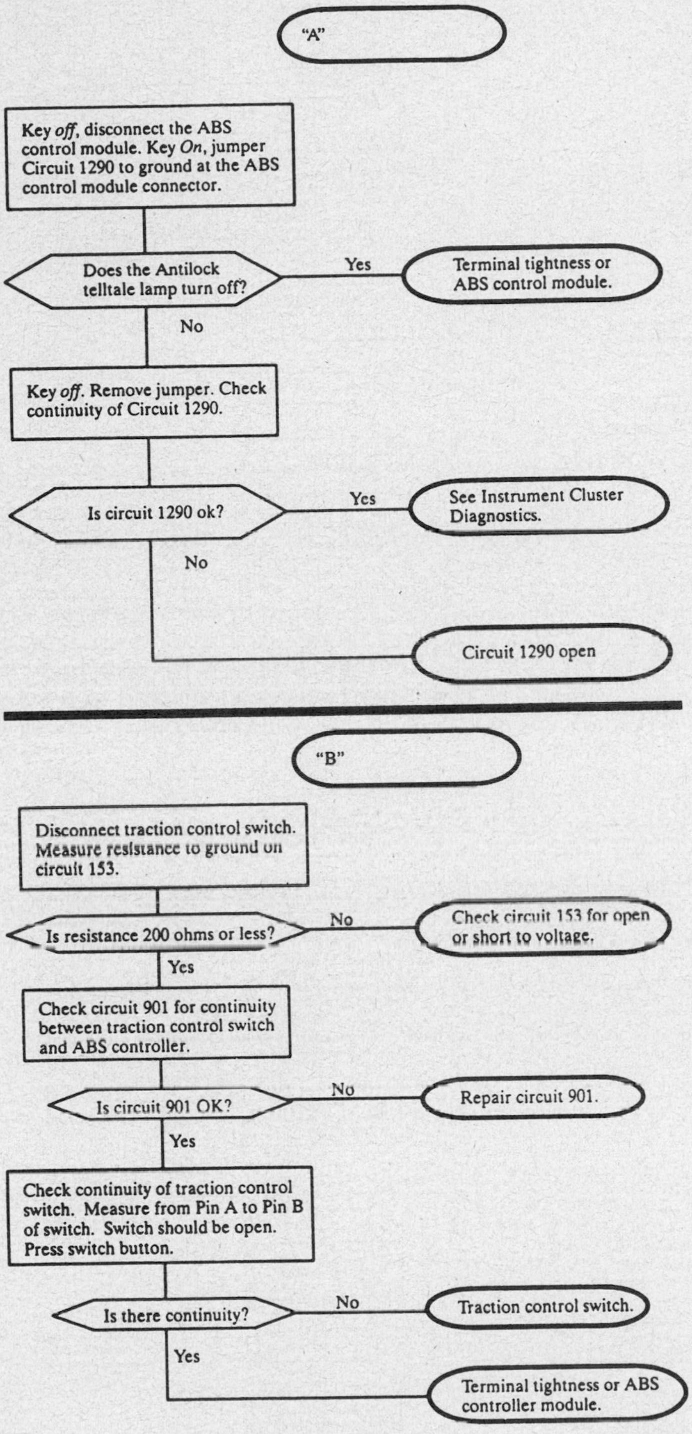
"A"
Key *off*, disconnect the ABS control module. Key *On*, jumper Circuit 1290 to ground at the ABS control module connector.
Does the Antilock telltale lamp turn off?
Yes
Terminal tightness or ABS control module.
No
Key *off*. Remove jumper. Check continuity of Circuit 1290.
Is circuit 1290 ok?
Yes
See Instrument Cluster Diagnostics.
No
Circuit 1290 open
"B"
Disconnect traction control switch. Measure resistance to ground on circuit 153.
Is resistance 200 ohms or less?
No
Check circuit 153 for open or short to voltage.
Yes
Check circuit 901 for continuity between traction control switch and ABS controller.
Is circuit 901 OK?
No
Repair circuit 901.
Yes
Check continuity of traction control switch. Measure from Pin A to Pin B of switch. Switch should be open. Press switch button.
Is there continuity?
No
Traction control switch.
Yes
Terminal tightness or ABS controller module.

G34029300009020X

Fig. 15 Code 12, telltale or traction LED fault (Part 2 of 2). 1993-95

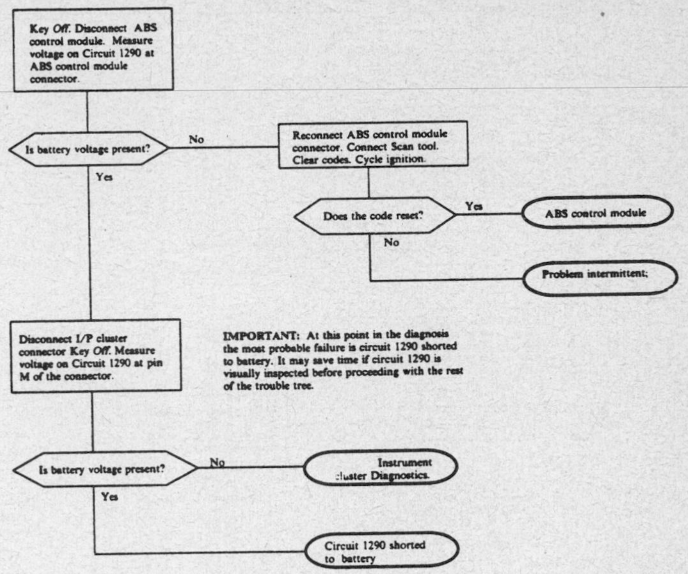
Key *Off*. Disconnect ABS control module. Measure voltage on Circuit 1290 at ABS control module connector.
Is battery voltage present?
No
Reconnect ABS control module connector. Connect Scan tool. Clear codes. Cycle ignition.
Does the code reset?
Yes
ABS control module
No
Problem intermittent;
Yes
Disconnect I/P cluster connector Key *Off*. Measure voltage on Circuit 1290 at pin M of the connector.
IMPORTANT: At this point in the diagnosis the most probable failure is circuit 1290 shorted to battery. It may save time if circuit 1290 is visually inspected before proceeding with the rest of the trouble tree.
Is battery voltage present?
No
Instrument cluster Diagnostics.
Yes
Circuit 1290 shorted to battery

G34029100010000X

Fig. 16 Code 13, telltale circuit shorted to B+. 1992

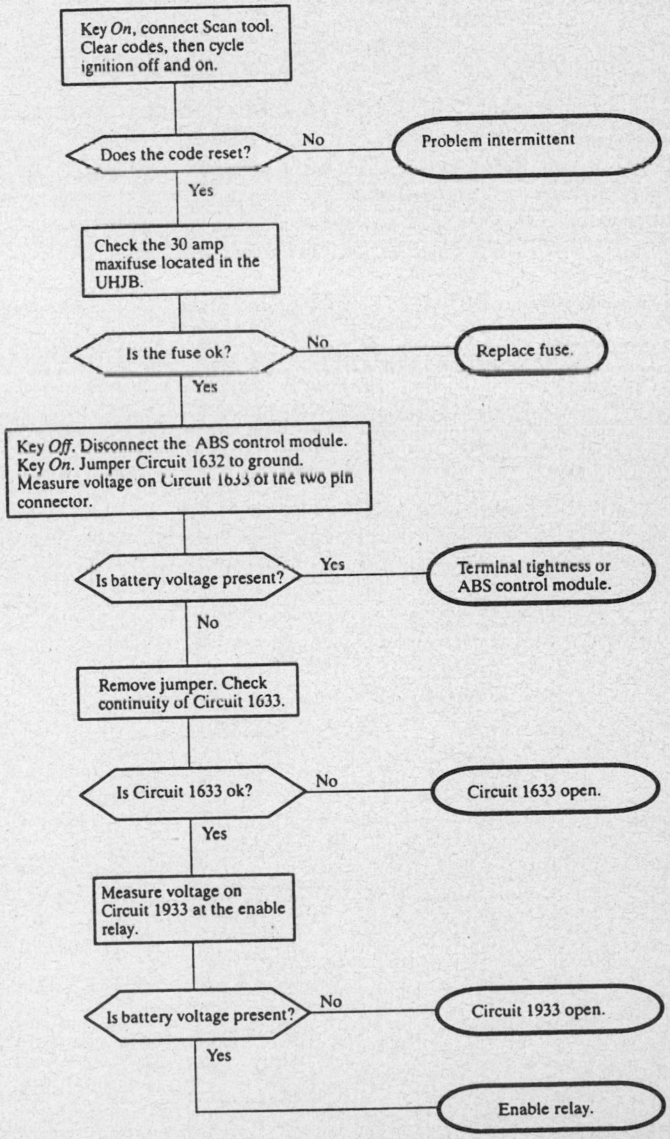
Key *On*, connect Scan tool. Clear codes, then cycle ignition off and on.
Does the code reset?
No
Problem intermittent
Yes
Check the 30 amp maxifuse located in the UHJB.
Is the fuse ok?
No
Replace fuse.
Yes
Key *Off*. Disconnect the ABS control module. Key *On*. Jumper Circuit 1632 to ground. Measure voltage on Circuit 1633 of the two pin connector.
Is battery voltage present?
Yes
Terminal tightness or ABS control module.
No
Remove jumper. Check continuity of Circuit 1633.
Is Circuit 1633 ok?
No
Circuit 1633 open.
Yes
Measure voltage on Circuit 1933 at the enable relay.
Is battery voltage present?
No
Circuit 1933 open.
Yes
Enable relay.

G34029100011000X

Fig. 17 Code 14, switched battery circuit open. 1992-93

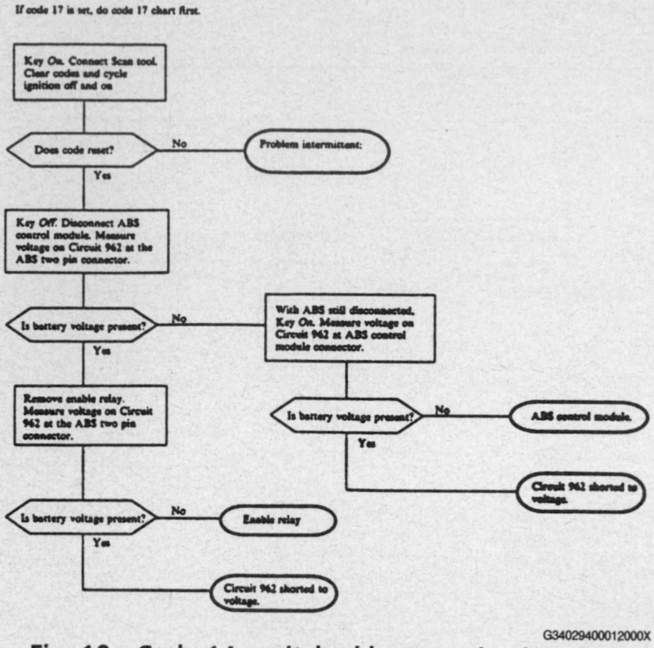
If code 17 is set, do code 17 chart first.
Key On. Connect Scan tool. Clear codes and cycle ignition off and on
Does code reset?
No
Problem intermittent:
Yes
Key Off. Disconnect ABS control module. Measure voltage on Circuit 962 at the ABS two pin connector.
Is battery voltage present?
No
With ABS still disconnected. Key On. Measure voltage on Circuit 962 at ABS control module connector.
Is battery voltage present?
No
ABS control module.
Yes
Circuit 962 shorted to voltage.
Yes
Remove enable relay. Measure voltage on Circuit 962 at the ABS two pin connector.
Is battery voltage present?
No
Enable relay
Yes
Circuit 962 shorted to voltage.
G34029400012000X

Fig. 18 Code 14, switched battery circuit open. 1994–95

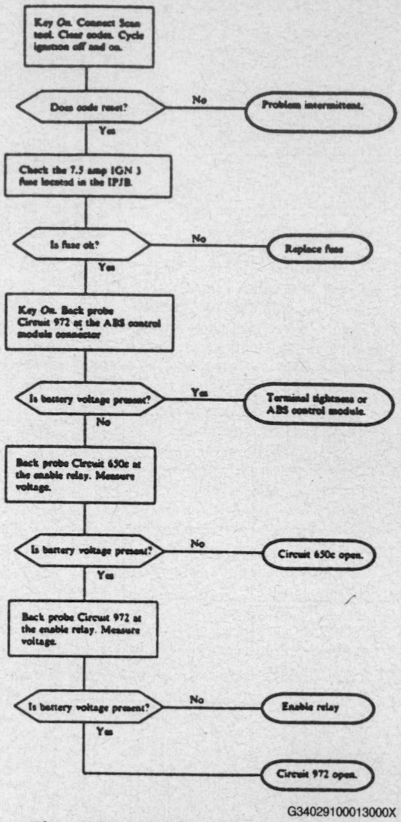
Key On. Connect Scan tool. Clear codes. Cycle ignition off and on.
Does code reset?
No
Problem intermittent.
Yes
Check the 7.5 amp IGN 3 fuse located in the IPJB.
Is fuse ok?
No
Replace fuse
Yes
Key On. Back probe Circuit 972 at the ABS control module connector
Is battery voltage present?
Yes
Terminal tightness or ABS control module.
No
Back probe Circuit 650c at the enable relay. Measure voltage.
Is battery voltage present?
No
Circuit 650c open.
Yes
Back probe Circuit 972 at the enable relay. Measure voltage.
Is battery voltage present?
No
Enable relay
Yes
Circuit 972 open.
G34029100013000X

Fig. 19 Code 15, switched battery circuit shorted to B+. 1992-93

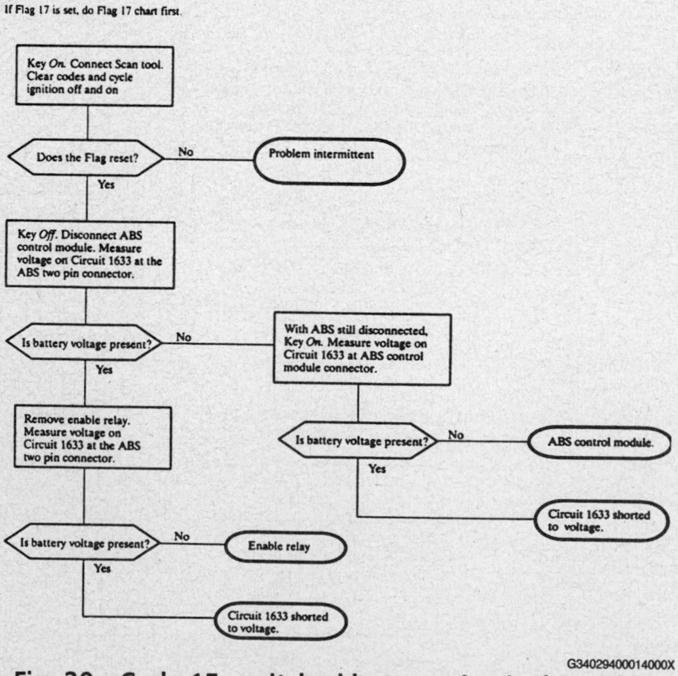
If Flag 17 is set, do Flag 17 chart first.
Key On. Connect Scan tool. Clear codes and cycle ignition off and on
Does the Flag reset?
No
Problem intermittent
Yes
Key Off. Disconnect ABS control module. Measure voltage on Circuit 1633 at the ABS two pin connector.
Is battery voltage present?
No
With ABS still disconnected. Key On. Measure voltage on Circuit 1633 at ABS control module connector.
Is battery voltage present?
No
ABS control module.
Yes
Circuit 1633 shorted to voltage.
Yes
Remove enable relay. Measure voltage on Circuit 1633 at the ABS two pin connector.
Is battery voltage present?
No
Enable relay
Yes
Circuit 1633 shorted to voltage.
G34029400014000X

Fig. 20 Code 15, switched battery circuit shorted to B+. 1994–95

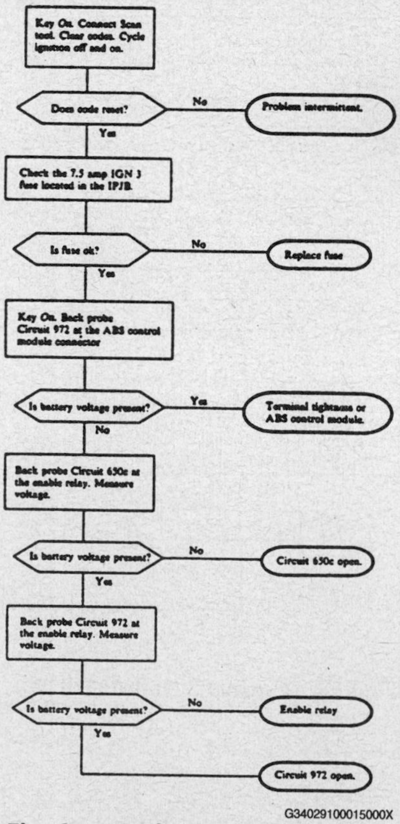
Key On. Connect Scan tool. Clear codes. Cycle ignition off and on.
Does code reset?
No
Problem intermittent.
Yes
Check the 7.5 amp IGN 3 fuse located in the IPJB.
Is fuse ok?
No
Replace fuse
Yes
Key On. Back probe Circuit 972 at the ABS control module connector
Is battery voltage present?
Yes
Terminal tightness or ABS control module.
No
Back probe Circuit 650c at the enable relay. Measure voltage.
Is battery voltage present?
No
Circuit 650c open.
Yes
Back probe Circuit 972 at the enable relay. Measure voltage.
Is battery voltage present?
No
Enable relay
Yes
Circuit 972 open.
G34029100015000X

Fig. 21 Code 16, enable relay coil circuit open. 1992-93

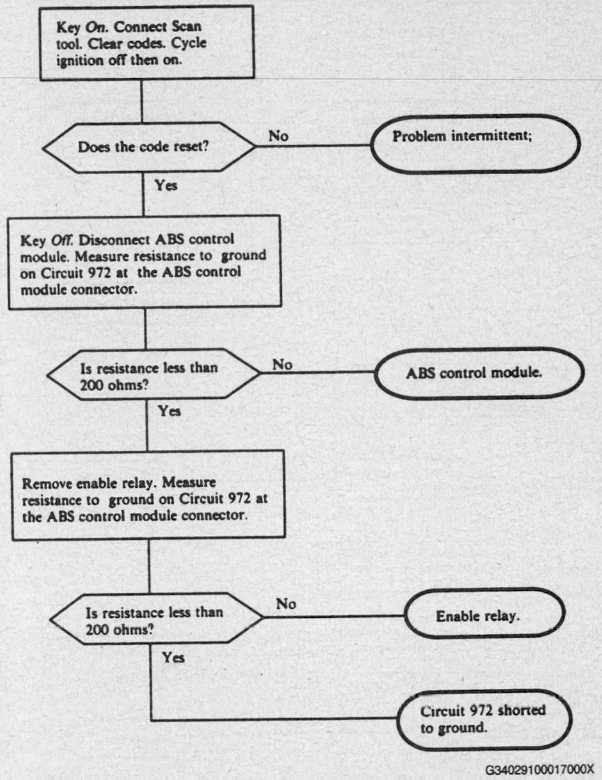
Key On. Connect Scan tool. Clear codes. Cycle ignition off then on.
Does the code reset?
No
Problem intermittent;
Yes
Key Off. Disconnect ABS control module. Measure resistance to ground on Circuit 972 at the ABS control module connector.
Is resistance less than 200 ohms?
No
ABS control module.
Yes
Remove enable relay. Measure resistance to ground on Circuit 972 at the ABS control module connector.
Is resistance less than 200 ohms?
No
Enable relay.
Yes
Circuit 972 shorted to ground.
G34029100017000X

Fig. 23 Code 17, enable relay coil circuit grounded. 1992-93

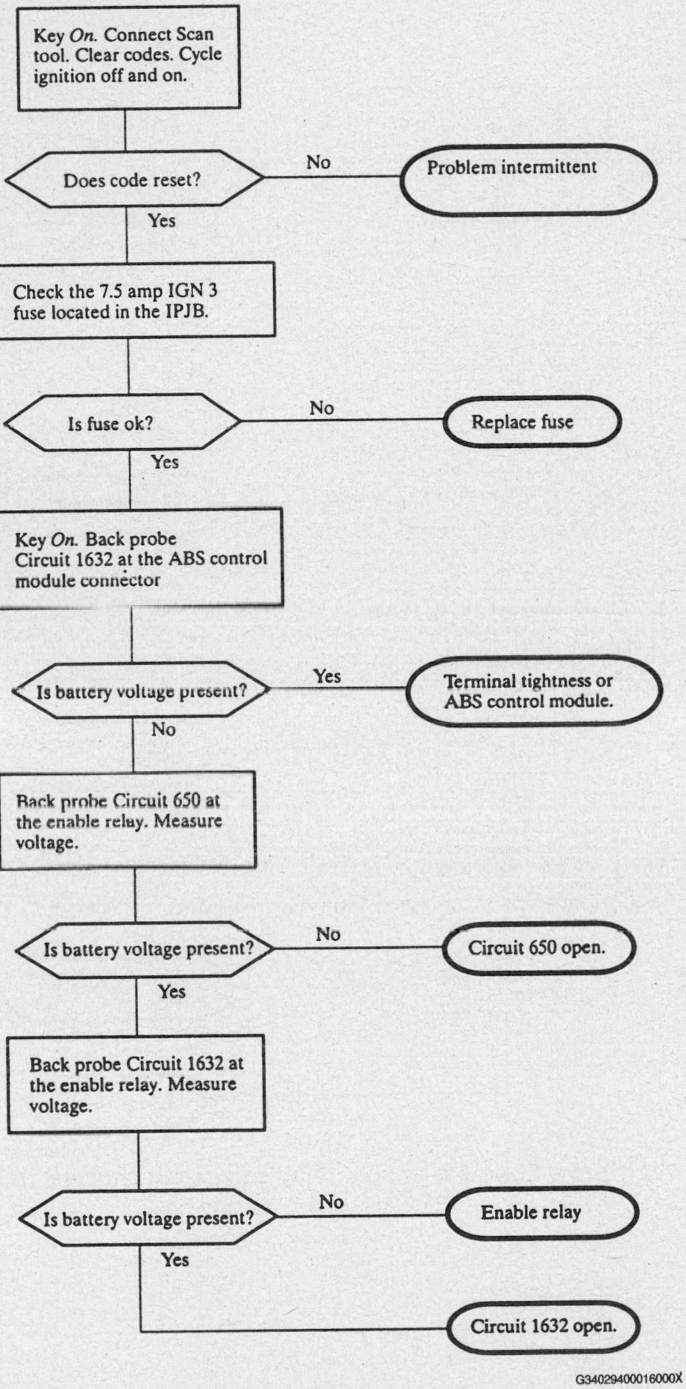
Key On. Connect Scan tool. Clear codes. Cycle ignition off and on.
Does code reset?
No
Problem intermittent
Yes
Check the 7.5 amp IGN 3 fuse located in the IPJB.
Is fuse ok?
No
Replace fuse
Yes
Key On. Back probe Circuit 1632 at the ABS control module connector
Is battery voltage present?
Yes
Terminal tightness or ABS control module.
No
Back probe Circuit 650 at the enable relay. Measure voltage.
Is battery voltage present?
No
Circuit 650 open.
Yes
Back probe Circuit 1632 at the enable relay. Measure voltage.
Is battery voltage present?
No
Enable relay
Yes
Circuit 1632 open.
G34029400016000X

Fig. 22 Code 16, enable relay coil circuit open. 1994–95

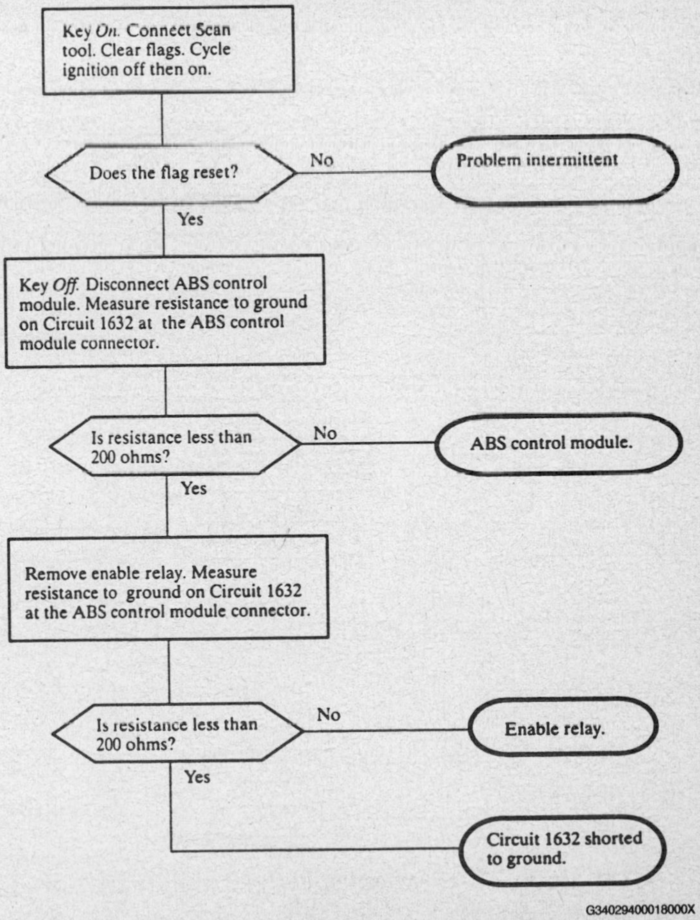
Key On. Connect Scan tool. Clear flags. Cycle ignition off then on.
Does the flag reset?
No
Problem intermittent
Yes
Key Off. Disconnect ABS control module. Measure resistance to ground on Circuit 1632 at the ABS control module connector.
Is resistance less than 200 ohms?
No
ABS control module.
Yes
Remove enable relay. Measure resistance to ground on Circuit 1632 at the ABS control module connector.
Is resistance less than 200 ohms?
No
Enable relay.
Yes
Circuit 1632 shorted to ground.
G34029400018000X

Fig. 24 Code 17, enable relay coil circuit grounded. 1994–95

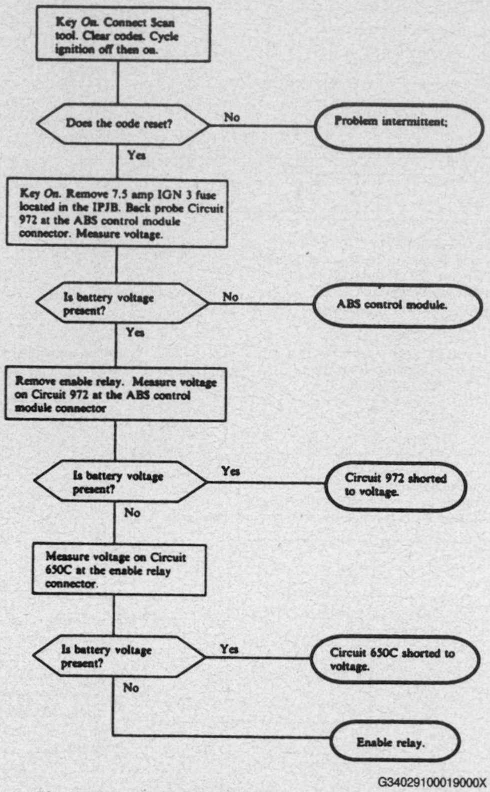
Key On. Connect Scan tool. Clear codes. Cycle ignition off then on.
Does the code reset?
No
Problem intermittent;
Yes
Key On. Remove 7.5 amp IGN 3 fuse located in the IPJB. Back probe Circuit 972 at the ABS control module connector. Measure voltage.
Is battery voltage present?
No
ABS control module.
Yes
Remove enable relay. Measure voltage on Circuit 972 at the ABS control module connector
Is battery voltage present?
Yes
Circuit 972 shorted to voltage.
No
Measure voltage on Circuit 650C at the enable relay connector.
Is battery voltage present?
Yes
Circuit 650C shorted to voltage.
No
Enable relay.
G34029100019000X

Fig. 25 Code 18, enable relay coil circuit shorted to B+. 1992-93

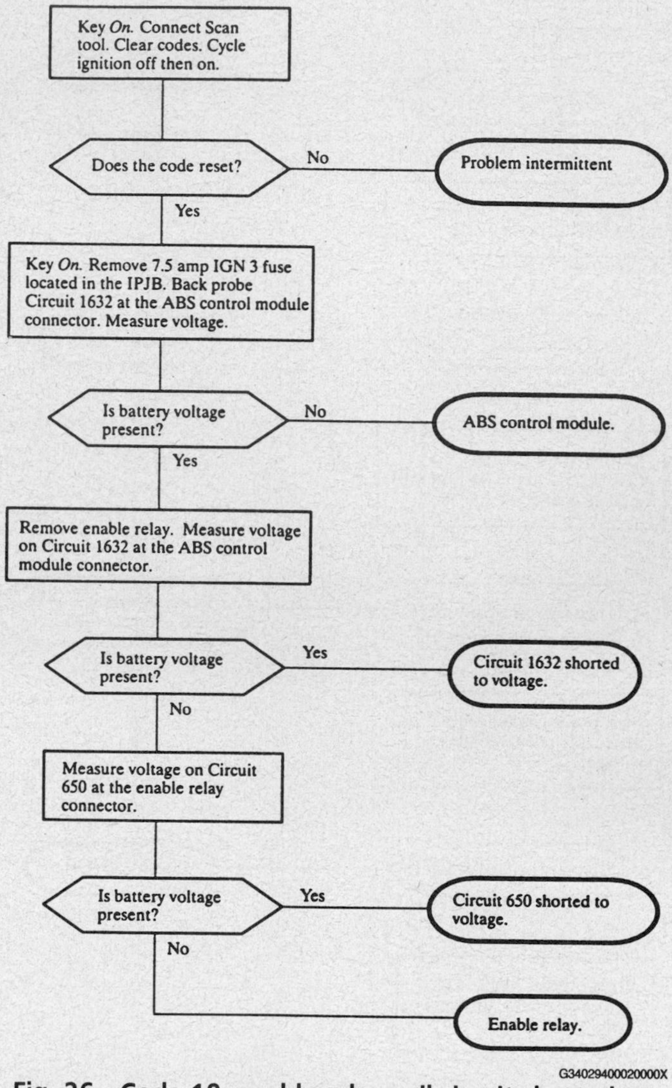
Key On. Connect Scan tool. Clear codes. Cycle ignition off then on.
Does the code reset?
No
Problem intermittent
Yes
Key On. Remove 7.5 amp IGN 3 fuse located in the IPJB. Back probe Circuit 1632 at the ABS control module connector. Measure voltage.
Is battery voltage present?
No
ABS control module.
Yes
Remove enable relay. Measure voltage on Circuit 1632 at the ABS control module connector.
Is battery voltage present?
Yes
Circuit 1632 shorted to voltage.
No
Measure voltage on Circuit 650 at the enable relay connector.
Is battery voltage present?
Yes
Circuit 650 shorted to voltage.
No
Enable relay.
G34029400020000X

Fig. 26 Code 18, enable relay coil circuit shorted to B+. 1994–95

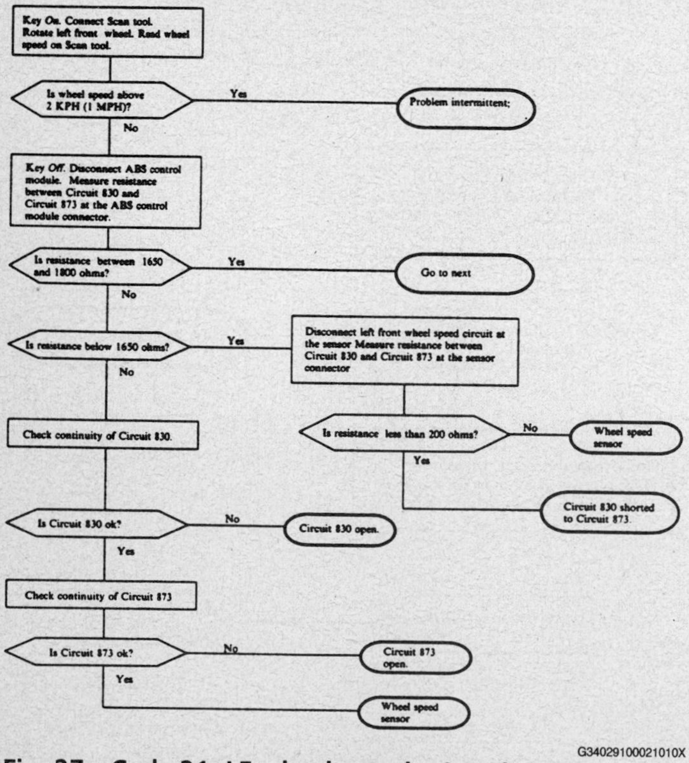
Key On. Connect Scan tool. Rotate left front wheel. Read wheel speed on Scan tool.
Is wheel speed above 2 KPH (1 MPH)?
Yes
Problem intermittent;
No
Key Off. Disconnect ABS control module. Measure resistance between Circuit 830 and Circuit 873 at the ABS control module connector.
Is resistance between 1650 and 1800 ohms?
Yes
Go to next
No
Is resistance below 1650 ohms?
Yes
Disconnect left front wheel speed circuit at the sensor Measure resistance between Circuit 830 and Circuit 873 at the sensor connector
Is resistance less than 200 ohms?
No
Wheel speed sensor
Yes
Circuit 830 shorted to Circuit 873.
No
Check continuity of Circuit 830.
Is Circuit 830 ok?
No
Circuit 830 open.
Yes
Check continuity of Circuit 873
Is Circuit 873 ok?
No
Circuit 873 open.
Yes
Wheel speed sensor
G34029100021010X

Fig. 27 Code 21, LF wheel speed = 0 mph (Part 1 of 2). 1992–95

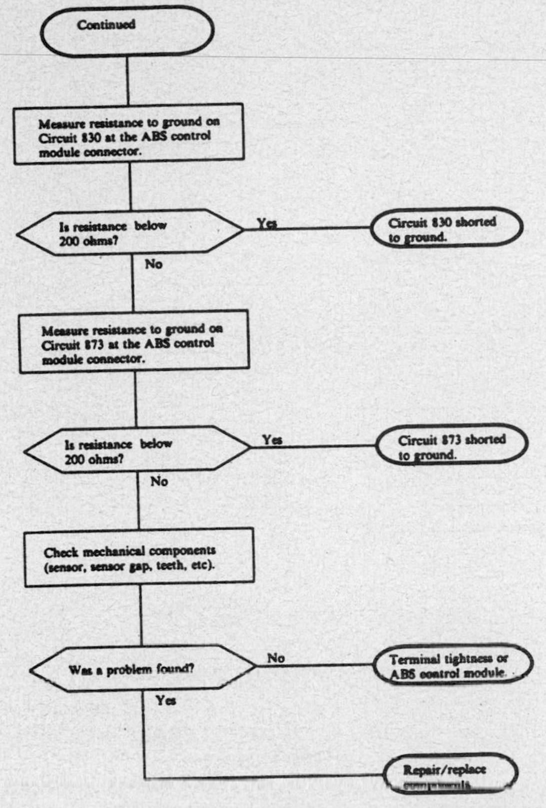
Continued
Measure resistance to ground on Circuit 830 at the ABS control module connector.
Is resistance below 200 ohms?
Yes
Circuit 830 shorted to ground.
No
Measure resistance to ground on Circuit 873 at the ABS control module connector.
Is resistance below 200 ohms?
Yes
Circuit 873 shorted to ground.
No
Check mechanical components (sensor, sensor gap, teeth, etc).
Was a problem found?
No
Terminal tightness or ABS control module.
Yes
Repair/replace

G34029100021020X

Fig. 27 Code 21, LF wheel speed = 0 mph (Part 2 of 2). 1992–95

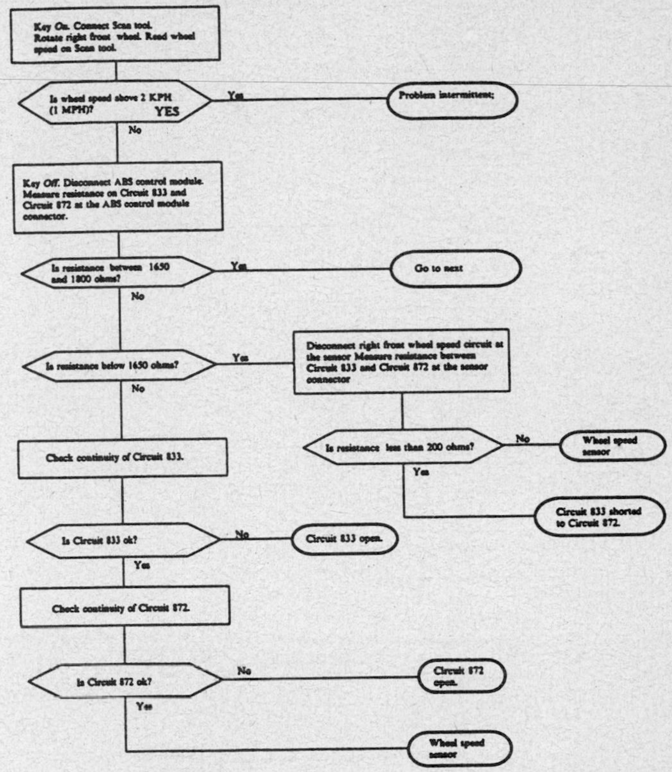
Key On. Connect Scan tool. Rotate right front wheel. Read wheel speed on Scan tool.
Is wheel speed above 2 KPH (1 MPH)?
YES
Yes
Problem intermittent;
No
Key Off. Disconnect ABS control module. Measure resistance on Circuit 833 and Circuit 872 at the ABS control module connector.
Is resistance between 1650 and 1800 ohms?
Yes
Go to next
No
Is resistance below 1650 ohms?
Yes
Disconnect right front wheel speed circuit at the sensor Measure resistance between Circuit 833 and Circuit 872 at the sensor connector
Is resistance less than 200 ohms?
No
Wheel speed sensor
Yes
Circuit 833 shorted to Circuit 872.
No
Check continuity of Circuit 833.
Is Circuit 833 ok?
No
Circuit 833 open.
Yes
Check continuity of Circuit 872.
Is Circuit 872 ok?
No
Circuit 872 open.
Yes
Wheel speed sensor

G34029100022010X

Fig. 28 Code 22, RF wheel speed – 0 MPH (Part 1 of 2)

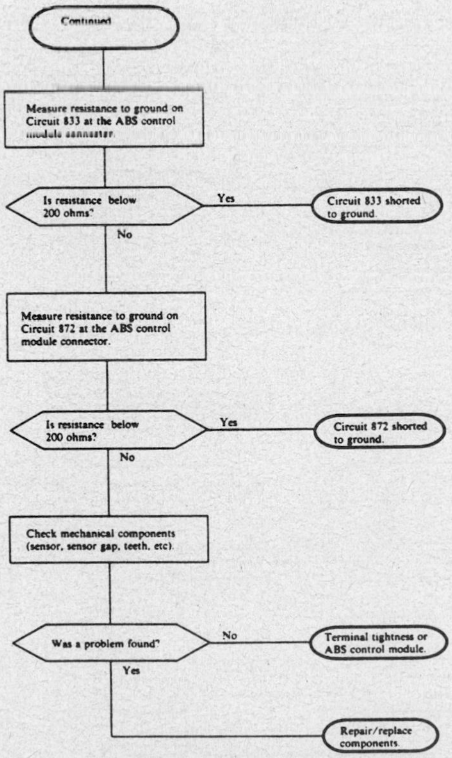
Continued
Measure resistance to ground on Circuit 833 at the ABS control module connector.
Is resistance below 200 ohms?
Yes
Circuit 833 shorted to ground.
No
Measure resistance to ground on Circuit 872 at the ABS control module connector.
Is resistance below 200 ohms?
Yes
Circuit 872 shorted to ground.
No
Check mechanical components (sensor, sensor gap, teeth, etc).
Was a problem found?
No
Terminal tightness or ABS control module.
Yes
Repair/replace components.

G34029100022020X

Fig. 28 Code 22, RF wheel speed = 0 MPH (Part 2 of 2)

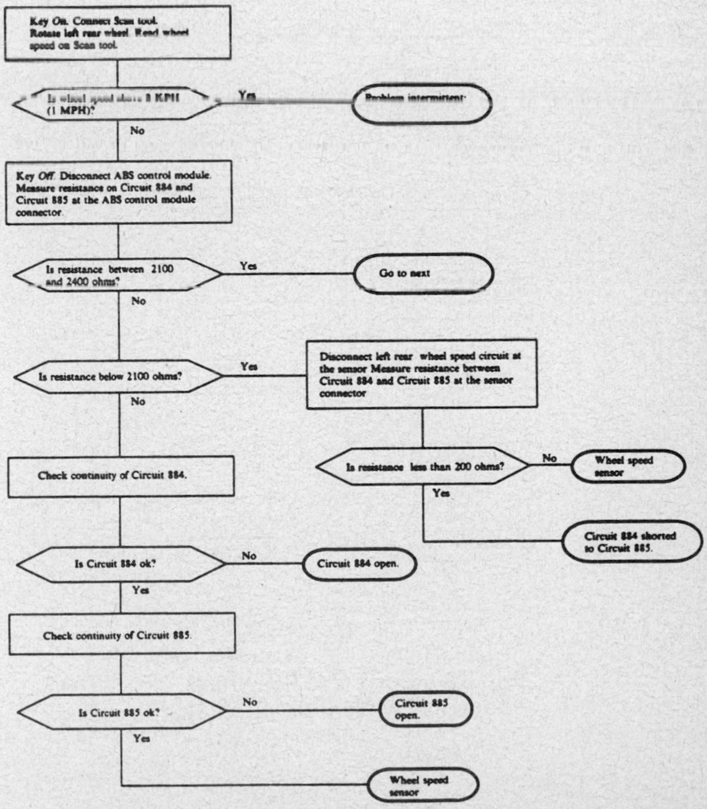
Key On. Connect Scan tool. Rotate left rear wheel. Read wheel speed on Scan tool.
(1 MPH)?
Yes
Problem intermittent:
No
Key Off. Disconnect ABS control module. Measure resistance on Circuit 884 and Circuit 885 at the ABS control module connector.
Is resistance between 2100 and 2400 ohms?
Yes
Go to next
No
Is resistance below 2100 ohms?
Yes
Disconnect left rear wheel speed circuit at the sensor Measure resistance between Circuit 884 and Circuit 885 at the sensor connector
Is resistance less than 200 ohms?
No
Wheel speed sensor
Yes
Circuit 884 shorted to Circuit 885.
No
Check continuity of Circuit 884.
Is Circuit 884 ok?
No
Circuit 884 open.
Yes
Check continuity of Circuit 885.
Is Circuit 885 ok?
No
Circuit 885 open.
Yes
Wheel speed sensor

G34029100023010X

Fig. 29 Code 23, LR wheel speed = 0 MPH (Part 1 of 2)

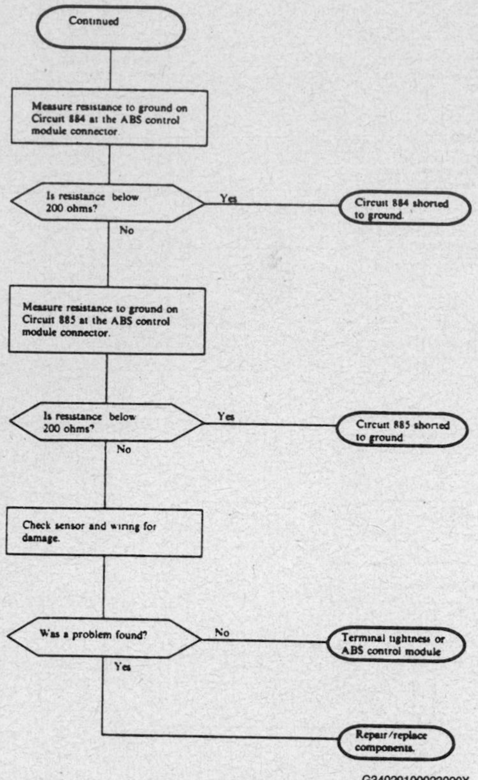
Continued
Measure resistance to ground on Circuit 884 at the ABS control module connector.
Is resistance below 200 ohms?
Yes
Circuit 884 shorted to ground.
No
Measure resistance to ground on Circuit 885 at the ABS control module connector.
Is resistance below 200 ohms?
Yes
Circuit 885 shorted to ground
No
Check sensor and wiring for damage.
Was a problem found?
No
Terminal tightness or ABS control module
Yes
Repair/replace components.

G34029100023020X

Fig. 29 Code 23, LR wheel speed = 0 MPH (Part 2 of 2)

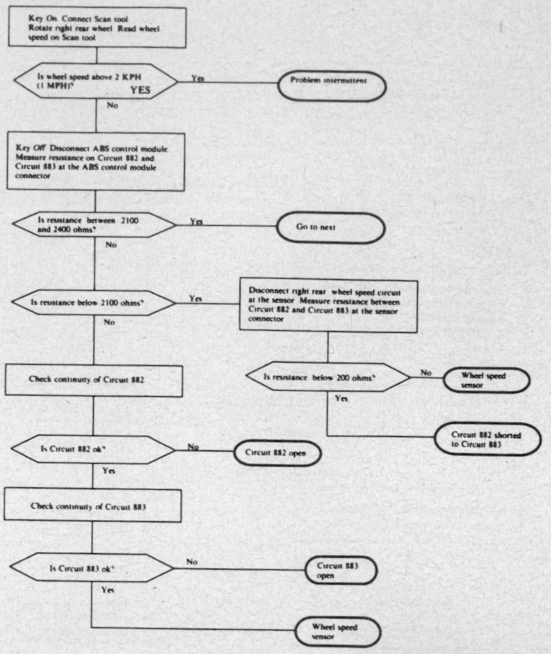
Key On. Connect Scan tool Rotate right rear wheel. Read wheel speed on Scan tool
Is wheel speed above 2 KPH (1 MPH)?
YES
Yes
Problem intermittent
No
Key Off. Disconnect ABS control module. Measure resistance on Circuit 882 and Circuit 883 at the ABS control module connector
Is resistance between 2100 and 2400 ohms?
Yes
Go to next
No
Is resistance below 2100 ohms?
Yes
Disconnect right rear wheel speed circuit at the sensor. Measure resistance between Circuit 882 and Circuit 883 at the sensor connector
Is resistance below 200 ohms?
No
Wheel speed sensor
Yes
Circuit 882 shorted to Circuit 883
No
Check continuity of Circuit 882
Is Circuit 882 ok?
No
Circuit 882 open
Yes
Check continuity of Circuit 883
Is Circuit 883 ok?
No
Circuit 883 open
Yes
Wheel speed sensor

G34029100024010X

Fig. 30 Code 24, RR wheel speed = 0 MPH (Part 1 of 2)

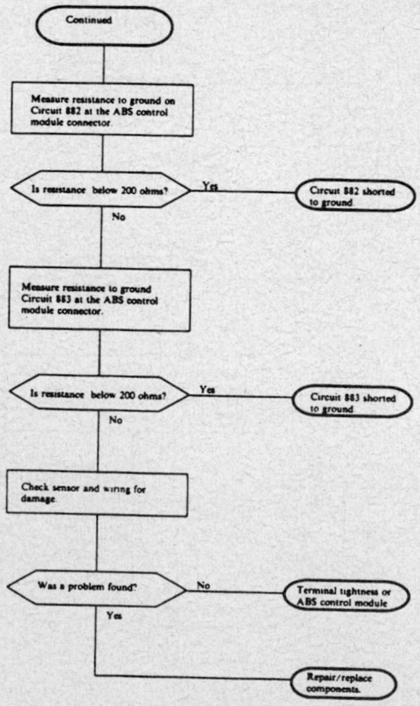
Continued
Measure resistance to ground on Circuit 882 at the ABS control module connector.
Is resistance below 200 ohms?
Yes
Circuit 882 shorted to ground.
No
Measure resistance to ground Circuit 883 at the ABS control module connector.
Is resistance below 200 ohms?
Yes
Circuit 883 shorted to ground
No
Check sensor and wiring for damage.
Was a problem found?
No
Terminal tightness or ABS control module
Yes
Repair/replace components.

G34029100024020X

Fig. 30 Code 24, RR wheel speed = 0 MPH (Part 2 of 2)

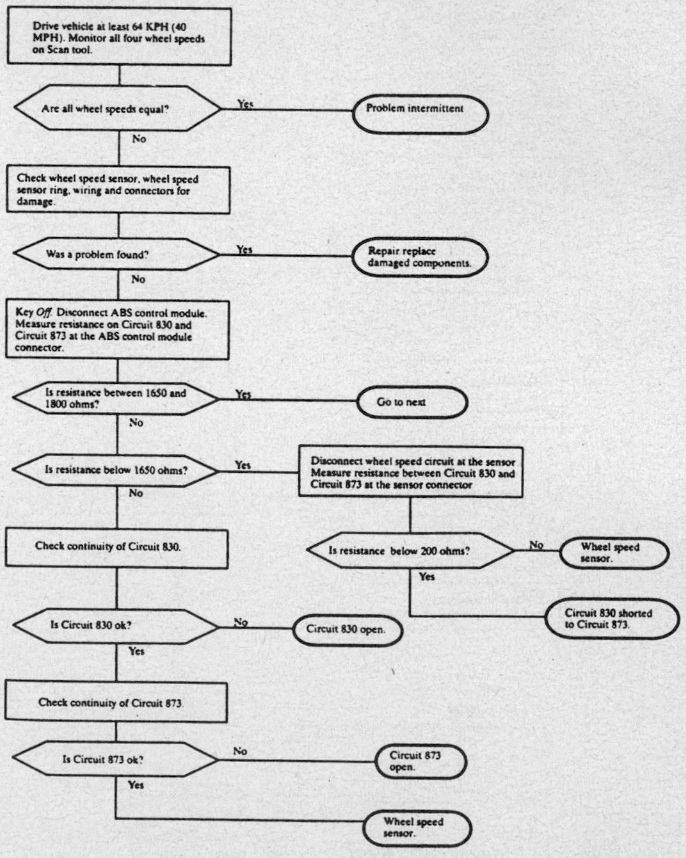
Drive vehicle at least 64 KPH (40 MPH). Monitor all four wheel speeds on Scan tool.
Are all wheel speeds equal?
Yes
Problem intermittent
No
Check wheel speed sensor, wheel speed sensor ring, wiring and connectors for damage.
Was a problem found?
Yes
Repair replace damaged components.
No
Key Off. Disconnect ABS control module. Measure resistance on Circuit 830 and Circuit 873 at the ABS control module connector.
Is resistance between 1650 and 1800 ohms?
Yes
Go to next
No
Is resistance below 1650 ohms?
Yes
Disconnect wheel speed circuit at the sensor. Measure resistance between Circuit 830 and Circuit 873 at the sensor connector
Is resistance below 200 ohms?
No
Wheel speed sensor.
Yes
Circuit 830 shorted to Circuit 873.
No
Check continuity of Circuit 830.
Is Circuit 830 ok?
No
Circuit 830 open.
Yes
Check continuity of Circuit 873.
Is Circuit 873 ok?
No
Circuit 873 open.
Yes
Wheel speed sensor.

G34029100025010X

Fig. 31 Code 25, LF wheel speed acceleration fault (Part 1 of 2)

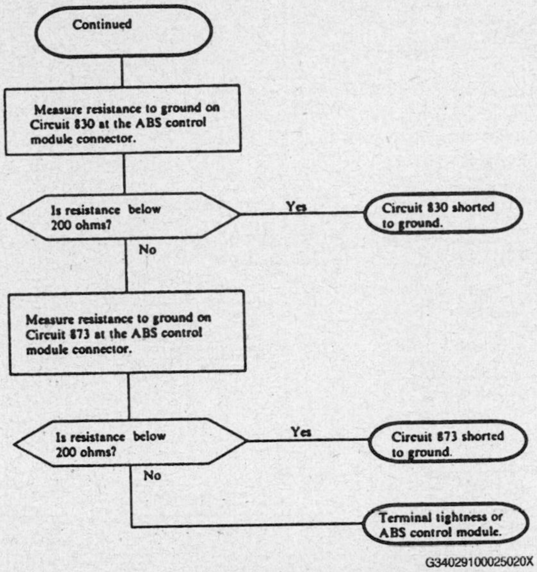
Continued
Measure resistance to ground on Circuit 830 at the ABS control module connector.
Is resistance below 200 ohms?
Yes
Circuit 830 shorted to ground.
No
Measure resistance to ground on Circuit 873 at the ABS control module connector.
Is resistance below 200 ohms?
Yes
Circuit 873 shorted to ground.
No
Terminal tightness or ABS control module.
G34029100025020X

Fig. 31 Code 25, LF wheel speed acceleration fault (Part 2 of 2)

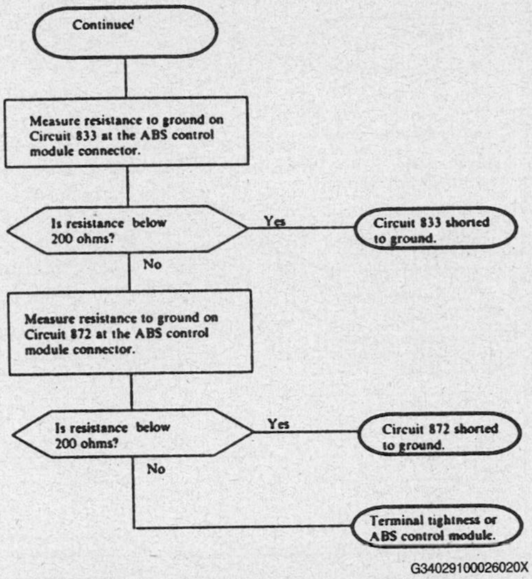
Continued
Measure resistance to ground on Circuit 833 at the ABS control module connector.
Is resistance below 200 ohms?
Yes
Circuit 833 shorted to ground.
No
Measure resistance to ground on Circuit 872 at the ABS control module connector.
Is resistance below 200 ohms?
Yes
Circuit 872 shorted to ground.
No
Terminal tightness or ABS control module.
G34029100026020X

Fig. 32 Code 26, RF wheel speed acceleration fault (Part 2 of 2)

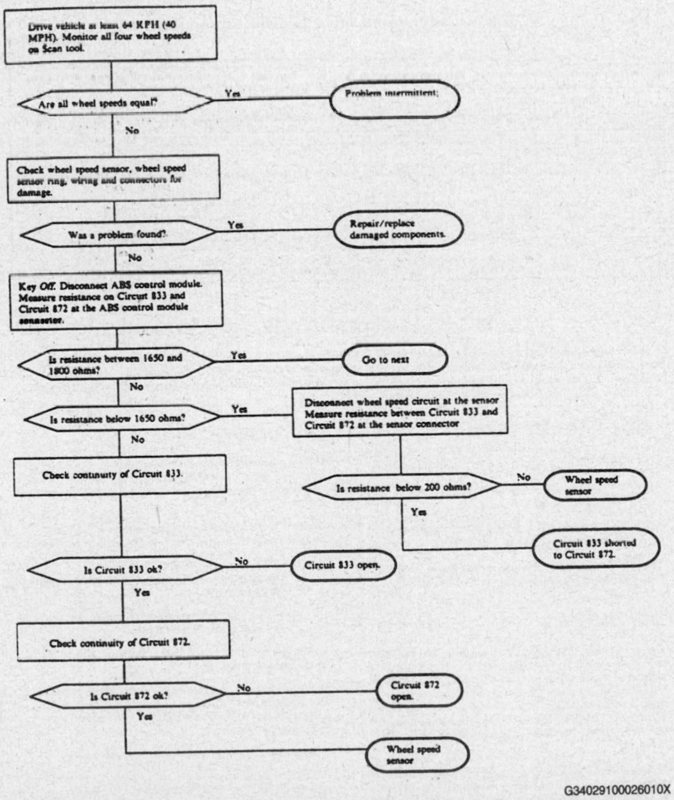
Drive vehicle at least 64 KPH (40 MPH). Monitor all four wheel speeds on Scan tool.
Are all wheel speeds equal?
Yes
Problem intermittent;
No
Check wheel speed sensor, wheel speed sensor ring, wiring and connectors for damage.
Was a problem found?
Yes
Repair/replace damaged components.
No
Key Off. Disconnect ABS control module. Measure resistance on Circuit 833 and Circuit 872 at the ABS control module connector.
Is resistance between 1650 and 1800 ohms?
Yes
Go to next
No
Is resistance below 1650 ohms?
Yes
Disconnect wheel speed circuit at the sensor Measure resistance between Circuit 833 and Circuit 872 at the sensor connector
Is resistance below 200 ohms?
No
Wheel speed sensor
Yes
Circuit 833 shorted to Circuit 872.
No
Check continuity of Circuit 833.
Is Circuit 833 ok?
No
Circuit 833 open.
Yes
Check continuity of Circuit 872.
Is Circuit 872 ok?
No
Circuit 872 open.
Yes
Wheel speed sensor
G34029100026010X

Fig. 32 Code 26, RF wheel speed acceleration fault (Part 1 of 2)

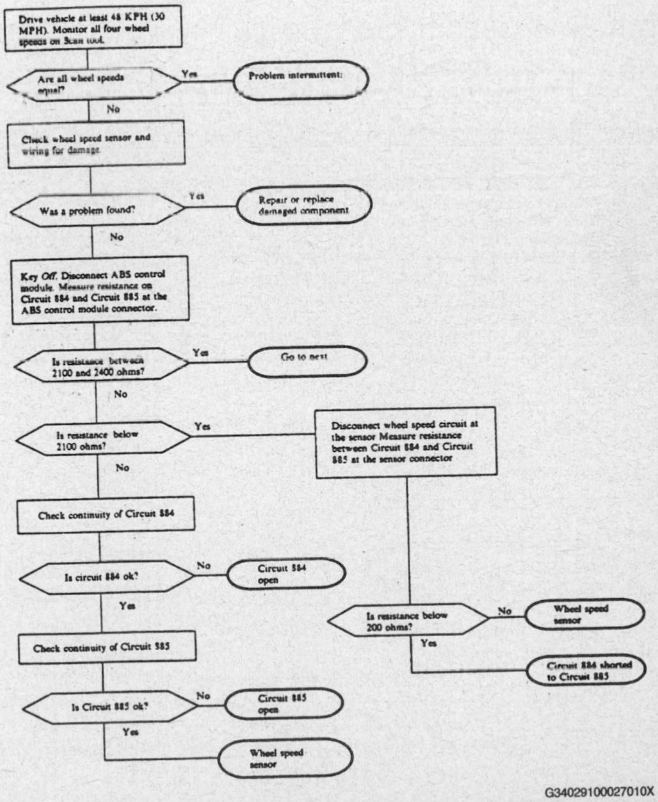
Drive vehicle at least 48 KPH (30 MPH). Monitor all four wheel speeds on Scan tool.
Are all wheel speeds equal?
Yes
Problem intermittent:
No
Check wheel speed sensor and wiring for damage.
Was a problem found?
Yes
Repair or replace damaged component
No
Key Off. Disconnect ABS control module. Measure resistance on Circuit 884 and Circuit 885 at the ABS control module connector.
Is resistance between 2100 and 2400 ohms?
Yes
Go to next
No
Is resistance below 2100 ohms?
Yes
Disconnect wheel speed circuit at the sensor Measure resistance between Circuit 884 and Circuit 885 at the sensor connector
Is resistance below 200 ohms?
No
Wheel speed sensor
Yes
Circuit 884 shorted to Circuit 885
No
Check continuity of Circuit 884
Is circuit 884 ok?
No
Circuit 884 open
Yes
Check continuity of Circuit 885
Is Circuit 885 ok?
No
Circuit 885 open
Yes
Wheel speed sensor
G34029100027010X

Fig. 33 Code 27, LR wheel speed acceleration fault (Part 1 of 2)

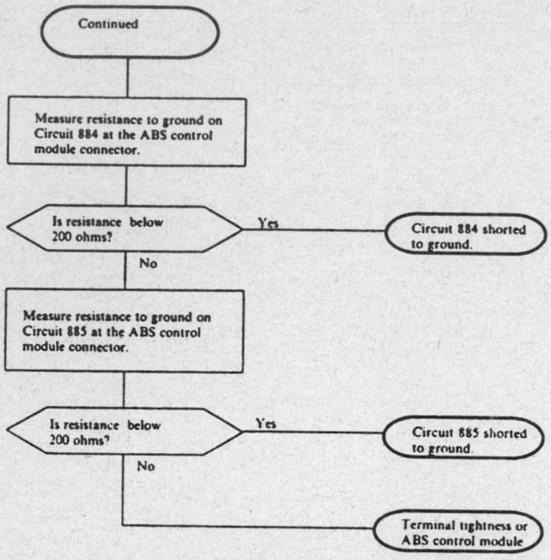
Continued
Measure resistance to ground on Circuit 884 at the ABS control module connector.
Is resistance below 200 ohms?
Yes
Circuit 884 shorted to ground.
No
Measure resistance to ground on Circuit 885 at the ABS control module connector.
Is resistance below 200 ohms?
Yes
Circuit 885 shorted to ground.
No
Terminal tightness or ABS control module

G34029100027020X

Fig. 33 Code 27, LR wheel speed acceleration fault (Part 2 of 2)

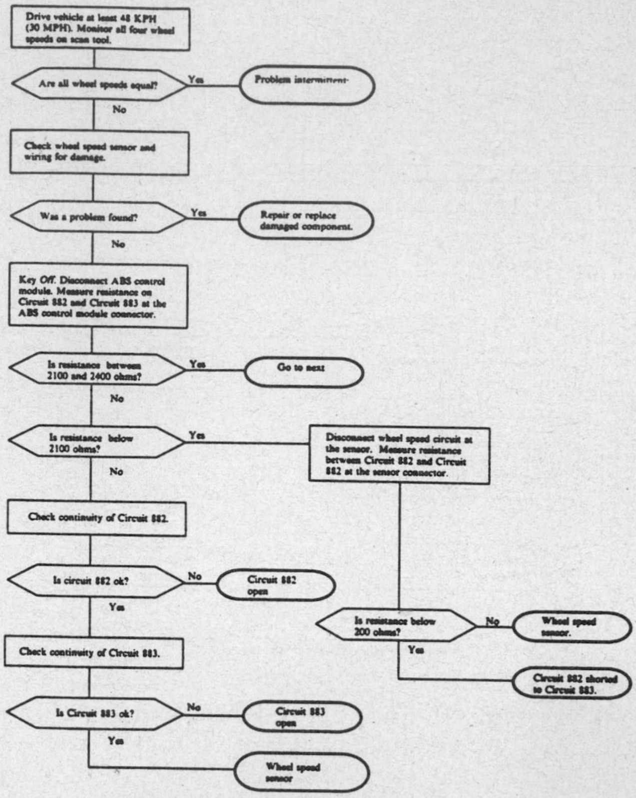
Drive vehicle at least 48 KPH (30 MPH). Monitor all four wheel speeds on scan tool.
Are all wheel speeds equal?
Yes
Problem intermittent
No
Check wheel speed sensor and wiring for damage.
Was a problem found?
Yes
Repair or replace damaged component.
No
Key Off. Disconnect ABS control module. Measure resistance on Circuit 882 and Circuit 883 at the ABS control module connector.
Is resistance between 2100 and 2400 ohms?
Yes
Go to next
No
Is resistance below 2100 ohms?
Yes
Disconnect wheel speed circuit at the sensor. Measure resistance between Circuit 882 and Circuit 882 at the sensor connector.
No
Check continuity of Circuit 882.
Is circuit 882 ok?
No
Circuit 882 open
Yes
Is resistance below 200 ohms?
No
Wheel speed sensor.
Yes
Circuit 882 shorted to Circuit 883.
Check continuity of Circuit 883.
Is Circuit 883 ok?
No
Circuit 883 open
Yes
Wheel speed sensor

G34029100028010X

Fig. 34 Code 28, RR wheel speed acceleration fault (Part 1 of 2)

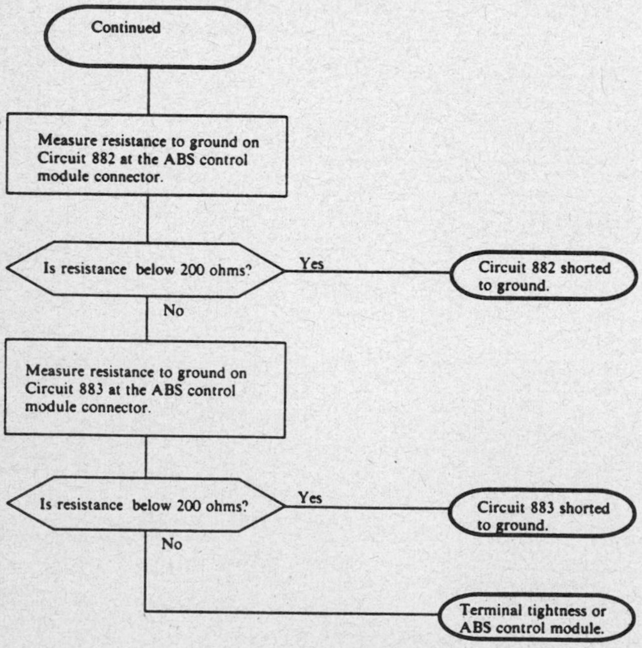
Continued
Measure resistance to ground on Circuit 882 at the ABS control module connector.
Is resistance below 200 ohms?
Yes
Circuit 882 shorted to ground.
No
Measure resistance to ground on Circuit 883 at the ABS control module connector.
Is resistance below 200 ohms?
Yes
Circuit 883 shorted to ground.
No
Terminal tightness or ABS control module.

G34029100028020X

Fig. 34 Code 28, RR wheel speed acceleration fault (Part 2 of 2)

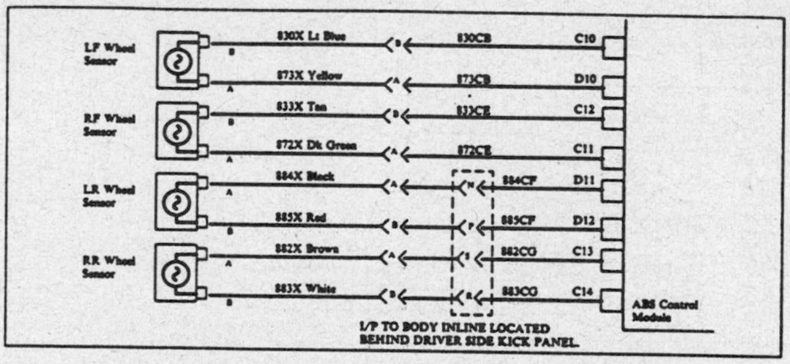
LF Wheel Sensor
RF Wheel Sensor
LR Wheel Sensor
RR Wheel Sensor
830X Lt Blue
873X Yellow
833X Tan
872X Dk Green
884X Black
885X Red
882X Brown
883X White
830CB
873CB
833CE
872CE
884CF
885CF
882CG
883CG
C10
D10
C12
C11
D11
D12
C13
C14
ABS Control Module
I/P TO BODY INLINE LOCATED BEHIND DRIVER SIDE KICK PANEL

ANY TWO WHEEL SPEEDS ARE 0 KPH (0 MPH)

The four wheel speed sensors monitor the speed of each wheel by placing a magnetic coupling next to a toothed ring mounted on the axle of each front wheel and in the hub and bearing of each rear wheel. The signal changes with the wheel speed. If the wheel speed signal is seen at 0 MPH on any two wheels while the car is moving, the control module will disable all ABS and turn on the Antilock telltale.

CODE PARAMETERS

Code 31 sets if:

Any two wheel speeds Are 0 KPH (0 MPH) for 60 seconds.

This code can set anytime vehicle is moving faster then 16 KPH (10 MPH) and not in ABS braking.

The vehicle should be driven at speeds above 16 KPH (10 MPH) to check for reappearance of this failure.

DIAGNOSIS

Diagnose Code 31 by connecting the Scan tool and either driving the vehicle or rotating each wheel by hand to determine which wheel speeds equal 0 KPH (0 MPH). When the faulty wheel sensors are identified, proceed with the corresponding Wheel Speed = 0 trouble tree (Codes 21, 22, 23, or 24). Closely inspect the connectors in the circuitry, since this is the most likely cause of a Code 31.

If both rear wheel speeds = 0 KPH (0 MPH), check the inline connector located behind the driver side kick panel for a bad connection or the body extension harness to the rear axle harness connector for a bad connection.

DIAGNOSTIC AIDS

Before proceeding make a thorough visual inspection of the wheel speed sensor circuitry. Closely inspect the inline connector(s) since this is the most likely area for opens or shorts.

Connect the Scan tool, spin the wheel by hand, and monitor the wheel speed. Make a comparison with other wheels.

- Visually inspect the sensors for a loose fastener or damage.
- Using an ohmmeter to check resistance, shake wires to locate intermittents.

Check the tightness of the female terminal grip with a spare male terminal.

When attempting to diagnose an intermittent problem, use the Scan tool* to review supplemental diagnostic information. The supplemental data can be used to duplicate a problem.

* Select Malf History from Scan tool ABS menu.

Intermittents or opens suspected to be at the connectors can be detected by using a Diagnostic Service Probe. Voltage can be read on wires without disconnecting any connectors.

G34029100029000X

Fig. 35 Code 31, any two wheel speeds = 0

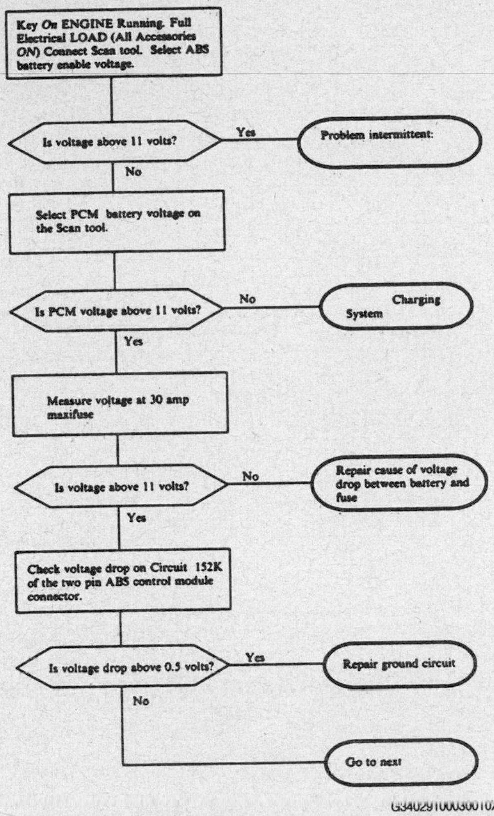

Key On ENGINE Running. Full Electrical LOAD (All Accessories ON) Connect Scan tool. Select ABS battery enable voltage.
Is voltage above 11 volts?
Yes
Problem intermittent:
No
Select PCM battery voltage on the Scan tool.
Is PCM voltage above 11 volts?
No
Charging System
Yes
Measure voltage at 30 amp maxifuse
Is voltage above 11 volts?
No
Repair cause of voltage drop between battery and fuse
Yes
Check voltage drop on Circuit 152K of the two pin ABS control module connector.
Is voltage drop above 0.5 volts?
Yes
Repair ground circuit
No
Go to next
G34029100030010X

Fig. 36 Code 36, ABS system voltage low (Part 1 of 2)

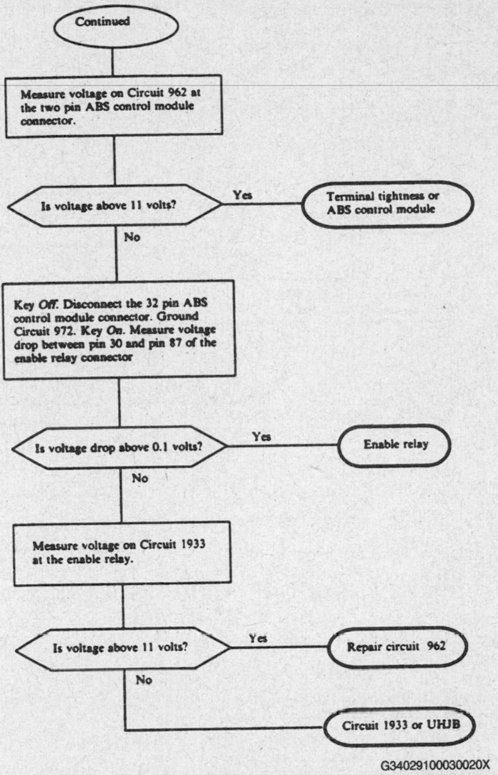

Continued
Measure voltage on Circuit 962 at the two pin ABS control module connector.
Is voltage above 11 volts?
Yes
Terminal tightness or ABS control module
No
Key Off. Disconnect the 32 pin ABS control module connector. Ground Circuit 972. Key On. Measure voltage drop between pin 30 and pin 87 of the enable relay connector
Is voltage drop above 0.1 volts?
Yes
Enable relay
No
Measure voltage on Circuit 1933 at the enable relay.
Is voltage above 11 volts?
Yes
Repair circuit 962
No
Circuit 1933 or UHJB
G34029100030020X

Fig. 36 Code 36, ABS system voltage low (Part 2 of 2)

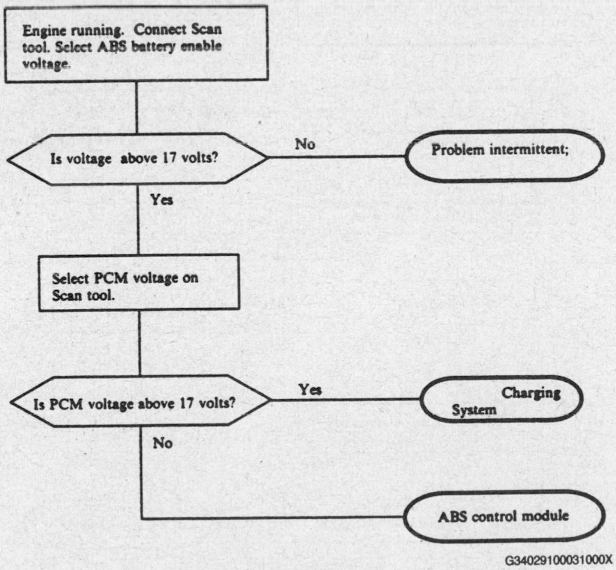

Engine running. Connect Scan tool. Select ABS battery enable voltage.
Is voltage above 17 volts?
No
Problem intermittent;
Yes
Select PCM voltage on Scan tool.
Is PCM voltage above 17 volts?
Yes
Charging System
No
ABS control module
G34029100031000X

Fig. 37 Code 37, ABS system voltage high

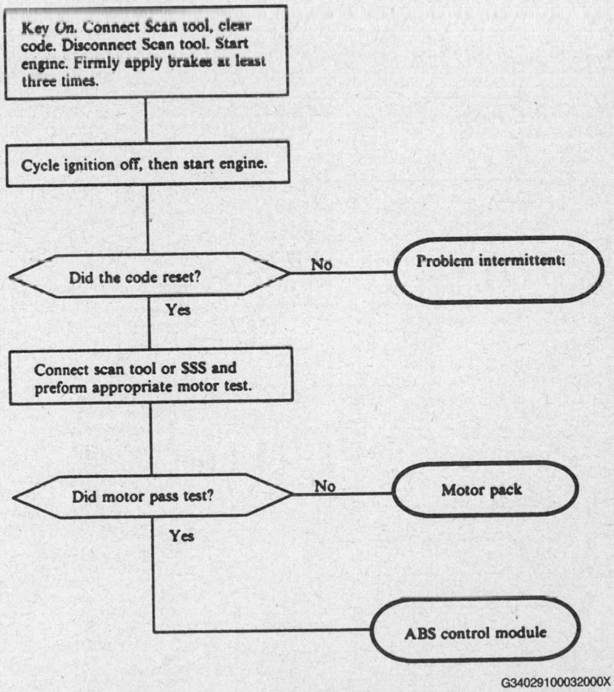

Key On. Connect Scan tool, clear code. Disconnect Scan tool. Start engine. Firmly apply brakes at least three times.
Cycle ignition off, then start engine.
Did the code reset?
No
Problem intermittent:
Yes
Connect scan tool or SSS and preform appropriate motor test.
Did motor pass test?
No
Motor pack
Yes
ABS control module
G34029100032000X

Fig. 38 Code 38, left front ESB does not hold motor

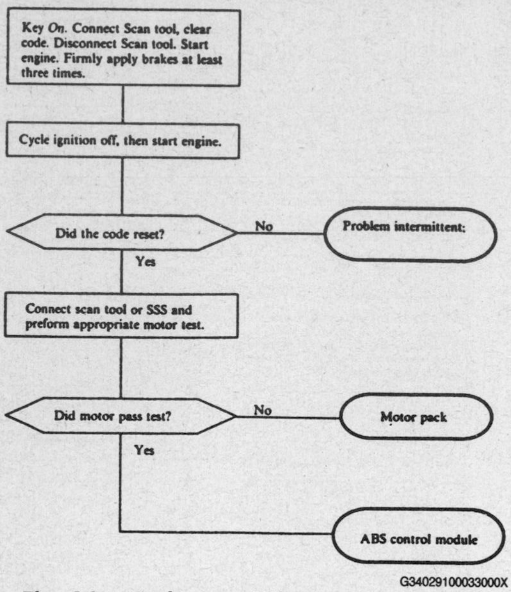
Key On. Connect Scan tool, clear code. Disconnect Scan tool. Start engine. Firmly apply brakes at least three times.
Cycle ignition off, then start engine.
Did the code reset?
No
Problem intermittent:
Yes
Connect scan tool or SSS and preform appropriate motor test.
Did motor pass test?
No
Motor pack
Yes
ABS control module
G34029100033000X

Fig. 39 Code 41, right front ESB does not hold motor

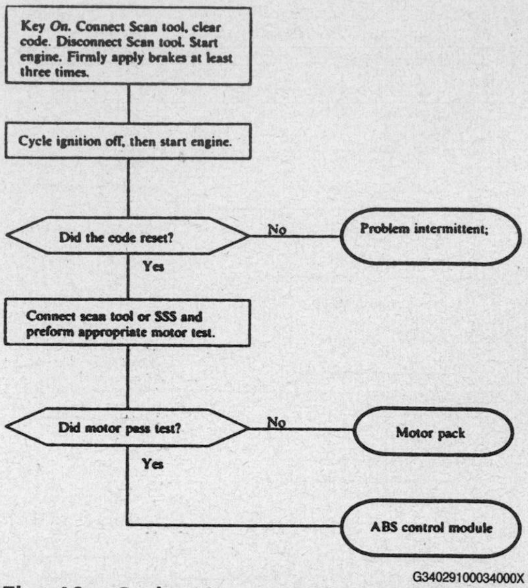
Key On. Connect Scan tool, clear code. Disconnect Scan tool. Start engine. Firmly apply brakes at least three times.
Cycle ignition off, then start engine.
Did the code reset?
No
Problem intermittent:
Yes
Connect scan tool or SSS and preform appropriate motor test.
Did motor pass test?
No
Motor pack
Yes
ABS control module
G34029100034000X

Fig. 40 Code 42, rear ESB does not hold motor

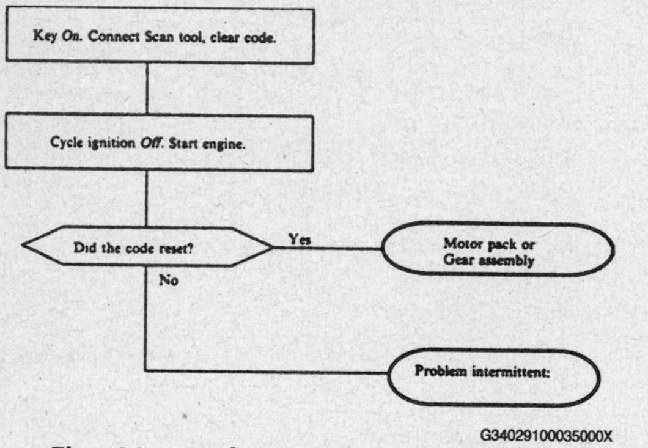
Key On. Connect Scan tool, clear code.
Cycle ignition Off. Start engine.
Did the code reset?
Yes
Motor pack or Gear assembly
No
Problem intermittent:
G34029100035000X

Fig. 41 Code 44, LF motor frozen

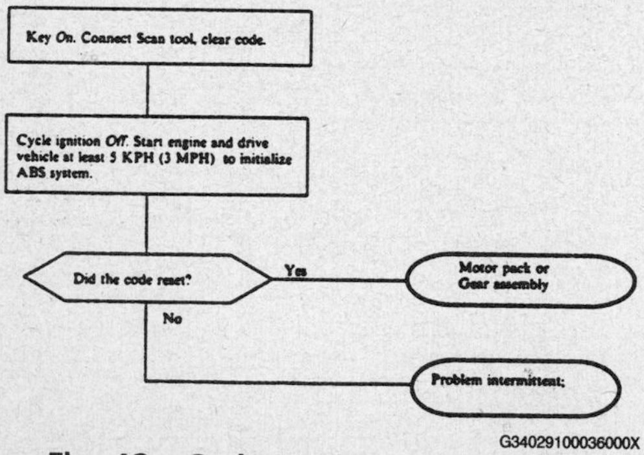
Key On. Connect Scan tool, clear code.
Cycle ignition Off. Start engine and drive vehicle at least 5 KPH (3 MPH) to initialize ABS system.
Did the code reset?
Yes
Motor pack or Gear assembly
No
Problem intermittent:
G34029100036000X

Fig. 42 Code 45, RF motor frozen

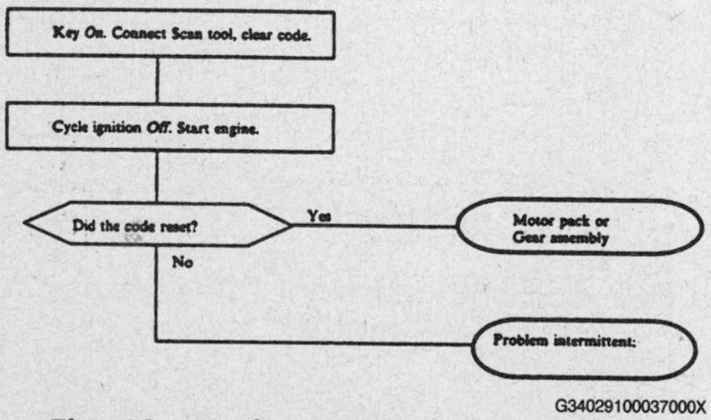
Key On. Connect Scan tool, clear code.
Cycle ignition Off. Start engine.
Did the code reset?
Yes
Motor pack or Gear assembly
No
Problem intermittent:
G34029100037000X

Fig. 43 Code 46, rear motor frozen

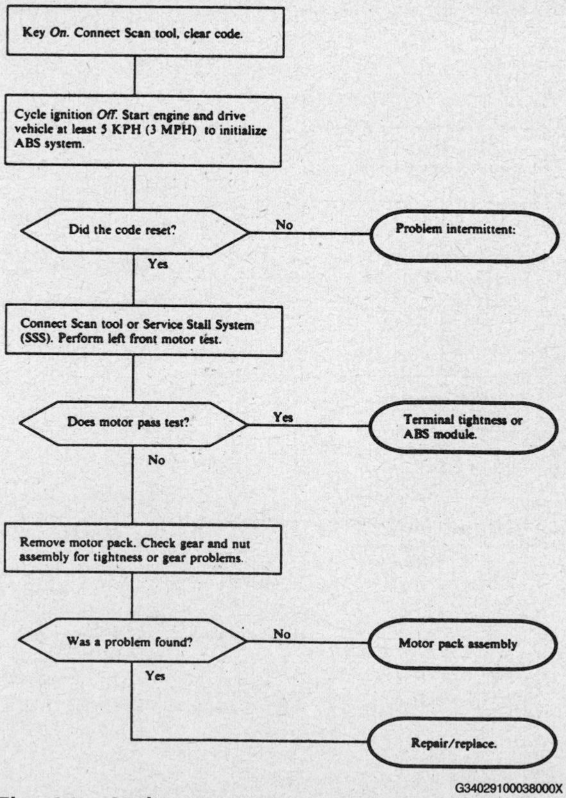
Key On. Connect Scan tool, clear code.
Cycle ignition Off. Start engine and drive vehicle at least 5 KPH (3 MPH) to initialize ABS system.
Did the code reset?
No
Problem intermittent:
Yes
Connect Scan tool or Service Stall System (SSS). Perform left front motor test.
Does motor pass test?
Yes
Terminal tightness or ABS module.
No
Remove motor pack. Check gear and nut assembly for tightness or gear problems.
Was a problem found?
No
Motor pack assembly
Yes
Repair/replace.
G34029100038000X

Fig. 44 Code 47, LF motor circuit current low

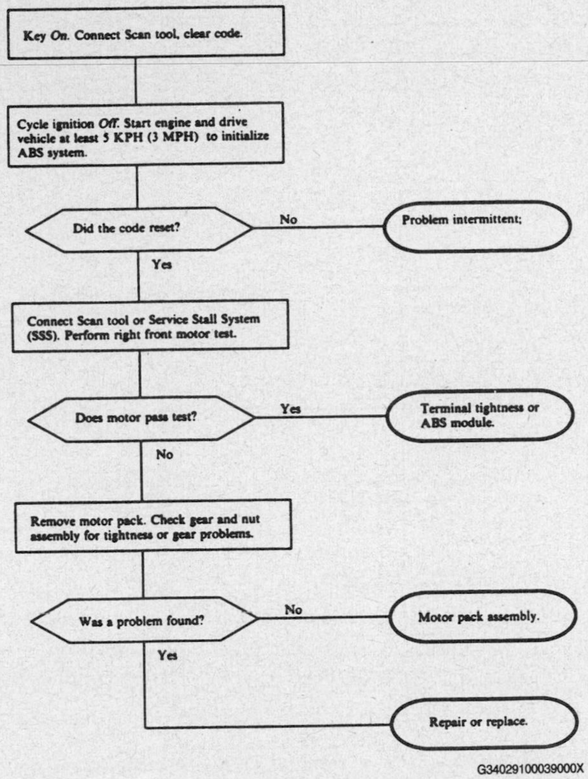
Key On. Connect Scan tool, clear code.
Cycle ignition Off. Start engine and drive vehicle at least 5 KPH (3 MPH) to initialize ABS system.
Did the code reset?
No
Problem intermittent;
Yes
Connect Scan tool or Service Stall System (SSS). Perform right front motor test.
Does motor pass test?
Yes
Terminal tightness or ABS module.
No
Remove motor pack. Check gear and nut assembly for tightness or gear problems.
Was a problem found?
No
Motor pack assembly.
Yes
Repair or replace.
G34029100039000X

Fig. 45 Code 48, RF motor circuit current low

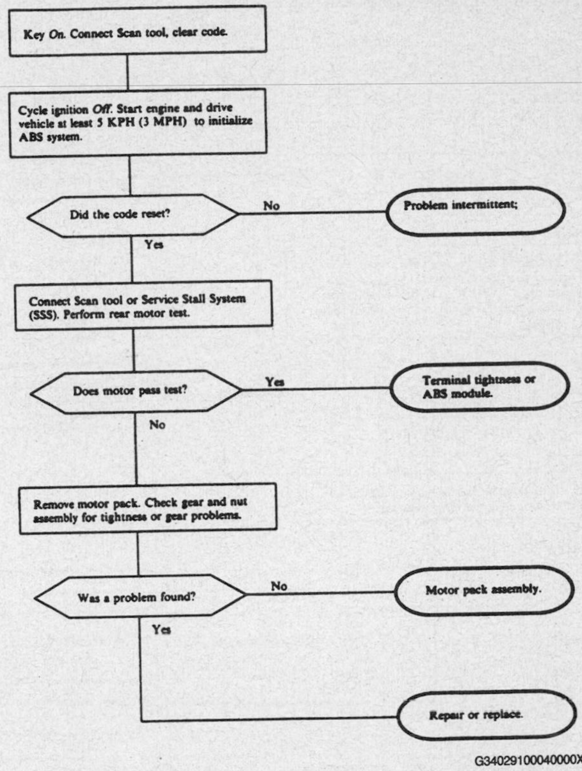
Key On. Connect Scan tool, clear code.
Cycle ignition Off. Start engine and drive vehicle at least 5 KPH (3 MPH) to initialize ABS system.
Did the code reset?
No
Problem intermittent;
Yes
Connect Scan tool or Service Stall System (SSS). Perform rear motor test.
Does motor pass test?
Yes
Terminal tightness or ABS module.
No
Remove motor pack. Check gear and nut assembly for tightness or gear problems.
Was a problem found?
No
Motor pack assembly.
Yes
Repair or replace.
G34029100040000X

Fig. 46 Code 51, rear motor circuit current low

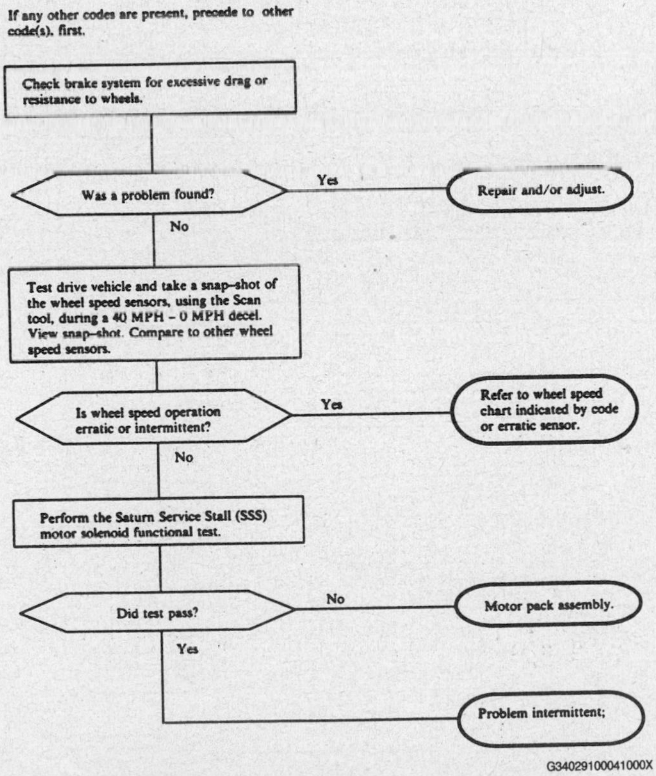
If any other codes are present, precede to other code(s) first.
Check brake system for excessive drag or resistance to wheels.
Was a problem found?
Yes
Repair and/or adjust.
No
Test drive vehicle and take a snap-shot of the wheel speed sensors, using the Scan tool, during a 40 MPH – 0 MPH decel. View snap-shot. Compare to other wheel speed sensors.
Is wheel speed operation erratic or intermittent?
Yes
Refer to wheel speed chart indicated by code or erratic sensor.
No
Perform the Saturn Service Stall (SSS) motor solenoid functional test.
Did test pass?
No
Motor pack assembly.
Yes
Problem intermittent;
G34029100041000X

Fig. 47 Code 52, LF in release too long

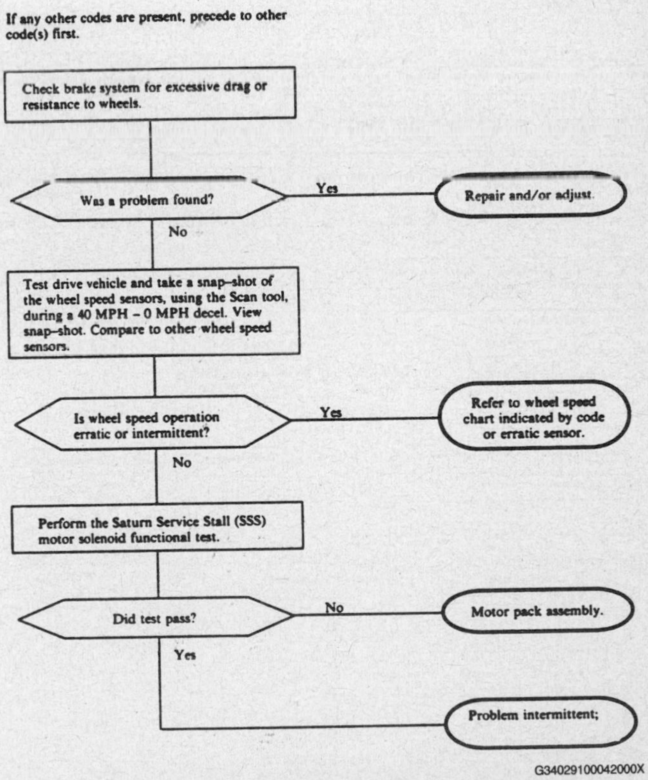
If any other codes are present, precede to other code(s) first.
Check brake system for excessive drag or resistance to wheels.
Was a problem found?
Yes
Repair and/or adjust.
No
Test drive vehicle and take a snap-shot of the wheel speed sensors, using the Scan tool, during a 40 MPH – 0 MPH decel. View snap-shot. Compare to other wheel speed sensors.
Is wheel speed operation erratic or intermittent?
Yes
Refer to wheel speed chart indicated by code or erratic sensor.
No
Perform the Saturn Service Stall (SSS) motor solenoid functional test.
Did test pass?
No
Motor pack assembly.
Yes
Problem intermittent;
G34029100042000X

Fig. 48 Code 53, RF in release too long

If any other codes are present, precede to code(s).

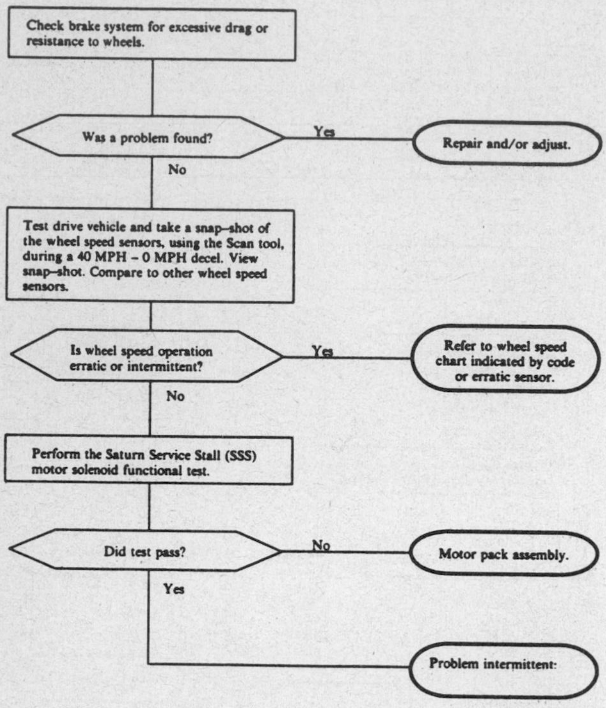
Check brake system for excessive drag or resistance to wheels.
Was a problem found?
Yes
Repair and/or adjust.
No
Test drive vehicle and take a snap–shot of the wheel speed sensors, using the Scan tool, during a 40 MPH – 0 MPH decel. View snap–shot. Compare to other wheel speed sensors.
Is wheel speed operation erratic or intermittent?
Yes
Refer to wheel speed chart indicated by code or erratic sensor.
No
Perform the Saturn Service Stall (SSS) motor solenoid functional test.
Did test pass?
No
Motor pack assembly.
Yes
Problem intermittent:

G34029100043000X

Fig. 49 Code 54, rear in release too long

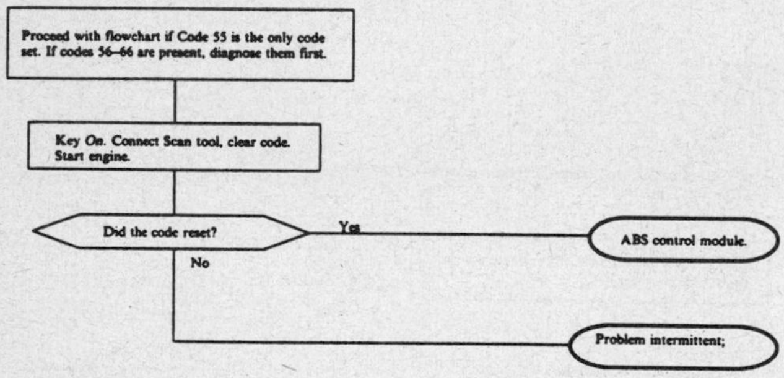
Proceed with flowchart if Code 55 is the only code set. If codes 56–66 are present, diagnose them first.
Key On. Connect Scan tool, clear code. Start engine.
Did the code reset?
Yes
ABS control module.
No
Problem intermittent;

G34029100044000X

Fig. 50 Code 55, motor circuit fault detected

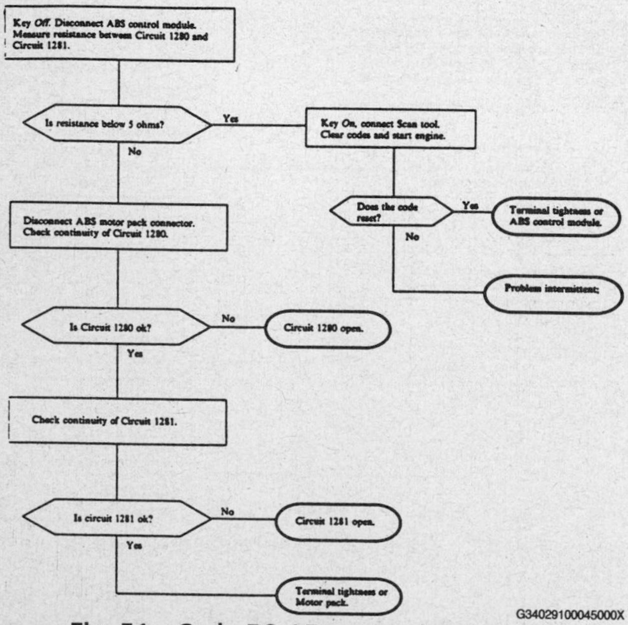
Key Off. Disconnect ABS control module. Measure resistance between Circuit 1280 and Circuit 1281.
Is resistance below 5 ohms?
Yes
Key On, connect Scan tool. Clear codes and start engine.
Does the code reset?
Yes
Terminal tightness or ABS control module.
No
Problem intermittent;
No
Disconnect ABS motor pack connector. Check continuity of Circuit 1280.
Is Circuit 1280 ok?
No
Circuit 1280 open.
Yes
Check continuity of Circuit 1281.
Is circuit 1281 ok?
No
Circuit 1281 open.
Yes
Terminal tightness or Motor pack.

G34029100045000X

Fig. 51 Code 56, LF motor circuit open

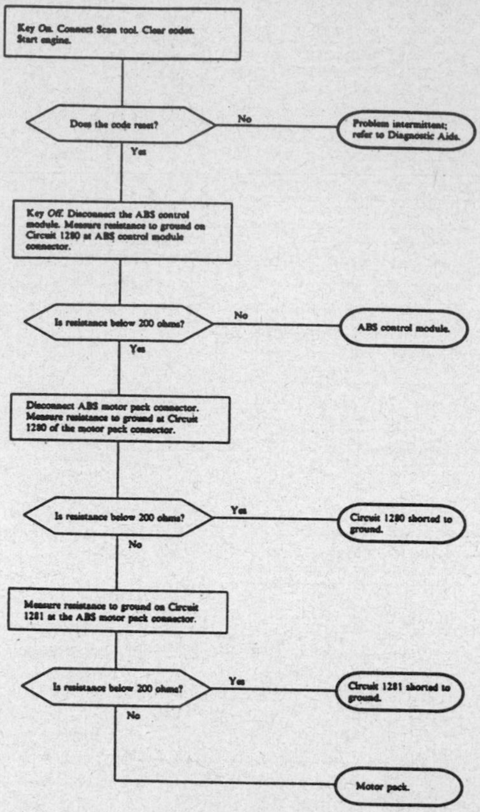
Key On. Connect Scan tool. Clear codes. Start engine.
Does the code reset?
No
Problem intermittent; refer to Diagnostic Aids.
Yes
Key Off. Disconnect the ABS control module. Measure resistance to ground on Circuit 1280 at ABS control module connector.
Is resistance below 200 ohms?
No
ABS control module.
Yes
Disconnect ABS motor pack connector. Measure resistance to ground at Circuit 1280 of the motor pack connector.
Is resistance below 200 ohms?
Yes
Circuit 1280 shorted to ground.
No
Measure resistance to ground on Circuit 1281 at the ABS motor pack connector.
Is resistance below 200 ohms?
Yes
Circuit 1281 shorted to ground.
No
Motor pack.

G34029100046000X

Fig. 52 Code 57, LF motor circuit grounded

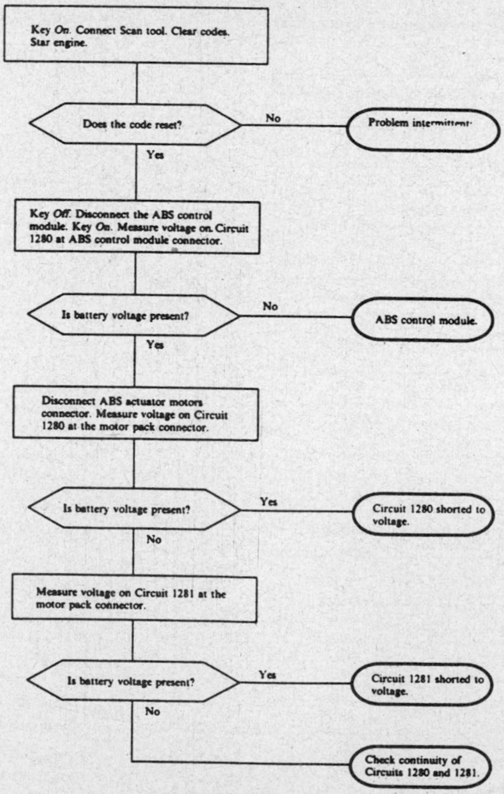
Key On. Connect Scan tool. Clear codes. Star engine.
Does the code reset?
No
Problem intermittent
Yes
Key Off. Disconnect the ABS control module. Key On. Measure voltage on Circuit 1280 at ABS control module connector.
Is battery voltage present?
No
ABS control module.
Yes
Disconnect ABS actuator motors connector. Measure voltage on Circuit 1280 at the motor pack connector.
Is battery voltage present?
Yes
Circuit 1280 shorted to voltage.
No
Measure voltage on Circuit 1281 at the motor pack connector.
Is battery voltage present?
Yes
Circuit 1281 shorted to voltage.
No
Check continuity of Circuits 1280 and 1281.

G34029100047000X

Fig. 53 Code 58, LF motor circuit shorted to B+. 1992

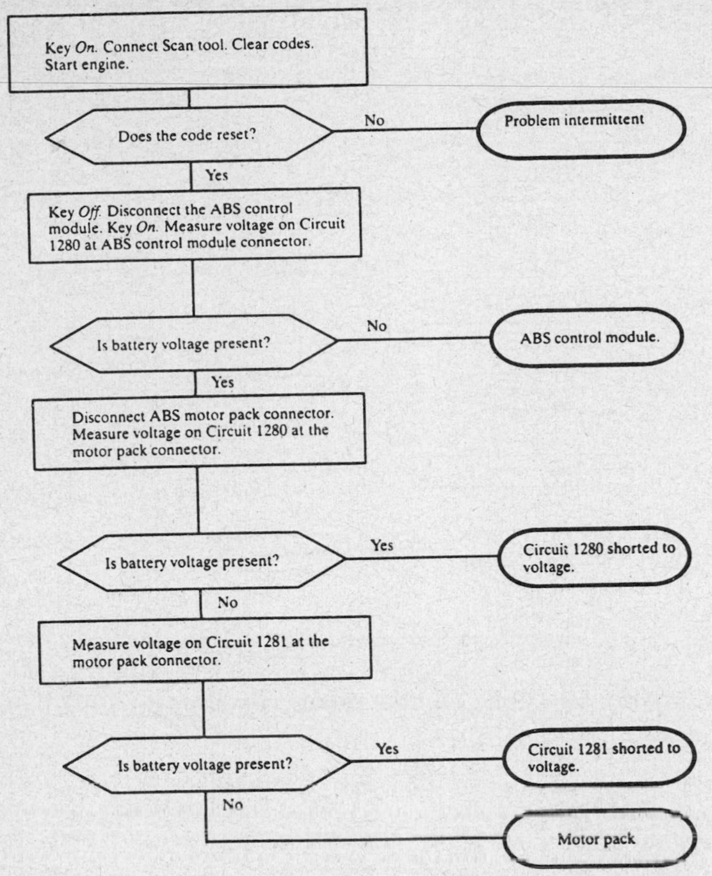
Key On. Connect Scan tool. Clear codes. Start engine.
Does the code reset?
No
Problem intermittent
Yes
Key Off. Disconnect the ABS control module. Key On. Measure voltage on Circuit 1280 at ABS control module connector.
Is battery voltage present?
No
ABS control module.
Yes
Disconnect ABS motor pack connector. Measure voltage on Circuit 1280 at the motor pack connector.
Is battery voltage present?
Yes
Circuit 1280 shorted to voltage.
No
Measure voltage on Circuit 1281 at the motor pack connector.
Is battery voltage present?
Yes
Circuit 1281 shorted to voltage.
No
Motor pack

G34029300048000X

Fig. 54 Code 58, LF motor circuit shorted to B+. 1993-95

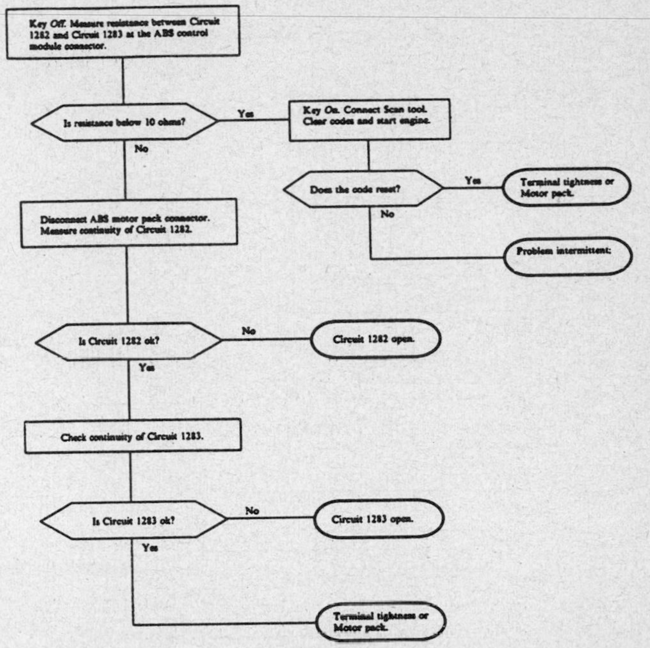
Key Off. Measure resistance between Circuit 1282 and Circuit 1283 at the ABS control module connector.
Is resistance below 10 ohms?
Yes
Key On. Connect Scan tool. Clear codes and start engine.
Does the code reset?
Yes
Terminal tightness or Motor pack.
No
Problem intermittent.
No
Disconnect ABS motor pack connector. Measure continuity of Circuit 1282.
Is Circuit 1282 ok?
No
Circuit 1282 open.
Yes
Check continuity of Circuit 1283.
Is Circuit 1283 ok?
No
Circuit 1283 open.
Yes
Terminal tightness or Motor pack.

G34029100049000X

Fig. 55 Code 61, RF motor circuit open. 1992

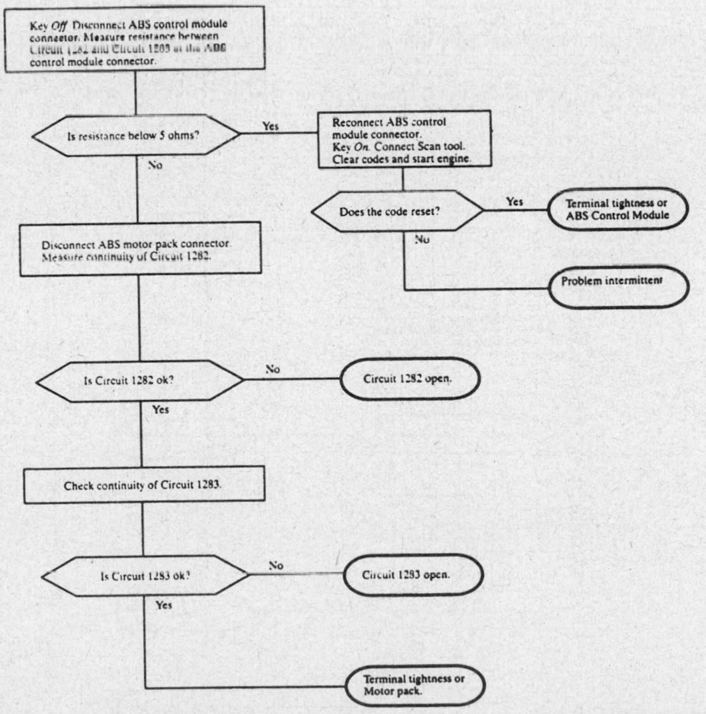
Key Off Disconnect ABS control module connector. Measure resistance between Circuit 1282 and Circuit 1283 at the ABS control module connector.
Is resistance below 5 ohms?
Yes
Reconnect ABS control module connector.
Key On. Connect Scan tool.
Clear codes and start engine.
Does the code reset?
Yes
Terminal tightness or ABS Control Module
No
Problem intermittent
No
Disconnect ABS motor pack connector.
Measure continuity of Circuit 1282.
Is Circuit 1282 ok?
No
Circuit 1282 open.
Yes
Check continuity of Circuit 1283.
Is Circuit 1283 ok?
No
Circuit 1283 open.
Yes
Terminal tightness or Motor pack.

G34029300050000X

Fig. 56 Code 61, RF motor circuit open. 1993-95

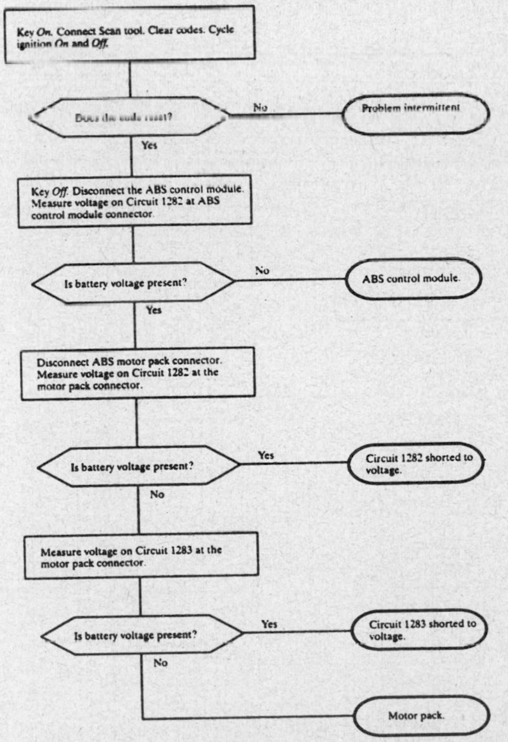
Key On. Connect Scan tool. Clear codes. Cycle ignition On and Off.
No
Problem intermittent
Yes
Key Off. Disconnect the ABS control module. Measure voltage on Circuit 1282 at ABS control module connector.
Is battery voltage present?
No
ABS control module.
Yes
Disconnect ABS motor pack connector. Measure voltage on Circuit 1282 at the motor pack connector.
Is battery voltage present?
Yes
Circuit 1282 shorted to voltage.
No
Measure voltage on Circuit 1283 at the motor pack connector.
Is battery voltage present?
Yes
Circuit 1283 shorted to voltage.
No
Motor pack.

G34029100051000X

Fig. 57 Code 62, RF motor circuit grounded

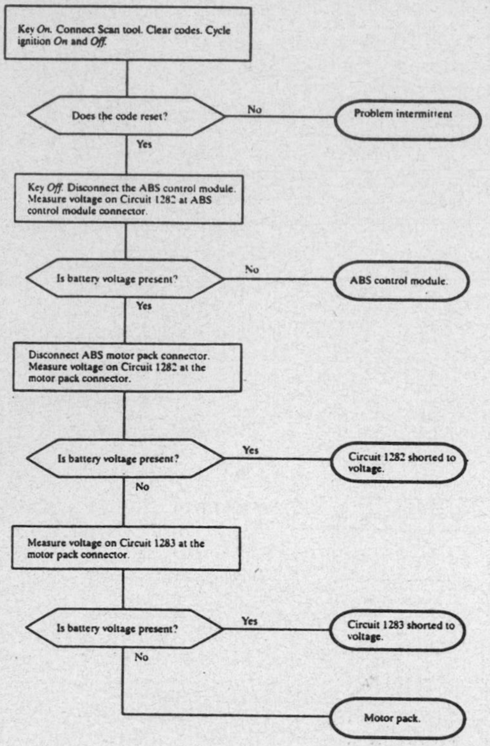

Key On. Connect Scan tool. Clear codes. Cycle ignition On and Off.
Does the code reset?
No
Problem intermittent
Yes
Key Off. Disconnect the ABS control module. Measure voltage on Circuit 1282 at ABS control module connector.
Is battery voltage present?
No
ABS control module.
Yes
Disconnect ABS motor pack connector. Measure voltage on Circuit 1282 at the motor pack connector.
Is battery voltage present?
Yes
Circuit 1282 shorted to voltage.
No
Measure voltage on Circuit 1283 at the motor pack connector.
Is battery voltage present?
Yes
Circuit 1283 shorted to voltage.
No
Motor pack.

G34029100052000X

Fig. 58 Code 63, RF motor circuit shorted to B+

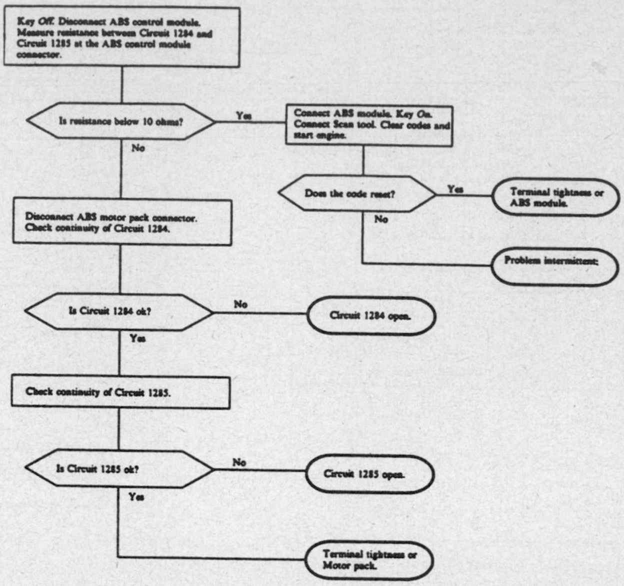

Key Off. Disconnect ABS control module. Measure resistance between Circuit 1284 and Circuit 1285 at the ABS control module connector.
Is resistance below 10 ohms?
Yes
Connect ABS module. Key On. Connect Scan tool. Clear codes and start engine.
Does the code reset?
Yes
Terminal tightness or ABS module.
No
Problem intermittent.
No
Disconnect ABS motor pack connector. Check continuity of Circuit 1284.
Is Circuit 1284 ok?
No
Circuit 1284 open.
Yes
Check continuity of Circuit 1285.
Is Circuit 1285 ok?
No
Circuit 1285 open.
Yes
Terminal tightness or Motor pack.

G34029100053000X

Fig. 59 Code 64, rear motor circuit open. 1992

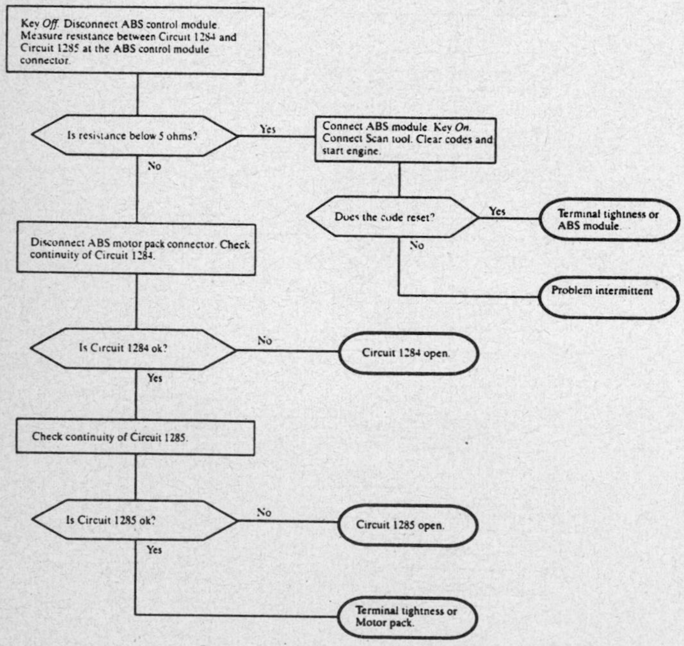

Key Off. Disconnect ABS control module. Measure resistance between Circuit 1284 and Circuit 1285 at the ABS control module connector.
Is resistance below 5 ohms?
Yes
Connect ABS module. Key On. Connect Scan tool. Clear codes and start engine.
Does the code reset?
Yes
Terminal tightness or ABS module.
No
Problem intermittent
No
Disconnect ABS motor pack connector. Check continuity of Circuit 1284.
Is Circuit 1284 ok?
No
Circuit 1284 open.
Yes
Check continuity of Circuit 1285.
Is Circuit 1285 ok?
No
Circuit 1285 open.
Yes
Terminal tightness or Motor pack.

G34029300054000X

Fig. 60 Code 64, rear motor circuit open. 1993-95

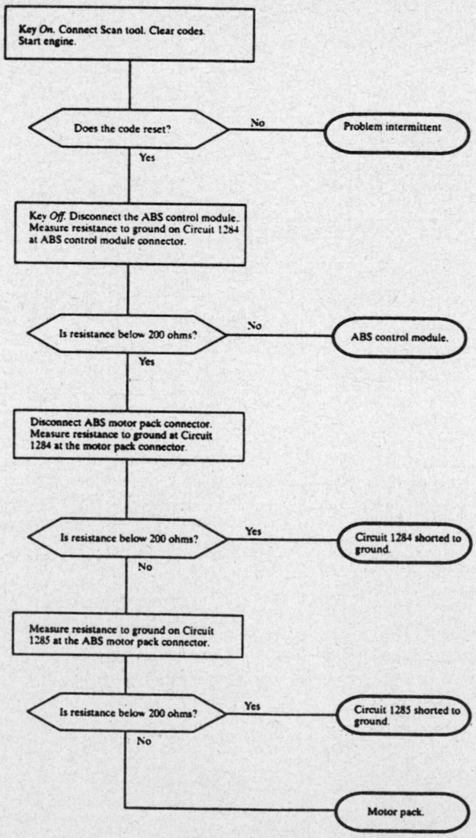

Key On. Connect Scan tool. Clear codes. Start engine.
Does the code reset?
No
Problem intermittent
Yes
Key Off. Disconnect the ABS control module. Measure resistance to ground on Circuit 1284 at ABS control module connector.
Is resistance below 200 ohms?
No
ABS control module.
Yes
Disconnect ABS motor pack connector. Measure resistance to ground at Circuit 1284 at the motor pack connector.
Is resistance below 200 ohms?
Yes
Circuit 1284 shorted to ground.
No
Measure resistance to ground on Circuit 1285 at the ABS motor pack connector.
Is resistance below 200 ohms?
Yes
Circuit 1285 shorted to ground.
No
Motor pack.

G34029100055000X

Fig. 61 Code 65, rear motor circuit grounded

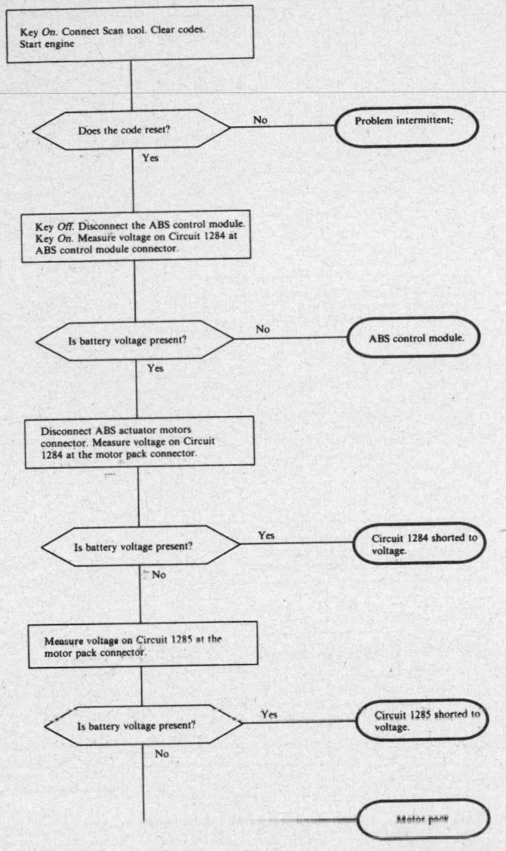
Key On. Connect Scan tool. Clear codes. Start engine
Does the code reset?
No
Problem intermittent;
Yes
Key Off. Disconnect the ABS control module. Key On. Measure voltage on Circuit 1284 at ABS control module connector.
Is battery voltage present?
No
ABS control module.
Yes
Disconnect ABS actuator motors connector. Measure voltage on Circuit 1284 at the motor pack connector.
Is battery voltage present?
Yes
Circuit 1284 shorted to voltage.
No
Measure voltage on Circuit 1285 at the motor pack connector.
Is battery voltage present?
Yes
Circuit 1285 shorted to voltage.
No
Motor pack

G34029100056000X

Fig. 62 Code 66, rear motor circuit shorted to B+

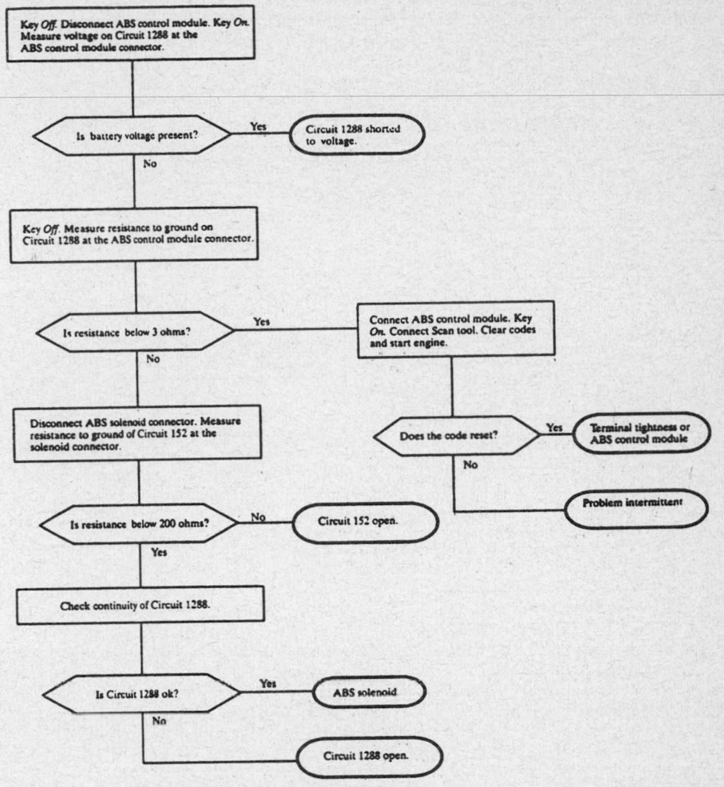
Key Off. Disconnect ABS control module. Key On. Measure voltage on Circuit 1288 at the ABS control module connector.
Is battery voltage present?
Yes
Circuit 1288 shorted to voltage.
No
Key Off. Measure resistance to ground on Circuit 1288 at the ABS control module connector.
Is resistance below 3 ohms?
Yes
Connect ABS control module. Key On. Connect Scan tool. Clear codes and start engine.
Does the code reset?
Yes
Terminal tightness or ABS control module
No
Problem intermittent
No
Disconnect ABS solenoid connector. Measure resistance to ground of Circuit 152 at the solenoid connector.
Is resistance below 200 ohms?
No
Circuit 152 open.
Yes
Check continuity of Circuit 1288.
Is Circuit 1288 ok?
Yes
ABS solenoid.
No
Circuit 1288 open.

G34029100057000X

Fig. 63 Code 76, solenoid circuit 1288 open or shorted to B+. 1992-93

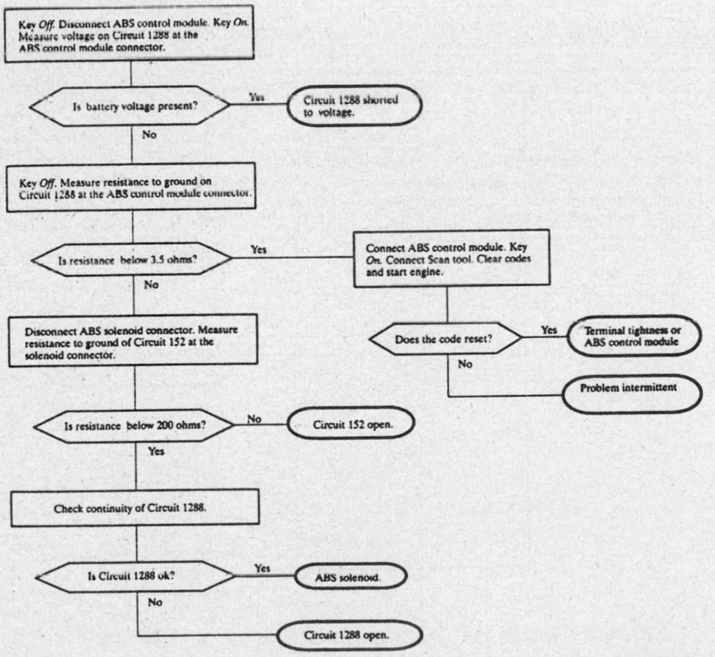
Key Off. Disconnect ABS control module. Key On. Measure voltage on Circuit 1288 at the ABS control module connector.
Is battery voltage present?
Yes
Circuit 1288 shorted to voltage.
No
Key Off. Measure resistance to ground on Circuit 1288 at the ABS control module connector.
Is resistance below 3.5 ohms?
Yes
Connect ABS control module. Key On. Connect Scan tool. Clear codes and start engine.
Does the code reset?
Yes
Terminal tightness or ABS control module
No
Problem intermittent
No
Disconnect ABS solenoid connector. Measure resistance to ground of Circuit 152 at the solenoid connector.
Is resistance below 200 ohms?
No
Circuit 152 open.
Yes
Check continuity of Circuit 1288.
Is Circuit 1288 ok?
Yes
ABS solenoid.
No
Circuit 1288 open.

G34029400058000X

Fig. 64 Code 76, solenoid circuit 1288 open or shorted to B+. 1994–95

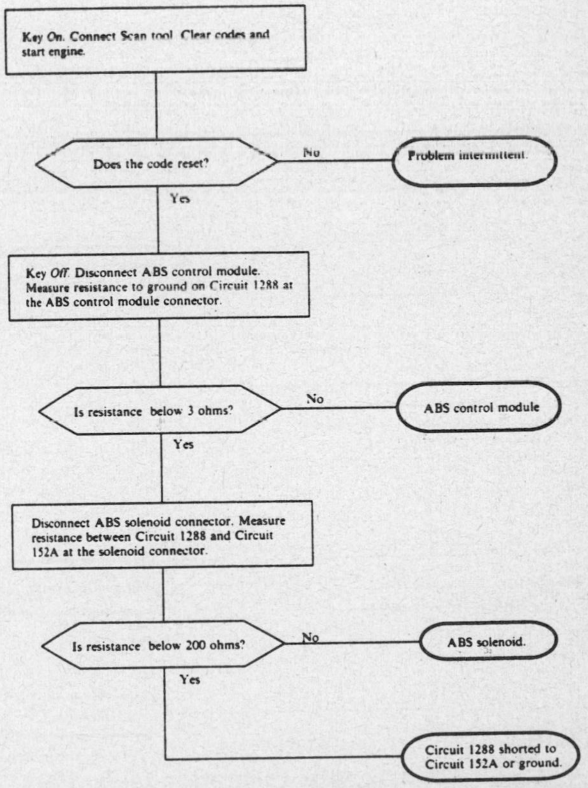
Key On. Connect Scan tool. Clear codes and start engine.
Does the code reset?
No
Problem intermittent.
Yes
Key Off. Disconnect ABS control module. Measure resistance to ground on Circuit 1288 at the ABS control module connector.
Is resistance below 3 ohms?
No
ABS control module
Yes
Disconnect ABS solenoid connector. Measure resistance between Circuit 1288 and Circuit 152A at the solenoid connector.
Is resistance below 200 ohms?
No
ABS solenoid.
Yes
Circuit 1288 shorted to Circuit 152A or ground.

G34029100059000X

Fig. 65 Code 77, solenoid circuit 1288 grounded

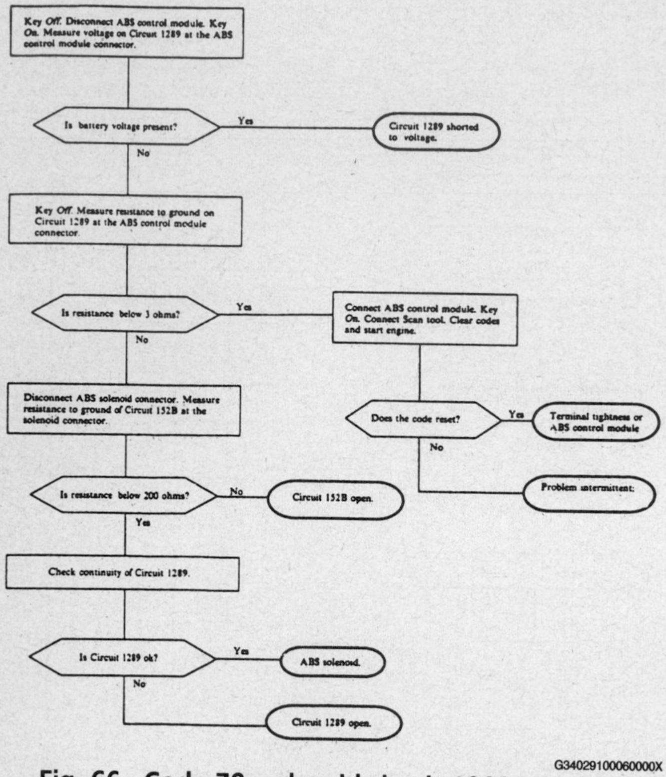
Key Off. Disconnect ABS control module. Key On. Measure voltage on Circuit 1289 at the ABS control module connector.
Is battery voltage present?
Yes
Circuit 1289 shorted to voltage.
No
Key Off. Measure resistance to ground on Circuit 1289 at the ABS control module connector.
Is resistance below 3 ohms?
Yes
Connect ABS control module. Key On. Connect Scan tool. Clear codes and start engine.
Does the code reset?
Yes
Terminal tightness or ABS control module
No
Problem intermittent:
No
Disconnect ABS solenoid connector. Measure resistance to ground of Circuit 152B at the solenoid connector.
Is resistance below 200 ohms?
No
Circuit 152B open.
Yes
Check continuity of Circuit 1289.
Is Circuit 1289 ok?
Yes
ABS solenoid.
No
Circuit 1289 open.
G34029100060000X

Fig. 66 Code 78, solenoid circuit 1289 open or shorted to B +

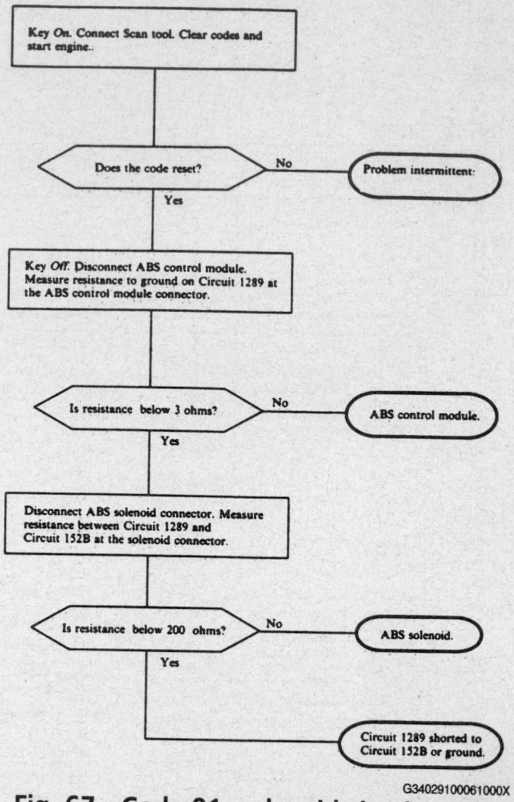
Key On. Connect Scan tool. Clear codes and start engine..
Does the code reset?
No
Problem intermittent:
Yes
Key Off. Disconnect ABS control module. Measure resistance to ground on Circuit 1289 at the ABS control module connector.
Is resistance below 3 ohms?
No
ABS control module.
Yes
Disconnect ABS solenoid connector. Measure resistance between Circuit 1289 and Circuit 152B at the solenoid connector.
Is resistance below 200 ohms?
No
ABS solenoid.
Yes
Circuit 1289 shorted to Circuit 152B or ground.
G34029100061000X

Fig. 67 Code 81, solenoid circuit 1289 grounded

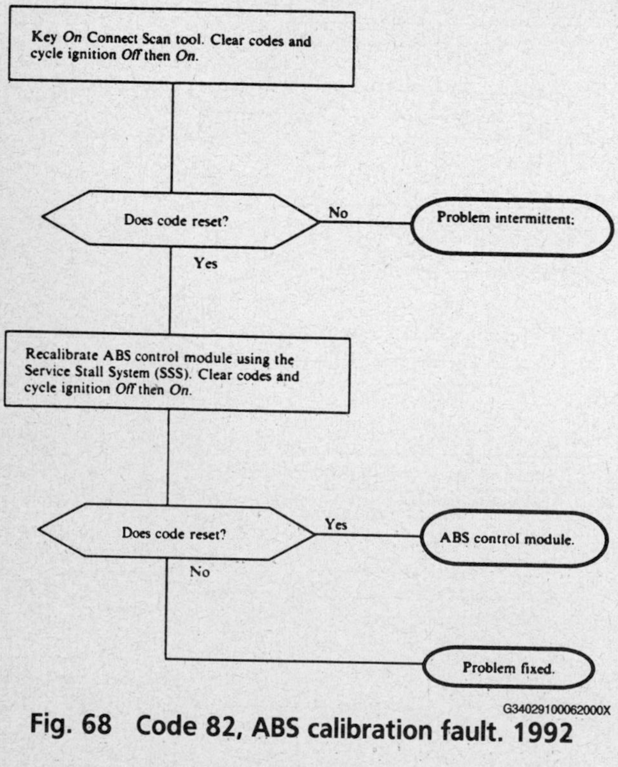
Key On Connect Scan tool. Clear codes and cycle ignition Off then On.
Does code reset?
No
Problem intermittent:
Yes
Recalibrate ABS control module using the Service Stall System (SSS). Clear codes and cycle ignition Off then On.
Does code reset?
Yes
ABS control module.
No
Problem fixed.
G34029100062000X

Fig. 68 Code 82, ABS calibration fault. 1992

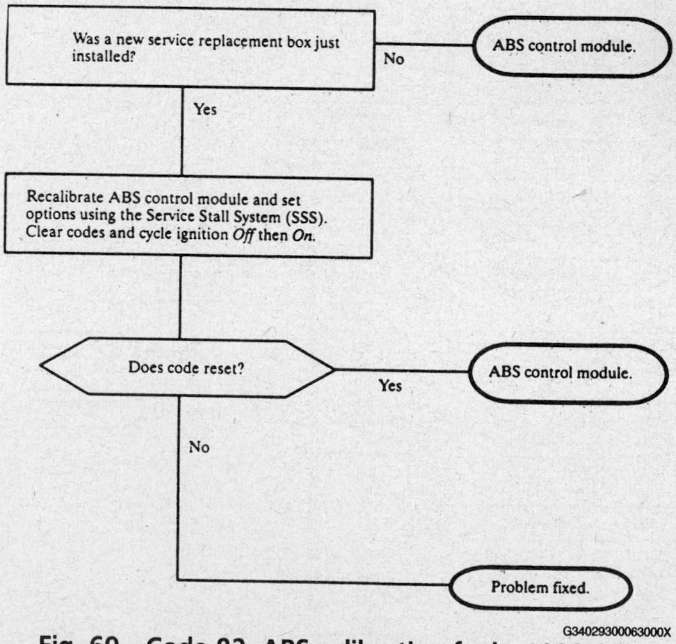
Was a new service replacement box just installed?
No
ABS control module.
Yes
Recalibrate ABS control module and set options using the Service Stall System (SSS). Clear codes and cycle ignition Off then On.
Does code reset?
Yes
ABS control module.
No
Problem fixed.
G34029300063000X

Fig. 69 Code 82, ABS calibration fault. 1993-95

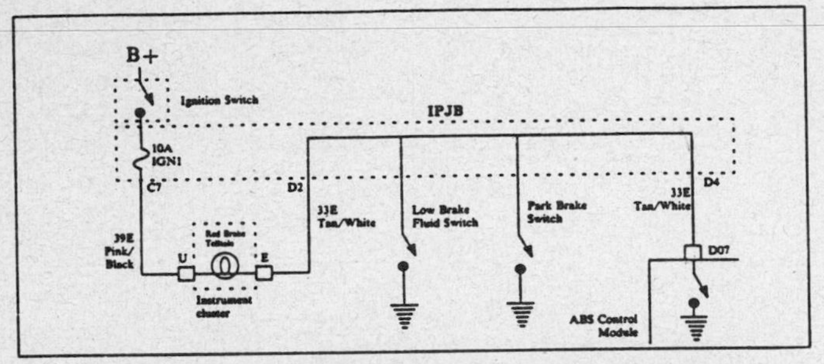
B+
Ignition Switch
IPJB
10A
IGN1
C7
D2
D4
33E
Tan/White
Low Brake
Fluid Switch
Park Brake
Switch
33E
Tan/White
39E
Pink/
Black
Red Brake
Telltale
U
E
D07
Instrument
cluster
ABS Control
Module

RED BRAKE TELLTALE COMMANDED ON BY ABS CONTROL MODULE

The Brake warning telltale can be turned on by the ABS control module in the event that base brake performance is degraded by an ABS fault (such as an open rear motor circuit when the piston is not home).

CODE PARAMETERS

ABS Code 86 will set if:

The ABS control module commands the Brake telltale to turn on.

DIAGNOSTIC AIDS

This code is set to provide notification that the ABS control module turned on the brake telltale.

Diagnose the accompanying ABS codes first. If the brake telltale remains on after the ABS fault is corrected, diagnose the problem associated with the brake telltale (park brake switch, low brake fluid, etc.).

Code 86 should only set in conjunction with another ABS code. If Code 86 sets alone, the ABS control module should be replaced.

G34029100064000X

Fig. 70 Code 86, ABS turned on red brake telltale

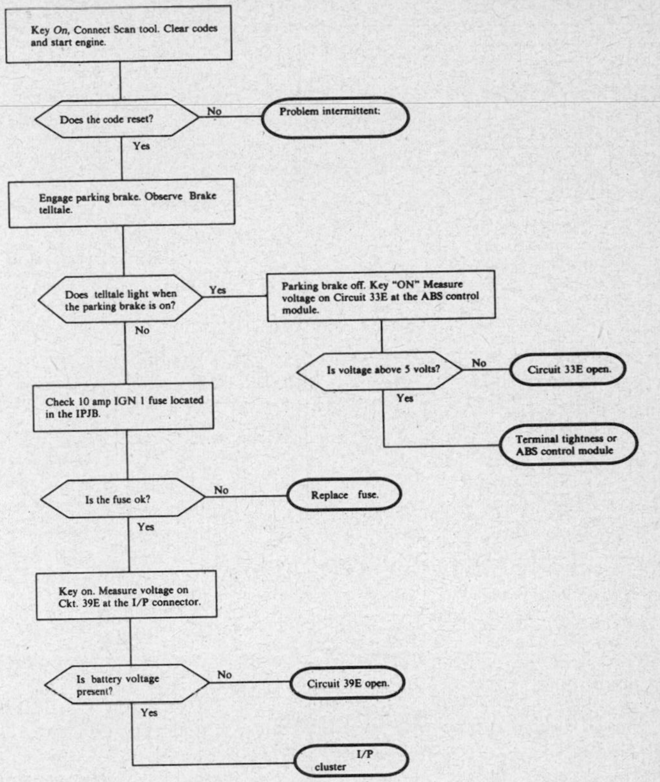
Key On, Connect Scan tool. Clear codes and start engine.
Does the code reset?
No
Problem intermittent.
Yes
Engage parking brake. Observe Brake telltale.
Does telltale light when the parking brake is on?
Yes
Parking brake off. Key "ON" Measure voltage on Circuit 33E at the ABS control module.
No
Is voltage above 5 volts?
No
Circuit 33E open.
Yes
Terminal tightness or ABS control module
Check 10 amp IGN 1 fuse located in the IPJB.
Is the fuse ok?
No
Replace fuse.
Yes
Key on. Measure voltage on Ckt. 39E at the I/P connector.
Is battery voltage present?
No
Circuit 39E open.
Yes
I/P cluster

G34029100065000X

Fig. 71 Code 87, red brake telltale circuit open

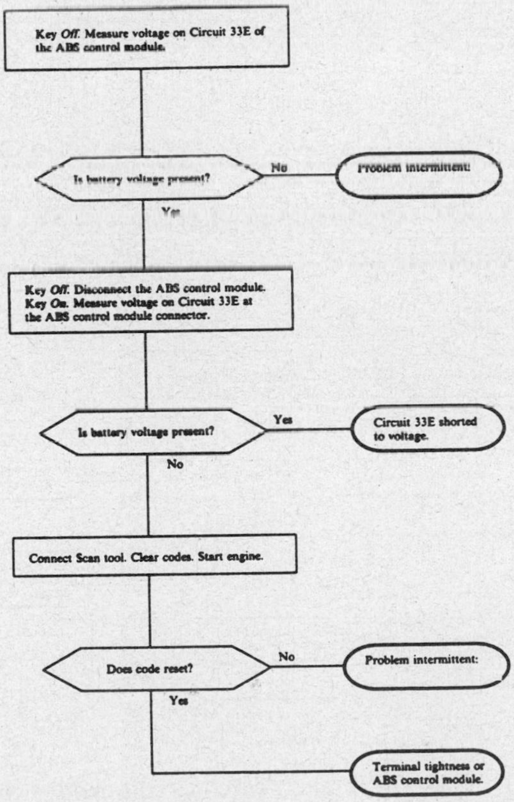
Key Off. Measure voltage on Circuit 33E of the ABS control module.
Is battery voltage present?
No
Problem intermittent.
Yes
Key Off. Disconnect the ABS control module. Key On. Measure voltage on Circuit 33E at the ABS control module connector.
Is battery voltage present?
Yes
Circuit 33E shorted to voltage.
No
Connect Scan tool. Clear codes. Start engine.
Does code reset?
No
Problem intermittent.
Yes
Terminal tightness or ABS control module.

G34029100066000X

Fig. 72 Code 88, red brake telltale circuit shorted to B+. 1992

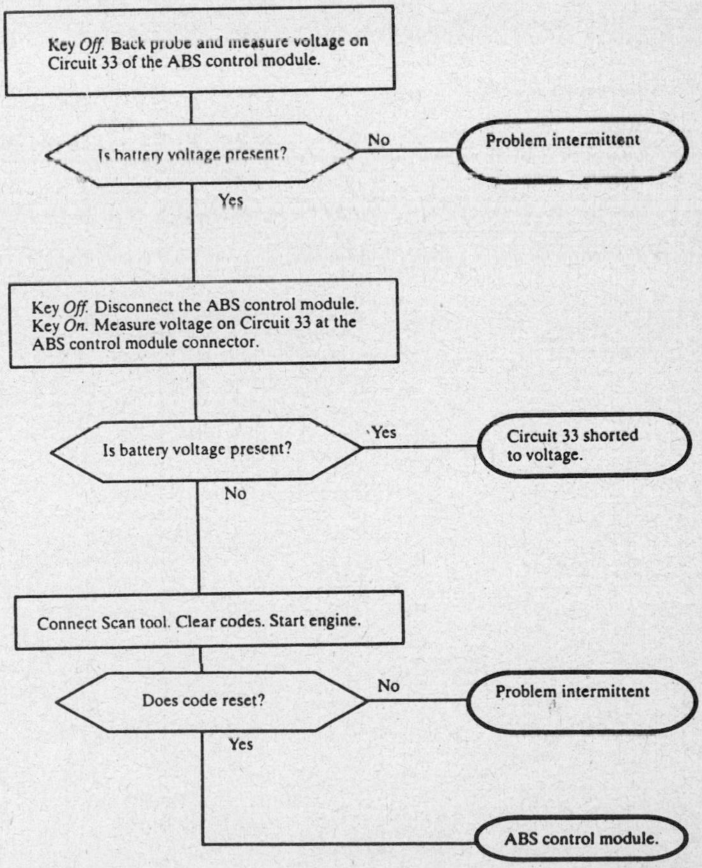
Key Off. Back probe and measure voltage on Circuit 33 of the ABS control module.
Is battery voltage present?
No
Problem intermittent
Yes
Key Off. Disconnect the ABS control module. Key On. Measure voltage on Circuit 33 at the ABS control module connector.
Is battery voltage present?
Yes
Circuit 33 shorted to voltage.
No
Connect Scan tool. Clear codes. Start engine.
Does code reset?
No
Problem intermittent
Yes
ABS control module.

G34029300067000X

Fig. 73 Code 88, red brake telltale circuit shorted to B+. 1993-95

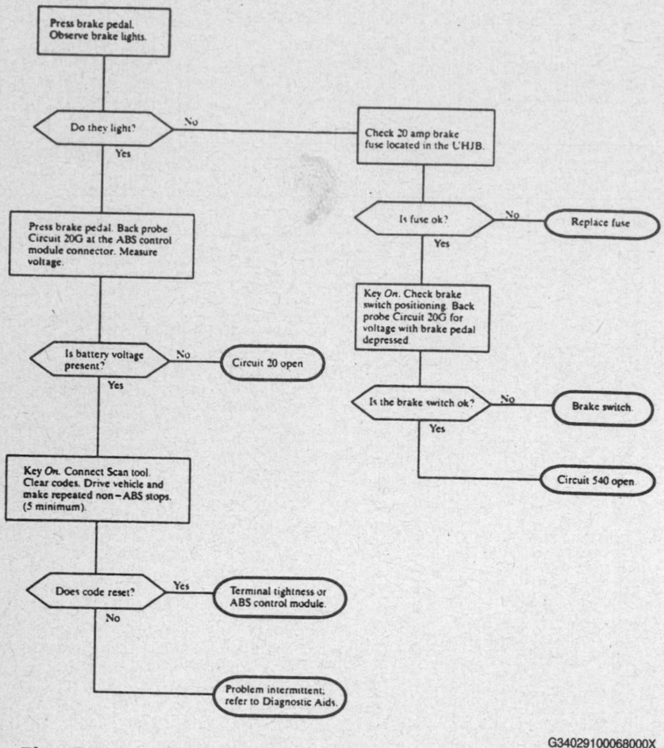
Press brake pedal. Observe brake lights.
Do they light?
No
Yes
Check 20 amp brake fuse located in the UHJB.
Is fuse ok?
Replace fuse
Press brake pedal. Back probe Circuit 20G at the ABS control module connector. Measure voltage.
Key On. Check brake switch positioning. Back probe Circuit 20G for voltage with brake pedal depressed
Is battery voltage present?
Circuit 20 open
Is the brake switch ok?
Brake switch.
Circuit 540 open.
Key On. Connect Scan tool. Clear codes. Drive vehicle and make repeated non-ABS stops. (5 minimum).
Does code reset?
Terminal tightness or ABS control module.
Problem intermittent; refer to Diagnostic Aids.
G34029100068000X

Fig. 74 Code 91, brake switch circuit open during normal stop

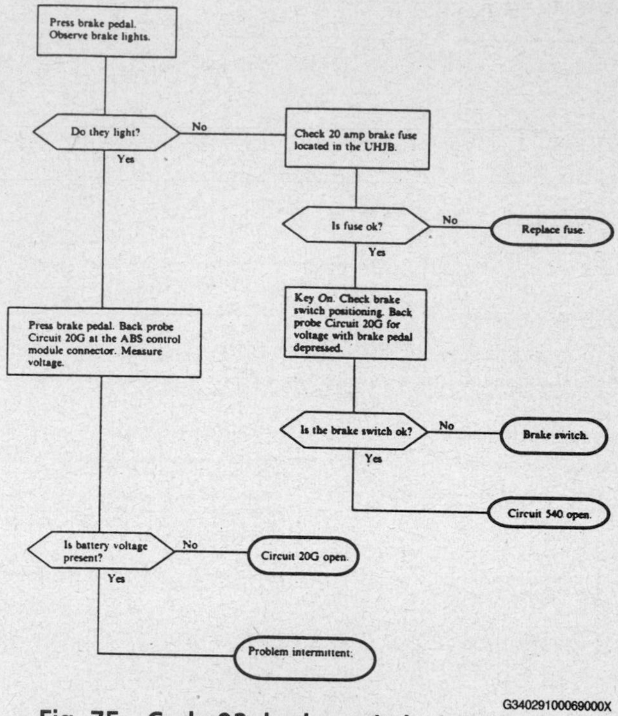
Press brake pedal. Observe brake lights.
Do they light?
No
Yes
Check 20 amp brake fuse located in the UHJB.
Is fuse ok?
Replace fuse.
Key On. Check brake switch positioning. Back probe Circuit 20G for voltage with brake pedal depressed.
Press brake pedal. Back probe Circuit 20G at the ABS control module connector. Measure voltage.
Is the brake switch ok?
Brake switch.
Circuit 540 open.
Is battery voltage present?
Circuit 20G open.
Problem intermittent;
G34029100069000X

Fig. 75 Code 92, brake switch circuit open during ABS stop

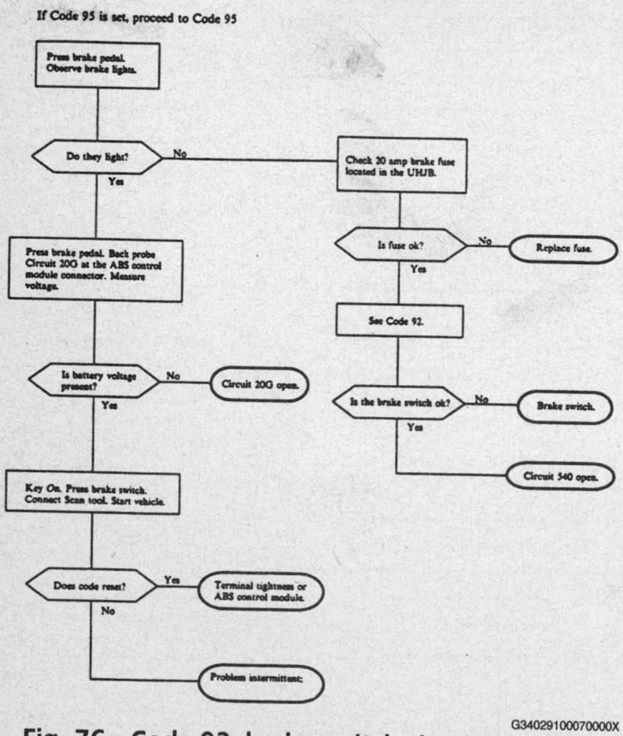
If Code 95 is set, proceed to Code 95
Press brake pedal. Observe brake lights.
Do they light?
No
Yes
Check 20 amp brake fuse located in the UHJB.
Is fuse ok?
Replace fuse.
Press brake pedal. Back probe Circuit 20G at the ABS control module connector. Measure voltage.
See Code 92.
Is battery voltage present?
Circuit 20G open.
Is the brake switch ok?
Brake switch.
Circuit 540 open.
Key On. Press brake switch. Connect Scan tool. Start vehicle.
Does code reset?
Terminal tightness or ABS control module.
Problem intermittent;
G34029100070000X

Fig. 76 Code 93, brake switch circuit open on initialization

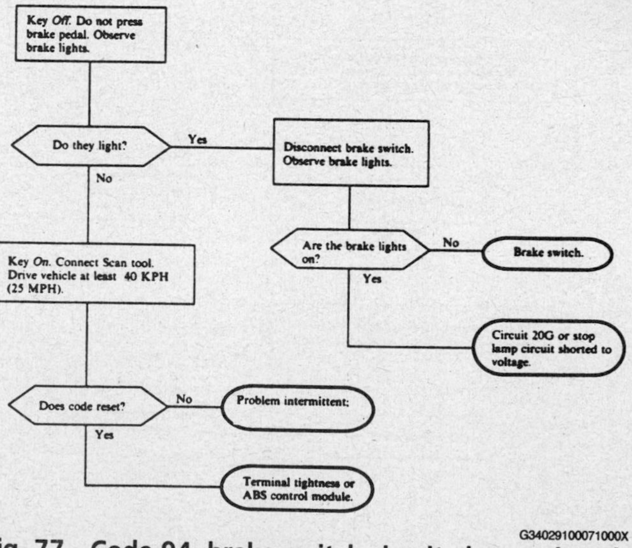
Key Off. Do not press brake pedal. Observe brake lights.
Do they light?
Yes
No
Disconnect brake switch. Observe brake lights.
Are the brake lights on?
Brake switch.
Key On. Connect Scan tool. Drive vehicle at least 40 KPH (25 MPH).
Circuit 20G or stop lamp circuit shorted to voltage.
Does code reset?
Problem intermittent;
Terminal tightness or ABS control module.
G34029100071000X

Fig. 77 Code 94, brake switch circuit always closed

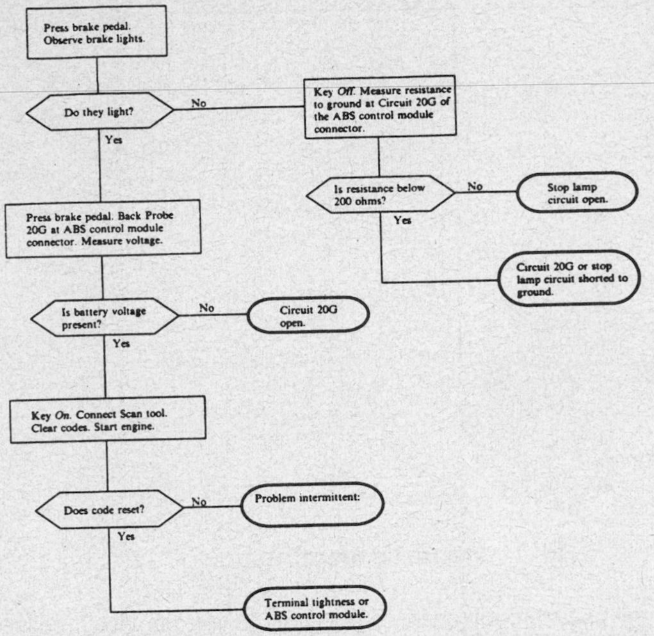
Press brake pedal.
Observe brake lights.
Do they light?
No
Yes
Key Off. Measure resistance to ground at Circuit 20G of the ABS control module connector.
Is resistance below 200 ohms?
No
Stop lamp circuit open.
Yes
Circuit 20G or stop lamp circuit shorted to ground.
Press brake pedal. Back Probe 20G at ABS control module connector. Measure voltage.
Is battery voltage present?
No
Circuit 20G open.
Yes
Key On. Connect Scan tool. Clear codes. Start engine.
Does code reset?
No
Problem intermittent.
Yes
Terminal tightness or ABS control module.
G34029100072000X

Fig. 78 Code 95, stop lamp circuit open NO TAG

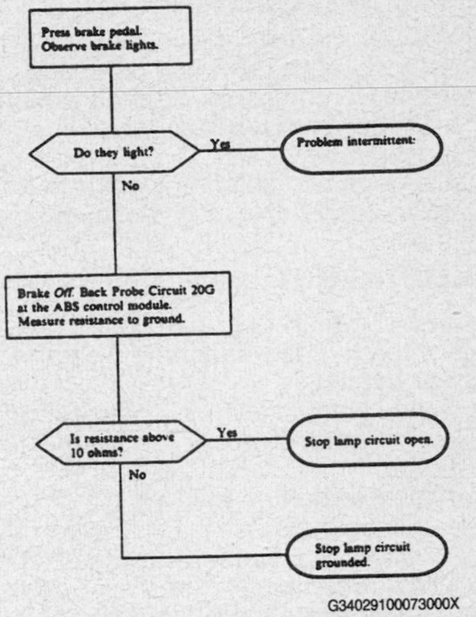
Press brake pedal.
Observe brake lights.
Do they light?
Yes
Problem intermittent.
No
Brake Off. Back Probe Circuit 20G at the ABS control module. Measure resistance to ground.
Is resistance above 10 ohms?
Yes
Stop lamp circuit open.
No
Stop lamp circuit grounded.
G34029100073000X

Fig. 79 Code 96, stop lamp circuit open or grounds open

AUTOMATIC TRANSAXLES

NOTE: On Air Bag Equipped Models, Refer To "Air Bag System Precautions" Located In The Front Of This Manual For System Disarming & Arming Procedures.

INDEX

PRECAUTIONS

AIR BAG SYSTEMS

Refer to "Air Bag System Precautions" in the front of this manual for system disarming and arming procedures.

IDENTIFICATION

The transaxle identification plate is located on the torque converter housing, **Fig. 1.**

DESCRIPTION

This automatic four speed transaxle is a fully automatic unit consisting of four multiple disc clutches, a four element torque converter with a lock up clutch, 1st gear sprag clutch and a servo actuated dog clutch.

The transaxle uses and electronic control system. The unit uses five electrohydraulic actuators in conjunction with a powertrain control module (PCM) and its sensors to control shift timing, shift feel and on-board diagnostics.

TROUBLESHOOTING

Refer to **Fig. 2,** for transaxle troubleshooting.

MAINTENANCE

FLUID CHECK

1. Start engine and allow to reach normal operating temperature.
2. Position vehicle on level surface.
3. Apply parking brake.
4. Move selector through all gears.
5. Move gear selector to P (park) position.
6. Allow engine to idle for three minutes with accessories off.
7. Check fluid level, color and condition.

FLUID CHANGE

1. Fluid may be drained when operating temperature of 190-200°F is reached.
2. Turn engine off, then raise and support vehicle.
3. Remove transaxle drain plug, then allow fluid five minutes to drain.
4. Install new drain plug washer and drain plug, the **torque** plug to 40 ft. lbs.
5. Fill transaxle with to correct fluid level.

IN-VEHICLE REPAIRS

SELECTOR SWITCH, REPLACE

Removal

1. Remove air induction tube.
2. **On models equipped with DOHC engine,** remove air filter box, then lift

resonator upward to disengage from service support bracket.

3. **On all models,** disconnect gear selector switch electrical connector.
4. Remove control lever shaft attaching nut, then remove manual lever, noting position.
5. Remove two selector switch to transaxle case attaching bolts, then remove.

Installation

1. Install switch to transaxle, then install switch to case attaching bolt and finger tighten.
2. Install manual lever to control shaft attaching nut, then tighten to specifications.
3. Adjust switch as follows:
   a. Place transaxle in D4 position, then using a suitable ohmmeter check for continuity across selector switch terminals, if continuity is not indicated, rotate switch until continuity is present.
   b. Tighten switch to case attaching bolts to specifications, then recheck for continuity.
4. Install cable to control lever, then adjust cable as outlined under "Shift Cable, Replace."
5. Connect switch electrical connector.
6. Install air induction tube and tighten attaching bolts to specifications.

SHIFT CABLE, REPLACE

Removal

1. Remove console assembly as follows:
   a. Tape release button on shifter lever handle.
   b. Remove rear storage tray liner, then remove two screws below liner.
   c. Remove two front console attaching screws.
   d. Apply parking brake, then remove trim panel below park brake lever.
   e. Remove ashtrays, then disconnect front ashtray electrical connector.
   f. **On models equipped with power window/mirrors,** lift window/lock/mirror switch rear edge, slide switch rearward, then disconnect electrical connectors.
   g. **On all models,** remove side trim panels.
   h. Lift rear of console, then from below console, release and push out seat belt bezels.
   i. Lift console while feeding seat belts through console.
2. Position shifter in second gear, then disconnect cable end from shifter.
3. Depress two cable tabs on cable housing, then remove cable from shifter assembly.
4. Remove air induction tube.
5. Disconnect cable from shifter lever.
6. Depress two cable retaining tabs, then remove cable from converter housing.
7. Raise and support vehicle.
8. Remove cable grommet from front of dash, then remove two attaching nuts and feed grommet plate through dash hole.

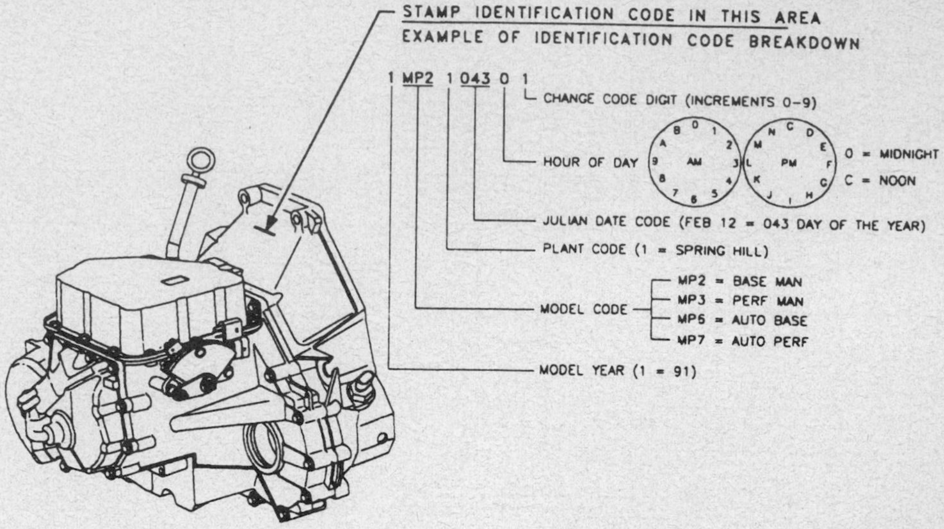
STAMP IDENTIFICATION CODE IN THIS AREA
EXAMPLE OF IDENTIFICATION CODE BREAKDOWN
1 MP2 1 043 0 1
CHANGE CODE DIGIT (INCREMENTS 0-9)
HOUR OF DAY
AM
PM
0 = MIDNIGHT
C = NOON
JULIAN DATE CODE (FEB 12 = 043 DAY OF THE YEAR)
PLANT CODE (1 = SPRING HILL)
MODEL CODE
MP2 = BASE MAN
MP3 = PERF MAN
MP6 = AUTO BASE
MP7 = AUTO PERF
MODEL YEAR (1 = 91)
G35029100001000X

Fig. 1 Transaxle identification

Installation

1. Feed cable and plate through front of dash, then install plat and tighten attaching nuts to specifications.
2. Connect cable to shift lever assembly.
3. Install cable housing to shifter assembly.
4. Install console assembly.
5. Install cable to converter housing.
6. Ensure transaxle and shifter are in park position.
7. Release cable adjustment lock tab, using a screwdriver, to pry lock tab up, then lift with hand.
8. Connect cable to shift lever, then install retainer.
9. Move cable housing back and forth in adjuster, noting endplay:
   a. Center cable housing in middle of endplay.
   b. Press in lock tab.
   c. Verify correct operation.
10. Install air induction tube.

PARK LOCK CABLE, REPLACE

Removal

1. Remove console assembly as outlined under "Shift Cable, Replace."
2. Remove three ignition switch bezel attaching screws, then remove bezel.
3. Place ignition switch on, depress cable retaining tab, then remove cable from ignition module.
4. Unsnap park lock cable end terminal from shifter plastic lock out lever.
5. Depress cable housing end fitting tabs, then remove cable from shifter assembly.
6. Remove cable, noting cable routing.

Installation

1. Ensure cable is routed through accelerator pedal bracket retainer.
2. Install cable, route cable same as cable was removed.
3. Turn ignition on, install cassette end of cable to ignition module, then turn ignition off.
4. Install park lock cable fitting end to shifter assembly, ensuring completely seated.
5. Using a screwdriver, lift cable end fitting lock tab to allow housing to move freely in end fitting.
6. Attach park lock cable end terminal to plastic lock out lever on shifter.
7. Adjust park lock cable as follows:
   a. With ignition off, shifter in park, depress cable end fitting lock and remove adjustment clip from new cable end terminal.
   b. If connecting a cable that does not have an adjustment clip, adjust clip to provide .005 inch gap between cable and end and cable to park lock connector.
8. Verify park lock operation as follows:
   a. With ignition off and shifter in park, attempt to shift lever out of park, lever should not shift out of park.
   b. Turn ignition to on position, then attempt to shift lever out of park, lever should shift out of park.
   c. With lever out of park, turn ignition to off position, key should be able to be removed from ignition.
   d. Attempt to shift lever to park, this should not be allowed.
   e. Turn ignition off, then attempt to remove ignition key, removal should occur.
   f. If steps a through e are not as indicated, readjust cable.
9. Install lower ignition switch bezel attaching screws.
10. Install console assembly.

VALVE BODY, REPLACE

Removal

1. Disconnect battery terminals. **Disconnect ground terminal first.**
2. Remove battery shield, then battery.
3. Remove battery tray.

X — Most Probable Cause(s)
• — Possible Causes

COMPLAINT–CONDITION / CAUSE	MAT	CTS	Dis. Primary	Dis. Secondary	Fuel Delivery System	EGR System	TPS	MAP Sensor	Eng. Vac.	Engine Mech. System	PCM/TC Calibration	Trans. 1st Gear Hyd./Mech.	Trans. Line Act. System	Trans. 2nd Act. System	Trans. 3rd Act. System	Trans. 4th Act. System	Trans. TCC Act. System	Trans. Hydra/Mech.	Trans. Perf/Norm Sw.	Shift to 2 Lt. Circuit	PRNDL Sel. Circuit	Brake Switch Circuit	Trans. Master Enable Circuit	Clutch Clearance	Gear Clearance Incorrect	1st Clutch Defective	2nd Clutch Defective	3rd Clutch Defective	4th Clutch Defective	Park Pawl Mech.	Reverse Fork Mech.	TCC Defective	Input Shaft Nut
Trans Hard Up-Shift:	X	•	•		•	X	•	X			•		X					•	•		•			X			•						
1st–2nd													X	•													•	•					
2nd–3rd													X	•	•													•	•				
3rd–4th													X		•	•																	
Trans Vibration:			•		•												X	X															
While Cruising				•	•												•	X															
Idling			•		•					•								X															
Accelerating			•		•												•	X															
Cold Ambient			•		•												•	X															
Normal Operating Temperature			•		•												•	X															
Cold Engine		X	•		•												•	•															
Decelerating						•											•	X															
Accessory Load			•		•												•	X															
Under Load			•		•												•	X															
Always			•		•												•	X															
Trans Shudder:			•	•	•	•				•				•	•	•	•	•															
Acceleration				X										•	•	•	•																
Normal Operating Temperature				•													•	•															
Deceleration																	•	•															
Braking																						•											
Under Load			•	X	•	•				•				•	•	•	•	•															
2nd Gear				X										•			X	•															
3rd Gear			X			•									•		X	•															
4th Gear				X		X										•	X	•															
Reverse				•										•				X															

G3602910006101OX

Fig. 2 Troubleshooting chart (Part 1 of 2)

4. Loosen transaxle connector bolt, then disconnect electrical connector.
5. **On models equipped with ABS,** remove master cylinder to booster attaching nuts, then lift cylinder slightly to remove valve body cover, then position cylinder back on booster studs.
6. **On all models,** remove valve body cover attaching bolts.
7. Remove eleven valve body to case bolts as shown in **Fig. 3.**

Installation

1. Install manual valve to manual link with manual valve flat facing upwards.
2. Lower valve body, then install manual link to manual valve.
3. Valve body to case attaching bolts must be placed in the valve body prior to installation, **Fig. 4.**
4. Clean and lubricate attaching bolts with Dexron II or equivalent.
5. Tighten valve body bolts in sequence, **Fig. 5,** to specifications.
6. Tighten valve body to case attaching bolts in sequence, **Fig. 6,** to specifications.
7. Using suitable carburetor cleaner, clean valve body cover gasket surface, then install valve body cover attaching bolts, in sequence, **Fig. 7,** and tighten to specifications.
8. **On models equipped with ABS,** install master cylinder to booster attaching nuts, then tighten to specifications.
9. **On all models,** connector transaxle electrical connector, then tighten connector attaching bolt to specifications.
10. Install battery tray, then tighten attaching bolts to specifications.
11. Install battery and battery shield attaching bolts, then tighten to specifications.
12. Connect battery terminals. **Connect positive terminal first to prevent arcing.**

TRANSAXLE
REPLACE

1. Remove air induction tube.
2. **On DOHC models,** lift resonator upward to disengage from engine service support bracket.
3. **On all models,** disconnect the following electrical connectors:
   a. Actuator connector.
   b. Vehicle and turbine speed sensor.
   c. Transaxle temperature sensor.
   d. Selector switch connector.
   e. Two ground terminals from top two converter housing bolts.
   f. Unclip oxygen sensor wire retainer from converter housing.
4. Remove top two converter housing to engine bolts, then insert suitable M12 x 1.75 x 100mm (4 inch) guide bolt with bolt head cut off, to top rear converter housing bolt hole.
5. Remove and discard DIS module to housing attaching bolts, then remove wire module coil to coolant outlet.
6. Loosen two front transaxle mount to transaxle bolts.
7. Secure radiator to upper radiator support with mechanics wire.
8. Install suitable engine support equipment, as follows:
   a. Install support bar feet on outer edge of shock tower.
   b. Connect bar hooks to engine support brackets.

X — Most Probable Cause(s)
● — Possible Causes

COMPLAINT–CONDITION / CAUSE	MAT	CTS	Dis. Primary	Dis. Secondary	Fuel Delivery System	EGR System	TPS	MAP Sensor	Eng. Vac.	Engine Mech. System	PCM/TCM Calibration	Trans. 1st Gear Hyd./Mech.	Trans. Line Act. System	Trans. 2nd Act. System	Trans. 3rd Act. System	Trans. 4th Act. System	Trans. TCC Act. System	Trans. Hydra/Mech.	Trans. Perf/Norm Sw.	Shift to 2 Lt. Circuit	PRNDL Sel. Circuit	Brake Switch Circuit	Trans. Master Enable Circuit	Clutch Clearance	Gear Clearance Incorrect	1st Clutch Defective	2nd Clutch Defective	3rd Clutch Defective	4th Clutch Defective	Park Pawl Mech.	Reverse Fork Mech.	TCC Defective	Input Shaft Nut
Trans Hard Downshift			●				●						X						●		●						●	●	●				
Accelerating													X						X								●	●	●				
Decelerating													X				X		X														
Shift to Two (2) Light													X				X																
Trans Slipping:													X	●	●	●	●									●	●	●	●			●	
Accelerating													X	●	●	●	●									●	●	●	●				
Normal Operating Temperature												●	X	●	●	●	●																
Cold Engine													X	●	●	●	●									●	●	●	●				
From Launch												●	X																				
1st Gear													X													X							
2nd Gear														X													X						●
3rd Gear															X													●					
4th Gear																X													●				
Reverse														X				X									X						
TCC																	X														X		
Trans Gear Missing:													X	●	●	●	●				●		●			●	●	●	●			X	
Reverse														●													X				X		●
Drives in Neutral																								X	●	●	●	●	●				
Trans No Park																														X			
Trans Stuck In Park																														X			
Trans Hunting/Gears, TCC:		●					X	X	X		●	●		X	X	X	X		●		●	X											
While Cruising		●					X	X	X		●				●																		
Cold Engine		X					●	●	●					●	●	●	●		●														
Under Load							X	X	X				●	●	●	●	●				●												

G35029100061020X

Fig. 2 Troubleshooting chart (Part 2 of 2)

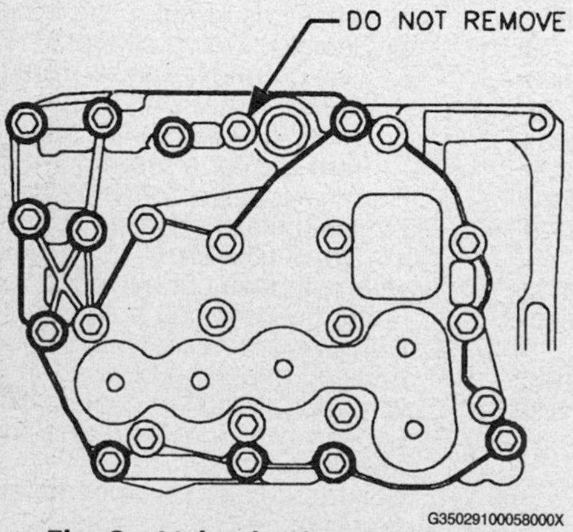
DO NOT REMOVE

G35029100058000X

Fig. 3 Valve body to case bolt removal

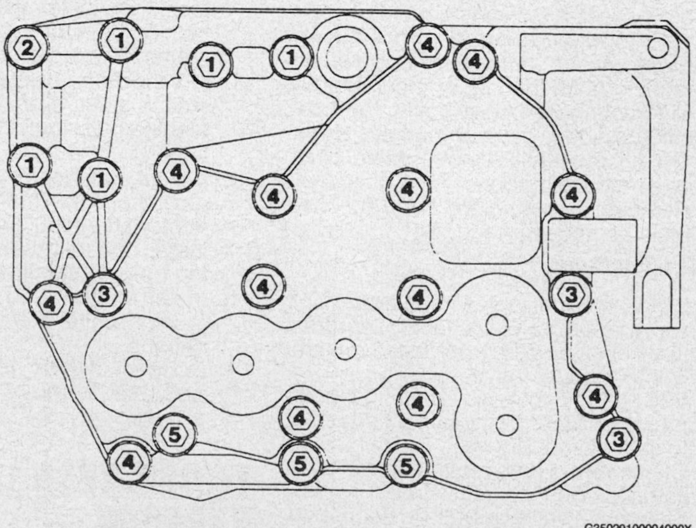

G35029100004000X

Fig. 4 Valve body to case bolt location

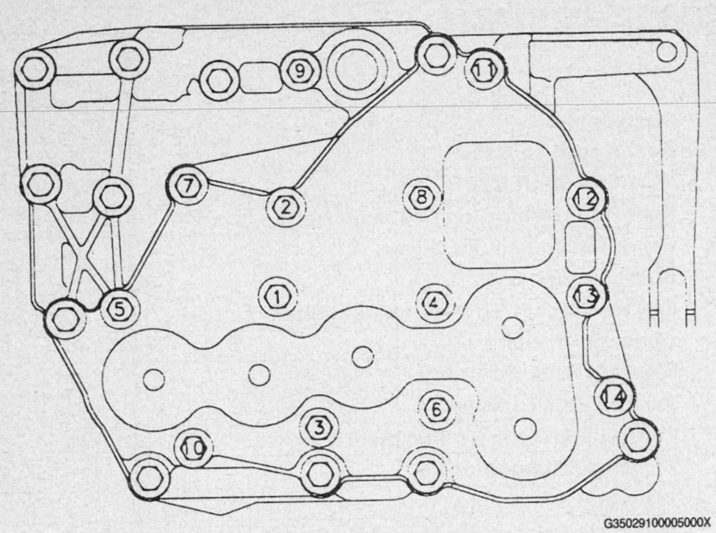
G35029100005000X

Fig. 5 Valve body bolt tightening sequence

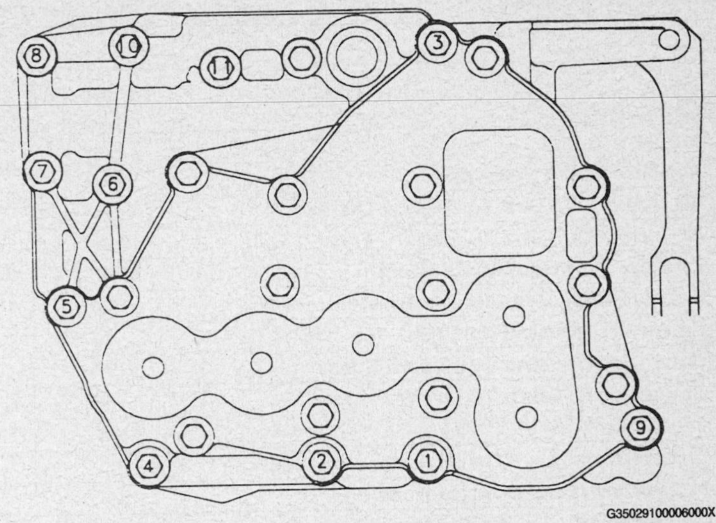
G35029100006000X

Fig. 6 Valve body to case bolt tightening sequence

c. Position stabilizer foot on engine block to right of engine oil dipstick.
d. Adjust hooks, then stabilize to remove looseness.

9. Raise and support vehicle, then drain transaxle fluid.
10. Remove front wheel assemblies.
11. Remove right, left and front splash shields.
12. Remove and discard outer cotter pin from lower ball joints, loosen attaching nut, then back off until top of nut is even with top of threads.
13. Using ball joint tool No. SA9132S or equivalent, separate ball joint from steering knuckle. **On models with ABS, outer CV joint has speed sensor ring, incorrect tool usage may result in ring damage or loss of ABS.**
14. Remove down pipe to manifold attaching nuts, then down pipe to powertrain stiffening bracket bolts, then down pipe to catalytic converter attaching bolts, then remove down pipe and discard front exhaust pipe to manifold and converter gaskets.
15. Remove engine to transaxle mount bracket attaching bolts, then remove bracket.
16. Remove rear transaxle mount bracket to transaxle bolts, then loosen mount attaching bolt to allow bracket to hang.
17. Remove right side steering rack to

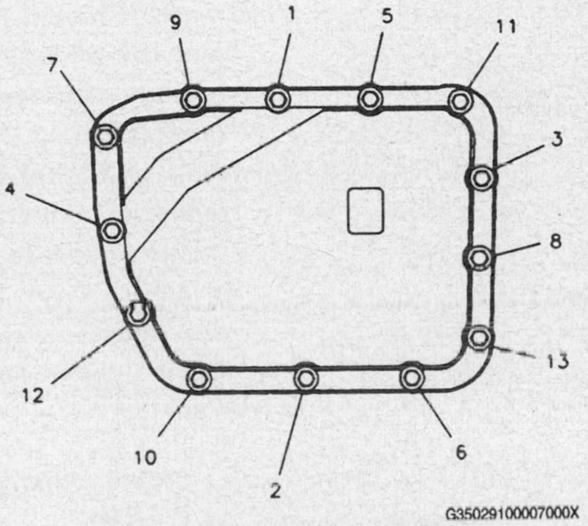
9
1
5
11
7
3
4
8
13
12
10
6
2
G35029100007000X

Fig. 7 Valve body cover bolt tightening sequence

cradle bolt, then back out bolt on left side as far as possible.

18. Disconnect brake line from rear cradle bracket.
19. Remove dust cover to converter housing attaching bolts, then remove cover.
20. Remove torque converter to flywheel attaching bolts.
21. Remove front transaxle mount to cradle attaching nuts.
22. Remove lower engine mount to cradle attaching nuts.
23. Remove lower transaxle mount to cradle attaching nuts.
24. Depress transaxle connector plastic tabs, then pull cooler lines from transaxle, then install 3/8 inch rubber hose between cooler lines to prevent leakage and dirt from entering lines.
25. Using suitable powertrain support dolly and two 4 inch x 4 inch x 36 inch pieces of wood support cradle on dolly.
26. Remove four cradle to body attaching bolts, then lower cradle from vehicle, ensuring two large spacing washers between cradle and body are attached to prevent loss.
27. Lower vehicle, lower transaxle side of engine support bar hook enough to allow valve body cover to clear frame rail, then raise vehicle. **It may be requires to lower rear of transaxle to clear body by adjusting engine support equipment.**
28. Support transaxle with a suitable jack.
29. Using a large screwdriver or pry bar, separate lefthand side axle from transaxle. **Do not allow pry tool to contact axle seal or seal damage may occur.**
30. Remove lower converter housing to engine attaching bolts, then install a suitable guide bolt to lower front converter housing.
31. Separate transaxle from engine, then lower enough to reach transaxle shifter cable.
32. Disconnect shifter cable, then remove shifter cable from converter housing.
33. Lower transaxle, then using cooler cleaner tool No. SA-165T or equivalent clean oil cooler and lines.
34. Reverse procedure to install, noting to tighten bolts and nuts to specifications.

TIGHTENING SPECIFICATIONS

Component	Torque/Ft. Lbs.
Actuator Cover	97①
Actuator Valve Body Bolts	97①
Air Induction Tube To Air Box Clamp	15①
Air Induction Tube To Battery Tray	62①
Bracket To Intermediate Shaft	40
Brake Master Cylinder To Booster	20
Converter Housing To Case	18
Converter Housing To Engine Studs	74
Converter Housing To Lower Engine	96
Cradle To Body	151
Distributorless Ignition System (DIS) Module	62①
Dust Cover To Converter Housing	89①
Engine Mount To Cradle Stud	67
Engine Mount	35
Exhaust Down Pipe To Catalytic Converter	33
Exhaust Down Pipe To Stiffening Bracket	23
Flywheel To Crankshaft	59
Ground Terminal To Converter Housing	18
Input Shaft Clamp	110
Input Shaft Nut	110
Intake Bracket	22
Intermediate Shaft Support	47
Lower Ball Joint Nut	55②
Oil Cooler Line Fitting	22
Oil Cooler Line To Radiator	20
Output Shaft Nut	110
Park Pawl Assembly	22
Park Sense Switch To Console	53①

Component	Torque/Ft. Lbs.
Rear Cover To Case	15
Rear Idle Shaft Cap	15
Rear Pitch Restrictor To Transaxle	40
Servo Cover Seal To Cover	15
Shifter To Floor	19
Starter Bracket To Intermediate Shaft	22
Stator Shaft Bolts	22
Steering Rack To Cradle	40
Tie Rod End To Knuckle	33②
Torque Converter To Flexplate	52
Transaxle Connector Bolt	27①
Transaxle Drain Plug	41
Transaxle Driver Side Mount To Cradle	40
Transaxle Front Cradle Nuts To Studs	35
Transaxle Mount To Transaxle	35
Transaxle Oil Indicator Tube	106①
Transaxle Passenger Side Mount To Cradle	40
Transaxle Pump Bolt	80①
Transaxle Shifter Cable To Plate	62①
Transaxle Temperature Sensor	70①
Turbine Speed Sensor	124①
Valve Body Cover Bolt	89①
Valve Body To Case	97①
Vehicle Speed Sensor	124①
Wheel Lug Nuts	103

①—Inch lbs.
②—Tighten, then align nut slot to cotter pin hole.

FRONT WHEEL DRIVE AXLES

INDEX

DESCRIPTION

The drive axle assembly, **Fig. 1**, consists of a tri-pot joint and an outer constant velocity (CV) joint, connected to an axle shaft. The outer CV joint has the ability to swivel, while the tri-pot joint has the ability to both swivel and move in and out. The right side of the vehicle incorporates an intermediate shaft, allowing the left and right axle shafts to be of equal length.

The drive axle should be inspected periodically for damage and wear.

TROUBLESHOOTING

CLICKING NOISE IN TURNS

Worn or damaged outboard joint(s).

CLUNK WHEN ACCELERATING FROM COAST TO DRIVE

Worn or damaged inboard tri-pot joint(s).

SHUDDER OR VIBRATION DURING ACCELERATION

1. Excessive C.V. joint angle.
2. Incorrect toe in or out.
3. Incorrect trim height.
4. Worn or damaged inboard or outboard C.V. joint(s).

VIBRATION AT HIGHWAY SPEEDS

1. Out of balance front tires or wheels.
2. Out of round front tires.

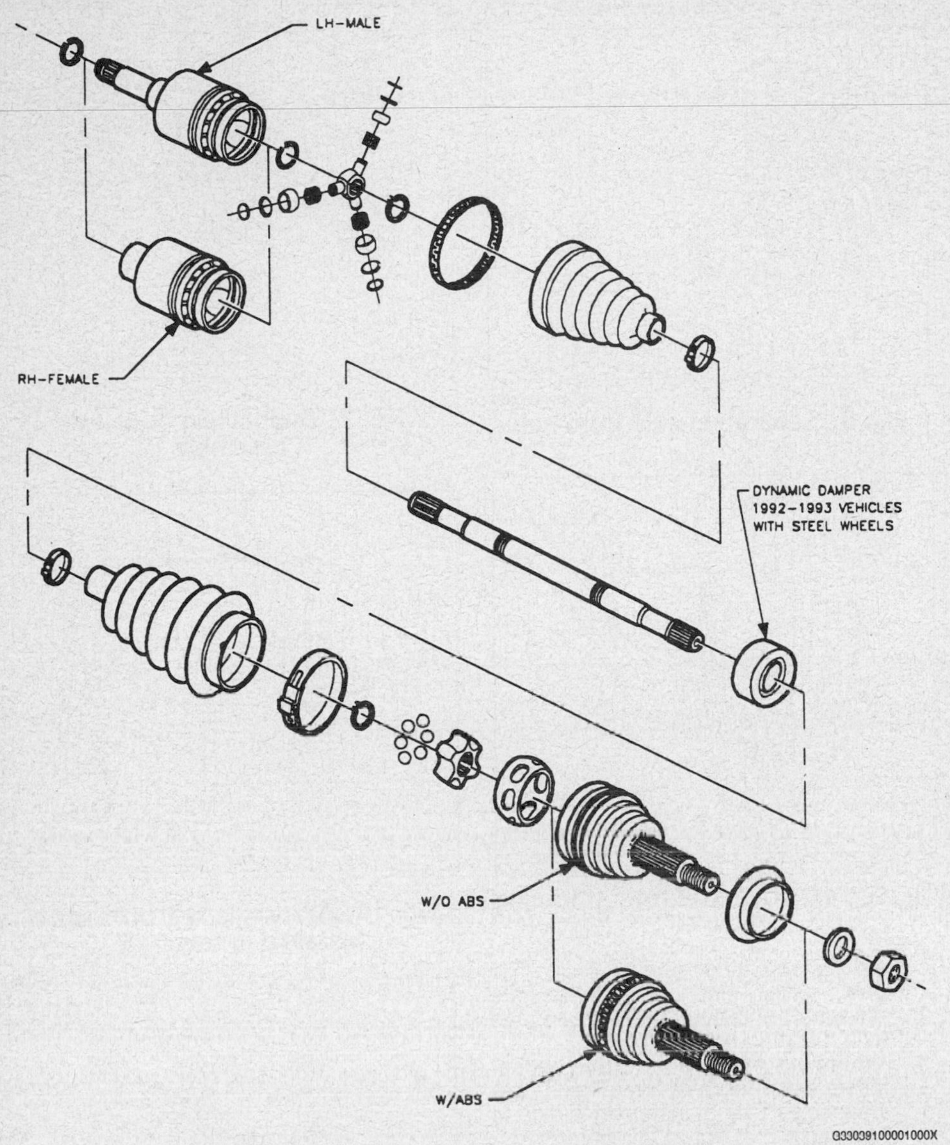
LH-MALE
RH-FEMALE
DYNAMIC DAMPER
1992-1993 VEHICLES
WITH STEEL WHEELS
W/O ABS
W/ABS
G33039100001000X

Fig. 1 Disassembled view of drive shaft

3. Worn C.V. joint(s).
4. Binding or tight C.V. joint(s).

DRIVESHAFT

REPLACE

REMOVAL

1. Depress brake pedal and loosen drive axle nut.
2. Raise and support vehicle, then remove front wheel and tire assembly and front inner splash shield. **If left drive axle or intermediate shaft is being removed, drain fluid from transaxle.**
3. Remove drive axle nut and washer, **Fig. 2.**
4. Remove and discard lower control arm to steering knuckle cotter pin.
5. Loosen lower control arm to steering knuckle castle nut to the point where top of castle nut is even with top of ball stud. **Do not remove castle nut at this time.**
6. Separate lower control arm from steering knuckle, using removal tool No. SA9132S or equivalent, **Fig. 3.** Do not use a wedge type tool to separate joint.
7. Remove and discard outer tie rod cotter pin, then remove tie rod end castle nut.
8. Separate tie rod end from steering knuckle, using removal tool No. SA91100C or equivalent, **Fig. 4. Do not use a wedge type tool to separate joint.**
9. Remove lower control arm to steering knuckle castle nut.
10. Position a long pry bar at the proper cradle and tension strut locations, then pull down on pry bar, separating lower control arm ball stud from steering knuckle, **Fig. 5.** Pull steering knuckle away from ball stud.
11. While pulling knuckle/strut assembly away from vehicle, pull outer end of drive axle out of wheel hub. If difficulty is encountered separating axle from hub, tap on end of drive axle shaft using a block of wood and a hammer, **Fig. 6.**
12. Support or suspend drive axle assembly with mechanics wire, **Fig. 7.**
13. **When removing right side drive axle,** remove drive axle from intermediate shaft by tapping axle at correct location with a hammer, using a block of wood between hammer and drive axle, **Fig. 8.** Separate drive axle from intermediate shaft and remove from vehicle.
14. **When removing left side drive axle,** remove drive axle by inserting a large screwdriver at correct location and prying axle out of transaxle, **Fig. 9.**

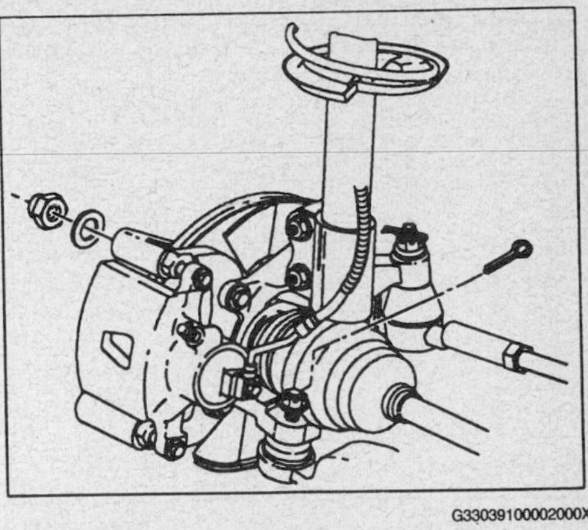
G33039100002000X

Fig. 2 Drive shaft nut & washer removal

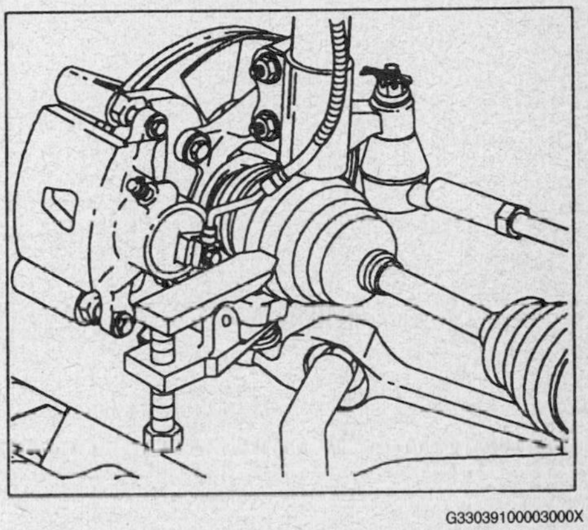
G33039100003000X

Fig. 3 Separating lower ball joint

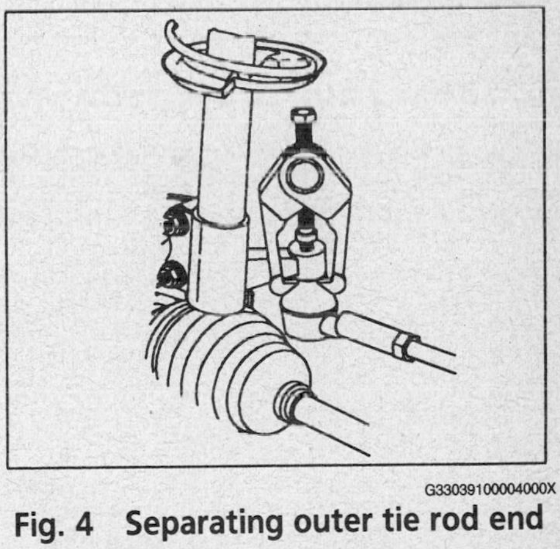
G33039100004000X

Fig. 4 Separating outer tie rod end

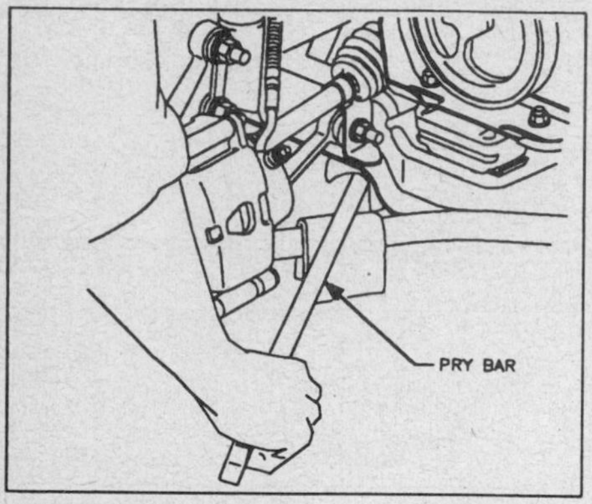
PRY BAR
G33039100005000X

Fig. 5 Separating lower ball joint from steering knuckle

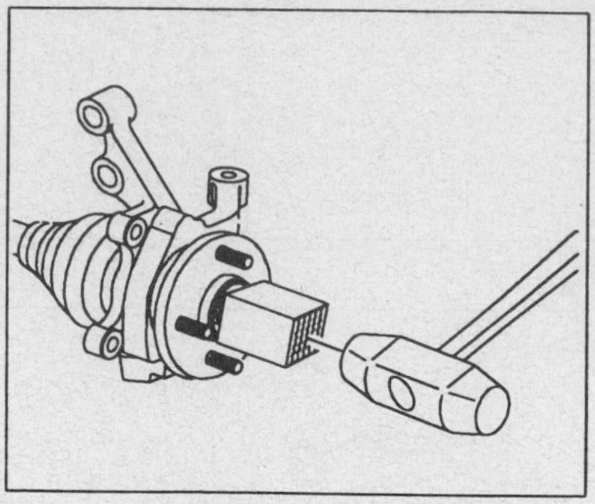
G33039100006000X

Fig. 6 Separating axle from hub

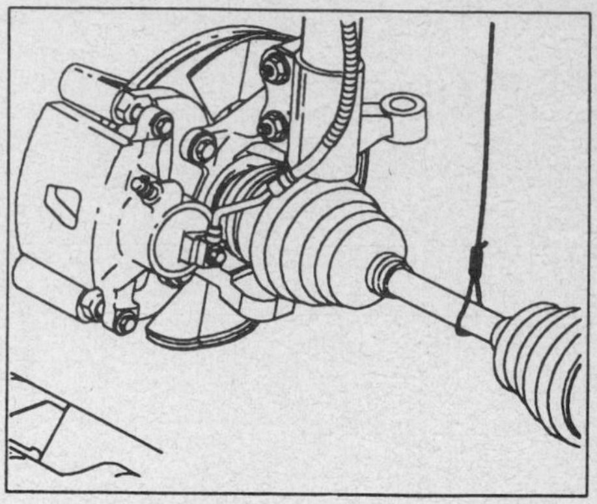
G33039100007000X

Fig. 7 Supporting drive axle assembly

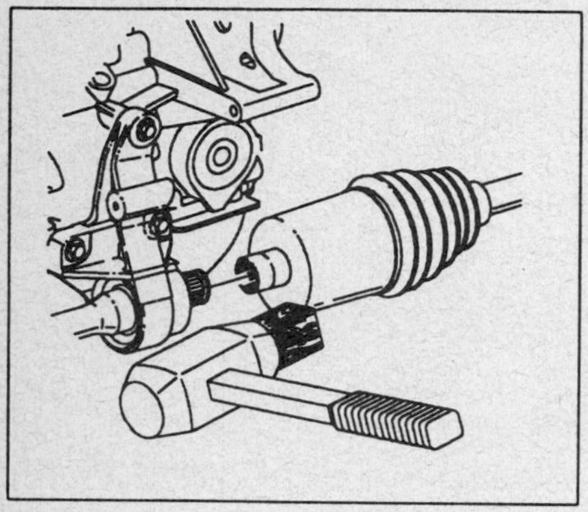
G33039100008000X

Fig. 8 Right drive axle from intermediate shaft removal

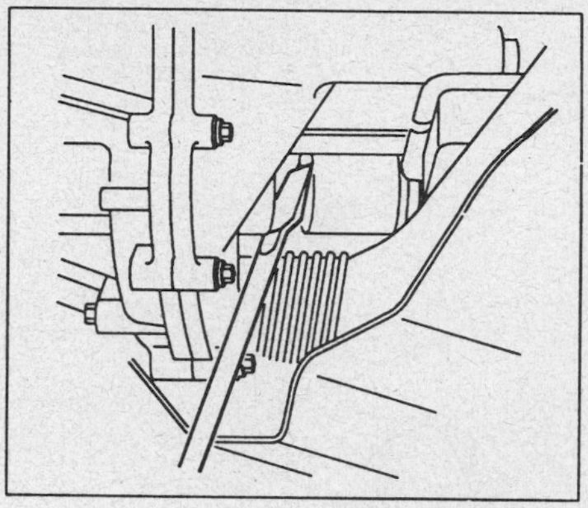
G33039100009000X

Fig. 9 Left drive axle from transaxle removal

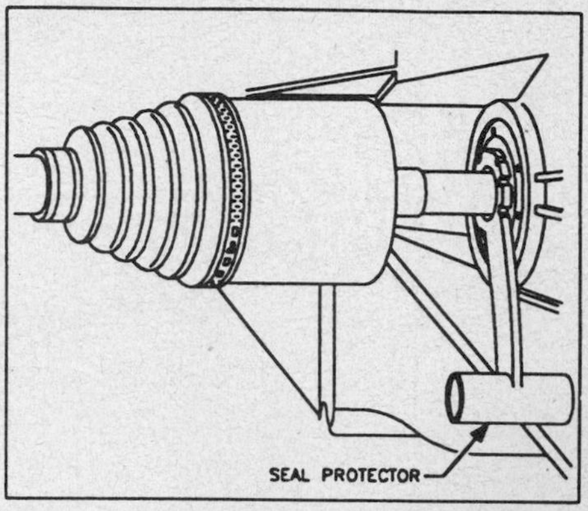
SEAL PROTECTOR
G33039100010000X

Fig. 10 Transaxle seal protector installed in transaxle

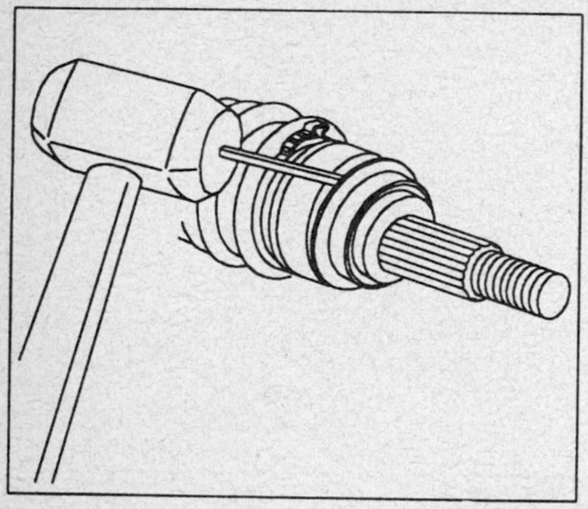
G33039100011000X

Fig. 11 Deflector ring from axle removal

When inserting screwdriver between transaxle and drive axle, do not contact transaxle oil seal. Remove drive axle from vehicle.

INSTALLATION

1. **When installing left side drive axle,** install transaxle seal protector tool No. SA91112T or equivalent, into transaxle, **Fig. 10.**
2. After drive axle splines have safely passed transaxle oil seal, remove seal protector and fully seat drive axle into transaxle.
3. **When installing right side drive axle,** insert inner end of drive axle onto outer end of intermediate driveshaft and push firmly to engage axle retaining ring.
4. **When installing both drive axles,** insert outer end or drive axle into wheel hub. Do not install drive axle to hub washer or nut at this time.
5. Install lower control arm ball stud into steering knuckle. Install ball stud castle nut but do not tighten at this time.
6. Install tie rod end to steering knuckle with castle nut and new cotter pin. **Torque** castle nut to 33 ft. lbs.
7. **Torque** ball joint stud castle nut to 55 ft. lbs. and install new cotter pin.
8. Install new axle to hub washer and nut. **Torque** axle nut to 145 ft. lbs.
9. Install front inner fender splash shield.
10. **Remove rust or corrosion from wheel mounting surfaces and brake rotors and drums. Failure to do so can cause wheel lug nuts to loosen in service.**
11. Position wheel onto hub and install wheel nuts. **Torque** nuts in a crossing pattern to 103 ft. lbs.
12. Lower vehicle from hoist and fill transaxle to correct level with proper lubricant, if necessary.
13. Connect battery ground cable.

DRIVESHAFT SERVICE

DISASSEMBLY

1. Clamp axle shaft in a vise.

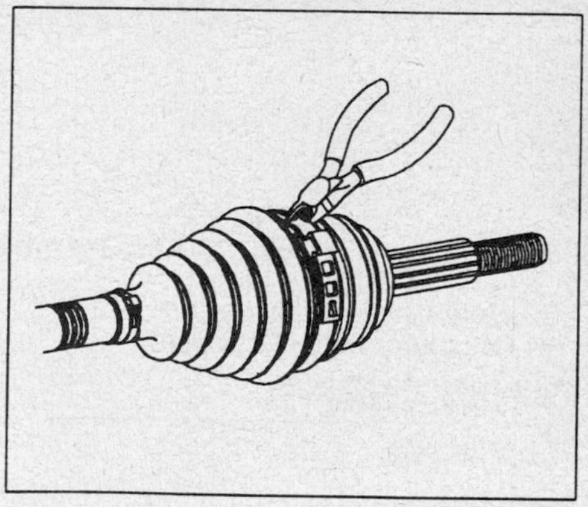
G33039100012000X

Fig. 12 Outer CV joint retaining clamps removal

2. If drive axle has a damaged deflector ring, remove ring from CV outer race using a brass drift and hammer and discard, **Fig. 11.**
3. Remove outer CV joint and seal as follows:
   a. Cut seal retaining clamps on CV joint seal with side cutters or a flat screw driver. Disengage outer band from inner band at retainer peg and discard clamp, **Fig. 12.**
   b. Separate joint seal from CV joint race at large diameter and slide seal along axle shaft away from joint.

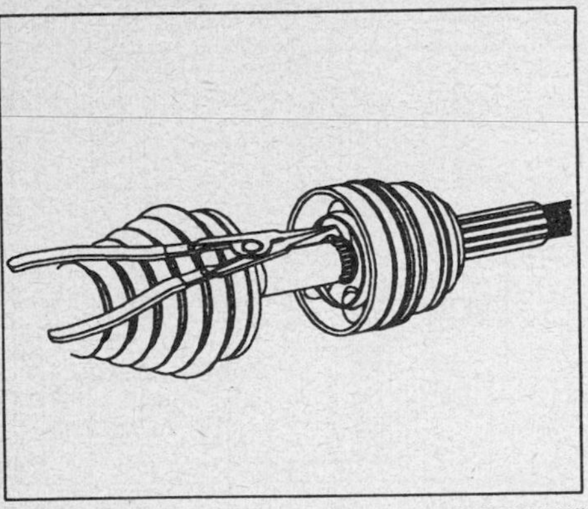

G33039100013000X

Fig. 13 Disconnecting race retaining ring

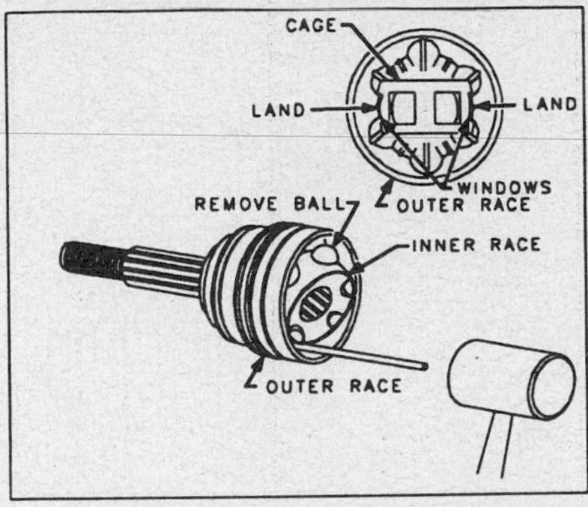
CAGE
LAND
LAND
WINDOWS
REMOVE BALL
OUTER RACE
INNER RACE
OUTER RACE

G33039100014000X

Fig. 14 CV joint ball removal

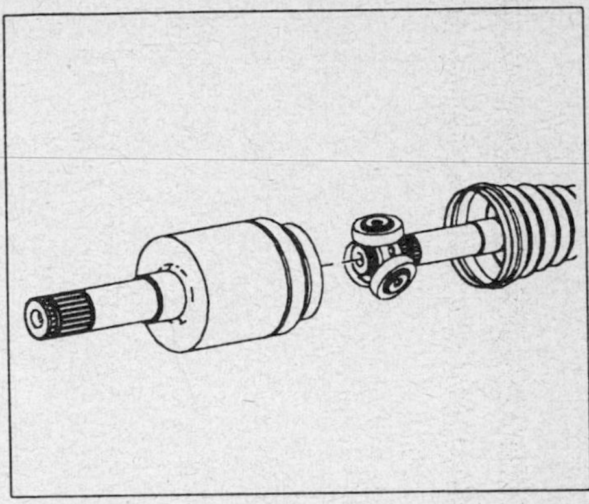

G33039100015000X

Fig. 15 Separating tri-pot housing from spider & shaft

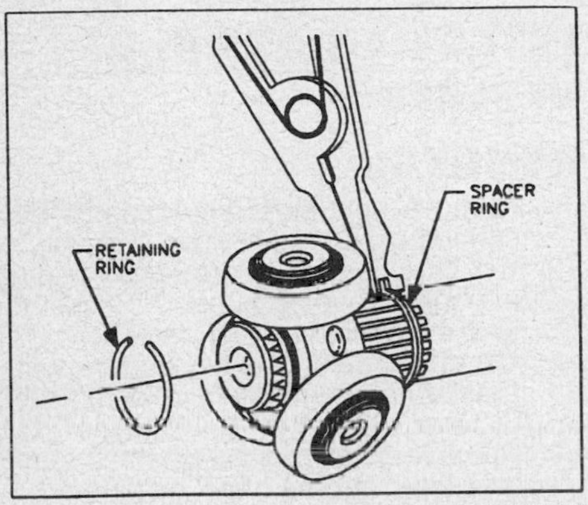
SPACER RING
RETAINING RING

G33039100016000X

Fig. 16 Spider assembly retaining ring from shaft removal

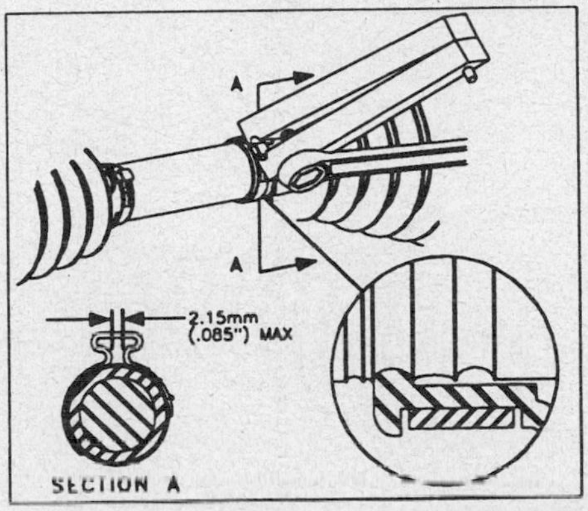
A
A
2.15mm (.085") MAX
SECTION A

G33039100017000X

Fig. 17 Crimping small CV joint retaining clamp

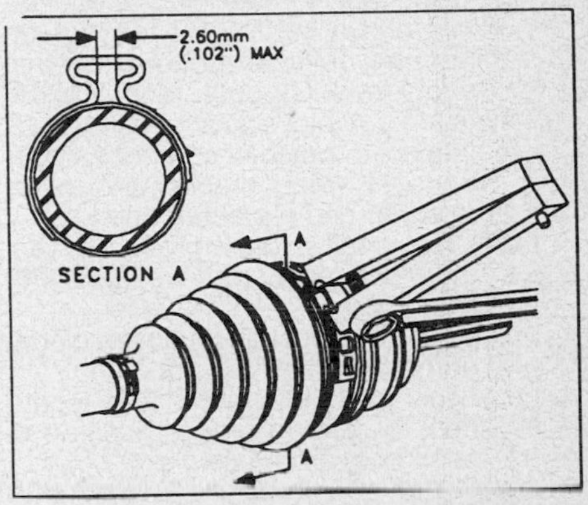
2.60mm (.102") MAX
SECTION A
A
A

G33039100018000X

Fig. 18 Crimping large CV joint retaining clamp

c. Wipe excess grease from face of CV inner race.
d. Spread ears on race retaining ring with snap ring pliers No. SA9198C or equivalent, and remove CV joint assembly from axle shaft, **Fig. 13.**
e. Remove axle seal from shaft.

4. Disassemble CV joint as follows:
   a. Using a brass drift, gently tap on cage until tilted enough to remove first ball, **Fig. 14.** Remove remaining balls in similar manner.
   b. With all balls removed, pivot cage and inner race 90° to center line of outer race with cage windows aligned with lands of outer race, then lift out cage and inner race.
   c. Rotate inner race up and out of cage.
   d. Thoroughly clean all CV joint parts and allow to dry.
5. Remove tri-pot joint and seal as follows:
   a. Cut eared seal retaining clamp on tri-pot seal using side cutters and discard.
   b. Remove and discard earless clamp, using a small bladed screwdriver.
   c. Separate seal from tri-pot housing at large diameter and slide seal along axle shaft away from joint.
   d. Wipe excess grease from face of tri-pot spider and inside of tri-pot housing, then remove tri-pot housing from spider and shaft, **Fig. 15.**
   e. Spread spacer ring with snap ring pliers SA9198C or equivalent and slide spacer ring and tri-pot spider back on axle, **Fig. 10.**
   f. Remove spider retaining ring from groove on axle shaft and slide spider assembly off shaft. **Handle tri-pot spider assembly with care. Tri-pot balls and needle rollers mat separate from spider trunnions.**
   g. Remove seal from axle shaft, then thoroughly degrease housing and allow to dry.

ASSEMBLY

1. Assembly CV joint as follows:
   a. Inspect parts for unusual wear, cracks and other damage. Replace joint assembly if needed.
   b. Place a light coat of grease on all inner and outer race grooves, then insert and rotate inner race into cage.
   c. Install cage and inner race into outer race with windows of cage aligned with lines of outer race.
   d. Install balls using a brass drift to gently rotate and position cage and inner race.
   e. Pack assembled joint with grease provided with service kit.
2. Install outer CV joint and seal as follows:
   a. Install small retaining clamp on neck of new seal. Do not crimp.
   b. Slide seal onto axle shaft and locate neck of seal in proper position in seal groove on axle shaft.
   c. Crimp seal retaining clamp with tool No. SA9203C or equivalent, **Fig 17.** Check clamp location during crimp operation to ensure it is positioned correctly around entire circumference.
   d. Measure clamp ear end gap dimension and recrimp if necessary.
   e. Place approximately half of grease provided in kit, inside seal and pack CV with remaining grease.
   f. Position large seal retaining clamp around seal. **Ensure retaining ring side of inner race faces axle shaft prior to installation.**
   g. Push CV joint onto axle shaft until retaining ring is seated in groove on axle shaft.
   h. Slide large diameter of seal over outside of CV joint race and locate lip of seal in housing groove.
   i. Crimp seal retaining clamp with tool No. SA9203C or equivalent, **Fig. 18.** Check clamp location during crimp operation to ensure it is positioned correctly around entire circumference.
   j. Measure clamp ear end gap dimension and recrimp if necessary.
   k. Position deflecting ring at CV joint outer race, if removed.

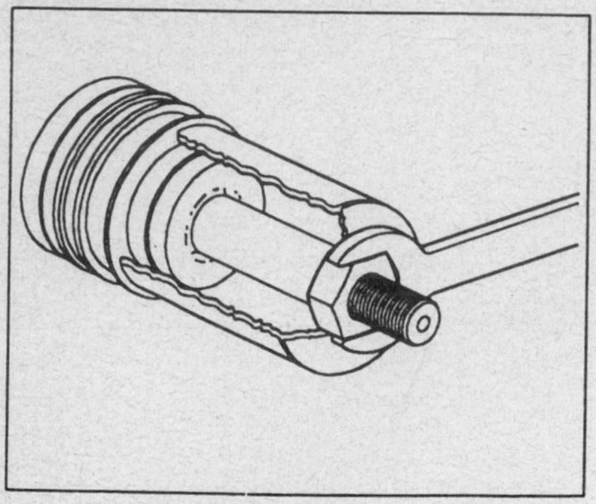

G33039100019000X

Fig. 19 Deflecting ring installation

l. Using tool No. SA9160C or equivalent and a M20 x 1.0 nut, tighten nut until deflector bottoms against shoulder of CV outer race, **Fig. 19.**

3. Install tri-pot joint and seal as follows:
   a. Inspect tri-pot joint components for unusual wear, cracks and other damage and replace if needed.
   b. Clean shaft. If rust is present in seal mounting area, remove rust with wire brush.
   c. Install small seal retaining clamp on neck of seal. Do not crimp.
   d. Slide seal onto shaft and locate neck of seal in proper position in seal groove on axle shaft.
   e. Crimp seal retaining clamp with tool No. SA9203C or equivalent, **Fig. 20.** Check clamp location during crimp operation to ensure it is positioned correctly around entire circumference.
   f. Measure clamp ear end gap dimension and recrimp if necessary, then install spacer ring on axle shaft and beyond second groove.
   g. Slide tri-pot spider assembly past spider retaining ring groove. **Ensure counterbored surface of tri-pot spider faces end of shaft after installation.**
   h. Install spider retaining ring in groove of axle shaft with snap ring pliers No. SA9198C or equivalent, then slide tri-pot spider towards end of shaft and reseat spacer ring in groove on axle.
   i. Place approximately half of the grease provided in kit in side seal and use the remainder to pack tri-pot housing.

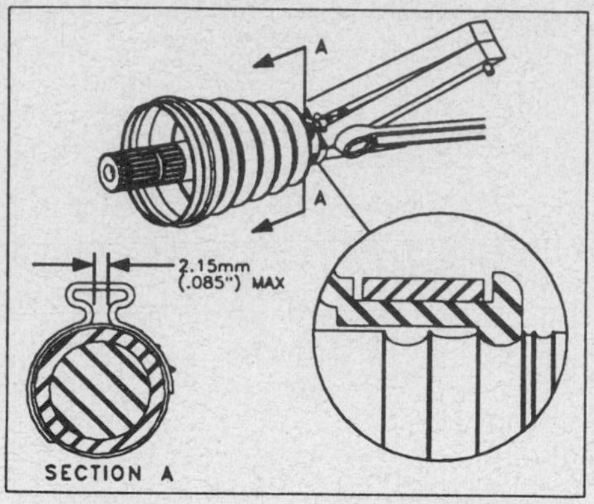
A
A
2.15mm
(.085") MAX
SECTION A

G33039100020000X

Fig. 20 Crimping small tri-pot seal retaining ring

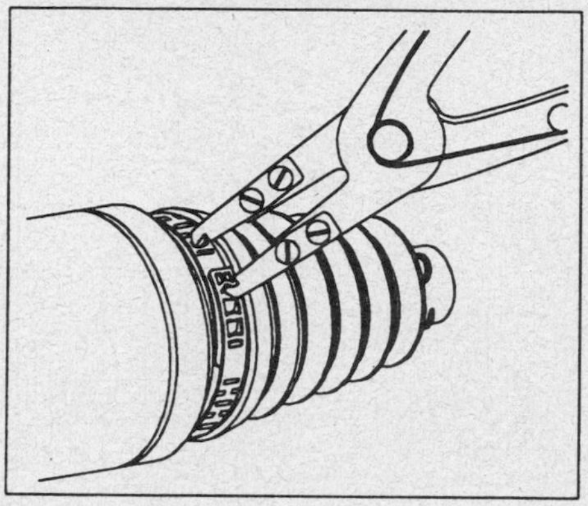

G33039100022000X

Fig. 22 Tri-pot large retaining clamp installation

   j. Install new convolute retainer over seal. **Joint must be assembled with convolute retainer in position . Seal damage will result if joint is not assembled to correct dimension.**
   k. Position seal retaining clamp around large diameter of seal, then slide tri-pot housing over tri-pot spider assembly on shaft.
   l. Slide large diameter of seal over outside of tri-pot housing and locate lip of seal in housing groove.
   m. Position tri-pot assembly at proper vehicle dimension, **Fig. 21.**
   n. Place large seal retaining clamp around seal and close with tool No. SA9161C or equivalent, **Fig. 22.**

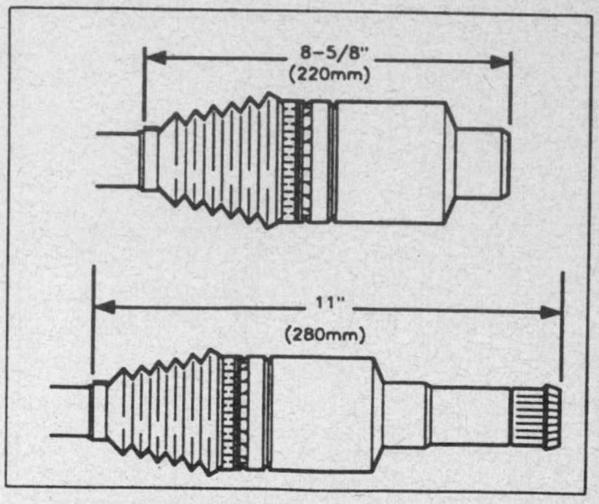
8-5/8"
(220mm)
11"
(280mm)

G33039100021000X

Fig. 21 Tri-pot assembly at proper vehicle dimension

INTERMEDIATE SHAFT REPLACE

REMOVAL

1. Remove right side drive axle as described under "Drive Axle, Replace."
2. **On DOHC engine models,** remove intermediate shaft support bracket to intake manifold bracket fasteners.
3. **On all models,** remove starter motor bracket to intermediate shaft bracket fastener.
4. Remove intermediate shaft support bracket to engine block fasteners.
5. Remove intermediate drive assembly from vehicle.

INSTALLATION

1. Install transaxle seal protector tool No. SA91112T or equivalent, **Fig. 10.**
2. Install intermediate driveshaft into transaxle. **Do not contact oil seal with shaft splines. The splines can damage oil seal.**
3. After intermediate driveshaft splines have safely passed transaxle oil seal, remove seal protector and fully seat intermediate driveshaft into transaxle.
4. Install intermediate driveshaft to engine block. **Torque** bolts to 40 ft. lbs.
5. **On DOHC engine models,** install intermediate shaft support bracket to intake manifold bracket. **Torque** bolts to 33 ft. lbs.
6. **On all models,** install starter motor bracket to intermediate shaft bracket. **Torque** bolts to 22 ft. lbs.

TROUBLESHOOTING

INDEX

X — Most Probable Cause(s)
• — Possible Causes

COMPLAINT–CONDITION / CAUSE	Engine Mechanical Operation		Head Gasket Blow–By or Seal Leakage	Faulty Damper, Flywheel, or	Torque Converter Ba ance	Valve Leakage	Broken or Scored Pistons/Rings	Worn Pistons/Rings	Incorrect Main or Rod Bearing Clearance	Damaged Crankshaft or Main/	Rod Bearings	Damaged/Worn Camshaft	Faulty Lifter or Guide Plate	Faulty Rocker Arm (Ease)	Worn/Misaligned Timing Gear,	Chain, or Key	Low Cylinder Compression	Worn or Scored Cylinder Bore	Throttle Linkage	Timing Retarded (Crankshaft/Ignition)	Timing Advanced (Crankshaft/Ignition)	Powertrain Mounts	Fuel Line or Clamps	Long Idle Periods	Cracked Cylinder Head or Wall	Engine Overloaded/Excessive Speed	Improper Starting Procedures	Debris or Fluid in Cylinder(s)	Faulty PCV Valve	Valve, Seals, and Guides	Starter, Cables, or Battery	Incorrect/Faulty Oil Filter	Powertrain Mounts/Adjustment	Trans. Second Gear Start	Lifter/Belt Tensioner Noisy
High Crankcase Pressure			•				X	X									•																		
Ticking Noise													X	•																		X			X
Mechanical Knocks							•	•	•	X			•	•								•	•					•				•			
Fuel Knocks															•						•														•
Excessive Engine Vibration			•	•					•					•	•							X											•		
Seized Engine Component							•	•	•	•																•		•				•			
Low Cylinder Compression			•			•	X	•					•		•			•							•										
High Cylinder Leakage			•			X	X	•					•					•							•										

G31139100005010X

Fig. 1 Engine mechanical (Part 1 of 2)

X — Most Probable Cause(s)
● — Possible Causes

COMPLAINT–CONDITION / CAUSE	Engine Mechanical Operation		Head Gasket Blow-By or Seal Leakage	Faulty Damper, Flywheel, or	Torque Converter Balance/Faulty	Valve Leakage/Valve Springs	Broken or Scored Pistons/Rings	Worn Pistons/Rings	Incorrect Main or Rod Bearing Clearance	Damaged Crankshaft or Main/	Rod Bearings	Damaged/Worn Camshaft	Faulty Lifter or Guide Plate	Faulty Rocker Arm (SOHC)	Worn/Misaligned Timing Gear,	Chain, or Key	Low Cylinder Compression	Worn or Scored Cylinder Bore	Throttle Linkage	Timing Retarded (Crankshaft/Ignition)	Timing Advanced (Crankshaft/Ignition)	Engine Mount/Bolts	Fuel Line or Clamps	Long Idle Periods	Cracked Cylinder Head or Wall	Engine Overloaded/Excessive Speed	Improper Starting Procedures	Debris or Fluid in Cylinder(s)	Faulty PCV Valve	Valve, Seals, and Guides	Starter, Cables, or Battery	Incorrect/Faulty Oil Filter	Powertrain Mounts/Adjustment	Trans. Second Gear Start	Lifter/Belt Tensioner Noisy
Low/Loss of Power			●		●	●	●	●				●	●	●	●		X	●	●	●	●					●							●	●	X
Hard to Start						●	●	●				●					●	●		●	●						X				●				
Will Not Start — Hot						●	●	●									●	●													X				
Will Not Start — Cold						●	●	●									●	●									X				●				
Engine Starts and Stalls																																			
Engine Misfires/Backfires						●						●			X																				
Rough/Erratic Idle																													●						
Poor Acceleration																			●																
Excessive Acceleration Smoke																				●	●														
Excessive White Smoke			X																						●										
Black Smoke Under Load												●	●	●	●		●	●																	
Blue Smoke							X	●					●	●			●	●							●					●					
Excessive Lube Consumption			●				●	●	●									●							●	●			●	●					
Excessive Fuel Consumption			●			●	●	●				●		●	●		●			●	●			●		●									●
Excessive Coolant Consumption			X																						●										
Lube Oil Leaks			●				●	●																					●						
Lube Oil Contaminated			●																																
Coolant Contaminated			●																																
High Coolant Temperature			●																																
Low Coolant Temperature																																			
High Oil Sump Temperature																																			
No Heat From Heater			●																																
Crankcase Sludge							●	●																●											
Low Oil Pressure									●	●			●																						
High Oil Pressure																																			

G31139100005020X

Fig. 1 Engine mechanical (Part 2 of 2)

X — Most Probable Cause(s)
● — Possible Causes

CAUSE

COMPLAINT–CONDITION	Cooling System	Quality/Grade of Coolant	Low Coolant Level	Faulty or Incorrect Pressure Cap	Inaccurate Temperature Gauge or Sensor	Obstructed Radiator/Heater Flow	Faulty Operation of Fan Motor/Relay	Faulty Thermostat	Faulty Water Pump/Seal	Restricted Coolant Flow or Leak	(Intake Manifold/Cylinder Head)	Faulty Fan Shroud	Faulty Air Inlet Duct	Plugged or Misrouted De-Aeration Line	High Coolant Temperature	Low Coolant Temperature	Radiator/Heater Core Damage	Obstructed Heater or Fill Hose	Faulty Accessory Drive Belt	Low Coolant Light On	Hose Clamps	Cylinder Block or Head	Intake Manifold
Low/Loss of Power																							
Hard to Start																							
Will Not Start — Hot																							
Will Not Start — Cold																							
Engine Starts and Stalls																							
Engine Misfires/Backfires																							
Rough/Erratic Idle																							
Poor Acceleration																							
Excessive Acceleration Smoke																							
Excessive White Smoke																						●	
Black Smoke Under Load																							
Blue Smoke																							
Excessive Lube Consumption																							
Excessive Fuel Consumption																							
Excessive Coolant Consumption/Leak									●	●							●			●	X	●	●
Lube Oil Leaks																							
Lube Oil Contaminated																							
Coolant Contaminated																							
High Coolant Temperature		●	X	X	X	●	X	●	●	●		●	X	●				●	●				
Low Coolant Temperature																							
High Oil Sump Temperature		●	●	●		●	●	●	●	●		●	●	●	●		●	●	●				
No Heat From Heater			●					●		●						●	●	●					●
Crankcase Sludge																							
Low Oil Pressure																							
High Oil Pressure																							

G31139100006000X

Fig. 2 Cooling system

X — Most Probable Cause(s)
● — Possible Causes

FUEL, EXHAUST AND EMISSION SYSTEMS

CAUSE

COMPLAINT–CONDITION			Fuel Quality/No Fuel	Throttle Shaft	Throttle Blade/Bore Dirty (Mir. Air)	Throttle Return Spring	Throttle Stop Lever	Throttle Cable	Faulty Injector	Injector Leak at Tip	Rich Injector	Lean Injector	Fuel Leak (Lines, Regulator, Tank)	IAC System	IAC Whistle	Injector Noise	Fuel Line/Fuel Pump Noise	Faulty Fuel Pump/Relay	Clogged/Pinched Fuel Line/Filter	Fuel Canister Purge System	Faulty Pressure Regulator	Low Fuel Pressure	High Fuel Pressure	EGR Valve Stuck Open	Oxygen Sensor	PCV Valve	PCM/EC (EEPROM)	Manifold Absolute Pressure Sensor	Throttle Position Sensor	EGR Valve/Passageway Closed	Crank Position Sensor	Coolant Temperature Sensor	Knock Sensor	Vacuum Leaks	Improper Starting Procedure
Hard Start/No Start			●						●	X	●	●		●				X	●	●	●	X	●	●				●	●		X	●			●
Stalling/Stumbling			●		X	●	●		●	●	●	●		●				●	●	●	●	●		X	●	●		●	●	X	●	X		●	
Rough/Erratic Idle			●	●	●	●	●		X	●	●	●		X					●	●	●	●		●	●	●		●		X	●	●		●	
High Idle				●		●	●	●		●	●			X							●					●		●				●		X	
Low Power			X					●	●									●	●			●		●				●		●	●		●		
Poor Fuel Economy			●						●	●	●	●	●								●		●									●	●	●	
Backfires											●	●							●			●									●	●		●	
Noises Miscellaneous															●	●	●																		
Sulfur Odor									●	●	●										●		●					●							
Fuel Odor													●							X					●										
Excessive Smoke									●		●	●														●									
Run On/Dieseling										●																									
Surges/Hesitates			●						●	●	●	●							X	●		●		●					X		●			●	
Engine Hydraulic Lock									●												●														
Sticky Throttle				●	X	●		X																					●						
Spark Knock			X																					X						X			●		

G31139100007010X

Fig. 3 Fuel, exhaust & emission systems (Part 1 of 2)

X — Most Probable Cause(s)
• — Possible Causes

FUEL, EXHAUST AND EMISSION SYSTEMS

COMPLAINT–CONDITION / CAUSE	Speedometer Calibration	Wheel Alignment	Tire Pressure	Overloading	Ignition System	Brake System	Air Temperature Sensor	Altitude (Thin Air)	Engine Mechanical	Induction Clog/Air Filter	Converter Plugged/Damaged	Exhaust Pipe Collapsed/Bent	Muffler Plugged/Damaged	A/C On	Excessive Speed	Cruise Control Cable Adj.	Powertrain Mounts/Adjustment	Restricted Air Intake	Plugged Air Filter	Emission Control Sensors	Spark Plugs/Wires	PCV Valve	Vacuum Lines	Fuel System	Exhaust System Leaks
Hard Start/No Start					X				•	•	•	•	•	•		•		•	•	•				X	
Stalling/Stumbling					X				•	•										X				X	
Rough/Erratic Idle (Vibration)					•				•								X								
High Idle																X				X		X	X		
Low Power				X	•	•		•	•	X	X	X	X	X						X				•	
Poor Fuel Economy	•	•	•	X	•	•	•		•	•				•	X					X				X	
Backfires					X						•	•	•							•					
Noises Miscellaneous											•	•	•											•	X
Sulfur Odor											•														
Fuel Odor																								X	
Excessive Smoke									•											•				•	
Run On/Dieseling																									
Surges/Hesitates					X					•						•				X				•	
Engine Hydraulic Lock									•															•	
Sticky Throttle																									
Spark Knock or Knock									•											X					
Failed Emission Test:					•													•	•	•	•	•	•	•	X
High HC					X				X											•	X	X	X		•
High CO																		•	X	•		X		X	•

G31139100007020X

Fig. 3 Fuel, exhaust & emission systems (Part 2 of 2)

Complaint/Condition	Possible Cause(s)	Correction(s)
Vehicle pulls	Mismatched, unevenly worn or improperly inflated tire(s).	Replace or inflate tire(s) correctly.
	Improper front or rear wheel alignment.	Correct wheel alignment.
	Worn or bent suspension component(s).	Replace component(s).
	Worn wheel bearings.	Replace wheel bearings.
	Steering gear out of adjustment or worn.	Replace or adjust steering gear.
	Sagging spring(s).	Replace damaged spring(s).
	Worn strut(s).	Replace worn strut(s).
Abnormal or excessive tire wear	Worn suspension component(s).	Replace component(s).
	Hard driving.	Advice customer.
	Tire(s) improperly inflated.	Inflate tire(s) correctly.
	Worn strut(s).	Replace worn strut(s).
Excessive body roll/pitching	Tension strut bent or broken.	Replace tension strut.
	Rear stabilizer bar or stabilizer bar links bent or broken.	Replace stabilizer bar/stabilizer bar links.
	Broken or sagging spring(s).	Replace damaged spring(s).
	Tire(s) improperly inflated.	Inflate tire(s) correctly.
	Strut(s) worn.	Replace worn strut(s).
Suspension bottoming	Weak spring(s).	Replace weak spring(s).
Front wheel shimmy	Tire(s) worn, out of round or improperly inflated.	Replace or inflate tire(s).
	Wheel(s) out of balance.	Balance wheel(s).
	Worn strut(s).	Replace worn strut(s).
	Wheel alignment incorrect.	Correct front wheel alignment.
	Wheel bearing(s) worn.	Replace worn bearing(s).
	Ball stud(s) worn.	Replace worn ball stud(s).
	Lower control arm bushing(s) worn or damaged.	Replace lower control arm(s).
	Tension strut bushing(s) worn or damaged.	Replace worn or damaged bushing(s).

Fig. 4 Front suspension

G31139100008000X

Complaint/Condition	Possible Cause(s)	Correction(s)
Vehicle pulls	Mismatched, unevenly worn or improperly inflated tire(s).	Replace or inflate tire(s) correctly.
	Improper front or rear wheel alignment.	Correct wheel alignment.
	Worn or bent front or rear suspension component(s).	Replace component(s).
	Worn wheel bearing(s).	Replace wheel bearing(s).
	Steering gear out of adjustment or worn.	Replace or adjust steering gear
	Damaged or sagging spring(s).	Replace spring(s).
Abnormal or excessive tire wear	Improper front or rear wheel alignment.	Correct wheel alignment.
	Worn strut(s).	Replace strut(s).
	Worn or bent front or rear suspension component(s).	Replace component(s).
	Hard driving.	Advise customer.
	Tire(s) improperly inflated.	Inflate tire(s) correctly.
Excessive body roll/pitching	Worn strut(s).	Replace worn strut(s).
	Tension strut bent or broken.	Replace tension strut.
	Rear stabilizer bar or stabilizer bar links bent or broken.	Replace stabilizer bar/stabilizer bar links.
	Broken or sagging springs(s).	Replace damaged spring(s).
	Tire(s) improperly inflated.	Inflate tire(s) correctly.

Fig. 5 Rear suspension

ENGINE REBUILDING SPECIFICATIONS

NOTE: For Engine Tightening Specifications, Refer To The Engine Section In The Appropriate Chassis Chapter Of This Manual.

INDEX

CYLINDER HEAD, VALVE GUIDE & VALVE SEATS

All Specifications Given In Inches, Unless Otherwise Specified.

Engine, Liter/CID	Cylinder Head Warpage Limit	Cylinder Head Overall Thickness	Valve Guides			Valve Seats			
			Standard I.D.	Stem To Guide Clearance		Seat Angle	Seat Width		Runout
				Intake	Exhaust		Intake	Exhaust	
1.9L/4-116 SOHC	①	4.444–4.454	.2751–.2761	.0010–.0025	.0015–.0032	44.5–45.5°	.0394–.0512	.0512–.0630	—
1.9L/4-116 DOHC	①	4.4449–4.428	.275–.276	.0010–.0025	.0015–.0032	44.5–45.5°	.031–.048	.041–.058	—

SOHC—single overhead cam.
DOHC—dual overhead cam.
①—Longitudinal deck, .004 inch; transverse deck, .002 inch.

VALVE SPRINGS

Engine, Liter/CID	Free Length	Seated Press., Lbs. @ Inches	Comp. Press., Lbs. @ Inches	Out Of Square Limit
1.9L/4-116 SOHC	1.8898–1.9134	76–87 @ 1.61	202–211@1.28	.100
1.9L/4-116 DOHC	1.61	66–77@1.34	163–180 @ .984	.100

SOHC—Single overhead cam.
DOHC—Dual overhead cam.

VALVES

All Specifications Given In Inches, Unless Otherwise Specified.

Engine, Liter/CID	Stem Diameter		Clearance①		Face Angle	Margin Min.
	Intake	Exhaust	Intake	Exhaust		
1.9L/4-116 SOHC	.2736-.2741	.2736-.2741	.001-.0025	.③	44.75-45.25°	②
1.9L/4-116 DOHC	.2736-.2741	.2729-.2736	.001-.0025	.0015-.0032	45-45.5°	.0295

SOHC—Single overhead cam.
DOHC—Dual overhead cam.
①—Between valve guide bushing & valve.
②—Intake width, .035 inch; exhaust width, .039 inch.
③—1992-94 models, .0015-.0020 inch, 1995 models, .0015-.0032 inch.

CAMSHAFT

All Specifications Given In Inches, Unless Otherwise Specified.

Engine, Liter/CID	Camshaft Journal Diameter	Maximum Journal Runout	Camshaft Bearing Clearance	Camshaft Endplay	Rocker Arm Oil Clearance	Lifter Bore Diameter	Lifter Diameter	Lifter To Bore Clearance
1.9L/4-116 SOHC	1.7480-1.7490	.①	.0020-.0040	.0028-.0079	—	—	.8420-.8427	.007-.0024
1.9L/4-116 DOHC	1.1398-1.1406	②	.0012-.0030	.0020-.008	—	—	1.2976-1.2982	.0010-.0026

SOHC—Single overhead cam.
DOHC—Dual overhead cam.
①—1992-94 models, .0028 inch, 1995 models, .0020 inch.
②—1992-94 models, .0040 inch, 1995 models, .0020 inch.

CRANKSHAFT, BEARINGS & RODS

All Specifications Given In Inches, Unless Otherwise Specified.

Engine, Liter/CID	Crankshaft				Bearing Clearance			Connecting Rod	
	Standard Journal Diameter		Out Of Round, All①	Taper, All①	Main Bearings	Connecting Rod Bearings	Thrust Bearing Clearance	Pin Bore Diameter	Side Clearance
	Main Bearing	Crank Pin							
1.9L/4-116	2.2438-2.2444	1.8500-1.8508	.0004	.0004	.0002-.002	.0002-.0009	—	.7679-.7685	.0065-.0222

①—Maximum.

PISTONS, PINS & RINGS

All Specifications Given In Inches, Unless Otherwise Specified.

Model	Piston Diameter (Std.)①	Piston Clearance	Piston Pin Diameter②③	Piston Pin To Piston Clearance	Piston Ring End Gap, Min.		Piston Ring Side Clearance	
					Comp.	Oil	Comp.	Oil
1.9L/4-116	3.2270-3.2277	④	.7676-.7677	.0001-.0004	⑥	.⑦	⑤	—

①—Measured at .20 inch from bottom of piston.
②—Pistons & pins are matched set and should be replaced as an assembly.
③—Minimum.
④—Bore 1, 2 & 3, .0002-.0017 inch; bore 4, .0006-.0021 inch.
⑤—Top ring, .0016-.0035 inch, on 1992-94 models & .0016-.0032 inch on 1995 models, 2nd ring, .0012-.0031 inch.
⑥—1992-94 models, .0098 inch: 1995 models, .0098-.0157 inch.
⑦—1992-94 models, .0098 inch: 1995 models, .0098-.0492 inch.

CYLINDER BLOCK

All Specifications Given In Inches, Unless Otherwise Specified.

Engine	Cylinder Bore Dia. (Std.)	Cylinder Bore Taper, Max.	Cylinder Bore Out Of Round, Max.
1.9L/4-116	①	.0020	.0020

①—Cylinder bores 1, 2 & 3; 3.2280–3.2287 inches. Cylinder bore No. 4; 3.2283–3.2291 inches.

OIL PUMP

All Specifications Given In Inches, Unless Otherwise Specified.

Engine, Liter/CID	Body To Side Clearance	Gear To Body Clearance	Tip Clearance	Gear Pocket		Pump Gear Thickness	Pump Gear Diameter	Relief Valve To Body Clearance
				Depth	Diameter			
1.9L/4-116	.0042	.005	.006	—	—	—	—	—

DECIMAL & MILLIMETER EQUIVALENTS

INCH	INCH	MM
1/64	.015625	.397
1/32	.03125	.794
3/64	.046875	1.191
1/16	.0625	1.587
5/64	.078125	1.984
3/32	.09375	2.381
7/64	.109375	2.778
1/8	.125	3.175
9/64	.140625	3.572
5/32	.15625	3.969
11/64	.171875	4.366
3/16	.1875	4.762
13/64	.203125	5.159
7/32	.21875	5.556
15/64	.234375	5.953
1/4	.25	6.350
17/64	.265625	6.747
9/32	.28125	7.144
19/64	.296875	7.541
5/16	.3125	7.937
21/64	.328125	8.334
11/32	.34375	8.731

INCH	INCH	MM
23/64	.359375	9.128
3/8	.375	9.525
25/64	.390625	9.922
13/32	.40625	10.319
27/64	.421875	10.716
7/16	.4375	11.113
29/64	.453125	11.509
15/32	.46875	11.906
31/64	.484375	12.303
1/2	.5	12.700
33/64	.515625	13.097
17/32	.53125	13.494
35/64	.546875	13.890
9/16	.5625	14.287
37/64	.578125	14.684
19/32	.59375	15.081
39/64	.609375	15.478
5/8	.625	15.875
41/64	.640625	16.272
21/32	.65625	16.669
43/64	.671875	17.065

INCH	INCH	MM
11/16	.6875	17.462
45/64	.703125	17.859
23/32	.71875	18.265
47/64	.734375	18.653
3/4	.75	19.050
49/64	.765625	19.447
25/32	.78125	19.884
51/64	.796875	20.240
13/16	.8125	20.637
53/64	.828125	21.034
27/32	.84375	21.431
55/64	.859375	21.828
7/8	.875	22.225
57/64	.890625	22.622
29.32	.90625	23.019
59/64	.921875	23.415
15/16	.9375	23.812
61/64	.953125	24.209
31/32	.96875	24.606
63/64	.984375	25.003
1		25.400

Special Service Tools

Throughout this manual references are made to and illustrations may depict the use of special tools required to perform certain jobs. These special tools can generally be ordered through the dealers of the make vehicle being serviced. It is also suggested that you check with local automotive supply firms as they also supply tools manufactured by other firms that will assist in the performance of these jobs. The vehicle manufacturers special tools are supplied by:

Chrysler Corporation . . . . Miller Special Tools
SPX Corporation
12842 Farmington Rd.
Livonia, Michigan 48150

Ford Motor Company . . . . Owatonna Tool Company
Owatonna, Minnesota 55060

General Motors . . . . Kent-Moore
SPX Corporation
29784 Little Mack
Roseville, Michigan 48066

Manual Information Locator

Operation/Subject/Topic	Auto Repair Manual	Auto Engine Tune Up & Electronics (Engine Performance) Manual
Air Bags	X	—
Air Conditioning	X	—
AIR Systems	—	X
All-Wheel Drive Systems	X	—
Alternator Specifications	X	—
Alternator Systems	X	—
Anti-Lock Brake Systems	X	—
Automatic Transaxle In-Vehicle Service	X	—
Automatic Transmission In-Vehicle Service	X	—
Axle Shaft Service	X	—
Back-Up Light Switch, Replace	X	—
Balance Shaft Service	X	—
Ball Joint Service	X	—
Belt Tension Data	X	—
Blower Motor, Replace	X	—
Brake Booster Service	X	—
Brake Service	X	—
Camber Adjustment	X	—
Camshaft Service	X	—
Capacity Data	X	—
Carburetor Adjustments	—	X
Carburetor Overhaul	—	X
Caster Adjustment	X	—
Catalytic Converters	—	X
Clutch Service	X	—
Clutch Start Switch, Replace	X	—
Coil Spring, Replace	X	—
Compression Check	—	X
Compression Pressures	—	X
Computer System Diagnostics	—	X
Computer System Identification	—	X
Computer Terminal Connector Identification	—	X
Computerized Engine Control Systems	—	X
Control Arm Service	X	—
Cooling System Bleed	X	—
Cooling System Data	X	—
Crankshaft Pulley, Replace	X	—
Crankshaft Rear Oil Seal Service	X	—
Cruise Control Systems	X	—
Cylinder Block Specifications	X	—
Cylinder Head Service	X	—
Cylinder Head Specifications	X	—
Cylinder Head, Replace	X	—
Cylinder Liner, Replace	X	—
Dash Panel Service	X	—
Differential Service	X	—
Dimmer Switch, Replace	X	—
Disc Brake Service	X	—
Distributor Service	—	X
Distributor, Replace	X	X
Distributorless Ignition Systems	—	X
Drive Axle Service	X	—
Drive Belt Tension Data	X	—
Drum Brake Service	X	—
EGR System	—	X
Electric Engine Cooling Fans	X	—
Electric Fuel Pumps	X	X
Electrical Symbol Identification	X	X
Electronic Fuel Injection	—	X
Electronic Ignition	—	X
Electronic Instrumentation	—	X
Electronic Level Controls	X	—
Emission Control Application Charts	—	X
Emission Controls	—	X
Emission Vacuum Hose Routing	—	X
Engine Compartment Reference Diagrams	—	X
Engine Cooling Fans	X	—
Engine Electronic Control Module, Replace	—	X
Engine Electronic Control Unit, Replace	—	X
Engine Front Cover Service	X	—
Engine Mounts, Replace	X	—
Engine Oil Seal Service	X	—
Engine Rebuilding Specifications	X	—
Engine Repairs	X	—
Engine Sensor Location	—	X
Engine Sensor Replacement	—	X
Engine Sensor Specification Charts	—	X
Engine Specifications	X	—
Engine System Identification Charts	—	X
Engine Tightening Specifications	X	—
Engine, Replace	X	—
Evaporator Core, Replace	X	—
Exhaust Gas Recirculation (EGR) Systems	—	X
Exhaust Manifold, Replace	X	—
Fast Idle Speed Adjustment	—	X
Feedback Carburetors	—	X
Flasher Location	X	—
Front Drive Axle Service	X	—
Front Wheel Alignment	X	—
Fuel Control System Identification	—	X
Fuel Filter, Replace	X	—
Fuel Injection Systems	—	X
Fuel Injector Cleaning Procedures	—	X
Fuel Injector, Replace	—	X
Fuel Pump Pressure Specifications	X	X
Fuel Pump Pressure Test	—	X
Fuel Pump Replacement	X	X
Fuse Panel Location	X	—
General Engine Specifications	X	—
Headlight Switch, Replace	X	—
Heated Air Cleaners	—	X